AMERICAN MEN & WOMEN OF SCIENCE

AMERICAN MEN & WOMEN OF SCIENCE

PHYSICAL AND BIOLOGICAL SCIENCES

15TH EDITION
VOLUME IV
J-L

EDITED BY
JAQUES CATTELL PRESS

R. R. BOWKER COMPANY
NEW YORK & LONDON 1982

Copyright © 1982 by Xerox Corporation
Published by R.R. Bowker Co.
1180 Avenue of the Americas, New York, N.Y. 10036

International Standard Book Number
        Set: 0-8352-1413-3
    Volume I: 0-8352-1414-1
   Volume II: 0-8352-1416-8
  Volume III: 0-8352-1417-6
  Volume IV: 0-8352-1418-4
   Volume V: 0-8352-1419-2
  Volume VI: 0-8352-1420-6
 Volume VII: 0-8352-1421-4
International Standard Serial Number: 0192-8570
Library of Congress Catalog Card Number: 6-7326

CONTENTS

ADVISORY COMMITTEE

Dr. Dael L. Wolfle, Committee Chairman
Professor Emeritus,
Graduate School of Public Affairs
University of Washington

Dr. Carl D. Douglass
Director,
Division of Research Grants
National Institutes of Health

Mr. Alan Fechter
Head,
Scientific and Technical
Personnel Studies
National Science Foundation

Dr. Harold S. Ginsberg
Professor & Chairman,
Department of Microbiology
College of Physicians and Surgeons
Columbia University

Dr. Allen L. Hammond
Editor, *Science '81,*
American Association for the
Advancement of Science

Dr. Anna J. Harrison
Professor,
Department of Chemistry
Mt. Holyoke College

Dr. William C. Kelly
Executive Director,
Office of Scientific and
Engineering Personnel
National Research Council

Dr. H. William Koch
Director,
American Institute of Physics

Dr. Robert Krauss
Executive Director,
Federation of American Societies
for Experimental Biology

Dr. William J. LeVeque
Executive Director,
American Mathematical Society

Dr. Raymond P. Mariella
Executive Director,
American Chemical Society

Dr. James H. Mulligan, Jr.
Professor,
Department of Electrical Engineering
University of California, Irvine

Dr. Kenneth Prewitt
President,
Social Science Research Council

Dr. Helen M. Ranney
Professor & Chairman,
Department of Medicine
University of California, San Diego

Dr. Matthias Stelly
Executive Vice President,
American Society of Agronomy

Mr. William E. Zimmie
President,
Zimmite Corporation

PREFACE

American Men and Women of Science is without peer as a chronicle of North American scientific endeavor and achievement. It has recorded the careers of over 280,000 scientists and engineers since the first edition appeared in 1906, and continues to provide current information on the leaders in America's research and academic communities.

The Fifteenth Edition contains the biographies of 130,000 women and men; 7,500 appear for the first time. The names of new entrants were submitted for consideration at the editors' request by current entrants and by persons in charge of academic, government and private research programs. All of those included meet the following criteria:

1. Achievement, by reason of experience and training of a stature in scientific work equivalent to that associated with the doctoral degree, coupled with presently continued activity in such work;

    or

2. Research activity of high quality in science as evidenced by publication in reputable scientific journals; or, for those whose work cannot be published because of governmental or industrial security, research activity of high quality in science as evidenced by the judgment of the individual's peers;

    or

3. Attainment of a position of substantial responsibility requiring scientific training and experience to the extent described for (1) and (2).

This edition profiles living scientists in the physical and biological fields as well as public health scientists, engineers, mathematicians, statisticians, and computer scientists. The information is collected by means of direct communication whenever possible. Forms are sent to all entrants for corroboration and updating, and those whose biographies are appearing for the first time receive verification proofs before publication. The information submitted by entrants is included as completely as possible within the boundaries of editorial and space restrictions. Full entries are repeated for former listees who do not return forms but whose current location can be verified in secondary sources. References to the previous edition are given for those who do not return forms and cannot be located, but who are presumed to be still active in science or engineering. A notation is made when an entrant from the previous edition is known to be deceased. Non-citizens of the Americas are included if working in the United States or Canada for a reasonable duration. Information on former entrants who have entered fields other than science and engineering, or who have been retired for ten years and are no longer professionally active has been omitted.

American Men and Women of Science has experienced many changes in its long history, and this edition is no exception. Following the suggestion of the advisory committee, and based on the recommendation of a user survey, the geographic and discipline indexes have been discontinued in printed form. The Fifteenth Edition will be available for on-line searching, however, through BRS, DIALOG and the Jaques Cattell Press. All elements of an entry, including field of interest, experience and location, can be accessed by the use of key words. Although *American Men and Women of Science* is on a three year publication cycle, the on-line database will be updated at more frequent intervals. Previous users of the directory will be pleased to find that the type size has been enlarged in response to many requests.

The Social and Behavioral Sciences section of *American Men and Women of Science* was last published in 1978. The limited acceptance of this section caused the postponement of subsequent editions. Realizing the importance of maintaining current data on the disciplines, the publishers are considering several possibilities for the future. One is the inclusion of selected, appropriate fields in the *Directory of American Scholars,* also a Bowker/Cattell publication. Another plan under consideration is the systematic addition of social and behavioral scientists to the on-line database for eventual publication in an all-inclusive *American Men and Women of Science.*

The editors take this opportunity to thank the Fifteenth Edition advisory committee for their guidance, encouragement and support. Appreciation is expressed to the many scientific societies who provided their membership lists for the purpose of locating former entrants whose addresses had changed.

Comments and suggestions on any aspect of the Fifteenth Edition are encouraged and should be directed to The Editors, *American Men and Women of Science,* P.O. Box 25001, Tempe, Arizona 85282.

Martha Cargill, *Editor*
Renee Lautenbach, *Managing Editor*
Terence Basom, *General Manager*
JAQUES CATTELL PRESS

August, 1982

ABBREVIATIONS

AAAS—American Association for the
  Advancement of Science
abnorm—abnormal
abstr—abstract(s)
acad—academic, academy
acct—account, accountant, accounting
acoust—acoustic(s), acoustical
ACTH—adrenocorticotrophic hormone
actg—acting
activ—activities, activity
addn—addition(s), additional
Add—Address
adj—adjunct, adjutant
adjust—adjustment
Adm—Admiral
admin—administration, administrative
adminr—administrator(s)
admis—admission(s)
adv—adviser(s), advisory
advan—advance(d), advancement
advert—advertisement, advertising
AEC—Atomic Energy Commission
aerodyn—aerodynamic(s)
aeronaut—aeronautic(s), aeronautical
aerophys—aerophysical, aerophysics
aesthet—aesthetic(s)
AFB—Air Force Base
affil—affiliate(s), affiliation
agr—agricultural, agriculture
agron—agronomic, agronomical, agronomy
agrost—agrostologic, agrostological,
  agrostology
agt—agent
AID—Agency for International Development
Ala-Alabama
allergol—allergological, allergology
alt—alternate
Alta—Alberta
Am—America, American
AMA—American Medical Association
anal—analysis, analytic, analytical
analog—analogue
anat—anatomic, anatomical, anatomy
anesthesiol—anesthesiology
angiol—angiology
Ann—Annal(s)
ann—annual
anthrop—anthropological, anthropology
anthropom—anthropometric, anthropometri-
  cal, anthropometry
antiq—antiquary, antiquities, antiquity

antiqn—antiquarian
apicult—apicultural, apiculture
APO—Army Post Office
app—appoint, appointed
appl—applied
appln—application
approx—approximate(ly)
Apr—April
apt—apartment(s)
aquacult—aquaculture
arbit—arbitration
arch—archives
archaeol—archaeological, archaeology
archit—architectural, architecture
Arg—Argentina, Argentine
Ariz—Arizona
Ark—Arkansas
artil—artillery
asn—association
assoc(s)—associate(s), associated
asst(s)—assistant(s), assistantship(s)
Assyriol—Assyriology
astrodyn—astrodynamics
astron—astronomical, astronomy
astronaut—astronautical, astronautics
astronr—astronomer
astrophys—astrophysical, astrophysics
attend—attendant, attending
atty—attorney
audiol—audiology
Aug—August
auth—author
AV—audiovisual
Ave—Avenue
avicult—avicultural, aviculture

b—born
bact—bacterial, bacteriologic, bacteriological,
  bacteriology
BC—British Columbia
bd—board
behav—behavior(al)
Belg—Belgian, Belgium
bibl—biblical
bibliog—bibliographic, bibliographical,
  bibliography
bibliogr—bibliographer
biochem—biochemical, biochemistry
biog—biographical, biography
biol—biological, biology
biomed—biomedical, biomedicine

biomet—biometric(s), biometrical, biometry
biophys—biophysical, biophysics
bk(s)—book(s)
bldg—building
Blvd—Boulevard
Bor—Borough
bot—botanical, botany
br—branch(es)
Brig—Brigadier
Brit—Britain, British
Bro(s)—Brother(s)
byrol—byrology
Bull—Bulletin
bur—bureau
bus—business
BWI—British West Indies

c—children
Calif—California
Can—Canada, Canadian
cand—candidate
Capt—Captain
cardiol—cardiology
cardiovasc—cardiovascular
cartog—cartographic, cartographical,
  cartography
cartogr—cartographer
Cath—Catholic
CEngr—Corps of Engineers
cent—central
Cent Am—Central America
cert—certificate(s), certification, certified
chap—chapter
chem—chemical(s), chemistry
chemother—chemotherapy
chmn—chairman
citricult—citriculture
class—classical
climat—climatological, climatology
clin(s)—clinic(s), clinical
cmndg—commanding
Co—Companies, Company
coauth— coauthor
co-dir—co-director
co-ed—co-editor
coeduc—coeducation, coeducational
col(s)—college(s), collegiate, colonel
collab—collaboration, coloborative
collabr—collaborator
Colo—Colorado
com—commerce, commercial

ABBREVIATIONS

Comdr—Commander
commun—communicable, communication(s)
comn(s)—commission(s), commissioned
comnr—commissioner
comp—comparative
compos—composition
comput—computation, computer(s), computing
comt(s)—committee(s)
conchol—conchology
conf—conference
cong—congress, congressional
Conn—Connecticut
conserv—conservation, conservatory
consol—consolidated, consolidation
const—constitution, constitutional
construct—construction, constructive
consult(s)—consult, consultant(s) consultantship(s), consultation, consulting
contemp—contemporary
contrib—contribute, contributing, contribution(s)
contribr—contributor
conv—convention
coop—cooperating, cooperation, cooperative
coord—coordinate(d), coordinating, coordination
coordr—coordinator
corp—corporate, corporation(s)
corresp—correspondence, correspondent, corresponding
coun—council, counsel, counseling
counr—councilor, counselor
criminol—criminological, criminology
cryog—cryogenic(s)
crystallog—crystallographic, crystallograpical, crystallography
crystallogr—crystallographer
Ct—Court
Ctr—Center
cult—cultural, culture
cur—curator
curric—curriculum
cybernet—cybernetic(s)
cytol—cytological, cytology
Czech—Czechoslovakia

DC—District of Columbia
Dec—December
Del—Delaware
deleg—delegate, delegation
delinq—delinquency, delinquent
dem—democrat(s), democratic
demog—demographic, demography
demogr—demographer
demonstr—demonstrator
dendrol—dendrologic, dendrological, dendrology
dent—dental, dentistry
dep—deputy
dept—department(al)
dermat—dermatologic, dermatological, dermatology
develop—developed, developing, development, developmental
diag—diagnosis, diagnostic
dialectol—dialectological, dialectology
dict—dictionaries, dictionary
Dig—Digest
dipl—diploma, diplomate
dir(s)—director(s), directories, directory
dis—disease(s), disorders

Diss Abstr—Dissertation Abstracts
dist—district
distrib—distributed, distribution, distributive
distribr—distributor(s)
div—division, divisional, divorced
DNA—deoxyribonucleic acid
doc—document(s), documentary, documentation
Dom—Dominion
Dr—Drive

e—east
ecol—ecological, ecology
econ(s)—economic(s), economical, economy
economet—econometric(s)
ECT—electroconvulsive or electroshock therapy
ed—edition(s), editor(s), editorial
ed bd—editorial board
educ—education, educational
educr—educator(s)
EEG—electroencephalogram, electroencephalographic, electroencephalography
Egyptol—Egyptology
EKG—electrocardiogram
elec—electric, electrical, electricity
electrochem—electrochemical, electrochemistry
electrophys—electrophysical, electrophysics
elem—elementary
embryol—embryologic, embryological, embryology
emer—emeriti, emiritus
employ—employment
encour—encouragement
encycl—encyclopedia
endocrinol—endocrinologic, endocrinology
eng—engineering
Eng—England, English
engr(s)—engineer(s)
enol—enology
Ens—Ensign
entom—entomological, entomology
environ—environment(s), environmental
enzym—enzymology
epidemiol—epidemiologic, epidemiological, epidemiology
equip—equipment
ESEA—Elementary & Secondary Education Act
espec—especially
estab—established, establishment(s)
ethnog—ethnographic, ethnographical, ethnography
ethnogr—ethnographer
ethnol—ethnologic, ethnological, ethnology
Europ—European
eval—evaluation
evangel—evangelical
eve—evening
exam—examination(s), examining
examr—examiner
except—exceptional
exec(s)—executive(s)
exeg—exegeses, exegesis, exegetic, exegetical
exhib(s)—exhibition(s), exhibit(s)
exp—experiment, experimental
exped(s)—expedition(s)
explor—exploration(s), exploratory
expos—exposition
exten—extension

fac—faculty

facil—facilities, facility
Feb—February
fed—federal
fedn—federation
fel(s)—fellow(s), fellowship(s)
fermentol—fermentology
fertil—fertility, fertilitization
Fla—Florida
floricult—floricultural, floriculture
found—foundation
FPO—Fleet Post Office
Fr—French
Ft—Fort

Ga—Georgia
gastroenterol—gastroenterological, gastroenterology
gen—general
geneal—genealogical, genealogy
geod—geodesy, geodetic
geog—geographic, geographical, geography
geogr—geographer
geol—geologic, geological, geology
geom—geometric, geometrical, geometry
geomorphol—geomorphologic, geomorphology
geophys—geophysical, geophysics
Ger—German, Germanic, Germany
geriat—geriatric(s)
geront—gerontological, gerontology
glaciol—glaciology
gov—governing, governor(s)
govt—government, governmental
grad—graduate(d)
Gt Brit—Great Britain
guid—guidance
gym—gymnasium
gynec—gynecologic, gynecological, gynecology

handbk(s)—handbook(s)
helminth—helminthology
hemat—hematologic, hematological, hematology
herpet—herpetologic, herpetological, herpetology
Hisp—Hispanic, Hispania
hist—historic, historical, history
histol—histological, histology
HM—Her Majesty
hochsch—hochschule
homeop—homeopathic, homeopathy
hon(s)—honor(s), honorable, honorary
hort—horticultural, horticulture
hosp(s)—hospital(s), hospitalization
hq—headquarters
HumRRO—Human Resources Research Office
husb—husbandry
Hwy—Highway
hydraul—hydraulic(s)
hydrodyn—hydrodynamic(s)
hydrol—hydrologic, hydrological, hydrology
hyg—hygiene, hygienic(s)
hypn—hypnosis

ichthyol—ichthyological, ichthyology
Ill—Illinois
illum—illuminating, illumination
illus—illustrate, illustrated, illustration
illusr—illustrator
immunol—immunologic, immunological, immunology

Imp—Imperial
improv—improvement
Inc—Incorporated
in-chg—in charge
incl—include(s), including
Ind—Indiana
indust(s)—industrial, industries, industry
inf—infantry
info—information
inorg—inorganic
ins—insurance
inst(s)—institute(s), institution(s)
instnl—institutional(ized)
instr(s)—instruct, instruction, instructor(s)
instrnl—instructional
int—international
intel—intelligence
introd—introduction
invert—invertebrate
invest(s)—investigation(s)
investr—investigator
irrig—irrigation
Ital—Italian

J—Journal
Jan—January
Jct—Junction
jour—journal, journalism
jr—junior
jurisp—jurisprudence
juv—juvenile

Kans—Kansas
Ky—Kentucky

La—Louisiana
lab(s)—laboratories, laboratory
lang—language(s)
laryngol—laryngological, laryngology
lect—lecture(s)
lectr—lecturer(s)
legis—legislation, legislative, legislature
lett—letter(s)
lib—liberal
libr—libraries, library
librn—librarian
lic—license(d)
limnol—limnological, limnology
ling—linguistic(s), linguistical
lit—literary, literature
lithol—lithologic, lithological, lithology
Lt—Lieutenant
Ltd—Limited

m—married
mach—machine(s), machinery
mag—magazine(s)
maj—major
malacol—malacology
mammal—mammalogy
Man—Manitoba
Mar—March
Mariol—Mariology
Mass—Massachusetts
mat—material(s)
mat med—materia medica
math—mathematic(s), mathematical
Md—Maryland
mech—mechanic(s), mechanical
med—medical, medicinal, medicine
Mediter—Mediterranean
Mem—Memorial
mem—member(s), membership(s)

ment—mental(ly)
metab—metabolic, metabolism
metall—metallurgic, metallurgical,
　　metallurgy
metallog—metallographic, metallography
metallogr—metallographer
metaphys—metaphysical, metaphysics
meteorol—meteorological, meteorology
metrol—metrological, metrology
metrop—metropolitan
Mex—Mexican, Mexico
mfg—manufacturing
mfr(s)—manufacture(s), manufacturer(s)
mgr—manager
mgt—management
Mich—Michigan
microbiol—microbiological, microbiology
micros—microscopic, microscopical,
　　microscopy
mid—middle
mil—military
mineral—mineralogical, mineralogy
Minn—Minnesota
Miss—Mississippi
mkt—market, marketing
Mo—Missouri
mod—modern
monogr—monograph
Mont—Montana
morphol—morphological, morphology
Mt—Mount
mult—multiple
munic—municipal, municipalities
mus—museum(s)
musicol—musicological, musicology
mycol—mycologic, mycology

n—north
NASA—National Aeronautics & Space
　　Administration
nat—national, naturalized
NATO—North Atlantic Treaty Organization
navig—navigation(al)
NB—New Brunswick
NC—North Carolina
NDak—North Dakota
NDEA—National Defense Education Act
Nebr—Nebraska
nematol—nematological, nematology
nerv—nervous
Neth—Netherlands
neurol—neurological, neurology
neuropath—neuropathological, neuro-
　　pathology
neuropsychiat—neuropsychiatric, neuro-
　　psychiatry
neurosurg—neurosurgical, neurosurgery
Nev—Nevada
New Eng—New England
New York—New York City
Nfld—Newfoundland
NH—New Hampshire
NIH—National Institutes of Health
NIMH—National Institute of Mental Health
NJ—New Jersey
NMex—New Mexico
nonres—nonresident
norm—normal
Norweg—Norwegian
Nov—November
NS—Nova Scotia
NSF—National Science Foundation
NSW—New South Wales

numis—numismatic(s)
nutrit—nutrition, nutritional
NY—New York State
NZ—New Zealand

observ—observatories, observatory
obstet—obstetric(s), obstetrical
occas—occasional(ly)
occup—occupation, occupational
oceanog—oceanographic, oceanographical,
　　oceanography
oceanogr—oceanographer
Oct—October
odontol—odontology
OEEC—Organization for European
　　Economic Cooperation
off—office, official
Okla—Oklahoma
olericult—olericulture
oncol—oncologic, oncology
Ont—Ontario
oper(s)—operation(s), operational,
　　operative
ophthal—ophthalmologic, ophthalmological,
　　ophthalmology
optom—optometric, optometrical, optometry
ord—ordnance
Ore—Oregon
org—organic
orgn—organization(s), organizational
orient—oriental
ornith—ornithological, ornithology
orthod—orthodontia, orthodontic(s)
orthop—orthopedic(s)
osteop—osteopathic, osteopathy
otol—otological, otology
otolaryngol—otolaryngological, otolaryn-
　　gology
otorhinol—otorhinologic, otorhinology

Pa—Pennsylvania
Pac—Pacific
paleobot—paleobotanical, paleobotany
paleont—paleontological, paleontology
Pan-Am—Pan-American
parasitol—parasitology
partic—participant, participating
path—pathologic, pathological, pathology
pedag—pedagogic(s), pedagogical, pedagogy
pediat—pediatric(s)
PEI—Prince Edward Islands
penol—penological, penology
periodont—periodontal, periodontic(s),
　　periodontology
petrog—petrographic, petrographical,
　　petrography
petrogr—petrographer
petrol—petroleum, petrologic, petrological,
　　petrology
pharm—pharmacy
pharmaceut—pharmaceutic(s), pharmaceu-
　　tical(s)
pharmacog—pharmacognosy
pharamacol—pharmacologic, pharmaco-
　　logical, pharmacology
phenomenol—phenomenologic(al),
　　phenomenology
philol—philological, philology
philos—philosophic, philosophical,
　　philosophy
photog—photographic, photography
photogeog—photogeographic, photo-
　　geography

ABBREVIATIONS

photogr—photographer(s)
photogram—photogrammetric, photogrammetry
photom—photometric, photometrical,
  photometry
phycol—phycology
phys—physical
physiog—physiographic, physiographical,
  physiography
physiol—physiological, physiology
Pkwy—Parkway
Pl—Place
polit—political, politics
polytech—polytechnic(al)
pomol—pomological, pomology
pontif—pontifical
pop—population
Port—Portugal, Portuguese
postgrad—postgraduate
PQ—Province of Quebec
PR—Puerto Rico
pract—practice
practr—practitioner
prehist—prehistoric, prehistory
prep—preparation, preparative, preparatory
pres—president
Presby—Presbyterian
preserv—preservation
prev—prevention, preventive
prin—principal
prob(s)—problem(s)
proc—proceedings
proctol—proctologic, proctological,
  proctology
prod—product(s), production, productive
prof—professional, professor, professorial
Prof Exp—Professional Experience
prog(s)—program(s), programmed,
  programming
proj—project(s), projection(al), projective
prom—promotion
protozool—protozoology
prov—province, provincial
psychiat—psychiatric, psychiatry
psychoanal—psychoanalysis, psychoanalytic,
  psychoanalytical
psychol—psychological, psychology
psychomet—psychometric(s)
psychopath—psychopathologic, psychopathology
psychophys—psychophysical, psychophysics
psychophysiol—psychophysiological,
  psychophysiology
psychosom—psychosomatic(s)
psychother—psychotherapeutic(s),
  psychotherapy
Pt—Point
pub—public
publ—publication(s), publish(ed),
  publisher, publishing
pvt—private

Qm—Quartermaster
Qm Gen—Quartermaster General
qual—qualitative, quality
quant—quantitative
quart—quarterly

radiol—radiological, radiology
RAF—Royal Air Force
RAFVR—Royal Air Force Volunteer
  Reserve

RAMC—Royal Army Medical Corps
RAMCR—Royal Army Medical Corps
  Reserve
RAOC—Royal Army Ordnance Corps
RASC—Royal Army Service Corps
RASCR—Royal Army Service Corps Reserve
RCAF—Royal Canadian Air Force
RCAFR—Royal Canadian Air Force Reserve
RCAFVR—Royal Canadian Air Force
  Volunteer Reserve
RCAMC—Royal Canadian Army Medical
  Corps
RCAMCR—Royal Canadian Army Medical
  Corps Reserve
RCASC—Royal Canadian Army Service
  Corps
RCASCR—Royal Canadian Army Service
  Corps Reserve
RCEME—Royal Canadian Electrical &
  Mechanical Engineers
RCN—Royal Canadian Navy
RCNR—Royal Canadian Naval Reserve
RCNVR—Royal Canadian Naval Volunteer
  Reserve
Rd—Road
RD—Rural Delivery
rec—record(s), recording
redevelop—redevelopment
ref—reference(s)
refrig—refrigeration
regist—register(ed), registration
registr—registrar
regt—regiment(al)
rehab—rehabilitation
rel(s)—relation(s), relative
relig—religion, religious
REME—Royal Electrical & Mechanical
  Engineers
rep—represent, representative
repub—republic
req—requirements
res—research, reserve
rev—review, revised, revision
RFD—Rural Free Delivery
rhet—rhetoric, rhetorical
RI—Rhode Island
Rm—Room
RM—Royal Marines
RN—Royal Navy
RNA—ribonucleic acid
RNR—Royal Naval Reserve
RNVR—Royal Naval Volunteer Reserve
roentgenol—roentgenologic, roentgeno-
  logical, roentgenology
RR—Railroad, Rural Route
rte—route
Russ—Russian
rwy—railway

s—south
SAfrica—South Africa
SAm—South America, South American
sanit—sanitary, sanitation
Sask—Saskatchewan
SC—South Carolina
Scand—Scandinavia(n)
sch(s)—school(s)
scholar—scholarship
sci—science(s), scientific
SDak—South Dakota
SEATO—Southeast Asia Treaty Organization
sec—secondary
sect—section

secy—secretary
seismog—seismograph, seismographic,
  seismography
seismogr—seismographer
seismol—seismological, seismology
sem—seminar, seminary
sen—senator, senatorial
Sept—September
ser—serial, series
serol—serologic, serological, serology
serv—service(s), serving
silvicult—silvicultural, silviculture
soc(s)—societies, society
soc sci—social science
sociol—sociologic, sociological, sociology
Span—Spanish
spec—special
specif—specification(s)
spectrog—spectrograph, spectrographic,
  spectography
spectrogr—spectrographer
spectrophotom—spectrophotometer, spectrophotometric, spectrophotometry
spectros—spectroscopic, spectroscopy
speleol—speleological, speleology
Sq—Square
sr—senior
St—Saint, Street(s)
sta(s)—station(s)
stand—standard(s), standardization
statist—statistical, statistics
Ste—Sainte
steril—sterility
stomatol—stomatology
stratig—stratigraphic, stratigraphy
stratigr—stratigrapher
struct—structural, structure(s)
stud—student(ship)
subcomt—subcommittee
subj—subject
subsid—subsidiary
substa—substation
super—superior
suppl—supplement(s), supplemental,
  supplementary
supt—superintendent
supv—supervising, supervision
supvr—supervisor
supvry—supervisory
surg—surgery, surgical
surv—survey, surveying
survr—surveyor
Swed—Swedish
Switz—Switzerland
symp—symposia, symposium(s)
syphil—syphilology
syst(s)—system(s), systematic(s),
  systematical

taxon—taxonomic, taxonomy
tech—technical, technique(s)
technol—technologic(al), technology
tel—telegraph(y), telephone
temp—temporary
Tenn—Tennessee
Terr—Terrace
Tex—Texas
textbk(s)—textbook(s)
text ed—text edition
theol—theological, theology
theoret—theoretic(al)
ther—therapy
therapeut—therapeutic(s)

thermodyn—thermodynamic(s)
topog—topographic, topographical,
  topography
topogr—topographer
toxicol—toxicologic, toxicological, toxicology
trans—transactions
transl—translated, translation(s)
translr—translator(s)
transp—transport, transportation
treas—treasurer, treasury
treat—treatment
trop—tropical
tuberc—tuberculosis
TV—television
Twp—Township

UAR—United Arab Republic
UK—United Kingdom
UN—United Nations
undergrad—undergraduate
unemploy—unemployment
UNESCO—United Nations Educational
  Scientific & Cultural Organization
UNICEF—United Nations International
  Childrens Fund
univ(s)—universities, university
UNRRA—United Nations Relief &
  Rehabilitation Administration
UNRWA—United Nations Relief & Works
  Agency
urol—urologic, urological, urology
US—United States

USA—US Army
USAAF—US Army Air Force
USAAFR—US Army Air Force Reserve
USAF—US Air Force
USAFR—US Air Force Reserve
USAR—US Army Reserve
USCG—US Coast Guard
USCGR—US Coast Guard Reserve
USDA—US Department of Agriculture
USMC—US Marine Corps
USMCR—US Marine Corps Reserve
USN—US Navy
USNAF—US Naval Air Force
USNAFR—US Naval Air Force Reserve
USNR—US Naval Reserve
USPHS—US Public Health Service
USPHSR—US Public Health Service Reserve
USSR—Union of Soviet Socialist Republics
USWMC—US Women's Marine Corps
USWMCR—US Women's Marine Corps
  Reserve

Va—Virginia
var—various
veg—vegetable(s), vegetation
vent—ventilating, ventilation
vert—vertebrate
vet—veteran(s), veterinarian, veterinary
VI—Virgin Islands
vinicult—viniculture
virol—virological, virology
vis—visiting

voc—vocational
vocab—vocabulary
vol(s)—voluntary, volunteer(s), volume(s)
vpres—vice president
vs—versus
Vt—Vermont

w—west
WAC—Women's Army Corps
Wash—Washington
WAVES—Women Accepted for Voluntary
  Emergency Service
WHO—World Health Organization
WI—West Indies
wid—widow, widowed, widower
Wis—Wisconsin
WRCNS—Women's Royal Canadian Naval
  Service
WRNS—Women's Royal Naval Service
WVa—West Virginia
Wyo—Wyoming

yearbk(s)—yearbook(s)
YMCA—Young Men's Christian Association
YMHA—Young Men's Hebrew Association
yr(s)—year(s)
YWCA—Young Women's Christian Asso-
  ciation
YWHA—Young Women's Hebrew Asso-
  ciation

zool—zoological, zoology

AMERICAN MEN & WOMEN OF SCIENCE

J

JA, WILLIAM YIN, b Mar 5, 36; US citizen. ANALYTICAL CHEMISTRY. *Educ:* Univ Calif, Berkeley, BS, 60. *Prof Exp:* Chemist, Qual Assurance Tech Agency, US Army Chem Corps, 60-62; anal chemist, Hyman (Julius) Labs, Inc, 62-64; anal chemist, Philadelphia Quartz Co, Calif, 64-66; RES ASSOC, RICHMOND RES CTR, STAUFFER CHEM CO, 66- *Mem:* Am Chem Soc; Am Soc Testing & Mat; Assoc Official Anal Chem. *Res:* Analytical methods development; trace analysis; separations and purification techniques, especially preparation of high-purity pesticide standards and metabolites by large-scale, high-speed column chromatography. *Mailing Add:* 1314 Noble Ct El Cerrito CA 94530

JAANUS, SIRET DESIREE, b Tallinn, Estonia, May 17, 37; US citizen; m 73. PHARMACOLOGY, ENDOCRINOLOGY. *Educ:* City Col New York, BS, 60; Hunter Col, MA, 66; State Univ NY Downstate Med Ctr, PhD(pharmacol), 70. *Prof Exp:* Res asst pharmacol, Albert Einstein Col Med, 60-64; res asst, State Univ Downstate Med Ctr, 64-66, NIH fel pharmacol, 66-70, path, 70-71; asst prof basic sci, State Univ NY Col Optom, 71-72, chmn dept, 72-73; ASSOC PROF BASIC SCI, SOUTHERN CALIF COL OPTOM, 73-; CHAIRPERSON, DEPT BASIC & VISUAL SCI, 78- *Mem:* AAAS; Am Soc Pharmacol & Exp Therapeut; Am Soc Cell Biol. *Res:* Autonomic and endocrine pharmacology. *Mailing Add:* Dept Basic & Visual Sci Southern Calif Col of Optom 2001 Assoc Rd Fullerton CA 92631

JABALPURWALA, KAIZER E, b Surat, India, May 4, 32; m 60; c 2. INORGANIC CHEMISTRY, PHYSICAL CHEMISTRY. *Educ:* Univ Bombay, BSc, 54, MSc, 56, PhD(coord chem), 60. *Prof Exp:* Res asst phys chem, Inst Sci, Univ Bombay, 58-61; res assoc inorg chem, Boston Univ, 61-64; chief chemist, Zinc Oxide Co Can Ltd, Hudson Bay Mining & Smelting Co, Montreal, 64-68, tech dir, 68-74; tech mgr, Zochem Ltd, 74; EXEC TECH DIR, G H CHEM LTD, 74- *Mem:* AAAS; Am Chem Soc; British Chem Soc; Tech Asn Pulp & Paper Indust; Chem Inst Can. *Res:* Light scattering by colloid systems; solution stabilities of complex ions; electrophotography related to photoconductivity of zinc oxide; technology of zinc oxide. *Mailing Add:* G H Chem Ltd 1550 Brouillette St PO Box 456 St Hyacinthe PQ J2S 7B8 Can

JABARIN, SALEH ABD EL KARIM, b Haifa, Israel, Feb 7, 39; m 69; c 1. POLYMER CHEMISTRY. *Educ:* Dartmouth Col, BA, 66; Polytech Inst Brooklyn, MS, 68; Univ Mass, PhD(polymer sci & eng), 71. *Prof Exp:* SR SCIENTIST, OWENS-ILLINOIS TECH CTR, 71- *Mem:* Am Chem Soc; Soc Plastics Engrs. *Res:* Studies of thermal, mechanical and optical properties of polymers and polymer crystallization using light scattering, x-ray diffraction, infra-red dichroism and birefringence; molecular orientation and solution characterization. *Mailing Add:* Owens-Illinois Tech Ctr PO Box 1035 Toledo OH 43666

JABBOUR, J T, b Tiptonville, Tenn, Aug 5, 27; m; c 5. PEDIATRIC NEUROLOGY. *Educ:* Univ Tenn, Martin, BS, 48; Univ Tenn, Memphis, MD, 51; Am Bd Pediat, dipl, 60. *Prof Exp:* Rotating intern, Baylor Univ Hosp, Dallas, 52-53; gen pract, Tenn, 53-56; resident, Col Med, Univ Tenn, Memphis, 56-58, res assoc pediat, 57; co-dir pediat neurol & seizure clin, Sch Med, Univ Okla, 59-61, asst prof pediat & neurol & assoc dir clin study ctr birth defects, 61-65; asst prof, 65-67, chief sect, 67-76, PROF PEDIAT & NEUROL, CTR HEALTH SCI, UNIV TENN, MEMPHIS, 67- *Concurrent Pos:* Fel neurol, Univ Minn, Minneapolis, 58-61; consult, Oklahoma City Speech & Hearing Ctr, 61-65; consult, Oklahoma City Children's Ctr, 61-65; chief pediat neurol, Child Develop Ctr, Med Units, Univ Tenn, Memphis, 65-68; consult, Ment Retardation Br, Bur Chronic Dis, USPHS, 66-69. *Mem:* AMA; Am Acad Pediat; Am Acad Neurol; Am Acad Cerebral Palsy. *Mailing Add:* Univ of Tenn 800 Madison Ave Memphis TN 38163

JABBOUR, KAHTAN NICOLAS, b Safita, Syria, Aug 26, 34. ENGINEERING. *Educ:* Damascus Univ, cert math, 53 & 54; Sch Advan Eng, Beirut, BS, 57; Purdue Univ, MS, 60, PhD(struct), 62. *Prof Exp:* Field engr, Arabian Am Oil Co, Saudi Arabia, 57-58; design engr, El-Ghab Proj, Syria, 58-59; asst prof eng, Kans State Univ, 62-63; assoc prof eng sci, Tenn

Technol Univ, 63-67; staff engr, Fairchild Hiller Corp, 67-69; aerospace engr, Goddard Space Flight Ctr, NASA, 69-73; sr mech engr, 73-80, SR PROJ MGR, US NUCLEAR REGULATORY COMN, 80- *Concurrent Pos:* Nat Sci Found res grant, 65-66. *Mem:* Am Soc Eng Educ. *Res:* Structural mechanics and engineering; perforated plates. *Mailing Add:* 109 Lucas Lane Bethesda MD 20814

JABBUR, RAMZI JIBRAIL, b Beirut, Lebanon, Mar 9, 37; US citizen; div; c 1. INDUSTRIAL CHEMISTRY, ECONOMETRICS. *Educ:* Am Univ Beirut, BS, 58; Stanford Univ, MS, 60, PhD(high energy physics), 63. *Prof Exp:* Res assoc physics, Columbia Univ, 63-65; res physicist, Argonne Nat Lab, 65-67; asst prof physics, City Col New York, 67-70; sr supvr, Batten, Barton, Durstine & Osborne, 70-74; proj mgr, 74-78, MGT CONSULT, W R GRACE & CO, 78- *Concurrent Pos:* Founder & bd mem, Am Bank, New York City. *Mem:* Am Phys Soc; NY Acad Sci; Inst Mgt Sci; Middle East Inst. *Res:* Management of major petrochemical projects; operations research and applications to managerial decisions; econometric statistical and dynamic models; strategic corp planning; investments, acquisitions and divestments. *Mailing Add:* 1380 Riverside Dr New York NY 10033

JABBUR, SUHAYL JIBRA'IL, b Beirut, Lebanon, June 17, 31; m 57; c 3. NEUROPHYSIOLOGY. *Educ:* Am Univ Beirut, BA, 52, MD, 56; Univ Wash, PhD, 60. *Prof Exp:* Asst pharmacol, Col Physicians & Surgeons, Columbia Univ, 56-57; res assoc physiol & biophys, Sch Med, Univ Wash, 57-60; from asst prof to assoc prof neurophysiol, 60-77, PROF PHYSIOL, AM UNIV BEIRUT, 77- *Concurrent Pos:* Rockefeller Found fel, 57-59. *Mem:* Lebanese AAAS; Soc Neurosci; hon mem British Brain Res Asn; hon mem Europ Brain & Behav Soc. *Res:* Cerebral cortical control of sensory input in the cuneate and gracile nuclei; antidromic activation of the pyramidal tract; hypothalamic control of the cardiovascular system; brain control of the uterus; neuropharmacology of somatic sensory system; visual, auditory and somatic interactions in central nervous system; somatic sensory pathways to various central nervous system areas. *Mailing Add:* Dept of Physiol Am Univ of Beirut Beirut Lebanon

JABINE, THOMAS BOYD, b Brooklyn, NY, Jan 26, 25; m 50; c 4. APPLIED STATISTICS. *Educ:* Mass Inst Technol, BS & MS, 49. *Prof Exp:* Var pos, US Census Bur, 49-68, chief statist res div, 65-73; chief math statistician, Social Security Admin, 73-79; statist policy expert, Energy Info Admin, US Dept Energy, 79-80; STATIST CONSULT, 80- *Concurrent Pos:* Constituent mem, Inter-Am Statist Inst. *Mem:* Fel Am Statist Asn; Int Statist Inst. *Res:* Survey methodology; sampling; quality control. *Mailing Add:* 3231 Worthington St NW Washington DC 20015

JABLON, SEYMOUR, b New York, NY, June 2, 18; m 41; c 2. BIOSTATISTICS, EPIDEMIOLOGY. *Educ:* City Col New York, BS, 39; Columbia Univ, MA, 40. *Prof Exp:* Prof assoc, Med Follow-up Agency, Nat Res Coun, 48-60; chief dept statist, Atomic Bomb Casualty Comn, 60-63; assoc dir, Med follow-up Agency, Nat Res Coun, 63-68; chief dept statist, Atomic Bomb Casualty Comn, 68-71; assoc dir, 71-75, DIR MED FOLLOW-UP AGENCY, NAT RES COUN, 75- *Concurrent Pos:* Mem, Nat Comn Radiation Protection, 74- *Mem:* Fel Am Statist Asn; Am Epidemiol Soc; Radiation Res Soc; Biomet Soc; Soc Epidemiol Res. *Res:* Late effects of radiation; epidemiology of cancer; epidemiology of cardiovascular disease. *Mailing Add:* Div Med Sci Nat Res Coun 2101 Constitution Ave NW Washington DC 20418

JABLONER, HAROLD, b New York, NY, Oct 25, 37; m 61; c 3. POLYMER CHEMISTRY, ORGANIC CHEMISTRY. *Educ:* City Col New York, BS, 57; Polytech Inst Brooklyn, PhD(chem), 63. *Prof Exp:* Res chemist, Hercules Powder Co, 63-68; sr res chemist, 68-71, res scientist, 71-78, RES ASSOC, HERCULES INC, 78- *Concurrent Pos:* Adj prof, Drexel Univ, 78- *Mem:* Am Chem Soc. *Res:* Solution properties and synthesis of macromolecules; hydrocarbon oxidation kinetics and mechanisms; thermally stable polymers; food; taste perception; polymer taste perception; solution properties of polymers; paper and synthetic pulp. *Mailing Add:* Hercules Res Ctr Wilmington DE 19899

1

JABLONSKI, DAVID ALBERT, b Worcester, Mass, Apr 6, 52. MATERIAL SCIENCE. *Educ:* Univ Mass, BS, 74; Mass Inst Technol, SM, 76, PhD(mat eng), 78. *Prof Exp:* RES SCIENTIST, UNITED TECHNOL RES CTR, UNITED TECHNOL CORP, 78- *Mem:* Sigma Xi; Am Soc Metals. *Res:* Fatigue in metals and polymers; environmental effects in materials; micro mechanisms of deformation and fracture in materials. *Mailing Add:* 94D-4 Cynthia Lane Middletown CT 06101

JABLONSKI, FELIX JOSEPH, b Chicago, Ill, Jan 12, 25; m 56; c 3. MATHEMATICS, PHYSICS. *Educ:* Tex A&I Univ, BA, 55; US Navy Postgrad Sch, MS, 61. *Prof Exp:* Head, Naval Sci Opers Res Dept, US Naval Acad, 63-66; head opers res, LTV Electrosystems, 66-70; ASSOC DIV DIR, OPERS RES INC, 72- *Mem:* Sigma Xi. *Res:* Operations research and naval logistics. *Mailing Add:* ORI Inc 1400 Spring St Silver Spring MD 20910

JABLONSKI, FRANK EDWARD, b Brooklyn, NY, Feb 3, 15; m 49; c 3. ELECTROOPTICS. *Educ:* Fordham Univ, BS, 36; NY Univ, MS, 40; Harvard Univ, MS, 46. *Prof Exp:* Physicist bur ord, US Dept Navy, 40-43, active duty, US Navy, 43-46 physicist influence devices, US Naval Ord Lab, 46-57, ord engr, Spec Projs Off, 57-58; physicist, Nat Security Agency, 58-59; physicist, Goddard Space Flight Ctr & NASA Hqs, 59-61, physicist off long range plans & progs, 61-63; tech adv, Chief of Naval Opers, 63-73; CONSULT PHYSICIST, 73- *Concurrent Pos:* Mem, Polaris Re-entry Body Coord Comt, 57-58; res adv comt control, guid & navig, NASA, 59-60. *Mem:* Fel AAAS; Am Phys Soc; Wilderness Soc. *Res:* Degaussing of ships; proximity exploders and fuzes; warheads for missiles; communications; space electronics; sonar; infrared; lasers. *Mailing Add:* 9916 Julliard Dr Bethesda MD 20817

JABLONSKI, WERNER LOUIS, b Frankfurt, Ger, May 6, 24; m 54; c 5. ORGANIC CHEMISTRY. *Educ:* Univ Toronto, BA & MA, 49; McGill Univ, PhD(org chem), 53. *Prof Exp:* Chemist, Can Indust Ltd, 49-50; chemist, Dow Chem Co, 50-69 & US Plywood Champion Papers, Inc, 69-71; CHEMIST, FOSTER GRANT, INC, 71- *Mem:* Soc Plastics Engrs; Am Chem Soc; Sigma Xi. *Res:* Polymers. *Mailing Add:* 33 Wilder Lane Fitchburg MA 01420

JACCARINO, VINCENT, b Brooklyn, NY, May 12, 24; m 65; c 2. SOLID STATE PHYSICS. *Educ:* Brooklyn Col, BS, 48; Mass Inst Technol, PhD(physics), 52. *Prof Exp:* Res assoc, Mass Inst Technol, 52-54; mem tech staff, Bell Tel Labs, 54-63, head solid state phys res dept, 63-66; chmn dept, 69-72, PROF PHYSICS, UNIV CALIF, SANTA BARBARA, 66- *Concurrent Pos:* Guggenheim Found fel, 73-74, Lady Davis fel, 79, Yamada Found fel, Japan, 80. *Mem:* Fel Am Phys Soc. *Res:* Magnetic resonance in solids; magnetism; superionic conductors; critical phenomena. *Mailing Add:* Dept of Physics Univ of Calif Santa Barbara CA 93106

JACCHIA, LUIGI GIUSEPPE, b Trieste, Italy, June 4, 10; nat US. ASTRONOMY. *Educ:* Univ Bologna, PhD(physics), 32. *Prof Exp:* From asst to instr astron, Univ Bologna, 32-38; RES ASSOC, COL OBSERV, HARVARD UNIV, 39-; physicist, Smithsonian Astrophys Observ, 56-80; RETIRED. *Concurrent Pos:* Res assoc, Mass Inst Technol, 49-53. *Mem:* Am Astron Soc; Int Astron Union; Int Union Geod & Geophys. *Res:* Variable stars; meteors; upper atmosphere; artificial satellites. *Mailing Add:* Smithsonian Inst Astrophys Observ 60 Garden St Cambridge MA 02138

JACH, JOSEPH, b SAfrica, Dec 15, 29; m 64; c 2. PHYSICAL CHEMISTRY. *Educ:* Univ Cape Town, BSc, 50, MSc, 52; Oxford Univ, PhD, 55. *Prof Exp:* Lectr chem, Univ Cape Town, 53; res assoc, Brookhaven Nat Lab, 56-63; ASSOC PROF ENG, STATE UNIV NY STONY BROOK, 63- *Res:* Solid state chemistry, particularly thermal decomposition of solids and Szillard-Challmers reactions and chemical reactivity at defect sites in solids. *Mailing Add:* Dept of Mat Sci State Univ of NY Stony Brook NY 11790

JACHE, ALBERT WILLIAM, b Manchester, NH, Nov 5, 24; m 48; c 4. INORGANIC CHEMISTRY. *Educ:* Univ NH, BS, 48, MS, 50; Univ Wash, PhD(chem), 52. *Prof Exp:* Sr chemist, Air Reduction Co, Inc, 52-53; res assoc physics, Duke Univ, 53-55; from asst prof to assoc prof chem, Agr & Mech Col Tex, 55-61; assoc res dir, Ozark Mahoning Co, 61-64; sr res assoc, Olin Mathieson Chem Corp, 64-57, sect mgr, 65-67; chmn dept chem, 67-72, dean grad sch, 72-77, assoc acad vpres health sci, 74-77, ASSOC V PRES ACAD AFFAIRS, MARQUETTE UNIV, 77- *Concurrent Pos:* Consult, Olin Corp, 67-75. *Mem:* AAAS; Am Chem Soc; NY Acad Sci; Sigma Xi. *Res:* Fluorine chemistry; halogens; nonaqueous solvent systems; environmental problems. *Mailing Add:* Marquette Univ Acad Affairs Milwaukee WI 53233

JACHIMOWICZ, FELEK, b Peznan, Poland, July 2, 47; nat US; m 71; c 2. SPECTROSCOPY, PHOTOCHEMISTRY. *Educ:* Univ Basel, Switz, dipl, 71, PhD(phys org chem), 75. *Prof Exp:* Fel phys org chem, Col Environ Sci & Forestry, State Univ NY, 78; SR RES CHEMIST, RES DIV, W R GRACE & CO, 78- *Mem:* Am Chem Soc. *Res:* Physical organic chemistry; synthetic chemistry; homogeuous catalysis; syntos chemistry; rectrial ions chemistry; analytical chemistry; spectroscopy. *Mailing Add:* W R Grace & Co 7379 Rte 32 Columbia MD 21044

JACHOWSKI, LEO ALBERT, JR, b Baltimore Co, Md, Aug 17, 18; m 41; c 4. PARASITOLOGY. *Educ:* Univ Mich, BS, 41, MS, 42; Johns Hopkins Univ, ScD, 53. *Prof Exp:* Asst zool & parasitol, Univ Mich, 42-43; res assoc parasitol & entom, Johns Hopkins Univ, 50-57, officer-in-chg, Naval Unit, US Army Trop Res Med Lab, PR, 57-59, res parasitologist, Naval Med Res Inst, 59-64; assoc prof, 64-66, asst head dept, 66-68, actg head dept, 68-70, asst head dept, 70-71, PROF ZOOL, UNIV MD, COLLEGE PARK, 66- *Concurrent Pos:* Lectr, Univ PR, 57-63; mem adv panel parasitic diseases, WHO, 64-70. *Honors & Awards:* Ashford Award, Am Soc Trop Med & Hyg, 52; Gonzalez-Martinez Award, Puerto Rican Bilharzia Comt, 59. *Mem:* Am Soc Parasitologists; Am Soc Trop Med & Hyg; Royal Soc Trop Med & Hyg. *Res:* Medical entomology; insect physiology; helminthology. *Mailing Add:* Dept of Zool Univ of Md College Park MD 20742

JACK, HULAN E, JR, b New York, NY, May 6, 35; m; c 4. PHYSICS. *Educ:* NY Univ, BS, 60, MS, 64, PhD(physics), 71. *Prof Exp:* Instr physics, NY Inst Technol, 61-66 & Eng Sch, Pratt Inst, 66-68; lectr, Wash Sq Col, NY Univ, 68-70; instr, Finch Col, 70-71; ASST PROF PHYSICS, KANS STATE UNIV, 71- *Mem:* AAAS; Am Physics Teachers; Am Phys Soc; Asn Comput Mach. *Res:* Solid state and atomic physics. *Mailing Add:* Dept of Physics Kans State Univ Manhattan KS 66502

JACK, JOHN JAMES, b Trenton, NJ, Jan 11, 43; m 67; c 2. ANALYTICAL CHEMISTRY, TECHNICAL MARKETING. *Educ:* Princeton Univ, AB, 65; Mass Inst Technol, PhD(anal chem), 71. *Prof Exp:* RES CHEMIST, & TECH MGT, PLASTIC PRODS & RESINS DEPT, E I DU PONT DE NEMOURS & CO, INC, 70- *Res:* Development of instrumental methods of analysis, especially spectroscopic, and application to industrial analytical problems; automation of laboratory testing and efficient use of newly developing mini- and micro-computers. *Mailing Add:* Concord Plaza-Talley E I Du Pont De Nemours & Co Inc Wilmington DE 19707

JACK, ROBERT CECIL MILTON, b St Vincent, WI, Oct 10, 29; Brit citizen; m 59; c 2. BIOCHEMISTRY. *Educ:* McGill Univ, BSc, 56; Columbia Univ, PhD(plant biochem), 64. *Prof Exp:* Chemist, Cent Exp Sta, WI, 58-60; asst biochemist, Boyce Thompson Inst, 64-66, assoc biochemist, 67; assoc prof, 67-76, PROF BIOL, GRAD SCH, ST JOHN'S UNIV, 76- *Mem:* Am Chem Soc; Am Oil Chem Soc; Am Soc Plant Physiol; Am Soc Microbiol; NY Acad Sci. *Res:* Lipid chemistry and metabolism; lipids; biological membranes. *Mailing Add:* Dept of Biol St John's Univ Grad Sch Jamaica NY 11432

JACK, THOMAS RICHARD, b Toronto, Ont, Mar 4, 47. PETROLEUM MICROBIOLOGY, INORGANIC CHEMISTRY. *Educ:* Univ Toronto, BSc, 69, PhD(chem), 75. *Prof Exp:* fel bioeng, Fac Eng Sci, Univ Western Ont, 75-76; vis asst prof chem, Scarborough Col, Univ Toronto, 76-77, asst prof, 77-79; petrol microbiologist, BC Res, 80-81; RES SCIENTIST, HUSKY RES CORP, DIV NOVA CORP, 81- *Concurrent Pos:* Fel, Nat Res Coun Can, 75; indust assoc, Arctic Inst North Am, Univ Calgary, 81- *Mem:* Chem Inst Can; Am Soc Microbiol; Am Chem Soc. *Res:* Interface between inorganic chemistry and microbiology; biotechnology and inorganic chemistry in energy production. *Mailing Add:* Univ Calgary 2500 Univ Dr Northwest Calgary AB T2N 1N4 Can

JACKANICZ, THEODORE MICHAEL, b Chicago, Ill, Oct 6, 38; m 62; c 1. REPRODUCTIVE ENDOCRINOLOGY. *Educ:* Northwestern Univ, BA, 59; Mich State Univ, PhD(biochem), 65. *Prof Exp:* Res fel endocrinol, Harvard Med Sch & Karolinska Inst, Sweden, 65-68; proj specialist pop, Ford Found, 69-70; staff scientist 70-74, SCIENTIST REPROD, POP COUN, NY, 74- *Concurrent Pos:* NIH fel, Harvard Med Sch, 65-67; NIH fel, Karolinska Inst, 67-68. *Mem:* Sigma Xi; AAAS; NY Acad Sci. *Res:* Reproductive endocrinology and contraceptive development with emphasis on contraceptive techniques based upon the controlled release of steroid hormones. *Mailing Add:* Pop Coun Rockefeller Univ 66 St & York Ave New York NY 10021

JACKEL, LAWRENCE DAVID, b New York, NY, June 16, 48; m 69. EXPERIMENTAL SOLID STATE PHYSICS, MICROFABRICATION. *Educ:* Brandeis Univ, BA, 69; Cornell Univ, MA, 72, PhD(exp physics), 76. *Prof Exp:* Res asst, Sch Appl & Eng Physics, Cornell Univ, 71-75, res assoc, 75; MEM TECH STAFF EXP SOLID STATE PHYSICS, BELL LABS, 75- *Mem:* Am Phys Soc. *Res:* Physics and applications of microstructures. *Mailing Add:* 4D335 Bell Labs Holmdel NJ 07733

JACKEL, SIMON SAMUEL, b New York, NY, Nov 11, 17; m 54; c 2. FOOD SCIENCE. *Educ:* City Col New York, BS, 38; Columbia Univ, AM, 47, PhD(biochem), 50. *Prof Exp:* Anal chemist, Plymouth Labs, 38-41; instr instrumentation, Air Corps Tech Training Sch, Ill, 41-43; instr chem & instrumentation, Army Air Forces Eng Officers Sch, Yale Univ, 43-44; res chemist anal chem, Fleischmann Labs, 44-47; asst biochem, Columbia Univ, 47-50; head yeast dept, Fleischmann Labs, 50-54, head fermentation div, 54-59; vpres & dir res, Vico Prod Co, 59-61; dir res & develop lab, 61-76, VPRES & DIR RES & DEVELOP, QUAL BAKERS AM COOP INC, 76- *Concurrent Pos:* Am Bakers Asn tech liaison comt, USDA, 70-; USPHS res grant, 47-50; pres, Plymouth Tech Serv, 66-; tech ed, Bakery Prod & Mkt Mag, 68-; mem sci adv comt, Am Inst Baking, 70-; mem indust adv comt, NDak State Univ, 72- *Honors & Awards:* Army Air Force Except Civilian Serv Award, 43; Wisdom Hall of Fame Award, 75; Charles N Frey Award, Am Asn Cereal Chemists, 81. *Mem:* AAAS; Am Chem Soc; Am Asn Cereal Chemists; Inst Food Technologists; fel Am Inst Chemists. *Res:* Fermentation; yeast metabolism; baking technology; nutrition; research management; new product development; regulatory affairs compliance. *Mailing Add:* 46 Kings Highway N Westport CT 06880

JACKELS, CHARLES FREDERICK, b St Paul, Minn, Nov 3, 46; m 70. QUANTUM CHEMISTRY. *Educ:* Univ Minn, Minneapolis, BChem, 68; Univ Wash, PhD(chem), 75. *Prof Exp:* Fel theoret chem, Battelle Mem Inst, 75-77; ASST PROF CHEM, WAKE FOREST UNIV, 77- *Mem:* Am Chem Soc. *Res:* Ab initio quantum chemical investigations of small molecules; potential energy surface calculations using self-consistent-field and configuration-interaction methods; applications to atmospheric chemistry. *Mailing Add:* Dept of Chem Wake Forest Univ Winston-Salem NC 27109

JACKELS, SUSAN CAROL, b Wichita, Kans, July 12, 46; m 70. INORGANIC CHEMISTRY, BIO-INORGANIC CHEMISTRY. *Educ:* Carleton Col, BA, 68; Univ Wash, PhD(inorg chem), 73. *Prof Exp:* Res biochem, Univ Wash, 73-75 & inorg chem, Ohio State Univ, 75-77; ASST PROF CHEM, WAKE FOREST UNIV, 77- *Mem:* Am Chem Soc; Sigma Xi. *Res:* Design, synthesis and study of transition metal complexes relevant to biological systems; macrocyclic complexes; electrochemistry of transition metal complexes. *Mailing Add:* Dept of Chem Wake Forest Univ Winston-Salem NC 27109

JACKINS, PAUL DAVID, b Houlton, Maine, Apr 3, 40; m 62; c 4. SYSTEMS ANALYSIS, SYSTEMS SIMULATION. *Educ:* Lafayette Col, BS, 62; Catholic Univ, MS, 70, PhD(acoustics), 81. *Prof Exp:* PHYSICIST DEVELOP & DESIGN, NAVAL SURFACE WEAPONS CTR, 64- *Mem:* Acoust Soc Am. *Res:* Investigation of the scattering of acoustical and electromagnetic waves, direct and inverse, by homogeneous and inhomogenous composites; objects having simple configurations. *Mailing Add:* Naval Surface Weapons Ctr White Oak Silver Spring MD 20910

JACKISCH, PHILIP FREDERICK, b Oshkosh, Wis, June 25, 35; m 60; c 1. ORGANIC CHEMISTRY. *Educ:* Univ Wis, BS, 57; Univ Mich, PhD(chem), 65. *Prof Exp:* Dir, Tabor Hill Vineyard & Winecellar, 71-72; PRES, INT WINE CONSULTS, 73- *Concurrent Pos:* Res chemist, Res Labs, Ethyl Corp, Mich, 64-; sci consult to wine indust, 70-; tech ed, Am Wine Soc J, 73-81. *Mem:* Am Soc Enologists; Am Chem Soc; Soc Petrol Engrs; Am Wine Soc. *Res:* Gasoline additives; lubricant additives; computer applications; enology; viticulture; sensory evaluation of foods; enhanced petroleum recovery; wine marketing. *Mailing Add:* 4218 Rosewold Royal Oak MI 48073

JACKIW, ROMAN WLADIMIR, b Lublinec, Poland, Nov 8, 39; US citizen; c 2. THEORETICAL PHYSICS, HIGH ENERGY PHYSICS. *Educ:* Swarthmore Col, AB, 61; Cornell Univ, PhD(physics), 66. *Prof Exp:* Soc Fels jr fel physics, Harvard Univ, 66-69; asst prof, 69-72, assoc prof, 72-77, PROF PHYSICS, MASS INST TECHNOL, 77- *Concurrent Pos:* Sloan Found res fel, 69-71; J S Guggenheim Mem Found fel, 77-78; consult, Los Alamos Nat Lab, 78- *Mem:* Am Phys Soc; Am Acad Arts & Sci. *Mailing Add:* Ctr for Theoret Physics Mass Inst of Technol 6-320 Cambridge MA 02139

JACKLET, JON WILLIS, b Springfield Gardens, NY, Apr 16, 35; m 62; c 3. NEUROPHYSIOLOGY, ANIMAL BEHAVIOR. *Educ:* Univ Ore, BS, 62, MA, 64, PhD(biol), 66. *Prof Exp:* USPHS res fel neurophysiol, Calif Inst Technol, 67-68; asst prof, 68-74, assoc prof, 74-80, PROF BIOL SCI, STATE UNIV NY ALBANY, 81- *Mem:* Soc Neurosci; Am Physiol Soc. *Res:* Neurophysiology of behavior; plasticity and specificity of neural organization; cellular aspects of circadian rhythms. *Mailing Add:* Dept of Biol Sci State Univ of NY Albany NY 12222

JACKLIN, STANLEY WILLIAM, entomology, see previous edition

JACKMAN, ALBERT HAVENS, b Rosedale, Kans, Feb 15, 08; m 46; c 2. PHYSICAL GEOGRAPHY. *Educ:* Princeton Univ, BS, 31; Clark Univ, PhD(geog), 53. *Prof Exp:* From asst prof to prof geog, Western Mich Univ, 62-78, head dept, 64-72; RETIRED. *Concurrent Pos:* Consult, Arctic Inst NAm, 67, vis scientist, Montreal Div, 72; mem adv bd mil personnel & supplies, Nat Acad Sci-Nat Res Coun, 69-71. *Mem:* AAAS; Am Geog Soc; Arctic Inst NAm; Asn Am Geogr; Nat Coun Geog Educ. *Res:* Development of transportation techniques and routes in Alaska and the Canadian territories, including the total impact through time of new highways on wilderness areas of these regions; geography of North American Arctic & Sub-Arctic. *Mailing Add:* Dept of Geog Western Mich Univ Kalamazoo MI 49001

JACKMAN, DONALD COE, b Cleveland, Tenn, Nov 29, 40; m 65, 81; c 3. INORGANIC CHEMISTRY, ANALYTICAL CHEMISTRY. *Educ:* Maryville Col, BS, 62; Univ Tenn, Knoxville, PhD(inorg chem), 66. *Prof Exp:* asst prof, 66-70, assoc prof inorg & anal chem, 70-80, PROF CHEM, PFEIFFER COL, 80- *Concurrent Pos:* NSF res grant, 71. *Mem:* Am Chem Soc. *Res:* Reactions of the alkali metals in liquid ammonia and liquid ethylamine at room temperature; electron exchange mechanisms in Cobalt-III and Chromium-II systems. *Mailing Add:* Dept of Chem Pfeiffer Col Misenheimer NC 28109

JACKMAN, HERBERT LEWIS, b Chicago, Ill, May 27, 47; m 74. PSYCHOPHARMACOLOGY, NEUROCHEMISTRY. *Educ:* Loyola Univ, BS, 71; Univ Ill, PhD(pharmacol), 78. *Prof Exp:* Fel, 78-82, RES ASSOC DEPT PSYCHIAT, UNIV CHICAGO, 82-; RES SCIENTIST, LAB BIOL PSYCHIAT, ILL STATE PSYCHIAT INST, 78- *Mem:* Soc Neurosci; AAAS. *Res:* Neuropsychopharmacology and the chemical and physiological foundations of normal and abnormal behavior; mechanisms of drug action, drug development, and clinical pharmacology; physiology, biochemistry and pharmacology of sleep and wakefulness. *Mailing Add:* Dept Psychiat Rm M350 Univ Chicago 950 E 59th St Chicago IL 60637

JACKMAN, LAURENCE A, b Brockton, Mass, Apr 27, 38; m 71. METALLURGY, MATERIALS SCIENCE. *Educ:* Rensselaer Polytech Inst, BS, 61, PhD(mat sci), 66. *Prof Exp:* From instr to asst prof mat eng, Rensselaer Polytech Inst, 65-73; sect leader mech metall, 71-80, CHIEF METALLURGIST, SPEC METALS CORP, 80- *Mem:* Am Soc Metals; Am Inst Mining, Metall & Petrol Engrs. *Res:* Mechanical behavior of materials. *Mailing Add:* Harts Dr New Hartford NY 13413

JACKMAN, LLOYD MILES, b Goolwa, SAustralia, Apr 1, 26; m 50; c 3. ORGANIC CHEMISTRY. *Educ:* Univ Adelaide, BSc, 45, Hons, 46, MSc, 48, PhD(chem), 51. *Prof Exp:* Beit fel, Univ London, 51-52; asst lectr chem, Imp Col, Univ London, 52-53; lectr, 53-61; reader org chem, Univ, 61-62; prof, Univ Melbourne, 62-67; PROF CHEM, PA STATE UNIV, UNIVERSITY PARK, 67- *Concurrent Pos:* Royal Commonwealth Soc bursary, 60; consult, Monsanto Co, UK & Australia, 60-67; vis prof, Iowa State Univ, 62; NSF sr foreign fel, 65; vis prof, Univ Tenn, 65; consult, Esso Res & Eng Co, 67-70 & Smith, Kline & French Labs, 67-; Guggenheim Found fel, 73; Humbold fel, 77-78. *Mem:* Am Chem Soc; The Chem Soc; fel Royal Australian Chem Inst. *Res:* Applications of nuclear magnetic resonance spectroscopy in organic chemistry; organic reactions of transition metal ligands; structures of alkali metal salts of enols; enzymology of phenylethanolamine N-methyl transferase. *Mailing Add:* 152 Davey Lab Pa State Univ University Park PA 16802

JACKMAN, THOMAS EDWARD, b Thamesville, Ont, Mar 16, 51; m 77; c 2. SURFACE SCIENCE, ION-SOLID INTERACTIONS. *Educ:* Univ Guelph, BSc, 72, MSc, 74, PhD(physics), 79. *Prof Exp:* Guest scientist, Max Planck Inst, Stuttgart, 74-75; vis fel, 80, RES OFFICER, CHALK RIVER NUCLEAR LABS, ONT, 80- *Concurrent Pos:* Res asst, Dept Physics, Univ Guelph, Ont, 76-; resident vis, Bell Labs, Murray Hill, NJ, 77-78. *Mem:* Sigma Xi; Chem Inst Can; Can Asn Physicists; Böhmische Phys Soc. *Res:* Fundamental interactions between MeV ion beams and solids and their application to investigate structural and adsorption properties of surfaces, and modification of electronic and structural properties of the bulk. *Mailing Add:* Solid State Sci Br Chalk River Nuclear Labs Chalk River ON K0J 1J0 Can

JACKNOW, JOEL, b New York, NY, Dec 15, 37. PHYSICAL CHEMISTRY. *Educ:* City Col New York, BChE, 59; Univ Utah, PhD(phys chem), 63. *Prof Exp:* Res chemist fundamental res sect, Texaco Inc, 63-65; res assoc & fel chem, Polytech Inst Brooklyn, 65-66; res assoc med sch, Tufts Univ, 66-67; sr physiologist, Bioelectronics Br, Instrumentation Lab, NASA Electronics Res Ctr, 67-68; sr staff mem, Int Res & Technol, 68-71; phys sci adminr, Environ Protection Agency, Off Planning & Eval, 71-74; sr prog mgr, Environ Qual Systs Inc, 74-75; environ & energy consult, 75-79, PROJ MGR ENVIRON CONTAMINANT EVAL, US FISH & WILDLIFE SERV, 79- *Mem:* Am Chem Soc; Am Pub Works Asn. *Res:* Sources of water publication; economic and technical analysis of environmental alternatives; strategic guidance for research study; environmental contaminant impacts on fish and wildlife. *Mailing Add:* 8110 Timber Valley Ct Dunn Loring VA 22027

JACKO, MICHAEL GEORGE, b Windsor, Ont, Oct 11, 38; m 63; c 1. PHYSICS, CHEMISTRY. *Educ:* Assumption Univ, BSc, 61; Univ Windsor, PhD(phys chem), 64. *Prof Exp:* Phys chemist, Imp Oil Res Dept, Ont, 64-66; phys chemist, 66-79, sr prin chemist, Bendix Advan Technol Ctr, 79-80, PRIN CHEMIST, BENDIX MAT CTR, BENDIX RES LABS, 81- *Concurrent Pos:* Res assoc chem, Univ Windsor, 73-74. *Mem:* Am Chem Soc; Soc Automotive Engrs; fel Am Chem Inst. *Res:* Gas kinetics; radical reactions; gas chromatography; petroleum products; polymers; thermal analysis; friction materials; functional fluids; brake wear debris studies; brake interace reactions. *Mailing Add:* Bendix Mat Ctr 20800 Civic Center Dr Southfield MI 48037

JACKOBS, JOHN JOSEPH, b Hibbing, Minn, Mar 25, 39; m 65; c 3. PHYSICAL CHEMISTRY, X-RAY CRYSTALLOGRAPHY. *Educ:* Wis State Univ, Superior, BA, 61; Iowa State Univ, MS, 64; Ariz State Univ, PhD(phys chem), 67. *Prof Exp:* Res asst chem, Case Western Reserve Univ, 67-69; asst prof physics, Heidelberg Col, 69-75; REGISTR & DIR COMPUT CTR, COE COL, 75- *Mem:* AAAS; Am Crystallog Asn; Sigma Xi. *Res:* X-ray diffraction studies of organic and small biological molecules. *Mailing Add:* Off of Registr Coe Col Cedar Rapids IA 52402

JACKOBS, JOSEPH ALDEN, b Shell Lake, Wis, Oct 23, 17; m 40; c 3. AGRONOMY. *Educ:* Univ Wis, BS, 40, MS, 43, PhD(agron), 47. *Prof Exp:* Asst agronomist, Irrig Exp Sta, State Col Wash, 46-51; assoc prof agron, 51-55, PROF CROP PROD, UNIV ILL, URBANA, 55- *Concurrent Pos:* Grass & fodder specialist, Int Coop Admin, India, 58-60, crop prod agronomist, US AID, 67-69. *Mem:* Fel AAAS; fel Am Soc Agron. *Res:* Alfalfa management, cutting treatments; legume, grass and fertility interactions; seed rotting in sweetclover caused by Pythium; genetic shifts in forage species when grown outside region of adaptation; establishment of forage species; soybean production in the tropics; grassland ecology. *Mailing Add:* Dept of Agron Univ of Ill Urbana IL 61801

JACKOVITZ, JOHN FRANKLIN, b Greensburg, Pa, Nov 9, 39; m 64; c 2. PHYSICAL INORGANIC CHEMISTRY. *Educ:* St Vincent Col, BSc, 61; Univ Notre Dame, PhD(chem), 65. *Prof Exp:* NSF vis scholar chem, Northwestern Univ, 66-67; sr scientist, 67-73, sr res scientist, 73-76, FEL SCIENTIST, WESTINGHOUSE RES & DEVELOP LABS, 76- *Prof Exp:* Res assoc, Univ Pittsburgh, 67-73. *Mem:* Soc Appl Spectros (pres, 81); Am Chem Soc; Electrochem Soc. *Res:* Chelate chemistry, infrared and Raman spectra and force fields of inorganic molecules; uranium chemistry. *Mailing Add:* Res & Develop Ctr Westinghouse Elec Co Pittsburgh PA 15235

JACKS, THOMAS JEROME, b Chicago, Ill, Jan 24, 38. BIOCHEMISTRY, PLANT PHYSIOLOGY. *Educ:* Western Reserve Univ, BS, 60, PhD, 65. *Prof Exp:* Nat Acad Sci res fel biochem, 65-67, RES LEADER, SOUTHERN REGIONAL RES CTR, USDA, 67- *Concurrent Pos:* Res staff, Tulane Univ, 74-; assoc ed, Am Oil Chemist's Soc, 75- *Mem:* Am Oil Chemist's Soc; Electron Micros Soc Am; Am Chem Soc; Am Soc Plant Physiol; AAAS. *Res:* Protein chemistry; enzymology; electron microscopy. *Mailing Add:* PO Box 19687 Southern Regional Res Ctr New Orleans LA 70179

JACKS, THOMAS MAURO, b Harrisburg, Pa, Mar 13, 41; m 69; c 2. MEDICAL MICROBIOLOGY. *Educ:* Duquesne Univ, BS, 64; Pa State Univ, MS, 66, PhD(microbiol), 68. *Prof Exp:* Asst prof biol, State Univ NY Col New Paltz, 58-59; sr researcher, Vet Microbiol Sect, Norwich Pharmacal Co, 69-80. *Concurrent Pos:* Instr, State Univ NY Agr & Tech Col Morrisville, 69-70 & 74-75. *Mem:* NY Acad Sci; Conf Res Workers Animal Diseases. *Res:* Escherichia coli pathogenicity in man and animals; bovine antibodies against Escherichia coli; role of enterotoxigenic Escherichia coli in diarrhea of new born animals. *Mailing Add:* 842 Wallberg Ave Westfield NJ 07090

JACKSON, ALBERT S(MITH), b Sylvia, Kans, Feb 2, 27; m 47; c 3. COMPUTER SCIENCE, CONTROL SYSTEMS. *Educ:* Calif Inst Technol, BS, 51, MS, 52; Cornell Univ, PhD(elec eng), 56. *Prof Exp:* Engr, Bell Tel Labs, 52; instr, Cornell Univ, 52-55; asst prof, 56-59; mgr, Data Processing & Controls Dept, Thompson-Ramo-Wooldridge Prod Co, 59-61; pres, Control Technol, Inc, 61-65; chief scientist, Milgo Electronics Corp, 65-70; pres, Opto Logic Corp, 70-75; MICROCOMPUT SYSTS ENG, MOTOROLA, INC, 75- *Concurrent Pos:* Consult, Gen Elec Co, 53-59, Gen Dynamics/Convair, 56-58 & Naval Res Lab, 57-59; lectr, Univ Calif, Irvine, 71- & Univ Calif, Los Angeles, 78- *Mem:* Inst Elec & Electronics Engrs; Inst Mgr Sci. *Res:* Analog and digital computers; feedback control system theory; application of computers to control systems; human factors research. *Mailing Add:* 9 Aldergrove Irvine CA 92714

JACKSON, ANDREW, b Preston, Eng, Dec 5, 48. TRIBOLOGY. *Educ:* Imperial Col, London Univ, BSc, 70, PhD(mech eng), 74. *Prof Exp:* Res engr, 74-76, sr res engr, 76-80, ASSOC, CENT RES DIV, MOBIL RES & DEVELOP CORP, PRINCETON, NJ, 80- *Honors & Awards:* Hunt Award, Am Soc Lubrication Engrs, 77, Hodson Award, 82. *Mem:* Am Soc Lubrication Engrs; Am Soc Mech Engrs; Inst Mech Engrs. *Res:* Lubrication science (tribology); elastohydrodynamic lubrication; traction; rolling contact fatigue; internal combustion engine lubrication. *Mailing Add:* 22 Alta Vista Dr Princeton NJ 08540

JACKSON, ANDREW D, JR, b Orange, NJ, Dec 20, 41; m 66. THEORETICAL NUCLEAR PHYSICS. *Educ:* Princeton Univ, AB, 63, MA, 65, PhD(physics), 67. *Prof Exp:* Res assoc physics, Princeton Univ, 67; NATO res fel, Univ Sussex, 67-68; from asst prof to assoc prof, 68-76, PROF PHYSICS, STATE UNIV NY STONY BROOK, 76- *Concurrent Pos:* Alfred P Sloane Found fel, 71-72. *Mem:* Am Phys Soc. *Res:* Nucleon-nucleon interaction and nuclear structure calculations. *Mailing Add:* Dept of Physics State Univ of NY Stony Brook NY 11790

JACKSON, ANDREW OTIS, b Enterprise, Ala, Apr 14, 41. PLANT VIROLOGY. *Educ:* Okla State Univ, BS, 64, MS, 67; Univ Man, PhD(plant path), 70. *Prof Exp:* Fel plant virol, Dept Agr Biochem, Univ Ariz & Dept Plant Path, Univ Nebr, 70-73; asst prof, 73-77, ASSOC PROF PLANT VIROL, PURDUE UNIV, 77- *Mem:* Am Phytopathological Soc; AAAS; Sigma Xi; Soc Gen Microbiol. *Mailing Add:* Dept of Bot & Plant Path Purdue Univ West Lafayette IN 47907

JACKSON, ANNE LOUISE, b Watertown, NY. IMMUNOLOGY. *Educ:* Cornell Univ, BS, 56; Univ Mich, MS, 57, PhD(microbiol), 63. *Prof Exp:* Res assoc biochem, Univ Mich, 61-63; asst prof microbiol, Sch Med & Dent, Georgetown Univ, 63-68; dir tech serv, Meloy Labs, 68-74; dir res immunol, Kent Labs, 74-77; mem staff, Dept Microbiol, Univ BC, 77-80; MGR TECH SERV, BECTON DICKINSON MONOCLONAL CTR, 80- *Concurrent Pos:* Guest worker, Lab Immunol, Nat Inst Allergy & Infectious Dis, NIH, 63-65; asst guest prof, Univ BC, 75- *Mem:* Am Asn Immunol; Fedn Am Socs Exp Biol; Can Asn Immunol; Am Fedn Clin Res. *Res:* Production and development of immunologic tests for in vitro diagnostics. *Mailing Add:* 506 Clyde Ave Becton Dickinson & Co Mountain View CA 94043

JACKSON, BENJAMIN A, b Hillburn, NY, July 8, 29; m 55; c 4. TOXICOLOGY. *Educ:* NY State Col Teachers, Albany, BA, 50; Rensselaer Polytech Inst, MS, 51; NY Univ, PhD(biol), 57; Fairleigh Dickinson Univ, MBA, 78. *Prof Exp:* Res biologist, Am Cyanamid Co, 51-67; electron microscopist, Toxicol Dept, Sterling-Winthrop Res Inst, 67-69; sr res toxicologist, Reproductive Safety Eval Group, Toxicol Res, Lederle Labs, Am Cyanamid Co, 69-75, mgr Teratology & Mutagenicity, Toxicol Sect, 75-78; supvr, petitions reviewers, 78-80, CHIEF, COLOR & COSMETIC EVAL BR, BUR FOODS, FOOD & DRUG ADMIN, 80- *Concurrent Pos:* Res assoc, Cornell Med Col, 64-65; adj asst prof pharmacol & toxicol, Howard Univ, 80- *Mem:* Soc Toxicol; Teratology Soc; Environ Mutagen Soc; Soc Pharmacol & Environ Path. *Res:* Experimental liver tumors; short term effects of drugs; mitotic activity; drug toxicity; quantitation of morphological changes; electron microscopy; teratology; mutagenicity; correlation between mutagenicity and carcinogenic potential of drugs; regulatory toxicology; color additive toxicology; cosmetic ingredients safety evaluation. *Mailing Add:* Bur Foods Food & Drug Admin HFF 158 200 C St SW Washington DC 20204

JACKSON, BENJAMIN T, b Jacksonville, Fla, Apr 28, 29; m 53; c 4. SURGERY, PHYSIOLOGY. *Educ:* Duke Univ, MD, 54. *Prof Exp:* Intern med, Duke Univ Hosp, 54-55; asst resident surg, Univ Minn Hosps, 57-58; resident, Med Col Va, 58-62, instr, 63-64; from asst prof to prof surg, Sch Med, Boston Univ, 64-80; PROF SURG, PROG MED, BROWN UNIV, 80- *Concurrent Pos:* USPHS res fel, Med Col Va, 58-62; Am Heart Asn advan res fel, 61-63; estab investr, Am Heart Asn, 63-68; asst chief surg serv, Boston Vet Admin Hosp, 74-80; chief surg serv, Providence Vet Admin Med Ctr, 80. *Mem:* Soc Gynec Invest; Am Fedn Clin Res; Am Soc Exp Path; Soc Univ Surg; Am Col Surg. *Res:* Fetal cardiovascular and endocrine physiology; pathophysiology of congenital cardiovascular anomalies; fetal hematologic development. *Mailing Add:* 11 October Ln Weston MA 02193

JACKSON, CAREY BIRDSONG, b Meridian, Miss, July 4, 07; m 35; c 1. INORGANIC CHEMISTRY. *Educ:* Miss State Col, BS, 28; George Washington Univ, MS, 29; Johns Hopkins Univ, PhD(phys chem), 34. *Prof Exp:* Instr chem, George Washington Univ, 29-31; chemist, Carbon Monoxide Eliminator Corp, 31-34; res chemist, Armour & Co, Ill, 34-35, Catalyst Res Corp, Pa, 35-36 & Mine Safety Appliance Co, 36 & 48; dir res, Callery Chem Co, 48-57; vpres & dir res, MSA Res Corp, 57-60; assoc dir res, Burke Res Corp, 60-62; pres, Beach Chem Co, 62-64; ADJ PROF CHEM, FLA ATLANTIC UNIV, 64- *Honors & Awards:* Distinguished Pub Serv Award, US Navy, 46. *Mem:* Am Chem Soc; Am Soc Naval Engrs; Am Inst Chemists. *Res:* Catalysts; hydrogenation of fats; self contained re-breathers; alkali metals; peroxides; superoxides; liquid metal heat transfer; boron chemistry. *Mailing Add:* 471 SE 16th Ave Pompano Beach FL 33060

JACKSON, CARL WAYNE, b Carbondale, Ill, Nov 27, 42; m 63. EXPERIMENTAL HEMATOLOGY, RADIATION BIOLOGY. *Educ:* Southern Ill Univ, BA, 63; Univ Tenn, Knoxville, PhD(radiation biol), 71. *Prof Exp:* Biol lab specialist physiol, Oak Ridge Nat Lab, 63-71; Nat Cancer Inst traineeship fel hemat, 71-73, res assoc, 73-75, asst mem, 76-80, ASSOC MEM, ST JUDE CHILDREN'S RES HOSP, 80- *Mem:* Am Soc Hemat; Int Soc Exp Hemat. *Res:* Hemopoiesis; thrombopoiesis; cell kinetics; cell regulation and differentiation; radiation hematology; assay of megakaryocytopoiesis; megakaryocytopoieses; microspectrophotometry; identification of megakaryocyte precursors. *Mailing Add:* St Jude Children's Res Hosp 332 N Lauderdale Memphis TN 38101

JACKSON, CARLTON DARNELL, b Wiggins, Miss, Dec 1, 38; m 58; c 2. BIOCHEMISTRY, ONCOLOGY. *Educ:* Miss Col, BS, 61; Univ Tenn, MS, 63, PhD(biochem), 67. *Prof Exp:* Res trainee biochem, St Jude Children's Res Hosp, 64-67; USPHS fel, Univ Miami, 67-69; asst prof biochem, Univ Tenn, 69-72; res chemist carcinogenesis, 72-75, CHIEF, DIV CARCINOGENIC RES, NAT CTR TOXICOL RES, FOOD & DRUG ADMIN, 76-; ASSOC PROF BIOCHEM, MED SCH, UNIV ARK, LITTLE ROCK, 72- *Concurrent Pos:* Res biochemist carcinogenesis, Vet Admin Hosp, Memphis, 69-72; pharmacologist, Off Sci Intel, Nat Ctr Toxicol Res, Div Mollecular Biol, 81- *Mem:* Am Asn Cancer Res; Sigma Xi. *Res:* Mechanisms of chemical carcinogenesis; molecular mechanism of hormone action; protein and nucleic acid synthesis; molecular biology of cell division and differentiation. *Mailing Add:* Nat Ctr Toxicol Res Food & Drug Admin Jefferson AR 72079

JACKSON, CARMAULT B, JR, b Newton, Mass, Apr 19, 24; m 47; c 3. INTERNAL MEDICINE, HEMATOLOGY. *Educ:* Bucknell Univ, BS, 48; Univ Pa, MD, 52. *Prof Exp:* Mem, Proj Mercury, NASA Space Task Group, 58-61; pvt prac internal med, San Antonio, Tex, 61-76; assoc dir extramural progs, Univ Tex Syst, 77-79; EXEC VPRES & ADMIN, METROPOLITAN MED CTR, SAN ANTONIO, TEX, 79- *Concurrent Pos:* Mem bd, Tex Inst Med Assessment, 76-80, pres, 80-81. *Mem:* Inst Med Nat Acad Sci; Am Cancer Soc. *Res:* Cancer control information and technology dissemination. *Mailing Add:* 1310 McCullough Ave San Antonio TX 78212

JACKSON, CHARLES RICHARD, b Gary, Ind, Feb 19, 35; m 59; c 4. CHEMICAL ENGINEERING, METALLURGICAL ENGINEERING. *Educ:* Purdue Univ, BS, 58, MS, 60. *Prof Exp:* Res engr coal, 59-65, res engr casting, 65-69, asst supt operating, 69-75, RES CONSULT, INLAND STEEL CO, 75- *Mem:* Am Inst Mining, Metall & Petrol Engrs. *Res:* Coal beneficiation; coal carbonization; fluid transport; modeling theory continuous casting; plant design. *Mailing Add:* 3001 E Columbus Dr East Chicago IN 46312

JACKSON, CLARENCE E(VERT), b Graceville, Minn, Sept 4, 06; m 36; c 3. METALLURGY, WELDING ENGINEERING. *Educ:* Carleton Col, BA, 27. *Prof Exp:* Instr, pub sch, SDak, 27-30; jr metallurgist, Nat Bur Standards, 30-37; asst metallurgist, US Naval Gun Factory, 37-38; metallurgist & head welding sect, Naval Res Lab, 38-46; res metallurgist & mgr welding res group, Metals Res Labs, 46-57; assoc mgr elec welding, Newark Develop Lab, Linde Co Div, Union Carbide Corp, 57-64; from assoc prof to prof, 64-77, EMER PROF WELDING ENG, OHIO STATE UNIV, 77- *Concurrent Pos:* Mem Welding Res Coun & World Metall Cong, 48 & 57; US deleg, Int Inst Welding, var countries, 60-79; consult, 65- *Honors & Awards:* Miller Medal, Am Welding Soc, 55, Thomas Mem Award, 76. *Mem:* Am Welding Soc (vpres, 60, pres, 63-64); Am Soc Metals; Am Inst Mining, Metall & Petrol Engrs; hon fel Brit Inst Welding; hon mem Australian Welding Inst. *Res:* Physics and metallurgy of welding. *Mailing Add:* Dept of Welding Eng 190 W 19th Ave Columbus OH 43210

JACKSON, CRAIG MERTON, b Staples, Minn, Dec 2, 41; m 62; c 1. BIOCHEMISTRY. *Educ:* Wash State Univ, BS, 63; Univ Wash, PhD(biochem), 67. *Prof Exp:* Res assoc, Col Med, Univ Ariz, 67; Am Cancer Soc fel chem physics, Unilever Res Lab, Port Sunlight, Eng, 67-69; asst prof, 69-74, assoc prof, 74-77, PROF BIOL CHEM, SCH MED, WASH UNIV, 77- *Concurrent Pos:* Res grants, Nat Heart, Lung & Blood Inst; res reviewer, Am Heart Asn, 71-74, estab investr, 74-79, chmn, Int Comt Thrombosis, 82-84; mem coun thrombosis, Am Heart Asn, 71-, estab investr, 74-79. *Mem:* AAAS; Int Soc Thrombosis & Hemostasis; Nat Heart, Lung & Blood Inst; Am Chem Soc; Am Heart Asn. *Res:* Protein chemistry of blood coagulation, lipid-protein interactions in blood coagulation; physical chemistry of lipids; surface and interfacial chemistry of biological systems. *Mailing Add:* Dept of Biol Chem Wash Univ Sch of Med St Louis MO 63110

JACKSON, CRAWFORD GARDNER, JR, b Birmingham, Ala, Jan 5, 31; m 65; c 1. VERTEBRATE BIOLOGY, PALEONTOLOGY. *Educ:* Emory Univ, AB, 52; Univ Fla, MS, 59, PhD(biol), 64. *Prof Exp:* Instr biol, Armstrong Col, 52-53; asst prof, Univ S Ala, 65-67; assoc prof, Col Women, Miss State, 67-69, prof, 70-74; managing ed, Ecology & Ecol Monogram, 74-78; cur & actg dir, San Diego Natural Hist Mus, 78-80; PROF, DEPT BASIC & APPL SCI, NAT UNIV, 80- *Concurrent Pos:* Vis lectr, San Diego State Col, 70-71; ed-in-chief, Herpetologica, 73-79; adj prof biol, San Diego State Univ, 74-79; res assoc, Smithsonian Inst, 74- & San Diego Natural Hist Mus, 75; lectr, Sch Med & Continuing Educ, Univ Calif, San Diego, 77- *Mem:* Herpet League; Paleont Soc; Sigma Xi; Biometric Soc; Am Soc Ichthyologists & Herpetologists. *Res:* Ecology, morphology, ethology, pathobiology of amphibians and reptiles; paleobiology of reptiles and mammals. *Mailing Add:* Basic & Appl Sci Nat Univ San Diego CA 92108

JACKSON, CURTIS M(AITLAND), b New York, NY, Apr 20, 33; m 57; c 2. METALLURGY. *Educ:* NY Univ, BMetE, 54; Ohio State Univ, MS, 59, PhD(metall), 66. *Prof Exp:* Prin metallurgist, Alloy Develop Div, 54-61, proj leader, Specialty Alloys Div, 61-67, assoc chief, 67-70, assoc chief, Nonferrous Metall Div, 70-73, ASSOC MGR PHYS & APPL METALL, COLUMBUS LABS, BATTELLE MEM INST, 73- *Concurrent Pos:* Dir, Wire J, 73-78 & Wire Found, 74- *Honors & Awards:* IR-100 Award, Indust Res Mag, 76; Mordica Mem Award, Wire Asn Int, 77, J Edward Donnellan Award, 78. *Mem:* Am Inst Mining, Metall & Petrol Engrs; Am Soc Metals; Am Vacuum Soc; Wire Asn Int (second vpres, 73-74, first vpres, 74-76, pres, 76-77). *Res:* Physical metallurgy; alloy development; nucleation and growth of thin films; technical economics; Nitinol alloys; metal failure analysis; electrical and electronic alloys; melting, casting and mechanical working of metals; wire technology. *Mailing Add:* Battelle-Columbus 505 King Ave Columbus OH 43201

JACKSON, CURTIS RUKES, b Kansas City, Mo, July 25, 27; m 51; c 6. RESEARCH MANAGEMENT, FOREIGN AGRICULTURAL DEVELOPMENT. *Educ:* Univ Miami, BS, 49; Fla State Univ, MS, 51; Univ Fla, PhD(plant path), 58. *Prof Exp:* Asst plant pathologist, Gulf Coast Exp Sta, 58-61; head plant path, Ga Coastal Plain Exp Sta, 61-68; asst dir, 68-73, RESIDENT DIR, AGR EXP STA, UNIV GA, 68-, ASSOC DIR, 73- *Concurrent Pos:* Res award, Nat Peanut Coun; consult foreign agr develop proj, Indust & Govt, 80- *Mem:* Am Phytopath Soc. *Res:* Diseases of peanuts; vegetables and ornamental plants; soil microbiology; tropical agricultural development. *Mailing Add:* Univ of Ga Col of Agr Ga Sta Experiment GA 30212

JACKSON, DALE LATHAM, b Eng, May 20, 32; m 59; c 1. ZOOLOGY. *Educ:* Univ Durham, BSc, 55, PhD(entom), 59. *Prof Exp:* Asst prof zool, Univ Guelph, 59-61; from asst prof to assoc prof, 61-69, PROF BIOL, UNIV AKRON, 69-, HEAD DEPT, 68- *Mem:* Entom Soc Can; fel Royal Entom Soc London; Soc Syst Zool. *Res:* Host relationships and taxonomy of proctotrupoidea experimental taxonomy. *Mailing Add:* Dept of Biol Univ of Akron Akron OH 44325

JACKSON, DANIEL FRANCIS, b Pittsburgh, Pa, June 11, 25; m 51. LIMNOLOGY. *Educ:* Univ Pittsburgh, BS, 49, MS, 50; State Univ NY, PhD(fisheries, wildlife), 57. *Prof Exp:* Lectr biol, Univ Pittsburgh, 49-51; asst prof, Col of Steubenville, 51-52; hydrologist, US Army Corps Engrs, Pa, 52-53; asst col forestry, State Univ NY, 53-55; asst prof, Western Mich Univ, 55-59; from asst prof to assoc prof, Univ Louisville, 59-63; prof limnol, Syracuse Univ, 63-73, 73-78; DIR & PROF ENVIRON & URBAN SYSTS, SCH TECHNOL, FLA INT UNIV, 78-; MEM STAFF, JACKSON & JACKSON ASSOC, 78- *Concurrent Pos:* Dir, C C Adams Ctr, 55-59; dir, Drinking Water Quual Res Ctr, Fla Int Univ, 76-78. *Mem:* Am Soc Limnol & Oceanog; Ecol Soc Am; Am Micros Soc; Am Fisheries Soc; Int Asn Theoret & Appl Limnol. *Res:* Limnology, primary productivity; aquatic physiology, plankton and radiation ecology; pollution. *Mailing Add:* 3323 Guilford Ct Naples FL 33942

JACKSON, DARRYL DEAN, b Lexington, Okla, 1932; m 59; c 2. CHEMICAL INSTRUMENTATION. *Educ:* Univ Okla, BS, 55, MS, 56; Univ NMex, PhD(radiochem), 68. *Prof Exp:* STAFF MEM, LOS ALAMOS NAT LAB, 56- *Mem:* AAAS; Am Inst Chemists; Am Chem Soc; Sigma Xi. *Res:* Structure of optically active inorganic complexes; chemistry of solutions of carrier-free iodine-131; radiochemistry of transuranium elements and fission products; development of automated instruments for chemical analysis. *Mailing Add:* Box 1663 Los Alamos NM 87544

JACKSON, DAVID ARCHER, b New York, NY, Apr 29, 42; m 66. MOLECULAR BIOLOGY, VIROLOGY. *Educ:* Harvard Univ, AB, 64; Stanford Univ, PhD(molecular biol), 69. *Prof Exp:* USPHS fel, Med Sch, Stanford Univ, 69-70, Nat Cystic Fibrosis Res Found basic sci fel, 70-72; asst prof microbiol, Univ Mich, Ann Arbor, 72-76, assoc prof, 77-81; CHMN, SCI ADV BD, GENEX CORP, ROCKVILLE, MD, 77-, VPRES & SCI DIR, 80- *Concurrent Pos:* Consult, President's Comn for Study Ethical Probs in Med, Biomed, & Behav Res 81-; mem, Ad Hoc Comt on Nat Issues in Genetic Eng, NSF, 81-; mem, Adv Panel Comp Assessment Develop Biotechnol, Off Technol Assessment, 81-; adj prof appl molecular biol, Univ Md Baltimore County, 81- *Mem:* Am Soc Microbiol; Genetic Soc Am ; Asn Res Dirs. *Res:* Molecular biology of mammalian cells and their viruses; enzymes acting on nucleic acids. *Mailing Add:* Genex Corp Labs Gaithersburg MD 20877

JACKSON, DAVID DIETHER, b San Francisco, Calif, Sept 18, 43; m 68. GEOPHYSICS. *Educ:* Calif Inst Technol, BS, 65; Mass Inst Technol, PhD(geophys), 69. *Prof Exp:* Assoc prof, 69-80, PROF GEOPHYS, UNIV CALIF, LOS ANGELES, 80- *Concurrent Pos:* Mem, US Nat Comt Seismol, Panel on Crustal Movement Measurements & Comt Geodesy/Seismol; sr resident res associateship, Nat Acad Sci/Nat Res Coun, 81. *Mem:* AAAS; Am Geophys Union; Seismol Soc Am. *Res:* Seismology; solid earth geophysics; geophysical inverse problems; applications of solid state physics to geophysics; earthquake prediction and control. *Mailing Add:* Dept Geophys & Space Physics Univ Calif Los Angeles CA 90024

JACKSON, DAVID PHILLIP, b Toronto, Ont, Oct 2, 40; m 75; c 2. MATHEMATICAL PHYSICS. *Educ:* Univ Toronto, BSc, 62, MA, 64, MASc, 66, PhD(eng physics), 68. *Prof Exp:* Mathematician, IBM, Toronto, 62-63; res asst, Inst Aerospace Studies, Toronto, 65-68; asst res officer, 68-70, assoc, 70-80, SR RES OFFICER, ATOMIC ENERGY CAN LTD, 81- *Concurrent Pos:* Vis scientist, Max-Plank Inst for Plasmaphysics, 75-76; assoc prof eng physics, McMaster Univ, 78-81, mem staff, Inst Mat Res, 79-, mem staff, Inst Energy Studies, 80-, prof, 81-; vis prof, Bell Labs, Murray Hill, 81- *Mem:* Chem Inst Can; Can Asn Physicists; Am Phys Soc. *Res:* Mathematical modeling of particle-surface and particle-solid interactions; the wall problem in fusion reactors. *Mailing Add:* Atomic Energy Can Ltd Chalk River ON K0J 1J0 Can

JACKSON, DONALD CARGILL, b Philadelphia, Pa, May 4, 37. PHYSIOLOGY. *Educ:* Geneva Col, BS, 59; Univ Pa, PhD(physiol), 63. *Prof Exp:* Res asst physiol, John B Pierce Lab, Conn, 61-63; res asst, Duke Univ, 63-65; res fel physiol, Sch Med, Univ Pa, 65-68, asst prof, 68-73; assoc prof, 73-79, PROF MED SCI, BROWN UNIV, 79- *Concurrent Pos:* Pa Plan scholar, 68-71. *Mem:* AAAS; Am Soc Zool; Am Physiol Soc. *Res:* Respiratory control in reptiles. *Mailing Add:* Div of Biol & Med Brown Univ Box G Providence RI 02906

JACKSON, DUDLEY PENNINGTON, b Roanoke, Va, Apr 1, 24; m 48. MEDICINE, HEMATOLOGY. *Educ:* Johns Hopkins Univ, MD, 47. *Prof Exp:* Asst med, Sch Med, Johns Hopkins Univ, 48-49 & 51-52, USPHS res fel hemat, 52-54, from instr to prof, 54-72; PROF MED & CHMN DEPT, SCH MED, GEORGETOWN UNIV, 72-, PHYSICIAN IN CHIEF, HOSP, 72- *Concurrent Pos:* Intern, Osler Med Serv, Johns Hopkins Hosp, 47-48, asst resident physician, 48-49 & 51-52, asst physician, 52-53, physician, Hemat Clin, 53-72; Markle scholar med sci, 54-59; mem coun on circulation & coun on thrombosis, Am Heart Asn. *Mem:* Am Physiol Soc; fel Am Col Physicians; Am Soc Hemat; Am Soc Clin Invest; Asn Am Physicians. *Res:* Blood coagulation. *Mailing Add:* Georgetown Univ Hosp 3800 Reservoir Rd NW Washington DC 20007

JACKSON, EARL GRAVES, b Springfield, Mass, Mar 27, 20; m 43; c 3. PHYSICAL CHEMISTRY. *Educ:* Am Int Col, BS, 42; Clark Univ, AM, 43; Rutgers Univ, PhD(chem), 51. *Prof Exp:* Chemist, Merck & Co, 46-48; lubricants specialist, Gen Elec Co, 51-55, supvr bearings, lubrication & seals develop, 55-60; sr phys chemist, Nat Res Corp, Cambridge, 60-62 & United Shoe Mach Corp, 62-69; dir chem physics lab, Res Div, USM Corp, Mass, 69-73, head adhesives sect, Lexington Res Lab, 73-79, MGR ADMIN, KENDALL CO, 80- *Concurrent Pos:* Mem subcomt lubrication & wear, Nat Adv Comt Aeronaut, 56-58. *Mem:* AAAS. *Res:* Physical chemistry of polymeric soaps; properties and mechanisms of lubricating greases; high temperature lubrication and fatigue; structural sealants; shoe technology; pressure sensitive adhesives and tapes. *Mailing Add:* Lexington Res Lab Kendall Co 17 Hartwell Ave Lexington MA 02173

JACKSON, EARL KENNETH, b Provo, Utah, Mar 17, 39; m 62; c 4. PLANT PHYSIOLOGY. *Educ:* Brigham Young Univ, BA, 63; Ore State Univ, PhD(plant physiol), 66. *Prof Exp:* Res assoc, Cent Res Dept, E I du Pont de Nemours & Co, 66-68; plant physiologist, Univ Del, 68-69; plant physiologist, Shell Develop Co, 69-75; SR PLANT PHYSIOLOGIST, LILLY RES LABS, 75- *Mem:* Am Soc Plant Physiologists; Plant Growth Regulation Soc Am. *Res:* Plant growth regulator research and development. *Mailing Add:* Lilly Res Labs PO Box 708 Greenfield IN 46140

JACKSON, EARL ROGER, b Madison, Ind, Aug 6, 30; m 51; c 1. FOOD CHEMISTRY. *Educ:* Hanover Col, AB, 52. *Prof Exp:* Chemist, Am Can Co, 52-57; chemist, Heekin Can Co, 58-64, asst res dir, 64-77, VPRES & DIR RES, HEEKIN CAN DIV, DIAMOND INT CORP, 78- *Mem:* Inst Food Technologists; Am Soc Brewing Chemists; Soc Soft Drink Technologists. *Mailing Add:* Heerin Can Div Diamond Int Corp 8200 Bradwell Rd Cincinnati OH 45244

JACKSON, EDWARD MILTON, b Wheeling, WVa, June 4, 38; m 76. CELL PHYSIOLOGY, BIOCHEMISTRY. *Educ:* Cath Univ Am, BA, 61; MS, 64; PhD(biol), 73. *Prof Exp:* Chmn sci dept, Marist Prep Sch, 65-70; teaching asst, Cath Univ Am, 70-73; assoc prof, Northern Va Community Col, 74-77; TOXICOLOGIST, NOXELL CORP, 77- *Concurrent Pos:* Instr, Trinity Col, 72-73; fel dept path, Sinai Hosp, Baltimore, 73-74; NSF training grant, 68. *Mem:* AAAS; Am Chem Soc; Sigma Xi; Am Col Toxicol. *Res:* Interaction of polychlorinated biphenyls in host mediated systems; qualitative and quantitative structural analysis of lysosomes; cellular and molecular events of inflammation. *Mailing Add:* Noxell Corp PO Box 1799 Baltimore MD 21203

JACKSON, EDWIN ATLEE, b Lyons, NY, Apr 18, 31; m 54; c 2. PHYSICS. *Educ:* Syracuse Univ, BS, 53, MS, 55, PhD(physics), 58. *Prof Exp:* Asst, Syracuse Univ, 54-57; asst & instr, Brandeis Univ, 57-58; Nat Acad Sci res assoc, Air Res & Develop Command, Air Force Cambridge Res Ctr, Mass, 58-59; staff mem, Proj Matterhorn, Princeton Univ, 59-61; asst prof, 61-63, assoc prof physics & mech eng, 63-77, PROF PHYSICS, UNIV ILL, URBANA, 77- *Concurrent Pos:* Vis sr physicist, Found Fundamental Res Matter, Inst Plasma-Physics, Netherlands, 67-68; vis mem staff, Los Alamos Sci Lab, 71; mem adv bd, Physica D: Nonlinear Phenomena, 80- *Mem:* Am Phys Soc. *Res:* Nonlinear dynamics; plasma physics; kinetic theory of gases. *Mailing Add:* Dept Physics Univ Ill Urbana IL 61801

JACKSON, ELIZABETH BURGER, b Clay, WVa, Oct 20, 14; m 62. BIOLOGY, CHEMISTRY. *Educ:* Col William & Mary, BS, 34, MA, 35; Univ Va, DEd, 60. *Prof Exp:* prof natural sci, 40-80, EMER PROF NATURAL SCI, LONGWOOD COL, 80- *Concurrent Pos:* Res grant, Univ Ctr, Univ Va, 58-59. *Mem:* AAAS; Nat Sci Teachers Asn. *Res:* Science education through commercial television; science for elementary schools. *Mailing Add:* Dept of Natural Sci Longwood Col Farmville VA 23901

JACKSON, ERNEST BAKER, b Bicknell, Utah, Mar 31, 14; m 43; c 8. AGRONOMY, BOTANY. *Educ:* Brigham Young Univ, BSc, 46; Univ Nebr, MSc, 54, PhD(agron), 56. *Prof Exp:* Pub sch teacher, Utah, 35-42, prin, 47-51; soils technologist, Bur Reclamation, Colo, 46-47; Fling Asst, Univ Nebr, 52-55, asst agronomist, 55-58; from asst agronomist to assoc agronomist, 58-71, prof agron & agronomist, Agr Exp Sta, 71-76, PROF PLANT SCI & RES SCIENTIST, UNIV ARIZ, 76- *Mem:* Am Soc Agron. *Res:* Forage crops. *Mailing Add:* Univ of Ariz Agr Exp Sta 6425 W 8th St Yuma AZ 85364

JACKSON, ETHEL NOLAND, b Geneva, NY, Apr 27, 44; m 66. MOLECULAR BIOLOGY, RECOMBINANT DNA METHODOLOGY. *Educ:* Harvard Univ, BA, 66; Stanford Univ, PhD(biol sci), 73. *Prof Exp:* Fel biochem genetics, Dept Human Genetics, Sch Med, Univ Mich, 72-74, asst prof microbiol, 74-81; RES DIR, VECTORS DEPT, GENEX CO, 81- *Concurrent Pos:* Am Cancer Soc fel, 74. *Mem:* Am Soc Microbiol; Genetics Soc Am; AAAS; Am Women Sci. *Res:* Biological regulatory mechanisms and biochemical genetics of bacterial viruses; chromosome structure of viruses; viral DNA packaging; vector systems for gene cloning in gram-positive bacteria; protein secretion by prokaryotes. *Mailing Add:* Genex Co 16020 Industrial Dr Gaithersburg MD 20760

JACKSON, EUGENE BERNARD, b Frankfort, Ind, June 18, 15; m 41. INFORMATION SCIENCE, INDUSTRIAL INFORMATION SYSTEMS. *Educ:* Purdue Univ, BSc, 37; Univ Ill, BSLS, 38, MALS, 42. *Prof Exp:* Jr prof asst, Eng Libr, Univ Ill, 38-40, asst in chg newspaper div, Libr, 40-41; doc librn, Univ Ala, 41-42; prof asst, Detroit Pub Libr, 42-46; chief libr sect, Cent Air Doc Off, Army-Navy-Air Force, 46-49; chief res info div, Off Qm Gen, US Dept Army, 49; chief div res info, Nat Adv Comt Aeronaut, 49-56; head libr dept, Gen Motors Res Labs, 56-65; dir info retrieval & libr serv, IBM Corp, 65-71; PROF LIBR SCI, UNIV TEX, AUSTIN, 71-

Concurrent Pos: Chief, Wright Field Ref Libr, 46-49; US mem doc comt, Adv Group Aeronaut Res & Develop, NATO, Paris, 52-57; McBee lectr, Simmons Col, 55; mem, Kresge-Hooker Sci Libr Assocs, Wayne State Univ, 57-65, pres, 64-65; vis lectr, Simmons Col, 65; mem exec bd, US Nat Comt Int Fedn Doc, 65-70, chmn, 70-72; vpres, Eng Index, Inc, 68-69, pres, 69-73, secy, 75-77; vis lectr, Kans State Teachers Col, 70; Lincoln lectr, Bus Sch, Ariz State Univ, 70; proj leader, Centralized Processing Med Libr Res Proj, 71-72; ed, Spec Librarianship, New Reader, 80. *Mem:* Am Inst Aeronaut & Astronaut; Spec Libr Asn (pres, 61-62); Am Soc Info Sci; Am Rec Mgt Asn. *Res:* Analysis and use of scientific literature by and for physical scientists; application of conventional and nonconventional information retrieval procedures to scientific information problems; industrial information systems. *Mailing Add:* Univ of Tex PO Box 7576 Austin TX 78712

JACKSON, EVERETT DALE, geology, see previous edition

JACKSON, FRANCIS CHARLES, b Rutherford, NJ, Sept 2, 17; m 49; c 4. MEDICINE. *Educ:* Yale Univ, AB, 39; Univ Va, MD, 43. *Prof Exp:* Intern surg, New York Hosp, Cornell Med Ctr, 44, asst resident surgeon, 44-45 & 47-49; asst anat, Med Col, Cornell Univ, 46, instr surg, 50; chief surgeon & consult, Arabian-Am Oil Co, 51; asst chief surgeon, Vet Admin Ctr, Maine, 52; from asst prof to prof surg, Sch Med, Univ Pittsburgh, 53-70; dir surg serv, 70-72, dir emergency & disaster med serv staff, Vet Admin Cent Off, 72-75; chmn, Dept Surg, 75-80, PROF SURG, SCH MED, TEX TECH UNIV, 75-, ASSOC DEAN CLIN EDUC, 80-; MED DIR, SOUTH PLAINS EMERGENCY MED SERV SYSTS, 79- *Concurrent Pos:* Asst, Med Col, Cornell Univ, 45-49; chief resident surgeon, New York Hosp, Cornell Med Ctr, 50; chief surgeon, Vet Admin Hosp, 52-70; consult staff, Presby Univ Hosp, Pittsburgh, 59-70; mem ad hoc adv group emergency health serv, Bur Health Serv, USPHS, 67-75; chief surv teams, USPHS, 68-69; mem review comn, Vet Admin Res & Educ Trainee Progs, 68-70; consult & mem med surv team, Westinghouse Corp Proj New Generation Mil Hosps, 69-70; consult, Off Emergency Planning, 69-71; co-med dir & consult, Ctr Western Pa Health Res & Develop, Carnegie-Mellon Univ, 69-72; clin prof surg, Sch Med, Georgetown Univ, 70-75; mem surg adv group, Food & Drug Admin, 71-76; mem & vchmn comt emergency med serv, Nat Acad Sci-Nat Res Coun; mem, President's Comn Study Med Aspects of Los Angeles Earthquake, 71; clin prof surg, Sch Med, George Washington Univ, 71-75; mem ad hoc comt emergency med serv commun, Off Telecommun Policy, 73-74; mem interdept comt emergency med serv, Dept Health, Educ & Welfare, 73-75; chief surgeon, Lubbock Gen Hosp, 75-80. *Honors & Awards:* Billings Gold Medal, AMA, 66; Stitt Award, Asn Mil Surgeons US, 68; Distinguished Serv Citation, US Dept Defense, 69; Physician's Recognition Award, AMA, 70, 73, 76, 79. *Mem:* Fel Am Col Surg; Am Med Asn; Soc Surg Alimentary Tract; Soc Surg Chmn; Am Surg Asn. *Res:* Portal hypertension; cirrhosis; esophageal varices; vascular surgery; schistosomiasis; chemotherapy as an adjuvant to surgery in the control of cancer; percutaneous splenoportography; spleen pressure; portal hemodynamics in Wilson's and other diseases; emergency medical services; trauma; telecommunications; disaster medical care; mass casualty care. *Mailing Add:* Dean's Suite Tex Tech Univ Sch Med Lubbock TX 79430

JACKSON, FRANCIS J, b Providence, RI, May 23, 32; m 56; c 3. PHYSICS. *Educ:* Providence Col, BS, 54; Brown Univ, ScM, 57, PhD(physics), 60. *Prof Exp:* Res assoc physics, Brown Univ, 59-60; sr scientist, 60-70, vpres, Phys Sci Div, 70-75, vpres Underwater Technol Div, 75-77, CORP V PRES, BOLT BERANEK & NEWMAN, INC, 77- *Concurrent Pos:* Adj prof, Cath Univ Am, 68- *Mem:* Acoust Soc Am; Inst Elec & Electronics Engrs. *Res:* Nonlinear acoustics; underwater acoustics and sonar; ultrasonic propagation. *Mailing Add:* 1611 Woodmoor Lane McLean VA 22101

JACKSON, GARY LESLIE, b Minneapolis, Minn, Jan 5, 45; m 70; c 1. PLASMA PHYSICS, ELECTROMAGNETICS. *Educ:* Univ Idaho, BS, 67; Calif State Univ, Northridge, MS, 72; Univ Ariz, PhD(elec eng), 77. *Prof Exp:* SR ENGR, GEN ATOMICS CO, 77- *Mem:* Inst Elec & Electronics Engrs; Am Phys Soc. *Res:* Fusion plasmas. *Mailing Add:* 13424 Sebago Ave Poway CA 92064

JACKSON, GARY LOUCKS, b Skidmore, Mo, Nov 4, 38; m 70. ENDOCRINOLOGY, PHYSIOLOGY. *Educ:* Univ Mo, BS, 60, AM, 63; Univ Ill, Urbana, PhD(animal sci), 67. *Prof Exp:* NIH fel, 67-68, assoc prof, 68-77, PROF ENDOCRINOL, UNIV ILL, URBANA, 77- *Mem:* Soc Study Reproduction; Endocrine Soc; Soc Exp Biol Med; Brit Soc Study Fertil. *Res:* Hypothalamic control of gonadotropin and prolactin secretions; biosynthesis of luteinizing hormone. *Mailing Add:* Dept Vet Physiol & Pharmacol Univ of Ill Col of Vet Med Urbana IL 61801

JACKSON, GEORGE FREDERICK, III, b Brooklyn, NY, May 16, 43; m 66; c 2. PHYSICAL CHEMISTRY, ANALYTICAL CHEMISTRY. *Educ:* MacMurray Col, BA, 65; Northwestern Univ, PhD(chem), 69. *Prof Exp:* Asst prof chem, Lake Forest Col, 69-73; assoc prof, 73-80, PROF CHEM, UNIV TAMPA, 80-, DIV CHMN, 82- *Mem:* AAAS; Am Chem Soc. *Res:* Studies of atomic inversion; involving arsenic and phosphorus atoms; properties of the allenic bond; use of NMR shift reagents for determination of molecular structures. *Mailing Add:* Dept of Chem Univ of Tampa 401 W Kennedy Blvd Tampa FL 33606

JACKSON, GEORGE GEE, b Provo, Utah, Oct 5, 20; m 43; c 5. INTERNAL MEDICINE. *Educ:* Brigham Young Univ, AB, 42; Univ Utah, MD, 45. *Prof Exp:* Intern, II & IV Med Serv, Boston City Hosp, Harvard Univ, 45-46, house physician, II Med Serv, 46, asst resident med, Hosp & teaching fel, Med Sch, 48-49, res fel, Med Sch, 49-50, asst med, Hosp & res fel, Thorndike Mem Lab, 49-51, Milton fel, Med Sch, 50-51; from asst prof to assoc prof med, Col Med, 51-59, prof, 59-79, ATTEND PHYSICIAN, UNIV ILL HOSP, CHICAGO, 51- *Concurrent Pos:* Consult, West Side Vet Admin Hosp, Chicago; spec fel, Abteilung fur Virusforschung, Tropeninstitut, Hamburg, Ger, 68-69; vis prof, Max von Pettenkofer Inst, Univ Munich, Germany, 78-79; ed, J Infectious Dis, 79- *Mem:* AAAS; Am Asn Immunologists; Am Col Physicians; Am Epidemiol Soc; Infectious Diseases Soc Am (secy-treas, 67-72, pres, 74). *Res:* Infectious diseases; antibiotics; microbiology. *Mailing Add:* Dept of Med Univ of Ill Col of Med Chicago IL 60612

JACKSON, GEORGE JOHN, b Vienna, Austria, Dec 10, 31; nat US. PARASITOLOGY. *Educ:* Univ Chicago, AB, 51, MS, 54, PhD, 58. *Prof Exp:* Fel, La State Univ, 58; res assoc & instr, Univ Chicago, 58-59; USPHS res fel & guest investr, Rockefeller Inst, 59-63; fac mem, Rockefeller Univ, 63-72; head lab parasitol, 72-80, ACTG CHIEF FOOD & COSMETICS, MICROBIOL BR, BUR FOOD, US FOOD & DRUG ADMIN, 80- *Concurrent Pos:* Consult, Pathway Labs, 58-59; adj prof, Rockefeller Univ & Lehigh Univ, 72-; ed, Exp Parasitol, 76-; US deleg, Food Hyg Coun & Cordex Alimentarius Comn, UN Food & Agr Orgn, 80- *Mem:* Am Soc Parasitologists; Soc Protozoologists; Am Soc Trop Med & Hyg; Coun Biol Ed. *Res:* Immunity; invertebrate physiology; axenic culture; food parasitology; anisakiasis. *Mailing Add:* US Food & Drug Admin Lab Parasitol HFF124 200 C St SW Washington DC 20204

JACKSON, GEORGE RICHARD, b Chagrin Falls, Ohio, Sept 27, 20; m 43; c 3. CHEMISTRY. *Educ:* Baldwin-Wallace Col, BS, 42; Johns Hopkins Univ, MA, 43, PhD(org chem), 48. *Prof Exp:* From instr to asst prof chem, Western Reserve Univ, 47-53; dir res, H C Fisher Co, 53-55; pres, Cliffdale Prod Corp, 55-57, Top-Scor Prod Inc, 57-61 & SuCrest Corp, 61-69; pres, Southern Shortenings, 69-77; CONSULT, 78- *Mem:* Am Chem Soc; Am Oil Chem Soc; Am Asn Cereal Chem; Inst Food Technol. *Res:* Food chemistry; fats and oils; analytical chemistry. *Mailing Add:* Apt 1903 2828 N Atlantic Ave Daytona Beach FL 32018

JACKSON, GERALD JAMES, b Pen Argyl, Pa, Aug 13, 29; m 53; c 2. PHARMACY. *Educ:* Temple Univ, BS, 52; Univ Conn, MS, 60, PhD(pharm), 62. *Prof Exp:* Pharmaceut chemist, Merck & Co, Inc, 52-55; pharmaceut chemist, Lederle Labs, 61-62, group leader, 62-67; dir pharm develop, Geigy Chem Corp, 67-71, dir pharm res & develop, 71-74; vpres, Colorcon, Inc, West Point, 74-76; DIR PHARMACEUT TECHNOL, E R SQUIBB & SONS, NEW BRUNSWICK, NJ, 77- *Mem:* Am Pharmaceut Asn; Acad Pharmaceut Sci; Perenteral Drug Asn. *Mailing Add:* 27 Ramsey Rd Middletown NJ 07748

JACKSON, HAROLD, b Preston, Lancashire, Eng, Aug 10, 37; m 61; c 3. FOOD SCIENCE. *Educ:* Univ Nottingham, BSc, 59, MSc, 61; Univ Alta, PhD(dairy sci), 63. *Prof Exp:* Asst prof dairy & food microbiol, 63-69, assoc prof food sci, 69-74, PROF FOOD SCI & CHMN DEPT, UNIV ALTA, 74- *Mem:* Am Soc Microbiol; Can Inst Food Sci & Technol; Brit Soc Appl Bact; Brit Soc Gen Microbiol. *Res:* Food microbiology; effects of environmental stress on microbial growth and activity. *Mailing Add:* Dept Food Sci Univ Alta Edmonton AB T6G 2P5 Can

JACKSON, HAROLD E, JR, b Pittsburgh, Pa, Jan 5, 33; m 58; c 3. NUCLEAR PHYSICS. *Educ:* Princeton Univ, AB, 54; Cornell Univ, PhD(physics), 60. *Prof Exp:* Sr physicist, 59-81, RES PROJ DIR, ARGONNE NAT LAB, 81- *Concurrent Pos:* Mem nuclear cross sect adv comt, AEC, 67-, secy, 71-73; chmn, US Nuclear Data Comt, 74-75; mem, nuclear data comt, Nuclear Energy Agency, 74-77; mem bd dirs, Los Alamos Meson Physics Fac Users Group, 79-80, chmn, 82- *Mem:* Am Phys Soc. *Res:* High energy physics; photoproduction of mesons; nuclear physics; study of nuclear structure with thermal and resonant neutron interactions; photonuclear interactions; medium energy physics; pion interactions with complex nuclei. *Mailing Add:* Physics Div Argonne Nat Lab Argonne IL 60439

JACKSON, HAROLD LEONARD, b Wichita, Kans, Mar 13, 23; m 52; c 4. POLYMER CHEMISTRY, FLUORINE CHEMISTRY. *Educ:* Munic Univ Wichita, AB, 43, MS, 46; Univ Ill, PhD(chem), 49. *Prof Exp:* Res chemist, Cent Res Dept, 49-59 & Org Chem Dept, 59-65, res assoc, Org Chem Dept, 66-77, RES ASSOC, PETROCHEMICALS DEPT, E I DU PONT DE NEMOURS & CO, INC, 78- *Concurrent Pos:* Vis prof, Univ Kans, 62-63. *Mem:* AAAS; Am Chem Soc. *Mailing Add:* RD 3 Box 194 Canterbury Hills Hockessin DE 19707

JACKSON, HAROLD WOODWORTH, b Lawrence, Mass, Mar 14, 28; m 50; c 4. ANALYTICAL CHEMISTRY. *Educ:* Univ NH, BS, 49; Univ Conn, MS, 51, PhD(biochem, dairy technol), 55. *Prof Exp:* Instr dairy technol, Univ Conn, 52-53; prod leader cheese, Kraft Foods Res Lab, 54-55, res chemist, 55-59, group leader chromatog, 59-60; group leader chromatog & infrared spectros, Res & Develop Div, Fundamental Chem Sect, Nat Dairy Prod Corp, 60-69; group leader chromatog & instrumental anal, 69-75, sr group leader, Kraftco Corp, 75-78, SR GROUP LEADER, BASIC FLAVOR CHEM RES & DEVELOP DIV, KRAFT, INC, 78- *Mem:* Am Oil Chemist's Soc; Am Chem Soc. *Res:* Isolation and identification of natural flavor compounds; analytical methodology on fatty acid derivatives; gas chromatography; nuclear magnetic resonance; basic flavor chemistry; mass spectrometry. *Mailing Add:* Kraft Inc 801 Waukegan Rd Glenview IL 60025

JACKSON, HENRY WOODROW, theoretical physics, see previous edition

JACKSON, HERBERT LEWIS, b Sawyer, Kans, May 9, 21; m 46; c 2. NUCLEAR PHYSICS. *Educ:* Univ Wis, PhD(physics), 52. *Prof Exp:* Asst, Phys Inst, Univ Basel, 52-54; asst prof physics, Univ Nebr, 54-60; from asst prof to assoc prof, 60-68, PROF RADIOL, UNIV IOWA, 68- *Mem:* Am Phys Soc; Health Physics Soc; Am Asn Physicists in Med; Sigma Xi. *Res:* Scattering of protons and neutrons from light elements; radiological physics. *Mailing Add:* Dept of Radiol Univ of Iowa Iowa City IA 52240

JACKSON, HERBERT WILLIAM, b Durham, NH, Jan 5, 11; m 36; c 1. POLLUTION BIOLOGY. *Educ:* Dartmouth Col, AB, 34; Cornell Univ, PhD(zool), 39. *Prof Exp:* Asst zool, Cornell Univ, 36-39; from instr to assoc prof biol, Va Polytech Inst, 39-51, tobacco specialist, Agr Exten Serv, 45; biologist, Training Sect, Robert A Taft Sanit Eng Ctr, USPHS, 51-67; chief biologist, Nat Training Ctr, Water Pollution Control Admin, US Dept Interior, 67-69; chief biologist, Environ Protection Agency, 69-73; CONSULT WATER POLLUTION ECOL, 73- *Concurrent Pos:* Collabr, US Dept Interior, 47-51; Rockefeller Found fel, Mex, 49-50; consult biol &

pollution ecol, Pan Am Health Orgn, 74-77. *Honors & Awards:* Bronze Medal for Meritorious Serv, US Environ Protection Agency, 73. *Mem:* Am Soc Limnol & Oceanog; Am Pub Health Asn; Sigma Xi; Water Pollution Control Fedn. *Res:* Biological and engineering aspects of water supply and pollution control; pollution ecology; marine and freshwater; plankton analysis techniques. *Mailing Add:* Old Piscataqua Rd Durham NH 03824

JACKSON, HEZEKIAH, plant physiology, deceased

JACKSON, (CHARLES) IAN, b Keighley, Eng, Feb 11, 35; Can & UK citizen; m 63; c 1. SCIENCE ADMINISTRATION. *Educ:* Univ London, BA, 56; McGill Univ, MSc, 59, PhD(geog), 61. *Prof Exp:* Lectr geog, London Sch Econ & Polit Sci, 59-69; head, Econ Geog Sect, Can Dept Energy, Mines & Resources, 69-71; dir priorities & planning, Can Ministry State Urban Affairs, 71-75; exec dir, Can Habitat & Energy Secretariat, 75, tech officer, 75-78; sr econ affairs officer, UN Econ Comn Europe, 78-81; EXEC DIR, SIGMA XI, 81- *Honors & Awards:* Darton Prize, Royal Meteorol Soc, 62; Evan Durbin Prize, Inst Econ Affairs, 66. *Res:* Environmental protection; energy use; fur-trade history. *Mailing Add:* Sigma Xi 345 Whitney Ave New Haven CT 06511

JACKSON, IVOR MICHAEL DAVID, b Glasgow, Scotland, Apr 17, 36; US citizen; m 72; c 2. NEUROENDOCRINOLOGY, COMPARATIVE ENDOCRINOLOGY. *Educ:* Univ Glasgow Med Sch, MB & ChB, 60. *Prof Exp:* Res fel neuroendocrinol, Univ Conn, 71-72; res fel endocrinal, 72-73, asst prof med, 73-77, assoc prof, 77-80, PROF MED, SCH MED, TUFTS UNIV, 80- *Concurrent Pos:* Prin investr, Nat Inst Arthritis, Metab & Diag Dis, NIH, 78-; physician, New Eng Med Ctr, 78- *Mem:* Royal Col Physicians London; fel Am Col Physicians; AAAS; Soc Exp Biol & Med; Am Soc Clin Invest. *Res:* Isolation, characterization and determination of the functional significance of the hypothalamic releasing hormone and neural peptide, thyrotropin releasing hormone in neuronal and extra-neuronal tissues of mammalian and submammalian species. *Mailing Add:* New England Med Ctr 171 Harrison Ave Boston MA 02111

JACKSON, JAMES ALBERT, b Louisville, Ky, May 27, 38; m 66; c 2. BIOCHEMISTRY, LABORATORY MEDICINE. *Educ:* Auburn Univ, BS, 68, MS, 69, PhD(physiol pharm, biochem), 71; Registry Med Technologists, cert, 71. *Prof Exp:* Lab technician, US Naval Hosp, Portsmouth, Va, 61-64; med technician, Med Ctr, Columbus, Ga, 64-68, chief med technician, 68-70; asst prof med technol, Univ Ky, 70-73; tech training mgr, 74-76, DIR TECH TRAINING & PROD LABELING, AMES CO, DIV MILES LABS, INC, 76- *Mem:* Am Asn Clin Chemists; NY Acad Sci; Am Soc Clin Path; Am Soc Med Technol. *Res:* Cholesterol metabolism. *Mailing Add:* Ames Co Div Miles Labs Inc Elkhart IN 46514

JACKSON, JAMES EDWARD, b Rochester, NY, Jan 12, 25; m 47; c 3. MATHEMATICAL STATISTICS. *Educ:* Univ Rochester, AB, 47; Univ NC, MA, 49; Va Polytech Inst, PhD, 60. *Prof Exp:* Statistician, Eastman Kodak Co, 48-57; asst process engr, Hercules Powder Co, 57-58; asst prof, Va Polytech Inst, 58-59; STATISTICIAN, KODAK PARK, EASTMAN KODAK CO, 59- *Honors & Awards:* Brumbaugh Award, Am Soc Qual Control, 78. *Mem:* Psychomet Soc; fel Am Soc Qual Control; Biomet Soc; fel Am Statist Asn; Statist Soc Can. *Res:* Development of statistical methods, particularly multivariate analysis; quality control; sample survey techniques; psychometric methods and their associated computer techniques for use in industrial problems. *Mailing Add:* Eastman Kodak Co MSD Bldg 56 Kodak Park Works Rochester NY 14650

JACKSON, JAMES FREDERICK, ecology, evolution, see previous edition

JACKSON, JAMES OLIVER, b New Iberia, La, July 16, 39; m 64; c 1. MEDICAL MICROBIOLOGY, IMMUNOLOGY. *Educ:* Univ Southwestern La, BS, 66, MS, 67; Univ Kans, PhD(microbiol), 70. *Prof Exp:* Asst prof microbiol, Southern Univ, 70-72; From asst prof to assoc prof, 72-80, PROF MICROBIOL, CALIF STATE POLYTECH UNIV, POMONA, 80- *Concurrent Pos:* Ad hoc consult, NIH, 70- *Mem:* Am Soc Microbiol. *Res:* Metabolic changes in experimental Listeria monocytogenes infections; extracellular proteins produced by Listeria monocytogenes; pathogenic mechanisms of Chromobacterium violecium. *Mailing Add:* Dept of Biol Sci Calif State Polytech Univ Pomona CA 91768

JACKSON, JASPER ANDREW, JR, b Washington, DC, Jan 26, 23; m 61; c 1. EXPERIMENTAL PHYSICS. *Educ:* Univ Okla, BS, 48, MS, 50, PhD(physics), 55. *Prof Exp:* Asst, Univ Okla, 49-51; mem staff, Los Alamos Sci Lab, 51-52; sr nuclear engr, Convair Div, Gen Dynamics Corp, 55; MEM STAFF, LOS ALAMOS NAT LAB, 56- *Mem:* Fel AAAS; Am Phys Soc. *Res:* Nuclear magnetic resonance; infrared and Raman spectroscopy; dynamic nuclear polarization; mass spectrometry. *Mailing Add:* Box 1663 Los Alamos NM 87544

JACKSON, JEREMY BRADFORD COOK, b Louisville, Ky, Nov 13, 42. MARINE ECOLOGY, PALEOBIOLOGY. *Educ:* George Washington Univ, AB, 65, MA, 67; Yale Univ, MPhil, 70, PhD(geol), 71. *Prof Exp:* Asst prof, 71-77, assoc prof marine ecol, 77-81, PROF ECOL, JOHNS HOPKINS UNIV, 81- *Concurrent Pos:* Mem biol oceanog panel, NSF, 75 & 76; vis prof, Discovery Bay Marine Lab, Univ West Indies, 76 & 78, Marine Biol Lab, Woods Hole, 79-; res assoc, Smithsonian Inst, 76-; prin investr, NSF grants, 71- *Mem:* Am Soc Limnol & Oceanog; Brit Ecol Soc; Ecol Soc Am; Int Bryozoology Asn; Int Soc Reef Studies. *Res:* Population biology and evolution of marine clonal invertebrates; adaptive significance of form in sessile organisms; competitive theory. *Mailing Add:* Dept of Earth & Planetary Sci Johns Hopkins Univ Baltimore MD 21218

JACKSON, JEROME ALAN, b Ft Benning, Ga, Feb 4, 43; m 65; c 4. ORNITHOLOGY, ECOLOGY. *Educ:* Iowa State Univ, BS, 65; Univ Kans, PhD(zool), 70. *Prof Exp:* Asst prof, 70-74, ASSOC PROF ZOOL, MISS STATE UNIV, 74- *Concurrent Pos:* Mem scientists' adv comt, Environ Defense Fund, 71-; consult, US Environ Protection Agency, 73-74; ed, Wilson Bull, 74-78 & The Mississippi Kite, 76-; regional ed, Am Birds, 78-; pres, Eco-Inventory Studies, Inc, 78-; leader endangered species recovery team, US Fish & Wildlife Serv; ed, J Field Ornithol, 80- *Mem:* Am Ornith Union; Wilson Ornith Soc (treas, 73-74, vpres, 79-); Sigma Xi; Cooper Ornith Soc. *Res:* Population dynamics and adaptation in hole-nesting birds; biology of endangered species; behavior of rat snakes, Elaphe. *Mailing Add:* Dept of Biol Sci Miss State Univ Mississippi State MS 39762

JACKSON, JOHN DAVID, b London, Ont, Jan 19, 25; m 49; c 4. THEORETICAL PHYSICS. *Educ:* Univ Western Ont, BSc, 46; Mass Inst Technol, PhD(physics), 49. *Prof Exp:* Res assoc physics, Mass Inst Technol, 49; from asst prof to assoc prof math, McGill Univ, 50-56; from assoc prof to prof physics, Univ Ill, 57-67; group leader theoret physics, 74-78, chmn dept, 78-81, PROF PHYSICS, UNIV CALIF, BERKELEY, 67-, ASSOC DIR & HEAD PHYSICS COMPUT SCI & MATH DIV, LAWRENCE BERKELEY LAB, 82- *Concurrent Pos:* Guggenheim fel, Princeton Univ, 56-57; consult, Argonne Nat Lab, 62-65, 75-78; Ford Found fel, Europ Orgn Nuclear Res, 63-64; assoc ed, Rev of Modern Physics, 68-72; vis fel, Clare Hall, Cambridge Univ, 70; consult, Stanford Linear Accelerator Ctr, 71-73 & Nat Accelerator Lab, 71-75; mem vis comt, Dept Physics, Mass Inst Technol, 73-76; ed, Annual Rev Nuclear & Particle Sci, 77- *Mem:* Fel Am Phys Soc. *Res:* Theoretical physics of fundamental particles. *Mailing Add:* Dept of Physics Univ of Calif Berkeley CA 94720

JACKSON, JOHN EDWARD, b Terre Haute, Ind, Feb 18, 17; m 46; c 5. AGRICULTURAL BIOCHEMISTRY, ORGANIC CHEMISTRY. *Educ:* Univ Iowa, BS, 46; Univ Minn, PhD(agr biochem), 58. *Prof Exp:* Asst sci aide, Northern Regional Res Lab, USDA, 41-42, jr chemist, 42-47; res chemist, Gen Mills Res Lab, 47-52; sr res chemist, Archer Daniels Midland Co, 56-62; instr indust chem, St Paul Voc Sch, Minn, 60-62; assoc prof, 62-65, PROF CHEM, STATE UNIV NY COL GENESEO, 65- *Mem:* AAAS; Am Chem Soc; NY Acad Sci. *Res:* Chemistry and biochemistry of fatty acids and their derivatives; radiation effects. *Mailing Add:* Dept of Chem State Univ NY Geneseo NY 14454

JACKSON, JOHN ERIC, b Cincinnati, Ohio, July 25, 37; m 60; c 1. CHEMICAL ENGINEERING. *Educ:* Purdue Univ, BS, 58; Univ Mich, MSE, 59. *Prof Exp:* Res engr, Speedway Labs, 59-63, group leader welding & lasers, 63-66, supvr, 66-68, LAB DIR, LINDE DIV, UNION CARBIDE CORP, 68- *Mem:* Am Inst Chem Engrs; Am Welding Soc. *Res:* Directing development of high performance materials for aircraft, nuclear, petroleum and related energy industries; wear and corrosion prevention; thermal barriers; composites; fossil fuel production and utilization; oil and gas extraction. *Mailing Add:* Linde Div 1500 Polco St Indianapolis IN 46224

JACKSON, JOHN FENWICK, b Kosciusko, Miss, Nov 19, 28; m 54; c 3. INTERNAL MEDICINE, GENETICS. *Educ:* Univ Miss, BA, 50; Tulane Univ, MD, 53; Am Bd Internal Med, dipl, 65. *Prof Exp:* Intern, Philadelphia Gen Hosp, 53-54; gen pract, Minter City, Miss, 54-56; resident res physician internal med, Med Ctr, Univ Miss, 58-60, chief resident physician, 60; from instr to asst prof internal med, Tulane Univ, 61-64; asst prof internal med & assoc prof prev med, 64-67, PROF PREV MED & ASSOC PROF INTERNAL MED, SCH MED, UNIV MISS, 67- *Concurrent Pos:* Res fel cancer, Univ Miss, 60-61; trainee, Inst Med Genetics, Univ Uppsala, 62-63; vis physician, Charity Hosp La, New Orleans, 63-64; attend physician, Univ Miss Hosp, Jackson, 64-; consult, Vet Admin Hosp, Jackson, 64-; vis investr, Pop Genetics Lab, Univ Hawaii, 70-71. *Mem:* Am Fedn Clin. *Res:* Am Soc Hemat; Soc Human Genetics. Res: Hematology; medical genetics; cytogenetic investigations in human disease; human linkage studies. *Mailing Add:* 2024 Southwood Jackson MS 39211

JACKSON, JOHN MATHEWS, b Chicago, Ill, July 9, 08; m 31; c 7. FOOD SCIENCE. *Educ:* Univ Chicago, BS, 29, PhD(chem), 32. *Prof Exp:* Chemist, Thermal Eng Group, Am Can Co, Ill, 32-37, supvr, 38-41, asst chief packaging res, 42-49, asst mgr res, Pac Div, 49-51, mgr, Res Div Lab, 52-55, Ill, 55-57, sect mgr, 57-63; dir res, Green Giant Co, 63-67, dir packaging res, 68-73; CONSULT, 73- *Concurrent Pos:* Mem, Comt Foods, Subcomt Radiation Sterilization, Nat Res Coun, 55-57; pres, Res & Develop Assocs Food & Container Inst, 62-63; mem, Sci Res Comt, Nat Canners Asn, 65-72; mem, Comt Microbiol Food, Adv Bd Mil Personnel Supplies, Nat Acad Sci, 65-68, Container Comt, 68-71; consult, Process Rev Comt, Bur Foods, Food & Drug Admin, 74- *Mem:* Am Chem Soc; fel Inst Food Technologists (pres, 62-63). *Res:* Decomposition of organic compounds in electrical discharges; heat penetration in canned foods; sterilization of canned foods; packaging of frozen foods; aerosol packaging. *Mailing Add:* PO Box 87 Lakeside MI 49116

JACKSON, JOHN PHILIP, physics, mathematics, see previous edition

JACKSON, JOHN RANICAR, b Eng, July 9, 16; m 42; c 2. PATHOLOGY. *Educ:* London Sch Trop Med, DTM & H, 42; Univ Toronto, DPH, 53; Univ Ottawa, MSc, 57; Royal Col Physicians & Surgeons, cert path, 58, FRCP(C), 72. *Prof Exp:* Instr parasitol, Univ Alta, 48-50; from asst prof to assoc prof path, Univ, 59-71, assoc registr, Can Tumour Ref Ctr, Dept Path, Univ Ottawa, 69-78; CONSULT PATHOLOGIST, ROYAL JUBILEE HOSP, VICTORIA, CAN, 78- *Mem:* Can Asn Path. *Res:* Pathological anatomy. *Mailing Add:* 1114-211 Wurtemburg Ottawa ON K1N 8M5 Can

JACKSON, JOHN STERLING, b Bowling Green, Ky, Nov 3, 22; m 49; c 5. ECONOMIC SYSTEM MODELING. *Educ:* Calif Inst Technol, BS, 46, MS, 54. *Prof Exp:* Asst prof, 56-59, ASSOC PROF ELEC ENG, UNIV KY, 59- *Concurrent Pos:* Ed of proceedings, Carnahan Conf Crime Countermeasure, 67-, Carnahan Conf Electronic Prosthetics, 72-73 & Int Conf Crime Countermeasure, 73-; consult, Off Opportunity in Sci, AAAS, 77- *Mem:* Inst Elec & Electronics Engrs; Am Soc Eng Educ; AAAS; Sigma Xi. *Res:* Social implications of technology; crime countermeasures. *Mailing Add:* Col of Eng Univ of Ky Lexington KY 40506

JACKSON, JOHNNY, plant physiology, biochemistry, see previous edition

JACKSON, JULIUS, b New York, NY, Apr 20, 16; m 41; c 1. INORGANIC CHEMISTRY. *Educ:* Polytech Inst Brooklyn, BS, 37, MS, 39, PhD(inorg chem), 41. *Prof Exp:* Res chemist, Otto H Henry, Brooklyn, 41-42; chemist-metallurgist, Nat Prod Refining Co, NJ, 42-44; res chemist, E I Du Pont De Nemours & Co, Inc, 44-65, sr res chemist, 65-66, res assoc, 66-80; CONSULT PIGMENTS, 80- *Concurrent Pos:* Eve instr, Polytech Inst Brooklyn, 42-47 & Brooklyn Col, 47. *Mem:* Am Chem Soc. *Res:* Inorganic chemistry; metallurgy of chromium alloys; nonaqueous solvents; chromium chemicals; selenium oxycholoro compounds of pyridine and related compounds; inorganic pigments; phthalocyanine pigments; quinacridone pigments; flame retardants; light stabilizers. *Mailing Add:* 224 Charles St Westfield NJ 07090

JACKSON, KENNETH ARTHUR, b Connaught, Ont, Oct 23, 30; m 52; c 3. MATERIALS SCIENCE. *Educ:* Univ Toronto, BASc, 52, MASc, 53; Harvard Univ, PhD(appl physics), 56. *Prof Exp:* Res fel, Harvard Univ, 56-58, asst prof metall, 58-62; mem tech staff, 62-67, HEAD MAT PHYSICS RES DEPT, BELL LABS, 67- *Mem:* AAAS; Am Phys Soc; Am Soc Metals; Am Inst Mining, Metall & Petrol Engrs; Mat Res Soc (vpres, 75-77, pres, 78). *Res:* Crystal growth; crystalline defects; surfaces. *Mailing Add:* Bell Labs Murray Hill NJ 07974

JACKSON, KENNETH LEE, b Berkeley, Calif, Jan 6, 26; m 48; c 4. PHYSIOLOGY. *Educ:* Univ Calif, Berkeley, AB, 49, PhD(physiol), 54. *Prof Exp:* Res asst physiol, Donner Lab, Univ Calif, Berkeley, 49-51; res physiologist, Off Naval Res Unit One, 51-53; sr investr, Biochem Br, US Naval Radiol Defense Lab, 54-60; head radiobiol group, Bioastronaut Sect, Boeing Co, 60-63; from asst prof to assoc prof, 63-76, PROF ENVIRON HEALTH & HEAD DIV, UNIV WASH, 76-, CHMN RADIOL SCI GROUP, 67- *Mem:* AAAS; Am Physiol Soc; Radiation Res Soc; Health Physics Soc; Am Pub Health Asn. *Res:* Biochemical and physiological mechanisms in mammalian radiation biology; cell and intestinal physiology. *Mailing Add:* Radiol Sci SB-30 Univ of Wash Seattle WA 98105

JACKSON, KERN CHANDLER, b Kansas City, Mo, Oct 13, 20; m 70; c 4. GEOLOGY. *Educ:* Mich Technol Univ, BS, 47, MS, 50; Univ Wis, PhD(geol), 51. *Prof Exp:* From instr to asst prof geol, Univ Maine, 50-52; from asst prof to assoc prof, 52-61, chmn dept, 55-59, PROF GEOL, UNIV ARK, FAYETTEVILLE, 61- *Mem:* AAAS; Am Mineral Soc; Geol Soc Am. *Res:* Petrology and petrography; petrography of Arkansas syenites and lamprophyres. *Mailing Add:* 235 Baxter Lane Fayetteville AR 72701

JACKSON, LAIRD G, b Seattle, Wash, Oct 10, 30; m 56; c 3. MEDICINE. *Educ:* Pomona Col, BA, 51; Univ Cincinnati, MD, 55. *Prof Exp:* Resident internal med, 59-62, instr med, 62-64, assoc, 64-66, PROF MED, JEFFERSON MED COL, 66-, PROF GYNEC-OBSTET & PEDIAT, 71-, DIR DIV MED GENETICS, 71- *Concurrent Pos:* NIH fel, 61-62; Leukemia Soc fel, 63-65, scholar, 65-; Nat Cancer Inst res grants, 64-66 & 65-68; Nat Found res grant, 64-66. *Mem:* Am Fedn Clin Res; Tissue Cult Asn; Am Soc Human Genetics; Am Asn Cancer Res. *Res:* Lymphangiography and dynamics of lymphatic system; chromosome morphology and nucleic acid and histone function in chromosomes. *Mailing Add:* Jefferson Med Col Dept of Med Thomas Jefferson Univ Philadelphia PA 19107

JACKSON, LARRY LAVERN, b Charlotte, Mich, June 2, 42; m 63; c 2. VETERINARY ANESTHESIOLOGY. *Educ:* Mich State Univ, BS, 64, DVM, 66; Iowa State Univ, MS, 71. *Prof Exp:* Vet, Miller Animal Clin, Lansing, Mich, 66-68; instr, 68-71, ASSOC PROF VET MED, IOWA STATE UNIV, 71- *Mem:* Am Vet Med Asn; Am Soc Vet Anesthesiol. *Res:* Cardio-pulmonary function of the equine and bovine species while under the influence of various anesthetic agents. *Mailing Add:* ISU Col Vet Med Iowa State Univ Ames IA 50011

JACKSON, LARRY LEE, b Livingston, Mont, Oct 8, 40; m 62; c 4. BIOCHEMISTRY. *Educ:* Mont State Univ, BS, 62; NDak State Univ, PhD(biochem), 65. *Prof Exp:* From asst prof to assoc prof, 65-75, PROF CHEM, MONT STATE UNIV, 75- *Mem:* Am Oil Chemist's Soc. *Res:* Lipid chemistry and biochemistry; surface lipids of insects and plants; hydrocarbon biosynthesis; microbial cell wall chemistry; disteria monocytoge genes; insect sterols. *Mailing Add:* Dept of Chem Mont State Univ Bozeman MT 59715

JACKSON, LARRY LYNN, b Defiance, Ohio, Aug 21, 40; m 62; c 3. POLYMER CHARACTERIZATION. *Educ:* Va Mil Inst, BS, 62; Ohio State Univ, PhD(org chem), 67. *Prof Exp:* RES MGR, DOW CHEM CO, 69- *Honors & Awards:* John C Vaaler, Chem Processing Mag, 72 & 78; IR-100, Indust Res Mag, 76. *Mem:* Am Chem Soc; Sigma Xi. *Res:* New product and process research with emphasis on advanced analytical instrumentation and technology. *Mailing Add:* 1010 Pepperidge Ct Midland MI 48640

JACKSON, LELAND BROOKS, b Atlanta, Ga, July 23, 40; m 68; c 1. ELECTRICAL ENGINEERING, ELECTRONICS ENGINEERING. *Educ:* Mass Inst Technol, SB & SM, 63; Stevens Inst Technol, ScD, 70. *Prof Exp:* Res eng radar, Sylvania Electronic Systs, 64-66; mem tech staff digital filters, Bell Tel Labs, 66-70; vpres instruments, Rockland Systs Corp, 70-74; assoc prof, 74-80, PROF ELEC ENG, UNIV RI, 80- *Concurrent Pos:* Res grants, NSF & Air Force Off Sci Res, 76 & Off Naval Res, 77. *Mem:* Fel Inst Elec & Electronics Engrs. *Res:* Optimum synthesis of digital filter structures; estimation of signal parameters and its application to speech analysis, sonar and bioengineering. *Mailing Add:* Kelley Hall Univ of RI Kingston RI 02881

JACKSON, LIONEL ERIC, JR, b San Mateo, Calif, Jan 20, 47; Can citizen; m 69. QUATERNARY GEOLOGY, ENVIRONMENTAL GEOLOGY. *Educ:* San Francisco State Univ, AB, 68; Stanford Univ, MS, 73; Univ Calgary, PhD(geol), 77. *Prof Exp:* Geologist, Hudson Bay Oil & Gas Ltd, 69-70; hydrologist, US Geol Surv, 71-73; GEOLOGIST, GEOL SURV CAN, 77- *Concurrent Pos:* Consult, Calif Dept Transp, 79; instr, Univ Calgary, 81- *Mem:* Fel Geol Asn Can; Am Quaternary Asn; Can Soc Petrol Geologists. *Res:* Quaternary geology and paleo-ecology of western interior plains and Rocky Mountain Foothills; natural hazards in northern Montane regions; quaternary geology of Yukon Territory. *Mailing Add:* Geol Surv Can 3303 33rd St NW Calgary AB T2L 2A7 Can

JACKSON, LLOYD K, b Fairbury, Nebr, Aug 25, 22; m 43; c 1. MATHEMATICS. *Educ:* Univ Nebr, AB, 43, MA, 48; Univ Calif, Los Angeles, PhD, 50. *Prof Exp:* From asst prof to assoc prof, 50-59, PROF MATH, UNIV NEBR, LINCOLN, 59- *Mem:* Am Math Soc; Math Asn Am. *Res:* Partial differential equations; function theory. *Mailing Add:* Dept of Math Univ of Nebr Lincoln NE 68508

JACKSON, M(ELBOURNE) L(ESLIE), b Wisdom, Mont, Sept 27, 15; m 44; c 4. CHEMICAL ENGINEERING. *Educ:* Mont State Col, BS, 41; Univ Minn, PhD(chem eng), 48. *Hon Degrees:* Dr, Montana State Univ, 80. *Prof Exp:* Instr chem eng, Mont State Col, 42-44 & Univ Minn, 44-48; asst prof, Univ Colo, 48-50; head process develop br, US Naval Ord Test Sta, Calif, 50-53; prof chem eng & head dept, 53-65, dean, Grad Sch, 65-70, res prof chem eng, 71-80, dean eng, 78-80, EMER PROF & DEAN, UNIV IDAHO, 80- *Concurrent Pos:* Consult, indust firms, 53-; E L Phillips intern, univ admin, Pa State Univ, 63-64. *Res:* Particle-molecular mass transfer applied to environmental control systems. *Mailing Add:* Dept of Chem Eng Univ of Idaho Moscow ID 83843

JACKSON, MARGARET E, b Zanesville, Ohio, Sept 2, 28. INORGANIC CHEMISTRY, PHYSICAL CHEMISTRY. *Educ:* Muskingum Col, BS, 50; Auburn Univ, MS, 58, PhD(phys chem), 64. *Prof Exp:* Chemist, Dow Chem Co, Mich, 51-52, Atlantic Supply Co, Md, 53 & Calverton Chem Co, Md, 53-56; asst chem, Auburn Univ, 56-62, instr, 62-64; asst prof, Delta State Col, 64-65; asst prof chem, 65-77, ASSOC PROF CHEM, UNIV S ALA, 77- *Mem:* Am Chem Soc; The Chem Soc. *Res:* The preparation and properties of organo-niobium compounds; determination of stability constants for metal diketo chelates and other coordination compounds. *Mailing Add:* Dept of Chem Univ of SAla Mobile AL 36608

JACKSON, MARION LEROY, b Reynolds, Nebr, Nov 30, 14; m 37; c 4. AGRONOMY, SOIL SCIENCE. *Educ:* Univ Nebr, BS, 36, MS, 37; Univ Wis, PhD(soil chem), 39. *Hon Degrees:* DSc, Univ Nebr, 74. *Prof Exp:* Land classification aide, Resettlement Admin, USDA, Nebr, 36-37; Alumni Res Found & univ fel, Univ Wis, 39-41, from instr to asst prof soils, 41-45; assoc prof agron, Exp Sta, Purdue Univ, 45-46; from assoc prof to prof soils, 46-74, chmn phys sci div, 52-55, FRANKLIN HIRAM KING PROF SOILS, UNIV WIS-MADISON, 74- *Concurrent Pos:* Vis prof, Cornell Univ, 59, Univ Calif, 60, Univ Nebr, 61, Va Polytech Inst, 62, Can Dept Agr, 64, Univ Thesaloniki, 66, Univ Tex, 67, Kyushu Univ, 69, Ohio Univ, 71 & distinguished vis prof, Univ Wash, 73; Nat Res Coun panel radioactive wastes, 76-77. *Honors & Awards:* Soil Sci Achievement Award, Am Soc Agron, 58. *Mem:* AAAS; Clay Minerals Soc (vpres, 65, pres, 66); fel Soil Sci Soc Am (vpres, 67, pres, 68); fel Am Soc Agron; fel Am Mineral Soc. *Res:* Crystal chemistry of soil colloids responsible for soil acidity; cation exchange, phosphate fixation and other chemical reactions; electron microscopy of soil minerals; world distribution of radioactive elements in global dust; soil influence on trace elements in the food chain and human health. *Mailing Add:* 309 Ozark Trail Madison WI 53705

JACKSON, MARION T, b Versailles, Ind, Aug 19, 33; m 55. PLANT ECOLOGY. *Educ:* Purdue Univ, BS, 61, PhD(plant ecol), 64. *Prof Exp:* From asst prof to assoc prof, 64-71, PROF LIFE SCI, IND STATE UNIV, TERRE HAUTE, 71- *Mem:* AAAS; Sigma Xi; Ecol Soc Am. *Res:* Forest ecology of Midwest; flowering phenology; biotic inventories of natural areas and national parks; ecological life histories; regional plant geography. *Mailing Add:* Dept of Life Sci Ind State Univ Terre Haute IN 47809

JACKSON, MARTIN PATRICK ARDEN, b Salisbury, Rhodesia, May 14, 47; US citizen; m 69; c 2. SEDIMENTARY TECTONICS, PRECAMBRIAN GEOLOGY. *Educ:* Univ London, BSc, 68, BSc, 69; Univ Cape Town, PhD(geol), 76. *Prof Exp:* Proj geologist, Eland Explor, SAfrica, 70-72; res assoc, Precambrian Res Unit, Univ Cape Town, 72-76; lectr, Geol Dept, Univ Natal, 76-79; res sci assoc, 80-81, RES SCIENTIST, BUR ECON GEOL, UNIV TEX, AUSTIN, 81- *Concurrent Pos:* Prin investr, Dept Energy, Tex Bur Econ Geol, 80- *Res:* Diapirism and halokinesis; tectonic evolution of sedimentary basins; syndepositional deformation; strain analysis; lineament analysis; structural analysis of Precambrian gneisses and greenstone belts; metamorphic petrology and geochemistry; curstal evolution of Southern Africa. *Mailing Add:* Bur Econ Geol Univ Tex Austin Univ Station Box X Austin TX 78712

JACKSON, MARVIN ALEXANDER, b Dawson, Ga, Oct 28, 27; m 57; c 2. MEDICINE, PATHOLOGY. *Educ:* Morehouse Col, BS, 47; Meharry Med Col, MD, 51; Univ Mich, MA, 56. *Prof Exp:* Intern, US Naval Hosp, St Albans, NY, 51-52, mem staff, 52-53; asst resident, Univ Mich Hosp, 53-54, teaching asst path, 54-55, instr, 55-56; from asst prof to assoc prof, 57-68, PROF PATH, COL MED, HOWARD UNIV, 68-, CHMN DEPT, 60- *Concurrent Pos:* Resident, Hosp Joint Dis, New York, 56-57; attend physician, Howard Univ Hosp, 57; consult physician, Vet Admin Hosp, Washington, DC, 60 & NIH, 68. *Mem:* Fel Col Am Path; Am Asn Anatomists; Am Asn Path & Bact; Int Acad Path; Tissue Cult Asn. *Mailing Add:* 1428 Iris St NW Washington DC 20012

JACKSON, MELVIN ROBERT, b Norwood, Pa, Nov 21, 43; m 68; c 1. METALLURGY, MATERIALS SCIENCE. *Educ:* Lehigh Univ, BS, 65, MS, 67, PhD(metall & mat sci), 71. *Prof Exp:* Metallurgist, Paul D Merios Res Labs, Int Nickel, 71-72; METALLURGIST, CORP RES & DEVELOP, GEN ELEC CO, 72- *Mem:* Am Inst Mining, Metall & Petrol Engrs; Sigma Xi. *Res:* Phase equilibria of high temperature metal and metal-ceramic systems, metallurgical coatings, tool materials. *Mailing Add:* Gen Elec Corp Res & Develop Schenectady NY 12301

JACKSON, MEYER B, b Iowa City, Iowa, Mar 24, 51; m 80; c 1. NEUROSCIENCE, DEVELOPMENTAL NEUROBIOLOGY. *Educ:* Brandeis Univ, BA, 73; Yale Univ, PhD(molecular biophys & biochem), 77. *Prof Exp:* NIH fel, 78-81; ASST PROF BIOL, UNIV CALIF, LOS ANGELES, 81- *Mem:* Biophys Soc; Soc Neurosci. *Res:* Physical and chemical factors which guide the electrical and morphological development of nerve cells. *Mailing Add:* Dept Biol Univ Calif 405 Hilgard Ave Los Angeles CA 90024

JACKSON, MICHAEL J, b Walton, Eng, Apr 12, 38; m 60. PHYSIOLOGY. *Educ:* Univ London, BSc, 63; Univ Sheffield, PhD(physiol), 66. *Prof Exp:* Asst exp officer biochem, Vet Lab, Ministry Agr, Eng, 57-63; res asst physiol, Univ Sheffield, 63-65, from asst lectr to lectr, 65-67; from asst prof to assoc prof, 67-77, PROF PHYSIOL, GEORGE WASHINGTON UNIV, 77- *Concurrent Pos:* USPHS Res Career Develop Award, 72-77; guest worker, Sect Gastroenterol, NIAMDD, 75-76; consult, Vet Admin Merit Rev Bd Basic Sci, 78-80; assoc ed, Am J Philol, Gastrointestinal & Liver Physics, 79- *Mem:* Brit Physiol Soc; Am Gastroenterol Asn; Am Physiol Soc; Soc Exp Biol & Med; Biophys Soc. *Res:* Epithelial transport of drugs and electrolytes; gastro-intestinal physiology. *Mailing Add:* Dept of Physiol George Washington Univ Med Ctr Washington DC 20037

JACKSON, NOEL, b Northallerton, Eng, Dec 25, 31; m 56; c 2. PLANT PATHOLOGY. *Educ:* Univ Durham, BSc, 53, Hons, 54, PhD, 61. *Prof Exp:* Biologist, Sports Turf Res Inst, Eng, 58-65; from asst prof to assoc prof, 65-75, PROF PLANT PATH, UNIV RI, 75-, PROF ENTOM, 77- *Mem:* Brit Asn Appl Biol; Am Phytopath Soc; Trans Brit Mycol Soc; Brit Soc Plant Path; Int Turfgrass Soc. *Res:* Diseases of turf grasses and ornamentals. *Mailing Add:* 234 Woodward Hall Univ of RI Kingston RI 02881

JACKSON, PETER RICHARD, b New York, NY, Dec 9, 48; m 76. PARASITOLOGY. *Educ:* Seton Hall Univ, BA, 70; Univ Tex, Austin, MA, 73; Rice Univ, PhD(biol), 76. *Prof Exp:* NIH assoc parasitol dept biol, Rice Univ, 76 & dept zool, Univ Mass, 76-78; NAT RES COUN ASSOC IMMUNOL, WALTER REED ARMY INST RES, 78- *Mem:* Am Soc Parasitologists; Soc Protozoologists; AAAS; Am Inst Biol Sci; Am Soc Zoologist. *Res:* Immunology of parasitic infections; biochemistry and physiology of parasites, especially parasitic protozoa. *Mailing Add:* Dept Immunol & Commun Dis Walter Reed Army Inst of Res Washington DC 20012

JACKSON, PHILIP LARKIN, b Grosse Point Park, Mich, Oct 20, 21; m 47; c 3. GEOPHYSICS, GEOLOGY. *Educ:* Univ Ore, BA, 50; Univ Mich, AM, 52, MS, 58, PhD(geol, mineral), 70. *Prof Exp:* Asst gas dynamics, Univ Mich, 53-56, res asst, 56-58; staff engr, Bendix Aerospace Div, 58-60; res assoc acoust & seismics, Univ Mich, Ann Arbor, 60-62, assoc res engr, 62-66, res geophysicist, 66-73; res geophysicist, Environ Res Inst, Mich, 73-78; RES SCIENTIST, UNIV MICH, 80- *Mem:* Am Geophys Union. *Res:* Seismology, gravity, electromagnetic sounding and remote sensing. *Mailing Add:* 3194 Lakewood Ann Arbor MI 48103

JACKSON, PRINCE A, JR, b Savannah, Ga, Mar 17, 25; m 50; c 4. PHYSICS, MATHEMATICS. *Educ:* Savannah State Col, BS, 49; NY Univ, MS, 50; Boston Col, PhD(sci, ed), 66. *Prof Exp:* Instr high sch, Ga, 50-55; instr physics, Savannah State Col, 55-61, asst prof math & physics, 61-64, assoc prof phys sci, 66-69, prof math & physics, 71-80, pres, 71-80. *Concurrent Pos:* Chmn div natural sci, Savannah State Col, 69-71. *Mem:* AAAS; Nat Sci Teachers Asn; Nat Inst Sci. *Res:* Improvement of science and mathematics education at all levels of instruction; differential equations of mathematical physics; pedagogical interrelationship between science and mathematics; philosophy of science. *Mailing Add:* 1215 E Duffy Savannah GA 31401

JACKSON, RAY DEAN, b Shoshone, Idaho, Sept 28, 29; m 52, 68; c 7. SOIL PHYSICS. *Educ:* Utah State Univ, BS, 56; Iowa State Univ, MS, 57; Colo State Univ, PhD(soil sci), 60. *Prof Exp:* Soil scientist soil physics, Soil & Water Conserv Res Div, 57-60, soil scientist, US Water Conserv Lab, 60-62, PHYSICIST, US WATER CONSERV LAB, AGR RES SERV, USDA, 62- *Concurrent Pos:* Orgn Econ Coop & Develop Sci fel, Eng, 64. *Honors & Awards:* Superior Serv Unit Award, USDA, 63. *Mem:* Fel AAAS; fel Soil Sci Soc Am; Am Soc Photogrammetry; fel Am Soc Agron. *Res:* Heat, water and water vapor transfer in soils; remote sensing of soil water and crop stress. *Mailing Add:* US Water Conserv Lab 4331 E Broadway Phoenix AZ 85040

JACKSON, RAY WELDON, b Toronto, Ont, Nov 11, 21; m 51; c 4. PHYSICS, SCIENCE POLICY. *Educ:* Univ Toronto, BASc, 44; McGill Univ, PhD(physics), 50. *Prof Exp:* Res asst physics, McGill Univ, 50-51; Am Coun Learned Soc fel, Yale Univ, 51-52, asst, 52-54; sr engr physics res, Sprague Elec Co, 54-56; assoc labs dir, RCA Victor Co, Ltd, 56-65; sci adv to sci secretariat, Privy Coun Off, Ottawa, 66-69; SCI ADV, SCI COUN CAN, 69- *Concurrent Pos:* Vis prof, McMaster Univ, 64-65 & Carleton Univ, 78-80. *Mem:* AAAS; sr mem Inst Elec & Electronics Engrs; Can Asn Physicists. *Res:* Semiconductor physics; electronic circuitry; nuclear detectors; philosophy of science and technology; appropriate technology for development. *Mailing Add:* 208 Clemow Ottawa ON K1S 2B4 Can

JACKSON, RAYMOND CARL, b Medora, Ind, May 7, 28; m 47; c 2. CYTOGENETICS. *Educ:* Ind Univ, AB, 52, AM, 53; Purdue Univ, PhD, 55. *Prof Exp:* Asst, Purdue Univ, 53-55; from instr to assoc prof biol, Univ NMex, 55-58; from asst prof to prof bot, Univ Kans, 58-71; PROF BIOL, TEX TECH UNIV, 71- *Mem:* AAAS; Bot Soc Am; Am Soc Plant Taxon; Int Asn Plant Taxon. *Res:* Systematic studies of the Compositae, particularly evolutionary mechanisms in Haplopappus and Machaeranthera; cytogenetics of Haplopappus gracilis. *Mailing Add:* Dept of Biol Sci Tex Tech Univ Lubbock TX 79409

JACKSON, RAYMOND JOHN, b Newark, NJ, Mar 13, 41; m 64. MEMBRANE BIOCHEMISTRY. *Educ:* Fairleigh Dickinson, BS, 63; Seton Hall Univ, MS, 65; Rutgers Univ, PhD(microbiol), 69. *Prof Exp:* Res assoc, 69-72, asst prof microbiol, 72-76, MEM FAC, MEMBRANE BIOL LAB, MED CTR, UNIV ALA, BIRMINGHAM, 76- *Mem:* AAAS; NY Acad Sci; Am Soc Microbiol. *Mailing Add:* Lab of Membrane Biol Univ of Ala Med Ctr Birmingham AL 35294

JACKSON, RICHARD LEE, b Indianapolis, Ind, Oct 8, 32; m 58; c 2. BIOCHEMISTRY, PHARMACY. *Educ:* Butler Univ, BS, 58, MS, 62; Ind Univ, Indianapolis, PhD(biochem), 65. *Prof Exp:* Assoc scientist, 60-62, sr scientist, 65-71, RES SCIENTIST BIOCHEM, ELI LILLY & CO, 71- *Mem:* Am Diabetes Asn; Am Soc Neurochem. *Res:* Diabetes; insulin chemistry; neurochemistry; glucagon protein chemistry. *Mailing Add:* Eli Lilly & Co 307 E McCarty St Indianapolis IN 46285

JACKSON, RICHARD LEE, b Springfield, Ill, Dec 30, 39. BIOCHEMISTRY, PROTEIN CHEMISTRY. *Educ:* Univ Ill, BS, 63, PhD(microbiol), 67. *Prof Exp:* Res assoc protein chem, Biol Dept, Brookhaven Nat Lab, 67-69; Nat Heart & Lung Inst jr staff fel, 69-70; Nat Inst Arthritis & Metab Dis sr staff fel, 70-71; asst prof exp med, 71-73, assoc prof exp med & cell biol, Baylor Col Med, 73-77; PROF PHARMACOL & CELL BIOPHYS, UNIV CINCINNATI COL MED, 77- *Concurrent Pos:* Estab investr, Am Heart Asn, 72-77, mem coun arteriosclerosis. *Mem:* AAAS; Am Soc Biol Chem; Biophys Soc; Am Chem Soc; Am Heart Asn. *Res:* Structure and function of human plasma lipoproteins and their relationship to atherosclerosis. *Mailing Add:* Rm 5006 Med Sci Bldg Univ Cincinnati Col Med Cincinnati OH 45267

JACKSON, RICHARD THOMAS, b Detroit, Mich, Jan 19, 30; m 55; c 2. PHYSIOLOGY. *Educ:* Univ Detroit, BS, 52, MS, 54; Fla State Univ, PhD(physiol), 60. *Prof Exp:* Asst physiol, Fla State Univ, 54-57, instr, 57-59; from asst prof to assoc prof, Loyola Univ, La, 59-63; res assoc, Lab Ophthal Res, 63-67; instr ophthal & physiol, 63-71, assoc prof, 71-76, PROF SURG & ASSOC PROF ALLIED HEALTH, EMORY UNIV, 76-, DIR, OTOLARYNGOL LAB, 67- *Concurrent Pos:* Consult, Comt Drugs, Am Acad Otolaryngol. *Mem:* Asn Res Otolaryngol; Am Acad Ophthal & Otolaryngol. *Res:* Nasal and eustachian tube physiology; control of blood flow to the nose and ear; clinical and animal testing of drugs that effect blood flow. *Mailing Add:* Dept of Surg Emory Univ Atlanta GA 30322

JACKSON, ROBERT BRUCE, JR, b Drakes Branch, Va, June 5, 29. MATHEMATICS. *Educ:* Davidson Col, BS, 50; Duke Univ, PhD(math), 57. *Prof Exp:* Teacher math, Battle Ground Acad, 50-51; asst, Duke Univ, 53-56; from asst prof to assoc prof, 56-66, PROF MATH, DAVIDSON COL, 66-, CHMN DEPT, 78- *Mem:* Math Asn Am. *Res:* Algebra; probability. *Mailing Add:* Dept of Math Davidson Col Davidson NC 28036

JACKSON, ROBERT DEWEY, b Nelson, Mo, Sept, 30, 29; m 51; c 3. ENTOMOLOGY. *Educ:* Univ Mo, BS, 52, MS, 57; Iowa State Univ, PhD(entom), 67. *Prof Exp:* Res entomologist, Agr Res Serv, USDA, 60-71, leader sugarcane insects invests, Entom Res Div, 71-73, res leader, Sugarcane Pests Res, 73-76; STAFF SCIENTIST, NAT PROG STAFF, AGR RES SERV, USDA, 76- *Mem:* Entom Soc Am; Int Soc Sugarcane Technologists; Am Soc Sugarcane Technologists. *Res:* Economic control of field crop insect pests, especially corn, soybean and sugarcane insects. *Mailing Add:* Nat Prog Staff Bldg 005 Barc-West Beltsville MD 20705

JACKSON, ROBERT HOWARD, food science, see previous edition

JACKSON, ROSCOE GEORGE, II, b Eureka, Kans, May 14, 48. SEDIMENTOLOGY, FLUID DYNAMICS. *Educ:* Univ Kans, BS, 70; Univ Ill, Urbana-Champaign, MS, 73, PhD(geol), 75. *Prof Exp:* Instr, Northwestern Univ, Evanston, 74-75, asst prof geol, 75-80; MEM FAC, DEPT GEOL SCI, UNIV MICH, ANN ARBOR, 80- *Mem:* Geol Soc Am; Int Asn Sedimentologists; Am Geophys Union; AAAS; Soc Econ Paleontologists & Mineralogists. *Res:* Ancient and modern alluvial sediments; mathematical models and mechanics of bedforms, sediment transport and fluid flow in modern sedimentary environments; flow structures of geophysical turbulent boundary layers. *Mailing Add:* Dept Geol Sci 1006 CC Little Bldg Univ Mich Ann Arbor MI 48109

JACKSON, ROY, b Manchester, Eng, Oct 6, 31; m 57; c 2. CHEMICAL ENGINEERING. *Educ:* Cambridge Univ, BA, 54, MA, 58; Univ Edinburgh, DSc(chem eng), 68. *Prof Exp:* Tech officer, Imp Chem Industs Ltd, 55-61; lectr chem eng, Univ Edinburgh, 61-64, reader, 64-68; prof, Rice Univ, 68-77; PROF CHEM ENG, UNIV HOUSTON, 77- *Concurrent Pos:* Consult, Shell Oil Co, 69- *Mem:* Brit Inst Chem Engrs; Am Inst Chem Engrs. *Res:* Chemical reaction engineering; fluid-particle systems. *Mailing Add:* Dept of Chem Eng Univ of Houston Houston TX 77004

JACKSON, ROY JOSEPH, b Cotton Port, La, Feb 8, 44. PHOTOCHEMISTRY. *Educ:* Southern Univ, Baton Rouge, BS, 65, MS, 69; Univ Calif, San Diego, PhD(chem), 75. *Prof Exp:* Instr chem, Southern Univ, Baton Rouge, 69-70; RES CHEMIST, SHELL DEVELOP CO, 75- *Mem:* Am Chem Soc. *Res:* Norish type II photoelimination, photocylization reactions, especially new aryl-alkyl systems; photocure of resins; development of new photocure systems. *Mailing Add:* Shell Develop Co PO Box 1380 Houston TX 77001

JACKSON, SALLY WOMACK, b El Paso, Tex, Jan 18, 44; m 66; c 3. MICROBIOLOGY. *Educ:* Baylor Univ, BA, 65; Baylor Col Med, PhD(microbiol), 69. *Prof Exp:* USDA fel microbiol, Univ Ky, 69-70; NIH fel, Baylor Col Med, 70-71, instr microbiol & dermat, 71-74. *Mem:* Am Soc Microbiol. *Res:* Microbial membranes, both biochemical and ultrastructural studies; microbial ultrastructure in general. *Mailing Add:* 2530 Wooddale Circle Waco TX 76710

JACKSON, SHARON WESLEY, b Topeka, Kans, June 15, 36; m 57; c 3. GENETICS, ENVIRONMENTAL SCIENCES. *Educ:* Kans Wesleyan Univ, BA, 58; Univ Kans, MA, 60; NC State Univ, PhD(genetics), 67. *Prof Exp:* Teacher high sch, Kans, 60-62; instr biol, Kans Wesleyan Univ, 62-64, from asst prof to assoc prof, 67-71; prof environ studies & chmn dept, Sacramento State Col, 71; dir, Environ Studies Ctr, 74-76; CO-DIR, LAND INST, 76- *Mem:* AAAS; Int Asn Plant Taxon. *Res:* Development of perennial grain crops. *Mailing Add:* Land Inst RR 3 Salina KS 67401

JACKSON, SHIRLEY ANN, b Washington, DC, Aug 5, 46. THEORETICAL SOLID STATE PHYSICS. *Educ:* Mass Inst Technol, SB, 68, PhD(physics), 73. *Prof Exp:* Res assoc theoret physics, Fermi Nat Accelerator Lab, 73-74; vis sci assoc, Europ Orgn Nuclear Res, 74-75; res assoc theoret physics, Fermi Nat Accelerator Lab, 75-76; MEM TECH STAFF, BELL TEL LABS, 76- *Concurrent Pos:* Adv study fel, Ford Found, 71-73; fel, Martin Marietta Corp, 72-73; grant, Ford Found, 74-75; mem bd trustees, MIT Corp, 75-85 & Lincoln Univ, 80-; mem, Comt Educ & Employ Women Sci & Eng, Nat Acad Sci, 81-82. *Mem:* Am Phys Soc; AAAS; NY Acad Sci; Sigma Xi; Nat Inst Sci. *Res:* Landau theories of charge density waves in one and two dimensions; transport properties of random systems; correlation effects in electron-hole plasmas; channeling in metals and semiconductors. theory; two dimensional yang-mills gauge theories; neutrino reactions. *Mailing Add:* Bell Tel Labs 600 Mountain Ave Murray Hill NJ 07974

JACKSON, SYDNEY VERN, b Kalamazoo, Mich, Aug 12, 48. NUCLEAR CHEMISTRY. *Educ:* Mass Inst Technol, BS, 70; Univ Md, College Park, PhD(chem), 75. *Prof Exp:* Fel nuclear chem, Cyclotron Inst, Tex A&M Univ, 75-76; res nuclear chem, 76-78, res laser fusion, 78-80, MEM STAFF SYSTS ANALYSIS & TECHNOL ASSESSMENT, LOS ALAMOS NAT LAB, 80- *Concurrent Pos:* Consult, Tech Systs, Santa Fe, NMex, 81- *Mem:* Am Phys Soc. *Res:* Technology assessment of magnetic confinement fusion; nuclear fuel reprocessing; alternative energy technologies; electric power technologies; risk analysis and assessment for energy technologies. *Mailing Add:* Los Alamos Nat Lab Los Alamos NM 87544

JACKSON, THOMAS EDWIN, b Amarillo, Tex, May 7, 44; m 69. MEDICINAL CHEMISTRY. *Educ:* Rice Univ, BA, 66; Mass Inst Technol, PhD(org chem), 71. *Prof Exp:* Fel org chem, Univ SC, 71-73; sr scientist med chem, Sandoz Inc, 73-75; RES CHEMIST MED CHEM, BIOMED RES, ICI-AMERICAS, INC, 75- *Mem:* Am Chem Soc; The Chem Soc; NY Acad Sci. *Res:* Biochemical consideration in drug design; selectivity in organic synthesis; heterocyclic chemistry. *Mailing Add:* Biomed Res Dept ICI-Americas Inc Wilmington DE 19897

JACKSON, THOMAS GERALD, b Mt Sterling, Ala, Dec 26, 36; m 67. ORGANIC CHEMISTRY. *Educ:* Univ Southern Miss, BS, 59, MS, 61; Univ Tenn, Knoxville, PhD(org chem), 65. *Prof Exp:* Asst org chem, Univ Southern Miss, 59-61; PROF CHEM, UNIV S ALA, 65- *Concurrent Pos:* Consult, Res Prod, Inc, Ala, 71- *Mem:* Am Chem Soc; Sigma Xi; Royal Soc Chem; Nat Asn Prev Health Prog Advisors. *Res:* Synthesis of organic compounds of potential medicinal interest; metalation studies of nitrogen containing heterocycles; investigations of compounds containing the nitrogen-silicon bond. *Mailing Add:* Dept of Chem Univ of S Ala Mobile AL 36608

JACKSON, THOMAS LLOYD, b Dayton, Wash, Jan 13, 22; m 43; c 2. SOILS, AGRONOMY. *Educ:* Wash State Univ, BS, 43, MS, 48, PhD, 52. *Prof Exp:* Jr agronomist, Wash State Univ, 47-52; exten soils specialist, 52-56, assoc soil scientist, 56-61, soil scientist, 61-77, PROF, ORE STATE UNIV, 77- *Mem:* Am Soc Agron; Soil Sci Soc Am. *Res:* Soil fertility and pasture management of legume crops; production of small grain crops; vegetable crop nutrition research. *Mailing Add:* Dept of Soil Sci Ore State Univ Corvallis OR 97331

JACKSON, THOMAS W(OODROW), b Chicago, Ill, Apr 3, 17; m 43; c 2. MECHANICAL ENGINEERING, HEAT TRANSFER. *Educ:* Univ Ill, BSME, 41; Univ Calif, MSME, 46; Purdue Univ, PhD(heat transfer), 49. *Prof Exp:* Engr inspection & design, Standard Oil Co, 41-42; res scientist, Lewis Flight Propulsion Lab, Nat Adv Comt Aeronaut, 49-51; prof mech eng, 54-78, chief div mech sci, Eng Exp Sta, 54-67, assoc dean eng res, 65-67, actg dean grad div, 66-67, EMER PROF MECH ENG, GA INST TECHNOL, 78- *Concurrent Pos:* Dir, Skidway Inst Oceanog, 67-70; tech dir, President's Nat Indust Pollution Control Coun, US Dept Commerce, 70-73; consult, 78- *Mem:* Am Soc Mech Engrs. *Res:* Turbine cooling; fuel element design; free and forced convection; acoustic effects on fluid flow and heat transfer; research management; pollution control. *Mailing Add:* PO Box 611 Ava MO 65608

JACKSON, TOGWELL ALEXANDER, b New York, NY, Nov 1, 39; m 67; c 2. BIOGEOCHEMISTRY OF INLAND WATERS. *Educ:* Columbia Univ, BA, 61; Univ Wis, MSc, 63; Univ Mo-Columbia, PhD(geol), 69. *Prof Exp:* Fel org geochem, Woods Hole Oceanog Inst, Dept of Chem, 68-69; fel soil microbiol, Yale Univ Sch Forestry, 69-70; res assoc org geochem, Univ Calif, Santa Barbara, Dept Geol Sci, 70-72; RES SCIENTIST BIOGEOCHEM, FRESHWATER INST, INLAND WATERS DIRECTORATE, CAN DEPT ENVIRON, WINNIPEG, 72- *Mem:* Sigma Xi; Int Asn Theoret & Appl Limnol. *Res:* Humic complexes and other forms of heavy metals and phosphate in recent lakes and streams, and their ecological role; paleobiological significance of organic matter in ancient, especially pre-Cambrian, sediments; biogeochemistry of toxic heavy metals, especially mercury in freshwater environments; forms of metals in relation to bio-availibility. *Mailing Add:* Freshwater Inst 501 University Crescent Winnipeg MB R3T 2N6 Can

JACKSON, WARREN, JR, b Oak Park, Ill, May 8, 22; m 47; c 2. ELECTRICAL ENGINEERING. *Educ:* Purdue Univ, BS, 47; Case Inst Technol, MS, 54. *Prof Exp:* Radio engr, Police Dept, River Forest, Ill, 41-42 & Purdue Univ, 46-47; elec engr, Chem & Physics Res Div, 47-54, sr tech specialist, Process Eng Div, 54-61, sr proj leader, Mgt Sci Unit, 61-70, instrumentation supvr res & develop, 70-74, SR PROCESS CONTROL SPECIALIST, RES & DEVELOP LAB, STANDARD OIL CO, OHIO, 74- *Mem:* AAAS; Inst Elec & Electronics Engrs; Instrument Soc Am; Soc Comput Simulation. *Res:* On line digital computer process control; electronic instrumentation for petroleum research; electronic computers; analog computer simulation of physical and business systems. *Mailing Add:* Res & Develop Labs 4440 Warrensville Center Rd Cleveland OH 44128

JACKSON, WILLIAM ADDISON, b Castile, NY, Apr 24, 26; m 64. PLANT NUTRITION, SOIL FERTILITY. *Educ:* Cornell Univ, BS, 50; Purdue Univ, MS, 52; NC State Univ, PhD(soil sci), 57. *Prof Exp:* Res instr soil sci, NC State Univ, 52-57; Ford Found fel plant nutrit, Univ Mich, 57-58; from asst prof to prof, 58-72, WILLIAM NEAL REYNOLDS PROF SOIL SCI, NC STATE UNIV, 72- *Concurrent Pos:* Mem comt post-doctoral fel eval, Div Biol & Agr, Nat Acad Sci-Nat Res Coun, 65-68; vis prof, Univ Ill, Urbana, 70-71. *Honors & Awards:* Co-recipient, Campbell Award, Am Inst Biol Sci, 64. *Mem:* Soil Sci Soc Am; Crop Sci Soc Am; Am Soc Agron; Am Soc Plant Pathologists; Japan Soc Soil Sci & Plant Nutrit. *Res:* Absorption, assimilation and distribution of nitrogen by higher plants; effects of nitrogen assimilation on photosynthesis, respiration and mineral accumulation. *Mailing Add:* Dept of Soil Sci NC State Univ Raleigh NC 27607

JACKSON, WILLIAM ANDREW, b Crawfordsville, Ark, Feb 8, 25; m 50; c 3. ANALYTICAL CHEMISTRY. *Educ:* Ark State Teachers Col, BS, 49. *Prof Exp:* Chemist, Int Paper Co, 49-54; res chemist, Fertilizer Lab, 54-65, CHIEF CHEMIST, ANAL SERV LAB, SOUTHERN PIEDMONT CONSERV RES CTR, AGR RES SERV, USDA, 65-, LAB HEAD, 73- *Res:* Basic phase of soil and water conservation research dealing with analysis of soil, water and plant materials in support of field, laboratory and greenhouse experiments. *Mailing Add:* 500 Timothy Rd Athens GA 30606

JACKSON, WILLIAM BRUCE, b Milwaukee, Wis, Sept 10, 26; m 52; c 3. ANIMAL ECOLOGY. *Educ:* Univ Wis, BA, 48, MA, 49; Johns Hopkins Univ, ScD(hyg & vert ecol), 52. *Prof Exp:* Asst zool, Univ Wis, 47-49; asst vert ecol, Johns Hopkins Univ, 49-52; res assoc animal behav, Am Mus Natural Hist, 52; sr asst scientist ecol, USPHS, 52-55; biologist, Pac Sci Bd, 55-57; asst prof, 57-64, asst dean, Col Lib Arts, 64-69, asst dean grad sch, 69-70, dir, Environ Studies Ctr, 70-80, PROF BIOL, BOWLING GREEN STATE UNIV, 64-, DIR, CTR ENVIRON RES & SERV, 80- *Concurrent Pos:* Collabr, US Fish & Wildlife Serv & Nat Pest Control Asn, 64-; consult, WHO & Food & Agr Orgn, UN, 69- & Ford Found, 75; consult ed, J Environ Educ, 73-77; chmn, Exec Comt, Ohio Biol Surv, 70-; adj prof community med, Med Col Ohio, Toledo, 74-80. *Mem:* Fel AAAS; Animal Behav Soc; Am Inst Biol Sci; Nat Asn Environ Educ; Am Ornithologists' Union. *Res:* Effects of insecticides on vertebrate populations; microclimatic factors in army ant behavior; ecology of small mammals and of arthropod disease vectors; economic and environmental biology; rodent and bird control methods; studies of anticoagulant resistance. *Mailing Add:* Ctr Environ Res & Serv Bowling Green State Univ Bowling Green OH 43403

JACKSON, WILLIAM DAVID, b Edinburgh, Scotland, May 20, 27; div; c 2. ELECTRICAL ENGINEERING. *Educ:* Glasgow Univ, BSc, 47, PhD(elec eng), 60. *Prof Exp:* Asst, Royal Col Sci & Technol, Glasgow Univ, 47-51; asst lectr elec eng, Col Sci & Technol, Univ Manchester, 51-54, lectr, 54-58; from asst prof to assoc prof, Mass Inst Technol, 58-66; prof, Univ Ill, Chicago Circle, 66-67; prin res scientist, Avco-Everett Res Lab, 67-72; prof elec eng, Univ Tenn Space Inst, 72-73; mgr thermal-mech energy conversion & storage, Elec Power Res Inst, Palo Alto, 73-74; mgr, MHD Prog, Off Coal Res & Energy Res & Develop Admin, Washington, DC, 74-75, dir MHD Div, 75-77; dir, Div Tech Anal & Spec Projs, Dept Energy, Washington, DC, 77-79; PRES, ENERGY CONSULT INC, 79- *Concurrent Pos:* Vis lectr, Mass Inst Technol, 55-57, lectr, 68-72; consult various industs & labs, 60-; vis prof, Tech Univ Berlin, 66; mem int magnetohydrodynamics liaison group, Int Atomic Energy Agency-UNESCO, 66-, chmn, 68-73; mem, US Steering Comt Eng Aspects Magnetohydrodynamics, 67-, prog chmn, 68-69, chmn, 69-70; mem, US-Ger Natural Resources Panel Magnetohydrodynamic Power, 70-72; mem, Task Force Tech Aspects, Comt Conserv Energy, Nat Power Surv, Fed Power Comn, 73; chmn, Steering Comt, US-USSR Coop Prog on magnethydrodynamics Power Generation, 73-79; prof lectr, George Washington Univ, 79-; mem, Energy Resources Operating Bd, Am Soc Mech Engrs, 81- *Honors & Awards:* Energy Res & Develop Admin Spec Achievement Award, 76; SERI Award, 78. *Mem:* Sr mem Inst Elec & Electronics Engrs; Am Phys Soc; assoc fel Am Inst Aeronaut & Astronaut; fel Brit Inst Elec Engrs. *Res:* Electrical power systems; magnetohydrodynamic power generation; analysis of energy systems, especially electrical aspects; development of technology base and engineering design data for first of a kind technologies; engineering of magnetohydodynamic power systems. *Mailing Add:* 3509 McKinley St NW Washington DC 20015

JACKSON, WILLIAM GORDON, b Iron Mountain, Mich, Apr 22, 19; m 43; c 2. CHEMISTRY. *Educ:* Univ Mich, BS, 42; Univ Ill, MS, 43, PhD(org chem), 45. *Prof Exp:* Asst chem, Univ Ill, 42-43, spec asst, Nat Defense Res Comt Proj, 43-45; res chemist, Upjohn Co, 46-59; pres, 59-77, CONSULT, BURDICK & JACKSON LABS, 78- *Mem:* Am Chem Soc. *Res:* Antibiotics, vitamin B12; natural product fractionation and structure; chromatography; countercurrent distribution; organic synthesis; laboratory automation apparatus; high-purity solvents. *Mailing Add:* Burdick & Jackson Labs Inc 1953 S Harvey St Muskegon MI 49442

JACKSON, WILLIAM JAMES, b Houston, Tex, Aug 1, 40. NEUROPSYCHOLOGY. *Educ:* Univ Tex, El Paso, BA, 62; Tex Tech Col, PhD(psychol), 66. *Prof Exp:* Nat Acad Sci-Nat Res Coun fel psychol, Aeromed Res Lab, Holloman AFB, NMex, 66-68; res asst prof, Univ Houston, 68-69 & Univ S Fla, 69-71; asst prof, 71-77, PROF PHYSIOL, MED COL GA, 77- *Concurrent Pos:* USPHS grant, Univ SFla, 69-71. *Mem:* AAAS; Am Psychol Asn; Soc Neurosci; Sigma Xi. *Res:* Neural substrate of learning and motivation; operant conditioning of brain activity. *Mailing Add:* Dept Physiol Med Col Ga Augusta GA 30901

JACKSON, WILLIAM MORGAN, b Birmingham, Ala, Sept 24, 36; m 59; c 2. PHOTOCHEMISTRY, CHEMICAL PHYSICS. *Educ:* Morehouse Col, BS, 56; Cath Univ Am, PhD(phys chem), 61. *Prof Exp:* Chemist res, Nat Bur Standards, 60-61; res scientist, Martin-Marietta Corp, 61-63; assoc, Nat Bur Standards, 63-64; asst, Goddard Space Flight Ctr, NASA, 64-67, sr chemist, 67-69; vis assoc prof physics, Univ Pittsburgh, 69-70; sr chemist, Goddard

Space Flight Ctr, NASA, 70-74; PROF CHEM, HOWARD UNIV, 74- Concurrent Pos: Mem US comt, Int Comn Optics, 75-77. Mem: AAAS; Am Chem Soc; Am Phys Soc; Int Astron Union; Optical Soc Am. Res: Chemical kinetics; photochemistry; molecular beams; astrochemistry; mass spectroscopy; application of tunable lasers to problems in photochemistry and chemical kinetics; photochemistry of comets. Mailing Add: Dept of Chem Howard Univ Washington DC 20059

JACKSON, WILLIAM MORRISON, b Colbert Co, Ala, Aug 2, 26; m 54; c 2. INORGANIC CHEMISTRY, PHYSICAL CHEMISTRY. Educ: Univ Ala, BS, 50; Univ Tenn, MS, 52 & 60, PhD(chem), 53, Am Bd Health Physics, cert, 80. Prof Exp: Chemist, Goodyear Atomic Corp, 53-55 & Union Carbide Corp, Oak Ridge Nat Lab, 55-61; group leader, Diamond Alkali Co, Ohio, 61-66; sr scientist, Oak Ridge Assoc Univs, Tenn, 66-68; tech mgr, Am Nuclear Corp, 68-70; syst chemist, 70-74, ENVIRON & HEALTH PHYSICS COORDR, ALA POWER CO, 74- Mem: Am Chem Soc; Health Physics Soc. Res: Radiochemistry; health physics. Mailing Add: Nuclear Generation Dept PO Box 2641 Birmingham AL 35291

JACKSON, WILLIAM ROY, JR, b Port Lavaca, Tex, Nov 26, 36. NUCLEAR PHYSICS. Educ: Columbia Univ, BA, 59; Rice Univ, MA, 65, PhD(physics), 67. Prof Exp: Asst prof, 67-71, ASSOC PROF PHYSICS, SOUTHWEST TEX STATE UNIV, 71- Mem: Am Phys Soc. Res: Low energy experimental nuclear physics; reaction mechanisms. Mailing Add: Dept of Physics Southwest Tex State Univ San Marcos TX 78666

JACKSON, WILLIAM THOMAS, b Stockdale, Ohio, May 10, 23; m 49; c 3. PLANT PHYSIOLOGY. Educ: Ohio State Univ, BS, 47; Duke Univ, PhD(bot), 53. Prof Exp: Instr biol, WVa Univ, 49-50; asst & plant physiol, Duke Univ, 50-53; from instr to asst prof bot, Yale Univ, 53-59; from asst prof to prof bot, 59-66, PROF BIOL, DARTMOUTH COL, 66- Concurrent Pos: Mem fel panel, NIH, 63-66. Mem: Am Soc Plant Physiol; Bot Soc Am; Am Soc Cell Biol; Scand Soc Plant Physiol. Res: Mechanism of action of growth regulators, particularly effects of pesticides upon mitosis and other events of cell cycle. Mailing Add: Dept of Biol Sci Dartmouth Col Hanover NH 03755

JACKSON, WINSTON JEROME, JR, b Asheville, NC, Feb 4, 26; m 52; c 2. POLYMER CHEMISTRY. Educ: Va Polytech Inst, BS, 49; Duke Univ, PhD(chem), 52. Prof Exp: From res chemist to sr res chemist, 52-57, res assoc, 58-72, sr res assoc, 73-80, RES FEL, EASTMAN CHEMICALS DIV, EASTMAN KODAK CO, 80- Mem: Am Chem Soc. Res: Organic synthesis; preparation and evaluation of new polymers and new polymer-forming reactions; liquid crystalline polymers. Mailing Add: Res Labs Tenn Eastman Co Kingsport TN 37660

JACO, NICHOLAS TREVENEN, b Liskeard, Eng, Sept 25, 20; m; c 4. PEDIATRICS. Educ: Oxford Univ, BA, 41, BSc, 43, MA, BM, BCh, 45; FRCP, dipl child health, 48; Royal Col Physicians & Surgeons Can, cert, 55, FRCP(C), 72. Prof Exp: Res fel pediat, Univ Liverpool, 50-51; res fel, Metab Unit, Hosp for Sic Children, Toronto, 55-56; asst clin prof, Columbia Univ, 61-63; assoc prof, 66-72, PROF PEDIAT, UNIV WESTERN ONT, 72-; HEAD DEPT PEDIAT, ST JOSEPH'S HOSP, LONDON, ONT, 66- Concurrent Pos: Clin investr, NY Health Res Coun, 61-63. Res: Newborn care. Mailing Add: Dept of Pediat St Joseph's Hosp London ON N6A 4V2 Can

JACO, WILLIAM HOWARD, b Grafton, WVa, July 14, 40; m 78; c 3. TOPOLOGY. Educ: Fairmont State Univ, BA, 62; Pa State Univ, MA, 64; Univ Wis, PhD(math), 68. Prof Exp: Proj mathematician underwater activities, Ord Res Lab, 61-64; instr math, Univ Mich, 68-70; from asst prof to assoc prof, 70-78, PROF MATH, RICE UNIV, 78- Concurrent Pos: NSF fel math, Inst Advan Study, 71-72, 78-79. Mem: Am Math Soc; Math Asn Am. Res: Geometric topology with particular interest in classical three-manifold topology; classification problems for three-manifolds and the structure of groups which are fundamental groups of three-manifolds. Mailing Add: Dept of Math Rice Univ Houston TX 77001

JACOB, ARTHUR FRANK, sedimentary petrology, economic geology, see previous edition

JACOB, FIELDEN EMMITT, b Columbia, Mo, July 20, 10; m 37; c 3. ANALYTICAL CHEMISTRY, PHYSICAL CHEMISTRY. Educ: Univ Mo, AB, 32, BS & MA, 35, PhD(chem), 39. Prof Exp: Instr chem, Univ Mo, 39-42; asst prof, Mont Sch Mines, 42-45; assoc prof, Kans State Teachers Col, Emporia, 45-47; assoc prof, 47-75, prof, 75-80, EMER PROF CHEM, DRAKE UNIV, 80- Mem: Am Asn Univ Profs; Am Chem Soc. Res: Colorimetric analysis; carotinoid pigments of egg yolks from hens on various diets; spectrophotometry; stability constants. Mailing Add: 1520 48th St Des Moines IA 50311

JACOB, GARY STEVEN, b St Louis, Mo, Mar 18, 47; m 75. BIOCHEMISTRY, ENZYMOLOGY. Educ: Univ Mo-St Louis, BS, 69; Univ Wis-Madison, PhD(biochem), 76. Prof Exp: fel biophysics, Thomas J Watson Res Ctr, IBM Corp, 76-79. Mem: AAAS; Am Chem Soc. Res: Structure and function of metalloproteins, particularly molybdenum-containing proteins, and with a dependence on the mechanism of enzyme action. Mailing Add: 800 N Lindbergh Blvd St Louis MO 63167

JACOB, HARRY S, b San Francisco, Calif, Apr 6, 33; m 54; c 3. INTERNAL MEDICINE, HEMATOLOGY. Educ: Reed Col, BA, 54; Harvard Univ, MD, 58. Prof Exp: Intern med, Boston City Hosp, 58-59, resident, 59-60; NIH fels hemat, Thorndike Mem Lab, Harvard Univ, 60-63, tutor med sci, Harvard Med Sch, 63-65; assoc prof med, Sch Med, Tufts Univ, 65-68; assoc prof, 68-70, PROF MED & CHIEF SECT HEMAT, MED SCH, UNIV MINN, MINNEAPOLIS, 70- Concurrent Pos: NIH res grants, 65-; prof, Royal Postgrad Med Sch London, 66; prof, Med Sch, Univ Chicago, 71; prof med, Univ Man, 71. Honors & Awards: Conrad Elvehjem Mem Award, 71. Mem: Am Soc Clin Invest; Am Fedn Clin Res; Am Soc Hemat; Int Soc Hemat; Asn Am Physicians. Res: Red cell metabolism; hemoglobin function-structure relationships; granulocyte function; reticuloendothelial physiology. Mailing Add: Dept of Med Univ of Minn Med Ctr Minneapolis MN 55455

JACOB, HENRY GEORGE, JR, b New Haven, Conn, June 11, 22; m 44; c 3. MATHEMATICS. Educ: Yale Univ, BE, 43, ME, 47, PhD(math), 53. Prof Exp: Asst instr calculus, Yale Univ, 50-53; asst prof math, La State Univ, 53-56 & Johns Hopkins Univ, 56-57; assoc prof, La State Univ, 57-62; PROF MATH, UNIV MASS, AMHERST, 62- Mem: Am Math Soc; Math Asn Am. Res: Algebra. Mailing Add: Dept of Math Univ of Mass Amherst MA 01002

JACOB, HORACE S, b Varanasi, India, May 17, 31; US citizen; m 61; c 2. POULTRY SCIENCE, PHYSIOLOGICAL GENETICS. Educ: Univ Lucknow, BA, 54; Lucknow Christian Training Col, LT, 55; Sam Houston State Univ, BS, 58, MEd, 59; Pa State Univ, MS, 63; Tex A&M Univ, PhD(poultry sci & biol), 67. Prof Exp: Agr supvr & teacher, Ingraham Inst, 59-61; assoc prof biol & agr, Alcorn Agr & Mech Col, 67; ASST PROF BIOL, SOUTHWESTERN UNIV, 67- Mem: AAAS. Res: Population genetics through the aid of electrophoretic studies. Mailing Add: Dept of Biol Southwestern Univ Georgetown TX 78626

JACOB, JAMES THECATTIL, b Ranny, India, June 18, 36; US citizen; m 64; c 2. PHARMACEUTICS. Educ: Univ Rajasthan, India, BPharm, 58; Univ Wash, MS, 63, PhD(pharmaceut), 66. Prof Exp: Chemist, Bipha Drug Labs, India, 58-61; sr pharmacist, Merck & Co, 67-71; sr pharmacist, Cooper Labs, 72-73, sect head, Prod Develop, 73-75, assoc dir, 76-78, dir new prod develop, 78-79; dir prod develop, Berlex Labs, 79-81; VPRES, DURAMED PHARMACEUT INC, 82- Concurrent Pos: Fel, Drug Plastic Res Labs, Univ Tex, Austin, 66-67. Mem: Am Pharmaceut Asn; Acad Pharmaceut Sci; Sigma Xi. Res: Sustained release dosage forms; ophthalmic formulations; bioavailability; drug-plastic interactions. Mailing Add: Duramed Pharmaceut Inc Westbury NY 11590

JACOB, JONAH HYE, b Calcutta, India, May 15, 43; US citizen; m 77; c 1. LASER PHYSICS, PLASMA PHYSICS. Educ: London Univ, BSc, 64; Yale Univ, PhD(plasma physics), 70. Prof Exp: Res assoc plasma physics, Yale Univ, 70-71; PRIN RES SCIENTIST LASER & PLASMA PHYSICS, AVCO-EVERETT RES LAB, 71- Mem: Am Phys Soc; AAAS. Res: High power lasers; discharge physics; atomic physics. Mailing Add: Avco-Everett Res Lab 2385 Revere Beach Pkwy Everett MA 02149

JACOB, K THOMAS, b India, May 13, 44; m 70; c 3. EXTRACTIVE METALLURGY, PROCESS METALLURGY. Educ: Mysore Univ, India, BSc, 64; Indian Inst Sci, BE, 67; Univ London, PhD(eng), 70; Imperial Col Sci & Technol, DIC, 70. Prof Exp: Sr res assoc, 71-76, asst prof, 76-79, ASSOC PROF METALL & MAT SCI, UNIV TORONTO, 79- Concurrent Pos: Consult, Lawrence Berkeley Lab, 77-79. Mem: Metall Soc; Am Ceramic Soc; Electrochem Soc; Can Inst Mining & Metall; Nat Inst Ceramic Engrs. Res: Physical chemistry of extractive metallurgy; interrelations between structure and thermodynamics properties of inorganic materials, alloys and melts; mathematical modelling; phase stability; chemical aspects of ceramic processing; transport properties of ceramics. Mailing Add: Dept Metall & Mat Sci Univ Toronto Toronto ON M5S 1A4 Can

JACOB, KLAUS H, Stuttgart, Germany, Aug 20, 36. TECTONICS, GEOTHERMAL RESEARCH. Educ: Univ Frankfurt, PhD(gophys), 68. Prof Exp: Res assoc, 68-73, SR RES ASSOC SEISMOL & TECTONICS, LAMONT-DOHERTY GEOL OBSERV, COLUMBIA UNIV, 73- Mem: Am Geophys Union; Seismol Soc Am; Am Geol Inst. Res: Geophysics of active plate margins (subduction and continental collision zones) based on earthquake information; seismic and volcanic hazards; microearthquake studies in Alaska, Himalaya and Central America; earthquake prediction. Mailing Add: Lamont-Doherty Geol Observ Palisades NY 10964

JACOB, LEONARD STEVEN, b Philadelphia, Pa, Mar 18, 49; m 69; c 2. ANESTHESIOLOGY, PHARMACOLOGY. Educ: Temple Med Sch, PhD(pharmacol), 75; Med Col Pa, MD, 78. Prof Exp: ASSOC PROF PHARMACOL, PA COL PODIATRIC MED, 75- Concurrent Pos: Mem int speakers bur infectious dis, Smith Kline & French Lab, 77-; vis instr, Med Col Pa, 77-; house staff anesthesiol, Hosp Univ Pa, 78- Mem: AMA; AAAS; Sigma Xi. Res: Cardiovascular and autonomic pharmacology; antibiotic therapy. Mailing Add: Pa Col Podiatric Med Eighth Race Street Philadelphia PA 19107

JACOB, PAUL B(ERNARD), JR, b Columbus, Miss, June 9, 22; m 46; c 2. ELECTRICAL ENGINEERING. Educ: Miss State Col, BS, 44; Northwestern Univ, MS, 48. Prof Exp: Jr engr, Tenn Eastman Corp, 44-46; from instr to assoc prof elec eng, 46-56, PROF ELEC ENG, MISS STATE UNIV, 56-, ASSOC HEAD DEPT, 61- Mem: Am Soc Eng Educ; Inst Elec & Electronics Engrs; Power Eng Soc. Res: High voltage engineering; electric power system analysis. Mailing Add: PO Drawer EE Mississippi State MS 39762

JACOB, PEYTON, III, b Ann Arbor, Mich, Sept 23, 47. DRUG METABOLISM, ORGANIC SYNTHESIS. Educ: Univ Calif, BS, 69; Purdue Univ, PhD(chem), 75. Prof Exp: NIH fel, 75-78, ASST RES CHEMIST, DIV CLIN PHARMACOL, SCH MED, UNIV CALIF, SAN FRANCISCO & SAN FRANCISCO GEN HOSP MED CTR, 78- Mem: Am Chem Soc; Sigma Xi. Res: Tobacco alkaloid metabolites; development of new analytical methodology for drugs and their metabolites in biologic fluids. Mailing Add: 1995 Ascot Dr #5 Moraga CA 94556

JACOB, RICHARD JOHN, b Salt Lake City, Utah, Oct 9, 37; m 59; c 3. THEORETICAL PHYSICS. Educ: Univ Utah, BS, 58, PhD(physics), 63. Prof Exp: Asst prof, 63-69, assoc prof, 69-78, PROF PHYSICS, ARIZ STATE UNIV, 78- Mem: Am Phys Soc; Am Asn Physics Teachers. Res: Theoretical elementary particle physics. Mailing Add: Dept of Physics Ariz State Univ Tempe AZ 85281

JACOB, RICHARD L, b Ripon, Wis, July 6, 32; m 67; c 1. THEORETICAL PHYSICS. *Educ:* Stanford Univ, BS, 55; Univ Wis, MS, 56, PhD(physics), 59. *Prof Exp:* Res assoc, Univ Wis, 59-60; asst prof physics, Tufts Univ, 60-65; assoc prof, Claremont Men's Col, 65-68; ASSOC PROF PHYSICS, CORNELL COL, 68-, ACAD COMP COORDR, 72- *Mem:* Am Phys Soc; Am Asn Physics Teachers. *Res:* Elementary particle physics; relativistic quantum mechanics; field theory; philosophy of physics; computer science. *Mailing Add:* Dept of Physics Cornell Col Mt Vernon IA 52314

JACOB, ROBERT ALLEN, b Chicago, Ill, Dec 16, 42; m 71. ANALYTICAL CHEMISTRY, CLINICAL CHEMISTRY. *Educ:* Ill Col, BA, 65; Southern Ill Univ, MA, 67, PhD, 70. *Prof Exp:* res chemist, Human Nutrit Lab, 75-79, sr chemist, Midwest Res Inst, Kemo, 79-81, RES CHEMIST, NUTRIT RES CTR, USDA, 81- *Mem:* Am Chem Soc; Am Asn Clin Chem; Sigma Xi. *Res:* Trace metal analysis and metabolism; analytical chemistry of nutrients; clinical lab methods for assessing nutritional status; clinical chemistry. *Mailing Add:* Nutrit Res Ctr USDA 15 Kneeland St Boston MA 02111

JACOB, STANLEY W, b Philadelphia, Pa, Jan 7, 24; m 64; c 2. MEDICINE, SURGERY. *Educ:* Ohio State Univ, BA, 45, MD, 48. *Prof Exp:* Instr surg, Harvard Med Sch, 57-59; asst prof, 59-65, ASSOC PROF SURG, MED SCH, UNIV ORE, 65-, GERLINGER ASSOC PROF, 81- *Mem:* Am Col Surg; Soc Univ Surg; NY Acad Sci. *Res:* Preservation and transplantation of tissues; biologic applications of dimethyl sulfoxide. *Mailing Add:* Ore Health Sci Univ 3181 SN Sam Jackson Park Rd Portland OR 97201

JACOB, THEODORE AUGUST, b Braddock, Pa, Aug 22, 19; m 44; c 3. ORGANIC CHEMISTRY, BIOCHEMISTRY. *Educ:* Col Wooster, BA, 41; Rensselaer Polytech Inst, MS, 43; Purdue Univ, PhD(org chem), 49. *Prof Exp:* Asst org chem, Rensselaer Polytech Inst, 41-43; org chemist, Standard Oil Co, NJ, 43-46; asst, Purdue Univ, 46-48; sr chemist, 49-57, group leader natural prod develop, 57-69, mgr animal drug metab, 69-76, asst dir, 76-80, DIR ANIMAL DRUG METAB & RADIOCHEM, MERCK, SHARP & DOHME RES LABS, 80- *Mem:* Am Chem Soc. *Res:* Isolation, purification and identification of biologically active products from plant, animal and fermentation sources; preparation and isolation of synthetic peptides, steroids and nucleotides; isolation and identification of drug metabolites. *Mailing Add:* Merck Sharp & Dohme Res Labs Rahway NJ 07065

JACOBER, WILLIAM JOHN, b Newark, NJ, Feb 13, 17; m 42; c 4. CHEMISTRY. *Educ:* Union Col, NY, BS, 38; Brown Univ, PhD(chem), 42. *Prof Exp:* Res chemist, NY, 42-53, engr, 53-54, sr engr, 54-74, STAFF ENGR, E I DU PONT DE NEMOURS & CO, INC, 74- *Mem:* Am Chem Soc. *Res:* Physical chemistry of cellulose; conductance of aluminum bromide and substituted aluminum bromides in non aqueous solvents; separation of isotopes; tritium control technology. *Mailing Add:* 1022 Hitchcock Dr Aiken SC 29801

JACOBI, GEORGE (THOMAS), b Mannheim, Ger, May 19, 22; nat US; m 55; c 1. ELECTRONIC ENGINEERING. *Educ:* Ohio State Univ, BEE, 47, MSc, 48. *Prof Exp:* Asst, Betatron Lab, Ohio State Univ, 48; engr res lab, Gen Elec Co, NY, 48-50, mgr analog comput eng, Gen Eng Lab, 50-55, electronic recording mach acct systs lab, Comput Dept, Calif, 56-57, mgr spec comput eng, 57-59; dir comput & mgt sci res, ITT Res Inst, 59-77; DIR BLDG AUTOMOTIVE SYST, JOHNSON CONTROLS INC, 77- *Mem:* Sr mem Inst Elec & Electronics Engrs; Asn Comput Mach; NY Acad Sci; Sigma Xi. *Res:* Computer logic and storage devices; system theory; electronic component technology; engineering management. *Mailing Add:* 2375 N Wahl Ave Milwaukee WI 53211

JACOBI, PETER ALAN, b Abington, Pa, Sept 14, 45; m 75. SYNTHETIC ORGANIC CHEMISTRY. *Educ:* Univ NH, BS, 67; Princeton Univ, MS, 70, PhD(chem), 73. *Prof Exp:* ASST PROF CHEM, WESLEYAN UNIV, 75- *Concurrent Pos:* Corp appointee, Harvard Univ, 73-75; consult, Anderson Oil Co, 76- *Mem:* Am Chem Soc; Royal Soc Chem; Sigma Xi. *Res:* Mechanistic organic chemistry; chemistry of natural products. *Mailing Add:* Off of Chmn Dept Wesleyan Univ Middletown CT 06457

JACOBI, W(ILLIAM) M(ALLETT), b Elizabeth, NJ, Apr 27, 30; m 62; c 2. NUCLEAR ENGINEERING. *Educ:* Syracuse Univ, BChE, 51; Univ Del, MChE, 53, PhD(chem eng), 55. *Prof Exp:* Supvry engr nuclear design, Bettis Atomic Power Div, Westinghouse Elec Corp, 55-61; consult, Nuclear Utilities Serv, Inc, 61-63; mgr adv reactor design, Westinghouse Astronuclear Lab, 63-66, mgr design & anal, systs & tech eng, 66-68, mgr mark 48 design eng, weapons dept, 68-70, eng mgr, Fast Flux Test Facility, Westinghouse Advan Reactors Div, 70-73; proj mgr, Clinch River Breeder Reactor Plant, systs eng mgr, Westinghouse Pressurized Water Reactor Systs Div, 78-79, gen mgr, Westinghouse Nuclear Technol div, 79-80, GEN MGR, WESTINGHOUSE NUCLEAR FUEL DIV, 81- *Mem:* Am Nuclear Soc; Am Inst Aeronaut & Astronaut. *Res:* Reactor physics; fluid flow and mechanical design. *Mailing Add:* PO Box 3912 Westinghouse Nuclear Fuel Div Pittsburgh PA 15230

JACOBOWITZ, DAVID, b Brooklyn, NY, July 15, 31; m 57; c 2. PHARMACOLOGY. *Educ:* City Col New York, BS, 53; Ohio State Univ, MS, 58, PhD(pharmacol), 62. *Prof Exp:* NIH fel pharmacol, Sch Med, Univ Pa, 62-63, instr, 63-65, assoc, 65-67, from asst prof to assoc prof, 67-71; HEAD HISTOPHARMACOL SECT, LAB CLIN SCI, NIH, 71- *Concurrent Pos:* Pa Plan scholar, Sch Med, Univ Pa, 63-65; USPHS career develop award, 66; Lady Davis vis prof, Hebrew Univ Jerusalem, Israel, 81. *Mem:* Neurochem Soc; Am Soc Pharmacol & Exp Therapeut; Neurosci Soc; Histochem Soc; Am Col Neuropsychopharmacology. *Res:* Endocrine pharmacology; effect of stress on pituitary and hypothalamic metabolism and adrenocorticotropic hormone synthesis; cellular pharmacology; localization and mechanism of action of the autonomic neurotransmitters; histochemistry of catecholamines and acetylcholinesterase; immunohistochemistry of peptides; localization of neuromodulator and neurotransmitter pathways in the brain. *Mailing Add:* Lab of Clin Sci Bldg 10 Rm 2D-46 Nat Inst of Health Bethesda MD 20014

JACOBOWITZ, RONALD, b New York, NY, Oct 18, 34; m 60; c 3. LINEAR STATISTICAL MODELS. *Educ:* City Col New York, BA, 55; Univ Chicago, SM, 56; Princeton Univ, PhD(math), 60. *Prof Exp:* Instr math, Mass Inst Technol, 60-62; asst prof, Univ Ariz, 62-66; assoc prof, Univ Kans, 66-70; PROF MATH, ARIZ STATE UNIV, 70- *Concurrent Pos:* Vis statistician, NIH, 79-80. *Mem:* Math Asn Am; Am Statist Asn. *Res:* Mathematical statistics; algebra; number theory; theory of quadratic forms. *Mailing Add:* Dept of Math Ariz State Univ Tempe AZ 85287

JACOBS, ABIGAIL CONWAY, b St Louis, Mo, Nov 11, 42; m 69; c 2. BIOCHEMISTRY. *Educ:* Univ Mich, Ann Arbor, BS, 64; Univ Calif, Berkeley, PhD(biochem), 68. *Prof Exp:* Am Cancer Soc fel immunochem, 68-70, res assoc biochem, Weizmann Inst Sci, Rehovot, Israel, 70-71; res assoc biochem, Queen's Univ, Belfast, 71-72; SR TECH WRITER & RESEARCHER CHEM CARCINOGENESIS, TRACTOR JITCO, 79- *Concurrent Pos:* Res assoc, Nuffield Found, 71-72. *Mem:* Sigma Xi. *Res:* Biochemistry of the allergic response. *Mailing Add:* Tracor Jitco 1776 E Jefferson St Rockville MD 20852

JACOBS, ALAN M(ARTIN), b New York, NY, Nov 14, 32; m 55, 78; c 2. NUCLEAR ENGINEERING, STATISTICAL MECHANICS. *Educ:* Cornell Univ, BEngPhys, 55; Pa State Univ, MS, 58, PhD(physics), 63. *Prof Exp:* Res assoc, Pa State Univ, University Park, 56-63, assoc prof nuclear eng, 63-68, prof, 68-80; PROF & CHMN NUCLEAR ENG SCI, UNIV FLA, 80- *Concurrent Pos:* Consult, Allis-Chalmers Mfg Co, 56-59, Westinghouse Astronuclear Lab, 61-62, Millitron, Inc & HRB-Singer, Inc, 63- & Combustion Eng Inc, 75- *Mem:* Am Nuclear Soc; Sigma Xi; Am Asn Physicists Med; Am Health Physics Soc; Am Soc Eng Educ. *Res:* Many body problems, especially neutron transport and plasma physics; nuclear reactor theory; radiography. *Mailing Add:* Nuclear Eng Sci Dept Univ Fla Gainesville FL 32611

JACOBS, ALAN MARTIN, b New York, NY, Feb 17, 42; m 68; c 2. GEOLOGY. *Educ:* City Col New York, BS, 63; Ind Univ, MA, 65, PhD(geol), 67. *Prof Exp:* Teaching asst, Ind Univ, 63-64; teaching assoc, 64; asst geologist, Ill State Geol Surv, 67-74; asst proj geologist, 74-75, proj geologist, 75-80, SR PROJ GEOLOGIST, E D'APPOLONIA CONSULT ENGRS, INC, 80- *Concurrent Pos:* Pres, Geoprobe, Alan M Jacobs, Inc, 79- *Mem:* Geol Soc Am; Am Quaternary Asn; Am Inst Prof Geologists. *Res:* Engineering geology; glacial and quaternary geology; geomorphology; geologic factors in site selection; seismicity; age-dating; environmental geology; borehole camera surveys. *Mailing Add:* Geoprobe PO Box 17072 Pittsburgh PA 15235

JACOBS, ALBERT MICHAEL, b Roanoke, Va, Mar 17, 19; m 56; c 2. APPLIED CHEMISTRY. *Educ:* Roanoke Col, BS, 41; Frostburg State Col, MS, 73. *Prof Exp:* Res chemist, Hercules Powder Co, NJ, 41, gen lab supvr, Va, 41-46, res assoc, Allegany Ballistics Lab, 46-56, supvr propellant res group, 56-60, supt rocket develop, 60-64, prog mgr, 64-67, mgr advan plans & progs, Hercules Inc, 67-69; mgr spec studies, 69-73, PROG MGR, HERCULES INC/ABL, 73- *Mem:* Am Chem Soc; Am Inst Aeronaut & Astronaut; Am Defense Preparedness Asn. *Res:* Solid propellants; propellant thermodynamics, formulation, burning catalysis and interior ballistic phenomena; rocket development. *Mailing Add:* 800 Washington St Cumberland MD 21502

JACOBS, ALLAN EDWARD, b Toronto, Ont, Aug 7, 38; m 62. THEORETICAL SOLID STATE PHYSICS. *Educ:* Univ Toronto, BASc, 60; Univ Waterloo, MSc, 62; Univ Ill, Urbana, PhD(physics), 68. *Prof Exp:* Res asst phys metall, Univ Toronto, 60-61; Nat Res Coun Can fel, Univ Hamburg, 68-69; asst prof, 69-74, ASSOC PROF PHYSICS, UNIV TORONTO, 74- *Concurrent Pos:* Nat Res Coun Can res grants, 69- *Mem:* Am Phys Soc; Can Asn Physicists. *Res:* Theory of inhomogeneous superconductors; theory of superfluid helium. *Mailing Add:* Dept of Physics Univ of Toronto Toronto ON M5S 1A7 Can

JACOBS, ALLEN LEON, b New York, NY, May 22, 31; m 54; c 3. PHARMACEUTICAL CHEMISTRY. *Educ:* Columbia Univ, BS, 52, MS, 54, PhD(pharmaceut chem), 62. *Prof Exp:* Instr chem, Col Pharmacol, Columbia Univ, 60-62; res anal chemist, 62-63, MGR ANAL RES, SANDOZ PHARMACEUT, INC, 63- *Mem:* Am Chem Soc; Am Pharmaceut Asn. *Res:* Plant biochemistry; analytical chemistry. *Mailing Add:* 11 Alcor Rd RFD 2 Dover NJ 07801

JACOBS, ALLEN WAYNE, b Quincy, Ill, May 12, 42. ANATOMY. *Educ:* Southern Ill Univ, BA, 65, MA, 67; Univ Iowa, PhD(anat), 71. *Prof Exp:* Asst physiol, Southern Ill Univ, 66-67; asst prof, 71-74, ASSOC PROF ANAT, MICH STATE UNIV, 74-, ASST DEAN EDUC RESOURCES, COL OSTEOP MED, 75- *Mem:* Am Inst Biol Sci; Asn Am Med Cols; Nat Sci Teachers Asn; Am Soc Performance Improvement. *Res:* Design and evaluation of anatomical instruction programs for undergraduate, graduate and medical students. *Mailing Add:* Dept of Anat East Fee Hall Mich State Univ East Lansing MI 48824

JACOBS, ALMA ALICE, microbiology, immunology, see previous edition

JACOBS, BARBARA B, b Cambridge, Mass, July 23, 29; c 2. ENDOCRINOLOGY, IMMUNOLOGY. *Educ:* Mich State Univ, BS, 50, MS, 52; Ind Univ, PhD(zool), 56. *Prof Exp:* Res assoc cancer res, Med Ctr, Ind Univ, 56; Am Cancer Soc-NSF fel, Med Ctr, Univ Colo, 56-58; USPHS fel, State Univ NY Downstate Med Ctr, 58-59; sr res scientist, Roswell Park Mem Inst, 59-63; assoc res scientist, 63-70, dir immunol, Am Med Ctr Denver, 70-77; assoc prof, 78-79, PROF LIFE SCI CTR, NOVA UNIV, 79- *Concurrent Pos:* Lect consult, State Univ NY Buffalo, 63; adj assoc prof, Sch Med, Univ Colo, 76-78. *Mem:* Am Asn Cancer Res; Am Asn Immunol; Transplantation Soc; Soc Exp Biol & Med. *Res:* Endocrine and hormonally influenced neoplasms; growth of tumors in allogeneic hosts following passage in vitro; tumor-host immunologic interactions. *Mailing Add:* Life Sci Ctr Nova Univ Ft Lauderdale FL 33314

JACOBS, DAVID R, JR, b Brooklyn, NY, Apr 16, 45; m 68; c 3. CARDIOVASCULAR EPIDEMIOLOGY, PREVENTIVE CARDIOLOGY. *Educ:* Hofstra Univ, BA, 66; Johns Hopkins Univ, PhD(math statist), 71. *Prof Exp:* Asst prof, Towson State Col, 70-71; asst prof biostatist, Dept Social & Prev Med, Univ Md, 71-74; asst prof biostatist, Lab Physiol Hyg, Univ, Minn, Minneapolis, 74-79, assoc prof, 79-81. *Concurrent Pos:* Fel, Coun Epidemiol, Am Heart Asn. *Mem:* Am Statist Asn; Soc Epidemiol Res; Am Heart Asn. *Res:* Carrying out of large-scale, long-term clinical trials; general research in cardiovascular epidemiology, including intervention methodologies for lowering the risk factors and relevant statistical techniques. *Mailing Add:* 100 St Bedford SE Minneapolis MN 55414

JACOBS, DIANE MARGARET, b Port-of-Spain, Trinidad, Mar 24, 40; US citizen; div. IMMUNOLOGY. *Educ:* Radcliffe Col, AB, 61; Harvard Univ, PhD(bact), 67. *Prof Exp:* Instr immunol, Hadassah Med Sch, Hebrew Univ, Jerusalem, 67-68, lectr, 68-71; New York Cancer Res Inst fel, Dept Biol, Univ Calif, San Diego, 71-73, instr biol, 73-74; sr res assoc, Salk Inst Biol Sci, 74-76; assoc prof, 76-80, PROF MICROBIOL, STATE UNIV NY, BUFFALO, 80- *Concurrent Pos:* consult, Hoffman-LaRoche, 75-76 & 78-79; mem cause and prev sci rev comt, Nat Cancer Inst, 77-81; prin investr on res grants from NIH, 74- & Am Cancer Soc, 77-80. *Mem:* AAAS; NY Acad Sci; Am Asn Immunologists; Reticuloendothelial Soc; Am Soc Microbiol. *Res:* Immunomodulatory agents of bacterial origin, particularly lipopolysaccharide; mechanism of triggering lymphocytes; nature of interaction with lymphocytes; lymphocyte membrane determinants interacting with lipopolysaccharide; structural requirements for lipopolysaccharide biological activity. *Mailing Add:* Dept of Microbiol State Univ NY Buffalo NY 14214

JACOBS, DONALD, physical chemistry, health physics, see previous edition

JACOBS, EDWIN M, b San Francisco, Calif, Sept 8, 25; m 66. MEDICAL ONCOLOGY. *Educ:* Reed Col, BA, 50; Cornell Univ, MD, 54. *Prof Exp:* Intern med, Bellevue Hosp, 54-55, resident, 56-57; resident, Mem Ctr, Sloan-Kettering Inst Cancer Res, 55-56, resident hemat, 57-58, resident & fel med & cancer chemother, 58-59; clin instr med, Sch Med & jr res physician, Cancer Res Inst, Med Ctr, 60-63, asst clin prof & head clin serv & asst res physician, Med Ctr, 63-69, assoc res physician, Cancer Res Inst & assoc clin prof med & radiol, Med Ctr, Univ Calif, San Francisco, 69-76; prog dir, 76-78, ASSOC BR CHIEF, CLIN INVEST BR, DIV CANCER TREATMENT, NAT CANCER INST, 78- *Concurrent Pos:* Consult, Vet Admin Hosp, Martinez, 62-, USPHS Hosp, San Francisco, 62-, Claire Zellerbach Saroni Tumor Inst, Mt Zion Hosp, 65-, Kaiser Hosp, Oakland, 66- & Naval Hosp, Oak Knoll, 73-; co-prin investr, West Coop Cancer Chemother Group, 63-, vchmn, 69-; Squibb-Olin fel, 65; mem lymphoma task force, Nat Cancer Inst, 66; dep prog dir, Clin Cancer Training Grant, 69-71, proj dir, 71-; vis physician, Royal Marsden Hosp, London, Eng, 71; prin investr, Western Cancer Studies Group, 71; coordr testicular cancer, 76, mem, Working Cadre, Nat Prostate Cancer Proj, 76 & Found Advan Educ Sci, NIH, 76. *Mem:* Fel Am Col Physicians; Am Radium Soc; Am Asn Cancer Res; Am Asn Cancer Educ; Am Soc Hematol. *Res:* Internal medicine. *Mailing Add:* Clin Invest Br 7910 Woodmont Ave Rm c 803 Bethesda MD 20014

JACOBS, ELLIOTT WARREN, b Brooklyn, NY, Feb 10, 50; m 71. APPLIED MATHEMATICS. *Educ:* State Univ New York, Stony Brook, BS, 71; Adelphi Univ, MS, 73, PhD(math), 76. *Prof Exp:* Asst prof math, Muskingum Col, 76-77 & Mt Union Col, 77-78; ASST PROF MATH, EMBRY-RIDDLE AERONAUT UNIV, 78- *Mem:* Am Math Soc; Math Asn Am. *Res:* Differential equations; nonstandard analysis. *Mailing Add:* Div of Math & Phys Sci Embry-Riddle Aeronaut Univ Daytona Beach FL 32014

JACOBS, EMMETT S, b Selma, NC, Mar 17, 26; m 52; c 2. AIR POLLUTION. *Educ:* Univ NC, BS, 50; Lehigh Univ, MS, 55, PhD(anal chem), 58. *Prof Exp:* Chemist, Nitrogen Div, Allied Chem Corp, 50-52; instr anal chem, Lehigh Univ, 52-55; res chemist anal, Jackson Lab, 58-66, res supvr anal res, 66-69, supvr automotive emission studies, Petrol Lab, 69-71, supvr anal & environ studies, 71-74, div head, Emissions & Eng Test Div, Petrol Lab, 74-78, DIV HEAD, PETROL ADDITIVES & ENVIRON & MGR ANTIKNOCKS TECH SERV, PETROL LAB, PETROCHEM DEPT, E I DU PONT DE NEMOURS & CO, INC, 78- *Mem:* Am Chem Soc; Am Soc Testing & Mat. *Res:* Analytical chemistry, especially gas chromatography, electrochemistry, x-ray and infrared spectroscopy; atmospheric chemistry and analysis of automotive emissions; gasoline quality and volume demand; gasoline blinding; lead in gasoline environmental issues. *Mailing Add:* Petrol Lab E I du Pont de Nemours & Co Inc Wilmington DE 19898

JACOBS, FRANCIS ALBIN, b Minneapolis, Minn, Feb 23, 18; m 53; c 5. BIOCHEMISTRY. *Educ:* Regis Col, BS, 39; St Louis Univ, PhD(biochem), 49. *Prof Exp:* Asst chem, Univ Denver, 39-41; chemist, Shattuck Chem Co, 41; biochemist, Off Sci Res & Develop, 42-45; Nat Cancer Inst fel chemotherapeut, 49-50; from instr to asst prof biochem, Sch Med, Univ Pittsburgh, 51-54; from asst prof to assoc prof, 54-64, PROF BIOCHEM, SCH MED, UNIV NDAK, 64- *Concurrent Pos:* Dir res participation for teacher training prog, Univ NDak, 59-63; mem adv comt sci & math, Dept Pub Instr, NDak, 59-; mem rev & eval comt, NSF, 60- *Mem:* Fel AAAS; Am Chem Soc; Am Soc Biol Chem; Soc Exp Biol & Med; Am Inst Nutrit. *Res:* Antibiotics and antitumor agents from microorganisms; gastroenterology, intestinal transport of amino acids and lipids; audiovisual aids in the teaching of biochemistry and nutrition; trace metal nutrition. *Mailing Add:* Dept of Biochem Univ NDak Sch of Med Grand Forks ND 58202

JACOBS, GEORGE JOSEPH, b New York, NY, Aug 30, 17; m 47; c 3. SPACE BIOLOGY, FISH & WILDLIFE SCIENCE. *Educ:* Univ Miss, AB, 40; WVa Univ, MSc, 46; George Washington Univ, PhD(zool), 55. *Prof Exp:* Biologist oceanog, US Navy Hydrographic Off, 49-50, biologist hematol, Naval Med Res Inst, 50-56; res biologist, Atomic Bomb Casualty Comn, Nat Acad Sci-Nat Res Coun, Japan, 56-59; space biologist, NASA, 59-62, chief phys biol, 62-71, chief ecol, 71-79; CONSULT LIFE SCI, 79- *Concurrent Pos:* Collabr, Brookhaven Nat Lab, 55; managing ed, J Am Soc Ichthyologists & Herpetologists, 66-72; hon res assoc, Smithsonian Inst, 71-; herpetol ed, J Am Soc Ichthyol & Herpetol, 78-82; consult, Am Physiol Soc, 80- *Mem:* AAAS; Am Soc Ichthyologists & Herpetologists; Biophys Soc; Am Physiol Soc. *Res:* Space biology; herpetology; environmental quality; ecology; remote sensing; comparative animal physiology. *Mailing Add:* Rd 2 Box 300E3 West Meadow House Bethesda MD 20014

JACOBS, GERALD DANIEL, b Perrysburg, Ohio, Jan 19, 35; m 58; c 2. PHYSICAL CHEMISTRY, SPECTROSCOPY. *Educ:* Bowling Green State Univ, BA, 57; Mich State Univ, PhD(microwave spectros), 61. *Prof Exp:* Res chemist, Chem Div, Union Carbide Corp, 63-64; assoc prof, 64-70, PROF CHEM & HEAD DEPT, NORTHERN MICH UNIV, 70- *Mem:* Am Chem Soc. *Res:* Microwave spectroscopy as applied to molecular structure determinations; determination of crystal structure by x-ray diffraction; physical chemistry of clathrates. *Mailing Add:* Dept of Chem Northern Mich Univ Marquette MI 49855

JACOBS, HAROLD, b Portchester, NY, Nov 21, 17; m 43; c 4. PHYSICAL ELECTRONICS. *Educ:* Johns Hopkins Univ, BA, 38; NY Univ, MA, 42, PhD(physics, educ), 45. *Prof Exp:* Physicist, Lancaster Div, Radio Corp Am, Pa, 42-45; physicist, Sylvania Elec Co, NY, 45-49; physicist, 49-70, SR SCIENTIST, ELECTRONIC COMPONENTS LAB, US ARMY ELECTRONICS COMMAND, FT MONMOUTH, 70-; PROF ELECTRONICS ENG, MONMOUTH COL, NJ, 57- *Mem:* Am Phys Soc; fel Inst Elec & Electronics Engrs. *Res:* Solid state physics; electron tubes and microwave design; education. *Mailing Add:* Dept of Electronic Eng Monmouth Col West Long Branch NJ 07764

JACOBS, HAROLD ROBERT, b Portland, Ore, Nov 19, 36; m 61; c 3. MECHANICAL ENGINEERING, THERMAL SCIENCES. *Educ:* Univ Portland, BS, 58; Wash State Univ, MSME, 61; Ohio State Univ, PhD(mech eng), 65. *Prof Exp:* Res & develop engr, Gen Elec Co, 58-59 & Boeing Co, 61-62; mem tech staff, Aerospace Corp, 65-68; from asst prof to assoc prof mech eng, 67-74, chmn dept civil eng, 78-79, PROF MECH ENG, UNIV UTAH, 74-, ASSOC DEAN RES, COL ENG, 81- *Mem:* Assoc fel Am Inst Aeronaut & Astronaut; Am Soc Mech Engrs; Sigma Xi. *Res:* Heat transfer; fluid mechanics; geothermal energy; oil shale processing; direct contact processing; condensers; thermal stresses; fracture. *Mailing Add:* Univ of Utah Salt Lake City UT 84117

JACOBS, HARRY LEWIS, b Philadelphia, Pa, Apr 10, 25; m 50; c 4. PSYCHOPHYSIOLOGY, NUTRITION. *Educ:* Univ Del, BA, 50, MA, 51; Cornell Univ, PhD, 55. *Prof Exp:* Asst prof psychol, Bucknell Univ, 54-60; NIMH spec res fel physiol, Sch Med, Univ Rochester, 59-61, assoc prof psychol, Univ Ill, 61-67; ASSOC DIR BEHAV SCI DIV, US ARMY NATICK LABS, 66- *Concurrent Pos:* Vis lectr nutrit & food sci, Mass Inst Technol, 66-67; assoc prof physiol, Clark Univ, 66-69, prof, 70-76; affil scientist, Worcester Found Exp Biol, 71- *Mem:* AAAS; fel Am Psychol Asn; Am Physiol Soc; Am Inst Nutrit; Am Inst Biol Sci. *Res:* Appetite, hunger and food habits. *Mailing Add:* Food Sci Lab US Army Natick Develop Ctr Natick MA 01760

JACOBS, HARVEY, b Cleveland, Ohio, Aug 10, 28; m 53; c 3. PHYSICAL CHEMISTRY, ORGANIC CHEMISTRY. *Educ:* Ohio State Univ, BS, 50; Temple Univ, MA, 54, PhD(chem), 56. *Prof Exp:* Res chemist, Anal Lab, Rohm & Haas Co, 56-71; toxicologist, Philadelphia Med Exam Off, 71-72; ANAL CHEMIST, GLIDDEN-DURKEE, DIV SCM CORP, 72- *Mem:* Am Chem Soc; Soc Appl Spectros. *Res:* Gas chromatography; nuclear magnetic resonance; forensic toxicology. *Mailing Add:* Glidden-Durkee PO Box 8827 Strongsville OH 44136

JACOBS, HYDE SPENCER, b Declo, Idaho, May 15, 26; m 50; c 5. AGRONOMY. *Educ:* Univ Idaho, BS, 52, MS, 54; Mich State Univ, PhD(soil chem), 57. *Prof Exp:* Instr soils, Mich State Univ, 53-57; from asst prof to assoc prof, 57-66, dir, Kans Water Resources Res Inst, 64-74, prof soils, Kans State Univ, 66-80, dir, Kans Evapotranspiration Lab, 68-79, head dept agron, 71-80, ASST DIR EXTEN & DIR AGR PROGS, KANS STATE UNIV, 81- *Concurrent Pos:* Consult, Earth Sci Curric Proj, Am Geol Inst, 64-65; NSF fel, Utah State Univ, 68-69; assoc ed, J Agron Educ, 70-74. *Mem:* Fel Am Soc Agron; Soil Sci Soc Am. *Res:* Agronomy, soils; irrigation; water resources. *Mailing Add:* 117 Umberger Hall Kans State Univ Manhattan KS 66502

JACOBS, IRA, b Brooklyn, NY, Jan 3, 31; m 56; c 3. PHYSICS, TELECOMMUNICATIONS. *Educ:* City Col New York, BS, 50; Purdue Univ, MS, 52, PhD(physics), 55. *Prof Exp:* Summer physicist, Signal Corps Eng Labs, 52; mem tech staff, Mil Res Div, 55-60, supvr, 60-62, head electromagnetic res dept, 62-66, head mil commun res dept, 66-67, digital transmission anal dept, 67-69, dir transmission systs res ctr, 69-71, dir digital transmission lab, 71-76, DIR WIDEBAND TRANSMISSION FACIL LAB, TRANSMISSION DIV, BELL LABS, 76- *Mem:* AAAS; Am Phys Soc; Inst Elec & Electronics Engrs. *Res:* Study of radar and military communications systems; analysis of transmission systems performance; development and evaluation of pulse code modulation transmission systems; development of fiber optic communication systems. *Mailing Add:* Wideband Transmission Facil Lab Bell Labs Holmdel NJ 07733

JACOBS, IRWIN MARK, b New Bedford, Mass, Oct 18, 33; m 54; c 4. COMMUNICATION THEORY, COMPUTER SCIENCES. *Educ:* Cornell Univ, BEE, 56; Mass Inst Technol, MS, 57, ScD(elec eng), 59. *Prof Exp:* Res asst elec eng, Mass Inst Technol, 58-59, from asst prof to assoc prof, 59-66; assoc prof, 66-69, PROF INFO & COMPUT SCI, UNIV CALIF, SAN DIEGO, 69-; PRES, LINKABIT CORP, 68- *Concurrent Pos:* Consult, Appl Res Lab, Sylvania Elec Prod, Inc, 59-, Lincoln Lab, Mass Inst Technol, 61-62,

Indust Teaching, Minneapolis-Honeywell, Inc, 63 & Bolt Beranek & Newman, Inc, 65; NASA resident res fel, Jet Propulsion Lab, 64-65; mem, Defense Commun Agency Sci Adv Group, 74- *Mem:* Fel Inst Elec & Electronics Engrs; Asn Comput Mach. *Res:* Information theory, coding theory and applications to digital communications; satellite multiple access, microprogrammed communications systems and packet switching. *Mailing Add:* Linkabit Corp 10453 Roselle St San Diego CA 92117

JACOBS, ISRAEL S(AMSON), b Buffalo, NY, July 20, 25; m 50; c 2. SOLID STATE PHYSICS. *Educ:* Univ Mich, BS, 47; Univ Chicago, SM, 51, PhD(physics), 53. *Prof Exp:* Asst physics, Univ Chicago, 49-50; PHYSICIST, GEN ELEC RES & DEVELOP CTR, 54. *Concurrent Pos:* Mem adv comt, Conf Magnetism & Magnetic Mat, 59-, prog chmn, 61, pub chmn, 62-64, steering comt, 68-71; mem organizing comt, Int Cong Magnetism, 62-67, exec chmn, 66-67; res, Nat Ctr Sci Res, Univ Grenoble, 65-66. *Mem:* Fel Am Phys Soc; sr mem Inst Elec & Electronics Engrs; Magnetics Soc. *Res:* Magnetism and magnetic materials; high magnetic field phenomena; antiferromagnetism; low-dimensional magnetic model systems; industrial applications of magnetics research. *Mailing Add:* Gen Elec Res Develop Ctr PO Box 8 Schenectady NY 12301

JACOBS, J(AMES) H(ARRISON), b St Charles, Mo, Apr 13, 16; m 42; c 2. METALLURGICAL ENGINEERING. *Educ:* Pa State Univ, BS, 36; Univ Mo, BS, 39, MS, 40. *Prof Exp:* Chemist, Western Elec Co, Ill, 36-39; metallurgist, US Bur Mines, 41-51; mgr chem eng develop, Tech Dept, Union Carbide Metals Co Div, 51-63, tech mgr nickel-cadmium battery develop, Consumer Prod Div, 63-72, TECH MGR CARBON/ZINC BATTERIES, BATTERY PROD DIV, UNION CARBIDE CORP, 72- *Mem:* Electrochem Soc; Am Inst Mining, Metall & Petrol Engrs. *Res:* Hydrometallurgy and electrometallurgy of non-ferrous metals. *Mailing Add:* Battery Prod Div Union Carbide Corp Box 6056 Cleveland OH 44101

JACOBS, JACQUELINE E, b Wilkinsburg, Pa, June 17, 23; m 46; c 3. ENVIRONMENTAL BIOLOGY. *Educ:* Coker Col, AB, 44; Univ SC, MS, 61, PhD(biol), 68. *Prof Exp:* Teacher, Moultrie High, Mt Pleasant, SC, 57-58 & Dreher High Sch, Columbia, 58-64; asst, Univ SC, 64-68; instr specialist, Instr TV, SC State Dept Educ, 68-71; instr, Spring Valley High Sch, 71-73; EXEC DIR, SC WILDLIFE FEDN, 74- *Concurrent Pos:* Bd trustees, Coker Col, 71-77; fel botany, W Gordon Belser, Univ SC, 64-65; grant, Belle W Baruch Found, Univ SC, 67-68; mem bd trustees, Coker Col, SC, 71-77; mem, Wildlife Adv Comt, Col Agr Sci, Clemson Univ, 76-82. *Honors & Awards:* SC Conserv Educ of Year Award, SC Wildlife Fedn; Conserv Award of Year, SC, Woodmen of the World, 75; F Bartow Culp Award Distinguished Serv, SC Wildlife Fedn, 75. *Mem:* AAAS; Am Inst Biol Sci; The Wildlife Soc; Sigma Xi; Bot Soc Am. *Res:* Freshwater algae of South Carolina; a curriculum guide for life science on educational TV. *Mailing Add:* Arcadian Plaza 4949 Two Notch Rd PO Box 4186 Columbia SC 29240

JACOBS, JAMES ALBERT, physics, deceased

JACOBS, JOHN ALLEN, b Cumberland, Ky, Aug 8, 39; m 64; c 2. ANIMAL SCIENCE. *Educ:* Univ Ky, BS, 63, MS, 65; Univ Wyo, PhD(animal sci), 70. *Prof Exp:* Supt beef, Stadler Packing Co, Columbus, 65-67; instr animal sci, Univ Wyo, 68-69; asst prof, 70-74, ASSOC PROF ANIMAL SCI, UNIV IDAHO, 74- *Mem:* Am Soc Animal Sci; Am Meat Sci Asn. *Res:* Physiology and biochemistry of domestic animals as related to meat quality and quantity. *Mailing Add:* Dept of Animal Industs Univ of Idaho Moscow ID 83843

JACOBS, JOHN EDWARD, b Kansas City, Mo, June 15, 20; m 46; c 6. BIOMEDICAL ENGINEERING, ELECTRICAL ENGINEERING. *Educ:* Northwestern Univ, BS, 47, MS, 48, PhD(elec eng), 50. *Hon Degrees:* ScD, Univ Strathclyde, 71. *Prof Exp:* Supvry res engr, X-Ray Dept, Gen Elec Co, 50-53, mgr adv develop lab, 53-59, elec engr res lab, 59-60; prof elec eng, 60-69, WALTER P MURPHY PROF ELEC ENG, COMPUT SCI & ENG SCI, NORTHWESTERN UNIV, 69-, EXEC DIR BIOMED ENG CTR, 61- *Concurrent Pos:* Lectr grad sch, Northwestern Univ, 52-; McKay vis prof, Univ Calif, 57-58; adj prof, Rensselaer Polytech Inst, 59-; pres, Biomed Eng Resource Corp, 69-; mem automated clin lab comt, Nat Inst Gen Med Sci, NIH, 70-, mem biomed training comt consult radiol sect, Army Res Off; chmn manpower comt, President's Adv Coun Mgt Improv, 71-; consult, Fed Coun Sci & Technol, 71- *Honors & Awards:* Coffin Award, Gen Elec Co, 53; Silver Medal, Am Soc Nondestructive Testing, 68. *Mem:* Nat Acad Eng; Biomed Eng Soc (treas, 68-); Instrument Soc Am. *Res:* Photoconduction electron optics; biomedicine; transducers. *Mailing Add:* 631 Milburn Evanston IL 60201

JACOBS, JOHN JOSEPH, b Utica, NY, Dec 26, 44; m 71. NEUROENDOCRINOLOGY. *Educ:* Hobart Col, BS, 66; Univ Rochester, PhD(anat), 70. *Prof Exp:* USPHS fel, Med Sch, Univ Ore, 70-72; asst prof, 72-78, ASSOC PROF ANAT, LA STATE UNIV MED CTR, NEW ORLEANS, 78- *Mem:* Am Asn Anatomists. *Res:* Brain-pituitary-adrenal axis; neonatal development of neuroendocrine axes. *Mailing Add:* Dept of Anat La State Univ Med Ctr New Orleans LA 70121

JACOBS, JOHN TERENCE, b St Catharines, Ont, June 29, 40; m 63; c 2. SOLID STATE PHYSICS, ELECTRICAL ENGINEERING. *Educ:* Univ Toronto, BASc, 62; Univ Ill, Urbana, MS, 64, PhD(elec eng), 67. *Prof Exp:* Res engr, Coordr Sci Lab, Univ Ill, 67-68; RES STAFF INORG MAT RES, IBM CORP, 68- *Mem:* Am Phys Soc; Inst Elec & Electronics Engrs. *Res:* Thin film physics particularly their electrical properties and size effects; electrical switching properties of ferroelectric materials and magneto-optic materials; explored laser transfer printing and microfilm; laser addressed liquid crystal displays. *Mailing Add:* 1475 S Bascom Ave 108 Campbell CA 95008

JACOBS, JOSEPH DONOVAN, b Motley, Minn, Dec 24, 08; m 37; c 1. CIVIL ENGINEERING. *Educ:* Univ Minn, BSCE, 34. *Prof Exp:* Civil engr & construct supvr, Walsh Construct Co, New York & San Francisco, 34-54; chief engr, Kaiser-Walsh-Perini-Raymond, Australia, 54-55; SR OFFICER, JACOBS ASSOCS, 55- *Concurrent Pos:* Chmn US nat comt tunneling technol, Nat Acad Sci, 77. *Mem:* Nat Acad Eng; fel Am Soc Civil Engrs; Am Inst Mining, Metal & Petrol Engrs; Nat Soc Prof Engrs. *Mailing Add:* Jacobs Assocs 500 Sansome St San Francisco CA 94111

JACOBS, JOSEPH JOHN, b New York, NY, June 13, 16; m 42; c 3. CHEMICAL ENGINEERING. *Educ:* Polytech Inst Brooklyn, BChE, 37, MChE, 39, DChE, 42. *Prof Exp:* Res chem engr, Autoxygen, Inc, New York, 39-42; sr chem engr, Merck & Co, Rahway, NJ, 42-44; vpres & tech dir, Chemurgic Corp, Calif, 44-47; consult chem engr, 47-55; pres, Jacobs Eng Co, 55-74, CHMN BD & CHIEF EXEC OFFICER, JACOBS ENG GROUP INC, 74- *Mem:* AAAS; Am Chem Soc; Am Inst Chem Engrs. *Res:* Distillation; extraction; chlorination; plant design; unit processes; concentration of lactic acid; dehydration of caustic soda; continuous saponification; improved lubricating composition; deterioration of lubricating oils; economic surveys. *Mailing Add:* Jacobs Eng Group Inc 251 S Lake Ave Pasadena CA 91101

JACOBS, LAURENCE ALAN, b Mexico City, Mex, Dec 17, 49; m 74. THEORETICAL PHYSICS, ELEMENTARY PARTICLE PHYSICS. *Educ:* Nat Univ Mex, BS, 72; Mass Inst Technol, PhD(physics), 76. *Prof Exp:* Res assoc physics, Mass Inst Technol, 76-77; res assoc, Brookhaven Nat Lab, 77-79; asst prof physics, Nat Univ Mex, 79-81; ASST PROF, INST THEORET PHYSICS, UNIV CALIF, SANTA BARBARA, 81- *Concurrent Pos:* Sci adv physics, Nat Sci & Technol, Mex. *Mem:* Am Phys Soc; Soc Mex Physics; Acad Invert Sci Mex; NY Acad Sci. *Res:* Theoretical physics, field theory; mathematical physics; statistical mechanics; condensed-matter physics. *Mailing Add:* Inst Theoret Physics Univ Calif Santa Barbara CA 93106

JACOBS, LEON, b Brooklyn, NY, Mar 26, 15; m 46; c 3. MEDICAL PARASITOLOGY. *Educ:* Brooklyn Col, BA, 35; George Washington Univ, MA, 38, PhD(parasitol), 47. *Prof Exp:* Jr zoologist, Nat Inst Health, 37-40, from asst protozoologist to protozoologist, 40-48, scientist, Lab Trop Dis, 48-52, sr scientist, 52-56, sci dir, 56-59, chief, Lab Parasitic Dis, Nat Inst Allergy & Infectious Dis, 59-64, actg sci dir, 64-66, sci dir, Div Biol Standards, 66-67; dep asst secy sci, Dept Health, Educ & Welfare, DC, 67-69; asst dir, Fogarty Int Ctr, NIH, 69-72, assoc dir, 72-78, dir, 78-79; SCI DIR, NAT SOC MED RES, 81- *Concurrent Pos:* Ed, Trop Med & Hyg News, 50-55 & J Parasitol, Am Soc Parasitol, 58-59; Fulbright res scholar, 60-61; Guggenheim fel, 60-61. *Honors & Awards:* Ward Medal, Am Soc Parasitol, 63; Distinguished Service Medal, Pub Health Serv, 66. *Mem:* Am Soc Parasitol (pres, 78); Am Soc Trop Med & Hyg (vpres, 70); Am Asn Immunol. *Res:* Freeliving and parasitic nematodes; parasitic protozoa; cultivation of Entamoeba histolytica and Dientamoeba fragilis; pathogenicity of Trichomonas vaginalis; biology of Toxoplasma; diagnosis of toxoplasmosis; treatment of toxoplasmic chorioretinitis; biomedical science administration. *Mailing Add:* Nat Insts of Health Bldg 31 Rm 2 C02 Bethesda MD 20014

JACOBS, LOIS JEAN, b Portage, Wis, Mar 10, 47. GENETICS. *Educ:* Univ Wis-Madison, BS, 69, PhD(genetics), 77. *Prof Exp:* Res assoc genetics, Inst Med Res, 77-80; ASST SCIENTIST DEPT MED GENETICS, UNIV WIS-MADISON, 81- *Mem:* Environ Mutagen Soc. *Res:* Somatic cell genetics, specifically mutagenesis and carcinogenesis in diploid human cells. *Mailing Add:* Univ Wis Dept Med Genetics 445 Henry Mall Madison WI 53706

JACOBS, LOYD DONALD, b Wolcott, Ind, Nov 22, 32; m 56; c 3. ACOUSTICS. *Educ:* Emporia Kans State Col, BA, 54; Univ Nebr, MS, 58. *Prof Exp:* Engr, Wichita, Kans, 57-62, sr engr, Seattle, Wash, 62-71, GROUP ENGR, BOEING CO, SEATTLE, WASH, 71- *Mem:* Acoust Soc Am; Sigma Xi. *Res:* Control and reduction of aircraft noise; response of aircraft structure to noise; noise radiation from surfaces immersed in airflow. *Mailing Add:* 2004 128th Ave SE Bellevue WA 98005

JACOBS, MARC QUILLEN, b Chandler, Okla, June 28, 38. MATHEMATICS. *Educ:* Univ Okla, BS, 60, MA, 63, PhD(math), 66. *Prof Exp:* Jr mathematician, Int Bus Mach Corp, 60-61; instr math, Univ Okla, 65-66; res asst prof appl math, Brown Univ, 66-67; asst prof math, Rice Univ, 67-68 & appl math, Brown Univ, 68-71; assoc prof, 71-74, PROF MATH, UNIV MO-COLUMBIA, 74- *Mem:* Am Math Soc; Math Asn Am; Soc Indust & Appl Math. *Res:* Optimal control theory. *Mailing Add:* Dept of Math Univ of Mo Columbia MO 65201

JACOBS, MARIAN BECKMANN, b Teaneck, NJ, Dec 20, 35; m 59; c 2. CLAY MINERALOGY, OCEANOGRAPHY. *Educ:* Barnard Col, BA, 57; Columbia Univ, MA, 59, PhD(geol), 63. *Prof Exp:* Res asst mineral, 57-59, RES ASSOC, LAMONT-DOHERTY GEOL OBSERV, COLUMBIA UNIV, 63- *Concurrent Pos:* Assoc prof biol & oceanog, Ramapo Col NJ, 74-77. *Mem:* AAAS; Geol Soc Am; Mineral Soc Am. *Res:* Clay mineral and trace element studies of deep sea sediments; microscopic and x-ray diffraction studies of particulate matter suspended in sea water; paleoclimatic studies of biogenous deep-sea sediments by x-ray spectroscopic analysis. *Mailing Add:* 276 Tom Hunter Rd Ft Lee NJ 07024

JACOBS, MARK, b Princeton, NJ, May 19, 50; m 73; c 3. PLANT PHYSIOLOGY. *Educ:* Harvard Univ, BA, 71; Stanford Univ, PhD(biol), 76. *Prof Exp:* asst prof, 75-81, ASSOC PROF BIOL, SWARTHMORE COL, 81- *Concurrent Pos:* NATO fel, 76-77. *Mem:* Am Soc Plant Physiologists; Inst Biol Sci; Sigma Xi. *Res:* Biochemical mode of action of the plant growth regulators; hormonal control of plant development. *Mailing Add:* Dept of Biol Swarthmore Col Swarthmore PA 19081

JACOBS, MARTIN JOHN, b Chicago, Ill, June 28, 44; m 66; c 1. SYNTHETIC ORGANIC CHEMISTRY. *Educ:* Ill Inst Technol, BS, 69; Colo State Univ, PhD(org chem), 75. *Prof Exp:* RES CHEMIST, INT MINERALS & CHEM CORP, 75- *Mem:* Am Chem Soc. *Res:* Synthesis of compounds as products for use in animal health, care and nutrition; industrial intermediates and pharmaceutical application. *Mailing Add:* IMC Chem Group 1331 S First St Terre Haute IN 47808

JACOBS, MERLE EMMOR, b Hollsopple, Pa, Nov 30, 18; m 59. ZOOLOGY. *Educ:* Goshen Col, AB, 49; Univ Ind, PhD(zool), 53. *Prof Exp:* Instr zool, Goshen Col, 53-54; instr zool, Duke Univ, 54-57; asst prof biol, Bethany Col, WVa, 57-62; prof biol, EM Col, Va, 62-64; RES PROF ZOOL, GOSHEN COL, 64- *Concurrent Pos:* Grant, Nat Insts Health, 59- *Honors & Awards:* Lalor Award, Sigma Xi. *Res:* Behavior and biochemical genetics. *Mailing Add:* Dept of Biol Goshen Col Goshen IN 46526

JACOBS, MICHAEL MOISES, b Miami, Fla, June 21, 50; m 80. PHYSICS, ELECTRO-OPTICS. *Educ:* Univ Miami, BS, 72, MS, 73, PhD(physics), 75. *Prof Exp:* Res physicist laser optics, Sci Applns Inc, Atlanta, Ga, 76; physicist & mem tech staff electro-optics, Satellite Systs Div, Rockwell Int, Seal Beach, Calif, 77-80; PHYSICIST & MEM TECH STAFF, ADVAN SYSTS TECHNOL DIV, AEROSPACE CORP, EL SEGUNDO, CALIF, 80- *Concurrent Pos:* Instr physics, Orange Coast Col, 76-79. *Mem:* Am Inst Physics; Optical Soc Am. *Res:* Electro-optic infrared & laser physics; acousto-optics; radiative transfer; atmospheric and oceanic optics; systems engineering; infrared focal plane device physics. *Mailing Add:* Aerospace Corp El Segundo CA 90245

JACOBS, MORTON HOWARD, b Newark, NJ, June 28, 24; m 70; c 1. ANALYTICAL CHEMISTRY. *Educ:* Univ Pa, BA, 46. *Prof Exp:* Biochemist, Univ Hosp, Univ Mich, 50-52; chemist, Control Lab, 53-58, Res Dept, 58-60, PROJ LEADER SPECTROSCOPY, INSTRUMENTATION & ANAL RES DEPT, INT FLAVORS & FRAGRANCES INC, 60-, SR PROJ CHEMIST, CHROMATOGRAPHY & SPECTROSCOPY RES DEPT, 78- *Mem:* Am Chem Soc; Int Soc Magnetic Resonance; Soc Appl Spectroscopy. *Res:* Application of chromatographic and spectroscopic techniques, resonance to structure elucidation of flavor and aroma chemicals, both natural and synthetic. *Mailing Add:* Int Flavors & Fragrances Inc 1515 Hwy 36 Union Beach NJ 07735

JACOBS, MYRON SAMUEL, b Jersey City, NJ, May 17, 22; c 2. PATHOLOGY. *Educ:* Univ Pa, BA, 45; NY Univ, MS, 51, PhD, 55. *Prof Exp:* Asst anat, Col Dent, NY Univ, 51-54; lectr histol & embryol, Queen's Univ, Ont, 54-56; instr histol, embryol & neuroanat, NY Med Col, 56-57, asst prof, 57-63, assoc prof anat, 63-65; dir cetacean brain lab, 62-65; res assoc comp path, Osborn Lab Marine Sci, NY Aquarium, 66-72; assoc prof, 73-79, PROF PATH, COL DENT, NY UNIV, 79- *Mem:* Am Asn Anat; Am Soc Zool; Soc Neurosci; NY Acad Sci. *Res:* Skin grafts and thermal changes in transplantation, rat; alloxan diabetes, hamster; cetacean nervous system. *Mailing Add:* Dept Path Col Dent NY Univ 421 First Ave New York NY 10010

JACOBS, NICHOLAS JOSEPH, b Oakland, Calif, Mar 29, 33; m 59; c 1. BACTERIOLOGY. *Educ:* Univ Ill, BS, 55; Cornell Univ, PhD, 60. *Prof Exp:* Res assoc, Univ Ill, 59-61; from asst bacteriologist to assoc bacteriologist, Am Meat Inst Found, 61-64; from instr to assoc prof, 64-80, PROF MICROBIOL, DARTMOUTH MED SCH, 80- *Mem:* AAAS; Am Soc Microbiol. *Res:* Bacterial physiology; pathogenic bacteriology; heme synthesis in bacteria. *Mailing Add:* 1 Haskins Hanover NH 03755

JACOBS, PATRICIA ANN, b London, Eng, Oct 8, 34. GENETICS. *Educ:* Univ St Andrews, BSc, 56, DSc(cytogenetics), 66. *Prof Exp:* Scientist, Med Res Coun, 57-72; PROF ANAT, SCH MED, UNIV HAWAII, 73- *Mem:* Genetics Soc Gt Brit; Am Soc Human Genetics. *Res:* Human cytogenetics. *Mailing Add:* Dept of Anat Univ of Hawaii Sch of Med Honolulu HI 96822

JACOBS, PATRICIA ANNE, b Chicago, Ill, May 27, 47. OPERATIONS RESEARCH. *Educ:* Northwestern Univ, BS, 69, MS, 71, PhD(appl math), 73. *Prof Exp:* Asst prof opers res, Stanford Univ, 72-78; ASSOC PROF OPERS RES, NAVAL POSTGRAD SCH, 78- *Res:* Stochastic processes and their applications; Markov renewal processes, Markov additive processes, and Markov processes; probabilistic models including those of point processes, particle systems and random measures. *Mailing Add:* Dept of Opers Res Naval Postgrad Sch Monterey CA 93940

JACOBS, PATRICK W M, b Durban, SAfrica, Sept 15, 23; m 50; c 3. PHYSICAL CHEMISTRY, SOLID STATE CHEMISTRY. *Educ:* Univ Natal, BSc, 41, MSc, 43; Univ London, PhD(phys chem), 51, DSc(phys Chem), 63. *Prof Exp:* Lectr chem, Rhodes Univ, SAfrica, 46-48; Beit fel, Imp Col, London, 48-50; from asst lectr to sr lectr phys chem, 50-64, reader, 64-65; SR PROF CHEM, UNIV WESTERN ONT, 65- *Mem:* Fel Royal Soc Chem; Can Inst Chem; Faraday Soc. *Res:* Optical and electrical properties of solids; calculation of defect energies for ionic crystals. *Mailing Add:* 19 Grenfell Circle London ON N6A 5B8 Can

JACOBS, R(OY) K(ENNETH), b Continental, Ohio, Dec 10, 08; m 34; c 3. ENGINEERING MECHANICS. *Educ:* Ohio Northern Univ, BS, 31 & 33; Univ Mich, MS, 38, PhD(civil eng), 56. *Hon Degrees:* DEng, Ohio Northern Univ, 64. *Prof Exp:* Asst prof eng mech, Ga Inst Technol, 37-42; assoc, Univ Ill, 42-43; asst prof civil eng, Duke Univ, 43-44; prof eng mech, 46-63, prof eng graphics & head dept, 63-76, EMER PROF GRAPHICS & EMER HEAD DEPT, GA INST TECHNOL, 76- *Mem:* Am Soc Civil Engrs; Am Soc Eng Educ. *Res:* Reinforced concrete; teaching techniques. *Mailing Add:* 15800 Freemanville Rd Alpharetta GA 30201

JACOBS, RALPH R, b Niagara Falls, NY, Dec 31, 42; m 66; c 2. QUANTUM ELECTRONICS. *Educ:* NY Univ, BS, 64; Yale Univ, MS, 65, PhM, 67, PhD(physics), 69. *Prof Exp:* Lab instr physics, Yale Univ, 67-69; mem tech staff, GTE Labs, Inc, Bayside, NY, 69-72; sr physicist laser-prog, Lawrence Livermore Lab, Univ Calif, 72-80; MGR RES & ADVANCED DEVELOP, SPECTRA-PHYSICS, INC, 80- *Mem:* Sigma Xi; Am Phys Soc. *Res:* Basic and applied aspects of atomic, molecular and laser physics in gaseous, liquid and solid state media; quantum electronics; laser spectroscopy-linear and nonlinear (ultraviolet, visible, infrared); low and high pressure gas discharges; high resolution microwave spectroscopy; rotational, vibrational, and electronic relaxation in molecules. *Mailing Add:* Spectra-Physics Inc 1250 W Middlefield Rd Mountain View CA 94042

JACOBS, RICHARD L, b Elsberry, Mo, Dec 29, 30; m 54; c 3. ORTHOPEDIC SURGERY, BIOCHEMISTRY. *Educ:* State Univ Iowa, BA, 52, MD, 56, MS, 61. *Prof Exp:* Arthritis & Rheumatism Found fel, State Univ Iowa, 59-62, resident orthop surg, 62-65; from asst prof to prof orthop, Univ Ill Med Ctr, 66-74; PROF ORTHOP SURG & HEAD DIV, ALBANY MED COL, 74- *Concurrent Pos:* Orthop Res & Educ Found res fel orthop, Mass Gen Hosp-Harvard Univ, 61-62; consult, Ill Div Serv Crippled Children, 65-74, Dixon State Sch, 66-74 & US Vet Admin Hosps, 68- *Mem:* AAAS; AMA; Am Chem Soc; Am Inst Chem; Am Acad Orthop Surg. *Res:* Vitamin metabolism; collagen chemistry; immunology. *Mailing Add:* Div of Orthop Surg Albany Med Col Albany NY 12208

JACOBS, RICHARD LEE, b Perrysburg, Ohio, Aug 4, 31; m 56; c 4. ORGANIC CHEMISTRY. *Educ:* Bowling Green State Univ, BA, 53; Mich State Univ, MS, 55, PhD(org chem), 59. *Prof Exp:* Asst, Mich State Univ, 53-59; res chemist, Koppers Co, Inc, Pa, 59-62; sr chemist, Maumee Chem Co, 62-66; DIR LAB, SHERWIN WILLIAMS CHEMS, 66- *Mem:* AAAS; Am Chem Soc, fel Am Inst Chemists; Soc Heterocyclic Chemists; Sigma Xi. *Res:* Organic sulfur compounds, especially thiacyclopropanes and thiophene; nitriles preparation and reactions; alkylation and reaction mechanisms of aromatics; nitrogen heterocycles. *Mailing Add:* 948 Maple St Perrysburg OH 43551

JACOBS, RICHARD LEWIS, b Pelham, Tenn, Mar 31, 27; m 59; c 4. CHEMOTHERAPY, IMMUNOLOGY. *Educ:* Tenn Polytech Inst, BS, 51; Tex A&M Univ, MS, 53, PhD(biochem, nutrit), 55. *Prof Exp:* Res asst biochem & nutrit, Tex A&M Univ, 51-55; mem staff, US Navy Med Res Inst, 55-60; sr scientist, Lab Parasite Chemother, Nat Inst Allergy & Infectious Dis, 60-76; sr scientist clin immunol, Parke Davis, div Warner-Lambert Co, 76-81; ASSOC PROF, VET MICROBIOL, UNIV MO, 81- *Mem:* AAAS; Am Soc Microbiol; Am Soc Trop Med & Hyg. *Res:* Animal growth-promoting effect of dietary antibiotics; animal nutrition; connective tissues; tissue homograft rejection; infectious diseases; metabolic pathways and mechanism of drug action in microorganisms; development of resistance to drugs in microorganisms; methods for determining drug levels in biological materials; chemotherapy of malaria; in vitro culture of malarial; parasites; immunology of malaria. *Mailing Add:* 212 Connaway Hall Univ Mo Columbia MO 65211

JACOBS, RICHARD M, b Wloclawek, Poland, Oct 31, 24; US citizen; m 50; c 1. ORTHODONTICS, ANATOMY. *Educ:* Univ Munich, Dr med dent, 48; NY Univ, DDS, 52; Univ Calif, San Francisco, MPH, 51; Univ Va, PhD(anat), 64; Univ Ill, MS, 65. *Prof Exp:* Resident dent, NY State Dept Ment Hyg, 52-53; dentist, Nev State Dept Pub Health, 59-60; Nat Inst Dent Res fel, Univ Va, 61-63 & Univ Ill, 63-65; assoc prof orthod & head dept, Fac Dent, Univ BC, 65-66; asst dean col dent, 66-67; actg head dept oral biol & curriculum coordr, 66-71, assoc dean col, 67-71, PROF ORTHOD, COL DENT, UNIV IOWA, 66- *Mem:* Fel Am Pub Health Asn; Am Asn Anat; Am Asn Orthod; fel Sigma Xi; Am Educ Res Asn. *Res:* Effects effects of spontaneous muscular activity on fetal development; pressure sensitive devices for measuring muscular activity; cost effectiveness of professional education; organizational behavior and academic performance. *Mailing Add:* Col of Dent Univ of Iowa Iowa City IA 52242

JACOBS, ROBERT M(ORTON), mechanical engineering, see previous edition

JACOBS, ROSS, b Montreal, Que, Feb 27, 25; m 53; c 4. BIOCHEMISTRY. *Educ:* McGill Univ, BSc, 48, MSc, 52, PhD, 54. *Prof Exp:* Res biochemist, Ayerst Labs, Inc, 54-55, asst to dir pharmaceut develop labs, 55-57; res assoc med, Univ Southern Calif, 57-58; asst prof obstet & gynec, 58-64, ASST PROF BIOCHEM, COL MED, STATE UNIV NY UPSTATE MED CTR, 58- *Concurrent Pos:* Dir labs, Calif Found Med Res, 57-58. *Mem:* Biochem Soc; Endocrine Soc. *Res:* Biosynthesis and metabolism of steroid hormones; gonadotropins. *Mailing Add:* Dept of Biochem State Univ NY Upstate Med Ctr Syracuse NY 13210

JACOBS, S LAWRENCE, b New York, NY, Nov 27, 29; m 53; c 3. CLINICAL CHEMISTRY, ANALYTICAL TOXICOLOGY. *Educ:* Rensselaer Polytech Inst, BS, 51; Univ Ill, MS, 52, PhD(chem), 55. *Prof Exp:* Asst chem, Univ Ill, 52-55; res chemist, Northern Regional Lab, USDA, 55; chief spec projs div, 56-65, dir dept chem, 66-67, qual assurance officer, 68-71, asst to dir, 71-75, mgr prof rels & corp accounts, 76-77, dir, Dept Clin & Indust Toxicol, 78-81, DIR, LOS ANGELES BR LABS, BIO-SCI LABS, 81- *Mem:* Am Chem Soc; Am Asn Clin Chem; Sigma Xi; Int Asn Forensic Toxicologists. *Res:* Clinical chemistry; adrenal hormones; bile pigments; enzymes; lipids; quality assurance; analytical toxicology. *Mailing Add:* 1357 Lachman Lane Pacific Palisades CA 90272

JACOBS, SANFORD, b New York, NY, May 23, 35; m 61; c 3. INORGANIC CHEMISTRY. *Educ:* City Col New York, BS, 57; Univ Colo, PhD(inorg chem), 62. *Prof Exp:* Res chemist, US Naval Radiol Defense Lab, 62-63; res chemist, M&T CHEMS, INC, 63-74, RES DIR, M&T CHEMS, INC, 74- *Mem:* Am Chem Soc. *Res:* Inorganic chemical research and development. *Mailing Add:* M & J Chemicals Inc Rahway NJ 07065

JACOBS, SIGMUND JAMES, b Minneapolis, Minn, Mar 25, 12; m 44. PHYSICS, FLUID DYNAMICS. *Educ:* Univ Minn, BChE, 33, MS, 52; Univ Amsterdam, PhD(physics), 53. *Prof Exp:* Asst phys chem, Univ Minn, 36-39; res assoc, Carnegie Inst Technol, 42-45; res assoc physics, Woods Hole Oceanog Inst, 46; res physicist, Naval Ord Lab, 46-50, chief detonation div, 50-57, sr scientist explosives res dept, 57-75; SR SCIENTIST, EXPLOSIVES DIV, NAVAL SURFACE WEAPONS CTR, WHITE OAK LAB, 75- *Honors & Awards:* Meritorious Civilian Serv Award, US Navy, 51, 60; DuPont Medal, Soc Motion Picture & TV Eng, 64. *Mem:* Am Phys Soc; Am Chem Soc; Soc Motion Picture & TV Eng; Combustion Inst. *Res:* Association in gases; deflagration of propellants and explosives; detonation of solid explosives; high pressure instrumentation; rapid expansion of gases; shock wave phenomena; electronic and photographic instrumentation; equation of fluid and solid states at high pressure. *Mailing Add:* 1208 Ruppert Rd Silver Spring MD 20903

JACOBS, STANLEY J, b Milwaukee, Wis, Feb 11, 36; m 65; c 1. GEOPHYSICS, FLUID MECHANICS. *Educ:* Northwestern Univ, BS, 59; Harvard Univ, AM, 60, PhD(appl math), 63. *Prof Exp:* Res fel atmospheric sci, Harvard Univ, 63-64; asst prof oceanog, 64-68, assoc prof, 68-74, PROF OCEANOG, UNIV MICH, ANN ARBOR, 74- *Mem:* Am Meteorol Soc. *Res:* Geophysical fluid mechanics. *Mailing Add:* Dept Atmospheric & Oceanic Sci Univ of Mich Ann Arbor MI 48104

JACOBS, STANLEY S, b Rochester, NH, Apr 19, 40; m 79; c 1. ANTARCTIC OCEANOGRAPHY. *Educ:* Mass Inst Technol, BS, 62. *Prof Exp:* Res asst marine geophysics, Woods Hole Oceanog Inst, 61-62; from grad res asst to sr res asst, 62-72, res staff assoc, 72-73, SR STAFF ASSOC PHYS OCEANOG, LAMONT-DOHERTY GEOL OBSERV, COLUMBIA UNIV, 74- *Concurrent Pos:* Chief scientist oceanog res, NSF & US Coast Guard, 64-78; mem, Comt Polar Res & Panel Antartic Oceanog, Nat Acad Sci-Nat Res Coun, 71; NSF prin investr, 74- *Res:* Interaction between seawater and the Antartic ice shelves and sea ice. *Mailing Add:* Lamont-Doherty Geol Observ Palisades NY 10964

JACOBS, STEPHEN FRANK, b New York, NY, Oct 1, 28; m 63; c 3. PHYSICS. *Educ:* Antioch Col, BS, 51; Johns Hopkins Univ, PhD(physics), 56. *Prof Exp:* Engr, Perkin-Elmer Corp, 56-60; sr physicist, TRG, Inc, 60-65; PROF OPTICAL SCI, UNIV ARIZ, 65- *Mem:* Optical Soc Am; Am Phys Soc. *Res:* Infrared radiation detection; quantum electronics. *Mailing Add:* Optical Sci Ctr Univ of Ariz Tucson AZ 85721

JACOBS, SYDNEY, b New Orleans, La, Nov 23, 07; m 38, 70; c 4. MEDICINE. *Educ:* Tulane Univ, BS, 28, MD, 30; Am Bd Internal Med, dipl, 39; Am Bd Pulmonary Dis, dipl, 54. *Prof Exp:* Intern, Touro Infirmary, La, 30-31; resident med, Syracuse Gen Hosp, NY, 31-32; clin asst, Tulane Univ, 32-34, instr clin med, 35-38, instr med, 38-45, from asst prof to assoc prof clin med, clin prof med, 61-77; chief med, Touro Infirmary, 53 & 67-76; RETIRED. *Concurrent Pos:* Consult, Charity Hosp, La, 58; sr consult, Flint-Goodridge Hosp, Dillard, Methodist Home Hosp & Jewish Children's Home. *Honors & Awards:* South Tuberc Conf Award, 65. *Mem:* Fel Am Col Physicians; Am Col Chest Physicians; Am Thoracic Soc; Am Heart Asn; Nat Tuberc Asn (pres, 66). *Res:* Diseases of the chest, especially pulmonary tuberculosis. *Mailing Add:* 3704 Octavia St New Orleans LA 70125

JACOBS, THEODORE ALAN, b Atlanta, Ga, Oct 19, 27; m 61; c 1. CHEMICAL PHYSICS. *Educ:* Emory Univ, AB, 50; Univ Southern Calif, MSME, 54; Calif Inst Tech, PhD(chem physics), 60. *Prof Exp:* Designer, Douglas Aircraft Co, 51-52; res engr, G O Noville & Assocs, 53-55; res assoc & lectr mech eng, Univ Southern Calif, 55-57; sr res engr eng sci, Rocketdyne Div, NAm Aviation, Inc, 57-58; sr res fel, Calif Inst Tech, 60-61; head chem kinetics sect, Aerospace Corp, 61-67, head aerophys dept, 67-71; sr scientist & dir high energy laser technol, TRW, Inc, 71-76; supt, Optical Sci Div, Naval Res Lab, 76-78, DEPUTY ASST SECY NAVY, RES, ENG & SYSTS, 78- *Concurrent Pos:* Consult, Gen Appl Sci Labs, 58-60, Plasmadyne Corp, 60-61 & Vickers Div, Sperry Rand Corp, 61-62. *Mem:* Fel Am Phys Soc; fel Optical Soc Am; Am Chem Soc; Am Ord Asn; Sigma Xi. *Res:* High temperature chemical kinetics; chemical lasers; high energy lasers. *Mailing Add:* 4915 Loosestrife Ct Annandale VA 22003

JACOBS, THOMAS LLOYD, b Forest City, Iowa, Aug 18, 08; m 34; c 3. ORGANIC CHEMISTRY, POLYMER CHEMISTRY. *Educ:* Cornell Univ, AB, 30, PhD(org chem), 35. *Prof Exp:* Instr chem, Harvard Univ, 35-39; from instr to assoc prof, 39-51, prof, 51-76, EMER PROF CHEM, UNIV CALIF, LOS ANGELES, 76- *Concurrent Pos:* Guggenheim fel, Univ Ill & Imp Col, London, 47-48; consult, Minn Mining & Mfg Co, 56-76. *Mem:* Am Chem Soc; Royal Soc Chem. *Res:* Chemistry of substituted acetylenes and allenes; heterocyclic compounds; synthesis of compounds for testing as antimalarials; stereochemistry of alicyclic compounds. *Mailing Add:* Dept Chem 4037 Young Hall Univ of Calif Los Angeles CA 90024

JACOBS, VERNE LOUIS, b Los Angeles, Calif, Aug 30, 41; m 69; c 2. ATOMIC PHYSICS. *Educ:* Mass Inst Technol, BS, 64; Univ Calif, Berkeley, PhD(physics), 68. *Prof Exp:* Res fel appl math, Weizmann Inst Sci, 68-71; res fel atomic physics, Queen's Univ, Belfast, 71-72; Nat Res Coun assoc space physics, Goddard Space Flight Ctr, NASA, 72-74; scientist plasma physics, Sci Applns, Inc, 74-77; RES PHYSICIST, PLASMA PHYSICS DIV, NAVAL RES LAB, 77- *Mem:* Am Phys Soc. *Res:* Atomic radiation processes in plasmas. *Mailing Add:* Naval Res Lab Plasma Physics Div C7750 Washington DC 20375

JACOBS, VIRGIL LEON, b Odin, Kans, Dec 27, 35; m 70. NEUROSCIENCE. *Educ:* St Benedict's Col, BS, 57; St Louis Univ, MS, 59; Univ Kans, PhD(anat), 65. *Prof Exp:* Instr anat, China Med Bd, Philippines, 62-63; fel neuroanat, Cent Inst Brain Res, Netherlands, 65-66; asst prof anat, Sch Med, Wayne State Univ, 66-69; asst prof & adv anat, AMA Educ Proj, Fac Med, Univ Saigon, 69-71; assoc prof anat, Sch Med, Univ Hawaii, 71-75; assoc prof anat, Tex A&M Univ, 75-78, res assoc, 78-80; ASSOC PROF ANAT, MOREHOUSE SCHOOL MED, ATLANTA, 80- *Concurrent Pos:* Exchange instr, Col Med, Univ Philippines, 62-63. *Mem:* Am Asn Anatomists; AAAS; Soc Neurosci; Sigma Xi. *Res:* Neuroanatomical pathways in reptiles; anatomical and behavioral studies on Flehmen in the Bovine; N Accumbens connections in the rat. *Mailing Add:* Morehouse Sch Med 830 Westview Dr SW Atlanta GA 30314

JACOBS, WALTER WILLIAM, b Newark, NJ, Sept 26, 14; m 41. MATHEMATICAL STATISTICS. *Educ:* City Col, BS, 34; George Washington Univ, MA, 40, PhD(statist), 51. *Prof Exp:* Statistician, Securities & Exchange Comn, 40-43; analyst, War Dept, 46-47; chief prod & markets sect, Dept Com, 47-51; dep chief comput div, Dept Air Force, 51-57; dep chief off res, Nat Security Agency, 57-66, commandant nat cryptologic sch, 66-69; adj prof, 52-69, prof, 69-72, prof comput sci, 72-80, EMER PROF MATH, STATIST & COMP SCI, AM UNIV, 80- *Honors & Awards:* Legion of Merit, 46; Exceptional Civilian Serv Medal, US Air Force, 56; Exceptional Civilian Serv Award, Nat Security Agency, 68. *Mem:* Math Asn Am; Asn Comput Mach. *Res:* Application of digital computers to information processing; linear programming; artificial intelligence. *Mailing Add:* Dept of Math & Statist Am Univ Mass & Nebr Ave NE Washington DC 20016

JACOBS, WILLIAM DONALD, b Birmingham, Ala, Apr 18, 28; m 63; c 3. ANALYTICAL CHEMISTRY. *Educ:* Col Charleston, BS, 51; Clemson Col, MS, 54; Univ Va, PhD(chem), 58. *Prof Exp:* Instr chem, Clemson Col, 52-54; instr chem, Gordon Mil Col, 54-55 & Univ Va, 57-58; asst prof, Univ Ga, 58-65; assoc prof, WGa Col, 65-68; assoc prof & chmn dept, 68-78, PROF CHEM, STILLMAN COL, 78-, CHMN, DIV MATH & SCI, 81- *Mem:* Am Chem Soc. *Res:* Spectrophotometric trace analysis; analytical chemistry of the platinum group elements. *Mailing Add:* Dept of Chem Stillman Col Tuscaloosa AL 35401

JACOBS, WILLIAM PAUL, b Boston, Mass, May 25, 19; m 49; c 2. PLANT DEVELOPMENT. *Educ:* Harvard Univ, AB, 42, MA, 45, PhD(biol), 46. *Prof Exp:* Fel histogenesis in vascular plants, Harvard Univ, 46-47, mem, Soc Fels, 47-48; from asst prof to prof, 48-69, W L Schultz prof, 69-72, PROF BIOL, PRINCETON UNIV, 72- *Concurrent Pos:* Sheldon traveling fel, 45-46; Lalor fel, 50-51; sr fel, Nat Sci Found, 56-57, sci fac fel, 62; Guggenheim fel, 67; mem comt innovation in lab instr, Biol Sci Curriculum Study, Am Inst Biol Sci, 59-64. *Honors & Awards:* Morrison Award, NY Acad Sci, 51; Dimond Prize, Bot Soc Am, 75. *Mem:* Soc Develop Biol (secy, 58-60, pres, 60-61); Am Soc Plant Physiol; Bot Soc Am; Int Soc Plant Morphologists; Brit Soc Exp Biol. *Res:* Internal factors controlling cell and organ differentiation and longevity; hormone transport and polarity; gravitational effects on giant coenocytes. *Mailing Add:* Dept of Biol Princeton Univ Princeton NJ 08540

JACOBS, WILLIAM WESCOTT, b Madison, Wis, Sept 8, 43; m 77; c 1. INTERMEDIATE ENERGY NUCLEAR PHYSICS. *Educ:* Reed Col, Portland, BA, 65; Univ Wash, MS, 67, PhD(physics), 74. *Prof Exp:* res assoc nuclear & atomic physics, Univ NC, Chapel Hill, 74-76; res assoc, 76-79, ASSOC RES SCIENTIST INTERMEDIATE ENERGY NUCLEAR PHYSICS, CYCLOTRON FACIL, IND UNIV, 79- *Mem:* Am Phys Soc; AAAS; Am Fedn Scientists. *Res:* Intermediate-energy nuclear physics; polarization effects in nuclear reactions and scattering; nuclear astrophysics; heavy-ion x-ray production; tests of fundamental symmetries. *Mailing Add:* Cyclotron Facil Milo B Sampson Ln Ind Univ Bloomington IN 47405

JACOBS, WILLIAM WOOD, JR, b Harrisburg, Pa, May 23, 47; m 69; c 3. ANIMAL BEHAVIOR, ETHOLOGY. *Educ:* Pa State Univ, BS, 69; Univ Chicago, MS, 71, PhD(biopsychol), 73. *Prof Exp:* Biologist rodenticides, US Environ Protection Agency, 74-75; fel olfaction & taste, Monell Chem Senses Ctr, 75-78; BIOLOGIST RODENTICIDES, US ENVIRON PROTECTION AGENCY, 78- *Concurrent Pos:* Fel, US Nat Inst Neurol Dis & Stroke, 75-78. *Mem:* Am Soc Mammalogists. *Res:* Investigations of taste, food selection, social and individual behavior of small mammals; use of containers in closed system transfer of pesticides. *Mailing Add:* TS-767 Regist Div US Environ Protection Agency Washington DC 20460

JACOBS, WOODROW COOPER, b Pasadena, Calif, Sept 11, 08; m 33; c 1. OCEANOGRAPHY, METEOROLOGY. *Educ:* Univ Calif, Los Angeles, AB, 30, PhD(oceanog, meteorol), 48; Univ Southern Calif, MS, 34. *Prof Exp:* Meteorologist, US Weather Bur, Calif, 31-36; forecaster, Pomona & Asst, Scripps Inst Oceanog, 36-41; chief civilian meteorologist hqs, US Army Air Force, 42-46; head climat br, US Weather Bur, DC, 46-48; dir climat, Air Force Air Weather Serv, DC & Scott Air Force Base, Ill, 48-60; phys scientist, Library Cong, 60-61; dir, Nat Oceanog Data Ctr, 61-67; dir, environ data ctr, Environ Sci Serv Admin, 67-70; SR SCIENTIST, OCEAN DATA SYSTS, INC, 71- *Concurrent Pos:* Lectr, Inst Oceanog & Meteorol, USDA Grad Sch, 42-58, Mass Inst Technol, 50 & Univ Chicago, 56; mem two panels, Res & Develop Bd, US Dept Defense, 48-52; mem comt climat, Joint Meteorol Comt, Joint Chiefs Staff, 48-58; mem comn climat, World Meteorol Orgn, 48-62; mem three panels, Interagency Comt Oceanog, 61-67; mem adv comt oceanog, Smithsonian Inst, 62-67; mem adv coun, Oceanic Res Inst, San Diego, 64-; mem adv panel, Sea-Air Interaction Prog, US Dept Com, 64-67; chmn int working group ocean atmosphere res, Comn Maritime Meteorol, 65-68; US del & pres subcomt agr forecasts, Int Meteorol Orgn, 47-50. *Mem:* Fel Am Geophys Union; fel Am Meteorol Soc; Am Soc Limnol & Oceanog; Royal Meteorol Soc; NY Acad Sci. *Res:* Maritime meteorology; atmospheric radiation and chemistry; energy exchange processes applied climatology. *Mailing Add:* 6309 Bradley Blvd Bethesda MD 20034

JACOBSEN, BARRY JAMES, b Racine, Wis, Aug 6, 47; m 69; c 2. PLANT PATHOLOGY. *Educ:* Univ Wis-Madison, BSc, 69, MSc, 71; Univ Minn, PhD(plant path), 73. *Prof Exp:* Asst prof, 73-77, ASSOC PROF PLANT PATH, UNIV ILL, URBANA-CHAMPAIGN, 77-, PROJ LEADER, 79- *Honors & Awards:* Campbell Award, Am Phytopath Soc, 80. *Mem:* Sigma Xi; Am Phytopath Soc; Soc Nematologists. *Res:* Studies on generalized disease resistance in wheat and tomatoes; effects of pesticides on non-target plant pathogens and interactions of plant parasitic nematodes and fungi in plant diseases; chemical control of plant diseases. *Mailing Add:* Dept Plant Path Univ Ill N533 Turner Hall 1102 S Goodwin Urbana IL 61801

JACOBSEN, DONALD WELDON, b Portland, Ore, Apr 26, 39; m 62; c 2. BIOCHEMISTRY, CHEMISTRY. *Educ:* Univ Pa, BA, 61; Ore State Univ, MS, 64, PhD(biochem, cell biol), 67. *Prof Exp:* Nat Insts Health fel biochem, 67-71, ASSOC BIOCHEM, SCRIPPS CLIN & RES FOUND, 71- *Concurrent Pos:* Dernham Fel, Am Cancer Soc, Calif, 72. *Mem:* AAAS; Am Chem Soc; Biophys Soc; Am Soc Microbiol. *Res:* Purification and function of cobalamin-binding proteins; receptor-mediated transport of cobalamin-binding proteins; mechanisms of enzyme action, especially ribonucleotide reductase, methionine synthetase and other vitamin B12 dependent enzymes; cobalamin and cobinamide chemistry; synthesis and function of B12 coenzymes in mammalian cells; B12-folate interrelationships. *Mailing Add:* Dept Biochem Scripps Clin Res Found 10666 N Torrey Pines Rd La Jolla CA 92037

JACOBSEN, EDWARD HASTINGS, b Elizabeth, NJ, Jan 2, 26. PHYSICS, ELECTRON OPTICS. *Educ:* Mass Inst Technol, BS, 50, PhD(physics), 54. *Prof Exp:* Fulbright fel, Col France, 54-55; res physicist, Res Lab, Gen Elec Co, 55-61; Brit Dept Sci & Indust Res fel, Nottingham, 61; PROF PHYSICS, UNIV ROCHESTER, 62- *Concurrent Pos:* Vis scientist, Molecular Biol Lab, Harvard Med Sch, 65; vis prof, Mass Inst Technol, 67-68, vis scientist, Res Lab Electronics, 70-72. *Mem:* Am Phys Soc. *Res:* Magnetic resonance; x-ray and neutron diffraction; microwave ultrasonics; statistical mechanics; semiconductors; plasma physics; biophysics. *Mailing Add:* Dept Physics Univ Rochester Rochester NY 14627

JACOBSEN, FRED MARIUS, JR, b Brooklyn, NY, May 19, 25; m 49; c 1. COMPUTER SCIENCE, APPLIED STATISTICS. *Educ:* Polytech Inst Brooklyn, BChE, 44; Iowa State Univ, PhD(chem eng), 54. *Prof Exp:* Minor shift foreman, US Army, Carbide & Carbon Chem Corp, 45; staff mem phys chem, Los Alamos Sci Lab, 46-50; asst chem engr, Inst Atomic Res, 51-54; chem engr statist, Am Oil Co, 55-56, group leader comput, 57-60, tech comput supvr, 61-69; dir comput serv, 70-73, RES SUPVR COMPUT, STANDARD OIL CO, IND, 74- *Mem:* AAAS; Asn Comput Mach; Am Inst Chem Engrs; Am Statist Asn; Inst Math Statist. *Res:* Scientific computing; engineering statistics; applied mathematics; information retrieval. *Mailing Add:* Standard Oil Co Ind Box 400 Naperville IL 60540

JACOBSEN, LYNN C, b Montevideo, Minn, Mar 12, 18; m 44; c 4. GEOLOGY. *Educ:* Univ Minn, BA, 41; Univ Okla, MS, 48; Pa State Col, PhD(mineral), 53. *Prof Exp:* Jr geologist, Panama Canal, 41-42; jr & asst geologist, US Geol Surv, 42-45; geologist, Union Oil Co, Calif, 45-47; instr geol, Univ Ky, 48-50 & 52-53, asst prof, 53-55; sr res geologist, Sohio Petrol Co, 55-59, asst to sr vpres, 59-70, mgr uranium opers, 70-78. *Concurrent Pos:* Consult uranium indust, 78- *Mem:* AAAS; Geol Soc Am; Soc Econ Paleont & Mineral; Am Asn Petrol Geologists. *Res:* Sedimentary petrology; subsurface geology; fuel and mineral economics. *Mailing Add:* 1800 Coe Ct NE Albuquerque NM 87110

JACOBSEN, NADINE KLECHA, b Milwaukee, Wis, Dec 13, 41; m 67. PHYSIOLOGICAL ECOLOGY. *Educ:* Drake Univ, BA, 64; Ore State Univ, MS, 66; Cornell Univ, PhD(wildlife ecol), 73. *Prof Exp:* Instr biol, Blue Mountain Community Col, 66-67; res assoc, Dept Radiation Biol, Cornell Univ, 68-69, fel, Dept Natural Resources, 73-74; ASSOC PROF WILDLIFE BIOL, UNIV CALIF, DAVIS, 74- *Mem:* Sigma Xi; Am Soc Mammal; Wildlife Soc; Am Soc Animal Scientists; Ecol Soc Am. *Res:* Ecological energetics of wildlife, particularly deer, over the annual cycle and between birth and weaning of young; how energy and nutrient metabolism are affected by environmental, behavioral and physiological states. *Mailing Add:* Div Wildlife & Fisheries Biol Univ Calif Davis CA 95616

JACOBSEN, NEIL SOREN, b Waterloo, Iowa, June 13, 30; m 54; c 3. ACADEMIC ADMINISTRATION. *Educ:* Univ Iowa, BA, 52; Univ Denver, MS, 56; Okla State Univ, PhD(physiol), 65. *Prof Exp:* Teacher high schs, Calif, 57-62; Nat Insts Health fel, Univ Mass, 64-66; asst prof, 66-71, dir student acad affairs, 69-72, actg vpres acad affairs, 79-80, ASSOC PROF ZOOL, NDAK STATE UNIV, 71-, DEAN UNIV STUDIES, 72-, ASSOC VPRES ACAD AFFAIRS, 81- *Res:* Lipid metabolism of intestinal parasites; effect of pesticides on the cardiovascular system. *Mailing Add:* NDak State Univ Fargo ND 58105

JACOBSEN, RICHARD T, b Pocatello, Idaho, Nov 12, 41; m 73; c 5. MECHANICAL ENGINEERING, THERMODYNAMICS. *Educ:* Univ Idaho, BS, 63, MS, 65; Wash State Univ, PhD(eng sci), 72. *Prof Exp:* From instr to assoc prof eng, 64-77, prof eng, 77-80, ASSOC DIR, CTR APPL THERMODYN STUDIES, UNIV IDAHO, 75-, PROF & CHMN, DEPT MECH ENG, 80- *Concurrent Pos:* Mem correlating functions working panel, Int Union Pure & Appl Chem, 73- & carbon monoxide working panel, 76- *Mem:* Sigma Xi; Am Soc Mech Engrs; Soc Automotive Engrs. *Res:* Thermodynamics; thermodynamic properties of fluids; thermodynamic system analysis. *Mailing Add:* Janssen Eng Bldg 237 Univ of Idaho Moscow ID 83843

JACOBSEN, STEIN BJORNAR, b Baerum, Norway, Feb 12, 50. GEOCHEMISTRY. *Educ:* Univ Oslo, Norway, BS, 75, MS, 75; Calif Inst Technol, PhD(geochem), 80. *Prof Exp:* Fel geochem, Calif Inst Technol, 80-81; ASST PROF GEOCHEM, HARVARD UNIV, 81- *Mem:* Am Geophys Union. *Res:* Neodymium, strontium and lead isotope studies of mantle structure and differentiation, crustal evolution and chronology; petrological and geochemical studies of granulite and eclogite facies rocks, ophiolites, orogenic peridotites and chondritic meteorites. *Mailing Add:* Hoffman Lab Harvard Univ 20 Oxford St Cambridge MA 02138

JACOBSEN, TERRY DALE, b Nampa, Idaho, Aug 17, 50; m 79. PLANT SYSTEMATICS. *Educ:* Col Idaho, BS, 72; Wash State Univ, MS, 75, PhD(bot), 78. *Prof Exp:* Lectr, Biol Prog, Wash State Univ, 77-78, instr bot, 78-79; asst to dir & res scientist, 79-81, ASST DIR & SR RES SCIENTIST, HUNT INST BOT DOC, CARNEGIE-MELLON UNIV, 81- *Concurrent Pos:* Adj res scientist, Carnegie Mus Natural Hist, 79-; ed, Bull Hunt Inst Bot Doc, 81- *Res:* Cytotaxonomy, anatomy and numerical analysis of the genus Allium L in North America. *Mailing Add:* Hunt Inst Bot Doc Carnegie-Mellon Univ Pittsburgh PA 15213

JACOBS-LORENA, MARCELO, b Sao Paulo, Brazil, May 5, 42; m 70; c 1. MOLECULAR BIOLOGY, EMBRYOLOGY. *Educ:* Sao Paulo Univ, BS, 64; Osaka Univ, MS, 67; Mass Inst Technol, PhD(biol), 72. *Prof Exp:* Fel biol, Univ Geneva, 72-77; ASST PROF ANAT, CASE WESTERN RESERVE UNIV, 77- *Concurrent Pos:* Fel, Europ Molecular Biol Orgn, 72-74; asst prof, Am Cancer Soc Inst grant, 77-78 & NIH, 78-83. *Mem:* Soc Develop Biol. *Res:* Biochemical aspects of Drosophila oogenesis and embryogenesis, Drosophila development and control of gene expression. *Mailing Add:* Dept of Anat Case Western Reserve Univ Cleveland OH 44106

JACOBSMEYER, VINCENT PAUL, b St Louis, Mo, July 7, 06. SOLID STATE PHYSICS. *Educ:* Gonzaga Univ, AB, 31; St Louis Univ, MA, 33, MS, 35, PhD(physics), 45; St Mary's Col, STL, 40. *Prof Exp:* Instr high sch, Marquette Univ, 35-36; from instr to prof, 44-74, EMER PROF PHYSICS, ST LOUIS UNIV, 74- *Mem:* Am Asn Physics Teachers. *Res:* Photoelectricity; photoconductivity; Hall effect and resistivity studies of semiconductors. *Mailing Add:* DeSmet Jesuit High Sch 233 N New Ballas Rd St Louis MO 63141

JACOBSOHN, GERT MAX, b Berlin, Ger, Aug 1, 29; nat US; m 59; c 4. BIOCHEMISTRY. *Educ:* Ill Col, AB, 52; Purdue Univ, MS, 55, PhD(biochem), 57. *Prof Exp:* Fel, Col Physicians & Surgeons, Columbia Univ, 57-60; asst mem endocrinol, Albert Einstein Med Ctr, 60-61; asst prof, 62-67, assoc prof, 67-77, PROF BIOL CHEM, HAHNEMANN MED COL, 77- *Mem:* AAAS; fel Am Cancer Soc; Am Chem Soc; Endocrine Soc; Am Soc Biol Chem. *Res:* Metabolic control of blood enzymes; membrane transfer phenomena; steroid interconversion and function in plants; regulation of steroid, methods of steroid assay and instrumentation. *Mailing Add:* Dept of Biol Chem Hahnemann Med Col Philadelphia PA 19102

JACOBSOHN, MYRA K, b New York, NY, Feb 13, 39; c 4. SEED GERMINATION, CELL BIOLOGY. *Educ:* Columbia Univ, BA, 60; Univ Pa, MS, 62; Bryn Mawr Col, PhD(biol), 75. *Prof Exp:* Res assoc, Hahnemann Med Col, 71-74, fel biochem, 74-76; lectr, 74-76, ASST PROF BIOL, BEAVER COL, 74- *Mem:* Am Soc Plant Physiologists; AAAS; Am Inst Biol Sci. *Res:* Seed germination; plant sterols; membrane structure. *Mailing Add:* Dept of Biol Beaver Col Glenside PA 19038

JACOBSON, ADA LEAH , b Boston, Mass, Oct 8, 33; m 58. PHYSICAL CHEMISTRY, BIOCHEMISTRY. *Educ:* Mass Inst Technol, BS, 54; Yale Univ, PhD(chem), 57. *Prof Exp:* Chemist, Shell Develop Co, Calif, 57-58; instr phys chem, Albertus Magnus Col, 58-59; instr biochem, Dartmouth Med Sch, 59-60; from instr to asst prof chem, 60-68, ASSOC PROF CHEM, UNIV CALGARY, 68- *Concurrent Pos:* Fel phys org chem, Yale Univ, 58-59; sr fel, Can Heart Found, 65- *Mem:* Am Chem Soc; Can Biochem Soc; Sigma Xi; Biophys Soc. *Res:* Physical chemistry of proteins, solutions and polymers. *Mailing Add:* Dept of Chem Univ of Calgary Calgary AB T2N 1N4 Can

JACOBSON, ALBERT H(ERMAN), JR, b St Paul, Minn, Oct 27, 17; m 60; c 2. INDUSTRIAL ENGINEERING, SYSTEMS ENGINEERING. *Educ:* Yale Univ, BS, 39; Mass Inst Technol, SM, 52; Univ Rochester, MS, 54; Stanford Univ, PhD(mgt eng), 76. *Prof Exp:* Personnel asst, Yale Univ, 39-40; indust engr, Radio Corp Am, NJ, 40-43; from chief engr to tech dir, Bur Ord, Navy Ord Div, Eastman Kodak Co, 46-57, from staff engr to mgr field opers, Space Satellite Prog, Apparatus Div, 57-59; assoc dean, Col Eng & Archit, Pa State Univ, 59-61; pres & gen mgr, Knapic Electro-Physics Co, Calif, 61-62; prof eng, 62-69, PROF INDUST & SYSTS ENG, SAN JOSE STATE UNIV, 69-, COFOUNDER & COORDR CYBERNETIC SYSTS GRAD PROG, 67- *Concurrent Pos:* Consult numerous indust firms, 63-; NSF sci fac fel, Stanford Univ, 65-66. *Mem:* AAAS; Am Soc Eng Educ; Am Inst Indust Engrs; Am Prod & Inventory Control Soc. *Res:* Infrared; guided missiles; satellites; engineering management; management development; cybernetic systems; transportation systems; information systems. *Mailing Add:* Sch of Eng 125 S Seventh St San Jose CA 95192

JACOBSON, ALEXANDER DONALD, b New York, NY, Dec 1, 33; m 55; c 3. ELECTRICAL ENGINEERING. *Educ:* Univ Calif, Los Angeles, BS, 55, MS, 58; Calif Inst Technol, PhD(electro-magnetic theory), 64. *Prof Exp:* Mem tech staff optics res, Hughes Res Labs Div, Hughes Aircraft Co, 55-68, head unconventional imaging sect, 68-72, assoc mgr explor studies dept, 72-76, prog mgr liquid crystal displays progs, Indust Prod Div, 76-77; consult, 77-79; CO-FOUNDER & PRES, SYSTS COGNITION CORP, 79- *Res:* Laser technology; electromagnetic theory; x-ray diffraction studies of crystals; display technology; computer systems; telecommunications; computer software products. *Mailing Add:* 12256 Canna Rd Los Angeles CA 90049

JACOBSON, ALLAN JOSEPH, b Newcastle, Eng, May 28, 44; m 68; c 1. INORGANIC CHEMISTRY, SOLID STATE CHEMISTRY. *Educ:* Oxford Univ, BA, 65, MA, 69, DPhil, 69. *Prof Exp:* Lectr chem, Oxford Univ, 70-76; sr staff chemist, 76-80, RES ASSOC, EXXON RES & ENG CO, EXXON CORP, 80- *Mem:* Chem Soc; Am Chem Soc. *Res:* Synthetic and structural solid state inorganic chemistry; neutron x-ray and electron diffraction; intercalation chemistry. *Mailing Add:* Exxon Res & Eng Co PO Box 45 Linden NJ 07036

JACOBSON, ANN BEATRICE, b New York, NY, July 24, 38. CELL BIOLOGY. *Educ:* Univ Chicago, BS, 58, PhD(bot), 62; Purdue Univ, MS, 61. *Prof Exp:* Res assoc plant biochem, Univ Chicago, 63-67; biologist, Biol Div, Oak Ridge Nat Lab, 67-71; vis scientist, Max Planck Inst Biochem, Munich, 71-75; Europ Molecular Biol Orgn Fel, Dept Molecular Biol, Univ Geneva, Switz, 75-76; lectr, 76-80, RES ASST PROF, DEPT MICROBIOL, STATE UNIV NY, STONY BROOK, 80- *Mem:* AAAS; Am Soc Microbiol; Am Women Sci. *Res:* RNA folding computer modeling and electron microscopy. *Mailing Add:* Dept of Microbiol State Univ of NY Stony Brook NY 11794

JACOBSON, ANTONE GARDNER, b Salt Lake City, Utah, May 22, 29; m 63; c 2. DEVELOPMENTAL BIOLOGY. *Educ:* Harvard Univ, AB, 51; Stanford Univ, PhD(exp embryol, biol), 55. *Prof Exp:* From instr to assoc prof, 57-68, PROF ZOOL, UNIV TEX, AUSTIN, 68- *Mem:* AAAS; Am Soc Zool; Soc Develop Biol; Int Soc Develop Biol. *Res:* Embryonic induction, morphogenesis and development of reproduction control centers in embryos. *Mailing Add:* Dept of Zool Univ of Texas Austin TX 78712

JACOBSON, ARNOLD P, b Rawlins, Wyo, July 21, 32; m 65. RADIATION BIOLOGY. *Educ:* Univ Wyo, BS, 58, MS, 60; Univ Mich, MPH, 62, PhD(radiation biol), 66. *Prof Exp:* Asst prof environ health, 65-79, assoc prof, 71-79, PROF ENVIRON & INDUST HEALTH, SCH PUB HEALTH, UNIV MICH, ANN ARBOR, 79- *Concurrent Pos:* Assoc res scientist, Inst Environ & Indust Health, 74-80. *Mem:* Radiation Res Soc; Health Physics Soc. *Res:* Immediate and very early biological responses to ionizing radiation; low dose effects of radiations. *Mailing Add:* M6242 Sch Pub Health II Dept of Environ & Indust Hlth Univ Mich Ann Arbor MI 48109

JACOBSON, ARTHUR E, b New York, NY, May 2, 28; m 64; c 2. MEDICINAL CHEMISTRY. *Educ:* Fordham Univ, BS, 49; Rutgers Univ, MS(pharm chem), 52, MS(chem), 54, PhD(org & phys chem), 60. *Prof Exp:* Nat Insts Health, US Pub Health Serv fel & org chemist, Albert Einstein Col Med, 59-62; RES CHEMIST, NAT INST ARTHRITIS, METAB & DIGESTIVE DIS, NIH, 62- *Concurrent Pos:* Instr spectros, Found Adv Ed in Sci, Inc, 64-; mem comt probs drug dependence, Inc, 74-; biol coordr for comt probs drug dependence, 77- *Mem:* AAAS; Am Chem Soc; The Chem Soc. *Res:* Synthesis of alkaloids and heterocycles; biochemistry; organic reaction mechanisms; spectroscopy; QSAR. *Mailing Add:* Bldg 4 Rm 136 Nat Inst of Arthritis & Metab Dis Bethesda MD 20014

JACOBSON, AVROHM, b Toronto, Ont, July 12, 19; US citizen; m 48; c 3. PSYCHIATRY, PSYCHOANALYSIS. *Educ:* Univ Mich, BA, 41; Tulane Univ, MD, 44. *Prof Exp:* House physician intern, Newark Beth Israel Hosp, 44-45; resident physician psychiat, Middletown State Hosp, NY, 45-46; instr psychiat, Sch Med, Georgetown Univ, 49-54; assoc clin prof, NY Med Col, 57-62; prof clin psychiat, Col Med & Dent, Seton Hall Univ, 60-64; CONSULT PSYCHIAT, 55-; CLIN PROF PSYCHIAT, RUTGERS MED SCH, 70- *Concurrent Pos:* Cand training psychoanal, Washington-Baltimore Psychoanal Asn, 48-52; consult psychiat, Tuberc Prev Children, 53-57, Pollak Mem Clin, Long Branch, NJ, 55-64, Vet Admin Hosp, Lyons, 55-, US Army, Ft Monmouth, 56-65 & Jersey Shore Med Ctr, 57-; sr attend psychiatrist, Monmouth Med Ctr, 57-; consult psychiat, US Info Agency, 59-60; councilman, Borough Interlaken, 66-; trustee, Ranney Sch Found, 68-70; consult psychiat, Trenton Psychiat Hosp, 69-; mem, Monmouth County Ment Health Bd, 69-75; comnr, Deal Lake Comn, 71-74; ed, NJ Psychiat Asn Newsletter; consult psychiat, NJ Rehab Comn & Adv Comn Medicaid; fel, WHO. *Honors & Awards:* Physicians Recognition Award, Am Med Asn, 70, 71, 72, 73, 74 & 78. *Mem:* Fel AAAS; Am Med Asn; fel Am Psychiat Asn; fel Am Col Physicians; fel NY Acad Sci. *Res:* Psychotherapy and training in psychotherapeutic techniques; the dynamics of psychotherapy. *Mailing Add:* Franklin Ave at Hwy 35 Deal NJ 07712

JACOBSON, BARUCH S, b New York, NY, Nov 23, 25; m 51; c 4. BIOPHYSICS. *Educ:* Columbia Univ, AB, 51; Univ Calif, PhD(biophys), 56. *Prof Exp:* NSF fel, Donner Lab, Univ Calif, 56-58, biophysicist, 58; from instr to asst prof zool, Univ Tex, 58-61; asst prof radiol, Univ Minn, Minneapolis, 61-68; ASSOC PROF PHYSICS, CENT MICH UNIV, 68- *Concurrent Pos:* Vis res prof, Inst Ecol, Univ Calif, Davis, 75. *Mem:* AAAS; Biophys Soc; Radiation Res Soc; Sigma Xi. *Res:* Cellular radiobiology; effects of ionizing radiation on cell reproduction; metabolic reversal of radiation damage; ultraviolet photobiology; environmental systems analysis. *Mailing Add:* Dept of Physics Cent Mich Univ Mt Pleasant MI 48859

JACOBSON, BERNARD, b Cleveland, Ohio, Apr 7, 28; m 56; c 2. MATHEMATICS. *Educ:* Western Reserve Univ, BS, 51; Mich State Univ, MS, 52, PhD(math), 56. *Prof Exp:* From asst prof to assoc prof math, Franklin & Marshall Col, 56-61; assoc dir comt on undergrad prog in math, Math Asn Am, 62-63; assoc prof, 63-69, PROF MATH, FRANKLIN & MARSHALL COL, 69- *Mem:* Am Math Soc; Math Asn Am. *Res:* Number theory. *Mailing Add:* Dept of Math Franklin & Marshall Col Lancaster PA 17604

JACOBSON, BERNARD JEROME, biochemistry, see previous edition

JACOBSON, BRUCE SHELL, b Los Angeles, Calif, Jan 11, 40. BIOLOGICAL CHEMISTRY. *Educ:* Calif State Col, Los Angeles, BA, 62, MA, 64; Univ Calif, Los Angeles, PhD(plant biochem), 70. *Prof Exp:* Res biologist, Univ Calif, Riverside, 70-71; res biochemist, Univ Calif, Davis, 71-73; res assoc, Harvard Univ, 73-77; asst prof, 77-80, ASSOC PROF BIOCHEM, UNIV MASS, AMHERST, 81- *Mem:* Am Chem Soc; Am Soc Cell Biologists. *Res:* Membrane physiology and biochemistry; isolation of plasma membranes by their external binding to synthetic polymers and characterization of their internal surface interactions with cytoplasmic fibrous proteins; isolation and characterization of actin binding proteins in the plasma membrane which facilitate endocytosis and cell to substratum interactions. *Mailing Add:* Dept of Biochem Univ of Mass Amherst MA 01003

JACOBSON, EDMUND, b Chicago, Ill, Apr 22, 88; m 26; c 3. PHYSIOLOGY. *Educ:* Northwestern Univ, BS, 07; Harvard Univ, AM, 09, PhD, 10; Rush Med Col, Univ Chicago, MD, 15. *Hon Degrees:* LLD, George Williams Col, 62. *Prof Exp:* Hon fel, Cornell Univ, 10-11; diagnostician, North Chicago Hosp, Ill, 18-19; assoc attend physician, Michael Reese Hosp, 19-26; res assoc physiol, Univ Chicago, 26-32, asst prof, 32-36; DIR, LAB CLIN PHYSIOL, 36- *Mem:* AAAS; AMA; fel Am Col Physicians; Int Stress & Tension Control Asn. *Res:* Electrophysiology of mental activities; measurement of muscular states and nervous states in man; hypertension; progressive relaxation; measurement of energy expenditures in man in terms of oxygen usage correlated with action-potential curves from signigicant neruomuscular regions with computer methods; foundations of theoretical medicine. *Mailing Add:* Lab for Clin Physiol 55 E Washington St Chicago IL 60602

JACOBSON, ELAINE LOUISE, b Miller, Kans, Mar 29, 45; m 67. BIOCHEMISTRY. *Educ:* Kans State Univ, BS, 67, PhD(biochem), 71. *Prof Exp:* Res fel biochem, Mayo Clin, Found & Grad Sch Med, 72-73; res assoc biochem, Dept Chem, NTex State Univ, 74-77; asst prof, 77-81, ASSOC PROF BIOL, TEX WOMAN'S UNIV, 81- *Concurrent Pos:* NIH fel, Mayo Clin, Found & Grad Sch Med, 72-73; Extramanal Assoc, 79-80. *Res:* Regulation of poly (adenosine diphosphate ribose) synthesis with a particular interest in events following DNA damage by carcinogens. *Mailing Add:* Dept of Biol Tex Woman's Univ Denton TX 76204

JACOBSON, EUGENE DONALD, b Bridgeport, Conn, Feb 19, 30; m 53, 72; c 5. PHYSIOLOGY. *Educ:* Wesleyan Univ, BA, 51; Univ Vt, MD, 55; State Univ NY, MS, 60. *Prof Exp:* Intern, State Univ NY, 55-56, resident internal med, 57-60; assoc prof physiol, Sch Med, Univ Calif, Los Angeles, 64-66; prof & chmn dept, Sch Med, Univ Okla, 66-71; prof physiol & chmn dept, Univ Tex Med Sch, Houston, 71-77; ASSOC DEAN, COL MED, UNIV CINCINNATI, 77- *Concurrent Pos:* NIH spec fel, Univ Calif, Los Angeles, 64-66, NIH res career develop award, 66; consult, Gen Med Study Sect, NIH, 68-72, Vet Admin, 69-71 & Upjohn Co, Mich, 70-78; prof physiol, Baylor Col Med, 72-77; chairperson, Nat Comn Digestive Diseases, 77-79. *Mem:* Am Physiol Soc; Soc Exp Biol & Med; Am Fedn Clin Res; Am Soc Clin Invest; Am Gastroenterol Asn. *Res:* Splanchnic circulation; gastrointestinal physiology. *Mailing Add:* Col of Med 231 Bethesda Ave Cincinnati OH 45267

JACOBSON, FLORENCE DORFMAN, b Chicago, Ill, Mar 25, 18; m 42; c 2. MATHEMATICS. *Educ:* Univ Chicago, SB, 38, SM, 40. *Prof Exp:* Instr math, Univ NC, 42-43; lectr, 55-57, from asst prof to assoc prof, 58-66, PROF MATH, ALBERTUS MAGNUS COL, 66-, CHMN DEPT, 80- *Concurrent Pos:* Consult, Sch Math Study Group, 58-; mem adv panel, In-Serv Inst, NSF, 61-66; sci fac fel, 62-63. *Mem:* Am Math Soc; Math Asn Am. *Res:* Non-associative algebras; in-service and preservice education in mathematics for teachers from kindergarten through junior college. *Mailing Add:* Dept of Math Albertus Magnus Col New Haven CT 06511

JACOBSON, FRANK HENRY, b Providence, RI, Sept 11, 15; m 40; c 1. PHYSIOLOGY. *Educ:* Emory Univ, BA, 42; Univ Rochester, PhD(physiol), 51. *Prof Exp:* From instr to asst prof physiol, Jefferson Med Col, 51-59; physiologist, Aerospace Med Res Dept, US Naval Develop Ctr, 59-70, physiologist, Appl Physiol Lab, Aircraft Crew Systs Directorate, 70-81; RETIRED. *Mem:* Am Physiol Soc; Aerospace Med Asn. *Res:* Temperature regulation of mammals; hypothalamus; acceleration; mechanism and pharmacology of cerebral concussion, sleep, arousal and affective illness. *Mailing Add:* 1035 Gravel Hill Rd Southampton PA 18966

JACOBSON, GAIL M, b Bartlesville, Okla, Feb 6, 38; m 63; c 3. BIOCHEMISTRY. *Educ:* Mt Holyoke Col, BA, 60, MA, 62; Cornell Univ, PhD(biochem), 66. *Prof Exp:* Res fel biochem, Calif Inst Technol, 66-68; asst mem, Okla Med Res Found, 68-76; LECTR, DEPT CHEM, CALIF POLYTECH STATE UNIV, 76- *Concurrent Pos:* Vis asst prof nutrit, Univ Okla, 68-75. *Mem:* Enzymology; enzyme kinetics; coenzyme B12; enzymes; methylation of ribosomal RNA. *Mailing Add:* Dept of Chem Calif Polytech State Univ San Luis Obispo CA 93407

JACOBSON, GLEN ARTHUR, b Greensburg, Kans, Feb 10, 26; m 50; c 2. FOOD CHEMISTRY. *Educ:* Kans State Univ, BS, 48, MS, 49; Univ Ill, PhD(food technol, biochem), 53. *Prof Exp:* Res chemist, Res Labs, Swift & Co, 53-56; div head, Fat & Oil Res, Basic Res Dept, Campbell Soup Co, 56-70, DIV HEAD, LIPID CHEM RES, BASIC RES DEPT, CAMPBELL INST FOOD RES, 70- *Mem:* Am Chem Soc; Am Oil Chem Soc; Inst Food Technologists. *Res:* Fats and oil chemistry; biochemistry. *Mailing Add:* Basic Res Div Box 57L Campbell Soup Co Camden NJ 08101

JACOBSON, HAROLD, b New York, NY, Jan 15, 29; m 52; c 3. PHYSICAL CHEMISTRY, PHYSICAL PHARMACY. *Educ:* City Col NY, BS, 50; Polytech Inst Brooklyn, PhD(phys chem), 59. *Prof Exp:* Chemist pharmaceut, Robin Pharmacal Co, 50-51; analyst, Nat Bur Standards, 51-54; sr res chemist electrochem devices, Nat Cash Register Co, 59-62; mem tech staff, Bell Tel Labs, 62-63; sr res scientist pharmaceut & biophys, Squibb Inst Med Res, 63-76, DEPT HEAD METHODS DEVELOP & TESTING STANDARDS, E R SQUIBB CORP, 76- *Concurrent Pos:* Adj prof, Middlesex Community Col, 67-70. *Mem:* Am Pharmaceut Asn; Am Chem Soc; NY Acad Sci. *Res:* Ion-exchange membranes; electro- chemistry; solution chemistry; differential thermal analysis; ion-specific electrodes. *Mailing Add:* E R Squibb Corp New Brunswick NJ 08902

JACOBSON, HAROLD GORDON, b Cincinnati, Ohio, Oct 12, 12; m 42; c 2. RADIOLOGY. *Educ:* Univ Cincinnati, BS, 34, BM, 36, MD, 37. *Prof Exp:* Asst radiol, Sch Med, Univ Tex, 41-42; instr, Sch Med, Yale Univ, 42; assoc to chief radiol serv & assoc radiologist, Vet Admin Hosp, Bronx, 46-50, chief radiol serv, 50-52; from asst clin prof to clin prof radiol, Col Med, NY Univ, 52-59, prof clin radiol, 59-64; RADIOLOGIST-IN-CHIEF, MONTEFIORE HOSP & MED CTR, 55-; PROF RADIOL, ALBERT EINSTEIN COL MED, 64-, CHMN DEPT, 72- *Concurrent Pos:* Dir dept radiol, Hosp Spec Surg, 53-54; consult, Vet Admin Hosp, Bronx, 57-; vis prof, Col Med, Univ Cincinnati, 59; chmn comt on affairs, Am Inst Radiol, Am Col Radiol, 71, co-chmn comt diag coding index & Thesaurus, 73-; Crookshank lectr, London, Eng, 74; Holmes lectr, Boston, 74; consult, Nat Bd Med Examiners, 75-; vis prof radiol, Inst Orthop, Univ London, Eng, 75- *Mem:* Radiol Soc NAm (1st vpres, 64-65, pres, 66-67); Am Roentgen Ray Soc; Int Skeletal Soc (pres, 74-75); AMA; Am Col Radiol. *Res:* Bone and joint radiology; neuroradiology; radiology of skeletal disorders. *Mailing Add:* Dept of Radiology Albert Einstein Col of Med Bronx NY 10461

JACOBSON, HARRY C, b Bozeman, Mont, July 13, 31; m 64; c 4. PHYSICS. *Educ:* Col Holy Cross, BS, 53; Yale Univ, MS, 61; PhD(physics), 65. *Prof Exp:* Physicist, Nuclear Div, Combustion Engrs, Inc, 56-60; PHYSICIST, DEPT PHYSICS & ASTRON, UNIV TENN, KNOXVILLE, 64-, ASSOC

PROF PHYSICS & ASTRON, 80- *Mem:* Am Phys Soc; Am Asn Physics Teachers. *Res:* Theory of atomic and molecular structure; theory of spectral line shapes. *Mailing Add:* Dept of Physics & Astron Univ of Tenn Knoxville TN 37916

JACOBSON, HERBERT (IRVING), b Chicago, Ill, Mar 17, 23; m 53; c 3. REPRODUCTIVE ENDOCRINOLOGY, BIOCHEMISTRY. *Educ:* Univ Chicago, SB, 48, SM, 49, PhD(chem), 57. *Prof Exp:* Res assoc & instr, Univ Chicago, 52-57, res assoc & asst prof, 57-59, asst prof, Ben May Lab Cancer Res, 59-64; assoc prof obstet & gynec, 64-73, RES PROF & CHIEF SECT REPROD STUDIES, DEPT OBSTET & GYNEC, ALBANY MED COL, 73-, RES PROF BIOCHEM, 75- *Concurrent Pos:* Res partic chem div, Oak Ridge Nat Lab, 61; USPHS spec fel, Max Planck Inst Biochem, Munich, 62-63; Nat Inst Arthritis & Metabolic Dis res career develop award, 66-70; vis prof, Max Planck Inst Cell Biol, 75-76. *Honors & Awards:* US Sr Scientist Award, Fed Repub Ger & Alexander von Humboldt Found, 75. *Mem:* Endocrine Soc; Soc Exp Biol & Med; NY Acad Sci; Soc Study Reprod. *Res:* Steroid biochemistry; mechanism of hormone action; regulation of hormone receptor synthesis; control processes in mammalian reproduction; response mechanisms in hormone-dependent cancer. *Mailing Add:* Dept of Obstet & Gynec Albany Med Col Albany NY 12208

JACOBSON, HOMER, b Cleveland, Ohio, Nov 27, 22; m 57; c 3. PHYSICAL BIOCHEMISTRY. *Educ:* Calif Inst Technol, BS, 41; Columbia Univ, AM, 42, PhD(chem), 48. *Prof Exp:* Res scientist, Manhattan Proj, NY, 44-46; assoc chemist, Brookhaven Nat Lab, 47-49; instr chem, Hunter Col, 49-50; from instr to assoc prof, 50-65; PROF CHEM, BROOKLYN COL, 66- *Concurrent Pos:* Guggenheim fel, Calif Inst Technol, 59-60; NIH spec fel, 60-61. *Mem:* AAAS; Am Chem Soc. *Res:* Chemical mutagenesis in bacterial viruses; virus growth in continuous culture; steady-state kinetics; information theory in biological systems; configurational entropy of superhelical molecules. *Mailing Add:* Dept of Chem Brooklyn Col Brooklyn NY 11210

JACOBSON, HOWARD NEWMAN, b St Paul, Minn, Aug 13, 23; m 61. PHYSIOLOGY. *Educ:* Northwestern Univ, BS, 47, BM, 50, MD, 51. *Prof Exp:* Intern med, Presby Hosp, Chicago, 50-51; resident obstet & gynec, 51-52; Asn Aid Crippled Children fel, 52-55; resident, Boston Lying-in-Hosp & Free Hosp for Women, 55-57; obstetrician-physiologist, PR Proj, Nat Inst Neurol Dis & Blindness, 58-60; asst obstet & gynec, Harvard Med Sch, 60-61, instr, 61-64, assoc, 64-65; actg assoc prof obstet & gynec, Sch Med & lectr pub health, Sch Pub Health, Univ Calif, San Francisco, 65-67, assoc coord allied health professions, 67-69; assoc prof obstet & gynec, Boston Hosp for Women & dir Macy prog, Harvard Med Sch, 69-74; prof community med, Rutgers Med Sch, Col Med & Dent NJ, 74-79; DIR, INST NUTRIT, UNIV NC, CHAPEL HILL, 79- *Concurrent Pos:* Res fel physiol, Harvard Med Sch, 52-54; mem adv panel maternal & child health, Children's Bur, 64-; NIH res career develop award, 64-65; mem food & nutrit bd, Nat Res Coun, 70-; chmn comt on maternal nutrit, Nat Acad Sci-Nat Res Coun, 71- *Mem:* Am Soc Clin Nutrit; assoc Am Physiol Soc. *Res:* Fetal physiology and responses of fetuses to asphyxia and hypoxia; autonomic nervous system in reproduction; maternity services, with emphasis on maternal nutrition; health manpower needs, nutrition monitoring. *Mailing Add:* Inst of Nutrit Univ of NC Chapel Hill NC 27514

JACOBSON, IRA DAVID, b New York, NY, May 28, 42; m 54; c 2. FLIGHT MECHANICS, FLUID MECHANICS. *Educ:* New York Univ, BS, 63; Univ VA, MS, 67, PhD(aerospace eng), 70. *Prof Exp:* Aerospace engr, NASA, 63-67; res scientist & lectr, 70-73, asst prof, 73-75, assoc prof, 75-79, PROF AEROSPACE ENG, UNIV VA, 79- *Concurrent Pos:* Mem, Transp Res Bd, Nat Acad Eng. *Mem:* Am Inst Aeronaut & Astronaut; Am Soc Eng Educr; Sigma Xi. *Res:* Flight mechanics, especially stability and control; fluid mechanics, especially the magnus effect; vehicle systems, especially vehicle ride quality. *Mailing Add:* Dept of Mech & Aerospace Eng Univ of Va Charlottesville VA 22901

JACOBSON, IRVEN ALLAN, JR, b Denver, Colo, Apr 19, 28; m 64; c 1. PHYSICAL CHEMISTRY, CHEMICAL KINETICS. *Educ:* Univ Colo, BA, 50. *Prof Exp:* Chemist, Laramie Energy Res Ctr, Bur Mines, US Dept Interior, 50-60, res chemist, 60-75, RES CHEMIST & PROJ LEADER, LARAMIE ENERGY TECHNOL CTR, US DEPT ENERGY, 75- *Mem:* Fel AAAS; Am Chem Soc; Sigma Xi. *Res:* Directing research on the kinetics of oil shale thermal gasification and low temperature oxidation. *Mailing Add:* 2626 Park Ave Laramie WY 82070

JACOBSON, JAMES WILLIAM, molecular genetics, see previous edition

JACOBSON, JAY STANLEY, b New York, NY, Oct 5, 34; m 71. PLANT PHYSIOLOGY, AIR POLLUTION. *Educ:* Cornell Univ, BS, 55; Columbia Univ, MA, 57, PhD(plant biochem), 60. *Prof Exp:* Assoc plant biochemist, 60-70, PLANT PHYSIOLOGIST, BOYCE THOMPSON INST, 70- *Concurrent Pos:* Assoc referee fluorine in plants, Asn Off Anal Chemists, 69-; mem panel on effects of ambient environ qual, Nat Acad Sci, 75-76; plant ecologist, US Dept Energy, 77-78; mem subcomt sci criteria for photochem oxidants, US Environ Protection Agency. *Mem:* Am Chem Soc; Am Soc Plant Physiol; Am Inst Biol Sci; Air Pollution Control Asn; Am Inst Chem. *Res:* Effects of air pollutants and acid rain on growth, development, yield and quality of agricultural crops. *Mailing Add:* Boyce Thompson Inst Tower Rd Cornell Univ Ithaca NY 14853

JACOBSON, JIMMY JOE, b Lonepine, Wyo, Feb 11, 37; m 73; c 3. GEOPHYSICS, EARTH SCIENCES. *Educ:* Univ Wyo, BS, 59; Colo Sch Mines, MSc, 64, DSc(geophys), 69. *Prof Exp:* From jr to sr geophysicist, Deco Electronics, 60-65; sr geophysicist, Westinghouse Geores Labs, 65-67; asst prof physics & geophys, Mont Col Mineral Sci & Technol, 70-74; mgr field opers, Geonomics, Inc, 74-77; SR RES SCIENTIST GEOPHYS, PAC NORTHWEST DIV, BATTELLE MEM INST, 77- *Concurrent Pos:* Geophysicist, Group Seven, Inc, 69-73. *Mem:* Sigma Xi. *Res:* Exploration of the earth and earth materials utilizing electrical and other geophysical tools. *Mailing Add:* Pac Northwest Div Battelle Blvd Richland WA 99352

JACOBSON, JOAN, b Hull, Iowa, Apr 26, 24; div. AUDIOLOGY, SPEECH PATHOLOGY. *Educ:* Morningside Col, BA, 44; Syracuse Univ, MA, 48, PhD(speech corrections), 58. *Prof Exp:* Instr speech path, Syracuse Univ, 46-51; therapist, Brookline Pub Schs, Mass, 51-57; res asst speech path, Syracuse Univ, 57-58; asst prof speech path & audiol & audiologist, Eastern Ill Univ, 58-62; assoc prof, 62-72, PROF SPEECH SCI, PATH & AUDIOL, ST CLOUD STATE UNIV, 72- *Concurrent Pos:* Therapist, Mass Gen Hosp, Boston, 51-57; mem prof adv comt, Minn Soc Crippled Children & Adults, 63- & Minn Easter Seal Soc, 64-; mem, Gov Adv Comt Serv Hearing Impaired, 64-66 & Model Presch Ctr Hearing-Impaired Children & Families, 69-72. *Mailing Add:* Dept of Speech Sci Path & Audiol St Cloud State Univ St Cloud MN 56301

JACOBSON, KARL BRUCE, b Manning, Iowa, Mar 5, 28; m 51; c 4. BIOCHEMISTRY. *Educ:* St Bonaventure Col, BS, 48; Johns Hopkins Univ, PhD(biol), 56. *Prof Exp:* Am Cancer Soc fel chem, Calif Inst Technol, 56-58; BIOCHEMIST BIOL DIV, OAK RIDGE NAT LAB, 58-; PROF BIOMED SCI, UNIV TENN, 68- *Mem:* AAAS; Am Soc Biol Chem; Am Chem Soc; NY Acad Sci. *Res:* Development and differentiation in terms of biochemical changes; relationship of structure of transfer RNA to its function; biochemical genetics in Drosophila; mechanism of toxicity of cadmium and other metals. *Mailing Add:* Biol Div Oak Ridge Nat Lab PO Box Y Oak Ridge TN 37830

JACOBSON, KEITH HAZEN, b Yankton, SDak, Nov 4, 18. PHARMACOLOGY, TOXICOLOGY. *Educ:* Univ SDak, BA, 40, MA, 41; NY Univ, BS, 44; Univ Cincinnati, PhD(phys biochem), 49. *Prof Exp:* Chemist, Rustless Iron & Steel Corp, 41-43; biochemist, staff supv & coordr res, Res & Eng Div, US Army Chem Ctr, 49-51, indust toxicol res, Med Labs, Chem Corps, 51-56, coordr, Mil Chem Prog, 56-63, med res dir, Chem Warfare Labs, 57-63, asst to dir, 57-63; supvr res pharmacol, Div Pharmacol, Food & Drug Admin, DC, 63-64, chief lab invests, Div Toxicol Eval, 64-68, chief toxicol res, Div Pharmacol & Toxicol, 68-69; assoc prof med, Lab Environ Med, Sch Med, Tulane Univ, 69-72; chief criteria develop br, 72-74, sr scientist, div criteria doc & standards develop, 74-81, CONSULT, TOXICOL & ENVIRON HEALTH, NAT INST OCCUP SAFETY & HEALTH, 81- *Mem:* Am Indust Hyg Asn; Soc Toxicol; Conf Govt Indust Hygienists; Environ Mutagen Soc; Am Acad Indust Hyg. *Res:* Occupational toxicology; pesticide and food additive toxicology. *Mailing Add:* 840 Beall Ave Rockville MD 20850

JACOBSON, KENNETH ALLAN, b Milwaukee, Wis, Oct 29, 41; m 64; c 3. BIOPHYSICS. *Educ:* Univ Wis-Madison, BS, 64, MS, 66; State Univ NY Buffalo, PhD(biophys), 72. *Prof Exp:* Physicist mat sci, Dow Corning Corp, 66-69; sr cancer res scientist membrane biophys, Roswell Park Mem Inst, 72-77, cancer res scientist V, 77-80. *Concurrent Pos:* Chmn, Biomembranes Grad Study Group, State Univ NY, Buffalo. *Res:* Development of fluorescence techniques to probe the dynamic structure of membranes; structure of the mammalian cell surface and its role in neoplasia. *Mailing Add:* 412 Maynard Dr Amherst NY 14226

JACOBSON, LARRY A, b Madison, Wis, Oct 29, 40; m 65. NUCLEAR PHYSICS. *Educ:* Univ Wis, Madison, BS, 63; MS, 64, PhD(physics), 69. *Prof Exp:* Develop proj physicist, 69-74, sect mgr, Pulsed Neutron Sect, 74-76, dept mgr elec eng, 76-79, mgr sensor physsics, 80-81, MGR NUCLEAR LOGGING, SCHLUMBERGER WELL SERV CO, SCHLUMBERGER LTD, 81- *Mem:* AAAS; Am Phys Soc; Soc Prof Well Log Analysts; Soc Petrol Eng. *Res:* Negative ion source development; heavy ion nuclear elastic scattering; nuclear techniques in mineral and petroleum exploration and evaluation; data processing of nuclear data. *Mailing Add:* Rte 2 Box 62 NE Richmond TX 77469

JACOBSON, LEON ORRIS, b Sims, NDak, Dec 16, 11; m 38; c 2. MEDICINE. *Educ:* NDak State Univ, BS, 35, Univ Chicago, MD, 39; Am Bd Internal Med, dipl. *Hon Degrees:* DSc, NDak State Univ, 66, Acadia Univ, Can, 68. *Prof Exp:* Intern, Univ Clins, 39-40, asst resident med, 40-41, asst med, Univ, 41-42, from instr to prof, 42-65, assoc dean div biol sci, 45-51, head hemat sect, 51-61, chmn dept med, 61-65, dean div biol sci & Pritzker Sch Med, 66-75, dir, The Franklin McLean Mem Res Inst, 75-77, JOSEPH REGENSTEIN PROF BIOL & MED SCI, UNIV CHICAGO, 65- *Concurrent Pos:* From assoc dir to dir health, Plutonium Proj, Manhattan Dist, Univ Chicago, 43-46; consult, Div Biol & Med Res, Argonne Nat Lab; spec consult hemat study sect, USPHS, 49-53, mem comt radiation studies, 51-55, mem nat adv comt radiation, 61-66; mem comt cancer diag & ther, Panel Chemother, Nat Res Coun, 51-55; dir, Argonne Cancer Res Hosp, 51-67; R W Stewart Mem lectr, Pittsburgh Acad Med, 52; Janeway lectr, Am Radium Soc, 53; mem adv comt isotope distrib, USAEC, 52-56, mem adv comt to Yugoslavia, 60; Burrell O Ralston lectr, Univ Southern Calif, 57; Alice Messinger Band Mem lectr, Univ Md, 59; George Minot Mem lectr, AMA, 60; US rep, Int Conf Peaceful Uses of Atomic Energy, Geneva, 55 & 58; mem nat adv bd, Okla Med Res Found, 59-64; consult, Inst Cancer Res, Philadelphia, 59-70; mem expert adv panel radiation, WHO, 60-65 & adv comt biophys, Surgeon Gen Army, 61-70; Jacobaeus Mem lectr, Helsinki, 62; Malthe Found lectr, Oslo, 62; consult div radiol health, Univ Grant & Training Br, Dept Health Educ & Welfare, 62-65; mem sci adv bd, Inst Advan Learning Med Sci, City Hope Med Ctr, 62-; consult, Univ Calif, 62-; mem Morison panel, Wooldridge Comt, Off Sci & Technol, Exec Off President, 63-65; mem med & sci adv bd, Will Rogers Mem Fund, 63-66; mem erythropoietin comt, Nat Heart Inst, 63-67; mem bd sci counr, Nat Cancer Inst, 63-67; mem space biol adv subcomt, Space Sci & Appln Steering Comt, NASA, 68-70. *Honors & Awards:* Janeway Medal, Am Radium Soc, 53; Robert Roesler de Villiers Award, Leukemia Soc, 56; Ralston Award, Univ Southern Calif, 57; Borden Award, Asn Am Med Cols, 62; Mod Med Award, 63; Award, Am Nuclear Soc, 63; Citation, City of Hope Nat Med Ctr, 67; John Phillips Mem Award, 75; Theodore Roosevelt Rough Riders Award, State NDak, 76; Am Soc Contemp Med & Surg Award, 81. *Mem:* Nat Acad Sci; Am Asn Cancer Res; Am Nuclear Soc; Am Soc Clin Invest; master Am Col Physicians. *Res:* Hematology; chemotherapeutic agents and radioisotopes on neoplastic diseases of the blood forming tissues; protection against radiation injury; radiobiology. *Mailing Add:* Div Biol Sci Univ Chicago 950 E 59th St Box 420 Chicago IL 60637

JACOBSON, LEWIS A, b Brooklyn, NY, Oct 10, 42; m 67; c 2. MOLECULAR BIOLOGY, BIOCHEMISTRY. *Educ:* Amherst Col, AB, 63; Univ Ill, MS, 65, PhD(biochem), 67. *Prof Exp:* Asst prof biophysics, 67-73, admin officer, Dept Biophys & Microbiol, 73-74, assoc prof biophys & microbiol, 73-76, ASSOC PROF BIOL SCI, UNIV PITTSBURGH, 76- *Mem:* AAAS; Am Soc Microbiol; Am Soc Biol Chemists. *Res:* Regulation of gene expression in bacteria, biochemistry and genetics of lysosomal proteses; molecular mechanisms of aging. *Mailing Add:* Dept of Biol Sci 304 Langley Hall Univ Pittsburgh Pittsburgh PA 15260

JACOBSON, LOUIS, b Chicago, Ill, Nov 21, 15; m 38; c 3. PLANT PHYSIOLOGY. *Educ:* Univ Calif, Los Angeles, AB, 36; Univ Calif, PhD(plant physiol), 43. *Prof Exp:* Analyst, Div Plant Nutrit, 38-42, radiochemist, Radiation Lab, 42-46, from asst prof & asst plant biochemist to assoc prof nutrit & assoc plant biochemist, 45-58, PROF PLANT NUTRIT & PLANT PHYSIOLOGIST EXP STA, DEPT SOILS & PLANT NUTRIT, UNIV CALIF, BERKELEY, 58- *Mem:* Am Chem Soc; Am Soc Plant Physiol; Bot Soc Am. *Res:* Absorption and accumulation of ions by plants; inorganic nutrition of plants; plant physiology. *Mailing Add:* Dept of Soils & Plant Nutrit Univ of Calif Berkeley CA 94720

JACOBSON, MARCUS, b Houston, Tex, May 2, 30; m 65. ENGINEERING MECHANICS. *Educ:* Rice Univ, BA, 51, BSME, 52, MSME, 54; Univ Calif, Los Angeles, PhD(eng), 65. *Prof Exp:* Asst prof mech eng, Rice Univ, 52-62; design engr, Douglas Aircraft Co, 62; sr dynamics engr, Lockheed-Calif Co, 63-64; ENG SPECIALIST STRUCT DYNAMICS, AIRCRAFT DIV, NORTHROP CORP, 64- *Mem:* Am Inst Aeronaut & Astronaut. *Res:* Structural dynamics. *Mailing Add:* Aircraft Div Northrop Corp 3901 W Broadway Hawthorne CA 90250

JACOBSON, MARCUS, b Cape Town, SAfrica, Apr 2, 30; US citizen; m 60; c 2. PHYSIOLOGY, BIOPHYSICS. *Educ:* Univ Cape Town, BSc, 51, MB, ChB, 56; Univ Edinburgh, PhD(physiol), 60. *Prof Exp:* Intern med, Groote Schuur Hosp, Cape Town, 56-57; lectr physiol, Med Sch, Univ Edinburgh, 60-65; guest investr biophys, Naval Med Res Inst, Bethesda, 65-66; from assoc prof to prof, Johns Hopkins Univ, 67-73; prof physiol, Sch Med, Univ Miami, 73-77; PROF & CHMN DEPT ANAT, COL MED, UNIV UTAH, SALT LAKE CITY, 77- *Concurrent Pos:* Assoc ed, Brain Res, 71-74, J Neurosci Res, 74- & Exp Neurol, 81- *Mem:* Brit Physiol Soc; Am Physiol Soc; Soc Neurosci. *Res:* Development and growth of the nervous system. *Mailing Add:* Dept of Anat Col of Med Univ of Utah Salt Lake City UT 84132

JACOBSON, MARTIN MICHAEL, b New York, NY, Nov 24, 34; m 65. BIOCHEMICAL PHARMACOLOGY. *Educ:* City Col New York, BS, 57; Long Island Univ, MS, 68. *Prof Exp:* Res technician, Rockefeller Inst Med Res, 57-58; res biochemist, Wellcome Res Labs, Burroughs Wellcome & Co, 59-70; biochemist, 70-73, sr scientist, 74, coordr exp therapeut, 74-78, res planning mgr exp therapeut, 78-80, asst dir exp therapeut, 80-81, ASST DIR RES PLANNING & DEVELOP, HOFFMAN-LA ROCHE INC, 81- *Mem:* Am Soc Pharmacol & Exp Therapeut; NY Acad Sci; AAAS; Am Pharmaceut Asn; Acad Pharmaceut Sci. *Res:* Biochemical, pharmacologic and toxicologic effects and metabolism of drugs, carcinogens and steroids; involvement of the various disciplines in drug development. *Mailing Add:* Hoffmann-LaRoche Inc Nutley NJ 07110

JACOBSON, MELVIN JOSEPH, b Providence, RI, Nov 25, 28; m 52; c 2. APPLIED MATHEMATICS, UNDERWATER ACOUSTICS. *Educ:* Brown Univ, AB, 50; Carnegie Inst Technol, MS, 52, PhD(math), 54. *Prof Exp:* Res mathematician, United Aircraft Corp, 52; res assoc, Carnegie Inst Technol, 52-53, instr math, 53-54; mem tech staff, Bell Tel Labs, Inc, 54-56; from asst prof to assoc prof, 56-61; PROF MATH, RENSSELAER POLYTECH INST, 61- *Concurrent Pos:* Vis prof, Inst Marine Sci, Univ Miami, 63-64, adj prof, 69-72. *Mem:* Am Math Soc; fel Acoust Soc Am; Math Asn Am. *Res:* ocean environmental acoustics; array studies; source and receiver motions; acoustic oceanography. *Mailing Add:* Dept of Math Sci Rensselaer Polytech Inst Troy NY 12181

JACOBSON, MICHAEL F, b Chicago, Ill, July 29, 43. SCIENCE POLICY, MOLECULAR BIOLOGY. *Educ:* Univ Chicago, BA, 65; Mass Inst Technol, PhD(microbiol), 69. *Prof Exp:* Res assoc, Salk Inst Biol Studies, 70-71; EXEC DIR, CTR SCI PUBLIC INTEREST, 71- *Concurrent Pos:* Tech consult, Ctr Study Responsive Law, 70-71; dir, Ctr Sci Pub Interest, 71-; Americans Concerned About Corp Power, 79-81 & Nat Coalition Dis Prev & Environ Health, 79- *Res:* Impact of dietary and environmental factors on human health. *Mailing Add:* Ctr Sci Public Interest 1755 S St NW Washington DC 20009

JACOBSON, MURRAY M, b Boston, Mass, Jan 2, 15; m 62; c 1. CHEMICAL ENGINEERING, MATERIALS ENGINEERING. *Educ:* Tufts Univ, BS, 35. *Prof Exp:* Chemist, Whiting Labs, Mass, 36-39; chief corrosion & lubrication sect, Watertown Arsenal Labs, 40-46, chem engr, 46-49, chief, Surface Chem Sect, 49-54, Phys Chem Br, 54-56, Chem Metall Lab, 56-59 & Mat Sci Lab, 59-64; dep chief, Mat Eng Div, Army Mat Res Agency, 64-66, chief prototypes lab, Army Mat & Mech Res Ctr, 66-69, chief mat test div, 69-74; TECH MGR, JACON INDUSTS, 75- *Concurrent Pos:* Army liaison mem, Subgroup on Greases, Coord Res Coun, War Adv Comt & Adv Comt on Corrosion, Ord Dept, 42-45; liaison mem subpanel on chromium, Panel on Refractory Metals, Mat Adv Bd, 49 & Comt Coatings, 68-69. *Honors & Awards:* Cert Commendation, War Dept, 45. *Mem:* Am Chem Soc; Am Electroplaters Soc; Nat Asn Corrosion Engrs; Am Soc Metals; Am Soc Testing & Mat. *Res:* Research management; corrosion; erosion; oxidation; wear; lubrication; protective coatings and treatments; antigalling coatings; titanium surface metallurgy. *Mailing Add:* Jacon Industs PO Box 231 Boston MA 02146

JACOBSON, MYRON KENNETH, b Richland Center, Wis, Sept 20, 43; m 67. BIOCHEMISTRY. *Educ:* Univ Wis-Platteville, BS, 65; Kans State Univ, PhD(biochem), 70. *Prof Exp:* NIH fel biochem, Univ Utah, 70-72; from res asst to res assoc biochem, Mayo Clin & Found, 73-74; asst prof chem, 74-80, ASSOC PROF CHEM & BASIC HEALTH SCI, NTEX STATE UNIV, 80- *Mem:* AAAS; Am Soc Biol Chemists. *Res:* Nicotinamide nucleotide metabolism, chemical carcinogenesis and DNA repair mechanisms. *Mailing Add:* Dept of Chem NTex State Univ Denton TX 76203

JACOBSON, NATHAN, b Warsaw, Poland, Sept 8, 10; US citizen; m 42; c 2. MATHEMATICS. *Educ:* Univ Ala, AB, 30; Princeton Univ, PhD(math), 34. *Hon Degrees:* DSc, Univ Chicago, 72. *Prof Exp:* Asst math, Inst Advan Study, Princeton Univ, 33-34; Procter fel, 34-35; lectr, Bryn Mawr Col, 35-36; Nat Res Found fel, Univ Chicago, 36-37; from instr to asst prof, Univ NC, 37-40; vis assoc prof, Johns Hopkins Univ, 40-41; assoc prof, Univ NC, 41-42, assoc ground sch instr, US Navy preflight sch, 42-43; assoc prof of math, Johns Hopkins Univ, 43-47; from assoc prof to prof, 47-67, HENRY FORD II PROF MATH, YALE UNIV, 67- *Concurrent Pos:* Ed, Bull, Am Math Soc, 48-53; Guggenheim fel, 51-52; Fulbright res grant, Univ Paris, 51-52; vis prof, Univ Chicago, 64, Univ Tokyo, 65, Tata Inst Fundamental Res, India, 70, Univ Rome, 71, Hebrew Univ Jerusalem, 71, Rehovoth, 71 & Australian Nat Univ, 78. *Mem:* Nat Acad Sci; Am Math Soc (vpres, 57-58, pres, 71-73); French Math Soc; Math Soc Japan; Am Acad Arts & Sci. *Res:* Topological algebra; structure theory of rings; non-associative algebra, especially Lie and Jordan algebras; Galois theory. *Mailing Add:* Dept of Math Yale Univ Box 2155 Yale Sta New Haven CT 06520

JACOBSON, NORMAN LEONARD, b Eau Claire, Wis, Sept 11, 18; m 43; c 2. ANIMAL NUTRITION. *Educ:* Univ Wis, BS, 40; Iowa State Univ, MS, 41, PhD(nutrit), 47. *Prof Exp:* From asst prof to prof animal & dairy sci, 47-79, DISTINGUISHED PROF AGR, IOWA STATE UNIV, 63-, ASSOC DEAN, GRAD COL, 73-, ASSOC VPRES RES, 79- *Concurrent Pos:* Moorman travel fel nutrit, 66. *Honors & Awards:* Am Feed Mfgrs Award, 55; Borden Award, 60; Morrison Award, Am Soc Animal Sci, 70. *Mem:* AAAS; Am Dairy Sci Asn (vpres, 71, pres, 72); Am Inst Nutrit; Am Soc Animal Sci. *Res:* Animal nutrition, particularly nutrition and physiology of the ruminant. *Mailing Add:* Dept of Animal Sci Iowa State Univ Ames IA 50011

JACOBSON, RALPH ALLEN, b Jersey City, NJ, June 3, 40; m 63; c 3. BIOCHEMISTRY. *Educ:* Montclair State Col, BA, 62; Cornell Univ, PhD(biochem), 66. *Prof Exp:* NIH res fel biol, Calif Inst Technol, 66-68; asst prof biochem, Univ Okla, 68-75; asst prof, 75-78, ASSOC PROF BIOCHEM, CALIF POLYTECH STATE UNIV, 78- *Mem:* AAAS; Sigma Xi; Am Chem Soc; NY Acad Sci. *Res:* Nucleic acids, sequence and function; differentiation and morphogenesis. *Mailing Add:* Dept of Chem Calif Polytech State Univ San Luis Obispo CA 93407

JACOBSON, RAYMOND E, b St Paul, Minn, May 25, 22; m 59; c 3. ELECTRONICS, COMPUTER SCIENCE. *Educ:* Yale Univ, BE, 44; Harvard Univ, MBA, 48; Oxford Univ, BA, 50, MA, 54. *Prof Exp:* Asst to gen mgr, Polytech Res & Develop Co, 50-55; prod sales mgr, Curtiss Wright Corp, 55-57; from div sales mgr to dir mkt, Thompson-Ramo-Wooldridge Prod Co, 57-60; vpres opers, Electro-Sci Investors, Inc, 60-63; pres, Maxson Electronics, 63-64; mgr consult, 64-67; CHMN & PRES, ANDERSON JACOBSON, INC, 67- *Concurrent Pos:* Chmn, Staco, Inc & Gen Electronic Controls, 60-63 & Whitehall Electronics, Inc, 61-63; dir, Tamar Electronics, Inc, 60-63 & Micro-Radionics, Inc, 65-67. *Mem:* Am Electronics Asn. *Mailing Add:* 14358 Old Wood Rd Saratoga CA 95070

JACOBSON, RICHARD MARTIN, b New York, NY, Dec 23, 47; m 75. SYNTHETIC ORGANIC CHEMISTRY. *Educ:* Case Western Reserve Univ, BS, 69; Columbia Univ, PhD(org chem), 73. *Prof Exp:* Asst prof chem, Ind Univ, Bloomington, 75-80; SR RES CHEMIST, ROHM & HAAS RES LAB, 80- *Mem:* Am Chem Soc; Royal Soc Chem. *Res:* Total synthesis of biologically active natural products and the development of new synthetic methods and reagents. *Mailing Add:* Rohm & Haas Res Lab 727 Norristown Rd Spring House PA 19477

JACOBSON, ROBERT ANDREW, b Waterbury, Conn, Feb 16, 32; m 62; c 2. PHYSICAL CHEMISTRY. *Educ:* Univ Conn, BA, 54; Univ Minn, PhD(phys chem), 59. *Prof Exp:* From instr to asst prof chem, Princeton Univ, 59-64; assoc prof, 64-69, PROF CHEM, IOWA STATE UNIV, 69- *Concurrent Pos:* Chemist, 64-69, sr chemist, Energy & Mineral Resources Res Inst & Ames Lab, 69- *Mem:* Am Chem Soc; Am Crystallog Asn. *Res:* Molecular structure of solids; x-ray and neutron diffraction. *Mailing Add:* Dept of Chem Iowa State Univ Ames IA 50011

JACOBSON, ROBERT LEROY, b Miles City, Mont, Mar 11, 32; m 53; c 4. CHEMICAL ENGINEERING. *Educ:* Mont State Col, BS, 54, PhD(chem eng), 58. *Prof Exp:* RES ENGR PETROL PROCESS DEVELOP, CHEVRON RES CO, STANDARD OIL CO CALIF, 58-, SR ENG ASSOC, 72-, GROUP LEADER, 77- *Mem:* Am Inst Chem Engrs. *Res:* Petroleum process research and development. *Mailing Add:* Calif Res Corp 576 Standard Ave Richmond CA 94804

JACOBSON, STANLEY, b Chicago, Ill, Aug 24, 37; m 60; c 1. NEUROANATOMY. *Educ:* Univ Ill, BS, 59; Northwestern Univ, MS, 61, PhD(anat), 63. *Prof Exp:* Biologist, NIH, 63-65; biologist, Vet Admin Res Hosp, Chicago, 65-67; asst prof, 67-70, assoc prof, 70-80, PROF ANAT, SCH MED, TUFTS UNIV, 80- *Concurrent Pos:* Lectr, Sch Med, George Washington Univ, 64-65; assoc, Med Sch, Northwestern Univ, 65-67. *Mem:* AAAS; Am Asn Anatomists. *Res:* Structure of central nervous system in normal and diseased animals; connections between cerebral cortex and thalamus; degeneration of nerve fibers. *Mailing Add:* Dept of Anat Tufts Univ Sch of Med Boston MA 02111

JACOBSON, STEPHEN ERNEST, b State Center, Iowa, Apr 6, 45; m 75. INORGANIC CHEMISTRY, ORGANOMETALLIC CHEMISTRY. *Educ:* Iowa State Univ, BS, 67; Ohio State Univ, MS, 70, PhD(inorg chem), 72. *Prof Exp:* res chemist inorg & catalysis, Alllied Chem Corp, 75-80; RES CHEMIST, HALCON RES, 80- *Mem:* Am Chem Soc. *Res:* Synthesis of organometallic and transition metal complexes and the study of their catalytic properties. *Mailing Add:* 7 Ironwood Rd Morristown NJ 07960

JACOBSON, STEPHEN RICHARD, b New York, NY, Sept 25, 44; m 81. GEOLOGY, PALEONTOLOGY. *Educ:* Dickinson Col, BS, 69; Harvard Univ, MA, 72; Ohio State Univ, PhD(geol), 78. *Prof Exp:* Instr geol, Lehman Col, 71-72; lectr geol, Hunter Col, 72-73; GEOLOGIST, CHEVRON USA, INC, 78- *Concurrent Pos:* Geologist, US Geol Surv, Coal Geol Lab, 75-76. *Mem:* Paleont Soc; Am Asn Stratig Palynologists; Palaeont Asn; Int Paleont Asn; Am Asn Petrol Geologists. *Res:* Ordovician and Permian acritarchs; ordovician biostratigraphy, cretaceous-tertiary palynology, palynological techniques. *Mailing Add:* Chevron USA Inc PO Box 599 Denver CO 80201

JACOBSON, STUART LEE, b Chicago, Ill, Apr 29, 34; m 59; c 2. PHYSIOLOGY, BIOPHYSICS. *Educ:* Cornell Univ, BCE, 57; Univ Minn, Minneapolis, MS, 63, PhD(biophys), 68. *Prof Exp:* Proj engr, Aeromed Lab, Wright Air Develop Ctr, US Air Force, 57-59; asst prof, 68-75, ASSOC PROF BIOL, CARLETON UNIV, 75- *Mem:* Int Soc Heart Res; Biophys Soc. *Res:* Engineering of systems for maintaining life in sealed environments; instrumentation for ecological studies; sensory physiology; electrophysiology, culture and electrophysiology of myocardial cells. *Mailing Add:* Dept of Biol Carleton Univ Ottawa ON K1S 5B6 Can

JACOBSON, WILLARD JAMES, b Northfield, Wis, May 22, 22; m 46; c 3. SCIENCE EDUCATION. *Educ:* Wis State Univ, River Falls, BS, 46; Columbia Univ, AM, 48, EdD, 52. *Prof Exp:* Teacher pub schs, Wis, 46-49; PROF NATURAL SCI, TEACHERS COL, COLUMBIA UNIV, 52-, CHMN DEPT SCI EDUC, 65-, CO-DIR, POPULATION EDUC PROJ, 72-, DIR, CITIZENS & SCIENCE EDUC STUDY, 79- *Concurrent Pos:* Fulbright lectr, Univ London, 60; consult, Royal Afghan Ministry Educ, 54-56, Am Sch Guatemala, 58, 61 & 64, UNESCO, 65, Nat Coun Sci Educ India, 69 & Nat Textbook Comn Brazil, 71; chmn educ adv comt, NY Acad Sci, 75-, mem bd govs, 78- *Mem:* Fel AAAS (vpres, 68-69); Nat Asn Res Sci Teaching (pres, 68-69); NY Acad Sci; Asn Educ Teachers Sci (pres, 62-63). *Res:* Science for children and early adolescents; population education. *Mailing Add:* 106 Morningside Dr New York NY 10027

JACOBUS, DAVID PENMAN, b Boston, Mass, Feb 26, 27; m 56; c 5. MEDICINE, RADIOBIOLOGY. *Educ:* Harvard Univ, BA, 49; Univ Pa, MD, 53. *Prof Exp:* Resident & researcher, Hosp Univ Pa, 53-57; chief dept radiobiol, Div Nuclear Med, Walter Reed Army Inst Res, 59-63, chief dept med chem, 63-65, dir, Div Med Chem, 65-69; vpres basic res, Merck Sharp & Dohme Res Labs, vpres, 74-78; OWNER, JACOBUS PHARMACEUT CO, INC, 78- *Concurrent Pos:* Mem revision comt, US Pharmacopeia, 70-; trustee, Cold Spring Harbor Lab, 70-; consult, St Luke's Hosp Ctr, New York, 71-; chmn Nat Cancer Inst Comt on Info Handling, 78- *Mem:* Am Chem Soc; Am Soc Info Sci; Asn Comput Mach; NY Acad Sci. *Res:* Information handling. *Mailing Add:* 37 Cleveland Lane Princeton NJ 08540

JACOBUS, OTHA JOHN, b Phoenix, Ariz, Dec 23, 39; m 62; c 2. ORGANIC CHEMISTRY. *Educ:* Southwestern at Memphis, BS, 62; Univ Tenn, Knoxville, PhD(org chem), 65. *Prof Exp:* NIH fel org chem, Princeton Univ, 66-67, instr, 67-69; from asst prof to prof org chem, Clemson Univ, 74-76; PROF ORG CHEM, TULANE UNIV, 78-, CHMN DEPT, 80- *Mem:* Am Chem Soc. *Res:* Stereochemistry; NMR spectroscopy; reaction mechanisms. *Mailing Add:* Dept of Chem Tulane Univ New Orleans LA 70118

JACOBUS, WILLIAM EDWARD, b Cleveland, Ohio, Nov 30, 42; m 66. BIOCHEMISTRY. *Educ:* Ohio Wesleyan Univ, BA, 64; Ohio State Univ, PhD(bchem), 69. *Prof Exp:* Fel biochem, Sch Med, Johns Hopkins Univ, 70-73, Heart Asn Md res fel & NIH res grant, Myocardial Infarction Res Unit, 71-73; asst prof zool, Univ Calif, Davis, 73-77; ASST PROF MED & PHYSIOL CHEM, JOHNS HOPKINS SCH MED, 77- *Concurrent Pos:* Nat Heart & Lung Inst res grant, 74-77. *Mem:* AAAS; Am Chem Soc; Am Physiol Soc; Sigma Xi; Biophys Soc. *Res:* Mitochondrial oxidative phosphorylation and ion transport; mitochondrial compartmentation and enzymology; metabolic regulation; cardiac bioenergetics; tissue nuclear magnetic resonance. *Mailing Add:* Div of Cardiol Sch of Med 1385 Blalock Bldg 600 N Wolfe St Baltimore MD 21205

JACOBY, ALEXANDER ROBB, b St Louis, Mo, Oct 8, 22; m 45. MATHEMATICS. *Educ:* Univ Chicago, SB, 41, SM, 42, PhD(math), 46. *Prof Exp:* Res math, Univ Chicago, 43-45, instr, 45-47; asst prof, Univ Miami, 47-49 & Rutgers Univ, 49-57; with Gen Elec Corp, 57-61; PROF MATH, UNIV NH, 61- *Res:* Topology and algebra. *Mailing Add:* Dept of Math Univ of NH Durham NH 03824

JACOBY, JAY, b New York, NY, Dec 12, 17; m 42; c 3. ANESTHESIOLOGY. *Educ:* Univ Minn, BS, 39, MB, 41, MD, 42; Univ Chicago, PhD(anesthesiol), 47; Am Bd Anesthesiol, dipl. *Prof Exp:* Res assoc & instr anesthesia, Univ Chicago, 46-47; assoc prof surg & dir anesthesia, Ohio State Univ, 47-53, prof, 53-59; prof & chmn dept, Med Sch, Marquette Univ, 59-65; PROF ANESTHESIOL & CHMN DEPT, JEFFERSON MED COL, 65- *Mem:* Am Soc Anesthesiol; Am Col Anesthesiol; Int Anesthesia Res Soc; AMA; Asn Univ Anesthetists. *Res:* Anesthetic and analgesic drugs; gas therapy. *Mailing Add:* Jefferson Med Col Thomas Jefferson Univ Philadelphia PA 19107

JACOBY, LAWRENCE JOHN, b Portland, Ore, May 19, 43; m 65; c 2. ORGANIC CHEMISTRY, ANALYTICAL CHEMISTRY. *Educ:* Ore State Univ, BS, 65; Colo State Univ, PhD(org chem), 69. *Prof Exp:* Asst prof org chem, Portland State Univ, 69-71; asst prof org chem, Chemeketa Community Col, 71-76; ANAL CHEMIST, TELEDYNE WAH CHANG, ALBANY, 76- *Mem:* Am Chem Soc. *Res:* Valence tautomerism induced by electron transfer. *Mailing Add:* 3267 NW Wishram Albany OR 97321

JACOBY, ROBERT H(AROLD), b Camden, NJ, Jan 20, 23; m 49; c 2. CHEMICAL ENGINEERING. *Educ:* Univ Pa, BS, 44; Univ Mich, MS, 48. *Prof Exp:* From jr engr to staff res engr, Amoco Prod Co, Okla, 48-67; from sr res engr to res assoc, Gulf Res & Develop Co, Pittsburgh, 67-77; ASSOC PROF PETROL & NATURAL GAS ENG, PA STATE UNIV, 77- *Concurrent Pos:* Co-chmn thermodyn comn, Gas Processors Asn, 65; consult, Gas Processors Asn Data Bk, 77- *Mem:* Am Inst Chem Engrs; Soc Petrol Engrs; Am Chem Soc. *Res:* Research management; high pressure hydrocarbon phase equilibrium and fluid properties; application to petroleum reservoir engineering and oil and gas production processing; coal liquefaction processes. *Mailing Add:* Pa State Univ 205 Mineral Sci Bldg University Park PA 16802

JACOBY, ROBERT OTTINGER, b New York, NY, June 20, 39. COMPARATIVE PATHOLOGY, IMMUNOLOGY. *Educ:* Cornell Univ, DVM, 63; Ohio State Univ, MSc, 68, PhD(path), 69. *Prof Exp:* Asst prof path, Ohio State Univ, 69; NIH fel Univ Chicago, 69-71; asst prof, 71-77, ASSOC PROF COMPARATIVE MED, YALE SCH MED, 77-, CHMN, SECT COMPARATIVE MED & DIR, DIV ANIMAL CARE, 78- *Mem:* AAAS; Am Col Vet Pathologists; Int Acad Path; Am Vet Med Asn; Sigma Xi. *Res:* Immunopathology; mechanisms of immunologic injury; ontogeny of immunity; genetics of resistance to infections; diseases of laboratory animals. *Mailing Add:* Sect of Comparative Med Yale Univ 375 Congress Ave New Haven CT 06510

JACOBY, RONALD LEE, b Muskegon, Mich, Jan 30, 43; m 66; c 3. MEDICINAL CHEMISTRY. *Educ:* Ferris State Col, BSPharm, 66; Univ Conn, PhD(med chem), 71. *Prof Exp:* Asst prof med chem, 70-74, assoc prof, 74-80, PROF MED CHEM, FERRIS STATE COL, 80- *Mem:* Am Pharmaceut Asn; Am Chem Soc. *Res:* Narcotic analgetics and antagonists. *Mailing Add:* Sch of Pharm Ferris State Col Big Rapids MI 49307

JACOBY, RUSSELL STEPHEN, b Lehighton, Pa, June 23, 39; m 59; c 3. METAMORPHIC PETROLOGY, URANIUM GEOLOGY. *Educ:* Syracuse Univ, BS, 61, MS, 64; Queen's Univ, PhD(geol), 68. *Prof Exp:* Asst prof geol, Cent Mo State Univ, 68-71; asst prof, 71-73, ASSOC PROF GEOL, ST LAWRENCE UNIV, 73- *Mem:* Geol Soc Am; Geol Asn Can; Sigma Xi. *Res:* Structural geology and metamorphic petrology of precambrian metamorphic shield areas; uranium exploration. *Mailing Add:* Dept Geol St Lawrence Univ Canton NY 13617

JACOBY, SAMUEL LUDWIG S, b Breslau, Ger, Feb 3, 32; US citizen; m 55; c 3. APPLIED MATHEMATICS, ENGINEERING. *Educ:* Israel Inst Technol, BS, 58; Univ Calif, Davis, MS, 60, Berkeley, PhD(eng sci), 62. *Prof Exp:* Res engr, Comput Dept, Boeing Co, 62-65, supvr eng math, 65-67, mgr math anal, 68-70, mgr anal systs, 71-75, GEN MGR, ENERGY TECHNOL APPLN DIV, BOEING COMPUT SERV CO, 76- *Res:* Mathematical modeling in general and mathematical modeling of hydrologic and hydraulic systems; optimization techniques and applications; linear and nonlinear programming; engineering mathematics and computer applications to engineering problems. *Mailing Add:* Boeing Comput Serv Co PO Box 24346 Seattle WA 98124

JACOBY, WILLIAM R(ICHARD), b Columbia, NJ, Sept 8, 26; m 49; c 3. CERAMIC ENGINEERING. *Educ:* Dickinson Col, BS, 50; Rutgers Univ, MS, 53, PhD(ceramic eng). 56. *Prof Exp:* Asst instr ceramic eng, Rutgers Univ, 54-56; res assoc, Knolls Atomic Power Lab, Gen Elec Co, 57-59; sr ceramist, Reactor Mat Lab, Minn Mining & Mfg Co, 59-62, supvr, 62-63, res specialist, Nuclear Prod Dept, 63-64; sr engr, Atomic Power Div, Westinghouse Elec Corp, 65-67, mgr ceramic develop, Advan Reactors Div, 67-68, mgr plutonium fuel facil, 68-69, mgr, Cheswick Opers, 74-81; MGR DECONTAMINATION & DECOMISSIONING ENG, WEST VALLEY NUCLEAR SERV CO, INC, 80- *Concurrent Pos:* Mem staff, Argonne Nat Lab, 65- *Mem:* Fel Am Ceramic Soc. *Res:* Materials, fabrication processes and product development in areas of fuel and control materials for thermal and fast reactors. *Mailing Add:* West Valley Nuclear Serv Co PO Box 191 West Valley NY 14171

JACOLEV, LEON, b Libau, Latvia, Dec 16, 14; nat US; m 44; c 2. CHEMICAL ENGINEERING. *Educ:* Northeastern Univ, BS, 39; Univ Pittsburgh, MS, 45. *Prof Exp:* Chemist, Eastern Gas & Fuel Assocs, Mass, 36-39; rating examr, Tech Personnel Div, US Civil Serv Comn, 40-41; asst chem engr, High Explosives Res Div, US Bur Mines, 41-43; chem engr, Nat Defense Res Comt, Off Sci Res & Develop, 43-45; tech & res div, Texaco Inc, 45-53; consult chem engr & tech dir, 53-55, CONSULT CHEM ENGR, TECH DIR & PRES, ASSOC TECH SERV, INC, 55- *Concurrent Pos:* Consult, Engrs Joint Coun, NY, 59; Am Inst Chem Eng rep, Mendeleev Cong Gen & Appl Chem, Moscow, 59; dir, Eng Socs Libr, NY. *Honors & Awards:* Naval Ord Develop Award, 45. *Mem:* AAAS; Am Chem Soc; Am Inst Chem Engrs; Geosci Info Soc; Spec Libr Asn. *Res:* Synthesis gas generation by partial combustion; petroleum refining and petrochemicals; documentation; Russian chemical and geological sciences and technology; retrieval, translation and dissemination of scientific information. *Mailing Add:* 30 The Fairway Upper Montclair NJ 07043

JACOLI, GIULIO GUIDO, b Pavullo, Italy, Oct 10, 20; Can citizen; m 52; c 2. BIOCHEMISTRY, MOLECULAR BIOLOGY. *Educ:* Univ Bologna, PhD(biochem), 48. *Prof Exp:* Res asst biochem, Univ Bologna, 46-48, asst prof, 48-52; head res pharmaceut chem & biochem, Biochimici Alfa, Italy, 52-58; fel biochem, Georgetown Univ, 58-59; asst res prof biochem pharmacol, George Washington Univ, 59-61; investr biochem, Rutgers Univ, 61-62; Nat Cancer Inst fel, Univ BC, 62-65; IN-CHG LAB BIOCHEM, RES STA, CAN DEPT AGR, 65- *Mem:* AAAS; Can Biochem Soc; Tissue Cult Asn; Sigma Xi; NY Acad Sci. *Res:* Biochemical mechanism of action of anticancer drugs; synthesis and organization of plant viruses at the molecular level. *Mailing Add:* Res Sta Can Dept Agr 6660 NW Marine Dr Vancouver BC V6T 1X2 Can

JACOVIDES, LINOS J, b Paphos, Cyprus, May 10, 40; US citizen; div; c 2. ELECTRICAL ENGINEERING. *Educ:* Glasgow Univ, BSc, 61, MSc, 63; Univ London, PhD, 65. *Prof Exp:* Sr res engr, Defense Res Labs, 65-67, sr res engr, Res Labs, Warren, 67-75, DEPT RES ENGR, RES LABS, GEN MOTORS CORP, 75- *Mem:* Inst Elec & Electronics Engrs; Brit Inst Elec Engrs; Soc Automotive Engrs. *Res:* Electromagnetics and electromagnetic energy conversion; high performance electric drive systems; automotive electrical systems; electric vehicles and locomotive electric drives; electromechanical devices. *Mailing Add:* Res Labs Gen Motors Tech Ctr Warren MI 48090

JACOX, MARILYN ESTHER, b Utica, NY, Apr 26, 29. MOLECULAR SPECTROSCOPY, PHOTOCHEMISTRY. *Educ:* Syracuse Univ, BA, 51; Cornell Univ, PhD, 56. *Prof Exp:* Res assoc phys chem, Univ NC, 56-58; fel spectros of solids, Mellon Inst Sci, 58-62; PHYS CHEMIST, NAT BUR STANDARDS, 62- *Concurrent Pos:* Chief, Photochem Sect, Nat Bur Standards, 73-74; chief, Environ Chem Processes Sect, Nat Bur Standards, 74-78. *Honors & Awards:* Outstanding Alumnus Award, Utica Col, 63; Award Phys Sci, Washington Acad Sci, 68; Gold Medal Award for Distinguished Serv, US Dept Commerce, 70; Federal Woman's Award, Fed Woman's Award Bd of Trustees, 73; Samuel Wesley Stratton Award, Nat Bur Standards, 73. *Mem:* Am Phys Soc; Am Chem Soc; Int-Am Photochem Soc. *Res:* Chemistry of free radicals and molecular ions; molecular spectroscopy. *Mailing Add:* Nat Bur of Standards Washington DC 20234

JACOX, RALPH FRANKLIN, b Alfred, NY, Oct 30, 13; m 40; c 3. INTERNAL MEDICINE. *Educ:* Alfred Univ, BS, 35; Univ Rochester, MD, 38; Am Bd Internal Med, dipl. *Prof Exp:* Intern med, Strong Mem Hosp, Univ Rochester, 38-39, asst resident, 39-40, chief resident med, 41-42; asst bact, Sch Hyg, Johns Hopkins Univ, 40-41; from instr to assoc prof, 46-63, PROF MED, SCH MED & DENT, UNIV ROCHESTER, 63-, DIR ARTHRITIS CLIN, 58- *Concurrent Pos:* Consult, Genesee Hosp, Rochester & Rochester Gen Hosp; trustee, Alfred Univ, 64. *Mem:* Am Fedn Clin Res; fel Am Col Physicians; Am Soc Clin Invest. *Res:* Cationic detergent fractionation of plasma proteins; glucuronidase studies of hemolytic streptococci and human joint fluid; factors concerned in coagulation of blood; bactericidal activity of human serum for B subtilis; bacteriology; hematology; a new method for production of nonspecific capsular swelling of the pneumococcus; protein chemistry and immunology. *Mailing Add:* 601 Elmwood Ave Rochester NY 14620

JACQUES, FELIX ANTHONY, b Kansas City, Kans, July 17, 24. BIOLOGY. *Educ:* Univ Iowa, BA, 50, MS, 53; St Louis Univ, PhD(biol), 60. *Prof Exp:* Instr biol, Langston Univ, 53-55; lectr zool, Southern Ill Univ, 59-61; asst prof physiol & evolution, Webster Col, 61-62; asst prof, 62-64, ASSOC PROF PHYSIOL, ST BONAVENTURE UNIV, 64- *Concurrent Pos:* Nat Heart Inst fel, 60-62, res grant, 65-68. *Mem:* AAAS; Am Soc Zool; assoc Am Physiol Soc; Am Inst Biol Sci. *Res:* Comparative and environmental physiology; environmental effects on blood and other tissues. *Mailing Add:* Dept of Biol St Bonaventure Univ St Bonaventure NY 14778

JACQUES, RICHARD LEO, b Newark, NJ, Oct 27, 45. ENTOMOLOGY. *Educ:* St Peters Col, NJ, BS, 67; Iowa State Univ, MS, 69; Purdue Univ, PhD(entomol), 72. *Prof Exp:* ASSOC PROF ENTOM & ZOOL, FAIRLEIGH DICKINSON UNIV, 72- *Mem:* Entom Soc Am; Coleopterists Soc. *Res:* Insects; systematics of coleoptera; plants, especially edible and poisonous plants of North America. *Mailing Add:* Dept Biol Sci Fairleigh Dickinson Univ Rutherford NJ 07070

JACQUET, HERVE, b France, Aug 4, 39; m 69; c 1. NUMBER THEORY. *Educ:* Univ Paris, Lience, 61, PhD(math), 67. *Prof Exp:* Researcher, Cent Nat de la Recherche Scientifique, 63-65; assoc prof math, Univ Md, 69-70; prof math, Grad Sch City Univ New York, 70-74; PROF MATH, COLUMBIA UNIV, 74- *Concurrent Pos:* Mem, Inst Advan Studies, 67-69. *Honors & Awards:* Prix Petit d'Ormoy, Acad Sci, Paris, 79. *Mem:* Acad Sci Paris. *Res:* Automorphic L-functions. *Mailing Add:* Columbia Univ New York NY 10027

JACQUEZ, JOHN ALFRED, b Pfastatt, Alsace, France, June 26, 22; US citizen; m 48; c 4. PHYSIOLOGY, BIOMATHEMATICS. *Educ:* Cornell Univ, MD, 47. *Prof Exp:* Res fel, Sloan-Kettering Inst, 47-50, from asst to assoc exp chemother, 50-60, assoc mem, 60-62; from instr to assoc prof biol, Sloan-Kettering Div, Cornell Univ, 52-63; assoc prof physiol, Med Sch, 62-69, assoc prof biostatist, Sch Pub Health, 62-72, PROF PHYSIOL, MED SCH, UNIV MICH, 69-, PROF BIOSTATIST, SCH PUB HEALTH, 72- *Concurrent Pos:* Vis investr path & bact, Rockefeller Inst, 47-48; consult, Rand Corp, 59-64; mem sci adv comt, Ore Regional Primate Res Ctr, 65-68; mem comput res study sect, NIH, 66-70, chmn, 68-70, mem chem & biol info handling rev comt, 75-79 & biotech res adv comt, 77-79; assoc ed, Math Biosci, 67-75, ed, 75- *Mem:* AAAS; Am Physiol Soc; Biophys Soc; Soc Indust & Appl Math; Soc Math Biol. *Res:* Active transport; structure and function of membranes; mathematical modeling of physiological systems; compartmental systems; logical and probabilistic structure of the diagnostic process; respiratory physiology. *Mailing Add:* Dept of Physiol Univ of Mich Med Sch Ann Arbor MI 48109

JACQUOT, RAYMOND G, b Casper, Wyo, Nov 16, 38. MECHANICAL ENGINEERING, ELECTRICAL ENGINEERING. *Educ:* Univ Wyo, BS, 60, MS, 62; Purdue Univ, PhD(mech eng), 69. *Prof Exp:* Supply instr mech eng, Univ Wyo, 60-62, instr, 62-64; instr, Purdue Univ, 64-65; from asst prof to assoc prof elec eng, 69-77, PROF ELEC ENG, UNIV WYO, 77- *Mem:* Am Soc Mech Engrs; Am Soc Eng Educ; Inst Elec & Electronics Engrs. *Res:* Vibration of elastic systems; simulation of large scale systems by digital computer; digital control and signal processing; nonlinear system analysis; digital filtering. *Mailing Add:* Dept of Elec Eng Univ of Wyo Laramie WY 82070

JADUSZLIWER, BERNARDO, b Buenos Aires, Argentina, Oct 17, 43; m 68; c 1. ELECTRON SCATTERING, POSITRON SCATTERING. *Educ:* Univ Buenos Aires, Lic en physics, 68; Univ Toronto, MSc, 70, PhD(physics), 73. *Prof Exp:* Fel physics, Univ Toronto, 73-74; assoc res scientist, 74-78, asst res prof, 78-81, ASSOC RES PROF PHYSICS, NY UNIV, 81- *Mem:* Am Phys Soc; AAAS. *Res:* Low energy electron positron scattering on ground and excited state atoms and molecules; measurement of atomic and molecular polarizabilities; atom interactions. *Mailing Add:* NY Univ Physics Dept 4 Wash Pl New York NY 10003

JAECKER, JOHN ALVIN, b Troy, NY, Feb 21, 45; m 68; c 2. INORGANIC CHEMISTRY. *Educ:* Hope Col, BA, 68; Purdue Univ, MA & PhD(inorg chem), 73. *Prof Exp:* SR CHEMIST, ATLANTIC RICHFIELD CO, 73- *Mem:* Am Chem Soc; Catalysis Soc. *Res:* Development of petroleum catalysts and studies of catalysts. *Mailing Add:* Atlantic Richfield Co Harvey Tech Ctr 400 E Sibley Blvd Harvey IL 60426

JAECKS, DUANE H, b Wausau, Wis, Sept 24, 35; m 59; c 2. ATOMIC PHYSICS. *Educ:* Univ Wis, BS, 58; Miami Univ, MA, 60; Univ Wash, Seattle, PhD(physics), 64. *Prof Exp:* From asst prof to assoc prof, 66-74, PROF PHYSICS, UNIV NEBR-LINCOLN, 74-, CHAIRPERSON DEPT, 80- *Mem:* Fel Am Phys Soc. *Res:* Basic atomic collisions research. *Mailing Add:* Dept of Physics Univ of Nebr Lincoln NE 68588

JAEGER, BERNARD F, b Spokane, Wash, Jan 1, 20; m 42; c 2. MILITARY OPERATIONS RESEARCH. *Educ:* Univ Notre Dame, BS, 41; Univ Minn, MS, 47. *Prof Exp:* Aerodynamicist, US Naval Ord Test Sta, Calif, 48-51, head aerodyn br, 51-57; design specialist, Missiles Div, Douglas Aircraft Corp, 57-60; armaments systs analyst, Rand Corp, 60-68, head armament systs br, 68-70; consult armaments systs anal, 70-72; systs analyst, R & D Assocs, 72-79; RETIRED. *Mem:* Asst fel Am Inst Aeronaut & Astronaut; Am Defense Preparedness Asn. *Res:* Systems and operations analysis associated with the application of nonnuclear weapons systems technology in tactical warfare. *Mailing Add:* 1162 La Noche Dr Lake San Marcos CA 92069

JAEGER, CHARLES WAYNE, b Kissimmee, Fla, Sept 8, 43; m 65; c 2. INDUSTRIAL ORGANIC CHEMISTRY. *Educ:* Fla State Univ, BS, 66; Purdue Univ, PhD(org chem), 71. *Prof Exp:* Res fel org chem, Ga Inst Technol, 71-73; res chemist, Dyes & Chem Div, Crompton & Knowles Corp, 73-80; SR RES SCIENTIST, TEKTRONIX, INC, 80- *Mem:* Am Chem Soc; Am Asn Textile Chem & Colorists. *Res:* Industrialresearch and process development of disperse dyes, heat transfer printing dyes and fluorescent whitening agents primarily for textile applications; imaging research on hardcopy devices; ink-jet ink chemistry. *Mailing Add:* Tektronix Inc PO Box 500 Beaverton OR 97077

JAEGER, DAVID ALLEN, b San Diego, Calif, June 3, 44; m 68; c 1. ORGANIC CHEMISTRY. *Educ:* Stanford Univ, BS, 65; Univ Calif, Los Angeles, PhD(org chem), 70. *Prof Exp:* NSF fel chem, Stanford Univ, 70-71; asst prof, 71-76, ASSOC PROF CHEM, UNIV WYO, 76- *Mem:* Am Chem Soc. *Res:* Chemistry; micellar catalysis surfactant; aromatic photochemistry. *Mailing Add:* Dept of Chem Univ of Wyo Laramie WY 82071

JAEGER, HERBERT KARL, b Harpolingen-Saeckingen, Ger, June 29, 31; m 59; c 1. ORGANIC CHEMISTRY. *Educ:* Univ Basel, PhD(org chem), 58. *Prof Exp:* Res fel chem, Univ Basel, 58-59 & Univ Calif, Los Angeles, 60-61; res assoc, 61-65, sect head, 65-70, res mgr org chem, 70-78, GROUP MGR, UPJOHN CO, 78- *Mem:* Am Chem Soc. *Res:* Isolation and chemistry of cardiac glycosides; microbial production and chemistry of carotenoids; process research and development of steroidal and other chemical products. *Mailing Add:* Upjohn Co Unit 1500 Portage Rd Kalamazoo MI 49001

JAEGER, KLAUS BRUNO, b Lübeck, Ger, May 8, 38; US citizen; m 69; c 1. EXPERIMENTAL HIGH ENERGY PHYSICS. *Educ:* Syracuse Univ, BS, 65, MS, 68, PhD(physics), 70. *Prof Exp:* Fel exp high energy physics, Argonne Nat Lab, 70-71, asst physicist, 71-75, physicist, 75-80; physicist, Brookhaven Nat Lab, 80-81; PHYSICIST, LOCKHEED CO, 82- *Concurrent Pos:* Assoc group leader bubble chamber, Argonne Nat Lab, 71-77, proj mgr 12ft solenoid magnet, 77-80, dep group leader for measuring & testing superconducting magnets, 80-81. *Mem:* Am Phys Soc; Am Inst Physics. *Res:* Design and implementation of new particle detection techniques such as solenoidal magnets with shower counters; inclusive hadron physics at high and medium energies; colliding electron positron beams; design and implementation of measuring techniques for superconducting dipole and quadrapole magnets. *Mailing Add:* Lockheed Space & Missiles Labs 1111 Lockheed Way 0148-71 B1151 Sunnyvale CA 94086

JAEGER, MARC JULES, b Berne, Switz, Apr 4, 29; m 60; c 2. RESPIRATORY PHYSIOLOGY. *Educ:* Univ Berne, Baccalaureat, 48, MD, 54. *Prof Exp:* Res assoc med, Univ Berne, 57-61; res assoc physiol, Col Med, Univ Fla, 61-63; res asst med, Univ Berne, 63-65; asst prof physiol, Univ Fribourg, 65-70; PROF PHYSIOL & DENT, COL MED, UNIV FLA, 70- *Concurrent Pos:* Vis prof, Dept Med, McGill Univ, Montreal, 80-81. *Mem:* Swiss Med Asn; Swiss Asn Physiol & Pharmacol; Swiss Soc Advan Sci; Int Union Physiol Sci. *Res:* Mechanics of breathing; fluid dynamics; mechanical and analog computer modelling; environmental physiology, especially diving, smoking and air pollution. *Mailing Add:* Dept of Physiol Univ of Fla Col of Med Gainesville FL 32610

JAEGER, RALPH R, b Cincinnati, Ohio, Jan 30, 40. INORGANIC CHEMISTRY. *Educ:* Univ Cincinnati, BS, 62; Purdue Univ, PhD(inorg chem), 67. *Prof Exp:* SR RES CHEMIST, MOUND LAB, MONSANTO RES CORP, 67- *Mem:* Am Chem Soc; Am Inst Chemists. *Res:* Chemical vapor deposition of refractory metals; high temperature chemistry of plutonium; fuel forms containing plutonium. *Mailing Add:* 5092 Benner Rd Miamisburg OH 45342

JAEGER, ROBERT GORDON, b Baltimore, Md, Dec 16, 37; m 64. POPULATION ECOLOGY. *Educ:* Univ Md, BS, 60, PhD(ecol), 69; Univ Calif, Berkeley, MA, 63. *Prof Exp:* Fac res asst ecol, Univ Md, 69-70, instr zool, 70-71; res assoc zool, Univ Wis, Madison, 71-74; asst prof zool, State Univ NY, Albany, 74-80, adj asst prof, 80-81; ASST PROF BIOL, UNIV SOUTHWESTERN LA, 81- *Honors & Awards:* Stoye Award, Am Soc Ichthyol & Herpet, 69. *Mem:* Ecol Soc Am; Animal Behav Soc; Soc Study Evolution; Am Inst Biol Sci; Am Soc Ichthyol & Herpet. *Res:* Competitive exclusion and environmental pressures in the distributions of salamander species; comparative phototactic responses of anuran species in relation to their natural habitats. *Mailing Add:* Dept Biol Univ Southwestern La Lafayette LA 70504

JAEGER, RUDOLPH JOHN, b Weehawken, NJ, Jan 17, 44; m 66; c 2. TOXICOLOGY. *Educ:* Renesselaer Polytech Inst, BS, 66; Johns Hopkins Univ, PhD(biochem toxicol), 71. *Prof Exp:* Res assoc toxicol, Harvard Sch Pub Health, 71-73, asst prof, 73-78, assoc prof, 78-79; ASSOC PROF ENVIRON MED, SCH MED, NY UNIV, 79- *Concurrent Pos:* Anal consult, Boston Blood Preserv Lab, Children's Hosp, 72-75; consult indust toxicol, Boston Poison Control Info, 72-; instr & course coordr indust toxicol & prod safety eval, Northeastern Univ, 74-; anal consult, Gen Tire & Rubber Co, Akron, Ohio, 74-75; reviewer, ad hoc grants rev comt, Div Advan Environ Res & Technol, 75-; consult toxicologist toxic chem sub-comt, Polaroid Corp, Cambridge, 77-; Nat Inst Environ Health Sci, res career develop award, 77-; mem subcomt fldmmability di-electrics panel, Nat Acad Eng, 77- *Mem:* Soc Toxicol; AAAS; NY Acad Sci; Am Conf Govt Indust Hygienists; Am Indust Hygiene Asn. *Res:* Inhalation toxicology of plastics monomers, pulmonary toxicology of combustion products. *Mailing Add:* Inst Environ Med NY Univ Med Ctr 550 First Ave New York NY 10016

JAEHNING, JUDITH A, b Yakima, Wash, Oct 14, 50. BIOCHEMISTRY. *Educ:* Univ Wash, Seattle, BS, 72; Washington Univ, St Louis, PhD(biol chem), 77. *Prof Exp:* Fel biochem, Univ Calif, Berkeley, 77-78 & Stanford Univ, 78-80; ASST PROF BIOCHEM, UNIV ILL, URBANA, 81- *Concurrent Pos:* fel biochem, Univ Calif, Berkeley, 77-78, Stanford Univ, 78-80. *Res:* Regulation and mechanisms of eukaryotic transcription; RNA polymerase; saccharomyces cerevisiae. *Mailing Add:* Dept Biochem Univ Ill 1209 W California Urbana IL 61801

JAENIKE, JOHN ROBERT, b Osawatomie, Kans, Feb 13, 26; m 47; c 3. MEDICINE. *Educ:* Univ Rochester, MD, 48. *Prof Exp:* From instr to assoc prof, 52-68, asst dean, 71-73, PROF MED, SCH MED & DENT, UNIV ROCHESTER, 68-, ASSOC DEAN, 73- *Concurrent Pos:* Sr investr, Nat Heart Inst, 58-60; Fogarty fel award, Sabbatical to Eng, 75-76. *Mem:* Am Fedn Clin Res; Am Soc Clin Invest; Asn Am Physicians; Am Physiol Soc. *Res:* Hypertension. *Mailing Add:* Dept of Med Univ of Rochester Med Ctr Rochester NY 14642

JAESCHKE, WALTER HENRY, b Milwaukee, Wis, Nov 25, 09; m 38; c 1. PATHOLOGY. *Educ:* Univ Wis, BS, 32, MD, 34; Am Bd Path, dipl, 41. *Prof Exp:* Intern, Hosp Div, Med Col Va, 34-35; resident med, Wis Gen Hosp, 35-37, resident path, 37-38, asst, 38-39, instr clin path, 39-41; pathologist & dir labs, St Agnes Hosp, Wis, 41-42; from asst prof to prof clin path, 42-64, prof surg path & path, 64-80, DIR, LAB SURG PATH, GEN HOSP, UNIV WIS-MADISON, 58-, EMER PROF PATH & LAB MED, 80-; CONSULT SURG PATHOLOGIST, 80- *Concurrent Pos:* Consult pathologist, Hosp Clin Labs & State Lab Hyg, Wis, 64- *Mem:* Fel Am Soc Clin Path; fel AMA. *Res:* Liver function tests; frozen section handling of surgical tissues; training methods in medical technology and surgical pathology. *Mailing Add:* 2313 Kendall Ave Madison WI 53705

JAFFA, ROBERT E, b Berkeley, Calif, Nov 11, 35. MATHEMATICS. *Educ:* Univ Calif, BA, 57, MA, 60, PhD(math), 64. *Prof Exp:* Res mathematician, Univ Calif, 64-65; from asst prof to assoc prof, 65-76, PROF MATH, SACRAMENTO STATE UNIV, 76- *Mem:* Am Math Soc. *Res:* Abstract algebra; functional analysis. *Mailing Add:* Dept of Math Sacramento State Univ Sacramento CA 95819

JAFFE, ANNETTE BRONKESH, b Munich, Ger, July 25, 46; US citizen; m 70; c 2. PHYSICAL ORGANIC CHEMISTRY, ELECTROANALYTICAL CHEMISTRY. *Educ:* Douglass Col, Rutgers Univ, BA, 68; Yale Univ, MPhil, 70, PhD(chem), 72. *Prof Exp:* MEM RES STAFF RES LABS, IBM CORP, 74- *Mem:* Am Chem Soc. *Res:* Solid state chemistry; electro-organic chemistry in aprotic solvents; reaction mechanisms; ink chemistry. *Mailing Add:* Res Labs IBM Corp 5600 Cottle Rd San Jose CA 95163

JAFFE, ARTHUR MICHAEL, b New York, NY, Dec 22, 37; m 71. MATHEMATICAL PHYSICS. *Educ:* Princeton Univ, AB, 59, PhD(physics), 65; Cambridge Univ, BA, 61. *Hon Degrees:* MA, Harvard Univ, 70. *Prof Exp:* Res assoc physics, Princeton Univ, 65-66; actg asst prof math, Stanford Univ, 66-67; visitor natural sci, Inst Advan Study, 67; from asst prof to assoc prof, 67-70, PROF MATH PHYSICS, HARVARD UNIV, 70- *Concurrent Pos:* Nat Acad Sci-Nat Res Coun, Air Force Off Sci Res fel, 65-67; res assoc, Stanford Lineai Accelerator Ctr, 66-67; Alfred P Sloan Found fel, 68-70; John S Guggenheim Found fel, 77; ed, Comn Math Physics, 75-79, chief ed, 79-; ed, Progress in Physics, 80-, Selecta Mathematica Sovietica, 81- *Honors & Awards:* NY Acad Sci award, 79; Dannie Heineman Prize, Am Inst Physics & Phys Soc, 80. *Mem:* Am Math Soc; Am Phys Soc; NY Acad Sci; AAAS; Am Acad Arts Sci. *Res:* Mathematical foundations of physics. *Mailing Add:* Dept of Physics Harvard Univ Cambridge MA 02138

JAFFE, BERNARD MORDECAI, b New York, NY, Mar 7, 17; m 62; c 1. PHYSICS. *Educ:* City Col New York, BS, 36; NY Univ, PhD(photoconductivity), 62. *Prof Exp:* Engr, Amperex Electronic Prod Co, 40-41; physicist, Signal Corps Labs, 41-44; engr, Lloyd Rogers Co, 44-45 & Airborne Instruments Lab, 45-46; tutor physics, City Col New York, 46-49 & 52-56; instr, Stevens Inst Technol, 56-59; from asst prof to assoc prof, 59-65, PROF PHYSICS, ADELPHI UNIV, 65- *Mem:* Am Phys Soc; Optical Soc Am; Am Asn Physics Teachers. *Res:* Photoconductivity; photovoltaic effect; persistent internal polarization; physical optics; coherence of light. *Mailing Add:* Dept Physics Adelphi Univ Garden City NY 11530

JAFFE, DONALD, b New York, NY, May 17, 31; m 53; c 5. MATERIALS SCIENCE, ELECTRONIC ENGINEERING. *Educ:* Mass Inst Technol, BS, 52, MS, 53; Carnegie-Mellon Univ, PhD(metall eng), 63. *Prof Exp:* Engr, Gen Elec Co, 53-58 & Westinghouse Elec Co, 58-65; mem tech staff magnetic mat, 65-68, supvr thin film mat, 68-72, supvr encapsulation mat, 72-77, supvr integrated circuit technol, 77-81, HEAD, FILM TECHNOL DEPT, BELL LABS, INC, 81- *Concurrent Pos:* Instr eve sch, Carnegie-Mellon Univ. *Mem:* Inst Elec & Electronics Engrs; Int Soc Hybrid Microelectronics. *Res:* Structure, properties and assembly techniques relative to materials and components used for microelectronics applications. *Mailing Add:* Bell Tel Labs Inc 555 Union Blvd Allentown PA 18103

JAFFE, EDWARD E, b Poland, Sept 22, 28; nat US; m 53; c 3. ORGANIC CHEMISTRY. *Educ:* City Col NY, BS, 52; NY Univ, MS, 54, PhD(org chem), 57. *Prof Exp:* Tech asst res, Mt Sinai Hosp, NY, 51-54; from res chemist to sr res chemist, 57-65, res assoc, 65-73, res supvr, 73-75, tech supt, 75-78, res mgr, 78-80, RES FEL, E I DU PONT DE NEMOURS & CO, INC, 80- *Mem:* Am Chem Soc. *Res:* Heterocyclic chemistry and the characterization of colored organic compounds; varied organic syntheses in the fields of organophosphorus chemistry, pigments, polymers; organic microchemistry. *Mailing Add:* Jackson Lab E I du Pont de Nemours & Co Inc Deepwater NJ 08023

JAFFE, ERIC ALLEN, b New York, NY, Apr 7, 42; m 71; c 2. HEMATOLOGY, ONCOLOGY. *Educ:* Downstate Med Ctr, State Univ NY, MD, 66. *Prof Exp:* Intern internal med, Kings County Hosp, Brooklyn, 66-67, resident, 67-68; resident, New York Hosp, 68-69; guest investr, Rockefeller Univ, 69; sr resident, New York Hosp, 70, fel hemat, 70-72; from instr to asst prof, 71-77, ASSOC PROF MED, MED COL, CORNELL UNIV, 77- *Concurrent Pos:* Res fel, Nat Hemophilia Found, 74-76; career scientist, Health Res Coun City New York, 74-75, Irma T Hirschl Career Scientist Award, 76-81 & NIH Res Career Develop Award, 76-81. *Honors & Awards:* Passano Found Young Scientist Award, 77. *Mem:* AAAS; Am Soc Hemat; Coun Arteriosclerosis & Thrombosis; Soc Exp Biol & Med; Am Fedn Clin Res. *Res:* Role of endothelial cells in coagulation and the relationship of enothelial cells to platelets, white cells, and atherosclerosis. *Mailing Add:* Med Col Cornell Univ 1300 York Ave New York NY 10021

JAFFE, ERNST RICHARD, b Chicago, Ill, Jan 4, 25; m 50; c 2. MEDICINE. *Educ:* Univ Chicago, BS, 45, MD & MS, 48; Am Bd Internal Med, dipl & dipl hemat. *Prof Exp:* Asst path, Univ Chicago, 46 & 47-48, asst physiol, 47; intern, Med Serv, Presby Hosp, New York, 48-49, asst resident, 49-51 & 53-55; from instr to assoc prof, 56-69, actg dean, 72-74, PROF MED, ALBERT EINSTEIN COL MED, 69-, HEAD DIV HEMAT, 70-, SR ASSOC DEAN, 74-, ASSOC DEAN FAC, 76- *Concurrent Pos:* Clin asst vis physician, Med Serv, Bronx Munic Hosp Ctr, 55-56, from asst vis physician to assoc vis physician, 55-63, attend physician, 63-; Nat Found Infantile Paralysis fel, 55-57; Health Res Coun, New York career scientist, 61-71; assoc vis physician, Lincoln Hosp, New York, 61-73; co-ed, Sem in Hemat, 68-; ed-in-chief, Blood, 75-77. *Mem:* Am Soc Hemat; Am Fedn Clin Res; Am Physiol Soc; Asn Am Physicians; Am Med Writers' Asn. *Res:* Internal medicine and hematology; metabolism of the mammalian erythrocyte and alterations occurring with aging of the erythrocyte. *Mailing Add:* Dept of Med Albert Einstein Col of Med Bronx NY 10461

JAFFE, FRED, b Cleveland, Ohio, Apr 5, 30; m 60; c 3. ORGANIC CHEMISTRY. *Educ:* Western Reserve Univ, BS, 52; Cornell Univ, PhD, 57. *Prof Exp:* Sloan fel, Cornell Univ, 57-58; res chemist, Washington Res Ctr, W R Grace & Co, Md, 58-63, sr res chemist, 63-65, coordr oxidation chem, 64-65; res chemist, Miami Valley Labs, Procter & Gamble Co, 65-68; sr res chemist, 68-75, RES ASSOC, EASTERN RES CTR, STAUFFER CHEM CO, 75- *Mem:* AAAS; Am Chem Soc; Royal Soc Chem. *Res:* Synthesis, stabilization and modification of formaldehyde polymers and copolymers; synthesis of para-bridged benzenes, liquid phase autoxidation, oxidation of decalin; hydroperoxides; carbanion oxidations; organometallic alkali chemistry; phosphorus and silicon; lubricant and hydraulic base stocks and additives; flame retardants. *Mailing Add:* Stauffer Chem Co Eastern Res Ctr Dobbs Ferry NY 10522

JAFFE, HANS, b Marburg, Ger, Apr 17, 19; US citizen; div; c 3. PHYSICAL CHEMISTRY, THEORETICAL CHEMISTRY. *Educ:* State Univ Iowa, BS, 41; Purdue Univ, MS, 42; Univ NC, PhD(chem), 52. *Prof Exp:* Phys chemist, USPHS, 46-54; from asst prof to assoc prof, 54-62, head dept, 66-71, PROF CHEM, UNIV CINCINNATI, 62- *Concurrent Pos:* Sect ed, Chem Abstr, 58-61; mem adv panel, Nat Bur Standards, 59-65; Fulbright fel, France, 61-62. *Mem:* Am Chem Soc; Am Phys Soc. *Res:* Quantum chemistry; basicities of weak bases; spectroscopy; excited state chemistry; physical organic chemistry; Hammett equation. *Mailing Add:* Dept of Chem Univ of Cincinnati Cincinnati OH 45221

JAFFE, HAROLD, b Chicago, Ill, May 8, 30; m 51; c 3. NUCLEAR SCIENCE. *Educ:* Univ Ill, BS, 51, PhD(nuclear chem), 54. *Prof Exp:* Asst res chemist, Union Oil Co, 54-55; sr chemist, Tracerlab, Inc, 55-56; prin nuclear chemist, Aerojet-Gen Nucleonics Div, Aerojet-Gen Corp, 56-57, prog mgr gas-cooled reactor exp, 57-59, mgr fuel develop dept, 60-62, asst mgr nuclear tech div, 62-64, mgr appl sci div, 64-66, asst to vpres, Nuclear Div, 66-69; Mgr San Ramon Plant & asst to pres, 69-70; chief isotope power systs proj br, Space Nuclear Systs Div, US Atomic Energy Comn, 70-72, mgr Isotope Flight Systs, 72-75; tech asst to asst admin nuclear energy, Energy Res & Develop Agency, 75-76; dep dir, Off Int Tech Coop, 76-81, DIR, OFF INT NUCLEAR COOP, DEPT ENERGY, 81- *Concurrent Pos:* Asst prof, John F Kennedy Univ, 66-70; mem bd dirs, Idaho Nuclear Corp, 68-70. *Honors & Awards:* Exceptional Serv Medal, NASA, 74. *Mem:* AAAS; Am Nuclear Soc; Am Chem Soc; fel Am Inst Chemists. *Mailing Add:* 10702 Great Arbor Dr Potomac MD 20854

JAFFE, HOWARD WILLIAM, b New York, NY, Feb 16, 19; m 50; c 3. GEOLOGY. *Educ:* Brooklyn Col, BA, 42; Univ Geneve, DSc, 72. *Prof Exp:* Sr engr aid, US Geol Surv, 42-44; petrographer, US Bur Mines, 44-51; geologist, US Geol Surv, 51-58; res sect leader mineral & geochem, Union Carbide Nuclear Co Div, Union Carbide Corp, 58-65; assoc prof, 65-70, PROF GEOL, UNIV MASS, AMHERST, 70- *Concurrent Pos:* Vis prof, Univ Geneva, 71-72 & 78-79. *Mem:* Fel Am Mineral Soc; fel Geol Soc Am; Geochem Soc; Am Geophys Union; Mineral Soc Gt Brit & Ireland. *Res:* Optical properties and crystal chemistry of rockforming minerals; petrography of igneous and metamorphic rocks; physical and chemical mineralogy of ores; geochronology; geochemistry of minor elements; Precambrian geology of the Hudson highlands and Adirondacks in New York. *Mailing Add:* Dept of Geol Univ of Mass Amherst MA 01002

JAFFE, ISRAELI AARON, b New York, NY, Dec 21, 27; m 52; c 3. INTERNAL MEDICINE. *Educ:* NY Univ, BS, 46; Columbia Univ, MD, 50; Am Bd Internal Med, dipl. *Prof Exp:* Clin assoc, NIH, 53-55; CLIN ASSOC INSTR MED, COLUMBIA UNIV, 57-, PROF CLIN MED, COL PHYSICIANS & SURGEONS, 78- *Concurrent Pos:* Asst prof instr med, New York Med Col, 60-63, prof instr med & dir rheumatic dis serv, 63-78. *Mem:* Am Col Physicians; AMA; Am Rheumatism Asn. *Res:* Rheumatic diseases. *Mailing Add:* 161 Ft Washington Ave New York NY 10032

JAFFE, JAMES MARK, b New York, NY, Apr 11, 43; m 64; c 2. PHARMACEUTICS. *Educ:* Univ Pittsburgh, BS, 68, BA, 69, MS, 70, PhD(pharmaceut), 72. *Prof Exp:* Asst pharmaceut, Sch Pharm, Univ Pittsburgh, 68-70, from instr to asst prof pharmaceut, 70-75, assoc prof, 75-80. *Concurrent Pos:* Reviewer, J Pharmaceut Sci, 74- & Am J Hosp Pharm. *Mem:* Am Pharmaceut Asn; Acad Pharmaceut Sci; Sigma Xi. *Res:* Physiological and formulation factors that influence the absorption and excretion of drugs. *Mailing Add:* 60 West Main St Brookside NJ 07926

JAFFE, JEROME HERBERT, psychopharmacology, see previous edition

JAFFE, JOSEPH, chemical engineering, see previous edition

JAFFE, JULIAN JOSEPH, b New York, NY, Feb 17, 26; m 53; c 4. PHARMACOLOGY. *Educ:* Univ Conn, BA, 49; Harvard Univ, MA, 51, PhD(biol), 55. *Prof Exp:* Asst, Harvard Univ, 52-53; instr biol, Brown Univ, 54-55, USPHS fel, 55-56; from instr to asst prof pharmacol, Sch Med, Yale Univ, 56-61; assoc prof, 61-67, PROF PHARMACOL, COL MED, UNIV VT, 67- *Concurrent Pos:* Wellcome res travel grants, Oxford Univ, 58 & Nuffield Inst Comp Med, London, 67, guest worker, Nuffield Inst Comp Med, 67-68; mem panel parasitic dis, US-Japan Coop Med Sci Prog, 71-76, mem trop med parasitol study sect, 77-81. *Mem:* Am Asn Cancer Res; Am Soc Pharmacol & Exp Therapeut; Am Soc Parasitol; Am Soc Trop Med & Hyg; NY Acad Sci. *Res:* Biochemical pharmacology; biochemistry of parasites. *Mailing Add:* Dept of Pharmacol Univ of Vt Col of Med Burlington VT 05405

JAFFE, LAURINDA A, b Pasadena, Calif, Jan 9, 52. DEVELOPMENTAL ELECTROPHYSIOLOGY. *Educ:* Purdue Univ, BS, 73; Univ Calif, Los Angeles, PhD(biol), 77. *Prof Exp:* NIH fel electrophysiol fertil, Marine Biol Lab, Woods Hole, Mass, 78-79; NSF fel electrophysiol fertil, Univ Calif, San Diego, 79-81; ASST PROF PHYSIOL, UNIV CONN, 81- *Mem:* Am Soc Cell Biol. *Res:* Electrical properties of eggs and embryos; electrical polyspermy blocks. *Mailing Add:* Dept Physiol Univ Conn Health Ctr Farmington CT 06032

JAFFE, LEONARD DAVID, b New York, NY, June 25, 19; m 45; c 4. SOLAR ENERGY, PLANETARY EXPLORATION. *Educ:* Mass Inst Technol, SB, 39, SM, 40; Harvard Univ, ScD(phys metall), 47. *Prof Exp:* Metallurgist, Watertown Arsenal, 40-42, metallurgist & supvr res on phase transformation in steel, 42-46, chief phys metall sect, 46-54; mgr, Mat Res Sect, Jet Propulsion Lab, 54-64, res specialist, Space Sci Div, 64, proj scientist surveyor proj, 65-68, mem tech staff, Space Sci & Energy Conversion Div, 68-81, SYST ENGR SOLAR THERMAL POWER SYSTS, JET PROPULSION LAB, CALIF INST TECHNOL, 81- *Mem:* AAAS; Am Geophys Union; Am Inst Aeronaut & Astronaut; Am Astron Soc; Am Inst Mining, Metall & Petrol Eng. *Res:* Solar thermal energy conversion; exploration of planetary surfaces; properties of the lunar surface. *Mailing Add:* Jet Propulsion Lab 4800 Oak Grove Dr Pasadena CA 91109

JAFFE, LIONEL, b New York, NY, Dec 28, 27; m 49; c 3. DEVELOPMENTAL PHYSIOLOGY, BIOPHYSICS. *Educ:* Harvard Univ, SB, 48; Calif Inst Technol, PhD(embryol), 54. *Prof Exp:* Fel, Nat Res Coun, Marine Sta, Johns Hopkins Univ, 53-54, Nat Sci Found, 54-55; fel marine biol, Scripps Inst, Calif, 55-56; asst prof biol, Brandeis Univ, 56-60; from asst prof to assoc prof, Univ Pa, 60-67; PROF BIOL, PURDUE UNIV, 67- *Mem:* AAAS; Biophys Soc; Am Soc Cell Biol; Am Soc Plant Physiol; Soc Gen Physiol. *Res:* Development and nature of morphogenetic polarity; cellular tropisms; bioelectric aspects of development. *Mailing Add:* Dept of Biol Purdue Univ West Lafayette IN 47907

JAFFE, MARVIN RICHARD, b New York, NY, May 23, 38. ANALYTICAL CHEMISTRY, INORGANIC CHEMISTRY. *Educ:* Brooklyn Col, BS, 60, MA, 65; Fordham Univ, PhD(anal chem), 70. *Prof Exp:* Qual control chemist, Schrafft's, New York, 60-62; prod develop chemist, 62-63; supvr prod develop, 63-65; instr chem, Bronx Community Col, 65-68; res asst, Fordham Univ, 68-70; guest jr res assoc, Brookhaven Nat Lab, 69-70; asst prof, 71-77, ASSOC PROF, SCI DEPT, MANHATTAN COMMUNITY COL, 77- *Mem:* Sigma Xi; Nat Sci Teachers Asn; Am Chem Soc. *Res:* Consumer science; science education of non-scientists; kinetics and mechanisms of beta-diketones. *Mailing Add:* Dept Sci Manhattan Community Col 1633 Broadway New York NY 10019

JAFFE, MICHAEL, b New York, NY, May 10, 42. POLYMER PHYSICS, PHYSICAL CHEMISTRY. *Educ:* Cornell Univ, BA, 63; Rensselaer Polytech Inst, PhD(chem), 67. *Prof Exp:* Res chemist, Celanese Res Co, 67-71, sr res chemist, 71-73, res assoc, 73-74, res supvr, 74-78; group leader, Res & Develop Lab, Fiber Industs, Inc, 78-80, res supvr, Celanese Res Co, 81-82, RES MGR, CELANESE RES CO, 82- *Mem:* Am Chem Soc; Am Phys Soc; NAm Thermal Anal Soc. *Res:* Morphology of crystalline high polymers; transition behavior of polymers; structure-property relationships of polymers and related materials. *Mailing Add:* 86 Mollis Ave Celanese Res Co Summit NJ 07901

JAFFE, MIRIAM WALTHER, b Clinton, Ind, Feb 6, 22; m 49; c 3. ASTRONOMY. *Educ:* Ind Univ, AB, 43; Univ Va, MA, 45; Radcliffe Col & Harvard Univ, PhD(astron), 48. *Prof Exp:* Instr astron, Wellesley Col, 48-49 & Univ Southern Calif, 49-51; asst prof astron, Haverford Col, 65-66; ASST PROF ASTRON, PURDUE UNIV, 68- *Mem:* Am Astron Soc. *Res:* Photographic photometry; classification of stellar spectra. *Mailing Add:* Dept of Geosci Purdue Univ West Lafayette IN 47906

JAFFE, MORDECAI J, b New York, NY, July 7, 33; m 61; c 3. PLANT PHYSIOLOGY. *Educ:* City Col New York, BS, 58; Cornell Univ, PhD(veg physiol), 64. *Prof Exp:* Lectr & res assoc biol, Yale Univ, 64-67; from asst prof to assoc prof plant physiol, Ohio Univ, 67-76, prof, 76-81; BABCOCK PROF BOTANY, WAKE FOREST UNIV, 81- *Concurrent Pos:* NSF res grant, 67-74 & 75-82; NASA res grant, 77-83; Bard res grant, 81-83; vis prof, Hebrew Univ, Jerusalem, 75; vis scientist, Boyce Thompson Inst Cornell Univ, 80. *Mem:* AAAS; Am Soc Plant Physiologists; Soc Develop Biol; Phytochem Soc NAm; Japanese Soc Plant Physiol. *Res:* Sensory physiology and biochemistry; rapid movements in plants; biochemistry of touch mediated processes in plants; physiology of stress in plants. *Mailing Add:* Biol Dept Wake Forest Univ Winston-Salem NC 27109

JAFFE, MORRY, b New York, NY, Oct 10, 40. EXPERIMENTAL PHYSICS. *Educ:* City Col New York, BS, 62; Boston Univ, MA, 64; City Univ New York, PhD(physics), 71. *Prof Exp:* Asst, Boston Univ, 62-64; lectr, City Col New York, 64-65, res asst, 65-69 & 70-71; LAB ASST, NEW YORK CITY DEPT AIR RESOURCES, 73- *Concurrent Pos:* Asst transit mgt analyst, Manhattan & Bronx Surface Transit Operating Authority, 78- *Mailing Add:* 65 Park Terr E New York NY 10034

JAFFE, PHILIP MONLANE, b Bronx, NY, Aug 14, 27; m 50; c 3. INORGANIC CHEMISTRY. *Educ:* City Col NY, BS, 48; Polytech Inst Brooklyn, MS, 53, PhD, 62. *Prof Exp:* Chemist, City Chem Corp, NY, 48-51; res chemist, Westinghouse Elec Co, 53-63; sr staff scientist, Aerospace Res Ctr, Gen Precision, Inc, 63-66; sr res chemist, Zenith Radio Corp, 66-72; PROF CHEM, OAKTON COMMUNITY COL, 70- *Concurrent Pos:* Mem comt chem technicians activities, Am Chem Soc, 73-78. *Mem:* Fel AAAS; Am Chem Soc; fel Am Inst Chem. *Res:* Inorganic phosphors and preparations; semiconductors; photoconductors; technical and educational writing. *Mailing Add:* Dept of Chem Oakton Community Col Morton Grove IL 60053

JAFFE, RANDAL CRAIG, b St Louis, Mo, Dec 18, 47; m 70; c 3. ENDOCRINOLOGY, BIOCHEMISTRY. *Educ:* Univ Southern Calif, BS, 68; Univ Calif, Davis, PhD(biochem), 72. *Prof Exp:* Fel endocrinol, Sch Med, Vanderbilt Univ, 72-73; fel cell biol, Baylor Col Med, 73-75; ASST PROF PHYSIOL, MED CTR, UNIV ILL, 75- *Concurrent Pos:* NIH fel, 74-75. *Mem:* AAAS; Endocrine Soc. *Res:* Mechanism of hormone action; comparative endocrinology; hormonal control of development. *Mailing Add:* Dept Physiol & Biophysics Med Ctr Univ Ill PO Box 6998 Chicago IL 60680

JAFFE, RICHARD ANDREW, b Oakland, Calif. NEUROPHYSIOLOGY, NEUROTOXICOLOGY. *Educ:* Univ Calif, Berkeley, AB, 69; Calif State Univ, Hayward, MA, 71; Univ Calif, San Francisco Med Ctr, PhD(neurophysiol), 76. *Prof Exp:* SR RES SCIENTIST & DIR, NEUROPHYSIOL LAB, BATTELLE MEM INST, 76- *Concurrent Pos:* Assoc prof, Joint Ctr Grad Study, Univ Wash, Wash State Univ & Ore State Univ, 76- *Mem:* Soc Neurosci; Inst Elec & Electronics Engrs; AAAS; Nat Soc Med Res; Bioelectromagnetics Soc. *Res:* Characterization of the physiological and pharmacological properties of mammalian peripheral sensory neurons; neurotoxicology of environmental contaminates; effects of electromagnetic radiation on the mammalian nervous system. *Mailing Add:* Neurosci Group Biol Dept Battelle Mem Inst Richland WA 99352

JAFFE, ROBERT B, b Detroit, Mich, Feb 18, 33; m 54; c 2. ENDOCRINOLOGY, OBSTETRICS & GYNECOLOGY. *Educ:* Univ Mich, MD, 57; Univ Colo, MS, 66; Am Bd Obstet & Gynec, dipl, 67 & Reproductive Endocrin cert. *Prof Exp:* Lab asst biochem, Univ Mich, 53-54; rotating intern, Univ Colo, 57-58, resident obstet & gynec, 59-63; from asst prof to prof obstet & gynec, Med Ctr, Univ Mich, Ann Arbor, 64-73; PROF OBSTET & GYNEC & CHMN DEPT, MED SCH, UNIV CALIF, SAN FRANCISCO, 73-, DIR, REPRODUCTIVE ENDOCRINOL CTR, 77- *Mem:* Fel Am Col Obstet & Gynec; Endocrine Soc; Am Fedn Clin Res; Soc Gynec Invest (pres). *Res:* Endocrinology; gynecology. *Mailing Add:* Dept of Obstet Gynec & Reprod Sci Univ Calif Med Sch San Francisco CA 94143

JAFFE, ROBERT LOREN, b Bath, Maine, May 23, 46. ELEMENTARY PARTICLE PHYSICS. *Educ:* Princeton Univ, AB, 68; Stanford Univ, MS, 71, PhD(physics), 72. *Prof Exp:* Res assoc physics, Stanford Linear Accelerator Ctr, 72; res assoc, 72-74, ASST PROF PHYSICS, MASS INST TECHNOL, 74- *Concurrent Pos:* Alfred P Sloan Found fel, 75-77; vis assoc theoret physics, Calif Inst Technol, 76; vis scientist, Stanford Accelerator Ctr, 76. *Mem:* Am Phys Soc; AAAS. *Res:* Theory of the structure of strongly interacting particles. *Mailing Add:* Dept of Physics 6-316 Mass Inst Technol Cambridge MA 02139

JAFFE, SIGMUND, b New Haven, Conn, Mar 1, 21; m 46; c 2. PHYSICAL CHEMISTRY. *Educ:* Wesleyan Univ, AB, 49; Iowa State Univ, PhD(chem), 53. *Prof Exp:* Asst phys chem, Ames Lab, Atomic Energy Comn, 49-53; sr engr, Air Reduction Res Lab, 53-58; from asst prof to assoc prof, 58-64, PROF CHEM, CALIF STATE UNIV, LOS ANGELES, 64- *Concurrent Pos:* NIH fel, Weizmann Inst, 64-65; res grant, Environ Protection Agency-US Pub Health, 66; res fel, Weizmann Inst Sci, 71-72; res scientist, Jet Propulsion Lab, Calif, 72-; vis prof, Queen Mary Col, Univ London, 78-79. *Mem:* Am Chem Soc. *Res:* Chemical kinetics; photo-chemical reactions of stratosphere and atmosphere including the reactions of Cl, NO2 and O3. *Mailing Add:* Dept of Chem Calif State Univ Los Angeles CA 90032

JAFFE, SOL SAMSON, b Ft Wayne, Ind, Feb 7, 20; m 52; c 2. ELECTROCHEMISTRY. *Educ:* Drew Univ, AB, 41; Stevens Inst Technol, MS, 45. *Prof Exp:* Chemist, Fidelity Chem Prod Corp Div, Maas & Waldstein Co, NJ, 42-46; res labs, Thomas A Edison, Inc, 46-51, res chemist, 51-57, Thomas A Edison Res Labs Div, McGraw Edison Co, 57-64; sr res chemist, Res & Develop Lab, Alkaline Battery Div, Gulton Industs, 64-65; chief chemist, Bright Star Industs, 65-70; formulating chemist, Nitine, Inc, 70-72; electrochem engr, Mallory Battery Co Div, P R Mallory & Co, Inc, 72-79; SECT HEAD ELECTROCHEM ENG, BATTERY TECHNOL CO DIV, DURACELL INT INC, 80- *Mem:* Electrochem Soc. *Res:* Leclanche, air-zinc, mercury-zinc, divalent silver-zinc, and fuel cells; nickel-iron, nickel-cadmium, silver-cadmium and lead-acid storage batteries; hermetically sealed cells; charge control electrodes; state-of-charge indicators; electrochemical devices; metal finishing; electroless plating. *Mailing Add:* 7 Nance Rd West Orange NJ 07052

JAFFE, WALTER JOSEPH, b Newton, Mass, Aug 23, 47; m 74. ASTRONOMY. *Educ:* Calif Inst Technol, BS, 68; Leiden Univ, Drs, 69, Dr, 74. *Prof Exp:* Staff scientist astron, Leiden Observ, 72-76; mem astron, Inst Advan Study, 76-77; ASST SCIENTIST, NAT RADIO ASTRON OBSERV, 77- *Res:* Radioastronomical and astrophysical studies of clusters of galaxies. *Mailing Add:* Nat Radio Astron Observ Edgemont Rd Charlottesville VA 22901

JAFFE, WERNER G, b Frankfurt, Ger, Oct 27, 14; m 46; c 6. NUTRITION, BIOCHEMISTRY. *Educ:* Univ Zurich, PhD(chem), 39; Cent Univ Venezuela, DrSc(biochem), 50. *Prof Exp:* Asst prof org chem, Sch Pharm, 47-50, assoc prof biochem, Sch Sci, 50-58, PROF BIOCHEM, SCH SCI, CENT UNIV VENEZUELA, 58-; RES ASSOC, NAT NUTRIT INST, 50-; DIR POSTGRAD COURSE NUTRIT PLANNING, 74- *Concurrent Pos:* Ed, Arch Latinoamerican Nutrit. *Honors & Awards:* Nat Sci Award, Ministry of Educ, 58; Gold Medal Sci Res, Cent Univ Venezuela, 60; Nat Sci Award of Venezuela, 78. *Mem:* AAAS; Venezuelan Asn Advan Sci (pres, 56); Venezuelan Chem Soc (pres, 53); cor mem Peruvian Chem Soc; cor mem Mex Chem Soc. *Res:* Enzymology; toxicology; lectins, enzyme inhibition; toxic food constituents. *Mailing Add:* Nat Nutrit Inst Apantado 2049 Caracas 10 Venezuela

JAFFE, WILLIAM J(ULIAN), b Passaic, NJ, Mar 22, 10. INDUSTRIAL ENGINEERING. *Educ:* NY Univ, BS, 30, Engr ScD(indust eng), 53; Columbia Univ, MA, 31, MS, 41. *Prof Exp:* Naval architect, Philadelphia Navy Yard, US Dept Navy, 41-45; instr math, 46, from instr to asst prof indust eng, 46-50, from asst exec assoc to exec assoc, 49-60, from assoc prof to prof eng, 50-73, distinguished prof, 73-75, EMER PROF ENG, NJ INST TECHNOL, 75- *Concurrent Pos:* Adj assoc prof col eng, NY Univ, 53-54; mem, Inst Bus Admin & Mgt, Japan, Comn on Manpower, Israel & Clark Bd Int Mgt, Comt Int Orgn Sci, Bd Standards Rev, Am Nat Standards Inst. *Mem:* Fel AAAS; fel Am Soc Mech Engrs; fel Am Inst Indust Engrs; fel Soc Advan Mgt; assoc fel NY Acad Med. *Res:* Industrial and management engineering. *Mailing Add:* 1175 York Ave New York NY 10021

JAFFEE, OSCAR CHARLES, b New York, NY, Sept 26, 16; m 62; c 1. EXPERIMENTAL EMBRYOLOGY. *Educ:* NY Univ, BA, 46, MS, 48, Ind Univ, PhD(zool), 52. *Prof Exp:* Instr anat, Sch Med, Univ Ark, 52-56; embryologist, Chronic Dis Res Inst, State Univ NY Buffalo, 58-60, from lectr to assoc prof, 60-68, PROF BIOL, UNIV DAYTON, 68- *Concurrent Pos:* Mem staff, Mt Desert Island Biol Lab; mem, Am Heart Asn Coun. *Mem:* Am Asn Anat; Teratology Soc; Int Soc Stereology; Int Soc Biorheol. *Res:* Cardiovascular embryology; teratology; physiology of the embryonic heart. *Mailing Add:* 300 College Park Ave Dayton OH 45469

JAFFEE, ROBERT I(SAAC), b Chicago, Ill, July 11, 17; m 45; c 2. METALLURGY. *Educ:* Ill Inst Technol, BS, 39; Harvard Univ, SM, 40; Univ Md, PhD(metall) 43. *Prof Exp:* Lectr, Univ Md, 42; res metallurgist, Leeds & Northrup Co, Pa, 42-43 & Univ Calif, 44; res engr, Battelle-Columbus, 43-44, asst supvr, 45-50, div chief, 50-60, tech mgr, 60-65, chief mat scientist, 65-75; tech mgr, 75-80, SR TECH ADV, ELEC POWER RES INST, 80- *Concurrent Pos:* Consult, President's Sci Adv Comt, 66; chmn adv comt mat, NASA, 66-71, mem mat & struct comt, 71-74; panel magnetohydrodynamics, Off Sci & Technol, 68-69; Nat Mat Adv Bd, Nat Acad Sci-Nat Acad Eng, 71-74; consult prof, Stanford Univ, 74- *Honors & Awards:* Bronze Medal, Am Ord Asn, 66. *Mem:* Nat Acad Eng; fel Metall Soc; Am Inst Mining, Metall & Petrol Engrs (pres, 78); fel & hon mem Am Soc Metals; fel Brit Soc Metals. *Res:* Physical metallurgy in titanium and refractory metals; oxidation of superalloys and refractory metals; stress corrosion of titanium; protective coatings. *Mailing Add:* 3851 May Ct Palo Alto CA 94304

JAFFEY, ARTHUR HAROLD, b Chicago, Ill, Dec 25, 14; m 45; c 2. NUCLEAR CHEMISTRY. *Educ:* Univ Chicago, BS, 36, PhD(phys chem), 41. *Prof Exp:* Instr chem lab, Univ Chicago, 37-40, res assoc detection poisonous gases, Off Sci Res & Develop Proj, 41-42 & Metall Lab, Manhattan Dist, 42-46; res assoc, 46-50, GROUP LEADER & SR CHEMIST, ARGONNE NAT LAB, 50- *Concurrent Pos:* Jr chemist, Rock Island Arsenal, US War Dept, Ill, 41; res assoc, Off Sci Res & Develop, Columbia Univ, 42. *Mem:* Am Phys Soc; Sigma Xi. *Res:* Measurement of disintegration properties of radioactive isotopes; measurement of thermal neutron reactions with heavy elements; statistical analysis of nuclear measurement data; development of superconducting heavy ion linear accelerator. *Mailing Add:* Bldg 200 Argonne Nat Lab Argonne IL 60439

JAGANNATHAN, SINGANALLUR N, b Coonoor, India, Mar 10, 34; m 68; c 2. NUTRITIONAL BIOCHEMISTRY, BIOCHEMICAL PATHOLOGY. *Educ:* Univ Bombay, BSc, 54, MSc, 59, PhD(biochem), 62. *Prof Exp:* Res asst to sr res officer nutrit, Indian Coun Med Res, Nat Inst Nutrit, 56-70; res scientist lipid, lipoprotein & biochem, Col Med, Univ Iowa, 70-74; asst prof biochem & exp path, 74-77, ASSOC PROF BIOCHEM & NUTRIT PATH, DEPT PATH & BIOCHEM, SCH MED, WVA UNIV, MORGANTOWN, 77-, ASSOC PROF COMMUN DENT, 79- *Concurrent Pos:* Nat Res Coun Can fel nutrit biochem, Queen's Univ, Ont, 62-64; Brit Coun fel, 64; fel, Coun Arteriosclerosis, Am Heart Asn, 72. *Mem:* Am Inst Nutrit; Am Soc Clin Nutrit. *Res:* Lipid and lipoprotein metabolism in relation to atherosclerosis; platelet function; human nutrition. *Mailing Add:* Dept Path Med Sch WVa Univ Morgantown WV 26506

JAGEL, KENNETH I(RWIN), JR, b Jamaica, NY, Feb 2, 27; m 51; c 2. CHEMICAL ENGINEERING. *Educ:* Columbia Univ, BSc, 51, MSc, 53, DEngSc, 61. *Prof Exp:* Asst chem eng, Columbia Univ, 51-53, res asst, 55-57; res engr, Socony Mobil Oil Co, Inc, 57-59, sr res engr, 59-65, group leader, Mobil Res & Develop Corp, 65-68, eng assoc, 68-71; mgr mfg, Engelhard Minerals & Chem Corp, 71-72, mgr process eng & develop, 72-73, dir prod assurance, 73-81, DIR QUAL & TECH SERV, ENGELHARD INDUST DIV, ENGELHARD CORP, 81- *Mem:* Fel AAAS; Am Inst Chem; Am Chem Soc; Am Inst Chem Engrs; Am Soc Testing & Mat. *Res:* Catalyst manufacture; auto-exhaust emission control catalysts; cracking catalysts; oil shale retorting processes; distillation equipment. *Mailing Add:* Engelhard Corp 70 Wood Ave S Iselin NJ 08830

JAGENDORF, ANDRE TRIDON, b New York, NY, Oct 21, 26; m 52; c 3. PLANT PHYSIOLOGY, BIOCHEMISTRY. *Educ:* Cornell Univ, AB, 48; Yale Univ, PhD(plant sci), 51. *Prof Exp:* Res assoc bot, Univ Calif, Los Angeles, 51-53; from asst prof to prof biol, Johns Hopkins Univ, 53-66, with McCollum-Pratt Inst, 53-66; PROF PLANT PHYSIOL, CORNELL UNIV, 66- *Concurrent Pos:* Merck fel, 51-53, Weizmann fel, 62. *Honors & Awards:* Award, Md Acad Sci, 61; Kettering Res Award, 63, Kettering Award in Photosyn, Am Soc Plant Physiologists, 78. *Mem:* Nat Acad Sci; Am Soc Photobiol; Am Soc Cell Biol; Am Soc Plant Physiol(pres, 67-68); fel AAAS. *Res:* Photosynthetic phosphorylation; biochemistry; chloroplast biogenesis. *Mailing Add:* Biol Div Cornell Univ Ithaca NY 14853

JAGERMAN, DAVID LEWIS, b Aug 27, 23; m 51; c 3. MATHEMATICS, ELECTRICAL ENGINEERING. *Educ:* Cooper Union Univ, BEE, 49; NY Univ, MS, 54, PhD(math), 62. *Prof Exp:* Sr engr analog comput, Reeves Instrument Corp, NY, 51-55; staff scientist math guided missiles, Stavid Eng, NJ, 55-57 & 57-59; design specialist trajectories, Gen Dynamics/Convair, Calif, 57; staff mem math control systs, Syst Develop Corp, NJ, 59-64; MEM TECH STAFF, BELL LABS, 64- *Concurrent Pos:* Assoc prof math, Fairleigh Dickinson Univ, 59-66; prof, Stevens Inst Technol, 67-72. *Mem:* Am Math Soc. *Res:* Diophantine analysis and numerical quadrature theory with application to the mathematical properties of pseudo-random numbers; information theory; telephone traffic theory. *Mailing Add:* Bell Labs Rm 3B-510 Holmdel NJ 07733

JAGGARD, DWIGHT LINCOLN, b Oceanside, NY, Apr 14, 48; m 68; c 2. OPTICS, ELECTROMAGNETISM. *Educ:* Univ Wis-Madison, BSEE, 71, MSEE, 72; Calif Inst Technol, PhD(elec eng & appl physics), 76. *Prof Exp:* Res asst geophys & elec eng, Univ Wis-Madison, 68-72; engr imaging radar & DFB lasers, Jet Propulsion Lab, Calif Inst Technol, 73-76, res fel, 76-78; asst prof optics & electromagnetics, Dept Elec Eng, Univ Utah, 78-80; ASST PROF OPTICS & ELECTROMAGNETICS, DEPT ELEC ENG & SCI, UNIV PA, 80- *Concurrent Pos:* Res asst optics & electromagnetics, Calif Inst Technol, 75-76, consult, Jet Propulsion Lab, 76-; consult, Environ Studies Lab, 78-81. *Mem:* Inst Elec & Electronic Engrs; Int Union Radio Sci; Optics Soc Am. *Res:* Wave propagation in periodic and almost periodic structures and gratings; integrated and fiber optics; optical processing light scattering from aerosols; microwave biohazards; remote sensing and inverse scattering and the effect of topology on electromagnetism. *Mailing Add:* Dept Elec Eng & Sci Univ Pa Philadelphia PA 19104

JAGGER, JOHN, b New Haven, Conn, Feb 22, 24; m 56; c 2. BIOPHYSICS, PHOTOBIOLOGY. *Educ:* Yale Univ, BS, 49, MS, 53, PhD(biophys), 54. *Prof Exp:* Asst, Mem Hosp, NY, 50-51; asst, Yale Univ, 53-54; Nat Found Infantile Paralysis fel, Radium Inst, France, 54-55; biophysicist, Biol Div, Oak Ridge Nat Lab, 56-65; from assoc prof to prof, Southwest Ctr Advan Studies, 65-69, prof biol, 69-81, PROF GEN STUDIES & BIOL, UNIV TEX, DALLAS, 81- *Concurrent Pos:* Lectr, Univ Tenn, 61-65; vis prof, Pa State Univ, 63 & Univ Kyoto, Japan, 79; consult, Aerojet Med & Biol Systs, 71-73; mem, US Nat Comt Photobiol, Nat Res Coun, 75-80, pres, 78-80. *Mem:* Fel AAAS; Biophys Soc; Radiation Res Soc; Am Soc Microbiol; Am Soc Photobiol. *Res:* Effects of radiations on large molecules and cells; effects of ultraviolet on bacteria; photoprotection; effects of near ultraviolet on cell growth and membrane function; history and social impact of biological science. *Mailing Add:* Sch Gen Studies, GR 2 6 Univ of Tex at Dallas Box 688 Richardson TX 75080

JAGIELLO, GEORGIANA MARY, b Boston, Mass, Aug 2, 27; m 57. GENETICS. *Educ:* Boston Univ, AB, 49; Tufts Univ, MD, 55. *Prof Exp:* Exchange fel surg, St Bartholomew's Hosp, London, 54; intern med, Res & Educ Hosps, Univ Ill, 55-56; resident, New Eng Med Ctr, Boston, 56-57; res fel endocrinol, Scripps Clin, La Jolla, 57-58; res fel, New Eng Med Ctr, Boston, 58-60; USPHS res fel cytogenetics, Guy's Hosp, London, 60-61; asst prof, Sch Med, Univ Ill, Chicago Circle, 61-66; sr lectr cytogenetics, Guy's Hosp, London, 66-69; res prof pediat, Sch Med, Univ Ill, Chicago Circle, 69-70; PROF OBSTET, GYNEC & HUMAN GENETICS, COL PHYSICIANS & SURGEONS, COLUMBIA UNIV, 70- *Concurrent Pos:* Mem, Inst Advan Study, Univ Ill, 64; NIH career develop award, 65; consult, Guy's Hosp, London, 66-69. *Mem:* Endocrine Soc; Teratology Soc; Environ Mutagen Soc; Am Soc Cell Biol; Soc Study Reproduction. *Res:* Mammalian meiosis; reproductive endocrinology. *Mailing Add:* Col of Physicians & Surgeons 630 W 168th St New York NY 10032

JAHAN-PARWAR, BEHRUS, b Ghoochan, Iran, May 26, 38, nat US; m 66; c 2. NEUROBIOLOGY. *Educ:* Univ Gottingen, MD, 64, DMSc(physiol), 65. *Prof Exp:* Res assoc neurophysiol, Dept Physiol, Univ Gottingen, 64-66; asst res neurophysiologist, Mental Health Res Inst, Univ Mich, 66-68; from asst prof to assoc prof physiol, Dept Biol, Clark Univ, 68-73; SR SCIENTIST NEUROBIOL, WORCESTER FOUND EXP BIOL, 73- *Concurrent Pos:* Prin investr NIH grants, 69-73, 74-77, 75-83 & 78-81; NIH res career develop award, 70-73; Grass Found grant, 75-78; NSF grant, 78-82. *Mem:* Soc Neurosci; Am Physiolog Soc; Am Soc Zoologist; Europ Chemoreception Res Orgn. *Res:* The elucidation of the principles of neuronal organization underlying processing of sensory information and generation and modification of behavior; neural mechanisms of chemoreception, learning and rhythmic behaviors such as feeding and locomotion . *Mailing Add:* Worcester Found Exp Biol 222 Maple Ave Shrewsbury MA 01545

JAHIEL, RENE, b France, Mar 29, 28; nat US; m 55; c 3. HEALTH SERVICES RESEARCH, MICROBIOLOGY. *Educ:* NY Univ, BA, 46; State Univ NY, MD, 50; Columbia Univ, PhD(microbiol), 57. *Prof Exp:* Intern, Montefiore Hosp, NY, 50-51; res, Mt Sinai Hosp, 51-52, fel, 52-55; asst prof microbiol, Sch Med, Univ Colo, 57-59; asst prof path, Columbia Univ, 59-61; asst prof pub health, Med Col, Cornell Univ, 61-67; res assoc prof prev med, 67-70, res prof prev med, 70-76, RES PROF MED, NY UNIV, 76- *Concurrent Pos:* Exp immunologist, Nat Jewish Hosp, Denver, Colo, 57-59; asst attend pathologist, Mt Sinai Hosp, New York, 59-61; career scientist, Health Res Coun New York, 62-66. *Mem:* NY Acad Sci; Am Soc Microbiol; Tissue Cult Asn; Am Pub Health Asn; Gerontol Soc Am. *Res:* Immunopathology; autoantibodies; tissue culture virology; tissue culture; interferon; community medicine; sociology of knowledge. *Mailing Add:* Dept Med NY Univ Sch of Med 550 First Ave New York NY 10016

JAHN, ALEX KARL, b Ger, Sept 4, 20; US citizen; m 60. ORGANIC & POLYMER CHEMISTRY. *Educ:* Univ Gottingen, dipl, 45, PhD(chem), 48. *Prof Exp:* Chemist polymer & org chem, Farbwerke Hoechst AG, Ger, 49-53; sci asst org chem, Univ Heidelberg, 54-57; sr res chemist polymer chem & technol, Dow Chem Co, 57-65, ASSOC SCIENTIST, BADISCHE CO, 65- *Res:* Organic and physical polymer chemistry; polymer and fiber technology; spin finishes; microbiology; chemotherapy of cancer. *Mailing Add:* 118 Dover Rd Williamsburg VA 23185

JAHN, EDWIN CORNELIUS, b Oneonta, NY, Sept 6, 02; m 27, 70; c 2. ORGANIC CHEMISTRY. *Educ:* NY State Col Forestry, BS, 25, MS, 26; McGill Univ, PhD(org chem), 29. *Hon Degrees:* DSc, Syracuse Univ, 72- *Prof Exp:* Asst, NY State Col Forestry, 25-26 & McGill Univ, 26-29; fel, Am-Scand Found, 29-30; from assoc prof to prof forestry, Univ Idaho, 30-38; prof forest chem, State Univ NY Col Environ Sci & Forestry, 38-72, dir res, 49-52, assoc dean phys sci, 52-66, exec dean, 66-67, dean, 67-69; EXEC SECY, EMPIRE STATE PAPER RES ASSOCS, INC, 70- *Concurrent Pos:* Consult, USDA, Sweden, 43-44; sr econ analyst, US Dept Com, 45-46; tech attache to US State Dept for Sweden, Finland, Norway & Denmark, 45-46; mem wood chem comt, Food & Agr Orgn, UN, 47-64. *Honors & Awards:* Tech Asn Pulp & Paper Indust Award, 70. *Mem:* Am Chem Soc; fel Soc Am Foresters; fel Tech Asn Pulp & Paper Indust; AAAS. *Res:* Cellulose, wood and polymer chemistry. *Mailing Add:* State Univ NY 316 Walters Hall Syracuse NY 13210

JAHN, ERNESTO, b Yumbel, Chile, Mar 29, 42; m 72. ANIMAL SCIENCE, RUMINANT NUTRITION. *Educ:* Univ Concepcion, MgAgr, 65; Va Polytech Inst & State Univ, MS, 69, PhD(ruminant nutrit), 74. *Prof Exp:* Agr engr ruminants, Inst Land & Cattle Invests, Chile, 65-72; res asst animal sci, Va Polytech Inst & State Univ, 72-74; SR RES BIOLOGIST ANIMAL SCI, RES LABS, MERCK & CO, INC, 74- *Mem:* Latin Am Soc Animal Prod; Agron Soc Chile. *Mailing Add:* 960 Potter Ave Union NJ 07083

JAHN, J RUSSELL, b Spirit Lake, Iowa, Dec 2, 26; m 50; c 3. ANIMAL SCIENCE. *Educ:* SDak State Univ, BS, 59, MS, 60, PhD(animal sci), 63. *Prof Exp:* Assoc prof, 62-66, PROF ANIMAL SCI & HEAD DEPT AGR SCI, UNIV WIS-PLATTEVILLE, 66- *Mem:* Am Soc Animal Sci. *Res:* Artificial insemination of beef cattle. *Mailing Add:* Dept of Agr Sci Univ of Wis Platteville WI 53818

JAHN, LAURENCE ROY, b Jefferson, Wis, June 24, 26; m 47; c 2. WILDLIFE ECOLOGY, ZOOLOGY. *Educ:* Univ Wis, BS, 49, MS, 58, PhD(wildlife ecol), 65. *Prof Exp:* Biologist migratory bird populations & habitats, Wis Dept Natural Resources, 49-59; N Cent field rep, 59-69, VPRES RESOURCE MGT & RES, WILDLIFE MGT INST, 69- *Concurrent Pos:* Mem, Bd Dir, Citizens Comt Natural Resources, 70-78; chmn steering comt, Nat Watershed Cong, 71-; mem, Adv Comt Wildlife, Dept State, 72-77, Adv Comt Water Data for Pub Use, US Geol Surv, 72- & Adv Panel on Tuna-Porpoise, Nat Marine Fisheries Serv, 74-; secy NAM Wildlife Found, 74-; mem, Adv Comt Fish, Wildlife & Parks, US Dept Interior, 75-78; mem, Environ Adv Bd, Dept Defense, US Army Corps Engrs, 79-; mem, Bd Agr & Renewable Resources, Nat Res Coun, Nat Acad Sci, 79- *Honors & Awards:* Commendation Awards, Soil Conserv Soc Am, 69. *Mem:* Fel AAAS; Wildlife Soc; Am Fisheries Soc; Am Water Resources Asn; Soil Conserv Soc Am. *Res:* Wildlife populations and habitats, particularly projects designed to provide information for strengthening management programs, especially guidelines for avoiding and minimizing adverse impacts on wildlife as development proceeds. *Mailing Add:* 2435 Riviera Dr Vienna VA 22180

JAHN, LAWRENCE A, b Cudahy, Wis, Dec 2, 41; m 66. AQUATIC BIOLOGY, FISHERIES MANAGEMENT. *Educ:* Univ Wis, BS, 63; Mont State Univ, MS, 66, PhD(zool), 68. *Prof Exp:* From asst prof to assoc prof, 68-81, PROF BIOL SCI, WESTERN ILL UNIV, 81- *Mem:* Am Fisheries Soc; Am Soc Ichthyol & Herpet. *Res:* Fish orientation, management and behavior; fish ecology and life histories. *Mailing Add:* Dept of Biol Sci Western Ill Univ Macomb IL 61455

JAHN, ROBERT G(EORGE), b Kearny, NJ, Apr 1, 30; m 53; c 4. ENGINEERING PHYSICS. *Educ:* Princeton Univ, BS, 51, MA, 53, PhD(physics), 55. *Prof Exp:* Asst prof physics. Lehigh Univ, 55-58; asst prof jet propulsion, Calif Inst Technol, 58-61; from asst prof to assoc prof, 62-67, dir grad studies, Dept Aerospace & Mech Sci, 68-70, PROF AEROSPACE SCI, PRINCETON UNIV, 67-, DEAN SCH ENG & APPL SCI, 71- *Concurrent Pos:* Mem res & technol adv subcomt electrophys, NASA, 68-71, mem res & technol adv comt space propulsion & power, 71-72, mem res & technol adv coun comt space propulsion & power, 76-77, mem nat adv coun space systs & technol adv comt, 78-; mem bd trustees, Assoc Univs, Inc, Washington, DC, 71-74, chmn bd, 77-79, trustee rep, 74-, mem nominating comt, 78-79. *Honors & Awards:* Curtis W McGraw Res Award, Am Soc Eng Educ, 69. *Mem:* Am Inst Aeronaut & Astronaut; Am Phys Soc. *Res:* Plasma propulsion; high temperature gasdynamics and fluid mechanics; shock tubes; plasmajets; ionization phenomena; electromagnetic wave propagation in ionized gases. *Mailing Add:* C-230 Eng Quadrangle Princeton Univ Princeton NJ 08544

JAHNGEN, EDWIN GEORG EMIL, JR, b Pittsburgh, Pa, Jan 8, 46. ORGANIC CHEMISTRY, BIORGANIC CHEMISTRY. *Educ:* Bates Col, BSc, 68; Univ Vt, PhD(org chem), 74. *Prof Exp:* Chemist, Water Improv Comn, Maine, 67-68; chemist org synthesis, Polaroid Corp, 68-70; res assoc nat prod, Univ BC, 74-76; groupleader, New Eng Nuclear Corp, 76-78; ASST PROF ORG CHEM, WILKES COL, 78- *Concurrent Pos:* NIH fel, Nat Res Coun, Univ BC, 74-76; consult Med Sch, Univ Conn, 78- *Mem:* Am Chem Soc. *Res:* Studies of bio-organic systems; synthesis and modification of exogenous; endogenous drugs and hormones. *Mailing Add:* Dept of Chem Wilkes Col Wilkes-Barre PA 18766

JAHNS, HANS O(TTO), b Kamen, Ger, Sept 4, 31; m 59; c 4. PETROLEUM ENGINEERING, ARCTIC ENGINEERING. *Educ:* Clausthal Tech Univ, dipl, 55, dipl, 56, Dr(Ing), 61. *Prof Exp:* Res asst petrol eng, Inst Drilling & Petrol Prod, Clausthal Tech Univ, 56-59; reservoir engr, Reservoir Lab, Wintershall AG, Ger, 59-62; res engr prod res, Jersey Prod Res Co, Standard Oil Co NJ, Okla, 62-65, res engr, 65-68, res assoc, 68-73, res adv, 73-77, sr res adv, 77-80, RES SCIENTIST, EXXON PROD RES CO, 80- *Concurrent Pos:* Mem permafrost comt, Nat Res Coun, 75-80, mem polar res bd, 76- ; mem adv bd, Geophys Inst, Univ Alaska, 78- *Mem:* Soc Petrol Engrs; AAAS; Am Petrol Inst. *Res:* Petroleum reservoir description; oceanography; arctic research; arctic engineering; sea ice mechanics. *Mailing Add:* c/o Exxon Prod Res Co PO Box 2189 Houston TX 77001

JAHNS, MONROE FRANK, b Seguin, Tex, May 16, 28; m 54; c 2. PHYSICS. *Educ:* Tex A&M Univ, BS, 49; Univ Tex, Austin, MA, 64, PhD(physics), 66. *Prof Exp:* Instr physics, Unit Tex, Austin, 65-66; asst prof, Sam Houston State Col, 66-67; advan sr fel med physics, 67-68, ASSOC PHYSICIST & ASSOC PROF BIOPHYS, UNIV TEX M D ANDERSON HOSP & TUMOR INST HOUSTON, 68- *Mem:* Am Phys Soc; Soc Nuclear Med; Am Asn Physicists Med. *Mailing Add:* Dept Biophys Univ Tex M D Anderson Hosp & Tumor Inst Houston TX 77025

JAHNS, RICHARD HENRY, b Los Angeles, Calif, Mar 10, 15; m 36; c 2. GEOLOGY. *Educ:* Calif Inst Technol, BS, 35, PhD(geol), 43, Northwestern Univ, MS, 37. *Prof Exp:* Asst, Northwestern Univ, 35-36, asst instr, 36-37; from jr geologist to sr geologist, US Geol Surv, 37-65; prof geol & dean, Sch Earth Sci, 65-79, W J & M L CROOK PROF GEOL & APPL EARTH SCI, STANFORD UNIV, 79- *Concurrent Pos:* From asst prof to prof, Calif Inst Technol, 46-60; asst ed Econ Geol, 52-68; assoc ed, Am Mineralogist, 57-63; vis prof, Pa State Univ, 58, prof & chmn div earth sci, 60-62, dean col mineral indust, 62-65; nat lectr, Sigma Xi, 65; mem, Calif State Mining & Geol Bd, 66-75; consult, US Geol Surv, 67-; mem task force reduction of earthquake risk, Off Sci & Technol, 70-71; mem, Calif State Seismic Safety Comn, 75- *Honors & Awards:* Ian Campbell Medal, Am Geol Inst, 81. *Mem:* Fel AAAS; fel Am Geophys Union, fel Geol Soc Am (pres, 70-71); fel Mineral Soc Am; Am Inst Mining, Metall & Petrol Eng. *Res:* Economic geology of industrial minerals; glacial geology; igneous and metamorphic petrology; geology of pegmatite deposits; structural and engineering geology; geology of California. *Mailing Add:* Sch of Earth Sci Stanford Univ Stanford CA 94305

JAHODA, FRANZ CARL, b Vienna, Austria, Sept 16, 30; nat US; m 55; c 2. EXPERIMENTAL PHYSICS. *Educ:* Swarthmore Col, BA, 51; Cornell Univ, PhD, 57. *Prof Exp:* MEM STAFF, LOS ALAMOS NAT LAB, 57-, GROUP LEADER, 74- *Concurrent Pos:* Mem staff, Culham Lab, Abingdon, Eng, 64-65; mem staff, Inst voor Plasmafysica, Jutphaas, Neth, 72-73. *Mem:* Optical Soc Am; Inst Elec & Electronics Engrs. *Res:* Plasma physics; spectroscopy; lasers; optical diagnostics. *Mailing Add:* Los Alamos Nat Lab Univ of Calif PO Box 1663 Los Alamos NM 87544

JAHODA, GERALD, b Vienna, Austria, Oct 22, 25; US citizen; m 52. INFORMATION SCIENCE. *Educ:* NY Univ, AB, 47; Columbia Univ, MS, 52, DLS, 60. *Prof Exp:* Instr & chem librn, Univ Wis, 52-53; group leader, Colgate-Palmolive Co, 53-57; sect head, Esso Res & Eng Co, 57-63; PROF INFO SCI & LIBRARIANSHIP, FLA STATE UNIV, 63- *Concurrent Pos:* Instr, Polytech Inst Brooklyn, 53-54 & Rutgers Univ, 61-62; Air Force Sci Res grant, 65-66; mem, Sci Inst Pub Info; US Off Educ grant, 74-; NSF grant, 76- *Mem:* Am Libr Asn; Spec Libr Asn; Am Soc Info Sci. *Res:* Information needs of scientists; organization of the literature of science and technology; use of data processing equipment in the operations of libraries and technical information centers. *Mailing Add:* Libr Sch Fla State Univ Tallahassee FL 32306

JAHODA, JOHN C, b Dalhart, Tex, Feb 9, 44. ECOLOGY, MAMMALOGY. *Educ:* Univ Conn, BA, 66; Okla State Univ, PhD(zool), 69. *Prof Exp:* Asst prof biol, State Univ NY Col Geneseo, 69-70; from asst prof to assoc prof, 70-81, PROF BIOL, BRIDGEWATER STATE COL, 81- *Concurrent Pos:* Consult, Raytheon Serv Co, 70-; mem, Corp Bermuda Biosta Res. *Mem:* Am Soc Mammal; Ecol Soc Am; Sigma Xi. *Res:* Ecology and ethology of mammals; salt marsh ecology; pollution of salt marshes. *Mailing Add:* Dept of Biol Sci Bridgewater State Col Bridgewater MA 02324

JAHSMAN, WILLIAM EDWARD, b Detroit, Mich, May 13, 26; m 49; c 3. MECHANICAL ENGINEERING. *Educ:* Cornell Univ, BEng, 51; Stanford Univ, MS, 53, PhD(eng mech), 54. *Prof Exp:* Mech specialist, Knolls Atomic Power Lab, Gen Elec, 54-56; consult scientist missiles & spacecraft, Lockheed Missiles & Space Co, 56-67; prof mech eng & chmn dept, Univ Colo, Boulder, 67-80; WITH INTEL CORP, 80- *Concurrent Pos:* Liaison scientist, Off Naval Res, 69-70; prin investr NSF grant, 70-76. *Mem:* Am Soc Mech Engrs; Am Soc Eng Educ; Am Acad Mech. *Res:* Wave propagation in inelastic materials; dynamic mechanical properties of coal and oil shale. *Mailing Add:* Intel Corp Santa Clara CA 95051

JAIKRISHNAN, KADAMBI RAJGOPAL, b Bangalore, India. FLUID DYNAMICS, MECHANICAL ENGINEERING. *Educ:* Univ Jodhpur, BE, 64; Univ Pittsburgh, MS, 70, PhD(mech eng), 76. *Prof Exp:* Planning engr mech eng, APEE Corp, Hyderabad, India, 65-67; grad student asst mech eng, Univ Pittsburgh, 68-71; engr heat transfer & fluid dynamics, 71-75, SR ENGR FLUID DYNAMICS, WESTINGHOUSE RES & DEVELOP CTR, 75- *Concurrent Pos:* Lectr mech eng dept, Univ Pittsburgh, 77. *Mem:* Am Soc Mech Engrs. *Res:* Compressible fluid dynamics; transonic flow of steam in blade passages of turbomachinery; laser doppler anemometry; flow visualization systems; flutter of blades; unstalled flutter. *Mailing Add:* Westinghouse Res & Develop Ctr 1310 Beulah Rd Pittsburgh PA 15235

JAIN, ANANT VIR, b Sardhana, India, March 15, 40; US citizen; m 71; c 1. TOXICOLOGY. *Educ:* Agra Univ, India, BS, 59, MS, 62; Purdue Univ, PhD(chem), 72. *Prof Exp:* Lectr chem, DAV Col, India, 62-64; res asst, Purdue Univ, 64-66, chem analyst, 66-72, res assoc, 72-74; anal chemist, 74-81, ASSOC ANAL TOXICOLOGIST, UNIV GA, 81- *Mem:* Am Chem Soc; Soc Toxicol; Asn Off Anal Chemists. *Res:* Analytical methods for the detection of poisons, drugs,and metals from biological and agricultural materials; analytical chemistry and toxicology of poisons; mycotoxin decontamination; diagnostic laboratory service. *Mailing Add:* Diag Asst Lab Col Vet Med Univ Ga Athens GA 30602

JAIN, ANIL KUMAR, b India, Jan 21, 46. ELECTRICAL ENGINEERING. *Educ:* Indian Inst Technol, Kharahpur, BTech Hons, 67; Univ Rochester, MS, 69, PhD(elec eng), 71. *Prof Exp:* Fel, Univ Southern Calif, 70-71, asst prof, 71-74; assoc prof elec eng, State Univ NY, Buffalo, 74-78; actg assoc prof, 78-79, PROF ELEC ENG, UNIV CALIF, DAVIS, 79- *Concurrent Pos:* Proj dir, NASA res grant, 75-76, Naval Undersea Ctr, San Diego, 76-77, Army Res Off grant, 76-78, Naval Ocean Syst Ctr grant, San Diego, 78-79 & Army Res Off, 78-82. *Honors & Awards:* Image Coding Achievement Award, Int Picture Coding Symp, Tokyo, 77. *Mem:* Inst Elec & Electronics Engrs; Optical Soc Am. *Res:* Digital image processing; signal processing; pattern recognition; communication theory; systems theory; computer applications; real time systems. *Mailing Add:* Dept of Elec Eng Univ of Calif Davis CA 95616

JAIN, ANRUDH KUMAR, b India, Oct 23, 41; m 71; c 2. BIOSTATISTICS, POPULATION STUDIES. *Educ:* Agra Univ, BSc, 58; Delhi Univ, MA, 60; Univ Mich, Ann Arbor, MA, 65, PhD(sociol), 68. *Prof Exp:* Res assoc pop studies & asst prof sociol, Univ Mich, Ann Arbor, 68-70; prog assoc family planning, Ford Found, India, 70-71; staff assoc family planning, Pop Coun, India, 71-73; asst dir biostatist, 73-76, assoc, 76-79, SR ASSOC, DEMOGRAPHIC IMPACTS DEVELOP PROG, POP COUN, 80-, DEP DIR, INT PROGS, 81- *Mem:* Int Union Sci Study Pop; Pop Asn Am; AAAS; Indian Asn Study Pop. *Res:* Determinants and consequences of population growth and its components, especially fertility, fecundability, lactation and postpartum amenorrhea; assessment of the safety and effectiveness of contraceptive methods currently available and those being developed. *Mailing Add:* Population Coun One Dag Hammarskjold Plaza New York NY 10017

JAIN, ARIDAMAN KUMAR, b Delhi, India, Apr 14, 38; m 63; c 2. APPLIED STATISTICS. *Educ:* Delhi Univ, BSc, 57; Purdue Univ, PhD(statist & indust eng), 68. *Prof Exp:* Statistician, SQC Units Indian Statist Inst, Baroda & Bombay, 60-61; Tata Oil Mills, Bombay, 61-63; MEM TECH STAFF, BELL LABS, 67- *Mem:* Am Statist Asn; Oper Res Soc Am. *Res:* Data analysis; design of experiments; statistical modelling; monte-carlo simulation; survey sampling. *Mailing Add:* Bell Labs Rm WB 1A369 Holmdel NJ 07733

JAIN, DULI CHANDRA, b Mungaoli, India, Feb 11, 29; m 51; c 2. MOLECULAR SPECTROSCOPY, DATABASE SYSTEMS. *Educ:* Banaras Hindu Univ, BS, 49; Univ Calcutta, MS, 51, DPhil(sci), 63; City Univ New York, MS, 74. *Prof Exp:* Lectr physics, Holkar Sci Col, India, 54-60, asst prof, 60-62; res fel, Saha Inst Nuclear Physics, India, 62-64; asst res scientist chem, NY Univ, 64-68; lectr, 68-70, asst prof, 71-77, ASSOC PROF PHYSICS, YORK COL, NY, 78- *Concurrent Pos:* Adj assoc prof comput sci, Queens Col, 78-; vis prof admin comput systs, Hofstra Univ, Hempstead, NY, 80-81. *Mem:* Am Phys Soc; Sigma Xi. *Res:* Intensity distribution in molecular band systems; potential energy curves and vibrational wave functions of diatomic molecules; programming systems for computers. *Mailing Add:* Dept of Physics York Col 150-14 Jamaica Ave Jamaica NY 11432

JAIN, MAHAVIR, b Barther, India, Jan 1, 41; US citizen; m 66. EXPERIMENTAL NUCLEAR PHYSICS. *Educ:* Agra Univ, BSc, 57; Univ Delhi, MSc, 59; Univ Md, College Park, PhD(physics), 69. *Prof Exp:* Fel nuclear physics, Univ Man, 69-71; res assoc nuclear physics, Tex A&M Univ, 71-78; MEM STAFF, LOS ALAMOS NAT LAB, 78- *Concurrent Pos:* Guest scientist, Los Alamos Sci Lab, 74-78. *Honors & Awards:* Res Publ Award, Naval Res Lab, 75. *Mem:* Am Phys Soc. *Res:* Direct interactions, especially quasi-free scattering from nucleons and clusters; excited states, breakup and polarization in three nucleon systems, neutron-proton scattering; polarization and pion production at LAMPF energies and transport calculations. *Mailing Add:* Los Alamos Nat Lab Mail Stop 540 Q-1 Los Alamos NM 87545

JAIN, MAHENDRA KUMAR, b Ujjain, India, Oct 12, 38; m 74; c 1. BIOPHYSICS, NEUROSCIENCES. *Educ:* Vikram Univ, India, MSc, 59; Weizmann Inst Sci, PhD(chem), 67. *Prof Exp:* Lectr chem, Educ Dept, Govt Madhya Pradesh, India, 59-64 & Punjabi Univ, 64-65; res assoc biochem, Ind Univ, Bloomington, 67-73; asst prrof, 73-75, assoc prof, 75-81, PROF BIOCHEM, UNIV DEL, 81- *Mem:* Biophys Soc; Fed Am Soc Exp Biol. *Res:* Membrane structure and function; mode of action of phospholipases on bilayers; reconstitution; effect of drugs on the phase properties of membrane. *Mailing Add:* Dept of Chem Univ Del Newark DE 19711

JAIN, MAHENDRA KUMAR, b Muzaffarnagar, India, Jan 4, 29; m 49; c 4. MATHEMATICAL ANALYSIS. *Educ:* Univ Lucknow, BS, 48, MS, 51, PhD(math), 55. *Prof Exp:* Lectr math, M J Inter Col Asara, 51-52; Vidyant Col, Univ Lucknow, 52-55; H D Jain Col, Magadh Univ, 55-59; res instr, WVa Univ, 67-69, asst prof, 69-70; ASSOC PROF MATH, UNIV TENN, MARTIN, 75- *Concurrent Pos:* Asst prof, Bihar Inst Technol, Sindri, 59-72; Agency Int Develop fel, Univ Wis, 63-64. *Mem:* Am Math Soc. *Res:* Complex variables; integral transforms. *Mailing Add:* Math Dept Univ Tenn Martin TN 38238

JAIN, NARESH C, b Meerut, India, Dec 30, 32. TOXICOLOGY, ANALYTICAL CHEMISTRY. *Educ:* Univ Lucknow, BS, 51, MS, 54; Univ Calif, Berkeley, PhD(criminol), 65. *Prof Exp:* Sci Officer toxicol, Govt Brit Guiana, 59-62; res toxicologist, Univ Calif, Berkeley, 63-66; assoc dir toxicol, Sch Med, Ind Univ, 66-71; assoc prof pharmacol & toxicol, 71-78, assoc prof community med & pub health, 72-78, PROF PHARMACOL & TOXICOL & PROF COMMUNITY MED & PUB HEALTH, SCH MED, UNIV SOUTHERN CALIF, 78-; DIR TOXICOL, RANCHO LOS AMIGOS HOSP, 71- *Mem:* Soc Toxicol; Am Acad Forensic Sci; Int Asn Toxicol; Brit Forensic Sci Soc. *Res:* Toxicology both clinical and forensic; application of instrumentation in the detection of drugs from biological fluids; drug metabolism; interaction of drugs, marijuana and alcohol; laboratory services to drug abuse and overdose patients; environmental monitoring of herbicides and pesticides. *Mailing Add:* Rancho Los Amigos Hosp 7601 E Imperial Hwy Downey CA 90242

JAIN, PIYARE LAL, b Punjab, India, Dec 11, 21; US citizen; m 55. PHYSICS. *Educ:* Punjab Univ, India, BA, 44, MA, 48; Mich State Univ, PhD(physics), 54. *Prof Exp:* Asst physics, Mich State Univ, 51-53; res assoc chem, Univ Minn, 53-54; from instr to assoc prof physics, 54-67, PROF PHYSICS, STATE UNIV NY BUFFALO, 67- *Concurrent Pos:* Res assoc, Univ Chicago, 59-60; mem staff, Lawrence Radiation Lab, Univ Calif & Bristol Univ, 61-62; Fulbright prof, Univ Rajasthan, India, 65-66. *Mem:* Fel Am Phys Soc. *Res:* Solid state, electron and nuclear magnetic resonance; nuclear physics; cosmic radiation and high energy physics. *Mailing Add:* Dept of Physics State Univ of NY Buffalo NY 14200

JAIN, RAJ K, b Baraut, India, Apr 19, 34; US citizen; m 56; c 3. PALYNOLOGY, PALEOBOTANY. *Educ:* Delhi Univ, India, BSc, 54; Rahasthan Univ, MSc, 56; Lucknow Univ, PhD(paleobot), 61. *Prof Exp:* Res asst paleobot, Inst Paleobot, India, 56-61; asst prof bot, Birla Inst Technol & Sci, India, 61-63 & Punjab Agr Univ, 63-65; res fel bot, Yale Univ, 65-67 & Univ Alta, 68-69; lectr bot, Univ Minn, 67-68; assoc prof bot, Univ Sierra Leone, West Africa, 69-74; PETROL PALEONTOLOGIST, BIOSTRATIGRAPHIC LAB, TEX INC, 74- *Mem:* Am Asn Stratigraphic Palynol; Sigma Xi; Bot Soc Am; Int Org Paleobot. *Res:* Fossil plants, pollen grain, spores and dinoflagellates in relation to evolutionary relationships as well as stratigraphy. *Mailing Add:* 13623 W 66th Way Arvada CO 80004

JAIN, RAVINDER KUMAR, b Punjab, India, Oct 12, 35; US citizen; m 61; c 2. ENVIRONMENTAL ENGINEERING, WATER RESOURCES. *Educ:* Calif State Univ, Sacramento, BS, 61, MS, 68; Tex Tech Univ, PhD(civil eng), 71; Harvard Univ, MPA, 80. *Prof Exp:* Civil engr design, Spink Eng Corp, 61-64; assoc engr water resources, Calif Dept of Water Resources, 64-68; civil engr, Develop & Resources Corp, 68-69; CHIEF ENVIRON DIV ENVIRON RES, US ARMY CORPS ENGRS, CONSTRUCT ENG RES LAB, 71- *Concurrent Pos:* Adj assoc prof, Univ Ill, Urbana-Champaign, 75-; exec & prof develop fellow, Harvard Univ, 79-80. *Honors & Awards:* Sustained Super Performance Awards, US Army Corps Engr, 72, 73 & 74. *Mem:* Am Soc Civil Engrs; Am Water Resources Asn; Soc Am Mil Engrs. *Res:* Environmental impact analysis, environ quality management related to solid waste, air, water and noise pollution; management of research and development organizations; science policy development. *Mailing Add:* US Army Construct Eng Res Lab Interstate Res Park Champaign IL 61820

JAIN, SUBODH K, b Nanauta, India, Dec 11, 34; m 57; c 3. POPULATION BIOLOGY, ECONOMIC BOTANY. *Educ:* Univ Delhi, BSc, 54; Indian Agr Res Inst, New Delhi, IARI, 56; Univ Calif, Davis, PhD(genetics), 60. *Prof Exp:* Pool off genetics, Coun Sci & Indust Res, New Delhi, 61-63; asst res geneticist, 63-67, assoc biologist, 67-72, PROF BIOL, UNIV CALIF, DAVIS, 72- *Concurrent Pos:* NSF res grant, 69-71, grassland study exped, Iberia, 70; Guggenheim Found fel & sr fel, Coun Sci & Indust Res Orgn, Australia, 71-72. *Mem:* Genetics Soc Am; Soc Study Evolution; Am Soc Naturalists; Ecol Soc Am. *Res:* Population genetics; biometry; plant breeding; plant evolution; dynamics of grassland communities; genetics and ecology of avena, bromus, trifolium species; human demography and ecology; current environmental crises. *Mailing Add:* Dept of Agronomy & Range Sci Univ of Calif Davis CA 95616

JAIN, VIJAY KUMAR, b Gwalior, India, Nov 15, 37; m 57; c 3. ELECTRICAL ENGINEERING. *Educ:* Univ Rajasthan, BE, 56; Univ Roorkee, ME dipl, 57; Mich State Univ, PhD(elec eng), 64. *Prof Exp:* Asst prof elec eng, Birla Eng Col, India, 57-61; asst prof, Mich State Univ, 64; asst prof, Birla Inst Technol & Sci, India, 65-66, assoc prof, 66-68; assoc prof, Univ South Fla, 68-74, prof, 74-79; prof, Ga Inst Technol, 79-80; PROF ELEC ENG, UNIV SOUTH FLA, 80- *Concurrent Pos:* Consult, Honeywell, Sperry, Vet Admin Hosp & A C Nielsen. *Mem:* Inst Elec & Electronics Engrs. *Res:*

Communication Electronics; bio-systems analysis; digital signal-processing; pattern recognition; speech signals analysis; electronic circuits; system identification control; optimization. *Mailing Add:* 531 Carriage Hills Dr Elec Engr Dept Univ South Fla Tampa FL 33617

JAIN, VINOD KUMAR, Indian citizen. POLYMER TRIBOLOGY, MACHINE DESIGN. *Educ:* Univ Roorkee, India, BE, 64, ME, 70; Iowa State Univ, PhD(mech eng), 80. *Prof Exp:* Lectr design, Univ Roorkee, India, 64-75; instr, 79-80, ASST PROF MAT & DESIGN, UNIV DAYTON, 80- *Mem:* Am Soc Mech Engrs; Inst Engrs India. *Res:* Friction and wear of polymers; characterization of surface topography; fatigue of polymeric composites. *Mailing Add:* Mech Eng Dept Univ Dayton Dayton OH 45469

JAINCHILL, JEROME, b New York, NY, Jan 27, 32; m 64; c 3. GENETICS, BIOCHEMISTRY. *Educ:* NY Univ, BA, 53, MS, 60, PhD(genetics), 63. *Prof Exp:* Res assoc radiobiol, Sloan-Kettering Inst, NY, 63-65; res assoc biochem carcinogens, NY Univ Med Ctr, 65-67; RES BIOCHEMIST, ENDO LABS, 67- *Mem:* AAAS; NY Acad Sci; Am Chem Soc. *Res:* Biochemistry of carcinogenic agents on DNA; drug metabolism; pharmacokinetics. *Mailing Add:* Endo Labs 1000 Stewart Ave Garden City NY 11530

JAKAB, GEORGE JOSEPH, b Budapest, Hungary, April 7, 39; m 63; c 2. PULMONARY IMMUNOLOGY, PULMONARY DISEASES. *Educ:* Univ Wis-Madison, BS, 65, MS, 67, PhD(med microbiol), 70. *Prof Exp:* Fel, Univ Vt, 70-72, res assoc, 72-77; ASSOC PROF, SCH HYG & PUB HEALTH, JOHNS HOPKINS UNIV, 77- *Concurrent Pos:* Res career develop award, Nat Heart, Lung & Blood Inst, 77. *Mem:* Infectious Dis Soc Am; Am Thoracic Soc; Reticuloendothelial Soc; Am Soc Microbiol. *Res:* Pulmonary defense mechanisms against infectious agents; interaction of infectious agents and environmental contaminants in the genesis and exacerbation of acute and chronic lung disease. *Mailing Add:* Dept Health Sci Sch Hyg Pub Health Johns Hopkins Univ Baltimore MD 21205

JAKES, KAREN SORKIN, b Washington, DC, June 18, 47; m 70; c 2. MOLECULAR BIOLOGY. *Educ:* Brown Univ, BSc, 69; Yale Univ, PhD(molecular biophys & biochem), 74. *Prof Exp:* Asst res genetics, 71-75, RES ASSOC GENETICS, ROCKEFELLER UNIV, 76- *Mem:* AAAS. *Res:* Mechanism of action and synthesis of colicin E3 and its immunity protein; export of colicins E1, E2 and E3; replication of bacteriophage fluid. *Mailing Add:* Dept of Genetics 1230 York Ave New York NY 10021

JAKES, W(ILLIAM) C(HESTER), JR, b Milwaukee, Wis, May 15, 22; m 48; c 2. ELECTRICAL ENGINEERING. *Educ:* Northwestern Univ, BS, 44, MS, 47, PhD(elec eng), 49. *Hon Degrees:* PhD, Iowa Wesleyan Univ, 61. *Prof Exp:* Mem tech staff, 49-62, head mobile radio res, 62-71, DIR RADIO TRANSMISSION LAB, BELL TEL LABS, 71- *Concurrent Pos:* Mem sci adv bd, Voice of Am, 60-62. *Mem:* Fel Inst Elec & Electronics Engrs. *Res:* Microwave propagation and antennas; satellite communication; microwave transmission systems development. *Mailing Add:* Radio Transmission Lab Bell Tel Labs 1600 Osgood St North Andover MA 01845

JAKLEVIC, JOSEPH MICHAEL, b Kansas City, Kans, Jan 16, 41; m 66; c 2. PHYSICS, ENVIRONMENTAL SCIENCES. *Educ:* Rockhurst Col, AB, 62; Univ Notre Dame, PhD(physics), 66. *Prof Exp:* Fel nuclear physics, Univ Notre Dame, 66-67; fel, 67-69, staff scientist eng, 69-78, SR STAFF SCIENTIST ENVIRON SCI & ENG, LAWRENCE BERKELEY LAB, 78- *Res:* Application of nuclear and atomic physics principles and techniques to problems of environmental sampling and analysis; x-ray and atomic physics techniques. *Mailing Add:* Lawrence Berkeley Lab No 1 Cyclotron Rd Berkeley CA 94720

JAKLEVIC, ROBERT C, b Kansas City, Kans, July 27, 34; m 62; c 2. EXPERIMENTAL SOLID STATE PHYSICS. *Educ:* Rockhurst Col, BS, 56; Univ Notre Dame, PhD(physics), 60. *Prof Exp:* Fel, Univ Notre Dame, 61-62; STAFF SCIENTIST SOLID STATE PHYSICS, FORD SCI LABS, 62- *Mem:* Fel Am Phys Soc; Sigma Xi. *Res:* Superconductivity; Josephson tunneling; normal metal tunneling; photoelectric effect in metals; thin film technology; tunneling in semiconductors; organic conductors; surface science. *Mailing Add:* Ford Scientific Labs PO Box 2053 Dearborn MI 48120

JAKOB, FREDI, b Horstein, Ger, Jan 11, 34; US citizen; m 57; c 4. ANALYTICAL CHEMISTRY. *Educ:* City Col NY, BS, 55; Rutgers Univ, PhD(anal Chem), 61. *Prof Exp:* Instr chem, Rutgers Univ, 60-61; from asst prof to assoc prof, 61-69, chmn dept, 65-68, PROF CHEM, CALIF STATE UNIV, SACRAMENTO, 69- *Concurrent Pos:* NSF grants, 61-; consult, St Bd Equalization, 62-78 & consult chemist, Anal Assocs Inc; vis assoc prof, Univ Wis, Madison, 68-69; vis prof, Victoria Univ, Wellington, NZ, 71. *Mem:* Am Chem Soc. *Res:* Theory and application of separation methods and chemical instrumentation; laboratory applications of computers. *Mailing Add:* 3227 Murchison Way Carmicheal CA 95608

JAKOB, KARL MICHAEL, b Berlin, Ger, Nov 5, 21; nat US; m 54; c 2. NUCLEIC ACIDS BIOLOGY, CELL BIOLOGY. *Educ:* Univ Ill, BS, 43, MS, 48; Univ Calif, PhD(cytogenetics, bot), 52. *Prof Exp:* Plant breeder, Marshall Farm Serv, Ill, 43-45; asst bot & cytol, Univ Ill & Univ Calif, 47-51; res assoc plant genetics, 53-68, sr scientist, 69-78, ASSOC PROF, WEIZMANN INST SCI, ISRAEL, 79- *Concurrent Pos:* Vis sr lectr, Univ Bar Ilan, Israel, 62-72; vis investr, Biol Div, Oak Ridge Nat Lab, 63-64. *Mem:* Sigma Xi. *Res:* Biochemistry of the cell division cycle of eukaryotes; mitotic synchronization; metabolism of nuclear-cytoplasmic and plastid RNA in plants; molecular biology of chromatin during DNA replication in vivo. *Mailing Add:* Dept of Plant Genetics Weizmann Inst of Sci Rehovot Israel

JAKOBSEN, ROBERT JOHN, b Chicago, Ill, Jan 29, 29; m 52. PHYSICAL CHEMISTRY. *Educ:* Col of Emporia, BS, 51. *Prof Exp:* Asst phys chem, Kans State Col, 51-55 & Univ Kans, 55-56; prin chemist, 56-64, SR CHEMIST, BATTELLE COLUMBUS LABS, 64- *Mem:* Soc Appl Spectros; Coblentz Soc. *Res:* Molecular spectroscopy, mainly infrared, Raman and nuclear magnetic resonance; application of molecular spectroscopy to structure and the correlation of spectra with physical and chemical properties. *Mailing Add:* Battelle-Columbus Labs 505 King Ave Columbus OH 43201

JAKOBSON, MARK JOHN, b Carlyle, Mont, May 4, 23; m 45; c 2. NUCLEAR PHYSICS. *Educ:* Univ Mont, AB, 44, MA, 47; Univ Calif, PhD(physics), 51. *Prof Exp:* Asst physics, Univ Calif, 47-49, physicist, Radiation Lab, 50-52; instr physics, Univ Wash, 52-53; from asst prof to assoc prof, 53-58, chmn dept astron & physics, 68-73, PROF PHYSICS, UNIV MONT, 58- *Mem:* Fel Am Phys Soc. *Res:* Photonuclear reactions; accelerator design; pion interactions. *Mailing Add:* 3000 Queen St Missoula MT 59801

JAKOBSSON, ERIC GUNNAR, SR, b New York, NY, Nov 18, 38; m 63; c 6. BIOPHYSICS, PHYSIOLOGY. *Educ:* Columbia Univ, BA, 59, BS, 60; Dartmouth Col, PhD(physics), 69. *Prof Exp:* Process engr cryog, Air Prod & Chem, 60-62; develop engr, Malaker Corp, 62-65; fel, Case Western Reserve Univ, 69-71; res assoc, 71-72, asst prof, 72-78, ASSOC PROF PHYSIOL & BIOPHYS, UNIV ILL, URBANA, 78-, ASSOC PROF BIOENG, 81- *Concurrent Pos:* Fel, NSF, 70-71; vis assoc prof physiol, Duke Univ, 79. *Mem:* Biophys Soc; AAAS. *Res:* Mechanisms and significance of ion movement across biological membranes; osmoregulation of animal cells; physics of ion movement; rhythmic and repetitive electrical activity in nerve; myocardial protection during surgery. *Mailing Add:* 803 W Main St Urbana IL 61801

JAKOBY, WILLIAM BERNARD, b Breslau, Ger, Nov 17, 28; nat US. BIOCHEMISTRY, MICROBIOLOGY. *Educ:* Brooklyn Col, BS, 50; Yale Univ, PhD(microbiol), 54. *Prof Exp:* Fel pharmacol, NY Univ-Bellevue Med Ctr, 53-54, fel biochem, 54-55; sr investr, 55-68, CHIEF SECT ENZYMES & INTERMEDIARY METAB, NAT INST ARTHRITIS, METAB & DIGESTIVE DIS, 68- *Concurrent Pos:* Mem bd dirs, Found Advan Educ in Sci, 68-; mem adv bd, John F Fogarty Int Ctr Advan Study Health Sci, NIH, 70-73; consult, Molecular Biol Panel, NSF, 70-73 & 76; mem, Enzyme Comn, Int Union Biochem, 69-71, Comn Biochem Nomenclature, 74-80; assoc ed, Anal Biochem, 78 & Hepatol, 80- *Mem:* Am Soc Biol Chemists. *Res:* Enzymology, detoxication. *Mailing Add:* Nat Inst of Health Bldg 10 Rm 9N109 Bethesda MD 20014

JAKOI, EMMA RAFF, b Cornwall, Ont, May 10, 46; US citizen; m 71. CELL BIOLOGY, MOLECULAR BIOLOGY. *Educ:* Wash State Univ, BS, 68; Duke Univ, PhD(physiol, pharmacol), 73. *Prof Exp:* ASST PROF ANAT, MED CTR, DUKE UNIV, 77- *Concurrent Pos:* Res assoc anat, Med Ctr, Duke Univ, 73-74; USPHS instnl res fel, 74-75, USPHS fel, 75-77. *Mem:* Am Soc Cell Biol; Biophys Soc; Sigma Xi. *Res:* Biochemical and morphological studies of ligatin, a membrane bound baseplate for cell surface proteins involved in intercellular adhesion during development of embryonic chick neural retina and in degradation of glycoproteins and glycolipids in suckling rat ileal epithelial cells. *Mailing Add:* Dept of Anat PO Box 3011 Durham NC 27710

JAKOWATZ, CHARLES V, b Kansas City, Kans, Feb 6, 20; m 47; c 2. ELECTRICAL ENGINEERING. *Educ:* Kans State Univ, BS, 44, MS, 47; Univ Ill, PhD(elec eng), 53. *Prof Exp:* Instr math, Kans State Univ, 45-46, asst prof mech eng, 46-48; asst prof elec eng, Univ Ill, 48-53; commun engr, Res Lab, Gen Elec Co, 53-63, liaison scientist, 63-65; prof elec eng & dean eng, 65-69, PROF ELEC ENGRS, WICHITA STATE UNIV, 70- *Concurrent Pos:* Adj prof, Rensselaer Polytech Inst, 58-63. *Mem:* Math Asn Am; Am Soc Eng Educ; sr mem Inst Elec & Electronics Engrs. *Res:* Cognitives processes; communication and information theory; network synthesis. *Mailing Add:* Col of Eng Wichita State Univ Wichita KS 67208

JAKOWSKA, SOPHIE, b Warsaw, Poland, Feb 12, 22; nat US; m 41; c 2. PATHOBIOLOGY. *Educ:* Lycee Warsaw, Poland, cert, 39; Univ Rome, cert, 42; Fordham Univ, MS, 45, PhD(biol), 47. *Prof Exp:* Instr bact, Col Mt St Vincent, 46; asst chemother div, Sloan-Kettering Inst Cancer Res, 47-48; from asst prof to assoc prof, Col Mt St Vincent, 48-58; asst to vpres med affairs, Nat Cystic Fibrosis Res Found, 61-62; head dept path, Food & Drug Res Labs, Inc, 64-67; tech adv & res coordr biol, Santo Domingo Univ, 67-68; spec proj dir, Nat Cystic Fibrosis Res Found, 68-69; biologist, Food & Drug Admin, 69-71; PROF BIOL SCI, COL STATEN ISLAND, CITY UNIV NY, 70-; SCI CONSULT, 77- *Concurrent Pos:* Collabr, NY Aquarium, NY Zool Soc, 48-59, res assoc exp biol, Dept Marine Biochem & Ecol, 59-62; collabr, Brookhaven Nat Lab, 52-62; vis prof grad sch, St Louis Univ, 57; res assoc dept labs, Beth Israel Hosp, 59- & Inst Crippled & Disabled, 62; NSF biol teacher inst lectr, Iona Col, 63-; consult, Inst Marine Biol, Santo Domingo Univ, 63-, res coordr & hon prof fac sci, 68-; consult, Animal Med Ctr, 64-68; pvt consult, 66-; consult, Span Dept, Grolier, Inc, NY, 68-75. *Mem:* Fel AAAS; Am Micros Soc; Soc Protozool; Am Soc Zoologists; Am Soc Ichthyologists & Herpetologists. *Res:* Plant and animal cytology; comparative pathology and hematology; experimental biology; parasitology; radiobiology; biochemical ecology; mucous secretions; conservation. *Mailing Add:* Col Staten Island Sunnyside Campus 715 Ocean Terrace Staten Island NY 10301

JAKUBIEC, ROBERT JOSEPH, b Detroit, Mich, June 19, 41; m 64; c 2. ANALYTICAL CHEMISTRY. *Educ:* Univ Detroit, BS, 63; Wayne State Univ, PhD(anal chem), 68. *Prof Exp:* Chemist, US Food & Drug Admin, 63-65; sr chemist, Corn Prod Co, 68-69; sr chemist, Armak Co, Div Akzona, 69-70, sect mgr anal chem, 70-76; PRES & LAB DIR, ENVIRO-TEST LABS, INC, 76-; VPRES & LAB DIR, PERRY LABS INC, 81- *Concurrent Pos:* Guest lectr, Northwestern Univ, 71- & Roosevelt Univ, 71-; instr, Chicago Gas Chromatog Sch, 73- *Mem:* Am Chem Soc; Am Oil Chem Soc; Am Soc Testing & Mat; Water Pollution Control Fedn. *Res:* General analytical methods development; gas chromatography; thin layer chromatography; atomic absorption spectroscopy; ultraviolet and visible spectroscopy; residue analysis; general instrumentation; high pressure liquid chromatography. *Mailing Add:* 5551 Lyman Downers Grove IL 60515

JAKUS, KARL, b Gyor, Hungary, Mar 21, 38; US citizen; div; c 1. MECHANICAL ENGINEERING, CERAMICS ENGINEERING. *Educ:* Univ Wis, Madison, BS, 63; Univ Calif, Berkeley, MS, 65, PhD(aerosci), 68. *Prof Exp:* Asst prof mech eng, Johns Hopkins Univ, 68-70; asst prof, 70-74, ASSOC PROF MECH ENG, UNIV MASS, AMHERST, 77- *Concurrent*

Pos: Consult govt labs and indust. *Mem:* Am Ceramics Soc; Am Soc Eng Educ. *Res:* Combustion; mechanical behavior of ceramics; electronics engineering. *Mailing Add:* Dept of Mech Eng Univ of Mass Amherst MA 01003

JAKUS, MARIE A, b Cleveland, Ohio, Oct 12, 14. BIOLOGY. *Educ:* Oberlin Col, AB, 37; Mass Inst Technol, PhD(biol), 45. *Prof Exp:* Asst zool, Wash Univ, 38-41; asst biol, Mass Inst Technol, 41-45, res assoc, 45-51; assoc, Retina Found, 51-61; res prog coordr, Extramural Progs, Nat Inst Neurol Dis & Blindness, NIH, 61-62, exec secy, Visual Sci B Study Sect, Div Res Grants, 62-77; RETIRED. *Concurrent Pos:* Rockefeller fel, Karolinska Inst, Sweden, 47-48. *Mem:* Electron Micros Soc Am; Asn Res Vision & Opthal. *Res:* Electron microscopy; biological electron microscopy; fine structure and properties of trichocysts, striated muscle, actin, myosin and actomyosin, paramyosin, cornea, sclera and lens. *Mailing Add:* 2370 Opalo Way San Diego CA 92111

JAKWAY, GEORGE ELMER, b Twin Falls, Idaho, July 3, 31; div. VERTEBRATE PALEONTOLOGY. *Educ:* Idaho State Col, BA, 53; Univ Kans, MS, 58; Univ Nebr, PhD, 63. *Prof Exp:* Asst vert paleont, State Mus, Univ Nebr, 57-60, asst instr zool, Univ, 60-61; asst prof, 61-68, ASSOC PROF ZOOL, CALIF STATE UNIV, LOS ANGELES, 68- *Concurrent Pos:* Consult, Idaho State Univ Mus, 62; res & field assoc, State Mus, Univ Nebr, 64-; res assoc, Los Angeles County Mus, 65- & George Page Mus, 80- *Mem:* AAAS; Soc Vert Paleont; Soc Study Evolution; Am Soc Mammal. *Res:* Pleistocene paleomammalogy, speciation and ecology. *Mailing Add:* Dept of Biol Calif State Univ Los Angeles CA 90032

JAKWAY, JACQUELINE SINKS, b San Juan, PR, Dec 13, 28; div. ANATOMY. *Educ:* Park Col, AB, 50; Univ Kans, PhD(anat), 58. *Prof Exp:* Asst histochem, Sch Med, Univ Kans, 50-52, asst anat, Univ, 52-57; asst animal path & hyg, Col Agr, Univ Nebr, 58, res assoc animal husb, 59, res assoc animal path & hyg, 59-61; from instr to asst prof anat, Sch Dent, Univ Southern Calif, 61-67; ASST PROF ANAT, STATE UNIV NY DOWNSTATE MED CTR, 67- *Concurrent Pos:* Nat Cancer Inst fel, 59-61. *Mem:* Fel AAAS; Am Asn Anat; NY Acad Sci; Am Soc Cell Biol; Soc Neurosci. *Res:* Comparative neuroanatomy; animal behavior. *Mailing Add:* Dept of Anat State Univ NY Downstate Med Ctr Brooklyn NY 11203

JALAL, SYED M, b Ranchi, India, Dec 2, 38; m 66. CYTOGENETICS. *Educ:* Univ Bihar, BSc, 59; Univ Wis, MS, 62, PhD(cytogenetics), 65. *Prof Exp:* Asst prof, 64-69, assoc prof, 69-77, PROF BIOL, UNIV N DAK, 77- *Concurrent Pos:* Vis prof, Univ Tex Cancer Ctr, Houston, 74; consult, Dept Pediat, 80- *Mem:* Am Genetic Asn; Am Inst Biol Sci; Am Soc Cell Biol; Genetic Soc Can; Sigma Xi. *Res:* Human and small mammal analysis of chromosomes based on standard and banded karyotypes; clastogenic effect of certain insecticides on small mammals; cytogenetics of tall grass prairie polyploid species of grasses. *Mailing Add:* Dept of Biol Univ N Dak Grand Forks ND 58202

JALBERT, JEFFREY SCOTT, b Bridgeport, Conn, Jan 9, 40; m 66; c 2. NUCLEAR PHYSICS. *Educ:* Fairfield Univ, BS, 61; Va Polytech Inst, PhD(physics), 67. *Prof Exp:* Asst prof physics, Hollins Col, 66-67; assoc prof, 67-75, PROF PHYSICS, DENISON UNIV, 75-, DIR COMPUT CTR, 76- *Mem:* Am Phys Soc; Am Math Soc; Sigma Xi. *Res:* Siting of power plants. *Mailing Add:* Denison Univ Granville OH 43023

JALIFE, JOSE, b Mex City, Mex, Mar 7, 47; m 71. CARDIAC ELECTROPHYSIOLOGY, ARRHYTHMIAS. *Educ:* Nat Univ Mex, BA, 65, MD, 72. *Prof Exp:* Fel pharmacol, Inst Cardiol, Mex, 68-70, instr, Univ Mex, 72-73; fel pharmacol, Upstate Med Ctr, State Univ NY, Syracuse, 73-75 & cardiac elec, Masonic Med Res Lab, Utica, 75-77; asst prof, 80-81, ASSOC PROF PHARMACOL, UPSTATE MED CTR, STATE UNIV NY, SYRACUSE, 81- *Concurrent Pos:* Res scientist cardiac elec, Masonic Med Res Lab, Utica, NY, 77-; estab investr, Am Heart Asn, 82-87. *Honors & Awards:* Dr Harold Lamport Award, Am Physiol Soc, 80. *Mem:* Am Physiol Soc; NY Acad Sci; AAAS; Electrophysiol Soc. *Res:* Theoretical and experimental work related to three major areas of experimental cardiology; cellular mechanism of cardiac arrhythmias; mechanism of pacemaker synchronization in heart cells; nervous control of heart rate and atrioventricular conduction. *Mailing Add:* Med Ctr State Univ NY 766 Irving Ave Syracuse NY 13210

JALIL, MAZHAR, b India, June 22, 33; US citizen; m 70; c 2. ACAROLOGY, BACTERIOLOGY. *Educ:* Univ Agra, BSc, 52, MSc, 54; Univ Nottingham, MSc, 63; Univ Waterloo, PhD(biol), 67; Am Registry Prof Entomologist cert, 71. *Prof Exp:* Farm supt, R A K Agr Inst, Sehore, India, 55-56; teacher & lectr agr, Govt Col, Sehore, 56-60; instr zool, Univ Nottingham, 62-64; instr biol, Univ Waterloo, 64-67; res assoc acarology, Univ Ky, 67-69; ENTOMOLOGIST & MICROBIOLOGIST, OHIO DEPT HEALTH, 69- *Concurrent Pos:* NIH consult, Govt Pakistan, 80-81. *Mem:* Acarological Soc Am; Entom Soc Am; Royal Agr Soc Eng. *Res:* Bionomics and ecology of oribatid mites; genetic control of mites and insects; biology, ecology and reproductive physiology of mosquitoes; diagnosis of streptococcal infection. *Mailing Add:* Ohio Dept Health PO Box 2568 Columbus OH 43216

JALUFKA, NELSON WAYNE, b Austwell, Tex, Dec 2, 32; m 62; c 2. ATOMIC PHYSICS, PLASMA PHYSICS. *Educ:* Lamar Univ, BS, 62; Col William & Mary, MA, 67; Univ Colo, Boulder, PhD(physics), 72. *Prof Exp:* RES SCIENTIST ATOMIC & PLASMA PHYSICS, LANGLEY RES CTR, NASA, 62- *Mem:* Am Phys Soc. *Res:* Nuclear pumped lasers, experimental; solar pumped lasers, experimental; basic atomic processes in plasmas. *Mailing Add:* MS 160 Langley Res Ctr NASA Hampton VA 23665

JAMBOR, PAUL EMIL, b Olomouc, Czechoslovakia, March 29, 37 . RINGS & MODULES. *Educ:* Inst Advan Technol, Prague, Dipl Ing, 62; Columbia Univ, MA, 70; Charles Univ, Prague, PhD(math), 73. *Prof Exp:* Assoc prof math, Charles Univ, Prague, 71-76; vis position, Math Inst, Tubingen, 76-77; lectr, Univ Mich, 77-80; ASSOC PROF MATH, UNIV NC, 81- *Concurrent Pos:* Assoc ed, Math Rev, 77-80. *Mem:* Am Math Soc. *Res:* Homological properties and structure theory of associative unitary rings. *Mailing Add:* Dept Math Univ NC Wilmington NC 28406

JAMERSON, FRANK EDWARD, b Lowell, Mass, Nov 5, 27; m 50; c 5. PHYSICS. *Educ:* Mass Inst Technol, BS, 48; Univ Notre Dame, PhD(physics), 52. *Prof Exp:* Physicist atomics br, US Naval Res Lab, Washington, DC, 51-52, head neutron physics sect reactors br, 54-57; sr scientist atomic power div, Westinghouse Elec Corp, 53; sr res physicist, Nuclear Power Eng Dept, 57-61, physics dept, 61-63, supvry res physicist & supv phys electronics group, Physics Dept, 63-69, HEAD, PHYSICS DEPT, GEN MOTORS CORP, 69- *Concurrent Pos:* Mem Nat Acad Sci-Nat Bur Standards eval panel, Off Air & Water Measurement, 71-72, chmn, 73-77; mem Nat Acad Sci-Nat Bur Standards eval panel, Inst Mat Res, 74-78 & panel Nat Measurement Lab, 78-80; chmn adv comt corp assoc, Am Inst Physics, 79-81; corp assoc, Gen Motors, 70- *Mem:* AAAS; Am Phys Soc; Soc Automotive Engrs; Sigma Xi; Am Vacuum Soc. *Res:* Plasma physics, nuclear reactor physics, energy conversion, research management solid state physics, surface physics, chemical physics, coherent optics and metal physics. *Mailing Add:* Physics Dept Gen Motors Res Labs Warren MI 48090

JAMES, ALAN THOMAS, organic geochemistry, see previous edition

JAMES, ALLEN PINSENT, b Lacolle, Que, Jan 2, 19; m 50; c 4. GENETICS. *Educ:* McGill Univ, BSc, 41, MSc, 43; Iowa State Col, PhD(genetics), 49. *Prof Exp:* Instr genetics, Iowa State Col, 49-51; res officer, Atomic Energy Can, Ltd, Chalk River, Ont, 51-74; MEM STAFF, DIV BIOL, NAT RES COUN CAN, OTTAWA, ONT, 74- *Mem:* Genetics Soc Am; Radiation Res Soc. *Res:* Yeast genetics; effects of radiation. *Mailing Add:* Div of Biol Nat Res Coun Ottawa ON K1A 0K6 Can

JAMES, ALTON EVERETTE, JR, b Oxford, NC, Aug 22, 38; m 60; c 3. RADIOLOGY, NUCLEAR MEDICINE. *Educ:* Univ NC, AB, 59; Duke Univ, MD, 63; Johns Hopkins Univ, MS, 71; Am Bd Radiol, dipl, 69; Am Bd Nuclear Med, cert, 72, Vanderbilt Law Sch, 77-79, Harvard Bus Sch, 79. *Prof Exp:* Intern med, Univ Fla, 63-64; resident radiol, Mass Gen Hosp, 66-68; chief res & fel, Harvard Med Sch, 68-69; from asst prof to assoc prof radiol sci, Med Sch, Johns Hopkins Univ, 69-75, dir res radiol dept, 73-75; PROF RADIOL & RADIOL SCI & CHMN DEPT, VANDERBILT UNIV, 75-, PROF MED ADMIN & LECTR LEGAL MED, 79-, SR RES ASSOC, INST PUB POLICY, 80-, PROF BIOMED ENG, 81- *Concurrent Pos:* Nat Acad Sci-Nat Res Coun James Picker fel, Sch Hyg & Pub Health, Johns Hopkins Univ, 69-71; consult, Walter Reed Army Hosp, 73-75, Armed Forces Radiobiol Res Inst, 73-, Nat Zool Park, Smithsonian Inst, 73-, Nat Naval Med Ctr, 74-75 & Nuffield Inst Comp Zool, London, 74; hon fel, Royal Soc Med, 74; hon res fel, Univ Col, London, 74. *Honors & Awards:* Gold medal, Soc Nuclear Med; Silver medal, Am Roentgen Ray Soc; Bronze medal, Soc Nuclear Med. *Mem:* AAAS; Am Soc Clin Invest; Radiol Soc NAm: Soc Chmn Acad Radiol Depts; Am Roentgen Ray Soc; Am Inst Ultrasound Med (treas, 78-81). *Res:* Cerebrospinal fluid physiology; avian respiration; computerized axial tomography; ultrasonography; medical jurisprudence; paleradiology; nuclear magnetic resonance; positron emission tomography; evaluation of authenticity of paintings; xerography; medical jurisprudence; author or coauthor of over 100 publications. *Mailing Add:* Dept of Radiol & Radiol Sci Vanderbilt Univ Med Sch Nashville TN 37232

JAMES, BELA MICHAEL, b Wichita Falls, Tex, Jan 20, 40; m 68; c 1. BIOLOGICAL OCEANOGRAPHY. *Educ:* Tarleton State Col, BS, 63; Tex A&M Univ, MS, 66, PhD(oceanog), 72. *Prof Exp:* Res asst oceanog, Tex A&M Univ, 68-70, res scientist, 70-73; EXEC VPRES & CHIEF RESEARCHER, TERECO CORP, 73- *Mem:* AAAS; Am Inst Biol Sci; Am Soc Zool. *Res:* Marine ecology; taxonomy and ecology of euphausiacean crustaceans and palaeotaxodont mollusks; deep-sea oceanography; water quality and pollution control. *Mailing Add:* TerEco Corp Box 2848 College Station TX 77840

JAMES, BRIAN ROBERT, b Birmingham, Eng, Apr 21, 36; m 62; c 4. INORGANIC CHEMISTRY. *Educ:* Oxford Univ, BA, 57, MA, DPhil(chem), 60. *Prof Exp:* Fel inorg reaction mechanisms, Univ BC, 60-62; sr sci officer, UK Atomic Energy Auth, 62-64; from asst prof to assoc prof, 64-74, PROF INORG CHEM, UNIV BC, 74- *Concurrent Pos:* Mem Nat Res Coun chem grants selection comt, 74-77; ed, Catalysis by Metal Complexes, 75- & Can J Chem, 78-; vis prof, Univ Pisa, 79. *Honors & Awards:* Noranda Award, Chem Inst Can, 75. *Mem:* Fel Chem Soc; fel Chem Inst Can; NY Acad Sci. *Res:* Synthesis, homogeneous catalytic properties of, and mechanistic studies on, coordination compounds, organometallics, and bioinorganic model systems. *Mailing Add:* Dept of Chem Univ BC Vancouver BC V6T 1Y6 Can

JAMES, CHARLES FRANKLIN, JR, b Des Arc, Mo, July 16, 31. INDUSTRIAL ENGINEERING. *Educ:* Purdue Univ, BSc, 58, MSc, 60, PhD(indust eng), 63. *Prof Exp:* Sr indust engr, McDonnell Aircraft Co, 63; asst prof indust eng, Univ RI, 63-66; assoc prof, Univ Mass, 66-67; PROF INDUST ENG & CHMN DEPT, UNIV RI, 67- *Concurrent Pos:* Labor arbitrator, Am Arbit Asn & Fed Mediation & Conciliation Serv; indust consult. *Mem:* Am Inst Indust Engrs; Am Soc Mech Engrs; Soc Mfg Engrs; Am Foundrymen's Soc; Inst Mgt Sci. *Res:* Materials processing; robotics; highway safety. *Mailing Add:* Dept of Indust Eng Univ of RI Kingston RI 02881

JAMES, CHARLES WILLIAM, b Dade City, Fla, Aug 13, 29; m 60; c 3. SYSTEMATIC BOTANY. *Educ:* Univ Fla, BS, 50, MS, 52; Duke Univ, PhD(bot), 55. *Prof Exp:* Instr bot, Univ Tenn, 55-56; res botanist herbarium, Harvard Univ, 56-57; from asst prof to assoc prof bot, 57-70, asst to dean, 63-70, PROF BOT & ASSOC DEAN COL ARTS & SCI, UNIV GA, 70- *Mem:* Am Soc Plant Taxon; Int Asn Plant Taxon. *Res:* Taxonomy of seed plants primarily of the southeastern United States. *Mailing Add:* 1175 Whit Davis Rd Athens GA 30605

JAMES, CHRISTOPHER ROBERT, b Vancouver, BC, Nov 15, 35; m 56; c 5. PLASMA PHYSICS, ELECTROMAGNETICS. *Educ:* Univ BC, BASc, 60, MASc, 61, PhD(elec Eng), 64. *Prof Exp:* Nat Res Coun-NATO fel, Oxford Univ, 64-65; from asst prof to assoc prof, 65-71, PROF PLASMAS, UNIV ALTA, 71-, CHMN DEPT, 74- *Concurrent Pos:* Nat Res Coun grant, 65-81; mem, Dept External Affairs Negotiating Team, 78-; bd examiners, Asn Prof Engrs, Geologists & Geophysicists Alta, 74-; dir negotiated develop grant, Nat Res Coun, 71-75. *Mem:* Can Asn Physicists; Eng Inst Can; Eng Inst Can; Am Phys Soc; AAAS. *Res:* Nonlinear laser heating of plasmas; laser-plasma interaction studies. *Mailing Add:* Dept of Elec Eng Univ of Alta Edmonton AB T6G 2E8 Can

JAMES, DANIEL SHAW, b Institute, WVa, May 23, 33; m 59; c 3. ORGANIC CHEMISTRY. *Educ:* Univ Ill, BA; Ill Inst Technol, PhD(org chem), 63. *Prof Exp:* Chemist org chem, Julian Labs, Ill, 58; NIH fel, Mass Inst Technol, 62-63; from res chemist to sr res chemist, 63-72, res supvr, 72-75, RES ASSOC, E I DU PONT DE NEMOURS & CO, INC, 75- *Mem:* AAAS; Am Chem Soc. *Res:* Chemistry of heterocyclic compounds; studies of aromatic substitution reactions; organic syntheses; chemistry involving new and unusual ring closures; dye research and development for textile and paper products. *Mailing Add:* Rte 1 Box 290 Hockessin DE 19707

JAMES, DAVID EUGENE, b Washington, Iowa, June 19, 45. ORGANIC CHEMISTRY. *Educ:* Cornell Col, BA, 67; Univ Iowa, PhD(org chem), 75. *Prof Exp:* Instr chem, Linn Mar Community Sch Dist, 67-71; RES & DEVELOP CHEMIST, AMOCO CHEM CORP, 75- *Mem:* Sigma Xi; Am Chem Soc. *Res:* Liquid chromatographic separations of industrially important compounds; photochemistry of aromatic hydrocarbons; homogeneous catalysis using transition metals; oxidation of aromatic hydrocarbons. *Mailing Add:* 1133 Woodland Hills Rd Batavia IL 60510

JAMES, DAVID EVAN, b Bellingham, Wash, Dec 14, 39; m 63. GEOPHYSICS. *Educ:* Stanford Univ, BS, 62, MS, 63, PhD(geophysics), 67. *Prof Exp:* Fel geophys, 66-68, assoc staff mem, 68-70, STAFF MEM GEOPHYS, DEPT TERRESTRIAL MAGNETISM, CARNEGIE INST, 70- *Mem:* AAAS; Am Geophys Union; Seismol Soc Am; Soc Explor Geophys; Geol Soc Am. *Res:* Seismic and gravity studies of crust and upper mantle; evolution of central Andean volcanic arc; isotope and trace element geochemistry of igneous rocks of volcanic arcs; precise hypocenter determinations; paleomagnetism. *Mailing Add:* Dept of Terrestrial Magnetism 5241 Broad Branch Rd NW Washington DC 20015

JAMES, DAVID F, b Belleville, Ont, July 9, 39. FLUID MECHANICS, BIOMEDICAL ENGINEERING. *Educ:* Queen's Univ, Ont, BSc, 62; Calif Inst Technol, MS, 63, PhD(mech eng), 67; Univ Cambridge, MA, 74. *Prof Exp:* Asst prof, 67-71, assoc prof, 71-79, PROF MECH ENG, UNIV TORONTO, 79- *Res:* Flow of dilute polymer solutions; behavior of viscoelastic fluids; fluid mechanics of physiological systems; flow around submerged bodies. *Mailing Add:* 8 St Thomas Apt 42 Toronto ON M5S 2B8 Can

JAMES, DAVID WINSTON, b Logan, Utah, Apr 10, 29; m 52; c 6. AGRICULTURE. *Educ:* Utah State Univ, BS, 56, MS, 57; Ore State Univ, PhD(soil chem), 62. *Prof Exp:* Instr soil chem, Ore State Univ, 60-62; asst soil scientist, Wash State Univ, 62-67, assoc soil scientist, 67-69; assoc prof soils & biometeorol, 69-75, PROF, DEPT SOILS SCI & BIOMETEROL, UTAH STATE UNIV, 75- *Concurrent Pos:* Tech adv & assoc dir, On-Farm Water Management Res in Develop Countries, Latin Am, USAID contract & Utah State Univ, 75-; res dir, Agr Res & Develop Prog for Utah State Univ, Bolivia, 77-80 & Consortium for Int Develop. *Mem:* Am Soc Agron; Soil Sci Soc Am; Am Soc Sugar Beet Technol; Soil Conserv Soc Am; AAAS. *Res:* Chemistry of plant nutrients in soils and the interactions between plant nutrients, soil moisture and other factors of plant growth; modeling of crop yield responses to soil fertility and soil moisture. *Mailing Add:* Dept of Soils UMC 48 Utah State Univ Logan UT 84322

JAMES, DEAN B, b Ames, Iowa, June 14, 34; m 60; c 2. PHYSICAL INORGANIC CHEMISTRY. *Educ:* Iowa State Univ, BS, 56, PhD, 60. *Prof Exp:* Res asst, Ames Lab, Atomic Energy Comn, 52-60; staff mem, Los Alamos Sci Lab, 60-66; group leader rare-earth res, Mich Chem Corp, 66-68; fel scientist res & develop, Nuclear Mat & Equip Corp, Atlantic Richfield Co, Apollo, 68-71; prin engr, 72-75, MGR, SAFEGUARDS AUDITS, NUCLEAR ENERGY GROUP, GEN ELEC CO, 75- *Res:* Ion exchange; waste treatment; process development; technical management; nuclear materials safeguards systems. *Mailing Add:* Nuclear Safety & Safeguards Gen Elec Co 175 Curtner Ave San Jose CA 95070

JAMES, DENNIS BRYAN, b Ruthin, Gt Brit, July 14, 24; US citizen; c 4. PHYSICS. *Educ:* Univ Wales, BSc, 48; Univ Cambridge, PhD(physics), 53. *Prof Exp:* Mem tech staff switching res, 54-62, head dept lunar explor, Bellcomm, 62-70, HEAD DEPT CUSTOMER TEL SYSTS, BELL LABS, 70- *Concurrent Pos:* Fel, Univ BC, 52-54. *Mem:* Sr mem Inst Elec & Electronics Eng. *Res:* Business communication methods. *Mailing Add:* Customer Tel Systs Lab Bell Labs Holmdel NJ 07733

JAMES, DONALD GORDON, b Auckland, NZ, Mar 18, 38; m 67; c 1. MATHEMATICS. *Educ:* New Zealand Univ, BSc, 59, MSc, 60; Mass Inst Technol, PhD(math), 63. *Prof Exp:* Lectr math, Univ Auckland, 64-65; asst prof, 66-69, assoc prof, 69-76, PROF MATH, PA STATE UNIV, 76- *Concurrent Pos:* Fel Alexander von Humboldt Stiftung, Germany, 69-70. *Mem:* Am Math Soc; Australian Math Soc; London Math Soc. *Res:* Algebra and number theory, particularly quadratic and hermitian forms, orthogonal and unitary groups. *Mailing Add:* Dept of Math Pa State Univ University Park PA 16802

JAMES, DOUGLAS GARFIELD LIMBREY, b London, Eng, Oct 31, 24; m 59; c 3. CHEMISTRY. *Educ:* Cambridge Univ, BA, 48, MA & PhD(chem), 55. *Prof Exp:* Lectr chem, Univ St Andrews, 54-59; from asst prof to assoc prof, 59-68, PROF CHEM, UNIV BC, 68- *Concurrent Pos:* Vis fel chem, Aberdeen Univ, 65-66. *Mem:* Fel Chem Inst Can; fel Royal Soc Chem. *Res:* Chemical kinetics; addition of free radicals to unsaturated molecules. *Mailing Add:* Dept of Chem Univ of BC Vancouver BC V6T 1W5 Can

JAMES, EDWARD, JR, b El Paso, Tex, July 14, 17; m 40; c 1. PHYSICAL CHEMISTRY, EXPLOSIVES. *Educ:* Univ Mich, BS, 37. *Prof Exp:* Chemist, Sherwin Williams Co, 37-46; chemist, Los Alamos Sci Labs, 46-49, sect leader, 49-60; sect leader, Lawrence Livermore Nat Lab, Univ Calif, 60-63, asst div leader, 63-80; CONSULT, 80- *Mem:* Am Chem Soc; AAAS. *Res:* Resin bonded pigments for textiles; emulsion paints; polyester resins; plastic bonded explosives; explosives, polymer synthesis and manufacture; detonation hydrodynamics. *Mailing Add:* 1085 Peary Ct Livermore CA 94550

JAMES, FLOYD LAMB, b W Lafayette, Ind, July 20, 11; m 39; c 3. ORGANIC CHEMISTRY. *Educ:* Univ Ind, AB, 31, AM, 32, PhD(org chem), 37. *Prof Exp:* Instr chem, Kokomo Jr Col, 35-36; instr, exten, Univ Ind, 36-41 & Univ Ohio, 41-44; from asst prof to prof, 44-81, EMER PROF CHEM, MIAMI UNIV, 81- *Concurrent Pos:* Consult, US Naval Res Lab, 57-69; lectr, Univ Mich, Dearborn, 81-82. *Mem:* Am Chem Soc. *Res:* Molecular rearrangements; ester syntheses; alternation in homologous series; organic nomenclature. *Mailing Add:* Dept of Chem Miami Univ Oxford OH 45056

JAMES, FRANCES CREWS, b Philadelphia, Pa, Sept 29, 30; c 3. ECOLOGY. *Educ:* Mt Holyoke Col, AB, 52; La State Univ, MS, 56; Univ Ark, PhD(zool), 70. *Prof Exp:* Instr zool & bot, Univ Ark, 60-70, res assoc, Mus, 71-73; asst prog dir, Ecol Prog, NSF, 73-76, assoc prog dir, 76-77; ASSOC PROF DEPT BIOL SCI, FLA STATE UNIV, TALLAHASSEE, 77- *Concurrent Pos:* Res assoc, Smithsonian Inst, 75- *Honors & Awards:* E P Edwards Prize, Wilson Ornith Soc. *Mem:* Ecol Soc Am; Am Ornithologists Union; Soc Syst Zool; AAAS; Cooper Ornith Soc. *Res:* Geographic variation in vertebrates; analysis of avian communities; habitat selection in birds; thermal behavioral ecology of lizards; avian systematics; allometry. *Mailing Add:* Dept of Biol Sci Fla State Univ Tallahassee FL 32306

JAMES, FRANKLIN WARD, b Montrose, Miss, Sept 2, 22; m 58; c 2. ANALYTICAL CHEMISTRY. *Educ:* Miss Col, BS; Univ NC, PhD(chem), 52. *Prof Exp:* From assoc prof to prof chem, Millsaps Col, 51-58; sr chemist, Res & Tech Dept, Texaco, Inc, 58-61; prof, 61-70, chmn dept, 61-80, FULLER E CALLAWAY PROF CHEM, MERCER UNIV, 70- *Mem:* Am Chem Soc. *Res:* Standard electrode potentials of electrodes in aqueous glycerol solutions. *Mailing Add:* Dept of Chem Mercer Univ Macon GA 31207

JAMES, GARTH A, b Malad City, Idaho, Aug 1, 26; m 47; c 7. ENDODONTICS. *Educ:* Utah State Univ, BS, 48, MS, 51; Univ Nebr, DDS, 60. *Prof Exp:* Teacher pub sch, Idaho, 47-49; res technician, Naval Biol Lab, Univ Calif, 52; instr bact & pub health, Utah State Agr Col & bacteriologist, Exp Sta, 52-56; res assoc bact, 56-60, assoc prof endodontics, 60-69, PROF ENDODONTICS, COL DENT, UNIV NEBR-LINCOLN, 69-, CHMN DEPT, 70- *Concurrent Pos:* Dir bact, St Elizabeth Hosp, 56-60. *Mem:* Am Dent Asn; Am Asn Endodont; Am Soc Microbiol; fel Am Col Dentists; fel Int Col Dentists. *Mailing Add:* Dept of Endodont Col Dent Univ of Nebr Lincoln NE 68508

JAMES, GEORGE ELLERT, b Douglas, Alaska, Apr 26, 17; m 53. ELECTRONICS ENGINEERING. *Educ:* Univ Wash, BS, 40; George Washington Univ, MS, 62, DSc(eng sci), 69. *Prof Exp:* Electronic develop engr, Gen Elec Co, 40-45; chief engr, Gen Commun Co, 46-47; asst proj engr, Hughes Aircraft Co, 47-48; chief engr, Lab for Electronics, Inc, 48-56; dir, Boston Div, Ramo-Wooldridge Corp, 56-57; tech staff mem, Inst Defense Anal, 58-70; vpres, Adcole Corp, 70-71; consult scientist, Missile Systs Div, Bedford Lab, Raytheon Co, 71-72; VPRES, ADCOLE CORP, 72- *Mem:* Sr mem Inst Elec & Electronics Engrs; Am Inst Aeronaut & Astronaut. *Res:* Electromagnetic field theory; electronic circuit design; radar and control systems; applied mathematics; operations analysis; computer software development. *Mailing Add:* 14 Temple St Apt 3-B Framingham MA 01701

JAMES, GEORGE WALTON, toxicology, radiobiology, see previous edition

JAMES, GEORGE WATSON, III, b Richmond, Va, July 3, 18; m 43; c 3. MEDICINE. *Educ:* Washington & Lee Univ, AB, 40; Med Col Va, MD, 43. *Prof Exp:* USPHS fel, 48-49; from asst prof to assoc prof, 49-65, PROF MED, MED COL VA, 65-, CHMN, DIV HEMAT, 57- *Concurrent Pos:* Markle scholar, Med Col Va, 49-54; consult, McGuire Vet Admin Hosp, Keecoughtan Vet Hosp. *Mem:* AAAS; Am Soc Clin Invest; Am Fedn Clin Res; Am Clin & Climat Asn; Am Soc Clin Nutrit. *Res:* Clinical investigations; bile pigment metabolism; red cell survival with N-15 label; leukemia and lymphoma chemotherapy; hematology. *Mailing Add:* Dept of Med Med Col of Va Richmond VA 23219

JAMES, GIDEON T, b Kansas City, Mo, July 10, 27; m 50; c 3. VERTEBRATE PALEONTOLOGY. *Educ:* Univ Houston, BS, 53, MS, 56; Univ Calif, Berkeley, PhD(paleont), 61. *Prof Exp:* Instr paleont, Univ Calif, Berkeley, 61-62; res paleontologist, 62-63; asst prof geol, Univ Ariz, 63-64, res assoc physics, 64-65; asst prof earth sci, 65-71, PROF EARTH SCI, E TEX STATE UNIV, 71-, V PRES PLANNING & INSTNL ADVAN, 74- *Concurrent Pos:* Dir, NSF Earth Sci Inst Secondary Sch Sci Teachers, Univ Calif, Berkeley, 62-65; adj prof, Southern Methodist Univ, 71- *Mem:* Soc Vert Paleont; Soc Econ Paleont & Mineral; Paleont Soc; NY Acad Sci; Int Paleont Union. *Res:* Vertebrate paleontology and biostratigraphy of Tertiary deposits of North America; geochemical dating of Tertiary rocks and Tertiary geochronology; histologic and ultrafine anatomy of fossil vertebrate tissues. *Mailing Add:* 2312 Bonney View Greenville TX 75401

JAMES, HAROLD LEE, b Taylorsville, NC, Oct 31, 39; m 65; c 1. BIOCHEMISTRY. *Educ:* ETenn State Univ, BS, 62; Univ Tenn, PhD(biochem), 68. *Prof Exp:* Res technician, Med Units, Univ Tenn, 62-63, res instr biochem, 68; res instr med & biochem, Sch Med, Temple Univ, 68-70; res scientist, Blood Res Lab, Am Nat Red Cross, 70-72; asst prof biochem, Univ Tenn Ctr for Health Sci, 72-75; res asst prof, 76-80, RES ASSOC PROF MED, PULMONARY DIV, SCH MED, TEMPLE UNIV, 80- *Concurrent Pos:* Res assoc, Lab Hemat, St Jude Children's Res Hosp, 72-75. *Mem:* Sigma Xi; Am Physiol Soc . *Res:* Methods for producing high-potency antihemophilic factor concentrates; analytical studies of antihemophilic factor; biochemistry and physiology of plasma and platelet fibrinogens; structural analysis of proteins; mechanism of interaction of alpha-1-antitrypsin with elastase; lung physiology of alpha-1-antitrypsin. *Mailing Add:* Temple Univ Sch Med 3400 N Broad St Philadelphia PA 19140

JAMES, HAROLD LLOYD, b Nanaimo, BC, June 11, 12; US citizen; m 36; c 4. GEOLOGY. *Educ:* State Col Wash, BS, 38; Princeton Univ, PhD(geol), 45. *Prof Exp:* Field asst, 38-40, from geologist to chief geologist, 40-71, RES GEOLOGIST, US GEOL SURV, 71- *Concurrent Pos:* Instr, Princeton Univ, 42; vis lectr, Northwestern Univ, Ill, 53-54; prof, Univ Minn, 61-65. *Honors & Awards:* Penrose Medal, Soc Econ Geologists, 76. *Mem:* Nat Acad Sci; fel Geol Soc Am; Soc Econ Geol; Geochem Soc; Mineral Soc Am. *Res:* Iron formations and iron ores of the Lake Superior region; Precambrian history and time classification; Precambrian geology of southwestern Montana. *Mailing Add:* 1617 Washington St Port Townsend WA 98368

JAMES, HELEN JANE, b Nebraska City, Nebr, June 15, 43. ANALYTICAL CHEMISTRY. *Educ:* Univ Nebr, BS, 65, PhD(anal chem), 70. *Prof Exp:* Fel, Univ Ariz, 70-71; asst prof, 71-75, assoc prof chem, 75-80, PROF CHEM, WEBER STATE COL, 80- *Mem:* Sigma Xi; Am Chem Soc. *Res:* Development and application of ion selective electrodes; the use of coated wire electrodes containing liquid membranes. *Mailing Add:* Dept of Chem Weber State Col Ogden UT 84408

JAMES, HERBERT I, b St Thomas, VI, Mar 30, 33; US citizen; m 62; c 2. PHYSICAL CHEMISTRY. *Educ:* Hampton Inst, BS, 55; Clark Univ, MA, 58, PhD(chem), 65. *Prof Exp:* Teacher, Elec Storage Battery Co, 65-76; SCIENTIST, XEROX CORP, 76- *Mem:* Electrochem Soc. *Res:* Diffusion and sedimentation studies of macromolecules; nuclear and radiochemistry; electrochemistry. *Mailing Add:* 107 Panorama Trail Rochester NY 14625

JAMES, HUBERT MAXWELL, b Clarksburg, WVa, Mar 10, 08; m 32; c 1. THEORETICAL SOLID STATE PHYSICS. *Educ:* Randolph-Macon Col, AB, 28; Harvard Univ, AM, 30, PhD(physics), 34. *Hon Degrees:* DSc, Randolph-Macon Col, 55; DSc, Otterbein Col, 71. *Prof Exp:* Instr physics, Harvard Univ, 31-34, fel, 34-36; from asst prof to prof physics, 36-74, head dept, 58-66, EMER PROF PHYSICS, PURDUE UNIV, 74- *Concurrent Pos:* Guggenheim Mem Found fel, Univ Oslo, 39-40; mem staff, Radiation Lab, Mass Inst Technol, 41-46. *Mem:* Fel Am Phys Soc; Am Asn Physics Teachers. *Res:* Quantum theory of atoms and molecules; statistical mechanics of high polymers; radar; quantum theory of solid state; order-disorder transitions. *Mailing Add:* Dept of Physics Purdue Univ West Lafayette IN 47906

JAMES, HUGO A, b Bridgeport, Conn, May 24, 30. PARASITOLOGY, HELMINTHOLOGY. *Educ:* Univ Bridgeport, BA, 57, MS, 58; Univ Va, MA, 61; Iowa State Univ, PhD(parasitol), 68. *Prof Exp:* From instr to assoc prof, 58-73, PROF BIOL, UNIV BRIDGEPORT, 73- *Concurrent Pos:* NSF res grant, Univ Va, 69. *Mem:* Am Inst Biol Sci; Am Soc Parasitol; Wildlife Dis Asn; Am Micros Soc (treas, 79-81); World Asn Advan Vet Parasitol. *Res:* Host-parasite interrelationships of helminths, specifically the Cestoda; zoonotic associations, particularly aspects of taxonomy, morphology, pathology and evolution. *Mailing Add:* Dept of Biol Univ of Bridgeport Bridgeport CT 06601

JAMES, JACK ALEXANDER, b Yale, Okla, Jan 24, 19; m 39; c 2. GEOLOGY. *Educ:* Drury Col, AB, 40; Mo Sch Mines, MS, 48, PhD(geol), 51. *Prof Exp:* Geologist, State Geol Surv, Mo, 46-48, econ geologist, 48-51, asst state geol, 51-52; geologist, Econ Geol, Am Metal Co, Ltd, 52-55; mgr explor div, Am Metal Climax, Inc, 55-60; consult geologist, 60-64; vpres, Callahan Mining Corp, 64-68; pres, Kurtz Mat Corp, 68-77; VCHMN, HIGH INDUST INC, 77- *Mem:* Geol Soc Am; Soc Econ Geol; Am Inst Mining, Metall & Petrol Eng; Mining & Metall Soc. *Res:* Economic geology. *Mailing Add:* 1501 Old Mill Rd Wyomissing PA 19610

JAMES, JACK N, b Dallas, Tex, Nov 22, 20; m 44; c 4. ELECTRICAL ENGINEERING. *Educ:* Southern Methodist Univ, BS, 42; Union Col, MS, 49. *Prof Exp:* Test engr, Gen Elec Co, 42-43 & 46-49; res engr, Radio Corp Am, 49-50; res engr, Jet Propulsion Lab, 50- 54, eng group supvr, 54-56, sect mgr, 56-58, div mgr, 58-60, dep prog mgr, 60-61, proj mgr, 61-65, dep asst lab dir, lunar & planetary projs, 65-67, asst lab dir, Tech Divs, 67-76, ASST LAB DIR, TECH & SPACE PROPULSION DEVELOP, JET PROPULSION LAB, 76- *Honors & Awards:* Pub Serv Award, NASA, 63; Hill Award, Am Inst Aeronaut & Astronaut, 63; Except Sci Achievement Medal, 65; Stuart Ballantine Medal, Franklin Inst, 67. *Mem:* Am Inst Aeronaut & Astronaut; Inst Elec & Electronics Engrs. *Res:* Management of Mariner II to Venus and Mariner IV to Mars projects; guidance systems for Corporal and Sergeant missiles. *Mailing Add:* Jet Propulsion Lab 4800 Oak Grove Dr Pasadena CA 91103

JAMES, JEFFREY, b Savannah, Ga, Aug 27, 44. ANALYTICAL CHEMISTRY, INORGANIC CHEMISTRY. *Educ:* Savannah State Col, BS, 66; Tuskegee Inst, MS, 70; Howard Univ, PhD(inorg chem), 73. *Prof Exp:* asst prof, 72-78, ASSOC PROF, SAVANNAH STATE COL, 78- *Concurrent Pos:* Res chemist, Agronne Nat Lab, 65; Eli Lily & Co, 69, Savannah River Lab, 75 & 80, Lawrence Livermore Lab, 78. *Mem:* Am Chem Soc; AAAS. *Res:* Kinetic study of metalloporphyrina and oxidation of dithionite by manganese; hematoporphyzins in basic solution; characterization of mercury; electnodes. *Mailing Add:* Savannah State Col PO Box 20443 Savannah GA 31404

JAMES, JESSE, b Haynesville, La, Jan 26, 37; m 59; c 5. BIOCHEMISTRY. *Educ:* Tex Southern Univ, BSc, 61, MSc, 62; Univ Tex, PhD(biochem), 65. *Prof Exp:* Assoc prof, 65-73, chmn dept, 73-76, PROF CHEM, KNOXVILLE COL, 73- *Concurrent Pos:* Consult, Union Carbide Corp, Tenn, 66-70; res chemist, Nat Bur Standards, 70- *Res:* Kinetics and mechanisms of enzyme-catalyzed reactions; standardization of reference materials for clinical chemistry. *Mailing Add:* 8500 Farmington Dr Knoxville TN 37919

JAMES, JOHN ALEXANDER, b Eng, Mar 26, 25; m 52; c 3. MEDICINE. *Educ:* Oxford Univ, BA, 50; Univ Edinburgh, MB, ChB, 47. *Prof Exp:* Asst physician, Brookhaven Nat Lab Hosp, 55-56; from asst prof to assoc prof pediat, Univ Tex Southwestern Med Sch Dallas, 56-64; prof pediat, Univ Southern Calif, 64-75,; PROF PEDIAT, UNIV CALIF, IRVINE, 76- *Mem:* Am Acad Pediat; Am Pediat Soc; Am Soc Pediat Res. *Res:* Renal disease in childhood; pediatrics. *Mailing Add:* Nephrology Sect 1109 W La Veta Ave Orange CA 92668

JAMES, JOHN CARY, b Ceredo, WVa, May 8, 26; m 58; c 1. ORGANIC CHEMISTRY. *Educ:* WVa Wesleyan Col, BS, 49; Univ Del, PhD(org chem), 60. *Prof Exp:* Teacher, Callao High Sch, Peru, 50-53; sr res chemist, Boston Labs, Monsanto Res Corp, 59-66; sr chemist, Northrop Carolina, Inc, 66-67; exec secy med chem fel rev comt, Div Res Grants, NIH, 67-70, chief sci eval sect, Res Anal & Eval Br, 70-71; CHIEF RES ANAL & EVAL BR, DIV RES GRANTS, NIH, 71- *Mem:* AAAS. *Res:* Synthesis of anti-oxidants; research on jet fuels and jet engine lubricants; antiradiation drug research; high temperature explosives; health sciences administration; research analysis and information science. *Mailing Add:* 4874 Chevy Chase Dr Chevy Chase MD 20815

JAMES, KENNETH EUGENE, b Los Angeles, Calif, Sept 14, 42; c 2. BIOMETRICS, BIOSTATISTICS. *Educ:* Walla Walla Col, Col Place, Wash, BS, 65; Univ Minn, MS, 67, PhD(biomet), 69. *Prof Exp:* Biometrician, Alaska Dept Fish & Game, 69-71; staff biostatistician, Vet Admin Coop Studies Analgesic Study, Palo Alto, Calif, 71-74; chief, Hines, Ill, 74-78, CHIEF, VET ADMIN COOP STUDIES PROG COORD CTR, PALO ALTO, CALIF, 78- *Concurrent Pos:* Lectr, Dept Preventive Med, Stanford Univ, 71-75, res assoc, Dept Anesthesia, Med Ctr, 71-74; asst prof, Dept Pharmacol, Stritch Sch Med, Loyola Univ, Chicago, 77-79; consult, Task Force Drug Develop, Muscular Dystrophy Asn, 77-, Chief Western Res & Develop Off, Vet Admin Med Ctr, Livermore, Calif, 78-81. *Mem:* Am Statist Asn; Biomet Soc; Int Soc Clin Biostatist; Soc Controlled Clin Trials. *Res:* Administration and conduct of multi-center trials, including the design, conduct and analyses of such trials. *Mailing Add:* Coop Studies Prog Coord Ctr, 151-K Vet Admin Med Ctr 3801 Miranda Ave Palo Alto CA 94304

JAMES, LARRY GEORGE, b Bellingham, Wash, May 1, 47; m 68; c 4. AGRICULTURAL ENGINEERING, IRRIGATION ENGINEERING. *Educ:* Wash State Univ, BS, 70; Univ Minn, PhD(agr eng), 75. *Prof Exp:* Asst prof agr eng, Cornell Univ, 75-77; ASST PROF AGR ENG, WASH STATE UNIV, 77- *Mem:* Am Soc Agr Engrs; Am Soc Engr Educ. *Res:* Plant water requirements; energy requirements for irrigation; sprinkler irrigation; infiltration. *Mailing Add:* Dept of Agr Eng Wash State Univ Pullman WA 99164

JAMES, LAURENCE BERESFORD, b Hollywood, Calif, Aug 20, 16; m 39; c 4. GEOLOGY. *Educ:* Stanford Univ, AB, 40. *Prof Exp:* Mining geologist, Consol Coppermines Corp, Nev, 40-41; mining engr, Anaconda Copper Co, Mont, 41; eng geologist, Calif State Dept Water Resources, 46-56, chief eng geologist, 56-76; CONSULT GEOLOGIST, 76- *Concurrent Pos:* Mem, nat comt rock mech, Nat Acad Sci, 67; consult geologist, United Nations, 69-; mem, US Comt Large Dams; consult, US Army Corps Engrs, US Bur Reclamation & World Bank. *Mem:* AAAS; fel Geol Soc Am; Seismol Soc Am; fel Am Soc Civil Eng; Asn Eng Geol. *Res:* Engineering and groundwater geology. *Mailing Add:* 120 Grey Canyon Dr Folsom CA 95630

JAMES, LAYLIN KNOX, JR, b Pittsburgh, Pa, Sept 17, 27; m 52; c 4. SURFACE CHEMISTRY. *Educ:* Univ Mich, BS, 50, MS, 52; Univ Ill, PhD(chem), 58. *Prof Exp:* Chemist, Shell Chem Co, div Shell Oil Co, 52-54; asst, Univ Ill, 54-56 & Wash State Univ, 57-58; res chemist, Procter & Gamble Co, 58-59; asst prof, 59-66, actg head dept, 70-71, assoc prof, 66-77, PROF CHEM, LAFAYETTE COL, 77-, DEPT HEAD, 79- *Concurrent Pos:* Chemist, US Naval Res Lab, 63; asst res prof, Biophys Dept, Mich State Univ, 64-65, vis prof, 69. *Mem:* AAAS; Am Chem Soc. *Res:* Surface chemistry of proteins and lipoproteins. *Mailing Add:* Dept of Chem Lafayette Col Easton PA 18042

JAMES, LEE MORTON, b New York, NY, Dec 14, 16; m 46. FORESTRY. *Educ:* Pa State Col, BS, 37; Univ Mich, MF, 43, PhD(forest econ), 45. *Prof Exp:* Instr forestry, Pa State Col, 37-38; unit supvr, New Eng Forest Emergency Proj, US Forest Serv, 38-40; forester, Appalachian Forest Exp Sta, 40-41 & 43-46, forest economist in charge unit resource anal, Div Forest Econ, Southern Forest Exp Sta, 46-51; assoc prof, 51-58, chmn dept, 66-78, PROF FORESTRY, MICH STATE UNIV, 58- *Concurrent Pos:* Consult, Resources for the Future, Inc, Forest Indust Coun, US Dept Interior, US Dept Com, Pub Land Law Rev Comt & President's Coun Environ Qual. *Mem:* Soc Am Foresters. *Res:* Forest resource and forest industry analysis; timber products marketing; forest policy. *Mailing Add:* Dept of Forestry Mich State Univ East Lansing MI 48824

JAMES, LEONARD STANLEY, b Te Awamutu, NZ, Nov 2, 24; US citizen. MEDICINE, PEDIATRICS. *Educ:* Univ Otago, NZ, MB, ChB, 48; Am Bd Pediat, dipl, 55. *Prof Exp:* Intern & resident pediat & obstet, Auckland Hosps, NZ, 49-51; gen pract med, 51-52; resident pediat, Hosp Sick Children, Toronto, 52-53; chief resident, Bellevue Med Ctr, New York, 53-54; res fel, State Univ NY Downstate Med Ctr, 54-55; res fel anesthesia & pediat, 55-59, from asst prof to assoc prof, 59-67, PROF ANESTHESIA & PEDIAT, COL PHYSICIANS & SURGEONS, COLUMBIA UNIV, 67- *Concurrent Pos:*

From asst attend pediatrician to assoc attend pediatrician, Babies Hosp, Columbia-Presby Med Ctr, 61-67, attend pediatrician, 67, dir div perinatology, 72-; Nat Inst Gen Med Sci grant, Columbia Univ, 61-73, Nat Heart & Lung Inst grant, 71-76. *Honors & Awards:* Mead Johnson Award, 65. *Mem:* Soc Pediat Res (vpres, 70); Am Pediat Soc; fel Am Acad Pediat; Perinatal Res Soc (pres, 72). *Res:* Physiology of the fetus and newborn; birth asphyxia and brain damage. *Mailing Add:* Dept of Anesthesia Col of Physician & Surgeons New York NY 10027

JAMES, MARLYNN REES, b Spanish Fork, Utah, Nov 20, 33; m 61; c 5. PHYSICAL CHEMISTRY. *Educ:* Brigham Young Univ, BS, 58, MS, 61; Univ Utah, PhD(theoret gas chromatography), 65. *Prof Exp:* Res asst chem, Purdue Univ, 64-66; PROF CHEM, UNIV NORTHERN COLO, 66- *Mem:* Am Chem Soc; Sigma Xi; Nat Sci Teachers Asn. *Res:* Kinetics of fast reactions by stopped-flow methods; computer applications to data acquisition and treatment; chemical education and curriculum development. *Mailing Add:* Dept of Chem Univ of Northern Colo Greeley CO 80639

JAMES, MARY FRANCES, b Clarksburg, WVa, Apr 21, 13. MEDICAL EDUCATION, LABORATORY MEDICINE. *Educ:* Randolph-Macon Woman's Col, AB, 35; Univ Ala, MS, 61. *Prof Exp:* Res technician cellular physiol, Univ Hosp, Duke Univ, 36-37, head technician out-patient lab, Sch Med, 37-45; instr bact & clin path, Med Col Ala & Jefferson-Hillman Hosp, 45-54; teaching supvr, Div Med Tech, Med Ctr, Univ Miss, 55-63; instr, Sch Med, 55-59, asst prof, Clin Lab Sci, 59-63; teaching supvr, Univ Hosp Sch Med Technol & asst prof path, Col Med, 63-66, assoc prof, 68-73, prof, 73-78, chmn dept, 66-78, EMER PROF MED TECHNOL, COL ALLIED HEALTH PROFESSIONS, UNIV KY, 78- *Concurrent Pos:* Mem Coun Med Technol Educ, 64-69. *Mem:* Am Soc Med Technol; Am Soc Allied Health Professions; Sigma Xi. *Res:* Immunology; responses to penicillin; medical technology. *Mailing Add:* 2008 B Fontaine Rd Lexington KY 40502

JAMES, MAURICE THEODORE, b Elwood, Ind, Sept 16, 05; m 29; c 2. INSECT TAXONOMY. *Educ:* Univ Colo, AB, 32, AM, 34, PhD(zool), 38. *Prof Exp:* Instr bot, zool & entom, Univ Colo, 32-34; cur mus & asst prof zool & entom, Colo State Col, 34-45, asst prof entom, 45-47; from asst prof to prof, 47-70, EMER PROF ENTOM, WASH STATE UNIV, 70- *Concurrent Pos:* Assoc entomologist, Bur Entom & Plant Quarantine, USDA, Wash, 42-44, entomologist, 44-45; managing ed, Annals, Entom Soc Am, 48-57. *Honors & Awards:* C W Woodworth Award, Entom Soc Am, 69. *Mem:* AAAS; Soc Syst Zoologists; hon Entom Soc Am; Entom Soc Can; Brazilian Entom Soc. *Res:* Taxonomy of Diptera; myiasisproducing flies; medical entomology; biology of disease-producing Diptera. *Mailing Add:* Dept of Entom Wash State Univ Pullman WA 99164

JAMES, MERLIN LEHN, b Lincoln, Nebr, Sept 27, 22; m 44; c 3. ENGINEERING MECHANICS. *Educ:* Univ Nebr, BSME, 49, MSEM, 60. *Prof Exp:* Sales engr, Phillips Petrol Co, 49-51; salesman, Harrington Co, 51-57; from instr to assoc prof eng mech, 57-76, MEM FAC ENG MECH, UNIV NEBR, LINCOLN, 76- *Concurrent Pos:* NSF grant analog comput, 69. *Mem:* Sigma Xi. *Res:* Analog computation; damping characteristics of structural members. *Mailing Add:* 4620 Mohawk Lincoln NE 68588

JAMES, MICHAEL ROYSTON, b London, Eng, Sept 11, 50; US citizen; m 72; c 2. MATERIALS SCIENCE. *Educ:* Tulane Univ, BS, 72; Northwestern Univ, PhD(mat sci), 77. *Prof Exp:* Fel, Lab Metal Physics, State Univ Groningen, Neth, 77-78; consult, Am Anal Corp, 78; MEM TECH STAFF, ROCKWELL INT SCI CTR, ROCKWELL INT CORP, 78- *Mem:* Soc Exp Stress Anal; Metall Soc; Am Soc Metals. *Res:* Nondestructive testing and component life prediction especially with residual stress measurement and its influence on metal fatigue; microstructural phenomena influencing microcrack initiation. *Mailing Add:* Rockwell Int Sci Ctr 1049 Camino Des Rios Thousand Oaks CA 91361

JAMES, NORMAN IVAN, agronomy, see previous edition

JAMES, ODETTE BRICMONT, b San Jose, Calif, Feb 7, 42. LUNAR PETROLOGY, IGNEOUS PETROLOGY. *Educ:* Stanford Univ, BS, 63, PhD(geol), 67. *Prof Exp:* GEOLOGIST, US GEOL SURV, 67- *Concurrent Pos:* Mem, Lunar Sample Anal Planning Team, NASA, 73-74, prin investr, 75-, chmn, 81- *Mem:* Mineral Soc Am (treas, 81-); Geol Soc Am; Am Geophys Union; Meteoritical Soc. *Res:* Petrology of lunar highland rocks; lunar highland breccias; igneous petrology; shock metamorphism. *Mailing Add:* 959 Nat Ctr US Geol Surv Reston VA 22092

JAMES, PHILIP BENJAMIN, b Kansas City, Mo, Mar 18, 40; m 65; c 2. PLANETARY ATMOSPHERES. *Educ:* Carnegie-Mellon Univ, BS, 61; Univ Wis, Madison, MS, 63, PhD(physics), 66. *Prof Exp:* Off Naval Res res assoc physics, Univ Ill, Urbana, 66-68; asst prof, 68-72, assoc prof, 72-79, PROF PHYSICS, UNIV MO-ST LOUIS, 79- *Concurrent Pos:* Nat Res Coun assoc, Jet Propulsion Lab, Calif Inst Technol, 77-78; mem, Viking Mars Proj, 77-78. *Mem:* Am Geophys Union; Am Astron Soc; Am Phys Soc. *Res:* Theoretical elementary particle physics; chemical physics. *Mailing Add:* Dept of Physics Univ of Mo St Louis MO 63121

JAMES, PHILIP NICKERSON, b Boston, Mass, Aug 16, 32; m 54; c 2. DATA PROCESSING. *Educ:* Mass Inst Technol, SB, 54; Univ Ill, PhD(org chem), 57. *Prof Exp:* Instr chem, Univ Calif, Berkeley, 57-58, asst prof, 58-59; res chemist, Lederle Labs, Am Cyanamid Co, 59-60; col rels rep, 60-62; photog chemist, Systs Res Div, Technicolor Corp, 62-63, proj leader, 63, sr res chemist, 63-66, staff asst to dir, 64-66; asst vchancellor grad studies & res, Univ Calif, San Diego, 66-69, exec asst to chancellor, 69-74; dir, Univ Southern Calif, Idyllwild Campus, 74-77; dir admin & planning, Deluxe Gen Inc, 20th Century-Fox, 77-78; dir mgt systs, Teledyne Systs Co, 78-79; sr res engr, Electronics Div, 79-80, DIR STRATEGY PLANNING DATA PROCESSING, NORTHROP CORP, 80- *Mem:* Am Chem Soc; Fedn Am Scientists; AAAS; Sigma Xi; Asn Comput Mach. *Res:* Biologically interesting compounds; structure; synthesis; chemical mechanisms; photographic chemistry; computer assisted solutions to synthetic problems; higher education. *Mailing Add:* Northrop Corp One Northrop Ave Hawthorne CA 90250

JAMES, RALPH L, b Portland, Ore, Apr 12, 41; m 69; c 2. MATHEMATICS, NUMERICAL ANALYSIS. *Educ:* Univ Wash, BS, 63; Ore State Univ, MS, 65, PhD, 70. *Prof Exp:* Vis asst prof math, Col of Idaho, 65-68; asst prof, 70-74, ASSOC PROF MATH, CALIF STATE COL, STANISLAUS, 74- *Mem:* Am Math Soc. *Res:* Functional analysis; ordered topological vector spaces; positive operators; approximation theory. *Mailing Add:* Dept of Math Calif State Col Stanislaus Turlock CA 95380

JAMES, RICHARD STEPHEN, b Hamilton, Ont, Feb 20, 40; m 64; c 2. GEOCHEMISTRY, PETROLOGY. *Educ:* McMaster Univ, BSc, 62, MSc, 64; Victoria Univ Manchester, PhD(geol), 67. *Prof Exp:* Fel, Univ Toronto, 67-69, lectr geol, 69-70; asst prof geol, 70-80, ASSOC PROF GEOL, LAURENTIAN UNIV, 80- *Mem:* Mineral Soc Am; Mineral Asn Can; Mineral Soc Gt Brit & Ireland. *Res:* Igneous and metamorphic petrology, application of experimental phase equilibria data to natural systems. *Mailing Add:* Dept of Geol Laurentian Univ Sudbury ON P3E 2C6 Can

JAMES, ROBERT CLARKE, b Bloomington, Ind, July 30, 18; m 45; c 4. MATHEMATICAL ANALYSIS. *Educ:* Univ Calif, Los Angeles, BA, 40; Calif Inst Technol, PhD(math), 47. *Prof Exp:* Benjamin Pierce instr math, Harvard Univ, 46-47; from instr to asst prof, Univ Calif, 47-51; assoc prof, Haverford Col, 51-57; prof & chmn dept, Harvey Mudd Col, 57-67; prof, State Univ NY Albany, 67-68; chmn dept, 76-81, PROF MATH, CLAREMONT GRAD SCH, 68- *Concurrent Pos:* Mem, Inst Advan Study, Princeton Univ, 62-63, Jerusalem, 76-77 & Mittay-Leffler Inst, Sweden, 78-79; chmn dept math, Claremont Grad Sch, 68-72. *Mem:* Am Math Soc; Soc Indust & Appl Math; Math Asn Am; AAAS; Fedn Am Scientists. *Res:* Normed vector spaces. *Mailing Add:* Dept of Math Claremont Grad Sch Claremont CA 91711

JAMES, RONALD VALDEMAR, b Oakland, Calif, Apr 27, 43; m 64; c 2. SOIL CHEMISTRY. *Educ:* Univ Calif, Davis, BS, 64; Univ Colo, Boulder, MS, 67, PhD(inorg chem), 69. *Prof Exp:* RES CHEMIST, US GEOL SURV, 68- *Mem:* Am Chem Soc; AAAS. *Res:* Chemistry and transport of solutes in the unsaturated zone and ground water; mathematical modeling; fate of pollutants in environmental waters; kinetics and mechanisms of inorganic reactions; ion exchange. *Mailing Add:* US Geol Surv 345 Middlefield Rd Menlo Park CA 94025

JAMES, STANLEY D, b Cardiff, UK, Aug 25, 32; m 61; c 2. ELECTROCHEMISTRY. *Educ:* Univ Wales, BSc, 53, PhD(phys chem), 59. *Prof Exp:* Vis scientist phys chem, NIH, 59-60; res fel phys & inorg chem, Univ Melbourne, 61-63; asst chemist electrochem, Brookhaven Nat Lab, 63-65, assoc chemist, 65-67; CHEMIST, ELECTROCHEM BR, US NAVAL SURFACE WEAPONS CTR, 67- *Mem:* Electrochem Soc; Inst Elec & Electronics Engrs. *Res:* Ion exchange membranes; electrokinetics; electrode kinetics; fused salt electrochemistry. *Mailing Add:* Electrochem Br US Naval Surface Weapons Ctr White Oak MD 20910

JAMES, TED RALPH, b La Crosse, Wis, June 26, 36; m 62; c 2. ECOLOGY, VERTEBRATE ZOOLOGY. *Educ:* Wis State Univ, La Crosse, BS, 58; Univ NDak, MST, 63, PhD(ecol), 67. *Prof Exp:* Teacher, La Crosse City Sch Syst, Wis, 58-61 & 62-63; from instr to asst prof biol, Univ NDak, 66-68; asst prof, 68-70, assoc prof, 71-76, PROF BIOL, UNIV TENN, MARTIN, 77-,CHMN DEPT BIOL SCI, 73- *Mem:* Am Soc Mammalogists; Wildlife Soc. *Res:* Vertebrate ecology and mammalogy, especially population dynamics and radio telemetric evaluation of movement and habitat utilization in game species. *Mailing Add:* Dept of Biol Sci Univ Tenn Martin TN 38238

JAMES, THOMAS LARRY, b North Platte, Nebr, Sept 8, 44; div; c 2. BIOPHYSICAL CHEMISTRY. *Educ:* Univ NMex, BS, 65; Univ Wis-Madison, PhD(anal chem), 69. *Prof Exp:* NIH trainee biochem, Univ Wis-Madison, 65-66, NIH fel anal chem, 66-69; res chemist, Tech Ctr, Celanese Chem Co, 69-71; NIH fel biophys, Johnson Res Found, Univ Pa, 71-73; asst prof, 73-79, ASSOC PROF PHYS CHEM, UNIV CALIF, SAN FRANCISCO, 80- *Mem:* Am Chem Soc. *Res:* Nuclear magnetic resonance applications to biochemical and biological systems; nucleic acids; enzyme mechanisms. *Mailing Add:* Dept of Pharmaceut Chem Univ of Calif San Francisco CA 94143

JAMES, THOMAS NAUM, b Amory, Miss, Oct 24, 25; m 48; c 3. CARDIOVASCULAR DISEASES. *Educ:* Tulane Univ, BS, 46, MD, 49; Am Bd Internal Med, dipl, 57, cert cardiovasc dis, 60; Am Col Chest Physicians, dipl. *Prof Exp:* Intern & resident med & cardiol, Henry Ford Hosp, 49-53; cardiologist, Ochsner Clin, New Orleans, La, 55-59; chmn sect cardiovasc res, Henry Ford Hosp, 59-68; sr scientist & dir res, Cardiovasc Res & Training Ctr, 68-70, prof path, 68-73, dir cardiovasc res & training ctr, 70-77, PROF MED, MED CTR, UNIV ALA, BIRMINGHAM, 68-, CHMN DEPT MED, 73-, MARY GERTRUDE WATERS PROF CARDIOL, 77- *Concurrent Pos:* From instr to asst prof, Tulane Univ, 55-59; vis physician, Charity Hosp, New Orleans, 55-59; secy, Cardiac Electrophysiol Group, 64-65, pres, 65-66. *Mem:* Am Heart Asn; fel Am Col Physicians; fel Am Col Cardiol (vpres, 70-71); fel Am Col Chest Physicians; Soc Exp Biol & Med. *Res:* Anatomy, pathology, physiology and pharmacology of the heart, particularly coronary arteries and conduction system. *Mailing Add:* Dept of Med Univ of Ala Med Ctr Birmingham AL 35294

JAMES, THOMAS RAY, b Dayton, Ohio, Mar 23, 46; m 68; c 1. MATHEMATICS. *Educ:* Otterbein Col, BA, 68; Ohio Univ, MS, 71, PhD(math), 74. *Prof Exp:* Teaching asst, Ohio Univ, 70-74; instr math & physics, Sewickley Acad, 74-75; asst prof math, Lake Erie Col, 75-79; ASST PROF MATH, OTTERBEIN COL, 79- *Mem:* Am Math Soc; Asn Comput Mach; Math Asn Am; Inst Elec & Electronics Engrs. *Res:* Point set topology. *Mailing Add:* Dept Math Otterbein Col Westerville OH 43081

JAMES, THOMAS WILLIAM, b Haugen, Wis, July 30, 18; m 49; c 3. ZOOLOGY. *Educ:* Univ Minn, BA, 48; Univ Mo, MA, 51; Univ Calif, PhD(zool), 54. *Prof Exp:* From instr to assoc prof zool, 53-66, chmn dept, 66-68, PROF CELL BIOL, UNIV CALIF, LOS ANGELES, 66- *Concurrent Pos:* Lalor fel, 55; USPHS spec res fel, 62-63. *Mem:* Biophys Soc; Am Soc Protozool; Am Soc Zool; Int Soc Cell Biol. *Res:* Surface chemistry of biological molecules; electron microscopy of cellular components; nuclear physiology and synchronization of cell division; rotary dispersion of biological molecules; cell growth kinetics; yeast mtDNA; chloroplast DNA; evolution in a chemostat. *Mailing Add:* Dept of Biol Univ of Calif 405 Hilgard Ave Los Angeles CA 90024

JAMES, V(IRGIL) EUGENE, b Braxton Co, WVa, May 6, 29; m 55; c 1. CHEMICAL ENGINEERING. *Educ:* WVa Univ, BS, 51, MS, 56, PhD(chem eng), 58. *Prof Exp:* Chem engr, nitrogen div, Allied Chem & Dye Corp, Va, 53-54; chem engr, Bur Mines, US Dept Interior, WVa, 54-58; res engr, Film Dept, Yerkes Res Lab, 58-61, res supvr, 61-65, process supvr, 65-67, SR SUPVR, TEXTILE FIBERS DEPT, E I DU PONT DE NEMOURS & CO, INC, 67- *Mem:* AAAS; assoc mem Am Inst Chem Engrs. *Res:* Film forming and polymer research; coal gasification research; synthetic fibers. *Mailing Add:* Textile Fibers Dept E I du Pont de Nemours & Co Inc Chattanooga TN 37401

JAMES, W(ILBUR) GERALD, b Parmele, NC, Oct 27, 22; m 44; c 2. SYSTEMS ENGINEERING, ELECTRONIC WARFARE ENGINEER. *Educ:* NC State Col, BS, 47; Univ Tenn, MS, 51. *Prof Exp:* Develop engr instrumentation dept, Oak Ridge Nat Lab, 47-51, group leader circuitry develop, 51-53; chief radio frequency sect, US Dept of Defense, Washington, DC, 53-54; mgr components develop sect, ACF Electronics Div, ACF Indust Inc, 54-56; proj mgr opers res sect, Am Mach & Foundry Co, Va, 56-58, mgr mil systs sect, 58-59, asst dept mgr electronics dept, 59-61; mgr appl sci lab, Melpar, Inc, 61-65; mem tech dirs staff, John Hopkins Univ, 65-66, head, Electronic Countermeasures Proj Off, Appl Physics Lab, 66-71, head, Oper Eval Group & Rep on Dir of Navy Labs Advan Tech Objectives Working Group Electronic Warfare, 71-75; asst dir, Systs Develop Dept, 75-80, SR STAFF ENGR, CTR FOR SYSTS DEVELOP, SRI INT, 80- *Concurrent Pos:* Lectr appl electronics counter measures, George Washington Univ, Sch Continuing Educ, 79-81. *Mem:* Inst Elec & Electronics Engrs. *Res:* Design and analysis for electronic warfare equipment and systems; threat studies and systems design for electronic warfare threat simulator; system design and analysis for military range instrumentation systems; electronic warfare systems and test and evaluation. *Mailing Add:* 7312 Redd Rd Falls Church VA 22043

JAMES, WILLIAM HOLDEN, b Ellijay, Ga, Apr 14, 09; m 47; c 1. FOOD SCIENCE. *Educ:* Emory Univ, BS, 28, MS, 29; Pa State Univ, PhD(org chem), 43. *Prof Exp:* Asst chem, Pa State Univ, 29-34; res chemist, Socony-Vacuum Oil Co, NJ, 34-41; asst chem, Pa State Univ, 41-43, instr org res, 43-44, animal nutrit, 44-45, asst prof, 45-48; assoc prof agr biochem, 48-62, prof, 62-77, EMER PROF FOOD SCI, LA STATE UNIV, 77- *Mem:* Fel AAAS; Am Chem Soc; Am Inst Nutrit; Inst Food Technologists; fel Royal Soc Health. *Res:* Energy metabolism; nutritional utilization of carotene and vitamin A; metabolic patterns in preadolescent children; use of electronic computers in searching out nutritional interrelationships; processing effects on rice quality. *Mailing Add:* Dept of Food Sci La State Univ Baton Rouge LA 70803

JAMES, WILLIAM JOSEPH, b Providence, RI, Sept 17, 22; m 42; c 2. SOLID STATE CHEMISTRY, ELECTROCHEMISTRY. *Educ:* Tufts Univ, BS, 49; Iowa State Univ, MS, 52, PhD(chem), 53. *Prof Exp:* Asst physics, Pa State Univ, 52-53; assoc prof chem, 53-60, dir grad ctr mat res, 64-75, assoc dir, 75-76, PROF CHEM, UNIV MO-ROLLA, 60-, SR INVESTR GRAD CTR MAT RES, 76- *Concurrent Pos:* Fulbright res fel, 61-62. *Mem:* Electrochem Soc; fel Am Inst Chemists; Am Chem Soc; Am Crystallog Asn. *Res:* Lattice imperfections; magnetic and crystal structure determinations by x-ray and neutron diffraction; electrochemical kinetics and corrosion science; plasma polymerization. *Mailing Add:* Grad Ctr for Mat Res Univ of Mo Rolla MO 65401

JAMESON, A KEITH, b Provo, Utah, June 11, 33; m 63; c 2. PHYSICAL CHEMISTRY. *Educ:* Brigham Young Univ, BS, 56, BSE & MS, 57; Univ Ill, Urbana, PhD(phys chem), 63. *Prof Exp:* Res chemist, Esso Res & Eng Co, 62-65; vis assoc prof chem, Ateneo de Manila Univ, 65-67; vis asst prof, Univ Ill, Urbana, 67-68; asst prof, 68-73, assoc prof chem, 73-80, PROF CHEM, LOYOLA UNIV, CHICAGO, 80- *Mem:* Am Chem Soc; Am Phys Soc. *Res:* Nuclear magnetic resonance; intermolecular interactions and spectroscopic observables; energy and environmental chemistry. *Mailing Add:* Dept of Chem Loyola Univ Chicago IL 60611

JAMESON, ARTHUR GREGORY, b Branford, Conn, Mar 26, 15; m 50; c 2. MEDICINE. *Educ:* Harvard Col, AB, 37; Mass Inst Technol, MS, 40; Columbia Univ, MD, 50. *Prof Exp:* Asst prof med, Col Med, State Univ NY Downstate Med Ctr, 57-59; asst prof pediat, 59-66, assoc clin prof med, 66-72, PROF CLIN MED, COL PHYSICIANS & SURGEONS, COLUMBIA UNIV, 72-; ACTG DIR, DEPT MED, ROOSEVELT HOSP, NEW YORK, 78- *Concurrent Pos:* Dir cardiovasc lab, Columbia-Presby Med Ctr, 59-66; consult, Brooklyn Hosp; dir cardiol, Dept Med, Roosevelt Hosp, 66-78. *Mem:* Fel Am Col Physicians; fel Am Col Cardiol. *Res:* Cardiovascular hemodynamics. *Mailing Add:* Dept of Med 428 W 59th St New York NY 10019

JAMESON, CHARLES WILLIAM, b LaPlata, Md, Feb 3, 48; m 69; c 1. ORGANIC CHEMISTRY, CHEMICAL CARCINOGENESIS. *Educ:* Mt St Mary's Col, BS, 70; Univ Md, PhD(org chem), 76. *Prof Exp:* Fac grad asst, Univ Md, 75-76; chemist bioassay, Tracor Jitco Inc, Tracor, Inc, 76-78, sr chemist, 78-79; expert chem, 79-80, PROG LEADER CHEM, NAT TOXICOL PROG, NAT CANCER INST, 80- *Concurrent Pos:* Sr chemist Bioassay Prog & consult, Chem Selection Group, Nat Cancer Inst, 76- *Mem:* Am Chem Soc. *Res:* Structure activity relationships. *Mailing Add:* PO Box 12233 Nat Toxicol Prog Research Triangle Park NC 27709

JAMESON, DAVID LEE, b Ranger, Tex, June 3, 27; m 49; c 4. EVOLUTION. *Educ:* Southern Methodist Univ, BS, 48; Univ Tex, MA, 49, PhD(zool), 52. *Prof Exp:* Asst prof biol, Pacific Univ, 52-53; from instr to asst prof, Univ Ore, 53-57; from asst prof to prof zool, San Diego State Col, 57-67; dir coastal ctr, 72-76, PROF BIOL, UNIV HOUSTON, 67- *Concurrent Pos:* Assoc dean grad sch, Univ Houston, 71-72, dean, 72-74; managing ed, Copeia, Am Soc Ichthyologists & Herpetologists; Nat Acad Sci Exchange scholar, Bulgarian Acad Sci, 77 & USSR Acad Sci, 78. *Mem:* Am Soc Mammal; Ecol Soc Am; Soc Study Evolution (secy, 68-73); Am Soc Ichthyologists & Herpetologists; Am Inst Biol Sci. *Res:* Genetics; amphibians; population genetics; mitochondrial DNA evolution. *Mailing Add:* Dept of Biol Univ of Houston Houston TX 77004

JAMESON, DONALD ALBERT, b Pueblo, Colo, Nov 18, 29; m 54; c 5. ECOLOGY. *Educ:* Colo State Univ, BS, 50; Mont State Col, MS, 52; Tex A&M Univ, PhD(range mgt), 58. *Prof Exp:* Range scientist, Rocky Mt Forest & Range Exp Sta, US Forest Serv, 56-68; assoc prof range sci, 68-71, assoc dean, Col Forestry & Natural Resources, 74-78, PROF RANGE SCI, COLO STATE UNIV, 71- *Mem:* Soc Range Mgt; Ecol Soc Am. *Res:* Ecology of native plants; quantitative natural resource management. *Mailing Add:* Dept Range Sci Colo State Univ Ft Collins CO 80521

JAMESON, DOROTHEA, b Newton, Mass, Nov 16, 20; m 48. NEUROSCIENCE. *Educ:* Wellesley Col, BA, 42. *Hon Degrees:* MA, Univ Pa, 72. *Prof Exp:* Res asst, Harvard Univ, 41-47; res psychologist, Eastman Kodak Co, 47-57; res scientist, NY Univ, 57-62; res assoc, 62-68, res prof, 68-72, prof psychol, 72-74, PROF PSYCHOL & VISUAL SCI, UNIV PA, 75- *Concurrent Pos:* Prin investr res grant, NIH & NSF, 57-; mem, Nat Acad Sci-Nat Res Coun Vision Comt, 70-72 & 76-; vis prof, Univ Rochester, 74-75 & Columbia Univ, 74-76; mem, Visual Sci B Study Sect, NIH, 75-78 & Comn Human Resources, Nat Acad Sci-Nat Res Coun, 77-80; fel Ctr Adv Study Behav Sci, 81-82. *Honors & Awards:* Warren Medal, Soc Exp Psychologists, 71; Distinguished Sci Achievement Award, Am Psychol Asn, 72; Godlove Award for Res in Color Vision, Inter-Soc Color Coun, 73; Tillyer Medal, Optical Soc Am, 82. *Mem:* Nat Acad Sci; Am Acad Arts & Sci; Soc Neurosci; Optical Soc Am; Asn Res Vision & Ophthal. *Res:* Visual mechanisms; human perception. *Mailing Add:* Dept of Psychol Univ of Pa 3815 Walnut St Philadelphia PA 19104

JAMESON, EVERETT WILLIAMS, JR, b Buffalo, NY, May 2, 21; m 69; c 5. VERTEBRATE ZOOLOGY, MEDICAL ENTOMOLOGY. *Educ:* Cornell Univ, BS, 43, PhD(vert zool), 48; Univ Kans, MA, 46. *Prof Exp:* Field observer, Hastings Reservation, Calif, 42; lab asst zool, Univ Kans, 45-46 & Cornell Univ, 46-48; from instr to assoc prof zool, 48-69, from asst zoologist to assoc zoologist exp sta, 48-65, vchmn dept, 69-74, PROF ZOOL, UNIV CALIF, DAVIS, 69- *Concurrent Pos:* Guggenheim fel, 58-59. *Mem:* Am Soc Mammalogists; assoc Am Soc Ichthyologists & Herpetologists; assoc Am Soc Parasitologists. *Res:* Population investigations of small mammals; food habits of vertebrates; fat and reproductive cycles of reptiles; oxygen consumption of reptiles; ecological, zoogeographic and taxonomic investigations of fleas and mites in North America and the Far East. *Mailing Add:* Dept of Zool Univ of Calif Davis CA 95616

JAMESON, PATRICIA MADOLINE, b Rhinelander, Wis, Mar 17, 39. MICROBIOLOGY, VIROLOGY. *Educ:* Carroll Col, Wis, BS, 61; Ind Univ, MS, 63, PhD(microbiol), 65. *Prof Exp:* Microbiologist viruses, US Army Biol Labs, Ft Detrick, 65-69; instr, 69-70, asst prof, 70-80, ASSOC PROF MICROBIOL, MED COL WIS, 80- *Mem:* AAAS; Am Soc Microbiol; Sigma Xi. *Res:* Arboviruses; comparison of neuraminidases of neurotropic and nonneurotropic influenza virus strains, especially with respect to substrate specificity; interferon, especially standards, assay and inducers; feline leukemia virus. *Mailing Add:* 2351 N 62nd of Wis Milwaukee WI 53213

JAMESON, ROBERT A, b Schenectady, NY, May 3, 37; m 59; c 2. PARTICLE ACCELERATOR PHYSICS & ENGINEERING, ELECTRICAL ENGINEERING. *Educ:* Univ Nebr, BS, 58; Univ Colo, MS, 62, PhD(elec eng), 65; Univ NMex, MMgt, 77. *Prof Exp:* From asst group leader to assoc group leader, 63-71, group leader, Accelerator Systs, Group MP-9, MP-Div, Lampf, 72-80, DEP DIV LEADER, ACCELERATOR TECHNOL DIV, LOS ALAMOS NAT LAB, 78- *Res:* Application of automatic control theory to high power microwave systems; systems analysis and development of particle accelerator control and rf-accelerator systems; particle accelerator beam dynamics. *Mailing Add:* AT-Div MS 820 Los Alamos Nat Lab Los Alamos NM 87545

JAMESON, WILLIAM J, JR, b Billings, Mont, June 8, 30; m 53; c 2. NUMERICAL MATHEMATICS, SYSTEMS ANALYSIS. *Educ:* Univ Mont, BA, 52; Univ Tex, MA, 54; Iowa State Univ, PhD(math), 62. *Prof Exp:* Physicist, Lockheed Missiles & Space Co, 58-59; fel & teaching asst appl math, Iowa State Univ, 59-62; mathematician, Collins Radio Co, 62-72, V PRES, SPECTRA ASSOCS, INC, 72- *Concurrent Pos:* Part-time asst prof math, Iowa State Univ, 62-67, assoc prof, 68-72, 80-; corresp consult, Nat Acad Sci-Nat Acad Eng Comt Sci & Tech Commun, 67-69; mem, Comn Nat Info Syst Math, 68-70; mem, Pub Info Comt, Fedn Info Processing Socs, 69-72; chmn, Math Sect, Res Div, Am Defense Preparedness Asn, 69-78. *Mem:* Am defense Preparedness Asn; Soc Indust & Appl Math (secy, 64-69, vpres, 69-74); Asn Comput Mach; Inst Elec & Electronics Engrs. *Res:* Numerical analysis and computation; systems analysis. *Mailing Add:* Spectra Assocs, Inc PO Box 2044 Cedar Rapids IA 52406

JAMIESON, ALEXANDER MACRAE, b Glasgow, Scotland, Sept 19, 44; m 71; c 2. CHEMICAL PHYSICS, POLYMER SCIENCE. *Educ:* Univ Glasgow, BS, 66; Oxford Univ, PhD(chem physics), 69. *Prof Exp:* Res assoc, 69-72, sr res assoc, 72-74, ASST PROF POLYMER SCI, DEPT MACROMOLECULAR SCI, CASE WESTERN RESERVE UNIV, 74- *Mem:* Biophys Soc; Am Chem Soc. *Res:* Physical characterization of polymer solutions; hydrodynamic properties of macromolecules; molecular relaxation phenomena in solutions; structure and function of polysaccharides and proteoglycans; quasielastic and differential laser light scattering. *Mailing Add:* 705 Olin Bldg Case Western Reserve Univ Cleveland OH 44106

JAMIESON, DEREK MAITLAND, b Dundee, Scotland, Nov 27, 30; Can citizen; m 55. MATHEMATICS, STATISTICS. *Educ:* St Andrews Univ, BSc, 51, Hons, 53. *Prof Exp:* Statistician, Can Industs, Ltd, 53-57; sci off math & statist, Defence Res Bd Can, 57-60; mem tech staff, Mitre Corp, 60-65; chief indust models div, Nat Energy Bd, 65-66; planning exec, Simpac Div, Treas Bd, 66-68; RES ADV, UNIV GUELPH, 68- *Mem:* Fel AAAS; Soc Gen Systs Res; Can Opers Res Soc; Opers Res Soc Am. *Res:* Computer aided analysis and study of large systems. *Mailing Add:* Univ of Guelph Guelph ON N1G 2W1 Can

JAMIESON, GLEN STEWART, b Montreal, Que. FISHERIES MANAGEMENT, INVERTEBRATE ECOLOGY. *Educ:* McGill Univ, BSc, 67; Univ BC, MSc, 70, PhD(zool), 73. *Prof Exp:* Fel, Dalhousie Univ, 74-75; sr marine biologist, Appl Marine Res Ltd, Halifax, 75-77; res scientist, Resource Br, 77-81, res scientist, Resource Serv Br, 81-82, PROG HEAD SHELLFISH, RESOURCE SERV BR, FISHERIES & OCEANS CAN, 82- *Res:* Fisheries management, emphasizing invertebrates; spatial and temporal distributions; stock assessment methodology; predator-prey interactions. *Mailing Add:* Pac Biol Sta Fisheries & Oceans Can Nanaimo BC V9R 5K6 Can

JAMIESON, GRAHAM ARCHIBALD, b Wellington, NZ, Aug 14, 29; m 60; c 1. BIOCHEMISTRY. *Educ:* Univ Otago, NZ, MSc, 51; Univ London, PhD(chem), 54, DSc(org chem), 72. *Prof Exp:* Res assoc org chem, Royal Inst Technol, Sweden, 55-56 & Med Col, Cornell Univ, 56-57; vis scientist, NIH, 57-61; res biochemist, 61-64, asst dir res, 65-69, res dir, Blood Prog, Blood Res Lab, 69-79, ASSOC DIR, BLOOD SERVICES, AM NAT RED CROSS, 79- *Concurrent Pos:* Adj prof, Sch Med & Dent, Georgetown Univ, 74-; mem exec comt, Thrombosis Coun, Am Heart Asn; mem, Blood Res Study Sect, NIH; mem adv comt, Res Blood Prod & Preserv, Letterman Army Inst Res; ed, Thrombosis Res, Am Soc Biol Chemists. *Honors & Awards:* Winzler Mem lectr, Univ Fla, 75. *Mem:* AAAS; Am Soc Biol Chem; Int Soc Thrombosis & Haemostasis; Am Chem Soc; Soc Exp Biol & Med. *Res:* Platelet function and membrane biochemistry. *Mailing Add:* Blood Res Lab Am Nat Red Cross Bethesda MD 20814

JAMIESON, J(OHN) A(NTHONY), b Barnet, Eng, Mar 16, 29; nat US; m 56; c 3. INFRARED PHYSICS, ENGINEERING. *Educ:* Univ London, BSc, 52; Stanford Univ, MS, 55, PhD(elec eng), 57. *Prof Exp:* Head detector systs anal, Avionics Div, Aerojet-Gen Corp, 56-59; sr scientist, Aeronutronic Div, Ford Motor Co, 59-62; mgr res, Astrionics Div, Aerojet-Gen Corp, 62-66, mgr electronic systs div, 66-70; asst dir & chief, Optics Div, US Army Advan Ballistic Missile Defense Agency, 70-73; PRES, JAMIESON SCI & ENG INC, 73- *Mem:* Optical Soc Am; sr mem Inst Elec & Electronics Engrs. *Res:* Information theory; applied infrared physics; noise analysis. *Mailing Add:* Suite 350 W 7315 Wisconsin Ave Washington DC 20014

JAMIESON, JAMES DOUGLAS, b Armstrong, BC, Jan 22, 34; m 64; c 2. CELL BIOLOGY. *Educ:* Univ BC, MD, 60; Rockefeller Univ, PhD(cell biol), 66. *Prof Exp:* Res assoc cell biol, Rockefeller Univ, 66-67, from asst prof to assoc prof, 67-73; assoc prof, 73-75, PROF CELL BIOL, YALE UNIV MED SCH, 75- *Mem:* Am Soc Cell Biol; Am Soc Biol Chemists. *Res:* Intracellular transport of secretory proteins; membrane formation and function; cell-hormone interactions; immunocytochemistry; pathophysiology of vascular smooth muscle; cytodifferentiation of glandular epithelia. *Mailing Add:* Sect of Cell Biol Yale Univ Med Sch New Haven CT 06510

JAMIESON, JOHN CALHOUN, b St Joseph, Mo, Jan 5, 24; m 49, 78; c 3. GEOPHYSICS, HIGH PRESSURE PHYSICS. *Educ:* Univ Chicago, SB, 47, SM, 51, PhD(geol), 52. *Prof Exp:* Fel, NSF, 52-53; from instr to assoc prof, 53-65, PROF GEOPHYS, UNIV CHICAGO, 65- *Concurrent Pos:* consult, Stanford Res Inst, 59-63 & 67, Los Alamos Sci Lab, 64- & Batelle Mem Lab, 69-70; mem ed bd, J High Temperatures-High Pressures, 73- *Mem:* Am Geophys Union; Sigma Xi; Am Phys Soc. *Res:* Properties of the earth's interior; high pressure x-ray techniques; shock wave studies. *Mailing Add:* Dept of Geophys Sci Univ of Chicago Chicago IL 60637

JAMIESON, NORMAN CLARK, b Edinburgh, Scotland, Nov 21, 35; US citizen; m 64; c 1. ORGANIC CHEMISTRY. *Educ:* Univ Edinburgh, BSc, 58; Univ Alta, MSc, 61; Univ Adelaide, PhD(org chem), 66. *Prof Exp:* Fel org chem, Rensselaer Polytech Inst, 66-67; sr res scientist, Merck & Co, Inc, 67-70; sr chemist, Thiokol, 70-77, res assoc, 77-80, DIR RES & DEVELOP, SCI PRODS DIV, MALLINCKRODT, INC, 80- *Mem:* Am Chem Soc; Royal Soc Chem. *Res:* Photochemistry; carbohydrates. *Mailing Add:* Mallinckrodt Inc PO Box 5840 St Louis MO 63134

JAMIESON, WILLIAM DAVID, b Toronto, Ont, Aug 6, 29; m 51; c 1. ANALYTICAL MASS SPECTROMETRY, PHYSICAL CHEMISTRY. *Educ:* Dalhousie Univ, BSc, 50, MSc, 51; Cambridge Univ, PhD(phys chem), 54. *Prof Exp:* Asst to dir, 64-75, SR RES OFFICER, ATLANTIC REGIONAL LAB, NAT RES COUN CAN, 54-, HEAD MARINE ANAL CHEM, 75- *Concurrent Pos:* Coordr, Atlantic Prov Interuniv Comt Sci, 63-65; head clean-up technol coord, Oper Oil, 70; mgr, Marine Anal Chem Standards Prog, 79- *Mem:* Fel Chem Inst Can; Am Soc Mass Spectrometry; Spectros Soc Can. *Res:* Mass spectrometry; instrumentation development; analytical chemistry; kinetics of gas phase ion reactions; oil pollution clean-up technology; marine analytical chemistry; development of analytical chemistry reference materials and standards. *Mailing Add:* Atlantic Res Lab Nat Res Coun Can 1411 Oxford St Halifax NS B3H 3Z1 Can

JAMISON, HOMER CLAUDE, b Marion, NC, Apr 14, 21; c 3. EPIDEMIOLOGY, DENTISTRY. *Educ:* Western Carolina Teachers Col, AB, 42; Emory Univ, DDS, 50; Univ Mich, MPH, 57, DrPH(epidemiol), 61; Am Bd Dent Pub Health, dipl. *Prof Exp:* Pub health dentist, NC State Bd Health, 51-54; dent officer, Mecklenburg Health Dept, 54-56; pub health dentist, Mich Dept Health, 57-58; from asst prof to prof dent, Med Ctr, Univ Ala, Birmingham, 60-68, dir grad prog, 62-63, dir comput res lab, 63-64; prof dent, Sch Dent, Univ Mo-Kansas City, 68-72; PROF DENT, SCH DENT,

UNIV ALA, BIRMINGHAM, 72- *Concurrent Pos:* Consult, Div Radiol Health, USPHS, 64-66; mem bd dirs, Jefferson County Anti-Tuberc Asn, 64-68. *Mem:* Fel Am Pub Health Asn; Am Dent Asn; Biomet Soc; Am Statist Asn. *Res:* Clinical studies of potential prophylactic and therapeutic agents; applications and uses of computers in health research; patterns and trends in oral health and diseases. *Mailing Add:* Sch of Dent Univ of Ala Birmingham AL 35294

JAMISON, JOEL DEXTER, b Roanoke, Va, Nov 22, 32; m 59; c 3. ORGANIC CHEMISTRY. *Educ:* Col William & Mary, BS, 55; Northwestern Univ, PhD(org chem), 60. *Prof Exp:* Res chemist, 60-72, res scientist, 72-79, TECH DIV MGR, HERCULES INC, 79- *Mem:* Am Chem Soc. *Res:* Molecular structure elucidation; synthesis and investigation of condensation reactions in strong acid; synthesis of biologically active organic compounds for screening as pesticides; synthesis of lubrication base stocks. *Mailing Add:* Hercules Inc 910 Market St Newport DE 19804

JAMISON, KING W, JR, b Meridian, Miss, Aug 8, 31; m 53; c 4. MATHEMATICS. *Educ:* Union Univ, Tenn, BS, 52; George Peabody Col, MA, 53, PhD(math educ), 62. *Prof Exp:* Lectr math, Vanderbilt Univ, 61-62; from asst prof to assoc prof, 62-72, PROF MATH, MIDDLE TENN STATE UNIV, 72- *Res:* Mathematics education, especially the relationship of mathematical symbols to English words; variable base abacus as a visual aid. *Mailing Add:* Dept of Math Middle Tenn State Univ Box 163 Murfreesboro TN 37130

JAMISON, RICHARD MELVIN, b Rayne, La, Oct 28, 38; div; c 3. VIROLOGY. *Educ:* Univ Southwestern La, BS, 58; Baylor Univ, MS, 62, PhD(virol), 66; Am Bd Med Microbiol, dipl, 76. *Prof Exp:* Res assoc biol div, Oak Ridge Nat Lab, 65-67; asst prof path, Univ Colo, Denver, 67-70; assoc prof, 70-78, PROF MICROBIOL & IMMUNOL, SCH MED, LA STATE UNIV, SHREVEPORT, 78-, DIR, DIAG VIROL LAB, 79- *Concurrent Pos:* Vis prof microbiol, Fac Med, Al Fetah Univ, Tripoli, Libya, 81-82. *Mem:* Am Soc Microbiol; Electron Micros Soc Am; Sigma Xi; Am Fedn Clin Res. *Res:* Replication of picornaviruses; viral oncology; rapid diagnosis of viral infections. *Mailing Add:* Dept of Microbiol & Immunol La State Univ Sch of Med Shreveport LA 71130

JAMISON, ROBERT EDWARD, b Tampa, Fla, Dec 21, 48. ABSTRACT CONVEXITY. *Educ:* Clemson Univ, BS, 70; Univ Wash, MS, 73, PhD(math), 74. *Prof Exp:* Asst prof, La State Univ, 74-79; ASSOC PROF MATH SCI, CLEMSON UNIV, 79- *Concurrent Pos:* Vis asst, Inst Avand Math, Univ Bonn, 75-76; Alexander von Humboldt fel, Univ Erlangen, 76-77; vis prof, Tech Univ Darmstadt, 79. *Mem:* Am Math Soc; Math Asn Am; German Math Union. *Res:* Combinatorial problems of a geometric nature, primarily those concerned with the theory of convex sets. *Mailing Add:* Math Sci Dept Clemson Univ Clemson SC 29631

JAMISON, STEVEN LYLE, b Pocatello, Idaho, Mar 18, 23; m 45; c 4. MATHEMATICS, COMPUTER SCIENCES. *Educ:* Univ Calif, Los Angeles, BA, 44; Univ Calif, PhD(math), 50. *Prof Exp:* Asst math, Univ Calif, 45-49, lectr, 49-50; asst prof, Fla State Univ, 50-54; appl sci rep, Int Bus Mach Corp, 54-57, univ & res inst rep, 57-59, math & programming mgr, 59-63, mgr, Western Data Processing Ctr, 63-64, asst mgr systs res & develop ctr, Los Angeles, 64-68, mgr, 68-70, mgr, IBM Develop Ctr, Palo Alto, 70-73, CONSULT, IBM CORP, 73- *Mem:* Asn Comput Mach. *Res:* Communication, education and employment problems of the deaf; digital computer systems; simulation; linear spaces; computer science. *Mailing Add:* IBM Corp 555 Bailey Ave San Jose CA 95150

JAMISON, WILLIAM H, b Burlington, Iowa, May 4, 32; m 62. MATHEMATICS. *Educ:* Mont State Col, BS, 59, MS, 61. *Prof Exp:* Instr math, Mont State Col, 59-62; assoc prof, 62-68, PROF MATH & CHMN DIV NATURAL SCI & MATH, ROCKY MT COL, 68- *Mem:* Math Asn Am; Am Math Soc; Am Asn Physics Teachers. *Res:* Boolean algebra; logic; fossil fuel utilization. *Mailing Add:* Div of Natural Sci & Math Rocky Mountain Col Billings MT 59102

JAMMU, K S, b India, Jan 1, 35; m 59; c 2. PHYSICS. *Educ:* Aligarh Muslim Univ, India, MSc, 57; Univ Toronto, MA, 60, PhD(physics), 65. *Prof Exp:* Lectr physics, Khalsa Col, Amritsar, India, 57-59; asst prof, Mem Univ, 65-67; from asst prof to assoc prof, St Dunstan's Univ, 67-69; ASSOC PROF PHYSICS, UNIV PRINCE EDWARD ISLAND, 69- *Mem:* Am Asn Physics Teachers; Can Asn Physicists. *Res:* Molecular physics; spectroscopy. *Mailing Add:* Dept of Physics Univ of Prince Edward Island Charlottetown PE C1A 4P3 Can

JAMNBACK, HUGO ANDREW, JR, b Fitchburg, Mass, Sept 18, 26; m 53; c 3. MEDICAL ENTOMOLOGY. *Educ:* Boston Univ, BA, 48; Univ Mass, MS, 51, PhD, 53; London Sch Hyg & Trop Med, dipl, 66. *Prof Exp:* Scientist entom, NY State Mus & Sci Serv, 53-59, sr scientist, 59-67, assoc scientist, 67-71, DIR, NY STATE SCI SERV, 71- *Concurrent Pos:* Consult, WHO, 67-; sr res assoc, Col Environ Sci & Forestry, Syracuse Univ, 73- *Mem:* Entom Soc Am; Am Mosquito Control Asn. *Res:* Taxonomy, biology and control of biting flies. *Mailing Add:* NY State Sci Serv State Educ Bldg Albany NY 12224

JAMPEL, ROBERT STEVEN, b New York, NY, Nov 3, 26; m 52; c 4. OPHTHALMOLOGY, ANATOMY. *Educ:* Columbia Univ, AB, 47, MD, 50; Univ Mich, MS, 57, PhD(anat), 58. *Prof Exp:* Clin instr ophthal, Univ Mich, 56-57, instr neurol, 57-58; asst prof, State Univ NY Downstate Med Ctr, 58-62; assoc ophthal, Columbia Univ, 62-70; PROF OPHTHAL & CHMN DEPT & DIR, KRESGE EYE INST, WAYNE STATE UNIV, 70- *Concurrent Pos:* Chief dept ophthal, Harper Hosp & Detroit Gen Hosp, 70- *Mem:* Asn Res Vision & Ophthal; Am Acad Ophthal & Otolaryngol; Am Acad Neurol. *Res:* Physiology of the ocular muscles. *Mailing Add:* Kresge Eye Inst Wayne State Univ Detroit MI 48201

JAMPOLSKY, ARTHUR, b Bismarck, NDak, Apr 24, 19; m 57; c 3. OPHTHALMOLOGY. *Educ:* Univ Calif, AB, 40; Stanford Univ, MD, 44; Am Bd Ophthal, dipl, 50. *Prof Exp:* Chief strabismus clin, 50-60, DIR SMITH-KETTLEWELL INST VISUAL SCI, PRESBY MED CTR, 60- *Concurrent Pos:* Mem comt on vision, Armed Forces-Nat Res Coun, 58-, exec coun, comt on vision, 60-64; vis sci study sect, NIH, 67-71, chmn, 70-71; regional consult ophthal, Oak Knoll Naval Hosp, Oakland & Travis AFB; consult, Letterman Gen Hosp, San Francisco & Calif State Bd Health; spec consult, Nat Inst Neurol Dis & Blindness. *Mem:* Am Optom Asn; Am Acad Ophthal & Otolaryngol; Am Ophthal Soc; Am Asn Ophthal; fel Am Col Surg. *Res:* Binocular vision; strabismus; physiological optics. *Mailing Add:* Smith-Kettlewell Inst Visual Sci 2232 Webster St San Francisco CA 94115

JAMRICH, JOHN XAVIER, b Muskegon Heights, Mich, June 12, 20; m 44; c 3. ACADEMIC ADMINISTRATION, STATISTICS. *Educ:* Univ Chicago, AB; Marquette Univ, MS, 48; Northwestern Univ, PhD(admin), 51. *Hon Degrees:* LLD, Northern Mich Univ, 68. *Prof Exp:* Instr math, Marquette Univ, 46-48; asst inst, Univ Wis, 48-49; asst dean of men, Northwestern Univ, 49-51; dean of students, Coe Col, 51-55; dean of fac, Doane Col, 55-57; prof & dir, Ctr Study Higher Educ, Mich State Univ, 57-63, assoc dean, Col Educ, 63-68; PRES, NORTHERN MICH UNIV, 68- *Concurrent Pos:* From asst dir to assoc dir, Legis Surv Higher Educ in Mich, 57-61; dir, Surv Higher Educ Grand Rapids, 59, Saginaw Valley, 62 & Study of Capital Outlay Needs for Ohio's State Insts Higher Educ, 62-63; accreditation examr & consult, NCent Asn Cols & Sec Schs, 62-; consult, Ford Found on Univ Nigeria, 64, State Bd Regents of Ohio, 65, Study of Capital Outlay Needs for Va State Comn Higher Educ, 65 & Facil Study for SC Comn Hihgher Educ, 66. *Mem:* AAAS; Am Math Soc; Am Educ Res Asn. *Res:* Educational statistics in connection with administration of the university. *Mailing Add:* Off of the pres Northern Mich Univ Marquette MI 49855

JAN, JEAN-PIERRE, solid state physics, deceased

JANAK, JAMES FRANCIS, b Yonkers, NY, Dec 5, 38; m 65; c 2. ELECTRICAL ENGINEERING, PHYSICS. *Educ:* Mass Inst Technol, SB, 60, SM, 62, ScD(elec eng), 64. *Prof Exp:* Instr elec eng, Mass Inst Technol, 62-64, asst prof, 64-65; MEM RES STAFF THEORET PHYSICS, THOMAS J WATSON RES CTR, IBM CORP, 65- *Concurrent Pos:* Ford Found fel, 64-65; adj assoc prof math, Pace Univ, 78- *Mem:* AAAS; Am Phys Soc. *Res:* Solid state physics. *Mailing Add:* T J Watson Res Ctr IBM Corp Box 218 Yorktown Heights NY 10598

JANARDAN, BANGALORE ANANTHAMURTHY, aerospace engineering, combustion engineering, see previous edition

JANARDAN, KONANUR G, b Konanur, India, Oct 15, 34; m 57; c 3. MATHEMATICAL STATISTICS, APPLIED STATISTICS. *Educ:* Univ Mysore, BSc, 56, MSc, 57; Pa State Univ, MA, 68, PhD(statist), 70. *Prof Exp:* Econ investr, Prog Eval Orgn, Govt of India, 57-60; lectr statist, Sri Venkateswara Univ, India, 60-64 & Univ Mysore, 64-66; asst statist & math, Pa State Univ, 66-70; instr statist, 70; asst prof math & statist, Montclair State Col, 70-71; assoc prof math & dir statist lab & tech servs, 71-80, PROF MATH & STATIST, SANGAMON STATE UNIV, 80- *Concurrent Pos:* Consult, Ill Environ Protection Agency, 72- *Mem:* Am Statist Asn; Biomet Soc; Math Asn Am. *Res:* Classical and contagious discrete distributions developed and used for the analysis of the random plot counts; analysis and interpretation of random counts in scientific work; statistical problems of biological importance, environment and ecology; analysis and study of environmental data related to water quality; biostatistics; stochastic modelling. *Mailing Add:* Dept of Math Systs Sangamon State Univ Springfield IL 62708

JANATA, JIRI, b Podebrady, Czech, July 12, 39; Brit citizen; m 62; c 2. ELECTROANALYTICAL, SOLID STATE DEVICES. *Educ:* Charles Univ, Pargue, MSc, 61, PhD(anal chem), 65. *Prof Exp:* Res fel, Univ Mich, 66-68; sr chemist, Imperial Chem Indust, 68-76; PROF BIOENG, UNIV UTAH, 76- *Concurrent Pos:* Prin investr, NSF, NIH & Dept Defense, 76-; consult, Johnson & Johnson, 79-; prin investr, Dept Chem, Univ Utah, 80- *Mem:* Royal Soc Chem; Electrochem Soc; Am Chem Soc. *Res:* Electroanalytical chemistry: solid state chemically inactive devices and in flow through electrochemical detectors. *Mailing Add:* Dept Bioeng Univ Utah Salt Lake City UT 84112

JANAUER, GILBERT E, b Vienna, Austria, Feb 26, 31; m 58; c 1. PHYSICAL ANALYTICAL CHEMISTRY. *Educ:* Univ Vienna, PhD(chem), 62. *Prof Exp:* Jr chemist, Oemvag, Austria, 58-60; res asst, Anal Inst, Univ Vienna, 60-61, instr anal chem, 61-62; res assoc chem, Clarkson Tech, 63-64; asst prof, 64-69, ASSOC PROF CHEM, STATE UNIV NY BINGHAMTON, 69- *Concurrent Pos:* Speaker, Gordon Res Conf Ion Exchange, 69, 75, 77 & vchmn, 79; NSF grant, 69-71; NSF fac adv, 73 & 76; vis prof, Graz State Technol, Austria, 71-72. *Mem:* AAAS; Am Chem Soc; Austrian Chem Soc. *Res:* Ion exchange equilibria and kinetics in aqueous and aqueous-organic solvents; separation methods; trace preconcentration and analysis; reactive ion exchange; analysis in biofluids. *Mailing Add:* Dept of Chem State Univ of NY Binghamton NY 13901

JANCA, FRANK CHARLES, b Chicago, Ill, Oct 27, 46. GENETICS. *Educ:* Western Mich Univ, BA, 68; MA, 72; La State Univ, PhD(zool), 78. *Prof Exp:* Fel genetics, Univ Alta, 78-81. *Mem:* Genetics Soc Am; Environ Mutagen Soc. *Res:* Mutagen testing and mutagenesis; bacteria; maize; Drosophila and mammalian systems. *Mailing Add:* Rte 1 76 Ave Decatur MI 49045

JANCARIK, JIRI, b Brno, Czech, Oct 9, 41; m 63; c 2. PLASMA PHYSICS. *Educ:* Charles Univ, Prague, RNDr(exp physics), 63; Czech Acad Sci, CSc(plasma physics), 68. *Prof Exp:* Fel electron beam & plasma physics, Inst Plasma Physics, Czech Acad Sci, 63-68; res officer plasma turbulence, Culham Lab, UK Atomic Energy Authority, 68-72; res assoc beam-plasma

interactions, Eng Dept, Univ Oxford, 69-72; res scientist, Fusion Res Ctr, Univ Tex, Austin, 72-81; PHYSICIST, LAWRENCE LIVERMORE NAT LAB, UNIV CALIF, LIVERMORE, 81- *Mem:* Am Phys Soc. *Res:* Plasma heating and containment for thermonuclear applications; study of plasma waves; turbulence using x-ray, magnetic and electromagnetic diagnostics; computer simulation of relativistic beams, plasma turbulence; collective ion accelerators; laser isotope separation; plasma microwave diagnostics. *Mailing Add:* Lawrence Livermore Nat Lab PO Box 808 Livermore CA 94550

JANDA, KENNETH CARL, b Denver, Colo, Nov 28, 50; m 71; c 1. MOLECULAR SPECTROSCOPY, SURFACE CHEMISTRY. *Educ:* Hope Col, AB, 73; Harvard Univ, AM, 75, PhD(phys chem), 77. *Prof Exp:* Fel, Univ Chicago, 77-78; A A Noyes res instr, 78-80, ASST PROF CHEM PHYSICS, CALIF INST TECHNOL, 80- *Mem:* Am Chem Soc; Am Phys Soc. *Res:* Spectroscopy of weakly bound molecules in molecular beams and on solid surfaces; dynamics of energy transfer from strong to weak bonds. *Mailing Add:* 127-72 Calif Inst Technol Pasadena CA 91125

JANDE, SOHAN SINGH, b Pialan, India, Mar 2, 33; m 60; c 2. ANATOMY, HISTOLOGY. *Educ:* Panjab Univ, India, BSc, 53, MSc, 56, PhD(zool), 61; Univ Alta, PhD, 64. *Educ:* Lectr biol, Khalsa Col, Mahilpur, India, 56-57; Panjab Univ, 59-61 & Univ Alta, 61-64; Nat Res Coun Can fel, 64-65; asst prof zool, Howard Univ, 65-67; asst prof, 67-71, assoc prof histol & embryol, 71-76, PROF ANAT, UNIV OTTAWA, 76- *Mem:* Can Asn Anat; Am Asn Anat; Am Soc Cell Biol. *Res:* Chromosome studies of insects and spiders; electron miscroscopy of skin; electron microscopy of hard tissues resorption; cellular mechanism of calcium homeostasis. *Mailing Add:* Dept Anat Fac Health Scis Univ of Ottawa Ottawa ON K1N 9A9 Can

JANDL, JAMES HARRIMAN, b Racine, Wis, Oct 30, 25; m 50; c 5. MEDICINE. *Educ:* Franklin & Marshall Col, BS, 45; Harvard Med Sch, MD, 49. *Prof Exp:* Res fel med, Harvard Med Sch, 52-55, instr med, 55-57, assoc, 57-59, from asst prof to assoc prof, 59-68, dir, Harvard Med Unit, 68-70, GEORGE RICHARDS MINOT PROF MED, HARVARD MED SCH, BOSTON CITY HOSP, 68-, HEAD, DEPT HEMAT, HARVARD MED SCH, 73- *Mem:* Am Soc Clin Invest; Am Fedn Clin Res; Asn Am Physicians; Am Clin & Climat Asn; Am Soc Hemat. *Res:* Hematology; mechanisms of the anemias, especially the hemolytic anemias; immune hematology; functions of the reticuloendothelial system. *Mailing Add:* Harvard Med Sch 25 Shattuck St E-2 Boston MA 02115

JANDORF, BERNARD JOSEPH, b Berlin, Ger, May 19, 15; nat US; m 46; c 1. BIOCHEMISTRY. *Educ:* Cambridge Univ, BA, 38; Harvard Univ, AM, 40, PhD(biochem), 42. *Prof Exp:* Asst, Lilly Res Labs, Woods Hole, 41; Commonwealth Fund sr fel, Thorndike Mem Lab, Boston City Hosp, 42-44; res biochemist, Chem Corps, Med Labs, US Army Chem Center, 44-49, chief enzyme chem br, 49-56, biochem res div, Chem Warfare Labs, 56-62; dep dir res directorate weapons systs, Edgewood Arsenal, 62-65, chief chem res div, 65-74, SR SCIENTIST, FREDERICK CANCER RES CTR, 75- *Concurrent Pos:* Fel, Harvard Univ, 42-44; lectr, Sch Hyg & Pub Health, Johns Hopkins Univ, 46-49; assoc prof, Univ Md, 59-62. *Mem:* AAAS; Am Chem Soc; Am Soc Biol Chem:. *Res:* Biological oxidations in mammalian tissues; intermediary carbohydrate metabolism; enzyme isolations; action of toxic agents on enzymes. *Mailing Add:* 6017 Baywood Ave Baltimore MD 21209

JANE, JOHN ANTHONY, b Chicago, Ill, Sept 21, 31; m 60; c 3. NEUROSURGERY. *Educ:* Univ Chicago, BA, 51, MD, 56, PhD(biol, psychol), 67. *Prof Exp:* From instr to assoc prof neurosurg, Sch Med, Case Western Reserve, 65-69; PROF NEUROSURG, SCH MED, UNIV VA, 69-, CHMN DEPT, 80- *Mem:* Am Asn Anat; Am Physiol Soc. *Res:* Physiological psychology; comparative neuroanatomy. *Mailing Add:* Dept of Neurosurg Univ of Va Sch of Med Charlottesville VA 22903

JANECKE, JOACHIM WILHELM, b Heidelberg, Ger, Feb 5, 29; m 54; c 2. PHYSICS. *Educ:* Univ Heidelberg, Dipl Physics, 52, Dr rer nat(physics), 55. *Prof Exp:* Res asst, Max Planck Inst Nuclear Res, 55-60; res assoc, Univ Mich, 60-62; res assoc, Nuclear Res Ctr, Karlsruhe, Ger, 62-65; assoc prof, 65-69, PROF PHYSICS, UNIV MICH, ANN ARBOR, 69- *Mem:* Fel Am Phys Soc; Ger Phys Soc. *Res:* Nuclear physics; nuclear astrophysics; nuclear reactions; accelerators; nuclear structure and masses; cosmo-chronology. *Mailing Add:* Dept of Physics Univ of Mich Ann Arbor MI 48109

JANEFF, JAN DIMITROFF, serology, bacteriology, see previous edition

JANES, DONALD LUCIAN, b Fresno, Calif, July 1, 39. SOLID STATE CHEMISTRY. *Educ:* Grinnell Col, AB, 61; Purdue Univ, PhD(inorg chem), 66. *Prof Exp:* Sr chemist, Cent Res Lab, Minn Mining & Mfg Co, 65-71, res specialist, 71-73, supvr, Magnetic Audio-Video Prod Div, 73-79, mgr, 79-81, MGR, INFO STORAGE LAB, 3M CO, 81- *Mem:* Am Chem Soc. *Res:* Preparation and properties of magnetic materials. *Mailing Add:* Info Storage Lab Bldg 201 3M Ctr St Paul MN 55144

JANES, DONALD WALLACE, b Kansas City, Mo, June 12, 29; m 53; c 4. BACTERIOLOGY, BIOLOGY. *Educ:* Baker Univ, AB, 51; Univ Kans, MA, 56; Kans State Univ, PhD(zool), 62. *Prof Exp:* Instr biol, Washburn Univ, 57-60; asst prof, Parsons Col, 61-62; from asst prof to assoc prof, 62-78, assoc vpres acad affairs & dean grad sch, 68-78, PROF BIOL, UNIV SOUTHERN COLO, 78- *Concurrent Pos:* Consult & examr, NCent Asn Cols & Sec Schs, 72- *Mem:* AAAS; Am Soc Zoologists; Am Soc Microbiol; Am Soc Mammal. *Res:* Problems of vertebrate distribution and histology; reproduction; vertebrate fauna of Colorado; chemistry and biosynthesis of bacterial pigments, particularly pigments of Serratia marscens. *Mailing Add:* Grad Sch Univ of Southern Colo Pueblo CO 81001

JANES, GEORGE SARGENT, b Brooklyn, NY, Apr 12, 27; m 52; c 5. PHYSICS. *Educ:* Cornell Univ, AB, 49; Mass Inst Technol, PhD(physics), 53. *Prof Exp:* Mem res staff, Nuclear Sci Div Indust Coop, Mass Inst Technol, 53-56; prin res scientist, 56-77, V PRES, AVCO-EVERETT RES LAB DIV, AVCO CORP, 77- *Concurrent Pos:* Mem adv comt, Regional Laser Ctr, Mass Inst Technol, 81- *Mem:* Fel Am Phys Soc; assoc fel Am Inst Aeronaut & Astronaut; Sigma Xi. *Res:* Meson physics and cosmic rays; magnetohydrodynamics; high temperature gas physics; plasma physics; ionization phenomena; lasers. *Mailing Add:* Avco Everett Res Lab 2385 Revere Beach Pkwy Everett MA 02149

JANES, RAY LOW, b Providence, Utah, Apr 26, 08; m 35; c 3. ENTOMOLOGY. *Educ:* Utah State Col, BS, 32, MA, 41; Univ Wis, PhD(entom), 43. *Prof Exp:* Lab asst zool, Utah State Col, 29-32, zool & entom, 38-40; farmer, Utah, 33-38; asst entom, Univ Wis, 40-42; entomologist, Pittsburgh Plate Glass Co, Wis, 42-46; exten entomologist, 46-71, prof, 63-71, EMER PROF ENTOM, MICH STATE UNIV, 71- *Concurrent Pos:* Field asst, Utah State Col, 30-31. *Mem:* Entom Soc Am. *Res:* Insects affecting alfalfa seed production; spittlebugs in alfalfa and clovers; insect control specialist on all agricultural crops; registration and use of agricultural pesticides; author of over 30 publications on insect control. *Mailing Add:* 246 East 1140 North Orem UT 84057

JANES, ROBERT L(EE), b St Paul, Minn, Dec 11, 14; m 38; c 5. CIVIL ENGINEERING. *Educ:* Calif Inst Technol, BS, 36, MS, 44; Ill Inst Technol, PhD, 55. *Prof Exp:* Hwy engr, Calif Div Hwy, 36-41; chief engr, Santa Fe Dam Construct Co, 41-43; instr & res engr, Calif Inst Technol, 43-45; res engr, Armour Res Found, Ill Inst Technol, 45-51, asst mgr mech eng res, 51-58; sr develop engr, Portland Cement Asn, 58-63; assoc prof civil eng, 63-69, PROF CIVIL ENG, OKLA STATE UNIV, 69- *Mem:* Am Soc Civil Engrs; Am Concrete Inst. *Res:* Highways; rigid pavement research; driving stresses in piles; physical behavior of soils under load. *Mailing Add:* Dept of Civil Eng Okla State Univ Stillwater OK 74074

JANEWAY, CHARLES ALDERSON, JR, b Boston, Mass, Feb 5, 43; m 77; c 2. IMMUNE RECOGNITION, IMMUNOGLOBULIN IDIOTYPES. *Educ:* Harvard Col, BA, 63; Harvard Univ, MD, 69. *Prof Exp:* Res assoc, NIH, 70-75; Moseley fel, Univ Uppsala, 75-77; asst prof, 77-81, ASSOC PROF PATH, SCH MED, YALE UNIV, 81- *Concurrent Pos:* Investr, Howard Hughes Med Inst, 77-; lectr biol, Yale Univ, 79-; mem, Immunobiol Study Sect, NIH, 82- *Mem:* AAAS; Am Asn Immunologists. *Res:* Molecular basis of specific immune recognition and the genes that control it, focusing primarily on T cells that activate all immune responses. *Mailing Add:* Dept Path Sch Med Yale Univ New Haven CT 06510

JANEWAY, RICHARD, b Los Angeles, Calif, Feb 12, 33; m 55; c 3. MEDICINE, NEUROLOGY. *Educ:* Colgate Univ, AB, 54; Univ Pa, MD, 58. *Prof Exp:* Intern, Hosp Univ Pa, 58-59; resident neurol, NC Baptist Hosp, 63-66; from instr to assoc prof neurol, 66-71, actg chmn, Dept Neurol, 69-70, prog dir, Cerebral Vascular Res Ctr, 69-71, PROF NEUROL & DEAN, BOWMAN GRAY SCH MED, WAKE FOREST UNIV, 71- *Concurrent Pos:* Prog admin, Cerebral Vascular Res Ctr, 66-69; Markle scholar, 68; mem spec task force, Joint Coun Subcomt, Cerebrovascular Dis, 68; coun cerebrovascular dis, Am Heart Asn, 69; mem spec procedures & equip study group, Joint Comt for Stroke Facil, 70; mem nat adv coun regional med prog, Dept Health, Educ & Welfare; consult, US-Egypt Collab Prog on Stroke; mem, Comn Deans, Asn Am Med Cols, 71-; mem, Asn Am Med Col, exec coun, 77-, coun deans, 71-, admin bd, 77-, chmn-elect, 81- *Mem:* Inst Med-Nat Acad Sci; fel Am Heart Asn; fel Am Col Physicians; Am Asn Neurol Surg; Am Neurol Asn. *Res:* Neurology; cerebrovascular disease. *Mailing Add:* Bowman Gray Sch Med Wake Forest Univ Winston-Salem NC 27103

JANG, ROLAND, b Calif, Nov 5, 22; m 45; c 2. CHEMICAL ENGINEERING. *Educ:* Univ Calif, BS, 48, MS, 50. *Prof Exp:* Mgr chem eng, Cutter Labs, 50-57; chief engr, Bioferm Corp, 57-64, dir eng bioferm div, Int Minerals & Chem Corp, 64-66; vpres, 66-72, pres, Int Med Technol, 72-74, PRES, INT DIAG TECHNOL, MEMOREX CORP, SANTA CLARA, 74- *Mem:* Am Chem Soc; Am Instrument Soc; Am Inst Chem Engrs. *Res:* Chemical engineering in pharmaceuticals and fermentation products. *Mailing Add:* Int Diag Technol 2551 Walsh AVe Santa Clara CA 95050

JANGAARD, NORMAN OLAF, b Seattle, Wash, Oct 11, 41; m 63; c 2. BIOCHEMISTRY. *Educ:* San Diego State Univ, BS, 62; Univ Calif, Los Angeles, PhD(biochem), 66; Univ Denver, JD, 76. *Prof Exp:* Lab technician, Scripps Inst Oceanog, Univ Calif, San Diego; biochemist, Pfizer, Inc, 66-68 & Shell Develop Co, 68-72; dir res, 72-74, dir qual assurance, 74-78, vpres qual assurance & res & develop, 78-80, vpres eng & res & develop, 80-81, VPRES QUAL ASSURANCE, REGULATORY AFFAIRS RES & DEVELOP, ADOLPH COORS CO, 81- *Mem:* Am Soc Brewing Chemists; Am Chem Soc; Inst Food Technologists; Am Asn Cereal Chemists; Master Brewer's Asn Am. *Res:* Fermentation and yeast physiology; microbiological control; brewing and malting technology; packaging materials; breeding and growing of hops, barley and rice; waste treatment technology. *Mailing Add:* Qual Assurance & Res & Develop Adolph Coors Co Dept 344 Golden CO 80401

JANGHORBANI, MORTEZA, b Isfahan, Iran, Sept 29, 43; US citizen; m 69; c 1. STABLE ISOTOPES, NEUTRON ACTIVATION. *Educ:* Am Univ Beirut, Lebanon, BS, 66; Oregon State Univ, MS, 68, PhD(chem), 72. *Prof Exp:* Assoc vis asst prof chem, Univ Ky, 72-73; res chemist, Univ Marburg, Ger, 73-75; group leader, Environ Trace Substances Res Ctr, Univ Mo, 75-77; PRIN RES SCIENTIST, MASS INST TECHNOL, 77- *Mem:* Am Chem Soc; AAAS. *Res:* Trace element research in relation to biology and human nutrition; analytical chemistry of trace elements. *Mailing Add:* Nuclear Reactor Lab Mass Inst Technol 138 Albany St Cambridge MA 02139

JANIAK, DANIEL ROBERT, b Buffalo, NY, May 31, 31; m 53. LASERS. *Educ:* Univ Buffalo, BS, 59; State Univ NY Buffalo, PhD(physics), 66. *Prof Exp:* RES PHYSICIST, TEXTRON BELL AEROSPACE, 62- *Mem:* Am Phys Soc. *Res:* Chemical characterization of high pressure gaseous system discharges; electric discharge augmented chemical lasers; chemical reactant generation by electric discharge and nozzle design for mixing laser systems; advanced laser systems research. *Mailing Add:* 21 Roswell Rd Buffalo NY 14215

JANICK, JULES, b New York, NY, May 16, 31; m 52; c 2. PLANT GENETICS, PLANT BREEDING. *Educ:* Cornell Univ, BS, 51; Purdue Univ, MS, 52, PhD(plant genetics & breeding), 54. *Prof Exp:* From instr to assoc prof, 54-63, PROF HORT, PURDUE UNIV, 63- *Concurrent Pos:* Hon res assoc bot, Univ Col, Univ London, 63; horticulturist, Agr Univ Minas Gerais, 63-65; vis colleague, Univ Hawaii, 69; consult, World Bank, 73- *Honors & Awards:* Paul Howe Shepard Award, Am Pomol Soc, 60 & 70; Marion W Meadows Award, Am Soc Hort Sci, 71; Kenneth Post Award, Am Soc Hort Sci, 81. *Mem:* Am Pomol Soc; Am Soc Hort Sci; fel Portuguese Hort Asn; AAAS. *Res:* Genetics and breeding of horticultural crops. *Mailing Add:* Dept Hort Purdue Univ West Lafayette IN 47906

JANICKI, BERNARD WILLIAM, b Wilmington, Del, Oct 14, 31; m 54; c 5. IMMUNOLOGY, MICROBIOLOGY. *Educ:* Univ Del, BA, 53, MA, 55; George Washington Univ, PhD(microbiol), 60. *Prof Exp:* Microbiologist, Tuberc Res Lab, Vet Admin Hosp, DC, 55-60, chief, 60-63, chief microbiol res lab, 63-72, chief pulmonary immunol res lab, 72-74; chief immunol br, 74-77, HEALTH SCI ADMINR, NAT INST ALLERGY & INFECTIOUS DIS, 74-, CHIEF, IMMUNOBIOL & IMMUNOCHEM BR, 78- *Concurrent Pos:* Lectr microbiol, Univ Md, 69-79; consult, Nat Inst Allergy & Infectious Dis, 69-75; mem US tuberc panel, US-Japan Coop Med Sci Prog, 69-75; spec lectr med, George Washington Univ, 74-79. *Mem:* Am Soc Microbiol; Soc Exp Biol & Med; NY Acad Sci; Am Asn Immunol; Am Thoracic Soc. *Res:* Immunity and hypersensitivity in infectious diseases. *Mailing Add:* Rm 757 Westwood Bldg Nat Inst Allergy & Infect Dis Bethesda MD 20205

JANICKI, CASIMIR A, b Milwaukee, Wis, Sept 20, 34; m 59; c 2. ANALYTICAL CHEMISTRY. *Educ:* LaSalle Col, BA, 56; Marquette Univ, MS, 58; Loyola Univ, PhD(anal chem), 64. *Prof Exp:* Anal chemist, Smith, Kline & French Labs, 57-60; sr anal chemist, 63-66, group leader, 66-74, sect head, McNeil Labs, Ft Washington, 74-80, SECT HEAD, MCNEIL PHARMACEUT, SPRING HOUSE, PA, 74-, TECH DIR ANAL CONTROL, 82- *Mem:* Am Chem Soc; Am Pharmaceut Asn; Acad Pharmaceut Sci. *Res:* Pharmaceutical analytical chemistry, including thinlayer, paper and ion exchange chromatography, ultra violet visible and infrared spectrometry, separation techniques including high performance liquid and gas liquid chromatography; kinetics and drug stability. *Mailing Add:* Hickory Hill Dr R D 1 Norristown PA 19401

JANICZEK, PAUL MICHAEL, b Hazleton, Pa, Oct 5, 37. ASTRONOMY, NAVIGATION. *Educ:* King's Col, BA, 60; Georgetown Univ, MA, 65, PhD(astron), 70. *Prof Exp:* Supvr qual control, Lansdale Div, Philco Corp, 60-61; programmer analyst sci satellites, Fed Syst Div, IBM Corp, 61-66; ASTRONR, US NAVAL OBSERV, 67-, ED, NAVIG, 78- *Mem:* Am Astron Soc; AAAS; Inst Navigation. *Res:* Dynamical astronomy; celestial navigation. *Mailing Add:* US Naval Observ Washington DC 20390

JANIK, BOREK, b Brno, Czech, Oct 29, 33; m 65; c 2. CLINICAL CHEMISTRY, ELECTROPHORESIS. *Educ:* Purkyne Univ, Brno, MS, 56; Czech Acad Sci, Brno, PhD(chem, biophys), 64. *Prof Exp:* Res assoc org chem, Lachema, Pure Chem Corp, Czech, 56-60; fel, Inst Biophys, Czech Acad Sci, Brno, 60-64, res scientist electrochem & biophys, 64-66 & 67-68; fel chem, Univ Mich, Ann Arbor, 66-67, res assoc electrochem, 68-69; sr res scientist phys biochem, Ames Div, Miles Lab, Inc, 69-74, mem staff, Res Prod Div, 75-78, mgr res & develop, 78-79; DIR CLIN RES & DEVELOP, GELMAN SCI, 79- *Mem:* Am Chem Soc; Am Asn Clin Chem; Asn Clin Scientists; Int Soc Clin Enzym. *Res:* Test and instrument programs in protein chemistry, immunochemistry, enzymology and hematology utilizing separation technolgies. *Mailing Add:* Gelman Sci Inc 6005 Wagner Rd Ann Arbor MI 48106

JANIS, ALLEN IRA, b Chicago, Ill, Sept 11, 30; m 53; c 2. PHYSICS. *Educ:* Northwestern Univ, BS, 51; Syracuse Univ, PhD(physics), 57. *Prof Exp:* From instr to assoc prof, 57-68, PROF PHYSICS, UNIV PITTSBURGH, 68-, ASSOC DIR, PHILOS SCI CTR, 75- *Concurrent Pos:* Sr res assoc, Philos Sci Ctr, Univ Pittsburgh, 67-75. *Mem:* AAAS; Am Phys Soc; Am Asn Physics Teachers; Philos Sci Asn. *Res:* General relativity. *Mailing Add:* Dept of Physics Univ of Pittsburgh Pittsburgh PA 15260

JANIS, F TIMOTHY, b Chicago, Ill, Apr 11, 40; m 62; c 3. THEORETICAL CHEMISTRY, COMPUTER SCIENCE. *Educ:* Wichita State Univ, BS, 62, MS, 63; Ill Inst Technol, PhD(chem), 68. *Prof Exp:* Res assoc chem, Argonne Nat Lab, 66-68; instr chem & data processing, Col DuPage, 68-69; from asst prof to assoc prof chem, Ill Benedictine Col, 69-74; assoc prof & asst acad dean/registr, Franklin Col, 74-77; admin mgr, 77-78, actg dir indust liaison off, 78-80, DIR, BUS DEVELOP DIV, INDIANAPOLIS CTR ADVAN RES, 80- *Concurrent Pos:* Fel, Argonne Nat Lab, 68, consult, 68- *Mem:* Am Chem Soc. *Res:* Ab-initio calculations on molecules, market research, entrepreneurial development. *Mailing Add:* Indianapolis Ctr Advan Res PO Box 647 Indianapolis IN 46223

JANISCHEWSKYJ, W, b Prague, Czech, Jan 21, 25; Can citizen; m 51; c 2. ELECTRICAL ENGINEERING. *Educ:* Univ Toronto, BASc, 52, MASc, 54. *Prof Exp:* Demonstr elec eng, Univ Toronto, 52-54, instr, 54-55; elec engr, Aluminum Labs, Ltd, 55-59; lectr elec eng, 59-62, from asst prof to assoc prof, 62-70, asst head Elec Eng Dept, 65-70, assoc dean fac, Appl Sci & Eng, 78-82, PROF ELEC ENG, UNIV TORONTO, 70- *Concurrent Pos:* Nat Res Coun Can res grant, 61-; consult, Elec Eng Consociates, 68- *Mem:* Inst Elec & Electronic Engrs; Can Elec Asn; Coun Int Grandes Res Elec. *Res:*

Distribution of mechanical stress in composite transmission-line conductors; extra high voltage transmission of electric power; radio interference caused by high voltage corona; fault behavior of complex electric power systems; methods of testing underground cable; lightning studies. *Mailing Add:* Dept of Elec Eng Univ of Toronto Toronto ON M5S 1A1 Can

JANKE, NORMAN C, b Milwaukee, Wis, Sept 5, 23; m 52; c 1. ENVIRONMENTAL GEOLOGY. *Educ:* Univ Chicago, MS, 52; Univ Calif, Los Angeles, PhD(geol), 63. *Prof Exp:* Consult geologist, Geo-Sci Inc, Tex, 53; instr geol, Fresno State Col, 55; instr geol & math, 56-60, from asst prof to assoc prof, 60-68, head dept, 68-74, PROF GEOL, CALIF STATE UNIV, SACRAMENTO, 68- *Concurrent Pos:* trustee bd mem, Moss Landing Marine Lab, 67-71; consult mining & forensic geology. *Mem:* NY Acad Sci; Sigma Xi; Asn Eng Geologists; Soc Econ Paleont & Mineral; Int Asn Sedimentol; Nat Asn Geol Teachers; Am Soc Photogram. *Res:* Slumping and land sliding mechanisms; effects of shape upon settling velocity and sieving; photogrammetric uses of ordinary camera equipment; particle size and shape analysis, sieving and settling methods; swelling clays genesis and effects. *Mailing Add:* 2670 Fair Oaks Blvd Sacramento CA 95825

JANKE, ROBERT A, b Detroit, Mich, Aug 19, 22; m 44; c 4. PLANT ECOLOGY, PHYSICS. *Educ:* Univ Mich, AB, 44, MS, 52; Mich Technol Univ, BS, 48; Univ Colo, PhD(ecol), 68. *Prof Exp:* Teacher pub sch, 44; from instr to assoc prof physics, 44-62, ASSOC PROF BIOL, MICH TECHNOL UNIV, 62- *Concurrent Pos:* NSF sci fac fel, 63-65. *Mem:* AAAS; Ecol Soc Am; Sigma Xi; Bot Soc Am. *Res:* Ecology; fire ecology, l boreal forest ecology. *Mailing Add:* Dept of Biosci Mich Technol Univ Houghton MI 49931

JANKE, WILFRED EDWIN, b Morris, Man, Dec 24, 32; m 58; c 4. SOIL SCIENCE. *Educ:* Univ Man, BSA, 55, MSc, 57; Univ Wis-Madison, PhD(soils, geol), 62. *Prof Exp:* Pedologist, Soil Surv Div, Can Dept Agr, 57-59, res scientist, Res Sta, 62-63; dir, Soil Testing Lab, Univ Man, 63-66; res agronomist & mkt coordr, fertilizer mkt div, Sherritt Gordon Mines Ltd, 66-78; fertilize prod mgr, Federated Cooperatives Ltd, 78-81, MKT RES SR ANALYST, POTASH CORP, SASKATOON, 81- *Mem:* Am Soc Agron; Can Soc Soil Sci; Agr Inst Can; Int Soc Soil Sci; Western Can Fertilizer Asn. *Res:* Soil fertility, nutrient requirements of various crops under various soil and climatic conditions; fertilizer research, development of new fertilizer products, determining agronomic uses and effectiveness. *Mailing Add:* Potash Corp Sales LTD Saskatoon Sq 410-22nd St E Saskatoon SK S7K 5T7 Can

JANKOVICS, LAWRENCE ROBERT, see Johnson, Lawrence Robert

JANKOWSKI, CHRISTOPHER K, b Warsaw, Poland, July 31, 40; m 66; c 1. ORGANIC CHEMISTRY. *Educ:* Univ Warsaw, MSc, 63; Univ Montreal, PhD(chem), 68. *Prof Exp:* Asst org chem, Univ Warsaw, 63-64; fel, Univ Montreal, 67-68, asst prof, 68-69; from asst prof to assoc prof, 69-78, PROF ORG CHEM, UNIV MONCTON, 78- *Concurrent Pos:* Res fel chem, Syntex, SA, Mexico, 75; res fel, Nuclear Studies Ctr, Saclay, France, 75-79; chmn dept chem, Univ Moncton, 78-81. *Mem:* Fel Chem Inst Can; Fr-Can Asn Advan Sci. *Res:* Synthesis of organic compounds with physiological activity; organic application of mass spectrometry and nuclear magnetic resonance; natural products; alkaloids, sugars or carbohydrates. *Mailing Add:* Dept of Chem Univ of Moncton Moncton NB E1A 3E9 Can

JANKOWSKI, CONRAD M, b Chicago, Ill, Feb 25, 28; m 53. ENVIRONMENTAL CHEMISTRY, HIGH TEMPERATURE REACTION. *Educ:* Mich State Univ, BS, 51, MS, 53; State Univ Iowa, PhD(anal chem), 60. *Prof Exp:* Chief anal chemist, Rayovac Corp, 53-55; group leader instrumentation res, Cent Sci Co, 55-58; asst prof anal chem, 60-63, ASSOC PROF ANAL CHEM & CHEM OCEANOG, NORTHEASTERN UNIV, 63- *Concurrent Pos:* Indust consult. *Mem:* AAAS; Am Chem Soc; fel Royal Soc Chem. *Res:* Electroanalytical chemistry; high temperature reactions; chemical instrumentation; air and water pollution measurements; chemical oceanography. *Mailing Add:* Dept of Chem Northeastern Univ Boston MA 02115

JANKOWSKI, FRANCIS JAMES, b Amsterdam, NY, Nov 22, 22; m 46; c 1. DESIGN ENGINEERING, NUCLEAR ENGINEERING. *Educ:* Union Col, NY, BScCE, 43; Univ Cincinnati, MSE, 47, ScD(physics), 49. *Prof Exp:* Res engr nuclear, Battelle Mem Inst, 49-50; adv scientist, Westinghouse Elec Corp, 50-55; consult, Battelle Mem Inst, 55-59; prof nuclear & mech, Rutgers Univ, 59-69; chmn dept eng, 69-74, PROF SYSTS ENG, WRIGHT STATE UNIV, 69- *Concurrent Pos:* Consult, Englehard Industs, NJ, 59-62, United Nuclear Corp, 59-65, Picatinny Arsenal, US Army, 64-69, Westinghouse Elec Corp, 60- & US Dept Energy, 73-78; sabbatical leave, Foreign Technol Div, US Air Force, 79-80. *Mem:* Sigma Xi; Am Nuclear Soc; Am Phys Soc; Am Soc Eng Educ. *Res:* Principles and methodologies of engineering design process, with emphasis on incorporating human factors variables, life cycle costs, and systems approach. *Mailing Add:* Wright State Univ Dayton OH 45435

JANKOWSKI, STANLEY JOHN, b Detroit, Mich, Dec 19, 28; m 54; c 4. ANALYTICAL CHEMISTRY. *Educ:* Washington & Jefferson Col, BA, 53; Univ Pittsburgh, PhD(anal chem), 60. *Prof Exp:* Supvr, Neville Chem Co, 58-60; anal chemist, Celanese Corp Am, 60-62, sr anal chemist, 62-66; sr res chemist, Atlas Chem Indust Inc, 66-70, res supvr, 70-81, RES SPECIALIST, ICI AMERICAS INC, 81- *Mem:* Am Chem Soc; Am Oil Chemists Soc. *Res:* Instrumental methods of analysis; chromatographic methods of analysis; drugs; organic chemicals; polymers. *Mailing Add:* 3329 Morningside Rd Wilmington DE 19810

JANKUS, EDWARD FRANCIS, b Chicago, Ill, Mar 17, 30; m 55; c 2. PHYSIOLOGY. *Educ:* Univ Minn, BS, 57, DVM, 59, PhD(vet physiol), 66. *Prof Exp:* Vet pvt pract, 59-61; from inst to asst prof, 61-71, ASSOC PROF VET PHYSIOL & PHARMACOL, UNIV MINN, ST PAUL, 71- *Mem:* NY Acad Sci; Am Vet Med Asn; Am Animal Health Asn. *Res:* Comparative cardiovascular physiology. *Mailing Add:* Dept of Vet Biol Univ of Minn St Paul MN 55101

JANKUS, VYTAUTAS ZACHARY, b Girvalakis, Lithuania, Sept 6, 19; US citizen; m 56; c 1. NUCLEAR SCIENCE. *Educ:* Univ Vilnius, Lithuania, dipl, 43; Stanford Univ, PhD(physics), 56. *Prof Exp:* Instr physics. Seattle Univ, 48-51; asst, Stanford Univ, 51-55; assoc physicist, Mat Sci Div, Argonne Nat Lab, 55-75, sr physicist, 75-81; RETIRED. *Mem:* Am Asn Physics Teachers; Am Phys Soc; Am Nuclear Soc; Sigma Xi. *Res:* Electron scattering; neutron thermalization; reactor safety; performance. fuel element. *Mailing Add:* 801 McCarthy Rd Lemont IL 60439

JANKY, DOUGLAS MICHAEL, b Hastings, Nebr, Nov 3, 46; m 70; c 3. FOOD SCIENCE & TECHNOLOGY, POULTRY SCIENCE. *Educ:* Univ Nebr, BS, 69, MS, 71, PhD(food sci & technol), 74. *Prof Exp:* Asst prof, 74-78, ASSOC PROF POULTRY PROD TECHNOL, UNIV FLA, GAINESVILLE, 78- *Concurrent Pos:* Consult qual control, USDA. *Mem:* Poultry Sci Asn; Inst Food Sci & Technol. *Res:* Poultry products technology; color and pigmentation of poultry products, meat tenderness and acceptability; mechanically deboned poultry; meat and emulsions. *Mailing Add:* Dept of Poultry Sci Univ of Fla Gainesville FL 32611

JANNASCH, HOLGER WINDEKILDE, b Holzminden, Ger, May 23, 27; m 56; c 1. MICROBIOLOGY. *Educ:* Univ Gottingen, PhD(microbiol), 55. *Prof Exp:* Res asst microbiol, Max Planck Soc, 57-60; pvt docent, Univ Gottingen, 61-63; SR SCIENTIST, WOODS HOLE OCEANOG INST, 63- *Concurrent Pos:* Fel, Scripps Inst Oceanog, Univ Calif, San Diego, 57-58; res assoc, Univ Wis, 58-59; dir microbiol ecol course & mem corp, Marine Biol Lab, Woods Hole, Mass, 71-80; mem panel water criteria, Nat Acad Sci & NSF, 75-78. *Honors & Awards:* Henry Bryant Bigelow Medal Oceanog, 80. *Mem:* Am Soc Microbiol; Am Soc Limnol & Oceanog; Int Asn Theoret & Appl Limnol. *Res:* Physiology and ecology of freshwater and marine bacteria; growth of microorganisms at low nutrient levels; steady state cultures; deep-sea microbiology. *Mailing Add:* Woods Hole Oceanog Inst Woods Hole MA 02543

JANNETTA, PETER JOSEPH, b Philadelphia, Pa, Apr 5, 32; m 54; c 6. SURGERY. *Educ:* Univ Pa, AB, 53, MD, 57; Am Bd Surg, dipl, 64; Am Bd Neurol Surg, dipl, 69. *Prof Exp:* From asst instr to instr surg, Sch Med, Univ Pa, 58-63, instr pharmacol, 60-63; assoc surg & neurosurg, Univ Calif, Los Angeles, 63-66; assoc prof surg & chmn div neurosurg, Med Ctr, La State Univ, 66-71; PROF NEUROL SURG & CHMN DEPT, SCH MED, UNIV PITTSBURGH, 71- *Concurrent Pos:* NIH training grant, Univ Pa, 60-63, res grants, Med Ctr, La State Univ, 67-70; develop training grant, 68-71. *Mem:* Fel Am Col Surg; Soc Neurol Surgeons; Am Asn Neurol Surgeons; Cong Neurol Surgeons; Neurosurg Soc Am. *Res:* Pheochromocytoma; catechol amine determinations; single unit recording in the vestibular system; mesoscopic central nervous system anatomy and pathology; trigeminal nerve function; trigeminal neuralgia; cranial nerve dysfunction syndromes-etiology and treatment; spinal cord injury. *Mailing Add:* Dept of Neurol Surg Univ of Pittsburgh Sch Med Pittsburgh PA 15261

JANNEY, CLINTON DALES, b Dover, NJ, Mar 10, 20; m 43. RADIOLOGICAL PHYSICS. *Educ:* Univ Ill, BS, 41; Univ Calif, PhD(physics), 45. *Prof Exp:* Physicist, Manhattan Proj, Univ Calif, 42-46 & 47; from asst prof to assoc prof physiol & med physics, Col Med, Univ Iowa, 47-53; sr physicist, Southwest Res Inst, 53-54; assoc cancer res scientist physics, Roswell Park Mem Inst, 54-59; assoc prof, 59-70, PROF RADIOL PHYSICS, UNIV VT, 70- *Concurrent Pos:* Am Cancer Soc fel, Nat Res Coun, 46-47. *Mem:* AAAS; Radiol Soc NAm; Am Asn Physicists in Med; Am Phys Soc; Biophys Soc. *Res:* Medical radiologic physics. *Mailing Add:* Dept of Radiol Univ of Vt Burlington VT 05405

JANNEY, DONALD HERBERT, b Kansas City, Mo, Nov 26, 31; m 53; c 2. PHYSICS. *Educ:* Univ Ill, BS, 52; Stanford Univ, MS, 53, PhD(appl physics), 57. *Prof Exp:* Asst, Los Alamos Sci Lab, 52; asst, Microwave Lab, Stanford Univ, 53-56; staff mem, 56-65, alternate group leader, 65-74, GROUP LEADER, LOS ALAMOS NAT LAB, 74- *Mem:* AAAS; Am Phys Soc; sr mem Inst Elec & Electronics Engrs. *Res:* Gamma ray measurements; flash radiography; image processing; image analysis. *Mailing Add:* Los Alamos Nat Lab PO Box 1663 Los Alamos NM 87545

JANNEY, GARETH MAYNARD, b Toledo, Ohio, Feb 19, 34; m 60; c 1. OPTICS. *Educ:* Columbia Univ, AB, 55; Georgetown Univ, MS, 62, PhD(physics), 65. *Prof Exp:* Physicist, US Army Night Vision Lab, US Army Electronics Command, 65-69; from mem tech staff lasers to sr staff physicist, 69-75, asst dept mgr lasers, Hughes Res Labs, 75-79, PROJ MGR, SPACE SENSORS DIV, HUGHES AIRCRAFT CO, 79- *Mem:* Am Optical Soc; Inst Elec & Electronics Engrs. *Res:* Diatomic molecular spectroscopy, gas laser research, laser mode control and diffractionoptics for high energy lasers, tunable electro-optical infrared filters. *Mailing Add:* Hughes Aircraft Co E01E1/A164 PO Box 902 El Segundo CA 90245

JANNEY, JAMES G, JR, b St Joseph, Mo, Jan 8, 18; m 43; c 4. CARDIOLOGY. *Educ:* Univ Kans, BA, 39, MD, 41; Am Bd Internal Med, dipl, 50. *Prof Exp:* Intern, St Louis City Hosp, 41-42, sr intern internal med, 42-43, resident, 43-44 & 47-48; from instr to sr instr internal med, 48-53, asst prof clin med, 53-65, dir div cardiol, 54-68, PROF CLIN MED, ST LOUIS UNIV, 65- *Concurrent Pos:* dir div cardiol, St Mary's Group of Hosps, 48-51, assoc physician, 51- *Mem:* Fel Am Col Physicians. *Mailing Add:* 950 Francis Pl St Louis MO 63105

JANOFF, AARON, b New York, NY, Jan 29, 30; m 52; c 3. EXPERIMENTAL PATHOLOGY. *Educ:* NY Univ, AB, 51, MS, 55, PhD(biol), 59. *Prof Exp:* From instr to assoc prof path, Sch Med, NY Univ, 58-71; PROF PATH, HEALTH SCI CTR, STATE UNIV NY STONY BROOK, 71- *Concurrent Pos:* USPHS fel, Sch Med, NY Univ, 58-61; USPHS career develop award, 61-71; consult, Nat Heart, Lung & Blood Inst; vis lectr, Cardiovasc Res Inst, Univ Calif, San Fransisco, 81. *Mem:* AAAS; Am Asn Path; Am Thoracic Soc; fel NY Acad Sci; Harvey Soc. *Res:* Elastolytic, neutral proteases of human neutrophile leukocytes and alveolar macrophages;

demonstration; isolation; characterization; study of possible role in emphysema; effects of tobacco cigarette smoking on activity of proteases and protease inhibitors in lung tissue. *Mailing Add:* Sch Med State Univ of NY Stony Brook NY 11794

JANOS, DAVID PAUL, b Chicago, Ill, Nov 24, 47. ECOLOGY, MYCOLOGY. *Educ:* Carleton Col, BA, 69; Univ Mich, Ann Arbor, MS, 71, PhD(bot), 75. *Prof Exp:* Herbarium asst trop bot, Field Mus Natural Hist, 70; FEL MYCORRHIZAE, SMITHSONIAN TROP RES INST, 76- *Concurrent Pos:* Field sta mgr, Orgn Trop Studies, Inc, 75. *Mem:* Mycological Soc Am; Asn Trop Biol; Sigma Xi; Ecol Soc Am; Int Soc TLop Ecol. *Res:* The evolutionary ecology of mutualistic associations, and the influences of mutualistic root associations on plant community composition and dynamics, especially those of vesicular-arbuscular mycorrhizae in the tropics. *Mailing Add:* Smithsonian Trop Res Inst PO Box 2072 Balboa Panama

JANOS, LUDVIK, b Brno, Czech, Oct 3, 22. MATHEMATICS. *Educ:* Charles Univ, Prague, Dr rer nat(math), 50. *Prof Exp:* Mathematician, Res Inst, Prague, 50-63; vis assoc prof math, George Washington Univ, 63-65; assoc prof, Dalhousie Univ, 65-66; vis assoc prof, Univ Fla, 66-69, assoc prof, 69-74; vis prof, Univ Mont, Missoula, 74-75; assoc prof math, Wash State Univ, 75-77; assoc ed, Math Rev, Univ Mich, 77-80; RES PROF, UNIV MD, 80- *Mem:* Am Math Soc. *Res:* Functional analysis applied to the theory of differential equations; theory of fixed points; general topology; mathematical statistics; algebraic topology applied to digital geometry and pattern recognition. *Mailing Add:* Comput Sci Ctr Univ Md College Park MD 20742

JANOS, WILLIAM AUGUSTUS, b Easton, Pa, Nov 9, 26; m 59. PHYSICS, INFORMATION SCIENCE. *Educ:* Rutgers Univ, BS, 51; Univ Calif, Berkeley, MA, 54, PhD(physics), 58. *Prof Exp:* Res physicist, Convair Astronaut Div, Gen Dynamics Corp, 51-60; staff physicist, Res Div & Advan Develop Lab, Raytheon Co, 60-63; sr tech specialist, NAm Space & Info Systs Div, 63-66; prin scientist, Philco-Ford Aeronutronic Appl Res Lab, 66-67; sr staff physicist, Missile Syst Div Labs, Raytheon Co, 67; sr scientist, Technol Serv Corp, 67-74; sr staff engr, McDonnell Douglas Astronautics Co, 74-76; prin electronics engr, Interstate Electronics Corp, 76-78; CONSULT, 78- *Concurrent Pos:* USAEC deleg, Int Conf Controlled Thermonuclear Fusion, 61; US deleg, Plasma Physics Symp, Int Union Pure & Appl Chem, USSR, 65. *Mem:* Sigma Xi; Am Phys Soc; Inst Elec & Electronics Eng. *Res:* Statistical physics and electromagnetics of Boltzmann and Fokker-Planck equations; Wiener-Hopf integral equations of statistical communications and information theory; systems analysis; phenomenology hydrodynamics; analytical modeling of physical systems, sensors and signal processing; mathematical physics. *Mailing Add:* 8381 Snowbird Dr Huntington Beach CA 92646

JANOTA, HARVEY FRANKLIN, b Gonzales, Tex, Nov 30, 35. ANALYTICAL CHEMISTRY. *Educ:* Tex Lutheran Col, BS, 57; Univ Tex, PhD(chem), 63. *Prof Exp:* Instr chem, Tex Lutheran Col, 60-63; asst prof, Muhlenberg Col, 63-68; assoc prof, 68-74, PROF CHEM, CALIF STATE UNIV, FULLERTON, 74- *Mem:* Am Chem Soc. *Res:* Spectrophotometry of the platinum elements; instrumental methods of analysis; infrared determination of minerals. *Mailing Add:* Dept of Chem Calif State Univ 800 N State College Blvd Fullerton CA 92631

JANOVY, JOHN, JR, b Houma, La, Dec 27, 37; m 61; c 3. ZOOLOGY. *Educ:* Univ Okla, BS, 59, MS, 62, PhD(zool), 65. *Prof Exp:* Trainee, Rutgers Univ, 65-66; assoc prof, 66-74, PROF ZOOL, UNIV NEBR, LINCOLN, 74-, ASST DEAN ARTS & SCI, 66- *Mem:* Am Soc Trop Med & Hyg; Am Soc Parasitol. *Res:* Epidemiology of parasitic protozoa; comparative metabolism and evolution and of parasitic flagellates. *Mailing Add:* Dept of Zool Univ of Nebr Lincoln NE 68506

JANOWITZ, GERALD S(AUL), b Bronx, NY, Apr 5, 43; m 68. FLUID MECHANICS. *Educ:* Polytech Inst Brooklyn, BS, 63; Johns Hopkins Univ, MS, 64, PhD(mech), 67. *Prof Exp:* Fel mech, Johns Hopkins Univ, 67-68; asst prof fluid mech, Case Western Reserve Univ, 68-76; assoc prof oceanog, 76-80, PROF MARINE SCI & ENG, NC STATE UNIV, 80- *Res:* Geophysical fluid mechanics; motion of bodies through stratified fluids; flows in lakes and the coastal boundary layers. *Mailing Add:* Dept of Marine Sci NC State Univ Raleigh NC 27607

JANOWITZ, HENRY DAVID, b Paterson, NJ, Mar 23, 15; m 42; c 2. GASTROENTEROLOGY. *Educ:* Columbia Univ, AB, 35, MD, 39, Univ Ill, MS, 49. *Prof Exp:* Intern, Mt Sinai Hosp, 39-41, fel path, 46, resident med, 47-48, asst physiol, Univ Ill, 48-49; asst gastroenterol, 50-54, chief gastro-intestinal clin, 56-62, dir NIH training prog gastroenterol, 59-75, HEAD DIV GASTROENTEROL, MT SINAI SCH MED, 56- *Concurrent Pos:* Hon lectr, Guy's Hosp, London, Eng, 56; McArthur lectr, Univ Edinburgh, 56; ed, Am J Digestive Dis, 56-65; asst clin prof med, Columbia Univ, 62-66; ed sect alimentary canal, Handbook Physiol, 65; Comfort Mem lectr, Mayo Found, 65; mem, Am Bd Gastroenterol, 65, chmn gastroenterol res group steering comt, 65; mem prog proj comt, Nat Inst Arthritis & Metab Dis, 65, chmn, 70; clin prof, Mt Sinai Sch Med, 66-; consult, Bronx Vet Admin Hosp, Horton Hosp, Middletown, NY & Englewood Hosp, NJ; pvt pract. *Mem:* Am Physiol Soc; Soc Exp Biol & Med; Am Soc Clin Investrs; Am Gastroenterol Asn (pres, 72); Asn Am Physicians. *Res:* Gastrointestinal physiology; clinical investigation in gastroenterology, especially the application of physiological methods to the study of intestinal function and disease. *Mailing Add:* Div Gastroenterol Mt Sinai Sch Med 11 E 100th St New York NY 10029

JANOWITZ, MELVIN FIVA, b Minneapolis, Minn, May 8, 29. ALGEBRA, CLUSTER ANALYSIS. *Educ:* Univ Minn, BA, 50; Wayne State Univ, PhD(math), 63. *Prof Exp:* Asst prof math, Univ NMex, 63-66; assoc prof, Western Mich Univ, 66-67; assoc prof, 67-70, PROF MATH, UNIV MASS, AMHERST, 70-, ASST DEAN, NATURAL SCI & MATH, 79- *Mem:* Am Math Soc; Math Asn Am; Classification Soc; Soc Systematic Zool. *Res:* Lattice theory; mathematical models for ordinal cluster analysis; application of cluster analysis in image segmentation and numerical taxonomy. *Mailing Add:* Dept of Math Univ of Mass Amherst MA 01002

JANOWSKY, DAVID STEFFAN, b San Diego, Calif, June 24, 39; m 62; c 4. PSYCHOPHARMACOLOGY. *Educ:* Univ Calif, San Francisco, BS, 61, MD, 64. *Prof Exp:* Asst prof, Dept Psychiat, Sch Med, Univ Calif, Los Angeles, 69-70; head physician, Crisis Clin, Psychiat Emergency Serv, Dept Psychiat, Harbor Gen Hosp, Calif, 69-70; asst prof pharmacol, Sch Med, Vanderbilt Univ, 70-73, asst prof psychiat, 70-72, assoc prof, 72-73; chief, Vet Admin Liaison Serv, 73-74, assoc prof, 73-76, PROF, DEPT PSYCHIAT, SCH MED, UNIV CALIF, SAN DIEGO, 76- *Concurrent Pos:* Chief psychiat serv, Univ Hosp, Univ Calif, San Diego, 74-78; prin investr, Mental Health Clin Res Ctr, NIMH, Univ Calif, Calif, San Diego. *Mem:* Am Col Neuropsychopharmacol; Am Psychiat Asn; Psychiat Res Soc; Soc Neurosci; Col Int Neuropsychopharmacol. *Res:* Effects of adrenergic-cholinergic balance in the affective disorders, using cholinesterase inhibitors and psychostimulant challenges as investigative probes, and correlating these results with pre-clinical animal models. *Mailing Add:* 2744 Inverness Court La Jolla CA 92037

JANS, JAMES PATRICK, b Detroit, Mich, Apr 6, 27; m 50; c 2. MATHEMATICS. *Educ:* Univ Mich, AB, 49, MA, 50, PhD(math), 55. *Prof Exp:* Jr instr math, Univ Mich, 53-54; instr, Yale Univ, 54-56; asst prof, Ohio State Univ, 56-57; asst prof, 57-64, PROF MATH, UNIV WASH, 64- *Mem:* Am Math Soc. *Res:* Algebra; structure of rings; homological and topological algebra. *Mailing Add:* Dept of Math Univ of Wash Seattle WA 98105

JANSEN, BERNARD JOSEPH, b Rockville, Minn, Aug 10, 27; m 55; c 4. MATHEMATICS, SOFTWARE. *Educ:* St John's Univ, Minn, BA, 50; St Louis Univ, MA, 52. *Prof Exp:* Instr math, St John's Univ, Minn, 54-56; comput analyst prog, 56-66, mgr Titan III software, 66-69, mgr avionics software, 69-75, mgr systs & software, Int Systs Div, 76-77, MGR PLANNING, CONTROL & CHANGE PROPOSALS, INT TELECOMMUN DIV, UNIVAC DEFENSE SYSTS DIV, SPERRY RAND CORP, 77- *Concurrent Pos:* Mem adv panel, Spaceborne Digital Comput Systs, NASA, 68- *Mem:* Math Asn Am; Sigma Xi. *Res:* Technical management of and application of computers to systems and software in the avionics, aerospace, command and control, and telecommunications fields. *Mailing Add:* 1859 Hillcrest St Paul MN 55116

JANSEN, GEORGE, JR, b Aloha, Ore, Nov 15, 34; m 56; c 4. CHEMICAL ENGINEERING. *Educ:* Ore State Univ, BS & BA, 55; Mass Inst Technol, SM, 57, ScD(chem eng), 59. *Prof Exp:* Chem engr, Hanford Labs, Gen Elec Co, Wash, 59-62, sr engr, 62-65; sr develop engr, Battelle-Northwest, 65-68, res assoc, 68-75; sr engr, Exxon Nuclear Co, Inc, 75-81; ANAL ENGR, BATTELLE MEM INST, 81- *Mem:* AAAS; Am Chem Soc; Am Inst Chem Engrs; Am Nuclear Soc. *Res:* Ion exchange; heat transfer; process development in nuclear fuel processing; solvent extraction; radioactive waste disposal; risk analysis; centrifuge enrichment. *Mailing Add:* 505 King Ave Columbus OH 43201

JANSEN, GEORGE JAMES, b Canton, Ohio, Apr 22, 25; m 53, 71; c 2. MINERALOGY. *Educ:* Univ Notre Dame, BS, 51; Bryn Mawr Col, MA, 52. *Prof Exp:* Hydrol field asst, US Geol Surv, 51, geologist, 52-57; prin geologist, Battelle Mem Inst, 57; supvr mineral & metallog, Res Ctr, Repub Steel Corp, Ohio, 57-69; mineralogist, Climax Molybdenum Lab, 69-76; mineralogist, Com Test & Eng Co, 76-78; VPRES PRIN INVESTS, ROCKY MOUNTAIN COAL PETROG, INC, 78- *Mem:* Geol Soc Am; Mineral Soc Am; Mineral Asn Can; Soc Independent Prof Earth Scientists. *Res:* Mineralogy of base metals; quantitative metallography; reflected light optics; coal petrography. *Mailing Add:* 12870 W 15th Dr Golden CO 80401

JANSEN, GERALD THOMAS, b Manitowoc, Wis, July 16, 26; c 5. DERMATOLOGY. *Educ:* Univ Wis, BS & MD, 50. *Prof Exp:* Intern, Med Col Va, 51; instr in med dermat, 56-58, from asst clin prof to assoc clin prof dermat, 58-68, clin prof in med dermat, 69-70, HEAD DIV DERMAT, MED CTR, UNIV ARK, LITTLE ROCK, 69-; CHIEF DIV DERMAT, VET ADMIN HOSP, 69- *Concurrent Pos:* Consult, Little Rock Consol Vet Admin Hosp, 56-69; spec consult, USPHS Venereal Dis Div, Atlanta, Ga, 64; dir, Sub-Coun Finance, Nat Prog for Dermat, 69-72, chmn, 72- *Mem:* Am Col Chemosurg (vpres, 74-75); Am Acad Dermat; Soc Invest Dermat; Am Venereal Dis Asn; Am Dermat Asn. *Res:* Tropical use of chemotherapy including 5-Fluorouracil; investigation of brown recluse spider venom reactions. *Mailing Add:* Dept of Dermat 4301 W Markham Little Rock AR 72201

JANSEN, GUSTAV RICHARD, b Staten Island, NY, May 19, 30; m 53; c 4. NUTRITION. *Educ:* Cornell Univ, BA, 50, PhD(biochem), 58. *Prof Exp:* Jr & assoc chemist, Am Cyanamid Co, 53-54; asst biochem, Cornell Univ, 54-58; res chemist, E I du Pont de Nemours & Co, 58-62; res assoc, Merck Inst Therapeut Res, 62-69; PROF FOOD SCI & NUTRIT & HEAD DEPT, COLO STATE UNIV, 69- *Concurrent Pos:* Prog mgr, USDA, competition grants prog human nutrit, 81-82. *Mem:* Am Inst Nutrit; Am Soc Biol Chem; Am Dietetic Asn; Inst Food Technologists; Soc Nutrit Educ. *Res:* Amino acid fortification; nutrition and early development; nutrition during lactation; nutrition education. *Mailing Add:* Dept of Food Sci & Nutrit Colo State Univ Ft Collins CO 80523

JANSEN, HENRICUS CORNELIS, b Bergen op Zoom, Holland, Aug 3, 42; US citizen; m 77. RANGE MANAGEMENT. *Educ:* Univ Calif, Berkeley, BS, 69, PhD(natural res sci & range mgt), 74. *Prof Exp:* Res forester range mgt, Pac Southwest Forest & Range Exp Sta, US Forest Serv, 72-76; asst prof, 76-80, ASSOC PROF RANGE MGT, CALIF STATE UNIV, CHICO, 80- *Concurrent Pos:* Consult range conservationist, Soil Conserv Serv, 79 & Bur Land Mgt, 81; botanist, Fish & Wildlife Serv, 80. *Mem:* Soc Range Mgt. *Res:* Computerized planning method including documentation for the management of federal grazing lands. *Mailing Add:* 598 E 4th St Chico CA 95926

JANSEN, IVAN JOHN, b Newton, Iowa, Mar 17, 41; m 60; c 4. AGRONOMY, SOIL SCIENCE. *Educ:* Iowa State Univ, BS, 63; Cornell Univ, MS, 71, PhD(soil sci), 72. *Prof Exp:* Soil scientist, Soil Conserv Serv, USDA, 63-67; soil technologist, Dept Agron, Cornell Univ, 67-68; soil scientist, Soil Conserv Serv, USDA, 72-74; asst prof, 74-80, ASSOC PROF PEDOLOGY, UNIV ILL, URBANA, 81- *Mem:* Am Soc Agron; Soil Sci Soc Am; Soil Conserv Soc Am. *Res:* Characterizing geographic bodies of soil and reclamation of surface-mined lands for rowcrop production. *Mailing Add:* N 411 Turner Hall Univ of Ill Urbana IL 61801

JANSING, JO ANN, b Louisville, Ky, Mar 23, 38. ANALYTICAL CHEMISTRY, PHYSICAL CHEMISTRY. *Educ:* Ursuline Col, Ky, BA, 65; Fordham Univ, MS, 67, PhD(anal & phys chem), 70. *Prof Exp:* Teacher high sch, Ky, 62-65; instr chem, Mt St Agnes Col, 69-70; asst prof, 70-74, assoc prof, 74-81, PROF CHEM, IND UNIV SOUTHEAST, 81-, CHAIR, DIV NATURAL SCI, 79- *Mem:* Am Chem Soc; Nat Sci Teachers Asn; Sigma Xi. *Res:* X-ray crystallographic structure studies of organic molecules. *Mailing Add:* Dept of Chem 4201 Grantline Rd New Albany IN 47150

JANSKI, ALVIN MICHAEL, b Braham, Minn, May 27, 49; m 71; c 2. BIOCHEMISTRY. *Educ:* St Cloud State Univ, Minn, BA, 71; NDak State Univ, PhD(biochem), 75. *Prof Exp:* Res assoc, Dept Biochem & Biophysics, Iowa State Univ, 75-78, NIH fel, 78; sr staff fel, Lab Metab, Nat Inst Alcohol Abuse & Alcoholism, 78-81; RES SCIENTIST, INT MINERALS & CHEM CORP, 81- *Concurrent Pos:* Prin investr, Int Minerals & Chem Corp, 81- *Mem:* Am Soc Biol Chemists; NY Acad Sci; Am Chem Soc; AAAS. *Res:* Protein vaccines by recombinant DNA technology; metabolic pathways through intracellular compartmentation of metabolites and enzymes and hormone-depedent phosphorylation of enzymes; in vitro study of growth. *Mailing Add:* Int Minerals & Chem Corp PO Box 207 Terre Haute IN 47808

JANSON, BLAIR F, b East Trumbull, Ohio, Jan 6, 18; m 44; c 3. PLANT PATHOLOGY. *Educ:* Ohio State Univ, BS, 40, MS, 47, PhD, 50. *Prof Exp:* Asst exten plant pathologist, 46, asst instr bot, 47-50, prof plant path, 62-80, EMER PROF PLANT PATH, OHIO STATE UNIV, 80-, EXTEN PLANT PATHOLOGIST, 50- *Mem:* Am Phytopath Soc. *Res:* Ornamental, fruit, cereal and forage crop diseases. *Mailing Add:* Dept of Plant Path Ohio State Univ 1735 Neil Ave Columbus OH 43210

JANSON, THOMAS RALPH, b Amarillo, Tex, Dec 31, 44; m 66; c 3. PHYSICAL CHEMISTRY, PHYSICAL BIOCHEMISTRY. *Educ:* St Louis Univ, BS, 66; Case Western Reserve Univ, PhD(chem), 71. *Prof Exp:* CHEMIST, ARGONNE NAT LAB, 70- *Concurrent Pos:* Ctr Educ Affairs fel, 70-71; AEC grant, 71- *Res:* Study of the structure of biological materials by nuclear magnetic resonance; nerve impulse activation; design and study of photovoltaic devices. *Mailing Add:* Argonne Nat Lab Chem Dept 9700 S Cass Ave Argonne IL 60439

JANSONS, VILMA KARINA, b Riga, Latvia; US citizen. MICROBIOLOGY. *Educ:* Brooklyn Col, BA, 61; Rutgers Univ, New Brunswick, PhD(microbiol), 67. *Prof Exp:* Lectr biol, Princeton Univ, 68-70, mem res staff biochem sci, 70-72; asst prof microbiol, 72-77, ASSOC PROF MICROBIOL, NJ MED SCH, COL MED & DENT NJ, 77- *Mem:* AAAS; Am Soc Microbiol. *Res:* Surface properties of normal and malignant cells; biochemistry of morphogenesis. *Mailing Add:* NJ Med Sch Col of Med & Dent of NJ Newark NJ 07103

JANSSEN, ALLEN S, b Boise, Idaho, Sept 12, 07; m 30; c 2. CIVIL ENGINEERING. *Educ:* Univ Idaho, BArch, 30, BS, 33, MS, 37. *Prof Exp:* Field draftsman, Idaho Dept Hwy, 30-31; from instr to asst prof civil eng, 31-42, assoc prof & actg head dept, 42-46, dean col eng & dir eng exp sta, 46-67, prof civil eng, 46-72, EMER PROF CIVIL ENG & EMER DEAN, SCH ENG, UNIV IDAHO, 72- *Concurrent Pos:* Testing engr, Idaho Dept Hwy, 36-42; eng consult, 36-72; mem, Hwy Res Bd, Nat Acad Sci-Nat Res Coun, 40-67; consult, Bur Yards & Docks, US Navy, 49; dir, western zone, Nat Coun State Bd Eng Exam, 52-54; mem regional adv coun, Bonneville Power Admin, 58-72. *Honors & Awards:* Distinguished Serv Cert, Nat Coun State Bd Eng Exam, 58; Merit Award, Am Soc Civil Engrs, 65. *Mem:* Am Soc Civil Engrs (pres, 57-58); Am Concret Inst; Nat Soc Prof Engrs (vpres, 62-64); Am Soc Eng Educ; Am Soc Testing & Mat. *Res:* Materials of construction; foundations and structures; engineering research and education. *Mailing Add:* 630 East C Moscow ID 83843

JANSSEN, FRANK WALTER, b St Paul, Minn, Sept 10, 26; m 52; c 2. DRUG METABOLISM. *Educ:* Col St Thomas, BS, 50; Iowa State Univ, MS, 52. *Prof Exp:* Asst scientist biochem, Hormel Inst, Univ Minn, 52-61; res scientist protein chem, 61-66, sr res scientist & group leader drug metab, 66-78, SUPVR PHARMACOKINETIC EVAL UNIT, WYETH LABS, INC, 78- *Mem:* Sigma Xi. *Res:* Drug disposition; biotransformation and pharmacokinetics of anti-inflammatory drugs; organ specific toxicity of drug metabolites; metabolism of unnatural amino acids; flavoprotein enzymes. *Mailing Add:* Drug Metab Wyeth Labs Inc PO Box 8299 Philadelphia PA 19101

JANSSEN, JERRY FREDERICK, b Mason City, Iowa, Mar 22, 36; m 59; c 2. ORGANIC CHEMISTRY. *Educ:* Iowa State Teachers Col, BA, 57, MA, 59; Mich State Univ, PhD(chem), 67. *Prof Exp:* Instr sci & math, Mason City Jr Col, Iowa, 59-61; asst instr, Mich State Univ, 61-63; asst prof chem, Antioch Col, 66-69; from asst prof to assoc prof, Eisenhower Col, 69-74; sr environ engr, GTE Sylvania, Inc, Seneca Falls, NY, 74-77, CHEM PATENT AGENT, GTE SERV CORP, 77- *Concurrent Pos:* Consult, Vernay Labs, Ohio, 68-69 & Sylvania Elec Prod, Inc, NY, 69- *Mem:* Am Chem Soc; fel Am Inst Chem. *Res:* Organic reaction mechanisms; molecular photochemistry; rearrangement reactions of aromatic compounds. *Mailing Add:* GTE Serv Corp 100 First Ave Waltham MA 02154

JANSSEN, JOHN E(DWARD), mechanical engineering, see previous edition

JANSSEN, MICHAEL ALLEN, b Boise, Idaho, Sept 30, 37; m; c 2. RADIO ASTRONOMY, PLANETARY SCIENCES. *Educ:* Univ Calif, AB, 63, PhD(atmospheric & space sci), 72. *Prof Exp:* Physicist, Lawrence Radiation Lab, 63-67; Nat Res Coun resident res assoc planetary radio astron, 72-74, sr scientist, 74-76, MEM TECH STAFF, JET PROPULSION LAB, CALIF INST TECHNOL, 76- *Concurrent Pos:* Prin investr, Microwave Atmospheric Exp, Venus Orbiting Imaging Radar Mission. *Mem:* Int Union Radio Sci; Am Astron Soc. *Res:* Development of radio interferometric techniques at millimeter wavelengths; investigation of the atmospheres of Venus and the outer planets by microwave techniques; spacecraft microwave radiometry; cosmic microwave background. *Mailing Add:* 183B-365 Jet Propulsion Lab 4800 Oak Grove Dr Pasadena CA 91103

JANSSEN, RICHARD WILLIAM, b Weehawken, NJ, June 22, 40; m 68; c 2. PHARMACEUTICAL CHEMISTRY, PHYSICAL PHARMACY. *Educ:* Ferris State Col, BS, 62; Rutgers Univ, MS, 66, PhD(pharmaceut chem), 69. *Prof Exp:* Sr anal chemist, Smith, Kline & French Labs, 69-71; res & develop chemist, Lescarden Ltd, 71-72, sr res scientist, 72-75; GROUP LEADER, WILLIAM H RORER INC, 75- *Mem:* Am Chem Soc; Am Pharmaceut Asn; Acad Pharmaceut Sci. *Res:* Drug preformulation; dissolution technology; analytical methods development. *Mailing Add:* William H Rorer Inc 500 Virginia Dr Ft Washington PA 19034

JANSSEN, ROBERT (JAMES) J, b Geneva, Ill, Feb 28, 31; m 57; c 2. VIROLOGY, IMMUNOLOGY. *Educ:* Cornell Col, BA, 53; State Univ Iowa, MS, 55, PhD(bact), 57. *Prof Exp:* Med bacteriologist virol, Biol Labs, US Army Chem Corps, Md, 57-61; asst prof, 61-67, assoc prof, 67-80, PROF MICROBIOL & MED TECHNOL, UNIV ARIZ, 80- *Mem:* Sigma Xi; Am Soc Microbiol. *Res:* Smallpox, influenza, enteroviruses, arboviruses; combined infections with two or more microbial agents; aerobiology studies with viral agents; serological techniques; effects of certain drugs on viral infections. *Mailing Add:* Dept Microbiol & Med Technol Univ of Ariz Tucson AZ 85721

JANSSEN, WILLIAM C, b Milwaukee, Wis, Aug 18, 25; m 52; c 4. MEDICINE. *Educ:* Marquette Univ, MD, 54. *Prof Exp:* Asst dir clin res, Lakeside Labs Inc, Div Colgate-Palmolive Co, 61-63, dir clin res, 63-65, dir med affairs, 66-75; with Glassner, Benner, Janssen & Lobel, 75-80; WITH ALLERGY CLIN OF MILWAUKEE, 80- *Concurrent Pos:* Mem, Wis Drug Qual Coun. *Mem:* Am Soc Internal Med; Am Acad Clin Toxicol; Soc Toxicol Can; Am Col Toxicol; NY Acad Sci. *Res:* Clinical pharmacology. *Mailing Add:* Allergy Clin Milwaukee SC 324 E Wisconsin Ave Milwaukee WI 53202

JANSSON, BIRGER, b Stockholm, Sweden, Sept 4, 21; m 54; c 4. BIOMATHEMATICS, EPIDEMIOLOGY. *Educ:* Univ Stockholm, FilKand, 46, FilLic, 65, FilDr(math statist), 66. *Hon Degrees:* Docent, Univ Stockholm, 67. *Prof Exp:* Head res math sci, Res Inst Nat Defense, Stockholm, Sweden, 48-73; BIOMATHEMATICIAN, NAT LARGE BOWEL CANCER PROJ & PROF BIOMATH, UNIV TEX M D ANDERSON HOSP & TUMOR INST, 73- *Concurrent Pos:* Consult mathematician, Swed Money Lottery, Stockholm, 66-73; consult biomath, Tumor Biol, Karolinska Inst, 66-73; Eleanor Roosevelt fel, Int Union Against Cancer, 70; vis assoc prof, Univ Tex, Houston, 70-71; assoc ed, Math Biosci, 74-; adj prof, Rice Univ, 74- *Mem:* AAAS; Soc Environ Geochem & Health; Int Soc Prev Oncol; Europ Study Group Cell Proliferation; Soc Swed Mathematicians. *Res:* Cancer, epidemiology and prevention, especially cancer of the colon, rectum, stomach and breast; mathematical models of the cell cycle and their use for finding rational protocols for cancer treatment. *Mailing Add:* Large Bowel Cancer Proj HMB 850 MD Anderson Hosp & Tumor Inst Houston TX 77030

JANSSON, DAVID GUILD, b Quincy, Mass. TECHNOLOGICAL INNOVATION. *Educ:* Mass Inst Technol, SB, 68, SM, 70, ScD, 73. *Prof Exp:* Scientific officer, Off Naval Res, 72-75; asst prof, 75-80, assoc prof, 80-81, ASSOC PROF, DEPT MECH ENG, MASS INST TECHNOL, 81-, DIR, INNOVATION CTR, 79- *Res:* Development of methodology for understanding and teaching the technological innovation process, including specific applications to energy conservation, unique electronic display devices and many other areas of innovation technology. *Mailing Add:* W91-209 Mass Inst Technol Massachusetts Ave Cambridge MA 02139

JANSSON, PETER ALLAN, b Teaneck, NJ, May 20, 42; m 67; c 2. OPTICAL PHYSICS, DIGITAL IMAGE PROCESSING. *Educ:* Stevens Inst Technol, BS, 64; Fla State Univ, PhD(physics), 68. *Prof Exp:* Instr physics, Fla State Univ, 67-68; res physicist, 68-71, sr res physicist, 71-76, res assoc, 76-80, SR RES ASSOC & TECH LEADER, DIGITAL IMAGE PROCESSING GROUP, EXP STA, E I DU PONT DE NEMOURS & CO, INC, 80- *Mem:* Am Phys Soc; fel Optical Soc Am; Soc Photog Instrumentation Engrs. *Res:* Infrared and optical physics; digital image processing; optical information processing; molecular spectroscopy; super resolving methodof deconvolution. *Mailing Add:* Room 212 Bldg 357 Du Pont Exp Sta Wilmington DE 19898

JANTZ, ORLO KENNETH, b Newton, Kans, June 16, 34; m 57; c 3. ENTOMOLOGY. *Educ:* Kans State Univ, BS, 57, MS, 62; Ore State Univ, PhD(entom), 65. *Prof Exp:* Lab asst entom, Kans State Univ, 52-53; field aide, Agr Mkt Serv, USDA, Kans, 53-55, biol aide, 55-57, entomologist, 57; res asst entom, Kans State Univ, 60-63; res asst, Ore State Univ, 63-65; entomologist, Agr Res Serv, USDA, Mich, 65-67; regional tech specialist, Dow Chem, Mich, 67-68; mgr field res sta, Ill, 68-71; develop specialist, 71-73; mgr res & develop agr & spec prods, Dow Chem Pac Ltd, Hong Kong, 73-77, mgr, tech serv & develop plant prod, Agr Prod Dept, 77-81, DIR, AGR PROD DEVELOP & REGIST, DOW CHEM USA, 81-; MGR RES & DEVELOP AGR & SPEC PROD, DOW CHEM PAC LTD, MGR, TS&D PLANT PRODS, AGR PRODS DEPT, DOW CHEM USA, 77- *Mem:* Entom Soc Am; Weed Sci Soc Am; Am Registry of Prof Entomologists. *Res:* Field development of agricultural chemicals; forest insects; stored grain pests; field crop insects. *Mailing Add:* Dow Chem USA PO Box 1706 Midland MI 48640

JANUARY, LEWIS EDWARD, b Haswell, Colo, Nov 14, 10; m 41; c 2. CARDIOLOGY. *Educ:* Colo Col, BA, 33; Univ Colo, MD, 37. *Hon Degrees:* DSc, Colo Col, 66. *Prof Exp:* Jr intern, Univ Hosp, 37-38, from asst resident to resident internal med, 38-41, asst physician, 41-42, from asst prof to assoc prof, 46-66, PROF MED, COL MED, UNIV IOWA, 46-, ASSOC CHMN DEPT, 73- *Concurrent Pos:* Chmn coun clin cardiol, Am Heart Asn, 61-63, fel coun clin cardiol; vchmn sect cardiovascular dis, AMA, 70-73; mem, Int-Soc Comn Heart Dis Resources; vis prof, Ain Shams Univ, Cairo, Egypt, 72. *Honors & Awards:* Honor Achievement Award, Angiol Res Found, 65; Distinguished Serv Citation, Coun Clin Cardiol, Am Heart Asn, 67, Gold Heart Award, Am Heart Asn, 69; Distinguished Serv Citation, Int-Soc Comn Heart Dis Resources, 71; Silver & Gold Award, Univ Colo, 71; Helen B Taussig Award, 72; Achievement Award, Am Heart Asn, 77, Citation Distinguished Serv to Cardiol, 78. *Mem:* Am Heart Asn (vpres, 63-65, pres, 66-67); fel Am Col Cardiol; Asn Univ Cardiol; Inter-Am Soc Cardiol; Int Cardiol Fedn (vpres, 70-76). *Res:* Diabetes insipidus; mercurial diuretics; electrocardiography; hypertension; heart diseases. *Mailing Add:* Dept of Med Univ of Iowa Hosp Iowa City IA 52244

JANUS, ALAN ROBERT, b Utica, NY, Dec 27, 37; m 59, 70. SOLID STATE SCIENCE. *Educ:* Utica Col, BA, 59; Syracuse Univ, PhD(inorg chem), 64. *Prof Exp:* Lab technician qual control, Utica Drop Forge & Tool Co, 56-59; res chemist organometallic, Solvay Process Div, Allied Chem Corp, 60; sr chemist thin films, Sprague Elec Co, Mass, 63-66, assoc prog mgr ceramic develop, 66-68; asst prof, Roanoke Col, 68-70; mgr thin film eng, Electronic Mat Div, Bell & Howell Res Labs, 70-71, dir eng, 71-74; sr scientist, Hughes Aircraft, Calif, 74-80; WITH BOURNE, INC, 80- *Concurrent Pos:* Res technician, Metals Div, Kelsey Hayes Co, 58-59; consult, Am Safety Razor Div, Philip Morris Co, 68-70, Electron Tube Div, Int Tel & Tel, 68-70, Bell & Howell, 73-74, Nat Micrometrics, 74- & Optifilm, 75- *Mem:* Am Vacuum Soc. *Res:* Thin film preparation and evaluation; magnetic susceptibilities; organometallic compound preparation and evaluation; coordination chemistry; chrome photoplates; III-IV compounds; ferrites; microanalytical services; surface acoustic wave device development; microwave hybrid device development. *Mailing Add:* Bourne Inc MS-94 1200 Columbia Ave Riverside CA 92507

JANUSZ, GERALD JOSEPH, b Aug 20, 40; US citizen; m 61. MATHEMATICS. *Educ:* Marquette Univ, BS, 62; Univ Wis, MS, 63; Univ Ore, PhD(math), 65. *Prof Exp:* Mem, Inst Advan Study, 65-66; instr math, Univ Chicago, 66-68; from asst prof to assoc prof, 68-73; PROF MATH, UNIV ILL, URBANA, 73- *Mem:* Am Math Soc; Math Asn Am. *Res:* Representations of finite groups; finite dimensional algebras. *Mailing Add:* Dept of Math 273 Altgeld Hall Univ of Ill Urbana IL 61801

JANUTOLO, DELANO BLAKE, b Bluefield, WVa, July 7, 52. PLANT PATHOLOGY, MYCOLOGY. *Educ:* WVa Univ, BS, 73; Va Polytech Inst & State Univ, PhD(plant path), 77. *Prof Exp:* ASST PROF BIOL, ANDERSON COL, 77- *Mem:* Am Phytopath Soc. *Res:* Evaluation and testing of fungicides; systemic fungicides. *Mailing Add:* Dept of Biol Anderson Col Anderson IN 46011

JANZ, GEORGE JOHN, b Russia, Aug 24, 17; nat US; m 51; c 4. PHYSICAL CHEMISTRY. *Educ:* Univ Man, BSc, 40; Univ Toronto, MA, 41, PhD(chem), 43; Univ London, DSc, 54. *Prof Exp:* Res chemist, Can Indust Ltd, 43-46; hon res assoc, Univ Col, London, 46-49; asst prof chem, Pa State Col, 49-50; from asst prof to assoc prof, 50-53, chmn dept chem, 62-72, prof, 53-80, WM WEIGHTMAN WALKER PROF CHEM, RENSSELAER POLYTECH INST, 80-, DIR, MOLTEN SALTS DATA CTR, 68- *Concurrent Pos:* Vis prof, Rockefeller Univ, 72-73. *Mem:* Am Chem Soc; Royal Soc Chem; Electrochem Soc; Faraday Soc; NY Acad Sci. *Res:* Electrochemistry; physical properties ties and spectroscopy of inorganic compounds in the molten state; aqueous and nonaqueous electrolytes; electrolysis of molten salts; thermodynamics and reaction energies of cyanogen-like compounds. *Mailing Add:* Dept of Chem Rensselaer Polytech Inst Troy NY 12181

JANZEN, ALEXANDER FRANK, b Einlage, Ukraine, Apr 19, 40; Can citizen; m 67; c 3. INORGANIC CHEMISTRY, ORGANOMETALLIC CHEMISTRY. *Educ:* McMaster Univ, BSc, 63; Western Ont Univ, PhD(chem), 66. *Prof Exp:* Fel chem, Univ London, 66-67; asst prof, 67-71, assoc prof, 71-78, PROF CHEM, UNIV MAN, 78- *Concurrent Pos:* Vis scientist, Max Planck Inst Exp Med, Ger, 73. *Mem:* Chem Inst Can; Am Chem Soc. *Res:* Synthesis of inorganic fluorine compounds and study of dynamic properties. *Mailing Add:* Dept of Chem Univ of Man Winnipeg MB R3T 2W2 Can

JANZEN, DANIEL HUNT, b Milwaukee, Wis, Jan 18, 39; c 2. ECOLOGY, EVOLUTION. *Educ:* Univ Calif, Berkeley, PhD(entom), 65. *Prof Exp:* Asst prof biol, Univ Kans, 65-68; from asst prof to assoc prof, Univ Chicago, 68-72; from assoc prof to prof, Univ Mich, 72-76; PROF BIOL, UNIV PA, 76- *Concurrent Pos:* Adv, Orgn Trop Studies, Costa Rica. *Honors & Awards:* Gleason Award, Am Bot Soc, 75. *Mem:* Soc Study Evolution; Ecol Soc Am; Am Soc Naturalists; Brit Ecol Soc; Asn Trop Biol. *Res:* Interactions of plants and animals, with emphasis on tropical field systems. *Mailing Add:* Dept of Biol Univ of Pa Philadelphia PA 19104

JANZEN, EDWARD GEORGE, b Winnipeg, Man, May 23, 32; m 52; c 2. PHYSICAL ORGANIC CHEMISTRY. *Educ:* Univ Man, BSc, 57, MSc, 60; Iowa State Univ, PhD(org chem), 63. *Prof Exp:* Fel dept chem, Iowa State Univ, 63-64; from asst prof to prof spectros, Univ Ga, 64-75; PROF & CHMN DEPT CHEM, UNIV GUELPH, 76- *Concurrent Pos:* Vis prof & scientist, Okla Med Res Found, 81 & IBM Instruments, Inc, San Jose, 82. *Honors & Awards:* Fulmer Award, Iowa State Univ. *Mem:* Fel Can Inst Chem. *Res:* Physical organic, biochemical and inorganic topics in electron spin resonance spectroscopy; spin trapping techniques, development and practice. *Mailing Add:* Dept of Chem Univ of Guelph Guelph ON N1G 2W1 Can

JANZEN, JACOB J, b Russia, Mar 29, 19; nat US; m 48; c 3. DAIRY SCIENCE. *Educ:* Univ Man, BSA, 44; Univ Wis, MS, 47, PhD(dairy indust, biochem), 52. *Prof Exp:* Asst, Dairy Prod Lab, Univ Man, 40-43, dairy sci, 44-45, lectr, 47-49; asst dairy indust, Univ Wis, 49-51, proj asst, 51-52, proj assoc, 52-53; proj engr res, Continental Can Co, 53-58; assoc prof, 58-68, PROF DAIRY SCI, CLEMSON UNIV, 68- *Concurrent Pos:* Asst, Univ Wis, 45-47. *Mem:* Am Dairy Sci Asn; Inst Food Technologists. *Res:* Cheesemaking; bacteriology of milk; physical and chemical properties of milk powder; canning of milk, whole and modified; blue cheese manufacture; study of milk flavor and methods of evaluation. *Mailing Add:* Dept of Dairy Sci Clemson Univ Clemson SC 29631

JANZEN, JAY, b Chickasha, Okla, Mar 24, 40; m 62; c 2. PHYSICAL CHEMISTRY. *Educ:* Univ Kans, BS, 62; Iowa State Univ, PhD(phys chem), 68. *Prof Exp:* SR RES CHEMIST, PHILLIPS PETROL CO, 68- *Mem:* Am Chem Soc. *Res:* Carbon black; reinforcement of elastopolymers; physics and chemistry of carbon surfaces; statistical morphology of particulate materials and composite media; random geometry; automatic image analysis; colloid physics. *Mailing Add:* 152 CPL Phillips Petrol Co Res Ctr Bartlesville OK 74004

JANZEN, WAYNE ROGER, b Herbert, Sask, Mar 8, 38; m 61; c 2. CHEMICAL PHYSICS. *Educ:* Univ BC, BSc, 61, MSc, 63, PhD(chem), 68. *Prof Exp:* Res chemist, Res Labs, Eastman Kodak Co, 67-71; teaching fel, Univ BC, 71-72; TEACHER, ALBERNI DIST SEC SCH, 73- *Res:* Nuclear magnetic resonance in solids. *Mailing Add:* 3827 Exton St Port Alberni BC V94 3Y1 Can

JANZOW, EDWARD F(RANK), b St Louis, Mo, Mar 19, 41; m 67; c 1. NUCLEAR ENGINEERING, MECHANICAL ENGINEERING. *Educ:* Washington Univ, BS, 63; Univ Mo, MS, 64; Univ Ill, Urbana, PhD(nuclear eng), 70; Univ Dayton, MBA, 81. *Prof Exp:* NASA traineeship, Univ Mo-Columbia, 63-64; Nat Sci Found traineeship, Univ Ill, Urbana, 64-68, asst, Off Water Resources, 68-69, nuclear eng prog, 69-70; sr res engr, 71-72, engr group leader, 72-75, supvr design & develop eng, 75-76, mgr eng & develop, 76-79, mgr eng & qual assurance, 79-81, MGR OPERATIONS, MONSANTO RES CORP, 81- *Concurrent Pos:* Mem comt, Sealed Radioactive Sources, Am Nat Standard Inst, 74- *Mem:* Am Nuclear Soc; Am Soc Testing & Mat. *Res:* Nuclear radiation and heat sources; research, development and design relating to such sources and techniques, apparatus and facilities for their fabrication; development and design of radioisotope shipping containers. *Mailing Add:* 2671 Crone Rd Xenia OH 45385

JAOUNI, KATHERINE COOK, b Alexandria, Va, Nov 8, 29; m 64; c 1. MICROBIOLOGY. *Educ:* Col William & Mary, BS, 49; George Washington Univ, MS, 52, PhD(microbiol), 57. *Prof Exp:* Bacteriologist, Alexandria Health Dept, 49-52; parasitologist, Trop Dis Lab, 52-57, virologist, Infectious Dis Lab, 57-78, RES MICROBIOLOGIST, NAT INST ALLERGY & INFECTIOUS DIS, 78- *Concurrent Pos:* Researcher, Pasteur Inst & St Vincent de Paul Hosp, France, 59-61 & Max Planck Inst, Tuebingen, Ger, 61-62; pres, Grad Women in Sci, Inc, 81-82. *Mem:* Am Soc Trop Med & Hyg; Am Soc Microbiol; Sigma Xi; AAAS. *Res:* Tissue culture of protozoa and mode of action of drugs against toxoplasma; characterization and antigenic analysis of respiratory viruses; oncogenic virology; viruses of protozoa; mode of action of drugs against protozoa and viruses; science administration. *Mailing Add:* Nat Inst Allergy & Infectious Dis Nat Insts Health Bethesda MD 20205

JAOUNI, TAYSIR M, b Jerusalem, Palestine, Aug 29, 24; US citizen; m 64; c 1. ORGANIC CHEMISTRY. *Educ:* Univ Calif, Berkeley, BA, 50, MA, 51, BSc, 60; Univ Colo, MSc, 63. *Prof Exp:* Asst chem, Univ Colo, 60-63; RES CHEMIST, LAB CHEM, NAT HEART & LUNG INST, 63- *Res:* Synthesis of diribonucleoside phosphates; RNA codewords and protein synthesis. *Mailing Add:* Lab of Chem Nat Heart & Lung Inst Bethesda MD 20205

JAPAR, STEVEN MARTIN, New York, NY, Nov 11, 44. PHOTOCHEMISTRY, CHEMICAL KINETICS. *Educ:* City Col New York, BS, 65; Case Inst Technol, PhD(phys chem), 69. *Prof Exp:* Fel, Div Physics, Nat Res Coun Can, 69-71; fel, Chem Dept, Univ Calif, Riverside, 71-72; instr, Chem Dept, Drexel Univ, 72-73; sr res scientist, 73-80, PRIN RES SCIENTIST ASSOC, RES STAFF, FORD MOTOR CO, 81- *Concurrent Pos:* Instr, Natural Sci Dept, Univ Mich, Dearborn, 75-76. *Mem:* Am Chem Soc; Air Pollution Control Asn; Sigma Xi; Optical Soc Am; Inter-Am Photochem Soc. *Res:* Chemistry and physics of gas phase aerosols generated from combustion sources; photochemistry, spectroscopy and chemical kinetics of species important in atmospheric chemistry; development of analytical methods for the measurement of such species. *Mailing Add:* 7628 Merriman Rd Westland MI 48185

JAPPE, NICHOLAS A(DOLF), b Seattle, Wash, Aug 31, 25; m 56; c 1. ENGINEERING, TECHNOLOGY. *Educ:* Univ Wash, Seattle, BS, 45; Lawrence Col, MS, 54, PhD, 56. *Prof Exp:* Tech dir, Scott Paper Co, 45-52; res assoc, Inst Paper Chem, Lawrence Col, 56-59 & Paramonga Agr Corp, Ltd, Peru, 59-63; mem res staff, 63-76, SECT LEADER PAPER RES, SCOTT PAPER CO, PHILADELPHIA, PA, 76- *Mem:* Tech Asn Pulp & Paper Indust. *Res:* Formation of chromophoric groups induced in cellulose by heat; interrelation of fiber and sheet properties for conventional paper and nonwoven structures. *Mailing Add:* Paper Res Scott Paper Co Scott Plaza Philadelphia PA 19113

JAQUES, LOUIS BARKER, b Toronto, Ont, July 10, 11; m 37; c 1. PHYSIOLOGY, PHARMACOLOGY. *Educ:* Univ Toronto, BA, 33, MA, 35, PhD(physiol), 41; Univ Sask, DSc, 74. *Prof Exp:* Asst physiol, Univ Toronto, 34-42, lectr & res assoc, 43-44, asst prof, 44-46; prof physiol & pharmacol & head dept, 46-71, Lindsay res prof, 71-79, EMER PROF, COL MED, RES ASSOC COL DENT, UNIV SASKATOON, 79- *Concurrent Pos:* Claude Bernard vis prof, Univ Montreal, 48; mem, Int Conf Thrombosis & Embolism, Univ Basel, 54; mem adv comt, Med Div, Nat Res Coun Can,

52-55 & 59-61, mem Int comt nomenclature of blood clotting factors, 54-66, chmn subcomt hemostasis, 62-65; chmn, Can Nat Comt, Int Union Physiol Sci, 62-64; mem Can nat comt, Int Coun Sci Unions, 63-64. *Mem:* Am Physiol Soc; Am Soc Pharmacol & Exp Therapeut; fel NY Acad Sci; fel Royal Soc Can; Pharmacol Soc Can. *Res:* Pharmacology of blood coagulation; anticoagulants; hemorrhage and thrombosis. *Mailing Add:* Col Dent Univ of Sask Saskatoon AB S6N 0W0 Can

JAQUES, ROBERT PAUL, b Caledonia, Ont, Jan 1, 31; m 54; c 3. INSECT PATHOLOGY. *Educ:* Univ Toronto, BSA, 52, MSA, 54; Cornell Univ, PhD(insect ecol), 60. *Prof Exp:* Res scientist, Kentville, NS, 54-67, RES SCIENTIST INSECT PATH, RES STA, CAN DEPT AGR, HARROW, ON, 67- *Concurrent Pos:* Res assoc biol, Acadia Univ, 62-65, assoc prof, 65-67; assoc fac, Univ Guelph, 76- *Mem:* Entom Soc Can; Am Entom Soc; Soc Invert Path. *Res:* Factors affecting development of disease in populations of insects; persistence of insect viruses in the environment; control of insects using pathogens and viruses. *Mailing Add:* Res Sta Can Dept of Agr Harrow ON N0R 1G0 Can

JAQUES, WILLIAM EVERETT, b Newbury, Mass, July 11, 17; m 68; c 7. PATHOLOGY. *Educ:* McGill Univ, MD & CM, 42. *Prof Exp:* Intern, Bridgeport Hosp, 42-43; asst resident path, Mass Mem Hosp, 47-49; instr, Harvard Med Sch, 49-53; assoc prof, La State Univ, 53-57, prof & chmn dept, Sch Med, Univ Okla, 57-66; prof path & chmn dept, Sch Med, Univ Ark, Little Rock, 66-74; prof path, Okla Col Osteop Med & Surg, Tulsa, Okla, 74-81; PROF PATH, AM UNIV CARIBBEAN, 81- *Concurrent Pos:* Resident, Children's Med Ctr, Boston, 49-50, assoc pathologist, Peter Bent Brigham Hosp, 51-53; res fel, Children Med Ctr, Boston, 50-51; vis prof, Nat Defense Med Ctr, Taiwan, 65-66; consult, Vet Admin, Oklahoma City , Muskogee & Little Rock; dir path, Nat Ctr Toxicol Res, Jefferson, Ark, 71-74; clin prof path, Univ Okla, 74-81. *Mem:* Am Soc Exp Path; Am Soc Clin Path; Am Asn Path & Bact; Int Acad Path; Am Col Angiol. *Res:* Pathological physiology; lesser circulation; embolism; mitral stenosis. *Mailing Add:* Leslie Pierce Trust Dept Utica Nat Bank & Trust PO Box 1559 Tulsa OK 74101

JAQUISS, DONALD B G, b Ramsgate, Eng, Nov 28, 29; m 56; c 4. ORGANIC CHEMISTRY. *Educ:* Univ Wales, BSc, 50; Univ Liverpool, PhD(org chem), 53. *Prof Exp:* Res & develop, UK Atomic Energy Authority, 54-56; res & develop dyestuffs div, Imp Chem Industs, 56; res & develop polychem div, E I du Pont de Nemours & Co, Tex, 56-59, Del, 59-60; develop chemist, Chem Mat Dept, 60-63, specialist, 63-69, mgr res & advan develop, Polycarbonate Res Develop, 69-75, MGR RES & DEVELOP, VALOX PROD SECT, GEN ELEC CO, 75- *Mem:* Am Chem Soc; Royal Soc Chem. *Res:* Polymer and intermediates syntheses and characterization; polyethylene; nylon; chemistry of carbonates and polycarbonates; phenols. *Mailing Add:* Valox Prod Sect Gen Elec Co One Plastics Ave Pittsfield MA 01201

JAQUITH, RICHARD HERBERT, b Newton, Mass, Mar 31, 19; m 42; c 5. INORGANIC CHEMISTRY. *Educ:* Univ Mass BS, 40, MS, 42; Mich State Univ, PhD(inorg chem), 55. *Prof Exp:* Instr chem, Univ Conn, 42-44 & 46-47; asst prof, Colby Col, 47-54; from asst prof to assoc prof, 54-65, PROF CHEM, UNIV MD, COLLEGE PARK, 65-, ASST VCHANCELLOR ACAD AFFAIRS, 73- *Mem:* Sigma Xi. *Res:* Nonaqueous inorganic solvents; rare earth compounds. *Mailing Add:* Dept of Chem Univ of Md College Park MD 20742

JARAMILLO, JORGE, b Chinchina, Colombia, Jan 7, 34; m 61; c 4. PHARMACOLOGY. *Educ:* Univ Caldas, MD, 58; Tulane Univ, MS, 62, PhD(pharmacol), 66. *Prof Exp:* Instr, Tulane Univ, 66-67; asst prof, Univ Conn, 67-68; sr pharmacologist, 68-70, res assoc, 70-77, SR RES ASSOC PHARMACOL, AYERST RES LABS, 77- *Mem:* Pharmacol Soc Can; Soc Toxicol Can. *Res:* Electropharmacology. *Mailing Add:* Ayerst Res Labs PO Box 6115 Montreal PQ H3C 3J2 Can

JARBOE, CHARLES HARRY, b Louisville, Ky, Oct 3, 28. CHEMICAL PHARMACOLOGY. *Educ:* Univ Louisville, BSc, 51, PhD(chem), 56. *Prof Exp:* Chemist, E I du Pont de Nemours & Co, 51-53; asst, AEC, Univ Louisville, 56, res asst prof org chem, 56-58, res assoc pharmacol, Sch Med, 58-62, assoc prof, health sci ctr, 62-72, PROF PHARMACOL, SCH MED & DIR THERAPEUT & TOXICOL LAB, UNIV LOUISVILLE, 72- *Concurrent Pos:* Consult, Brown & Williamson Tobacco Corp, 57-58, chief scientist, 58-61, consult, 62-64; spec fel, Nat Heart Inst, 61-; asst dean planning & proj coordr, Univ Louisville, 65-67, actg chmn dept pharmacol, 68; vis scientist, Sci Div, Abbott Labs, 70-71; consult, Am Horse Shows Asn, 73-; vis prof, Med Col Va, Va Commonwealth Univ, 74; Ky Med Assistance Prog Formulary Subcomt & Pest Control Adv Bd, Ky Environ Qual Comn, 78-; vis prof, Med Sch, Aucklund Univ, 79 & Univ Utah, 80. *Mem:* Am Chem Soc; The Chem Soc; Am Acad Clin Toxicol; Am Soc Pharmacol & Exp Therapeut; NY Acad Sci. *Res:* Chemical aspects of drug action; human pharmacokinetics; design of synthetic drugs with selective action. *Mailing Add:* Dept of Pharmacol Sch of Med Univ of Louisville Louisville KY 40202

JARBOE, THOMAS RICHARD, b Paxton, Ill, Aug 23, 45; m 70; c 4. PLASMA PHYSICS. *Educ:* Univ Ill, BS, 67; Univ Calif, Berkeley, PhD(plasma physics), 75. *Prof Exp:* Physicist optics, Naval Weapons Ctr, China Lake, Calif, 68; physicist fusion res, 74-80, ASSOC GROUP LEADER, LOS ALAMOS NAT LAB, 80- *Res:* Interaction of plasma and magnetic field in an implosion heated theta pinch; goal is to understand and improve this method of plasma heating. *Mailing Add:* 172 Piedra Loop White Rock NM 60627

JARCHO, LEONARD WALLENSTEIN, b New York, NY, Aug 12, 16. NEUROLOGY. *Educ:* Harvard Univ, AB, 36; Columbia Univ, MA, 37, MD, 41. *Prof Exp:* Instr physiol, Col Physicians & Surgeons, Columbia Univ, 41; Denison fel, Johns Hopkins Univ, 46-47, asst med, 48-51, instr, 51-52; from asst prof med to assoc prof neurol, 53-63, chmn neurol div, Sch Med, 59-65, chmn dept, 65-81, neurologist-in-chief, Med Ctr, 65-81, PROF NEUROOL, COL MED, UTAH UNIV, 63- *Concurrent Pos:* Archbold fel med, Johns Hopkins Univ, 48-50, asst physician, Outpatient Dept, 48-52, Nat Found Infantile Paralysis fel, 50-52; asst chief med, Vet Admin Hosp, Salt Lake City, Utah, 53-57, chief med serv, 57, neurol serv, 59; spec clin trainee, NIH, Nat Hosp, London, 58 & Mass Gen Hosp, Boston, 58-59; neurologist-in-chief, Salt Lake County Gen Hosp, 59-65. *Mem:* Am Physiol Soc; Am Neurol Asn; Am Asn Res Nerv & Ment Dis; Am Acad Neurol; Am Fedn Clin Res. *Res:* Neurophysiology; neuromuscular disease. *Mailing Add:* 1497 Devonshire Dr Salt Lake City UT 84108

JARDETZKY, OLEG, b Belgrade, Yugoslavia, Feb 11, 29; nat US; m 52, 65; c 3. MOLECULAR BIOLOGY, PHARMACOLOGY. *Educ:* Macalester Col, BA, 50; Univ Minn, MD, 54, PhD(chem physiol), 56. *Hon Degrees:* DSc, Macalester Col, 74; LLD, Calif Western Univ, 78. *Prof Exp:* Res asst physiol, Univ Minn, 50-54; Nat Res Coun fel chem, Calif Inst Technol, 56-57; assoc pharmacol, Harvard Med Sch, 57-59, asst prof, 59-66; dir dept biophys & pharmacol, Merck Sharp & Dohme Res Labs, NJ, 66-68, exec dir basic med sci, Merck Inst Therapeut Res, 68-69; actg chmn, 73-74, PROF PHARMACOL, SCH MED, STANFORD UNIV, 69-, DIR, MAGNETIC RESONANCE LAB, 75- *Concurrent Pos:* Irvine McQuarrie scholar award, 54; consult, Mass Gen Hosp, 61-67; vis prof, State Univ NY Buffalo, 63; consult coun drugs, AMA, 64; Japan Chem Soc lectr, Univ Tokyo, 65; vis scientist, Cambridge Univ, 65-66; Chem Students Asn lectr, Univ Amsterdam, 66; basic sci lectr, Med Ctr, Univ Calif, San Francisco, 68; vis prof, State Univ NY Albany, 70; USSR Acad Sci lectr, 70; chmn, Nat Comn, 10th Int Conf on Magnetic Resonance Biol Syst, Stanford Univ, 82; adv bd mem, 22nd Cong Appl Mgt Planning & Eng Resources Eval, 82. *Mem:* AAAS; Am Chem Soc; Am Soc Biol Chemists; Biophys Soc; Int Soc Magnetic Resonance. *Res:* Molecular mechanisms of protein function; biological applications of nuclear magnetic resonance. *Mailing Add:* Dept of Pharmacol Stanford Univ Stanford CA 94305

JARDINE, D(ONALD) A(NDREW), b Kingston, Ont, July 23, 30; div; c 2. COMPUTER SCIENCE. *Educ:* Queen's Univ Ont, BSc, 52, MSc, 54; Univ Del, PhD, 57. *Prof Exp:* Res engr, Du Pont Can Ltd, 56-68, res assoc, 68-70; assoc prof, 70-73, head dept, 73-78, PROF COMPUT SCI, QUEEN'S UNIV ONT, 73- *Concurrent Pos:* Pres, Common Comput Users Group, 66-68. *Mem:* Asn Comput Mach. *Res:* Data base management systems; data description languages. *Mailing Add:* 53 Silver St Kingston ON K7M 2P6 Can

JARDINE, DOUGLAS MARSHALL, b Colorado Springs, Colo, Dec 12, 29; m 50; c 3. MECHANICAL ENGINEERING. *Educ:* Univ Colo, BS, 52. *Prof Exp:* Proj mgr eng construct, Douglas Jardine Construct, 52-60, pres, 61-75; PROG MGR SOLAR ENERGY SYSTS, KAMAN SCI CORP, KAMAN CORP, 75- *Concurrent Pos:* Consult, Metrek Div, Mitre Corp, 76-77; mem, Int Comt Energy Conserv As-Built Community, Nat Acad Sci/Eng Building Res Adv Bd, 76-; mem, Gov Solar Adv Comt, Colo, 77- *Mem:* Am Soc Heat Refrig & Air-Conditioning Engrs. *Res:* Commercialization of preferred solar heating and cooling systems and combined photovoltaic power systems. *Mailing Add:* Kaman Sci Corp PO Box 7463 Colorado Springs CO 80933

JARDINE, IAN, b Glasgow, Scotland, Sept 17, 48. MASS SPECTROMETRY, IMMUNOPHARMACOLOGY. *Educ:* Univ Glasgow, BSc, 70, PhD(chem), 73. *Prof Exp:* Fel pharmacol, Med Sch, Johns Hopkins Univ, 73-76; asst prof med chem & pharmacog, Sch Pharm & Pharmacol Sci, Purdue Univ, West Lafayette, 76-79; assoc prof, 79-80, CONSULT PHARMACOL, MAYO CLINIC, 79-; ASSOC PROF PHARMACOL, UNIV MINN, 79- *Mem:* Am Chem Soc; Am Soc Mass Spectrometry; Sigma Xi. *Res:* Development of mass spectrometric methods for pharmacological and biochemical analysis; drug metabolism, particularly cancer chemotherapeutic and immunoactive agents. *Mailing Add:* Dept Pharmacol Mayo Clin Rochester MN 55901

JARDINE, JOHN MCNAIR, b Moncton, NB, June 25, 19; m 45; c 2. ATOMIC ENERGY, MATHEMATICAL STATISTICS. *Educ:* Mt Allison Univ, BSc, 40; McGill Univ, MSc, 48. *Prof Exp:* Res chemist, Refining Div, Eldorado Mining & Refining Ltd, 48-51, chief analyst, 51-53, chief chemist, 53-62, supt metall lab, Res & Develop Div, 62-69, res supt, Eldorado Nuclear Ltd, 69-72; scientific adv mining, Atomic Energy Control Bd, Can, 72-81. *Honors & Awards:* Can Forces Decoration, Can Govt, 60. *Mem:* Fel Chem Inst Can; Can Soc Chem Eng. *Res:* Analytical chemistry in the Canadian uranium industry; solvent extraction of uranium and thorium; separation of copper, cobalt and nickel by solvent extraction; development of process for production of hafnium free zirconium metal from zircon sands; transportation of radioactive materials; uranium mining and milling. *Mailing Add:* Eng 467 Broadview Ave Ottawa ON K2A 2L2 Can

JAREM, JOHN, b Jarembina, Czech, July 4, 21; US citizen; m; c 4. ELECTRICAL ENGINEERING. *Educ:* Polytech Inst Brooklyn, BEE, 47, MEE, 50; Univ Pa, MS, 57, PhD(plasma physics), 60. *Prof Exp:* Electronic res engr, Tele-Register Corp, NY, 47; asst prof elec eng & math, US Naval Postgrad Sch, 48-51; math specialist, Lockheed Aircraft Corp, Calif, 51-54; mem systs eng tech staff, Radio Corp Am, NJ, 54-59, engr, 59-62; sr staff mem, Inst Defense Anal, 62-63; staff engr dir & systs engr, Radio Corp Am, 63-64; head dept elec eng, 64-68, PROF ELEC ENG, DREXEL UNIV, 64- *Concurrent Pos:* Consult, Radio Corp Am, 64-65, Inst Defense Anal, 64- & Aero Chem, 66- *Mem:* Sr mem Inst Elec & Electronics Engrs; Am Phys Soc. *Res:* Systems engineering; applied mathematics; plasma physics. *Mailing Add:* Dept of Elec Eng 32nd & Chestnut Sts Philadelphia PA 19104

JARETT, LEONARD, b Lubbock, Tex, Aug 25, 36; m 62; c 3. CLINICAL PATHOLOGY, BIOCHEMISTRY. *Educ:* Rice Univ, BA, 58; Wash Univ, MD, 62. *Prof Exp:* Intern path, Barnes Hosp, St Louis, Mo, 62-63, resident, 63-64; res assoc, Sect Cellular Physiol, Lab Biochem, Nat Heart Inst, 64-66; from instr path to assoc prof path & med, Washington Univ, 66-75, head div lab med, 69-75, prof path & med, Sch Med, 75-80; PROF & CHMN DEPT PATH & LAB MED, SCH MED, UNIV PA, 80- *Concurrent Pos:* Dir labs & head div lab med, Barnes Hosp, 69-80; mem sci adv bd, St Jude Children's

Res Hosp, 80. *Honors & Awards:* David Rumbough Award, Juv Diabetes Found, 80. *Mem:* Endocrine Soc; Acad Clin Lab Physicians & Scientists; Am Soc Biol Chemists; Am Fedn Clin Res; fel Am Soc Clin Path. *Res:* Biochemical and ultrastructural techniques in the study of the mechanism of insulin action. *Mailing Add:* Dept Path & Lab Med Box 671 HUP 3400 Spruce Street Philadelphia PA 19104

JARGIELLO, PATRICIA, b Erie, Pa, July 9, 44. MOLECULAR GENETICS. *Educ:* Mercyhurst Col, BA, 66; Univ Pittsburgh, PhD(microbiol), 73. *Prof Exp:* Lab asst, Fed Bur Invest, 66-67; teaching asst biol, Univ Pittsburgh, 67-68; instr, Univ Parana, Brazil, 72-73; fel pediat, 73-76, instr, 74-76, RES ASST PROF MICROBIOL, MED SCH, UNIV PITTSBURGH, 77- *Concurrent Pos:* Vis fel cytogenetics, Southbury Training Sch Hosp, 74. *Mem:* Am Soc Human Genetics; Genetics Soc Am; Tissue Cult Asn; Am Soc Microbiol; AAAS. *Res:* Regulation of genes coding for enzymes involved in deoxynucleoside catabolism and deoxyribose utilization in salmonella; regulation of globin chain synthesis and hemoglobin formation in human fibroblast-rabbit erythroblast heterokaryons; ribose metabolism in hepatoma; metaphase chromosome isolation. *Mailing Add:* Dept Microbiol Sch Med Univ Pittsburgh Pittsburgh PA 15206

JARGON, JERRY ROBERT, b Beckemeyer, Ill, Aug 2, 39; m 63; c 3. PETROLEUM ENGINEERING, CHEMICAL ENGINEERING. *Educ:* Univ Ill, BS, 63; Univ Denver, MS, 67. *Prof Exp:* Assoc engr res, Chicago Bridge & Iron Co, 62; assoc engr, 63-66, engr, 66-72, adv engr prod res, 72-77, SR ENGR PETROL TECHNOL, MARATHON OIL CO, 77- *Concurrent Pos:* Lectr continuing educ courses, Soc Petrol Engrs, 73-74, prog comt, Rocky Mt Region, 74-75, formation evalu comt, Nat Meeting, 75, mem, Monogr Rev Comt Gas Well Performance, 77- *Mem:* Soc Petrol Engr Assoc Inst Mech Engrs; Res Soc Am. *Res:* Reservoir modeling and engineering; pressure transient testing in wells; multiphase flow in wells and pipelines. *Mailing Add:* Marathon Oil Co PO Box 269 Littleton CO 80160

JARIWALA, SHARAD LALLUBHAI, b Bombay, India, Oct 15, 40; m 69. CHEMICAL ENGINEERING. *Educ:* Univ Bombay, BSChE, 62; Johns Hopkins Univ, PhD(chem eng), 66. *Prof Exp:* Res engr, Tenneco Chem, Inc, 66-70; sr scientist, Fermentation Res & Develop, 70-75, head, Fermentation Prods Production, 75-76, mgr, 77-79, GROUP MGR, FERMENTATION PRODS PRODUCTION, THE UPJOHN CO, 80- *Mem:* Am Inst Chem Engrs. *Res:* Developing new technology for the separation and recovery of antibiotics from fermentation broths; separations technology; reaction engineering in fixed and fluidized beds; liquid phase oxidations. *Mailing Add:* 512 Barberry Kalamazoo MI 49002

JARKE, FRANK HENRY, b Bloomington, Ill, Mar 28, 46; m 71. PHYSICAL CHEMISTRY, ANALYTICAL CHEMISTRY. *Educ:* Southern Ill Univ, BA, 69; Ill Inst Technol, MS, 74. *Prof Exp:* Asst chemist, ITT Res Inst, 69-73, assoc chem, 73-78, res chemist odor sci, 78-81; MGR ANAL SERV, CHEM WASTE MGT, RIVERDALE, ILL, 81- *Mem:* Am Chem Soc; AAAS; Soc Appl Spectros; Am Soc Heating, Refrig & Air-Conditioning Engrs; NY Acad Sci. *Res:* Fundamental and applied research of odors and air pollution; development and use of both subjective and objective methods using humans as detectors. *Mailing Add:* Chem Waste Mgt Inc 150 W 137th St Riverdale IL 60627

JARMAKAN, JAY M, US citizen. PEDIATRIC CARDIOLOGY. *Educ:* Damascus Univ, BCP, 56, MD, 62. *Prof Exp:* Pediat resident, Buffalo Children's Hosp & Children's Hosp Philadelphia, 63-65; fel pediat cardiol, Children's Hosp Pittsburgh, 65-66; fel, Med Ctr, Duke Univ, 66-68, asst prof pediat, 68-73; assoc prof, 73-78, DIR CARDIOPULMONARY LAB & PROF PEDIAT, MED CTR, UNIV CALIF, LOS ANGELES, 78- *Mem:* Soc Pediat Res; fel Am Col Cardiol; Am Heart Asn. *Res:* Developmental myocardial function with emphasis on congenital heart disease and the effect of hypoxia on cardiac cell function. *Mailing Add:* Dept of Pediat Univ of Calif Med Ctr Los Angeles CA 90024

JARMIE, NELSON, b Santa Monica, Calif, Mar 24, 28; m 52; c 2. NUCLEAR PHYSICS. *Educ:* Calif Inst Technol, BS, 48; Univ Calif, PhD(physics), 53. *Prof Exp:* Res physicist, Radiation Lab, Univ Calif, 50-53; PROF PHYSICS, LOS ALAMOS GRAD CTR, UNIV NMEX, 57-; MEM STAFF, LOS ALAMOS NAT LAB, 53- *Concurrent Pos:* Vis asst prof, Univ Calif, 59-60; partic, Vis Scientist Prog, 65- *Mem:* Fel AAAS; fel Am Phys Soc. *Res:* Low energy nuclear physics; low and medium energy particle physics; astrophysics. *Mailing Add:* Dept AS Mail Stop 456 Los Alamos Nat Lab Los Alamos NM 87545

JARMOLOW, KENNETH, b Lebanon, Conn, Sept 15, 24; m 47; c 2. FLUID & SOLID MECHANICS. *Educ:* Mass Inst Technol, SB & AE, 48. *Prof Exp:* Engr aeronaut, Martin Co, 48-53, design specialist, 53-54, group engr, 54-56, chief aeronaut staff, 56-58, res staff, 58-60, mgr res & develop, aeronaut, physics & mat, 60-63, dir metals, physics, biol & math, Res Inst Advan Studies, 63-74, CORP DIR, RES & DEVELOP, MARTIN MARIETTA LABS, 74- *Concurrent Pos:* Mem adv comts res & technol, NASA, 71-77 & Nat Adv Coun Space Systs & Technol, 77- *Mem:* AAAS; Am Inst Aeronaut & Astronaut; Am Astronaut Soc. *Res:* Supersonic aerodynamics; solid body mechanics; aircraft and rocket design; space physics; stability and control of aircraft and rockets; trajectory analysis; optimization. *Mailing Add:* Martin Marietta Labs 1450 S Rolling Rd Baltimore MD 21227

JARNAGIN, RICHARD CALVIN, b Dallas, Tex, Aug 26, 30; m 52; c 2. PHYSICAL CHEMISTRY. *Educ:* Southern Methodist Univ, BS, 52; Yale Univ, PhD, 58. *Prof Exp:* Res chemist, Wright Air Develop Ctr, US Air Force, 53-55; from instr to assoc prof, 58-68, PROF CHEM, UNIV NC, CHAPEL HILL, 68- *Concurrent Pos:* Guggenheim fel, 67-68 & NSF fel, Sandia Nat Labs, 78-79. *Mem:* Am Chem Soc; fel Am Phys Soc. *Res:* Electrical and optical properties of molecular systems; photo conduction in organic solids and liquids; kinetics of excited molecular states; electronic and geometric structure of surface complexes. *Mailing Add:* Dept of Chem Univ of NC Chapel Hill NC 27514

JAROLMEN, HOWARD, b New York, NY, Oct 19, 37; m 66; c 2. MEDICAL MICROBIOLOGY, GENETICS. *Educ:* Alfred Univ, BA, 58; Hahnemann Med Col, MS, 60, PhD(microbiol), 64. *Prof Exp:* NIH fel genetics, Cornell Univ, 64-67; res bacteriologist, Am Cyanamid Co, 67-70, group leader bact chemother, 70-74, head dept microbiol & chemother, 74-76, GROUP LEADER FERMENTATION PROCESS RES & DEVELOP DEPT, LEDERLE LABS DIV, AM CYANAMID CO, 76- *Mem:* Am Soc Microbiol; Soc Indust Microbiol. *Res:* In vitro and vivo studies of transferable resistance amongst the Enterobacteriaceae; veterinary microbiology; prophylaxis and therapy of experimental infections; bacterial mutagenicity testing; antibiotic discoveries, discovery of antimycobacterials and antiparasitics; strain and media improvement for antibiotic-producing cultures. *Mailing Add:* Lederle Labs Pearl River NY 10965

JARON, DOV, b Tel-Aviv, Israel, Oct 29, 35; US citizen. BIOMEDICAL ENGINEERING. *Educ:* Univ Denver, BS, 61; Univ Pa, PhD(biomed eng), 67. *Prof Exp:* Sr res assoc, Maimonides Med Ctr, 67-70; dir surg res lab, Sinai Hosp, Detroit, 70-73; assoc prof biomed eng, Univ RI, 73-77, prof, 77-80; PROF & DIR BIOMED ENG & SCI, INST DREXEL UNIV, 80- *Concurrent Pos:* Consult circultory syst devices panel, Food & Drug Admin, 76-79; chmn, Sixth Ann New Eng Bioeng Conf, 78. *Mem:* Biomed Eng Soc; AAAS; NY Acad Sci; Inst Elec & Electronics Engrs; Am Soc Artificial Internal Organs. *Res:* Development, evaluation and implementation of cardiac assist devices; control and optimization of assisted circulation; cardiovascular modeling and assessment of function; biomedical instrumentation; computer applications to health care. *Mailing Add:* Biomed Engr & Sci Inst Drexel Univ Philadelphia PA 19104

JAROS, STANLEY E(DWARD), b Syracuse, NY, Mar 23, 19; m 42, 59; c 6. CHEMICAL ENGINEERING. *Educ:* Syracuse Univ, BChE, 40, MChE, 42. *Prof Exp:* Chem engr, Exxon Res & Eng Co, 42-55, asst dir, Chem Develop Div, 55-57, dir, 57-61, assoc dir, Process Eng Div, 61-65, res coordr, Chem Planning Staff, 65-66, res coordr, New Projs Develop, 66-72, res coordr, Corp Res Feasibility Unit, 72-78; CONSULT, 78- *Mem:* Am Chem Soc; Am Inst Chem Engrs. *Res:* Translating research results to commercial projects in the process industries. *Mailing Add:* 1199 Monticello Rd Lafayette CA 94549

JAROSLOW, BERNARD NORMAN, b New York, NY, Nov 4, 24; m 46; c 2. IMMUNOLOGY. *Educ:* City Col New York, BS, 47; Univ Iowa, MS, 48; Univ Chicago, PhD(immunol), 53. *Prof Exp:* Asst bacteriologist, 53-57, ASSOC bacteriologist, 57-69, immunologist, 69-77, ECOLOGIST, BIOL DIV, ARGONNE NAT LAB, 77- *Concurrent Pos:* La State Univ fel trop med, 59; Guggenheim fel, Walter Eliza Hall Inst, Australia, 64-65. *Mem:* Am Asn Immunol; Radiation Res Soc; Ecol Soc Am. *Res:* Immunity to parasites; antibody formation; effects of radiation and hibernation on immunity; aging and the immune response; cellular immunity; evolution. *Mailing Add:* Div Environ Impact Studs Argonne Nat Lab Argonne IL 60439

JAROWSKI, CHARLES I, b Baltimore, Md, July 29, 17; m 45; c 3. PHARMACEUTICAL CHEMISTRY. *Educ:* Univ Md, BS, 38, PhD(pharmaceut chem), 43. *Prof Exp:* Fel, Univ Ill, 42-44; res chemist, Wyeth Inc, Pa, 44-46; chief chemist, Vick Chem Co, NY, 46-48; res chemist, Chas Pfizer & Co, Inc, 48-50, mgr pharmaceut res & develop, 50-60, dir, 60-69; assoc prof, 69-75, PROF PHARMACEUT, ST JOHNS UNIV, NY, 75-, CHMN, DEPT ALLIED HEALTH & INDUST SCI, 78- *Mem:* Am Pharmaceut Asn. *Res:* Synthesis of antibacterial agents, antioxidants, and medicinals; antioxidant for food and drug industry; germicidal steam aerosolic compounds; antibiotic derivatives; drug detoxification; scientific nutrition; drug delivery systems. *Mailing Add:* Dept of Pharmaceut St Johns Univ New York NY 11439

JARRETT, HOWARD STARKE, JR, b Charleston, WVa, Oct 24, 27; m 51; c 4. MAGNETISM, SOLID STATE PHYSICS. *Educ:* Rensselaer Polytech Inst, BS, 47, MS, 48; Mass Inst Technol, PhD(physics), 51. *Prof Exp:* Res physicist, 51-55, RES SUPVR, CENT RES DEPT, E I DU PONT DE NEMOURS & CO, INC, 55- *Concurrent Pos:* Prog co-chmn, Conf Magnetism & Magnetic Mat, 65, conf chmn, 69, chmn adv comn, 70. *Mem:* Fel Am Phys Soc. *Mailing Add:* 805 Sycamore Lane Wilmington DE 19807

JARRETT, NOEL, b Long Eaton, Eng, Nov 17, 21; nat US; m 49; c 4. CHEMICAL ENGINEERING. *Educ:* Univ Pittsburgh, BS, 48; Univ Mich, MS, 51. *Prof Exp:* Sales engr indust oil sales, Freedom-Valvoline Oil Co, 49-50; res engr smelting, 51-55, sect head chem eng, 55-59, asst chief process metall div, 60-69, mgr, 69-73, TECH DIR SMELTING RES & DEVELOP, ALCOA LABS, ALUMINUM CO AM, 73- *Mem:* Nat Acad Eng; Am Inst Chem Engrs; Am Inst Mining, Metall & Petrol Engrs; Electrochem Soc; Am Soc Metals. *Res:* Electrochemical cell development; optimization of Hall-Heroult Process; coker reactor; cell development of Alcoa Smelting Process; pollution control by scrubbing of chlorine from furnace effluent; high purity Al via crystallization. *Mailing Add:* Aluminum Co of Am Alcoa Labs Alcoa Center PA 15069

JARRETT, STEVEN MICHAEL, b New York, NY, Mar 17, 36; m 61; c 4. PHYSICS. *Educ:* City Col New York, BS, 56; Univ Mich, MS, 58, PhD(physics), 63. *Prof Exp:* Res assoc physics, Univ Mich, 62-63; sr scientist, TRG, Inc, Control Data Corp, NY, 63-66; sr res, Coherent Radiation Labs, Calif, 66-71; pres, Quantum Systs Corp, 71-75; ENG PROJ MGR, SPECTRA PHYSICS, 75- *Mem:* Am Phys Soc; Optical Soc Am. *Res:* Lasers, especially gas, solid state and dye lasers; optics; spectroscopy. *Mailing Add:* Spectra Physics 1250 W Middlefield Rd Mountain View CA 94042

JARROLL, EDWARD LEE, JR, b Huntington, WVa, Jan 4, 48; m 75. BIOLOGY, PARASITOLOGY. *Educ:* WVa Univ, AB, 69, MS, 71, PhD(biol), 77. *Prof Exp:* From instr to asst prof biol, Salem Col, 73-77; microbiologist, WVa Dept Health, 77; FEL MICROBIOL, HEALTH SCI CTR, UNIV ORE, 77- *Mem:* Am Soc Trop Med & Hyg; Am Soc Parasitologists; AAAS. *Res:* Giardia and Trichomonas culture; physiology, immunology, and epidemiology; efficacy of disinfectants on Giardia cyst viability; helminth population biology. *Mailing Add:* Dept of Microbiol & Immunol 3181 SW Sam Jackson Park Rd Portland OR 97201

JARUZELSKI, JOHN JANUSZ, b Poland, Oct 4, 26; nat US; m 56; c 1. INDUSTRIAL ORGANIC CHEMISTRY. *Educ:* Alliance Col, BS, 51; Pa State Univ, PhD(chem), 54. *Prof Exp:* Res chemist, Pittsburgh Plate Glass Co, 54-56; fel, Mellon Inst, 56-59; res chemist prod develop div, US Steel Corp, 59-60; sr chemist, Esso Res & Eng Co, 60-74, SR STAFF CHEMIST, EXXON CHEM CO, 74- *Mem:* Am Chem Soc. *Res:* Substitution reactions of aromatic hydrocarbons, especially chloroalkylations; esterification and polyesterification of alcohols and phenols; epoxydation and epoxy resins; thermosetting resins and reinforced plastics; chemistry of lubricants and additives. *Mailing Add:* 475 Channing Ave Westfield NJ 07090

JARVIK, JONATHAN WALLACE, b Charleston, SC, Mar 18, 45. ORGANELLE MORPHOGENESIS. *Educ:* Columbia Col, BA, 67; Mass Inst Technol, PhD(biol), 75. *Prof Exp:* Helen Hay Whitney fel, Yale Univ, 75-78; ASST PROF BIOL SCI, CARNEGIE-MELLON UNIV, 78- *Mem:* Genetics Soc Am; Am Soc Microbiol; Am Soc Cell Biol. *Res:* Genetic biochemical and ultrastructural analysis of eucaryotic flagellar morphogenesis. *Mailing Add:* Dept Biol Sci Carnegie-Mellon Univ 4400 5th Ave Pittsburgh PA 15213

JARVIK, LISSY F, b The Hague, Neth; nat US; m 54; c 2. HUMAN GENETICS. *Educ:* Hunter Col, AB, 46; Columbia Univ, MA, 47, PhD(physiol), 50; Western Reserve Univ, MD, 54; Am Bd Pediat, dipl. *Prof Exp:* Asst psychiat, Columbia Univ, 46-48, res assoc, 48-50; asst, Sch Med, Western Reserve Univ, 53; intern, Mt Sinai Hosp, New York, 54-55; sr res scientist med genetics, Radiation Safety Officer, NY State Psychiat Inst, 55-62, assoc res scientist & assoc attend psychiatrist, 63-72; PROF PSYCHIAT, UNIV CALIF, LOS ANGELES, 72- *Concurrent Pos:* NSF traveling fel, Int Cong Human Genetics, Denmark, 56; fel, Vanderbilt Clin, 57-58; resident pediat, Columbia-Presby Med Ctr, 55-56, from asst clin prof to assoc clin prof psychiat, Columbia Univ, 62-72; res psychiatrist, NY State Psychiat Inst, 69-72; vis assoc prof, Univ Calif, Los Angeles, 70-71; chief psychogenetics unit, Vet Admin Hosp Brentwood, Los Angeles, 70-; mem joint psychotomimetic adv comt, Nat Inst Ment Health-Food & Drug Admin, 70-72; tech comt res & develop, White House Conf Aging, 71-73; vis McCleod prof, Univ Adelaide, SAustralia, 81. *Mem:* Fel Am Psychol Asn; Am Soc Human Genetics; Soc Study Social Biol; Am Psychopath Asn; Am Psychiat Asn. *Res:* Psychiatric genetics and aging, especially twin studies; gerontology; cytogenetics; psychiatric, psychological, gerontological and pediatric aspects of medical genetics. *Mailing Add:* 760 Westwood Plaza Los Angeles CA 90024

JARVIK, MURRAY ELIAS, b New York, NY, June 1, 23; m 54; c 2. PHARMACOLOGY. *Educ:* City Col New York, BS, 44; Univ Calif, Los Angeles, MA, 45; Univ Calif, Berkeley, MD, 51, PhD, 52. *Prof Exp:* Res technician phys chem, Rockefeller Inst, 43-44; asst exp psychol, Univ Calif, Los Angeles, 44-45; asst physiol psychol, Univ Calif, Berkeley, 45-46, comp psychol, 47 & pharmacol, Med Sch, 51; res assoc comp physiol psychol, Yerkes Labs, Fla, 51-53; lectr physiol psychol, Columbia Univ, 53-55; vis asst prof, Univ Calif, 55; res assoc psychopharmacol, Long Island Biol Asn, NY, 55-56; from asst prof to prof pharmacol, Albert Einstein Col Med, 56-72, prof psychiat, 69-72; PROF PSYCHIAT & PHARMACOL, UNIV CALIF, LOS ANGELES, 72- *Concurrent Pos:* Res assoc, Mt Sinai Hosp, NY, 53-55; adj asst prof physiol psychol, Grad Div, NY Univ, 57; managing ed, Psychopharmacologia, 65; mem psychopharmacology study sect, NIMH, 65-70; adv comt abuse of stimulant & depressant drugs, Bur Drug Abuse Control, Food & Drug Admin, 66-68; chief res, Psychopharmacol Unit, Vet Admin Hosp, Los Angeles, 72- *Mem:* Am Soc Pharmacol & Exp Therapeut; fel Am Psychol Asn; fel NY Acad Sci; Am Col Neuropsychopharmacol; Int Brain Res Orgn. *Res:* Effects of drugs upon learning and retention; neurophysiological basis of learning; localization of drug effects in the central nervous system; psychopharmacology; primate behavior; techniques for chronic implantation of arterial catheters. *Mailing Add:* Dept of Psychiat Univ Calif Ctr for Health Sci Los Angeles CA 90024

JARVINEN, RICHARD DALVIN, b Virginia, Minn, Dec 5, 38; m 61; c 2. MATHEMATICS. *Educ:* St John's Univ, Minn, BA, 60; Vanderbilt Univ, MAT, 61; Syracuse Univ, PhD(math), 71. *Prof Exp:* Analyst missile simulations, Remington Rand Univac, 61-62; asst prof math, Carleton Col, 67-72; assoc prof math, 72-80, PROF MATH & STATIST, ST MARY'S COL, 80- *Concurrent Pos:* Researcher math & statist, St Mary's Col, 75- *Mem:* Math Asn Am; Sigma Xi. *Res:* Bases in topological linear spaces; applications of undergraduate mathematics; computer generated movies and slides for learning mathematics. *Mailing Add:* Dept of Math St Mary's Col Winona MN 55987

JARVIS, ALBERT E, pharmaceutical chemistry, see previous edition

JARVIS, BRUCE B, b Van Wert, Ohio, Sept 30, 42; m 63; c 2. ORGANIC CHEMISTRY. *Educ:* Ohio Wesleyan Univ, BA, 63; Univ Colo, PhD(chem), 66. *Prof Exp:* Instr chem, Northwestern Univ, 66-67; asst prof, 67-71, assoc prof, 71-79, PROF CHEM, UNIV MD, COLLEGE PARK, 79- *Mem:* AAAS; Am Chem Soc; Sigma Xi. *Res:* Natural product chemistry; nucleophilic displacements; sulfur chemistry and molecular rearrangements; mycotoxins. *Mailing Add:* Dept of Chem Univ of Md College Park MD 20742

JARVIS, CHRISTINE WOODRUFF, b Raleigh, NC, June 19, 49; m 71. TEXTILE SCIENCE, PHYSICAL CHEMISTRY. *Educ:* Univ NC, Chapel Hill, 71; Mass Inst Technol, PhD(phys chem), 76. *Prof Exp:* Res assoc textiles, 76, instr chem, 76-78, ASST PROF TEXTILES, CLEMSON UNIV, 78- *Mem:* Am Chem Soc; Am Phys Soc; Am Asn Textile Technologists; Sigma Xi; Am Asn Textile Chemists & Colorists. *Res:* Fiber physics; nonwovens; chemical kinetics of polymer flammability; cotton dust analysis. *Mailing Add:* Dept of Textiles Sirrine Hall Clemson Univ Clemson SC 29631

JARVIS, FLOYD ELDRIDGE, JR, b Richmond, Va, Aug 15, 21; m 53; c 1. GENETICS. *Educ:* Univ Richmond, AB, 47; Va Polytech Inst, PhD(biol), 56. *Prof Exp:* Assoc prof, 55-65, PROF BIOL, RADFORD UNIV, 65- *Mem:* Entom Soc Am. *Res:* Inheritance of insecticidal resistance; residual effectiveness of insecticide formulations. *Mailing Add:* Dept of Biol Radford Univ Radford VA 24142

JARVIS, FRANCIS GEORGE, b St Paul, Minn, Mar 13, 15; m 45. BACTERIOLOGY, BIOCHEMISTRY. *Educ:* Univ Wash, Seattle, BS, 45; Univ Wis, MS, 46, PhD(biochem), 49. *Prof Exp:* Asst prof bact, Univ Kans, 49-50; assoc prof, Idaho State Col, 50-57; bacteriologist, Rocky Mt Lab, 57-60; prof bact, Idaho State Univ, 60-76, prof microbiol & biochem, 76-80; RETIRED. *Mem:* AAAS; Am Soc Microbiol; Sigma Xi. *Res:* Biochemical research with penicillin; Pseudomonas aeruginosa and macromolecules of viruses and bacteria. *Mailing Add:* 2569 N E 85th St Seattle WA 98115

JARVIS, JACK REYNOLDS, b Menomonie, Wis, Oct 31, 15; m 45; c 2. MEDICINE. *Educ:* Birmingham-South Col, BS, 34; Vanderbilt Univ, MD, 38; Am Bd Psychiat & Neurol, dipl, 45. *Prof Exp:* Assoc prof psychiat, Med Col Ala, 48-61; ASST PROF PSYCHIAT, SCH MED, EMORY UNIV, 61- *Concurrent Pos:* Chief psychiat serv, Vet Admin Hosp, Birmingham, Ala, 55-61; area chief psychiat, Vet Admin Ga, 61-65; staff physician, Regional Off, Vet Admin, 65-; staff physician, Vet Admin Hosp, 66- *Mem:* AMA; Am Psychiat Asn. *Res:* Psychiatry. *Mailing Add:* Vet Admin Hosp 1670 Clairmont Rd Decatur GA 30033

JARVIS, JAMES GORDON, b Aultsville, Ont, July 13, 24; nat US; m 47; c 2. PHYSICS. *Educ:* Queen's Univ, Can, BSc, 45; Univ Rochester, MS, 54. *Prof Exp:* Instr, Queen's Univ, Can, 45-46; res assoc, Photomat Div, 46-69, SR LAB HEAD, RES LABS, EASTMAN KODAK CO, 69- *Honors & Awards:* Jour Award, Soc Motion Picture & TV Eng, 57. *Mem:* Optical Soc Am; Am Soc Photog Sci & Eng. *Res:* Colorimetry; physiological optics; solid state physics; electrophotography. *Mailing Add:* Res Labs B-81 Eastman Kodak Co Rochester NY 14650

JARVIS, JOHN FREDERICK, b Montreal, Can, June 22, 41; US citizen; m 63; c 2. COMPUTER SCIENCE. *Educ:* Univ Fla, BS, 62; Duke Univ, PhD(physics), 67. *Prof Exp:* Res assoc physics, Duke Univ, 67-68; MEM TECH STAFF SYSTS RES, BELL LABS, 68- *Concurrent Pos:* Vis lectr, Princeton Univ, 78-79. *Mem:* Inst Elec & Electronics Engrs; AAAS; Am Astron Soc; Soc Mfg Engrs. *Res:* Computer graphics, computer vision, automated inspection, pattern recognition; robotics; astronomy. *Mailing Add:* Bell Labs 4E610 Holmdel NJ 07733

JARVIS, JOHN J, b Donnelson, Tenn, Aug 7, 41; m 63. OPERATIONS RESEARCH, SYSTEMS ANALYSIS. *Educ:* Univ Ala, BSIE, 63, MSIE, 65; Johns Hopkins Univ, PhD(opers res), 68. *Prof Exp:* Numerical analyst, NASA, 63; res asst, Univ Ala, 63-65; res assoc, Johns Hopkins Univ, 65-68; assoc prof, 68-76, PROF INDUST & SYSTS ENG, GA INST TECHNOL, 76- *Concurrent Pos:* Consult, Southern Rwy Syst, 69-, Quant Systs Assoc, Inc, 70-, Schimpeler/Corradino Assoc, 70- & Environ Protection Agency, 78- *Mem:* Opers Res Soc Am; Inst Mgt Sci; Soc Indust & Appl Math; Am Inst Indust Engrs. *Res:* Modeling and methodology in operations research and network theory-analysis. *Mailing Add:* 4912 Vermack Rd Atlanta GA 30338

JARVIS, LACTANCE AUBREY, b Homer, Mich, Sept 7, 21; m 43; c 2. ORGANIC POLYMER CHEMISTRY. *Educ:* Mich State Univ, BS, 43. *Prof Exp:* Chem engr, Firestone Rubber & Tire Co, 43-49; chemist rubber & plastics, Wyandotte Chem Corp, 49-55; chem engr, Whirlpool Corp, 55-60; dir res, Modern Plastics Corp, Mich, 60-66; MGR MAT RES, CLARK EQUIP CO, 66- *Mem:* Am Chem Soc; Soc Plastics Engrs; Sigma Xi. *Res:* Development and application of plastic materials and processes. *Mailing Add:* PO Box 64 Buchanan MI 49107

JARVIS, NELDON LYNN, b Salt Lake City, Utah, Nov 16, 35; m 53; c 4. SURFACE CHEMISTRY. *Educ:* Brigham Young Univ, BS, 52; Kans State Univ, PhD(agron), 58. *Prof Exp:* Nat Acad Sci-Nat Res Coun res assoc, US Naval Res Lab, 57-59, phys chemist, 59-69, HEAD SURFACE CHEM BR, CHEM DIV, US NAVAL RES LAB, 69- *Concurrent Pos:* Lectr, Am Univ, 64 & 69- *Mem:* Sigma Xi. *Res:* Adsorption-desorption phenomena at solid-liquid and liquid-air interfaces; wetting and spreading phenomena; tribology; surface chemistry of ocean; surface analysis. *Mailing Add:* 7915 Fort Hunt Rd Alexandria VA 22308

JARVIS, RICHARD STANLEY, b Nottingham, Eng, Feb 13, 49; m 78. HYDROLOGY. *Educ:* Cambridge Univ, BA, 70, PhD(geog), 75. *Prof Exp:* Lectr geog, Durham Univ, 73-74; ASSOC PROF GEOG, STATE UNIV NY BUFFALO, 74- *Mem:* Am Geophys Union; Asn Am Geogrs; Inst Brit Geogrs. *Res:* Network analysis of hydrologic systems; fluvial geomorphology; digitized data systems in hydrology and geomorphology; computer applications in geography; biogeography. *Mailing Add:* Dept of Geog 415 Fronczak Hall Buffalo NY 14260

JARVIS, ROGER GEORGE, b Hugglescote, Eng, Apr 26, 28; Can citizen; m 54; c 2. MATHEMATICS. *Educ:* Oxford Univ, BA, 49, MA & DPhil(physics), 53. *Prof Exp:* Fel nuclear physics, Nat Res Coun, Chalk River, 53-54; res fel, Imp Chem Indust, Univ Liverpool, 55; mem, Atomic Power Div, Gen Elec Co, Eng, 56; SR RES OFF, APPL MATH BR, ATOMIC ENERGY CAN, LTD, 56- *Mem:* Can Appl Math Soc; Am Math Soc; Math Asn Am. *Res:* Operations research, mainly in nuclear energy; risk analysis; mathematical modeling. *Mailing Add:* Box 1570 Deep River ON K0J 1P0 Can

JARVIS, STEPHEN, JR, applied mathematics, see previous edition

JARVIS, WILLIAM ROBERT, b Olney, Eng, Nov 15, 27; m 52; c 1. PLANT PATHOLOGY, MYCOLOGY. *Educ:* Univ Sheffield, BSc, 51; Univ London, PhD(plant Path), 53, DIC, 53. *Prof Exp:* Prin sci officer, Scottish Hort Res Inst, 53-74; asst specialist, Univ Calif, 63-64; scientist, Dept Sci & Indust Res, New Zealand, 69-70; HEAD, PLANT PATH SECT, CAN DEPT AGR, 74- *Mem:* Am Phytopath Soc; Mycol Soc Am; Brit Fedn Plant Pathologists; Brit Mycol Soc; Can Phytopathol Soc. *Res:* Biology of botrytis species; powdery mildews; biological control; diseases of field and greenhouse vegetables, small berry fruits and ornamental bulb crops. *Mailing Add:* Agr Can Res Sta Harrow ON N0R 1G0 Can

JARZEN, DAVID MACARTHUR, b Cleveland, Ohio, Oct 19, 41; m 62; c 2. PALYNOLOGY, PALEOBOTANY. *Educ:* Kent State Univ, BS, 67, MA, 69; Univ Toronto, PhD(geol), 73. *Prof Exp:* CUR FOSSIL PLANTS, NAT MUS CAN, 73- *Mem:* Can Asn Palynologists; Am Asn Stratig Palynologists; Asn Trop Biol; Int Asn Angiosperm Paleobot; Bot Soc Am. *Res:* Palynological investigations of terminal cretaceous and lower Tertiary floras, to discover the paleoenvironmental setting based on the botanical affinities of the fossil pollen and spores. *Mailing Add:* Nat Mus of Natural Sci Ottawa ON K1A 0M8 Can

JARZYNSKI, JACEK, b Warsaw, Poland, Mar 28, 35; US citizen. PHYSICS. *Educ:* Imp Col, Univ London, BS, 57, PhD(physics), 61. *Prof Exp:* Fel phys acoustics, Cath Univ Am, 61-62; tech officer optics, Imp Chem Industs, Ltd, Gt Brit, 63; assoc prof physics, Am Univ, 63-71; RES PHYSICIST, NAVAL RES LAB, 71- *Concurrent Pos:* Consult, Naval Ord Lab, 67-70. *Mem:* Acoust Soc Am; Am Phys Soc. *Res:* Parametric underwater acoustic arrays and sound propagation; development of ultrasonic methods for study of materials; measurement of thermodynamic properties of metals and alloys and comparison with pseudopotential theory. *Mailing Add:* Naval Res Lab 4555 Overlook Ave SW Washington DC 20375

JASCH, LAURA GWENDOLYN, b Chicago, Ill, June 17, 45. DEVELOPMENTAL BIOLOGY. *Educ:* Univ Ill, BSc, 67, BA, 67, PhD(anat), 72. *Prof Exp:* Res assoc biochem, Univ Ill, 72-73, assoc anat, 73-74, asst prof anat, 74-76; ASST PROF ANAT, UNIV BC, 76- *Mem:* Am Asn Anatomists; Am Zool Soc; Can Fed Biol Soc; Soc Develop Biol; Soc Develop Biol. *Res:* Biochemical basis for morphogenesis in limb regeneration; proteins in normal and dystrophic muscle. *Mailing Add:* 360 E 37th Vancouver BC V5W 1E7 Can

JASELSKIS, BRUNO, b Suraitciai, Lithuania, Mar 9, 24; nat US; m 55; c 6. ANALYTICAL CHEMISTRY, INORGANIC CHEMISTRY. *Educ:* Union Univ, NY, BS, 52; Iowa State Univ, MS, 54, PhD, 55. *Prof Exp:* Instr chem, Univ Mich, 56-59, asst prof, 59-62; from asst prof to assoc prof, 62-69, PROF CHEM, LOYOLA UNIV CHICAGO, 69- *Mem:* Am Chem Soc; AAAS; Sigma Xi. *Res:* Complex ions and their application to analytical problems; solution chemistry of Xenon compounds; determination of micro amounts of various substances. *Mailing Add:* Dept of Chem Loyola Univ Chicago IL 60626

JASHNANI, INDRA, b Ghotki, Pakistan, Nov 2, 44. CHEMICAL ENGINEERING. *Educ:* Indian Inst Technol, Bombay, BTech, 67; Univ Cincinnati, PhD(chem eng), 71. *Prof Exp:* Fel chem & nuclear eng, Univ Cincinnati, 71-72; sr engr, A P T, Inc, 72-74; staff mem, Arthur D Little, Inc, 74-77; SR STAFF ENGR, MARTIN MARIETTA CORP, 77- *Mem:* Am Inst Chem Engrs; Am Chem Soc; Air Pollution Control Asn. *Res:* Environmental control, particularly air, water and solid, for process industries and utility boilers. *Mailing Add:* 5060 Ten Mills Rd Columbia MD 21044

JASIN, HUGO E, b Buenos Aires, Arg, Jan 22, 33; US citizen; m 66; c 3. INTERNAL MEDICINE, IMMUNOLOGY. *Educ:* Univ Buenos Aires, MD, 56. *Prof Exp:* Fel internal med, Univ Tex Southwestern Med Sch, 59-62 & 64-65; Nuffield fel, Med Res Coun Rheumatism Res Unit, Eng, 62-64; from instr to asst prof, 65-71, assoc prof, 71-78, PROF INTERNAL MED, UNIV TEX SOUTHWESTERN MED SCH, 78- *Concurrent Pos:* Arthritis Found fel, 70-72; USPHS career develop award, 73-77; mem, Gen Med Study Sect, USPHS, 74-78. *Mem:* Fel Am Col Physicians; Am Asn Immunologists; Am Rheumatism Asn; Am Soc Clin Invest. *Res:* Immunological mechanisms in rheumatic diseases and chronic inflammation. *Mailing Add:* Univ of Tex Southwestern Med Sch 5323 Harry Hines Blvd Dallas TX 75235

JASINSKI, DONALD ROBERT, b Chicago, Ill, Aug 27, 38; m 64; c 4. CLINICAL PHARMACOLOGY. *Educ:* Loyola Univ, Ill, 56-59; Univ Ill, MD, 63. *Prof Exp:* Intern, Res & Educ Hosps, Univ Ill, Chicago, 63-64, fel neuropharmacol, 64-65; staff physician, 65-67, chief opiate unit, 67-68, chief clin pharmacol sect, 69-77, DIR, ADDICTION RES CTR, NAT INST DRUG ABUSE, 77- *Concurrent Pos:* Assoc mem grad fac, Dept Pharmacol, Col Med, Univ Ky; clin asst prof pharmacol, Univ Ky; clin prof pharmacol & toxicol & mem grad fac, Univ Louisville, Ky. *Mem:* AAAS; Am Soc Clin Pharmacol & Therapeut; Am Soc Pharmacol & Exp Therapeut; Soc Neurosci; Int Brain Res Orgn. *Res* Neuropharmacology; psychopharmacology. *Mailing Add:* Nat Inst Drug Abuse Addiction Res Ctr PO Box 5200 Baltimore MD 21224

JASINSKI, JERRY PETER, b Newport, NH, July 28, 40; m 66; c 2. X-RAY CRYSTALLOGRAPHY, BIOCHEMISTRY. *Educ:* Univ NH, BA, 64, MST, 68; Worcester Polytech Inst, MNS, 68; Univ Wyo, PhD(chem), 74. *Prof Exp:* Teacher, high schs, NY, NH & Vt, 64-70; teaching & res assoc chem, Univ Wyo, 70-73; Assoc Western Univs fel, Los Alamos Sci Lab, 73-74; res assoc, Univ Va, 74-75; teacher chem & physics, Springfield High Sch, Vt, 75-78; ASST PROF CHEM, KEENE STATE COL, NH, 78-, COORDR, PHYSICAL SCI, 81- *Mem:* Sigma Xi; Am Chem Soc; AAAS; Am Asn Physics Teachers. *Res:* Experimental and theoretical molecular electronic spectroscopy; solid state and coordination chemistry; x-ray crystallography; bioinorganic chemistry; industrial chemistry. *Mailing Add:* 12 Orchard Lane Springfield VT 05156

JASKOSKI, BENEDICT JACOB, b Velva, NDak, July 25, 15; m 56; c 1. PARASITOLOGY. *Educ:* Jamestown Col, AB, 39; Univ Notre Dame, MS, 42, PhD(zool), 50. *Hon Degrees:* DSc, Ill Col Podiatry, 64. *Prof Exp:* Prin pub sch, NDak, 39-40; asst instr biol, Univ Notre Dame, 49-50; asst prof, Creighton Univ, 50-54; assoc prof, 54-63, PROF BIOL, LOYOLA UNIV CHICAGO, 63- *Concurrent Pos:* Fel trop med, La State Univ, 61; assoc Am Univ Beirut, 66; USPHS res award; Am Cancer Soc inst grant partic. *Mem:* Fel AAAS; Am Soc Parasitologists; Am Soc Zoologists; Am Micros Soc; fel Am Pub Health Asn. *Res:* Parasites of captive animals; nematode parasites; biochemistry and physiology of parasitic nematodes; human parasitology; culture of metazoan parasites. *Mailing Add:* Dept of Biol Loyola Univ Chicago IL 60626

JASMIN, GAETAN, b Montreal, Que, Nov 24, 24; m 52; c 3. PATHOLOGY. *Educ:* St Laurent Col, BA, 45; Univ Montreal, MD, 51, PhD(exp med), 56; CSPQ, 68; FRCP(C), 78. *Prof Exp:* From asst prof exp path to assoc prof path, 56-67, PROF PATH, UNIV MONTREAL, 67-, CHMN DEPT, 70- *Concurrent Pos:* Med res assoc, Nat Res Coun Can, 58-; ed, Revue Canadienne de Biologie. *Mem:* Soc Exp Biol & Med; Am Physiol Soc; Histochem Soc; Can Soc Clin Invest; Int Acad Path. *Res:* Endocrinology; muscle diseases and cancer. *Mailing Add:* Dept of Path Fac Med Univ Montreal Montreal PQ H3C 3J7 Can

JASNY, GEORGE R, b Katowice, Poland, June 6, 24; US citizen; m 51; c 2. CHEMICAL ENGINEERING. *Educ:* Univ Wash, Seattle, BS, 49; Mass Inst Technol, ScM, 52. *Prof Exp:* Engr, Y-12 plant, 50-56, eng dept head, 56-62, tech div head, 62-65, chief engr, 65-71, dir eng, 71-80, VPRES ENG & COMPUT SCI, NUCLEAR DIV, UNION CARBIDE CORP, 80- *Mem:* Fel Am Inst Chem Engrs; AAAS; Sci Res Soc NAm; Nat Soc Prof Engrs. *Res:* Solvent extractions; enriched uranium scrap processing; plant design; quality control; uranium enrichment. *Mailing Add:* 106 Dixie Lane Oak Ridge TN 37830

JASON, ANDREW JOHN, b Detroit, Mich, Jan 27, 38; m 62; c 1. MOLECULAR PHYSICS, SURFACE PHYSICS. *Educ:* Mass Inst Technol, SB, 59; Univ Chicago, MS, 60, PhD(physics), 67. *Prof Exp:* Res assoc physics, Univ Chicago, 67-68; asst prof, 68-73, ASSOC PROF PHYSICS, UNIV ALA, 73- *Mem:* AAAS; Am Phys Soc. *Res:* Field ionization; atomic physics; high field studies of atoms and molecules; kinetics of evaporation; ion optics; mass spectrometry; optical properties of surfaces. *Mailing Add:* Dept of Physics Univ of Ala University AL 35486

JASON, EMIL FRED, b Edwardsville, Ill, Aug 7, 27; m 55; c 2. CHEMISTRY. *Educ:* Lincoln Univ, Mo, BS, 49; Washington Univ, St Louis, MA, 55, PhD(chem), 57. *Prof Exp:* Teacher pub sch, Ethiopia, 49-51; fel, Wash Univ, St Louis, 57-58; asst proj chemist, Stand Oil Co, Ind, 58-60, proj chemist, 60; asst prof chem, Lincoln Univ, Mo, 60-71; PROF CHEM & ASST VPRES, SOUTHERN ILL UNIV, 71- *Mem:* Am Chem Soc. *Res:* Organic syntheses; oxidation; free radical reactions. *Mailing Add:* Dept of Chem Southern Ill Univ Edwardsville IL 62025

JASPER, DONALD EDWARD, b La Grande, Ore, Dec 30, 18; m 43; c 2. VETERINARY MEDICINE, CLINICAL PATHOLOGY. *Educ:* State Col Wash, BS, 40, DVM, 42; Iowa State Col, MS, 44; Univ Minn, PhD(vet med), 47. *Prof Exp:* Asst clinician, Iowa State Col, 42-44; from asst prof to assoc prof, 47-54, PROF CLIN PATH, SCH VET MED, UNIV CALIF, DAVIS, 54- *Concurrent Pos:* Dean sch vet med & asst dir exp sta, Univ Calif, Davis, 54-62; sr NIH fel, 68; Fulbright Hays sr res scholar, 75; Fulbright Hays Distinguished Prof, 78. *Honors & Awards:* Borden Award, 67. *Mem:* US Animal Health Asn; Am Vet Med Asn; Am Soc Microbiol. *Res:* Bovine mastitis; mycoplasma infections. *Mailing Add:* Sch of Vet Med Univ of Calif Davis CA 95616

JASPER, DONALD KOHEN, b Miami, Fla. BIOLOGY. *Educ:* Howard Univ, BS, 52; Univ York, PhD(cell ultrastruct & physiol), 69. *Prof Exp:* Electron microscopist, Rockefeller Inst Med Res, 56-60; res asst cytol, Columbia Univ, 60-66; res fel cell biol, Univ York, 66-69; asst prof, 69-75, ASSOC PROF CELL BIOL, ILL INST TECHNOL, 75- *Concurrent Pos:* NSF grant, 70; fac res fel, Argonne Nat Lab, 81. *Mem:* AAAS; Am Soc Cell Biol; Electron Microscopy Soc Am; Am Inst Biol Sci. *Res:* Cellular ultrastructure as related to function, especially as mucosal epithelial and muscle cell structure and function. *Mailing Add:* Dept of Biol Ill Inst of Technol Chicago IL 60616

JASPER, HERBERT HENRY, b La Grande, Ore, July 27, 06; nat Can; m 40; c 2. NEUROPHYSIOLOGY. *Educ:* Reed Col, BA, 27; Univ Ore, MA, 29; Univ Iowa, PhD(psychol), 31; Univ Paris, Dr es Sc(physiol), 35; McGill Univ, MDCM, 43. *Hon Degrees:* Dr, Univ Bordeaux, 49, Univ Aix-Marseille, 60, McGill Univ, 71, Univ Western Ont, 77 & Queens Univ, 79. *Prof Exp:* Instr psychol, Univ Ore, 27-29; instr, Univ Iowa, 29-31; asst prof, Brown Univ, 33-38; asst prof neurol & neurosurg, McGill Univ, 38-46; prof exp neurol & dir neurophysiol & electroencephalog labs, Montreal Neurol Inst, 46-64; res prof neurophysiol, Labs Neurol Sci, 65-76, & dir med res coun group neurol sci, Dept Physiol, 67-76, EMER PROF NEUROPHYSIOL, UNIV MONTREAL, 76- *Concurrent Pos:* First pres, Int Fedn Socs Electroencephalog & Clin Neurophysiol, 47-49; founding ed-in-chief & publisher, Int J Electroencephalog & Clin Neurophysiol, 49-62. *Honors & Awards:* Ralph Gerard Prize, Soc Neurosci, 81. *Mem:* Am Physiol Soc; Am Neurol Asn; Am Electroencephalog Soc (1st pres, 46-48); fel Royal Soc Can; Int Brain Res Orgn (1st exec secy, 61-63, hon exec secy, 71-72). *Res:* Brain research; behavioral sciences; neurology. *Mailing Add:* 4501 Sherbrooke W #1F Westmount PQ H3Z 1E7 Can

JASPER, MARTIN THEOPHILUS, b Hazlehurst, Miss, Mar 19, 34; m 63; c 5. MECHANICAL & CHEMICAL ENGINEERING. *Educ:* Miss State Univ, BS, 55, MS, 62; Univ Ala, PhD(mech eng), 67. *Prof Exp:* Engr, Am Cast Iron Pipe Co, 55-56; plant metallurgist, Vickers, Inc, 57-59; design engr, Missile Div, Chrysler Corp, 59-60; from instr to assoc prof, 60-75, PROF

MECH ENG, MISS STATE UNIV, 75- *Mem:* Am Soc Eng Educ; Am Soc Mech Engrs; Soc Mfg Engrs; NY Acad Sci. *Res:* Parametric analysis, modeling and optimization of thermal and hydrodynamic systems. *Mailing Add:* Dept of Mech Eng Miss State Univ State College MS 39762

JASPER, N(ORMAN) H(ANS), b Ger, May 10, 18; nat US; m 40; c 2. MECHANICS, NAVAL ARCHITECTURE. *Educ:* City Col New York, BME, 41; Univ Md, MS, 52; Cath Univ Am, DEng(aeronaut eng), 56. *Prof Exp:* Naval architect, Sci & Test Sect, Puget Sound Naval Shipyard, 41-46; proj engr & supvr exp sect, David Taylor Model Basin, US Navy, 46-48, proj engr & dep div head, 48-57, supvry physicist & head vibrations & seaworthiness br, 57-60, head ship dynamics div & asst to lab dir, 60-61, tech dir, US Navy Mine Defense Lab, 61-68, tech dir, Naval Ship Res & Develop Lab, 68-72, chief tech adv, Comdr, Operational Test & Eval Force, US Navy, 72-73; RETIRED. *Concurrent Pos:* Consult, Nat Acad Sci. *Honors & Awards:* US Dept Navy & US Dept Defense Distinguished Civilian Serv Awards, 62. *Mem:* Fel Am Soc Mech Engrs; Soc Naval Archit & Marine Engrs; Am Soc Naval Engrs. *Res:* Vibrations; dynamics of structures; structural seaworthiness; mine warfare; underwater technology; administration of research and development. *Mailing Add:* 100 Cherry St 103 Panama City FL 32401

JASPER, ROBERT LAWRENCE, b Windsor, Ky, Apr 24, 18; m 44, 62; c 1. ENDOCRINOLOGY, TOXICOLOGY. *Educ:* Berea Col, AB, 49; Univ Ky, MS, 50; Purdue Univ, PhD, 55. *Prof Exp:* Instr physiol, Univ Ky, 50-51; sect chief environ physiol, Army Med Res Lab, Ky, 54-58; co-dir endocrinol, Endocrine Consult Lab, 58-62; pharmacologist-in-chg, Pharm Lab, Agr Res Serv, USDA, Md, 62-64, asst chief staff officer pharmacol, Pesticides Regulation Div, 64-67, pharmacologist-in-chg, Pharm Lab, 67-70, head safety & biol sect, Chem & Biol Invest Br, Tech Serv Div, Off Pesticides Progs, 70-73, ASST BR CHIEF, CHEM & BIOL INVEST BR, TECH SERV DIV, OFF PESTICIDES PROGS, ENVIRON PROTECTION AGENCY, 73- *Mem:* Am Inst Chemists; Am Chem Soc; Am Soc Zoologists; Am Asn Lab Animal Sci; NY Acad Sci. *Res:* Effect of low environmental temperature on fat metabolism; tissue and steroid metabolism; development and clinical application of hormone assays; pesticides toxicology. *Mailing Add:* Environ Protection Agency Bldg 402 Agr Res Ctr Beltsville MD 20705

JASPER, SAMUEL JACOB, b Lancaster, Ohio, Nov 1, 21; m 44; c 3. MATHEMATICS. *Educ:* Univ Ohio, AB, 43; Ohio State Univ, MA, 46; Univ Ky, PhD(math), 48. *Prof Exp:* Instr math, Univ Ohio, 43-44 & Univ Ky, 46-48; asst prof, Kent State Univ, 48-51 & East Tenn State Col, 51-54; from asst prof to assoc prof, 54-67, PROF MATH, OHIO UNIV, 67- *Concurrent Pos:* Asst dean col arts & sci, Ohio Univ, 58-63, dir hon col, 63-66, chmn dept math, 67-68. *Mem:* Math Asn Am. *Res:* Differential geometry; homogeneous functions; calculus of variations. *Mailing Add:* Dept of Math Ohio Univ Athens OH 45701

JASPERSE, JOHN R, b Seattle, Wash, May 8, 35; m 58; c 2. PLASMA PHYSICS, SPACE PHYSICS. *Educ:* Harvard Univ, BA, 57; Northeastern Univ, MS, 63, PhD(physics), 66. *Prof Exp:* Res physicist, Arthur D Little, Inc, 59-65; RES PHYSICIST, AIR FORCE GEOPHYSICS LAB, 65- *Concurrent Pos:* Lectr, Northeastern Univ, 68-71; vis scientist, Mass Inst Technol, 79- *Honors & Awards:* Marcus D O'Day Mem Award. *Mem:* Am Geophys Union; Sigma Xi; Am Phys Soc. *Res:* Quantum theory of atoms and molecules; scattering theory; three-body problem; electromagnetic theory; plasma theory; space physics. *Mailing Add:* Air Force Geophysics Lab Bedford MA 01731

JASPERSON, STEPHEN NEWELL, b Wisconsin Rapids, Wis, May 10, 41; m 65; c 1. SOLID STATE PHYSICS. *Educ:* Univ Wis, BS, 63; Princeton Univ, MA, 65, PhD(physics), 68. *Prof Exp:* Res assoc physics, Princeton Univ, 67-68 & Univ Ill, 68-70; asst prof, 70-74, ASSOC PROF PHYSICS, WORCESTER POLYTECH INST, 74- *Concurrent Pos:* Res scientist, Physics Br, Naval Weapons Ctr, 71- *Mem:* AAAS; Am Phys Soc. *Res:* Optical properties of metals and semiconductors; modulation spectroscopy techniques such as electroreflectance and polarization modulation. *Mailing Add:* Dept of Physics Worcester Polytech Inst Worcester MA 01609

JASS, HERMAN EARL, b Chicago, Ill, Mar 30, 18; m 47; c 2. BIOCHEMISTRY, PHARMACOLOGY. *Educ:* Univ Ill, BS, 39; Northwestern Univ, MS, 50, PhD(chem), 53. *Prof Exp:* Org chemist, Gas Res Dept, People's Gas Co, Ill, 40-41; chief biochemist, Helene Curtis Indust, Inc, 42-51; group leader biochem, Armour & Co, 53-55; assoc res dir, Revlon, Inc, 55-64; vpres res, Carter Prod Div, Carter-Wallace, Inc, 64-76; TECH MGT CONSULT, 76- *Concurrent Pos:* Guest lectr, Columbia Col Pharm, 64 & 65. *Honors & Awards:* Cosmetic Indust Buyers & Suppliers Award, 78. *Mem:* AAAS; Am Chem Soc; Soc Cosmetic Chem. *Res:* Proprietary drugs and toiletries; biochemistry and physiology of the skin; synthesis of topical therapeutic agents. *Mailing Add:* 29 Platz Dr Somerville NJ 08558

JASTAK, J THEODORE, b Astoria, NY, Dec 1, 36; m 62; c 3. ORAL SURGERY, ANESTHESIA. *Educ:* Seton Hall Col, DDS, 62; Univ Rochester, PhD(exp path), 67. *Prof Exp:* Resident oral surg, Henry Ford Hosp, Detroit, 67-69; ASSOC PROF ORAL SURG, DENT SCH & CLIN ASSOC PROF, MED SCH, UNIV ORE, 69- *Concurrent Pos:* Vis asst prof, Dent Sch, Univ Detroit, 68-69. *Mem:* AAAS; Am Soc Oral Surg; Am Dent Asn; Am Dent Soc Anesthesiol; Int Asn Dent Res. *Res:* Effects of renal failure on parathyroid function and calcium homeostasis; ketamine and innovar as outpatient anesthetic agents. *Mailing Add:* Ore Health Sci Univ Portland OR 97201

JASTRAM, PHILIP SHELDON, b Providence, RI, Feb 28, 20; m 47; c 2. PHYSICS. *Educ:* Harvard Univ, SB, 43; Univ Mich, PhD(physics), 48. *Prof Exp:* Res assoc, Radio Res Lab, Harvard Univ, 43-45; instr, Univ Mich, 48-49, res physicist, US Navy Proj, 49; asst prof physics, Wash Univ, St Louis, 49-55; from asst prof to assoc prof, 55-64, PROF PHYSICS, OHIO STATE UNIV, 64- *Concurrent Pos:* Orgn European Econ Coop fel, Copenhagen, 61; consult, US Agency Int Develop, India, 64, 65 & 68. *Mem:* AAAS; fel Am Phys Soc; Inst Elec & Electronics Eng; Am Asn Physics Teachers; Fedn Am Sci. *Res:* Nuclear structure and spectroscopy; angular and polarization correlation measurements; nuclear orientation at low temperatures; Mossbauer scattering. *Mailing Add:* Dept of Physics Ohio State Univ 174 W 18th Ave Columbus OH 43210

JASTROW, ROBERT, b New York, NY, Sept 7, 25. ATMOSPHERIC PHYSICS. *Educ:* Columbia Univ, BA, 44, MA, 45, PhD(physics), 48. *Prof Exp:* Fel, Univ Leiden, 48-49; mem, Inst Advan Study, Princeton Univ, 49-50; mem fac, Univ Calif, Berkeley, 50-53; asst prof physics, Yale Univ, 53-54; consult nuclear physics, US Naval Res Lab, 54-58; head theoret div, 58-61, DIR INST SPACE STUDIES, GODDARD SPACE FLIGHT CTR, NASA, 61- *Concurrent Pos:* Chmn lunar explor comt, NASA, 59-60, mem comt, 60-62; adj prof, Columbia Univ, 61- & Dartmouth Col, 74-; ed, J Atmospheric Sci, Am Meteorol Soc, 62-74. *Honors & Awards:* Arthur S Fleming Award, 65; NASA Medal, 68. *Mem:* Fel AAAS; fel Am Geophys Union; fel Am Phys Soc; Am Astron Soc. *Res:* Nuclear physics; physics of atmosphere, the moon and terrestrial planets. *Mailing Add:* 22 Riverside Dr New York NY 10023

JASTRZEBSKI, Z(BIGNIEW) D(AMAZY), b Warsaw, Poland, Sept 15, 10; nat US; m 48; c 2. CHEMICAL ENGINEERING. *Educ:* Warsaw Tech Univ, Dipl Ing, 35, DSc, 61. *Prof Exp:* Sr asst lectr & res engr, Road Res Inst, Warsaw Tech Univ, 34-39; dir, Res Labs, Kabul, Afghanistan, 39-43; prof appl chem & chem eng, head depts & vprin, Polish Univ Col, Eng, 46-53; prof chem eng, 53-76, head dept, 61-76, EMER PROF CHEM ENG, LAFAYETTE COL, 76- *Mem:* Am Soc Eng Educ; Asn Corrosion Engrs; Am Inst Chem Engrs; Brit Inst Chem Engrs. *Res:* Rheology; corrosion; process design; materials. *Mailing Add:* Dept of Chem Eng Lafayette Col Easton PA 18042

JASWAL, SITARAM SINGH, b Bham, India, Sept 15, 37. PHYSICS, MATHEMATICS. *Educ:* Univ Panjab, India, BSc, 58, MSc, 59; Mich State Univ, PhD(physics), 64. *Prof Exp:* Asst geophys, Oil & Natural Gas Comn, India, 59-60; asst physics, Univ Alta, 60-61 & Mich State Univ, 61-64; fel, Univ Pa, 64-66; from asst prof to assoc prof, 66-74, PROF PHYSICS, UNIV NEBR, LINCOLN, 74- *Concurrent Pos:* Vis scientist, Max Planck Inst Solid State Res, 74-75. *Mem:* Am Phys Soc. *Res:* Lattice dynamics of perfect and imperfect crystals; point defects in solids; electronic properties of metallic glasses; Raman scattering. *Mailing Add:* Behlen Lab of Physics Univ of Nebr Lincoln NE 68588

JATLOW, J(ACOB) L(AWRENCE), b Poland, Apr 7, 03; nat US; m 36; c 1. ELECTRONICS, COMMUNICATIONS ENGINEERING. *Educ:* Rensselaer Polytech Inst, EE, 24. *Prof Exp:* Develop engr, Conner Crouse Corp, 24-32; asst chief engr, F A D Andrea Radio Corp, 32-35; develop engr, Photo Positive Corp, 35-40; chief engr photochem res, Repub Eng Prod, Inc, 40-42; chief engr, Wire Transmission Div, Defense Commun Div, Int Tel & Tel, Inc, 42-54, assoc dir, Radio Transmission Lab, 54-60, dir, Systs Eng Lab, 60-64, tech dir commun, 64-77; RETIRED. *Mem:* Fel Inst Elec & Electronics Engrs; fel AAAS; NY Acad Sci. *Res:* Communications systems engineering; wire and radio transmission; switching systems; command and control systems; communication and electronic equipment. *Mailing Add:* 166 E 61st St New York NY 10021

JAUHAR, PREM P, b India, Sept 15, 39. GENETICS, PLANT BREEDING. *Educ:* Agra Univ, India, BS, 57, MS, 59; Indian Agr Res Inst, New Delhi, PhD, 65. *Prof Exp:* Asst cytogeneticist, Indian Agr Res Inst, 63-70, asst prof genetics, 70-72 & 75-76; sr sci officer cytology, Univ Col Wales, Welsh Plant Breeding Sta, UK, 72-75; res assoc agron, Univ Ky, 76-78; res geneticist bot & plant sci, Univ Calif, Riverside, 78-81; CYTOGENETICIST, DIV CYTOGENETICS & CYTOL, CITY HOPE NAT MED CTR, DUARTE, CALIF, 81- *Concurrent Pos:* Vis scientist, Welsh Plant Breeding Sta, UK, 72-75; post grad fac, Indian Agr Res Inst, New Delhi, 60-70; Genetics Soc Am travel award, 78. *Mem:* Genetics Soc Am; Crop Sci Soc Am; Am Genetic Asn; Fel Linnean Soc London; Indian Soc Genetics & Plant Breeding. *Res:* Regulatory mechanism that controls chromosome pairing in the polyploid species of Festuca; breeding work on Panicum and Pennisetum; tropical and temperature herbage crops; polyploidy and mutation breeding techniques. *Mailing Add:* 230 W Campus View Dr Riverside CA 92507

JAUMOT, FRANK EDWARD, JR, b Charleston, WVa, Aug 3, 23; m 47; c 2. SOLID STATE PHYSICS. *Educ:* Western Md Col, BS, 47, DSc, 66; Univ Pa, PhD(physics), 51. *Prof Exp:* Instr physics, Univ Pa, 51-52; chief physics, Metals Sect, Labs Res & Develop, Franklin Inst, 52-56; dir res & eng semiconductors, Delco Radio Div, 56-70, dir res & eng, 70-79, DIR ADVAN ENG, DELCO ELECTRONICS DIV, GEN MOTORS CORP, 79- *Concurrent Pos:* Instr asst, Univ Pa, 52-54, vis asst prof, 54-56. *Mem:* Am Phys Soc; Am Inst Aeronaut & Astronaut; Inst Elec & Electronics Engrs; Soc Auto Engrs; Am Asn Physics Teachers. *Res:* Order-disorder phenomena and other cooperative phenomena; diffusion in metals; thermoelectricity; semiconductors. *Mailing Add:* Delco Electronics Div Motors Corp PO 1104 Kokomo IN 46901

JAUSSI, AUGUST WILHELM, b Paris, Idaho, Aug 26, 25; m 55; c 6. PHYSIOLOGY. *Educ:* Univ Idaho, BS, 53; Brigham Young Univ, MS, 55; Okla State Univ, PhD, 60. *Prof Exp:* From instr to asst prof physiol, Okla State Univ, 56-62; from asst prof to assoc prof, 62-72, prof physiol, 72-77, PROF ZOOL, BRIGHAM YOUNG UNIV, 77- *Res:* Environmental effects on physiological activity. *Mailing Add:* Dept of Zool Brigham Young Univ Provo UT 84601

JAVAHER, JAMES N, b Tehran, Iran, Jan 1, 24; US citizen; m 63; c 4. MATHEMATICS. *Educ:* Univ Tehran, LLB, 46; San Jose State Col, BA, 50; Univ Calif, Berkeley, MA, 52; Stanford Univ, BS, 54; Univ Paris, ScD(math, physics), 60. *Prof Exp:* Instr math & eng, Sacramento City Col, 55-59 & 60-61; asst prof math & physics, 61-62, assoc prof, 62-66, PROF MATH, CALIF STATE COL, STANISLAUS, 66- *Concurrent Pos:* Chmn dept math, Stanislaus State Col, 61-70. *Mem:* Am Math Soc; Math Asn Am; Am Asn Physics Teachers. *Res:* Foundations of mathematics; applied mathematics. *Mailing Add:* Dept of Math 800 Monte Vista Ave Turlock CA 95380

JAVAID, JAVAID IQBAL, biochemistry, psychopharmacology, see previous edition

JAVAN, ALI, b Tehran, Iran, Dec 27, 26; nat US; m 62; c 1. PHYSICS. *Educ:* Columbia Univ, PhD(physics), 54. *Prof Exp:* Res assoc physics, Columbia Univ, 54-59; mem tech staff, Bell Tel Labs, Inc, 59-62; assoc prof, 62-64, prof, 64-78, FRANCIS WRIGHT PROF PHYSICS, MASS INST TECHNOL, 78- *Concurrent Pos:* Sr US Scientist Award, Humboldt Found, 80. *Honors & Awards:* Stuart Ballentine Medal, 62; Hertz Found Award, 66; Sepas Medal, Govt Iran, 71; Frederic Ives Medal, Optical Soc Am, 75. *Mem:* Fel Nat Acad Sci; fel Am Phys Soc; fel Optical Soc Am; Sigma Xi; fel Am Acad Arts & Sci. *Res:* Atomic spectroscopy and physics of quantum electronics. *Mailing Add:* Dept of Physics Mass Inst of Technol Cambridge MA 02139

JAVEL, ERIC, b Elizabeth, NJ, Mar 2, 47; m 68; c 2. NEUROPHYSIOLOGY. *Educ:* Johns Hopkins Univ, BA, 68; Univ Pittsburgh, PhD(bioacoust), 72. *Prof Exp:* DIR AUDITORY PHYSIOL, BOYS TOWN INST COMMUN DIS IN CHILDREN, 76- *Concurrent Pos:* NIH fel, Dept Neurophysiol, Med Sch, Univ Wis, 73-75; assoc prof otolaryngol & physiol, Sch Med, Creighton Univ; mem comt hearing & bioacoustics, Nat Acad Sci. *Mem:* Acoust Soc Am; Soc Neurosci; Asn Res Otolaryngol; Sigma Xi. *Res:* Stimulus coding in auditory nuclei; computer applications in physiology; developmental neurophysiology. *Mailing Add:* Boys Town Inst 555 N 30th St Omaha NE 68131

JAVICK, RICHARD ANTHONY, b Plains, Pa, Aug 29, 32; m 61; c 10. ANALYTICAL CHEMISTRY. *Educ:* King's Col, Pa, BS, 54; Pa State Univ, PhD(chem), 58. *Prof Exp:* Res chemist, E I du Pont de Nemours & Co, Del, 58-59; asst prof chem, King's Col, Pa, 59-61 & State assoc prof, 62-69; res assoc, Pa Univ, 61-62; sr res chemist, 69-80, RES ASSOC, CHEM RES & DEVELOP CTR, FMC CORP, 80- *Concurrent Pos:* Chmn dept chem, King's Col, Pa, 67-69. *Mem:* Am Chem Soc; Chem Mfg Asn. *Res:* Application of instrumental methods to analytical investigations; electrochemical kinetics; polymer chemistry, synthesis and applications thereof; applications of analytical methods to wastewater analysis. *Mailing Add:* Chem Res & Develop Ctr FMC Corp Box 8 Princeton NJ 08540

JAVID, MANSOUR, b Hamadan, Iran, Mar 25, 19; nat US. ELECTRICAL ENGINEERING. *Educ:* Univ Birmingham, BSc, 41; McGill Univ, MEng, 50, PhD, 56. *Prof Exp:* Consult engr, 45-49; lectr elec eng, McGill Univ, 50-52; asst prof, Ill Inst Technol, 53-55; from asst prof to assoc prof, 55-70, PROF ELEC ENG, CITY COL NEW YORK, 70- *Concurrent Pos:* Mem, Nat Electronic Conf, 54. *Mem:* Inst Elec & Electronics Engrs. *Res:* Field and circuit analysis; computer aided design. *Mailing Add:* Dept of Elec Eng City Col of New York New York NY 10031

JAVID, MANUCHER J, b Tehran, Iran, Jan 11, 22; nat US; m 51; c 4. NEUROSURGERY. *Educ:* Univ Ill, MD, 46; Am Bd Neurol Surg, dipl, 55. *Prof Exp:* Intern, Augustana Hosp, Ill, 46-47; resident gen surg, 47-48; resident neurosurg, 48-49; resident, New Eng Ctr Hosp, 50 & Mass Gen Hosp, 51-53; from instr to assoc prof, 53-62, chmn div, 63, PROF NEUROL SURG, SCH MED, UNIV WIS-MADISON, 62- *Concurrent Pos:* Fel neurosurg, Lahey Clin, Mss, 49; fel neuropath, Ill Neuropsychiat Inst, 49; res fel, Mass Gen Hosp, 50; teaching fel, Harvard Med Sch, 52. *Mem:* AAAS; AMA; fel Am Col Surg; Am Asn Neurol Surg; Soc Neurol Surgeons. *Res:* Intracranial pressure, cerebrovascular diseases and intracranial neoplasms. *Mailing Add:* Div Neurosurg Univ Wis Med Ctr Madison WI 53792

JAVINSKY, MARTIN A, b Chicago, Ill, Aug 26, 41; m 64; c 3. CHEMICAL ENGINEERING. *Educ:* Ill Inst Technol, BSChE, 63; Univ Mich, Ann Arbor, MSE, 65 & 66; PhD(chem eng), 67. *Prof Exp:* Res engr, Comput Systs Div, Chevron Res Co, 67-71; sr res engr, 71-73; econ analyst, Standard Oil of Calif, 73-77; supvr financial anal, 77-78, PLANNING CONSULT, CHEVRON USA, INC, 78- *Mem:* Am Inst Chem Engrs; Instrument Soc Am. *Res:* Computer control, process modelling and simulation, application of linear and nonlinear programming techniques; operations research; finance and economic analysis. *Mailing Add:* Chevron USA Inc 575 Market San Francisco CA 94103

JAVITT, NORMAN B, b New York, NY, Mar 9, 28; m 55; c 4. MEDICINE, PHYSIOLOGY. *Educ:* Syracuse Univ, AB, 47; Univ NC, PhD(physiol), 51; Duke Univ, MD, 54; Am Bd Internal Med, dipl, 62. *Prof Exp:* Intern med, Mt Sinai Hosp, New York, 54-55, asst resident, 57-58; Am Heart Asn adv fel, Col Physicians & Surgeons, Columbia Univ, 58-59; chief resident med, Mt Sinai Hosp, 60, res assoc, 61-62; from instr to asst prof, Sch Med, NY Univ, 62-68; assoc prof, 68-72, PROF MED, MED COL, CORNELL UNIV, 72-, HEAD DIV GASTROENTEROL, 70- *Concurrent Pos:* USPHS spec fel, Mt Sinai Hosp, 61-62; career investr, Health Res Coun City New York, 62- *Mem:* Am Fedn Clin Res; fel Am Col Physicians; Am Soc Clin Invest; Am Gastroenterol Asn; Am Asn Study Liver Dis. *Res:* Biochemical and physiological investigations related to human liver disease. *Mailing Add:* Dept of Med Cornell Univ Med Col NY Hosp New York NY 10021

JAVOR, GEORGE TIBOR, biochemistry, see previous edition

JAWA, MANJIT S, b Patiala, India, Aug 5, 34; m 64; c 2. APPLIED MATHEMATICS, CONTINUUM MECHANICS. *Educ:* Indian Inst Technol, PhD(appl math), 67. *Prof Exp:* Res asst statist, Panjab Govt, India, 56-58; lectr math Univ Cols, India, 58-63 & Indian Inst Technol, 66-67; asst prof appl math & eng mech, Univ Mo-Rolla, 67-70; assoc prof, Hartwick Col, 70-71; PROF MATH, FAYETTEVILLE STATE UNIV, 71- *Res:* Exact numerical analysis of fluid dynamics, heat transfer and magnetohydrodynamics problems on digital computers. *Mailing Add:* Dept of Math Fayetteville State Univ Fayetteville NC 28301

JAWAD, MAAN HAMID, b Baghdad, Iraq, Dec 2, 43; US citizen; m 68; c 2. STRUCTURAL ENGINEERING, ENGINEERING MECHANICS. *Educ:* Al-Hikma Univ, BSc, 64; Univ Kans, MS, 65; Iowa State Univ, PhD(struct eng), 69. *Prof Exp:* Bridge engr, Iowa State Hwy Comn, 67-68; design engr, 68-70, staff consult, 70-77, MGR ENG DESIGN, NOOTER CORP, 77- *Mem:* Am Soc Civil Engrs; Am Soc Mech Engrs. *Res:* Pressure vessels area, mainly layered vessels, expansion joints, and high pressure gaskets. *Mailing Add:* Nooter Corp PO Box 451 St Louis MO 63166

JAWED, INAM, b Sagar, India, Sept 27, 47; Pakistan citizen. PHYSICAL CHEMISTRY, CEMENT CHEMISTRY. *Educ:* Karachi Univ, BS, 66, MS, 68; Oxford Univ, PhD(chem), 71. *Prof Exp:* Asst prof phys chem, Peshawar Univ, 72-74; vis prof cement chem, Tokyo Inst Technol, 74-76; res scientist, 76-78, sr scientist cement chem, 78-80, HEAD ANAL CHEM DEPT, MARTIN MARIETTA LABS, 80- *Concurrent Pos:* Unesco fel, 74; Brit Coun fel, 68. *Mem:* Am Chem Soc; Am Ceramic Soc; Royal Inst Chem Brit. *Res:* Analytical chemistry of silicates and refractory materials; cement chemistry; kinetics of clinker formation and hydration of clinker minerals. *Mailing Add:* Dept Anal Chem Martin Marietta Labs Baltimore MD 21227

JAWETZ, ERNEST, b Vienna, Austria, June 9, 16; nat US; m 54; c 4. MICROBIOLOGY, MEDICINE. *Educ:* Univ Vienna, 37; Univ NH, MA, 40; Univ Calif, PhD(microbiol), 42; Stanford Univ, MD, 46. *Prof Exp:* Lectr bact, Univ Calif, 42-44; sr asst surgeon, NIH, 46-48; from asst prof to assoc prof bact, 48-53, chmn dept microbiol, 62-78, PROF MICROBIOL & MED & LECTR PEDIAT, SCH MED, UNIV CALIF, 54- *Concurrent Pos:* Almroth Wright lectr, London, 52 & 58; vis prof, Univ Shiraz, Iran, 77. *Honors & Awards:* Florey Mem lectr, Adelaide, 81. *Mem:* Am Soc Clin Invest; Am Soc Microbiol; Soc Exp Biol & Med; Am Asn Immunol; Am Acad Microbiol. *Res:* Clinical bacteriology; antibiotics; chemotherapy; infectious diseases; virology. *Mailing Add:* Dept of Microbiol & Med Univ of Calif Med Ctr San Francisco CA 94143

JAWOROWSKI, ANDRZEJ EDWARD, b Lublin, Poland, Dec 28, 42; m 65; c 1. SOLID STATE PHYSICS. *Educ:* Univ Warsaw, MSc, 66, PhD(physics), 74. *Prof Exp:* Teaching asst, Dept Physics, Univ Warsaw, 66-68, asst lectr exp physics, 68-74 & lectr solid state physics, 74-78; SR FEL, PHYSICS DEPT, INST STUDY DEFECTS SOLIDS, STATE UNIV NY, ALBANY, 78- *Concurrent Pos:* Res assoc, Radiation Physics Lab, Solid State Div, Inst Nuclear Res, Swierk, 67-74; prog head, Inst Physics, Polish Acad Sci, Warsaw, 76-77. *Honors & Awards:* Prize of Ministry Sci, Schs Acad Rank & Technol, Warsaw, Poland, 75. *Mem:* Europ Phys Soc; Am Phys Soc; Polish Phys Soc. *Res:* Defects in solids; radiation effects and damage; ion implantation; deep levels spectroscopy; positron annihilation in semiconductors. *Mailing Add:* Physics Dept State Univ NY Albany NY 12222

JAWOROWSKI, JAN W, b Augustow, Poland, Mar 2, 28; m 54. TOPOLOGY. *Educ:* Univ Warsaw, Magister, 52; Polish Acad Sci, PhD(math), 55. *Prof Exp:* Asst math, Univ Warsaw, 50-52, from adj to docent, 52-63; extraordinary prof, Math Inst, Polish Acad Sci, 63-64; assoc prof, Cornell Univ, 64-65; PROF MATH, IND UNIV, 65- *Concurrent Pos:* Fel, Polish Acad Sci, 57-58; NSF grant, Inst Advan Study, 60-61. *Mem:* Am Math Soc; Polish Math Soc. *Res:* Algebraic and geometric topology. *Mailing Add:* Dept of Math Ind Univ Bloomington IN 47401

JAWORSKI, CASIMIR A, b South Bend, Ind, Aug 1, 30. SOIL SCIENCE, HORTICULTURE. *Educ:* Purdue Univ, BSc, 52, MSc, 57; Rutgers Univ, PhD(soil sci), 62. *Prof Exp:* Resident hall counr, Purdue Univ, 54-56, res asst agron, 55-57, fac adv resident halls, 56-57; res fel soil, Rutgers Univ, 57-60, SOIL SCIENTIST, SOUTHERN REGION, SCI & EDUC ADMIN, AGR RES, USDA, 62- *Mem:* Am Soc Agron; Soil Sci Soc Am; Int Soc Hort Sci; Int Soc Soil Sci; AAAS. *Res:* Plant nutrition, chemistry and cultural practices; cultural practices for vegetable transplant production; systems for vegetable production; developing potatoes for the warm-humid regions of the world. *Mailing Add:* Ga Coastal Plain Sta Tifton GA 31794

JAWORSKI, ERNEST GEORGE, b Minneapolis, Minn, Jan 10, 26; m 50; c 3. BIOLOGICAL CHEMISTRY, MOLECULAR BIOLOGY. *Educ:* Univ Minn, BChem, 48; Ore State Col, MS, 50, PhD(biochem), 52. *Prof Exp:* Asst chem, Ore State Col, 48-49, asst biochem, 49-52; res biochemist, 52-54, res group leader, 54-60, scientist, 60-62, sr scientist, 62-70, DISTINGUISHED SCI FEL, MONSANTO CO, 70- *Concurrent Pos:* Mem, Frasch Found Awards Comt, Am Chem Soc, 69-; chmn, Gordon Conf Plant Cell & Tissue Culture, 73-75, trustee, Gordon Res Conf, Inc, 75-81; mem ed bd, J Am Soc Plant Physiologists, 73-83; mem panel, Int Cell Res Orgn UNESCO, 77-; chmn bd trustees, Gordon Res Conf Inc, 78-79. *Mem:* AAAS; Am Chem Soc; Sigma Xi; Am Soc Plant Physiologists; Weed Sci Soc Am. *Res:* Plant growth regulation, hormones and metabolism; plant chemotherapeutic investigations; mechanism of action of herbicides; radioisotope techniques; biosynthesis of chitin; plant cell and tissue culture; plant organogenesis; cell biology; molecular biology. *Mailing Add:* 11 Clerbrook Ladue MO 63124

JAWORSKI, JAN GUY, b Woonsocket, RI, Dec 7, 46; m 69; c 2. BIOCHEMISTRY. *Educ:* Col of the Holy Cross, BA, 68; Purdue Univ, PhD(biochem), 72. *Prof Exp:* Res biochemist, Dept Biochem & Biophys, Univ Calif, Davis, 72-74; ASST PROF CHEM, MIAMI UNIV, 74- *Mem:* AAAS. *Res:* Metabolism of prostaglandins, long chain fatty acids and lipids. *Mailing Add:* Dept of Chem Miami Univ Oxford OH 45056

JAY, GEORGE EDGAR, JR, public health administration, see previous edition

JAY, JAMES MONROE, b Ben Hill Co, Ga, Sept 12, 27; m 59; c 3. BACTERIOLOGY, MICROBIAL ECOLOGY. *Educ:* Paine Col, AB, 50; Ohio State Univ, MSc, 53, PhD(bact), 56. *Prof Exp:* Asst, Ohio State Univ, 53-55, Agr Exp Sta, 55-56, res assoc, 56-57; from asst prof to prof bact, Southern Univ, 57-61; from asst prof to assoc prof, 61-69, PROF BACT,

WAYNE STATE UNIV, 69- *Mem:* AAAS; Am Soc Microbiol; Inst Food Technologists; Am Chem Soc; Am Pub Health Asn. *Res:* Biochemistry of beef spoilage, rapid techniques for measuring meat spoilage; lysozyme production by bacteria; extracellular proteins of staphylococci; rapid determination of microorganisms in foods; microbial ecology; limulus lysate test; lipopolysaccharides in foods; selective culture media for gram positive and gram negative bacteria. *Mailing Add:* Dept of Biol Wayne State Univ Detroit MI 48202

JAYACHANDRAN, TOKE, b Madras, India; US citizen. STATISTICS, MATHEMATICS. *Educ:* V R Col, Nellore, India, BA, 51; Univ Wyo, MS, 62; Case Inst Technol, PhD(math statist), 67. *Prof Exp:* Res asst statist, Univ Wyo, 61-62; grad asst math, Case Inst Technol, 62-67; asst prof math, 67-70, ASSOC PROF MATH, NAVAL POSTGRAD SCH, 70- *Concurrent Pos:* Consult, Litton Sci Support Labs, Ft Ord, 68-72, BDM Corp, 72-75 & Sci Appln Inc, Monterey, 78-; opers analyst, Off Naval Res, Arlington, 75-77. *Mem:* Sigma Xi; Am Statist Asn; Am Math Soc. *Res:* Design of experiments, prediction intervals, reliability and life testing. *Mailing Add:* Dept of Math Naval Postgrad Sch Monterey CA 93940

JAYADEV, T S, b Bangalore, India; US citizen. ELECTRICAL ENGINEERING, PHYSICS. *Educ:* Univ Mysore, BSE, 58; Ill Inst Technol, MS, 62; Univ Notre Dame, PhD(elec eng), 68. *Prof Exp:* Asst prof elec eng, Karnatak Univ, India, 62-64, prof, 64-65; from asst prof to assoc prof, Univ Wis-Milwaukee, 68-76, prof elec eng, 76-78, mem lab surface studies, 68-78; MGR, THERMOELEC, ENERGY CONVERSION DEVICES, 80- *Concurrent Pos:* Sr to prin scientist, Solar Energy Res Inst, 78- *Mem:* Inst Elec & Electronics Engrs; Am Phys Soc; Am Vacuum Soc; Int Solar Energy Soc. *Res:* Solar, wind, geothermal energy conversion systems; solid state energy conversion; thermoelectrics; power electronics; electromechanical conversion systems; electrical properties of thin films; thin film devices; device physics; surface physics. *Mailing Add:* Mgr Thermoelectrics Energy Conversion Devices 1675 W Maple Milwaukee MI 68084

JAYANT, NUGGEHALLY S, b Bangalore, India, Jan 9, 46. COMMUNICATIONS SCIENCE. *Educ:* Univ Mysore, BSc, 62; Indian Inst Sci, Bangalore, BE, 65, PhD(elec commun), 70. *Prof Exp:* Res assoc commun, Stanford Univ, 67-68; MEM TECH STAFF SPEECH & ACOUST RES, BELL TEL LABS, 68- *Concurrent Pos:* Fel Coun Sci & Indust Res, India, 66-67; vis scientist, Indian Inst Sci, Bangalore, 72, 75. *Mem:* Inst Elec & Electronics Engrs. *Res:* Communication and information systems. *Mailing Add:* Bell Tel Labs Room 2D 524 600 Mountain Ave New Providence NJ 07974

JAYARAMAN, AIYASAMI, b Madras, India, Dec 5, 26; m 45; c 2. HIGH PRESSURE PHYSICS. *Educ:* Univ Madras, BSc, 46, MSc, 54, PhD(solid state physics), 60. *Prof Exp:* Res asst physics, Raman Res Inst, India, 49-54, asst prof, 54-60; asst res geophysicist, Inst Geophys, Univ Calif, Los Angeles, 60-63; MEM TECH STAFF, BELL LABS, NJ, 63- *Concurrent Pos:* Guggenheim fel, 70-71; vis prof, Indian Inst Sci, Bangalore, 70-71; vis scientist, Nat Aeronaut Lab, India, 70-71; vis prof, Max Planck Inst, 79-80; US sr scientist award, Alexander Von Humboldt Found, 78. *Mem:* fel Am Phys Soc; fel Indian Acad Sci (treas, 56-60). *Res:* Optical, x-ray crystallography and luminescence; phase transitions in solids at high pressures; transport properties in semiconductors, magnetic and superconducting properties of metals and alloys. *Mailing Add:* Bell Labs Murray Hill NJ 07974

JAYARAMAN, H, b Gudiattam, India, Dec 21, 36; US citizen; m 69; c 1. ORGANIC CHEMISTRY. *Educ:* Univ Madras, BSc, 56, MA, 58, PhD(chem), 63. *Prof Exp:* Lectr, Madras Christian Col, India, 57-65; Fulbright-Hays res fel, Univ Kans, 65-66; res assoc, Pa State Univ, 66-68; Pool off, Madras Christian Col, India, 69-70; res assoc, Univ Kans, 70-72 & Univ Pa, 72-73; info scientist, 73-80, SR INFO SCIENTIST, PHILLIPS PETROL CO, OKLA, 80- *Mem:* Am Chem Soc; Asn Info Mgrs. *Res:* Computerized retrieval and dissemination of technical information; oxidation and solvolytic reactions; enzyme model reactions; kinetic isotope effects; mechanistic organic and bio-organic chemistry. *Mailing Add:* 184 Res Bldg 1 110-A PLB Phillips Petrol Co Bartlesville OK 74004

JAYARAMAN, NARAYANAN, b Tamilnadu, India, June 30, 48; m 77. CREEP-FATIGUE-ENVIRONMENT. *Educ:* Indian Inst Sci, Bangalore, India, BE, 70, ME, 72, PhD(metal), 79. *Prof Exp:* Res fel metal, Indian Inst Sci, 72-77; scientist, Nat Aeronaut Lab, India, 77-79; fel, 79-80, vis asst prof, 80-81, ASST PROF METAL, UNIV CINCINNATI, 81- *Mem:* Am Soc Metals; Metal Soc. *Res:* Fracture and fatigue behavior of ni-base superalloys in relationship with their microstructures; stress generation due to oxidation of metals and alloys; life prediction models for high temperature materials. *Mailing Add:* Rm 498 Dept Mat Sci & Metall Eng M L 12 Rhodes Hall Univ Cincinnati Cincinnati OH 45221

JAYAWEERA, KOLF, b Kalutara, Ceylon, Dec 2, 38; m 65; c 3. CLOUD PHYSICS. *Educ:* Univ Ceylon, BS, 60; Univ London, PhD(physics), 65, Imp Col, Univ London, DIC(cloud physics), 65. *Prof Exp:* Asst lectr physics, Univ Ceylon, 60-62, lectr, 65-67; scientist, Commonwealth Sci & Indust Res Orgn res fel, Sydney, 67-70; asst prof, 70-74, assoc prof, 74-81, PROF GEOPHYS, GEOPHYS INST, UNIV ALASKA, 81- *Concurrent Pos:* Res grants, NSF, Geophys Inst, Univ Alaska, 71-, Nat Oceanog & Atmospheric Admin, 73-75 & Off Naval Res, 72-75; prog assoc meteorol, NSF, 78-79 & Air Force Off Sci Res, 79- *Mem:* AAAS; fel Royal Meteorol Soc; Am Meteorol Soc; Am Geophys Union. *Res:* Nucleation, growth and aerodynamics of ice crystals in clouds; weather modification; satellite meteorology and sea ice; atmosphere turbulence. *Mailing Add:* Geophys Inst Univ of Alaska College AK 00701

JAYCOX, ELBERT RALPH, b Miami, Ariz, Oct 13, 23; m 47; c 4. ENTOMOLOGY. *Educ:* Univ Calif, BS, 49, MS, 51, PhD(entom, apicult), 56. *Prof Exp:* Supvr apiary inspection, Calif Dept Agr, 53-58; entomologist apicult, wild bee pollination invests, USDA, Utah State Univ, 58-63; assoc prof hort, Univ Ill, Urbana, 63-69, prof hort & entom, 69-80, prof entom, 80-81; ADJ PROF ENTOM, NMEX STATE UNIV, 81- *Concurrent Pos:* Vis prof, Univ Bern, Switz, 73-74; assoc ed, J Apicult Res. *Mem:* Sigma Xi; Entom Soc Am; Int Bee Res Asn. *Res:* Honey bee diseases and parasites; pesticides and bees; bee behavior and biology; pollination; taxonomy of Anthidium. *Mailing Add:* Entom & Plant Path Dept Box 3BE NMex State Univ Las Cruces NM 88003

JAYE, MURRAY JOSEPH, b New York, NY, Aug 17, 37; m 60; c 2. FOOD SCIENCE, MICROBIOLOGY. *Educ:* Univ Ga, BS, 59; Univ Ill, Urbana, MS, 61, PhD(food sci), 64. *Prof Exp:* Res scientist, Hercules Inc, 64-67; sr scientist, Frito-Lay Inc, 67-68, sect mgr, 69-70, prin scientist, 71-73, mgr corp develop, 74-75; MGR NEW FOOD PROD, CLOROX CO, 75-; TECH DIR, FAIRMONT FOODS CO, 80- *Mem:* Am Chem Soc; Inst Food Technologists; Am Mgt Asn. *Res:* New food products research; flavor chemistry and utilization; starch and hydrocolloid chemistry and utilization; food systems development; research administration. *Mailing Add:* 2517 Via Verde Walnut Creek CA 94598

JAYE, SEYMOUR, b Chicago, Ill, Oct 1, 31; m 58; c 3. ENGINEERING PHYSICS, NUCLEAR ENGINEERING. *Educ:* Univ Ill, BS, 54, MS, 55. *Prof Exp:* Asst radiant heating, Univ Ill, 54-55; assoc physicist nuclear reactor design, Oak Ridge Nat Lab, 55, physicist, 56-60; group leader nuclear design & reactor physics, high temperature gas-cooled reactor, Gen Atomic Div, Gen Dynamics Corp, 60-66, mgr off high temperature gas-cooled reactor planning & asst dept chmn nuclear anal & reactor physics, 66-70, mgr nuclear fuel mkt, Gulf Gen Atomic, 70-71; mgr fuel studies, 71-73, DIR, VPRES & GEN MGR, S M STOLLER CORP, 74-; PRES, URANIUM SUPPLY SERV CORP, 75- *Concurrent Pos:* Lectr, Univ Tenn, 60. *Mem:* Am Nuclear Soc. *Res:* Nuclear design of power reactors; nuclear reactor fuel; reactor physics. *Mailing Add:* S M Stoller Corp Suite 800 Colorado Bldg Boulder CO 80303

JAYME, DAVID WOODWARD, b Peterson, NJ, Dec 30, 50; m 73; c 4. MEMBRANE TRANSPORT, SOMATIC CELL GENETICS. *Educ:* Brigham Young Univ, BS, 74, MS, 75; Univ Mich, PhD(biol chem), 79. *Prof Exp:* Fel human genetics, Yale Univ, 79-81; ASST PROF PHARMACOL, MED COL VA, VA COMMONWEALTH UNIV, 81- *Mem:* NY Acad Sci. *Res:* Membrane transport of ions and metabolites in mammalian cells; isolation and characterization of transport and regulatory mutants; Mechanism of drug therapy, toxicity and resistance. *Mailing Add:* Med Col Va Va Commonwealth Univ Box 663 Med Col Va Sta Richmond VA 23298

JAYNE, BENJAMIN A, b Enid, Okla, Oct 10, 28; m 50; c 3. FOREST PRODUCTS, THEORETICAL ECOLOGY. *Educ:* Univ Idaho, BS, 52; Yale Univ, MF, 53, DFor, 55. *Prof Exp:* From instr to asst prof wood technol, Yale Univ, 55-58; assoc wood technologist, Wash State Univ, 59-61; NSF sr fel physics & phys chem, Univ Calif, San Diego, 61-62; prof wood technol, NC State Univ, 62-66; prof wood physics, Univ Wash, 66-76, dir ctr quantitative sci in forestry, Fisheries & Wildlife, 71-76; DEAN, SCH FORESTRY & ENVIRON STUDIES, DUKE UNIV, 76- *Concurrent Pos:* Assoc dean, Col Forest Resources, Univ Wash, 68-71; ed, Wood & Fiber. *Mem:* Forest Prod Res Soc; Soc Wood Sci & Technol (pres elect, 60). *Res:* Theoretical and experimental physics of wood and wood composites; mass and energy transport in ecosystems; development of a general theoretical framework for the physical properties of wood and fiber composite materials; application of mathematical modeling to management of natural resource systems. *Mailing Add:* Sch of Forestry & Environ Studies Duke Univ Durham NC 27706

JAYNE, EDGAR PLEASANT, b Flat Gap, Ky, Aug 17, 13; m 54; c 1. ANATOMY, PHYSIOLOGY. *Educ:* Univ Ky, AB, 36, MS, 40; Washington Univ, PhD(anat), 50. *Prof Exp:* Prin pub sch, Ky, 37-38; asst zool, Univ Ky, 38-40, chem, 41; chemist, E I du Pont de Nemours & Co, 41-42; metallographer, Ford Motor Co, 43-46; from assoc prof to prof anat, George Washington Univ, 50-53; assoc prof, 53-73, prof anat, 73-77, dir basic sci, 73-77, EMER PROF, SCH ALLIED HEALTH PROFESSIONS, 78- *Concurrent Pos:* Instr, Wayne State Univ, 45-48. *Mem:* Asn Schs Allied Health Professions; Am Asn Anat. *Res:* Gerontology; circulatory and endocrine systems, especially the adrenal gland. *Mailing Add:* Sch of Allied Health Univ of Conn Storrs CT 06268

JAYNE, JACK EDGAR, b Spokane, Wash, Dec 18, 25; m 47; c 4. CHEMISTRY. *Educ:* Univ Wis, BS, 47, MS, 48, PhD, 53; Lawrence Univ, MS, 50. *Prof Exp:* Sr res scientist, Kimberly-Clark Corp, 52-74; MGR ENVIRON SERV, GREEN BAY PACKAGING, INC, 74- *Mem:* Tech Asn Pulp & Paper Indust. *Res:* Environmental research on effluents and emissions from pulp and paper manufacture. *Mailing Add:* Green Bay Packaging Inc 1700 N Webster Box 1107 Green Bay WI 54305

JAYNE, JERROLD CLARENCE, b Stevens Point, Wis, Feb 8, 31; m 60; c 2. ANALYTICAL CHEMISTRY, INORGANIC CHEMISTRY. *Educ:* Univ Wis, BS, 52, PhD(anal chem), 63. *Prof Exp:* From asst prof to assoc prof, 63-74, PROF CHEM, SAN FRANCISCO STATE UNIV, 75- *Concurrent Pos:* Partic, Water Chem Prog, Univ Wis, 70-72. *Mem:* Am Chem Soc. *Res:* Coordination chemistry; water chemistry. *Mailing Add:* Dept of Chem San Francisco State Univ San Francisco CA 94132

JAYNES, EDWIN THOMPSON, b Waterloo, Iowa, July 5, 22. THEORETICAL PHYSICS. *Educ:* Univ Iowa, BA, 42; Princeton Univ, MA, 48, PhD(physics), 50. *Prof Exp:* Proj engr, Sperry Gyroscope Co, 42-44; actg asst prof, Stanford Univ, 50-55; assoc prof physics, 55-60; assoc prof, 60-63, prof physics, 63-76, WAYMAN CROW PROF PHYSICS, WASHINGTON UNIV, 76- *Mem:* AAAS; Am Phys Soc; Am Asn Physics Teachers. *Res:* Electromagnetic theory; statistical mechanics. *Mailing Add:* Dept of Physics Col of Arts & Sci Wash Univ St Louis MO 63130

JAYNES, HUGH OLIVER, b Greeneville, Tenn, Aug 14, 31; m 53; c 2. FOOD SCIENCE. *Educ:* Univ Tenn, BS, 53, MS, 54; Univ Ill, PhD(food sci), 70. *Prof Exp:* Bacteriologist, Res & Develop Ctr, Pet, Inc, 56-63, sect leader chem, 63-67; res fel food sci, Univ Ill, 67-70; assoc prof, 70-79, PROF FOOD TECHNOL & SCI, UNIV TENN, KNOXVILLE, 79- *Concurrent Pos:* Vis prof, Univ Alexandria, Egypt, 80. *Mem:* Inst Food Technologists; Am Dairy Sci Asn; Sigma Xi. *Res:* Applied research in food color, food chemistry and food product development. *Mailing Add:* Food Technol & Sci Dept Univ of Tenn PO Box 1071 Knoxville TN 37901

JAYNES, JOHN ALVA, b Bonham, Tex, Sept 27, 29; m 55; c 2. FOOD SCIENCE. *Educ:* Sam Houston State Teachers Col, BS, 51; Tex Tech Col, BS, 56, MS, 57; Mich State Univ, PhD(dairy), 60. *Prof Exp:* Proj leader food res, 60-63, assoc dir res, 63-67, prod mgr, Canned Milk Prod, 67-73, pres beverage prod, 73-75, vpres foods div, 75-76, pres refrigerated prod, 77-79, vpres, 80-81, VPRES OPERS GROCERY PROD, BORDEN INC, 81- *Mem:* Am Dairy Sci Asn. *Res:* Canned sterile milk and milk based drinks. *Mailing Add:* Borden Inc 180 E Broad St Columbus OH 43215

JAYNES, RICHARD ANDRUS, b New Iberia, La, May 27, 35; m 59; c 3. PLANT BREEDING. *Educ:* Wesleyan Univ, BA, 57; Yale Univ, MS, 59, PhD(bot), 61. *Prof Exp:* Asst geneticist, 61-65, assoc geneticist, 65-75, geneticist, 75-80, HORTICULTURIST, CONN AGR EXP STA, 80- *Mem:* AAAS; Am Soc Hort Sci; Int Plant Propagators Soc. *Res:* Development of hybrid chestnut trees resistant to the chestnut blight fungus; biological control of the chestnut blight fungus; breeding improved woody ornamentals, especially laurel (Kalmia); vegetative propagation of woody plants. *Mailing Add:* Conn Agr Exp Sta Box 1106 New Haven CT 06504

JEAN, BENOIT, plasma physics, see previous edition

JEAN, GEORGE NOEL, b New York, NY, Aug 2, 29. ORGANIC CHEMISTRY. *Educ:* Fordham Univ, BS, 49, MS, 51, PhD(chem), 57. *Prof Exp:* Dye chemist, J P Stevens & Co, Inc, NY, 48; asst phys sci, Med Labs, Army Chem Ctr, Md, 53-55; asst chem, Fordham Univ, 55-56; patent chemist, Patent Dept, Legal Div, Chas Pfizer & Co, Inc, 56-71, patent chemist, 71-76, SR PATENT CHEMIST, PATENT DEPT, LEGAL DIV, PFIZER INC, 76- *Mem:* AAAS; Am Chem Soc. *Res:* Synthesis and stereochemistry of biaromatic heterocycles; analytical detection of mercaptans; dye chemistry; chemical pharmaceutical patents. *Mailing Add:* 6739 Ingram St Forest Hills NY 11375

JEAN-BAPTISTE, EMILE, b Port-au-Prince, Haiti, Mar 15, 47; m 68; c 2. PHYSIOLOGY, ENDOCRINE PHARMACOLOGY. *Educ:* Fordham Univ, BS, 71, MS, 72, PhD(physiol), 76. *Prof Exp:* res assoc metab & endocrinol, 76-80, ASST PROF LAB CELL BIOCHEM & PHARMACOL, ROCKEFELLER UNIV, 80- *Concurrent Pos:* Adj asst prof, Col New Rochelle, 75-76 & City Univ New York, 75- *Mem:* Am Soc Zoologists; Sigma Xi; AAAS; NY Acad Sci. *Res:* Hormonal regulation of lipolysis in adipose tissue; steroidogenesis in adrenal cortes; magnesium flux in plasma membranes; ACTH and glucagon analogs, endorphins, enkephelins and their mechanism of action through the cyclic adenosine monophosphate system. *Mailing Add:* Rockefeller Univ 1230 York Ave New York NY 10021

JEANES, JACK KENNETH, b McKinney, Tex, July 2, 23; m 47; c 4. CHEMISTRY. *Educ:* NTex State Col, BS, 47, MS, 48; Oak Ridge Inst Nuclear Studies, cert, 52; Univ Tex, Austin, PhD(biophys), 57. *Prof Exp:* Assoc prof chem, Southwestern State Col, Okla, 48-51; res assoc, Tex Res Found, 51-54; res asst biophys, Southwestern Med Sch, Univ Tex, 54-56, from instr to asst prof, 56-60; assoc prof chem & chmn dept, Univ Dallas, 60-69; PRES & CHIEF EXEC OFF, INDUST RI CHEM LAB, INC, 69- *Concurrent Pos:* Chem consult, 57-; NIH grant geront, 57-60. *Mem:* Am Chem Soc. *Res:* Biophysics; organic chemistry. *Mailing Add:* Indust Ri Chem Lab Inc 726 S Sherman St Richardson TX 75080

JEANLOZ, RAYMOND, b Winchester, Mass, Aug 18, 52. MINERAL PHYSICS. *Educ:* Amherst Col, BA, 75; Calif Inst Technol, PhD(geol & geophysics), 79. *Prof Exp:* Asst prof, Harvard Univ, 79-81; ASST PROF GEOL & GEOPHYS, UNIV CALIF, BERKELEY, 81- *Mem:* AAAS; Am Geophys Union; Geol Soc Am. *Res:* Experimental and theoretical study of mineral properties, especially elastic and thermodynamic, with particular application to the state of the earth's deep interior. *Mailing Add:* Dept Geol & Geophysics Univ Calif Berkeley CA 94720

JEANLOZ, ROGER WILLIAM, b Berne, Switz, Nov 3, 17; nat US; m 45; c 5. BIOCHEMISTRY. *Educ:* Univ Geneva, ChE, 41, PhD(org chem), 43. *Hon Degrees:* AM, Harvard Univ, 61; DSc, Univ Paris, 80. *Prof Exp:* Instr chem, Univ Geneva, 41-44; assoc chem, Univ Montreal, 47; sr mem & head biochem lab, Worcester Found Exp Biol, 49-51; res assoc, 51-57, assoc org chem, Dept Med, 57-60, from asst prof to assoc prof, 60-69, PROF BIOL CHEM, HARVARD MED SCH, 69-; BIOCHEMIST, MASS GEN HOSP, 61- *Concurrent Pos:* Swiss Found fel, Univ Basel, 43-45; NIH sr res fel, 48; lectr Swiss-Am Found Sci exchange, 53-54; NSF sr fel, 59-60; guest prof, Univ Cologne, 59-60, Univ Freiburg, 60, Univ Tokyo & Univ Kyoto, 75; tutor, Harvard Univ, 61; mem study sect physiol chem, NIH, 64-68 & 69-70; Nat Acad Sci & Acad Sci USSR exchange fel, 70; physiol chem B res study comn, Am Heart Asn, 72-75; lectr, Grenoble, 72 & Lille, 73. *Honors & Awards:* Fr Soc Biol Chem Medal, 60; Liege Univ Medal, 64; Prix Jaubert, Univ Geneva, 73; Hudson Prize, Am Chem Soc, 73. *Mem:* Am Chem Soc; Am Soc Biol Chemists; Royal Soc Chem; Swiss Chem Soc; Biochem Soc. *Res:* Chemistry of carbohydrates; amino sugars; mucopolysaccharides; glycolipids; glycoproteins; bacterial cell walls; deoxysugars; ribose derivatives; glycogen; steroids; metabolism of corticosteroids. *Mailing Add:* Mass Gen Hosp Boston MA 02114

JEANMAIRE, ROBERT L, b Rockford, Ill, Feb 28, 20; m 58; c 3. SCIENCE EDUCATION. *Educ:* Univ Ill, BS, 50, MS, 52; Rensselaer Polytech Inst, MS, 65. *Prof Exp:* Teacher, Melvin Sibley High Sch, 50-52, W Sr High Sch, 52-60 & Auburn High Sch, 60-64; instr physics & math, San Joaquin Delta Col, 64-65; ASSOC PROF PHYSICS, CARTHAGE COL, 65- *Concurrent Pos:* Writer and teacher oper jet engine control, Woodward Governor Co, 57-58. *Mem:* Am Asn Physics Teachers. *Res:* Teaching general physics using a computer. *Mailing Add:* Dept of Physics Carthage Col Kenosha WI 53140

JEANNOTTE, ANTHONY CHARLES, II, b Milwaukee, Wis, Apr 20, 47; m 70; c 2. PHYSICAL CHEMISTRY. *Educ:* Univ Wis, Milwaukee, BS, 70; Univ Minn, PhD(phys chem), 75. *Prof Exp:* Appointee chem div, Argonne Nat Lab, 75-78; SR DEVELOP ENG OPTICAL MEASUREMENT, FOXBORO-WILKS INFRARED CTR, 78- *Mem:* Am Chem Soc; AAAS. *Res:* Vibrational anharmonicity and vibration-rotation interactions; solvent-solute interactions; chemical kinetics; interfacial chemistry-ATR, catalysis; optical measurement systems; numerical analysis. *Mailing Add:* Chem Div Foxboro-Wilks 140 S Water St Norwalk CT 06856

JEARLD, AMBROSE, JR, b Annapolis, Md, Mar 6, 44; m 76; c 1. FISHERIES BIOLOGY, FISHERIES RESEARCH. *Educ:* Univ Md, Eastern Shore, BS, 65; Okla State Univ, MS, 70, PhD(zool), 75. *Prof Exp:* Chemist, Publickers Indust Inc, 65-67; biol asst med res, US Army Edgewood Arsenal, 69-71; asst prof biol & anat, Lincoln Univ, 75-77; asst prof animal behav & ecol, Howard Univ, 77-78; SUPVRY RES FISHERY BIOLOGIST, NORTHEAST FISHERIES CTR, WOODS HOLE LAB, US DEPT OF COM, 78- *Concurrent Pos:* Fel, Nat Sci, Okla State Univ, 73; fac mem, Sandy Hook Lab, Dept Com, 77-78; mem, Annapolis Environ Comn, 77-78. *Mem:* Sigma Xi; Animal Behav Soc; Am Fisheries Soc; Int Asn Fish Ethologists. *Res:* Animal behavior with emphasis on behavioral ecology in an aquatic environment; aging and growth problems and their influence on conservation and management of fishery resources in the northeast Atlantic. *Mailing Add:* US Dept of Com Woods Hole Lab Woods Hole MA 02543

JEBE, EMIL H, b Clutier, Iowa, Feb 26, 09; m 41. EXPERIMENTAL STATISTICS, APPLIED STATISTICS. *Educ:* Iowa State Univ, BS, 38, MS, 41; NC State Univ, PhD(exp statist), 50. *Prof Exp:* Agr statistician, USDA, 38-40 & 46-49, supvr, USDA-Works Progress Admin & agr statistician, Pilot Res Survey, 40-41; assoc prof statist, Iowa State Univ, 49-59; res mathematician, Infrared & Optics Div, Willow Run Labs, Univ Mich, Ann Arbor, 59-72; res mathematician & consult statistician, 73-79, EMER STATISTICIAN, ENVIRON RES INST MICH, 79- *Concurrent Pos:* Consult Statistician, 74- *Mem:* Am Statist Asn; Int Biomet Soc; Int Asn Statist Phys Sci & Eng; Int Asn Survey Statist; Am Soc Testing & Mat. *Res:* Application of sampling theory to the design and analysis of sample surveys and experiments; computer programing of least squares and ANOVA; systems analysis and operations research; property assessment analyses. *Mailing Add:* 2650 Laurentide Dr Ann Arbor MI 48103

JEBENS, HAROLD J, sanitary engineering, bacteriology, see previous edition

JEBSEN, ROBERT H, b New York, NY, Sept 5, 31; m 51; c 3. PHYSICAL MEDICINE & REHABILITATION. *Educ:* Brooklyn Col, BA, 53; State Univ NY Downstate Med Ctr, MD, 56; Ohio State Univ, MMS, 60. *Prof Exp:* Intern, Harrisburg Hosp, Pa, 56-57; resident phys & rehab med, Ohio State Univ, Hosp, 57-60; chief phys med & rehab serv, Carswell AFB Hosp, Fort Worth, Tex, 60-62; dir rehab ctr & muscular dystrophy clin, St Luke's Hosp, Cedar Rapids, Iowa, 62-63; from asst prof to assoc prof phys med & rehab, Univ Wash, 63-68; prof phys med & rehab & dir, 68-74, CLIN PROF PHYS MED & REHAB, UNIV CINCINNATI, 74- *Concurrent Pos:* Attend physician, Iowa City Vet Admin Hosp, 62-63; consult, Knoxville Vet Admin Hosp, Iowa, 62-63. *Mem:* Am Acad Phys Med & Rehab; Am Asn Electromyog & Electrodiag (pres, 74-75); Am Cong Rehab Med; Asn Acad Physiatrists. *Res:* Neuromuscular electrodiagnosis; orthotics; objective measurements of physical function. *Mailing Add:* Suite 324 2825 Burnet Ave Cincinnati OH 45219

JECK, RICHARD KAHR, b Iola, Kans, Oct 6, 38; m 63; c 2. CLOUD PHYSICS, AEROSOL PHYSICS. *Educ:* Rockhurst Col, Kansas City, BA, 60; St Louis Univ, MS, 63, PhD(physics), 68. *Prof Exp:* Fel, Nat Acad Sci, Nat Res Coun, US Naval Res Lab, 68-70; res & develop physicist, Bruker Physik Agr, Ger, 70-71; staff scientist, Smithsonian Radiation Biol Lab, 71-73; RES PHYSICIST, US NAVAL RES LAB, 73- *Concurrent Pos:* Res assoc prof, US Naval Acad, Annapolis, Md, 80-81. *Mem:* Am Phys Soc; Am Meteorol Soc; Am Inst Aeronaut & Astronaut. *Res:* Airborne measurements of cloud characteristics related to aircraft icing; shipboard, airborne, and island based measurements of particulate aerosol size distributions in the maritime environment; onboard tests of air filtration systems for gas turbine powered vessels. *Mailing Add:* Naval Res Lab Code 4323 4555 Overlook Ave Southwest Washington DC 20375

JEDLINSKI, HENRYK, b Bialystok, Poland, Feb 15, 24; nat US; m 58. PLANT PATHOLOGY. *Educ:* Univ Nebr, BS, 50, MS, 54, PhD, 59. *Prof Exp:* Asst, Univ Nebr, 51-59; asst prof, 59-80, ASSOC PROF PLANT PATH, UNIV ILL, URBANA, 80-; PLANT PATHOLOGIST, AGR RES SERV, USDA, 59- *Mem:* Phytopath Am Soc; Int Soc Plant Path; Am Soc Virol. *Res:* Virus diseases of oats and cereals; insect transmission; epidemiology; vectors; disease resistance. *Mailing Add:* Dept of Plant Path Univ Ill 1102 S Goodwin Ave Urbana IL 61801

JEDYNAK, LEO, b Flint, Mich, Sept 15, 28; m 54; c 4. ELECTRICAL ENGINEERING. *Educ:* Mich State Univ, BSc, 54; Mass Inst Technol, MSc, 56, ScD(elec eng), 62. *Prof Exp:* Prog engr, Gen Elec Co, 54; res asst elec eng, Mass Inst Technol, 54-56; instr, Mich State Univ, 56-57; teaching asst, Mass Inst Technol, 57-58, instr, 58-62; from asst prof to assoc prof, Univ Wis-Madison, 62-76, prof elec eng, 76-80; SR VPRES CORP RES & DEVELOP, OAK INDUST INC, 80- *Concurrent Pos:* Dir corp res, Oak Electro/netics

Corp, 69-71, sci & eng consult, 71-; mem bd dirs, Oak Industs Inc, 70- *Mem:* AAAS; Inst Elec & Electronics Engrs. *Res:* Insulation of high voltages in high vacuum; electric switches, contacts and relays; real time applications of microcomputer systems. *Mailing Add:* Oak Indust Inc 16935 W Bernardo Dr Rancho Bernardo CA 92127

JEE, WEBSTER SHEW SHUN, b Oakland, Calif, June 25, 25; m 51; c 1. ANATOMY. *Educ:* Univ Calif, BA, 49, MA, 51; Univ Utah, PhD(anat), 59. *Prof Exp:* Asst zool, Univ Calif, 49-51; asst anat, 52-58, actg bone group leader, Radiol Div, 56-58, instr, 59-60, asst res prof, 60-61, assoc prof, 63-67, dir training prog mineralized tissues, 64-74, actg chmn anat div radiobiol, 73-77, PROF ANAT, COL MED, UNIV UTAH, 67-, BONE GROUP LEADER RADIOBIOL DIV, 58-, ACTG DIR DIV RADIOBIOL, 73- *Concurrent Pos:* Spec consult, Int Atomic Energy Agency, 60 & 64; mem staff, Radiol Health Res Activ, 63-; mem training comt, Nat Inst Dent Res, 66-70, chmn, 68-70; mem sci comt 33, Nat Coun Radiation Protection & Measurements, 69-; assoc ed, Anat Rec, 69-; consult ed var jour, 70-; assoc ed, Calcified Tissue Res, 77-78; mem, Comt Animal Models for Res on Aging, Nat Res Coun, 78-81; mem peer rev comt musculoskeletal physiol, Am Inst Biol Sci & NASA, 78- *Mem:* Radiation Res Soc; Reticuloendothelial Soc; Orthop Res Soc; Am Asn Anat; Int Asn Dent Res. *Res:* Physiology and metabolism of bone and teeth; radiation biology. *Mailing Add:* Radiobiol Lab Bldg 351 Univ of Utah Col of Med Salt Lake City UT 84112

JEFFAY, HENRY, b Brooklyn, NY, Feb 9, 27; m 57; c 5. BIOCHEMISTRY. *Educ:* Univ Wis, BS, 48, MS, 49, PhD(biochem), 53. *Prof Exp:* Instr biochem, Sch Med, Univ PR, 53-55; res assoc, 55-56, from asst prof to assoc prof, 56-68, asst dean fac affairs, 70-72, assoc dean basic sci, 72-74, PROF BIOCHEM, UNIV ILL COL MED, 68- *Concurrent Pos:* Consult, Vet Admin Hosp, Chicago & Norwegian Am Hosp; consult, Roosevelt Mem Hosp, dir med educ; dir basic sci, Rockford Sch Med, Univ Ill, 74-76, actg dean basic sci, 76-79. *Mem:* AAAS; Am Chem Soc; Am Soc Biol Chemists; Int Asn Dent Res. *Res:* Protein metabolism; metabolism of oral tissue; obesity. *Mailing Add:* Dept of Biochem Univ of Ill Col of Med Chicago IL 60612

JEFFCOAT, MARJORIE KAPLAN, b Boston, Mass, June 14, 51; m 73. PERIODONTOLOGY, RADIOLOGY. *Educ:* Mass Inst Technol, SB, 72; Harvard Sch Dent Med, DMD, 76, cert periodont, 78. *Prof Exp:* Res fel, 75-78, instr, 78-79, ASST PROF PERIODONT, HARVARD SCH DENT MED, 79- *Concurrent Pos:* Consult, Brigham & Womens Hosp, 80- & Children's Hosp Med Ctr, 81. *Mem:* Am Dent Asn; Am Acad Periodont; Int Asn Dent Res. *Res:* Bone resorption and periodontal disease utilizes the following approaches, bone scanning, radiolabeled microsphere measurements of blood flow, studies of chemotherapeutic agents for treatment of periodontal disease, studies of the effects of local factors on periodontal disease. *Mailing Add:* Harvard Sch Dent Med 188 Longwood Ave Boston MA 02115

JEFFERIES, JOHN TREVOR, b Kellerberrin, Western Australia, Apr 2, 25; m 49; c 3. ASTROPHYSICS. *Educ:* Western Australia Univ, BSc, 46, DSc(physics), 61; Cambridge Univ, MA, 49. *Prof Exp:* Res off solar physics, Commonwealth Sci & Indust Res Orgn, NSW, 49-56, prin res off astrophys, 59-60; res assoc, Harvard Col Observ, 56-57, res staff, High Altitude Observ, Colo, 57-58 & Sacramento Peak Observ, 58-59; consult to dir, Nat Bur Standards, Colo, 60-62; fel, Joint Inst Lab Astrophys, 62-64; PROF ASTROPHYS, UNIV HAWAII, 64-, DIR INST ASTRON, 67- *Concurrent Pos:* Adj prof, Univ Colo, 61-64; res assoc, High Altitude Observ, 61-64; prof, Col France, 70 & 77; Guggenheim fel, 70-71. *Mem:* Am Astron Soc; Int Astron Union; Royal Astron Soc. *Res:* Solar physics; radiative transfer; spectral line information; analysis of stellar spectra. *Mailing Add:* Inst for Astron 2680 Woodlawn Dr Honolulu HI 96822

JEFFERIES, MICHAEL JOHN, b London, Eng, Feb 2, 41; m 69; c 1. TECHNICAL MANAGEMENT. *Educ:* Univ Nottingham, BSc, 63, PhD(elec eng), 67. *Prof Exp:* elec engr, 67-76, mgr, Cryogenics Br, 76-77, mgr, Power Systs Lab, 77-79, mgr, Elec Systs Tech Lab, 79-80, RES & DEVELOP MGR, ENERGY SCI ENG, CORP RES & DEVELOP, GEN ELEC CO, 80- *Mem:* Inst Elec & Electronics Engrs; Brit Inst Elec Engrs; Inst Elec Engrs UK. *Res:* Power system equipment: generators, motors, transformers, switchgear; electrical energy generation, transmission and utilization. *Mailing Add:* Gen Elec Co Corp Res & Develop PO Box 8 Schenectady NY 12301

JEFFERS, DANIEL L, agronomy, plant physiology, see previous edition

JEFFERS, THOMAS KIRK, b Syracuse, NY, Apr 30, 41; m 69; c 2. PARASITOLOGY, POULTRY SCIENCE. *Educ:* Cornell Univ, BS, 63; Univ Wis, PhD(zool & poultry sci), 69. *Prof Exp:* Geneticist, Animal Res Inst, Can Dept Agr, 68-69; dept head parasitol, Hess & Clark Div, Rhodia, Inc, 69-74; SR PARASITOLOGIST, LILLY RES LABS, 74- *Honors & Awards:* P P Levine Award, Am Asn Avian Pathologists, 74. *Mem:* Am Soc Parasitologists; Soc Protozoologists; Sigma Xi; Am Asn Avian Pathologists; Am Genetic Asn. *Res:* Avian coccidiosis; anticoccidial chemotherapy; intraspecific variation in the coccidia; anticoccidial drug resistance; host response to coccidia. *Mailing Add:* Lilly Res Labs PO Box 708 Greenfield IN 46140

JEFFERS, WILLIAM ALLEN, JR, b Philadelphia, Pa, May 4, 36; m 58; c 3. LOW TEMPERATURE PHYSICS. *Educ:* Amherst Col, AB, 57; Mass Inst Technol, PhD(physics), 62. *Prof Exp:* Sr physicist, Battelle Mem Inst, 62-66; asst prof, 66-76, ASSOC PROF PHYSICS, LAFAYETTE COL, 76-, DEAN COL, 78- *Concurrent Pos:* Dean studies, Lafayette Col, 72-75. *Mem:* Am Phys Soc; Am Asn Physics Teachers. *Res:* Ultrasonic absorption in liquid helium; superconductivity; transport properties in metals. *Mailing Add:* Dept of Physics Lafayette Col Easton PA 18042

JEFFERSON, CAROL ANNETTE, b Minneapolis, Minn, July 4, 48; m 75; c 1. PLANT ECOLOGY. *Educ:* St Olaf Col, BA, 70; Ore State Univ, PhD(bot), 74. *Prof Exp:* Asst prof biol, Eckerd Col, 74-76; asst prof biol, ASSOC PROF BIOL, WINONA STATE UNIV, 81- *Mem:* AAAS; Ecol Soc Am. *Res:* Great Lakes sand vegetation; driftless area-relict communities; flood plain vegetation; wetland ecotones. *Mailing Add:* Dept of Biol Winona State Univ Winona MN 55987

JEFFERSON, DAVID KENOSS, b Pasadena, Calif, Dec 21, 38; m 67; c 2. COMPUTER SCIENCE. *Educ:* Calif Inst Technol, BS, 60; Columbia Univ, AM, 62; Univ Mich, PhD(comput sci), 69. *Prof Exp:* Vis prof comput sci, Naval Postgrad Sch, 72-73; mathematician, Naval Weapons Lab, 60-72, res mathematician, 73-75; PROJ LEADER INFO SYST DESIGN, DAVID W TAYLOR NAVAL SHIP RES & DEVELOP CTR, 75- *Mem:* Sigma Xi; Asn Comput Mach; Inst Elec & Electronics Engrs. *Res:* Design, implementation and optimization of very large and complex information processing systems; analysis of user requirements and data base design. *Mailing Add:* Code 1821 David W Taylor Naval Ship Res & Develop Ctr Bethesda MD 20084

JEFFERSON, DONALD EARL, b Homeland, Fla, Sept 27, 27; m 51; c 2. SCIENCE POLICY, PHYSICAL OCEANOGRAPHY. *Educ:* Morehouse Col, BS, 48; Howard Univ, MS, 50. *Prof Exp:* Instr physics, Va Union Univ, 49-51; physicist, US Naval Ord Lab, 51-52, elec engr, 54-72, elec engr, Naval Surface Weapon Ctr, 72-81, SCI ADV TO COMMANDER SECOND FLEET, NAVAL ASSISTANCE PROG, 81- *Concurrent Pos:* Vpres eng, Copycomposer Corp, 69-71. *Res:* Review of naval operational systems for modification or replacement as needed; design and modification of instrumentation for measuring ocean currents; statistical analysis and prediction of system and environment interactions; underwater acoustics. *Mailing Add:* 13321 Bea Kay Dr Silver Spring MD 20904

JEFFERSON, JAMES WALTER, b Mineola, NY, Aug 14, 37; m 65; c 3. PSYCHOPHARMACOLOGY. *Educ:* Bucknell Univ, BS, 58; Univ Wis, MD, 64. *Prof Exp:* Intern, St Lukes Hosp, NY, 64-65; resident internal med, Univ Wis, 65-67; fel, Univ Chicago, 67-68; resident psychiat, 71-74, asst prof, 74-78, assoc prof, 78-81, PROF PSYCHIAT, UNIV WIS-MADISON, 81- *Concurrent Pos:* Staff psychiatrist, Vet Admin Hosp, Wis, 74-81; dir, Lithium Info Ctr, Madison, 74- *Mem:* Am Psychiat Asn; Am Psychopath Asn; Int Neuropsychopharmacologium Soc; Drug Info Asn; Sigma Xi. *Res:* Clinical psychopharmacology; compilation and dissertation of information through interactive computer programs in psychiatry; neuropsychiatric aspects of medical disorders. *Mailing Add:* Dept Psychiat Clin Sci Ctr Univ Wis 600 Highland Ave Madison WI 53792

JEFFERSON, LEONARD SHELTON, b Maysville, Ky, Jan 14, 39. PHYSIOLOGY. *Educ:* Eastern Ky Univ, BS, 61; Vanderbilt Univ, PhD(physiol), 66. *Prof Exp:* Vis scientist, Cambridge Univ, 66-67; res assoc physiol, Col Med, Vanderbilt Univ, 67; from instr to assoc prof, 67-75, PROF PHYSIOL, COL MED, PA STATE UNIV, 75- *Concurrent Pos:* USPHS fel, 66-67. *Honors & Awards:* Lilly Award, Am Diabetes Asn, 79. *Mem:* Am Soc Biol Chemists; Biochem Soc; Am Physiol Soc; Am Diabetes Asn. *Res:* Regulation of skeletal muscle and hepatic carbohydrate and protein metabolism by hormones and other factors, especially mechanism of action of insulin and growth hormone. *Mailing Add:* Milton S Hershey Med Ctr Pa State Univ Hershey PA 17033

JEFFERSON, MARGARET CORREAN, b Eau Claire, Wis, Aug 22, 47. GENETICS. *Educ:* Univ Dubuque, BS, 69; Univ Colo, MA, 71; Univ Ariz, PhD(genetics), 77. *Prof Exp:* Asst prof, 77-81, ASSOC PROF BIOL, CALIF STATE UNIV, LOS ANGELES, 81- *Concurrent Pos:* Consult, Compton Sickle Cell Educ & Detection Ctr, 77-; prin invester biomed res support grants, NIH, 77- & res apprenticeships minority high sch students, NSF, 81-82. *Mem:* AAAS; Am Genetics Soc; Genetics Soc Am; Soc Study Evolution. *Res:* Ecological and behavioral genetics of desert-adapted Drosophila; specifically, pheromonal regulation of reproductive strategies in desert-adapted Drosophila; genetics of learning behavior; cytogenetics of Cycads. *Mailing Add:* Dept of Biol Calif State Univ 5151 State Univ Dr Los Angeles CA 90032

JEFFERSON, ROLAND NEWTON, b Washington, DC, Nov 7, 11; m 46; c 3. ENTOMOLOGY. *Educ:* Va Polytech Inst, BS, 34, MS, 36; Iowa State Col, PhD(entom), 42. *Prof Exp:* Asst entomologist, Va Exp Sta, 36-39; instr entom, Va Polytech Inst, 39-40; asst entomologist, Va Exp Sta, 41-42; from asst prof & asst entomologist to prof & entomologist, Exp Sta, Univ Calif, Los Angeles, 46-60; prof entom, 60-76, EMER PROF ENTOM & ENTOMOLOGIST, EXP STA, UNIV CALIF, RIVERSIDE, 76- *Mem:* Entom Soc Am. *Res:* Insect morphology; insects affecting floricultural crops. *Mailing Add:* 5499 Grassy Trail Dr Riverside CA 92504

JEFFERSON, THOMAS BRADLEY, b Urich, Mo, Nov 25, 24; m 46; c 3. MECHANICAL ENGINEERING. *Educ:* Kans State Col, BS, 49; Univ Nebr, MS, 50; Purdue Univ, PhD, 55. *Prof Exp:* Instr mech eng, Univ Nebr, 49-52; from instr to asst prof, Purdue Univ, 52-58; prof & head dept, Univ Ark, Fayetteville, 58-69; dean, Sch Eng & Technol, 69-78, PROF THERMAL & ENVIRON ENG, SOUTHERN ILL UNIV, 78- *Concurrent Pos:* Consult, Allison Div, Gen Motors Corp, 56-57. *Mem:* Am Soc Mech Engrs; Am Soc Eng Educ. *Res:* Heat transfer. *Mailing Add:* Sch of Eng & Technol Southern Ill Univ Carbondale IL 62901

JEFFERSON, THOMAS HUTTON, JR, b Mineola, NY, June 6, 41. NUMERICAL ANALYSIS, COMPUTER SCIENCE. *Educ:* Rensselaer Polytech Inst, BS, 63; NC State Univ, MAM, 65; Univ Calif, PhD(appl math), 69. *Prof Exp:* MEM TECH STAFF, APPL MATH DIV, SANDIA LABS, LIVERMORE, 69- *Mem:* Soc Indust & Appl Math. *Res:* Nonlinear parameter determination; function minimization; numerical quadrature; computer software libraries. *Mailing Add:* Sci Comput Div 8332 Sandia Labs Livermore CA 94550

JEFFERSON, WILLIAM EMMETT, JR, b Franklin Co, Va, Mar 10, 25; m 47; c 5. BIOCHEMISTRY. *Educ:* Va Polytech Inst, BS, 45, MS, 48; Univ Tex, PhD(bact), 55. *Prof Exp:* Instr biol, Va Polytech Inst, 46-48; jr biologist, Oak Ridge Nat Lab, 48-50; res scientist, Univ Tex, 53-55; from asst prof to assoc prof, 55-69, PROF BIOCHEM & DEP CHMN DEPT, UNIV TENN CTR HEALTH SCI, MEMPHIS, 69- *Mem:* Am Chem Soc; Am Soc Microbiol; Am Soc Biol Chem; Am Asn Dent Schs. *Res:* Fermentation mechanisms; fungal metabolism; function of steroids in fungi. *Mailing Add:* Dept of Biochem Univ of Tenn Ctr for Health Sci Memphis TN 38163

JEFFERTS, KEITH BARTLETT, b Raymond, Wash, May 10, 31; m 53; c 4. ATOMIC PHYSICS, FISHERIES MANAGEMENT. *Educ:* Univ Wash, PhD(physics), 62. *Prof Exp:* Mem tech staff physics, Bell Tel Labs, 63-75; PRES, NORTHWEST MARINE TECHNOL, 72- *Mem:* Am Phys Soc. *Res:* Structure of simple molecules; molecular astrophysics; application of physical techniques to problems of fishery management. *Mailing Add:* PO Box 363 Shaw Island WA 98286

JEFFERY, DUANE ELDRO, b Delta, Utah, Sept 28, 37; m 61; c 3. GENETICS, EVOLUTIONARY BIOLOGY. *Educ:* Utah State Univ, BS, 62, MS, 63; Univ Calif, Berkeley, MA, 66, PhD(zool, genetics), 72. *Prof Exp:* Asst prof, 69-77, ASSOC PROF ZOOL, BRIGHAM YOUNG UNIV, 77- *Concurrent Pos:* Vis colleague genetics, Univ Hawaii, 74-75. *Mem:* Soc Study Evolution; Genetics Soc Am; Am Soc Human Genetics; AAAS. *Res:* Developmental and evolutionary genetics in Drosophila populations; human transmission genetics; cytogenetics. *Mailing Add:* Dept of Zool Brigham Young Univ Provo UT 84602

JEFFERY, GEOFFREY MARRON, b Dundee, NY, May 13, 19; m 41; c 4. MALARIOLOGY. *Educ:* Hobart Col, BA, 40; Syracuse Univ, MA, 42; Johns Hopkins Univ, ScD(parasitol), 44; Yale Univ, MPH, 61. *Prof Exp:* Biol aide, Tenn Valley Authority, Wilson Dam, Alta, 44; asst sanitarian, USPHS, 44-45, asst sanitarian, Commun Dis Ctr, Ga, 45-46; from asst sanitarian to sr asst scientist, Sch Trop Med, PR, 46-47; from sr asst scientist to scientist, Malaria Res Lab, Lab Trop Dis, NIH, Ga, 48-54, from scientist to sr scientist, SC, 54-60, sci dir, 60-63, asst chief, Lab Parasite Chemother, Nat Inst Allergy & Infectious Dis, 63-66, actg chief, 66, chief, 67-68; chief, Cent Am Res Sta, 69-74, asst dir, 74-75, dir, Vector Biol & Control Div, Bur Trop Dis, 75-81, ASST DIR, DIV PARASITIC DIS, BUR TROP DIS, CTR DIS CONTROL, 81- *Concurrent Pos:* Asst prof, Univ Bridgeport, 47-48; mem expert panel malaria, WHO, 63-, scientific group on chemother of malaria, Geneva, 67, parasitol of malaria, Teheran, 68 & Cent Am Malaria Assessment Mission, AID, 64; assoc mem comn malaria, Armed Forces Epidemiol Bd, 65-69, mem, 69-73; deleg, Int Cong Trop Med & Malaria, Lisbon, 58, Rio de Janeiro, 63, Teheran, 68, Int Cong Parasitol, Rome, 64, Wash, 70 & Latin Am Cong Parasitol, 73. *Honors & Awards:* USPHS Commendation Medal, 66; Ashford Medal, Am Soc Trop Med & Hyg, 59. *Mem:* AAAS; Am Soc Parasitol; Am Soc Trop Med & Hyg (secy-treas, 61-67, vpres, 71 & pres, 75); Am Mosquito Control Asn; Royal Soc Trop Med & Hyg. *Res:* Malarias of man and lower animals; chemotherapy of malaria and parasitic infections; epidemiology of malaria and intestinal parasites; biology of human malarias; immunology and pathology of malaria; diagnosis of parasitic infections; drug resistant strains of malaria parasites; methodology of malaria eradication and control. *Mailing Add:* 1093 Blackshear Dr Atlanta GA 30304

JEFFERY, LARRY S, b Delta, Utah, June 21, 36; m 59; c 7. WEED SCIENCE, WEED BIOLOGY. *Educ:* Utah State Univ, BS, 62; NDak State Univ, PhD(plant sci), 66. *Prof Exp:* Asst prof weed sci, Univ Nebr Lincoln & Bogota, Colombia, 66-69; ASSOC PROF WEED SCI, UNIV TENN, 69- *Concurrent Pos:* Consult, Univ Wis & EMBRAPA-Ministry Agr Brazil, Lordrina, 76. *Mem:* Weed Sci Soc Am; Coun Agr Sci & Technol; Int Weed Sci Soc. *Res:* Weed control in economic crops; development of weed control systems in corn, soybeans, grain sorghum, tobacco, alfalfa, small grains and pastures. *Mailing Add:* Plant & Soil Sci Dept Univ Tenn Knoxville TN 37996

JEFFERY, LAWRENCE R, b Memphis, Tenn, June 30, 27; m 48; c 5. SYSTEMS DESIGN, SYSTEMS SCIENCE. *Educ:* Univ Chicago, MS, 53. *Prof Exp:* Instr electronic eng & math, Am TV Inst, Ill, 46-51; engr, Raytheon Mfg Co, Mass, 53-54; staff mem command & control systs, Lincoln Lab, Mass Inst Technol, 54-58, sect leader, 58; assoc dept head, Mass, 59-61, dept head, 61-63, assoc tech dir, 63-73, TECH DIR COMMUN, MITRE CORP, 73- *Mem:* Sr mem Inst Elec & Electronics Engrs. *Res:* Design and evaluation of computer-based command; control and communication systems; military operations research; digital computer engineering. *Mailing Add:* Mitre Corp Burlington Rd Bedford MA 01730

JEFFERY, RONDO NELDEN, b Provo, Utah, Apr 16, 40; m 65; c 5. SOLID STATE PHYSICS. *Educ:* Brigham Young Univ, BS, 63, MS, 65; Univ Ill-Urbana, PhD(physics), 70. *Prof Exp:* Res assoc physics, Rensselaer Polytech Inst, 70-73; asst prof physics, Wayne State Univ, 73-80; MEM FAC, DEPT PHYSICS, WEBER STATE COL, 80- *Concurrent Pos:* Asst prof, Cottrell res grant, Res Corp, 75-78 & NSF res grant, 78-81. *Mem:* Am Phys Soc; Am Asn Physics Teachers; Sigma Xi. *Res:* High pressure effects in solids; properties of point defects such as vacancies under high-pressure, high-temperature conditions using diffusion and positron annihilation techniques. *Mailing Add:* Dept Physics Weber State Col Ogden UT 84408

JEFFERY, SEYMOUR, computer science, electronics, see previous edition

JEFFERY, WILLIAM RICHARD, b Chicago, Ill, June 9, 44; m 75. DEVELOPMENTAL BIOLOGY, CELL BIOLOGY. *Educ:* Univ Ill, BS, 67; Univ Iowa, PhD(zool), 71. *Prof Exp:* Res asst biol, Univ Ill, 65-66; NIH fel zool, Univ Iowa, 67-71; Am Cancer Soc fel oncol, Univ Wis, 71-72; res assoc biochem, Sch Med, Tufts Univ, 72-74; asst prof biophys, Univ Houston, 74-77; asst prof, 77-80, ASSOC PROF ZOOL, UNIV TEX, 80- *Concurrent Pos:* Corp mem, Marine Biol Lab, Woods Hole 75-, instr embryol, 80-82. *Mem:* AAAS; Am Soc Cell Biol; Asn Develop Biol. *Res:* Molecular and cellular mechanisms of cell development and differentiation. *Mailing Add:* Dept of Zool Univ of Tex Austin TX 78712

JEFFERYS, WILLIAM H, III, b New Bedford, Mass, July 8, 40. ASTRONOMY. *Educ:* Wesleyan Univ, BA, 62; Yale Univ, MS, 64, PhD(astron), 65. *Prof Exp:* Instr astron, Wesleyan Univ, 64-65; asst prof, 65-68, assoc prof, 68-79, PROF ASTRON, UNIV TEX, AUSTIN, 79- *Concurrent Pos:* Alfred P Sloan fel, 65-67. *Mem:* AAAS; Am Astron Soc; Royal Astron Soc; Int Astron Union. *Res:* Astrometry; celestial mechanics. *Mailing Add:* Dept of Astron Univ of Tex Austin TX 78712

JEFFORDS, RUSSELL MACGREGOR, b Shinglehouse, Pa, May 11, 18; m 43; c 1. GEOLOGY. *Educ:* Syracuse Univ, AB, 39; Univ Kans, MA, 41, PhD(geol), 46. *Prof Exp:* Asst geologist, Kans Geol Surv, 39-42; geologist, US Geol Surv, 42-54 & Humble Oil & Refining Co, 54-64; res adv, 64-79, CONSULT, EXXON PROD RES CO, 79- *Concurrent Pos:* Instr, Brown Univ, 46-47; asst prof, Univ Tex, 47-48; assoc ed, Paleont Inst, Univ Kans, 69- *Mem:* Soc Tech Commun; Geol Soc Am; Paleont Soc; Soc Econ Paleontologists & Mineralogists; Am Asn Petrol Geologists. *Res:* Stratigraphic paleontology; ground-water hydrology and geochemistry; Paleozoic corals; crinoids; chitinozoans; editing. *Mailing Add:* 8002 Beverly Hill Houston TX 77063

JEFFREY, GEORGE ALAN, b Cardiff, Eng, July 29, 15; nat US; m 42; c 2. CRYSTALLOGRAPHY. *Educ:* Univ Birmingham, BSc, 36, PhD(chem), 39, DSc, 53. *Prof Exp:* X-ray crystallographer, Brit Rubber Producers Res Asn, 39-45; lectr inorg & phys chem, Univ Leeds, 45-53; prof chem & physics, 53-64, UNIV PROF CRYSTALLOG, UNIV PITTSBURGH, 65-, CHMN DEPT, 69- *Concurrent Pos:* Vis prof crystallog, Univ Pittsburgh, 50-51; mem exec comt gov bd, Am Inst Physics, 71- Award, Am Chem Soc, 78. *Honors & Awards:* Hudson Award, Am Chem Soc, 80. *Mem:* Am Chem Soc; Am Crystallog Asn (treas, 54-58, pres, 63); The Chem Soc; Brit Inst Physics & Phys Soc. *Res:* Structure of hydrates and carbohydrates; biochemical crystallography; crystallographic computing. *Mailing Add:* Dept of Crystallog Univ of Pittsburgh Pittsburgh PA 15260

JEFFREY, JACKSON EUGENE, b Oakhurst, NJ, May 28, 31; m 54; c 3. BIOLOGICAL STRUCTURE. *Educ:* Col William & Mary, BS, 54; Va Polytech Univ, MS, 59; Med Col Va, PhD(anat), 63. *Prof Exp:* Asst prof, 62-65, ASSOC PROF BIOL, VA COMMONWEALTH UNIV, 65- *Mem:* AAAS. *Res:* Fatty acid oxidation in cattle; effects of avitaminosis C on enzyme activity; interaction of various sex hormones on the reproductive system of the golden hamster; serum protein polymorphism in fish. *Mailing Add:* Dept of Biol Va Commonwealth Univ S7N 0W0 Richmond VA 23220

JEFFREY, JAMES GEORGE, b Scott, Sask, May 3, 17; m 48; c 5. PHARMACEUTICAL CHEMISTRY. *Educ:* Univ Sask, BSP, 43, MSc, 46; Univ Wis, PhD(pharmaceut chem), 55. *Prof Exp:* From instr to assoc prof, 45-56, PROF PHARM, COL PHARM, UNIV SASK, 56- *Concurrent Pos:* Asst secy, Can Conf Pharmaceut Facs, 47-51, chmn, 59-60. *Mem:* Am Pharmaceut Asn; Asn Facs Pharm Can. *Res:* Organic pharmaceutical chemistry. *Mailing Add:* Col of Pharm Univ of Sask Saskatoon SK S7N 0W0 Can

JEFFREY, JOHN J, b Worcester, Mass, May 3, 37; m 72. BIOLOGICAL CHEMISTRY, ENDOCRINOLOGY. *Educ:* Col of the Holy Cross, BS, 58; Georgetown Univ, PhD(chem), 65. *Prof Exp:* From instr to assoc prof, 67-81, PROF MED, SCH MED, WASHINGTON UNIV, 81- *Res:* Enzymatic mechanisms of collagen degradation; hormonal regulation of mammalian collagenase activity. *Mailing Add:* Div of Dermat Dept of Med Wash Univ Sch of Med St Louis MO 63110

JEFFREY, KENNETH ROBERT, b Toronto, Ont, May 7, 41; m 67. NUCLEAR MAGNETIC RESONANCE. *Educ:* Univ Toronto, BSc, 64, MA, 66, PhD(physics), 69. *Prof Exp:* Asst prof physics, 69-75, assoc prof, 75-81, PROF PHYSICS, UNIV GUELPH, 81- *Mem:* Can Asn Physicists; Biophys Soc. *Res:* Nuclear magnetic resonance studies of molecular reorientation and phase transitions in solids and lyotropic liquid crystals; biophysical techniques (nuclear magnetic resonance, x-ray diffraction, calorimetry dielectric relaxation), applied to model and biological membranes. *Mailing Add:* Dept of Physics Univ of Guelph Guelph ON W1G 2W1 Can

JEFFREY, NORRIS BODDIE, fisheries management, see previous edition

JEFFREYS, DONALD BEARSS, b Sackets Harbor, NY, Apr 15, 25; m 54; c 2. PLANT PHYSIOLOGY, MICROBIOLOGY. *Educ:* Roanoke Col, BS, 51; Univ NC, MA, 55, PhD(bot), 63. *Prof Exp:* Instr biol, Furman Univ, 54-56; asst prof, 60-63, ASSOC PROF BIOL, EAST CAROLINA UNIV, 63- *Mem:* Bot Soc Am; Am Soc Microbiol. *Res:* Plant growth; microbiology of estaurine organisms. *Mailing Add:* Dept of Biol ECarolina Univ Greenville NC 27834

JEFFRIES, CARSON DUNNING, b Lake Charles, La, Mar 20, 22; div; c 2. SOLID STATE PHYSICS. *Educ:* La State Univ, BS, 43; Stanford Univ, PhD(physics), 51. *Prof Exp:* Res assoc, Radio Res Lab, Harvard Univ, 43-45; instr physics, Phys Inst, Univ Zurich, 51; from instr to assoc prof, 52-63, PROF PHYSICS, UNIV CALIF, BERKELEY, 63- *Concurrent Pos:* NSF fels, 58 & 65-66; Fulbright res scholar, 59; Miller res prof, 61. *Mem:* Am Phys Soc. *Res:* Nuclear and electronic paramagnetism and magnetic resonance; nuclear orientation; low temperature and solid state physics; paramagnetic relaxation; optical properties of semi-conductors; excitons; chaotic behavior of physical systems. *Mailing Add:* Dept of Physics LeConte Hall Univ of Calif Berkeley CA 94720

JEFFRIES, CHARLES DEAN, b Rome, Ga, Apr 9, 29; m 53. MICROBIOLOGY. *Educ:* NGa Col, BS, 50; Univ Tenn, MS, 55, PhD(bact), 58. *Prof Exp:* Technician, Div Labs, State Dept Pub Health, Ga, 50-51; from instr to assoc prof, 58-70, from actg dep chmn to assoc chmn dept, 70-75, asst dean curric affairs & dir grad progs, 75-80, PROF IMMUNOL & MICROBIOL, SCH MED, WAYNE STATE UNIV, 70- *Concurrent Pos:* Fulbright lectr, Cairo Univ, 65-66; mem bd exam basic sci, State Mich, 67-72, vpres, 71-72; guest res, Mycol Div, Ctr Dis Control, US Pub Health Serv, Atlanta, Ga, 80-81. *Mem:* Fel Am Acad Microbiol; Am Soc Microbiol; Soc Exp Biol & Med; Brit Soc Gen Microbiol; Int Soc Human & Animal Mycol. *Res:* Bacterial identification; medical mycology. *Mailing Add:* Dept of Immunol & Microbiol Wayne State Univ Sch of Med Detroit MI 48201

JEFFRIES, GRAHAM HARRY, b Barmera, S Australia, May 31, 29; m 55; c 4. INTERNAL MEDICINE, GASTROENTEROLOGY. *Educ:* Univ NZ, BMedSc, 49, MB, ChB, 53; Oxford Univ, DPhil(physiol), 55. *Prof Exp:* Assoc prof med, Med Col, Cornell Univ, 64-69; PROF MED & CHMN DEPT, COL MED, MILTON S HERSHEY MED CTR, PA STATE UNIV, 69- *Mem:* Am Fedn Clin Res; Am Gastroenterol Asn; Am Soc Clin Invest; fel Am Col Physicians. *Res:* Gastric secretion; vitamin B-12 metabolism; intestinal absorption; liver disease. *Mailing Add:* Milton S Hershey Med Ctr Pa State Univ Hershey PA 17033

JEFFRIES, HARRY PERRY, b Newark, NJ, Apr 15, 29; m 51; c 5. ZOOLOGY. *Educ:* Univ RI, BS, 51, MS, 55; Rutgers Univ, PhD(zool), 59. *Prof Exp:* Asst biol oceanog, Univ RI, 51-55; pharmacologist, Ciba Pharmaceut Prod, Inc, NJ, 55-56; asst, Rutgers Univ, 56-59; from asst prof to assoc prof, 59-73, PROF BIOL OCEANOG, UNIV RI, 73- *Concurrent Pos:* Grants, Fed Water Qual Admin, USPHS, Dept Energy & Nat Oceanog & Atmospheric Admin; Environ Protection Agency Sea Grant, Am Petroleum Inst; pres, Estuarine Res Fedn, 73-75. *Mem:* Fel AAAS; Am Soc Limnol & Oceanog. *Res:* Comparative ecology of estuarine habitats; biological fertility of inshore marine areas and characterization of community structure; chemical homeostasis of marine organisms in relation to environmental stress; biochemical systematics. *Mailing Add:* Grad Sch Oceanog Univ of RI Kingston RI 02881

JEFFRIES, NEAL POWELL, b Indianapolis, Ind, Aug 25, 35; m 58; c 2. MECHANICAL ENGINEERING. *Educ:* Purdue Univ, BS, 57; Mass Inst Technol, MS, 58; Univ Cincinnati, PhD(mech eng), 69. *Prof Exp:* Res asst heat transfer, Stanford Univ, 61-63; engr, Gen Elec Co, Ohio, 63-65, proj mgr heat transfer, 65-67; res assoc mech eng, Univ Cincinnati, 67-69, asst prof, 69-74; MGR EDUC MECH ENG DEPT, STRUCT DYNAMICS RES CORP, 74- *Concurrent Pos:* Lectr, Gen Elec Co, 63-74; consult, Struct Dynamics Res Corp, 68-74, Honeywell Res Lab & Am Laundry Mfg, 69-70, Vortex Corp, 70-, & Avco Electronics, 71-; US Navy grant, 70-71. *Mem:* Am Soc Mech Engrs; Soc Mfg Engrs; Am Soc Eng Educ. *Res:* Heat transfer; fluid flow; thermodynamics; boiling phenomena; heat pipe; manufacturing engineering. *Mailing Add:* 3112 Cooper Cincinnati OH 45241

JEFFRIES, QUENTIN RAY, b Terre Haute, Ind, Feb 28, 20; m 51; c 2. CHEMICAL ENGINEERING. *Educ:* Rose Polytech Inst, BS, 41; Univ Mich, MS, 47; Univ Ill, PhD(chem eng), 53. *Prof Exp:* Asst chem engr, Commercial Solvents Corp, 48-49, shift supvr, Penicillin Plant, 49-51; prin chem engr, Battelle Mem Inst, 53-56; prin chem engr, 56-59, tech develop engr, 59-65, CHEM ENGR RES, ENG DEPT, INT MINERALS CORP, 65- *Mem:* Am Chem Soc. *Res:* Gaseous diffusion. *Mailing Add:* Int Minerals Corp 1331 S First St Terre Haute IN 47801

JEFFRIES, ROBERT ALAN, b Indianapolis, Ind, Nov 11, 33; m 54; c 2. OPTICAL PHYSICS. *Educ:* Univ Okla, BS, 54, MS, 61, PhD(ionization kinetics), 65. *Prof Exp:* Proj engr, Pontiac Motor Div, Gen Motors Corp, 54-55; staff mem, 57-76, group leader, 76-77, asst div leader, 77-79, LEADER, LOS ALAMOS NAT LAB, 77- *Mem:* Am Phys Soc; Sigma Xi. *Res:* Ionization kinetics; shock hydrodynamics; laser produced plasmas; electro optical instrumentation. *Mailing Add:* Los Alamos Nat Lab NSP/TV Los Alamos NM 87544

JEFFRIES, THOMAS WILLIAM, b New Orleans, La, Oct 31, 47; m 74. MICROBIOLOGY. *Educ:* Calif State Univ, Long Beach, BS, 69, MS, 72; Rutgers Univ, PhD(microbiol), 75. *Prof Exp:* Asst microbiol, Calif State Univ, Long Beach, 69-71; res intern, Rutgers Univ, 72-75; staff mem microbiol, Lawrence Livermore Lab, Univ Calif, 75-77; res assoc chem eng & appl chem, Columbia Univ, 77-79; MICROBIOLOGIST, FOREST PROD LAB, USDA, 79- *Mem:* Am Soc Microbiol; Soc Indust Microbiol; AAAS; Am Chem Soc; Tech Pulp & Paper Indust. *Res:* Applied microbial ecology; polysaccharide biochemistry; biochemical engineering; biochemistry; biotechnology; enzymology; microbial photosynthesis; biofuels; environmental toxicology; lignin biodegradation; peutose fermentation; yeasts. *Mailing Add:* USDA Forest Prod Lab PO Box 5130 Madison WI 53705

JEFFRIES, WILLIAM BOWMAN, b Chicago, Ill, Mar 5, 26; div; c 3. INVERTEBRATE ZOOLOGY. *Educ:* Univ Pittsburgh, BS, 49; Univ NC, MA, 52, PhD(zool), 55. *Prof Exp:* Asst zool, Univ NC, 50-55; Nat Cancer Inst fel, Ind Univ, 55-56; from instr to asst prof microanat, Med Col Ga, 56-59; from asst prof to assoc prof biol, 59-68, chmn dept, 65-68 & 74-77, PROF BIOL, DICKINSON COL, 68- *Concurrent Pos:* NIH spec res fel, Vet Admin Hosp, Miami, 68-69; res assoc biochem, Sch Med, Univ Miami, 68-69; res assoc, Dept Zool, Field Mus Natural Hist, 76- *Mem:* AAAS; Am Soc Zool; Soc Protozool. *Res:* Physiology; parasitology; protozoology; biology of the barnacle genus octolasmis. *Mailing Add:* Dept of Biol Dickinson Col Carlisle PA 17013

JEFFS, PETER W, b Luton, Eng, Jan 9, 33; m 57; c 3. ORGANIC CHEMISTRY. *Educ:* Univ Natal, PhD(chem), 61. *Prof Exp:* Res asst, Akers Res Labs, Imp Chem Indust, Eng, 50-57; lectr org chem, Univ Natal, 60-62; from asst prof to assoc prof, 64-71, PROF ORG CHEM, DUKE UNIV, 71- *Mem:* Am Chem Soc; fel The Chem Soc; assoc Royal Inst Chem. *Res:* Chemistry of alkaloids, terpenes and mould metabolites; alkaloid biosynthesis; application of nuclear magnetic resonance to structure determination. *Mailing Add:* Dept of Chem Duke Univ Durham NC 27706

JEFIMENKO, OLEG D, b USSR, Oct 14, 22; m 45. PHYSICS. *Educ:* Lewis & Clark Col, BA, 52; Univ Ore, MA, 54, PhD(physics), 56. *Prof Exp:* Asst physics, Univ Ore, 52-55; from asst prof to assoc prof, 56-67, PROF PHYSICS, WVA UNIV, 67- *Mem:* Am Phys Soc; Am Asn Physics Teachers; Electrostatic Soc Am. *Res:* Electromagnetic theory; cosmical electrodynamics; electrostatics; electrets; atomic physics. *Mailing Add:* Dept of Physics WVa Univ Morgantown WV 26506

JEGLA, THOMAS CYRIL, b St Johns, Mich, July 5, 35; m 65; c 2. COMPARATIVE PHYSIOLOGY, MARINE BIOLOGY. *Educ:* Mich State Univ, BS, 58; Univ Ill, MS, 60, PhD(zool), 64. *Prof Exp:* Asst prof biol, Univ Minn, 63-64 & Yale Univ, 64-66; asst prof, 66-68, ASSOC PROF BIOL, KENYON COL, 68- *Concurrent Pos:* NSF res grants, 70 & 73; vis assoc prof, Yale Univ, 81-83. *Mem:* AAAS; Am Soc Zool; Soc Europ Comp Endocrinol. *Res:* Molting physiology of arthropods; environmental physiology; invertebrate biology; endocrinology. *Mailing Add:* Dept Biol Kenyon Col Gambier OH 43022

JEGLUM, JOHN KARL, b Medford, Wis, Dec 9, 38; m 64; c 2. FOREST ECOLOGY, SILVICULTURE. *Educ:* Univ Wis, BS, 60, MS, 62; Univ Sask, PhD(plant ecol), 68. *Prof Exp:* Asst prof bot, Eastern Ill Univ, 65-66; RES SCIENTIST FORESTRY ECOL, CAN FORESTRY SERV, 68- *Mem:* Can Bot Asn; Can Inst Forestry; Ecol Soc Am; Int Peat Soc. *Res:* Wetland classification and ecology; boreal vegetational ecology; autecology of black spruce; regeneration silviculture; strip cutting in black spruce; environmental impacts of harvesting. *Mailing Add:* Great Lakes Forest Res Ctr Box 490 Sault Ste Marie ON P6A 5M7 Can

JEHLE, HERBERT, b Stuttgart, Ger, Mar 5, 07; nat US; m 52; c 2. THEORETICAL PHYSICS. *Educ:* Inst Technol, Stuttgart, Dipl Ing, 30; Inst Technol, Berlin, Dr Ing, 33. *Prof Exp:* Ed collaborator, Jahrbuch Fortschritte d Math, Berlin, 35-36; res asst, Univ Southampton, 37; res assoc, Univ Brussels, 38-40; instr Harvard Univ, 42-46; guest Franklin Inst, Nat Res Coun seeing-aid proj, 46; mem, Inst Adv Study, Princeton, 47; asst prof physics, Univ Pa, 47-49; from assoc prof to prof, Univ Nebr, 49-59; res assoc, Calif Inst Technol, 56-57; prof, 59-72, EMER PROF PHYSICS, GEORGE WASHINGTON UNIV, 72-; GUEST, INST THEOR PHYSICS, UNIV AMSTERDAM, 75-; VIS PROF THEOR PHYS, UNIV MUNICH, 77- *Concurrent Pos:* NIH fel, 65-66; consult, Nat Cancer Inst, 72-77; sr fel Univ Md, 72-; guest, Max Planck Inst Physics & Astrophys, Munich, 73-74 & Uppsala Univ, Sweden, 75 & 76. *Mem:* Fel Am Phys Soc; Am Astron Soc; Biophys Soc; Am Math Soc; Soc Quantum Biol. *Res:* Charge fluctuation forces; nucleic acid replication, bilateral symmetry in morphogenesis; statistical hypotheses in gravitational systems; intermolecular forces and biological specificity; flux quantization and particle physics; elementary particle physics. *Mailing Add:* 1208 Sherwood Rd Charlottesville 22901 West Germany

JEHN, KENNETH HARTMEIER, meteorology, deceased

JEHN, LAWRENCE A, b Dayton, Ohio, Aug 7, 21; m 44; c 9. APPLIED MATHEMATICS. *Educ:* Dayton Univ, BS, 43; Univ Mich, ScM, 49. *Prof Exp:* Instr math, Univ Dayton, 46-47, asst prof, 50-56; res assoc, Univ Mich, 56-57; assoc prof, 57-63, RES MATHEMATICIAN, RES INST, UNIV DAYTON, 63-, PROF COMPUT SCI, 74- *Concurrent Pos:* Consult, Univ Dayton, 51-56 & 57-63, assoc prof comput sci & mech eng, 68-74. *Mem:* Asn Comput Mach; Inst Elec & Electronics Engrs; Comput Soc; Am Soc Eng Educ. *Res:* Computer science education; numerical analysis and simulation. *Mailing Add:* Dept Comput Sci Univ Dayton 300 College Park Dayton OH 45469

JEKEL, EUGENE CARL, b Holland, Mich, Dec 19, 30; m 60; c 2. INORGANIC CHEMISTRY. *Educ:* Hope Col, AB, 52; Purdue Univ, MS, 55, PhD(inorg chem), 64. *Prof Exp:* From instr to assoc prof, 55-69, chmn dept, 67-70 & 73-76, PROF CHEM, HOPE COL, 69-, CHIEF HEALTH PROFESSIONS ADV, 77- *Concurrent Pos:* Vis prof, Univ Calif, Berkeley, 70-71. *Mem:* Asn Am Med Cols; Nat Sci Teachers Asn; Am Chem Soc; Am Sci Affiliation. *Res:* Thermodynamics of aqueous solutions at high temperature. *Mailing Add:* Dept of Chem Hope Col Holland MI 49423

JEKEL, JAMES FRANKLIN, b St Louis, Mo, Oct 14, 34; m 58; c 4. EPIDEMIOLOGY, PUBLIC HEALTH. *Educ:* Wesleyan Univ, AB, 56; Wash Univ, MD, 60; Yale Univ, MPH, 65. *Prof Exp:* Res asst pub health, St Louis County Health Dept, 58; asst prof, 67-71, assoc prof pub health, 71-80, PROF EPIDEMOL & PUB HEALTH, YALE UNIV, 80- *Mem:* Am Pub Health Asn; fel Am Col Prev Med; fel Am Sci Affiliation. *Res:* Epidemiology of infectious diseases, especially tuberculosis, diphtheria and the venereal diseases; program evaluation, especially health programs for teenage mothers. *Mailing Add:* Dept of Epidemiol & Pub Health Yale Univ 60 College St New Haven CT 06510

JEKELI, CHRISTOPHER, b Marburg, WGer, Dec 21, 53. GEODESY. *Educ:* McGill Univ, BA, 76; Ohio State Univ, MSc, 78, PhD(geod), 81. *Prof Exp:* Res assoc geod, Ohio State Univ, 77-81; GEODESIST, AIR FORCE GEOPHYSICS LAB, 81- *Mem:* Am Geophys Union; Am Congress Surveying & Mapping. *Res:* Physical geodesy: methods to analyze and improve knowledge of the earth's external gravity field and application of these methods to gravimetric data. *Mailing Add:* Air Force Geophysics Lab Hanscom AFB MA 01731

JEKELI, WALTER, b Wiesbaden, Ger, Feb 23, 25; m 52; c 2. PHYSICS. *Educ:* Univ Marburg, dipl physics, 52, PhD(nuclear physics), 55. *Prof Exp:* Teacher, High Schs, Ger, 55-62; from asst prof to assoc prof physics, Clarkson Col Technol, 62-66; chmn dept physics, 67-76, PROF PHYSICS, STATE UNIV NY COL POTSDAM, 66- *Mem:* Am Phys Soc; Am Asn Physics Teachers; Ger Phys Soc. *Res:* Optics; spectroscopy; philosophy of physics. *Mailing Add:* Dept of Physics State Univ of NY Col Potsdam NY 13676

JELEN, FREDERIC CHARLES, b Chelsea, Mass, Jan 17, 10; m 43; c 2. CHEMICAL ENGINEERING. *Educ:* Mass Inst Technol, SB, 31, SM, 32; Harvard Univ, AM, 34, PhD(phys chem), 35. *Prof Exp:* Chemist phosphates, Monsanto Co, 35-41; engr electrochem, Battelle Mem Inst, 42-43; chief engr silicates, Cowles Chem Co, 43-49; engr corrosion, Allied Chem Co, 49-61; prof chem eng, Lamar Univ, 61-80; PROF CHEM ENG, MCNEESE STATE UNIV, 81- *Concurrent Pos:* Consult cost eng, 61-, PPG Industs, Inc, 62-75, Int Nickel, 63, Mobil Oil Corp, 63-, Mobil Chem Co, 64-71 & E I du Pont de Nemours & Co, Inc, 75; chmn continuing educ, Am Asn Cost Engrs, 71- *Mem:* Am Inst Chem Engrs; fel Am Asn Cost Engrs. *Res:* Cost engineering. *Mailing Add:* 6170 Pansy Dr Beaumont TX 77706

JELENKO, CARL, III, b Baltimore, Md, Sept 8, 31; c 2. SURGERY. *Educ:* Loyola Col, Md, BS, 53; Univ Md, MD, 57, MS, 68. *Prof Exp:* From intern to resident surg, Sinai Hosp Baltimore, John Hopkins Hosp & Univ Md Hosp, 63-64; instr surg, Sch Med, Univ Md, 64-68; assoc prof, 68-73, prof surg, Med Col Ga, 73-78; PROF EMERGENCY MED, COMMUNITY MED & SURG, WRIGHT STATE UNIV SCH MED, DAYTON, OHIO, 78- *Concurrent Pos:* Consult, US Army Hosp, Fort Gordon, Ga, 73- *Mem:* Fel Am Col Surg; Am Burn Asn; Soc Univ Surg; Am Asn Surg of Trauma; Asn Acad Surg. *Res:* Biophysics of burn trauma; surface water loss and caloric metabolism in burns and denuding traumata and control of these parameters; microcirculation in burn victims; fluid management shock; resuscitation. *Mailing Add:* Dept of Emergency Med Wright State Univ Sch of Med Dayton OH 45324

JELINEK, ARTHUR GILBERT, b Milwaukee, Wis, May 6, 17; m 45; c 3. SYNTHETIC ORGANIC CHEMISTRY. *Educ:* Univ Wis, BS, 40, PhD(org chem), 44. *Prof Exp:* Res & control chemist, Fox River Paper Corp, Wis, 40-41; asst org chem, Univ Wis, 41-44; res chemist, Grasselli Chem Dept, E I du Pont de Nemours & Co Inc, 44-55, sr res chemist, Biochem Dept, 55-79; RETIRED. *Mem:* Emer mem Am Chem Soc. *Res:* Agricultural chemicals. *Mailing Add:* 2500 Lindell Rd Garden Farm Wilmington DE 19808

JELINEK, BOHDAN, b Jimaramov, Czech, June 21, 10; nat US; m 65; c 1. BIOCHEMISTRY, CLINICAL MEDICINE. *Educ:* Brno Tech Univ, BS, 32, DSc(chem), 35; Masaryk Univ, BSc, 33, MD, 39. *Prof Exp:* French Govt Scholar, Institut Pasteur, Paris, France, 35-37; asst prof appl biochem, Brno Tech Univ, 38-39; res assoc, Sugar Res Inst, 40-45; Brit Res Coun scholar, Univ Birmingham, Eng, 45-46, Univ res fel, 48-49; prof fermentation chem & indust mycol & chmn dept, Univ Prague, 46-48; asst prof biochem, Univ Alta, 49-52; assoc prof, Univ Mo, 52-54; res assoc, Med Res Inst, City of Hope Med Res Ctr, 54-64; head biochemist & asst to dir res, Adolph's Food Prod Mfg Co, 57-70; CONSULT, 70- *Concurrent Pos:* Intern, Sante Fe Mem Hosp, Los Angeles, 72-73; med dir, Alcohol Prog, Los Angeles County Health Serv, 74-75; med consult, Dept Rehab, State Calif, 75- *Mem:* AAAS; Am Chem Soc; Inst Food Technologists; NY Acad Sci; Royal Soc Chem. *Res:* Chemistry and biochemistry of carbohydrates and their derivatives; fermentations, physical chemistry and enzymatic degradation of starch and its components; nutritional and industrial aspects of carbohydrates; dietetic foods; papain. *Mailing Add:* 231 N Primrose Ave Monrovia CA 91016

JELINEK, CHARLES FRANK, b Miles City, Mont, Feb 6, 17; m 44; c 2. ORGANIC CHEMISTRY. *Educ:* Mont State Col, BS, 38; Oxford Univ, BSc, 41; Univ Ill, PhD(org chem), 44. *Prof Exp:* Res chemist, Gen Aniline & Film Corp, 46-47, asst to dir res, 47-49, sales engr & asst dir cent sales develop dept, 49-50, sect leader appln res, 50-52, mgr surfactants res, 52-55, mgr process res & develop dept, 55-59, dir dyestuff & chem div, Cent Res Lab, 59-63; sr staff adv, Chem Staff, Esso Res & Eng Co, 63-66; coordr new ventures, Enjay, 66-71; coordr tech opportunities div, Dart Industs, Inc, 71-72; dir div chem technol, 72-75, dept assoc dir technol, 75-79, DEPT ASSOC DIR PHYS SCI, BUR FOODS, FOOD & DRUG ADMIN, 79- *Mem:* Am Chem Soc; Asn Off Anal Chemists; Am Inst Chemists; Commercial Develop Asn. *Res:* Derivatives of acetylene; dyes; pigments; surfactants; polymers; solvents; coatings; chemical contaminants in foods. *Mailing Add:* Food & Drug Admin 200 C St SW Washington DC 20204

JELINEK, FREDERICK, b Prague, Czech, Nov 18, 32; nat US; m 61; c 2. ELECTRONIC ENGINEERING. *Educ:* Mass Inst Technol, SB, 56, SM, 58, PhD(elec eng), 62. *Prof Exp:* Instr elec eng, Mass Inst Technol, 59-62; from asst prof to prof, Cornell Univ, 62-74; SR MGR CONTINUOUS SPEECH RECOGNITION, T J WATSON RES CTR, IBM CORP, 72- *Concurrent Pos:* Vis lectr, Harvard Univ, 62; NSF grant, 64-66; vis scientist, IBM T J Watson Res Ctr, 68-69; NASA contracts, 66-72. *Mem:* Fel Inst Elec & Electronics Engrs. *Res:* Transmission of information; coding; data compression; speech recognition; information theory. *Mailing Add:* T J Watson Res Ctr IBM Corp Yorktown Heights NY 10598

JELINEK, ROBERT V(INCENT), b New York, NY, Mar 5, 26; m 55; c 3. CHEMICAL ENGINEERING. *Educ:* Columbia Univ, BS, 45, MS, 47, PhD(chem eng), 53. *Prof Exp:* Asst drafting, Columbia Univ, 43-45, instr chem eng, 49-51; chem engr, Develop Div, Standard Oil Develop Co, 51-53; asst prof chem eng, Columbia Univ, 53-54; from asst prof to prof, Syracuse Univ, 54-72, dir summer res prog high sch teachers, 64-69, asst to dean eng, 55-60, fac secy, 62-64, chmn eng fac, 64-65; prof & dean, Sch Environ & Resource Eng, 72-80, PROF DEPT PAPER SCI & ENG, STATE UNIV NY COL ENVIRON SCI & FORESTRY, 80- *Concurrent Pos:* Assoc, Danforth Found, 56-60; NSF res grant, 59-61; prog dir eng chem, NSF, 71-72. *Mem:* Am Chem Soc; Electrochem Soc; Nat Asn Corrosion Engrs; Am Inst Chem Engrs. *Res:* Reaction kinetics; corrosion; electrochemistry; adsorption; process design and computer simulation. *Mailing Add:* Col Environ Sci & Forestry State Univ New York Syracuse NY 13210

JELLARD, CHARLES H, b Abergavenny, Wales, Dec 25, 16; m 50; c 4. MEDICAL BACTERIOLOGY, PUBLIC HEALTH. *Educ:* Oxford Univ, BA & BM, BCh, 42; Univ London, dipl bact, 51; FRCPath, 65; Oxford Univ, DM, 75. *Hon Degrees:* MA, Cambridge Univ, 48. *Prof Exp:* Dir, Pub Health Lab Serv, Plymouth, UK, 53-68; ASSOC PROF BACT & DEP DIR, PROV LAB PUB HEALTH, UNIV ALTA, 68- *Concurrent Pos:* Hon consult bacteriologist, Plymouth Hosps, UK, 53-68. *Mem:* Path Soc Gt Brit & Ireland; Brit Soc Gen Microbiol. *Res:* Diagnostic medical bacteriology; epidemiology. *Mailing Add:* Prov Lab of Pub Health Univ of Alta Edmonton AB T6H 4L5 Can

JELLIFFE, DERRICK BRIAN, b Rochester, UK, Jan 20, 21; m 42. NUTRITION, PEDIATRICS. *Educ:* Univ London, MB, BS, 43, MRCP, 44, DCH & MD, 45, DTH & H, 47; Am Bd Pediat, dipl, 58; FRCP, 61. *Prof Exp:* Lectr med, Univ Ibadan, 49-52; sr lectr pediat, Univ WI, 52-54; WHO vis prof, All-India Inst Hyg & Pub Health, Calcutta, 54-56; vis prof trop med, Med Sch, Tulane Univ, 56-59; prof pediat, Med Sch, Makerere Univ, Uganda, 59-66; prof community nutrit & dir, Caribbean Food & Nutrit Inst, Jamaica, 67-71; prof pub health, 71-77, PROF ECON PUB HEALTH, SCH PUB HEALTH, UNIV CALIF, LOS ANGELES, 77- *Concurrent Pos:* Fulbright fel, Med Sch, Tulane Univ, 51; vis prof, Sch Pub Health, Univ Calif, Berkeley, 63; chmn comt ecol prev young child malnutrit, Int Union Nutrit Sci, 70- *Honors & Awards:* Rosen von Rosenstein Medal, Swed Pediat Soc, 69. *Mem:* Fel Am Pub Health Asn; fel Am Acad Pediat; Am Inst Nutrit; Asn Pediat India (pres, 54); Asn Physicians E Africa (pres, 63). *Res:* Health and nutrition in young children in developing countries, particularly the epidemiology field assessment and evaluation of programs. *Mailing Add:* Sch of Pub Health Univ of Calif Los Angeles CA 90024

JELLIFFE, ROGER WOODHAM, b Cleveland, Ohio, Feb 18, 29; m 54; c 4. CARDIOLOGY, CLINICAL PHARMACOLOGY. *Educ:* Harvard Col, AB, 50; Columbia Univ, MD, 54; Am Bd Internal Med, dipl, 62; Am Bd Cardiovasc Dis, dipl, 65. *Prof Exp:* Intern med, Univ Hosps, Cleveland, Ohio, 54-55, asst resident, 55-56; Nat Found Infantile Paralysis fel exp med, Sch Med, Western Reserve Univ, 56-58; staff physician, Vet Admin Hosp, Cleveland, 58-60, resident med, 60-61; from instr to assoc prof, 61-76, PROF MED, SCH MED, UNIV SOUTHERN CALIF, 76- *Concurrent Pos:* Los Angeles County Heart Asn res fel, Sch Med, Univ Southern Calif, 61-63; NIH res grants digitalis, 64- *Mem:* fel Am Col Physicians; fel Am Col Cardiol; fel Am Heart Asn; Am Soc Pharmacol & Exp Therapeut. *Res:* Cardiovascular pharmacology; chemical measurements of digitalis glycosides and mathematical descriptions of the kinetics of digitalis, kanamycin, gentamicin, streptomycin, procainamide, lidocaine and other drugs in man; computer assistance for planning, monitoring and adjusting dosage regimens of the above drugs. *Mailing Add:* Univ of Southern Calif Sch Med 2025 Zonal Ave Los Angeles CA 90033

JELLINCK, PETER HARRY, b Paris, France, Feb 20, 28; m 54; c 3. BIOCHEMISTRY, ENDOCRINOLOGY. *Educ:* Cambridge Univ, BA, 48; Univ London, BSc, 50, MSc, 52, PhD(biochem), 54. *Prof Exp:* Can Nat Res Coun fel biochem, McGill Univ, 55-56; lectr chem, Norwood Tech Col, Eng, 56-57; lectr biochem, St Bartholomew's Hosp Med Col, London, 57-58 & Middlesex Hosp Med Sch, 58-59; from asst prof to prof, Univ BC, 60-67; head dept, 67-78, PROF BIOCHEM, QUEEN'S UNIV, ONT, 67- *Concurrent Pos:* Nat Cancer Inst Can-Med Res Coun Can res grant, 59-; vis prof, Rockefeller Univ, 78-79. *Mem:* Am Asn Cancer Res; Brit Biochem Soc; Can Biochem Soc; Endocrine Soc. *Res:* Estrogen action; role of steroid hormones in breast cancer. *Mailing Add:* Dept of Biochem Queen's Univ Kingston ON K7L 3N6 Can

JELLINEK, HANS HELMUT GUNTER, b Free City of Danzig, Mar 25, 17; m 48; c 1. PHYSICAL CHEMISTRY. *Educ:* Univ London, DIC, 41, PhD(phys chem), 42; Cambridge Univ, PhD(colloid & phys chem), 45, ScD, 64. *Prof Exp:* Sect head phys chem, J Lyons & Co, Eng, 45-50; assoc prof, Univ Adelaide, 50-54; vis prof, Polytech Inst Brooklyn, 54-57; assoc prof, Univ Cincinnati, 57-59; prof chem, Univ Windsor, 59-64, head dept, 59-63; PROF CHEM, CLARKSON COL, 64- *Concurrent Pos:* Sci expert, US Dept Army, 54-63 & 70-; mem comt high polymer res, Nat Res Coun Can, 62-64. *Mem:* AAAS; Am Chem Soc; fel Am Inst Chem; fel Chem Inst Can; fel Royal Inst Chem. *Res:* Stability of high polymers; reaction kinetics; surface chemistry; energy production; adhesive and rheological properties of ice; author of over 160 publications. *Mailing Add:* Dept of Chem Clarkson Col Potsdam NY 13676

JELLING, MURRAY, b Brooklyn, NY, Jan 7, 18; m 41; c 1. ORGANIC CHEMISTRY, PATENT LICENSING. *Educ:* Brooklyn Col, BS, 37; Polytech Inst, NY, MS, 41, PhD(chem), 45. *Prof Exp:* Res chemist, Autoxygen, Inc, 38-41; res chemist, Nopco Chem Co, Inc, 41-43; res assoc, polymer, Polytech Inst, NY, 43-45; res dir org chem, Maguire Industs, Inc, 45-47; pres, Cidex Corp, 48-57; CONSULT CHEMIST, 57- *Concurrent Pos:* Pres, Jonelle Indust Prod Inc, 67-72. *Mem:* Am Chem Soc; Sigma Xi. *Res:* Improvement, modification and cost reduction of existing products; industrial organic chemistry; polymers; textile maintenance (dry-cleaning and laundry) products; chemical specialties. *Mailing Add:* 21 Spring Hill Rd Roslyn Heights NY 11577

JELLINGER, THOMAS CHRISTIAN, b Seaton, Ill, Sept 17, 23; m 46; c 3. CONSTRUCTION ENGINEERING. *Educ:* Univ Ill, Urbana-Champaign, BS, 49; Iowa State Univ, MS, 63. *Prof Exp:* Engr, various consult firms, Cincinnati, 49-52 & Wagner, Inc, 52-57; proprietor eng & architect, Thomas C Jellinger, 57-60; PROF-IN-CHARGE CONSTRUCT ENG, IOWA STATE UNIV, 60- *Concurrent Pos:* Dir & vpres, Assoc Gen Contractor Educ & Res Found, 70; founding dir, Am Inst Constructors. *Mem:* Nat Soc Prof Engrs; Am Soc Eng Educ. *Res:* Construction management, techniques, and advanced methods of construction scheduling. *Mailing Add:* Dept of Construct Eng Iowa State Univ Ames IA 50010

JELLISON, GERALD EARLE, JR, b Bangor, Maine, Mar 27, 46; m 70; c 2. OPTICS. *Educ:* Bowdoin Col, BA, 68; Brown Univ, ScM, 73, PhD(physics), 77. *Prof Exp:* Nat Res Coun fel, Naval Res Lab, 76-78; STAFF SCIENTIST, OAK RIDGE NAT LAB, 78- *Mem:* Am Phys Soc. *Res:* Physics of semiconductors as related to laser annealing mechanisms; measurement of optical properties of materials as a function of doping and temperature, as well as time-released optical measurements. *Mailing Add:* Bldg 2000 Solid State Div Oak Ridge Nat Lab Oak Ridge TN 37830

JELLUM, MILTON DELBERT, b Starbuck, Minn, Oct 26, 34; m 57; c 2. AGRONOMY, PLANT BREEDING. *Educ:* Univ Minn, BS, 56; Univ Ill, MS, 58, PhD(agron), 61. *Prof Exp:* Asst agronomist, 60-67, assoc prof, 67-72, PROF AGRON, GA EXP STA, UNIV GA, 72- *Mem:* AAAS; Am Soc Agron; Crop Sci Soc Am; Am Oil Chem Soc; Am Asn Cereal Chem. *Res:* Environmental and genetic study of oil content and fatty acid composition of corn grain oil; study of yield components of corn and corn breeding. *Mailing Add:* Dept of Agron Ga Exp Sta Univ of Ga Experiment GA 30212

JEMAL, MOHAMMED, Ethiopian citizen. PHARMACEUTICS, MEDICINAL CHEMISTRY. *Educ:* Haile Sellassie Univ, BS, 70; Purdue Univ, PhD(pharm anal), 76. *Prof Exp:* Assoc pharm anal, Purdue Univ, 76-77; RES INVESTR ANAL RES & DEVELOP, SQUIBB INST MED RES, 78- *Mem:* Am Chem Soc; Am Pharmaceut Asn. *Res:* Method development for medicinal and pharmaceutical agents. *Mailing Add:* Squibb Inst Med Res New Brunswick NJ 08903

JEMIAN, WARTAN A(RMIN), b Lynn, Mass, Dec 31, 25; m 51; c 4. PHYSICAL METALLURGY. *Educ:* Univ Md, BS, 50; Rensselaer Polytech Inst, MS, 53, PhD(metall eng), 56. *Prof Exp:* Engr, Semiconductor Dept, Westinghouse Elec Corp, 55-57; sr fel & head power rectifiers fel, Mellon Inst, 57-62; dir res & develop, Rectifier-Capacitor Div, Fansteel Metall Corp, 62; assoc prof, 62-65, PROF MECH ENG, AUBURN UNIV, 65-, CHMN MAT ENG CURRICULUM COMT, 63-, PROF MAT ENG, 75- *Concurrent Pos:* Lectr & adj prof, Univ Pittsburgh, 56-62. *Mem:* Am Inst Mining, Metall & Petrol Engrs; Am Soc Metals; Am Soc Eng Educ; Biomat Res Soc; Int Asn Math & Comput Simulation. *Res:* Education; structure and properties of composite materials; computer analysis of materials; education in materials science and engineering. *Mailing Add:* Dept of Mat Eng Auburn Univ Auburn AL 36830

JEMSKI, JOSEPH VICTOR, b Blackstone, Mass, Mar 19, 20; m 43; c 1. MEDICAL MICROBIOLOGY. *Educ:* Fordham Univ, BS, 42; Univ Pa, PhD(med microbiol), 52. *Prof Exp:* Head bact dept, Maltine Co, 46-49; chief animal path unit, Ralph M Parsons Co, 52-55; chief animal path sect, Chem Corps, 55-59, chief test sphere br, US Army Biol Defense Res Labs, 59-72, SR INVESTR, US ARMY RES INST INFECTIOUS DIS, 72- *Mem:* AAAS; Am Soc Microbiol; Am Asn Lab Animal Sci; Sigma Xi; fel Am Acad Microbiol. *Res:* Experimental aerosol induced diseases in laboratory animals; aerobiology; biological safety; immunogenesis and immunoprophylaxis of respiratory diseases. *Mailing Add:* US Army Med Res Inst Infectious Dis Ft Detrick Frederick MD 21701

JEN, CHIH KUNG, b Chin Yuan, China, Aug 15, 06; nat US; m 37; c 4. MICROWAVE PHYSICS. *Educ:* Mass Inst Technol, SB, 28; Univ Pa, SM, 29; Harvard Univ, PhD(physics), 31. *Prof Exp:* Asst physics, Harvard Univ, 30-32, instr, 32-33; prof, Shuntung Univ, China, 33-34; prof, Tsing Hua Univ, Peking, China, 34-37, dir radio res int, 37-45; res lectr physics, Harvard Univ, 46-50; vchmn res ctr, 58-74, William S Parsons vis prof chem physics, 66-67, physicist & prin staff mem, Appl Physics Lab, 50-76, CONSULT, JOHNS HOPKINS UNIV, 78- *Concurrent Pos:* Fel, China Found, 31-32. *Mem:* Fel Am Phys Soc. *Res:* Ionosphere; quantum mechanics; electron tube phenomena; microwave spectroscopy. *Mailing Add:* Johns Hopkins Univ Appl Phys Lab Johns Hopkins Rd Laurel MD 20707

JEN, JOSEPH JWU-SHAN, b China, May 8, 39; m 65; c 2. FOOD SCIENCE, BIOCHEMISTRY. *Educ:* Nat Taiwan Univ, BS, 60; Wash State Univ, MS, 64; Univ Calif, Berkeley, PhD(comp biochem), 69. *Prof Exp:* Asst prof, 69-74, assoc prof, 74-80, PROF FOOD SCI & BIOCHEM, CLEMSON UNIV, 80- *Concurrent Pos:* Res food technician, USDA, 75; vis prof, Nat Taiwan Univ, 76. *Mem:* AAAS; Inst Food Technol; Sigma Xi; Am Chem Soc; Am Soc Plant Physiologists. *Res:* Pectic enzymes and texture of fruits; biochemistry of plant pigments including chlorophylls, carotenoids and anthocyanins; biochemistry of fruit ripening in peaches and tomatoes; studies of food enzymology and nutritive qualities of vegetables and legumes. *Mailing Add:* Dept of Food Science Clemson Univ Clemson SC 29631

JEN, PHILIP HUNGSUN, b Hunan, China, Jan 11, 44; US citizen; m 71. AUDITORY PHYSIOLOGY, NEUROETHOLOGY. *Educ:* Tunghai Univ BS, 67; Washington Univ, MA, 71, PhD(biol), 74. *Prof Exp:* res assoc, Washington Univ, 74-75; asst prof, 75-81, ASSOC PROF NERVOUS SYSTEM, UNIV MO, COLUMBIA, 81- *Concurrent Pos:* Vis prof, J W Goethe Univ, Frankfurt, 79; prin investr, NSF, 78- & NIH, 80-; guest lectr, Inst Acoust, Chinese Acad Sci, 80; NIH res career develop award, 80. *Mem:* Am Soc Zoologists; Acoust Soc Am; Soc Neurosci; AAAS; NY Acad Sci. *Res:* Neuroethological investigation of acoustic signal encoding, processing and control in the auditory system of echo locating bats. *Mailing Add:* 208 Leferre Hall Div Biol Sci Univ Mo Columbia MO 65211

JEN, SHEN, b Shanghai, China, Dec 8, 47; m 75. APPLIED PHYSICS. *Educ:* Nat Taiwan Univ, BS, 68; Harvard Univ, MS, 70, PhD(appl physics), 75. *Prof Exp:* Res assoc light scattering spectros, Dept Chem, State Univ NY Stony Brook, 75-76; PROJ MGR, XEROX CORP, 77- *Mem:* Soc Photog Scientists & Engrs. *Res:* Quasielastic light scattering study of liquid crystals and polymers; electrophotography. *Mailing Add:* Xerox Corp MS-101 1341 W Mockingbird Lane Dallas TX 75247

JEN, YUN, b China, Oct 5, 27; nat US; m 51; c 2. ORGANIC CHEMISTRY. *Educ:* Shanghai Univ, BS, 48; Carnegie Inst Technol, MS, 49. *Prof Exp:* Res chemist, Am Cyanamid Co, 51-56; mgr eng, Anaheim Plant, Oronite Chem Co Div, Calif Chem Co, Standard Oil Co, Calif, 56-60; res engr, Gen Elec Co, 60-63; dir res & develop, Tenneco Chem Co, 63-75; mem staff, Chem Div, Union Camp Corp, 75-77; PRES, J J CHEM, INC, 77- *Mem:* Am Chem Soc. *Res:* Polymers; water soluble resins; alkyds; acrylics; polyesters; pulp and paper; naval stores products; ore benefication. *Mailing Add:* 16 Gale Break Circle Savannah GA 31406

JENCKS, WILLIAM PLATT, b Bar Harbor, Maine, Aug 15, 27; m 50; c 2. BIOCHEMISTRY, ORGANIC CHEMISTRY. *Educ:* Harvard Univ, MD, 51. *Prof Exp:* Intern, Peter Bent Brigham Hosp, 51-52; res fel biochem, Res Lab, Mass Gen Hosp, 52-53; res fel pharmacol, Army Med Serv Grad Sch, Walter Reed Army Med Ctr, 53-55, chief dept pharm, 54-55; res fel biochem, Res Lab, Mass Gen Hosp, 55-56; res fel, Harvard Univ, 56-57; from asst prof to assoc prof, 57-63, PROF BIOCHEM, BRANDEIS UNIV, 63- *Honors & Awards:* Eli Lilly Co Award, Am Chem Soc, 62. *Mem:* Nat Acad Sci; AAAS; Am Soc Biol Chem; Am Chem Soc; Am Acad Arts & Sci. *Res:* Mechanism and catalysis of carbonyl, acyl, phosphate transfer and other reactions; mechanism of enzyme action; intermolecular forces in aqueous solution; mechanism of coupled vectorial processes. *Mailing Add:* Grad Dept Biochem Brandeis Univ Waltham MA 02254

JENDEN, DONALD JAMES, b Horsham, Eng, Sept 1, 26; nat US; m 50; c 3. PHARMACOLOGY, ANALYTICAL CHEMISTRY. *Educ:* Univ London, BSc, 47, MB, BS, 50. *Hon Degrees:* Dr, Univ Uppsala, Sweden, 80. *Prof Exp:* Demonstr physiol & pharmacol, Univ London, 47-50; lectr pharmacol, Univ Calif, 50-51; from asst prof to prof pharmacol, 53-67, PROF BIOMATH, UNIV CALIF, LOS ANGELES, 67-, CHMN DEPT PHARMACOL, 68- *Concurrent Pos:* Mem, Brain Res Inst, Univ Calif, Los Angeles, 61-; hon res assoc, Univ Col, Univ London, 61-62; consult, US Vet Admin Hosp, Long Beach, Calif, 63- *Mem:* Soc Neurosci; Am Soc Pharmacol & Exp Therapeut; Am Physiol Soc; Am Soc Med Sch Pharmacol; fel Am Col Neuropsychopharmacol. *Res:* Chemical and biochemical pharmacology; applications of mass spectrometry and stable isotopes in pharmacology and toxicology; cholinergic mechanisms; mathematical biology. *Mailing Add:* Dept of Pharmacol Sch Med 23-273 Ctr Hlth Sci Univ Calif Los Angeles CA 90024

JENDRESEN, MALCOLM DAN, b Janesville, Wis, June 6, 33; m 54; c 1. BIOMATERIALS. *Educ:* Marquette Univ, DDS, 61; Univ Lund, Sweden, PhD(surface sci), 80. *Prof Exp:* Instr & res assoc dent mat, Marquette Univ, Wis, 61-64; chief restoration dent, US Air Force Sch Aerospace Med, 64-68; PROF BIOMAT SCI, SCH DENT, UNIV CALIF, SAN FRANCISCO, 68-, ASST DENT RES, 72- *Concurrent Pos:* Consult, US Air Force Sch Aerospace Med, 68-72, Vet Admin Hosp, San Francisco, 68-, WHO, 72-, Nordisk Inst Odontologisk Mat, 78-, Surg Gen, US Army, 79 & Dept Health & Human Serv, Pub Health Serv, Nat Inst Dent Res, NIH; vis prof, Univ Lund, Sweden, 78-79. *Mem:* Fel Int Asn Dent Res; fel Am Col Dentists; fel Int Col Dentists; fel AAAS; fel Sigma Xi. *Res:* General materials with emphasis on adhesion in biological environments; characterization of biofilm and the clinical adhesiveness of intact biological surfaces and subsequent adhesive events. *Mailing Add:* Biomat Sci 507-S Sch Dent Univ Calif San Francisco CA 94143

JENERICK, HOWARD PETER, b Cicero, Ill, May 20, 23; m 47; c 3. PHYSIOLOGY. *Educ:* Univ Chicago, PhB, 46, SB, 48, PhD(physiol), 51. *Prof Exp:* From instr biol to asst prof gen physiol, Mass Inst Technol, 51-58; exec secy, Res Training Br, Div Gen Med Sci, NIH, 58-60; assoc prof physiol, Emory Univ, 60-64; chief spec res resources br, Div Res Facil & Resources, NIH, 64-65, chief res grants br, 65-67, prog dir biophys sci, 67-72, spec asst to the dir, 72-76; CHIEF OFF PROG ANAL, NAT INST GEN MED SCI, NIH, 76- *Mem:* Biophys Soc; Am Physiol Soc. *Res:* Electrophysiology; scientific administration. *Mailing Add:* Nat Inst Gen Med Sci NIH Bethesda MD 20205

JENG, DUEN-REN, b Taipei, Taiwan, China, Mar 1, 32; nat US; m 66; c 3. FLUID MECHANICS. *Educ:* Nat Univ Taiwan, BS, 55; Univ Ill, MS, 60, PhD(mech eng), 65. *Prof Exp:* Asst mech eng, Nat Univ Taiwan, 56-69 & Univ Ill, 60-64; asst prof, Univ Ala, 65-67; from asst prof to assoc prof, 65-77, PROF MECH ENG, UNIV TOLEDO, 77- *Mem:* Assoc Am Soc Mech Engrs. *Res:* Metal cutting; thermal contact resistance and transient heat transfer in laminar boundary layer; wind energy. *Mailing Add:* Dept of Mech Eng Col of Eng 2801 W Bancroft Toledo OH 43606

JENG, RAYMOND ING-SONG, b Taipei, Taiwan, Jan 1, 40; m 71. HYDROLOGY, HYDRAULICS. *Educ:* Nat Taiwan Univ, BS, 62; Colo State Univ, MS, 65, PhD(civil eng), 68. *Prof Exp:* Res asst hydrol invest, Colo State Univ, 64-67; asst prof civil eng, 68-77, assoc prof, 77-80, PROF CIVIL ENG, CALIF STATE UNIV, LOS ANGELES, 80- *Concurrent Pos:* Consult, Boise Cascade Property Inc, 70 & Los Angeles County Flood Control Dist, 71- *Mem:* Am Soc Civil Engrs; Am Geophys Union; Am Water Works Asn; Am Soc Eng Educ. *Res:* Hydrologic system analysis; statistical and stochastic hydrology. *Mailing Add:* Dept of Civil Eng 5151 State University Dr Los Angeles CA 90032

JENICEK, JOHN ANDREW, b Chicago, Ill, 22. ANESTHESIOLOGY. *Educ:* Univ Ill, MD, 46; Am Bd Anesthesiol, cert, 57. *Prof Exp:* Intern, St Mary Nazareth Hosp, Chicago, 46-47; resident anesthesiol, Brooke Army Hosp, 49-51; chief anesthesiol & oper serv, Tripler Army Hosp, 52-54, asst chief, 54-55; asst chief anesthesiol & oper serv, Walter Reed Army Hosp, 55-57; chief anesthesiol & oper serv, Brooke Army Hosp, 57-61; chief anesthesiol & oper serv, Walter Reed Army Hosp, 62-67; assoc prof, 67-72, PROF ANESTHESIOL, UNIV TEX MED BR, GALVESTON, 72- *Concurrent Pos:* Consult anesthesiol, Surgeon Gen, US Army, 62-67. *Mem:* AMA; Am Soc Anesthesiol; fel Am Col Anesthesiol. *Mailing Add:* 2802 Beluche Dr Galveston TX 77551

JENIKE, ANDREW W(ITOLD), b Warsaw, Poland, Apr 16, 14; nat US; m 43; c 2. MECHANICAL ENGINEERING. *Educ:* Warsaw Tech Univ, Dipl, 39; Univ London, PhD(struct eng), 48. *Hon Degrees:* DTech, Univ Bradford, Eng, 72. *Prof Exp:* Design & develop engr, Poland, Can & US, 39 & 48-51; res prof mech & mining eng & dir bulk solids flow proj, Eng Exp Sta, Univ Utah, 56-62; consult engr, 62-66; pres, Jenike & Johanson Inc, 66-79; CONSULT ENGR, 80- *Concurrent Pos:* von Humboldt Found sr US scientist award, WGer, 76. *Res:* Storage and flow of solids; manufacture of solids flowability testing equipment. *Mailing Add:* 2 Exec Park Dr North Billerica MA 01862

JEN-JACOBSON, LINDA, b Kunming, China, Oct 29, 41; US citizen; m 67. BIOCHEMISTRY, BIOPHYSICS. *Educ:* Radcliffe Col, AB, 62; Univ Ill, MS, 65, PhD(biochem), 67. *Prof Exp:* Res assoc, 67-69, lectr, 69-70, res assoc biophys, 70-80, ASSOC PROF BIOL SCI, UNIV PITTSBURGH, 80- *Res:* Physicochemical determinants of protein conformation; regulation of macromolecular metabolism. *Mailing Add:* Dept of Biol Sci Univ of Pittsburgh Pittsburgh PA 15260

JENKIN, HOWARD M, b New York, NY, May 1, 25; m 56; c 3. MICROBIOLOGY. *Educ:* Univ Wis, BS, 49; Univ Chicago, PhD(microbiol), 60. *Prof Exp:* Nat Res Coun fel microbiol, Virus-Rickettsiae Div, Biol Labs, Ft Detrick, Md, 60-61, mem staff, Immunol Br, 61-62; res asst prof prev med, Sch Med, Univ Wash, 62-66; assoc prof microbiol, Med Sch & assoc prof, Hormel Inst, Grad Sch, 66-71, PROF MICROBIOL, MED SCH, UNIV MINN, MINNEAPOLIS, 71-, PROF, HORMEL INST, GRAD SCH, 71-, HEAD SECT, 66- *Concurrent Pos:* Head virol-tissue cult dept, US Naval Med Res Unit 2, Taiwan, 63-66. *Mem:* Am Soc Microbiol; Sigma Xi; Tissue Cult Asn; Soc Exp Biol & Med. *Res:* Comparative lipid biochemistry; biology and serology of members of Chlamydia; herpes virus; treponema and arbovirus groups of microorganisms; tumor-lipid membrane studies. *Mailing Add:* Hormel Inst Univ of Minn Austin MN 55912

JENKINS, ALFRED MARTIN, b Boston, Mass, July 27, 17. ORGANIC CHEMISTRY. *Educ:* Tufts Univ, BS, 42; Boston Univ, AM, 47; Okla State Univ, PhD(chem), 52. *Prof Exp:* Metallurgist, Watertown Arsenal, 42; res chemist, E I du Pont de Nemours & Co, 52-60; PROF SCI, GLASSBORO STATE COL, 60- *Mem:* Am Chem Soc. *Res:* Cyclic polymerization of aldehydes. *Mailing Add:* 1212 N Main St Glassboro NJ 08028

JENKINS, ALVIN WILKINS, JR, b Raleigh, NC, Dec 30, 28; m 51; c 2. PLASMA PHYSICS, ASTROPHYSICS. *Educ:* NC State Col, BEE, 51, MS, 55; Univ Va, PhD, 58. *Prof Exp:* Sr physicist theoret physics, Ord Res Lab, Univ Va, 58-59; res physicist, Univ Res Inst, Denver, 59-61; assoc prof physics, Wichita State Univ, 61-66; assoc prof, 66-70, PROF PHYSICS, NC STATE UNIV, 70-, HEAD DEPT, 76- ACTG CHMN DEPT, 75- *Mem:* Am Phys Soc; Am Geophys Union; Am Astron Soc. *Res:* Atmospheric and magnetospheric physics; plasma physics. *Mailing Add:* Dept of Physics NC State Univ Raleigh NC 27607

JENKINS, BURTON CHARLES, b New Westminster, BC, June 13, 20; m 47; c 4. CYTOGENETICS. *Educ:* Univ Alta, BSc, 41, MSc, 44; Univ Calif, PhD(genetics), 50. *Prof Exp:* Asst field crops, Univ Alta, 39-44; asst cerealist, Exp Sta, Swift Current, Sask, 44-48; chief asst, Lab Cereal Breeding, Exp Farm, Lethbridge, Alta, 48-50; assoc prof field husb, Univ Sask, 50-54; prof, Div Plant Sci & Rosner Chair Agron, Univ Man, 54-66; cytogeneticist & head basic res, World Seeds, Inc, 66-68; dir res, Jenkins Found Res, 68-80; RES PROF PLANT SCI, GRACELAND COL, 68-; STA HEAD & SR PLANT BREEDER TRITICALE, DESSERT SEED CO INC, 80- *Concurrent Pos:* Mem, Wartime Bur Tech Personnel, 44-46; spec sci aide, Wheat Improv Prog, Rockefeller Found, Mex, 64. *Mem:* AAAS; Agr Inst Can; Am Soc Agron; Sigma Xi. *Res:* Crop improvement, with special reference to breeding grains; fundamental cytogenetic study in wheats and related species. *Mailing Add:* Dessert Seed Co Inc PO Box 801 Salinas CA 93902

JENKINS, CHARLES ROBERT, b Newton, Ill, Aug 17, 30; m 53; c 4. SANITARY ENGINEERING, AQUATIC BIOLOGY. *Educ:* Eastern Ill State Col, BS, 52; Univ Ill, MS, 59; Okla State Univ, PhD(zool), 64. *Prof Exp:* From asst prof to assoc prof sanit eng, 61-77, prof environ eng, 77-80, PROF CIVIL ENG, WEST VA UNIV, 80- *Mem:* Am Soc Limnol & Oceanog; Water Pollution Control Fedn; Am Water Works Asn. *Res:* Water pollution control; waste treatment. *Mailing Add:* Dept of Civil Eng WVa Univ Morgantown WV 26506

JENKINS, DALE WILSON, b Wapakoneta, Ohio, June 17, 18; m 42; c 5. ECOLOGY. *Educ:* Ohio State Univ, BSc, 38, MA, 39, PhD, 47. *Prof Exp:* Ecologist, Soil Conserv Serv, 35; instr, Ohio State Univ, 38-39, Univ Chicago, 39-40, Univ Ill, 40-41 & Univ Minn, 41-42; agr specialist, Foreign Econ Admin, Washington, DC, 42-43; entomologist & chief animal ecol br, Army Med Labs, Md, 46-52, dep chief allied sci div, 54-56, chief entom div, 53-62; chief environ biol prog, NASA Hq, 62-66, asst dir biosci progs, 66-70; dir ecol prog, Smithsonian Inst, 70-74; dep dir, Ctr Human Ecol & Health, Pan Am Health Orgn, 75-78; ECOL CONSULT, 78- *Concurrent Pos:* Lectr, Sch Pub Health & Hyg, Johns Hopkins Univ, 50-; consult, USDA, Alaska, 47, USPHS, 48, Northern Insect Surv, Defence Res Bd Can, 49-50 & US Air Force, 59-; planning conf partic, Life Sci Prog, NASA, 60 & WHO, Bangkok, 60; mem, Armed Forces Pest Control Bd, 55- & Interdept Pest Control Comt, 58-; chmn bd gov, Inst Lab Animal Resources, Nat Res Coun, 55-60, adv to UNESCO, 57-; US Dept State deleg, Int Conf Peaceful Uses Atomic Energy, Geneva, 55; Nat Acad Sci-Nat Res Coun deleg, Int Cong Entom, Montreal, 56. *Mem:* Fel AAAS; Ecol Soc Am; Am Mosquito Control Asn; Am Asn Lab Animal Sci. *Res:* Ecology of plants and animals; radioisotope tracers; laboratory animals; epidemiology; environmental impacts. *Mailing Add:* 3028 Tanglewood Dr Sarasota FL 33579

JENKINS, DANIEL EDWARDS, b Omaha, Nebr, July 19, 16; m 42; c 3. MEDICINE. *Educ:* Univ Tex, BA, 37, MD, 40. *Prof Exp:* Asst prof med, Med Sch, Univ Mich, 45-47; chief lung dis sect, Jefferson Davis & Ben Taub Gen Hosps, 47-74; PROF MED, BAYLOR COL MED, 58- *Concurrent Pos:* Attend physician, Methodist Hosp, 56-; consult, Vet Admin Hosps, Houston & Temple, 49-, Hermann Hosp, Houston, 56- & Brooke Army Hosp, 56- *Mem:* Am Thoracic Soc (pres, 58-59); fel Am Col Physicians; Am Lung Asn (pres, 67-68); Royal Soc med; hon mem Mex Tuberc Asn. *Res:* Internal medicine; respiratory diseases. *Mailing Add:* Baylor Col of Med 1200 Moursund Ave Houston TX 77030

JENKINS, DAVID BRUCE, b Pittsburgh, Pa, Feb 22, 49; m 69; c 2. GROSS ANATOMY. *Educ:* Univ Pittsburgh, BS, 71; Pa State Univ, PhD(anat), 75. *Prof Exp:* Asst prof gross anat, Med Ctr, George Washington Univ, 75-77; ASST PROF GROSS ANAT, SCH MED, UNIV NC, 77- *Mem:* Am Asn Anatomists; AAAS; Asn Res Otolaryngol; Sigma Xi. *Res:* Comparative studies of the vertebrate inner ear utilizing light microscopy and transmission and scanning electromicroscopy. *Mailing Add:* Dept of Anat 102 Bldg D Univ of NC Chapel Hill NC 27514

JENKINS, DAVID H, b Philadelphia, Pa, Jan 19, 18; m 42; c 2. WILDLIFE MANAGEMENT. *Educ:* Pa State Univ, BS, 40, MS, 42; Univ Mich, PhD(wildlife mgt), 64. *Prof Exp:* Biologist, US Soil Conserv Serv, 39; asst, Pa Coop Wildlife Res Unit, 40-42; asst, Univ Mich, 48-49; mammalogist, Mich Dept Natural Resources, 49-64, supvr game res, 64-65, chief, Div Res & Develop, 65-72, dep dir natural resources, 72-75, chief, Wildlife Div, 75-80; RETIRED. *Concurrent Pos:* Shoen-Rene fel, 49. *Mem:* Wildlife Soc. *Res:* Conservation of renewable natural resources; white-tailed deer management; upland game and fur bearer research and management. *Mailing Add:* 1906 Gordon St Lansing MI 48910

JENKINS, DAVID ISAAC, b Shropshire, Eng, Oct 4, 35; m 60; c 2. SANITARY ENGINEERING. *Educ:* Univ Birmingham, BSc, 57; Univ Durham, PhD(sanit eng), 60. *Prof Exp:* Res chemist, 60-61, from asst prof to assoc prof, 63-74, PROF SANIT ENG, UNIV CALIF, BERKELEY, 74-, DIR, SANIT ENG RES LAB, 61- *Concurrent Pos:* Sabbatical leave, Dept Eng & Appl Physics, Harvard Univ, 69-70. *Mem:* Am Chem Soc; Water Pollution Control Fedn; Asn Environ Eng Prof; fel Royal Inst Chem; Brit Inst Water Pollution Control. *Res:* Chemistry and biochemistry of processes and phenomena associated with the control of environment, especially the upgrading of water quality; biological waste treatment processes; activated sludge operation. *Mailing Add:* 11 Yale Circle Kensington CA 94804

JENKINS, DAVID R(ICHARD), b Lima, Ohio, Oct 24, 24; m 47; c 3. CIVIL ENGINEERING, ENGINEERING MECHANICS. *Educ:* Case Inst Technol, BSc, 48; Ohio State Univ, MSc, 54; Univ Mich, PhD(eng mech), 62. *Prof Exp:* Stress analyst, Airplane Div, Curtiss-Wright Corp, 48, tech asst, Battelle Mem Inst, 48-50, prin mech engr, 50-55, proj leader, 55-58; instr eng mech, Univ Mich, 58-62, asst prof, 62-65; sr res fel, Tech Ctr, Owens-Corning Fiberglas Corp, 65-69; assoc prof, 69-71, prof & chmn engr mech & mat sci, 71-75, prof civil eng & environ sci & actg chmn, 75-76, actg chmn mech eng & aerospace sci, 81-82, PROF ENG, UNIV CENT FLA, 76- *Concurrent Pos:* Fac res grant, Univ Mich, 65; on sabbatical leave, mat res eng, Nat Bur Standards, Ctr for Bldg Technol, 78-80. *Mem:* AAAS; Am Soc Civil Engrs; Soc Exp Stress Anal; Am Soc Metals; Soc Eng Sci. *Res:* Structural performance of buildings, behavior of roofing materials; high temperature structural behavior; crack propagation in steel shells; aircraft structural investigations; yielding and strain hardening in metallic materials; composite materials. *Mailing Add:* Univ Cent Fla Col Eng PO Box 25000 Orlando FL 32816

JENKINS, EDGAR WILLIAM, b Columbus, Ohio, Apr 29, 33; m 59; c 3. HIGH ENERGY PHYSICS. *Educ:* Harvard Univ, AB, 55; Columbia Univ, PhD(physics), 62. *Prof Exp:* From asst physicist to assoc physicist, Brookhaven Nat Lab, 60-64; from asst prof to assoc prof, 64-71, PROF PHYSICS, UNIV ARIZ, 71- *Mem:* Am Phys Soc; Am Asn Physics Teachers. *Res:* Interactions, properties and decays of elementary particles. *Mailing Add:* Dept of Physics Univ of Ariz Tucson AZ 85721

JENKINS, EDWARD BEYNON, b San Francisco, Calif, Mar 20, 39; m 63; c 2. ASTROPHYSICS. *Educ:* Univ Calif, Davis, BA, 62; Cornell Univ, PhD(physics), 66. *Prof Exp:* Res assoc astrophys, 66-67, res staff mem, 67-73, res astronomer, 73-79, SR RES ASTRONOMER, PRINCETON UNIV OBSERV, 79- *Mem:* Am Astron Soc; Int Astron Union. *Res:* Rocket and satellite ultraviolet astronomy; interstellar medium; image sensor development. *Mailing Add:* Princeton Univ Observ Princeton NJ 08544

JENKINS, EDWARD FELIX, b Baltimore, Md, Aug, 17, 06. ASTRONOMY. *Educ:* Villanova Col, AB, 27; Cath Univ, MS, 33, PhD(chem), 39. *Prof Exp:* From instr to prof chem, 35-60, head dept astron, 61-74, PROF ASTRON, VILLANOVA UNIV, 58- *Mem:* Am Chem Soc; Am Astron Soc; Royal Astron Soc Can. *Res:* Reagents for organic analysis; catalytic hydrogenation; history of chemistry and astronomy. *Mailing Add:* Dept of Astron Villanova Univ Villanova PA 19085

JENKINS, EMERSON D, b Utica, NY, Jan 13, 09. ALGEBRA. *Educ:* Colgate Univ, AB, 31; Ohio State Univ, MA, 32, PhD(math), 35. *Prof Exp:* Instr math, Univ Ky, 35-37; assoc prof, Eastern Ky State Col, 37-47; from assoc prof to prof, 47-76, EMER PROF MATH, KENT STATE UNIV, 76- *Mem:* Am Math Soc; Math Asn Am. *Res:* Modern abstract algebra. *Mailing Add:* 2641 Dunham Rd Utica NY 13501

JENKINS, FARISH ALSTON, JR, b New York, May 19, 40; m 63; c 2. VERTEBRATE PALEONTOLOGY, ANATOMY. *Prof Exp:* Princeton Univ, AB, 61; Yale Univ, MSc, 66, PhD(geol), 68. Prof Exp: From instr to asst prof anat, Col Physicians & Surgeons, Columbia Univ, 68-71; assoc prof biol & assoc cur vert paleont, 71-74, PROF BIOL & CUR VERT PALEONT, MUS COMP ZOOL, HARVARD UNIV, 74- *Res:* Vertebrate anatomy and evolution, especially reptiles and mammals; biomechanics of musculoskeletal system. *Mailing Add:* Mus Comp Zool Labs Harvard Univ Cambridge MA 02138

JENKINS, FLOYD ALBERT, b Los Angeles, Calif, Aug 14, 16. COMPARATIVE ANATOMY, VERTEBRATE PALEONTOLOGY. *Educ:* St Louis Univ, AB, 40, MA, 42, MS, 43, PhD, 54; Alma Col, Calif, STL, 49. *Prof Exp:* Lab instr biol, St Louis Univ, 41-43; instr, 43-45 & 53-55, asst prof, 55-60, assoc prof, 60-77, PROF BIOL, LOYOLA MARYMOUNT UNIV, 77- *Mem:* Paleont Soc; Soc Study Evolution; Soc Vert Paleont. *Res:* Functional anatomy of machairodont cats; early evolution of mammals. *Mailing Add:* Dept of Biol Loyola Marymount Univ Los Angeles CA 90045

JENKINS, GEORGE LOVELL, nuclear physics, deceased

JENKINS, GEORGE ROBERT, b Denver, Colo, Dec 14, 14; m 41; c 2. GEOLOGY. *Educ:* Univ Colo, AB, 36; Univ Wis, PhM, 38. *Prof Exp:* Asst geog, Univ Colo, 36-37; asst, Univ Wis, 37-40; instr, Univ Mo, 40-42; officer in chg, US Weather Bur, Madison, Wis, 46-47; from asst prof to assoc prof geol, 48-63, from asst dir to assoc dir, Inst Res, 56-63, prof geol, 63-80, EMER DIR, INST RES, 80- *Mem:* AAAS; Am Meteorol Soc; Am Geophys Union. *Res:* Water resources. *Mailing Add:* Off of Res Lehigh Univ Bethlehem PA 18015

JENKINS, HOWARD BRYNER, b Arimo, Idaho, Jan 30, 28; m 51; c 3. MATHEMATICS. *Educ:* Mass Inst Technol, BS, 50; Univ Southern Calif, PhD(math), 58. *Prof Exp:* Lectr math, Univ Southern Calif, 54-57; instr, Calif Inst Technol, 57-58; temp mem, Inst Math Sci, NY Univ, 58-59, res assoc, 59-60; vis asst prof math, Stanford Univ, 60-61; asst prof, 61-65, ASSOC PROF MATH, UNIV MINN, MINNEAPOLIS, 65-, ASSOC HEAD SCH MATH, 71- *Concurrent Pos:* Vis assoc prof, Stanford Univ, 66-67. *Mem:* Am Math Soc. *Res:* Partial differential equations; variational problems; minimal surfaces. *Mailing Add:* Sch of Math Inst Technol Univ of Minn Minneapolis MN 55455

JENKINS, HOWARD JONES, b Oak Hill, Ohio, Sept 14, 16; m 51; c 4. PHARMACOLOGY. *Educ:* Ohio State Univ, PhD(pharmacol), 50. *Prof Exp:* Res pharmacologist, Armour Labs, 51-53; from asst prof to assoc prof, 53-67, dir div pharmacol & allied sci, 64-73, PROF PHARMACOL, MASS COL PHARM, 67- *Mem:* AAAS; Acad Pharmaceut Sci; Sigma Xi; Am Pharmaceut Asn. *Res:* Cardiovascular pharmacology; autonomic pharmacology; structure-activity relationships involved in antispasmodic and antihistaminic responses; analgetic potentiation; biological assay. *Mailing Add:* Dept of Pharmacol Mass Col of Pharm Boston MA 02115

JENKINS, HUGHES BRANTLEY, JR, b Jacksonville, Fla, Oct 17, 27. THEORETICAL PHYSICS. *Educ:* Univ Ga, AB, 48, MS, 55; Univ Ky, PhD(physics), 63. *Prof Exp:* Instr math & physics, Univ Ga, 52-55; asst physicist, Oak Ridge Nat Lab, Union Carbide Corp, Tenn, 55-57, asst mathematician, 57-58; intr physics, Univ Ky, 58-62; assoc prof, Ga State Col, 62-68; ASSOC PROF PHYSICS & ASTRON, VALDOSTA STATE COL, 68- *Res:* Statistical mechanics and mathematical physics. *Mailing Add:* Dept of Physics Valdosta State Col Valdosta GA 31601

JENKINS, JAMES ALLISTER, b Toronto, Ont, Sept 23, 23; nat US. MATHEMATICS. *Educ:* Toronto, BA, 44, MA, 45; Harvard Univ, PhD(math), 48. *Prof Exp:* Jewett fel, Harvard Univ, 48-49 & Inst Advan Study & Princeton Univ, 49-50; asst prof math, Johns Hopkins Univ, 50-54; from assoc prof to prof, Univ Notre Dame, 54-59; PROF MATH, WASHINGTON UNIV, 59- *Concurrent Pos:* Mem, Inst Advan Study, 57-59, 61-62, 73-74 & 80-81; Fulbright vis prof, Imp Col, Univ London, 62. *Mem:* Am Math Soc; Math Soc France; Ger Math Asn. *Res:* Geometrical and analytical function theories; topological theory functions. *Mailing Add:* Dept of Math Washington Univ St Louis MO 63130

JENKINS, JAMES HOBART, b Mt Vernon, Ohio, Jan 28, 19; m 42; c 3. WILDLIFE MANAGEMENT. *Educ:* Ohio State Univ, BSc, 40; Univ Ga, MSc, 49, PhD(animal ecol), 55. *Prof Exp:* Game biologist, State Div Conserv, Ohio, 40-41; res biologist, Ben Venue Labs, Inc, Ohio, 41-47; field biologist, State Game & Fish Comn, Ga, 47-49; asst zool, 48-49, from instr to assoc prof, 50-64, prof wildlife mgt, 64-76, PROF FOREST RESOURCES, SCH FORESTRY, UNIV GA, 76- *Mem:* Soc Am Foresters; Am Soc Mammal; Wildlife Soc; Am Fisheries Soc. *Res:* Deer management; small mammals; doves; small impoundments; automatic projectile syringe for live capture of animals; telemetry; radiation bioaccumulation. *Mailing Add:* Univ of Ga Sch of Forest Resources Athens GA 30602

JENKINS, JAMES WILLIAM, b Jamestown, NY, May 5, 21; c 3. ORGANIC CHEMISTRY. *Educ:* Allegheny Col, BS, 44; Univ Buffalo, MS, 48, PhD(chem), 50. *Prof Exp:* Asst prof chem, Lafayette Col, 49-51; res anal chemist, Gen Aniline & Film Corp, 51-52; res anal chemist, Colgate Palmolive Co, 52-54, group leader anal sect, 54-58, sr group leader, 59-60, sect head, 60-63, res mgr, 63-64; dir, 65-69, VPRES, RES & DEVELOP, CONSUMER PROD DIV, PFIZER INC, 69- *Mem:* Am Chem Soc; Soc Cosmetic Chem. *Res:* Product development; proprietary pharmaceuticals; toiletries and cosmetics; hair and skin research. *Mailing Add:* Res & Develop Consumer Prod Div Pfizer Inc 100 Jefferson Rd Parsippany NJ 07054

JENKINS, JEFF HARLIN, b Gamaliel, Ky, Mar 8, 37; m 59; c 2. PLANT PATHOLOGY. *Educ:* Western Ky Col, BS, 59; La State Univ, MS, 61, PhD(plant path), 63. *Prof Exp:* From asst prof to assoc prof bot, 63-74, PROF BIOL, WESTERN KY UNIV, 74- *Mem:* Am Phytopath Soc. *Res:* Taxonomic mycology; fusarium wilt of alfalfa; bacterial leaf spot of bell pepper. *Mailing Add:* Dept of Biol Western Ky Univ Bowling Green KY 42101

JENKINS, JIMMY RAYMOND, b Selma, NC, Mar 18, 43; m 65; c 2. BIOLOGICAL STRUCTURE. *Educ:* Elizabeth City State Univ, BS, 65; Purdue Univ, MS, 70, PhD(biol educ), 72. *Prof Exp:* Teacher high schs, Md, 65-69; fel biol, Purdue Univ, 69-70, teaching fel & res asst instrnl develop, 70-72; asst prof biol & asst acad dean, 72-74, ASSOC PROF BIOL & DEAN, ELIZABETH CITY STATE UNIV, 73-, V CHANCELLOR ACAD AFFAIRS, 77- *Concurrent Pos:* Adv coun mem, Albemarle Regional Planning & Develop Comn, 74-; proposal reviewer, NSF, 74; individualized instr, Region 15, Northeastern NC, 75; instrnl consult, Halifax County Schs, NC, 75-76; mem, Health Manpower Develop Corp. *Mem:* Nat Asn Res Sci Teaching. *Res:* Instructional development and design geared to biology and the facilitation of biological concepts. *Mailing Add:* Elizabeth City State Univ Parkview Dr Elizabeth City NC 27909

JENKINS, JOE WILEY, b Bronaugh, Mo, Oct 17, 41; m 65; c 2. MATHEMATICS. *Educ:* Univ Ill, Urbana, PhD(math), 68. *Prof Exp:* asst prof, 68-80, ASSOC PROF MATH, STATE UNIV NY ALBANY, 80- *Concurrent Pos:* Mem, Inst Advan Study, 71-72. *Mem:* Am Math Soc. *Res:* Functional analysis; amenable groups; symmetric group algebras. *Mailing Add:* Dept of Math State Unv NY 1400 Washington Ave Albany NY 12203

JENKINS, JOHN BRUNER, b Springfield, Mass, July 20, 41; m 63. GENETICS. *Educ:* Utah State Univ, BS, 64, MS, 65; Univ Calif, Los Angeles, PhD(zool), 68. *Prof Exp:* Asst prof, 68-74, assoc prof, 74-80, PROF & CHMN BIOL, SWARTHMORE COL, 80- *Mem:* AAAS; Genetics Soc Am; Am Genetic Asn. *Res:* Chemical mutagenesis in Drosophila and its relation to genetic fine structure. *Mailing Add:* Dept of Biol Swarthmore Col Swarthmore PA 19081

JENKINS, JOHNIE NORTON, b Barton, Ark, Nov 3, 34; m 59; c 2. PLANT GENETICS, AGRONOMY. *Educ:* Univ Ark, BSA, 56; Purdue Univ, MS, 58, PhD(genetics), 60. *Prof Exp:* Res assoc agron, Univ Ill, 60-61; RES GENETICIST, CROP SCI & ENG LAB, AGR RES SERV, USDA, 61- *Concurrent Pos:* secondary prof & mem grad fac, Miss State Univ, 64- *Mem:* Am Soc Agron; Crop Sci Soc Am; Entom Soc Am; investigations of basic causes of boll weevil resistance in cotton plants and development of factors which will confer resistance. *Res:* Host plant resistance to cotton insects; investigations of basic causes of insect resistance in cotton plants and development of factors which will confer resistance. *Mailing Add:* Crop Sci & Eng Res Lab PO Box 5367 Mississippi State MS 39762

JENKINS, KENNETH DUNNING, b New York, NY, Apr 8, 44. DEVELOPMENTAL BIOLOGY. *Educ:* San Fernando Valley State Col, BA, 66; Univ Calif, Los Angeles, PhD(develop biol), 70. *Prof Exp:* Asst prof develop biol, 70-74, ASSOC PROF BIOL, CALIF STATE COL, LONG BEACH, 74- *Mem:* AAAS; Soc Develop Biol. *Res:* Translational control mechanisms in early development. *Mailing Add:* Dept of Biol Calif State Univ Long Beach CA 90840

JENKINS, KENNETH JAMES WILLIAM, b Montreal, Que, Oct 1, 29; m 69; c 1. BIOCHEMISTRY, NUTRITION. *Educ:* McGill Univ, BSc, 51; Univ Sask, MSc, 53; Univ Wis, PhD(biochem), 58. *Prof Exp:* Head res & develop emergency rations, Defense Res Med Labs, Dept Nat Defence, Can, 53-54; asst biochem, Univ Wis, 54-58; asst prof biochem & nutrit, Ont Agr Col, Guelph, 58-65; res officer, 65-73, head trace mineral nutrit sect, Trace Minerals & Pesticide Div, 73-80, SR SCIENTIST, ANIMAL RES INST, CENT EXP FARM, CAN DEPT AGR, 80- *Honors & Awards:* Borden Award, Can, 74. *Mem:* Can Nutrit Soc; Can Biochem Soc. *Res:* Nutritional requirements of animals; biochemical role of mineral elements; tocopherol and selenium metabolism; dental caries. *Mailing Add:* Trace Minerals & Pesticides Div Can Dept of Agr Ottawa ON K1A 0Y9 Can

JENKINS, LEONARD CECIL, b Vancouver, BC, June 23, 26; m 66. ANESTHESIOLOGY, PHARMACOLOGY. *Educ:* Univ BC, BA, 48; McGill Univ, MD, CM, 52; FRCP(C), 59. *Prof Exp:* McLaughlin travel fel, 58-59; clin instr, 59-61, clin asst prof, 61-67, assoc prof, 67-70, ASSOC PROF PHARMACOL, FAC MED, UNIV BC, 68-, PROF ANESTHESIA & HEAD DEPT, 70-; DIR ANESTHESIA, VANCOUVER GEN HOSP, 70- *Concurrent Pos:* Med Res Coun res grant, 66-68. *Mem:* Am Soc Anesthesiol; Can Anesthetists Soc. *Res:* Anesthesia and the central nervous system; mechanisms of anesthesia; shock. *Mailing Add:* Dept of Anesthesia Univ of BC Vancouver BC V6T 1E1 Can

JENKINS, LESLIE HUGH, b Bryson City, NC, Sept 26, 24; m 51; c 2. SURFACE PHYSICS. *Educ:* Univ NC, BS, 49, PhD(phys chem), 54. *Prof Exp:* Group leader, Va-Carolina Chem Corp, 54-56; mem res staff, 56-73, SECT HEAD, OAK RIDGE NAT LAB, 73- *Mem:* AAAS; Am Phys Soc; Sigma Xi. *Res:* Surface physics; secondary electron emission and Auger spectroscopy; low energy electron diffraction; particle-solid interactions at surfaces. *Mailing Add:* Oak Ridge Nat Lab PO Box X Oak Ridge TN 37830

JENKINS, MAMIE LEAH YOUNG, b Washington, DC, July 10, 40; m 73. NUTRITION, BIOCHEMISTRY. *Educ:* Howard Univ, BS, 62, MS, 65, PhD(nutrit), 80. *Prof Exp:* Chemist, Agr Res Serv, US Dept Agr, 64-67; RES CHEMIST, DIV NUTRIT, FOOD & DRUG ADMIN, BUR FOODS, 67- *Mem:* Animal Nutrit Res Coun; Am Chem Soc; Am Inst Nutrit. *Res:* Protein quality, amino acid fortification, amino acid derivatives and vitamins; emphasis on the metabolic role of lecithin as a dietary choline source, and its interrelationships with other nutrients. *Mailing Add:* Food & Drug Admin (HFF-268) 200 C St SW Washington DC 20204

JENKINS, MARIE MAGDALEN, b Eldorado, Ill, Sept 26, 09. INVERTEBRATE ZOOLOGY. *Educ:* Phillips Univ, BA, 29; Cath Univ Am, MA, 51; Univ Okla, PhD(zool), 61. *Prof Exp:* Asst prof biol, Benedictine Heights Col, 54-57, registr, 55-57; instr zool, Univ Okla, 60-62; from assoc prof to prof biol, 62-75, EMER PROF BIOL, MADISON COL, VA, 75- *Concurrent Pos:* Sigma Xi grant, 64-66; NIH grant, 66-69; writer of sci books for young people, 69- *Mem:* AAAS; Am Soc Zool; Soc Children's Book Writers; Authors Guild; Sigma Xi. *Res:* Planarian physiology, reproductive activity and behavior; life history of sexual versus asexual strains; ageing. *Mailing Add:* Rte 2 Box 19B1 Strasburg VA 22657

JENKINS, MARION THOMAS, b Hughes Springs, Tex, Feb 11, 17; m 42; c 3. ANESTHESIOLOGY. *Educ:* Univ Tex, BA, 37, MD, 40; Am Bd Anesthesiol, dipl, 52; Royal Col Surg, fel fac anesthetics, 68. *Prof Exp:* Prof, 51-66, MARGARET MILAM McDERMOTT PROF ANESTHESIOL, UNIV TEX HEALTH SCI CTR, DALLAS, 66-, CHMN DEPT, 51- *Concurrent Pos:* Chief, Dept Anesthesiol, Parkland Mem Hosp, 48-; chief, Children's Med Ctr, 53-; assoc chief anesthesiol, Presby Hosp, Dallas, 65-; consult, Vet Admin Hosp, 53-; consult, Baylor Univ Med Ctr, 55- *Mem:* Am Soc Anesthesiologists (pres, 72). *Res:* Physiological derangements due to trauma. *Mailing Add:* Univ of Tex Health Sci Ctr 5323 Harry Hines Blvd Dallas TX 75235

JENKINS, MELVIN EARL, b Kansas City, Mo, June 24, 23; m 48; c 3. METABOLISM. *Educ:* Univ Kans, AB, 44, MD, 46. *Prof Exp:* From instr to assoc prof pediat, Col Med, Howard Univ, 50-69; prof, Col Med, Univ Nebr Med Ctr, Omaha, 69-73; PROF PEDIAT & CHMN DEPT PEDIAT & CHILD HEALTH, COL MED, HOWARD UNIV, 73- *Mem:* Am Acad

Pediat. *Res:* Gonadal function; human growth and development; sickle cell hemoglobin; fetal and newborn physiology; steroid metabolism. *Mailing Add:* Dept of Pediat & Child Health Howard Univ Col of Med Washington DC 20059

JENKINS, PHILIP WINDER, b Birmingham, Ala, Nov 7, 33; m 56; c 4. ORGANIC CHEMISTRY. *Educ:* Univ Ill, BS, 55; Mass Inst Technol, PhD(chem), 59. *Prof Exp:* Asst, Mass Inst Technol, 55-59; res chemist, 59-61, sr res chemist, 61-65, res assoc, 65-68, lab head, 68-71, res assoc, Emulsion Res Div, Res Labs, 71-74, res assoc, Anal Sci Div, Res Labs, 74-80, TECH ASSOC, HEALTH SAFETY & HUMAN FACTORS LAB, EASTMAN KODAK CO, 78- *Concurrent Pos:* Inst fel, Mass Inst Technol, 59. *Mem:* Am Chem Soc; Royal Inst Chem; Soc Environ Toxicol & Chem; Sigma Xi; NY Acad Sci. *Res:* Cyclooctatetraene derivatives; proximity effects in medium ring compounds; gas chromatography; heterocycles; photographic sensitizing dyes; photochemistry; excited state energy processes; environmental fate and effects of chemicals. *Mailing Add:* Eastman Kodak Co Bldg 320 Kodak Park Rochester NY 14650

JENKINS, RICHARD LEOS, b Brookings, SDak, June 3, 03; m 27; c 3. PSYCHIATRY. *Educ:* Stanford Univ, BA, 25; Rush Med Col, MD, 30. *Prof Exp:* Intern med, surg, pediat & obstet, Res & Educ Hosps, Chicago, 29-30; instr physiol, Univ Chicago, 30-32; pediatrician, Inst Juvenile Res, Chicago, 32-36; Rockefeller Found fel psychiat, Henry Phipps Clin, Johns Hopkins Hosp, 36-37; psychiatrist, NY State Training Sch Boys, 38-41; psychiatrist, Mich Child Guid Inst, Ann Arbor, 41-43; psychiatrist, Inst Juvenile Res, Chicago, 43-44, actg dir, 44-46; psychiatrist, Health Serv, Univ Ill, 46-49; chief psychiat res, Cent Off Vet Admin, Washington, DC, 49-55, dir psychiat eval proj, 55-61; prof child psychiat & chief, Child Psychiat Serv, Univ Iowa, 61-71, EMER PROF CHILD PSYCHIAT, UNIV IOWA, 71- *Concurrent Pos:* From asst prof to assoc prof criminol, social hyg & med jurisp, Col Med, Univ Ill, 43-46, actg head dept, 44-46, assoc prof psychiat, 45-49; mem comt area-wide planning facilities for ment retarded, Dept Health, Educ & Welfare, 62-64; mem comt ment retardation grant rev, 65-66; consult, Iowa Training Sch Boys, Edora, 71- & Ment Health Inst, Mt Pleasant, 71-81. *Mem:* Fel Am Orthopsychiat Asn; Am Psychiat Asn; Am Acad Child Psychiat. *Res:* Diagnostic grouping and treatment in child psychiatry. *Mailing Add:* Dept of Psychiat Univ of Iowa Iowa City IA 52240

JENKINS, ROBERT ALLAN, b Logan, Utah, Apr 1, 34; m 56; c 2. CELL BIOLOGY. *Educ:* Utah State Univ, BS, 57; Syracuse Univ, MS, 61; Iowa State Univ, PhD(cell biol), 64. *Prof Exp:* Teacher, Jr High Sch, Utah, 56-60, instr & assoc cell biol & electron micros, Iowa State Univ, 63-66; from asst prof to assoc prof zool, 66-74, PROF ZOOL, UNIV WYO, 74- *Mem:* AAAS; Am Soc Cell Biol; Soc Protozool. *Res:* Use of electron microscopy, cytochemistry and biochemical techniques for cytological studies of filamentous structures related to morphogenetic processes typical of dividing, regenerating and excysting ciliates. *Mailing Add:* Dept of Zool Univ of Wyo Laramie WY 82070

JENKINS, ROBERT EDWARD, space sciences, see previous edition

JENKINS, ROBERT ELLSWORTH, JR, b Lewistown, Pa, Sept 30, 42; m 64; c 2. ECOLOGICAL CONSERVATION. *Educ:* Rutgers Univ, AB, 64; Harvard Univ, PhD(biol), 70. *Prof Exp:* V PRES SCI PROGS, NATURE CONSERV, 70- *Concurrent Pos:* Mem US comt, Conserv Ecosysts Sect, Int Biol Prog, 70-75; mem, Fed Comt Res Natural Areas, 70-; res assoc, Smithsonian Inst, 71-72; assoc dir, Ctr Appl Res & Environ Sci, 71-73; mem, US Nat Comn, UNESCO, 74-76; mem bd, Rare Animal Relief Effort, 74-76; founder & nat dir, State Natural Heritage Progs, 75-; mem, US Man & the Biosphere Directorate, Proj 8, 78- *Honors & Awards:* Am Motors Prof Conserv Award, 78. *Mem:* Fel AAAS; Am Inst Biol Sci; Ecol Soc Am; Soc Study Evolution; Wildlife Soc. *Res:* Animal and plant ecology and evolution; human population and environment; applied research in land management, ecosystem preservation and restoration; ecological inventory and data banking. *Mailing Add:* Nature Conserv Suite 800 1800 N Kent St Arlington VA 22209

JENKINS, ROBERT M, b Kansas City, Mo, June 18, 23; m 56; 4. FISH BIOLOGY. *Educ:* Univ Okla, BS, 48, MS, 49. *Prof Exp:* Regional fishery biologist, Okla Game & Fish Dept, 49-50; dir fishery res, Okla Fishery Res Lab, 52-57; asst exec vpres fish conserv, Sport Fishing Inst, 58-62; DIR NAT RESERVOIR RES PROG, US FISH & WILDLIFE SERV, 63- *Concurrent Pos:* Mem panel fishery experts, Food & Agr Orgn, 63-; mem bd dirs, Sport Fishery Res Found, 63- *Mem:* Am Fisheries Soc; Am Soc Limnol & Oceanog. *Res:* Large reservoir fish production nationally as influenced by various environmental parameters. *Mailing Add:* US Fish & Wildlife Serv 113 S East St Fayetteville AR 72701

JENKINS, ROBERT WALLS, JR, b Richmond, Va, June 12, 36; m 58; c 3. RADIOCHEMISTRY, PLANT ECOLOGY. *Educ:* Va Mil Inst, BS, 58; Purdue Univ, MS, 61; Calif Western, PhD, 80. *Prof Exp:* Instr chem, Purdue Univ, 58-60; asst prof, Va Mil Inst, 60-61; chief nuclear chem div, Nuclear Defense Lab, 61-63; res scientist, Naval Res Lab, 63-65; res scientist, 65-67, CHIEF RADIOCHEM GROUP, PHILIP MORRIS INC RES CTR, 67- *Honors & Awards:* Philip Morris Award Distinguished Achievement Tobacco Sci, 70. *Mem:* Am Chem Soc; Am Nuclear Soc. *Res:* Radioisotopes; biosynthetic production of radiochemicals and their use in experimentation; gas radiochromatography; neutron activation analysis; smoke formation mechanisms; smoke aerosol generation; smoke chemistry. *Mailing Add:* Philip Morris Inc Res Ctr PO Box 26583 Richmond VA 23261

JENKINS, RODMAN, b San Francisco, Calif, June 24, 29. CHEMICAL ENGINEERING. *Educ:* Mass Inst Technol, BS, 46; Univ Del, MChE, 47; Calif Inst Technol, PhD(chem eng), 50. *Prof Exp:* Sr res engr, Mobil Oil Co, 49-59; proj leader, IBM Corp, 59-61, spec rep, 61-63, mkt rep, 63-68, systs analyst, 68-72; SR CHEM ENGR, TRW SYSTS, 72- *Mem:* Am Chem Soc; Am Inst Chem Engrs; Am Inst Mining, Metall & Petrol Engrs. *Res:* Petroleum production and refining. *Mailing Add:* 20809B Allen St Tejas Simulation Int Dallas TX 75204

JENKINS, SAMUEL FOREST, JR, b Oxford, NC, June 15, 30; m 51; c 3. PLANT PATHOLOGY. *Educ:* NC State Univ, BS, 58, MS, 60, PhD(plant path), 62. *Prof Exp:* Res asst plant path, NC State Univ, 58-61; asst plant pathologist, Univ Ga Coastal Plain Exp Sta, 62-65; from asst prof to assoc prof, 65-75, PROF PLANT PATH, NC STATE UNIV, 75- *Mem:* Am Phytopath Soc. *Res:* Diseases of vegetable crops; genetics of microorganisms; breeding plants for disease resistance. *Mailing Add:* NC State Univ Dept Plant Path PO Box 5397 Raleigh NC 27650

JENKINS, SIDNEY HARTMAN, JR, b Chicago, Ill, Aug 6, 22; m 47; c 3. ORGANIC POLYMER CHEMISTRY. *Educ:* Northwestern Univ, BS, 45, MS, 49; Univ Okla, PhD(chem), 53. *Prof Exp:* RES ASSOC, PLASTICS DEPT, E I DU PONT DE NEMOURS & CO, INC, 52- *Res:* Ketimines and organic polymers. *Mailing Add:* E I du Pont de Nemours & Co Inc PO Box 1089 Sabine River Works Orange TX 77630

JENKINS, TED R, mathematics, see previous edition

JENKINS, TERRY LLOYD, b Beresford, SDak, Nov 7, 35; m 57; c 6. MATHEMATICS. *Educ:* Univ SDak, BA, 57; Univ Iowa, MS, 59; Univ Nebr, PhD(math), 66. *Prof Exp:* Instr math, Univ SDak, 59-60; from instr to asst prof, Univ Nebr, 61-66; from asst prof to assoc prof, 66-74, PROF MATH, UNIV WYO, 74- *Mem:* Am Math Soc; Math Asn Am. *Res:* Ring theory; radicals of rings. *Mailing Add:* Dept of Math Univ of Wyo Laramie WY 82071

JENKINS, THOMAS GORDON, b Ft Lewis, Wash, Jan 28, 47; m 68; c 2. SYSTEMS ANALYSIS. *Educ:* Univ Ark, BS, 72, MS, 74; Tex A&M Univ, PhD(animal breeding), 77. *Prof Exp:* Res assoc, Tex A&M Univ, 77-78; RES GENETICIST, US MEAT & ANIMAL RES CTR, AGR RES SERV, USDA, 78- *Concurrent Pos:* Consult, Wintock Int Livestock Res & Training Ctr, 76. *Mem:* Am Soc Animal Sci. *Res:* Development and validation of the impact of innovative technologies on the efficiency of production of beef cattle and sheep production systems. *Mailing Add:* US Meat & Animal Res Ctr PO Box 166 Clay Center NE 68933

JENKINS, THOMAS LLEWELLYN, b Cambridge, Mass, July 16, 27; m 51; c 4. ASTROPHYSICS. *Educ:* Pomona Col, BA, 50; Cornell Univ, PhD(physics), 56. *Prof Exp:* Physicist, Lawrence Radiation Lab, Univ Calif, 55-60; from asst prof to assoc prof, 60-68, PROF PHYSICS, CASE WESTERN RESERVE UNIV, 68- *Mem:* AAAS; Am Phys Soc. *Res:* Neutrino induced reactions; low level counting; electron pair production; photoproduction of mesons; shock hydrodynamics; experimental elementary particle physics; gamma ray astronomy. *Mailing Add:* Dept of Physics Case Western Reserve Univ Cleveland OH 44106

JENKINS, THOMAS WILLIAM, b Adrian, Mich, Jan 25, 22; m 48; c 3. ANATOMY, NEUROPATHOLOGY. *Educ:* Kent State Univ, BS, 47; Mich State Col, MS, 50, PhD(zool, anat), 54. *Prof Exp:* Asst biol, Kent State Univ, 41-43, 46-47; asst zool, 48-52, from instr to assoc prof anat, 52-73, PROF ANAT & PATH, MICH STATE UNIV, 73- *Concurrent Pos:* NIH spec fel, Sch Med, Temple Univ, 62-63. *Mem:* Am Asn Anat; Am Asn Vet Anat; Am Acad Neurol; Soc Neurosci; Sigma Xi. *Res:* Functional anatomy of the nervous system. *Mailing Add:* Dept of Anat Mich State Univ Col Osteop Med East Lansing MI 48824

JENKINS, VERNON KELLY, b Chattanooga, Tenn, Dec 29, 32; m 54; c 2. RADIOLOGICAL HEALTH, RADIOBIOLOGY. *Educ:* Carson-Newman Col, BS, 54; Univ Tenn, Knoxville, MS, 65, PhD(zool), 67. *Prof Exp:* Res assoc, Biol Div, Oak Ridge Nat Lab, 59-65, res scientist, 67-68; NIH fel exp biol, Baylor Col Med, 68-69, asst prof, 69-70; asst prof, 70-76, ASSOC PROF RADIATION BIOL, UNIV TEX MED BR GALVESTON, 76- *Mem:* Radiation Res Soc; Am Soc Exp Path; Soc Exp Hemat; Reticuloendothelial Soc; NY Acad Sci. *Res:* Effects of radiation on hemopoiesis in mammals, including effects on the immune mechanism; studies of the interrelationships among radiation, immunity, hemopoiesis and the carcinogenic process. *Mailing Add:* Div of Radiother Unv of Tex Med Br Galveston TX 77550

JENKINS, WILLIAM A, b Ft Worth, Tex, June 18, 25; m 53; c 1. PHYSICAL CHEMISTRY, INORGANIC CHEMISTRY. *Educ:* Univ Tex, BS, 47, PhD(phys inorg chem), 50. *Prof Exp:* Res chemist nuclear chem, 52-56, res sect head inorg chem, Exp Sta, 56-58, res sect head metall, Eastern Lab, Gibbstown, NJ, 58-60, supvr govt contracts, 60-63, asst dir, 63-66, asst mgr sales, 66-68, mgr clad metal sales, 68-70, res mgr, Fluorocarbons Div, Plastics Dept, 70-73, MGR RES & MFG, PLASTICS PROD DIV, E I DU PONT DE NEMOURS & CO, 73- *Mem:* Am Chem Soc; Am Soc Metals. *Res:* Nuclear chemistry; physical metallurgy. *Mailing Add:* 104 Augustine Cutoff Wilmington DE 19803

JENKINS, WILLIAM FRANK, b Bangor, Ala, Feb 11, 20; m 49; c 4. HORTICULTURE. *Educ:* Ala Polytech Inst, BS, 43, MS, 47; Univ Md, PhD(hort), 54. *Prof Exp:* Asst horticulturist, Miss Agr Exp Sta, 51-57; PROF AGR, E TEX STATE UNIV, 57- *Mem:* Am Soc Hort Sci. *Res:* Olericulture. *Mailing Add:* Dept of Agr ETex State Univ Commerce TX 75428

JENKINS, WILLIAM KENNETH, b Pittsburgh, Pa, Apr 12, 47; m 70. ELECTRICAL ENGINEERING. *Educ:* Lehigh Univ, BSEE, 69; Purdue Univ, MSEE, 71, PhD(elec eng), 74. *Prof Exp:* Res scientist assoc elec eng, Lockheed Missiles & Space Co, Inc, 74-77; asst prof, 77-80, ASSOC PROF ELEC ENG, UNIV ILL, URGANA-CHAMPAIGN, 80- *Concurrent Pos:* Consult, Ill State Water, 78, Siliconix, Inc, 78- *Mem:* Inst Elec & Electronics Engrs, (secy & tres, 82-84). *Res:* Circuit and system theory; digital signal processing and digital filters. *Mailing Add:* 1913 Moraine Dr Champaign IL 61920

JENKINS, WILLIAM L, b Johannesburg, SAfrica, Jan 29, 37; m 61; c 4. VETERINARY PHARMACOLOGY, VETERINARY PHYSIOLOGY. *Educ:* Univ Pretoria, BVSc, 58, M Med Vet, 68; Univ Mo, PhD(pharmacol), 70. *Prof Exp:* Asst pvt pract, 59-62; lectr vet med, Univ Pretoria, 62-66, sr lectr, 69-71, prof & head physiol & pharmacol, 71-75, prof & head vet physiol & pharmacol, 76-78; res assoc pharmacol, Univ Mo, 66-69; vis prof physiol & pharmacol, 75-76, PROF VET PHYSIOL & PHARMACOL, TEX A&M UNIV, 78- *Concurrent Pos:* Mem, Efficacy Subcomt & Scheduling Comt, SAfrican Med Control Coun, 74-78; mem, Subcomt Radiation Appln, Agr SAfrican Atomic Energy Bd, 75-78. *Mem:* Am Acad Vet Pharmacol & Therapeut; Am Col Vet Toxicologists; Am Soc Vet Physiologists & Pharmacologists. *Res:* Veterinary pharmacology and therapeutics including comparative pharmacokinetics; physiopathology of stress in cattle and sheep; ruminant physiology and pharmacology. *Mailing Add:* Dept of Vet Physiol & Pharmacol Tex A&M Univ College Station TX 77843

JENKINS, WILLIAM ROBERT, b Hertford, NC, Sept 12, 27; m 51; c 3. NEMATOLOGY. *Educ:* Col William & Mary, BS, 50; Univ Va, MS, 52; Univ Md, PhD(hort, plant path), 54. *Prof Exp:* Asst biol, Univ Va, 50-51; asst plant path, Univ Md, 51-54, from instr to asst prof, 54-60; assoc res specialist, 60-63, res specialist, 63-65, res prof, 65-69, assoc dean, col, 74-77, PROF BIOL & CHMN DEPT, LIVINGSTON COL, RUTGERS UNIV, 69-, DEAN, COL, 77- *Mem:* Soc Nematologists. *Res:* Nematodes in relation to water pollution; transmission of human pathogens in nematodes borne by domestic water supplies; nematodes in soil. *Mailing Add:* Livingston Col Rutgers Univ New Brunswick NJ 08903

JENKINS, WILLIAM WESLEY, b Chicago, Ill, Oct 22, 17; m 52; c 3. PHARMACEUTICAL CHEMISTRY. *Educ:* DePauw Univ, AB, 39; Loyola Univ, Ill, MS, 42; Northwestern Univ, PhD(chem), 50. *Prof Exp:* Res chemist, 39-42 & 49-53, res admin asst, 53-60, head new prod develop, 60-63, dir, 63-67, dir res serv, 67-69, dir develop, 69-71, dir prod affairs, 71-79, DIR PRECLIN OPER, SEARLE RES & DEVELOP DIV, G D SEARLE & CO, 79- *Mem:* Am Chem Soc. *Res:* Heterocycles; nitrogen compounds; steroids. *Mailing Add:* 623 Washington Ave Wilmette IL 60091

JENKINS, WILMER ATKINSON, II, b Chicago, Ill, Feb 10, 28; m 49; c 3. PHYSICAL CHEMISTRY, INORGANIC CHEMISTRY. *Educ:* Swarthmore Col, BA, 49; Calif Inst Technol, PhD(chem), 53. *Prof Exp:* Res chemist, 52-57, res supvr, 57-60, asst dir res, 60-62, tech mgr, 62-66, asst plant mgr, 66-68, plants tech mgr, 68-70, dir res & develop, 70-76, dir, Polyester & Acrylics Div, 76-78, DIR, FLEXIBLE PKG DIV, E I DU PONT DE NEMOURS & CO, INC, 78- *Mem:* Am Chem Soc. *Res:* Extractive metallurgy; catalytic processes for polymer intermediates; explosives compositions; polymer chemistry. *Mailing Add:* 107 W Baynard Blvd Carrcroft Wilmington DE 10903

JENKINS, WINBORNE TERRY, b Waupun, Wis, Mar 23, 32; m 58; c 3. BIOLOGICAL CHEMISTRY, ENZYMOLOGY. *Educ:* Cambridge Univ, BA, 53; Mass Inst Technol, PhD(biol), 57. *Prof Exp:* Instr, Mass Inst Technol, 57-58; instr biochem, Univ Calif, Berkeley, 58-66; instr chem, 66-68, PROF CHEM, IND UNIV, BLOOMINGTON, 68- *Concurrent Pos:* Spec res fel, NIH, 61-62, career develop award, 69-74. *Mem:* Am Soc Biol Chemists. *Res:* Intermediary metabolism of amino acids, especially the purification, characterization and general enzymological properties of transaminases. *Mailing Add:* Dept of Chem Ind Univ Bloomington IN 47401

JENKS, GLENN HERBERT, b Savanna, Ill, June 8, 16; m 45; c 2. PHYSICAL CHEMISTRY. *Educ:* Mich State Col, BS, 39; Northwestern Univ, PhD(phys chem), 45. *Prof Exp:* Res assoc, Metall Lab, Univ Chicago, 43; SR CHEMIST, OAK RIDGE NAT LAB, 43- *Mem:* AAAS; Sigma Xi; Am Chem Soc; Am Phys Soc. *Res:* Calorimetry; radiation chemistry; radiation effects in solids. *Mailing Add:* 369 East Dr Oak Ridge TN 37830

JENKS, RICHARD D, b Chicago, Ill, Nov 16, 37; m 60; c 3. MATHEMATICS. *Educ:* Univ Ill, BS, 60, PhD(math), 66. *Prof Exp:* Res asst, Coordinated Sci Lab, Univ Ill, 60-66; fel math, Brookhaven Nat Lab, 66-68; RES STAFF MEM MATH SCI, THOMAS J WATSON RES CTR, IBM CORP, 68-; PROF COMPUT SCI, NY UNIV, 80- *Concurrent Pos:* Adj assoc prof math, NY Univ, 69-72; vis lectr comput sci, Yale Univ, 64 & 74; vis prof, Univ Utah, 76; Nat lectr, Asn Comput Mach, 78-80. *Mem:* Asn Comput Mach. *Res:* Computer language and system design, translator writing systems, computer algebra, non-numerical computation; study of very high level languages and their compilation. *Mailing Add:* Thomas J Watson Res Ctr IBM Corp PO Box 218 Yorktown Heights NY 10598

JENKS, ROBERT L, applied physics, see previous edition

JENKS, THEODORE EUGENE, wood science & technology, deceased

JENKS, WILLIAM FURNESS, b Philadelphia, Pa, June 28, 09; m 35; c 3. ECONOMIC GEOLOGY. *Educ:* Harvard Univ, AB, 32, PhD(struct geol), 36; Univ Wis, MA, 33. *Prof Exp:* Jr geologist, Tex Col, 36-38; geologist, Cerro de Pasco Copper Corp, Peru, 38-45; US Dept State vis prof, Univ San Agustin, Peru, 45-46; from asst prof to assoc prof geol, Univ Rochester, 46-55; head dept & dir univ mus, 55-68, prof geol, 55-79, CONSULT GEOLOGIST, UNIV CINCINNATI, 79- *Concurrent Pos:* Lectr, Univ San Agustin, Peru, 43; Fulbright lectr, Univ Tokyo, 62-63. *Mem:* Fel Geol Soc Am; Soc Econ Geol; Ital Soc Geol; Am Asn Petrol Geol; Am Geophys Union. *Res:* Mineral deposits of South America; disseminated copper deposits; tertiary volcanic rocks of western North America; massive concordant sulfide ore deposits. *Mailing Add:* 19 Munroe St Newburyport MA 01950

JENNE, EVERETT A, b Beattie, Kans, Mar 2, 30; m 58; c 3. GEOCHEMICAL MODELING. *Educ:* Univ Nebr, BS, 52, MS, 53; Ore State Univ, PhD, 60. *Prof Exp:* Res fel soil chem & clay mineral, Ore State Soil Dept, 56-60; res fel rheology, Univ Calif, Berkeley, 60-62; soil scientist, US Geol Surv, Colo, 62-68, Calif, 68-79; SR SCIENTIST AQUATIC GEOCHEM, PAC NORTHWEST LAB, BATTELLE MEM INST, RICHLAND, 80- *Concurrent Pos:* Mem ad hoc comt trace elements & uralithiasis incidence, Nat Acad Sci, 75-76; mem subcomt, 76-81, Geochem Environ Rel Health & Dis Comt, Nat Acad Sci, 81- *Mem:* Soil Sci Soc Am; Geol Soc Am; Soc Environ Geochem & Health; Am Geophys Union; Am Soc Limnol & Oceanog. *Res:* Trace element geochemistry; geothermal trace elements; trace element analyses and partitioning processes among solute, sediment and biota; adsorption phenomenon; colloid chemistry of metal oxides; mineral-water reactions of fossil and nuclear fuel wastes; bioavailability of trace elements. *Mailing Add:* Pac NW Lab Battelle Mem Inst 999 Battelle Blvd Richland WA 99352

JENNEMANN, VINCENT FRANCIS, b St Louis, Mo, Nov 27, 21; m 46; c 7. COMPUTER SCIENCE, EXPLORATION GEOPHYSICS. *Educ:* St Louis Univ, BS, 47, MS, 49; Univ Tulsa, PhD(earth sci), 72. *Prof Exp:* Instr math, St Louis Univ, 46-48; res computer, Seismog Dept, Sun Oil Co, 48-51; instr math, Lamar Col, 49-51; asst, Lamont Geol Observ, Columbia Univ, 51-54; res engr, Amoco Prod Co, 54-58, sr res engr, 58-64, sr res scientist, 64-66, comput analyst, 66-74, STAFF COMPUTER ANALYST, STANDARD OIL CO (IND), 74- *Mem:* Seismol Soc Am; Soc Explor Geophys; Am Geophys Union. *Res:* Computerized mapping system; use of preferred numbers with the metric system. *Mailing Add:* Standard Oil Co (Ind) Box 591 Tulsa OK 74102

JENNER, CHARLES EDWIN, b Indianola, Iowa, Nov 5, 19; m 42; c 2. BIOLOGY. *Educ:* Cent Col, Mo, AB, 41; Harvard Univ, MA, 49, PhD(biol), 51. *Prof Exp:* From asst prof to assoc prof & chmn dept, 50-60, PROF ZOOL, UNIV NC, CHAPEL HILL, 60- *Concurrent Pos:* Instr, Marine Biol Lab, Woods Hole, 52-54 & 61. *Mem:* AAAS; Ecol Soc Am; Am Soc Limnol & Oceanog; Am Soc Zool. *Res:* Aquatic ecology; animal photoperiodism. *Mailing Add:* Dept of Zool Univ of NC Chapel Hill NC 27514

JENNER, DAVID CHARLES, b Seattle, Wash, Oct 21, 43; m 69; c 2. ASTRONOMY, COMPUTER SCIENCE. *Educ:* Univ Wash, BS(physics) & BS(math), 66; Univ Wis-Madison, PhD(astron), 70. *Prof Exp:* Asst prof astron, NMex State Univ, Las Cruces, 70-72; adj asst prof astron, Univ Calif, Los Angeles, 72-78; RES ASSOC, DEPT ASTRON & PHYSICIST, APPL PHYSICS LAB, UNIV WASH, 78- *Mem:* Am Astron Soc; Int Astron Union; Astron Soc Pac; AAAS; Inst Elec & Electronics Engrs. *Res:* Masses of galaxies; stellar populations in galaxies; the nuclei of active galaxies; planetary nebulae; observational instrumentation and techniques; software systems; hardware systems; laboratory data acquisition and instrument control. *Mailing Add:* Dept of Astron Univ of Wash Seattle WA 98195

JENNER, EDWARD L, b Pontiac, Mich, Mar 27, 18; m 42; c 3. AGRICULTURAL BIOCHEMISTRY. *Educ:* Lake Forest Col, AB, 39; Univ Mich, MS, 40, PhD(chem), 42. *Prof Exp:* Res chemist, Univ Mich, 41-45; RES CHEMIST, EXP STA, E I DU PONT DE NEMOURS & CO, INC, 45- *Concurrent Pos:* Res assoc cell physiol, Univ Calif, 62-63. *Mem:* Am Chem Soc. *Res:* Synthesis of nitramines; acid-catalyzed telomerizations; reactions of hydroxyl and amino radicals, halogen atoms and aliphatic free radicals; catalysis by soluble derivatives of transition metals; oxidative and photosynthetic phosphorylation; biochemistry of phytochrome; ozone damage to vegetation. *Mailing Add:* Exp Sta E I du Pont de Nemours & Co Wilmington DE 19898

JENNESS, ROBERT, b Rochester, NH, Sept 21, 17; m 40; c 3. BIOCHEMISTRY. *Educ:* Univ NH, BS, 38; Univ Vt, MS, 40; Univ Minn, PhD(agr biochem), 44. *Prof Exp:* From instr to assoc prof, 40-53, PROF AGR BIOCHEM, UNIV MINN, ST PAUL, 53- *Honors & Awards:* Borden Award, 53. *Mem:* AAAS; Am Soc Biol Chem; Am Dairy Sci Asn; Am Chem Soc; Am Soc Mammalogists. *Res:* Biosynthesis of ascorbate by mammals; chemistry of milk proteins and salts; comparative biochemistry of milks of various species. *Mailing Add:* Dept of Biochem Univ Of Minn St Paul MN 55108

JENNESS, STUART EDWARD, b Ottawa, Ont, Aug 22, 25; m 49, 80; c 2. GEOLOGY. *Educ:* Queens Univ, Ont, 48; Univ Minn, MS, 50; Yale Univ, PhD(geol), 55. *Prof Exp:* Instr geol, Muhlenberg Col, 49-51; geologist, Nfld Geol Surv, 52-53; geologist, Geol Surv Can, 54-67; PUBL SUPVR, CAN JOUR RES, NAT RES COUN CAN, 67- *Mem:* Geol Soc Am; Mineral Asn Can; Geol Asn Can. *Mailing Add:* 9 2051 Jasmine Crescent Ottawa ON K1J 7W2 Can

JENNETT, JOSEPH CHARLES, b Dallas, Tex, June 11, 40; m 63. CIVIL & ENVIRONMENTAL ENGINEERING. *Educ:* Southern Methodist Univ, BSCE, 63, MSCE, 66; Univ NMex, PhD(sanit eng), 69; Am Acad Environ Engrs, Dipl, 78. *Prof Exp:* Engr, Southwestern Design Br, US Corp Engrs, 62-63; construct engr, Calif State Dept Water Resources, Orville, 63-64; consult engr, Pitotmeter Assocs, 65-66 & 69; from asst prof to assoc prof civil eng, Univ Mo-Rolla, 69-75; PROF CIVIL ENG & CHMN DEPT, SYRACUSE UNIV, 75- *Concurrent Pos:* Chmn task force on toxic trace substances in water, 75 & comt of water treatment and water resources mgt, 76; mem, Prof Coord Comt, 77-; mem, Environ Eng Div, Res Coun, 78-; ed, E N Am Minerals Environ J, 78. *Mem:* Am Soc Civil Engrs; Am Water Works Asn; Am Soc Eng Educ; Water Pollution Control Fedn; Nat Soc Prof Engrs. *Res:* Urban and rural runoff pollutants; drying of digested sludge; industrial waste treatment techniques; effects of heavy metals on aquatic ecosystems and treatment devices; biological operations on domestic and industrial wastes; analysis and treatment of toxic metals and trace organics; urban and rural run-off quality. *Mailing Add:* Dept of Civil Eng Syracuse Univ Syracuse NY 13210

JENNETTE, KAREN WETTERHAHN, see Wetterhahn, Karen E

JENNEY, DAVID S, b Mattapoisett, Mass, May 18, 31; m 53; c 3. MECHANICS, AERODYNAMICS. *Educ:* Worcester Polytech Inst, BS, 53; Univ Conn, MS, 56; Rensselaer Polytech Inst, PhD(mech), 68. *Prof Exp:* Res engr, Res Labs, United Aircraft Corp, 53-58, supvr rotary wing aerodyn, 58-62, eng mgt pos, 62-77, CHIEF TECH ENG, SIKORSKY AIRCRAFT DIV, UNITED TECHNOL CORP, 77- *Mem:* Am Helicopter Soc. *Res:* Helicopter and vertical take-off aircraft aerodynamics and dynamics. *Mailing Add:* 109 Wilbrook Rd Stratford CT 06497

JENNEY, ELIZABETH HOLDEN, b Bennington, Vt, Nov 4, 12. PHARMACOLOGY. *Educ:* Mt Holyoke Col, AB, 34; Univ Ill, MS, 47. *Prof Exp:* Asst pharmacol, Sch Med, Boston Univ, 35-36; med technologist, Rutland Hosp, Vt, 37-41; med technologist, Cooly Dickinson Hosp, Northampton, Mass, 41-43; res assoc, Univ Ill Col Med, 48-54; instr, Sch Med, Emory Univ, 54-60; res scientist, Sect Pharmacol, Bur Res, NJ Neuropsychiat Inst, 60-73; PHARMACOLOGIST, BRAIN BIO CTR, 73- *Mem:* Sigma Xi; Am Soc Pharmacol & Exp Therapeut. *Res:* Neuropharmacology; psychopharmacology; schizophrenia. *Mailing Add:* Brain Bio Ctr 862 Route 518 Skillman NJ 08558

JENNEY, JOE ALLEN, optical physics, see previous edition

JENNI, DONALD ALISON, b Pueblo, Colo, June 20, 32; m 56; c 4. ETHOLOGY. *Educ:* Ore State Univ, BS, 53; Utah State Univ, MS, 56; Univ Fla, PhD(zool), 61. *Prof Exp:* Asst prof zool, Univ Fla, 61-62 & Eastern Ill Univ, 62-66; assoc prof, 66-71, chmn dept, 72-75, PROF ZOOL, UNIV MONT, 71- *Concurrent Pos:* NIH fel & res biologist, Univ Leiden, 64-66; vis prof, Cornell Univ, 75 & Univ Wash, 79-80. *Mem:* Animal Behav Soc; Am Ecol Soc; Am Ornith Union; Wilson Ornith Soc; Am Soc Mammal. *Res:* Ethology and behavioral ecology, especially the behavioral approach to classic ecological problems; adaptation and evolution of behavioral patterns including social organization in response to ecological pressures; evolution of mateship systems, especially non-inonogamous systems; behavioral problems of territoriality. *Mailing Add:* Dept of Zool Univ of Mont Missoula MT 59812

JENNINGS, ALBERT RAY, b Grosvenor, Tex, Nov 11, 26; m 42; c 2. GEOLOGY. *Educ:* Hardin-Simmons Univ, BA, 58; Tex A&M Univ, MS, 60, PhD(geol), 64. *Prof Exp:* Res asst hydrol, Tex Eng Exp Sta, Tex A&M Univ, 60-63; explor geologist, Mobil Oil Co, 64-68; from asst prof to prof geol, ECarolina Univ, 68-74, chmn dept, 70-74; assoc prof, 74-76, HEAD DEPT GEOL, HARDIN-SIMMONS UNIV, 76-, PROF, 78- *Concurrent Pos:* Consult geologist, 74- *Mem:* Am Inst Prof Geol; Am Asn Petrol Geol; fel Geol Soc Am. *Res:* Utilization of radioisotopes as ground-water tracers. *Mailing Add:* Dept of Geol Box 970 Hardin Simmons Univ Abilene TX 79698

JENNINGS, ALFRED S(TONEBRAKER), b St Louis, Mo, Sept 30, 25; m 49; c 4. CHEMICAL ENGINEERING. *Educ:* Washington Univ, St Louis, BS, 48, MS, 49, DSc(chem eng), 51. *Prof Exp:* Chem engr, 51-57, res supvr, 57-68, res mgr separations eng div, 68-80, SR RES ASSOC, SAVANNAH RIVER LAB, E I DU PONT DE NEMOURS & CO, INC, 80- *Mem:* Am Chem Soc; Am Inst Chem Engrs. *Res:* Radiochemical separations and solvent extraction process development; isotope separation processes; high-level waste immobilization. *Mailing Add:* 1469 Canterbury Ct SE Aiken SC 29801

JENNINGS, ALLEN LEE, b Quincy, Ill, July 5, 43; m 67; c 1. BIOCHEMISTRY, ENZYMOLOGY. *Educ:* Western Ill Univ, BS, 65; Univ Ark, PhD(chem), 70. *Prof Exp:* Res assoc biochem, Iowa State Univ, 70-71; RES ASSOC BIOCHEM, US ENVIRON PROTECTION AGENCY, 71- *Mem:* AAAS; Am Chem Soc. *Mailing Add:* 2306 S Dinwiddie St Arlington VA 22206

JENNINGS, BILLY RAY, microbiology, immunology, see previous edition

JENNINGS, BOJAN HAMLIN, b Waukegan, Ill, Apr 4, 20; m 42; c 3. ORGANIC CHEMISTRY. *Educ:* Bryn Mawr Col, AB, 42; Radcliffe Col, MA, 43, PhD(chem), 55. *Prof Exp:* Res chemist, Dewey & Almy Chem Co, 42-43; from instr to assoc prof, 43-62, PROF CHEM, WHEATON COL, MASS, 62-, CHMN DEPT, 68- *Mem:* Am Chem Soc; NY Acad Sci; Asn Women Sci. *Res:* Steroid chemistry; cancer research; physical organic chemistry; photochemistry. *Mailing Add:* Dept of Chem Wheaton Col Norton MA 02766

JENNINGS, BURGESS H(ILL), b Baltimore, Md, Sept 12, 03; m 25; c 1. MECHANICAL ENGINEERING. *Educ:* Johns Hopkins Univ, BE, 25; Lehigh Univ, MS, 28, MA, 35. *Prof Exp:* Mem fac, Lehigh Univ, 26-35, assoc prof, 35-40; prof, 40-73, chmn dept, 41-57, assoc dean eng, 62-70, EMER PROF MECH ENG, NORTHWESTERN UNIV, 73- *Concurrent Pos:* Consult, var US co & labs, 34-71; mem, Refrig Res Found, 44-57; ed, Lubricating Eng, Am Soc Mech Engrs, 44-51; vpres, Int Inst Refrig, 57-67. *Honors & Awards:* Off Sci Res & Develop Citation, 45; Richards Mem Award, 50; Am Soc Heat, Refrig & Air-Conditioning Engrs Plaque, 61; Worcester Reed Warner Medal, 72; F Paul Anderson Medal, 80. *Mem:* Nat Acad Engrs; fel Am Soc Heat, Refrig & Air-Conditioning Engrs (treas & vpres, 46-48, pres, 49); hon mem Am Soc Mech Engrs; Am Soc Lubrication Engrs (secy & vpres, 44-49); Am Soc Eng Educ. *Res:* Applied thermodynamics; refrigeration; environmental control. *Mailing Add:* Dept Mech Eng Northwestern Univ Evanston IL 60201

JENNINGS, CARL ANTHONY, b Harrisburg, Ill, Dec 28, 44; m 65; c 2. ORGANIC CHEMISTRY, CHEMICAL MANUFACTURING MANAGEMENT. *Educ:* Southern Ill Univ, BS, 67, PhD(org chem), 71. *Prof Exp:* Res assoc org chem, Univ Ill, 71-72; from res chemist to mgr, Photog Emulsion Mfg, GAF Corp, 72-77; from asst to vpres, Ind Chem, 77-78, mgr develop chem, 78-80, MGR AGR CHEM MFG, BASF WYANDOTTE CORP, 80- *Mem:* Am Chem Soc; Am Inst Chem Engrs; Soc Photog Scientists & Engrs. *Res:* Agricultural chemicals; chemical manufacturing management; polyoxyalkylenes and organic oxide chemicals; urethanes; organic synthesis; photographic emulsion theory; organometallics. *Mailing Add:* 12638 Warwick Dr Baton Rouge LA 70815

JENNINGS, CHARLES DAVID, b Newtonia, Mo, May 21, 39; c 2. OCEANOGRAPHY. *Educ:* Northwest Nazarene Col, BA, 61; Ore State Univ, MS, 66, PhD(oceanog), 68. *Prof Exp:* Instr physics, Ore Col Educ, 62-63; instr oceanog, World Campus Afloat, 66, asst prof, 68; oceanogr, US Bur Com Fisheries, 68-70; asst prof oceanog, Ore Col Educ, 70-74, assoc prof physics, 74-78; PROF PHYSICS, WESTERN ORE STATE COL, 78- *Mem:* AAAS; Am Soc Limnol & Oceanog. *Res:* Radioactivity and trace elements in the marine environment; circulation of estuaries; marine radioecology. *Mailing Add:* Natural Sci Western Ore State Col Monmouth OR 97361

JENNINGS, CHARLES WARREN, b Toledo, Ohio, Dec 3, 18; m 49; c 3. ELECTROCHEMISTRY. *Educ:* Univ Toledo, BEng, 40; Univ Calif, MS, 43; Duke Univ, PhD(chem), 51. *Prof Exp:* Res chemist, Dow Chem Co, Calif, 42-43; chemist, Nat Bur Standards, 46-47, res assoc, 47-48; res assoc, Res Proj, Duke Univ, 48-50; assoc prof chem, NC State Col, 50-57; MEM STAFF, SANDIA CORP, 57- *Mem:* Am Chem Soc. *Res:* Physical properties of electrodeposited metals; electrochemistry of batteries and fused salt systems; chlorination of hydrocarbons; thermal batteries; printed circuit boards; adhesives. *Mailing Add:* 1209 Mesilla NE Albuquerque NM 87110

JENNINGS, DANIEL THOMAS, b Fulton, Ky, July 4, 35; m 55; c 2. FOREST ENTOMOLOGY, ARACHNOLOGY. *Educ:* Colo State Univ, BS, 60; Univ NMex, MS, 67, PhD(biol), 72. *Prof Exp:* Entomologist, Forest Serv, 62-65, res entomologist, NC Forest Exp Sta, 65-68, res entomologist, Rocky Mountain Forest & Range Exp Sta, 68-76, PRIN RES ENTOMOLOGIST, NORTHEASTERN FOREST EXP STA, FOREST SERV, USDA, 76- *Concurrent Pos:* Collabr, Environ Qual Inst, Biol Active Natural Prod Lab, Agr Res Serv, Beltsville, Md, 73-; adj asst prof biol, Univ NMex, 74-77; fac assoc, Univ Maine, 76- *Honors & Awards:* Sigma Xi. *Mem:* Entom Soc Am; Am Entom Soc; Am Arachnological Soc; Brit Arachnological Soc; Entom Soc Can. *Res:* Life histories and habits of forest insects, their biological control by natural enemies and pheromones; the arachnid fauna associated with forest trees. *Mailing Add:* Northeastern Forest Exp Sta Univ of Maine USDA Bldg Orono ME 04473

JENNINGS, DAVID PHIPPS, b Columbia, Mo, Aug 3, 41; m 64; c 2. PHYSIOLOGY, VETERINARY MEDICINE. *Educ:* Univ Mo, BS, 63, DVM, 65; Okla State Univ, PhD(physiol), 69. *Prof Exp:* NIH trainee, 65-66, fel, 66-68, from asst prof to assoc prof physiol, Okla State Univ, 68-77; PROF PHYSIOL, MISS STATE UNIV, 77- *Concurrent Pos:* NIH spec fel anat, Sch Med, Univ Calif, Los Angeles, 71-72; clin neurol trainee, Univ Ga, 78. *Mem:* AAAS; Am Vet Med Asn; Am Asn Vet Anatomists; Am Asn Vet Cols; Am Soc Vet Physiol & Pharmacol. *Res:* Interdisciplinary approach to isolating and studying central nervous system mechanisms for processing input information into appropriate reflex control of physiologic systems. *Mailing Add:* Col of Vet Med Miss State Univ Mississippi State MS 39762

JENNINGS, DONALD ALFRED, solid state physics, see previous edition

JENNINGS, DONALD B, b Windsor, Ont, July 20, 32; m 57; c 4. MEDICINE, PHYSIOLOGY. *Educ:* Queen's Univ, Ont, MD, CM, 57, MSc, 60, PhD(physiol), 62. *Prof Exp:* Jr intern, Montreal Gen Hosp, 57-58, jr asst res med, 58-59; res fel med & physiol, Cardiovasc Res Inst, Med Ctr, Univ Calif, San Francisco, 62-64; from asst prof to assoc prof, 64-74, PROF PHYSIOL, QUEEN'S UNIV, ONT, 74- *Concurrent Pos:* George Christian Hoffman fel path, 62-63; Can Heart Found sr res fel physiol, 64-69; assoc ed, Can J Physiol Pharmacol, 78; fel, Max Planck Inst Exp Med, 81; vis prof, Med Sch, Dartmouth Col, 81. *Mem:* Can Physiol Soc (secy, 75-78); Am Physiol Soc; Can Soc Clin Invest. *Res:* Humoral and nervous regulation of cardiovascular, respiratory, metabolic and erythropoietic adjustments to high carbon dioxide and low oxygen environments and anaemic anoxia; interaction of temperature regulation with the cardio-respiratory admustment to acute and chronic hypercapnia and hypoxia. *Mailing Add:* Dept of Physiol Queen's Univ Kingston ON K7L 3N6 Can

JENNINGS, DONALD EDWARD, b New Rochelle, NY, May 30, 48; m 70. MOLECULAR SPECTROSCOPY. *Educ:* Northern Ariz Univ, BS, 70; Univ Tenn, PhD(physics), 74. *Prof Exp:* Res assoc physics, Univ Tenn, Knoxville, 74-75; Nat Acad Sci-Nat Res Coun res assoc, 76-77, SPACE SCIENTIST, GODDARD SPACE FLIGHT CTR, NASA, 77- *Res:* Molecular spectroscopy; fourier transform, tuneable diode laser, and grating spectroscopy; planetary infrared astronomy; radio astronomy of interstellar molecules. *Mailing Add:* NASA Goddard Space Flight Ctr Code 693 Greenbelt MD 20771

JENNINGS, FEENAN DEE, b Los Angeles, Calif, Aug 11, 23; m 47, 65; c 2. OCEANOGRAPHY. *Educ:* NMex State Univ, BS, 50. *Prof Exp:* Asst oceanog, Scripps Inst, Univ Calif, 50-51, asst chem, 52-53, res chemist, 53-55, sr engr oceanog, 55-58; head oceanog sect, Geophys Br, US Naval Res, 58-70; heaad, Int Decade Ocean Explor, NSF, 70-78; DIR SEAGRANT COL PROG, TEX A&M UNIV, 78- *Mem:* AAAS; Am Geophys Union. *Res:* Physical oceanography; nuclear and atomic instrumentation; chemical engineering. *Mailing Add:* Seagrant Tex A & M Univ College Station TX 77843

JENNINGS, FRANK LAMONT, b Minneapolis, Minn, Apr 25, 21; m 48; c 4. PATHOLOGY. *Educ:* Ind Univ, AB, 42, MD, 47. *Prof Exp:* asst path, Univ chicago, 48, atomic energy fel, 48-51, from instr path, 52-60; assoc prof path, Univ Tex Med Br, Galveston, 60-63, prof & chmn dept, 63-76. *Concurrent Pos:* mem staff, Armed Forces Inst Path, 55-57. *Mem:* Am Soc Exp Path; Radiation Res Soc; Col Am Path; Am Soc Clin Path; Int Acad Path. *Res:* Radiation pathology and recovery; protein nutrition; tumor metabolism. *Mailing Add:* Wright State Univ Sch of Med PO Box 927 Dayton OH 45401

JENNINGS, HARLEY YOUNG, JR, b Clio, Mich, Sept 29, 26; m 50; c 3. CHEMISTRY. *Educ:* Univ NC, BS, 48; Univ Mich, MS, 49, PhD(chem), 52. *Prof Exp:* Res chemist, Parker Pen Co, 50-52; res chemist, Chevron Res Co, 52-59, group supvr, 59-62, sr res chemist, 62-67, SR RES ASSOC, CHEVRON OIL FIELD RES CO, LA HABRA, 67- *Mem:* AAAS; Am Chem Soc; Am Inst Mining, Metall & Petrol Engrs. *Res:* Surface energy relationships, contact angle and interfacial tension; capillarity; fluid flow and enhanced recovery of petroleum; colloid and surface chemistry; oil well stimulation and stimulation and damage prevention mechanisms; phase behavior and fluid analysis. *Mailing Add:* 2501 Terraza Pl Fullerton CA 92635

JENNINGS, LAURENCE DUANE, b New Haven, Conn, Nov 14, 29; m 51; c 3. SOLID STATE PHYSICS. *Educ:* Mass Inst Technol, SB, 50, PhD(physics), 55. *Prof Exp:* Asst prof chem, Iowa State Univ, 55-59; SOLID STATE PHYSICIST, US ARMY MAT & MECH RES CTR, 59- *Mem:* Am Phys Soc; Am Crystallog Asn; Inst Elec & Electronic Engr. *Res:* Diffraction; equilibrium properties of solids. *Mailing Add:* US Army Mat & Mech Res Ctr Watertown MA 02172

JENNINGS, MICHAEL LEON, b Cleveland, Ohio, June 10, 48; m 76. TRANSPORT PHYSIOLOGY, MEMBRANE BIOCHEMISTRY. *Educ:* Mass Inst Technol, SB, 70; Harvard Univ, PhD(biophysics), 76. *Prof Exp:* Fel, Max Planck Inst Biophysics, 77-78; ASST PROF PHYSIOL, COL MED, UNIV IOWA, 78- *Mem:* Biophys Soc; Am Physiol Soc; Sigma Xi. *Res:* Structure and function of biological ion transport proteins, especially the inorganic anion transport protein of the erythrocyte membrane. *Mailing Add:* Dept Physiol & Biophysics Univ Iowa Iowa City IA 52242

JENNINGS, PAUL BERNARD, JR, b Medford, Mass, Oct 13, 38; m 64; c 4. VETERINARY SURGERY, COMPARATIVE MEDICINE. *Educ:* Tufts Univ, BS, 60; Univ Pa, VMD, 64, M Med Sci, 70; Am Col Vet Surgeons, dipl, 73. *Prof Exp:* US Army, 65-, res investr surg, Walter Reed Army Inst Res, 65-67, asst chief, Clin Invest Serv, Madigan Army Med Ctr, Tacoma, Wash, 71-77, staff officer animal med, US Army Health Serv Command, Directorate Vet Serv, Ft Sam Houston, 78-79, chief, Div Res Support, Letterman Army Inst Res, San Francisco, 79-81, COMMANDER, 167TH MED DETACHMENT, US ARMY, STUTTGART, WGER, 81- *Concurrent Pos:* Consult to surgeon gen, US Army Med Dept, 72-; Am Cancer Soc grant, 69-70; ed consult, J Vet Surg, 77- *Honors & Awards:* Gold Medal-Sci Exhib, Am Acad Pediat, 76 & 78; Cert Merit-Sci Exhib, AMA, 77 & 78. *Mem:* AAAS; Am Col Vet Surgeons; Sigma Xi; Am Vet Med Asn; Asn Mil Surgeons US. *Res:* Shock, trauma & surgical infections; transplantation immunology; comparative medical aspects of human disease, including animal models. *Mailing Add:* 167th Med Detachment APO New York NY 09154

JENNINGS, PAUL C(HRISTIAN), b Brigham City, Utah, May 21, 36; m 81; c 2. CIVIL ENGINEERING, APPLIED MECHANICS. *Educ:* Colo State Univ, BS, 58; Calif Inst Technol, MS, 60, PhD(civil eng), 63. *Prof Exp:* From instr to assoc prof mech, US Air Force Acad, 63-66; from asst prof to prof appl mech, 66-76, PROF CIVIL ENG & APPL MECH, CALIF INST TECHNOL, 76- *Concurrent Pos:* Tech asst to eng panel, Nat Acad Sci Comt on Alaskan Earthquake, 65-; Erskine fel, Univ Canterbury, 70; pres, Earthquake Eng Res Inst, 80- *Honors & Awards:* Huber Res Prize, Am Soc Civil Engrs, 76. *Mem:* Am Soc Civil Engrs; Seismol Soc Am; Earthquake Eng Res Inst; Am Soc Eng Educ; Am Geophys Union. *Res:* Structural dynamics and engineering seismology, especially response of structures to earthquake motion; earthquake engineering. *Mailing Add:* Mail Code 104-44 Calif Inst of Technol Pasadena CA 91125

JENNINGS, PAUL HARRY, b Brockton, Mass, Jan 31, 38; m 60; c 3. PLANT PHYSIOLOGY. *Educ:* Univ Mass, Amherst, BVA, 60; NC State Univ, MS, 62, PhD(plant physiol), 65. *Prof Exp:* Asst res plant physiol, Univ Calif, Davis, 67-69; from asst prof to assoc prof plant physiol, Univ Mass, Amherst, 69-82, secy fac senate, 80-82; PROF & HEAD, DEPT HORT, KANS STATE UNIV, 82- *Mem:* Am Soc Plant Physiol; Am Soc Hort Sci; Crop Sci Soc Am. *Res:* Physiology of disease resistance; anabolic and catabolic pathways of carbohydrate metabolism as related to genetic potential, stage development and isozymic differences in plants; effects of low temperatures on germination and growth of crop plants susceptible to chilling injury. *Mailing Add:* Dept Hort Waters Hall Kans State Univ Manhattan KS 66506

JENNINGS, PAUL W, b Denver, Colo, Sept 24, 36; m 61; c 2. ORGANOMETALLLIC CHEMISTRY. *Educ:* Univ Colo, BA, 58, MS, 61; Univ Utah, PhD(org chem), 65. *Prof Exp:* Res fel chem, Calif Inst Technol, 64-66; from asst prof to assoc prof, 66-75, PROF CHEM, MONT STATE UNIV, 75- *Mem:* Am Chem Soc. *Res:* Organometallic photochemistry, photochemical energy transfer, and elucidation of the structure of medicinal components of plants having physiological activity. *Mailing Add:* Dept of Chem Mont State Univ Bozeman MT 59715

JENNINGS, RICHARD LOUIS, b Newark, NJ, July 28, 33; m 56; c 2. CIVIL ENGINEERING, APPLIED MECHANICS. *Educ:* Univ Ohio, BS, 56, BSCE, 57; Univ Ill, MS, 58, PhD(civil eng), 64. *Prof Exp:* Asst prof, 63-67, ASSOC PROF CIVIL ENG, UNIV VA, 67- *Concurrent Pos:* Consult, Babcock & Wilcox Corp, Va. *Mem:* Am Soc Civil Engrs. *Res:* Earthquake and nuclear blast resistant design structures; mechanical vibrations of thin shells; structural design of large steerable radio telescopes; rehabilitation engineering; highway pavement analysis. *Mailing Add:* Dept of Civil Eng Thornton Hall Univ of Va Charlottesville VA 22903

JENNINGS, ROBERT BURGESS, b Baltimore, Md, Dec 14, 26; m 52; c 5. PATHOLOGY, EXPERIMENTAL PATHOLOGY. *Educ:* Northwestern Univ, BS, 47, MS & BM, 49, MD, 50. *Prof Exp:* Intern, Passavant Mem Hosp, Chicago, Ill, 49-50, resident path, 50-51; from instr to prof, Med Sch, Northwestern Univ, Ill, 53-69, Magerstadt prof path & chmn dept, 69-75; prof, 75-80, JAMES B DUKE PROF PATH, MED SCH, DUKE UNIV, 80-, CHMN DEPT, 75- *Concurrent Pos:* Markle scholar, 58-63; attend physician, Vet Admin Res Hosp, Chicago, Ill, 55-69, consult physician, 69-75; pathologist, Community Hosp, Evanston, Ill, 57-67; vis scientist, Middlesex Hosp Med Sch, London, 61-62; mem path A study sect, USPHS, 60-65; attend physician & chief labs, Passavant Mem Hosp, 69-72; attend staff, Northwestern Mem Hosp, 72-75. *Mem:* Am Asn Pathologists; Soc Exp Biol & Med; Int Soc Heart Res; Am Soc Cell Biol; Am Heart Asn. *Res:* Cardiovascular and renal disease; cell physiology; cell injury; electron microscopy. *Mailing Add:* Dept of Path Duke Univ Med Ctr Durham NC 27710

JENNINGS, TED VERNON, b Council Bluffs, Iowa, May 5, 31; m 49; c 2. STRUCTURAL GEOLOGY, PETROLEUM GEOLOGY. *Educ:* Univ Iowa, BA, 56, MS, 58, PhD(geol), 67. *Prof Exp:* Geologist, Standard Oil Co, Tex, 58-61, econ geologist, 61-63, analyst, 63-64; asst prof, 67-73, assoc prof geol, Purdue Univ, West Lafayette, 73-80; CONSULT GEOLOGIST, 66- *Mem:* Am Inst Prof Geologists; Am Asn Petrol Geol; Geol Soc Am. *Res:* Early Paleozoic structure, Central High Andes, Peru; structural evolution of Bighorn Mountain region, Wyoming; fracture development controls; stratigraphy of the Minnelusa Formation, Black Hills, South Dakota; petroleum geologyy, Southwest Utah. *Mailing Add:* 56 Inverness Dr E Englewood CO 80112

JENNINGS, WALTER GOODRICH, b Sioux, Iowa, Mar 2, 22; m 47; c 3. GAS CHROMATOGRAPHY. *Educ:* Univ Calif, BS, 50, MS, 52, PhD(agr chem), 54. *Prof Exp:* Instr dairy indust, 54-59, from asst prof to assoc prof food sci, 59-65, from jr chemist to assoc chemist, 54-65, PROF FOOD SCI & CHEMIST EXP STA, UNIV CALIF, DAVIS, 65- *Concurrent Pos:* NIH sr scientist award, Vienna, Austria, 67-68; spec award sr Am scientist, Alexander von Humboldt Found, 74-75; consult, several indust firms; ed, J High Resolution Chromatography & Chromotography Commun, J Food Chem & Chemi, Mikrobiologie, Technologie der Lebensmittel; Founder & co-owner of J & W Sci, Inc, Rancho Cordova, Calif. *Honors & Awards:* Medal, Univ Bologna, 67; Medal, Fr Asn Agr Chemists, 71. *Mem:* Am Chem Soc; Inst Food Technol; Sigma Xi; hon mem Soc Flavor Chemists. *Res:* Isolation and characterization of trace volatiles; flavor chemistry; glass capillary gas chromatography; author of over 150 publications. *Mailing Add:* Dept of Food Sci & Technol Univ of Calif Chem Annex Davis CA 95616

JENNINGS, WILLIAM HARNEY, JR, b Ames, Iowa, Dec 6, 31; m 57; c 2. BIOPHYSICS. *Educ:* Duke Univ, BS, 54; George Washington Univ, MS, 59. *Prof Exp:* Physicist, Naval Med Res Inst, 54-58; RES PHYSICIST, NAT INST ARTHRITIS, METAB & DIGESTIVE DIS, 61- *Mem:* AAAS; Chem Soc. *Res:* Laboratory computers, dedicated, multi-user and networks. *Mailing Add:* Nat Inst of Arthritis Metab & Digestive Dis Bethesda MD 20014

JENNISON, DWIGHT RICHARD, b Teaneck, NJ, June 11, 43; m 68; c 3. THEORETICAL PHYSICS. *Educ:* Rensselaer Polytech Inst, BS, 65, MS, 73, PhD(physics), 74. *Prof Exp:* Res asst physics, Univ NDak, 69-70; teaching asst, Rensselaer Polytech Inst, 71, NIH trainee, 71-74; res assoc, Dept Physics & Mat Res Lab, Univ Ill, Urbana, 74-75, res asst prof physics, 76; MEM TECH STAFF, SOLID STATE THEORY DIV, SANDIA LABS, 77-; ASSOC PHYSICS, DEPT PHYSICS & MAT RES LAB, UNIV ILL, URBANA, 74- *Mem:* Am Phys Soc. *Res:* Electronic properties of solids, surfaces and molecules; theory of auger electron spectroscopy and stimulated desorption. *Mailing Add:* Sandia Nat Labs Albuquerque NM 87185

JENNISON, JAMES H(ENRY), b Mason City, Iowa, June 8, 11; m 42; c 4. ENGINEERING. *Educ:* Calif Inst Technol, BS, 35, MS, 36. *Prof Exp:* Engr, bridge dept, Calif Div Hwys, 36-43; engr underwater ord res & develop, Calif Inst Technol, 43-45; head prod eng div, US Naval Ord Test Sta, 45-67, head comput sci & eng dept, Naval Undersea Ctr, 67-77; head prod eng dept, Naval Ocean Systs Ctr, 77-79; CONSULT, 79- *Honors & Awards:* First Award, Int Bridge Design Competition, Lincoln Arc Welding Found, 50. *Mem:* Fel Am Soc Civil Engrs. *Res:* Welded steel structures; dynamic response of structures; unusual structural design problems. *Mailing Add:* 1418 Walnut Creek Dr Encinitas CA 92024

JENNRICH, ELLEN COUTLEE, b Kankakee, Ill, Dec 16, 39; m 71; c 2. ANIMAL BEHAVIOR, ECOLOGY. *Educ:* Wayne State Univ, BA, 60, MS, 62; Univ Calif, Los Angeles, PhD(zool), 66. *Prof Exp:* Lectr biol, Mt St Mary's Col, 63-64; lectr, Univ Calif, Riverside, 66-68; lectr zool, Univ Calif, Los Angeles, 68-72. *Res:* Population biology of starlings; comparative breeding behavior of goldfinches, fluctuations in population size, avian communication, maintenance and agonistic behavior. *Mailing Add:* 3400 Purdue Ave Los Angeles CA 90066

JENNRICH, ROBERT I, b Milwaukee, Wis, Feb 11, 32. STATISTICS. *Educ:* Univ Wis, BS, 54, MS, 56; Univ Calif, Los Angeles, PhD(math), 60. *Prof Exp:* Asst prof math, Univ Wis, 60-62; asst prof math & asst res statistician, 62-70, assoc prof math & biomath, 70-74, PROF MATH & BIOMATH, UNIV CALIF, LOS ANGELES, 74- *Mem:* Am Statist Asn; Inst Math Statist. *Res:* Computer algorithms for data analysis; non-linear least squares, methods and statistical properties; factor analysis, rotation and maximum likelihood algorithms; analysis of variance, properties of the mixed model; time series analysis. *Mailing Add:* Dept of Math Univ of Calif Los Angeles CA 90024

JENNY, HANS K, b Glarus, Switz, Sept 14, 19; nat US; m 49; c 3. ELECTRONIC & ELECTRICAL ENGINEERING. *Educ:* Swiss Fed Inst Technol, MSEE, 43. *Prof Exp:* Asst prof & res engr, Swiss Fed Inst Technol, 43-46; microwave tube develop engr, Radio Corp Am, Pa, 46-50, eng leader, Harrison, 50-53, mgr, Microwave Tube Develop Dept, 53-57, mgr microwave eng, 57-67, mgr microwave solid state devices oper, 67-72, chief tech adv, Indust Tube Div, 72-74, MGR, RCA TECH INFO PROGS, RCA CORP RES & ENG, 75- *Mem:* Fel Inst Elec & Electronics Engrs. *Res:* Parametric amplifiers; variable capacitance and tunnel amplifiers; phase shifters; microwave laser modulators and detectors; microwave devices and systems; engineering organizations; technical information, including communications, publications and information systems. *Mailing Add:* RCA Corp 204-2 Cherry Hill NJ 08358

JENNY, NEIL ALLAN, b Milwaukee, Wis, Sept 6, 36; m 60; c 4. PESTICIDE CHEMISTRY. *Educ:* Univ Wis, BS, 58; Univ Kans, PhD(med chem), 63. *Prof Exp:* Res chemist, Polymer Div, Morton Chem co, Ill, 63-66, res chemist, Org Div, 66-69, contract mfg coordr, Div Schering Agr, 77-79, SUPVR ANAL RES, NOR-AM AGR PROD, DIV SCHERING AGR, BERLIN, 69- *Mem:* Am Chem Soc; Am Pharmaceut Asn. *Res:* Resistance factors of crops; pesticide residue analytical methods; pesticide metabolism; effect of pesticide residues on environment; retail pharmacy; pesticide formulation; quality control; production and contract manufacturing; residue chemistry. *Mailing Add:* 350 W Shuman Blvd Nor-Am Agr Prod Inc Naperville IL 60540

JENNY, ROBERT B, b Utica, NY, Nov 30, 23; m 50; c 4. AERODYNAMICS. *Educ:* Univ Detroit, BAeroE, 49. *Prof Exp:* Aeronaut engr, Douglas Aircraft Co, 49-57, proj aerodynamics eng, McDonnell Aircraft Co, 57-65, sect mgr, 65-70, BR MGR AERODYNAMICS, MCDONNELL AIRCRAFT CO, MCDONNELL DOUGLAS CORP, 70- *Mem:* Am Inst Aeronaut & Astronaut; Am Helicopter Soc. *Mailing Add:* McDonnell Aircraft Co PO Box 516 St Louis MO 63166

JENS, WAYNE H(ENRY), b Manitowoc, Wis, Dec 20, 21; m 46; c 4. MECHANICAL ENGINEERING, NUCLEAR ENGINEERING. *Educ:* Univ Wis, BS, 43; Purdue Univ, MS, 48, PhD(mech eng), 49. *Prof Exp:* Eng designer, NAm Aviation, Inc, 43-44; eng asst heat transfer, Purdue Univ, 46-49; head eng anal group, Argonne Nat Lab, 49-53; proj leader & mgr, Nuclear Develop Corp Am, 53-57; gen mgr, Atomic Power Develop Assocs, Inc, 57-71; mgr eng & construct, 76-78, asst vpres eng & construct, 78-80, VPRES NUCLEAR OPER, DETROIT EDISON CO, 80- *Concurrent Pos:* Mem bd trustees, Argonne Univ Asn, 77-; mem nuclear power div comn, Elec Power Res Inst, 78- *Honors & Awards:* Gold Award, Eng Soc of Detroit, 78. *Mem:* Fel Am Nuclear Soc; Am Soc Mech Engrs. *Res:* Boiling heat transfer; nuclear fuel irradiation stability; reactor design. *Mailing Add:* 1246 Balfour Rd Grosse Pointe Park MI 48230

JENSEN, ADOLPH ROBERT, b Elmhurst, Ill, Apr 14,15; m 50; c 2. ANALYTICAL CHEMISTRY. *Educ:* Wheaton Col, BS, 37; Univ Ill, MS, 40, PhD(anal chem), 42. *Prof Exp:* Asst chem, Wheaton Col, 37-38; asst anal chem, Univ Ill, 38-42; asst chemist & head anal chem sect, Aircraft Engine Res Lab, Nat Adv Comt Aeronaut, 42-46; from asst prof to assoc prof, 46-55, chmn dept, 56-71, PROF CHEM, BALDWIN-WALLACE COL, 55- *Mem:* AAAS; Am Chem Soc. *Res:* Analytical chemistry of foods; analytical chemistry of fuels and lubricants; instrumental methods of analysis. *Mailing Add:* Dept of Chem Baldwin-Wallace Col Berea OH 44017

JENSEN, ALBERT CHRISTIAN, b New York, NY, Jan 26, 24; m 47; c 3. FISHERY BIOLOGY, MARINE ENVIRONMENTAL SCIENCE. *Educ:* State Univ NY Syracuse, BS, 51, MS, 54. *Prof Exp:* Res biologist marine fisheries, US Fish & Wildlife Serv, Woods Hole, Mass, 54-65; managing ed marine sci, Marine Lab, Univ Miami, 65-67; asst dir coastal environ, NY State Dept Environ Conserv, 67-77; CONSULT COASTAL ENVIRON, ENVIRON ASSOCS, 77- *Concurrent Pos:* Adv, Atlantic States Marine Fisheries Comn, Washington, DC, 67-80 & US Deleg to Int Comn Northwest Atlantic Fisheries, 72-75; asst prof, Grad Dept Marine Sci, C W Post Col, 75-77; instr, Cent Fla Community Col, 78- *Mem:* Am Fisheries Soc; Am Inst Fishery Res Biologists; Gulf & Caribbean Fisheries Inst. *Res:* Marine science; coastal zone management; fisheries management. *Mailing Add:* Environ Assocs PO Box 223 Inglis FL 32649

JENSEN, ALDON HOMAN, b Massena, Iowa, Dec 20, 22; m 48; c 3. ANIMAL NUTRITION. *Educ:* Univ Ill, BS, 49, MS, 50; Iowa State Col, PhD, 53. *Prof Exp:* Asst, Iowa State Col, 52-54, asst prof, 54-60; from asst prof to assoc prof, 60-68, PROF ANIMAL SCI, UNIV ILL, URBANA, 68- *Mem:* Am Soc Animal Sci; Animal Nutrit Res Coun. *Res:* Animal physiology and environment. *Mailing Add:* Dept of Animal Sci Univ of Ill Urbana IL 61801

JENSEN, ANDREW O, b Delavan, Minn, Aug 3, 27; m 52; c 4. ELECTRICAL ENGINEERING, MATHEMATICS. *Educ:* Univ Minn, BSEE, 50, MSEE, 53, PhD(elec eng), 56. *Prof Exp:* Instr elec eng, Univ Minn, 53-56; res engr, Gen Elec Co, 56-61; mgr dept energy conversion, 61-63, mgr spec tube dept, 63-65, mgr lab electro-optical technol, 65-67, mgr div electro-optical & solid state, 67-69, vpres advan technol div, 69-73, vpres radiation systs div, Electro-Optical Systs, 73-76, vpres advan technol, 76-79, vpres corp prog, 79-82, VPRES CHEM SCI, XEROX CORP, 81- *Concurrent Pos:* Mem, President's Comn Energy Resources, 63-64. *Mem:* Inst Elec & Electronics Engrs. *Res:* Physical acoustics; gaseous electronics; physical electronics; thermionic energy conversion; light production research and development. *Mailing Add:* Electro-Optical Systs 300 N Halstead Pasadena CA 91107

JENSEN, ARNOLD WILLIAM, b Racine, Wis, Apr 30, 28; m 60. ORGANIC CHEMISTRY, POLYMER CHEMISTRY. *Educ:* Dana Col, Nebr, BA, 50; Okla State Col, PhD(chem), 58. *Prof Exp:* Res chemist, Dow Chem Co, Tex, 52-53; RES CHEMIST, TEXTILE FIBERS DEPT, E I DU PONT DE NEMOURS & CO, INC, 58- *Mem:* AAAS; Am Chem Soc. *Res:* Nuclear magnetic resonance; infrared; synthetic fibers. *Mailing Add:* Anal Res Textile Fibers Dept E I du Pont de Nemours & Co Inc Waynesboro VA 22980

JENSEN, ARTHUR SEIGFRIED, b Trenton, NJ, Dec 24, 17; m 41; c 3. ELECTRONIC PHYSICS. *Educ:* Univ Pa, BS, 38, MS, 39, PhD(physics), 41;. *Prof Exp:* Lab asst physics, Univ Pa, 38-39; res physicist, Naval Res Lab, Washington, DC, 41; res physicist labs, Radio Corp Am, 45-57; mgr spec electron devices, Electronic Tube Div, Appl Res Dept, Westinghouse Elec Corp, 57-65, sr adv physicist, 65-77; RETIRED. *Concurrent Pos:* Instr physics, US Naval Acad, 41-46. *Honors & Awards:* Westinghouse Spec Corp Patent Award, 72. *Mem:* AAAS; Am Phys Soc; Am Asn Physics Teachers; fel Inst Elec & Electronics Eng; Soc Photo-Optical Instrumentation Engrs. *Res:* Solid state electro-optical imaging systems; imaging techniques and sensing devices; image quality and information theory; noise and image sensor detection limitations; electron optics and integrated circuits; infrared image sensors and systems; modeling solid state devices. *Mailing Add:* Defense & Electronics Systs Ctr Westinghouse Elec Corp PO Box 1521 Baltimore MD 21203

JENSEN, BARBARA LYNNE, US citizen; c 2. PHYSICS, MATHEMATICS. *Educ:* Univ Utah, BS, 64; Columbia Univ, MA, 72, PhD(physics), 73. *Prof Exp:* Res assoc physics, IBM Thomas J Watson Res Ctr, Yorktown Heights, NY, 70-73; instr, Univ Lowell, 74-77; ASST PROF PHYSICS, BOSTON UNIV, 78- *Mem:* AAAS; Am Phys Soc; Optical Soc Am. *Res:* Solid state physics; condensed matter physics; plasma physics; interaction of radiation and matter; optical and electronic properties of semiconductors and metals at high frequencies. *Mailing Add:* Dept of Physics 111 Cummington St Boston MA 02215

JENSEN, BRUCE A, b Spencer, Iowa, Aug 6, 30; m 51; c 2. MATHEMATICS. *Educ:* Dana Col, BA, 52; Univ Wis-Madison, MS, 55; Univ Nebr-Lincoln, PhD(math), 66. *Prof Exp:* Instr math & physics, Dana Col, 55-58, asst prof math, 58-59; from asst prof to assoc prof, Nebr Wesleyan Univ, 59-66; assoc prof, 66-73, PROF MATH, PORTLAND STATE UNIV, 73- *Mem:* Am Math Soc; Math Asn Am. *Res:* Algebraic semigroups; finiteness conditions on infinite semigroups; extensions of semigroups; decompositions of semigroups. *Mailing Add:* Dept Math PO Box 751 Portland State Univ Portland OR 97207

JENSEN, BRUCE L, b Three Rivers, Mich, Aug 6, 44; m 65; c 2. ORGANIC CHEMISTRY. *Educ:* Western Mich Univ, BS, 66, PhD(org chem), 70. *Prof Exp:* Instr chem, Univ Maine, Orono, 72-73; Nat Cancer Inst fel, Univ Mich, Ann Arbor, 70-72; asst prof, 73-78, ASSOC PROF CHEM, UNIV MAINE, ORONO, 78- *Mem:* Am Chem Soc. *Res:* Organic synthesis; infrared, nuclear magnetic resonance and mass spectroscopy; heterocycles; natural products; medicinal chemistry; halonium ion chemistry; steroids; antineoplastic drugs; antiarrhythmic drugs. *Mailing Add:* 69 Webster Ave Bangor ME 04401

JENSEN, CHESTER E, b Detroit, Mich, Mar 31, 21; m 48; c 2. BIOMETRICS. *Educ:* Mich State Col, BS, 46, MF, 48. *Prof Exp:* Mensurationist, US Forest Serv, 48-54, silviculturist, 54-56, statistician, Cent States Forest Exp Sta, Ohio, 56-67, statistician, Northeast Forest Exp Sta, Pa, 67, math statistician, Inter-Mountain Forest & Range Exp Sta, Utah, 67-80; RETIRED. *Concurrent Pos:* Consult, Turkish Forest Res Inst, Ankara, 65. *Mem:* Soc Am Foresters; Am Statist Asn. *Mailing Add:* Intermt Forest & Range Exp Sta US Forest Serv 25th & Adams Ogden UT 84401

JENSEN, CLAYTON EVERETT, b Hartford, Conn, Oct 23, 20; m 77; c 3. METEOROLOGY, COMPUTER SCIENCE. *Educ:* Trinity Col, Conn, BS, 44; Mass Inst Technol, SM, 51, PhD(meteorol), 60. *Prof Exp:* Chief eval & develop div, Hq, Air Weather Serv, 51-53, detachment comdr & staff weather officer, Air Force Cambridge Res Labs, 56-58, meteorol systs analyst, Strategic Air Command, 60-63; assoc prof math & dir comput ctr, Va Mil Inst, 63-65; chief supporting res group, Off Fed Coord Meteorol, Environ Sci Serv Admin, 65-69, chief fed plans & coord div, 69-71, chief environ monitoring div, Nat Oceanic & Atmospheric Admin, 71-73, dep assoc adminr, 73-75; CONSULT & WEATHER ANALYST, WINK TV, CBS, FT MYERS, 78- & US DEPT STATE, 80- *Concurrent Pos:* Lectr, Univ Omaha, 60-63; consult, Nat Environ Satellite Ctr, 64-65; chmn, Interdept Comt Appl Meteorol Res, 65-73 & Interdept Comt Meteorol Serv; observer, Interdept Comt Atmospheric Sci, Fed Coun Sci & Technol; fed coordr meteorol, Dept Com, 73-75; govt & acad consult. *Mem:* Am Meteorol Soc; Sigma Xi. *Res:* General circulation of the atmospheres; cloud physics; instrumentation for atmospheric electricity and airborne measurement of liquid water; satellite meteorology; computer education; global environmental research. *Mailing Add:* 4419 SE 20th Pl Cape Coral FL 33904

JENSEN, CLYDE B, b Rigby, Idaho, Aug 14, 48; m 69; c 2. PHARMACOLOGY. *Educ:* Brigham Young Univ, BS, 70; Univ NDak, MS, 73, PhD(pharmacol), 74. *Prof Exp:* ASST PROF PHARMACOL, OKLA COL OSTEOP MED & SURG, 74-, ASST DEAN STUDENT AFFAIRS, 77- *Concurrent Pos:* Consult pharmacol, Nat Bd Examrs Osteop Physicians & Surgeons Inc, 75- *Mem:* Sigma Xi. *Res:* The effects of centrally-acting and ototoxic drugs on the vestibulo-ocular reflex arc. *Mailing Add:* Okla Col of Osteop Med & Surg 1111 W 17th St Tulsa OK 74101

JENSEN, CRAIG LEEBENS, b Rochester, Minn, Dec 8, 50. METALLURGY. *Educ:* Univ Minn, BS, 73; Iowa State Univ, PhD(metall), 77. *Prof Exp:* ASST PROF MAT SCI, UNIV MINN, 77- *Mem:* Am Soc Metals; Am Inst Mining, Metall & Petrol Engrs. *Res:* Transport properties of hydrogen in transition metals. *Mailing Add:* Dept of Chem Eng & Mat Sci 151 Chem Eng Univ of Minn Minneapolis MN 55455

JENSEN, CREIGHTON RANDALL, b Harlan, Iowa, Dec 27, 29; div. SOIL PHYSICS. *Educ:* Calif State Polytech Col, BS, 56; Iowa State Univ, MS, 59, PhD(agron), 61. *Prof Exp:* Res asst soil physics, Iowa State Univ, 56-61; soil physicist, Univ Calif, Riverside, 62-63 & 64-68; DIR, JENSEN INSTRUMENTS, 68- *Mem:* AAAS; Am Soc Agron; Soil Sci Soc Am. *Res:* Soil aeration. *Mailing Add:* 3612 Sixth Ave Tacoma WA 98406

JENSEN, CYNTHIA G, b Wheeling, WVa, Nov 7, 38; m 60; c 2. CELL BIOLOGY. *Educ:* Brown Univ, AB, 60; Univ Minn, PhD(zool), 66. *Prof Exp:* Res assoc biol, Univ Ore, 66-68; asst prof path, Univ Utah, 68-71; SR LECTR ANAT, SCH MED, UNIV AUCKLAND, 72- *Mem:* AAAS; Am Soc Cell Biol; Electron Micros Soc Am. *Res:* Ultrastructural studies of cell division and microtubule organization. *Mailing Add:* Dept Anat Sch Med Univ Auckland Auckland New Zealand

JENSEN, DAVID, b San Francisco, Calif, Oct 14, 26; m 50; c 2. MEDICAL PHYSIOLOGY. *Educ:* Univ Calif, Berkeley, BA, 48, MA, 50, PhD(physiol), 54. *Prof Exp:* Asst res physiol chemist, Sch Med, Univ Calif, Los Angeles & Vet Admin Hosp, 55-56, Am Heart Asn estab investr & res assoc, Scripps Inst, Univ Calif, 56-57; asst prof physiol, Med Ctr, Univ Colo, Denver, 67-71; SCI AUTHOR, 71- *Concurrent Pos:* Los Angeles Co Heart Asn estab investr, Univ Calif, Los Angeles, 55-56, Riverside Co Heart Asn fel, 56-58 & San Diego Co Heart Asn res fel, 58-60; Am Heart Asn advan res fel, Scripps Inst, Univ Calif, 60-62, estab investr, 62-67. *Mem:* AAAS; Soc Gen Physiol. *Res:* Basic mechanisms of cardiac automatism using electrophysiological techniques as well as biochemical approach; comparative physiological studies on a variety of species; intrinsic cardiac rate regulation; neuroanatomy; neurophysiology. *Mailing Add:* 1040 S Madison St Denver CO 80209

JENSEN, DAVID EDWARD, b Penn Yan, NY, June 25, 09; m 41. MINERALOGY. *Educ:* Cornell Univ, AB, 30; Univ Rochester, MS, 32. *Prof Exp:* Asst biologist, 31-34, asst mineralogist, 34-37, head mineral dept, 47-50, dir geol div, 50-74, secy, 62-70, vpres, 69-74, CONSULT, WARD'S NAT

SCI ESTAB, INC, 74- *Mem:* Fel Geol Soc Am; fel Mineral Soc Am; Mineral Asn Can; Mineral Soc Gt Brit & Ireland. *Res:* Minerals and mineral localities of New York State; geochemistry; audiovisual materials. *Mailing Add:* 199 E Brook Rd Pittsford NY 14534

JENSEN, DAVID JAMES, b Racine, Wis, May 10, 35; m 56; c 5. ANALYTICAL CHEMISTRY. *Educ:* Univ Wis-Milwaukee, BS, 58; Purdue Univ, MS, 65, PhD(biochem), 67. *Prof Exp:* Instr chem, Univ Wis-Milwaukee, 57-61; instr anal chem & state chemist of Ind, Purdue Univ, 61-67; RES CHEMIST ANAL CHEM, DOW CHEM USA, 67- *Mem:* Asn Off Anal Chemists; Am Chem Soc; Sigma Xi. *Res:* Studies on pesticide residues, herbicides, dioxin, fumigants and nitrogen conserver; analysis of pesticide formulations and associated analytical methods development. *Mailing Add:* 4553 S Saginaw Rd Midland MI 48640

JENSEN, DONALD RAY, b Nashville, Tenn, Apr 25, 32; m 64; c 3. MATHEMATICAL STATISTICS. *Educ:* Univ Tenn, BS, 55; Iowa State Univ, MS, 57, PhD(statist, soils), 62. *Prof Exp:* Asst prof statist, Ore State Univ, 62-65; from asst prof to assoc prof, 65-73, PROF STATIST, VA POLYTECH INST & STATE UNIV, 73- *Concurrent Pos:* NIH career develop award, 67-72. *Mem:* Biomet Soc; Am Statist Asn; Am Inst Math Statist; Soc Indust Appl Math; Math Asn Am. *Res:* Probability inequalities; multivariate statistical analysis; multivariate distributions; simultaneous statistical inference; large-sample theory. *Mailing Add:* Dept of Statist Va Polytech Inst & State Univ Blacksburg VA 24061

JENSEN, DONALD REED, b Pocatello, Idaho, May 4, 31; m 56; c 3. MAMMALIAN PHYSIOLOGY. *Educ:* Idaho State Univ, BS, 53; Univ Wash, BA, 54; Utah State Univ, MS, 61, PhD(physiol), 64. *Prof Exp:* NIH fel, Inst Physiol Chem, Univ Cologne, 64-66; asst prof, 66-69, asst to chmn dept biol sci, 68-78, ASSOC PROF PHYSIOL, ILL STATE UNIV, 69- *Mem:* Fel AAAS; Am Soc Zool; Sigma Xi. *Res:* Endocrinology of reproduction; biochemistry of sialic acids; toxic effect of gossypol on physiological processes; reproductive physiology of micropthalmic rats. *Mailing Add:* Dept of Biol Ill State Univ Normal IL 61761

JENSEN, DOUGLAS ANDREW, b Muskegon, Mich, Oct 18, 40; m 65; c 2. ELEMENTARY PARTICLE PHYSICS. *Educ:* Kalamazoo Col, AB, 63; Univ Chicago, MS, 65, PhD(physics), 70. *Prof Exp:* NSF fel, Joseph Henry Labs, Princeton Univ, 70-71; asst prof physics, 71-77; ASSOC PROF PHYSICS, UNIV MASS, AMHERST, 77- *Mem:* Am Asn Physics Teachers; Am Phys Soc. *Res:* Elementary particle physics; weak interaction and symmetries; hadron production of strange and charmed particles. *Mailing Add:* Dept of Physics & Astron Univ of Mass Amherst MA 01003

JENSEN, EDWIN HARRY, b Phillips, Wis, Aug 29, 22; m 47; c 2. AGRONOMY. *Educ:* Univ Wis, BS, 49, MS, 50, PhD(agron & soil), 52. *Prof Exp:* Soil scientist, Soil Conserv Serv, USDA, 48-49; asst agronomist & asst prof agron, Univ Nev, 52-54; exten agronomist, Univ Minn, 54-56; assoc agronomist & assoc prof agron, 56-64, PROF AGRON & AGRONOMIST, UNIV NEV, RENO, 64- *Mem:* Am Soc Agron; Crop Sci Soc; Sigma Xi. *Res:* Forage crop management; forage quality; grass seed production. *Mailing Add:* Div Plant Soil & Water Sci Univ of Nev Reno NV 89507

JENSEN, ELWOOD VERNON, b Fargo, NDak, Jan 13, 20; m 41; c 2. BIOCHEMISTRY. *Educ:* Wittenberg Col, AB, 40; Univ Chicago, PhD(org chem), 44. *Hon Degrees:* DSc, Wittenberg Univ, 63, Acadia Univ, 76. *Prof Exp:* Asst prof, Dept Surg, 47-51, from asst prof to assoc prof, Dept Biochem, 51-60, from asst prof to prof, Ben May Lab Cancer Res, 51-63, Am Cancer Soc-Charles Hayden Found res prof, Dept Physiol & Ben May Lab Cancer Res, 63-69, PROF BIOPHYS, UNIV CHICAGO, 73-, PROF PHYSIOL, 77-, PROF BIOCHEM & CHAS B HUGGINS DISTINGUISHED SERV PROF BIOL SCI, 80-, DIR, BEN MAY LAB CANCER RES, 69- *Concurrent Pos:* Guggenheim fel, Swiss Fed Inst Technol, 46-47; USPHS spec fel, 58; vis prof, Max Planck Inst, Munich, Ger, 58 & Kyoto Univ, 65. *Honors & Awards:* D R Edwards Medal, 70; La Madonnina Prize, 73; GHA Clowes Award, 75; Papanicolaou Award, 75; Prix Roussel, 76; Nat Award, Am Cancer Soc, 76; Amory Prize, 77; Gregory Pincus Mem Award, 78; Gairdner Award, 79; C F Kettering Prize, 80; Lucy Wortham James Award, 80; Nat Acad Clin Biochem Award, 81. *Mem:* Nat Acad Sci; Am Acad Arts & Sci; Am Chem Soc; Am Soc Biol Chemists; Endocrine Soc (pres, 80-81); Am Asn Cancer Res. *Res:* Steroid hormones; breast cancer; proteins; organophosphorus chemistry. *Mailing Add:* Ben May Lab for Cancer Res Univ of Chicago Chicago IL 60637

JENSEN, EMRON ALFRED, b Richfield, Utah, Jan 5, 25; m 49; c 8. PARASITOLOGY, PROTOZOOLOGY. *Educ:* Utah State Univ, BS, 50, MS, 61, PhD(zool), 63. *Prof Exp:* Teacher high sch, Idaho, 50-52; technician, Am Cyanamid Co, 52-53; teacher elem sch, Utah, 54-59; lab instr zool, Utah State Univ, 59-63; from asst prof to assoc prof, 63-70, PROF ZOOL & CHMN DEPT, WEBER STATE COL, 70- *Res:* Parasite protozoa, particularly trichomonads. *Mailing Add:* Dept of Zool Weber State Col Ogden UT 84408

JENSEN, ERIK HUGO, b Fredericia, Denmark, June 27, 24; nat US; m 49; c 3. PHARMACY. *Educ:* Royal Danish Sch Pharm, BSc, 45, MS, 48, PhD, 54. *Prof Exp:* Res assoc, Upjohn Co, 50-56; head pharmaceut res & develop dept, Ferrosan Inc, Malmo, Sweden, 56-57; res assoc pharm, 57-62; sect head qual control, 62-63, mgr, 63-66, asst dir qual control, 66-81, DIR, CONTROL DEVELOP & ADMIN, UPJOHN CO, 81- *Honors & Awards:* W E Upjohn Award, 62. *Mem:* Am Chem Soc; Am Pharmaceut Asn; Acad Pharmaceut Sci; Pharmaceut Mfr Asn. *Res:* Controlled release of pharmaceuticals; stability of pharmaceuticals; assays of pharmaceuticals; analytical applications of sodium borohydride; analytical chemistry; quality control procedures. *Mailing Add:* Control Div Upjohn Co Kalamazoo MI 49001

JENSEN, ERLING, b Petersburg, Alaska, Jan 9, 23; m 51. MICROBIOLOGY. *Educ:* State Col Wash, BS, 50; Cornell Univ, MS, 51, PhD(bact), 53. *Prof Exp:* Sr microbiologist, Smith Kline & French Labs, Pa, 53-62; head viral oncol dept, Chas Pfizer & Co, Inc, 62-70; mgr virol dept, Hazleton Labs, 70-71; SCI MGR WASHINGTON LAB, EG&G/MASON RES INST, 73- *Mem:* AAAS; Am Soc Microbiol; Soc Exp Biol & Med; Tissue Cult Asn; Environ Mutagen Soc. *Res:* Tissue culture; viral oncology; chemical carcinogenesis. *Mailing Add:* EG&G/Mason Res Inst 1530 E Jefferson St Rockville MD 20852

JENSEN, ERLING N, b Des Moines, Iowa, Sept 3, 08; m 36; c 4. NUCLEAR PHYSICS. *Educ:* Drake Univ, BA, 32; Columbia Univ, AM, 33; Iowa State Univ, PhD(physics), 47. *Hon Degrees:* LittD, Lafayette Col, 62; LLD, Drake Univ, Lehigh Univ & Muhlenberg Col, 69. *Prof Exp:* Teacher & prin, Pub Sch, Iowa, 34-35; prof sci, Grand View Col, 35-43; from asst prof to prof physics, Iowa State Univ, 43-61; pres, Muhlenberg Col, 61-69; prof, 69-73, EMER PROF PHYSICS, IOWA STATE UNIV, 73-; EMER PRES, MUHLENBERG COL, 69- *Concurrent Pos:* Assoc physicist, Inst Atomic Res, 48-56, sr physicist, 56-61. *Honors & Awards:* Double D Award, Drake Univ, 68. *Mem:* Fel Am Phys Soc; Am Asn Physics Teachers; Fedn Am Scientists; Sigma Xi. *Res:* Nuclear spectroscopy; determination of nuclear energy levels with magnetic spectrometers. *Mailing Add:* 2522 Pierce Ave Ames IA 50010

JENSEN, GARY LEE, b Hyrum, Utah, Sept 5, 33; m 58; c 5. EXPERIMENTAL NUCLEAR PHYSICS. *Educ:* Utah State Univ, BS, 58; Univ Mich, MS, 60, PhD(physics), 64. *Prof Exp:* Asst prof, 66-70, ASSOC PROF PHYSICS, BRIGHAM YOUNG UNIV, 70- *Mem:* Am Phys Soc. *Res:* Decay modes and branching ratios for the K-plus meson; low-energy nuclear physics; moderating lithium glass neutron detector development. *Mailing Add:* 57 S Eastwood Dr Orem UT 84057

JENSEN, GARY RICHARD, b Miles City, Mont, Mar 19, 41; m 65; c 3. DIFFERENTIAL GEOMETRY. *Educ:* Mass Inst Technol, BS, 63; Univ Calif, Berkeley, PhD(math), 68. *Prof Exp:* Asst prof math, Carnegie-Mellon Univ, 68-69; fel math, Washington Univ, St Louis, 69-70, asst prof, 70-75, assoc prof, 75-76; vis assoc prof math, Univ Calif, Berkeley, 76-77; ASSOC PROF MATH, WASHINGTON UNIV, ST LOUIS, 77- *Mem:* Am Math Soc; Math Asn Am. *Res:* Differential geometry, especially of submanifolds of homogeneous spaces. *Mailing Add:* Math Dept Box 1146 Wahington Univ St Louis MO 63130

JENSEN, GORDON D, b Seattle, Wash, Jan 28, 26; m 57; c 3. PEDIATRICS, PSYCHIATRY. *Educ:* Yale Univ, MD, 49. *Prof Exp:* Asst prof pediat, Sch Med, Univ Wash, 57-60; res asst prof psychiat, 61-62, asst psychiat, 62-65, from asst prof to assoc prof, 65-69; PROF PSYCHIAT & PEDIAT, SCH MED, UNIV CALIF, DAVIS, 69- *Concurrent Pos:* Mem core staff, Regional Primate Res Ctr, Univ Wash, 67-69; sr consult child psychiat, Sacramento Med Ctr, 69-74. *Mem:* Soc Biol Psychiat; Animal Behav Soc; Am Acad Pediat; Am Col Psychiat; Psychiat Res Soc. *Res:* Primate behavior; sexuality; aging. *Mailing Add:* Div of Ment Health Univ of Calif Sch Med Davis CA 95616

JENSEN, GORDON E(UGENE), chemical engineering, see previous edition

JENSEN, HANNE MARGRETE, b Copenhagen, Denmark, Dec 9, 35; US citizen; m 57; c 4. PRECANCER. *Educ:* Univ Wash, MD, 61; Am Bd Path, cert anatomic & clin path, 68, cert blood banking, 79. *Prof Exp:* Fel exp path, Dept Path, Sch Med, Univ Wash, 65-67; asst prof, 69-79, ASSOC PROF PATH, DEPT PATH, SCH MED, UNIV CALIF, DAVIS, 79- *Concurrent Pos:* Mem Treatment Comt, Breast Cancer Task Force, Nat Cncer Inst, 77-81, prin investr, Contract Breast Cancer Task Force, 78-81. *Mem:* Am Asn Blood Banks; AAAS; Am Soc Clin Pathologists; Int Acad Path. *Res:* Assessment of precancer of breast parenchyma, using assays for angiogenesis factor; assays of breast fluids for angiogenesis factor; prediction of high cancer risk; morphologic studies of precancer of the prostate gland. *Mailing Add:* Dept Path Sch Med Univ Calif Davis CA 95616

JENSEN, HARBO PETER, b Boston, Mass, Mar 27, 48. ORGANIC CHEMISTRY. *Educ:* Northeastern Univ, BA, 71; Mass Inst Technol, PhD(org chem), 74. *Prof Exp:* Tech aide, Polaroid Corp, 67-70; res chemist, Chevron Res Co, Standard Oil Co Calif, 74-78, proj supvr, Huntington Beach Co, 78-80; pres, Timoc, 75-80; govt affairs coordr, Chevron USA, 80-81, FOREIGN STAFF ADV, STANDARD OIL CO CALIF, 81- *Concurrent Pos:* Pres & chmn, Cal Bionics, 81- *Mem:* AAAS; Am Chem Soc; Sigma Xi; Contact Lens Mgrs Asn. *Res:* Petroleum science and synthetic fuels; polymer science, especially hydrophilic polymers for soft contact lenses. *Mailing Add:* Standard Oil Co Calif 225 Bush St San Francisco CA 94104

JENSEN, HAROLD JAMES, b Sunnyside, Wash, Sept 16, 21; m 46; c 3. NEMATOLOGY. *Educ:* Univ Calif, BS, 47, PhD(nematol), 50. *Prof Exp:* Instr & asst, 50-51, from asst prof to assoc prof & from asst nematologist to assoc nematologist, 51-65, PROF BOT & NEMATOLOGIST, ORE STATE UNIV, 65- *Concurrent Pos:* Consult, Hawaiian Sugar Planters Asn, 58. *Mem:* Am Phytopath Soc; Soc Nematol (vpres, 70-71, pres, 71-72). *Res:* Identification, symptomatology and pathology of plant diseases caused by nematodes; nematological control techniques, taxonomy, and teaching; relationships of nematodes with other plant pathogens. *Mailing Add:* Dept of Plant Path Ore State Univ Corvallis OR 97331

JENSEN, J(OHN) H(ENRY), JR, b Aurora, Ill, June 17, 16; m 48. CHEMICAL ENGINEERING. *Educ:* SDak Sch Mines & Tech, BS, 39; Iowa State Univ, MS, 42, PhD(chem eng), 48. *Prof Exp:* Instr, Iowa State Univ, 40-48; sr chem engr, Tenn Eastman Co, 48-81; RETIRED. *Mem:* Instrument Soc Am. *Res:* Production of acetic anhydride; application of a digital computer to a chemical manufacturing process; process control by analog instruments or by digital computer; analog computing; interactive computer graphics system. *Mailing Add:* 4560 Old Stage Rd Kingsport TN 37664

JENSEN, JAMES EJLER, b Neenah, Wis, Mar 12, 30; m 53; c 6. NUCLEAR ENGINEERING, MANAGEMENT. *Educ:* Univ Wis, BSChE, 53; Univ Pittsburgh, MBA, 61, PhD(finance, mgt), 65. *Prof Exp:* Engr chem processing, Hanford Atomic Prods, Gen Elec Co, 53-56; engr, Bettis Atomic Power Lab, 56-65, supvr mech design, 65-69, mgr, 69-75, mgr prog control & design integration, Clinch River Breeder Reactor Plant, Advan Reactors Div, Walts Mill, 75-77, MGR COMPONENT DEVELOP, WATER REACTORS DIVS, POWER SYSTS, WESTINGHOUSE ELEC CORP, 77- *Mem:* Am Inst Chem Engrs. *Res:* Economics of nuclear power generation; A Pricing Model for the Convertible Debenture. *Mailing Add:* Power Systs Westinghouse Elec Box 355 Pittsburgh PA 15230

JENSEN, JAMES LE ROY, b Hopkins, Minn, July 2, 15; m 40; c 5. CHEMISTRY. *Educ:* Univ Minn, BS, 37, MS, 38, PhD(agr biochem), 41. *Prof Exp:* Asst dir biol dept, Distillation Prod, Inc, NY, 42-45; sales rep, Nutrena Mills, Inc, Minn, 47-52, asst div mgr, Nebr, 52-54, div sales mgr, 54-55, qual control mgr, Minn, 56-59; gen mgr, Beebe Labs, Inc, 59-60; tech dir & div sales mgr, Ulmer Pharmacal Co, 60-70; dist sales mgr, Physicians & Hosp Supply Co, 70-74, sales mgr, 74-77; RETIRED. *Mem:* Fel Am Chem Soc; Sigma Xi. *Res:* Role of vitamins A, C and E in nutrition and physiology; pharmaceuticals and biologicals. *Mailing Add:* 4639 Williston Rd Minnetonka MN 55343

JENSEN, JAMES LESLIE, b Tulare, Calif, Oct 17, 39; m 60; c 2. PHYSICAL ORGANIC CHEMISTRY. *Educ:* Westmont Col, BA, 61; Univ Calif, Santa Barbara, MA, 63; Univ Wash, PhD(org chem), 67. *Prof Exp:* Instr chem, Westmont Col, 62-64; instr, Univ Wash, 68; from asst prof to assoc prof, 68-76, PROF CHEM, CALIF STATE UNIV, LONG BEACH, 76- *Concurrent Pos:* Calif State Col, Long Beach Found & Long Beach Heart Asn grants, 69-71; vis scientist biochem, Brandeis Univ, 74-75; NSF grant, 77-; vis prof chem, Univ Calif, Irvine, 81. *Mem:* AAAS; NY Acad Sci; Am Chem Soc; Royal Soc Chem. *Res:* Solution kinetics; deuterium isotope effects; acid catalysis; acidity functions; mechanisms of hydration and hydrolysis reactions; linear free energy relationships; analytical organic chemistry. *Mailing Add:* 3301 Huntley Dr Los Alamitos CA 90720

JENSEN, JENS TRYGVE, b Grimstad, Norway, Dec 29, 19; US citizen; m 49; c 2. RADIOCHEMISTRY. *Educ:* Wagner Col, BS, 43; Univ Minn, MA, 48; Columbia Univ, EdD, 53. *Prof Exp:* Res chemist & group leader, Kellex Corp, New York & Oak Ridge, 43-45; instr chem, Glendive Jr Col, Mont, 46-47; from instr to assoc prof, 47-58, chmn dept, 60-74, PROF CHEM, WAGNER COL, 58- *Concurrent Pos:* Lectr med physics, Teachers Col, Columbia Univ, 52-64. *Mem:* Am Chem Soc; fel Am Inst Chem. *Res:* Use of radioactive tracers in analytical chemistry; training nuclear medicine technologists. *Mailing Add:* Dept of Chem Wagner Col Staten Island NY 10301

JENSEN, JOERG, b Gottingen, Ger, Sept 10, 16; nat US; m 47; c 3. IMMUNOBIOLOGY, TRANSPLANTATION BIOLOGY. *Educ:* Univ Berlin, Lic, 40; Univ Gottingen, MD, 46, Dr habil, 50. *Prof Exp:* Asst prof microbiol, Univ Gottingen, 50-54;; from asst prof to assoc prof, Sch Med, Marquette Univ, 54-64; investr, Howard Hughes Med Inst, 64-66; assoc prof, 66-70, PROF MICROBIOL, SCH MED, UNIV MIAMI, 70- *Concurrent Pos:* Lederle med fac award, 58; consult immunol, Vet Admin Hosp, Miami, 69-; dir, Histocampatibility Testing Lab, Med Ctr, Univ Miami, & Vet Admin Hosp, Miami, 73- *Mem:* Am Soc Zoologists; Am Asn Immunol; Am Asn Histocompatibility Testing; NY Acad Sci; Transplantation Soc. *Res:* Antibody formation; complement components, their chemical nature, origin and biological function; transplantation immunology; chemotaxis of leucocytes; cytophilic and natural antibodies. *Mailing Add:* Univ of Miami Sch of Med PO Box 520875 Biscayne Annex Miami FL 33152

JENSEN, JOHN NEIL, b St George, Utah, Sept 29, 36; m 59; c 5. POPULATION GENETICS, MAMMALOGY. *Educ:* Univ Utah, BS, 64, MS, 65; Ariz State Univ, PhD(zool), 69. *Prof Exp:* Assoc prof, 70-77, PROF ZOOL, WEBER STATE COL, 77- *Mem:* Am Soc Mammal. *Res:* Population genetics and ecology of mammalian Peromyscus. *Mailing Add:* 5396 South 300 W Ogden UT 84403

JENSEN, KEITH EDWIN, b Council Grove, Kans, Sept 6, 24; m 43; c 4. CANCER. *Educ:* Univ Kans, AB, 48, MA, 49; Jefferson Med Col, PhD, 51. *Prof Exp:* Asst bacteriologist, State Bd Health, Kans, 49; asst instr, Univ Kans, 49; asst, Jefferson Med Col, 49-51; res assoc epidemiol, Univ Mich, 51-55, asst prof, 55-56; dir, Int Influenza Ctr, USPHS, 56-58; mgr Respiratory Dis Sect, 58-61, asst dir, Biol Res, 61-65; dir virol, 65-68, dir virol & oncol, Med Prod Res & Develop, 68-72, exec dir cancer res, 72-80, SR SCI ADV, PFIZER INC, 80- *Mem:* Am Soc Microbiol; Am Acad Microbiol; Am Asn Immunol. *Res:* Epidemiology and immunology of mycoplasmal and viral respiratory diseases; viral oncology; interferon inducers; tumor immunology; cancer chemotherapy; chemical carcinogenesis; antimicrobiols; immunotherapeutics; rheumatology. *Mailing Add:* Sr Sci Adv Cent Res Pfizer Inc Groton CT 06340

JENSEN, KEITH FRANK, b Fontanelle, Iowa, Apr 9, 38; m 60; c 3. FORESTRY. *Educ:* Iowa State Univ, BS, 60, PhD(plant physio physiol, silvicult), 63. *Prof Exp:* PLANT PHYSIOLOGIST, DIS DIV, US FOREST SERV, 63- *Concurrent Pos:* Res fel, Univ Wis, 73-74. *Mem:* Am Phytopath Soc; Sigma Xi. *Res:* Effect of air pollution and environmental stresses on growth and development of forest trees. *Mailing Add:* Forest Insect & Dis Lab PO Box 365 Delaware OH 43015

JENSEN, LAWRENCE CRAIG-WINSTON, b New York, NY, Oct 5, 36; m 60; c 2. PLANT ANATOMY, CYTOLOGY. *Educ:* Brown Univ, BA, 60; Univ Minn, MSc, 62, PhD(bot), 66. *Prof Exp:* NIH fel, 66-68; asst prof biol, Univ Utah, 68-72; MEM FAC DEPT BOT, UNIV AUCKLAND, 72- *Mem:* Bot Soc Am. *Res:* Ultrastructure of the mitotic spindle. *Mailing Add:* Dept of Bot Univ of Auckland Auckland New Zealand

JENSEN, LEO STANLEY, b Bellingham, Wash, Feb 28, 25; m 54; c 4. ANIMAL NUTRITION. *Educ:* Wash State Univ, BS, 49; Cornel Univ, PhD(animal nutrit), 54. *Prof Exp:* Jr poultry scientist, Wash State Univ, 49-51, from asst prof to prof poultry sci, 54-73, chmn grad prog nutrit, 70-73; PROF POULTRY SCI, UNIV GA, 73- *Concurrent Pos:* Oak Ridge Inst Nuclear Studies res partic, AEC, Univ Tenn, 64-65. *Honors & Awards:* AFMA Award, Poultry Sci Asn, 66; Merck Award, Poultry Sci Asn, 79. *Mem:* Poultry Sci Asn; Am Inst Nutrit; Soc Exp Biol & Med. *Res:* Vitamins, minerals, fatty acids and unidentified factors in poultry nutrition; nutritional factors affecting hepatic lipid accumulation; nutrition-endocrine interactions in avian species. *Mailing Add:* Dept of Poultry Sci Univ of Ga Athens GA 30602

JENSEN, LYLE HOWARD, b East Stanwood, Wash, Nov 24, 15; m 40; c 3. BIOPHYSICAL CHEMISTRY. *Educ:* Walla Walla Col, BA, 39; Univ Wash, PhD(phys chem), 43. *Prof Exp:* Res assoc, Univ Chicago, 43-44; assoc prof chem, Emmanuel Missionary Col, 44-46; res assoc, Ohio State Univ, 46-47; actg asst prof, 47-48, Anderson fel x-ray diffraction, 48-49, from instr to assoc prof anat, 49-61, PROF ANAT, UNIV WASH, 61- *Mem:* AAAS; Am Chem Soc; Am Crystallog Asn; Am Asn Anat. *Res:* Chemistry of heavy metals; low temperature thermodynamics of gases; molecular structure; x-ray diffraction studies of biologically important molecules. *Mailing Add:* Dept of Biol Structure Univ of Wash Seattle WA 98195

JENSEN, MARCUS MARTIN, b Mantua, Utah, May 26, 29; m 59; c 3. MEDICAL MICROBIOLOGY. *Educ:* Utah State Univ, BS, 52, MS, 54; Univ Calif, Los Angeles, PhD(med microbiol), 61. *Prof Exp:* Res virologist, Res Serv, Vet Admin Ctr, 61-63; asst prof med microbiol, Sch Med, Univ Calif, Los Angeles, 63-69; assoc prof, 69-78, PROF MICROBIOL, BRIGHAM YOUNG UNIV, 78- *Concurrent Pos:* Assoc mem, Brain Res Inst, Med Sch, Univ Calif, Los Angeles, 68-69; pres, Robbins Aseptic Air Systs Inc, Calif, 68-69 & Jensen Res Labs, Utah, 69- *Honors & Awards:* George N Raines Award, Am Psychiat Asn, 62. *Mem:* AAAS; Am Soc Microbiol; Am Asn Avian Pathologists. *Res:* Natural resistance to infectious diseases, influence of emotional stress on suscepsusceptibility to viral infections; role of viruses in kidney diseases; methods of controlling the airborne spread of microorganisms in hospitals; development of vaccines for turkey diseases. *Mailing Add:* Dept of Microbiol Brigham Young Univ Provo UT 84602

JENSEN, MARVIN E(LI), b Clay Co, Minn, Dec 23, 26; m 47; c 3. AGRICULTURAL ENGINEERING. *Educ:* NDak State Univ, BS, 51, MS, 52; Colo State Univ, PhD, 65. *Prof Exp:* Asst, NDak State Univ, 51-52, instr & asst agr engr, 52-54, asst prof agr eng & asst agr engr, 54-55; agr eng, 55-59, invests leader irrig, drainage & water storage facil, 59-61, invests leader water mgt, Northwest Br, 61-69, dir, Snake River Conserv Res Ctr, Sci & Educ Admin, 69-79, NAT RES PROG LEADER, WATER MGT, AGR RES SERV, USDA, 79- *Concurrent Pos:* Mem, Int Comn Irrig & Drainage. *Honors & Awards:* Huber Res Prize, Am Soc Civil Engrs, 68; Hancor Soil & Water Eng Award, Am Soc Agr Engrs, 74. *Mem:* Am Soc Agr Engrs; Soil Sci Soc Am; Am Soc Civil Engrs; AAAS; Soil Conserv Soc Am. *Res:* Irrigation engineering research. *Mailing Add:* Drake Exec Plaza 2625 Redwing Rd Suite 130 Ft Collins CO 80526

JENSEN, MEAD LEROY, b Salt Lake City, Utah, June 11, 25; m 47; c 5. ECONOMIC GEOLOGY. *Educ:* Univ Utah, BS, 48; Mass Inst Technol, PhD(geol), 51. *Prof Exp:* From instr to assoc prof geol, Yale Univ, 51-64, dir grad studies, 64-65; PROF GEOL, UNIV UTAH, 65- *Mem:* Fel Geol Soc Am; Am Inst Mining, Metall & Petrol Eng; Am Geophys Union; Soc Petrol Eng; Mineral Soc Am. *Res:* Isotopic and economic geology, metallic, nonmetallic and petroleum; exploration geology. *Mailing Add:* Dept of Geol & Geophys Sci Univ of Utah Salt Lake City UT 84112

JENSEN, OTTO GERHARD, b Rushford, Minn, June 22, 05; m 35; c 2. CHEMISTRY. *Educ:* St Olaf Col, AB, 27; Pa State Col, MS, 29; Univ Minn, PhD(biochem), 31. *Prof Exp:* Asst, Pa State Col, 27-29; asst, Univ Minn, 29-31; res chemist, Gen Foods Corp, Mich, 32-37; res chemist, Borden Co, NY, 37-43; phys chemist, Boyce Thompson Inst, 43-46; res chemist, Bowey's, Inc, Ill, 46-52; head prod & processes res div, Nat Biscuit Co, New York, 52-70; CONSULT, 70- *Mem:* Am Chem Soc; Am Asn Cereal Chem. *Res:* Streaming potentials; gelatin; dairy chemistry; chocolate products; Irish moss; cereal chemistry. *Mailing Add:* 111 E Allendale Ave Saddle River NJ 07458

JENSEN, PAUL, population ecology, see previous edition

JENSEN, PAUL ALLEN, b Chicago, Ill, Aug 27, 36; m 63; c 3. OPERATIONS RESEARCH, ELECTRICAL ENGINEERING. *Educ:* Univ Ill, BS, 59; Univ Pittsburgh, MS, 63; Johns Hopkins Univ, PhD(opers res), 67. *Prof Exp:* Engr, Surface Div, Westinghouse Elec Corp, 59-63; from asst prof to assoc prof, 67-73, PROF OPERS RES, UNIV TEX, AUSTIN, 73- *Mem:* Opers Res Soc Am; Inst Mgt Sci. *Res:* Mathematical optimization theory and application; network flow techniques used for optimization; reliability engineering; transportation systems; water resources. *Mailing Add:* Dept of Mech Eng Univ of Tex Austin TX 78712

JENSEN, PAUL EDWARD T, b New Orleans, La, Apr 27, 26; m 53; c 3. SYSTEMS ANALYSIS, OPERATIONS RESEARCH. *Educ:* Tulane Univ, BS, 47, BBA, 49; Golden Gate Univ, MBA, 75. *Prof Exp:* Asst mgr, Atlantic Gulf Sugar Co, Cuba, 52-55; sr engr, 55-59, develop engr, 59-60, supvr tech pub, 60-63, mgr tech pub, 63-64, eng specialist, 64-76, SR ENG SPECIALIST, ELECTRONIC DEFENSE LABS, GTE PROD CORP, 76- *Concurrent Pos:* Consult, Asn Continuing Educ, Stanford, Calif, 74-, Stanford Univ, 77- & GTE Prod Corp, 80-; instr, Cogswell Col, San Francisco, 79- *Mem:* Am Phys Soc; Inst Elec & Electronics Engrs; Soc Tech Commun. *Res:* Systems analysis of tactical and strategic communications and electronics systems; electronic warfare vulnerability analysis. *Mailing Add:* GTE-Sylvania Inc PO Box 205 Mountain View CA 94042

JENSEN, PHILIP WRIGHT, b Hollister, Calif, Dec 10, 27; m 51; c 3. ANALYTICAL CHEMISTRY. Educ: San Francisco State Col, AB, 50; Univ Wash, MS, 52. Prof Exp: Res chemist, Yerkes Res Lab, Deepwater, NJ, 53-67, res chemist org chem dept, Jackson Lab, 67-71, res chemist, Gen Anal Lab, 71-76, SR CHEMIST, ANTIOCH WORKS, E I DU PONT DE NEMOURS & CO, 76- Res: Bromate reactions; analytical methods for polymers. Mailing Add: 1112 Granada Ct Antioch CA 94509

JENSEN, RANDOLPH A(UGUST), b Lyon Co, Minn, May 25, 19; m 42; c 3. CHEMICAL ENGINEERING, POLLUTION CONTROL. Educ: Univ Minn, BChE, 40; Univ Iowa, MSChE, 46. Prof Exp: Res chem engr, Cliffs Dow Chem Co, Mich, 40-42; proj engr, eng exp sta, Pa State Col, 42-43; res assoc, Inst Hydrol Res, Univ Iowa, 43-46; proj engr, US Govt Synthetic Rubber Labs, Ohio, 46-47; res engr, Battelle Mem Inst, 47-51; chem engr, Houston Plant, Rohm & Haas Ky Inc, 51-62, chief chem engr, Louisville Plant, 62-71, pollution control engr, 71-79; PRES, JENSEN CONSULT INC, 79- Concurrent Pos: Mem, Nat Adv Comt Aeronaut, 42-43. Mem: Am Inst Chem Engrs; Air Pollution Control Asn; Water Pollution Control Asn. Res: Fluid flow low and high velocity gas streams; chemical plant process improvement; air and water pollution control; solid waste disposal; numerous publications on air and water pollution control, electropolishing, heat transfer and crystallization. Mailing Add: Jensen Consult Inc PO Box 43079 Louisville KY 40243

JENSEN, REED JERRY, b Dec 16, 36; m 60; c 6. PHYSICAL CHEMISTRY. Educ: Brigham Young Univ, BA, 60, PhD(phys chem), 65. Prof Exp: Fel phys chem, Univ Calif, Berkeley, 65-66; staff mem, Los Alamos Sci Lab, 66-67; asst prof, Brigham Young Univ, 67-69; staff mem phys chem, 69-72, group leader chem lasers, 72-76, ALT DIV LEADER LASER CHEM, LOS ALAMOS NAT LAB, 76- Mem: Am Chem Soc. Mailing Add: Los Alamos Nat Lab PO Box 1663 Los Alamos NM 87545

JENSEN, RICHARD ARTHUR, b Ogden, Utah, Oct 24, 36. PHARMACOLOGY. Educ: Univ Ore, BS, 60; Univ Wash, MS, 63, PhD(pharmacol), 66. Prof Exp: Fel, Univ Calif, San Francisco, 66-68, asst prof pharmacol, 69-74; sr pharmacologist, 74-78, DIR CARDIOVASC PHARMACOL PROG, STANFORD RES INST, 78- Mem: Am Soc Pharmacol & Exp Therapeut. Res: Evaluation of the effects of drugs and other chemicals on cardiac electrical and mechanical activity; antiarrhythmic drug action, the electrophysiological action of drugs that induce cardiac arrhythmias; drug induced cardiac muscle dis; hemodynamic studies in conscious dogs using biotelemetry. Mailing Add: Stanford Res Inst Menlo Park CA 94025

JENSEN, RICHARD DONALD, b Hartington, Nebr, Oct 6, 36; m 57; c 4. VETERINARY PATHOLOGY. Educ: Iowa State Univ, DVM, 64; Univ Minn, St Paul, PhD(vet path), 70. Prof Exp: Res fel path, 70-76, DIR TOXICOL & PATH, MERCK INST THERAPEUT RES, MERCK & CO, INC, 77- Mem: Am Col Vet Path; Int Acad Path; Am Vet Med Asn. Res: Avian mycoplasma infection; toxicologic and pathologic evaluation of potential therapeutic agents. Mailing Add: 463 Ferry Rd Doylestorm PA 18901

JENSEN, RICHARD ERLING, b Des Moines, Iowa, Apr 3, 38; m 60; c 2. ANALYTICAL CHEMISTRY. Educ: Iowa State Univ, BS, 60; Univ Iowa, MS, 64, PhD(anal chem), 65. Prof Exp: Asst prof anal chem, Mankato State Col, 65-66; asst prof, 66-71, ASSOC PROF ANAL CHEM, GUSTAVUS ADOLPHUS COL, 71- Mem: Am Chem Soc. Res: Synthesis and development of organic analytical reagents; trace analysis of metals using spectrophotometry, fluorescence and atomic absorption. Mailing Add: Dept of Chem Gustavus Adolphus Col St Peter MN 56082

JENSEN, RICHARD EUGENE, b Unity, Sask, June 30, 27; US citizen; m 63. PHYSICS. Educ: Univ Sask, BS, 49, MS, 52; Ariz State Univ, PhD(physics), 66. Prof Exp: Proj engr physics, Motorola Inc, 56-59 & Nuclear Corp Am, 59-63; RES PHYSICIST, NAVAL SURFACE WEAPONS CTR, 67- Mem: Am Phys Soc; Optical Soc Am; Inst Elec & Electronics Engrs. Res: Lasers and optical propagation. Mailing Add: Naval Surface Weapons Ctr Silver Spring MD 20910

JENSEN, RICHARD GRANT, b Los Angeles, Calif, Apr 16, 36; m 61; c 4. BIOCHEMISTRY. Educ: Brigham Young Univ, BA, 61, PhD(biochem), 65. Prof Exp: Chas F Kettering res fel biochem, Chas F Kettering Res Lab, Ohio, 63-65; NIH fel, Lawrence Radiation Lab, Univ Calif, 65-67; from asst prof to assoc prof biochem, 67-79, assoc prof plant sci, 76-79, PROF BIOCHEM & PLANT SCI, UNIV ARIZ, 79- Concurrent Pos: Vis prof, Chem Inst Tech Univ Munich, Freising-Weihens Tephan, West Ger, 74-75; vis prof, Bot Inst, Univ Brone, Switz, 75; consult, Agr Div, Monsanto Co, 76; prog dir, Photosynthesis Prog, Competitive Res Grants Off, Sci & Educ Admin, US Dept Agr, 81. Mem: Am Soc Biol Chemists; Am Chem Soc; Am Soc Plant Physiol; fel AAAS. Res: Cell biology and metabolism; photosynthesis; metabolic regulation in plant cells; carbon dioxide fixation. Mailing Add: Dept of Biochem Univ of Ariz Tucson AZ 85721

JENSEN, RICHARD HARVEY, b Estherville, Iowa, June 14, 41; m; c 2. ANATOMY, IMMUNOLOGY. Educ: Univ Northern Iowa, BA, 63; Univ Iowa, MA, 69, PhD(anat), 73. Prof Exp: Instr math & sci, Charles City High Sch, Iowa, 63-66; clin phys therapist, Univ Iowa, 67-68, from teaching asst to instr gross anat, 69-73; grant seed res, Univ Nebr Med Ctr, Omaha, 73-75, asst prof gross anat, 73-77; MEM STAFF PROG PHYS THER, MARQUETTE UNIV, 77- Concurrent Pos: Vis instr gross anat, Univ Miami, 72; consult design & orgn gross anat prog phys ther, Fla Int Univ, 73. Mem: Am Phys Ther Asn; Am Asn Anatomists; Am Col Sports Med. Res: Hematology, especially stimulation of bone marrow; biomechanics, with emphasis on kinetic and kinematic analysis of extremities. Mailing Add: Phys Ther Prog Marquette Univ Milwaukee WI 53233

JENSEN, RICHARD JORG, b Erie Co, Ohio, Jan 17, 47; m 70. SYSTEMATIC BOTANY, PLANT ECOLOGY. Educ: Austin Peay State Univ, BS, 70, MS, 72; Miami Univ, PhD(bot), 75. Prof Exp: Asst prof biol, Wright State Univ, 75-80; MEM FAC BIOL, ST MARYS COL, 80- Concurrent Pos: NSF res grant, 73 & 78; Sigma Xi grant in aid of res, 74. Mem: Torrey Bot Club; Int Asn Plant Taxon; Bot Soc Am; Sigma Xi; Am Soc Plant Taxonomists. Res: Systematic and ecological studies of Quercus subgenus Erythrobalanus, or red oaks, emphasizing numerical analyses of hybrid-containing populations. Mailing Add: Dept Biol St Marys Col Notre Dame IN 46556

JENSEN, ROBERT ALAN, b Bainbridge, NY, Sept 25, 40. NEUROBIOLOGY, PSYCHOBIOLOGY. Educ: Col Wooster, Ohio, BA, 65; Kent State Univ, MA, 70; Northern Ill Univ, PhD(biopsychol), 76. Prof Exp: Instr psychol, Kent State Univ, 68-71; asst res psychobiologist, Univ Calif, Irvine, 76-81; ASST PROF, DEPT PSYCHOL, SOUTHERN ILL UNIV, CARBONDALE, 81- Concurrent Pos: Fel, Univ Calif, Irvine, 75-78; managing ed, Behav & Neural Biol, 78-81. Mem: AAAS; NY Acad Sci; Soc Neurosci; Sigma Xi. Res: Neurobiological aspects of memory modulation; physiological basis of memory deficits seen in aged animals; the role of catecholamine and opioid systems in the control of learning and memory processes. Mailing Add: Dept Psychol Southern Ill Univ Carbondale IL 62901

JENSEN, ROBERT GORDON, b Carthage, Mo, Jan 2, 26; m 47; c 2. BIOCHEMISTRY. Educ: Univ Mo, BS, 50, MS, 51, PhD(dairy bact), 54. Prof Exp: From instr to asst prof dairy bact, Univ Mo, 54-56; asst prof, 56-66, prof dairy mfg, 66-70, PROF NUTRIT SCI, UNIV CONN, 70- Mem: AAAS; Am Oil Chem Soc; Am Dairy Sci Asn; Am Inst Nutrit; Am Chem Soc. Res: Lipases, human milk lipids. Mailing Add: Dept of Nutrit Sci Univ of Conn Storrs CT 06268

JENSEN, RONALD HARRY, b Chicago, Ill, Nov 25, 38; m 58; c 3. BIOPHYSICAL CHEMISTRY, CYTOCHEMISTRY. Educ: Lawrence Col, BS, 60; Calif Inst Technol, PhD(chem), 64. Prof Exp: Res fel biol, Calif Inst Technol, 64-67; res scientist molecular biol, Int Minerals & Chem Corp, 67-69; sr investr microbiol, Smith Kline & French Labs, 70-74; life scientist biol & med, 75-79, SECT LEADER CYTOCHEMISTRY, LAWRENCE LIVERMORE NAT LAB, 79- Res: Fluorescent probes of cellular structure and the use of flow and image cytometry of stained cells or chromosomes to study mutagenisis and carcinogenisis. Mailing Add: Biomed Div Lawrence Livermore Nat Lab PO Box 5507 Livermore CA 94550

JENSEN, ROY A, b Racine, Wis, Apr 8, 36; m 56; c 5. MICROBIOLOGY, BIOCHEMISTRY. Educ: Ripon Col, BA, 58; Univ Tex M D Anderson Hosp & Tumor Inst, PhD(biochem, genetics), 63. Prof Exp: Res instr, Sch Med, Univ Wash, 65; asst prof biol, State Univ NY Buffalo, 66-68; assoc prof microbiol, Baylor Col Med, 68-73; prof biol, Univ Tex M D Anderson Hosp & Tumor Inst Houston, 73-76; PROF BIOL, STATE UNIV NY BINGHAMTON, 76-, DIR CTR SOMATIC-CELL GENETICS & BIOCHEM, 78- Concurrent Pos: USPHS fel microbiol, Sch Med, Univ Wash, 64-66. Mem: Am Soc Microbiol; Tissue Cult Asn. Res: Biochemical genetics; gene-enzyme relationships; regulation of gene and enzyme activities; metabolic interlock; plant tissue culture. Mailing Add: Dept of Biol State Univ NY Binghamton NY 13901

JENSEN, RUE, b Vermillion, Utah, Oct 24, 11; m 42; c 2. VETERINARY PATHOLOGY. Educ: Utah State Univ, BS, 37, MS, 39; Colo State Univ, DVM, 42; Univ Minn, PhD, 53; Kasetsart Univ, Bangkok, DVSc, 65. Prof Exp: Instr vet sci, La State Univ, 42-43; from asst prof to assoc prof, 43-48, PROF PATH, COLO STATE UNIV, 48-, DIR DIAG LAB, 73- Concurrent Pos: From asst pathologist exp sta to pathologist exp sta, Colo State Univ, 43-57, chief animal dis sect & dean col vet med & biomed sci, 57-66, dir exp sta, 66-69, vpres res, 66-73; consult, USDA, 57-, Agency Int Develop, Univ Teheran, 62 & Kasetsart Univ, Bangkok, 64; USDA del, USSR, 58; mem, Agr Res Inst; consult pathologist, Monfort Colo, Inc, 77- & Univ Wyo, 78- Mem: Soc Exp Biol & Med; Am Vet Med Asn; Am Col Vet Path; Int Acad Path. Res: Necrobacillosis of cattle; vibriosis of sheep; diseases of feedlot cattle; diseases of sheep. Mailing Add: Diag Lab Colo State Univ Ft Collins CO 80521

JENSEN, STANLEY GEORGE, b Homer, Nebr, Sept 22, 34; m 58; c 3. PLANT PATHOLOGY. Educ: Univ Nebr, BS, 57, PhD(bot), 62. Prof Exp: PLANT PATHOLOGIST, UNIV NEBR, AGR RES SERV, USDA, 62- Mem: Am Phytopath Soc. Res: Diseases of sorghum; pathophysiology. Mailing Add: 406 M Plant Sci Bldg Univ Nebr Lincoln NE 68583

JENSEN, THOMAS E, b Waverly, Iowa, Sept 21, 32; m 56; c 2. CELL BIOLOGY. Educ: Wartburg Col, BA, 58; SDak State Univ, MA, 62; Iowa State Univ, PhD(cytol), 65. Prof Exp: Res assoc, Iowa State Univ, 64-65; asst prof biol, Wayne State Univ, 65-70; assoc prof, 70-72, PROF BIOL, LEHMAN COL, 73- Mem: AAAS; Electron Micros Soc Am; Am Soc Cell Biol; Bot Soc Am. Res: Ultrastructure of cells. Mailing Add: Dept of Biol Sci Lehman Col City Univ New York Bronx NY 10468

JENSEN, THORKIL, b Vejle, Denmark, Jan 23, 19; nat US; m 43; c 1. MICROBIOLOGY. Educ: Gustavus Adolphus Col, BA, 41; Univ Minn, MS, 49, PhD(zool), 52. Prof Exp: Instr embryol & histol, Vet Sch, Univ Minn, 51-52; from asst prof to assoc prof, 52-63, PROF MICROBIOL, SCH MED, UNIV KANS, 63- Concurrent Pos: China Med Bd fel, 55; consult, St Mary's Hosp, Kansas City, 53-58, Vct Admin Hosp, Mo, 54-61, Midwest Res Inst, 61-63 & Baptist Mem Hosp, Kansas City, 65- Mem: Am Soc Parasitol; Am Trop Med & Hyg. Res: In vitro culture of some parasitic protozoa and helminths; possible host-parasite relationships between viruses and protozoa and helminths; biochemistry of excystation in acanthamoeba. Mailing Add: 7029 Glenwood Ave Overland Park KS 66204

JENSEN, TIMOTHY B(ERG), b Willmar, Minn, Oct 25, 39; m 61; c 2. CHEMICAL ENGINEERING. *Educ:* Univ Minn, Minneapolis, BS, 61; Princeton Univ, PhD(chem eng), 65. *Prof Exp:* Sr chem engr, 64-68, res supvr, 68-73, res mgr, 73-74, TECH MGR, MINN MINING & MFG CO, 74- *Mem:* Am Soc Testing & Mat; Am Inst Chem Engrs. *Res:* Optimal control theory; reactor design; urethane chemistry; oriented polyester; packaging products. *Mailing Add:* 2011 W 67th St Minneapolis MN 55423

JENSEN, TORKIL HESSELBERG, b Kolding, Denmark, Apr 9, 32; m 56; c 3. PLASMA PHYSICS. *Educ:* Tech Univ Denmark, MS, 56. *Prof Exp:* Staff mem reactor & plasma physics, Danish Atomic Energy Comn, 56-60; MEM STAFF PLASMA PHYSICS, GULF GEN ATOMIC CO, 64- *Mem:* Am Phys Soc. *Res:* Experimental plasma physics. *Mailing Add:* Gen Atomic Co PO Box 81608 San Diego CA 92138

JENSEN, VARON, plant physiology, see previous edition

JENSEN, WALLACE NORUP, b Moroni, Utah, Aug 31, 21; m 47; c 3. HEMATOLOGY. *Educ:* Univ Utah, BS, 42, MD, 45; Am Bd Internal Med, dipl. *Prof Exp:* Intern med, Johns Hopkins Hosp, 45-46; asst resident, Univ Utah Hosps, 48-49, resident, 49-50; fel hemat, Univ Utah, 50-52, sr Damon Runyon fel med, Med, Ctr, 50-53; asst prof med, Sch Med, Duke Univ, 53-55; asst prof to prof Univ Pittsburgh, 58-67, prof med & chmn dept, head div hemat, 55-69; prof med & chmn dept, Sch Med, George Washington Univ, 69-76, Eugene Meyer prof med, 71-75; PROG CHMN, DEPT MED, ALBANY MED COL, 76- *Concurrent Pos:* Chief hemat sect, Vet Admin Hosp, Durham, 53-55; mem study sect hemat, NIH, 57-61; mem study sect, Grad Training Grants Hemat, USPHS, 62-66; NIH spec fel, Nat Transfusion Ctr & Sch Advan Studies, France, 63-64; mem bd exam, Am Bd Internal Med, 70-78; nat consult internal med-hemat, Off Surg Gen, 70-; Asn Prof Med, Liaison Comt, NIH, 71. *Mem:* Am Soc Hemat; Am Col Physicians; Am Fedn Clin Res; Soc Nuclear Med; Int Soc Hemat. *Res:* Medicine. *Mailing Add:* Dept of Med Albany Med Col 47 New Scotland Ave Albany NY 12208

JENSEN, WAYNE IVAN, b Taylor, Nebr, Mar 24, 14; m 44; c 2. VETERINARY MICROBIOLOGY, WILDLIFE DISEASES. *Educ:* Univ Nebr, BA, 41; Cornell Univ, DVM, 49, MS, 52; Am Col Vet Microbiol, dipl. *Prof Exp:* Res asst microbiol, Johns Hopkins Univ, 49-52, res assoc, 52-54; bacteriologist, Denver Wildlife Res Ctr, US Bur Sport Fisheries & Wildlife, 55-63, chief sect wildlife dis res, 63-69, MICROBIOLOGIST IN CHARGE, BEAR RIVER RES STA, US FISH & WILDLIFE SERV, 70- *Honors & Awards:* Meritorius Serv Award, US Dept Interior, 78. *Mem:* AAAS; Am Vet Med Asn; Wildlife Dis Asn; Am Soc Microbiol. *Res:* Avian botulism; avian cholera; Pasteurella and similar infections in wild birds and mammals. *Mailing Add:* Bear River Res Sta PO Box 459 Brigham City UT 84302

JENSEN, WILLIAM AUGUST, b Chicago, Ill, Aug 22, 27; m 48; c 2. BOTANY. *Educ:* Univ Chicago, PhB, 49, MS, 50, PhD(bot), 53. *Prof Exp:* USPHS fel, Calif Inst Technol, 53-55; NSF fel, Univ Brussels, 55-56; asst prof biol, Univ Va, 56-57; asst prof, 57-59, assoc prof, 59-61, chmn dept, 71-73, PROF BOT, UNIV CALIF, BERKELEY, 61-, CHMN DEPT, 74- *Concurrent Pos:* Prog dir develop biol, NSF, 73-74. *Mem:* Bot Soc Am (vpres, 75-76); Am Soc Cell Biol; Soc Study Develop Biol (secy, 62-64). *Res:* Botanical histochemistry; botanical cytology; plant embryology. *Mailing Add:* Dept of Bot Univ of Calif Berkeley CA 94720

JENSEN, WILLIAM PHELPS, b Minneapolis, Minn, May 22, 37; m 62; c 3. CHEMISTRY. *Educ:* Univ Minn, BS, 59; Univ Iowa, MS, 62, PhD(inorg chem), 64. *Prof Exp:* Res chemist, Pittsburgh Plate Glass Co, 63-66; vis asst prof, La State Univ, 66-67; assoc prof, 67-77, PROF CHEM, SDAK STATE UNIV, 77- *Mem:* Am Chem Soc. *Res:* Chemistry of lanthanide and actinide elements; structure determination of complex compounds by x-ray diffraction. *Mailing Add:* Dept of Chem SDak State Univ Brookings SD 57007

JENSH, RONALD PAUL, b New York, NY, June 14, 38; m 62; c 2. EXPERIMENTAL EMBRYOLOGY, BEHAVIORAL TERATOLOGY. *Educ:* Bucknell Univ, BA, 60, MA, 62; Jefferson Med Col, PhD(anat), 66. *Prof Exp:* Instr anat & res assoc radiol, 66-68, asst prof radiol & anat, 68-74, ASSOC PROF RADIOL & ANAT, JEFFERSON MED COL & THOMAS JEFFERSON UNIV, 74- *Concurrent Pos:* Investr, NIH grants, Stein Res Ctr & Dept Anat, Jefferson Med Col, 66- *Mem:* AAAS; Am Asn Anat; Teratology Soc; NY Acad Sci. *Res:* Teratology; embryology, statistical applications; behavioral toxicology; reproductive biology, developmental biology and radiobiology. *Mailing Add:* Dept Anat 561 JAH Thomas Jefferson Univ Philadelphia PA 19107

JENSSEN, THOMAS ALAN, b South Bend, Ind, Mar 18, 39; m 62; c 3. ANIMAL BEHAVIOR, ECOLOGY. *Educ:* Univ Redlands, BS, 62; Southern Ill Univ, MA, 64; Univ Okla, PhD(zool), 69. *Prof Exp:* Nat Inst Ment Health assoc herpet, Harvard Univ, 69-71; asst prof, 71-77, ASSOC PROF BIOL, VA POLYTECH INST & STATE UNIV, 77- *Concurrent Pos:* Res asst, Med Ctr, Univ Okla, 69-70. *Mem:* AAAS; Am Soc Ichthyol & Herpet; Animal Behav Soc; Ecol Soc Am; Soc Study Amphibians & Reptiles. *Res:* Behavior and ecology of various species of anurans and lizards, especially communicative value of anoline lizard displays. *Mailing Add:* Dept of Biol Va Polytech Inst & State Univ Blacksburg VA 24061

JENTGEN, RICHARD LOUIS, b Columbus, Ohio, Dec 9, 27; m 53; c 5. RESEARCH MANAGEMENT. *Educ:* Ohio State Univ, BA, 49. *Prof Exp:* Chemist, Ariz Portland Cement Co, 49-50; prin chemist, 53-61, sr res chemist, 61-65, proj leader, 65-67, assoc chief struct & lubrication physics div & appl physics div, 67-69, CHIEF LUBRICATION ENG, LUBRICATION MECH DIV, COLUMBUS LABS, BATTELLE MEM INST, 69- *Mem:* Am Soc Lubrication Eng; Soc Mfg Eng. *Res:* Petroleum chemistry; formulation, evaluation and application of functional fluids and lubricants; the chemistry and physics of lubrication; tribology. *Mailing Add:* 2745 Welsford Columbus OH 43221

JENTOFT, JOYCE EILEEN, b Canton, Ohio, Mar 10, 45; m. STRUCTURE-FUNCTION RELATIONSHIPS, PHYSICAL BIOCHEMISTRY. *Educ:* Capital Univ, BS, 66; Univ Minn, PhD(inorg chem), 71. *Prof Exp:* Fel phys biochem, Univ Minn, 72; fel phys biochem, 77, immunol, 78, sr res assoc phys biochem, Dept Pediat, 79-81, ASST PROF, DEPT BIOCHEM, SCH MED, CASE WESTERN RESERVE UNIV, 81- *Concurrent Pos:* Instr biochem, Case Western Univ, 79-81. *Mem:* Am Chem Soc; Biophys Soc. *Res:* Structure-function relationships in proteins and enzymes; role of amino groups in proteins using carbon 13 nuclear magnetic resonance. *Mailing Add:* Dept Biochem Sch Med Case Western Reserve Univ Cleveland OH 44106

JENTOFT, RALPH EUGENE, JR, b Tacoma, Wash, Nov 30, 18; m 54; c 2. PHYSICAL CHEMISTRY, ANALYTICAL CHEMISTRY. *Educ:* Univ Wash, BS, 41, PhD(chem), 52. *Prof Exp:* Chemist, Oceanog Surv Philippines, US Fish & Wildlife Serv, 47-48; res assoc oceanog, Office Naval Res, Univ Wash, 49-52; res chemist, Chevron Res Co, Standard Oil Co Calif, 52-60, sr res chemist, 60-64, sr res assoc phys & anal chem, 64-79; CONSULT, 80- *Mem:* AAAS; Am Chem Soc. *Res:* Phase studies and thermodynamic measurements in field of petroleum chemistry; separation and purification; trace analysis for hydrocarbons and petrochemicals; analytical separations; liquid chromatography and supercritical fluid chromatography. *Mailing Add:* 11601 Occidental Rd Sebastopol CA 95472

JENZANO, ANTHONY FRANCIS, b Philadelphia, Pa, May 20, 19; m 40; c 2. ASTRONOMY, PHYSICS. *Prof Exp:* Head technician, Fels Planetarium, Pa, 46-49; head technician, Univ NC, Chapel Hill, 49-51, mgr, 51-60, dir, Morehead Planetarium, 60-81; PLANETARIUM COUNR US & CAN, CARL ZEISS OPTICAL CO, 81- *Concurrent Pos:* Consult, London Planetarium, Eng, 55-57, Buhl Planetarium, Pa, 59, var proposed planetaria, 63-, Carl Zeiss Optical Co, 65- & Fernbank Sci Ctr, Ga, 66- *Mem:* Assoc Am Astron Soc; Am Asn Mus. *Res:* Initiation and direction of celestial training program for United States Mercury, Gemini, Apollo, Skylab and Apollo-Soyuz astronauts. *Mailing Add:* 37 Oakwood Dr Chapel Hill NC 27514

JEON, KWANG WU, b Korea, Nov 10, 34; m 58; c 2. CELL BIOLOGY, DEVELOPMENTAL BIOLOGY. *Educ:* Seoul Nat Univ, BS, 57, MS, 59; Univ London, PhD(cell physiol), 64. *Prof Exp:* Res fel electron micros, Middlesex Hosp, Univ London, 64-65; res asst prof cell physiol, State Univ NY Buffalo, 65-69; assoc prof, 70-75, PROF ZOOL, UNIV TENN, KNOXVILLE, 76- *Concurrent Pos:* Asst ed, Int Rev Cytol, 67-; Am Cancer Soc res grant, Univ Tenn, Knoxville, 71, Am Heart Asn & Nat Inst Child Health & Human Develop res grants, 71-73; Nat Inst Gen Med Sci res grant, 74-77; NSF res grant, 77- *Mem:* AAAS; Am Soc Cell Biol, Soc Develop Biol; Soc Protozoologists. *Res:* Cell growth and division; nucleocytoplasmic interactions; cell organelle structure and function. *Mailing Add:* Dept of Zool Univ of Tenn Knoxville TN 37996

JEONG, TUNG HON, b Kwangtung, China, Dec 19, 35; US citizen; m 63; c 3. NUCLEAR PHYSICS. *Educ:* Yale Univ, BS, 57; Univ Minn, PhD(physics), 62. *Prof Exp:* Res assoc physics, Univ Minn, 62-63; from asst prof to assoc prof, 63-78, PROF PHYSICS & CHMN DEPT, LAKE FOREST COL, 78- *Concurrent Pos:* Tech consult; fel, Optical Soc Am. *Honors & Awards:* Robert Millikin Medal, Am Asn Physics Teachers, 76. *Mem:* Am Asn Physics Teachers; Laser Inst Am; AAAS; Soc Photo-Optical Instrumentation Engrs; Am Phys Soc. *Res:* Precision proton-nuclear elastic scattering; linear proton accelerator injector; H-source for pre-injectors; optics; physics education; lasers and holography; non-destructive testing; laser applications and holography. *Mailing Add:* 745 N Waukegan Rd Lake Forest IL 60045

JEPPSON, LEE RALPH, b Brigham City, Utah, Feb 17, 10; m 36; c 6. ENTOMOLOGY. *Educ:* Brigham Young Univ, BS, 31; Utah State Univ, MS, 40; Univ Calif, PhD(entom), 43. *Prof Exp:* Teacher, Utah Pub Schs, 31-36; entomologist, Calif Conserv Co, 40-42; assoc, Exp Sta, 42-45, from jr entomologist to assoc entomologist, Res Ctr & Exp Sta, 45-60, lectr, Univ, 66-74, prof, 74-77, ENTOMOLOGIST, CITRUS RES CTR & AGR EXP STA, UNIV CALIF, RIVERSIDE, 60-, EMER PROF ENTOM, UNIV, 77- *Mem:* AAAS; Entom Soc Am; Acarol Soc Am. *Res:* Biology; ecology; morphology; taxonomy; host specificity and control of phytophagous mites. *Mailing Add:* Citrus Res Ctr & Agr Exp Sta Univ of Calif Riverside CA 92502

JEPPSON, ROLAND W, b Brigham City, Utah, Aug 30, 33; m 59; c 8. CIVIL ENGINEERING. *Educ:* Utah State Univ, BS, 58, MS, 60; Stanford Univ, PhD(civil eng), 67. *Prof Exp:* Res engr, Utah State Univ, 58-60; asst prof civil eng, Humboldt State Col, 60-64; res engr, summers, 61-64, head, Dept Civil & Environ Eng, 73-77, assoc prof, 66-71, PROF CIVIL ENG, UTAH STATE UNIV, 71- *Honors & Awards:* J C Stevens Award, Am Soc Civil Engrs, 68; Horton Award, Am Geophys Union, 76. *Mem:* Am Soc Civil Engrs; Am Soc Eng Educ; Am Geophys Union. *Res:* Numerical solutions to free surface fluid and porous media flow problems; water resource planning and design; hydrologic research. *Mailing Add:* Dept Civil & Environ Eng Utah State Univ Logan UT 84321

JEPSEN, DONALD WILLIAM, b Lincoln, Nebr, Jan 14, 32. SURFACE PHYSICS, STATISTICAL MECHANICS. *Educ:* Univ Rochester, BS, 53; Univ Wis, MS, 56, PhD(theoret chem), 59. *Prof Exp:* Gen Motors fel, Inst Fluid Dynamics & Appl Math, Univ Md, 59-60; STAFF MEM, IBM CORP RES CTR, 60- *Mem:* Am Phys Soc; Am Chem Soc. *Res:* Theoretical chemical physics; nonequilibrium properties of large systems; properties of solid surfaces and low energy electron diffraction. *Mailing Add:* IBM Corp Box 218 Yorktown Heights NY 10598

JEPSON, CARL HENRY, b Des Moines, Iowa, Mar 21, 22; m 44. POLYMER CHEMISTRY, PLASTICS ENGINEERING. *Educ:* Iowa State Univ, BS, 44. *Prof Exp:* Engr, 44-51, supvr, 51-53, SR SUPVR, PLASTICS PROD & RESINS DEPT, E I DU PONT DE NEMOURS & CO, 53- *Mem:* Am Chem Soc; Soc Plastics Engrs. *Res:* New plastics development; economic evaluations; processing research. *Mailing Add:* Du Pont Co Plastics Dept 1007 Market St Wilmington DE 19898

JEPSON, WILLIAM W, b Minneapolis, Minn, Apr 14, 26; m 51; c 4. MEDICINE, PSYCHIATRY. *Educ:* Swarthmore Col, BA, 47; Cornell Univ, MD, 50. *Prof Exp:* Res psychiat, Cincinnati Gen Hosp, 56; from instr to asst prof, 57-68, ASSOC PROF PSYCHIAT, MED SCH, UNIV MINN, MINNEAPOLIS, 68- *Concurrent Pos:* Chief psychiat, Hennepin County Med Ctr, 59-, prog dir, Ment Health Ctr, 60-; mem psychiat training rev comt, NIMH, 67-71. *Mem:* Am Psychiat Asn. *Mailing Add:* Hennepin County Med Ctr 619 S Fifth St Minneapolis MN 55415

JEREMIAH, LESTER EARL, b Walla Walla, Wash, Dec 9, 41; m 66; c 3. MEAT SCIENCES. *Educ:* Wash State Univ, BS, 65; Univ Mo, MS, 67; Tex A&M Univ, PhD(meat sci), 71. *Prof Exp:* Exten agent, Wash State Univ, 67-69; grad asst meat sci, Tex A&M Univ, 69-71; salesman real estate, David A Gamache Real Estate Co, 72-73; co exten dir, Colo State Univ, 73-74; tech writer human nutrit, Agriserv Found, 74-75; RES SCIENTIST MEAT SCI, CAN DEPT AGR, 75- *Mem:* Am Soc Animal Sci; Inst Food Technologists; Am Meat Sci Asn. *Res:* Beef tenderness, quality, preservation, retail case-life, and meat handling systems; frozen storage and display of meat. *Mailing Add:* Agr Can Res Br Animal Sci Sect Res Sta Lacombe AB T0C 1S0 Can

JEREMIAS, CHARLES GEORGE, b Marlborough, Mass, July 8, 20; m 80; c 2. ORGANIC CHEMISTRY, INORGANIC CHEMISTRY. *Educ:* Univ Ga, BS, 42; Tulane Univ, PhD(chem), 49. *Prof Exp:* Chemist, US Rubber Co, 42-45; res chemist, Tenn Eastman Co, 48-60; group leader res, Southern Dyestuff Co, Martin-Marietta Co, 60-62; assoc prof & actg head dept, 62-64, PROF CHEM & HEAD DEPT, NEWBERRY COL, 64- *Concurrent Pos:* Consult, Delta 2 Finishing Plant, J P Stevens Co, 65-70 & James Flett Orgn, Inc, 77-79. *Mem:* Am Chem Soc; Am Inst Chemists. *Res:* Organic intermediates for synthetic fibers, dyes and insecticides; sulfur dyes and intermediates. *Mailing Add:* Dept of Chem Newberry Col Newberry SC 29108

JERGER, E(DWARD) W, b Milwaukee, Wis, Mar 13, 22; m 44; c 2. MECHANICAL ENGINEERING. *Educ:* Marquette Univ, BS, 46; Univ Wis, MS, 47; Iowa State Univ, PhD(theoret & appl mech), 51. *Prof Exp:* Dir process eng, Wis Malting Co, 46-48; asst prof mech eng, Iowa State Col, 48-55; assoc prof, 55-61, prof & head dept, 61-68, ASSOC DEAN ENG, UNIV NOTRE DAME, 68- *Mem:* Am Soc Mech Engrs; Am Soc Eng Educ; Nat Fire Protection Asn; Int Asn Arson Investr. *Res:* Thermal systems; fire protection engineering; protective construction; fire research. *Mailing Add:* Col of Eng Univ of Notre Dame Notre Dame IN 46556

JERINA, DONALD M, b Chicago, Ill, Jan 17, 40; m 64. ORGANIC CHEMISTRY, BIOCHEMISTRY. *Educ:* Knox Col, Ill, BA, 62; Northwestern Univ, PhD(org chem), 66. *Prof Exp:* Fel org chem & biochem, 66-68, sr fel, 69-70, res chemist, 70-73, CHIEF, OXIDATION MECHANISMS SECT, NAT INST ARTHRITIS, DIABETES, DIGESTIVE & KIDNEY DIS, NIH, 73- *Mem:* AAAS; Am Chem Soc; Am Cancer Soc; Fedn Am Socs Exp Biol. *Res:* Synthesis of peptides and oligonucleotides on polymer supports; enzymes drug metabolism; microsomal hydroxylation; biochemical mechanisms; migration of ring substituents during aryl hydroxylation, particularly the NIH shift; chemistry and biochemistry of arene oxides; chemical carcinogenesis. *Mailing Add:* Lab of Bioorg Chem Bldg 4 Nat Inst Arthritis Diabetes & Digestive & Kidney Dis Bethesda MD 20014

JERIS, JOHN S(TRATIS), b Boston, Mass, June 6, 30; m 58; c 2. ENVIRONMENTAL ENGINEERING, SCIENCE. *Educ:* Mass Inst Technol, BS, 53, MS, 54, ScD(sanit eng), 63. *Prof Exp:* Proj engr, Stearns & Wheler, NY, 56-59; res asst, Mass Inst Technol, 59-62; from asst prof to assoc prof, 62-71, dir environ eng & sci grad prog, 66-78, PROF CIVIL ENG, MANHATTAN COL, 71- *Concurrent Pos:* Vpres res & develop, Ecolotrol Inc, 70- *Honors & Awards:* Kenneth Allen Mem Award, NY Water Pollution Control Asn, 75; Thomas R Camp Medal, Water Pollution Control Fedn, 79. *Mem:* Sigma Xi; Am Water Works Asn; Water Pollution Control Fedn; Am Soc Civil Engrs; Asn Environ Eng Prof. *Res:* Biological waste treatment; use of biological fluid beds, transport of polychlorinated biphenyl through sediment; anaerobic and aerobic stabilization of sludges. *Mailing Add:* 57 Pietro Dr Yonkers NY 10710

JERISON, HARRY JACOB, b Bialystok, Poland, Oct 13, 25; US citizen; m 50; c 3. NEUROBIOLOGY, MEDICAL PSYCHOLOGY. *Educ:* Univ Chicago, BS, 47, PhD(psychol), 54. *Prof Exp:* Res psychologist, AeroMed Lab, US Air Force, 49-57; assoc prof psychol, Antioch Col, 57-64, dir, Behav Res Lab, 57-69, prof psychol, 64-68, prof biol, 68-69; PROF BIOBEHAV SCI, DEPT PSYCHIAT, SCH MED & PROF, DEPT PSYCHOL, UNIV CALIF, LOS ANGELES, 69- *Concurrent Pos:* Fel, Ctr Advan Study Behav Sci, 67-68; hon res assoc, Dept Vert Paleont, Los Angeles County Mus, 70-; vis scientist, Med Res Coun, Appl Psychol Unit, Cambridge, Eng, 78-79. *Mem:* Psychonomic Soc; Am Psychol Asn; Soc Neurosci; Soc Study Attention & Performance; Soc Vert Paleont. *Res:* Paleoneurology; evolutionary biopsychology; neurolinguistics; attention and vigilance; quantitative neuroanatomy. *Mailing Add:* Dept of Psychiat Univ of Calif Los Angeles CA 90024

JERISON, MEYER, b Bialystok, Poland, Nov 28, 22; nat US; m 45; c 2. MATHEMATICS. *Educ:* City Col New York, BS, 43; Brown Univ, MS, 47; Univ Mich, PhD(math), 50. *Prof Exp:* Physicist, Nat Adv Comt Aeronaut, 44-46; res instr math, Univ Ill, 49-51; from asst prof to assoc prof math, 51-60, chmn div math sci & head dept math, 69-75, PROF MATH, PURDUE UNIV, WEST LAFAYETTE, 60- *Concurrent Pos:* Lectr, Case Inst Technol, 45-46; res engr, Lockheed Aircraft Corp, 52; mem, Inst Advan Study, 58-59; mem comt undergrad prog in math, Math Asn Am, 68-71. *Mem:* Am Math Soc; Math Asn Am. *Res:* Linear topological spaces; spaces of continuous functions; group algebra. *Mailing Add:* Dept of Math Purdue Univ West Lafayette IN 47907

JERKOFSKY, MARYANN, b Alameda, Calif, Feb 18, 43. VIROLOGY, MOLECULAR GENETICS. *Educ:* Univ Tex, BA, 65; Baylor Col Med, PhD(virol), 69. *Prof Exp:* Fel microbiol, Col Med, Pa State Univ, 69-72, res assoc, 72-73, instr, 73-74; res asst prof, Sch Med, Univ Miami, 74-75; asst prof, 76-81, ASSOC PROF MICROBIOL, UNIV MAINE, ORONO, 81- *Mem:* Am Soc Microbiol; Sigma Xi. *Res:* Herpesviruses interaction between unrelated animal viruses, genetics of DNA tumor viruses, defective DNA viruses, cell transformation by DNA tumor viruses. *Mailing Add:* Dept of Microbiol Univ of Maine Orono ME 04469

JERMANN, WILLIAM HOWARD, b Cleveland, Ohio, June 29, 35; m 63; c 3. ELECTRICAL ENGINEERING. *Educ:* Univ Detroit, BEE, 58, MA, 62; Univ Conn, PhD(elec eng), 67. *Prof Exp:* Jr engr, Toledo Edison Co, Ohio, 58; instr elec eng, Univ Detroit, 61-62; asst prof, US Coast Guard Acad, 62-67; from asst prof to assoc prof, 67-77, PROF, DEPT ELEC ENG, MEMPHIS STATE UNIV, 77- *Concurrent Pos:* NSF res grant, 69-70. *Mem:* Am Soc Eng Educ; Simulation Coun. *Res:* Hybrid Monte-Carlo solutions to partial differential equations; development of engineering concepts curriculum project. *Mailing Add:* Dept Elec Eng Memphis State Univ Memphis TN 38152

JERNER, R CRAIG, b St Louis, Mo, Oct 12, 38; m 57; c 3. METALLURGICAL ENGINEERING, MATERIALS SCIENCE. *Educ:* Univ Wash, St Louis, BS, 60, MS, 61; Univ Denver, PhD(metall), 65. *Prof Exp:* Res assoc, Univ Denver, 61-64; from asst prof to assoc prof metall eng, Univ Okla, 65-76, asst dean grad col, 71-72; SR PARTNER, EMTEC CORP, 73- *Concurrent Pos:* Consult, var indust co; assoc staff mem, Transp Safety Inst, US Dept Transp, 73-78; adj prof metall eng, Univ Okla, 76- *Mem:* Microbeam Anal Soc; Am Acad Forensic Sci. *Res:* Application of scanning electron microscopy and energy dispersive x-ray spectroscopy to the analysis of metallic and non-metallic failures. *Mailing Add:* Emtec Corp 3503 Charleston Rd Norman OK 73069

JERNIGAN, ROBERT LEE, b Portales, NMex, May 4, 41; m 68; c 1. PHYSICAL CHEMISTRY, POLYMER CHEMISTRY. *Educ:* Calif Inst Technol, BS, 63; Stanford Univ, PhD(phys chem), 67. *Prof Exp:* NIH fel, Univ Calif, San Diego, 68-70; sr staff fel chem, 70-75, THEORET CHEMIST, NIH, 75- *Mem:* AAAS; Am Chem Soc; Biophys Soc; Am Phys Soc. *Res:* Protein and polypeptide conformational transitions; theories of equilibrium and dynamic properties of linear macromolecules in solution; dimensional, electrical and optical properties; conformations of biopolymers; biophysics. *Mailing Add:* Lab Math Biol Nat Insts of Health Bethesda MD 20205

JERNOW, JANE L, b Shanghai, China; US citizen. ORGANIC CHEMISTRY. *Educ:* Univ Ill, Urbana, BS, 58, MS, 61; Pa State Univ, PhD(org chem), 63. *Prof Exp:* Res chemist, Sterling Winthrop Res Inst, 68-69; res assoc, State Univ NY Albany, 69-70; SR CHEMIST, HOFFMANN-LA ROCHE INC, 71- *Concurrent Pos:* NIH fel chem, Cornell Univ, 64-65. *Mem:* Am Chem Soc. *Res:* Mechanism study in organic chemistry; synthetic and medicinal chemistry. *Mailing Add:* Hoffmann-La Roche Inc 340 Kingsley St Nutley NJ 07110

JEROME, JOSEPH WALTER, b Philadelphia, Pa, June 7, 39; m 67; c 2. APPLIED MATHEMATICS. *Educ:* St Joseph's Col, Pa, BS, 61; Purdue Univ, MS, 63, PhD(math), 66. *Prof Exp:* Asst prof math, Math Res Ctr, Univ Wis-Madison, 66-68; asst prof, Case Western Reserve Univ, 68-70; from asst prof to assoc prof, 70-76, PROF MATH, NORTHWESTERN UNIV, 76- *Concurrent Pos:* Vis sr fel, Oxford Univ, 74-75; vis prof, Univ Tex, 78-79; vis mem tech staff, Bell Labs, NJ, 81. *Mem:* Am Math Soc; Soc Indust Appl Math. *Res:* Approximation of nonlinear partial differential equation models. *Mailing Add:* Dept of Math Northwestern Univ Evanston IL 60201

JEROME, NORGE WINIFRED, b Grenada, WI, Nov 3, 30; US citizen. NUTRITION, PUBLIC HEALTH. *Educ:* Howard Univ, BS, 60; Univ Wis-Madison, MS, 62, PhD(nutrit, anthrop), 67. *Prof Exp:* Instr foods & nutrit, Howard Univ, 62-63; res assoc nutrit & anthrop, Univ Wis-Madison, 66-67; asst prof nutrit, 69-70, asst prof human ecol, 70-72, assoc prof human ecol & community health, Col Health Sci, 72-78, dir, Educ Resources Ctr, Div Learning Resources, 74-77, PROF, DEPT COMMUNITY HEALTH, SCH MED, UNIV KANS MED CTR, KANSAS CITY, 78-, DIR, DEPT COMMUNITY HEALTH, COMMUNITY NUTRIT DIV, 81- *Concurrent Pos:* Mem, Inst Res on Poverty, Univ Wis-Madison, 66-67; mem awards bd, Am Dietetic Asn, 68-71; assoc ed, J Nutrit Educ, 71-77, mem, Nat Adv Coun, 77-; mem nat adv panel, Children's Advert Rev Unit, 74-; mem nat adv coun, Children's TV Workshop, 74-75; chairperson comt nutrit anthrop, 74-77; mem, Food & Nutrit Coun, Am Pub Health Asn, 75-78; mem study panel 12, World Food & Nutrit Study, Nat Acad Sci, 76, Cancer & Nutrit Sci Review Comt, Diet, Nutrit & Cancer Prog, Nat Cancer Inst, NIH, 76-78 & Lipid Metab Adv Comt, Nat Heart, Lung & Blood Inst, NIH, 78-82, man-food systs interaction comt, Nat Res Coun, 80- *Mem:* Fel Am Anthrop Asn; Am Dietetic Asn; Am Pub Health Asn; Soc Med Anthrop; Am Inst Nutrit. *Res:* Dietary patterns of population groups; modernization, diet and health; compliance to medical regimen; consumer response to nutritional and health prescriptions. *Mailing Add:* Dept of Community Health Univ of Kans Med Ctr Kansas City KS 66103

JEROSLOW, ROBERT G, b Bronx, NY, Sept 13, 42; c 1. OPERATIONS RESEARCH, MATHEMATICAL LOGIC. *Educ:* Columbia Univ, BS, 64; Cornell Univ, PhD(math logic), 69. *Prof Exp:* asst prof math, Inst Technol, Univ Minn, Minneapolis, 69-72; assoc prof math, Grad Sch Indust Admin, Carnegie-Mellon Univ, 72-76, prof, 76-80; PROF, COL MGT, GEORGIA INST TECHNOL, 78- *Concurrent Pos:* Vis asst prof, Grad Sch Indust Admin & Sch Urban Affairs, Carnegie-Mellon Univ, 70; NSF grant math logic, Univ Minn, Minneapolis, 70-72; NSF res grant opers res, 72- *Mem:* Opers Res Soc Am; Inst Mgt Sci; Am Math Soc; Math Prog Soc. *Res:* Self-referential statements; Godel's second underrivability theorem; integer programming; generalized linear complementary; nonlinear programming; convex analysis; cutting-plane theory. *Mailing Add:* Col Mgt Ga Inst Technol Atlanta GA 30332

JERRARD, RICHARD PATTERSON, b Evanston, Ill, July 23, 25; m 51; c 3. FIXED POINTS, MULTIPLE-VALUED FUNCTIONS. *Educ:* Univ Wis, BS, 49, MS, 50; Univ Mich, PhD(math), 58. *Prof Exp:* Engr, Gen Elec Co, 50-54; instr math, Univ Mich, 56-57; mathematician, Bell Labs, 57-58; from asst prof to assoc prof, 58-69, PROF MATH, UNIV ILL, URBANA-CHAMPAIGN, 69- *Concurrent Pos:* Vis fel, Univ Warwick, 65-66 & 77 & Cambridge Univ, 72-73. *Mem:* Am Math Soc; Math Asn Am. *Mailing Add:* Dept of Math Univ of Ill at Urbana-Champaign Urbana IL 61803

JERRELLS, THOMAS RAY, b Wickenburg, Ariz, Feb 28, 44; m 65; c 2. TUMOR IMMUNOLOGY, CELLULAR IMMUNOLOGY. *Educ:* Univ Ariz, BS, 72; Wash State Univ, MS, 74, PhD(microbiol), 76. *Prof Exp:* Tumor immunologist, Litton Bionetics, Inc, 76-78, head, Immunoregulation Sect, 78-80; MEM STAFF, DEPT RICKETTSIAL DIS, WALTER REED ARMY INST RES, 80- *Mem:* Am Soc Microbiol; Am Med Technologists; Nat Registry Microbiol. *Res:* Defining immunoregulatory cells involved in cell-mediated immune responses and role in the immunodepression associated with tumor burden. *Mailing Add:* Dept Rickettsial Dis Bldg 40 Rm B060 Walter Reed Army Inst Res Washington DC 20012

JERRI, ABDUL J, b Amarah, Iraq, July 20, 32; div; c 2. APPLIED MATHEMATICS. *Educ:* Univ Baghdad, BSc, 55; Ill Inst Technol, MSc, 60; Ore State Univ, PhD(math), 67. *Prof Exp:* Instr physics, Baquba Teacher Col, Iraq, 56-58; asst physicist, IIT Res Inst, 59-62; asst prof, 67-70, ASSOC PROF MATH, CLARKSON COL, 70- *Concurrent Pos:* Head dept, Am Univ Cairo, 72-73; vis assoc prof, 73-74; assoc prof, Kuwait Univ, 78-79. *Mem:* Am Math Soc; Soc Indust & Appl Math; Pattern Recognition Soc. *Res:* Mathematical physics; integral transforms. *Mailing Add:* Dept of Math Clarkson Col Potsdam NY 13676

JERSEY, GEORGE CARL, b Highland Park, Mich, Aug 20, 40; m 58; c 2. VETERINARY PATHOLOGY. *Educ:* Eastern Mich Univ, BA, 64; Mich State Univ, BS, 65; DVM, 67, MS, 69, PhD(vet path), 73. *Prof Exp:* Upjohn fel, Dept Path, Mich State Univ, 67-68, instr, 68-70; clin path, 70-72; res specialist path, Toxicol Res Lab, Dow Chem Co, 72-80. *Mem:* Am Vet Med Asn. *Res:* Pathological and toxicological evaluation of industrial, agricultural and consumer chemicals; chemical products in laboratory animals to help establish safe production, handling, transportation and use of these materials. *Mailing Add:* 1418 North Rd Lake Jackson TX 77566

JERSILD, RALPH ALVIN, JR, b Janesville, Wis, Sept 29, 31; m 53; c 2. MICROSCOPIC ANATOMY, CELL BIOLOGY. *Educ:* St Olaf Col, BA, 53; Univ Ill, MS, 57, PhD(zool), 61. *Prof Exp:* From instr to assoc prof, 61-71, PROF ANAT, SCH MED, IND UNIV INDIANAPOLIS, 71- *Mem:* AAAS; Am Asn Anat; Electron Micros Soc Am; Am Soc Cell Biol. *Res:* Electron microscopy; intestinal lipid absorption and transport; glycoprotein synthesis and transport; golgi apparatus; cell surface. *Mailing Add:* Dept of Anat Ind Univ Med Ctr Indianapolis IN 46223

JERVIS, HERBERT HUNTER, b Wilmington, Del, June 25, 42. MOLECULAR GENETICS. *Educ:* Springfield Col, BS, 64, MEd, 66; Fla State Univ, MS, 71, PhD(genetics), 73. *Prof Exp:* Res assoc biochem, VA Polytech Inst & State Univ, 73-75; asst prof, 75-80, ASSOC PROF BIOL, ADELPHI UNIV, 81- *Mem:* Genetics Soc Am; Am Soc Microbiol; Brit Mycol Soc; Sigma Xi; Am Genetic Asn. *Res:* Role of transfer RNAs in the development and differentiation of fungi, especially Neurospora and Allomyces. *Mailing Add:* Dept of Biol Adelphi Univ Garden City NY 11530

JERVIS, ROBERT ALFRED, b Wilmington, Del, May 15, 38; m 81; c 2. BOTANY, ECOLOGY. *Educ:* Dartmouth Col, BA, 60; Rutgers Univ, MS, 62, PhD(ecol), 64. *Prof Exp:* From asst prof to assoc prof biol, Emory & Henry Col, 64-68; prof biol, Goddard Col, 68-81; PROF BIOL, COMMUNITY COL VT, 81- *Concurrent Pos:* Dir Goddard Col non-resident ecol study projs, Southeast & Southwest US, 71-72 & Northwest & Alaska, 76 & Bahamas, 78; dir, Goddard Col Raptor Rehab Ctr; dir, Summer Prog in Outdoor Educ, Goddar Col. *Mem:* Ecol Soc Am; Am Nature Study Soc. *Res:* Freshwater marsh vegetation and productivity; vegetation patterns in the south Appalachians; New England ecology; ornithology. *Mailing Add:* Dept Biol Community Col Vt State St Montpelier VT 05602

JERVIS, ROBERT E, b Toronto, Int, May 21, 27; m 50; c 2. RADIOCHEMISTRY, APPLICATIONS. *Educ:* Univ Toronto, BA, 49, MA, 50, PhD(phys chem), 52. *Prof Exp:* Assoc res officer, Atomic Energy Can, Ltd, Ont, 52-58; assoc prof, 58-67, assoc dean res eng, 74-78, res chmn, 81, PROF APPL CHEM, DEPT CHEM ENG, UNIV TORONTO, 66- *Concurrent Pos:* Vchmn, Can Sci Fairs Coun, 63-65; vis prof, Fac Sci, Univ Tokyo, 65-66; vis prof, Energy Res Group, Cambridge Univ, 78, Nat Univ Malaysia, 79. *Mem:* AAAS; Can Soc Forensic Sci; fel Chem Inst Can; Can Nuclear Asn; fel Indian Acad Forensic Sci. *Res:* Radioactivation research, especially application of nuclear detection methods to crime detection and to environmental pollution problems from heavy metals, mercury, arsenic, cadmium and lead. *Mailing Add:* Dept of Chem Eng Univ of Toronto Toronto ON M5S 1A1 Can

JESAITIS, ALGIRDAS JOSEPH, b Fed Repub Ger, Aug 21, 45; US citizen; m 79; c 2. IMMUNOPATHOLOGY. *Educ:* Sch Eng & Sci, NY Univ, BS, 67; Calif Inst Technol, PhD(biophysics), 73. *Prof Exp:* Fel, Univ Freiburg, WGer, 73-75; fel, Univ Calif, San Diego, 75-79; RES ASSOC, SCRIPPS CLIN & RES FOUND, 79- *Mem:* Biophys Soc; AAAS. *Res:* Biophysics and cell biology of sensory transduction mechanisms; role of membrane in inflammation, chemotaxis and phototropism. *Mailing Add:* Dept Immunopath Scripps Clin & Res Found 10666 N Torrey Pines Rd La Jolla CA 92037

JESAITIS, MARGERIS ADOMAS, b Smolensk, Russia, Sept 16, 19; nat US. MOLECULAR BIOLOGY, BIOCHEMISTRY. *Educ:* Vilnius Univ, Dipl Chem, 41; Univ Tübingen, ScD(chem), 48. *Prof Exp:* Asst org chem, Vilnius Univ, 41-44; asst biochem, Kaiser Wilhelm Inst, Univ Tübingen, 49; from asst to assoc, 50-57, ASSOC PROF BIOCHEM, ROCKEFELLER UNIV, 57- *Mem:* Am Chem Soc; Am Soc Biol Chemists; Am Soc Microbiol; NY Acad Sci. *Res:* Bacterial antigens; viruses; nucleic acids; bacteriocins. *Mailing Add:* Rockefeller Univ E 66th St & York Ave New York NY 10021

JESAITIS, RAYMOND G, b Vilnius, Lithuania, Jan 20, 43; m 65; c 4. PHYSICAL ORGANIC CHEMISTRY. *Educ:* Cooper Union, BChE, 63; Cornell Univ, PhD(org chem), 67. *Prof Exp:* Res fel chem, Univ Calif, Berkeley, 67-68; asst prof, State Univ NY Stony Brook, 68-74; assoc prof, 74-80, PROF CHEM, STATE UNIV NY COL TECHNOL, UTICA, 80- *Mem:* Am Chem Soc; Royal Soc Chem. *Res:* Physical and theoretical organic chemistry, including molecular structure; molecular interactions; carbonium ion chemistry; ecological systematics. *Mailing Add:* Dept of Chem State Univ NY Col of Technol Utica NY 13502

JESKA, EDWARD LAWRENCE, b Erie, Pa, Aug 6, 23; m 50; c 4. IMMUNOLOGY. *Educ:* Gannon Col, BA, 51; Marquette Univ, MS, 54; Univ Pa, PhD, 66. *Prof Exp:* Chief parasitologist, Pa Dept Health, 55-63; fel, Univ Pa, 65-67, res asst prof parasitol, Sch Vet Med, 67; from asst prof to assoc prof, 67-74, chmn dept immunobiol, 75-80, PROF VET PATH & VET MED, RES INST, IOWA STATE UNIV, 74- *Mem:* Reticuloendothelial Soc; Soc Exp Biol & Med; Am Asn Immunologists. *Res:* Characterization of parasitic nematode antigens involved in white cell reactions of vertebrate hosts; macrophage as effector mechanisms of resistance to infection. *Mailing Add:* 1451 Truman Pl Ames IA 50010

JESKEY, HAROLD ALFRED, b St Louis, Mo, Aug 18, 12; m 39; c 2. ORGANIC CHEMISTRY. *Educ:* St Louis Col Pharm, BS, 33; Wash Univ, BA, 37; Univ Wis, PhD(org chem), 42. *Prof Exp:* Asst chemist, James F Ballard, Inc, 33-35; instr chem, St Louis Col Pharm, 35-38; asst, Univ Wis, 38-41; from instr to asst prof, Univ Tenn, 41-44; from asst prof to assoc prof, 45-57, chmn dept, 62-72, prof, 57-79, EMER PROF CHEM, SOUTHERN METHODIST UNIV, 79-; PROF BIOCHEM, SOUTHWESTERN MED SCH, UNIV TEX, 80- *Mem:* Am Chem Soc. *Res:* Organic synthesis; carbonation of phenols. *Mailing Add:* Dept of Chem Southern Methodist Univ Dallas TX 75222

JESPERSEN, JAMES, b Weldona, Colo, Nov 17, 34; c 3. RADIOPHYSICS, COMMUNICATION THEORY. *Educ:* Colo Univ, BA, 56, MS, 61. *Prof Exp:* Proj leader radio astron, Cent Radio Propagation Lab, 56-61; group leader satellite ionospheric scintillation studies, 64-66; exchange scientist theory of VLF radio propagation, Radio Res Lab, Slough, Eng, 62-63; consult time broadcast studies, Nat Bur Standards, 67-68, chief time & frequency, Dissemination Res Group, Exp & Theoret Studies Time Dissemination, 69-72; Dept Comm Sci fel & consult tele-commun, 72-73; CONSULT THEORET RADIO PROPAGATION STUDIES, NAT BUR STANDARDS, 74- *Concurrent Pos:* Consult, Inst-Range Instrumentation Group, 73-79, Korean Standards Res Inst, 77-78 & UN Develop Plan, 78-79. *Honors & Awards:* Bronze Plaque, Korean Standards Res Inst, 78. *Mem:* Sr mem Inst Elec & Electronics Engrs; Sigma Xi; Inst Navig. *Res:* Radio astronomy; ionospheric physics; radio propagation; communication and information theory; time dissemination and navigation systems; communication aids for the deaf. *Mailing Add:* Nat Bur of Standards 325 S Broadway Boulder CO 80302

JESPERSEN, NEIL DAVID, b Brooklyn, NY, Mar 5, 46; m 70; c 2. ANALYTICAL CHEMISTRY. *Educ:* Washington & Lee Univ, BS, 67; Pa State Univ, PhD(chem), 71. *Prof Exp:* Asst prof chem, Univ Tex, Austin, 71-77; asst prof, 77-80, ASSOC PROF CHEM, ST JOHN'S UNIV, NY, 80- *Mem:* Am Chem Soc; AAAS; Sigma Xi. *Res:* Thermometric titrimetry; clinical analysis; environmental mutagens. *Mailing Add:* Dept of Chem St John's Univ Jamaica NY 11439

JESS, EDWARD ORLAND, b Westbrook, Maine, Oct 9, 17; m 44. METEOROLOGY. *Educ:* Univ Southern Maine, BS, 39; NY Univ, MS, 48; Univ Stockholm, Fil Lic(meteorol), 58. *Prof Exp:* Comdr, 15th Weather Squadron, Far East Air Forces, Manila, US Air Force, 46, comdr, Weather Control Detachment, Berlin Airlift, 48-49, opers officer & chief tech serv, Rhein Main Weather Cent, Air Weather Serv, Ger, 49-52, chief extended forecasting, Global Weather Cent, Strategic Air Command, Offutt Air Force Base, Nebr, 52-55, opers officer, Joint Task Force 7 Weather Ctr, Oper RED WING, Eniwetok, 55-56, chief support tech serv, 4th Weather Group, Air Weather Serv, Andrews Air Force Base, Md, 58-64, comdr, Asian Weather Cent, Air Weather Serv, Tokyo, 64-66, comdr, 20th Weather Squadron, 67, dir aerospace servs directorate, Hq Air Weather Serv, Scott Air Force Base, 67-72; STAFF METEOROLOGIST & DIR STATE AIR POLLUTION EPISODE CONTROL CTR, VA STATE AIR POLLUTION CONTROL BD, 72- *Honors & Awards:* Legion of Merit Award, US Air Force, 72. *Mem:* Fel Am Meteorol Soc. *Res:* Role of the physical environment in the genesis, transport, intensification and dissipation of air pollution. *Mailing Add:* 4712 Monument Ave Richmond VA 23230

JESSE, KENNETH EDWARD, b Chicago, Ill, Jan 3, 33; m 59; c 3. SOLID STATE PHYSICS. *Educ:* Univ Ill, BS, 61; Univ Wyo, MS, 62; Ariz State Univ, PhD(physics), 67. *Prof Exp:* Res physicist, Aerospace Res Lab, Wright-Patterson Air Force Base, 66-67; ASSOC PROF PHYSICS, ILL STATE UNIV, 67-, RADIATION SAFETY OFFICER, 71- *Mem:* Am Asn Physics Teachers. *Res:* Thermoelectrical and electrical properties of nonmetallic materials. *Mailing Add:* Dept of Physics Ill State Univ Normal IL 61761

JESSEN, CARL ROGER, b Fairmont, Minn, Jan 12, 33; m 55; c 3. RADIOLOGY, GENETICS. *Educ:* Univ Minn, BS, 54, DVM, 56, PhD(genetics), 69. *Prof Exp:* Pvt pract, 56-64; assoc prof vet clin sci, 74-77, RADIOLOGIST, DEPT CLIN SCI, COL VET MED, UNIV MINN, ST PAUL, 69-, PROF VET CLIN SCI, 77-, ASSOC DEAN VET MED SERV, 78- *Mem:* Am Vet Med Asn; Am Vet Radiol Soc; Genetics Soc Am. *Res:* Canine hip dysplasia; bone dysplasias in general. *Mailing Add:* 1947 Rosedale Dr St Paul MN 55113

JESSEPH, JOHN ERVIN, b Pasco, Wash, Nov 6, 25; m 48; c 2. SURGERY. *Educ:* Whitman Col, AB, 49; Univ Wash, MD, 53, MS, 56. *Hon Degrees:* DSc, Whitman Col, 75. *Prof Exp:* USPHS res fel, 56-58; asst prof surg, Sch Med, Univ Wash, 59-62; assoc scientist, Med Dept, Brookhaven Nat Lab, 62-65; from assoc prof to prof surg, Col Med, Ohio State Univ, 65-71; PROF SURG & CHMN DEPT, SCH MED, IND UNIV INDIANAPOLIS, 71- *Concurrent Pos:* Res collabr, Med Dept, Brookhaven Nat Lab, 65- *Mem:* Am Surg Asn; Soc Univ Surgeons; Am Col Surg. *Res:* Gastrointestinal physiology; extracorporeal circulation; radiation biology. *Mailing Add:* Dept of Surg Ind Univ Sch of Med Indianapolis IN 46202

JESSER, WILLIAM AUGUSTUS, b Waynesboro, Va, Dec 20, 39; m 62; c 2. METAL PHYSICS, MATERIALS SCIENCE. *Educ:* Univ Va, BA, 62, MS, 64, PhD(physics), 66. *Prof Exp:* Lectr physics, Univ Witwatersrand, 66-68; from asst prof to assoc prof, 68-78, PROF MAT SCI, UNIV VA, 78- *Concurrent Pos:* Mem, Ctr Advan Studies, Univ Va, NSF, 68-70; vis prof, Nagoya Univ, Japan, 78. *Honors & Awards:* Alan Talbott Gwathmey Award, 67. *Mem:* Am Soc Metals; Electron Micros Soc Am. *Res:* Growth and properties of thin films; transmission electron microscopy and diffraction; surface and interface properties; radiation damage; mechanical properties of irradiated materials. *Mailing Add:* Dept of Mat Sci Thornton Hall Univ of Va Charlottesville VA 22901

JESSOP, ALAN MICHAEL, b Wellingborough, UK, Feb 4, 34; m 59; c 3. GEOPHYSICS. *Educ:* Univ Nottingham, BSc, 55, PhD(mining), 58. *Prof Exp:* Res officer, Brit Cotton Indust Res Asn, 58-60; Nat Res Coun Can fel geophysics, Univ Western Ont, 60-62; sci officer, Dominion Observ, 62-65, res scientist, 65-80; MEM STAFF, DIV SEISMOL/EARTH PHYS BR, DEPT ENERGY MINES & RESOURCES, OTTAWA, 80- *Concurrent Pos:* Mem, Int Heat Flow Comt, 63-75, secy, 71-75. *Mem:* Geol Asn Can; Am Geophys Union. *Res:* Geothermics; permafrost; geothermal energy. *Mailing Add:* Earth Physics Br Dept Energy Mines & Resources Ottawa ON K1A 0Y3 Can

JESSOP, NANCY MEYER, b Pasadena, Calif, Dec 24, 26; m 47; c 2. ZOOLOGY. *Educ:* Univ Redlands, BA, 45; Univ Ore, MA, 47; Univ Calif, Berkeley, PhD(zool), 53. *Prof Exp:* Asst zool & biol, Univ Ore, 45-46; asst exp zool, Univ Calif, 46-48; teacher, Calif Pub Schs, 53-55; teacher biol, Oceanside-Carlsbad Col, 55-60; from asst prof to prof, US Int Univ, Calif Western Campus, 60-75, chmn dept, 67-73; PROF LIFE SCI, PALOMAR COL, 75- *Mem:* Am Soc Zoologists; Am Soc Naturalists; Animal Behavior Soc (secy, 72-75). *Res:* Peromyscus genetics; tissue reactions to deep freezing; evolution and ontogeny of behavior; sociobiology. *Mailing Add:* Dept of Life Sci Palomar Col San Marcos CA 92069

JESSUP, DANIEL CLIFFORD, b Sudbury, Ont, Oct 5, 24; m 49; c 1. PHYSIOLOGY, PHARMACOLOGY. *Educ:* Univ Western Ont, BA, 49, MSc, 52, PhD(endocrinol), 56. *Prof Exp:* Sr res fel pharmacol, Columbia Univ, 56-57; res fel, Univ Edinburgh, 57-58; chemist, Food & Drug Directorate, Ottawa, 58-60, pharmacologist, 60-62, toxicologist, 62-64, head pharmacol eval, Invest New Drug Sect, 64-65; res coordr drug toxicol, Hazelton Labs, Inc, 65-67, assoc dir toxicol div, 67-69, dir toxicol biosci lab, 69-72; chief toxicologist, Rohm and Haas Co, 72-73; res dir, Bio/Tox Res Labs, Inc, 73-75; asst dir, 75-76, ASSOC DIR RES, INT RES & DEVELOP CORP, 76- *Mem:* Soc Toxicol; Pharmacol Soc Can; fel Am Inst Chemists. *Res:* Endocrinology, method development concerned with neurohypophysis and insulin; toxicology of pesticides; drug toxicology. *Mailing Add:* 6630 Isbell Kalamazoo MI 48910

JESSUP, GORDON L, JR, b Hampton, Va, Apr 29; 22; m 55; c 5. BIOSTATISTICS. *Educ:* Univ Md, BS, 50, MS, 55; Ore State Univ, PhD(genetics, statist), 63. *Prof Exp:* Animal husbandman, Southwest Range Sheep Breeding Lab, USDA, Ft Wingate, NMex, 52-57 & 60-61; math statistician, Biomath Div, US Army Biol Labs, Ft Detrick, 61-67; math statistician, Div Biol Effects, Bur Radiol Health, Food & Drug Admin, HEW, 67-81; RETIRED. *Mem:* Am Statist Asn; Biomet Soc. *Res:* Biostatistics and epidemiology in radiological health. *Mailing Add:* 207 Locust St Frederick MD 21701

JESTER, DOUGLAS BREWER, fisheries management, see previous edition

JESTER, GUY EARLSCORT, b Dyersburg, Tenn, Oct 20, 29; m 53; c 4. STRUCTURAL DYNAMICS, SOIL MECHANICS. *Educ:* US Mil Acad, BS, 51; Univ Ill, MS, 58, PhD(civil eng), 69. *Prof Exp:* chief, Eng Branch, US Army, Europ, 59-61, asst prof civil eng, US Mil Acad, 62-65, dir, Dept Res & Mgt, US Army Waterways Exp Sta, 65-67, div engr, Vietnam, 68-69, off chief res & develop, Info Systs, US Army, 69-71, dist engr, St Louis Dist Corp Engrs, 71-73; VPRES, J S ALBERICI CONSTRUCT CO INC, 73- *Concurrent Pos:* Pres, Asn Improvement Mississippi River, 74-78; vchmn, Prof Code Comt Metrop St Louis, 74-; comnr, Bldg & Indust Develop Comn, 78- *Mem:* Am Soc Civil Engrs; Soc Am Mil Engrs; Sigma Xi. *Res:* Soil-structure interaction; soils; structure design under dynamic loading conditions. *Mailing Add:* 13093 Greenbough Creve Coeur MO 63141

JESTER, JAMES VINCENT, b Riverside, Calif, Sept 7, 50; m 77. EXPERIMENTAL PATHOLOGY, OPHTHALMOLOGY. *Educ:* Univ Southern Calif, BS, 72, PhD(exp path), 78. *Prof Exp:* Fel ophthal path, Estelle Doheny Eye Found, 78, INSTR, DEPT OPHTHAL & PATH & VIS PROF, DEPT BIOL, UNIV SOUTHERN CALIF, 81- *Concurrent Pos:* Prin investr, Fight for Sight-Grant-in-Aid, 81-82. *Mem:* Asn Res Vision & Ophthal; AAAS. *Res:* Ophthalmic experimental pathology with specific emphasis on elucidating the pathogenetic mechanism involved in corneal and lid margin disease using morphologic and biochemical techniques. *Mailing Add:* Estelle Doheny Eye Found Univ Southern Calif Med Sch 1355 San Pablo St Los Angeles CA 90033

JESTER, WILLIAM A, b Philadelphia, Pa, June 16, 34; m 67; c 1. CHEMICAL & NUCLEAR ENGINEERING. *Educ:* Drexel Inst, BS, 57; Pa State Univ, MS, 61, PhD(chem eng), 65. *Prof Exp:* Asst prof, 65-76, ASSOC PROF NUCLEAR ENG, PA STATE UNIV, 76- *Concurrent Pos:* Consult. *Mem:* Am Nuclear Soc; fel Am Inst Chem; Am Chem Soc; Am Sci Affiliation; AAAS. *Res:* Development of radio-nuclear techniques for the solution of scientific and engineering problems. *Mailing Add:* Breazeale Nuclear Reactor Pa State Univ University Park PA 16802

JESURUN, CARLOS ANTONIO, b San Antonio, Tex, Feb 18, 49; m 71; c 2. PEDIATRICS, NEONATOLOGY. *Educ:* Univ Mich, Ann Arbor, BA, 70; Baylor Col Med, MD, 73; Am Bd Pediat, cert, 78. *Prof Exp:* Intern pediat, Children's Hosp, Detroit, Mich, 73-74, resident, 74-76; fel neonatology, Hutzel Hosp, 76-78, DIR NEWBORN FOLLOW-UP CLIN & ASSOC NEONATOLOGIST, HUTZEL HOSP & INSTR PEDIAT, WAYNE STATE UNIV, 78- *Mailing Add:* Hutzel Hosp 4707 St Antoine Detroit MI 48201

JESURUN, HAROLD MENDEZ, b San Juan, PR, Dec 24, 15; m 47; c 4. OBSTETRICS & GYNECOLOGY. *Educ:* Columbia Col, BA, 37; Univ Mich, MD, 40; Am Bd Obstet & Gynec, dipl, 53 & 78. *Prof Exp:* Area med dir, Eng Hosp, Brit Guiana, 41-42; malariologist, New Guinea, 43-44; dist pub health dir, Taegu, Korea, 45; exec officer & dir cholera control prog, Pub Health Dept, Korea, 46; resident obstet & gynec, Fitzsimmons Gen Hosp, Denver, Colo, 47-48; resident & sr resident, Brooke Gen Hosp, San Antonio, Tex, 48-50; chief dept obstet & gynec, Percy Jones Gen Hosp, Battle Creek, Mich, 51-52; asst chief obstet & gynec serv, Brooke Gen Hosp, 52-55; asst prof obstet & gynec, Baylor Univ, 54-55; chief obstet & gynec serv, Rodriguez Gen Hosp, PR, 55-58; chief serv, Letterman Gen Hosp, San Francisco, 58-62; chief serv, US Gen Hosp, Frankfurt, Ger, 62-66; chief obstet & gynec serv & asst chief prof serv, Madigan Gen Hosp, Tacoma, Wash, 66-67; assoc clin prof obstet & gynec, Col Med & Dent NJ, 67-69; clin dir, Thomason Gen Hosp, El Paso, Tex, 69-73. *Concurrent Pos:* Prog dir obstet & gynec, St Michael Hosp, Newark, NJ, 67-69; consult, US Army Hosp, Ft Dix, 68-69 & William Beaumont Gen Hosp, 69-73; Am Col Obstet & Gynec proj dir family planning grant, Off Econ Opportunity Family Planning, 71-72; clin investr grant, Inst Surg Res, Temple Univ, 72-; proj dir family planning grant, Dept Health, Educ & Welfare, 72-; bd mem, Am Cancer Soc, 75-; mem prof adv comt, March of Dimes, 76-; vchmn, Retired Sect, Armed Forces Dist Am Col Obstetricians & Gynecologists, 76- *Honors & Awards:* Physician's Recognition Award, AMA, 69. *Mem:* AAAS; fel Am Col Obstet & Gynec; fel Am Col Surg; Asn Mil Surg US; Am Soc Trop Med & Hyg. *Res:* Obstetric and gynecologic oncology; patient education. *Mailing Add:* Dept of Obstet & Gynec Univ of Tex Med Sch Houston TX 77025

JETER, HEWITT WEBB, b Cincinnati, Ohio, Sept 9, 41; m 66; c 2. ENVIRONMENTAL RADIOCHEMISTRY, GEOPHYSICS. *Educ:* Yale Univ, BE, 63; Ore State Univ, PhD(oceanog), 72. *Prof Exp:* Scientist oceanog, 72-74, LAB MGR RADIOCHEM, TELEDYNE ISOTOPES, 74-, SR SCIENTIST GEOPHYS, 78- *Concurrent Pos:* Consult, Ocean Systs Div, Sippican Corp, 77- *Res:* Mathematical modeling geophysics and oceanography. *Mailing Add:* Teledyne Isotopes 50 Van Buren Ave Westwood NJ 07675

JETER, WAYBURN STEWART, b Cooper, Tex, Feb 16, 26; m 47; c 3. MEDICAL MICROBIOLOGY, IMMUNOLOGY. *Educ:* Univ Okla, BS, 48, MS, 49; Univ Wis, PhD(med microbiol), 50; Am Bd Med Microbiol, dipl. *Prof Exp:* Instr plant sci, Univ Okla, 48; asst med microbiol, Univ Wis, 48-50; instr bact, Col Med, Univ Iowa, 50-51, assoc, 51-52, from asst prof to assoc prof, 52-63; dir, Med Technol Prog, 75-77, PROF MICROBIOL, UNIV ARIZ, 63-, HEAD DEPT MICROBIOL 68-, DIR LAB CELLULAR IMMUNOL, 76- *Mem:* AAAS; Am Soc Microbiol; Soc Exp Biol & Med; Am Asn Immunol; Sigma Xi. *Res:* Hypersensitivity; complement; transfer factor; tissue transplantation; pathogenic bacteria. *Mailing Add:* Dept of Microbiol Univ of Ariz Tucson AZ 85721

JETT, JAMES HUBERT, b Washington, DC, Nov 27, 38; m 62; c 2. FLOW CYTOMETRY. *Educ:* Univ NMex, BS, 60, MS, 61; Univ Colo, PhD(nuclear physics), 69. *Prof Exp:* Fel, Physics Div, 69-71, MEM STAFF, EXP PATHOL GROUP, LIFE SCI DIV, LOS ALAMOS NAT LAB, 71- *Mem:* Am Phys Soc; AAAS; Soc Anal Cytometry; Cell Kinetics Soc. *Res:* Instrumentation application and data interpretation; interpretation of biological experiments and computer applications. *Mailing Add:* Los Alamos Nat Lab MS 888 Los Alamos NM 87545

JETTE, ARCHELLE NORMAN, b Portland, Ore, May 15, 34; m 72; c 1. PHYSICS. *Educ:* Univ Calif, Riverside, AB, 61, MA, 63, PhD(physics), 65. *Prof Exp:* Res assoc fel physics, Columbia Univ, 65; RES PHYSICIST, APPL PHYSICS LAB, JOHNS HOPKINS UNIV, 65- *Concurrent Pos:* Vis scientist, Ctr Interdisciplinary Res, Univ Bielefeld, WGer, 80. *Mem:* Am Phys Soc. *Res:* Color centers; molecular atomic physics. *Mailing Add:* Appl Physics Lab Johns Hopkins Univ Laurel MD 20707

JETT-TILTON, MARTI, b Springfield, Ohio, July 22, 41; m 71; c 2. CELL SURFACE RECEPTORS, GLYCOCONJUGATES. *Educ:* Marion Col, BA, 62; Georgetown Univ PhD(biochem), 73. *Prof Exp:* Fel biochem, Blood Res Lab, Am Red Cross, 73-75, res scientist, 75-80; sr Nat Res Coun fel, Walter Reed Army Inst Res, 80-81; ADJ PROF, CATHOLIC UNIV, 80- *Mem:* NY Acad Sci; Am Chem Soc; AAAS; Am Tissue Cult Asn; Am Women Sci. *Res:* Cell surface receptor isolation; characterization and quantitation; mechanisms of entry of ligands into cultured and peripheral blood cells; effects of certain liposome preparations on virally transformed cells. *Mailing Add:* 3446 Oakwood Terr NW Washington DC 20010

JEUTTER, DEAN CURTIS, b Bradford, Pa, Dec 27, 44; m 67; c 1. BIOMEDICAL ENGINEERING. *Educ:* Drexel Univ, BS, 67, MS, 69, PhD(biomed eng), 74. *Prof Exp:* Chief engr, Electronics Div, Ventron Corp, 69-70; res assoc bioteletry, Dept Biomed Eng, Drexel Univ, 70-74, fel reprod biol, Dept Obstet & Gynec, Univ Pa, 74-76; ASST PROF BIOMED ENG, DEPT ELEC ENG, MARQUETTE UNIV, 76- *Concurrent Pos:* Adj asst prof physiol, Dept Biol, Drexel Univ, 75-76 & Dept Physiol, Med Col Wis, 77-; asst clin prof neurosurg, Med Col Wis, 78- *Mem:* Inst Elec & Electronics Engrs; Biomed Engrs Soc (secy & treas, 78-); Sigma Xi. *Res:* Unencumbered monitoring of reproductive tract parameters in the mammal using implanted multichannel biotelemetry, computer processing and statistical assessment. *Mailing Add:* Dept Elec Eng 1515 Wisconsin Ave Milwaukee WI 53233

JEWELL, FREDERICK FORBES, SR, b Oil City, Pa, June 4, 28; m 51; c 5. HISTOPATHOLOGY. *Educ:* Mich State Col, BS, 51, MS, 52; Univ WVa, PhD, 55. *Prof Exp:* Asst plant path, Univ WVa, 52-55; prin plant pathologist forest tree dis, Southern Inst Forest Genetics, 55-67; assoc prof, 67-69, PROF FOREST PROTECTION, LA TECH UNIV, 69- *Mem:* Am Phytopath Soc. *Res:* Disease resistance in forest treas; rust-resistance in Southern pines; pathological anatomy. *Mailing Add:* La Tech Univ Sch of Forestry Ruston LA 71270

JEWELL, NICHOLAS PATRICK, b Paisley, Scotland, Sept 3, 52; m 80. BIOSTATISTICS, TIME SERIES. *Educ:* Univ Edinburgh, BSc, 73, PhD(math), 76. *Prof Exp:* Harkness fel, Commonwealth Fund, NY, 76-78; res fel, Univ Edinburgh, UK, 78-79; asst prof statist, Princeton Univ, 79-81; ASST PROF BIOSTATIST, UNIV CALIF, BERKELEY, 81- *Mem:* Am Statist Asn; Inst Math Statist; Biomet Soc; Am Math Soc; London Math Soc. *Res:* Biostatistics; mathematical statistics; functional analysis; function theory. *Mailing Add:* Prog Biostatist Sch Pub Health Univ Calif Berkeley CA 94720

JEWELL, WILLIAM R, b Evanston, Ill, Oct 7, 35; m 60; c 4. SURGERY. *Educ:* Blackburn Col, BA, 57; Univ Ill, BS, 59, MD, 61. *Prof Exp:* Asst prof surg, Med Ctr, Univ Ky, 68-71; assoc prof med, 71-78, PROF MED & CHIEF GEN SURG, UNIV KANS MED CTR, 78- *Concurrent Pos:* Consult, US Vet Admin Hosp, Lexington, Ky, 68- *Honors & Awards:* Meade Johnson Sr Res Award Surg, 66, Health Sci Achievement Award, 71. *Res:* Carcinogenesis; protein metabolism in cancer bearing hosts; oncologic immunology; wound healing. *Mailing Add:* Dept of Surg Univ of Kans Med Ctr Kansas City KS 66103

JEWELL, WILLIAM S(YLVESTER), b Detroit, Mich, July 2, 32; m 56; c 4. OPERATIONS RESEARCH, ACTUARIAL SCIENCE. *Educ:* Cornell Univ, BEngPhys, 54; Mass Inst Technol, SM, 55, ScD, 58. *Prof Exp:* Asst, Mass Inst Technol, 55-58; assoc prof, Mgt Sci Div, Broadview Res Corp, 58-60; from asst prof to assoc prof indust eng, 61-67, chmn dept, 67-69 & 76-80, PROF INDUST ENG & OPERS RES, UNIV CALIF, BERKELEY, 67- *Concurrent Pos:* Fulbright res scholar, France, 65; chmn bd, Teknekron, Inc, Berkeley, 68-; res scholar, Int Inst Appl Systs Anal, 74-75; guest prof, Fed Inst Technol, Switzer, 80-81. *Mem:* Opers Res Soc Am; Inst Mgt Sci; Swiss Actuarial Asn; Sigma Xi. *Res:* Operations research; optimization; network models; stochastic processes; prediction and estimation; reliability; risk theory. *Mailing Add:* Dept of Indust Eng & Opers Res Univ of Calif Berkeley CA 94720

JEWETT, DON L, b Eureka, Calif, Jan 28, 31; m 54; c 2. ORTHOPEDIC SURGERY, NEUROPHYSIOLOGY. *Educ:* San Francisco State Col, AB, Univ Calif, Berkeley, 54-56; Univ Calif, San Francisco, MD, 60; Oxford Univ, DPhil(physiol), 63. *Prof Exp:* NIH fel, Yale Univ, 63-64; asst prof physiol & neurosurg, 64-72, clin instr orthop surg, 72-75, ASSOC PROF ORTHOP SURG, MED SCH, UNIV CALIF, SAN FRANCISCO, 75- *Mem:* Am Physiol Soc; Soc Neurosci; Sigma Xi. *Res:* Central and peripheral nervous system physiology related to clinical conditions; bioengineering; averaged far field potentials. *Mailing Add:* Rm U-471 Univ of Calif San Francisco CA 94143

JEWETT, F(RANK) B(ALDWIN), JR, b New York, NY, Apr 4, 17; m 42; c 4. MECHANICAL ENGINEERING. *Educ:* Calif Inst Technol, BS, 38; Harvard Univ, MBA, 40. *Prof Exp:* Asst, Grad Sch Bus Admin, Harvard Univ, 40-41; vpres & mgr venture new div, Nat Res Corp, 41-47; managing dir eng res & develop, Mech Div, Gen Mills, Inc, 47-55; dir, Vitro Corp Am, 56-69, exec vpres, 59, pres & chief exec officer, 59-69; FOUNDER & PRES, TECH AUDIT ASSOCS, INC, 69- *Mem:* Am Soc Mech Engrs; NY Acad Sci; AAAS. *Res:* High vacuum processing and metallurgy; high altitude phenomena and meteorology; plasma physics and chemistry; remote controlled mechanisms; systems engineering; range operation; extractive metallurgy; exploration and mining; technical auditing; technical management. *Mailing Add:* Tech Audit Assocs Inc 420 Lexington Ave New York NY 10017

JEWETT, HUGH JUDGE, b Baltimore, Md, Sept 26, 03; m 41; c 1. UROLOGY. *Educ:* Johns Hopkins Univ, AB, 26, MD, 30. *Prof Exp:* Assoc prof, 51-66, PROF UROL, SCH MED, JOHNS HOPKINS UNIV, 66-, UROLOGIST, JOHNS HOPKINS HOSP, 36- *Concurrent Pos:* Emer ed, J Urol; ed-in-chief, Urol Surv; pres, Md Med Serv, 50-54; trustee, Am Urol Res Found, 52; counsr med & chirurgical fac, State Md, 53-55; chmn registry genito-urinary path, Armed Forces Inst Path, 58-64; mem bd gov, Am Col Surg, 58-64 & Am Bd Urol, 59-66. *Honors & Awards:* Barringer Medal, Am Asn Genito-Urinary Surg, 62; Ramon Guiteras Award, Am Urol Asn, 63. *Mem:* Fel Am Col Surg; Am Urol Asn (pres, 65-66); Am Asn Genito-Urinary Surg (pres, 70-71); Clin Soc Genito-Urinary Surg (pres, 68-69); Int Soc Urol. *Res:* Clinical research on cancer of the bladder and prostate. *Mailing Add:* Dept of Urol Johns Hopkins Univ Baltimore MD 21205

JEWETT, JOHN GIBSON, b Birmingham, Ala, Jan 21, 37; m 62. ORGANIC CHEMISTRY. *Educ:* Harvard Univ, AB, 58; Mass Inst Technol, PhD(org chem), 62. *Prof Exp:* Res assoc org chem, Ind Univ, 62-64; from asst prof to prof chem, Ohio Univ, 64-77; PROF CHEM & DEAN COL ARTS & SCI, UNIV VT, 77- *Mem:* Am Chem Soc. *Res:* Reaction mechanisms; isotope effects; simple displacement reactions; highly strained ring systems; fragmentation reactions. *Mailing Add:* Col Arts & Sci Univ Vt Burlington VT 05405

JEWETT, JOHN WILLIAM, mathematical analysis, deceased

JEWETT, ROBERT ELWIN, b Jackson, Mich, Feb 3, 34. PHARMACOLOGY. *Educ:* Univ Mich, MD, 58. *Prof Exp:* Intern, Toledo Gen Hosp, Ohio, 58-59; asst resident ophthal, Univ Hosp, Ann Arbor, Mich, 59-60; physician, Ciba Pharmaceut Co, 60-62; instr pharmacol, Med Sch, Univ Kans, 64-65; from instr to prof, Med Sch, Emory Univ, 65-74; prof pharmacol & dean, Col Med, ETenn State Univ, 74-76; assoc dean, 76-80, PROF PHARMACOL, SCH MED, WRIGHT STATE UNIV, 76-, SR ASSOC DEAN ACAD AFFAIRS, 80- *Concurrent Pos:* Nat Inst Neurol Dis & Blindness spec fels, 63-65. *Mem:* AAAS; Am Soc Pharmacol & Exp Therapeut. *Res:* Neuropharmacology; pharmacology of sleep, amines and behavior. *Mailing Add:* Wright State Univ Sch of Med PO Box 927 Dayton OH 45401

JEWETT, SANDRA LYNNE, b Lone Pine, Calif, Nov 13, 45; m 70. BIOCHEMISTRY, BIO-ORGANIC CHEMISTRY. *Educ:* Univ Calif, Santa Barbara, BA, 67, PhD(chem), 71. *Prof Exp:* Res fel biochem, Stanford Univ, 71-73; res fel enzyme immunoassays, Syva Co, Palo Alto, Calif, 74-75; asst prof chem, Williams Col, 75-77; ASST PROF CHEM, CALIF STATE UNIV, NORTHRIDGE, 77- *Concurrent Pos:* NIH fel, 72-73. *Mem:* AAAS; Am Chem Soc; Sigma Xi. *Res:* Studies of erythrocyte superoxide dismutase; chemical studies of active site and intersubunit interactions; formation of and properties of metal deficient enzymes. *Mailing Add:* Dept of Chem Calif State Univ Northridge CA 91330

JEWSBURY, WILBUR, b Jacksonville, Ill, Dec 13, 06; m 33; c 3. CHEMISTRY. *Educ:* Ill Col, BA, 27; Western Ill Univ, MS, 45; NDak State Univ, PhD(chem), 65. *Prof Exp:* Teacher pub schs, Ill, 28-55; instr chem, Western Ill Univ, 55 & State Col Wash, 55-58; from asst prof to prof, 58-77, EMER PROF CHEM, MANKATO STATE COL, 77- *Mem:* AAAS; Am Chem Soc. *Res:* Inorganic and organic chemistry; phase selenate; humic acids. *Mailing Add:* 202 Long St Mankato MN 56001

JEX, VICTOR BIRD, b Salt Lake City, Utah, Apr 17, 19; m 46; c 3. PHYSICAL ORGANIC CHEMISTRY. *Educ:* Univ Utah, AB, 43, MA, 47; Mass Inst Technol, PhD(chem), 50. *Prof Exp:* Asst, Sugar Res Found, Inc, 46-47; asst, Mass Inst Technol, 47-50; res chemist, Linde Air Prods Co Div, Union Carbide & Carbon Corp, 50-58, asst mgr, Tonawanda Labs, Linde Co Div, Union Carbide Corp, 58-62, mgr, Tonawanda Labs, Consumer Prods Div, 62-65, dir, Tarrytown Labs, 65-72, dir home & automotive prods div, 72-78, SR RES ASSOC, TARRYTOWN LABS, UNION CARBIDE CORP, 78- *Mem:* AAAS; Am Chem Soc. *Res:* Catalysis; organometallic and silicon chemistry. *Mailing Add:* Tarrytown Tech Ctr Tarrytown NY 10591

JEYAPALAN, KANDIAH, b Sri Lanka, June 24, 38; m 64; c 2. PHOTOGRAMMETRY. *Educ:* Univ Ceylon, BSc, 60; Univ London, MSc, 67, PhD(photogram), 72. *Prof Exp:* Asst supt, Surv Dept, Sri Lanka, 61-67, chief photogrammetrist, 67-69; res assoc, Dept Geodetic Sci, Ohio State Univ, 69-72; asst prof surv, geod & photogram, Calif State Univ, Fresno, 72-74, assoc prof, 74-78, prof, 78-79; PROF SURV, GEOD & PHOTOGRAM, IOWA STATE UNIV, 79- *Concurrent Pos:* UN fel, UN Educ & Sci Orgn, 66; Lectr, Dept Geod Sci, Ohio State Univ, 69-72; admin asst, Highway Dept, Columbus, Ohio, 72; sr lectr, Univ Dar-es-Salaam, Tanzania, 73 & 74; res civil engr, US Geol Surv, 77. *Mem:* Am Soc Photogram; Am Congress Surv & Mapping; Sigma Xi. *Res:* Photogrammetry: development of analytical plotter, calibration of cameras, analytical triangulation, shortwave photogrammetry and digital terrain model; geodesy: electronic surveying, Doppler surveying and geoposition system; numerical cadastral survey. *Mailing Add:* 3201 Oakland Ames IA 50010

JEZAK, EDWARD V, b Czestochowa, Poland, Mar 29, 34; US citizen; m 62; c 2. PHYSICS. *Educ:* Harvard Univ, AB, 57; Univ Minn, PhD(physics), 62. *Prof Exp:* Asst prof physics, Boston Col, 62-68; ASSOC PROF MATH, ROYAL MIL COL CAN, 68- *Mem:* Am Phys Soc. *Res:* Nuclear theoretical physics; three body problem; molecular dynamics. *Mailing Add:* Dept of Math Royal Mil Col of Can Kingston ON K7L 2W3 Can

JEZESKI, JAMES JOHN, b Minneapolis, Minn, June 8, 18; m 43. MICROBIOLOGY, FOOD SCIENCE. *Educ:* Univ Minn, BS, 40, MS, 42, PhD(bact), 47. *Prof Exp:* Asst dairy bact, Univ Minn, St Paul, 41-43, from asst prof to prof, 48-69; prof bot & microbiol, Mont State Univ, 69-73; dir res & develop, Monarch Chem Div, H B Fuller Co, 73-78; MEM STAFF EXTEN FOOD TECHNOL, UNIV FLA, 78- *Mem:* Am Soc Microbiol; Am Dairy Sci Asn; Nat Environ Health Asn; Int Asn Milk, Food & Environ Sanit; Inst Food Technol. *Res:* Role of microorganisms in manufacturing and deterioration of foods; quality assurance and public health safety of foods. *Mailing Add:* Dept Food Sci & Human Nutrit Univ Fla Gainesville FL 32611

JEZL, JAMES LOUIS, b Tobias, Nebr, Dec 12, 18; m; c 6. ORGANIC CHEMISTRY, RESEARCH ADMINISTRATION. *Educ:* Univ Nebr, AB, 41; Pa State Col, MS, 42; Univ Del, PhD(org chem), 49. *Prof Exp:* Supvry chemist, US Rubber Co, 42-43; jr anal chemist, Sun Oil Co, Ohio, 43-45, sr anal chemist, 45-47, develop chemist, Pa, 47-49, res chemist, 49-54, res group leader, 54-58, sect chief, 58-60, mgr res div, Avisun Corp, 60-68, dir res, 68-70; div dir, 70-76, MGR EXPLOR RES, RES & DEVELOP DEPT, NAPERVILLE TECH CTR, AMOCO CHEM CORP, 76- *Mem:* AAAS; Am Chem Soc. *Res:* Petrochemicals; polyolefins; petroleum processing. *Mailing Add:* Naperville Tech Ctr Amoco Chem Corp Naperville IL 60540

JEZOREK, JOHN ROBERT, b Baltimore, Md, June 12, 42; m 67; c 1. ANALYTICAL CHEMISTRY, INORGANIC CHEMISTRY. *Educ:* Loyola Col, Md, BS, 64; Univ Del, PhD(anal chem), 69. *Prof Exp:* Res assoc, Univ Mich, 69-70; asst prof, 70-77, ASSOC PROF ANAL CHEM, UNIV NC, GREENSBORO, 77- *Mem:* Am Chem Soc. *Res:* Thermometric titrimetry of aqueous-nonaqueous solutions; water structure; reactions and complexes in nonaqueous solvents. *Mailing Add:* Dept of Chem Univ of NC Greensboro NC 27412

JEZYK, PETER FRANKLIN, b Ware, Mass, Nov 7, 39; c 2. VETERINARY MEDICINE. *Educ:* Univ Mass, BS, 61, PhD(zool), 66; Univ Pa, VMD, 75. *Prof Exp:* NIH fel biol chem & res assoc, Univ Mich, 66-67; asst prof biochem, Med Col Va, 67-71; asst prof, 75-81, ASSOC PROF MED GENETICS, SCH VET MED, UNIV PA, 75- *Concurrent Pos:* Dir, Metab Screening Lab, Children's Hosp Philadelphia, 76- *Mem:* AAAS; Am Vet Med Asn. *Res:* Metabolic aspects of inherited disease in companion animals. *Mailing Add:* Dept of Med Genetics Univ of Pa Sch of Vet Med Philadelphia PA 19104

JHA, MAHESH CHANDRA, b Biha, India, March 13, 45; US citizen; m 64; c 2. EXTRACTIVE METALLURGY, PROCESS DEVELOPMENT. *Educ:* Bihan Inst Technol, India, BScEng, 65; Mich Tech Univ, MS, 70; Iowa State Univ, Ames, PhD(metall & chem eng), 74. *Prof Exp:* Lectr extractive metall, Biha Inst Technol, India, 65-66 & Univ Rorkee, India, 66-69; grad res asst, Inst Mineral Res, Mich Tech Univ, 69-70 & Ames Lab, Iowa State Univ, 70-73; res metallurgist, 73-75, group leader, 75-78, SECT SUPVR RES & DEVELOP, AMAX EXTRACTIVE RES & DEVELOP, INC, 78- *Mem:* Mech Inst Mech Eng; Am Inst Chem Engrs. *Res:* Improving the processes for extraction of non-ferrous metals such as nickel, cobalt, molybdenum, tnugsten, gold, silver from low-grade ores. *Mailing Add:* Amax Res & Develop Inc 5950 McIntyre St Golden CO 80403

JHA, SHACHEENATHA, b Darbhanga, Bihar, India, Nov 15, 18; m 55; c 4. EXPERIMENTAL NUCLEAR PHYSICS. *Educ:* Patna Univ, BS, 39, MS, 41; Univ Edinburgh, PhD(nuclear physics), 50. *Prof Exp:* Res scholar physics, Patna Sci Col, 41-44, lectr, 44-46, asst prof, 51; Govt Bihar scholar nuclear physics, Univ Edinburgh, 46-51; res fel physics, Tata Inst Fundamental Res, India, 51-56, fel, 56-61; asst prof, Carnegie Inst Technol, 61-66; assoc prof, Case Western Reserve Univ, 66-69; PROF PHYSICS, UNIV CINCINNATI, 69- *Mem:* Fel Am Phys Soc; Am Asn Physics Teachers. *Res:* Nuclear spectroscopy and reaction; Mossbauer effect; molecular spectroscopy. *Mailing Add:* Dept of Physics Univ of Cincinnati Cincinnati OH 45221

JHAMANDAS, KHEM, b EAfrica, May 11, 39; m 71. PHARMACOLOGY. *Educ:* Univ London, BSc, 64; Univ Alta, MSc, 66, PhD(pharmacol), 69. *Prof Exp:* Med Res Coun Can fel pharmacol & therapeut, Univ Man, 69-70; asst prof, 70-75, ASSOC PROF PHARMACOL, FAC MED, QUEEN'S UNIV, ONT, 75- *Concurrent Pos:* Vis scientist, Mayo Clinic & Killam res fel, 80-81. *Mem:* Pharmacol Soc Can; Am Soc Pharmacol & Exp Therapeut; Int Narcotic Res Conf. *Res:* Neuropharmacology; action of drugs on transmitter substances in the central nervous system; mechanisms underlying drug dependence on psychotropic agents; neuropharmacology of enkephalins, endorphins and neuropeptides. *Mailing Add:* Dept of Pharmacol Queen's Univ Kingston ON K7L 3N6 Can

JHIRAD, DAVID JOHN, PHYSICS. *Educ:* Cambridge Univ, BA, 61, MA, 64; Harvard Univ, PhD(appl physics), 72. *Prof Exp:* Asst prof physics, Boston Univ & Univ Mass, 70-75; staff dir energy, Union Concerned Scientists, 75-78; sr res scientist energy, Jet Propulsion Lab, Calif Inst Technol, 78-80; DIR, INT ENERGY PROG, BROOKHAVEN NAT LAB, 80- *Mem:* Am Phys Soc; AAAS; NY Acad Sci; Int Solar Energy Soc; Scientists Inst Pub Info. *Res:* Renewable energy technology, energy technology assessment and policy analysis, international energy planning and technology transfer; thermodynamics and statistical mechanics. *Mailing Add:* Bldg 475 Brookhaven Nat Lab Upton NY 11973

JI, SUNGCHUL, b Sheenweejoo, Korea, Dec 17, 37; c 67; c 1. BIOPHYSICS, CELL PHYSIOLOGY. *Educ:* Univ Minn, Duluth, BA, 65; State Univ NY Albany, PhD(org chem), 70. *Prof Exp:* Asst prof chem, Mankato State Col, 68-70; NIH trainee & res asst prof, Inst Enzyme Res, Univ Wis-Madison, 70-74; res assoc, Johnson Res Found, Univ Pa, 74-76; res scientist, Max Planck Inst Systs Physiol, 76-; RES ASST PROF, DEPT PHARMACOL, UNIV NC, 79- *Mem:* Am Chem Soc; AAAS. *Res:* Anion radical chemistry; electron transfer reactions in organic solvents; energy-coupling mechanism in mitochondria; nicotinamide-adenine dinucleotide fluorescence photography; micro-light guide tissue photometry; flow-metabolism coupling in the liver; alcohol-induced liver injury; lobular oxygen gradient in the liver. *Mailing Add:* Dept Pharmacol Sch Med Univ NC Chapel Hill NC 27514

JI, TAE HWA, b Andong, Korea, Apr 7, 41; m 65; c 2. BIOCHEMISTRY. *Educ:* Seoul Nat Univ, BS, 64; Univ Calif, San Diego, PhD(biol), 68. *Prof Exp:* Fel, Inst Biomed Res, AMA, 68-69; fel, Univ Minn, 69-70; from asst prof to assoc prof, 70-77, PROF BIOCHEM, UNIV WYO, 77- *Concurrent Pos:* Vis prof, Harvard Univ, 77-78; scholar cancer res, Am Cancer Soc, 77-78; mem, Neurobiol Study Sect, NIH, 80. *Mem:* Biophys Soc; Am Soc Biol Chemists; Am Chem Soc. *Res:* Chemical crosslinking of cell membranes; hormone receptors. *Mailing Add:* Dept of Biochem Univ of Wyo Laramie WY 82071

JIANG, JACK BAU-CHIEN, b Sze-chuan, China, Nov 15, 47; m; m 73; c 1. ORGANIC CHEMISTRY, MEDICINAL CHEMISTRY. *Educ:* Nat Cheng Kung Univ, BS, 70; Mich State Univ, PhD(org chem), 75. *Prof Exp:* Res specialist, Univ Minn, 75-77; res chemist drug synthesis, Am Cyanamid Co, 77-79; scientist, 79-81, SR SCIENTIST, ORTHO PHARM CORP, 81- *Mem:* Am Chem Soc. *Res:* Design and synthesis of medicinal agents; isolation and structural elucidation of natural product; development of new synthetic methods. *Mailing Add:* Ortho Pharmaceut Corp Rte 202 Raritan NJ 08869

JIANG, NAI-SIANG, b Nanking, China, June 6, 31; m 58; c 2. BIOCHEMISTRY. *Educ:* Nat Taiwan Univ, BS, 55; Emory Univ, MS, 59, PhD(biochem), 62. *Prof Exp:* Instr biochem, Emory Univ, 62-66; res assoc, Mayo Found, Mayo Clin, 66-67, consult, Dept Endocrine Res, 67-70, asst prof biochem, Mayo Grad Sch Med, 67-75, assoc prof biochem & lab med, Mayo Med Sch, 75-80, PROF LAB MED, MAYO MED SCH, UNIV MINN, 80-, DIR & CONSULT, ENDOCRINE LAB, DEPT LAB MED, MAYO CLIN & FOUND, 71- *Mem:* AAAS; Am Chem Soc; Endocrine Soc. *Res:* Measurement of hormones in body fluid. *Mailing Add:* Mayo Med Sch Univ of Minn Rochester MN 55901

JICHA, HENRY LOUIS, JR, b New York, NY, June 25, 28; m 51; c 3. ECONOMIC GEOLOGY. *Educ:* Columbia Univ, BA, 48, MA, 51, PhD(econ geol), 52. *Prof Exp:* Geologist, Mineral Deposits Br, US Geol Surv, Colo, 48-49 & Fla, 49; field asst, NMex Bur Mines & Mineral Resources, 50-51, econ geologist, 51-56; asst prof geol, Colo Sch Mines, 56-58; analyst mining & metal stocks, Baker, Weeks & Co, 58-61; ed-analyst, Value Line Invest Surv, Metals, Oils, Brewing, 61-62; mgr, New York Res, Courts & Co, 62-70; sr analyst, Newberger, Loeb & Co, 70-71; mgr res, Jesup & Lamont, 71-73; VPRES & SR ANALYST, BACHE HALSEY STUART SHIELDS, INC, NEW YORK, 74- *Concurrent Pos:* Consult, Baumgartner Oil Co, Colo, 57-58. *Mem:* Geol Soc Am; Soc Econ Geol; Sigma Xi. *Res:* Uranium deposits in Colorado, phosphate deposits in Florida; lead-zinc deposits in Europe; tertiary volcanics, lead-zinc-silver deposits, Mesa del Oro Quadrangle and manganese deposits in New Mexico. *Mailing Add:* 12 Western Dr Ardsley NY 10502

JILEK, ANTHONY FRANCIS, animal science, see previous edition

JILES, CHARLES WILLIAM, b Vienna, La, Aug 11, 27; m 50; c 4. ELECTRICAL ENGINEERING. *Educ:* La Polytech Inst, BS & BA, 49; Okla State Univ, MS, 50, PhD, 55. *Prof Exp:* Asst physics, La Polytech Inst, 47-49; res instr, Okla State Univ, 50-55; sr aerophysics engr, Convair Div, Gen Dynamics Corp, 55-58, proj aerophysics engr, 58-60, design specialist, 60; PROF ELEC ENG, UNIV TEX, ARLINGTON, 60- *Mem:* Inst Elec & Electronics Engrs; Am Astronaut Soc. *Res:* Application of matrix algebra and tensor analysis to electric circuits and machines; network analysis and synthesis; design of automatic control systems. *Mailing Add:* Dept of Elec Eng Univ of Tex Arlington TX 76019

JILLIE, DON W, b San Lois Opsipo, Calif, May 19, 48; m 72; c 1. JOSEPHSON DIGITAL TECHNOLOGY, SUERCONDUCTIVITY. *Educ:* Stanford Univ, BS, 70; State Univ NY Stony Brook, PhD(physics), 76. *Prof Exp:* MEM TECH STAFF, SPERRY RES CTR, 76- *Mem:* Am Phys Soc; Inst Elec & Electronics Engrs. *Res:* Small-scale applications of superconductivity, particularly microwave properties and coherent effects in thin-film microbridge Josephson junctions; integrated Josephson circuits for use in high speed computers. *Mailing Add:* Sperry Res Ctr 100 North Rd Sudbury MA 01776

JIMENEZ-MARIN, DANIEL, b Sevilla, Colombia, Dec 14, 36; m 68; c 1. ANATOMY, GENETICS. *Educ:* Nat Univ Colombia, MD, 62; La State Univ Med Ctr, New Orleans, PhD(anat & biochem), 71. *Prof Exp:* Pvt pract, Cali, Colombia, 65; from instr to asst prof anat & cytochem, Sch Med, Cali, Colombia, 65-67, dir, Histol & Cytochem Lab, 66-67; asst prof, 71-73, ASSOC PROF ANAT & CYTOCHEM, FAC MED, DALHOUSIE UNIV, 74- *Mem:* AAAS. *Res:* Molecular properties of tissue proteins in relation to genetic variation and evolutionary change. *Mailing Add:* 37-52 83rd St Jackson Heights NY 11372

JIMERSON, GEORGE DAVID, b Little Rock, Ark, May 12, 44; m 65; c 2. INORGANIC CHEMISTRY, ANALYTICAL CHEMISTRY. *Educ:* Ouachita Baptist Univ, BS, 66; Ind Univ, Bloomington, PhD(chem), 70. *Prof Exp:* Asst prof, 75, ASSOC PROF CHEM, ARK STATE UNIV, 75- *Concurrent Pos:* Prin investr res grant, Ark Educ Res & Develop Proj, 71-72; co-prin investr res contract, Ark Highway Dept, 72- *Honors & Awards:* Hon Sci Award, Bausch & Lomb, 62. *Mem:* Am Chem Soc; Sigma Xi. *Res:* Waste utilization and resource conservation, specifically the development and evaluation of a substitute for petroleum asphalt that can be produced from wood and other cellulosic wastes; preparation and identification of cyano-halo complexes of chromium III. *Mailing Add:* Dept of Physical Sci Ark State Univ State University AR 72467

JIMESON, ROBERT M(ACKAY), JR, b Charleroi, Pa, Jan 29, 21; m 46; c 4. CHEMICAL ENGINEERING. *Educ:* Pa State Univ, BS, 42; George Washington Univ, MS, 65. *Prof Exp:* Engr, Glenn L Martin Co, 42-45; res assoc org synthesis, Mellon Inst Indust Res, 45-47; res assoc sales admin, Union Carbide Corp, 47-49; chem engr, US Bur Mines, US Dept Interior, 49-59, phys sci adminstr, 59-64; phys sci adminstr, US Pub Health Serv, HEW, 64-70; asst adv environ qual, Fed Power Comn, 70-74; staff off technol assessment, US Cong, 74-76; mgr, Fossil Technol Overview, Dept Energy, 76-78; CONSULT, ENERGY FUELS, ENVIRON MGT, INT ACTIV & CHEM ENG, 78- *Concurrent Pos:* Lectr, McKeesport Ctr, Pa State Univ, 57-59 & George Washington Univ Grad Sch Eng, 77-79. *Honors & Awards:* Award, US Dept Interior, 57. *Mem:* Am Chem Soc; Am Inst Chem Engrs (treas, 64-65); Nat Soc Prof Engrs. *Res:* Engineering administration; processes for production of natural fuels, synthetic fuels and chemicals; formulation of plans and policies affecting federal program for prevention and control of air pollution. *Mailing Add:* 1501 Gingerwood Ct Vienna VA 22180

JIN, RONG-SHENG, b Foochow, Fukien, China, Dec 4, 33; US citizen; m 62. PHYSICS. *Educ:* Denison Univ, BS, 57; Ohio State Univ, PhD(physics), 65. *Prof Exp:* Instr physics, Denison Univ, 59-60; asst prof, Loyola Univ, Calif, 65-67; assoc scientist, Lockheed Missiles & Space Co, Calif, 67-69; ASSOC PROF SPACE SCI & PHYSICS, FLA INST TECHNOL, 69- *Mem:* Sigma Xi; Am Phys Soc; Am Inst Physics; Am Inst Aeronaut & Astronaut; Am Geophys Soc. *Res:* Nuclear and space physics; planetary magnetism. *Mailing Add:* Dept of Space Sci & Mech Eng Fla Inst of Technol Melbourne FL 32901

JIN, SUNGHO, b Daejon, Korea, Nov 6, 45; US citizen; m 72; c 2. MATERIALS SCIENCE ENGINEERING. *Educ:* Seoul Nat Univ, BS, 69; Univ Calif, Berkeley, MS, 72, PhD(phys metall), 74. *Prof Exp:* Res staff, Univ Calif, Berkeley, 74-76; mem tech staff, 76-81, SUPVR, BELL LABS, MURRAY HILL, 81- *Mem:* Am Soc Metals; Am Inst Mining, Metall & Petroleum Engrs Metall Soc. *Res:* New alloys and thin films with unique magnetic, mechanical, electrical or thermal properties useful for applications in electronics or telecommunications industry. *Mailing Add:* Bell Labs 600 Mountain Ave Murray Hill NJ 07974

JINDRAK, KAREL, b Merin, Czech, Mar 29, 26; m 51; c 1. PATHOLOGY. *Educ:* Charles Univ, Prague, MUC, 47, MUDr, 50; Chalres Univ, Hradec Kralove, CSc, 65; Educ Coun Foreign Med Grad, cert, 68. *Prof Exp:* Intern med, Gen Hosp, Roznava, Czech, 51; pathologist & asst prof path, Med Fac, Charles Univ, Hradec Kralove, 56-65; pathologist & head dept path, Res Inst Pharm & Biochem, Prague, 66-67; pathologist, Dept Animal Sci, Univ Hawaii, 67-68; res pathologist, Mt Sinai Hosp, New York, 68-71; PATHOLOGIST, METHODIST HOSP, NEW YORK, 71-; CLIN ASST PROF PATH, STATE UNIV NY DOWNSTATE MED CTR, 72- *Concurrent Pos:* Ministry Health app head dept path, Czech Hosp, Haiphong, Vietnam, 58-60; consult, Med Fac, Charles Univ, Hradec Kralove, 61-64; Czech Ministry Health res grant, 63-65; NIH grant, Univ Hawaii, 66. *Honors & Awards:* Slovak Nat Coun Award, 51; Czech Ministry Health Award, 66. *Mem:* Am Soc Trop Med & Hyg; Czech Med Soc; Am Asn Pathologists; fel Col Am Path. *Res:* Pathology of infectious and parasitic diseases of man and animals; neuropathology; pathology of chronic drug toxicity; problems related to cerebral nematodiasis. *Mailing Add:* Dept of Path Methodist Hosp 506 Sixth St Brooklyn NY 11215

JIRGENSONS, ARNOLD, b Latvia, Dec 2, 06; nat US; m 42. POLYMER CHEMISTRY. *Educ:* Univ Latvia, Chem Eng, 32. *Prof Exp:* Instr chem, Univ Latvia, 32-44; res chemist, Zellwolle & Kunstseide Ring, Ger, 44-45; res chemist, Boston Blacking Co, Sweden, 47-50, B B Chem Co, Can 50-54, Endicott Johnson Corp, NY, 54-60 & Jersey State Chem Co, NJ, 60-61; res chemist, RA Chem Corp, 61-73, chief tech dir, 73-77; CONSULT, 77- *Mem:* Am Chem Soc. *Res:* Emulsion polymerization; water base coatings; new emulsion polymers for flame retardant textile coatings; new emulsion copolymers capable of self-crosslinking. *Mailing Add:* Skyview Circle Meadow Lake Park Sciota PA 18354

JIRGENSONS, BRUNO, b Adazhi, Latvia, May 16, 04; nat US; m 27; c 2. BIOCHEMISTRY. *Educ:* Univ Latvia, Mag Chem, 26, Dr Chem, 33, Dr Chem Habil, 34. *Prof Exp:* Instr, Univ Latvia, 26-34, asst prof, 34-40, prof, 40-41, asst prof, 41-44; assoc prof, UN Relief & Rehab Admin, Univ Munich, 46-47; Imp Chem Industs res fel, Manchester Univ, 47-49; prof chem, Tex Lutheran Col, 49-52; assoc biochemist, Hosp & assoc prof biochem, Post-Grad Sch Med, 52-58, prof & biochemist, 58-74, chief sect protein struct, Grad Sch Biomed Sci, 63-70, prof, 64-74, EMER PROF BIOCHEM, UNIV TEX M D ANDERSON HOSP & TUMOR INST HOUSTON, 74- *Concurrent Pos:* Fel, Univ Freiburg, 39. *Honors & Awards:* Univ Tex Distinguished Serv Award, 70. *Mem:* Am Chem Soc; Am Soc Biol Chemists; hon mem Am Asn Clin Chemists. *Res:* Optical rotation of amino acids and proteins; viscosity of proteins and polymers; denaturation of proteins; characterization of proteins in diseases; optical rotary dispersion and circular dichroism of proteins in relation to conformation. *Mailing Add:* Univ of Tex M D Anderson Hosp Tex Med Ctr Houston TX 77030

JIRKOVSKY, IVO, b Prague, Czech, June 26, 35; Can citizen; m 65. MEDICINAL CHEMISTRY, ORGANIC CHEMISTRY. *Educ:* Col Chem Technol, Prague, Dipl eng, 58; Czech Acad Sci, PhD(org chem), 63. *Prof Exp:* Asst res chemist, Res Inst Pharm & Biochem, Prague, 58-60, assoc res chemist, 63-68; sr res chemist, 68-73, sect head med chem, 73-77, SR RES ASSOC, AYERST RES LABS, 77- *Concurrent Pos:* Fel, Univ NB, 66-67. *Mem:* Am Chem Soc; fel Chem Inst Can. *Res:* Organic syntheses; alkaloids; heterocycles; physical organic chemistry; hypotensive, psychotherapeutic and anti-inflammatory agents; antiallergy drugs; hypolipidemic agents. *Mailing Add:* Ayerst Labs Res PO Box 6115 Montreal PQ H5B 1A9 Can

JIRSA, JAMES O, b Lincoln, Nebr, July 30, 38; m 65. CIVIL ENGINEERING, STRUCTURAL ENGINEERING. *Educ:* Univ Nebr, BS, 60; Univ Ill, MS, 62, PhD(civil eng), 63. *Prof Exp:* Asst prof civil eng, Univ Nebr, 64-65; from asst prof to assoc prof, Rice Univ, 65-71; assoc prof, 72-77, PROF CIVIL ENG, UNIV TEX, AUSTIN, 72- *Concurrent Pos:* Fulbright scholar, Inst Appl Res Reinforced Concrete, France, 63-64; Portland Cement Asn, 65 & H J Degenkolb Assocs, 80. *Honors & Awards:* Rees Award, Am Soc Civil Engr, 70; Wason Medal, Am Concrete Inst, 77; Reese Structural Award, Am Concrete Inst, 77 & 69; Huber Res Prize, Am Soc Civil Engr, 78. *Mem:* Am Concrete Inst; Am Soc Civil Engrs. *Res:* Reinforced concrete behavior and design of reinforced concrete structures. *Mailing Add:* Dept of Civil Eng Univ of Tex Austin TX 78712

JISCHKE, MARTIN C(HARLES), b Chicago, Ill, Aug 7, 41; m 70. FLUID MECHANICS. *Educ:* Ill Inst Technol, BS, 63; Mass Inst Technol, SM, 64, PhD(aeronaut & astronaut), 68. *Prof Exp:* Asst aeronaut & astronaut, Mass Inst Technol, 66-68; from asst prof to assoc prof aerospace & mech eng, 68-75, prof, 75-81, DEAN ENG, UNIV OKLA, 81-; PROF AEROSPACE & MECH ENG, UNIV OKLA, 75- *Concurrent Pos:* On leave, White House fel, US Dept Transp, 75-76; prin investr, US Air Force, 77- & US Nuclear Regulatory Comn, 77- *Honors & Awards:* Ralph R Teetor Award, Soc Automotive Engrs, 70. *Mem:* Am Inst Aeronaut & Astronaut; Am Phys Soc; Soc Automotive Engrs. *Res:* Viscous flows; aerodynamics; geophysical; fluid dynamics; heat transfer. *Mailing Add:* Col Eng Univ Okla Norman OK 73019

JIU, JAMES, b Oakland, Calif, July 7, 29; m 56; c 4. MICROBIAL BIOCHEMISTRY. *Educ:* Univ Calif, BS, 52, PhD, 55. *Prof Exp:* Res scientist, 55-80, HEAD, G D SEARLE & CO, 80- *Mem:* Am Chem Soc; Am Soc Pharmacog; Am Soc Microbiol. *Res:* Analytical chemistry; microbial metabolites; chemotherapy; microbial transformation; synthetic drugs; natural products. *Mailing Add:* G D Searle & Co PO Box 5110 Chicago IL 60680

JIUSTO, JAMES E, b Schenectady, NY, Apr 5, 29; m 52; c 4. METEOROLOGY, ATMOSPHERIC PHYSICS. *Educ:* State Univ NY Albany, AB, 53, MA, 62; Pa State Univ, PhD(meteorol), 67. *Prof Exp:* Physicist, Cornell Aeronaut Lab, 56-61, sect head atmospheric physics, 61-67; assoc prof atmospheric sci, 68-78, SR RES ASSOC, ATMOSPHERIC SCI RES CTR, STATE UNIV NY ALBANY, 68-, RES PROF ATMOSPHERIC SCI, 78-, HEAD ATMOSPHERIC PHYSICS SECT, 74-

Concurrent Pos: Consult, US Army Res Off, 69-70, Environ Protection Agency, 71, Atmospheric Sci Adv Panel, NSF, 71-74 & Fed Aviation Admin, 73-81; mem, Int Comt Nucleation, 75- *Mem:* Fel Am Meteorol Soc; Royal Meteorol Soc. *Res:* Cloud and precipitation physics; weather modification; aerosol physics and nucleation. *Mailing Add:* Atmospheric Sci Res Ctr State Univ of NY Albany NY 12222

JIZBA, ZDENEK VACLAV, b Prague, Czech, Feb 25, 27; nat US; m 60; c 3. EXPLORATION GEOLOGY. *Educ:* State Col Wash, BS, 49, MS, 50; Univ Wis, PhD, 53. *Prof Exp:* Res geologist, Chevron Res Co, 55-62, sr res geologist, 62-67, SR RES ASSOC, CHEVRON OIL FIELD RES CO, STANDARD OIL CO CALIF, 67- *Mem:* Geol Soc Am; Int Asn Math Geol. *Res:* Mathematical geology; man-machine interaction to solve complex geological problems; computer applications in geology. *Mailing Add:* 1341 N Rebecca Dr La Habra CA 90631

JOACHIM, FRANK G, b Budapest, Hungary, Feb 17, 20; m 47; c 5. ENTOMOLOGY. *Educ:* Joseph Nador Tech & Agr Sci Univ, Hungary, CE, 44. *Prof Exp:* Sci res worker, Res Inst Plant Protection, Hungary, 47-51; chief lectr & entom expert, Quarantine Lab Plant Protection, 51-56; asst state entomologist, Mo State Dept Agr, 59-64; res asst agr entom, NDak State Univ, 64-66; MEM STAFF METAB & RADIATION RES LAB, AGR RES SERV, USDA, 66- *Mem:* AAAS; Entom Soc Am. *Res:* Insect endocrinology; biology and control of destructive insects; insect growth and development. *Mailing Add:* 709 S 11th St Fargo ND 58102

JOANNOPOULOS, JOHN DIMITRIS, b New York, NY, Apr 26, 47. SURFACES, AMORPHOUS MATERIALS. *Educ:* Univ Calif, Berkeley, BA, 68, PhD(physics), 74; Univ Calif, Davis, MA, 70. *Prof Exp:* Asst prof, 74-78, ASSOC PROF PHYSICS, MASS INST TECHNOL, 78- *Concurrent Pos:* Fel, Alfred P Sloan Found, 76-80, John Simon Guggenheim Found, 81-82. *Mem:* Am Phys Soc; Am Vacuum Soc. *Res:* Condensed matter physics: including properties of crystalline solids, surfaces of solids, defects and amorphous solids. *Mailing Add:* Dept Physics 13-2037 Mass Inst Technol Cambridge MA 02139

JOB, ROBERT CHARLES, b Honolulu, Hawaii, May 19, 43. INORGANIC CHEMISTRY. *Educ:* Univ Calif, Berkeley, BS, 67; Univ Mich, PhD(inorg chem), 71. *Prof Exp:* Assoc chem, Univ Calif, Santa Barbara, 71-74, res chemist, 74-75; ASST PROF CHEM, COLO STATE UNIV, 75- *Res:* Inorganic analogs of biological systems; organometallic chemistry of transition metals with Group IV-a prosthetics; asymmetric induction involving optically active transition metal systems; coordination chemistry. *Mailing Add:* Dept of Chem Colo State Univ Ft Collins CO 80521

JOBE, JOHN M, b Ponca City, Okla, June 9, 33; m 54; c 5. TOPOLOGY. *Educ:* Univ Tulsa, BS, 55; Okla State Univ, MS, 63, PhD(math), 66. *Prof Exp:* Teacher high sch, Okla, 55-62; from asst prof to assoc prof, 74-77, PROF MATH, OKLA STATE UNIV, 77- *Mem:* Math Asn Am; Am Math Soc. *Res:* Point set topology. *Mailing Add:* Dept of Math Okla State Univ Stillwater OK 74074

JOBE, LOWELL A(RTHUR), b Lead, SDak, Aug 28, 14; m 42; c 2. CHEMICAL ENGINEERING. *Educ:* SDak Sch Mines & Technol, BS, 38; Univ Iowa, MS, 39. *Prof Exp:* Asst metall, Univ Iowa, 38-39; chief chemist & chem engr, Graver Tank & Mfg Co, Inc, 39-47; from asst prof to assoc prof chem eng, Univ Idaho, 47-60; process control engr, Atomic Energy Div, Phillips Petrol Co, 60-66; sr process control engr, Idaho Nuclear Corp, 66-71; sr process control engr, Idaho Chem Prog, Allied Chem Corp, 71-77; mem staff, Exxon Nuclear, 77-80; INSTR PROCESS TECHNOL, EASTERN IDAHO VOC TECH SCH, 80- *Mem:* Instrument Soc Am; Am Inst Chem Engrs. *Res:* Automatic process control; industrial water and waste treatment; nuclear engineering. *Mailing Add:* 150 S Corner Ave Idaho Falls ID 83402

JOBE, PHILLIP CARL, b Carlsbad, NMex, Jan 9, 40; m 59; c 2. NEUROPHARMACOLOGY. *Educ:* Univ NMex, BS, 63; Univ Ariz, PhD(pharmacol), 70. *Prof Exp:* Teaching asst, Univ Ariz, 60-63, assoc, 63-67; asst prof pharmacol, Univ Nebr, 69-70; asst prof, Northeast La Univ, 70-74, dir, Drug Abuse Ctr, 71-74; asst prof, 74-75, assoc prof, 75-80, PROF PHARMACOL, THERAPEUT & PSYCHIAT, SCH MED, LA STATE UNIV, SHREVEPORT, 80- *Concurrent Pos:* Consult neuropharmacol & clin pharmacologist, Vet Admin Hosp, 74- *Mem:* Soc Neurosci; Sigma Xi. *Res:* Role of central nervous system neurotransmitters in the regulation of seizure intensity and susceptibility with special emphasis on the relative importance of discrete catecholaminergic neuron systems. *Mailing Add:* Med Ctr La State Univ PO Box 3932 Shreveport LA 71130

JOBES, FORREST CROSSETT, JR, b Trenton, NJ, Nov 26, 35; m 58; c 1. PHYSICS. *Educ:* Oberlin Col, AB, 57; Yale Univ, MS, 58, PhD(physics), 62. *Prof Exp:* Asst physics, Yale Univ, 57-62; res physicist cent res div lab, Mobil Oil Co, 62-65, sr res physicist, Mobil Oil Corp, 65-71; MEM RES STAFF, PLASMA PHYSICS, PHYSICS LAB, PRINCETON UNIV, 71- *Mem:* Am Phys Soc. *Res:* Plasma and nuclear physics. *Mailing Add:* Plasma Physics Lab Princeton Univ PO Box 451 Princeton NJ 08540

JOBIN, LUC JOSEPH, b Masson, Que, Mar 6, 35; m 59; c 5. ENTOMOLOGY, FORESTRY. *Educ:* Univ Montreal, BSc, 58; McGill Univ, MSc, 61; Laval Univ, PhD(biol), 68. *Prof Exp:* Res scientist, Dept Agr, Quebec, 61-72; RES SCIENTIST FORESTRY, ENVIRONMENT CAN, 72- *Concurrent Pos:* Consult, Food & Agr Org, UN, 75- *Res:* Forest insect control; biology and ecology of forest insect pests. *Mailing Add:* 2925 Summerside Ste-Foy PQ G1W 2E9 Can

JOBIN, RALPH ALFRED, organic chemistry, food technology, see previous edition

JOBIN, WILLIAM ROGER, tropical public health, see previous edition

JOBSIS, FRANS FREDERIK, b Batavia, Indonesia, Apr 1, 29; nat US; m 51; c 5. PHYSIOLOGY. *Educ:* Univ Md, BS, 51; Univ Mich, MS, 53, PhD(zool), 58. *Prof Exp:* Res fel biophys, Johnson Found, Univ Pa, 58-59, res assoc, 61-62, asst prof biophys & physiol, Univ, 62-64; fel biochem, Univ Amsterdam, 59-60; fel, Nobel Inst Neurophysiol, Sweden, 60-61; from asst prof to assoc prof, 64-69, PROF PHYSIOL, DUKE UNIV, 69- *Concurrent Pos:* Guggenheim fel, 71-72. *Mem:* Fel AAAS; Am Physiol Soc; Biophys Soc; Soc Neurosci. *Res:* Physiology, biochemistry and biophysics of muscle and nervous tissue; comparative physiology; physiology of behavior. *Mailing Add:* Dept of Physiol Duke Univ Durham NC 27710

JOBST, JOEL EDWARD, b South Milwaukee, Wis, May 13, 36; m 59; c 3. NUCLEAR PHYSICS. *Educ:* Marquette Univ, BS, 59; Univ Wis, MS, 61, PhD(physics), 66. *Prof Exp:* SCI SPECIALIST, EG & G, 66- *Mem:* Am Phys Soc; Am Nuclear Soc; Solar Energy Soc. *Res:* Nuclear research; detector technology; operation and development of particle accelerators and neutron generators; airborne remote sensing, including infrared scanner; preparation of terrestrial radiation maps from gamma data recorded on an aerial survey platform. *Mailing Add:* 3013 Bryant Ave Las Vegas NV 89125

JOCHIM, KENNETH ERWIN, b St Louis, Mo, July 30, 11; m 37; c 2. PHYSIOLOGY. *Educ:* Univ Chicago, BS, 39, PhD, 41. *Prof Exp:* Res assoc cardiovasc dept, Michael Reese Hosp, Chicago, 31-42; from instr to asst prof physiol, Sch Med, St Louis Univ, 42-46; prof & chmn dept, Univ Kans, 46-61, asst dean, Sch Med, 52-57; sr res scientist biol sci dept, Defense Systs Div, Gen Motors Corp, Mich, 61-63; PROF PHYSIOL, UNIV MICH, ANN ARBOR, 63- *Concurrent Pos:* Fulbright res scholar, Univ Munich, 56-57. *Mem:* Soc Exp Biol & Med. *Res:* Coronary circulation; electrocardiography; cardiodynamics; peripheral circulatory dynamics. *Mailing Add:* 2066 Chaucer Dr Ann Arbor MI 48103

JOCHLE, WOLFGANG, b Munich, Ger, Oct 5, 27; m 64. VETERINARY SCIENCE, THERIOGENOLOGY. *Educ:* Univ Munich, DrMedVet, 53; Am Col Theriogenologists, dipl, 75. *Prof Exp:* Ger Res Asn fel endocrinol, Vet Fac, Univ Munich, 53-54; vet res scientist, Hormon-Chemie, 54-56; asst animal husb, Vet Fac, Free Univ Berlin, 56-59; vet res scientist, Schering AG, 59-63; res dir vet med, Fecunda AG, Switz, 64-65; dir inst vet sci, Syntex Corp, Mex, 66-68, Calif, 68-73, vpres int vet sect, Syntex Res Div, 73-75; DIR, WOLFGANG JÖCHLE ASSOCS, CONSULT VET SCIENTISTS & THERIOGENOLOGISTS, 75- *Concurrent Pos:* Vet res, Syntex Int, Mex, 66-68. *Mem:* Am Vet Med Asn; Asn Gnotobiotics; Am Soc Animal Sci; Am Vet Soc Study Breeding Soundness; NY Acad Sci. *Res:* Interaction between environment and reproductive functions in animals; use of hormones as therapeutic and managerial tools in veterinary medicine and animal industry; comparative reproductive neuroendocrinology; endocrinology pf parturition; new drug development in the animal health field; animal models for clinical conditions. *Mailing Add:* Wolfgang Jöchle Assocs Old Boonton Rd Denville Township NJ 07834

JOCHMAN, RICHARD LEE, b Appleton, Wis, Jan 10, 48; m 69. MEDICINAL CHEMISTRY, ORGANIC CHEMISTRY. *Educ:* St Norbert Col, BS, 70; Univ Kans, MS, 74, PhD(med chem), 78. *Prof Exp:* Instr chem, 77-80, ASST PROF CHEM, COL ST BENEDICT, 80- *Mem:* AAAS; Am Chem Soc. *Res:* Synthesis of metabolically stable analogs of neuropeptides. *Mailing Add:* Dept of Chem Col of St Benedict St Joseph MN 56374

JOCHSBERGER, THEODORE, b New York, NY, Mar 6, 40; m 63; c 1. PHYSICAL ORGANIC CHEMISTRY. *Educ:* Hunter Col, BA, 61, MA, 63; City Univ New York, PhD(phys chem), 69. *Prof Exp:* ASSOC PROF PHARMACEUT, ARNOLD & MARIE SCHWARTZ COL PHARM & HEALTH SCI, LONG ISLAND UNIV, 68- *Mem:* AAAS; Am Chem Soc; *Res:* Kinetics and mechanisms of free radical reactions; polymers and polymerization mechanisms; metal-peroxide catalyzed reactions. *Mailing Add:* Long Island Univ Brooklyn NY 11201

JOCKUSCH, CARL GROOS, JR, b San Antonio, Tex, July 13, 41; m 64; c 3. MATHEMATICAL LOGIC. *Educ:* Swarthmore Col, BA, 63; Mass Inst Technol, PhD(math), 66. *Prof Exp:* Instr math, Northeastern Univ, 66-67; from asst prof to assoc prof, 67-75, PROF MATH, UNIV ILL, URBANA-CHAMPAIGN, 75- *Concurrent Pos:* Ed, J Symbolic Logic, 74-75. *Mem:* Am Math Soc; Math Asn Am; Asn Symbolic Logic. *Res:* Recursion theory. *Mailing Add:* Dept of Math Univ of Ill at Urbana-Champaign Urbana IL 61801

JOCOY, EDWARD HENRY, b Buffalo, NY, Oct 24, 33; m 68; c 1. ELECTRICAL ENGINEERING. *Educ:* Rensselaer Polytech Inst, BEE, 55; Univ Buffalo, MS, 59; Cornell Univ, PhD(elec eng), 69. *Prof Exp:* Electronics engr, 55-64, head radar & electronics sect, 64-65, 71-74, PRIN ENG, CALSPAN CORP, 74- *Mem:* Inst Elec & Electronics Engrs. *Res:* Radar and communications; analytical and experimental research of radar and communications systems; mathematical modeling; signal processing. *Mailing Add:* Calspan Corp Box 400 Buffalo NY 14225

JODEIT, MAX A, JR, b Tulsa, Okla, Apr 14, 37; m 61; c 3. MATHEMATICS. *Educ:* Rice Univ, BA, 62, MA, 65, PhD(math), 67. *Prof Exp:* Instr math, Univ Chicago, 67-69, vis asst prof, 69-70, asst prof, 70-73; ASSOC PROF MATH, UNIV MINN, MINNEAPOLIS, 73- *Mem:* AAAS; Am Math Soc; Math Asn Am. *Res:* Mathematical analysis; singular integrals in boundary value problems. *Mailing Add:* 127 Vincent Hall Univ of Minn Sch of Math Minneapolis MN 55455

JODRY, RICHARD L, b Toledo, Ohio, May 17, 22; m 45; c 7. EXPLORATION GEOLOGY. *Educ:* Mich State Univ, BS, 45, MS, 54. *Prof Exp:* Geologist, Magnolia Petrol Co, 45-47 & Ohio Oil Co, 47-50; chief geologist, Rex Oil & Gas Co, 50-55; from res geologist & group supvr to sr res geologist, Billings Res Group, Sun Oil Co, 55-70, chief geologist geothermal energy, 70-77; PRES, ENERGY & NATURAL RESOURCE CONSULTS, INC, 77- *Concurrent Pos:* Mem, Bd Mineral Resources, Nat

Res Coun, 75-78. *Honors & Awards:* Distinguished Lectr Award, Am Asn Petrol Geologist, 67-68. *Mem:* Am Asn Petrol Geologists; Geol Soc Am; Soc Econ Paleontologists & Mineralogists; Soc Explor Geophys; Geothermal Resources Coun (vpres, 74-75). *Res:* Deposition of carbonate sediments; formation of carbonate rocks and their petrographic and petrophysical characteristics; unexplored basin evaluation; world hydrocarbon resource evaluation; coal and geothermal exploration and development. *Mailing Add:* 641 Strings San Antonio TX 78216

JOEBSTL, JOHANN ANTON, b Graz, Australia, July 17, 27; US citizen; m 57; c 1. ENERGY CONVERSION. *Prof Exp:* Res chemist, Electronic Res & Develop Lab, 58-68, Mobility Equip Res & Develop Ctr, 68-76, br chief, 76-81, DIV CHIEF, ELECTROCHEM DIV, MOBILITY EQUIP RES & DEVELOP COMMAND, US ARMY, 81- *Mem:* Am Chem Soc; Am Vacuum Soc; Electrochem Soc. *Res:* Electrocatalysis; novel electrolytes; advanced fuel conditioning techniques; fundamental investigations in electrochemistry. *Mailing Add:* Mobility Equip Res & Develop Command Electrochem Div DRDME-EC Ft Belvoir VA 22060

JOEDICKE, INGO BERND, b Grossfurra, Ger, May 17, 48; US citizen; m 68; c 2. INORGANIC CHEMISTRY. *Educ:* Univ Wash, BS, 70; Ore State Univ, PhD(inorg chem), 76. *Prof Exp:* Res asst inorg chem, Ore State Univ, 71-76; SR INORG CHEMIST, GAF CORP, 76- *Mem:* Am Chem Soc; Sigma Xi. *Res:* Homogeneous catalysis of coordinated phosphorus ester autoxidation; high temperature chemistry of silicates and clays; silicate films and coatings. *Mailing Add:* Rte 1 Box 245 V Hedgesville WV 25427

JOEL, AMOS EDWARD, JR, b Philadelphia, Pa, Mar 12, 18; m; c 3. ELECTRICAL ENGINEERING. *Educ:* Mass Inst Technol, BS, 40, MS, 42. *Prof Exp:* Switching systs develop engr, 54-60, head, Electronic Switching Planning Dept, 60-61, dir, Switching Systs Develop Lab, 61-62 & Local Switching Lab, 62-67, SWITCHING CONSULT, BELL TEL LABS, INC, 67- *Honors & Awards:* Outstanding Patent Award, NJ Coun Res & Develop, 72; Alexander Graham Bell Medal, Inst Elec & Electronics Engrs, 76. *Mem:* Asn Comput Mach; fel Inst Elec & Electronics Engrs; AAAS. *Res:* Design of automatic telephone switching systems; communication privacy systems; design of research computer systems; relay and transistor switching circuits; design of automatic accounting systems; teaching telephone switching circuit design and system principles; electronic information processing systems. *Mailing Add:* Bell Tel Labs Holmdel NJ 07733

JOEL, CLIFFE DAVID, b Saskatoon, Sask, Aug 10, 32; US citizen; m 58; c 3. BIOCHEMISTRY. *Educ:* Pomona Col, AB, 53; Harvard Univ, MA, 55, PhD(biochem), 59. *Prof Exp:* Res fel biol chem, Harvard Med Sch, 59-60, from instr to asst prof, 60-68; chmn dept, 71-73, ASSOC PROF CHEM, LAWRENCE UNIV, 68- *Concurrent Pos:* NIH res fel, 59-60; biochemist, Mass Ment Health Ctr, 63-68; career develop award, Nat Inst Neurol Dis & Stroke, 68. *Mem:* AAAS; Am Chem Soc; Am Soc Neurochem; Int Soc Neurochem. *Res:* Chemistry and metabolism of lipids, especially polyunsaturated fatty acids; neurochemistry; chemistry of the eye. *Mailing Add:* Dept of Chem Lawrence Univ Appleton WI 54912

JOEL, DARREL DEAN, b Woodlake, Minn, Apr 26, 33; m 65. EXPERIMENTAL PATHOLOGY, IMMUNOLOGY. *Educ:* Univ Minn, BS, 56, DVM, 58, PhD(vet path), 64. *Prof Exp:* Instr vet path, Univ Minn, 58-60, res fel exp path, 60-64; from asst scientist to assoc scientist, 64-72, SCIENTIST, BROOKHAVEN NAT LAB, 72- *Concurrent Pos:* Assoc prof, State Univ NY Stony Brook, 72- *Mem:* AAAS; Am Soc Hemat; Am Physiol Soc; Am Soc Vet Clin Pathologists; Conf Res Workers Animal Dis. *Res:* Physiology of the lymphoid system; regulation of lymphocyte kinetics and its relationship to the immune response; experimental hematology. *Mailing Add:* Med Res Ctr Brookhaven Nat Lab Upton NY 11973

JOENK, RUDOLPH JOHN, JR, b St Louis, Mo, Aug 17, 32; m 53; c 5. SOLID STATE PHYSICS. *Educ:* Wash Univ, AB, 53; Univ Wash, MS, 57; Univ Pittsburgh, PhD(physics), 62. *Prof Exp:* Physicist, Bettis Atomic Power Lab, Westinghouse Elec Corp, 57-61; res staff mem, Thomas J Watson Res Ctr, 62-68, assoc ed, 68-71, ed, IBM J Res & Develop, Armonk, NY, 71-78, MEM STAFF PATENT OPERS, IBM J RES & DEVELOP, IBM CORP, 78- *Concurrent Pos:* Ed, Transactions on Prof Commun, Inst Elec & Electronics Engrs, 77-, publ bd mem, 78- *Mem:* Sr mem Inst Elec & Electronics Engrs; Am Phys Soc. *Res:* Technical information and communication. *Mailing Add:* IBM Corp PO Box 1900 Boulder CO 80302

JOENSUU, OIVA I, b Finland, May 6, 15; nat US; m 41; c 3. GEOLOGY. *Educ:* Univ Helsinki, MS, 46, Fil Lic, 68. *Prof Exp:* Spectrochemist, Geol Surv, Finland, 45-47, Dept of Geol, Univ Chicago, 48-57 & Vitro Chem Co, 57-60; from res asst prof to res assoc prof geochem, 60-76, assoc prof, 76-80, EMER ASSOC PROF MARINE GEOL & GEOPHYS, INST MARINE SCI, UNIV MIAMI, 80- *Mem:* Am Geochem Soc; Geol Soc Finland. *Res:* Geochemistry. *Mailing Add:* Inst of Marine Sci Univ of Miami Miami FL 33124

JOERN, JAMES ANTHONY, b Omaha, Neb, Sept 6, 48; m 79. POPULATION BIOLOGY, INSECT ECOLOGY. *Educ:* Univ Wis, BS, 70; Univ Tex, PhD(pop biol), 77. *Prof Exp:* ASST PROF ECOL, UNIV NEBR, 78- *Mem:* Ecol Soc Am; Soc Study Evolution; Entom Soc Am; Pan Am Acridological Soc. *Res:* Factors responsible for resource use by assemblages of grasshoppers; factors influencing the population dynamics of grasshoppers; the evolution of diet by herbivores. *Mailing Add:* Sch Life Sciences Univ Nebr Lincoln NE 68588

JOESTEN, MELVIN D, b Rochelle, Ill, Oct 27, 32; m 53; c 2. INORGANIC CHEMISTRY. *Educ:* Northern Ill Univ, BS, 54; Univ Ill, MS, 59, PhD(inorg chem), 62. *Prof Exp:* Teacher, Ill High Sch, 56-58; asst prof chem, Southern Ill Univ, 62-66; assoc prof, 66-75, PROF CHEM & CHMN DEPT, VANDERBILT UNIV, 75- *Mem:* Am Chem Soc; Sigma Xi. *Res:* Jahn-Teller effect; hydrogen bonding; coordination chemistry. *Mailing Add:* Dept of Chem Vanderbilt Univ Nashville TN 37235

JOESTEN, RAYMOND, b San Francisco, Calif, Sept 12, 44; m 67; c 2. METAMORPHIC PETROLOGY. *Educ:* San Jose State Col, BS, 66; Calif Inst Technol, PhD, 74. *Prof Exp:* ASSOC PROF GEOL & GEOPHYSICS, UNIV CONN, 71- *Concurrent Pos:* Vis scholar, Dept Microbiol & Petrol, Cambridge Univ, 79. *Mem:* Geol Soc Am. *Res:* Analysis of mass transport inmetamorphic rocks through study of natural systems and modelling using methods of non-equilibrium thermodynamics. *Mailing Add:* Dept Geol & Geophysics U-45 Univ Conn Storrs CT 06268

JOFFE, ANATOLE, b Belg, Sept 1, 32; c 2. MATHEMATICS. *Educ:* Univ Brussels, Lic Sc & advan teaching degree agr, 54, Lic Sc, 55; Cornell Univ, PhD(sci math), 59. *Prof Exp:* Asst prof math, McGill Univ, 60-61; from asst prof to assoc prof, 61-73, PROF MATH & DIR, MATH RES CTR, UNIV MONTREAL, 73- *Concurrent Pos:* Mem, Comt Aid Nat Res Coun, 74-77, Comt Basic Sci Coun Univ, 74- *Mem:* Am Math Soc; Inst Math Statist; Math Soc Can. *Res:* Theory of pure and applied probability; Galton-Watson process; some of independent random variables index by a tree and applications to biology. *Mailing Add:* Math Res Ctr Univ of Montreal Montreal PQ H3C 3J4 Can

JOFFE, FREDERICK M, b Chicago, Ill, Oct 26, 36; m 59; c 4. BIOCHEMISTRY, FOOD TECHNOLOGY. *Educ:* Mich State Univ, BS, 58, MS, 59; Rutgers Univ, PhD(food sci), 61. *Prof Exp:* Basic develop scientist, Foods Div, Procter & Gamble Co, 62-63, process develop group leader, Folger Coffee Co, 63-64, prod res group leader, 64-68, head prod res & prof serv, 68-70, head shampoo prod develop, Procter & Gamble, 70-72, assoc dir toilet goods prod develop, Procter & Gamble, 72-76, ASSOC DIR PAPER PROD DEVELOP, PROCTER & GAMBLE INT, 77- *Res:* Kinetics of enzyme activity; autooxidation of lipids; instant coffee processes; extraction; spray and freeze drying; sensory perception effects on food acceptability; products research; process development and packaging management. *Mailing Add:* Procter & Gamble Int 301 E Sixth St Cincinnati OH 45202

JOFFE, JOSEPH, b Moscow, Russia, Oct 14, 09; nat US; m 31; c 3. PHYSICAL CHEMISTRY. *Educ:* Columbia Univ, AB, 29, BS, 30, MA, 31, PhD(chem), 33. *Prof Exp:* Asst physics, Columbia Univ, 31, asst chem, Univ Exten, 32-33; from instr to assoc prof math, Newark Col Eng, 32-40, from prof to distinguished prof chem eng, 40-75, res dir, Res Found, 59-61, chmn dept, 63-75, EMER PROF CHEM ENG, NJ INST TECHNOL, 75- *Concurrent Pos:* Sr asst, Div War Res, S A M Labs, Manhattan Proj, Columbia Univ, 43; develop phys chemist, Fed Tel & Radio Corp, 44. *Mem:* Am Chem Soc; Am Inst Chem Engrs; Am Soc Eng Educ. *Res:* Absorption spectroscopy; selenium rectifiers; thermodynamics of gases and gas mixtures; combustion of carbon; flow of gases in pipelines; thermal cracking of hydrocarbons; chemical reaction kinetics; equations of state; vapor-liquid equilibria. *Mailing Add:* 77 Parker Ave Maplewood NJ 07040

JOFFE, MORRIS H, b Odessa, Russia, June 26, 00; nat US; m 26, 42; c 2. CHEMISTRY. *Educ:* Univ Ill, BS, 22. *Prof Exp:* Instr chem, Siebel Inst Technol, 22-23; instr, Am Inst Baking, 23-26; head baker's serv dept, Colonial Salt Co, 26-30; chem engr, Emulsol Corp, 30-55, pres, Emulsol Egg Prod Corp, 55-65; partner, 56-65, PRES, M H JOFFE & ASSOCS, INC, 65- *Mem:* AAAS; Am Chem Soc; Am Inst Chem Engrs; fel Am Inst Chemists; Inst Food Technologists. *Res:* Bread baking; mayonnaise and salad dressing products. *Mailing Add:* M H Joffe & Assocs Inc 434 S Wabash Ave Chicago IL 60605

JOFFEE, IRVING BRIAN, b Rochester, NY, Sept 9, 46; m 68; c 3. ORGANIC CHEMISTRY, SURFACE CHEMISTRY. *Educ:* Mass Inst Technol, SB, 68; Brandeis Univ, MA, 71, PhD(org chem), 73. *Prof Exp:* Fel, Hebrew Univ, Israel, 73; sr chemist res & develop, Dead Sea Bromine Co, Ltd, Israel, 74-75; RES CHEMIST RES & DEVELOP, PALL CORP, 75- *Mem:* Am Chem Soc. *Res:* Polymer modification. *Mailing Add:* Pall Corp 30 Sea Cliff Ave Glen Cove NY 11542

JOFTES, DAVID LION, b Brooklyn, NY, Apr 30, 24; m 48; c 1. PHYSIOLOGY, DEVELOPMENTAL BIOLOGY. *Educ:* Tufts Col, BS, 44, MS, 47; Boston Univ, PhD(physiol), 51. *Prof Exp:* Asst physiol, Tufts Col, 47; res assoc radiation, Boston Univ, 50-52; res assoc, Col Med, Univ Ill, 52-53; radiobiologist, US Air Force Atomic Warfare Directorate, 53-54 & Cancer Res Inst, 54-67; biomed sci adminr, Ment Retardation Prog, Nat Inst Child Health & Human Develop, 68-74; chief, Nat Organ Site Progs Br, 74-76, chief, Rev & Referral Br, 76-78, CHIEF, CONTRACTS REV BR, NAT CANCER INST, 78- *Concurrent Pos:* Collab scientist, Brookhaven Nat Lab, 58-61; res assoc path, Harvard Med Sch, 61-66; adj prof, Boston Univ, 66-67. *Mem:* Am Soc Cell Biologists; Tissue Cult Asn; Soc Develop Biol. *Res:* Cancer; radiation effects; radioautography; circulation physiology. *Mailing Add:* 11113 Hunt Club Dr Potomac MD 20854

JOHAM, HOWARD ERNEST, b Los Angeles, Calif, Oct 12, 19; m 42; c 2. PLANT PHYSIOLOGY. *Educ:* Univ Calif, BA, 41; Agr & Mech Col, Tex, MS, 43; Iowa State Col, PhD(plant physiol), 50. *Prof Exp:* Jr plant physiologist, USDA, Calif, 43-44; instr bot, 46-47, from asst prof to prof plant physiol, 47-75, sect leader, 59-75, prof plant sci & head dept, 74-80, EMER PRO PLANT SCI, TEX A&M UNIV, 80- *Concurrent Pos:* Mem, Nat Cotton Task Force, 70-72. *Mem:* Am Soc Agron; Am Soc Plant Physiol; Scand Soc Plant Physiol. *Res:* Plant nutrition; role of calcium in translocation of carbohydrates; cation interactions in cotton nutrition. *Mailing Add:* Dept of Plant Sci Tex A&M Univ College Station TX 77843

JOHANNES, ROBERT, b Philadelphia, Pa, Jan 16, 27; m 61; c 3. PHYSICS. *Educ:* Dickinson Col, BS, 50; Lehigh Univ, MS, 52, PhD(physics), 61. *Prof Exp:* Asst physics, Lehigh Univ, 52-58, res asst, 58-60; proj scientist res lab, Philco Corp, Ford Motor Co, 60-64, res specialist, Appl Res Lab, 64-66; sr scientist, Westinghouse Res Lab, 66-70; sr scientist, Superior Electronics Res Lab, Que, 70-72; res physicist, 72-77, PRIN SCIENTIST, CALSPAN CORP, 77- *Mem:* Am Phys Soc. *Res:* Electro-optics; ferroelectrics; infrared spectroscopy; optical data processing; optical properties; transition metal oxides; lasers; optics; system analysis. *Mailing Add:* 1217 Edgewood Ave Las Cruces NM 88001

JOHANNES, ROBERT EARL, b North Battleford, Sask, Sept 26, 36; m 59; c 1. MARINE ECOLOGY. *Educ:* Univ BC, BSc, 58, MSc, 59; Univ Hawaii, PhD(zool), 63. *Prof Exp:* Res asst, Univ BC, 58-59; res asst, Univ Hawaii, 60-63; res assoc, Marine Inst, Univ Ga, 63-65, res assoc, Dept Zool, Univ, 65-66, from asst prof to assoc prof, 66-77; vis assoc researcher, Hawaii Inst Marine Biol, 77-79; SR RES SCIENTIST, COMMONWEALTH SCI & INDUST RES ORGN DEPT, FISHERIES DIV, 79- *Concurrent Pos:* Guggenheim fel, 74-75. *Mem:* Am Soc Limnol & Oceanog. *Res:* Fisheries, ethnobiology and pollution in tropical marine communities; flux of energy and nutrients through coral reef and seagrass communities. *Mailing Add:* Commonwealth Sci & Indust Res Orgn Fisheries Div PO Box 20 North Beach 6020 Western Australia

JOHANNESEN, ROLF BRADFORD, b Ann Arbor, Mich, Nov 3, 24; m 47; c 2. INORGANIC CHEMISTRY. *Educ:* Wayne Univ, BS, 45, MS, 48; Purdue Univ, PhD(inorg chem), 51. *Prof Exp:* CHEMIST, NAT BUR STANDARDS, 51- *Mem:* AAAS; Am Chem Soc; Am Soc Testing & Mat. *Res:* Nuclear magnetic resonance; analysis of high-resolution spectra; structural studies by broad-line nuclear magnetic resonance; chemistry of group IV metals and metal-metal bonding; chemical applications of computer programming. *Mailing Add:* Div 561 Nat Bur Standards Washington DC 20234

JOHANNESSEN, CARL L, b Santa Ana, Calif, July 28, 24; m; c 1. BIOGEOGRAPHY, CULTURAL GEOGRAPHY. *Educ:* Univ Calif, Berkeley, BA, 50, MA, 53, PhD(geog), 59. *Prof Exp:* Instr geog, Univ Calif, Davis, 59; PROF GEOG, UNIV ORE, 59- *Concurrent Pos:* Agr Develop Coun grant, Costa Rica, 65, Guggenheim Found fel, 65-66; pres, Neopropagations, Inc, 69-; mem, Conf Latin Am Geogr. *Mem:* AAAS; Asn Am Geogr; Am Geog Soc; Soc Econ Bot; Sigma Xi. *Res:* Ways in which man has modified plants and animals and their distributions; Latin America. *Mailing Add:* Dept of Geog Univ of Ore Eugene OR 97403

JOHANNESSEN, GEORGE ANDREW, b Seattle, Wash, Jan 10, 19; m 49; c 4. HORTICULTURE, PLANT BREEDING. *Educ:* Rutgers Univ, BS, 41; Purdue Univ, MS, 48; Cornell Univ, PhD(veg crops, plant breeding, physiol), 50. *Prof Exp:* Asst soil technologist, Va Truck Exp Sta, 46; asst hort, Purdue Univ, 46-48; asst hort, NY Exp Sta, Cornell Univ, Geneva, 48-50; assoc prof veg crops & pomol, Cornell Univ, 50-53; western area agronomist, Am Can Co, 53-60; head plant breeding dept & affil mem grad fac, Pineapple Res Inst Hawaii, Univ Hawaii, 60-64; dir raw prod res, Calif Canners & Growers, 64-67; dir, Calif Tomato Res Inst, 68-72; mgr, Calif Processing Tomato Adv Bd, 72-78; DIR, CALIF TOMATO RES INST, 78- *Concurrent Pos:* Affil mem grad fac, Univ Hawaii, 60-64; vis assoc prof, Cornell Univ, 63-64; consult tomato & pineapple prod, Agency Int Develop, Africa, 68; mem gov bd, Agr Res Inst, Washington, DC, 71-73; consult, Food & Agr Orgn, UN, Ivory Coast, Africa, 80. *Mem:* Fel Am Soc Hort Sci; Sigma Xi. *Res:* Vegetable crops; physiology; tomato fruit cracking; histology of tomato fruit skin; fruit and vegetable crop production; post-harvest handling and storage of fruit and vegetable crops; tomato and pineapple breeding; research administration. *Mailing Add:* 333 Hartford Rd Danville CA 94526

JOHANNESSEN, JACK, b Alameda, Calif, June 22, 15; m 34; c 2. ELECTRICAL ENGINEERING. *Educ:* Calif Inst Technol, BS, 38. *Prof Exp:* Asst recorder geophys surv party, Tex Co, Calif, 38-39; elec distrib engr, Imp Irrig Dist, 39, elec inspector, 39-40; elec engr, Basic Magnesium Co, Nev, 42; elec engr, Imp Irrig Dist, Calif, 42, supt generation, 42-45; consult elec engr, 45-50; gen supvr, NAm Aviation, 50-62; consult engr & property develop, 62-65; res engr, Saturn V, Boeing Co, 65-67; design specialist, Lockheed, 67-80; CONSULTING ENGR, 80- *Mem:* Assoc Inst Elec & Electronics Engrs. *Res:* Design of remote control of central stations and of machine tools; basic principles of electrical engineering; electronics; electro-mechanical devices. *Mailing Add:* PO Box 1661 PO Box 551 Rancho Sante Fe CA 92067

JOHANNESSEN, PAUL ROMBERG, b Oslo, Norway, Aug 12, 26, nat US; m 50; c 2. SOLID STATE ELECTRONICS. *Educ:* Mass Inst Technol, SB & SM, 53, ScD, 58. *Prof Exp:* Res engr, Electronic Systs Lab, Mass Inst Technol, 53-56, res asst & instr, 56-58, asst prof, 58-59; sr scientist, Sylvania Elec Prod Inc, 59-69; vpres, Symbionics, 69-70; PRES, MEGAPULSE, INC, 70- *Mem:* Sr mem Inst Elec & Electronics Engrs. *Res:* Solid state power sources; automatic controls; nonlinear circuits; electronics. *Mailing Add:* 40 Tyler Rd Lexington MA 02173

JOHANNINGSMEIER, ARTHUR GEORGE, b Lafayette, Ind, Nov 5, 30; m 56; c 2. ECOLOGY. *Educ:* Purdue Univ, BS, 56, MS, 62, PhD, 66. *Prof Exp:* Teacher, High Sch, Mich, 56-58; instr biol, bot & zool, Purdue, 58-62, teaching asst biol & zool, 62-64; asst prof biol, Boston Univ, 64-71; NSF fac fel, Grasslands IBP, Colo State Univ, 71-72; CHMN SCI DEPT, CUSHING ACAD, 72- *Concurrent Pos:* Consult water qual, New Eng Interstate Water Pollution Control Comn, Boston, 75-78. *Mem:* Ecol Soc Am; Am Inst Biol Scientists; Sigma Xi; AAAS; Am Soc Mammal. *Res:* Food and energy relationships of small mammals in natural communities; development of field methods for the study of small mammal movements and physiology; water quality assessment. *Mailing Add:* Dept of Sci Cushing Acad Ashburnham MA 01430

JOHANNSEN, CHRISTIAN JAKOB, b Randolph, Nebr, July 24, 37; m 59; c 2. AGRONOMY. *Educ:* Univ Nebr, Lincoln, BS, 59, MS, 61; Purdue Univ, PhD(soil physics, agron), 69. *Prof Exp:* Area agronomist, Chevron Chem Co, 61-62; exten agronomist, Purdue Univ, 63-65, res asst soil physics, 65-66, res agronomist, Lab Applns Remote Sensing, 66-69, prog leader, 69-72; EXTEN AGRONOMIST, UNIV MO-COLUMBIA, 72- *Mem:* Am Soc Agron; Soil Sci Soc Am; Soil Conserv Soc Am; Int Soil Sci Soc; Am Soc Photogram. *Res:* Providing natural resources data and information to agricultural and nonagricultural users; emphasis on remote sensing and soil survey data for land use planning. *Mailing Add:* 214 Waters Hall Univ of Mo Columbia MO 65201

JOHANNSEN, FREDERICK RICHARD, b St Louis, Mo, Feb 17, 46. TOXICOLOGY, OCCUPATIONAL TOXICOLOGY. *Educ:* William Jewell Col, AB, 68; Univ Mo, MS, 70, PhD(toxicol), 73; Am Bd Toxicol, dipl, 81. *Prof Exp:* Grad res asst toxicol, Toxicol Lab, Univ Mo, 68-72, res assoc, 72-73; sr toxicologist, 73-78, toxicologist specialist, 78-79, group leader, Environ Health Lab, 79-80, TOXICOL MGR, MONSANTO CO, 79- *Concurrent Pos:* Lectr, Am Indust Hyg Asn, 79- *Mem:* Soc Toxicol; Am Indust Hyg Asn; Am Chem Soc; Entom Soc Am; Am Asn Lab Animal Sci. *Res:* Toxicology and hazard assessment for use in support of environmental and occupational safety. *Mailing Add:* Monsanto Co 800 N Lindbergh Blvd St Louis MO 63166

JOHANSEN, ERLING, b Overhalla, Norway, Apr 8, 23; nat US; m 52; c 3. DENTISTRY, ORAL PATHOLOGY. *Educ:* Tufts Col, DMD, 49; Univ Rochester, PhD, 55. *Prof Exp:* Asst, Dent Sch, Tufts Col, 46-49; instr histol, Eastman Sch Dent Hyg, 52-64; from asst prof to prof dent res, Sch Med & Dent, Univ Rochester, 55-66, Margaret & Cy Welcher prof, 66-80, chmn dept, 55-80, prof clin dent, 74-80; PROF & DEAN DENT SCI, SCH DENT MED, TUFTS UNIV, 80- *Concurrent Pos:* Consult, Nat Inst Dent Res; consult, Bur Environ Health, mem clin fel rev panel & anat & path fel comt, USPHS; lectr, XIVth World Dent Cong, Paris, France, First Pan-Pac Cong Dent Res, Tokyo, Japan & Asian Pac Regional Orgn Cong, Bangkok, Thailand; spec consult, Comt Asn Role & Function, mem comt advan educ, Task Force on Advan Educ & Exec Comt, chmn sect advan educ & vpres, Advan Educ Prog, Am Asn Dent Schs; hon guest prof, Kanagawa Dent Sch, Japan; int lectr & adv, Pan-Am Health Orgn, WHO, Colombia, Peru & Chile, 73; int lectr, Venezuela, 74; ed, J Dent Educ; USPHS grants. *Mem:* Fel AAAS; fel Am Pub Health Asn; Am Dent Asn; Norweg Dent Asn; Int Asn Dent Res. *Res:* Experimental dental caries; electron microscopy; mineralized tissues; graduate education. *Mailing Add:* Sch Dent Med Tufts Univ 136 Harrison Ave Boston MA 02111

JOHANSEN, HANS WILLIAM, b Worcester, Mass, June 11, 32; c 2. MARINE PHYCOLOGY. *Educ:* San Jose State Col, BA, 55; San Francisco State Col, MA, 61; Univ Calif, Berkeley, PhD(phycol), 66. *Prof Exp:* Teacher, San Mateo High Sch, 56-60; USPHS fel, 66-68; asst prof bot, 68-72, ASSOC PROF BOTANY, DEPT BIOL, CLARK UNIV, 72- *Mem:* Phycol Soc Am; Int Phycol Soc. *Res:* Systematics, structure, reproduction and morphogenesis of Corallinaceae; ecology of marine benthic algae. *Mailing Add:* Dept of Biol Clark Univ Worcester MA 01610

JOHANSEN, PETER HERMAN, b Moncton, NB, Dec 24, 39; m 65; c 4. ZOOLOGY. *Educ:* Univ NB, BSc, 61, MSc, 63; Univ BC, PhD(zool), 66. *Prof Exp:* ASSOC PROF BIOL, QUEEN'S UNIV, 66- *Mem:* Can Soc Zoologists. *Res:* Environmental physiology of teleost fish and aquatic toxicology. *Mailing Add:* Dept of Biol Queen's Univ Kingston ON K7L 3N6 Can

JOHANSEN, ROBERT H, b Grafton, NDak, July 25, 22; m 48; c 4. HORTICULTURE. *Educ:* NDak State Univ, BS, 49, MS, 56; La State Univ, PhD(hort), 64. *Prof Exp:* From asst horticulturist to assoc horticulturist, 53-65, HORTICULTURIST, NDAK STATE UNIV, 65-, PROF HORT & FORESTRY, 73- *Res:* Potato breeding. *Mailing Add:* Col of Agr NDak State Univ Fargo ND 58102

JOHANSEN, ROBERT TOROLF, b Minneapolis, Minn, June 13, 24; m 51; c 3. PHYSICAL CHEMISTRY. *Educ:* Jamestown Col, BS, 48; Okla State Univ, MS, 51. *Prof Exp:* Res chemist, Bur Mines, Dept Interior, 51-59, proj leader, 59-60, from asst proj coordr to prof coordr, 60-72, res supvr, 72-74; res supvr, Energy Res & Develop Admin, US Dept Energy, 75-81; RETIRED. *Honors & Awards:* Meritorious Serv Awards, Dept Interior, 68 & Energy Res & Develop Admin, 76. *Mem:* Am Chem Soc; Soc Petrol Engrs; Am Gas Asn; Interstate Oil Compact Comn; Am Petrol Inst. *Res:* Petroleum research, particularly in the development of secondary and tertiary recovery mechanisms and techniques, including related chemical and reservoir reactions. *Mailing Add:* 3502 Price Rd Bartlesville OK 74003

JOHANSON, CHRIS ELLYN, b Tacoma, Wash, June 18, 45; m 72. PSYCHOPHARMACOLOGY. *Educ:* Univ Ill, Chicago, BS, 68; Univ Chicago, PhD(psychol), 72. *Prof Exp:* USPHS trainee psychol, 68-72, RES ASSOC, DEPT PSYCHIAT, UNIV CHICAGO, 72- *Concurrent Pos:* Consult behav res, Behav Res & Action Social Res, 72-74, Schering Labs, 72-76 & Merrell-Nat Labs, 74-76. *Mem:* Am Psychol Asn; Behav Pharmacol Soc; Int Asn Study Drug Dependence. *Res:* The effects in the rhesus monkey of a variety of environmental and pharmacological variables on drug self-administration and effect of chronic drug administration on behavior. *Mailing Add:* Dept of Psychiat Univ Chicago 950 E 59th St Chicago IL 60637

JOHANSON, JERRY RAY, b Salt Lake City, Utah, Aug 29, 37; m 57; c 5. MECHANICAL ENGINEERING, APPLIED MECHANICS. *Educ:* Univ Utah, BS, 59, PhD(mech eng), 62. *Prof Exp:* Res engr, Appl Res Lab, US Steel Corp, 62-65, sr res engr, 65-66; vpres, 66-72, sr vpres, 72-80, PRES, JENIKE & JOHNSON, INC, 80- *Honors & Awards:* Henry Hess Award, Am Soc Mech Engrs, 66. *Mem:* Am Soc Mech Engrs; Int Briguetting Asn. *Res:* Flow of solids; agglomeration of solids; fluid flow in bulk solids; testing bulk properties of solids. *Mailing Add:* 2 Exec Park Dr North Billerica MA 01862

JOHANSON, L(ENNART) N(OBLE), b Salt Lake City, Utah, May 3, 21; m 48; c 3. CHEMICAL ENGINEERING. *Educ:* Univ Utah, BS, 42; Univ Wis, MS, 43, PhD(chem eng), 48. *Prof Exp:* Chem engr, US Bur Mines, Utah, 42; assoc process engr, Richfield Oil Corp, Calif, 44-45, process engr, 48-51; instr chem eng, Univ Wis, 47-48; from asst prof to assoc prof, 51-61, PROF CHEM ENG, UNIV WASH, 61- *Concurrent Pos:* Consult. *Mem:* Am Chem Soc; Am Soc Eng Educ; Am Inst Chem Engrs; Tech Asn Pulp & Paper Indust. *Res:* Pulp, paper technology; chemical engineering kinetics; reactor design; fluidization; high temperature technology. *Mailing Add:* Dept of Chem Eng Univ of Wash Seattle WA 98105

JOHANSON, LAMAR, b Kyle, Tex, Oct 31, 35; m 60. PLANT PHYSIOLOGY. *Educ:* Southwest Tex State Col, BS, 57, MA, 58; Tex A&M Univ, PhD(plant physiol), 67. *Prof Exp:* Asst biol, Southwest Tex State Col, 56-58; instr, Tarleton State Univ, 61-63; asst plant physiol, Tex A&M Univ, 63-65; assoc prof, 67-71, PROF BIOL & HEAD DEPT BIOL SCI, TARLETON STATE UNIV, 71- *Mem:* AAAS; Am Soc Plant Physiologists; Scandinavian Soc Plant Physiologists; Am Inst Biol Sci; Am Oil Chemists' Soc. *Res:* Nutrition of excised plant tissues and algae, especially calcium and sodium requirements; lateral root formation; biochemistry and physiology of the peanut; mineral nutrition, oil quality and response to irrigation. *Mailing Add:* Dept of Biol Sci Tarleton State Univ Stephenville TX 76402

JOHANSON, ROBERT GAIL, b San Francisco, Calif, Aug 26, 36; m 64; c 5. ANALYTICAL CHEMISTRY. *Educ:* Reed Col, AB, 60; Univ Vt, PhD(org chem), 69. *Prof Exp:* Chemist, Aerojet-Gen Corp, 61-66; fel org chem, Case Western Reserve Univ, 69-70; staff mem, Raychem Corp, 70-76; sr mem staff, Signetics Corp, 76-81; MGR HEAD & DISK DEVELOP, DATAPOINT CORP, 81- *Mem:* Am Chem Soc; Royal Soc Chem; Sigma Xi; Inst Elec & Electronics Engrs. *Res:* Analytical methods development; instrumental analysis; computer interfacing of analytical instruments. *Mailing Add:* Datapoint Corp 686 E Maude Sunnyvale CA 94086

JOHANSON, WALDEMAR GUSTAVE, JR, b St Paul, Minn, Sept 9, 37; m 60; c 3. INTERNAL MEDICINE, PULMONARY DISEASES. *Educ:* Gustavus Adolphus Col, BS, 59; Univ Minn, Minneapolis, MD, 62. *Prof Exp:* Intern med, Med Ctr, Univ Calif, Los Angeles, 62-63; resident, Minneapolis Vet Admin Hosp & St Paul Ramsey Hosp, 65-67; from instr to assoc prof med, Univ Tex Health Sci Ctr, Dallas, 69-74; assoc prof, 74-78, PROF MED, UNIV TEX HEALTH SCI CTR, SAN ANTONIO, 78-, CHIEF, PULMONARY DIS SECT, 74- *Concurrent Pos:* Nat Inst Arthritis & Infectious Dis fel, Univ Tex Health Sci Ctr, Dallas, 68-71. *Mem:* Am Thoracic Soc; Am Fedn Clin Res. *Res:* Pulmonary disease models; infectious disease of the lungs. *Mailing Add:* Univ of Tex Health Sci Ctr 7703 Floyd Curl Dr San Antonio TX 78284

JOHANSSON, KARL RICHARD, b Bay City, Mich, June 28, 20; m 43; c 3. MICROBIOLOGY. *Educ:* Univ Wis, BS, 42, MS, 46, PhD(bact), 48. *Prof Exp:* Anal chemist, Swift & Co, 42; asst bact, Univ Wis, 42-43, asst vet sci, 46, asst bact, 46-48; instr dairy bact, Univ Calif, 48-49; from asst prof to assoc prof bact & immunol, Univ Minn, 49-59; exec secy virol & rickettsiol study sect, Div Res Grants, NIH, 59-61; assoc prof environ health eng, Calif Inst Technol, 61-63; chief res grants br, Nat Inst Neurol Dis & Blindness, NIH, 63-65, exec secy virol study sect, Div Res Grants, 65-69; prof microbiol, Univ Tex Med Sch San Antonio, 69-70; dep dir sci affairs, Wistar Inst, 70-73; PROF BIOL SCI & CHMN DEPT, N TEX STATE UNIV, 73- *Concurrent Pos:* Consult, Gen Mills, Inc, 53, Minneapolis-Honeywell, 58-59 & Tex Col Osteop Med, 73- *Mem:* AAAS; Am Soc Microbiol; Soc Exp Biol & Med; Soc Gen Microbiol; Am Acad Microbiol. *Res:* Microbial ecology; oxidation of methane; microbial transformations in natural ecosystems. *Mailing Add:* Dept of Biol Sci NTex State Univ Denton TX 76203

JOHANSSON, MILDRED P, b Altamont, NY, Aug 31, 18; m 50. BIOLOGY, ENTOMOLOGY. *Educ:* State Univ NY, Albany, BA, 40; Cornell Univ, MA, 45. *Prof Exp:* Teacher high schs, 40-46; instr biol, Centenary Col, 46-49; asst prof physiol, Miami Univ, Ohio, 49-50; res aide anat, Col Med, State Univ, NY, 52-53; instr, Adelphi Col, 54-60; lectr, Queens Col, NY, 60-61; from asst prof to assoc prof, 61-70, PROF BIOL, QUEENSBOROUGH COMMUNITY COL, 70- *Mem:* AAAS; Int Bee Res Asn; Entom Soc Am. *Res:* Pollen residues in honey; honeybee forage plants; honeybee behavior and caste differentiation; population studies of Tribolium confusum. *Mailing Add:* Dept of Biol Queensborough Community Col Bayside NY 11364

JOHANSSON, TAGE SIGVARD KJELL, b Kalstad, Sweden, Aug 8, 19; nat US; m 50. ZOOLOGY. *Educ:* Beloit Col, BS, 42; Univ Wis, MS, 44, PhD(zool), 47. *Prof Exp:* Asst zool, Univ Wis, 42-46; instr, Grinnell Col, 47-48; instr, Dartmouth Col, 48-50; instr, NY Univ, 50-52; chmn dept, 60-63, PROF BIOL, QUEENS COL, NY, 52- *Concurrent Pos:* Entomologist, Bee Cult Lab, Agr Res Serv, USDA, Ariz, 56-57; vis assoc prof, Dept Environ Biol, Univ Guelph, 71-72; mem coun, Int Comn Bee Bot, 71- *Mem:* Entom Soc Am; Bee Res Asn. *Res:* Entomology; apiculture. *Mailing Add:* Dept of Biol Queens Col Flushing NY 11367

JOHAR, JOGINDAR SINGH, b Rawalpindi, West Pakistan, Jan 1, 35; m 60; c 3. ENVIRONMENTAL CHEMISTRY, FLUORINE CHEMISTRY. *Educ:* Panjab Univ, India, BSc, 57, MSc, 59; Univ Fla, PhD(chem), 66. *Prof Exp:* Lectr chem, Govt Col, Ludhiana, India, 59-62; chmn sci & math div, Cleveland State Community Col, 67-68; PROF CHEM, WAYNE STATE COL, 68- *Concurrent Pos:* Fel, Univ Idaho, 66-67. *Mem:* AAAS; Am Chem Soc. *Res:* Synthesis and study of fluorine compounds containing nitrogen sulfur and phosphorus; volatile products and use of non-aqueous solvents. *Mailing Add:* Dept of Chem Wayne State Col Wayne NE 68787

JOHARI, OM, b Jodhpur, India, Aug 13, 40; m 67; c 1. ELECTRON MICROSCOPY, METALLURGY. *Educ:* Indian Inst Technol, Kharagpur, BTech, 62; Univ Calif, Berkeley, MS, 63, PhD(metall), 65. *Prof Exp:* Res asst metall, Univ Calif, Berkeley, 62-65, res fel & lectr, 65; asst prof, Drexel Inst Technol, 65-66; res metallurgist, IIT Res Inst, 66-68, mgr metal physcis, 68-77; SECY & TREAS, SEM INC, 77-; PRES, JOHARI ASSOCS INC, 78- *Concurrent Pos:* Consult, Lockheed-Ga Co, 65-66; ed, Scanning Electron Micros, 68-, Food Microstruct, 81- *Honors & Awards:* Grossman Award, Am Soc Metals, 66. *Mem:* Microbeam Anal Soc. *Res:* Relationship between structure and properties of materials; applications of scanning and transmission electron microscopy in material sciences and other branches of science and technology; failure analysis of metallic materials. *Mailing Add:* Johari Assocs Inc 1034 Ala Dr Elk Grove Village IL 60007

JOHN, ANDREW, b Baltimore, Md, Jan 5, 34; m 54; c 2. PHOTOCHEMISTRY, CATALYSIS. *Educ:* Johns Hopkins Univ, BA, 54; Univ Del, MS, 56, PhD(phys chem), 57. *Prof Exp:* Res chemist, High Pressure Lab, 57-64, supvr cent res div, 64-73, supvr mat sci div, 73-74, supvr org res div, 74-78, mgr, Appln Develop Div, 78-81, SR RES ASSOC, HERCULES INC, 81- *Mem:* Am Chem Soc. *Res:* Heterogeneous and homogeneous catalysis; high pressure reactions; boron hydrides; photopolymerization; printing plates prepared by photopolymerization. *Mailing Add:* 23 Mars Rd North Star Newark DE 19711

JOHN, DAVID THOMAS, b Kano, Nigeria, Apr 25, 41; m 63; c 2. PARASITOLOGY. *Educ:* Asbury Col, AB, 63; Univ NC, Chapel Hill, MSPH, 66, PhD(parasitol), 70. *Prof Exp:* NIH malariology training prog grant, Univ Ga, 70-72; asst prof microbiol, 72-78, ASSOC PROF MICROBIOL, MED COL VA, VA COMMONWEALTH UNIV, 78- *Concurrent Pos:* Mem, Raptor Res Found; partic tour, People's Repub China, Am Soc Trop Med & Hyg, 78. *Mem:* Am Soc Parasitol; Wildlife Dis Asn; Soc Protozool; Am Soc Trop Med & Hyg; Sigma Xi. *Res:* Host-parasite relations. *Mailing Add:* Dept of Microbiol Med Col of Va Richmond VA 23298

JOHN, E ROY, b Brownsville, Pa, Aug 14, 24; m; c 6. NEUROPHYSIOLOGY, PSYCHOPHYSIOLOGY. *Educ:* Univ Chicago, BS, 48, PhD(physiol psychol), 54. *Prof Exp:* Sr res technician radiochem, Argonne Nat Labs, AEC, 46-51; res asst psychol, Univ Chicago, 51-54; res assoc, Comn Behav Sci, 54-56; assoc res anatomist, Univ Calif, Los Angeles, 56-57; assoc res physiologist, 57-58; assoc prof psychol, Univ Rochester, 59-60, prof psychol & dir, Ctr Brain Res, 60-63; prof psychiat & dir brain res labs, New York Med Col, 63-77, prof physiol, 72-77; PROF PSYCHIAT & DIR BRAIN RES LABS, NEW YORK UNIV MED CTR, 77- *Concurrent Pos:* Res consult chem, C F Pease Co, Chicago, 52-55; City New York Health Res Coun career scientist awards, 64-75; mem, Nat Adv Coun Brain Res; assoc ed, Brain & Behav Res. *Mem:* Am Physiol Soc; Am Psychopath Soc; Int Brain Res Orgn; Soc Neurosci. *Res:* Mechanisms of learning and memory; automatic computer evaluation of brain activity; assessment of minimal brain dysfunction in children; cognitive deficit in aging. *Mailing Add:* Brain Res Labs New York Univ Med Ctr New York NY 10016

JOHN, FRITZ, b Berlin, Ger, June 14, 10; nat US; m 33; c 2. MATHEMATICS. *Educ:* Univ Göttingen, PhD(math), 33. *Prof Exp:* Asst, Univ Göttingen, 32; res scholar, Cambridge Univ, 34-35; from asst prof to assoc prof math, Univ Ky, 35-42; mathematician, US War Dept, 43-45; assoc prof, 46-60, prof, 60-80, EMER PROF MATH, NY UNIV, 80- *Concurrent Pos:* Rockefeller Found fel, NY, 42; dir res, Inst Numerical Anal, Nat Bur Standards, Calif, 50-51; Josiah Willard Gibbs Lectr, Am Math Soc, 75, Courant prof math sci, 77. *Honors & Awards:* George David Birkhoff Prize Appl Math, Am Math Soc & Soc Indust & Appl Math, 73. *Mem:* Nat Acad Sci; Leopoldina Ger Acad Researchers Natural Sci; Am Math Soc; Math Asn Am. *Res:* Partial differential equations; non-linear elasticity; analysis; geometry. *Mailing Add:* Courant Inst Math Sci 251 Mercer St New York NY 10012

JOHN, GEORGE, b Nov 24, 21. NUCLEAR ENGINEERING. *Educ:* Ohio State Univ, PhD(nuclear chem), 52. *Prof Exp:* ASSOC PROF NUCLEAR ENG & PHYSICS, AIR FORCE INST TECHNOL, 56- *Mem:* Am Chem Soc; Am Asn Physics Teachers. *Mailing Add:* Dept of Physics Air Force Inst of Technol Wright-Patterson AFB OH 45433

JOHN, GEORGE SWISHER, b Lima, Ohio, May 16, 20; m 43; c 3. CHEMICAL PHYSICS, CHEMICAL ENGINEERING. *Educ:* Bowling Green State Univ, BS, 41; Ohio State Univ, PhD(phys chem), 49. *Prof Exp:* Asst chem, Bowling Green State Univ, 41-42 & Ohio State Univ, 42-43; res chemist, Manhattan Proj, SAM Labs, Columbia Univ, 43-44, Houdialle Hershey Co, 44-45 & Tenn Eastman Corp, 45-46; asst chem, Ohio State Univ, 46-48, res assoc, Res Found, 48-50; res chemist, Standard Oil Co Ind, 50-58; assoc prof chem eng, Univ Notre Dame, 58-62; CONSULT GOVT AGENCIES, 62- *Mem:* Am Chem Soc; Am Inst Chem Eng. *Res:* Electron scattering; kinetics and heterogeneous catalysis. *Mailing Add:* 800 S Campus Pl Princess Anne MD 21853

JOHN, JAMES EDWARD ALBERT, b Montreal, Ont, Nov 6, 33; US citizen; m 58; c 4. MECHANICAL ENGINEERING. *Educ:* Princeton Univ, BSE, 55, MSE, 57; Univ Md, PhD(mech eng), 63. *Prof Exp:* Res engr metall div, Air Reduction Co, Inc, NJ, 56-59; from instr to prof mech eng, Univ Md, 59-71; chmn dept, Univ Toledo, 71-77; PROF & CHMN DEPT MECH ENG, OHIO STATE UNIV, 77- *Concurrent Pos:* Consult Goddard Space Flight Ctr, NASA, 63-68; exec dir, Nat Acad Sci comt motor vehicle emissions, 71-72. *Mem:* Am Soc Mech Engrs; Am Soc Eng Educ. *Res:* Space simulation; vacuum; cryogenics; automotive emissions; thermal pollution; fluid dynamics. *Mailing Add:* Dept of Mech Eng Ohio State Univ Columbus OH 43210

JOHN, JOSEPH, b Madura, India, Mar 14, 38; m 67. NUCLEAR SCIENCE, INSTRUMENTATION. *Educ:* Madras Christian Col, India, BSc, 58; Univ Madras, MA, 60; Fla State Univ, PhD(nuclear physics), 68. *Prof Exp:* Indian AEC fel, Bhabha Atomic Res Ctr, Govt India, 58-59, sci officer nuclear physics, 59-62, jr res officer, 62-68; sr scientist, Gulf Gen Atomic, San Diego, 68-70; staff scientist, 71-72; prog mgr technol appln dept, Gulf Radiation Tech, San Diego, 72-73; mgr NDT technol dept, Intelcom Rad Tech, 73-75, mgr, NDI Systs Dept, 75-76, mgr, NDI Systs Div, 76-78, MGR NUCLEAR SYSTS DIV, IRT CORP, 78-, V PRES, 77- *Concurrent Pos:* Mgr, Californium-252 Demonstration Ctr, San Diego, 72-78. *Mem:* Am Phys Soc; Am Nuclear Soc; Am Soc Nondestructive Test; Am Mgt Asn; Am Soc Test & Mat. *Res:* Applied nuclear physics; applications of nuclear techniques for nondestructive evaluation; neutron radiography, radiation gauging, mineral exploration technology, nuclear materials measurement, automation and computer control of nondestructive inspection systems. *Mailing Add:* IRT Corp PO Box 80817 San Diego CA 92138

JOHN, KENNETH RYDAL, b Anaconda, Mont, Apr 10, 25; m 49; c 3. LIMNOLOGY. *Educ:* Univ Wyo, BS, 50; Univ Wis, MS, 52, PhD(limnol), 54. *Prof Exp:* Asst fish ecol, Univ Wis, 50-52, asst zool, 52-54; asst spec sensory functions in fishes, Am Mus Natural Hist, 54-55; instr, Northern Ill Univ, 55-56; assoc prof, 56-74, prof biol & chmn dept, 74-80, DR E PAUL & FRANCIS H RUFF PROF BIOL, FRANKLIN & MARSHALL COL, 80- *Mem:* Am Soc Limnol & Oceanog; Am Soc Ichthyol & Herpet; Ecol Soc Am. *Res:* Ecology of fishes; genetics. *Mailing Add:* 550 State St Lancaster PA 17603

JOHN, PETER WILLIAM MEREDITH, b Porthcawl, Wales, Aug 20, 23; nat US; m 54; c 2. MATHEMATICAL STATISTICS. *Educ:* Oxford Univ, BA, 44, MA, 48, dipl, 49; Univ Okla, PhD(math), 55. *Prof Exp:* Instr math, Univ Okla, 49-52 & 53-55; math master, Casady Sch, Okla, 52-53; asst prof, Univ NMex, 55-57; assoc res statistician, Calif Res Corp, Stand Oil Calif, 57-58, res statistician, 58-61; from assoc prof to prof, Univ Calif, Davis, 61-67; PROF MATH, UNIV TEX, AUSTIN, 67- *Concurrent Pos:* Vis prof, Univ Calif, Berkeley, 58-61; vis prof, Univ Ky, 70-71. *Mem:* Am Statist Asn; Inst Math Statist; Royal Statist Soc. *Res:* Design of experiments; engineering applications of mathematical statistics. *Mailing Add:* Dept of Math Univ of Tex at Austin Austin TX 78712

JOHN, WALTER, b Okla, Feb 16, 24; m 54; c 4. ENVIRONMENTAL PHYSICS. *Educ:* Univ Calif, PhD, 55. *Prof Exp:* Instr physics, Univ Ill, 55-58; physicist, Lawrence Radiation Lab, Univ Calif, 58-71; prof physics & phys sci & chmn dept, Stanislaus State Col, 71-74; RES SPECIALIST, AIR & INDUST HYG LAB, CALIF DEPT HEALTH, 74- *Concurrent Pos:* Res assoc, Univ Calif, Berkeley, 75- *Mem:* Am Phys Soc. *Res:* Experimental nuclear physics, especially nuclear reactions, fission and bent-crystal gamma ray spectroscopy; photonuclear reactions; x-rays; air pollution; aerosol physics; particulate matter in the atmosphere. *Mailing Add:* Air & Indust Hyg Lab Calif Dept of Health Berkeley CA 94704

JOHNK, CARL T(HEODORE) A(DOLF), b Lutterbeck, Ger, Oct 22, 19; US citizen; m 53; c 4. ELECTRICAL ENGINEERING. *Educ:* Shurtleff Col, BS, 41; Mo Sch Mines, BS, 42; Univ Ill, MS, 48, PhD(elec eng), 54. *Prof Exp:* Elec engr, Radio Corp Am, NJ, 42; instr elec eng, Univ Mo, Rolla, 42-44, from instr to asst prof, 45-49; res assoc, Univ Ill, 49-54; assoc prof, 54-65, PROF ELEC ENG, UNIV COLO, BOULDER, 65- *Concurrent Pos:* Consult, Denver Res Inst, 59-62 & Ramo-Wooldridge Corp, 60-61. *Mem:* Inst Elec & Electronics Engrs; Am Soc Eng Educ. *Res:* Antenna and array theory; modeling of antennas above lossy surfaces; modeling of very low frequency propagation in earthionosphere waveguide; electromagnetic fields; passive and active network theory. *Mailing Add:* Dept of Elec Eng Univ of Colo Boulder CO 80302

JOHNS, ANTHONY, b Neath, Wales, June 2, 47; m 72. PHARMACOLOGY. *Educ:* Univ London, BS, 70; Univ Wales, PhD(physiol), 73. *Prof Exp:* Tutorial fel physiol, Univ Col, Cardiff, Wales, 70-73; fel, WHO, 73-75; FEL, CAN HEART FOUND, 75- *Mem:* Soc Drug Res; Brit Pharmacol Soc. *Res:* Smooth muscle physiology and pharmacology; reproductive physiology; characteristics of catecholamine release. *Mailing Add:* Dept of Pharmacol Med Sci Univ of Alta Edmonton AB T6G 2E1 Can

JOHNS, DAVID GARRETT, b Prince Rupert, BC, Oct 18, 29; m 62; c 2. PHARMACOLOGY, BIOCHEMISTRY. *Educ:* McGill Univ, BSc, 54, MD, 58, PhD(biochem), 63. *Prof Exp:* Asst prof med, McGill Univ, 62-63; vis fel pharmacol, Sch Med, Yale Univ, 63-65; from asst prof to assoc prof, 65-70; head drug metab sect, Lab Chem Pharmacol, 70-75, actg chief lab med chem & biol, 75-78, CHIEF LAB MED CHEM & BIOL, NAT CANCER INST, 78- *Mem:* Am Soc Clin Invest; Asn Cancer Res; Am Soc Pharmacol & Exp Therapeut; Fedn Clin Res; Can Soc Clin Invest. *Res:* Mode of action and metabolism of cancer chemotherapeutic agents; megaloblastic anemias. *Mailing Add:* Nat Cancer Inst Bldg 37 Rm 5-C-02 NIH Bethesda MD 20205

JOHNS, DON HERBERT, analytical chemistry, see previous edition

JOHNS, HAROLD E, b Chengtu, W China, July 4, 15; m 40; c 3. PHYSICS, BIOPHYSICS. *Educ:* McMaster Univ, BA, 36; Univ Toronto, MA, 37, PhD(physics), 39. *Hon Degrees:* LLD, Univ Sask, 59; DSc, McMaster Univ, 68, Carleton Univ, 76 & Univ Western Ont, 78. *Prof Exp:* Lectr physics, Univ Alta, 39-45; from asst prof to prof, Univ Sask, 45-56; head dept med biophys, 62-71, PROF PHYSICS & MED BIOPHYS, UNIV TORONTO, 58-; HEAD PHYSICS DIV, ONT CANCER INST, 56- *Concurrent Pos:* Physicist, Sask Cancer Comn, 45-56; mem int comn radiol units, Int Cong Radiol, 52; mem, Nat Cancer Inst Can; Charles Mickle fel, Fac Med, Univ Toronto, 66. *Honors & Awards:* Roentgen Award, Brit Inst Radiol, 53; Medal, Can Asn Physicists, 65; Henry Marshall Tory Medal, Royal Soc Can, 71; Gairdner Int Award, 73; Coolidge Award, Am Asn Physicists in Med, 76; Officer of the Order of Can, 77; Gold Medal, Am Col Radiol, 80. *Mem:* Am Radium Soc; hon fel Am Col Radiol; Can Asn Physicists; Can Asn Med Physicists (pres, 55); Brit Inst Radiol. *Res:* Physical basis of radiotherapy; interaction of radiation with matter; development of cobalt-60 for radiotherapy; physics of radiation therapy and radiology; molecular biology; effects of ultraviolet light on deoxyribonucleic acid and its components; new methods of imaging in diagnostic radiology. *Mailing Add:* Ont Cancer Inst Physics Div 500 Sherbourne St Toronto ON M4X 1K9 Can

JOHNS, LEWIS E(DWARD), JR, b Pittsburgh, Pa, Dec 13, 35; m 57; c 3. CHEMICAL ENGINEERING. *Educ:* Carnegie Inst Technol, BS, 57, PhD(chem eng), 64. *Prof Exp:* Chem engr, Dow Chem Co, 62-67; asst prof, 67-76, assoc prof, 76-80, PROF CHEM ENG, UNIV FLA, 80- *Concurrent Pos:* Instr, Saginaw Valley Col, 64. *Mem:* Am Inst Chem Engrs. *Res:* Fluid mechanics; diffusion. *Mailing Add:* Dept of Chem Eng Univ of Fla Gainesville FL 32601

JOHNS, MARTIN WESLEY, b Chengtu, West China, Mar 23, 13; nat Can; m 81; c 4. NUCLEAR PHYSICS. *Educ:* McMaster Univ, BA, 32, MA, 34; Univ Toronto, PhD, 38. *Hon Degrees:* DSc, Brandon Univ, 75. *Prof Exp:* Prof physics, Brandon Col, 37-46; assoc res physicist, Nat Res Coun Can, 46-47; from asst prof to prof physics, McMaster Univ, 47-81, chmn dept, 61-67 & 70-77; RETIRED. *Concurrent Pos:* Nuffield travel grant, Oxford Univ, 59-60; vis scientist, Atomic Energy Can, 67-68. *Mem:* Am Phys Soc; Am Asn Physics Teachers; fel Royal Soc Can; Can Asn Physicists. *Res:* Atomic spectroscopy; neutron physics; nuclear decay schemes; angular correlation of gamma rays; nuclear structure spectroscopy. *Mailing Add:* Dept of Physics McMaster Univ Hamilton ON L8S 4L8 Can

JOHNS, MILTON VERNON, JR, b Berkeley, Calif, Sept 27, 25; m 54; c 2. MATHEMATICAL STATISTICS. *Educ:* Stanford Univ, BA, 49; Columbia Univ, PhD(math, statist), 56. *Prof Exp:* Res assoc, 56-57, from asst prof to assoc prof, 57-66, PROF STATIST, STANFORD UNIV, 66- *Mem:* AAAS; Am Math Soc; Math Asn Am; Inst Math Statist; Am Statist Asn. *Res:* Statistical decision theory. *Mailing Add:* Dept of Statistics Stanford Univ Stanford CA 94305

JOHNS, PHILIP TIMOTHY, b Bismarck, NDak, July 17, 43. BIOCHEMISTRY. *Educ:* Gustavus Adolphus Col, BA, 65; Univ NDak, PhD(biochem), 70. *Prof Exp:* Fla Heart Asn fel biochem, Col Med, Univ Fla, 70-72; asst prof chem, Va Union Univ, 72-76; ASST PROF CHEM, UNIV WIS-WHITEWATER, 76- *Mem:* Am Chem Soc. *Res:* Metabolic control; biosynthesis of plasma lipoproteins; enzymology and control of carbohydrate metabolism. *Mailing Add:* Dept of Chem Univ of Wis Whitewater WI 53190

JOHNS, RICHARD JAMES, b Pendleton, Ore, Aug 19, 25; m 53; c 3. MEDICINE. *Educ:* Univ Ore, BS, 47; Johns Hopkins Univ, MD, 48; Am Bd Internal Med, dipl. *Prof Exp:* Intern med, Johns Hopkins Hosp, 48-49; asst, 51-53, fel, 53-55, from instr to assoc prof, 55-66, asst dean admis, 62-66, dir sub-dept biomed eng, 66-70, prof med, Johns Hopkins Univ, 66-80, MASSEY PROF BIOMED ENG, JOHNS HOPKINS UNIV, 80-, PRIN PROF STAFF, APPL PHYSICS LAB, 67-, DIR DEPT BIOMED ENG, 70- *Concurrent Pos:* Asst resident physician, Johns Hopkins Hosp, 51-53, resident physician, 55-56, physician, 56- *Mem:* Fel AAAS; Am Soc Clin Invest; Am Clin & Climatol Asn; Biomed Eng Soc; fel Am Col Physicians. *Res:* Biomedical engineering; clincial support systems; neuromuscular function in man. *Mailing Add:* Dept of Biomed Eng Johns Hopkins Univ Sch of Med Baltimore MD 21205

JOHNS, THOMAS RICHARDS, II, b Fairmont, WVa, Aug 25, 24; m 46; c 3. NEUROLOGY, NEUROPHYSIOLOGY. *Educ:* Univ WVa, AB, 45; Harvard Univ, MD, 48; Am Bd Psychiat & Neurol, dipl, 56. *Prof Exp:* Intern, Faulkner Hosp, Boston, Mass, 48-49; resident neurol, Jefferson Hosp, Philadelphia, Pa, 49-51; from asst resident to chief resident, Neurol Inst, Presby Hosp, New York, 53-55; from neurologist to actg chief, Univ Hosp, 56-57, from asst prof to assoc prof, 56-64, PROF NEUROL, SCH MED, UNIV VA, 64-, NEUROLOGIST-IN-CHIEF, UNIV HOSP, 58- *Concurrent Pos:* Vis fel & asst neurol, Col Physicians & Surgeons, Columbia Univ, 54-55; Markle scholar, 57-62; res fel, Inst Pharmacol, Univ Lund, 60; consult, Vet Admin Hosp, Richmond, 57-65; mem med adv bd, Nat Mult Sclerosis Asn, 60-; mem staff, med res study sect, Voc Rehab Admin, 61-67, chmn, 65-67; mem rev panel, Neurol & Sensory Dis Br, Div Chronic Dis, Bur State Serv, asst examr, Am Bd Psychiat & Neurol, 62-65, assoc examr, 65- *Mem:* AAAS; Asn Nerv & Ment Dis; Am Acad Neurol; AMA. *Res:* Physiology and pharmacology of neuromuscular transmission; use of intra-cellular electrodes to elucidate nature of disease. *Mailing Add:* Dept of Neurol Univ of Va Sch of Med Charlottesville VA 22901

JOHNS, VARNER JAY, JR, b Denver, Colo, Jan 27, 21; m 44; c 3. INTERNAL MEDICINE. *Educ:* La Sierra Col, BS, 44; Col Med Evangelists, MD, 45; Am Bd Internal Med, dipl, 51, cert, 74; Am Bd Cardiovasc Dis, dipl, 66. *Prof Exp:* Intern, White Mem Hosp, 44-45, resident internal med, 45-47; resident path, Loma Linda Sanitarium & Hosp, 47-48; instr internal med, Sch Med, Loma Linda Univ, 48-51, asst clin prof & assoc dean, 51-54, asst prof, 54-55, assoc clin prof, 55-56, assoc prof, 56-57, chmn dept med, 56-69, chief, Med Serv, Univ Hosp, 64-69, PROF MED, SCH MED, LOMA LINDA UNIV, 57-, SR PHYSICIAN, 64-, ASSOC DEAN CONTINUING EDUC, UNIV, 75- *Concurrent Pos:* Consult, Off Surg Gen, US, 56-67; sr attend physician, Los Angeles County Hosp, 56-64, physician-in-chief internal med, 58-64; vis colleague, Inst Cardiol, London, 62-63; hon vis physician, Nat Heart Hosp, London, 62-63; co-chmn dept med, White Mem Hosp, 78- *Mem:* Am Heart Asn; AMA; Am Fedn Clin Res; fel Am Col Physicians; Int Soc Internal Med. *Res:* Cardiology. *Mailing Add:* Loma Linda Univ Med Ctr Loma Linda CA 92354

JOHNS, WILLIAM DAVIS, b Waynesburg, Pa, Nov 2, 25; m 46; c 3. GEOCHEMISTRY. *Educ:* Col Wooster, AB, 47; Univ Ill, MS, 51, PhD(geol), 52. *Prof Exp:* Spec asst petrol, Eng Exp Sta, Univ Ill, 49-52, asst geol, 52-55; from asst prof to prof, Wash Univ, 55-70, chmn dept earth sci, 62-69; PROF GEOL, UNIV MO-COLUMBIA, 70- *Concurrent Pos:* Fulbright scholar, Univ Göttingen, 59-60 & Univ Heidelberg, 68-69. *Honors & Awards:* Alexander von Humboldt US Sr Scientist Award, 77. *Mem:* Fel Geol Soc Am; Am Mineral Soc; Mineral Soc Gt Brit & Ireland; Geochem Soc; Clay Minerals Soc. *Res:* Mineralogy of clays; recent sediments; diagenesis; organic geochemistry; burial diagenesis of pelitic sediments and dispersed organic matter. *Mailing Add:* Dept of Geol Univ of Mo Columbia MO 65201

JOHNS, WILLIAM FRANCIS, b Chicago, Ill, Aug 31, 30; m 50; c 3. ORGANIC CHEMISTRY, MEDICINAL CHEMISTRY. *Educ:* Univ Chicago, PhB, 48, MS, 51; Univ Wis, PhD(org chem), 55. *Prof Exp:* Jr res chemist org synthesis, Merck & Co, 51-53; sr res chemist pharmaceut, 55-65, res fel, 65-71, asst dir chem res, 71-73, DIR CHEM RES, SEARLE LABS, G D SEARLE & CO, 73- *Mem:* Am Chem Soc; AAAS; Am Pharm Asn; NY Acad Sci. *Res:* Organic synthesis, especially steroids, antialdosterone agents. *Mailing Add:* 1360 Sanford Lane Glenview IL 60025

JOHNS, WILLIS MERLE, b Spokane, Wash, June 23, 21; m 50; c 1. ECONOMIC GEOLOGY, GEOCHEMISTRY. *Educ:* Mont Sch Mines, BS, 52, MS, 58. *Prof Exp:* Geologist, Am Smelting & Refining Co, 52-54, resident geologist, 54-56, proj geologist, 58-64, chief geologist, 64-74, CHIEF ECON GEOL DIV, MONT BUR MINES & GEOL, 74- *Concurrent Pos:* From asst prof to assoc prof econ geol, Mont Col Mineral Sci & Technol, 64-73, prof, 74- *Mem:* Soc Econ Geologists; Asn Prof Geol Scientists. *Res:* Regional geology of Precambrian Belt rocks in northwest Montana. *Mailing Add:* Mont Bur of Mines & Geol Mont Col Mineral Sci & Technol Butte MT 59701

JOHNSEN, DENNIS O, b Santa Monica, Calif, Apr 2, 37; m 62; c 3. LABORATORY ANIMAL MEDICINE, VETERINARY MEDICINE. *Educ:* Univ Calif, Davis, BS, 59, DVM, 61; Ohio State Univ, MS, 65. *Prof Exp:* Chief vet med br lab animal med, US Army Res Inst Environ Med, Natick, Mass, 62-63; chief vet med serv, Naval Radiol Defense Lab, San Francisco, 65-68; chief vet med br, SEATO Med Res Lab, Bangkok, 68-72; chief animal resources br, Letterman Army Inst Res, San Francisco, 72-76; exec secy animal resources rev comt, Div Res Resource, NIH, 76-80; SCIENCE ATTACHE & INT HEALTH REP, AM EMBASSY, NEW DELHI, INDIA, 80- *Concurrent Pos:* Coun mem & consult, Am Asn Accreditation of Lab Animal Care, 74-76; bd dirs & ed newsletter, Am Col Lab Animal Med, 77-79. *Mem:* Am Vet Med Asn; Am Soc Lab Animal Practitioners; Am Col Lab Animal Med; Am Asn Lab Animal Sci. *Res:* Nonhuman primatology and breeding; spontaneous diseases of laboratory animals; laboratory animal quality assurance. *Mailing Add:* Dept State New Delhi Washington DC 20520

JOHNSEN, ELMER L, b Lake Forest, Ill, June 28, 30; m 58; c 4. ELECTRICAL ENGINEERING. *Educ:* Harvard Univ, BA, 52; Univ Mich, Ann Arbor, MSEE, 54, PhD(elec eng), 64. *Prof Exp:* Sr engr, Cook Res Labs, 56-58, res asst radar systs, Univ Mich, Ann Arbor, 58-60, res assoc, 60-63, assoc res engr, 63-65, res engr, 65-77, lectr elec eng, 66-70; RES ENGR, ENVIRON RES INST MICH, 73- *Honors & Awards:* Barry Carleton Award, Inst Elec & Electronics Engrs Group on Aerospace & Electronic Systs, 73. *Mem:* Inst Elec & Electronics Engrs; Sigma Xi. *Res:* Radar systems; electromagnetic scattering properties of radar targets. *Mailing Add:* Environ Res Inst of Mich Box 8618 Ann Arbor MI 48107

JOHNSEN, EUGENE CARLYLE, b Minneapolis, Minn, Jan 27, 32; m 57. ALGEBRA. *Educ:* Univ Minn, BChem, 54; Ohio State Univ, PhD(math), 61. *Prof Exp:* Instr chem & math, Univ Minn, 56-57; instr math, Ohio State Univ, 62; Nat Acad Sci-Nat Res Coun res assoc, Nat Bur Standards, 62-63; lectr, 63-64, from asst prof to assoc prof, 64-74, PROF MATH, UNIV CALIF, SANTA BARBARA, 74- *Concurrent Pos:* Air Force Off Sci res grants, 64-73, vis lectr, Univ Mich, 68-69; Fulbright Hays res grant, Univ of Tübingen, 69; NSF res grant, 77-; gen ed, DISCOVERY, Univ Calif, Santa Barbara, J Undergrad Res. *Mem:* AAAS; Am Math Soc; Math Asn Am; Soc Indust & Appl Math. *Res:* Combinatorial designs and matrices; finite geometries; algebraic structures; matrix theory; mathematical models in biological and social sciences. *Mailing Add:* Dept of Math Univ of Calif Santa Barbara CA 93106

JOHNSEN, JOHN HERBERT, b Staten Island, NY, Aug 19, 23; m 48; c 3. GEOLOGY. *Educ:* Syracuse Univ, AB, 47, MSc, 48; Lehigh Univ, PhD(geol), 57. *Prof Exp:* Asst geol, Syracuse Univ, 46-48; mining geologist, NJ Zinc Co, Va, 48-49; from instr to assoc prof, 51-67, PROF GEOL, VASSAR COL, 67-, CHMN DEPT, 63-66 & 68- *Concurrent Pos:* Vis prof, Sci Camp, Univ Wyo, 53; del, Int Geol Cong Mex, 56 & Australia, 76; eng geologist, NY State Dept Pub Works, 59; vis prof, St Augustine's Col, 60 & State Univ NY Col New Paltz, 60 & 64-65; assoc dir, Summer Inst Earth Sci, 61, dir, Summer Inst Geol, 62-72; part time geologist-consult, Hudson River Valley Comn, 65, NY State Off of Planning Coord, 66-67, Cent New Region Planning & Develop Bd, 69-70; mem, NSF Conf Geol Lake Superior Region, 63, NSF Conf Geol Southern Can Rockies, 67 & Environ Task Force, 25th Cong Dist, NY, 74-; part time dir, Ecol-Conserv Prog, Vassar Col, 73- *Mem:* AAAS; fel Geol Soc Am; Soc Econ Paleontologists & Mineralogists; Am Geophys Union; Sigma Xi. *Res:* Stratigraphy and petrography of early and middle Paleozoic carbonate rocks of New York; geology of aggregate materials and reclamation studies of mined lands. *Mailing Add:* Dept of Geol & Geog Vassar Col Poughkeepsie NY 12601

JOHNSEN, RAINER, b Kiel, Ger, Jan 23, 40; m 65; c 2. PHYSICS. *Educ:* Univ Kiel, dipl physics, 65, Dr rer nat, 66. *Prof Exp:* Res assoc physics, 66-68, res asst prof, 68-71, RES ASSOC PROF PHYSICS, UNIV PITTSBURGH, 71- *Mem:* Am Geophys Union. *Res:* Atomic physics; atomic collisions; physics of upper atmosphere; mass spectroscopy; laser plasma research. *Mailing Add:* Dept of Physics Univ of Pittsburgh Pittsburgh PA 15260

JOHNSEN, RICHARD EMANUEL, b Brooklyn, NY, Feb 8, 36; m 57; c 3. INSECTICIDE TOXICOLOGY. *Educ:* St Olaf Col, BA, 57; Iowa State Univ, MS, 59, PhD(entom), 62. *Prof Exp:* Asst entom, Iowa State Univ, 62; asst prof, 65-70, ASSOC PROF ENTOM, COLO STATE UNIV, 70- *Mem:* AAAS; Am Chem Soc; Entom Soc Am; Am Soc Microbiol; NY Acad Sci. *Res:* Pesticides and their residues, particularly their metabolism, distribution and persistence in plants, soils and the physical environment; microbial pesticide degradation; analytical methodology for pesticide studies. *Mailing Add:* Dept of Zool & Entom Colo State Univ Ft Collins CO 80523

JOHNSEN, ROGER CRAIG, b Warren, Pa, Apr 25, 38; m 65. GENETICS. *Educ:* Ohio Wesleyan Univ, BA, 60; Univ Ore, MS, 63; Brown Univ, PhD(genetics), 68. *Prof Exp:* Asst prof, 67-73, ASSOC PROF BIOL, ADELPHI UNIV, 73- *Mem:* AAAS; Soc Study Social Biol; Genetics Soc Am; Am Genetics Asn. *Res:* Chromosome behavior and mechanics; effects of structure and gene action on chromosome recovery during gametogenesis; genetic controls on the competitive behavior of reciprocal gametic types. *Mailing Add:* Dept of Biol Adelphi Univ Garden City NY 11530

JOHNSEN, RUSSELL HAROLD, b Chicago, Ill, Aug 5, 22; m 48; c 2. RADIATION CHEMISTRY, ACADEMIC ADMINISTRATION. *Educ:* Univ Chicago, BS, 47; Univ Wis, PhD(chem), 51. *Prof Exp:* Res chemist, Ninol Lab, 46-47; from asst prof to assoc prof, 51-61, PROF CHEM, FLA STATE UNIV, 61-, ASSOC DEAN, GRAD STUDIES, 77- *Concurrent Pos:* Assoc provost, Col Arts & Sci, Fla State Univ, 74-77. *Mem:* Fel AAAS; Am Chem Soc; Am Phys Soc; Radiation Res Soc; Am Soc Mass Spectrometry. *Res:* Kinetics of reactive intermediates, mechanistic studies; free radical reactions in the atmosphere; electron spin resonance studies. *Mailing Add:* 1425 Devil's Dip Tallahassee FL 32308

JOHNSEN, SHERMAN EDWARD JEROME, b Minneapolis, Minn, July 23, 20; m 43; c 3. APPLIED MATHEMATICS. *Educ:* Univ Minn, BChem, 42; Purdue Univ, MS, 62. *Prof Exp:* Res chemist phys chem, Monsanto Chem Co, Tex, 42-47, res group leader, 47-53, res sect leader, 53-57; asst math, Purdue Univ, 57-62; sr mathematician, 62-70, SR DEVELOP ENGR, DETROIT DIESEL ALLISON DIV, GEN MOTORS CO, 70- *Res:* Monte Carlo simulations. *Mailing Add:* 790 W Oak St Zionsville IN 46077

JOHNSEN, THOMAS NORMAN, JR, b Chicago, Ill, July 3, 29; m 56; c 2. ECOLOGY, RANGE MANAGEMENT. *Educ:* Univ Ariz, BS, 50, MS, 54; Duke Univ, PhD(bot), 60. *Prof Exp:* Res scientist range weed control, 56-72, res leader, Agr Res Serv, US Dept Agr, 72-78; RES SCIENTIST RANGE ECOL, TUCSON, ARIZ, 78- *Mem:* AAAS; Ecol Soc Am; Weed Sci Soc Am; Soc Range Mgt; Am Soc Agron. *Res:* Evaluation and development of grazing land weed and brush control methods; fate of herbicides in soils and water; plant life history; plant population changes and trends; plant biomass production; development of crimson poppy as a crop. *Mailing Add:* USDA, Sci Educ Admin 2000 E Allen Rd Tucson AZ 85719

JOHNSGARD, PAUL AUSTIN, b Fargo, NDak, June 28, 31; m 56; c 4. ZOOLOGY. *Educ:* NDak State Univ, BS, 53; Wash State Univ, MS, 55; Cornell Univ, PhD(vert zool), 59. *Prof Exp:* NSF fel zool, Bristol Univ, 59-60, USPHS fel, 60-61; from instr to assoc prof, 61-68, FOUND PROF, UNIV NEBR-LINCOLN, 68- *Concurrent Pos:* NSF res grants, 63-67 & 68-71; Guggenheim Found fel, 71; mem bd dirs, Int Wild Waterfowl Asn, 72- *Honors & Awards:* Outstanding Publ Award, Wildlife Soc, 74. *Mem:* Am Ornith Union; Wilson Ornith Soc; Cooper Ornith Soc. *Res:* Systematics of birds, especially the family Anatidae; comparative behavior of birds; ecology of vertebrates; speciation and isolating mechanisms; sympatry and hybridization in birds. *Mailing Add:* 7431 Holdrege Lincoln NE 68505

JOHNSON, A(LFRED) BURTON, JR, b Salt Lake City, Utah, Apr 8, 29; m 54; c 4. CORROSION, NUCLEAR MATERIALS. *Educ:* Univ Utah, BS, 54, PhD(fuel technol), 58. *Prof Exp:* Mem staff, Hanford Labs, Gen Elec Co, 61-65; staff scientist, 65-81, SR STAFF SCIENTIST, PAC NORTHWEST DIV, BATTELLE MEM INST, 81- *Concurrent Pos:* Lectr, Univ Dayton, 60-61, Richland Grad Ctr, 74-; mem staff, Univ Wis, 73. *Mem:* Am Chem Soc; Nat Asn Corrosion Engrs; Am Soc Testing & Mat. *Res:* Corrosion in fission and fusion reactors; atmospheric corrosion; corrosion of ancient metals; spent nuclear fuel storage; author or coauthor of over 100 publications. *Mailing Add:* Pacific Northwest Div Battelle Mem Inst Richland WA 99352

JOHNSON, ADRIAN EARL, JR, b Port Arthur, Tex, Dec 17, 28; m 49; c 3. CHEMICAL ENGINEERING, MATHEMATICS. *Educ:* La State Univ, BS, 48; Mass Inst Technol, SM, 49; Univ Fla, PhD(chem eng), 58. *Prof Exp:* Process engr, Mobil Oil Co, Tex, 49-53; asst prof chem eng, Lamar State Univ, 53-54; instr, Univ Fla, 54-57; appl scientist, Int Bus Mach Corp, La, 57-60; asst dir comput res ctr-eng res ctr, La State Univ, 60-62; consult & mgr mgt serv dept, Union Carbide Corp, NY, 62-67; staff consult, Real Time Systs, Inc, 67-68; PROF CHEM ENG, LA STATE UNIV, BATON ROUGE, 68- *Mem:* Am Inst Chem Engrs. *Res:* Computer control of petrochemical processes; optimization and control of distillation columns and methanol plants. *Mailing Add:* 14115 Harrell's Ferry Rd Baton Rouge LA 70816

JOHNSON, ALAN ARTHUR, b Beckenham, Eng, Aug 18, 30; m 58; c 5. MATERIALS SCIENCE & ENGINEERING. *Educ:* Univ Reading, BSc, 52; Univ Toronto, MA, 54; Univ of London, Dipl & PhD(metal physics), 60. *Prof Exp:* Demonstr physics, Univ Toronto, 52-54; sci officer, Royal Naval Sci Serv, 54-56; res asst metall, Imp Col, Univ London, 56-57, lectr, 60-62; dir res, Mat Res Corp, NY, 63-65; prof phys metall, Polytech Inst Brooklyn, 65-71, head dept phys & eng metall, 67-71; prof mat sci & chmn dept mat sci & eng, Wash State Univ, 71-75; dean grad sch, 75-76, PROF MAT SCI, UNIV LOUISVILLE, 75- *Mem:* Metall Soc; Am Soc Metals. *Res:* Low temperature physics; oceanography; underwater acoustics; biomedical materials. *Mailing Add:* Speed Sci Sch Univ of Louisville Louisville KY 40292

JOHNSON, ALAN CLAIR, b Washington, DC, Jan 1, 46; m 81. SOLID STATE PHYSICS, MICROELECTRONIC ENGINEERING. *Educ:* Colgate Univ, BA, 67; Tulane Univ, MS, 71, PhD(physics), 75. *Prof Exp:* Engr, Westinghouse Elec Corp, Baltimore, Md, 67-69; instr physics, Univ New Orleans, 75-79; MICROELECTRONIC PROCESS ENGR, ROCKWELL INT, NEWPORT BEACH, CALIF, 79- *Mem:* Am Phys Soc. *Res:* Thin film superconductivity. *Mailing Add:* Rockwell Int 4311 Jamboree Rd Newport Beach CA 92660

JOHNSON, ALAN J, b Washington, DC, Mar 19, 19; m 52; c 3. HEMATOLOGY, BIOCHEMISTRY. *Educ:* Dartmouth Col, BA, 40; Univ Wis, MA, 42; Lond Island Col Med, MD, 45. *Prof Exp:* Fel med, 48-49, asst med, 49-50, from instr med to assoc prof exp med, 50-71, PROF EXP MED, SCH MED, NY UNIV, 71- *Concurrent Pos:* Clin asst vis physician, Bellevue Hosp, New York, 49-52, asst vis physician, 52-; assoc res dir blood prog, Am Nat Red Cross Res Lab, 61-70; assoc attend, Univ Hosp, NY Univ Med Ctr, 61-; mem comt plasma fractionation & related processes, Blood Res Inst, 61-71; mem comt thrombolytic agts, Nat Heart & Lung Inst, 62-68, mem thrombosis adv comt, 68-70, 72- & comt thrombosis, 68-74; consult, Med Serv, Vet Admin Hosp, New York, 64-; consult, WHO, 66-, Community Blood Coun Gtr New York, 68-, Protein Fractionation Ctr, Nat Transfusion Asn Scotland, 69-, Protein Fractionation Unit, Oxford Haemophilia Ctr, Med Res Coun, Eng, 69-, Iranian Nat Transfusion Soc, 71 & Nat Heart & Lung Inst, 72-; mem subcomt factor VIII & IX prep & co-chmn subcomt fibrinolysis, thrombolysis and intravascular coagulation, Int Comt Thrombosis & Haemostasis, 66-71, co-chmn & chmn subcomt standardization, 71-; mem subcomt protocol & standardization & anal biochem data, Streptokinase-Urokinase Pulmonary Embolism Trial, 68-73; mem coun thrombosis, Am Heart Asn; career scientist, NY Health Res Coun, 70-75. *Mem:* Soc Exp Biol & Med; Am Soc Clin Invest; Am Soc Exp Pathologists; Am Fedn Clin Res; Am Physiol Soc. *Res:* Fibrinolysis; blood coagulation; fibrinolytic agents and inhibitors; thromboembolic disease; plasma fractionation with solid-phase reagents; isolation, purification, function and kinetics of proteolytic enzymes and blood coagulation components for clinical and laboratory use; concentration and removal of hepatitis-associated antigen from plasma and plasma fractions; standardization of coagulation and fibrinolytic agents and reagents. *Mailing Add:* Dept of Med NY Univ Med Ctr New York NY 10016

JOHNSON, ALAN KIM, b Altoona, Pa, Aug 15, 42; m 65; c 1. BEHAVIORAL BIOLOGY. *Educ:* Pa State Univ, BS, 64; Temple Univ, MA, 66; Univ Pittsburgh, PhD(psychobiol), 70. *Prof Exp:* Fel psychobiol, Inst Neurol Sci, Univ Pa, 70-73; asst prof, 73-77, ASSOC PROF PSYCHOL, UNIV IOWA, 77- *Concurrent Pos:* NIH fel, 70. *Honors & Awards:* Res Scientist Develop Award, NIMH, 75. *Mem:* Sigma Xi; AAAS; Soc Neurosci. *Res:* Neurobiology and endocrinology of feeding and drinking; physiological bases of motivation and reinforcement. *Mailing Add:* Dept of Psychol Univ of Iowa Iowa City IA 52240

JOHNSON, ALAN LEN, plant breeding, see previous edition

JOHNSON, ALBERT SYDNEY, III, b Clarkston, Ga, Dec 27, 33; m 59; c 4. WILDLIFE BIOLOGY, WILDLIFE MANAGEMENT. *Educ:* Univ Ga, BS, 59; Auburn Univ, MS, 62, PhD(zool), 69. *Prof Exp:* Fire control aide, US Forest Serv, 58; res asst wildlife biol, Auburn Univ, 59-62, instr wildlife biol & zool, 63-68; wildlife biologist, Ala State Dept Conserv, 62-63; ASSOC DIR BIOL RESOURCES, INST NATURAL RESOURCES, UNIV GA, 68- *Mem:* AAAS; Ecol Soc Am; Wildlife Soc; Am Soc Mammalogists; Soc Am Foresters. *Res:* Wildlife habitat biology and management; ecological impacts of land management practices. *Mailing Add:* Inst of Natural Resources Univ of Ga 13 Ecol Bldg Athens GA 30602

JOHNSON, ALBERT W, b Belvidere, Ill, July 29, 26; m 45; c 3. PLANT ECOLOGY. *Educ:* Colo Agr & Mech Col, BS, 49; Univ Colo, MS, 51, PhD(bot), 56. *Prof Exp:* Instr biol, Univ Colo, 54-55; from instr to assoc prof bot, Univ Alaska, 56-62, NSF fac sci fel, 60-61; jr res botanist, Univ Calif, Los Angeles, 62-64; from asst prof to assoc prof, 64-69, dean, Col Sci, 69-77, actg vpres, acad affairs, 77-80, PROF BIOL, SAN DIEGO STATE UNIV, 69-, VPRES, ACAD AFFAIRS, 80- *Mem:* AAAS; Ecol Soc Am. *Res:* Arctic and alpine plant ecology and taxonomy; cytogenetics; physiological ecology. *Mailing Add:* Dept of Biol San Diego State Univ San Diego CA 92115

JOHNSON, ALBERT WAYNE, b Mullins, SC, July 19, 44; m 65; c 3. ENTOMOLOGY. *Educ:* Clemson Univ, BS, 66, MS, 68; Auburn Univ, PhD(entom), 71. *Prof Exp:* assoc prof tobacco insects, 70-80, assoc prof entom, 74-80, PROF TOBACCO INSECTS & ENTOM, PEE DEE EXP STA, CLEMSON UNIV, 80- *Mem:* Entom Soc Am. *Res:* Insecticide screening, economic thresholds, scouting techniques, insect surveys of pests and beneficials, cultural control practices, biological control, host-plant resistance studies and development of insect-resistant varieties; insect control using insecticides and parasites, predators, and pathogens. *Mailing Add:* 3043 Larkspur Rd Florence SC 29501

JOHNSON, ALDIE E(DWIN), JR, b Moline, Ill, Apr 8, 25; m 47; c 3. MECHANICAL & AEROSPACE ENGINEERING. *Educ:* Iowa State Col, BS, 47. *Prof Exp:* Aerospace res scientist, res engr, Struct Res Div, Langley Aeronaut Labor, Nat Adv Comt Aeronaut, 48-57; group leader struct test, Res & Adv Develop Div, Avco Corp, 57-59, asst sect chief, 59, sect chief, 59-64, dept mgr struct, 64-68; mgr engr, Teledyne Mt Res, 68-76, V PRES, TELEDYNE ENG SERV, 76- *Mem:* Assoc fel Am Inst Aeronaut & Astronaut; fel Soc Exp Stress Anal (pres, 71). *Res:* Analytical mechanics; nuclear power generation component design; aerospace structural testing technology. *Mailing Add:* 130 Second Ave Waltham MA 02254

JOHNSON, ALEXANDER LAWRENCE, b Gisborne, NZ, Oct 13, 31; nat US; m 61; c 3. ORGANIC CHEMISTRY. *Educ:* Victoria Univ, Wellington, BSc, 54, MSc, 55; Univ Rochester, PhD(org chem), 64. *Prof Exp:* Sec sch teacher chem, Rongotai Col, NZ, 55-60; RES CHEMIST, CENT RES DEPT, E I DU PONT DE NEMOURS & CO, INC, 63- *Honors & Awards:* Eastman Kodak Prize, Univ Rochester, 62. *Mem:* Am Chem Soc; The Chem Soc; NZ Inst Chemists. *Res:* Elucidation of the structures of natural products; synthetic organic chemistry relating to these and to heterocyclic systems; application of physical methods to the solution of organic chemical problems. *Mailing Add:* Cent Res Dept Exp Sta E I du Pont de Nemours & Co Inc Wilmington DE 19898

JOHNSON, ALFRED THEODORE, JR, b Phila, Pa, June 24, 41. ELECTRICAL ENGINEERING. *Educ:* Drexel Univ, BSEE, 63; Univ Pa, PhD(elec eng), 69. *Prof Exp:* Asst prof, 74-78, ASSOC PROF ENG, WIDENER COL, 78- *Mem:* Inst Elec & Electronics Engrs. *Res:* Approximation problem using analog and digital filters; analog fault analysis; circuit theory. *Mailing Add:* Ctr of Eng Widener Col Chester PA 19013

JOHNSON, ALICE RUFFIN, b Charlottesville, Va, Sept 22, 36; div; c 2. PHARMACOLOGY, IMMUNOLOGY. *Educ:* Univ Va, BS, 58; Emory Univ, MS, 60, PhD(pharmacol), 68. *Prof Exp:* From instr to asst prof pharmacol, Sch Med, Emory Univ, 68-72; vis scientist, Scripps Clin & Res Found, 72-74; ASST PROF PHARMACOL, SOUTHWESTERN MED SCH, UNIV TEX HEALTH SCI CTR, DALLAS, 74- *Concurrent Pos:* Nat

Inst Allergy & Infectious Dis res grant, 69-72; NIH spec fel, Scripps Clin & Res Found, 72-74; Nat Heart Lung & Blood Inst res grant, 75- *Mem:* AAAS; Am Soc Pharmacol & Exp Therapeut. *Res:* Release of pharmacologically active substances; mast cells; endothelial cells; peptides; allergy. *Mailing Add:* Dept of Pharmacol Univ of Tex Health Sci Ctr Dallas TX 75325

JOHNSON, ALLAN ALEXANDER, b Georgetown, Guyana. INTERNATIONAL NUTRITION, FOOD SCIENCE. *Educ:* McGill Univ, BSc, 72; Cornell Univ, MNS, 74, PhD(int nutrit), 78. *Prof Exp:* Res asst, Cornell Univ, 72-78, nutrit sci, 74, biochem, 74-75, ref asst, Albert R Mann Libr, 75-78; ASST PROF HUMAN NUTRIT, HOWARD UNIV, 78- *Concurrent Pos:* Int Health grant, Howard Univ, 78- *Mem:* Am Pub Health Asn. *Res:* Prevalence and etiology of nutritional anemias; programs for control of nutritional anemias; methods for assessment of nutritional status. *Mailing Add:* Prog in Human Nutrit & Food Howard Univ Washington DC 20059

JOHNSON, ALLAN M, b Apr 3, 21; US citizen; m 42; c 9. MECHANICAL ENGINEERING. *Educ:* Brigham Young Univ, ME, 56. *Prof Exp:* Combustion engr, Aircraft Gas Turbine Div, Gen Elec Co, 56-58; sr engr, Marquardt Corp, Van Nuys, 58-62, mem adv tech staff electrochem, 62-72; INDUST CONSULT, 72- *Mem:* AAAS. *Res:* Combustion research for propulsion applications; fuel cell electrochemistry and electrochemical water desalting; sorbent based recirculating dialysate artificial kidney system; industrial heat transfer systems. *Mailing Add:* 7423 Balcom Ave Reseda CA 91335

JOHNSON, ALLEN NEILL, b Colfax, Wash, Dec 19, 44; m 71; c 2. PATHOLOGY. *Educ:* Wash State Univ, DVM, 69; Univ Wis, PhD(vet sci), 77; Am Col Vet Pathologists, dipl, 78. *Prof Exp:* Res asst, Univ Wis-Madison, 71-74; vet path, Univ Ga Vet Med Col, 74-76; pathologist, Lederle Labs, 76-78; GROUP LEADER PATH, ORTHOPHARMACEUT CORP, 78- *Mem:* Am Col Vet Pathologists; Int Acad Path; Am Vet Med Asn; Soc Toxicol Pathologists; Am Vet Clin Pathologists. *Res:* Evaluation of tissues from laboratory animals and farm species to determine and resolve pathologic lesions associated with dosing of experimental drugs. *Mailing Add:* 75 Ambar Pl Bernardsville NJ 07924

JOHNSON, ALVA WILLIAM, b Tifton, Ga, Nov 8, 36; m 60; c 1. NEMATOLOGY, PLANT PATHOLOGY. *Educ:* Univ Ga, BSA, 63, MS, 64; NC State Univ, PhD(plant path), 67. *Prof Exp:* SUPVRY RES NEMATOLOGIST, COASTAL PLAIN EXP STA, SCI & EDUC ADMIN, US DEPT AGR, 67- *Mem:* Soc Nematologists; Am Phytopath Soc; Orgn Trop Am Nematologists. *Res:* Nematode control; population dynamics; nematode-fungus interactions; multiple plant-pest control; nematode resistance in plants; development of integrated pest management systems to manage nematode populations that are effective, economical and environmentally sound. *Mailing Add:* Plant Path Dept US Dept of Agr Coastal Plain Exp Sta Tifton GA 31794

JOHNSON, ALYN WILLIAM, b Calgary, Alta, Dec 16, 33; m 56; c 4. ORGANIC CHEMISTRY. *Educ:* Univ Alta, BSc, 54; Cornell Univ, PhD(chem), 57. *Prof Exp:* Asst chem, Cornell Univ, 55; fel org chem, Carnegie-Mellon Inst, 57-60; from asst prof to assoc prof, Univ NDak, 60-65; assoc prof & chmn dept, Univ Sask, Regina, 65-67; dir res & develop, 67-75, PROF CHEM & DEAN GRAD SCH, UNIV NDAK, 75- *Concurrent Pos:* Dir, NDak Regional Environ Assessment Prog, 75-77. *Mem:* Fel AAAS; Am Chem Soc; Sigma Xi; fel Chem Inst Can. *Res:* Chemistry of ylids; d-orbital interactions; synthetic organic chemistry; environmental assessment; system design; polynuclear aromatic hydrocarbons. *Mailing Add:* Grad Sch Univ of NDak Grand Forks ND 58202

JOHNSON, ARCHIE DOYLE, reproduction physiology, biochemistry, see previous edition

JOHNSON, ARLO F, b Franklin, Idaho, Dec 2, 15; m 47; c 4. MECHANICAL ENGINEERING. *Educ:* Calif Inst Technol, BS & MS, 42; Stanford Univ, PhD, 52. *Prof Exp:* Aerodynamicist, Douglas Aircraft Corp, 42-45; asst prof aeronaut eng, Univ Ill, 46-47; instr, Univ Utah, 47-48; asst, Stanford Univ, 48-51; assoc prof, 51-60, head dept, 55-57, PROF MECH ENG, UNIV UTAH, 60- *Concurrent Pos:* Prof, Bandung Technol Inst, 61-63; aeronaut res engr, Ames Lab, NASA, 57; mem staff, Sandia Corp, 59. *Mem:* Am Soc Eng Educ. *Res:* Boundary layer theory; gas dynamics; applied mechanics. *Mailing Add:* Dept of Mech Eng Univ of Utah Salt Lake City UT 84112

JOHNSON, ARMEAD, b Waco, Tex, Dec 16, 42. IMMUNOGENETICS, HISTOCOMPATIBILITY. *Educ:* Univ Tex, BS, 64; Baylor Col Med, MS, 70, PhD(microbiol & immunol), 71. *Prof Exp:* Assoc, Med Ctr, Duke Univ, 74-75, asst prof, 75-80; ASST PROF PEDIAT & MICROBIOL, SCH MED, GEORGETOWN UNIV, 80- *Concurrent Pos:* Consult, Blood Bank, Charity Hosp La, New Orleans, 75-; consult, Human Leucocyte Antigen Factor Tissue Typing Lab, Georgetown Univ, 80- *Mem:* Transplantation Soc; Am Asn Immunologists; Am Asn Clin Histocompatibility; Sigma Xi. *Res:* Serological identification, characterization and genetics of antigens within the human major histocompatibility complex and investigation of their role in the immune response. *Mailing Add:* Sch Med Georgetown Univ Box 63 3900 Reservoir Rd NW Washington DC 20007

JOHNSON, ARNOLD I(VAN), b Madison, Nebr, June 3, 19; m 41; c 3. HYDROLOGY, SOIL MECHANICS. *Educ:* Univ Nebr, BS, 49, AB, 50. *Prof Exp:* Supvr mat testing, Omaha Steel Works, Nebr, 41-44; testing engr soils, Nebr Hwy Testing Lab, 46-48; chief hydrol lab, US Geol Surv, Denver, 48-67, staff hydrologist, Water Resources Div, 67, chief, Water Res Div Training Ctr, 68-70, asst chief, Off Water Data Coord, Washington, DC, 71-79; WATER RESOURCES CONSULT, WOODWARD-CLYDE CONSULTS, DENVER, 79- *Concurrent Pos:* UNESCO consult, Turkey, 65; UN consult, 79; fac affiliate, Colo State Univ, 69-70; pres, Int Comn

Subsurface Water, 72-75; dir, Renewable Natural Resources Found, 79. *Honors & Awards:* Award of Merit, US Dept Interior, 62, Meritorious Serv Award, 77; Prof Engrs in Govt Engr of Year Award, 69. *Mem:* Am Geophys Union; Int Asn Hydrol Sci (vpres, 75-79); fel Am Soc Civil Engrs; fel Am Soc Testing & Mat; fel Am Water Resources Asn (pres, 72). *Res:* Soil moisture; permeability and specific yield of rock and soil materials. *Mailing Add:* Woodward-Clyde Consults 7600 E Orchard Rd Englewood CO 80111

JOHNSON, ARNOLD RICHARD, JR, b Allen, Kans, Jan 12, 29; m 53; c 3. ANALYTICAL CHEMISTRY. *Educ:* Fresno State Col, BS, 51; Ore State Univ, PhD(anal chem), 62. *Prof Exp:* Anal chemist, Lab, Socony Mobil Oil Co, Inc, NJ, 54-56; asst prof anal chem, Univ Wyo, 62-65; assoc prof, 65-70, PROF CHEM & HEAD DEPT, MINOT STATE COL, 70- *Mem:* Am Chem Soc; Sigma Xi. *Res:* Differential spectrophotometry; combustion methods of analysis; analytical chemistry of hafnium and zirconium; trace analysis; spot tests. *Mailing Add:* Dept of Chem Minot State Col Minot ND 58701

JOHNSON, ARTHUR ALBIN, b Chicago, Ill, Feb 24, 25; m 51; c 5. PARASITOLOGY. *Educ:* Univ Minn, AB, 50; Univ Ill, MS, 52, PhD(zool), 55. *Prof Exp:* From asst prof to assoc prof, 55-59, prof biol, 59-81, HAROLD & LUCY CABE DISTINGUISHED PROF BIOL, HENDRIX COL, 81- *Concurrent Pos:* Vis lectr, Univ Ill, 63 & 64; mem, NSF Radiation Biol Inst, Argonne Nat Lab, 65. *Mem:* Fel AAAS; Am Micros Soc; Soc Nematologists; Am Soc Parasitol; Nat Audubon Soc. *Res:* Mermithidae; sex determination mechanisms; ecology and physiology of helminths. *Mailing Add:* 53 Meadow Brook Dr Conway AR 72032

JOHNSON, ARTHUR CLARK, b Vancouver, BC, Oct 11, 22; m 52; c 4. NUCLEAR PHYSICS. *Educ:* Univ BC, BA, 44, MA, 46; Purdue Univ, PhD(exp nuclear physics), 51. *Prof Exp:* Reactor physicist, Atomic Energy Can, Ltd, Ont, 51-55; projs mgr, Nuclear Div, Canadair, Ltd, Que, 55-59; mem staff, Off Proj Develop, Gen Atomic Div, Gen Dynamics Corp, 59-60; asst to pres, 60-61, dir campus planning, 61-66, asst vpres, 66-69, vpres acad serv, 69-73, PROF ENERGY STUDIES, YORK UNIV, 74- *Concurrent Pos:* Exec coordr technol, Ministry Energy, Govt Ont; chmn, Ont Hydrogen Energy Task Force, 80-81. *Mem:* Am Phys Soc; Am Nuclear Soc; Can Asn Physicists. *Res:* Design and economics of reactors; experimental nuclear physics. *Mailing Add:* York Univ 4700 Keele St Downsview ON M3J 1P3 Can

JOHNSON, ARTHUR EDWARD, b Graceville, Minn, July 4, 42; m 65; c 3. BIOPHYSICAL CHEMISTRY. *Educ:* Calif Inst Technol, BS, 64; Univ Ore, PhD(biochem), 73. *Prof Exp:* Instr sci, Milton Acad, Mass, 64-69; Helen Hay Whitney res assoc, Chem Dept, Columbia Univ, 74-77; ASST PROF, CHEM DEPT, UNIV OKLA, 77- *Concurrent Pos:* Prin investr, NIH, Am Heart Asn, Am Chem Soc & Res Corp grants, 79- *Res:* Structure annd function of macromolecules and macromolecular multicomponent complexes; fluorescence spectroscopy; affinity labeling; singlet-singlet energy transfer; blood coagulation and clotting factors; ribosomes; elongation factors; chemically modified transfer RNAs; protein-nucleic acid interactions. *Mailing Add:* Dept Chem Univ Okla Norman OK 73019

JOHNSON, ARTHUR FRANKLIN, b Can, Oct 8, 17; US citizen; m 43; c 4. PHYSICS. *Educ:* Univ Alta, BSc, 38; Univ Toronto, MA, 47, PhD(physics), 49. *Prof Exp:* Res physicist tire eng res, US Rubber Co, 49-52 & Honeywell Res Ctr, Minneapolis-Honeywell Regulator Co, 52-55; res supvr, Minn Mining & Mfg Co, 55-64; prof physics, Gustavus Adolphus Col, 64-66; prof physics & chmn dept, Monmouth Col, Ill, 66-78; ASST DEAN, SCH OF ENG & APPL SCI, WASHINGTON UNIV, 78- *Mem:* AAAS; Sigma Xi; Am Phys Soc; Am Asn Physics Teachers. *Res:* Magnetism; photoconductivity and electrical properties of solids. *Mailing Add:* 222 Wildbrier Dr Ballwin MO 63011

JOHNSON, ARTHUR FREDERICK, b Laconia, NH, Nov 20, 22; m 44; c 4. EXPERIMENTAL STATISTICS. *Educ:* Antioch Col, BS, 43; Ohio State Univ, PhD(org chem), 48. *Prof Exp:* Res assoc, Wayne State Univ, 48-50; assoc dir, Res Div, Buckeye Cellulose Corp, 50-60; chief statist, Res & Develop Div, Procter & Gamble, 60-62; sr biostatistician, Midwest Res Support Ctr, Vet Admin Hosp, 63-72; Hines Coop Studies Support Ctr, 72-76; ASSOC DIR BIOSTATIST, SMITH KLINE & FRENCH LABS, 76- *Concurrent Pos:* Adj assoc prof indust eng, Ill Inst Technol, 63-68 & 71-75. *Res:* Planning of experimental and nonexperimental investigations. *Mailing Add:* 1211 W Flora Philadelphia PA 19122

JOHNSON, ARTHUR GILBERT, b Eveleth, Minn, Feb 1, 26; m 51; c 4. IMMUNOLOGY. *Educ:* Univ Minn, BA, 50, MSc, 51; Univ Md, PhD(bact), 55. *Prof Exp:* Biochemist, Immunol Div, Walter Reed Army Inst Res, DC, 52-55; from instr to assoc prof, Med Sch, Univ Mich, 55-66; prof bact & immunol, 66-78; PROF & HEAD, DEPT MED MICROBIOL & IMMUNOL, SCH OF MED, UNIV MINN, DULUTH, 78- *Concurrent Pos:* Mem, Nat Inst Dent Res Coun, 72-75. *Mem:* Am Soc Microbiol; Am Asn Immunologists; Soc Exp Biol & Med. *Res:* Antibody formation; mode of action of bacterial endotoxins; host resistance factors. *Mailing Add:* Dept of Med Microbiol & Immunol Sch of Med Univ of Minn Duluth MN 55812

JOHNSON, ARTHUR LEE, b Eufaula, Okla, June 10, 35; m 70; c 2. CHEMISTRY. *Educ:* Langston Univ, BS, 57; Univ Pittsburgh, MS, 60. *Prof Exp:* Chemist, 60-64; res chemist, 64-71; SR RES CHEMIST, EASTMAN KODAK CO, 71- *Res:* Design and synthesis of organic compounds for use in silver and non-silver imaging systems. *Mailing Add:* Eastman Kodak Co Kodak Park Rochester NY 14650

JOHNSON, ARTHUR THOMAS, b East Meadow, NY, Feb 21, 41; m 63; c 2. BIOENGINEERING, AGRICULTURAL ENGINEERING. *Educ:* Cornell Univ, BAE, 64, MS, 67, PhD(bioeng), 69. *Prof Exp:* Res bioengr, Dept Army, Edgewood Arsenal, Md, 71-75; asst prof, 75-80, ASSOC PROF AGR ENG, UNIV MD, 80-, ASST PROF PHYS EDUC, 78- *Concurrent Pos:* Am Soc Agr Engrs rep to coun, Alliance Eng in Med & Biol, 75-; grant,

Nat Inst Occup Safety & Health, HEW, 78-; consult, Nat Broadcasting Syst Energy Related Devices Prog, 78- *Mem:* Am Soc Agr Engrs; Inst Elec & Electronics Engrs; Am Indust Hygiene Asn; Am Conf Govt Indust Hygienists; Alliance Engrs Med & Biol. *Res:* Instrumentation and control; biological process engineering; respiratory stress and modelling. *Mailing Add:* Dept of Agr Eng Univ of Md College Park MD 20742

JOHNSON, B CONNOR, b Regina, Sask, Apr 28, 11; US citizen. BIOCHEMISTRY, NUTRITION. *Educ:* McMaster Univ, BA, 33, MA, 34; Univ Wis-Madison, PhD(biochem), 40. *Prof Exp:* From asst prof to prof animal nutrit, Univ Ill, 43-65; MEM BIOCHEM, OKLA MED RES FOUND, 65-; PROF BIOCHEM & HEAD DEPT, COL MED, UNIV OKLA HEALTH SCI CTR, 65- *Concurrent Pos:* Guggenheim Found fel, Nat Inst Res Dairying, Reading, Eng, 55; consult mem, President's Second Atom for Peace Mission to SAm, 56; consult, Cent Res Labs, Armour & Co, Chicago, 57-63; US Dept State consult, Orgn Europ Econ Coop, Paris, 58; consult, Merck & Co, NJ, 60, Agr Res Coun of Fedn Rhodesia & Nyasaland, 62, Nutrit Div, US Army Natick Labs, 63-72 & SE Asian Ministers Educ-Univ Indonesia, 74, Nutrit Inst, USDA, 77; NSF sr fel, Inst Chem Natural Substances, Nat Ctr Sci Res, Paris, 61-62; vis prof, Inst Biol Chem, Univ Strasbourg, 72. *Honors & Awards:* Am Feed Mfg Asn-Nutrit Coun US Award, 60; Purkyne Medal, Czech Acad Sci, 69; Osborne-Mendel Award, Am Inst Nutrit, 74. *Mem:* Am Soc Biol Chemists; Am Inst Nutrit; Am Chem Soc; Brit Biochem Soc; Soc Exp Biol & Med. *Res:* Nutritional biochemistry; metabolic functions of vitamins A, K, B-12 and E; starvation-refeeding; nutrition and enzyme induction. *Mailing Add:* Dept of Biochem & Molecular Biol Univ of Okla Health Sci Ctr Oklahoma City OK 73190

JOHNSON, B LAMAR, JR, b Minneapolis, Minn, May 31, 30; m 54; c 4. INTERNAL MEDICINE, INFECTIOUS DISEASES. *Educ:* Denison Univ, BA, 51; Univ Calif, Los Angeles, MD, 55. *Prof Exp:* Asst prof, 62-69, asst dean, 63-65, PROF MED, SCH MED, UNIV CALIF, LOS ANGELES, 69- *Concurrent Pos:* Attend med, Wadsworth Vet Admin Hosp, 63- *Res:* Drug induced nephropathy; endocarditis. *Mailing Add:* Sch of Med Univ of Calif Los Angeles CA 90024

JOHNSON, B(ENJAMIN) M(ARTINEAU), b Chiralla, South India, Oct 28, 30; nat US; m 54; c 2. CHEMICAL ENGINEERING, MECHANICAL ENGINEERING. *Educ:* Cornell Univ, BChE, 52; Univ Wis, MS, 53, PhD(chem eng), 56. *Prof Exp:* Sr engr, Chem Res & Develop, Hanford Labs, Gen Elec Co, 56-64; mgr, Eng Anal Unit, 65-67, mgr, Sodium Fluid Syst Sect, Fast Flux Text Facil, 67-69, mgr, Fluid & Energy Systs, 69-74, SR ENGR PROG MGR, PAC NORTHWEST LABS, 74- *Concurrent Pos:* Coordr chem eng joint ctr grad study, Univ Wash & Wash State Univ, 65-, affiliate assoc prof, 65-74, affiliate prof, 74-; mem, Coord Comt, US/USSR Coop Prog in Thermal Power Plant Heat Rejection Systs, 75- *Mem:* Am Inst Chem Engrs; Sigma Xi; Am Nuclear Soc. *Res:* Heat and mass transfer; fluid mechanics; economic analysis; nuclear reactor technology; project (development, design, construction) management. *Mailing Add:* Battelle Mem Inst Pac Northwest Labs Richland WA 99352

JOHNSON, BARRY LEE, b Sanders, Ky, Oct 24, 38; m 60; c 4. ELECTRICAL ENGINEERING, BIOMEDICAL ENGINEERING. *Educ:* Univ Ky, BS, 60; Iowa State Univ, MS, 62, PhD(elec eng), 67. *Prof Exp:* Biomed engr, USPHS, 62-64, 67-74; BIOMED ENGR, NAT INST OCCUP SAFETY & HEALTH, 74- *Concurrent Pos:* Lectr, Univ Cincinnati, 68-69. *Res:* Behavioral toxicology; sensory evoked potentials; electroencephalography; mathematical modelling of physiological systems; occupational safety and health; neurotoxicology. *Mailing Add:* Nat Inst Occup Safety & Health 4676 Columbia Pkwy Cincinnati OH 45226

JOHNSON, BECKY BEARD, b Denver, Colo, May 4, 42; m 62. PHYSIOLOGY. *Educ:* Okla State Univ, BS, 64; Univ Ill, Urbana, MS, 66, PhD(physiol), 68. *Prof Exp:* asst prof biol, 74-80, ASSOC PROF BOT, OKLA STATE UNIV, 80- *Concurrent Pos:* NIH fel, 69-70. *Mem:* Am Soc Plant Physiologists; Am Tissue Cult Asn. *Res:* Plant tissue culture and protoplast fusion for use in plant breeding and genetics. *Mailing Add:* 211 Life Sci West Okla State Univ Stillwater OK 74074

JOHNSON, BEN BUTLER, b Brooklyn, NY, May 23, 20; m 62; c 5. INTERNAL MEDICINE. *Educ:* Harvard Univ, AB, 42; Harvard Med Sch, MD, 44; Am Bd Internal Med, dipl & cert nephrology. *Prof Exp:* Intern path, NY Hosp, 44-45; asst, Med Col, Cornell Univ, 46-47; asst resident med, NY Univ Div, Bellevue Hosp, 47-49; from instr to asst prof med, Stanford Univ, 55-59; asst prof, 59-62, ASSOC PROF MED, SCH MED, UNIV MISS, 62-, HEAD DIV RENAL DIS, 59- *Concurrent Pos:* Res fels, Bassett Hosp, Cooperstown, NY, 49-50 & Sch Med, Stanford Univ, 50-53; head diabetes clin, Univ Hosps, Stanford Univ, 56-59, dir, Grad Training Prog Metab Dis, Univ, 55-59. *Mem:* Int Soc Nephrology; Am Soc Nephrology; fel Am Col Physicians; Endocrine Soc; AMA. *Res:* Renal disease; aldosterone and edema; metabolic diseases. *Mailing Add:* Dept of Med Univ of Miss Med Ctr Jackson MS 39216

JOHNSON, BEN FRANCIS, b Sacramento, Calif, Jan 4, 43; m 65; c 2. MICROBIAL GENETICS. *Educ:* Univ Calif, Davis, BA, 65, Berkeley, MA, 67, PhD(bact), 70. *Prof Exp:* Fel microbial genetics, 71-74, ACTG CHIEF MICROBIOL DIV, PALO ALTO MED RES FOUND, 74- *Mem:* Genetics Soc Am; Am Soc Microbiol; Sigma Xi. *Res:* Genetical and biochemical investigation into the nature of the processes of DNA repair, mutagenesis and regulation of cell division. *Mailing Add:* Palo Alto Med Res Found 860 Bryant St Palo Alto CA 94301

JOHNSON, BEN S(LEMMONS), JR, b Greensburg, Pa, Nov 25, 17; m 43; c 3. CHEMICAL ENGINEERING. *Educ:* Univ WVa, BS, 39, BSChE, 40. *Prof Exp:* Asst to metallurgist, Weirton Steel Co, WVa, 40-42; process control engr, Morgantown Ord Works, 42-44, asst chief chemist, 44-45, instrument engr, Belle Works, 45-51, process control supvr, Dana Plant, Ind, 51-53, res supvr, Savannah River Lab, 53-61, PROCESS CONTROL SUPVR, SAVANNAH RIVER PLANT, E I DU PONT DE NEMOURS & CO, INC, 61- *Mem:* Am Chem Soc. *Res:* Chemical and isotope separation and purification from atomic reactor fuels and targets; analytical and process control instrumentation; radioactive waste management. *Mailing Add:* 203 Dunbarton Circle Aiken SC 29801

JOHNSON, BERTIL LENNART, b Dawson, Minn, June 11, 09; m 35; c 2. GENETICS. *Educ:* Univ Minn, BS, 38, PhD(bot), 43. *Prof Exp:* Assoc geneticist, USDA, 43-47; asst prof floricult, Univ Calif, Los Angeles, 47-50, assoc prof, 50-56, prof genetics, 56-69; prof genetics, 69-76, EMER PROF GENETICS, UNIV CALIF, RIVERSIDE, 76- *Honors & Awards:* Vaughan Award, Am Soc Hort Sci, 55; Award, Am Carnation Soc, 60. *Mem:* Bot Soc Am; Genetics Soc Am; Am Soc Agron. *Res:* Genetics of Matthiola; cytogenetics of the Gramineae; biochemical-phylogenetic studies in the Triticinae. *Mailing Add:* Dept of Bot & Plant Sci Univ of Calif Riverside CA 92502

JOHNSON, BOB DUELL, b Pocahontas, Ark, June 24, 36; c 2. CYTOLOGY, TOXINOLOGY. *Educ:* Ark State Univ, BS, 58; Ariz State Univ, MS, 64, PhD(zool), 67. *Prof Exp:* Teacher, Northeast Independent Sch Dist, Tex, 58-62; partic zool, Acad Year Inst, Ariz State Univ, 62-63, res asst toxinol, 63-66, res assoc, 66-67; asst prof, 67-74, assoc prof, 74-80, PROF ZOOL, ARK STATE UNIV, 80- *Mem:* Int Soc Toxinol. *Res:* Effects of toxins on enzyme systems and morphology of cells. *Mailing Add:* Box VV Col of Sci Ark State Univ State University AR 72467

JOHNSON, BOBBY RAY, b Oakwood, Okla, Oct 30, 41; m 62; c 2. LIPID SCIENCE, FLAVOR CHEMISTRY. *Educ:* Okla State Univ, BS, 63, MS, 66, PhD(biochem), 70. *Prof Exp:* Instr chem, Okla Christian Col, 66-67; instr biochem, Okla State Univ, 67-68; USPHS fel, Univ Calif, Davis, 69-70; asst prof food sci, NC State Univ, 70-76; SR RES CHEMIST, CAMPBELL INST RES TECHNOL, CAMPBELL SOUP CO, 76- *Mem:* Am Chem Soc; Am Oil Chemists Soc; Inst Food Technol. *Res:* Fats and oil chemistry; natural antioxidants. *Mailing Add:* 129 Kipling Rd Cherry Hill NJ 08003

JOHNSON, BRANN, b Annapolis, Md, Dec 4, 46; c 2. STRUCTURAL GEOLOGY. *Educ:* Univ Calif, Berkeley, BA, 68; Pa State Univ, MEng, 73, PhD(geol), 75. *Prof Exp:* Geologist, Marine Geol & Hydrol Div, US Geol Surv, 68; asst geol, Dept Geol & Geophysics, Pa State Univ, 68-71; instr geol, Div Geol & Planetary Sci, Calif Tech, 74-75; asst prof geol, 75-80, civil eng, 76-79 & geophysics, 79-80, ASSOC PROF GEOL & GEOPHYSICS, DEPT GEOL & GEOPHYSICS, TEX A&M UNIV, 80- *Concurrent Pos:* Vis staff scientist, Los Alamos Sci Lab, 76-81; subpanel mem, Nat Res Coun, 79-80; prin investr, Cambridge Labs, US Air Force, Cambridge Labs, 75-77, Los Alamos Sci Lab, 76-78 & Div Basic Energy Res, Dept Energy, 79-; res assoc, Ctr Tectonophysics, Tex A&M Univ, 75- *Mem:* Int Glaciol Soc; Am Geophys Union. *Res:* Crustal geologic processes; development of mathematical models; glacial abrasion cracks; landslide mechanics; thermal cracking of rock; fracture permeability; water and rock interaction; mechanics of geologic discontinuites. *Mailing Add:* Ctr Tectonophysics Tex A&M Univ College Station TX 77843

JOHNSON, BRANT MONTGOMERY, b Houston, Tex, Aug 25, 49; m 73; c 2. ATOMIC PHYSICS. *Educ:* Univ Tex, Austin, BS, 71, MA, 74, PhD(physics), 75. *Prof Exp:* Res sci assoc II, Univ Tex, Austin, 71-73, Welch Found Fel, 73-75; res assoc, Physics Dept, 75-77, asst physicist, 77-79, assoc physicist, 79-80, PHYSICIST, PHYSICS DEPT, BROOKHAVEN NAT LAB, 81- *Concurrent Pos:* Vis scientist, Lawrence Berkeley Lab, Oak Ridge Nat Lab, 77 & Triumf Lab, BC, 80; lectr, Brookhaven Semester Prog, Brookhaven Nat Lab, 81. *Mem:* AAAS; Am Phys Soc. *Res:* Ion-atom, ion-electron and ion-photon (synchrotron radiation) collisions and the structure of highly ionized atoms with emphasis on atomic processes relevant to high temperature plasma research. *Mailing Add:* Physics Dept Bldg 901A Brookhaven Nat Lab Upton NY 11973

JOHNSON, BRIAN JOHN, b Reading, Eng, Oct 28, 38; m 68. BIOCHEMISTRY, EDUCATIONAL ADMINISTRATION. *Educ:* Univ Leeds, BSc, 60; Univ London, PhD(org chem) & dipl, Imp Col, 63; Univ London, DSc, 77; Inst Educ Mgt, Harvard, 81. *Prof Exp:* Res assoc org chem, State Univ NY Buffalo, 63-64; res assoc, St John's Univ, 64-65; res assoc, Mass Inst Technol, 65-66; asst prof chem, Tufts Univ, 66-71; ASSOC PROF MICROBIOL, MED SCH, UNIV ALA, BIRMINGHAM, 71-, CO-DIR GRAD PROG, 78- *Mem:* Am Chem Soc. *Res:* Synthesis, structure and biological properties of peptides and proteins; biochemistry of lipid-protein interactions; immunopharmacology; complement; allergy. *Mailing Add:* Univ Ala Univ Sta Birmingham AL 35294

JOHNSON, BRUCE, b Hawarden, Iowa, Sept 4, 32; m 55; c 2. NAVAL ARCHITECTURE, OCEAN ENGINEERING. *Educ:* Iowa State Univ, BSME, 55; Purdue Univ, MSME, 62, PhD(mech eng), 65. *Prof Exp:* Instr marine eng, US Naval Acad, 57-59; mech eng, Purdue Univ, 59-64; assoc prof, 64-70, PROF ENG & DIR HYDROMECH LAB, US NAVAL ACAD, 70- *Concurrent Pos:* Western Elec Fund award eng teaching, 71; chmn, 18th Am Towing Tank Conf, 77; trustee, Bauman Bible Telecasts; US Rep Info Comt of Int Towing Tank Conf. *Mem:* AAAS; Am Soc Mech Engrs; Am Soc Eng Educ; Soc Naval Architects & Marine Engrs; Am Soc Naval Engrs. *Res:* Hydrodynamics, ship model testing and brain wave analysis. *Mailing Add:* Dept of Naval Systs Eng US Naval Acad Annapolis MD 21402

JOHNSON, BRUCE MCDOUGALL, b Ottawa, Ill, Sept 24, 43; m 63; c 3. ANALYTICAL CHEMISTRY, CANCER. *Educ:* Univ Wis-Madison, BS, 66, MS, 67, PhD(chem), 72. *Prof Exp:* Asst prof clin oncol, Ctr Health Sci, Univ Wis-Madison, 72-75, asst prof human oncol, 75-77; res scientist, 77-80, SR RES SCIENTIST, ANAL RES DEPT, PFIZER INC, 80- *Mem:* AAAS; Am Chem Soc; Am Soc Mass Spectrometry; Am Asn Cancer Res. *Res:* Metabolism of antineoplastic drugs and carcinogens; analysis of pharmaceuticals; application of gas chromatography and mass spectrometry to biomedical and biological problems. *Mailing Add:* 30 Bobwhite Trail Gales Ferry CT 06335

JOHNSON, BRUCE MCK, b New Brunswick, NJ, Jan 28, 33; m 55; c 3. STATISTICS. *Educ:* Rutgers Univ, BS, 55; Cornell Univ, PhD(opers res), 64. *Prof Exp:* Asst prof, Northwestern Univ, 60-65; ASSOC PROF STATIST, UNIV CONN, 65- *Mem:* Inst Math Statist. *Res:* Stochastic processes; inference. *Mailing Add:* Inst Math Statist State Univ of Conn Storrs CT 06268

JOHNSON, BRUCE PAUL, b Lewiston, Maine, Aug 8, 38; m 61; c 4. SOLID STATE ELECTRONICS. *Educ:* Bates Col, BS, 60; Univ NH, MS, 63; Univ Mo-Columbia, PhD(physics), 67. *Prof Exp:* Instr physics, Hobart & William Smith Cols, 62-64; advan physicist, Gen Elec Co, 67-72, supvr, Solid State Lamp Proj, 72-74; ASSOC PROF ELEC ENG, UNIV NEV, RENO, 74- & CHMN, 78- *Mem:* Inst Elec & Electronic Engr; Am Soc Eng Educ; Sigma Xi; Am Phys Soc; Electrochem Soc. *Res:* Color centers; x-ray photoconductivity and luminescent materials; liquid epitaxy of III-V materials; solid state electronic materials and devices. *Mailing Add:* 3190 W Seventh Reno NV 89503

JOHNSON, BRYAN HUGH, b Hammond, La, Aug 15, 40; m 62; c 2. ENDOCRINE PHYSIOLOGY. *Educ:* Southeastern La Univ, BS, 63; La State Univ, MS, 66; Okla State Univ, PhD(reproduction), 69. *Prof Exp:* NIH res fel, Okla State Univ, 60-71; ASSOC PROF ENDOCRINE PHYSIOL, NC STATE UNIV, 71- *Concurrent Pos:* Biomed res grant, NDak State Univ, 76 & 78. *Mem:* Soc Study Reproduction; Am Soc Animal Sci; Sigma Xi. *Res:* Testicular steroidogenesis; adrenal-testicular interrelationship. *Mailing Add:* Dept of Animal Sci NC State Univ Raleigh NC 27607

JOHNSON, BRYCE VINCENT, b Minneapolis, Minn, Oct 24, 49; m 71. INORGANIC CHEMISTRY, ORGANOMETALLIC CHEMISTRY. *Educ:* St Olaf Col, BA, 71; Yale Univ, MS & MPhil, 72, PhD(chem), 75. *Prof Exp:* asst prof chem, Univ Louisville, 75-79; MEM STAFF, AMOCO RES CTR, AMOCO CHEM CORP, 79- *Mem:* Am Chem Soc; Sigma Xi. *Res:* Organometallic synthesis; transition metal isocyanide complexes; homogeneous catalysis; fluxional systems. *Mailing Add:* Amoco Res Ctr Amoco Chem Corp Naperville KY 60566

JOHNSON, BYRON ANDREW, b Muskegon, Mich, June 13, 21; m 46; c 3. PHARMACEUTICAL CHEMISTRY. *Educ:* Mich State Univ, BS, 43. *Prof Exp:* Cellulose chemist, Dow Chem Co, 43; org chemist, Upjohn Co, 46-67, ADMIN ASST TO RES DIR, UPJOHN INT, 67- *Mem:* Am Chem Soc. *Res:* Organic chemistry as applied to pharmaceuticals; steroids. *Mailing Add:* Upjohn Int 320 Portage St Kalamazoo MI 49006

JOHNSON, BYRON F, b St Mary's, Pa, July 25, 28; Can citizen; m 52, 67; c 4. CELL BIOLOGY, MICROBIOLOGY. *Educ:* Pa State Univ, BS, 50; Univ Calif, Los Angeles, MA, 58, PhD(zool), 60. *Prof Exp:* Nat Cancer Inst fel zool, Univ Edinburgh, 60-62; RES OFFICER, DIV BIOL SCI, NAT RES COUN CAN, 62- *Concurrent Pos:* Vis scientist, Nat Inst Med Res, London, Eng, 68-69; mem, Int Comn Yeast & Yeast-Like Organisms, 80- *Mem:* Am Soc Cell Biol; Am Soc Microbiol; Can Soc Cell Biol; Genetics Soc Can; Int Cell Cycle Soc. *Res:* Cell cycle; cellular growth and division; growth of cell organelles; biosynthesis of wall polysaccharides; regulation of cell size; temperature effects in biological systems; cytoplasmic genetics; anaerobiosis; cagmostat culture. *Mailing Add:* Div of Biol Sci Nat Res Coun of Can Ottawa ON K1A 0R6 Can

JOHNSON, C(HARLES) BRUCE, b Sioux City, Iowa, Aug 5, 35; m 56; c 2. PHYSICS, ELECTRICAL ENGINEERING. *Educ:* Iowa State Univ, BS, 57; Univ Minn, Minneapolis, MSEE, 63, PhD(elec eng), 67. *Prof Exp:* Assoc scientist, Electronics Group, Gen Mills, Inc, 58-61; res asst gaseous electronics, Univ Minn, 61-63, res fel, 63-67; engr, RCA Electronics Components, 67-70; sr staff engr, Bendix Res Labs, 70-74; prin engr, 74-77, TECH DIR, ELECTRO-OPTICAL PRODS DIV, INT TEL & TEL, FT WAYNE, 78- *Mem:* AAAS; Am Phys Soc; Inst Elec & Electronics Engrs; Optical Soc Am; Soc Photo-Optical Instrumentation. *Res:* Space-charge-effects in vacuum and gases; charged particle optics; electro-optical image transfer characteristics, especially modulation transfer function studies; high resolution image-intensifier/camera-tube development; charged particle transport in gases; high altitude instrumentation; infrared studies; electrical-optical sensor analysis. *Mailing Add:* Int Tel & Tel 3700 E Pontiac St Ft Wayne IN 46803

JOHNSON, C SCOTT, b Sullivan, Mo, Feb 4, 32. PHYSICS, BIOPHYSICS. *Educ:* Univ Mo-Rolla, BS, 54; Wash Univ, PhD(physics), 59. *Prof Exp:* Res assoc physics, Fermi Inst Nuclear Studies, Univ Chicago, 59-63; physicist, Naval Ord Test Sta, 63-67; sr res scientist, 67-69, HEAD MARINE BIOSCI DIV, NAVAL UNDERSEA CTR, 69- *Mem:* Am Phys Soc; Acoust Soc Am. *Res:* Marine mammal bioacoustics; shark behavioral studies; nuclear physics. *Mailing Add:* 1876 Sefton Pl San Diego CA 92107

JOHNSON, CALVIN KEITH, b Litchfield, Minn, Dec 15, 37; m 60; c 3. ORGANIC CHEMISTRY. *Educ:* Olivet Nazarene Col, AB, 59; Mich State Univ, PhD(org chem), 63. *Prof Exp:* NIH fel org chem, Columbia Univ, 63-64; res chemist, Minn Mining & Mfg Co, 64-67; group leader polymer res, CPC Int, 67-69; tech dir res, 69-77, V PRES RES & DEVELOP, ACME RESIN CORP, 77- *Res:* Organic photochemistry; synthesis and reactions of small ring compounds; mechanisms of polymer decomposition; latent curing resin systems; phenolic, thermosetting and foundry resins; polymers; molding compounds. *Mailing Add:* Acme Resin Co 1401 Circle Ave Forest Park IL 60130

JOHNSON, CARL ARNOLD, b Bend, Ore, Mar 5, 25; m 49; c 2. ORGANIC CHEMISTRY. *Educ:* Reed Col, BA, 50; State Col Wash, MS, 52, PhD(chem), 56. *Prof Exp:* Fel org synthesis, Mellon Inst, 56-59; chief forest prod res, Owens-Ill Co, 59-60, chief org chem res, 60-64, mgr appln res, 64-68, consult coatings & optical mat, 68-69, proj mgr glass fiber reinforcements technol & chem develop, Owens Corning Fiberglas Co, 69-74, sr scientist chem support, 74-75, RES ASSOC CHEM SUPPORT, TEXTILE OPERS, TECH CTR, OWENS CORNING FIBERGLAS CO, 75- *Concurrent Pos:* Dir, Bd of Dirs, Toastmasters Int, 78-80. *Mem:* Am Chem Soc; Sigma Xi; AAAS. *Res:* Development of new glass fiber size systems. *Mailing Add:* Owens Corning Fiberglas Tech Ctr PO Box 415 Granville OH 43023

JOHNSON, CARL BOONE, b Jacksonville, Fla, Mar 11, 38; m 64; c 1. TOXICOLOGY, ENVIRONMENTAL HEALTH. *Educ:* Fla State Univ, Tallahassee, BS, 59; Am Univ, MS, 67; Georgetown Univ, PhD(biochem), 74. *Prof Exp:* Res chemist, Nat Naval Med Ctr, 63-72; res scientist, Microbiol Assocs, 74-76; sci adminr, 76-81, TOXICOLOGIST, BUR FOODS, FOOD & DRUG ADMIN, 81- *Mem:* AAAS. *Res:* Solubilized and partially purified a glucagon-binding protein from rat liver plasma membranes; uptake of drugs by rat kidney lysosomes. *Mailing Add:* 2420 Eccleston St Silver Spring MD 20902

JOHNSON, CARL EDWARD, b Marshalltown, Iowa, Nov 27, 46; m 73; c 2. SEISMICITY, SEISMIC NETWORKS. *Educ:* Mass Inst Technol, BS & MS, 72; Calif Inst Technol, PhD(geophysics), 79. *Prof Exp:* GEOPHYSICIST, OFF EARTHQUAKE STUDIES, US GEOL SURV, 79- *Concurrent Pos:* Vis res assoc, Seismol Lab, Calif Inst Technol, 79- *Mem:* Seismol Soc; Am Geophys Union. *Res:* Seismicity studies related to earthquake prediction research including the development of real-time data acquisition and earthquake data base systems. *Mailing Add:* 252-21 Calif Inst Technol Pasadena CA 91125

JOHNSON, CARL EDWIN, b Jamestown, Kans, June 24, 17; m 46; c 2. ORGANIC CHEMISTRY. *Educ:* Bethany Col, Kans, BS, 38; Univ Kans, MA, 41, PhD(chem), 43. *Prof Exp:* Chemist, Standard Oil Co Ind, 43-46; dir res, Mich Chem Corp, 46-47; sect leader, Standard Oil Co Ind, 47-59, dir new chem res, 59-61; dir org chem res, Amoco Chem Corp, 61-65; coordr res & develop, Standard Oil Co Ind, 65-67; gen mgr, Amoco Chem Corp, 67-69, vpres res & develop, 69-80. *Mem:* Am Chem Soc; Am Inst Chem Engrs; Am Inst Chemists. *Res:* Chemicals; polymers; hydrocarbon separations; conversions. *Mailing Add:* 1217 Somerset Lane Elk Grove Village IL 60007

JOHNSON, CARL EMIL, JR, b Coleraine, Minn, Dec 11, 21; m 50; c 2. PHYSICAL CHEMISTRY. *Educ:* Univ Calif, BS, 43; Univ Calif, Los Angeles, PhD(chem), 50. *Prof Exp:* Instr chem, Univ Ill, 50-52; from res chemist to supv res chemist, Calif Res Corp, 52-68; SR RES ASSOC, CHEVRON OIL FIELD RES CO, LA HABRA, 68- *Concurrent Pos:* Lectr, Univ Southern Calif, 60-; mem city coun, Laguna Beach, Calif, 72-78. *Mem:* Am Chem Soc; Soc Petrol Engrs. *Res:* Kinetics of reactions in solution; chemistry of surfaces and surface active agents; fluid flow through porous media. *Mailing Add:* Chevron Oil Field Res Ctr 3282 Beach Blvd La Habra CA 90631

JOHNSON, CARL ERICK, b Chicago, Ill, Feb 17, 14; m 41; c 2. ORGANIC CHEMISTRY. *Educ:* Univ Chicago, BS, 38, MS, 49. *Prof Exp:* Chemist, Western Shade Cloth Co, Ill, 33-45; chief org chemist, Nat Aluminate Corp, 45-52, dir inorg res, 52-56, sr technol adv, 56-59; sect head, Cent Res, 59-60, res mgr, Metal Indust Div, 60-68, res assoc, 68-71, res assoc, Miss, 71-74, RES MGR, BROOKHAVEN RES LAB, NALCO CHEM CO, 74- *Mem:* AAAS; Am Chem Soc; Nat Asn Corrosion Engrs; Am Asn Textile Chemists & Colorists; Am Tech Asn Pulp & Paper Indust. *Res:* Water and textile treatment; flotation of minerals; synthesis of organic compounds; measurement of the film pressure of insoluble films; organic chemistry of boiler water treatment; aqueous corrosion; ion exchange; industrial lubrication, especially metal rolling and emulsion technology. *Mailing Add:* 401 McNair Ave Brookhaven MS 39601

JOHNSON, CARL LYNN, b Beaumont, Tex, Aug 22, 41. PHARMACOLOGY, BIOCHEMISTRY. *Educ:* Rice Univ, BA, 64; Univ Houston, MS, 68; Baylor Col Med, PhD(pharmacol), 71. *Prof Exp:* Instr, 71-72, asst prof pharmacol, 72-73, asst prof pharmacol, Mt Sinai Sch Med, 73-77; ASSOC PROF PHARMACOL, UNIV OF CINCINNATI COL OF MED, 77- *Res:* Hormone receptors and adenylate cyclase; molecular pharmacology. *Mailing Add:* Dept of Pharmacol & Cell Biophys Univ of Cincinnati Col of Med Cincinnati OH 45267

JOHNSON, CARL RANDOLPH, b Charlottesville, Va, Apr 28, 37; m 66; c 1. ORGANIC CHEMISTRY. *Educ:* Med Col Va, BS, 58; Univ Ill, PhD(chem), 62. *Prof Exp:* NSF res fel chem, Harvard Univ, 62; from asst prof to assoc prof, 62-68, PROF CHEM, WAYNE STATE UNIV, 68- *Concurrent Pos:* Alfred P Sloan fel, 65-68; bd of eds, Org Synthesis, 75-82; adv bd, J of Org Chem, 76-81. *Mem:* Am Chem Soc; The Chem Soc. *Res:* Organic sulfur chemistry, especially sulfoxides & sulfoximines; sulfur and nitrogen containing heterocycles; exploratory synthetic chemistry; synthesis of compounds of potential medicinal activity. *Mailing Add:* Dept of Chem Wayne State Univ Detroit MI 48202

JOHNSON, CARL WILLIAM, b Mound Valley, Kans, Feb 11, 42; m 68; c 2. PLANT BREEDING. *Educ:* Coffeyville Jr Col, AA, 62; Kans State Univ, BS, 65; NDak State Univ, MS, 67; Univ Nebr, PhD(agron), 74. *Prof Exp:* PLANT BREEDER, CALIF COOP RICE RES FOUND, 74- *Mem:* Crop Sci Soc Am; Am Soc Agronomy; Coun Agr Sci & Technol. *Res:* Development of rice varieties for the California rice industry. *Mailing Add:* Rice Exp Sta PO Box 306 Biggs CA 95917

JOHNSON, CARLOS SIGFRID, JR, b Ann Arbor, Mich, July 11, 42; m 67. MATHEMATICS. *Educ:* Calif Inst Technol, BS, 63; Univ Mass, MA, 68, PhD(math), 70. *Prof Exp:* Asst prof, 70-75, ASSOC PROF MATH, BOWLING GREEN STATE UNIV, 75- *Mem:* Am Math Soc; Math Asn Am. *Res:* Lattice theory; algebraic theory of semigroups. *Mailing Add:* Dept of Math Bowling Green State Univ Bowling Green OH 43403

JOHNSON, CARLTON E(GBERT), b Paintsville, Ky, Nov 26, 17; m 48; c 5. AGRICULTURAL ENGINEERING. *Educ:* Berea Col, BS, 38; Iowa State Univ, MS, 48, PhD(voc educ), 56. *Prof Exp:* Teacher, pub sch, Ky, 38-42; from instr to asst prof agr eng, Iowa State Univ, 47-55; assoc prof, Ohio State Univ, 55-66, prof agr eng, 66-80. *Concurrent Pos:* Vis prof, Univ Minn, 52; Am Soc Agr Engrs rep, nat safety coun sect, Z531 safety comt, Am Nat Standards Inst; mem, Ohio State Adv Comt Tech Educ in Agr; past chmn, subject matter comt, Am Asn Voc Instrnl Mat. *Mem:* Am Soc Agr Engrs. *Res:* Vocational agriculture teacher training; vocational education. *Mailing Add:* 869 Havendale Dr Columbus OH 43220

JOHNSON, CARLTON ROBERT, b Chicago, Ill, Sept 19, 26; m 51; c 2. PETROLEUM GEOLOGY, GROUNDWATER GEOLOGY. *Educ:* Monmouth Col, Ill, BA, 49; Univ Iowa, MS, 54, PhD, 56. *Prof Exp:* Geologist, US Geol Surv, 50-56; res geologist, Jersey Prod Res Co, 56-65; sr res geologist, Esso Prod Res Co, 65-69, res assoc, Exxon Prod Res Co, 69-72, SR RES ASSOC, EXXON PROD RES CO, 72- *Mem:* Geol Soc Am; Soc Petrol Engrs. *Res:* Computer mapping and modeling programs; geology and performance of oil, gas and water reservoirs; well testing procedures and instrumentation. *Mailing Add:* Exxon Prod Res Co PO Box 2189 Houston TX 77001

JOHNSON, CARROLL KENNETH, b Greeley, Colo, Sept 18, 29; m 51; c 5. CRYSTALLOGRAPHY, BIOPHYSICS. *Educ:* Colo State Univ, BS, 55; Mass Inst Technol, PhD(biophys), 59. *Prof Exp:* Asst biol, Mass Inst Technol, 55-56, asst biophys, 56-59; Am Cancer Soc res fel x-ray crystallog, Inst Cancer Res, Pa, 59-62; RES CHEMIST NEUTRON CRYSTALLOG, CHEM DIV, OAK RIDGE NAT LAB, 62- *Mem:* Am Crystallog Asn. *Res:* Neutron diffraction; stereochemistry of enzyme substrates; diffraction theory of biological polymers, crystallographic computing; automated graphics for illustrating crystal structures; crystallographic thermal-motion analysis; basic crystallographic theory. *Mailing Add:* 344 East Dr Oak Ridge TN 37830

JOHNSON, CECIL GRAY, b Nanafalia, Ala, Feb 26, 22; m 48; c 3. INDUSTRIAL & SYSTEMS ENGINEERING. *Educ:* Ga Inst Technol, BS, 48 & 49, MS, 57. *Prof Exp:* Indust engr, Gen Shoe Corp, 49-50 & Am Art Metals Co, 50-55; PROF INDUST & SYSTS ENG, GA INST TECHNOL, 55- *Concurrent Pos:* Mgt & systs eng consult, 55-; ed-in-chief, J Am Inst Indust Engrs, 55-65; res assoc, Off Naval Res, Univ Calif, Los Angeles, 59; consult, HEW, Univ Ga, 69. *Honors & Awards:* Award, Am Inst Indust Engrs. *Mem:* Am Inst Indust Engrs (vpres, 65-67); Nat Soc Prof Engrs. *Res:* Human performance and organizational theory; educational systems, especially American universities; analysis and design methodology for complex systems. *Mailing Add:* 3211 Argonne Dr NW Atlanta GA 30305

JOHNSON, CHARLES A, b Buffalo, NY, Nov 10, 31; m 53. CHEMICAL ENGINEERING. *Educ:* Syracuse Univ, BChE, 53, PhD(chem eng), 57. *Prof Exp:* Sr engr, Bettis Atomic Power Lab, Westinghouse Elec Corp, 56-60; chief chem engr, Carrier Res & Develop Co, 60-71, CHIEF DEVELOP ENGR, AIR QUAL SYSTS DEPT, CARRIER CORP, 71- *Mem:* Am Inst Chem Engrs. *Res:* Air pollution abatement; air filtration and odor control. *Mailing Add:* 1908 W Genesee Syracuse NY 13204

JOHNSON, CHARLES ANDREW, b Chicago, Ill, May 8, 15; m 40; c 2. MATHEMATICS. *Educ:* Northern Ill Univ, BEd, 37; Northwestern Univ, MA, 40; Univ Kans, PhD(math), 50. *Prof Exp:* Teacher & prin pub schs, Ill, 38-40, teacher, 40-43; PROF MATH, UNIV MO-ROLLA, 46- *Concurrent Pos:* Instr, Univ Kans, 48-50; res assoc, Argonne Nat Lab, 62. *Mem:* Am Soc Eng Educ; Am Math Asn. *Res:* Mathematical education. *Mailing Add:* Dept of Math Univ of Mo Rolla MO 65401

JOHNSON, CHARLES EDWARD, b Pennington Gap, Va, Nov 19, 40; m 70. ATOMIC PHYSICS. *Educ:* Yale Univ, BS, 62, MS, 65, PhD(physics), 67. *Prof Exp:* Res physicist, Lawrence Radiation Lab, Univ Calif, Berkeley, 67-72; ASST PROF PHYSICS, NC STATE UNIV, 73 *Mem:* Am Phys Soc. *Res:* Measurement of the fundamental properties of free atoms and molecules using the techniques of optical pumping and atomic beam magnetic resonance. *Mailing Add:* Dept of Physics NC State Univ Raleigh NC 27607

JOHNSON, CHARLES F, b Chicago, Ill, Sept 15, 27; m 61; c 1. MEDICINE, ELECTRON MICROSCOPY. *Educ:* Univ Chicago, PhB, 49, MD, 54; Am Bd Internal Med, dipl, 62. *Prof Exp:* From instr to asst prof, Sch Med, Univ Chicago, 58-67; ASSOC PROF MED, IND UNIV-PURDUE UNIV, INDIANAPOLIS, 67- *Concurrent Pos:* Asst head gastroenterol, Vet Admin Hosp, Indianapolis, 67-71, head, 71-, consult; head sect gastroenterol, St Vincent's Hosp, Indianapolis. *Mem:* AAAS; Am Soc Cell Biologists; Electron Micros Soc Am. *Res:* Electron microscopy of lipid absorption and various human gastrointestinal diseases. *Mailing Add:* 8402 Harcourt Rd Indianapolis IN 46260

JOHNSON, CHARLES HENRY, b Chicago, Ill, June 12, 25; m 48; c 3. MATHEMATICAL STATISTICS. *Educ:* Bradley Univ, BA, 49, MS, 50; Okla State Univ, PhD(math), 63. *Prof Exp:* Asst math, Univ Pittsburgh, 50-52; sect chief, Continental Casualty Co, 52-55; from asst prof to assoc prof math & astron, DePauw Univ, 55-67; PROF MATH & CHMN DEPT, UNIV WIS-STEVENS POINT, 67- *Res:* Astronomy. *Mailing Add:* Dept of Math Wis State Univ Stevens Point WI 54481

JOHNSON, CHARLES MINOR, b Nashville, Tenn, May 31, 23; m 48; c 1. PHYSICS. *Educ:* Vanderbilt Univ, BE, 44; Duke Univ, PhD(physics), 51. *Prof Exp:* Res assoc, Radiation Lab, Johns Hopkins Univ, 51-53, res scientist, 53-56; res mgr, Electronic Commun, Inc, 56-61; res dir, Emerson Res Lab, 60-61; res mgr, IBM Corp, 61-67; dep safeguard syst mgr, Sci & Technol, Dept Army, 67-73; DEP DIR WORLD WIDE MIL COMMAND & CONTROL SYST ARCHIT DEVELOP, IBM CORP, 73- *Concurrent Pos:* Consult, Sperry-Rand Corp, 55 & Eng Res & Develop Lab, US Army, 59-; sci adv, Joint Strategic Target Planning Staff, 72-; consult, Develop & Readiness Command, US Army, 76. *Honors & Awards:* Dept Army Medal Exceptional Civilian Serv, 73. *Mem:* Am Phys Soc; Inst Elec & Electronics Engrs. *Res:* Microwave physics, ferrite devices, electronic scanning radars, millimeter wave techniques, microwave spectroscopy; radiation scattering, lasers and optics; semiconductor devices; ballistic missile defense; command and control systems. *Mailing Add:* IBM Corp 1701 N Ft Myer Dr Rosslyn VA 22209

JOHNSON, CHARLES NELSON, JR, b Mt Hope, Kans, June 17, 15; m 41; c 3. APPLIED PHYSICS. *Educ:* Friends Univ, AB, 38. *Prof Exp:* Jr instr eng physics, Johns Hopkins Univ, 38-41; physicist, Bur Ord, US Dept Navy, Washington, DC & Naval Operating Base, Norfolk, Va, 41-42, physicist, Norfolk Navy Yard, Va, 42-46, sr physicist, Aviation Ord Dept, 46-51, sr physicist, Ballistic Instrumentation Dept, Naval Proving Ground, 51-55; supvry res physicist, US Army Engr Res & Develop Ctr, 55-67, chief detection br, Intrusion, Detection & Sensor Lab, 67-71, chief phys sci group, Countermine/Counter Intrusion Dept, 71-73; CONSULT PHYSICIST, 74- *Mem:* AAAS; Am Phys Soc; Sigma Xi. *Res:* Interior and exterior ballistic measurements; weapons systems evaluation and counter-measures; barrier and intrusion detection systems; remote multiband sensor systems; land mines, concealed explosives, letter bombs and booby trap detectors. *Mailing Add:* 3100 N Oxford St Arlington VA 22207

JOHNSON, CHARLES ROBERT, b Ft Collins, Colo, June 8, 41; m 64; c 2. ORNAMENTAL HORTICULTURE. *Educ:* Colo State Univ, BS, 64; Ore State Univ, PhD(ornamental plant physiol), 70. *Prof Exp:* Res floricult, K Stormly Hansen Greenhouses, Copenhagen, Denmark, 64-65; res & teaching, Dept Hort, Clemson Univ, 69-73; res & teaching ornamental hort, 73-80, ASSOC PROF ORNAMENTAL HORT, UNIV FLA, 80- *Mem:* Am Soc Hort Sci. *Res:* Ornamental plant physiology with emphasis on biochemical aspects of vegetative propagation, growth and development, nutrition and applied research on media, watering and timing of plants for rapid production. *Mailing Add:* Dept of Ornamental Hort Univ of Fla Gainesville FL 32611

JOHNSON, CHARLES ROYAL, b Elkhart, Ind, Jan 28, 48; m 72. ALGEBRA, APPLIED MATHEMATICS. *Educ:* Northwestern Univ, BA, 69; Calif Inst Technol, PhD(math, econ), 72. *Prof Exp:* Res assoc math, Appl Math Div, Nat Bur Stand, 72-74; asst prof math & econ, 74-75, ASSOC PROF, APPL MATH & ECON, INST FOR PHYS SCI & TECHNOL, UNIV MD, COLLEGE PARK, 76- *Concurrent Pos:* Consult, Appl Math Div, Nat Bur Stand, 74-; vis staff mem, Los Alamos Sci Labs, 74- *Mem:* Am Math Soc; Soc Indust & Appl Math; Am Econ Asn. *Res:* Matrix theory and applications; combinatorics and mathematical economics. *Mailing Add:* Inst for Phys Sci & Technol Univ of Md College Park MD 20742

JOHNSON, CHARLES SIDNEY, JR, b Albany, Ga, Mar 7, 36; m 58; c 2. PHYSICAL CHEMISTRY. *Educ:* Ga Inst Technol, BS, 58; Mass Inst Technol, PhD(phys chem), 61. *Prof Exp:* Nat Acad Sci-Nat Res Coun fel, 61-62; from asst prof to assoc prof phys chem, Yale Univ, 62-67; PROF CHEM, UNIV NC, CHAPEL HILL, 67- *Concurrent Pos:* Sloan Found res fel, 66-; ed bd, J Magnetic Resonance, 71-; Guggenheim Found fel, 72. *Mem:* AAAS; fel Am Phys Soc. *Res:* Nuclear magnetic and electron spin resonance; spin relaxation; chemical rate processes; laser light scattering. *Mailing Add:* Dept of Chem Univ of NC Chapel Hill NC 27514

JOHNSON, CHARLES WILLIAM, b Ennis, Tex, Jan 25, 22; m 43; c 3. MICROBIOLOGY. *Educ:* Prairie View State Col, BS, 42; Univ Southern Calif, MS, 47; Meharry Med Col, MD, 53. *Prof Exp:* Instr bact & parasitol, 47-49, from asst prof to assoc prof, 49-59, chmn dept, 59-73, PROF MICROBIOL, MEHARRY MED COL, 59-, DEAN DIV GRAD STUDIES & RES, 66- *Concurrent Pos:* Actg chmn dept microbiol, Meharry Med Col, 53-59; Rockefeller Found fel, 57-59; consult, Hubbard Hosp, 52-54. *Mem:* AAAS; Am Soc Microbiol; Am Acad Allergy; Am Fedn Clin Res. *Res:* Immunology and mycology. *Mailing Add:* Div of Grad Studies & Res Meharry Med Col 1005 18th Ave North Nashville TN 37208

JOHNSON, CHRIS ALAN, b Roseburg, Ore, Oct 1, 49; m 71. PSYCHOPHYSICS, PHYSIOLOGICAL OPTICS. *Educ:* Univ Ore, BA, 70; Pa State Univ, MSc, 72, PhD(psychol), 74. *Prof Exp:* NIH res fel, Nat Eye Inst, 75. *Concurrent Pos:* Res fel ophthal, Univ Fla, 74-76; Nat Eye Inst, NIH fels, 75 & 77, academic investr award, 78. *Mem:* Sigma Xi; AAAS; Asn Res Vision & Ophthal; Optical Soc Am; Int Perimetric Soc. *Res:* Visual psychophysics, analysis of the accommodation mechanism, examination of peripheral visual functions and development and adaptation of psychophysical tests to quantitative perimetry and visual field testing. *Mailing Add:* Dept of Ophthal Univ of Calif Davis CA 95616

JOHNSON, CLARENCE DANIEL, b Exeter, Calif, July 20, 31; m 51; c 4. SYSTEMATIC ENTOMOLOGY. *Educ:* Fresno State Univ, BA, 53; Ariz State Univ, MS, 61; Univ Calif, Berkeley, PhD(entom), 66. *Prof Exp:* High sch teacher, Calif, 56-63; asst prof, 66-70, PROF ZOOL, NORTHERN ARIZ UNIV, 70- *Mem:* Soc Study Evolution; Ecol Soc Am; Entom Soc Am; Soc Syst Zool. *Res:* Systematics, ecology and behavior of the beetle family Bruchidae; insect-plant interactions; effects of habitat modification on arthropods. *Mailing Add:* Dept of Biol Sci Northern Ariz Univ Flagstaff AZ 86011

JOHNSON, CLARENCE EUGENE, b Elk City, Okla, Nov 1, 41. ENGINEERING, AGRICULTURE. *Educ:* Okla State Univ, BS, 63; Iowa State Univ, MS, 68, PhD(agr eng), 69. *Prof Exp:* Instr agr eng, Iowa State Univ, 64-69; assoc prof, SDak State Univ, 70-77; agr engr, Columbia Plateum Conserv Res Ctr, USDA Sci Educ Admin-Agr Res, Ore, 77-79; PROF AGR ENG, AUBURN UNIV, 79- *Mem:* Am Soc Agr Engrs; Am Soc Eng Educ. *Res:* Soil dynamics; tillage and traction; harvesting systems; machinery system simulation; similitude. *Mailing Add:* Dept of Agr Eng Auburn Univ Auburn AL 36830

JOHNSON, CLARENCE L(EONARD), b Ishpeming, Mich, Feb 27, 10; m 36. AERONAUTICAL ENGINEERING. *Educ:* Univ Mich, BS, 32, MS, 33; Univ Calif, Los Angeles, LLD, 65. *Hon Degrees:* DE, Univ Mich, 64; DSc, Univ Southern Calif, 64. *Prof Exp:* Consult, Studebaker Corp, 32-33; chief res engr, 33-52, chief engr, 52-56, vpres in charge res & advan develop, 56-58, vpres advan develop projs, 58-69, SR V PRES, LOCKHEED AIRCRAFT CORP, 69- *Honors & Awards:* Sperry Award, Am Inst Aeronaut & Astronaut, 37, Reed Award, 56, Collier Trophy, 59 & 64; Wright Bros Medal, Soc Automotive Engrs, 41; Sylvanus Albert Reed Award, 56 & 66; Medal of Freedom, 64; Nat Medal Sci, 66; Thomas D White Nat Defense Award, 66; William Mitchell Mem Award, 69; Spirit of St Louis Medal, 70; Eng Achievement Award, Am Soc Metals; Theodore Von Karman Award; Founders Medal, Nat Acad Eng, 71. *Mem:* Nat Acad Sci; Nat Acad Eng; fel Am Inst Aeronaut & Astronaut (vpres, 48); fel Am Acad Arts & Sci; fel Royal Aeronaut Soc. *Res:* Aeronautical design; boundary layer control; power plants. *Mailing Add:* Lockheed Aircraft Corp Dept 01-02 PO Box 551 Burbank CA 91503

JOHNSON, CLARK E, JR, b Minneapolis, Minn, Aug 3, 30; m 51, 65; c 7. MAGNETISM. *Educ:* Univ Minn, Minneapolis, BS, 50, MS, 61. *Prof Exp:* Sr physicist, Cent Res Labs, Minn Mining & Mfg Co, 50-59; pres res & develop, Leyghton-Paige Corp, 59-61; pres, Telostat Corp, 61-63; vpres, Minnetech Labs, 63-66; vpres eng, Vibrac Corp Div, USM Corp, 67-72; pres, Micro-Commun Corp, 72-77; dir, res & develop, Buckeye Int, Inc, 77-80; PRES, VERTMAG SYSTS CORP, 81- *Concurrent Pos:* Consult physicist, Graham Magnetics, Inc, 68-74; dir & tech adv, Trans Data Syst; finance comt chmn, Magnetics Soc, 75-; dir Sciencare Corp. *Mem:* AAAS; Inst Elec & Electronics Engrs; Am Phys Soc; Instrument Soc Am; NY Acad Sci. *Res:* Magnetic theory; magnetic recording and recording materials; fine particle magnetic theory; electromagnetic transducers and devices; electro-optic transducers and devices; new techniques for recording information using magnetic properties of materials; perpendicular magnetic recordings. *Mailing Add:* 4112 Massachusetts Long Beach CA 90814

JOHNSON, CLAYTON HENRY, JR, b Denver, Colo, Feb 13, 16; m 40; c 2. PETROLOGY. *Educ:* Univ Mo, AB, 37, MA, 39; Cornell Univ, PhD(petrog), 43. *Prof Exp:* Chief writer, State Mineral Surv, Ark, 39-40; mineral microscopist, Am Cyanamid Chem Corp, NY, 43-45; asst prof, 45-50, ASSOC PROF GEOL, UNIV MO-COLUMBIA, 50- *Concurrent Pos:* Geologist, Foreign Opers Admin, US State Dept, 54. *Mem:* Fel Geol Soc Am; Asn Prof Geol Scientists; Nat Asn Geol Teachers; Nat Sci Teachers Asn. *Res:* Igneous and metamorphic petrology; metallic ore deposits; earth science education. *Mailing Add:* 205 Geol Bldg Univ of Mo Columbia MO 65211

JOHNSON, CLELAND HOWARD, b Pierpont, SDak, Sept 16, 22; m 44; c 3. NUCLEAR PHYSICS. *Educ:* Hastings Col, BA, 44; Univ Wis, PhD(physics), 51. *Prof Exp:* PHYSICIST, OAK RIDGE NAT LAB, 51- *Mem:* Am Phys Soc. *Res:* Experimental nuclear structure physics. *Mailing Add:* Oak Ridge Nat Lab Oak Ridge TN 37831

JOHNSON, CLIFTON W, b Lewisville, Idaho, Sept 23, 24; m 52; c 6. CIVIL & AGRICULTURAL ENGINEERING. *Educ:* Utah State Univ, BS, 56, MS, 57. *Prof Exp:* Water distribution engr, State Engrs Off, Utah, 57-60; HYDRAUL ENGR, AGR RES SERV, 60- *Mem:* Am Soc Civil Engrs; Am Soc Agr Engrs; Am Geophys Union. *Res:* Hydrology, erosion and sediment transport; design, construction and operation of water measuring devices; irrigation water diversion and use; sediment transport, measurement and studies of arid lands hydrology. *Mailing Add:* 3907 Whitehead Boise ID 83703

JOHNSON, CLINTON CHARLES, b Hector, Minn, Aug 15, 27; m 52; c 5. DENTISTRY, ORAL PATHOLOGY. *Educ:* Macalester Col, BA, 53; Univ Minn, BS & DDS, 57, MSD, 65; Am Bd Oral Path, dipl, 67. *Prof Exp:* Staff dentist, Vet Admin Hosp, Minneapolis, Minn, 60-62; asst chief dent, Dent Training Ctr, Washington, DC, 65-66; oral pathologist, Armed Forces Inst Path, 66-67; chief dent serv, Vet Admin Hosp, Buffalo, NY, 67-72; chief dent serv, Vet Admin Hosp, Dallas, 72-74; CHIEF DENT SERV, VET ADMIN OUTPATIENT CLIN, LUBBOCK, 74- *Concurrent Pos:* Vis lectr, Howard Univ, 66-67; from asst prof to assoc prof oral path, Sch Dent, State Univ NY Buffalo, 67-72. *Mem:* Am Dent Asn; fel Am Acad Oral Path. *Res:* Forensic dentistry. *Mailing Add:* 4713 78th St Lubbock TX 79424

JOHNSON, CLYDE EDGAR, JR, physiology, zoology, see previous edition

JOHNSON, CORINNE LESSIG, b Wilmington, Del, Oct 29, 38. MICROBIOLOGY, BIOCHEMISTRY. *Educ:* Wellesley Col, AB, 60; Univ Rochester, MS, 64, PhD(biol), 69. *Prof Exp:* Sci Res Coun res asst & fel biochem, Univ Leicester, 69-70; fel, Albert Einstein Col Med, 70-72; assoc res scientist & instr biochem, Dent Ctr, NY Univ, 72-74, asst prof microbiol, 75; vis asst prof biol, Vassar Col, 75-77; asst prof biol, Carleton Col, 77-78; res assoc microbiol, Sch Med, Boston Univ, 78-79; BIOL ED & GEN MGR, EDUTECH INC, 81- *Concurrent Pos:* Treas, Alliance Independent Scholars, 80- *Mem:* AAAS; Am Soc Microbiol; Am Chem Soc; Asn Women Sci; NY Acad Sci. *Res:* Microbial membrane transport and metabolism. *Mailing Add:* EduTech Inc 634 Commonwealth Ave Newton Centre MA 02159

JOHNSON, CORWIN MCGILLIVRAY, b Berthold, NDak, Mar 30, 24; m 46; c 4. AGRONOMY. *Educ:* State Col Wash, BS, 50, MSA, 51; Cornell Univ, PhD, 53. *Prof Exp:* Res asst agron, State Col Wash, 50-51, asst agronomist, Northwestern Wash Exp Sta, 53-56; asst agronomist & asst prof agron, Miss State Univ, 56-61; asst prof crops prod, 61-62, HEAD CROP SCI DEPT, CALIF POLYTECH STATE UNIV, SAN LUIS OBISPO, 62-, PROF, 74- *Mem:* Am Soc Agron; Crop Sci Soc Am. *Res:* Effect of management practices and soil fertility on the yield and quality of field crops. *Mailing Add:* Rte 2 Box 407 San Luis Obispo CA 93401

JOHNSON, CURTIS ALAN, b Johnstown, Pa, Jan 22, 48; m 69; c 2. MATERIAL SCIENCE, CERAMIC SCIENCE. *Educ:* Pa State Univ, BS, 69, PhD(metall), 74. *Prof Exp:* STAFF SCIENTIST CERAMICS, GEN ELEC CORP RES & DEVELOP CTR, 73- *Mem:* Am Ceramics Soc. *Res:* Mechanical and physical properties of metals and ceramics, in particular high temperature structural ceramics; fabrication methods; densification processes and phase transformations of ceramics. *Mailing Add:* Gen Elec Corp Res & Develop Ctr PO Box 8 Schenectady NY 12301

JOHNSON, CURTIS ALLEN, b Mead, Nebr, Apr 3, 17; m 54; c 2. AGRICULTURAL ENGINEERING. *Educ:* Univ Nebr, BSc, 40; Iowa State Univ, MS, 55. *Prof Exp:* Test engr, Tractor Testing Lab, Int Harvester Co, 40-41; asst prof agr eng, Univ Del, 46-48; prin, Friendsville Acad, Tenn, 49-50; instr agr eng, Iowa State Univ, 50-55; agr workshop adv, US State Dept, Int Coop Admin, Pakistan, 55-57; ASSOC PROF AGR ENG, UNIV MASS, AMHERST, 57- *Mem:* Am Soc Agr Engrs. *Res:* Relationship of milking machines to mastitis; liquid handling of agricultural wastes; world-wide water resources planning; farm homes and buildings; design of economical houses for minimal waste of structural materials and fossil fuel energy inputs. *Mailing Add:* Dept of Food & Agr Eng Univ of Mass Amherst MA 01002

JOHNSON, D(AVID) LYNN, b Provo, Utah, Apr 2, 34; m 59; c 5. MATERIALS SCIENCE. *Educ:* Univ Utah, BS, 56, PhD(ceramic eng), 62. *Prof Exp:* Mining engr trainee, US Smelting, Ref & Mining Co, 56; from asst prof to assoc prof, 62-71, PROF MAT SCI, NORTHWESTERN UNIV, 71- *Concurrent Pos:* Consult. *Mem:* Am Electrochem Soc; fel Am Ceramic Soc; Am Inst Mining, Metall & Petrol Engrs. *Res:* Mechanisms of material transport in the sintering of oxides and metals; impurity effects in sintering; grain boundary diffusion in sintering; fracture. *Mailing Add:* Dept of Mat Sci Northwestern Univ Evanston IL 60201

JOHNSON, DALE A, b Chicago, Ill, Nov 18, 37; m 60; c 2. PHYSICAL CHEMISTRY, INORGANIC CHEMISTRY. *Educ:* Univ Ill, BS, 59; Northwestern Univ, PhD(chem), 64. *Prof Exp:* Asst prof, 63-67, assoc prof, 67-73, PROF CHEM, UNIV ARK, FAYETTEVILLE, 73- *Mem:* Am Chem Soc. *Res:* Thermal and photochemical reactions of transition metal complexes; reactions of coordinated molecules; spectroscopy of inorganic compounds. *Mailing Add:* Dept of Chem Univ of Ark Fayetteville AR 72701

JOHNSON, DALE HOWARD, b Los Angeles, Calif, Feb 23, 45; m 77; c 1. ORAL HYGIENE, COSMETIC CHEMISTRY. *Educ:* Univ Redlands, BS, 66; Northwestern Univ, PhD(org chem), 71. *Prof Exp:* Res chemist toiletries, Alberto-Culver Co, 71-73; sect head, Appln Lab, Armak Indust Chem, Div Akzona Inc, 73-77; mgr prod develop, Helene Curtis Indust Inc, 77-81; SECT HEAD ORAL HYG, VICKS DIV RES, RICHARDSON-VICKS INC, 81- *Mem:* Am Chem Soc; Soc Cosmetic Chemists. *Res:* New oral hygiene and dental products for both the dental profession and the consumer. *Mailing Add:* 25 Governors Lane Bethel CT 06801

JOHNSON, DALE WALDO, b Nelson, Wis, Apr 11, 15; m 45; c 3. FOOD SCIENCE. *Educ:* Univ Minn, BCh, 37, PhD(bact), 41. *Prof Exp:* Res & teaching asst, Univ Minn, 37-41, Hormel fel, 41-42; chief bacteriologist, Res Lab, Pillsbury Mills, 42-45 & Diversey Corp, 45-48; microbiologist & head dept, Soya Div, Glidden Co, 48-53, liaison & head biol, Cent Org Res Labs, 53-55, res consult, Chemurgy Div, 53-58; mgr edible protein prod, Cent Soya Co, 58-63; vpres, Soypro Int, Inc, 63-69; exec vpres, Crest Prod Inc, 63-73; PRES, FOOD INGREDIENTS INC, ELK GROVE VILLAGE, 73- *Concurrent Pos:* Consult, 37-45 & 62-; bacteriologist, State Dept Health, Minn, 40-41. *Mem:* Am Chem Soc; Am Asn Cereal Chemists; Inst Food Technologists; Am Oil Chemist's Soc. *Res:* Microbiology of meat and cereals; development of germicides; sewage treatment and analysis; nutrition of yeast, molds and bacteria; fermentation; vitamin B12; antibiotics; fish solubles; bioconversions; micro-biological assays; soy products; nutrition; foods and feeds; enzymes; milk proteins; sesame products; soybean products and processing technology. *Mailing Add:* 3039 Payne St Evanston IL 60201

JOHNSON, DALLAS EUGENE, b Central City, Nebr, Oct 14, 38. DATA ANALYSIS, LINEAR MODELS. *Educ:* Kearney State Teachers Col, BS, 60; Western Mich Univ, MS, 66; Colo State Univ, PhD(statist), 71. *Prof Exp:* Instr statist, Colo State Univ, 66-68; asst prof, Univ Mo-Rolla, 71-75; assoc prof, 75-81, PROF STATIST, KANS STATE UNIV, 81- *Mem:* Am Statist Asn; Inst Math Statist. *Res:* Linear models; data analysis; statistical design; biased regression methods. *Mailing Add:* Dept of Statist Kans State Univ Manhattan KS 66506

JOHNSON, DANIEL LEON, b Manistee, Mich, Jan 24, 36; m 63; c 4. BIOACOUSTICS. *Educ:* US Mil Acad, BS, 58; Univ Mich, MSE, 60; Univ Colo, PhD(aerospace eng), 71. *Prof Exp:* Aero engr, Serv Eng, 60-69, bioengr, 71-72, PROJ OFFICER, AEROSPACE MED LAB, US AIR FORCE, 71- *Concurrent Pos:* Mem, Environ Impact Statements on Noise, Comt Hearing Bioacoust & Biomech, Nat Acad Sci-Nat Res Coun, 73-, Noise Induced Hearing Loss, Comt S-3 Bioacoust, Am Nat Standards, 74- *Honors & Awards:* Sci Achievement Award, US Air Force, 74. *Mem:* Acoust Soc Am; AAAS. *Res:* The effect of infrasound on man; typical noise exposure of the American population; evaluation of environmental noise; the various effects of noise on hearing. *Mailing Add:* 4037 Forest Ridge Dayton OH 45424

JOHNSON, DAVID AARON, b Fairfax, Minn, June 11, 26; m 50; c 4. ORGANIC CHEMISTRY. *Educ:* Univ Minn, BA, 49; Mass Inst Technol, PhD(org chem), 52. *Prof Exp:* Res chemist pharmaceut chem, Bristol Labs Div, 52-53, dir chem develop lab, 53-75, dir chem develop, 75-78, VPRES DEVELOP, INDUST DIV, BRISTOL-MYERS CO, 75- *Mem:* Am Chem Soc. *Res:* Research and development in pharmaceutical industry. *Mailing Add:* Bristol-Myers Co Inc PO Box 657 Syracuse NY 13201

JOHNSON, DAVID ALFRED, b Muskegon, Mich, Mar 13, 38; m 60; c 3. PHYSICAL INORGANIC CHEMISTRY. *Educ:* Greenville Col, AB, 60; La State Univ, PhD(chem), 66. *Prof Exp:* Chemist, Pet Milk Res Labs, summer 60; asst prof chem, Greenville Col, 62-64; instr, La State Univ, 64-65; PROF CHEM, SPRING ARBOR COL, 66- *Concurrent Pos:* Fel, Dept Chem, La State Univ, 70-71. *Mem:* Am Chem Soc. *Res:* Physical chemistry of electrolytes in mixed solvent systems, medium effects of such systems; five coordinate complexes of transition metals; thermodynamics of biological systems. *Mailing Add:* Dept of Chem Spring Arbor Col Spring Arbor MI 49283

JOHNSON, DAVID ASHBY, b Asheville, NC, Sept 6, 43; m 67. OCEANOGRAPHY. *Educ:* Mass Inst Technol, SB & SM, 66; Univ Calif, San Diego, PhD(oceanog), 71. *Prof Exp:* NSF fel oceanog, 71-72, asst scientist, 72-75, ASSOC SCIENTIST, WOODS HOLE OCEANOG INST, 75- *Mem:* AAAS; Geol Soc Am; Am Geophys Union. *Res:* Ocean floor processes; biostratigraphy of pelagic sediments; interactions of sea floor topography, abyssal circulation and bottom sediments. *Mailing Add:* Woods Hole Oceanog Inst Woods Hole MA 02543

JOHNSON, DAVID B, b Big Spring, Tex, Jan 11, 40; m 62; c 3. MECHANICS. *Educ:* Univ Tex, Austin, BSME, 63, MSME, 64; Stanford Univ, PhD(eng mech), 68. *Prof Exp:* Assoc prof mech eng, Southern Methodist Univ, 68-73; ASSOC PROF ENG SCI & MECH, IOWA STATE UNIV, 75- *Mem:* Am Soc Mech Engrs; Am Soc Eng Educ; Soc Exp Stress Anal; Soc Eng Sci. *Res:* Dynamics; vibrations; space mechanics; phytomechanics. *Mailing Add:* Dept of Eng Sci & Mech Iowa State Univ Ames IA 50011

JOHNSON, DAVID BARTON, b Providence, RI, June 5, 46; m 70; c 2. BIO-ORGANIC CHEMISTRY, BIO-ANALYTICAL CHEMISTRY. *Educ:* Univ RI, BS, 69; Duke Univ, PhD(org chem), 75. *Prof Exp:* NIH fel biochem pharmacol, Med Sch, Duke Univ, 74-76; assoc chemist bio-org chem, Midwest Res Inst, 76-80; RES SCIENTIST II, UPJOHN CO, 80- *Mem:* Am Chem Soc; Sigma Xi. *Res:* Bio-organic chemistry dealing in the synthesis, biosynthesis, analysis, and structural elucidation of xenobiotic metabolites; analysis of metabolites in biological samples; in vitro studies of xenobiotic metabolizing enzymes; radiochemical synthesis. *Mailing Add:* Upjohn Co 301 Henrietta St Kalamazoo MI 49001

JOHNSON, DAVID EDSEL, b Chatham, La, Aug 16, 27; m 59; c 4. ELECTRICAL ENGINEERING, APPLIED MATHEMATICS. *Educ:* La Tech Univ, BS & BA, 49; Auburn Univ, MS, 52, PhD(math), 58. *Prof Exp:* Draftsman, La Power & Light Co, 49-50; mathematician, Nat Bur Standards, 52; assoc prof math, 54-62, PROF ELEC ENG, LA STATE UNIV, 62- *Concurrent Pos:* NSF fac fel, Stanford Univ, 61-62. *Mem:* Sigma Xi. *Res:* Electric circuits and systems. *Mailing Add:* Dept of Elec Eng La State Univ Baton Rouge LA 70803

JOHNSON, DAVID EDWIN, b Newark, NJ, Sept 3, 44. HIGH ENERGY PHYSICS. *Educ:* Univ Calif, Berkeley, AB, 66; Iowa State Univ, PhD(high energy physics), 72. *Prof Exp:* Res assoc & instr physics, Iowa State Univ, Ames Lab, USAEC, 67-72, assoc & instr physics, 72-73; PHYSICIST, FERMI NAT ACCELERATOR LAB, UNIV RES ASSOC, 73- *Mem:* AAAS; Sigma Xi; Am Phys Soc. *Res:* High energy accelarator design and research; high energy experimental research. *Mailing Add:* Advan Projs PO Box 500 Fermi Nat Accelerator Lab Batavia IL 60510

JOHNSON, DAVID FREEMAN, b Nashville, Tenn, Jan 28, 25; m 47; c 2. BIOCHEMISTRY. *Educ:* Allegheny Col, BS, 47; Howard Univ, MS, 49; Georgetown Univ, PhD(biochem), 57. *Hon Degrees:* DSc, Allegheny Col, 72. *Prof Exp:* Instr chem, Howard Univ, 49-50; res chemist, Freedman's Hosp, Washington, DC, 50-52; res chemist, 52-71, CHIEF MICROANAL SERV & INSTRUMENT SECT, NAT INST ARTHRITIS & METAB DISEASES, 71- *Concurrent Pos:* Instr, USDA Grad Sch, 58-60 & Found Advan Educ in Sci, Inc, NIH, 60- *Mem:* AAAS; Am Chem Soc; Fedn Am Socs Exp Biol; Am Phys Soc. *Res:* Hormones; plant and animal steroids; metabolism; analytical methods; partition chromatography. *Mailing Add:* Rm 130 Bldg 4 Nat Inst Arthritis & Metab Diseases Bethesda MD 20014

JOHNSON, DAVID GREGORY, b Belvidere, Ill, July 11, 40; m 65; c 3. ENDOCRINOLOGY, CLINICAL PHARMACOLOGY. *Educ:* Yale Univ, BA, 62; Dartmouth Med Sch, BMed Sci, 64; Harvard Univ, MD, 67. *Prof Exp:* Resident, Univ Calif, San Francisco, 67-69; res assoc, NIH, 69-71; fel, Univ Wash, 71-73; asst prof, 73-77, assoc prof, 77-78; ASSOC PROF, DEPT INTERNAL MED, UNIV ARIZ HEALTH SCI CTR, 78- *Concurrent Pos:* Assoc ed, Life Sci, 81-82. *Mem:* Am Diabetes Asn; Am Soc Pharmacol & Exp Therapeut; Endocrine Soc; Am Fedn Clin Res. *Res:* Experimental and clinical research regarding diabetes, pancreatic endocrine secretion, gastro intestinal hormones and catecholamine physiology; development and testing of drugs, particularly for the treatment of diabetes. *Mailing Add:* Dept Internal Med Univ Ariz Health Sci Ctr Tucson AZ 85724

JOHNSON, DAVID HARLEY, b Brooklyn, NY, May 31, 41; m 61; c 2. HEAT TRANSFER, FLUID MECHANICS. *Educ:* Purdue Univ, BS, 63, MS, 64; Cornell Univ, PhD(appl physics), 75. *Prof Exp:* Staff mem, Sandia Corp, 64-67; adj instr hydraul, Tompkins-Cortland Community Col, 69-70; teaching asst statist thermodyn, Cornell Univ, 70-72; sr staff physicist, Appl Physics Lab, Johns Hopkins Univ, 73-79, asst group leader, 78-79; PRIN ENGR, SOLAR ENERGY RES INST, 79-, GROUP MGR, 80- *Concurrent Pos:* Consult, Appl Physics Lab, Johns Hopkins Univ, 79-80 & Flow Industs Inc, 81- *Mem:* Am Soc Mech Engrs. *Res:* Dynamics of stratified fluids in the ocean and in solar ponds; direct contact heat transfer phenomena important to the design of open-cycle thermal energy conversion power plants and other heat exchangers. *Mailing Add:* 14183 W Expos Dr Lakewood CO 80228

JOHNSON, DAVID L(IVINGSTONE), b Gustavus, Ohio, Feb 17, 15; m 54. ELECTRICAL ENGINEERING. *Educ:* Berea Col, AB, 36; Univ Iowa, MA, 38, BS, 42; Okla State Univ, MS, 50, PhD(elec eng), 57. *Prof Exp:* Speech & lab asst elec eng, Univ Iowa, 36-42; instr, US Naval Training Sch, Okla State Univ, 42-44; US field engr, radio & radar, Airborne Coord Group, 44-45; instr radio, Spartan Sch Aeronaut, 45-47, head radio sch, 47-48; asst prof elec eng, Okla State Univ, 48-55; PROF & HEAD DEPT ELEC ENG, LA TECH UNIV, 55- *Mem:* AAAS; Soc Indust & Appl Math; Nat Soc Prof Engrs; Asn Comput Mach; Inst Elec & Electronics Engrs. *Res:* Switching circuits, computers. *Mailing Add:* Dept of Elec Eng La Tech Univ Ruston LA 71272

JOHNSON, DAVID LEROY, b Truman, Ark, Sept 10, 47. SOLAR ENERGY. *Educ:* Ark State Univ, BS, 69; Univ Ill Urbana-Champaign, MS, 71, PhD(physics), 78. *Prof Exp:* Fel dept physics, Univ Ill, 78-80; PRIN INVESTR, CONSTRUCTION ENG RES LAB, CORPS ENGRS, 80- *Concurrent Pos:* Adj res asst prof physics, Univ Ill, 81- *Mem:* Am Soc Heating, Refrigerating & Airconditioning Engrs; Int Solar Energy Soc. *Res:* Experimental studies of fundamental defect properties in solids; solar energy systems for space heating and cooling of buildings; heating, ventilating and air conditioning controls and energy conservation techniques for heating, ventilating and air conditioning systems. *Mailing Add:* 1808 Cypress Dr Champaign IL 61820

JOHNSON, DAVID LINTON, b Chicago, Ill, July 9, 45; m 72; c 2. THEORETICAL SOLID STATE PHYSICS. *Educ:* Univ Notre Dame, BS, 67; Univ Chicago, MS, 69, PhD(physics), 74. *Prof Exp:* Fel physics, Michelson Lab, Naval Weapons Ctr, 72-74; fel, Ames Lab, Iowa State Univ, 74-76; asst prof physics, Northeastern Univ, 76-79; RES PHYSICIST, SCHLUMBERGER DOLL RES CTR, 79- *Mem:* Am Phys Soc; Acoust Soc Am; Soc Exp Geol. *Res:* Optical properties of solids; electronic structure of solids. *Mailing Add:* Schlumberger Doll Res Ctr PO Box 307 Ridgefield CT 06877

JOHNSON, DAVID NORSEEN, b Bronx, NY, Sept 28, 38; m 60; c 2. PHARMACOLOGY. *Educ:* N Park Col, Ill, BS, 60; Univ Louisville, Ky, MS, 67; Med Col Va, PhD(pharmacol), 76. *Prof Exp:* Res scientist pharmacol, 66-69, sr res scientist, 69-75, MGR NEUROPHARMACOL, A H ROBINS PHARMACEUT CO, 66- *Mem:* Am Soc Pharmacol & Exp Therapeut; Am Chem Soc; Soc Neurosci. *Res:* Basic mechanisms underlying mental illness and the methodologies for testing new chemical entities for treating disorders. *Mailing Add:* A H Robins Res Labs 1211 Sherwood Ave Richmond VA 23220

JOHNSON, DAVID ROBERT, agronomy, crop physiology, see previous edition

JOHNSON, DAVID RUSSELL, b Manaus, Brazil, Oct 23, 45; m 67; c 1. PHYSICAL CHEMISTRY. *Educ:* Austin Col, BA, 67; Tex Christian Univ, PhD(chem), 70. *Prof Exp:* Fel radiation chem, Baylor Univ, 70-72 & Univ Fla, 72-73; res chemist textile fibers, DuPont, Waynesboro, Va, 73-75; res chemist separations chem, 75-78, staff chemist, 78-79, res supvr anal chem, 79-81, RES SUPVR HYDROGEN TECHNOL, ENVIRON EFFECTS, SAVANNAH RIVER LAB, E I DU PONT DE NEMOURS & CO, INC, 81- *Mem:* Am Chem Soc. *Res:* Plutonium soil migration studies; environmental dose-to-man modelling methods; uranium fuel fabrication methods; chemical separations processes for nuclear fuel recycle and waste management programs. *Mailing Add:* 1695 Huckleberry Dr Aiken SC 29801

JOHNSON, DAVID SIMONDS, b Porterville, Calif, June 29, 24; m 74. METEOROLOGY. *Educ:* Univ Calif, Los Angeles, AB, 48, MA, 49. *Prof Exp:* Meteorol aid, US Weather Bur, 46-47; asst meteorol, Univ Calif, Los Angeles, 48-52; assoc meteorologist, Pineapple Res Inst, Univ Hawaii, 52-56; chief observ testing & develop ctr, US Weather Bur, 56-58, asst chief meteorol satellite lab, 58-60, chief, 60-62, from dep dir to dir, Nat Weather Satellite Ctr, 62-65, dir, Nat Environ Satellite Ctr, Environ Sci Serv Admin, 65-70; dir, Nat Environ Satellite Serv, 70-80, ASST ADMIN SATELLITES, NAT OCEANIC & ATMOSPHERIC ADMIN, 80- *Concurrent Pos:* Spec asst to pres, Univ Corp Atmospheric Res, 82-; consult to secy gen, World Meteorol Orgn, 82- *Honors & Awards:* Gold Medal, Dept Com, 65; William T Pecora Award, Dept of Interior, 78; Fed Career Serv Award for Sustained Excellence, Nat Civil Serv League, 74; William T Pecora Award, NASA & Dept of Interior, 78. *Mem:* AAAS; Am Meteorol Soc (pres, 74); Am Geophys Union; Int Acad Astronaut; Sigma Xi. *Res:* Meteorological instruments and observing techniques; environmental satellites. *Mailing Add:* 3061 Mimon Rd Annapolis MD 21403

JOHNSON, DAVID STIFLER, computer science, mathematics, see previous edition

JOHNSON, DAVID W, JR, b Windber, Pa, Sept 23, 42; m 64; c 2. CERAMIC & MATERIALS SCIENCE. *Educ:* Pa State Univ, BS, 64, PhD(ceramic sci), 68. *Prof Exp:* MEM TECH STAFF, BELL TEL LABS, 68- *Mem:* Am Ceramic Soc; Fine Particle Soc. *Res:* Dielectric relaxation in doped strontium titanate; characterization of fine oxide particles; magnetic ceramics; ionic conductors. *Mailing Add:* Bell Tel Labs Rm 6D-305 Murray Hill NJ 07974

JOHNSON, DELWIN PHELPS, b Rocky Mountain, NC, Mar 24, 26; m 54; c 2. ANALYTICAL CHEMISTRY. *Educ:* NC State Univ, BS, 48. *Prof Exp:* Chemist, NC Dept Agr, 48-57; res chemist, Chem Div, Union Carbide Corp, 57-63, res chemist, Olefins Div, 63-64; res staff chemist, 64-69, group leader new prod develop sect, 69-70, HEAD NEW PROD DEVELOP SECT, R J REYNOLDS TOBACCO CO, 70- *Mem:* Am Chem Soc. *Res:* Development of new and novel micro-analytical techniques for trace constituents in complex mixtures; experimental and commercial pesticide residues in animal and plant products, utilizing ultraviolet, infrared and visible spectrophotometry, gas and liquid phase chromatography. *Mailing Add:* 3021 St Claire Rd Winston-Salem NC 27106

JOHNSON, DENNIS ALLEN, b Pocatello, Idaho, May 10, 49; m 71; c 3. PLANT PATHOLOGY. *Educ:* Brigham Young Univ, BS, 74; Univ Minn, MS, 75, PhD(plant path), 78. *Prof Exp:* Res & teaching asst bot, Brigham Young Univ, 72-74; teaching asst mycol, Univ Minn, 75-76, res asst plant path, 74-78; ASST PROF PLANT PATH, TEX AGR EXP STA, 78- *Concurrent Pos:* Mem, Hard Red Winter Wheat Improv Comt, USDA, 78- *Mem:* Am Phytopath Soc; Mycol Soc Am; Sigma Xi. *Res:* Disease resistance and epidemiology of small grain diseases. *Mailing Add:* Tex Agr Exp Sta PO Box 1658 Vernon TX 76384

JOHNSON, DEWAYNE CARL, b Minneapolis, Minn, Sept 15, 35. PHYSICS. *Educ:* Univ Minn, Minneapolis, BS, 57, MS, 60, PhD(elec eng), 63. *Prof Exp:* Mem tech staff physics, Bell Tel Labs, 64-65; asst prof, 65-69, ASSOC PROF PHYSICS, UNIV WIS-MILWAUKEE, 70- *Mem:* Am Phys Soc. *Res:* Low energy electron diffraction. *Mailing Add:* Dept of Physics Univ Of Wis Milwaukee WI 53201

JOHNSON, DEWEY, JR, b Sapulpa, Okla, Sept 23, 26; m 53; c 4. BIOCHEMISTRY, NUTRITION. *Educ:* Colo State Univ, BS, 50; Univ Conn, MS, 55; Rutgers Univ, PhD, 58; Nat Registry Clin Chemists. *Prof Exp:* Asst poultry nutrit, Rutgers Univ, 55-58; assoc animal nutrit, Lime Crest Res Lab, Limestone Prod Corp Am, NJ, 58-62; nutritionist, Food & Drug Res Lab, 62-63; biochemist, 63-68, DIR CLIN LAB, EQUITABLE LIFE ASSURANCE SOC US, NEW YORK, 68- *Mem:* Am Soc Animal Sci; Am Dairy Sci Asn; Poultry Sci Asn. *Res:* Metabolism of amino acids; metabolism of drugs; biochemical changes in alcoholism; automated clinical chemistry techniques; folic acid and vitamin B12 metabolism. *Mailing Add:* 12 Barbara Pl Edison NJ 08817

JOHNSON, DIANE MARY, b Winnipeg, Man, Feb 21, 35. MATHEMATICS. *Educ:* Univ Man, BSc, 55, MSc, 56; Univ Toronto, PhD(math), 59. *Prof Exp:* Lectr, 58-62, from asst prof to assoc prof, 62-75, PROF MATH, UNIV MAN, 75- *Mem:* Am Math Soc; Math Asn Am; Can Math Cong; Soc Indust & Appl Math. *Res:* Modular representation theory; graph theory; combinatorics. *Mailing Add:* Dept of Math Univ of Man Winnipeg MB R3T 2N2 Can

JOHNSON, DONAL DABELL, b Rigby, Idaho, July 20, 22; m 45; c 3. SOILS, MICROBIOLOGY. *Educ:* Brigham Young Univ, BS, 48; Cornell Univ, MS, 50, PhD(soils), 52. *Prof Exp:* Asst agron, Cornell Univ, 48-51; from asst prof to assoc prof, 52-62, coordr, Nigeria Proj, 64-69, PROF AGRON, COLO STATE UNIV, 62-, DEAN COL AGR SCI, 68-, ASSOC & DEP DIR EXP STA, 69- *Concurrent Pos:* Trustee & chmn, Consortium Int Develop, 74-; chmn, Great Plains Agr Coun, 77. *Mem:* Sigma Xi; Fel AAAS; Am Soc Agron; Soil Sci Soc Am. *Res:* Nitrogen transformations in soil. *Mailing Add:* Col of Agr Sci Colo State Univ Ft Collins CO 80523

JOHNSON, DONALD CHARLES, b Black River Falls, Wis, Jan 30, 27; m 52; c 1. ENDOCRINOLOGY. *Educ:* Univ Wis, BS, 49; Univ Iowa, MS, 50, PhD(zool), 56. *Prof Exp:* Asst zool, Univ Iowa, 53-56, res assoc, 56-58, res asst prof, 59-63; from asst prof to assoc prof, 63-69, PROF OBSTET, GYNEC & PHYSIOL, SCH MED, UNIV KANS, 69- *Mem:* AAAS; Endocrine Soc; Am Physiol Soc; Soc Gynec Invest; Soc Study Reprod. *Res:* Reproductive physiology and endocrinology; comparative physiology of gonadotrophins; spontaneous and experimental ovarian and testicular tumors. *Mailing Add:* Dept of Obstet & Gynec Univ of Kans Med Ctr Kansas City KS 66103

JOHNSON, DONALD CURTIS, b Minneapolis, Minn, Mar 21, 35; m 56; c 3. ORGANIC CHEMISTRY. *Educ:* Hamline Univ, BS, 57; Univ Minn, PhD(org chem), 62. *Prof Exp:* Res aide org chem, 61-67, res assoc & chmn dept chem, Inst Paper Chem, 67-77 prof org chem, 70-77; SCIENTIFIC SPECIALIST FIBER CHEM, WEYERHAEUSER CO, 77- *Concurrent Pos:* Chmn, Gordon Res Conf Chem & Physics of Paper, 72-74. *Mem:* Am Chem Soc; Tech Asn Pulp & Paper Indust. *Res:* Cellulose chemistry, including reactions in solution and mechanisms of chain degradation; lignin chemistry, particularly delignification processes with selective oxidants. *Mailing Add:* Weyerhaeuser Technol Ctr Tacoma WA 98401

JOHNSON, DONALD EDGAR, biochemistry, analytical chemistry, see previous edition

JOHNSON, DONALD ELWOOD, b Joliet, Ill, July 23, 35; m 56; c 2. MATHEMATICS. *Educ:* N Cent Col, BA, 57; Univ Wis-Madison, MS, 59; Ill Inst Technol, PhD(math), 73. *Prof Exp:* Asst mathematician, Argonne Nat Lab, 59-61; from instr to assoc prof, 61-78, chairperson math, 69-73 & 75-78, PROF MATH, N CENT COL, 78-, CHAIRPERSON, DIV NATURAL SCI & MATH, 78- *Mem:* Math Asn Am; Nat Coun Teachers Math; Soc Indust Appl Math; Am Asn Univ Prof. *Res:* Geometry of polygenic functions. *Mailing Add:* Dept of Math N Cent Col Naperville IL 60540

JOHNSON, DONALD EUGENE, b Sykeston, NDak, Nov 17, 38; m 61; c 3. ANIMAL NUTRITION. *Educ:* NDak State Univ, BS, 60, MS, 63; Colo State Univ, PhD(animal nutrit), 66. *Prof Exp:* Res asst animal nutrit, NDak State Univ, 61-63 & Colo State Univ, 63-66; res assoc, Cornell Univ, 66-68; asst prof ruminant nutrit, Univ Ill, Urbana, 68-72; assoc prof, 72-80, PROF ANIMAL NUTRIT & DIR METAB LAB, COLO STATE UNIV, FOOTHILLS CAMPUS, 80- *Mem:* AAAS; Am Soc Animal Sci; Am Dairy Sci Asn. *Res:* Animal energy metabolism. *Mailing Add:* Colo State Univ Metab Lab Foothills Campus Ft Collins CO 80521

JOHNSON, DONALD GLEN, b Detroit, Mich, Jan 29, 31; m 53; c 2. MATHEMATICS. *Educ:* Albion Col, AB, 53; Mich State Univ, MS, 57; Purdue Univ, PhD(math), 59. *Prof Exp:* From asst prof to assoc prof math, Pa State Univ, 59-65; assoc prof, 65-70, PROF MATH, NMEX STATE UNIV, 70- *Mem:* Am Math Soc; Math Asn Am; Nat Coun Teachers Math. *Res:* Lattice ordered rings; rings of continuous functions. *Mailing Add:* Dept of Math NMex State Univ University Park NM 88001

JOHNSON, DONALD HASKALL, b Livingston, Mont, June 15, 22; m 47; c 4. MINERALOGY, CRYSTALLOGRAPHY. *Educ:* Mont Sch Mines, BS, 43; Harvard Univ, MA, 48; Colo Sch Mines, DSc(mining geol), 61. *Prof Exp:* Geologist, US Geol Surv, 50-54; from instr to asst prof geol, Colo Sch Mines, 54-61; chief mineralogist, Rhoanglo Mine Serv Ltd, Zambia, 61-65; tech adv UN Develop Prog Spec Fund, 65-66; geologist, For Br, US Geol Surv, Liberia, 67-69, geologist-mineralogist, Off Int Geol, Saudi Arabia, 69-74; MEM FAC, DEPT MINERAL, PETROL & MINERALS UNIV, SAUDI ARABIA, 74- *Mem:* AAAS; Am Inst Mining, Metall & Petrol Eng; Am Soc Testing & Mat; Mineral Soc Am; Mineral Asn Can. *Res:* Determinative mineralogy; studies of radioactive minerals; mineralogical studies in support of mining and metallurgical operations; forensic mineralogy; geological and mineralogical studies of ore deposits. *Mailing Add:* Dept of Mineral Petrol & Minerals Univ Dhahran Saudi Arabia

JOHNSON, DONALD L(EE), b Denver, Colo, Feb 19, 27; m 47; c 4. METALLURGICAL ENGINEERING. *Educ:* Colo Sch Mines, MetE, 50, MS, 56; Univ Nebr, Lincoln, PhD(chem eng), 68. *Prof Exp:* Trainee, Allis Chalmers Mfg Co, 50-51; metall engr, Mine & Smelter Supply Co, 53-56; asst prof metall eng, Wash State Univ, 56-59; sr metallurgist, NAm Rockwell Corp, 60-63; assoc prof metall, 63-75, PROF MECH ENG, METALL PROG, UNIV NEBR, LINCOLN, 75- *Concurrent Pos:* Consult, Brunswick Corp, 69-; Univ Nebr Res Coun-NASA-Ames Res Ctr fel, Univ Nebr, Lincoln, 71-72. *Mem:* Am Soc Metals; Nat Asn Corrosion Engrs. *Res:* Gas-metal equilibria; hydrogen transport in metallic alloys; polarization analysis of corrosion in aqueous systems; leaching kinetics. *Mailing Add:* 1840 Pinedale Ave Lincoln NE 68508

JOHNSON, DONALD LEE, b Aurora, Ill, Mar 9, 35; m 60; c 4. CHEMICAL ENGINEERING, POLYMER CHEMISTRY. *Educ:* Univ Ill, Urbana, BS, 62; Wash Univ, DSc(chem eng), 66. *Prof Exp:* Res engr, Eng Res Dept, 65-67, group leader, Spec Prod Develop Dept, 67-70 & Indust Prod Dept, 70-75, DIR INDUST PROD RES & DEVELOP DEPT, A E STALEY MFG CO, 75- *Mem:* Am Chem Soc; Am Inst Chem Engrs; Tech Asn Pulp & Paper Industs. *Res:* Physical chemistry of surfaces; polymer engineering as applied to paper, film and foil converting; biochemical engineering; biomass utilization. *Mailing Add:* Indust Prod Dept Cent Res Labs A E Staley Mfg Co Decatur IL 62521

JOHNSON, DONALD R, b McPherson, Kans, Apr 1, 30; m 53; c 2. METEOROLOGY. *Educ:* Bethany Col, BS, 52; Univ Wash, BS, 53; Univ Wis, MS, 60, PhD(meteorol), 65. *Prof Exp:* From proj asst to proj assoc, 59-64, from asst prof to assoc prof, 64-70, chmn dept, 73-76, PROF METEOROL, UNIV WIS-MADISON, 70-, ASSOC DIR, SPACE SCI & ENG CTR, 77- *Concurrent Pos:* Vis assoc prof, Pa State Univ, 69; chief ed, Monthly Weather Review, 77- *Mem:* Meterol Soc Japan; Nat Weatherr Asn; Am Meteorol Soc; Royal Meteorol Soc. *Res:* Dynamic climatology and meteorology; secondary and general circulation studies. *Mailing Add:* Dept of Meteorol & Space Sci Bldg Univ of Wis Madison WI 53706

JOHNSON, DONALD RALPH, b Newport, Wash, Aug 18, 31; m 55; c 3. VERTEBRATE ECOLOGY. *Educ:* Univ Idaho, BS, 53, MS, 58; Colo State Univ, PhD(wildlife ecol), 62. *Prof Exp:* From asst prof to assoc prof biol, Ft Lewis Col, 61-65; assoc prof, Minot State Col, 65-68; assoc prof, 68-75, PROF BIOL, UNIV IDAHO, 75- *Mem:* Am Soc Mammal. *Res:* Small mammal ecology; effects of 2, 4-D on rodent food habits; energy relations of pikas; diets of sympatric lizards; osprey ecology. *Mailing Add:* Dept of Biol Sci Univ of Idaho Moscow ID 83843

JOHNSON, DONALD REX, molecular spectroscopy, radio astronomy, see previous edition

JOHNSON, DONALD RICHARD, b Duluth, Minn, Jan 15, 29; m 56; c 2. ANALYTICAL CHEMISTRY. *Educ:* Univ Minn, BA, 49; Univ Wis, PhD(anal chem), 54. *Prof Exp:* Chemist, Mat Packaging Sect, Forest Prod Lab, USDA, 52-53; res chemist, Polychem Dept, Res & Develop Div, 53-59, res supvr, 59-62, prod mgr, Instrument Prod Div, 62-65, res mgr, 65-71, mgr res & eng, Photo Prod Dept, 71-74, MGR RES & DEVELOP, E I DU PONT DE NEMOURS & CO, INC, 53- *Mem:* AAAS; Am Chem Soc; Sigma Xi; Am Asn Clin Chemists. *Res:* Chemical instrumentation; thermal analysis; clinical, analytical, physical and polymer chemistry; infrared spectroscopy. *Mailing Add:* Photo Prod Dept Exp Sta 334 E I du Pont de Nemours & Co Inc Wilmington DE 19898

JOHNSON, DONALD W, b Worthington, Minn, May 4, 29; m 50; c 2. VETERINARY MEDICINE. *Educ:* Univ Minn, BS, 51, DVM, 53, PhD(microbiol), 63. *Prof Exp:* From instr to assoc prof vet med & clins, Col Vet Med, Univ Minn, 55-67; prof vet med, Univ Mo-Columbia, 67-69; PROF VET MED, UNIV MINN, ST PAUL, 69-, DIR GRAD STUDY, 80- *Res:* Viral and bacterial respiratory diseases of cattle and horses; host response to infectious diseases; cell mediated immune response of the bovine. *Mailing Add:* Dept of Vet Med Col Vet Med Univ of Minn St Paul MN 55101

JOHNSON, DONALD WAYNE, organic chemistry, photochemistry, see previous edition

JOHNSON, DONALD WILLIAM, b Norwalk, Iowa, Nov 10, 35; m 56; c 5. ENVIRONMENTAL PHYSIOLOGY, FISH BIOLOGY. *Educ:* Wash State Univ, BS, 58; Univ Mont, MST, 64; Ariz State Univ, PhD(zool), 69. *Prof Exp:* Wildlife biologist, Boise Nat Forest, US Forest Serv, 58-59; fisheries res asst, Fisheries Res Inst, Univ Wash, 59-60; high sch instr, Wash, 60-65; NIH res fel, Bodega Marine Lab, Univ Calif, Berkeley, 69-71; asst prof biol, Idaho State Univ, 71-77; PROF BIOL & DIR, HANCOCK BIOL STA, MURRAY STATE UNIV, 77- *Concurrent Pos:* NSF/SEED res fel, Univ Nairobi, 74-75; consult, Food Agr Orgn/UN Environ Prog Med Pol, 77. *Mem:* AAAS; Am Soc Zoologists; Am Fisheries Soc; Am Soc Ichthyologists & Herpetologists; Ecol Soc Am. *Res:* Endocrine control of hydromineral balance in fishes; possible sublethal effects of environmental contaminants. *Mailing Add:* Dept of Biol Murray State Univ Murray KY 42071

JOHNSON, DONOVAN EARL, b Holdrege, Nebr, June 26, 42; m 65; c 2. MICROBIOLOGY, BIOCHEMISTRY. *Educ:* Univ Nebr, BS, 64, MS, 66; Univ Wis-Madison, PhD(microbiol), 72. *Prof Exp:* From res asst to res assoc microbiol, 66-74, proj leader microbiol, Northern Regional Res Lab, 74-81, RES MICROBIOLOGIST, US GRAIN MKT RES LAB, AGR RES SERV, USDA, 81- *Concurrent Pos:* Adj prof chem, Bradley Univ, 74. *Mem:* Sigma Xi; Am Soc Microbiol; Soc Invert Path. *Res:* Biological insecticides; microbiology of insect pathogens; physiology of bacterial sporulation. *Mailing Add:* 3130 Amherst Ave Manhattan KS 66502

JOHNSON, DOUGLAS ALLAN, b Montevideo, Minn, Dec 6, 49; m 72; c 1. PLANT PHYSIOLOGY, RANGE ECOLOGY. *Educ:* Augustana Col, SDak, BA, 71; Utah State Univ, MS, 73, PhD(range ecol), 75. *Prof Exp:* Res asst tundra plant water relations, Dept Range Sci, Utah State Univ, 73-75; res assoc, Dept Biol, Augustana Col, 75-76; PLANT PHYSIOLOGIST RANGE PLANT IMPROV, CROPS RES LAB, SCI & EDUC ADMIN, USDA, 76- *Concurrent Pos:* NSF grant, 75-76; Nat Defense Educ Act fel, 71-73. *Mem:* Am Soc Plant Physiol; Crop Sci Soc Am; Am Soc Agron; Soc Range Mgt. *Res:* Development of superior forage plants for the Intermountain West; defining physiological basis of range plant resistance to drought stress. *Mailing Add:* Crops Res Lab UMC 63 Utah State Univ Logan UT 84322

JOHNSON, DOUGLAS L, b Minneapolis, Minn, Jan 21, 25; m 48; c 3. CHEMICAL ENGINEERING. *Educ:* Univ Wis-Madison, BS, 47, MS, 48, PhD(chem eng), 56. *Prof Exp:* Engr chem develop, Procter & Gamble Co, Ohio, 48-51; engr res & develop chem, F G Findley Co, Wis, 51-52; instr chem eng, Univ Wis-Madison, 52-56; sr process chem engr, Courtaulds Inc, Ala, 56-58; group leader fiber develop, Fla, 58-59, develop supvr acrylic fibers, 59-63, develop mgr, 63-68, TECH DIR, AM CYANAMID, NJ, 68- *Mem:* Am Inst Chem Engrs. *Res:* Kinetics of gas-liquid reactions in stirred batch reactors; hydrogenation of vegetable oils; adhesion to cold metallic surfaces; cellulose chemistry; extrusion and orientation of cellulose fibers; acrylic polymer chemistry; polymer solutions; acrylic fibers. *Mailing Add:* Am Cyanamid Co 701 Rivenwood Rd Franklin Lakes NJ 07417

JOHNSON, DUDLEY PAUL, b Burbank, Calif, Sept 22, 40; m 64; c 2. MATHEMATICS, MATHEMATICAL STATISTICS. *Educ:* Yale Univ, BA, 62; Mass Inst Technol, PhD(math), 66. *Prof Exp:* Asst prof math, Univ Calif, Riverside, 66-71; from asst prof to assoc prof math, 71-77, ASSOC PROF STATIST, UNIV CALGARY, 77- *Mem:* Am Math Soc; Inst Math Statist. *Res:* Stochastic processes. *Mailing Add:* 16 Varsplain Pl NW Calgary PQ T3A 0A8 Can

JOHNSON, E(WELL) CALVIN, b Tampa, Fla, Apr 18, 26. ELECTRICAL ENGINEERING. *Educ:* Ga Inst Technol, BEE, 47; Mass Inst Technol, SM, 49, EE, 50, ScD(elec eng), 51. *Prof Exp:* Res asst, Mass Inst Technol, 47-51; sr engr, Res Labs Div, Bendix Corp, 51-54, proj engr, 54-56, supvry engr, 56-58, head comput dept, 58-62, mgr info & control systs lab, 62-65, asst gen mgr, 65-67, vpres res & dir labs div, 67-69, vpres eng & res, 69-73; vpres res & develop, Gould, Inc, 73-75; CONSULT, 75- *Mem:* Fel Inst Elec & Electronics Engrs. *Res:* Feedback control systems; analog and digital computers; machine-tool control; photogrammetric instruments; aerospace information and control systems; automotive electronics; industrial automation systems. *Mailing Add:* 4807 Culbreath Isles Rd Tampa FL 33609

JOHNSON, E(DWARD) O, b Hartford, Conn, Dec 21, 19; m 47; c 2. PHYSICAL ELECTRONICS. *Educ:* Pratt Inst, BS, 48. *Prof Exp:* Res engr, RCA Labs, 48-59, chief engr, Semiconductor & Mat Div, 59-64, mgr tech prog, Electronic Components Div, 64-70, mgr spec prod, Solid State Div, 70-71, MGR TECH LIAISON, INT LICENSING, RCA CORP, NEW YORK, 71- *Concurrent Pos:* Mem panel elec powered vehicles, Dept Com, 67. *Honors & Awards:* Award, Inst Elec & Electronics Engrs, 53. *Mem:* Fel Inst Elec & Electronics Engrs. *Res:* Gaseous electronics; hot cathode arcs; semiconductor surfaces and devices. *Mailing Add:* RCA Res Lab Inc 971-2 A2a 4-90 Zushi-Machi Machida City Tokyo 194-02 Japan

JOHNSON, EARNEST J, b Phillipsburg, Pa, Feb 23, 31, m 56; c 7. SOLID STATE PHYSICS. *Educ:* Pa State Univ, BS, 53; Purdue Univ, MS, 54, PhD(physics), 64. *Prof Exp:* Staff mem, NAm Aviation, Inc, 55-56 & Hughes Aircraft Co, 56-58; mem res staff, Lincoln Lab, Mass Inst Technol, 64-74; MEM STAFF, GTE LAB, WALTHAM, MASS, 74- *Mem:* Optical Soc Am; Am Phys Soc. *Res:* Study of band structure of solids by observation of optical absorption and luminescence and effects of doping, magnetic fields and strains; laser materials; quantum electronics. *Mailing Add:* GTE Lab 40 Sylvan Rd Waltham MA 02154

JOHNSON, EDGAR GUSTAV, b St Cloud, Minn, Sept 16, 22; m 49; c 5. OPTICS. *Educ:* Univ Minn, BS, 47, MS, 49. *Prof Exp:* Res asst physics, Univ Minn, Minneapolis, 47-49; technologist-physicist, Inst Nuclear Studies, Chicago, 49; from physicist to sr physicist, Minn Mining & Mfg Co, 49-58, physics specialist, 58-68, sr physics specialist, 68-81; RETIRED. *Mem:* Optical Soc Am. *Res:* Photometry; geometric optics; retroreflective optics; vacuum vapor deposition. *Mailing Add:* 910 Bartelmy Lane St Paul MN 55119

JOHNSON, EDWARD MICHAEL, b Kenosha, Wis, Apr 9, 45. CHROMOSOME STRUCTURE, GENE REGULATION. *Educ:* Pomona Col, BA, 67; Yale Univ, PhD(pharmacol), 71. *Prof Exp:* Fel, Rockefeller Univ, 71-73, asst prof cell biol, 75-81; res assoc, 73-75, ASSOC SCIENTIST, MEM SLOAN-KETTERING CANCER CTR, 75-; ASSOC PROF CELL BIOL, ROCKEFELLER UNIV, 81- *Concurrent Pos:* Adj prof genetics, Cornell Grad Sch Med Sci, 79; fac res award, Am Cancer Soc, 81. *Mem:* Am Soc Cell Biol; Am Soc Pharmacol & Exp Therapeut; NY Acad Sci. *Res:* Regulation of gene expression in higher organisms; structure and chromosomal organization of individual genes, including ways in which hormones and other developmental signals regulate gene activity during development. *Mailing Add:* Rockfeller Univ 1230 York Ave New York NY 10021

JOHNSON, EDWARD MILES, JR, microbial genetics, see previous edition

JOHNSON, EDWIN WALLACE, b New Ulm, Minn, May 2, 23; m 55; c 2. PHYSICAL CHEMISTRY. *Educ:* Harvard Univ, BS, 44, MA, 48, PhD(phys chem), 50. *Prof Exp:* Res phys chemist, 49-55, adv phys chemist, 55-74, ADV ENG, METALL DEPT, WESTINGHOUSE ELEC CORP, 74- *Mem:* Am Chem Soc; Electrochem Soc; Am Inst Mining, Metall & Petrol Eng. *Res:* Molecular state of carboxylic acid vapors; solubility and diffusivity of hydrogen in metals; hydrogen embrittlement of steels; process metallurgy of titanium base alloys; vacuum arc melting; low pressure arc phenomena; properties of thermoelectric materials; measurement of thermal conductivity of liquid semiconductors at high temperatures; coated-electrode welding of austenitic high temperature alloys. *Mailing Add:* Westinghouse Res Labs Beulah Rd Pittsburgh PA 15235

JOHNSON, EINER WESLEY, JR, b Bemidji, Minn, July 5, 19; m 51; c 4. ORTHOPEDIC SURGERY. *Educ:* Univ Minn, BA, 41, BS, 42, BM, 44, MD, 45, MA, 50. *Prof Exp:* From instr to assoc prof orthop surg, 52-71, PROF ORTHOP SURG, MAYO GRAD SCH MED, UNIV MINN, 71- *Concurrent Pos:* Consult, Mayo Clin, Rochester Methodist Hosp & Rochester-St Mary's Hosp. *Mem:* Am Acad Orthop Surgeons; Clin Orthop Soc; Am Orthop Asn. *Mailing Add:* Mayo Clin Rochester MN 55901

JOHNSON, ELIJAH, b Eutawville, SC, Jan 1, 48. PHYSICAL CHEMISTRY. *Educ:* Penn State Univ, BS, 69; Univ Ill, PhD(chem), 76. *Prof Exp:* CHEMIST, OAK RIDGE NAT LAB, 76- *Concurrent Pos:* E P Wigner fel, Oak Ridge Nat Lab, 77- *Mem:* Am Chem Soc. *Res:* Theoretical and experimental studies of liquids using statistical mechanics and x-ray and neutron scattering. *Mailing Add:* Div Chem Oak Ridge Nat Lab PO Box X Oak Ridge TN 37830

JOHNSON, ELIZABETH BRIGGS, b Bowling Green, Ky, 1921; div; c 1. PHYSICS. *Educ:* Western Ky Univ, BS, 43; Vanderbilt Univ, MS, 52. *Prof Exp:* Res asst, SAM Lab, Columbia Univ, 44-45; res asst, SAM Lab, Union Carbide & Chem Corp, 45, assoc physicist, Oak Ridge Gaseous Diffusion Plant, Union Carbide Corp, 48-50, physicist, Oak Ridge Nat Lab, 50-68, physicist, Oak Ridge Y-12 Plant, 68-75; PHYSICIST, OAK RIDGE NAT LAB, 75- *Concurrent Pos:* Secy standards comt N16, Am Nat Standards Inst; mem, Atomic Safety & Licensing Bd Panel, US Nuclear Regulatory Comn. *Mem:* Am Physics Soc; fel Am Nuclear Soc; Sigma Xi; NY Acad Sci. *Res:* Nuclear criticality safety and nuclear reactors. *Mailing Add:* Oak Ridge Lab PO Box X Oak Ridge TN 37830

JOHNSON, ELIZABETH COX, b Joliet, Ill, Nov 1, 17; m 50; c 4. NUTRITION. *Educ:* Univ Ariz, BS, 40, MS, 42; Ore State Univ, PhD(foods & nutrit), 50. *Prof Exp:* Pub health nutritionist, Vis Nurse Asn, Boston, 42-43; asst prof nutrit, Iowa State Univ, 49-51; asst prof nutrit res, 51-52, asst prof nutrit, summer 56, asst prof foods & nutrit, 65-72, ASSOC PROF FOODS & NUTRIT, ORE STATE UNIV, 72- *Res:* Basal metabolic rate of Arizona women; thiamine metabolism of women on controlled diets, daily levels of thiamine in the blood. *Mailing Add:* Dept of Foods & Nutrit Ore State Univ Sch of Home Econ Corvallis OR 97331

JOHNSON, ELLIS LANE, b Athens, Ga, July 26, 38; m 62; c 1. OPERATIONS RESEARCH. *Educ:* Ga Inst Technol, BS, 60; Univ Calif, Berkeley, MA, 62, PhD(eng sci), 65. *Prof Exp:* Asst prof admin sci, Yale Univ, 64-68; MEM RES STAFF MATH SCI, THOMAS J WATSON RES CTR, IBM CORP, 68- *Concurrent Pos:* Vis assoc prof, Univ Waterloo, 60-61, adj prof, 72-; vis engr, Sci Develop, IBM, France, 73-74. *Mem:* Math Prog Soc. *Res:* Theory and algorithms for integer programming; study of combinatorial polyhedra; character recognition. *Mailing Add:* Thomas J Watson Res Ctr IBM Corp PO Box 218 Yorktown Heights NY 10598

JOHNSON, ELMER MARSHALL, b Midlothian, Ill, June 16, 30; m 51; c 4. ANATOMY. *Educ:* Agr & Mech Col Tex, BS, 54, MS, 55; Univ Calif, Berkeley, PhD(anat), 59. *Prof Exp:* Asst zool, microtech & bot, Agr & Mech Col Tex, 53-55; asst gross anat & histol, Univ Calif, 55-58; instr anat & physiol, Contra Costa Col, 58-59; assoc prof anat, Univ Fla, 60-68, prof anat sci, 68-71; prof human morphol & chmn dept, Col Med, Univ Calif, Irvine, 71-72; PROF ANAT & CHMN DEPT, JEFFERSON MED COL, THOMAS JEFFERSON UNIV, 72-, DIR, DANIEL BAUGH INST ANAT, 72- *Concurrent Pos:* Asst researcher histochem, Surg Gen, US Army, 54. *Mem:* AAAS; Teratology Soc (pres, 74-75); Am Asn Anatomists. *Res:* Experimental teratology and nutrition; reproductive physiology; molecular biology; electron microscopy; histochemistry. *Mailing Add:* Dept of Anat Jefferson Med Col Philadelphia PA 19107

JOHNSON, ELMER ROGER, b Erwin, SDak, Oct 4, 11; m 40; c 4. CHEMISTRY. *Educ:* SDak State Col, BS, 33; Univ Wis, PhD(chem), 40. *Prof Exp:* Asst gen chem, Univ Wis, 37-40; res chemist, Tex Co, NY, 40-46; assoc prof, 46-55, prof, 55-78, EMER PROF CHEM, SDAK STATE UNIV, 78- *Mem:* AAAS; Am Chem Soc. *Res:* Fuel composition and antiknock quality; synthesis of fuel components and additives; synthesis of additives for lubricating oils; the Lange gold sol test; factors influencing the preparation of the gold sol and its use in the Lange test. *Mailing Add:* Dept of Chem SDak State Univ Brookings SD 57006

JOHNSON, ELSIE ERNEST, b Hackensack, NJ; m 64; c 3. ANESTHESIOLOGY. *Educ:* Women's Med Col Pa, MD, 64; Am Bd Anesthesiol, dipl, 75. *Prof Exp:* Intern, Philadelphia Gen Hosp, 64-65; resident anesthesiol, New Eng Deaconess Hosp, 65-67; narcos underlakare, Malmo Almana Stukhusset, Sweden, 67-68; res fel, 71-73, instr, 73-77, ASST PROF ANESTHESIA, HARVARD MED SCH, 77- *Concurrent Pos:* Staff anesthetist, Beth Israel Hosp, Boston, 73- *Mem:* Am Soc Anesthesiologists; Am Physiol Soc. *Res:* Splanchnic effects of mechanical ventilation with regard to circulation; biliary and hepatic function; opiate effects on biliary pressure; splanchnic endogenous opiate release. *Mailing Add:* Dept Anesthesiol Beth Israel Hosp 303 Brookline Ave Boston MA

JOHNSON, ELTON LOYD, b Florence, Colo, June 6, 18; m 42; c 2. ANIMAL NUTRITION. *Educ:* Okla State Univ, BSA, 40; Purdue Univ, MS, 42, PhD(animal nutrit), 48. *Prof Exp:* Asst poultry, Purdue Univ, 40-42, poultry & agr chem, 42-48; from asst prof to assoc prof poultry, Iowa State Col, 48-49; prof poultry sci & head dept, Univ Minn, 53-64; dir, Int Rural Develop Off, Nat Asn State Univs & Land Grant Cols, 64-66; dir res, Ralston Purina Int, 67-71, pres Ralston Purina Eastern & managing dir, Agri-prod, Asian Develop Region, 71-73; dir res & tech serv, Cosby-Hodges Milling Co, 74-78; ASSOC PROF POULTRY SCI, UNIV MD, 78- *Mem:* Am Soc Animal Sci; Poultry Sci Asn; Am Inst Nutrit; Am Inst Biol Sci. *Res:* Poultry nutrition; vitamin, mineral, protein and unidentified factor studies; vitamin A requirement of young chickens; administration. *Mailing Add:* 12211 Valerie Lane Laurel MD 20811

JOHNSON, ELWIN LEROY, b Hillsboro, Ill, July 20, 35; m 67; c 3. CERAMIC ENGINEERING, CHEMISTRY. *Educ:* Univ Ill, BS, 56, MS, 57, PhD(ceramic eng), 60. *Prof Exp:* From res asst to res assoc ceramic eng, Ceramic Eng Dept, Univ Ill, 56-59; mem tech staff mat sci, Cent Res Lab, 60-65, eng sect mgr advan circuits, Semiconductor Div, 65-68, FCC mgr circuits & packaging, 68-75, PROG MGR NEW PROD, CENT RES LABS, TEX INSTRUMENTS, INC, 75- *Concurrent Pos:* Fel, Owens-Corning Fiberglass Corp, Ceramic Eng Dept, Univ Ill, 57-60; chmn, JC-11 Comt, Joint Electron Device Eng Coun, Electronic Indust Asn, 74- *Mem:* Am Ceramic Soc; Nat Inst Ceramic Engrs; Electronic Indust Asn; Am Soc Testing & Mat. *Res:* Materials science; thick film hybrids; electronic packaging; electronic display devices; solar energy conversion. *Mailing Add:* PO Box 225303 Tex Instruments Inc MS 158 Dallas TX 75265

JOHNSON, EMMETT JOHN, b New Orleans, La, Apr 17, 29; m 55; c 2. MICROBIOLOGY. *Educ:* Loyola Univ of the South, BS, 52; La State Univ, MS, 54, PhD(bact), 57. *Prof Exp:* Nat Res Coun fel, Med Sch, Stanford Univ, 57-58; from asst prof to assoc prof microbiol, Med Sch, Univ Miss, 58-65; res scientist, Exobiol Div, Ames Res Ctr, NASA, 65-66; res assoc, Bruce Lyon Mem Res Inst, Oakland, Calif, 66-67; assoc prof, 67-70, PROF MICROBIOL & IMMUNOL, MED SCH, TULANE UNIV, 70- *Concurrent Pos:* Res assoc microbiol, Stanford Med Sch, 57-68; teaching assoc, 65-66, lectr, 66-67; Lederle Med Fac award, 62-65; res consult, Oak Ridge Nat Lab, 63-64 & 67-; res assoc molecular biol, Pasteur Inst, Paris, France, 74-75. *Mem:* AAAS; fel Am Acad Microbiol; Am Soc Microbiol; Am Soc Biol Chemists; Am Chem Soc. *Res:* Molecular mechanisms of genetic and biochemical regulation; biochemical basis of chemolithotrophic autotrophy; genetic and biochemical characterization of common enterobacterial antigens. *Mailing Add:* Dept of Microbiol & Immunol Tulane Univ Med Sch New Orleans LA 70112

JOHNSON, EMORY EMANUEL, b Ceresco, Nebr, May 3, 14; m 39; c 2. CIVIL ENGINEERING. *Educ:* Univ Nebr, BSc, 36; Univ Mich, MS, 41. *Prof Exp:* Instr math, Mo Sch Mines, 37-41; asst prof civil eng, SDak State Univ, 41-43 & Univ Kans, 43-46; assoc prof, Colo State Univ, 46; PROF CIVIL ENG & HEAD DEPT, S DAK STATE UNIV, 47- *Concurrent Pos:* Spec consult, Boeing Airplane Co, 52-58. *Mem:* Am Soc Civil Engrs; Am Concrete Inst; Am Soc Eng Educ; Nat Soc Prof Engrs. *Res:* Structures; mechanics. *Mailing Add:* 515 13th Ave Brookings SD 57006

JOHNSON, ERIC G, JR, b Klamath Falls, Ore, June 17, 36; m 59; c 2. LASERS. *Educ:* Mass Inst Technol, BS, 57; Harvard Univ, MA, 60, PhD(physics), 63. *Prof Exp:* GEN PHYSICIST, BOULDER LABS, NAT BUR STANDARDS, 62- *Mem:* Am Phys Soc. *Res:* Measurement theory; unitary matrix field theory; laser power and energy measurements. *Mailing Add:* Nat Bur of Standards 325 S Broadway Boulder CO 80302

JOHNSON, ERIC RICHARD, b Elkhart, Ind, Mar 11, 47; m 68; c 1. BIOCHEMISTRY. *Educ:* Rose-Hulman Inst Technol, BS, 69; Univ Minn, PhD(biochem), 74. *Prof Exp:* Asst chemist, Uniroyal, Inc, 68; USPHS fel biochem, Univ Minn, 69-74; res assoc biochem, Duke Univ Med Ctr, 74-76; ASST PROF CHEM, BALL STATE UNIV, 76- *Concurrent Pos:* Fel, Nat Inst Environ Health Sci, Duke Univ Med Ctr, 75-76. *Mem:* Am Chem Soc; Sigma Xi. *Res:* Protein and peptide chemistry; mechanisms of protein folding; oxygen toxicity; superoxide free radical production and decomposition in biological systems. *Mailing Add:* Dept of Chem Ball State Univ Muncie IN 47306

JOHNSON, ERIC ROBERT, b Windom, Minn, Nov 17, 47; m 69. ANALYTICAL CHEMISTRY, CHEMICAL INSTRUMENTATION. *Educ:* Hamline Univ, BS, 69; Fla State Univ, PhD(anal chem), 75. *Prof Exp:* Res assoc anal chem, Mich State Univ, 74-76; mem staff, Mass Spectrometry Div, Varian Assocs, 76-77; MGR LAB COMPUT NETWORK, WAYNE STATE UNIV, 77- *Mem:* Am Chem Soc; Soc Appl Spectros. *Res:* Application of minicomputers to laboratory instrumentation; design of special purpose digital, analog and hybrid instrumentation systems; study of atomic absorption, emission and fluorescence spectroscopic methods of trace metal analysis. *Mailing Add:* Dept of Chem Wayne State Univ Detroit MI 48202

JOHNSON, ERIC VAN, b Medford, Mass, Mar 11, 43; c 2. ORNITHOLOGY. *Educ:* Brown Univ, AB, 64; Cornell Univ, PhD(wildlife sci), 69. *Prof Exp:* Asst prof, 69-74, assoc prof, 74-80, PROF BIOL, CALIF POLYTECH STATE UNIV, SAN LUIS OBISPO, 80- *Mem:* Cooper Ornith Soc; Am Ornith Union; Wilson Ornith Soc. *Res:* Avian taxonomy, behavior and population ecology. *Mailing Add:* Dept of Biol Sci Calif Polytech State Univ San Luis Obispo CA 93407

JOHNSON, ERIC WILLIAM, b Harrow, Eng, Oct 30, 23; m 56; c 1. APPLIED MECHANICS, MECHANICAL ENGINEERING. *Educ:* Univ London, BSc, 50; Univ Alta, MSc, 65; Univ BC, PhD(appl mech), 70. *Prof Exp:* Asst engr, Brit Oxygen Co, 50-57; asst prof mech eng, Univ Alta, 58-67; ASSOC PROF MECH ENG, UNIV CALGARY, 70-, ASSOC DEAN FAC OF ENG, 77- *Mem:* Inst Mech Engrs. *Res:* Numerical control of machine tools using stereoscopic photography; photoelasticity; engineering optics. *Mailing Add:* 1311 Windsor St NW Calgary PQ T2N 3X2 Can

JOHNSON, ERNEST F(REDERICK), (JR), b Jamestown, NY, Apr 4, 18; m 44; c 4. CHEMICAL ENGINEERING. *Educ:* Lehigh Univ, BS, 40; Univ Pa, PhD(chem eng), 49. *Prof Exp:* From res & develop engr to tech supvr synthetic org chem mfg, Barrett Div, Allied Chem & Dye Corp, 40-46; from asst prof to assoc prof, 48-59, assoc dean fac, 62-66, dir grad studies, Dept Chem Eng, 69-74, chmn dept, 77-78, ASSOC, PLASMA PHYSICS LAB, 55-, PROF CHEM ENG, PRINCETON UNIV, 59- *Concurrent Pos:* Consult chem engr, 50-; trustee, Assoc Univs, Inc, 62-68, chmn, 65-67; dir, Autodynamics, Inc, 67- *Mem:* Fel AAAS; Am Chem Soc; Am Soc Eng Educ; fel Am Inst Chem Engrs; fel Am Inst Chemists. *Res:* Thermodynamic and transport properties of fluids; automatic process control; catalysis; technological aspects of controlled thermonuclear fusion. *Mailing Add:* Dept of Chem Eng Princeton Univ Eng Quadrangle Princeton NJ 08540

JOHNSON, ERNEST WALTER, physiology, biophysics, see previous edition

JOHNSON, EUGENE A, b Crosby, Minn, Feb 24, 25; m 47; c 4. BIOSTATISTICS. *Educ:* Univ Minn, BA, 49, MA, 50, PhD(biostatist), 56. *Prof Exp:* From asst prof to assoc prof biostatist, Univ Minn, Minneapolis, 56-60, assoc prof indust eng, 60-62; prof math & head dept, Gustavus Adolphus Col, 62-64; assoc prof & dir biomed data processing unit, 64-69, PROF BIOMET, COL MED SCI, UNIV MINN, MINNEAPOLIS, 69-, DIR GRAD STUDY, 80- *Mem:* Am Statist Asn; Biomet Soc; Inst Math Statist. *Res:* Biomedical computing; computing in biology; mathematics; operations research. *Mailing Add:* Dept of Biomet Univ of Minn Col of Med Sci Minneapolis MN 55455

JOHNSON, EUGENE MALCOLM, JR, b Baltimore, Md, Oct 20, 43; m 65; c 2. PHARMACOLOGY. *Educ:* Univ Md, BS, 66, PhD(med chem), 70. *Prof Exp:* Fel pharmacol, Sch Med, Wash Univ, 70-73; asst prof pharmacol, Med Col Pa, 73-76; asst prof, 76-78, ASSOC PROF PHARMACOL, SCH MED, WASH UNIV, 78- *Res:* Autonomic pharmacology; role of sympathetic nervous system in hypertension; effect of drugs on development of the sympathetic nervous system. *Mailing Add:* Dept of Pharmacol Wash Univ Sch Med St Louis MO 63110

JOHNSON, EUGENE W, b El Paso, Tex, May 25, 39; m 59; c 1. ALGEBRA. *Educ:* Univ Calif, Riverside, BA, 63, MA, 64, PhD(algebra), 66. *Prof Exp:* Asst prof math, Eastern NMex Univ, 66; from asst prof to assoc prof, 66-75, PROF MATH, UNIV IOWA, 75- *Mem:* Am Math Soc. *Res:* Noetherian rings and abstract ideal theory. *Mailing Add:* Dept of Math Univ of Iowa Iowa City IA 52240

JOHNSON, EVERT WILLIAM, b Astoria, NY, Apr 6, 21; m 50; c 3. FORESTRY, PHOTOGRAMMETRY. *Educ:* Univ NH, BS, 43; Yale Univ, MF, 47; Syracuse Univ, PhD, 57. *Prof Exp:* Forester chg aerial surv, Sable Mt Corp, Vt, 47-50; from instr to assoc prof forestry, Auburn Univ, 50-67, asst, 50-53, asst forester, 53-57, prof forestry, 67-80. *Mem:* AAAS; Forest Hist Soc; Soc Am Foresters; Am Soc Photogram. *Res:* Applications of photogrammetry, statistics and computer science to forest measurements. *Mailing Add:* 743 Heard Ave Auburn AL 36830

JOHNSON, F BRENT, b Monroe, Utah, Mar 31, 42; m 65; c 4. VIROLOGY. *Educ:* Brigham Young Univ, BS, 66, MS, 67, PhD(microbiol), 70. *Prof Exp:* Fel virol, NIH, 70-72; asst prof, 72-75, assoc prof, 75-80, PROF MICROBIOL, BRIGHAM YOUNG UNIV, 80- *Concurrent Pos:* NIH res grants, 73 & 76. *Mem:* Am Soc Microbiol; AAAS. *Res:* Viral replication; structure and biology of virus infections. *Mailing Add:* 887 Widtsoe Bldg Brigham Young Univ Provo UT 84602

JOHNSON, F CLIFFORD, b Ft Worth, Tex, Nov 4, 32; m 58; c 3. GENETICS, ECOLOGY. *Educ:* Univ Tex, BA, 55, MA, 60, PhD(zool), 61. *Prof Exp:* Instr zool, Duke Univ, 60-61; asst prof genetics, Va Polytech Inst, 61-62; asst prof biol & chmn dept, NMex Inst Mining & Technol, 62-66, assoc prof, 67-70; PROF ZOOL, UNIV FLA, 70- *Res:* Genetics of polymorphic variation. *Mailing Add:* Dept of Zool Univ of Fla Gainesville FL 32601

JOHNSON, FATIMA NUNES, b Rizal, Philippines, Jan 1, 39; m 67; c 2. ORGANIC CHEMISTRY. *Educ:* Adamson Univ, Manila, BS, 59; Boston Col, MS, 61, PhD(org chem), 64. *Prof Exp:* Proj leader org med chem, Arthur D Little, Inc, Mass, 64-69; res chemist, Org Chem Labs, Edgewood Arsenal, Md, 69-70; SCIENTIST DRUG STANDARDS, US PHARMACOPEIA, 71- *Mem:* Am Chem Soc. *Res:* Organo-fluorine compounds; organometallics; molecular rearrangements; nitrogen heterocyclics. *Mailing Add:* 5314 Dunleer Lane Burke VA 22015

JOHNSON, FRANCIS, b Bristol, Eng, Mar 12, 30; m 55; c 3. ORGANIC CHEMISTRY. *Educ:* Glasgow Univ, BSc, 51, PhD(org chem), 54. *Prof Exp:* Fel org chem, Boston Univ, 54-57; from res chemist to assoc scientist, Eastern Res Lab, Dow Chem Co, 57-69, res scientist, 69-74; PROF PHARMACOL & CHEM, STATE UNIV NY STONY BROOK, 74- *Concurrent Pos:* Eve lectr, Boston Univ, 56-70; consult, Qm Res Corps, US Army, 56-58 & Dow Chem Co, 74-; vis scientist, Oxford Univ, 66-67. *Mem:* Am Chem Soc; Royal Soc Chem; assoc Royal Inst Chem; fel Royal Soc Arts. *Res:* Synthetic organic chemistry, especially natural product and aliphatic areas; medicinal chemistry. *Mailing Add:* Dept of Pharmacol Sci State Univ of NY Stony Brook NY 11794

JOHNSON, FRANCIS SEVERIN, b Omak, Wash, July 20, 18; m 43; c 1. SPACE PHYSICS, METEOROLOGY. *Educ:* Univ Alta, BSc, 40; Univ Calif, Los Angeles, MA, 42, PhD(meteorol), 58. *Prof Exp:* Physicist, US Naval Res Lab, 46-55; space physicist, Lockheed Missiles & Space Co, 55-62 & dir, Earth & Planetary Sci Lab, Southwest Ctr Advan Studies, 62-69; actg pres, Univ, 69-71, prof & dir, Ctr Advan Studies, 71-74, CECIL H & IDA M GREEN HONS PROF NATURAL SCI, UNIV TEX, DALLAS, 74-; ASST DIR ASTRON, ATMOSPHERIC, EARTH & OCEAN SCI, NAT SCI FOUND, WASHINGTON, DC, 79- *Concurrent Pos:* Consult, NASA,

60-79; mem, Panel Adv Cent Radio Propagation Lab, Nat Bur Standards, 62-65, mem panel on weather & climate modification, 64-70, mem adv comt to Air Force Systs Command panel on re-entry physics, 65-68, mem comt solar-terrestrial res, 66-79, chmn, 71-74, mem comt adv to Environ Sci Serv Admin, 66-71, mem space sci bd, 67-80, mem geophys res bd, 71-75, mem comt adv to Nat Oceanic & Atmospheric Admin, 71-72, mem, Climate Res Bd, 77-79; mem adv panel atmospheric sci, NSF, 62-66; chmn, US Comn IV, Int Union Radio Sci, 64-67, secy, US Nat Comt, 67-70, vchmn, 70-73, chmn, 73-76; mem res adv comt, Coord Bd Tex Col & Univ Syst, 66-68; mem, Air Force Sci Adv Bd, 68-79; mem, Nat Adv Comt Oceans & Atmosphere, 71-73; mem climatic impact comt, Nat Acad Sci, 72-76; pres, Spec Comt Solar-Terrestrial Physics, 74-77; vpres, Comt Space Res, Int Coun Sci Unions, 75- *Honors & Awards:* Space Sci Award, Am Inst Aeronaut & Astronaut, 66; Henryk Arctowski Medal, Nat Acad Sci, 72; Except Sci Achievement Medal, NASA, 73; John A Fleming Award, Am Geophys Union, 77. *Mem:* Am Meteorol Soc; Am Physical Soc; Am Geophys Union; Am Inst Aeronaut & Astronaut; Inst Elec & Electronics Engrs. *Res:* Upper atmospheric and magnetospheric physics; space science; planetary atmospheres; upper atmosphere and space physics; planetary science; solar radiation; synoptic and physical meteorology. *Mailing Add:* 1806 24th St Arlington VA 22202

JOHNSON, FRANK BACCHUS, b Washington, DC, Feb 1, 19; m 47; c 2. PATHOLOGY. *Educ:* Univ Mich, BS, 40; Howard Univ, MD, 44. *Prof Exp:* From intern to resident path, Med Ctr, Jersey City, 44-46; dir clin labs, Howard Univ, 46-48; res assoc, Univ Chicago, 50-52; pathologist, 52-60, chief basic sci div, 60-72, chief, Histochem Br, 72-74, CHMN, DEPT CHEM PATH, ARMED FORCES INST PATH, 74- *Concurrent Pos:* AEC fel med sci, Univ Chicago, 48-50. *Honors & Awards:* Citation Admin & Tech Proficiency, Vet Admin, 58, Commendation Outstanding Contributions Histochem, 64. *Mem:* Am Crystallog Soc; Histochem Soc. *Res:* Histochemistry in pathology. *Mailing Add:* Armed Forces Inst Path Washington DC 20306

JOHNSON, FRANK HARRIS, b Raleigh, NC, July 31, 08; m 33; c 3. MOLECULAR BIOLOGY. *Educ:* Princeton Univ, AB, 31, PhD(biol), 36; Duke Univ, AM, 32. *Prof Exp:* From instr to prof, 37-69, Edwin Grant Conklin prof, 69-77, EMER PROF BIOL, PRINCETON UNIV, 77-, SR RES BIOLOGIST, 77- *Concurrent Pos:* Rockefeller fel, Univs Delft & Utrecht, 39; Guggenheim fel, Calif Inst Technol & Marine Biol Lab, Woods Hole, 44-46 & Univ Utah, 50-51; prog dir Develop, Environ & Syst Biol, NSF, 52-53, consult, 53-56. *Honors & Awards:* Sci Prize, AAAS, 41. *Mem:* fel Explorer's Club; Soc Gen Physiol; Am Physiol Soc; Soc Exp Biol & Med; Am Soc Microbiol. *Res:* Physical chemistry of biological reactions; action of temperature, hydrostatic pressure, drugs and other factors in luminescence, respiration, growth, enzyme reactions, cell division and other processes; kinetic basis of molecular biology; theory of rate processes in biology. *Mailing Add:* Dept of Biol Princeton Univ Princeton NJ 08540

JOHNSON, FRANK JUNIOR, b Rosendale, Mo, Aug 24, 30; m 51; c 3. ANALYTICAL CHEMISTRY. *Educ:* Northwest Mo State Col, BS, 52; Univ Mo, MSc, 61. *Prof Exp:* Instr agr chem, Univ Mo, 55-62; anal chemist, 62-69, HEAD, ANAL LAB, TENN VALLEY AUTHORITY, 69- *Mem:* Asn Off Anal Chemists; Am Chem Soc. *Res:* Fertilizer chemistry; investigation of new or improved analytical methods pertaining to fertilizer and related materials. *Mailing Add:* 1915 Hermitage Dr Florence AL 35630

JOHNSON, FRANK WALKER, b St Augustine, Fla, May 22, 09; m 53; c 2. GEOLOGY. *Educ:* Univ Nebr, BA, 34. *Hon Degrees:* DSc, 79. *Prof Exp:* Asst fossil collecting, Childs Frick Lab, Am Mus Natural Hist, 35-36; jr geologist, Lago Petrol Corp, Venezuela, 36-37, resident geologist, 38-41; dist geologist, Standard Oil Co, 41-42, sr geologist spec studies, 42-43; dist geologist, Creole Petrol Corp, 43-44, div geologist, 44-52; regional geologist, SAm, Standard Oil Co NJ, NY, 52-53; div geologist, Western Venezuela, Creole Petrol Corp, 53-54, asst explor mgr, 54-58; vpres chg explor res, Jersey Prod Res Co, 58-61; dep mgr explor, Standard Oil Co, NJ, 62-67; chmn adv comt explor res, Esso Prod Res Co, 62-67, sr explor adv, 67-68; mgr explor Esso East, 68-71; CONSULT GEOLOGIST, 71- *Concurrent Pos:* Chmn, Inland Wetlands & Water Courses Agency, Greenwich, Conn, 73-76 & chmn, Conserv Comn, 73-78. *Mem:* AAAS; Am Geog Soc; fel Geol Soc Am; Soc Vert Paleont; Am Asn Petrol Geologists. *Res:* Exploration for hydrocarbons; geology, geophysics and geochemistry as applied to petroleum exploration; stratigraphy of late Tertiary along Niobizia River in northern Nebraska as related to fossil vertebrates collecting localities. *Mailing Add:* 5 W 86th St Apt 8-C New York NY 10024

JOHNSON, FRANKFORD MILAM, mathematics, see previous edition

JOHNSON, FRANKLIN M, b Cloquet, Minn, Nov 1, 40. GENETICS. *Educ:* Univ Minn, Duluth, BA, 62; Univ Hawaii, MS, 64; Univ Tex, Austin, PhD(zool), 66. *Prof Exp:* NIH fel, 66-67; res scientist, Univ Tex, Austin, 67-68; asst prof genetics, NC State Univ, 68-74, sr geneticist, Res Triangle Inst, 74-77; RES GENETICIST, NAT INST ENVIRON HEALTH SCI, 77- *Mem:* AAAS; Genetics Soc Am; Am Soc Naturalists; Am Soc Human Genetics. *Res:* Patterns of genetic variability in natural populations; adaptive relationships between environment and genetically controlled enzyme variation; comparative biochemistry of allelic enzymes; methods in mutagenesis testing. *Mailing Add:* Lab of Biochem Genetics Nat Inst of Environ Health Sci Research Triangle Park NC 27709

JOHNSON, FRED LOWERY, JR, b San Angelo, Tex, Oct 24, 27; m 49; c 3. INDUSTRIAL ORGANIC CHEMISTRY. *Educ:* Univ Tex, BS, 51, PhD(chem), 59. *Prof Exp:* Sr process chemist, Am Cyanamid Co, La, 59-62; res chemist, Jefferson Chem Co, Inc, 62-64, sr res chemist, 64-68, proj chemist, 68-76, SR PROJ CHEMIST, TEXACO CHEM CO, 76- *Mem:* Am Chem Soc; Sigma Xi. *Res:* Catalytic research and process development for petrochemicals. *Mailing Add:* Texaco Chem Co Inc PO Box 15730 Austin TX 78761

JOHNSON, FRED TULLOCH, b Peoria, Ill, Aug 23, 21; m 61; c 1. PHYSICS. *Educ:* Johns Hopkins Univ, AB, 44, PhD, 52. *Prof Exp:* Res assoc physics, Johns Hopkins Univ, 48-51; staff physicist electronics, Bendix Corp, 52-61, head navig dept, Conductron Corp, 61-64, dir res sensor dynamics, 64-65; head adv infrared systs, Tex Instruments Inc, 65-67; assoc prof, 67-74, PROF PHYSICS & ASTRON, EASTERN MICH UNIV, 74- *Res:* X-rays; x-ray diffraction; information theory; electronics; signal processing; radar; infrared. *Mailing Add:* Dept of Physics Eastern Mich Univ Ypsilanti MI 48197

JOHNSON, FREDERIC ALLAN, b Concord, NH, Mar 6, 32; m 56; c 3. INORGANIC CHEMISTRY, PHYSICAL CHEMISTRY. *Educ:* Univ NH, BS, 54, MS, 55; Univ Wis, PhD(chem), 58. *Prof Exp:* Lab instr, Univ NH, 54; chemist, Redstone Arsenal Res Div, Rohm & Haas Co, 58-62, group leader anal chem, 62-70; ASSOC PROF CHEM, AUBURN UNIV, 70- *Mem:* Am Chem Soc. *Res:* Fluorine and metal coordination chemistry; nuclear magnetic resonance; kinetics. *Mailing Add:* Dept of Chem Auburn Univ Auburn AL 36830

JOHNSON, FREDERIC DUANE, b Chicago, Ill, Oct 24, 25; m 48; c 5. FOREST ECOLOGY. *Educ:* Ore State Col, BS, 50; Univ Idaho, MS, 52. *Prof Exp:* Radioisotopes technologist, 52-56, from instr to asst prof forest mgt, 56-67, assoc prof forest ecol, 67-72, PROF FOREST ECOL, UNIV IDAHO, 72- *Mem:* Ecol Soc Am; Soc Am Foresters. *Res:* Forest and wetlands ecology and plant distribution; temperate and tropical dendrology. *Mailing Add:* Col of Forestry Univ of Idaho Moscow ID 83843

JOHNSON, FREDERICK ALLAN, b Winnipeg, Man, Nov 7, 23. NUCLEAR PHYSICS. *Educ:* Univ Man, BSc, 45; McGill Univ, PhD(nuclear physics), 52. *Prof Exp:* Res assoc nuclear physics, Radiation Lab, McGill Univ, 52-53; sr engr, Can Aviation Electronics Co, 53-55; Defence Sci Serv officer nuclear physics, Suffield Exp Sta, 55-59, Defence Sci Serv Officer Chem, Biol & Radiation Labs, 59-71, DEFENCE SCI SERV OFFICER NUCLEAR PHYSICS, DEFENCE RES BD, DEFENCE RES ESTAB, 71- *Mem:* Am Phys Soc; Can Asn Physicists. *Res:* Spectroscopy of nuclear radiations from cyclotron-produced cadmium and silver isotopes; auger transitions in silver; industrial design of radiation detectors; nanosecond pulse electronics; neutron time-of-flight spectroscopy; beam pulsing and deflection; pulse-shape discrimination circuits for neutron identification; neutron activation; radiological protection and health physics. *Mailing Add:* Defence Res Estab Ottawa ON K1A 0K2 Can

JOHNSON, FREDERICK ARTHUR, JR, b Pittsburgh, Pa, Sept 8, 23; m 46; c 1. GEOLOGY. *Educ:* Harvard Univ, BS, 44; Univ Chicago, MS, 49, PhD(geol), 51. *Prof Exp:* From assoc geologist to sr geologist stratig sect, Explor Dept, Humble Oil & Ref Co, 51-60, supvry geologist, 60-66; sect supvr struct geol & basin interpretation, Esso Prod Res Co, 66-67; sr explor geologist, Humble Oil & Refining Co, 67-76; GEOL ADV, EXXON CO, 76- *Mem:* Sigma Xi; AAAS; Geol Soc Am; Soc Econ Paleont & Mineral; Am Asn Petrol Geol. *Res:* Carbonate rock; stratigraphic and structural geology of Permian Basin, west Texas; structural geology of Rocky Mountains; regional geology of Alaska, eastern USSR and western Canada. *Mailing Add:* Exxon Co USA PO Box 2180 Rm 2227 Houston TX 77001

JOHNSON, FREDERICK CARROLL, b Sheridan, Wyo, Oct 23, 40; m 64; c 1. APPLIED MATHEMATICS, RESOURCE MANAGEMENT. *Educ:* Univ NDak, BS, 62; Univ Wash, MS & PhD(appl math), 66. *Prof Exp:* Res analyst real-time data processing, DBA Systs, Inc, 66-68; res scientist appl math, Boeing Sci Res Labs, 68-73; mathematician, 73-77, CHIEF, MATH ANAL DIV, NAT BUR STANDARDS, 77- *Mem:* Soc Indust & Appl Math; Inst Elec & Electronics Engrs; Asn Comput Mach; Am Fisheries Soc. *Res:* Applications of mathematical modeling to natural resource management; computational methods for constrained optimization problems; economic and biological consequences of fisheries management. *Mailing Add:* Math Anal Div Nat Bur of Stand Washington DC 20234

JOHNSON, FREEMAN KEITH, b Redmond, Utah, Feb 2, 33; m 56; c 9. GENETICS, PLANT BREEDING. *Educ:* Brigham Young Univ, BA, 56; Univ Minn, MS, 61, PhD(genetics), 64. *Prof Exp:* From asst to assoc prof agron, Univ Minn, 63-66; mgr sunflower res, Cargill Inc, 66-76, dir res sunflower breeding, 76-80; WITH RED RIVER COMMODITIES, INC, 80- *Mem:* Am Soc Agron. *Res:* Sunflower, breeding and cultural practices for the United States and Argentina. *Mailing Add:* Red River Commodities Inc 2506 E Brentwood Mission TX 78576

JOHNSON, GARLAND A, b Laona, Wis, July 16, 36; m 58; c 4. BIOCHEMISTRY, PHARMACOLOGY. *Educ:* Carroll Col, Wis, BS, 58; Ohio State Univ, MSc, 60, PhD(physiol chem), 63. *Prof Exp:* Res assoc biochem, Res Found, Ohio State Univ, 63; staff fel, Nat Inst Neurol Dis & Blindness, 63-64; RES ASSOC, UPJOHN CO, 64- *Mem:* AAAS; Am Soc Pharmacol Exp Therapeut. *Res:* Metabolism of catecholamines and serotonin; effect of drugs on biogenic amines; biochemistry of nerve transmission. *Mailing Add:* Cardiovasc Dis Res Upjohn Co Kalamazoo MI 49001

JOHNSON, GARY DEAN, b Sioux City, Iowa, Dec 2, 42; m 65; c 1. GEOLOGY. *Educ:* Iowa State Univ, BS, 64, MS, 67, PhD(geol), 71. *Prof Exp:* Instr geol, Iowa State Univ, 69-71; asst prof, 71-77, ASSOC PROF GEOL, DARTMOUTH COL, 77- *Concurrent Pos:* Res assoc, Iowa State Univ, 71-72. *Mem:* Geol Soc Am; Soc Econ Paleont & Mineral; Soil Sci Soc Am. *Res:* Stratigraphy and sedimentology; Cenozoic terrestrial deposits of Asia and Africa; geology of the Himalayas; paleopedology; geochronology. *Mailing Add:* Dept of Earth Sci Dartmouth Col Hanover NH 03755

JOHNSON, GARY LEE, b Osage City, Kans, Nov 20, 38; m 60; c 2. ELECTRICAL ENGINEERING. *Educ:* Kans State Univ, BS, 61, MS, 63; Okla State Univ, PhD, 66. *Prof Exp:* Asst prof, 66-73, ASSOC PROF ELEC ENG, KANS STATE UNIV, 73- *Concurrent Pos:* Consult, Kansas City Power & Light Co, 71- *Mem:* Inst Elec & Electronics Engrs; Am Wind Energy Asn; Int Solar Energy Soc. *Res:* Power systems; wind electric systems. *Mailing Add:* Dept of Elec Eng Kans State Univ Manhattan KS 66506

JOHNSON, GARY R, comparative pathology, see previous edition

JOHNSON, GEORGE, JR, b Wilmington, NC, Apr 6, 26; m 50; c 4. MEDICINE, SURGERY. *Educ:* Univ NC, BS, 49; Cornell Univ, MD, 52; Am Bd Surg, dipl, 60; Am Bd Thoracic Surg, dipl, 63. *Prof Exp:* Instr surg, Cornell Univ, 58-59; from asst prof to prof, 61-73, ROSCOE B G COWPER PROF SURG, SCH MED, UNIV NC, CHAPEL HILL, 73-, CHIEF, DIV GEN SURG, 69-, V CHMN, DEPT SURG, 77- *Concurrent Pos:* Ed, NC Med J. *Mem:* Am Col Surgeons; Soc Univ Surgeons; Soc Vascular Surgeons; Am Asn Surg of Trauma; Asn Acad Surgeons. *Res:* Vascular and thoracic surgery; hemodynamics associated with cirrhosis of the liver; local and systematic hemodynamics of an arteriovenous fistula; gall bladder surgery. *Mailing Add:* Dept of Surg Univ of NC Sch of Med Chapel Hill NC 27515

JOHNSON, GEORGE CARVER, engineering mechanics, see previous edition

JOHNSON, GEORGE CHRYSLER, b Junction City, Kans, Apr 13, 15; m 45; c 2. CHEMISTRY. *Educ:* Univ Kans, AB, 37; Yale Univ, PhD(phys chem), 40. *Prof Exp:* res chemist, Mobil Res & Develop Corp, 40-80; CONSULT, 80- *Mem:* Am Chem Soc. *Res:* Thermodynamics of solutions; gasoline, lubricating oils; chemicals from petroleum; catalysts; separation processes; zeolites; oil shale; research administration; coal processes; phosphates. *Mailing Add:* 15 Bayberry Rd RR 2 Princeton NJ 08540

JOHNSON, GEORGE FREDERICK, b Harmony, Minn, July 15, 16; m 41. ORGANIC CHEMISTRY. *Educ:* Iowa State Univ, BS, 38; Ohio State Univ, PhD(chem), 43. *Prof Exp:* Proj leader, Process Develop Lab, Carbide & Carbon Chem Co, 53-55, group leader, Chem Div, 55-71, develop scientist chem & plastics, Res & Develop Dept, 71-76, SITE ADMINR, AGR PROD DIV, RES & DEVELOP DEPT, UNION CARBIDE CORP, 76- *Mem:* Am Chem Soc; Am Inst Chem Engrs. *Mailing Add:* 1336 Morningside Dr Charleston WV 25314

JOHNSON, GEORGE LEONARD, b Englewood, NJ, May 18, 31; m 65; c 3. GEOLOGICAL OCEANOGRAPHY. *Educ:* Williams Col, BA, 53; NY Univ, MS, 65; Univ Copenhagen, PhD(marine geol), 75. *Prof Exp:* Res asst marine geol, Lamont-Doherty Geol Observ, 57-65; oceanogr, US Naval Oceanog Off, Md, 65-75; SCI ADMINR ARCTIC PROG, PHYS SCI ADMIN, OFF NAVAL RES, 75- *Concurrent Pos:* Consult, Int Geol Comn Mediter Region of Europe, 70-, Comn Invest of Mediter, 70-75, Polar Res Bd, Natural Acad Sci, 75-, Panel Polar Eng, Nat Res Coun, 77- & Comn Tectonic Chart of World, 77-; sci consult, Intergovt Oceanog Comn, Int Hydrographic Off, 75-; agency rep, Global Atmospheric Res Prog. *Mem:* Am Geophys Union; Arctic Inst NAm; Polar Soc. *Res:* Geophysics with specialization in marine geomorphology and physiography of the world's oceans; arctic and antarctic marine geology; naval arctic research; polar regions. *Mailing Add:* Code 461 Off of Naval Res 800 N Quincy St Arlington VA 22217

JOHNSON, GEORGE PATRICK, b Pine Bluff, Ark, June 16, 32; m 67; c 3. TECHNOLOGY ASSESSMENT, CIVIL ENGINEERING. *Educ:* Univ Miss, BSCE, 54; Stanford Univ, MS, 67, Engr, 69, PhD(civil eng), 71. *Prof Exp:* Res civil engr int develop, C S McCandless & Co, 65-67; oper analyst housing res, Stanford Res Inst, 67-69; res engr water resources, INTASA, Inc, 69-71; water resource engr, US Army Eng Inst Water Resources, 71-74; PROG MGR TECH ASSESSMENT, NSF, 74- *Concurrent Pos:* Consult, Rand Corp, 70-71. *Mem:* AAAS; Soc Gen Syst Res; Int Water Resources Asn; Sigma Xi. *Res:* Technology assessment methods and utilization; policy research and analysis; water resources planning; technological forecasting; futures research; structural modeling; decision analysis for public policy. *Mailing Add:* 3614 34TH St Washington DC 20550

JOHNSON, GEORGE PHILIP, b Minneapolis, Minn, Nov 13, 26; m 51; c 4. MATHEMATICAL ANALYSIS. *Educ:* Univ Minn, BS, 48, MA, 49, PhD(math), 56. *Prof Exp:* Asst math & statist, Univ Minn, 48-51; instr math, 55-56; mathematician, Nat Security Agency, 51-54; sr mathematician, Standard Oil Co Calif, 56-60; assoc prof math, Wesleyan Univ, 60-64 & Univ of the South, 64-65; chmn dept, 65-70, PROF MATH, OAKLAND UNIV, 65-, DEAN GRAD SCH, 69- *Concurrent Pos:* Off Naval Res assoc, 63-64; consult-evaluator, NCent Asn Cols & Schs, 72- *Mem:* Am Math Soc; Math Asn Am; Sigma Xi. *Res:* Abstract harmonic analysis; numerical analysis and computing. *Mailing Add:* Off of Grad Study Oakland Univ Rochester MI 48063

JOHNSON, GEORGE ROBERT, b Caledonia, NY, Aug 2, 17; m 42; c 4. ANIMAL HUSBANDRY. *Educ:* Cornell Univ, BS, 39; Mich State Univ, MS, 47, PhD, 54. *Prof Exp:* Pub sch teacher, NY, 39-42; asst county agt agr, Canton, NY, 42-43; from instr to assoc prof animal husb, Cornell Univ, 43-55; assoc prof animal sci, 55-58, PROF ANIMAL SCI & CHMN DEPT, OHIO STATE UNIV, 58- *Mem:* Am Soc Animal Sci. *Res:* Administration in animal science, especially teaching, research and extension; sheep production and management. *Mailing Add:* Col of Agr Ohio State Univ Columbus OH 43210

JOHNSON, GEORGE THOMAS, b Greenwood, Ark, Mar 26, 16; m 41; c 2. BOTANY, BACTERIOLOGY. *Educ:* Univ Ark, BA, 36; Wash Univ, MS, 38, PhD(mycol), 39. *Prof Exp:* Asst bot, Univ Ark, 34-35, tech asst hort & forestry, 35-36; asst & lectr bot, Wash Univ, 39-40; Guggenheim Mem Found traveling fel, Mex, Cent Am, WIndies & SAm, 40-42; asst biol, Mass Inst Technol, 42-46, from instr to asst prof, 46-51; assoc prof bot & bact, 51-56, chmn dept biol, 54-58 & 61-64, vchmn, 58-61, PROF BOT & BACT, UNIV ARK, FAYETTEVILLE, 64- *Concurrent Pos:* Mem expeds, US, 36-40, Mex, 40, Panama & Cuba, 40-41, SAm, 41-42 & Alaska Hwy, 42-44; res partic & consult, Oak Ridge Inst Nuclear Studies, 53-57 & 59-68; vis prof, La State Univ, 60. *Mem:* Bot Soc Am; Am Soc Microbiol; Mycol Soc Am. *Res:* Microbiology; mycology; radioisotope techniques. *Mailing Add:* Dept of Bot & Bact Univ of Ark Fayetteville AR 72701

JOHNSON, GERALD GLENN, JR, b Renovo, Pa, Nov 10, 39; m 63; c 2. MATERIALS SCIENCE. *Educ:* John Carroll Univ, BS, 62; Pa State Univ, PhD(mat sci, physics), 65. *Prof Exp:* Jr physicist, Erie Registor Corp, 60-62; asst prof solid state sci, 65-71, ASSOC PROF COMPUT SCI, PA STATE UNIV, 71- *Concurrent Pos:* Mem, Nat Res Coun. *Mem:* AAAS; Am Phys Soc; Am Crystallog Asn; Am Soc Testing & Mat. *Res:* Information retrieval as applied to x-ray powder diffraction identification systems; high resolution powder diffraction techniques using Guinier Cameras and automatic microdensitometers. *Mailing Add:* Dept of Comput Sci Col of Sci Pa State Univ University Park PA 16802

JOHNSON, GERALD WINFORD, b Minneapolis, Minn, Oct 31, 32; m 58; c 3. CIVIL ENGINEERING. *Educ:* Purdue Univ, BS, 55; Ohio State Univ, MS, 60; Univ Wis-Madison, PhD(civil eng), 69. *Prof Exp:* Field serv engr, Boeing Co, Wash, 60-61; programmer analyst, Syst Develop Corp, Calif, 61-65; ASST PROF CIVIL ENG, UNIV MINN, MINNEAPOLIS, 69- *Mem:* Am Soc Civil Engrs; Am Cong Surv & Mapping; Am Soc Photogram; Arctic Inst N Am; Am Inst Navig. *Res:* Reliability of atmospheric refraction in polar astronavigation; cartography and map rectification in north Greenland; application of computers to survey net adjustments. *Mailing Add:* Dept of Civil Eng Univ of Minn Minneapolis MN 55455

JOHNSON, GLEN ERIC, b Rochester, NY, May 29, 51; m 75; c 2. OPTIMAL MECHANICAL DESIGN. *Educ:* Worcester Polytech Inst, BS, 73; Ga Inst Technol, MSME, 74; Vanderbilt Univ, PhD(mech eng), 78. *Prof Exp:* Mech eng, Machine Design, Tenn Eastman Co, 74-76; asst prof, Vanderbilt Univ, 78-79 & Univ Va, 79-81; ASSOC PROF MECH ENG, VANDERBILT UNIV, 81- *Concurrent Pos:* Co-prin investr, US Dept Transp, 80-81; prin investr, Nat Sci Found, 80-; assoc ed, Transp J Mech Design, Am Soc Mech Engrs, 81- *Mem:* Am Soc Mech Engrs; Acoust Soc Am; Math Prog Soc; Sigma Xi. *Res:* Development of algorithmic and ad hoc optimization strategies; application of optimization theory to the design of mechanical systems and machines; machine design; system modeling and analysis; noise and vibration control. *Mailing Add:* Vanderbilt Univ Box 8-B Nashville TN 37235

JOHNSON, GLENN M, b US citizen. ENGINEERING. *Educ:* Pa State Univ, BS, 64; Northwestern Univ, MS, 65; Am Acad Environ Engrs, dipl. *Prof Exp:* Surveyor, US Forest Serv, 60; designer & draftsman, Chicago Bridge & Iron Co, 61-62; asst proj engr, Nat Forge Co, 62-63; proj engr, 65-68, GROUP MGR, ROY WESTON INC, 72- *Mem:* Am Soc Civil Engrs; Am Water Resources Asn. *Res:* Water resources engineering; resource economics; wastewater management systems design. *Mailing Add:* Roy Weston Inc Weston Way West Chester PA 19380

JOHNSON, GLENN RICHARD, b Geneseo, Ill, Feb 19, 38. PLANT BREEDING. *Educ:* Iowa State Univ, BS, 60, PhD(plant breeding), 65. *Prof Exp:* PLANT BREEDER MAIZE, DEKALB AGRES, INC, 65- *Mem:* AAAS; Sigma Xi; Am Soc Agron. *Res:* Plant breeding, including applied statistical techniques in relation to plant breeding problems. *Mailing Add:* DeKalb AgRes Inc Thomasboro IL 61878

JOHNSON, GORDON CARLTON, b Newport, RI, Feb 9, 29; m 56; c 3. CHEMICAL ENGINEERING, PHYSICAL CHEMISTRY. *Educ:* City Col New York, BChE, 52. *Prof Exp:* Develop engr, Silicones Div, 52-62, proj leader silicone prod develop & tech serv, 62-66, group leader, 66-77, TECHNOL MGR, UNION CARBIDE CORP, 77- *Mem:* Am Chem Soc; Tech Asn Pulp & Paper Indust; Am Asn Textile Technologists. *Res:* Silicone chemistry; polymer synthesis and characterization; emulsification; resin catalysis and cure; rheology; textile applications; paper release coating; fiber lubricant; surfactants; fiber intermediates; ethylene oxide derivates. *Mailing Add:* Tech Ctr Union Carbide Corp Tarrytown NY 10591

JOHNSON, GORDON E, b Welland, Ont, Sept 21, 34; m 58; c 6. PHARMACOLOGY. *Educ:* Univ Toronto, BScPhm, 57, MA, 59, PhD(pharmacol), 61. *Prof Exp:* Med Res Coun Can fel physiol, Karolinska Inst, Sweden, 62-63; from asst prof to prof pharmacol, Univ Toronto, 63-73; PROF PHARMACOL & HEAD DEPT, UNIV SASK, 73- *Mem:* Am Soc Pharmacol & Exp Therapeut; Pharmacol Soc Can; fel Am Col Clin Pharmacol; Am Soc Clin Pharmacol; Can Soc Clin Pharmacol. *Res:* Catecholamines; thermoregulation and influence of environmental temperature on drug action; drug metabolism. *Mailing Add:* Dept of Pharmacol Univ of Sask Saskatoon SK S7N 0W0 Can

JOHNSON, GORDON GUSTAV, b Chicago, Ill, June 23, 36; m 57; c 4. MATHEMATICS. *Educ:* Ill Inst Technol, BS, 58; Univ Tenn, PhD(math), 64. *Prof Exp:* Asst prof math, Univ Ga, 64-69; assoc prof, Va Polytech Inst, 69-71, assoc prof, 71-74, PROF MATH, UNIV HOUSTON, 74- *Concurrent Pos:* Managing ed, Houston J Math, 74-; fel, Oak Ridge Inst Nuclear Studies, 63-64; sr research assoc, Nat Res Coun, 78-79; assoc, Johnson Space Ctr, NASA, 78-80 & NASA Hq, 80-81; ed, Houston J Math, 74- *Mem:* Swedish Math Soc; Sigma Xi; Am Math Soc. *Res:* Analysis. *Mailing Add:* 2010 Fairwind Rd Houston TX 77062

JOHNSON, GORDON LEE, b Denver, Colo, Jan 26, 37; m 66; c 1. PHARMACOLOGY, PHYSIOLOGY. *Educ:* Carthage Col, BA, 59; Northwestern Univ, PhD(pharmacol), 65. *Prof Exp:* Vis asst prof physiol, Univ Ill, Chicago, 65-66; asst prof pharmacol & toxicol, Univ Tex Med Br, Galveston, 68-74; prin scientist, Dept Pharmacol, Schering Corp, 74-78; PHARMACOLOGIST, FOOD & DRUG ADMIN, ROCKVILLE, 78- *Concurrent Pos:* Fel pharmacol, Northwestern Univ, 65-66 & Emory Univ, 66-68; adj asst prof pharmacol & toxicol, Univ Tex Med Br, Galveston, 74- *Mem:* AAAS; NY Acad Sci. *Res:* Cardiovascular actions of dopamine; antihistaminic compounds and their ability to alter cardiovascular effects of sympathomimetic agents; influence of thyroxine on tone and responsiveness of vascular smooth muscle; hypertension and antihypertensive drugs. *Mailing Add:* 817 Diamond Dr Gaithersburg MD 20760

JOHNSON, GORDON OLIVER, b Portland, Ore, June 2, 44; m 71; c 3. SOLID STATE PHYSICS. *Educ:* Walla Walla Col, BS, 66; Calif Inst Technol, MS, 67, PhD(elec eng), 72. *Prof Exp:* Res assoc elec eng, Purdue Univ, 72-74; asst prof, 74-77, assoc prof, 77-80, PROF PHYSICS, WALLA WALLA COL, 80- *Mem:* Inst Elec & Electronics Engrs. *Res:* Magnetic materials; processes of magnetization; magneto resistance phenomena. *Mailing Add:* Dept of Physics Walla Walla Col College Place WA 99324

JOHNSON, GORDON V, b Harvey, NDak, Jan 9, 40; m 62; c 1. SOIL FERTILITY. *Educ:* NDak State Univ, BS, 63; Univ Nev, MS, 66; Univ Nebr, PhD(agron), 69. *Prof Exp:* From asst prof to assoc prof agr chem & soils, Univ Ariz, 69-77; ASSOC PROF AGRON, OKLA STATE UNIV, 77-, DIR AGRON SERV & STATE SOIL SPECIALIST, EXTEN, 78- *Mem:* Int Turfgrass Soc; Crop Sci Soc Am; Am Soc Agron; Soil Sci Soc Am. *Res:* Evaluation of micro-nutrient supplying status of soils; evaluation of interferences in the spectrophotometric determination of iron with ethylenediamine Di (o-hydroxyphenylacetic acid); turfgrass management and nutrition; subirrigation of turfgrass; soil-turfgrass systems for tertiary sewage effluent treatment; effects of temperature and nitrogen on turfgrass root decline. *Mailing Add:* Dept of Agron Okla State Univ Stillwater OK 74074

JOHNSON, GORDON VERLE, b Long Beach, Calif, Sept 5, 33; m 60; c 4. PLANT PHYSIOLOGY. *Educ:* Univ Calif, Berkeley, BS, 55, MS, 59; Univ Ariz, PhD(agr chem, soils), 65. *Prof Exp:* Res assoc bot, Ore State Univ, 63-64, asst prof, 64-65; asst prof biol, 65-70, ASSOC PROF BIOL, UNIV NMEX, 70- *Mem:* AAAS; Am Soc Plant Physiol. *Res:* Metabolism of micronutrients by plants; physiological effects of stress on plants; algal nutrition; biological nitrogen fixation. *Mailing Add:* Dept of Biol Univ of NMex Albuquerque NM 87131

JOHNSON, GROVER LEON, b Bunn, Ark, Jan 9, 31; m 62; c 3. PHYSICAL CHEMISTRY. *Educ:* Rice Inst, BA, 53; Univ Tex, PhD(phys chem), 60. *Prof Exp:* Sr res chemist corrosion, Socony Mobil Oil Co, 60-64; ASST PROF CHEM, UNIV TEX, ARLINGTON, 64- *Concurrent Pos:* Consult, Socony Mobil Oil Co, 64- *Mem:* Am Chem Soc. *Res:* Electrochemistry; corrosion. *Mailing Add:* Dept of Chem Univ of Tex Arlington TX 76019

JOHNSON, GUY, JR, b Dallas, Tex, Mar 11, 22; m 42; c 3. MATHEMATICAL ANALYSIS. *Educ:* Agr & Mech Col Tex, BS, 43, MS, 52; Harvard Univ, MBA, 47; Rice Inst, PhD, 55. *Prof Exp:* Asst eng, Tex Eng Exp Sta, 48-50; from instr to assoc prof math, Rice Univ, 54-66; assoc prof, 66-69, PROF MATH, SYRACUSE UNIV, 69- *Concurrent Pos:* Vis prof, Syracuse Univ, 64-66. *Mem:* Am Math Soc; Math Asn Am. *Res:* Potential theory. *Mailing Add:* Dept of Math Syracuse Univ Syracuse NY 13210

JOHNSON, HAL G(USTAV), b Saginaw, Mich, Apr 30, 15; m 40; c 3. ORGANIC CHEMISTRY, MARKETING. *Educ:* Beloit Col, BS, 36, MS, 38; Univ Wis, PhD(org chem), 41. *Prof Exp:* Instr chem, Beloit Col, 35-38; asst, Univ Wis, 38-41; org chemist, Com Solvents Corp, Ind, 41-45; asst gen mgr, Dykem Co, St Louis, Mo, 45-46; mgr org intermediate & pharmaceuts, Org Develop Dept, Monsanto Chem Co, 46-49, asst dir, Gen Develop Dept, 49-52, dir res & develop, Western Div, Calif, 52-54; dir develop dept, Res & Eng Div, 54-57; dir chem & rubber div, Bus & Defense Serv Admin, US Dept Com, Washington, DC, 57; vpres, Vick Chem Co, 57-59; chem & mgt consult, 59-62; vpres mkt & sales, Southwest Potash Div, Am Metal Climax, Inc, 62-66; mgt consult, Hal Johnson Assocs & Barnes Res Assocs, 66-69; dir chem develop, Chem Plastics Group, Develop Div, Borg Warner Corp, 69-71; assoc prof, 71-80, PROF MKT, NORTHERN ILL UNIV, 80- *Concurrent Pos:* Educ & mgt consult; guest prof int & indust mkt, Linköping Univ, Sweden, 77-78. *Mem:* AAAS; Am Chem Soc; Com Develop Asn; Am Mkt Asn. *Mailing Add:* Dept of Mkt Northern Ill Univ De Kalb IL 60115

JOHNSON, HAMILTON MCKEE, b Orlando, Fla, June 7, 15; m 37; c 2. GEOLOGY, GEOPHYSICS. *Educ:* La State Univ, BS, 33, MS, 36; Univ Okla, PhD(geol), 54. *Prof Exp:* Asst physics, Purdue Univ, 36-37; engr subsurface geophys, Schlumberger Well Surv Corp, 37-47; mgr logging div, Seismograph Serv Corp, Venezuela, 47-50; instr geol, Univ Okla, 52-53; dist geologist, Tex Petrol Co, Venezuela, 54-56; well logging coordr, Creole Petrol Corp, Venezuela, 56-58; head dept geol, 62-69, univ chmn, 66-69, PROF GEOL & GEOPHYS, TULANE UNIV, LA, 58- *Concurrent Pos:* Well logging consult, Jersey Prod Res Corp, Okla, 58-64 & var oil co, 64-; ed, Log Analyst, 62; distinguished scientist lectr, Sinclair Res Corp, Okla, 64; consult, Cabinet Task Force Oil Import Control, 69; mem, President's Panel, Santa Barbara Oil Spill, 69. *Mem:* AAAS; Soc Prof Well Logging Analysis (vpres, 64, pres, 65); Seismol Soc Am; Geol Soc Am; Am Soc Explor Geophys. *Res:* Subsurface geophysical methods and interpretations; seismic and gravity interpretation. *Mailing Add:* Dept of Geol Tulane Univ New Orleans LA 70118

JOHNSON, HARLAN BRUCE, b Indianapolis, Ind, July 3, 22; m 44; c 4. PHYSICAL CHEMISTRY. *Educ:* Purdue Univ, BS, 43; Iowa State Col, MS, 48; Kans State Col, PhD(chem), 52. *Prof Exp:* Org res chemist, Eastman Kodak Co, 43-44; prod supvr, Tenn Eastman Corp, 44-46; asst, Atomic Res Inst, 46-48; from instr to asst prof chem, Ft Hays Kans State Col, 48-52; prof & head dept, Washburn Univ, 52-57, chmn sci div, 56-57; res supvr, Petro-Tex Chem Corp, 57-67, asst dir res, 66-67; dir res, Columbia Nitrogen Corp, 67-70; MEM STAFF, PPG INDUSTS, INC, 70- *Mem:* Am Chem Soc; Am Inst Chem Engrs. *Res:* Electrolytic solutions; thermodynamics; petrochemicals; electrochemistry. *Mailing Add:* PPG Industs Inc PO Box 31 Barberton OH 44204

JOHNSON, HARLAN PAUL, b Chicago, Ill, Dec 18, 39; m 72; c 2. OCEANOGRAPHY. *Educ:* Univ Ill, BS, 63; Southern Ill Univ, MS, 66; Univ Wash, PhD(geophysics), 72. *Prof Exp:* RES ASSOC PROF, UNIV WASH, 80- *Concurrent Pos:* Vis prof, Inst Geol, Univ Rennes, France, 81. *Res:* Origin and evolution of oceanic crust; rock magnetism; source of marine magnetic anomalies. *Mailing Add:* Sch Oceanog Univ Wash Seattle WA 98195

JOHNSON, HAROLD DAVID, b Verona, Mo, Feb 28, 24; m 49; c 4. PHYSIOLOGY. *Educ:* Drury Col, BS, 49; Univ Mo, MA, 52, PhD(dairy husb), 56. *Prof Exp:* Asst biol, Drury Col, 48-49; drug rep, Kendall Co, Ind, 49-50; asst zool, 51-52, from asst to prof dairy husb, 52-77, PROF ENVIRON PHYSIOL, UNIV MO-COLUMBIA, 77- *Concurrent Pos:* Mem comt bioclimatol & meteorol, Agr Bd, Nat Acad Sci. *Honors & Awards:* Animal Biometeorol Award, Am Meteorol Soc, 72; Peterson Award, Int Soc Biometeorol, 72; Gamma Sigma Delta Fac Res Award, 75. *Mem:* AAAS; Am Soc Animal Sci; Am Physiol Soc; Am Dairy Sci Asn; Int Soc Biometeorol. *Res:* Environmental physiology; investigations on effects of climate and environment on growth and production; related biochemical and physiological reactions of cattle and smaller laboratory mammals. *Mailing Add:* Dept of Dairy Husb 104 Eckles Hall Univ of Mo Columbia MO 65201

JOHNSON, HAROLD HUNT, b Gary, Ind, Sept 20, 29; m 58; c 1. MATHEMATICS. *Educ:* San Jose State Col, BA, 51; Univ Calif, MA, 56, PhD(math), 57. *Prof Exp:* Instr math, Stanford Univ, 57-58 & Princeton Univ, 58-61; assoc prof, Univ Wash, 61-74; vis assoc prof math, George Washington Univ, 74-76; PROF MATH, TRINITY COL, 77- *Mem:* Am Math Soc; Math Asn Am; Soc Indust & Appl Math. *Res:* Differential geometry; systems of exterior differential forms; infinite pseudo-groups. *Mailing Add:* 590 S Brys Grosse Pointe Woods MI 48236

JOHNSON, HAROLD LESTER, astronomy, deceased

JOHNSON, HARRY MCCLURE, b Chicago, Ill, May 15, 25; m 48; c 4. METEOROLOGY, OCEANOGRAPHY. *Educ:* Mass Inst Technol, BS, 46; Cornell Univ, MS & PhD(environ ecol, physics), 54. *Prof Exp:* Officer-in-chg, Navy Weather Unit, Alaska, 46; asst physics & math, Cornell Univ, 47-48, math, 48-50 & zool, 50-52, asst prof meteorol & in chg div meteorol, 54-59; assoc meteorologist & oceanogr, Meteorol Div, Inst Geophys, Univ Hawaii, 60-61; res meteorologist, Nat Environ Satellite Ctr, 61-68 & Nat Hurricane Ctr, Fla, 68-74, RES METEOROLOGIST, NAT OCEANIC & ATMOSPHERIC ADMIN, NAT ENVIRON SCI SERV, MD, 74- *Mem:* AAAS; Ecol Soc Am; Wilderness Soc; Cooper Ornith Soc. *Res:* Satellite meteorology; arctic, subarctic, subtropical and tropical meteorology; oceanography; micrometeorology and ocean-atmosphere interactions; environmental ecology and physiology; wilderness and habitat preservation. *Mailing Add:* Nat Oceanic & Atmospheric Admin Fed Off Bldg 4 Suitland MD 20233

JOHNSON, HARRY WILLIAM, JR, b Waverly, Fla, Jan 2, 27; m 57; c 3. ORGANIC CHEMISTRY. *Educ:* Mass Inst Technol, SB, 51; Univ Ill, PhD(chem), 54. *Prof Exp:* From instr to assoc prof & chmn dept, 54-67, PROF CHEM, UNIV CALIF, RIVERSIDE, 67-, DEAN GRAD DIV, 74- *Mem:* AAAS; Am Chem Soc; Royal Soc Chem. *Res:* Organic reaction mechanisms; reactions of heterocycles; isocyanate and isocyanide chemistry. *Mailing Add:* Dept of Chem Univ of Calif Riverside CA 92521

JOHNSON, HENRY DOUGLAS, pharmacology, see previous edition

JOHNSON, HENRY STANLEY, JR, b Augusta, Ga, Apr 16, 26; m 54; c 4. EXPLORATION GEOLOGY, ECONOMIC GEOLOGY. *Educ:* Univ SC, BS, 47. *Prof Exp:* Geologist, Minerals Deposits Br, US Geol Surv, 48-49 & 52-57; geologist, Zonolite Co, 49-52; chief geologist, Div Geol, SC State Develop Bd, 57-61; state geologist, 61-69; CONSULT ECON GEOLOGIST & PRES, SANDHILL RESOURCES, INC, 69- *Mem:* Geol Soc Am; Soc Econ Geologists; Am Inst Mining & Metall Engrs; Am Inst Prof Geol Scientists; Am Asn Petrol Geologists. *Res:* Economic geology; metallic and non-metallic mineral deposits and petroleum; petrology; structure; stratigraphy; general geology. *Mailing Add:* Sandhill Resources Inc PO Box 877 Charleston SC 29402

JOHNSON, HENRY WILSON, JR, chemical instrumentation, see previous edition

JOHNSON, HERBERT GORDON, b Granite Falls, Minn, Apr 11, 16; m 41; c 2. PLANT PATHOLOGY. *Educ:* Univ Minn, BS, 39, PhD, 53. *Prof Exp:* Agt barberry eradication, USDA, 39-40; plant pathologist & horticulturist, Yoder Bros, Inc, 40-42 & 45-48; asst plant path, Univ Minn, 48-53; plant pathologist, Green Giant Co, 53-56; assoc prof plant path, Univ Minn, St Paul, 56-64, prof, 64-80, exten plant pathologist, 56-80; RETIRED. *Mem:* Am Phytopath Soc; Sigma Xi. *Res:* Applied plant pathology. *Mailing Add:* 2175 Rosewood Lane St Paul MN 55113

JOHNSON, HERBERT HARRISON, b Cleveland, Ohio, July 16, 31; m 55; c 4. MATERIALS SCIENCE, ENGINEERING. *Educ:* Case Inst Technol, BS, 52, MS, 54, PhD(metall), 57. *Prof Exp:* Asst prof metall, Lehigh Univ, 57-60; assoc prof mat sci & eng, 50-67, dir dept, 70-74, PROF MAT SCI & ENG, CORNELL UNIV, 67-, DIR, MAT SCI CTR, 74- *Mem:* Am Inst Mining, Metall & Petrol Engrs; Am Soc Metals; Am Phys Soc; AAAS. *Res:* Deformation of solids; dislocation mechanics; physical metallurgy; fracture and fatigue; gases in solids. *Mailing Add:* Dept of Mat Sci & Eng Bard Hall Cornell Univ Ithaca NY 14850

JOHNSON, HERBERT WINDAL, b Tenn, July 3, 20; m 48; c 3. GENETICS, PLANT BREEDING. *Educ:* Univ Tenn, BSc, 43; Univ Nebr, MSc, 48, PhD(agron), 50. *Prof Exp:* Instr genetics, Univ Nebr, 47-48; agronomist plant breeding, USDA, NC, 48-53; res agronomist, Crops Res Div, Agr Res Serv, 53-64; PROF AGRON & HEAD DEPT AGRON & PLANT GENETICS, INST AGR, UNIV MINN, ST PAUL, 64- *Mem:* Fel Am Soc Agron. *Res:* Quantitative genetics; plant breeding procedures. *Mailing Add:* Dept of Agron & Plant Genetics Univ of Minn Inst of Agr St Paul MN 55101

JOHNSON, HILDING REYNOLD, b Sweden, Feb 14, 20; US citizen; m 47. ANALYTICAL CHEMISTRY. *Educ:* Clarkson Col Technol, BS, 42. *Prof Exp:* Chemist, Heyden Chem Corp, 42-48; group leader anal chem, Heyden Newport Chem Corp, 48-70; supvr, Tenneco Chem, Inc, 70-75, mgr anal serv, 75-81; RETIRED. *Mem:* Am Chem Soc. *Mailing Add:* 19 Lois Ct Packanack Lake Wayne NJ 07470

JOHNSON, HOLLIS RALPH, b Tremonton, Utah, Dec 2, 28; m 54; c 6. ASTROPHYSICS. *Educ:* Brigham Young Univ, BA, 55, MA, 57; Univ Colo, PhD(astrophys), 60. *Prof Exp:* NSF fel, Paris, France, 60-61; res assoc astron, Yale Univ, 61-63; assoc prof, 63-69, PROF ASTRON, IND UNIV, BLOOMINGTON, 69-, CHMN DEPT, 78- *Concurrent Pos:* Vis scientist, High Altitude Observ, Nat Ctr Atmospheric Res, 71-72. *Mem:* Am Astron Soc; Int Astron Union; Sigma Xi. *Res:* Theory of spectral line formation; transfer of radiation in a hot gas; solar chromosphere; cool giant stars; chemical composition of stars. *Mailing Add:* Dept of Astron Ind Univ Swain Hall W Bloomington IN 47401

JOHNSON, HOLLISTER, JR, b Watertown, NY, Jan 14, 29; m 51; c 2. CHEMISTRY. *Educ:* Univ Rochester, BS, 59. *Prof Exp:* SR RES CHEMIST, EASTMAN KODAK CO RES LABS, 53- *Mem:* Am Chem Soc. *Res:* Solution formulation and coating technology. *Mailing Add:* Eastman Kodak Co Res Labs 1669 Lake Ave Rochester NY 14650

JOHNSON, HOMER F(IELDS), JR, b Lynchburg, Va, Sept 8, 20; m 47; c 4. CHEMICAL ENGINEERING. *Educ:* Univ Va, BChE, 42; Yale Univ, MEng, 44, DEng, 46. *Prof Exp:* Asst, Yale Univ, 42-43, instr, 43-45; chem engr, Standard Oil Develop Co, 45-49; from asst prof to assoc prof, 49-58, PROF CHEM ENG, UNIV TENN, KNOXVILLE, 58-, HEAD DEPT, 60- *Concurrent Pos:* Consult, Oak Ridge Nat Lab, 51- *Mem:* Am Soc Eng Educ; Am Inst Chem Engrs; Sigma Xi. *Res:* Thermodynamics; mass transfer. *Mailing Add:* Dept of Chem Metall & Polymer Eng Univ of Tenn Knoxville TN 37916

JOHNSON, HORACE RICHARD, b Jersey City, NJ, Apr 26, 26; m 50; c 5. PHYSICS, ELECTRICAL ENGINEERING. *Educ:* Cornell Univ, BEE, 46; Mass Inst Technol, PhD(physics), 52. *Prof Exp:* Asst physics, Cornell Univ, 46-47; asst, Mass Inst Technol, 51; head microwave tube dept, Res Lab, Hughes Aircraft Co, 52-57; exec vpres, 58-68, PRES, WATKINS-JOHNSON CO, 68- *Concurrent Pos:* Lectr, Univ Calif, Los Angeles, 56-57; lectr, Stanford Univ, 58-68, assoc, Dept Elec Eng, 68- *Mem:* Am Phys Soc; Sigma Xi; fel Inst Elec & Electronics Engrs. *Res:* Microwave spectroscopy; electron devices; microwave systems. *Mailing Add:* Watkins-Johnson Co 3333 Hillview Ave Palo Alto CA 94304

JOHNSON, HORTON ANTON, b Cheyenne, Wyo, Nov 12, 26. MEDICINE, PATHOLOGY. *Educ:* Colo Col, AB, 49; Columbia Univ, MD, 53; Am Bd Path, dipl, 58. *Prof Exp:* Intern, Univ Mich, 53-54, resident path, 54-57; resident, Pondville Hosp, Walpole, Mass, 57-58; res assoc, Brookhaven Nat Lab, 58-60; asst prof, Univ Utah, 60-63; scientist & attend pathologist, Brookhaven Nat Lab, 63-70; prof path, State Univ NY Stony Brook, 70-72; prof, Sch Med, Ind Univ, Indianapolis, 72-75; PROF PATH & CHMN DEPT, SCH MED, TULANE UNIV, 75- *Concurrent Pos:* Lederle Med fac award, 61-63; sr vis pathologist, Charity Hosp, New Orleans. *Mem:* Radiation Res Soc; Am Asn Path & Bact; Am Soc Exp Pathologists; Biophys Soc. *Res:* Radiation pathology; kinetics of cell proliferation; thermal injury; information theory. *Mailing Add:* Dept of Path Tulane Univ Sch of Med New Orleans LA 70112

JOHNSON, HOWARD (LAURENCE), b San Leandro, Calif, Jan 4, 33; m 56; c 4. MEDICINAL CHEMISTRY, PHARMACOLOGY. *Educ:* Univ Calif, BS, 56. *Prof Exp:* Pharmaceut Educ fel, 59-61; fel chem pharmacol, Nat Heart Inst, 63-65; chemist pharmaceut chem, 65-71, sr pharmacol chemist, 72-78, MGR BIOPHYS CHEMOMETRICS, LIFE SCI RES, STANFORD RES INST, 78- *Concurrent Pos:* Res assoc, Med Ctr, Univ Calif, 72- *Mem:* AAAS; Am Chem Soc; Am Pharmaceut Asn; Acad Pharmaceut Sci; Am Soc Pharmacol & Exp Therapeut. *Res:* Chemistry, pharmacology of autonomic agents; extrapyramidal central nervous system pharmacology; drug distribution, metabolism and mechanisms of action; structure activity relationships; biochemical pharmacology of biogenic amines; histamine; drug-receptor interaction. *Mailing Add:* Dept of Pharmaceut Chem Life Sci Res Stanford Res Inst Menlo Park CA 94025

JOHNSON, HOWARD ARTHUR, SR, b Ind, Dec 16, 23; m 47; c 2. MATHEMATICS, OPERATIONS RESEARCH. *Educ:* Franklin Col, AB, 49; Wesleyan Univ, MA, 50. *Prof Exp:* Physicist, Naval Ord Plant, Ind, 50-54; opers analyst, Air Proving Ground Command, 54-58; chief opers anal, Hq, 3rd Air Force, Eng, 58; dept chief opers anal, Hq, US Air Forces Europe, 58-61, dir, Opers Model Eval Group Air Force (OMEGA), 61-63; sr staff scientist & mgr comp effectiveness res div, Spindle Top Res, Inc, 63-67; res dir, Vitro Servs Div, Vitro Corp Am, 67-68; sci asst to dir testing, Hq, Armament Develop & Test Ctr, 68-70, sci asst electronics test, 70-73, SR OPERS RES SCIENTIST OPERS ANAL, HQ, US AIR FORCE TACTICAL AIR WARFARE CTR, EGLIN AFB, 73- *Concurrent Pos:* Consult, Supreme Hq, Allied Powers Europ, 59-61, Ministry Defense, Fed Repub Ger, 61, US Air Force, 64-65 & Gulf South Res Inst, 68- *Mem:* Opers Res Soc Am; Mil Opers Res Soc; Am Statist Asn; NY Acad Sci; AAAS. *Res:* Solution of non-recurring operational problems for command or management decision utilizing the scientific method and a quantitative multidisciplinary approach. *Mailing Add:* 309 Yacht Club Dr NE Ft Walton Beach FL 32548

JOHNSON, HOWARD B(EATTIE), b Willits, Calif, Apr 27, 36; m 62; c 4. CERAMICS ENGINEERING, PHYSICAL CHEMISTRY. *Educ:* Univ of the Pac, BS, 58; Univ Minn, MS, 66; Univ Utah, PhD(ceramic eng), 66. *Prof Exp:* Res chemist, PPG Indust, Inc, 60-63; sr ceramist, Pittsburgh Corning Corp, 66-69, dir process develop, 69-77; DIR RES, VESUVIUS CRUCIBLE CO, 77- *Mem:* Am Ceramic Soc; Am Chem Soc; Sigma Xi. *Res:* Manufacturing inorganic thermal insulation materials and special refractory materials; kinetics and thermodynamics of gas-solid reactions; electrical properties of ceramic materials. *Mailing Add:* 21 Delaware Trail Venetia PA 15367

JOHNSON, HOWARD ERNEST, b Livingston, Mont, Sept 21, 35; m 59; c 3. FRESH WATER ECOLOGY, TOXICOLOGY. *Educ:* Mont State Univ, BS, 59, MS, 61; Univ Wash, PhD(fisheries), 67. *Prof Exp:* From asst prof to assoc prof, 67-75, PROF FISHERIES, MICH STATE UNIV, 75-, COORDR ENVIRON CONTAMINATION, PESTICIDE RES CTR, 78- *Concurrent Pos:* Panel mem comt water qual criteria, Nat Acad Sci, 71-72; coordr toxic substances, Mich Serv & Educ Admin Grant Prog, 78- Am Fisheries Soc; Am Inst Fisheries Res Biologists. *Res:* Toxicity tests with aquatic organisms; production and culture of fish. *Mailing Add:* Pesticide Res Ctr Mich State Univ East Lansing MI 48823

JOHNSON, HOWARD JAMES, JR, clinical chemistry, see previous edition

JOHNSON, HOWARD M, b Annapolis, Md, May 30, 36; m 58; c 2. IMMUNOLOGY, MICROBIOLOGY. *Educ:* Ohio State Univ, BS, 58, MS, 59, PhD(immunohemat), 62. *Prof Exp:* Res assoc immunohemat, Ohio State Univ, 62-63; res microbiologist, USPHS, 63-69; res immunologist, Food & Drug Admin, Cincinnati, 69-77, PROF, DEPT MICROBIOL, UNIV TEX MED BR, GALVESTON, 77- *Mem:* AAAS; Am Soc Microbiol; Am Asn Immunologists. *Res:* Immunochemistry; haptens; immune response; allergens; tissue immunology; immunological methods; microbial antigens; haptenic properties of small molecular weight toxins; immunobiology; in vitro immune response. *Mailing Add:* Dept of Microbiol Univ of Tex Med Br Galveston TX 77550

JOHNSON, HOWARD P, b Odebolt, Iowa, Jan 27, 23; m 52; c 3. AGRICULTURAL ENGINEERING. *Educ:* Iowa State Univ, BS, 49, MS, 50, PhD(agr & civil eng), 59; Univ Iowa, MS, 54. *Prof Exp:* Lab asst, 49-50, res assoc, 51-53, 55-58, from asst prof to assoc prof, 59-62, PROF AGR ENG, IOWA STATE UNIV, 62- *Honors & Awards:* Hancor Soil & Water Eng Award, Am Soc Agr Engrs, 78. *Mem:* AAAS; fel Am Soc Agr Engrs; Am Geophys Union; Soil Conserv Soc Am; Am Soc Eng Educ. *Res:* Hydrologic, water quality and soil mechanics problems related to irrigation, drainage, erosion control and small watersheds. *Mailing Add:* Dept of Agr Eng Iowa State Univ Ames IA 50010

JOHNSON, HUGH MITCHELL, b Des Moines, Iowa, Mar 4, 23; m 51. ASTRONOMY. *Educ:* Univ Chicago, AB, 48, SB, 49, PhD(astron), 53. *Prof Exp:* Asst astron, Yerkes Observ, Univ Chicago, 50-53; asst prof, Univ Iowa, 54-59; assoc prof & assoc astronr, Univ Ariz, 60-62; assoc scientist, Nat Radio Astron Observ, 62-63; STAFF SCIENTIST & MEM RES LAB, LOCKHEED MISSILES & SPACE CO, 63- *Concurrent Pos:* Res assoc, Yerkes Observ, Univ Chicago, 53-60; vis fel, Australian Nat Univ, 58-59; lectr, Stanford Univ, 71-75 & 80-81. *Mem:* Am Astron Soc; Royal Astron Soc; Int Astron Union. *Res:* Nebulae; galaxies; x-ray astronomy. *Mailing Add:* Lockheed Missiles & Space Co Bldg 255 3251 Hanover St Palo Alto CA 94304

JOHNSON, HUGH SWANEY, poultry science, see previous edition

JOHNSON, IRVING, b Chicago, Ill, Oct 23, 18; m 42; c 2. PHYSICAL CHEMISTRY. *Educ:* Cornell Col, BA, 41; Columbia Univ, MA, 43, PhD(phys chem), 47. *Prof Exp:* Asst chem, Columbia Univ, 41-42, lect demonstr, 42-43, lectr chem, 43-44, asst, Div War Res, 44-45; from asst prof to assoc prof chem, Okla Agr & Mech Col, 46-53; prin res engr, Ford Motor Co, 53-57; chemist, 57-79, SR CHEMIST, ARGONNE NAT LAB, 79- *Mem:* Am Chem Soc; Am Inst Chemists. *Res:* Kinetics; light scattering; aerosols; thermodynamics of high temperature systems; electrochemistry; chemistry of nuclear fuels; fuelreprocessing. *Mailing Add:* 276 Woodstock Ave Clarendon Hills IL 60514

JOHNSON, IRVING STANLEY, b Grand Junction, Colo, June 30, 25; m 49; c 4. CANCER, RESEARCH ADMINISTRATION. *Educ:* Washburn Univ, AB, 48; Univ Kans, PhD(zool), 53. *Prof Exp:* Asst instr anat, Washburn Univ, 47-48; asst instr parasitol, embryol & zool, Univ Kans, 48-50, asst zool, 50-53; asst dir biol-pharmacol res div, 53-68, dir biol res div, Lilly Res Lab, 68-72, exec dir, Eli Lilly Res Labs, 72-73, VPRES RES, ELI LILLY RES LABS, 73- *Concurrent Pos:* Ed bd, Chemico-Biol Interactions, 68-73; mem consult panel, Nat Cancer Prog, 71; ed adv bd, Cancer Res, 71-73; assoc ed, 74-; mem develop therapeut comt, Nat Cancer Inst, 78- *Mem:* AAAS; Am Asn Cancer Res; Am Soc Cell Biologists; Environ Mutagen Soc; Soc Exp Biol & Med. *Res:* Anti-tumor chemotherapy; antiviral chemotherapy; tissue culture techniques; experimental embryology; oncogenic viruses; maintenance of biological function in tissue culture; recombinant DNA and public policy. *Mailing Add:* Eli Lilly & Co 740 S Alabama St Indianapolis IN 46206

JOHNSON, IVAN M, b Mansfield, Wash, May 30, 40; m 62; c 2. ZOOLOGY, PHYSIOLOGY. *Educ:* Whitworth Col, Wash, BS, 62; Univ Mont, PhD(zool), 69. *Prof Exp:* Asst zool, Univ Mont, 63-69; Nat Inst Gen Med Sci fel biol, Yale Univ, 69-71; asst prof, 71-78, ASSOC PROF BIOL, CONCORDIA COL, 78- *Mem:* Sigma Xi; Raptor Res Found. *Res:* Osmoregulation of vertebrates. *Mailing Add:* Dept of Biol Concordia Col Moorhead MN 56560

JOHNSON, J(AMES) R(OBERT), b Cincinnati, Ohio, Jan 2, 23; m 45; c 6. CERAMICS ENGINEERING. *Educ:* Ohio State Univ, BCerE, 47, MSc, 48, PhD(ceramic eng), 50. *Prof Exp:* Asst instr ceramic eng, Ohio State Univ, 49-50; asst prof, Univ Tex, 50-51; tech adv, Ceramic Lab, Oak Ridge Nat Lab, 51-56; dir phys sci lab, Cent Res Labs, 3M Co, 56-62, dir phys sci res, 62-72, exec scientist & dir adv res progs lab, 72-79; CONSULT, 79- *Concurrent Pos:* Adj prof, Univ Minn & Univ Wis-Stout. *Honors & Awards:* Pace Award, 59; Texnikoi Award, 62. *Mem:* Nat Acad Eng; hon mem Am Ceramic Soc (pres, 73); Sigma Xi; Nat Inst Ceramic Engrs. *Res:* Ceramics; metallurgy; solid state physics; quantum electronics; inorganic chemistry; diffusion; glass. *Mailing Add:* Rte 1 Box 231B River Falls WI 54022

JOHNSON, J(OSEPH) STUART, b Gower, Mo, May 8, 12; m 34; c 3. ELECTRICAL ENGINEERING. *Educ:* Univ Mo, BS, 32, MS, 34; Iowa State Col, PhD(elec eng), 37. *Hon Degrees:* DSc, Lawrence Inst Technol, 63. *Prof Exp:* Asst elec eng, Iowa State Col, 34-36, instr mech, 36-37; elec eng, Mo Sch Mines, 37-39, asst prof, 39-46; assoc res engr, Univ Fla, 46-47, prof elec eng & asst dean, 47-54; prof elec eng & head sch, Purdue Univ, 54-57; prof elec eng & dean col eng, Wayne State Univ, 57-67; dean sch eng, Univ Mo-Rolla, 67-77; RETIRED. *Concurrent Pos:* Instr eng sci mgt defense & war training, Army spec training prog & Sig Corps, Mo Sch Mines, 40-44. *Mem:* Am Soc Eng Educ (vpres, 63-65); Inst Elec & Electronics Engrs; Nat Soc Prof Engrs. *Res:* Induction motor design; electromagnetic wave propagation; correlation of electrical and thermal properties of building brick; power system analysis. *Mailing Add:* 1000 Vista Dr Rte 3 Rolla MO 65401

JOHNSON, JACK (LAMAR), b Elkhart, Ind, Mar 30, 30; m 56; c 2. ANALYTICAL CHEMISTRY. *Educ:* Western Mich Univ, BS, 52; Wayne State Univ, MS, 54, PhD(anal chem), 59. *Prof Exp:* Anal chemist, Ethyl Corp, Mich, 54; SR RES CHEMIST, RES LABS, GEN MOTORS CORP, 59- *Mem:* AAAS; Am Chem Soc; Am Microchem Soc. *Res:* Trace analysis of constituents in ferrous and non-ferrous materials; chemical microscopy; microchemical techniques of analysis; development of instrumental methods for microanalysis and characterization of micro samples; development of methods for analysis of pollutants in air and water; x-ray diffraction analysis of materials. *Mailing Add:* Dept of Anal Chem Res Lab Gen Motors 12 Mile & Mound Rds Warren MI 48090

JOHNSON, JACK DONALD, b Huntington, Ore, Aug 23, 31; m 58; c 4. RESEARCH ADMINISTRATION, ENVIRONMENTAL SCIENCE. *Educ:* San Diego State Col, BA, 59; Univ Minn, MS, 67, PhD(environ health), 71. *Prof Exp:* Proj engr, Humphrey, Inc, 56-60; sect chief aerospace, Martin-Marietta Corp, 60-63; syst engr, Jet Propulsion Labs, Calif Inst Technol, 63-66; res fel, Univ Minn, 67-70; DIR, OFF ARID LANDS STUDIES, UNIV ARIZ, 71-, DIR AID NATURAL RESOURCES PROG, 74-, ASST COORDR, INTERDISCIPLINARY PROGS, 75-, ASSOC DEAN, COL AGR, 81- *Concurrent Pos:* Desertification consult, AID, 74. *Mem:* AAAS; Am Water Resources Asn; Am Geophys Union; Inst Environ Sci; Inst Int Develop. *Res:* Desertification; less developed country development; utilization of arid land resources; hydrology; natural resources mangement; biomass and bioenergy development. *Mailing Add:* 845 N Park Tucson AZ 85719

JOHNSON, JACK WAYNE, b Cannon Falls, Minn, July 8, 50; m 73. SYNTHETIC INORGANIC, ORGANOMETALLIC CHEMISTRY. *Educ:* Carleton Col, BA, 72; Univ Wis-Madison, MS, 74, PhD(inorg chem), 76. *Prof Exp:* NSF fel inorg chem, Cornell Univ, 76-77; res chemist, 77-79, sr chemist, 79-81, STAFF CHEMIST, INORG CHEM, CORP RES LABS, EXXON RES & ENG, 81- *Mem:* Am Chem Soc; Sigma Xi. *Res:* Organometallic chemistry; solid state chemistry; layered solids. *Mailing Add:* Corp Res Sci Labs PO Box 45 Linden NJ 07036

JOHNSON, JAMES AUGUSTUS, JR, b Macon, Ga, May 19, 22; m 49; c 3. PETROLEUM CHEMISTRY, CHEMICAL ENGINEERING. *Educ:* Univ Ga, BS, 42; Univ Wis, MS, 44, PhD(chem), 49. *Prof Exp:* Asst, Univ Wis, 43-44; sr chemist, Southern Res Inst, 48-57; chemist, Esso Stand Oil Co, 57-62, sr chemist, Esso Res Labs, Humble Oil & Refining Co, 62-69, staff analyst, Math Comput & Systs Dept, 69-72, staff engr, Exxon Co USA, 69-76, SR STAFF CHEMIST, EXXON RES & DEVELOP LABS, 76- *Mem:* Am Chem Soc; Am Inst Chem Engrs. *Res:* Synthesis of steroids and purine ribosides; petroleum fuel processes; petrochemical process development; application of automatic analyzers and data systems. *Mailing Add:* Exxon Res & Develop Labs Box 2226 Baton Rouge LA 70821

JOHNSON, JAMES CARL, b Madison, Wis. VIROLOGY. *Educ:* Iowa State Univ, BS, 64; Mich State Univ, MS, 67, PhD(microbiol), 71. *Prof Exp:* Fel biochem, Mich State Univ, 71-72; Jane Coffin Childs fel molecular biol, Albert Einstein Col Med, 72-75; ASST PROF BIOL SCI, OLD DOMINION UNIV, 75- *Mem:* Am Soc Microbiol; Tissue Cult Asn. *Res:* Molecular biology of tumor viruses; ecology of viruses; DNA and RNA synthesis in prokaryotes and eukaryotes. *Mailing Add:* Dept of Biol Sci Old Dominion Univ Norfolk VA 23508

JOHNSON, JAMES DANIEL, b Toledo, Ohio, Mar 21, 44; m 66; c 1. THEORETICAL PHYSICS, STATISTICAL MECHANICS. *Educ:* Case Inst Technol, BS, 66; State Univ NY, Stony Brook, MA, 68, PhD(physics), 72. *Prof Exp:* Res assoc physics, Rockefeller Univ, 72-74; fel, 74-76, STAFF MEM PHYSICS, LOS ALAMOS NAT LAB, 76- *Mem:* Am Phys Soc. *Res:* Exact models and rigorous results in statistical mechanics; equation of state studies for materials of interest to energy development programs and to detonation physics. *Mailing Add:* T-4 MS-212 Los Alamos Nat Lab Los Alamos NM 87545

JOHNSON, JAMES DEAN, biochemistry, infectious diseases, see previous edition

JOHNSON, JAMES DONALD, b Inglewood, Calif, Aug 1, 35; m 55; c 2. CHEMISTRY. *Educ:* Univ Calif, Los Angeles, BS, 57; Univ NC, PhD(anal chem), 62. *Prof Exp:* From asst prof to assoc prof water chem, 61-72, PROF ENVIRON CHEM, SCH PUB HEALTH, UNIV NC, CHAPEL HILL, 72- *Concurrent Pos:* Vis lectr, NC Wesleyan Col, 63-64; environ fel, Gothenburg Univ, Sweden, 70-71 & Nobel symp, 71. *Mem:* Am Asn Univ Professors; Am Chem Soc; Water Pollution Control Fedn. *Res:* Chemistry of natural aqueous solutions; analysis and kinetics of chlorine and bromine hydrolysis; fluoride and fluoride complexes in seawater; drinking, cooling, and waste-water disinfection chemistry. *Mailing Add:* Dept Environ Sci & Eng Sch Pub Health Univ NC Chapel Hill NC 27515

JOHNSON, JAMES EDWARD, b Warren, Pa, Jan 3, 36; m 59; c 3. RADIATION BIOPHYSICS. *Educ:* Houghton Col, BS, 57; Univ Rochester, MS, 59; Colo State Univ, PhD(radiation biol), 65. *Prof Exp:* Chemist, E I du Pont de Nemours & Co, summer 57; res asst biophys, Univ Rochester, 59-62; instr radiation physics & radiation safety officer, Colo State Univ, 62-66, asst prof animal sci & radiation biol, 66-67; res assoc biophys, Harvard Med Sch, 67-68; from asst prof to assoc prof, 68-74, PROF ANIMAL SCI & RADIATION BIOL, COLO STATE UNIV, 74- *Concurrent Pos:* Lectr, Oak Ridge Mobile Lab, 65-73. *Mem:* Health Physics Soc. *Res:* Alkali metal metabolism; whole-body counting; environmental radioactivity. *Mailing Add:* Dept of Animal Sci 135 BRB Colo State Univ Ft Collins CO 80521

JOHNSON, JAMES EDWARD, b Indianapolis, Ind, May 25, 40; m 62; c 1. FISH BIOLOGY, AQUATIC ECOLOGY. *Educ:* Purdue Univ, BS, 62; Butler Univ, MS, 65; Ariz State Univ, PhD(zool), 69. *Prof Exp:* Teacher jr high sch, 62-65; res assoc zool, Ariz State Univ, 69-70; fac growth & res grants, Univ Mass, Amherst, 71, asst prof fish biol, 70-77; BIOLOGIST ENDANGERED SPECIES, US FISH & WILDLIFE SERV, 77- *Mem:* Am Soc Ichthyologists & Herpetologists; Am Fisheries Soc. *Res:* Biology of Dorosoma petenense; population movement and growth of Catostomus commersoni and Alosa pseudoharengus. *Mailing Add:* US Fish & Wildlife Serv 292 Alamosa NW Albuquerque NM 87107

JOHNSON, JAMES EDWIN, b Berwind, WVa, June 5, 17; m 55; c 2. PHYSICAL CHEMISTRY. *Educ:* Emory & Henry Col, BS, 42; Va Polytech Inst, MS, 49, PhD, 52. *Prof Exp:* Instr chem, Emory & Henry Col, 46-48; res chemist, Chemstrand Corp, 52-62; assoc prof, 62-65, PROF CHEM, APPALACHIAN STATE UNIV, 65- *Mem:* Am Chem Soc. *Res:* Solid State physics; physical chemistry of high polymers. *Mailing Add:* Dept of Chem Appalachian State Univ Boone NC 28608

JOHNSON, JAMES ELVER, b Montevideo, Minn, Dec 27, 37; m 78; c 3. ORGANIC CHEMISTRY. *Educ:* Univ Minn, BChem, 61, MS, 62; Univ Mo, PhD(chem), 66. *Prof Exp:* Asst prof chem, Sam Houston State Univ, 66-70; asst prof, 70-71, assoc prof, 71-77, PROF CHEM, TEX WOMAN'S UNIV, 77- *Mem:* Am Chem Soc; Royal Soc Chem; Sigma Xi; Int Am Photochem Soc. *Res:* Kinetics and mechanisms in organic nitrogen chemistry. *Mailing Add:* Dept of Chem Tex Woman's Univ Denton TX 76204

JOHNSON, JAMES HOWARD, b Monmouth, Ill, June 2, 25; m 51; c 3. OCEANOGRAPHY, FISHERIES. *Educ:* US Naval Acad, BS, 47; Univ Mich, MS, 56. *Prof Exp:* Fishery biologist, US Bur Com Fisheries, Ann Arbor, 56-59, oceanogr fisheries, San Diego, 59-65 & Washington, DC, 65-69; chief pac environ group fisheries, Nat Marine Fisheries Serv, Monterey, Calif, 69-76, regional fisheries attache, Tokyo, 76-80; CONSULT, 80- *Mem:* Oceanog Soc Japan. *Res:* Changing ocean climate and effects on abundance and distribution of marine resources. *Mailing Add:* 3548 Greenfield Pl Carmel CA 96923

JOHNSON, JAMES LESLIE, b Kipling, NC, Feb 13, 21; m 45; c 2. CHEMISTRY. *Educ:* Univ NC, BS, 43; Univ Ill, PhD(chem), 49. *Prof Exp:* Chemist, Stamford Res Labs, Am Cyanamid Co, 43-46; CHEMIST, UPJOHN CO, 49- *Mem:* AAAS; Am Chem Soc; Coblentz Soc. *Res:* Natural products; spectroscopy; quality control; clinical chemistry. *Mailing Add:* UpJohn Co 7000 Portage Rd Kalamazoo MI 49001

JOHNSON, JAMES M(ELTON), b Pittsboro, NC, Dec 29, 15; m 54. CHEMICAL ENGINEERING. *Educ:* NC State Col, BS, 37. *Prof Exp:* Chem engr, Res & Develop Dept, Socony Vacuum Labs, Socony Mobil Oil Co, Inc, 37-44, chief chemist, Bead Catalyst Plant Lab, 44-49, asst chief chemist, Refinery Labs, 49-62, SR PROCESS ENGR CATALYST & SULFUR MFG, MOBIL OIL CO, INC, 62- *Mem:* Am Chem Soc; Am Inst Chem Engrs. *Res:* Bead catalyst; petroleum refinery control; Claus sulfur plant and tail gas unit design and operation. *Mailing Add:* Mobil Oil Co Inc Paulsboro NJ 08066

JOHNSON, JAMES NORMAN, b Tacoma, Wash, Sept 6, 39; m 59; c 3. SOLID MECHANICS. *Educ:* Univ Puget Sound, BS, 61; Wash State Univ, PhD(physics), 66. *Prof Exp:* Res fel physics, Wash State Univ, 66-67; mem tech staff, Sandia Labs, 67-73; staff consult, Terra Tek, Inc, 73-76; MEM TECH STAFF, LOS ALAMOS NAT LAB, 76- *Mem:* Am Geophys Union; Sigma Xi; Am Phys Soc. *Res:* Theory of wave propagation and dynamic failure in solids including geophysical materials; constitutive relations for solids over a wide range of strain rates and experimental situations. *Mailing Add:* Los Alamos Nat Lab MS-214 Los Alamos NM 87545

JOHNSON, JAMES STEVEN, JR, b Marion, SC, Oct 30, 21; m 50; c 2. PHYSICAL CHEMISTRY. *Educ:* The Citadel, BS, 42; Univ NC, PhD(chem), 49. *Prof Exp:* CHEMIST, OAK RIDGE NAT LAB, 49-, GROUP LEADER, 58- *Concurrent Pos:* Guggenheim & Fulbright res fels, Univ Gottingen & Utrecht, 58-59. *Mem:* AAAS; Soc Petrol Engrs; Am Chem Soc. *Res:* Solution thermodynamics; desalination by hyperfiltration; filtration; adsorption on inorganic solids; enhanced oil recovery; micelier system. *Mailing Add:* 918 W Outer Dr Oak Ridge TN 37830

JOHNSON, JAMES W(INSTON), b Quinton, Okla, May 25, 30; m 53; c 2. CHEMICAL ENGINEERING, ELECTROCHEMISTRY. *Educ:* Univ Mo-Rolla, BS, 57, MS, 58; Univ Mo-Columbia, PhD(chem eng), 61. *Prof Exp:* From instr to assoc prof, 58-67, PROF CHEM ENG, UNIV MO-ROLLA, 67-, CHMN, DEPT CHEM ENG, 79- *Concurrent Pos:* Fel electrochem lab, Univ Pa, 62-63. *Mem:* Am Inst Chem Engrs; Nat Asn Corrosion Engrs; Electrochem Soc; Am Soc Eng Educ. *Res:* Electrochemical oxidation and reduction of hydrocarbons; kinetics of metal dissolution and deposition; corrosion. *Mailing Add:* Dept of Chem Eng Univ of Mo Rolla MO 65401

JOHNSON, JANICE KAY, b Burke, SDak, Apr 12, 46; m 68. PHYSICAL SCIENCE, SCIENCE EDUCATION. Educ: Dakota State Col, BS, 68; Southern Ill Univ, MS, 69; Syracuse Univ, PhD(sci educ), 76. Prof Exp: Grad intern educ, Southern Ill Univ, 68-69; teacher sci, Pine Grove Middle Sch, NY, 69-74; grad intern sci educ, Syracuse Univ, 74-76; instr phys sci, Mesa Community Col, 77-79; prog developer, Rio Salado Col, 78-79; COORDR INFO SYSTS, ARIZ STATE UNIV, 79- Concurrent Pos: Consult, Ariz State Dept Educ, Energy Res, 78; NSF grant proposal reviewer, 78. Mem: Nat Sci Teachers Asn. Res: Cognitive development and its relation to science education. Mailing Add: 116 Gammage Hall Ariz State Univ Tempe AZ 85287

JOHNSON, JAY ALLAN, b Two Harbors, Minn, July 15, 41; m 71. WOOD SCIENCE, ENGINEERING MECHANICS. Educ: Univ Minn, BS, 64; Col Environ Sci & Forestry, Syracuse Univ, MS, 71; Univ Wash, PhD(wood sci), 73. Prof Exp: Asst prof wood physics, Va Polytech Inst & State Univ, 73-77; SCI SPECIALIST WOOD COMPOSITE MAT, WEYERHAEUSER CO, 77- Mem: AAAS; Soc Wood Sci & Technol; Forest Prods Res Soc; Am Soc Testing & Mat. Res: Development of wood particulate materials; modeling stress development in wood during drying; evaluation of fracture mechanics for testing procedures for wood and wood based materials. Mailing Add: Weyerhaeuser Co WTC-1B4 Tacoma WA 98401

JOHNSON, JAY WOLBERT, b Decatur Co, Tenn, Nov 12, 43; m 64; c 2. AGRONOMY. Educ: Univ Tenn, Knoxville, BS, 67, MS, 69; Univ Ill, Urbana-Champaign, PhD(agron), 72. Prof Exp: Res assoc agron, Univ Ill, Urbana-Champaign, 72-74; ASST PROF AGRON, OHIO STATE UNIV, 75- Mem: Am Soc Agron; Soil Sci Soc Am. Res: Applied research correlating soil test and plant analysis to crop yields; basic research on environmental factors affecting denitrification. Mailing Add: Dept of Agron Townshend Hall Ohio State Univ 1880 Neil Ave Columbus OH 43210

JOHNSON, JEAN ELAINE, psychosomatic medicine, see previous edition

JOHNSON, JEFFERY LEE, b Milwaukee, Wis, Mar 6, 41; m 68; c 1. NEUROPHYSIOLOGY. Educ: Lakeland Col, BS, 64; Ind Univ, Indianapolis, PhD(physiol), 68. Prof Exp: Asst prof, 70-76, ASSOC PROF PHYSIOL & PHARMACOL, SCH MED, UNIV S DAK, 76- Concurrent Pos: NIH grants, Inst Psychiat Res, Med Ctr, Ind Univ, Indianapolis, 68-70. Mem: AAAS; Soc Neurosci. Res: Axoplasmic flow; regeneration; transmitter systems; topographic distribution of amino acids and enzymes in nervous system; electrophysiological analysis of nervous system activity. Mailing Add: Dept of Physiol & Pharmacol Univ of SDak Sch of Med Vermillion SD 57069

JOHNSON, JEROME H, b Moscow, Idaho, Nov 22, 18; m 43; c 3. ELECTRICAL ENGINEERING. Educ: Univ Idaho, BS, 42; Ore State Univ, MS, 47, PhD(elec eng), 53. Prof Exp: Asst prof elec eng, Univ Wyo, 46-47 & Wash State Univ, 47-53; staff mem res, Sandia Corp, 53-58; prof & coordr eng sci, 58-77; EMER PROF ENG, UNIV REDLANDS, 77- Mem: Inst Elec & Electronics Engrs. Res: High energy shock excited pulse generators; solid state lasers; digital-analog computer elements. Mailing Add: Dept of Eng Sci Univ of Redlands Redlands CA 92373

JOHNSON, JERRY MICHAEL, environmental health, see previous edition

JOHNSON, JERRY WAYNE, b Perry, Ga, July 22, 48; m 68. AGRONOMY. Educ: Univ Ga, BSA, 70; Purdue Univ, MS, 72, PhD(agron), 74. Prof Exp: Res asst hybrid wheat, Purdue Univ, 70-74; asst prof plant breeding & genetics, Univ Md, 74-77; asst prof, 77-80, ASSOC PROF PLANT BREEDING & GENETICS, UNIV GA, 80- Mem: Am Soc Agron; Crop Sci Soc Agron. Res: Development of barley and wheat varieties that are early and have disease resistance and milling and baking quality; a better feed barley being developed with a higher protein content. Mailing Add: Dept of Agron Ga Exp Sta Experiment GA 30212

JOHNSON, JOE W, b July 19, 08; US citizen. HYDRAULIC ENGINEERING. Educ: Univ Calif, Berkeley, BSCE, 31, MSCE, 34. Prof Exp: Res sediment transport by flowing water, Waterways Exp Sta, Vicksburg, Miss, 34-35 & Soil Conserv Serv, Washington, DC, 42-75; from instr to prof, 42-75, EMER PROF HYDRAUL ENG, UNIV CALIF, BERKELEY, 75- Concurrent Pos: Ed, Proc Int Conf Coastal Eng, 50-76 & Shore & Beach, Am Shore & Beach Preserv Asn, 74- Mem: Nat Acad Eng; hon mem Am Soc Civil Engrs. Mailing Add: 266 Lake Dr Berkeley CA 94708

JOHNSON, JOHN ALAN, b Gary, Ind, Jan 30, 43; m 65; c 2. ULTRASONICS. Educ: Grinnell Col, BA, 65; Carnegie-Mellon Univ, MS, 67, PhD(physics), 70. Prof Exp: Asst prof physics, Kenyon Col, 69-76; asst prof physics, Wittenberg Univ, 76-79; SCIENTIST, EG&G IDAHO, 79- Honors & Awards: ISEP, NSF, 74. Mem: Am Phys Soc; Am Asn Physics Teachers. Res: Nondestructive evaluation; ultrasonics; microcomputers. Mailing Add: Box 1625 EG&G Idaho Idaho Falls ID 83415

JOHNSON, JOHN ALEXANDER, b St Cloud, Minn, May 15, 24; m 46; c 4. PHYSIOLOGY. Educ: Univ Minn, BS, 46, PhD(physiol), 50, MD, 58. Prof Exp: Instr physiol, Univ Minn, 51-52; assoc pharmacol, Harvard Med Sch, 53-54; from asst prof to assoc prof, 54-60, PROF PHYSIOL, UNIV MINN, MINNEAPOLIS, 60- Concurrent Pos: Guggenheim fel, 63-64. Mem: AAAS; Am Phys Soc; Biophys Soc. Res: Transport, circulation and metabolism. Mailing Add: Dept of Physiol Univ of Minn Minneapolis MN 55455

JOHNSON, JOHN ARNOLD, b Cusson, Minn, Dec 6, 24; m 51; c 6. SKIN METABOLISM, PHOTOSENSITIVITY. Educ: Univ Minn, BA, 51, MS, 64, PhD(med biochem), 71. Prof Exp: Chemist, Bemis Bros Bag Co, 55-60; scientist biomed res, Univ Minn, 60-71; asst prof dermat, 71-73, ASSOC PROF DERMAT & BIOCHEM, MED CTR, UNIV NEBR, OMAHA, 73-; ASSOC PROF DERMAT, SCH MED, CREIGHTON UNIV, 75- Mem:

AAAS; Am Chem Soc; Soc Invest Dermat. Res: In vivo skin glucose metabolism in humans; enzymic determination of glucose, oligoglucosides and glycogen in animal tissues; mechanisms of photoprotection. Mailing Add: Dept of Dermat Univ of Nebr Med Ctr Omaha NE 68105

JOHNSON, JOHN CHARLES, geophysics, deceased

JOHNSON, JOHN CHRISTOPHER, JR, b Gunnison, Colo, Nov 28, 24; m 48; c 3. ZOOLOGY, PARASITOLOGY. Educ: Ohio State Univ, BS, 47; Univ Okla, PhD(zool), 57. Prof Exp: Pub sch teacher, Ohio, 48; teacher, Sch Dependents, Ramey AFB, PR, 48-49; instr, Univ Okla, 50-56; from asst prof to assoc prof zool, 56-62, actg chmn dept biol, 60-62, PROF ZOOL, PITTSBURG STATE UNIV, 62- Concurrent Pos: Actg dir, Rocky Mountain Biol Lab, Colo, 54-, trustee, 64-, dir, 68-77. Mem: Am Ornithologists' Union; Soc Syst Zool; Am Inst Biol Sci. Res: Vertebrate zoology; parasites of birds; bioecology; ornithology. Mailing Add: Dept of Biol Pittsburg State Univ Pittsburg KS 66762

JOHNSON, JOHN CLARK, b Waterbury, Conn, Aug 17, 19; m 41; c 2. APPLIED PHYSICS. Educ: Middlebury Col, AB, 41; Mass Inst Technol, SM, 46, ScD(meteorol), 48. Prof Exp: From instr to asst prof meteorol, Mass Inst Technol, 47-53; res assoc & lectr physics, Tufts Univ, 53-54; PROF PHYSICS, WORCESTER POLYTECH INST, 54- Concurrent Pos: Res assoc ed, Harvard Univ, 66-67. Mem: Am Phys Soc; Optical Soc Am; Am Meteorol Soc; Am Asn Physics Teachers. Res: Physical meteorology; scattering theory. Mailing Add: Dept of Physics Worcester Polytech Inst Worcester MA 01609

JOHNSON, JOHN E(DWIN), b Detroit, Mich, Jan 18, 31; m 53; c 4. CIVIL & STRUCTURAL ENGINEERING. Educ: Gonzaga Univ, BSCE, 56; Stanford Univ, MSCE, 57; Purdue Univ, PhD, 63. Prof Exp: Design engr, Detroit Edison Co, 58-60; instr, Purdue Univ, 60-62; res engr, Dow Chem Co, 62-65; from asst prof to assoc prof civil eng, 65-77, PROF CIVIL & ENVIRON ENG, UNIV WIS-MADISON, 77- Concurrent Pos: Consult, Dow Chem Co, 65- Mem: Am Soc Civil Engrs; Am Soc Eng Educ; Am Concrete Inst; Nat Soc Prof Engrs; Sigma Xi. Res: Composite behavior; folded plates and thin shells made from plastics or laminate materials; use of plastics as structural materials. Mailing Add: Dept of Civil Eng Univ of Wis Madison WI 53706

JOHNSON, JOHN ENOCH, b Osage City, Kans, May 4, 14; m 42; c 2. PHYSICAL ORGANIC CHEMISTRY. Educ: Univ Kans, AB, 36, MA, 38; Univ Wis, PhD(chem), 42. Prof Exp: Asst instr chem, Univ Kans, 36-38; asst instr, Univ Wis, 38-39, asst, 39-41; group leader chem warfare res, Naval Res Lab, 41-46, group leader petrol chem, 46-52, head distillate fuels & combustion, 52-72, head org chem br, 72-74; CONSULT, 74- Honors & Awards: Navy Meritorious Civilian Serv Award. Mem: AAAS; Am Chem Soc; Combustion Inst. Res: Bond strength; fuels; oxidation and ignition phenomena; analysis and control of closed atmospheres; catalytic oxidation; chemi-ionization; reactions of atomic oxygen; free radicals. Mailing Add: Rte 3 Box 212 Montross VA 22520

JOHNSON, JOHN HAL, b Benjamin, Utah, July 1, 30; m 58; c 4. ORGANIC & FOOD CHEMISTRY. Educ: Brigham Young Univ, BS, 55, MS, 57; Ohio State Univ, PhD(food sci), 63. Prof Exp: Lab instr chem, Brigham Young Univ, 59-60; res asst food chem, Agr Exp Sta, Ohio State Univ, 60-63; asst biochemist food sci, Agr Exp Sta, Univ Fla, 63-68; ASSOC PROF FOOD SCI & NUTRIT, BRIGHAM YOUNG UNIV, 69- Honors & Awards: Virginia F Cutler lectr, 78. Mem: Inst Food Technologists; Sigma Xi. Res: Chemical reactions occurring in foods during processing and storage; effects on functional qualities of cooker extruded soy enriched cereal flours; development of cereal-based complemented foods. Mailing Add: Dept of Food Sci & Nutrit Brigham Young Univ Provo UT 84602

JOHNSON, JOHN HAROLD, b Chicago, Ill. LIQUID CHROMATOGRAPHY, SPECTROSCOPY. Educ: Monmouth Col, Ill, BA, 68; Univ Ark, PhD(organ chem), 74. Prof Exp: Sr scientist, US Environ Protection Agency, 73-77; res investr, Nalco Environ & Chem Sci Corp, 77-78; supvr chem anal, G D Searle Co, 78-80; SR RES INVESTR, AM CRITICAL CARE, 80- Concurrent Pos: Lectr, Fac Inst, Argonne Nat Lab, 76-79 & Am Chem Soc Speakers Tour, 77. Mem: Acad Pharmaceut Sci; Am Chem Soc; Am Inst Chemists. Res: Chromatographic separation techniques as applied to pharmaceuticals and water soluble polymers; basic studies into new chromatographic separation/spectroscopic techniques as applied to pharmaceutical stability programs and structure identification. Mailing Add: 320 Juniper Parkway Libertyville IL 60048

JOHNSON, JOHN HARRIS, b Fond du Lac, Wis, Feb 10, 37; m 57; c 2. MECHANICAL ENGINEERING, AIR POLLUTION. Educ: Univ Wis-Madison, BS, 59, MS, 60, PhD(mech eng), 64. Prof Exp: Res asst mech eng, Univ Wis-Madison, 59-64; chief engr appl eng res, Int Harvester Co, Ill, 66-70; from asst prof to assoc prof, 70-75, prof 75-80, DISTINGUISHED PRESIDENTIAL PROF, MICH TECHNOL UNIV, 81- Concurrent Pos: Coord res coun-air pollution res comt, 68-; mem emissions standards comt, Engine Mfg Asn, 68-70, fuels & lubricants activ, Soc Automotive Engrs, 73-, vchmn, 79-81; mem Mine Health Res Adv Comt, Dept Health, Educ & Welfare, 79-81; consult, US Environ Protection Agency, 71- & US Bur Mines, 77-, Nat Acad Sci, 79-81, NASA, 78-, Off Tech Assess, Us Cong, 79, Stanford Res Inst, 81-, A D Little, 80- Mem: Soc Automotive Engrs; Combustion Inst; Am Soc Mech Engrs; Air Pollution Control Asn; Am Soc Eng Educ. Res: Experimental combustion studies; computer calculations of single fuel drop motion and vaporization; computer cycle analysis; hybrid engine research; emissions and air pollution; instantaneous temperature measurements in internal combustion engines; tribology; diesel particulate emissions; pollutants in underground mining. Mailing Add: Dept of Mech Eng & Eng Mech Mich Technol Univ Houghton MI 49931

JOHNSON, JOHN IRWIN, JR, b Salt Lake City, Utah, Aug 18, 31. NEUROBIOLOGY. *Educ:* Univ Notre Dame, AB, 52; Purdue Univ, MS, 55, PhD(psychol), 57. *Prof Exp:* Instr psychol, Purdue Univ, 56-57; from instr to asst prof, Marquette Univ, 57-60; USPHS spec res fel lab neurophysiol, Univ Wis, 60-63; Fulbright res scholar physiol, Univ Sydney, 64-65; from assoc prof to prof biophys, psychol & zool, 65-81, PROF ANAT, MICH STATE UNIV, 81- *Concurrent Pos:* NIH career develop award, 65-72. *Mem:* AAAS; Am Psychol Asn; Am Soc Zool; Soc Nuerosci; Am Asn Anat. *Res:* Brain function; neuroanatomy; animal behavior. *Mailing Add:* Dept Anat Mich State Univ East Lansing MI 48824

JOHNSON, JOHN LEROY, b Kanawha, Iowa, Oct 28, 36; m 70; c 2. MICROBIOLOGY. *Educ:* Concordia Col, Moorhead, Minn, BA, 58; Mont State Univ, MS, 60, PhD(bact). 64. *Prof Exp:* Fel microbiol, Univ Wash, 64-68; asst prof bact, 68-71, assoc prof microbiol, 71-77, PROF MICROBIOL, VA POLYTECH INST & STATE UNIV, 77- *Mem:* AAAS; Am Soc Microbiol. *Res:* Obligate anaerobic bacteria; bacterial taxonomy; nucleic acids. *Mailing Add:* Dept Anaerobic Microbiol Va Polytech Inst & State Univ Blacksburg VA 24061

JOHNSON, JOHN LOWELL, b Butte, Mont, Mar 18, 26; m 51; c 3. PLASMA PHYSICS. *Educ:* Mont State Univ, BS, 49; Yale Univ, MS, 50, PhD(physics). 54. *Prof Exp:* Sr scientist, Atomic Power Dept, 54-64, fel physicist, Res Labs, 64-68, ADV SCIENTIST, RES & DEVELOP CTR, WESTINGHOUSE ELEC CORP, 68- *Concurrent Pos:* Vis mem res staff, Plasma Physics Lab, Princeton Univ, 55-70, vis sr res physicist, 70- *Mem:* Am Phys Soc; Am Nuclear Soc. *Res:* Theoretical plasma physics associated with the controlled thermonuclear program with principal emphasis directed towards investigation of the magnetohydrodynamic properties of toroidal confinement configurations. *Mailing Add:* Princeton Univ Plasma Physics Lab Box 451 Princeton NJ 08544

JOHNSON, JOHN MARSHALL, b McCamey, Tex, Aug 10, 44; m 70; c 2. PHYSIOLOGY. *Educ:* Rice Univ, BA, 66; Univ Tex Southwestern Med Sch, PhD(physiol). 72. *Prof Exp:* Sr fel, Sch Med, Univ Wash, 72-74, res assoc physiol, 74-75; asst prof, 75-80, ASSOC PROF PHYSIOL, UNIV TEX HEALTH SCI CTR, SAN ANTONIO, 80- *Mem:* Am Heart Asn; Am Physiol Soc. *Res:* Reflex control of the circulatory system; cardiovascular physiology regulation of cutaneous blood flow. *Mailing Add:* Dept of Physiol Univ of Tex Health Sci Ctr San Antonio TX 78284

JOHNSON, JOHN MORRIS, b Boise, Idaho, Mar 16, 37; m 59; c 2. BOTANY, CYTOLOGY. *Educ:* Col Idaho, BS, 59; Ore State Univ, MS, 61, PhD(bot, tissue cult). 64. *Prof Exp:* From asst prof to assoc prof biol, Cent Col Iowa, 64-69; assoc prof, 69-74, PROF BIOL, WESTERN ORE STATE COL, 74- *Concurrent Pos:* USPHS fel, Univ Chicago, 65-66. *Mem:* AAAS; Bot Soc Am; Am Soc Cell Biologists. *Res:* Plant tissue culture; behavior and function of nucleus and nucleolar vacuoles. *Mailing Add:* Dept of Sci & Math Western Ore State Col Monmouth OR 97361

JOHNSON, JOHN PETER, applied statistics, see previous edition

JOHNSON, JOHN PETER, physical geography, see previous edition

JOHNSON, JOHN RAVEN, b Chicago, Ill, Aug 9, 00; m 29; c 2. ORGANIC CHEMISTRY. *Educ:* Univ Ill, BS, 19, MS, 20, PhD(org chem). 22. *Prof Exp:* Fel, Am Field Serv, Col de France, 22-24; instr chem, Univ Ill, 24-27; asst prof, 30-52, Todd prof, 52-65, EMER PROF CHEM, CORNELL UNIV, 65- *Concurrent Pos:* Consult, E I du Pont de Nemours & Co, 37-67; liaison sci officer, Off Sci Res & Develop, London, 42-45. *Honors & Awards:* Medaille d'Honneur, France. *Mem:* Nat Acad Sci. *Res:* Organic boron compounds; explosives; ketene derivatives; furan derivatives; dienes; mechanism of reactions; structure of gliotoxin; biosynthesis of isoprene derivatives. *Mailing Add:* Deer Valley Rd Townshend VT 05353

JOHNSON, JOHN RAYMOND, b Bureau, Ill, Mar 16, 05; m 28; c 4. PHYSIOLOGY, PHARMACOLOGY. *Educ:* Washburn Col, BS, 26; Univ Chicago, 26-28; Tulane Univ, PhD(physiol). 34. *Prof Exp:* Instr anat & physiol, Battle Creek Col, 28-30; asst physiol, Sch Med, Tulane Univ, 30-34, instr, 34-35; fel, Sch Med, Western Reserve Univ, 35-36; from instr to assoc prof physiol & pharmacol, Long Island Col Med, 36-48, actg dir dept, 45-48; prof physiol & dir dept, Fac Med, Univ Ottawa, 48-53; dir dept, 53-65, physiologist, Hosp, 53-65, asst dean, Sch Med, 65-72, prof physiol & pharmacol, 53-76, EMER PROF PHYSIOL, SCH MED, CREIGHTON UNIV, 76- *Concurrent Pos:* Asst physiologist, Long Island Col Hosp, 38-46, consult, Dept Med, 46-48. *Mem:* AAAS; Soc Exp Biol & Med; Am Physiol Soc; Harvey Soc; Am Heart Asn. *Res:* Cardiovascular physiology; cardiodynamics; intramyocardial pressure. *Mailing Add:* Dept of Physiol Creighton Univ Sch of Med Omaha NE 68178

JOHNSON, JOHN RICHARD, b Edmonton, Alta, July 6, 42; m 67; c 2. BIOPHYSICS, HEALTH PHYSICS. *Educ:* Univ BC, BS, 67, MS, 70, PhD(physics). 73. *Prof Exp:* med res officer, 73-81, HEAD, BIOMED RES BR, CHALK RIVER NUCLEAR LAB, ATOMIC ENERGY CAN, 81- *Mem:* Can Asn Physicists; Health Physics Soc; Radiation Protection Asn. *Res:* Development of mathematical models for the retention of, and dose from, radioactive materials in humans; improvement of instrumentation for measuring internal radioactive contamination in humans. *Mailing Add:* Med Res Br Chalk River Nuclear Lab Chalk River ON K0J 1J0 Can

JOHNSON, JOHN RONALD, parasitology, see previous edition

JOHNSON, JOHN WEBSTER, JR, b Pawhuska, Okla, Sept 29, 25. ORGANIC CHEMISTRY. *Educ:* Univ Wichita, BA, 52, MS, 53; Univ Ill, PhD(chem). 56. *Prof Exp:* Asst prof, 56-64, ASSOC PROF CHEM, WICHITA STATE UNIV, 64- *Mem:* Am Chem Soc. *Res:* Nucleophilic displacement reactions on epoxides and lactones; synthetic high molecular weight polymers, especially their preparation, properties and uses. *Mailing Add:* Dept of Chem Wichita State Univ Wichita KS 67208

JOHNSON, JOHNNY ALBERT, b El Paso, Tex, Mar 6, 38; m 55; c 2. LATTICES, RINGS. *Educ:* Univ Calif, Riverside, BA, 65, MA, 66, PhD(math). 68. *Prof Exp:* NSF fel, Univ Calif, Riverside, 65-68; from asst prof to assoc prof, 68-78, PROF MATH, UNIV HOUSTON, 78- *Concurrent Pos:* Univ Houston res initiation grant, 69; sr engr, Jet Propulsion Lab, Calif Inst Technol, 69; assoc managing ed, Houston J Math, 74-; Univ Houston res grant, 78, leave grant, 80. *Mem:* Math Asn Am; Am Math Soc. *Res:* Commutative algebra. *Mailing Add:* Dept of Math Univ of Houston Houston TX 77004

JOHNSON, JOHNNY R(AY), b Chatham, La, Dec 19, 29; m 60; c 3. APPLIED MATHEMATICS, ELECTRICAL ENGINEERING. *Educ:* La Polytech Inst, EE, 51. *Prof Exp:* Electronic engr, Pitman-Dunn Lab, Frankford Arsenal, 53-54; asst prof math, La Polytech Inst, 58-62; assoc prof, Appalachian State Teachers Col, 62-63; assoc prof, 63-70, PROF ELEC ENG, LA STATE UNIV, BATON ROUGE, 70- *Mem:* Sr mem Inst Elec & Electronics Engrs; Am Asn Univ Professors. *Res:* Special functions; boundary value problems; analog and digital filters. *Mailing Add:* Dept of Elec Eng La State Univ Baton Rouge LA 70803

JOHNSON, JOSEPH ALAN, b West Palm Beach, Fla, Feb 1, 33; m 56; c 2. PHYSIOLOGY. *Educ:* Butler Univ, BA, 63; Ind Univ Med Ctr, PhD(physiol). 68. *Prof Exp:* USPHS fel, 69-71, asst prof, 71-78, ASSOC PROF PHYSIOL, UNIV MO-COLUMBIA, 78-, RES PHYSIOLOGIST, VET ADMIN HOSP, 74- *Mem:* Am Physiol Soc; Endocrine Soc; Am Soc Nephrol; Soc Exp Biol & Med; Am Fedn Clin Res. *Res:* Renal, endocrine and cardiovascular physiology; renal hypertension; renin-angiotensin system; estrogens and sodium retention. *Mailing Add:* Res Serv 151 Truman Mem Vet Admin Hosp Columbia MO 65201

JOHNSON, JOSEPH ANDREW, III, b Nashville, Tenn, May 26, 40; m 61; c 4. TURBULENCE, STATISTICAL MECHANICS. *Educ:* Fisk Univ, BA, 60; Yale Univ, MS, 61, PhD(physics). 65. *Prof Exp:* Mem tech staff, Bell Labs, Whippany, NJ, 65-68; vis asst prof eng & appl sci, Yale Univ, 68-69; chmn & prof physics, Southern Univ, Baton Rouge, La, 69-72; assoc prof physics, Rutgers Univ, 73-81; PROF PHYSICS, CITY COL NEW YORK, 81- *Concurrent Pos:* Consult, Sikorsky Aircraft Corp, 62-65; Gen Appl Sci Lab, 68-69, vonKharman Gas Dynamic Facil, 69-77, Fermi Nat Lab, 73, Yale Univ, 73-75, Bell Labs, 75-76, Res & Develop Ctr, Gen Elec Corp, 78-80 & Grambling State Univ, 80- *Mem:* Am Inst Aeronaut & Astronaut; Am Phys Soc. *Res:* Non-strange elementary particle interactions; noise propagation; ionized re-entry trails; plasma-photon absorption processes; new approaches to the physics of turbulence. *Mailing Add:* Dept Physics City Col NY Convent Ave 138th St New York NY 10031

JOHNSON, JOSEPH EGGLESTON, III, b Elberton, Ga, Sept 17, 30; m 56; c 3. INTERNAL MEDICINE, INFECTIOUS DISEASE. *Educ:* Vanderbilt Univ, BA, 51, MD, 54. *Prof Exp:* Intern, Osler Med Serv, Johns Hopkins Hosp, 54-55, fel med, 58-59, asst resident, 57-58 & 59-60, res physician, 60-61; from instr to asst prof, Sch Med, Johns Hopkins Univ, 61-66, asst dean student affairs, 63-66; from assoc prof to prof, Col Med, Univ Fla, 66-72, chief infectious dis div, 68-72, assoc dean, 70-72; PROF MED & CHMN DEPT, BOWMAN GRAY SCH MED, 72- *Concurrent Pos:* Am Col Physicians Mead Johnson scholar, 60-61; John & Mary R Markle scholar acad med, 62-67; prog dir, USPHS Med Student Res Training Grant, 63-66; prin investr, Off Surgeon Gen, US Dept Army res grant, 66-71; consult, US Army Biol Lab, Ft Detrick, Md, 66-71; dir, Nat Insts Allergy & Infectious Dis training grant & contract Food & Drug Admin, 67-72; sabbatical, London Clin Res Ctr, 70-71, Royal Soc Med traveling fel, 70-71; mem, Federated Coun Internal Med, 78-, vchmn, 81- *Mem:* Am Asn Immunologists; Am Soc Microbiol; Soc Exp Biol & Med; fel Royal Soc Med; Am Clin & Climat Asn. *Res:* Pathogenesis of staphylococcal infection; role of bacterial hypersensitivity and immunity in infection; epidemiology of hospital and laboratory acquired infection; pulmonary host defense mechanisms; adverse drug reactions; epidemiology and mechanisms. *Mailing Add:* Dept of Med Bowman Gray Sch of Med Winston-Salem NC 27103

JOHNSON, JOSEPH RICHARD, b Fond du Lac, Wis, June 13, 22; m 46; c 3. MEDICINE. *Educ:* Univ Wis, BS & MD, 46. *Prof Exp:* Asst prof internal med, Univ Mich, 56-57; from clin asst prof to clin assoc prof, Univ Wis, 57-66; ASSOC PROF MED, UNIV MINN, MINNEAPOLIS & MEM SR STAFF, PULMONARY DIS SECT, VET ADMIN HOSP, MINNEAPOLIS, 66- *Concurrent Pos:* Chief sect, Vet Admin Hosp, Ann Arbor, Mich, 54-57 & Madison, Wis, 57-66; dir, Hennepin County Chest Clin & mem staff, Hennepin County Gen Hosp. *Mem:* Am Thoracic Soc; fel Am Col Chest Physicians; fel Am Col Physicians; Am Fedn Clin Res. *Mailing Add:* 9901 Dellridge Rd Minneapolis MN 55420

JOHNSON, JUDITH LYNNE HUNTINGTON, b Casper, Wyo, Jan 25, 42; m 67; c 2. BIOCHEMISTRY, MEDICINAL CHEMISTRY. *Educ:* Lindenwood Col, Mo, BA, 64; Iowa State Univ, Ames, MS, 67. *Prof Exp:* Res assoc, Food & Nutrition Dept, Iowa State Univ, 66-67; assoc scientist, Parke Davis & Co, 67-77; SR ASSOC SCIENTIST, WARNER-LAMBERT CO, DIV PARKE DAVIS CO, 77- *Mem:* Am Chem Soc. *Res:* Studies of chlorophyll and ribonucleic acids and enzymatic studies; chemotherapy of parasitic infections; cancer chemotherapy; novel heterocyclic ring systems. *Mailing Add:* Warner-Lambert Co 2800 Plymouth Rd Ann Arbor MI 48105

JOHNSON, JULIAN FRANK, b Baxter, Kans, Aug 20, 23; m 43. POLYMER CHEMISTRY. *Educ:* Col Wooster, BA, 43; Brown Univ, PhD(chem). 50. *Prof Exp:* Supvry res chemist, Chevron Res Corp, 50-68; assoc prof, 68-70, PROF CHEM, UNIV CONN, 70-, ASSOC DIR, INST MAT SCI, 71- *Concurrent Pos:* Lectr, Exten Div, Univ Calif, Berkeley, 60-68. *Honors & Awards:* Am Chem Soc Award in Chromatog, 70. *Mem:* Am Chem Soc; Am Phys Soc; Am Soc Rheol; Brit Soc Rheol. *Res:* Physics of polymers; rheology; chromatography. *Mailing Add:* Inst of Mat Sci U-136 Univ of Conn Storrs CT 06268

JOHNSON, K JEFFREY, b Olean, NY, Oct 5, 42; m 66. INORGANIC CHEMISTRY. *Educ:* Col St Thomas, BS, 65; Wash State Univ, PhD(inorg chem), 69. *Prof Exp:* Asst prof, 69-76, ASSOC PROF CHEM, UNIV PITTSBURGH, 76- *Concurrent Pos:* Consult comput assisted instr, NSF Grant, 69- *Mem:* AAAS; Am Chem Soc; Asn Comput Mach. *Res:* Computer application and computer assisted instruction in chemistry; numerical analysis; wide line nuclear magnetic resonance and electron spin resonance. *Mailing Add:* Dept of Chem Univ of Pittsburgh Pittsburgh PA 15260

JOHNSON, KAREN LOUISE, b Flint, Mich, Feb 4, 41. BOTANY, PLANT ECOLOGY. *Educ:* Swarthmore Col, BA, 63; Univ Ill, Urbana, MS, 65, PhD(bot), 70. *Prof Exp:* Instr biol, Colby Col, 66-68; fel bot, Univ Man, 69-72; CUR BOT, MANITOBA MUS MAN & NATURE, 72- *Mem:* Ecol Soc Am. *Res:* Alpine plant communities and soils; vegetation mapping and description; establishment of ecological reserves and natural areas; Boreal forest plant geography. *Mailing Add:* Manitoba Mus Man & Nature 190 Rupert St Winnipeg MB R3B 0N2 Can

JOHNSON, KEITH EDWARD, b Feltham, Eng, Jan 4, 35; m 60; c 2. HIGH TEMPERATURE CHEMISTRY. *Educ:* Univ London, BSc & ARCS, 56; Univ London, DIC & PhD(phys chem), 59, DSc(chem), 74. *Prof Exp:* Res assoc anal chem, Univ Ill, 59-62; asst lectr phys chem, Sir John Cass Col, Eng, 62-63, lectr, 63-66; from asst prof to assoc prof, 66-72, PROF INORG & ANAL CHEM, UNIV REGINA, 72- *Concurrent Pos:* Vis prof, Univ Calif, Riverside, 72-73 & Sask Power Corp, 79-80. *Mem:* Electrochem Soc; fel Chem Inst Can; fel Royal Soc Arts; The Chem Soc; Am Chem Soc. *Res:* Molten salt electrochemistry; coordination of transition metal ions in melts; structural studies of inorganic complexes; water and soil analysis; electrochemical coal gasification. *Mailing Add:* Dept of Chem Univ of Regina Regina SK S4S 0A2 Can

JOHNSON, KEITH HUBER, b Reading, Pa, May 1, 36; m 62; c 1. QUANTUM CHEMISTRY. *Educ:* Princeton Univ, AB, 58; Temple Univ, MA, 61, PhD(physics), 65. *Prof Exp:* Res fel quantum theory proj, Univ Fla, 65-67; PROF MAT SCI, MASS INST TECHNOL, 67- *Concurrent Pos:* Consult, Gen Elec Corp Res & Develop, 72- & Exxon Res & Eng Co, 75- *Honors & Awards:* Medal, Int Acad Quantum Molecular Sci, 73. *Mem:* Am Phys Soc. *Res:* Electronic structure of molecules and solids; surface chemistry; catalytic chemistry. *Mailing Add:* Ctr for Mat Sci & Eng Mass Inst Technol Cambridge MA 02139

JOHNSON, KENNETH, b Putnam Co, Ind, Aug 18, 07; m 39; c 2. RESEARCH MANAGEMENT, ORGANIC CHEMISTRY. *Educ:* Ind State Teachers Col, AB, 31; Purdue Univ, PhD(org chem), 37. *Prof Exp:* Asst chem, Purdue Univ, 31-35; res chemist, Com Solvents Corp, 36-40, develop chemist & supt prod scale develop plant, 40-51; area supt in charge polymerization, Nylon Plant, Chemstrand Corp, 51-55, from asst plant mgr to plant mgr, Acrilan Plant, 55-58, dir acrilan mfg, 58-60, dir res admin, Chemstrand Res Ctr, Inc, 60-68; prof, 68-74, EMER PROF RES MGT, GEORGE WASHINGTON UNIV, 74- *Mem:* Am Chem Soc; fel Am Inst Chemists. *Res:* Aminohydroxy compounds from nitrohydroxy compounds; plant development for manufacturing nitroparaffins; polymers; chemical fibers; management of technical information. *Mailing Add:* 25317 Carmel Knolls Dr Carmel CA 93923

JOHNSON, KENNETH ALAN, b Duluth, Minn, Mar 26, 31; m 54. THEORETICAL PHYSICS. *Educ:* Ill Inst Technol, BS, 52; Harvard Univ, AM, 54, PhD(physics), 55. *Prof Exp:* Res fel & lectr physics, Harvard Univ, 55-57; NSF fel, Univ Copenhagen, 57-58; from asst prof to assoc prof, 58-65, PROF PHYSICS, MASS INST TECHNOL, 65- *Concurrent Pos:* Guggenheim fel, 71-72. *Mem:* fel Am Phys Soc; fel Am Acad Arts & Sci. *Res:* Quantum electrodynamics; quantum field theory; elementary particle physics. *Mailing Add:* Dept of Physics Mass Inst of Technol Cambridge MA 02139

JOHNSON, KENNETH ALLEN, b Davenport, Iowa, Mar 10, 49; m 70; c 2. CELL MOTILITY. *Educ:* Univ Iowa, BS, 71; Univ Wis, PhD(molecular biol), 75. *Prof Exp:* Fel biophysics, Univ Chicago, 75-79; ASST PROF BIOCHEM, PA STATE UNIV, 79- *Concurrent Pos:* Guest scientist, Brookhaven Nat Lab, 81- *Mem:* Biophys Soc; Am Soc Cell Biol. *Res:* Cell motility, especially structure, mechanism and regulation of the dynein adenosine triphosphatase in cilia and flagella; microtubule assembly pathway; rapid transient kinetic analysis of enzyme reaction pathways. *Mailing Add:* Biochem Prog 301 Althouse Lab Pa State Univ University Park PA 16802

JOHNSON, KENNETH DELFORD, b Minneapolis, Minn, Sept 8, 11; m 37; c 4. AIR POLLUTION, INDUSTRIAL HYGIENE. *Educ:* Andrews Univ, BS, 32; Calif Inst Technol, PhD(chem), 54; Am Bd Clin Chemists, dipl, 54. *Prof Exp:* Teacher, Pub Schs, Wis, 33-36; clin chemist, White Mem Hosp, 36-38; chemist, Los Angeles County Gen Hosp, 39-43; asst dir, Albert L Chaney Chem Lab, Inc, 46-56, vpres, 56-57; tech asst to sr vpres, Atlantic Res Corp, 57-67; asst tech dir spec proj, Mfg Chemists Asn, Washington, DC, 67-76; RETIRED. *Concurrent Pos:* Consult, Environ Mgt, 76- *Mem:* Fel AAAS; fel Am Inst Chem; fel Am Clin Chem; Am Chem Soc; Air Pollution Control Asn. *Res:* Air pollution control engineering; industrial hygiene engineering; analytical toxicology. *Mailing Add:* Box 284 C RR 3 Big Pine Key FL 33043

JOHNSON, KENNETH DUANE, b Los Angeles, Calif, Jan 18, 44; m 66; c 2. PLANT PHYSIOLOGY. *Educ:* Univ Calif, Santa Barbara, BA, 66, PhD(biol), 69. *Prof Exp:* NSF fel plant physiol, Mich State Univ, 69-71; res fel, Dept Biol, Univ Calif, San Diego, 71-72; asst prof, 72-76, assoc prof, 76-80, PROF BOT, SAN DIEGO STATE UNIV, 80- *Mem:* Am Soc Plant Physiol. *Res:* Mechanism of plant hormones action; biochemistry of growth and development. *Mailing Add:* Dept of Bot San Diego State Univ San Diego CA 92182

JOHNSON, KENNETH EARL, b Worcester, NY, July 24, 21; m 43; c 2. CHEMISTRY. *Educ:* NY State Col Teachers, Albany, BA, 42; Stanford Univ, MA, 43. *Prof Exp:* Res chemist natural & synthetic rubber, Am Anode Inc, 43-45, tech salesman, 45-47; res chemist, Fabrics & Finishes Dept, 47-58, group leader, 58-60, tech supvr, 60-63, sales prod mgr, 63-67, venture mgr high temp-sheet struct, 67-70, sales mgr adhesives & coatings, 70-71, prod mgr pkg mat sales, 71-77, RES ASSOC, E I DU PONT DE NEMOURS & CO, INC, 77- *Mem:* Am Chem Soc. *Res:* Solubilization and micellar formation of soaps; locus of polymerization of synthetic rubber; rubber and polymer chemistry. *Mailing Add:* 1413 Ivy Dr Webster Farm Wilmington DE 19803

JOHNSON, KENNETH EUGENE, physical chemistry, organic chemistry, see previous edition

JOHNSON, KENNETH GEORGE, b Oneonta, NY, Feb 22, 30; m 53; c 3. GEOMORPHOLOGY. *Educ:* Union Col, NY, BS, 52; Mich State Univ, MS, 57; Rensselaer Polytech Inst, PhD(geol), 68. *Prof Exp:* Geologist, Western Hemisphere Explor Div, Gulf Oil Corp, 58-61 & Bolivian Gulf Oil Co, 61-64; from asst prof to assoc prof, 66-78, PROF GEOL, SKIDMORE COL, 78-, CHMN DEPT, 69- *Honors & Awards:* Scidmore Fac Res Lectr, 81. *Mem:* Am Asn Petrol Geologists; Soc Econ Paleontologists & Mineralogists; Nat Asn Geol Teachers; Geol Soc Am. *Res:* Applications of geomorphology to military geology and petroleum exploration; photogeology in petroleum exploration; coastal depositional systems and nearshore marine processes. *Mailing Add:* Dept of Geol Skidmore Col Saratoga Springs NY 12866

JOHNSON, KENNETH GERALD, b New York, NY, Feb 12, 25; m 50. INTERNAL MEDICINE. *Educ:* Manhattan Col, BS, 44; State Univ NY, MD, 50. *Hon Degrees:* MA, Dartmouth Col, 74. *Prof Exp:* From intern to chief resident internal med, Yale-New Haven Med Ctr, 50-54; from instr to assoc prof, Sch Med, Yale Univ, 54-64; chief of med, Atomic Bomb Casualty Comn, Japan, 64-67; prof community med & dir div epidemiol res, Med Col, Cornell Univ, 67-71; prof community med, chmn dept & assoc dean, Dartmouth Med Sch, 71-74; PROF COMMUNITY MED, MT SINAI SCH MED, 74- *Concurrent Pos:* James Hudson Brown fel med physics, 51-52; Nat Heart trainee, 53-54; consult cardiologist, Yale-New Haven Med Ctr & Hosp of St Raphael, New Haven, Conn, 55-65; vis lectr, Col Med, Hiroshima Univ, 64-67; assoc attend physician, New York Hosp, 67-; sr prog consult, Robert Wood Johnson Found, 75-; chmn, NY State Comn Formulate Plan for Pub Med Schs, 75-76; sr prog consult, Robert Wood Johnson Found, 75-; consult, Am Col Obstet & Gynecol, 76-, Mid-Hudson Consortium Hosps, 76-, Surgeon Army, 77-, Dean, State Univ NY Binghamton clin campus, 77- & NY State Dept Health, 77- *Mem:* Fel Am Col Cariol; Am Fedn Clin Res; Soc Epidemiol Res; fel Am Col Prev Med; Am Pub Health Asn. *Res:* Research and development of health services. *Mailing Add:* Dept of Community Med Mt Sinai Sch of Med New York NY 10029

JOHNSON, KENNETH HARVEY, b Hallock, Minn, Feb 17, 36; m 60; c 3. VETERINARY PATHOLOGY. *Educ:* Univ Minn, BS, 58, DVM, 60, PhD(vet path), 65. *Prof Exp:* NIH training fel, 60-65, from asst prof to assoc prof, 65-73; head sect path, 74-76, act chmn dept vet pathobiol, 76-77, PROF VET PATH, COL VET MED, UNIV MINN, ST PAUL, 73-, CHMN DEPT VET PATHOBIOL, 77- *Concurrent Pos:* Path consult, Minn Mining & Mfg Co, 66-71 & Medtronic, Inc, 72-; USPHS biomed sci support grant, 68- *Honors & Awards:* Norden Award, 70. *Mem:* Electron Micros Soc Am; Am Asn Feline Practitioners. *Res:* Amyloidosis; feline diseases; ultrastructural studies; polymer tumorigenesis in mice; diabetes mellitus in cats. *Mailing Add:* Dept of Vet Pathobiol Univ of Minn Col of Vet Med St Paul MN 55108

JOHNSON, KENNETH MAURICE, JR, b Houston, Tex, Dec 7, 44; m 68; c 2. PHARMACOLOGY, BIOCHEMISTRY. *Educ:* Stephen F Austin State Univ, BS, 67; Univ Houston, PhD(biophys sci), 74. *Prof Exp:* Instr physics, Houston Independent Sch Dist, 67-69; fel pharmacol, Med Col Va, 75-77; ASST PROF PHARMACOL, UNIV TEX MED BR, 77- *Concurrent Pos:* Fel, Nat Inst Drug Abuse, 76-77; prin investr, Pharmaceut Mfrs Asn Found, 78-79 & Nat Inst Drug Abuse, 79-82. *Mem:* AAAS; NY Acad Sci; Soc Neurosci; Sigma Xi. *Res:* Neurochemical and behavioral pharmacology of cannabinoids, opiates, hallucinogens and psychomotor stimulants; biochemistry of neuronal transport, synthesis and regulation of indoleamines and catecholamines; neuroendocrine effects of psychoactive drugs. *Mailing Add:* Dept of Pharmacol Univ of Tex Med Br Galveston TX 77550

JOHNSON, KENNETH OLAFUR, US citizen. NEUROPHYSIOLOGY, BIOMEDICAL ENGINEERING. *Educ:* Univ Wash, BS, 61; Syracuse Univ, MS, 65; Johns Hopkins Univ, PhD(biomed eng), 70. *Prof Exp:* Engr, Gen Elec Co, 61-65; asst prof physiol & biomed eng, Sch Med, Johns Hopkins Univ, 71-72; staff mem, Univ Melbourne, 72-80; MEM STAFF, JOHNS HOPKINS UNIV, 81- *Mem:* AAAS; Soc Neurosci. *Res:* Neural mechanisms in sensation and perception. *Mailing Add:* Dept Physiol Johns Hopkins Univ 725 N Wolfe St Baltimore MD 21205

JOHNSON, KENNETH SUTHERLAND, b Brooklyn, NY, Sept 16, 34; m 59; c 3. GEOLOGY. *Educ:* Univ Okla, BS, 59 & 61, MS, 62; Univ Ill, Urbana, PhD(geol), 67. *Prof Exp:* GEOLOGIST, OKLA GEOL SURV, 62-, ASSOC DIR, 78- *Concurrent Pos:* Teaching asst, Univ Okla, 58-61; teaching asst, Univ Ill, Urbana, 65-67; consult geologist, 68-; dir, Okla Mining & Mineral Resources Res Inst, 78-80. *Mem:* AAAS; Geol Soc Am; Am Asn Petrol Geologists; Am Inst Prof Geologists; Am Inst Mining, Metall & Petrol Engrs. *Res:* Economic geology; stratigraphy; field mapping of geologic structures and mineral resources; photogeology; environmental geology; earth-science education; geology of evaporites and redbeds; disposal of radioactive and industrial wastes. *Mailing Add:* Okla Geol Surv Norman OK 73019

JOHNSON, KURT EDWARD, b Needham, Mass, July 6, 43; m 67; c 1. DEVELOPMENTAL BIOLOGY. *Educ:* Johns Hopkins Univ, BS, 65; Yale Univ, MPhil, 69, PhD(develop biol), 70. *Prof Exp:* Fel develop biol, Yale Univ, 70-71; asst prof anat, Med Ctr, Duke Univ, 71-77; ASSOC PROF

ANAT, MED CTR, GEORGE WASHINGTON UNIV, 77- *Mem:* AAAS; Sigma Xi; Am Soc Cell Biologists; Soc Develop Biologists. *Res:* Experimental morphogenesis; experimental analysis of amphibian gastrulation. *Mailing Add:* Med Ctr Dept of Anat 2300 Eye St NW Washington DC 20037

JOHNSON, KURT P, b Chicago, Ill, Oct 6, 38; m 61; c 1. MECHANICAL ENGINEERING. *Educ:* Northwestern Univ, BS, 60, PhD(mech eng), 63. *Prof Exp:* Sr staff engr, McDonnell Douglas Astronaut Co, 63-75, DIR CORP DIVERSIFICATION TECHNOL, McDONNELL DOUGLAS CORP, 76- *Concurrent Pos:* NSF fel. *Mem:* Am Inst Aeronaut & Astronaut. *Res:* Nuclear rocket propulsion; direct energy conversion; plasma dynamics and magnetohydrodynamics; energy systems technology; transportation systems technology. *Mailing Add:* McDonnell Douglas Corp PO Box 516 St Louis MO 63166

JOHNSON, L(AWRENCE) D(AVID), b Tacoma, Wash, Jan 26, 37; m 71. CIVIL ENGINEERING, MATERIAL SCIENCE. *Educ:* Univ Wash, Seattle, BS, 59; Univ Calif, Berkeley, MS, 61, PhD(eng sci), 63; Miss State Univ, MCE, 73. *Prof Exp:* Sr engr graphite res & develop, Gen Elec Co, Wash, 62-64; res scientist, Pac Northwest Labs, Battelle Mem Inst, 64-65; civil engr, 66-74, RES CIVIL ENGR, WATERWAYS EXP STA, US ARMY CORPS ENGRS, 74- *Mem:* Soc Am Mil Engrs; Am Soc Civil Engrs; Am Soc Testing & Mat. *Res:* Mechanical behavior of ceramic materials; soil mechanics and foundation engineering. *Mailing Add:* US Army Eng Waterways Exp Sta PO Box 631 Vicksburg MS 39180

JOHNSON, L(EE) ENSIGN, b New River, Tenn, May 26, 31; m 55; c 4. ELECTRICAL ENGINEERING, BIOENGINEERING. *Educ:* Vanderbilt Univ, BE, 53, BD, 59; Case Western Reserve Univ, MS, 63, PhD, 64. *Prof Exp:* Prod line mgr, Aladdin Electronics, Div Aladdin Indust, 55-59; from instr to assoc prof, 59-72, assoc provost, 70-75, PROF ELEC ENG, VANDERBILT UNIV, 72- *Mem:* Inst Elec & Electronics Engrs (secy-treas, 75-77). *Res:* Physiological control systems; iron kinetics in humans. *Mailing Add:* Vanderbilt Univ PO Box 1722 Sta B Nashville TN 37203

JOHNSON, LADON JEROME, b Gardner, NDak, Sept 11, 34. ANIMAL HUSBANDRY. *Educ:* NDak State Univ, BS, 56, MS, 57; Ohio State Univ, PhD(animal sci), 65. *Prof Exp:* Res asst animal sci, Ohio State Univ, 56-57; asst county agent com agr, NDak Coop Exten Serv, 59-61; res asst animal sci, Ohio Agr Res & Develop Ctr, 61-64, tech aide, 64-65; from asst exten animal husbandman to exten animal husbandman, 66-74, PROF ANIMAL HUSB, COOP EXTEN SERV, N DAK STATE UNIV, 74- *Mem:* AAAS; Am Soc Animal Sci. *Res:* Physiological differences associated with different gaining ability of beef cattle; effect of stage of maturity on yield and nutritive value of corn silage; improvement of corn silage by chemical additives. *Mailing Add:* Dept of Animal Husb NDak State Univ Fargo ND 58102

JOHNSON, LARRY CLAUD, b Roby, Tex, Aug 24, 36; m 56; c 2. PHYSICS. *Educ:* Tex Christian Univ, BA, 58; Mass Inst Technol, SM, 60; Princeton Univ, PhD(astrophys), 66. *Prof Exp:* Res assoc, 66-69, MEM RES STAFF PLASMA PHYSICS, PLASMA PHYSICS LAB, PRINCETON UNIV, 69- *Mem:* AAAS; Am Phys Soc. *Res:* Plasma physics; plasma spectroscopy and laser scattering; atomic collision cross sections. *Mailing Add:* 1040 Mercer Rd Princeton NJ 08540

JOHNSON, LARRY DON, b Winnfield, La, Nov 20, 40; m 62. PHYSICS. *Educ:* La Polytech Inst, BS, 62; Univ Tenn, MS, 64, PhD(physics), 67. *Prof Exp:* ASSOC PROF PHYSICS, NORTHEAST LA UNIV, 67- *Mem:* Am Asn Physics Teachers; Am Phys Soc; AAAS; Sigma Xi. *Res:* Statistical mechanics and phase transitions; human biomechanics. *Mailing Add:* Dept of Physics Northeast La Univ Monroe LA 71209

JOHNSON, LARRY K, b Howard, Kans, Aug 6, 36; m 57; c 5. MATHEMATICS. *Educ:* Kans State Teachers Col, BSEd & AB, 58, MS, 60; Univ Ga, EdD(math educ), 63. *Prof Exp:* Instr math educ, Univ Ga, 61-63; asst prof, 63-67, ASSOC PROF MATH, CENT MO STATE COL, 67- *Mem:* Math Asn Am. *Res:* Mathematics education. *Mailing Add:* Dept of Math Cent Mo State Col Warrensburg MO 64093

JOHNSON, LARRY RAY, b Atlanta, Ga, Dec 18, 35; m 58; c 3. INDUSTRIAL ENGINEERING. *Educ:* Ga Inst Technol, BCerE, 58, BIE, 60, MSIE, 62; Okla State Univ, PhD(indust eng), 69. *Prof Exp:* Assoc mfg res engr, Lockheed-Ga Co, 61-63; from asst prof to assoc prof indust eng, 63-76, PROF INDUST ENG, MISS STATE UNIV, 76- *Mem:* Am Inst Indust Engrs. *Res:* Hospital systems; occupational safety and health; energy conservation; work methods. *Mailing Add:* 415 Oktibbeha Dr Starkville MS 39759

JOHNSON, LAVELL R, b Salt Lake City, Utah, Jan 16, 35; m 58; c 6. BIOCHEMISTRY, ORGANIC CHEMISTRY. *Educ:* Univ Utah, BS, 59; Brigham Young Univ, PhD(biochem), 65. *Prof Exp:* Sr scientist biochem, Ames Co Div, Miles Labs, 64-68; assoc res dir dept med, Latter-Day Saints Hosp, 68-71; PRES, JOHNSON RES, 71- *Mem:* AAAS; Am Chem Soc. *Res:* Mechanism of action of adrenocorticotropic hormone; pregnenolone synthesis by adrenal preparations; analysis of growth hormone, testosterone, metanephrine, insulin and adrenocorticotropic hormone. *Mailing Add:* Johnson Res 3201 Teton Dr Salt Lake City UT 84109

JOHNSON, LAWRENCE ALAN, b Columbus, Ohio, Apr 30, 47; m 69; c 2. FOOD SCIENCE, CEREAL CHEMISTRY. *Educ:* Ohio State Univ, BSc, 69; NC State Univ, MSc, 71; Kans State Univ, PhD(food sci), 78. *Prof Exp:* Res asst food sci, NC State Univ, 69-71; food adv, US Army QM Corps, 71-73; res chemist food prod develop, Dwight P Joyce Res Ctr, Durkee Foods, 73-75; res asst grain sci, Food Sci, Kans State Univ, 75-78; ASST RES CHEMIST FOOD SCI, FOOD PROTEIN RES & DEVELOP CTR, TEX A&M UNIV, 78- *Mem:* Am Asn Cereal Chemists; Inst Food Technologists; Am Oil Chemists Soc; Am Peanut Res & Educ Asn. *Res:* Vegetable protein utilization; oilseed processing; cereal chemistry and baking technology; oil extraction. *Mailing Add:* Food Protein Res & Develop Ctr Tex A&M Univ College Station TX 77843

JOHNSON, LAWRENCE ARTHUR, b Luck, Wis, July 9, 36; m 59; c 3. REPRODUCTIVE PHYSIOLOGY. *Educ:* Wis State Univ, River Falls, BS, 61; Univ Minn, St Paul, MS, 63; Univ Md, PhD(animal sci & biochem), 68. *Prof Exp:* Chemist, 64-66, res chemist, 66-72, RES PHYSIOLOGIST ANIMAL SCI, AGR RES SERV, USDA, 72- *Mem:* Soc Study Reproduction; Am Soc Animal Sci; Soc Cryobiol; Am Soc Andrology. *Res:* Reproductive physiology and biochemistry of porcine and bovine semen; artificial insemination; acrosomal enzymes; frozen semen; antifertility. *Mailing Add:* Reproduction Lab USDA Agr Res Serv Beltsville MD 20705

JOHNSON, LAWRENCE LLOYD, b Bangor, Maine, Dec 30, 41; m 76. IMMUNOGENETICS. *Educ:* Univ Maine, BA, 64, MA, 73, PhD(zool), 80. *Prof Exp:* FEL, MCARDLE LAB, UNIV WIS-MADISON, 80- *Res:* Genetics of mammalian histocompatibility antigens; developmental immunogenetics; theoretical genetics. *Mailing Add:* McArdle Lab Cancer Res Univ Wis 450 N Randall Ave Madison WI 53706

JOHNSON, LAWRENCE ROBERT, b Gyor, Hungary, Feb 14, 31; US citizen. ANALYTICAL CHEMISTRY, PHYSICAL CHEMISTRY. *Educ:* Eotvos Lorand Univ, Budapest, dipl, 53; Columbia Univ, PhD(chem), 61. *Prof Exp:* Res chemist, Lever Bros Res Ctr, NJ, 56-57; AEC res asst, Columbia Univ, 57-59; group leader polymer res radioisotopes, Rohm and Hass Co, Pa, 60-62; asst prof instrumental, anal & phys chem, Lafayette Col, 62-65; assoc prof anal & phys chem, Union Col, Ky, 65-78, actg head dept, 69-73; consult, 78-81; CONSULT WATER TREAT, CITY UTILITIES CO, CORBIN, KY, 81- *Res:* Kinetics of polymer adsorption, flocculation and deflocculation; radioisotopes; instrumental analysis. *Mailing Add:* PO Box 272 Barbourville KY 40906

JOHNSON, LEANDER FLOYD, b Lecompte, La, Aug 3, 26; m 48; c 2. PLANT PATHOLOGY. *Educ:* Southwestern La Inst, BS, 48; La State Univ, MS, 51, PhD(plant path), 53. *Prof Exp:* Instr bot, 53-54; from asst prof to assoc prof plant path, 54-70, PROF PLANT PATH, UNIV TENN, KNOXVILLE, 70- *Concurrent Pos:* Sci teacher, 48-49. *Mem:* Am Phytopath Soc. *Res:* Biological control of plant diseases; methods of approach and basic concepts of soil microbiology. *Mailing Add:* Dept Entom & Plant Path Univ of Tenn Knoxville TN 37916

JOHNSON, LEE FREDERICK, b Philadelphia, Pa, Jan 10, 46; m 67; c 2. MOLECULAR BIOLOGY. *Educ:* Muhlenberg Col, BS, 67; Yale Univ, MPhil, 69, PhD(molecular biophysics), 72. *Prof Exp:* Fel cell biol, Mass Inst Technol, 71-75; asst prof, 75-80, ASSOC PROF BIOCHEM, OHIO STATE UNIV, 80- *Concurrent Pos:* Am Cancer Soc fel, 72-74; fac res award, Am Cancer Soc, 80-85; mem, molecular, cellular & develop biol progs, Ohio State Univ, 76-, molecular biol panel, NSF, 80- *Mem:* Am Soc Cell Biol; Am Soc Biol Chemists. *Res:* Regulation of growth, RNA metabolism and gene expression in cultured mammalian cells. *Mailing Add:* Dept of Biochem Ohio State Univ Columbus OH 43210

JOHNSON, LEE H(ARNIE), b Houston, Tex, Jan 4, 09; m 40; c 2. CIVIL ENGINEERING. *Educ:* Rice Inst, BA, 30, MA, 31; Harvard Univ, MS, 32, ScD(civil eng), 35. *Prof Exp:* Asst civil eng, Harvard Univ, 32-35; asst eng aide, US Waterways Exp Sta, Miss, 35-36; jr engr & asst to engr in charge design & specifications, US Eng Off, Ala, 36-37; prof civil eng & dean, Sch Eng, Univ Miss, 37-50; prof civil eng & dean, Sch Eng, 50-72, EMER DEAN & W R IRBY PROF ENG, TULANE UNIV LA, 72- *Mem:* Am Soc Civil Engrs; Am Soc Eng Educ. *Res:* Mathematical simplification of design of statically indeterminate structures; new technique of slide rule operation for duplex-type slide rules; simplified nomography; creative approach to engineering education. *Mailing Add:* Sch of Eng Tulane Univ of La New Orleans LA 70118

JOHNSON, LEE MURPHY, b Lufkin, Tex, Sept 11, 34; m 57; c 1. MATHEMATICS. *Educ:* Univ Tex, Austin, BSChE, 57, MA, 65, PhD(math), 68. *Prof Exp:* Res chem engr, Humble Oil & Refining Co, 57-62; asst prof, 67-71, ASSOC PROF MATH, NORTHERN ARIZ UNIV, 71- *Mem:* Am Math Soc; Math Asn Am. *Res:* General measure theory. *Mailing Add:* Dept of Math Northern Ariz Univ Flagstaff AZ 86011

JOHNSON, LEE W, b Appleton, Minn, Oct 25, 38; m 63. MATHEMATICS. *Educ:* La State Univ, BS, 63, MS, 65; Mich State Univ, PhD(math), 67. *Prof Exp:* Asst prof, 67-74, ASSOC PROF MATH, VA POLYTECH INST & STATE UNIV, 74- *Mem:* Am Math Soc; Soc Indust & Appl Math. *Res:* Numerical analysis and approximation theory. *Mailing Add:* Dept of Math Va Polytech Inst & State Univ Blacksburg VA 24061

JOHNSON, LELAND GILBERT, b Roseau, Minn, Oct 16, 37; m 78; c 3. COMPARATIVE PHYSIOLOGY, EMBRYOLOGY. *Educ:* Augustana Col, SDak, BA, 59; Northwestern Univ, MS, 61, PhD(biol sci), 65. *Prof Exp:* From asst prof to assoc prof, 64-73, PROF BIOL, AUGUSTANA COL, SDAK, 73- *Concurrent Pos:* NSF sci fac fel, Queen Mary Col, 70-71; George C Marshall fel, Biol Inst, Odense Univ, Denmark, 77. *Mem:* AAAS; Am Soc Zool; Soc Develop Biol. *Res:* Developmental physiology; effects of temperature on developmental processes. *Mailing Add:* Dept of Biol Augustana Col Sioux Falls SD 57197

JOHNSON, LELAND PARRISH, b Ponemah, Ill, Nov 14, 10; m 40; c 2. ZOOLOGY. *Educ:* Monmouth Col, BS, 32; Univ Iowa, MS, 37, PhD(zool), 42. *Prof Exp:* High sch teacher, Ill, 33-36; from instr to assoc prof biol, 37-47, dean, Col Liberal Arts, 71-76, prof, 47-81, chmn dept, 56-81, coordr, Sci Div, 57-81, EMER PROF BIOL, DRAKE UNIV, 81- *Concurrent Pos:* Lectr, Iowa Lutheran Hosp, 38-41; mem, Iowa Bd Basic Sci Exam, 49-61, chmn, 61-; coop study eval in gen educ, Am Coun Educ, 51-54; Ford fac fel, 55-56. *Mem:* AAAS; Am Micros Soc; Am Soc Zool; Soc Protozool; Nat Asn Res Sci Teaching. *Res:* Taxonomic, cytological and physiological protozoology; history of science. *Mailing Add:* 6340 Harwood Ct Des Moines IA 50312

JOHNSON, LEO FRANCIS, b White Plains, NY, Nov 6, 28; m 62; c 4. LASERS. *Educ:* Univ Vt, BA, 51; Syracuse Univ, MS, 55, PhD(physics), 59. *Prof Exp:* Tech engr, Gen Elec Co, 51-53; res asst physics, Syracuse Univ, 54-59; MEM TECH STAFF PHYSICS, BELL TEL LABS, 59- *Mem:* Fel Am Phys Soc. *Res:* Photoconductivity of semiconductors; optical spectroscopy of rare earth and transition metal ions in crystals; investigations of laser phenomena in crystals; interference diffraction gratings; sub-micron surface structures. *Mailing Add:* Bell Tel Labs Room ID-463 Dept 1151 Murray Hill NJ 07974

JOHNSON, LEON JOSEPH, b Detroit, Mich, Jan 17, 29; m 52; c 3. SOIL MINERALOGY. *Educ:* Pa State Univ, BS, 54, MS, 55 PhD(agron), 57. *Prof Exp:* Res geologist, Cities Serv Res & Develop Co, 57-59; asst prof soil technol, 59-67, assoc prof, 67-80, PROF SOIL MINERAL, PA STATE UNIV, 80- *Mem:* Am Soc Agron; Clay Minerals Soc. *Res:* Weathering of soil minerals; formation of soil profiles; clay mineralogy. *Mailing Add:* 119 Tyson Bldg Pa State Univ University Park PA 16802

JOHNSON, LEONARD EVANS, b Ogden, Utah, Nov 13, 40. GEOPHYSICS. *Educ:* Mass Inst Technol, BS, 62; Univ Calif, San Diego, MS, 67, PhD(geophys), 71. *Prof Exp:* Res assoc geophys, Boeing Sci Res Labs, 62-65; vis fel, Coop Inst Res Environ Sci, Univ Colo, 71-73; vis prof, Univ Calif, Berkeley, 73-74; assoc prog dir, 74-79, PROG DIR GEOPHYS, NSF, 79- *Concurrent Pos:* Prof lectr, George Washington Univ, 77-; mem comt math geophys, Int Union Geod & Geophys. *Mem:* Am Geophys Union; Seismol Soc Am; fel Royal Astron Soc; AAAS. *Res:* Theoretical and observational seismology, inverse problems in geophysics. *Mailing Add:* Div Earth Sci NSF Washington DC 20550

JOHNSON, LEONARD GUSTAVE, b Negaunee, Mich, Mar 12, 18; m 44; c 1. APPLIED STATISTICS. *Educ:* Northern Mich Univ, AB, 40; Univ Mich, AM, 41. *Prof Exp:* Mathematician, Gen Motors Corp, 45-52, sr mathematician, Res Lab, 53-55, sr res mathematician, 56-69, prod assurance statistician, Environ Activities Staff, 69-74; CONSULT, DETROIT RES INST, 74- *Concurrent Pos:* Ed, Statist Bull, 71- *Mem:* NY Acad Sci; Indust Math Soc (treas, 52); Soc Automotive Engrs; Am Soc Qual Control. *Res:* Statistical design and analysis of fatigue experiments and their optimum programming; reliability; brake design mathematics; engineering and biomedical applications of statistics, with emphasis on reliability, together with computer programs to facilitate such work. *Mailing Add:* 31811 Bretz Dr Warren MI 48093

JOHNSON, LEONARD N, dental materials, metallurgical engineering, see previous edition

JOHNSON, LEONARD ROY, b Chicago, Ill, Jan 31, 42. PHYSIOLOGY. *Educ:* Wabash Col, BA, 63; Univ Mich, Ann Arbor, PhD(physiol), 67. *Prof Exp:* NIH fel & instr physiol, Sch Med, Univ Calif, Los Angeles, 67-69; from asst prof to assoc prof, Sch Med, Univ Okla, 69-72; PROF PHYSIOL, UNIV TEX MED SCH, HOUSTON, 72- *Concurrent Pos:* Res grant, Univ Okla, 70-73; G A Manahan Trust grant, 70-72; NIH res career develop award, 72-77, grant, 73-82. *Mem:* Am Gastroenterol Asn; Am Physiol Soc; Endocrine Soc; Soc Exp Biol & Med. *Res:* Regulation of gastric and pancreatic secretion action of gastrointestinal hormones; regulation of growth of gastrointestinal mucosa and gastrin receptor binding. *Mailing Add:* Dept of Physiol Univ of Tex Med Sch Houston TX 77025

JOHNSON, LEROY DENNIS, b Langhorne, Pa, Oct 4, 08; m 40; c 2. ORGANIC CHEMISTRY. *Educ:* Lincoln Univ, Pa, AB, 31; Univ Pa, MS, 34, PhD(chem), 54. *Prof Exp:* Prof chem, Storer Col, 34-55, dean, 40-55; assoc prof, 55-56, actg dean, 56-57, DEAN, LINCOLN UNIV, PA, 57-, PROF CHEM, 56-, REGISTR, 69- *Mem:* Am Chem Soc. *Res:* General chemistry demonstrations; general science demonstrations; analytical organic chemistry; environmental science. *Mailing Add:* Lincoln University PA 19352

JOHNSON, LEROY FRANKLIN, b Seattle, Wash, Feb 4, 33; m 56; c 2. NUCLEAR MAGNETIC RESONANCE. *Educ:* Ore State Univ, BS, 54, MS, 56. *Prof Exp:* Dept mgr, Varian Assocs, 57-72; VPRES, NICOLET MAGNETICS CORP, 72- *Concurrent Pos:* Prof-in-charge interpretation nuclear magnetic resonance spectra short course, Am Che, Soc, 66-; mem subcomt E-13 molecular spectros, Am Testing & Mat, 70-; mem exec comt, Exp Nuclear Magnetic Resonance Conf, 77-79. *Mem:* Am Chem Soc; AAAS; Soc Appl Spectros. *Res:* Applications of nuclear magnetic resonance spectroscopy; development of nuclear magnetic resonance instrumentation; utilization of minicomputers with nuclear magnetic resonance instruments. *Mailing Add:* Nicolet Technol Corp 145 E Dana St Mountain View CA 94041

JOHNSON, LESLIE KILHAM, b New York, NY, June 9, 45. ZOOLOGY. *Educ:* Harvard Univ, BA, 67; Univ Calif, Berkeley, PhD(zool), 74. *Prof Exp:* Grad fel zool, NSF, 71-74; res fel, Alexander von Humboldt, Zool Inst, Wurzburg, Ger, 74-75; ASST PROF ZOOL, UNIV IOWA, 75- *Mem:* Sigma Xi; Animal Behav Soc; Brit Arachnological Soc; Am Soc Naturalists. *Res:* Behavioral ecology; aggressive behavior; learning; foraging patterns of social insects. *Mailing Add:* Dept of Zool Univ of Iowa Iowa City IA 52242

JOHNSON, LEWIS WARREN, b Ottumwa, Iowa, Mar 18, 22; m 48; c 6. GENETICS. *Educ:* Cornell Col, AB, 47; Auburn Univ, MS, 51; Tex A&M Univ, PhD(genetics), 56. *Prof Exp:* Assoc prof poultry sci, Auburn Univ, 55-80. *Mem:* Fel AAAS; Am Genetic Asn; Poultry Sci Asn. *Res:* Genetics and physiology of avian blood group antigens; genetic resistance to infectious diseases; structure and function of cellular membranes; microbiological variation in population structure. *Mailing Add:* 682 Heard Ave Auburn AL 36830

JOHNSON, LIONEL, b Linslade, Eng, Aug 12, 24; m 54; c 3. LIMNOLOGY, FISHERIES. *Educ:* Univ Leeds, BSc, 49, MSc, 58, PhD(zool), 60. *Prof Exp:* Econ botanist, Dept Agr, Govt Trinidad, 50-54; sr agr officer, Govt Mauritius, 54-58; scientist limnol & fisheries, Arctic Biol Sta, Fisheries Res Bd Can, 61-66; sci leader, Fisheries Resources Sect, 66-72, RES SCIENTIST, FRESHWATER INST, 72- *Concurrent Pos:* Mem, Can Freshwater subcomt, Int Biol Prog, 65-73. *Mem:* Can Soc Zoologists; Arctic Inst NAm; Am Fisheries Soc; Int Asn Theoret & Appl Limnol. *Res:* Population ecology of Arctic fishes; limnology of Arctic freshwaters; distribution and biology of marine-glacial relicts; management of northern fisheries. *Mailing Add:* Freshwater Inst 501 University Crescent Winnipeg MB R3T 2N6 Can

JOHNSON, LITTLETON WALES, b Concord Wharf, Va, Oct 17, 29; m 51; c 3. FOOD SCIENCE. *Educ:* Va Polytech Inst, BS, 56, MS, 58. *Prof Exp:* Asst processing engr, Hercules Powder Co, 55-58; assoc prof food technol, Va Polytech Inst, 58-61; plant mgr, Dulany Foods, Inc, 61-67; opers mgr, Glidden-Durkee Div, SCM Corp, 67-69, dir mfg, Food Serv Group, 69-71, Regional mgr, 71-76; vpres, 76-80, SR VPRES MFG, MRS SMITH'S FROZEN FOOD CO, KELLOGG CO, 80- *Mem:* Inst Food Technologists; Am Frozen Food Inst; Inst Food Mfr Asn; Sigma Xi; Am Mgt Asn. *Res:* Food processing techniques; statistical quality control; submerged acetic fermentations. *Mailing Add:* 292 Continental Dr Pottstown PA 19464

JOHNSON, LLOYD N(EWHALL), b Eureka, Kans, Nov 16, 21; m 45; c 1. PETROLEUM & CHEMICAL ENGINEERING. *Educ:* Univ Kans, BS, 44; Univ Tex, Austin, PhD(petrol eng), 70. *Prof Exp:* Indust chemist, Hercules Powder Co, 44-45; res engr, Core Labs, Inc, 46-52; supvr reservoir fluids lab, Venezuela, 52-55; res engr, petrol res comt, Univ Tex, 55-63, instr math, 63-64; asst prof petrol & natural gas eng, Tex A&I Univ, 65-77; COORDR OIL & GAS TECHNOL, BEE COUNTY COL, 79- *Concurrent Pos:* Consult engr, 64- *Mem:* Simulation Coun; Soc Petrol Engrs; Geochem Soc; Asn Comput Mach. *Res:* Drilling problems; reserves; completion methods; production methods and controls; mathematical models; scientific data processing; economic development and improved recovery in petroleum reservoirs; engineering methods. *Mailing Add:* PO Box 2254 Station One Kingsville TX 78363

JOHNSON, LOUISE H, b Minneota, Minn, Oct 22, 27. MATHEMATICS EDUCATION. *Educ:* Augsburg Col, BA, 49; Univ Northern Colo, MA, 61, DEduc, 71; Univ Ill, MA, 63. *Prof Exp:* Teacher high schs, Minn, 49-62; assoc dean lib arts & sci, 74-76, PROF MATH, ST CLOUD STATE UNIV, 63-, DEAN LIB ARTS & SCI, 76- *Mem:* Nat Coun Teachers Math. *Mailing Add:* Whitney Hall St Cloud State Univ St Cloud MN 56301

JOHNSON, LOWELL BOYDEN, b Dwight, Ill, Oct 12, 35; m 56; c 2. PLANT PATHOLOGY, PLANT PHYSIOLOGY. *Educ:* Univ Ill, BS, 57; Purdue Univ, West Lafayette, MS, 62, PhD(plant path), 64. *Prof Exp:* Asst res plant pathologist, Univ Calif, Davis, 64-68; asst prof plant path, 68-71, ASSOC PROF PLANT PATH, KANS STATE UNIV, 71- *Mem:* AAAS; Am Phytopath Soc; Am Soc Plant Physiol. *Res:* Plant dispase physiology; plant cell culture and regeneration. *Mailing Add:* Dept of Plant Path Kans State Univ Manhattan KS 66506

JOHNSON, LOYD, b Somerville, Ala, Mar 18, 27; m 52; c 3. AGRICULTURAL ENGINEERING, SOIL & WATER MANAGEMENT. *Educ:* Ala Polytech Inst, BS, 50, MS, 55. *Prof Exp:* Asst dist supt farm develop, Tela RR Co, 51-52 & 56; asst agr eng, Ala Agr Exp Sta, Auburn, 53-54; asst engr, Gen Off, United Fruit Co, 56-57, sr proj engr, Cia Agricola Guatemala, 56-60; AGR ENGR, ROCKEFELLER FOUND, 60- *Concurrent Pos:* Agr engr, Int Rice Res Inst, 60-68 & NC State Univ, 67-68; agr engr, Int Ctr Trop Agr, Colombia, 68-77; vis scientist, La State Univ, 74-75; rice specialist, Ecuador Nat Inst for Land & Cattle Investigations, 77- & Int Agr Develop Serv, 78-81; vis scientist, Int Fertilizer Develop Ctr, 81-82. *Mem:* Am Soc Agr Engrs; Indian Soc Agr Eng. *Res:* Rice specialist and development of irrigation, fertilizer, drainage, roads, bridges, sanitation, machine and processing systems for agricultural experiment stations and food production in the lowland tropics; machinery management. *Mailing Add:* The Rockefeller Found 1133 Ave of the Americas New York NY 10036

JOHNSON, LUTHER ELMAN, b Corpus Christi, Tex, July 26, 10; m 41; c 5. ELECTRICAL ENGINEERING. *Educ:* Tex A&M Univ, BS, 35, MS, 40. *Prof Exp:* Observer seismic explor, Texaco Develop Corp, 35-39; instr elec eng, NMex State, 40-41; var assigments including asst prof, US Mil Acad & chief spec projs, Signal Corps, US Army, 41-61; assoc prof elec eng, The Citadel, 61-76; RETIRED. *Mem:* Inst Elec & Electronics Engrs. *Res:* Engineering analyses. *Mailing Add:* 1832 N Somerset Circle Charleston SC 29407

JOHNSON, LYNWOOD ALBERT, b Macon, Ga, Oct 4, 33. INDUSTRIAL ENGINEERING, OPERATIONS RESEARCH. *Educ:* Ga Inst Technol, BIE, 55, MS, 59, PhD(indust eng), 65. *Prof Exp:* Indust engr, E I du Pont de Nemours & Co, Inc, 55-57; from instr to asst prof indust eng, Ga Inst Technol, 58-64; supvr opers res, Kurt Salmon Assocs, 64-66; assoc prof, 66-68, PROF INDUST ENG, GA INST TECHNOL, 68- *Concurrent Pos:* Vis prof, Thayer Sch Eng, Dartmouth Col, 67; Dept Systs & Indust Eng, Univ Ariz, 81-82; assoc ed, J Forecasting, 81- *Mem:* Am Inst Indust Engrs; Opers Res Soc Am; Inst Mgt Sci; Am Soc Qual Control; Am Prod & Inventory Control Soc. *Res:* Production systems analysis; systems modeling and simulation; optimization methods; decision theory; engineering design processes. *Mailing Add:* Sch of Indust & Systs Eng Ga Inst of Technol Atlanta GA 30332

JOHNSON, MALCOLM JULIUS, b Portland, Ore, Dec 12, 17; m 42; c 2. AGRONOMY. *Educ:* Ore State Univ, BS, 41, MS, 55; Purdue Univ, PhD(crop physiol, ecol), 61. *Prof Exp:* From assoc prof to prof, 49-80, EMER PROF AGRON & SUPT, CENT ORE EXP STA, ORE STATE UNIV, 49-80. *Mem:* Am Soc Agron; Crop Sci Soc Am. *Res:* Crop adaptation and management practices, especially crop fertility on pumice soils. *Mailing Add:* Cent Ore Exp Sta Ore State Univ Redmond OR 97756

JOHNSON, MALCOLM PRATT, b New Haven, Conn, Aug 9, 41; m 64; c 2. INORGANIC CHEMISTRY. *Educ:* Amherst Col, BA, 63; Northwestern Univ, PhD(inorg chem), 67. *Prof Exp:* Res chemist, Chem Div, Union Carbide Corp, 66-69, res chemist, Linde Div, Tarrytown, NY, 69-71; gen mgr Gulf Coast Div, Humphrey Chem Co, 71-77; mgr com develop, Southwest Specialty Chem Inc, 77-80; MGR MKT, DIXIE CHEM CO, 80- *Mem:* Am Chem Soc; NY Acad Sci. *Res:* Oxygen and nitrogen complexes of transition metals; organometallic chemistry; homogeneous catalysis; Lewis basicity; polyethylenimine chemistry; infrared spectroscopy. *Mailing Add:* 3 Thunderbird Circle Baytown TX 77521

JOHNSON, MARIE-LOUISE TULLY, b New York, NY, July 26, 27; m 50. MEDICINE, EPIDEMIOLOGY. *Educ:* Manhattanville Col, AB, 48; Yale Univ, PhD(microbiol), 54, MD, 56. *Prof Exp:* Asst prof dermat, Sch Med, Yale Univ, 61-64; chief dermat, Atomic Bomb Casualty Comn, Nat Acad Sci, 64-67; from asst prof to assoc prof, Sch Med, NY Univ, 67-70, assoc prof, Dartmouth Med Sch, 71-74; PROF DERMAT, SCH MED, NY UNIV, 75- *Concurrent Pos:* Consult, Med Sch, Cornell Univ, 67-70 & HEW 68-; chief dermat, White River Junction Vet Admin Hosp, 71-74. *Mem:* Soc Invest Dermat; Am Acad Dermat; Dermat Found; Am Dermat Asn. *Res:* Prevalence of dermatological disease in populations; disease, disability, discomfort and need for care. *Mailing Add:* NY Univ Sch of Med 560 First Ave New York NY 10016

JOHNSON, MARK EDWARD, b Chicago, Ill, June 27, 52; m 76. STATISTICS, OPERATIONS RESEARCH. *Educ:* Univ Iowa, BA, 73, MS, 74, PhD(indust & mgt eng), 76. *Prof Exp:* STAFF MEM STATIST, LOS ALAMOS NAT LAB, 76- *Mem:* Am Statist Asn; Math Asn Am; Inst Math Statist. *Res:* Applied statistics; random variate generation; Monte Carlo methods; probability distributions. *Mailing Add:* Statist Group S-1 Los Alamos Nat Lab MS 600 Box 1663 Los Alamos NM 87545

JOHNSON, MARVIN ELROY, b Red Wing, Minn, Nov 3, 45; m 70. PARTICLE PHYSICS. *Educ:* Univ Minn, BS, 67; Yale Univ, MPhil, 69, PhD(physics), 73. *Prof Exp:* PHYSICIST, FERMI NAT ACCLERATOR LAB, 73- *Mem:* Sigma Xi. *Res:* Strong interactions using hybrid bubble chamber techniques. *Mailing Add:* Fermi Nat Accelerator Lab PO Box 500 Batavia IL 60510

JOHNSON, MARVIN FRANCIS LINTON, b Chicago, Ill, June 6, 20; m 43; c 3. PHYSICAL CHEMISTRY. *Educ:* Loyola Univ, Ill, BS, 40, MS, 42. *Prof Exp:* Res chemist, Res & Develop Dept, Sinclair Refining Co, 41-50, res chemist, Sinclair Res Labs, 50-69, sr res chemist, 69-73, res assoc, 73-79, SR RES ASSOC, HARVEY TECH CTR, ATLANTIC RICHFIELD CO, 79- *Mem:* Catalysis Soc; Am Chem Soc; Am Soc Testing & Mat. *Res:* Heterogeneous catalysis; adsorption of gases by catalysts; pore structures of catalysts; physical-chemical characterizations of catalysts. *Mailing Add:* 1124 Elder Rd Homewood IL 60430

JOHNSON, MARVIN M, b Salt Lake City, Utah, Mar 21, 28; m 51; c 4. KINETICS, CATALYSIS. *Educ:* Univ Utah, BS, 50, PhD(chem eng), 56. *Prof Exp:* Sr res engr, 56-65, mgr hydorcarbon process, 65-68, res assoc, 68-74, sr res assoc, 74-78, SR SCIENTIST CATALYSIS, PHILLIPS RES CTR, 78- *Concurrent Pos:* Adj prof chem eng, Univ Kans, 81- *Mem:* Am Chem Soc; Am Inst Chem Engrs; Sigma Xi. *Res:* New catalysts and processes related to production and refining of petroleum and petrochemicals. *Mailing Add:* 206 CPL Phillips Res Ctr Bartlesville OK 74004

JOHNSON, MARVIN MELROSE, b Neligh, Nebr, Apr 21, 25; m 51; c 5. INDUSTRIAL ENGINEERING, ENGINEERING STATISTICS. *Educ:* Purdue Univ, BS, 49; Univ Iowa, MS, 66, PhD(indust eng), 68. *Prof Exp:* Supvr qual control, Chicago Bumper Div, Houdaille Hershey, 49-52; sr indust engr, Bell & Howell Co, 52-54; chief indust engr, Pioneer Cent Div, Bendix Corp, 54-57, supvr systs & procedures, 57-59, staff asst to asst gen mgr, 59-64; lectr indust & mgt eng, Univ Iowa, 64, instr, 65-66; assoc prof mech eng, 68-70, assoc prof indust & mgt systs eng, 70-77, PROF INDUST & MGT SYSTS ENG, UNIV NEBR, LINCOLN, 77- *Concurrent Pos:* Indust eng consult, Lincoln, Nebr & Davenport, Iowa, 64-; consult, Pioneer Cent Div, Bendix Corp, 64-68 & Brunswick Corp, 69-; prof & advisor, USAID|Univ Nebr-Omaha Contract|Kabul Univ, Afghanistan, 75-76. *Mem:* Fel Am Inst Indust Engrs; Am Soc Mech Engrs; Am Statist Asn; Am Soc Eng Educ; Inst Mgt Sci. *Res:* Systems; vegetable protein isolate; replaceable energy sources; operations research; applied statistics; simulation; quality control and reliability; production planning and control. *Mailing Add:* 175 Nebraska Hall Univ of Nebr Lincoln NE 68588

JOHNSON, MARY FRANCES, b Green Bay, Wis, Nov 17, 40. INORGANIC CHEMISTRY. *Educ:* Marquette Univ, BS, 63, MS, 65; St Louis Univ, PhD(inorg chem), 72. *Prof Exp:* PROF & CHAIRPERSON CHEM DEPT, FONTBONNE COL, 72- *Mem:* Am Chem Soc; Sigma Xi. *Res:* Spectroscopy and synthesis of lanthanide chelates involving nitrogen donor ligands. *Mailing Add:* Fontbonne Col 6800 Wydown Blvd St Louis MO 63105

JOHNSON, MARY FRANCES, b Milford, Conn, Nov 21, 51; m 78. CLINICAL TRIALS, SURVIVAL ANALYSIS. *Educ:* Tufts Univ, BS, 73; Yale Univ, MPH, 75, PhD(biostatist), 78. *Prof Exp:* Data analyst, Dept Epidemiol & Public Health, Yale Univ, 73-74, res asst, Conn Cancer Epidemiol Unit, 75-76; consult, Waterford Conserv Comn, Conn, 74-75; MATH STATISTICIAN, DIV BIOMET, BUR DRUGS, FOOD & DRUG ADMIN, 78- *Concurrent Pos:* Student ed, Yale J Biol & Med, 75-78, teaching asst, Div Biostatist, 75-77. *Mem:* Am Statist Asn; Biomet Soc. *Res:* Design and statistical analysis of therapeutic drug trials and epidemiological studies; applications of parametric and non-parametric models for failure time data. *Mailing Add:* Div Biomet HFD-232 Bur Drugs Food & Drug Admin 5600 Fishers Lane Rockville MD 20857

JOHNSON, MARY IDA, b Harlingen, Tex, Oct 30, 42; m 75; c 1. NEUROBIOLOGY, PEDIATRIC NEUROLOGY. *Educ:* Wash State Univ, BS, 64; Johns Hopkins Univ, MD, 68. *Prof Exp:* Intern & resident, Johns Hopkins Hosp, 68-71; fel neurol, 71-74, RES ASST PROF NEUROBIOL, WASH UNIV SCH MED, 74- *Mem:* Soc Neurosci; Child Neurol Soc; Am Acad Neurol. *Res:* Early synapse formation in tissue culture; development of neurotransmitter function in the autonomic nervous system. *Mailing Add:* Dept Anat & Neurobiol 660 S Euclid Ave St Louis MO 63110

JOHNSON, MARY KNETTLES, b Detroit, Mich, Sept 2, 29; m 55; c 2. BACTERIOLOGY. *Educ:* La State Univ, BS, 54, MS, 55, PhD(bact), 57. *Prof Exp:* Res assoc pharmacol, Stanford Univ, 57-58; asst prof microbiol, Sch Med, Univ Miss, 58-65; assoc prof, 67-80, PROF MICROBIOL, SCH MED, TULANE UNIV, LA, 80- *Concurrent Pos:* Instr, Millsaps Col, 58-61. *Mem:* fel Am Acad Microbiol; Am Soc Microbiol. *Res:* Bacterial physiology; mechanisms of pathogenicity. *Mailing Add:* Dept of Microbiol Tulane Univ Sch of Med New Orleans LA 70112

JOHNSON, MARY LYNN MILLER, b Pampa, Tex, Mar 12, 38; m 57; c 2. FUEL SCIENCE, AIR POLLUTION. *Educ:* Univ Tex, El Paso, BS, 58; NMex State Univ, MS, 61; Pa State Univ, PhD(fuel sci), 70. *Prof Exp:* Chemist, El Paso City-County Health Unit, Tex, 59-60 & 61-63 & Tex State Health Dept, 63-64; independent consult air pollution, 64-68; asst prof chem, Univ Tex, Arlington, 68-75; INSTR CHEM, HOCKADAY SCH, DALLAS, 75- *Mem:* Combustion Inst; Am Chem Soc; Air Pollution Control Asn. *Res:* Investigation of odor counteractants; combustion reactions, especially in the afterburning region, oxides of carbon and sulfur; analytical methods for measurement of air pollutants; air pollution chemistry; flame chemistry; combustion, new energy sources and air pollution. *Mailing Add:* 3004 Croydon Denton TX 76201

JOHNSON, MAURICE VERNER, JR, b Duluth, Minn, Sept 13, 25; m 44; c 2. RESEARCH ADMINISTRATION, AGRICULTURAL ENGINEERING. *Educ:* Univ Calif, Berkeley, BS, 53. *Prof Exp:* Engr, 53-59, chief engr, 59-66, MGR FRESH FRUIT RES & DEVELOP, SUNKIST GROWERS, INC, 66- *Concurrent Pos:* Mem, Pres Eng Adv Coun, Univ Calif, 75-, Chancellor's Adv Comt Col Nat & Agr Sci & Exp Sta, Univ Calif, Riverside, 78- *Mem:* AAAS; fel Am Soc Agr Engrs; Am Soc Mech Engrs; Am Inst Indust Engrs. *Res:* Handling of fresh citrus fruit; chemicals; electronics; mechanical research. *Mailing Add:* Sunkist Res Ctr 760 E Sunkist St Ontario CA 91761

JOHNSON, MELVIN ANDREW, JR, b Springfield, Ohio, Sept 4, 29; m 53; c 2. MEDICAL PHYSIOLOGY. *Educ:* Cent State Univ, BS, 50; Miami Univ, MS, 55; Jefferson Med Col, PhD(med physiol), 69. *Prof Exp:* Asst anat, Western Reserve Univ, 51-53; grad asst zool, Miami Univ, 54-55; instr biol, Grambling Col, 55-59; from instr to assoc prof, 61-72, PROF BIOL, CENT STATE UNIV, 72-, CHMN DEPT, 69-; PROF PHYSIOL, SCH MED, WRIGHT STATE UNIV, 74- *Concurrent Pos:* Am Heart Asn res grant, 70-72; prog dir minority biomed support grant, NIH, 72-77; prin investr 72-77 & 80-, ad hoc consult, Div Res Resources, 73-; item writer, Educ Testing Serv, 75-; prog dir, NASA grant, 77-79. *Mem:* Am Col Sports Med; AAAS; Am Physiol Soc; Sigma Xi. *Res:* Hemodynamic and metabolic responses to hemorrhagic stress following surgical alterations in liver and splenic tissue; effect of certain atmospheric pollutants on small mammals. *Mailing Add:* Dept of Biol Cent State Univ Wilberforce OH 45384

JOHNSON, MELVIN CLARK, b Newark, NJ, Aug 29, 38; m 75; c 2. TOXICOLOGY, PHARMACOLOGY. *Educ:* Rutgers Univ, BS, 62; McGill Univ, MS, 68; Howard Univ, PhD(pharmacol), 72. *Prof Exp:* From assoc scientist to scientist pharmacol, Warner-Lambert Res Inst, 62-70; toxicologist med dept, Hercules, Inc, 72-76; DIR TOXICOL, AGR DIV, AM CYANIMID CO, 77- *Mem:* Am Inst Biol Sci; Am Acad Clin Toxicol; NY Acad Sci. *Res:* Toxicology and pharmacology; safety of food additives, pesticides, animal drugs, food packaging materials and other consumer products; evaluation of potential exposures. *Mailing Add:* Am Cyanamid Co Agr Div PO Box 400 Princeton NJ 08540

JOHNSON, MELVIN WALTER, JR, b Chicago, Ill, May 27, 28; m 54; c 2. AGRONOMY, GENETICS. *Educ:* Univ Ill, BS, 50; Univ Wis, MS, 51, PhD(plant breeding), 54. *Prof Exp:* Asst agron, Univ Wis, 50-54; asst prof & asst agronomist, WVa Univ, 56-60, assoc prof & assoc agronomist, 60-65; ASSOC PROF AGRON, PA STATE UNIV, UNIVERSITY PARK, 65- *Mem:* Am Soc Agron; AAAS. *Res:* Plant breeding; plant genetics; corn breeding; basic and applied corn breeding and genetics research. *Mailing Add:* Dept of Agron Tyson Bldg Pa State Univ University Park PA 16802

JOHNSON, MICHAEL DAVID, b Chicago, Ill, Jan 6, 45; m 67; c 1. INSECT ECOLOGY. *Educ:* Northern Ill Univ, BS, 67; Northwestern Univ, PhD(biol), 70. *Prof Exp:* Res asst entom, Walter Reed Army Inst Res, 71-73; asst prof, 73-79, ASSOC PROF ZOOL, DEPAUW UNIV, 79- *Concurrent Pos:* Model implementation prog res grant, Environ Protection Agency, 78-80. *Res:* Ecology and biology of the solitary bees of central Indiana; benthic research in central Indiana. *Mailing Add:* Dept of Zool DePauw Univ Greencastle IN 46135

JOHNSON, MICHAEL EVART, b Cody, Wyo, Sept 4, 45. BIOPHYSICS. *Educ:* Univ Wyo, BS, 68; Northwestern Univ, MS, 70, PhD(biophys), 73. *Prof Exp:* Res assoc & NIH fel biophys, Univ Pittsburgh, 73-75; asst prof, 75-79, ASSOC PROF MED CHEM, UNIV ILL MED CTR, 79- *Concurrent Pos:* Guest scientist, Argonne Nat Lab, 75-; investr, Am Heart Asn, 79-84. *Mem:* Biophys Soc; AAAS; Am Chem Soc; Sigma Xi. *Res:* Sickling mechanism in sickle cell anemia; general application of magnetic resonance to biological systems. *Mailing Add:* Dept of Med Chem Univ of Ill Med Ctr PO Box 6998 Chicago IL 60680

JOHNSON, MICHAEL PAUL, b Oakland, Calif, Sept 13, 37; m 71; c 3. PLANT ECOLOGY. *Educ:* Univ Calif, Davis, BS, 59; Univ Ore, PhD(biol), 66. *Prof Exp:* Instr bot, San Francisco State Col, 60-61; asst prof ecol, Kent State Univ, 65-68; asst prof biol sci, Fla State Univ, 68-72; assoc prof biol, Kans State Univ & assoc dir, Konza Prairie Res Natural Area, 72-80; MEM STAFF, SCI EDUC ADMIN, USDA, 80- *Mem:* Soc Study Evolution; Ecol Soc Am; Brit Ecol Soc; Am Soc Naturalists; Sigma Xi. *Res:* Population biology; ecological genetics; botany; ecology. *Mailing Add:* PO Box 267 Sci Educ Admin Southwestern Ctr Res USDA Weslaco TX 78596

JOHNSON, MICHAEL ROSS, b Detroit, Mich, Oct 27, 44; m 64; c 2. ORGANIC CHEMISTRY. *Educ:* Univ Calif, Berkeley, BS, 67; Univ Calif, Santa Barbara, PhD(org chem), 70. *Prof Exp:* Res chemist, 71-73, sr res scientist, 73-76, sr res investr & proj leader, 76-80, MGR, CENT NERV SYST RES, PFIZER INC, 81- *Concurrent Pos:* NSF undergrad res fel, Calif State Col, Los Angeles, 64; NDEA Title IV fel, Univ Calif, Santa Barbara, 68-70; NIH fel, Univ Calif, Berkeley, 70-71. *Mem:* Am Chem Soc; Sigma Xi. *Res:* Mechanism and stereochemistry of carbonium ion, carbanion, organometallic and hydride reduction reactions; synthesis of pharmacalogically active heterocycles and natural products; synthesis of cannabinoid derived therapeutants. *Mailing Add:* Pfizer Cent Res Pfizer Inc Groton CT 06340

JOHNSON, MIKKEL BORLAUG, b Waynesboro, Va, Jan 2, 43; m 65; c 2. THEORETICAL NUCLEAR PHYSICS. *Educ:* Va Polytech Inst, BS, 66; Carnegie-Mellon Univ, MS, 68, PhD(physics), 71. *Prof Exp:* Consult physics, Rand Corp, 67 & 68; res assoc, Cornell Univ, 70-72; STAFF MEM PHYSICS, LOS ALAMOS NAT LAB, UNIV CALIF, 72- *Concurrent Pos:* Assoc ed nuclear physics, North-Holland Publ Co, 75-; vis prof, Dept Physics, State Univ NY, Stony Brook, 81-82. *Mem:* Am Phys Soc. *Res:* Effective interactions in nuclear physics; theory of dense nuclear matter; intermediate energy nuclear theory. *Mailing Add:* 118 Piedra Coop Los Alamos NM 87544

JOHNSON, MILES F, b Frederic, Wis, Mar 9, 36; m 63, 81. SYSTEMATIC BOTANY. *Educ:* Wis State Univ, River Falls, BS, 58; Univ Wis-Madison, MS, 62; Univ Minn, Minneapolis, PhD(bot), 68. *Prof Exp:* High sch teacher, Wis, 58-60; teaching asst bot, Univ Wis-Madison, 60-62, instr bot & zool, 62-64; teaching asst bot, Univ Minn, Minneapolis, 64-67, instr, 68; from asst prof to assoc prof, 68-80, PROF BIOL, VA COMMONWEALTH UNIV, 80- *Mem:* Bot Soc Am; Am Soc Plant Taxon; Int Soc Plant Taxon. *Res:* Taxonomy and systematics of Compositae; genus Ageratum; flora of Virginia. *Mailing Add:* Dept of Biol Va Commonwealth Univ Acad Ctr Richmond VA 23284

JOHNSON, MILLARD WALLACE, JR, b Racine, Wis, Feb 1, 28; m 53; c 4. MATHEMATICS. *Educ:* Univ Wis, BS, 52, MS, 53; Mass Inst Technol, PhD(math), 57. *Prof Exp:* Instr math, Mass Inst Technol, 53-58; from asst prof to assoc prof eng mech, 59-64, PROF ENG MECH & MATH, UNIV WIS-MADISON, 64- *Concurrent Pos:* Mem staff, Math Res Ctr, Univ Wis, 58-59, 60-61 & 75-76; mem exec comt, Rheol Res Ctr, Univ Wis, 69-; mem adv bd, Int Math & Statist Libr, 71- *Mem:* Soc Rheol; Soc Indust & Appl Math; Am Soc Mech Engrs; Soc Eng Sci. *Res:* Applied mathematics; rheology. *Mailing Add:* Dept of Math Univ of Wis Madison WI 53706

JOHNSON, MILTON R(AYMOND), JR, b Shreveport, La, Nov 5, 19; m 42; c 3. ELECTRICAL ENGINEERING. *Educ:* La Polytech Inst, BS, 40; Okla State Univ, MS, 51; Tex A&M Univ, PhD, 63. *Prof Exp:* Design engr, Gen Elec Co, 41-47; from asst prof to assoc elec eng, 47-54, PROF ELEC ENG, LOS ANGELES TECH UNIV, 54-, HEAD DEPT, 80- *Concurrent Pos:* Consult, Delta Res & Develop Corp, 52- *Mem:* Am Soc Eng Educ; Inst Elec & Electronics Engrs. *Res:* Electromechanical energy converters; automatic control systems. *Mailing Add:* Dept of Elec Eng La Tech Univ Ruston LA 71270

JOHNSON, MONTGOMERY HUNT, b Utica, NY, Nov 21, 07; m 46; c 2. PHYSICS. *Educ:* Harvard Univ, AB, 29, MA, 31, PhD(physics), 32. *Prof Exp:* Instr & tutor physics, Harvard Univ, 29-31; Nat Res Coun fel, NY Univ, 32-34, instr physics, 34-37, asst prof, 38-41; proj engr, Sperry Gyroscope Co, 41-42; mem staff, Radiation Lab, Mass Inst Technol, 42-45; head absorbent mat, Radio Div, Naval Res Lab, 45-47, consult physics div, 47, supt nucleonics div, 47-48, consult, 48-53; physicist, Radiation Lab, Univ Calif, 53-54; assoc dir res lab, Missile Systs Div, Lockheed Aircraft Corp, 54-56; gen opers mgr, Space Tech Opers, Aeronutronic Div, Ford Motor Co, 56-66, sr staff scientist, 60-63, mgr physics lab, Appl Res Lab, Philco Corp, 63-66, dir develop planning, Philco-Ford Corp, 66-73; CONSULT, LAWRENCE LIVERMORE LAB, 73- *Concurrent Pos:* Prof, Univ Md, 48-52. *Mem:* Fel Am Phys Soc; Sigma Xi. *Res:* Atomic and nuclear physics; quantum theory; electrodynamics; relativistic hydrodynamics; astrophysics. *Mailing Add:* 19002 E Dodge Ave Santa Ana CA 92705

JOHNSON, MORRIS ALFRED, b International Falls, Minn, Aug 3, 37; m 61; c 4. PLANT BIOCHEMISTRY. *Educ:* NDak State Univ, BS, 60, MS, 62; Ore State Univ, PhD(biochem), 66. *Prof Exp:* Asst prof & res fel biochem, 66-73, chmn dept biol, 70-79, ASSOC PROF BIOCHEM, INST PAPER CHEM, 73-, RES ASSOC, 74- *Mem:* Am Chem Soc; Am Soc Plant Physiol; fel Am Inst Chemists; Sigma Xi. *Res:* Intermediary metabolism and oxidative phosphorylation in plants; natural plant growth and development regulators; biochemistry of tree callus and suspension cultures. *Mailing Add:* Forest Biol Sect Inst of Paper Chem Appleton WI 54912

JOHNSON, MURRAY LEATHERS, b Tacoma, Wash, Oct 16, 14; m 42; c 4. MEDICINE, MAMMALOGY. *Educ:* Univ Ore, BA, 35, MD, 39; Am Bd Surg, dipl. *Prof Exp:* Res surg, Union Mem Hosp, Baltimore, Md, 39-43; CUR MAMMALS, PUGET SOUND MUS NATURAL HIST, UNIV PUGET SOUND, 48- *Concurrent Pos:* Comnr, US Marine Mammal Comn, 79-; mem, Nongame Adv Coun, Wash State Dept Game. *Mem:* AAAS; Am Soc Ichthyol & Herpet; Ecol Soc Am; Am Soc Mammalogists; Am Col Surg. *Res:* Clinical medicine and surgery in relation to the basic sciences; natural history of the mammals of the Pacific Northwest; basic biologic relationships of mammals. *Mailing Add:* Puget Sound Mus Natural Hist 501 Tacoma Ave Tacoma WA 98403

JOHNSON, MYRLE F, b Jerico Springs, Mo, Dec 12, 18; m 57; c 2. PHYSICAL CHEMISTRY. *Educ:* Southwest Mo State Col, AB, 41; Univ Wis, PhD(phys chem), 50. *Prof Exp:* Assoc prof chem, Southwest Mo State Col, 50-53; res chemist, 53-65, sr res chemist, 65-71, RES ASSOC, EASTMAN KODAK CO, 71- *Mem:* Am Chem Soc. *Res:* Rheology and colloid chemistry. *Mailing Add:* 41 Old North Hill Rochester NY 14617

JOHNSON, NED KEITH, b Reno, Nev, Nov 3, 32; m 52; c 4. ORNITHOLOGY. *Educ:* Univ Nev, BS, 54; Univ Calif, PhD(zool), 61. *Prof Exp:* From asst prof to assoc prof, 62-74, asst cur birds, Mus Vertebrate Zool, 62-63, PROF ZOOL, UNIV CALIF, BERKELEY, 74-, VCHMN DEPT, 68-, CUR BIRDS, MUS VERTEBRATE ZOOL, 63- *Concurrent Pos:* NSF res grant, 65-67. *Mem:* Am Soc Zool; Am Ornith Union; Cooper Ornith Soc; Soc Study Evolution; Soc Syst Zool. *Res:* Biosystematics; molt cycles; distribution and ecology of New World birds. *Mailing Add:* Mus of Vertebrate Zool Univ of Calif Berkeley CA 94720

JOHNSON, NOAH R, b Kingsport, Tenn, Oct 15, 28; m 50; c 3. NUCLEAR CHEMISTRY. *Educ:* ETenn State Univ, BS, 50; Fla State Univ, PhD, 56. *Prof Exp:* Pub sch teacher, Tenn, 50-52; nuclear chemist, 56-80, NUCLEAR PHYSICIST & GROUP LEADER, OAK RIDGE NAT LAB, 80- *Concurrent Pos:* Fulbright & Guggenheim fels, Niels Bohr Inst, Copenhagen & Danish Atomic Energy Comn, Riso, 62-63. *Mem:* Fel Am Phys Soc; Sigma Xi; Am Chem Soc. *Res:* Nuclear spectroscopy and reactions; coulomb excitation; Doppler-shift lifetime measurements; studies of high-angular momentum behavior in nuclei. *Mailing Add:* Oak Ridge Nat Lab PO Box X Oak Ridge TN 37830

JOHNSON, NORMAN ELDEN, b Mesa, Ariz, Apr 26, 33; m 54; c 1. FOREST MANAGEMENT, SILVICULTURE. *Educ:* Ore State Univ, BSF, 55, MS, 57; Univ Calif, PhD, 61. *Prof Exp:* Forestry aid, US Forest Serv, 51-52; forest engr, Southwest Lumber Mills, 54-55, forest entom asst, 55; forest entomologist, Forestry Res Ctr, Weyerhaeuser Co, Wash, 56-66, forest bioprotection leader, 66-69, forestry res mgr, Southern Forestry Res Ctr, Ark, 69-75, mgr tropical forestry & res, 75-78, vpres, Far East Region, Weyerhaeuser Co, Singapore, 78-80, vpres, NC Region, Weyerhaeuser Co, New Bern, NC, 80- *Concurrent Pos:* Assoc prof dept entom, Cornell Univ, 67-69; adj prof, Sch Forestry Resources, NC State Univ, 72; assoc ed, J Appl Forestry. *Mem:* Entom Soc Am; Soc Am Foresters; Entom Soc Can. *Res:* Forest plantation management. *Mailing Add:* PO Box 1391 New Bern NC Singapore

JOHNSON, NORMAN L, b Tillamook, Ore, July 27, 39; m 64; c 3. GEOMETRY. *Educ:* Portland State Univ, BA, 64; Wash State Univ, MA, 66, PhD(math), 68. *Prof Exp:* Asst prof math, Eastern Wash State Col, 68-69; asst prof, 69-78, PROF MATH, UNIV IOWA, 78- *Concurrent Pos:* Researcher, NSF fel, 71-72; res fel, Univ Bergen, 73-74; Sci Res Coun researcher, Great Britain, 78- *Res:* Finite projective planes; classification of semitranslation planes and their construction; translation planes; collineation groups. *Mailing Add:* Dept of Math Univ of Iowa Iowa City IA 52240

JOHNSON, NORMAN LLOYD, b Ilford, Eng, Jan 9, 17; m 64. STATISTICS. *Educ:* Univ Col London, BSc, 36 & 37, MSc, 38, PhD(statist), 48, DSc, 63. *Prof Exp:* Asst lectr statist, Univ Col London, 38-39, 45-46, lectr, 46-56, reader, 56-62; chmn dept, 71-76, PROF STATIST, UNIV NC, CHAPEL HILL, 62- *Concurrent Pos:* Vis assoc prof, Univ NC, Chapel Hill, 52-53; vacation consult, Road Res Lab, Eng, 56-59; vis prof, Case Inst Technol, 60-61. *Mem:* Fel Inst Math Statist; fel Am Statist Asn; Am Soc Qual Control; fel Royal Statist Soc; Biomet Soc. *Res:* Systems of frequency distributions; checks on completeness of samples; reliability. *Mailing Add:* Dept of Statistics Univ of NC Chapel Hill NC 27514

JOHNSON, NOYE MONROE, b Milwaukee, Wis, Dec 12, 30; m 53; c 2. GEOCHRONOLOGY, HYDROGEOLOGY. *Educ:* Univ Kans, BS, 53; Univ Wis, MS, 59, PhD(geol), 62. *Prof Exp:* PROF GEOL, DARTMOUTH COL, 62- *Concurrent Pos:* AEC res study contract, 62-; NSF res grants, 63- *Mem:* AAAS; Am Geophys Union; Geol Soc Am. *Res:* Remanent magnetic stratigraphy; physical limnology. *Mailing Add:* Dept of Earth Sci DartmouthCol Hanover NH 03755

JOHNSON, OGDEN CARL, b Rockford, Ill, Aug 15, 29; m 55; c 4. FOOD TECHNOLOGY, RESEARCH ADMINISTRATION. *Educ:* Univ Ill, BS, 51, MS, 52, PhD(food technol), 56. *Prof Exp:* Res assoc, Univ Ill, 56-57; sr res chemist, A E Staley Mfg Co, 57-60; asst secy, Coun Foods & Nutrit, AMA, 60-64, assoc secy, 64-66; nutrit sect, NIH, 66-68, nutrit prog, Pub Health Surv, Dept Health Educ & Welfare, 68-70; dir div nutrit, Food & Drug Admin, 70-74; vpres sci affairs, 74-80, EXEC VPRES, HERSHEY FOODS CORP, 80- *Mem:* Am Chem Soc; Am Oil Chem Soc; Inst Food Technologists. *Res:* Food product development; nutritive value of processed foods; nutrition survey; human nutrition; nutrition education. *Mailing Add:* RD 1 Box 400 Palmyra PA 17078

JOHNSON, OLIVER WILLIAM, b Maud, Okla, Mar 30, 30; m 58; c 1. VERTEBRATE ZOOLOGY, PHYSIOLOGY. *Educ:* Fresno State Col, AB, 55; Ore State Univ, MS, 59, PhD(zool), 65. *Prof Exp:* Instr ecol, Ore State Univ, 59-61; asst prof zool, Ariz State Col, 61-63; res assoc entom, Ore State Univ, 63-64; assoc prof, 64-74, PROF ZOOL, NORTHERN ARIZ UNIV, 74- *Mem:* AAAS; Am Soc Mammalogists; Am Soc Ichthyologists & Herpetologists. *Res:* Amphibian and reptilian temperature adaptation; biochemical taxonomy. *Mailing Add:* Dept of Biol Sci Northern Ariz Univ Flagstaff AZ 86001

JOHNSON, ORLAND EUGENE, b Gary, Ind, July 25, 23; m 46. NUCLEAR PHYSICS. *Educ:* Ind Univ, AB, 49, MS, 51, PhD(physics), 56. *Prof Exp:* Res assocj 56, from asst prof to assoc prof, 56-65, PROF PHYSICS, PURDUE UNIV, 65- *Mem:* Am Phys Soc. *Res:* Beta and gamma spectroscopy; nuclear scattering and reactions. *Mailing Add:* Dept of Physics Purdue Univ West Lafayette IN 47906

JOHNSON, OSCAR HUGO, b Hartford, Ohio, Aug 30, 14; m 40; c 4. ORGANIC CHEMISTRY. *Educ:* Hiram Col, AB, 36; Univ Nebr, MS, 39, PhD(org chem), 41. *Prof Exp:* Asst chem, Univ Nebr, 36-39; res chemist, Merck & Co, Inc, 41-46; res chemist, Niagara Chem Div, FMC Corp, 46-49, Westvaco Chem Div, 49-50, asst dir res, 50-53, dir res, Niagara Chem Div, 54-58, dir res & develop, Org Chem Dept, 58-59, asst to div mgr, Niagara Chem Div, 59-61, mkt dir, 61-63, vpres & dir res, Chem Div, 63-71; vpres & regional mgr, Nat Exec Search, Inc, 71-74; sr indust economist, Stanford Res Inst, 74-79; CONSULT AGR CHEM, 79- *Mem:* Am Chem Soc; Indust Res Inst. *Res:* Medicinal, agricultural and industrial chemicals; economic research in agricultural chemicals. *Mailing Add:* 16337 Swartz Canyon Rd Ramona CA 92065

JOHNSON, OSCAR WALTER, b Chicago, Ill, Mar 28, 35; m 55; c 2. ORNITHOLOGY, ECOLOGY. *Educ:* Mich State Univ, BS, 57; Wash State Univ, MS, 59, PhD(zool), 64. *Prof Exp:* Asst prof biol, Western State Col Colo, 63-65; from asst prof to assoc prof, 65-73, PROF BIOL, MOORHEAD STATE UNIV, 73- *Concurrent Pos:* NSF res grants, 65-66, 67-69, Ariz State Univ, 71-72 & Med Sch, Univ Ariz, 75; Res Corp grant, 73; Agr Econ Div & Dept Energy res grants, Univ Hawaii, 70, 73, 78, 79, & 80; mem, Int Comn Avian Anatomical Nomenclature, 73- *Mem:* AAAS; Am Ornith Union; Cooper Ornith Soc; Wilson Ornith Soc. *Res:* Ecology and behavior in shorebirds, particularly long-distance migrant species of the insular Pacific; microanatomical and physiological studies of the bird kidney. *Mailing Add:* Dept of Biol Moorhead State Univ Moorhead MN 56560

JOHNSON, OWEN W, b Provo, Utah, Mar 31, 31; m 57; c 3. SOLID STATE PHYSICS. *Educ:* Univ Utah, BA, 57, PhD(physics), 62. *Prof Exp:* Asst res prof physics, 62-64, asst prof ceramic eng, 64-65, from asst prof to assoc prof physics, 65-76, PROF PHYSICS, UNIV UTAH, 76-, ADJ ASSOC PROF MAT SCI, 68- 68- *Mem:* Am Phys Soc. *Res:* Electronic and optical properties of oxides and semiconductors; infrared spectroscopy; electronic properties of thin films. *Mailing Add:* Dept of Physics Univ of Utah Salt Lake City UT 84112

JOHNSON, PATRICIA ANN J, b New York, NY, Oct 10, 43; m 64; c 2. CLINICAL NEUROPSYCHOLOGY, CLINICAL PSYCHOLOGY. *Educ:* Univ Houston, BS, MA, PhD(psychol), 77. *Prof Exp:* exec dir & clin neuropsychologist, Found Lang & Learning Opportuunities, 77-80. *Concurrent Pos:* NIH fel, 74-77; clin asst prof psychol, Univ Houston, 78- *Mem:* AAAS; Int Neuropsychol Soc; Soc Neurosci; Am Psychol Asn; Biofeedback Soc Am. *Res:* Etiology and neuropsychology of learning and language disorders in children. *Mailing Add:* 3406 N Main Baytown TX 77521

JOHNSON, PATRICIA R, b Waco, Tex, Feb 28, 31; div; c 2. CELL CULTURE, GENETIC OBESITY. *Educ:* Baylor Univ, AB, 52, MA, 58; Rutgers Univ, PhD(biochem), 67. *Prof Exp:* Health physicist, Rocky Flats Plant, Dow Chem Corp, 52-53; anal chemist, Va Carolina Chem Corp, Tex, 53-54; high sch teacher, Tex, 56-60; instr biol & chem, Malone Col, 60-61; res asst, Bur Biol Res, Rutgers Univ, 61-64; from instr to assoc prof biol, 64-75, PROF BIOL, VASSAR COL, 75-, CHMN, DEPT BIOL, 75-, WILLIAM R KEENAN CHAIR, 81- *Concurrent Pos:* Adj assoc prof, Rockefeller Univ, 71-75, adj prof, 75-80. *Mem:* AAAS; NY Acad Sci; Am Inst Nutrit. *Res:* Adipose tissue growth and development in genetically obese mice and rats: behavior; metabolism; cell culture of fetal hepatocytes and precursor adipocyres from the genetically obese zucker rat. *Mailing Add:* Dept of Biol Vassar Col Poughkeepsie NY 12601

JOHNSON, PAUL A(MOS), chemical engineering, physical chemistry, see previous edition

JOHNSON, PAUL BENNETT, b Lewiston, Idaho, Jan 13, 18; m 43; c 2. MATHEMATICS. *Educ:* Univ Wash, BA, 38, MS, 44; Calif Inst Technol, PhD(math), 47. *Prof Exp:* Asst prof math, Occidental Col, 47-50, from assoc prof to prof, 50-59, chmn dept, 50-59; assoc prof, 59-65, PROF MATH, UNIV CALIF, LOS ANGELES, 65- *Concurrent Pos:* Vis prof, Haverford Col, 53-54; assoc, Ebeling Assocs, 73-74, consult, NY Dept Ment Health, 73-74. *Mem:* Am Math Soc; Math Asn Am; Sigma Xi. *Res:* Geometry; statistics; hydrology; mathematics education; engineering; African mathematics; mathematical modeling. *Mailing Add:* Dept of Math Univ of Calif Los Angeles CA 90024

JOHNSON, PAUL CHRISTIAN, b Ironwood, Mich, Feb 3, 28; m 55; c 3. PHYSIOLOGY. *Educ:* Univ Mich, BS, 51, MA, 53, PhD(physiol), 55. *Prof Exp:* Instr physiol, Univ Mich, 55-56; instr, Western Reserve Univ, 56-58; from asst prof to assoc prof, Sch Med, Ind Univ, 58-67; PROF PHYSIOL & HEAD DEPT, COL MED, UNIV ARIZ, 67- *Concurrent Pos:* NIH fel, 65-66; mem physiol study sect, NIH, 68-72; mem steering comt, circulation sect, Am Physiol Soc, 71-74, chmn, 74, mem coun, 78-82. *Mem:* AAAS; Am Physiol Soc; Microcirc Soc (pres, 67-68). *Res:* Local regulation of blood flow, microcirculation; capillary filtration and exchange. *Mailing Add:* Dept of Physiol Univ of Ariz Col of Med Tucson AZ 85724

JOHNSON, PAUL H(ILTON), b Nevis, Minn, May 2, 16; div; c 2. CHEMICAL ENGINEERING. *Educ:* Univ Minn, BChE, 38. *Prof Exp:* Process engr, Minn Gas Co, 38-41; res engr, Phillips Petrol Co, 41-54, sect chief, Res & Develop Dept, 54-60, mgr, Petrol Process Br, 60-69, mgr, Carbon Black Br, Res Ctr, 69-81; CONSULT CARBON BLACK ENVIRON HEALTH, PROCESS & RAW MAT, 81- *Mem:* Am Chem Soc. *Res:* Process development; petroleum refining; petrochemicals; carbon black; carbon black environmental health. *Mailing Add:* 1325 Osage Bartlesville OK 74003

JOHNSON, PAUL HICKOK, b Syracuse, NY, Mar 3, 43; m 67; c 2. BIOCHEMISTRY, MOLECULAR BIOLOGY. *Educ:* State Univ NY Buffalo, BA, 65, PhD(biochem), 70. *Prof Exp:* Am Cancer Soc fel, Calif Inst Technol, 70-74; asst prof biochem & molecular biol, 74-78, ASSOC PROF BIOCHEM, WAYNE STATE UNIV, 78- *Concurrent Pos:* USPHS grant molecular biol, Wayne State Univ, 74-77. *Mem:* AAAS; Biophys Soc; Am Chem Soc; Am Asn Microbiol; Sigma Xi. *Res:* Nucleic acid biochemistry and enzymology. *Mailing Add:* Dept of Biochem Wayne State Univ Sch of Med Detroit MI 48201

JOHNSON, PAUL LORENTZ, b Hawarden, Iowa, Sept 19, 41; m 71; c 3. COMPUTER SOFTWARE. *Educ:* St Olaf Col, BA, 63; Wash State Univ, PhD(phys chem), 68. *Prof Exp:* Fel, Univ Ill, Urbana-Champaign, 68-69; res assoc, Univ Ariz, 69-71, Mich State Univ, 71-72; Royal Norwegian Coun Sci & Indust res fel, Univ Bergen, Norway, 72-73; res assoc, Univ Ariz, 73-75; res assoc, 75-77, COMPUT SCIENTIST, ARGONNE NAT LAB, 77- *Concurrent Pos:* Instr, Lansing Community Col, 72. *Mem:* Asn Comput Mach; Am Crystallog Asn; Sigma Xi. *Res:* Neutron and x-ray crystallographic experiments applied to structures of organic, biological and inorganic interest; one-dimensional conducting compounds; portability of computer software; scientific applications of computers. *Mailing Add:* Nat Energy Software Ctr Argonne Nat Lab 9700 S Cass Ave Argonne IL 60439

JOHNSON, PAUL ROBERT, b Kenosha, Wis, Sept 13, 10; m 35; c 4. RUBBER CHEMISTRY, POLYMER CHEMISTRY. *Educ:* Univ Wis, BA, 34; Univ Minn, PhD(org chem), 38. *Prof Exp:* Asst instr chem, Univ Minn, 35-38; du Pont res fel, Univ Wis, 38-40; res chemist, E I du Pont de Nemours & Co Inc, 40-54, res supvr elastomers res, 54-75; INDEPENDENT RES CONSULT, 75- *Mem:* Am Chem Soc. *Res:* Pyrolysis of indene hydrocarbons; electrochemistry; vapor-liquid equilibria; gas phase reactions; synthetic elastomers; process development; rubber chemicals; flammability of materials; toxicity of chemicals. *Mailing Add:* 525 Hanover Rd Wilmington DE 19809

JOHNSON, PETER DEXTER, b Norwich, Conn, July 1, 21; div; c 3. APPLIED PHYSICS. *Educ:* Harvard Univ, SB, 42; Univ NC, MA, 48, PhD(phys chem), 49. *Prof Exp:* Supvr ballistic testing, Hercules Powder Co, Va, 42-43; RES ASSOC, GEN ELEC CO, 49- *Concurrent Pos:* Vis assoc prof, Cornell Univ, 58-59; patent agent, 81- *Mem:* Fel AAAS; fel Am Inst Chemists; Am Chem Soc; fel Am Phys Soc; Optical Soc Am. *Res:* Optical properties of phosphors and semiconductors; luminescence theory; optics and optical instrument design; optical properties of gas discharges. *Mailing Add:* Gen Elec Co Corp R&D Room 5 B31 K-1 Schenectady NY 12301

JOHNSON, PETER GRAHAM, b St Helens, Eng, Aug 28, 45; m 67. GEOMORPHOLOGY. *Educ:* Univ Leeds, BSc, 66, PhD(geog), 69. *Prof Exp:* Asst prof, 69-74, ASSOC PROF GEOMORPHOL, UNIV OTTAWA, 74- *Mem:* Inst Brit Geog; Glaciol Soc; Asn Am Geog; Arctic Inst NAm; Can Asn Geog. *Res:* Environmental controls on geomorphic processes in an alpine type environment; rock glacier mechanics and drainage systems; ice cored landform formation and degradation; southwest Yukon Territory; glacier hydrology. *Mailing Add:* Dept of Geog & Regional Plan Univ of Ottawa Ottawa ON K1N 6N5 Can

JOHNSON, PETER WADE, b Chatham, Ont, Mar 25, 42; m 67. PLANT PATHOLOGY, PLANT NEMATOLOGY. *Educ:* Ont Agr Col, BSc, 64; Univ Guelph, MSc, 66; Univ Calif, Riverside, PhD(plant path), 69. *Prof Exp:* RES SCIENTIST, CAN DEPT AGR, 69- *Mem:* Soc Nematol; Can Phytopath Soc. *Res:* Nematode problems in greenhouse vegetables fruit orchards and tobacco. *Mailing Add:* Res Sta Agr Can Vineland Station ON L0R 2E0 Can

JOHNSON, PHILIP CARL, b White Plains, NY, Nov 12, 24; m 50; c 2. MEDICINE. *Educ:* Univ Mich, BS, 48, MD, 49; Am Bd Internal Med, cert, 56, cert endocrinol, 73; Am Bd Nuclear Med, cert, 72. *Prof Exp:* From intern to resident, Univ Mich Hosp, 49-52, jr clin instr, 52, instr & asst dir radioisotope unit, 54-55; from asst prof to assoc prof med, Med Sch, Univ Okla, 55-60; assoc prof, 60-67, PROF MED, BAYLOR COL MED, 67-; DIR RADIOISOTOPE LAB, METHODIST HOSP, 60- *Concurrent Pos:* Asst dir prof servs res & chief radioisotope unit, Vet Admin Hosp, Oklahoma City, 55-60; mem state radiation adv bd, Tex; mem bioelectronics adv bd, Hoffmann-La Roche Co; attend nuclear med, Vet Admin Hosp; sr attend internal med, Methodist Hosp, Houston, attend endocrinol serv. *Mem:* Fel Am Col Angiol; fel Am Col Physicians; Am Fedn Clin Res; Soc Exp Biol & Med; fel Am Col Nuclear Med. *Res:* Use of radioisotopes in study of intra-organ blood flow; thyroid function; drug testing; studies of hypodynamic states including space flight. *Mailing Add:* Methodist Hosp Radioisotope Lab 6516 Bertner Blvd Houston TX 77030

JOHNSON, PHILIP L, b Oneonta, NY, May 26, 31. ECOLOGY. *Educ:* Purdue Univ, BS, 53, MS, 55; Duke Univ, PhD(bot), 61. *Prof Exp:* Instr bot, Univ Wyo, 59-61; res botanist, Range Res, US Forest Serv, Wyo, 61-62; res ecologist, Cold Regions Res & Eng Lab, NH, 62-67; assoc prof forest resources, Univ Ga, 67-70; div dir environ systs & resources, NSF, 70-74; exec dir, Oak Ridge Assoc Univs, 74-81; EXEC DIR, JOHN E GRAY INST, LAMAR UNIV, 81- *Concurrent Pos:* Vis asst prof biol, Dartmouth Col, 63 & 65-; res collabr, Brookhaven Nat Lab, 63-65; mem NH Pesticide control Bd, 65-67; mem primary productivity comt, Int Biol Prog, 67-68, adv comt tundra biome, 68-70, deciduous forest biome coord comt, 68-70; assoc prog dir, environ biol prog, NSF, 68-69; mem environ biol panel foreign currency prog, Smithsonian Inst, 69-70; vchmn interagency comt ecol res, Fed Coun Sci & Technol-Coun Environ Qual, 72; mem US Comt Man & Biosphere Prog, 73-74; mem fel adv panel environ affairs, Rockefeller Found, 74-; mem exec comt, East Tenn Cancer Res Ctr, Knoxville, 75-78; mem regional comt Southeastern Plant Environ Lab, 75- *Mem:* AAAS; Am Inst Biol Sci; Ecol Soc Am; Brit Ecol Soc; fel Arctic Inst NAm. *Res:* Production and processes in arctic and alpine tundra; aerial sensing of ecological patterns; mineral cycling in ecosystems applications of environmental sciences; interdisciplinary research and training. *Mailing Add:* John E Gray Inst Lamar Univ PO Box 10067 Beaumont TX 77710

JOHNSON, PHILIP M, b Vancouver, Wash, Oct 22, 40; m 64; c 2. PHYSICAL CHEMISTRY, MOLECULAR SPECTROSCOPY. *Educ:* Univ Wash, BS, 62; Cornell Univ, PhD(phys chem), 67. *Prof Exp:* NIH fel, Univ Chicago, 66-68; from asst prof to assoc prof, 68-78, PROF CHEM, STATE UNIV NY STONY BROOK, 78- *Concurrent Pos:* Vis fel, Joint Inst Lab Astrophys, Colo, 75-76. *Mem:* Am Phys Soc; Am Chem Soc. *Res:* Ultraviolet and vacuum ultraviolet spectroscopy; evolution of electronic energy in molecules; multiphoton ionization spectroscopy. *Mailing Add:* Dept of Chem State Univ of NY Stony Brook NY 11794

JOHNSON, PHILIP MARTYN, radiology, nuclear medicine, deceased

JOHNSON, PHILLIP EUGENE, b Bostic, NC, Feb 25, 37; m 59; c 1. MATHEMATICS. *Educ:* Appalachian State Teachers Col, BS, 59; George Peabody Col, MA, 63, PhD(math), 68; Am Univ, MA, 66. *Prof Exp:* High sch teacher, Va, 60-63; instr math, Univ Richmond, 63-65; from instr to asst prof, Vanderbilt Univ, 66-71; asst prof, 71-76, ASSOC PROF MATH, UNIV NC, CHARLOTTE, 76- *Concurrent Pos:* Vis asst prof, NC State Univ, 71. *Mem:* Math Asn Am; Nat Coun Teachers Math. *Res:* Mathematics history and education. *Mailing Add:* Dept of Math Univ of NC Charlotte NC 28213

JOHNSON, PHYLLIS ELAINE, b Grafton, NDak, Feb 19, 49; m 69; c 2. MASS SPECTROMETRY, TRACE METAL NUTRITION. *Educ:* Univ NDak, BS, 71, PhD(phys chem), 76. *Prof Exp:* Lab instr chem & biochem, Mary Col, NDak, 71-72; CHEMIST, SCI EDUC ADMIN-USDA HUMAN NUTRIT LAB, UNIV N DAK, 75- *Concurrent Pos:* Fel, Univ NDak, 75-77. *Mem:* Am Chem Soc; Am Inst Nutrit; Am Soc Mass Spectrometry; Asn Women in Sci. *Res:* Trace metal absorption; biological metal-ligand complexes; lactation and infant nutrition; absorption, metabolism and bioavailability of trace metals, especially iron, zinc, and copper, are investigated in humans using stable metal isotopes as tracers. *Mailing Add:* SEA-USDA Human Nutrit Lab Box 7166 Univ Sta Grand Forks ND 58202

JOHNSON, PHYLLIS TRUTH, b Salem, Ore, Aug 8, 26. INVERTEBRATE PATHOLOGY. *Educ:* Univ Calif, PhD(parasitol), 54. *Prof Exp:* Parasitologist med entom, Bur Vector Control, State Dept Health, Calif, 48-50; entomologist, Dept Entom, Walter Reed Army Inst Res, Washington, DC, 50-55; entomologist, Entom Res Br, USDA, 55-58; med entomologist, Gorgas Mem Lab, 59-63; from asst res pathobiologist to assoc res pathobiologist, Univ Calif, Irvine, 64-70; res fel, Calif Inst Technol, 70-71; consult, Off Environ Sci, Smithsonian Inst, 71-72; BIOLOGIST, NAT MARINE FISHERIES SERV, 72- *Concurrent Pos:* Consult, US Naval Med Res Unit 3, Cairo, Egypt, 57-; res assoc, USDA, 58-63; mem comt animal models & genetic stocks, Nat Res Coun, 71-75. *Mem:* Sigma Xi; fel AAAS; Soc Invert Path (vpres, 78-80 & pres, 81-82); Am Soc Trop Med & Hyg; Am Soc Parasitol. *Res:* Leishmaniasis; taxonomy of Siphonaptera and Anoplura; pathological processes in invertebrates; viruses in crustaceans; histopathology of crustaceans. *Mailing Add:* Nat Marine Fisheries Serv Oxford Lab Oxford MD 21654

JOHNSON, PIERCE, JR, electrical engineering, see previous edition

JOHNSON, PORTER W, b Chattanooga, Tenn, Sept 4, 42; m 63; c 2. HIGH ENERGY PHYSICS, MATHEMATICAL PHYSICS. *Educ:* Case Inst Technol, BS, 63; Princeton Univ, MA, 65, PhD(physics), 67. *Prof Exp:* Fel, Case Western Reserve Univ, 67-69; asst prof physics, 69-74, ASSOC PROF PHYSICS, ILL INST TECHNOL, 74- *Mem:* Am Phys Soc. *Res:* Study of mathematical structure of nonlinear equations involved in applications of general principles to elementary particle scattering data. *Mailing Add:* Dept of Physics Ill Inst of Technol Chicago IL 60616

JOHNSON, PRESTON BENTON, b Benson, NC, Mar 7, 32; m 54; c 3. ELECTRICAL ENGINEERING. *Educ:* NC State Univ, BSEE, 58, MS, 62; Va Polytech Inst, PhD(elec eng), 66. *Prof Exp:* Instr elec eng, NC State Univ, 61-62; asst prof, Va Polytech Inst, 62-66; ASSOC PROF ELEC ENG, OLD DOMINION UNIV, 66- *Concurrent Pos:* Chmn, Dept Elec Eng, Old Dominion Univ, 74-77; vpres, Sigma Consults, Inc, 75- *Mem:* Inst Elec & Electronics Engrs; Am Soc Eng Educ; Instrument Soc Am. *Res:* Negative-resistance electronic devices based on superconductive tunneling between thin films; oceanographic instrumentations. *Mailing Add:* Sch of Eng Old Dominion Univ Norfolk VA 23508

JOHNSON, QUINTIN C, b Excelsior, Minn, July 24, 35; m 57; c 2. CRYSTALLOGRAPHY. *Educ:* St Olaf Col, BA, 57; Univ Calif, Berkeley, PhD(chem), 61. *Prof Exp:* Chemist, 60-75, actg dep dept head chem, 75-76, assoc dept head chem, 76-80, DIV LEADER, LAWRENCE LIVERMORE NAT LAB, 80- *Mem:* AAAS; Am Crystallog Asn (vpres, 80, pres, 81); Am Phys Soc. *Res:* Flash x-ray diffraction studies; automation of powder diffraction; high pressure crystallography. *Mailing Add:* Lawrence Livermore Nat Lab L-326 Livermore CA 94550

JOHNSON, R(ICHARD) A(LLAN), b Winnipeg, Man, Mar 21, 32; m 57; c 3. ELECTRICAL ENGINEERING. *Educ:* Univ Man, BSc, 54, MSc, 56. *Prof Exp:* From asst prof to assoc prof, 55-66, PROF ELEC ENG, UNIV MAN, 66- *Mem:* Inst Elec & Electronics Engrs. *Res:* Circuits and systems theory; nonlinear oscillations. *Mailing Add:* Dept of Elec Eng Univ of Man Winnipeg MB R3T 2N2 Can

JOHNSON, RALEIGH FRANCIS, JR, b Hazard, Ky, Jan 24, 41; m 63; c 2. NUCLEAR MEDICINE, RADIOLOGICAL PHYSICS. *Educ:* Berea Col, AB, 64; Univ Miami, MS, 65; Purdue Univ, PhD(radiol physics), 69. *Prof Exp:* Assoc radiol & nuclear med & physicist, Duke Univ & Vet Admin Hosp, 69-72; ASST PROF RADIOL & NUCLEAR MED & PHYSICIST, UNIV TEX MED BR GALVESTON, 72- *Concurrent Pos:* Consult, Scientists & Engrs for Appalachia, 71- *Mem:* Health Physics Soc; Nuclear Med Soc; Sigma Xi; Creation Res Soc; Am Asn Physicists in Med. *Res:* Evaluation of microprocession controlled automatic well-type scintillation counting system; quality control of scintillation counting and imaging systems; evaluation of multipeak scintillation imaging; evaluation of large detection scintillation gamma cameras. *Mailing Add:* Nuclear Med Div Univ of Tex Med Br Galveston TX 77550

JOHNSON, RALPH ALTON, b Alton, Ill, Sept 14, 19; m 54; c 1. ANALYTICAL CHEMISTRY. *Educ:* Hastings Col, BA, 40; Univ Colo, MS, 42; Univ Minn, PhD(chem), 49. *Prof Exp:* Jr chemist, Manhattan Proj, Hanford Eng Works, E I du Pont de Nemours & Co, 44-45; from instr to asst prof anal chem, Univ Ill, 48-55; SR RES CHEMIST, SHELL DEVELOP CO, 55- *Mem:* Am Chem Soc; Air Pollution Control Asn. *Res:* Psychophysics, odor measurement; wastewater processing and analysis; precipitation studies; spectrophotometric and electron microscopic investigations; neutron activation analysis. *Mailing Add:* 13135 Boheme Houston TX 77079

JOHNSON, RALPH BERNARD, b Brainerd, Minn, May 9, 18. MATHEMATICS. *Educ:* Gustavus Adolphus Col, 40; Columbia Univ, MA, 41. *Prof Exp:* Instr math, Univ Tenn, 46-49; asst prof, Clemson Col, 50-55; assoc prof, Catawba Col, 55-66; INSTR MATH, UNIV SOUTH ALA, 66- *Mem:* Am Math Soc; Inst Math Statist. *Res:* Estimation of intervals which contain an assigned proportion of a normal univariate population; postage stamps of the world that are related to mathematics. *Mailing Add:* Dept of Math Univ of South Ala Mobile AL 36688

JOHNSON, RALPH E, b Ashtabula, Ohio, Dec 1, 24; m 64; c 2. PHYSICAL CHEMISTRY. *Educ:* Univ Detroit, BS, 47, MS, 49; Mich State Univ, PhD(phys chem), 55. *Prof Exp:* Sr nuclear engr, Gen Dynamics/Convair, 55-57; sr res engr high temperature chem, Atomics Int Div, NAm Aviation, Inc, 57-64; STAFF SCIENTIST BATTERY TECHNOL, LOCKHEED MISSILE & SPACE CO, 65- *Mem:* Am Chem Soc; Electrochem Soc. *Res:* Development of batteries for spacecraft applications. *Mailing Add:* 205 Mistletoe Rd Los Gatos CA 95030

JOHNSON, RALPH M, JR, b Ririe, Idaho, Apr 19, 18; m 40; c 3. BIOLOGICAL CHEMISTRY. *Educ:* Utah State Agr Col, BS, 40; Univ Wis, MS, 44, PhD(biochem), 48. *Prof Exp:* Asst prof biochem, Col Med, Wayne State Univ, 48-59; from assoc prof to prof physiol chem, Ohio State Univ, 59-68, dir & res prof, Inst Nutrit & Food Technol, 60-68, dir, 63-68, dean col biol sci, 66-68, res assoc prof, 59-60, dir labs, 59-63; DEAN COL SCI & PROF CHEM, UTAH STATE UNIV, 68- *Mem:* Am Soc Biol Chemists; Am Inst Nutrit. *Res:* Lipid metabolism; metabolism of phosphorous compounds; hormonal and hereditary factors in carcinogenesis; biochemical role of vitamin E. *Mailing Add:* Col of Sci Utah State Univ Logan UT 84321

JOHNSON, RALPH STERLING, JR, b Shickshinny, Pa, Apr 2, 26; m 51; c 1. MATERIALS SCIENCE, METALLURGICAL ENGINEERING. *Educ:* Univ Akron, BS, 57, MS, 60; Univ Mich, Ann Arbor, PhD(mat sci & metall eng), 70. *Prof Exp:* Sr res engr mat & mfg res, Res & Develop Dept, Goodyear Aerospace Corp, 49-61; sr staff engr, Seismic Equip Dept, Bendix Aerospace Systems Div, Ann Arbor, 62-72; consult mat corrosion & mfg processes, Res & Eng Dept, Bechtel Nat, Inc, San Francisco, 73-79 & Aramco, Dhahran, Saudi Arabia, 79-81; CONSULT MAT CORROSION & MFG PROCESSES & MEM, CORROSION TASK FORCE, SOHIO ALASKA PETROL CO, ANCHORAGE, 81- *Concurrent Pos:* Mem water qual task force, Bechtel Power Corp, 75- *Honors & Awards:* Apollo Achievement Award, NASA, 69. *Mem:* NY Acad Sci; Am Inst Mining, Metall & Petrol Engrs; Nat Asn Corrosion Engrs; Sigma Xi; Am Soc Metals. *Res:* Materials performance and corrosion of materials in flue gas desulfurization systems; feedwater and steam generating systems in steam electric plants; oil field production facilities materials of construction and corrosion control. *Mailing Add:* 5063 Sillary Circle Anchorage AK 99054

JOHNSON, RALPH T, JR, b Salina, Kans, Apr 29, 35; m 58; c 4. SOLID STATE PHYSICS, RESEARCH SUPERVISION. *Educ:* Kans State Univ, BS, 57, MS, 59, PhD(physics), 64. *Prof Exp:* Physicist, Aircraft Nuclear Propulsion Dept, Gen Elec Co, 57-58; asst physics, Kans State Univ, 58-63; proj officer, Air Force Weapons Lab, 63-65; staff mem solid state physics, 65-70, RES SUPVR ELEC TRANSPORT & ELECTRONIC PROPERTIES MAT, SANDIA LABS, 70- *Concurrent Pos:* Mem energy conversion panel, NMex Gov Energy Task Force, 74. *Mem:* Am Phys Soc; Sigma Xi. *Res:* X-ray diffraction topography; dislocations and martensitic transformations; rocketborne magnetometers and optical spectrometers; semiconductor radiation defects, ionization effects and neutron detectors; electrical properties of amorphous semiconductors; thermoelectrics; solid electrolytes; electronic properties of dielectric materials. *Mailing Add:* 6601 Arroyo del Oso NE Albuquerque NM 87109

JOHNSON, RANDALL ARTHUR, b Los Angeles, Calif, Sept 28, 46; m 77; c 2. AGRICULTURE, COMPUTER SOFTWARE. *Educ:* Calif State Polytech Univ, Pomona, BS, 68; Univ Mo, MS, 73, PhD(animal sci), 77. *Prof Exp:* Res asst animal sci, Univ Mo, 72-73; dir placement & asst dean, 73-76; mgr qual control & nutrit, Nat Pet Food Corp, 76-79; PRES, AGR-DATA SYST, INC, 79- *Concurrent Pos:* Dir res, Nat Pet Food Corp, 78-79; consult, Toxicol Prog, Agro-Am Corp, 81- *Mem:* Am Soc Animal Sci; Am Dairy Sci Asn. *Res:* Ruminant nutrition and management systems utilizing computers; de-toxification of dairy lactating cows of long chain hydrocarbon residues from adipose tissue. *Mailing Add:* Suite 203 2001 E Campbell Phoenix AZ 85016

JOHNSON, RANDY ALLAN, b Minneapolis, Minn, Feb 9, 47; m 78. HIGH ENERGY PHYSICS. *Educ:* Princeton Univ, AB, 69; Univ Calif, Berkeley, PhD(physics), 75. *Prof Exp:* Fel physics, Lawrence Berkeley Lab, 75-76; ASSOC PHYSICIST, BROOKHAVEN NAT LAB, 76- *Mem:* Sigma Xi. *Res:* Particle scattering at high energies. *Mailing Add:* Brookhaven Nat Lab Upton NY 11973

JOHNSON, RAY C(LIFFORD), mechanical engineering, see previous edition

JOHNSON, RAY EDWIN, b East View, Ky, Aug 9, 36; m 64. SOIL FERTILITY. *Educ:* Univ Ky, BS, 57, MS, 59; NC State Univ, PhD(mineral nutrit), 62. *Prof Exp:* Res assoc, Mineral Nutrit Pioneering Res Lab, USDA, 62-63; res plant physiologist, US Regional Soybean Lab, Crops Res Div, Agr

Res Serv, Ill, 63-67; from asst prof to assoc prof agron, soil fertil & soil chem, 67-73, PROF AGRON, SOIL FERTIL & SOIL CHEM, WESTERN KY UNIV, 73- Mem: Am Soc Agron; Sigma Xi. Res: Mineral nutrition and interaction in plants; relationship of fertilizer response to soil test results. Mailing Add: Dept of Agr Western Ky Univ Bowling Green KY 42101

JOHNSON, RAY LELAND, b LaGrange, Ohio, Nov 7, 39; m 62; c 2. PHYSICAL CHEMISTRY, ENVIRONMENTAL CHEMISTRY. Educ: Kent State Univ, BS, 61; Ohio Univ, PhD(phys chem), 66. Prof Exp: Sr res chemist, PPG Industs Inc, 66-69; asst prof, 69-77, ASSOC PROF CHEM & ACTG CHMN, DIV NATURAL SCI, HILLSDALE COL, 77- Concurrent Pos: Consult, Hillsdale Waste Water Treatment Plant, 70-; W K Kellogg Found res grant water qual studies, 71-73. Mem: AAAS; Am Chem Soc. Res: Thermodynamics and kinetics; surface and colloid chemistry; interaction of pigments with polymers; solution chemistry; chemical investigations of water quality in lakes and streams; chemical methods of waste water treatment. Mailing Add: Dept of Chem Hillsdale Col Hillsdale MI 49242

JOHNSON, RAYMOND C, JR, b Galveston, Tex, Sept 29, 22; c 9. ELECTRONICS. Educ: Tex A&M Univ, BS, 45; Univ Fla, MS, 49. Prof Exp: From asst prof to assoc prof, 46-68, PROF ELEC ENG, UNIV FLA, 68-, SECT HEAD, ELECTRONIC RES SECT, 59-, DIR ELECTRONIC COMMUN LAB, 76- Res: Electronics systems. Mailing Add: Electron Commun Lab PO Box 1253 Gainesville FL 32602

JOHNSON, RAYMOND EARL, b Peru, Nebr, Oct 26, 14; m 41. ZOOLOGY. Educ: Doane Col, BA, 36; Univ Nebr, MA, 38; Univ Mich, PhD(zool), 42. Prof Exp: Aquatic biologist, US Fish & Wildlife Serv, Univ Minn, 45-46, fisheries res supvr, 47-51, asst fed aid supvr, Bur Sport Fisheries & Wildlife, 51-56, chief fish div, 56-58, chief br fed aid, 58-59, asst dir, Bur Sport Fisheries & Wildlife, 59-71, chief off environ qual, 71-72; dep div dir, NSF, 72-74; CONSULT, NAT WILDLIFE FEDN, 74- Mem: Am Soc Ichtyologists & Herpetologists; Am Fisheries Soc; Am Soc Limnol & Oceanog; Wildlife Soc. Res: Taxonomy and distribution of freshwater fishes in North America; fisheries management; life history of freshwater fishes. Mailing Add: Nat Wildlife Fedn Washington DC 20036

JOHNSON, RAYMOND LEWIS, b Alice, Tex, June 25, 43; m 65; c 1. MATHEMATICS. Educ: Univ Tex, Austin, BA, 63; Rice Univ, PhD(math), 69. Prof Exp: Asst prof, 68-72, assoc prof, 72-78, PROF MATH, UNIV MD, COLLEGE PARK, 78- Concurrent Pos: Gen Res Bd grant, 68 & 71; sabbatical leave, Inst Mittag-Leffler, DJursholm, 74-75 & Howard Univ, 76-78. Mem: Am Math Soc. Res: Parabolic partial differential equations; representation theorems; spaces of functions defined by difference conditions. Mailing Add: Dept of Math Univ of Md College Park MD 20742

JOHNSON, RAYMOND NILS, b New York, NY, July 26, 41; m 65; c 2. ANALYTICAL CHEMISTRY. Educ: Franklin & Marshall Col, AB, 63; Middlebury Col, MS, 65; Clarkson Technol Col, PhD(chem), 69. Prof Exp: From res assoc anal chem to group leader, 69-75, sect head anal chem, 75-78, ASST DIR ANAL RES & DEVELOP, AYERST LABS, INC, 78- Mem: Am Chem Soc; Acad Pharmaceut Sci; Sigma Xi. Res: Pharmaceutical analysis using gas chromatography, polarography, mass spectrometry and mass fragmentography; emphasis placed on preparation of novel chemical derivatives and development of analytical methods that are precise, accurate and specific. Mailing Add: Anal Res & Develop Lab Ayerst Labs Inc Rouses Point NY 12979

JOHNSON, RAYMOND ROY, b Phoenix, Ariz, June 19, 32; m 76; c 5. SYSTEMATIC BOTANY, VERTEBRATE ZOOLOGY. Educ: Ariz State Univ, BS, 55; Univ Ariz, MS, 60; Univ Kans, PhD(bot), 64. Prof Exp: Asst prof biol, Western NMex Univ, 64-65 & Univ Tex, El Paso, 65-68; from assoc prof to prof biol, Prescott Col, 68-74; res scientist, Grand Canyon, 74-75,sr res scientist, 76-80, SR RES SCIENTIST, COOP NAT PARK RESOURCES STUDY UNIT, NAT PARK SERV, UNIV ARIZ, 80- Concurrent Pos: Adj prof, Renewble Nat Res Studies Unit, Univ Ariz, 80- Mem: Am Ornith Union; Am Soc Mammal; Cooper Ornith Soc; Sigma Xi. Res: Plant taxonomy and cytogenetics; animal distribution; riparian ecology; desertification and arid land ecology. Mailing Add: Coop Nat Park Res Studies Unit 125 Biol Sci E Univ Ariz Tucson AZ 85721

JOHNSON, RICHARD ALLEN, b Panama City, Fla, Aug 13, 45; m 68; c 2. PHYSICAL CHEMISTRY. Educ: Ill Inst Technol, BS, 67; Mich State Univ, PhD(chem physics), 71. Prof Exp: Scientist, Control Anal Res & Develop Unit, 71-73, res scientist, 73-74, sr res scientist, 74-76, MGR PROD CONTROL, UPJOHN CO, 76- Mem: Am Chem Soc; Am Phys Soc. Res: Molecular spectroscopy of solids; solid state chemistry; physical characterization of pharmaceutical solids; application of computers to online data acquisition from analytical laboratory instrumentation. Mailing Add: Dept 7820-41-1 Upjohn Co Kalamazoo MI 49001

JOHNSON, RICHARD CARL, synthetic organic chemistry, see previous edition

JOHNSON, RICHARD CLAYTON, b Eveleth, Minn, May 9, 30; div; c 2. APPLIED PHYSICS. Educ: Ga Inst Technol, BS, 53, MS, 58, PhD(physics), 61. Prof Exp: From asst res physicist to sr res physicist, 56-79, head radar br, 63-68, prin res physicist, 67-79, chief electronics div, 68-72, mgr systs & tech dept, 72-75, assoc dir eng exp sta, 75-79, PRIN RES ENGR, GA INST TECHNOL, 79- Concurrent Pos: Distinguished lectr, Inst Elec & Electronics Engrs, Antennas & Propagation Soc, 78-79, pres, 80. Mem: Am Phys Soc; fel Inst Elec & Electronics Engrs; Sigma Xi. Res: Radar and radiometry systems; antenna research and development; microwave theory and techniques; microwave spectroscopy; electromagnetic compatibility. Mailing Add: Eng Exp Sta Ga Inst of Technol Atlanta GA 30332

JOHNSON, RICHARD D, b Zanesville, Ohio, Oct 28, 34; m 57; c 1. CHEMISTRY. Educ: Oberlin Col, BA, 56; Carnegie Inst Technol, MS, 59, PhD(chem), 61; Mass Inst Tech, bus, 81- Prof Exp: Fel phys org chem, Univ Calif, Los Angeles, 61-62; sr scientist, Jet Propulsion Lab, Calif Inst Technol, 62-63; chief flight exp off, Life Sci, 75-76, RES SCIENTIST, AMES RES CTR, NASA, 76- Concurrent Pos: Lectr, Stanford Univ, 74-; Sloan fel, 81-82. Mem: AAAS; Am Inst Aeronaut & Astronaut; Am Chem Soc. Res: Exobiology and the detection of extraterrestrial life, especially chemical aspects, physical, organic and analytical; Apollo lunar sample analysis; 1976 Viking Mars life detection experiment; space colonies; 1976 Stanford/Ames study on space settlements; space shuttle experiments; space biomedical experiments. Mailing Add: 11564 Arroyo Oaks Los Altos Hills CA 94022

JOHNSON, RICHARD DEAN, b DeKalb, Ill, July 8, 36; m 69; c 4. PRODUCT LICENSING, TECHNOLOGY TRANSFER. Educ: Univ Calif, Berkeley, BS, 60, PharmD, 61, MS, 62; Univ Calif, San Francisco, PhD(pharm chem), 65. Prof Exp: Pharmacist, Alta Vista Drug Co, 60-61; res chemist & sect head, Allergan Pharmceut Co, 65-67; assoc dir med serv, Syntex Labs, Inc, 67-68, dir regulatory affairs, 68-73; dir corp licensing, 73-79, VPRES LICENSING, MARION LABS, INC, 80- Concurrent Pos: Borden Co grad award, Univ Calif, San Francisco, 61-62; fels, Am Found Pharmaceut Educ & Henry S Wellcome Mem, 63-65; mem, Pres Comn Exec Interchange, US Dept Com, 70-71; lectr, Bus Sch, Univ SC, 75-77. Honors & Awards: Marion Labs President's Award, 80. Mem: AAAS; Am Pharmaceut Asn; Am Chem Soc; Acad Pharmaceut Sci; Licensing Exec Soc. Res: Thermal titration; thermal electric methods for studying physical and chemical properties of solutions. Mailing Add: Marion Labs Inc 9221 Ward Pkwy Kansas City MO 64114

JOHNSON, RICHARD EVAN, b Pomona, Calif, Nov 9, 36. ORNITHOLOGY, ZOOGEOGRAPHY. Educ: Univ Calif, Berkeley, BS, 58; Univ Mont, MS, 68; Univ Calif, Berkeley, PhD(zool), 72. Prof Exp: Asst prof, 72-78, ASSOC PROF ZOOL, WASH STATE UNIV, 78- DIR, CHARLES R CONNER MUS, 72- Concurrent Pos: Ed, The Murrelet, 76-80. Mem: Am Ornithologists Union; Cooper Ornith Soc; Wilson Ornith Soc; Soc Study Evolution; Soc Syst Zool. Res: Zoogeography, ecology and speciation of birds; evolution of arctic and alpine ecosystems; mammals of the Northwest. Mailing Add: Dept of Zool Wash State Univ Pullman WA 99164

JOHNSON, RICHARD HARLAN, b Portland, Ore, Nov 4, 45; m 65; c 2. METEOROLOGY. Educ: Ore State Univ, BS, 67; Univ Chicago, MS, 69; Univ Wash, PhD(atmospheric sci), 75. Prof Exp: Res meteorologist, Nat Hurricane Res Lab, 76-77; asst prof atmospheric sci, Univ Wis-Milwaukee, 77-79; ASST PROF ATMOSPHERIC SCI, COLO STATE UNIV, 80- Mem: Am Meteorol Soc; AAAS; Japan Meteorol Soc. Res: Atmospheric convection and the planetary boundary layer; mesoscale meteorology; synoptic meteorology; study of precipitating clouds and their interaction with the atmospheric circulation on various scales. Mailing Add: 2500 Wyandotte Dr Ft Collins CO 80526

JOHNSON, RICHARD JAMES, b Tonasket, Wash, Sept 29, 23; m 49; c 4. ANIMAL NUTRITION, BIOCHEMISTRY. Educ: Wash State Univ, BS, 60, MS, 63, PhD(animal sci), 67. Prof Exp: Sr exp aide agron, Wash State Univ, 56-60, county agent, 60-62, from instr to prof animal sci, 63-76, actg chmn dept, 75-76; PROF & HEAD DEPT, SOUTHEAST KANS EXP STA, KANS STATE UNIV, 77- Concurrent Pos: Consult, World Bank, Univ Develop, Pakistan, 76. Mem: Am Soc Agron; Coun Agr Sci & Technol; Sigma Xi; AAAS; Am Soc Animal Sci. Res: Beef cattle nutrition; composition of feedstuffs; equine nutrition; mineral metabolism. Mailing Add: Southeast Kans Exp Sta Br of Kans State Univ Parsons KS 67357

JOHNSON, RICHARD LAWRENCE, b Glendale, WVa, Feb 3, 39; m 60; c 2. ORGANIC CHEMISTRY. Educ: Washington & Jefferson Col, BA, 60; Univ Ky, MS, 62; Univ Iowa, PhD(org chem), 66. Prof Exp: Chemist, Rayonier, Inc, 65-66; chemist, 66-73, SR RES CHEMIST, E I DU PONT DE NEMOURS & CO INC, 73- Concurrent Pos: Lectr, Parkersburg Br, WVa Univ, 70-71 & Parkersburg Community Col, 71-73. Mem: Am Chem Soc; Sigma Xi. Res: Fluorocarbon polymers and fluorocarbon synthesis; nylon polymerization and extrusion compounding; fluorocarbon dispersion applications. Mailing Add: E I du Pont de Nemours & Co Inc Plastics Res Washington WV 26181

JOHNSON, RICHARD LEON, b Enid, Okla, June 12, 38; m 62; c 2. SIGNAL PROCESSING, ATMOSPHERIC ELECTRICITY. Educ: Univ Tex, Arlington, BSEE, 64; Southern Methodist Univ, MSEE, 66; Okla State Univ, PhD(elec eng), 70. Prof Exp: Aerosyst engr electronics, Gen Dynamics Corp, Ft Worth, Tex, 64-66; res asst, Okla State Univ, 66-70; STAFF ENGR ELECTROMAGNETICS, SOUTHWEST RES INST, 70- Mem: Int Union Radio Sci; Inst Elec & Electronic Engrs. Res: Communication and information systems analysis; signal detection and estimation; atmospheric electricity in severe storms. Mailing Add: Dept of Radiolocation Sci Southwest Res Inst San Antonio TX 78284

JOHNSON, RICHARD NORING, b Wethersfield, Conn, Apr 12, 34; m 60; c 2. BIOMEDICAL ENGINEERING. Educ: Tri-State Col, BSc, 61; Worcester Polytech Inst, MSc, 65; Univ Va, DSc(biomed eng), 69. Prof Exp: Instr elec technol, Hartford State Tech Col, 61-65; res assoc neurol, Schs Eng & Med, Univ Va, 69-70, instr, 70-71, asst prof biomed eng & neurol, 72-77, assoc prof, 77-79; PROF BIOMED ENG & NEUROLOGY, SCH MED, UNIV NC, CHAPEL HILL, 79- Concurrent Pos: Fel biomed eng, Johns Hopkins Univ, 71-72. Mem: AAAS; Am Soc Eng Educ; Soc Neurosci; Biomed Eng Soc; Am Epilepsy Soc. Res: Neurophysiological control systems; neural models. Mailing Add: Dept Neurology Univ NC Chapel Hill Chapel Hill NC 27514

JOHNSON, RICHARD RAY, b Carrol, Iowa, Nov 18, 47; m 68. AGRONOMY. *Educ:* Iowa State Univ, BS, 69, MS, 70; Univ Minn, PhD(plant physiol), 74. *Prof Exp:* Asst prof crop prod, Univ Ill, Urbana, 74-77, assoc prof, 77-80; STAFF AGRONOMIST, DEERE & CO, 80- *Mem:* Crop Sci Soc Am; Am Soc Agron; Soil Sci Soc Am; Weed Sci Soc. *Res:* Applying new technology in crop production to the design and marketing of agricultural equipment. *Mailing Add:* Deere & Co Tech Ctr 3300 River Dr Moline IL 61265

JOHNSON, RICHARD STEBBINS, b Maywood, Ill, Oct 18, 22; m 53, 67; c 1. PHYSICAL ORGANIC CHEMISTRY. *Educ:* Ill Inst Technol, BS, 46, MS, 48; Duke Univ, PhD(chem), 51. *Prof Exp:* Res chemist, Nat Carbon Res Labs, 51-55; sr res chemist, Riegel Textile Corp, 55-60; sr scientist, Southern Res Inst, 60-65; ASST PROF BIOCHEM, MED COL & ASSOC PROF CHEM, UNIV ALA, BIRMINGHAM, 65- *Mem:* AAAS; Am Chem Soc; Electrochem Soc. *Res:* Electrochemistry and chemical kinetics; surface phenomena. *Mailing Add:* Univ Col Dept of Chem Univ of Ala Birmingham AL 35294

JOHNSON, RICHARD T, b Grosse Pointe Farms, Mich, July 16, 31; m 54; c 4. NEUROLOGY, VIROLOGY. *Educ:* Univ Colo, AB, 53, MD, 56. *Prof Exp:* Teaching fel neurol & neuropath, Harvard Med Sch, 59-61; fel microbiol, John Curtin Sch Med, Canberra, Australia, 62-64; from asst prof to assoc prof neurol, Sch Med, Case Western Reserve Univ, 64-69; assoc prof microbiol, 69-74, DWIGHT D EISENHOWER-UNITED CEREBRAL PALSY PROF NEUROL, SCH MED, JOHNS HOPKINS UNIV, 69-, PROF MICROBIOL, 74-; NEUROLOGIST, JOHNS HOPKINS HOSP, 69- *Concurrent Pos:* First neurol asst, Univ Newcastle, Eng, 61-62; assoc neurologist, Cleveland Metrop Gen Hosp, Ohio, 64-69; asst neurologist, Highland View Hosp, Cleveland, 64-69; mem comn, Asn Res Nervous & Ment Dis, 64, 69-77; hon prof, Univ Peruana Cayetano Heredia, 80. *Honors & Awards:* Weil Award, Am Asn Neuropath, 67; Sydney Farber Res Award, 74 & 76; Humboldt Prize, 75; Weinstein-Goldson Award, 79; Gordon Wilson Medal, 80. *Mem:* Am Fedn Clin Res; Am Soc Clin Invest; Int Brain Res Orgn; Am Asn Neuropath; Am Neurol Asn. *Res:* Clinical neurology; pathogenesis of viral infections of the nervous system. *Mailing Add:* Dept of Neurol Johns Hopkins Univ Med Sch Baltimore MD 21205

JOHNSON, RICHARD T(ERRELL), b Shreveport, La, July 28, 39; m 61; c 2. MECHANICAL ENGINEERING. *Educ:* Mo Sch Mines, BSME, 62, MS, 64; Univ Iowa, PhD(mech eng), 67. *Prof Exp:* Instr eng mech, Univ Mo-Rolla, 62-64; instr mech eng, Univ Iowa, 64-66; from asst prof to assoc prof, 67-77, PROF MECH ENG, UNIV MO-ROLLA, 77- *Mem:* Am Soc Mech Engrs; Instrument Soc Am; Soc Automotive Engrs; Sigma Xi. *Res:* Mechanical engineering design; control systems and instrumentation; alternate fuels for transportation engines; improved efficiency of combustion engines. *Mailing Add:* Dept of Mech & Aerospace Eng Univ of Mo Rolla MO 65401

JOHNSON, RICHARD WILLIAM, b Denver, Colo, July 11, 50; m 75; c 1. BIO-ORGANIC CHEMISTRY, ELECTRO-ORGANIC CHEMISTRY. *Educ:* Northwestern Univ, BA & MS, 72; Columbia Univ, MPhil, 74, PhD(chem), 76. *Prof Exp:* ASST PROF ORG CHEM, HARVARD UNIV, 77- *Mem:* Am Chem Soc. *Res:* New synthetic procedures based on organic electrochemical reactions; haptea-antibody interactions as model systems for enzymes. *Mailing Add:* 12 Oxford St Cambridge MA 02138

JOHNSON, ROBERT ALAN, b New York, NY, Jan 2, 33; m 54; c 3. SOLID STATE PHYSICS, MATERIALS SCIENCE. *Educ:* Harvard Univ, AB, 54; Rensselaer Polytech Inst, PhD(physics), 62. *Prof Exp:* Scientist physics, Brookhaven Nat Lab, 62-69; PROF MAT SCI, UNIV VA, 69- *Mem:* Am Phys Soc; AAAS; Am Inst Mining, Metall & Petrol Engrs. *Res:* Theoretical study of interatomic forces, defects and radiation damage in metals; use is made of computer simulation techniques and computer solutions of kinetic equations. *Mailing Add:* Dept of Mat Sci Univ of Va Charlottesville VA 22901

JOHNSON, ROBERT BRITTEN, b Cortland, NY, Sept 24, 24; m 47; c 3. GEOLOGY. *Educ:* Syracuse Univ, AB, 49, MS, 50; Univ Ill, PhD(geol), 54. *Prof Exp:* Asst, Syracuse Univ, 47-50; asst, State Geol Surv, Ill, 51-53, asst geologist, 53-54; asst prof geol & staff geologist, Syracuse Univ, 54-55; sr geologist & geophysicist, C A Bays & Assocs, 55-56; from asst prof to prof geol, Purdue Univ, 56-66; prof geol & head dept geol & geog, DePauw Univ, 66-67; chmn dept geol, 69-73, prof geol prog, 73-77, head earth resources actg dept, 79-80, PROF GEOL, COLO STATE UNIV, 67- *Concurrent Pos:* Lectr, Univ Ill, 55-56; indust consult, 62-; mem comt A2L01, Transp Res Bd; mem comt A2L05, Transp Res Bd, 75-, chmn comt A2L01, 76-82; geologist, US Geol Surv, 76- *Mem:* Fel Geol Soc Am; Int Asn Math Geol. *Res:* Engineering geology, especially landslides and geophysical and remote sensing applications; statistical geology. *Mailing Add:* Dept of Earth Resources Colo State Univ Ft Collins CO 80523

JOHNSON, ROBERT CHANDLER, b Detroit, Mich, Oct 19, 30; m 55; c 4. SOLID STATE PHYSICS, ANALYTICAL CHEMICAL PHYSICS. *Educ:* Univ Mich, BS, 52; State Univ Iowa, MA, 57; Stanford Univ, PhD(physics), 62. *Prof Exp:* Res physicist, 62-73, res physicist res & develop planning, 73-75, res physicist thermal anal, 75-78, SUPVR ANAL CHEM PHYSICS, CENT RES & DEVELOP DEPT, E I DU PONT DE NEMOURS & CO INC, 78- *Concurrent Pos:* Vis scientist, Am Inst Physics, 72-75. *Mem:* NAm Thermal Anal Soc (secy, 79-); Am Phys Soc; Am Chem Soc; Sigma Xi. *Res:* Magnetic field effects on triplet excitons; exciton physics of organic crystals; Kapitza resistance in liquid helium; low temperature physics; thermal analysis. *Mailing Add:* Exp Sta E I Du Pont de Nemours & Co Inc Wilmington DE 19898

JOHNSON, ROBERT ED, b Highland Park, Ill, Nov 14, 42; m 64; c 2. MEDICINAL CHEMISTRY. *Educ:* Univ Wis, BS, 64; Univ Minn, PhD(org chem), 68. *Prof Exp:* RES CHEMIST & GROUP LEADER MED CHEM, STERLING-WINTHROP RES INST, STERLING DRUG CO, 68- *Mem:* Am Chem Soc. *Res:* Synthesis of novel heterocyclic and aromatic compounds that may have useful medicinal properties. *Mailing Add:* Sterling-Winthrop Res Inst Rensselaer NY 12144

JOHNSON, ROBERT EDWARD, b Chicago, Ill, July 3, 39; m 70; c 2. PLANETARY SCIENCE. *Educ:* Colo Col, BA, 61; Wesleyan Univ, MA, 63; Univ Wis, Madison, PhD(physics), 68. *Prof Exp:* Res fel, Queen's Univ, Belfast, Ireland, 68-69; asst prof physics, Southern Ill Univ, 69-71; ASSOC PROF ENG PHYSICS, UNIV VA, 71- *Concurrent Pos:* NATO fel, Univ Copenhagen, 76; vis scinetist, Ctr Earth & Planetary Physics, Harvard Univ, 77-78; fac fel, Argonne Nat Lab, 82; NSF & NASA grants prin investr, 78-; consult, Dept Physics, Denver Univ, 70 & Bell Tel Lab, 79- *Mem:* Am Phys Soc; Am Geol Phys Union; Am Astron Soc. *Res:* Atomic and molecular physics; problems of interest in the Jovian magnetosphere, and interaction of ionizing radiations with solids and surfaces. *Mailing Add:* Dept Nuclear Eng & Eng Physics Univ Va Charlottesville VA 22901

JOHNSON, ROBERT EUGENE, b Conrad, Mont, Apr 8, 11; m 35; c 2. PHYSIOLOGY, ANIMAL NUTRITION. *Educ:* Univ Wash, BS, 31; Oxford Univ, BA, 34, PhD(biochem), 35; Harvard Univ, MD, 41. *Prof Exp:* Asst & assoc, Fatigue Lab, Harvard Univ, 35-42, asst prof indust physiol, 42-46; dir, Med Nutrit Lab, US Army, 46-49; prof physiol, Univ Ill, Urbana, 49-73; prof biol, Knox Col, 73-79, coordr, Knox-Rush Med Prog, 73-79; PRES, HORN OF THE MOON ENTERPRISES, MONTPELIER, VT, 79- *Concurrent Pos:* Head dept physiol, Univ Ill, 49-60, dir hons prog, 58-67; NSF sr res fel, 57-58; Guggenheim fel, 64-65; consult physician, Presby-St Lukes Hosp, Chicago, 73- *Mem:* Am Physiol Soc; Am Soc Clin Invest. *Res:* Physiological responses in man to stresses of work, environment and diet; metabolism of poikilotherms; history of environmental physiology. *Mailing Add:* Horn of the Moon RFD 1 Montpelier VT 05602

JOHNSON, ROBERT F, b Crestwood, Ky, Mar 20, 29; m 53; c 4. TEXTILE ENGINEERING. *Educ:* Univ Ky, BS, 51; Ga Inst Technol, MS, 58; Swiss Fed Inst Technol, PhD(indust & eng chem), 63. *Prof Exp:* Res chemist, Dow Chem Co, 58-65; assoc prof textile eng, Ga Inst Technol, 65-66; res sect mgr, Phillips Petrol Co, 66-68, consult, 69-70; prof textile eng & dir, Chem Processes Lab, Textile Res Ctr, Tex Tech Univ, 68-72; PROF TEXXTILES & CLOTHING, UNIV MINN, 72-, ASSOC DIR, GRAD STUDIES, 80- *Mem:* Am Asn Textile Chem & Colorists; Am Chem Soc; Brit Soc Dyers & Colourists; Am Coun Consumer Interests. *Res:* Physical and chemical properties of textile materials; textile chemical unit operations and processes; chemistry of dyes; modification of visually- and tactily-sensed properties of natural and synthetic fibers. *Mailing Add:* PO Box 80025 St Paul MN 55108

JOHNSON, ROBERT GLENN, b Green Mountain, Iowa, Dec 12, 22; m 49; c 5. ELECTROPHYSICS. *Educ:* Case Inst Technol, BS, 47; Iowa State Col, PhD(physics), 52. *Prof Exp:* Asst physics, Iowa State Col, 49-52; proj engr, Bendix Aviation Corp, 52-55; sr res physicist, 55-67, STAFF SCIENTIST, HONEYWELL RES CTR, HOPKINS, 67- *Mem:* Inst Elec & Electronics Engrs; Am Phys Soc; AAAS; Sigma Xi. *Res:* Corona degradation of materials; climatology; gas discharge phenomena; ultraviolet light sensor technology. *Mailing Add:* 12814 March Circle Minnetonka MN 55343

JOHNSON, ROBERT GUDWIN, b Milwaukee, Wis, Nov 23, 27; m 58; c 4. ORGANIC CHEMISTRY. *Educ:* Marquette Univ, BS, 49; Iowa State Col, PhD(chem), 54. *Prof Exp:* Asst chem, Iowa State Col, 49-53; from instr to assoc prof, 54-65, chmn dept, 66-75, PROF CHEM, XAVIER UNIV, OHIO, 65- *Mem:* AAAS; Am Chem Soc. *Res:* Hunsdiecker/Borodine reaction; oxygen-containing heterocycles; hypolipidemic agents; anti-cancer compounds; aromatic substitution. *Mailing Add:* Dept of Chem Xavier Univ Cincinnati OH 45207

JOHNSON, ROBERT H(OWARD), b Chicago, Ill, Mar 16, 20; m 42; c 2. MECHANICAL ENGINEERING. *Educ:* Univ Ill, BS, 42; Rensselaer Polytech Inst, PhD, 58. *Prof Exp:* Student engr adv eng prog, Gen Elec Co, 42-43, engr, Gas Turbine Div, 43-45, mech engr, Res Lab, 45-68, mgr combustion develop, Gas Turbine Prod Div, 68-76; BLDG SUPT ENG, GILLEY CO, INC, 76- *Mem:* AAAS; Am Soc Mech Engrs; Air Pollution Control Asn. *Res:* Hypersonic gas dynamics; general fluid mechanics; turbomachinery; combustion; physical chemistry. *Mailing Add:* Gilley Co Inc 421 SW Sixth Ave Portland OR 97204

JOHNSON, ROBERT H, b Montreal, Que, June 23, 36. DENTISTRY. *Educ:* McGill Univ, BSc, 58, DDS, 62; Ind Univ, MSD, 64; Univ Wash, cert periodontics, 71; Am Bd Oral Med, dipl; FRCD(C). *Prof Exp:* Asst prof dent, McGill Univ, 64-66; asst prof dent & dir hosp dent serv, Med Ctr, Univ Ky, 66-69; from assoc prof to prof dent, Univ Western Ont, 71-80, chmn div periodont, 78-80; PROF PERIODONT & CHMN DEPT PERIODONT, UNIV WASHINGTON SCH DENT, SEATTLE, 80- *Concurrent Pos:* Chief oral diag clin, Montreal Gen Hosp, 64-66. *Mem:* Am Acad Periodont; fel Am Acad Oral Path. *Res:* Effects of tetracyclines on teeth and bone; dentinal hypersensitivity; pulpal hyperemia; effects of restorative materials on the dental pulp; chemotherapeutic plaque control. *Mailing Add:* Dept Periodont sm-44 Univ Wash Sch Dent Seattle WA 98195

JOHNSON, ROBERT HALL, organic chemistry, see previous edition

JOHNSON, ROBERT HUGH, b Chicago, Ill, Nov 25, 29; m 54; c 4. ENGINEERING. *Educ:* Univ Ill, BS, 52; Univ Mich, MS(aeronaut eng) & MS(instrumentation eng), 54. *Prof Exp:* Test engr, Pratt & Whitney Div, United Aircraft Corp, 52; engr, Bendix Systs Div, Bendix Corp, 57-61; mgr display systs, Strand Eng Co, 61-62; prod mgr, Data Display Inc, 62-64; mgr systs anal, 64-68, mgr long range planning, 68-69, dir earth resource surv progs, 69-70, DIR EARTH RESOURCES TECHNOL SATELLITE, SATELLITE IMAGE PROCESSING SYST DEVELOP PROG, BENDIX AEROSPACE SYSTS DIV, BENDIX CORP, 70- *Res:* Engineering program management; engineering development of advanced systems for remote sensing and image data processing. *Mailing Add:* 3641 Larchmont Ann Arbor MI 48105

JOHNSON, ROBERT JOSEPH, b Toppenish, Wash, Feb 8, 15; m 41; c 3. ANATOMY. *Educ:* Iowa State Teachers Col; Univ Iowa, MD, 43. *Prof Exp:* Asst anat, Col Med, Univ Iowa, 38-41; from instr to assoc prof, Sch Med, Univ Wash, 46-57, prof anat & surg, 57; prof gross & neurol anat & head dept, Sch Med, WVa Univ, 57-63; PROF ANAT & CHMN DEPT, GRAD SCH MED, UNIV PA, 63-. *Concurrent Pos:* Consult, Madigan Army Hosp, Tacoma, Wash, 49-57 & Vet Admin Hosp, Seattle, Wash, 50-57; lectr, Western State Hosp, Tacoma, 51-57; consult, USPHS Hosp, 52-57; assoc prof surg, Sch Med, Univ Wash, 55-57. *Mem:* Fel Am Acad Forensic Sci; Am Asn Anatomists. *Res:* Human anatomy; peripheral nerves; venous system of lower limb; congenital anomalies. *Mailing Add:* Dept of Anat Univ of Pa Grad Sch of Med Philadelphia PA 19104

JOHNSON, ROBERT KARL, b Worthington, Minn, May 7, 44; m 75. ICHTHYOLOGY. *Educ:* Occidental Col, AB, 66; Univ Calif, San Diego, PhD(marine biol), 72. *Prof Exp:* Res assoc ecol, Chesapeake Biol Lab, Univ Md, 71-72; asst cur fishes, 72-75, assoc cur, 75-81, CUR FISHES & CHMN DEPT ZOOL, FIELD MUS NATURAL HIST, 81- *Concurrent Pos:* Asst prof earth sci, Univ Notre Dame, 74; adj asst prof biol sci, Northern Ill Univ, 74-79, adj assoc prof, 79- *Mem:* Am Soc Ichthyologists & Herpetologists; Soc Syst Zool; AAAS. *Res:* Systematics, ecology and zoogeography of marine fishes. *Mailing Add:* Div Fish Field Mus Natural Hist Roosevelt Rd at Lake Shore Dr Chicago IL 60605

JOHNSON, ROBERT L(AWRENCE), b Glasgow, Mont, June 18, 19; m 45; c 3. MECHANICAL ENGINEERING. *Educ:* Mont State Univ, BS, 42. *Prof Exp:* Mech engr, Langley Mem Aeronaut Lab, Nat Adv Comt Aeronaut, 42-43, from mech engr to supvry mat res engr, 43-71, chief lubrication br, Lewis Res Ctr, NASA, 63-75; RETIRED. *Concurrent Pos:* Lubrication consult, 62-; chmn, Gordon Res Conf Friction, Lubrication & Wear, 74; US deleg & chmn group experts wear eng mat, Orgn Econ Coop & Develop, 64-73; adj prof mech eng, Rensselaer Polytech Inst, 75- *Honors & Awards:* IR 100 Award, 66 & 73; Alfred E Hunt Award, Am Soc Lubrication Engrs, 61 & 65, Nat Award, 71; Tribology Gold Medal, Brit Inst Mech Engrs, 76; Mayo D Hersey Award, Am Soc Mech Engrs, 77. *Mem:* AAAS; Am Soc Testing & Mat; Soc Automotive Engrs; fel Am Soc Lubrication Engrs (pres, 68-69); fel Brit Inst Mech Engrs. *Res:* Lubrication, friction and wear in seals, bearings and other mechanical components and lubricants for extreme environments. *Mailing Add:* 5304 W 62nd St Edina MN 55436

JOHNSON, ROBERT L, b Winslow, Ariz, 1920. ENGINEERING. *Educ:* Univ Calif, Berkeley, BS, 41, MS, 42. *Prof Exp:* From mem staff to vpres manned orbiting lab, Douglas Aircraft Co, 46-69; asst secy army for res & develop, Dept of Army, 69-73; corp vpres eng & res, McDonnell Douglas Corp, 73-75; pres, McDonnell Douglas Astronaut Co, 75-80, CORP VPRES-GROUP EXEC, McDONNELL DOUGLAS CORP, 80- *Concurrent Pos:* Mem eng adv coun, Univ Calif. *Honors & Awards:* James H Wyld Mem Award, Am Rocket Soc. *Mem:* Nat Acad Eng; fel Am Inst Aeronaut and Astronaut. *Mailing Add:* McDonnell Douglas Corp 3855 Lakewood Blvd Long Beach CA 90846

JOHNSON, ROBERT LEE, b Dallas, Tex, Apr 28, 26; m 52; c 2. PHYSIOLOGY. *Educ:* Southern Methodist Univ, BS, 47; Northwestern Univ, MD, 51. *Prof Exp:* Intern, Cook County Hosp, Chicago, 51-55; res fel internal med, Southwestern Med Sch, Univ Tex, 55-56; res fel physiol, Grad Sch Med, Univ Pa, 56-57; from instr to assoc prof, 57-69, PROF INTERNAL MED, UNIV TEX HEALTH SCI CTR, DALLAS, 69- *Concurrent Pos:* Assoc ed, J Clin Invest, 72-77; prog chmn, Cardiopulmonary Coun, Am Heart Asn, 79-81, mem, Cardiovascular Develop Res Study Comt, 81-83. *Mem:* Am Asn Physicians; Am Fedn Clin Res; Am Thoracic Soc; Am Physiol Soc; Am Soc Clin Invest. *Res:* Exercise physiology; adaptation to high altitude; control of capillary circulation and diffusing surface in the lung. *Mailing Add:* Univ of Tex Health Sci Ctr 5323 Harry Hines Blvd Dallas TX 75235

JOHNSON, ROBERT LEROY, b Chicago, Ill, Sept 22, 40; m 63; c 2. MATHEMATICS. *Educ:* Augustana Col, Ill, AB, 62; Univ Kans, MA, 65, PhD(math), 67. *Prof Exp:* Asst prof math, Iowa State Univ, 67-68; asst prof, 68-72, assoc prof, 72-80, PROF MATH, AUGUSTANA COL, ILL, 80- *Mem:* Math Asn Am; Am Math Soc. *Res:* Topological rings. *Mailing Add:* Dept of Math Augustana Col Rock Island IL 61201

JOHNSON, ROBERT M, b Oklahoma City, Okla, Mar 28, 39; m 63; c 1. METALLURGICAL ENGINEERING. *Educ:* Univ Okla, BS, 62, MMetEng, 65, PhD(eng sci), 67. *Prof Exp:* Asst prof eng mech & mat sci, 67-71, assoc prof mat sci, 71-79, PROF MECH ENG & MAT SCI, UNIV TEX, ARLINGTON, 79-, ASSOC DEAN GRAD SCH, 80- *Concurrent Pos:* Sr scientist, Vought Corp Advanced Technol Ctr, 77-78. *Mem:* Am Soc Metals; Am Soc Eng Educ; Soc Exp Stress Anal. *Res:* Basic deformation processes in mechanical metallurgy; dislocation mechanisms; fracture mechanics; corrosion. *Mailing Add:* Mech Eng Dept Univ of Tex Arlington TX 76019

JOHNSON, ROBERT MICHAEL, b Brooklyn, NY. BIOCHEMISTRY. *Educ:* Fordham Col, AB, 61; Columbia Univ, PhD(biochem), 70. *Prof Exp:* NIH fel, Cornell Univ, 71-72; instr, 72-73; asst prof, 73-79, ASSOC PROF BIOCHEM, MED SCH, WAYNE STATE UNIV, 79- *Res:* Biochemistry of biological membranes; enzymic catalysis. *Mailing Add:* Dept of Biochem Wayne State Univ Med Sch Detroit MI 48201

JOHNSON, ROBERT O, b Eau Claire, Wis, Feb 27, 21; m 49; c 5. SURGERY, ONCOLOGY. *Educ:* Univ Wis, BS, 44, MD, 48; Am Bd Surg, dipl, 62. *Prof Exp:* Pvt pract, NDak, 51-57; resident physician, Univ Wis Hosps, 57-61; from instr to assoc prof surg, 61-71, from asst prof to assoc prof clin oncol, 63-71, PROF SURG & CLIN ONCOL, CHMN CENT ONCOL GROUP & DIR DIV CLIN ONCOL, SCH MED, UNIV WIS-MADISON, 71- *Concurrent Pos:* Consult, Vet Admin Hosps, Madison, Wis, 63-71. *Mem:* Am Col Surgeons; Am Soc Clin Oncol; Am Asn Cancer Res; Pan-Pac Surg Asn; Am Asn Cancer Educ. *Res:* Improvement in clinical care of the cancer patient. *Mailing Add:* Div of Clin Oncol Univ of Wis Sch of Med Madison WI 53706

JOHNSON, ROBERT OSCAR, b Detroit, Mich, May 7, 26; m 61; c 3. APPLIED MATHEMATICS. *Educ:* Univ Mich, Ann Arbor, BS(eng) & BS(math), 46, MS, 49; Univ Ill, Urbana, MS, 52; Ohio State Univ, PhD(math), 75. *Prof Exp:* Sr engr, ITT Labs, 50-52; procurement rep aircraft systs, Repub Aviation, Inc, 52-53; admin engr, Teterboro Div, Bendix Corp, 54-58; proposal mgr altitude control systs, Aerospace Div, Walter Kidde & Co, Inc, 58-62; res specialist, Columbus Div, NAm Rockwell, Inc, 64-68; PROF MATH, FRANKLIN UNIV, 68-, DIV CHMN, ENG TECHNOL, 81- *Concurrent Pos:* Teaching assoc, asst math, Ohio State Univ, 64-69; prof engr, Data Control Ctr, Ohio State Hwy Dept, 69-75. *Mem:* NY Acad Sci. *Res:* Mathematical modeling of transportation systems. *Mailing Add:* PO Box 30722 Gahanna OH 43230

JOHNSON, ROBERT R(OYCE), b Madison, Wis, June 20, 28; m 53; c 3. ENGINEERING. *Educ:* Univ Wis, BS, 50; Yale Univ, MEng, 51; Calif Inst Technol, PhD, 56. *Prof Exp:* Res physicist, Hughes Aircraft Co, Calif, 51-55; engr, Gen Elec Co, 55-56, mgr, Comput Lab, 56-59, mgr eng, Comput Dept, 59-64; dir eng, 64-68, vpres eng, 68-80, VPRES ADVAN TECHNOL, BURROUGHS CORP, DETROIT, 80- *Mem:* Fel Inst Elec & Electronics Engrs. *Res:* Computer technology; logic design; sequential analysis. *Mailing Add:* Burroughs Corp Burroughs Pl Detroit MI 48232

JOHNSON, ROBERT REINER, b Chicago, Ill, June 8, 32; m 67; c 1. ORGANIC CHEMISTRY. *Educ:* Brown Univ, ScB, 54; Rice Univ, PhD(chem), 58. *Prof Exp:* Res assoc chem, Johns Hopkins Univ, 58-59; group leader, 59-67, SCIENTIST, BROWN & WILLIAMSON TOBACCO CORP, 67- *Mem:* Am Chem Soc; Phytochem Soc NAm. *Res:* Physical organic chemistry and chemistry of natural products. *Mailing Add:* Brown & Williamson Tobacco Corp Res Dept PO Box 539 Louisville KY 40201

JOHNSON, ROBERT S, b Pikeville, Ky, Nov 23, 37. MATHEMATICS. *Educ:* Georgetown Col, BS, 59; Univ NC, MA, 62, PhD(ring theory), 66. *Prof Exp:* From instr to assoc prof, 65-75, PROF MATH & HEAD DEPT, WASHINGTON & LEE UNIV, 75- *Mem:* Am Math Soc; Math Asn Am. *Res:* Group theory and ring theory; conditions implying commutativity. *Mailing Add:* Dept of Math Washington & Lee Univ Lexington VA 24450

JOHNSON, ROBERT SHEPARD, b Wilkinsburg, Pa, Nov 24, 28; m 59; c 3. NUMERICAL ANALYSIS. *Educ:* Northwestern Univ, BS, 50, MS, 51; Univ Pa, PhD(math), 59. *Prof Exp:* Res assoc, Inst Coop Res, 53-59; ENGR, RCA CORP, 59- *Mem:* Am Math Soc; Soc Indust & Appl Math. *Res:* Approximation theory; moments. *Mailing Add:* 2102 Brandeis Ave Riverton NJ 08077

JOHNSON, ROBERT W, JR, b Staunton, Va, Sept 12, 24; m 50; c 2. GEOLOGY, GEOPHYSICS. *Educ:* Univ Ky, BS, 51; Univ Wis, MS, 58. *Prof Exp:* Geophysicist, US Geol Surv, 51-56, geologist, 57-61; supvr, Mineral Resources Sec, Tenn Valley Authority, 61-79; CHIEF GEOLOGIST, TENN DIV GEOL, 79- *Mem:* Geol Soc Am; Soc Econ Geologists; Geophys Union; Am Inst Mining, Metall & Petrol Engrs; Am Inst Prof Geologists. *Res:* Airborne geophysical surveys; Precambrian mineral deposits; geological studies to interpret geophysics; mineral resources in economic development program. *Mailing Add:* Tenn Div Geology Dempster Bldg 305 W Springdale Ave Knoxville TN 37917

JOHNSON, ROBERT WALTER, b New York, NY, Mar 11, 30; m 61; c 2. ECOLOGY. *Educ:* Hofstra Univ, BA, 58, MA, 59; Cornell Univ, PhD(wildlife mgt), 73. *Prof Exp:* Res asst nematol, USDA, 56-57; ASSOC PROF BIOL, HOFSTRA UNIV, 59-61 & 65- *Concurrent Pos:* Marine conserv biologist, Town Oyster Bay, NY, 67-; terrestrial ecologist, Grumman Ecosyst Corp, 74-; pres, R W Johnson & Assoc, Environ Anal Inc, 74- *Mem:* Wildlife Soc; Ecol Soc Am. *Res:* Estuarine ecology; ecology of marsh birds; environmental impact analysis. *Mailing Add:* Dept of Biol Hofstra Univ Hempstead NY 11550

JOHNSON, ROBERT WARD, b Hampton, Va, Dec 19, 29; m 55; c 4. MARINE SCIENCES, OPERATIONS RESEARCH. *Educ:* Va Polytech Inst & State Univ, BS, 50; Pa State Univ, MS, 54; NC State Univ, PhD(marine sci), 75. *Prof Exp:* Develop engr, Philco Corp, 52-53, E I du Pont de Nemours & Co, Inc, 54-57; design develop res engr, Carrier Corp, 57-63; res & develop engr, 63-70, RES SCIENTIST MARINE SCI, LANGLEY RES CTR, NASA, 70- *Mem:* Am Soc Photogram. *Res:* Application of remote sensing (aircraft and satellite) techniques to monitor pollution sources and to study processes in marine ecosystems. *Mailing Add:* Langley Res Ctr NASA Mail Stop 272 Hampton VA 23665

JOHNSON, ROBERT WELLS, b Hartford, Conn, Apr 21, 38; m 64; c 3. MATHEMATICS. *Educ:* Amherst Col, AB, 59; Mass Inst Technol, MS, 61, PhD(math), 64. *Prof Exp:* From instr to assoc prof, 64-75, PROF MATH, BOWDOIN COL, 75- *Mem:* Math Asn Am; Am Math Soc. *Res:* Algebra and number theory. *Mailing Add:* Dept of Math Bowdoin Col Brunswick ME 04011

JOHNSON, ROBERT WILLIAM, polymer science, see previous edition

JOHNSON, ROBERT WILLIAM, JR, b Jacksonville, Fla, Oct 9, 27; m 57; c 4. ORGANIC CHEMISTRY. *Educ:* Univ Fla, BS, 53, PhD(org chem), 59; Purdue Univ, MS, 56. *Prof Exp:* Res chemist, Ethyl Corp, 59-62; supt compound develop dept, Chem Div, Union Bag-Camp Paper Corp, 62-65, supt prod develop dept, 65-67; mgr chem div, Prod Develop Dept, 67-73, SR CHEMIST, CHEM APPLN DEVELOP DEPT, UNION CAMP CORP, 73- *Mem:* Am Chem Soc; Am Oil Chemists Soc; NY Acad Sci. *Res:* Tall oil; fatty acids; organic synthesis; organometallics; organofluorine compounds; instrumental methods of analysis; Ziegler type catalysts; stereoregular polymers. *Mailing Add:* Chem Div Union Camp Corp Savannah GA 31402

JOHNSON, ROGER ALVIN, b Chicago, Ill, Jan 15, 26; m 56; c 1. INDUSTRIAL ORGANIC CHEMISTRY. *Educ:* Univ Fla, BSc, 50, MS, 52, PhD, 55. *Prof Exp:* PHYS ORG CHEMIST, E I DU PONT DE NEMOURS & CO, INC, 54- *Concurrent Pos:* Vis instr, Univ Del. *Res:* Organic pigments; quinacridones. *Mailing Add:* E I du Pont de Nemours & Co Inc Newport DE 19804

JOHNSON, ROGER D, JR, b Richmond, Va, May 27, 30; m 55; c 3. MATHEMATICS. *Educ:* Dartmouth Col, AB, 51; Univ Va, MA, 53, PhD(math), 56. *Prof Exp:* Instr math, Univ Va, 55-56; asst prof, 56-61, ASSOC PROF MATH, GA INST TECHNOL, 61- *Mem:* Am Math Soc; Math Asn Am. *Res:* Homology theory and its relationship to certain topics of general topology such as connectedness and dimension. *Mailing Add:* Ga Inst of Technol Sch of Math Atlanta GA 30332

JOHNSON, ROGER W, b Kalamazoo, Mich, May 4, 29; m 58; c 2. VIROLOGY. *Educ:* Valparaiso Univ, BS, 52; Univ Ky, MS, 58, PhD(microbiol), 63. *Prof Exp:* Microbiologist, US Army Biol Labs, 63-69; prin investr, US Army Biol Defense Res Ctr, 69-72; HEAD DEPT VIRUS PROD, FREDERICK CANCER RES CTR, NAT CANCER INST, 72- *Mem:* AAAS; Am Soc Microbiol; Sigma Xi. *Res:* Parameters of seed stock development; scale up and production of oncogenic or suspected oncogenic viruses from tissue culture. *Mailing Add:* 7003 Summerfield Dr Frederick MD 21701

JOHNSON, ROLAND NORMAN, medicinal chemistry, organic chemistry, see previous edition

JOHNSON, ROLLAND PAUL, b Stewartville, Minn, Jan 1, 41; div; c 2. PHYSICS. *Educ:* Univ Calif, Berkeley, AB, 64, PhD(physics), 70. *Prof Exp:* Res asst physics, Lawrence Berkeley Lab, Univ Calif, Berkeley, 67-70, res assoc, 70-74; PHYSICIST, FERMI NAT ACCELERATOR LAB, 74- *Concurrent Pos:* Vis scientist, Inst High Energy Physics, Serpukhov, USSR, 72-73 & Europ Orgn Nuclear Res, Geneva, Switzerland, 80-81. *Mem:* Am Phys Soc. *Res:* Accelerators; experimental particle physics; experimental high energy physics. *Mailing Add:* Fermilab PO Box 500 Batavia IL 60510

JOHNSON, RONALD CARL, b Milwaukee, Wis, Sept 5, 35; m 60; c 2. INORGANIC CHEMISTRY. *Educ:* Lawrence Col, BS, 57; Northwestern Univ, PhD(chem), 61. *Prof Exp:* From asst prof to assoc prof, 61-73, PROF CHEM, EMORY UNIV, 73- *Mem:* AAAS; Am Chem Soc. *Res:* Reactions of compounds of transition metals; mechanisms of reactions. *Mailing Add:* Dept of Chem Emory Univ Atlanta GA 30322

JOHNSON, RONALD DOYLE, b Collinsville, Okla, Feb 9, 45; div; c 1. NATURAL PRODUCTS CHEMISTRY. *Educ:* Okla State Univ, BS, 67, PhD(biochem), 72. *Prof Exp:* Res fel bio-org chem, Univ Ill, 72-74; SR CHEMIST, RES LABS, ELI LILLY & CO, 74- *Mem:* Am Chem Soc; Sigma Xi. *Res:* Antimicrobial agents research; high performance liquid chromatography; marine natural products. *Mailing Add:* Eli Lilly & Co Bldg BB M539 Indianapolis IN 46206

JOHNSON, RONALD ERNEST, b Portland, Ore, Oct 14, 39; m 68; c 2. PHYSICAL OCEANOGRAPHY. *Educ:* Ore State Univ, BS, 62, MS, 63, PhD(phys oceanog), 72. *Prof Exp:* Assoc sr engr, Lockheed-Calif Co, 63-64; asst prof oceanog, 68-78, ASSOC PROF OCEANOG, OLD DOMINION UNIV, 78- *Mem:* AAAS; Am Geophys Union. *Res:* Circulation and distribution of intermediate waters of the worlds oceans. *Mailing Add:* Dept Oceanog Old Dominion Univ Norfolk VA 23508

JOHNSON, RONALD GENE, b Detroit, Mich, Nov 14, 41; m 64; c 2. RADIATION BIOPHYSICS, RADIOLOGICAL HEALTH. *Educ:* Eastern Mich Univ, AB, 63; Univ Kans, MS, 68, PhD(radiation biophys), 70. *Prof Exp:* High sch teacher, Mich, 64 & Ohio, 64-65; asst prof, 70-74, assoc prof, 74-78, PROF PHYSICS, MALONE COL, 78-, EXEC VPRES, 81- *Concurrent Pos:* Radiation biologist, Aultman Hosp, 73-; consult, Med Physics Serv, Inc, 73-; vis assoc prof radiation biophys, Univ Kans, 76-77; assoc prof clin radiation biophys radiol, Northeastern Ohio Univs Col Med, 78-. *Mem:* Am Asn Physics Teachers; Sigma Xi. *Res:* Effect of glucose on the sensitivity of Escherichia coli to Mitomycin C; radiation repair mechanisms; radiation-induced atrophy of bone; quality control in diagnostic radiology; effects of diagnostic x-rays during first trimester of pregnancy. *Mailing Add:* Off Acad Affairs Malone Col Canton OH 44709

JOHNSON, RONALD GORDON, b Embro, Ont, Feb 7, 39; m 69. NUCLEAR PHYSICS, BIOPHYSICS. *Educ:* Queen's Univ, Ont, BSc, 60, MSc, 62; Univ Liverpool, PhD(particle physics), 68. *Prof Exp:* Asst prof, 66-71, ASSOC PROF PHYSICS, TRENT UNIV, 71- *Concurrent Pos:* Nat Res Coun Can res grant, 71-72. *Mem:* AAAS; Can Asn Physicists; Am Phys Soc; Am Asn Physics Teachers. *Res:* Neutron spectroscopy; weak interactions; photonuclear reactions; radiation effects on cells. *Mailing Add:* Dept of Physics Trent Univ Peterborough ON K9J 7B8 Can

JOHNSON, RONALD ROY, b De Smet, SDak, Dec 8, 28; m 55; c 4. BIOCHEMISTRY, ANIMAL NUTRITION. *Educ:* SDak State Col, BS, 50, MS, 52; Ohio State Univ, PhD(biochem), 54. *Prof Exp:* Asst, Exp Sta, SDak State Col, 50-52; from asst prof to prof animal sci, Ohio Agr Res & Develop Ctr, 55-69; prof animal sci & indust, Okla State Univ, 69-74; prof animal sci & head dept, Univ Tenn, Knoxville, 74-81; ASSOC DIR, OKLA AGR EXP STA, OKLA STATE UNIV, 81- *Concurrent Pos:* Consult, Nutrit Surv Team, Comt Nutrit Nat Defense, Spain, 58 & Chile, 60; USPHS sr fel, Univ Calif, Berkeley, 65-66. *Mem:* Am Soc Animal Sci; Am Dairy Sci Asn; Am Inst Nutrit. *Res:* Nutrition, physiology and biochemistry of Rumen microorganisms and ruminant animals; nutrition of farm livestock. *Mailing Add:* 139 Agr Hall Okla State Univ Stillwater OK 74074

JOHNSON, RONALD SANDERS, b Chicago, Ill, March 9, 52. PHYSICAL BIOCHEMISTRY, INORGANIC BIOCHEMISTRY. *Educ:* Northwestern Univ, BA, 73, PhD(biochem & molecularbiol), 78. *Prof Exp:* Instr biochem & res tech, Northwestern Univ, 78; fel, NIH & Miller Inst Basic Res Sci, Univ Calif, Berkeley, 78-81; ASST PROF BIOCHEM & PHYS BIOCHEM, SCH MED, EAST CAROLINA UNIV, 81- *Mem:* Am Chem Soc; Sigma Xi. *Res:* Application of biophysical techniques to explore the mechanism of gene regulation in the bacterium B subtilis during sporulation, encompassing protein-nucleic acid as well as protein-protein interactions. *Mailing Add:* Dept Biochem Sch Med East Carolina Univ Greenville NC 27834

JOHNSON, ROSE MARY, b Ashland, Ky, July 14, 27. ZOOLOGY. *Educ:* Hood Col, AB, 49; Univ Va, MA, 56, PhD(biol), 62. *Prof Exp:* Res asst microbiol, Sch Med, Univ Va, 51-55; instr biol, Sweet Briar Col, 59-61; asst prof, Old Dom Col, 61-62; assoc prof, 62-74, PROF BIOL, MARY WASHINGTON COL, 74- *Mem:* Fel AAAS; Am Soc Zoologists. *Res:* Taxonomic relationships of crayfishes using serological techniques such as agar diffusion and precipitin reactions; calcium deposition and dissolution during the molting cycle of crayfishes. *Mailing Add:* Dept of Biol Mary Washington Col Fredericksburg VA 22401

JOHNSON, ROSS BYRON, b Ladd, Ill, June 4, 19; m 42. ENVIRONMENTAL GEOLOGY, FUELS GEOLOGY. *Educ:* Univ NMex, BS, 46, MS, 48. *Prof Exp:* Geologist, US Geol Surv, 48-62, res geologist, 62-74; CONSULT GEOLOGIST, 74- *Mem:* Fel Geol Soc Am; Sigma Xi. *Res:* Formation of sand dunes, rock glaciers, joints, and faults and their effects on the environment and engineering structures; stratigraphic, structural, and igneous geology; geologic mapping and photo-geology; petroleum and coal resources of the Southern Rocky Mountains and adjacent high plains of Colorado and New Mexico. *Mailing Add:* 240 Quay St Lakewood CO 80226

JOHNSON, ROSS GLENN, b McKeesport, Pa, Oct 5, 42; m 64; c 2. CELL BIOLOGY. *Educ:* Augustana Col, Ill, BA, 64; Iowa State Univ, MS, 66, PhD(cell biol), 68. *Prof Exp:* Asst prof cytol & zool, 68-73, assoc prof zool, Univ Minn-Minneapolis, 73-76, assoc prof, 76-80, PROF GENETICS & CELL BIOL, UNIV MINN-ST PAUL, 80- *Mem:* AAAS; Am Soc Cell Biol. *Res:* Involvement of cell junctions in cell communication; structure and function of cell organelles. *Mailing Add:* Dept of Genetics & Cell Biol Univ of Minn St Paul MN 55108

JOHNSON, ROTHER RODENIOUS, b Victoria, Va, Sept 2, 18; m 45; c 1. BACTERIOLOGY, IMMUNOLOGY. *Educ:* Va State Col, BS, 48; Mich State Univ, MS, 50, PhD(bact, immunol), 54. *Prof Exp:* Asst prof bact, Meharry Med Col, 54-63; PROF BACT, TENN STATE UNIV, 63- *Concurrent Pos:* Lederle med fac award, 56-59. *Mem:* Am Soc Microbiol. *Res:* Electron microscopic observations on primary and serially passaged radiation-induced myeloid leukemias of the RF mouse. *Mailing Add:* 4110 Hydes Ferry Rd Nashville TN 37218

JOHNSON, ROWLAND EDWARD, b Detroit, Mich, Sept 7, 22; m 46; c 4. SOLID STATE CHEMISTRY. *Educ:* Univ Calif, BS, 47; Ore State Col, PhD(chem), 51. *Prof Exp:* From instr to asst prof chem, Fla State Univ, 50-57; sect leader, Br Mat Res, Cent Res Labs, Tex Instruments Inc, 57-71, br head, Phys Sci Res Lab, 71-78; CONSULT, 78- *Mem:* Am Chem Soc. *Res:* Semiconductors; high purity materials; inorganic reactions and mechanisms; magnetic materials. *Mailing Add:* 4323 Middleton Road Dallas TX 75229

JOHNSON, ROY ALLEN, b Bemidji, Minn, July 26, 37; m 63; c 2. ORGANIC CHEMISTRY. *Educ:* Univ Minn, BCh, 59, PhD(org chem), 65; Univ BC, MSc, 61. *Prof Exp:* SR RES SCIENTIST CHEM, UPJOHN CO, 65- *Mem:* Am Chem Soc; AAAS. *Res:* Synthetic organic chemistry; prostaglandin chemistry; microbial oxidations; stereochemistry. *Mailing Add:* Exp Chem Res Upjohn Co Kalamazoo MI 49001

JOHNSON, ROY ANDREW, b Oak Park, Ill, Mar 20, 39; m 67; c 2. MATHEMATICS. *Educ:* St Olaf Col, BA, 60; Univ Iowa, PhD(math), 64. *Prof Exp:* Asst lectr math, Univ Lagos, 64-65; asst prof, Univ Col, Addis Ababa, 65-66; asst prof, 66-73, ASSOC PROF MATH, WASH STATE UNIV, 73- *Mem:* Am Math Soc; Math Asn Am. *Res:* Measure theory and integration. *Mailing Add:* Dept of Math Wash State Univ Pullman WA 99164

JOHNSON, ROY MELVIN, b Chicago, Ill, Sept 8, 26; m 52; c 4. MICROBIOLOGY. *Educ:* Univ Chicago, AB, 49, MS, 51; Univ NMex, PhD(bact), 55. *Prof Exp:* Instr biol, Ariz State Univ, 52-53; asst, Univ NMex, 53-55; from asst prof to assoc prof microbiol, 55-65, PROF MICROBIOL, ARIZ STATE UNIV, 65- *Concurrent Pos:* NIH fel, Ind Univ, 63-64. *Mem:* AAAS; Am Soc Microbiol; fel Am Acad Microbiol. *Res:* Bacterial physiology and systematics. *Mailing Add:* Dept of Microbiol Ariz State Univ Tempe AZ 85281

JOHNSON, ROY RAGNAR, b Chicago, Ill, Jan 23, 32; m 63. PLASMA PHYSICS, SOLID STATE PHYSICS. *Educ:* Univ Minn, BEE, 54, MSEE, 56, PhD(elec eng), 59. *Prof Exp:* Asst solid state physics, Univ Minn, 54-56; res scientist, Boeing Sci Res Lab, 59-70; asst prof, 70-74, ASSOC PROF PHYSICS, UNIV BC, 74- *Concurrent Pos:* Vis scientist, Royal Inst Technol, Sweden, 63-64. *Mem:* AAAS; Am Phys Soc; Inst Elec & Electronics Eng. *Res:* Fluids physics; solids fluctuations. *Mailing Add:* Dept of Physics Univ of BC Vancouver BC V6T 1W5 Can

JOHNSON, RULON EDWARD, JR, b Logan, Utah, June 5, 29; m 54; c 6. PHYSICAL CHEMISTRY. *Educ:* Utah State Univ, BS, 51; Stanford Univ, PhD(phys chem), 57. *Prof Exp:* From res chemist to sr res chemist, Jackson Lab, 57-69, RES ASSOC, ORG CHEM DEPT, EXP STA, E I DU PONT DE NEMOURS & CO, INC, 69- *Mem:* AAAS; fel Am Chem Soc. *Res:* Thermodynamics, especially application to interfaces; molecular interactions at interfaces. *Mailing Add:* Cent Res & Develop Dept E I du Pont de Nemours & Co Inc Wilmington DE 19899

JOHNSON, RUSSELL CLARENCE, b Wausau, Wis, Aug 3, 30; m 55; c 3. MICROBIOLOGY. *Educ:* Univ Wis, BS, 57, MS, 58, PhD(microbiol), 60. *Prof Exp:* Res assoc microbiol, Univ Wis, 60; Nat Acad Sci-Nat Res Coun res assoc, 60-61; res microbiologist, Ft Detrick, Md, 61-62; from instr to assoc prof, 62-74, PROF MICROBIOL, MED SCH, UNIV MINN, MINNEAPOLIS, 74- *Concurrent Pos:* USPHS spec fel, 63-65, res grant, 66-; mem subcomt taxon Leptospira & subcomt taxon Spirochaetales, Int Comt Syst Bact, 69-; mem comn viral infections, Armed Forces Epidemiol Bd, 70-73. *Mem:* AAAS; Am Soc Microbiol; Soc Exp Biol & Med. *Res:* Biology of pathogenic and nonpathogenic spirochetes. *Mailing Add:* Dept of Microbiol Univ of Minn Med Sch Minneapolis MN 55455

JOHNSON, RUSSELL DEE, JR, b Granite City, Ill, Dec 10, 28; m 53; c 4. OPERATIONS RESEARCH. *Educ:* Univ Rochester, BS, 50; Univ Calif, PhD(phys chem), 54. *Prof Exp:* Chemist, Dow Chem Co, Mich, 53-56; physicist, 56-62, SR SCIENTIST, OPERS RES, INC, 62- *Mem:* Am Chem Soc; Am Phys Soc; Inst Mgt Sci. *Res:* Weapons systems analysis; applied game theory. *Mailing Add:* 1902 Ventura Ave Silver Spring MD 20902

JOHNSON, RUSSELL TINGEY, b Brigham, Utah, Oct 3, 19; m 46; c 4. PLANT GENETICS, AGRONOMY. *Educ:* Utah State Agr Col, BS, 44; Univ Minn, MS, 48, PhD(agron, plant genetics), 50. *Prof Exp:* Plant breeder sugar beets, Spreckels Sugar Co, Amstar Corp, 50-54, dir agr res, 54-60, dir res, 60-62, vpres agr & res, 62-74, vpres & dir res & develop, Spreckels Sugar Div, 74-81; RETIRED. *Concurrent Pos:* Adj exec lectr, Santa Clara Univ, Ca. *Mem:* Am Soc Agron; Soil Sci Soc Am; Am Soc Sugar Beet Technologists. *Res:* Inheritance of disease and insect resistance in sugar beets; utilization of male sterility and polyploidy for the commercial utilization of hybrid vigor in sugar beets. *Mailing Add:* 255 Darrell Rd Hillsborough CA 94010

JOHNSON, SAMUEL BRITTON, b Canyon, Tex, Apr 25, 26; m 49; c 3. OPHTHALMOLOGY. *Educ:* WTex State Col, BS, 46; Tulane Univ, MD, 48, dipl ophthal, 50; Am Bd Ophthal, dipl. *Prof Exp:* PROF OPHTHAL, UNIV MISS MED CTR, 56- *Concurrent Pos:* trustee, Miss Sch for Deaf, Miss Sch for Blind & Miss Voc Rehab for Blind. *Mem:* Am Col Surgeons; Asn Res Vision & Ophthal. *Mailing Add:* Div of Ophthal Univ of Miss Med Ctr Jackson MS 39216

JOHNSON, SAMUEL EDGAR, II, b San Jose, Calif, Sept 27, 44; m 70. MARINE ECOLOGY. *Educ:* Stanford Univ, BS, 66, PhD(biol), 73. *Prof Exp:* Scholar biophys ecol, Dept Bot, Univ Mich, 72-73; ASST PROF ZOOL, CLARK UNIV, 73- *Concurrent Pos:* Res assoc, New Eng Res Inc, 73- *Honors & Awards:* Arthur C Giese Award, Stanford Univ, 73. *Mem:* Am Soc Zoologists; Ecol Soc Am; Am Meteorol Soc; Sigma Xi; Int Biometeorol Soc. *Res:* Biophysical ecology, microclimatology and biometeorology of the marine rocky intertidal region with emphasis on heat and mass transfer processes as they affect intertidal organisms, particularly amphipods and molluscs; estuarine ecology and coastal zone resource management. *Mailing Add:* Dept of Biol Clark Univ Worcester MA 01610

JOHNSON, SHARON LEIJOY, organic chemistry, biochemistry, see previous edition

JOHNSON, SHIRLEY A(NDERSON), JR, b Lansing, Mich, Sept 13, 19; m 43; c 3. MECHANICAL ENGINEERING. *Educ:* Duke Univ, BS, 42; Univ Denver, MS, 60. *Hon Degrees:* DSc, Oglethorpe Univ, 65. *Prof Exp:* Engr, Gen Elec Co, 42-46; instr mech eng, Col Eng, 47-49, with Denver Res Inst, 48-52, DIR, DENVER RES INST, UNIV DENVER, 52- *Concurrent Pos:* Ed, Proceedings, Nat Conf Admin Res, 61-; dir, Cent Investment Corp, 64- & Denver Chamber of Commerce, 64-; mem, Governor's Adv Comt Oil Shale, 64-, vchmn, Governor's Sci Comn, 65-; mem exec comt, Eng Col Res Coun. *Mem:* Am Inst Aeronaut & Astronaut; Am Soc Eng Educ. *Res:* Research administration. *Mailing Add:* Denver Res Inst Univ of Denver University Park Denver CO 80210

JOHNSON, SHIRLEY MAE, b Ironwood, Mich, May 26, 40; m 75. REPRODUCTIVE PHYSIOLOGY. *Educ:* Northern Mich Col, BS, 62; Mich State Univ, MS, 65, PhD(physiol), 70; Univ Mich, MPH, 72. *Prof Exp:* Teacher pub sch, Grand Rapids, Mich, 62-63; lab technician, Endocrine Res Unit, 65-70, asst to vpres, Off Res Develop, 71, UNIV PROF FAMILY MED, COL OSTEOP MED, MICH STATE UNIV, 72- *Concurrent Pos:* Res consult, Mich Cancer Found, 70; educ consult, Tri-County Family Planning Ctr, Lansing, Mich, 75- *Mem:* Am Pub Health Asn; Am Asn Sex Educr, Counr & Therapists; Sigma Xi. *Res:* influence on health care of knowledge, attitudes, concerns and beliefs patients have toward reproductive physiology and family planning; contraceptive use and advertising. *Mailing Add:* Dept of Family Med Mich State Univ East Lansing MI 48824

JOHNSON, STANLEY HARRIS, b Fresno, Calif, Dec 3, 38; m 65; c 1. AUTOMATIC CONTROL SYSTEMS. *Educ:* Univ Calif, Berkeley, BS, 62, MS, 67, PhD(mech eng), 73. *Prof Exp:* Design engr physics res, Lawrence Radiation Lab, 61-65; syst engr comput sales, Int Bus Mach Co, 65-67; sr engr comput control, Mobil Res & Develop Corp, 67-70; from asst prof to assoc prof, 73-79, PROF, DEPT MECH ENG & MECH, LEHIGH UNIV, 79- *Concurrent Pos:* Fac fel, Dryden Flight Res Ctr, 74 & 75; DuPont assoc prof, DuPont Univ Sci & Eng grant, 78-80. *Mem:* Am Soc Mech Engrs; Am Asn Univ Prof. *Res:* Numerical simulation of dynamical systems; development of the methodology of simulation; simulation validity and verification; numerical solution of partial differential equations; application of optimal control theory. *Mailing Add:* Dept of Mech Eng & Mech Lehigh Univ Bethlehem PA 18015

JOHNSON, STANLEY O(WEN), b Bismarck, NDak, Dec 28, 30; m 57; c 2. NUCLEAR ENGINEERING, ARCHITECTURAL ACOUSTICS. *Educ:* Univ Colo, BS, 53. *Prof Exp:* Student engr, Westinghouse Elec Corp, 53-54, scientist, Bettis Atomic Power Lab, 54-60, supvr nuclear reactor kinetics, 60-61; group leader reactor safety & dynamics anal, Atomic Energy Div, Phillips Petrol Co, 61-63, sect chief anal & data processing, 63-68, mgr, Spert Proj, 68-69; mgr, Idaho Nuclear Corp, 69-71; mgr, Aerojet Nuclear Co, 71-73; PRES, INTERMOUNTAIN TECHNOL, INC, 73-, DIR, ITI-JAPAN, INC, 81-; DIR, ENE-CON, INC, 78- *Concurrent Pos:* Dir, Ene-Con, Inc, 78-81. *Mem:* AAAS; fel Am Nuclear Soc. *Res:* Nuclear reactor safety research; nuclear reactor dynamics; computer simulation of nuclear reactors. *Mailing Add:* PO Box 1604 Idaho Falls ID 83401

JOHNSON, STEPHEN CURTIS, b Philadelphia, Pa, July 13, 44; m 68; c 2. COMPUTER SCIENCE. *Educ:* Haverford Col, AB, 63; Columbia Univ, MS, 64, PhD(math), 68. *Prof Exp:* MEM TECH STAFF COMPUT SCI, BELL TEL LABS, 68- *Mem:* AAAS; Asn Comput Mach; Ny Acad Sci. *Res:* Cluster analysis; computerized algebra systems; design and implementation of computer languages and systems; integrated circuit design. *Mailing Add:* Bell Tel Labs Rm 2C-559 600 Mountain Ave Murray Hill NJ 07974

JOHNSON, STURE ARCHIE MANSFIELD, b Morgan, Ore, Apr 24, 07; m 36. MEDICINE. *Educ:* Univ Ore, BA, 34, MD, 38; Am Bd Dermat & Syphilol, dipl. *Prof Exp:* Fel dermat & syphilol, Univ Ore, 39-41; res assoc, Univ Mich, 41-44, asst prof, 44-46; prof dermat & syphilol & head dept, 46-77, EMER PROF DERMAT & SYPHILOL, UNIV WIS-MADISON, 77- *Concurrent Pos:* Consult, Vet Admin Hosp, Madison. *Mem:* Soc Invest Dermat; Am Dermat Asn; AMA; fel Am Col Physicians; fel Am Acad Dermat. *Res:* Mycology; syphilis; dermatology. *Mailing Add:* 10306 Hutton Dr Sun City AZ 85351

JOHNSON, TERRELL KENT, b Inglewood, Calif, Nov 23, 47. GENETICS. *Educ:* Univ Calif, San Diego, BA, 70; Calif State Univ, Northridge, MS, 72; Univ Tex, Austin, PhD(zool), 76. *Prof Exp:* Res fel genetics, Calif Inst Technol, 76-77; USPHS trainee, 77-79, RES ASSOC GENETICS, KANS STATE UNIV, 79- *Mem:* Genetics Soc Am; Soc Develop Biol; Sigma Xi. *Mailing Add:* Div of Biol Kans State Univ Manhattan KS 66506

JOHNSON, TERRY CHARLES, b St Paul, Minn, Aug 8, 36; m 58; c 3. MOLECULAR BIOLOGY, VIROLOGY. *Educ:* Hamline Univ, BS, 58; Univ Minn, Minneapolis, MS, 61, PhD(microbiol), 64. *Prof Exp:* USPHS res asst, Univ Minn, Minneapolis, 58-64; USPHS fel molecular biol, Univ Calif, Irvine, 64-66; from asst prof to assoc prof, Med Sch, Northwestern Univ, Chicago, 66-73, prof virol, 73-77; PROF & DIR, DIV BIOL, KANS STATE UNIV, 77- *Mem:* AAAS; Teratology Soc; Am Soc Neurochem; Am Soc Microbiol. *Res:* Developmental aspects of macromolecular synthesis of mammalian cells and its role in host resistance to viral infection; regulation of protein and nucleic acid metabolism in brain; neural development. *Mailing Add:* Div of Biol Kans State Univ Manhattan KS 66506

JOHNSON, TERRY R(OBERT), b Chicago, Ill, Nov 16, 32; m 56; c 4. CHEMICAL ENGINEERING. *Educ:* Rice Univ, BA, 54, BS, 55; Univ Mich, MS, 56, PhD(chem eng), 59. *Prof Exp:* Assoc chem engr, Argonne Nat Lab, 58-74; sr process engr, Aglomet, Inc, 74-75; CHEM ENGR, ARGONNE NAT LAB, 75- *Concurrent Pos:* Vis prof, Iowa State Univ, 70. *Mem:* Am Inst Chem Engrs; Am Nuclear Soc. *Res:* Radiation chemistry of aqueous systems; nuclear fuel recovery; chemistry of liquid metals and salts; open-cycle MHD. *Mailing Add:* Argonne Nat Lab 9700 S Cass Ave Argonne IL 60439

JOHNSON, TERRY WALTER, JR, b Waukegan, Ill, Jan 13, 23; m 48; c 3. MYCOLOGY. *Educ:* Univ Ill, BS, 48; Univ Mich, MS, 49, PhD(bot), 51. *Prof Exp:* Instr bot, Univ Mich, 50-51; mycologist, Chem Corps Biol Labs, Camp Detrick, 51-53; asst prof biol, Univ Miss, 53-54; from asst prof to assoc prof bot, 54-65, chmn dept, 63-71, PROF BOT, DUKE UNIV, 65- *Concurrent Pos:* Guggenheim fel, 60-61; mem systs panel, NSF, 63-66; ed-in-chief, Mycologia, 81- *Mem:* Bot Soc Am; Mycol Soc Am; Brit Mycol Soc. *Res:* Aquatic phycomycetes; Mycetozoa; marine fungi. *Mailing Add:* Dept of Bot Duke Univ Durham NC 27706

JOHNSON, THEODORE REYNOLD, b Willmar, Minn, Mar 20, 46; m 70; c 3. MICROBIOLOGY, IMMUNOLOGY. *Educ:* Augsburg Col, BA, 68; Univ Ill Med Ctr, MS, 70, PhD(microbiol), 73. *Prof Exp:* Res asst microbiol, Rush-Presby St Lukes Hosp, 68-72; asst prof biol, Mankato State Univ, 72-77; ASST PROF BIOL, ST OLAF COL, 77- *Concurrent Pos:* Consult virol, St Joseph's Hosp, 74-77, microbiol, Donaldson Corp, 77- *Mem:* Am Soc Microbiol; AAAS. *Res:* Study of the immune response of humans to colonic cancer and screening the excretory products for carcinogens; cancer and immune systems of hibernating animals. *Mailing Add:* Dept of Biol St Olaf Col Northfield MN 55057

JOHNSON, THOMAS, b Hallitsville, Tex, Feb 12, 36; m 56; c 3. ECONOMETRICS, RESOURCE ECONOMICS. *Educ:* Univ Tex, Austin, BA, 57; Tex Christian Univ, MA, 62; NC State Univ, MES, 67, PhD(economet & statist), 69. *Prof Exp:* Nuclear engr, Convair, Fortworth, Tex, 57-61; eng specialist, LTV-Vought Aeronaut Div, Dallas, Tex, 61-64; oper analyst, Res Triangle Inst, 64-69; assoc prof, 74-78, PROF ECON & STATIST, NC STATE UNIV, 78- *Mem:* Am Statist Asn; Am Econ Asn; Economet Soc; Southern Econ Asn. *Res:* Statistics and mathematics applications to economic questions; analysis of qualitative and limited variables in analysis of problems in renewable resources, human, natural and agricultural. *Mailing Add:* 1217 Wellington Lane Cary NC 27511

JOHNSON, THOMAS CHARLES, b Virginia, Minn, Aug 15, 44; m 66; c 2. LIMNOLOGY. *Educ:* Univ Wash, BS, 67; Univ Calif, San Diego, PhD(oceanog), 75. *Prof Exp:* Officer, Off Res & Develop, US Coast Guard, 69-71; res asst, Scripps Inst Oceanog, 71-74, fel, 75; asst prof geol, Univ Minn, Minneapolis, 75-80, assoc prof, 80-81; ASSOC PROF GEOL, UNIV MINN, DULUTH, 81- *Concurrent Pos:* Prin investr, res grants, NSF, Environ Protection Agency & Nat Oceanic & Atmospheric Admin, 75- *Mem:* AAAS; Am Soc Limnologists & Oceanographers; Geol Soc Am. *Res:* Sedimentological processes in large lakes, including physical processes in deep offshore regions and chemical processes including studies of silica budgets, total organic carbon and lead geochronology. *Mailing Add:* Dept Geol Univ Minn Duluth MN 55812

JOHNSON, THOMAS EUGENE, b Denver, Colo, June 19, 48. DEVELOPMENTAL GENETICS. *Educ:* Mass Inst Technol, BS, 70; Univ Wash, PhD(genetics), 75. *Prof Exp:* Fel genetics, Cornell Univ, 75-77; FEL MOLECULAR, CELLULAR, DEVELOP BIOL, UNIV COLO, 77- *Mem:* Genetics Soc Am; Soc Develop Biol; AAAS; Gerontol Soc Am. *Res:* Genetics of aging in the nematode; control of early embryonic development in the nematode caenorhabditis elegans; Caenorhabditis elegans. *Mailing Add:* Molecular Cellular & Develop Biol Univ of Colo Boulder CO 80309

JOHNSON, THOMAS HAWKINS, b Boston, Mass, Nov 11, 43; m 74; c 1. PHYSICS. *Educ:* US Mil Acad, BS, 65; Univ Calif, Davis, MS, 68, PhD(appl physics), 74. *Prof Exp:* Physicist nuclear weapons design, US Air Force Weapons Lab, 65-67 & US Defense Nuclear Agency, 69-71; physicist magnetic fusion energy, Lawrence Livermore Lab, Univ Calif, 72-74; chief physics sect high power lasers, US Air Force Weapons Lab, 75-77; instr & assoc prof lit, physics & philos, US Mil Acad, 77-80, dir sci res lab & asst dean acad res, 80-81; SPEC ASST TO PRESIDENT'S SCI ADV, WASHINGTON, DC, 81- *Concurrent Pos:* Consult, US Defense Nuclear Agency, 74-81, Lawrence Livermore Lab, Univ Calif, 75-78, Los Alamos Lab, Univ Calif, 79-, US Defense Advan Res Projs Agency, 75-, Defense Sci Bd, 79-, dir energy res & under secy energy, 79-; mem staff fusion rev comt, Off Energy Res, US Dept Energy, 78-79. *Mem:* Am Phys Soc; AAAS. *Res:* Computational physics; high power gas lasers; magnetic confinement fusion; inertial confinement fusion; plasma instabilities and diffusion; nuclear weapons design and atmospheric effects; hydrodynamics. *Mailing Add:* Off Sci & Technol Policy Exec Off of the Pres Washington DC 20500

JOHNSON, THOMAS L, b Little Rock, Ark, Dec 18, 32. BIOLOGY. *Educ:* Lynchburg Col, BA, 56; Univ Va, MA, 58, PhD(biol), 64. *Prof Exp:* From instr to assoc prof, 59-74, PROF BIOL, MARY WASHINGTON COL, UNIV VA, 74- *Mem:* Am Micros Soc. *Res:* Invertebrate histology; understanding of evolutionary relationships through studies of male reproductive systems of decapod crustaceans. *Mailing Add:* Dept of Biol Mary Washington Col Fredericksburg VA 22401

JOHNSON, THOMAS LYNN, b Westmount, Que, June 20, 19; nat US; m 56. ORGANIC CHEMISTRY. *Educ:* Amherst Col, BA, 42; Univ Wis, MS, 44, PhD(org chem), 46. *Prof Exp:* PATENT AGENT, STERLING-WINTHROP RES INST, 46- *Mem:* Am Chem Soc. *Res:* Medicinal chemistry; steroids; patent law. *Mailing Add:* Sterling-Winthrop Res Inst Rensselaer NY 12144

JOHNSON, THOMAS NICK, b Davenport, Iowa, Aug 20, 23; m 55. NEUROANATOMY. *Educ:* St Ambrose Col, BS, 44; Mich State Col, MS, 49; Univ Mich, PhD(neuroanat), 52. *Prof Exp:* From instr to asst prof physiol, Mich State Col, 46-54; from asst prof to assoc prof, 54-69, PROF ANAT, SCH MED, GEORGE WASHINGTON UNIV, 69- *Concurrent Pos:* Nat Inst Neurol Dis & Blindness spec trainee, Dept Anat, Med Ctr, Univ Calif, Los Angeles, 58-59. *Mem:* AAAS; Am Asn Anatomists; assoc Am Acad Neurologists. *Res:* Comparative neurology of mammalian midbrain and forebrain; experimental neurology of extrapyramidal motor systems; electron microscopy of human primary brain tumors. *Mailing Add:* Sch of Med George Washington Univ Washington DC 20037

JOHNSON, THOMAS RAYMOND, b Washington, DC, July 8, 44; m 73; c 1. CELL BIOLOGY. *Educ:* Harvard Univ, BA, 66; Case Western Reserve Univ, PhD(biol), 71. *Prof Exp:* Instr, Univ Ill, Chicago Med Ctr, 71-73; SR RES ASSOC, CASE WESTERN RESERVE UNIV, 73- *Res:* The contribution of ribosomal RNA to ribosome structure and protein synthesis in eukaryotes. *Mailing Add:* 3062 Huntington Shaker Heights OH 44120

JOHNSON, THOMAS W, dermatology, see previous edition

JOHNSON, THYS B(RENTWOOD), b Duluth, Minn, Mar 20, 34; m 58; c 3. MINING ENGINEERING, OPERATIONS RESEARCH. *Educ:* Univ Minn-Minneapolis, BS, 56, MS, 58; Univ Calif, Berkeley, PhD(opers res), 68. *Prof Exp:* Mining engr, Minn Ore Opers, US Steel Corp, 58-61, mathematician, 61-64; mining methods res engr, US Bur Mines, 64-68, mining engr, 68, supvry mining engr, 68-69, supvry opers res analyst, 69-72; PROF MINING ENG, COLO SCH MINES, 72-, HEAD DEPT, 74- *Mem:* Opers Res Soc Am; Am Inst Mining, Metall & Petrol Engrs. *Res:* Research and development of operations research techniques as applied to problems of the mineral industry; developed mathematical and dynamic programming techniques for open pit mine planning and production scheduling. *Mailing Add:* Dept of Mining Eng Colo Sch of Mines Golden CO 80401

JOHNSON, TOM MILROY, b Northville, Mich, Jan 16, 35; m 59; c 2. INTERNAL MEDICINE. *Educ:* Col Wooster, BA, 56; Northwestern Univ, Ill, MD, 61. *Prof Exp:* Am Thoracic Soc fel pulmonary dis, Med Ctr, Univ MIch, 67-68; asst prof med, 68-71, assoc prof med, Col Human Med, Mich State Univ, 71-77; PROF INTERNAL MED & DEAN SCH MED, UNIV NDAK, 77- *Concurrent Pos:* Asst dean, Grand Rapids Campus, Univ Mich, 71-77. *Mem:* Am Thoracic Soc; fel Am Col Physicians; Am Col Chest Physicians. *Res:* Relationship of community and university medical education; pulmonary disease. *Mailing Add:* Univ NDak Sch Med Rm 125 Grand Fork ND 58202

JOHNSON, TORRENCE VAINO, b Rockville Centre, NY, Dec 1, 44; m 67. PLANETARY SCIENCES, ASTRONOMY. *Educ:* Washington Univ, BS, 66; Calif Inst Technol, PhD(planetary sci), 70. *Prof Exp:* Mem res staff planetary astron, Planetary Astron Lab NASA, Mass Inst Technol, 69-71; Nat Res Coun resident res assoc planetology, 71-73, sr scientist, 73-74, res scientist, 80-81, SR RES SCIENTIST, JET PROPULSION LAB, CALIF INST TECHNOL, 81-, GROUP SUPVR OPTICAL ASTRON GROUP, 74- *Concurrent Pos:* Mem Uranus sci adv comt, NASA, 73-75, mem outer planets probe working group, 74-76; scientist, Proj Galileo, NASA, 77- & mem, Voyager Imaging Sci Team, 78-; vis assoc prof planetary sci, Calif Inst Technol, 81-83. *Mem:* Sigma Xi; AAAS; Am Astron Soc (secy-treas, 77-); Int Astron Union; Am Geophys Union. *Res:* Telescopic observations of planetary surfaces and atmospheres; laboratory studies of silicates and ices; interpretation of planetary spacecraft data. *Mailing Add:* Jet Propulsion Lab 183-301 4800 Oak Grove Dr Pasadena CA 91101

JOHNSON, VANCLIFF, b Jamaica, West Indies, Oct 2, 39; m 60; c 4. SOLID STATE CHEMISTRY. *Educ:* Howard Univ, BSc, 65; Brown Univ, PhD(chem), 69. *Prof Exp:* RES CHEMIST, CENT RES DEPT, E I DU PONT DE NEMOURS & CO, INC, 68- *Mem:* Sigma Xi. *Res:* Synthesis, crystal growth and crystal chemistry of covalent inorganic compounds. *Mailing Add:* Cent Res Dept E I du Pont de Nemours & Co Inc Wilmington DE 19898

JOHNSON, VARD HAYES, b Pleasant Grove, Utah, Sept 17, 09; m 46; c 2. GEOLOGY. *Educ:* Brigham Young Univ, BS, 32, MS, 33; Univ Ariz, PhD(econ geol), 41. *Prof Exp:* Student instr mineral & geol, Brigham Young Univ, 31-33; jr engr & geologist, New Park Mines Co, Utah, 36 & Park City Consol Mining, 37-39; recorder, US Geol Surv, Ariz, 40-42, geologist, Washington, DC, 43-53; geologist, Columbia Geneva Steel, 53-64; CONSULT GEOLOGIST, 64- *Mem:* Geol Soc Am; Soc Econ Geol; Am Inst Prof Geol; Am Inst Mining, Metall & Petrol Eng; Can Inst Mining & Metall. *Res:* Geology of coal, especially coking coals of western North America; geology and ore deposits of Helvetia mining district, Pima County, Arizona; ferrous and non-ferrous ores of western North America. *Mailing Add:* 2784 Bryant Palo Alto CA 94306

JOHNSON, VERN RAY, b Salt Lake City, Utah, Feb 25, 37; m 59; c 4. ELECTRICAL ENGINEERING, SOCIAL TECHNOLOGY. *Educ:* Univ Utah, BS, 60, PhD(elec eng, physics), 65. *Prof Exp:* Res asst, Microwave Devices Lab, Utah, 60-64; res engr, Microwave Electronics Div, Teledyne, Inc, 64-67; assoc prof elec eng, 67-79, ASST DEAN, COL ENG, UNIV ARIZ, 79- *Honors & Awards:* Achievement Award, Inst Elec & Electronics Engrs, 71; Anderson Prize, Univ Ariz, 77. *Mem:* Inst Elec & Electronics Engrs; Am Soc Eng Educ. *Res:* Microwave acoustic amplification; photoelastic interactions in solid materials; surface wave acoustics; engineering manpower system simulation and demand projections; communication; application of engineering techniques to social problems. *Mailing Add:* Dept of Elec Eng Univ of Ariz Tucson AZ 85721

JOHNSON, VERNER CARL, b Chicago, Ill, Sept 14, 43. EXPLORATION GEOLOGY, EXPLORATION GEOPHYSICS. *Educ:* Southern Ill Univ, BA, 67, MS, 70; Univ Tenn, PhD(geol), 75. *Prof Exp:* Instr, Calif State Univ, 72-74; proj geophysicist, Gulf Res & Develop Corp, 74-76; asst prof, Mesa Col, 76-77; GEOLOGIST, BENDIX FIELD ENG CORP, 77- *Concurrent Pos:* Asst prof, Mesa Col, 77- *Mem:* Am Asn Petrol Geologists; Am Geophys Union; Geol Soc Am; Soc Explor Geophysicists. *Res:* Geologic information; rock formation in field; determination of favorable environment for uranium occurrences. *Mailing Add:* Bendix Field Eng Corp PO Box 1569 Grand Junction CO 81502

JOHNSON, VINCENT ARNOLD, b York, Nebr, Jan 5, 28; m 53; c 3. ZOOLOGY, PHYSIOLOGY. *Educ:* Univ Nebr, BSc, 52, MSc, 55, PhD(zool, physiol), 64. *Prof Exp:* Spec instr biol, Univ Tex, 57-61; asst prof, Augustana Col, Ill, 64-67; from asst prof to assoc prof, 67-72, PROF BIOL, ST CLOUD STATE UNIV, 72- *Mem:* Am Soc Zool; Soc Protozoologists; AAAS; Sigma Xi. *Res:* Cellular growth and metabolism. *Mailing Add:* Dept of Biol Sci St Cloud State Univ St Cloud MN 56301

JOHNSON, VIRGIL ALLEN, b Newman Grove, Nebr, June 28, 21; m 43; c 4. AGRONOMY. *Educ:* Univ Nebr, BSc, 48, PhD(agron), 52. *Prof Exp:* Asst agronomist, Univ Nebr, 52-54; RES AGRONOMIST, NCENT REGION, AGR RES SERV, USDA & PROF AGRON, UNIV NEBR-LINCOLN, 54- *Concurrent Pos:* Mem comt genetic vulnerability major crops, Nat Acad Sci, 71, chmn organizing comt for int workshop on seed proteins, 73-74; co-chmn resource comt cereals, NSF/MIT Protein Resources Study, 75. *Honors & Awards:* Gamma Sigma Delta Int Distinguished Serv Award, 69; Crop Sci Soc Am Award, 75. *Mem:* NY Acad Sci; Am Soc Agron; Am Genetics Asn; AAAS; Crop Sci Soc Am (pres, 78). *Res:* Wheat breeding and genetics; genetics and physiology of wheat; protein quantity and nutritional quality. *Mailing Add:* Dept of Agron Univ of Nebr Lincoln NE 68583

JOHNSON, VIVIAN ANNABELLE, b Portland, Ore, July 1, 12. SOLID STATE PHYSICS. *Educ:* Reed Col, BA, 32; Purdue Univ, MS, 34, PhD(physics), 37. *Prof Exp:* Asst physics, 32-37, asst instr, 37-38, from instr to prof physics, 38-79, asst head dept, 73-79, EMER PROF PHYSICS, PURDUE UNIV, WEST LAFAYETTE, 79- *Mem:* AAAS; Am Phys Soc; Am Asn Physics Teachers. *Res:* Solid state physics; theory of electrical semiconductors; transport phenomena. *Mailing Add:* Dept of Physics Purdue Univ West Lafayette IN 47907

JOHNSON, W(ILLIAM) C, b Jamestown, NY, Aug 20, 27; m 55; c 3. CHEMICAL ENGINEERING. *Educ:* Univ Wis, BS, 51, MS, 53, PhD(chem eng), 60. *Prof Exp:* Instr chem eng, Univ Wis, 53-58; sr engr, 58-63, chem engr res specialist, 63-75, SR ENGR SPECIALIST, MINN MINING & MFG CO, 75- *Concurrent Pos:* Adj prof chem eng, Univ Minn, 77- *Mem:* Am Chem Soc; Am Inst Chem Engrs. *Res:* Organic chemical purification and separations; fine particle characterization; reaction kinetics and catalysis; ultraviolet light catalyzed polymerization. *Mailing Add:* Minn Mining & Mfg Co 3M Center 518-1 St Paul MN 55144

JOHNSON, W REED, b Chattanooga, Tenn, Sept 3, 31; m 56; c 3. NUCLEAR ENGINEERING. *Educ:* Va Mil Inst, BS, 53; Univ Va, DSc(eng physics), 62. *Prof Exp:* Shielding engr, Elec Boat Div, Gen Dynamics Corp, 54-55; nuclear engr, Alco Prod, Inc, 55-57; proj engr reactor facility, Va, 58-62, proj dir, Univ Va-Philippine Atomic Energy Comn Proj, 62-64; res dir, 64-66, assoc prof, 66-68, asst dir reactor facil, 66-74, PROF NUCLEAR ENG, UNIV VA, 68- *Concurrent Pos:* Proj engr, Div Reactor Licensing, US Atomic Energy Comn, 68-69; mem, Atomic Safety & Licensing Appeal Bd, 74- *Mem:* Fel Am Nuclear Soc; Am Soc Eng Educ. *Res:* Radiation shielding; reactor safety; experimental engineering. *Mailing Add:* Dept of Nuclear Eng Univ of Va Charlottesville VA 22903

JOHNSON, WALLACE DELMAR, b Idaho Falls, Idaho, June 5, 39; m 58; c 6. ORGANIC CHEMISTRY. *Educ:* Brigham Young Univ, BS, 61; Univ Utah, PhD(org chem), 69. *Prof Exp:* Res chemist, 61-64 & 68-72, PATENT LIAISON, PHILLIPS PETROL CO, 72- *Mem:* Am Chem Soc; Sigma Xi. *Res:* Organophosphorus chemistry; synthesis of rubbers and plastics. *Mailing Add:* 3700 Redbud Lane Bartlesville OK 74003

JOHNSON, WALLACE E, b Chisolm, Minn, Feb 28, 25; m 46; c 5. COMPUTER SCIENCE. *Educ:* Univ Minn, BS, 50. *Prof Exp:* Res engr, High Speed Flight Sta, Nat Adv Comt Aeronaut, 51-53; staff mem, Los Alamos Sci Lab, 53-58; staff mem, Gen Atomic Div, Gen Dynamics Corp, 58-59; staff mem, Los Alamos Sci Lab, 59-60; staff mem, Gen Atomic Div, Gen Dynamics Corp, 60-65; prin res scientist, Honeywell Inc, 65-67, Systs, Sci & Software, 67-71 & Sci Applns Inc, 71-73; CONSULT, COMPUT CODE CONSULTS, 73- *Mem:* Am Phys Soc; Am Sci Affiliation. *Res:* Use of high speed computers for the numerical treatment of radiation flow, neutronics and hydrodynamics; one, two and three dimensional hydrodynamic, strength of materials and radiation codes to solve problems in high energy fluid dynamics. *Mailing Add:* 1680 Camino Redondo Los Alamos NM 87544

JOHNSON, WALLACE W, b LaMoure, NDak, Nov 23, 26; m 51; c 4. PHARMACOLOGY, DENTISTRY. *Educ:* NDak State Col, BS, 50; Univ Iowa, DDS, 57, MS, 58. *Prof Exp:* Asst dent, 57-58; from instr to assoc prof oper dent, 58-65, PROF OPER DENT, COL DENT, UNIV IOWA, 65- *Mem:* Am Dent Asn; Am Col Dentists; Am Asn Dent Res; Am Asn Dent Schs. *Res:* Drugs and their use in dentistry; educational research; dental materials research. *Mailing Add:* Univ of Iowa Col of Dent Iowa City IA 52240

JOHNSON, WALTER C(URTIS), b Weikert, Pa, Jan 6, 13; m 34; c 3. ELECTRONICS. *Educ:* Pa State Col, BSE, 34, EE, 42. *Prof Exp:* Student elec engr, Gen Elec Co, NY, 34-37; from instr to assoc prof, 37-43, chmn dept, 51-65, PROF ELEC ENG, PRINCETON UNIV, 43- *Concurrent Pos:* Resident vis, Bell Labs, 68. *Honors & Awards:* Nat Best Initial Paper Award, Am Inst Elec Engrs, 39; Western Elec Award, Am Soc Eng Educ, 67. *Mem:* Am Soc Eng Educ; Am Phys Soc; fel Inst Elec & Electronics Engrs. *Res:* Semiconductor materials and devices; charge transport and trapping in insulators; insulator reliability. *Mailing Add:* Dept of Elec Eng Eng Quad Princeton Univ Princeton NJ 08540

JOHNSON, WALTER CURTIS, JR, b Princeton, NJ, Feb 11, 39; m 60; c 2. BIOPHYSICAL CHEMISTRY. *Educ:* Yale Univ, BA, 61; Univ Wash, PhD(phys chem), 66. *Prof Exp:* NSF fel, Univ Calif, Berkeley, 66-68; asst prof biophys, 68-72, assoc prof biophys, 72-78, PROF BIOPHYS, ORE STATE UNIV, 78- *Concurrent Pos:* NSF grant circular dichroism & conformation of biopolymers, 68-; USPHS grant, nucleic acid conformation & function, 74-; mem panel equip, NIH, 79; mem panel biol instrumentation, NSF, 80-82. *Mem:* Biophys Soc. *Res:* Spectroscopic properties of biopolymers, principally their circular dichroism, their conformation and resulting biological function. *Mailing Add:* Dept of Biochem & Biophys Ore State Univ Corvallis OR 97331

JOHNSON, WALTER HEINRICK, JR, b Minneapolis, Minn, Sept 20, 28; m 58; c 2. PHYSICS, MASS SPECTROMETRY. *Educ:* Univ Minn, BA, 50, MA, 52, PhD(physics), 56. *Prof Exp:* Res assoc, Univ Minn, 56-57; exp physicist, Knolls Atomic Power Lab, Gen Elec Co, 57-58; from asst prof to assoc prof physics, 58-68, actg chmn physics, 69-70, assoc dean, 71-77, actg dean, 77-79, PROF PHYSICS, UNIV MINN, MINNEAPOLIS, 68-, . *Concurrent Pos:* Mem, Comn on Atomic Classes & Fundamental Constants, Int Union Pure & Appl Physics, 66-72, secy, 72-75; mem, Int Union Pure Appl Chem, 71-73, Comn on Atomic Weights, 75-78. *Mem:* AAAS; fel Am Phys Soc; Am Vacuum Soc; Am Asn Physics Teachers. *Res:* Mass spectroscopy; measurement of atomic masses; nuclear binding energy; neutron cross-section measurements. *Mailing Add:* Sch of Physics 116 Church St SE Minneapolis MN 55455

JOHNSON, WALTER HENRY, b Montreal, Que, Feb 9, 11; m 36; c 2. PHYSIOLOGY. *Educ:* McGill Univ, BSc, 33; Univ Toronto, PhD(physiol), 37. *Prof Exp:* Asst biol, Univ Toronto, 33-37; from instr to asst prof, Sch Med, Georgetown Univ, 39-44; asst prof zool, Univ Western Ont, 44-48; asst prof, Royal Can Air Force Inst Aviation Med, 48-49; physiologist, Defence Res Med Labs, 49-65; assoc prof otolaryngol & dir res, Univ Toronto, 65-76; DIR RES, CONN SMYTHE RES FOUND, 76- *Concurrent Pos:* Fel physiol, McGill Univ, 34-39; hon assoc prof physiol, Univ Toronto; mem staff, St Michael's Hosp; res assoc, Toronto Gen Hosp; consult, US Naval Inst Aerospace Med. *Honors & Awards:* Tuttle Award, Aerospace Med Asn, 56; Skylab Achievement Award, NASA, 74. *Mem:* Can Soc Aviation Med (pres, 73-74); Aerospace Med Asn (vpres, 74); Can Soc Otolaryngol; Int Acad Astronaut; Can Soc AV Med. *Res:* Physiology of vision; physiology of semicircular canals; motion sickness; aerospace medicine. *Mailing Add:* Dept Otolaryngol Univ Toronto 92 College Ct Toronto ON M5S 2R8 Can

JOHNSON, WALTER K, b Minneapolis, Minn, Aug 28, 23; m 50; c 3. ENVIRONMENTAL & CIVIL ENGINEERING. *Educ:* Univ Minn, BCE, 48, MSCE, 51, PhD(sanit eng), 63; Am Acad Environ Eng, dipl, 65. *Prof Exp:* Civil engr, Greeley & Hansen, Consult Engrs, 48-49; asst, Univ Minn, 49-51; sanit engr, Infilco, Inc, Ariz, 51-52 & Toltz, King, Duvall & Anderson, Consult Engrs, Minn, 52-55; lectr civil eng, Univ Minn, Minneapolis, 55-63, from asst prof to prof, 63-75; DIR QUAL CONTROL, METRO WASTE CONTROL COMN, ST PAUL, 75- *Concurrent Pos:* Environ Protection Agency res fel, Brit Water Pollution Res Lab, Steverage, Eng, 70. *Honors & Awards:* Radebaugh Award, Cent States Water Pollution Control Asn, 65. *Mem:* Am Soc Civil Water Pollution Control Asn; Int Asn Water Pollution Res; Am Water Works Asn. *Res:* Biological treatment of waste waters and the removal of nitrogen and phosphorus from waste waters by biological and chemical means. *Mailing Add:* 5321 29th Ave S Minneapolis MN 55417

JOHNSON, WALTER LEE, b Greensboro, NC, May 23, 18; m 50; c 1. AGRONOMY. *Educ:* Agr & Tech Col NC, BS, 42; Univ Ill, MS, 47, PhD, 53. *Prof Exp:* Agronomist, Southern Univ, 47-50; prof agron, 53-77, head dept, 53-67, head dept earth & plant sci, 62-72, PROF & DIR, DIV AGR SCI, FLA A&M, 73- *Mem:* Am Soc Agron; Soil Sci Soc Am. *Res:* Field crops; soils. *Mailing Add:* Dept of Earth & Plant Sci Fla A&M Univ Tallahassee FL 32307

JOHNSON, WALTER RICHARD, b Richmond, Va, Feb 25, 29; m 52. PHYSICS. *Educ:* Univ Mich, BSE, 52, MS, 53, PhD(physics), 58. *Prof Exp:* In str physics, Univ Mich, 57-58; from asst prof to assoc prof, 58-67, PROF PHYSICS, UNIV NOTRE DAME, 67- *Res:* Hydrodynamics; atomic physics; quantum electrodynamics. *Mailing Add:* Dept of Physics Univ of Notre Dame Notre Dame IN 46556

JOHNSON, WARREN CHARLES, b Otter Lake, Mich, Sept 22, 01; m 28; c 3. CHEMISTRY. *Educ:* Kalamazoo Col, BS, 22; Clark Univ, MA, 23; Brown Univ, PhD(chem), 25. *Hon Degrees:* DSc, Kalamazoo Col, 46 & Brown Univ, 60. *Prof Exp:* Res instr chem, Brown Univ, 25-27; from instr to prof, 27-67, chmn dept, 45-55, assoc dean div phys sci, 46-55, dean, 55-59, vpres in chg spec sci progs, 58-67, EMER PROF CHEM & EMER VPRES, UNIV CHICAGO, 67- *Concurrent Pos:* Dir chem div, Clinton Labs, Oak Ridge, 43-46; consult, AEC, 46-; mem gen adv comt, 54-60, chmn, 56-60; mem bd trustees, Kalamazoo Col, 50-; Mellon Inst, 58- & Oak Ridge Inst Nuclear Studies, 58-, Inst Defense Anal, 60- & Atomic Indust Forum, 63-65; mem defense sci bd, Dept Defense, 57-60; mem div comt, NSF, 58-60; consult, Union Carbide Corp, 62- *Honors & Awards:* Presidential Award, Cert Merit, 48; Citation & Medal, AEC, 61. *Mem:* AAAS; Am Chem Soc; Am Nuclear Soc. *Res:* Inorganic chemistry; liquid ammonia solutions; hydrides; rare earths and elements. *Mailing Add:* 946 Bellclaire SE Grand Rapids MI 49506

JOHNSON, WARREN THURSTON, b Charleston, WVa, Apr 22, 25; m 49; c 2. ENTOMOLOGY. *Educ:* Morris Harvey Col, 47; Ohio State Univ, MS, 52; Univ Md, PhD(entom), 56. *Prof Exp:* Asst entom, USPHS, 48-50; from instr to asst prof, Col Agr, Univ Md, 52-62; from asst prof to assoc prof, 62-71, PROF ENTOM, COL AGR, CORNELL UNIV, 71- *Concurrent Pos:* Vis res prof, Univ Calif, Berkeley, 69-70; vis res scientist, Forest Pest Mgt Inst, Can Forest Serv, Ottawa, 77. *Mem:* Entom Soc Am; Entom Soc Can. *Res:* Biology and control of insects and diseases of woody ornamental plants. *Mailing Add:* 1444 Hanshaw Rd Ithaca NY 14850

JOHNSON, WARREN W, b Ackerman, Miss, Jan 13, 23; m 52; c 1. PATHOLOGY. *Educ:* Millsaps Col, BS, 50; Univ Miss, MS, 52, MD, 57. *Prof Exp:* Instr anat, Univ Miss, 52-55; from instr to asst prof path, Col Med, Univ Tenn, Memphis, 64-79; PROF PATH, SCH MED, UNIV MISS, 79- *Mem:* AMA; NY Acad Sci; Int Acad Path; Am Asn Cancer Res. *Res:* Ultrastructural diagnosis of neoplasia; immunohistologic study of tumors containing myosin; collagenous tumors; complications in leukemia; pituitary cytology in steroid therapy; pathology of neuromuscular diseases. *Mailing Add:* Dept Path Univ Miss Med Ctr 2500 N State St Jackson MS 39216

JOHNSON, WAYNE JON, b Elroy, Wis, May 14, 39; m 64; c 3. AUTOMOTIVE ENGINEERING. *Educ:* Univ Wis, BS, 61, MS, 62, PhD(elec eng), 68. *Prof Exp:* Engr, Res Dept, Collins Radio Co, Cedar Rapids, 60 & 61, res engr, 62-64; sr res engr, Lab di Cibernetica, Naples, Italy, 68-69; sr res engr, 69-73, PRIN RES ENG ASSOC, DEPT PHYSICS, FORD MOTOR CO, 73- *Mem:* Inst Elec & Electronics Engrs; Soc Automotive Engrs. *Res:* Nonlinear wave propagation; superconducting devices; semiconductor device physics; combustion research on internal combustion engines; plasma probing techniques; electromagnetic interference phenomena; networking and distributed computing techniques applied to the automobile. *Mailing Add:* 1044 Charlesworth Dearborn Heights MI 48127

JOHNSON, WAYNE ORRIN, b Valley City, NDak, May 26, 42; m 65; c 1. AGRICULTURAL CHEMISTRY. *Educ:* Concordia Col, BA, 64; Mich State Univ, MS, 66; Univ Ore, PhD(org chem), 69. *Prof Exp:* Group leader, 69-76, mgr res farms & liasion activ, 76-79, MGR HYBRID CROPS, AGR PROD RES, AGR-CHEM, ROHM & HAAS CO, 79- *Mem:* Am Chem Soc; Plant Growth Regulator Working Group; Am Seed Trade Asn. *Res:* Synthetic structure-activity chemistry related to biological sciences, especially pesticidal research. *Mailing Add:* 346 Centennial Rd Warminster PA 18974

JOHNSON, WENDEL J, b Oak Park, Ill, July 13, 41; m 64; c 2. ANIMAL ECOLOGY, ZOOGEOGRAPHY. *Educ:* Mich State Univ, BS, 63, MS, 65; Purdue Univ, PhD(mammalian ecol), 69. *Prof Exp:* Asst prof, 69-75, ASSOC PROF BIOL, UNIV WIS CTR-MARINETTE, 75- *Concurrent Pos:* Sigma Xi grant-in-aid, 64, 70; Wis Alumni Res Found fel, 70. *Mem:* AAAS; Ecol Soc Am; Am Soc Mammal; Am Inst Biol Sci. *Res:* Zoogeographical analysis of reptiles and amphibians in the Northern Peninsula of Michigan; population dynamics of small mammals in Isle Royale National Park; population regulation in small mammals; environmental problems from human numbers. *Mailing Add:* Dept of Biol Univ of Wis Ctr Marinette WI 54143

JOHNSON, WENDELL EUGENE, b Minneapolis, Minn, Sept 23, 10; m 46; c 2. CIVIL ENGINEERING. *Educ:* Univ Minn, BSCE, 31. *Prof Exp:* Field off engr, Minn Hwy Dept, 31-33; off engr & specifications writer, Corps Engrs, Dept Army, Conchas Dam, NMex & Caddoa, Colo, 38-40, chief sect civil design, Third Locks, Panama Canal, Diablo Heights, CZ, 40-42, asst construct chief to construct chief, 42-43, chief div eng, Omaha Dist, 46-49, chief eng div, Mo River Div, Omaha, 49-61, chief eng div for civil works, Off Chief of Engrs, Washington, DC, 61-70; INT CONSULT ENGR DAMS & WATER RESOURCES, 70- *Mem:* Nat Acad Eng; Am Soc Civil Engrs; Soc Am Mil Engrs; Nat Soc Prof Engrs. *Mailing Add:* 1524 Woodacre Dr McLean VA 22101

JOHNSON, WENDELL GILBERT, b Wichita, Kans, Feb 19, 22; m 48; c 4. MATHEMATICS. *Educ:* Phillips Univ, BA, 47; Univ Mich, MA, 48; Syracuse Univ, PhD(math), 55. *Prof Exp:* Asst prof math, Phillips Univ, 48-50; asst, Syracuse Univ, 52-55; asst prof, Southern Ill Univ, 55-57; vpres & dean col, 64-69, PROF MATH, HIRAM COL, 57- *Concurrent Pos:* NSF sci fac fel, 61-62. *Mem:* Am Math Soc; Math Asn Am; Asn Comput Mach. *Res:* Algebra; geometry. *Mailing Add:* Dept of Math Hiram Col Hiram OH 44234

JOHNSON, WHITNEY LARSEN, b Brigham City, Utah, July 11, 27; m 54; c 10. STATISTICS, COMPUTER SCIENCE. *Educ:* Utah State Univ, BS, 54; Univ Minn, Minneapolis, MS, 57. *Prof Exp:* Assoc prof statist, Va Polytech Inst & State Univ, 62-68; adminr automated data processing systs, State Coun Higher Educ, Va, 69-72; DIR MGT INFO SERV, NORTHERN MICH UNIV, 72- *Concurrent Pos:* Coordr comput ctr, Va Polytech Inst & State Univ, 62-64 & dir, 64-68. *Mem:* Am Statist Asn; Asn Comput Mach; Asn Educ Data Systs. *Res:* Moments of serial correlation coefficients and computing networks on regional and statewide basis; management information for education. *Mailing Add:* Mgt Info Serv Northern Mich Univ Marquette MI 49855

JOHNSON, WILBUR VANCE, b Bellingham, Wash, Jan 14, 31; m 53. CHEMICAL PHYSICS. *Educ:* Univ Wash, Seattle, BS, 53; Ore State Univ, PhD, 60. *Prof Exp:* Instr chem, Univ Mont, 57-59; asst prof physics, Cent Wash State Col, 60-62; physicist, Res Anal Corp, 62-65; assoc prof physics & chmn dept, Cent Wash State Col, 65-70; exec officer, Am Asn Physics Teachers, Washington, DC, 70-72; assoc prof physics, 72-77, chmn dept geol & physics, 74-78, PROF PHYSICS, CENT WASH UNIV, 77- *Mem:* Fel AAAS. *Res:* Crystallography; color centers in alkali halides; quantum chemistry; solid state physics. *Mailing Add:* 209 E Tenth Ave Ellensburg WA 98926

JOHNSON, WILEY CARROLL, JR, b Asheville, NC, Jan 1, 30; m 51; c 2. PLANT BREEDING. *Educ:* Wake Forest Col, BS, 49; NC State Col, BS, 51, MS, 53; Cornell Univ, PhD(plant breeding), 56. *Prof Exp:* Res agronomist, Cornell Univ, 56-57; assoc prof, 57-69, PROF PLANT BREEDING, AUBURN UNIV, 69- *Mem:* Am Soc Agron; Crop Sci Soc Am; Am Genetics Asn. *Res:* Genetics and breeding of clovers. *Mailing Add:* Dept of Agron & Soils Auburn Univ Auburn AL 36830

JOHNSON, WILFRID E(STILL), b Whitley Bay, Eng, May 24, 05; nat US; c 3. MECHANICAL ENGINEERING. *Educ:* Ore State Col, BS, 30, ME, 39. *Hon Degrees:* DSc, Ore State Col, 59. *Prof Exp:* Design engr household refrigerator, Gen Elec Co, 30-36, commercial refrig, 36-40, sect engr aircraft supercharger, 40-44, engr, Aircraft Gas Turbine Dept, 44-45, mgr eng, Air Conditioning Dept, 45-48, mgr eng design & construct, Hanford Atomic Prod Opers, 48-51, asst gen mgr, 51-52, gen mgr, 52-66; mem, US Atomic Energy Comn, Washington, DC, 66-76; RETIRED. *Honors & Awards:* Citation, Atomic Energy Comn, 65; Gold Medal Award, Am Soc Mech Engrs. *Mem:* Nat Acad Engrs; fel Am Nuclear Soc; fel Am Soc Mech Engrs; Am Acad Polit & Soc Sci; assoc Am Soc Eng Educ. *Mailing Add:* PO Box 963 Richland WA 99352

JOHNSON, WILLARD JESSE, b Theodore, Sask, Apr 27, 16; m 57; c 1. BIOCHEMISTRY. *Educ:* McGill Univ, BSc, 49, PhD(biochem), 52. *Prof Exp:* Dir biochem res, Frank W Horner, Ltd, Que, 55-64; biochemist & head biochem sect, Food & Drug Directorate, 65-77; WITH PHARMACOL HEALTH, PROTECTION BR, HEALTH & WELFARE, CAN, 78- *Mem:* AAAS; Soc Exp Biol & Med; Am Soc Biol Chemists; Can Biochem Soc; Can Physiol Soc. *Res:* Drug metabolism. *Mailing Add:* Pharmacol Health Protection Br Health & Welfare Can Ottawa ON KIN 6N5 Can

JOHNSON, WILLIAM, b Boston, Mass, Oct 6, 41; m 65; c 1. MICROBIOLOGY. *Educ:* Marietta Col, BS, 63; Miami Univ, MS, 65; Rutgers Univ, PhD(microbiol), 68. *Prof Exp:* Nat Acad Sci-Nat Res Coun fel, Army Biol Res Ctr, Ft Detrick, Md, 68-70; asst prof microbiol, 70-74, assoc prof, 74-80, PROF MICROBIOL, COL MED, UNIV IOWA, 80- *Mem:* AAAS; Am Soc Microbiol; NY Acad Sci; Am Acad Microbiol. *Res:* Pathogenic microbiology; microbial toxins. *Mailing Add:* Dept of Microbiol Univ of Iowa Col of Med Iowa City IA 52240

JOHNSON, WILLIAM ALEXANDER, b Ennis, Tex, June 22, 22; m 46; c 2. POULTRY SCIENCE. *Educ:* La State Univ, BS, 43, MS, 47; Univ Minn, PhD(poultry breeding), 52. *Prof Exp:* Instr poultry husb, La State Univ, 47-49, asst, Univ Minn, 49-52; from asst prof to assoc prof poultry breeding, 52-65, PROF POULTRY BREEDING, LA STATE UNIV, BATON ROUGE, 65-, HEAD DEPT, 81- *Mem:* Poultry Sci Asn; World Poultry Sci Asn; Am Genetics Asn; Sigma Xi; Nat Asn Cols & Teachers Agr. *Res:* Poultry breeding and genetics; environmental physiology; catfish breeding and genetics. *Mailing Add:* Dept of Poultry Sci La State Univ Baton Rouge LA 70803

JOHNSON, WILLIAM ARTHUR, b Beverly, Mass, Apr 26, 51; m 78. ELECTROMAGNETISM, APPLIED MATHEMATICS. *Educ:* Univ Ariz, BS, 72, MA, 74, PhD(math), 78. *Prof Exp:* Teaching assoc math, Univ Ariz, 73-77, res assoc electromagnetics, 77-78, instr, 78; ass prof elec eng, Univ Miss, 78-79; staff scientist, Sci Applns, Inc, 79-81; ENGR, LAWRENCE LIVERMORE NAT LAB, 81- *Mem:* Inst Elec Engrs; Am Math Soc. *Res:* Electromagnetic theory. *Mailing Add:* Lawrence Livermore Nat Lab Livermore CA 94550

JOHNSON, WILLIAM BRADFORD, b Philadelphia, Pa, Sept 16, 20; m 43; c 4. HORTICULTURE. *Educ:* Pa State Col, BS, 42; Univ Mass, MS, 51; Harvard Univ, MA, 56. *Prof Exp:* Asst trial grounds, Ritter Seed Co, NJ, 46-47; instr olericulture, Univ Mass, 47-56; assoc exten specialist, 56-67, EXTEN SPECIALIST VEG CROPS, DEPT HORT & FORESTRY, EXTEN SERV, COOK COL, RUTGERS UNIV, NEW BRUNSWICK, 67- *Mem:* Am Soc Hort Sci; Am Hort Soc; Sigma Xi. *Res:* Production information and development of cultural practices of vegetables, especially processing crops including variety testing. *Mailing Add:* 6 Orchard Rd Piscataway NJ 08854

JOHNSON, WILLIAM BUHMANN, b Palo Alto, Calif, Dec 5, 44; m 68; c 2. MATHEMATICAL ANALYSIS. *Educ:* Southern Methodist Univ, BA, 66; Iowa State Univ, PhD(math), 69. *Prof Exp:* Asst prof math, Univ Houston, 69-71; from asst prof to assoc prof, 71-74, PROF MATH, OHIO STATE UNIV, 74- *Concurrent Pos:* Vis prof math, Univ Tex, Austin, 75 & Tex A&M Univ, College Station, 81; fel Inst Advan Studies, Hebrew Univ, Jerusalem, 77-78; ed, Trans Am Math Soc, 82-85. *Mem:* Am Math Soc; London Math Soc. *Res:* Functional analysis; isomorphic theory of Banach spaces. *Mailing Add:* Dept of Math Ohio State Univ Columbus OH 43210

JOHNSON, WILLIAM CONE, b Eastland, Tex, Nov 20, 26; m 56; c 3. INTERNAL MEDICINE. *Educ:* NTex State Univ, BS, 49; Univ Tex, MD, 54; Am Bd Internal Med, dipl, 63; Am Bd Pulmonary Dis, dipl, 68. *Prof Exp:* From intern to chief resident, John Sealy Hosp, Univ Tex Hosps, 54-58; chief med serv, 1604th US Air Force Hosp, 58-60, pulmonologist, Wilford Hall Hosp, Aerospace Med Div, Lackland AFB, Tex, 60-61, chief pulmonary & infectious dis serv, 61-63; med dir inhalation ther serv, Scott & White Mem Hosp, Temple, Tex, 63-65, dir pulmonary physiol labs, 63-68; dir respiratory ther serv & pulmonary physiol labs, Hendrick Mem Hosp, Abilene, 68-69; CLIN ASST PROF MED, UNIV TEX HEALTH SCI CTR, DALLAS, 69-; MED DIR RESPIRATORY THER SERV & PULMONARY FUNCTION LABS, WTEX MED CTR HOSP, ABILENE, 70- *Concurrent Pos:* Consult, Sect Clin Physiol, Scott & White Clin, Temple, 63-68, inhalation ther serv, Scott & White Mem Hosp, 65-68; med examr, Fed Aviation Agency, 66-; consult, Vet Admin Hosps, 65-, WTex Med Ctr Hosp, 68-, Hendrick Mem Hosp, Abilene, 68-69 & 70- & Shannon WTex Mem Hosp, San Angelo, 69; mem bd dirs, WTex Med Ctr Res Found, 69; med dir work eval & rehab unit, Methodist Hosp Dallas, 69-70; med dir respiratory ther serv, Cox Mem Hosp, Abilene, 70-75, Rolling Plains Mem Hosp, Sweetwater, 70-, Root Mem Hosp, Colorado City, Tex, 70, Med Ctr Hosp, Big Spring, 73-74, Shepperd Mem Hosp, Burnet, Tex, 76-80, Morris Mem Hosp, Coleman, Tex, 80-; clin asst prof med, Univ Tex Southwestern Med Sch Dallas, 69-; clin assoc prof med, Tex Tech Univ Sch Med, 74- *Mem:* AAAS; Am Asn Inhalation Therapists; fel Am Col Chest Physicians; fel Am Col Physicians; Am Fedn Clin Res. *Res:* Pulmonary physiology. *Mailing Add:* 1026 N 21st St Abilene TX 79601

JOHNSON, WILLIAM E, JR, b Plano, Tex, July 20, 30; m 53; c 3. MEDICAL ENTOMOLOGY. *Educ:* Huston-Tillotson Col, BS, 51; Univ Okla, MS, 53, PhD(zool), 61. *Prof Exp:* Instr biol, Tuskegee Inst, 55-57; mus asst, Univ Okla, 57-60; chmn div sci & math, Albany State Col, 60-69; asst vpres acad affairs, Ala State Univ, 69-74, dean grad studies, 74-80, prof biol, 69-80. *Mem:* Am Mosquito Control Asn. *Res:* Mosquito ecology. *Mailing Add:* 4606 Lawnwood Dr Montgomery AL 36108

JOHNSON, WILLIAM EVERETT, b Wallowa, Ore, Oct 22, 21; m 46; c 4. PHARMACOLOGY. *Educ:* Wash State Univ, BS, 51, MS, 53, PhD(pharmacol), 58. *Prof Exp:* From instr to asst prof pharm, Col Pharm, Univ Wyo, 53-58, from assoc prof to prof pharmacol, 58-65; assoc prof, 65-72, PROF PHARMACOL, COL PHARM, WASH STATE UNIV, 72- *Res:* Pharmacology of the cardiovascular system and mechanism of action of teratogens. *Mailing Add:* Col of Pharm Wash State Univ Pullman WA 99163

JOHNSON, WILLIAM HARDING, b Lockport, Ill, July 4, 21; m 46; c 2. PHYSIOLOGY, BIOPHYSICS. *Educ:* Univ Chicago, BS, 49, PhD, 52. *Prof Exp:* Instr physiol, Univ Ill, 52-54, from asst prof to assoc prof physiol & exec secy biophys div, 54-62; PROF BIOL, RENSSELAER POLYTECH INST, 62- *Concurrent Pos:* Lalor fel, Marine Biol Lab, Woods Hole, Mass, 54. *Mem:* AAAS; Biophys Soc. *Res:* Mechanical properties of muscles in an attempt to determine the molecular changes occurring in the contractile system during contraction; molecular basis of smooth muscle tonus. *Mailing Add:* 1100 Argo Blvd Schenectady NY 12303

JOHNSON, WILLIAM HILTON, b Indianapolis, Ind, Feb 14, 35; m 56; c 3. QUATERNARY GEOLOGY. *Educ:* Earlham Col, AB, 56; Univ Ill, MS, 61, PhD(geol), 62. *Prof Exp:* From instr to asst prof, 62-68, ASSOC PROF GEOL, UNIV ILL, URBANA, 68- *Mem:* Geol Soc Am; Soc Econ Paleontologists & Mineralogists; Nat Asn Geol Teachers; Am Quaternary Asn; Glaciol Soc. *Res:* Mineralogy and stratigraphy of Pleistocene deposits and glacial geology. *Mailing Add:* Dept Geol Univ Ill 1301 W Green St Urbana IL 61803

JOHNSON, WILLIAM HOWARD, b Sidney, Ohio, Sept 3, 22; m 43; c 3. AGRICULTURAL ENGINEERING. *Educ:* Ohio State Univ, BS, 48, MS, 53; Mich State Univ, PhD(agr eng), 60. *Prof Exp:* From instr to prof agr eng, Ohio Agr Res & Develop Ctr, assoc chmn dept, 53-68, actg chmn dept, 68-69; prof agr eng & head dept, 70-81, DIR ENG EXP STA, KANS STATE UNIV, 81- *Concurrent Pos:* Agr eng consult, 57-; vis scientist & lectr, Tex A&M Univ, 69-70. *Mem:* Fel Am Soc Agr Engrs. *Res:* Power and machinery area of agricultural engineering; determination of functional requirements and design; efficiency of harvesting and tillage machine components. *Mailing Add:* Eng Exp Sta Kans State Univ Manhattan KS 66506

JOHNSON, WILLIAM HUGH, b Fayetteville, NC, Sept 14, 32; m 58; c 2. CROP PROCESS ENGINEERING, SYSTEM DESIGN AND ANALYSIS. *Educ:* NC State Univ, BS, 54, MS, 56, PhD(agr eng), 61. *Prof Exp:* Res instr, 56-61, from asst prof to assoc prof, 61-69, PROF AGR ENG, NC STATE UNIV, 69- *Concurrent Pos:* Partic & spec reporter, 4th Int Tobacco Sci Cong, Athens, 66, 5th Int Tobacco Sci Cong, Hamburg, 70; consult, Indian Inst Technol, Ford Found Proj, Kharagpur, India, 66; ed, Tobacco Sci, 80- *Honors & Awards:* Philip Morris Distinguished Achievement Award Tobacco Sci, 73. *Mem:* Am Soc Agr Engrs. *Res:* Bioengineering of plant materials; energy and mass transfer relations during processing; physical, chemical and enzymatic changes in response to dynamic process variables; health-related modifications of tobacco; systems engineering; biological engineering. *Mailing Add:* Dept of Biol & Agr Eng Box 5906 NC State Univ Raleigh NC 27607

JOHNSON, WILLIAM JACOB, b Gladwin, Mich, June 23, 14; m 44; c 2. INORGANIC CHEMISTRY. *Educ:* Univ Calif, Davis, BS, 37; Kans State Univ, MS, 48, PhD(plant biochem), 62. *Prof Exp:* Sci teacher, Kans High Sch, 44-46; instr, 47-50, bus mgr, 50-52, from asst prof to assoc prof, 52-62, PROF CHEM, TABOR COL, 62-, CHMN DIV NATURAL SCI & MATH, 63- *Concurrent Pos:* Vis sr lectr, Univ Zambia, 70-71. *Mem:* Am Chem Soc. *Res:* Nature of zinc and other micronutrients in plant extracts. *Mailing Add:* 212 S Madison Hillsboro KS 67063

JOHNSON, WILLIAM K, b Kalamazoo, Mich, Jan 4, 27; m 52; c 1. ORGANIC CHEMISTRY. *Educ:* Univ Mich, BS, 50, MS, 51, PhD(pharm chem), 54. *Prof Exp:* Chemist res & eng div, Monsanto Co, 53-60, proj mgr, Org Develop Dept, 60-65, mgr mkt res, Org Div, 65-67, mgr commercial develop plasticizers & gen chem, 67-69, mgr technol gen chem, 69-71, dir res & commercial develop, Process Chem Group, Monsanto Indust Chem Co, 71-76, mgr markets & prod, 76-79, MGR MKT RES & PLANNING, MONSANTO INTERMEDIATES CO, 79- *Mem:* Am Chem Soc; Commercial Develop Asn; Ger Chem Soc; Chem Mkt Res Asn. *Res:* Organometallics and organic synthesis; intermediates and fine chemicals. *Mailing Add:* Monsanto Intermediates Co 800 N Lindbergh Blvd St Louis MO 63166

JOHNSON, WILLIAM LAWRENCE, b Keene, NH, Aug 28, 36; c 3. RUMINANT NUTRITION, FORAGE UTILIZATION. *Educ:* Univ NH, BS, 58; Cornell Univ, MS, 64, PhD(dairy cattle nutrit), 66. *Prof Exp:* Asst prof, 66-74, ASSOC PROF ANIMAL SCI, NC STATE UNIV, 74- *Concurrent Pos:* Dairy husb res specialist, NC State Univ, 66-69, co-leader forage & animal nutrit prog, Agr Mission to Peru, 70-73; prin investr small ruminants collab res, Indonesia & Brazil, 78- *Mem:* Am Dairy Sci Asn; Am Soc Animal Sci; Latin Am Asn Animal Prod. *Res:* Factors influencing utilization of forages, and roughage by products, including tropical feedstuffs, by cattle, sheep and goats. *Mailing Add:* Dept of Animal Sci NC State Univ Raleigh NC 27650

JOHNSON, WILLIAM LEWIS, b Bryan, Tex, July 6, 40; m 63; c 1. SOLID STATE PHYSICS. *Educ:* Univ Southern Miss, BA, 62; Naval Postgrad Sch, MS, 66, PhD(physics), 69. *Prof Exp:* Instr physics, Naval Postgrad Sch, 63-69; res assoc, Univ Ill, 69-71; ASSOC PROF PHYSICS & CHMN DEPT, WESTMINSTER COL, PA, 71- *Mem:* Am Phys Soc; Am Asn Physics Teachers; Sigma Xi. *Res:* Critical point phenomena; microcomputers; laboratory automation. *Mailing Add:* Dept of Physics Westminster Col New Wilmington PA 16142

JOHNSON, WILLIAM LEWIS, b Bowling Green, Ohio, July 26, 48. SOLID STATE PHYSICS, MATERIALS SCIENCE. *Educ:* Hamilton Col, BA, 70; Calif Inst Technol, PhD(appl physics), 74. *Prof Exp:* Fel appl physics, Calif Inst Technol, 74-75; fel, T J Watson Res Ctr, IBM Corp, 75-77; asst prof, 77-80, ASSOC PROF MAT SCI, CALIF INST TECHNOL, 80- *Concurrent Pos:* Consult, Adv Technol Ctr, Dresser Industs, 78-, Oak Ridge Nat Lab, 80- & Jet Propulsion Lab, Calif Inst Technol, Pasadena, 80- *Mem:* Am Phys Soc; AAAS. *Res:* Low temperature physics; superconductivity; amorphous materials; properties of metastable metallic materials. *Mailing Add:* Keck Lab of Eng Calif Inst of Technol Pasadena CA 91125

JOHNSON, WILLIAM MCCRAY, b Pittsville, Va, Mar 17, 50; m 72. PLANT DISEASE EPIDEMIOLOGY, PLANT RESISTANCE BREEDING. *Educ:* Univ Md, Eastern Shore, BS, 72; Okla State Univ, BS, 76, PhD(plant path), 76. *Prof Exp:* Asst prof, 76-79, ASSOC PROF, LANGSTON UNIV & OKLA STATE UNIV, 80- *Mem:* Am Phytopath Soc; Sigma Xi. *Res:* Synthesis and characterization of stable plant disease resistance in cotton. *Mailing Add:* Rte 5 Box 139 Stillwater OK 74074

JOHNSON, WILLIAM PIERRE, physics, see previous edition

JOHNSON, WILLIAM RANDOLPH, JR, b Oxford, NC, July 25, 30; m 54; c 3. POLYMER CHEMISTRY, THEORETICAL CHEMISTRY. *Educ:* NC Col Durham, BS, 50; Univ Notre Dame, MS, 52; Univ Pa, PhD(chem), 58. *Prof Exp:* Instr, Prairie View A&M Col, 52-53; prof, Fla A&M Univ, 58-61; chemist, W R Grace & Co, 61-63; chemist, Philip Morris Res Div, 75-79, MGR SPECIAL AFFAIRS, PHILIP MORRIS RES CTR, 81- *Concurrent Pos:* Adj prof chem, Va Union Univ, 63-73, exec in residence, 79-81. *Res:* Polymer synthesis; smoke chemistry; smoke formation mechanisms; pyrolysis mechanisms. *Mailing Add:* Philip Morris USA PO Box 26603 Richmond VA 23261

JOHNSON, WILLIAM ROBERT, b Buffalo, Okla, Sept 24, 39; m 61; c 2. MATERIALS SCIENCE. *Educ:* San Jose State Col, BS, 64; Stanford Univ, MS, 67, PhD(mat sci), 69. *Prof Exp:* Scientist & prod mgr vacuum metallization, St Clair-Field Inc, Mt View, Calif, 69-70; assoc scientist, 70-71, staff assoc, 71-72, sr engr, 72-73, staff engr, 73-81, MGR MATS EVAL, GEN ATOMIC CO, 81- *Mem:* Am Soc Metals. *Res:* Structure of materials; mechanical behavior of materials (fracture, creep and stress rupture); environmental effects on materials. *Mailing Add:* 12243 Riesling Ct San Diego CA 92131

JOHNSON, WILLIAM S(TANLEY), b Camden, Tenn, Dec 9, 39; m 67; c 2. MECHANICAL & ENVIRONMENTAL ENGINEERING. *Educ:* Univ Tenn, Knoxville, BS, 61; Clemson Univ, MS, 65, PhD(eng), 67. *Prof Exp:* Asst design engr, Pratt & Whitney Aircraft Div, United Aircraft Corp, 61-62; asst prof mech eng, Univ Tenn, 67-70; assoc prof, 70-77, PROF MECH ENG, UNIV TENN, 77- *Mem:* Am Soc Mech Engrs; Am Inst Aeronaut & Astronaut; Am Soc Eng Educ. *Res:* Application of pulse-jet flow in low area ratio ejectors; determination of velocity characteristics of two-dimensional fluid jets; boundary layer control on submarine surfaces; energy conservation analysis in buildings. *Mailing Add:* Dept of Mech & Aerospace Eng Univ of Tenn Knoxville TN 37916

JOHNSON, WILLIAM SUMMER, b New Rochelle, NY, Feb 24, 13; m 40. ORGANIC CHEMISTRY. *Educ:* Amherst Col, AB, 36; Harvard Univ, AM, 38, PhD(org chem), 40. *Hon Degrees:* DSc, Amherst Col, 56 & Long Island Univ, 68. *Prof Exp:* Instr chem, Amherst Col, 36-37; asst to Prof R P Linstead, Harvard Univ, 40; from instr to prof org chem, Univ Wis, 40-54, Homer Adkins prof, 54-60; exec head dept chem, 60-69, prof, 60-68, Jackson-Wood prof, 65-68, EMER PROF CHEM, STANFORD UNIV, 68- *Concurrent Pos:* Secy org sect, Int Cong Pure & Appl Chem, 51, invited lectr, Eng, 63; Am-Swiss Found lectr, Switz, 51; Coover lectr, Univ Iowa, 52; mem chem adv panel, NSF, 52-56; Edward Clark Lee lectr, Univ Chicago, 56, Am Chem Soc Julius Stieglitz mem lectr, 63; Bachmann lectr, Univ Mich, 57; Max Tishler lectr, Harvard Univ, 64; Andrews lectr, Univ New South Wales, 65; mem US-Brazil study group grad teaching & res in chem, US-Brazil Sci Coop Prog, Off Foreign Secy, Nat Acad Sci, 68; consult, Zoecon Corp, 68- & Organon, 74-; Phillips lectr, Haverford Col, 69; mem med chem A study sect, NIH, 70-; Treat B Johnson lectr, Yale Univ, 71; Falk-Plaut lectr, Columbia Univ, 71; Centenary lectr, Univ UK, 73-74; Van't Hoff Centenary lectr, Univ Leiden, 74. *Honors & Awards:* Am Chem Soc Award Creative Work in Synthetic Org Chem, 58; Mfg Award Creative Res, 63; Nichols Medal Award, 68, Roussel Prize, 70 & Roger Adams Award, 77, Am Chem Soc. *Mem:* Nat Acad Sci; Am Chem Soc; Am Acad Arts & Sci. *Res:* conformational principles; biomimetic polyene cyclizations. *Mailing Add:* Dept of Chem Stanford Univ Stanford CA 94305

JOHNSON, WILLIAM THOMAS MITCHELL, physical chemistry, cardiovascular physiology, see previous edition

JOHNSON, WILLIAM W, b Provo, Utah, July 11, 34; m 69; c 2. GEOPHYSICS. *Educ:* Brigham Young Univ, BS, 56; Univ Utah, MS, 58; Univ Pittsburgh, PhD(geophys), 65. *Prof Exp:* Sr res scientist, Sinclair Oil Corp, 65-69; PRIN RES GEOPHYSICIST, ATLANTIC RICHFIELD CO, 69- *Concurrent Pos:* Res assoc, Lamont-Doherty Geol Observ, Columbia Univ, 66-67. *Mem:* AAAS; Soc Explor Geophysicists. *Res:* Propagation of elastic waves in anisotropic media; geological interpretation of gravity and magnetic data; seismic wave propagation. *Mailing Add:* Atlantic Richfield Co PO Box 2819 Dallas TX 75221

JOHNSON, WILLIAM WAYNE, b Minneapolis, Minn, Oct 12, 34. GENETICS. *Educ:* Univ Minn, BS, 57, MS, 59, PhD(zool), 63. *Prof Exp:* Interim asst prof biol, Univ Fla, 62-63; asst prof, 63-68, ASSOC PROF BIOL, UNIV NMEX, 68- *Mem:* AAAS; Genetics Soc Am; Am Inst Biol Sci. *Res:* Experimental population genetics of Drosophila. *Mailing Add:* Dept of Biol Univ of NMex Albuquerque NM 87131

JOHNSON, WILLIS HUGH, b Parkersburg, Ind, Dec 21, 02; m 29; c 2. ZOOLOGY. *Educ:* Wabash Col, AB, 25; Univ Chicago, MS, 29, PhD(zool), 32. *Hon Degrees:* DSc, Wabash Col, 74. *Prof Exp:* From instr to assoc prof zool, Wabash Col, 25-35; from asst prof to assoc prof biol, Stanford Univ, 35-41, prof biol & dir army specialized training prog, 41-46; prof zool, 46-65, chmn dept biol & sci div, 46-68; Treves Prof biol, 65-73, EMER PROF BIOL, WABASH COL, 73- *Concurrent Pos:* Instr, US Army Univ, Eng, 44-45; vchmn, Comn Undergrad Educ in Biol Sci, 65-66. *Mem:* Am Soc Zool; Am Soc Naturalists; Soc Protozool; fel NY Acad Sci. *Res:* Populations and sterile culture of protozoa; encystment and nutrition in protozoa; nutrition and regeneration in Planaria. *Mailing Add:* Dept of Biol Wabash Col Crawfordsville IN 47933

JOHNSON, WINFORD B(LAIR), b Lineville, Ala, Nov 7, 12; m 40; c 1. CHEMICAL ENGINEERING. *Educ:* Ala Polytech Inst, BS, 32, MS, 33; Yale Univ, DEng, 40. *Prof Exp:* Teacher, pub sch, Ala, 33-35; jr chem engr, Wilson Dam Tenn Valley Authority, 35-38; instr chem eng, Yale Univ, 38-40; chem engr, Eastern Lab, 40-50, head chem eng sect, 50-55, res assoc, 55-56, asst lab dir, 56-58, mgt develop coord, 58-61, tech asst to res dir, 61-70, CHEM ENGR, E I DU PONT DE NEMOURS & CO, 70- *Mem:* Am Inst Chem Engrs; Am Ord Asn; Inst Mgt Sci. *Res:* Heat transfer and compressibility of fluids; chemical processes for dye intermediates, rubber chemicals and polymer intermediates; development of modern chemical processes; catalysts; new product development; explosives; solid propellants. *Mailing Add:* Fireside Farm Unionville PA 19375

JOHNSON, WOODROW ELDRED, b Forest Lake, Minn, Oct 22, 17; m 42; c 4. PHYSICS. *Educ:* Hamline Univ, BS, 37; Brown Univ, MS, 39, PhD(physics), 42. *Hon Degrees:* DS, Hamline Univ, 61. *Prof Exp:* Asst, Brown Univ, 37-40; from instr to asst prof physics, Syracuse Univ, 41-44, asst prof, 46-47; sr physicist, Tenn Eastman Corp, 44-46 & Manhattan Proj, Oak Ridge Nat Lab, 47-49; sect mgr, Bettis Atomic Power Lab, 49-51, mgr tech opers, Prototype Reactor Facil, Idaho, 51-53, asst to dir develop, 53-54, corp tech consult, Matahorn Proj, Princeton Univ, 54, corp mem, Indust Atomic Power Study Group, 54-55, proj mgr, Pa Adv Reactor Proj, Atomic Power Dept, 55-59, dir projs, 59-61, gen mgr, 61-64, gen mgr, Astronuclear Lab, 64-68, vpres & gen mgr, Astronuclear/Underseas Div, 68-71, VPRES, WESTINGHOUSE CORP, 67-, VPRES & GEN MGR, TRANSP DIV, 71- *Mem:* Nat Acad Eng; Inst Elec & Electronics Engrs; Am Nuclear Soc; Nat Asn Mfg; Am Phys Soc. *Res:* Photoelectricity; electron diffraction; physics of thin metallic films; effect of radiation on solids. *Mailing Add:* Westinghouse Elec Corp Transp Div 2001 Lebanon Rd West Mifflin PA 15122

JOHNSON-LUSSENBURG, CHRISTINE MARGARET, b Hawkesbury, Ont, Jan 29, 31; m 53, 72; c 6. VIROLOGY, MOLECULAR BIOLOGY. *Educ:* McGill Univ, BSc, 52, MSc, 53; Univ Ottawa, PhD, 67. *Prof Exp:* Asst prof, 67-78, ASSOC PROF MICROBIOL, UNIV OTTAWA, 78- *Mem:* Can Soc Microbiologists; Am Soc Microbiol. *Res:* Structural and antigenic studies of components involved in virus replication, including myxoviruses, herpesvirus and coronavirus. *Mailing Add:* Dept of Microbiol Univ of Ottawa Ottawa ON K1N 9A9 Can

JOHNSRUD, ALAN EDWIN, b Manitowoc, Wis, Dec 4, 30. OPERATIONS RESEARCH. *Educ:* Univ Wis, BA, 53, MA, 54, PhD(physics), 58. *Prof Exp:* Physicist, Hughes Aircraft Co, 58-60; sr staff physicist, Nat Eng Sci Co, 60-62; res scientist, Northrop Space Labs, 62-64; sr staff physicist, Nat Eng Sci Co, Calif, 64-66; mem tech staff, TRW Systs, Inc, 66-67; sr eng specialist, Litton Data Systs, 67-68; opers res analyst, Control Data Corp, 68-69; OPERS RES ANALYST, HQ, US DEPT ARMY, 69- *Mem:* Am Phys Soc. *Res:* Neutron cross section measurements; Van de Graaff accelerator; electron linac; vacuum technology; charged particle detection; magnetometry; underwater acoustics; antisubmarine and antimissile warfare; operations research; testing of military equipment. *Mailing Add:* 1319 S Randolph St Arlington VA 22204

JOHNSSON, LARS-GORAN, b Tampere, Finland, Mar 2, 30; div; c 1. OTORHINOLARYNGOLOGY. *Educ:* Turku Univ, Med Lic, 57; Univ Helsinki, Odontologie Lic, 60, Dr Med Sci, 79. *Prof Exp:* Resident, Univ Ear, Nose & Throat Hosp, Univ Helsinki, 61-64; stipend study, Brit Coun, London, 65; Fulbright fel, Med Sch, Univ Mich, Ann Arbor, 65-66, res assoc ear res, 66-70, assoc prof, 70-78, PROF OTORHINOLARYNGOL, KRESGE HEARING RES INST, MED SCH, UNIV MICH, ANN ARBOR, 78- *Concurrent Pos:* Docent otorhinolarynyol, Univ Helsinki, 80- *Res:* Ear anatomy and pathology. *Mailing Add:* Kresge Hearing Res Inst Univ of Mich Med Sch Ann Arbor MI 48109

JOHNSTON, A SIDNEY, b Hinton, WVa, Apr 4, 37. NUCLEAR PHYSICS. *Educ:* Va Polytech Inst, BS, 59; Carnegie-Mellon Univ, MS, 61, PhD(physics), 65; Chicago Kent Col Law, JD, 78. *Prof Exp:* Sr scientist physics, Westinghouse Astronuclear, 65-68; asst prof, Pratt Inst, 68-74; MEM STAFF, DEPT NUCLEAR MED, MICHAEL REESE HOSP, 74- *Concurrent Pos:* Private law pract, 78- *Mem:* Am Bar Asn; Am Asn Physicists Med; Health Physics Soc; AAAS; Am Phys Soc. *Res:* Nuclear engineering; solid state physics; science and society. *Mailing Add:* Rm 1250 135 S La Salle St Chicago IL 60603

JOHNSTON, ALAN ROBERT, b Long Beach, Calif, June 26, 31; m 56; c 3. OPTICAL PHYSICS. *Educ:* Calif Inst Technol, BS, 52, PhD(physics), 56. *Prof Exp:* Res scientist, 56-62, res group supvr optical physics res, 62-71, MEM TECH STAFF, JET PROPULSION LAB, 71- *Mem:* Optical Soc Am; Am Phys Soc. *Res:* Fiber optic systems; optoelectronic sensors. *Mailing Add:* Jet Propulsion Lab 4800 Oak Grove Dr Pasadena CA 91103

JOHNSTON, ANDREA, b Minneapolis, Minn, Mar 13, 21. MATHEMATICS. *Educ:* St Mary Col, Kans, BA, 48; Cath Univ, MS, 52, PhD(math), 54. *Prof Exp:* CHMN DEPT MATH, ST MARY COL, KANS, 54- *Mem:* Math Asn Am. *Res:* Mathematics teaching; preparation of elementary and secondary teachers. *Mailing Add:* St Mary Col Leavenworth KS 66048

JOHNSTON, BARBARA JANE, b Brooklyn, NY, Nov 27, 21. MEDICINE. *Educ:* William Smith Col, BA, 43; NY Univ, MD, 51. *Hon Degrees:* DSc, Hobart Col, 64. *Prof Exp:* Asst prof med, Med Ctr, NY Univ, 53-60; dir cancer res, Women's Hosp Div, St Luke's Hosp, 60-68; chief med oncol serv, St Vincent's Hosp Med Ctr, 68-77; CONSULT, 77- *Concurrent Pos:* Luis Guerrero Mem lectr, Univ Santo Tomas, Manila. *Mem:* AAAS; fel Am Col Physicians; fel Am Col Angiol; Harvey Soc; AMA. *Res:* Internal medicine; oncology. *Mailing Add:* St Vincent's Hosp Med Ctr 153 W 11th St New York NY 10011

JOHNSTON, BRUCE (GILBERT), b Detroit, Mich, Oct 13, 05; m 39; c 3. CIVIL ENGINEERING. *Educ:* Univ Ill, BS, 30; Lehigh Univ, MS, 34; Columbia Univ, PhD(civil eng), 38. *Prof Exp:* Testing inspector, US Indian Serv Construct, Coolidge Dam, 27-29; concrete designer, Roberts & Schaefer Eng Co, Ill, 30-31; asst civil eng, Lehigh Univ, 32-34; instr, Columbia Univ, 34-38; asst prof, Lehigh Univ, 38-41, assoc prof, 41, engr, Bur Yds & Docks, US Navy, 42; engr & proj supvr, Appl Physics Lab, Johns Hopkins Univ, 42-45; prof, Lehigh Univ, 45-50; prof, 50-68, EMER PROF STRUCT ENG, UNIV MICH, ANN ARBOR, 68- *Concurrent Pos:* Asst dir, Fritz Lab, Lehigh Univ, 38-41; from assoc dir to dir, 47-50; chmn, Column Res Coun, Eng Found, 56-62, ed, Guide to Design Criteria for Metal Compression Members, 60-, 66 & 76. *Honors & Awards:* Croes Medal, Am Soc Civil Engrs, 37 & 54, Res Prize, 57, Ernest E Howard Award, 74. *Mem:* Nat Acad Eng; hon mem Am Soc Civil Engrs. *Res:* Strength of steel structures and structural members. *Mailing Add:* 5025 E Calle Barril Tucson AZ 85718

JOHNSTON, C EDWARD, b Ont. AQUACULTURE. *Educ:* Univ NB, BA, 64, PhD(biol), 68. *Prof Exp:* Asst prof, Prince Wales Col, 68-69; asst prof, 69-76, ASSOC PROF BIOL, UNIV PEI, 76- *Concurrent Pos:* Vis prof, Biol Sta, NB, 79-80. *Mem:* Am Fisheries Soc. *Res:* Effect of low pH on parr-smolt transformation of atlantic salmon; effect of termperature regimes on salmonid physiology; rapid and slow acclimation procedures on ionoregulatory mechanisms of rainbow trout. *Mailing Add:* Biol Dept Univ PEI Charlottetown PI C1A 4P3 Can

JOHNSTON, CARTER D(UPUY), b Lexington, Ky, Oct 17, 15; m 41; c 3. BIOCHEMISTRY. *Educ:* Univ Ky, BS, 37; Univ Chicago, PhD(biochem), 42. *Prof Exp:* Asst, Univ Chicago, 42-44; pharmacologist, Food & Drug Admin, 44-53; biochemist, Hazleton Lab, Va, 53-58; toxicologist, Woodard Res Corp, 58-75, SRI Int, 76-77 & Litton Bionetics, 78-81; RETIRED. *Mem:* AAAS; Sigma Xi. *Res:* Toxicology; enzymatic reactions; cholinesterase inhibitors; drug metabolism. *Mailing Add:* 6412 Newman Rd Clifton VA 22024

JOHNSTON, CHARLES LOUIS, JR, b Danville, Pa, Nov 4, 23; m 51; c 4. CLINICAL PATHOLOGY. *Educ:* Univ NC, AB, 47, MS, 49; Univ Pa, MD, 53. *Prof Exp:* Southeastern Pa Heart Asn fel med, Sch Med, Univ Pa, 55-56; res assoc physiol, Sch Med, Univ NC, 56-59, asst prof, 60-65; PROF CLIN PATH, MED COL VA, VA COMMONWEALTH UNIV, 65- *Concurrent Pos:* Fulbright res fel hemat, Univ Oslo Hosp, 59-60; USPHS res career

develop award, 60-65. *Mem:* Am Physiol Soc; Soc Exp Biol & Med; Am Asn Path; Am Soc Hemat; Am Soc Clin Path. *Res:* Basic mechanisms operating in blood coagulation; morphological hematology. *Mailing Add:* Dept of Clin Path Med Col of Va Richmond VA 23298

JOHNSTON, CHRISTIAN WILLIAM, b Brooklyn, NY, Jan 9, 11; m 46; c 2. PHYSICAL CHEMISTRY. *Educ:* Columbia Univ, AB, 34. *Prof Exp:* Anal chemist, Martin Dennis Co, NJ, 27-28; res chemist, Darco Corp, NY, 28-40; asst to vpres in chg prod, US Indust Chem Co, 40-50, dir resin res & head tech serv, 50-58; supvr polymer appln res, Food Mach & Chem Corp, 58-63; mgr polymer appln res, Plastics Div, Tenneco Mfg Co, 63-68, sr scientist, Tenneco Chem Co, 68-76; CONSULT, 76- *Concurrent Pos:* Tech dir, Tyndale Plains Hunter Ltd, 80- *Mem:* Soc Plastics Engrs; Am Soc Qual Control; Am Chem Soc; Soc Rheology. *Res:* Adsorption form solution; optical method colorimetry; reaction rates; rheology; electronic circuits measurements and control; polymer chemistry; chemical engineering equipment design and plant operating statistical analysis; hydrophyllic polymers. *Mailing Add:* RD 1 Box 19 Amwell Rd Neshanic Station NJ 08853

JOHNSTON, CLAIR C, b Beaver Falls, Pa, Jan 13, 99; m 28. CIVIL ENGINEERING. *Educ:* Univ Detroit, BCE, 23, CE, 33; Univ Mich, MCE, 36. *Prof Exp:* From asst prof to prof civil eng, Univ Detroit, 27-42; staff engr, Stevenson, Jordan & Harrison, Mgt Consult, 42-47; training dir, Square D Co, Mich, 48-59; supvr eng develop, Chrysler Missile Plant, 59-61; prof civil eng, Univ Detroit, 61-62; prof, Detroit Inst Technol, 62-70; civil eng consult, 70-75; RETIRED. *Concurrent Pos:* Chmn dept civil eng, Detroit Inst Technol, 62-69, dean col eng, 68-69. *Mem:* Am Soc Civil Engrs. *Res:* Reinforced concrete and indeterminate structures. *Mailing Add:* 475 Colonial Ct Grosse Point Farms MI 48236

JOHNSTON, COLIN DEANE, b Northern Ireland, Apr 28, 40; m 67; c 1. CIVIL ENGINEERING, MATERIALS SCIENCE. *Educ:* Queen's Univ, Belfast, BSc, 62, PhD(civil eng), 67. *Prof Exp:* Site engr, Govt of Northern Ireland, 66-67; tech mgr concrete prod, Pre-Mix Concrete, Ltd, 67; assoc prof, 67-78, PROF CIVIL ENG, UNIV CALGARY, 78- *Honors & Awards:* Wason Medal, Am Concrete Inst, 77. *Mem:* Am Concrete Inst; Am Soc Testing & Mat; Brit Concrete Soc. *Res:* Properties of concrete, fiber reinforced concrete, ferrocement, sulphur concrete and asphalt concrete; structural and paving applications. *Mailing Add:* Dept of Civil Eng Univ of Calgary Calgary AB T2N 1N4 Can

JOHNSTON, CYRUS CONRAD, JR, b Statesville, NC, July 16, 29; m 60; c 2. INTERNAL MEDICINE, ENDOCRINOLOGY. *Educ:* Duke Univ, AB, 51, MD, 55; Am Bd Internal Med, dipl. *Prof Exp:* Intern med, Duke Hosp, 55-56; resident, Barnes Hosp, St Louis, 56-57; fel endocrinol & metab, 59-61, USPHS career res develop award, 63-68, from instr to assoc prof med, 61-69, assoc dir gen clin res ctr, 62-67, PROF MED, MED CTR, IND UNIV, INDIANAPOLIS, 69-, DIR DIV ENDOCRINOL & METAB, 68- *Mem:* AAAS; Am Fedn Clin Res; Endocrine Soc; fel Am Col Physicians; Am Diabetes Asn. *Res:* Metabolism of bone both in human subjects and in the experimental animal. *Mailing Add:* 5002 Buttonwood Crescent Indianapolis IN 46208

JOHNSTON, DAVID HERVEY, b Syracuse, NY, Aug 25, 51; m 72. GEOPHYSICS. *Educ:* Mass Inst Technol, SB, 73, PhD(geophysics), 79. *Prof Exp:* SR RES GEOPHYSICIST ROCK PHYSICS, EXXON PROD RES CO, 79- *Mem:* Am Geophys Union; Soc Explor Geophysicists; Soc Exp Stress Anal; Int Soc Rock Mech. *Res:* Rock physics; relation of microstructure and fluid content to measurable acoustic, electrical, flow and nuclear properties of rocks; structure and evolution of planetary interiors. *Mailing Add:* Exxon Prod Res Co PO Box 2189 Houston TX 77001

JOHNSTON, DAVID OWEN, b Franklin, Tenn, July 27, 30; m 50; c 4. PHYSICAL CHEMISTRY. *Educ:* George Peabody Col, BS, 51; Mid Tenn State Col, MA, 58; Univ Miss, PhD(chem), 63. *Prof Exp:* Teacher pub schs, Tenn, 51-53 & 54-58; instr phys sci, Mid Tenn State Col, 58-60; from asst prof to assoc prof chem, 63-71, PROF CHEM, DAVID LIPSCOMB COL, 71- *Concurrent Pos:* Fel res, Vanderbilt Univ, 65, 66, 69. *Mem:* Am Chem Soc. *Res:* Transport properties of rare earth salts in nonaqueous solvents; kinetics of inorganic oxidation-reduction reactions. *Mailing Add:* Dept of Chem David Lipscomb Col Nashville TN 37203

JOHNSTON, DAVID WARE, b Miami, Fla, Nov 23, 26; m 48; c 3. AVIAN PHYSIOLOGY, AVIAN ECOLOGY. AVIAN. *Educ:* Univ Ga, BS, 49, MS, 50; Univ Calif, PhD, 54. *Prof Exp:* Assoc prof, Mercer Univ, 54-59 & Wake Forest Col, 59-63; assoc prof biol sci & zool, 63-74, PROF ZOOL, UNIV FLA, 74- *Mem:* Ecol Soc Am; Cooper Ornith Soc; Am Ornith Union; Nat Audubon Soc. *Res:* Fat deposition in birds; pesticide levels in birds; ecology of insular avifaunas. *Mailing Add:* Dept of Zool Univ of Fla Gainesville FL 32611

JOHNSTON, DENNIS ADDINGTON, b Oak Ridge, Tenn, Sept 17, 44; m 66; c 2. BIOSTATISTICS. *Educ:* Arlington State Col, BS, 65; Univ Tex, Austin, MS, 66; Tex Tech Univ, PhD(math), 71. *Prof Exp:* Asst biomathematician & asst prof biomath, 72-78, ASSOC BIOMATHEMATICIAN & ASSOC PROF BIOMATH, M D ANDERSON HOSP & TUMOR INST, 78- *Concurrent Pos:* adj asst prof, Dept Math Sci, Rice Univ, 73-78; adj assoc prof, 79-; mem fac, Grad Sch Biomed Sci, Univ Tex, Houston, 73- *Mem:* Am Statist Asn. *Res:* Biomedical image processing; consultant in mathematical and statistical models; biostatistics; automated chromosome analysis. *Mailing Add:* Dept Biomath M D Anderson Hosp & Tumor Inst Houston TX 77030

JOHNSTON, DON RICHARD, b Union City, Ind, Aug 10, 37; c 2. CHEMICAL PHYSICS. *Educ:* Earlham Col, BA, 57; Brown Univ, PhD(chem), 61. *Prof Exp:* Insulation engr, M&P Lab, Gen Elec Co, 60-67; unit mgr phys chem, 68-70, SUBSECT MGR CHEM & ELEC INSULATION, GEN ELEC CO, 70- *Mem:* Am Chem Soc; Inst Elec & Electronic Engrs; Metals Properties Coun. *Res:* Mechanism of corona degradation of electrical insulation; electrical polarization currents for metallic corrosion. *Mailing Add:* RD 1 Bliss Rd Ballston Spa NY 12020

JOHNSTON, E(LWOOD) RUSSELL, JR, b Philadelphia, Pa, Dec 26, 25; m 51; c 2. CIVIL ENGINEERING. *Educ:* Univ Del, BCE, 46; Mass Inst Technol, MS, 47, ScD(civil eng), 49. *Prof Exp:* Asst civil eng, Mass Inst Technol, 46-47; struct designer, Fay, Spofford & Thorndike, 47-49; from asst prof to assoc prof, prof civil eng, Lehigh Univ, 49-57; prof, Worcester Polytech Inst, 57-63; head dept, 72-77, PROF CIVIL ENG, UNIV CONN, 63- *Concurrent Pos:* Guest prof, Swiss Fed Inst Technol, Zurich, 70 & 77. *Honors & Awards:* Western Elec Teaching Award, Am Soc Eng Educ, 69. *Mem:* Am Soc Civil Engrs; Am Soc Eng Educ; Nat Soc Prof Engrs; Int Asn Bridge & Struct Engrs; Am Acad Mech. *Res:* Structural engineering; applied mechanics; vibrations. *Mailing Add:* Dept of Civil Eng Univ of Conn Storrs CT 06268

JOHNSTON, ERNEST RAYMOND, b Dahinda, Ill, Feb 9, 07; m 39. MATHEMATICS. *Educ:* Ill State Norm Univ, BEd, 38; Univ Ill, MS, 39; Univ Minn, PhD(math), 54. *Prof Exp:* Teacher & prin, Pub Schs, Ill, 26-37; teacher, High Sch, Ill, 39-40; instr math, Austin Jr Col, Minn, 40-42 & Univ Minn, 42-44; mech engr, Naval Ord Lab, Md, 44-47; asst prof math & mech, Univ Minn, 47-51, lectr math, 51-53; prof, Wis State Col, Whitewater, 53-55; from assoc prof to prof math, 55-76, head dept math sci, 63-72, EMER PROF MATH, IND UNIV-PURDUE UNIV, INDIANAPOLIS, 76- *Mem:* Am Math Soc; Math Asn Am. *Mailing Add:* 215 Valley View Dr Kerrville TX 78028

JOHNSTON, FRANCIS E, b Paris, Ky, Oct 9, 31; m 55; c 3. PHYSICAL ANTHROPOLOGY. *Educ:* Univ Ky, BA, 59, MA, 60; Univ Pa, PhD(anthrop), 62. *Prof Exp:* From instr phys anthrop to asst prof anthrop, Univ Pa, 60-66, asst cur phys anthrop, Univ Mus, 63-66; fel, Univ London Inst Child Health, 66-67; assoc prof anthrop, Univ Tex, Austin, 68-71; prof anthrop, Temple Univ, 71-73; PROF ANTHROP, UNIV PA, 73- *Concurrent Pos:* Consult growth & develop, Nat Ctr Health Statist, 63-; fel, Inst Cancer Res, 67-68 & 75-; managing ed, Am J Phys Anthrop, 77- *Mem:* Am Asn Phys Anthrop (secy-treas, 64-68, vpres, 70-72); Am Anthrop Asn; Brit Soc Study Human Biol; Human Biol Coun; fel Royal Soc Med. *Res:* Child growth and development; population biology; human genetics; ecology of nutrition in human populations. *Mailing Add:* Dept of Anthrop Univ of Pa Philadelphia PA 19104

JOHNSTON, FRANCIS J, b Ferryville, Wis, Sept 20, 24; m 48; c 1. PHYSICAL CHEMISTRY. *Educ:* Univ Wis, BS, 47, PhD(chem), 52. *Prof Exp:* Chemist, E I du Pont de Nemours & Co, 52-54; from asst prof to assoc prof chem, Univ Louisville, 54-60; ASSOC PROF CHEM, UNIV GA, 60- *Mem:* Am Chem Soc. *Res:* Radiation and surface chemistry; reaction kinetics. *Mailing Add:* Dept of Chem Univ of Ga Athens GA 30602

JOHNSTON, G(ORDON) W(ILLIAM), b Toronto, Ont, Dec 10, 26; m 55; c 2. ENGINEERING PHYSICS. *Educ:* Univ Toronto, BSc, 48, MASc, 50, PhD(aerophys), 53. *Prof Exp:* Design engr, A V Roe, Co, Ltd, Can, 49-51; asst, Defense Res Bd Can, 52-53; res supvr sci lab, Res Div, Ford Motor Co, Mich, 53-54, head gas dynamics sect, 54-55; proj engr, De Haviland Aircraft Can, Ltd, 55-63, dir short take off & landing res proj, 60-63, head adv proj group, 63-70; ASSOC PROF AEROACOUST, INST AEROSPACE STUDIES, UNIV TORONTO, 70- *Concurrent Pos:* Mem assoc comt aerodyn noise, Nat Res Coun Can; lectr, Inst Aerophys, Univ Toronto, 57-59; aerodyn consult, Plasma Dynamics Dept, United Aircraft Res Labs, Conn, 67-70. *Mem:* Can Aeronaut Inst. *Res:* Transonic and low-speed aerodynamics; boundary layer control; stability and control of fixed and rotating wing aircraft configurations; slipstream wing aerodynamics. *Mailing Add:* Inst Aerospace Studies Univ Toronto Toronto ON M5S 2R8 Can

JOHNSTON, GEORGE I, b Bryn Mawr, Pa, May 29, 29; m 61; c 1. ELECTRICAL ENGINEERING. *Educ:* Johns Hopkins Univ, BS, 55. *Prof Exp:* Electronics technician, Sch Med, Johns Hopkins Univ, 48-55; med electronics engr, NIH, 55-58; dir res, Instrument Serv, Med Sch, 58-76, ASSOC PROF & DIR, INSTRUMENT & SAFETY SERV, UNIV ORE, 76- *Concurrent Pos:* Asst sanit engr, USPHS. *Mem:* Inst Elec & Electronics Engrs. *Res:* Biomedical engineering. *Mailing Add:* Instrument & Safety Serv Health Sci Ctr Portland OR 97201

JOHNSTON, GEORGE LAWRENCE, b Los Angeles, Calif, Nov 11, 32; m 59. PLASMA PHYSICS, ASTROPHYSICS. *Educ:* Calif Inst Technol, BS, 54; Harvard Univ, JD, 57; Univ Calif, Los Angeles, MS, 62, PhD(physics), 67. *Prof Exp:* Mem tech staff, Space Technol Labs, Inc, 57-60 & Aerospace Corp, 60-64; asst res physicist, Univ Calif, Los Angeles, 67-69; asst prof physics, Sonoma State Univ, 69-74, assoc prof, 74-80; RES PHYSICIST, PLASMA FUSION CTR, MASS INST TECHNOL, 80- *Concurrent Pos:* Res assoc, Mass Inst Technol, 75-77; adv comnr, Calif Energy Comn, 77-78. *Mem:* Am Phys Soc; AAAS; Sigma Xi. *Res:* Plasma kinetic theory; nonlinear plasma theory; plasma astrophysics; free electron lasers. *Mailing Add:* Plasma Fusion Ctr Mass Inst Technol NW16-232 Cambridge MA 02139

JOHNSTON, GEORGE ROBERT, b Salt Lake City, Utah, July 4, 34; m 59; c 3. CYTOGENETICS. *Educ:* Univ Utah, BS, 59, MS, 61, PhD(genetics), 64. *Prof Exp:* Fel genetics, Univ Calif, Berkeley, 64-65; asst prof zool, Univ Wyo, 65-67; from asst prof to assoc prof, 67-77, PROF BIOL, CALIF STATE UNIV, HAYWARD, 77- *Concurrent Pos:* Consult pediat, Kaiser Hosp, Oakland, Calif, 73-; consult, Biomed Div, Lawrence Livermore Lab, 75- *Mem:* Fel AAAS; Asn Cytogenetics Technologists. *Res:* Human chromosome identification linked to clinical defects and the structure of mammalian chromosomes. *Mailing Add:* Dept of Biol Calif State Univ Hayward CA 94542

JOHNSTON, GEORGE TAYLOR, b Princeton, WVa, Apr 18, 42; m 66; c 2. OPTICAL PHYSICS. *Educ:* Mich State Univ, BS, 62, MS, 65, PhD(physics), 67; Univ Dayton, MS, 74. *Prof Exp:* Res assoc physics, Brown Univ, 67-69; asst prof, Univ Dayton, 69-72, res physicist, Res Inst, 72-81; SR SCIENTIST, ROCKETDYNE, DIV ROCKWELL INT, 81- *Mem:* Optical Soc Am; Soc Photo-optical Instrumentation Engrs; Am Asn Physics Teachers. *Res:* Optical properties of materials; optical instrumentation and metrology; analysis, test and evaluation of high energy laser optical components and component materials, including optical thin films and laser damage mechanisms in coatings, mirrors and transparent materials. *Mailing Add:* Rocketdyne AFWL/ARAD Kirtland AFB NM 87117

JOHNSTON, GERALD SAMUEL, b Johnstown, Pa, Aug 4, 30; m 56; c 6. NUCLEAR MEDICINE. *Educ:* Univ Pittsburgh, BS, 52, MD, 56. *Prof Exp:* Intern rotating, Walter Reed Gen Hosp, US Army, 56-57, resident internal med, Brooke Gen Hosp, San Antonio, 57-60, comdr, Mobile Army Surg Hosp, Korea, 61-62, chief nuclear medicine, Walter Reed Gen Hosp, 63-69, chief colonel, Letterman Gen Hosp, San Francisco, 69-71; PROF MED & RADIOL NUCLEAR MED, UNIV MD, BALTIMORE, 76-; DIR NUCLEAR MED, NIH, 71- *Concurrent Pos:* Clin assoc prof med, Georgetown Univ, 74-; prof radiol & nuclear med, Uniformed Serv, Univ Health Sci, Bethesda, Md, 79- *Mem:* Soc Nuclear Med; Am Col Physicians; Am Med Asn. *Res:* Renal function; renal transplantation; nuclear medicine applications to renal function and cardiac function. *Mailing Add:* 9423 Holland Ave Bethesda MD 20814

JOHNSTON, GORDON ROBERT, b Portland, Ore, July 13, 28; m 60; c 4. ORGANIC CHEMISTRY. *Educ:* Univ Portland, BS, 50, MS, 52; Univ Ill, PhD(org chem), 56. *Prof Exp:* Res org chemist, Dow Chem Co, 56-58; res assoc org chem, Med Sch, Univ Ore, 58-60; res chemist, Crown Zellerbach Corp, 60-62; res chemist, Aerojet-Gen Corp, 62-63; res fel, Calif Inst Technol, 63-64; asst prof org chem, Col Women, San Diego, 64-66; ASST PROF CHEM, PA STATE UNIV, 66- *Concurrent Pos:* Trainee, Mass Inst Technol, 76-77. *Mem:* Am Chem Soc; Am Inst Chemists; Royal Soc Chem. *Mailing Add:* 1709 10th Ave Beaver PA 15009

JOHNSTON, HARLIN DEE, b Ogden, Utah, Mar 16, 42; m 63; c 2. PETROLEUM CHEMISTRY, LABORATORY AUTOMATION. *Educ:* Brigham Young Univ, BA, 65, PhD(inorg chem), 68. *Prof Exp:* RES CHEMIST CATALYSIS, PHILLIPS RES CTR, PHILLIPS PETROL CO, 68- *Mem:* Am Chem Soc; Sigma Xi. *Res:* Heterogeneous catalysis and solution thermodynamics; studies of solid-gas interaction using differential thermal analysis and thermogravimetric analysis; coal gasification; coal gasification. *Mailing Add:* Phillips Res Ctr Phillips Petrol Co Bartlesville OK 74004

JOHNSTON, HAROLD SLEDGE, b Woodstock, Ga, Oct 11, 20; m 48; c 4. PHYSICAL CHEMISTRY. *Educ:* Emory Univ, AB, 41; Calif Inst Technol, PhD(chem), 48. *Hon Degrees:* DSc, Emory Univ, 65. *Prof Exp:* Asst, Nat Defense Res Comt, Calif Inst Technol, 42-45, assoc prof chem, 56-57; from instr to assoc prof, Stanford Univ, 48-56; dean, Col Chem, 66-70, PROF CHEM, UNIV CALIF, BERKELEY, 57- *Concurrent Pos:* Guggenheim fel, Belg, 61; NATO vis prof, Italy, 64. *Mem:* Nat Acad Sci; AAAS; Am Chem Soc; Am Phys Soc; Am Acad Arts & Sci. *Res:* Fast gas phase reactions; kinetic isotope effects; photochemistry; unimolecular reactions; atmospheric chemistry. *Mailing Add:* Dept of Chem Univ of Calif Berkeley CA 94720

JOHNSTON, HARRY HENRY, b Chicago, Ill, Feb 1, 29; m 52; c 4. MICROBIOLOGY, BIOCHEMISTRY. *Educ:* Mich State Univ, BS, 52, PhD(soils), 58; Univ Mo, MS, 54. *Prof Exp:* Assoc prof biol, Wilmington Col, Ohio, 58-68; PROF BIOL, UNIV NC, ASHEVILLE, 68- *Concurrent Pos:* Fulbright grant, Spain, 62-63. *Mem:* AAAS; Am Soc Microbiol. *Res:* Breakdown of organic matter in soils; uptake of amino acids by plants. *Mailing Add:* Div of Sci & Math Univ of NC Asheville NC 28804

JOHNSTON, HERBERT NORRIS, b Cleveland, Ohio, Aug 9, 28; m 50; c 2. CHEMISTRY. *Educ:* Ohio Univ, BS, 49. *Prof Exp:* Res chemist coatings res, Glidden Co, 49-52; assoc chief, 52-68, chief polymer & paper technol div, Columbus Lab, 68-72, mgr polymer & paper chem, 72-78, MGR INDUST MKT OFF, COLUMBUS LABS, BATTELLE MEM INST, 78- *Mem:* Am Chem Soc; Sigma Xi; Tech Asn Pulp & Paper Indust; Fedn Socs Paint Technol; Am Soc Testing & Mat. *Res:* Coatings, polymers, adhesives and inks for paper, wood and metals; powdered polymers, service life of polymeric materials, processing of plastics. *Mailing Add:* Polymer & Paper Chem Battelle-Columbus 505 King Ave Columbus OH 43201

JOHNSTON, HUGH WILLIAM, b Butte, Mont, Feb 24, 20; m 69; c 1. ORGANIC CHEMISTRY. *Educ:* Mont State Col, BS, 41; Univ Ill, MS, 44; Ind Univ, PhD(chem), 48. *Prof Exp:* Res chemist plastics, Bakelite Co, 48-53; asst prof chem, Newark Cols, Rutgers Univ, 53-57; from assoc prof to prof chem, 64-75, DIR DEVELOP SERV, WHITWORTH COL, 75- *Res:* Friedel-Crafts catalysis of cyanoethylation, coumarins and dihydrocoumarins; degradation of ketones. *Mailing Add:* N 4532 Royal Ct Spokane WA 99205

JOHNSTON, JAMES BAKER, b Baton Rouge, La, Sept 10, 46; m 70; c 3. MARINE SCIENCES, SCIENCE EDUCATION. *Educ:* La State Univ, Baton Rouge, BS, 70, MEd, 71; Univ Southern Miss, PhD(sci educ, biol), 73. *Prof Exp:* Oceanographer marine biol, Bur Land Mgt, New Orleans, 74-76; ECOLOGIST, US FISH & WILDLIFE SERV, US DEPT INTERIOR, MISS, 76- *Concurrent Pos:* Math instr & NSF consult, Prentiss Inst & Jr Col, 72-73; marine res asst, Univ Southern Miss, Gulf Univs Res Consortium, 72-73; marine fisheries mgt consult, Miss Marine Res Coun, 73-74. *Honors & Awards:* Edward H Hillard Award, Nat Wildlife Fedn, 72. *Mem:* Ecol Soc Am; Explorers Club; Estuarine Res Fedn. *Res:* Characterization and geophysical mapping of offshore reefs and banks; marine fisheries management; ecosystem characterization and system analysis of coastal regions; development of marine science education programs. *Mailing Add:* US Fish & Wildlife Serv 1010 Gause BN4 Slidell LA 70458

JOHNSTON, JAMES BENNETT, b San Diego, Calif, Dec 31, 43; m 69; c 2. BIODEGRADATION, GENETIC ENGINEERING. *Educ:* Univ Md, College Park, BS, 66; Univ Wis-Madison, PhD(biochem), 70. *Prof Exp:* Fel, Inst Pasteur, Paris, 70-71; res fel, Univ Kent, Canterbury, UK, 71-74; vis asst prof, 74-76, ASST PROF, UNIV ILL, URBANA, 76- *Concurrent Pos:* Consult, Cetus Corp, 76-80, Ill Environ Protection Agency, 76-81, Pan Am Health Orgn, 80-, AgroBiotics Corp, 81-; prin investr, var grants, 77- *Mem:* Am Chem Soc; Am Soc Microbiol; US Fedn Culture Collections; AAAS; Environ Mutagen Soc. *Res:* Recovery, detection and identification of environmental mutagens, especially in potable waters, and the genetics of hydrocarbon degradation by bacteria; manipulation of bacterial DNA to improve biodegradations for waste treatment or for the production of specialty chemicals. *Mailing Add:* 2310 Glenoak Champaign IL 61820

JOHNSTON, JAMES DOUGLAS, b Meadville, Pa, Aug 4, 24; m 50; c 4. ORGANIC CHEMISTRY. *Educ:* Purdue Univ, BS, 48, MS, 49; Pa State Univ, PhD(chem), 52. *Prof Exp:* Res chemist, 52-57, res assoc, 57, supvr chem res, 58-65, res adv, Pioneering Res, 65-67, SR RES ADV, PIONEERING RES, ETHYL CORP, 67- *Mem:* AAAS; Am Chem Soc. *Res:* Organic syntheses; organometallic compounds of transition metals; free radical reactions; insecticides; fungicides; detergents and detergent intermediates; chemistry of olefins; aluminum alkyls; pharmaceutical products; genetic engineering. *Mailing Add:* Ethyl Corp PO Box 341 Baton Rouge LA 70821

JOHNSTON, JAMES P(AUL), b Pittsburgh, Pa, May 11, 31; m 57; c 5. MECHANICAL ENGINEERING, FLUID DYNAMICS. *Educ:* Mass Inst Technol, BS & MS, 54, ScD(mech eng), 57. *Prof Exp:* Res engr, Ingersoll-Rand Co. NJ, 58-61; from asst prof to assoc prof, 61-73, PROF MECH ENG, STANFORD UNIV, 73- *Concurrent Pos:* Instr, Night Grad Sch Prog, Lehigh Univ, 59-60; Am Soc Mech Engrs-Freeman fel, 67; vis res scientist, Nat Phys Lab, Teddington, Eng, 67-68. *Honors & Awards:* Robert T Knapp Award, Am Soc Mech Engrs, 75. *Mem:* AAAS; Am Soc Mech Engrs; Am Inst Aeronaut & Astronaut. *Res:* Fluid dynamics of real fluids, particularly two and three dimensional turbulent boundary layers; effects of coordinate system rotation on the turbulent boundary layer; fluid flow in ducts, diffusers and tubomachinery, especially internal flow. *Mailing Add:* Dept of Mech Eng Stanford Univ Stanford CA 94305

JOHNSTON, JEAN VANCE, b Shippensburg, Pa, Feb 17, 12. ORGANIC CHEMISTRY. *Educ:* Smith Col, AB, 34; Yale Univ, PhD(org chem), 38. *Prof Exp:* Asst chem, Smith Col, 39; instr pvt sch, Conn, 40; asst prof chem, Furman Univ, 40-42; from instr to assoc prof chem, 42-74, EMER ASSOC PROF CHEM, CONN COL, 74- *Concurrent Pos:* Fel, Pa State Univ, 69-70. *Mem:* Am Chem Soc. *Res:* Synthesis of organic compounds of medicinal interest; amidines. *Mailing Add:* 505 W King St Shippensburg PA 17257

JOHNSTON, JOHN, b Newcastle-on-Tyne, Eng, Nov 8, 25; US citizen; m 47; c 3. RUBBER CHEMISTRY. *Educ:* Hull Col Technol, BSc, 58. *Prof Exp:* Teacher, County Educ Authorities, Hull, Eng, 48-49; chemist, Standard Oil Co, Saltend, 49-50 & T J Smith & Nephew Ltd, Hull, 50-58; res chemist, Arno Adhesive Tape Inc, 59-67, asst dir res pressure sensitive adhesives, 67, dir res, 68-71, dir res & develop, 71-73, vpres res, Develop & Tech Opers, 73-77; dir tech serv, Johnson & Johnson, 77-78; DIR RES, TUCK INDUSTS, 78- *Concurrent Pos:* lectr, Purdue Univ, North Regional Campus, 65-71; chmn, Pressure Sensitive Tape Coun Tech Comt, 74-76. *Mem:* Am Chem Soc. *Res:* Theory and practice of pressure sensitive adhesives. *Mailing Add:* Tuck Industs 1 Lefeyre Lane New Rochelle NY 10801

JOHNSTON, JOHN B(EVERLEY), b Los Angeles, Calif, Aug 11, 29; m 66; c 1. COMPUTER SCIENCE. *Educ:* Calif Inst Technol, BS, 51, PhD(math), 55. *Prof Exp:* Instr math, Cornell Univ, 55-57; asst prof, Univ Kansas City, 57-58; from asst prof to assoc prof, Univ Kans, 58-64; mathematician, Gen Elec Res & Develop Ctr, NY, 64-68; assoc prof comput sci, Ind Univ, Bloomington, 68-69; info scientist, Gen Elec Res & Develop Ctr, NY, 69-71; PROF COMPUT SCI, NMEX STATE UNIV, 71- *Mem:* Asn Comput Mach. *Res:* Structure of computation; computer languages; structure of computer systems. *Mailing Add:* Dept of Comput Sci NMex State Univ Las Cruces NM 88001

JOHNSTON, JOHN ERIC, b Detroit, Mich, Feb 5, 48. POLYMER CHEMISTRY, ANALYTICAL CHEMISTRY. *Educ:* Univ Notre Dame, BS, 70; Univ Akron, PhD(polymer sci), 75. *Prof Exp:* Fel polymer sci, Ctr Macromolecular Res, 75; sr chemist polymer synthesis & characterization, Union Carbide Corp, 76-80; HEAD, VISCOSITY INDEX MODIFIER RES GROUP, EXXON CHEM CO, 81- *Mem:* Am Chem Soc; Soc Automotive Engrs. *Res:* Novel polymer processes and polymer characterization techniques; polymer structure, process and property correlations; polymer colloid morphology; process relationships; lubricant additives. *Mailing Add:* Exxon Chem Co PO Box 536 Linden NJ 07036

JOHNSTON, JOHN MARSHALL, b North Platte, Nebr, Nov 14, 28; m 53; c 3. BIOCHEMISTRY. *Educ:* Hastings Col, BA, 49; Univ Colo, PhD, 53. *Prof Exp:* Res assoc, Walter Reed Inst Res, 53-55; from instr to assoc prof, 55-66, PROF BIOCHEM, UNIV TEX HEALTH SCI CTR, DALLAS, 66-, PROF OBSTET & GYNEC, 74- *Concurrent Pos:* NSF sr res fel, Univ Lund, 62-63. *Mem:* AAAS; Am Chem Soc; Am Soc Biol Chemists. *Res:* Lipid metabolism in absorption; fetal lung maturation, partuition and membranes. *Mailing Add:* Dept of Biochem Univ of Tex Health Sci Ctr Dallas TX 75235

JOHNSTON, JOHN O'NEAL, b Baltimore, Md, July 21, 39. REPRODUCTIVE ENDOCRINOLOGY, NEUROPHARMACOLOGY. *Educ:* Univ Md, College Park, BS, 61, MS, 65, PhD(reproductive physiol), 70. *Prof Exp:* Res asst reproductive physiol, Agr Res Serv, USDA, 61-65; res asst, Dept Animal Sci, Univ Md, 65-69; res scientist fertil res, Upjohn Co, 69-71; res endocrinology, 71-73, sect head endocrinol, 73-81, SR RES ENDOCRINOLOGIST, BIOCHEM DEPT, MERRELL RES CTR, MERRELL DOW PHARMACEUTICALS INC, DOW CHEM CO, 81- *Concurrent Pos:* Biol adv, Life Sci Div, Res Triangle Park, NC, 75-78; consult, Vet Pharmaceut, Jensen-Salsbery Labs, 72-79. *Mem:* Soc Study Reproduction; Am Soc Andrology; Int Soc Psychoneuroendocrinol; NY Acad Sci; AAAS. *Res:* Development of therapeutic agents for control of male

and female fertility; regulation of hormonal action via receptor mechanism in target tissues; animal growth stimulants; neuroendocrine pharmacology of animal behavior; enzyme inhibitors for regulation of endocrine dependent cancer and reproductive processes. *Mailing Add:* Merrell Res Ctr Merrell Dow Pharmaceut Inc 2110 Galbraith Cincinnati OH 45215

JOHNSTON, JOHN SPENCER, b Phoenix, Ariz, May 27, 44; m 66; c 1. GENETICS. *Educ:* Univ Wash, BS, 66; Univ Ariz, PhD(genetics), 72. *Prof Exp:* NIH fel, Univ Tex, Austin, 72-75; asst prof biol, Baylor Univ, Waco, 75-79; ASSOC PROF GENETICS, TEX A&M UNIV, 79- *Concurrent Pos:* Res grant, Energy Res Develop Asn & Univ Tex, Austin, 73- *Mem:* AAAS; Genetics Soc Am; Evolution Soc Am; Soc Am Naturalists. *Res:* Ecological genetics of Drosophila species. *Mailing Add:* Dept Plant Sci Tex A&M Univ College Station TX 77843

JOHNSTON, KATHARINE GENTRY, b Minneapolis, Kans, Jan 19, 21; m 50; c 2. INDUSTRIAL ORGANIC CHEMISTRY. *Educ:* Kans State Univ, BS, 42, MS, 50. *Prof Exp:* Res chemist, Org Div, Monsanto Chem Co, 51-71; RES SCIENTIST CLIN DIAG, AMES CO, DIV MILES LABS, 71- *Mem:* Sigma Xi; AAAS; Am Chem Soc. *Res:* Organic and enzymatic reactions in clinical diagnostic systems; complex formation and stabilization; ion temperature polymerization. *Mailing Add:* Ames Co Div Miles Labs 1127 Myrtle St Elkhart IN 46514

JOHNSTON, KENNETH JOHN, b New York, NY, Oct 9, 41; m 66. ASTRONOMY. *Educ:* Manhattan Col, BEE, 64; Georgetown Univ, PhD(astron), 69. *Prof Exp:* Nat Acad Sci-Nat Res Coun res assoc astron, 69-71, ASTRONOMER, NAVAL RES LAB, 71- *Mem:* Am Astron Soc. *Res:* Radio astronomy; variable stars. *Mailing Add:* Naval Res Lab Code 7132 Washington DC 20390

JOHNSTON, LAURANCE S, b St Paul, Minn, Aug 4, 50; m 75. HEALTH SCIENCE ADMINISTRATION. *Educ:* Hamline Univ, BS, 72; Northwestern Univ, Evanston, MS, 73, PhD(biochem & molecular biol), 77. *Prof Exp:* Fel, Dept Biochem & Molecular Biol, Northwestern Univ, 76-77; fel, Chicago Med Sch, 77-78; consumer safety officer, Div Food & Color Additives, Bur Foods, Food & Drug Admin, Washington, DC, 78-79, mem, food animal additives staff, 79-81; HEALTH SCIENTIST ADMINR, NAT INST CHILD HEALTH & HUMAN DEVELOP, NIH, 81- *Mem:* Am Chem Soc; AAAS. *Res:* Health science administration; regulatory science; bacterial cell wall and membrane biochemistry; the role of cell-surface glycosaminoglycans and carbohydrates in cellular interactions and growth. *Mailing Add:* Nat Inst Child Health & Human Develop 7910 Woodmont Ave Rm C608 Bethesda MD 20205

JOHNSTON, LAVERNE ALBERT, b Hallettsville, Tex, Mar 7, 30; m 61; c 2. BOTANY. *Educ:* Baylor Univ, AB, 51, MA, 57; Southwestern Baptist Theol Sem, MRE, 54. *Prof Exp:* Teacher, Gonzales Ind Sch Dist, 51-52; instr & asst prof biol, Baylor Univ, 54-60; res asst bot, Univ Tex, Austin, 76-80; TECH WRITER, 80- *Mem:* Am Inst Biol Sci; Bot Soc Am. *Res:* Phycology; angiosperm taxonomy. *Mailing Add:* 3905 Ave G Austin TX 78751

JOHNSTON, LAWRENCE HARDING, b Tse-Nan-Fu, China, Feb 11, 18; US citizen; m 42; c 5. OPTICAL PHYSICS. *Educ:* Univ Calif, AB, 40, PhD(physics), 50. *Prof Exp:* Res assoc, Radiation Lab, Mass Inst Technol, 40-43; res assoc, Los Alamos Sci Lab, Univ Calif, 43-45; asst, Lawrence Radiation Lab, Univ Calif, 45-50; from instr to assoc prof physics, Univ Minn, Minneapolis, 50-61; sr scientist, Aerospace Corp, 61-63; sr staff mem, Stanford Linear Accelerator Ctr, 63-67; PROF PHYSICS, UNIV IDAHO, 67- *Mem:* Fel Am Phys Soc; fel Am Sci Affil. *Res:* Far infrared physics; molecular spectroscopy; microwave radar; atom bomb development; proton linear accelerator development; nuclear and high energy particle physics; proton-proton scattering. *Mailing Add:* 917 E Eighth St Moscow ID 83843

JOHNSTON, MALCOLM CAMPBELL, b Montague, PEI, Feb 13, 31; m 55. TERATOLOGY, DEVELOPMENTAL BIOLOGY. *Educ:* Univ Toronto, DDS, 54, MScD, 56; Univ Rochester, PhD(anat), 65. *Prof Exp:* Res assoc clin res, Cleft Palate Res & Treat Ctr, Hosp Sick Children, Toronto, 56-60; asst & assoc prof hist, Sch Dent & Med, Univ Toronto, 64-69; vis scientist, NIH, Bethesda, Md, 69-76; PROF ORTHODONT & ANAT, SCH DENT & MED, UNIV NC, 76- *Concurrent Pos:* Sect ed, Cleft Palate J, 81- *Mem:* Sigma Xi; Am Cleft Palate Asn; Teratology Soc; Am Asn Anatomists. *Res:* Normal and abnormal embryonic craniofacial development in mice, with limited studies on man. *Mailing Add:* Dent Res Ctr Univ NC Chapel Hill NC 27514

JOHNSTON, MANLEY RODERICK, b Edmonton, Alta, Oct 2, 42; m 67. ORGANIC POLYMER CHEMISTRY. *Educ:* Univ Alta, BSc, 64; Univ Ill, Urbana, MS, 66, PhD(org chem), 69. *Prof Exp:* Sr chemist, 68-72, res specialist, 72-73, supvr, 73-78, tech mgr, Bldg Serv & Cleaning Prod Div, 78-82, LAB MGR, NONWOVENS TECHNOL CTR, 3M CO, 82- *Mem:* Am Chem Soc; Royal Soc Chem. *Res:* Small ring compounds; organic coatings; metal finishing; adhesion; high temperature polymers; fibers; polymerization catalysts; fluorine chemistry. *Mailing Add:* 531 Robert Ct St Paul MN 55115

JOHNSTON, MARILYN FRANCES MEYERS, b Buffalo, NY, Mar 30, 37. BIOCHEMISTRY, IMMUNOLOGY. *Educ:* Rosary Hill Col, BS, 66; St Louis Univ, PhD(biochem), 70, MD, 75. *Prof Exp:* NIH fel, Washington Univ, 70-72; instr biochem, Sch Med, St Louis Univ, 72-75; resident path, Sch Med, Wash Univ, 75-77; resident path, St John's Mercy Med Ctr, 77-79; fel path & med, 79-80, ASST PROF PATH, MED SCH, ST LOUIS UNIV, 80- *Concurrent Pos:* AMA J Goldberger fel, St Louis Univ, 74. *Mem:* Am Chem Soc; Col Am Pathologists; Am Asn Immunologists. *Res:* Biosynthesis of vitamin K dependent clotting proteins; immunoglobulin biosynthesis; antibody active site structure; pathology. *Mailing Add:* Sch Med St Louis Univ St Louis MO 63104

JOHNSTON, MARSHALL CONRING, b San Antonio, Tex, May 10, 30; m 61; c 2. SYSTEMATIC BOTANY. *Educ:* Univ Tex, BS, 51, MA, 52, PhD(bot), 55. *Prof Exp:* Fel, Rice Inst, 55; asst prof biol, Sul Ross State Col, 58-59; res scientist bot, 59-61, assoc prof, 61-72, PROF BOT, UNIV TEX, AUSTIN, 72- *Concurrent Pos:* Sci asst, Univ Munich, 68-69; dir, Rare Plant Study Ctr, 72- *Mem:* AAAS; Bot Soc Am; Am Soc Plant Taxon; Int Soc Plant Taxon; Am Inst Biol Sci. *Res:* Distribution of vegetation types; systematics and historical biogeography of vascular plants of southwestern United States and northern Mexico; flora of Texas. *Mailing Add:* Dept of Bot Univ of Tex Austin TX 78712

JOHNSTON, MARTHA M, b Pittsburgh, Pa, Sept 28, 42; div; c 1. BIOCHEMISTRY. *Educ:* Carnegie Inst Technol, BS, 64; Univ Pittsburgh, PhD(biochem), 69. *Prof Exp:* Res fel biochem, Sloan-Kettering Inst, 69-71; res fel pharmacol, Columbia Univ, 71-74; sr biochemist, USV Pharmaceut Corp, Revlon, Inc, 74-76, sect head drug disposition, 76-80, ASST DIR, DRUG REGULATORY AFFAIRS, REVLON HEALTH CARE GROUP, REVLON, INC, 80- *Mem:* Am Chem Soc; AAAS; Acad Pharmaceut Sci; Am Soc Pharmacol & Exp Therapeut. *Res:* Development of analytical methods for the analysis of drugs, drug metabolism, pharmacokinetics and biopharmaceutics. *Mailing Add:* Dept Regulatory Affairs 1 Scarsdale Rd Tuckahoe NY 10707

JOHNSTON, MARY HELEN, b WPalm Beach, Fla, Sept 17, 45. FAILURE ANALYSIS. *Educ:* Fla State Univ, BS, 66, MS, 69; Univ Fla, PhD(metal eng), 73. *Prof Exp:* MAT ENGR, GEORGE C MARSHALL SPACE FLIGHT CTR, NASA, 69-; MEM STAFF METALL, UNIV ALA, HUNTSVILLE, 80- *Concurrent Pos:* Prin investr, Marshall Space Flight Ctr, NASA, 76-; pres, Metall Eng Technol Ala, Inc, 82- *Mem:* Am Soc Metals; Nat Soc Prof Engrs. *Res:* Directional solidification of metallic (in situ), including immiscible systems and superalloys; influence of gravity effects on solidification structures in castings; single crystal; undercooling; x-ray diffraction. *Mailing Add:* Mat Sci EH 22 Marshall Space Flight Ctr Huntsville AL 35812

JOHNSTON, MELVIN ROSCOE, b McAlester, Okla, June 23, 21; m 46; c 2. FOOD TECHNOLOGY. *Educ:* Agr & Mech Col Tex, BS, 48; Ore State Col, MS, 50; Univ Mo, PhD, 56. *Prof Exp:* Instr food technol, Ore State Col, 48-50; food technologist, Libby, McNeil & Libby, 50-52; from instr to asst prof hort, Univ Mo, 52-59; prof food technol & adv dept, Univ Tenn, Knoxville, 59-73; CHIEF, FRUIT & VEG BR, DIV FOOD TECHNOL, BUR FOODS, FOOD & DRUG ADMIN, HEW, 73- *Mem:* Fel Inst Food Technologists; Sigma Xi. *Res:* Implementation and support of regulatory action; food color technology; freezing; freeze-drying and thermal processing of foods. *Mailing Add:* Plant & Protein Technol Br HFF-214 200 C St SW Washington DC 20204

JOHNSTON, MICHAEL ADAIR, b May 26, 46; US citizen. BIOORGANIC CHEMISTRY, MEDICINAL CHEMISTRY. *Educ:* Colo Col, BA, 68; Univ Glasgow, MS, 69; Yale Univ, MPhil, 71, PhD(biochem), 73. *Prof Exp:* Asst prof biochem, Holy Cross Col, 73-78; NIH res fel, Dept Chem, Mass Inst Technol, 78-80; ASST PROF CHEM & BIOCHEM, UNIV CHICAGO, 81- *Concurrent Pos:* Vis scientist, Dept Chem, Mass Inst Technol, 77-78. *Mem:* AAAS; Am Chem Soc. *Res:* enzyme active-site chemistry and bioorganic reaction mechanisms; design and synthesis of enzyme inactivators; design of drug delivery systems. *Mailing Add:* Dept Chem Univ Chicago 5735 Ellis Ave Chicago IL 60037

JOHNSTON, MILTON DWYNELL, JR, b Hillsboro, Ore, Nov 4, 43. PHYSICAL CHEMISTRY, MOLECULAR SPECTROSCOPY. *Educ:* Portland State Univ, BA, 65, Princeton Univ, AM, 68, PhD(chem), 69. *Prof Exp:* Res assoc nuclear magnetic resonance, Univ Ariz, 70-71; res assoc, Tex A&M Univ, 71-73; asst prof, 73-80, ASSOC PROF CHEM, UNIV SOUTH FLA, 80- *Mem:* Am Chem Soc; Am Phys Soc; The Chem Soc; Sigma Xi; NY Acad Sci. *Res:* Nuclear magnetic resonance solvent effects; theory of nuclear magnetic resonance spectral parameters; theory of liquids and liquid solutions and of intermolecular forces. *Mailing Add:* Dept of Chem Univ of SFla Tampa FL 33620

JOHNSTON, MURIEL EVELYN, radiobiology, see previous edition

JOHNSTON, NAOMI LEMKEY, b Oak Park, Ill, Jan 16, 32; m 64. NEUROANATOMY, ANATOMY. *Educ:* Univ Mich, BS, 54; Northwestern Univ, MS, 55, PhD(histochem), 62. *Prof Exp:* Res asst histochem, Sch Med, Northwestern Univ, 55-58; from instr to asst prof histol, Loyola Univ, 62-64; NIMH training grant, 64-66; asst prof, 66-69, ASSOC PROF ANAT, UNIV ILL COL MED, 69- *Concurrent Pos:* From res assoc to sr investr anat, Ill State Pediat Inst, 66-75. *Mem:* AAAS; Soc Cell Biologists; Asn Am Anatomists; Asn Neurosci. *Res:* Developmental neurobiology; analysis of structure and chemical composition of subcellular fractions of cerebellum, especially conducting membranes and synaptic membranes; electron microscopy of developing nervous system. *Mailing Add:* Dept of Anat Univ of Ill Col of Med Chicago IL 60612

JOHNSTON, NORMAN JOSEPH, b Charles Town, WVa, Dec 15, 34; m 57; c 4. ORGANIC POLYMER CHEMISTRY. *Educ:* Shepherd Col, BS, 56; Univ Va, PhD(org chem), 63. *Prof Exp:* Chemist insulating mat dept, Gen Elec Co, 61-63; asst prof chem, Va Polytech Inst & State Univ, 66-67; Nat Acad Sci-Nat Res Coun resident res fel, Langley Res Ctr, 66-67, aerospace technologist & chemist, 67-70, head polymer sect, 70-80. *Mem:* Am Chem Soc; Soc Aerospace Mat & Process Engrs. *Res:* Synthesis and characterization of high performance polymers and their evaluation as composite matrices, adhesives and space stable films. *Mailing Add:* Langley Res Ctr NASA Mail Stop 226 Hampton VA 23665

JOHNSTON, NORMAN PAUL, b Salt Lake City, Utah, Apr 5, 41; m 66; c 5. ANIMAL NUTRITION, REPRODUCTION BIOLOGY. *Educ:* Brigham Young Univ, BA, 66; Ore State Univ, MS, 67, PhD(avian nutrit), 71; Univ Utah, MBA, 69. *Prof Exp:* Animal nutritionist, Brookfield Prod Inc, 69-70; PROF ANIMAL SCI, BRIGHAM YOUNG UNIV, 71- *Mem:* Sigma Xi; Poultry Sci; Am Soc Animal Sci; World Poultry Sci. *Res:* Poultry reproduction, in particular artificial insemination. *Mailing Add:* 1795 South 340E Orem UT 84057

JOHNSTON, NORMAN WILSON, b Pittsburgh, Pa, June 18, 42; m 65; c 3. POLYMER CHEMISTRY. *Educ:* Clarion State Col, BS, 64; Univ Akron, PhD(polymer sci), 68. *Prof Exp:* Chemist polymer chem, Ethyl Corp, 65; sr chemist, Union Carbide Corp, 68-71, proj scientist, 71-72, group leader adhesives, coatings & moldings, 72-76; assoc dir res & develop, 76-77, lab dir, 77-79, res dir, 78-81, MGR BUS & TECH PLANNING, OWENS-CORNING FIBERGLAS CORP, 81- *Mem:* Am Chem Soc. *Res:* Polymer structure--property relationships, polymer synthesis, coatings, adhesives, fire retardance, molding and extrusion, composites, polymer blends, degradable plastics, cement, foams, insulation. *Mailing Add:* Owens-Corning Fiberglas Corp Fiberglas Tower One Levis Sq Toledo OH 43659

JOHNSTON, PAUL BRUNS, b Chicago. Ill, Apr 2, 27; wid; c 3. MEDICAL MICROBIOLOGY. *Educ:* Northwestern Univ, BS, 49; Loyola Univ, Ill, MS, 51; Univ Chicago, PhD(microbiol), 57. *Prof Exp:* Virologist, US Naval Med Res Unit 2, Taiwan, 57-60; asst prof microbiol, Jefferson Med Col, 60-64; ASSOC PROF MICROBIOL, SCH MED, UNIV LOUISVILLE, 64- *Concurrent Pos:* Instr, Univ Chicago, 57-60. *Mem:* Am Soc Microbiol; Soc Exp Biol & Med; Tissue Cult Asn; Am Asn Immunol. *Res:* Nature of latent virus infections; simian foamy virus immunology; adenoviruses. *Mailing Add:* Dept of Microbiol Sch of Med Univ of Louisville Louisville KY 40232

JOHNSTON, PERRY MAX, b Edgewood, Tex, Feb 6, 21; m 43; c 4. VERTEBRATE EMBRYOLOGY. *Educ:* NTex State Col, BS, 40, MS, 42; Univ Mich, PhD(zool), 49. *Prof Exp:* From asst prof to assoc prof zool, 49-54, PROF ZOOL, UNIV ARK, FAYETTEVILLE, 54-, CHMN DEPT, 66- *Concurrent Pos:* Res partic, Oak Ridge Inst Nuclear Studies, 53-54. *Mem:* Am Soc Zool; Am Micros Soc. *Res:* Vertebrate embryology; embryology of centrarchid fishes; utilization of radioisotopes by vertebrate embryos. *Mailing Add:* Dept of Zool Univ of Ark Fayetteville AR 72701

JOHNSTON, RAYMOND F, b Fenton, Mo, June 29, 13; m 35; c 1. PHYSIOLOGY, PHARMACOLOGY. *Educ:* Univ Mo, BS, 35; Mich State Univ, MS, 48, DVM, 49; Univ Minn, PhD, 59. *Prof Exp:* Instr voc agr, Univ Mo, 35-45; asst path, 45-47, asst physiol, 47-49, PROF PHYSIOL, MICH STATE UNIV, 49- *Concurrent Pos:* Sr mem team vet to Indonesia, 60-62. *Mem:* Fel Am Vet Med Asn. *Res:* Toxicology; cardiovascular physiology; neurophysiology; biomedical communications. *Mailing Add:* Dept of Physiol Mich State Univ East Lansing MI 48823

JOHNSTON, RICHARD BOLES, JR, b Atlanta, Ga, Aug 23, 35; m 60; c 3. PEDIATRICS. *Educ:* Vanderbilt Univ, BA, 57, MD, 61. *Prof Exp:* NIH fel, Harvard Med Sch, 67-68, USPHS training grant, 68-69, NIH spec fel, 69-70; from asst prof to assoc prof pediat & microbiol, Univ Ala, Birmingham, 70-77; DIR DEPT PEDIAT, NAT JEWISH HOSP & RES CTR, DENVER, 77-; PROF PEDIAT, SCH MED, UNIV COLO, 77-, VCHMN DEPT, 80- *Concurrent Pos:* Macy Found scholar, Rockefeller Univ, NY, 76-77. *Mem:* Soc Pediat Res (pres, 80-81); Am Asn Immunologists; Infectious Dis Soc Am; Am Soc Clin Invest; Am Pediat Soc. *Res:* Mechanisms of resistance to infection; phagocyte function; complement. *Mailing Add:* Nat Jewish Hosp & Res Ctr 3800 E Colfax Denver CO 80206

JOHNSTON, RICHARD FOURNESS, b Oakland, Calif. July 27, 25; m 48; c 3. SYSTEMATICS, ECOLOGY. *Educ:* Univ Calif, BA, 50, MA, 53, PhD, 55. *Prof Exp:* Instr biol, NMex State Univ, 56-57; from asst prof to assoc prof zool, 58-67, assoc cur, 63-67, chmn dept, 79-82, PROF ZOOL, UNIV KANS, 67-, CUR BIRDS, MUS NATURAL HIST, 67- *Concurrent Pos:* Ed, Syst Zool, Syst Cur Syst Zool, 67-70; prog dir syst biol, NSF, 68-69; ed, Annual Rev Ecol & Systematics, 68-, Current Ornith, 81- *Honors & Awards:* Coues Award, Am Ornith Union, 75. *Mem:* Fel AAAS; Ecol Soc Am; fel Am Ornith Union; Soc Study Evolution; Am Soc Naturalists. *Res:* Taxonomy; evolutionary biology; behavior and ecology of birds, especially passerines. *Mailing Add:* Mus of Natural Hist Univ of Kans Lawrence KS 66045

JOHNSTON, RICHARD W(RAY), b Delaware, Ohio, July 27, 25; m 46; c 2. ELECTRICAL & ELECTRONIC ENGINEERING. *Educ:* Ind Inst Technol, BS, 49. *Prof Exp:* Instr electronics, Electronic Inst Inc, 49-51; res assoc, Willow Run Res Ctr, Univ Mich, 51-53; sr proj engr, Electronics Dept, Mfg Develop Staff, 53-61, sr res engr elec propulsion, Res Labs, 61-70, supvr res eng, 70-76, DEPT RES ENGR ELEC ENG, RES LABS, GEN MOTORS CORP, 76- *Mem:* Inst Elec & Electronics Engrs; Soc Automotive Engrs. *Res:* Solid state inverters and control circuits for high performance electric drives; propulsion for electric cars, torpedos, and submarines; variable speed drives for industrial applications. *Mailing Add:* Res Labs 12 Mile & Mound Rds Warren MI 48092

JOHNSTON, ROBERT BENJAMIN, b North Platte, Nebr, Mar 21, 22; m 44; c 2. BIOCHEMISTRY. *Educ:* Hastings Col, AB, 44; Univ Chicago, PhD(biochem), 49. *Prof Exp:* Instr physiol chem, Yale Univ, 53; from asst prof to assoc prof, 53-65, PROF CHEM, UNIV NEBR-LINCOLN, 65- *Concurrent Pos:* USPHS spec fel, Max Planck Inst Cell Chem, Munich, 61-62 & Inst Microbiol Biochem, Erlansen, 78-79. *Mem:* AAAS; Am Chem Soc; Brit Biochem Soc; Am Soc Biol Chemists; NY Acad Sci. *Res:* Enzyme mechanisms and biological synthesis of peptide bonds; amino acid racemases; releasing factors; enkephalins; peptide antibiotics. *Mailing Add:* Dept of Chem Univ of Nebr Lincoln NE 68510

JOHNSTON, ROBERT E, b Philadelphia, Pa, Apr 16, 42; m 70; c 2. BEHAVIOR, ETHOLOGY. *Educ:* Dartmouth Col, AB, 64; Rockefeller Univ, PhD(behav & life sci), 70. *Prof Exp:* Asst prof, 70-78, ASSOC PROF PSYCHOL & BIOL, CORNELL UNIV, 78- *Mem:* AAAS; Animal Behav Soc; Sigma Xi; Am Soc Mammalogists. *Res:* Mechanisms and evolution of behavior, especially reproductive and agressive behavior; communication, including olfactory (pheromones), auditory and visual signals; relationships between hormones and behavior; neural mechanisms of olfaction; human ethology. *Mailing Add:* Dept Psychol Uris Hall Cornell Univ Ithaca NY 14853

JOHNSTON, ROBERT EDWARD, b Houston, Tex, Sept 19, 47; m 76. MICROBIOLOGY, VIROLOGY. *Educ:* Rice Univ, BA, 68; Univ Tex, Austin, PhD(microbiol), 73. *Prof Exp:* Med Res Coun fel microbiol, Queens Univ, 73-76; asst prof microbiol, 76-80, ASSOC PROF MICROBIOL, NC STATE UNIV, 80- *Concurrent Pos:* NIH Young investr grant, NC State Univ, 78-81. *Mem:* Am Soc Microbiol. *Res:* Host cell influence on virus replication. *Mailing Add:* Dept of Microbiol NC State Univ Raleigh NC 27650

JOHNSTON, ROBERT HOWARD, b Martinsville, Ohio, Feb 7, 24; m 56; c 4. MATHEMATICS. *Educ:* Miami Univ, BSEd, 47, MA, 50. *Prof Exp:* From asst & instr math to asst prof air sci, Miami Univ, 47-54; res assoc math & dir res br, Weapons Employ Br, Armed Forces Spec Weapons Command, Albuquerque, 54-57; from instr to asst prof math, US Air Force Acad, 57-61, res assoc, Frank J Seker Res Lab, Off Aerospace Res, 63-64; from asst prof to assoc prof, Dept Math, 64-70, dep head dept, 69-70; ASST PROF MATH SCI, VA COMMONWEALTH UNIV, 70-, DIR MATH AUDIO TUTORIAL LAB, 72- *Concurrent Pos:* Reader, Educ Testing Serv, 69-74, consult calculus & anal geom tests, 73- *Mem:* Am Math Soc; Nat Coun Teachers Math. *Res:* Mathematical audio tutorial laboratories as a vehicle to enable greater background development in the basic mathematics areas. *Mailing Add:* Dept of Math Sci Va Commonwealth Univ Richmond VA 23284

JOHNSTON, ROBERT R, b Oakland, Calif, June 10, 29; m 50; c 3. THEORETICAL PHYSICS. *Educ:* Univ Calif, Berkeley, AB, 54, MA, 56, PhD(physics), 61. *Prof Exp:* Staff mem theoret physics, Los Alamos Sci Lab, 56-63; res scientist res labs, Lockheed Missiles & Space Co, Calif, 63-64; res consult theoret physics, Systs Res & Develop Ctr, Int Bus Mach Corp, 64-65; res scientist, Lockheed Palo Alto Res Labs, 65-73; SCIENTIST, SCI APPLICATIONS, INC, 73- *Concurrent Pos:* Consult, Los Alamos Sci Lab, Univ Calif, 64- *Mem:* Am Phys Soc. *Res:* Computer applications in theoretical physics; atomic and nuclear reaction phenomena; neutron physics; Monte Carlo techniques. *Mailing Add:* Sci Applications Inc 2680 Hanover St Palo Alto CA 94304

JOHNSTON, ROBERT WARD, b Buffalo, NY, May 27, 25; m 59; c 2. PHYSICS, ACADEMIC ADMINISTRATION. *Educ:* Cornell Univ, BEE, 46, PhD(physics), 52. *Prof Exp:* Asst physics, Cornell Univ, 46-51, physicist, Aeronaut Lab, 47-48; physicist, Electronics Lab, Gen Elec Co, NY, 51-57; mgr sci & tech rels, Adv Res & Develop Div, Avco Corp, Mass, 57-59; asst prog dir physics, NSF, 59-60, assoc prog dir, 60-61, spec asst to asst dir math, phys & eng sci div, 61, spec asst to assoc dir res, 61-65, exec asst to dir, Washington, DC, 65-69; VChancellor res, Washington Univ, 69-73; ASSOC EXEC OFFICER, NAT ACAD SCI, 73- *Mem:* AAAS; Am Phys Soc. *Res:* Soft x-ray spectroscopy; magnetic materials; solid state physics; research administration. *Mailing Add:* Nat Acad Sci 2101 Constitution Ave Washington DC 20418

JOHNSTON, RONALD HARVEY, b Drumheller, Alta, May 11, 39; m 69. ELECTRONIC ENGINEERING. *Educ:* Univ Alta, BSc, 61; Univ London, DIC & PhD(elec eng), 67. *Prof Exp:* Eng trainee, Can Gen Elec, 61-62; res asst electronics, Queen's Univ, Belfast, 64-67; mem scientific staff res & develop, Northern Elec Co Ltd, 67-69; asst prof, 70-77, ASSOC PROF ELECTRONICS, UNIV CALGARY, 77- *Mem:* Inst Elec & Electronics Engrs. *Res:* Frequency multipliers; transistor amplifiers and multipliers; microwave measurements; semiconductor circuits. *Mailing Add:* Dept of Elec Eng Univ of Calgary Calgary 45 AB T2N 1N4 Can

JOHNSTON, RUSSELL SHAYNE, b Ft William, Ont, Nov 4, 48. PLASMA PHYSICS, APPLIED MATHEMATICS. *Educ:* McGill Univ, BSc, 70; Princeton Univ, PhD(plasma physics), 74. *Prof Exp:* Res asst plasma physics, Plasma Physics Lab, Princeton Univ, 70-74; res fel plasma physics, Lawrence Berkeley Lab, Univ Calif, 74-76; ASST PROF APPL PHYSICS, COLUMBIA UNIV, 76- *Mem:* Sigma Xi; Am Phys Soc. *Res:* Theoretical plasma physics, particularly nonlinear interactions among waves and particles. *Mailing Add:* Dept of Appl Physics & Nuclear Eng Columbia Univ New York NY 10027

JOHNSTON, SAMUEL PAUL, aeronautical engineering, see previous edition

JOHNSTON, STEWART ARCHIBALD, b Ft William, Ont, Aug 22, 11; nat US; m 32; c 3. PHYSICAL CHEMISTRY. *Educ:* Univ Man, BSc, 32, MSc, 37; Stanford Univ, PhD(phys chem), 49. *Prof Exp:* Demonstr chem, Univ Man, 29-33; lectr physics, United Col, 34-38; asst phys sci, Stanford Univ, 38-39; res chemist, Va Chem Corp, 40-41 & United Color & Pigment Co, 41; develop engr, Western Elec Co, 41-42; instr physics & math, Western Wash Col Educ, 42-43; vis asst prof physics, Univ Southern Calif, 43-44; res engr & actg chief chem sect, Jet Propulsion Lab, Calif Inst Technol, 44-46; chmn div sci & math, Calif State Univ, 53-64, dir res & govt rels, 64-67; prof chem, 52-77; RETIRED. *Concurrent Pos:* Staff engr, Calif Inst Technol, 52-53; chmn dept math, Western Wash Col Educ, 46-52. *Mem:* AAAS; Am Chem Soc. *Res:* Rocket propellants; colloidal electrolytes; phase rule diagrams; direct current amplification. *Mailing Add:* 181 White Oak Dr Arcadia CA 91006

JOHNSTON, TAYLOR JIMMIE, b Newbern, Tenn, May 11, 40; m 66. AGRONOMY, PLANT PHYSIOLOGY. *Educ:* Univ Tenn, Martin, BS, 63; Univ Ill, MS, 65, PhD(agron), 68. *Prof Exp:* From instr to assoc prof, 68-76, PROF CROP SCI, MICH STATE UNIV, 76-, ASST DEAN, COL AGR & NATURAL RESOURCES, 81- *Mem:* Am Soc Agron; Crop Sci Soc Am. *Res:* Photosynthesis of soybeans and general crop physiology and ecology. *Mailing Add:* Col Agr & Natural Resources 121 Agr Hall Mich State Univ East Lansing MI 48823

JOHNSTON, THOMAS M(ATKINS), b Okmulgee, Okla, Dec 8, 21; m 43; c 4. ENGINEERING. *Educ:* US Mil Acad, BS, 43; NY Univ, MS, 49. *Prof Exp:* Instr, Eng Sch, US Army, Va, 47-48, instr math, US Mil Acad, 49-52, commanding officer, 14th Eng Battalion, 53-54, exec officer, Ryukyus Command Eng Serv, Okinawa, 54-55, mem staff, Off Dep Chief of Staff Mil Opers, Pentagon, 56-58; res engr systs eng eval & res, Radio Corp Am, NJ, 58-66, mgr systs anal, 66-67; mgr, Info Systs Dept, Raytheon Co, 67-71; chief, Tech Prog Div, Fed Aviation Admin, 71-79; mgr, Air Traffic Control Systs, Westinghouse Elec Corp, 79-81; PRES, ENREAL ENTERPRISES INC, 81- *Concurrent Pos:* Lectr, Univ Calif, 54-55, Univ Md, 56-57 & Am Univ, 56-58. *Res:* Strategic warning systems; advanced missile systems; military communications systems; satellite systems; air defense systems; command, control and communications systems; ground transportation systems; air traffic control. *Mailing Add:* 3720 Carriage House Ct Alexandria VA 22309

JOHNSTON, TUDOR WYATT, b Montreal, Que, Jan 17, 32; m 58; c 3. PLASMA PHYSICS. *Educ:* McGill Univ, BEng, 53; Cambridge Univ, PhD(eng physics), 58. *Prof Exp:* Sr res scientist, Microwave & Plasma Physics Lab, RCA Victor Co, Ltd, 58-67, plasma & space physics lab, 67-69; assoc prof physics, Univ Houston, 69-73; PROF, INST NAT RES SCI ENERGIE, UNIV QUE, 73- *Concurrent Pos:* Vis prof, Tex A&M Univ, 67; consult, RCA, 70, Can Dept Commun, 71; KMS Fusion, 80-81, Laser Lab, Univ Rochester, 81-82. *Mem:* Fel Am Phys Soc; Can Asn Physicists. *Res:* Plasma theory; computer simulation; nonlinear wave-plasma; laser-plasma interaction. *Mailing Add:* INRS-Energie CP 1020 Varennes PQ J0L 2P0 Can

JOHNSTON, WALTER EDWARD, b Clarksville, Ark, Apr 8, 39; m 60; c 3. STATISTICS. *Educ:* Tex A&M Univ, BS, 60, MS, 65, PhD(statist), 70. *Prof Exp:* Teacher, Tex High Sch, 60-61; from asst prof to prof exp statist, Clemson Univ, 67-78; ASSOC PROF, SOUTHWEST TEX STATE UNIV, SAN MARCOS, 80- *Mem:* Am Statist Asn. *Res:* Application of statistical methods in agricultural and biological research. *Mailing Add:* Dept Statist 203-DH Southwest Tex State Univ San Marcos TX 78666

JOHNSTON, WILBUR DEXTER, JR, b New Haven, Conn, July 6, 40; m 63; c 2. PHYSICS, ELECTRICAL ENGINEERING. *Educ:* Yale Univ, BS, 61; Mass Inst Technol, PhD(physics), 66. *Prof Exp:* Res asst electronics, Mass Inst Technol, 61-66; mem tech staff, 66-79, SUPVR, SOLID STATE MAT, BELL TEL LABS, 80- *Mem:* AAAS; Inst Elec & Electronics Engrs; Electrochem Soc. *Res:* Optical communications; laser physics; non-linear optics; semiconductor lasers; solar cells; heterojunction and compound semiconductor device physics; vapor phase epitaxial growth of semiconductor materials; materials science. *Mailing Add:* Bell Tel Labs MH-7C-317 Murray Hill NJ 07974

JOHNSTON, WILLIAM CARGILL, b Clarinda, Iowa, Aug 31, 17; m 47; c 4. SOLID STATE PHYSICS. *Educ:* Davidson Col, BA, 39; Univ Va, MA, 42, PhD(physics), 43. *Prof Exp:* Res engr, Westinghouse Elec Corp, 43-68; chmn dept, 68-74, PROF PHYSICS, GEORGE MASON UNIV, 74-, DEAN SUMMER SESSION, 70- *Concurrent Pos:* Instr physics, Carnegie Inst Technol, 45- *Res:* Flame velocity measurements; fundamental combustion; solidification of metals. *Mailing Add:* Dept of Physics George Mason Univ Fairfax VA 22030

JOHNSTON, WILLIAM DWIGHT, b Bellevue, Pa, Jan 17, 28; m 50; c 3. INORGANIC CHEMISTRY. *Educ:* Univ Pittsburgh, BS, 49, MS, 51, PhD(chem), 53. *Prof Exp:* Res engr, Res Labs, Westinghouse Elec Corp, 53-57, adv chemist, 57-62; res chemist, 62-65, asst dir res, 65-69, dir res & develop, 69-74, TECH DIR INT OPERS, PITTSBURGH CORNING CORP, 74- *Mem:* Am Chem Soc; Am Ceramic Soc. *Res:* Glass research; solid state chemistry; crystallography; semiconductors; magnetic materials; inorganic preparations; phase diagrams; thermodynamics; metal chelates. *Mailing Add:* Pittsburgh Corning Corp 800 Presque Isle Dr Pittsburgh PA 15239

JOHNSTON, WILLIAM GEORGE, b CZ, Dec 6, 21; m 46. SOLID STATE PHYSICS. *Educ:* Univ Chicago, BS, 49, MS, 52, PhD(physics), 54. *Prof Exp:* Physicist, Res & Develop Ctr, 54-63, mgr personnel & admin, Gen Physics Res, 63-65 & Metal & Ceramic Physics, 65-69, PHYSICIST, RES & DEVELOP CTR, GEN ELEC CO, 69- *Concurrent Pos:* Coolidge fel, Gen Elec Co, 75. *Mem:* Fel Am Phys Soc; Am Inst Mining, Metall & Petrol Eng. *Res:* Defects in crystals; crystal plasticity; fracture of crystals; ionic conductivity; radiation damage; radiation metallurgy. *Mailing Add:* Corp Res & Develop Ctr Gen Elec Co PO Box 8 Schenectady NY 12301

JOHNSTON, WILLIAM V, b Berkeley, Calif, May 6, 27; m 51; c 4. PHYSICAL CHEMISTRY & METALLURGY. *Educ:* Col Wooster, BA, 50; Univ Pittsburgh, PhD(phys chem), 55. *Hon Degrees:* Cert of Recognition, NASA, 73. *Prof Exp:* Asst, Univ Pittsburgh, 50-55; sr cryogenic operator, Ohio State Univ, 52; res assoc, Knolls Atomic Power Lab, Gen Elec Co, 55-61; res specialist, Atomics Int Div, N Am Aviation Corp, 61-62; group leader phys metall, Sci Ctr, 62-69, prin scientist, N Am Rockwell Corp, 69, mem tech staff, Rocketdyne Div, 69-72; nuclear engr, US Atomic Energy Comn, 72-74; br chief, Fuel Behav Res Br, 74-80, ASST DIR, DIV ENG, US NUCLEAR REGULATORY COMN, 80- *Concurrent Pos:* Chmn working group on nuclear safety, Orgn Econ Coop & Develop/Int Energy Agency, 75; chmn, Halden Reactor Proj, Orgn Econ Coop & Develop, 81. *Mem:* Am Chem Soc; Am Inst Mining, Metall & Petrol Engrs; AAAS; Am Nuclear Soc. *Res:* Metal physics; calorimetry; nuclear fuels; solid electrolytes; solution thermodynamics; bound water; nuclear safety; nuclear materials. *Mailing Add:* 17600 Stoneridge Ct Gaithersburg MD 20878

JOHNSTON, WILLIAM WEBB, b Statesville, NC, Aug 26, 33. PATHOLOGY, CYTOLOGY. *Educ:* Davidson Col, BS, 54; Duke Univ, MD, 59; Am Bd Path, dipl. *Prof Exp:* Res training prog grant, Duke Univ, 60-61, res fel path, 61-63, assoc, 63-65, from asst prof to assoc prof, 65-72, PROF PATH, MED CTR, DUKE UNIV, 72-, DIR CYTOPATH, 66-, FAC CLIN CANCER TRAINING PROG, 66- *Concurrent Pos:* Consult path, Durham Vet Admin Hosp, 66-; mem bd dirs, Am Cancer Soc, Durham County. *Honors & Awards:* Ortho Award, Can Soc Cytol, 72. *Mem:* Am Asn Path; Am Soc Cytol (pres, 81-82); fel Am Soc Clin Path; fel Int Acad Cytol. *Res:* Basic diagnostic methods in cytopathology. *Mailing Add:* Dept of Path Duke Univ Med Ctr Durham NC 27710

JOHNSTONE, C(HARLES) WILKIN, b Alamosa, Colo, Aug 22, 16; m 47; c 2. NUCLEAR PHYSICS, INSTRUMENTATION. *Educ:* Colo Col, AB, 38; Dartmouth Col, AM, 40. *Prof Exp:* Asst physics, Colo Col, 37-38, Dartmouth Col, 38-40 & Pa State Col, 40-41; proj engr, Navy Dept Proj, Sperry Gyroscope Co, NY, 41-44, Naval Res Lab, Washington, DC, 44-45, in charge marine radar design & develop, NY, 45-47; mem staff electronics res, Los Alamos Sci Lab, Calif, 47-56; develop proj engr, 56-60, sect head nuclear physics, 60-68, SR DEVELOP PROJ ENGR, ENG PHYSICS DEPT, SCHLUMBERGER WELL SERV, 68- *Mem:* Inst Elec & Electronics Engrs. *Res:* Specialized electronic circuits for IFF, radar and nuclear research, and instrumentation; radioactivity techniques and apparatus for well logging. *Mailing Add:* Eng Physics Dept PO Box 2175 Houston TX 77001

JOHNSTONE, DONALD BOYES, b Newport, RI, July 25, 19; m 49; c 3. MICROBIOLOGY. *Educ:* RI State Col, BS, 42; Rutgers Univ, MS, 43, PhD(microbiol), 48. *Prof Exp:* Bacteriologist, Woods Hole Oceanog Inst, 42-43 & 46; from asst prof to assoc prof microbiol, 48-58, PROF MICROBIOL, UNIV VT, 58-, CHMN DEPT AGR BIOCHEM, 59-, MICROBIOLOGIST, AGR EXP STA, 48-, DEAN GRAD COL, 69- *Mem:* AAAS; Am Soc Microbiol; fel Am Acad Microbiol. *Res:* Marine bacteriology; antibiotics from higher plants; isolation of streptomycin producing actinomycetes; vitamin B-12 sources; whey utilization; azotobacter metabolism; classification; fluorescent pigments; extra-cellular polysaccharides; pesticide degradation. *Mailing Add:* Dept Microbiol & Biochem Univ Vt Burlington VT 05401

JOHNSTONE, DONALD LEE, b Bluefield, WVa, Feb 4, 39; m 62; c 1. BACTERIOLOGY. *Educ:* Eastern Wash State Col, BA, 64; Wash State Univ, MS, 66, PhD(aquatic bact), 70. *Prof Exp:* Asst prof civil eng & asst sanit scientist, Res Div, Col Eng, 69-76, ASSOC PROF CIVIL & ENVIRON ENG, WASH STATE UNIV, 76- *Concurrent Pos:* Mem, Int Conf Dis Nature Communicable to Man, 64. *Mem:* AAAS; Am Soc Microbiol; Water Pollution Control Fedn. *Res:* Interaction of bacteria and soil; survival of intestinal bacteria in the aquatic environment; bacterial aerosols generated during waste disposal practices; ecology of fresh water bacteria. *Mailing Add:* Environ Eng Sloan Hall 141 Wash State Univ Pullman WA 99164

JOHNSTONE, FRANCIS ELLIOTT, JR, b Georgetown Co, SC, Apr 22, 11; m 36; c 2. HORTICULTURE, PLANT BREEDING. *Educ:* Clemson Col, BS, 32; La State Univ, MS, 36; Cornell Univ, PhD(plant breeding), 40. *Prof Exp:* Truck farmer, 32-33; teacher, Pub Schs, SC, 33-34; tech asst plant path, Clemson Truck Agr Exp Sta, 35; admin officer, Civilian Conserv Corps, 35-36; from asst prof to prof hort, Ala Polytech Inst, 40-47; geneticist, Educ Serv, Nat Cottonseed Prod Asn, 47-48; prof hort, Ohio State Univ, 48-50; head, Dept Hort & chmn div, 51-68, prof hort, 51-78, actg dir, Bot Gardens, 68-70, dir, 70-78, EMER DIR, BOT GARDENS & EMER PROF HORT, UNIV GA, 78- *Mem:* Fel AAAS; Am Asn Hort Sci; Am Asn Bot Gardens & Arboreta. *Res:* Breeding camellias; horticultural crop breeding; effects of microclimates; breeding and testing peach rootstocks; development of vegetative propagation method for peaches. *Mailing Add:* 395 Parkway Dr Athens GA 30601

JOHNSTONE, FREDERICK ROBERT CARLYLE, b Colwyn Bay, Wales, Oct 8, 22; m 54; c 4. SURGERY. *Educ:* Univ Edinburgh, MB & ChB, 45; Univ BC, MSc, 54; FRCS, 50. *Prof Exp:* From asst prof to assoc prof, 55-67, PROF SURG, FAC MED, UNIV BC, 67-, LECTR ANAT, 55- *Concurrent Pos:* Fel anat, Fac Med, Univ BC, 50-51. *Mem:* Am Asn Anatomists; fel Am Col Surgeons; Can Asn Anatomists. *Res:* Anatomy. *Mailing Add:* 700 W 10th Vancouver BC V52 1L5 Can

JOHNSTONE, JAMES G(EORGE), b LaPorte, Ind, July 29, 20; m 46; c 1. GEOLOGY, CIVIL ENGINEERING. *Educ:* Colo Sch Mines, Geol Eng, 48; Purdue Univ, MSE, 52. *Prof Exp:* Asst prof geol & civil eng & res engr, Purdue Univ, 48-55; eng geologist, Geophoto Servs, Colo, 55-57; from asst prof to assoc prof, 57-70, PROF CIVIL ENG, COLO SCH MINES, 70- *Mem:* Am Soc Civil Engrs; Geol Soc Am; Nat Soc Prof Engrs; Am Soc Eng Educ. *Res:* Soil mechanics; engineering geology; applications of geology to engineering projects; computer science. *Mailing Add:* Dept of Basic Eng Colo Sch of Mines Golden CO 80401

JOHNSTONE, ROSE M, b Lodz, Poland, May 14, 28; Can citizen; m 53; c 2. BIOCHEMISTRY. *Educ:* McGill Univ, BSc, 50, PhD(biochem), 53. *Prof Exp:* Res assoc biochem, McGill Univ & Montreal Gen Hosp Res Inst, 53-65, asst prof, 61-65; from asst prof to assoc prof, 65-76, PROF CHEM, McGILL UNIV, 77- *Concurrent Pos:* Nat Cancer Inst Can fel, 54-57, res grant, 65- *Mem:* Can Fedn Biol Soc; Can Biochem Soc; Am Soc Biol Chemists; Brit Biochem Soc. *Res:* Transport of organic substances into mammalian cells; development of transport systems; reconstitution of transport systems; transport in membrane vesicles. *Mailing Add:* Dept of Biochem McGill Univ Montreal PQ H3A 2T5 Can

JOINER, HARRY FRANCIS, II, geophysics, mathematics, see previous edition

JOINER, JASPER NEWTON, b Winter Garden, Fla, June 1, 21; m 44; c 3. HORTICULTURE. *Educ:* Univ Fla, BSA, 47, MAgr, 55; Ohio State Univ, PhD(plant physiol, biochem), 58. *Prof Exp:* Asst ed, Agr Exten Serv & Exp Sta, 50-53, asst hort specialist, Agr Ext en Serv, 54-58, assoc prof ornamental hort & assoc horticulturist, Inst Food & Agr Sci, 58-66, PROF ORNAMENTAL HORT & HORTICULTURIST, INST FOOD & AGR SCI, UNIV FLA, 66- *Mem:* Am Soc Hort Sci. *Res:* Nutrition of floricultural and woody ornamental crops; growth regulators, photoperiodism and mycorrhizae. *Mailing Add:* Dept of Ornamental Hort Univ of Fla Rm 111 Rolfs Hall Gainesville FL 32611

JOINER, ROBERT RUSSELL, b Belleville, NJ, May 3, 16; m 42; c 3. FOOD CHEMISTRY. *Educ:* Polytech Inst Brooklyn, BS, 41. *Prof Exp:* Anal chemist, Wallace & Tiernan, Inc, 35-37, res chemist, 37-45, group leader, 45-54, asst dir chem res, 54-59; assoc dir res, Process Div, Pennwalt Corp, 60-62, Newark Res Lab, 62-65, mgr, Process Div Res, 65-69, mgr, Food & Agr Div Res, 69-71, tech dir, 71-79, tech dir, Flour Div, 80-81; CONSULT, 81- *Mem:* Am Chem Soc; Am Asn Cereal Chemists; Inst Food Technol. *Res:* Flour treatment; food preservation; cereal and food chemistry; agricultural chemicals. *Mailing Add:* 136 Antietam Rd Cherry Hill NJ 08034

JOINER, WILLIAM CORNELIUS HENRY, b Camden, NJ, June 8, 36; m 64. SOLID STATE PHYSICS. *Educ:* Rutgers Univ, BA, 57, PhD(physics), 62. *Prof Exp:* Sr physicist, Aerospace Div, Westinghouse Elec Co, 61-65, fel physicist, 65; from asst prof to assoc prof, 65-73, PROF PHYSICS, UNIV CINCINNATI, 73-, HEAD DEPT, 74- *Mem:* Am Phys Soc. *Res:* Superconductivity; low temperature physics. *Mailing Add:* Dept of Physics Univ of Cincinnati Cincinnati OH 45221

JOKELA, JALMER JOHN, b Ely, Minn, Sept 20, 21; m 53; c 3. FOREST GENETICS. *Educ:* Univ Minn, BSF, 47, MS, 51; Univ Ill, PhD(agron), 63. *Prof Exp:* Agr aide, Lake States Forest Exp Sta, 46; asst, Univ Minn, 49-51; asst, 47-49 & 51-59, res assoc & instr, 59-63, asst prof, 63-69, ASSOC PROF FOREST RES, UNIV ILL, URBANA, 69- *Mem:* Soc Am Foresters. *Res:* Genetics and breeding of cottonwoods; silviculture; mensuration. *Mailing Add:* 203 Forest Sci Lab Univ of Ill Urbana IL 61801

JOKINEN, EILEEN HOPE, b Detroit, Mich, July 22, 43. INVERTEBRATE ZOOLOGY, PARASITOLOGY. *Educ:* Wayne State Univ, BS, 65, PhD(zool), 71. *Prof Exp:* Instr introd biol, Wayne County Community Col, Detroit, Mich, 71-72; instr comp anat, Univ Mich, Dearborn, Mich, 72; asst & assoc prof invert zool, ecol, parasitol, comp anat, embryol & introd zool, Suffolk Univ, Boston, Mass, 72-80; VIS ASST PROF GEN ECOL & INVERT ZOOL, UNIV CONN, STORRS, 80- *Mem:* Am Malacol Soc; Am Soc Zoologists; Am Inst Biol Sci. *Res:* Freshwater malacology; community ecology of freshwater littoral zone benthos; biogeography of freshwater snails. *Mailing Add:* U-42 Ecol Sect Univ Conn Storrs CT 06226

JOKIPII, JACK RANDOLPH, b Ironwood, Mich, Sept 10, 39; m 64. THEORETICAL PHYSICS, ASTROPHYSICS. *Educ:* Univ Mich, BS, 61; Calif Inst Technol, PhD(physics), 65. *Prof Exp:* Res assoc physics, Enrico Fermi Inst Nuclear Studies, Univ Chicago, 65-67, asst prof, Inst & Univ, 67-69; assoc prof theoret physics, Downs Lab Physics, Calif Inst Technol, 69-73; PROF ASTRON & PLANETARY SCI, UNIV ARIZ, 74- *Concurrent Pos:* Alfred P Sloan Found fel, 69. *Mem:* Am Phys Soc; Am Geophys Union; Am Astron Soc; Int Astron Union. *Res:* Theoretical space physics; cosmic ray acceleration and propagation; interpretation of space vehicle observations; solar physics; interstellar physics. *Mailing Add:* Dept of Planetary Sci Univ of Ariz Tucson AZ 85721

JOKL, ERNST, b Breslau, Ger, Aug 3, 07; nat US; m 33; c 2. PHYSIOLOGY. *Educ:* Breslau Univ, MD, 31; Univ Witwatersrand, MB & BCh, 36. *Prof Exp:* Asst exp med, Breslau Univ, 30-31; sr res fel, Int Inst High Altitude Physics, Switz, 31; dir, Res Inst Med & Sport, Breslau Univ, 31-33; sr med officer, Dept Educ & mem, Nat Adv Coun Phys Educ, Union SAfrica, 38-44, med consult, Dir Gen Med Serv & Aviation Med, Union Defense Force, 40-44; DISTINGUISHED PROF REHAB, PHYSIOL & PHYS EDUC, UNIV KY, 54- *Concurrent Pos:* Pres res comt, Int Coun Sport & Phys Educ, UNESCO; hon prof physiol & med, Univs WBerlin & Frankfurt; Nat Libr Med res grant fel, Bethesda. *Honors & Awards:* Buckston Browne Brit Empire Prize, 42; Medal, Brit Harveian Soc, 42; Res Awards, Ger Soc Sports Med & Int Coun Mil Sport; Order of Merit, Ger Fed Repub, 72. *Mem:* Fel Am Col Cardiol; Brit Med Asn. *Res:* Clinical physiology of exercise and rehabilitation. *Mailing Add:* Univ of Ky Lexington KY 40506

JOKLIK, WOLFGANG KARL, b Vienna, Austria, Nov 16, 26; m 55, 77; c 2. BIOCHEMISTRY, VIROLOGY. *Educ:* Univ Sydney, BSc, 48, MSc, 49; Oxford Univ, DPhil(biochem), 52. *Prof Exp:* Fel microbiol, Australian Nat Univ, 52-62; USPHS traveling fel, 59-60; from assoc prof to prof cell biol, Albert Einstein Col Med, 62-68; JAMES B DUKE PROF MICROBIOL & IMMUNOL & CHMN DEPT, MED CTR, DUKE UNIV, 68- *Concurrent Pos:* Mem microbiol test comt, Nat Bd Med Examrs; mem exec comt virol sect, Int Asn Microbiol Socs; ed, Virology; chmn, First Gordon Conf Animal Cells & Viruses, 67; mem exec comn, Int Comn Taxonomy of Viruses, 78-; assoc ed, J Biol Chem, 78- *Mem:* Nat Acad Sci; Am Asn Immunologists; Am Soc Microbiol; Am Am Med Sch Microbiol Chmns Asn (pres, 79); Soc Cell Biologists. *Res:* Biochemistry of virus multiplication, including the mechanisms of nucleic acid replication, transcription and translation of genetic information, regulation of genetic expression and the mechanisms of protein synthesis. *Mailing Add:* Dept of Microbiol & Immunol Duke Univ Med Ctr Durham NC 27710

JOLICOEUR, PIERRE, b Montreal, Que, Apr 5, 34; m 69; c 3. BIOMATHEMATICS, BIOMETRICS. *Educ:* Univ Montreal, BA, 53, BSc, 56; Univ BC, MA, 58; Univ Chicago, PhD(paleozool), 63. *Prof Exp:* From asst prof to assoc prof biol, 61-72, chmn dept biol sci, 73-77, PROF BIOL, UNIV MONTREAL, 72- *Concurrent Pos:* Vis assoc prof, Univ Kans, 66; vis assoc scientist, NIH, 67. *Mem:* AAAS; Soc Study Evolution; Biomet Soc; Ecol Soc Am. *Res:* Biological applications of mathematics and statistics, multivariate analysis; vertebrate zoology; ecology of animal populations. *Mailing Add:* Dept Biol Sci Univ of Montreal PO Box 6128 Montreal PQ H3C 3J7 Can

JOLLES, MITCHELL IRA, b Bronx, NY, Feb 10, 53. SOLID MECHANICS. *Educ:* Polytech Inst, Brooklyn, BS & MS, 73; Va Polytech Inst & State Univ, PhD(eng mech), 76. *Prof Exp:* Lectr eng sci & mech, 73-74, instr, Va Polytech Inst & State Univ, 74-76; asst prof aerospace & mech eng, Univ Notre Dame, 77-79; assoc prof mech & aero eng/nuclear eng, Univ Mo, 79-82; HEAD, FRACTURE MECH SECT, NAVAL RES LAB, 82- *Concurrent Pos:* Res assoc, Nat Aeronaut & Space Admin, 73-74, Dept Defense, 73-74, NSF, 73-76, Energy Res & Develop Admin, 75-76, Air Force Flight Dynamics Lab, 75, & Cabot Corp, 77; prin investr, NSF, 78-82, Exxon Educ Found, 78-79, Student Competition Relevant Eng, 78-79 & Argonne Nat Lab, 80-82. *Honors & Awards:* Ralph R Teetor Award, Soc Automotive Engrs, 79. *Mem:* Soc Exp Stress Anal; Am Soc Testing & Mat; Am Soc Eng Educ; Soc Eng Sci. *Res:* Fracture mechanics; experimental stress analysis; fatigue. *Mailing Add:* Code 6382 Naval Res Lab Washington DC 20375

JOLLEY, HOMER RICHARD, b Morgan City, La, May 28, 16; m 72. PUBLIC HEALTH ADMINISTRATION, RESEARCH ADMINISTRATION. *Educ:* Univ Gonzaga, AB, 38, MA, 39; Fordham Univ, MS, 41; St Louis Univ, STL, 46; Princeton Univ, PhD(chem), 51. *Prof Exp:* Instr chem, Spring Hill Col, 39-40 & 41-42; asst instr, Princeton Univ, 48-49; from asst prof to prof chem, Loyola Univ, La, 51-70, chmn dept, 56-64, vpres, Univ, 64-66, pres, 66-70; dir, Off Innovation, Med Serv Admin, HEW, 70-75, spec asst to comnr health serv delivery systs, 75-77; asst acad vpres & vis prof admin med, Med Univ SC, 77-81; CO-FOUNDER & EXEC DIR, CHARLESTON RES INST, 82- *Concurrent Pos:* Res partic, Oak Ridge Inst Nuclear Studies, 47, 59 consult, 61-; co-prin investr, Res Prog, US Off Saline Water; mem, Interagency Comt Ment Retardation, 75- & Interagency Regulatory Group Health Maintenance Orgns, 75- *Mem:* Am Chem Soc; Am Inst Chemists. *Res:* Electrophoresis of polyelectrolytes; assymetric resins; properties of aqueous solutions under high pressure and temperature; cost-effectiveness and quality of care in organized forms of the health care delivery system. *Mailing Add:* Charleston Res Inst 701 E Bay St Charleston SC 29403

JOLLEY, JOHN ERIC, b Blackpool, Eng, June 26, 29; nat US; m 55; c 3. MATERIALS SCIENCE. *Educ:* Univ Liverpool, BS, 50, PhD(phys chem), 53. *Prof Exp:* Fel, Univ Rochester. 53-55 & Univ Calif, Berkeley, 55-57; res chemist film dept, Res Lab, 58-60, res chemist cent res dept, 60, res supvr, 60-64, tech mgr develop dept, Exp Sta, 64-67, RES FEL, PHOTOG PROD DEPT, EXP STA, E I DU PONT DE NEMOURS & CO, INC, 67- *Mem:* Sigma Xi. *Res:* Kinetics; radical reactions; solubility; polymer chemistry; electronic materials; magnetism; photographic science. *Mailing Add:* Photog Prod Dept Exp Sta E I du Pont de Nemours & Co Inc Wilmington DE 19898

JOLLEY, ROBERT LOUIS, b Little Rock, Ark, July 11, 29; m 50; c 2. ENVIRONMENTAL CHEMISTRY. *Educ:* Friends Univ, BA, 50; Univ Tenn, Knoxville, PhD(ecol), 73. *Prof Exp:* Asst chem, Friends Univ, 49-50 & Univ Chicago, 50-51; chemist, Southwest Grease & Oil Co, 51-55; chemist, 56-73, CHEM ECOLOGIST, OAK RIDGE NAT LAB, 73- *Mem:* Am Chem Soc; AAAS; Sigma Xi. *Res:* Measurement and identification of organic constituents in natural and polluted waters; determination of chlorination effects and analysis of chloro-organics in process effluents and condenser cooling waters for electric power plants. *Mailing Add:* Oak Ridge Nat Lab Oak Ridge TN 37830

JOLLEY, WELDON BOSEN, b Gunnison, Utah, Sept 8, 26; m 54; c 3. PHYSIOLOGY. *Educ:* Brigham Young Univ, AB, 52; Univ Southern Calif, PhD(cell physiol), 59. *Prof Exp:* Res assoc, Univ Southern Calif, 53-59, instr, 58-59, asst prof physiol & co-dir, Surg Res Lab, 59-71, PROF PHYSIOL, BIOPHYS & SURG & ASSOC DIR SURG RES LAB, LOMA LINDA UNIV, 71- ; PROF PHYSIOL, JERRY L PETTIS VET ADMIN HOSP, 80- *Concurrent Pos:* Instr, Compton Col, 56; dir, Bio Nuclear Corp; mem bd, Life Resources, Inc & ICN Pharmaceut Inc. *Mem:* AAAS; AMA; Am Fedn Clin Res; Am Physiol Soc; Transplantation Soc. *Res:* Tissue transplantation; nucleic acid metabolism; cancer chemotherapy; biological effects of pulsed electromagnetic fields. *Mailing Add:* Dept of Physiol Loma Linda Univ Sch of Med Loma Linda CA 92354

JOLLICK, JOSEPH DARRYL, b Denbo, Pa, May 15, 41; m 63; c 2. MICROBIAL GENETICS, MEDICAL MICROBIOLOGY. *Educ:* Calif State Col, BS, 63, Am Univ, MS, 66; WVa Univ, PhD(microbiol), 69. *Prof Exp:* Biologist, Nat Cancer Inst, 63-64; Nat Res Coun grant, Biol Sci Lab, Ft Detrick, 69-70; instr, 70-72, asst prof microbiol, Sch Med, Wayne State Univ, 72-77; asst prof microbiol, Sch Med Ohio Univ, 78-80; ASSOC PROF MICROBIOL, COL OSTEOP MED, OHIO UNIV, 80- *Concurrent Pos:* NIH grant, Wayne State Univ, 74- *Mem:* AAAS; Am Soc Microbiol; Am Asn Univ Prof. *Res:* Genetics of Caulobacter; mechanism and transfer of antibiotic resistance in Serratia and Pseudomonas. *Mailing Add:* Dept Basic Sci Col Osteop Med Ohio Univ Athens OH 45701

JOLLIE, MALCOLM THOMAS, b Lakewood, Ohio, July 11, 19; m 50; c 2. COMPARATIVE ANATOMY. *Educ:* Western Reserve Univ, BS, 41; Univ Colo, MS, 43; Stanford Univ, PhD(comp anat), 54. *Prof Exp:* Asst biol, Univ Colo, 41-43; mus technician birds & asst zool, Univ Calif, 43-45; instr sci, Western NMex Teachers Col, 45-47; asst prof zool, Univ Idaho, 47-56 & Univ Pittsburgh, 56-65; PROF BIOL, NORTHERN ILL UNIV, 65- *Res:* Comparative anatomy relating to origin and phylogeny of chordates and vertebrates; systematic ornithology and ichthyology. *Mailing Add:* Dept of Biol Sci Northern Ill Univ De Kalb IL 60115

JOLLIE, WILLIAM PUCETTE, b Passaic, NJ, June 27, 28; m 50; c 2. ANATOMY. *Educ:* Lehigh Univ, BA, 50, MS, 52; Harvard Univ, PhD(biol), 59. *Prof Exp:* Lectr histol & embryol, Queen's Univ, Ont, 59-61; from asst prof to prof anat, Sch Med, Tulane Univ, 61-69; PROF ANAT & CHMN DEPT, MED COL VA, VA COMMONWEALTH UNIV, 69- *Mem:* Am Asn Anatomists; Am Soc Cell Biologists; Soc Study Reproduction. *Res:* Electron microscopy of placental barriers; visualization of placental transport; maternal accommodations to implantation and placental formation; viviparity in submammalian vertebrates. *Mailing Add:* Dept of Anat Med Col of Va Richmond VA 23298

JOLLIFFE, ALFRED WALTON, b Winnipeg, Man, May 8, 07; m 37; c 4. GEOLOGY. *Educ:* Queen's Univ, Ont, BA, 29, MA, 31; Princeton Univ, PhD(geol), 35. *Prof Exp:* Asst geologist, Geol Surv Can, 35-36, from assoc geologist to geologist, 36-45; assoc prof geol, McGill Univ, 46-50; PROF GEOL, QUEEN'S UNIV, ONT, 50- *Mem:* Fel Geol Soc Am; fel Am Mineral Soc; Royal Soc Can. *Res:* History of science and technology; Pre-Cambrian structural and economic geology; iron and uranium deposits; geochemistry. *Mailing Add:* 68 Collingwood Kingston ON K7L 3X4 Can

JOLLS, CLAUDIA LEE, b Detroit, Mich, May 20, 53. PLANT ECOLOGY, PLANT POPULATION BIOLOGY. *Educ:* Univ Mich, Ann Arbor, BS, 75; Univ Colo, Boulder, PhD(biol), 80. *Prof Exp:* Teaching asst ecol, bot & human physiol, Dept Environ Pop & Organismic, Univ Colo, 75-80; fel plant pop biol, Mich State Univ, 80-81; RESIDENT TERRESTRIAL ECOLOGIST, BIOL STA, UNIV MICH, 81- *Concurrent Pos:* Gardeners asst, Matthaei Bot Gardens, Univ Mich, 72-73; res asst plant ecol, Dept Environ, Pop & Organismic, Univ Colo at Audubon-Whittel Res Ranch, Ariz, 76; adv, Traineeship Prog, Mt Res Sta, Inst Arctic & Alpine Res, Univ Colo, NSF, 77 & 78; prog coordr, Naturalist-Ecologist Training Prog, Biol Sta, Univ Mich, 81- *Mem:* Am Women Sci; Bot Soc Am; Ecol Soc Am; Torrey Bot Club. *Res:* Plant ecology and population biology: resource allocation patterns, population dynamics, breeding systems, life histories, wetland community structure, forest succession, alpine ecology. *Mailing Add:* Biol Sta Univ Mich Pellston MI 49769

JOLLS, KENNETH ROBERT, b Baltimore, Md, Oct 19, 33. CHEMICAL ENGINEERING. *Educ:* Duke Univ, AB, 58; NC State Univ, BSChE, 61; Univ Ill, MS, 63, PhD(chem eng), 66. *Prof Exp:* Asst chem eng, Univ Ill, 61-65; from asst prof to assoc prof, Polytech Inst Brooklyn, 65-70; ASSOC PROF CHEM ENG, IOWA STATE UNIV, 70- *Mem:* Am Inst Chem Engrs; Am Soc Eng Educ; Sigma Xi; Am Chem Soc. *Res:* Fluid mechanics; thermodynamics; application of electronic instrumentation in chemical engineering research; analog computation. *Mailing Add:* Dept of Chem Eng Sweeney Hall Iowa State Univ Ames IA 50011

JOLLY, ALISON BISHOP, b Ithaca, NY, May 9, 37; m 63; c 4. ANIMAL BEHAVIOR. *Educ:* Cornell Univ, BA, 58; Yale Univ, PhD(zool), 62. *Prof Exp:* Res assoc zool, NY Zool Soc, 62-64; res assoc, Sch Biol, Univ Sussex, 68-81; GUEST INVESTR, ROCKEFFELLER UNIV, 82- *Concurrent Pos:* NSF res grant, 62-64. *Mem:* AAAS; Am Soc Zool; Am Asn Phys Anthropologists; Am Anthrop Asn; Sigma Xi. *Res:* Conservation of natural ecosystems in Madagascar; primate behavior, particulrly that of prosimians; evolution of human behavior. *Mailing Add:* Rockefeller Univ 1230 York Ave New York NY 10021

JOLLY, CLIFFORD J, b Southend, Eng, Jan 21, 39; m 61; c 2. PHYSICAL ANTHROPOLOGY, PRIMATOLOGY. *Educ:* Univ London, BA, 60, PhD(phys anthrop), 65. *Prof Exp:* Res asst phys anthrop, Univ Col, London, 63-65, asst lectr, 65-67; from asst prof to assoc prof, 67-75, PROF PHYS ANTHROP, NY UNIV, 75- *Concurrent Pos:* Vis res fel, Makerere Univ Col, Uganda, 65-66. *Mem:* Soc Study Human Biol; Zool Soc London; Royal Anthrop Inst. *Res:* Primate functional anatomy; serology and biology. *Mailing Add:* Dept of Anthrop NY Univ 25 Waverly Pl New York NY 10003

JOLLY, JANICE LAURENE WILLARD, b Bakersfield, Calif, July 23, 31; m 56; c 3. ECONOMIC GEOLOGY, PETROLOGY. *Educ:* Univ Ore, BA, 56, MS, 57. *Prof Exp:* Geologist, US Geol Surv, 58-67; res geologist, RST Tech Serv Ltd, Zambia, 67-72; mineral commodity area specialist, US Bur Mines, 73-80, intern, Exec Managerial Develop Prog, Dept Interior, 80-81, SR PHYS SCIENTIST, US BUR MINES, 81- *Mem:* Fel Geol Soc Am; Am Inst Mining, Metall & Petrol Engrs. *Res:* Geology of the Monument Quadrangle, Oregon; petrography of the crystalline rocks, Potomac River gorge, Maryland-Virginia; ore deposit controls in Mississippi and Appalachian Valleys lead-zinc deposits; eastern United States heavy metal and massive sulfide deposits; geochemistry of copper deposits of Zambia; commodity surveys of iron oxide and carajas iron ore (Brazil); international mineral industry studies in Africa and Middle East; supply and demand of strategic and critical minerals; mineral economics. *Mailing Add:* US Bur of Mines 2401 E St NW Washington DC 20241

JOLLY, RAMESH C, food science, dairy science, see previous edition

JOLLY, STUART MARTIN, b London, Eng, Aug 29, 46; US citizen. SYSTEMS DESIGN. *Educ:* Haverford Col, BA, 68; Cornell Univ, MS, 71. *Prof Exp:* Mem staff, Robinson Assocs Inc, 72-74, vpres, res & develop, 74-77; mem tech staff, 77-79, GROUP LEADER, MITRE CORP, 79- *Res:* Analysis and design of communications systems, security systems and speech processing. *Mailing Add:* Rte 101 RFD 3 Amherst NH 03031

JOLLY, WAYNE TRAVIS, b Jacksonville, Tex, Aug 15, 40. PETROLOGY, VOLCANOLOGY. *Educ:* Univ Tex, Austin, BFA, 63, MA, 67; State Univ NY Binghamton, PhD(geol), 70. *Prof Exp:* Fel geol, Univ Sask, 70-71; asst prof, 71-75, ASSOC PROF GEOL, BROCK UNIV, 75- *Mem:* Geol Soc Am; Geol Asn Can; Mineral Asn Can. *Res:* Geochemical petrology and metamorphic petrology of volcanic rocks with emphasis on prehnite-pumpellyite facies and origin of Archean volcanics. *Mailing Add:* Dept of Geol Sci Brock Univ St Catharines ON L2S 3A1 Can

JOLLY, WILLIAM LEE, b Chicago, Ill, Dec 27, 27; m 50; c 3. INORGANIC CHEMISTRY. *Educ:* Univ Ill, BS, 48, MS, 49; Univ Calif, PhD(chem), 52. *Prof Exp:* Instr, 52-53, chemist, Radiation Lab, 53-55, from asst prof to assoc prof, 55-62, PROF CHEM, UNIV CALIF, BERKELEY, 62- *Mem:* AAAS; Am Chem Soc; Royal Soc Chem. *Res:* Liquid ammonia chemistry; chemistry of the volatile hydrides; studies of the bonding in transition metal complexes; x-ray photoelectron spectroscopy. *Mailing Add:* Dept of Chem Univ of Calif Berkeley CA 94720

JOLY, DANIEL JOSE, b Buenos Aires, Arg, Mar 11, 21; m 45; c 2. EPIDEMIOLOGY, ONCOLOGY. *Educ:* Univ Buenos Aires, MD, 44; NY Univ, 54-55; Johns Hopkins Univ, MPH, 66, DRPH(epidemiol), 73. *Prof Exp:* Res fel surg, Harvard Med Sch, 51; from asst resident to sr resident oncol surg, Mem Hosp Cancer, New York, 52-56; prof surg & chmn dept, Univ of the Andes, Venezuela, 60-61; chmn dept surg, Inst Oncol, Univ Buenos Aires, 62-64; regional adv cancer control, Pan Am Health Orgn-WHO, 68-75, rep in Cuba, 75-81; CONSULT EPIDEMIOL & PUB HEALTH, 81- *Concurrent Pos:* Res fel surg physiol, Sloan-Kettering Inst Cancer Res, 53-58; assoc, dept epidemiol, Sch Hyg & Pub Health, Johns Hopkins Univ, 73- *Mem:* Arg Soc Cancerology; Am Pub Health Asn. *Res:* Epidemiology of chronic diseases with special emphasis in cancer and environmental factors, such as cigarette smoking. *Mailing Add:* 8413 Westmount Terrace Bethesda MD 20817

JOLY, GEORGE W(ILFRED), b Montreal, Que, June 5, 17. CIVIL ENGINEERING. *Educ:* Loyola Col, Can, BA, 38; McGill Univ, BEng, 49, MEng, 50. *Prof Exp:* Asst dean faculty eng, McGill Univ, 57-63; dean, Loyola Col, Montreal, 63-77, PROF ENG & ASSOC DEAN FAC ENG, LOYOLA CAMPUS, CONCORDIA UNIV, MONTREAL, 77- *Mem:* Am Soc Eng Educ; Eng Inst Can. *Res:* Structural engineering; steel; mechanics. *Mailing Add:* Fac of Eng Loyola Campus Concordia Univ Montreal PQ H3G 1M8 Can

JOLY, LOUIS PHILIPPE, b Montreal, Que, July 23, 28; m 54; c 3. PHARMACEUTICAL CHEMISTRY. *Educ:* Laval Univ, BA, 49, BSc, 53; Univ Bordeaux, France, PhD, 65. *Prof Exp:* Lectr, 57-58, assoc prof, 58-71, PROF MED CHEM, COL PHARM, UNIV LAVAL, 71- *Concurrent Pos:* Chief pharmacist, Robert Giffard Hosp Ctr, 57-69; consult, Neuropsychopharmacol Res Univ, 69- *Mem:* AAAS; NY Acad Sci; Am Pharmaceut Asn; Can Pharmaceut Asn. *Res:* Synthesis and essay by cell culture methods of new alkylating agents as antineoplastics; biotransforms of long acting psychotropic drugs. *Mailing Add:* 1324 Rue Marechal Foch Quebec PQ G1S 2C4 Can

JOMAIN-BAUM, MIREILLE, biochemistry, nutrition, deceased

JONA, FRANCO PAUL, b Pistoia, Italy, Oct 10, 22; nat US; m 52; c 2. SURFACE PHYSICS, SURFACE CHEMISTRY. *Educ:* Swiss Fed Inst Technol, dipl, 45, PhD(physics), 49. *Prof Exp:* Instr physics, Univ Bern, 45-46 & Swiss Fed Inst Technol, 46-52; res assoc, Pa State Univ, 52-54, asst prof, 54-57; res physicist res labs, Westinghouse Elec Corp, 57-59; staff physicist res lab, Int Bus Mach Corp, NY, 59-69; PROF ENG, STATE UNIV NY STONY BROOK, 69- *Mem:* Fel Am Phys Soc; Ital Phys Soc; Swiss Phys Soc; Phys Soc Japan. *Res:* Ferroelectricity; crystallography; elasticity; piezoelectricity; crystal growth; surface studies. *Mailing Add:* Dept of Mat Sci Col of Eng State Univ NY Stony Brook NY 11790

JONAH, CHARLES D, b Lafayette, Ind, Mar 19, 43; m 69. RADIATION CHEMISTRY. *Educ:* Oberlin Col, BA, 65; Columbia Univ, PhD(chem), 70. *Prof Exp:* Fel phys chem, Columbia Univ, 69-71; fel, 71-74, asst scientist, 74-77, CHEMIST RADIATION CHEM, ARGONNE NAT LAB, 77- *Mem:* Am Phys Soc; Am Chem Soc. *Res:* Mechanism of reactions; fast kinetic measurements; instrumentation; radiation chemistry of aqueous systems solvation of electrons. *Mailing Add:* Chem Div Argonne Nat Lab 9700 S Cass Ave Argonne IL 60439

JONAS, ALBERT MOSHE, b New Haven, Conn, Oct 3, 31; m 54; c 3. PATHOLOGY, COMPARATIVE MEDICINE. *Educ:* Univ Toronto, DVM, 55; Am Col Vet Path, dipl. *Prof Exp:* Pvt pract, 55-61; res asst path, Sch med, Yale Univ, 61-63, from instr to asst prof, 63-68, assoc prof animal sci & chief lab, 68-73, assoc prof path, 71-73, prof animal sci & path, 73-74, prof comp med, Div Health Sci Res & Path & chief sect comp med, 74-77, prof comp med & path & chmn sect comp med, 77-78, dir animal care, 61-78; first dean, Vet Sch, 78-81, CHMN COMP MED & LAB ANIMAL SCI, VET SCH, TUFTS UNIV, 81-, PROF EXP PATH, MED SCH, 78- *Concurrent Pos:* Mem coun, Inst Lab Animal Resources, Nat Acad Sci, 65-69; mem, Am Asn Accreditation Lab Animal Care, 68-75; mem animal res adv comt, Div Res Resources, NIH, 72-76; mem adv comt comp path, Armed Forces Inst Path, 73-76; chmn comt, Longterm Holding of Lab Rodents, Inst Lab Animal Res, Nat Acad Sci, 73-76 & mem, Orgn Comt Symp on Lab Animal Housing, 74-75; mem tech rev comt, Bioassay Prog, Nat Cancer Inst, 77-78, eval panel, Primate Res Ctrs Prog, NIH, 77-78, cause & prev sci rev comt, Nat Cancer Inst, 78-81, adv bd, Northeast Regional Primate Ctr, 79-82, comt vet med sci, Nat Acad Sci, 79- *Mem:* Am Asn Lab Animal Sci; Am Vet Med Asn; Int Acad Path; Am Col Vet Path; Soc Pharmacol & Environ Path. *Res:* Naturally occurring diseases in laboratory animals with specific interests in animal model systems; pulmonary pathology including pulmonary hemodynamics and infectious diseases with emphasis in pathogenesis. *Mailing Add:* 203 Harrison Ave Boston MA 02111

JONAS, ANA, b Rokiskis, Lithuania, Nov 24, 43; US citizen; m 68. BIOCHEMISTRY. *Educ:* Univ Ill, Chicago, BS, 66, Urbana, PhD(biochem), 70. *Prof Exp:* NIH trainee, 70-72, asst prof, 72-79, ASSOC PROF BIOCHEM, UNIV ILL, URBANA, 79- *Concurrent Pos:* NATO fel, Max Planck Med Res Inst, Heidelberg, WGer, 73; res grants, Nat Heart Lung & Blood Inst, 73-, consult, 78-; estab investrship, Am Heart Asn, 74-79; res grants, Am Heart Asn, 80-83; Max Baer res award, 78-; coun arteriosclerosis fel, Am Heart Asn; Fogarty fel, Centre Biophysique Moleculaire, Cent Nat de la Rech Sci, Orleans, France, 81. *Mem:* NY Acad Sci; Am Heart Asn; Am Soc Biol Chemists. *Res:* Structure and function of high density serum lipoproteins; protein-lipid interactions; transport function of serum proteins; applications of fluorescence spectroscopy. *Mailing Add:* 190 Med Sci Bldg Univ of Ill Urbana IL 61801

JONAS, EDWARD CHARLES, b San Antonio, Tex, July 24, 24; m 49; c 3. CLAY MINERALOGY. *Educ:* Rice Inst, BS, 44; Univ Ill, MS, 52, PhD(geol), 54. *Prof Exp:* Asst geologist, Ill State Geol Surv, 52-54; from asst prof to assoc prof geol, 54-66, PROF GEOL, UNIV TEX, AUSTIN, 66- *Concurrent Pos:* Fulbright sr res award, NZ, 60-61. *Mem:* Fel AAAS; fel Geol Soc Am; fel Mineral Soc Am; Geochem Soc; Mineral Soc Gt Brit & Ireland. *Res:* Mineralogy of clays and uranium deposits in the Texas Gulf Tertiary. *Mailing Add:* Dept of Geol Sci Univ of Tex Austin TX 78712

JONAS, HERBERT, b Düsseldorf, Ger, May 23, 15; nat US; m. PLANT PHYSIOLOGY. *Educ:* Univ Calif, BS, 41, PhD(plant physiol), 50. *Prof Exp:* Nat Res Coun & AEC fel plant physiol, Biol Div, Oak Ridge Nat Lab, 51-52; res assoc pharmacol, Sch Med, Univ Va, 52-54, res assoc, Cancer Res Lab, 54-58; from assoc prof bot & pharmacog to assoc prof bot, Col Pharm, 58-69, chmn dept pharmacog, 58-68, PROF BOT, COL BIOL SCI, UNIV MINN, ST PAUL, 69- *Concurrent Pos:* Electronics instr, US Naval Installations, Calif, 42-46. *Mem:* AAAS; Am Soc Plant Physiol; Bot Soc Am; Soc Econ Bot. *Res:* Physiology, biophysics; medicinal plants; secondary plant metabolites; sensitive plants; teaching; plant-man interrelations; economic botany. *Mailing Add:* Dept of Bot Univ of Minn St Paul MN 55108

JONAS, JIRI, b Prague, Czech, Apr 1, 32; US citizen; m 68. PHYSICAL CHEMISTRY. *Educ:* Tech Univ Prague, BS, 56; Czech Acad Sci, PhD(chem), 60. *Prof Exp:* Res assoc chem, Czech Acad Sci, 60-63; vis scientist, 63-65, from asst prof to assoc prof, 66-72, PROF CHEM, UNIV ILL, URBANA, 72-, SR STAFF MEM MAT RES, 70- *Concurrent Pos:* Fels, Alfred P Sloan Found, 67-69 & Guggenheim Found, 72-73; assoc mem ctr advan study, Univ Ill, 76-77. *Mem:* Am Chem Soc; Am Phys Soc; AAAS. *Res:* Nuclear magnetic resonance; raman spectroscopy; dynamic structure of liquids; fused salts, molecular solids and polymers; high pressure research; behavior of materials under extreme conditions of pressure and temperature. *Mailing Add:* Dept of Chem Univ of Ill Urbana IL 61801

JONAS, JOHN JOSEPH, b Budapest, Hungary, Dec 9, 14; nat US; m 41; c 3. ORGANIC CHEMISTRY. *Educ:* Pazmany Peter Univ, PhD(chem, physics. math), 37. *Prof Exp:* Asst & instr org & pharmaceut chem, Pazmany Peter Univ, 36-39; chemist, Darmol Pharmaceut Co, Budapest, 39-43; chemist, Hungary Viscose Corp, 43-45; asst div leader pharmaceut & nutrit res, Inst Heiligenberg, Ger, 46-51; assoc mgr indust prod, Res & Develop Div, Kraft Inc, 51-77, SCI MGT CONSULT, RES & DEVELOP DIV, DART & KRAFT, INC, 77- *Concurrent Pos:* Consult, Protein Resources Study, NSF, 75-76. *Mem:* Am Chem Soc; Inst Food Technol; Am Inst Chemists. *Res:* Metabolic diseases of dairy cattle; seaweed hydrocolloids; food emulsifying systems; high protein foods; dairy analogues, vegetable proteins, synthetic nutrients. *Mailing Add:* Box 183/c Rte 1 Laurel Fork VA 24352

JONAS, JOHN JOSEPH, b Montreal, Que, Dec 12, 32; m 60; c 4. PHYSICAL METALLURGY, MECHANICAL METALLURGY. *Educ:* McGill Univ, BEng, 54; Cambridge Univ, PhD(mech sci), 60. *Prof Exp:* From asst prof to assoc prof, 60-73, assoc dean, Fac Grad Studies & Res, 71-75, PROF PHYS METALL, McGILL UNIV, 73- *Honors & Awards:* Reaumur Medal, French Soc Metall, 80. *Mem:* Am Soc Metals; Am Inst Mining, Metall & Petrol Engrs; Brit Inst Metals. *Res:* Mechanical metallurgy; elevated temperature deformation of metals and crystalline materials; microstructural changes and stress-strain rate-temperature relationships during hot working; plastic instability; thermal activation analysis. *Mailing Add:* Dept of Metall Eng McGill Univ Montreal PQ H3Z 2J2 Can

JONAS, LEONARD ABRAHAM, b New York, NY, Feb 6, 20; m 42; c 2. PHYSICAL CHEMISTRY. *Educ:* Brooklyn Col, AB, 40; Univ Md, MS, 69, PhD(phys chem), 70. *Prof Exp:* SR RES SCIENTIST, NAT CANCER INST, FREDERICK CANCER RES FAC, LITTON BIONETICS, INC, 80- *Mem:* Am Carbon Soc; Am Soc Testing & Mat; AAAS; Am Chem Soc; Sigma Xi. *Res:* Equilibrium gas adsorption; adsorption kinetics; aerosol physics and filtration; heterogeneous catalysis; physical protection against carcinogens. *Mailing Add:* 6612 Baythorne Rd Baltimore MD 21209

JONAS, ROBERT JAMES, b Marinette, Wis, June 8, 26; m 50; c 3. ANIMAL ECOLOGY, WILDLIFE MANAGEMENT. *Educ:* Univ Idaho, BS, 50, MS, 55; Mont State Univ, PhD(wildlife mgt), 64. *Prof Exp:* Instr biol, Lewis-Clark Norm Col, 55-57; asst prof, Whitman Col, 64-65 & Univ Idaho, 65-66; coordr wildlife biol, 79-81, PROF ZOOL, WASH STATE UNIV, 66- *Concurrent Pos:* Danforth Assoc, 68-; environ specialist, Nat Park Serv, 75-76. *Honors & Awards:* Meritorious Serv Award, Dept Interior, 69. *Mem:* AAAS; Sigma Xi (vpres, 74-75); Wildlife Soc. *Res:* Populations of wild animals; human impact on natural ecosystems. *Mailing Add:* Dept of Zool Wash State Univ Pullman WA 99164

JONASSEN, HANS BOEGH, b Seelze, Ger, Aug 18, 12; nat US; m 39; c 3. INORGANIC CHEMISTRY. *Educ:* Tulane Univ, BS, 42, MS, 44; Univ Ill, PhD(chem), 46. *Prof Exp:* From instr gen & anal chem to asst prof chem, Tulane Univ, 43-48, assoc prof inorg chem, 48-52, chmn dept chem, 62-68, prof inorg chem, 52-80. *Concurrent Pos:* Sci liaison officer, London Br, Off Naval Res, 58-59; mem adv coun col chem, NSF-Am Chem Soc, 62-67; Reilly centennial lectr, Univ Notre Dame, 65; Francis P Dwyer Mem lectr, Univ New South Wales, 67; Australian-Am Educ Found sr scholar, Univ Sydney, 71. *Mem:* AAAS; Am Chem Soc. *Res:* Inorganic and metalorganic chemistry; complex ions; homogenous and heterogeneous catalysis. *Mailing Add:* 7729 Belfast New Orleans LA 70125

JONCAS, JEAN HARRY, b Montreal, Que, June 27, 30; m 55; c 5. VIROLOGY, INFECTIOUS DISEASES. *Educ:* Jean de Brebeuf Col, BA, 48; Univ Montreal, MD, 55, PhD(microbiol, immunol), 67; Royal Col Physicians & Surgeons, Can, cert pediat, 59, cert microbiol, 76. *Prof Exp:* Fel, Sch Med, Wayne State Univ, 56; res asst, 60-70, RES ASSOC VIROL, INST MICROBIOL & HYG, UNIV MONTREAL, 71-, PROF MICROBIOL & IMMUNOL, SCH MED, 70-, HEAD INFECTIOUS DIS SECT, STE JUSTINE HOSP, MONTREAL, 70-, HEAD DEPT MICROBIOL, 77- *Concurrent Pos:* Clin asst, Montreal Children's Hosp, 59-70, consult, 70-; lectr, Sch Med, Univ Montreal, 64-67, asst prof, 67-70; demonstr, Dept

Pediat, McGill Univ, 70-; mem adv comt infection, Immunity & Ther, Defence Res Bd Can, 70-74; Med Res Coun Can grant, 70-; Nat Defence Res grant, 70-76; Fed Prov pub health res grant, 71-75; Nat Cancer Inst Can grant, 75- *Mem:* Can Soc Microbiol; Can Pub Health Asn; Am Soc Microbiol; Can Paediat Soc; fel Am Acad Pediat. *Res:* Etiology and epidemiology of infectious mononucleosis; the Epstein-Barr herpes virus; cell-virus relationship; Epstein-Barr virus and oncogenesis; diagnosis of viral infections by rapid immunological methods and electron microscopy; pediatric infectious diseases, epidemiology, diagnosis and treatment. *Mailing Add:* Dept Microbiol & Immunol St Justine Hosp 3175 Ste-Catherine Rd Montreal PQ H3T 1C5 Can

JONEJA, MADAN GOPAL, b Lyallpur, India, Dec 25, 36; Can citizen; m 65. TERATOLOGY, ULTRASTRUCTURAL CELL BIOLOGY. *Educ:* Panjab Univ, India, MSc, 58; Queen's Univ, Ont, PhD(biol), 65. *Prof Exp:* From lectr to assoc prof, 65-76, chmn grad studies anat, 70-80, PROF ANAT, QUEEN'S UNIV, ONT, 81- *Mem:* AAAS; Teratology Soc; Am Asn Anatomists; Can Asn Anatomists. *Res:* Cytology; mammalian; embryogenesis; role of chromosome aberrations in neoplastic transformations and cytological mechanisms of teratogenesis; stereoscan electron microscope and transmission electron microscope of in vitro differentiation of alveolar type II cells. *Mailing Add:* Dept Anat Queen's Univ Kingston ON K7L 3W6 Can

JONES, A(NDREW) R(OSS), b Mt Sterling, Ill, May 3, 21; m 44; c 2. ELECTRICAL ENGINEERING. *Educ:* Clemson Col, BEE, 47; Univ Pittsburgh, MSEE, 53. *Prof Exp:* Engr, 47-58, mgr preliminary plant eng, Atomic Power Dept, 58-64, mgr advan develop & planning, 64-66, mgr projs syst & technol, Astronuclear Labs, 66-71, mgr spec proj, 71-76, mgr eng, Adv Energy Syst Div, 76-78, MGR EMERGING SYSTS STUDIES, WESTINGHOUSE ELEC CORP, 78- *Honors & Awards:* Norris & Riggs Medals, Clemson Col. *Mem:* Am Nuclear Soc; Soc Naval Archit; Inst Elec & Electronics Engrs; Am Inst Aeronaut & Astronaut. *Res:* Nuclear, solar and fuel cell power plant design and economics, particularly electric utility and cogeneration applications. *Mailing Add:* Adv Energy Systs Div PO Box 10864 Pittsburgh PA 15236

JONES, ALAN A, b Jamestown, NY, Nov 15, 44; m 72. POLYMER CHEMISTRY. *Educ:* Colgate Univ, AB, 66; Univ Wis, PhD(phys chem), 72. *Prof Exp:* Res instr polymer chem, Dartmouth Col, 72-74; asst prof, 74-78, ASSOC PROF CHEM, CLARK UNIV, 78-, DEPT CHAIR, 81- *Mem:* Am Chem Soc. *Res:* The dynamic properties of macromolecules in solution are probed by nuclear magnetic resonance spectroscopy or dielectric response and discussed in terms of models relating specific motions to the experimental observations. *Mailing Add:* Dept of Chem Clark Univ Worcester MA 01610

JONES, ALAN LEE, b Albion, NY, June 23, 39; m 67; c 2. PLANT PATHOLOGY. *Educ:* Cornell Univ, BS, 61, MS, 63; NC State Univ, PhD(plant path), 68. *Prof Exp:* From asst prof to assoc prof, 68-77, PROF PLANT PATH, MICH STATE UNIV, 77- *Concurrent Pos:* Sabbatical leaves, Plant Protection Inst, Agr Res Ctr, USDA, Beltsville, Md, 74-75 & Bayer Agr, Leverkusen, Fed Repub Germ, 82. *Honors & Awards:* Nat Award in Agr, Am Phytopath Soc, 78. *Mem:* AAAS; Can Phytopath Soc; Am Phytopath Soc. *Res:* Epidemiology and control of tree fruit diseases; disease pest management systems; fungicide tolerance in tree fruit pathogens; identification, transmission and control of mycoplasma diseases of tree fruit. *Mailing Add:* Dept of Bot & Plant Path Mich State Univ East Lansing MI 48824

JONES, ALAN RICHARD, b Denver, Colo, Dec 25, 39; m 64; c 2. PHYSICAL CHEMISTRY, CHEMICAL ENGINEERING. *Educ:* Univ Colo, BSChE, 62; Lawrence Univ, MA, 64, PhD, 67. *Prof Exp:* Res scientist, 67-69, leader paper prod group, 69-74, leader chem processes group, 74-78, ASST TECH DIR, UNION CAMP CORP, 78- *Honors & Awards:* Hugh D Camp Award, Union Camp Corp, 73. *Mem:* Am Inst Chem Engr; Tech Asn Pulp & Paper Indust. *Res:* Mechanical and optical properties of paper, characterization of papermaking pulps, development and optimization of pulping, by-product chemical, and papermaking processes. *Mailing Add:* Union Camp Corp Franklin VA 23851

JONES, ALBERT CLEVELAND, b Coalinga, Calif, Aug 18, 29; m 55; c 3. FISHERIES. *Educ:* Univ Wash, BS, 51; Univ Calif, MA, 54, PhD(zool), 59. *Prof Exp:* Asst, Ore Fish Comn, 49-50, biologist, 51; biologist, Fisheries Res Inst, Univ Wash, 52; asst, Sagehen Creek Wildlife Fisheries Sta, Univ Calif, 53-54, asst zool, Univ, 54-58; asst ichthyol, Calif Acad Sci, 58-59; res asst prof fisheries, Univ Miami, 59-65; asst dir, 65-71, prog mgr, Off-in-Chg, 72-76, ASST DIR FISHERY MGT, SOUTHEAST FISHERIES CTR, MIAMI LAB, NAT MARINE FISHERIES SERV, 76- *Concurrent Pos:* Ministry of Agr, Fisheries & Food fel, Eng, 64-65; adj assoc prof, Univ Miami, 68-76, adj prof, 76- *Mem:* Am Fisheries Soc; Am Soc Ichthyol & Herpet; Am Inst Fishery Res Biologists. *Res:* Population dynamics; biometrics; ecology. *Mailing Add:* 8950 SW 62 CT Miami FL 33156

JONES, ALFRED, b Richmond, Va, Mar 25, 32; m 62; c 2. PLANT GENETICS. *Educ:* Va Polytech Inst, BS, 53; NC State Col, MS, 57, PhD(plant breeding & path), 61. *Prof Exp:* Res asst cotton breeding, field crops dept, NC State Col, 61-62; RES GENETICIST VEG & ORNAMENTALS RES BR, PLANT SCI RES DIV, US VEG BREEDING LAB, USDA, 62- *Concurrent Pos:* L M Ware Res Award, Am Soc Hort Sci, 79. *Mem:* Am Soc Hort Sci; Am Genetic Asn; Crop Sci Soc Am; Am Soc Agron. *Res:* Cytogenetics of sweetpotato, especially nature of ploidy in Ipomoea and its relation to speciation, recombination and breeding systems; quantitative genetic techniques of breeding for disease and insect resistant types. *Mailing Add:* Sci & Educ Admin 2875 Savanah Hwy Charleston SC 29407

JONES, ALFRED RUSSELL, b Chicago, Ill, Oct 23, 20; m 45. ORGANIC CHEMISTRY. *Educ:* Univ Chicago, BS, 42; Univ Wis, PhD(org chem), 48. *Prof Exp:* Jr chemist, Gen Elec Co, Mass, 42; contract employee, US Naval Res Lab, DC, 42-44; chemist, 48-53, SR CHEMIST, OAK RIDGE NAT LAB, 53- *Concurrent Pos:* Lectr, Univ Panjab & sci adv, AEC, Pakistan, 63-64; vis scientist, Hahn-Meitner Inst Berlin, 64-65. *Mem:* Am Chem Soc. *Res:* Synthesis of compounds containing radioactive carbon and developmental work on such syntheses; radiation chemistry of organic compounds; energy transfer in solid and liquid systems; separations and analytical procedures for the characterization of cigarette smoke condensates and coal hydrogenolysis products. *Mailing Add:* 7217 Wellswood Ln Knoxville TN 37919

JONES, ALISTER VALLANCE, b Christchurch, NZ, Feb 4, 24; m 51; c 3. AERONOMY. *Educ:* Univ NZ, BSc, 45, MSc, 46; Cambridge Univ, PhD(physics), 50. *Prof Exp:* Nat Res Coun Can fel, 49-51; from asst prof to prof physics, Univ Sask, 53-68; sr res officer, Upper Atmosphere Res Sect, Astrophys Br, 68-76, PRIN RES OFFICER, PLANETARY SCI SECT, HERZBERG INST ASTROPHYS, NAT RES COUN CAN, 76- *Concurrent Pos:* Ed, Physics Can, Can Asn Physicists, 63-66, assoc ed, Aeronomy & Space Physics, Can J Physics, 79- *Mem:* Can Asn Physicists; Royal Soc Can. *Res:* Infrared, auroral and airglow spectroscopy. *Mailing Add:* Herzberg Inst of Astrophys Nat Res Coun Can Ottawa ON K1A 0R6 Can

JONES, ALLAN W, b Scranton, Pa, June, 3, 37; m 62; c 4. BIOLOGY, PHYSIOLOGY. *Educ:* Princeton Univ, BSE, 59; Univ Pa, PhD(physiol), 65. *Prof Exp:* Trainee & instr physiol, Sch Med, Univ Pa, 65-66; fel, Oxford Univ, 66-68; assoc, Sch Med, Univ Pa, 68-69, asst prof, 69-72, assoc dir, Bockus Res Inst, Grad Hosp, 70-72; assoc prof, 72-78, PROF PHYSIOL, SCH MED, UNIV MO-COLUMBIA, 78- *Concurrent Pos:* Estab investr, Am Heart Asn, 74-79; mem, Coun High Blood Pressure Res. *Mem:* Am Pharmacol Soc; Am Physiol Soc. *Res:* Hypertension; electrolyte metabolism of arteries; cardiovascular research. *Mailing Add:* Dept of Physiol Univ of Mo Columbia MO 65212

JONES, ALMUT GITTER, b Oldenburg, WGer, Sept 8, 23; US citizen; wid. PLANT TAXONOMY. *Educ:* Univ Ill, Urbana, BS, 58, MS, 60, PhD(bot), 73. *Prof Exp:* CUR HERBARIUM, UNIV ILL, URBANA, 73- *Concurrent Pos:* Asst prof bot, Univ Ill, Urbana, 74-75 & 79- *Mem:* Am Soc Plant Taxonomists; Am Bot Soc; Int Asn Plant Taxon. *Res:* Taxonomy, phytogeography and biosystematics of Aster, Compositae; flora of Illinois. *Mailing Add:* Dept of Bot Univ of Ill-Champaign Urbana IL 61801

JONES, ALUN RICHARD, b Ipoh, Malaya, May 6, 28; Can citizen; m 55; c 2. PHYSICS, INSTRUMENTATION. *Educ:* Univ Bristol, BSc, 52; McGill Univ, MSc, 54. *Prof Exp:* Mem physics div electronics, Atomic Energy Can Ltd, 54-56, mem biol & health physics div radiation dosimetry, 56-72; exchange worker, Inst Cancer Res, UK, 62-63; SR RES OFFICER, BIOL & HEALTH PHYSICS DIV, ATOMIC ENERGY CAN LTD, 65- *Mem:* Health Physics Soc; Can Radiation Protection Asn. *Res:* External dosimetry of gamma and beta rays; thermoluminescence dosimetry; monitoring of alpha, beta and gamma contamination; detectors of ionising radiation (Geiger Mueller counters and silicon junction detectors); radiation protection. *Mailing Add:* Health Sci Div Atomic Energy of Can Ltd CRNL Chalk River ON K0J 1J0 Can

JONES, ANITA KATHERINE, b Ft Worth, Tex. COMPUTER SCIENCE. *Educ:* Rice Univ, AB, 64; Univ Tex, MA, 66; Carnegie-Mellon Univ, PhD(comput sci), 73. *Prof Exp:* Programmer, IBM Corp, 66-68; asst prof, 73-78, ASSOC PROF COMPUT SCI, CARNEGIE-MELLON UNIV, 78- *Concurrent Pos:* Consult, NSF, 73 & Rand Corp, 75-; Nat Res Coun travel grant, 74. *Mem:* Asn Comput Mach; Inst Elec & Electronics Engrs. *Res:* Design and implementation of programmed systems on computers, including enforcement of security policies on computers, operating systems, programming languages. *Mailing Add:* Dept of Comput Sci Carnegie-Mellon Univ Pittsburgh PA 15213

JONES, ARTHUR EUGENE, b Plymouth, Ind, Feb 6, 32; m 59; c 3. VISION. *Educ:* Ind Univ, AB, 60, PhD(physiol psychol), 64. *Prof Exp:* Res psychologist, US Army Med Res Lab, Ft Knox, Ky, 63-66; sr prin res scientist, Systs & Res Ctr, Honeywell, Inc, Minn, 66-69; ASSOC PROF OPTOM & PHYSIOL OPTICS, IND UNIV, BLOOMINGTON, 69- *Concurrent Pos:* Mem Nat Res Coun comt on vision, 64-66; bd dirs, Laser Indust Asn, 67-70; Gast prof, Univ Karlsruhe, 73-74. *Honors & Awards:* US Sr Scientist, Alexander von Humboldt-Stiftung, 73. *Mem:* AAAS; Asn Res Vision & Ophthal; Psychonomic Soc; Optical Soc Am; Soc Neurosci. *Res:* Comparative anatomy and physiology of the visual system; ocular hazards of ionizing and non-ionizing radiation; mechanisms of color vision. *Mailing Add:* Sch of Optom Physiol Optics Ind Univ Bloomington IN 47401

JONES, ARTHUR LETCHER, b New Canton, Va, May 2, 14; m 46; c 4. PETROLEUM CHEMISTRY. *Educ:* Hampden-Sydney Col, BS, 36; Univ Va, PhD(anal chem), 43. *Prof Exp:* Instr chem, Hampden-Sydney Col, 36-39 & Cornell Univ, 43-46; res group supvr, 46-52, res sect supvr, 52-64, coordr long-range planning res & develop, 64-67, SR RES ASSOC, STANDARD OIL CO, OHIO, 67- *Mem:* AAAS; Am Chem Soc. *Res:* Organic analytical reagents; magnetic susceptibility; separations of hydrocarbons; liquid thermal diffusion; properties of petroleum fuels; physical techniques in petroleum research; fuel cells; radio satellite tracking. *Mailing Add:* 32340 Woodsdale Lane Cleveland OH 44139

JONES, ARTHUR WYNNE, b Washington, DC, Dec 10, 13; m 38; c 4. PARASITOLOGY. *Educ:* Univ Va, BA, 34, LLB, 36, MA, 41, PhD(biol), 43. *Prof Exp:* Lab asst, Univ Va, 32-33; asst prof biol, Southwestern Univ, Tex, 43-45; actg assoc prof zool, Univ Tenn, Knoxville, 45-46, from assoc prof to prof, 46-78. *Concurrent Pos:* Actg head dept, 75-77. *Mem:* Am Soc Parasitol; Am Micros Soc. *Res:* Cytotaxonomy of cestodes; cestody cytology; radiation of parasites; immunology of trypanosomes. *Mailing Add:* 1603 Swain Dr Long Beach NC 28461

JONES, BARBARA, b Salt Lake City, Utah, Feb 8, 28. PEDIATRICS. *Educ:* Stanford Univ, AB, 49; Univ Utah, MD, 52; Am Bd Pediat, dipl, cert pediat hemat-oncol, 74. *Prof Exp:* From intern to asst resident pediat, St Louis Children's Hosp, 52-55; from instr to asst prof, Sch Med, Washington Univ, 55-61; from asst prof to assoc prof, 61-68, PROF PEDIAT, MED CTR, WVA UNIV, 68-, VCHMN DEPT, 70- *Mem:* Am Pediat Soc; Am Soc Hemat; Am Acad Pediat; Am Soc Clin Oncol; Soc Pediat Res. *Res:* Pediatric hematology and oncology; medical genetics. *Mailing Add:* Dept of Pediat WVa Univ Med Ctr Morgantown WV 26506

JONES, BARBARA ELLEN, b Philadelphia, Pa, Dec 19, 44; m 72; c 1. NEUROSCIENCE, NEUROANATOMY. *Educ:* Univ Del, BA, 66, PhD(psychol), 71. *Prof Exp:* Fel neurochem, Col France, Paris, 70-72; res assoc neuroanat, Univ Chicago, 72-74; vis lectr med physiol, Univ Nairobi, 74-75; res assoc & asst prof psychiat, Univ Chicago, 75-77; ASST PROF NEUROL, McGILL UNIV, 77- *Concurrent Pos:* Scholar, Med Res Coun Can, 78. *Mem:* Soc Neurosci; Am Asn Anat; Asn Psychophysiol Study Sleep. *Res:* Neuroanatomical organization of the brain stem reticular formation and of brain stem neurons that contain particular neurotransmitters, including monamines and acetylcholine; importance of these systems in mechanisms of sleep and wakefulness. *Mailing Add:* Dept Neurol & Neurosurg McGill Univ Montreal Neurol Inst Montreal PQ H3A 2B4 Can

JONES, BARCLAY G(EORGE), b Lafleche, Sask, May 6, 31; US citizen; m 59; c 3. NUCLEAR ENGINEERING, MECHANICAL ENGINEERING. *Educ:* Univ Sask, BE, 54; Univ Ill, MS, 60, PhD(nuclear eng), 66. *Prof Exp:* Athlone fel, Eng Elec Co, Rugby, Eng, 54-55; Atomic Energy Res Estab, Harwell, 55-57; engr, Nuclear Div, Canadair Ltd, Montreal, Que, 57-58; res asst, 58-60, instr nuclear eng, 63-66, from asst prof to assoc prof, 66-72, PROF NUCLEAR & MECH ENG, UNIV ILL, URBANA-CHAMPAIGN, 72-, ASSOC CHAIRPERSON, NUCLEAR ENG, 81- *Concurrent Pos:* Consult, WVa Pulp & Paper Co, Va, 68, Arnold Res Orgn, Inc, Tullahoma, Tenn, 74-80, Argonne Nat Lab, 76- & Fauske & Assocs, Burr Ridge, Ill, 81- *Mem:* Am Nuclear Soc; Can Soc Mech Engrs; Am Soc Mech Engrs; Eng Inst Can; Am Inst Aeronaut & Astronaut. *Res:* Heat transfer, fluid dynamics and turbulence as related to liquid metal coolants, reactor safety, two-phase flow, water pollution and statistical turbulence measurements; aerodynamic noise generation. *Mailing Add:* Nuclear Eng Prog Univ of Ill Urbana IL 61801

JONES, BENJAMIN A(NGUS), JR, b Mahomet, Ill, Apr 16, 26; m 49; c 2. AGRICULTURAL ENGINEERING. *Educ:* Univ Ill, BS, 49, MS, 50, PhD(civil eng), 58. *Prof Exp:* Asst agr eng, Univ Ill, 49-50; actg chmn, Dept Agr Eng, Univ Vt, 50-51, asst prof & asst agr engr, Agr Exten Serv, 50-52; from instr to assoc prof, 52-64, prof agr eng & head soil & water div, 64-73, ASSOC DIR, ILL AGR EXP STA, UNIV ILL, URBANA-CHAMPAIGN, 73- *Concurrent Pos:* Consult engr, Ill Drainage Dists. *Honors & Awards:* Hancor Award, Am Soc Agr Engrs, 77. *Mem:* Am Soc Agr Engrs; Am Soc Eng Educ; Soil Conserv Soc Am. *Res:* Agricultural land drainage and irrigation; agricultural hydrology and the hydraulics of erosion control structures. *Mailing Add:* 211 Mumford Hall Univ of Ill Urbana IL 61801

JONES, BENJAMIN FRANKLIN, JR, b Apr 15, 36; US citizen; m 57; c 3. MATHEMATICS. *Educ:* Rice Univ, BA, 58, PhD(math), 61. *Prof Exp:* Temp mem, Courant Inst Math Sci, NY Univ, 61-62; from asst prof to assoc prof math, 62-68, PROF MATH, RICE UNIV, 68- *Concurrent Pos:* Mem, Inst Advan Study, 65-66; vis prof, Univ Minn, 69-70. *Mem:* Am Math Soc; Math Asn Am. *Res:* Partial differential equations; singular integral operators. *Mailing Add:* Dept of Math Rice Univ Houston TX 77001

JONES, BERNARD R, b Grand Rapids, Minn, Jan 8, 23; m 50; c 5. FISH BIOLOGY. *Educ:* Univ Minn, BS, 49. *Prof Exp:* Pub health biologist, Minn Dept Health, 51-56; res biologist, Minn Dept Conserv, 56-66; resaquatic biologist & team coordr, 66-76, chief res br, 76-81, ASSOC DIR, ENVIRON RES LAB, ENVIRON PROTECTION AGENCY, 81- *Mem:* Am Fisheries Soc; Am Inst Fisheries Res Biologists. *Res:* Management. *Mailing Add:* Environ Res Lab of Duluth 6201 Congdon Blvd Duluth MN 55804

JONES, BERNE LEE, b Rochester, Ind, May 30, 41; m 63; c 3. BIOCHEMISTRY, PROTEIN CHEMISTRY. *Educ:* Wabash Col, BA, 63; Wash State Univ, PhD(chem), 67. *Prof Exp:* Fel biochem, Univ Colo, 67-69 & Univ Alta, 69-72; asst prof plant sci, Univ Man, 72-77; RES CHEMIST BIOCHEM, USDA, 77- *Mem:* Am Asn Cereal Chem; Am Chem Soc. *Res:* Biochemistry of cereal proteins; protein sequencing; genetic inheritance of wheat proteins. *Mailing Add:* Grain Mkt Res Lab USDA 1515 College Ave Manhattan KS 66502

JONES, BERWYN E, b Scottsbluff, Nebr, Mar 11, 37; m 58; c 2. ANALYTICAL CHEMISTRY. *Educ:* Nebr Wesleyan Univ, BA, 58; Kans State Univ, PhD(anal chem), 65. *Prof Exp:* From instr to assoc prof chem, Monmouth Col, Ill, 63-75; prof, Upper Iowa Univ, Fayette, 75-77; assoc prof, Longwood Col, 77-78; res chemist, 78-80, ASST LAB DIR, NAT WATER QUAL LABB, US GEOL SURV, ATLANTA, 80- *Concurrent Pos:* Vis asst prof, Univ Ill, 69-70; res assoc, Argonne Nat Lab, 70-71. *Mem:* AAAS; Am Chem Soc; Soc Appl Spectros. *Res:* Absorption and fluorescence spectroscopy; chromatography; atomic emission spectroscopy; molecular fluorescence spectroscopy. *Mailing Add:* US Geol Surv 6481-H Peachtree Indust Blvd Doraville GA 30340

JONES, BETTY RUTH, b Hernando, Miss, Mar 20, 51; m 73. CELL BIOLOGY, ELECTRON MICROSCOPY. *Educ:* Rust Col, BS, 73; Atlanta Univ, MS, 75, PhD(biol), 78. *Prof Exp:* MBS partic res biol, Atlanta Univ, 73-78; ASST PROF BIOL, MOREHOUSE COL, 78- *Concurrent Pos:* Student nurse, Methodist Hosp Sch Nursing, 71-72; anal chem lab tech trainee, Polaroid Corp, 70; res asst microbiol, Argonne Nat Lab, 73; lab coordr, Atlanta Jr Col, 75; Biomed Res Sci grant, 78-79. *Mem:* Am Soc Parasitol; Am Micros Soc; Electron Micros Soc; Am Soc Microbiol. *Res:* Parasitology; sickle cell membranes. *Mailing Add:* Apt #35 600 Huntington Ave Boston MA 02115

JONES, BILL EDSON, experimental psychology, see previous edition

JONES, BLAIR FRANCIS, b Apr 14, 34; m 55; c 2. GEOLOGY. *Educ:* Beloit Col, BA, 55; Johns Hopkins Univ, PhD, 63. *Prof Exp:* Lab instr geol, Beloit Col, 54-55; geologist, US Geol Surv, 55, geologist, Mineral Deposits Br, 56-57, res geologist, Water Resources Div, 58-74, res adv geochem, Washington, DC, 74-77, RES ADV GEOCHEM, WATER RESOURCES DIV, US GEOL SURV, NAT CTR, RESTON, 77- *Concurrent Pos:* Instr, Rockford Col, 54; vis prof, State Univ NY Binghamton, 70. *Mem:* Fel Geol Soc Am; Geochem Soc; fel Mineral Soc Am; Am Geophys Union; Soc Econ Paleontologists & Mineralogists. *Res:* Hydrogeochemistry; sedimentary petrology; geochemistry of weathering; brines, lacustrine sediments and evaporites; solutes in natural water. *Mailing Add:* 7905 Glenbrook Rd Bethesda MD 20014

JONES, BRIAN HERBERT, b Chester, Eng, Apr 23, 37; US citizen; m 74. MATERIALS SCIENCE, MECHANICAL ENGINEERING. *Educ:* Univ Liverpool, BEng, 61, PhD(appl mech), 65; Univ Calif, Los Angeles, cert bus admin, 69. *Prof Exp:* Group leader mat technol, Douglas Aircraft Co, 66-69; consult, ARAP, Inc, 69-72; vpres eng, Goldsworthy Eng, Inc, 72-75; PRES & GEN MGR ENG, COMPOSITEK ENG CORP, KELSEY-HAYES-FRUEHAUF CORP, 75- *Concurrent Pos:* Clayton fel, Inst Mech Engrs, London, 63-65; Busk fel, Royal Aeronaut Soc, London, 63-64; mem advan composites comt, Soc Plastics Indust, 76- *Mem:* Am Inst Aeronaut & Astronaut; Am Soc Mech Engrs; Soc Plastics Indust. *Res:* Composite materials product design and analysis; lightweight structures; plasticity of metals; process development; machine design. *Mailing Add:* 407 Country Club Dr San Gabriel CA 91775

JONES, BRIAN MCCOY, plant pathology, see previous edition

JONES, BRYANT LEE, b McLeansboro, Ill, Apr 17, 20; m 43; c 2. MEDICINE, CANCER. *Educ:* Univ Md, BS, 41, MD, 44. *Prof Exp:* Intern, Franklin Square Hosp, Baltimore, 44-45, asst resident med, 45-46, resident, 48-49; pvt pract, 49-59; sr med assoc pharmaceut res, Ciba Pharmaceut Co, NJ, 60-63; head endocrine sect, Clin Br Collab Res, Nat Cancer Inst, Md, 63-66; res investr, Div Oncol & Radiopharmaceut, Off New Drugs, Food & Drug Admin, 66-68; opers officer, Div Regional Med Progs, Health Serv & Ment Health Admin, 68-69, assoc cancer & nuclear med, 69-71; DEP DIR DIV ONCOL & RADIOPHARMACEUT DRUG PROD, OFF SCI EVAL, BUR DRUGS, FOOD & DRUG ADMIN, 71- *Mem:* AMA; Am Soc Clin Oncol; Soc Nuclear Med. *Res:* Collaborative research concerned with the acquisition and testing of new compounds showing potential as cancer chemotherapeutic agents. *Mailing Add:* Div of Oncol & Radiopharmaceut Drug Prod Food & Drug Admin Rockville MD 20857

JONES, BURTON FREDRICK, b Manistique, Mich, Oct 28, 42. ASTROMETRY. *Educ:* Univ Chicago, BS, 65, MS, 68, PhD(astron), 70. *Prof Exp:* Fel astron, Lick Observ, Univ Calif, 70-71; sr res fel, Royal Greenwich Observ, 72-74; res fel, Univ Tex, 74-75; asst res astronomer, 75-79, ASST ASTRONOMER & PROF, LICK OBSERV, CALIF, 79- *Mem:* Int Astron Union; Am Astron Soc. *Res:* Stellar proper motions; cluster membership. *Mailing Add:* Lick Observ Univ Calif Santa Cruz CA 95054

JONES, BURTON WADSWORTH, b Redwood Falls, Minn, Oct 1, 02; m 32; c 3. MATHEMATICS. *Educ:* Grinnell Col, AB, 23, DSc, 70; Harvard Univ, AM, 24; Univ Chicago, PhD(math), 28. *Prof Exp:* Instr math, Western Reserve Univ, 24-26 & Univ Chicago, 28-29; Nat Res Coun fel, Univ Chicago & Calif Inst Technol, 29-30; from asst prof to prof math, Cornell Univ, 30-48; prof math, 48-71, EMER PROF MATH, UNIV COLO, BOULDER, 71- *Concurrent Pos:* Mem, Inst Advan Study, 39-40; Res Corp grant, NY, 48-49; vis prof, Univ PR, 59-60; US-AID math regional specialist, Cent Am. 64-65; vis prof, Univ Col Cayey, PR, 71-72. *Mem:* Am Math Soc; Math Asn Am (assoc secy, 46-48). *Res:* Quadratic forms; matrices; theory of numbers. *Mailing Add:* Dept of Math Univ of Colo Boulder CO 80309

JONES, C ROBERT, b Scranton, Pa, May 8, 33; m 57; c 4. CELL PHYSIOLOGY. *Educ:* Univ Scranton, BS, 54; Fordham Univ, MS, 56, PhD(physiol), 62. *Prof Exp:* Res asst chemother, Sloan-Kettering Inst Cancer Res, 58-59; fel, Fordham Univ, 62-63; from instr to asst prof physiol, 63-68, assoc prof cell biol, 68-74, PROF CELL BIOL, LEHMAN COL, 74-, CHMN DEPT BIOL SCI, 68- *Concurrent Pos:* Lectr, Bronx Community Col, 62-63; NSF res grant, Div Metab Biol, 64-66. *Mem:* AAAS; Entom Soc Am. *Res:* Activity of respiratory enzymes during the metamorphosis of holometabolous insects; identification of Lysosomes in insect tissues; mammalian physiology. *Mailing Add:* Dept of Biol Sci Herbert H Lehman Col Bronx NY 10468

JONES, CARL TRAINER, b Allentown, Pa, Dec 31, 10; m 38; c 2. CHEMISTRY. *Educ:* Washington Missionary Col, BA, 33; Cath Univ, MS, 39; Ore State Col, PhD, 59. *Prof Exp:* Head dept chem, Atlantic Union Col, 37-38; asst prof chem, Washington Missionary Col, 38-46; head dept sci, Philippine Union Col, 47-52; asst prof chem, Walla Walla Col, 52-76, chmn dept, 60-76; RETIRED. *Concurrent Pos:* Teacher, Takoma Acad, 38-46. *Mem:* Am Chem Soc. *Res:* Analytical chemistry. *Mailing Add:* 207 NE A St College Place WA 99324

JONES, CAROL A, b Kremmling, Colo, Sept 10, 36; m 55; c 7. BIOPHYSICS. *Educ:* Univ Colo, BA, 63, PhD(biophys), 69. *Prof Exp:* Fel biophys, US Pub Health Serv, 69-71, res assoc biophys & genetics, 71-74, asst prof, 74-80, ASSOC PROF BIOPHYS & GENETICS, UNIV COLO HEALTH SCI CTR, 80-, SR FEL, ELEANOR ROOSEVELT INST CANCER RES, 80- *Mem:* Am Soc Cell Biol. *Res:* Cell biology; somatic cell genetics; cell surface molecules. *Mailing Add:* E Roosevelt Inst Cancer Res Univ Colo Med Ctr 4200 E 9th Ave Denver CO 80220

JONES, CHARLES, b New York, NY, Feb 27, 26; m 46; c 2. MECHANICAL ENGINEERING. *Educ:* Columbia Univ, BS, 50, MS, 53. *Prof Exp:* Design engr stress anal & test engr, 50-55, sect head stress & appl mech, 55-57, gas turbine design sect head, 57-58, lead proj engr, 58-62, chief design engr, 62-68, chief engr, 68-69, dir eng, 69-81, DIR RES, ROTARY COMBUSTION

ENG FAC, CURTISS-WRIGHT CORP, 81- *Concurrent Pos:* Geust mem, Adv Comt, Nat Adv Space Agency, 81; mem, Adv Comt, NSF, 74-75. *Mem:* Soc Automotive Engrs. *Res:* Rotary combustion engine. *Mailing Add:* Rotary Eng Fac Curtiss-Wright Corp One Passaic St Woodbridge NJ 07075

JONES, CHARLES DINGEE, b Hammond, Ind, July 12, 25; m 47; c 2. MECHANICAL ENGINEERING. *Educ:* Lehigh Univ, BS, 47; Univ Ky, MS, 48; Ohio State Univ, PhD(mech eng), 52. *Prof Exp:* Instr mech eng, Univ Ky, 48-49; res assoc, 50-53, from asst prof to assoc prof, 56-64, PROF MECH ENG, OHIO STATE UNIV, 64-, RES SUPVR, 54- *Mem:* Am Soc Eng Educ; Am Soc Mech Engrs; Nat Soc Prof Engrs. *Res:* Heat transfer; thermodynamics; fluid dynamics. *Mailing Add:* Dept of Mech Eng 206 W 18th Ave Columbus OH 43210

JONES, CHARLES E, b Oklahoma City, Okla, June 10, 28; m 49; c 5. MOLECULAR PHYSICS, ATOMIC PHYSICS. *Educ:* Univ Ark, Fayetteville, BS, 51, MS, 55; Tex A&M Univ, PhD(physics), 65. *Prof Exp:* Jr thermo engr, Convair Aircraft Co, 51-52; aerodyn engr, McDonnell Aircraft Co, 52-53; instr physics, Mo Sch Mines, 55-57 & Tex A&M Univ, 57-61; asst & assoc prof, Univ Ark, 61-70; PROF PHYSICS & HEAD DEPT, E TEX STATE UNIV, 70- *Concurrent Pos:* Consult, NSF-Agency Int Develop Summer Inst, 69. *Mem:* Am Asn Physics Teachers; Am Phys Soc. *Res:* Atoms and molecules in inert matrices at low temperatures by means of absorption and emission spectroscopy. *Mailing Add:* Dept of Physics ETex State Univ Commerce TX 75428

JONES, CHARLES E(DWARD), b New York, NY, Apr 20, 20; m 44; c 4. HEAT TRANSFER. *Educ:* City Col New York, BS, 47; Agr & Mech Col Tex, MS, 51; Cornell Univ, PhD, 57. *Prof Exp:* Instr, City Col New York, 47-49; asst prof & asst res engr, Agr & Mech Col Tex, 49-52; res engr, Res Ctr, Babcock & Wilcox Co, Ohio 54-57, head anal eng sect, 58, supt tech serv, 59-61, mgr anal lab, 61-65, mgr thermodynamics lab, 65-67, asst dir, 67-68, dir res ctr, 68-71; vpres opers, Bailey Meter Co, 71, pres, 71-74; asst to exec vpres technol, Indust Prod Group, Babcock & Wilcox Co, 75-80; RETIRED. *Mem:* Fel Am Soc Mech Engrs (pres, 80-81); Sigma Xi. *Res:* Thermodynamics; fluid mechanics; automatic data acquisition. *Mailing Add:* Babcock & Wilcox Co 29801 Euclid Ave Wickliffe OH 44092

JONES, CHARLES M(AURICE), b Bernie, Mo, Feb 12, 25; m 47; c 2. ELECTRONICS. *Educ:* NC State Col, BSEE, 50; Purdue Univ, MS, 54. *Prof Exp:* Elec engr, Hunt Oil Co, Ala, 50-51; electronic engr res & develop, US Air Force Cambridge Res Ctr, 54-58, chief recognition sect, 58-61; sr electronic systs engr, Syst Develop Corp, Mass, 61-67; STUDY DIR, RAYTHEON CO, 67- *Mem:* NY Acad Sci. *Res:* Unusual data processing problems; conceptual system design; systems analysis; technical writing. *Mailing Add:* 18 Colonial Dr Chelmsford MA 01824

JONES, CHARLES MILLER, JR, b Atlanta, Ga, Feb 25, 35; m 57; c 2. PHYSICS. *Educ:* Ga Inst Technol, BS, 57; Rice Univ, MA, 59, PhD(physics), 61. *Prof Exp:* Res assoc, Rice Univ, 61-62; PHYSICIST, OAK RIDGE NAT LAB, 62- *Mem:* AAAS; Am Phys Soc; Am Vacuum Soc. *Res:* Nuclear structure, especially reactions and scattering in the light nuclei; tests of fundamental symmetries using nuclear reactions; application of superconductivity to particle accelerators; physics and technology of electrostatic particle accelerators. *Mailing Add:* Bldg 6000 Oak Ridge Nat Lab Oak Ridge TN 37830

JONES, CHESTER GEORGE, b Utica, NY, May 14, 36; m 61; c 3. OPERATIONS RESEARCH, SYSTEMS ANALYSIS. *Educ:* Syracuse Univ, BS, 60; Univ Ill, Urbana, MS, 64; Ohio State Univ, PhD(indust eng), 71. *Prof Exp:* Mfg engr, Remington Rand Div, Sperry Rand Corp, 60-63; design engr, Nat Cash Register Co, 64-66; SYSTEMS ANALYST, DEP DEVELOP PLANNING, WRIGHT-PATTERSON AFB, DAYTON, 66- *Res:* Optimization of the design and use of advanced systems; development of solutions to constrained optimization problems. *Mailing Add:* 446 Lincoln Park Blvd Kettering OH 45429

JONES, CHRISTINE, x-ray astronomy, see previous edition

JONES, CLAIBORNE STRIBLING, b Petersburg, Va, Dec 20, 14; m 40; c 3. ZOOLOGY. *Educ:* Hampden-Sydney Col, AB, 35; Univ Va, MA, 40, PhD(biol), 44. *Prof Exp:* From asst prof to assoc prof, Univ NC, Chapel Hill, 44-56, asst to chancellor, 77-80, 66-74, vchancellor bus & finance, 74-77, prof zool, 56-80, exec asst to chancellor,; RETIRED. *Mailing Add:* 103 S Bldg Univ of NC Chapel Hill NC 27514

JONES, CLARENCE S, b Rigby, Idaho, Aug 21, 26; m 48; c 3. PHYSICS, ENGINEERING. *Educ:* Univ Utah, BA, 50, MA, 52. *Prof Exp:* Mem staff, Los Alamos Sci Lab, 52-55; mem tech staff, Ramo-Wooldridge Corp, Calif, 55-57; chief engr, Res & Develop Labs, Link Div, Gen Precision, Inc, 57-62; mgr equip eng, Sylvania Elec Prod Inc, 62-64; vpres eng, ESL Inc, 64-70; pres, Anal Develop Assocs Corp, 70-76, CHMN BD, ADAC LABS, 76- *Mem:* AAAS. *Res:* Design and execution of physical experiments in nuclear physics and electronics; design of electronic systems and circuits; administration of scientific and engineering activities. *Mailing Add:* ADAC Labs 255 San Geronimo Way Sunnyvale CA 94086

JONES, CLAUDE KITCHENER, physics, see previous edition

JONES, CLIVE GARETH, b Cirencester, Eng, March 3, 51; m 77. CHEMICAL ECOLOGY, PLANT-INSECT INTERACTIONS. *Educ:* Univ Salford, Eng, BSc, 74; Univ York, Eng, DPhil(biol), 78. *Prof Exp:* Fel res, Dept Entom, Univ Ga, 78-80; CHEM ECOLOGIST & DEPT HEAD RES, NY BOT GARDEN CARY ARBORETUM, MILLBROOK, 80- *Concurrent Pos:* Adj asst prof, Marist Col, Poughkeepsi, 80-; consult, Ctr Semiochem Res & Technol, Res Productivity Coun Can, Fredericton, NB, 82- *Mem:* AAAS; Entomol Soc Am. *Res:* Chemical ecology and plant-insect interactions; chemical defenses of insects and plants; plant-mammal interactions. *Mailing Add:* NY Bot Garden Cary Arboretum Millbrook NY 12545

JONES, CLYDE JOE, b Scottsbluff, Nebr, Mar 3, 35; m 55; c 2. MAMMALIAN ECOLOGY, TAXONOMY. *Educ:* Hastings Col, BA, 57; Univ NMex, MS, 60, PhD(biol). 64. *Prof Exp:* Asst cur biol, Univ NMex, 62-65; asst prof, Tulane Univ, 65-70; res assoc, Delta Regional Primate Res Ctr, 67-70; zoologist, Bur Sport Fisheries & Wildlife, Nat Mus Natural Hist, 70-73, dir, Nat Fish & Wildlife Lab, 73-79; DIR, DENVER WILDLIFE RES CTR, 79- *Concurrent Pos:* Res investr field studies, Rio Muni, WAfrica, Nat Geog Soc, 66-68; biologist, Antarctic Inspection, Oper Deepfreeze, 71-; res assoc, Smithsonian Inst, 71- *Honors & Awards:* Antarctic Serv Medal, Oper Deepfreeze, US Navy, 71. *Mem:* AAAS; Am Soc Mammal; Soc Syst Zool; Ecol Soc Am. *Res:* Systematics and ecology of mammals, especially rodents and bats of America; bats, primates and rodents of West Africa. *Mailing Add:* US Fish & Wildlife Serv Bldg 16 Fed Ctr Denver CO 80225

JONES, COLIN ELLIOTT, solid state physics, see previous edition

JONES, CREIGHTON CLINTON, b Mt Oliver, Pa, Feb 13, 13; m 39; c 2. PHYSICS. *Educ:* Carnegie Inst Technol, BS, 34, MS, 35; Univ NC, PhD(physics), 38. *Prof Exp:* Am Philos Soc res assoc, Univ NC, 38-39; res physicist, Nat Carbon Co Div, Union Carbide Corp, 39-40 & 49-54, physicist, 40-49, tech rep, 54-62, appln mgr brush prod, Carbon Prod Div, 62-78; CONSULT, 78- *Mem:* Am Phys Soc; Inst Elec & Electronics Eng. *Res:* Nuclear physics; energy loss of electrons in collision with nuclei; processing of carbon products; testing and application of carbon and carbon metal brushes on electrical equipment; sliding contacts. *Mailing Add:* 112 Highland Dr Chapel Hill NC 27574

JONES, DALE ROBERT, b Galesburg, Ill, June 17, 24. PHYSICS. *Educ:* Univ Cincinnati, BSc, 48; Wash Univ, PhD, 53. *Prof Exp:* From asst prof to assoc prof, 53-62, PROF PHYSICS, UNIV CINCINNATI, 62- *Mem:* Am Phys Soc. *Res:* Cosmic rays; atomic physics. *Mailing Add:* Dept of Physics Univ of Cincinnati Cincinnati OH 45221

JONES, DALLAS WAYNE, b Tiplersville, Miss, Sept 13, 38. PHYSICS. *Educ:* Memphis State Univ, BS, 60; Univ Va, MS, 62, PhD(physics), 66. *Prof Exp:* Teaching asst physics, Univ Va, 60-63, res asst, 63-65; res physicist, US Naval Res Lab, 65-69; ASSOC PROF PHYSICS, MEMPHIS STATE UNIV, 69-, DIR, CTR NUCLEAR STUDIES, 73- *Res:* Quantum physics; nuclear spectroscopy; reactor technology. *Mailing Add:* Ctr for Nuclear Studies Memphis State Univ Memphis TN 38152

JONES, DANE ROBERT, b Park City, Utah, Nov 27, 47; m 74. PHYSICAL CHEMISTRY. *Educ:* Univ Utah, BA, 69; Stanford Univ, PhD(phys chem), 74. *Prof Exp:* Res assoc phys chem, Phys Chem Inst, Univ Uppsala, 74-75; res assoc & instr phys chem, Univ Utah, 75-76; asst prof, 76-80, ASSOC PROF CHEM, CALIF POLYTECH STATE UNIV, SAN LUIS OBISPO, 80- *Mem:* Am Chem Soc. *Res:* Light scattering; molecular complexes in solution. *Mailing Add:* Dept of Chem Calif Polytech State Univ San Luis Obispo CA 93407

JONES, DANIEL DAVID, b Olney, Ill, Feb 23, 43; m 65. PLANT PHYSIOLOGY, PHYCOLOGY. *Educ:* Purdue Univ, BS, 65, MS, 67; Mich State Univ, PhD(plant physiol), 70. *Prof Exp:* ASSOC PROF BIOL, UNIV ALA, BIRMINGHAM, 70- *Mem:* Am Soc Plant Physiol; Am Inst Biol Scientists. *Res:* Golgi apparatus mediated polysaccharide secretion by outer root cap cells of Zea mays; isolation, chemical characterization and ultrastructural and conformational changes of gasvacuole membranes from Microcystis aeruginosa Kuetz emend Elenkin. *Mailing Add:* Dept of Biol Univ of Ala 1919 Seventh Ave S Birmingham AL 35294

JONES, DANIEL ELVEN, b New Orleans, La, Sept 9, 43; m 65. PHYSICAL CHEMISTRY, COMPUTER SCIENCE. *Educ:* La State Univ, Baton Rouge, BS, 65; Univ Calif, Berkeley, PhD(phys chem), 70. *Prof Exp:* Res chemist, Am Cyanamid Co, 70-71, res comput specialist, 71-76; res chemist, 76-78, SR RES CHEMIST, FREEPORT MINERALS CO, 79- *Mem:* Am Chem Soc; Clay Minerals Soc; Sigma Xi. *Res:* Metal ion-nucleotide binding; carbon-13 Fourier transform nuclear magnetic resonance; application of digital computers and computing techniques for improvement of analytical instrumentation; uranium recovery from phosphoric acid; sulfur purification; inorganic chemistry. *Mailing Add:* Freeport Minerals Co PO Box 26 Belle Chasse LA 70037

JONES, DANIEL PATRICK, b Lima, Ohio, Aug 21, 41; m 64; c 1. HISTORY OF SCIENCE. *Educ:* Univ Louisville, BS, 63; Harvard Univ, AM, 65; Univ Wis-Madison, PhD(hist sci), 69. *Prof Exp:* Macy fel hist med & biol sci, Johns Hopkins Univ, 69-70; asst prof hist sci, Ore State Univ, 70-78; vis prof, 78-80, ASST PROF HIST SCI, CTR HUMANISTIC STUDIES, UNIV ILL MED CTR, 80- *Mem:* AAAS; Hist Sci Soc; Am Chem Soc. *Res:* History of biochemistry and organic chemistry, 19th and early 20th century; relationships between science and society; history of public health. *Mailing Add:* Ctr for Humanistic Studies Univ Ill Med Ctr Chicago IL 60612

JONES, DAVID, b Gardiner, Mont, Nov 20, 12; m 40; c 1. METALLURGICAL ENGINEERING. *Educ:* Mont Sch Mines, BS, 35. *Prof Exp:* Mining engr, 35-43; supt, Cloverdale Quicksilver Mine, Calif, 43; mining engr, Union Mines Develop Corp, 43-46; consult mining engr, Nev, 46; chief mining br, Real Estate Div, Corps Eng, US Army, 47-64; valuation engr, Br Real Estate Appraisal, Bur Indian Affairs, US Dept Interior, Washington, DC, 64-70; mining engr, Nat Park Serv, San Francisco, 70-81; CONSULT MINING ENGR, 81- *Mem:* Am Inst Mining, Metall & Petrol Engrs. *Res:* Fair market valuation of mineral interests in land; title to mining claims in public land. *Mailing Add:* Nat Park Serv 450 Golden Gate Ave San Francisco CA 94102

JONES, DAVID A, JR, b McCook, Nebr, Feb 9, 37; c 3. ORGANIC CHEMISTRY. *Educ:* Tex A&M Univ, BS, 58; NMex State Univ, MS, 64; Purdue Univ, PhD(org chem), 68. *Prof Exp:* Mem staff, Dept Med Chem, 68-81, RES SCIENTIST II, G D SEARLE & CO, 77- *Mem:* AAAS; Am Chem Soc. *Res:* Organometallic chemistry of silicon, magnesium, lithium; organic chemistry of phosphorus; amino acid and peptide chemistry. *Mailing Add:* G D Searle & Co Box 5110 Chicago IL 60680

JONES, DAVID B, b Canton, China, Dec 1, 21; US citizen; m 44; c 3. PATHOLOGY. *Educ:* Syracuse Univ, AB, 43, MD, 45; Am Bd Path, dipl. *Prof Exp:* From asst prof to assoc prof, 50-62, PROF PATH, STATE UNIV NY UPSTATE MED CTR, 62- *Mem:* Am Asn Pathologists & Bacteriologists; Am Soc Cytol. *Res:* Electron microscopy. *Mailing Add:* State Univ of NY Upstate Med Ctr Syracuse NY 13210

JONES, DAVID CHARLES LLOYD, b Oakland, Calif, Jan 13, 23; m 43; c 3. TOXICOLOGY. *Educ:* Univ Calif, AB, 43, MA, 48, PhD(physiol), 54. *Prof Exp:* Asst, Univ Calif, 47-48; res physiologist, US Naval Radiol Defense Lab, Calif, 48-69; sr physiologist life sci, 69-78, DIR TOXICOL LAB, SRI INT, 78- *Mem:* Am Physiol Soc; Radiation Res Soc; Geront Soc. *Res:* Biological effects of radiation; performance and environmental physiology; gerontology; carcinogenesis. *Mailing Add:* Dept of Life Sci SRI Int Menlo Park CA 94025

JONES, DAVID H(UNTER), b Youngstown, Ohio, Jan 7, 31; m 54; c 2. NUCLEAR ENGINEERING. *Educ:* Oberlin Col, AB, 52; Univ Wash, MS, 56. *Prof Exp:* Nuclear design scientist, Bettis Atomic Power Lab, Westinghouse Elec Corp, 56-65; supvr & mgr light water breeder reactor nuclear design, West Mifflin, 65-76, mgr operation planning, Fast Flux Testing Facil, Westinghouse Hanford Co, 76-81; REP POWER REACTOR & NUCLEAR FUEL DEVELOP CORP, US DEPT ENERGY, JAPAN, 81- *Mem:* Am Nuclear Soc. *Res:* Nuclear design and analysis; fast reactor testing and operations. *Mailing Add:* Westinghouse Hanford Co PO Box 1970 Richland WA 99352

JONES, DAVID HARTLEY, b Kansas City, Mo, Feb 10, 39; m 65; c 3. BIOCHEMISTRY. *Educ:* Bethany Nazarene Col, BS, 61; Univ Okla, MS, 64; Cornell Univ, PhD(biochem), 68. *Prof Exp:* USPHS fel biochem, Univ Calif, Los Angeles, 67-69; asst prof, Albany Med Col, Union Univ, 69-75, assoc prof, 75-78; assoc prof biochem, Oral Roberts Univ, 78-80. *Mem:* AAAS. *Res:* Oxidative phosphorylation in mitochondria; functional state transitions in the mammary gland; mitochondrial biogenesis during functional state transitions in the mammary gland. *Mailing Add:* 1719 S Gary Tulsa OK 74104

JONES, DAVID LAWRENCE, b Chicago, Ill, Nov 12, 30; m 53; c 4. GEOLOGY, PALEONTOLOGY. *Educ:* Yale Univ, BS, 52; Stanford Univ, MS, 53, PhD, 56. *Prof Exp:* GEOLOGIST, WESTERN REGION, US GEOL SURV, 55- *Mem:* Geol Soc Am; Paleont Soc. *Res:* Molluscan paleontology; Cretaceous of the Pacific coast region of North America; stratigraphy, structural, biostratigraphy and molluscan paleontology of upper Mesozoic rocks of the Pacific Coast of North America. *Mailing Add:* US Geol Surv 345 Middlefield Rd Menlo Park CA 94025

JONES, DAVID LLOYD, b Sapporo, Japan, Apr 11, 19; US citizen; m 42; c 3. ENERGY PLANNING, METEOROLOGY & CLIMATOLOGY. *Educ:* Carleton Col, BA, 41; Pa State Univ, MS, 53, PhD(meteorol), 60. *Prof Exp:* Unit leader meteorol, Statist Dept, US Nat Weather Serv, 43-46; instr math, Fisk Univ, 46; meteorologist, Am Airlines, 46-51; asst meteorol, Pa State Univ, 51-55, instr, 55-56; lectr & assoc res meteorologist, Univ Mich, 56-61; sr res scientist, Travelers Res Ctr, 61-65; assoc prof meteorol, Cent Conn State Col, 65; assoc prof, 65-71, dir Europ earth sci study prog, 74 & 76, PROF METEOROL & ENERGY PLANNING SOUTHERN ILL UNIV, CARBONDALE, 71- *Concurrent Pos:* Lectr, NSF vis Scientist Prog, Am Meteorol Soc & Mich State Univ, 60-61; lectr, Mus Art, Sci & Indust, Conn, 63-65; consult, Educ Film Proj, Am Meteorol Soc, Boston, 64; consult world weather data syst, US Nat Weather Serv, Washington, DC, 65; partic writing conf, Earth Sci Curric Proj, Am Geol Inst, Colo, 65; chmn sect meteorol & climat, Ill State Acad Sci, 70; dir, US Dept Energy Summer Inst on Energy, 77, staff mem, 78. *Mem:* Am Meteorol Soc; Sigma Xi. *Res:* Large scale atmospheric vertical motion; atmospheric pollution by aeroallergens; atmosphere-hydrosphere interactions; meteorological data-processing system design; laboratory and classroom instructional devices; educational films; interdisciplinary problems in the environmental sciences; science museum design; energy planning and community energy planning; alternate energy resources; oceanography. *Mailing Add:* Dept Geog & Environ Planning Southern Ill Univ Carbondale IL 62901

JONES, DAVID STEVENS, b Detroit, Mich, Sept 13, 38; m 63; c 1. IMMUNOPATHOLOGY, IMMUNOLOGY. *Educ:* Albion Col, BA, 60; Mich State Univ, MS, 61; Univ Western Ont, PhD(path), 69. *Prof Exp:* From res biologist to asst res microbiologist, Parke, Davis & Co, 63-65; from lectr to asst prof path, Univ Western Ont, 69-72; asst dir clin res, Hoechst Pharmaceut, Inc, 72-73; dir diag eval, Behring Diag, 74-77; DIR CLIN AFFAIRS, ZIMMER USA, 77- *Concurrent Pos:* Nat Cancer Inst Can res grant, 70-72; Ont Heart Found res grant, 71-72; consult immunopath, Renal Unit, Victoria Hosp, 69-72. *Mem:* Am Soc Clin Path; Am Asn Clin Chemists; Asn Clin Scientists. *Res:* Immunomicroscopy; enzyme labeled antibody; enzyme immunoassay. *Mailing Add:* PO Box 70 Miles Labs Inc Elkhart IN 46515

JONES, DEAN GRAEME, b Pine Village, Ind, Aug 30, 17; m 42; c 4. POULTRY BREEDING. *Educ:* Purdue Univ, BSA, 39; Cornell Univ, MS, 41, PhD(animal breeding), 46. *Prof Exp:* Asst animal breeding, Cornell Univ, 39-43 & 46; from asst prof to prof poultry husb, SDak State Col, 46-53; POULTRY GENETICIST, DE KALB AGRESEARCH, INC, 54- *Concurrent Pos:* Agent poultry husb, Bur Animal Indust, USDA, DC, 48-53. *Mem:* AAAS; Am Genetic Asn; Poultry Sci Asn. *Res:* Poultry genetics; physiology of avian reproduction; relationships between development of the comb, body size and reproductive capacity in white leghorn males. *Mailing Add:* De Kalb Poultry Res Ctr Sycamore Rd De Kalb IL 60115

JONES, DENNY ALAN, metallurgy, electrochemistry, see previous edition

JONES, DEREK WILLIAM, b Birmingham, Eng, Dec 9, 33; Can citizen; m 57; c 4. DENTAL MATERIALS. *Educ:* Univ Birmingham, BSc, 65, PhD(dent mat sci), 70; Inst Ceramics, AICeram, 70, FICeram, 78. *Prof Exp:* Instr dent technol & mat, Univ Birmingham, 65-75; assoc prof dent biomat, 75-77, prof-in-chg dent biomat, 77-79, PROF & HEAD, DIV DENT BIOMAT SCI FAC DENT, DALHOUSIE UNIV, 79- *Concurrent Pos:* Vis lectr, Mathew Boulton Tech Col, 61-68; examr, City & Guilds London Inst, 66-73; mem comt & consult, Brit Stand Comt Dent Mat, 70-75; Brit expert rep, Int Stand Orgn, 73-75, Can rep, 75-, comt mem coun dent mat & devices, 77-, chmn Can adv comt, tech comt 106; chmn comt dent, Can Stand Asn, 78-; mem, Can Standards Steering Comt Health Care Technol, Can Standards Comt Implant Mat, 79 & Med Res Coun; dent schs rep, Dent Mat Group, Int Asn Dent Res. *Mem:* Can Asn Dent Res; Int Asn Dent Res; Soc Biomat; Inst Ceramics. *Res:* Development of test methodology; evaluating mechanical-physical properties of materials to optomize clinical and laboratory use; biological factors relative to clinical performance; studies of hard and soft polymers, ceramics and metals; author of over 60 scientific publications. *Mailing Add:* Fac of Dent Dalhousie Univ Halifax NS B3H 4H6 Can

JONES, DON B(ARBER), b Minneapolis, Minn, Mar 3, 24; m 49; c 2. HYDRAULIC ENGINEERING, OCEAN ENGINEERING. *Educ:* Univ Kans, BS, 51; Univ Iowa, MS, 54. *Prof Exp:* Engr, Phillips Petrol Co, 51-52; asst prof civil eng, Ga Inst Technol, 54-62; RES ENGR, NAVAL CIVIL ENG LAB, 65- *Concurrent Pos:* Nat Sci Found fac fel, 62-65. *Mem:* Am Soc Civil Engrs. *Res:* Incompressible fluid dynamics including effects of water waves. *Mailing Add:* Code L42 Naval Civil Eng Lab Naval Construct Battalion Ctr Port Hueneme CA 93043

JONES, DONALD AKERS, b Topeka, Kans, Dec 27, 30; m 56; c 4. ACTUARIAL SCIENCE. *Educ:* Iowa State Univ, BS, 52; Univ Iowa, MS, 56, PhD(math), 59. *Prof Exp:* Asst prof, 59-65, ASSOC PROF MATH, UNIV MICH-ANN ARBOR, 65- *Mem:* Am Statist Asn; Soc Actuaries. *Res:* Statistics and actuarial mathematics. *Mailing Add:* Dept of Math Univ of Mich Ann Arbor MI 48109

JONES, DONALD EUGENE, b South Bend, Ind, Aug 1, 34; m 55; c 3. ANALYTICAL CHEMISTRY. *Educ:* Manchester Col, AB, 57; Purdue Univ, PhD(anal chem), 60. *Prof Exp:* Chemist, Bendix Corp, Ind, 57; res chemist, E I du Pont de Nemours & Co, 60; instr chem, Wabash Col, 61-63; asst prrof, 63-67, assoc prof, 67-76, PROF CHEM, WESTERN MD COL, 76-, HEAD DEPT, 76- *Concurrent Pos:* Vis assoc prof, Purdue Univ, 71-72; chem consult, Carroll County Gen Hosp, 74- *Mem:* Am Chem Soc. *Res:* Fluorescence of materials as applied to analytical procedures; trace analysis of materials; computer applications to chemical analysis; analytical chemistry as applied to clinical situations. *Mailing Add:* Dept of Chem Western Md Col Westminster MD 21157

JONES, DONLAN F(RANCIS), b San Francisco, Calif, Feb 5, 30; m 57; c 4. ELECTRICAL ENGINEERING, COMPUTER SCIENCES. *Educ:* Univ Santa Clara, BEE, 52; Univ Calif, Los Angeles, MS, 54; Stanford Univ, Engr, 72. *Prof Exp:* Res engr, Hughes Aircraft Co, 52-56; asst prof elec eng, Univ Santa Clara, 56-63; adv develop engr, Sylvania Electronics Systs Div, Gen Tel & Electronics Corp, 63-65; eng specialist, 65-69; eng mgr, Comput Terminal Prods, 69-74, eng mgr, 4081 & MEG systs, 74-78, engr mgr, mass storage syst, 78-81, ENGR MGR, DATA COMMUN, INFO DISPLAY DIV, TEKTRONIX, INC, BEAVERTON, 81- *Concurrent Pos:* Adv develop engr, Sylvania Electronics Systs Div, Gen Tel & Electronics Corp, 57-63; NSF sci fac fel, 61-62; consult, Sonoma State Hosp, Calif, 62-63. *Mem:* Inst Elec & Electronics Engrs. *Res:* Application of computers to engineering and non-scientific problems; threshold logical design; graphic computer systems. *Mailing Add:* 427 Laurel St Lake Oswego OR 97034

JONES, DOUGLAS EMRON, b Long Beach, Calif, Aug 19, 30; m 55; c 5. PHYSICS. *Educ:* Brigham Young Univ, BS, 57, MS, 59, PhD(physics), 64. *Prof Exp:* Technician radio repair, Southern Calif Edison Co, 54-55; apprentice engr, Collins Radio Co, 56, group supvr, 57; space scientist, Jet Propulsion Lab, Calif Inst Technol, 59-62; from asst prof to assoc prof, 64-74, PROF PHYSICS, BRIGHAM YOUNG UNIV, 74- *Mem:* Am Geophys Union; Am Phys Soc. *Res:* Solar physics; interplanetary magnetic fields; planetary atmospheres. *Mailing Add:* Dept of Physics Brigham Young Univ Provo UT 84602

JONES, DOUGLAS EPPS, b Tuscaloosa, Ala, May 28, 30; m 55; c 3. GEOLOGY, PALEONTOLOGY. *Educ:* Univ Ala, BS, 52; La State Univ, PhD(geol), 59. *Prof Exp:* Res geologist, La Geol Surv, 55-58; from asst prof to assoc prof geol, 58-66, head, Dept Geol & Geog, 66-69, PROF GEOL, UNIV ALA, 69- *Mem:* Geol Soc Am; Soc Econ Paleontologists & Mineralogists; Am Asn Petrol Geologists. *Res:* Stratigraphy and paleontology of Gulf Coastal region of the United States. *Mailing Add:* PO Box 2906 University AL 35486

JONES, DOUGLAS LINWOOD, b Limeton, Va, Dec 26, 37. ENGINEERING, SOLID MECHANICS. *Educ:* George Washington Univ, BME, 63, MSE, 65, DSc, 70. *Prof Exp:* Univ fel eng, 66-67, from instr to asst prof eng & appl sci, 67-71, from asst res prof to assoc res prof, 71-77, assoc prof, 77-82, PROF ENG & APPL SCI, GEORGE WASHINGTON UNIV, 82- *Concurrent Pos:* Consult, Seal & Co, 70-71, Comsat Labs, 74-76, Eng Servs Co, 76-81, Ensco, Inc, 77-78 & Systs Technol Labs, Inc, 80-82. *Mem:* Am Acad Mech; Am Soc Testing & Mat; Am Soc Mech Engrs; Soc Eng Sci; Soc Exp Stress Anal. *Res:* Fatigue, fracture and fracture mechanics of metals and composite materials; statistical methods; fractography and failure analysis; experimental stress analysis; evaluation and development of constitutive relations in continuum mechanics; nondestructive inspection methods; composite materials. *Mailing Add:* Sch of Eng & Appl Sci George Washington Univ Washington DC 20052

JONES, DUANE ARNOLD, b Rice Co, Minn, July 18, 33; m 54; c 3. RESEARCH ADMINISTRATION. *Educ:* St Olaf Col, BA, 57; Univ Minn, Minneapolis, PhD(org chem), 61. *Prof Exp:* Sr res chemist, 61-62, proj leader carbohydrate chem, 62-69, group leader, 69-74, res assoc, 74-77, MGR PROD REGULATION & SAFETY, GEN MILLS CHEM INC, 77- *Mem:* Am Chem Soc. *Res:* Preparation, characterization and utilization of semi-synthetic hydrocolloid products derived from reproducible and readily available natural products, such as starch, tamarind, guar and cellulose, with particular interest in their graft copolymers. *Mailing Add:* Henkel Corp 4620 W 77th St Minneapolis MN 55435

JONES, DUVALL ALBERT, b Hurlock, Md, Oct 17, 33; m 66; c 2. VERTEBRATE ZOOLOGY. *Educ:* Western Md Col, AB, 55; Univ Md, MS, 61; Univ Fla, PhD(zool), 67. *Prof Exp:* Asst prof biol, Madison Col, Va, 60-62; asst prof biol, head dept & chmn div natural sci & math, Ferrum Jr Col, 62-65; asst prof biol & actg head dept, West Liberty State Col, 66-67; asst prof, Carnegie-Mellon Univ, 67-73; ASSOC PROF BIOL, ST JOSEPH'S COL, 73- *Concurrent Pos:* Scaife grant. *Mem:* AAAS; Am Soc Zool; Am Soc Ichthyol & Herpet; Genetics Soc Am; Ecol Soc Am. *Res:* Physiological ecology of amphibians; environmental genetics; bile pigments and their effects. *Mailing Add:* Dept of Biol St Joseph's Col Rensselaer IN 47978

JONES, E(DWARD) M(CCLUNG) T(HOMPSON), b Topeka, Kans, Aug 19, 24; m 49; c 3. MICROWAVE ELECTRONICS. *Educ:* Swarthmore Col, BS, 44; Stanford Univ, MS, 48, PhD(elec eng), 50. *Prof Exp:* Res assoc elec eng, Stanford Univ, 48-50; sr res engr, Stanford Res Inst, 50-57, head microwave group, 57-61; dir eng, Menlo Park Div, TRG, Inc, Control Data Corp, 61-67; eng mgr, Antennas & Transmission Lines Div, Granger Assocs, 67-68; vpres eng & technol, 68-71, EXEC VPRES, TCI, 71- *Mem:* Inst Elec & Electronics Engrs; Sigma Xi. *Res:* Microwave components and antennas; antennas. *Mailing Add:* 2161 Via Escalera Los Altos CA 94022

JONES, EARLE DOUGLAS, b Birmingham, Ala, Apr 10, 31; m 61. ELECTRONICS. *Educ:* Ga Inst Technol, BS, 56; Stanford Univ, MS, 58. *Prof Exp:* Asst math, Ga Inst Technol, 55-56; res engr, 56-65, mgr electronics & optics, 65-76, exec dir, 76-80, VPRES & DIR ADVAN DEVELOP, STANFORD RES INST, 80- *Mem:* Inst Elec & Electronics Engrs; Sigma Xi. *Res:* Space electronics; communication systems research in satellite meteorology; display devices and digital control research; bioengineering. *Mailing Add:* Stanford Res Inst Menlo Park CA 94025

JONES, EDWARD DAVID, b Rockland, Wis, May 8, 20; m 47; c 4. PLANT PATHOLOGY. *Educ:* Univ Wis, BS, 46, MS, 47, PhD(plant path), 53. *Prof Exp:* Instr plant path, Univ Wis, 48-53; plant pathologist, Red Dot Foods, Inc, 53-58; from asst prof to assoc prof plant path, 58-74, PROF PLANT PATH, CORNELL UNIV, 74- *Concurrent Pos:* In-chg found & cert seed potato prog NY state, 60-, Uihlein Farm, Cornell Univ, 61-, Henry Uihlein II tissue cult facil at Uihlein Farm, Lake Placid, NY, 77- *Mem:* Am Phytopath Soc; Potato Asn Am (vpres, 81-82); Sigma Xi. *Res:* Production of disease-free nuclear seed stocks by tissue culture; disease problems relating to the production of seed potatoes. *Mailing Add:* Dept of Plant Path Cornell Univ Ithaca NY 14853

JONES, EDWARD EUGENE, b Culpeper, Va, Feb 2, 20; m 47; c 3. PROTOZOOLOGY. *Educ:* Univ SC, AB, 47; Univ NC, PhD(zool), 51. *Prof Exp:* Asst zool, Univ NC, 48-49, teaching fel, 49-50, instr, 50-51; instr microanat, Med Col Va, 51-52; prof biol, Tift Col, 54-57; from asst prof to prof, Ga State Col, 57-64; assoc prof, Jacksonville Univ, 64-67; assoc prof, 67-69, PROF BIOL, UNIV S ALA, 69- *Mem:* Am Micros Soc; Soc Protozool; Am Soc Zool. *Res:* Nuclear phenomena and cystment in ciliates; protozoan ecology; survey of protozoa of Mobile Bay, Alabama. *Mailing Add:* Dept of Biol Sci Univ of SAla Mobile AL 36688

JONES, EDWARD GEORGE, b Upper Hutt, NZ, Mar 26, 39; m 63; c 2. NEUROBIOLOGY. *Educ:* Univ Otago, NZ, MB, ChB, 62, MD, 70; Oxford Univ, DPhil(anat), 68. *Prof Exp:* Demonstr anat, Univ Otago, NZ, 64-65, from asst lectr to lectr, 65-70, assoc prof, 71-72; assoc prof anat, 72-75, PROF ANAT & NEUROBIOL, SCH MED, WASHINGTON UNIV, 75-, PROF NEUROSCI, 81- *Concurrent Pos:* Nuffield Dom demonstr, Oxford Univ, 65, 65-68, lectr, Balliol Col, 66-68; NZ Med Res Coun grant, Sch Med, Otago Univ, 69-71; assoc ed, J Comp Neurol, 75-80; Macy Found sr fac scholar, Monash Univ, Australia, 78-79; Green vis prof, Univ Tex Med Br, Galveston, 78, Beale Mem Lectr, 80; assoc ed, J Neurosci, 81-; dir, James O'Leary Div Exp Neurol & Neurological Surg, Washington Univ, George H & Ethel Ronzon scholar in neurosci & sr scientist, McDonnell Ctr for Study of Higher Brain Function. *Honors & Awards:* Symington Mem Prize, Anat Soc Gt Brit & Ireland, 68; Rolleston Mem Prize, Oxford Univ, 70. *Mem:* Anat Soc Gt Brit & Ireland; Am Asn Anatomists; Soc Neurosci; Anat Soc Australia & NZ; NZ Med Asn. *Res:* Structure and development of sensory systems particularly in primates and with emphasis on cerebral cortex and somatic sensory system. *Mailing Add:* Dept of Anat Wash Univ Sch of Med St Louis MO 63110

JONES, EDWARD GOMER, b Lawton, Okla, Oct 22, 12; m 45; c 4. MEDICINE. *Educ:* Pomona Col, AB, 34; Univ Rochester, MD, 40. *Prof Exp:* Intern, Baltimore City Hosps, 40-41; resident, Univ Md Hosp, 41-45; asst gynec, 45-47, instr, 47-52, assoc prof clin gynec, 52-62, prof clin gynec, Sch Med, Univ Southern Calif, 62-76; RETIRED. *Concurrent Pos:* Consult, Olive View Sanatorium & Los Angeles County Hosp. *Mem:* AAAS; AMA; fel Am Col Surg. *Res:* Tumor therapy. *Mailing Add:* PO Box 978 Kaunakaka HI 96748

JONES, EDWARD GRANT, b Toronto, Ont, Feb 16, 42; m 72; c 3. CHEMICAL PHYSICS. *Educ:* Univ Toronto, BSc, 65, MSc, 67, PhD(phys chem), 69. *Prof Exp:* Vis res scientist, Ohio State Univ Res Found, 69-71; res assoc, Purdue Univ, 71-72; consult, Systs Res Labs, 71-72, sr res chemist & proj mgr, 72-75; res asst prof chem, 75-77, RES ASSOC PROF CHEM, WRIGHT STATE UNIV, 77- *Concurrent Pos:* Consult, Systs Res Labs, 75- *Mem:* Sr mem Am Chem Soc; sr mem Am Soc Mass Spectrometry. *Res:* Gas phase kinetics; ion-neutral collision phenomena; unimolecular decomposition; chemiluminescence; thermal degradation of polymers; kinetics of polymerization. *Mailing Add:* Dept of Chem Wright State Univ Dayton OH 45435

JONES, EDWARD O(SCAR), JR, b Dothan, Ala, June 18, 22; m 47; c 2. MECHANICAL ENGINEERING. *Educ:* Auburn Univ, BS, 43 & 46; Univ Ill, MS, 49. *Prof Exp:* Tooling engr, Consol Vultee Aircraft Corp, 43-45; from instr to assoc prof mech eng, 46-61, asst dean eng, 74-78, PROF MECH ENG, AUBURN UNIV, 61-, ASST HEAD DEPT, 65-, ASSOC DEAN ENG, 78- *Mem:* Soc Automotive Engrs; Soc Exp Stress Anal. *Res:* Experimental stress analysis, especially thin-shell pressure vessels. *Mailing Add:* Sch of Eng Ramsay Hall Auburn Univ Auburn AL 36830

JONES, EDWARD RAYMOND, b Steubenville, Ohio, Jan 27, 43; m 64; c 1. AGRONOMY. *Educ:* Ohio State Univ, BS, 65; Pa State Univ, MS, 67, PhD(agron), 69. *Prof Exp:* Assoc prof, 71-77, PROF AGRON, DEL STATE COL, 77- *Mem:* Am Soc Agron; Am Forage & Grassland Coun. *Res:* Forage crop management. *Mailing Add:* Box 77 Del State Col Dover DE 19901

JONES, EDWARD STEPHEN, b Boston, Mass, Apr 17, 31; m 56; c 2. ORGANIC CHEMISTRY. *Educ:* Northeastern Univ, BS, 53; Purdue Univ, MS, 56; Wayne State Univ, PhD(org chem), 61. *Prof Exp:* Res chemist, Gen Chem Div, Allied Chem Corp, NJ, 60-69, sr res chemist, Specialty Chem Div, Buffalo, 69-80; SR RES CHEMIST, HALOCARBON PROD CORP, 80- *Mem:* Am Chem Soc. *Res:* Organic fluorine chemistry; applications, process research and development; basic research; product research and development. *Mailing Add:* 11 Gristmill Rd Cedar Knolls NJ 07927

JONES, EDWIN C, JR, b Parkersburg, WVa, June 27, 34; m 60; c 3. ELECTRICAL ENGINEERING, EDUCATION. *Educ:* WVa Univ, BS, 55; Imp Col, Univ London, Dipl, 56; Univ Ill, Urbana, PhD(elec eng), 62. *Prof Exp:* Teaching asst elec eng, Univ Ill, 58-59; from instr to asst prof elec eng, Univ Ill, 60-66; from asst prof to assoc prof, 66-72, PROF ELEC ENG, IOWA STATE UNIV, 72- *Concurrent Pos:* Engr, Gen Elec Co, 57, 62 & Westinghouse Elec Co, 59; proc chmn, Nat Electronics Conf, 65, prog chmn, 68, secy, 69, awards chmn, 69-70, vpres continuing educ, 71. *Mem:* AAAS; Inst Elec & Electronics Engrs; Am Soc Eng Educ; AAAS; Soc Hist Technol. *Res:* Circuit theory; experimental engineering techniques; educational methods; technology and social change. *Mailing Add:* Dept of Elec Eng Iowa State Univ Ames IA 50011

JONES, EDWIN RUDOLPH, JR, b Lumberton, NC, Aug 3, 38; m 60; c 4. SOLID STATE PHYSICS. *Educ:* Clemson Univ, BS, 60; Univ Wis, MS, 62, PhD(physics), 65. *Prof Exp:* Asst prof physics, 65-72, assoc prof, 72-77, PROF PHYSICS, UNIV SC, 77- *Concurrent Pos:* Vis prof, Univ de El Salvador, 78. *Mem:* Am Phys Soc; Am Asn Physics Teachers. *Res:* Low temperature magnetic properties of solids. *Mailing Add:* Dept of Physics Univ of SC Columbia SC 29208

JONES, ELBERT ELLERY, b Warren Co, NC, May 28, 12; m 36; c 2. PHYSICS. *Educ:* Agr & Tech Col NC, BS, 41; NY Univ, MA, 45; Columbia Univ, EdD(sci educ), 61. *Prof Exp:* High sch teacher, 42-45; assoc prof physics, Shaw Univ, 45-50 & Md State Teachers Col, 50-60; prof phys sci & physics, Va State Col, 60-65; prof phys sci, 65-77, PROF PHYSICS, BOWIE STATE COL, 65- *Mem:* Am Asn Physics Teachers. *Res:* Nuclear magnetic resonance and paramagnetic resonance. *Mailing Add:* Dept of Sci Bowie State Col Bowie MD 20715

JONES, ELDON MELTON, b Chenoa, Ill, Feb 1, 14; m 39; c 5. MEDICINAL CHEMISTRY. *Educ:* Univ Ill, BS, 36; Pa State Col, MS, 37, PhD(org chem), 40. *Prof Exp:* Asst, Pa State Col, 40-41; res chemist, Parke, Davis & Co, 41-58, head tech info, 58-69, mgr res libr serv, 69-76, mgr sci info, 76-77; RETIRED. *Mem:* AAAS; Am Chem Soc. *Res:* Steroidal compounds; antimalarials; analgesic drugs; polymerization of olefins. *Mailing Add:* 2023 Day St Ann Arbor MI 48104

JONES, ELEANOR GREEN, b Norfolk, Va, Aug 10, 29; m 51, 67; c 2. MATHEMATICS. *Educ:* Howard Univ, BS, 49, MS, 50; Syracuse Univ, PhD(math), 66. *Prof Exp:* Instr, Hampton Inst, 55-62, assoc prof, 66-67; teaching asst, Syracuse Univ, 64-66; PROF MATH, NORFOLK STATE COL, 67- *Mem:* Am Math Soc; Math Asn Am; Nat Asn Math (vpres, 75-); Sigma Xi. *Res:* Abelian groups and their endomorphism rings; direct decompositions and quasi-endomorphisms of torsion free abelian groups. *Mailing Add:* 6301 Bucknell Circle Virginia Beach VA 23462

JONES, ELIZABETH W, b Seattle, Wash, Mar 8, 39. MICROBIAL GENETICS. *Educ:* Univ Wash, BS, 60, PhD(genetics), 64. *Prof Exp:* USPHS trainee, Univ Wash, 60-64; res assoc & USPHS training grant microbiol, Mass Inst Technol, 64-67, instr, 67-69; asst prof biol & microbiol, Case Western Reserve Univ, 69-74; ASSOC PROF BIOL SCI, CARNEGIE MELLON UNIV, 74- *Concurrent Pos:* USPHS res grant, 70-, re career develop award, 71. *Mem:* AAAS; Genetics Soc Am. *Res:* Organization and expression of genetic material in yeast; metabolic regulation in eucaryotes. *Mailing Add:* Dept of Biol Sci Carnegie Mellon Univ Pittsburgh PA 15213

JONES, ELMER EVERETT, b Hinsdale, Ill, Sept 2, 26; m 56; c 1. ORGANIC CHEMISTRY. *Educ:* Univ Chicago, PhB, 48, BS, 50; Washington Univ, PhD, 57. *Prof Exp:* Asst, Washington Univ, 50-55; res assoc, Tannhauser Lab, Boston Dispensary, 56-58; asst prof chem, 58-62, ASSOC PROF CHEM, NORTHEASTERN UNIV, 62- *Mem:* AAAS; Am Chem Soc; Sigma Xi. *Res:* Amino acids; ester solvolysis; phosphates. *Mailing Add:* Dept of Chem Northeastern Univ Boston MA 02115

JONES, ERIC DANIEL, b Oakland, Calif, Jan 6, 36; m 57; c 5. SOLID STATE PHYSICS. *Educ:* Ore State Univ, BS, 57; Univ Wash, MS, 59, PhD(physics), 62. *Prof Exp:* Mem tech staff, Bell Tel Labs, NJ, 62-65; mem staff solid state physics res, Sandia Corp, 65-68, supvr laser effects res, 68-82,

MEM STAFF LASER RES, SANDIA NAT LABS, 82- *Mem:* Fel Am Phys Soc. *Res:* Study of ferromagnetism, antiferromagnetism, paramagnetism in insulators and metals by the use of nuclear magnetic resonance techniques; high power laser energy deposition in solids; ultrashort laser pulse generation and applications. *Mailing Add:* Sandia Corp Orgn 5124 PO Box 5800 Albuquerque NM 87112

JONES, ERIC MANNING, b Goldsboro, NC, Mar 25, 44. HYDRODYNAMICS, ASTROPHYSICS. *Educ:* Calif Inst Technol, BS, 66; Univ Wis-Madison, PhD(astron), 69. *Prof Exp:* STAFF MEM HYDRODYN, LOS ALAMOS NAT LAB, 69- *Mem:* Am Astron Soc. *Res:* Supernova remnants; interstellar medium; nuclear explosion phenomenology; volcanology and cratering. *Mailing Add:* Los Alamos Nat Lab MS 665 PO Box 1663 Los Alamos NM 87545

JONES, ERIC WYNN, b St Martins, Eng, Sept 24, 24; US citizen; m 48; c 1. VETERINARY SURGERY. *Educ:* MRCVS, 46; Cornell Univ, PhD(vet surg), 50; Am Col Vet Surg, dipl, 71; Am Col Vet Anesthesiol, dipl, 78. *Prof Exp:* consult, Col Vet Med, Miss State Univ, 74-78; VDEAN COL VET MED, MISS STATE UNIV, 78- *Concurrent Pos:* Dir clin res, 56-77. Concurrent. *Mem:* Am Vet Med Asn; Brit Vet Asn; Asn Vet Anaesthetists Gt Brit & Ireland; Am Soc Anesthesiol; Am Soc Vet Anesthesiol. *Res:* Inhalation anesthesia techniques; bovine anaplasmosis; spleen function in infectious anemia; enteritis; mechanical ventilators; malignant hyperthermia; drug testing. *Mailing Add:* Col Vet Med Drawer V Miss State Univ Mississippi State MS 39762

JONES, ERNEST ADDISON, b Columbia, Ky, June 5, 18; m 43. PHYSICS. *Educ:* Western Ky State Teachers Col, BS, 42; Vanderbilt Univ, MS, 43; Ohio State Univ, PhD(phys chem), 48. *Prof Exp:* Res physicist, Manhattan Dist, Columbia Univ, 43-45; res chemist, Carbide & Carbon Chem Co, 48-50; from asst prof to assoc prof, 50-65, PROF PHYSICS, VANDERBILT UNIV, 65- *Mem:* Am Phys Soc; Optical Soc Am. *Res:* Infrared and Raman spectroscopy. *Mailing Add:* Dept of Physics Vanderbilt Univ Nashville TN 37240

JONES, ERNEST OLIN, b Atlanta, Ga, Feb 1, 23; m 46; c 2. RADIOLOGICAL PHYSICS. *Educ:* Emory Univ, AB, 48, MS, 49; US Naval Postgrad Sch, MS, 59; NC State Univ, PhD(nuclear eng), 64; Am Bd Radiol, dipl radiol physics, 75. *Prof Exp:* Dep dir nuclear med, Walter Reed Army Inst Res, 64-67, dir div biometrics, 67-68; assoc prof radiol, Col Med, 68-72, PROF RADIOL, COL MED, UNIV NEBR, OMAHA, 72-, ASSOC PROF RADIO, COL DENT, 69- *Mem:* Soc Nuclear Med; Am Asn Physicists in Med; Asn Mil Surgeons US; Am Col Radiol; Am Col Nuclear Physicians. *Res:* Radiation therapy dosimetry; diagnostic x-ray dosage reduction, medical computer applications. *Mailing Add:* Dept of Radiol Univ of Nebr Col of Med Omaha NE 68105

JONES, EUGENE LAVERNE, b Adona, Ark, Sept 20, 28; m 50; c 4. GEOLOGY. *Educ:* Univ Ark, BS, 51, MS, 52; Univ Okla, PhD, 61. *Prof Exp:* Petrol geologist, Gulf Oil Corp, 52-54; asst prof geol & head dept, Ark Polytech Col, 54-60; sr res geologist, Field Res Lab, Socony Mobil Oil Co, Inc, 60-64, mgr geol-geochem res & tech serv, Mobil Res & Develop Corp, 64-71, vpres & explor mgr, Mobil North Sea Inc, London, 71-73 & Mobil Explor Norway, Inc, 73-75, Adv, 78-79 MGR EXPLOR RES, MOBIL RES & DEVELOP CORP, 75-, MGR EXPLOR, PROD RES DIV, 79- *Concurrent Pos:* Instr, Oklahoma City Univ, 58; fel, NSF, 58-59. *Mem:* AAAS; Am Asn Petrol Geologists; Sigma Xi; Geol Soc London. *Res:* Palynology; sedimentation; petroleum exploration, geology, geochemistry and geophysics; stratigraphy. *Mailing Add:* Mobil Res & Develop Corp PO Box 900 Dallas TX 75221

JONES, EVAN EARL, b Wray, Colo, June 8, 35; m 55. BIOCHEMISTRY. *Educ:* Colo State Univ, BS, 60; Univ Ill, MS, 62, PhD(biochem), 64. *Prof Exp:* Fel biochem, Inst Microbiol, Rutgers Univ, 64-66; asst prof nutrit biochem, 66-69, asst prof animal sci & biochem, 69-71, ASSOC PROF BIOCHEM, 71- & PROF ANIMAL SCI, NC STATE UNIV, 77- *Concurrent Pos:* Vis scholar, Stanford Univ, 75-76. *Mem:* AAAS; Am Chem Soc; Am Soc Biol Chemists; Am Soc Microbiol. *Res:* Amino acid biosynthesis, arginine; metabolic control mechanisms. *Mailing Add:* Dept of Animal Sci NC State Univ Raleigh NC 27607

JONES, EVAN THOMAS, organic chemistry, see previous edition

JONES, EVERET CLYDE, b West Plains, Mo, Jan 26, 23; m 70; c 1. MARINE BIOLOGY. *Educ:* Hastings Col, AB, 49; Univ Miami, Fla, MS, 52. *Prof Exp:* Fishery biologist, Nat Marine Fisheries Serv, 55-73; asst prof biol, 74-77, ASST PROF SCI, NORTHEAST MO STATE UNIV, 79- *Mem:* Am Inst Fishery Res Biologists. *Res:* Systematics, ecology and zoogeography of marine copepods; mechanisms controlling distribution of marine plankton and tunas; behavior and systematics of sharks; chemistry of marine algae. *Mailing Add:* Rte 2 Box 29A Norwood MO 65717

JONES, EVERETT, b Albany, NY, Jan 25, 30; m 57; c 3. AEROSPACE ENGINEERING, COMPUTATIONAL MECHANICS. *Educ:* Rensselaer Polytech Inst, BAE, 56, MAE, 60; Stanford Univ, PhD(aeronaut & astronaut sci), 68. *Prof Exp:* Advan study scientist, Lockheed Missiles & Space Co, 56-57; res asst aeronaut eng, Rensselaer Polytech Inst, 57-59; sr thermodynamicist, Lockheed Missiles & Space Co, 59-61, sr engr, 61-64, res specialist, 64-69; ASST PROF AEROSPACE ENG, UNIV MD, COLLEGE PARK, 69- *Concurrent Pos:* Res asst, dept aeronaut & astronaut sci, Stanford Univ, 66-68, res assoc, 68-69; asst prof, dept mech eng, San Jose State Col, 67-68. *Mem:* Am Inst Aeronaut & Astronaut; NY Acad Sci. *Res:* Research on analysis of wave transmission in blood vessels, flowmeter analysis and analysis of low density wind tunnels; ocean vehicles, heat transfer and viscous flow. *Mailing Add:* Dept of Aeronaut Eng Univ of Md College Park MD 20742

JONES, EVERETT BRUCE, b Ft Collins, Colo, Sept 23, 33; m 56; c 2. HYDROLOGY, WATER RESOURCES ENGINEERING. *Educ:* Univ Wyo, BS, 55; Pa State Univ, MS, 59; Colo State Univ, PhD(watershed mgt), 64. *Prof Exp:* Chief water develop, Wyo Natural Resources Bd, 59-61; engr-hydrologist, Douglas W Barr, Consult Hydraul Engrs, Minn, 64-65; asst dir inst for res on land & water resources, in-chg of water resources ctr & asst prof meteorol, Pa State Univ, 65-68; coordr water resources, Environ Serv Oper, EG&G, Inc, 69; vpres, 70-77, PRES, M W BITTINGER & ASSOCS, INC, 77-; PRES, RESOURCE CONSULTS, INC, 77- *Concurrent Pos:* Asst interstate streams comnr, State of Wyo, 61; vpres, Wyo Well Serv, Inc, 61-70. *Mem:* Am Soc Civil Engrs; Am Meteorol Soc; Am Geophys Union. *Res:* Groundwater hydrology; surface-water hydrology and hydrometeorology, especially water resources management aspects. *Mailing Add:* Resource Consults Inc PO Box Q Ft Collins CO 80522

JONES, EVERETT LINN, b Lima, Ohio, Aug 20, 30; m 60; c 3. DERMATOLOGY, CLINICAL PHARMACOLOGY. *Educ:* Ohio State Univ, BA & MD, 55. *Prof Exp:* Intern, Orange County Gen Hosp, 55-56; sr asst surgeon, USPHS, 56-58; resident dermat, Sch Med, Yale Univ, 60 & Univ Chicago, 60-63; clin investr, Lilly Res Lab, 63-77; med dir, Hill Top Res, Inc, 77-79. *Concurrent Pos:* Assoc dir clin pharmacol, Cintest, Inc, 77-79; med adv, Psoriasis Res Asn, 77-; consult, Proctor & Gamble, 81-82; mem adv comt, Betamed Pharmaceut, Inc, 81- *Mem:* Am Acad Dermat; Am Fedn Clin Res; Soc Invest Dermat. *Res:* Drug development; clinical testing of dermatological products. *Mailing Add:* 1017 Carew Tower Cincinnati OH 45202

JONES, FABER BENJAMIN, b Dec 4, 32; US citizen; m 54; c 4. POLYMER CHEMISTRY. *Educ:* Ohio State Univ, BSc, 54. *Prof Exp:* Asst div chief polymer res, Battelle Mem Inst, 53-63; tech dir adhesives res, Evans Adhesives Corp, 63-64; mgr, Chem Appln Br, 64-79, mgr, Polymer Appln Br, 79, DIR POLYMER MAT RES, PHILLIPS PETROL CO, 80- *Mem:* Am Chem Soc; Adhesion Soc; Soc Plastic Engrs. *Res:* Polymer research and technology, especially on adhesives, coatings and reinforced plastic systems. *Mailing Add:* Rm 264RF Res Ctr Phillips Petrol Co Bartlesville OK 74004

JONES, FLOYD BURTON, b Cisco, Tex, Nov 22, 10; m 36; c 4. TOPOLOGY. *Educ:* Univ Tex, BA, 32, PhD(math), 35. *Prof Exp:* Instr pure math, Univ Tex, 32-40, asst prof, 40-43, assoc prof, 43-50; prof math, Univ NC, 50-62; prof math, 62-78, EMER PROF MATH, UNIV CALIF, RIVERSIDE, 78- *Concurrent Pos:* Res assoc, Underwater Sound Lab, Harvard Univ, 42-44; sr fel, NSF, 57-58; mem, Inst Advan Study, 57-58; vis fel, Inst Advan Studies, Australian Nat Univ, 68; Fulbright-Hays Fel, NZ, 75; vis fel, Univ Houston, 77. *Mem:* Am Math Soc; Math Asn Am. *Res:* Pointset theoretic topology. *Mailing Add:* Dept of Math Univ of Calif Riverside CA 92521

JONES, FRANCIS THOMAS, b Pottsville, Pa, Oct 19, 33. PHYSICAL CHEMISTRY. *Educ:* Pa State Univ, BS, 55; Polytech Inst Brooklyn, PhD(phys chem), 60. *Hon Degrees:* MEng, Stevens Inst Technol, 75. *Prof Exp:* Gen Elec Co Ltd fel radiation chem, Univ Leeds, 60-62; chemist, Union Carbide Corp, 62-64; from asst prof to assoc prof chem, 64-71, PROF CHEM, STEVENS INST TECHNOL, 71-, HEAD DEPT CHEM & CHEM ENG, 79- *Concurrent Pos:* Adj assoc prof anesthesiol, New York Med Col, 77- *Mem:* Am Chem Soc. *Res:* Radiation chemistry; photochemistry; catalysis; mass spectrometry; kinetics; instrumentation design. *Mailing Add:* Dept of Chem Stevens Inst of Technol Hoboken NJ 07030

JONES, FRANCIS TUCKER, b Rocklin, Calif, Jan 17, 05; m 42; c 3. CHEMISTRY. *Educ:* Pac Univ, Ore, AB, 28; Univ Ore, AM, 31; Cornell Univ, PhD(chem micros), 34. *Prof Exp:* Asst chem, Pac Univ, Ore, 26-28; teacher pub sch, Ore, 28-29; asst chem, Univ Ore, 29-31 & Cornell Univ, 32-34; prof, Pac Univ, Ore, 34-42; chemist, Mkt & Nutrit Div, Agr Res Serv, USDA, 42-74; RETIRED. *Mem:* Am Chem Soc. *Res:* Physical and analytical chemistry; chemical microscopy applied to determination of optical and crystallographic properties and phase relations; scanning electron microscopy. *Mailing Add:* 244 Trinity Ave Berkeley CA 94708

JONES, FRANK CULVER, b Ft Worth, Tex, July 30, 32; m 55; c 1. COSMIC RAY PHYSICS, THEORETICAL ASTROPHYSICS. *Educ:* Rice Inst, BA, 54; Univ Chicago, MS, 55, PhD(physics), 61. *Prof Exp:* Res assoc physics, Univ Chicago, 60; res assoc, Princeton Univ, 60-61, instr, 61-63; Nat Acad Sci-Nat Res Coun resident res assoc, Theoret Studies Group, 63-65, physicist, 65-77, ASTROPHYSICIST, LAB HIGH ENERGY ASTROPHYS, GODDARD SPACE FLIGHT CTR, NASA, 77- *Concurrent Pos:* Vis scientist, Max Planck Inst Nuclear Physics, 77. *Mem:* AAAS; fel Am Phys Soc; Am Astron Soc. *Res:* Physics of the origin of cosmic rays and related astrophysical problems; statistical physics of cosmic ray origin and propagation in the galaxy. *Mailing Add:* Code 660 Lab for High Energy Astrophys NASA Goddard Space Flight Ctr Greenbelt MD 20771

JONES, FRANK NORTON, b Columbia, Mo, Dec 27, 36; m 61; c 1. PLASTICS, PROTECTIVE COATINGS. *Educ:* Oberlin Col, AB, 58; Duke Univ, PhD(org chem), 62. *Prof Exp:* Instr org chem, Duke Univ, 61-62; fel, Mass Inst Technol, 62-63; res chemist, Cent Res Dept, E I Du Pont de Nemours Co, 63-68, staff chemist, 68-70, res supvr, 70-73; tech mgr, Celanese Polymer Specialties Co, 73-79; RES & DEVELOP MGR, CARGILL, INC, 79- *Mem:* Am Chem Soc; Soc Plastics Engrs; Fedn Soc Coatings Technol; Nat Paint & Coatings Asn. *Res:* Synthetic organic organometallic and polymer chemistry; coatings; plastics; agricultural chemicals. *Mailing Add:* Cargill Inc Res Dept Box 9300 Minneapolis MN 55440

JONES, FRANKLIN M, b Reidsville, NC, Mar 10, 33; m 63; c 2. SCIENCE EDUCATION. *Educ:* Appalachian State Teachers Col, BS, 55, MA, 60; Univ NC, MEd, 60; Univ Ga, EdD(sci educ), 66. *Prof Exp:* Teacher, High Sch, Va, 55-56 & NC, 56-58; prof chem, Ferrum Jr Col, 60-64; assoc prof, 66-68, PROF PHYS SCI, RADFORD COL, 68- *Mailing Add:* Dept of Phys Sci Radford Col Radford VA 24142

JONES, FRED O(SCAR), b Harper Co, Kans, Mar 26, 12; m 34; c 2. ENGINEERING GEOLOGY. *Educ:* Colo Col, AB, 33. *Prof Exp:* Engr construct & ref, Sinclair Oil Co, Wyo, 35-40; proj geologist, US Bur Reclamation, Wash, 40-47; chief geologist, Nat Hydroelec Eng Bur, Nat Resources Cmn, China, 47; dist geologist, US Bur Reclamation, Nebr, 48; geologist, US Geol Surv, Wash, 48-55; consult geol, 55-81; RETIRED. *Concurrent Pos:* Consult, Ministry Hydraul Resources, Mex, 48-50, UN, Thailand, 59 & 60 & US Agency Int Develop, Brazil, 66-67. *Mem:* Geol Soc Am; Am Soc Civil Engrs; Asn Eng Geol. *Res:* Landslide processes; nature of ground water and basalt terrain; damsite geology. *Mailing Add:* 57 Sahuaro Dr Queen Valley Apache Junction AZ 85220

JONES, FREDERICK GOODWIN, b Utica, NY, Nov 6, 35; m 59; c 3. PERMANENT MAGNETS, POWDER METALLURGY. *Educ:* Cornell Univ, BMetE, 59; Univ Mich, Ann Arbor, MSE & PhD(metall), 69. *Prof Exp:* Staff engr, Crucible Steel Co Am, 59-65; sr develop engr, magnetism, Gen Elec Co, 69-73; SR DEVELOP ENGR, HITACHI MAGNETICS CORP, 73- *Mem:* Am Inst Mining, Metall & Petrol Engrs; Am Foundrymen's Soc; Am Inst Elec & Electronics Engrs; Sigma Xi. *Res:* Permanent magnet materials; rare earth-cobalt alloys; hydrogen-metal reactions; low alloy steels; high temperature alloys. *Mailing Add:* Hitachi Magnetics Corp Edmore MI 48829

JONES, GALEN EVERTS, b Milwaukee, Wis, Sept 9, 28; m 54; c 3. MARINE MICROBIOLOGY. *Educ:* Dartmouth Col, AB, 50; Williams Col, MA, 52; Rutgers Univ, PhD(microbiol), 56. *Prof Exp:* Asst, Williams Col, 50-52; from jr res microbiologist to asst res microbiologist, Div Marine Biol, Scripps Inst Oceanog, Univ Calif, 55-63, Rockefeller fel, 55-57; assoc prof biol, Boston Univ, 63-66; dir, Jackson Estuarine Lab, 66-72, PROF MICROBIOL, UNIV NH, 66-, CHMN DEPT, 75- *Concurrent Pos:* Res grants, Nat Inst Allergy & Infectious Dis, 57-59, div water supply & pollution control, USPHS, 59-62, 63-66 & NSF 72-74, 75-76 & 77-78; consult, Eli Lilly & Co, Ind, 58-59, Bendix-Pac, Calif, 60, Arthur D Little Co, Mass, 69-70 & 73-74 & Normandeau Assocs, Inc, NH, 70-71; Off Naval Res contract, 63-64 & 66-68; nonresident assoc microbiol, Woods Hole Oceanog Inst, 64-72, lectr, Marine Biol Lab, Woods Hole, 71-72, 74-75 & 76-77; mem, Nat Sea-Grant Univ Comt, 65-67; mem, Santa Barbara Oil Spill Panel, Exec Off of the President, 69-70; mem adv panel biol oceanog, NSF, 71-72 & mem oceanog adv panel, 74-75; vis prof oceanog, Univ Liverpool, 72-73; mem, Inst Ecol Adv Panel to Nat Comn Water Qual, Washington, DC, 74-76; mem exec panel oceanog div, NSF, 80; vis prof, Scripps Inst Oceanog, Univ Calif, 81. *Mem:* Fel AAAS; Am Inst Biol Sci; Sigma Xi; Soc Gen Microbiol; fel Am Acad Microbiol. *Res:* Biochemicals and trace elements in sea water; chemosynthesis; fractionation of stable isotopes in microorganisms; biogeochemistry; elemental composition of bacteria. *Mailing Add:* Dept of Microbiol Univ of NH Durham NH 03824

JONES, GARETH HUBERT STANLEY, b Cardiff, Wales, Aug 28, 24. EARTH SCIENCE. *Educ:* Univ Wales, BSc, 51; Univ Toronto, MA, 57; Univ Alta, PhD(physics), 63. *Prof Exp:* Asst engr, DeHavilland Propellers Ltd, Hatfield, 52-54; scientist, Mining Res Estab, Middlesex, 54-56; scientist, Suffield Exp Sta, 57-65, head geophys & struct sect, 65-69; dep dir, Maritime Command, Oper Res Div, 69-71; sci adv to comdr & dep chief staff, Res Develop Training Command Hq, 71-75, planning officer (land), Defence Res Bd, 75-79; MEM DEFENSE RES STAFF, CAN EMBASSY, WASHINGTON, DC, 81- *Mem:* Am Geophys Union; Am Astron Soc; Can Soc Exp Geophys; Asn Geoscientists Int Develop. *Res:* Strong motion seismology; cratering by high explosives; structural response to blast; airborne dust suppression and monitoring; missile guidance by infrared; scale model studies on blast waves; heat capacity of minerals at liquid helium temperatures. *Mailing Add:* Can Embassy 2450 Massachusetts Ave Washington DC 20008

JONES, GARTH, b Victoria, BC, Mar 27, 32. NUCLEAR PHYSICS. *Educ:* Univ BC, BA, 53, MSc, 55, PhD(physics), 59. *Prof Exp:* Jr sci officer electronics, Atomic Energy Can, Ltd, 55-56; Rutherford Mem fel, Clarendon Lab, Oxford Univ, 60, Nat Res Coun Can overseas fel nuclear physics, 60-61; from asst prof to assoc prof, 61-69, PROF PHYSICS, UNIV BC, 69- *Concurrent Pos:* Guggenheim fel, 67-68. *Mem:* Can Asn Physicists; Am Phys Soc. *Res:* Nuclear reactions; positron annihilation; intermediate energy physics. *Mailing Add:* Dept of Physics Univ of BC Vancouver Can

JONES, GARTH WICKS, b Aberdare, Wales, Sept 23, 40; m 64; c 3. MICROBIOLOGY. *Educ:* Univ Reading, BSc, 69, PhD(microbiol), 72. *Prof Exp:* Sr sci officer microbiol, Inst Res Animal Dis, Brit Agr Res Coun, 72-75; ASST PROF MICROBIOL, UNIV MICH, ANN ARBOR, 75- *Concurrent Pos:* Scholar, Univ Mich, Ann Arbor, 74-75. *Mem:* Soc Gen Microbiol; Brit Soc Appl Bact; Am Soc Microbiol. *Res:* Nature and function of the adhesive properties of bacteria, particularly enteric pathogens, and the composition of the eukaryotic cell components with which bacterial adhesive substances interact. *Mailing Add:* Dept Microbiol 6643 Med Sci Bldg Univ of Mich Ann Arbor MI 48109

JONES, GARY EDWARD, b Metropolis, Ill, June 2, 40; m 64; c 1. GENETICS, CELL BIOLOGY. *Educ:* Univ Ill, Urbana, BS, 62, MS, 64; Univ Calif, Berkeley, PhD(biophys), 70. *Prof Exp:* NIH fel biophys, Pa State Univ, 70-71; staff geneticist, Hosp for Sick Children, Toronto, Ont, 71-73; asst prof biol, 73-78, asst prof genetics, 78-79, ASSOC PROF GENETICS, UNIV CALIF, RIVERSIDE, 79- *Mem:* Sigma Xi; AAAS; Genetic Soc Am; Am Soc Microbiol. *Res:* Biochemical genetics of amino acid utilization in yeast; somatic cell genetics of cultured animal and plant cells. *Mailing Add:* Dept of Bot & Plant Sci Univ of Calif Riverside CA 92521

JONES, GEOFFREY MELVILL, b Shelford, Eng, Jan 14, 23; m 53; c 4. NEUROSCIENCES, AEROSPACE MEDICINE. *Educ:* Univ Cambridge, MA, 48, MB, BCh, 49. *Prof Exp:* House surgeon, Middlesex Hosp, London, 49-50; surgeon, Ear, Nose & Throat, Addenbrookes Hosp, Cambridge, 50-51; sci officer, Med Res Coun, Gt Brit, 55-61; dir aviation med, Aviation Med Res Unit, 61-75; assoc prof, 61-67, PROF PHYSIOL, MCGILL UNIV, 67- *Concurrent Pos:* Vis prof, Stanford Univ, 71-72 & Col de France, Paris, 79; sr res assoc, Nat Acad Sci, 71-72. *Honors & Awards:* Harry G Armstrong Award res in aerospace med, 69; Arnold D Tuttle Award, 71. *Mem:* Can Physiol Soc; fel Can Aeronaut & Space Inst; fel Royal Soc Can. *Res:* Neurophysiology of postural control, vestibular and oculomotor systems; respiration at high altitude; long duration flying fatigue; high altitude bail out; pilot disorientation; adaptive plasticity in brainstem reflexes. *Mailing Add:* 3265 Glencoe Ave Montreal PQ H3R 2C5 Can

JONES, GEORGE HENRY, b Muskogee, Okla, Feb 21, 42; m 65. BIOCHEMISTRY, MOLECULAR BIOLOGY. *Educ:* Harvard Univ, BA, 63; Univ Calif, Berkeley, PhD(biochem), 68. *Prof Exp:* Helen Hay Whitney Found fels, NIH, 68-70 & Univ Geneva, 70-71; asst prof zool, 71-74, ASSOC PROF BIOL SCI & CELL & MOLECULAR BIOL, UNIV MICH, ANN ARBOR, 74- *Mem:* AAAS. *Res:* Mammalian protein biosynthesis, specifically initiation mechanisms; immunoglobulin biosynthesis; cellular regulatory mechanisms. *Mailing Add:* Dept of Zool Univ of Mich Ann Arbor MI 48109

JONES, GEORGE R, b Los Angeles, Calif, Aug 16, 30; m 52; c 6. THEORETICAL PHYSICS, PSYCHOPHYSICS. *Educ:* Western Md Col, BS, 51; Cath Univ, MS, 53, PhD(physics), 63. *Prof Exp:* Jr electronics engr, Davies Labs, Inc, 52-54; physicist, Diamond Ord Fuze Labs, 54-63, res physicist, Harry Diamond Labs, 63-66; RES PHYSICIST, VISIONICS TECH AREA, NIGHT VISION LABS, 66- *Concurrent Pos:* Consult, Am Mach & Foundry, 61-62; lectr, Am Univ, 69- *Mem:* Am Phys Soc; Inst Elec & Electronics Eng. *Res:* Optical spectra of rare earth doped solids; magnetic properties of solids; electromagnetic theory; electromagnetic instrumentation for solid state measurements; artificial intelligence (visual) and mathematical modeling of human vision processes; applied mathematics. *Mailing Add:* 113 Northway Rd Greenbelt MD 20770

JONES, GERALD MURRAY, b Gouverneur, NY, Apr 17, 41; m 63; c 3. DAIRY SCIENCE. *Educ:* Cornell Univ, BS, 62; Univ Maine, MS, 64; Pa State Univ, PhD(dairy sci), 68. *Prof Exp:* Asst prof animal sci, Macdonald, Col, McGill Univ, 68-74; assoc prof, 74-80, PROF DAIRY SCI, VA POLYTECH INST & STATE UNIV, 80-, EXTEN DAIRY SCIENTIST, 74- *Mem:* Nat Mastitis Coun; Am Dairy Sci Asn; Am Soc Animal Sci. *Res:* Milking management, practices and systems; mastitis; calf nutrition and management; dairy cattle nutrition; dairy herd management. *Mailing Add:* Dept of Dairy Sci Va Polytech Inst & State Univ Blacksburg VA 24061

JONES, GERALD WALTER, b Utica, NY, June 25, 42. PHOTOGRAPHIC CHEMISTRY, POLYMER APPLICATIONS. *Educ:* Hartwick Col, BA, 64; Syracuse Univ, PhD(org chem), 70. *Prof Exp:* Lab asst chem, Hartwick Col. 64-65; fel, Ohio State Univ, 70-74; res chemist, GAF Corp, 74-81; ADV ENGR, IBM CORP, 81- *Mem:* Am Chem Soc. *Res:* Photolysis of alpha, beta-unsaturated ketones and carbene chemistry; photographic science, resilient sheet vinyl flooring and photoresists. *Mailing Add:* 1112 Reynolds Rd Johnson City NY 13790

JONES, GIFFIN DENISON, b Fond du Lac, Wis, Dec 16, 18; m 39; c 4. ORGANIC CHEMISTRY. *Educ:* Univ Wis, BS, 39; Univ Ill, PhD(org chem), 42. *Prof Exp:* Instr org chem, Univ Iowa, 42-44; res chemist, Cent Res Labs, Gen Aniline & Film Corp, Pa, 44-47; res chemist, Phys Res Lab, 47-56, dir. 56-68, dir, E C Britton Lab, 68-70, RES SCIENTIST, PHYS RES LAB, DOW CHEM CO, 70- *Concurrent Pos:* Civilian with Off Sci Res & Develop, 44. *Mem:* Am Chem Soc. *Res:* Polymers; organic reaction mechanism. *Mailing Add:* Phys Res Lab 1712 Bldg Dow Chem Co Midland MI 48640

JONES, GILBERT FRED, b Oakland, Calif, Apr 3, 30; m 51; c 6. MARINE ECOLOGY, HISTOLOGY. *Educ:* Col of the Pac, AB, 52; Univ Wis, MS, 54; Univ Southern Calif, PhD(biol), 67. *Prof Exp:* Biologist, Mainland Shelf Surv, Allan Hancock Found, 57-64, from instr to asst prof, 64-70, ASSOC PROF BIOL, UNIV SOUTHERN CALIF, 70- *Mem:* Am Soc Limnol & Oceanog; Marine Biol Asn UK. *Res:* Benthic marine ecology, particularly population ecology; marine nematodes. *Mailing Add:* Dept of Biol Sci Univ of Southern Calif Los Angeles CA 90007

JONES, GILDA LYNN, b Water Valley, Miss, May 16, 27. BACTERIOLOGY. *Educ:* Miss State Univ for Women, BS, 51; Univ Mich, MPH, 67; Univ NC, Chapel Hill, PhD(pub health), 74. *Prof Exp:* Med technologist & chief, Bact Lab, Grady Mem Hosp, Atlanta, Ga, 52-60; SUPVY MICROBIOLOGIST, CENTERS DIS CONTROL, ATLANTA, 61- *Honors & Awards:* Betty King Award, Am Soc Microbiol, 79. *Mem:* Am Soc Microbiol; Am Pub Health Asn; Sigma Xi. *Res:* Development of training materials in bacteriology for use by the clinical laboratory worker. *Mailing Add:* Ctr Dis Control 1600 Clifton Rd Atlanta GA 30333

JONES, GLENN CLARK, b Raleigh, NC, Aug 22, 35; m 65. ORGANIC CHEMISTRY, POLYMER CHEMISTRY. *Educ:* Wake Forest Col, BS, 57; Duke Univ, PhD(chem), 62. *Prof Exp:* Res assoc org chem, Duke Univ, 61-62; res chemist, 62-64, SR RES CHEMIST, TENN EASTMAN CO, 64- *Mem:* Am Chem Soc. *Res:* Base catalyzed rearrangements; polymer feasibility studies; free radical chemistry; organic electrochemistry. *Mailing Add:* 3620 Hemlock Park Dr Kingsport TN 37663

JONES, GORDON ERVIN, b Greenwood, Miss, July 23, 36; m 61; c 1. PHYSICS. *Educ:* Miss State Univ, BS, 58; Duke Univ, PhD(physics), 64. *Prof Exp:* From asst prof to assoc prof physics, 64-72, PROF PHYSICS, MISS STATE UNIV, 72- *Mem:* Am Phys Soc; Am Asn Physics Teachers. *Res:* Microwave spectroscopy. *Mailing Add:* Dept of Physics Miss State Univ Mississippi State MS 39762

JONES, GORDON HENRY, b Stockport, Eng, Apr 2, 40; m 63; c 2. ORGANIC CHEMISTRY. *Educ:* Cambridge Univ, BA, 62, PhD, 65, MA, 66. *Prof Exp:* Fel org chem, 65-66, RES CHEMIST, SYNTEX INST ORG CHEM, 66- *Mem:* Am Chem Soc; Royal Soc Chem. *Res:* Application of new reactions in carbohydrate and nucleoside chemistry; peptide chemistry. *Mailing Add:* Syntex Inst of Org Chem 3401 Hillview Palo Alto CA 94304

JONES, GRAHAM ALFRED, b London, Eng, May 8, 35; m 63; c 4. AGRICULTURAL MICROBIOLOGY. *Educ:* Univ Leeds, BSc, 57; McGill Univ, MSc, 58, PhD(agr bact), 63. *Prof Exp:* Lectr agr bact, McGill Univ, 58-60; asst prof dairy sci, 63-67, assoc prof dairy & food sci, 67-73, PROF DAIRY & FOOD SCI, UNIV SASK, 73-, LECTR MICROBIOL, 75-, HEAD DEPT, 81- *Concurrent Pos:* Vis prof, Nat Res Coun Can, 74; vis scientist, Agr Res Coun Inst Animal Physiol, Babraham, Eng, 78-79. *Honors & Awards:* Queen's Jubilee Medal, 77. *Mem:* Am Soc Microbiol; Can Soc Microbiol (secy-treas, 70-73, second vpres, 80-81, first vpres, 81-82); Can Inst Food Sci & Technol. *Res:* Rumen microbiology; agricultural fermentations; biomass utilization. *Mailing Add:* Dept of Dairy & Food Sci Univ of Sask Saskatoon SK S7N 0W0 Can

JONES, GROVER STEPHEN, mathematics, see previous edition

JONES, GUILFORD, II, b Jackson, Tenn, Nov 24, 43; m 66; c 2. PHYSICAL ORGANIC CHEMISTRY, PHOTOCHEMISTRY. *Educ:* Southwestern at Memphis, BS, 65; Univ Wis-Madison, PhD(chem), 70. *Prof Exp:* Asst prof, 71-77, ASSOC PROF CHEM, BOSTON UNIV, 77- *Concurrent Pos:* NIH fel, Yale Univ, 69-71. *Mem:* Am Chem Soc; The Chem Soc; Int Solar Energy Soc. *Res:* Photochemical conversion of solar energy; small ring chemistry; mechanisms and applications of photochemical and thermal reactions; photochemical synthesis of natural products. *Mailing Add:* Dept of Chem Boston Univ Boston MA 02215

JONES, GUY LANGSTON, b Kinston, NC, June 7, 23; m 48; c 2. PLANT BREEDING. *Educ:* NC State Col, BS, 47, MS, 50; Univ Minn, PhD, 52. *Prof Exp:* Supt br sta, NC Agr Exp Sta, 47-49; asst dept agron & plant genetics, Univ Minn, 50-52; asst prof dept agron, 52-58, assoc prof field crops, 58-61, prof crop sci, 61-65, head agron exten, 65-75, PROF CROP SCI & SOIL SCI, NC STATE UNIV, 69- CONSULT, TOBACCO PROD & AGRON EXTEN PROGS, 71-, HEAD CROP SCI EXTEN, 75- *Concurrent Pos:* With Ministry Agr, Venezuela, 59, Inst Tobacco, Dominican Repub, 63, Agency Int Develop, Guatemala, 64-65 & Philippines, 64-65 & Food & Agr Orgn, Argentina, 74; assoc ed, Agron J. *Mem:* Fel Am Soc Agron; Sigma Xi. Crop Sci Soc Am. *Res:* Tobacco genetics; tobacco variety evaluation; agronomy extension. *Mailing Add:* Dept of Crop Sci NC State Univ Raleigh NC 27650

JONES, GWILYM STRONG, b Cincinnati, Ohio, May 4, 42; m 67; c 3. MAMMALOGY, VERTEBRATE ECOLOGY. *Educ:* Hanover Col, BA, 64; Purdue Univ, MS, 67; Ind State Univ, PhD(mammal syst), 79. *Prof Exp:* Res investr, Naval Med Res Unit 2, Taiwan, 67-69; mus specialist, Smithsonian Inst, 70-71; ASST PROF BIOL, NORTHEASTERN UNIV, 76- *Concurrent Pos:* Collabr mammal div, Smithsonian Inst, 70; adv, Chinese Asn Conserv Nature & Natural Resources, 69-70; grants, Am Inst Biol Sci, 70, Theodore Roosevelt Mem Fund & Am Mus Natural Hist, 74, US Dept Health & Human Serv, 78 & 81, NH Fish Game Dept, 80-81 & Pub Archeol Lab, Brown Univ, 80. *Mem:* Am Soc Mammalogists; Soc Syst Zool; Sigma Xi. *Res:* Mammalian systematics; vertebrate food habits; ectoparasites and demographics. *Mailing Add:* Dept of Biol Northeastern Univ Boston MA 02115

JONES, HAROLD LESTER, b Nampa, Idaho, June 19, 43; m 65; c 2. ORGANIC CHEMISTRY. *Educ:* Ore State Univ, BS, 65; Univ Colo, PhD(chem), 69. *Prof Exp:* Res asst, Univ Colo, 68; asst prof, 69-76, ASSOC PROF CHEM, COLO COL, 76-, CHMN, 81- *Concurrent Pos:* Res assoc, Univ Colo, 72. *Mem:* Am Chem Soc. *Res:* Nuclear magnetic resonance; small ring chemistry, bicyclic systems and cyclopropanols; free radical reactions in cyclopropanols; photochemistry of bicyclic-spiro-compounds. *Mailing Add:* Dept of Chem Colo Col Colorado Springs CO 80903

JONES, HAROLD TRAINER, b Allentown, Pa, Dec 22, 25; m 53; c 2. MATHEMATICAL ANALYSIS. *Educ:* Washington Missionary Col, BA, 46; Lehigh Univ, MA, 49; Brown Univ, PhD(appl math), 58. *Prof Exp:* Instr math, Pac Union Col, 46-48; fel appl math, Brown Univ, 49-51, asst, 51-52; from asst prof to assoc prof math, 52-64, PROF MATH, ANDREWS UNIV, 64- *Concurrent Pos:* NSF fac fel, 65-66. *Mem:* Am Math Soc; Soc Indust & Appl Math; Math Asn Am. *Res:* Potential theory; functional analysis. *Mailing Add:* 146 Woodland Dr Berrien Springs MI 49103

JONES, HARRIS CLEVE, solid state physics, low temperature physics, see previous edition

JONES, HAYDN, b Muskogee, Okla, Feb 15, 11; m 38; c 3. INDUSTRIAL CHEMISTRY. *Educ:* Lake Forest Col, AB, 32; Univ Chicago, MS, 32, PhD(physics), 39. *Prof Exp:* Res dir, Hizone Prod, 39-42; res assoc metall lab, Univ Chicago, 42-43; sr physicist, Manhattan Proj, Clinton Labs, Tenn, 43-45; res dir, Hizone Prod, 45-81. *Mem:* Am Chem Soc; fel Am Inst Chem. *Res:* Magnetic permeability of iron at ultra radio frequencies; energy distribution of cosmic rays; atomic pile; nuclear physics; preservation of animal tissues at ordinary temperatures; chemistry. *Mailing Add:* Hizone Prods Inc 1211 Washington Ave Wilmette IL 60091

JONES, HELENA SPEISER, b Columbus, Ohio, June 26, 40; m 65; c 2. ANATOMY, MEDICAL SCIENCES. *Educ:* Ohio State Univ, BSc, 62, PhD(anat) 68. *Prof Exp:* Instr anat, Med Ctr, Ind Univ, Indianapolis, 68-69; NIH staff fel, Nat Inst Environ Health Sci 72-75; ASST PROF BIOL, UNIV WIS-EAU CLAIRE, 75- *Concurrent Pos:* Consult, Adv Comt Estab Med Histol Technicians Assoc Degree, 76-; fels biomed sci, Washington, DC, 77 & 78; mem review panels, NSF; Eau Claire Community cancer grant, 80, 81 & 82. *Mem:* Am Asn Anatomists; Sigma Xi; NY Acad Sci. *Res:* Skin cancer; endocrinology; bone. *Mailing Add:* Dept Biol Univ Wis Eau Claire WI 54701

JONES, HOBART WAYNE, b Logansport, Ind, Apr 15, 21; m 43; c 4. ANIMAL BREEDING. *Educ:* Purdue Univ, BSA, 43; Ohio State Univ, MSA, 46, PhD(animal prod), 60. *Prof Exp:* Assoc prof, 50-61, PROF ANIMAL SCI, PURDUE UNIV, 61- *Mem:* Am Soc Animal Sci. *Res:* Animal production; swine nutrition and environmental studies. *Mailing Add:* Dept of Animal Sci Purdue Univ West Lafayette IN 47907

JONES, HOWARD, b Bolton, Eng, Apr 6, 37; m 69; c 2. MEDICINAL CHEMISTRY, ORGANIC CHEMISTRY. *Educ:* Univ Leeds, BSc, 59, PhD(org chem), 62. *Prof Exp:* Fel org chem, Univ Calif, Los Angeles, 62-64; asst dir, Merck Sharp & Dohme Res Labs, 64-78; DIR MED CHEM, USV PHARMACEUT CORP, 78- *Mem:* Royal Soc Chem; Am Chem Soc. *Res:* Inflammation and rheumatoid arthritis; vitamin D and bone metabolism; immunology. *Mailing Add:* USV Pharmaceut Corp One Scarsdale Rd Tuckahoe NY 10707

JONES, HOWARD ST CLAIRE, JR, b Richmond, Va, Aug 18, 21; m 46. ELECTRONIC ENGINEERING, MICROWAVE PHYSICS. *Educ:* Va Union Univ, BS, 43; Howard Univ, cert eng, 44; Bucknell Univ, MSEE, 73. *Hon Degrees:* DSc, Va Union Univ, 71. *Prof Exp:* Electronic scientist microwave electronics, Diamond Ord Fuze Lab, Washington, DC, 53-59, supvry electronic engr, 59-68, chief microwave res & develop, 68-80, TECH CONSULT, HARRY DIAMOND LABS, MD, 80- *Concurrent Pos:* Instr physics & math, Hilltop Radio-Electronics Inst, Washington, DC, 46-53; asst prof electronic eng, Sch Eng, Howard Univ, 58-63; tech consult, Phelps Dodge Electronics, Conn, 68-69; Sccy of Army fel, 72. *Mem:* Fel Inst Elec & Electronics Engrs; fel AAAS; Antenna & Propagation Soc; Microwave Theory & Techniques Soc. *Res:* Microwave research and development--directing, planning and coordinating research and development programs which involve theoretical and applied microwave research; management of programs and projects relating to major electronic systems. *Mailing Add:* 6200 Sligo Mill Rd NE Washington DC 20011

JONES, IRA, b Bartow, Fla, Jan 22, 34; m 57; c 2. ZOOLOGY, PARASITOLOGY. *Educ:* Benedict Col, BS, 55; Atlanta Univ, MS, 57; Wayne State Univ, PhD(biol), 66. *Prof Exp:* Instr biol, Savannah State Col, 57-59; assoc prof, Fla Agr & Mech Univ, 64-66 & Inter-Am Univ PR, 66-69; from asst prof to assoc prof, 69-77, PROF BIOL, CALIF STATE UNIV, LONG BEACH, 77- *Concurrent Pos:* USPHS fel, 61; grant, Caribbean Inst & Study Ctr for Latin Am, 68-69; Sigma Xi res grant, 68-69; PR Nuclear Ctr grant, 69; consult, Nat Commun Dis Ctr, 69; Calif State Univ Long Beach Found grant, 69-71; dir & consult parasitol, Jones Biomed & Lab, Long Beach, Ca, 77- *Mem:* Am Soc Parasitol; Am Inst Biol Sci; Soc Protozool. *Res:* Research on the endosymbionts of Sipunculids, including, zoogeography of parasitism, host specificity, life cycles of parasites and the cytochemistry and ultra-structure of Sipunculids sporozoa. *Mailing Add:* Dept of Biol Ca State Univ 6101 E Seventh St Long Beach CA 90840

JONES, IRVING WENDELL, b Washington, DC. STRUCTURAL ENGINEERING & MECHANICS. *Educ:* Howard Univ, BS, 53; Columbia Univ, MS, 57; Polytech Inst Brooklyn, PhD(appl mech), 67. *Prof Exp:* Asst civil eng, Columbia Univ, 56-57; struct engr, Grumman Aerospace Corp, 57-62; asst aerospace & mech, Polytech Inst Brooklyn, 62-63; asst dir & partner, Appl Technol Assocs, Inc, 63-69; assoc prof civil eng, 69-72, PROF CIVIL ENG & CHMN DEPT, HOWARD UNIV, 72- *Concurrent Pos:* Consult, space div, Fairchild-Hiller Corp, 62-64 & Dist Eng Serv, Inc, 77-; mem pressure vessel res coun, Welding Res Found, 64-69; lectr, grad sch, Stevens Inst Technol, 68-69. *Mem:* Am Soc Civil Engrs (pres, 69); Am Soc Mech Engrs (pres, 64); Am Soc Eng Educ (pres, 69). *Res:* Developed methods for computer-aided structural analysis including high temperature effects; helped develop shock-absorbing mounts and foundations for sensitive shipboard equipment; developed analysis methods for effects of high temperature on aerospace structures. *Mailing Add:* Dept of Civil Eng Sch of Eng Howard Univ Washington DC 20001

JONES, IVAN DUNLAVY, b Holdrege, Nebr, Dec 10, 03; m 30; c 2. FOOD SCIENCE. *Educ:* Nebr Wesleyan Univ, AB, 26; Univ Minn, PhD(agr biochem), 31. *Prof Exp:* Instr agr biochem, Univ Minn, 29-30; assoc horticulturist, Exp Sta, 31-45; prof hort, 45-61 & food sci, 61-70, EMER PROF FOOD SCI, NC STATE UNIV, 70- *Concurrent Pos:* Consult food sci & technol, 70-; vis prof, Middle East Tech Univ, Ankara, Turkey 79-80. *Mem:* Am Chem Soc; fel Inst Food Technol; fel Am Pub Health Asn; fel Am Inst Chem; Sigma Xi. *Res:* Chemical composition of fruits and vegetables and their processing by freezing, canning, dehydration and brining; estimation of chlorophylls and their metal derivatives; influence preservation technique on chlorophyll. *Mailing Add:* 2710 Rosedale Ave Raleigh NC 27607

JONES, J(AMES) B(EVERLY), b Kansas City, Mo, Aug 21, 23; m 45; c 2. MECHANICAL ENGINEERING. *Educ:* Va Polytech Inst, BS, 44; Purdue Univ, MS, 47, PhD(mech eng), 51. *Prof Exp:* Asst mech engr, Eng Bd, US War Dept, Va, 44-45; asst instr mech eng, Purdue Univ, 45-47, instr, 47-51; serv engr, Babcock & Wilcox Co, 48; develop engr, Gen Elec Co, 51-52; asst prof mech eng, Purdue Univ, 51-54; sr proj engr, Allison Div, Gen Motors Corp, 53; assoc prof mech eng, Purdue Univ, 54-57, prof, 57-64; PROF MECH ENG & HEAD DEPT, VA POLYTECH INST & STATE UNIV, 64- *Concurrent Pos:* NSF faculty fel, Swiss Fed Inst Technol, 61-62. *Mem:* Am Soc Mech Engrs; Am Soc Eng Educ; Am Inst Aeronaut & Astronaut. *Res:* Fluid mechanics; thermodynamics. *Mailing Add:* Dept of Mech Eng Va Polytech Inst & State Univ Blacksburg VA 24061

JONES, J BENTON, JR, b Tyrone, Pa, Apr 4, 30; m 55; c 1. SOIL FERTILITY, PLANT NUTRITION. *Educ:* Univ Ill, BS, 52; Pa State Univ, MS, 56, PhD(agron), 59. *Prof Exp:* From assoc prof to prof agron, Ohio Agr Res & Develop Ctr, 59-68; div chmn, Dept Hort, 74-79, PROF AGRON, AGR EXTEN-AGRON, UNIV GA, 68-, MEM, INST ECOL, 75-, PROF, DEPT HORT, 79- *Concurrent Pos:* Chmn, Coun Soil Testing & Plant Anal, 67-69, secy-treas, 69-; mem bd, Coun Agr Sci & Technol, 73-78. *Mem:* AAAS; Am Soc Agron; Soil Sci Soc Am; Int Soc Soil Sci; Am Soc Hort Sci. *Res:* Soil and plant chemistry, especially the micronutrients; soil fertility and plant nutrition related to crop production. *Mailing Add:* Dept of Hort Univ of Ga Athens GA 30602

JONES, J KNOX, JR, b Lincoln, Nebr, Mar 16, 29; m 53; c 3. VERTEBRATE ZOOLOGY. *Educ:* Univ Nebr, BS, 51; Univ Kans, MA, 53, PhD, 62. *Prof Exp:* From instr to assoc prof zool, Univ Kans, 59-68, prof systs & ecol, 68-71, from asst cur to assoc cur, Mus Natural Hist, 59-68, assoc dir & cur mammals, 68-71; PROF BIOL, COORD MUS STUDIES & DEAN GRAD SCH TEX TECH UNIV, 71-, VPRES RES & GRAD STUDIES, 74- *Concurrent Pos:* Managing ed, Soc Study Evolution, 65-66 & Am Soc Mammal, 67-72. *Honors & Awards:* C Hart Merriam Award, Am Soc Mammal, 77. *Mem:* Am Soc Mammal (vpres, 68-72, pres, 72-74); Soc Syst Zool; Soc Study Evolution. *Res:* Mammalogy, especially systematics and biogeography of North and Middle American mammals. *Mailing Add:* Off of the Dean Grad Sch Tex Tech Univ Lubbock TX 79409

JONES, J(OHN) L(LOYD), JR, b Henry, Ill, June 5, 18; m 47; c 3. ELECTRICAL ENGINEERING. *Educ:* Univ Ill, BS, 40, MS, 41; Univ Md, MS, 49, PhD, 63. *Prof Exp:* Physicist, US Naval Ord Lab, 42-63; assoc prof elec eng, Bradley Univ, 63-77; RETIRED. *Mem:* Acoust Soc Am; Am Soc Eng Educ. *Res:* Acoustics; circuit theory; electromagnetic theory; shock and vibration. *Mailing Add:* 1110 Warren St Henry IL 61537

JONES, J P, b Los Angeles, Calif, Sept 9, 41; m 64. MATHEMATICS. *Educ:* Univ Wash, BS, 63, MS, 66, PhD(math), 68. *Prof Exp:* Asst prof, 68-75, ASSOC PROF MATH, UNIV CALGARY, 75- *Honors & Awards:* Lester R Ford Award, Math Asn Am, 77. *Mem:* Am Math Soc; Math Asn Am; Asn Symbolic Logic; Can Math Cong. *Res:* Mathematical logic. *Mailing Add:* Dept Math & Statist Univ of Calgary Calgary AB T2N 1N4 Can

JONES, JACK COLVARD, b Birmingham, Ala, Nov 25, 20; m 46; c 3. INSECT PHYSIOLOGY. *Educ:* Auburn Univ, BS, 42, MS, 47; Iowa State Col, PhD(entom), 50. *Prof Exp:* Lab asst comp anat, Auburn Univ, 46-48; med entomologist insect physiol, Lab Trop Dis, Nat Microbiol Inst, 50-58; assoc prof entom, Univ Md, College Park, 58-64, prof, 64-80. *Concurrent Pos:* Lectr, George Washington Univ, 51-53; NIH career development award, 64-74; Guggenheim fel, 65. *Mem:* AAAS; Entom Soc Am. *Res:* Insect hemocytes; physiology of feeding of mosquitoes; physiology reproduction in mosquitoes; anatomy grasshopper. *Mailing Add:* 5609 Rollins Lane District Heights MD 20027

JONES, JACK EARL, b Middleton, Ga, July 30, 25; m 46; c 1. AGRONOMY. *Educ:* Univ Ga, BS, 48, MS, 50; La State Univ, PhD, 61. *Prof Exp:* From asst prof to assoc prof, 50-68, PROF COTTON BREEDING & GENETICS, LA STATE UNIV, BATON ROUGE, 68- *Mem:* Am Soc Agron; Crop Sci Soc Am; Sigma Xi. *Res:* Cotton breeding for superior fiber properties; resistance to diseases and insects; genetics of quantitative characters of cotton; cotton production practices. *Mailing Add:* Dept of Agron La State Univ Baton Rouge LA 70803

JONES, JACK EDENFIELD, b Jacksonville, Fla, Oct 24, 29; m 59; c 3. POULTRY SCIENCE. *Educ:* Univ Fla, BS, 51, MS, 64, PhD(physiol), 66. *Prof Exp:* Supvr farm mgt, Farmers Home Admin, 56-58; sanitarian, St Johns County Health Dept, 58-61; asst dir res, Coop Mills, 66-68; from asst prof to assoc prof, 68-76, PROF POULTRY, CLEMSON UNIV, 76- *Mem:* Poultry Sci Asn. *Res:* Nutrition; physiological-environmental relationships with turkeys and game birds. *Mailing Add:* 501 Isaqueena Trail Clemson SC 29631

JONES, JAMES DAVID, b Newark, NJ, Dec 21, 28; m 53; c 6. PEDIATRICS, PSYCHIATRY. *Educ:* Va Mil Inst, BS, 50; Duke Univ, MD, 54; Am Bd Pediat, dipl, 60; Am Bd Psychiat & Neurol, dipl, 63. *Prof Exp:* Fel child psychiat, NIMH, 61-63; assoc pediat, 63-71, asst prof psychiat, 63-73, ASST PROF PEDIAT, SCH MED, DUKE UNIV, 71-, ASSOC PROF PSYCHIAT, DIV CHILD & ADOLESCENT PSYCHIAT, 73- *Mem:* Am Psychiat Asn. *Res:* Clinical research in child psychiatry, especially in pediatrics. *Mailing Add:* Dept of Psychiat Duke Univ Durham NC 27710

JONES, JAMES DONALD, b Fond du Lac, Wis, Oct 5, 30; m 56; c 3. BIOCHEMISTRY. *Educ:* Ripon Col, AB, 52; Univ Wis, MS, 56, PhD(biochem), 58. *Prof Exp:* Asst prof animal nutrit, Iowa State Univ, 58-60; asst to staff sect biochem, 60-61, CONSULT, SECT CLIN CHEM, MAYO CLIN, 61- *Mem:* Am Chem Soc; Am Inst Nutrit; Am Asn Clin Chem; fel Am Inst Chemists. *Res:* Nitrogen and electrolyte metabolism in animals; biochemistry of the young; metabolism of guanidines. *Mailing Add:* Sect of Clin Chem Mayo Clin 200 First St S W Rochester MN 55901

JONES, JAMES EDWARD, b Columbus, Ohio, June 5, 24; m 44; c 5. VETERINARY MEDICINE. *Educ:* Ohio State Univ, DVM, 50, MS, 75. *Prof Exp:* Gen pract vet med, 50-68; CLINICIAN, OHIO AGR RES & DEVELOP CTR, 68- *Mem:* Am Vet Med Asn. *Res:* Atrophic rhinitis in swine; epizootiology. *Mailing Add:* 1133 Summerset Dr RR 1 Camelot Estates Wooster OH 44691

JONES, JAMES HOLDEN, b Parkersburg, WVa, Feb 2, 28; m 51; c 2. ORGANIC CHEMISTRY. *Educ:* WVa Univ, BS, 50; Duke Univ, PhD(chem), 58. *Prof Exp:* Process chemist, Merck & Co, Inc, 58-60, res chemist, 60-64, res fel, 64-80, SR RES FEL, MERCK SHARP & DOHME RES LABS, 80- *Mem:* Am Chem Soc. *Res:* Diuretics; central nervous system. *Mailing Add:* 649 Midway Lane Blue Bell PA 19422

JONES, JAMES JORDAN, b Palo Alto, Calif, Nov 19, 38; m 69; c 2. ATMOSPHERIC ELECTRICITY. *Educ:* Stanford Univ, BS, 60; Univ Ariz, MS, 63, PhD(physics), 69. *Prof Exp:* Res assoc cosmic ray particle physics, Univ Chicago, 69-72; proj assoc, Univ Wis, 72-73; res physicist, Univ Ariz, 73-81; RES PHYSICIST ATMOSPHERIC ELEC & ADJ ASST PROF PHYSICS, NMEX INST MINING & TECHNOL, 81- *Mem:* Am Phys Soc; Am Geophys Union. *Res:* Investigation of the electrical structure of convetive clouds by means of electric field meters mounted on research aircraft; testing of models of electric charge distribution in study coulds by direct comparison with measured electric fields. *Mailing Add:* Physics Dept NMex Inst Mining & Technol Socorro NM 87801

JONES, JAMES L, b Spokane, Wash, Sept 26, 26; m 51; c 5. ELECTRONICS, COMMUNICATIONS. *Educ:* US Mil Acad, BS, 48; Univ Ill, MS, 54; Stanford Univ, PhD(elec eng), 58. *Prof Exp:* US Army, 48-72, proj officer radar div, Army Electronics Lab, 54-56, asst dir, 58-59, chief tech staff, 59-61, prog mgr surveillance & commun, Advan Res Proj Agency, 62-65, asst dir develop, Off Secy Defense, Res & Develop Ctr, Thailand, 66-68, dep dir, 68-70, mem, 160th Signal Group, Vietnam, 70-71, dep dir eng, Defense Spec Proj Group, 71-72; mem staff, 72-81, dir, Tactical Warfare Opers, 75-81, VPRES, GEN RES CORP, 80- *Mem:* Sr mem Inst Elec & Electronics Engrs. *Res:* Radar; microwave tubes; sensor technology and military applications; navigation. *Mailing Add:* Gen Res Corp 7655 Old Springhouse Rd McLean VA 22102

JONES, JAMES OGDEN, b Punkin Center, Tex. STRATIGRAPHY, SEDIMENTOLOGY. *Educ:* Midwestern State Univ, BS, 62; Baylor Univ, MS, 66; Univ Iowa, PhD(geol), 71. *Prof Exp:* Geologists helper, Shell Oil Co, 59-60; lab asst geol, Midwestern State Univ, 60-62; teaching asst, Baylor Univ, 62-64 & Univ Iowa, 64-68; asst prof, Univ Southern Miss, 71; from asst prof to assoc prof geol, Southern Ark Univ, 71-77, head dept, 71-77; ASST PROF & DIR GEOL PROG, UNIV TEX, SAN ANTONIO, 78- *Concurrent Pos:* Vis asst prof, Univ Tex, San Antonio, 77-78. *Mem:* Am Asn Petrol Geologists; Soc Econ Paleontologists & Mineralogists; Nat Asn Geol Teachers; Geol Soc Am; Sigma Xi. *Res:* Stratigraphy and paleontology of lower Permian shelf deposits of west Texas; Cretaceous stratigraphy and paleontology of Gulf Coastal Plain; paleontology. *Mailing Add:* 8638 Bristlecone Dr San Antonio TX 78240

JONES, JAMES PRESTON, b Mendenhall, Miss, Feb 1, 35; m 62; c 2. SOIL FERTILITY, PLANT NUTRITION. *Educ:* Miss State Col, BS, 57; Univ Ariz, MS, 60, PhD(soils), 66. *Prof Exp:* Asst agriculturist, Agr Exten, Univ Calif, 61-66; asst prof soils, Fresno State Col, 66-67; assoc prof soils, Univ Idaho, 67-75, prof, 75-80, asst head dept, 73-80. *Mem:* Am Soc Agron; Soil Sci Soc Am; Int Soc Soil Sci; Coun Soil Testing & Plant Anal. *Res:* Soil fertility evaluation; plant tissue analysis. *Mailing Add:* 1011 Harding Moscow ID 83843

JONES, JAMES RICHARD, b Orange, NJ, Apr 23, 18; m 48; c 3. HYDROLOGY. *Educ:* Princeton Univ, AB, 40; Syracuse Univ, MS, 48. *Prof Exp:* Field geologist, City of Syracuse, 40-41; geologist, US Geol Surv, 48-58, tech adv ground water geol, US Opers Mission to Libya, 58-64, geologist, 64-68, tech adv groundwater geol, US Agency Int Develop, Ethiopia, 68-70, sr hydrologist, EPakistan, 70-71, Afghanistan, 81-72, India, 72-73 & Yeman Arab Repub, 74-75, chief, Off Int Activities, Water Resources Div, 75-81; HYDROGEOLOGIST, TETRA TECH INT, INC, 81- *Concurrent Pos:* Instr, Univ NDak, 48-49. *Mem:* Geol Soc Am; Am Asn Petrol Geol. *Res:* Groundwater geology. *Mailing Add:* Tetra Tech Int Inc 1911 Fort Meyer Dr Suite 403 Arlington VA 22209

JONES, JAMES ROBERT, b Quicksand, Ky, Dec 8, 31; m 58; c 3. ANIMAL HUSBANDRY, NUTRITION. *Educ:* Univ Ky, BS, 53, MS, 57; Cornell Univ, PhD(animal husb), 61. *Prof Exp:* Experimentalist animal husb, Cornell Univ, 61-64; EXTEN SPECIALIST, NC STATE UNIV, 64-, HEAD, SWINE EXTEN, 80- *Mem:* Am Soc Animal Sci. *Res:* Swine nutrition. *Mailing Add:* Dept of Animal Sci NC State Univ Raleigh NC 27607

JONES, JAMES WILSON, b Muskogee, Okla, Oct 13, 41; m 58; c 4. CARDIAC SURGERY, VASCULAR SURGERY. *Educ:* Tulane Med Ctr, MD, 66; Tulane Grad Sch, PhD(anat), 79. *Prof Exp:* Instr anat, 69-72, instr surg, 75-76, asst prof, 76-80, ASSOC PROF SURG, TULANE MED CTR, 80- *Mem:* Am Col Surgeons; Am Col Cardiol; Am Col Chest Physicians; Soc Thoracic Surgeons. *Res:* Throacic injuries; myocardiac preservation; infections in cardiac surgery; bioenergetics. *Mailing Add:* 1430 Tulane Ave New Orleans LA 70112

JONES, JANICE LORRAINE, b Takoma Park, Md, Mar 10, 43; m 67; c 2. BIOPHYSICS, CELL PHYSIOLOGY. *Educ:* St Bonaventure Univ, BS, 65; Johns Hopkins Univ, PhD(biophys), 70. *Prof Exp:* Asst prof med technol, Univ Vt, 70-74, res assoc, Dept Med, 78; ASST PROF PHYSIOL, SCH MED, CASE WESTERN RESERVE UNIV, 78- *Concurrent Pos:* Mem comt interdisciplinary grad prog cell biol, Univ Vt, 71- *Mem:* Biophys Soc; Int Soc Heart Res. *Res:* Cardiac physiology; physiology of cardiac cells in tissue culture; electrically induced myocardial damage. *Mailing Add:* Dept of Physiol Sch of Med Case Western Reserve Univ Cleveland OH 44106

JONES, JEANETTE, b Ft Valley, Ga, Sept 19, 50. MEDICAL MYCOLOGY, FUNGAL PHYSIOLOGY. *Educ:* Ft Valley State Col, BSc, 72; Ohio State Univ, MSc, 73, PhD(bot/med mycol), 76. *Prof Exp:* Instr biol, Ft Valley State Col, 72; univ fel, Ohio State Univ, 72-73, teaching assoc, 73-75, dissertation year fel, 75-76; asst prof, 76-78, ASSOC PROF BIOL, ALA A&M UNIV, 79- *Concurrent Pos:* Consult, Minority Biomed Support Prog, NIH, 78-81, Ft Valley State Col, 76, NSF, 79-80, Sixteen Inst Health Sci Consortium, Nat Adv Coun, 79-81 & Grad Traineeship Prog, NSF, 81. *Mem:* Med Mycol Soc Am; Sigma Xi; Int Soc Human & Animal Mycosis; Am Soc Microbiol; Am Soc Allied Health Professionals. *Res:* Isolation and control of growth of pathogenic fungi; nutirtion and morphogenesis of the ascomycetes. *Mailing Add:* Dept Biol Ala A&M Univ PO Box 207 Normal AL 35762

JONES, JENNINGS HINCH, b Petrolia, Pa, Aug 19, 13; m 40; c 2. ORGANIC CHEMISTRY. *Educ:* Pa State Col, BS, 34, MS, 37, PhD(chem), 41. *Prof Exp:* Chemist, Org Labs, Pa Coal Prod Co, 34-36; asst petrol ref, 41-44, from instr to assoc prof chem 44-52, assoc res prof, 53-64, prof chem, 64-69, EMER PROF CHEM ENG, PA STATE UNIV, 69- *Mem:* Am Chem Soc; Am Inst Chem Eng; fel Am Inst Chem; Combustion Inst; Sigma Xi. *Res:* Petroleum chemistry; identification and separation of the products from the vapor phase oxidation of normal heptane; oxidation of organic chemicals, hydrocarbons and petroleum fractions; chemical behavior of hydroperoxides and perfluoroacids; sulfonates from oxidized paraffins. *Mailing Add:* Dept Chem Engr Pa State Univ University Park PA 16802

JONES, JEROLD W, b Salt Lake City, Utah, July 6, 37; m 61; c 4. THERMAL SYSTEMS, FLUID SYSTEMS. *Educ:* Univ Utah, BSME, 62, PhD(mech eng), 70; Stanford Univ, MS, 65. *Prof Exp:* Res scientist heat transfer, Ames Res Ctr, NASA, 62-66; fel, Ohio State Univ, 69-70, asst prof mech eng, 70-73; asst prof arch eng, 73-76, ASSOC PROF MECH ENG, UNIV TEX, AUSTIN, 76- *Concurrent Pos:* Chmn, Tech Adv Group, Am Inst Architects Res Corp, 77-80; asst dir & prin investr, Ctr Energy Studies, Univ Tex, Austin, 75-; mem, Steering Comt Energy Conserv Bldg, Nat Res Coun, 79- *Mem:* Am Soc Heating, Refrig & Air-Conditioning Engrs; Am Soc Mech Engrs. *Res:* Heat transfer and thermodynamics with particular applications in systems modeling; design and analysis for improving energy use efficiency of buildings and heating and air conditioning equipment. *Mailing Add:* Dept Mech Eng Taylor Hall 167 Univ Tex Austin TX 78712

JONES, JERRY LATHAM, b St Louis, Mo, Oct 20, 46; m 73. ENVIRONMENTAL ENGINEERING, BIOCHEMICAL ENGINEERING. *Educ:* Cornell Univ, BS, 68, ME, 69; Stanford Univ, MS, 76. *Prof Exp:* Pilot plants supvr, Monsanto Biodize Systs, 69-71; eng serv mgr, Monsanto Envirochem, 71-73; environ engr, 73-75, sr chem engr, 75-76, mgr environ control group, 76-78, DIR ENVIRON & BIOCHEM ENG, SRI INT, 78- *Mem:* Am Inst Chem Engrs; Am Chem Soc; Water Pollution Control Fedn. *Res:* Development and evaluation of pollution control technologies, primarily biochemical and thermal processes; fermentation processes. *Mailing Add:* Chem Eng Lab SRI Int 333 Ravenswood Ave Menlo Park CA 94025

JONES, JERRY LYNN, b Grandfield, Okla, Mar 28, 33; m 54; c 3. ANALYTICAL CHEMISTRY, EDUCATIONAL ADMINISTRATION. *Educ:* Okla State Univ, AB, 57, MS, 60; Univ Ark, PhD(chem), 63. *Prof Exp:* Res asst chem, Puget Sound Pulp & Timber, 56; res partic, Oak Ridge Nat Lab, 64; asst prof, Tex A&M Univ, 62-68; assoc prof, 68-72, coordr acad grants & contracts, 73-78, interim dean res & grad sch, 76-77, PROF CHEM, CENT WASH UNIV, 72-, SPEC ASST TO PRES, 79- *Concurrent Pos:* Assoc ed sci & technol, USA Today, 75- *Mem:* Am Chem Soc; fel Am Inst Chemists. *Res:* Electroanalytical methods; trace metal analysis; atomic absorption spectroscopy; computers in chemistry; electrode reactions; environmental analysis; research design and evaluation. *Mailing Add:* Off Pres Cent Wash Univ Ellensburg WA 98926

JONES, JESS HAROLD JOSEPH, b Melville, La, Mar 30, 35; m 58; c 4. PHYSICS, MECHANICS. *Educ:* La State Univ, BS, 58. *Prof Exp:* Engr, Brown Eng Co, 61-64, sr engr, 64; aerospace engr, 64-66, chief, Acoust Sect, 66-72, LEAD ENGR ENVIRON ASSESSMENT TECHNOL, GEORGE C MARSHALL SPACE FLIGHT CTR, NASA, 72- *Mem:* Acoust Soc Am; Am Soc Mech Engrs. *Res:* Theoretical and experimental investigations of the basic noise generation mechanisms of rocket exhaust flows and fluctuating pressure fields associated with space vehicles; analysis of random processes; fluid mechanics; wave propagation; sonic boom analysis; structural dynamics; rotating machinery; turbomachinery analysis; diagnostic analysis of dynamic data; fast fourier transforms analysis; ignition overpressure analysis and testing. *Mailing Add:* George C Marshall Space Flight Ctr ED24 S&E-AERO-AU NASA Huntsville AL 35812

JONES, JESSE W, b Troup, Tex, Jan 16, 31; m 55; c 5. CHEMISTRY. *Educ:* Tex Col, BS, 54; NMex Highlands Univ, MS, 56; Ariz State Univ, PhD(org chem), 63. *Prof Exp:* Asst chem, NMex Highlands Univ, 54-55; asst biochem, Univ Utah, 55-56; asst prof chem, Tex Col, 56-58; res assoc, Ariz State Univ, 58-63; prof, Tex Col, 63-67, head dept, 63-64, head div natural sci, 64-67; PROF CHEM, BISHOP COL, 67- *Concurrent Pos:* Nat Inst Gen Med Sci & Welch Found grants, 63-65. *Mem:* AAAS; Am Chem Soc. *Res:* Synthesis, mechanism of action and biochemical studies of certain nitrogen heterocycles. *Mailing Add:* Dept of Chem Bishop Col Dallas TX 75241

JONES, JIMMY BARTHEL, b Selmer, Tenn, Dec 1, 33; m 54; c 3. INTERNAL MEDICINE, LABORATORY ANIMAL MEDICINE. *Educ:* Univ Tenn, Martin, BS, 56; Univ Ill, BS, 61, DVM, 63. *Prof Exp:* Soil conservationist, USDA, 56-59, dist vet, Animal Health Div, 63-64; pvt practice, 64-67; vet biol div, Oak Ridge Nat Lab, 67-68; vet dir, Col Liberal Arts Animal Facil, 68-73, dir animal facil, Mem Res Ctr, 68-76, assoc prof, 76-80, PROF, DEPT URBAN PRACT, COL VET MED & HEAD, DEPT ENVIRON PRACT, UNIV TENN, 81- *Concurrent Pos:* Vet-consult, Biol Div, Oak Ridge Nat Lab, 68-69. *Mem:* Am Vet Med Asn; Int Soc Exp Hematol; Soc Exp Biol & Med. *Res:* Internal diseases of animals; administration and design of animal facilities as they interact with research projects; canine cyclic neutropenia; mechanisms of hematologic changes and management of affected animals. *Mailing Add:* Dept Eviron Pract Univ Tenn PO Box 1071 Knoxville TN 37901

JONES, JOE MAXEY, b Herpel, Ark, Mar 20, 42. IMMUNOPATHOLOGY. *Educ:* Wichita State Univ, BS, 64, MS, 66; Univ NC, Chapel Hill, PhD(immunol), 70. *Prof Exp:* Fel immunopath, Scripps Clin Res Found, 70-73, assoc, 73-77; head immunol & immunochem, Nat Ctr Toxicol Res, 77-80; ASST PROF IMMUNOL, UNIV ARK MED SCI, 80- *Mem:* Am Asn Immunologists; AAAS. *Res:* Tumor immunology; genetic control of immune responses. *Mailing Add:* Univ Ark Med Sci 4301 W Markham Little Rock AR 72205

JONES, JOHN, JR, b Antioch, Tenn, Nov 19, 17; m 49; c 1. MATHEMATICS. *Educ:* Peabody Col, MA, 46; George Washington Univ, PhD(math), 70. *Prof Exp:* Assoc prof math, Southern Miss Univ, 46-55, head dept, 50-55; instr, Univ Tenn, 55-57; assoc prof, US Air Force Inst Technol, 57-60; mathematician, Hq, US Air Force, 60-64; asst prof lectr, George Washington Univ, 64-66; prof lectr, Am Univ, 66-68; assoc prof, 68-70, PROF MATH, AIR FORCE INST TECHNOL, 70- *Mem:* Am Math Soc; Math Asn Am. *Res:* Matrix theory; differential equations; functional analysis. *Mailing Add:* 2101 Matrena Dr Dayton OH 45431

JONES, JOHN A(RTHUR), b Port Chester, NY, Apr 6, 32; c 1. ENVIRONMENTAL SCIENCES, AQUATIC ECOLOGY. *Educ:* Univ Ill, Urbana, BS, 54; Tex A&M Univ, MS, 60; Univ Miami, PhD(marine sci), 68. *Prof Exp:* Res assoc marine biol, Univ Miami, 64-67; acting dir, Lake Erie Environ Studies & adj asst prof biol, State Univ NY Col, Fredonia, 68-70; assoc prof environ technol, 70-80, PROF ENVIRON TECHNOL & NATURAL SCI, MIAMI-DADE COMMUNITY COL, 80- *Concurrent Pos:* Seminar assoc, Columbia Univ, 68-; consult, 71- *Mem:* AAAS; Am Geophys Union; Am Soc Limnol & Oceanog. *Res:* Environmental measurements; graphic and statistical analysis of enviromental data, especially in aquatic enviroments; comparative properties of environmental fluids. *Mailing Add:* Miami-Dade Community Col 11011 SW 104th St Miami FL 33176

JONES, JOHN ACKLAND, b Alexandria, Va, Nov 6, 34; m 60; c 1. ENTOMOLOGY. *Educ:* Univ of the South, BS, 56; Univ Va, MS, 63; Iowa State Univ, PhD(entom), 73. *Prof Exp:* Instr biol, Univ of the South, 57-58; med lab technician histol, US Army Med Serv Corps, 58-60; assoc prof biol, Parsons Col, 63-66; state entomologist regulatory, Nebr Dept Agr, 73-78; ASST PROF ENTOM, UNIV NEBR-LINCOLN, 78- *Mem:* Entom Soc Am; Sigma Xi. *Res:* Insect morphology and development; insect pests of shelter belts; horticultural pests. *Mailing Add:* Dept of Entom Univ of Nebr Lincoln NE 68583

JONES, JOHN BRYAN, b Colwyn Bay, NWales, Dec 11, 34; m 62; c 2. ORGANIC CHEMISTRY, ORGANIC BIOCHEMISTRY. *Educ:* Univ Wales, BSc, 55, PhD(chem), 58; Oxford Univ, DPhil(chem), 60. *Prof Exp:* Fel org chem, Mass Inst Technol, 60-61; NIH res fel, Calif Inst Technol, 61-62; Imp Chem Indust fel, Oxford Univ, 62-63; from asst prof to assoc prof, 63-74, PROF ORG CHEM, UNIV TORONTO, 74- *Mem:* Fel Am Chem Soc; Chem Inst Can. *Res:* Organic chemical applications of enzymes; immobilized enzymes. *Mailing Add:* Dept of Chem Univ of Toronto Toronto ON M5S 1A1 Can

JONES, JOHN DEWI, b Carmarthen, Wales, May 3, 26; m 55; c 4. PLANT BIOCHEMISTRY. *Educ:* Univ Wales, BSc, 46, MSc & PhD, 54. *Prof Exp:* Asst biochem, Univ Col Wales, Aberystwyth, 47 & 50-51, asst agr chem, Bangor, 51-54; sci off & chemist, Plant Path Lab, Ministry Agr, Fisheries & Food, Harpenden, Eng, 54-55; res assoc biol, Queen's Univ, Ont, 55-59; res plant biochemist, Ditton Lab, Agr Res Coun, Maidstone, Eng, 60-65; plant biochemist & head sect storage res fruits & veg, 66-70, res scientist, 70-71, plant biochemist, 71-73, SR RES SCIENTIST, FOOD RES INST, CAN DEPT AGR, 73- *Concurrent Pos:* Chemist, Mauritius-Seychelles Fisheries Res Surv, London, Eng, 48-50; fel, Nat Res Coun Can, 57-59. *Mem:* Am Soc Plant Physiol; Can Soc Plant Physiol; The Chem Soc; Fel Royal Inst Chem; fel Inst Food Sci & Technol UK. *Res:* Chemical and physical methods of removing toxic substances from cruciferous oil seeds; chemistry of glucosinolates, myrosinases, vegetable protein research and development; food ingredients; nutrition of plant proteins; toxicology of oilseeds; evaluation of novel sources of food proteins. *Mailing Add:* Food Res Inst Cent Exp Farm Can Agr Ottawa ON K1A 0C6 Can

JONES, JOHN EVAN, b Mt Pleasant, Utah, Oct 29, 30; m 54; c 3. INTERNAL MEDICINE, ENDOCRINOLOGY. *Educ:* Univ Utah, BS, 52, MD, 55; Am Bd Internal Med, dipl, cert endocrinol & metab, 73. *Prof Exp:* Dir USPHS trainee endocrinol, Univ Minn Hosps, 59; dir USPHS trainee, 60-61, from instr to asst prof med, 61-63, from asst prof to assoc prof endocrinol, 63-70, chmn div metab-endocrinol, 67-74, PROF MED & ENDOCRINOL, SCH MED, WVA UNIV, 70-, DEAN SCH MED, 74- *Mem:* Fel Am Col Physicians; Endocrine Soc; Am Fedn Clin Res; Am Soc Clin Nutrit. *Res:* Mineral metabolism; thyroid metabolism; adrenal hormone metabolism. *Mailing Add:* Dept of Med WVa Univ Sch of Med Morgantown WV 26506

JONES, JOHN F(REDERICK), b Scranton, Pa, Aug 19, 32; m 62; c 3. CHEMICAL ENGINEERING. *Educ:* Pa State Univ, BS, 54; Univ Del, MS, 56; Univ Colo, PhD(chem eng), 60. *Prof Exp:* Chem engr, Esso Res & Eng Co, 56-58; instr chem eng, Univ Colo, 58-60; res chem engr, 60-63, sr res chem engr, 63-68, asst mgr, Proj COED, 68-72, mgr, 72-74, dir, coal & coke technol, 74-75, bus venture & tech mgr, Philadelphia, 75-77, DIR RES & DEVELOP, INDUST CHEM GROUP, FMC CORP, 77- *Mem:* Am Chem Soc; Am Inst Chem Engrs; Indust Res Inst; AAAS; Sigma Xi. *Res:* Petroleum refining; carbonization; gasification and liquefaction of coal; sewage and water treatment; industrial chemicals. *Mailing Add:* FMC Corp Chem Res & Develop Ctr PO Box 8 Princeton NJ 08540

JONES, JOHN FRANKLIN, b Superior, Wis, Oct 16, 33; m 77. SPACE SCIENCES, ASTRODYNAMICS. *Educ:* Univ Wis, BSME, 59; Univ Cincinnati, MS, 61. *Prof Exp:* Engr appl math, 59-69, supvr orbit mech, Viking Support Orgn, 69-73, SR ENGR RADAR SYST, ELECTRONIC SYST DIV, GEN ELEC CO, 73- *Mem:* Inst Elec & Electronics Engrs; Am Inst Aeronaut & Astronaut. *Res:* Orbit mechanics; statistical decision theory; modern control theory; large systems analysis. *Mailing Add:* 7339 Palomino Path Liverpool NY 13088

JONES, JOHN PAUL, b Warren, Ohio, Dec 10, 24; m 50; c 3. PLANT PATHOLOGY. *Educ:* Ohio Univ, BS, 50; Univ Nebr, MA, 53, PhD, 56. *Prof Exp:* Plant pathologist, Delta Exp Sta, Agr Res Serv, USDA, 55-60, PROF PLANT PATH, UNIV ARK, FAYETTEVILLE, 60- *Concurrent Pos:* Plant pathologist, Arab Repub Egypt, 81- *Mem:* Am Phytopath Soc. *Res:* Phytopathology; diseases of field crops; etiology and control of cereal crops diseases. *Mailing Add:* Dept of Plant Path Univ of Ark Fayetteville AR 72701

JONES, JOHN PAUL, b Stockdale, Ohio, Feb 24, 32; m 61; c 3. PLANT PATHOLOGY. *Educ:* Ohio State Univ, BS, 53, MS, 55, PhD(plant path), 58. *Prof Exp:* Asst plant path, Ohio Agr Exp Sta, 54-58; from asst prof to assoc prof, 58-69, PROF PLANT PATH, AGR RES & EDUC CTR, UNIV FLA, 69- *Mem:* Am Phytopath Soc. *Res:* Nature and control of vegetable diseases; biology of plant pathogens. *Mailing Add:* Agr Res & Educ Ctr Univ of Fla 5007 60th St E Bradenton FL 33508

JONES, JOHN PAUL, b Takoma Park, Md, Nov 17, 40; m 66; c 1. MATHEMATICS. *Educ:* Alderson-Broaddus Col, BS, 62; WVa Univ, MA, 64; Pa State Univ, DEd(math), 71. *Prof Exp:* Instr math, Allegheny Col, 64-67; asst prof, 71-74, ASSOC PROF MATH & HEAD DEPT, FROSTBURG STATE COL, 74- *Mem:* Am Math Soc; Math Asn Am. *Res:* Algebra-groups and rings. *Mailing Add:* Dept of Math Frostburg State Col Frostburg MD 21532

JONES, JOHN PAUL, JR, b Memphis, Tenn, Sept 1, 26. MEDICINE. *Educ:* Southwestern Col, Tenn, 48-52; Univ Tenn, MD, 56. *Prof Exp:* Intern, White Plains Hosp, New York, 56-57; intern gen surg res, Lenox Hill Hosp, New York, 57-61; Orthop fel & res instr, Columbia-Presby Med Ctr, New York, 61-62; surgeon, Am Export Lines, 62-63; assoc med dir, Med Dept, Pfizer Inc, 64-71; dir med affairs, Ethicon Inc, 71-80; CORP DIR HEALTH SCI, JOHNSON & JOHNSON, INC, 80- *Concurrent Pos:* Pvt pract, Tenn, 63-64; fel, Col Med, Univ Tenn, 63-64. *Mem:* AAAS; AMA; Am Soc Microbiol; Inst Elec & Electronics Engrs; Sigma Xi. *Res:* Surgery and antibiotics. *Mailing Add:* 501 George St Plaza II Johnson & Johnson Inc New Brunswick NJ 08903

JONES, JOHN R, b Pandora, Ohio, Feb 18, 24; m 46; c 4. MEDICINE, ANESTHESIOLOGY. *Educ:* Univ Mich, MD, 51. *Prof Exp:* From instr to asst prof anesthesia, Ohio State Univ, 54-59; assoc prof, Marquette Univ, 60-62; prof, Med Ctr, Univ Nebr, Omaha, 62-70, Shackelford prof surg, 70-72, chmn dept anesthesia, 72; exec assoc dean, Med Col Va, 72-78, dir clin serv, 73-78, PROF ANESTHESIOL, MED COL VA, VA COMMONWEALTH UNIV, 72-, EDUC DIR, DEPT ANESTHESIOL, 78- *Concurrent Pos:* Consult, Great Lakes Naval Hosp, 60-62, Omaha Vet Admin, 62- & Lincoln Vet Admin, 69- *Mem:* Am Soc Anesthesiol; AMA; Int Anesthesia Res Soc; fel Am Soc Clin Pharmacol & Therapeut; Am Col Anesthesiol. *Res:* Effects of pH on drug action; effects of hypoxia; hypercarbia and pH on heart rate; respiratory physiology; stress. *Mailing Add:* Dept of Anesthesiol Med Col of Va Box 923 Richmond VA 23219

JONES, JOHN RICHARD, b Bremerton, Wash, Aug 23, 47; m 69; c 1. LIMNOLOGY. *Educ:* Western Wash State Col, BA, 69; Iowa State Univ, MS, 72, PhD(limnol), 74. *Prof Exp:* Fel, Iowa State Univ, 74-75; asst prof, 75-80, ASSOC PROF LIMNOL, UNIV MO-COLUMBIA, 80- *Mem:* Am Soc Limnol & Oceanog; Ecol Soc Am; Am Fisheries Soc; Sigma Xi. *Res:* Eutrophication process in lakes and reservoirs; attention to phosphorous and algal biomass. *Mailing Add:* Sch of Forestry Fish & Wildlife 112 Stephens Hall Univ of Mo Columbia MO 65201

JONES, JOHN TAYLOR, b Salt Lake City, Utah, Jan 4, 32; m 53; c 4. CERAMICS ENGINEERING, METALLURGY. *Educ:* Univ Utah, BS, 57, PhD(ceramic eng, metall), 65. *Prof Exp:* Res engr, Coors Porcelain Co, Colo, 57-60, prod supt, 60-61, develop engr, 61-62; asst dir res, Vesuvius Crucible Co, Pa, 65-66; assoc prof ceramic eng, Iowa State Univ, 66-74; process develop mgr, Interspace Corp, Calif, 74; res & develop mgr, Pfaltzgraff Co, Pa, 74-78; res & develop mgr, 78-80, TECH DIR, LENOX CHINA CO, NJ, 80- *Mem:* Nat Inst Ceramic Engrs; Am Ceramic Soc; Ceramic Educ Coun; Brit Ceramic Soc; Can Ceramic Soc. *Res:* Diffusion, strength, stoichiometry properties and fabrication of oxides; ceramic whitewares. *Mailing Add:* Lenox China Co Tilton Rd Pomona NJ 08240

JONES, JOHNNYE M, b Henderson, Tex, Apr 3, 43. ELECTRON MICROSCOPY, MYCOLOGY. *Educ:* Prarie View A&M Univ, BS, 65; Atlanta Univ, MA, 70, PhD(bot & mycol), 79. *Prof Exp:* Instr biol & math, Carthage Public Schs, 65-67, Chicago Public Schs, 67-69, Morgan State Univ, Baltimore, Md, 70-74 & Mercer Univ, Atlanta, Ga, 75-79; ASST PROF BIOL, HAMPTON INST, 79- *Concurrent Pos:* Fac fel, Nat Inst Gen Med Sci, NIH, 74; res assoc, Brookhaven Nat Lab, 79-81. *Mem:* Bot Soc Am; Mycol Soc Am; Nat Minority Health Affairs Asn. *Res:* Ultrastructural studies on certain species of fungi Ascomycetes and Oomycetes, especially developmental and physiological aspects. *Mailing Add:* Dept Biol Sci Hampton Inst Hampton VA 23668

JONES, JOYCE HOWELL, b Roanoke, Va, May 4, 44; m 68. EMBRYOLOGY, ANIMAL SCIENCE & NUTRITION. *Educ:* Va Polytech Inst & State Univ, BS, 66, MS, 71, PhD(genetics), 74. *Prof Exp:* Jr high sch phys sci teacher, 69-70; asst prof biol, Ferrum Col, 74-77; EXTEN SPECIALIST & ASST PROF POULTRY, VA POLYTECH INST & STATE UNIV, 77- *Mem:* Poultry Sci Asn; Am Genetic Asn; AAAS; Sigma Xi. *Res:* Genetical, physiological and behavioral relationships in avian and mammalian pre and post natal development. *Mailing Add:* Dept of Poultry Sci Va Polytech Inst & State Univ Blacksburg VA 24061

JONES, JUSTINE H, b Brooklyn, NY, Feb 10, 24. PROTOZOOLOGY. *Educ:* St John's Univ, NY, BS, 54, MS, 57, PhD(zool), 64. *Prof Exp:* Teacher, Sacred Heart Sch, 45-52 & Bishop McDonnell Mem High Sch, 52-57; from instr to assoc prof, 57-66, PROF BIOL, MOLLOY COL, 66-, CHMN DEPT, 65- *Mem:* AAAS; Soc Protozool; Am Soc Zool; Am Inst Biol Sci. *Res:* Isolation of species of Paramecium trichium; establishment of axenic cultures of these organisms; development of a defined medium for Paramecium trichium and studies on the vitamin requirements of these protozoa. *Mailing Add:* Dept of Biol Molloy Col 1000 Hempstead Ave Rockville Centre NY 11570

JONES, KAY H, b US citizen. ENGINEERING. *Educ:* Univ Washington, BS, 56; Univ Calif, Berkeley, MS, 61, PhD(sanit eng), 68. *Prof Exp:* Mem staff, Nat Air Pollution Control Admin, Dept Health, Educ & Welfare, 67-70; mem, Off Air Prog, Environ Protection Agency, 70-74; consult, WHO, 74-75; mem, Coun Environ Qual, Exec Off Pres, 75-79; prof environ eng, Drexel Univ, Pa, 79-81; VPRES, ROY WESTON INC, 81- *Honors & Awards:* State-of-the-Art Civil Eng Award, Am Soc Civil Engrs, 75. *Mem:* Am Soc Civil Engrs. *Res:* Ambient air quality data analysis; air pollution impact analysis; population exposure modeling; environmental epidemiology; environmental toxicology; industrial hygiene. *Mailing Add:* Roy Weston Inc Weston Way West Chester PA 19380

JONES, KEITH WARLOW, b Lincoln, Nebr, Aug 30, 28; m 54; c 3. EXPERIMENTAL ATOMIC PHYSICS, APPLIED PHYSICS. *Educ:* Princeton Univ, AB, 50; Univ Wis, MS, 51, PhD(physics), 55. *Prof Exp:* Asst prof physics, Univ NC, 54-55; res assoc, Columbia Univ, 55-58; from asst prof to assoc prof, Ohio State Univ, 58-63; from assoc physicist to physicist, 63-75, SR PHYSICIST, BROOKHAVEN NAT LAB, 75- *Mem:* Fel Am Phys Soc. *Res:* Beam foil spectroscopy; heavy ion-atom collisions; trace element and isotope identification techniques; micro-beam methods and applications. *Mailing Add:* Dept of Physics Brookhaven Nat Lab Upton NY 11973

JONES, KENNETH CHARLES, b San Pedro, Calif, July 20, 34; m 56; c 2. ALGOLOGY, MOLECULAR GENETICS. *Educ:* Univ Calif, Los Angeles, BA, 57, MA, 62, PhD(plant sci), 65. *Prof Exp:* From asst prof to assoc prof, 64-71, actg dean grad studies & res, 77-78, dept chmn, 79-80, PROF BIOL, CALIF STATE UNIV, NORTHRIDGE, 71- *Mem:* AAAS; Sigma Xi. *Res:* Chemical regulation of plant growth; genetic control mechanisms; physiology of germination of Chara. *Mailing Add:* Dept of Biol Calif State Univ Northridge CA 91324

JONES, KENNETH LA MAR, b Ogden, Utah, May 31, 31; m 59; c 2. BIOLOGICAL SCIENCES. *Educ:* Utah State Univ, BS, 58, MS, 60. *Prof Exp:* Teacher, Los Angeles City Schs, 60-62; PROF BIOL, MT SAN ANTONIO COL, 62-, COORD HEALTH EDUC, 64- *Mem:* AAAS; Am Pub Health Asn; Nat Sci Teachers Asn; Am Col Health Asn; Am Acad Polit & Soc Sci. *Res:* Parasites of rainbow trout; drug abuse education. *Mailing Add:* Planetary Research Inst Pasadena CA 91106

JONES, KENNETH LESTER, b Keweenaw Bay, Mich, Dec 3, 05; m 29; c 2. SOIL MICROBIOLOGY, HISTORY. *Educ:* Syracuse Univ, AB, 28; Univ Mich, PhD(bot), 33. *Prof Exp:* Instr, 29-37, from asst prof to prof, 37-77, chmn dept, 50-63, EMER PROF BIOL SCI, UNIV MICH, ANN ARBOR, 77- *Concurrent Pos:* Researcher, Commercial Solvents Corp, 48-50. *Mem:* AAAS; Am Soc Microbiol; Bot Soc Am; Am Acad Microbiol. *Res:* Variation, morphology and distribution of streptomyces. *Mailing Add:* 607 W Davis Ann Arbor MI 48103

JONES, KENNETH WAYNE, b Decatur, Ill, Dec 22, 46; m 68; c 2. CLINICAL MICROBIOLOGY, ENVIRONMENTAL MICROBIOLOGY. *Educ:* Southern Conn State Col, BS, 70; Univ NC, MPH, 74, PhD(public health microbiol), 76. *Prof Exp:* Microbiologist, Conn Health Dept, Greenwich, 71-73; res asst, Centers Dis Control, 75-76; CHIEF MICROBIOLOGIST, RI DEPT HEALTH, 76- *Mem:* Sigma Xi; Am Soc Microbiol; Am Public Health Asn. *Res:* Diagnostic procedures in clinical and public health microbiology; microbiological methods for monitoring environmental quality. *Mailing Add:* 1 Newcastle Dr East Greenwich RI 02818

JONES, KIRKLAND LEE, b Amarillo, Tex, Oct 1, 41; m 64; c 2. POPULATION ECOLOGY, HERPETOLOGY. *Educ:* Baylor Univ, BA, 64; Univ NMex, MS, 70, PhD(biol), 74. *Prof Exp:* asst prof biol, Southern Methodist Univ, 74-81; MEM STAFF, LOS ALAMOS TECH ASSOCS, 81- *Concurrent Pos:* Collabr, Nat Park Serv, 70-73; consult, Environ Protection Agency, 72-73; consult, 76- *Mem:* Sigma Xi; Ecol Soc Am; Am Soc Ichthyologists & Herpetologists. *Res:* Effects of competition on niche dimensionality and morphology; energetics of feeding strategies; endangered species. *Mailing Add:* Los Alamos Tech Assocs Los Alamos NM 87544

JONES, L(EWELLYN) E(DWARD), b Montreal, Can, Mar 25, 10; m 38; c 2. HYDRAULIC ENGINEERING. *Educ:* Univ Man, BScCE, 31, Univ Toronto, MASc, 33, PhD(hydraul), 41. *Prof Exp:* Jr engr, Can Pac Rwy Co, 29-30 & Man Prov Govt, 31-33; instr & lectr, appl physics, 36-44, from ast prof to prof mech eng, 44-75, EMER PROF MECH ENG, UNIV TORONTO, 75-, ENG ARCHIVIST & CUR, 70-, ASSOC, INST ENVIRON STUDIES, 71- *Concurrent Pos:* Hydraul engr, Hydro-Elec Power Comn Ont, 41-57; Ford Found res grant, 63; gen consult, 57- *Honors & Awards:* Queen's Silver Jubilee Medal, 77. *Mem:* Am Soc Civil Eng; Am Soc Mech Engrs; Eng Inst Can; Royal Can Inst; Brit Inst Mech Engrs. *Res:* Applied physics; optics; photography; metrology; fluid mechanics; water resources; applied mathematics; data processing and interpretation; computers and numerical methods; technical publication; engineering history; optimal interpretation of experimental data. *Mailing Add:* 29 Prince George Dr Islington ON M9A 1X9 Can

JONES, LARRY HUDSON, b Dillon, SC, July 3, 48. PLANT PHYSIOLOGY, BOTANY. *Educ:* Wofford Col, BS, 70; Univ NC, Chapel Hill, PhD(bot), 76. *Prof Exp:* Res assoc biochem & microbiol, Cook Col, Rutgers Univ, 75-76; vis asst prof biol, Swarthmore Col, 76-77; ASST PROF BIOL, UNIV OF THE SOUTH, 77- *Mem:* Am Soc Plant Physiologists; Sigma Xi. *Res:* Tissue culture; effects of methylation of RNA on biological systems; coordination of protein synthesis in chloroplasts and mitochondria; plant hormones; genetics. *Mailing Add:* Dept of Biol Univ of the South Sewanee TN 37375

JONES, LARRY PHILIP, b Hamilton, Mont, Dec 11, 34; m 59; c 2. VETERINARY PATHOLOGY. *Educ:* Wash State Univ, BA, 57, DVM, 58; Am Col Vet Path, dipl, 68. *Prof Exp:* Res assoc path, Agr Res Lab, Univ Tenn, 58-60; asst prof vet path, Inst Trop Vet Med, 65-69; PATHOLOGIST & HEAD DEPT PATH, TEX VET MED DIAG LAB, 69- *Mem:* Am Vet Med Asn; Wildlife Dis Asn; Wildlife Soc. *Res:* Infectious diseases of domestic and wild ruminants. *Mailing Add:* Tex Vet Diagnostic Lab Drawer 3040 College Station TX 77840

JONES, LARRY W, b Huntington Co, Ind, Feb 14, 34; m 57; c 3. PLANT PHYSIOLOGY. *Educ:* Univ Ariz, BS, 55, MS, 59; Univ Tex, PhD(bot), 64. *Prof Exp:* Res scientist, Res Inst Adv Studies, Div Martin Co, 64-65; from asst prof to assoc prof, 65-73, PROF BOT, UNIV TENN, KNOXVILLE, 73- *Concurrent Pos:* Vis prof, Ore State Univ, 74-75; consult, Waterways Exp Sta, US Army Corps Engrs, Vicksburg, Miss, 77- *Mem:* Am Soc Plant Physiol; Phycol Soc Am; Am Soc Photobiol. *Res:* Photosynthetic mechanisms and algal physiology; photosynthesis and hydrogen production. *Mailing Add:* Dept of Bot Univ of Tenn Knoxville TN 37916

JONES, LAWRENCE RYMAN, b Terre Haute, Ind, Jan 8, 21; m 43; c 2. ANALYTICAL CHEMISTRY. *Educ:* Ind State Univ, BS, 46. *Prof Exp:* Res chemist, Com Solvents Corp, 43-75; RES CHEMIST, INT MINERAL & CHEM CORP, 75- *Res:* Analytical method research. *Mailing Add:* 1539 S Sixth St Terre Haute IN 47802

JONES, LAWRENCE WILLIAM, b Evanston, Ill, Nov 16, 25; m 50; c 3. HIGH ENERGY PHYSICS. *Educ:* Northwestern Univ, BS, 48, MS, 49; Univ Calif, PhD(physics), 52. *Prof Exp:* Asst, Univ Calif, 50-52; from instr to assoc prof, 52-63, PROF PHYSICS, UNIV MICH, ANN ARBOR, 63- *Concurrent Pos:* Physicist, Lawrence Radiation Lab, Univ Calif; physicist, Midwestern Univs Res Asn, 56-57; consult, Space Tech Labs, Inc, Thompson-Ramo-Wooldridge, Inc; Ford Found fel, Europ Orgn Nuclear Res, 61-62, Guggenheim Found fel, 65; vis prof, Westfield Col, London, 77 & Tata Inst, Bombay, 79. *Mem:* Am Phys Soc; AAAS; Int Asn Hydrogen Energy. *Res:* Strong interactions of elementary particles at high energies; cosmic ray physics at very high energies; hadron production of dilepions and prompt neutrinos; hydrogen energy systems; medical physics instrumentation. *Mailing Add:* Dept of Physics Univ of Mich Ann Arbor MI 48109

JONES, LEE BENNETT, b Memphis, Tenn, Mar 14, 38; m 64; c 2. ORGANIC CHEMISTRY. *Educ:* Wabash Col, BA, 60; Mass Inst Technol, PhD(org chem), 64. *Prof Exp:* NSF fel chem, Calif Inst Technol, 64; from asst prof to assoc prof, 64-72, asst head dept, 71-73, head dept, 73-77, dean grad col, 77-80, PROF CHEM, UNIV ARIZ, 72-, PROVOST, GRAD COL & HEALTH SCI, 80- *Mem:* AAAS; Am Chem Soc; The Chem Soc. *Res:* Photochemistry; carbonium ion reactions; nucleophilic substitutions; isotope effects. *Mailing Add:* Grad Col Univ of Ariz Tucson AZ 85721

JONES, LEEROY GEORGE, b Flint, Mich, Aug 15, 29; m 53; c 4. ENVIRONMENTAL MEDICINE, INTERNAL MEDICINE. *Educ:* Mich State Col, AB, 52; Wayne Univ, MD, 56. *Prof Exp:* Intern med, Holy Cross Hosp, Salt Lake City, 56-57; US Army, 57-, resident, Detroit Receiving Hosp, 58-61, asst chief dept gastroenterol, Walter Reed Army Inst Res, 61-62, asst chief med res br, Hq, US Army Med Res & Develop Command, 62-64, chief outpatient serv & dept med, DeWitt Army Hosp, Ft Belvoir, 64-65, team chief trop med, US Army Med Res Team, Vietnam, 67-68, dir physiol lab, Inst Environ Med, 68-70, cmndg officer & sci-tech dir, US Army Res Inst Environ Med, 71-76, dir med res, 76-77, dep comdr, Med Res & Develop Command, Md, 77-80, COMDR, MED DEPT ACTIVITY, US ARMY, 80- *Concurrent Pos:* Asst instr, Wayne State Univ, 58-61; fel, Harvard Med Sch, 65-67, res assoc, 69-70, lectr physiol, 73-; army liaison rep appl physiol study sect, NIH, 71-; panel on self regulation, Advan Res Proj Agency, Dept Defense, 71-; consult environ med, Surgeon Gen, USA, 71-76. *Mem:* AAAS; Am Physiol Soc; Asn Mil Surgeons US; Am Fedn Clin Res; fel Am Col Physicians. *Res:* Cardiovascular physiology; psychophysiology; environmental physiology; exercise physiology. *Mailing Add:* Irwin Army Hosp Ft Riley MEDDAC Ft Riley KS 66442

JONES, LEO EDWARD, b Dunsmuir, Calif, Feb 12, 18; m 58; c 4. PLANT MORPHOGENESIS. *Educ:* Chico State Col, AB, 42; Ore State Univ, PhD(bot), 50. *Prof Exp:* Asst horticulturist, Plant Introd Garden, USDA, 40-42, 45-46; from asst prof to assoc prof, Ore State Univ, 50-71; PROF BIOL, BOISE STATE UNIV, 72- *Mem:* Bot Soc Am; Sigma Xi. *Res:* Host-parasite relationships; plant tissue and cell culture; growth and differentiation; developmental cytology; plant tissue and cell culture and growth and morphogenesis; plant tissue culture; video-cinemicrography in freshwater biology. *Mailing Add:* Dept of Biol Boise State Univ Boise ID 83725

JONES, LEON LLOYD, physical chemistry, theoretical chemistry, see previous edition

JONES, LEONARD CLIVE, b Kimmswick, Mo, Jan 26, 21; m 39; c 5. ENGINEERING, PHYSICS. *Educ:* Southeast Mo State Teachers Col, BS, 42; St Louis Univ, MS, 49, PhD(physics), 52. *Prof Exp:* Res chemist, Mo-Tac Co, 50-52; engr-physicist, McDonnell Aircraft Corp, 52-54; design engr, Universal Match Corp, 54-56; head radar engr, Emerson Elec Mfg Co, 56-57, adv design engr, appl res lab, 57-61; prof eng, St Louis Univ, 61-65; PROF ENG, SOUTHERN ILL UNIV, EDWARDSVILLE, 65- *Concurrent Pos:* Lectr, eng grad prog, St Louis Univ, 54-61. *Mem:* Inst Elec & Electronics Engrs. *Res:* Communications statistics; operations research; systems analysis; microprocessor systems; applied science and mathematics. *Mailing Add:* Dept of Eng Southern Ill Univ Edwardsville IL 62025

JONES, LEONIDAS JOHN, b Warrenton, NC, May 17, 37; m 63; c 3. SOFTWARE SYSTEMS. *Educ:* Duke Univ, BS, 58; MS, 60, PhD(elec eng), 66. *Prof Exp:* Scientist, 66-77, adminr, 77-79, MGR, RES & DEVELOP CTR, GEN ELEC CO, 79- *Concurrent Pos:* Gen Elec rep, Conf Data Syst Lang, 71-77. *Mem:* Asn Comput Mach. *Res:* Computer-aided design and database systems for industrial automation. *Mailing Add:* RD2 Devils Lane Ballston Spa NY

JONES, LESTER TYLER, JR, b Des Moines, Iowa, Dec 5, 39; m 62; c 3. PHYSICAL CHEMISTRY, HEALTH SCIENCES. *Educ:* Univ Iowa, BS, 61; Wash State Univ, PhD(phys chem), 66. *Prof Exp:* Sr chemist, 65-72, res specialist, 72-73, supvr, 73-74, mgr, Cent Res Labs, 74-81, MGR, HEMAT SECT, LIFE SCI SECTOR, 3M CO, 81- *Mem:* Am Chem Soc. *Res:* Corrosion of metals; nuclear quadruple resonance; charge transfer complexes; dye adsorption; controlled release; biomaterials; hematology and blood. *Mailing Add:* 3M Co 3M Ctr Bldg 201-2W St Paul MN 55144

JONES, LEWIS HAMMOND, IV, b Cleveland, Ohio, Feb 26, 41. SEMICONDUCTOR PHYSICS. *Educ:* Ohio Wesleyan Univ, BA, 63; Univ Ill, MS, 65, PhD(physics), 71. *Prof Exp:* Vis scientist physics, Ctr Nuclear Energy, Saclay, France, 71-72 & Nat Lab, Frascati, Italy, 72-74; res assoc physics, Univ Md, College Park, 74-77; Park, 74-76; asst res physicist, Univ Calif, Irvine, 78-79; MEM RES STAFF, FAIRCHILD CAMERA & INSTRUMENT CORP, PALO ALTO, 79- *Mem:* AAAS; Am Phys Soc; Inst Elec & Electronics Engrs. *Res:* Development of semiconductor memory and logic devices. *Mailing Add:* Fairchild Semiconductor 4001 Miranda Ave Palo Alto CA 94304

JONES, LEWIS POSEY, b Sheridan, Ind, Jan 23, 21; m 42; c 3. INFORMATION SYSTEMS, AUDIOVISUAL COMMUNICATIONS. *Educ:* Purdue Univ, BS, 43. *Prof Exp:* Design engr, Aeronca Aircraft Corp, Ohio, 43-44; design engr, aeroprod div, Gen Motors Corp, Ohio, 44; aeronaut engr, eval div, bur aeronaut, US Navy Dept, Washington, DC, 46-49, head airframe components design, airborne equip div, 50-54; chief engr, Thompson Trailer Corp, Va, 49-50; tech adv to comdr, US Naval Aviation Safety Ctr, Naval Air Sta, Norfolk, Va, 54-60; exec asst to asst dir appln & manned space flight, off space flight prog, NASA, 60-62; dep dir prog reports div, off programming, 62-70; PROG REV OFFICER, NSF, 70- *Concurrent Pos:* Mem data processing comt, adv bd, Bur Aeronaut Indust; Dir, Orgn Media Systs, Inc, Ft Worth, 78- *Mem:* Int Tape Asn (secy, 75-); Am Inst Aeronaut & Astronaut; AAAS; Am Soc Pub Admin; Nat Comput Graphics Asn. *Res:* Aviation safety operations research; material reliability analysis; management information systems development; visual information communication; teleconferencing; business computer graphic system development. *Mailing Add:* NSF 1800 G St NW Rm 540 Washington DC 20550

JONES, LEWIS WILLIAM, b Malad, Idaho, July 6, 06; m 28; c 1. BACTERIOLOGY. *Educ:* Utah State Agr Col, BS, 36, MS, 37; Stanford Univ, PhD(bact, physiol), 52. *Prof Exp:* Pub sch prin, Idaho, 26-34; from instr to prof, 37-75, actg head dept, 60-63, EMER PROF BACT, UTAH STATE UNIV, 75- *Concurrent Pos:* NSF fac fel, 59-60. *Mem:* AAAS; Am Soc Microbiol; Am Pub Health Asn. *Res:* Effects of temperature, alkali salts, insecticides and herbicides upon soil microorganisms; gas production in pasteurized dairy products; anaerobic metabolism; denitrification. *Mailing Add:* 320 N 100 W Malad ID 83252

JONES, LILY ANN, b Montevideo, Minn, July 6, 38; div; c 2. MICROBIAL GENETICS, MOLECULAR BIOLOGY. *Educ:* Univ Minn, BA, 60, MS, 63, PhD(microbiol), 64. *Prof Exp:* Sr lab technician, Univ Minn, 60-64; instr, 64-70, asst prof microbial genetics, 70-76, ASST PROF IMMUNOL & MICROBIOL, WAYNE STATE UNIV, 76- *Mem:* AAAS; Soc Indust Microbiol; Am Inst Biol Sci; NY Acad Sci; Japanese Soc Plant Physiol. *Res:* Genetics of Streptomyces; phylogeny of actinomycetes; mode of action of antibiotics; life-cycle and structure of actinophage. *Mailing Add:* Dept Immunol & Microbiol Wayne State Univ Med Sch Detroit MI 48202

JONES, LINCOLN D, b Los Angeles, Calif, Dec 4, 23; m 44; c 3. ELECTRICAL ENGINEERING. *Educ:* Univ Ariz, BS, 51, MS, 56; Stanford Univ, Engr, 64. *Prof Exp:* Instr elec eng, Univ Ariz, 51-54; asst prof, Calif State Polytech Col, 54-56; from asst prof to assoc prof, 56-65, PROF ELEC ENG, SAN JOSE STATE UNIV, 65- *Mem:* Inst Elec & Electronics Engrs; Am Soc Eng Educ; Soc Comput Simulation. *Res:* Finding system models for second order nonlinear systems that exhibit jump resonance. *Mailing Add:* Dept of Elec Eng San Jose State Univ San Jose CA 95192

JONES, LLEWELLYN CLAIBORNE, JR, b Chester, Pa, Nov 4, 19; m 45; c 3. ANALYTICAL CHEMISTRY. *Educ:* Harvard Univ, BS, 43. *Prof Exp:* Res chemist, Houston Res Lab, Shell Oil Co, 43-44 & Wood River Res Lab, 44-46, group leader, 46-56, res chemist, Thorton Res Ctr, Shell Res, Ltd, Eng, 56-57, asst chief res physicist, Wood River Res Lab, 57-65, head anal dept, Emeryville Res Ctr, Shell Develop Co, 65-69, head process develop dept, Res Ctr, Shell Berre, France, 69-70, head, Anal Dept, Royal Dutch Shell Lab, Netherlands, 70-72, ANALYTICAL MGR, SHELL DEVELOP CO, 72- *Res:* Absorption spectroscopy; infrared and vacuum ultraviolet; ion exchange chromatography; instrumental methods of analysis. *Mailing Add:* 2505 Broadway Houston TX 77012

JONES, LLEWELLYN HOSFORD, b Oberlin, Ohio, Nov 14, 19; m 48; c 5. PHYSICAL CHEMISTRY. *Educ:* Univ Mich, BS, 42; Univ Buffalo, AM, 47; Calif Inst Technol, PhD(chem), 51. *Prof Exp:* MEM STAFF, LOS ALAMOS NAT LAB, UNIV CALIF, 51- *Mem:* Am Chem Soc. *Res:* Infrared spectroscopy; molecular ionic structure. *Mailing Add:* Los Alamos Nat Lab Univ Calif Los Alamos NM 87544

JONES, LLOYD GEORGE, b Hobart, La, Aug 6, 19. HORTICULTURE. *Educ:* La State Univ, BS, 49, MS, 50; Purdue Univ, PhD(hort), 53. *Prof Exp:* Asst, La State Univ, 46-49; asst, Purdue Univ, 50-53; asst horticulturist, 53-55, assoc prof, 56-61, PROF HORT, AGR EXP STA, LA STATE UNIV, BATON ROUGE, 62- *Mem:* AAAS; Am Soc Plant Physiol; Am Soc Hort Sci. *Res:* Plant nutrition; soil fertility. *Mailing Add:* 137 Agron-Hort Bldg La State Univ Baton Rouge LA 70803

JONES, LOIS MAE, b Waukesha, Wis, Feb 28, 24. BACTERIOLOGY. *Educ:* Carroll Col, BA, 45; Univ Wis, MS, 47, PhD(agr bact), 50; Am Bd Microbiol, dipl. *Prof Exp:* Fulbright fel, Vet Lab, Ministry Agr, Weybridge, Eng, 50-51, res officer, 53-57; proj assoc prev med, Univ Wis, 51-53; brucellosis consult, WHO, UN, 57, Food & Agr Orgn, Japan, 57-58 & African region, 58; res assoc, Dept Bact, 59-67, RES ASSOC, DEPT VET SCI, UNIV WIS-MADISON, 67- *Concurrent Pos:* Secy subcomt taxon Brucellae, Int Comt Bact Nomenclature, 58-70; WHO brucellosis consult, Iran, 61 & 62 & Argentina, 70-71, mem adv panel brucellosis, WHO, 64- *Mem:* Am Soc Microbiol. *Res:* Improvement of serological and bacteriological methods for detection of brucellosis; taxonomy of Brucella; development of vaccines against Brucella melitensis infection. *Mailing Add:* Dept of Vet Sci Univ of Wis-Madison Madison WI 53706

JONES, LOIS MARILYN, b Berea, Ohio, Sept 6, 34. GEOCHEMISTRY, GEOLOGY. *Educ:* Ohio State Univ, BS, 55, MS, 59, PhD(geochem), 69. *Prof Exp:* Lab asst chem, Ohio State Univ, 53-55, asst, 55-59; res anal chem, Exp Sta, E I du Pont de Nemours & Co, Inc, 59-61; asst, Ohio State Univ, 61; lectr, Mem Univ Nfld, 61-63; res anal chemist, US Geol Surv, 63-66; res asst geochem, Ohio State Univ, 66-67, res assoc isotope geol, 69; asst prof geol, Univ Ga, 69-77; SR RES SCIENTIST, RES & DEVELOP DEPT, CONTINENTAL OIL CO, 77- *Concurrent Pos:* Prin investr, Tenn Copper Co grant, 69; proj leader, NSF grant, Inst Polar Studies, Ohio State Univ, & Univ Ga, 69-70. *Mem:* Geol Asn Can; Am Geophys Union; Geochem Soc;

Geol Soc Am; Int Asn Geochem & Cosmochem. *Res:* Geochemistry of trace elements in igneous rocks; rubidium-strontium geochronology; strontium isotopes as natural tracers; geochronology, geochemistry, and glacial history of the ice-free valleys and paleolimnology of the saline lakes; Antarctica. *Mailing Add:* Res & Develop Dept Continental Oil Co Ponca City OK 74601

JONES, LORELLA MARGARET, b Toronto, Ont, Feb 22, 43; US citizen. ELEMENTARY PARTICLE PHYSICS. *Educ:* Radcliffe Col, BA, 64; Calif Inst Technol, MSc, 66, PhD(physics), 68. *Prof Exp:* Instr & fel high energy theory, Calif Inst Technol, 67-68; from asst prof to assoc prof, 68-78, PROF PHYSICS, UNIV ILL, URBANA, 78- *Concurrent Pos:* Ann Horton vis res fel, Newnham Col, Univ Cambridge, 74-75; vis scientist, Ger El Synch & Orgn Europ Res Nuclear labs, 81-82. *Mem:* AAAS. *Res:* Phenomenological applications of high energy theory to strong interactions. *Mailing Add:* Dept of Physics Univ of Ill Urbana IL 61801

JONES, LOUISE HINRICHSEN, b Ames, Iowa, Dec 24, 30; m 52. APPLIED MATHEMATICS, COMPUTER SCIENCE. *Educ:* Radcliffe Col, AB, 52, MA, 53; Univ Del, MA, 68, PhD(appl math), 70. *Prof Exp:* Physicist, Textile Fibers Dept, E I du Pont de Nemours & Co, Inc, 53-59, res physicist, 59-66; asst prof appl math & comput sci, Univ Del, 69-74; mem staff, 74-76, SUPVR E I DU PONT DE NEMOURS & CO, INC, 76- *Mem:* Am Math Soc; Soc Indust & Appl Math; Asn Comput Mach. *Res:* Nonlinear eigenvalue problems; numerical solution of integral equations; automata theory; microprogramming; optimization. *Mailing Add:* 233 Cheltenham Rd Newark DE 19711

JONES, LUCILE MERRILL, b Santa Monica, Calif, Feb 13, 55; m 81. SEISMOLOGY, ROCK MECHANICS. *Educ:* Brown Univ, AB, 76; Mass Inst Technol, PhD(geophysics), 81. *Prof Exp:* Res asst seismol, Mass Inst Technol, 76-81; RES ASSOC SEISMOL, LAMONT-DOUHERTY GEOL OBSERV, COLUMBIA UNIV, 81- *Concurrent Pos:* Fulbright fel, Inst Geophysics, State Seismol Bur, Beijing, China, 79. *Mem:* Am Geophys Union. *Res:* Earthquake mechanics and prediction through laboratory rock deformation studies and field studies of earthquake mechanisms and precursory activity including foreshocks, ground water changes and abnormal animal behavior. *Mailing Add:* Lamont-Doherty Geol Observ Palisades NY 10964

JONES, MAITLAND, JR, b New York, NY, Nov 23, 37; m 60; c 3. ORGANIC CHEMISTRY. *Educ:* Yale Univ, BS, 59, MS, 60, PhD(chem), 63. *Prof Exp:* Fel chem, Univ Wis, 63-64; from instr to assoc prof, 64-73, PROF CHEM, PRINCETON UNIV, 73- *Concurrent Pos:* Vis prof, Free Univ, Amsterdam, 73-74 & 78. *Mem:* Am Chem Soc; Chem Soc Japan; Royal Soc Chem. *Res:* Chemistry of reactive intermediates; thermal and photochemical reorganizations. *Mailing Add:* Dept of Chem Princeton Univ Princeton NJ 08540

JONES, MALCOLM DAVID, b Orange, Calif, Feb 16, 23; m 45; c 5. RADIOLOGY. *Educ:* Univ Calif, AB, 43, MD, 46. *Prof Exp:* Intern, San Diego Naval Hosp, 46-47; from resident to resident radiol, Med Ctr, Univ Calif, San Francisco, 50-53, from asst prof to assoc prof, 54-65, from asst radiologist to assoc radiologist, 54-65, prof radiol & radiologist, 65-74; PROF RADIOL & CHMN DEPT, UNIV TEX HEALTH SCI CTR SAN ANTONIO, 74-, PROF DEPT DIAG & ROENTGENOL, 77- *Mem:* AMA; Am Col Radiol. *Res:* Radiographic assessment of age changes in the primate spine. *Mailing Add:* Dept of Radiol Univ of Tex Health Sci Ctr San Antonio TX 78284

JONES, MARGARET ZEE, b Swedesboro, NJ, June 24, 36; m 59; c 3. NEUROPATHOLOGY, PATHOLOGY. *Educ:* Univ Pa, BA, 57; Med Col Va, MD, 61. *Prof Exp:* Clin asst, Sch Med, Univ Wash, 62-65; resident neuropath, Med Col Va, 66-67, from instr to asst prof, 67-69, actg dir div neuropath, 68-69; from asst prof to assoc prof path, 70-78, PROF PATH, MICH STATE UNIV, 78- *Concurrent Pos:* From intern to resident path & neuropath, Univ Wash, 62-65; lectr, Sch Med, Yale Univ, 69-; fel biochem, Nat Inst Neurol Dis & Stroke, Mich State Univ, 70-71, grant, 80-83; grant, Nat Multiple Sclerosis Soc, 71-72. *Mem:* Am Fedn Clin Res; Am Asn Neuropath; Soc Neurosci; Am Soc Clin Path; Am Asn Pathologists. *Res:* Developmental neurobiology; neurochemistry; medical education; neuropathology, particularly developmental and neuromuscular disorders. *Mailing Add:* Dept of Path Mich State Univ East Lansing MI 48823

JONES, MARK MARTIN, b Scranton, Pa, Jan 7, 28; m 51; c 2. INORGANIC CHEMISTRY. *Educ:* Lehigh Univ, BS, 48, MS, 49; Univ Kans, PhD(chem), 52. *Prof Exp:* Fel hydrazine chem, Univ Ill, 52-53, instr chem, 53-55; chemist, Picatinny Arsenal, 55-57, chief develop unit, Explosives Res Sect, 57; from asst prof to assoc prof, 57-64, PROF INORG CHEM, VANDERBILT UNIV, 64- *Mem:* AAAS; Am Chem Soc. *Res:* Methods of studying complexes in solution; structural factors determining stability of complexes and variations in their reactivity; therapeutic chelating agents for toxic heavy metals. *Mailing Add:* Dept of Chem Vanderbilt Univ PO Box 1583 Nashville TN 37203

JONES, MARK WALLON, b Wheeling, WVa, Dec 20, 16; m 66; c 1. PHYSICS, MATHEMATICS. *Educ:* Univ Wva, AB, 38; Univ Fla, MS, 48, PhD(physics, math), 53. *Prof Exp:* Observer dept terrestrial magnetism, Carnegie Inst Washington, 39-47; fel-sr physicist, Geophys Inst, Univ Alaska, 48-50; sr physicist, Ord Eng Corp, 53-55; pres, Geo-Sci Inc, 55-70; PRES, DESIGN SYSTS INC, 71-; TEACHER PHYSICS & MATH, CHAPMAN COL, 77- *Concurrent Pos:* Pres, NMex Res Inst, 60-73; bd chmn, 73- *Mem:* Sr mem Inst Elec & Electronics Engrs; Sigma Xi. *Res:* Geophysics, especially atmospheric and ionospheric physics; biophysics, particularly radiation effects and bio-electric potentials; geophysics and physics of water resources; physical mathematics. *Mailing Add:* Design Systs Inc 1610 Juniper Dr Alamogordo NM 88310

JONES, MARTHA OWNBEY, b Colfax, Wash, Dec 10, 40; m 68; c 1. BIOLOGICAL CHEMISTRY, ORGANIC CHEMISTRY. *Educ:* Grinnell Col, BA, 62; Purdue Univ, PhD(chem), 75. *Prof Exp:* Instr, Purdue Univ, 66-67; from instr to asst prof chem, Drew Univ, 68-78; lectr org chem, Princeton Univ, 78-82; ASST PROF CHEM, UNION COL, 82- *Mem:* Am Chem Soc; AAAS; Sigma Xi; Am Asn Univ Profs. *Res:* Protein chemistry and enzymology; protein folding and the relationship between structure and biological activity of proteolytic enzymes. *Mailing Add:* Dept of Chem Union Col Cranford NJ 07016

JONES, MARVIN THOMAS, b St Louis, Mo, Apr 20, 36; m 58; c 2. PHYSICAL CHEMISTRY. *Educ:* Wash Univ, St Louis, AB, 58, PhD(phys chem), 61. *Prof Exp:* Res chemist, Exp Sta, Cent Res Dept, E I du Pont de Nemours & Co, Inc, 61-66; assoc prof chem, St Louis Univ, 66-69; assoc prof, 69-71, actg dean, Col Arts & Sci, 78-79, PROF CHEM, UNIV MO-ST LOUIS, 71-, ASSOC DEAN, COL ARTS & SCI, 76- *Concurrent Pos:* Res assoc, Univ Groningen, Neth, 75-76 & Sheffield Univ, Eng, 76. *Mem:* AAAS; Am Chem Soc; Am Phys Soc; Sigma Xi. *Res:* Spectroscopic techniques, especially magnetic resonance to study problems of chemical and physical interest. *Mailing Add:* Dept of Chem Univ of Mo-St Louis St Louis MO 63121

JONES, MARY ELLEN, b La Grange, Ill, Dec 25, 22; c 2. BIOCHEMISTRY. *Educ:* Univ Chicago, BS, 44; Yale Univ, PhD, 51. *Prof Exp:* Res chemist, Armour & Co, 42-48; AEC fel, Biochem Res Lab, Mass Gen Hosp, 51-53, Am Cancer Soc fel, 53-55; assoc biochemist, Biochem Res Lab, Mass Gen Hosp, 55-57; from asst prof to assoc prof biochem, Brandeis Univ, 57-66; from assoc prof to prof, Univ NC, Chapel Hill, 66-71, partic assoc prof zool, 67-69, prof, 69-71; prof biochem, Univ Southern Calif, 71-78; prof, 78-80, KENAN PROF, UNIV NC, CHAPEL HILL, 80-, CHMN BIOCHEM, 78- *Concurrent Pos:* Am Cancer Soc scholar, 57-62; dir NIH dent training grant, Brandeis Univ, 62-66; assoc ed, Can J Biochem, 69-74; mem grants comt, Am Cancer Soc, 71-73; mem biochem study sect, NIH, 71-75; mem merit rev bd basic serv, Vet Admin, 75-78; mem, Life Sci Comt, NASA, 76-78; mem metabolic biol study sect, NSF, 78-81; mem sci adv bd Nat Heart, Lung & Blood Inst, NIH, 80- *Mem:* Inst Med-Nat Acad Sci; AAAS; Am Chem Soc; Am Soc Biol Chemists; NY Acad Sci. *Res:* Enzymology; biosynthetic and transfer reactions; metabolic regulation of enzymes; multifunctional proteins; pyrimidine and amino acid biosynthesis; carbamyl phosphate; acetyl-coenzyme A. *Mailing Add:* Dept of Biochem Univ of NC Sch Med Chapel Hill NC 27514

JONES, MAURICE HARRY, b London, Eng, Jan 7, 27; m 52; c 2. PHYSICAL CHEMISTRY, ORGANIC CHEMISTRY. *Educ:* Univ London, BSc, 47, PhD(chem), 50. *Prof Exp:* Fel photochem, Nat Res Coun, Can, 50-52; Bakelite res fel polymerization, Univ Birmingham, 52-53; asst dir dept chem, 54-63, dir dept phys chem, 63-72, dir, Dept Res Coord & Planning, 72-77, VPRES INTERDEPT PROGS, ONT RES FOUND, CAN, 77- *Mem:* Am Chem Soc; fel Chem Inst Can; Am Electroplaters Soc. *Res:* Polymerization; membranes; electroplating; pollution; research administration. *Mailing Add:* Dept of Res Coord & Planning Sheridan Park Mississauga ON L5K 1B3 Can

JONES, MELTON RODNEY, b Richmond, Va, Jan 13, 45; m 68; c 2. GENETICS, BIOLOGY. *Educ:* Am Univ, BS, 66; Howard Univ, MS, 68, PhD(zool), 72. *Prof Exp:* Chmn biol, Shaw Univ, 74-75; asst prof, Univ Colo, Boulder, 76-77; ASSOC PROF BIOL & CHMN DEPT SCI, COMMUNITY COL BALTIMORE, 78-; ASST TO DEAN, COL OSTEOP MED, OHIO UNIV, 78- *Mem:* AAAS; Am Inst Biol Sci; Sigma Xi. *Res:* Biochemical genetics with respect to enzyme activity and gene dosage. *Mailing Add:* Dept of Sci 2901 Liberty Heights Ave Baltimore MD 21209

JONES, MELVIN D, b Hardisty, Alta, Nov 16, 43; m 66; c 1. PROSTHODONTICS. *Educ:* Univ Alta, DDS, 66; Ind Univ, Indianapolis, MSD, 69. *Prof Exp:* Asst prof dent, Univ Alta, 66-67; instr, Ind Univ, Indianapolis, 68-69; assoc prof dent, Univ Alta, 69-75; MEM STAFF, UNIV CALGARY, 75- *Concurrent Pos:* Can Fund Dent Educ fel, 67-69; mem, Am Asn Dent Schs, 69-70; supvr audiovisual sect, Fac Dent, Univ Alta, 70-71. *Mem:* AAAS; Am Dent Asn; Can Dent Asn. *Res:* Phosphate-bonded investments for regular gold castings; three dimensional recordings of mandibular movement; aduiovisual education; failures of cast restorations long term clinical study; myofacial pain syndrome clinical study. *Mailing Add:* 702 Mission Med Ctr 2303 Fourth St SW Calgary AB T2S 2S7 Can

JONES, MERRELL ROBERT, b Salt Lake City, Utah, June 27, 38; m 59; c 6. COMPUTER SCIENCE, PHYSICS INSTRUCTION. *Educ:* Univ Utah, BS, 60, PhD(physics), 70. *Prof Exp:* From asst prof to assoc prof, 66-80, chmn dept eng & phys sci, 73-76, PROF PHYSICS, SOUTHERN UTAH STATE COL, 81-, DIR COMPUT CTR, 74- *Mem:* Am Phys Soc; Am Asn Physics Teachers; Asn Comput Mach; Digital Equip Corp Users Soc. *Res:* Computer science; computers in undergraduate instruction; methods and curricula in astronomy physics and computer science in elementary and secondary schools; piezoelectricity; point defects in crystals. *Mailing Add:* Dept of Physics Southern Utah State Col Cedar City UT 84720

JONES, MERRIAM ARTHUR, b Hankinson, NDak, Jan 4, 13; m 33; c 1. ORGANIC CHEMISTRY, AGRICULTURAL CHEMISTRY. *Educ:* Univ NDak, BA, 33; George Washington Univ, PhD(chem), 50. *Prof Exp:* Agr chemist, Mayaguez Exp Sta, USDA, PR, 39-46 & Allergens Div, 46-51; agr chemist, US Agency Int Develop, Guatemala, 51-58, Iraq, 58-59, Haiti, 59-60, Lebanon, 60-62, Iran, 62-63, Turkey, 63-65 & DC, 65-68; from asst prof to assoc prof, 68-73, asst chmn phys sci, Div Natural Sci & Math, 70-79, PROF CHEM, NORTHERN VA COMMUNITY COL, 73- *Mem:* Am Chem Soc; Nat Sci Teachers Asn. *Res:* NOCl reaction with normal pentenes; chemistry of curing processes, other processing; plant constituents; technical assistance; chemical education. *Mailing Add:* 5936 N Third St Arlington VA 22203

JONES, MERRILL C(ALVIN), b Salona, Pa, Jan 4, 25; m 50; c 4. PHYSICS, COMPUTER SCIENCE. *Educ:* Univ NMex, BS, 52, MA, 70. *Prof Exp:* Eng technician, indust apparatus div, Sylvania Elec Prod, Inc, 44-48; electronics technician, 48-52, measurement engr, 52-53, sect supvr metrol, 53-55, sect supvr & mem tech staff, 55-65, mem tech staff, 65-77, DIV SUPVR, SANDIA NAT LABS, 77- *Mem:* Comput Soc; Inst Elec & Electronics Engrs. *Res:* Metrology; standards and precision measurement of electrical and physical quantities; application of computers to scientific and administrative problems of metrology; standards program management. *Mailing Add:* Sandia Nat Labs 2553 Albuquerque NM 87185

JONES, MICHAEL BAXTER, b Seattle, Wash, Oct 19, 44; m 66; c 2. ECONOMIC GEOLOGY. *Educ:* Univ Wash, BS, 66, MS, 69; Ore State Univ, PhD(geol), 75. *Prof Exp:* Geologist, Kennecott Explor Inc, Kennecott Copper Corp, 73-77; GEOLOGIST, FREEPORT EXPLOR CO, 77- *Mem:* Sigma Xi; Geol Soc Am; Asn Explor Geophysicists. *Res:* Structural, lithological, mineralogical and chemical manifestations of base and precious metal ore deposits. *Mailing Add:* Freeport Explor Co PO Box 1911 Reno NV 89505

JONES, MILLARD LAWRENCE, JR, b Aug 14, 33; m 59; c 2. CHEMICAL ENGINEERING. *Educ:* Univ Utah, BS, 55; Univ Mich, Ann Arbor, MS, 58, PhD(chem eng), 61. *Prof Exp:* Res engr, Dow Chem Corp, 61-66; asst prof chem eng, 66-71, ASSOC PROF CHEM ENG, UNIV TOLEDO, 71- *Concurrent Pos:* Consult, Owens-Ill Corp, 67-71. *Mem:* Am Inst Chem Engrs. *Res:* Process dynamics and controls. *Mailing Add:* 2318 Densmore Toledo OH 43606

JONES, MILTON BENNION, b Cedar City, Utah, Jan 15, 26; m 51; c 6. SOIL FERTILITY. *Educ:* Utah State Univ, BS, 52; Ohio State Univ, PhD(soil fertil), 55. *Prof Exp:* Assoc agronomist, Sta, 55-69, AGRONOMIST, HOPLAND FIELD STA & LECTR, UNIV CALIF, 69- *Concurrent Pos:* Res mineral nutrit of trop legumes, IRI Res Inst, Brazil, 63-65; teacher forage crops & range mgt, Univ Calif, Davis, 67-; res sulfur nutrit forage crops, CSIRO, Canberra, Australia, 74. *Mem:* Am Soc Agron; Am Soc Range Mgt. *Res:* Range plant nutrition; range soils; range fertilization. *Mailing Add:* 4070 University Rd Univ of Calif Hopland CA 95449

JONES, MORRIS THOMPSON, b St Louis, Mo, Dec 17, 16; m 48; c 2. BACTERIOLOGY. *Educ:* Univ Ill, AB, 40, MS, 41, PhD(bact), 44. *Prof Exp:* Appl res bacteriologist, Swift & Co, 44; res bacteriologist & food technologist, Automatic Canteen Co Am, 46-50; phys sci res adminr, Off Naval Res, 50-56; asst to chief extramural progs, Nat Inst Allergy & Infectious Dis, 56-57, asst chief, Nat Inst Arthritis & Metab Dis, 57-60, dep chief training br, 60-64, asst head spec foreign currency prog, Off Int Res, NIH, 64-68, CHIEF SPEC FOREIGN CURRENCY PROG, FOGARTY INT CTR, NIH, 68- *Mem:* AAAS; Am Soc Microbiol; Am Chem Soc; Am Pub Health Asn. *Res:* High frequency cooking of foods; bacteriology of meat food products; solubility of dehydrated cream; incidence and distribution of Clostridum botulinium in soils of Illinois; sanitation and corrosion of stainless steels. *Mailing Add:* 6622 Fernwood Ct Bethesda Washington DC 20014

JONES, MORTON EDWARD, b Alhambra, Calif, Apr 12, 28; m 51; c 4. PHYSICAL CHEMISTRY. *Educ:* Univ Calif, BS, 49; Calif Inst Technol, PhD(chem), 53. *Prof Exp:* Mem tech staff, 53-61, sr scientist, Semiconductor Device Tech Sect, Device Res Dept, 61-65, dir, Mat Sci Res Lab, 65-71, dir, Phys Sci Res Lab, 71-79, DIR, RESOURCE DEVELOP, TEX INSTRUMENTS, INC, 79- *Mailing Add:* Phys Sci Res Lab Tex Instrum Inc PO Box 225936 MS 145 Dallas TX 75265

JONES, NOEL DUANE, b Omaha, Nebr, Aug 4, 37; m 63; c 2. CRYSTALLOGRAPHY. *Educ:* Rensselaer Polytech Inst, BS, 59; Calif Inst Technol, PhD(chem), 64. *Prof Exp:* NIH fel, Univ Berne, 64-66; RES SCIENTIST, PHYS CHEM RES DIV, ELI LILLY & CO, 67- *Mem:* Am Chem Soc; Am Crystallog Asn. *Res:* Crystals and molecular structure of biologically active compounds. *Mailing Add:* Phys Chem Res Div Eli Lilly & Co Indianapolis IN 46206

JONES, NOLAN T(HOMAS), b Manhattan, Kans, May 5, 27; m 52; c 3. ELECTRICAL ENGINEERING. *Educ:* Univ Nebr, BSc, 51; Mass Inst Technol, SM, 54. *Prof Exp:* Res engr electronic eng, Lincoln Lab, Mass Inst Technol, 51-58; proj leader, 64-66, SUB-DEPT HEAD, MITRE CORP, BEDFORD, 59- *Mem:* Inst Elec & Electronics Engrs. *Res:* Applications of digital computers for real-time automatic control. *Mailing Add:* 22 Squire Rd Winchester MA 01890

JONES, OLIVER PERRY, b West Chester, Pa, May 13, 06; m 35; c 4. ANATOMY. *Educ:* Temple Univ, AB, 29; Univ Minn, PhD(anat), 35; Univ Buffalo, MD, 56. *Prof Exp:* Asst zool, Ind Univ, 29-31; asst anat, Univ Minn, 34-35, instr, 35-37; from asst prof to prof, 37-71, head dept, 43-71, asst dean, 46-54, distinguished prof, 71-76, EMER DISTINGUISHED PROF, SCH MED, STATE UNIV NY BUFFALO, 76- *Concurrent Pos:* Historian, Int Soc Hemat, 62-80; distinguished lectr, Sch Med, Tulane Univ, 64; hon mem med staff, Sister of Charity Hosp. *Mem:* Histochem Soc; Electron Micros Soc Am; Am Asn Anatomists; Nat Soc Med Res; Am Soc Hemat. *Res:* Hematology; phase microscopy; electron microscopy and cytochemistry of blood cells under normal and pathologic conditions; medical history of early 19th century. *Mailing Add:* 23 Berkley Pl Buffalo NY 14209

JONES, OLIVER WILLIAM, b Ft Smith, Ark, Feb 7, 32; m 55; c 4. MEDICINE, BIOCHEMISTRY. *Educ:* Northeastern State Col, Okla, BS, 54; Univ Okla, MD, 57. *Prof Exp:* From intern to jr resident med, Med Ctr, Duke Univ, 57-59, sr resident, 60-61; res assoc biochem genetics, Nat Heart Inst, 61-63; asst prof med, Duke Univ, 65-66, asst prof biochem, 66-67, co-dir, Res Training Prog, Med Ctr, 66-68, assoc prof med & biochem, 67-68; assoc prof, 68-73, PROF MED & PEDIAT, SCH MED, UNIV CALIF, SAN DIEGO, 73-, DIR DIV MED GENETICS, 68- *Concurrent Pos:* Arthritis & Rheumatism Asn fel, Duke Univ, 59-60; fel biochem, Stanford Univ, 63-65;

NIH career develop award, 63-68; Nat Inst Arthritis & Metab Dis res grant, 65-68; Damon Runyon Found res grant, 68-71; Am Cancer Soc res grant, 69-73; NIH grants, 69-75. *Mem:* AAAS; Am Soc Human Genetics; Am Soc Cell Biol; Am Soc Biol Chemists; Soc Pediat Res. *Res:* Genetic counseling; regulation of pyrimidine biosynthesis; cytogenetics. *Mailing Add:* Dept of Med M-013 Univ of Calif at San Diego La Jolla CA 92037

JONES, ORVAL ELMER, b Ft Morgan, Colo, Apr 9, 34; m 54; c 3. APPLIED MECHANICS. *Educ:* Colo State Univ, BS, 56; Calif Inst Technol, MS, 57, PhD(mech eng), 61. *Prof Exp:* Tech staff mem, Res & Develop Labs, Hughes Aircraft Co, Calif, 56-57; res engr, Hydromech Lab, Calif Inst Technol, 60-61; staff mem, Sandia Corp, 61-64, div supvr dynamic stress res, 64-68, mgr phys res dept, 68-71, dir solid state sci res, 71-74, dir nuclear security systs, 74-77, dir nuclear waste and environ programs, 77-78, DIR ENG SCI, SANDIA NAT LABS, 78- *Concurrent Pos:* NSF fel, 59-60; vis lectr, Univ NMex, 64 & 68. *Mem:* AAAS; Am Soc Mech Eng; Am Phys Soc. *Res:* electrical and mechanical response of piezoelectrics, ferroelectrics and semiconductors to shock loading; nuclear security safeguards systems for transportation and storage of nuclear materials and weapons; underground repository and technology development for nuclear waste isolation; engineering applications of structural dynamics, transport phenomena, and rock mechanics. *Mailing Add:* Eng Sci Dir 5500 Sandia Nat Labs Kirtland AFB E Albuquerque NM 87115

JONES, OTHA CLYDE, b Emporia, Kans, May 16, 08; m 31. CHEMICAL ENGINEERING, PHYSICAL CHEMISTRY. *Educ:* Univ Utah, BS, 30, MS, 31. *Prof Exp:* Res engr, Monsanto Co, 31-37, group leader, 38-50, asst dir res, 50-64, mgr process tech monomers, 64-70, sr planning analyst, 70-73; mech engr, Arthur G McKee, Inc, 75-77; process engr, Fishstone, Inc, 78-79; CONSULT ENG CONTRACTOR, 79- *Mem:* Am Chem Soc Am; Inst Chem Engrs. *Res:* Production of phosphorus, inorganic phosphates, fluosilicates, phosphorus sulfides, vinyl chloride, polyethylene, and other polymers. *Mailing Add:* 12358 Ironstone Rd Des Peres MO 63131

JONES, OWEN LLOYD, b Hackensack, NJ, July 31, 35; m; c 6. PHYSICAL CHEMISTRY, RADIOCHEMISTRY. *Educ:* Drew Univ, AB, 57; WVa Univ, MS, 60, PhD(phys chem), 67. *Prof Exp:* Instr chem, WVa Univ, 60-65; asst prof, 65-73, ASSOC PROF CHEM, US NAVAL ACAD, 73- *Mem:* Am Chem Soc; Sigma Xi. *Res:* Solution kinetics; exchange rate studies using isotopic tracer techniques. *Mailing Add:* Dept of Chem US Naval Acad Annapolis MD 21402

JONES, P(HILIP) H(ARRHY), b Tredegar, Eng, Jan 30, 31; Can citizen; m 54; c 4. SANITARY ENGINEERING. *Educ:* Univ Toronto, BASc, 58, Univ Northwestern, MS, 63, PhD(sanit eng), 65. *Prof Exp:* Asst munic eng, Borough Engr's Off, Surbiton, Eng, 50-51; asst engr to Sir William Halcrow, Volta River Proj, Ghana, 51-54; proj engr, Town Planning Consult, Toronto, Ont, 54-58; prin munic engr, Franklin McArthur Assocs, 58-62; from asst prof to assoc prof, 64-70, sch hyg, 65-66, chmn inst environ studies, 71-74, dir environ educ, 74-80, PROF CIVIL ENG, UNIV TORONTO, 70-, DIR INT PROG OFF, 81- *Mem:* Am Soc Civil Engrs; Am Water Works Asn; Eng Inst Can. *Res:* Microbiology of waste treatment, stream, river and lake pollution; ecology of complex living systems and their relationship to man's environment; management of toxic and hazardous wastes. *Mailing Add:* Inst of Environ Studies Univ of Toronto Toronto ON M5S 1A1 Can

JONES, PATRICK RAY, b Austin, Tex, Oct 22, 43; m 68; c 2. PHYSICAL CHEMISTRY. *Educ:* Univ Tex, Austin, BA & BS, 66; Stanford Univ, PhD(chem), 71. *Prof Exp:* Res fel chem, Nat Acad Sci, 71-73; res fel chem, Calif Inst Technol, 73-74; MEM FAC CHEM, UNIV PAC, 74- *Concurrent Pos:* Vis scholar chem, Stanford Univ, 79-80. *Mem:* Am Chem Soc. *Res:* Matrix isolation studies of oxygen, fluorine and chlorine atom reactions; electron-impact excitation of gases; combined liquid chromatography and mass-spectrometry; physical chemistry of organometallics. *Mailing Add:* Chem Dept Univ Pac Stockton CA 95211

JONES, PAUL HASTINGS, b Fostoria, Mich, Aug 31, 18; m 41; c 4. GEOLOGY. *Educ:* Mich State Col, BS, 41; La State Univ, MS, 51, PhD, 68. *Prof Exp:* Geophysicist, Halliburton Oil Well Cementing Co, Tex, 41-42; from geologist to geologist in charge groundwater invests, US Geol Surv, La, 42-52, dist geologist in charge, Pa, 52-55, tech adv, Groundwater Geol Surv, Int Co-op Admin, India, 55-57, dist geologist, Tenn, 58-59, res proj chief, Ground Water Br, Nat Reactor Testing Sta, Idaho, 59-62, chief radiohydrol sect, Water Resources Div, DC, 62-64, res hydrologist, Gulf Coastal Plain, 65-74; mem fac, Dept Geol, La State Univ, 74-77; CONSULT, 77- *Concurrent Pos:* Consult, World Bank, 66 & UN, 70; mem Nat Acad Sci adv team, India, 71. *Mem:* Soc Econ Geol; fel Geol Soc Am; Am Asn Petrol Geol; Soc Petrol Eng; Am Soc Test & Mat. *Res:* Quantitative interpretation of borehole geophysical logs; hydrogeology of deep sedimentary basins; role of geopressure in the fluid hydrocarbon regime; hydrology of waste disposal; enhanced production of petroleum and natural gas; geothermal resources of Northern Gulf of Mexico Basin. *Mailing Add:* 3256 McConnell Dr Baton Rouge LA 70809

JONES, PAUL KENNETH, b Des Moines, Iowa, Jan 5, 43; m 71. BIOSTATISTICS. *Educ:* Grinnell Col, BA, 64; Univ Iowa, MS, 69, PhD(statist), 72. *Prof Exp:* Teacher math, Troy Mills, Iowa, 66-67; res asst statist, Am Col Testing, 68-72; sr instr, 72-73, asst prof, 73-80, ASSOC PROF BIOMET, CASE WESTERN RESERVE UNIV, 80- *Mem:* Am Statist Asn; Biomet Soc. *Res:* Quantitative differentiation of normal and diseased states in blood clotting; log linear analysis of factors related to perinatal mortality. *Mailing Add:* Dept of Biomet Case Western Reserve Univ Hosps Cleveland OH 44106

JONES, PAUL RAYMOND, b Chicago, Ill, July 19, 30; m 58; c 3. ORGANIC CHEMISTRY. *Educ:* Albion Col, BA, 52; Univ Ill, PhD, 56. *Prof Exp:* From asst prof to assoc prof, 56-65, PROF CHEM, UNIV NH, 65- *Concurrent Pos:* NSF sci fac fel, Max-Planck Inst, Gottingen, 64-65; Fulbright res fel, Chem Inst, Univ Freiburg, Ger, 73. *Mem:* Am Chem Soc. *Res:* Macrocycles; ring-chain tautomerism. *Mailing Add:* Dept Chem Univ NH Durham NH 03824

JONES, PAUL RONALD, b York, Pa, Dec 19, 40; m 67; c 2. ORGANOMETALLIC CHEMISTRY. Educ: Pa State Univ, BS, 62; Purdue Univ, PhD(chem), 66. Prof Exp: Res assoc chem, Univ Wis-Madison, 66-67; asst prof, 68-73, assoc prof, 73-79, PROF CHEM, NTEX STATE UNIV, 79- Mem: Am Chem Soc. Res: Organometallic chemistry, especially involving synthesis structure and reactions of group IV compounds; bonding in organometallic compounds; stereochemistry and mechanism of the reactions of subvalent organosilicon in termediates. Mailing Add: Dept of Chem N Tex State Univ Denton TX 76203

JONES, PETER DAVID, b Palmerston North, NZ, Apr 27, 40; m 67; c 3. BIOCHEMISTRY, NUTRITION. Educ: Victoria Univ Wellington, BS, 61, MS, 63; Duke Univ, PhD(biochem), 68. Prof Exp: Res assoc, Univ Ariz, 68-69; lectr, Victoria Univ Wellington, 69-72; asst prof, 72-75, ASSOC PROF BIOCHEM, UNIV TENN CTR HEALTH SCI, 75-, ASST DEAN ACAD AFFAIRS, COL MED, 79- Mem: AAAS; Sigma Xi; Nutrit Today Soc. Res: Oxidative desaturation of long chain fatty acids; structure and function of the electron transport chains of the endoplasmic reticulum; nutritional role of fatty acids and lipids. Mailing Add: Dept of Biochem Univ of Tenn Ctr for Health Sci Memphis TN 38163

JONES, PETER FRANK, b Brooklyn, NY, Mar 15, 37; m 78; c 5. PHYSICAL CHEMISTRY, ANALYTICAL CHEMISTRY. Educ: Univ Kans, BA, 60; Univ Chicago, MS, 61; Univ Calif, Los Angeles, PhD(high pressure spectros), 67. Prof Exp: Mem tech staff, 66-73, head, Forensic Sci Sect, 73-74, HEAD, ANAL SCI DEPT, AEROSPACE CORP, 74- Mem: Am Chem Soc; AAAS. Res: Nonradiative transitions in molecules; radiation effects on polymers; analytical applications of photoluminescence. Mailing Add: Aerospace Corp PO Box 92957 Los Angeles CA 90009

JONES, PETER HADLEY, b Cleveland, Ohio, Aug 14, 34; m 57; c 3. ORGANIC CHEMISTRY, CARDIOVASCULAR DISEASES. Educ: Harvard Univ, AB, 56; Univ Calif, Los Angeles, PhD(org chem), 60. Prof Exp: Sr res chemist, Abbott Labs, 60-70, assoc res fel, 70-71, mgr med chem, 71-75, head cardiovasc res, 75-79; vpres & dir res, Interx Corp, 79-80; SECT HEAD GASTROINTESTINAL DIS, SEARLE LABS, G D SEARLE & CO, 80- Concurrent Pos: Instr, Dept Biochem, Med Sch, Northwestern Univ, 69-73. Mem: Am Chem Soc; AAAS. Res: Reactions of diphenylcarbenes; chemistry of macrolide antibiotics; chemistry of hypertensive agents; development of new drugs for hypertension angina; chemical drug delivery systems; gastrointestinal drugs. Mailing Add: Dept of Med Chem Searle Labs Box 5110 Chicago IL 60680

JONES, PHILIP ARTHUR, b Prince George, BC, Mar 1, 24. ENTOMOLOGY. Educ: Univ BC, BSA, 49; Univ Wis-Madison, MS, 56, PhD(entom), 63. Prof Exp: Asst forest biologist can serv, Can Dept Agr, 49-52; res asst forest entom, Univ Wis, 52-58; res officer, Forest Biol Div, Can Dept Agr, 58-60; from proj asst to proj assoc biol control, Univ Wis, 60-64; from asst prof to assoc prof entom, SDak State Univ, 65-74; tech dir, Agr Chem Div, FMC of Can Ltd, 74-77; ENVIRON SCIENTIST, ENVIRON CAN, 77- Concurrent Pos: Mem tech comt, Can Agr Chem Asn, 74-77. Mem: Entom Soc Am; Am Registry Prof Entomologists. Res: environmental assessment of toxic chemicals. Mailing Add: Box 6221 Station J Ottawa ON K2A 1T3 Can

JONES, PHILLIP SANFORD, b Elyria, Ohio, Feb 26, 12; m 35; c 4. MATHEMATICS. Educ: Univ Mich, AB, 33, AM, 35, PhD(math), 48. Hon Degrees: LHD, Northern Mich Univ, 72. Prof Exp: Teacher pub sch, Mich, 34-37; teacher math, Edison Inst Technol, 37-43, Univ Mich, 43-44 & Ohio State Univ, 44-45; from instr to assoc prof, 47-58, PROF MATH, UNIV MICH, ANN ARBOR, 58- Concurrent Pos: Vis prof, Ain Shams Univ, Cairo, Egypt, 78. Mem: Nat Coun Teachers Math (pres, 60-62); Am Math Soc; Hist Sci Soc; Math Asn Am. Res: History and teaching of mathematics; development of the mathematical theory of linear perspective; development of number systems. Mailing Add: Dept of Math Univ of Mich Ann Arbor MI 48109

JONES, PHILLIPS RUSSELL, b Troy, NY, Aug 25, 30; m 52; c 3. PHYSICS. Educ: Univ Mass, BS, 51; Univ Conn, MA, 56, PhD(physics), 59. Prof Exp: Teacher, Mass Pub Sch, 52; asst physics, Univ Conn, 54-58; from asst prof to assoc prof, 58-68, PROF PHYSICS, UNIV MASS, AMHERST, 68- Mem: Am Phys Soc. Res: Experimental atomic physics. Mailing Add: Dept of Physics Univ of Mass Amherst MA 01002

JONES, PHYLLIS EDITH, b Barrie, Ont, Sept 16, 24. NURSING. Educ: Univ Toronto, BScN, 50, MSc, 69. Prof Exp: Asst prof, 63-70, assoc prof, 70-72, PROF NURSING, UNIV TORONTO, 72-, DEAN NURSING, 79- Mem: Can Pub Health Asn; Am Pub Health Asn. Res: Innovations in community health nursing, in collaboration with physician services. Mailing Add: 50 St George St Toronto ON M5S 1A1 Can

JONES, R E DOUGLAS, b Kansas City, Mo, Nov 28, 33; m 54; c 4. MATHEMATICS. Educ: Univ Okla, BA, 55, MA, 57; Iowa State Univ, PhD(math), 62. Prof Exp: Aerophys engr, Convair-Ft Worth, 56-58; instr math, Iowa State Univ, 58-62; asst prof, Wichita State Univ, 62-65; assoc prof, Univ Mo-Rolla, 65-71; PROF MATH, McKENDREE COL, 71- Concurrent Pos: Consult, Boeing Co, Kans, 62-64. Mem: Am Math Soc; Math Asn Am. Res: Topologies generated by metric densities; opaque sets. Mailing Add: Div of Sci & Math McKendree Col Lebanon IL 62254

JONES, R H B, b Victoria, BC, Oct 24, 98; nat US; m 31; c 2. ECONOMIC GEOLOGY. Educ: Univ BC, BASc, 23; Univ Wis, PhD(geol), 27. Prof Exp: From instr to asst prof geol, State Col Wash, 26-29; asst prof, Ind State Teachers Col, 29-30; from geologist to chief geologist, Oliver Iron Mining Div, US Steel Corp, 30-53, consult geologist, 53-54, staff geologist, Columbia-Geneva Steel Div, 54-62; consult geologist, 62-80; RETIRED. Mem: Fel Geol Soc Am; Soc Econ Geol; Am Inst Mining, Metall & Petrol Eng; Can Inst Mining & Metall. Res: Exploration for and development of raw materials for steel industry, North America, South America and Africa. Mailing Add: 3023 Hillside Dr Burlingame CA 94010

JONES, R(ICHARD) JAMES, b Detroit, Mich, Sept 6, 21. ELECTRICAL ENGINEERING, MECHANICAL ENGINEERING. Educ: Mich Col Mining, BS, 44 & 54, EE, 50, MS, 54. Prof Exp: Elec equip tester, Allen-Bradley Co, 44; equip design engr, standardization & correlation eng, Globe-Union, Inc, 44-47; from instr to assoc prof elec eng, 47-76, EMER ASSOC PROF ELEC ENG, MICH TECHNOL UNIV, 76- Mem: Inst Elec & Electronics Engrs. Res: Automatic controls; servomechanisms; electrical illumination; electrical machinery. Mailing Add: 305 W Calverley Ave Houghton MI 49931

JONES, R NORMAN, b Manchester, Eng, Mar 20, 13; nat Can; m 39; c 2. SPECTROCHEMISTRY. Educ: Univ Manchester, BSc, 33, MSc, 34, PhD(chem), 36, DSc(chem), 54. Hon Degrees: DSc, Univ Poznan, 72. Prof Exp: Tutor biochem, Harvard Univ, 39-41; lectr chem, Queen's Univ, Can, 42-43, asst prof, 43-46; from assoc res officer to prin res officer, Nat Res Coun Can, 46-77; PVT CONSULT CHEM SPECTROS, 77- Concurrent Pos: Chmn molecular spectros comn, Int Union Pure & Appl Chem, 67-71, from vpres to pres phys chem div, 71-77, emer pres, 77-; secy task group comput use, Comt Data Sci & Technol, Int Coun Sci Unions, 67-75, mem bur, 70-74, mem exec comt, 75-78, mem adv comt, UNISIST-UNESCO, 74-77; guest prof, Tokyo Inst Technol, Japan, 79-82. Honors & Awards: Herzberg Award, Spec Soc Can; Fisher Award, Chem Soc Can. Mem: Am Chem Soc; Royal Soc Can; Chem Inst Can; Royal Soc Chem; Int Union Pure & Appl Chem. Res: Molecular spectroscopy; use of ultraviolet, infrared and Raman spectroscopy for the elucidation of molecular structure, with special reference to steroids and other natural products; use of computers for data logging and as aids in evaluation, storage and retrieval of spectral data; molecular structure determination and analysis by vibrational spectroscopy. Mailing Add: Suite 601 71 Somerset St W Ottawa ON K2P 2G2 Can

JONES, RALPH, JR, b Parkersburg, WVa, Mar 16, 18; m 44; c 2. INTERNAL MEDICINE. Educ: WVa Univ, AB, 39; Univ Pa, MD, 43; Am Bd Internal Med, dipl, 58. Prof Exp: Intern, Univ Hosp, Univ Pa, 43-44; res assoc med, Univ Chicago, 44-46, res assoc urol & biochem, 46-47; resident, Univ Hosp, Univ Pa, 47-49, instr med, Univ, 49-50, assoc, 50-51, asst prof clin med, 51-54, assoc prof med, 55, dir, C Willard Robinson Found, 50-54; prof med & chmn dept, Sch Med, Univ Miami, 55-63; chief cancer res internist, Roswell Park Mem Inst, NY, 65-69; PROF BIOCHEM PHARM, STATE UNIV NY BUFFALO & CHIEF INTERNIST, RANSOMVILLE MED GROUP, 69- Concurrent Pos: Nat Res Coun fel, Univ Hosp, Univ Pa, 48-49, Markle scholar med sci, 49-54; consult res & develop bd, Surgeon Gen, US Army, 51-57; consult, Surgeon Gen, USPHS, 55- Mem: AAAS; Am Soc Pharmacol & Exp Therapeut; Am Asn Cancer Res; AMA; fel Am Col Physicians. Res: Cancer chemotherapy; human pharmacology. Mailing Add: 549 Fourth St Niagara Falls NY 14301

JONES, RALPH WILLIAM, b Coin, Iowa, Aug 29, 21; m 45; c 3. PHARMACEUTICAL CHEMISTRY. Educ: St Louis Col Pharm, BS, 48; Purdue Univ, MS, 51. Prof Exp: Res pharmacist, 51-57, group leader sterile prod res, 57-61, sect head liquid-ointment prod res, 61-64, secy new prod comt, 63-64, dept mgr allied prod res, 64-66 & radiopharmaceutical prod res & develop, 66-67, DEPT MGR, LIQUID PRODS RES & DEVELOP, ABBOTT LABS, 67- Mem: Am Pharmaceut Asn; Am Chem Soc. Res: Basic and applied research on new pharmaceutical dosage forms and products; pharmacy, chemistry and allied medical sciences. Mailing Add: Dept 497 Abbott Labs North Chicago IL 60064

JONES, RANDALL JEFFERIES, b Gould, Okla, Oct 16, 15; m 37; c 2. SOIL CHEMISTRY. Educ: Okla State Univ, BS, 36; Univ Wis, MS, 37, PhD(soils), 39. Prof Exp: From asst to assoc prof soils, Exp Sta, Auburn Univ, 39-44; chief, Soils & Fertilizer Res Sect, Agr Rels Div, Tenn Valley Authority, 44-49; assoc dir, Exp Sta, Miss State Col, 49-50; DEAN INSTR AGR, OKLA STATE UNIV, 50- Mem: Am Soc Agron; Soil Sci Soc Am. Res: Methods for determination of phosphorus and potassium in soils and plants; chemistry of potash fixation in soils; utilization of nitrogen under various soil conditions; crop response to phosphate fertilizers. Mailing Add: Col of Agr Okla State Univ Stillwater OK 74074

JONES, RAYMOND F, plant physiology, see previous edition

JONES, REBECCA ANNE, b Menominee, Mich, Jan 23, 51. WATER QUALITY CONTROL, AQUATIC CHEMISTRY. Educ: Southern Methodist Univ, BS, 73; Univ Tex, Dallas, MS, 75, PhD(environ sci), 78. Prof Exp: Res asst environ sci, Colo State Univ, 78-80. Concurrent Pos: Proj assoc, EnviroQual Consults & Labs, 76- Mem: Am Soc Testing & Mat; Am Water Works Asn; Am Soc Civil Engrs; Am Chem Soc; Am Soc Limnol & Oceanog. Res: Environmental chemistry especially fate modeling, water quality control. Mailing Add: 4027 Medford Dr 101 Annandale VA 22003

JONES, REESE TASKER, b Philadelphia, Pa, June 7, 32; m 56; c 3. PSYCHIATRY. Educ: Univ Mich, BS, 54, MD, 58. Prof Exp: Res psychiat, Langley Porter Neuropsychiat Inst, 62-67; asst prof, 67-73, assoc prof res, Med Ctr, 73-76, PROF PSYCHIAT, SCH MED, UNIV CALIF, SAN FRANCISCO, 76- Concurrent Pos: Staff psychiatrist, Langley Porter Neuropsychiat Inst, 67-; Nat Inst Ment Health res career develop award, 67- Mem: Am Psychiat Asn; Psychiat Res Soc; Am Col Neuropsychopharmacol. Res: Objective indices of psychopathology; human neurophysiology; psychopharmacology. Mailing Add: Dept of Psychiat Univ of Calif Sch of Med San Francisco CA 94143

JONES, RENA TALLEY, b Chipley, Ga, Aug 3, 37. MICROBIOLOGY. Educ: Morris Brown Col, BA, 60; Atlanta Univ, MS, 67; Wayne State Univ, PhD(microbiol), 74. Prof Exp: Instr biol, Morris Brown Col, Ga, 60-66; NSF grant, Atlanta Univ, 66; INSTR BIOL, CHMN DEPT & PROJ DIR HEALTH CAREERS PROG, SPELMAN COL, 73- Mem: Am Soc Microbiol; AAAS; Sigma Xi. Res: Staphylococcal and slime molds; enzymes; immunochemistry. Mailing Add: Dept of Biol Spelman Col 350 Spelman Lane SW Atlanta GA 30314

JONES, REX H, b Mapleton, Iowa, Dec 22, 32; m 55; c 3. VETERINARY MEDICINE. *Educ:* Iowa State Univ, DVM, 56. *Prof Exp:* Practitioner, Moorhead Vet Clinic, 56-71, Twin Valley Vet Clinic, 71-77; mem tech serv, Syntex Agribusiness, 77-80; clin researcher, 80-81, HEAD VET VACCINE RES, SYNTEX RES, 81- *Mem:* Am Vet Med Asn; Am Bovine Practitioners Asn; Am Swine Practitioners Asn. *Mailing Add:* Syntex Res PO Box 653 Des Moines IA 50303

JONES, RICHARD BRADLEY, b Norristown, Pa, June 21, 47. NUCLEAR SCIENCE, APPLIED MATHEMATICS. *Educ:* Va Polytech Inst & State Univ, BS, 70, MS, 71, PhD(nuclear eng), 74. *Prof Exp:* Lectr nuclear eng, Univ Calif, Santa Barbara, 74-75; fel appl math, Univ Ill, 75-77; mem tech staff, nuclear risk anal, Sandia Lab, 77-78; asst prof comput sci, State Univ NY, Plattsburgh, 78-81; CONSULT, 81- *Concurrent Pos:* Consult, W Alton Jones Cell Sci Ctr, 78, Chem-Nuclear Syst Inc, 78; vis prof appl math, Univ Florence, Italy, 81. *Mem:* Am Nuclear Soc; Am Soc Eng Educ; Soc Indust & Appl Math; AAAS. *Res:* Applied mathematics; mathematical modeling of cell regeneration; computer animation effects in education; systems design. *Mailing Add:* W Alten Jones Cell Sci Ctr Old Barn Rd Lake Placid NY 12946

JONES, RICHARD CONRAD, b Lebanon, NH, Feb 25, 16; m 41; c 1. BOTANY. *Educ:* Dartmouth Col, AB, 38; State Col Wash, PhD(bot), 44. *Prof Exp:* Asst, Agr Exp Sta, Univ NH, 44-45, instr bot, 45-46, asst, 46-48; prof biol, State Univ NY Col New Paltz, 48-66, actg dean, 66-67, dean col, 67-68, vpres acad affairs, 68; assoc univ dean, State Univ NY Albany, 68; pres, State Univ NY Col Cortland, 68-78; EXEC DIR, MONTSHIRE MUS SCI, 79- *Concurrent Pos:* With NSF Inst Bot, Cornell Univ, 57 & NSF Genetics, Cold Springs Harbor, 59; res fel, State Univ NY Col New Paltz, 58 & 60. *Mem:* AAAS; Bot Soc Am; Mycol Soc Am. *Res:* Genetics; alteration of generations in biological systems. *Mailing Add:* Box 223 Etna NH 03750

JONES, RICHARD ELMORE, b Rochester, NY, July 16, 44; m 69; c 1. PHYSICAL PHARMACY. *Educ:* Dartmouth Col, AB, 65; Stanford Univ, PhD(phys chem), 70. *Prof Exp:* Sr progammer & analyst, Syntex Corp, 69-71; staff researcher, 71-77, sr staff researcher, 77-78, DEPT HEAD, INST PHARMACEUT SCI, SYNTEX RES, 78- *Concurrent Pos:* Adj prof, Univ Pac Sch Pharm, 74-75, 80- *Mem:* Am Chem Soc; Am Pharmaceut Asn; Acad Pharmaceut Sci. *Res:* Percutaneous absorption; experimental design in formulation problems; pharmaceutical aerosols. *Mailing Add:* Syntex Res 3401 Hillview Ave Palo Alto CA 94304

JONES, RICHARD EVAN, b Sacramento, Calif, May 13, 40; m 80; c 4. COMPARATIVE ENDOCRINOLOGY, REPRODUCTIVE BIOLOGY. *Educ:* Univ Calif, Berkeley, BA, 61, MA, 64, PhD(zool), 68. *Prof Exp:* Asst prof behav sci, Hershey Med Ctr, Pa State Univ, 68-69; from asst prof to assoc prof, 69-80, PROF BIOL, UNIV COLO, BOULDER, 80- *Concurrent Pos:* Res career develop award, NIH, 74-79. *Res:* Control of ovarian follicular growth; reptilian reproduction; control of uterine contraction. *Mailing Add:* Lab of Comp Reproduction Univ of Colo Boulder CO 80309

JONES, RICHARD EVAN, JR, b Oak Park, Ill, Aug 3, 40; m 64; c 1. PHYSICAL CHEMISTRY, INORGANIC CHEMISTRY. *Educ:* Monmouth Col, BA, 62; Univ Hawaii, PhD(chem), 70. *Prof Exp:* Lab asst qual control, Ralph Wells & Co, 61-62; res scientist, Continental Can Co, 62-64; lab mgr plastics, Gat Ke Corp, 64-66; NDEA Title IV fel, 67; assoc prof, 70-80, PROF CHEM, LEWIS & CLARK COMMUNITY COL, 80- *Mem:* Am Chem Soc; AAAS; Nat Sci Teachers Asn. *Res:* Aqueous-nonaqueous solvent extraction of metals; better methods for presentation of chemistry in lower division courses. *Mailing Add:* Div of Health & Life Sci Lewis & Clark Community Col Godfrey IL 62035

JONES, RICHARD HAMILTON, b Greenfield, Mass, Feb 4, 28; m 52. POLYMER CHEMISTRY. *Educ:* Mass Inst Technol, SB, 48; Harvard Univ, AM, 51, PhD(chem), 52. *Prof Exp:* Res fel chem, Harvard Univ, 52-53; from res chemist to sr res chemist, 53-68, res assoc, Plastics Dept, 68-80, RES ASSOC, POLYMER PROD DEPT, E I DU PONT DE NEMOURS & CO, INC, 80- *Mem:* Am Chem Soc. *Res:* Polymerization kinetics; reaction mechanisms; high polymer chemistry. *Mailing Add:* E I du Pont de Nemours & Co Inc 1007 Market St Newark DE 19711

JONES, RICHARD HENRY, b Starkville, Miss, Jan 21, 39. SANITARY ENGINEERING. *Educ:* Miss State Univ, BS, 61; Univ Fla, MS, 63, PhD(sanit eng), 66. *Prof Exp:* Sanit engr, Environ Eng, Inc, 67-68, pres, 68, vpres, 68-76; PRES, JONES, EDMUNDS & ASSOCS, 76- *Mem:* Water Pollution Control Asn. *Res:* Waste treatment processes for industrial and domestic wastewater; wastewater reuse for domestic consumption; ocean disposal and diffusion of sewage and industrial waste. *Mailing Add:* Jones Edmunds & Assocs 1511 NW Sixth St Gainesville FL 32601

JONES, RICHARD HUNN, b Ridley Township, Pa, Oct 31, 34; m 81; c 2. BIOSTATISTICS, COMPUTER SCIENCE. *Educ:* Pa State Univ, BS, 56, MS, 57; Brown Univ, PhD(appl math), 61. *Prof Exp:* NSF fel, Univ Stockholm, 61-62; from asst prof to assoc prof statist, Johns Hopkins Univ, 62-68; prof info & comput sci, Univ Hawaii, 68-75, chmn dept, 70-73; PROF BIOMET & DIR SCI COMPUT CTR, UNIV COLO MED CTR, DENVER, 75- *Concurrent Pos:* Consult, Swed Meteorol & Hydrol Inst, 62, RCA Serv Co, Fla, 62-66 & Tripler Army Hosp, Hawaii, 69-73. *Mem:* Biomet Soc; Am Statist Asn; Bernoulli Soc Math Statist & Probability. *Res:* Time series analysis; stochastic processes; statistical data analysis. *Mailing Add:* Dept Biomet Box B-119 Sch Med Univ Colo Denver CO 80262

JONES, RICHARD LAMAR, b Charleston, Miss, May 31, 39; m 64; c 2. INSECT PHYSIOLOGY, INSECT BEHAVIOR. *Educ:* Miss State Univ, BS, 63, MS, 65; Univ Calif, Riverside, PhD(insect toxicol), 68. *Prof Exp:* Insect physiologist, Southern Grain Insect Res Lab, Agr Res Serv, USDA, 68-77; res assoc, Univ Ga, 69-77; ASSOC PROF INSECT PHYSIOL, DEPT OF ENTOM, FISHERIES & WILDLIFE, UNIV MINN, 77- *Mem:* AAAS; Entom Soc Am; Am Chem Soc. *Res:* Investigation of chemicals associated with insect behavior. *Mailing Add:* Dept of Entom Fisheries & Wildlife Univ of Minn St Paul MN 55108

JONES, RICHARD LEE, b Warren, Ohio, Apr 9, 29; m 55; c 2. MATERIALS SCIENCE ENGINEERING, METALLURGICAL ENGINEERING. *Educ:* Wayne State Univ, BS, 52; Univ Mich, MS, 53, PhD(metall), 59. *Prof Exp:* Res asst, eng res inst, Univ Mich, 53-56; staff scientist, Gen Dynamics/Astronaut, 58-61; head metallics res br, 61-62, chief mat res, 62-65, mgr res & technol, 65-70, mgr struct & mat res & technol, 70-75, MGR, MAT & PROCESS RES & TECHNOL, AIRCRAFT DIV, NORTHROP CORP, 75- *Mem:* Am Soc Metals; Am Inst Mining, Metall & Petrol Engrs; Am Inst Aeronaut & Astronaut; Soc Advan Mat & Process Eng. *Res:* Structures and materials research. *Mailing Add:* Aircraft Div Northrop Corp 1 Northrup Ave Hawthorne CA 90250

JONES, RICHARD LEE, b Mendota, Ill, June 27, 44; m 80; c 1. LUNG PHYSIOLOGY. *Educ:* St Thomas Col, BS, 66; Marquette Univ, MS, 69, PhD(physiol), 70. *Prof Exp:* Lectr, 71-73, asst prof, 73-77, ASSOC PROF PHYSIOL, UNIV ALBERTA, 77- *Concurrent Pos:* Lab dir, Univ Hosp, 73-; sci assoc, Royal Alexandria Hosp, 77- *Mem:* Sigma Xi; Am Physiol Soc; Am Col Chest Physicians; Northwest Soc Clin Res; NY Acad Sci. *Res:* Very high frequency ventilation; regional lung function in asthma; exercise training in patients with cystic fibrosis. *Mailing Add:* 6-104 Clin Sci Bldg Univ Alberta Edmonton AB T6G 2G3 Can

JONES, RICHARD THEODORE, b Portland, Ore, Nov 9, 29; m 53; c 3. MEDICINE, BIOCHEMISTRY. *Educ:* Univ Ore, BS, 53, MS & MD, 56; Calif Inst Technol, PhD(chem), 61. *Prof Exp:* Intern med, Hosp Univ Pa, 56-57; from asst prof to assoc prof exp med & biochem, 61-66, PROF BIOCHEM & CHMN DEPT, MED SCH, UNIV ORE, 66- *Concurrent Pos:* Former mem biochem comt, Nat Bd Med Examrs; med scientist, Training Comt, Nat Inst Gen Med Serv; mem, Biochem Training Comt, NIH, Med Scientist Training Comt, Sickle Cell Ctr Rev Comt & Blood Res Rev Group; actg pres, Univ Ore Health Sci Ctr, 77-78, spec consult to pres, 78-79. *Mem:* Am Soc Hemat; Int Soc Hemat; Am Fedn Clin Res; Am Soc Biol Chemists. *Res:* Medical and biochemical genetics, structure and function of normal and abnormal hemoglobins and other human proteins. *Mailing Add:* Dept of Biochem Univ of Ore Med Sch Portland OR 97201

JONES, RICHARD VICTOR, b Oakland, Calif, June 8, 29; m; c 3. SOLID STATE PHYSICS. *Educ:* Univ Calif, AB, 51, PhD(physics), 56. *Hon Degrees:* MA, Harvard, 61. *Prof Exp:* Sr engr, Shockley Semiconductor Lab, Beckman Instruments, Inc, 55-57; from asst prof to assoc prof appl physics, 57-71, assoc dean div eng & appl physics, 69-71, dean grad sch arts & sci, 71-72, PROF APPL PHYSICS, HARVARD UNIV, 71- *Concurrent Pos:* Guggenheim fel, 60-61; vis MacKay Prof, Univ Calif, Berkeley, 67-68. *Mem:* Am Phys Soc; Inst Elec & Electronics Engrs. *Res:* Optical physics and electromagnetic phenomena; electronic and optical materials; ceramics; theory and application of magnetism and ferroelectricity. *Mailing Add:* Gordon McKay Lab Harvard Univ Cambridge MA 02138

JONES, ROBERT CLARK, b Toledo, Ohio, June 30, 16; m 38, 77. THEORETICAL PHYSICS. *Educ:* Harvard Univ, AB, 38, AM, 39, PhD(physics), 41. *Prof Exp:* Mem tech staff, Bell Tel Labs, 41-44; sr physicist, 44-67, RES FEL PHYSICS, POLAROID CORP, 67- *Honors & Awards:* Lomb Medal, Optical Soc Am, 44, Frederic Ives Medal, 72; Thomas Young Medal & Prize, Brit Inst Physics, 77. *Mem:* Fel Optical Soc Am; fel Acoust Soc Am; fel Soc Photog Sci & Eng (vpres, 59-63); fel Am Acad Arts & Sci. *Res:* Theoretical physics; theoretical optics; detectivity and detective quantum efficiency of radiation detectors; theoretical models of photographic films; theory of absorption of light by developed photographic films. *Mailing Add:* Polaroid Corp Location 750M-4J Cambridge MA 02139

JONES, ROBERT EDWARD, b Yonkers, NY, Jan 14, 23; m 48; c 2. PHYSICS. *Educ:* Oberlin Col, BA, 48; Univ Mich, MA, 49; Pa State Univ, PhD(physics), 53. *Prof Exp:* Res asst eng res, Ionosphere Res Lab, Pa State Univ, 52-53, assoc prof & actg dir, 54-55, instr physics, Univ, 53-54; assoc prof, 55-63, from actg head dept to head dept, 56-74, chmn Div Natural Sci & Math, 74-79, PROF PHYSICS, LINFIELD COL, 63- *Concurrent Pos:* Physicist, Linfield Res Inst, 56-, actg dir, 65-68; physicist, Field Emission Corp, 61-63. *Mem:* AAAS; Am Asn Physics Teachers; Am Geophys Union; Optical Soc Am. *Res:* Physics of the upper atmosphere. *Mailing Add:* Dept Physics Linfield Col McMinnville OR 97128

JONES, ROBERT ERWIN, b Upper Darby, Pa, Oct 20, 30. PSYCHIATRY. *Educ:* Williams Col, BA, 52; Univ Pa, MD, 57. *Prof Exp:* Instr clin psychiat, Univ Pa, 62, asst prof, 64-76: asst clin dir, Inst Pa Hosp, 63-65, clin dir, 65-69, assoc med dir, 69-76; PROF PSYCHIAT, JEFFERSON MED COL, 76- *Mem:* Am Psychiat Soc. *Res:* Schizophrenia; medical history. *Mailing Add:* 15th Fl Thompson Annex Jefferson Med Col Philadelphia PA 19107

JONES, ROBERT F, b Dallas, Tex, Dec 30, 26; m 53; c 4. ONCOLOGY. *Educ:* Univ Tex, Dallas, MD, 52; Am Bd Surg, cert, 64. *Prof Exp:* Res fel surg, Univ Tex Southwestern Med Sch, Dallas, 55, USPHS fel, 62-63; from instr to assoc prof, Univ Tex Health Sci Ctr Dallas, 63-74; assoc prof, 74-79, PROF SURG, MED SCH, UNIV WASH, 79- *Concurrent Pos:* Am Cancer Soc advan clin fel, 63-66. *Mem:* Am Col Surgeons; AMA; Am Asn Cancer Educ; Am Cancer Soc; Soc Surg Oncol. *Res:* Viral and surgical oncology; tumor immunology; clinical cancer. *Mailing Add:* Dept of Surg RF-25 Univ of Wash Med Sch Seattle WA 98195

JONES, ROBERT JAMES, b Dawson, Ga, June 10, 51; m 70; c 1. CROP PHYSIOLOGY, AGRONOMY. *Educ:* Ft Valley State Col, BS, 73; Univ Ga, MS, 75; Univ Mo, PhD(crop physiol), 78. *Prof Exp:* Soil conservationist, Soil Conserv Serv, 70-73; asst prof corn physiol, 78-80, ASSOC PROF ENTOM, FISHERIES & WILDLIFE, UNIV MINN, 80- *Mem:* Crop Sci Soc Am; Am Soc Agron; Am Soc Plant Physiologists. *Res:* Corn physiology; major interest in the relationship between photosynthesis and dark respiration during plant ontogeny and as affected by nutritional and environmental stress factors. *Mailing Add:* Dept of Agron & Plant Genetics 303 Agron Bldg Univ of Minn St Paul MN 55108

JONES, ROBERT L, b Wellston, Ohio, Jan 26, 36; m 58; c 3. SOIL MINERALOGY. *Educ:* Ohio State Univ, BSc, 58, MSc, 59; Univ Ill, PhD(soil mineral), 62. *Prof Exp:* Res assoc, 62-64, from asst prof to assoc prof, 64-73, PROF SOIL MINERAL & ECOL, UNIV ILL, URBANA, 73- *Mem:* Am Soc Agron; Mineral Soc Am; Wildlife Soc. *Res:* Soil mineral analysis techniques; applied mineralogy in soil genesis studies; biogeochemistry. *Mailing Add:* Dept of Agron Univ of Ill Urbana IL 61801

JONES, ROBERT LEROY, b Allentown, Pa, May 28, 39; m 64; c 2. HUMAN BIOLOGY, PHYSIOLOGY. *Educ:* Millersville State Col, BS, 61; Univ Okla, MS, 65; Pa State Univ, EDD(biol), 70. *Prof Exp:* Res scientist physiol, Pillsburg Co, 65-66; instr biol, Pa State Univ, 66-68; chmn math & sci & assoc prof biol, Am Col Switz, 68-69; assoc prof, Plymouth State Col, 69-72; dean acad affairs, prof life sci & chmn div, Harrisburg Area Community Col, 72-78; ASSOC PROF HUMAN BIOL & BASIC MED SCI, COL MED, PA STATE UNIV, 78- *Mem:* AAAS; Am Inst Biol Sci; Am Asn Univ Profs; Am Col Sports Med. *Res:* Cardiovascular physiology; health promotion and disease prevention; studies on continuing physical exercise during pregnancy: implications of changes in maternal heat balance, body fat storage, and metabolism on the well-being of mother and unborn child. *Mailing Add:* Dept of Family Med M S Hershey Med Ctr Hershey PA 17033

JONES, ROBERT MILLARD, b Mattoon, Ill, Aug 8, 39; m 63; c 3. SOLID MECHANICS. *Educ:* Univ Ill, Urbana, BS, 60, MS, 61, PhD(theoret & appl mech), 64. *Prof Exp:* Instr theoret & appl mech, Univ Ill, Urbana, 63-64; mem tech staff, Aerospace Corp, 64-70; assoc prof solid mech, Inst Technol, Southern Methodist Univ, 70-74, prof, 75-81; PROF ENG SCI & MECH, VA POLYTECH INST & STATE UNIV, 81- *Concurrent Pos:* Consult, Lockheed Missile & Space Ctr, 76 & 79, US Air Force Mat Lab, 71-79. *Mem:* Assoc fel Am Inst Aeronaut & Astronaut; Am Acad Mech; Am Soc Mech Engrs. *Res:* Shell buckling; shell stress analysis; mechanics of composite materials; finite element; stress analysis of axisymmetric solids. *Mailing Add:* Eng Sci & Mech Dept Va Polytech Inst & State Univ Blacksburg VA 24061

JONES, ROBERT ORVILLE, b Digby, NS, Mar 31, 14; m 37; c 2. PSYCHIATRY. *Educ:* Dalhousie Univ, BSc, 33, MDCM, 37; FRCPS(C). *Hon Degrees:* DrEng, NS Tech Col, 70. *Prof Exp:* Rockefeller fel psychiat, Henry Phipps Psychiat Clin, Johns Hopkins Hosp, Baltimore, Md, 39-41; assoc prof, 41-49, head dept, 49-75, prof, 49-76, EMER PROF PSYCHIAT, DALHOUSIE UNIV, 76- *Concurrent Pos:* Consult, NS Hosp, Dartmouth, Izaak Walton Killam Hosp, Halifax & Can Forces Hosp, 49-; psychiatrist, Victoria Gen Hosp, 49-, head dept psychiat, 49-75; psychiatrist, Camp Hill Hosp, Halifax, 49-, head dept psychiat, 49-75; vis prof, Royal Free Hosp, London, Eng. *Honors & Awards:* Can Centennial Medal, 67; Can Queen's Jubilee Medal, 77. *Mem:* Hon mem Can Psychiat Asn (charter pres); Can Med Asn (past pres); Can Ment Health Asn (past pres); fel Am Psychiat Asn; charter fel Am Col Psychiat. *Res:* Geriairic psychiatry; evaluation psychiatric treatment, follow-up studies. *Mailing Add:* Dept of Psychiat Victoria Gen Hosp Halifax NS B3H 2Y9 Can

JONES, ROBERT SIDNEY, b Gatesville, Tex, Dec 17, 36; c 2. MARINE BIOLOGY, ICTHYOLOGY. *Educ:* Univ Tex, BA, 59, MA, 63, PhD(zool), 67. *Prof Exp:* Dir & prof biol, Univ Guam Marine Lab, 67-74; fisheries biologist, Harbor Br Found Inc, 74-76; prog mgr admin, Univ Tex, 76; DIR JOHNSON SCI LAB, HARBOR BR FOUND, INC, 76- *Mem:* Am Soc Ichthyologists & Herpetologists; Sigma Xi. *Res:* Ecology and behavior of marine fishes. *Mailing Add:* Harbor Br Found Inc RR1 Box 196 Ft Pierce FL 33450

JONES, ROBERT THOMAS, b Macon, Mo, May 28, 1910; m 64; c 6. AERONAUTICAL ENGINEERING. *Hon Degrees:* ScD, Univ Colo, 71. *Prof Exp:* Aeronaut res scientist, NACA, Langley Field, Va, 34-46, res scientist, Ames Res Ctr, NACA-NASA, Moffett Field, Calif, 46-62; sr staff scientist, Avco-Everett Res Lab, Everett, Mass, 62-70; sr staff scientist, 70-81, RES ASSOC, NASA, AMES RES CTR, CALIF, 81- *Concurrent Pos:* Consult prof, Stanford Univ, 81. *Honors & Awards:* Reed Award, Inst Aeronaut Sci, 46; Inventions & Contrib Award, NASA, 75; Langley Medal, Smithsonian Inst, 81. *Mem:* Nat Acad Eng; fel Am Inst Aeronaut & Astronaut; AAAS. *Res:* High speed wing theory. *Mailing Add:* Ames Res Ctr NASA Moffett Field CA 94035

JONES, ROBERT WILLIAM, b Seattle, Wash, Jan 20, 27; m 53; c 3. GEOLOGY. *Educ:* Univ Wash, Seattle, BS, 50, MS, 57, PhD(geol), 59. *Prof Exp:* Ground water geologist, US Geol Surv, 51-55; from instr to asst prof, 58-66, ASSOC PROF GEOL, UNIV IDAHO, 66- *Mem:* Geol Soc Am; Am Asn Petrol Geol; Nat Asn Geol Teachers; Int Asn Volcanology; AAAS. *Res:* Petrology and structure of igneous and metamorphic rocks. *Mailing Add:* Dept of Geol Univ of Idaho Moscow ID 83843

JONES, ROBERT WILLIAM, b Wenatchee, Wash, Dec 18, 40. THEORETICAL PHYSICS, ENERGY ANALYSIS. *Educ:* Univ Wash, BS, 64; Univ Colo, PhD(physics), 69. *Prof Exp:* Asst prof, 69-74, ASSOC PROF PHYSICS, UNIV SDAK, 74- *Concurrent Pos:* Res assoc, Univ Ariz, 71-72; assoc prof physics, petroleum & minerals, Univ Dhahran, Saudi Arabia, 74-76; vis staff mem, Los Alamos Sci Lab, 78; consult, Oak Ridge Nat Lab, 78. *Mem:* Int Solar Energy Soc. *Res:* Nuclear many-body theory; statistical mechanics; theory of quantum liquids; solar energy applications to heating and cooling of buildings including passive heating and absorption air-conditioning. *Mailing Add:* Dept of Earth Sci & Physics Univ of SDak Vermillion SD 57069

JONES, ROBIN L(ESLIE), b Stanley, Eng, May 19, 40; m 65. PHYSICAL METALLURGY, MATERIALS ENGINEERING. *Educ:* Cambridge Univ, BA, 62, MA, 66, PhD(metall), 66. *Prof Exp:* Sr res metallurgist, Res Labs, Franklin Inst, 66-71, group leader, Metall Lab, 71-72; mgr metall prog, SRI Int, 72-78; proj mgr, 78-80, PROG MGR NUCLEAR SYSTS & MAT, ELEC POWER RES INST, 80- *Mem:* Am Soc Mech Engrs; Nat Asn Corrosion Engrs; Am Inst Mining, Metall & Petrol Engrs; Am Soc Testing & Mat. *Res:* Physical and mechanical metallurgy, particularly the relations between mechanical properties and fine microstructure; fracture mechanics; ductile fracture of metallic materials; corrosion; environmentally assisted fracture of metals and ceramics. *Mailing Add:* Elec Power Res Inst 3412 Hillview Ave Palo Alto CA 94303

JONES, ROBIN RICHARD, b Little Rock, Ark, Oct 18, 37. PATHOLOGY, BIOCHEMISTRY. *Educ:* Univ Ark, BS, 61, MD, 62, MS, 66, PhD(biochem), 67. *Prof Exp:* Spec instr, 65-69, ASST PROF PATH, MED SCH, UNIV ARK, 67-, ASST PROF MED TECHNOL, SCH ALLIED HEALTH SCI, 74- *Res:* Vitamin E deficiency; muscular dystrophy. *Mailing Add:* Dept of Path Univ of Ark Med Sch Little Rock AR 77701

JONES, ROGER, b Kimbolton, Herefordshire, Eng, Mar 19, 40; m 65; c 2. BOTANY. *Educ:* Univ Wales, BSc, 62, PhD(ecol), 67; Kans State Univ, MSc, 64. *Prof Exp:* Asst prof, 67-73, ASSOC PROF BIOL, TRENT UNIV, 73- *Mem:* Brit Ecol Soc; Am Soc Limnol & Oceanog; Soc Int Limnol. *Res:* Heavy metals in soils and plants; paleolimnology. *Mailing Add:* Dept of Biol Trent Univ Peterborough ON K9J 7B8 Can

JONES, ROGER ALAN, b York, Pa, Mar 25, 47; m 68; c 1. ORGANIC CHEMISTRY. *Educ:* Univ Del, BS, 69; Univ Alta, PhD(chem), 74. *Prof Exp:* NIH fel, Dept Chem, Mass Inst Technol, 75-76; ASST PROF CHEM, DOUGLASS COL, RUTGERS UNIV, 77- *Mem:* AAAS; Am Chem Soc. *Res:* Development of new concepts for oligonucleotide synthesis and synthetic transformations of nucleic acid components and related compounds. *Mailing Add:* Dept of Chem Douglass Col New Brunswick NJ 08903

JONES, ROGER C(LYDE), b Lake Andes, SDak, Aug 17, 19; m 52; c 2. ELECTRICAL ENGINEERING, PLASMA PHYSICS. *Educ:* Univ Nebr, BS, 49; Univ Md, MS, 53, PhD, 63. *Prof Exp:* Electronic engr, Naval Res Lab, 49-50, electronic scientist, 50-57; sr staff engr, Melpar Inc, Westinghouse Air Brake Co, 57-58, consult proj engr, antenna & radiation systs lab, 58-59, head physics sect, phys sci lab, 59-64, chief scientist for physics, electronics-physics res ctr, 64; acting dir, appl res lab, 64-65, PROF ELEC ENG, UNIV ARIZ, 64-, ADJ PROF RADIOL, 78- *Mem:* Fel AAAS; Am Phys Soc; sr mem Inst Elec & Electronics Engrs; Optical Soc Am; Bioelectromagnetics Soc. *Res:* General physical electronics; infrared engineering; gas and solid state lasers; hyperthermia; bioelectromagnetics. *Mailing Add:* 5809 E Third St Tucson AZ 85711

JONES, ROGER STANLEY, b New York, NY, June 17, 34; m 56; c 2. HIGH ENERGY PHYSICS. *Educ:* City Col New York, BS, 55; Univ Ill, MS, 57, PhD(physics), 61. *Prof Exp:* Res assoc physics, Univ Ill, 61-62; US Air Force Off Sci Res fel, Nat Comt Nuclear Energy Labs, Frascati, 62-63; from asst physicist to assoc physicist, Brookhaven Nat Lab, 64-67; ASSOC PROF PHYSICS, UNIV MINN, MINNEAPOLIS, 67- *Mem:* Am Phys Soc. *Res:* High energy experimental physics and elementary particle physics; epistemology and symbolism of physics. *Mailing Add:* Sch of Physics & Astron Univ of Minn Minneapolis MN 55455

JONES, RONALD DALE, b Stillwater, Okla, July 18, 32; div; c 2. COMPUTER SCIENCE. *Educ:* Okla State Univ, BA, 55; Univ Kans, MPA, 60; Univ Southern Calif, DPA, 64. *Prof Exp:* Admin aide budget & mgt, City of Wichita, Kans, 59-60; admin intern, City of Beverly Hills, Calif, 60-61; sr res engr, Los Angeles Div, NAm Aviation, Inc, 61-63; engr, Rand Corp, 63-65; PROF COMPUT SCI, SCH ADMIN, UNIV MO-KANSAS CITY, 66- *Concurrent Pos:* Lectr, Kansas City Art Inst, 72- *Mem:* Asn Comput Mach. *Res:* Simulation of social-psychological systems, particularly bureaucracies; security of computer systems. *Mailing Add:* Univ of Mo Sch of Admin Kansas City MO 64110

JONES, RONALD GOLDIN, b Yorkville, Ga, Nov 29, 33; m 57. ORGANIC CHEMISTRY. *Educ:* Emory Univ, BA, 55, MS, 57; Ga Inst Technol, PhD(org chem), 61. *Prof Exp:* Lab technician prod develop & control, Southern Latex Corp, Ga, 51-53, develop chemist prod develop, 55; from asst prof to assoc prof, 61-67, PROF ORG CHEM, GA STATE UNIV, 67- *Concurrent Pos:* NSF acad year exten grant, 63-65; dir NSF grant, Ga Jr Col Coop Chem Proj, 69-70. *Mem:* Am Chem Soc; Sigma Xi. *Res:* Catalytic hydrogenation; applications of nuclear magnetic resonance spectroscopy in organic chemistry; organic reaction mechanisms. *Mailing Add:* Ga State Univ University Plaza Atlanta GA 30303

JONES, RONALD MCCLUNG, b Palo Alto, Calif, May 6, 51; m 74; c 1. PHYSIOLOGICAL ECOLOGY, RESPIRATORY PHYSIOLOGY. *Educ:* Swarthmore Col, BA, 72; Univ Calif, Riverside, PhD(biol), 78. *Prof Exp:* FEL PHYSIOL, DARTMOUTH MED SCH, HANOVER, 78- *Mem:* AAAS; Am Inst Biol Sci; Am Soc Zool; Sigma Xi. *Res:* Physiological ecology of vertebrates. *Mailing Add:* Dept of Physiol Dartmouth Med Sch Hanover NH 03755

JONES, ROY CARL, JR, b New York, NY, Aug 3, 39; m 64; c 4. MATHEMATICS. *Educ:* Case Inst Technol, BS, 62; Western Reserve Univ, MS, 64, PhD(math), 66. *Prof Exp:* Asst prof, Univ Fla, 66-69; ASST PROF MATH, FLA TECHNOL UNIV, 69- *Mem:* Am Math Soc; Math Asn Am. *Res:* Approximation theory, characterizing and finding best uniform or Tchebycheff approximations; numerical methods including developing algorithms or iterative procedures that converge to the best approximations. *Mailing Add:* Dept of Math PO Box 25000 Fla Technol Univ Orlando FL 32816

JONES, ROY WINFIELD, b Shawnee, Okla, Sept 16, 05; m 28; c 2. EXPERIMENTAL EMBRYOLOGY. *Educ:* Okla City Univ, AB, 27; Kans State Univ, MS, 28; Univ Okla, PhD(zool), 37. *Prof Exp:* Asst, Oklahoma City Univ, 25-27; asst parasitol, Kans State Col, 27-28; teacher pub sch, La, 28; from asst prof to prof biol, Cent State Teachers Col, 29-47, dean col & actg dean men, 39-47; prof zool, 47-71, head dept, 51-71, chmn gen educ courses biol sci, 47-51, EMER PROF ZOOL & HEAD DEPT, OKLA STATE UNIV, 71- *Concurrent Pos:* Collecting Net scholar, Marine Biol Lab, Woods Hole, 34. *Mem:* Am Soc Zool; Am Micros Soc; Soc Exp Biol & Med; Am Inst Biol Sci; Nat Asn Retired Teachers. *Res:* Resistance to parasitism; experimental embryology and cytology; mitotic index; effects of different chemicals, ultrasound and radiation on cell division and embryonic differentiation using fish embryo. *Mailing Add:* 2030 W Admiral Stillwater OK 74074

JONES, RUFUS SIDNEY, b Warrenton, NC, May 9, 40; m 68; c 1. ORGANIC CHEMISTRY, POLYMER CHEMISTRY. *Educ:* Duke Univ, BS, 62; Purdue Univ, PhD(org chem), 68. *Prof Exp:* Res chemist, 68-72, sr res chemist, 72-80, RES ASSOC, CELANESE RES CO, 81- *Mem:* Am Chem Soc. *Res:* Condensation and cationic polymerization; organic synthesis; preparation and characterization of synthetic membranes. *Mailing Add:* Celanese Res Co 86 Morris Ave Summit NJ 07901

JONES, RUSSEL C(AMERON), b Tarentum, Pa, Oct 18, 35; m 58. CIVIL ENGINEERING. *Educ:* Carnegie Inst Technol, BS, 57, MS, 60, PhD(sci of mat), 64. *Prof Exp:* Struct designer, Hunting, Larsen & Dunnels Engrs, Pa, 57-59, assoc engr, Missiles & Space Systs Div, Douglas Aircraft Co, 60; asst prof civil eng, Mass Inst Technol, 63-66, assoc prof, 66-71; prof & chmn dept, Ohio State Univ, 71-77; dean, Sch Eng, Univ Mass, 77-81; VPRES ACAD AFFAIRS, BOSTON UNIV, 81- *Mem:* AAAS; Am Soc Eng Educ; Nat Soc Prof Engrs; Metall Soc; Am Soc Testing & Mat. *Res:* Science of materials; composite materials; building systems; housing; construction management; engineering education. *Mailing Add:* 145 Bay State Rd Boston Univ Boston MA 02215

JONES, RUSSELL HOWARD, b Oakland, Calif, July 7, 44; m 68; c 3. MATERIALS SCIENCE, METALLURGY. *Educ:* Calif State Polytech Col, BS, 67; Univ Calif, Berkeley, MS, 68, PhD(metall), 71. *Prof Exp:* Engr metall, Westinghouse Elec Corp, 71-73; sr res scientist, 73-80, STAFF SCIENTIST METALL, PAC NORTHWEST DIV, BATTELLE MEM INST, 80- *Mem:* Am Soc Metals; Am Inst Mining, Metall & Petrol Engrs. *Res:* High temperature alloys; radiation damage and stress corrosion. *Mailing Add:* Pac Northwest Div PO Box 999 Richland WA 99352

JONES, RUSSELL K, b Port Chester, NY, Aug 17, 22; m 49; c 4. VETERINARY PUBLIC HEALTH. *Educ:* Cornell Univ, DVM, 45; Purdue Univ, PhD(path), 54. *Prof Exp:* From instr to assoc prof, Agr Exp Sta, 48-60, assoc prof path, Sch Vet Sci & Med, 60-65, PROF VET PATH, SCH VET SCI & MED, PURDUE UNIV, 65- *Mem:* Am Vet Med Asn; Conf Res Workers Animal Dis. *Res:* Diagnostics, including microbiology and pathology; zoonoses. *Mailing Add:* Sch of Vet Med Purdue Univ West Lafayette IN 47906

JONES, RUSSELL LEWIS, b Dyserth, Wales, May 10, 41; c 3. PLANT PHYSIOLOGY. *Educ:* Univ Col Wales, BSc, 62, PhD(bot), 65. *Prof Exp:* AEC fel, Mich State Univ–AEC Plant Res Lab, 65-66; from asst prof to assoc prof, 66-74, PROF BOT, UNIV CALIF, BERKELEY, 74- *Concurrent Pos:* Peer panel mem, adv, Panel Develop Biol, NSF, 71-73; assoc ed, Annual Rev Plant Physiol, 71-; Guggenheim Mem Found fel, 72-73. *Mem:* Am Soc Plant Physiol; Int Plant Growth Substances Asn. *Res:* Biochemistry and physiology of the action of gibberellic acid and other plant hormones. *Mailing Add:* Dept of Bot Univ of Calif Berkeley CA 94720

JONES, RUSSELL STINE, b Corvallis, Ore, June 5, 14; m 40; c 8. PATHOLOGY. *Educ:* Univ Ore, MD, 40; Am Bd Path, dipl, 48. *Prof Exp:* Intern, Ancker Hosp, Minn, 40-41; resident path, Hosp & Clins, Univ Ore, 41-44; from instr to asst prof, Col Med, Univ Tenn, 47-52; assoc prof, Med Sch, Univ Ore, 52-54; prof path, Col Med, Univ Utah, 54-66, dir clin labs, 60-66; prof path, Univ Mo-Kansas City, 66-70; dir labs, Dept Path, Providence Hosp, Ore, 70-72; DIR LABS, DEPT PATH, IMPERIAL POINT MED CTR, FT LAUDERDALE, 72- *Concurrent Pos:* Dir labs, WTenn Tuberc Hosp, Memphis, 48-52; consult, Vet Admin Hosp, Memphis, 48-52. *Mem:* Am Asn Cancer Res; Am Rheumatism Asn; Am Soc Clin Pathologists; Am Asn Blood Banks; Int Acad Path. *Res:* Arthritis and rheumatic diseases; experimental tumors; adrenal steroids; scurvy; mycoplasmal infections; activation analysis; radiobiology. *Mailing Add:* Imperial Point Med Ctr 6401 N Federal Hwy Ft Lauderdale FL 33308

JONES, SAMUEL B, JR, b Roswell, Ga, Dec 18, 33; m 55; c 3. BOTANY. *Educ:* Auburn Univ, BS, 55, MS, 61; Univ Ga, PhD(bot), 64. *Prof Exp:* Teacher, South Cobb High Sch, 58-59; instr bot, Auburn Univ, 59-61; asst prof, Univ Southern Miss, 64-67; from asst prof to assoc prof, 67-74, PROF BOT, UNIV GA, 74-, DIR, BOT GARDEN, 81- *Concurrent Pos:* NSF res grants; Calloway Found res grant. *Mem:* Bot Soc Am; Am Soc Plant Taxonomists; Int Asn Plant Taxon; Soc Study Evolution; Torrey Bot Club. *Res:* Systematics of higher plants; tribe Vernonieae (compositae), especially Vernonia; flora of southeastern United States, especially Georgia. *Mailing Add:* Dept of Bot Univ of Ga Athens GA 30602

JONES, SAMUEL O'BRIEN, b Louisburg, NC, Mar 14, 11; m 37; c 2. CHEMISTRY, CHEMICAL ENGINEERING. *Educ:* NC State Col, BS, 32; Johns Hopkins Univ, PhD(org chem), 36. *Prof Exp:* Dir org res, R J Reynolds Tobacco Co, 36-52; dir tobacco eng, 52-64, mgr tobacco prod develop, 64-70, dir tobacco develop, 70-76; RETIRED. *Mem:* Am Chem Soc; Am Inst Chem Engrs. *Res:* Tobacco research and process development; reactions of sulfur, hydrogen sulfide and mercaptans with unsaturated hydrocarbons. *Mailing Add:* 310 Plymouth Ave Winston-Salem NC 27104

JONES, SAMUEL STIMPSON, b Buckingham Co, Va, Apr 9, 23. PHYSICAL CHEMISTRY. *Educ:* Hampden-Sydney Col, BS, 43; Cornell Univ, PhD(phys chem), 50. *Prof Exp:* Chemist, Manhattan Proj, Monsanto Chem Co, 44-46; res assoc phys chem, Knolls Atomic Power Lab, Gen Elec Co, 50-57, radiation chemist, Vallecitos Atomic Lab, 57-61, radiation effects specialist, Defense Syst Dept & Electronics Lab, 61-63 & tech specialist,

Hanford Labs, 63-65; res assoc Pac Northwest Lab, Battelle Mem Inst, Wash, 65-70; sr staff res scientist, Ctr Technol, Kaiser Aluminum & Chem Corp, 70-81; MGR, CARBON & MAT RES, ANACONDA ALUMINUM CO, 81- *Mem:* AAAS; Am Chem Soc; NY Acad Sci; Am Carbon Soc. *Res:* Radiochemistry; complex ions; radiation chemistry; radiation effects on electronic materials; graphite physics and chemistry; chemistry and physics of carbon. *Mailing Add:* PO Box 43698 Tucson AZ 85733

JONES, SANFORD L, b Bulan, Ky, Sept 22, 25; m 56; c 3. REPRODUCTIVE ENDOCRINOLOGY. *Educ:* Eastern Ky State Col, BS, 50; Univ Ky, MS, 56; Univ Tenn, PhD(physiol, biochem), 60. *Prof Exp:* Secondary teacher, Perry County Schs, Ky, 50-55; res assoc physiol, Univ Tenn, 60-61; from asst prof to assoc prof, 61-65, PROF BIOL, EASTERN KY UNIV, 66- *Mem:* Am Soc Zool. *Res:* Effects of antithyroid compounds on metabolism of thyroxine; absorption of iodinated compounds in amphibians and reptiles; radioimmunoassay of luteinizing hormone. *Mailing Add:* Dept of Biol Sci Eastern Ky Univ Richmond KY 40475

JONES, STANLEY BENNETT, b San Francisco, Calif, Jan 14, 22; m 46; c 2. GEOPHYSICS. *Educ:* Univ Calif, PhD(physics), 50. *Prof Exp:* Physicist, Radiation Lab, Univ Calif, 48-50; res physicist oil field res, 50-58, sect supvr, Well Logging & Basic Prod Sect, 58-63, sect supvr, Geophys Sect, 63-68, mgr, Geophhys Div, Chevron Oil Field Res Co, 68-76, geophys res consult, 79-80, mgr, Develop & Implementation Div, Chevron Geosci Co, 77-78, geophys res consult, Chevron Oil Field Res Co, 79-80, MGR, SYSTS & ENG SERV DIV, CHEVRON OIL FIELD RES CO, 81- *Mem:* Am Phys Soc; Am Geophys Union; Soc Explor Geophys; Europ Asn Explor Geophys. *Res:* Cosmic rays; meson physics; oil well logging, producing and geophysics research. *Mailing Add:* 7823 S California Ave Whittier CA 90602

JONES, STANLEY C(ULVER), b Spokane, Wash, Aug 31, 33; m 57; c 3. CHEMICAL ENGINEERING. *Educ:* Wash State Univ, BSE, 56; Univ Mich, MSE, 59, PhD(chem eng), 62. *Prof Exp:* Engr, Kaiser Aluminum & Chem Corp, 56-58; adv res engr, 62-71, sr res scientist, 71-75, RES ASSOC, DENVER RES CTR, MARATHON OIL CO, 75- *Mem:* Soc Petrol Engrs; Sigma Xi; Am Inst Chem Engrs. *Res:* Anodizing processes for aluminum alloys; behavior of a pulsed extraction column; movement of water through aquifers in contact with natural gas; secondary and tertiary oil recovery processes; reservoir rock properties; petroleum production. *Mailing Add:* Denver Res Ctr Marathon Oil Co PO Box 269 Littleton CO 80160

JONES, STANLEY E, b Mt Vernon, NY, July 20, 39; m 80; c 1. APPLIED MATHEMATICS, ENGINEERING MECHANICS. *Educ:* Univ Del, BA, 63, MS, 66, PhD(appl sci), 67. *Prof Exp:* ASSOC PROF ENG MECH, UNIV KY, 67- *Concurrent Pos:* Vis prof, Univ Iowa, 69 & Ga Inst Tech, 79-80; consult, Marshall Space Flight Ctr, NASA, 70 & US Air Force, Eglin AFB, Fla, 81. *Res:* Fluid transients, plasticity analysis and nonlinear mechanics. *Mailing Add:* Col of Eng Univ of Ky Lexington KY 40506

JONES, STANLEY LESLIE, b Waltham, Mass, Mar 22, 19; m 48; c 5. ANALYTICAL CHEMISTRY. *Educ:* Tufts Col, BS, 41, MS, 47; Harvard Univ, AM, 49, PhD(anal chem), 51. *Prof Exp:* Res chemist drying oils, Bird & Son, Inc, 41-42; jr chemist chem anal, US Navy Yard, Mass, 42-44; res chemist, Merck & Co, Inc, 50-55; appl res chemist, Knolls Atomic Power Lab, Gen Elec Co, 55-60, consult chemist, 60-80; RETIRED. *Mem:* Am Chem Soc; AAAS. *Res:* Analytical research; colloid science. *Mailing Add:* 37 Saratoga Dr Scotia NY 12302

JONES, STANLEY TANNER, b Palo Alto, Calif, Mar 10, 45; m 77; c 2. PHYSICS. *Educ:* Stanford Univ, BS, 66; Univ Ill, Urbana, MA, 68, PhD(physics), 70. *Prof Exp:* Asst prof, 70-76, ASSOC PROF PHYSICS, UNIV ALA, 76- *Mem:* Am Phys Soc; Am Asn Physics Teachers. *Res:* Elementary particle physics. *Mailing Add:* Dept of Physics Univ of Ala PO Box 1921 University AL 35486

JONES, STEPHEN BENDER, b Lansing, Mich, Oct 19, 45; m 70; c 2. PHYSIOLOGY. *Educ:* Cent Mich Univ, BS, 67, MS, 69; Univ Mo, PhD(physiol), 75. *Prof Exp:* Teaching asst biol, Cent Mich Univ, 67-68, asst instr, 68-69, instr, 69-71; res assoc physiol, 75-76, ASST PROF PHYSIOL, STRITCH SCH MED, LOYOLA UNIV, CHICAGO, 76- *Mem:* Sigma Xi; assoc Am Physiol Soc. *Res:* Neural control of the heart; peripheral catecholamine metabolism; hibernation; environmental physiology. *Mailing Add:* Dept of Physiol Loyola Univ of Chicago Maywood IL 60153

JONES, STEPHEN THOMAS, b Washington, NC, Feb 12, 42; m 63; c 1. ORGANIC CHEMISTRY. *Educ:* E Carolina Univ, AB, 64; Emory Univ, PhD(org chem), 68. *Prof Exp:* Res chemist, Lorillard, 68-70, supvr prod develop, 70-72, mgr prod develop, 72-77, MGR OPERS & RES PLANNING, INT, LORILLARD, LOEWS CORP, 77- *Mem:* Sigma Xi; Am Chem Soc. *Res:* Steroid synthesis; syntheses of hydroazulenes; syntheses of heterocyclic compounds; tobacco chemistry. *Mailing Add:* 1208 King George Dr Greensboro NC 27410

JONES, T(HOMAS) BENJAMIN, b Madison, Md, Aug 26, 12; m 47; c 2. ELECTRICAL ENGINEERING. *Educ:* Johns Hopkins Univ, BE, 33, Dr Eng, 37. *Prof Exp:* Asst instr elec eng, Johns Hopkins Univ, 36-37; mem tech staff, Bell Tel Lab, NY, 37-41; foreign wire rels engr, C & P Tel Co, Md, 41-44, personnel supvr, 44-45, commercial mgr, 45-46; asst prof elec eng, Johns Hopkins Univ, 46-50, assoc prof, 50-56; mem tech staff, Bell Tel Labs, 56-58, tech supvr, 58-67, dielectrics specialist, 67-73; SR ASSOC, TRIDENT ENG ASSOCS, 73- *Concurrent Pos:* Proj engr bur ships, US Navy, 46-50, res contract dir, Off Naval Res, 48-54; res contract dir, Army Ord Corps, 54-56; consult, E I du Pont de Nemours & Co, Inc, 54-56. *Mem:* Inst Elec & Electronics Engrs. *Res:* Dielectrics and insulation; electrical capacitors; electrical discharges, arcs and welding; electrical measurements; oxidation of impregnated paper insulation. *Mailing Add:* Skywater Rd Gibson Island MD 21056

JONES, TERRY LEE, b Marysville, Kans, Oct 12, 45. REAL-TIME IMAGE PROCESSORS, PHYSICS. *Educ:* Rutgers Univ, BA, 68; Am Univ, MS, 74. *Prof Exp:* Physicist elec sources, Night Vision Lab, Far Infrared Tech Area, 68-74; res physicist MIS Structures, Night Vision Lab, Image Intensification Tech Area, 74-78; RES PHYSICIST IMAGE PROCESS, NIGHT VISION & ELECTROOPTICS LAB, 78- *Mem:* Inst Elec & Electronics Engrs Comput Soc. *Res:* Automatic target recognition; image processing; electron sources, photo electric emmision, metal oxide or metal insulated semiconductor photocathodes, field assisted photocathodes, night vision devices, infrared sensors, ultra high vacuum. *Mailing Add:* Night Vision & Electro Optics Lab DELNV Ft Belvoir VA 22060

JONES, THEODORE CHARLES, b Pittsburgh, Pa, Nov 9, 39; m 62; c 2. GENETICS, BIOCHEMISTRY. *Educ:* Amherst Col, AB, 61; Univ Wash, PhD(genetics), 67. *Prof Exp:* Fel, Univ Wis, 67-69; asst prof biol, Amherst Col, 69-72; asst prof biol sci, Mt Holyoke Col, 72-79. *Mem:* Genetics Soc Am; Am Soc Microbiol. *Res:* Regulation of enzyme synthesis and enzyme localization in microorganisms. *Mailing Add:* Environ Protection Agency TS-778 Washington DC 20460

JONES, THEODORE HAROLD DOUGLAS, b Belfast, North Ireland, Oct 30, 38. BIOCHEMISTRY, MICROBIOLOGY. *Educ:* Univ Edinburgh, BSc, 59; Mass Inst Technol, PhD(biochem), 66. *Prof Exp:* Res asst biochem, Detroit Inst Cancer Res, 59-61; Damon Runyon Fund Cancer Res fel, Harvard Med Sch, 66-68; NIH traineeship aging res, Retina Found, 68-70; asst prof, 70-75, ASSOC PROF CHEM, UNIV SAN FRANCISCO, 75- *Res:* Biochemistry of differentiation, particularly events occurring during germination of spores of the cellular slime molds; biochemistry of membrane proteins and their changes during differentiation; clinical enzymology; development of diagnostic enzyme patterns in blood serum. *Mailing Add:* Dept of Chem Univ of San Francisco San Francisco CA 94117

JONES, THEODORE SIDNEY, b East Orange, NJ, Apr 28, 11; m 36; c 2. PETROLEUM GEOLOGY. *Educ:* Rutgers Univ, AB, 32; Univ Mich, PhD(geol), 35. *Prof Exp:* Jr soil surveyor, Soil Conserv Serv, USDA, 35-37; geologist, Humble Oil & Refining Co, 37-48; dist geologist, Sohio Petrol Co, 48-50; staff geologist, 50-53, chief stratigrapher, 53-60, mem staff, 60-69, regional stratigrapher, Union Oil Co Calif, 69-76; INDEPENDENT GEOLOGIST, 76- *Mem:* Fel Geol Soc Am; Am Asn Petrol Geol. *Res:* Paleozoic stratigraphy. *Mailing Add:* 1204 W Storey Midland TX 79701

JONES, THOMAS CARLYLE, b Boise, Idaho, Sept 29, 12; m 35; c 3. VETERINARY PATHOLOGY, COMPARATIVE PATHOLOGY. *Educ:* Wash State Univ, BS & DVM, 35. *Hon Degrees:* DSc, Ohio State Univ, 70. *Prof Exp:* Officer in chg, US Army Vet Res Lab, Front Royal Qm Depot, Va, 39-46, chief vet path sect, Armed Forces Inst Path, Washington, DC, 46-50, chief vet dept, Army Med Field Lab, Heidelberg, Ger, 50-53, chief vet path sect, Armed Forces Inst Path, 53-57; dir dept path, Angell Mem Animal Hosp, Boston, 57-67; clin assoc, Med Sch, 57-63, assoc clin prof path, 63-71, PROF COMP PATH, NEW ENG REGIONAL PRIMATE RES CTR, HARVARD MED SCH, 71- *Concurrent Pos:* Master res, Grad Coun, George Washington Univ, 47-51; res assoc path, Cancer Res Inst, New Eng Deaconess Hosp, 57-67; consult, Armed Forces Inst Path, 58- & Nat Cancer Inst, 61-62; mem comt path training, Nat Inst Gen Med Sci, 60-63; mem comt animal health, Nat Acad Sci-Nat Res Coun, 62-65; mem consult staff, Peter Bent Brigham Hosp, Boston, 62-78; mem adv comt animal resources, NIH, 65-68. *Mem:* Am Vet Med Asn; Am Col Vet Pathologists (secy-treas, 48-50 & 53-60, pres, 62-63); Am Asn Pathologists & Bacteriologists; Int Acad Path (pres, 70-71); Conf Res Workers Animal Dis. *Res:* Genetics and cytogenetics applied to disease in animals. *Mailing Add:* New Eng Regional Primate Res Ctr Harvard Med Sch Southborough MA 01772

JONES, THOMAS EVAN, b Basin, Miss, Dec 26, 44. ANALYTICAL CHEMISTRY, INORGANIC CHEMISTRY. *Educ:* Col Great Falls, BS, 70; Wash State Univ, PhD(chem), 74. *Prof Exp:* Teaching asst chem, Wash State Univ, 70-74; res assoc, Wayne State Univ, 74-75; asst prof chem, Univ NMex, 75-80; SR CHEMIST, ROCKWELL HANFORD OPERS, 80- *Mem:* Am Chem Soc; Sigma Xi. *Res:* Kinetic and mechanisms of redox and complexation reactions and their analytical applications. *Mailing Add:* Rockwell Hanford Opers PO Box 800 Richland WA 99352

JONES, THOMAS F(RANKLIN), JR, electrical engineering, deceased

JONES, THOMAS HUBBARD, b Batavia, Ill, June 8, 36; m 58; c 2. PHYSICAL CHEMISTRY, LIGHT-SENSITIVE MATERIALS. *Educ:* Augustana Col, Ill, BA, 58; Univ Minn, Minneapolis, PhD(phys chem), 63. *Prof Exp:* Res chemist, Photo Prod Res Lab, E I du Pont de Nemours & Co, Inc, 63-69; proj chemist, 69-78, res supvr, 78-80, RES ASSOC, RICHARDSON CO, MELROSE PARK, 80- *Mem:* Soc Photog Sci & Eng. *Res:* Photopolymerization; photolithography; synthesis of organic polymers and photopolymers; evaluation of photopolymers and other light-sensitive materials for lithographic printing. *Mailing Add:* 1032 Douglas Ave Naperville IL 60540

JONES, THOMAS OSWELL, b Oshkosh, Wis, May 13, 08; m 50; c 2. CHEMISTRY. *Educ:* Wis State Col, Oshkosh, BE, 30; Univ Wis, PhM, 34, PhD(inorg chem), 37. *Prof Exp:* Instr chem, Haverford Col, 38-40, from asst prof to assoc prof, 40-54, prof, 54-56; actg head, Off Sci Info, NSF, 56-58, head, Off Antarctic Prog, 58-65, div dir environ sci, 65-69, dep asst dir nat & int progs, 69-75, spec dep asst dir int activities, 75-78; RETIRED. *Concurrent Pos:* Asst to sect chief, Metall Lab, Univ Chicago, 44-45, sect chief, Info Div, 45-46. *Honors & Awards:* Order al Merito, Chile. *Mem:* Am Chem Soc; Am Geophys Union. *Res:* Cryoscopy; isotopes; micro-analytical methods; solubilities; preparation, properties and reactions of isotopes of hydrogen and oxygen; radiation chemistry. *Mailing Add:* 7504 Holiday Terr Bethesda MD 20034

JONES, THOMAS S, b Oakland, Md, Nov 11, 29; m 55; c 3. METALLURGY. *Educ:* Univ Ill, BS, 50, MS, 51; Pa State Univ, PhD(metall), 61. *Prof Exp:* Res asst metall, Gen Elec Res Lab, 51-56; res assoc, Pa State Univ, 61-62; sr res metallurgist, Allegheny Ludlum Res Ctr, 62-70; staff metallurgist, 71-74, PHYS SCIENTIST, US BUR MINES, 74- *Res:* Phase equilibria in metal and oxide systems at high temperatures; kinetics of reduction in metallurgical systems; steelmaking. *Mailing Add:* 4212 Braeburn Dr Fairfax VA 22032

JONES, THOMAS WALTER, b Odessa, Tex, June 22, 45; m 68; c 1. THEORETICAL ASTROPHYSICS. *Educ:* Univ Tex, Austin, BS, 67; Univ Minn, MS, 69, PhD(physics), 72. *Prof Exp:* Asst res physicist, Univ Calif, San Diego, 72-75; asst scientist, Nat Radio Astron Observ, 75-77, assoc scientist, 77; asst prof, 78-80, ASSOC PROF ASTRON, UNIV MINN, 80- *Mem:* Am Astron Soc; Int Astron Union. *Res:* Studies of physical processes in cosmic radio and infrared sources; nuclei of galaxies and quasars; radiation transfer in circumstellar environments. *Mailing Add:* Dept of Astron Univ Minn Minneapolis MN 55455

JONES, TRUMAN R(OSS), JR, b Gainesville, Tex, Apr 15, 21; div; c 6. CIVIL ENGINEERING. *Educ:* Tex A&M Univ, BS, 43, MS, 55. *Prof Exp:* Instr civil eng, Tex A&M Univ, 47-51; consult engr, 51-54; asst prof struct & asst res engr, Tex A&M Univ, 54-56, assoc prof civil eng & assoc res engr, 57-60, prof, 60-63; TECH DIR, VULCAN MAT CO, 63- *Concurrent Pos:* Instr, Eng Sch, Ft Belvoir, Va, 43-45, chief construct, Honolulu Dist Eng Off, 45-47; consult engr, 47-53; mem, Transp Res Bd, Nat Acad Sci-Nat Res Coun. *Mem:* Fel Am Soc Civil Engrs; Nat Soc Prof Engrs; fel Am Concrete Inst; Am Soc Testing & Mat. *Res:* Construction materials. *Mailing Add:* Vulcan Mat Co PO Box 7497 Birmingham AL 35223

JONES, ULYSSES SIMPSON, JR, b Portsmouth, Va, Feb 14, 18; m 41; c 1. SOIL FERTILITY. *Educ:* Va Polytech Inst, BS, 39; Purdue Univ, MS, 42; Univ Wis, PhD(soils), 47. *Prof Exp:* Chemist, F S Royster, 42; asst, Univ Wis, 46-47; assoc agronomist, State Agr Exp Sta, State Col Miss, USDA, 47-53; agronomist, Olin Mathieson Chem Corp, 53-60; head dept agron & soils, 60-71, PROF AGRON & SOILS, CLEMSON UNIV, 71- *Concurrent Pos:* Guest prof, Oak Ridge Inst Nuclear Studies, 50 & Univ Arkansas, 52; vis scientist, Int Rice Res Inst; vis prof, Univ Philippines, 79-80. *Honors & Awards:* Spokesman of Year, Chevron Chem Co & Farm Chem Mag, 75; Fulbright lectr, Aegean Univ, 76-77. *Mem:* Fel Soil Sci Soc Am; fel Am Soc Agron; Am Chem Soc; Entom Soc Am. *Res:* Availability of phosphates in soils; soil acidity and organic matter; limestone availability to crops and reaction in soil; use of radioactive elements for soil and fertilizer studies; insecticide and fertilizer mixtures for leaf feeding and insect control; trends in sulfur supply in air, rainwater and soil; environmental impact of acid rain. *Mailing Add:* Dept of Agron & Soils Clemson Univ Clemson SC 29631

JONES, VERNON DOUGLAS, b Florence, Ala, July 15, 37; m 61; c 1. PHARMACOLOGY. *Educ:* Florence State Univ, BA, 58; Vanderbilt Univ, PhD(pharmacol), 64; Univ NMex, JD, 74. *Prof Exp:* NIH fel pharmacol, Sch Med, Vanderbilt Univ, 64-65; NIH fel, Med Col, Cornell Univ, 65-67; asst prof pharmacol, 67-71, asst prof psychiat, 71-73, CLIN ASSOC, DEPT PSYCHIAT, SCH MED, UNIV NMEX, 73-, PHARMACOLOGIST, MENT HEALTH CTR, 73- *Res:* Drugs in criminal and civil law. *Mailing Add:* 318 Louisiana SE Albuquerque NM 87108

JONES, VICTOR ALAN, b Fremont, Mich, Feb 24, 30; m 54; c 4. FOOD ENGINEERING, FOOD SCIENCE. *Educ:* Mich State Univ, BS, 52, MS, 59, PhD(agr eng), 62. *Prof Exp:* From asst prof to assoc prof, 62-78, PROF FOOD ENG, NC STATE UNIV, 78- *Concurrent Pos:* Vis prof, Ore State Univ, 71. *Mem:* Am Soc Agr Engrs; Inst Food Technologists; Am Dairy Sci Asn; Sigma Xi. *Res:* Unit operations and control for ultrahigh temperature pasteurization or sterilization of foods; packaging materials and equipment. *Mailing Add:* Dept Food Sci NC State Univ Raleigh NC 27650

JONES, WALTER H(ARRISON), b Griffin, Sask, Sept 21, 22; US citizen; Wid. CHEMISTRY, SYSTEMS ANALYSIS. *Educ:* Univ Calif, Los Angeles, BS, 44, PhD(phys org chem), 48. *Prof Exp:* Res assoc, Univ Calif, Los Angeles, 48; chemist, Western Regional Res Lab, USDA, 48-51; chemist, Los Alamos Sci Lab, 51-54; sr res engr, NAm Aviation, Inc, 54-56; mgr chem dept, Aeronutronic Div, Ford Motor Co, 56-60; panel chmn, Inst Defense Anal, 60-63; head propulsion dept, Aerospace Corp, 63-64; sr scientist & head adv tech, Hughes Aircraft Co, 64-68; assoc prof, 69-70, prof aeronaut syst, 70-75, dir Corpus Christi Ctr, 69-75, PROF CHEM, UNIV WEST FLA, 75- *Concurrent Pos:* Chmn thermochem panel, Joint Army-Navy-Air Force-Adv Res Proj Agency-NASA, 60-62; consult, Fla Energy Comt & Solar Fla Solar Energy Ctr, 74-79; vis prof, Univ Toronto, 78-79. *Mem:* Am Chem Soc; fel Am Inst Chemists; NY Acad Sci; AAAS; Int Solar Energy Soc. *Res:* Chemical kinetics; polymer chemistry; thermodynamics; combustion; propulsion; missile and space systems analysis and engineering; energy systems analyses; quantum chemistry. *Mailing Add:* Dept Chem Univ of W Fla Pensacola FL 32504

JONES, WALTER LARUE, b Houston, Tex, Nov 20, 25. ENTOMOLOGY. *Educ:* Prairie View Agr & Mech Col, BS, 47; Ohio State Univ, MS, 49, PhD(entom), 60. *Prof Exp:* Instr biol, Tuskegee Inst, 49-50; res asst zool & entom, Ohio State Univ, 52-54; instr, 56-58, chmn dept, 60-74, dir div arts & sci, 67-74, PROF BIOL, LANGSTON UNIV, 60-, DEAN ACAD AFFAIRS & ACTG DIR DIV ARTS & SCI, 74- *Concurrent Pos:* Intern, Am Coun Educ, 68-69. *Mem:* AAAS; Entom Soc Am. *Res:* Gnotobiology and germ free techniques; mosquito biology; botany. *Mailing Add:* Dept of Biol Langston Univ Langston OK 73050

JONES, WESLEY MORRIS, b Raymond, Wash, Apr 29, 19; m 54; c 3. PHYSICAL CHEMISTRY. *Educ:* Univ Calif, AB, 40, PhD(chem), 46. *Prof Exp:* Asst chem, Univ Calif, 40-42; STAFF MEM, LOS ALAMOS NAT LAB, 43- *Concurrent Pos:* Res fel, Calif Inst Technol, 57-58. *Mem:* Am Chem Soc. *Res:* Low temperature specific heats; thermodynamics; gas kinetics; physical chemistry of tritium and hydrogen isotope effects; diffusion; thermochemical cycles for hydrogen production. *Mailing Add:* 4753 Sandia Dr Los Alamos CA 87544

JONES, WILBER CLARK, b Grove City, Pa, Jan 21, 41; m 62; c 2. INORGANIC CHEMISTRY. *Educ:* Westminster Col, Pa, BS, 62; Univ Tenn, PhD(chem), 66. *Prof Exp:* Asst prof, 66-70, assoc prof, 70-77, PROF CHEM, CONCORD COL, 77-, CHMN PHYS SCI DEPT, 74- *Mem:* Am Chem Soc. *Res:* Synthesis and structural studies on coordination compounds. *Mailing Add:* Dept of Phys Sci Concord Col Athens WV 24712

JONES, WILBUR DOUGLAS, JR, b Augusta, Ga, July 3, 27; m 52; c 2. MICROBIOLOGY. *Educ:* Emory Univ, AB, 49; WVa Univ, MS, 51; Med Col Ga, PhD(microbiol), 68. *Prof Exp:* Asst, WVa Univ, 51; instr sci, Truett-McConnell Jr Col, 51-53; bacteriologist, Ga State Health Dept, 53-60, chief bacteriologist, Training Lab, 60-62; RES MICROBIOLOGIST, CTR DIS CONTROL, USPHS, 62- *Mem:* Am Soc Microbiol; fel Am Acad Microbiol. *Res:* Genetics and phage typing of the mycobacteria; genetics and molecular biology of the mycobacteriophages. *Mailing Add:* Mycobacteriol Br Ctr for Disease Control Atlanta GA 30333

JONES, WILLIAM B, b Spring Hill, Tenn, Sept 24, 31; m 56; c 5. NUMERICAL ANALYSIS, COMPLEX ANALYSIS. *Educ:* Jacksonville State Col, BA, 53; Vanderbilt Univ, MA, 55, PhD(math), 63. *Prof Exp:* Mathematician, Nat Bur Standards, 58-63; actg asst prof math, 63-64, asst prof appl math, 64-68, assoc prof math, 68-73, assoc chmn dept, 72-74, PROF MATH, UNIV COLO, BOULDER, 73- *Concurrent Pos:* Consult, Nat Bur Standards, 64-65 & Environ Sci Servs Admin, 65-70; consult, Off Telecommun-Inst Telecommun Sci, 70-73, mathematician, 70-71. *Honors & Awards:* Gold Medal Award, US Dept Com, 65. *Mem:* Am Math Soc; Math Asn Am; Soc Indust & Appl Math. *Res:* Complex analysis; numerical analysis; approximation theory; continued fractions; Pade Approximants. *Mailing Add:* 455 Erie Dr Boulder CO 80303

JONES, WILLIAM B(ENJAMIN), JR, b Fairburn, Ga, Sept 17, 24; m 48; c 3. ELECTRICAL ENGINEERING. *Educ:* Ga Inst Technol, BS, 45, MS, 48, PhD(elec eng), 53. *Prof Exp:* Engr, radar develop, R I Sarbacher & Assoc, 47-48; from instr to assoc prof elec eng & res assoc, Ga Inst Technol, 48-54; res engr, Hughes Aircraft Co, 54-58; prof elec eng, Ga Inst Technol, 58-67; PROF ELEC ENG & HEAD DEPT, TEX A&M UNIV, 67- *Mem:* Sr mem Inst Elec & Electronics Engrs; Nat Soc Prof Engrs; Soc Mfg Engrs; Am Soc Eng Educ. *Res:* Communications theory and systems; engineering education. *Mailing Add:* Dept of Elec Eng Tex A&M Univ College Station TX 77843

JONES, WILLIAM BARCLAY, b San Francisco, Calif, Aug 18, 19; m 46; c 3. PHYSICS. *Educ:* Univ Calif, AB, 47, PhD(physics), 64. *Prof Exp:* Accelerator supvr, Crocker Lab, Univ Calif, 55-62; nuclear physicist, Tech Measurement Corp, 62-67; res assoc physics, Yale Univ, 68-75; PHYSICIST, BROOKHAVEN NAT LAB, 75- *Mem:* Am Phys Soc; Am Nuclear Soc; AAAS. *Res:* Low and intermediate energy; experimental nuclear physics. *Mailing Add:* Brookhaven Nat Lab Bldg 901A Upton NY 11973

JONES, WILLIAM DENVER, b Jenkinjones, WVa, Apr 14, 35; m 58; c 2. PLASMA PHYSICS, SOLAR PHYSICS. *Educ:* Berea Col, BA, 58; Vanderbilt Univ, MA, 61, PhD(physics), 63. *Prof Exp:* Res assoc plasma physics, Thermonuclear Div, Oak Ridge Nat Lab, 63-70; assoc prof, 70-72, PROF PHYSICS, UNIV SOUTH FLA, 72- *Concurrent Pos:* AEC & Energy Res Develop Admin res contracts, 71-76; Air Force Cambridge Res Labs contract, 72-74; consult, Solarkit of Fla, Tampa, 75- *Mem:* Fel Am Phys Soc; Am Asn Physics Teachers; Sigma Xi. *Res:* Basic and applied research in plasmas; applied research in alternative energy sources, with emphasis on solar energy. *Mailing Add:* Dept of Physics Univ of SFla Tampa FL 33620

JONES, WILLIAM ERNEST, b Sackville, NB, Can, Aug 7, 36; m 58; c 4. PHYSICAL CHEMISTRY. *Educ:* Mt Allison Univ, BSc, 58, MSc, 59; McGill Univ, PhD(phys chem), 63. *Prof Exp:* Res assoc, Mt Allison Univ, 59-60; from asst prof to assoc prof, 62-73, PROF PHYS CHEM, DALHOUSIE UNIV, 73-, CHMN DEPT CHEM, 74- *Mem:* Chem Inst Can; Chem Inst Can; NY Acad Sci; Can Asn Physicists; Int Am Photochem Soc. *Res:* Kinetics; spectroscopy. *Mailing Add:* Dept of Chem Dalhousie Univ Halifax NS B3H 4J3 Can

JONES, WILLIAM F, b Sanford, NC, Sept 5, 27; m 51; c 1. GENETICS, SCIENCE EDUCATION. *Educ:* Davis & Elkins Col, BA, 51; Madison Col, MS, 58; Univ Va, EdD(sci educ), 68. *Prof Exp:* Teacher, Louisa County High Sch, Va, 51-53 & Handley High Sch, Winchester, 53-58; assoc prof, 58-78, PROF BIOL, JAMES MADISON UNIV, 78- *Concurrent Pos:* Dir, NSF Inst. *Res:* General zoology; genetics; population genetics; evolution; biometrics; psychometrics; marine sciences; curriculum and instruction. *Mailing Add:* 725 S Main St Harrisonburg VA 22801

JONES, WILLIAM HENRY, JR, b Waycross, Ga, Mar 3, 04; m 61; c 1. CHEMISTRY. *Educ:* Emory Univ, BS, 24; Princeton Univ, MA, 25, PhD(phys chem), 29. *Prof Exp:* Asst, Princeton Univ, 24-27; instr chem, 27-30, from asst prof to prof, 30-72, EMER PROF CHEM & ADMIN ASST, EMORY UNIV, 72- *Concurrent Pos:* Fel, Calif Inst Technol, 41-42; lab dir, thermal diffusion plant, Manhattan Proj, 44-45; dir progs, NSF, Emory Univ, 59-66; dir progs, Ford Found, 62-67. *Honors & Awards:* Thomas Jefferson Award, 67. *Mem:* AAAS; Am Chem Soc; Am Phys Soc; fel Am Inst Chemists. *Res:* Chemical reaction kinetics; x-rays and molecular structure; precise calorimetry of latent heats; thermal diffusion of liquids; yields in proton-induced fission; chemical education. *Mailing Add:* Dept of Chem Emory Univ Atlanta GA 30322

JONES, WILLIAM HOWRY, b Lancaster, Pa, Nov 6, 20; m 59; c 4. ORGANIC CHEMISTRY. *Educ:* Juniata Col, BS, 42; Columbia Univ, MA, 44; Mass Inst Technol, PhD(org chem), 47. *Prof Exp:* Lab asst chem, Juniata Col, 39-42; lab asst, Columbia Univ, 42-44; lectr, 43, asst, Manhattan Proj, SAM Labs, 44-45; asst, Anti-Malarial Proj, Mass Inst Technol, 45-46; Du Pont fel nuclear alkylation, Univ Ill, 47-48; instr chem, Univ Ill, 48-49; res chemist, Merck Inc, 49-59, RES ASSOC, MERCK SHARP & DOHME RES LABS, 59- *Mem:* Am Chem Soc; fel NY Acad Sci. *Res:* Synthesis of physiologically active compounds; reaction mechanisms; synthesis of substituted diamines and quinoline derivatives; catalytic hydrogenation; high pressure research. *Mailing Add:* Merck Sharp & Dohme Res Labs Rahway NJ 07065

JONES, WILLIAM J, b New York, NY, Mar 23, 15; m 42; c 3. ENGINEERING PHYSICS. *Educ:* Tufts Univ, BS, 41; Newark Col Eng, MS, 50. *Prof Exp:* Lectr physics, Harvard Univ, 63-72; SR STAFF RES ASSOC, ENERGY LAB, MASS INST TECHNOL, 72- *Res:* High energy physics; energy technologies issues and policies. *Mailing Add:* 92 Bullough Park Newton MA 02160

JONES, WILLIAM JONAS, JR, b Whaleyville, Va, Nov 18, 41; m 80. ORGANIC CHEMISTRY, TEXTILE FIBERS. *Educ:* Col William & Mary, BS, 63; Duke Univ, PhD(org chem), 66. *Prof Exp:* RES CHEMIST, DACRON RES LAB, E I DU PONT DE NEMOURS & CO, INC, 66- *Mem:* Am Chem Soc. *Res:* Heterocyclic organic compounds; polymers; chemistry of textile fibers; fiber engineering. *Mailing Add:* Dacron Res Lab E I du Pont de Nemours & Co Inc Kinston NC 28501

JONES, WILLIAM LOUIS, b Chicago, Ill, Nov 23, 46. OPTOMETRY. *Educ:* Univ NMex, BS, 69; Univ Houston, OD(optom), 76. *Prof Exp:* Optom resident, Vet Admin Hosp, Kansas City, Mo, 76-77; asst prof optom, Univ Houston, 77-78; CHIEF OPTOM, VET ADMIN, HOSP, 78- *Mem:* Am Acad Optom; Nat Asn Vet Admin Optometrists. *Res:* Anatomy; physiology; pathology of the eye; systemic conditions which effect the eye; contact lenses and their physiological effects on the eye. *Mailing Add:* Dept of Ophthal 2100 Ridgecrest Dr Albuquerque NM 87108

JONES, WILLIAM MAURICE, b Campbellsville, Ky, Jan 12, 30; m 56; c 3. ORGANIC CHEMISTRY. *Educ:* Union Univ, Tenn, BS, 51; Univ Ga, MS, 53; Univ Southern Calif, PhD(org chem), 55. *Prof Exp:* Instr chem, Univ Southern Calif, 55-56; from asst prof to assoc prof, 56-65, chmn dept, 68-73, PROF CHEM, UNIV FLA, 65- *Concurrent Pos:* Sloan fel, 63-67; NATO sr sci fel, 71; mem ed bd, Chem Rev, 71-74, J Organic Chem, 74-79. *Mem:* Am Chem Soc. *Res:* Mechanisms of organic reactions; carbocyclic aromatic carbenes; transition metal complexes of conjugated carbocyclic carbenes; carbene-carbene rearrangements. *Mailing Add:* Dept of Chem Univ of Fla Gainesville FL 32601

JONES, WILLIAM PHILIP, b Chicago, Ill, Oct 2, 42; m 64; c 2. EXPERIMENTAL NUCLEAR PHYSICS. *Educ:* Univ Notre Dame, BS, 64; Univ Mich, MS, 65, PhD(physics), 69. *Prof Exp:* Res assoc, 69-71, STAFF SCIENTIST PHYSICS, IND UNIV, BLOOMINGTON, 71- *Mem:* Am Phys Soc; Sigma Xi; AAAS. *Res:* Medium energy nuclear physics; charged-particle reactions; properties of nuclear energy levels; cyclotron orbit dynamics. *Mailing Add:* Cyclotron Facil Ind Univ Milo B Sampson Lane Bloomington IN 47401

JONES, WILLIAM VERNON, b Yellville, Ark, Jan 25, 35; m 55; c 3. COSMIC RAY PHYSICS. *Educ:* Univ Tulsa, BS, 63; La State Univ, Baton Rouge, PhD(physics), 67. *Prof Exp:* Res assoc physics, La State Univ, Baton Rouge, 67; guest res assoc, Max Planck Inst Extraterrestrial Physics, 67-68; res instr, 69-70, asst prof, 70-74, ASSOC PROF PHYSICS & ASTRON, LA STATE UNIV, BATON ROUGE, 74- *Concurrent Pos:* Alexander von Humboldt res stipend, 67-68. *Mem:* Am Inst Physics; Am Phys Soc. *Res:* Electromagnetic cascade measurements; properties of high-energy nuclear interactions in cosmic rays; Monte Carlo calculations to study nuclear cascades; use of ionization spectrometers for cosmic ray energy measurements. *Mailing Add:* Dept of Physics & Astron La State Univ Baton Rouge LA 70803

JONES, WINSTON WILLIAM, b Eclectic, Ala, Jan 18, 10; m 33; c 2. HORTICULTURE. *Educ:* Ala Polytech Inst, BS, 31; Purdue Univ, MS, 33; Univ Chicago, PhD(plant physiol), 36. *Prof Exp:* Asst, Purdue Univ, 33; asst plant physiologist, Exp Sta, Univ Hawaii, 36-38, asst horticulturist, 38-42; from assoc horticulturist to horticulturist, Univ Ariz, 42-46; assoc horticulturist, 46-51, prof & horticulturist, 51-77, EMER PROF HORT & HORTICULTURIST, UNIV CALIF, RIVERSIDE, 77- *Mem:* AAAS; Am Soc Plant Physiol; Am Soc Hort Sci. *Res:* Mineral and organic nutrition of citrus; respiration in etiolated wheat seedlings as influenced by phosphorus nutrition. *Mailing Add:* Dept Bot & Plant Sci Univ of Calif Riverside CA 92521

JONES, WINTON D, JR, b Terre Haute, Ind, June 23, 41; m 64; c 2. MEDICINAL CHEMISTRY, ORGANIC CHEMISTRY. *Educ:* Butler Univ, BS, 63, MS, 66; Univ Kans, PhD(med chem), 71. *Prof Exp:* org chemist, Merrell-Dow Pharmaceut, Inc, Dow Chem Co, 80- *Concurrent Pos:* Cong sci consult. *Mem:* Am Chem Soc. *Res:* Medicinal chemistry, antiallergic agents; synthesis of central nervous system, cardiovascular coxasackie virus and immunological agents. *Mailing Add:* Merrell-Nat Labs 110 E Amity Rd Cincinnati OH 45215

JONES WITTERS, PATRICIA H, b Elizabeth, NJ, Nov 9, 38; m 58, 67; c 2. REPRODUCTIVE PHYSIOLOGY. *Educ:* NMex State Univ, BS, 62; Purdue Univ, PhD(reprod physiol), 67. *Prof Exp:* Asst prof, 67-74, ASSOC PROF ZOOL, OHIO UNIV, 74- *Concurrent Pos:* Consult, Schering Corp, 67. *Mem:* Soc Study Reproduction. *Res:* Reproductive physiology in domestic pig, dairy cow and laboratory rat. *Mailing Add:* Dept Zool Ohio Univ Zool Bldg Athens OH 45701

JONG, ING-CHANG, b Yunlin, Taiwan, Feb 5, 38; m 66; c 2. SOLID MECHANICS. *Educ:* Nat Taiwan Univ, BS, 61; SDak Sch Mines & Technol, MS, 63; Northwestern Univ, Chicago, PhD(theoret & appl mech), 65. *Prof Exp:* From asst prof to assoc prof, 65-74, PROF ENG SCI, UNIV ARK, FAYETTEVILLE, 74- *Concurrent Pos:* Prin investr, eng res initiation grant, NSF, 67-69, eng mech res grant, 69-71. *Mem:* Am Soc Mech Engrs; Am Soc Eng Educ; Am Acad Mech; Sigma Xi. *Res:* Nonconservative stability of damped structures; vibrations and dynamic stability of structural systems exhibiting yielding and hysteresis. *Mailing Add:* Dept of Eng Sci Univ of Ark Fayetteville AR 72701

JONG, SHUNG-CHANG, b Taiwan, Nov 12, 36; US citizen; m 65; c 3. MYCOLOGY. *Educ:* Nat Taiwan Univ, BS, 60; Western Ill Univ, MS, 66; Wash State Univ, PhD(mycol), 69. *Prof Exp:* Asst plant pathologist, Taiwan Agr Res Inst, 61-63; asst instr mycol, Nat Taiwan Univ, 63-65; sr mycologist, 69-71, cur fungi, 71-73, CUR & HEAD MYCOL DEPT, AM TYPE CULTURE COLLECTION, 74- *Concurrent Pos:* Sci Found grants, 75- *Mem:* Am Phytopath Soc; Am Soc Microbiol; Int Soc Human & Animal Mycol; Med Mycol Soc Am; Mycol Soc Am. *Res:* Preservation and industrial applications of living fungi; biology of fungi in culture. *Mailing Add:* Mycol Dept 12301 Parklawn Dr Am Type Cult Collection Rockville MD 20852

JONGEDYK, HOWARD ALBERT, b Chicago, Ill, Sept 6, 26; m 55; c 1. CIVIL ENGINEERING. *Educ:* Univ Ill, BS, 47, MS, 48; Univ Minn, MS, 58, PhD(civil eng), 68. *Prof Exp:* Asst soil conservationist, Soil Conserv Serv, USDA, 48-53; asst soil conservationist, Water Resources Div, US Geol Survey, 55-62; res scientist, Carbon Prods Div, Union Carbide Corp, 62-66; staff engr, SD Lab, IBM Corp, 68-69; HYDRAULIC ENGR, FED HWY ADMIN, DC, 69- *Mem:* Am Geophys Union; Am Chem Soc; Am Soc Civil Engrs. *Res:* Soils; sediments; carbons; particulate matter; drainage, permeability; structure, strength, sizing, fluid flow patterns, electrokinetic effects; air and water pollution. *Mailing Add:* Off of Res Fed Hwy Admin 400 Seventh St SW Washington DC 20590

JONGENBURGER, HUIBERT S, physical chemistry, chemical engineering, see previous edition

JONI, SAJ-NICOLE A, US citizen. COMPUTER SCIENCE. *Educ:* Univ Calif, San Diego, BA, 73, MS, 75, PhD(math), 77. *Prof Exp:* Instr appl math, Mass Inst Technol, 77-78; asst prof math, Carnegie-Mellon Univ, 78-80 & Mass Inst Technol, 80-81; ASST PROF COMPUT SCI & MATH, WELLESLEY COL, 81- *Mem:* Am Math Soc; Asn Women Math; Asn Comput Mach. *Res:* Formal languages; combinatorial and algebraic solutions to automata-theortic problems; integration and intersection of feminist theory and mathematics computer science; aritifical intelligence. *Mailing Add:* Dept Comput Sci Wellesley Col Wellesley MA 02181

JONNARD, AIMISON, b Sewanee, Tenn, Aug 3, 16; m 61; c 4. CHEMICAL ENGINEERING. *Educ:* Kans State Univ, BS, 38; Columbia Univ, MS, 39; Univ Pittsburgh, PhD(chem eng), 49. *Prof Exp:* Engr, Exp Sta, E I du Pont de Nemours & Co, 39-41; instr chem eng, Kans State Univ, 41-45; sr technologist, Shell Chem Co, 49-54, mgr mkt anal, 54-59; mgr mkt res & develop, US Indust Chem Co Div, Nat Distillers & Chem Co, 59-61; vpres, Celanese Chem Co, 61-63; sr corp planner, Exxon Chem Co, 63-71; CHIEF, ENERGY & CHEM DIV, US INT TRADE COMN, 71- *Mem:* Am Chem Soc; Am Inst Chem Engrs. *Res:* Chemical economics. *Mailing Add:* 1202 Old Stable Rd McLean VA 22102

JONSSON, BJARNI, b Draghals, Iceland, Feb 15, 20. MATHEMATICS. *Educ:* Univ Calif, AB, 43, PhD(math), 46. *Prof Exp:* Instr, Brown Univ, 46-48, from asst prof to assoc prof, Univ Minn, Minneapolis, 48-59, prof, 59-66; DISTINGUISHED PROF MATH, VANDERBILT UNIV, 66- *Mem:* Am Math Soc; Icelandic Math Soc; Asn Symbolic Logic. *Res:* Algebra. *Mailing Add:* Dept of Math PO Box 1541 Sta B Vanderbilt Univ Nashville TN 37235

JONSSON, HALDOR TURNER, JR, b State College, Pa, Jan 5, 29; m 64; c 2. BIOCHEMISTRY. *Educ:* Tex A&M Univ, BS, 52, MS, 61; Baylor Univ, PhD(biochem), 65. *Prof Exp:* Res asst plastics & resins, Shell Chem Corp, 56-59; res asst biochem, Tex A&M Univ, 59-61 & Col Med, Baylor Univ, 61-65; res assoc, Sch Med, Boston Univ, 65-66; asst prof chem, 66-70, ASSOC PROF BIOCHEM, MED UNIV SC, 70- *Concurrent Pos:* Clin chem consult, Vet Admin Hosp, Charleston, 66- *Mem:* Am Chem Soc; Am Soc Biol Chem; Am Oil Chemists' Soc; NY Acad Sci. *Res:* Gonadotropins and their influence on ovarian function; role of prostoglandins and essential fatty acids in wounds; gas-liquid chromatography; long term effects of pesticides on mammals. *Mailing Add:* Dept of Biochem Med Univ of SC Charleston SC 29425

JONSSON, JENS J(OHANNES), b Mildstedt, Ger, Apr 4, 22; m 45; c 5. ELECTRICAL ENGINEERING. *Educ:* Univ Utah, BS, 44 & 46; Purdue Univ, MS, 47, PhD(elec eng), 51. *Prof Exp:* Instr elec eng, Univ Utah, 47; instr, Purdue Univ, 47-51; assoc prof, 51-53, chmn eng sci dept, 54-55, chmn elec eng sci dept, 55-60, mgr, Eng Anal Ctr, 64-72, PROF ELEC ENG, BRIGHAM YOUNG UNIV, 53- *Concurrent Pos:* Asst, Purdue Univ, 50-51; supvr res & develop, NAm Aviation Corp, 51-53; vis res prof, Polytech Inst Brooklyn, 60-61; UNESCO field expert, Mid East Tech Univ, Ankara, 67-68 & chief tech adv, Romania, 74-76. *Mem:* Am Soc Eng Educ; Inst Elec & Electronics Engrs; Sigma Xi. *Res:* Automatic control; systems engineering; computers. *Mailing Add:* Dept of Elec Eng Brigham Young Univ 123 FELB Provo UT 84601

JONSSON, JOHN ERIK, b New York, NY, Sept 6, 01; m 23; c 3. ENGINEERING. *Educ:* Rensselaer Polytech Inst, ME, 22. *Hon Degrees:* DEng, Rensselaer Polytech Inst, 59; DSc, Hobart & William Smith Col, 61, Austin Col, 63; LLD, Southern Methodist Univ, 64, Carnegie-Mellon Univ, 72, Skidmore Col, 72; DCL, Univ Dallas, 68, Okla Christian Col, 73. *Prof Exp:* Mem mgt staff, Aluminum Co Am, 22-27 & Dumont Motor Car Co, 27-30; mem mgt staff, Tex Instruments, Inc, 30-42, pres, 51-58, chmn bd, 58-66, hon chmn bd, 67-77, HON DIR, TEX INSTRUMENTS, INC, 77- *Concurrent Pos:* Dir, Repub of Tex Corp. *Honors & Awards:* Bene Merenti Medal, 66; Gantt Medal, 68; Hoover Medal, 70; Chauncey Rose Medal, Rose-Hulman Inst, 72; Founders Medal, Nat Acad Eng, 74, Bus Hall of Fame, 75; John Ericsson Award, Am Soc Swedish Engrs. *Mem:* Nat Acad Eng; Soc Explor Geophysicists; Newcomen Soc; Am Mgt Asn. *Mailing Add:* Tex Instruments Inc 3300 Republic Bank Tower Dallas TX 75201

JONSSON, WILBUR JACOB, b Winnipeg, Man, Sept 18, 36. MATHEMATICS. *Educ:* Univ Man, BSc, 58, MSc, 59; Univ Tübingen, Dr rer nat(math), 63. *Prof Exp:* Lectr math, Univ Man, 59-60, asst prof, 62-65; lectr, Univ Birmingham, 65-66; ASSOC PROF MATH, McGILL UNIV, 66- *Res:* Projective planes; group theory; combinatory mathematics; foundations of geometry. *Mailing Add:* Dept of Math McGill Univ Montreal PQ H3A 2T5 Can

JONTE, JOHN HAWORTH, b Moscow, Idaho, Oct 21, 18; m 42; c 4. GEOCHEMISTRY, INORGANIC CHEMISTRY. *Educ:* Univ of the Pac, AB, 40; Wash State Univ, MS, 42; Univ Ark, PhD(chem), 56. *Prof Exp:* Jr chemist, US Bur Mines, Nev, 42-44 & Shell Develop Co, Calif, 44-46; instr chem, Iowa State Univ, 46-51; instr geol, Univ Ark, 54-55; res chemist, Texaco Inc, Tex, 55-61, group leader geochem, 61-66; assoc prof geochem & anal chem, 66-69, PROF CHEM & HEAD DEPT, SDAK SCH MINES & TECHNOL, 69- *Mem:* AAAS; Am Chem Soc; Geochem Soc; Am Inst Chemists; NY Acad Sci. *Res:* Geochemistry of petroleum and of sedimentary rocks; nuclear reactions in the earth's crust and geochemistry of thermal waters; radioactive tracer techniques in inorganic chemistry. *Mailing Add:* Dept of Chem SDak Sch of Mines & Technol Rapid City SD 57701

JOOS, HOWARD ARTHUR, b Albany, NY, May 27, 22; m 46; c 3. PEDIATRICS, PEDIATRIC CARDIOLOGY. *Educ:* Univ Rochester, MD, 45. *Prof Exp:* Intern pediat, Harriet Lane Home, Johns Hopkins Univ, 45-46; asst resident, Strong Mem Hosp, Univ Rochester, 48-49, chief resident, 50-51, asst pediatrician, 51-54, from instr to asst prof, 51-55; assoc prof, Sch Med, Univ Southern Calif, 55-61; clin asst prof, Univ Colo, 61-64; prof pediat, State Univ NY Downstate Med Ctr, 64-73; prof pediat & chmn dept, Sch Med, Univ NDak, 73-76; clin prof pediat, Med Col Ohio, 76-79; CLIN PROF PEDIAT, STATE UNIV NY DOWNSTATE MED CTR, 80- *Concurrent Pos:* Vet fel, Sch Med, Univ Rochester, 48-49, 50-51; Masonic res fel, 49-50, Markle Found scholar, 51-55; mem staff, Convalescent Hosp Children, Rochester, NY; consult staff, Genesee Hosp; dir cardiovasc res, physiol res & pvt serv, Children's Hosp, Los Angeles, 55-59; chief pediat, Nat Jewish Hosp, Denver, Colo, 61-64; dir pediat serv, Maimonides Hosp Brooklyn, 64-73; dir med educ & pediat, Toledo Hosp, 76-79; dir pediat, Staten Island Hosp, 79- *Mem:* AAAS; Soc Pediat Res; AMA; Am Acad Pediat. *Res:* Cardiovascular diseases of infancy and childhood. *Mailing Add:* Staten Island Hosp 475 Seaview Ave Staten Island NY 10305

JOOS, RICHARD W, b Cologne, Minn, Sept 22, 34; m 60; c 4. BIOCHEMISTRY. *Educ:* Col St Thomas, BS, 58; Univ Minn, PhD(biochem), 64. *Prof Exp:* Teaching asst biochem, Univ Minn, 58-62, res assoc med, 62-66; biochemist, Vet Admin Hosp, Minneapolis, 66-67; RES SPECIALIST, 3M CTR, MINN MINING & MFG CO, 67- *Concurrent Pos:* Instr, Univ Minn Dent Sch, 71- *Mem:* Int Asn Dent Res. *Res:* Ion binding to macromolecules; humoral factors against bacteria; preventive agents for dental disease; dental materials. *Mailing Add:* 3M Co 3M Ctr 2501 Hudson Rd St Paul MN 55101

JOPLING, ALAN VICTOR, b Sydney, Australia, Oct 3, 24; m 50; c 2. GEOMORPHOLOGY, SEDIMENTOLOGY. *Educ:* Univ Sydney, BSc, 46, BE, 47; Harvard Univ, AM, 58, PhD(geol), 61. *Prof Exp:* Asst engr, Water Conserv Comn, NSW, 42-47; teaching fel geol, Univ Sydney, 47-49; lectr, NSW Univ Tech, 49-53; seismologist, Frontier Geophys Co, Alta, 53-54; geologist, Mobil Oil Can Ltd, 54-56 & water resources, US Geol Surv, 58-61; from asst prof to assoc prof, 61-68, PROF GEOG, UNIV TORONTO, 68-, PROF GEOL, 80- *Concurrent Pos:* NSF grant photogeol, Harvard Univ, 61. *Honors & Awards:* Best Paper Award, Soc Econ Paleont & Mineral, 65. *Mem:* Geol Soc Am; Soc Econ Paleont & Mineral; Int Asn Sedimentol; Can Asn Geog; Eng Inst Can. *Res:* fluid mechanics of sedimentation; physics of surface processes; processes of erosion, transportation and deposition of sedimentary materials; hydrology and water resources. *Mailing Add:* Dept of Geog Univ of Toronto Toronto ON M5S 1A1 Can

JOPPA, LEONARD ROBERT, b Billings, Mont, Sept 29, 30; m 59; c 4. GENETICS. *Educ:* Mont State Univ, BS, 57, PhD(genetics), 67; Ore State Univ, MS, 62. *Prof Exp:* Asst agron, Mont Agr Exp Sta, 57-62, asst agronomist, 62-64, res asst agron, 64-67; RES GENETICIST PLANTS, SCI & EDUC ADMIN, AGR RES, USDA, 67- *Mem:* AAAS; Am Soc Agron; Crops Sci Soc Am; Genetics Soc Am; Genetics Soc Can. *Res:* Genetics and cytogenetics of wheat and its relatives. *Mailing Add:* Agr Res Serv Dept of Agron State University Sta Fargo ND 58102

JOPPA, RICHARD M, b Littleton, Colo, Sept 29, 29; m 52; c 2. ELECTRICAL ENGINEERING, ELECTRONICS. *Educ:* Colo State Univ, BS, 51; Univ Ill, MS, 57, PhD(elec eng), 63. *Prof Exp:* US Air Force, 51-71, instr elec eng, US Air Force Inst Technol, 57-59, chief space physics br, res directorate, Air Force Spec Weapons Ctr, NMex, 60-61, asst chief space vehicle div, test directorate, 62-64, asst prof elec eng, US Air Force Acad, 64-66, assoc prof, 66-68, chief anal br, survivability div & dir, vulnerability assessment directorate, Air Force Spec Weapons Ctr, Kirtland AFB, 68-71; ELEC-ELECTRONICS ENGR, LOS ALAMOS NAT LABS, UNIV CALIF, 71- *Concurrent Pos:* NSF fel, Univ Santa Clara, 67. *Mem:* Sr mem Inst Elec & Electronics Engrs; Nat Soc Prof Engrs. *Res:* Telemetry; instrumentation; information theory; circuit theory; experiment design, test and integration; control systems; electromagnetic environment energy conversion; research and development financial management. *Mailing Add:* Los Alamos Nat Lab MS-124 PO Box 1663 Los Alamos NM 87544

JOPSON, HARRY GORGAS MICHENER, b Philadelphia, Pa, June 23, 11; m 33; c 2. ZOOLOGY. *Educ:* Haverford Col, BS, 32; Cornell Univ, MA, 33, PhD(vert zool), 36. *Hon Degrees:* ScD, Bridgewater Col, 77. *Prof Exp:* Instr biol, Iowa State Teachers Col, 36; from asst prof to assoc prof, 36-46, prof biol, 46-81, EMER PROF, BRIDGEWATER COL, 81- *Concurrent Pos:* Asst dir, Overseas Oper, United Seamen's Serv, 43-46; trustee, Rockingham County Bd Educ, 57-76, chmn, 74-76; trustee, Nat Parks & Consrv Asn, 65-80. *Mem:* Soc Study Amphibians & Reptiles; Am Soc Ichthyol & Herpet; Am Soc Mammal; Am Ornith Union. *Res:* Salamanders of southeastern United States; vertebrate natural history. *Mailing Add:* PO Box 26 Bridgewater VA 22812

JORAM, PHILIP ROBERT, b Longview, Tex, Apr 30, 25; m 52; c 5. BIOLOGY. *Prof Exp:* Preparator & curator, Path Mus, Sch Med, La State Univ, 46; sr technician & asst, Med Mus, Armed Forces Inst Path, 52-53; head, Plastics Univ, Div Res Serv, Med Arts Sect, NIH, 54-80; RETIRED. *Concurrent Pos:* Preparator, Path Mus, Sch Med, George Washington Univ, 53-; consult, Med Plastics Tech Serv, 69- *Res:* Application of plastics technology for medical research; medical museum technology. *Mailing Add:* 4416 Yuma St NW Washington DC 20016

JORCH, HAROLD HENRY, b WGer, Feb 17, 51; Can citizen; m 75; c 2. PHYSICS, SEMICONDUCTOR SURFACE. *Educ:* Univ Waterloo, BSc(sci), 74, BSc(physics), 75; Univ Guelph, MSc, 77, PhD(physics), 82. *Prof Exp:* FEL, CHALK RIVER NUCLEAR LAB, ATOMIC ENERGY CAN CO, 81- *Concurrent Pos:* Tech collabr, Brookhaven Nat Lab, 79-81. *Res:* Properties of surfaces and interfaces using particle beams (ions and positrons). *Mailing Add:* Chalk River Nuclear Lab Atomic Energy Can Ltd Chalk River ON K0J 1J0 Can

JORDAN, A(NGEL) G(ONI), b Pamplona, Spain, Sept 19, 30; m 56; c 3. SOLID STATE ELECTRONICS, UNIVERSITY ADMINISTRATION. *Educ:* Univ Zaragoza, MS, 52; Carnegie Inst Technol, MS & PhD(elec eng), 59. *Prof Exp:* Res assoc physics, Navy Res Inst, Spain, 52-53, res fel electronics, 53-56; instr elec eng, Carnegie Inst Technol, 56-58; res fel semiconductors, Mellon Inst, 58-59; asst prof elec eng, Carnegie Inst Technol, 59-62, assoc prof, 62-66, prof phys electronics, 66-69, prof elec eng & head dept, 69-79, V A & Helen Whitaker prof electronics & elec eng, 72-79, DEAN CARNEGIE INST TECHNOL, CARNEGIE-MELLON UNIV, 79- *Concurrent Pos:* Consult var companies, 60-; mem res adv comt, Allegheny-Singer Corp; Sr scientist award, NATO, 77. *Mem:* Fel Inst Elec & Electronics Engrs; Am Phys Soc; Am Soc Eng Educ; AAAS. *Res:* Solid state devices; integrated circuits; thin films; joining of materials; coal mine electronics; gas sensing devices and systems; environmental and biomedical instrumentation; robotics; applied electronics; semiconductor devices. *Mailing Add:* Dean's Off Carnegie Inst Technol Carnegie-Mellon Univ Pittsburgh PA 15213

JORDAN, ALBERT GUSTAV, b Oak Park, Ill, Jan 7, 41; m 64; c 2. MATERIALS SCIENCE, NUCLEAR METALLURGY. *Educ:* Purdue Univ, BS, MetE, 62; Univ Ill, Urbana, MS, 63, PhD(mat sci), 69. *Prof Exp:* ENGR, NUCLEAR METALL, KNOLLS ATOMIC POWER LAB, GEN ELEC CO, 68- *Mem:* Am Soc Metals; Am Nuclear Soc. *Res:* Behavior of nuclear fuel systems; prediction of performance of fuel systems. *Mailing Add:* 1134 Waverly Pl Schenectady NY 12308

JORDAN, ALBERT RAYMOND, b Alma, Kans, Oct 4, 06; m 32; c 3. PHYSICS. *Educ:* Univ Colo, BA, 29, MA, 33, PhD(physics), 40. *Prof Exp:* Instr physics, Univ Colo, 30-36 & Colo Agr & Mech Col, 36-37; from asst prof to assoc prof, Mont State Col, 37-41; physicist, Naval Ord Lab, Washington, DC, 41-42; from assoc prof to prof physics, Mont State Col, 42-52; sr res physicist, Denver Res Inst, Colo, 52-57; dean, 57-72, EMER DEAN, GRAD SCH, COLO SCH MINES, 72- *Concurrent Pos:* Physicist, Curtiss-Wright Res Lab, 44-45. *Mem:* Am Geophys Union; Am Meteorol Soc. *Res:* Barometry and anemometry, atmospheric acoustics; geophysics. *Mailing Add:* 1603 S Uinta Way Denver CO 80231

JORDAN, ALEXANDER WALKER, III, b Richmond, Va, Apr 12, 45; m 72. ENDOCRINOLOGY, REPRODUCTIVE PHYSIOLOGY. *Educ:* Roanoke Col, BS, 67; Univ Richmond, MA, 69; Rutgers Univ, PhD(zool), 75. *Prof Exp:* Fel endocrinol, Dept Physiol & Biophysics, Colo State Univ, 75-78; STAFF FEL ENDOCRINOL, FOOD & DRUG ADMIN, HEW, 78- *Concurrent Pos:* Fel, Rockefeller Found, 75-77. *Mem:* Sigma Xi; Soc Study Reproduction. *Res:* Reproductive endocrinology; investigation into the mechanism of action of peptide hormones and prostaglandins on steroidogenesis. *Mailing Add:* Div of Drug Biol HFD-412 200 C St SW Washington DC 20204

JORDAN, ANDREW STEPHEN, b Mezokovesd, Hungary, May 1, 36; US citizen; m 68; c 1. METALLURGY, PHYSICAL CHEMISTRY. *Educ:* Pa State Univ, BS, 59; Univ Pa, PhD(metall), 65. *Prof Exp:* Engr, Philco Corp, Pa, 59-62; res engr, Westinghouse Res Labs, Pa, 62-63; MEM TECH STAFF, BELL TEL LABS, 65- *Mem:* Electrochem Soc. *Res:* Crystal growth of compound semiconductors; chemical thermodynamics of optoelectronic materials with special emphasis on phase diagrams; impurity incorporation and defect chemistry; reliability of devices; crystal growth modeling. *Mailing Add:* Bell Tel Labs Murray Hill NJ 07974

JORDAN, BERNARD WILLIAM, JR, b Kansas City, Mo, Nov 10, 37; m 64; c 2. CONTROL ENGINEERING. *Educ:* Univ Calif, Berkeley, BS, 59, MS, 61, PhD(elec eng), 64. *Prof Exp:* Mem tech staff, Control Systs Dept, Aerospace Corp, Calif, 64-67; asst prof hybrid comput, 67-71, ASSOC PROF COMPUT ORGN, COMPUT GRAPHICS, HYBRID COMPUT, NORTHWESTERN UNIV, 71- *Concurrent Pos:* Consult, Aerospace Corp, 67- *Mem:* Inst Elec & Electronics Engrs. *Res:* Multi and parallel processors; computer graphics systems; application of connection networks to automatically patched hybrid computers. *Mailing Add:* Northwestern Univ Technol Inst Comput Sci Evanston IL 60201

JORDAN, BRIGITTE, b Ger. MEDICAL ANTHROPOLOGY, CROSSCULTURAL OBSTETRICS. *Educ:* Calif State Univ, Sacramento, BA, 69, MA, 71; Univ Calif, Irvine, PhD(soc sci), 75. *Prof Exp:* Asst prof, 75-80, ASSOC PROF, DEPT ANTHROP & COMMUNITY MED, MICH STATE UNIV, 80- *Concurrent Pos:* Res assoc, Feminist Women's Health Ctr, Santa Ana, Calif, 72-75. *Honors & Awards:* Margaret Mead Award, Soc Appl Anthrop, 80. *Mem:* Fel Am Anthrop Asn; Soc Appl Anthrop; Soc Med Anthrop; Soc Visual Anthrop. *Res:* Design of culturally appropriate maternal and child health care delivery systems; test of basic assumptions; integration of traditional and western medicine in developing countries; methodology, including videographic methods for documentation and analysis; patient-practitioner relationship; alternate systems of health care delivery; symbolic language of advertising; status of women; Maya Indians of Yucatan, Mexico. *Mailing Add:* Dept of Anthrop Mich State Univ East Lansing MI 48824

JORDAN, CARL FREDERICK, b New Brunswick, NJ, Dec 10, 35; m 67; c 2. ECOLOGY. *Educ:* Univ Mich, BS, 58; Rutgers Univ, MS, 64, PhD(ecol), 66. *Prof Exp:* Assoc sceintist, P R Nuclear Ctr, AEC, 66-69; from asst ecologist to assoc ecologist, Radiol & Environ Res Div, Argonne Nat Lab, 69-74; RES ASSOC, INST ECOL, UNIV GA, 74-, SR ECOLOGIST, 79- *Concurrent Pos:* Vis Scientist, Ecol Ctr, Venezuelan Inst Sci Invest, 74- *Honors & Awards:* Mercer Award, Ecol Soc Am, 73. *Mem:* AAAS; Ecol Soc Am; Soil Sci Soc Am. *Res:* Movement of chemical elements in soil; radiation recovery and mineral cycling in the tropical rain forest; application of systems analysis techniques to ecology; shifting agriculture in the Amazon Basin. *Mailing Add:* Inst of Ecol Univ of Ga Athens GA 30602

JORDAN, CHARLES EDWIN, b South Charleston, Ohio, Jan 2, 27; m 54; c 3. ANIMAL NUTRITION. *Educ:* Ohio State Univ, BS, 51; Purdue Univ, MS, 55, PhD, 58. *Prof Exp:* Instr animal sci, Purdue Univ, 56-58, asst prof, 58-59; sr sceintist animal nutrit res, 59-61, from asst head to head, 61-71, dir agr res, Lilly Res Ctr Ltd, Eng, 71-74, dir prod info, Elanco Prod Co Div, 74-75, EXECUTIVE DIR, LILLY RES LAB DIV, ELI LILLY CO, 75- *Mem:* AAAS; Am Soc Animal Sci; Animal Nutrit Res Coun; Am Inst Biol Sci. *Res:* Swine nutrition and physiology; quality control of rations and feedstuffs; chemical regulation of growth. *Mailing Add:* Lilly Res Lab Greenfield IN 46140

JORDAN, CHARLES LEMUEL, b Ash Grove, Mo, May 28, 22; m 51; c 6. METEOROLOGY. *Educ:* Univ Chicago, PhB, 48, BS, 49, SM, 51, PhD(meteorol), 56. *Prof Exp:* Meteorol aide, US Weather Bur, Philippines & Japan, 46-47, res meteorologist, Nat Hurricane Res Proj, 56-57; asst meteorol, Chicago, 51-54; tech consult, Air Weather Serv, US Air Force, Washington, DC, 54-55; assoc prof meteorol, 57-63, chmn dept, 63-70, PROF METEOROL, FLA STATE UNIV, 63- *Mem:* AAAS; fel Am Metoerol Soc; Am Geophys Union. *Res:* Tropical meteorology and climatology; synoptic meteorology; hurricanes. *Mailing Add:* Dept of Meteorology Fla State Univ Tallahassee FL 32306

JORDAN, CHRIS SULLIVAN, b Yangchow, China, Aug 6, 24; US citizen; m 47; c 3. BIOL^GY. *Educ:* Drake Univ, BA, 48; Univ Iowa, MS, 51, PhD(zool), 55. *Prof Exp:* Clin lab technologist, Vet Admin Hosp, Iowa City, Iowa, 52-55; supvr bact & parasitol, Terrell's Labs, Tex, 55-56; prof biol, Howard Payne Col, 56-63; prof, Houston Baptist Col, 63-67; CHMN DIV SCI & MATH, DALLAS BAPTIST COL, 67- *Concurrent Pos:* Res grant, NIH, 59-62. *Mem:* Am Inst Biol Sci; AAAS; Am Soc Parasitol; Am Soc Microbiol. *Res:* Parasitology and medical bacteriology. *Mailing Add:* 3838 Picturline Dr Dallas TX 75233

JORDAN, CONSTANCE (LOUISE) BRINE, b Newton, Mass, Dec 26, 19; m 57; c 5. NUTRITION. *Educ:* Harvard Univ, MPH, 48; Cornell Univ, PhD(food, nutrit), 54. *Prof Exp:* Chief dietitian, Newton-Wellesley Hosp, 43-45; asst dir sch lunch, Pub Schs, Newton, 45-46; asst nutrit, Harvard Univ, 46-48; assoc prof food & nutrit, Univ RI, 48-56; prof home econ & head dept, 56-73, dean grad studies, 73-78, PROF FOOD & NUTRIT, FRAMINGHAM STATE COL, 78- *Concurrent Pos:* Consult, Arthur D Little, Inc & Mkt Res Corp Am, 54-58. *Mem:* AAAS; Am Dietetic Asn; Am Home Econ Asn. *Res:* Absorption of calcium; institutional dietary studies; nutritional status; nontraditional education at graduate level. *Mailing Add:* 8 Beacon Natick MA 01760

JORDAN, DAVID CARLYLE, b Brampton, Ont, July 11, 26; m 54; c 3. BACTERIOLOGY. *Educ:* Univ Toronto, BSA, 50, MSA, 51; Mich State Univ, PhD, 55, Can Col Microbiol, RM, 79. *Prof Exp:* Asst res, Ont Agr Col, 50-52, lectr bact, 52-56, from asst prof to assoc prof, 56-68, Chmn Dept, 71-81, PROF MICROBIOL, UNIV GUELPH, 68- *Concurrent Pos:* Nuffield traveling fel, 59. *Mem:* AAAS; Am Soc Microbiol; Can Soc Microbiol; Brit Soc Gen Microbiol. *Res:* Bacterial physiology as related to rhizobium species; arctic and subarctic microbiology. *Mailing Add:* 8 Young St Guelph ON N1G 2W1 Can

JORDAN, DAVID M, b Ashtabula, Ohio, Aug 19, 37; m 61; c 2. ORGANIC CHEMISTRY. *Educ:* Col Wooster, BA, 59; Ohio State Univ, PhD(chem), 65. *Prof Exp:* ASSOC PROF CHEM, STATE UNIV NY COL POTSDAM, 65- *Mem:* Am Chem Soc. *Res:* Diazoacetophenone decompositions; reaction of ketenes; techniques for thin-layer chromatography on cylindrical surfaces; styryl azide decompositions. *Mailing Add:* Rte 4 Potsdam NY 13676

JORDAN, DONALD J, b New York, NY, 1916. ENGINEERING. *Educ:* NY Univ, BS, 38. *Prof Exp:* Power plant staff engr, Chance Vought Aircraft, 44-48; mem staff, Pratt & Whitney, 48-71, eng mgr, 71-75; eng mgr, Power Systs Div, United Technologies, 75-78; RETIRED. *Mem:* Nat Acad Sci. *Mailing Add:* 113 Evergreen Lane Glastonbury CT 06033

JORDAN, DUANE PAUL, b Glendale, Calif, July 17, 35; c 2. MECHANICAL ENGINEERING. *Educ:* Stanford Univ, BS, 57, MS, 58, PhD(mech eng), 61. *Prof Exp:* Mech engr, Lawrence Radiation Lab, Univ Calif, 60-63; sr engr, integrated controls dept, Electronics Assocs, Inc, 63-64; asst prof mech eng, 64-67, ASSOC PROF MECH ENG, TEX TECH UNIV, 67- *Concurrent Pos:* Consult, Lawrence Radiation Lab, 63-65, Profit Index Systs, Inc, 66-, Fanning, Fanning, Agnes Consult Engrs, 76- & Tex Indust Comn, 78- *Mem:* Am Soc Mech Engrs; Am Soc Heat, Refrig & Air Conditioning Engrs; Am Soc Eng Educ. *Res:* Thermal, physical and social economic systems analysis and simulation using digital and analog computer techniques. *Mailing Add:* Dept of Mech Eng Tex Tech Univ Lubbock TX 79409

JORDAN, EDWARD C(ONRAD), b Edmonton, Alta, Can, Dec 31, 10; nat US; m 41; c 3. ELECTRICAL ENGINEERING. *Educ:* Univ Alta, BSc, 34, MSc, 36; Ohio State Univ, PhD(elec eng), 40. *Prof Exp:* Operator radio sta, CKUA, 28-36; elec engr, Int Nickel Co, 36-37; instr elec eng, Worcester Polytech Inst, 40-41; from instr to asst prof, Ohio State Univ, 41-45; assoc prof, 45-47, prof, 47-54, PROF ELEC ENG & HEAD DEPT, UNIV ILL, URBANA, 54- *Mem:* Int Union Radio Sci; Am Soc Eng Educ; fel Inst Elec & Electronics Engrs. *Res:* Antennas and radio direction finding. *Mailing Add:* Dept of Elec Eng Univ of Ill Urbana IL 61801

JORDAN, EDWARD DANIEL, b Bridgeport, Conn, Mar 14, 31; m 57; c 5. NUCLEAR ENGINEERING. *Educ:* Fairfield Univ, BS, 53; NY Univ, MS, 55; Univ Md, PhD(nuclear eng), 65. *Prof Exp:* Reactor physicist nuclear eng, Foster Wheeler Corp, 55-57; US Atomic Energy Comn, 57-59; assoc prof, 59-64, PROF NUCLEAR ENG, CATH UNIV AM, 64-, DIR, INFO SYST & PLANNING OFF, 68- *Mem:* AAAS; Am Nuclear Soc; Sigma Xi; Am Soc Eng Educ. *Res:* Nuclear engineering; academic planning; futuristics. *Mailing Add:* Cath Univ of Am Washington DC 20064

JORDAN, EDWARD HILL, plant morphogenesis, see previous edition

JORDAN, ELKE, b Ger, Apr 8, 37. MOLECULAR BIOLOGY, GENETICS. *Educ:* Goucher Col, BA, 57; Johns Hopkins Univ, PhD(biochem), 62. *Prof Exp:* Fel, Harvard Univ, 62-64; fel, Univ Cologne, 64-68; res assoc, Univ Wis-Madison, 68-69; res assoc, Univ Calif, Berkeley, 69-72; grants assoc, 72-73, coordr collab res, Nat Cancer Inst, 73-76, prog admin, 76-78, DEP DIR, GENETICS PROG, NAT INST GEN MED SCI, NIH, 78- *Concurrent Pos:* NIH fel, 62-65; fel, Helen Hay Whitney Found, 65-68. *Mem:* Genetics Soc Am; AAAS. *Res:* Gene regulation in prokaryotes, genetic recombination. *Mailing Add:* Genetics Prog Nat Inst Gen Med Sci NIH Bethesda MD 20205

JORDAN, FRANK, b Budapest, Hungary, Jan 28, 41; US citizen; m 75; c 2. BIO-ORGANIC CHEMISTRY, BIOPHYSICAL CHEMISTRY. *Educ:* Drexel Univ, BS, 64; Univ Pa, PhD(chem), 67. *Prof Exp:* NATO fel quantum chem, Univ Paris, France, 67-68; NIH fel bio-org chem, Chem Dept, Harvard Univ, 68-70; asst prof, 70-75, assoc prof, 75-79, PROF CHEM, RUTGERS UNIV, NEWARK, 79- *Concurrent Pos:* NIH grants, USPHS, 74-82. *Mem:* Am Chem Soc; AAAS; Sigma Xi; Biophys Soc; Am Soc Biol Chem. *Res:* Enzyme mechanism studies on enzymes sythesizing and utilizing thiamine diphosphate, purine nucleoside phosphorylase, glyoxalase I and serine proteases. *Mailing Add:* Dept of Chem Rutgers Univ 73 Warren St Newark NJ 07102

JORDAN, GEORGE LYMAN, JR, b Kinston, NC, July 10, 21; m 45; c 4. SURGERY. *Educ:* Univ NC, BS, 42; Univ Pa, MD, 44; Tulane Univ, MS, 49. *Prof Exp:* From instr to assoc prof, 52-64, PROF SURG, BAYLOR COL MED, 64- *Concurrent Pos:* Fel surg, Mayo Found, 49-52; from asst chief to chief surg, Vet Admin Hosp, 52-59, actg chief, 59-60, consult, 60-; attend surgeon, Jefferson Davis Hosp, Methodist Hosp, St Luke's Episcopal Hosp & Tex Children's Hosp; dep chief surg, Ben Taub Gen Hosp, 64-; chief of staff, Harris County Hosp Dist, 68- *Mem:* Soc Univ Surgeons; AMA; Am Col Surgeons; Am Surg Asn; Am Asn Surg of Trauma. *Res:* Postgastrectomy syndromes; pancreatic disease; experimental production of atherosclerosis; aortic homografts and prostheses; homotransplantation. *Mailing Add:* Baylor Col of Med 1200 Moursund Ave Houston TX 77030

JORDAN, GEORGE SAMUEL, b Dallas, Tex, Apr 11, 44; m 66. MATHEMATICS. *Educ:* Southern Methodist Univ, BA, 66; Univ Wis-Madison, MS, 69, PhD(math), 71. *Prof Exp:* Asst prof, 71-76, ASSOC PROF MATH, UNIV TENN, KNOXVILLE, 76- *Mem:* Am Math Soc. *Res:* Integral equations; Tauberian theory; functions of a complex variable. *Mailing Add:* Dept of Math Univ of Tenn Knoxville TN 37916

JORDAN, GILBERT LEROY, b Portland, Ore, July 1, 24; m 43; c 4. RANGE SCIENCE. *Educ:* Ore State Univ, BS, 51, MS, 52; Univ Calif, PhD(bot), 62. *Prof Exp:* Chemist, Chipman Co, 52-56, plant supt, 56-57; res asst agron, Univ Calif, 58-62; asst specialist, 62-67, assoc prof, 67-71, PROF RANGE MGT, UNIV ARIZ, 71-, SPECIALIST, 67- *Mem:* Fel AAAS; Soc Range Mgt. *Res:* Improvement of semi-arid rangelands through shrub control; revegetation and studies to promote effective utilization of precipitation; revegetation of mine tailings. *Mailing Add:* Sch Renewable Natural Res Univ of Ariz Tucson AZ 85721

JORDAN, HANS, b Gottingen, Ger, Oct 17, 39; US citizen; m 65; c 2. CHEMICAL ENGINEERING, PHYSICS. *Educ:* Johns Hopkins Univ, AB, 61. *Prof Exp:* Res scientist reactor safety, Karlsruhe Nuclear Res Ctr, 71-75; PRIN RES SCIENTIST AEROSOL SCI, BATTELLE COLUMBUS LABS, 75- *Mem:* Gesellshaft fur Aerosolforschung; Kerntechnischegesellschaft im Deutschen Atomforum. *Res:* Basic aerosol mechanics research, theory and experiment. *Mailing Add:* Battelle Columbus Labs 505 King Ave Columbus OH 43201

JORDAN, HAROLD VERNON, b Boston, Mass, Aug 18, 24; m 50; c 3. MICROBIOLOGY. *Educ:* Univ NH, BS, 49; Univ Md, MS, 52, PhD(microbiol), 56. *Prof Exp:* Res scientist oral microbiol, Nat Inst Dent Res, 49-69; RES SCIENTIST ORAL MICROBIOL, FORSYTH DENT CTR, 69- *Concurrent Pos:* Vis scientist, Royal Dent Sch, Malmo, Sweden, 65-66. *Mem:* AAAS; fel Am Col Dent; Am Soc Microbiol; Int Asn Dent Res. *Res:* Lactic acid bacteria, metabolism and taxonomy; microbiology of dental caries and periodontal disease; gnotobiotic techniques in dental research; oral microbiology. *Mailing Add:* Forsyth Dent Ctr 140 Fenway Boston MA 02115

JORDAN, HARRY FREDERICK, b Tacoma Park, Md, Mar 6, 40; m 62; c 2. COMPUTER SCIENCE, ELECTRICAL ENGINEERING. *Educ:* Rice Univ, BA, 61; Univ Ill, MS, 63, PhD(physics), 68. *Prof Exp:* From asst prof to assoc prof, 66-80, PROF ELEC ENG & COMPUT SCI, UNIV COLO, BOULDER, 80- *Mem:* Asn Comput Mach; Am Phys Soc; Inst Elec & Electronics Engrs. *Res:* Monte Carlo computational methods; numerical evaluation of functional integrals; computer graphics; parallel processor design. *Mailing Add:* Dept of Elec Eng Univ of Colo Boulder CO 80309

JORDAN, HELEN ELAINE, b Bridgewater, Va, July 19, 26. VETERINARY PARASITOLOGY. *Educ:* Bridgewater Col, BA, 46; Va Polytech Inst, MS, 55; Univ Ga, DVM, 55, PhD(parasitol), 62 62. *Prof Exp:* From asst prof to assoc prof vet parasitol, Univ Ga, 55-69; PROF VET PARASITOL, COL VET MED, OKLA STATE UNIV, 69- *Mem:* AAAS; Am Soc Parasitol; Am Vet Med Asn; Am Soc Vet Parasitol; Asn Am Vet Med Cols. *Res:* Life cycle study of flukes; surveillance and epidemiology parasites in wild and domestic animals; parasite-host interactions and parasite ecology. *Mailing Add:* Dept of Vet Parasitol & Pub Health Okla State Univ Col of Vet Med Stillwater OK 74074

JORDAN, HOWARD EMERSON, b State College, NMex, May 14, 26; m 49; c 2. ELECTRICAL ENGINEERING. *Educ:* Univ Wis, BS, 46; Case Inst Technol, MS, 58, PhD(elec eng), 62. *Prof Exp:* Appln engr, Rao-O-Vac Co, Wis, 46-52; develop engr, Reliance Elec & Eng Co, Cleveland, 54-63, sr develop engr, 63-66, sr engr advan systs develop, 66-71; CHIEF ENGR, AC MACH, 71-, MGR ADVAN DEVELOP, 81- *Mem:* Inst Elec & Electronics Engrs. *Res:* Development and design of electrical rotating machinery and electromechanical devices; development of computer methods for design. *Mailing Add:* 25300 Chatworth Dr Euclid OH 44117

JORDAN, IAN BERNARD, b June 22, 23; Can citizen. ELECTRICAL ENGINEERING. *Educ:* Warsaw Tech Univ, MSc, 52; Polish Acad Sci, DSc, 60; Laval Univ, DSc, 66. *Prof Exp:* Scientist & head sect power systs & apparatus, Inst Elec, Warsaw, 49-60; PROF ELEC ENG, LAVAL UNIV, 61- *Concurrent Pos:* Nat Res Coun Can grants, 63- & Electricite de France, Paris, 70; consult, Inst Technol, Warsaw, 52-60 & Nucletron, Montreal, 63-65; vis prof, Nat Inst Sci Res, Varennes, 70- & Univ Que, 70- *Mem:* Inst Elec & Electronics Engrs. *Res:* Power systems and apparatus; gaseous electronics; dielectrics; atmospheric electricity. *Mailing Add:* 1255 Charles Huot Ave Quebec PQ G1T 2L9 Can

JORDAN, JAMES A, JR, b Berkeley, Calif, Dec 28, 36; m 61; c 2. APPLIED MATHEMATICS. *Educ:* Ohio State Univ, BSc, 58; Univ Mich, MSc, 59, PhD(physics), 64. *Prof Exp:* Physicist, US Air Force Aeronaut Res Lab, 60; asst res physicist, Univ Mich, 60-64; asst prof atomic physics, Rice Univ, 64-70; sci staff mem, IBM Houston Sci Ctr, 69-71, mgr appl math, 71-74, MGR POWER SYSTEMS ANALYSIS, IBM PALO ALTO SCI CTR, 74- *Mem:* Inst Elec & Electronic Engrs. *Res:* Optical data processing, computer holography; network analysis; atomic collisions; atomic spectroscopy; scientific computations; simulation and control of power systems; data management. *Mailing Add:* 975 Glenbar Ave Sunnyvale CA 94087

JORDAN, JAMES HENRY, b Sacramento, Calif, Oct 16, 31; m 58; c 3. MATHEMATICS. *Educ:* Southern Ore Col, BS, 53; Univ Ore, MA, 58; Univ Colo, PhD(math), 62. *Prof Exp:* Teacher elem sch, Ore, 53-56; from asst prof to assoc prof, 62-70, PROF MATH, WASH STATE UNIV, 70-, CHMN, PROG SCI & MATH TEACHING, 77- *Mem:* Math Asn Am; Am Math Soc. *Res:* Number theory in general, specifically Kth power reciprocity, consecutive residues, Gaussian integers and simple continued fractions. *Mailing Add:* Dept of Math Wash State Univ Pullman WA 99163

JORDAN, JAMES N, b Whiteville, NC, Jan 30, 25; m 58; c 2. EARTH SCIENCE. *Educ:* Univ NC, BS, 47. *Prof Exp:* Lab instr geol, Univ NC, 47-48; geologist, Creole Petrol Corp, Venezuela, 48-50; self employed, mining, Venezuela, 50-52; geophysicist, US Coast & Geodetic Surv, 53-66, chief spec seismol anal br, Earth Sci Lab, Environ Res Labs, Nat Oceanic & Atmospheric Admin, 66-73; SUPVRY GEOPHYSICIST, OFF EARTHQUAKE STUDIES, US GEOL SURV, 73- *Concurrent Pos:* Mem, NSF Earthquake Eng Res Inst Mission to Chile, 60. *Honors & Awards:* US Dept Com Bronze Award, 66. *Mem:* Am Geophys Union; Seismol Soc Am; Earthquake Eng Res Inst. *Res:* Geological field studies; field investigations of earthquake damage; earthquake location studies; travel times of seismic waves; magnitude and energy studies of earthquakes; seismic studies relating to nuclear disarmament. *Mailing Add:* US Geol Surv Stop 967 Box 25046 Denver Fed Ctr Denver CO 80225

JORDAN, JOHN EMMETT, physical chemistry, see previous edition

JORDAN, JOHN PATRICK, b Salt Lake City, Utah, Apr 23, 34; m 54; c 8. BIOCHEMISTRY. *Educ:* Univ Calif, Davis, BS, 55, PhD(comp biochem), 63. *Prof Exp:* From asst prof to assoc prof chem, Okla City Univ, 62-68; assoc prof biochem, 68-71, assoc prof biochem, 68-71, assoc dean Col Natural Sci & dir biol core curriculum, 68-72, DIR, PROJ BIOCOTIE, COLO STATE UNIV, 70-, PROF BIOCHEM, 71-, DIR, UNIV EXP STA, 72- *Concurrent Pos:* Grant dir, NASA res grant, 63-; Prin investr, Frontiers Sci Found Okla, Inc res grant, 64-65; Okla Heart Asn res grant, 65-66; NIH res grant, 65-68; consult space med, NASA, 65-70; NIH biomed sci support grant, 69-; Nat Sci Found curriculum res grant, 71-; Boettcher Found res grant, 70-71; gen chmn annual meeting, Am Inst Biol Sci, 71. *Honors & Awards:* Bond Award, Am Oil Chem Soc, 67. *Mem:* Fel AAAS; fel Am Inst Chem; Brit Biochem Soc; Am Physiol Soc; Soc Exp Biol & Med. *Res:* Intermediary metabolism, particularly the effects of artificial atmospheres on metabolism; curricular development, especially in biology and chemistry; research administration. *Mailing Add:* Dir Office Exp Sta Colo State Univ Ft Collins CO 80523

JORDAN, JOHN WILLIAM, b Pittsburgh, Pa, Apr 25, 12; m 36, 79; c 5. INDUSTRIAL CHEMISTRY. *Educ:* Marietta Col, AB, 34; Columbia Univ, PhD(chem), 38. *Hon Degrees:* ScD, Marietta Col, 59. *Prof Exp:* Asst food anal & colloid chem, Columbia Univ, 35-38; fel asst tech glassware, Mellon Inst, 38-39, sr fel lead, 41-51; chemist, Pittsburgh Corning Corp, Pa, 39-41; mgr res labs, 51-56, tech dir, 57-76, CONSULT, BAROID DIV, NL INDUSTS, INC, 76- *Concurrent Pos:* Dir, Enenco, Inc, 62-76. *Mem:* AAAS; Am Chem Soc; Clay Minerals Soc (pres, 73-74). *Res:* Chemistry of hydrous ferric oxides; structural glass products; synthetic resins and coatings; oil well drilling fluids; organic complexes of clay minerals. *Mailing Add:* 1505 Butlercrest Houston TX 77080

JORDAN, JOSEPH, b Timisoara, Rumania, June 29, 19; nat US; m 52; c 4. ANALYTICAL CHEMISTRY. *Educ:* Hebrew Univ, Israel, MSc, 42, PhD, 45. *Prof Exp:* Asst & instr, Hebrew Univ, Israel, 45-49; res fel, Harvard, Univ, 50; res fel & instr, Univ Minn, 51-54; from asst prof to assoc prof chem, 54-60, PROF CHEM, PA STATE UNIV, UNIVERSITY PARK, 60- *Concurrent Pos:* Vis prof, Univ Calif, Berkeley, 59, Swiss Fed Inst Technol, Zurich, 60-61, Cornell Univ, 65 & Ecole Superieure de Physique et Chimie Indust & Pierre & Marie Curie Univ, Paris, 75-76 ; res collabr, Brookhaven Nat Lab, 60-63; consult, Am Instrument Co, 60-, Marcel Dekker, Inc, 65- & Int Paper Co, 79-; chmn comn electrochem, Int Union Pure & Appl Chem, 67-71, mem phys chem div comt, 69-73, mem, Electroanal Chem Comn, 73-, chmn, 81-; mem comt symbols, units & terminology, Numerical Data Adv Bd, Nat Res Coun, Nat Acad Sci, 73-76; mem eval panel phys chem div, Nat Bur Standards, 75-78; res assoc, Nat Ctr Sci Res, Paris, 75-76. *Honors & Awards:* Bennedetti-Pichler Award, Am Microchem Soc, 78. *Mem:* Fel AAAS; Am Chem Soc; fel Am Inst Chemists. *Res:* Polarography; kinetics and mechanisms of electron transfer; electrode reactions; molten salts; thermochemical titrations; enthalpimetric analysis; thermochemistry of immunological and enzymatic processes; instrumental analysis of sulfur compounds in coal process streams; electrochemical photovoltaic cells. *Mailing Add:* Dept of Chem 152 Davey Lab Pa State Univ University Park PA 16802

JORDAN, KENNETH A(LLAN), b Palinfield, NJ, June 30, 30; m 52; c 4. AGRICULTURAL ENGINEERING. *Educ:* Purdue Univ, BS, 52, MS, 54, PhD(agr eng), 59. *Prof Exp:* Asst, Purdue Univ, 54-57, res instr, 57-58; from asst prof to assoc prof farm struct, NC State Univ, 58-67; PROF FARM STRUCT, UNIV MINN, ST PAUL, 67- *Mem:* AAAS; Am Soc Eng Educ; Am Soc Agr Engrs. *Res:* Animal shelter and greenhouse simulation; weather pattern frequency; environmental, pathogenic and nutritional factors in animal production; plant and animal modeling; computer controlled respiratory calorimetry for homeothermic assessment; simulation and modeling. *Mailing Add:* Dept of Agr Eng Univ of Minn St Paul MN 55108

JORDAN, KENNETH DAVID, b Norwood, Mass, Feb 25, 48. PHYSICAL CHEMISTRY. *Educ:* Northeastern Univ, BA, 70; Mass Inst Technol, PhD(chem), 74. *Prof Exp:* J W Gibbs instr eng & appl sci, Yale Univ, 74-76, asst prof, 76-78; asst prof, 78-80, ASSOC PROF CHEM, UNIV PITTSBURGH, 80- *Concurrent Pos:* Vis asst prof, Univ Utah, 76 & 77; Alfred P Sloan Found fel, 77; Camille & Henry Dreyfus Found teacher scholar, 77; John Simon Guggenheim fel, 81. *Mem:* Am Chem Soc; Am Phys Soc; Fedn Am Scientists; Sigma Xi. *Res:* Theoretical studies of the electronic structure of molecules; electron transmission spectroscopic studies of hydrocarbons; positron-molecule interactions; energy transfer in reactions of excited atoms with molecules. *Mailing Add:* Dept of Chem Univ of Pittsburgh Pittsburgh PA 15260

JORDAN, KENNETH GARY, b Anderson, SC, Nov 18, 35; m 57; c 2. PHYSICAL CHEMISTRY. *Educ:* Clemson Univ, BS, 57, MS, 61, PhD(phys chem), 63. *Prof Exp:* Chemist, 57, res chemist, Dacron Technol Div, NC, 63-68, sr res chemist, 69-70, Dacron Textile Res Lab, Wilmington, 70-75, textile fibers end use mkt specialist, 75-77, develop assoc, 77-78, mkt rep, 78-81, SR MKT REP, INDUST FIBERS DIV, E I DU PONT DE NEMOURS & CO, INC, 81- *Mem:* Am Chem Soc. *Res:* Semiconductor properties of polymers; polyester catalysis and kinetics; new polymer technology; synthetic fiber and fabric characterization and evaluation; industrial fiber sales and development. *Mailing Add:* 384 M Holly Knoll Hockessin DE 19707

JORDAN, KENNETH L(OUIS), b Portland, Maine, May 10, 33; m 62; c 3. ELECTRICAL ENGINEERING, COMMUNICATIONS. *Educ:* Rensselaer Polytech Inst, BEE; Mass Inst Technol, SM, 56, ScD(elec eng), 61. *Prof Exp:* Staff mem commun, Lincoln Lab, Mass Inst Technol, 60-67, asst group leader, 67-68, group leader, 68-76; PRIN DEP ASST SECY RES & DEVELOP, OFF SECY AIR FORCE, THE PENTAGON, 76- *Mem:* Inst Elec & Electronics Engrs. *Res:* Random processes; modulation and coding; satellite communications. *Mailing Add:* Off Secy of Air Force The Pentagon Washington DC 20330

JORDAN, LOWELL STEPHEN, b Vale, Ore, Apr 23, 30; m 50; c 4. PLANT PHYSIOLOGY. *Educ:* Ore State Univ, BS, 54; Univ Minn, PhD(agron, bot), 57. *Prof Exp:* Asst agron, Univ Minn, 54-57; asst prof plant industs, Southern Ill Univ, 57-59; from asst plant physiologist to assoc plant physiologist, 59-70, PLANT PHYSIOLOGIST & PROF PLANT SCI, UNIV CALIF, RIVERSIDE, 70- *Mem:* Fel Weed Sci Soc Am; Am Soc Plant Physiol; Am Soc Hort Sci. *Res:* Weed science; herbicide physiology, mechanism of action and metabolism in plants. *Mailing Add:* Dept of Bot & Plant Sci Univ of Calif Riverside CA 92502

JORDAN, MARK H(ENRY), b Lawrence, Mass, Apr 10, 15; m 39; c 2. CIVIL ENGINEERING. *Educ:* US Naval Acad, BS, 37; Rensselaer Polytech Inst, BCE, 41, MCE, 42, MS, 65, PhD(mgt), 68. *Prof Exp:* Officer in charge, Naval Civil Engrs Corps Officers Sch, Pt Hueneme, Calif, 60-63; assoc prof civil eng, construct & mgt, Univ Mo, 66-67; dean continuing studies, Rensselaer Polytech Inst, 67-72; prof civil eng, 68-77; CONSULT ENGR, 76- *Concurrent Pos:* Mem, Rensselaer County Charter Comn, 69-71. *Mem:* Fel Am Soc Civil Engrs; Am Soc Eng Educ; Nat Soc Prof Engrs; Soc Am Mil Engrs. *Res:* Industrial management, application of contemporary management concepts to engineering construction. *Mailing Add:* 40 Steuben St Sixth Floor Albany NY 12207

JORDAN, NEAL F(RANCIS), b Franklinville, NY, July 8, 32; m 55; c 2. ENGINEERING PHYSICS. *Educ:* Cornell Univ, BEngPhys, 55; Purdue Univ, MS, 59, PhD(eng sci), 63. *Prof Exp:* Instr continuum mech, Purdue Univ, 60-63; res assoc geophys, Jersey Prod Res Co, Okla, 63-65, RES ASSOC GEOPHYS, EXXON PROD RES CO, 65- *Concurrent Pos:* Consult, Gen Tech Corp, Ind, 59-63. *Mem:* Soc Eng Sci; Soc Explor Geophys. *Res:* Geophysics; nonlinear theories of continuous media; elastic wave propagation. *Mailing Add:* 330 Knipp Houston TX 77024

JORDAN, PAUL H, JR, b Bigelow, Ark, Nov 22, 19; m 44; c 3. PHYSIOLOGY, SURGERY. *Educ:* Univ Chicago, BS, 41, MD, 44; Univ Ill, MS, 50. *Prof Exp:* Asst prof surg, Sch Med, Univ Calif, Los Angeles, 55-58; assoc prof, Sch Med, Univ Fla, 59-64; chief staff, 69-70, CHIEF SURG, VET ADMIN HOSP, HOUSTON, 64-; PROF SURG, BAYLOR COL MED, 64- *Concurrent Pos:* Fel, NIH, 58-59. *Mem:* Am Surg Asn; Soc Exp Biol & Med; Soc Univ Surg; Am Col Surg; Am Gastroenterol Asn. *Res:* Gastrointestinal physiology. *Mailing Add:* Baylor Col of Med 1200 Moursund Houston TX 77030

JORDAN, PETER ALBION, b Oakland, Calif, Jan 2, 30; m 62; c 3. ECOLOGY, WILDLIFE MANAGEMENT. *Educ:* Univ Calif, Berkeley, AB, 55, PhD(zool), 67. *Prof Exp:* Asst specialist studies migratory deer, Sch Forestry, Univ Calif, Berkeley, 55-61, teaching asst zool, 61-62, instr, 62-63; res assoc ecol moose & wolves, Purdue Univ, 63-66; asst prof wildlife ecol, Sch Forestry, Yale Univ, 67-74; ASSOC PROF, DEPT ENTOM, FISHERIES & WILDLIFE, UNIV MINN, ST PAUL, 74- *Mem:* Wildlife Soc; Am Soc Naturalists; Ecol Soc Am; Am Soc Mammal. *Res:* Behavior, population dynamics and food habits of wild ungulates and carnivores; impact of herbivorous mammals upon forest vegetation; sodium acquisition and aquatic feeding by forest herbivores; management of big game; ecosystem processes; conservation practices and ethics. *Mailing Add:* Dept of Entom, Fish & Wildlife Univ of Minn St Paul MN 55108

JORDAN, PETER C H, b London, Eng, May 3, 36; US citizen. THEORETICAL CHEMISTRY. *Educ:* Calif Inst Technol, BS, 57; Yale Univ, PhD(quantum mech), 60. *Prof Exp:* NSF fel, 60-62; asst res chemist, Univ Calif, San Diego, 62-64; asst prof chem, 64-70, assoc prof, 70-81, PROF CHEM, BRANDEIS UNIV, 81- *Concurrent Pos:* Guggenheim fel, 71-72; Marion & Jaspar Whiting fel, 78-79; vis prof, Dept Biol, Konstanz Univ, 78-79. *Mem:* AAAS; Am Phys Soc. *Res:* Statistical mechanics; quantum chemistry; irreversible thermodynamics; membrane transport. *Mailing Add:* Dept Chem Brandeis Univ Waltham MA 02154

JORDAN, RICHARD CHARLES, b Minneapolis, Minn, Apr 16, 09; m 35; c 3. MECHANICAL ENGINEERING. *Educ:* Univ Minn, BAeroE, 31, MS, 33, PhD(mech eng), 40. *Prof Exp:* Head air conditioning div, Minneapolis Br, Am Radiator & Standard Sanit Corp, 33-36; instr petrol eng, Univ Tulsa, 36-37; eng exp sta, 37-41, asst dir eng exp sta, 41-44, from asst prof to prof mech eng, 41-76, dir indust labs, 44-45, head dept mech eng, 50-76, head sch mech & aerospace eng, 66-76, actg assoc dean, Inst Technol, 77-80, EMER PROF MECH ENG, UNIV MINN, MINNEAPOLIS, 76-, ASSOC DEAN, INST TECHNOL, 80- *Concurrent Pos:* Consult, Corps Engrs, US Army, 51-52; adv panel eng sci, NSF, 54-57, chmn, 56-57; mem, Div Eng & Indust Res, Nat Acad Sci-Nat Res Coun, 54-74, chmn div, 61-65, mem-at-large, 65-74, chmn ad hoc comt eng in developing countries, 59-61, chmn ad hoc comt eng & soc sci, 61-65; deleg, Int Cong Refrig, Paris, 55, Copenhagen, 59, Munich, 63, Madrid, 67, Washington, 71 & Moscow, 75; Nat Res Coun deleg to exec comt of sci coun, Int Inst Refrig, Paris, 55-71, US deleg, 57-63, US nat comt, Moscow & Prague, 58, exec comt, 59-63, tech bd, 63-67; Am Standards Asn deleg, Int Standards Orgn, London, 58; deleg, World Power Conf, Melbourne, 62; mem, CENTO Surv Mission, Iran, Pakistan & Turkey, 63; vchmn eng & accreditation comt, Region VII, Eng Coun Prof Develop, 64-66, chmn & eng accreditation comt, Region VIII, 66-69; consult, AID, 64- & var indust orgns; mem adv comt int orgns & progs, Off Int Rels, Nat Acad Sci, 65-; mem, Fulbright Prog Long-Range Planning Team, US-Brazil Prog, 67; chmn study group indust res, US-Brazil Sci Coop Prog, Nat Acad Sci, Rio de Janeiro & Washington, DC, 67 & Belo Horizonte, Brazil & Houston, 68; mem conf strategy for technol develop Latin-Am, 69; mem, bd dirs, Onan Corp Div, McGraw-Edison Corp, 72-; energy consult, Control Data Corp, 77-; World Bank Consult alt energy resources Brazil, 76; chmn, Comt Rev Prog Dept Energy, Div Conserv & Community Syst, Nat Res Coun, 80- *Honors & Awards:* Wolverine Award, Am Soc Heat, Refrig & Air-Conditioning Engrs, 49, F Paul Anderson Medal & E K Campbell Award, 66. *Mem:* Nat Acad Eng; fel AAAS; fel Am Soc Mech Engrs; Nat Soc Prof Engrs; fel Am Soc Heat, Refrig & Air-Conditioning Engrs (treas, 50, vpres, 51-52, pres, 63). *Res:* Air filtration; dust analyses; conditions of comfort; heat transmission; refrigeration; quantitative and qualitative analysis of atmospheric dust; solar energy; engineering. *Mailing Add:* 209 Mech Eng Univ of Minn Minneapolis MN 55455

JORDAN, ROBERT, JR, b Macon, Ga, Sept 11, 20; m 42; c 3. PEDIATRICS. *Educ:* Vanderbilt Univ, BA, 41, MD, 43. *Prof Exp:* Intern pediat, Duke Univ Hosp, Durham, NC, 44; resident pediat, Henrietta Egleston Mem Hosp, Atlanta, Ga, 44-45; res fel pediat, 48-49, from asst prof to assoc prof, 54-66, PROF PEDIAT, UNIV TENN COL MED, 66-; DIR, CHILD DEVELOP CTR, UNIV TENN, 57-; PROF CHILD DEVELOP, 66- *Concurrent Pos:* Supt Arlington Develop Ctr, Tenn, 74-75; mem, President's Comt Ment Retardation. *Mem:* Am Acad Pediat; fel Am Med Asn; Am Asn Mental Deficiency; Asn Univ Affiliated Facil (past pres). *Res:* Neurologically handicapped children. *Mailing Add:* Univ Tenn Child Develop Ctr 711 Jefferson Ave Memphis TN 38105

JORDAN, ROBERT BEATTY, inorganic chemistry, see previous edition

JORDAN, ROBERT LAWRENCE, b Miami, Fla, May 7, 41; div; c 2. ANATOMY, TERATOLOGY. *Educ:* Fla Southern Col, BS, 65; Univ Fla, 65-66; Univ Cincinnati, PhD(anat), 69. *Prof Exp:* Asst prof, 70-74, ASSOC PROF ANAT, MED COL VA, 74- *Concurrent Pos:* USPHS fel teratology & toxicol, Kettering Lab, Univ Cincinnati, 69-70; vis prof anat, St George's Med Sch, Greneda, West Indies, 79- *Mem:* Teratology Soc; Am Asn Anat; Sigma Xi. *Mailing Add:* Dept Anat Med Col Va Box 709 MCV Station Richmond VA 23298

JORDAN, ROBERT MANSEAU, b Minneapolis, Minn, Feb 13, 20; m 42; c 3. ANIMAL HUSBANDRY. *Educ:* Univ Minn, BS, 42; SDak State Col, MS, 49; Kans State Col, PhD(animal nutrit), 53. *Prof Exp:* Instr animal husb, Univ Minn, 42; sales rep, Lyon Chem, Minn, 45; instr, SDak State Col, 48-49, from asst prof to assoc prof, 49-54; from asst prof to assoc prof, 54-64, PROF ANIMAL HUSB, UNIV MINN, ST PAUL, 64- *Concurrent Pos:* Mem comt, Nutrient Req Horses, Nat Res Coun, 78, chmn comt, Nutrient Req Sheep, 80-82. *Mem:* Am Soc Animal Sci; Brit Soc Animal Prod; Equine Nutrit & Physiol Soc; Acad Natural Sci. *Res:* Use of hormones in animal production; digestibility studies; sheep nutrition; protein, calcium and phosphorus energy requirements for growth, reproduction, lactation and work of horses; copper toxicity studies with horses; pasture research involving development of low alkaloid varieties of canary grass and energy intakes by lamb grazing legume or grass pastures; silage studies and non-protein sources of nitrogen for horses. *Mailing Add:* Dept of Animal Sci Univ of Minn St Paul MN 55101

JORDAN, ROBERT R, b New York, NY, June 5, 37; m 58; c 2. GEOLOGY. *Educ:* Hunter Col, AB, 58; Bryn Mawr Col, MA, 62, PhD(geol), 64. *Prof Exp:* From geologist to asst state geologist, Del Geol Surv, 58-69; from instr to asst prof geol, Univ Del, 62-68; STATE GEOLOGIST & DIR, DEL GEOL SURV, 69-; ASSOC PROF GEOL, UNIV DEL, 68- *Concurrent Pos:* Registered prof geologist in Delaware, 72-; gov rep, Outer Continental Shelf Res Mgt Adv Bd, Dept Interior, 74-77; mem, Comt Offshore Energy Technol, Nat Acad Sci/Nat Res Coun, 78-; regional coordr, Asn Am Petrol Geologists, 78-; nAm comn stratig Nomenclature, 78- *Mem:* Asn Am State Geol (secy-treas, 77-81, vpres, 81-); Am Inst Prof Geol; fel Geol Soc Am; Soc Econ Paleont & Mineral. *Res:* Sedimentary petrology; stratigraphy; geology of the Atlantic Coastal Plain; micropaleontology; ground water supplies. *Mailing Add:* Del Geol Surv Univ of Del Newark DE 19711

JORDAN, RUSSELL THOMAS, b Geneseo, NY; m 46; c 6. VIROLOGY, IMMUNOCHEMISTRY. *Educ:* Univ Ark, BS, 49, MS, 51; Univ Mich, PhD(virol), 53. *Prof Exp:* Rackham res fel, Sch Med, Univ Mich, 53, asst prof bact, 53-54; clin asst prof infectious dis, Sch Med, Univ Calif, Los Angeles, 54-59; chief, Dept Exp Immunol, Nat Jewish Hosp, Denver, 60-63; dir res & labs, Biomed Res Labs Div, Bio-Organic Chem Inc, 63-71; vpres sci & technol, C F Kettering Found, dir, C F Kettering Lab & vpres, Kettering Sci Res, Inc, 71-73; pres & chmn bd, Vipont Chem & Res Ctr, 73-75; res dir, Chemex Corp, 75-77; PRES, MED-X-CONSULT, FT COLLINS, 77- *Concurrent Pos:* Chmn dept microbiol, City of Hope Med Ctr, Calif, 54-60; lectr, Univ Calif, Los Angeles, 56-59; res fel immunochem, Calif Inst Technol, 58-59; asst prof, Sch Med, Univ Colo, Denver, 61-71; chief space biomed res, Aerospace Group, Martin-Marietta Corp, Colo, 66-71. *Mem:* Am Asn Immunol; Soc Exp Biol & Med; Am Asn Cancer Res; Sigma Xi; NY Acad Sci. *Res:* Microbiology; interference phenomenon; infection and resistance; virus induced neoplasms; immunochemistry of cancer; immunochemical properties of tumor specific antigens and antibodies. *Mailing Add:* Med-X-Consult 1809 Indian Meadows Lane Ft Collins CO 80521

JORDAN, SCOTT WILSON, b Iola, Kans, Aug 22, 34; m 55; c 3. PATHOLOGY. *Educ:* Univ Kans, AB, 56, MD, 59. *Prof Exp:* From intern to resident path, Med Ctr, Univ Kans, 59-63; pathologist, Nat Acad Sci-Nat Res Coun Atomic Bomb Casualty Comn, 63-65; asst prof, 65-69, ASSOC PROF PATH, SCH MED, UNIV NMEX, 69- *Concurrent Pos:* USPHS fel, Med Ctr, Univ Kans, 60-63; consult, Midwest Res Inst, Mo, 62-63 & Nat Cancer Inst, 74-77. *Mem:* Am Soc Cytol; Am Asn Path; Int Acad Path. *Res:* Pathology of radiation injury; diagnostic cytology. *Mailing Add:* Dept of Path Univ of NMex Sch of Med Albuquerque NM 87131

JORDAN, STANLEY CLARK, b Elkin, NC, Apr 13, 47; m 76; c 1. PEDIATRICS, PEDIATRIC NEPHROLOGY. *Educ:* Univ NC, Chapel Hill, AB, 69, MD, 73. *Prof Exp:* Asst clin prof pediat, Univ Southern Calif, 79-80; ASST PROF PEDIAT, UNIV CALIF, LOS ANGELES, 80- *Concurrent Pos:* Prin investr, NIH clin investr award, 80-83. *Mem:* Am Soc Pediat Nephrol. *Res:* Renal immmunopathology and transplantation immunology. *Mailing Add:* A2-331 MDCC Univ Calif Los Angeles Hosp Los Angeles CA 90024

JORDAN, STEVEN LEE, b Jersey City, NJ, Feb 17, 43; m 66; c 2. DIFFERENTIAL GEOMETRY, MATHEMATICS EDUCATION. *Educ:* Princeton Univ, AB, 65; Univ Calif, Berkeley, MA, 67, PhD(math), 70. *Prof Exp:* Asst prof, 70-76, ASSOC PROF MATH, UNIV ILL, CHICAGO CIRCLE, 76- *Concurrent Pos:* NSF res grant, 70-72; Carnegie Found res grant, 75-76; HEW res grant, 80- *Mem:* Am Math Soc; Math Asn Am; Sigma Xi; Nat Coun Teachers Math. *Res:* Differential geometry and complex manifolds; all levels of mathematics teacher education; history of mathematics. *Mailing Add:* Dept of Math Box 4348 Univ of Ill at Chicago Circle Chicago IL 60680

JORDAN, STUART DAVIS, b St Louis, Mo, July 25, 36; m 61; c 2. SOLAR PHYSICS. *Educ:* Wash Univ, BS, 58; Univ Colo, Boulder, PhD(physics, astrophys), 68. *Prof Exp:* Res adminr plasma dynamics, Air Force Off Sci Res, 59-63; actg chief solar physics, NASA HQ, 74; RES SCIENTIST, LAB ASTRON & SOLAR PHYSICS, GODDARD SPACE FLIGHT CTR, NASA, 68- *Mem:* Am Phys Soc; Am Astron Soc; Int Astron Union; AAAS; Sigma Xi. *Res:* Radiative transfer in solar atmosphere; shock wave heating of high temperature, low density gases; energy balance and temperature structure of stellar atmospheres; solar ultraviolet and radio astronomy. *Mailing Add:* Code 682 Lab for Astron & Solar Physics Goddard Space Flight Ctr NASA Greenbelt MD 20771

JORDAN, THOMAS FREDRICK, b Duluth, Minn, June 4, 36; div. THEORETICAL PHYSICS. *Educ:* Univ Minn, Duluth, BA, 58; Univ Rochester, PhD(physics), 62. *Prof Exp:* Res assoc physics, Univ Rochester, 61-62, instr, 62-63; NSF fel, Berne, 63-64; from asst prof to assoc prof, Univ Pittsburgh, 64-70; PROF PHYSICS, UNIV MINN, DULUTH, 70- *Concurrent Pos:* Sloan Found fel, 65-67. *Res:* Mathematical physics; quantum mechanics; field theory; relativistic particle dynamics; scattering theory; elementary particle interactions; quantum theory of optical coherence; hydrodynamics of Great Lakes circulation. *Mailing Add:* Dept of Physics Univ of Minn Duluth MN 55812

JORDAN, THOMAS HILLMAN, b Coco Solo, CZ, Oct 8, 48; m 73. GEOPHYSICS. *Educ:* Calif Inst Technol, BS, 69, MS, 70, PhD(geophys), 72. *Prof Exp:* Asst prof geophys, Princeton Univ, 72-75; ASSOC PROF GEOPHYS, SCRIPPS INST OCEANOG, UNIV CALIF, SAN DIEGO, 75- *Mem:* Am Geophys Union; Geol Soc Am. *Res:* Structure of the earth's interior; plate tectonics; mantle dynamics; wave propagation; inverse theory. *Mailing Add:* Mail Code A-015 Scripps Inst Oceanog Univ Calif La Jolla CA 92093

JORDAN, THOMAS NEWTON, b Darlove, Miss, Mar 29, 47; m 73; c 1. WEED SCIENCE, AGRONOMY. *Educ:* Miss State Univ, BS, 70, MS, 71; Purdue Univ, PhD(plant physiol), 74. *Prof Exp:* Fel weed control, Miss Agr & Forestry Exp Sta, Miss State Univ, 74, asst plant physiologist, 74-78; assoc prof bot, Purdue Univ, 78-80. *Mem:* Weed Sci Soc Am; AAAS. *Res:* Integrated pest management and weed control in agronomic crops. *Mailing Add:* 3331 Soldiers Home Rd WL West Lafayette IN 47906

JORDAN, TRUMAN H, b Wayne, Mich, Nov 18, 37; m 61; c 3. PHYSICAL CHEMISTRY. *Educ:* Albion Col, BA, 59; Harvard Univ, MA, 62, PhD(chem), 64. *Prof Exp:* NASA fel & res assoc crystallog, Univ Pittsburgh, 64-66; from to assoc prof, 66-77, PROF CHEM, CORNELL COL, 77- *Mem:* AAAS; Am Chem Soc; Am Crystallog Asn; Int Asn Dent Res. *Res:* Molecular structure by means of x-ray crystallography; dental chemistry. *Mailing Add:* Dept of Chem Cornell Col Mt Vernon IA 52314

JORDAN, WADE HAMPTON, JR, electrochemistry, physical chemistry, see previous edition

JORDAN, WALTER HARRISON, b Whitehall, Mont, Apr 22, 08; m 34; c 1. PHYSICS, NUCLEAR ENGINEERING. *Educ:* Univ Okla, AB, 30, MS, 31; Calif Inst Technol, PhD(physics), 34. *Prof Exp:* Assoc prof, Univ SDak, 34-41; res assoc, Mass Inst Technol, 41-46; physicist, Oak Ridge Nat Lab, 46-59, asst dir, 59-70, sr res adv, 70-73; RETIRED. *Concurrent Pos:* Part-time prof, Univ Tenn, 65-78; mem, Atomic Safety License Bd, 70- *Mem:* AAAS; fel Am Phys Soc; fel Am Nuclear Soc. *Res:* Nuclear power plant safety. *Mailing Add:* 881 W Outer Dr Oak Ridge TN 37830

JORDAN, WAYNE ROBERT, b Kankakee, Ill, Jan 7, 40; m 60; c 6. PLANT PHYSIOLOGY, BIOCHEMISTRY. *Educ:* Univ Ill, Urbana, BS, 61, MS, 62; Univ Calif, Davis, PhD(plant physiol), 68. *Prof Exp:* From asst prof to assoc prof, 68-75, PROF CROP PHYSIOL, TEX AGR EXP STA, 75-, RESIDENT DIR, BLACK LAND RES CTR, 80- *Concurrent Pos:* Assoc ed, Agron J, 78-81. *Mem:* Am Soc Plant Physiol; Crop Sci Soc Am; Am Soc Agron. *Res:* Plant water relations; drought resistance; seed germination; protein synthesis; hormonal regulation of abscission. *Mailing Add:* Tex Agr Exp Sta Tex A&M Univ Temple TX 77843

JORDAN, WILLARD CLAYTON, b Richmond, Ind, May 13, 22; m 46; c 2. NUCLEAR PHYSICS. *Educ:* Miami Univ, BA, 45; Univ Mich, MS, 48, PhD, 54. *Prof Exp:* Res assoc, Argonne Nat Lab, 51-53, asst physicist, Exp Nuclear Physics, 53-54; physicist, Res Labs, Bendix Corp, 54-64; SCIENTIST, LOCKHEED MISSILES & SPACE RES LABS, PALO ALTO, 64- *Concurrent Pos:* Asst, Univ Mich, 48-53; vis physicist, Lawrence Radiation Lab, Univ Calif, 58-64. *Mem:* Am Phys Soc; Am Nuclear Soc; Am Asn Physics Teachers. *Res:* Radioactive decay; nuclear reactors; thermonuclear research; space physics. *Mailing Add:* Lockheed Palo Alto Labs Bldg 203 3251 Hanover St Palo Alto CA 94304

JORDAN, WILLIAM D(ITMER), b Selma, Ala, Feb 5, 22; m 47; c 3. ENGINEERING MECHANICS. *Educ:* Univ Ala, BS, 42, MS, 49; Univ Ill, PhD(theoret & appl mech), 52. *Prof Exp:* Asst prof eng mech, Univ Ala, 46-50, asst theoret & appl mech, Univ Ill, 50-52; assoc prof eng mech, 52-57, PROF ENG MECH, UNIV ALA, 57-, HEAD DEPT ENG MECH, 61- *Mem:* Am Soc Eng Educ; Am Soc Mech Engrs; Am Inst Aeronaut & Astronaut; Am Acad Mech. *Res:* Strength of materials; structures; stress analysis; thermal stresses; buckling. *Mailing Add:* Dept of Aerospace Eng Mech Eng & Eng Mech PO Box 2908 University AL 35486

JORDAN, WILLIAM KIRBY, b New York, NY, May 24, 23; m 44; c 4. FOOD SCIENCE. *Educ:* Cornell Univ, BS, 47, MS, 48, PhD(daily sci), 50. *Prof Exp:* From asst prof to assoc prof, 50-59, PROF FOOD SCI, CORNELL UNIV, 59- *Mem:* Am Dairy Sci Asn; Inst Food Technol. *Res:* Food engineering. *Mailing Add:* Dept of Food Sci Cornell Univ Ithaca NY 14850

JORDAN, WILLIAM MALCOLM, b Brooklyn, NY, June 19, 36; m 63; c 1. GEOLOGY. *Educ:* Columbia Univ, BA, 57, MA, 61; Univ Wis, PhD(geol), 65. *Prof Exp:* Res geologist, Jersey Prod Res Co, Okla, 64-65; res geologist, Esso Prod Res Co, Tex, 65-66; assoc prof, 66-69, PROF EARTH SCI, MILLERSVILLE STATE COL, 69- *Concurrent Pos:* Chmn dept earth sci, Millersville State Col, 67-72. *Mem:* Am Asn Petrol Geologists; Geol Soc Am; Hist Sci Soc; Nat Asn Geol Teachers; Soc Econ Paleont & Mineral. *Res:* Mature clastic sediments; paleocurrents and paleoclimatology; sedimentary facies and petroleum accumulation; history of geology. *Mailing Add:* Dept of Earth Sci Millersville State Col Millersville PA 17551

JORDAN, WILLIAM STONE, JR, b Fayetteville, NC, Sept 28, 17; m 47; c 2. MEDICINE. *Educ:* Univ NC, AB, 38; Harvard Univ, MD, 42. *Prof Exp:* From intern to asst resident, 2nd Med Serv, Boston City Hosp, 42-43, resdient, 46-47; from instr to assoc prof prev med, Sch Med, Western Reserve Univ, 48-58, from instr to asst prof med, 48-58; prof prev & internal med & chmn dept prev med, Sch Med, Univ Va, 58-67; prof med & community med, Univ Ky, 67-74, dean Col Med, 67-74; DIR MICROBIOL & INFECTIOUS DIS PROG, NAT INST ALLERGY & INFECTIOUS DIS, 76- *Concurrent Pos:* Teaching fel prev med & med, Sch Med, Western Reserve Univ, 47-48; dir comn acute respiratory dis, Epidemiol Bd, US Armed Forces; consult, Surgeon Gen; mem, comn epidemiol & vet follow-up studies, Nat Acad Sci, 65-72; mem infectious dis adv comt, Nat Inst Allergy & Infectious Dis, 67-71; mem, Panel on Review of Viral & Rickettsial Vaccines, Food & Durg Admin, 73-76; dir microbiol & infectious dis prog, Nat Inst Allergy & Infectious Dis, NIH, 79- *Mem:* Soc Exp Biol & Med; Am Epidemiol Soc; Am Soc Clin Invest; Am Pub Health Asn; Am Asn Immunol. *Res:* Etiology and epidemiology of acute respiratory disease. *Mailing Add:* Nat Inst Health Bldg 31 Rm 7A52 Bethesda MD 20205

JORDAN, WILLIS POPE, JR, b Rossville, Ga, Oct 7, 18; m 52; c 3. UROLOGY. *Educ:* Emory Univ, BS, 39, MD, 43. *Prof Exp:* Intern, Emory Univ Hosp, 43-44; from asst resident to chief resident, Columbus Med Ctr, Ga, 44-45; preceptorship urol under Dr W P Jordan, Sr, 47-52; asst resident surg, Vet Admin Hosp, Atlanta, 52-53, from asst resident to sr resident urol, New Orleans, 53-55; sect chief, Lake City, Fla, 55-68; assoc prof, 68-77, PROF UROL, COL MED, UNIV TENN, MEMPHIS, 77-; SECT CHIEF, VET ADMIN HOSP, MEMPHIS, 68- *Concurrent Pos:* Asst prof, Col Med, Univ Fla, 65-68. *Mem:* Am Urol Asn; Am Col Surg; AMA; Int Soc Urol; Soc Univ Urol. *Res:* Cancer of the prostate and bladder; hydrodynamics of micturition. *Mailing Add:* Vet Admin Hosp 1030 Jefferson Ave Memphis TN 31804

JORDAN-MOLERO, JAIME E, b Utuado, PR, Jan 5, 41; m 72; c 3. PLANT PHYSIOLOGY, WEED CONTROL. *Educ:* Univ PR, BS, 63, MS, 70; Univ Ill Urbana-Champaign, PhD(agron), 77. *Prof Exp:* Res asst agr, 63-69, asst agronomist agr res, 69-79, asst dir, Agr Exp Sta, 77-79, ASSOC PROF AGR RES, ASST DEAN & DIR, AGR EXP STA, UTUADO REGIONAL COL, UNIV PR, 79- *Concurrent Pos:* Prof crop physiol, Mayaguez Campus, Univ PR, 77- *Mem:* Am Soc Agr Sci. *Res:* Crop nutrition; coffee genetics and selection; plant physiology; weed control physiology and ecology. *Mailing Add:* Agr Exp Sta Univ PR PO Box H Rio Piedras PR 00928

JORDEN, ROGER M, b Carthage, Mo, Nov 15, 35. ENVIRONMENTAL ENGINEERING, WATER CHEMISTRY. *Educ:* Univ Tex, Austin, BS, 59; Univ Ariz, MS, 62; Univ Ill, Urbana, PhD(civil eng), 68. *Prof Exp:* Res asst hydrol, Inst Water Utilization, Univ Ariz, 59-62; res assoc, Travelers Res Inst, 62-64; res assoc sanit eng, Univ Ill, Urbana, 64-67, res fel, 67-68; asst prof environ eng, Univ Colo, Boulder, 68-75, assoc prof, 75-76; proj mgr, Elec Power Res Inst, Calif, 76-79; proj mgr water mgt, Colo Ute Elec Asn, Inc, 79-81; CONSULT WATER MGT, 82- *Honors & Awards:* Eddy Award, Water Pollution Control Fedn, 76. *Mem:* Water Pollution Control Fedn. *Res:* Water management of zero discharge water systems in power plants; coagulation-flocculation of dilute colloidal suspensions; physical-chemical removal of trace elements; environmental transport of trace elements. *Mailing Add:* Water Systs Eng PO Box 770545 Steamboat Springs CO 80477

JORDIN, MARCUS WAYNE, b Idaho Falls, Idaho, May 23, 27; m 56; c 2. PHARMACOLOGY. *Educ:* Idaho State Col, BS, 49; Purdue Univ, MS, 52, PhD(pharmacol), 54. *Prof Exp:* Assoc prof, 54-62, PROF PHARMACOL & HEAD DEPT, SCH PHARM, UNIV ARK, LITTLE ROCK, 62- *Mem:* Am Pharmaceut Asn. *Res:* Central nervous system drugs; tranquilizers and psychic energizers. *Mailing Add:* 309 Brookside Dr Little Rock AR 72205

JORDON, ROBERT EARL, b Buffalo, NY, May 7, 38; m 69; c 1. DERMATOLOGY, IMMUNOLOGY. *Educ:* Hamilton Col, BA, 60; State Univ NY Buffalo, MD, 65; Univ Minn, Minneapolis, MS, 70. *Prof Exp:* Asst prof dermat & immunol, Mayo Med Sch Med, Univ Minn, Rochester, 71-77; PROF & CHMN SECT DERMAT, MED COL WIS, 77- *Concurrent Pos:* Training grant dermat, Mayo Clin, 68-69; Nat Inst Arthritis, Metab & Digestive Dis res fel, Univ Minn, 72-73; vis asst prof & assoc mem grad fac, Univ Minn, Minneapolis, 71- *Mem:* AAAS; Am Asn Immunol; Am Fedn Clin Res; Soc Invest Dermat. *Res:* Immunopathology of bullous skin diseases using immunofluorescence, and complement research technics. *Mailing Add:* Dept of Dermat Med Col of Wis Milwaukee WI 53193

JORGENS, JOSEPH, b Minneapolis, Minn, Jan 23, 18; m 44; c 5. MEDICINE, RADIOLOGY. *Educ:* Univ Minn, BS, 41, MB, 43, MD, 44, MS, 52, PhD, 54; Am Bd Radiol, dipl. *Prof Exp:* Res instr, Univ Minn, Minneapolis, 49-52, from assoc prof to prof radiol, 58-68; PROF RADIOL SCI, UNIV CALIF, LOS ANGELES, 68-; HEAD RADIOL, VET ADMIN CTR, LOS ANGELES, 68- *Concurrent Pos:* Chief radiol, Minneapolis Vet Admin Hosp, 52-68. *Mem:* Radiol Soc NAm; AMA; Am Col Radiol. *Res:* Diagnostic cardiovascular roentgenology. *Mailing Add:* Dept Radiol Sci Univ Calif Los Angeles CA 90024

JORGENSEN, CLIVE D, b Orem, Utah, July 14, 31; m 55; c 3. ENTOMOLOGY. *Educ:* Brigham Young Univ, BS, 54, MS, 57; Ore State Univ, PhD(entom), 64. *Prof Exp:* Field dir ecol res, 60-63, from instr to assoc prof zool & entom, 63-73, PROF ZOOL, BRIGHAM YOUNG UNIV, 73-, CHMN DEPT, 74- *Concurrent Pos:* US Atomic Energy Comn res grant, 63-66; USDA res grant, 65-67; NSF grant, asst prof zool, Iowa State Univ, 71-72; coordr biol instr, Brigham Young Univ, 72-74. *Mem:* AAAS; Entom Soc Am; Am Soc Mammal. *Res:* Ecological research. *Mailing Add:* Dept of Zool Brigham Young Univ Provo UT 84601

JORGENSEN, ERIK, b Denmark, Oct 28, 21; nat Can; m 46; c 2. ENVIRONMENTAL MANAGEMENT, FORESTRY. *Educ:* Royal Vet & Agr Col, Denmark, MF, 46. *Prof Exp:* Asst forest path, Royal Vet & Agr Col, Denmark, 49-53, amanuensis, col & proj leader, Forest Exp Sta, 53-55; res officer in chg plantation dis, Can Dept Agr, 55-59; agr prof forest path, Univ Toronto, 59-63, assoc prof, Shade Tree Res Lab, 63-67, prof forestry, 67-73, in chg lab, 63-72; chief urban forestry prog, Forest Mgt Inst, Can Forestry Serv, Dept Environ, 73-78; DIR, UNIV GUELPH ARBORETUM & PROF ENVIRON BIOL, 78- *Mem:* AAAS; Can Phytopath Soc; NY Acad Sci; Arboricult Res & Educ Acad (pres, 76-78). *Res:* Urban forestry management and planning; environmental impact on/and by trees; tree diseases, physiology and breeding; forest botany and ecology; arboriculture. *Mailing Add:* Univ of Guelph Arboretum Guelph ON N1G 2W1 Can

JORGENSEN, EUGENE CLIFFORD, organic chemistry, medicinal chemistry, deceased

JORGENSEN, GEORGE NORMAN, b Omaha, Nebr, Feb 22, 36; m 70; c 2. BIOCHEMISTRY, VIROLOGY. *Educ:* Univ Nebr, BS, 57; Univ Ill, MS, 68, PhD(biochem), 72. *Prof Exp:* Lab technician, Shell Chem Co, 57-58; res asst radiation biol, M D Anderson Hosp & Tumor Inst, 59-66; res assoc biochem virol, Baylor Col Med, 72-76; RES ASSOC BIOL, RICE UNIV, 77- *Mem:* Am Chem Soc; AAAS; Sigma Xi. *Res:* Studies of enzymes of snail metabolism such as urease, super oxide desmutase and mannitol oxidase concerned with comparative aspects of nitrogen metabolism and energy sources of snails. *Mailing Add:* 8302 Greenbush Houston TX 77025

JORGENSEN, HELMUTH ERIK MILO, b Odense, Denmark, June 19, 27; nat US; m 53; c 3. PHYSICAL CHEMISTRY. *Educ:* Polytech Inst Brooklyn, BS, 50; Rutgers Univ, PhD(phys chem), 59. *Prof Exp:* Develop chemist, Sterling-Winthrop Res Inst, 50-51; res chemist, Schering Corp, 52-53; develop chemist, Am Cyanamid Co, 53-54; asst, Rutgers Univ, 54-58; res chemist, Distillation Prod Industs, Eastman Kodak Co, 58-60; assoc res chemist, Sterling-Winthrop Res Inst, NY, 60-69; assoc prof, 69-80, PROF CHEM, HUDSON VALLEY COMMUNITY COL, 80- *Mem:* Am Chem Soc. *Res:* Physical chemistry of polymers and colloids; new methods of teaching chemistry. *Mailing Add:* Van Leuven Dr S RD 1 Rensselaer NY 12144

JORGENSEN, JACQUES R, b Oak Park, Ill, Apr 29, 31; m 58. SOIL SCIENCE. *Educ:* Mich Col Mining & Technol, BS, 52; Mich State Univ, MS, 57; Univ Minn, PhD(soil microbiol), 61. *Prof Exp:* Geogr, US Dept Interior, 52-55; res forester, Southern Forest Exp Sta, 57-58; res asst soil microbiol, Univ Minn, 58-61; soil scientist, Southern Forest & Range Exp Sta, US Forest Serv, La, 61-66; PRIN SOIL SCIENTIST, SOUTHEASTERN FOREST & RANGE EXP STA, US FOREST SERV, USDA, 66- *Mem:* AAAS; Soc Am Foresters; Soil Sci Soc Am. *Res:* Soil biochemistry and microbiology; forest soil investigations; nutrient cycling; nitrogen fixation. *Mailing Add:* SE Forest & Range Exp Sta Box 12254 Research Triangle Park NC 27709

JORGENSEN, JAMES D, b Salina, Utah, Mar 23, 48; m 70. SOLID STATE PHYSICS. *Educ:* Brigham Young Univ, BS, 70, PhD(physics), 75. *Prof Exp:* Fel, 75-77, asst physicist neutron diffraction, 77-78, PHYSICIST, ARGONNE NAT LAB, 79-, GROUP LEADER NEUTRON SCATTERING, 81- *Mem:* Am Phys Soc. *Res:* Pressure induced phase transitions in solids; mechanical properties and structure of solids; time of flight neutron diffraction at high pressure; pulsed source neutron diffraction; fast ionic transport. *Mailing Add:* Solid State Sci Div Argonne Nat Lab Argonne IL 60439

JORGENSEN, JENS ERIK, b Oslo, Norway, July 2, 36; US citizen; m 62; c 2. MECHANICAL ENGINEERING, SYSTEMS ANALYSIS. *Educ:* Mass Inst Technol, SB, 59, MS, 63, ScD(mech eng), 69. *Prof Exp:* Res engr, Cadilac Gage Co, Calif, 59-61; res engr, MHD Inc, Calif, 62; res asst mech eng, Mass Inst Technol, 63-65, instr, 65-68; asst prof, 68-73, assoc prof, 73-79, PROF MECH ENG, UNIV WASH, 79- *Concurrent Pos:* Nat Insts Health fel bioeng, 69; consult, Wash Iron Works, 69-70; Pac Northwest Forest & Range Exp Sta, US Forest Serv, 71-77, Weyerhaeuser Co, 79-81 & Metro, 81- *Honors & Awards:* Ralph Teetor Award, Soc Automotive Engrs, 71. *Mem:* Am Soc Mech Engrs; Instrument Soc Am. *Res:* Fluid power systems analysis; design and analysis of fluidic devices; control systems analysis; instrumentation design and performance analysis; design and control of large scale off road equipment for logging in national forests; manufacturing systems analysis and automechanics of manufacturing processes. *Mailing Add:* Dept of Mech Eng FU-10 Univ of Wash Seattle WA 98105

JORGENSEN, P(AUL) J, b Midway, Utah, Sept 1, 30; m 59; c 6. MATERIALS SCIENCE, CHEMISTRY. *Educ:* Brigham Young Univ, BS, 54; Univ Utah, PhD(ceramics eng), 60. *Prof Exp:* Ceramist, Gen Elec Res Lab, 60-68; chmn, Ceramics Dept, Stanford Res Inst, 68-74, dir, Mat Res Ctr, 74-76, exec dir phys sci, 76-77, vpres phys & life sci, 77-80, SR VPRES, SCI GROUP, SRI INT, 80- *Concurrent Pos:* Lectr, Univ Calif, Berkeley, 69-70; consult, GTE Sylvania, Inc, 71- *Honors & Awards:* I R 100 Award, 67. *Mem:* Fel Am Ceramic Soc; AAAS. *Res:* Kinetics of transport processes in ceramics, including sintering, solute segregation, grain growth, diffusion, electrical conductivity, oxidation, corrosion and permeation. *Mailing Add:* 333 Ravenswood Ave Menlo Park CA 94025

JORGENSEN, ROBERT ROTHNICK, SR, b Columbus, Wis, Sept 26, 35; m 58; c 4. VETERINARY PUBLIC HEALTH, OPERATIONS RESEARCH. *Educ:* Univ Minn, BS, 57, DVM, 59, MPH, 65; Naval Postgrad Sch, MS, 71; Am Bd Vet Pub Health, dipl, 73. *Prof Exp:* Chief, Prog Eval & Studies Off, Off Surgeon Gen, Dept Army, 71-72, chief, Mgt & Studies Off, 71-76, chief, Vet Corps Career Activ, Med Dept, Personnel Support Agency, 76-77, CHIEF, VET SCI DIV, ACAD HEALTH SCI, US ARMY, 78- *Concurrent Pos:* Adj lectr, Am Univ, 72-78; consult, Surgeon Gen for Vet Pub Health, 76-, Comt on Lab Animal Facil, Nat Acad Sci-Nat Res Coun, 77-; Conf Pub Health Vets (pres, 77-); adj prof, Univ Tex, Health Sci Ctr, 79- *Mem:* Am Vet Med Asn; Am Public Health Asn; Asn Mil Surgeons US. *Res:* Data analysis; epidemiology; computer science. *Mailing Add:* Acad of Health Sci HSA-IVS Ft Sam Houston TX 78234

JORGENSEN, WILLIAM L, b New York, NY, Oct 5, 49. ORGANIC CHEMISTRY, THEORETICAL CHEMISTRY. *Educ:* Princeton Univ, AB, 70; Harvard Univ, PhD(chem physics), 75. *Prof Exp:* From asst prof to assoc prof, 75-82, PROF ORG CHEM, PURDUE UNIV, 82- *Concurrent Pos:* Dreyfus teacher-scholar, Camille & Henry Dreyfus Found Inc, 78-83; A P Sloan Found fel, 79-81. *Mem:* Am Chem Soc. *Res:* Theoretical organic chemistry; computer simulations of molecular liquids and solutions; computer assisted synthetic analysis. *Mailing Add:* Dept of Chem Purdue Univ West Lafayette IN 47907

JORGENSEN, EDSEL CARPENTER, b Kamas, Utah, Mar 11, 26; m 47; c 6. ZOOLOGY, NEMATOLOGY. *Educ:* Univ Utah, BS, 53, MS, 56. *Prof Exp:* Nematologist, USDA, 54-62, res nematologist, Utah State Univ, 62-67, zoologist, Utah Exp Sta, 67-70, ZOOLOGIST, CALIF EXP STA, USDA, 70- *Mem:* Soc Nematol; Orgn Trop Am Nematol; Am Phytopath Soc. *Res:* Nematode ecology, control, biology and interactions. *Mailing Add:* USDA Agr Res Sta 17053 Shafter Ave Shafter CA 93263

JORGENSON, GORDON VICTOR, b Sunburg, Minn, Jan 3, 33; m 57; c 2. THIN FILMS. *Educ:* St Olaf Col, BA, 54. *Prof Exp:* Physicist, Wright Air Develop Ctr, Wright-Patterson AFB, 54-55; prin lab attendant, Univ Minn, 56-57; assoc scientist, Gen Mills, Inc, 57-61; sr scientist, 61-63; sr scientist, Appl Sci Div, Litton Indust, Inc, 63-66; sr physicist, NStar Res & Develop Inst, 66-75; sr physicist, Midwest Res Inst, 75-78; prin res scientist, 78-79, SR PRIN RES SCIENTIST, HONEYWELL INC, 80- *Mem:* AAAS; Am Vacuum Soc. *Res:* Surface physics research utilizing sputtering; effects of solar-wind bombardment of bodies in space; electrohydrodynamics; research in vacuum deposited thin films; optical coating technology. *Mailing Add:* Honeywell Inc MS 17-2345 2600 Ridgway Pkwy Minneapolis MN 55413

JORGENSON, JAMES WALLACE, b Kenosha, Wis, Sept 9, 52; m 78. CHROMATOGRAPHY, ELECTROPHORESIS. *Educ:* Northern Ill Univ, BS, 74; Ind Univ, PhD(chem), 79. *Prof Exp:* ASST PROF CHEM, UNIV NC, CHAPEL HILL, 79- *Mem:* Am Chem Soc. *Res:* Chemical separations: fundamental studies of gas chromatogrphy; liquid chromatogrphy and electrophoresis. *Mailing Add:* Chem Dept Venable Hall 045A Univ NC Chapel Hill NC 27514

JORNA, SIEBE, b Harlingen, The Netherlands, July 8, 38; m 64; c 1. THEORETICAL PHYSICS. *Educ:* Univ Western Australia, BS, 58 & 59, MS, 62; St Andrews Univ, PhD(theoret physics), 65. *Prof Exp:* Res asst theoret physics, St Andrews Univ, 61-62, asst lectr, 62-65; res asst, Univ Calif, San Diego, 65-67; asst prof, Georgetown Univ, 67-71; ASSOC RES PHYSICIST, UNIV CALIF, SAN DIEGO, 71- *Concurrent Pos:* Laser consult, Naval Res Lab, Washington, DC, 67-69; sr scientist, KMS Fusion, Inc, 72-74; staff scientist, Phys Dynamics, Inc, 74- *Mem:* Am Phys Soc. *Res:* Mathematical, nuclear, high energy and solid state physics; nonlinear optics; plasma physics; particle beam fusion; laser-driven fusion. *Mailing Add:* Phys Dynamics Inc Box 556 La Jolla CA 92037

JORNS, MARILYN SCHUMAN, b New York, NY, Aug 24, 43; m 71. ENZYMOLOGY. *Educ:* State Univ NY Binghamton, BA, 65; Univ Mich, MS, 67, PhD(biochem), 70. *Prof Exp:* Am Cancer Soc fel chem, Univ Konstanz, 70-72; res assoc biochem, Univ Tex Health Sci Ctr Dallas, 72-75; ASST PROF CHEM, OHIO STATE UNIV, 75- *Mem:* Sigma Xi; Am Chem Soc; Am Soc Biol Chemists; AAAS. *Res:* Elucidating the mechanisms by which various flavoenzymes promote catalysis via chemical characterization of reaction intermediates and correlations with model flavin chemistry. *Mailing Add:* Dept of Chem Ohio State Univ 140 W 18th Ave Columbus OH 43210

JORY, FARNHAM STEWART, b Berkeley, Calif, Dec 6, 26; div; c 3. PHYSICS. *Educ:* Univ Calif, AB, 48; Swiss Fed Inst Technol, dipl, 51; Univ Chicago, MS, 54, PhD(physics), 55. *Prof Exp:* Asst, Enrico Fermi Inst Nuclear Studies, Ill, 52-55; researcher physics, Univ Md, 56-57; res geophysicist, Inst Geophys, Univ Calif, Los Angeles, 57-58; mem tech staff, Space Tech Labs, Thompson-Ramo-Wooldridge Corp, 58-59; asst prof physics, Long Beach State Col, 59-60; physicist, Lawrence Radiation Lab, 60; CONSULT PHYSICS, 60- *Concurrent Pos:* Vis asst prof, Univ Calif, Los Angeles, 57-58. *Mem:* Am Phys Soc; Am Geophys Union. *Res:* Cosmic-ray and upper-atmosphere physics; geomagnetism and solarterrestrial relationships; experimental spectroscopy. *Mailing Add:* Apt 302 2558 Fruitvale Ave Oakland CA 94601

JOSE, JORGE VALENZUELA, b Mexico City, Mex, Sept 13, 49. PHYSICS. *Educ:* Nat Univ Mex, BS, 72, MS, 73, PhD(physics), 76. *Prof Exp:* Res assoc physics, Brown Univ, 74-76; asst prof res, 76-77; James Franck fel physics, Univ Chicago, 77-79; asst prof res, Rutgers Univ, 79-80; ASST PROF PHYSICS, NORTHEASTERN UNIV, 80- *Concurrent Pos:* Guest scholar, Kyoto Univ, Japan, 79. *Mem:* Am Phys Soc. *Res:* Phase transitions in condensed matter physics. *Mailing Add:* Physics Dept Northeastern Univ Boston MA 02115

JOSEFOWICZ, JACK YITZHAK, biophysics, see previous edition

JOSELOW, MORRIS M, b New York, NY, Apr 26, 23; m 48; c 3. PUBLIC HEALTH. *Educ:* City Col New York, BS, 43; Columbia Univ, MA, 46, PhD(biochem), 49; Bd Cert Safety Prof, cert; Am Intersoc Acad, cert environ sci. *Prof Exp:* Res assoc chem, Columbia Univ, 45-46, lectr, 46-47; instr, City Col New York, 47-49; lab dir, US Naval Res, 50-55 & Consumers Union, 55-65; asst prof pub health, Columbia Univ, 65-70; assoc prof, 70-75, PROF PREV MED, COMMUNITY HEALTH, COL MED & DENT NJ, NEWARK, 75- *Concurrent Pos:* Fel, Sloan-Kettering Inst, 49-50; NSF fel, Oak Ridge Inst Nuclear Studies, 54, 67; fels, USPHS, 59, 68 & WHO, 68; guest investr, Rockefeller Univ, 68. *Mem:* Fel NY Acad Sci; Am Chem Soc; fel Am Pub Health Asn; Am Indust Hyg Asn; fel Royal Soc Health. *Res:* Environmental sciences; toxicology; industrial hygiene and safety; clinical chemistry; food and nutrition; trace metals; biological monitoring; air pollution. *Mailing Add:* 607 Fern St Westwood NJ 07675

JOSELYN, JO ANN CRAM, b St Francis, Kans, Oct 5, 43. SOLAR PHYSICS, SPACE PHYSICS. *Educ:* Univ Colo, BS, 65, MS, 67, PhD(astrogeophys), 78. *Prof Exp:* Physicist res ionospheric physics, 68-75, physicist res magnetospheric physics, 75-76, physicist res solar wind, 76-78, PHYSICIST SOLAR & GEOMAGNETIC FORECASTING, SPACE ENVIRON SERVS CTR, SPACE ENVIRON LAB, NAT OCEANIC & ATMOSPHERIC ADMIN, 78- *Mem:* Am Geophys Union; Union Radio Scientists Int; AAAS; Sigma Xi. *Res:* Astro geophysics, especially solar physics and solar wind physics; also solar-terrestrial relationships, especially geomagnetism. *Mailing Add:* NOAA/ERL/SEL R43 325 Broadway Boulder CO 80303

JOSENHANS, JAMES GROSS, b Toledo, Ohio, Dec 19, 32; m 61; c 2. SOLID STATE ELECTRONICS. *Educ:* Univ Toledo, BSc, 56; Ohio State Univ, MSc, 58, PhD(elec eng), 62. *Prof Exp:* Engr, Storer Broadcasting Co, Ohio, 51-53; teaching asst physics, Univ Toledo, 53-56; from res asst to res

assoc, Electron Device Lab, Ohio State Univ, 57-62, asst prof elec eng, 62-63; MEM TECH STAFF, BELL TEL LAB, 63- *Mem:* Am Phys Soc; Inst Elec & Electronics Engrs. *Res:* Silicon integrated circuit development strategies to satisfy projected telephone systems needs. *Mailing Add:* Room 2A343 Div 21 Bell Tel Lab Murray Hill NJ 07974

JOSENHANS, WILLIAM T, b Wildbad, Ger, Feb 19, 22; Can citizen; m 44; c 4. RESPIRATORY PHYSIOLOGY, RESPIRATORY DISEASES. *Educ:* Univ Tubingen, MD, 50. *Prof Exp:* Physician student health, Univ Bonn, 51-54; asst prof physiol, 54-58; from asst prof to assoc prof, 58-64, PROF PHYSIOL, DALHOUSIE UNIV, 64- *Concurrent Pos:* Dir, Pulmonary Function Lab, Halifax Infirmary. *Mem:* Can Physiol Soc; Am Physiol Soc; Ger Physiol Soc; fel Am Col Chest Physicians. *Res:* Mechanisms of respiration; ballisto cardiography; physiology of exercise. *Mailing Add:* Dept Physiol Dalhousie Univ Halifax NS B3H 3J5 Can

JOSEPH, ALFRED S, b Cortland, NY, June 27, 32; m 56; c 2. PHYSICS. *Educ:* Union Col, NY, BS, 56; Case Inst Technol, MS, 60, PhD(physics), 62. *Prof Exp:* Instr, Case Inst Technol, 58-62; sr physicist, Atomics Int Div, Corp Eng, Rockwell Int, 62, mem tech staff, 62-68, group leader, sci ctr, 68-72, dir solid state electronics, 72-76, sr tech adv, Autonetics, 76-77, sr eng exec technol appln, 77-80. *Concurrent Pos:* Consult, Gen Elec Co, Ohio, 59-61. *Mem:* Am Phys Soc. *Res:* Studies of the electronic properties of metals through the de Haas-van Alphen effect; superconducting phenomena; semiconductors and semiconductor devices. *Mailing Add:* 9515 Sawyer Los Angeles CA 90035

JOSEPH, BERNARD WILLIAM, b Detroit, Mich, June 7, 29; m 51; c 3. VEHICLE EMISSION. *Educ:* Wayne State Univ, BA, 68. *Prof Exp:* assoc sr res physicist, Res Labs, 51-80, SR DEVELOP ENGR, ENG STAFF, GEN MOTORS CORP, 80- *Honors & Awards:* Arch T Colwell Award, Soc Automotive Engrs, 74. *Mem:* Optical Soc Am; Soc Photog Scientists & Engrs. *Res:* Optical properties of materials, optical design, radiometry, photometry and photochemistry; exhaust emmision measurement; optical engineering. *Mailing Add:* 1949 Franklin Berkley MI 48072

JOSEPH, DANIEL D, b Chicago, Ill, Mar 26, 29; m 50; c 3. MECHANICAL ENGINEERING. *Educ:* Univ Chicago, MA, 50; Ill Inst Technol, BS, 59, MS, 60, PhD(mech eng), 63. *Prof Exp:* Asst mech eng, Ill Inst Technol, 59-62, asst prof, 62-63, from asst prof to assoc prof fluid mech, 63-68, PROF AEROSPACE ENG & MECH, UNIV MINN, MINNEAPOLIS, 68- *Concurrent Pos:* Guggenheim fel, 69-70; assoc ed arch rational mech anal, J Appl Mech & J Appl Math, Soc Indust & Appl Math. *Mem:* Am Soc Mech Engrs; Am Phys Soc; Soc Natural Philol. *Res:* Fluid mechanics, flow through porous media and hydrodynamic stability; applied mathematics; theory of hydrodynamic stability and bifurcation theory; rheology of viscoelastic fluids. *Mailing Add:* Dept of Mech & Aerospace Eng Univ of Minn Minneapolis MN 55455

JOSEPH, DAVID WINRAM, b Evanston, Ill, June 28, 30; m 60; c 3. ELEMENTARY PARTICLE PHYSICS. *Educ:* Roosevelt Col, BS, 52; Univ Chicago, MS, 57, PhD(elem particle physics), 59. *Prof Exp:* Physicist, Ballistic Res Labs, Aberdeen Proving Ground, Md, 53-55; res assoc physics, Purdue Univ, 59-61; res assoc, US Naval Res Lab, Washington, DC, 61-63; from asst prof to assoc prof, 63-68, PROF PHYSICS, UNIV NEBR-LINCOLN, 68- *Mem:* Fel Am Phys Soc. *Res:* Group and algebraic methods. *Mailing Add:* Dept of Physics & Astron Univ of Nebr Lincoln NE 68588

JOSEPH, DONALD J, b Summerfield, Ill, Sept 24, 22; m 45; c 2. OTOLARYNGOLOGY. *Educ:* St Louis Univ, MD, 46; Baylor Univ, MS, 53. *Prof Exp:* Assoc prof, 67-71, PROF SURG, SCH MED, UNIV MO-COLUMBIA, 71-, CHIEF OTOLARYNGOL, 67- *Concurrent Pos:* Consult, US Army Surgeon Gen, 61-64; mem comt hearing & bioacoust, Nat Res Coun, 61-67; communicative sci study sect, NIH, 62-64. *Honors & Awards:* Bronze Star Medal, 57; Legion of Merit, 67. *Mem:* Fel Am Acad Ophthal & Otolaryngol; fel Am Col Surg; fel Am Laryngol, Rhinol & Otol Soc. *Res:* Communicative sciences; audiology; speech pathology. *Mailing Add:* Otolaryngology Sect Univ of Mo-Columbia Sch of Med Columbia MO 65201

JOSEPH, EARL CLARK, b St Paul, Minn, Nov 1, 26; m 55; c 4. ANTICIPATORY SCIENCES, COMPUTER SCIENCE. *Educ:* Univ Minn, Minneapolis, BA, 51. *Prof Exp:* Mathematician, programmer & analyst, Univac, Sperry Rand Corp, 51-55, proj supvr & mgr, 55-58, systs mgr, 58-63, STAFF SCIENTIST, SPERRY UNIVAC, 63-, FUTURIST, 75-; FUTURIST-IN-RESIDENCE, SCI MUS MINN, 77- *Concurrent Pos:* Vis lectr, Univ Minn, 71- *Mem:* AAAS; sr mem Inst Elec & Electronics Engrs; Asn Comput Mach. *Res:* Computer system design research, reliability and availability; multiprocessors; self repairable systems; microprogramming; impact of computers on society; time sharing; real time control; computer architecture; technological forecasting; systems management; information systems; operating systems, microprocessors, smart machines for education, agriculture, health, delivery and research of the future. *Mailing Add:* Sperry Univac PO Box 3525 St Paul MN 55165

JOSEPH, EDWARD DAVID, b Pittsburgh, Pa, Aug 26, 19; m 42; c 3. PSYCHIATRY, PSYCHOANALYSIS. *Educ:* McGill Univ, BSc, 42, MD, CM, 43. *Prof Exp:* Intern med, Montreal Gen Hosp, 43-44; resident psychiat, 47-48, clin asst, 49-66, ATTEND PSYCHIATRIST, MT SINAI HOSP, 66-; PROF PSYCHIAT, MT SINAI SCH MED, 68- *Concurrent Pos:* Kastor fel, Mt Sinai Hosp, 48-49; cand, NY Psychoanal Inst, 48-55, mem fac, 63- *Mem:* AAAS; Am Psychoanal Asn (pres, 71-73); Int Psychoanal Asn (treas, 73-77, pres, 77-81); Am Psychiat Asn; Am Psychosom Soc. *Res:* Psychology of twins; psychoanalytic clinical studies; psychosomatic problems; psychiatric education of medical students and residents. *Mailing Add:* Mt Sinai Sch of Med 11 E 100 St New York NY 10029

JOSEPH, J MEHSEN, b Whitesville, WVa, Sept 30, 28; m 51; c 5. MEDICAL MICROBIOLOGY. *Educ:* WVa Univ, BA, 48, MSc, 49; Univ Md, PhD(bact, chem), 54; Univ Toledo, BSc, 55. *Prof Exp:* Asst zool & anat, WVa Univ, 48-49; asst prof microbiol, Univ Toledo, 51-54; dir res, Biol Res Inst, 54-57; asst dir bur labs, 63- 76, DIR LABS, LABS, MD STATE DEPT HEALTH & MENT HYG, 77- *Concurrent Pos:* Sect head bur labs, Md State Dept Health & Ment Hyg, 57-63. *Mem:* Am Soc Microbiol (secy, 74-); Brit Soc Microbiol; Tissue Cult Asn; Am Pub Health Asn. *Res:* Disinfectants; antiseptics; microbiology of acid mine waters; lysozyme activity in relation to oral infections; public health microbiology; isolation methods for genus Clostridium; acute and chronic toxicity of chlorinated phenols; disease transmission by anesthetizing apparatus; evaluation of fungicidal compounds; diagnostic virology and tissue culture. *Mailing Add:* Md State Labs Admin 201 W Preston St Baltimore MD 21201

JOSEPH, J WALTER, JR, b Oak Park, Ill, Oct 8, 28; m 53; c 2. MECHANICAL ENGINEERING. *Educ:* NC State Col, BS, 50; Pa State Univ, MS, 54. *Prof Exp:* Asst eng res, Pa State Univ, 50-51, thermal res lab, 53-54; mech engr, Savannah River Lab, 54-65, mech engr, reactor tech dept, 65-71, asst chief supvr, 71-76, chief supvr, 76-78, supt, Traffic & Transp Dept, 78-80, SUPT, EQUIP ENG DEPT, SAVANNAH RIVER PLANT, E I DU PONT DE NEMOURS & CO, INC, 80- *Res:* Nuclear reactor project management; mechanical and welding development supporting nuclear operations; remote equipment, nuclear waste management; isotopic heat sources; shipping containers; resistance welding; high pressure gas technology. *Mailing Add:* Savannah River Plant E I du Pont de Nemours & Co Inc Aiken SC 29801

JOSEPH, JAMES, b Los Angeles, Calif, Oct 28, 30; m 58; c 2. MARINE BIOLOGY. *Educ:* Humboldt State Col, BS, 56, MS, 58; Univ Wash, PhD, 66. *Hon Degrees:* Dr, Universite de Bretagne Occidental, France Nautilus Award. *Prof Exp:* Scientist, Inter-Am Trop Tuna Comn, 58-63, prin scientist, 64-69, dir invests, 69, RES ASSOC, INST MARINE RES, SCRIPPS INST OCEANOG, 69-; AFFIL PROF, UNIV WASH, 69- *Concurrent Pos:* Served on various panels, comts, etc concerning marine sci and fisheries & as adv to all levels of govt. *Mem:* Am Inst Fishery Res Biol; Sigma Xi. *Res:* Relationship exploitation by man on the dynamics of the stocks of marine fishes; development of international arrangements for the conservation and management of living marine resources. *Mailing Add:* Inst of Marine Res Scripps Inst of Oceanog La Jolla CA 92037

JOSEPH, JAMES, b Berlin, Ger, Feb 3, 26; nat US; m 52; c 2. PHYSICS. *Educ:* Brooklyn Col, BS, 49; Univ Iowa, PhD, 56. *Prof Exp:* Asst prof, Iowa State Univ, 55-57; assoc prof, 57-65, chmn dept, 66-72, PROF PHYSICS, ST JOHNS UNIV, 65- *Concurrent Pos:* Res grant, Air Force Off Sci Res, 59, Nat Sci Found, 61, NASA, 62; vis prof physics, Inst Theoret Physics, Univ Geneva, 63-64; vis prof physics, Inst Nuclear Physics, Univ Karlsruhe, W Ger, 75. *Mem:* NY Acad Sci; Am Phys Soc. *Res:* Theoretical physics; quantum electrodynamics; particle physics. *Mailing Add:* 150-02 88th Ave Jamaica NY 11432

JOSEPH, JOHN MUNDANCHERIL, b Kerala, India, Feb 21, 47; US citizen; m 81; c 1. CHROMATOGRAPHY, SPECTROSCOPY. *Educ:* Kerala Univ, India, BS, 68; Univ Jabalpur, India, MS, 71; Drexel Univ, Philadelphia, MS & PhD(biochem), 80. *Prof Exp:* Lectr chem, Kerala Univ, India, 68-69; Chemist, McDowell Distillery, Kerala, 71-73; Midvale Heppenstal, Philadelphia, 73-75; teaching & res asst biochem, Drexel Univ, Philadelphia, 75-80; RES INVESTR ANAL CHEM, SQUIBB INST MED RES, 81- *Concurrent Pos:* Fel biochem, Drexel Univ, Philadelphia, 75-81. *Mem:* Sigma Xi; AAAS; Am Chem Soc; Am Pharmaceut Asn. *Res:* Examination of the stereochemical requirements for the biological activity of cholesterol in terms of its metabolism to other functional sterols and its proper fit into biological membranes, investigated in both enzymatic and functional membranous systems; chemical synthesis of cholesterol analogues; conformational and configurational analysis of sterols by hydrogen and carbon 13-nuclear magnetic resonance. *Mailing Add:* Anal Res & Develop Squibb Inst Med Res New Brunswick NJ 08903

JOSEPH, MARJORY L, b Milan, Ohio, Oct 10, 17; m 41; c 1. TEXTILE CHEMISTRY. *Educ:* Ohio State Univ, BS, 39, MS, 52; Pa State Univ, PhD(textile chem), 62. *Prof Exp:* High sch teacher, Ohio, 48-51; teaching asst clothing & textiles, Ohio State Univ, 51-52; from instr to assoc prof, Juniata Col, 52-62, chmn div, 54-58, chmn dept home econ, 58-62; assoc prof clothing & textiles, 62-66, actg chmn dept home econ, 68-69, PROF CLOTHING & TEXTILES, CALIF STATE UNIV, NORTHRIDGE, 66-, CHMN DEPT HOME ECON, 69- *Concurrent Pos:* Part-time instr clothing & textile res, Pa State Univ, 57-62; consult, Southern Calif Gas Co, 63-, Southern Counties Gas Co, 64, Mattel Toy Corp, 67-68, Springs Mills Inc, 73- & US Borax Co, 74- *Mem:* Fel Am Inst Chemists; Am Soc Testing & Mat; Am Asn Textile Chemists & Colorists; Home Econ Asn; Brit Soc Dyers & Colourists. *Res:* Evaluation of durability; correlation of actual wear to laboratory testing methods; application and end-use of new fabrics, textiles and finishes; flammability of textiles; author or co-author of various publications. *Mailing Add:* Calif State Univ 18111 Nordhoff St Northridge CA 91324

JOSEPH, PETER D(ANIEL), b Brooklyn, NY, Jan 21, 36; m 57; c 1. ELECTRICAL ENGINEERING. *Educ:* Mass Inst Technol, SB & SM, 58; Purdue Univ, PhD(elec eng), 61. *Prof Exp:* Instr elec eng, Purdue Univ, 58-61; mem tech staff, 61-64, head guidance sect, 64-66, mgr syst anal & software dept, 66-70, mgr sensor design & anal dept, 70-76, LAB MGR, TRW SYSTS & ENERGY GROUP, 76- *Mem:* Inst Elec & Electronics Engrs; Am Inst Aeronaut & Astronaut. *Res:* Guidance of missiles and space vehicles; optimal control theory; optimal filter theory; electro-optical sensors. *Mailing Add:* TRW Inc One Space Park Redondo Beach CA 90278

JOSEPH, PETER MARON, b Ridley Park, Pa, Mar 26, 39. MEDICAL PHYSICS. *Educ:* Lafayette Col, BS, 59; Harvard Univ, MA, 61, PhD(physics), 67. *Prof Exp:* Instr physics, Cornell Univ, 67-70; asst prof, Carnegie-Mellon Univ, 70-72; NIH fel, Memorial-Sloan Kettering Cancer Ctr, 72-73; instr radiol, Columbia-Presby Med Ctr, 73-75, asst prof, 75-80; ASSOC PROF DIAG IMAGES PHYSICS, UNIV MD, BALTIMORE, 80- *Mem:* AAAS; Am Phys Soc; Am Asn Physicists in Med. *Res:* High energy electromagnetic phenomena; experimental tests of quantum electrodynamics; photo production of vector mesons; energy range relations; x-ray spectra and attenuation curves; radiographic image quality; computerized axial tomography. *Mailing Add:* Radiol Dept Univ Md Hosp Baltimore MD 21201

JOSEPH, RAMON R, b New York, NY, May 17, 30; m 56; c 3. GASTROENTEROLOGY, ENZYMOLOGY. *Educ:* Manhattan Col, BS, 52; Cornell Univ, MD, 56. *Prof Exp:* Intern med, Meadowbrook Hosp, Hempstead, 56-57; resident, 59-62, staff physician, 62-64, asst dir dept med, Wayne County Gen Hosp, 64-73; assoc prof, 68-75, PROF INTERNAL MED, UNIV MICH, ANN ARBOR, 75-, ASST DEAN MED SCH, 73-; DIR GASTROENTEROL SECT, WAYNE COUNTY GEN HOSP, WESTLAND, 62-, DIR DEPT MED, 73- *Concurrent Pos:* Fel, Wayne County Gen Hosp, 61-62; consult, Annapolis Hosp, Wayne, 62-, St Mary Hosp, Livonia, 62-, Mich Dept Educ, 69-73; from instr to assoc prof internal med, Univ Mich, Ann Arbor, 62-75; chmn res dept, Wayne County Gen Hosp, 64-, pres med staff, 71-72. *Mem:* AAAS; fel Am Col Physicians; NY Acad Sci; Asn Am Med Col; AMA. *Res:* Origin and nature of human serum lactic dehydrogenase; multiple molecular forms of enzyme amylase; biochemical diagnosis in gastroenterology; radiographic aspects of gastroenterology. *Mailing Add:* Dept Med Wayne County Gen Hosp Westland MI 48185

JOSEPH, RICHARD ISAAC, b Brooklyn, NY, May 25, 36; m 61; c 3. SOLID STATE PHYSICS. *Educ:* City Col New York, BS, 57; Harvard Univ, PhD(physics), 62. *Prof Exp:* Sr res scientist solid state physics, Raytheon Co, 61-66; from asst prof to assoc prof, 66-70, PROF ELEC ENG, JOHNS HOPKINS UNIV, 70- *Mem:* AAAS; Am Phys Soc. *Res:* Statistical mechanics; theory of magnetism and properties of magnetic materials; microwave physics; theory of solid state; exchange interactions in solids; critical phenomena; solitons; non-linear wave equations. *Mailing Add:* Dept of Elec Eng Johns Hopkins Univ Baltimore MD 21218

JOSEPH, ROSALINE RESNICK, b New York City, NY, Aug 21, 29; m 54; c 2. MEDICINE, HEMATOLOGY & ONCOLOGY. *Educ:* Cornell Univ, AB, 49; Women's Med Col Pa, MD, 53; Temple Univ, MS, 58. *Prof Exp:* Instr hematol, Med Ctr, Temple Univ, 57-60, assoc med, 60-63, assoc prof med, 63-77, course coordr retinculo-endothelial, Syst Interdisciplinary Course Comt, 68-73; PROF MED & CHIEF HEMATOL & ONCOL DEPT, MED COL PA, 77- *Mem:* Am Fedn Clin Res; Am Soc Hematol; Fel Am Col Physicians; Am Asn Cancer Educ; Am Soc Clin Oncol. *Res:* New modalities in the treatment of cancer and hematologic disorders. *Mailing Add:* Med Col Pa 3300 Henry Ave Philadelphia PA 19129

JOSEPH, ROY D, b Fremont, Ohio, July 26, 37; m 69. APPLIED MATHEMATICS. *Educ:* Fenn Col, BEE, 60; Case Inst Technol, MSEE, 62, PhD(eng), 65. *Prof Exp:* Res assoc, Case Inst Technol, 65-66; asst prof eng, State Univ NY Stony Brook, 66-72; asst prof, 73-80, ASSOC PROF ELEC ENG, SPACE INST, UNIV TENN, 80- *Mem:* Inst Elec & Electronics Eng; Soc Indust & Appl Math; Am Asn Univ Professors. *Res:* active network synthesis; optimal control signal processing. *Mailing Add:* Space Inst Univ of Tenn Tullahoma TN 37388

JOSEPH, SAMMY WILLIAM, b Jacksonville, Fla, Oct 10, 34; m 67; c 2. MICROBIOLOGY, MEDICAL BACTERIOLOGY. *Educ:* Univ Fla, BSA, 56; St John's Univ, NY, MS, 64, PhD(microbiol), 70. *Prof Exp:* Asst head serol br, US Naval Med Sch, Nat Naval Med Ctr, 57-58, head bact, serol & mycol br, US Naval Hosp, St Albans, NY, 58-63, head bact & mycol br, Naval Med Sch, Nat Naval Med Ctr, 63-67; Navy contract fel bact, St John's Univ, NY, 67-70; microbiologist & exec officer, Naval Med Res Unit 2, Jakarta Detachment, Indonesia, 70-73, comndg officer bact, Naval Unit, Ft Detrick, 73-75, dep chmn microbiol dept, Naval Med Res Inst, 75-78, prog mgr infectious dis, Naval Med Res & Develop Command, Nat Naval Med Ctr, 78-81; PROF & CHMN, DEPT MICROBIOL, UNIV MD, 81- *Concurrent Pos:* Vis scientist, Off Naval Res, London, 77. *Mem:* Am Soc Microbiol; Am Acad Microbiol; AAAS; NY Acad Sci; Am Soc Clin Path. *Res:* Studies on bacteria of clinical significance, particularly those causing gastroenteritis; purification and characterization of toxic substances; role of antibiotics in treatment; bacterial adherence to surfaces. *Mailing Add:* Dept Microbiol Univ Md College Park MD 20742

JOSEPH, SOLOMON, b Brooklyn, NY, Nov 3, 10; m 35; c 2. INDUSTRIAL CHEMISTRY. *Educ:* Columbia Univ, BS, 35, MA, 37; Polytech Inst Brooklyn, PhD(chem), 44. *Prof Exp:* Lab instr chem, Yeshiva Col, 35-38; chemist, New York Bd Transportation, 39-45; dir res, Bri-Test, Inc, 45-50; chief chemist, Camp Chem Co, 51-52; chemist, Res Div, Penetone Co, NJ, 52-60; chief chemist, Chem Div, John Sexton & Co, Mich, 60-63; teacher chem, New York City Bd Educ, 63-80. *Concurrent Pos:* Instr, Yeshiva Col, 45-50; lectr & adj prof chem, City Univ New York, 67-70. *Res:* Emulsion of waxes, resins and polishes; cryoscopic studies of acids and bases in selenium oxychloride; protective coatings; synthetic detergents; corrosion prevention; sanitation chemicals; chemical specialties. *Mailing Add:* 1044 E Fifth St Brooklyn NY 11230

JOSEPH, STANLEY ROBERT, b Jacobus, Pa, May 21, 30; m 56; c 3. MEDICAL ENTOMOLOGY. *Educ:* Gettysburg Col, BA, 52; Pa State Univ, MS, 54; Univ Md, PhD(entom), 68. *Prof Exp:* From asst entomologist to assoc entomologist, Md State Bd Agr, 56-73; entomologist, pest mgt sect, 73-79, CHIEF, MOSQUITO CONTROL SECT, MD DEPT AGR, 80- *Mem:* Entom Soc Am; Am Mosquito Control Asn. *Res:* Methods and insecticides for use in mosquito control in Maryland; ultra low volume insecticide applications with air and ground equipment; biology of Culiseta melanura in Maryland; insect physiology; toxicology of malathion to vertebrates. *Mailing Add:* Md Dept Agr Mosquito Control Sect Annapolis MD 21401

JOSEPHS, JESS J, b New York, NY, Jan 4, 17; m 62; c 2. MUSICAL ACOUSTICS. *Educ:* NY Univ, AB, 38, MSc, 40, PhD(phys chem), 43. *Prof Exp:* Res assoc, Northwestern Univ, 45-46, instr phys chem, 46-47; asst prof phys sci, Univ Chicago, 47-50; asst prof physics, Boston Univ, 50-56; PROF PHYSICS, SMITH COL, 56- *Mem:* Am Phys Soc; Am Asn Physics Teachers; Acoust Soc Am; Audio Eng Soc; Sigma Xi. *Res:* Solid state physics. psychoacoustics; acoustical study of the violin; distortion in electronically reproduced music. *Mailing Add:* 56 Ward Ave Northampton MA 01060

JOSEPHS, MELVIN JAY, b New York, NY, Apr 26, 26; m 48; c 2. PLANT PHYSIOLOGY: INFORMATION SCIENCE. *Educ:* Rutgers Univ, BSc, 50, MSc, 52, PhD(plant physiol, bot), 54. *Prof Exp:* Plant physiologist, Dow Chem Co, Mich, 54-60; assoc ed, Chem & Eng News, Am Chem Soc, 60-66, managing ed, Environ Sci & Technol, 66-69, managing ed, 69-73; asst dir, Prod & Prog Mgt, Nat Tech Info Serv, US Dept Com, 73-76; chief, Toxicol Data Bank, Nat Libr Med, HEW, 76-78; DIR, NAT TECH INFO SERV, OFF GOVT AGENCY SUPPORT, DEPT COM, 78- *Mem:* Am Chem Soc; Sigma Xi. *Res:* Boron nutrition and organic acid content; growth regulators; herbicides; algae; aquatic plants. *Mailing Add:* 9109 Friars Rd Bethesda MD 20817

JOSEPHS, ROBERT, b Philadelphia, Pa, June 29, 37; m 74; c 1. BIOPHYSICS, STRUCTURAL BIOLOGY. *Educ:* Univ Ill, BS, 59; Hebrew Univ, MSc, 62; Johns Hopkins Univ, PhD(biol), 66. *Prof Exp:* Res assoc muscle biol, Johns Hopkins Univ, 66-67; fel, MRC Lab Molecular Biol, 68-69; fel struct biol, 70-73, scientist, 73-77, SR SCIENTIST & ASSOC, POLYMER DEPT, WEIZMAN INST, 77-; ASSOC PROF BIOPHYS & THEORET BIOL, UNIV CHICAGO, 77- *Concurrent Pos:* NIH grant, 78-81. *Res:* Structural biology; sickle cell anemia; electron crystallography. *Mailing Add:* Dept of Biophys 920 E 58th St Chicago IL 60637

JOSEPHSON, ALAN S, b Bronx, NY, Nov 30, 30; m 55; c 3. MEDICINE, IMMUNOLOGY. *Educ:* NY Univ, AB, 52, MD, 56; Am Bd Internal Med, dipl, 66. *Prof Exp:* from asst prof to assoc prof, 63-73, PROF MED, STATE UNIV NY DOWNSTATE MED CTR, 73- *Concurrent Pos:* Nat Inst Allergy & Infectious Dis trainee fel, NY Univ, 58-60. *Mem:* Am Fedn Clin Res; Am Rheumatism Asn; Am Asn Immunologists. *Res:* Immunologic properties of penicillin; proteins of secretions; immunologic properties of air pollutants. *Mailing Add:* Dept of Med State Univ of NY Downstate Med Ctr Brooklyn NY 11203

JOSEPHSON, EDWARD SAMUEL, b Boston, Mass, Sept 30, 15; m 38; c 3. FOOD SCIENCE, RESEARCH ADMINISTRATION. *Educ:* Harvard Univ, AB, 36; Mass Inst Technol, PhD(biochem), 40; Indust Col Armed Forces, dipl, 62. *Prof Exp:* Williams-Waterman fel, Mass Inst Technol, 40-43; biochemist, NIH, 44-52 & US Army Chem Corp, 52-54; chief, Biol & Chem Br, Qm Res & Eng Command, 54, asst chief, Chem & Plastics Div, 54-56, assoc sci dir develop, 56-61, spec asst food & food irradiation, 61-62; assoc dir food radiation, Food Div & dir, Radiation Lab, 62-72, dep tech dir food serv systs prog, US Army Natick Res & Develop Labs, 72-75; SR LECTR, DEPT NUTRIT & FOOD SCI, MASS INST TECHNOL, 76- *Concurrent Pos:* Asst prof, Oglethorpe Univ, 43-44 & Med Sch, Emory Univ, 45; lectr, Am Univ, 50-54; adv on preserving food by ionizing radiation, Int Atomic Energy Agency, UN, 64-, Food & Agr Orgn, UN, 64-, Israel AEC, 65-, Inter-Am Nuclear Energy Comn, Orgn Am States, 68-, Ministry Econ, Iran, 69- & Dept Atomic Energy, India, 67-; vchmn, Inter-Dept Comt Radiation Preservation Food, 70-71; consult, Universal Sci & Eng, 76-; lectr, Ctr Lifelong Learning, Harvard Univ, 77- *Mem:* AAAS; Am Chem Soc; Inst Food Technol; Sigma Xi; Am Col Nuclear Med. *Res:* Chemotherapy of malaria and other tropical diseases; enzymes; vitamins; nutrition; microbiology; food preservation by ionizing radiations. *Mailing Add:* Dept Nutrit & Food Sci Mass Inst Technol Cambridge MA 02139

JOSEPHSON, LEONARD MELVIN, b Ashland, Wis, Dec 4, 13; m 40; c 2. PLANT BREEDING, AGRONOMY. *Educ:* Univ Wis, BS, 36, PhD(plant path, agron), 41. *Prof Exp:* Agt, USDA, Wis, 33-36, purchasing seed grain agt, Minn, 36-37; asst, Univ Wis, 37-39; secy & field rep, Malt Res Inst, 39-43; from asst agronomist to agronomist, Exp Sta, Univ Ky, 43-51; maize breeder, Union SAfrica, 51-54; prof agron, 54-71, PROF PLANT & SOIL SCI, UNIV TENN, KNOXVILLE, 71- *Concurrent Pos:* Consult, Univ Tenn-AID, India; res agronomist, USDA, 54-71. *Mem:* AAAS; fel Am Soc Agron; Am Phytopath Soc; Am Genetics Asn; Genetics Soc Am. *Res:* Corn breeding, breeding methods and genetics; corn pathology; corn insects. *Mailing Add:* Dept of Plant & Soil Sci Univ of Tenn Knoxville TN 37916

JOSEPHSON, ROBERT KARL, b Somerville, Mass, July 12, 34; m 56; c 3. COMPARATIVE PHYSIOLOGY. *Educ:* Tufts Univ, BS, 56; Univ Calif, Los Angeles, PhD(zool), 60. *Prof Exp:* NATO fel, Univ Tübingen, 61; from asst prof to assoc prof zool, Univ Minn, 62-65; from assoc prof to prof biol, Case Western Reserve Univ, 65-71; PROF BIOL, UNIV CALIF, IRVINE, 71- *Concurrent Pos:* Guggenheim fel, 77-78. *Mem:* AAAS; Am Soc Zool; Brit Soc Exp Biol; Soc Gen Physiol; Soc Neurosci. *Res:* Physiological mechanisms controlling behavior in lower animals. *Mailing Add:* Sch of Biol Sci Univ of Calif Irvine CA 92664

JOSEPHSON, RONALD VICTOR, b Bellefonte, Pa, May 19, 42; m 69; c 2. FOOD CHEMISTRY, BIOCHEMISTRY. *Educ:* Pa State Univ, BS, 64; Univ Minn, St Paul, MS, 66, PhD(food sci), 70. *Prof Exp:* Asst prof dairy technol, Ohio State Univ, 70-71, asst prof food sci & nutrit, 71-75; ASSOC PROF & PROF FAM STUDIES & CONSUMER SCI, SAN DIEGO STATE UNIV, 75- *Concurrent Pos:* Prin investr grants, Nat Oceanic & Atmospheric Admin, US Army, Nat Fisheries Inst & Inst Food Technologists, 77- *Mem:* Am Dairy Sci Asn; Inst Food Technol; Sigma Xi; AAAS. *Res:* Chemistry, analysis and storage stability of foods; milk and diary foods, fish and seafoods, medical foods, and vegetable proteins. *Mailing Add:* Sch Fam Studies & Consumer Sci San Diego State Univ San Diego CA 92182

JOSHI, ARAVIND KRISHNA, b Poona, India, Aug 5, 29; m 63. COMPUTER & INFORMATION SCIENCE. *Educ:* Univ Poona, BE, 51; Indian Inst Sci, Bangalore, dipl, 52; Univ Pa, MS, 58, PhD(elec eng), 60. *Prof Exp:* Res asst electronics, Indian Inst Sci, Bangalore, 52-53 & Tata Inst Fundamental Res, Bombay, 53; prof engr, Radio Corp Am, NJ, 54-58; assoc ling anal, 58-61, from asst prof to assoc prof elec eng & ling, 61-72, PROF COMPUT & INFO SCI & CHMN DEPT, UNIV PA, 72- *Concurrent Pos:* Assoc, transformations & discourse anal proj, NSF, 58-; consult info theory & ling, Philco Res Lab, Pa, 62-63; ling consult, Western Reserve, 64-; Guggenheim fel, 71-72; mem, Inst Advan Study, 71-72. *Mem:* Asn Comput Mach; fel Inst Elec & Electronics Engrs; Am Math Soc. *Res:* Information theory; structural analysis of natural languages and formal linguistics; natural language processing; artificial intelligence; mathematical linguistics. *Mailing Add:* Moore Sch of Elec Eng Univ of Pa Philadelphia PA 19104

JOSHI, BHAIRAV DATT, b Dungrakot, Almora, India, Mar 5, 39; m 67. PHYSICAL CHEMISTRY, QUANTUM CHEMISTRY. *Educ:* Univ Delhi, BS, 59, MS, 61; Univ Chicago, MS, 63, PhD(chem), 64. *Prof Exp:* Fel chem, Dept Phys, Univ Chicago, 65-66, lectr, Indian Inst Technol, Kanpur, 66-67; reader, Univ Delhi, 67-69; res assoc, State Univ NY Stony Brook, 69-70; asst prof, 70-77, ASSOC PROF CHEM, STATE UNIV NY COL GENESEO, 78- *Mem:* Am Phys Soc; AAAS; Am Chem Soc. *Res:* Quantum mechanical studies of the electronic structure of small atoms and molecules; use of computers in undergraduate education. *Mailing Add:* 3 Mohawk Ave Geneseo NY 14454

JOSHI, JAYANT GOPAL, b Poona, India, July 22, 32; m 58; c 2. BIOCHEMISTRY. *Educ:* Univ Poona, BSc, 52, MSc, 54, PhD(biochem), 57. *Prof Exp:* Indian Coun Med Res-Rockefeller Found fel biochem, Nutrit Res Labs, Coonoor, India, 56-58; jr sci officer, Cent Food Tech Res Inst, Mysore, 58-59; res fel, Duke Univ, 59-64; sci pool officer, Nat Chem Labs, Poona, India, 64-66; assoc, Duke Univ, 66-68, asst prof, 68-70; assoc prof, 70-79, PROF BIOCHEM, UNIV TENN, KNOXVILLE, 79- *Concurrent Pos:* Vis scientist, Inst Clin Chem, Uppsala, Sweden, 72 & 73; consult, Biol Div, Oak Ridge Nat Labs. *Mem:* Am Soc Biol Chemists; Am Soc Microbiol. *Res:* Comparative biochemistry; mechanism of enzyme action--pyridine nucleotide, metabolism, biosynthesis and regulation, biochemical change induced by ultraviolet light; metal toxicity. *Mailing Add:* Dept of Biochem Univ of Tenn Knoxville TN 37916

JOSHI, MADHUSUDAN SHANKARRAO, b Jamkandi, India, Oct 21, 28; m 53; c 2. REPRODUCTIVE PHYSIOLOGY, ENDOCRINOLOGY. *Educ:* Karnatak Univ, India, BSc, 49; Univ Bombay, MSc, 53; Weizmann Inst Sci, PhD(biol), 70. *Prof Exp:* Asst res officer physiol reprod, Cancer Res Ctr, Parel, Bombay, 56-66; asst prof anat, State Univ NY Downstate Med Ctr, 70-77; mem fac, 77-80, ASSOC PROF, DEPT ANAT, UNIV NDAK, 80- *Mem:* Soc Study Fertil UK; Soc Study Reproduction; Am Asn Anat; Sigma Xi; Am Physiol Soc. *Res:* Mechanisms involved in fertilization and implantation; study of hormone dependent enzymes in uterus; proteins in cerebrospinal fluid. *Mailing Add:* Dept of Anat Univ NDak Grand Forks ND 58202

JOSHI, MUKUND SHANKAR, b India, June 11, 47; m 73; c 2. PHARMACEUTICAL CHEMISTRY, ORGANIC CHEMISTRY. *Educ:* VJ Tech Inst, Bombay, India, 69; Univ Md, MS, 73, PhD(chem engr), 76. *Prof Exp:* Vis scientist, Danish Atomic Energy Comn, 75-76; RES SCIENTIST, UPJOHN CO, 76- *Mem:* Am Inst Chem Engrs; Am Chem Soc. *Res:* Chemical process research and development work to commercially manufacture pharmaceutical products; synthesis of steroids and prostaglandins; feasibility studies risk analysis, economic evaluation and supervision of laboratory. *Mailing Add:* Upjohn Co Portage Rd Kalamazoo MI 49001

JOSHI, SEWA RAM, b Baluana, Punjab, Oct 15, 33; US citizen; m 54; c 1. TOXICOLOGY, VETERINARY MEDICINE. *Educ:* Punjab Univ, BVSc, 54; Cornell Univ, MS, 63, PhD(animal physiol), 65. *Prof Exp:* State vet, Civil Vet Dept, Punjab, 54-55; res assoc animal reprod, Ind Vet Res Inst, Izathnagar, 55-61; res assoc path & toxicol, Cancer Res Found, Harvard Med Sch, 65-71; sr staff fel cancer, Nat Cancer Inst, 71-76; PHYSIOLOGIST PHARM & TOXICOL, BUR DRUGS, FOOD & DRUG ADMIN, 76- *Concurrent Pos:* Assoc prof, Howard Univ, Washington, DC, 72-75. *Mem:* Soc Study Reproduction; NY Acad Sci; Environ Mutagen Soc; Sigma Xi; Soc Toxicol. *Res:* Reproductive toxicology; chemical carcinogenesis and mutagenesis of chemicals in the environmental toxicology. *Mailing Add:* Div Anti-infective Drug Prod 5600 Fishers Lane Rm 12B16 Rockville MD 20857

JOSHI, SHARAD GOPAL, b Nagpur, India. REPRODUCTIVE ENDOCRINOLOGY, REPRODUCTIVE PHYSIOLOGY. *Educ:* Univ Nagpur, India, BS, 52, MS, 54; Univ Bombay, PhD(biochem), 59. *Prof Exp:* Fel endocrinol, Worcester Fedn & Harvard Med Sch, 59-63; assoc prof reproductive physiol, Inst Med Sci, India, 63-65; staff scientist endocrinol, Syntex Inst Hormone Biol, 65-66 & Southwest Fedn Res & Educ, 66-73; assoc prof obstet, gynec & biochem, 73-82, PROF OBSTET & GYNEC, ALBANY MED COL, 82- *Honors & Awards:* Edward Tyler Award, Int Soc Reproductive Med, 81. *Mem:* Endocrine Soc; Soc Study Reproduction; Int Soc Reproductive Med; NY Acad Sci. *Res:* Hormonal control and role of endometrium in human pregnancy; fertility control in human subjects; effects of toxic agents on human pregnancy. *Mailing Add:* Dept Obstet & Gynec Albany Med Col 47 New Scotland Ave Albany NY 12208

JOSHI, VASUDEV CHHOTALAL, b Borsad, Gujarat, June 26, 38; m 65; c 3. BIOCHEMISTRY. *Educ:* Madras Univ, BPharm, 59; Andhra Univ, MPharm, 61; Indian Inst Sci, PhD(biochem), 65. *Prof Exp:* Res assoc biochem, Med Ctr, Duke Univ, 66-70, assoc in pediat, 70-72; asst prof, 72-78, ASSOC PROF BIOCHEM, BAYLOR COL MED, 78- *Concurrent Pos:* Ford Found fel, Indian Inst Sci, Bangalore, 65-66; Fulbright fel, US Educ Found in India, 66; NIH grant, Med Ctr, Duke Univ, 66-70; vis assoc prof, Mass Inst Technol, 80-81; res career develop award, USPHS, 78-83. *Mem:* Brit Biochem

Soc; Am Soc Biol Chemists; Soc Biol Chemists, India. *Res:* Enzymatic mechanism of fatty acid synthesis in bacteria and animal tissues; hormonal regulation of fatty acid synthetase and stearoyl coenzyme A desaturase in liver; lipid metabolism in cultured cells; mechanism of insulin action. *Mailing Add:* Dept of Biochem Baylor Col of Med Houston TX 77030

JOSHUA, HENRY, b Hamburg, Ger, Dec 8, 34; US citizen; m 68; c 3. ORGANIC CHEMISTRY, SEPARATION SCIENCE. *Educ:* Bar-Ilan Univ, Israel, BS, 59; NY Univ, MS, 62, PhD(chem), 64. *Prof Exp:* Res chemist, Res Div, Col Eng, NY Univ, 60-61; res fel chem, Princeton Univ, 64-65; sr res chemist, 65-78; RES FEL, MERCK SHARP & DOHME RES LABS, 78- *Mem:* Am Chem Soc. *Res:* Isolation of active compounds from biological sources and purification of organic synthetic reaction products; development of instrumentation for liquid chromatography and laboratory automation. *Mailing Add:* Merck Sharpe & Dohme Res Lab PO Box 2000 Rahway NJ 07065

JOSIAS, CONRAD S(EYMOUR), b New York, NY, June 12, 30; m 63; c 3. ELECTRICAL ENGINEERING. *Educ:* NY Univ, BEE, 51; Polytech Inst Brooklyn, MEE, 55. *Prof Exp:* Engr electronic develop, Airborne Instruments Lab, Inc, NY, 51-56; from res engr, missile guid systs to eng group supvr, space electronics group, space sci div, Jet Propulsion Lab, Calif Inst Technol, 56-65; pres, Analog Technol Corp, Pasadena, 65-79; PRES, JOSIAS ASSOCS, INC, 79- *Concurrent Pos:* Instr, Pasadena City Col, 59-61. *Honors & Awards:* Award, NASA Inventions & Contrib Bd, 64. *Mem:* Inst Elec & Electronics Engrs. *Res:* Electronic devices and systems; scientific instruments for laboratory and space applications; analytical instruments for industrial laboratories. *Mailing Add:* 4733 Hillard Ave La Canada CA 91011

JOSLIN, ROBERT SCOTT, b Indianapolis, Ind, May 28, 29; m 56; c 3. PHARMACEUTICAL CHEMISTRY. *Educ:* Purdue Univ, BS, 51, MS, 55, PhD(phys pharm), 59. *Prof Exp:* Assoc pharmaceut chemist, Eli Lilly & Co, 53-54, sr pharmaceut chemist, 58-65; dir prod improv, William H. Rorer, Inc, 65-68, dir depts pharmaceut sci, Res Div & asst dir res, 68-74; assoc dir pharmaceut & chem develop, G D Searle & Co, 74-78; dir pharmaceut & anal res & develop, Baxter Labs, 78; CONSULT, 78- *Honors & Awards:* Lunsford Richardson Award, 57. *Mem:* Fel Am Inst Chemists; Am Chem Soc; fel Acad Pharmaceut Sci; Int Pharmaceut Fedn; NY Acad Sci. *Res:* Pharmaceutical formulation; biopharmaceutics; process and product development. *Mailing Add:* 3264-D Sanders Northbrook IL 60062

JOSLYN, DENNIS JOSEPH, b Chicago, Ill, Apr 29, 47; m 76. INSECT CYTOGENETICS, BIOCHEMICAL GENETICS OF INSECTS. *Educ:* St Procopius Col, BS, 69; Univ Ill, Urbana, MS, 73, PhD(zool), 78. *Prof Exp:* Asst res scientist insect genetics, Univ Fla, 76-79; res assoc, Insects Affecting Man & Animals Res Lab, USDA, 78-79; ASST PROF ZOOL, RUTGERS UNIV, 79- *Concurrent Pos:* Res assoc, Insects Affecting Man & Animals Res Lab, USDA, 76-79. *Mem:* Genetics Soc Am; Am Genetic Asn; Am Mosquito Control Asn. *Res:* Evolutionary genetics and experimental population genetics of insects; genetic control of insects of medical, veterinary and agricultural importance; genetics, isozymology and cytology of insect pathogens. *Mailing Add:* Dept Biol Camden Col Arts & Sci Rutgers Univ Camden NJ 08102

JOSS, PAUL CHRISTOPHER, b Brooklyn, NY, May 7, 45; m 70; c 1. THEORETICAL ASTROPHYSICS, X-RAY ASTRONOMY. *Educ:* Cornell Univ, BA, 66, PhD(astron, space sci), 71. *Prof Exp:* Mem, Inst Advan Study, 71-73; asst prof, 73-78, ASSOC PROF, DEPT PHYSICS, MASS INST TECHNOL, 78- *Concurrent Pos:* Vis scientist, Dept Nuclear Physics, Weizmann Inst Sci, 74-75 & 78, Inst Astron, Univ Cambridge, 77; Alfred P Sloan res fel, 76-80; vis staff mem, Los Alamos Nat Lab, 79; consult, Visidyne, Inc, 79- & Los Alamos Nat Lab, 80- *Honors & Awards:* Helen B Warner Prize, Am Astron Soc, 80. *Mem:* Am Astron Soc. *Res:* Theoretical and observational studies of compact x-ray sources; theoretical research on stellar structure and evolution, extragalactic astrophysics, the spectra of quasars, and the origin and orbital evolution of comets. *Mailing Add:* Rm 6-203 Mass Inst of Technol Cambridge MA 02139

JOSSEM, EDMUND LEONARD, b Camden, NJ, May 19, 19. PHYSICS. *Educ:* City Col New York, BS, 38; Cornell Univ, MS, 39, PhD(physics), 50. *Prof Exp:* Asst physics, Cornell Univ, 40-42, instr, 42-45; mem staff, Los Alamos Sci Lab, 45-46; asst physics, Cornell Univ, 46-50, res assoc, 50-55, actg asst prof, 55-56; from asst prof to assoc prof, 56-64, chmn dept, 67-80, PROF PHYSICS, OHIO STATE UNIV, 64- *Concurrent Pos:* Staff physicist, Comn Col Physics, 63-64, exec secy, 64-65, chmn, 66-71; mem, Nat Adv Coun Educ Professions Develop, 67-70; mem bd dirs, Mich-Ohio Educ Lab, 67-69; adv coun educ & manpower, Am Inst Physics, 69-72; mem physics survey comt, panel on educ, Nat Acad Sci-Nat Res Coun, 70-72; mem comn physic educ, Int Union Pure & Applied Physics, 81-; mem hon bd, Int Conf X-ray & Atomic Inner Shell Physics, 81-82. *Honors & Awards:* Distinguished Serv Citation, Am Asn Physics Teachers, 70. *Mem:* Fel AAAS; Am Phys Soc; Am Asn Physics Teachers (vpres, 71-72, pres, 73-74); fel Royal Acad Arts. *Res:* Solid state physics; x-ray physics. *Mailing Add:* Dept Physics Ohio State Univ 174 W 18th Ave Columbus OH 43210

JOSSI, JACK WILLIAM, b Portland, Ore, Apr 4, 37; c 3. OCEANOGRAPHY, ECOLOGY. *Educ:* Pac Univ, BS, 59; Univ Wash, Seattle, BS, 62; Univ Miami, MS, 72. *Prof Exp:* Phys oceanogr trop oceanog, Washington Biol Lab, US Dept Interior, 62-65, oceanogr, Trop Atlantic Biol Lab, 65-70, mgr fishery climat prog, Southeast Fisheries Ctr, 71-72, chief, Continuous Plankton Recorder Surv, Marine Resources Monitoring, Assessment & Prediction Field Group, US Dept Commerce, 72-74, asst chief, 74-78, RES OCEANOGR OCEAN CLIMAT, ATLANTIC ENVIRON GROUP, NAT OCEANIC & ATMOSPHERIC ADMIN, US DEPT COMMERCE, 78- *Concurrent Pos:* Fel, Univ Miami, 67-68; consult, Smithsonian Inst, 70; mem, Standing Comt Oceanog, Nat Marine Fisheries Serv, US Dept Commerce, 71- *Mem:* Marine Biol Asn UK. *Res:* Ocean climatology; modeling and forecasting of distribution and abundance of living marine resources. *Mailing Add:* Eastshore Rd Jamestown RI 02835

JOST, DANA NELSON, b Arlington, Mass, May 11, 25; m 47; c 2. PHYCOLOGY, ENVIRONMENTAL BIOLOGY. *Educ:* Univ Mass, BS, 49; Harvard Univ, PhD(biol), 53. *Prof Exp:* Instr, 53-55, from asst prof to assoc prof, 55-59, chmn dept, 64-76, PROF BIOL, FRAMINGHAM STATE COL, 59- *Mem:* AAAS; Phycol Soc Am; Bot Soc Am; Int Phycol Soc. *Res:* Growth and reproduction of chlorophycean algae; evolution of microorganisms; environmental influences of algal growth. *Mailing Add:* Dept Biol Hemenway Hall P.O. Box 2000 Framingham MA 01701

JOST, DONALD E, b Chicago, Ill, Nov 5, 36; m 57; c 3. CHEMICAL ENGINEERING. *Educ:* Univ Del, BS, 58; Princeton Univ, PhD(chem eng), 64. *Prof Exp:* Instr chem eng, Princeton Univ, 61-62; asst prof, Ore State Univ, 62-64 & Univ Pa, 64-67; res engr, 67-70, mgr, eng res, 70-75, mgr, resource develop, res & develop, Sun Oil Co, 75-79, spec assignment, chem strategic planning, Sun Petrol Prod Co, 79-80, MGR, CHEM GROUP, RES & DEVELOP, SUNTECH, INC, 80- *Concurrent Pos:* Chem res engr, US Bur Mines, 63-64; Ford Found fel, 65-66. *Mem:* Am Inst Chem Engrs; Commercial Develop Asn. *Mailing Add:* Suntech Inc PO Box 1135 Marcus Hook PA 19061

JOST, ERNEST, b El Ferrol, Spain, Sept 6, 28; US citizen; m 55; c 4. PHYSICAL CHEMISTRY. *Educ:* Univ Berne, license, 55, PhD(phys chem), 58. *Prof Exp:* Mem tech staff, Metals & Controls Div, Tex Instruments Inc, 58-61; mgr develop, Ciba A G, Switz, 61-62; dir res & develop, Mat & Elec Prod Group, 62-74, DIR PROD RES DEPT, TEX INSTRUMENTS INC, ATTLEBORO, 74- *Concurrent Pos:* Consult, Nat Acad Sci, 71. *Mem:* Electrochem Soc; The Chem Soc. *Res:* Metallurgy; electrochemistry; diffusion; solid state physics; semiconducting ceramics. *Mailing Add:* Prod Res Dept Tex Instruments Inc 34 Forest St Attleboro MA 02703

JOST, JEAN-PIERRE, b Avenches, Switz, Oct 10, 37; US citizen; m 68; c 2. BIOCHEMISTRY, CELL BIOLOGY. *Educ:* Swiss Fed Inst Technol, MS, 61, PhD(biol, biochem), 64. *Prof Exp:* Proj assoc, McArdle Mem Lab Cancer Res, Univ Wis-Madison, 64-66, fel, Lab Molecular Biol, 67-68; molecular biologist, Nat Jewish Hosp & Res Ctr, Denver, 68-71; GROUP LEADER, FRIEDRICH MIESCHER INST, SWITZ, 71- *Concurrent Pos:* Asst prof, Dept Biophys & Genetics, Med Sch, Univ Colo, Denver, 68-71; res grants, Am Cancer Soc, 69, NIH, Health, Educ & Welfare & NSF, 70. *Res:* Mode of action of steroid hormones; hormonal regulation of the expression of specific genes in eukaryotes. *Mailing Add:* Friedrich Miescher Inst Postfach 273 CH-4002 Basel Switzerland

JOST, PATRICIA COWAN, b St Louis, Mo. BIOPHYSICAL CHEMISTRY, MOLECULAR BIOLOGY. *Educ:* Memphis State Univ, BS, 52; Univ Ore, PhD(biol), 66. *Prof Exp:* Res assoc molecular genetics, 66-68, SR RES ASSOC MOLECULAR BIOL, INST MOLECULAR BIOL, UNIV ORE, 68- *Concurrent Pos:* NIH fel, Univ Ore, 66-68. *Mem:* Biophys Soc. *Res:* Membrane structure; reporter groups and magnetic resonance; membrane biology, lipid-lipid and lipid-protein interactions. *Mailing Add:* Inst of Molecular Biol Univ of Ore Eugene OR 97403

JOSTEN, JOHN JAMES, bacteriology, see previous edition

JOSTLEIN, HANS, b Munich, WGer, Dec 27, 40; m 67; c 3. VACUUM ENGINEERING, EXPERIMENTAL PHYSICS. *Educ:* Ludwigs Maximilian Univ, WGer, PhD(physics), 69. *Prof Exp:* Fel high energy res, Univ Munich, 69-70; res asst, Univ Rochester, 70-73; asst prof, State Univ NY, Stony Brook, 73-79; PHYSICIST RES & ACCELERATION SUPPORT, FERMI NAT ACCELERATOR LAB, 79- *Res:* High energy particle physics, specifically muon; muon inelastic scattering; high mass pair production for leptons and hadrons to test quark theory; drell-yan processes and resonance production; very high lumosity pair production. *Mailing Add:* Fermi Nat Accelerator Lab MS I11 Box 500 Batavia IL 60510

JOSWICK, HARRY LOREN, microbiology, see previous edition

JOUBIN, FRANC RENAULT, b San Francisco, Calif, Nov 15, 11; nat Can; m 38; c 1. CHEMISTRY. *Educ:* Univ BC, BA, 36, MA, 41. *Hon Degrees:* DSc, Univ BC, 57. *Prof Exp:* From mine geologist to explor geologist, Pioneer Gold Mines Co, 38-48; pres & managing dir, Algom Uranium Mines, 53-56, dir, Rio Algom Mines, 56-58; pres, Bralorne Pioneer Mines, 58-60; CONSULT TO ADMINR, UN DEVELOP PROG, 68- *Concurrent Pos:* Managing dir, Pronto, Pater, Rixahabasca, Rexspar, Lake Nordic, Spanish-Am & Panel Uranium Mines, 53-56; geol consult, Rio Tinto Co, Eng, 56-58; dir, Guaranty Trust of Can, 57-60. *Honors & Awards:* Leonard Gold Medal, Eng Inst Can, 55; Blaylock Gold Medal, Can Inst Mining & Metall, 57. *Mem:* Am Inst Mining, Metall & Petrol Eng; Can Inst Mining & Metall (vpres, 57-58); Geol Asn Can; Royal Can Inst. *Res:* Geology; geophysics. *Mailing Add:* 500 Avenue Rd Toronto ON M4V 2J6 Can

JOULLIE, MADELEINE M, b Paris, France, Mar 29, 27; nat US; m 59. ORGANIC CHEMISTRY. *Educ:* Simmons Col, BS, 49; Univ Pa, MS, 50, PhD, 53. *Prof Exp:* From instr to asst prof, 53-68, assoc prof, 68-77, PROF CHEM, UNIV PA, 77- *Mem:* AAAS; Am Chem Soc. *Res:* Mechanisms of organic reactions; heterocyclic chemistry; synthesis of potential antimetabolites. *Mailing Add:* Dept of Chem Univ of Pa Philadelphia PA 19104

JOUNG, JOHN JONGIN, b Korea, June 29, 41; m 68; c 2. CHEMICAL PROCESS ENGINEERING, BIOENGINEERING. *Educ:* Seoul Nat Univ, BS, 63, MS, 67; Univ NMex, PhD(chem eng), 70. *Prof Exp:* Res fel, Ames Lab, 70-71; res supvr, Univ Chicago, 71-76; sr scientist, Colgate-Palmolive Co, 76-78; sci adv, Am Hosp Supply Corp, 78-81; STAFF RES ENGR, STANDARD OIL CO, IND, 81- *Concurrent Pos:* Vcmndg officer, Chem Smoke Generator Co, Korea, 63-65; assst investr, Korea Inst Sci & Technol, 67-68. *Mem:* Am Inst Chem Engrs; Am Chem Soc; Soc Plastics Engrs; Am Mgt Asn. *Res:* Process and product research in the areas of chemical, polymer, energy and health care business; cancer and clinical pathology. *Mailing Add:* 234 E Bailey Rd Unit-G Naperville IL 60565

JOURDIAN, GEORGE WILLIAM, b Northampton, Mass, Apr 21, 29; m 54; c 2. BIOCHEMISTRY, MICROBIOLOGY. *Educ:* Amherst Col, BA, 49; Univ Mass, MS, 53; Purdue Univ, PhD(bact), 58. *Prof Exp:* From instr to assoc prof biol chem & biochem, 61-74, res assoc internal med, 65-74, PROF BIOL CHEM, MED SCH, UNIV MICH, ANN ARBOR, 65- *Concurrent Pos:* Arthritis Found fel, 58-61; Fogarty Sr Int fel, 78-79. *Mem:* Am Soc Biol Chem; Am Chem Soc; Soc Complex Carbohydrates. *Res:* Biochemistry of glycosaminoglycans and glycoproteins. *Mailing Add:* Rackham Arthritis Res Unit Univ of Mich Med Ctr Ann Arbor MI 48104

JOVANOVIC, M(ILAN) K(OSTA), b Belgrade, Yugoslavia, Oct 29, 13; nat US; m 54; c 1. MECHANICAL ENGINEERING. *Educ:* Univ Belgrade, Dipl Ing, 38, Dipl Phys, 45; Northwestern Univ, MS, 54, PhD(mech eng), 57. *Prof Exp:* Asst thermodyn & physics, Univ Belgrade, 39-46, instr physics, 46-47, asst prof thermodyn, 47-51, assoc prof thermodyn & refig mach & asst dean, Sch Mech Eng, 51-52; instr physics, Univ Ill, 55; assoc prof mech eng, SDak Sch Mines & Technol, 56-58; from assoc prof to prof, Okla State Univ, 58-63; prof, Univ Alaska, 63-65; prof, US Naval Acad, 65-68; PROF MECH ENG, WICHITA STATE UNIV, 68- *Mem:* Am Soc Mech Engrs; Am Soc Eng Educ. *Res:* Thermodynamics. *Mailing Add:* Dept of Mech Eng Wichita State Univ Wichita KS 67208

JOVANOVICH, JOVAN VOJISLAV, b Belgrade, Yugoslavia, July 30, 28; m 55; c 2. HIGH ENERGY PHYSICS, NUCLEAR PHYSICS. *Educ:* Univ Belgrade, BSc, 50; Univ Man, MSc, 56; Washington Univ, St Louis, PhD(physics), 61. *Prof Exp:* Asst physics, Inst Brois Kidric, Belgrade, Yugoslavia, 50-54, Univ Belgrade, 53-55 & Univ Man, 55-57; asst, Wash Univ, 57-61, res assoc, 61; res assoc, Brookhaven Nat Lab, 61-63, vis asst physicist, 63-64, develop officer, Nuclear Physics Lab, Oxford Univ, 64-65; asst prof, 65-67, assoc prof, 67-79, PROF PHYSICS, UNIV MAN, 79- *Concurrent Pos:* Vis scientist, Orgn Europ Nuclear Res, 71-72, 78-79. *Mem:* Am Phys Soc; Can Asn Physicists. *Res:* Investigation of properties of neutral K mesons; elementary inelastic proton-proton interaction; search for quarks, pion properties. *Mailing Add:* Dept of Physics Univ of Man Winnipeg MB R3T 2N2 Can

JOVANOVITCH, DRASKO D, high energy physics, see previous edition

JOWETT, DAVID, b Liverpool, Eng, Oct 14, 34; m 57; c 2. STATISTICS, BOTANY. *Educ:* Univ Wales, BSc, 56, PhD(bot), 59. *Prof Exp:* Demonstr agr bot, Univ Col NWales, 56-59; sr sci officer, Plant Breeding, EAfrican Agr & Forestry Res Orgn, Uganda, 59-65; from asst prof to assoc prof statist, Iowa State Univ, 65-70; assoc prof, 70-77, PROF MATH, UNIV WIS-GREEN BAY, 77- *Concurrent Pos:* Rockefeller Found fel, Iowa State Univ, 62-63; Intern, Acad Admin, Am Coun Educ, 76-77. *Mem:* AAAS; Brit Ecol Soc; Am Statist Asn; Biomet Soc; Am Soc Nat; fel Royal Statist Soc. *Res:* Heavy metal resistance and tolerance of low nutrient levels in plants; improved varieties hybrids of sorghum for Africa; sorghum agronomy crown rust epiphytology; biostatistics; biomathematics; statistical computing. *Mailing Add:* Col of Environ Sci Univ of Wis Green Bay WI 54305

JOY, DAVID CHARLES, b Colchester, Eng, Nov 15, 43. ELECTRON MICROSCOPY, MATERIALS SCIENCE. *Educ:* Cambridge Univ, BA, 66; Oxford Univ, DPhil(metall), 69. *Prof Exp:* Fac metall, Oxford Univ, 69-74; MEM TECH STAFF ELECTRON MICROS, BELL TEL LABS, 74- *Concurrent Pos:* Res fel, Imperial Chem Industs, 69-71 & Oxford Univ, 69-72; Warren res fel, Royal Soc London, 72-74. *Honors & Awards:* Burton Medal, Electron Micros Soc Am, 78. *Mem:* Electron Micros Soc Am; Royal Micros Soc London. *Res:* Electron microscopy and electron spectroscopy applied to microstructural and microchemical analysis. *Mailing Add:* Bell Tel Labs 600 Mountain Ave Murray Hill NJ 07974

JOY, GEORGE CECIL, III, b Lincoln, Nebr, Apr 22, 48; m 70; c 1. INORGANIC CHEMISTRY. *Educ:* Grinnell Col, BA, 70; Northwestern Univ, MS, 71, PhD(inorg chem), 75. *Prof Exp:* res chemist, 74-76, groupleader, 76-81, MGR APPL CATALYSIS RES, CORP RES DIV, UOP INC, 81- *Mem:* Am Chem Soc; Nat Catalysis Soc; Soc Automotive Engrs. *Res:* Studies in heterogeneous catalysis; inorganic aspects of preparation and characterization of catalysts. *Mailing Add:* Corp Res Ctr UOP Inc 10 UOP Plaza Des Plaines IL 60016

JOY, JOSEPH WAYNE, b Iowa City, Apr 12, 30; m 58; c 3. PHYSICAL OCEANOGRAPHY. *Educ:* State Col Wash, BA, 55; Univ Calif, San Diego, MS, 58. *Prof Exp:* Res oceanogr, Marine Phys Lab, Univ Calif, San Diego, 56-61; oceanogr, Marine Adv, Bendix Corp, 61-66; res oceanogr, Meteorol Res, Inc, 66-67; sr scientist, Westinghouse Ocean Res Lab, Calif, 67-70; specialist oceanog, Scripps Inst Oceanog, Univ Calif, San Diego, 70-74; STAFF OCEANOGR, INTERSEA RES CORP, 74- *Mem:* AAAS; Am Geophys Union; Am Meteorol Soc. *Res:* Surface waves and currents; radar oceanography; radar as oceanographic tool. *Mailing Add:* 1210 Agate St San Diego CA 92109

JOY, KENNETH WILFRED, b Sunderland, Eng, May 13, 35; m; c 2. PLANT PHYSIOLOGY. *Educ:* Bristol Univ, BSc, 56, PhD(plant physiol), 59. *Prof Exp:* Res assoc plant physiol, Imp Col, Univ London, 59-64; vis res assoc agron, Univ Ill, Urbana, 64-65; assoc prof bot, Univ Toronto, 66-68; PROF BIOL, CARLETON UNIV, 68- *Concurrent Pos:* Fulbright travel fel, 64-65. *Mem:* Am Soc Plant Physiol; Can Soc Plant Physiol (secy, 68-69). *Res:* Nitrogen metabolism of plants, especially amino acid metabolism; synthesis and utilization of amides. *Mailing Add:* Dept of Biol Carleton Univ Ottawa ON K1S 5B6 Can

JOY, MICHAEL LAWRENCE GRAHAME, b Toronto, Ont, July 31, 40; m 67; c 2. BIOMEDICAL ENGINEERING. *Educ:* Univ Toronto, BSc, 63, MASc, 68, PhD(elec eng), 70. *Prof Exp:* Asst prof elec eng, 70-76, ASSOC PROF BIOMED & ELEC ENG, UNIV TORONTO, 76- *Concurrent Pos:* Univ & Nat Res Coun Can grants, 70-71; vpres, Facets Inc, 70-74, pres, 74- *Mem:* Can Med & Biol Eng Soc. *Res:* Nuclear medical scintigraphy. *Mailing Add:* 118 Burnhamthorpe Rd Toronto ON M9A 1H7 Can

JOY, ROBERT JOHN THOMAS, b South Kingstown, RI, Apr 5, 29; m 52; c 2. INTERNAL MEDICINE, PHYSIOLOGY. *Educ:* Univ RI, BS, 50; Yale Univ, MD, 54; Harvard Univ, MA, 65. *Prof Exp:* Med Corps, US Army, 54-81, intern, Walter Reed Gen Hosp, 54-55, resident, 56-58, chief, Bioastronaut Br, Army Med Res Lab, Ft Knox, Ky, 59-61, comdr & mem res staff, Army Res Inst Environ Med, 61-63, chief med res team, Walter Reed Army Inst Res, Vietnam, 65-66, dep dir, US Army Res Inst Environ Med, Mass, 66-68, chief Med Res Div, US Army Med Res & Develop Command, Washington, DC, 68-69, dep biol & med res, Directorate of Defense Res & Eng, 69-71, dep dir, 71-75, dir & comdr, Walter Reed Army Inst Res, 75-76; prof mil med & hist & chmn dept, 76-81, PROF MED HIST & CHMN DEPT, UNIFORMED SERV UNIV SCH MED, 81- *Honors & Awards:* Osler Medal, Am Asn Hist Med, 54; Hoff Mem Medal Mil Med, 59; J S Billings Award, 66. *Mem:* Am Asn Hist Med; Hist Sci Soc; Am Physiol Soc; fel Am Col Physicians; Osler Soc. *Res:* Environmental physiology and medicine; history of medicine; research administration and management. *Mailing Add:* Uniformed Serv Univ Sch Med 4301 Jones Bridge Rd Bethesda MD 20814

JOY, ROBERT MCKERNON, b Troy, NY, May 9, 41; m 69. NEUROPHARMACOLOGY, NEUROTOXICOLOGY. *Educ:* Ore State Univ, BS, 64; Stanford Univ, PhD(pharmacol), 70; Am Bd Toxicol, dipl. *Prof Exp:* Res pharmacologist, 69-70, asst prof pharmacol, Sch Vet Med, Univ Calif, Davis, 70-77; assoc prof neuropath, Harvard Med Sch, Harvard Univ, 77-78; ASSOC PROF PHARMACOL, SCH VET MED, UNIV CALIF, DAVIS, 78- *Concurrent Pos:* Assoc res neurosci, Children's Hosp, Boston, 77-78. *Mem:* AAAS; Soc Neurosci; Am Soc Pharmacol & Exp Therapeut; Soc Toxicol. *Res:* Epilepsy, anticonvulsant and convulsant drugs; mechanism of action; insecticide actions on central nervous system. *Mailing Add:* Dept of Physiol Sci Univ of Calif Sch of Vet Med Davis CA 95616

JOY, VINCENT ANTHONY, b New York, NY, Feb 22, 20; m 52; c 7. INTERNAL MEDICINE. *Educ:* Fordham Univ, BS, 46; Duke Univ, MD, 50. *Prof Exp:* Staff internist, Vet Admin Hosp, East Orange, NJ, 53-54; staff internist & admitting officer, Vet Admin Hosp, New York, 54-59; med dir clin res, Int Div, E R Squibb & Sons, 59-67; SR MED DIR, BASIC CLIN RES, INT DIV, MERCK SHARP & DOHME, RAHWAY, NJ, 67-; CLIN ASST PROF MED, MED COL, CORNELL UNIV, 69- *Concurrent Pos:* Asst physician, Bellevue Hosp, 60-69; clin asst physician, New York Hosp, 69- *Honors & Awards:* Physicians Recognition Award, AMA, 70-71; Cert Spec Merit, Am Bd Dipl Pharm, 71. *Res:* Gastroenterology; influence of the vagus nerve on gastric secretion; various classes of drugs on the parietal cell; action of decarboxylase inhibitor in the treatment of patients with Parkinson's disease, including administration of L-dopa to determine action of inhibitor as a means of reducing requirements; lipid-lowering and uricosuric effects of clofibrate-type drugs; beta-blockers. *Mailing Add:* 700 Scranton Ave East Rockaway NY 11518

JOYCE, BLAINE R, b Jeannette, Pa, Nov 13, 25; m 55; c 3. PHYSICAL CHEMISTRY. *Educ:* Univ Pittsburgh, BS, 49; Univ Toledo, MS, 65. *Prof Exp:* Res assoc activated carbon, Mellon Inst, 49-51; develop engr, 53-60, group leader activated carbon, 60-65, mgr activated carbon prod eng, 65-68, sr develop engr, Carbon Prod Div, 68-80, ASST TECH DIR ACTIVATED CARBON, CARBON-GRAPHITE TECH SALES SERV, UNION CARBIDE CORP, 80- *Mem:* Am Chem Soc. *Res:* Production and applications of arc carbons for lighting and metal processing applications; development of activated carbon products and cost studies for business product planning. *Mailing Add:* 453 Cranston Dr Cleveland OH 44118

JOYCE, ELAINE C ELDER, b Louisville, Ky. ENVIRONMENTAL PHYSIOLOGY, ELECTRON MICROSCOPY. *Educ:* Ursuline Col, BA, 63; Georgetown Univ, PhD(biol), 70. *Prof Exp:* Asst prof biol, Bellarmine Col, 70-71; res assoc electron micros, Microbiol Assocs, 71-72; asst prof, 72-78, ASSOC PROF BIOL, GEORGE MASON UNIV, 78- & ASST DEAN, COL ARTS & SCI, 80- *Concurrent Pos:* Danforth Assoc. *Mem:* Am Soc Zoologists; AAAS; Sigma Xi. *Res:* Ultrastructure of the barbels of the channel catfish, Ictalurus punctatus, and the effects of pollutants on this species; morphophysiology of vascular smooth muscle and renal tissue in cadmium treated rats. *Mailing Add:* Col Arts & Sci George Mason Univ Fairfax VA 22030

JOYCE, GLENN RUSSELL, b St Louis, Mo, June 24, 39; m 62; c 1. PLASMA PHYSICS. *Educ:* Cent Methodist Col, BA, 61; Univ Mo, MS, 63, PhD(physics), 66. *Prof Exp:* Res assoc, Univ Iowa, 66-68, assoc prof physics, 68-77, prof physics, 77-81; SR RES SCIENTIST, NAVAL RES LAB, 81- *Concurrent Pos:* Vis assoc prof, Hunter Col, 74; res scientist physics, Max Planck Inst Plasma Physics, 69; vis res scientist, Goddard Space Flight Ctr, NASA, 75-79. *Mem:* Am Phys Soc. *Res:* Plasma theory; interaction of test particles with plasmas; particle simulation of plasmas; numerical simulation and kinetic theory of plasmas. *Mailing Add:* 6916 Tulsa Ct Alexandria VA 22307

JOYCE, JAMES MARTIN, b Bayonne, NJ, Jan 27, 42; m 65. NUCLEAR PHYSICS. *Educ:* LaSalle Col, BA, 63; Univ Pa, MS, 64, PhD(physics), 67. *Prof Exp:* Res assoc nuclear physics, Univ NC, Chapel Hill, 67-70; ASSOC PROF PHYSICS & DIR ACCELERATOR LAB, E CAROLINA UNIV, 70- *Mem:* Am Phys Soc. *Res:* Experimental nuclear physics, spectroscopy, reactions; experimental atomic physics and applied physics; computer systems and interface design. *Mailing Add:* Dept of Physics ECarolina Univ Greenville NC 27834

JOYCE, RICHARD ROSS, b Wilmington, Del, June 28, 44. ASTRONOMY. *Educ:* Williams Col, BA, 65; Univ Calif, Berkeley, PhD(physics), 70. *Prof Exp:* Res asst physics, Lawrence Radiation Lab, Univ Calif, Berkeley, 66-70; fel astron, State Univ NY, Stony Brook, 70-72, lectr, 72-73; SUPPORT SCIENTIST ASTRON, KITT PEAK NAT OBSERV, 73- *Mem:* Am Phys Soc; Am Astron Soc. *Res:* Infrared detector development; telescope optimization for infrared use; study of heavily obscured and/or cool sources in infrared; study of infrared emission line sources. *Mailing Add:* Kitt Peak Nat Observ PO Box 26732 Tucson AZ 85726

JOYCE, ROBERT MICHAEL, b Lincoln, Nebr, Sept 19, 15; m 41; c 2. ORGANIC CHEMISTRY. *Educ:* Univ Nebr, BS, 35, MS, 36; Univ Ill, PhD(org chem), 38. *Prof Exp:* Res chemist, Cent Res Dept, E I DuPont de Nemours & Co, Inc, 38-45, res supvr, 45-50, lab dir, 50-53, asst dir res, 53-62, dir res, 63-65, dir res & develop, Film Dept, 65-72, dir sci affairs pharmaceut div, Biochem Dept, 72-78; RETIRED. *Mem:* AAAS; Am Chem Soc. *Res:* Synthetic polymers; plastic films. *Mailing Add:* RD 1 Box 86 Hockessin DE 19707

JOYCE, RONALD STONE, b Dundee, Scotland, Aug 31, 22; US citizen; m 51; c 2. PHYSICAL CHEMISTRY. *Educ:* McMaster Univ, BSc, 46, MSc, 47. *Prof Exp:* Res chemist, Imp Oil Co, Ltd, 47-49 & Int Minerals & Chem Corp, 49-53; sr res chemist, Nalco Chem Co, 53-57 & Pittsburgh Coke & Chem Co, 57-59; supvr activated carbon res, 59-70, mgr activated carbon res, 70-74, SR RES ASSOC, PITTSBURGH ACTIVATED CARBON CO, CALGON CORP, DIV MERCK & CO, INC, 74- *Mem:* Am Chem Soc; Am Soc Testing & Mat; Water Pollution Control Fedn. *Res:* Production and application of granular activated carbons and in adsorption technology; applications of ion exchange resins. *Mailing Add:* Calgon Corp Div Merck & Co Inc PO Box 1346 Pittsburgh PA 15241

JOYCE, WILLIAM B(AXTER), b Columbus, Ohio, Oct 17, 32; m 58; c 4. THEORETICAL PHYSICS. *Educ:* Cornell Univ, BEP, 55; Univ Iowa, PhD(physics), 66. *Prof Exp:* Mgr advan technol, Indust Nucleonics Corp, Ohio, 63-66; MEM TECH STAFF, BELL LABS, 66- *Mem:* Am Phys Soc. *Res:* Applied theoretical physics. *Mailing Add:* Bell Labs Murray Hill NJ 07974

JOYNER, ALAN E, JR, microbiology, see previous edition

JOYNER, BOBBY GERALD, plant pathology, gnotobiology, see previous edition

JOYNER, CLAUDE REUBEN, b Winston-Salem, NC, Dec 4, 25; m 50; c 2. MEDICINE. *Educ:* Univ NC, BS, 47; Univ Pa, MD, 49; Am Bd Internal Med, dipl, 57; Am Bd Cardiovasc Dis, dipl, 63. *Prof Exp:* Resdient med, Bowman Gray Sch Med, 50; Nat Heart Inst trainee & asst instr, Sch Med, Univ Pa, 52-53, from instr to assoc prof, 53-71; prof med, Hahnemann Med Col, 71-72; CLIN PROF MED, UNIV PITTSBURGH, 72-; DIR DEPT MED, ALLEGHENY GEN HOSP, PITTSBURGH, 72- *Concurrent Pos:* Attend cardiologist, Vet Admin Hosp, Philadelphia, 63-; mem coun arteriosclerosis, Am Heart Asn. *Mem:* Fel AAAS; Am Heart Asn; fel Am Col Physicians; Am Fedn Clin Res; fel Am Col Cardiol. *Res:* Academic medicine; cardiology; phonocardiography; ultrasound. *Mailing Add:* Allegheny Gen Hosp Dept of Med 320 E North St Pittsburgh PA 15212

JOYNER, HOWARD SAJON, b Ft Worth, Tex, June 6, 39; m 69; c 3. ENGINEERING. *Educ:* Univ Tex, Austin, BS, 62, MA, 64; Univ Mo-Rolla, MS, 67, PhD, 70. *Prof Exp:* Nuclear engr, Gen Dynamics/Ft Worth, 64; asst prof mech eng, Wichita State Univ, 69-75; dir planning, res & develop, Univ Kans Sch Med, Wichita, 75-77; PRES, KINETIC CORP, 77- *Mem:* Am Soc Mech Engrs. *Mailing Add:* Kinetic Corp PO Box 8161 Wichita KS 67208

JOYNER, JOHN T, III, b Winston-Salem, NC, June 27, 28; m 50; c 3. INTERNAL MEDICINE. *Educ:* Wake Forest Col, BS, 48, MD, 52; Am Bd Internal Med, 62. *Prof Exp:* Chief resident med, Hosp, Emory Univ, 57-58; staff physician, 58-61, chief nuclear med, 65-75, CHIEF GEN MED, VET ADMIN HOSP, ASHVILLE, 61-, CHIEF MED SERV, 75-; ASST PROF CLIN MED, DUKE UNIV, 77- *Mem:* AMA; Am Col Physicians; Am Soc Nuclear Med. *Mailing Add:* Vet Admin Hosp Asheville NC 28805

JOYNER, POWELL AUSTIN, b Dallas, Tex, July 20, 25; m 52. RESEARCH MANAGEMENT. *Educ:* Centenary Col, BS, 46; Univ Iowa, PhD(phys chem), 51. *Prof Exp:* Asst, Univ Iowa, 46-50; res chemist, Minneapolis-Honeywell Regulator Co, 50-52; head anal sect, Callery Chem Co, 52-53; head measurements div, 53-54; sr res scientist, Res Ctr, Minneapolis-Honeywell Regulator Co, 54-56, res supvr, 56-58, head chem sect, 58-60, proj mgr fuel cell controls, 60-62, staff scientist, Honeywell Res Ctr, 62-63; asst dir, Res Div, Allis Chalmers Mfg Co, 63-64, gen mgr space & defense sci, 64-67, dir planning & eval, 67-68; dir res, 68-79, VPRES RES, TRANE CO, 79- *Mem:* Am Chem Soc; AAAS. *Res:* Raman effect; humidity instrumentation; hydrophyllic films; phase studies; thermochemistry; molten salts; fuel cells; air pollution; air conditioning; combustion. *Mailing Add:* Trane Co 3600 Pammel Creek Rd La Crosse WI 54601

JOYNER, RALPH DELMER, b Derby, Va, Aug 31, 28; m 50; c 3. INORGANIC CHEMISTRY. *Educ:* Miami Univ, BS, 50, MS, 51; Case Inst Technol, PhD(inorg chem), 61. *Prof Exp:* Chemist, Monsanto Co, Ohio, 51-52, res chemist, Mound Lab, 52-58; chemist, Solvay Process Div, Allied Chem Corp, NY, 61; sr res chemist, Chem Div, Pittsburgh Plate Glass Co, Ohio, 61-62, res assoc, 62, res supvr, 62-65; from asst prof to assoc prof inorg chem, 65-73, PROF INORG CHEM, BALL STATE UNIV, 73- *Concurrent Pos:* Instr night sch, Univ Dayton, 52-54; res assoc & grad student adv, Case Inst Technol, 62-63. *Mem:* Am Chem Soc. *Res:* Silicon and germanium coordination compounds. *Mailing Add:* Dept of Chem Ball State Univ Muncie IN 43706

JOYNER, RONALD WAYNE, b Wake Forest, NC, Mar 21, 47; m 69; c 1. CARDIAC ELECTROPHYSIOLOGY, NEUROPHYSIOLOGY. *Educ:* Univ NC, BS, 69; Duke Univ, MD, 74, PhD(physiol), 73. *Prof Exp:* Asst prof physiol, Duke Univ, 76-77; ASST PROF PHYSIOL, UNIV IOWA, 77- *Mem:* Biophys Soc. *Res:* Mechanisms of propagation of cardiac action potentials related to cardiac arrythmias, by electrophysiological and numerical simulation techniques; synaptic transmission and motor control in squid. *Mailing Add:* Dept Physiol Univ Iowa Iowa City IA 52242

JOYNER, WEYLAND THOMAS, JR, b Suffolk, Va, Aug 8, 29; m 55; c 2. NUCLEAR PHYSICS, ELECTRONICS. *Educ:* Hampden-Sydney Col, BS, 51; Duke Univ, MA, 52, PhD(physics), 55. *Prof Exp:* Asst physics, Duke Univ, 51-53, fel, 53-54; physicist, Dept of Defense, 54-57; asst prof, Hampden-Sydney, Col, 57-59, assoc prof, 59-63, prof, 63-66; staff physicist, Univ Mich, Ann Arbor, 66-67; PROF PHYSICS, HAMPDEN-SYDNEY COL, 67-, CHMN DEPT, 69- *Concurrent Pos:* Consult, Oak Ridge Inst Nuclear Studies, 60-66; res partic, Ames Lab, AEC, 64, 65; dir col physics prog, Am Inst Physics, 67-68; chmn physics comn, Col Entrance Exam Bd, 71-72. *Mem:* Am Phys Soc; Am Asn Physics Teachers; Inst Elec & Electronics Engrs. *Res:* positron lifetimes; nanosecond circuitry; x-ray fluorescence. *Mailing Add:* Hampden-Sydney Col Hampden-Sydney VA 23943

JOYNER, WILLIAM B, b Casper, Wyo, Dec 27, 29; m 52. GEOPHYSICS. *Educ:* Harvard Univ, AB, 51, AM, 52, PhD(geophys), 58. *Prof Exp:* Geophysicist, Humble Oil & Refining Co, 58-63; sr scientist, Vela Uniform Prog, Dunlap & Assocs, Inc, 64; GEOPHYSICIST, US GEOL SURV, 64- *Mem:* Am Geophys Union; Soc Explor Geophys; Geol Soc Am; Seismol Soc Am; Earthquake Eng Res Inst. *Res:* Solid earth geophysics; gravity and terrestrial magnetism; terrestrial heat flow and temperatures within the earth; engineering seismology. *Mailing Add:* 472 Virginia Ave San Mateo CA 94402

JOYNER, WILLIAM HENRY, JR, b Washington, DC, Sept 21, 46; m 68; c 2. COMPUTER SCIENCE. *Educ:* Univ Va, BS, 68; Harvard Univ, SM, 69, PhD(appl math), 73. *Prof Exp:* RES STAFF MEM COMPUT SCI, IBM THOMAS J WATSON RES CTR, 73- *Mem:* Asn Comput Mach. *Res:* Computer program verification; automated theorem proving; machine description languages. *Mailing Add:* 144 Valley Rd Ktonah NY 10536

JOYNER, WILLIAM LYMAN, b Farmville, NC, June 10, 39; m 64; c 2. PHYSIOLOGY. *Educ:* Davidson Col, BS, 65; Univ NC, MSPH, 67, PhD(physiol), 71. *Prof Exp:* Res technician animal med, Univ NC, 65-67, res assoc physiol, 67-69; trainee, Med Ctr, Duke Univ, 71-73; asst prof, 73-77, ASSOC PROF PHYSIOL, COL MED, UNIV NEBR MED CTR, 77- *Concurrent Pos:* Pharm travel grant, Microcirculatory Soc, 75. *Mem:* Am Physiol Soc; Microcurculatory Soc. *Res:* Cardiovascular physiology particularly the microcirculation, molecular transport, vascular reactivity and controlling mechanisms; alterations in blood coagulation and hemostasis related to hemodynamic responses of the microcirculation in various tissues. *Mailing Add:* Dept of Physiol Col of Med Univ of Nebr Med Ctr Omaha NE 68105

JOYNSON, REUBEN EDWIN, JR, b Winfield, Kans, Dec 27, 26. PHYSICS. *Educ:* Kans State Univ, BS, 49, MS, 50; Mass Inst Technol, PhD(physics), 54. *Prof Exp:* Res physicist, Continental Oil Co, 54-60; consult physicist, Comput Lab, 60-63, PHYSICIST, RES & DEVELOP CTR, GEN ELEC CO, 63- *Mem:* AAAS; Am Phys Soc. *Res:* X-ray diffraction; digital computer design and programming; cryogenics; thin film devices; artificial intelligence; visual image processing. *Mailing Add:* 4C1 K-1 Res & Develop Ctr Gen Elec Co Schenectady NY 12301

JOYNT, ROBERT JAMES, b LeMars, Iowa, Dec 22, 25; m 53; c 6. NEUROLOGY. *Educ:* Westmar Col, BA, 49; Univ Iowa, MD, 52, MS, PhD(anat), 63; Am Bd Psychiat & Neurol, dipl, 59. *Prof Exp:* Assoc neurol, Univ Iowa, 57-58, from asst prof to assoc prof, 58-66; PROF NEUROL & ANAT & CHMN DEPT NEUROL, MED CTR, UNIV ROCHESTER, 66- *Concurrent Pos:* Mem res training grant comt, Nat Inst Neurol Dis & Blindness, 63-67 & neurol study sect, div res grants, NIH, 67-72; bd adv, off biometry & epidemiol, NINCDS, 76- *Honors & Awards:* DSc, Westmar Col, 64. *Mem:* Am Neurol Asn; Am Acad Neurol; Am Electroencephalog Soc. *Res:* Investigation of fluid control by central nervous system; correlation of performance tests with lesions in brain damaged patients. *Mailing Add:* Dept of Neurol Univ of Rochester Med Ctr Rochester NY 14642

JU, FREDERICK D, b Shanghai, China, Sept 21, 29; US citizen; m 56; c 3. THEORETICAL & APPLIED MECHANICS. *Educ:* Univ Houston, BS, 53; Univ Ill, MS, 56, PhD(theoret & appl mech), 58. *Prof Exp:* From asst prof to assoc prof, 58-67, chmn, 73-76, PROF MECH ENG, UNIV NMEX, 67- *Concurrent Pos:* Consult, Los Alamos Sci Lab, 62-, vis staff mem, 72-; nat vis prof, Nat Sci Coun, Repub of China, 71-72; prin investr, Air Force Off Sci Res, 61-72 & 81- & Off Naval Res, 81- *Mem:* Am Soc Mech Engrs; Soc Eng Sci; Sigma Xi. *Res:* Fracture diagnosis in structures; fracture in bearing seals; structural safety of reactor; boundary layor theory; finite element methods; dislocation theory. *Mailing Add:* Dept of Mech Eng Univ of NMex Albuquerque NM 87131

JUANG, LING LING, b Taipei, Taiwan, Oct 10, 49; m 73; c 1. NUMERICAL ANALYSIS. *Educ:* Nat Taiwan Univ, BS, 72; State Univ NY Stony Brook, MS, 73, PhD(appl math), 76. *Prof Exp:* Syst analyst heat transfer prob, KLD Assoc, Inc, 75-76; asst mathematician energy models, Brookhaven Nat Lab, 76-80; COMPUT PROCESS CONTROL SPECIALIST, GEN ELEC CO, 80- *Mem:* Am Commun Mach; Soc Mfg Eng. *Res:* Economic-energy modeling of depletable resources; computer aided manufacturing system design. *Mailing Add:* 4293 Berryhill Lane Cincinnati OH 45242

JUBB, GERALD LOMBARD, JR, b Ayer, Mass, Jan 3, 43; m 67; c 2. PEST MANAGEMENT. *Educ:* NMex Highlands Univ, BA, 65; Univ Ariz, MS, 67, PhD(entom), 70. *Prof Exp:* NSF trainee entom, Univ Ariz, 67-70; asst prof, 70-76, ASSOC PROF ENTOM, ERIE COUNTY FIELD RES LAB, PA STATE UNIV, 76- *Mem:* Entom Soc Am; Int Orgn Biol Control; Acarological Soc Am; Am Soc Enol; Sigma Xi. *Res:* Insects and mites attacking grapes; economic injury levels; monitoring techniques; pesticide impact in vineyards; grape pest management. *Mailing Add:* Pa State Univ Dept of Entom Erie County Field Res Lab North East PA 16428

JUBERG, RICHARD CALDWELL, b Bismarck, NDak, Sept 26, 30; m 57; c 6. HUMAN GENETICS, PEDIATRICS. *Educ:* Carleton Col, BA, 52; Univ Mich, Ann Arbor, MD, 56, MS, 63, PhD(human genetics), 66. *Prof Exp:* Intern, Charity Hosp La, New Orleans, 56-57; resident pediat, Tulane Univ & Charity Hosp, La, 57-59; chief resident, Univ Chicago Clin, 59-60; instr pediat, Univ Mich, Ann Arbor, 61-66; asst prof, WVa Univ, 66-69; assoc prof med genetics & pediat, Univ Ore, 69-70; assoc prof pediat, Sch Med, La State Univ, Shreveport, 70-73, prof, 73-76; PROF PEDIAT, SCH MED, WRIGHT STATE UNIV, DAYTON, 76- *Concurrent Pos:* Appalachian Lab Occup Respiratory Dis, Inst Environ Health Sci, NIH res contract, 67-68; mem staff, Dept Med Genetics & Birth Defects, Children's Med Ctr, Dayton, 76- *Mem:* Am Pediat Soc; Am Soc Human Genetics; Sigma Xi; Soc Pediat Res. *Res:* Human cytogenetics, clinical genetics and dermatoglyphics; orgin of chromosomal abnormalities; recognition of new chromosomal syndromes; inheritance of finger, palm, and sole patterns. *Mailing Add:* Dept of Med Genetics & Birth Defects One Children's Plaza Dayton OH 45404

JUBERG, RICHARD KENT, b Cooperstown, NDak, May 14, 29; m 56; c 4. MATHEMATICS. *Educ:* Univ Minn, BS, 52, PhD(math), 58. *Prof Exp:* Temporary mem, Courant Inst Math Sci, NY Univ, 57-58; instr, Univ Minn, 58-60, from asst prof to assoc prof, 60-75, PROF MATH, UNIV CALIF, IRVINE, 75- *Concurrent Pos:* NSF sci faculty fel, Pisa, 65-66; vis prof, Univ Sussex, 72-73, Math Inst Technol, Göteburg, Sweden, 81. *Mem:* Am Math Soc. *Res:* Problems in analysis and partial differential equations. *Mailing Add:* Dept Math Univ Calif Irvine CA 92717

JUBY, PETER FREDERICK, b Great Yarmouth, Eng, Oct 27, 35; US citizen; m 70; c 2. MEDICINAL CHEMISTRY. *Educ:* Univ Nottingham, BSc, 57, PhD(org chem), 61. *Prof Exp:* Nat Res Coun Can fel, 60-62; sr res scientist, 62-76, PRIN INVESTR, BRISTOL LABS, INC, 76- *Mem:* Am Chem Soc. *Res:* Natural product chemistry; biosynthesis of alkaloids; synthesis of medicinal agents. *Mailing Add:* Medicinal Chem Res Bristol Labs PO Box 657 Syracuse NY 13201

JUCHAU, MONT RAWLINGS, b Virginia, Idaho, Nov 11, 34; m 60; c 4. PHARMACOLOGY. *Educ:* Idaho State Univ, BS, 60; Wash State Univ, MS, 63; Univ Iowa, PhD(pharmacol), 66. *Prof Exp:* Pharmacist, Trolinger Pharm, Tick Klock Drug, 60-63; from instr to asst prof biochem pharmacol, State Univ NY Buffalo, 66-69; asst prof, 69-73; assoc prof, 73-80, PROF PHARMACOL, SCH MED, UNIV WASH, 80- *Honors & Awards:* Delbert-Putnam Award, 59; Rexall Award, 60. *Mem:* AAAS; Am Soc Pharmacol & Exp Therapeut; Int Soc Biochem Pharmacol. *Res:* Investigation of the biotransformation of drugs in the human foetoplacental unit. *Mailing Add:* Dept of Pharmacol Univ of Wash Sch of Med Seattle WA 98195

JUD, HENRY G, b Rochester, NY, Sept 19, 34; m 58; c 4. ELECTRICAL ENGINEERING. *Educ:* Valparaiso Univ, BS, 56; Univ Pittsburgh, MS, 59, PhD(elec eng), 62. *Prof Exp:* Electronics technician, Western Elec Co, 56-57; specialist missile systs, Autonetics Div, NAm Aviation Inc, 62-64; from asst prof to assoc prof elec eng, Valparaiso Univ, 64-68; staff engr, IBM Fed Systs Div, NY, 68-70, advan engr, 70-71, develop engr, 71-76, DEVELOP ENGR, IBM CORP, MD, 76- *Mem:* Inst Elec & Electronics Engrs. *Res:* Missile system error analysis; automatic control; random input control systems; computer systems design. *Mailing Add:* IBM Corp 18100 Frederick Pike Gaitherburg MD 20760

JUDAY, GLENN PATRICK, b Elwood, Ind, May 4, 50; m 71; c 2. FOREST ECOLOGY, CONSERVATION. *Educ:* Purdue Univ, BS, 72; Ore State Univ, Phd(plant ecol), 77. *Prof Exp:* Fel ecol & conserv, Ore State Univ, 76-77; coordr ecol reserves, Joint Fed-State Land Use Planning Comn, Alaska, 77-78, Arctic Environ Info & Data Ctr, Univ Alaska, 78 & Inst Northern Forestry, Forest Serv, USDA, 78-81; VIS ASSOC PROF, AGR EXP STA, UNIV ALASKA, 81- *Mem:* AAAS; Ecol Soc Am; Soc Am Foresters. *Res:* Systematic plan for conserving ecological reserves using vegetation, wildlife, and geologic classifications; old-growth forest structure, including stocking, basal area, age height and spacing. *Mailing Add:* Inst Northern Forestry 308 Tanana Dr Fairbanks AK 99701

JUDAY, RICHARD EVANS, b Madison, Wis, May 28, 18. ORGANIC CHEMISTRY. *Educ:* Harvard Univ, BA, 39; Univ Wis, PhD(org chem), 43. *Prof Exp:* Asst res chemist, Gen Chem Co, NY, 43-45 & Ortho Pharmaceut Corp, 44-47; from asst prof to prof chem, 47-77, EMER PROF CHEM, UNIV MONT, 77- *Mem:* Fel AAAS; Am Chem Soc; Am Soc Limnol & Oceanog. *Res:* Water quality; chemical limnology. *Mailing Add:* Dept of Chem Univ of Mont Missoula MT 59801

JUDD, BRIAN RAYMOND, b Chelmsford, Eng, Feb 13, 31. THEORETICAL PHYSICS, ATOMIC PHYSICS. *Educ:* Oxford Univ, BA, 52, MA & DPhil, 55. *Prof Exp:* Fel, Magdalen Col, Oxford Univ, 55-62; instr physics, Univ Chicago, 57-58; chemist, Lawrence Radiation Lab, Univ Calif, Berkeley, 59-62; assoc prof spectros, Univ Paris, 62-64; staff mem nuclear chem, Lawrence Radiation Lab, Univ Calif, Berkeley, 64-66; PROF PHYSICS, JOHNS HOPKINS UNIV, 66-, CHMN DEPT, 79- *Concurrent Pos:* Consult, Argonne Nat Lab, 77- *Res:* Theoretical studies of atoms, molecules and solid state physics, particularly application of group theory. *Mailing Add:* Dept of Physics Johns Hopkins Univ Baltimore MD 21218

JUDD, BURKE HAYCOCK, b Kanab, Utah, Sept 5, 27; m 53; c 3. GENETICS. *Educ:* Univ Utah, BS, 50, MS, 51; Calif Inst Technol, PhD(genetics), 54. *Prof Exp:* Am Can Soc Fel, Univ Tex, Austin, 54-56, from instr to assoc prof zool, 56-69, prof, 69-79; CHIEF, LAB GENETICS, NAT INST ENVIRON HEALTH SCI, RESEARCH TRIANGLE PARK, NC, 79- *Concurrent Pos:* Geneticist, AEC, Washington, DC, 68-69; mem panel genetic biol, NSF, 69-72; consult, Tex Educ Agency, 71; Gosney vis prof, Div Biol, Calif Inst Technol, 75-76; adj prof zool, Univ NC, Chapel Hill, 79- & Prog Genetics, Duke Univ, Durham, NC, 80- *Mem:* Fel AAAS; Genetics Soc Am (vpres, 79 & pres, 80); Am Soc Nat (secy, 68-70). *Res:* Chromosome organization; gene function and regulation; recombination mechanism; genetics of Drosophila. *Mailing Add:* Lab Genetics Nat Inst Environ Health Sci PO Box 12233 Research Triangle Park NC 27709

JUDD, CLAUDE IVAN, b Wausau, Wis, Aug 28, 24; m 47; c 5. MEDICINAL CHEMISTRY. *Educ:* Univ Wis, BS, 54, PhD(org chem), 57. *Prof Exp:* Res chemist, Dow Chem Co, 57-59; res chemist, Lakeside Labs Div, Colgate-Palmolive Co, Wis, 59, sect chief chem dept, 59-60, dir med chem dept, 61-66, dir res, 66-75; dir lab sci res, 75-78, vpres drug develop, Merrell-Nat Labs, 78-81, DIR RES & DEVELOP, MERRELL DOW PHARMACEUTICALS, 81- *Mem:* Am Chem Soc; NY Acad Sci. *Res:* Natural products; water soluble polymers; synthetic medicinal chemistry with primary interest in agents affecting the cardiovascular and central nervous systems and blood; mechanism of biological reactions. *Mailing Add:* Merrell Dow Pharmaceuticals Inc 110 E Galbraith Rd Cincinnati OH 45215

JUDD, DAVID LOCKHART, b Chehalis, Wash, Jan 8, 23; m 45; c 2. THEORETICAL PHYSICS. *Educ:* Whitman Col, AB, 43; Calif Inst Technol, MS, 47, PhD(physics), 50. *Prof Exp:* Staff mem, Physics Div, Los Alamos Sci Lab, 45-46; staff mem theoret physics, Nuclear Energy Div, Rand Corp, 49-51; group leader theoret physics, Lab, 51-66, lectr, Univ, 53-62, from dep head to head physics div, 63-70, ASSOC DIR PHYSICS, LAWRENCE BERKELEY LAB, UNIV CALIF, 67-, SR LECTR PHYSICS, UNIV, 62- *Concurrent Pos:* Consult, Northrop Aircraft Co, 47-49, Radiation Lab, Univ Calif, 50-51, Rand Corp, 51-55 & W M Brobeck & Assocs, 60; mem adv comt, Electronuclear & Physics Div, Oak Ridge Nat Lab, 63-65. *Mem:* Am Phys Soc. *Res:* Theoretical and mathematical physics; accelerator theory; ion optics; plasma and particle physics; nonlinear mechanics. *Mailing Add:* Dept of Physics Univ of Calif 366 Le Conte Hall Berkeley CA 94720

JUDD, FLOYD L, b Janesville, Wis, Jan 25, 34; m 62; c 3. HIGH ENERGY PHYSICS, OPTICS. *Educ:* Carroll Col, BS, 56; Iowa State Univ, MS, 60, PhD, 66. *Prof Exp:* Asst prof, Northwestern State Col, La, 59-62, 64-67; asst prof, 67-70, assoc prof physics, Fresno State Col, 70-71; PROF PHYSICS & CHMN, CALIF STATE UNIV, FRESNO, 71- *Mailing Add:* Dept of Physics Calif State Univ Fresno CA 93740

JUDD, GARY, b Humene, Czech, Sept 24, 42; US citizen; m 64. PHYSICAL METALLURGY, ELECTRON MICROSCOPY. *Educ:* Rensselaer Polytech Inst, BMetE, 63, PhD(phys metall), 67. *Prof Exp:* Res asst, 66-67, from asst prof to assoc prof, 72-76, actg chmn dept mat eng, 74-75, vprovost, Plans & Resources, 75-79, PROF MAT ENG, RENSSELAER POLYTECH INST, 72-, VPROVOST, ACAD AFFAIRS & DEAN GRAD SCH, 79- *Concurrent Pos:* Consult, Oak Ridge Nat Lab, 67-70 & Watervliet Arsenal, 68-78; metall eng consult ed, McGraw-Hill Sci & Technol Encycl, 75- *Mem:* Am Inst Mining, Metall & Petrol Engrs; Am Soc Metals; Sigma Xi; Microbeam Anal Soc; Soc Col & Univ Planning. *Res:* Structure sensitive properties of materials, particularly strengthening mechanisms, precipitation kinetics, defect structures, biomaterials and corrosion; electron probe micro-analysis; scanning electron microscopy; forensic science. *Mailing Add:* Pittsburgh Bldg Rensselaer Polytech Inst Troy NY 12181

JUDD, JANE HARTER, b Pittsburgh, Pa, Oct 24, 25; m 72. SPECTROSCOPY, ANALYTICAL CHEMISTRY. *Educ:* Carlow Col, BA, 47. *Prof Exp:* Chemist, Dept Res Med, Univ Pittsburgh, 48-50; SR SCIENTIST, WESTINGHOUSE BETTIS ATOMIC POWER PLANT, 51- *Concurrent Pos:* Exec secy, Pittsburgh Conf Anal Chem & Appl Spectroscopy, 64-, pres, 78. *Mailing Add:* Westinghouse Bettis PO Box 79 West Mifflin PA 15122

JUDD, LEWIS LUND, b Los Angeles, Calif, Feb 10, 30; m 74; c 3. PSYCHIATRY, CHILD PSYCHIATRY. *Educ:* Univ Utah, BS, 54; George Washington Univ, 54-56; Univ Calif, Los Angeles, MD, 58. *Prof Exp:* Intern internal med, Ctr Health Sci, Univ Calif, Los Angeles, 58-59, resident psychiat, 59-60, 62-64; asst prof psychol & psychiat, 65-70; assoc prof, 70-73, actg chmn dept, 74-75, co-chmn dept, 75-77, CHMN DEPT PSYCHIAT, UNIV CALIF, SAN DIEGO, 77- PROF PSYCHIAT, 73- *Concurrent Pos:* Fel child psychiat, Ctr Health Sci, Univ Calif, Los Angeles, 62-64, State of Calif fel, 66, NIMH fels, 67-69, Scottish Rites Comt on Res in Schizophrenics, 69; supvr psychiat, Adolescent Outpatient Unit, Marion Davies Pediat Clin, Ctr Health Sci, Univ Calif, Los Angeles, 65-70, supvr psychiat consult serv to dept pediat, 65-70, attend physician, Hosp, 65-70, psychiat consult, Dept Phys Med & Rehab, 65-70, dir educ, Child & Adolescent Psychiat, Dept Psychiat, 65-70; psychiat consult, Calif State Bd Rehab, Sacramento, 65-70; mem adv comt eval of drug abuse progs, County of San Diego, 70; dir, Univ Calif Drug Abuse Progs, 70-73; vchmn & dir clin progs, Dept Psychiat, Univ Calif, San Diego, 70-73, chmn Social & Behavioral Sci Course, Sch Med, 70-; psychiat consult, San Diego County Dept Pub Health, 72-; chief psychiat serv, Vet Admin Hosp, San Diego, 72-77. *Mem:* Am Psychiat Asn; Am Orthopsychiat Asn; Soc Res Child Develop; Am Soc Adolescent Psychiat; Psychiat Res Soc. *Res:* Substance abuse in adolescents; developmental psychopathology; epidemiology of deviant populations; clinical psychopharmacology. *Mailing Add:* Dept of Psychiat Univ of Calif San Diego La Jolla CA 92037

JUDD, O'DEAN P, b Austin, Minn, May 26, 37; m 68; c 3. LASERS AND OPTICS, ATOMIC AND MOLECULAR PHYSICS. *Educ:* St Johns Univ, BS, 59; Univ Calif, Los Angeles, MS, 61, PhD(physics), 68. *Prof Exp:* Staff physicist, Hughes Res Lab, 59-67 & 69-72; consult, 72-74; fel plasma physics, Univ Calif, Los Angeles, 68-69; assoc group leader, theoret div, 72-75, group leader advan laser res, 75-77, MEM STAFF, APPL PHOTOCHEM DIV, LOS ALAMOS NAT LAB, UNIV CALIF, 77- *Concurrent Pos:* consult, 80-; adj prof physics, Univ NMex, 81- *Mem:* Am Phys Soc; Inst Elec & Electronics Engrs; AAAS. *Res:* Non-linear optics; laser physics, atomic and molecular physics; quantum electronics and laser chemistry, theoretical and experimental. *Mailing Add:* Los Alamos Nat Lab Group AP-DO MS 563 Los Alamos NM 87545

JUDD, ROSS LEONARD, b London, Ont, June 3, 36; m 62; c 2. HEAT TRANSFER. *Educ:* Western Ont Inst Technol, BESc, 58; McMaster Univ, MEng, 63; Univ Mich, PhD(heat transfer), 68. *Prof Exp:* Develop engr, Civilian Atomic Power Dept, Can Gen Elec, 58-61; lectr, 63-67, asst prof, 67-

74, assoc prof, 74-80, PROF HEAT TRANSFER & THERMODYN, MCMASTER UNIV, 80- *Honors & Awards:* R R Teetor Award, Soc Automotive Engrs. *Mem:* Am Soc Mech Engrs; Soc Automotive Engrs. *Res:* Boiling heat transfer; heat transfer in internal passages. *Mailing Add:* Dept of Mech Eng McMaster Univ Hamilton ON L8S 4L8 Can

JUDD, ROY WHITLOCK, JR, plant pathology, see previous edition

JUDD, STANLEY H, b Denver, Colo, Feb 12, 28; m 50, 77; c 2. ENVIRONMENTAL HEALTH. *Educ:* Univ Calif, Los Angeles, BS, 49; Univ Calif, Berkeley, MPH, 56. *Prof Exp:* Chemist, State of Calif Dept Pub Health, 49-50, 53-56 & US Army Environ Health Lab, 50-52; res chemist, Chevron Res Corp, 56-58, indust hygienist, 58-65, sr indust hygienist, 65-69, environ health & pollution engr, 69-78, staff indust hygienist, 78-80, MGR, HEALTH SURVEILLANCE SERV, STANDARD OIL CO, CALIF, 80- *Concurrent Pos:* Mem fac, Inst Noise Control Eng & Inst Safety & Syst Mgt, Univ Southern Calif Extension. *Mem:* Am Indust Hyg Asn; Am Acad Indust Hyg; Acoust Soc Am; Am Chem Soc. *Res:* Engineering noise control at the source to prevent hearing loss, interference with communications and annoyance; safe handling of pesticide and petrochemical products including facilities designs; occupational health information systems design; epidemiology; biomedical surveillance. *Mailing Add:* Standard Oil Co of Calif 225 Bush St San Francisco CA 94120

JUDD, WALTER STEPHEN, b Fairbanks, Alaska, Apr 14, 51; m 72. PLANT SYSTEMATICS. *Educ:* Mich State Univ, BS, 73, MS, 74; Harvard Univ, PhD(biol), 79. *Prof Exp:* ASST PROF BOT, DEPT BOT, UNIV FLA, 78- *Mem:* Am Soc Plant Taxonomists; Int Asn Plant Taxon; Am Bryological & Lichenological Soc; Bot Soc Am. *Res:* Systematics and evolution of flowering plants with specific interest in the Ericaceae and Melastomataceae; floras of the West Indies and Florida. *Mailing Add:* Dept Bot Univ Fla Gainesville FL 32611

JUDD, WILLIAM ROBERT, b Denver, Colo, Aug 16, 17; m 42; c 5. ROCK MECHANICS, GEOTECHNICAL ENGINEERING. *Educ:* Univ Colo, AB, 41. *Prof Exp:* Eng geologist, US Bur Reclamation, 38-41, head geol sect I, Off Chief Engr, 44-48; head basing technol group, Rand Corp, Calif, 60-65; prof soil mech & geol, 66-67, PROF ROCK MECH, SCH CIVIL ENG, PURDUE UNIV, 67-, HEAD GEOTECH ENG, 76- *Concurrent Pos:* Eng geologist, Water Conserv Bd, Colo, 41-42 & Denver & Rio Grande West Rwy, 42-44; instr, Lowry AFB, 46-51; consult geologist & engr, 50-; mem adv bd, mountain & arctic warfare, US Army, 56-62; consult to various US & foreign govt agencies & comts & pvt industs, 58-; chmn, US Nat Comt Rock Mech, 63-69, chmn panel awards, 71-, sr adv panel res, 77-81; mem panel geophys, US Air Force Sci Adv Bd, 64-68; geo-sci ed, Am Elsevier Publ Co, Inc, 66-71; Alex du Toit mem lectr, Univ SAfrica, 67; reviewer, Appl Mech Reviews, 68-73; ed in chief, Int J Eng Geol, 72-; tech dir, Underground Explor & Rock Properties Info Ctr, 72-80; mem, Nat Res Coun Comt on Dam Safety, 77-78 & Exec Coun, US Comt on Large Dams, 77-83. *Mem:* Fel SAfrican Inst Mining & Metall; fel Am Soc Civil Engrs; fel Geol Soc Am; Int Soc Rock Mech (vpres, 67-70); Am Arbit Asn. *Res:* Reservoir-induced seismicity; rock tunnels; geotechnics. *Mailing Add:* Sch of Civil Eng Purdue Univ West Lafayette IN 47907

JUDD, WILLIAM WALLACE, b Windsor, NS, Oct 22, 15; m 46; c 4. ENTOMOLOGY. *Educ:* McMaster Univ, BA, 38; Univ Western Ont, MA, 40; Univ Toronto, PhD(zool), 46. *Prof Exp:* Agr asst, Can Dept Agr, 37-42; asst meteorol, Dept Transport, Ottawa, 42-45; lectr zool, McMaster Univ, 46-48, asst prof, 48-50; asst prof, 50-51, assoc prof, 52-64, prof, 65-81, EMER PROF ZOOL, UNIV WESTERN ONT, 81- *Res:* Aquatic insects; insect morphology. *Mailing Add:* Dept of Zool Univ of Western Ont London ON N6A 5B7 Can

JUDGE, DARRELL L, b Albion, Ill, Nov 2, 34; m 59; c 3. PHYSICS. *Educ:* Eastern Ill State Col, BS, 56; Univ Southern Calif, MS, 63, PhD(physics), 65. *Prof Exp:* Mem tech staff, Thompson-Ramo-Wooldridge Corp, 58-59; lectr math, 61-63, vis asst prof, 65-66, from asst prof to assoc prof, 66-75, PROF PHYSICS, UNIV SOUTHERN CALIF, 75- *Concurrent Pos:* Consult, Space Physics Dept, Thompson-Ramo-Wooldridge Corp, 60-71; Douglas Aircraft Co, 61 & Planetary Atmospheres Adv Subcomt, Space Sci & Applns Steering Comt, NASA, 69-70. *Honors & Awards:* NASA Except Scientific Achievement Medal & NASA Pub Serv Group Achievement Award to Pioneer 10 Scientific Instrument Team, 74. *Mem:* Am Geophys Union; Am Phys Soc. *Res:* Space physics and spectroscopy. *Mailing Add:* Dept of Physics Univ of Southern Calif Univ Park Los Angeles CA 90007

JUDGE, JOSEPH MALACHI, b Carbondale, Pa, June 10, 30; m 57; c 5. POLYMER CHEMISTRY. *Educ:* Kings Col, Pa, BS, 52; Univ Notre Dame, PhD(chem), 58. *Prof Exp:* Res chemist, Polychems Dept, E I du Pont de Nemours & Co, 55-58; res chemist, Armstrong Cork Co, 58-80, MGR TECH INFO SERV, ARMSTRONG WORLD INDUST, INC, 80- *Mem:* AAAS; Am Soc Info Sci; Am Chem Soc. *Res:* Vinyl polymerization; polymeric blends; polyvinyl chloride modifications; structure to dynamic properties relationships; elastomer synthesis; high energy radiation; information retrieval. *Mailing Add:* Res & Develop Ctr Armstrong World Indust Inc Lancaster PA 17604

JUDGE, LEO FRANCIS, JR, b Washington, DC, Jan 6, 27; m 49; c 4. MICROBIOLOGY. *Educ:* Univ Md, BS, 53, MS, 55, PhD(bact), 58. *Prof Exp:* Asst bact, Univ Md, 53-57; MGR MICROBIOL SERV, PROCTER & GAMBLE CO, 57- *Mem:* Am Soc Microbiol; Soc Indust Microbiol; Am Soc Testing & Mat; Cosmetic Toiletry & Fragrance Asn. *Res:* Bacterial metabolism and physiology; microbial associations; medical microbiology; antiseptics and disinfectants. *Mailing Add:* 5359 Sanrio Ct Cincinnati OH 45239

JUDGE, MAX DAVID, b Shirley, Ind, Oct 14, 32; m 53; c 3. ANIMAL SCIENCE, FOOD SCIENCE. *Educ:* Purdue Univ, BS, 54, PhD(animal physiol), 62; Ohio State Univ, MSc, 58. *Prof Exp:* From instr to assoc prof, 58-68, PROF ANIMAL SCI, PURDUE UNIV, 68- *Concurrent Pos:* Res fel, Univ Wis, 64-65. *Mem:* Am Meat Sci Asn; Am Soc Animal Sci; Inst Food Technol. *Res:* Physiological and endocrine control of muscle properties and subsequent utilization of muscle as a food. *Mailing Add:* Dept of Animal Sci Smith Hall Purdue Univ West Lafayette IN 47906

JUDGE, ROGER JOHN RICHARD, b London, Eng, Nov 22, 38; US citizen; m 74; c 2. AERONAUTICAL ENGINEERING, ASTRONAUTICAL ENGINEERING. *Educ:* Univ Nottingham, BSc, 60, PhD(physics), 64. *Prof Exp:* Staff scientist, Bell Can Labs, 63-67; fel, Nat Res Coun Can, 67-69; res physicist, Univ Calif, San Diego, 69-75; prin engr, Orincon Corp, 78-79; STAFF SCIENTIST, IRT CORP, 79- *Concurrent Pos:* Vis prof, Univ Ottawa, 67-69 & Univ Calif, San Diego, 75- *Mem:* Am Geophys Union. *Res:* Upper atmosphere and space physics; spacecraft technology; nuclear survivability. *Mailing Add:* IRT Corp 7650 Convoy Ct PO Box 80817 San Diego CA 92138

JUDIS, JOSEPH, b Toledo, Ohio, Sept 23, 29; m 55; c 2. BIOCHEMICAL PHARMACOLOGY. *Educ:* Univ Toledo, BS, 49; Purdue Univ, MS, 51, PhD(bact), 54. *Prof Exp:* Res assoc microbiol, Sch Med, Western Reserve Univ, 53-55; res bacteriologist, Toledo Hosp Inst Med Res, 55-56; chmn dept biol, 64-66, dean, Col Pharm, 66-76, PROF PHARM, COL PHARM, UNIV TOLEDO, 62-, PROF BIOL, COL ARTS & SCI, 64- *Mem:* AAAS; Am Soc Microbiol; Am Chem Soc; Am Pharmaceut Asn; Brit Soc Gen Microbiol. *Res:* Microbial physiology. *Mailing Add:* Col of Pharm Univ of Toledo Toledo OH 43606

JUDISH, JOHN PAUL, b Canonsburg, Pa, May 23, 26; m 58; c 3. CHEMICAL PHYSICS. *Educ:* Univ Pittsburgh, BS, 50; Univ Tenn, PhD(physics), 74. *Prof Exp:* Engr Van de Graaff accelerator, 51-74, RES STAFF MEM PHYSICS, OAK RIDGE NAT LAB, 75- *Mem:* Am Phys Soc; Inst Elec & Electronics Engrs. *Res:* Atomic and molecular physics; visible and vuv spectroscopy; interaction of optical radiation with gases; lasers; excitation and ionization of gases by high energy ions; superconducting resistance at high frequencies. *Mailing Add:* Bldg 5500 Oak Ridge Nat Lab Oak Ridge TN 37830

JUDKINS, JOSEPH FAULCON, JR, b Richmond, Va, May 12, 38; m 61; c 3. SANITARY ENGINEERING. *Educ:* Va Polytech Inst, BS, 61, MS, 65, PhD(civil eng), 67. *Prof Exp:* Asst prof civil eng, 67-71, Gottlieb assoc prof, 71-77, GOTTLIEB PROF CIVIL ENG, AUBURN UNIV, 77- *Mem:* Am Soc Civil Engrs; Water Pollution Control Fedn; Am Water Works Asn. *Res:* Industrial and domestic waste treatment; water supply engineering. *Mailing Add:* Dept of Civil Eng Ramsay Hall Auburn Univ Auburn AL 36830

JUDKINS, MELVIN P, b Los Angeles, Calif, May 3, 22; m 46. CARDIOVASCULAR RADIOLOGY. *Educ:* La Sierra Col, BS, 43; Loma Linda Univ, MD, 47. *Prof Exp:* Instr radiol, Med Sch, Univ Ore, 64, from assoc prof to prof, 66-70; dir cardiovasc radiol, 66-69; dir cardiovasc labs, prof radiol & chmn dept, 70-78, PROF RADIOL, LOMA LINDA UNIV, 78- *Concurrent Pos:* NIH fel, Univ Lund, 65. *Mem:* Fel Am Col Radiol; fel Am Col Cardiol; Soc Cardiac Angiography; Intersoc Comns Heart Dis Resources; NAm Soc Cardiac Radiol. *Res:* Coronary artery disease and arteriography. *Mailing Add:* 25850 Hudson Ct Loma Linda CA 92354

JUDKINS, RODDIE REAGAN, b Sunbright, Tenn, Dec 31, 41; m 64; c 3. COAL CONVERSION SYSTEMS, COAL LIQUEFACTION PROCESSES. *Educ:* Tenn Polytech Inst, BS, 63, MS, 65; Ga Inst Technol, PhD(phys chem), 70. *Prof Exp:* Eng assoc, Union Carbide Corp, 64, 65 & 66; instr chem, Ga Inst Technol, 65-70; plant mgr, Nuclear Chem & Metals Corp, 70-73; tech assoc, E R Johnson Assocs, Inc, 73-77; develop engr, 77-81, TASK LEADER, UNION CARBIDE CORP, 81- *Mem:* Am Chem Soc; Sigma Xi. *Res:* Materials of construction for coal conversion systems; thorium metal process development and improvement; corrosion mechanisms in coal liquefaction processes; nuclear fuel fabrication technology and economics. *Mailing Add:* Bldg 4508 Oak Ridge Nat Lab PO Box X Oak Ridge TN 37830

JUDSON, BURTON FREDERICK, b Boston, Mass, Aug 7, 28; m 51; c 2. CHEMICAL ENGINEERING. *Educ:* Mass Inst Technol, BS, 48. *Prof Exp:* Engr & mgr processing, Hanford Atomic Prods Oper, 48-65, mgr chem eng & plutonium fuels, Vallecitos Nuclear Ctr, 65-72, plant mgr, Midwest Fuel Recovery Oper, 72-75, mgr advan eng, Nuclear Energy Progs, 75-77, VPRES & MGR ENG, GEN ELEC URANIUM MGT CORP, GEN ELEC CORP, 77- *Mem:* Am Inst Chem Engrs; Am Nuclear Soc; AAAS. *Res:* Reprocessing and refabrication of irradiated nuclear fuels. *Mailing Add:* Gen Elec Uranium Mgt Corp 175 Curtner Ave ME858 San Jose CA 95125

JUDSON, CHARLES LEROY, b Lodi, Calif, Oct 21, 26; m 50; c 3. INSECT PHYSIOLOGY. *Educ:* Univ Calif, BA, 51, PhD(entom), 56. *Prof Exp:* Asst prof, 62-70, assoc prof, 70-77, ASSOC, EXP STA, UNIV CALIF, DAVIS, 55-, PROF ENTOM, 77-; VECTOR CONTROL SPECIALIST, CALIF DEPT PUB HEALTH, 55- *Mem:* Entom Soc Am. *Res:* Insect biochemistry; physiology of hatching; mosquito eggs. *Mailing Add:* Dept of Entom Univ of Calif Davis CA 95616

JUDSON, CHARLES MORRILL, b Washington, DC, July 2, 19; m 44; c 2. PHYSICAL CHEMISTRY. *Educ:* Swarthmore Col, BA, 40; Univ Pa, MS, 42, PhD(phys chem), 47. *Prof Exp:* Asst instr chem, Univ Pa, 40-42; res chemist, Columbia Univ, 42-44; res chemist, Standard Oil Co (Ind), 44-45; res chemist, Am Cyanamid Co, 47-54; group leader, 54-57; mgr chem physics sect, 57-62; chief anal develop sect, Anal & Control Div, Consol Electrodyn Corp, 62-63; dir eng, 63-70; res scientist, Granville Phillips Co, 70-71; consult mass spectrometry, 71-73; scientist, 73-76, CHIEF SCIENTIST, ANALOG TECHNOL CORP, 76-; mgr, Microtrace Anal Serv, 75-80. *Mem:* Am Chem Soc; Am Phys Soc; Am Soc Testing & Mat; Am Soc Mass Spectrometry; Soc Appl Spectros. *Res:* Mass spectrometry; instruments; radio-tracers; electrolytes; surface agents. *Mailing Add:* 608 Seabrooke Pl Lawrence KS 66044

JUDSON, HORACE AUGUSTUS, b Miami, Fla, Aug 7, 41. ORGANIC CHEMISTRY. *Educ:* Lincoln Univ, AB, 63; Cornell Univ, PhD(org chem), 70. *Prof Exp:* Asst prof chem, Bethune-Cookman Col, 69; asst prof, 69-74, PROF CHEM & VPRES ACAD AFFAIRS, MORGAN STATE UNIV, 74- *Mem:* Am Chem Soc; Nat Inst Sci. *Res:* Decomposition mechanisms of organic peroxides and peresters; synthesis of strained ring compounds via peresters. *Mailing Add:* Dept of Chem Box 525 Morgan State Col Baltimore MD 21212

JUDSON, SHELDON, JR, b Utica, NY, Oct 18, 18; m 43; c 3. GEOLOGY. *Educ:* Princeton Univ, AB, 40; Harvard Univ, AM, 46, PhD(geol), 48. *Prof Exp:* From instr to assoc prof geol, Univ Wis, 48-55; assoc prof, 55-64, chmn, Dept Geol & Geophys Sci, 70-82, chmn univ res bd, 72-77, KNOX TAYLOR PROF GEOL, PRINCETON UNIV, 64- *Concurrent Pos:* Fund Advan Educ fel, 54-55; Guggenheim & Fulbright fels, Italy, 60-61; Guggenheim fel, 66-67. *Mem:* AAAS; Geol Soc Am; assoc Arctic Inst NAm. *Res:* Glacial geology; geomorphology. *Mailing Add:* Dept of Geol & Geophys Sci Princeton Univ Princeton NJ 08540

JUDSON, WALTER EMERY, b Roxbury, Mass, June 5, 16; m 43; c 3. MEDICINE. *Educ:* Tufts Univ, BS, 38; Johns Hopkins Univ, MD, 42; Am Bd Internal Med, dipl, 50; Am Bd Cardiovasc Dis, cert, 50. *Prof Exp:* Asst med, Sch Med, Boston Univ, 48-49, from instr to asst prof, 50-55; assoc prof, 56-65, PROF MED, SCH MED, UNIV IND, INDIANAPOLIS, 65- *Mem:* Fel Am Col Physicians; AMA; Am Heart Asn; Am Fedn Clin Res. *Res:* Cardiovascular research. *Mailing Add:* Ind Univ Med Ctr 1100 W Michigan St Indianapolis IN 46207

JUDY, KENNETH JAMES, insect physiology, see previous edition

JUENGE, ERIC CARL, b Weehawken, NJ, Jan 12, 27; m 54, 71; c 3. ORGANOMETALLIC CHEMISTRY. *Educ:* NY Univ, BA, 51, PhD(chem), 57. *Prof Exp:* Jr chemist pharmaceut, Hoffmann-La Roche, Inc, 51-52; asst, NY Univ, 55-56; res chemist organometallic field, Ethyl Corp, La, 56-59; sr chemist agr chem, Spencer Chem Co, 59-61; from assoc to prof chem, Kans State Col, Pittsburg, 61-74; res assoc, 74-75, asst res prof chem, Coop State Res Serv, Ft Valley State Col, 75-78; CHEMIST, NAT CTR FOR DRUG ANAL, FOOD & DRUG ADMIN, 78- *Mem:* Am Chem Soc. *Res:* Organic chemistry; agricultural chemistry; chemical nitrogen fixation. *Mailing Add:* Nat Ctr for Drug Anal 1114 Market St St Louis MO 63101

JUENKER, DAVID W, physics, deceased

JUERGENS, JOHN LOUIS, b Mankato, Minn, Mar 29, 25; m 48; c 4. INTERNAL MEDICINE. *Educ:* Univ Minn, Minneapolis, BS, 46, MS, 56; Harvard Univ, MD, 49. *Prof Exp:* Asst prof med, 62-67, assoc prof clin med, 67-78, PROF MED, MAYO SCH MED, UNIV MINN, 78-; CONSULT CARDIOVASC DIS & INTERNAL MED, MAYO CLIN, 56- *Concurrent Pos:* Fel internal med, Mayo Grad Sch Med, Univ Minn, 53-56. *Mem:* Fel Am Col Physicians. *Res:* Peripheral vascular diseases; atherosclerosis; lipid metabolism. *Mailing Add:* Mayo Clin 200 First St SW Rochester MN 55901

JUERGENS, R(AYMOND) J(OHN), JR, b St Louis, Mo, Sept 29, 24; m 61; c 4. COMPOSITES. *Educ:* Univ Mo-Rolla, BS, 48; Washington Univ, St Louis, MS, 60. *Prof Exp:* Metallurgist, qual labs, ACF Industs, Inc, 52-53; engr mat & processes, 53-60, res scientist, 60-68, sr group engr, 68-70, sect mgr, 70-74, BR CHIEF, McDONNELL AIRCRAFT CO, 74- *Mem:* Am Soc Metals; Am Inst Mining, Metall & Petrol Engrs; Am Inst Aeronaut & Astronaut. *Res:* Metallurgy; resistance welding; refractory metal application; composite and nonmetallic materials development. *Mailing Add:* McDonnell Aircraft Co Box 516 St Louis MO 63166

JUERGENSMEYER, ELIZABETH B, b Columbia, Mo, May 28, 40; m 63; c 2. CELL BIOLOGY, GENETICS. *Educ:* Ore State Univ, BS, 62; Univ Ill, Urbana, MS, 64, PhD(biol), 67. *Prof Exp:* Asst, Univ Ill, Chicago Circle, 65-68; asst prof, Harper Col, 68-69; assoc prof, 69-80, PROF BIOL & FAC MODERATOR, JUDSON COL, ILL, 80- *Mem:* AAAS; Am Inst Biol Sci; Soc Protozool; Genetics Soc Am; Am Soc Zool. *Res:* Genetics and genetic control mechanisms in Tetrahymena pyriformis, emphasizing serotypes. *Mailing Add:* Dept of Biol Judson Col Elgin IL 60120

JUGENHEIMER, ROBERT WILLIAM, b Scott Co, Iowa, Nov 6, 04; m 33; c 2. AGRONOMY. *Educ:* Iowa State Univ, BS, 34, MS, 36, PhD(genetics), 40. *Prof Exp:* Agent, Bur Plant Indust, USDA & Iowa State Univ, 28-38; assoc agronomist, USDA, Kans State Univ, 38-44; res dir, Pfister Asn Growers, Ill, 44-45; prof plant genetics, 45-72, dir, Off Overseas Proj, 56-72, asst coord, Int Coop Prog, 56-61, asst dean, Col Agr & asst dir, Exp Sta, 59-61, EMER PROF PLANT GENETICS & EMER DIR OFF OVERSEAS PROJS, UNIV ILL, URBANA-CHAMPAIGN, 72- *Concurrent Pos:* Spec adv hybrid corn, Turkish Ministry Agr & US Econ Coop Admin, Turkey, 50; consult in charge coop hybrid corn prog, Europc & Mediter areas, Food & Agr Orgn, Italy, 52-53; collab, USDA, 54-58; mem agr res inst & agr bd, Nat Acad Sci-Nat Res Coun; res admin adv, Uttar Pradesh Agr Univ, Pantnagar, India, 68-70. *Mem:* Fel AAAS; fel Am Soc Agron; Genetics Soc Am; Am Genetic Asn; Am Statist Asn. *Res:* Corn breeding, genetics and production; corn inbred lines and hybrids; resistance to diseases, insects and drought; technical aid programs in Asia, Europe, Africa & South America; author of over 220 publications. *Mailing Add:* 1307 W University Ave Champaign IL 61820

JUHASZ, STEPHEN, b Budapest, Hungary, Dec 26, 13; nat US. MECHANICS. *Educ:* Royal Inst Technol, Budapest, dipl Ing, 36; Royal Inst Technol, Sweden, MSc, 49, Tekn Lic, 51. *Prof Exp:* Mgr & engr, Oeconomia Ltd, Combustion & Salgotarjan Coal Mines, Hungary, 36-46; mem staff, Royal Inst Technol, Stockholm, 49-51 & Univ Toronto, 51-52; res assoc, Fuels Res Lab, Mass Inst Technol, 52-53; exec ed, 53-60, ED, APPL MECH REV, 60-, DIR, SOUTHWEST RES INST, 60- *Mem:* Fel Am Soc Mech Engrs; Sigma Xi; Am Inst Aeronaut & Astronaut; fel Am Asn Advan Sci. *Res:* Heat transfer; boiler availability; information retrieval. *Mailing Add:* PO Box 28510 San Antonio TX 78284

JUHASZ, STEPHEN EUGENE, b Kecskemet, Hungary, Sept 20, 23; Can citizen; m 65. PSYCHIATRY. *Educ:* Med Univ Budapest, MD, 51; McGill Univ, PhD, 62. *Prof Exp:* Instr bact, Med Univ Budapest, 51-54, lectr, 54-56, asst prof, 56; res assoc, Royal Edward Laurentian Hosp, 57; res asst, McGill Univ, 58-62; guest researcher, Univ Lausanne, 62-63; staff researcher, Res Inst Exp Biol & Med, Borstel, WGer, 63-64; asst prof microbiol, Univ BC, 64-66; assoc prof, 67-70, prof microbiol, Stritch Sch Med, Loyola Univ, 70-72; res microbiologist, Vet Admin Hosp, Hines, 67-72, resident psychiat, 72-75; INSTR PSYCHIAT, STRITCH SCH MED, LOYOLA UNIV, 75- *Mem:* Am Med Asn; Sigma Xi. *Res:* Bacterial cytology; spheroplasts and L forms of Salmonella; morphogenetics of mycobacteria; phage typing and lysogeny in mycobacteria; transduction and transformation in mycobacteria. *Mailing Add:* Alexian Brothers Med Plaza 850 Biesterfield Rd Suite 3001 Elk Grove Village IL 60007

JUHL, WILLIAM G, b Luverne, Minn, June 30, 24; m 56; c 2. CHEMICAL ENGINEERING. *Educ:* Univ Minn, BChE, 45; Iowa State Col, PhD(chem eng), 53. *Prof Exp:* Res engr, Lion Oil Co, 53-55; group leader res, 55-64, process tech mgr, 65-74, PROCESS TECHNOL DIR, MONSANTO CO, 74- *Mem:* Am Inst Chem Engrs; Am Chem Soc. *Res:* Process development studies of hydrocarbons, conversion and petrochemical production. *Mailing Add:* Monsanto Co PO Box 1311 Texas City TX 77590

JUHOLA, CARL, b Bismarck, NDak, Jan 28, 20; m 44; c 3. ELECTRICAL ENGINEERING. *Educ:* Univ Wash, Seattle, BSEE, 43. *Prof Exp:* Suveyor, US Bur Reclamation, 40-41; plant engr, Boeing Aircraft Co, Seattle, 41-43; eng exec, electronic develop, United Shoe Mach Corp, 46-61, dept mgr, indust & mach develop, 61-70; dir comput control lab, 70-73, MGR, ELECTRONICS LAB, USM CORP, 73- *Mem:* Sr mem Inst Elec & Electronics Engrs. *Res:* Management; electronic controls; dielectric heating; fasteners; packaging adhesive systems; development of minicomputer and micro-computer control systems; robotics and computer-aided design; computer-aided manufacturing systems. *Mailing Add:* 5 Ray St Beverly MA 01915

JUILLET, JACQUES ANDRE, ecology, biometry, see previous edition

JUKES, THOMAS HUGHES, b Hastings, Eng, Aug 25, 06; nat US; m 42; c 3. BIOCHEMISTRY, MOLECULAR EVOLUTION. *Educ:* Univ Toronto, BSA, 30, PhD(biochem), 33. *Hon Degrees:* DSc, Univ Guelph, 72. *Prof Exp:* Nat Res Coun fel biochem, Univ Calif, 33-34, instr poultry husb, 34-39, asst prof, 39-42; dir sect nutrit & physiol res, Am Cyanamid Co, 42-59, dir chem res, Agr Div, 59-63; PROF IN RESIDENCE MED PHYSICS, LECTR NUTTRIT SCI & RES BIOCHEMIST, SPACE SCI LAB, UNIV CALIF, BERKELEY, 63-, PROF BIOPHYSICS, 81- *Concurrent Pos:* Consult, Chem Warfare Serv, 43-45 & NASA, 69-70; vis sr res fel biochem, Princeton Univ, 62-63; chmn, Interdisciplinary Sci Comn F on Life Sci, Comt Space Res, Int Coun Sci Unions, 78- *Honors & Awards:* Borden Award, Poultry Sci Asn, 47; Kenneth A Spencer Award, Am Chem Soc, 76; Agr & Food Chem Award, Am Chem Soc, 79. *Mem:* Am Soc Biol Chem; Soc Exp Biol & Med; fel Am Soc Animal Sci; Poultry Sci Asn; fel Am Inst Nutrit. *Res:* Vitamin B complex; choline; pantothenic and folic acid; vitamin B12 and antibiotics in nutrition; folic acid antagonists; proteins; genetic code; biochemical evolution; exobiology. *Mailing Add:* Space Sci Lab Univ Calif Berkeley CA 94720

JULES, LEONARD HERBERT, b Cleveland, Ohio, Oct 5, 22; m 53; c 2. ORGANIC CHEMISTRY. *Educ:* Univ Southern Calif, AB, 48, MS, 49. *Prof Exp:* Res chemist, Sahyun Labs, 50-55; res chemist, Purex Corp, 55-58; res chemist, Nat Res & Chem Co, 58-62; res chemist, 62-69, PLANT MGR, PHILIP A HUNT CHEM CORP, 69- *Mem:* Am Chem Soc; Soc Photog Sci & Eng. *Res:* Pharmaceuticals; organic intermediates; organic chlorine bleaches; surfactants; asphalt additives; corrosion inhibitors; photographic chemicals. *Mailing Add:* 6035 Wooster Ave Los Angeles CA 90056

JULESZ, BELA, b Budapest, Hungary, Feb 19, 28; US citizen; m 53. VISION, PHYSIOLOGICAL OPTICS. *Educ:* Budapest Tech Univ, dipl, 50; Hungarian Acad Sci, Dr Ing, 56. *Prof Exp:* Asst, Dept Tel Commun, Budapest Tech Univ, 50-51; res engr microwave syst, Inst Telecommun Res, Budapest, 51-56; HEAD SENSORY & PERCEPTUAL PROCESSES DEPT, BELL TEL LABS, INC, 56- *Concurrent Pos:* Vis prof exp psychol, Mass Inst Technol, 69; Fed Tech Univ, Zurich, 75-76; Fairchild distinguished scholar, Calif Inst Technol, 77-79. *Mem:* Fel AAAS; Inst Elec & Electronics Engrs; fel Optical Soc Am; Psychonomic Soc; fel Am Acad Arts & Sci. *Res:* Visual perception; binocular depth perception; pattern recognition; optical data processing; psychophysics and neurophysiology of vision; mathematical models; clinical problems of strabismus. *Mailing Add:* Sensory and Percep Process Dept Bell Tel Labs Inc Murray Hill NJ 07974

JULIAN, DONALD BENJAMIN, b Pelham, Mass, June 6, 22; m 45; c 3. PHOTOGRAPHIC CHEMISTRY, CHEMICAL MICROSCOPY. *Educ:* Univ Mass, BS, 45. *Prof Exp:* Jr chemist, 45-48, from res chemist to sr res chemist, 48-62, res assoc, 62-74, sr res assoc chem, Eastman Kodak Co Res Labs, 74-80; RETIRED. *Mem:* Am Chem Soc; Soc Photog Scientists & Engrs. *Res:* Determination of image structure of color photographic films and papers by optical microscope methods; dispersions of oil soluble couplers and other components in aqueous gelatin; chemistry and physics of color photography. *Mailing Add:* 1079 Shoemaker Rd Webster NY 14580

JULIAN, EDWARD A, b San Francisco, Calif, June 22, 26; m 61; c 2. PHARMACY. *Educ:* Univ Utah, BSc, 51, BPharm, 53; Univ Wash, Seattle, MSc, 55, PhD(pharm), 58. *Prof Exp:* Asst prof pharmacog, Univ Colo, 58-60; from asst prof to assoc prof, 60-70, PROF PHARMACOG & PHARM, SCH PHARM, UNIV WYO, 70- *Res:* Pharmaceutical botany; optical chemical crystallography; chemical plant taxonomy. *Mailing Add:* Sch of Pharm Univ of Wyo Laramie WY 82071

JULIAN, GLENN MARCENIA, b Knoxville, Tenn, Oct 1, 39; m 68; c 3. NUCLEAR PHYSICS. *Educ:* Carnegie-Mellon Univ, BS, 61, MS, 63, PhD(physics), 67. *Prof Exp:* Asst prof, 68-72, ASSOC PROF PHYSICS, MIAMI UNIV, 72- *Mem:* Am Phys Soc; Am Geophys Union; Sigma Xi. *Res:* Studies of nuclear structure by means of gamma and beta radiation. *Mailing Add:* Dept of Physics Miami Univ Oxford OH 45056

JULIAN, GORDON RAY, b Wenatchee, Wash, May 29, 28; m 52; c 2. CHEMISTRY. *Educ:* Univ Utah, BS, 50; Univ Ore, MA, 55, PhD(chem), 60. *Prof Exp:* Res fel pharmacol, Harvard Med Sch, 60-62, res assoc, 62-64; from asst prof to assoc prof, 64-70, PROF CHEM, MONT STATE UNIV, 70- *Concurrent Pos:* NIH res grant, 65-68; foreign vis scientist, Szeged, Hungary, 74-75; vis prof, Friedrich Miescher Inst, Basel, Switz, 75-76. *Mem:* AAAS; Am Chem Soc. *Res:* Biochemical processes at elevated temperature; in vitro protein synthesis; early biochemical events in plant development. *Mailing Add:* Dept of Chem Mont State Univ Bozeman MT 59717

JULIAN, LOGAN M, b Ashland, Ore, Aug 12, 23; m 51. VETERINARY ANATOMY. *Educ:* State Col Wash, BS, 45, DVM, 46; Univ Calif, PhD(comp path), 51. *Prof Exp:* Assoc vet anat, 48-51, asst anatomist & asst prof, 51-56, assoc anatomist & assoc prof, 56-61, ANATOMIST & PROF VET SCI, UNIV CALIF, DAVIS, 61- *Mem:* Am Asn Anat; Am Vet Med Asn; Am Asn Vet Anat; World Asn Vet Anat. *Res:* Anatomy of domestic animals; anatomical bases of genetic and environmental influences upon growth; hereditary muscular dystrophy. *Mailing Add:* Dept of Anat Sch of Vet Med Univ of Calif Davis CA 95616

JULIAN, MAUREEN M, b New York, NY, July 3, 39; m 68; c 2. PHYSICAL CHEMISTRY, CRYSTALLOGRAPHY, COMPUTERS. *Educ:* Hunter Col, AB, 61; Cornell Univ, PhD(phys chem), 66. *Prof Exp:* Chemist, Univ Col, Univ London, 66-68; sr chemist, Kirtland AFB, NMex, 69-70, consult chem, 71-73; HEAD DEPT SCI, WOOD LAWN SCH, 74-; asst prof chem, Hollins Col, Va, 78-81; SR SCIENTIST, ENVIRON TESTING SYSTS, INC, ROANOKE, VA, 79- *Concurrent Pos:* Vis asst prof, Va Polytech Inst, Blacksburg, 78- *Mem:* Am Chem Soc; Am Phys Soc; Am Crystallog Asn; AAAS; The Chem Soc. *Res:* Zeolites, optical crystallography of anthracene; solid state reactions; photodimerization of anthracene; history of crystallography; teaching off crystallography for undergraduates; symmetry; chemistry in elementary schools; computers; software for environmental chemistry. *Mailing Add:* 3863 Red Fox Dr Roanoke VA 24017

JULIAN, ORMAND C, b Omaha, Nebr, May 6, 13; m 35; c 2. CARDIOVASCULAR SURGERY. *Educ:* Univ Chicago, BS, 34, MD, 37, PhD(surg), 41. *Prof Exp:* Asst surg, Univ Chicago, 37-41; asst surg, Univ Ill, 46-47, from instr to prof, 47-71; chmn dept cardiovasc thoracic surg, 71-72, PROF SURG, RUSH MED COL, 71-, ON LEAVE, 72- *Concurrent Pos:* Chmn, Sect Cardiovasc Thoracic Surg, Presby-St Lukes Hosp, Chicago. *Mem:* Soc Clin Surg; Soc Vascular Surg; Am Surg Asn; fel Am Col Surg; Int Cardiovasc Soc. *Res:* Vascular disease; coagulation; surgical treatment of portal hypertension. *Mailing Add:* 47-190 El Agadir Palm Desert CA 92260

JULIAN, PAUL R, b LaPorte, Ind, Oct 12, 29; m 58; c 6. METEOROLOGY. *Educ:* DePauw Univ, AB, 51; Pa State Univ, MS, 53, PhD(meteorol), 60. *Prof Exp:* Asst meteorol, Pa State Univ, 53 & 55-56, instr, 57-59; mem res staff, High Altitude Observ, Colo, 59-64; MEM RES STAFF, NAT CTR ATMOSPHERIC RES, 64- *Concurrent Pos:* Affiliate prof, Univ Chicago, 68-72. *Mem:* Fel Am Meteorol Soc; Am Geophys Union. *Res:* Statistical methods applied to meteorology; general circulation of tropics. *Mailing Add:* Nat Ctr Atmospheric Res Boulder CO 80303

JULIAN, RENE STEPHEN, b Omak, Wash, Mar 7, 14; m 40; c 3. PHYSICS. *Educ:* Univ Wash, Seattle, BS, 38; Mass Inst Technol, PhD(physics), 47. *Prof Exp:* Asst, Univ Wash, 38-40; mem tech staff, Bell Tel Labs, 40-46; res assoc, Mass Inst Technol, 46-48; res asst prof, Univ Ill, 48; head, Electronics Dept, Guided Missile Div, Hughes Aircraft Co, 49-59, sr scientist, 59-80. *Concurrent Pos:* Consult, AEC, 56-68. *Mem:* Am Phys Soc; Sigma Xi; Inst Elec & Electronics Engrs; Optical Soc Am; Am Astron Soc. *Res:* Microwave engineering; molecular beams; hyperfine separation of atomic deuterium; guided missile electronics; lasers; optics. *Mailing Add:* 10906 NE Bill Point Ct Bainbridge WA 98110

JULIANO, RUDOLPH LAWRENCE, b New York, NY, July 18, 41; m 63; c 2. CELL BIOLOGY, BIOPHYSICS. *Educ:* Cornell Univ, BS, 63; Univ Rochester, PhD(biophys), 70. *Prof Exp:* Engr, Radio Corp Am, 63-64; sci teacher, US Peace Corps, Philippines, 64-66; cancer res scientist cell biol, Roswell Park Mem Inst, 70-72; investr cell biol, Res Inst, Hosp Sick Children, Toronto, 72-80; MEM FAC, UNIV TEX MED SCH, 80- *Concurrent Pos:* Asst prof, Dept Med Biophys, Univ Toronto, 73-; assoc prof pharmacol, Univ Tex Med Sch, Houston, 78- *Mem:* AAAS; Biophys Soc; Can Biochem Soc. *Res:* Surface proteins of mammalian cells; drug delivery systems. *Mailing Add:* Univ Tex Med Sch PO Box 20708 Houston TX 77025

JULICH, PAUL M, electrical engineering, see previous edition

JULIEN, HIRAM PAUL, b Syracuse, NY, Oct 21, 29; m 51; c 4. PHYSICAL CHEMISTRY. *Educ:* DePauw Univ, AB, 51; Mass Inst Technol, PhD(phys chem), 55. *Prof Exp:* Asst phys chem, Mass Inst Technol, 51-55; res chemist, Prod Res, Esso Res & Eng Co, 55-58, group head, 58-59; mgr adv studies dept, Bonded Abrasives Div, Carborundum Co, 59-61, mgr develop dept, 62-64, mgr ceramics & metall dept, Res & Develop Div, 64-67; MGR ADVAN TECHNOL & TESTING DEPT, JIM WALTER RES CORP, 67- *Mem:* Am Chem Soc; Am Soc Testing & Mat. *Res:* Thermodynamics; automotive and jet fuels; bonded abrasives; high temperature materials and composites; building materials; cellular plastics; mineral fibers; inorganic fillers. *Mailing Add:* 6100 Bahama Shores Dr S St Petersburg FL 33705

JULIEN, HOWARD L, b Oak Park, Ill, Dec 13, 42; m 65; c 2. HEAT TRANSFER, FLUID MECHANICS. *Educ:* Ill Inst Technol, BS, 64, MS, 67; Stanford Univ, PhD(heat & mass transfer), 69. *Prof Exp:* Assoc sr res engr, Gen Motors Res Labs, 69-70, sr res engr, 70-77; PRIN ENGR, KAISER ENGRS, INC, 77- *Mem:* Am Soc Mech Engrs; Sigma Xi; Soc Automotive Engrs. *Res:* Basic experimental/analytical convective heat transfer research; gas turbine heat transfer; experimental fluid mechanics; thermodynamic cycle analysis of alternative automotive power plants; heat transfer in nuclear waste processing and storage facilities. *Mailing Add:* Kaiser Engrs Inc 300 Lakeside Dr Oakland CA 94623

JULIEN, JEAN-PAUL, b Quebec, Que, Jan 15, 18; m 55; c 3. FOOD CHEMISTRY. *Educ:* Univ Montreal, BA, 39; Laval Univ, MSc, 45. *Prof Exp:* Prof dairy sci, Dairy Sch, St Hyacinthe, PQ, 45-57; tech dir, Dalpe & Bros, Vercheres, 57-60; prof biochem, Oka Agr Inst, 60-62; dir, Dept Food Sci, 70-80, PROF FOOD CHEM, LAVAL UNIV, 62- *Mem:* Am Dairy Sci Asn; Inst Food Technol; Can Inst Food Sci & Technol. *Res:* Dairy technology relating to milk proteins, ice cream and milk powder. *Mailing Add:* Dept of Food Sci Laval Univ Quebec PQ G1K 7P4 Can

JULIEN, JULIEN BERNARD, phytopathology, see previous edition

JULIEN, LARRY MARLIN, b Nora Springs, Iowa, Aug 16, 37; m 59; c 2. PHYSICAL CHEMISTRY. *Educ:* Wis State Univ, River Falls, BS, 62; Univ Iowa, MS, 65, PhD(chem), 66. *Prof Exp:* Asst prof, 66-73, ASSOC PROF CHEM, MICH TECHNOL UNIV, 73- *Mem:* Am Chem Soc. *Res:* Thermodynamics; molecular spectroscopy and wood-bark surface properties. *Mailing Add:* Dept of Chem & Chem Eng Mich Technol Univ Houghton MI 49931

JULIENNE, PAUL SEBASTIAN, b Spartanburg, SC, May 8, 44; m 68; c 2. QUANTUM CHEMISTRY, ATMOSPHERIC CHEMISTRY. *Educ:* Wofford Col, BS, 65; Univ NC, Chapel Hill, PhD(chem), 69. *Prof Exp:* Nat Acad Sci-Nat Res Coun res assoc, Nat Bur Standards, 69-71, res chemist quantum chem, 71-73; res physicist, Plasma Physics Div, Naval Res Lab, Washington, DC, 73-74; res chemist, Phys Chem Div, 74-77, RES CHEMIST, MOLECULAR SPECTROS DIV, NAT BUR STANDARDS, 77- *Mem:* Am Phys Soc; Am Geophys Union. *Res:* Molecular spectroscopy, eximer lasers, ionospheric chemistry; application of ab initio calculations to study molecular dynamics. *Mailing Add:* B268 Physics Bldg Nat Bur Standards Washington DC 20234

JULIN, BRUCE GUSTAV, b Klippan, Sweden, Apr 14, 36; m 64; c 2. ANALYTICAL CHEMISTRY, PESTICIDE CHEMISTRY. *Educ:* Boston Univ, BA, 61; Univ Minn, Minneapolis, PhD(anal chem), 65. *Prof Exp:* Res chemist, 65-72, sr res chemist, 72-74, res supvr, Indust & Biochem Dept, 74-77, RES MGR, BIOCHEM DEPT, E I DU PONT DE NEMOURS & CO, INC, 77- *Res:* Stability constants; spectroscopy; chemistry of flames; metabolism and degradation of pesticides soil, water, plants and animals. *Mailing Add:* Indust & Biochem Dept Exp Sta E I du Pont de Nemours & Co Inc Wilmington DE 19898

JULINAO, PETER C, b New Kensington, Pa, Oct 10, 41; m 65; c 3. POLYMER CHEMISTRY. *Educ:* St Vincent Col, BS, 63; WVa Univ, MS, 65; Univ Akron, PhD(polymer sci), 68. *Prof Exp:* Chemist, 68-71, tech coordr, 71-72, MGR RES & DEVELOP, POLYMER PHYSICS & ENG BR, GEN ELEC CO, 76- *Concurrent Pos:* Chmn, Gordon Conf Elastomers, 81. *Mem:* Acct Control Syst; Soc Plastic Engrs. *Res:* Synthesis and properties of block polymers; use of organometallic and organosiloxane intermediates for polymer forming reactions. *Mailing Add:* Gen Elec Corp Res & Develop Gen Elec Co PO Box 8 Schenectady NY 12301

JULIS, ANTHONY JAY, plant pathology, genetics, see previous edition

JULIUS, STEVO, b Kovin, Yugoslavia, Apr 15, 29. MEDICINE. *Educ:* Univ Zagreb, MD, 53, DMSc, 64. *Prof Exp:* Intern, Univ Zagreb Hosp, 53-54, resident internal med, 55-60; res asst med, Med Ctr, Univ Mich, Ann Arbor, 61-62; sr instr, Univ Zagreb Hosp, 62-64; from instr to assoc prof, 64-74, PROF INTERNAL MED & DIR HYPERTENSION UNIT, MED CTR, UNIV MICH, ANN ARBOR, 74-, ASSOC PROF PHYSIOL, 80- *Concurrent Pos:* Mem coun epidemiol & med adv bd-coun high blood pressure res, Am Heart Asn. *Mem:* Am Col Cardiol; Am Heart Asn; Am Fedn Clin Res; Int Soc Cardiol; Am Physiol Soc. *Res:* Hemodynamics of borderline hypertensions; patho-physiology of hypertension. *Mailing Add:* 1328 Culiver Ann Arbor MI 49027

JULIUSSEN, J EGIL, b Stavanger, Norway, May 4, 43; US citizen; m 66; c 1. COMPUTER SCIENCE, INFORMATION SCIENCE. *Educ:* Purdue Univ, BS, 69, MS, 70, PhD(elec eng), 72. *Prof Exp:* Engr, Norden, Div United Technols, 72-73; SR MEM TECH STAFF ENG, TEX INSTRUMENTS, INC, 73- *Mem:* Inst Elec & Electronics Engrs; Asn Comput Mach. *Res:* Memory technologies, magnetic bubble memories, charge-coupled memories, computer system architecture, minicomputers, microprocessors, microprogramming, computer peripheral controllers. *Mailing Add:* 908 Dumont Dr Richardson TX 75080

JULL, EDWARD VINCENT, b Calgary, Alta, Aug 8, 34; m 65; c 4. ELECTRICAL ENGINEERING. *Educ:* Queen's Univ Ont, BSc, 56; Univ London, PhD(elec eng), 60. *Hon Degrees:* DSc, Univ London, 79. *Prof Exp:* Jr res officer, Radio & Elec Eng Div, Nat Res Coun Can, 56-57; asst prof elec eng, Univ Alta, 60-61; asst res officer, Radio & Elec Eng Div, Nat Res Coun Can, 61-72, assoc res officer, 67-72; assoc prof, 72-80, PROF ELEC ENG, UNIV BC, 80- *Concurrent Pos:* Guest researcher, lab electromagnetic theory, Tech Univ Denmark, 63-65 & microwave dept, Royal Inst Technol, Sweden, 65; chmn, Can comn VI, Int Union Radio Sci, 73-76, chmn Can Nat Comt, 80-; assoc ed, Radio Science, 80- *Honors & Awards:* J T Bolljahn Award, Inst Elec & Electronics Engrs, 65. *Mem:* Sr mem Inst Elec & Electronics Engrs; Can Soc Elec Eng. *Res:* Electromagnetic theory; diffraction theory; antennas. *Mailing Add:* Dept Elec Eng Univ BC Vancouver BC V6T 1W5 Can

JULL, GEORGE W(ALTER), b Calgary, Alta, Can, June 22, 29; m 56; c 1. ELECTRONIC ENGINEERING. *Educ:* Univ Alta, BS, 51; Univ London, DIC & PhD(elec eng), 55. *Prof Exp:* Defense scientist, High Frequency Systs, Defense Res Telecommun Estab, 55-71; prog mgr, Info Directorate, 71-75; SR CONSULT, COMMUN RES DIRECTORATE, 75- *Mem:* Optical Soc Am; Inst Elec & Electronics Engrs. *Res:* Advanced communications systems techniques; coherent optical systems; new voice, video and data systems analysis; telecommunications policy research. *Mailing Add:* Dept of Commun Commun Res Ctr PO Box 11490 Station H Ottawa ON K2H 8S2 Can

JULL, ROBERT KINGSLEY, geology, deceased

JULLIEN, GRAHAM ARNOLD, b Wolverhampton, Eng, June 16, 43; m 70; c 2. SIGNAL PROCESSING, ELECTRONIC SYSTEMS. *Educ:* Loughborough Univ Technol, BTech, 65; Univ Birmingham, MS, 67; Univ Aston, PhD(elec eng), 69. *Prof Exp:* Engr, English Elec Co, 65-66; res asst elec eng, Univ Aston, 67-69; from asst prof to assoc prof, 69-78, PROF ELEC ENG, UNIV WINDSOR, 78- *Concurrent Pos:* Univ grant, Windsor Univ, 69-70, Nat Res Coun Can grant, 69-72, operating grants, 69-, travel fel, 75; sr res engr, Cent Res Labs, EMI Ltd, UK, 75-76; Nat Sci & Eng Res Coun grant, Can, 80-83; pres, Micrel Ltd, 74- *Mem:* Inst Elec & Electronics Engrs; Am Soc Eng Educ. *Res:* Digital signal processing; image processing; high speed digital hardware; microprocessor systems. *Mailing Add:* Dept of Elec Eng Univ of Windsor Windsor ON N9B 3P4 Can

JULYAN, FREDERICK JOHN, b Cleveland, Ohio, May 21, 27; m 60; c 4. ANATOMY, HISTOLOGY. *Educ:* Western Reserve Univ, AB, 50; Ohio State Univ, PhD(zool), 62. *Prof Exp:* Instr zool, Capital Univ, 60-61; from instr to asst prof anat, Ohio State Univ, 62-66; from asst prof to assoc prof, 67-73, prof anat, Chicago Col Osteop Med, 74-75, chmn dept, 73-75; PROF & CHMN DEPT ANAT, KIRKSVILLE COL OSTEOP MED, KIRKSVILLE, MO, 75- *Mem:* AAAS. *Res:* Teaching techniques. *Mailing Add:* Dept of Anat Kirksville Col Osteop Med Kirksville MO 63501

JUMARS, PETER ALFRED, b Dinkelsbuhl, Ger, June 3, 48; US citizen. BIOLOGICAL OCEANOGRAPHY. *Educ:* Univ Del, BA, 69; Univ Calif, San Diego, PhD(oceanog), 74. *Prof Exp:* Res assoc oceanog, Allan Hancock Found, Univ Southern Calif, 74-75; asst prof, 75-80, ASSOC PROF OCEANOG, UNIV WASH, 80- *Mem:* AAAS; Am Soc Limnol & Oceanog; Am Statist Asn; Ecol Soc Am; Am Geophys Union. *Res:* Marine benthic community ecology and associated biometrics, particularly factors affecting local dispersion patterns and species diversity; sediment-organism interactions; biology of polychaetous annelids. *Mailing Add:* Dept of Oceanog WB-10 Univ of Wash Seattle WA 98195

JUMIKIS, ALFREDS RICHARDS, b Riga, Latvia, Dec 7, 07; US citizen; m 34; c 1. SOIL MECHANICS, CIVIL ENGINEERING. *Educ:* Univ Latvia, Riga, CE, 37, Dr EngSc, 42; Vienna Tech Univ, Dr Techn, 43; Univ Stuttgart, Dr Ing, 68. *Prof Exp:* Asst prof eng, mech, Univ Del, 48-52; assoc prof soil mech & found eng, 52-55, prof, 55-73, distinguished prof, 73-78, EMER PROF CIVIL ENG, RUTGERS UNIV, 78- *Concurrent Pos:* Dir joint hwy res proj, Rutgers Univ & NJ State Hwy Dept, 52-55; NSF res grants, 55-69; mem comt on frost action in soils, Hwy Res Bd, Nat Acad Sci-Nat Res Coun, 55-; consult, Jersey Power & Light Co, 62-63; GAF Corp, 70- & Nat Soil Serv, Inc, 70-; mem, Nat Comt on Rock Mech, 71-; mem, US Comt on Large Dams. *Mem:* Am Soc Civil Engrs; Nat Soc Prof Engrs; Int Soc Rock Mech; Am Soc Eng Educ. *Res:* Rupture surfaces in soil; thermal soil mechanics; foundation engineering; author or coauthor of more than 110 publications. *Mailing Add:* Dept of Civil Eng University Heights Campus New Brunswick NJ 08903

JUMP, J ROBERT, b Kansas City, Mo, Feb 15, 37; m 62; c 2. COMPUTER SCIENCE, ELECTRICAL ENGINEERING. *Educ:* Univ Cincinnati, BS, 60, MS, 62; Univ Mich, MS, 65, PhD(comput sci), 68. *Prof Exp:* Elec engr, Avco Corp, 60-61; elec engr, IBM Corp, 62-64; asst prof, 68-76, assoc prof, 76-79, PROF ELEC ENG, WILL RICE COL, 79- *Concurrent Pos:* Assoc ed, Inst Elec & Electronics Engrs Trans Computs, 79-81. *Mem:* Inst Elec & Electronics Engrs; Asn Comput Mach. *Res:* Digital systems design; parallel computing; asynchronous control of digital systems. *Mailing Add:* Dept of Elec Eng Rice Univ Houston TX 77001

JUMP, JOHN AUSTIN, b Easton, Md, Dec 28, 13; m 43; c 2. MYCOLOGY, PLANT PATHOLOGY. *Educ:* Swarthmore Col, AB, 34; Univ Pa, PhD(bot), 38. *Prof Exp:* Instr biol, Md State Teachers Col, Frostburg, 38-43; mem res dept, Jos E Seagram & Sons, 43-44; res assoc, Univ Pa, 44-46; from asst prof to assoc prof biol, Univ Notre Dame, 46-58; chmn dept, 58-78, prof biol, 58-78, EMER PROF, ELMHURST COL, 78- *Res:* Plant mimicry; Mesembryanthemacea. *Mailing Add:* Dept of Biol Elmhurst Col Elmhurst IL 60126

JUMP, LORIN KEITH, b Bloomington, Ill, Mar 7, 28; m 51; c 4. GENETICS, PLANT BREEDING. *Educ:* Univ Ill, BS & MS, 51. *Prof Exp:* Corn breeder, 51-56, mgr res cent corn belt, 57-62, asst mgr res opers, 62-68, mgr hybrid corn res, 68-70, assoc dir co res, 70-75, assoc res dir, 75-77, MGR SEED PROD RES & FOUND SEED, FUNK SEEDS INT, 78- *Concurrent Pos:* Mem, Agr Res Inst, Nat Acad Sci-Nat Res Coun. *Mem:* AAAS; Am Soc Agron. *Res:* Development of commercial corn, sorghum and wheat varieties for the United States and the world. *Mailing Add:* Co Res Funk Seeds Int Bloomington IL 61701

JUMPER, CHARLES FREDERICK, b Prosperity, SC, Nov 4, 34; m 67; c 1. PHYSICAL CHEMISTRY. *Educ:* Univ SC, BS, 56, MS, 57; Fla State Univ, PhD(phys chem), 61. *Prof Exp:* Instr chem, Univ SC, 60-61; res assoc, Bell Tel Labs NJ, 61-62; from asst prof to assoc prof, 62-69, PROF CHEM, THE CITADEL, 69- *Mem:* Am Chem Soc. *Res:* Hydrogen bonding; nuclear magnetic resonance; ion exchange; kinetics of very fast reactions; structure of liquids; vibrational spectroscopy. *Mailing Add:* Dept of Chem The Citadel Charleston SC 29409

JUMPER, ERIC J, b Washington, DC, Aug 18, 46; m 67; c 2. GAS DYNAMICS, LASER PHYSICS. *Educ:* Univ NMex, BS, 68; Univ Wyo, MS, 69; Air Force Inst Technol, PhD(mech eng, laser physics), 75. *Prof Exp:* Lab mech engr, Human Eng Div, 6570 Aerospace Med Res Lab, Wright-Patterson AFB, Ohio, 69-72, aerodynamicist fluid dynamics & laser physics, Technol Div, Air Force Weapons Lab, 74-76, assoc prof, Dept Aeronaut, Us Air Force Acad, 76-81, ASSOC PROF, DEPT AERONAUT & ASTRONAUT, AIR FORCE INST TECHNOL, WRIGHT-PATTERSON AFB, 81- *Concurrent Pos:* Co-coordr, Shroud of Turin Res Proj, 74-; consult laser probs, Air Force Weapons Lab, 76-; ed, Aeronaut Dig, US Air Force Acad, 78-81, assoc ed, 81-; consult heat transfer, Broadcast Prod Div, Harris Corp, 79- *Mem:* Am Inst Aeronaut & Astronaut. *Res:* Shroud of Turin; researching authenticity of cloth purported to be the burial cloth of Jesus of Nazereth; supersonic drag predictions; physical chemistry of heterogeneous reactions; gas dynamics of lasers; laser-target interaction physics. *Mailing Add:* Dept Aeronaut & Astronaut Air Force Inst Technol Wright-Patterson AFB OH 45433

JUN, CHOLL KYU, materials science, metallurgical engineering, see previous edition

JUNCOSA, MARIO LEON, b Lima, Peru, Sept 18, 21; US citizen; m 46; c 3. APPLIED MATHEMATICS, NUMERICAL ANALYSIS. *Educ:* Hofstra Col, BA, 43; Cornell Univ, MS, 45, PhD(appl math), 48. *Prof Exp:* Asst physics, Cornell Univ, 43-47, asst mech, 45-47, instr, 47-48; math, Johns Hopkins Univ, 48-50; mathematician, Exterior Ballistics Lab & Comput Lab, Ballistics Res Labs, Aberdeen Proving Ground, Md, 49-53; mathematician, 53-70, SR MATHEMATICIAN, RAND CORP, 70- *Concurrent Pos:* Instr, Univ Southern Calif Exten, 54; instr & lectr Univ Calif Exten, Los Angeles, 56-58; ed in chief, Asn Comput Mach J, 59-63; consult math & comput sci adv group, AEC, 63-72; chmn satellite tracking accuracy panel, Nat Acad Sci Adv Comt to Air Force Systs Command, 67-69; mem comput adv panel, Nat Ctr Atmospheric Res, 68-; mem adv coun, Southwest Regional Lab Educ Res & Develop, 68-72; consult, Div Comput Res, NSF, 71- *Mem:* Soc Indust & Appl Math. *Res:* Applied math, probability, ordinary and partial differential equations and applications, general numerical and problem analysis, digital computation, mathematical programing and applications, privacy in computerized data banks, and mathematical applications in medicine. *Mailing Add:* Rand Corp Phys Sci Dept 1700 Main St Santa Monica CA 90406

JUNG, GERALD ALVIN, b Milwaukee, Wis, July 16, 30; m 57. AGRONOMY, PLANT PHYSIOLOGY. *Educ:* Univ Wis, BS, 52, MS, 54, PhD, 58. *Prof Exp:* Biologist, Chem Warfare Lab, Ft Detrick, Md, 54-56; asst prof agron, WVa Univ, 58-62, assoc prof, 62-67, prof agron & genetics, 67-70; tech adv for soil fertility & physiol & biochem technol, 77-81, RES AGRONOMIST, US REGIONAL PASTURE RES LAB, AGR RES SERV, USDA, 70- *Concurrent Pos:* Adj prof agron, Pa State Univ. *Mem:* Am Soc Agron; Am Forage & Grassland Coun; Soc Cryobiol. *Res:* Forage crop adaptation and production on marginal lands; nutritional value of forage crops as influenced by soils and fertilizers; physiology of cold tolerance of alfalfa. *Mailing Add:* US Regional Pasture Res Lab University Park PA 16802

JUNG, GLENN HAROLD, b Lyons, Kans, Oct 11, 24; m 48; c 5. OCEANOGRAPHY, METEOROLOGY. *Educ:* Mass Inst Technol, SB, 49, SM, 52; Tex A&M Univ, PhD(phys oceanog), 55. *Prof Exp:* Asst meteorol, Mass Inst Technol, 50-51, mem staff, Div Indust Co-op, 52; asst oceanog, Tex A&M Univ, 53-54, assoc oceanog & asst prof phys oceanog & phys meteorol, 55-57; assoc prof oceanog, 58-65, PROF OCEANOG, NAVAL POSTGRAD SCH, 65- *Concurrent Pos:* Consult, Texas Co, La, 58 & US Naval Oceanog Off, 65 & 66; vis fac mem, Inst Phys Oceanog, Univ Copenhagen, 71-72. *Mem:* Sigma Xi; Am Geophys Union. *Res:* Energy transfer by sea and air, especially across air-sea boundary; oceanographic analysis and forecasting. *Mailing Add:* Dept of Oceanog Naval Postgrad Sch Monterey CA 93940

JUNG, HILDA ZIIFLE, b Gretna, La, Sept 7, 22; m 68. PHYSICAL CHEMISTRY, PLASMA PHYSICS. *Educ:* Tulane Univ, BS, 43. *Prof Exp:* Release clerk, Higgins Aircraft Co, 43-44; res physicist, Southern Regional Res Ctr, USDA, 44-79; RETIRED. *Mem:* Sigma Xi; Am Asn Textile Chemists & Colorists; Am Chem Soc; AAAS; NY Acad Sci. *Res:* Physical and physical chemical reactions and properties of natural polymers; kinetics of reactions; crystalline orientation; elasticity; low temperature plasma reactions; application of statistical techniques. *Mailing Add:* 109 Kennedy Dr Gretna LA 70053

JUNG, JAMES MOSER, b Kannapolis, NC, May 25, 28; m 58; c 5. ORGANIC CHEMISTRY. *Educ:* Davidson Col, BS, 49; Univ NC, PhD(org chem), 62. *Prof Exp:* PROF CHEM & CHMN DEPT, CAMPBELL COL, 62- *Mem:* AAAS. *Res:* Preparation, properties and cyclization of azomethines. *Mailing Add:* Dept of Chem Campbell Col Buies Creek NC 27506

JUNG, JOHN ANDREW, JR, b Jersey City, NJ, May 3, 38. ORGANIC CHEMISTRY, CATALYSIS. *Educ:* St Peter's Col, BS, 61; Univ Iowa, PhD(org chem), 66. *Prof Exp:* Res chemist, US Army Ballistic Res Labs, Md, 66-67; res chemist, M W Kellogg Co, 67-71; sr res chemist, Chem Systs Inc, 72-81; STAFF CHEMIST, NEW VENTURES DIV, EXXON CHEM, 81- *Mem:* Am Chem Soc; Catalysis Soc; Sigma Xi. *Res:* Petrochemical process developments. *Mailing Add:* 2 Coolidge Ave East Hanover NJ 07936

JUNG, MICHAEL ERNEST, b New Orleans, La, May 14, 47; m 69. SYNTHETIC ORGANIC CHEMISTRY, NATURAL PRODUCTS CHEMISTRY. *Educ:* Rice Univ, BA, 69; Columbia Univ, PhD(chem), 73. *Prof Exp:* NATO fel, Swiss Fed Inst Technol, 73-74; asst prof, 74-79, ASSOC PROF CHEM, UNIV CALIF, LOS ANGELES, 79- *Concurrent Pos:* Camille & Henry Dreyfus Teacher-Scholar grant, 78-83; Alfred P Sloan Found Res fel, 79-81; Fulbright-Mays grant, US Res Scholar Award, 80-81. *Mem:* Am Chem Soc; The Chem Soc; Sigma Xi. *Res:* Organic synthesis, particularly of biologically interesting natural products; development of new synthetic methods; chemistry of organic compounds of group IVb metals, such as silicon and tin, and their use in organic synthesis. *Mailing Add:* Dept of Chem Univ of Calif 405 Hilgard Ave Los Angeles CA 90024

JUNG, RODNEY CLIFTON, b New Orleans, La, Oct 9, 20. TROPICAL MEDICINE. *Educ:* Tulane Univ, BS, 41, MD, 45, MS, 50, PhD(parasitol), 53. *Prof Exp:* Asst zool, 39-42, asst parasitol, 48-50, from instr to prof trop med, 50-74, CLIN PROF MED, TULANE UNIV, 74- *Concurrent Pos:* Markle scholar, 53-58; dir health, City of New Orleans, 63-70 & 79-; sr vis physician, Charity Hosp, La; consult, US Quarantine Serv. *Honors & Awards:* Geiger Medal pub health. *Mem:* Am Soc Trop Med & Hyg; Am Soc Parasitologists; fel Am Col Physicians; Royal Soc Trop Med & Hyg. *Res:* Clinical aspects of parasitic infections. *Mailing Add:* 3600 Chestnut St New Orleans LA 70115

JUNGA, FRANK ARTHUR, b Patchogue, NY, May 15, 34; m 56. SOLID STATE PHYSICS. *Educ:* Yale Univ, BS, 56; Univ Calif, Berkeley, MA, 59, PhD(physics), 63. *Prof Exp:* Grad prog student, 56-63, RES SCIENTIST SOLID STATE PHYSICS, LOCKHEED RES LAB, 63- *Mem:* Am Phys Soc. *Res:* Basic mechanisms involved in optical and/or electrical phenomena in semiconductors; photoconductivity; photovoltaic effects; laser phenomena; radiation effects in semiconductors; research on surface phenomena in compound semiconductors. *Mailing Add:* Dept 52-40 B202 Lockheed Res Lab 3251 Hanover St Palo Alto CA 94304

JUNGALWALA, FIROZE BAMANSHAW, b India, Aug 28, 36; US citizen. BIOCHEMISTRY, NEUROCHEMISTRY. *Educ:* Gujarat Univ, India, BSc, 56, MSc, 58; Indian Inst Sci, Bangalore, PhD(biochem), 63. *Prof Exp:* BIOCHEMIST, EUNICE KENNEDY SHRIVER CTR MENT RETARDATION, INC, 71-; PRIN RES ASSOC NEUROL, HARVARD UNIV, 75- *Concurrent Pos:* Res fel physiol chem, Univ Wis-Madison, 64-66; res fel psychiat, Washington Univ, St Louis, 66-68; Nat Multiple Sclerosis Soc res fel, Inst Animal Physiol, Cambridge, Eng, 68-70; assoc ed, J Lipid Res. *Mem:* Int Soc Neurochem; Am Soc Neurochem; Fedn Am Soc Exp Biol. *Res:* Lipids; role of lipids in membrane formation and organization; cerebral membranes, systhesis function and breakdown of lipids in health and diseases. *Mailing Add:* Eunice Kennedy Shriver Ctr Ment Retardation Inc Waltham MA 02254

JUNGAS, ROBERT LEANDO, b Mt Lake, Minn, Sept 25, 34; m 57. BIOCHEMISTRY, PHYSIOLOGY. *Educ:* St Olaf Col, BA, 56; Harvard Univ, PhD(biochem), 61. *Prof Exp:* Instr biochem, 63-65, assoc 65-68, asst prof biol chem, 68-71, assoc prof biol chem, Harvard Med Sch, 71-74; PROF PHYSIOL, UNIV CONN HEALTH CTR, 74- *Concurrent Pos:* USPHS training grant biochem, Harvard Med Sch, 60-63. *Mem:* Am Soc Biol Chemists; Biochem Soc. *Res:* Action of hormones on adipose tissue metabolism. *Mailing Add:* Dept of Physiol Univ Conn Health Ctr Farmington CT 06032

JUNGBAUER, MARY ANN, b Phoenix, Ariz, Aug 10, 34. INORGANIC CHEMISTRY. *Educ:* Immaculate Heart Col, BA, 57; Univ Notre Dame, MS, 61, PhD(inorg chem), 64. *Prof Exp:* Teacher, Pub Schs, 56-59; teaching & res asst chem, Univ Notre Dame, 59-63; instr chem, Immaculate Heart Col, 63-67; asst prof chem, Drew Univ, 67-69; adj assoc prof, 69-72, ASSOC PROF CHEM, BARRY COL, 72-, CHMN, DEPT PHYS SCI, 80- *Mem:* Am Chem Soc; Sigma Xi. *Mailing Add:* 704 Jeronimo Dr Coral Gables FL 33146

JUNGCK, GERALD FREDERICK, b Dubuque, Iowa, Mar 1, 29; m 59; c 2. TOPOLOGY. *Educ:* Wartburg Col, BA, 56; Univ Wis, MA, 59; State Univ NY, Binghamton, PhD(math), 78. *Prof Exp:* Instr, 59-61, asst prof, 61-77, ASSOC PROF MATH, BRADLEY UNIV, 77- *Concurrent Pos:* NSF fac fel, Rutgers Univ, 68. *Mem:* Math Asn Am. *Res:* Fixed point theorems for commuting mappings on metric spaces; local homeomorphisms. *Mailing Add:* Dept of Math Bradley Univ Peoria IL 61625

JUNGCLAUS, GREGORY ALAN, b Yankton, SDak, Dec 16, 47; m 66; c 2. ANALYTICAL CHEMISTRY, ENVIRONMENTAL CHEMISTRY. *Educ:* Univ SDak, BA, 70, MA, 72; Ariz State Univ, PhD(chem), 75. *Prof Exp:* Res assoc chem, Mass Inst Technol, 75-77; sr res scientist, Ford Motor Co, 77-78; res chemist, Battelle Columbus Labs, 78-81; SR CHEMIST, MIDWEST RES INST, 81- *Mem:* Am Chem Soc; Am Soc Mass Spectrom; Meteoritical Soc; Sigma Xi. *Res:* Technical direction of projects concerning analytical method development and application; agent demilitarization and installation restoration; gas chromatographic mass spectrometry. *Mailing Add:* 425 Volker Blvd Midwest Res Inst Kansas City MO 64110

JUNGE, DOUGLAS, b Milwaukee, Wis, Jan 16, 38; m 60; c 2. NEUROPHYSIOLOGY. *Educ:* Calif Inst Technol, BS, 59; Univ Calif, Los Angeles, PhD(physiol), 65. *Prof Exp:* Asst res zoologist, Scripps Inst Oceanog, 65-67; asst prof, 67-73, assoc prof, 73-79, PROF ORAL BIOL, SCH DENT, UNIV CALIF, LOS ANGELES, 79- *Concurrent Pos:* NIH grant, 68-71 & contract, 69-71; NSF grant, 72-74; ed, J Theoret Neurobiol, 81- *Mem:* Am Physiol Soc; Biophys Soc; Soc Neurosci. *Res:* Electrophysiology of excitable membranes; ionic properties of nerve; receptor mechanisms in sensory systems, especially gustatory. *Mailing Add:* Dept of Oral Biol Univ of Calif Sch of Dent Los Angeles CA 90024

JUNGER, MIGUEL C(HAPERO), b Dresden, Ger, Jan 29, 23; nat US; m 46; c 2. ACOUSTICS, APPLIED MECHANICS. *Educ:* Mass Inst Technol, BS, 44, MS, 46; Harvard Univ, ScD(appl mech), 51. *Prof Exp:* res fel, Harvard Univ, 51-55; partner, 55-59, PRES, CAMBRIDGE ACOUSTICAL ASSOCS, 59- *Concurrent Pos:* Sr vis lectr, Mass Inst Technol, 68-78; vis prof, Compiegne Technol Univ, France 75 & 77-81; consult, Off Naval Res, London, 75. *Mem:* Fel Acoust Soc Am; fel Am Soc Mech Engr; Am Acad Mech. *Res:* Physical acoustics, particularly underwater sound; dynamics of elastic systems in an acoustic medium; noise control; mechanical vibrations and shock. *Mailing Add:* Cambridge Acoust Assocs Inc 54 Rindge Ave Ext Cambridge MA 02140

JUNGERMAN, JOHN (ALBERT), b Modesto, Calif, Dec 28, 21. PHYSICS. *Educ:* Univ Calif, AB, 43, PhD(physics), 49. *Prof Exp:* Asst physics, Univ Calif, 43-44, res physicist, Radiation Lab, 44-45, Los Alamos Sci Lab, 45-46 & Lawrence Berkeley Lab, 46-49; fel, AEC, Cornell Univ, 49-50; res physicist, Lawrence Berkeley Lab, Univ Calif, 50-51; res physicist, 51-69, dir, Crocker Nuclear Lab, 69-80, PROF PHYSICS, UNIV CALIF, DAVIS, 69- *Mem:* Fel Am Phys Soc. *Res:* Charged particle induced fission; beta ray spectroscopy; sector-focused cyclotrons; particle scattering; medical physics. *Mailing Add:* Dept of Physics Univ of Calif Davis CA 95616

JUNGERMANN, ERIC, b Mainz, Ger, Sept 8, 23; US citizen; m 51; c 1. SURFACE ACTIVE AGENTS, ANTIMICROBIAL AGENTS. *Educ:* City Col New York, BS, 49; Polytech Inst Brooklyn, MS, 53, PhD(org chem), 57. *Prof Exp:* Res chemist, Colgate-Palmolive Co, 46-57; sect head chem synthesis, Armour Indust Chem Co, 57-59, mgr surfactant res, Soap Div, 59-65, dir household res & develop, Armour & Co, 65-71, vpres res & develop, Armour Dial Inc, 71-75; Dir corp develop, Helene Curtis Indust, 75-78; PRES, JUNGERMANN ASSOCS, INC, 78- *Concurrent Pos:* Assoc ed, J Am Oil Chemists Soc; mem sci adv bd, Lowes Corp, 79-; mem bd dirs, Lee Pharmaceut Corp, 79- *Mem:* Am Oil Chemists' Soc; Soc Cosmetic Chemists; Am Chem Soc. *Res:* Soap, detergent and cosmetic technology, both from the fundamental and practical viewpoint; fat based surfactants; fatty acid derivatives; soaps; hair and skin care products; antimicrobials; organophosphorus compounds. *Mailing Add:* 2323 N Central Ave Suite 1001 Phoenix AZ 85004

JUNGKIND, DONALD LEE, b Washington, DC, Apr 16, 43; m 65; c 3. MEDICAL MICROBIOLOGY, MICROBIAL PHYSIOLOGY. *Educ:* Lamar State Univ, BS, 65; Univ Houston, MS, 68; Univ Tex Med Br Galveston, PhD(microbiol), 72. *Prof Exp:* Fel clin microbiol, Sch Med, Temple Univ, 72-73; asst prof, 73-81, ASSOC PROF PATH & MICROBIOL, SCH MED, THOMAS JEFFERSON UNIV, 81-, DIR, CLIN MICROBIOL LAB, 73- *Concurrent Pos:* Pres, Microbiol Consult, Inc, 78- *Mem:* Am Soc Microbiol; Am Soc Clin Path; Asn Clin Scientists. *Res:* Diagnostic microbiology and immunology with emphasis on automation of procedures; microbial physiology and effects of antimicrobial agents on cells. *Mailing Add:* Clin Microbiol Lab Thomas Jefferson Univ Hosp Philadelphia PA 19107

JUNGMANN, RICHARD A, b Volklingen, Switz, Oct 29, 28; nat US; m 61. BIOCHEMISTRY, ORGANIC CHEMISTRY. *Educ:* Univ Saarland, 48-50; Univ Basel, PhD, 58. *Prof Exp:* Res staff mem biochem, Worcester Found Exp Biol, Mass, 58-59; dir org res, McGean Chem Co, Ohio, 59-63; res assoc, 63-68, from asst prof to assoc prof biochem, 68-74, PROF BIOCHEM, MED SCH, NORTHWESTERN UNIV, 74-, PROF MOLECULAR BIOL, 80- *Concurrent Pos:* Lectr, Cleveland State Univ, 60-63; sr res investr biochem, Dept Res, Chicago Wesley Mem Hosp, 63-68; consult, McGean Chem Co, 63-64, dept med, Med Sch, Northwestern Univ, 65- *Mem:* AAAS; Am Chem Soc; fel Am Inst Chem; Swiss Chem Soc; Endocrine Soc. *Res:* Mechanism of action of hormones; regulation of nucleoprotein metabolism and gene expression. *Mailing Add:* 3122 Isabella St Evanston IL 60201

JUNGREIS, ARTHUR MARTIN, zoology, deceased

JUNI, ELLIOT, b NY, Aug 6, 21; m 44; c 2. BACTERIAL PHYSIOLOGY. *Educ:* City Col New York, BEE, 44; Western Reserve Univ, PhD(microbiol), 51. *Prof Exp:* Asst prof bact, Univ Ill, 51-56; from assoc prof to prof, Sch Med, Emory Univ, 56-66; PROF BACT, MED SCH, UNIV MICH, ANN ARBOR, 66- *Mem:* AAAS; Am Soc Microbiol; Am Soc Biol Chem. *Res:* Bacterial metabolism. *Mailing Add:* Dept of Microbiol Univ of Mich Med Sch Ann Arbor MI 48109

JUNIPER, KERRISON, JR, b St Petersburg, Fla, Aug 3, 24; m 43; c 2. MEDICINE. *Educ:* Emory Univ, MD, 49; Am Bd Internal Med, dipl; Am Bd Gastroenterol, dipl; Am Bd Microbiol, cert pub health & med lab parasitol, 68. *Prof Exp:* Asst med, Boston Univ, 54-56; from asst prof to prof med, Med Ctr, Univ Ark, Little Rock, 56-73, chief gastrointestinal sect, 56-70, dir postgrad training prog in gastroenterol, 56-71, dir off biomed commun, 69-70; PROF MED, SCH MED & CHIEF, GASTROINTESTINAL DIV, SOUTHERN ILL UNIV, 73- *Concurrent Pos:* USPHS fel gastroenterol, Mass Mem Hosps, 54-56; attend med, Vet Admin Hosp, Little Rock, 56-62; consult, 62-; coordr, Technol Res Med Educ, 70-; assoc dir, Continuing Educ Prog Physicians, 70-; vis prof internal med, Nat Defense Med Ctr, Taipei, 71-72; vis lectr, Trop Med Course, Walter Reed Army Inst Res, Washington, DC. *Mem:* AAAS; Am Fedn Clin Res; fel Am Col Physicians; Am Gastroenterol Asn; Am Soc Trop Med & Hyg. *Res:* Gastroenterology; gallstone formation and amebiasis; self-instructional audio visual units. *Mailing Add:* Dept of Med Southern Ill Univ Sch of Med Springfield IL 62708

JUNK, WILLIAM A(RTHUR), JR, b Uniontown, Pa, Mar 12, 24; m 56; c 2. CHEMICAL ENGINEERING. *Educ:* Pa State Col, BS, 48; Univ Ill, MS, 50, PhD(chem eng), 52. *Prof Exp:* CHEM ENGR, STANDARD OIL CO, 52- *Mem:* Am Chem Soc. *Res:* Physical properties of hydrocarbons; separation processes. *Mailing Add:* 18344 Aberdeen Ave Homewood IL 60430

JUNKER, BOBBY RAY, b San Antonio, Tex, Aug 29, 43. ATOMIC PHYSICS. *Educ:* Univ Southwestern La, BS, 65; Univ Tex, Austin, MA, 67, PhD(chem), 69. *Prof Exp:* Instr chem, Univ Tex, Austin, 69-70; res assoc physics, Univ Pittsburgh, 70-72; asst prof physics, Univ Ga, 72-76; PHYSICIST, OFF NAVAL RES, 77- *Mem:* Am Phys Soc. *Res:* Theoretical atomic physics, including electron-atom and ion-atom collisions. *Mailing Add:* Off Naval Res Code 412 800 N Quincy St Arlington VA 22217

JUNKHAN, GEORGE H, b Peoria, Ill, Jan 30, 29; m 56; c 2. MECHANICAL ENGINEERING. *Educ:* Iowa State Univ, BS, 55, MS, 59, PhD(mech eng, appl mech), 64. *Prof Exp:* From instr to asst prof, 57-66, ASSOC PROF MECH ENG, IOWA STATE UNIV, 66- *Mem:* Am Soc Mech Engrs; Am Soc Eng Educ. *Res:* Heat transfer and fluid mechanics, particularly testing of turbomachinery and experimental heat transfer. *Mailing Add:* Dept of Mech Eng Iowa State Univ Ames IA 50010

JUNKINS, DAVID R, b US citizen. ENGINEERING. *Educ:* Purdue Univ, BS, 68, MS, 73; Am Acad Environ Engrs, dipl. *Prof Exp:* MEM STAFF, ROY WESTON INC, 73- *Mem:* Am Soc Civil Engrs. *Res:* Evaluation and concept design for industrial wastewater treatment systems. *Mailing Add:* Roy Weston Inc Weston Way West Chester PA 19380

JUNKINS, JOHN LEE, b Carters, Ga, May 23, 43; m 65; c 2. AEROSPACE ENGINEERING, APPLIED MATHEMATICS. *Educ:* Auburn Univ, BSAE, 65; Univ Calif, Los Angeles, MS, 67, PhD(eng), 69. *Prof Exp:* Aerospace engr, NASA, 61-65; engr & scientist aerospace eng, McDonnell Douglas Astronaut Co, 65-69; assoc prof, Univ Va, 70-78; PROF ENG MECH, VA POLYTECH INST, 78- *Concurrent Pos:* Consult, US Naval Surface Weapons Labs, 70-73, US Army Topog Maps Command, 71-74, Univ Space Res Asn, 75-76, US Engr Topog Lab, 77-, US Defense Mapping Agency, 77-, Univ Va, 78-; assoc ed, J Astronaut Sci, 77- *Mem:* Am Inst Aeronaut & Astronaut; Am Geophys Union; Am Astronaut Soc; Am Soc Photogram. *Res:* Satellite dynamics and control; mathematical modeling of dynamical systems; geophysics; remote sensing. *Mailing Add:* Dept of Eng Sci & Mech Va Polytech Inst & State Univ Blacksburg VA 24061

JUO, PEI-SHOW, b Shantung, China, Feb 6, 30; m 65. BIOCHEMISTRY, MOLECULAR BIOLOGY. *Educ:* Taiwan Prov Chung Hsing Univ, BS, 57; Univ Toronto, MS, 63; Univ NH, PhD(virol), 66. *Prof Exp:* Res biochemist, Kitchawan Res Lab, 66-67 & Gulf South Res Inst, 67-68; assoc prof, 68-74, PROF BIOL, STATE UNIV NY COL, POTSDAM, 74- *Mem:* AAAS; Am Soc Microbiol. *Res:* Purification and characterization of proteins and other macromolecules; immunological and electrophoretic analysis of protein antigens. *Mailing Add:* Dept of Biol State Univ of N Y Potsdam NY 13676

JUOLA, ROBERT C, b Astoria, Ore, Aug 8, 40; m 63; c 2. STATISTICS, MATHEMATICS. *Educ:* Univ Ore, BS, 62; Mich State Univ, MS, 64, PhD(statist), 68. *Prof Exp:* Res engr, Boeing Co, 64-66; asst prof math, Univ Tex, Austin, 68-70; assoc chmn dept, 70-77, PROF MATH, BOISE STATE UNIV, 70- *Mem:* AAAS; Inst Math Statist; Am Statist Asn. *Res:* Design of experiments; sequential experimentation. *Mailing Add:* Dept of Math Boise State Univ Boise ID 83725

JUORIO, AUGUSTO VICTOR, b Buenos Aires, Arg, July 13, 34; m 61; c 2. NEUROPHARMACOLOGY. *Educ:* Univ Buenos Aires, BSP, 58, BSc, 61, PhD(pharmacol), 67. *Prof Exp:* Demonstr pharmacol, Fac Pharm Biochem, Univ Buenos Aires, 59-63; res fel, Inst Animal Physiol, Babraham, Cambridge, Eng, 63-66; asst prof, Fac Pharm Biochem, Univ Buenos Aires, 66-68; res fel Univ Col, Univ London, 68-73; res pharmacologist, 73-77, HEAD BASIC STUDIES, PSYCHIAT RES DIV, UNIV HOSP, SASKATOON, SASK, 77- *Mem:* Am Soc Pharmacol & Exp Therapeut; Brit Pharmacol Soc; Int Soc Neurochem. *Res:* Investigation of the phylogenetic evolution of neurotransmitters and the mechanism of action of drugs used to alleviate abnormal mental conditions. *Mailing Add:* Psychiat Res Div Rm 508A Univ Hosp Saskatoon SK S7N 0X0 Can

JUPNIK, HELEN, b Kenosha, Wis, Sept 30, 15. OPTICS. *Educ:* Univ Wis, BA & MA, 37; Univ Rochester, PhD(physics), 40. *Prof Exp:* Asst physics, Univ Wis, 37; asst instr, Univ Rochester, 37-40; Huff fel, Bryn Mawr Col, 40-41, Berliner res docentship fel, 41-42; asst, Princeton Univ, 42; physicist, Nat Res Corp, 42-43; res physicist, Am Optical Co, 43-48, sr res physicist, 48-58, supvr thin films, 58-59, chief physicist, 59-65, mgr thin film develop, 65-67, MGR THIN FILM TECH, SCI INSTRUMENT DIV, AM OPTICAL CORP, 67- *Mem:* Am Phys Soc; fel Optical Soc Am; Am Vacuum Soc; NY Acad Sci. *Res:* Physical optics; evaporation and properties of thin films; microscopy. *Mailing Add:* Am Optical Sci Instrument Div PO Box 123 Buffalo NY 14240

JURA, GEORGE, b New York, NY, Nov 18, 11; c 3. PHYSICAL CHEMISTRY. *Educ:* Ill Inst Technol, BS, 39; Univ Chicago, PhD, 42. *Prof Exp:* Res assoc chem, Univ Chicago, 42-46; from asst prof to assoc prof chem, Univ Calif, Berkeley, 46-53, prof, 53-80. *Concurrent Pos:* Guggenheim fel, 55. *Res:* Electric and magnetic properties of solids at high pressures and the surfaces of solids. *Mailing Add:* 36 Arlington Ave Kensington CA 94707

JURA, MICHAEL ALAN, b Oakland, Calif, Sept 11, 47; m 74; c 1. ASTROPHYSICS. *Educ:* Univ Calif, Berkeley, BA, 67; Harvard Univ, MA, 69, PhD(astron), 71. *Prof Exp:* Res assoc astron, Goddard Space Flight Ctr, NASA, 71 & Princeton Univ Observ, 73-74; asst prof, 74-77, assoc prof, 77-81, PROF ASTRON, UNIV CALIF, LOS ANGELES, 81- *Concurrent Pos:* Alfred P Sloan Found fel, 77-79. *Mem:* Int Astron Union; Am Astron Soc. *Res:* Physics of the interstellar medium and problems in star formation. *Mailing Add:* Dept of Astron Univ of Calif Los Angeles CA 90024

JURAND, JERRY GEORGE, b Gostyn, Poland, Apr 23, 23; US citizen; m 50; c 3. IMMUNOLOGY, PERIODONTOLOGY. *Educ:* Univ Erlangen, DMD, 56; Univ Tenn, Memphis, DDS, 65. *Prof Exp:* Cancer res scientist, Roswell Park Mem Inst, 58-62; res assoc immunol, St Jude Childrens Res Hosp, Memphis, 62-65; assoc prof, 65-70, PROF PERIODONT, COL DENT, UNIV TENN, MEMPHIS, 70- *Concurrent Pos:* Consult, St Jude Childrens Res Hosp, 65- *Mem:* AAAS; NY Acad Sci; Int Asn Dent Res; Am Dent Asn. *Res:* Immunohistochemical identification and localization of antibodies in human and in animal tissues; tumor immunology; role of immunological reactions in etiology of periodontal disease; growth factors in oro-facial development. *Mailing Add:* Col of Dent Univ of Tenn Memphis TN 38163

JURASEK, LUBOMIR, b Uzhorod, Czech, June 2, 31; m 57; c 3. PROTEIN CHEMISTRY, MICROBIOLOGY. *Educ:* Purkyne Univ Brno, MSc, 54, PhD(biol), 63. *Prof Exp:* Res officer mycol, State Forest Prod Res Inst, Bratislava, Czech, 54-64; fel enzymol, Nat Res Coun Can, 64-66; res scientist microbiol, State Forest Prod Res Inst, 66-68; res assoc protein chem, Univ Alta, Edmonton, 68-75; RES SCIENTIST MICROBIOL, PULP & PAPER RES INST CAN, 75- *Concurrent Pos:* Lectr, Dept Biochem, Univ Alta, 73-75. *Mem:* Am Soc Microbiol; Soc Indust Microbiol; Am Chem Soc; Can

Biochem Soc; Tech Asn Pulp & Paper Indust. *Res:* Molecular mechanism of biological degradation of cellulose, hemicelluloses and lignin; structure and function of cellulases and their production by microorganisms; pulp and paper biotechnology. *Mailing Add:* Pulp & Paper Res Inst of Can 570 St John's Blvd Pointe Claire PQ H9R 3J9 Can

JURASKA, JANICE MARIE, b Berwyn, Ill, Feb 9, 49. NEUROSCIENCE, BIOPSYCHOLOGY. *Educ:* Lawrence Univ, BA, 71; Univ Ill, Champaign, MA, 75; Univ Colo, PhD(biopychol), 77. *Prof Exp:* NIMH fel, Dept Psychol, Univ Ill, 78-79; ASST PROF BIOPSYCHOL, DEPT PSYCHOL, IND UNIV, 80- *Mem:* AAAS; Int Soc Develop Psychobiol; Soc Neurosci. *Res:* Plasticity and development of the nervous system (anatomy) and of behavior. *Mailing Add:* Dept Psychol Ind Univ Bloomington IN 47405

JURCH, GEORGE RICHARD, JR, b New Britain, Conn, Feb 1, 34; m 61; c 3. PHYSICAL ORGANIC CHEMISTRY. *Educ:* Univ Fla, BS, 57; Univ Ky, MS, 61; Univ Calif, San Diego, PhD(chem), 65. *Prof Exp:* Res chemist, IBM Corp, Ky, 61; NIH fel chem, Yale Univ, 65-66; res assoc, 66; asst prof, 66-71, assoc prof, 71-80, PROF CHEM, UNIV SOUTH FLA, 80- *Mem:* Am Chem Soc. *Res:* Radical-cation intermediates; free radicals; sulfur chemistry, nonaqueous solvent interactions with biological systems; nuclear magnetic resonance conformation studies. *Mailing Add:* Dept of Chem Univ of SFla Tampa FL 33620

JURD, LEONARD, b Sydney, Australia, Dec 3, 25; US citizen; m 61; c 2. CHEMISTRY. *Educ:* Univ Sydney, BSc, 47; Univ Nottingham, England, PhD(org chem), 53. *Hon Degrees:* DSc, Univ Sydney, 71. *Prof Exp:* Res chemist, 59-70, RES LEADER NAT PROD CHEM, AGR RES SERV, USDA, 70- *Honors & Awards:* Agr Chem Award, Am Chem Soc, 77. *Mem:* Phytochem Soc NAm, (pres, 62); Am Chem Soc. *Res:* Isolation and structure of biologically active plant products. *Mailing Add:* 800 Buchanan St Albany CA 94710

JURECIC, ANTON, b Mrasevo, Yugoslavia, Sept 21, 22; US citizen; m 59; c 3. DENTAL RESEARCH. *Educ:* Univ NC, BS, 53; State Univ NY Col Forestry, MS, 57. *Prof Exp:* Res chemist, Int Paper Co, 57-60 & Borden Inc, 60-67; SR RES CHEMIST, SS WHITE DIV, PENNWALT CORP, 67- *Mem:* Am Chem Soc; Int Asn Dent Res. *Res:* Dental materials; adhesion. *Mailing Add:* 237 Fairview Rd Springfield PA 19064

JURETSCHKE, HELLMUT JOSEPH, b Berlin, Ger, Aug 9, 24; nat US; m 50; c 2. SOLID STATE PHYSICS. *Educ:* Harvard Univ, BA, 44, MA, 47, PhD(physics), 50. *Prof Exp:* From instr to assoc prof, 50-59, actg head dept, 65-66, head dept, 66-77, PROF PHYSICS, POLYTECH INST NEW YORK, 59- *Mem:* Fel Am Phys Soc; Am Asn Physics Teachers. *Res:* Surface properties of metals; electronic structure of metals. *Mailing Add:* Dept of Physics Polytech Inst of New York Brooklyn NY 11201

JUREWICZ, ANTHONY THEODORE, b Chicago, Ill, July 30, 41; m 66; c 3. ORGANIC CHEMISTRY. *Educ:* St Mary's Col, Minn, BA, 63; Case Inst Technol, PhD(org chem), 67. *Prof Exp:* sr res chemist, 67-77, plannning mgr, 77-80, PHOSPHORUS DIV PLANNING MGR, MOBIL CHEM CO, MOBIL OIL CORP, 80- *Honors & Awards:* Am Chemists's Sr Award, 63. *Mem:* Am Chem Soc; NY Acad Sci. *Res:* Diazodization of aliphatic and cyclic amines in aprotic media and the catalytic oxidation of organic compounds. *Mailing Add:* Phosphorus Div Mobil Chem Co PO Box 26683 Richmond VA 23261

JURF, AMIN N, b Syria, Dec 3, 32; US citizen; m 58; c 3. PHYSIOLOGY. *Educ:* Western Md Col, BA, 59; Univ Md, PhD(physiol), 66. *Prof Exp:* Res scientist, 61-66, from instr to asst prof, 66-74, assoc prof renal physiol, 74-76, ASST PROF PHYSIOL, UNIV MD, BALTIMORE CITY, 76- *Res:* Neuro-renal physiology; salt and water metabolism. *Mailing Add:* Dept of Physiol Univ of Md Sch of Med Baltimore MD 21201

JURGELSKI, WILLIAM, JR, b Englishtown, NJ, May 25, 31; m 54; c 2. EXPERIMENTAL CARCINOGENESIS, TOXICOLOGY. *Educ:* Rutgers Univ, BS, 53, MS, 55, PhD(genetics), 58. *Prof Exp:* Geneticist, Fed Exp Sta in PR, Agr Res Serv, USDA, 57-60; pharmacologist, Food & Drug Admin, 60-63; res assoc path, Med Ctr, Duke Univ, 63-67, intern, 67-68; MED OFFICER, NAT INST ENVIRON HEALTH SCI, 68- *Concurrent Pos:* Fel neuropath, Duke Univ, 67-68. *Mem:* AAAS; Am Asn Pathologists; Am Asn Cancer Res. *Res:* Carcinogenesis and and pediatric cancer; the marsupial as an experimental animal. *Mailing Add:* Off Health Hazard Assessment Nat Inst of Environ Health Sci Research Triangle Park NC 27709

JURGENSEN, DELBERT F(REDERICK), JR, b St Paul, Minn, Mar 31, 09; m 28; c 3. CHEMICAL ENGINEERING. *Educ:* Univ Minn, BChE, 31, MS, 32, PhD(chem eng), 34. *Prof Exp:* Chemist, Pure Oil Co, 34-35; res supvr, US Gypsum Co, 35-42; chief engr, Chem Warfare Serv Develop Lab, Mass Inst Technol, 42-45; dir chem res & develop dept & chief engr, Spec Projs Dept, Am Mach & Foundry Co, NY, 45-52, spec asst to vpres, 52-56; vpres develop & res, Blaw-Knox Co, 56-60; CONSULT MGT ENGR, 64- *Mem:* Am Chem Soc; Asn Res Dirs; Am Inst Chemists; Am Inst Chem Engrs. *Res:* Technical administration; heat transfer; development of equipment and processes for industrial promotion; commercial development and research and development administration; chemical process industries. *Mailing Add:* 2700 Coral Springs Dr Coral Springs FL 33065

JURICA, GERALD MICHAEL, b Detroit, Mich, Sept 24, 41; m 78; c 3. ATMOSPHERIC PHYSICS. *Educ:* Univ Detroit, BEE, 63; Univ Ariz, MS, 66, PhD(atmospheric sci), 70. *Prof Exp:* Res assoc, Univ Ariz, 67-70; asst prof, Purdue Univ, 70-75; ASSOC PROF ATMOSPHERIC SCI, TEX TECH UNIV, 75- *Mem:* Am Meteorol Soc. *Res:* Satellite meteorology; cloud physical processes. *Mailing Add:* Atomosheric Sci Group Tex Tech Univ PO Box 4320 Lubbock TX 79409

JURICEK, DIANE KATHRYN, b Ft Benning, Ga, Feb 29, 44; c 2. GENETICS, CELL BIOLOGY. *Educ:* Emory Univ, BS, 69, PhD(biol), 73; Southern Conn State Col, MS, 80. *Prof Exp:* Vis instr genetics, Emory Univ, 74-75; fel DNA biochem, Yale Univ, 75-77, res assoc somatic cell genetics, 77-80; ASST PROF, EMORY UNIV, 80- *Concurrent Pos:* Am Cancer Soc Fel, Yale Univ, 76-77, fel NIH grant, 75-76; NSF grant, Emory Univ, 69-72; mem, Fertile & Gamete Physiol Training Prog, Marine Biol Lab, 74. *Mem:* Sigma Xi; Am Soc Cell Biol; Am Women Sci. *Res:* Cytogenetics; somatic cell genetics; chromosome structure; human genetics; virus-chromosome interactions; gene transfer; DNA biochemistry. *Mailing Add:* Dept Biol Emory Univ Atlanta GA 30322

JURICIC, DAVOR, b Split, Yugoslavia, Aug 2, 28; m 53; c 1. MECHANICAL SYSTEMS DESIGN, COMPUTER AIDED DESIGN. *Educ:* Univ Belgrade, BSc, 52, DSc, 64. *Prof Exp:* Analyst aircraft struct, Icarus-Belgrade, Yugoslavia, 53-58; res fel aeroelasticity, Inst Aeronaut, Zarkovo-Belgrade, 58-63; from asst prof to assoc prof aeronaut eng, Univ Belgrade, 63-68; from assoc prof to prof mech eng, SDak State Univ, 68-75; vis prof appl mech, Stanford Univ, 75-78; PROF MECH ENG, UNIV TEX, AUSTIN, 78- *Concurrent Pos:* Consult, Elec Power Res Inst, Palo Alto, Flow Res, Inc, Kent, Wash, 76-, Southern Res Inst, Birmingham, Joy Mfg Co, Los Angeles & Dresser Industs, Houston, 78- *Mem:* Am Soc Eng Educ; Ger Soc Appl Math & Mech; Am Soc Mech Engrs; Sigma Xi. *Res:* Aircraft vibration and flutter; dynamics of railway vehicles; dynamics and stability of bipedal locomotion; modeling and simulation of dynamic systems; mechanical systems design; electrostatic precipitators. *Mailing Add:* Dept of Mech Eng Univ of Tex Austin TX 78712

JURINAK, JEROME JOSEPH, b Cleveland, Ohio, June 3, 27; m 54; c 4. SOIL CHEMISTRY. *Educ:* Colo State Univ, BS, 51; Utah State Univ, MS, 54, PhD(soil chem), 56. *Prof Exp:* Jr soil chemist, Univ Calif, Davis, 56-58, from asst to assoc soil chemist, 58-67; PROF SOIL CHEM, UTAH STATE UNIV, 67-, DEPT HEAD, 78- *Concurrent Pos:* Danforth teaching fel; Consult, USAID, UNESCO, Orgn Am States & private indust; vis prof, Rural Univ Rio de Janeiro, Brazil, 75, 77. *Mem:* Fel Am Soc Agron; fel Soil Sci Soc Am; Int Soc Soil Sci; fel Am Inst Chem; Coun Agr Sci Technol. *Res:* Reclamation of disturbed soils and geologic material; heavy metal chemistry and transport in soils; salt-affected soils; irrigation and return flow water quality; surface chemistry. *Mailing Add:* Dept of Soil Sci and Biometeorol Utah State Univ Logan UT 84322

JURINSKI, NEIL B(ERNARD), b Peekskill, NY, Oct 28, 38; m 62; c 3. INDUSTRIAL HYGIENE, ENVIRONMENTAL CHEMISTRY. *Educ:* State Univ NY, Albany, BS, 60; Univ Miss, PhD(phys chem), 63; Am Bd Indust Hyg, cert, 74. *Prof Exp:* Res assoc chem, Mich State Univ, 63-64; asst prof, Boston Col, 64-69; res scientist, Chem Div, J M Huber Corp, 69-72; environ chemist, US Army Environ Hyg Agency, 72-76; sr indust hygienist, SRI Int, 76-77; indust hygienist, Tracor Jitco, Inc, 77-80; PRES, NUCHEM CO, INC, 75- *Concurrent Pos:* Consult, 70- *Mem:* Am Indust Hyg Asn; Am Acad Indust Hyg; Am Chem Soc; The Chem Soc; Int Hazard Control Mgt Asn. *Res:* Industrial hygiene surveys and consultation; hazardous and toxic chemical problems; waste disposal and processing; carcinogen/mutagen safety; environmental sampling and analysis; material handling and processing. *Mailing Add:* 9321 Raintree Rd Burke VA 22015

JURIST, JOHN MICHAEL, biophysics, see previous edition

JURKAT, MARTIN PETER, b Berlin, Ger, July 23, 35; m 58; c 3. MANAGEMENT SCIENCE, MATHEMATICS. *Educ:* Swarthmore Col, BA, 57; Univ NC, MA, 60; Stevens Inst Technol, PhD(math), 72. *Prof Exp:* Statistician, Marketer's Res Serv, Inc, 59-60; asst engr, Res Lab, Burroughs Corp, 60-61; sr systs analyst, ITT Info Systs Div, 61-64; staff scientist, Davidson Lab, 64-76, dir, Ctr Munic Studies & Servs, 76-78, prof, 78-80, ALEXANDER CROMBIC HUMPHREYS PROF MGT SCI, STEVENS INST TECHNOL, 80- *Concurrent Pos:* Consult, Tank Automotive Command, US Army. *Mem:* Opers Res Soc Am; Soc Indust & Appl Math; Sigma Xi. *Res:* Mathematical modelling; simulation; off-road vehicle design and modelling; computer graphics; transportation systems; operations research. *Mailing Add:* Dept Mgt Sci Syst Inst Tech Castle Point Sta Hoboken NJ 07030

JURKAT, WOLFGANG BERNHARD, b Gerdauen, Ger, Mar 26, 29. MATHEMATICAL ANALYSIS. *Educ:* Univ Tübingen, PhD(math), 50. *Prof Exp:* Asst math, Univ Tübingen, 50-52, dozent, 52-54; assoc prof, Univ Cincinnati, 54-56 & Ohio State Univ, 56-57; assoc prof, 57-58, JOHN RAYMOND FRENCH PROF MATH, SYRACUSE UNIV, 58- *Mem:* Am Math Soc; Ger Math Soc. *Res:* Analysis, particularly summability, Fourier series, analytic number theory, also combinatories and probability. *Mailing Add:* Dept of Math Syracuse Univ Syracuse NY 13210

JURKIEWICZ, MAURICE J, b Claremont, NH, Sept 24, 24; m 51; c 2. SURGERY. *Educ:* Univ Md, DDS, 46; Harvard Univ, MD, 52. *Prof Exp:* Instr surg, Sch Med, Washington Univ, 57-59; from asst prof to prof surg, Col Med, Univ Fla, 59-73, chief plastic surg, 64-73; PROF SURG, SCH MED, EMORY UNIV, 73- *Concurrent Pos:* Clin fel plastic surg, Barnes Hosp, St Louis, Mo, 58-59; mem bd sci counr, Nat Inst Dent Res, 66-71; chief surg serv, Vet Admin Hosp, Gainesville, 68-73; lectr & consult, Naval Hosp, Orlando, 69-70; consult plastic surg, Walter Reed Hosp, Washington, DC, 70- *Mem:* AAAS; Am Col Surg; AMA; Am Soc Plastic & Reconstruct Surg; Plastic Surg Res Coun. *Res:* Wound healing; congenital malformations; general and reconstructive surgery; head and neck surgery. *Mailing Add:* Dept of Surg Emory Univ Sch of Med Atlanta GA 30322

JURKUS, ALGIRDAS PETRAS, b Klaipeda, Lithuania, June 11, 35; Can citizen. ELECTRONICS. *Educ:* Univ Montreal, BASc, 57; Univ Sheffield, PhD(elec eng), 60. *Prof Exp:* RES SCIENTIST ELECTRONICS, NAT RES COUN CAN, 60- *Mem:* Inst Elec & Electronics Engrs. *Res:* Establishment and maintenance of primary national standards and development of precise methods of measurement, at high and microwave frequencies, of various electromagnetic quantities. *Mailing Add:* Div of Physics Nat Res Coun Ottawa ON K1A 0S1 Can

JURMAIN, ROBERT DOUGLAS, b Worcester, Mass, July 20, 48; m 74. PHYSICAL ANTHROPOLOGY. *Educ:* Univ Calif, Los Angeles, AB, 70; Harvard Univ, PhD(anthrop), 75. *Prof Exp:* asst prof, 75-79, ASSOC PROF ANTHROP, SAN JOSE STATE UNIV, 79- *Mem:* Am Asn Phys Anthropologists. *Res:* Paleopathology of prehistoric human osteological remains; comparative biomechanical studies of primate limb skeletons; paeloanthropological research of early hominids in East Africa. *Mailing Add:* Dept of Anthrop San Jose State Univ San Jose CA 95192

JURS, PETER CHRISTIAN, b Oakland, Calif, Apr 13, 43; m 67; c 3. ANALYTICAL CHEMISTRY. *Educ:* Stanford Univ, BS, 65; Univ Wash, PhD(chem), 69. *Prof Exp:* from asst prof to assoc prof, 69-78, PROF CHEM, PA STATE UNIV, 78- *Mem:* Am Chem Soc. *Res:* Computer methods in analytical chemistry; structure-activity studies. *Mailing Add:* Dept of Chem Pa State Univ University Park PA 16802

JURSINIC, PAUL ANDREW, b Joliet, Ill, June 13, 46. BIOPHYSICS. *Educ:* Univ Ill, BS, 69, MS, 71, PhD(biophys), 77. *Prof Exp:* RES SCIENTIST PLANT PHYSIOL, NORTHERN REGIONAL RES CTR, USDA, 77- *Mem:* Am Soc Photobiol. *Res:* The photochemical reactions which make up the light reactions of green plant photosynthesis. *Mailing Add:* Northern Regional Res Ctr 1815 N University St Peoria IL 61604

JURTSHUK, PETER, JR, b New York, NY, July 28, 29; m 71; c 2. MICROBIAL PHYSIOLOGY, BIOCHEMISTRY. *Educ:* NY Univ, AB, 51; Creighton Univ, MS, 53; Univ Md, PhD(microbiol), 57. *Prof Exp:* Asst microbiol, Univ Md, 53-56; asst prof pharmacol, Brooklyn Col Pharm, 57-59; fel enzyme chem, Inst Enzyme Res, Univ Wis, 59-63; from asst prof to assoc prof, Univ Tex, Austin, 63-70; assoc prof, 70-76, undergrad chmn biol, 77-81, PROF BIOL, UNIV HOUSTON, 76- *Mem:* AAAS; fel Am Acad Microbiol; Am Soc Microbiol; Am Chem Soc; Am Soc Biol Chem. *Res:* Isolation and characterization of particulate oxidases and oxygenating enzyme complexes from microorganisms; aspects of the microbiological oxidase reaction relating to cellular bioenergetics; particulate enzyme complexes of microorganisms, specifically the cytochrome oxidases of bacterial electron transport systems. *Mailing Add:* Dept of Biol Univ of Houston Houston TX 77004

JURY, ELIAHU I(BRAHAM), b Bagdad, Iraq, May 23, 23; nat US; m 49; c 2. ELECTRICAL ENGINEERING. *Educ:* Israel Inst Technol, EE, 47; Harvard Univ, MS, 49; Columbia Univ, EngScD, 53. *Prof Exp:* From instr to assoc prof, 53-64, PROF ELEC ENG, UNIV CALIF, BERKELEY, 64- *Concurrent Pos:* Res engr, Columbia Univ, 53-54; consult, Bell Tel Labs, 56 & Convair Div, Gen Dynamics Corp, 57; vis lectr, Northwestern Univ, 57, Univ Mich, 58 & Univ Paris, 58-59. *Mem:* Sr mem Inst Elec & Electronics Engrs. *Res:* Sampled-data and discrete systems; automatic control; circuit theory; transform methods; information theory; digital and sampled-data control systems. *Mailing Add:* Dept of Elec Eng Univ of Calif Berkeley CA 94720

JURY, STANLEY H(ENRY MARTIN), b Appleton, Wis, Mar 3, 16; m 42; c 1. CHEMICAL ENGINEERING. *Educ:* Univ Cincinnati, ChemE, 42, PhD, 49; Univ Louisville, MS, 47. *Prof Exp:* Secy chem eng, Palocoat, Inc, 46; PROF CHEM ENG, UNIV TENN, KNOXVILLE, 49- *Concurrent Pos:* Consult, Wright Patterson AFB & Oak Ridge Nat Lab. *Mem:* Am Soc Eng Educ; Am Inst Chem Engrs. *Res:* Diffusional operations; thermal diffusion; heat transfer; birefringent flows and fluids; adsorption and ion exchange; machine computation and automatic control. *Mailing Add:* Dept of Chem & Metall Eng Univ of Tenn Knoxville TN 37916

JURY, WILLIAM AUSTIN, b Highland Park, Mich, Aug 8, 46; m 72. SOIL PHYSICS, ENVIRONMENTAL PHYSICS. *Educ:* Univ Mich, BS, 68; Univ Wis, MS, 70, PhD(physics), 73. *Prof Exp:* Proj assoc soil physics, Dept Soil Sci, Univ Wis, 73-74; asst prof, 74-78, ASSOC PROF SOIL PHYSICS, DEPT OF SOIL & ENVIRON SCI, UNIV CALIF, RIVERSIDE, 78- *Concurrent Pos:* Mem, Nat Comn, Nat Res Coun/Inst Ecol, 74-75; consult, Rockwell Hanford Oper, 76-79 & County of San Diego, 78-79. *Mem:* Am Soc Agron; Soil Sci Soc Am; Int Soil Sci Soc; Am Geophys Union. *Res:* Measurement and modeling of water, heat and chemical transport through and reactions in soil. *Mailing Add:* Dept of Soil & Environ Sci Univ Calif Riverside CA 92521

JUSKEVICE, JOHN ANTHONY, paleontology, marine zoology, see previous edition

JUSKO, WILLIAM JOSEPH, b Salamanca, NY, Oct 26, 42; m 64; c 3. PHARMACY. *Educ:* State Univ NY Buffalo, BS, 65, PhD(pharmaceut), 70. *Prof Exp:* Pharmacologist, Vet Admin Hosp, Boston, 70-72; assoc prof, 72-77, PROF PHARMACEUT, SCH PHARM, STATE UNIV NY BUFFALO, 77-; DIR, DIV CLIN PHARMACOL SCI, MILLARD FILLMORE HOSP, BUFFALO, 81- *Concurrent Pos:* Dir, Clin Pharmacokinetics Lab, Millard Fillmore Hosp, Buffalo, 72-81. *Mem:* Am Pharmaceut Asn; Acad Pharmaceut Sci; AAAS; Am Soc Clin Pharmacol & Therapeut; Am Soc Microbiol. *Res:* Clinical pharmacokinetics, chemotherapy; biopharmaceutics; drug analysis and pharmacodynamics. *Mailing Add:* Sch Pharm State Univ NY Buffalo Amherst NY 14260

JUST, GEORGE, b Kobe, Japan, May 17, 29; nat Can; m 55; c 3. ORGANIC CHEMISTRY. *Educ:* Swiss Fed Inst Technol, Ing Chim, 51; Univ Western Ont, PhD(chem), 56. *Prof Exp:* Res chemist, Univ Calif, Los Angeles, 56-57 & Monsanto Can, Ltd, 57-58; from asst prof to assoc prof, 58-70, PROF ORG CHEM, McGILL UNIV, 70- *Mem:* Am Chem Soc; fel Chem Inst Can. *Res:* Natural products synthesis. *Mailing Add:* Dept Chem McGill Univ Montreal PQ H3A 2K6 Can

JUST, JOHN JOSEF, b Botschar, Jugoslavia, Nov 17, 38; US citizen; m 65; c 3. DEVELOPMENTAL BIOLOGY, ENDOCRINOLOGY. *Educ:* DePaul Univ, Chicago, BS, 62, MS, 64; Univ Iowa, PhD(zool), 68. *Prof Exp:* Fel biochem, Fla State Univ, 68-70; asst prof biol, 70-74, ASSOC PROF BIOL, UNIV KY, 74- *Concurrent Pos:* Schmitt fel, Dept Zool, Univ Iowa, 63-64;

NIH fel, Dept Chem, Fla State Univ, 68-70; vis prof, Univ Bern, 76-77. *Mem:* AAAS; Am Zoologist; Sigma Xi. *Res:* Biochemical and morphological methods are used to study hormonal influence on development with particular emphasis on amphibian metamorphosis; physiological triggers for hatching of embryos. *Mailing Add:* Sch Biol Morgan Bldg Univ of Ky Lexington KY 40506

JUST, KURT W, b Oels, Ger, May 19, 27; m 53; c 3. THEORETICAL PHYSICS. *Educ:* Free Univ Berlin, Dr rer nat, 54, Dr habil, 58. *Prof Exp:* Asst physics, Free Univ Berlin, 50-60; assoc prof, 61-66, PROF PHYSICS, UNIV ARIZ, 66- *Concurrent Pos:* Sci counsr, Free Univ Berlin, 60-63; consult, Edgerton, Germeshausen & Grier, NY, 63-64. *Honors & Awards:* Essay Prize, Gravity Res Found, 65. *Mem:* Int Soc Gen Relativity & Gravitation. *Res:* Quantum field theory; quantized theory of gravity. *Mailing Add:* Dept of Physics Univ of Ariz Tucson AZ 85721

JUST, RICHARD, b Tulsa, Okla, Feb 18, 48; m 67; c 2. AGRICULTURE ECONOMICS. *Educ:* Okla State Univ, BS, 69; Univ Calif, Berkeley, MA, 71, PhD(agr economics), 72. *Prof Exp:* Comput programmer, Okla State Univ, 66-69, assoc prof agr economics, 72-75; PROF AGR ECONOMICS, UNIV CALIF, BERKELEY, 75- *Concurrent Pos:* Consult, World Bank, 76, US Gen Acct Off, 79 & Oak Ridge Nat Lab, 76. *Mem:* Am Econ Asn; Economet Soc; Am Agr Econ Asn; Western Agr Econ Asn. *Mailing Add:* 207 Giannini Hall Univ Calif Berkeley CA 94720

JUSTEN, LEWIS LEO, b Tampa, Fla, June 24, 51; m 71; c 2. PHYSICAL CHEMISTRY, ANALYTICAL CHEMISTRY. *Educ:* Univ SFla, BA, 72; Northwestern Univ, MS, 73, PhD(chem), 78. *Prof Exp:* RES CHEMIST COAL ANAL, EXXON RES & ENG CO, 77- *Mem:* Am Chem Soc. *Res:* Coal science relating to synthetic fuels; thermodynamics of liquids; optical properties of liquids; gas-liquid chromatography. *Mailing Add:* Exxon Res & Eng Co PO Box 4255 Baytown TX 77520

JUSTER, ALLAN, b Albany, NY, Sept 8, 22; m 52; c 1. MECHANICAL ENGINEERING. *Educ:* Pratt Inst, BME, 47; Univ Del, MME, 51. *Prof Exp:* Design engr, Develop Eng Corp, 47-48; instr eng, Univ Conn, 48-51; supvr res, Diamond Ord Fuze Lab, Washington, DC, 51-53; res engr, Armour Res Found, Ill, 53-55; res engr, Sperry Gyroscope Corp, NY, 55-61; sr staff engr, Repub Aviation Corp, 61-66; prof eng ∶chnol & chmn dept, NY Inst Technol, 66-70; PROF ENG TECHNOL & CHMN DEPT, FAIRLEIGH DICKINSON UNIV, 70- *Res:* Cryogenics, educational and ultra high vacuum research. *Mailing Add:* Dept of Eng Technol Fairleigh Dickinson Univ Teaneck NJ 07666

JUSTER, NORMAN JOEL, b New York, NY, Feb 19, 24; m 60; c 5. ORGANIC CHEMISTRY. *Educ:* Univ Calif, Los Angeles, BA, 43, MS, 47, PhD(org chem), 56. *Prof Exp:* Mem chem fac, John Muir Col, 47-55; dept phys sci, Pasadena City Col, 56-60; sr chemist & head org sect, Motorola, Inc, 60-61, mgr org-polymer labs, Semiconductors Div, 61; PROF CHEM, PASADENA CITY COL, 61-, CHMN, DEPT CHEM & DIV PHYS SCI, 78- *Concurrent Pos:* Res dir & consult, Photo Prod Res Lab, E I du Pont de Nemours & Co, 49-52; consult, Witco Chem Co, 53; res dir & consult, Motorola Semiconductor Prod, Inc, 61-; Nat Defense Educ Act lectr, 63; res dir & consult, Energy Conversion Devices, 64; vis prof, Univ Ky, 65-66; consult, Silverton & Silverton, 68-, McInherry Enterprises, 69- & Oncol Div, Med Res Inst Calif, 74-; critical reviewer chem texts, 64-; vis prof chem, Univ Hawaii, 73-74 & 80. *Honors & Awards:* J Ray Risser Award, 78. *Mem:* AAAS; Am Chem Soc; Asn Consult Chemists & Chem Eng; Soc Plastics Eng. *Res:* Reactions, particularly polymerization of acetylenic studies; reaction mechanisms; organic semiconduction; solid state organic chemistry; electronic structure of molecules; management of cell growth and reproduction with organic semiconductors. *Mailing Add:* Dept of Chem Pasadena City Col Pasadena CA 91106

JUSTESEN, DON ROBERT, b Salt Lake City, Utah, Mar 8, 30; m 58; c 4. NEUROPSYCHOLOGY. *Educ:* Univ Utah, BA, 55, MA, 57, PhD, 60. *Prof Exp:* Asst prof psychol & head dept, Westminster Col, 59-62; DIR NEUROPSYCHOL RES LABS, VET ADMIN HOSP, 62-; PROF PSYCHIAT, MED SCH, UNIV KANS, 71- *Concurrent Pos:* From asst prof to assoc prof psychiat, Med Sch, Univ Kans, 63-71; lectr, Univ Mo-Kansas City, 63-66, assoc prof, 66-68, prof, 68-75; vis prof, Univ Colo, 65; consult, NASA, 70-72; mem, Comt C-95 Safety Stand for Non-ionizing Radiation, Am Nat Stand Inst, 75-; assoc ed, J Microwave Power, 75-; mem, comn A, Nat Acad Sci Int Union of Radio Sci & chmn, comt man & radiation, IEEE, 77- *Honors & Awards:* First Prize, Am Psychol Asn, 68. *Mem:* Fel Am Psychol Asn; fel AAAS; Soc Neurosci. *Res:* Neurophysiological correlates of behavior; biothermal correlates of emotion and arousal; biological and psychological response to non-ionizing electromagnetic radiation; philosophy of science. *Mailing Add:* Vet Admin Hosp 4801 Linwood Blvd Kansas City MO 64128

JUSTHAM, STEPHEN ALTON, b New Kensington, Pa, May 22, 37; m 68; c 2. CLIMATOLOGY, METEOROLOGY. *Educ:* Indiana Univ Pa, BS, 64, MA, 70; Univ Ill, PhD(geog), 74. *Prof Exp:* Teacher geog polit sci, Washington Twp Sch Dist, Apollo, Pa, 64-66; teacher civics, New Kensington-Arnold Sch Dist, 66-68; ASSOC PROF GEOG, BALL STATE UNIV, 71- *Mem:* Am Meteorol Soc; Am Geophys Union; Asn Am Geogr; Royal Meteorl Soc. *Res:* Climatology and meteorology of severe weather phenomena, specifically tornado preparedness programs; wind resource inventory and modeling. *Mailing Add:* Dept of Geog Ball State Univ Muncie IN 47306

JUSTICE, BENJAMIN, b Logansport, Ind, June 10, 26; m 48; c 3. PHYSICS. *Educ:* Purdue Univ, BS, 50. *Prof Exp:* Engr, 50-51, qual control mgr, Danville, Ky, 51-58, qual assurance mgr, Corning, NY, 58-60, res physicist, 60-71, SR RES PHYSICIST, CORNING GLASS WORKS, 71- *Res:* Measurement of physical properties of materials, primarily glass, of a non-routine nature or technique, such as microinstability of glasses and glass-ceramics. *Mailing Add:* Corning Glass Works SSPFR 4 Corning NY 14830

JUSTICE, JAMES HORACE, b Big Spring, Tex, Aug 31, 41. EXPLORATION GEOPHYSICS. *Educ:* Univ Tex, BA, 63; Univ Md, MA, 66, PhD(math), 68. *Prof Exp:* From asst prof to assoc prof math, Univ Tulsa, 68-78, prof, 78-82; CHAIR IN EXPLOR GEOPHYS, UNIV CALGARY, 82- *Concurrent Pos:* Consult, Amoco Prod Co, 69-80; fel, Amax, Inc, Colo Sch Mines, 69-80; geophys consult, 82- *Mem:* Am Math Soc; Math Asn Am. *Res:* Signal processing in exploration geophysics; multidimensional signal processing; digital signal processing. *Mailing Add:* Dept Geol Geophys Univ Calgary 2500 Univ Dr NW Calgary AB T2N 1N4 Can

JUSTICE, JOHN KEITH, b Martinsville, Tex, Aug 26, 20; m 43; c 4. SOIL FERTILITY. *Educ:* Stephen F Austin State Univ, BS, 42; Tex A&M Univ, BS, 48, MS, 49; Utah State Univ, PhD(soil sci), 61. *Prof Exp:* Instr agron, Tex A&M Univ, 49-50; from instr to assoc prof, 50-61, PROF AGRON & HEAD DEPT, ABILENE CHRISTIAN UNIV, 61- *Concurrent Pos:* NSF fel, Utah State Univ, 62. *Mem:* Am Soc Agron; Soil Sci Soc Am. *Res:* Effects of fertilizer application on the chemical composition of turnip greens; moisture and temperature effects on the transformation of nitrogen form applied ammonium sulfate in a calcareous soil. *Mailing Add:* Dept of Agr Abilene Christian Univ Abilene TX 79601

JUSTICE, KEITH EVANS, b Arkansas City, Kans, Feb 6, 30; m 57; c 3. ECOLOGY, EVOLUTIONARY BIOLOGY. *Educ:* Univ Ariz, BS, 55, MS, 56, PhD(zool), 60. *Prof Exp:* Res assoc pop genetics, Columbia Univ, 59-60 & Ariz-Sonora Desert Mus, 60-62; proj engr, Melpar Inc, 62-65; asst prof biol sci, 65-67, assoc dean grad div, 68-69, actg dean, 69-71, dean spec progs, 74-77, dean prof studies, 77-81, ASSOC PROF ECOL & EVOLUTIONARY BIOL, UNIV CALIF, IRVINE, 67- *Concurrent Pos:* Res assoc, Univ Ariz, 60-62; vpres, Rocky Mt Biol Lab, Crested Butte, Colo, 66-71. *Mem:* Am Soc Mammal; Soc Study Evolution; Am Soc Naturalists; AAAS. *Res:* Population dynamics and behavior of desert rodents; computer assisted instruction. *Mailing Add:* Dept of Ecol & Evolutionary Biol Univ of Calif Irvine CA 92717

JUSTICE, RAYMOND, b Logansport, Ind, Oct 14, 24; m 46; c 5. ELECTRICAL ENGINEERING. *Educ:* Purdue Univ, BS, 49; Ohio State Univ, MA, 50, PhD, 56. *Prof Exp:* Res assoc, Ohio State Univ, 50-56; sr group engr, Gen Dynamics/Convair, 56-59; supvry engr, Granger Assocs Elec Res, 59-62; staff mem weapons systs, Eval Div, Inst Defense Anal, 62-64; vpres eng, Andrew Corp, 64-69; pres, Justice Assocs, Inc, 69-76; SR DESIGN SPECIALIST, DEFENSE SYSTS, CUBIC CORP, 76- *Mem:* Inst Elec & Electronics Engrs. *Res:* Electromagnetics; radar; communication antennas. *Mailing Add:* Defense Systs Dept 9233 Balboa San Diego CA 92199

JUSTIN, JAMES ROBERT, b Scranton, Pa, Oct 14, 33; m 57; c 2. AGRONOMY, FIELD CROPS. *Educ:* Pa State Univ, BS, 55, MS, 57; Tex A&M Univ, PhD(plant breeding), 63. *Prof Exp:* Instr agron, Tex A&M Univ, 60-63; exten agronomist, Univ Minn, 63-67, from instr to asst prof agron, 64-67; assoc specialist, 67-75, SPECIALIST, CROPS & SOILS EXTEN, RUTGERS UNIV, NEW BRUNSWICK, 75- *Mem:* Am Forage & Grassland Coun; Am Soc Agron; Crop Sci Soc Am. *Res:* Improvement of field crop and seed production; variety testing and production research with soybeans and variety testing with forages. *Mailing Add:* Dept of Soils & Crops Rutgers Univ New Brunswick NJ 08903

JUSTINES, GUSTAVO, b Feb 5, 31; Panama citizen; m 54; c 4. VIROLOGY, IMMUNOPATHOLOGY. *Educ:* Univ Panama, Licenciodo, 61; Yale Univ, MPH, 67; Univ Wis, PhD(virol), 71. *Prof Exp:* Biologist, Mid Am Res Unit, 61-67, virologist, 67-75; VIROLOGIST, GORGAS MEM LAB, 75- *Mem:* Am Soc Trop Med & Hygiene; Soc Panamena de Microbiol & Parasitol (pres, 75); Soc Gen Microbiol. *Res:* Ecology of arbovirus; specially Venezuelon equine encephalitis; Newcastle disease. *Mailing Add:* Gorgas Mem Lab AP 6991 Panama 5 Panama

JUSTUS, CARL GERALD, b Atlanta, Ga, Oct 2, 39; m 63; c 2. ATMOSPHERIC PHYSICS, ATMOSPHERIC DYNAMICS. *Educ:* Ga Inst Technol, BS, 61, MS, 63, PhD(physics), 66. *Prof Exp:* Assoc prof, 65-74, prof aerospace eng, 74-78, PROF GEOPHYS, GA INST TECHNOL, 78- *Mem:* Am Geophys Union; Am Meteorol Soc; Royal Meteorol Soc. *Res:* Atmospheric turbulence; solar radiation; upper atmosphere meteorology; wind energy. *Mailing Add:* Sch Geophys Sci Ga Inst of Technol Atlanta GA 30332

JUSTUS, DAVID ELDON, b Van Buren, Mo, May 22, 36; m 60; c 5. IMMUNOLOGY, PARASITOLOGY. *Educ:* Southeast Mo State Col, BS, 63; Univ Mo-Columbia, MS, 65; Univ Okla, PhD(med parasitol), 68. *Prof Exp:* ASST PROF MICROBIOL & IMMUNOL, UNIV LOUISVILLE, 70- *Concurrent Pos:* Fel microbiol, Sch Med, Univ Louisville, 69-70. *Mem:* Am Soc Microbiol; Am Soc Trop Med & Hyg; Reticuloendothelial Soc. *Res:* Anaphylactic antibody and mast cell responses in mice infected with Trichinella spiralis. *Mailing Add:* Dept of Microbiol Univ of Louisville Sch of Med Louisville KY 40201

JUSTUS, JERRY T, b Chicago, Ill, Oct 13, 32; m. DEVELOPMENTAL BIOLOGY. *Educ:* Franklin Col, AB, 57; Ind Univ, MA, 62, PhD(endocrinol, develop biol), 65. *Prof Exp:* Teacher zool, Ind Univ, 60-61, res asst endocrinol, 61-63, res fel develop biol, 64-65; sr cancer res scientist, Springville Labs, Roswell Park Mem Inst, 66-68; asst prof, 68-70, ASSOC PROF ZOOL, ARIZ STATE UNIV, 70- *Concurrent Pos:* Am Cancer Soc Inst grant, 67-68; United Health Found grant, 67-68; Am Heart Asn grant, 67-69 & 76-78; estab investr, Am Heart Asn, 71-76. *Mem:* AAAS; NY Acad Sci; Am Soc Zool; Soc Develop Biol. *Mailing Add:* Dept of Zool Ariz State Univ Tempe AZ 85281

JUSTUS, NORMAN EDWARD, b Marionville, Mo, Jan 1, 26; m 46; c 3. AGRONOMY. *Educ:* Univ Ark, BSA, 54, MS, 55; Okla State Univ, PhD(genetics, plant breeding), 58. *Prof Exp:* Instr agron, Okla State Univ, 56-58; res agronomist, Cotton Genetics & Breeding Sect, USDA, 58-65;

SUPT SOUTHWEST CTR & PROF AGRON, UNIV MO-COLUMBIA, 65-
Res: Direction and coordination of all research and related activities of
University Southwest Missouri Center. *Mailing Add:* Rte 3 Mt Vernon MO
65712

JUSTUS, PHILIP STANLEY, b New York, NY, Jan 17, 41; m 62; c 2.
GEOLOGY, TECTONICS. *Educ:* City Col New York, BS, 62; Univ NC,
Chapel Hill, MS, 66, PhD, 71. *Prof Exp:* Teaching asst geol, Univ NC, 62-67,
student dir seismog sta, 64-66; instr astron & phys geog, US Mil Acad, 67-68,
asst prof astron & geol, 68-70; fel, Rice Univ, 70-71; asst prof, 71-77, ASSOC
PROF GEOL, FAIRLEIGH DICKINSON UNIV, 77- *Concurrent Pos:*
Assoc ed, Geol Sect, NJ Acad Sci Bull & contrib ed, NJ Sci Teachers Asn
Bull, 73- *Mem:* AAAS; Geol Soc Am; Am Geophys Union; Sigma Xi. *Res:*
Deciphering the sequence of textrual development and crystallization history
of diabase dikes; determining the structural and metamorphic evolution of the
Brevard fault zone and Blue Ridge Mountains in North Carolina. *Mailing
Add:* Dept of Earth Sci Fairleigh Dickinson Univ Rutherford NJ 07070

JUSTUSSON, WILLIAM M(ATT), b Bessemer, Mich, Jan 10, 30; m 48; c 6.
PHYSICAL METALLURGY. *Educ:* Mich Col Mining & Technol, BS, 51;
Univ Wis, MS, 52. *Prof Exp:* Scientist, Atomic Power Div, Westinghouse Elec
Corp, 52-53; nuclear engr, Convair Div, Gen Dynamics Corp, 53-54; res
metallurgist, Sci Lab, 54-65, supvr, Appl Res Lab, 65-70, asst plant mgr,
Vulcan Forge Plant, 70-72, ADVAN MFG RES SPECIALIST, CASTING
DIV, FORD MOTOR CO, 72- *Mem:* Am Soc Metals; Am Inst Mining,
Metall & Petrol Engrs. *Res:* Thermomechanical treatment of steels; powder
metallurgy; casting and processing of steels; research and development of new
materials and manufacturing concepts for specific applications and the
introduction of new technology. *Mailing Add:* 30146 Woodbrook Ct
Farmington Hills MI 48018

JUTILA, JOHN W, b Mullan, Idaho, May 21, 31; m 53; c 4.
IMMUNOLOGY, MEDICAL MICROBIOLOGY. *Educ:* Mont State Univ,
BA, 53, MA, 54; Univ Wash, PhD(microbiol), 60. *Prof Exp:* Fel, Univ Wash,
60-61; NIH grants, 62-69, 70-76. *Mem:* Fel AAAS; fel Am Acad Microbiol;
Am Soc Microbiol; Soc Ext Biol & Med; Am Asn Immunol. *Res:*
Pathogenesis of wasting syndromes in mice; immunobiology of the
congenitally athymic mouse and immune cell interactions with tumor cells in
vivo and tissue culture systems. *Mailing Add:* VPres Res Mont State Univ
Bozeman MT 59715

JUTRAS, MICHEL WILFRID, b Timmins, Ont, Can, May 11, 36; US
citizen; m 61; c 2. AGRONOMY. *Educ:* Univ Mass, BS, 58; Univ Conn, MS,
61; Iowa State Univ, PhD(crop physiol), 64. *Prof Exp:* Instr agron, Iowa State
Univ, 62-64; asst prof, 64-70, assoc prof, 70-78, PROF AGRON, CLEMSON
UNIV, 78- *Concurrent Pos:* Consult, Agr Serv Labs, Inc, Tex. *Mem:* AAAS;
Am Soc Agron; Crop Sci Soc Am; Soil Sci Soc Am; Int Soc Soil Sci. *Res:*
Photo-thermoperiodic responses of crop plants; crop drought and heat
resistance; microclimatology; crop morphology and development; grazing
systems; crop physiology and ecology. *Mailing Add:* Dept of Agron 277 Plant
& Animal Sci Clemson Univ Clemson SC 29631

JUVET, RICHARD SPALDING, JR, b Los Angeles, Calif, Aug 8, 30; m 55;
c 4. ANALYTICAL CHEMISTRY, CHROMATOGRAPHY. *Educ:* Univ
Calif, Los Angeles, BS, 52, PhD(chem), 55. *Prof Exp:* From instr to assoc prof
anal chem, Univ Ill, Urbana, 55-70; PROF ANAL CHEM, ARIZ STATE
UNIV, 70- *Concurrent Pos:* Vis prof, Univ Calif, Los Angeles, 60, Nat Taiwan
Univ, 68 & Ecole Polytechnique, France, 76-77; NSF sr fel, Cambridge Univ,
64-65; mem air pollution chem & physics adv comt, US Dept Health, Educ
& Welfare, 69-72; ed adv, J Chromatographic Sci, 69-, Analytica Chimica
Acta, 72-74 & Anal Chem, 74-76; Sci Exchange Agreement Award for lects
& travel Eastern Europe, 77; mem adv panel advan chem alarm technol,
Develop & Eng Directorate, Defense Systs Div, Edgewood Arsenal, 75.
Mem: Am Chem Soc (secy-treas, Div Anal Chem, 69-71, chmn, 72-73);
AAAS; fel Am Inst Chemists; Sigma Xi; Am Radio Relay League. *Res:* New
applications of gas chromatography; liquid chromatography detectors;
photochemistry; organic structural determinations and functional group
analysis; chelate chemistry of polyhydroxy compounds; optical rotation
measurements in study of metal chelates; inorganic gas chromatography;
computer interfacing. *Mailing Add:* Dept of Chem Ariz State Univ Tempe AZ
85287

JUVINALL, ROBERT C, b Danville, Ill, Apr 11, 17; m 45; c 2.
MECHANICAL ENGINEERING. *Educ:* Case Inst Technol, BS, 39;
Chrysler Inst Eng, MAE, 41; Univ Ill, MS, 50. *Prof Exp:* Proj engr, engine
develop & supvr eng staff, res design dept, Chrysler Corp, 39-48; asst prof
mech eng, Univ Ill, 48-50; assoc prof, Ill Inst Technol, 50-51; asst dir eng,
Ransburg Electro-Coating Corp, 51-57; assoc prof mech eng, 57-62, PROF
MECH ENG, UNIV MICH, ANN ARBOR, 62- *Concurrent Pos:* Consult
engr. *Mem:* Am Soc Mech Engrs; Am Soc Eng Educ. *Res:* Engineering stress
analysis and mechanical design. *Mailing Add:* 3545 Daleview Dr Ann Arbor
MI 48103

JYUNG, WOON HENG, b Korea, Mar 12, 34; m 61; c 2. PLANT
PHYSIOLOGY. *Educ:* Seoul Nat Univ, BS, 57; Mich State Univ, MS, 59,
PhD(hort physiol), 63. *Prof Exp:* Res assoc hort physiol, Mich State Univ,
63-64; from asst prof to assoc prof, 64-74, PROF BIOL, UNIV TOLEDO, 74-
Mem: AAAS; Am Soc Plant Physiol; Japanese Soc Plant Physiol. *Res:*
Mechanisms of ion uptake by plant cells; zinc metabolism in higher plants.
Mailing Add: Dept of Biol Univ of Toledo Toledo OH 43606

K

KAAE, JAMES LEWIS, b Bell, Calif, Oct 28, 36; m 65; c 1. MATERIALS
SCIENCE. *Educ:* Univ Calif, Los Angeles, BS, 59, MS, 61, PhD(eng), 65.
Prof Exp: Int res fel, Welding Inst, Eng, 65-67; staff mem, metall, Gulf Energy
& Environ Systs, Inc, 67-73; TECH ADV, GEN ATOMIC CO, 73- *Mem:*
Am Carbon Soc. *Res:* Structure, properties and irradiation behavior of
pyrolytic carbon; welding metallurgy of steels; behavior of materials under
high-temperature cyclic loading; behavior of coated particle nuclear fuels.
Mailing Add: Gen Atomic Co PO Box 81608 San Diego CA 92138

KAARSBERG, ERNEST ANDERSEN, b Denmark, Sept 5, 18; US citizen; m
51; c 3. GEOPHYSICS. *Educ:* Queens Univ, Ont, BSc, 49; Univ Toronto,
MA, 50; Univ Chicago, PhD(geol, geophys), 58. *Prof Exp:* Assoc prof
geophys, Univ Wash, 61-63; Fulbright lectr, Graz Tech Univ, 63-64; assoc
prof, Ga Inst Technol, 64-66; mgr geophys lab, Brown Eng Co, 66-69; prof
lectr continuing educ, Am Univ, 69-71; assoc prof earth sci, Staten Island
Community Col, 71-76; CONSULT, 76- *Concurrent Pos:* Geophysicist, Imp
Oil Co, Calgary, Alta, 50-51; geophys supvr, Brit Am Oil Co, 51-53 &
Standard Oil Calif, Calgary, 53-55; sr res geophysicist & geochemist, Geophys
Serv Inc, Dallas, Tex, 58-60; eng physicist, Shannon & Wilson Inc, Soil Mech
& Found Engrs, Seattle, 60-61. *Mem:* Am Geophys Union; Soc Explor
Geophysicists; NY Acad Sci; Explorors Club; Am Soc Mil Engrs. *Res:* Study
of earth and lunar-like material properties for use in dynamic simulation of
the development of many earth and lunar features; development of innovative
methods of teaching scientific principles to nonscience major college
students. *Mailing Add:* 52 Willow Rd W Apt 2-C Staten Island NY 10303

KAAS, JON HOWARD, b Fargo, NDak, Sept 13, 37; m 63; c 2.
PSYCHOPHYSIOLOGY. *Educ:* Northland Col, BA, 59; Duke Univ,
PhD(psychol), 65. *Prof Exp:* Trainee neurophysiol, Univ Wis-Madison, 65-
68, asst prof, 68-73; assoc prof, 73-79, PROF PSYCHOL, VANDERBILT
UNIV, 79- *Mem:* Soc Neurosci. *Res:* Visual and sensory systems; brain
functions and evolution. *Mailing Add:* Dept of Psychol Vanderbilt Univ
Nashville TN 37203

KAATZ, MARTIN RICHARD, b Cleveland, Ohio, Apr 16, 24; m 47; c 3.
PHYSICAL GEOGRAPHY. *Educ:* Univ Mich, BA, 48, MA, 49, PhD(geog),
52. *Prof Exp:* From asst prof to assoc prof, 52-64, chmn dept, 62-76, PROF
GEOG, CENT WASH STATE COL, 65- *Concurrent Pos:* Fulbright prof,
Trinity Col, Univ Dublin, 65-66; pres, Asn Pac Coast Geographers, 69-70.
Mem: Asn Am Geogr; Am Geog Soc; Am Quaternary Asn. *Res:* Significance
of mass wasting and periglacial landforms to the modern environment;
irrigation and drought in central Washington. *Mailing Add:* Dept of Geog &
Land Studies Cent Wash State Univ Ellensburg WA 98926

KABACK, DAVID BRIAN, b New York, NY, May 4, 50. RECOMBINANT
DNA, DEVELOPMENTAL BIOLOGY. *Educ:* State Univ NY Stony Brook,
BS, 71; Brandeis Univ, PhD(biol), 76. *Prof Exp:* Res fel chem, Calif Inst
Technol, 76-78; ASST PROF MICROBIOL, NJ MED SCH, UNIV MED &
DENT NJ, 78- *Mem:* Am Soc Microbiol. *Res:* Molecular genetics of yeast
meiosis and sporulation; organization of encaryotic genes and chromosomes.
Mailing Add: Dept Microbiol NJ Med Sch Univ Med & Dent NJ 100 Bergen
St Newark NJ 07103

KABACK, HOWARD RONALD, b Philadelphia, Pa, June 5, 36; m 57; c 3.
BIOCHEMISTRY. *Educ:* Haverford Col, BA, 58; Albert Einstein Col Med,
MD, 62. *Prof Exp:* Intern pediat, Bronx Munic Hosp Ctr, 62-63; sr res investr,
Lab Biochem, Nat Heart Inst, 66-69; HEAD, MEMBRANE BIOCHEM
LAB & ASSOC MEM, DIV BIOCHEM, ROCHE INST MOLECULAR
BIOL, 70- *Concurrent Pos:* Edward John Noble Found fel, 62-64; fel physiol,
Albert Einstein Col Med, 63-64; res fel biochem, Nat Heart Inst, 64-66.
Honors & Awards: S Waksman Award, 73; Lewis Rosenstiel Award, 74.
Mem: Am Soc Biol Chemists; Fedn Am Socs Exp Biol; NY Acad Sci; Am Soc
Microbiol; Biophys Soc. *Res:* Transport; membranes; genetics. *Mailing Add:*
Membrane Biochem Lab Roche Inst of Molecular Biol Nutley NJ 07110

KABACK, STUART MARK, b Elizabeth, NJ, June 12, 34; m 55; c 2.
ORGANIC CHEMISTRY. *Educ:* Columbia Univ, AB, 55, AM, 56, PhD(org
chem), 60. *Prof Exp:* Chemist, Tech Info Div, Esso Res & Eng Co, 60-63,
Chem Res Div, 63 & Tech Info Div, 63-68, sr res chemist, Chem Corp Serv,
68-70, sr res chemist, Res Corp Serv, 70-76, RES ASSOC, EXXON RES &
ENG CO, 76-, MEM STAFF, ANAL & INFO DIV, 78- *Mem:* Am Chem
Soc (asst secy div chem lit, 69-71, actg treas, 71-72). *Res:* Information
retrieval and analysis; patent information on petrochemicals, polymer
chemistry; petroleum technology. *Mailing Add:* 222 Denman Rd Cranford
NJ 07016

KABADI, BALACHANDRA N, b Gadag, Mysore, India, July 15, 33; m 50; c
4. PHYSICAL PHARMACY, PHARMACEUTICAL CHEMISTRY. *Educ:*
Karnatak Univ, India, BSc, 58; Univ Bombay, BSc, 60; Univ Wash, MS, 62,
PhD(pharm), 65. *Prof Exp:* Fel chem, Univ SC, 65-66 & Sch Pharm, Univ
Mich, 66-67; asst prof pharm, Col Pharm, Fla A&M Univ, 67-68; SR RES
SCIENTIST, TECH STANDARDS, E R SQUIBB & SONS, 68- *Mem:* Am
Pharmaceut Asn; Am Chem Soc. *Res:* Isolation, identification of compounds
from natural plant products; pharmaceutical complexation reactions of
phenols and water soluble hydrophilic polymers of nonionic nature; analytical
chemistry-analysis of pharmaceutical products involving spectrophotometric
methods. *Mailing Add:* Tech Standards Dept E R Squibb & Sons Inc New
Brunswick NJ 08903

KABAK, IRWIN WILLIAM, b New York, NY, May 21, 36; m 57; c 2.
OPERATIONS RESEARCH, INDUSTRIAL ENGINEERING. *Educ:* NY
Univ, BIndE, 56, MIndE, 58, PhD(opers res), 64. *Prof Exp:* Mfg trainee &
cost control analyst, Mergenthaler Linotype Co, 56-57; opers res engr, Esso
Res & Eng Co, 56-58; mem tech staff & specialist traffic studies, Bell Tel Labs,

58-64; from asst prof to assoc prof, 65-70, PROF OPERS RES, NY UNIV, 70-; PRES, MODELMETRICS, INC, 67- *Concurrent Pos:* Consult various indust & govt; instr & adj asst prof, NY Univ, 63-65; lectr, City Univ New York, 64-65, Am Mgt Asn, 66-69, Purchasing Agents Asn NY, 67 & Diebold Group, 67; corp dir, Taxtronics Inc, 69-; consult & corp dir, Hardboard Fabricators Inc, 70; vis prof, Polytech Inst NY & CW Post Col, 71-72, Rutgers Univ, 78. *Mem:* Am Inst Indust Engrs; Inst Mgt Sci; Opers Res Soc Am; Nat Soc Prof Engrs. *Res:* Applications of applied probability in queueing, inventory, reliability and simulation; operations management and finance; model building, testing and evaluating. *Mailing Add:* NY Univ Grad Sch of Bus Admin 100 Trinity Pl New York NY 10006

KABALKA, GEORGE WALTER, b Wyandotte, Mich, Feb 1, 43; m 68; c 2. ORGANIC CHEMISTRY, ORGANOMETALLIC CHEMISTRY. *Educ:* Univ Mich, BS, 65; Purdue Univ, PhD(chem), 70. *Prof Exp:* Res assoc, Purdue Univ, 69-70; ASSOC PROF CHEM, UNIV TENN, KNOXVILLE, 70- *Concurrent Pos:* Consult, Oak Ridge Nat Lab, 76-, Oak Ridge Assoc Univ, 77-, Mt Sinai Hosp, Miami, 81- & Brookhaven Nat Lab, 81- *Mem:* Am Chem Soc; Soc Nuclear Med. *Res:* Organic synthesis; synthesis of radiopharmaceuticals containing short-lived radionuclides; organometallic reaction mechanisms. *Mailing Add:* Dept of Chem Univ of Tenn Knoxville TN 37916

KABARA, JON JOSEPH, b Chicago, Ill, Nov 26, 26; m 70; c 6. PHARMACOLOGY, CLINICAL BIOCHEMISTRY. *Educ:* St Mary's Col, Minn, BS, 48; Univ Miami, MS, 50; Univ Chicago, PhD(pharmacol), 59. *Prof Exp:* Asst biochem, Univ Ill, 48; asst chem, Univ Miami, 48-49, microbiol, 50-53; asst med, Univ Chicago, 53-57; from asst prof to prof chem, Univ Detroit, 57-68; prof pharmacol & assoc dean, 69-70, PROF MED, COL OSTEOP MED, MICH STATE UNIV, 70- *Mem:* AAAS; Am Chem Soc; NY Acad Sci; Am Soc Clin Path; Am Asn Clin Chem. *Res:* Cancer and virus chemotherapy; sterol biogenesis and metabolism; biochemistry of the central nervous system; radiobiology and clinical chemistry; biochemistry; venom research; pharmacology in dental research of food preservation and cosmetic. *Mailing Add:* Dept Biomech Mich State Univ East Lansing MI 48824

KABASERVICE, THOMAS PETER, electrical engineering, see previous edition

KABAT, DAVID, b Minneapolis, Minn, Oct 15, 40; m 62; c 2. BIOCHEMISTRY, GENETICS. *Educ:* Brown Univ, ScB, 62; Calif Inst Technol, PhD(biochem), 67. *Prof Exp:* NIH res assoc biophys, Mass Inst Technol, 67-69; asst prof, 69-72, ASSOC PROF BIOCHEM, MED SCH, UNIV ORE, 72- *Mem:* Am Soc Biol Chemists. *Res:* Biochemical genetics of growth and differentiation. *Mailing Add:* 2335 NW Johnson West Portland OR 97210

KABAT, ELVIN ABRAHAM, b New York, NY, Sept 1, 14; m 42; c 3. BIOCHEMISTRY. *Educ:* City Col New York, BS, 32; Columbia Univ, AM, 34, PhD(biochem), 37. *Hon Degrees:* DL, Univ Glasgow, 76. *Prof Exp:* Lab asst immunochem, Presby Hosp, 33-37; instr path, Med Col, Cornell Univ, 38-41; res assoc biochem, 41-46, from asst prof to assoc prof bact, 46-52, PROF MICROBIOL, COL PHYSICIANS & SURGEONS, COLUMBIA UNIV, 52-, PROF HUMAN GENETICS & DEVELOP, 69- *Concurrent Pos:* Rockefeller Found fel, Inst Phys Chem, Univ Uppsala, 37-38; Fogarty scholar, NIH, 74-75; mem sci staff, Div War Res Instr, City Col New York, 46-47; Harvey lectr, 51; mem subcomt shock, Nat Res Coun, 51-53, panel on plasma, 53-59, comt plasma & plasma substitutes, 59-71; biochem adv panel, Am Inst Biol Sci, Off Naval Res, 57-62; Philips lectr, Haverford Col, 60, 74; prof, Col France, 64; mem expert adv panel on immunol, WHO, 65-82; expert, Nat Cancer Inst, NIH, 75-81. *Honors & Awards:* Lilly Award, Am Soc Microbiologists, 49; Award, Nat Multiple Sclerosis Soc, 62; Karl Landsteiner Mem Award, 66; Claude Bernard Medal, Univ Montreal, 68; City of Hope Res Award, 74; L G Horwitz Prize, Harvey Soc, 77; R E Dyer Lectr Award, NIH, 79; Alexander S Wiener lectr, New York Blood Ctr, New York, 79; Townsend Harris Medal, City Col, New York, 80. *Mem:* Nat Acad Sci; AAAS; Am Chem Soc; Am Soc Microbiol; Harvey Soc (vpres, 75-76, pres, 76-77). *Res:* Immunochemistry; organic reactions in qualitative analysis; mechanisms of immune reactions; antibody purification; physical chemistry of antibodies; serum and spinal fluid proteins; blood group substances; allergy; multiple sclerosis; dextrans; structure and immunological specificity; secondary structure of proteins; lectin; nature of antibody combining sites. *Mailing Add:* Col of Physicians & Surgeons Columbia Univ New York NY 10032

KABAT, HUGH F, b Manitowoc, Wis, Oct 3, 32; m 56, 80; c 3. PHARMACY ADMINISTRATION. *Educ:* Univ Mich, BS, 54, MS, 56, PhD(pharm admin), 61. *Prof Exp:* Chief pharm serv, Alaska Native Hosp, USPHS, 56-58; from asst prof to assoc prof pharm technol, 61-69, head dept clin pharm, 69-74, prof clin pharm, 69-80, asst dean admin, 74-80, PROF, COL PHARM, UNIV MINN, MINNEAPOLIS, 80-, ASSOC DEAN, ACAD AFFAIRS, 80- *Concurrent Pos:* Consult, Vet Admin Hosp, Minneapolis, Hennepin County Med Ctr, St Paul Ramsey Med Ctr, Data Dynamics & Mkt Measurements; contrib ed, Geriatric Nursing, 65-68, Drug Intel, 67-74 & Int Pharmaceut Abstr, 64-81. *Honors & Awards:* Mead-Johnson Award & Hallie Bruce Mem Lectr Award, Am Soc Hosp Pharmacists, 69. *Mem:* Am Pharmaceut Asn; Am Soc Hosp Pharmacists; Am Asn Cols Pharm. *Res:* Drug utilization review; patient compliance; clinical pharmacy; chronobiology. *Mailing Add:* Univ of Minn Col of Pharm Minneapolis MN 55455

KABAYAMA, MICHIOMI ABRAHAM, b Kanazawa, Japan, Apr 18, 26; m 51; c 5. POLYMER CHEMISTRY. *Educ:* Sir George Williams Col, BSc, 52; Univ Montreal, MSc, 56, DSc, 58. *Prof Exp:* Control chemist, Monsanto of Can, 51-53; demonstr, Univ Montreal, 53-56; res chemist, Dupont of Can, 58 & E I du Pont de Nemours & Co, 58-65; res chemist, Ethicon, Inc, 65-67; res chemist, Res & Develop Labs, Northern Elec Co, Ltd, 67-69; mgr transducer & polymer mat develop, 69-71, Bell-Northern Res Labs, 71-74, mgr plastics eng, Mfg Res Centre, Northern Elec Co, Ltd, 74-76; TECH DIR, SOC

PLASTICS INDUST OF CAN, 76- *Mem:* Soc Plastics Engrs; fel Chem Inst Can. *Res:* Physical properties and structure of polymers; thermodynamics of solutions of polymers; calorimetry of polymer solutions; plastic material and processing technology; new methods and applications; combustibility and toxicity of combustion products; occupational health and safety. *Mailing Add:* Soc of Plastics Indust Suite 104-1262 Don Mills Rd Don Mills ON M3B 2W7 Can

KABE, DATTATRAYA G, b Belgaum, India, Dec 30, 26; m 54; c 3. MATHEMATICAL STATISTICS, OPERATIONS RESEARCH. *Educ:* Univ Bombay, BSc, 48, MSc, 52; Univ Karnatak, India, MSc, 55; Wayne State Univ, PhD(statist), 64. *Prof Exp:* Lectr statist, Vijay Col, India, 52-53 & Karnatak Univ, India, 53-61; assoc math, Wayne State Univ, 61-64; assoc prof math & statist, Northern Mich Univ, 65-66 & Dalhousie Univ, 66-68; assoc prof, 68-75, PROF MATH & STATIST, ST MARY'S UNIV, NS, 75- *Concurrent Pos:* Nat Res Coun Can grants & Can Math Cong res scholar; prof statist, NMex State Univ, 80-81. *Mem:* Inst Math Statist. *Res:* Distribution theory; design of experiments; multivariate analysis; Pascal computer programming language; sampling techniques; math programming. *Mailing Add:* Dept of Math St Mary's Univ Halifax NS B3H 3C3 Can

KABEL, RICHARD HARVEY, b Detroit, Mich, Dec 18, 32; m 60; c 2. TRIBOLOGY, MECHANICAL ENGINEERING. *Educ:* Gen Motors Inst, BSME, 61. *Prof Exp:* Res engr eng oils, Gen Motors Res Labs, 61-67; sr res engr, 67-74, groupleader, 74-78, staff res engr eng oils, 78-81, SR STAFF RES ENGR ENG OILS, GEN MOTORS RES LABS, 81- *Concurrent Pos:* Gen Motors rep, Lub Rev Comt, US Army & Soc Automotive Engrs. *Mem:* Soc Automotive Engrs; Am Soc Testing & Mat. *Res:* Engine oils, formulation of engine oils, field performance, and methods to evaluate them. *Mailing Add:* Dept of Fuels & Lubs Gen Motors Res Labs Warren MI 48090

KABEL, ROBERT L(YNN), b Champaign, Ill, Apr 3, 32; m 58; c 2. CATALYTIC KINETICS, REACTOR DYNAMICS. *Educ:* Univ Ill, BS, 55; Univ Wash, PhD(chem eng), 61. *Prof Exp:* From asst prof to assoc prof, 63-74, PROF CHEM ENG, PA STATE UNIV, 74- *Concurrent Pos:* Royal Norweg Coun Sci & Indust Res fel, Tech Univ Norway, 71-72; consult, Exxon Res & Eng, 76-; vis lectr, Pahlavi Univ, Iran, 78. *Mem:* Am Chem Soc; Am Inst Chem Engrs; Am Asn Univ Professors; Am Soc Eng Educ. *Res:* Reaction kinetics; adsorption; thermodynamic equilibria; heterogeneous catalysis; chemical reactor dynamics; aerospace life support systems; thermal conductivity; mathematical modeling of natural processes; mass transfer at the earth's surface; air pollution meteorology. *Mailing Add:* 164 Fenske Lab Pa State Univ University Park PA 16802

KABELE, THOMAS J(OSEPH), chemical engineering, see previous edition

KABIK, IRVING, b Washington, DC, Aug 27, 21; m 59; c 2. CHEMICAL ENGINEERING. *Educ:* Univ Md, BS, 43. *Prof Exp:* Chem engr, US Bur Mines, 43-45; chem engr gun factory, US Naval Ord Lab, 45-46, supvry chem engr, 53-62, chief explosion dynamics div, 62-75, specialist explosive systs design, 75-80; RETIRED. *Honors & Awards:* Meritorious civilian serv award, US Navy, 51. *Mem:* AAAS; Am Chem Soc; Am Ord Asn. *Res:* Explosive processes. *Mailing Add:* US Naval Surface Weapons Ctr Silver Spring MD 20910

KABIR, PRABAHAN KEMAL, b Calcutta, India, June 30, 33. THEORETICAL PHYSICS. *Educ:* Univ Delhi, BSc, 51, MSc, 53; Cornell Univ, PhD(theoret physics), 57. *Prof Exp:* Mem Inst Advan Study, Princeton Univ, 56-57; res fel physics, Univ Birmingham, 57-58; sur reader nuclear physics, Univ Calcutta, 58-60; asst prof physics, Carnegie Inst Technol, 60-63; vis scientist, Europ Org Nuclear Res, Geneva, 63-65; prin sci officer, Sci Res Coun, UK, 65-71; PROF PHYSICS, UNIV VA, 71- *Concurrent Pos:* Mem, Ctr Advan Study, Univ VA, 70-73; sr res fel, Univ Sussex, 74; ed, Physics Letters B, 78-81. *Mem:* Am Phys Soc. *Res:* Application of concepts of symmetry to the classification of elementary particles and investigation of the broken mirror-symmetries of physical laws. *Mailing Add:* Dept of Physics Univ of Va Charlottesville VA 22901

KABISCH, WILLIAM THOMAS, b Bureau, Ill, Nov 10, 19; m 46; c 3. ANATOMY. *Educ:* Augustana Col, AB, 48; Univ Chicago, SM, 51, PhD(anat), 54. *Prof Exp:* Asst, Univ Chicago, 49-53, from instr to asst prof anat, 54-62; asst to exec officer, Am Asn Advan Sci, 62-67, asst exec officer, 67-70; assoc prof anat, 70-71; from asst dean to assoc dean, 70-72, PROF ANAT & ASSOC DEAN FOR RES, SCH MED, SOUTHERN ILL UNIV, 73- *Concurrent Pos:* Lederle med fac award, 56-59; dir, Eastern Tech Off & sr staff mem, Enviro-Med Calif, Inc, 72-73. *Mem:* AAAS; Am Asn Anat. *Res:* Gross anatomy; phagocytosis; bone regeneration; wound healing. *Mailing Add:* Southern Ill Univ Sch of Med Springfield IL 62708

KABLAOUI, MAHMOUD SHAFIQ, b Tarshiha, Palestine, Apr 15, 38; US citizen; m 65; c 3. CHEMISTRY. *Educ:* Am Univ Beirut, BSc, 60; Univ SC, PhD(org chem), 67. *Prof Exp:* From chemist to res chemist, 67-76, sr res chemist, 76-80, GROUP LEADER, BEACON RES LAB, TEXACO INC, 80- *Mem:* Am Chem Soc; Sigma Xi. *Res:* Organic synthesis, petrochemicals; aromatization reactions, organic nitrogen compounds and fuels and lubricants technology; biotechnology area involving fermentation, enzyme catalysis and photobioconversion. *Mailing Add:* Texaco Inc PO Box 509 Beacon NY 12508

KABLER, J D, b Wichita, Kans, Dec 29, 26; m 50; c 5. INTERNAL MEDICINE. *Educ:* Univ Kans, AB, 47, MD, 50; Am Bd Internal Med, dipl, 58, recertified, 74. *Prof Exp:* Intern Univ Hosp, 50-51, resident med, 51-52, 54-56, from instr to assoc prof, Med Sch, 57-70, PROF MED, MED SCH, UNIV WIS-MADISON, 70-, DIR HEALTH SERV, 68- *Concurrent Pos:* Fel, Univ Wis-Madison, 56-57. *Mem:* Am Psychosom Soc; AMA; fel Am Col Physicians; Am Venereal Disease Asn; Asn Mil Surgeons. *Res:* Clinical psychophysiology. *Mailing Add:* Univ Health Serv Univ of Wis Madison WI 53706

KABLER, MILTON NORRIS, b Roanoke, Va, Apr 30, 32; m 57; c 2. OPTICS. *Educ:* Va Polytech Inst, BS, 55; Univ NC, Chapel Hill, PhD(physics), 59. *Prof Exp:* Res asst prof physics, Univ Ill, Urbana, 59-62; physicist, 62-69, assoc supt mat sci div, 75-77, head, Optical Mat Br, 69-79, HEAD, OPTICAL PROBES BR, NAVAL RES LAB, 79- *Concurrent Pos:* Sabbatical leave, Clarendon Lab, Oxford Univ, 73-74. *Mem:* Fel Am Phys Soc; Sigma Xi; AAAS; Optical Soc Am. *Res:* Electronic properties of insulator materials; color centers, excitons, dislocations, radiation effects, surfaces, magneto-optic effects; optical technologies; synchrotron radiation. *Mailing Add:* Code 6510 Naval Res Lab Washington DC 20375

KABRA, POKAR MAL, b India, Nov 17, 42; m 66; c 2. CLINICAL CHEMISTRY, ANALYTICAL CHEMISTRY. *Educ:* Univ Bombay, BS, 66; Univ Kans, PhD(med chem), 72. *Prof Exp:* Trainee neuro-surg, Univ Calif, San Francisco, 73-74, trainee lab med, 74-75, assoc specialist, 75-77, asst prof, 77-81, ASSOC PROF LAB MED, UNIV CALIF, SAN FRANCISCO, 81- *Mem:* Am Chem Soc; AAAS; Am Asn Clin Chemists. *Res:* Drug metabolism; application of liquid chromatography in clinical sciences. *Mailing Add:* Dept of Lab Med M-507 Univ of Calif San Francisco CA 94143

KAC, MARK, b Krzemieniec, Poland, Aug 3, 14; nat US; m 42; c 2. MATHEMATICS. *Educ:* John Casimer Univ, Lwow, Magister Philos, 36, PhD(math), 37. *Hon Degrees:* DSc, Case Inst Technol, 66. *Prof Exp:* Asst, John Casimer Univ, 35-37; jr actuary, Phoenix Co, Lwow, 37-38; res fel, Parnas Found, Johns Hopkins Univ, 38-39; from instr to prof math, Cornell Univ, 39-61; PROF MATH, ROCKEFELLER UNIV, 61- *Concurrent Pos:* Guggenheim fel, Univ Mich & Cornell Univ, 46-47; mem, Inst Advan Study, 51-52; chmn div math sci, Nat Acad Sci-Nat Res Coun, 65-67. *Mem:* Nat Acad Sci; Am Acad Arts & Sci; Am Math Soc; Math Asn Am; fel Inst Math Statist. *Res:* Theory of probability; mathematical statistics; analysis; number theory; mathematical physics, especially statistical mechanics. *Mailing Add:* Dept Math Univ Southern Calif University Park Los Angeles CA 90007

KACHADOORIAN, REUBEN, b Fresno, Calif, Mar 30, 21; m 51. ENGINEERING GEOLOGY, GEOLOGY. *Educ:* Calif Inst Technol, BS, 51; Stanford Univ, MS, 69. *Prof Exp:* Inspector-geologist, 12th Naval Dist, 51-52; engr geol, 52-54, proj chief, 54-58, proj leader, 58-63, PROJ CHIEF, US GEOL SURV, 63- *Concurrent Pos:* Mem, Off Fed Inspector's Comt, Alaska Natural Gas Pipeline, 79- *Mem:* Geol Soc Am; Asn Eng Geol. *Res:* Engineering geology, including damsites, highways, airstrips, railroads, pipelines and landslides; earthquakes; nuclear geology; chemical and impact craters; Pleistocene and recent geology. *Mailing Add:* US Geol Survey 345 Middlefield Rd Menlo Park CA 94025

KACHHAL, SWATANTRA KUMAR, b India, July 7, 47; m 77; c 1. INDUSTRIAL ENGINEERING, OPERATIONS RESEARCH. *Educ:* Univ Roorkee, India, BS, 68; Univ Minn, MS, 71, PhD(indust eng & opers res), 74. *Prof Exp:* Instr, 73-74, asst prof, 74-78, ASSOC PROF INDUST & SYST ENG, UNIV MICH, DEARBORN, 78- *Concurrent Pos:* Consult, Corning Glass Works, 78-80, Henry Ford Hosp, 80- *Mem:* Am Inst Indust Eng; Opers Res Soc Am. *Res:* Facilities planning; warehaousing; automated and mechanized storage systems; applications of operations research. *Mailing Add:* Sch of Eng Univ of Mich Dearborn MI 48128

KACHIKIAN, ROUBEN, b Ardabil, Iran, Dec 19, 26; nat US; m 51; c 2. MICROBIOLOGY. *Educ:* Syracuse Univ, BS, 52; Univ Tenn, MS, 54; Univ Mass, PhD(food technol), 57. *Prof Exp:* Instr food technol, Univ Mass, 54-57; develop chemist, Chas Pfizer & Co, 57-61; sr develop engr, Air Prod & Chem Inc, 61-64; prod develop assoc, Merck & Co, Inc, 64-68; group leader, Pepsico Inc, 68-69; mgr res planning & admin, Beech-Nut-Life Savers, Inc, 69-72, mgr tech serv, 72-76, Mgr Planning Admin, Beechnut Inc, 76-80, ASSOC DIR TECH SERV, LIFE SAVERS, INC, 81- *Mem:* Am Soc Microbiol; Am Inst Chemists. *Res:* Food preservation; food additives; nutritional supplementation and development of high protein products; beverages; cryogenics in foods; confections; chewing gum and candy; baby foods; sensory testing; product and sanitary standards. *Mailing Add:* 48 Birchwood Rd Old Tappan NJ 07675

KACHMAR, JOHN FREDERICK, b Akron, Ohio, Jan 10, 16; m 46; c 1. BIOCHEMISTRY. *Educ:* Univ Akron, BS, 36; Univ Minn, MS, 47, PhD(biochem), 51. *Prof Exp:* Asst chemist rubber, Victor Gasket Co, 36-37; jr chemist sewage & stream pollution, USPHS, 37-41, asst chemist, 41-42 & 46; asst vitamins & enzymes, Dept Agr Biochem, Univ Minn, 47-50, assoc biochemist Rh serol, Dept Obstet & Gynec, 50-52; biochemist blood coagulation, South Div, Albert Einstein Med Ctr, 52-58; chief clin chem sect, Dept Biochem, 58-67, dir lab training, 67-69, asst dir clin lab, 69-72, CONSULT, CLIN CHEM LAB, RUSH-PRESBY-ST LUKE'S MED CTR, 72-; ASSOC PROF BIOCHEM, RUSH UNIV, 71- *Concurrent Pos:* Asst prof biochem, Univ Ill Med Sch, 65-71. *Honors & Awards:* Natelson Award, 80. *Mem:* AAAS; Am Chem Soc; Am Asn Clin Chemists. *Res:* Activation of enzymes and enzyme kinetics; blood coagulation; clinical chemistry. *Mailing Add:* Rush-Presby-St Luke's Med Ctr 1743 W Harrison St No 433 Chicago IL 60612

KACPRZYNSKI, JERRY JOZEF, applied mechanics, aeroelasticity, see previous edition

KACSER, CLAUDE, b 1934. THEORETICAL PHYSICS. *Educ:* Oxford Univ, BA, 55, MA & PhD(physics), 59. *Prof Exp:* Res fel physics, Magdalen Col, Oxford Univ, 58-59; instr, Princeton Univ, 59-61; res fel, Magdalen Col, Oxford Univ, 61-62; asst prof, Columbia Univ, 62-64; asst prof, 64-67, ASSOC PROF PHYSICS, UNIV MD, COLLEGE PARK, 67- *Mem:* Am Phys Soc; Am Asn Physics Teachers. *Res:* Elementary particle physics; three body final state interactions; analyticity properties of Feynman graphs; rescattering effects in nuclear physics. *Mailing Add:* Dept of Physics & Astron Univ of Md College Park MD 20742

KACZMARCZYK, ALEXANDER, b Krynica, Poland, Apr 1, 32; US citizen; m 59; c 2. INORGANIC CHEMISTRY. *Educ:* Am Univ, Beirut, BA, 54; Wash Univ, PhD(chem), 60. *Prof Exp:* Res asst, Purdue Univ, 60; res fel, Harvard, 60-62, tutor chem, 61-62; asst prof, Dartmouth Col, 62-68; ASSOC PROF CHEM, TUFTS UNIV, 68- *Concurrent Pos:* Grants, Air Force Off Sci Res & USPHS, 63; vis res fel, Res Lab Archaeol, Oxford Univ, 75-76. *Mem:* AAAS; Am Chem Soc. *Res:* Chemistry of boron hydrides and applications of chemistry to art and archaeology. *Mailing Add:* Dept of Chem Tufts Univ Medford MA 02155

KACZMARCZYK, WALTER J, b New Britain, Conn, Jan 3, 39; m 63; c 3. BIOCHEMICAL GENETICS. *Educ:* Fairfield Univ, BS, 61; St John's Univ, NY, MS, 63; Hahnemann Med Col, PhD(biochem genetics), 67. *Prof Exp:* Nat Acad Sci fel biochem, Plum Island Animal Dis Lab, USDA, 66-69; asst prof, 69-72, assoc prof genetics, 72-76, PROF GENETICS & BIOCHEM, WVA UNIV, 76-; BIOCHEM GENETICIST, 69- *Mem:* AAAS; Genetics Soc Am; Am Chem Soc. *Res:* Biochemistry and genetics of tyrosinase isoenzymes in Bacillus subtilus; isolation and characterization of foot and mouth disease; fungal viruses. *Mailing Add:* Dept of Genetics Rm 1104 WVa Univ Evansdale Campus Morgantown WV 26505

KADABA, PANKAJA KOOVELI, b Perumbavoor, India, May 15, 28; m 54; c 1. ORGANIC CHEMISTRY, MEDICINAL CHEMISTRY. *Educ:* Travancore Univ, India, BSc, 47, MSc, 49; Univ Delhi, PhD(org chem), 54. *Prof Exp:* Lectr chem, Am Mission Med Col, India, 49-50 & Univ Delhi, 50-53; guest scholar, Univ Ky, 54-55; res assoc, Brown Univ, 57-60; instr biochem, Univ Ky, 64-65; assoc prof chem, Morehead State Univ, 65-66; asst prof, Christian Bros Col, 66-68; RES ASSOC PROF PHARMACEUT CHEM, COL PHARM, UNIV KY, 68- *Concurrent Pos:* Vis res assoc prof chem, Univ Ljubljana, Yugoslavia, 73-74. *Mem:* Am Chem Soc. *Res:* Chemistry of heterocyclic compounds, their synthesis, reaction mechanisms and biological activity; flavones, flavanols, phenothiazines, xanthones and 1, 2, 3-triazolines; role of protic and dipolar aprotic solvents in heterocyclic synthesis via 1,3-cycloaddition reactions; borohydride reductions of heterocyclic compounds; esterification reactions using borontrifluoride-ehterate catalyst. *Mailing Add:* Div of Med Chem Univ of Ky Col of Pharm Lexington KY 40506

KADABA, PRASAD KRISHNA, b Bangalore, India, Feb 14, 24; m 54; c 1. PHYSICS, ELECTRONICS. *Educ:* Univ Mysore, BS, 43, MS, 44; Calif Inst Technol, MS, 46; Univ Calif, Los Angeles, PhD(physics), 49. *Prof Exp:* Sci officer electronics, Nat Phys Lab, India, 50-52, asst supt, Tech Develop Estab, 52-53; asst prof elec eng, Univ Ky, 54-57 & Newark Col Eng, 57-59; assoc prof, 59-62, PROF ELEC ENG & DIR RES, UNIV KY, 62- *Concurrent Pos:* Alumni fel physics, Mich State Univ, 53-54; consult, Fed Pac Elec Co, NJ, 58; scholar, Univ Calif, Los Angeles, 58-59; AEC traveling fel, India, 63-64; Ky Res Found spec fel, 63-64; mem conf elec insulation & dielec phenomena, Nat Res Coun; consult, IBM, Ky; resident assoc, Argonne Nat Lab; prin investr microwave proj, Ky Tobacco Res Inst, 71-72; res fel to Yugoslavia, Int Res & Exchange Bd, 73; sr Fulbright-Hays Award, Yugoslav-Am Bi-Nat Comn, 74; vis scientist, Johnson Space Ctr, Houston, 75; prin investr proj, Off Water Resources Res Inst, 76-; Oak Ridge Assoc Univs fel, 76; prin investr microwave spectros proj, Ky Tobacco Res Inst, 77-78; vis prof, intergovernment personnel act prog, Air Force Off Sci Res, Wright Patterson Air Force Base Mat Lab, 80-81, Avionics Lab, 81-82. *Mem:* Am Soc Eng Educ; Brit Inst Elec Eng; sr mem Inst Elec & Electronics Engrs. *Res:* Microwave absorption of organic liquids; non resonant absorption of compressed gases and molecular nature of materials; nuclear quadrupole resonance and nuclear magnetic resonance studies; biological effects of microwaves; pollution studies. *Mailing Add:* Dept of Elec Eng Univ of Ky Lexington KY 40506

KADABA, PRASANNA V, b Gundlupet, India, July 4, 31; US citizen; m 66; c 1. MECHANICAL ENGINEERING. *Educ:* Univ Mysore, BE, 52 & 54; Univ Ky, MS, 56; Ill Inst Technol, PhD(mech eng), 64. *Prof Exp:* Asst refrig, Univ Ky, 54-56; asst mech eng, Ill Inst Technol, 56-60, instr, 60-63; res engr, Roy C Ingersoll Res Ctr, Borg-Warner Corp, 63-66, sr res engr, 66-67; sr res scientist, Res & Develop Ctr, Westinghouse Elec Corp, Pa, 67-69; ASSOC PROF MECH ENG, GA INST TECHNOL, 69- *Mem:* Am Soc Mech Engrs; Am Soc Heating, Refrig & Air-Conditioning Engrs; Am Soc Eng Educ; Sigma Xi. *Res:* Solar energy; refrigeration; air conditioning; heat transfer; thermodynamics; mechanical systems for buildings; thermal systems design; energy conservation. *Mailing Add:* Dept of Mech Eng Ga Inst of Technol Atlanta GA 30332

KADAN, RANJIT SINGH, b Karnal, Haryana State, India, Jan 1, 35; m 66; c 1. FOOD BIOCHEMISTRY, MICROBIOLOGY. *Educ:* Punjab Univ, DVM, 58; Kans State Univ, MS, 62; Rutgers Univ, New Brunswick, PhD(food sci), 67. *Prof Exp:* Vet surgeon, Punjab State, India, 58-60; res asst food, Food Sci Dept, Rutgers Univ, 62-67, sr group leader, 67-73; group leader food res, Quaker Oats Co, Barrington, Ill, 66-69, sr group leader, 70-73; mgr, Food Products Res, Lubin Maselli Lab, Chicago, 73-75; SR FOOD SCIENTIST, SOUTHERN REGIONAL RES CTR, AGR RES SERV, USDA, NEW ORLEANS, 75- *Concurrent Pos:* Consult, Volunteers Tech Assistance, 66- *Mem:* Inst Food Technologists; Am Oil Chemists Soc; Am Asn Cereal Chemists; Am Dairy Sci Asn; NY Acad Sci. *Res:* Diversified food research activities in the areas of dairy, cereals, oil seeds, snacks, long shelf life food products, beverages, toxic constituents of foods include microbiol toxins, and nutritional attributes of foods. *Mailing Add:* 8554 Fordham Ct New Orleans LA 70127

KADANE, JOSEPH BORN, b Washington, DC, Jan 10, 41. APPLIED STATISTICS, MATHEMATICAL STATISTICS. *Educ:* Harvard Univ, BA, 62; Stanford Univ, PhD(statist), 66. *Prof Exp:* Asst prof statist, Yale Univ, 66-69, actg dir grad studies, 67-68; assoc prof social sci & statist, Carnegie-Mellon Univ, A69-72; APROF 69-72, PROF STATIST, SOCIAL SCI DEPT STATIST, CARNEGIE-MELLON UNIV, 72- *Concurrent Pos:* Res staff mem, Cowles Found Res Econ, Yale Univ, 66-69, co-prin investr NSF grant econ, 67-69 & Off Naval Res, 73- mem staff, Ctr Naval Anal, 68-71; consult, Long Island Lighting Co, 68, Nat Develop Corp, Govt Tanzania, 68, Ctr Naval Anal, 71- & Bur Labor Statist, US Dept Labor, 72-73. *Mem:* Fel Am Statist Asn; fel Inst Math Statist; Opers Res Soc; fel Royal Statist Soc; fel AAAS. *Res:* Theory and use of statistics in economics, political science, sociology and anthropology. *Mailing Add:* Dept of Statist Carnegie-Mellon Univ Pittsburgh PA 15213

KADANKA, ZDENEK KAREL, b Rajhrad, Czech, May 24, 33; m 60; c 2. CYTOGENETICS, BIOCHEMISTRY. *Educ:* Purkyne Univ, Brno, dipl chem & RNDr, 57, dipl med & MUDr, 63; Inst Postgrad Studies for Physicians & Pharmacists, Prague, dipl, 66. *Prof Exp:* Lectr histol & embryol, Med Fac, Purkyne Univ, Brno, 59-63; physician allergy & diabetes, Sanatorium, Luhacovice, Czech, 63-66, intern, 66-69; sr res asst, 69-71, RES ASSOC KARYOLOGY, CONNAUGHT MED RES LABS, UNIV TORONTO, 71- *Concurrent Pos:* Gertrude I'Anson fel, Connaught Med Res Labs, Univ Toronto, 69-70; NIH grants, 71-72. *Res:* Karyologic data; cell membrane changes; transformation of human and animal cells cultured in vitro. *Mailing Add:* 64 Givendolen Circle Willowdale ON M2N 2L7 Can

KADANOFF, LEO P, b New York, NY, Jan 14, 37; m 58; c 3. THEORETICAL PHYSICS. *Educ:* Harvard Univ, AB, 57, AM, 58, PhD(physics), 60. *Prof Exp:* NSF fel, 60-61; from asst prof to prof physics, Univ Ill, Urbana, 61-69; prof physics & eng, Brown Univ, 69-70, univ prof, 70-78; PROF PHYSICS, UNIV CHICAGO, 78- *Concurrent Pos:* A P Sloan Found fel, 63-67. *Honors & Awards:* Buckley Prize, Am Phys Soc, 76; Wolf Prize, Wolf Found, 80. *Mem:* Fel Am Phys Soc; Nat Acad Sci. *Res:* Solid state and many particle theory; development of urban growth models; phenomena near phase transitions; behavior of dynamical systems. *Mailing Add:* Brown Univ Providence RI 02912

KADAR, DEZSO, b Zazar, Transylvania, July 21, 33; Can citizen; m 57; c 2. PHARMACOLOGY. *Educ:* Univ Toronto, BS, 59, MS, 66, PhD(pharmacol), 68. *Prof Exp:* Res asst pharmacol & toxicol, Connaught Med Res Lab, 60-65, demonstr, 65-68, lectr, 68-70, asst prof, 70-76, ASSOC PROF PHARMACOL, UNIV TORONTO, 76- *Concurrent Pos:* Mem, Drug Adv Comt, Ont Col Pharmacists, 72-, Comt Drugs & Therapeut, St Joseph's Hosp, 74- & Coun Fac Pharm, Univ Toronto, 73- *Mem:* Pharmacol Soc Can. *Res:* Drug metabolism and disposition in man and animals; microsomal drug oxidation in vitro. *Mailing Add:* Dept of Pharmacol Univ of Toronto Toronto ON M5S 2R8 Can

KADE, CHARLES FREDERICK, JR, b Sheboygan, Wis, Apr 4, 14; m 46; c 6. MEDICAL & HEALTH SCIENCES. *Educ:* Carleton Col, BA, 36; NDak State Univ, MS, 38; Univ Ill, PhD(biochem), 41. *Prof Exp:* Asst chem, Carleton Col, 35-36 & NDak State Univ, 36-38; asst, Univ Ill, 38, 39-41, fel, 41-43; dir biochem res, Frederick Stearns & Co, 43-47; res chemist, Sterling-Winthrop Res Inst, 47-49; dir div med sci, McNeil Labs, Inc, 49-60, vpres & dir res, 60-66; vpres, Johnson & Johnson Int, 66-79; vpres, Janssen Res & Develop, Inc, 72-79; CONSULT, 79- *Mem:* AAAS; Am Chem Soc; Asn Res Dirs; Am Pharmaceut Asn; Soc Indust Chem. *Res:* Intermediary metabolism of amino acids; protein and amino acid requirements of the dog; preparation of hydrolysates for intravenous use. *Mailing Add:* 983 Butler Pike Blue Bell PA 19422

KADER, ADEL ABDEL, b Cairo, Egypt, Mar 1, 41; US citizen; m 63; c 2. PLANT PHYSIOLOGY, HORTICULTURE. *Educ:* Univ Ain Shams, Cairo, BSc, 59; Univ Calif, Davis, MSc, 62, PhD(plant physiol), 66. *Prof Exp:* Lectr hort, Univ Ain Shams, Cairo, 66-71; consult, Agr Inst, Kuwait, 71-72; asst res plant physiol, 72-77, asst prof, 78-79, ASSOC PROF POMOL, UNIV CALIF, DAVIS, 79- *Honors & Awards:* Asgrow Award, Am Soc Hort Sci, 78; Nat Food Processors Award, Am Soc Hort Sci, 80. *Mem:* Am Soc Hort Sci; Am Soc Plant Physiologists; Inst Food Technologists; Int Soc Hort Sci; Coun Agr Sci & Technol. *Res:* Postharvest biology and biotechnology of horticultural crops; quality evaluation and maintenance of harvested fruits and vegetables. *Mailing Add:* Dept of Pomol Univ of Calif Davis CA 95616

KADESCH, RICHARD GILMORE, b Annapolis, Md, Mar 1, 18; m 43; c 3. ORGANIC CHEMISTRY. *Educ:* Iowa State Teachers Col, BA, 38; Univ Chicago, PhD(org chem), 41. *Prof Exp:* Lab asst chem, Univ Chicago, 39-40; res chemist, Columbia Chem Div, Pittsburgh Plate Glass Co, Ohio, 41-45; dir res, Plastics Div, Reynolds Metals Co, Ind, 45-49; res dir, Emery Indust, 49-58, consult, 58-59; res dir, Nepera Chem Co, 59-61; mgr ozone processes div, Welsbach Corp, Pa, 61-63; vpres res & develop, Carter's Ink Co, Mass, 63-66; DIR, AM TECH SERV, 66- *Concurrent Pos:* Assoc prof chem, Emmanuel Col, Mass, 68-74. *Mem:* AAAS; Am Chem Soc; Am Oil Chem Soc; Com Develop Asn. *Res:* Steric effects in aromatic ketones; vinyl polymerization; monomer synthesis; cross-linked resins; thermoplastic resins; plastic film; reaction of certain epoxides; film coating from latex; fats and oils; fatty acids and alcohols; textile chemicals; plasticizers; dry cleaning; ozonolysis; pharmaceuticals; inks; marking devices; copying. *Mailing Add:* 15 Mayflower Rd Winchester MA 01890

KADESCH, ROBERT R, b Cedar Falls, Iowa, May 14, 22; m 43; c 3. PHYSICS. *Educ:* Iowa State Teachers Col, BS, 43; Univ Rochester, MS, 49; Univ Wis, PhD(physics), 55. *Prof Exp:* From asst prof to assoc prof physics, 56-65, assoc dean col lett & sci, 66-68, PROF PHYSICS, UNIV UTAH, 65- *Concurrent Pos:* Staff assoc, NSF, Washington, DC, 68-69; vis res physicist, Lawrence Hall Sci, Univ Calif, Berkeley, 73-74. *Res:* Personalized computer-assisted video disc instruction; learning theory; formal thinking. *Mailing Add:* Dept of Physics Univ of Utah Salt Lake City UT 84112

KADEY, FREDERIC L, JR, b Toronto, Ont, June 21, 18; US citizen; m 50; c 2. ECONOMIC GEOLOGY, EXPLORATION GEOLOGY. *Educ:* Rutgers Univ, BSc, 41; Harvard Univ, MA, 47. *Prof Exp:* Res petrogr, Res Lab, US Steel Corp, 47-51; mineralogist & petrogr, Johns-Manville Res & Eng Ctr, NJ, 51-66, chief fillers sect, 66-71, res assoc geol, Res Ctr, 71-72, explor mgr, Int Div, 72-73, explor mgr mining group, 73-81, EXPLOR MGR,

JOHNS-MANVILLE CORP, COLO, 81- *Concurrent Pos:* Nat exec reservist, Emergency Minerals Admin, US Dept Interior, 73- *Mem:* Fel AAAS; Soc Mining Engrs; Am Mineral Soc; NY Acad Sci; Am Inst Prof Geologists. *Res:* Microscopy, particle size analysis; technology of mineral fillers and hydro-thermal silicate reactions; economic evaluation of industrial minerals; exploration of diatomite, perlite, talc, kaolin deposits. *Mailing Add:* 7653 S Rosemary Circle Englewood CO 80112

KADIN, HAROLD, b New York, NY, Jan 12, 22; m 53; c 2. ANALYTICAL CHEMISTRY, BIOCHEMISTRY. *Educ:* City Col New York, BS, 48; NY Univ, MS, 53. *Prof Exp:* Chemist, NY Univ-Bellevue Med Ctr, 48-51; chief clin chemist, Meadowbrook Hosp, NY, 52-53; anal chemist, Hoffmann-La Roche Inc, NJ, 53-58; assoc technologist, Gen Foods Res Ctr, NY, 58-60; SR RES INVESTR PHARMACEUT, SQUIBB INST MED RES, 60- *Mem:* Assoc Acad Pharmaceut Sci; Am Chem Soc. *Res:* Methods of analysis involving spectrophotometry, spectrofluorometry and chromatography; pharmaceutical analysis involving testing purity and stability of drugs; residues analysis; high performance liquid chromatography. *Mailing Add:* Anal Res & Develop Dept Squibb Inst for Med Res New Brunswick NJ 08903

KADIS, BARNEY MORRIS, b Omaha, Nebr, Dec 26, 27. BIOCHEMISTRY. *Educ:* Univ Omaha, BA, 52; Iowa State Univ, PhD(chem), 57. *Prof Exp:* Asst chem, Iowa State Univ, 52-57; asst prof, Dubuque Univ, 57-58; res chemist, Col Med, Univ Nebr, 58-60; assoc prof chem, State Univ NY Albany, 60-61; res asst prof obstet & gynec, Col Med, Univ Nebr, Omaha, 61-66, asst prof biochem, 62-66; assoc prof biol sci, Southern Ill Univ, 69-70, assoc prof, 70-74, chmn dept dent med, 70-73, prof biochem, 74-82; PROF BIOCHEM, SCH MED, MERCER UNIV, 82- *Concurrent Pos:* Fel, Inst Hormone Biol, Syntex Res, 66-67; fel anat; Sch Med, Stanford Univ, 67-69; vis prof, Univ Calif Med Ctr, 75-76. *Mem:* AAAS; Int Asn Dent Res; Am Chem Soc; Endocrine Soc; Am Soc Biol Chemists. *Res:* Metabolism of bone cells in culture and the effects of endogenous, including hormones and exogenous, including endotoxins, substances; effect of the diabetic state. *Mailing Add:* Div Basic Med Sci Sch Med Mercer Univ Macon GA 31207

KADIS, SOLOMON, b Baltimore, Md, May 17, 23; m 58; c 3. MICROBIOLOGY. *Educ:* St John's Col, Md, BA, 50; Univ Va, MA, 51; Vanderbilt Univ, PhD(cellular physiol), 57. *Prof Exp:* Asst, Vanderbilt Univ, 55-57; res assoc cellular physiol & microbiol, US Vitamin & Pharmaceut Corp, NY, 57-60 & Geront Res Inst, 60-61; assoc prof microbiol & immunol, Sch Med, Temple Univ, 71-72; PROF MED MICROBIOL, COL VET MED, UNIV GA, 72- *Concurrent Pos:* Asst mem, Res Labs, Albert Einstein Med Ctr, 61-63; assoc mem, 63-73. *Mem:* AAAS; Am Soc Microbiol; Am Soc Cell Biol; Am Acad Microbiol. *Res:* Bacterial physiology and toxin production and action; bacterial virulence as related to urinary tract infections; role of dietary iron in susceptibility of animals to bacterial infectious diseases. *Mailing Add:* Dept of Med Microbiol Univ of Ga Col of Vet Med Athens GA 30602

KADIS, VINCENT WILLIAM, b Seinai, Lithuania, Sept 25, 22; Can citizen; m 58. MICROBIOLOGY, BIOCHEMISTRY. *Educ:* Univ Sask, BA, 55; Purdue Univ, MSc, 57, PhD(microbiol, biochem), 60. *Prof Exp:* Microbiologist, 57-61, DIR LAB, ALTA DEPT AGR, CAN, 61- *Mem:* Fel Am Pub Health Asn; Am Inst Food Technologists; NY Acad Sci; Can Inst Food Sci & Technol (pres, 77-78); Am Soc Microbiol. *Res:* Bacteriophage of lactic cultures; Q-fever infection in humans and animals; detection and persistence of chlorinated insecticides in human and animal blood; insecticide residues in food. *Mailing Add:* Alta Dept of Agr O S Longman Bldg 6909 116th St Edmonton AB T6H 4P2 Can

KADISH, ABRAHAM, mathematics, plasma physics, see previous edition

KADISH, KARL MITCHELL, b Detroit, Mich, Feb 4, 45. ANALYTICAL CHEMISTRY. *Educ:* Univ Mich, BS, 67; Pa State Univ, PhD(chem), 70. *Prof Exp:* Vis asst prof chem, Univ New Orleans, 70-71; res asst, Nat Ctr Sci Res, France, 71-72; asst prof chem, Calif State Univ, Fullerton, 72-76; asst prof, 76-77, assoc prof, 78-82, PROF CHEM, UNIV HOUSTON, 82- *Concurrent Pos:* Pres, Intersci Consults, USA, 75-; vis prof, Univ Strasbourg, 80-81; assoc mem, Int Union Pure & Appl Chem Comn 5, 80-84. *Mem:* Am Chem Soc; Electrochem Soc. *Res:* Electro- and bioanalytical chemistry; rates and mechanisms of electron transfer in biologically important compounds; reactions of porphyrin metal complexes; redox reactions of transition metal complexes; spectroelectrochemistry. *Mailing Add:* Dept of Chem Univ of Houston Houston TX 77004

KADISON, RICHARD VINCENT, b New York, NY, July 25, 25; m 56; c 1. MATHEMATICS. *Educ:* Univ Chicago, MS, 47, PhD, 50. *Prof Exp:* Nat Res Coun fel math, Inst Advan Study, 50-51, mem, Off Naval Res Contract, 51-52; from asst prof to prof, Columbia Univ, 52-64; KUEMMERLE PROF MATH, UNIV PA, 64- *Concurrent Pos:* Fulbright res grant, Denmark, 54-55; Sloan fel, 58-62; Guggenheim fel, 69-70. *Mem:* Am Math Soc; foreign mem Royal Danish Acad Sci & Lett. *Res:* Spectral theory; group representations; topological algebra; abstract analysis. *Mailing Add:* Dept of Math E1 Univ of Pa Philadelphia PA 19104

KADKADE, PRAKASH GOPAL, b Goa, India, Sept 10, 41; US citizen; m 70; c 1. PLANT PHYSIOLOGY, PLANT BIOCHEMISTRY. *Educ:* Bombay Univ, BSc, 62, MSc, 64; St Louis Univ, PhD(biol), 70. *Prof Exp:* Fel plant biochem, St Louis Univ, 70-71; vis scientist natural prod, Cent Am Res Inst, 71-73; sr res chemist cereal chem, Anheuser Busch, Inc, 73-74; MEM TECH STAFF PLANT PHYSIOL, GEN TEL & ELECTRONICS LAB, 74- *Concurrent Pos:* Vis scientist plant biochem, Cent Am Res Inst, 74; vis prof molecular biol, Cath Univ, PR, 74. *Mem:* AAAS; Am Inst Biol Sci; Am Inst Plant Physiologists; Int Soc Plant Cell & Tissue Cult; Sigma Xi. *Res:* Understanding of mechanisms of light actions on certain plant biological and chemical processes. *Mailing Add:* Gen Tel & Electronics Lab 40 Sylvan Rd Waltham MA 02154

KADLEC, JOHN A, b Racine, Wis, Sept 22, 31; m 54; c 4. WILDLIFE MANAGEMENT, ECOLOGY. *Educ:* Univ Mich, BSF, 52, MS, 56, PhD(wildlife mgt), 60. *Prof Exp:* Res biologist, Mich Dept Conserv, 58-63 & US Bur Sport Fisheries & Wildlife, 63-67; res assoc & asst prof wildlife mgt, Univ Mich, Ann Arbor & prog coordr anal ecosyst, Int Biol Prog, 68-71, from assoc prof to prof resource ecol, 71-74; head dept, 74-80, PROF WILDLIFE SCI, COL NATURAL RESOURCES, UTAH STATE UNIV, 74- *Mem:* AAAS; Wildlife Soc; Ecol Soc Am. *Res:* Applications of population ecology and systems ecology to resource management, especially wildlife; animal habitat studies; wetland ecology. *Mailing Add:* Dept of Wildlife Sci Utah State Univ Logan UT 84322

KADLEC, PAUL WILLIAM, b Chatfield, Minn, Feb 10, 25; m 48; c 2. METEOROLOGY. *Educ:* St Louis Univ, BS, 51. *Prof Exp:* Aeronaut meteorologist, Chicago & Southern Air Lines, 51-52; aeronaut meteorologist, Eastern Air Lines, 52-61, flight res meteorologist, 61-69; mgr meteorol, Continental Airlines Inc, 69-78, flight plan mkt rep, 78-80. *Concurrent Pos:* Gen chmn, Int Conf Aerospace & Aeronaut Meteorol. *Honors & Awards:* Gorrell Award, Air Transport Asn, 64; Robert M Losey Award, Am Inst Aeronaut & Astronaut, 75. *Mem:* Am Meteorol Soc; fel Am Inst Aeronaut & Astronaut. *Res:* Development of airborne sensing equipment for jet aircraft utilizing theory that atmospheric temperature gradients are associated with clear air turbulence at high altitudes. *Mailing Add:* 28631 Quail Hill Dr Rancho Palos Verdes CA 90274

KADLEC, ROBERT HENRY, b Racine, Wis, June 11, 38; m 57; c 3. CHEMICAL ENGINEERING. *Educ:* Univ Wis, BS, 58; Univ Mich, MS, 59, PhD(chem eng), 62. *Prof Exp:* From asst prof to assoc prof, 61-70, PROF CHEM ENG, UNIV MICH, ANN ARBOR, 70- *Concurrent Pos:* Ed, Am Inst Chem Engrs J, 76- *Mem:* Am Inst Chem Engrs; Am Soc Eng Educ; AAUP. *Res:* Chemical reactors, water quality; mathematical modelling; simulation; wetlands; wastewater; automobile emission control. *Mailing Add:* Dept of Chem Eng Univ of Mich Ann Arbor MI 48109

KADLUBAR, FRED F, b Dallas, Tex, Mar 1, 46; m 68; c 1. TOXICOLOGY, ONCOLOGY. *Educ:* Univ Dallas, BA, 68; Univ Tex, Austin, PhD(chem), 73. *Prof Exp:* Fel, McArdle Lab Cancer Res, Univ Wis, Madison, 73-76; chemist, Div Molecular Biol, 76-79, DIR, DIV CARCINOGENESIS RES, NAT CTR TOXICOL RES, 79- *Concurrent Pos:* Adj Prof, Dept Biochem, Pharmacol & Toxicol, Univ Ark, Little Rock, 77-; mem, Working Cadre Nat Bladder Cancer Proj, 80- *Mem:* Am Asn Cancer Res; Sigma Xi; AAAS; Am Chem Soc. *Res:* Biochemical mechanisms of chemical carcinogenesis with emphasis on aromatic amines and nitroaromatics and liver and bladder carcinogenesis; detoxification by glutathione and structure properties of carcinogen DNA adducts. *Mailing Add:* Div Carcinogenesis Res HFT-110 Nat Ctr Toxicol Res Jefferson AR 72079

KADNER, CARL GEORGE, b Oakland, Calif, May 23, 11; m 39; c 3. INSECT PHYSIOLOGY. *Educ:* Univ San Francisco, BS, 33; Univ Calif, Berkeley, MS, 36, PhD(med entom), 41. *Prof Exp:* Instr biol, 36-41, prof & chmn dept, 41-78, EMER PROF BIOL, LOYOLA MARYMOUNT UNIV, 78- *Mem:* Entom Soc Am; Am Soc Microbiol. *Res:* Nutritional requirements of Dipteran larvae. *Mailing Add:* 8100 Loyola Blvd Los Angeles CA 90045

KADNER, ROBERT JOSEPH, b Los Angeles, Calif, Mar 19, 42; m 67; c 2. BIOCHEMICAL GENETICS. *Educ:* Loyola Univ, Los Angeles, BS, 63; Univ Calif, Los Angeles, PhD(biol chem), 67. *Prof Exp:* Nat Cancer Inst fel microbiol, Med Sch, NY Univ, 67-69; from asst prof to assoc prof, 69-80, PROF MICROBIOL, SCH MED, UNIV VA, 80- *Mem:* Am Soc Microbiol; Genetics Soc Am; Am Soc Biol Chemists. *Res:* Genetics and biochemistry of transport in Escherichia coli; bacterial genetics and regulation. *Mailing Add:* Dept of Microbiol Sch of Med Univ of Va Charlottesville VA 22908

KADO, CLARENCE ISAO, b Santa Rosa, Calif, June 10, 36; m 63; c 2. MOLECULAR BIOLOGY, PLANT PATHOLOGY. *Educ:* Univ Calif, Berkeley, BS, 59, PhD, 64. *Prof Exp:* Res fel virus lab, Univ Calif, Berkeley, 64-67, asst res biochemist, 67-68; from asst prof to assoc prof, 66-76, PROF PLANT PATH, UNIV CALIF, DAVIS, 76- *Concurrent Pos:* NATO sr fel, Ctr Study Nuclear Energy, Mol, Belg, 74-75; sabbatical leave, Dept Molecular, Cellular & Develop Biol, Univ Colo, Boulder, 75. *Mem:* AAAS; Am Soc Microbiol; Am Phytopath Soc; NY Acad Sci; Sigma Xi. *Res:* Molecular biology of host-pathogen interactions; molecular mechanism of tumorigenesis and abnormal growth in higher cells; plant bacteriology and virology. *Mailing Add:* Dept Plant Path Univ Calif Davis CA 95616

KADOR, PETER FRITZ, b Regensburg, Ger, Oct 3, 49; US citizen; m 76. MEDICINAL CHEMISTRY. *Educ:* Capital Univ, BA, 72; Ohio State Univ, PhD(med chem), 76. *Prof Exp:* staff fel cataract res, 76-79, RES CHEMIST, NAT EYE INST, NIH, 79- *Concurrent Pos:* Rhoto Cataract Res Award, 81. *Mem:* Am Chem Soc; Asn Res Vision & Ophthal; AAAS. *Res:* Cataract development; lens transport systems; drug effects on the lens; aldose reductase inhibitors. *Mailing Add:* Nat Eye Inst NIH Rm 230 Bldg 6 Bethesda MD 20014

KADOTA, T THEODORE, b Ehime-ken, Japan, Nov 14, 30; US citizen; m 56; c 3. MATHEMATICS, COMMUNICATIONS. *Educ:* Yokohama Nat Univ, BS, 53; Univ Calif, Berkeley, MS, 56, PhD(elec eng), 60. *Prof Exp:* Teaching asst, Univ Calif, Berkeley, 55-56, res asst, 56-60; MEM STAFF MATH, BELL TEL LABS, INC, 60- *Mem:* Fel Inst Elec & Electronics Engrs. *Res:* Mathematical research in communication theory, specifically, application of probability theory and stochastic processes to detection, estimation, information theory and random ocean waves theory; model making; theorem proving. *Mailing Add:* Math Res Ctr 600 Mountain Ave Bell Tel Labs, Inc Murray Hill NJ 07974

KADOUM, AHMED MOHAMED, b Oct 28, 37; m 65; c 2. ENTOMOLOGY, TOXICOLOGY. *Educ:* Univ Alexandria, BSc, 58; Univ Nebr, MSc, 63, PhD(entom), 66. *Prof Exp:* Instr chem, Univ Alexandria, 58-60; res asst entom, Univ Nebr, 62-65, instr toxicol, 65-66; ASST PROF ENTOM, KANS STATE UNIV, 66- *Res:* Pesticidal chemistry and toxicology. *Mailing Add:* Dept of Entom Kans State Univ Manhattan KS 66502

KADYK, JOHN AMOS, b Springfield, Ill, Nov 10, 29; m 57; c 2. PHYSICS. *Educ:* Williams Col, AB, 52; Mass Inst Technol, BS, 52; Calif Inst Technol, PhD(physics), 57. *Prof Exp:* Instr physics, Univ Mich, 57-59; EXP PHYSICIST, LAWRENCE BERKELEY LAB, UNIV CALIF, 59- *Res:* High energy physics; colliding beams. *Mailing Add:* Lawrence Berkeley Lab Univ of Calif Berkeley CA 94720

KAEDING, WARREN WILLIAM, b Milwaukee, Wis, Apr 24, 21; m 48; c 4. ORGANIC CHEMISTRY. *Educ:* Wis State Univ, Oshkosh, BS, 42; Univ Calif, Los Angeles, MS, 49, Univ Calif, PhD(chem), 52. *Prof Exp:* Res chemist, Leffingwell Chem Co, 49 & Dow Chem Co, 52-65; res chemist, 65-68, mgr org chem res, 68-72, sr res assoc, 72-78, SR SCIENTIST, MOBILE CHEM CO, 78- *Mem:* Am Chem Soc. *Res:* Organic synthesis; catalytic oxidation; oxidation mechanisms, carbamate insecticides; hetero-catalysis with zeolites. *Mailing Add:* 700 Mountain Ave Westfield NJ 07090

KAELBER, WILLIAM WALBRIDGE, b Rochester, NY, Aug 6, 23; m 49; c 4. NEUROLOGY. *Educ:* NY Med Col, MD, 48. *Prof Exp:* Instr neurol, 55-56, assoc, 56-58, res asst prof, 58-61, assoc prof anat & neurol, 61-68, PROF ANAT & NEUROL, COL MED, UNIV IOWA, 68- *Concurrent Pos:* USPHS spec clin trainee, Univ Iowa, 56-58. *Mem:* Asn Res Nerv & Ment Dis. *Res:* Experimental neuroanatomy; neurophysiology; nociceptive aspects of nervous system. *Mailing Add:* Dept of Anat Univ of Iowa Col of Med Iowa City IA 52240

KAELBLE, DAVID HARDIE, b Pine City, Minn, June 2, 28; m 51; c 5. PHYSICAL CHEMISTRY, POLYMER PHYSICS. *Educ:* Univ Minn, Minneapolis, BSc, 51. *Prof Exp:* Polymer chemist, Cent Res Labs, 3M Co, 51-56, sr res chemist, 56-61, res specialist, 61-69; mem tech staff, 69-75, GROUP LEADER POLYMER & COMPOSITES GROUP, SCI CTR, ROCKWELL INT CORP, 75- *Concurrent Pos:* Mem comt damping nomenclature, Am Standards Asn, 63-65 & comt adhesion, Nat Res Coun, 71; chmn, Gordon Conf Adhesion, 71. *Honors & Awards:* Award, Am Soc Test & Mat, 63. *Mem:* Am Chem Soc; Am Phys Soc; Soc Rheol. *Res:* Adhesion phenomena including surface chemistry, rheology, and fracture mechanics; polymer physical chemistry and mechanical properties; biophysics and composite material properties. *Mailing Add:* Sci Ctr Rockwell Int Corp Thousand Oaks CA 91360

KAELBLE, EMMETT FRANK, b St Louis, Mo, July 31, 31; m 55; c 3. ANALYTICAL CHEMISTRY, SPECTROSCOPY. *Educ:* DePauw Univ, BA, 53; Univ Ill, MS, 55, PhD(anal chem), 57. *Prof Exp:* From res chemist to sr res chemist, 57-64; res group leader, Res Dept, Inorg Chem Div, Monsanto Co, 64-78, SR RES GROUP LEADER, APPL SCI, MONSANTO INDUST CHEM CO, 78- *Mem:* Am Chem Soc; Soc Appl Spectros. *Res:* X-ray spectroscopy; chromatography; other instrumental and chemical analytical techniques. *Mailing Add:* Monsanto Co 800 N Lindbergh Blvd St Louis MO 63166

KAELLIS, EUGENE, dentistry, see previous edition

KAEMPFFER, FREDERICK AUGUSTUS, b Gorlitz, Ger, Nov 29, 20; nat Can; m 44; c 2. THEORETICAL PHYSICS. *Educ:* Univ Gottingen, dipl physics, 43, Dr rer nat(physics), 48. *Prof Exp:* Lectr, 48, from asst prof to assoc prof, 49-58, PROF PHYSICS, UNIV BC, 58- *Mem:* Am Phys Soc. *Res:* Theory of fields. *Mailing Add:* 2054 Western Pkwy Vancouver BC V6T 1V5 Can

KAENEL, REGINALD A(LFRED), communication & computer sciences, see previous edition

KAESBERG, PAUL JOSEPH, b Engers, Ger, Sept 26, 23; nat US; m 53; c 3. BIOPHYSICS, BIOCHEMISTRY. *Educ:* Univ Wis, BS, 45, PhD(physics), 49. *Hon Degrees:* DSc, State Univ Leiden, 75. *Prof Exp:* From instr to asst prof biomet & physics, 49-54, from asst prof to prof biochem, 54-60, PROF BIOPHYS & BIOCHEM, UNIV WIS-MADISON, 64-, CHMN BIOPHYS LAB, 70- *Mem:* Am Soc Biol Chem Am Soc Microbiol; Biophys Soc. *Res:* Structure and synthesis of viruses and macromolecules. *Mailing Add:* Biophys Lab Univ of Wis Madison WI 53706

KAESLER, ROGER LEROY, b Ponca City, Okla, June 22, 37; m 61; c 3. MICROPALEONTOLOGY. *Educ:* Colo Sch Mines, GeolE, 59; Univ Kans, MS, 62, PhD(micropaleont), 65. *Prof Exp:* From asst prof to assoc prof, 65-73, PROF GEOL, UNIV KANS, 73- *Mem:* Paleont Soc; Soc Syst Zool; Geol Soc Am; Am Soc Naturalists; Ecol Soc Am. *Res:* Paleoecology of Ostracoda and Fusulinacea; quantitative methods in applied aquatic biology. *Mailing Add:* Dept of Geol Univ of Kans Lawrence KS 66044

KAESZ, HERBERT DAVID, b Alexandria, Egypt, Jan 4, 33; nat US; m 58. ORGANOMETALLIC CHEMISTRY. *Educ:* NY Univ, BA, 54; Harvard Univ, MA, 56, PhD, 59. *Prof Exp:* Fel inorg chem & adv prog high sch teachers, Harvard Univ, 58-60; from asst prof to assoc prof, 60-68, PROF INORG CHEM, UNIV CALIF, LOS ANGELES, 68- *Concurrent Pos:* Assoc ed, Inorg Chem, Am Chem Soc, 68- *Mem:* Am Chem Soc; Royal Soc Chem; fel AAAS. *Res:* Chemistry of transition metals, especially organometallic complexes, polynuclear metal carbonyl cluster complexes and hydrides; pathways of homogeneous catalysis. *Mailing Add:* Dept of Chem Univ of Calif Los Angeles CA 90024

KAFADAR, KAREN, b Evergreen Park, Ill, July 6, 53. DATA ANALYSIS, ROBUST METHODS. *Educ:* Stanford Univ, BS & MS, 75; Princeton Univ, PhD(statist), 79. *Prof Exp:* Asst prof statist, Ore State Univ, 79-80; MATH STATISTICIAN, STATIST ENG DIV, NAT BUR STANDARDS, 80- *Concurrent Pos:* Consult, OEA, Inc, 77- *Mem:* Am Statist Asn; Inst Math Statist. *Res:* New methodology in data analysis particularly robust methods and treatment of outliers; experimental design; spectrum analysis. *Mailing Add:* Statist Eng Div Admin A-337 Nat Bur Standards Washington DC 20234

KAFALAS, JAMES A, b Ipswich, Mass, Dec 28, 19; m 57; c 2. PHYSICAL INORGANIC CHEMISTRY. *Educ:* Harvard Univ, AB, 50. *Prof Exp:* Sr chemist, Tracerlab, Inc, Mass, 50-52; chemist, Lincoln Lab, Mass Inst Technol, 52-59 & Manlabs Inc, 59-61; chemist, Lincoln Lab, Mass Inst Technol, 61-80; WITH GEN TEL & ELECTRONICS LABS, 80- *Mem:* Am Chem Soc. *Res:* Behavior of matter at elevated pressures up to 100,000 atmospheres; chemistry of semiconductor surfaces; preparation of pure semiconducting compounds; effects of nuclear detonations; solid electrolytes with high ionic conductivity; exploitation of solar energy. *Mailing Add:* Gen Tel & Electronics Labs 40 Sylvan Rd Waltham MA 02254

KAFALAS, PETER, b Newburyport, Mass, Dec 6, 25; m 57; c 2. CHEMICAL PHYSICS. *Educ:* Harvard Univ, AB, 50; Mass Inst Technol, PhD(inorg chem), 54. *Prof Exp:* Assoc chemist, Argonne Nat Lab, 54-59; staff mem, Mitre Corp, Mass, 59-61; sr scientist, Tech Opers, Inc, 61-65; STAFF MEM, LINCOLN LAB, MASS INST TECHNOL, 65- *Mem:* Am Chem Soc; Optical Soc Am. *Res:* Nuclear chemistry, deuteron reactions and neutron reactions; spectroscopy, high-speed spectrography of plasmas; laser technology, laser Q-switching with saturable dyes; laser propagation studies; laser vaporization of fog droplets; laser beam diagnostics. *Mailing Add:* Lincoln Lab Mass Inst Technol PO Box 73 Lexington MA 02173

KAFATOS, FOTIS C, b Iraclion, Greece, Apr 16, 40; m 67; c 1. DEVELOPMENTAL BIOLOGY. *Educ:* Cornell Univ, BA, 61; Harvard Univ, MA, 62, PhD(biol), 65. *Prof Exp:* Tutor, 62-63, from instr to asst prof, 65-69, PROF BIOL, HARVARD UNIV, 69- *Mem:* AAAS; Am Soc Zool; Am Soc Cell Biol; Soc Develop Biol. *Res:* Molecular and cellular aspects of development, cell differentiation during insect metamorphosis. *Mailing Add:* Biol Labs Harvard Univ Cambridge MA 02138

KAFATOS, MINAS, b Crete, Greece, Mar 25, 45; m 71; c 2. ASTROPHYSICS. *Educ:* Cornell Univ, BA, 67; Mass Inst Technol, PhD(physics), 72. *Prof Exp:* Res assoc astrophysics, Joint Inst for Lab Astrophys, Univ Colo, 72-73 & Nat Res Coun, Nat Acad Sci, 73-75; asst prof, 75-79, ASSOC PROF ASTRON, GEORGE MASON UNIV, 79- *Concurrent Pos:* Res scientist astrophys, Goddard Space Flight Ctr, NASA, 75- *Mem:* Am Astron Soc; Am Phys Soc; Int Astron Union. *Res:* Black holes; quasars; active galaxies; interstellar medium; mass loss and long period variables; forbidden line calculations; symbiotic stars; cosmic rays; supernovae. *Mailing Add:* Dept of Physics George Mason Univ Fairfax VA 22030

KAFER, ENID ROSEMARY, b Sydney, Australia, May 27, 37. ANESTHESIOLOGY. *Educ:* Univ Sydney, BS, 59, MB & BS, 62, MD, 70. *Prof Exp:* Med resident, Royal Prince Alfred Hosp, Sydney, 62-63, anesthetic registr, 64; res fel, Dept Med, Univ Sydney, 65-66, lectr, 67, Life Ins Med Res fel, 68-69; sr registr, Dept Anesthetics, Royal Postgrad Med Sch, London, 69-71; fel physiol, Univ Calif, San Francisco, 71-72, asst prof, Dept Anesthesia, 72-73; ASSOC PROF PHYSIOL & ANESTHESIOL, SCH MED, UNIV NC, CHAPEL HILL, 73- *Concurrent Pos:* Mem, Res Rev Comt, NC Heart Asn, 76-79. *Mem:* Fel Royal Australian Col Physicians; fel Fac Royal Col Surgeons London; Am Physiol Soc; Am Soc Anesthesiologists; Am Thoracic Soc. *Res:* Load adjustment mechanisms of the respiratory system, including examination of neural and muscle factors, and the effects of changing chemical stimuli, chemoreceptor denervation and the effects of general anesthesia. *Mailing Add:* Dept of Anesthesiol Sch of Med Univ of NC Chapel Hill NC 27514

KAFER, ETTA (MRS E R BOOTHROYD), b Zurich, Switz, July 31, 25; m 57; c 3. GENETICS. *Educ:* Univ Zurich, dipl, 48, PhD(genetics), 52. *Prof Exp:* Res asst microbial genetics, Glasgow Univ, 53-55, res fel, 55-56; res fel, Carnegie Inst, 56; res assoc, 58-63, lectr, 59-62, asst prof, 62-67, assoc prof, 67-76, PROF MICROBIAL GENETICS, McGILL UNIV, 76- *Mem:* Genetics Soc Am; Genetics Soc Can; Swiss Genetics Soc. *Res:* Microbial genetics; mitotic and meiotic recombination; genetics of nucleases; mutagen sensitivity in fungi. *Mailing Add:* Biol Sci Bldg 1205 Dr Penfield Ave Montreal PQ H3A 1B1 Can

KAFESJIAN, R(ALPH), b Chicago, Ill, Mar 28, 34; m 55; c 3. CHEMICAL ENGINEERING, PHYSICAL CHEMISTRY. *Educ:* Purdue Univ, BS, 55; Univ Louisville, MChE, 57, PhD(chem eng), 61. *Prof Exp:* Instr chem physics & chem eng, Univ Louisville, 57-60; res chem engr, Monsanto Res Corp, 61-63, sr res chem engr, 63-67, res group leader, 67-69; biomed res lab, 69-71, task leader corp technol, 71-77, sr scientist, 78-80, PRIN SCIENTIST, AM HOSP SUPPLY CORP, 81- *Mem:* AAAS; Am Chem Soc; assoc Am Inst Chem Engrs; Nat Asn Corrosion Engrs; Biomat Soc. *Res:* High temperature materials, reactions, processes and technology; electrochemical energy conversion methods; corrosion; electrochemistry; biomedical materials and devices. *Mailing Add:* Med Specialties Am Hosp Supply Corp 2132 Michelson Irvine CA 92715

KAFFEZAKIS, JOHN GEORGE, b Athens, Greece, June 15, 29; US citizen; m 55; c 2. FOOD SCIENCE, MICROBIOLOGY. *Educ:* Col Agr, Athens, BS, 50; Iowa State Univ, MS, 52; Univ Md, PhD(food sci), 67. *Prof Exp:* Lab supt, Borden Co, Ltd, Can, 52-55; food technologist, Agr & Fisheries Br, Ottawa, Ont, 55-64; asst prof food technol, Auburn Univ, 64-66; res scientist, Joseph E Seagrams & Sons, Inc, 67-69; DIR TECH SERV, OVERSEAS DIV, NAT CAN CORP, 69- *Mem:* AAAS; Inst Food Technologists; Agr Inst Can. *Res:* Processing, microbiology, packaging, quality evaluation, development of new food products and marketing. *Mailing Add:* 29 Selefkou St Thrakomakedones Attiki Greece

KAFKA, MARIAN STERN, b Richmond, Va, Mar 30, 27; m 52; c 3. PHYSIOLOGY, NEUROSCIENCE. *Educ:* Conn Col, BA, 48; Univ Chicago, PhD(physiol), 52. *Prof Exp:* Teaching asst zool, Conn Col, 47-48; asst physiol, Sch Med, Univ Chicago, 48-52; res asst, Sch Med, Emory Univ, 52-53, Ill Neuropsychiat Inst, Univ Ill, Chicago, 53-54 & Sch Med, Yale Univ, 54-57; USPHS fel, Endocrinol Br, Nat Heart & Lung Inst, 65-68, physiologist, Hypertension-Endocrine Br, 68-74, PHYSIOLOGIST, SECT BIOCHEM & PHARMACOL, BIOL PSYCHIAT BR, NIMH, USPHS, 74- *Mem:* Am Physiol Soc; Endocrine Soc; Biophys Soc; AAAS; Sigma Xi. *Res:* Interaction between neurotransmitters, hormones and receptors on neurons and blood cells; central nervous system control of circadian rhythms. *Mailing Add:* Biol Psychiat Br Bldg 10 Rm 3N-256 NIMH Bethesda MD 20205

KAFKA, ROBERT W(ILLIAM), b Chicago, Ill, Oct 30, 37; m 66; c 1. DEFENSE ELECTRONICS SYSTEMS, COMMAND & CONTROL SYSTEMS. *Educ:* Univ Ill, BSEE, 58, MSEE, 59, PhD(elec eng), 63. *Prof Exp:* Instr elec eng, Univ Ill, 60-63; mem tech staff, Guid & Control Dept, Aerospace Corp, 63-66; MGR ADVAN TECHNOL PROGS OFF, SYSTS DIV, HUGHES AIRCRAFT CO, 66- *Mem:* Inst Elec & Electronics Engrs; Sigma Xi. *Mailing Add:* Systs Div B618/P325 Hughes Aircraft Co PO Box 3310 Fullerton CA 92634

KAFRAWY, ADEL, b Cairo, Egypt, Oct 15, 43; US citizen; m 75; c 2. ORGANIC CHEMISTRY, CELLULOSE TECHNOLOGY. *Educ:* Cairo Univ, BSc, 64; Univ Rochester, MS, 71; Univ Mo-Columbia, PhD(org chem), 74; Syracuse Univ, MBA, 82. *Prof Exp:* Demonstr chem, Cairo Univ, 64-68; assoc phys org chem, Syracuse Univ, 74-75; assoc org chem, State Univ NY Col Environ Sci & Forestry, Syracuse, 75-77; res chemist, Cellulose Res, ITT Rayonier, Inc, 77-81; SR SCIENTIST POLYMER RES, ETHICON, INC, 81- *Mem:* Am Chem Soc. *Res:* Polymer cellulose and organic chemical research and development. *Mailing Add:* Ethicon Inc Polymer Res & Develop Rte 22 Somerville NJ 08876

KAGAN, BENJAMIN, b New York, NY, Mar 9, 21; m 43; c 2. ORGANIC CHEMISTRY. *Educ:* DePaul Univ, BS, 47; Pa State Univ, MS, 50. *Prof Exp:* Org res chemist, Army Chem Ctr, Md, 50-62; res anal chemist, Div Food Chem, Bur Drugs, Food & Drug Admin, 62-66, chemist, Div Oncol & Radiopharmaceut Drug Prod, 66-73, supvry chemist, 73-77; CONSULT REGULATORY AFFAIRS, 77- *Concurrent Pos:* Lectr regulatory affairs, 79- *Mem:* AAAS; Am Chem Soc; fel Am Inst Chemists; Parenteral Drug Asn. *Res:* Organo-phosphorous and sulfur compounds; nitrogen heterocycles; radiopharmaceuticals. *Mailing Add:* 7916 Ivymount Terr Potomac MD 20854

KAGAN, BENJAMIN M, b Washington, Pa, July 15, 13; m 40; c 2. PEDIATRICS. *Educ:* Washington & Jefferson Col, AB, 33; Johns Hopkins Univ, MD, 37; Am Bd Nutrit & Am Bd Pediat, cert. *Prof Exp:* Instr, St Phillip Sch Pub Health Nursing, 40-42, instr, Marine Biol Lab, Woods Hole, 34; intern, Sinai Hosp, Baltimore, 37-38; res contagion, Willard Parker Hosp, 38; resident pediat, Babies Hosp, New York, 39-40; instr pediat, Med Col Va, 40-42; asst, Columbia Univ, 46; from clin asst prof to clin prof, Univ Ill, 47-54; prof, Northwestern Univ, 54-55; PROF-IN-RESIDENCE PEDIAT, SCH MED, UNIV CALIF, LOS ANGELES, 55-, VCHMN DEPT, 74- *Concurrent Pos:* Mem staff, Michael Reese Hosp, 46-51, attend pediatrician, & dir, Pediat Res Dept, Inst Med Res, 46-55, chmn dept pediat, 51-55; dir & chmn pediat, Cedars Sinai Med Ctr, 55-; official examr, mem exec comt & chmn written exam comt, Am Bd Pediat. *Mem:* AAAS; Am Pediat Soc; Soc Pediat Res; Soc Exp Biol & Med; AMA. *Res:* Nutrition and infectious disease. *Mailing Add:* 8700 Beverly Blvd Los Angeles CA 90048

KAGAN, FRED, b Chicago, Ill, Dec 24, 20; m 45; c 6. MEDICINAL CHEMISTRY, ORGANIC CHEMISTRY. *Educ:* Univ Ill, BS, 42; Mass Inst Technol, PhD(org chem), 49. *Prof Exp:* Res org chemist, Stand Oil Co Ind, 49-52; res org chemist, 52-68, mgr cent nerv syst res, 68-78, group mgr, 78-81, DIR, EXP SCI & THERAPEUTICS, UPJOHN CO, 81- *Mem:* Am Chem Soc; The Chem Soc; NY Acad Sci. *Res:* Synthesis; psychopharmacology, drug development from test tube through human testing to finally filing an NDA. *Mailing Add:* Upjohn Co 301 Henrietta St Kalamazoo MI 49001

KAGAN, HARVEY ALEXANDER, b New York, NY, Sept 25, 37; m 68. CIVIL ENGINEERING. *Educ:* Columbia Univ, BS, 58; Univ Ill, MS, 59; NY Univ, EngScD(civil eng), 65; Purdue Univ, MS, 80. *Prof Exp:* Struct engr, Repub Aviation Corp, 59-61; asst civil engr, New York City Bd Educ, 61; struct test engr, Martin Co Div, Martin-Marietta Corp, 61-62, eng specialist, 65-66; test engr, Vertol Div, Boeing Co, 62; struct mech engr, Grumman Aircraft Corp, 66; from asst prof to assoc prof civil eng, Rutgers Univ, 66-74; sr civil engr, C F Braun & Co, 74-75; assoc prof & prog chmn, Univ Evansville, 75-77; sr consult, Wager-Hohns-Inglis, 78-81; SR CONSULT, HILL INT, INC, 81- *Concurrent Pos:* NSF res grant, 67-68. *Mem:* Am Soc Civil Engrs; Am Concrete Inst; Sigma Xi. *Mailing Add:* Hill Int PO Box 397 Willingboro NJ 08046

KAGAN, HERBERT MARCUS, b Boston, Mass, Aug 18, 32; m 62; c 2. BIOCHEMISTRY. *Educ:* Univ Mass, Amherst, BS, 54, MS, 56; Tufts Univ, PhD(biochem), 66. *Prof Exp:* Instr microbiol, Purdue Univ, 56-58; res assoc pharmacol, Sch Med, Boston Univ, 59-60; biologist, Arthur D Little, Inc, 60-61; asst prof, 69-72, assoc prof, 72-80, PROF BIOCHEM, SCH MED, BOSTON UNIV, 80- *Concurrent Pos:* Am Cancer Soc res fel biochem, Harvard Med Sch, 66-69; fel, Arteriosclerosis Coun, Am Heart Asn. *Mem:* AAAS; Am Soc Biol Chemists; Am Heart Asn; Sigma Xi. *Res:* Enzymology; protein chemistry; structure-function relationships of enzymes; connective tissue proteins; stereospecifity in catalysis. *Mailing Add:* Dept Biochem Res Bldg Rm 420 Boston Univ Sch of Med Boston MA 02118

KAGAN, IRVING GEORGE, b New York, NY, June 1, 19; m 40; c 2. PARASITOLOGY, IMMUNOLOGY. *Educ:* Brooklyn Col, AB, 40; Univ Mich, MA, 47, PhD(zool), 50. *Prof Exp:* Asst prof zool, Univ Pa, 52-57; chief helminth unit, 57-62, chief parasitol unit, 62-66, DIR PARASITOL DIV,

CTR DIS CONTROL, 67- *Concurrent Pos:* Nat Res Coun fel, Univ Chicago, 50-52; mem, Scientific Working Group, Epidemiology, WHO, 78. *Honors & Awards:* Henry Baldwin Ward Medal, Am Soc Parasitol, 65; Behring-Bilharz Medal, 81. *Mem:* Am Soc Trop Med & Hyg; Am Soc Parasitol; Am Asn Immunol; Am Micros Soc; Sci Res Soc Am. *Res:* Immunodiagnosis of parasitic infections and the immunology of the host parasite interaction. *Mailing Add:* Parasitic Dis Div Ctr Infectious Dis Ctr Dis Control Atlanta GA 30333

KAGAN, JACQUES, b Paris, France, Nov 11, 33; US citizen. ORGANIC CHEMISTRY, BIOLOGICAL CHEMISTRY. *Educ:* Sorbonne, BS, 56; Rice Univ, PhD(chem), 60. *Prof Exp:* Res assoc, Mass Inst Technol, 60-61; res chemist, Amoco Chem Co, Ind, 61-62; res scientist & Welch Found fel, Univ Tex, 62-65; from asst prof to assoc prof, 65-73, PROF CHEM & BIOL, UNIV ILL, CHICAGO CIRCLE, 73- *Concurrent Pos:* Vis prof, Univ Geneva, 71-72 & Univ Haute-Alsace, 80; Fulbright grant, 80. *Honors & Awards:* Cooley Award, Am Soc Plant Taxon, 64. *Mem:* Am Chem Soc; Am Soc Photobiol. *Res:* Organic synthesis and reaction mechanisms; plant chemistry and biochemistry; photochemical reactions. *Mailing Add:* Dept of Chem Univ of Ill at Chicago Circle Chicago IL 60680

KAGAN, JOEL (DAVID), b New York, NY, Aug 18, 43; m 65; c 2. MATHEMATICS. *Educ:* Rutgers Col, BA, 66; Stevens Inst Technol, MS, 67, PhD(math), 70. *Prof Exp:* Instr math, Stevens Inst Technol, 68-70; ASST PROF MATH, UNIV HARTFORD, 70- *Mem:* Soc Symbolic Logic; Am Math Soc. *Res:* Algebraic logic; algebraic structures arising from theories in the sentential and predicate calculus with identity connective. *Mailing Add:* Dept of Math Univ Hartford West Hartford CT 06117

KAGANN, ROBERT HOWARD, b New York, NY, June 26, 46. CHEMICAL PHYSICS. *Educ:* NY Univ, BA, 69; Univ Colo, PhD(chem physics), 75. *Prof Exp:* Res fel physics, Univ BC, 75-77; NAT RES COUN ASSOC PHYSICS, MOLECULAR SPECTROS DIV, NAT BUR STANDARDS, 77- *Mem:* Am Phys Soc. *Res:* Molecular spectroscopy in the visible, infrared, and microwave regions; laser and heat pipe spectroscopy. *Mailing Add:* Nat Bur of Standards Washington DC 20234

KAGANOV, ALAN LAWRENCE, b Brooklyn, NY, Dec 7, 38. BIOENGINEERING, MECHANICAL ENGINEERING. *Educ:* Duke Univ, BS, 60; New York Univ, MBA, 67; Columbia Univ, MS, 72, ScD, 74. *Prof Exp:* Packaging engr, Amstar Co, 60-64; prod develop engr, Johnson & Johnson, 64-69; career fel, NIH, 69-74; DIR MED PROD RES & DEVELOP, DAVIS & GECK, AM CYANAMID CO, 74- *Mem:* Sigma Xi; Am Chem Soc; Am Soc Testing & Mat. *Res:* Development of new implantable materials and medical devices. *Mailing Add:* 150 Gary Rd Stanford CT 06903

KAGARISE, RONALD EUGENE, b East Freedom, Pa, July 17, 26; m 47; c 3. PHYSICS. *Educ:* Duke Univ, BA, 48; Pa State Col, MS, 49, PhD(physics), 51. *Prof Exp:* Res assoc physics, Pa State Col, 51-52; head chem spectros sect, Naval Res Lab, 52-66; prog dir phys chem, NSF, 66-68; supt chem div, Naval Res Lab, 68-76; DIR DIV MAT RES, NSF, WASHINGTON, DC, 76- *Mem:* Am Phys Soc; Sigma Xi; Am Chem Soc; Coblentz Soc. *Res:* Rotational isomerism; molecular constants; structure. *Mailing Add:* 602 Pine Rd Oxon Hill MD 20022

KAGAWA, CHARLES M, b Halaula, Hawaii, Feb 11, 23; m 49; c 3. MEDICAL RESEARCH. *Educ:* Univ Hawaii, BA, 45; Univ Wis, MS, 48, PhD, 53. *Prof Exp:* Investr biol res, G D Searle & Co, Ill, 53-64; dir biol res, 64-68, asst to dir res, 68-71, asst dir res, 71-72, mgr ophthal res, 72, SCI ADV-ADMIN ASST, ALCON LABS, INC, 73- *Mem:* AAAS; Soc Exp Biol & Med; Am Soc Pharmacol & Exp Therapeut; Am Chem Soc; Am Soc Zool. *Res:* Metabolic effects of adrenocortical and related steroids; renal physiology; diuretic agents; preclinical safety and efficacy evaluation of ophthalmic drugs; drug regulatory affairs. *Mailing Add:* Alcon Labs Inc PO Box 1959 Ft Worth TX 76101

KAGEL, RONALD OLIVER, b Milwaukee, Wis, Jan 16, 36; m 59; c 3. ANALYTICAL CHEMISTRY. *Educ:* Univ Wis, BS, 58; Univ Minn, PhD(chem), 64. *Prof Exp:* Res chemist, 64-67, proj leader, Chem Res Lab, 67-69, group leader, 69-71, sr res chemist, 71-72, sr anal specialist, 72-74, supvr spec anal group, 74-77, environ systs group leader surface anal, 77-78, res mgr surface anal, Anal Lab, 78-79, mgr, Regulatory Affairs-Water, 79-81, mgr states environ activities, 81, DIR ENVIRON QUALITY, DOW CHEM CO, 81- *Concurrent Pos:* Mem fac, Saginaw Valley Col, 64-67; mem adv bd, Raman Newslett, 68-75; secy, Ad-hoc Subpanel Laser Excited Raman Spectra, Nat Res Coun, 68, mem, Numerical Data Adv Bd, Joint Comt Atomic & Molecular Structure-Subcomt Laser Raman Spectros, 70-80; mem, Ad-hoc Panel Micro-Raman Spectros, Nat Bur Stand, 74; assoc ed, Appl Spectros, 75-80; secy, Int Fourier Trans Conf, 77; CMA Adv Comt, Task Group Anal Methods & Monitoring; mem adv comt, Critical Mat Register, State Mich Dept Nat Res, 76-79; liason coordr, Am Soc Testing & Mat, 79-81; chmn, Natural Resources Comt, State Govt Affairs Coun, 81- *Mem:* Optical Soc Am; Soc Appl Spectros; Coblentz Soc; Am Soc Testing & Mat. *Res:* Molecular structure elucidation, surface catalysis and bulk mechanistic studies; remote detection of ambient air emissions by infrared Fourier transform and Raman spectroscopy; infrared chemiluminescence applications; environmental measurements of trace compounds. *Mailing Add:* Environ Quality 2030 Bldg Dow Chem Co Midland MI 48640

KAGEN, HERBERT PAUL, b Worcester, Mass, May 6, 29; m 56; c 4. ORGANIC CHEMISTRY. *Educ:* Mass Inst Technol, SB, 52; Univ RI, MS, 54; Wayne State Univ, PhD, 60. *Prof Exp:* From asst prof to assoc prof chem, Detroit Inst Technol, 57-67; chmn dept chem, 68-71, PROF ORG CHEM, W VA STATE COL, 67-, DIR CHEM TECHNOL, 75- *Concurrent Pos:* Consult, Chem Serv Corp, 57-, Union Carbide Corp, WVa State Bd Educ & Kanawha County Bd Educ; Mich Heart Asn fel, 60; adj prof, WVa Univ, 70-71; dir, NSF-Coop Col Sch Sci Prog for high sch chem teachers, 70-71;

dir, WVa RESA III Prog Gifted High Sch Sr, 75; fac adv, NSF-SOS Prog, Kanawha Valley, 73. *Mem:* Am Chem Soc. *Res:* Reaction of amines with lactides; organic nitrogen chemistry; preparation of lactides. *Mailing Add:* Dept Chem W Va State Col Institute WV 25112

KAGETSU, T(ADASHI) J(ACK), b Vancouver, BC, Apr 22, 31; m 57; c 2. CHEMICAL ENGINEERING. *Educ:* Univ Toronto, BASc, 54, MASc, 55, PhD(appl chem), 57. *Prof Exp:* Asst res chem engr, metals div, 57-60, res chem engr, 60-61, assoc engr, nuclear div, 61-64, proj engr, mining & metals div, 64-67, staff engr, 67-75, mgr, process eng, 75-77, mgr design eng, 77-78, ASST DIR, ENG, METALS DIV, UNION CARBIDE CORP, 78- *Mem:* Am Inst Chem Engrs; Am Inst Mining, Metall & Petrol Engrs. *Res:* Kinetics of metal dissolution in aqueous media; fused salt electrolysis; gas-solid mass transfer and heat transfer; hydrometallurgy and pyrometallurgy; process simulation by computers. *Mailing Add:* Union Carbide Corp Metals Div Technol & Eng Dept PO Box 97 Niagara Falls NY 14302

KAGHAN, WALTER S(EIDEL), b New York, NY, Apr 16, 19; m 47; c 3. CHEMICAL ENGINEERING. *Educ:* City Col New York, BChE, 40; NY Univ, MChE, 48; Purdue Univ, PhD(chem eng), 52. *Prof Exp:* Res chem engr, St Regis Paper Co, 40-41; assoc chem engr, E I du Pont de Nemours & Co, 42-43; process engr, Kellex Corp, 44-45; dir, Resinous Res Assoc, 45-48; asst prof chem eng, Rose Polytech Inst, group leader & asst sect chief, Develop Sect, Olin Corp, 51-59, dir develop sect, Film Res & Develop Dept, 59-63, dir res & develop, Film Div, 63-75; CONSULT CHEM ENGR, 75- *Mem:* Am Soc Plastics Engrs; Am Inst Chem Engrs; NY Acad Sci; Am Chem Soc; Licensing Execs Soc. *Res:* Cellophane; polymers; plastics extrusion; rheology; polyolefins; packaging. *Mailing Add:* 4315 Brandywine Dr Sarasota FL 33583

KAGIWADA, HARRIET HATSUNE, b Honolulu, Hawaii, Sept 2, 37; m 61; c 2. APPLIED MATHEMATICS, SYSTEMS SCIENCE. *Educ:* Univ Hawaii, BA, 59, MSc, 60; Univ Kyoto, PhD(astrophys), 65. *Prof Exp:* Mathematician, Rand Corp, 61-71; res assoc math, Univ Southern Calif & consult, Rand Corp, 71-77; PRES, HFS ASSOCS, 77-; SR STAFF ENGR, HUGHES AIRCRAFT CO, 79- *Concurrent Pos:* Assoc ed, Appl Math & Comput. *Mem:* Inst Elec & Electronics Engrs; Soc Indust & Appl Math; Asn Old Crows; AAAS. *Res:* Optimization; control theory; team decision theory; command and control; operations research; atmospheric temperature estimation; mathematical models; system identification, mathematical and computational methods; dynamic programming, quasilinearization and invariant imbedding; integral equations; boundary value problems; initial value problems. *Mailing Add:* HFS Assocs 3117 Malcolm Ave Los Angeles CA 90034

KAGIWADA, REYNOLD SHIGERU, b Los Angeles, Calif, July 8, 38; m 61; c 2. ELECTRONICS ENGINEERING, SOLID STATE PHYSICS. *Educ:* Univ Calif, Los Angeles, BS, 60, MS, 63, PhD(physics), 66. *Prof Exp:* Asst prof physics, Univ Calif, Los Angeles, 67-69 & Univ Southern Calif, 69-72; mem prof staff, 72-75, scientist, 75-76, sect head, 76-77, sr scientist, 77-80, MGR, MICROWAVE PROD DEPT, MICROELECTRON CTR, TRW SYSTS GROUP, 80- *Mem:* Am Phys Soc; Acoustical Soc Am; Inst Elec & Electronic Engrs; Am Inst Aeronaut & Astronaut; Asn Old Crows. *Res:* Gallium-arsenic devices; integrated circuits; millimeter-wave devices; microwave acoustic devices; low temperature physics; superconductivity; liquid helium; ultrasonics; acoustics; microwave physics. *Mailing Add:* TRW Systs Group One Space Park Redondo Beach CA 90278

KAHAN, ARCHIE M, b Denver, Colo, Jan 18, 17; m 44; c 2. METEOROLOGY. *Educ:* Univ Denver, BA, 36, MA, 40; Calif Inst Technol, MS, 42; Agr & Mech Col Tex, PhD(meteorol oceanog), 59. *Prof Exp:* Jr engr, Denison Dist, Corps Engrs, 38-41; hydrologist, US Weather Bur, 45-46; supvr hydrologist in-chg, Mo River Forecast Ctr, 46-51; assoc dir, Am Inst Aerological Res, 51-53; asst prof meteorol, Agr & Mech Col Tex, 53-54; exec dir, Tex A&M Res Found, 54-63, dir, Tex Eng Exp Sta, 62-63; dir, Univ Okla Res Inst, 63-65; gen phys scientist, US Bur Reclamation, 65-70, chief off atmospheric resources mgt, 70-79, assoc chief, div res, 78-79; CONSULT METEOROLOGIST, 79- *Concurrent Pos:* Consult, President's Adv Comt Weather Control, 54 & NSF Panel Weather Modification, 65; mem, Adv Comt Weather Modification, State of Colo, 72- *Honors & Awards:* Award, Am Meteorol Soc, 62. *Mem:* Am Soc Civil Engrs; AAAS; Am Meteorol Soc; Am Geophys Union. *Res:* Hydrology; hydrometeorology; oceanography; research administration; development of cloud seeding technology for water resource enhancement. *Mailing Add:* 610 S Eldridge Lakewood CO 80228

KAHAN, BARRY D, b Cleveland, Ohio, July 25, 39; m 62. IMMUNOLOGY, SURGERY. *Educ:* Univ Chicago, BS, 60, PhD(physiol), 64, MD, 65. *Prof Exp:* Intern, Mass Gen Hosp, 65-66; staff assoc, NIH, 66-68; surg residency, 68-72; asst prof, 72-74, assoc prof surg, Northwestern Univ, 74-77; PROF, DEPT SURG, UNIV TEX MED SCH, 77- *Mem:* AAAS; Am Asn Immunol; Soc Univ Surg; fel Am Col Surg; Transplantation Soc. *Res:* Electron microscopy; protein biochemistry; transplantation antigens; delayed-typed hypersensitivity; transplantation and tumor-specific antyius. *Mailing Add:* Dept of Surg Univ Tex Med Sch Houston TX 77030

KAHAN, I HOWARD, b New York, NY, Jan 7, 23; m 54; c 3. AVIAN PATHOLOGY, BACTERIOLOGY. *Educ:* Queens Col, NY, BS, 43; Univ Pa, VMD, 49. *Prof Exp:* Dir vet med, Glenside Animal Hosp, 51-68; assoc prof, 68-76, PROF POULTRY PATH, ANIMAL DIS & BACT & DIR POULTRY DIAG LAB, DELAWARE VALLEY COL, 76- *Concurrent Pos:* Instr, Pa State Univ, Ogontz Campus, 60-63 & Roxborough Mem Hosp, 61-62; inspector poultry, USDA, 63-68. *Mem:* AAAS; Am Asn Avian Path; US Animal Health Asn. *Res:* All phases of avian diseases and pathology using disciplined microbiology, virology, serology and histopathology. *Mailing Add:* Dept of Poultry Path Delaware Valley Col Doylestown PA 18901

KAHAN, LAWRENCE, b Los Angeles, Calif, May 16, 44; m 69; c 2. BIOCHEMISTRY, IMMUNOLOGY. *Educ:* Univ Calif, Berkeley, BA, 65; Brandeis Univ, PhD(biochem), 71. *Prof Exp:* Fel biochem, 70-73, asst prof physiol chem, 73-78, ASSOC PROF PHYSIOL CHEM, UNIV WIS-MADISON, 78- *Concurrent Pos:* Fel, Am Cancer Soc, 70-72; res grant, NIH, 75-; consult, NSF, 77-; NSF res grant, 80- *Mem:* Am Soc Biol Chemists; Am Chem Soc. *Res:* Structure and function of bacterial and eukaryote ribosomes; cancer associated enzymes; molecular biology. *Mailing Add:* Dept of Physiol Chem Univ of Wis Madison WI 53706

KAHAN, LINDA BERYL, b San Francisco, Calif, Sept 28, 41. NEUROPHYSIOLOGY. *Educ:* Univ Calif, Berkeley, BA, 63; Stanford Univ, MA, 65, PhD(biol), 67. *Prof Exp:* Fel neurophysiol, Univ Miami, 67-68; asst prof, Antioch Col, 68-71; MEM FAC BIOL, EVERGREEN STATE COL, 71- *Mem:* AAAS. *Res:* Physiology and anatomy of invertebrate nervous systems; neural control of behavior. *Mailing Add:* Fac of Biol Evergreen State Col Olympia WA 98505

KAHAN, WILLIAM M, b Toronto, Ont, June 5, 33; m 54; c 2. MATHEMATICS, COMPUTER SCIENCE. *Educ:* Univ Toronto, BA, 54, MA, 56, PhD(numerical anal), 58. *Prof Exp:* Nat Res Coun Can fel, Cambridge Univ, 58-60; from asst prof to assoc prof math & comput sci, Univ Toronto, 60-67, prof, 68; prof comput sci, 69-72, PROF MATH, ELEC ENG & COMPUT SCI, UNIV CALIF, BERKELEY, 72- *Concurrent Pos:* Nat Res Coun Can res grant, 64-69; vis assoc prof, Stanford Univ, 66; consult, IBM Res, Yorktown Heights, NY, 67 & 72-73, Hewlett-Packard, Corvallis, Or, 74- & INTEL, Santa Clara, Calif, 77- *Mem:* Am Math Soc; Asn Comput Mach; Soc Indust & Appl Math; Inst Elec & Electronics Engrs. *Res:* Large matrix calculations; trajectory problems; error analysis; design computer arithmetic units; execution-time diagnostic systems for scientific computer systems; general purpose programs to solve standard problems in numerical analysis with highest reliability on electronic computer; standard for floating-point arithmetic. *Mailing Add:* Dept of Math Evans Hall Univ of Calif Berkeley CA 94720

KAHANA, SIDNEY H, b Winnipeg, Man, July 23, 33; m 57; c 2. THEORETICAL PHYSICS. *Educ:* Univ Man, BSc, 54, MSc, 55; Univ Edinburgh, PhD(physics), 57. *Prof Exp:* From asst prof to assoc prof physics, McGill Univ, 57-67; vis scientist, Niels Bohr Inst, 59-61; vis scientist, 65-66, SCIENTIST PHYSICS, BROOKHAVEN NAT LAB, 67- *Concurrent Pos:* Vis scientist, Atomic Energy Can, 57-62, 63 & 64; Guggenheim fel, John Simon Mem Found, 74-75. *Mem:* Fel, Am Phys Soc. *Res:* Nuclear theory; structure and reactions; intermediate energy; baryon-anti-baryon systems; many body problems. *Mailing Add:* Dept of Physics Brookhaven Nat Lab Upton NY 11973

KAHANDER, DAVID KENNETH, b New York, NY, Sept 12, 41; m 64; c 2. APPLIED MATHEMATICS, COMPUTER METHODS. *Educ:* City Col New York, BS, 62; Stevens Inst Technol, MS, 64, PhD(math), 68. *Prof Exp:* Mem staff numerical anal, Los Alamos Nat Lab, 68-80; MEM STAFF, NAT BUR STANDARDS, 80- *Concurrent Pos:* Vis prof, Univ Mich, 72-73, Univ Torino, Italy, 77, Swiss Fed Inst Technol, 77-78 & Vienna Tech Univ, 78. *Mem:* Am Math Soc; Asn Comput Mach. *Res:* Numerical analysis; computing methods; mathematical software. *Mailing Add:* Div 713 A151 Tech Bldg Nat Bur Standards Washington DC 20234

KAHLE, ANNE BETTINE, b Auburn, Wash, Mar 30, 34; m 57; c 4. GEOPHYSICS. *Educ:* Univ Alaska, BS, 55, MS, 61; Univ Calif, Los Angeles, PhD(meteorol), 75. *Prof Exp:* Res asst, Rand Corp, Calif, 61-63, from asst phys scientist to assoc phys scientist, 63-67, phys scientist, 67-74; mem tech staff, 74-75, SUPVR EARTH APPLNS & CLIMAT GROUP, JET PROPULSION LAB, 75- *Concurrent Pos:* Consult, Rand Corp, 74- *Mem:* Am Meteorol Soc; Sigma Xi; Am Geophys Union. *Res:* Remote sensing of geology; geomagnetic field; particles and fields in magnetosphere and interplanetary space; solar-terrestrial relationships; atmospheric physics; gravity; atmospheric radiation. *Mailing Add:* Jet Propulsion Lab 4800 Oak Grove Dr Pasadena CA 91103

KAHLE, CHARLES F, b Toledo, Ohio, June 2, 30; m 57; c 6. GEOLOGY. *Educ:* St Joseph's Col, Ind, BS, 53; Miami Univ, Ohio, MS, 57; Univ Kans, PhD(geol), 62. *Prof Exp:* Geologist, Mobil Petrol Co, Okla, 57-58; asst prof geol, Okla State Univ 62-63 & Univ Toledo, 63-65; from asst prof to assoc prof, 65-74, PROF GEOL, BOWLING GREEN STATE UNIV, 74- *Mem:* Geol Soc Am; Soc Econ Paleont & Mineral. *Res:* Carbonate geology; petroleum geology; scanning electron microscopy. *Mailing Add:* Dept of Geol Bowling Green State Univ Bowling Green OH 43402

KAHLER, ALBERT COMSTOCK, III, b Bay Shore, NY, June 10, 51; m 72; c 1. NUCLEAR PHYSICS. *Educ:* Gettysburg Col, BA, 73; Univ Tenn, PhD(physics), 78. *Prof Exp:* res assoc physics, Cyclotron Inst, Tex A&M Univ, 78-81; SR SCIENTIST EXP PHYSICS, WESTINGHOUSE ELEC CORP, BETTIS ATOMIC POWER LAB, 81- *Mem:* Am Phys Soc. *Res:* Nuclear structure studies using gamma-ray spectroscopy techniques. *Mailing Add:* Westinghouse Elec Corp Bettis Atomic Power Lab West Mifflin PA 15122

KAHLER, ALEX L, b Scottsbluff, Nebr, July 4, 39; m 63. GENETICS, PLANT BREEDING. *Educ:* Univ Calif, Davis, BS, 65, MS, 67, PhD, 73. *Prof Exp:* staff res assoc genetics, Univ Calif, Davis, 65-80; ASSOC PROF PLANT SCI, SDAK STATE UNIV, BROOKINGS, 80-; PLANT GENETICIST, NORTHERN GRAIN INSECTS RES LAB, AGR RES SERV, USDA, 80- *Mem:* AAAS; Am Genetics Asn; Soc Study Evolution; Genetics Soc Am; Crop Sci Soc Am. *Res:* Determining the extent and distribution of genetic variability within and between populations and with measuring the forces which are responsible for the observed variability; improving corn populations for resistance to insects and diseases. *Mailing Add:* Dept of Genetics Briggs Hall Univ of Calif Davis CA 95616

KAHLER, RICHARD LEE, b Milltown, NJ, Jan 2, 33; m 58; c 3. CARDIOVASCULAR PHYSIOLOGY. *Educ:* Yale Univ, MD, 57. *Prof Exp:* From asst prof to assoc prof med, Yale Univ, 65-68; ASSOC PROF MED, SCH MED, UNIV CALIF, SAN DIEGO, 68-; HEAD CARDIOVASCULAR DIV, SCRIPPS CLIN & RES FOUND, 68- *Concurrent Pos:* NIH res career develop award, 65-68. *Mem:* AAAS; Am Physiol Soc; Am Heart Asn; Am Col Physicians; Am Col Cardiol. *Res:* Cardiovascular pharmacology. *Mailing Add:* Scripps Clin & Res Found 10666 N Torrey Pines Rd La Jolla CA 92037

KAHLES, JOHN FRANK, b Chicago, Ill, Sept 11, 14; m 40; c 7. METALLURGY. *Educ:* Ill Inst Technol, BS, 36; Univ Cincinnati, PhD(metall), 46. *Prof Exp:* From instr to assoc prof metall, 39-51, res assoc, grad sch, 51-64, ADJ PROF METALL, COL ENG & GRAD SCH, UNIV CINCINNATI, 64-; vpres, 58-80, SR VPRES, METCUT RES ASSOCS, INC, DIR INFO TECHNOL, 67- *Concurrent Pos:* Consult metallurgist, 39- *Honors & Awards:* Joseph Whitworth Prize, Brit Inst Mech Engrs, 68. *Mem:* Fel Am Soc Metals; Am Soc Testing & Mat; Am Inst Mining, Metall & Petrol Engrs; Am Welding Soc; Am Soc Nondestructive Testing. *Res:* Heat treatment; metal processing; isothermal transformation studies; failure analysis; metallography; machinability; information science. *Mailing Add:* Metcut Res Assocs Inc 3980 Rosslyn Dr Cincinnati OH 45209

KAHLON, PREM SINGH, b Lyallpur, India, June 16, 36; m 67; c 2. BIOLOGY, PLANT GENETICS. *Educ:* Punjab Univ, India, BS, 56; La State Univ, MS, 62; Punjab Univ, PhD(plant breeding), 64. *Prof Exp:* Asst prof biol, Talladega Col, 64-65; prof, Alcorn Agr & Mech Col, 65-66; PROF BIOL, TENN STATE UNIV, 66- *Mem:* Genetics Soc Am; Environ Mutagen Soc; Indian Soc Genetics & Plant Breeding. *Res:* Inheritance studies in rice, especially cooking quality; mutation genetics; chemical mutagenesis. *Mailing Add:* Dept of Biol Tenn State Univ Nashville TN 37203

KAHN, A CLARK, b Pittsburgh, Pa, Dec 16, 37; m 60; c 2. BIOCHEMISTRY. *Educ:* Univ NH, BA, 61, MS, 63; Pa State Univ, PhD(biochem), 66. *Prof Exp:* Lab officer clin chem & biochemist, USPHS Hosp, 66-68; supvr clin path, ICI Am, 68-76; dir res & develop, Precision Systs, 76-77; dir labs, New Eng Med Labs, 77-78; DIR CLIN PATH, INT RES & DEVELOP CORP, 78- *Mem:* AAAS; Am Chem Soc; Am Asn Clin Chem; Am Soc Vet Clin Pathologists; Nat Registry Clin Chemists. *Res:* Clinical laboratory medicine, particularly electrolyte chemistry and intestinal absorption, malabsorption syndrome; laboratory animal clinical pathology. *Mailing Add:* Dept of Clin Path Main St Mattawan MI 49071

KAHN, ALAN RICHARD, b Chicago, Ill, Mar 1, 32; m 70; c 2. BIOENGINEERING, PHYSIOLOGY. *Educ:* Univ Ill, MD, 59. *Prof Exp:* Design engr, Offner Electronics, 58-59, dir physiol res, Offner Div, Beckman Instruments, Inc, 62-63, med dir, 63-66; dir biophys res, Hoffman LaRoche Inc, 66-68; vpres res & develop, Health Technol Corp, 68-70; sr vpres cardiovasc res, Medtronic Inc, 70-77; pres, Andersen Med Systs, 77-78; dir biomed res, Nicolet Instrument Corp, 78-80; CONSULT, APPL ELECTRONIC CONSULTS INC, 80- *Concurrent Pos:* Clin asst prof, Univ Minn; lectr, Univ Ill; chmn comt med devices, Am Nat Standards Inst. *Mem:* Neuroelec Soc (vpres); AMA; Biomed Eng Soc; Inst Elec & Electronics Eng; Asn Advan Med Instrumentation. *Res:* Cardiovascular neurological and rehabilitation instrumentation; aerospace medicine; biological electrode techniques, medical device standards, management for research and development programs. *Mailing Add:* Nicolet Instrument Corp 5225 Verona Rd Madison WI 53711

KAHN, ALBERT, b Wurburg, Ger, May 21, 31; nat US. DEVELOPMENTAL BIOLOGY. *Educ:* Cornell Univ, BS, 53; Univ Calif, Los Angeles, PhD(bot), 58. *Prof Exp:* Jr res botanist, Univ Calif, Los Angeles, 58-59; fels, NSF, Stockholm, 59-61 & USPHS, 61-62; res fel biol, Calif Inst Technol, 62-64; assoc prof, Purdue Univ, 64-70; ASSOC PROF BIOL, GENETICS INST, COPENHAGEN UNIV, 70- *Mem:* AAAS; Am Soc Cell Biol; Am Soc Plant Physiol. *Res:* Chloroplast pigments; genetic control of chloroplast development; mutagenesis and somatic recombinogenesis. *Mailing Add:* Genetics Inst Copenhagen Univ Oster Farimagsgade 2A DK 1353 Copenhagen Denmark

KAHN, ALFRED JEROME, b Chicago, Ill, Feb 1, 20; m 44; c 1. PHYSIOLOGY. *Educ:* Univ Chicago, PhD(physiol), 43, MD, 44. *Prof Exp:* Resident internal med, Billings Hosp, 45-46, 48; resident psychiat, Michael Reese Hosp, 48-49; pvt pract internal med, 50-60; mem staff physiol aging process, Argonne Nat Lab, 60-63; MEM STAFF, HINES VET ADMIN HOSP, 63- *Res:* Physiology of aging process; clinical problems of spinal cord injury. *Mailing Add:* 956 Second Ave Des Plaines IL 60016

KAHN, ARNOLD HERBERT, b New York, NY, Nov 5, 28; m 58. PHYSICS. *Educ:* Rensselaer Polytech Inst, BS, 50; Univ Calif, MA, 52, PhD(physics), 55. *Prof Exp:* Asst, Univ Calif, 50-52; res assoc, Univ Ill, 54-56; PHYSICIST, NAT BUR STANDARDS, 56- *Concurrent Pos:* Instr, Univ Md, 56-61. *Mem:* Am Phys Soc. *Res:* Theory of solids; electrical, magnetic, and optical properties of solids. *Mailing Add:* Nat Bur of Standards Washington DC 20234

KAHN, ARTHUR B, b New York, NY, Feb 11, 31; m 56; c 3. COMPUTER SCIENCE. *Educ:* City Col New York, BS, 51; Johns Hopkins Univ, MSE, 54, PhD(dynamic meteorol), 59. *Prof Exp:* Res asst dynamic meteorol, Johns Hopkins Univ, 51-54, staff asst, 54-58; sr engr, Air Arm Div, Westinghouse Elec Corp, 58-63, fel engr, Systs Div 63-68, fel engr, Info Processing Dept, 68-70, adv engr, 71-78; ASSOC PROF, INFO QUANT STUDIES, UNIV BALTIMORE, 78- *Concurrent Pos:* Founder & chmn prog eval & rev tech proj, SHARE, 62-64; vis assoc prof, Univ Wis-Madison, 68-71. *Mem:* Asn Comput Mach. *Res:* Determination of what the nonspecialist should know about computers and development of ways and means to educate him. *Mailing Add:* 4120 Balmoral Circle Pikesville MD 21208

KAHN, ARTHUR JOLE, b New York, NY, May 29, 21; m 50; c 4. PHYSIOLOGY. *Educ:* NY Univ, AB, 47, MS, 49, PhD(biophys), 52. *Prof Exp:* Res assoc, NY Univ, 48-51, instr, 51; asst prof physiol, Col Med & Dent, Georgetown Univ, 51-56; from asst prof to assoc prof, 56-69, PROF PHYSIOL, COL MED & DENT NJ, 69- *Mem:* Am Physiol Soc. *Res:* Elasticity and contractility of cardiac muscle. *Mailing Add:* Dept of Physiol Col of Med & Dent of NJ Newark NJ 07103

KAHN, BERND, b Pforzheim, Ger, Aug 16, 28; nat US; m 61; c 2. RADIOCHEMISTRY. *Educ:* Newark Col Eng, BS, 50; Vanderbilt Univ, MS, 52; Mass Inst Technol, PhD(chem), 60. *Prof Exp:* Assoc chemist radiochem, Oak Ridge Nat Lab, 51-54; radiochemist, USPHS, 54-69; radiochemist, Radiochem & Nuclear Eng Br, Environ Protection Agency, Nat Environ Res Ctr, 69-74; DIR, ENVIRON RESOURCES CTR & PROF NUCLEAR ENG & HEALTH PHYSICS, GA INST TECHNOL, 74- *Concurrent Pos:* Mem, Nat Coun Radiation Protection & Measurements. *Mem:* Health Physics Soc; Am Chem Soc; Am Phys Soc. *Res:* Analytical radiochemical methods; behavior of radionuclides in the environment; radioactive effluents from nuclear power stations. *Mailing Add:* Environ Resources Ctr Ga Inst of Technol Atlanta GA 30332

KAHN, CARL RONALD, b Louisville, Ky, Jan 14, 44; m 66; c 2. ENDOCRINOLOGY. *Educ:* Univ Louisville, BA, 64, MD, 68. *Prof Exp:* Sr investr, 73-78, chief cellular & molecular physiol, Diabetes Br, Nat Inst Arthritis & Metab Dis, NIH, 78-81; DIR RES, JOSLIN DIABETES CTR, 81- *Concurrent Pos:* Mem, Med Sci Adv Bd, Juv Diabetes Found, 78-; chief, Div Diabetes & Metabolism, Brigham & Women's Hosp, 81. *Honors & Awards:* Davis Rumbough Mem Award, Juv Diabetes Found, 77. *Mem:* Am Soc Clin Invest; Am Fedn Clin. *Res:* Endocrine Soc; Am Diabetes Asn. Res: Insulin action and alterations in insulin action in disease states; hypoglycemia and insulin-like peptides in blood. *Mailing Add:* Joslin Diabetes Ctr 1 Joslin Place Boston MA 02115

KAHN, CHARLES HOWARD, b Birmingham, Ala, Feb 10, 26; m 56; c 3. ARCHITECTURE, STRUCTURAL ENGINEERING. *Educ:* Univ NC, AB, 46; NC State Col, BCE, 48, BArch, 56; Mass Inst Technol, MS, 49. *Prof Exp:* Assoc prof struct design, sch design, NC State Univ, 52-59; from assoc prof to prof archit, 59-68, dean, Sch Archit & Urban Design, 68-80, PROF ARCHIT, SCH ARCHIT & URBAN DESIGN, UNIV KANS, 80- *Concurrent Pos:* Consult, 56-66; Fulbright fel, Italy, 57-58; pres, Charles H Kahn & Assoc & Cybertechnol, Ltd, 66-68; mem, Kans State Bldg Comn, 78-80. *Honors & Awards:* Annual res award, Nat Inst Archit Educ, 77. *Mem:* Am Soc Eng Educ; Am Soc Civil Engrs; Am Inst Archit; Asn Col Schs Archit. *Res:* Thin shells, membranal structures; architecture; history of the architectural structuralist movement, 1948 to 1965. *Mailing Add:* Sch of Archit & Urban Design Univ of Kans Lawrence KS 66045

KAHN, DANIEL STEPHEN, b Brooklyn, NY, Nov 20, 35. MATHEMATICS. *Educ:* Princeton Univ, AB, 57; Mass Inst Technol, PhD(math), 64. *Prof Exp:* Res instr math, Univ Chicago, 62-64; asst prof, 64-69, assoc prof, 69-78, PROF MATH, NORTHWESTERN UNIV, ILL, 78- *Mem:* Am Math Soc. *Res:* Algebraic topology, especially field of stable homotopy theory. *Mailing Add:* Dept of Math Northwestern Univ Evanston IL 60201

KAHN, DAVID, b Peoria, Ill, Feb 4, 26; m 57; c 3. SOLID STATE PHYSICS. *Educ:* Univ Ill, BS, 45; Univ Chicago, MS, 50, PhD(physics), 53. *Prof Exp:* Solid state physicist, Lewis Lab, Nat Adv Comt Aeronaut, 53-56; staff scientist, Res Inst Advan Study, 56-59, sr scientist, 59-70; RES ASSOC, AMP, INC, 70- *Concurrent Pos:* Am Cancer Soc res fel, Norsk Hydro's Inst Cancer Res, Norway, 54-55. *Mem:* Am Phys Soc; Radiation Res Soc; Am Soc Metals. *Res:* Nuclear magnetic resonance in solids; transition metal compounds; transport properties of solids; metallic semiconductor transitions; stress relaxation in metals. *Mailing Add:* Res Div AMP Inc 425 Prince St PO Box 3608 Harrisburg PA 17105

KAHN, DAVID, b New York, NY, Apr 27, 33; m 52; c 3. PHYSICS. *Educ:* Brooklyn Col, BS, 57; Yale Univ, MS, 59, PhD(physics), 62. *Prof Exp:* Sr scientist, Raytheon Co, 62-66 & electronics res ctr, NASA, 66-71; group head, Modelling & Anal Group, 71-74, SECT CHIEF TECHNOL, TRANSP SYSTS CTR, US DEPT TRANSP, 74- *Mem:* Am Phys Soc; sr mem Inst Elec & Electronics Eng. *Res:* Kinetic theory and plasma physics; wave propagation in highly rarefied gases; plasma density discontinuity wave coupling; traffic flow theory. *Mailing Add:* Transp Systs Ctr US Dept Transp 55 Broadway Kendall Square Boston MA 02142

KAHN, DONALD JAY, b Baltimore, Md, Aug 10, 30; m 60; c 3. ORGANIC CHEMISTRY. *Educ:* Princeton Univ, BA, 52; Univ Chicago, PhD(org chem), 57. *Prof Exp:* Asst org chem, Univ Chicago, 52-55; chemist, Esso Res & Eng Co, 57-60, proj leader & sr chemist, 60-63, sect head, 63-67, mgr aviation tech serv, Exxon Int Inc, 68-71, environ conserv sr adv, Exxon Corp, 71-77, solar energy gen mgr, Exxon Enterprises Inc, 78-81, SR TECHNOL ADV, EXXON CORP, 81- *Mem:* Am Chem Soc; Sigma Xi. *Res:* Reaction mechanisms; free radical organic chemistry and polymerization; chemical additives for lubricants; industrial lubricants, greases, wax products and asphalt products; solar photovoltics. *Mailing Add:* 62 Spring St Metuchen NJ 08840

KAHN, DONALD R, b Birmingham, Ala, May 21, 29; m; c 4. CARDIOVASCULAR SURGERY, THORACIC SURGERY. *Educ:* Birmingham-Southern Col, BA, 50; Univ Ala, BA, 57, MD, 54. *Prof Exp:* Intern, St Louis City Hosp, 54-55; resident, Med Ctr, Univ Mich, Ann Arbor, 55-59, instr thoracic surg, Med Sch, 63-64, from asst prof to assoc prof surg, 64-71; head div thoracic & cardiovasc surg, Med Ctr, Univ Wis-Madison, 71-80, prof surg & chmn cardiovasc med, Univ Wis Hosp, 71-80. *Concurrent Pos:* Am Thoracic Soc fel, 61-64; asst, Sch Med, Washington Univ, 54-55; dir clin invest lab, directorate med res, Chem Warfare Lab, 56-58. *Mem:* Fel Am Col Surg; Am Heart Asn; Am Thoracic Soc; Am Asn Thoracic Surg; Soc Thoracic Surg. *Mailing Add:* Suite 106 801 Princeton Ave Birmingham AL 35211

KAHN, DONALD W, b New York, NY, Nov 21, 35; m 56; c 2. MATHEMATICS. *Educ:* Cornell Univ, BA, 57; Yale Univ, PhD(math), 61. *Prof Exp:* Ritt instr math, Columbia Univ, 61-64; asst prof, 64-67, ASSOC PROF MATH, UNIV MINN, MINNEAPOLIS, 67- *Concurrent Pos:* Vis Fulbright prof, Univ Heidelberg, 65. *Mem:* Am Math Soc. *Res:* Algebraic topology. *Mailing Add:* Dept of Math Univ of Minn Minneapolis MN 55455

KAHN, ELLIOTT H, b Brooklyn, NY, Feb 27, 26; m 52; c 3. CIVIL ENGINEERING, APPLIED MECHANICS. *Educ:* City Col New York, BCE, 45; Polytech Inst Brooklyn, MCE, 48. *Prof Exp:* Res engr, Repub Aviation Corp, NY, 45-47; staff engr, D B Steinman, 47-51; sr engr, W L Maxson Corp, 51-57, mgr reliability anal sect, 57-61; sr tech staff scientist, Kollsman Instrument Corp, Syosset, 61-76; MGR, COOPERS & LYBRAND, 76- *Concurrent Pos:* Lectr & consult engr, various times. *Honors & Awards:* Robert Ridgeway Award, Am Soc Civil Engrs, 45. *Mem:* AAAS; NY Acad Sci; Nat Soc Prof Engrs; Am Soc Civil Engrs; Inst Elec & Electronics Engrs. *Res:* Applied mechanics and systems engineering in the fields of structures, reliability, traffic, instruments, laser safety and electro-optical systems. *Mailing Add:* Coopers & Lybrand 1251 Avenue of the Americas New York NY 10020

KAHN, FREDERIC JAY, b Brooklyn, NY, Sept 1, 41; m 67; c 2. ELECTRO-OPTICAL DEVICES, SUBMICRON LITHOGRAPHY. *Educ:* Rensselaer Polytech Inst, BEE, 62; Harvard Univ, AM, 63, PhD(solid state physics), 68. *Prof Exp:* Res asst reflection magnetooptics garnets & orthoferrites, Gordon McKay Lab, Harvard Univ, 65-68; spec researcher liquid crystal displays, Quantum Device Res Lab, Cent Res Lab, Nippon Elec Co, Kawasaki, Japan, 68-69; mem tech staff liquid crystal mat displays & related technol, Optical Control Devices Dept, Solid State Lab, Bell Labs, 70-73; lab proj mgr, 73-81, SUPVR OPTICAL MAT & POLYMERS GROUP, MAT RES DEPT, SOLID STATE LAB, HEWLETT PACKARD LABS, 81- *Mem:* Am Phys Soc; Inst Elec & Electronics Engrs; fel Soc Info Display. *Res:* Liquid crystal display materials, devices and systems; electron-beam and x-ray resists for high resolution lithography; optical memory materials and systems; optical fiber properties and devices; optical disc memories and erasable media. *Mailing Add:* Hewlett Packard Labs 1501 Page Mill Rd Palo Alto CA 94304

KAHN, HAROLD A, b New York, NY, Jan 4, 20; m 40; c 3. EPIDEMIOLOGY. *Educ:* City Col New York, BS, 39; Am Univ, MA, 49. *Prof Exp:* Statistician venereal dis control, USPHS, 42-50, heart dis res, Nat Heart & Lung Inst, 50-51, med care needs, USPHS, 51-57, res adminr, NIH, 57-60, heart dis res, Nat Heart & Lung Inst, 60-71, chief off biomet & epidemiol, Nat Eye Inst, 71-75; prof epidemiol, Sch Hyg & Pub Health, Johns Hopkins Univ, 75-78; CONSULT EPIDEMIOL, 78- *Concurrent Pos:* Fel Coun Epidemiol, Am Heart Asn, 64-; USPHS award, 57; Lady Davis vis prof epidemiol, Hebrew Univ, Jerusalem. *Honors & Awards:* Superior Serv Award, NIH, 74. *Mem:* Fel Am Statist Asn; Soc Epidemiol Res; Int Soc Geog Ophthal. *Res:* Nutrition and other risk factors in relation to chronic disease; problems of data collection in field surveys. *Mailing Add:* 3405 Pendleton Dr Silver Spring MD 20902

KAHN, HARRY ALBERT, chemical engineering, see previous edition

KAHN, JACK HENRY, b Bolivar, Tenn, Nov 1, 23; m 52; c 3. PHYSICS. *Educ:* Univ Tenn, BS, 47, MS, 49, PhD(physics), 51. *Prof Exp:* Classification analyst, Declassification Br, US AEC, 51-55, asst chief, 55-68, chief, 68-73, staff asst, 73-75, asst chief, Weapons Prog Br, Div Classification, 75-79, PHYSICIST, US DEPT ENERGY, 79- *Mem:* Am Phys Soc. *Res:* Nuclear physics. *Mailing Add:* Div of Classification US Dept of Energy Washington DC 20545

KAHN, JAMES STEVEN, b New York, NY, Oct 14, 31; m 54; c 3. EARTH SCIENCES. *Educ:* City Col New York, BS, 52; Pa State Univ, MS, 54; Univ Chicago, PhD(geol), 56. *Prof Exp:* From instr to asst prof geol, Univ RI, 57-60; chemist, Lawrence Radiation Lab, Univ Calif, Livermore, 60-66, group leader, K Div, 66-70; dept mgr, Corp Develop Div, Physics Int Co, 70-71; dep leader, K Div, 71-73, div leader earth sci, 73-75, asst assoc dir, Human Resources, 75-76, dep assoc dir, 76-78, ASSOC DIR NUCLEAR TEST, LAWRENCE LIVERMORE NAT LAB, 78-, LAB ASSOC DIR, 80- *Concurrent Pos:* Res assoc, Narragansett Marine Lab, 58-60. *Mem:* Fel Geol Soc Am; Am Phys Soc. *Res:* Microstructure of ceramics and glass-crystal melts; applied statistics; explosive containment and phenomenology; in situ energy resource recovery planning; human resource utilization; organizational development. *Mailing Add:* Lawrence Livermore Nat Lab Univ of Calif PO Box 808 Livermore CA 94550

KAHN, JOSEPH STEPHAN, b Ger, Aug 12, 29; m 70; c 2. PLANT BIOCHEMISTRY. *Educ:* Univ Calif, BS, 55; Univ Ill, PhD, 58. *Prof Exp:* Res assoc physiol, Univ Ill, 58-59; res assoc biol, Johns Hopkins Univ, 59-61; from asst prof to assoc prof, 61-71, PROF BOT & BIOCHEM, NC STATE UNIV, 71- *Mem:* Am Soc Plant Physiol; Am Soc Photobiol; Am Soc Cell Biol; Biophys Soc; Am Soc Biol Chem. *Res:* Electron transport and pathway of adenosine triphosphate formation in chloroplasts; localization of enzyme systems in chloroplasts; modification of protozoal mitochondria by drugs. *Mailing Add:* Dept of Biochem NC State Univ Raleigh NC 27607

KAHN, KENNETH, b Brooklyn, NY, July 27, 29; m 75; c 5. BIOCHEMISTRY. *Educ:* Gray Univ, MSc, 53; Univ Strasbourg, ScD(biochem), 55. *Prof Exp:* Lectr biochem, Liverpool Polytech, Eng, 68-76; vis prof micriobiol, Univ Barcebonn, Spain, 76-78; adj prof chem, Bloomfield Col, 78-79; PROF BIOCHEM, TOURO COL, 80- *Concurrent Pos:* Res assoc, Inst Appl Biol, 79. *Mailing Add:* Touro Col 30 W 44th St New York NY 10001

KAHN, LAWRENCE F, b Oakland, Calif, Jan 26, 45; m 71; c 2. STRUCTURAL ENGINEERING, CIVIL ENGINEERING. *Educ:* Stanford Univ, BS, 66; Univ Ill, Champaign-Urbana, MS, 67; Univ Mich, Ann Arbor, PhD(civil eng), 76. *Prof Exp:* Struct engr undersea struct, US Naval

Civil Eng Lab, 67-71; struct engr power plant, Bechtel Power Corp, 76; asst prof, 76-80, ASSOC PROF STRUCT ENG, GA INST TECHNOL, 80- *Concurrent Pos:* Prin investr, NSF grant, 77-78, Ga Dept Transp grant, 77-78. *Honors & Awards:* Raymond Reese Res Prize, Am Soc Civil Eng, 80. *Mem:* Am Soc Civil Engrs; Am Concrete Inst; Earthquake Eng Res Inst; Masonry Soc. *Res:* Earthquake engineering; ocean structures; reinforced concrete structures; masonry structures; experimental analysis. *Mailing Add:* Sch of Civil Eng Ga Inst of Technol Atlanta GA 30332

KAHN, LEO DAVID, b Everett, Mass. BIOPHYSICAL CHEMISTRY. *Educ:* Mass Inst Technol, SB, 54; Yale Univ, PhD(chem), 59. *Prof Exp:* RES CHEMIST, EASTERN REGIONAL RES & DEVELOP LAB, USDA, 58- *Mem:* AAAS; Am Chem Soc; Biophys Soc; NY Acad Sci. *Res:* Physical chemistry of proteins; electronic instrumentation for use in chemical investigations. *Mailing Add:* East Regional Res & Develop Lab USDA 600 E Mermaid Lane Philadelphia PA 19118

KAHN, LEONARD B, b Johannesburg, SAfrica, July 20, 37; m 63; c 3. SURGICAL PATHOLOGY. *Educ:* Witwaterstrand Univ, Johannesburg, MB, BCh, 60; Univ Cape Town, M Med Path, 65; MRCPath, 77. *Prof Exp:* Intern med & surg, Johannesburg Gen Hosp, 61-62; resident path, Univ Cape Town, 62-66; resident & fel clin asst, Sch Med, Washington Univ, St Louis, 67-69; assoc prof, Dept Path, Sch Med, Univ Cape Town, 74-77; prof & dir surg & path, Sch Med, Univ NC, Chapel Hill, 77-80; CHMN DEPT LABS, LONG ISLAND JEWISH-HILLSIDE MED CTR, 80-; PROF PATH, STATE UNIV NY STONY BROOK, 80- *Concurrent Pos:* Cecil John Adams Mem travelling fel, Univ Cape Town, 67. *Mem:* Int Acad Path; Gastrointestinal Path Club; Int Skeletal Soc. *Res:* Clinical pathologic, including immunologic and ultrastructural studies of a variety of human neoplasma, especially those involving lymphoreticular tissues, bone, soft tissue and gastrointestinal tract including salivary glands. *Mailing Add:* Long Island Jewish-Hillside Med Ctr 270-05 76th Ave New Hyde Park NY 11040

KAHN, MANFRED, b Frankfurt am Main, Ger, Feb 21, 26; nat US; m 60; c 3. CERAMIC SCIENCE, ELECTRICAL ENGINEERING. *Educ:* Univ Wis, BSEE, 54; Rensselaer Polytech Inst, MSEE, 59; Pa State Univ, PhD(ceramic sci), 69. *Prof Exp:* Mem tech staff, Ceramic Dept, Sprague Elec Co, 54-74; SR SCIENTIST, AVX CERAMICS INC, 74- *Mem:* Inst Elec & Electronics Engrs; Am Ceramic Soc. *Res:* Surface layer capacitors; ohmic contacts and hybrid microcircuits; multilayer capacitors; pilot plant production; base metal electrodes; process development; pilot plant and production; circuit design and applications engineering; test equipment design and distributed networks. *Mailing Add:* 606 44th Ave N Myrtle Beach SC 29577

KAHN, MILTON, b Philadelphia, Pa, Nov 21, 18; m 40; c 1. CHEMISTRY. *Educ:* Univ Calif, BS, 41; Wash Univ, PhD(chem), 50. *Prof Exp:* Anal chemist, Paraffine Co, Inc, 42-43; res chemist, Los Alamos Sci Lab, 43-46; from asst prof to assoc prof chem, Univ N Mex, 48-57, prof, 57-81; RETIRED. *Mem:* AAAS; Am Chem Soc. *Res:* Isotopic exchange reactions; hot atom chemistry; chemical behavior of substances at low concentrations; radiochemistry. *Mailing Add:* Dept of Chem Univ of NMex Albuquerque NM 87131

KAHN, NORMAN, b New York, NY, Dec 28, 32; m 58. NEUROPHARMACOLOGY, MEDICAL EDUCATION. *Educ:* Columbia Univ, AB, 54, DDS, 58, PhD(pharmacol), 64. *Prof Exp:* Dent intern, Montefiore Hosp, Bronx, NY, 58-59; from instr to asst prof, 62-72, assoc prof pharmacol, 72-80, assoc prof dent, 74-81, PROF PHARMACOL, COL PHYSICIANS & SURGEONS & DENT, SCH DENT & ORAL SURG, COLUMBIA UNIV, 81- *Concurrent Pos:* NIH trainee neuropharmacol, Columbia Univ, 59-62; Nat Inst Neurol Dis & Blindness spec fels, Columbia Univ, 62-64 & Pisa, 65-66; NIH career develop award, 67-71; vis assoc prof anesthesiol, Univ Calif, Los Angeles, 78. *Mem:* Am Dent Asn; Am Physiol Soc; Int Asn Dent Res. *Res:* Physiology and pharmacology of autonomic nervous system; medical and dental education. *Mailing Add:* Col of Physicians & Surgeons Columbia Univ New York NY 10032

KAHN, PETER B, b New York, NY, Mar 18, 35; m 56; c 3. THEORETICAL PHYSICS. *Educ:* Union Col, NY, BS, 56; Northwestern Univ, PhD(physics), 60. *Prof Exp:* Res assoc physics, Univ Iowa, 60-61; from asst prof to assoc prof, 61-71, PROF PHYSICS, STATE UNIV NY STONY BROOK, 71-, CHMN DEPT, 74- *Concurrent Pos:* Sr Weizmann fel, 67-68. *Mem:* Fel Am Phys Soc. *Res:* Mathematical biology; statistical theory of energy level distributions; innovation in physics curricula. *Mailing Add:* Dept of Physics State Univ of NY Stony Brook NY 11794

KAHN, PETER JACK, b Santiago, Chile, Dec 1, 39; US citizen; m 63. MATHEMATICS. *Educ:* Oberlin Col, BA, 60; Princeton Univ, PhD(math), 64. *Prof Exp:* Actg instr math, Univ Calif, Berkeley, 63, instr, 64-65; asst prof, 65-70, assoc prof, 70-75, PROF MATH, CORNELL UNIV, 75- *Concurrent Pos:* Mem, Inst Advan Study, 69-71; Humboldt sr scientist, Univ Heidelberg, 74-75. *Mem:* Am Math Soc. *Res:* Algebraic and differential topology. *Mailing Add:* Dept of Math Cornell Univ Ithaca NY 14850

KAHN, RAYMOND HENRY, b New York, NY, Aug 29, 26; m 50; c 3. ENDOCRINOLOGY, HISTOLOGY. *Educ:* Univ Calif, Los Angeles, BA, 48; Univ Calif, Berkeley, MS, 49, PhD(zool), 53. *Prof Exp:* From instr to assoc prof, 54-67, PROF ANAT, UNIV MICH, ANN ARBOR, 67-, DIR RES, HENRY FORD HOSP, 77- *Concurrent Pos:* Am Cancer Soc fel, Strangeways Res Lab, 53-54; USPHS spec fel, Inst Endocrinol, Gunma Univ, Japan, 67-68. *Mem:* Endocrine Soc; Soc Exp Biol & Med; Tissue Cult Asn (secy, 68-72, pres, 74-76); Am Asn Anat; Nat Coun Univ Res Admin. *Res:* Pseudo intimal linings of artificial prostheses; histochemistry; organ culture of prostate; tissue culture. *Mailing Add:* Dept of Anat Univ of Mich Ann Arbor MI 48109

KAHN, ROBERT PHILIP, b Chicago, Ill, Apr 20, 24; m 47; c 3. PLANT PATHOLOGY. *Educ:* Univ Ill, BA, 48, PhD(plant path), 51. *Prof Exp:* Asst bot, Univ Ill, 48-52; from plant pathologist to supvry plant pathologist, Chem Warfare Labs, Ft Detrick, 52-57; PLANT PATHOLOGIST, ANIMAL & PLANT HEALTH INSPECTION SERV, USDA, 57- *Concurrent Pos:* Officer-in-chg, EAfrican Plant Quarantine Sta, USDA, Kenya, 70-72. *Mem:* Am Phytopath Soc; Int Soc Plant Pathol. *Res:* Virology; plant quarantine pathology; plant tissue culture; agriculture; tropical plant pathology. *Mailing Add:* US Dept of Agr Fed Ctr Bldg Hyattsville MD 20782

KAHN, SAMUEL GEORGE, b Belleville, NJ, May 20, 29; m 60; c 2. NUTRITION. *Educ:* Ill Wesleyan Univ, BS, 51; Univ Ill, MS, 53 & 54, PhD(animal nutrit), 55. *Prof Exp:* Asst animal nutrit, Univ Ill, 52-55; res assoc, Radio Carbon Lab, 55-56; asst biochem, Squibb Inst Med Res, 56-58, sect head nutrit res, Div Agr Sci, 58-59, sr res scientist, 59-67, res supvr & head nutrit res, 67-69; assoc prof nutrit & food & actg chmn, Drexel Inst Technol, 69-71; nutrit adv, Res Off & Univ Rels, Tech Assistance Bur, 71-74; SR NUTRIT ADV OFF NUTRIT, 74- *Concurrent Pos:* Hon prof nutrit, Rutgers Univ, 67; adj prof, VA Polytech Inst & State Univ, 74- *Mem:* Am Inst Nutrit; fel NY Acad Sci; Am Physiol Sic; Soc Exp Biol & Med; Poultry Sci Asn. *Res:* Vitamin and lipid metabolism; atherosclerosis; animal nutrition; nutrition, health and population; international nutrition. *Mailing Add:* Off Nutrit Sci & Tech Bur AID US Dept of State Washington DC 20523

KAHN, WALTER K(URT), b Mannheim, Ger, Mar 24, 29; US citizen; m 62; c 2. ELECTRICAL ENGINEERING, ELECTROPHYSICS. *Educ:* Cooper Union, BEE, 51; Polytech Inst Brooklyn, MEE, 54, DEE, 60. *Prof Exp:* Engr radar, Wheeler Labs, NY, 51-54; res assoc, microwave res inst, Polytech Inst Brooklyn, 54-60, asst prof elec eng, 60-62, from assoc prof to prof electrophysics, 62-69; chmn dept elec eng & comput sci, 70-74, PROF ELEC ENG & APPL SCI, GEORGE WASHINGTON UNIV, 69- *Concurrent Pos:* Liaison scientist, Off Naval Res, London, 67-68; mem comn 6, Int Union Radio Sci; ed, trans, Inst Elec & Electronics Engrs, 77- *Honors & Awards:* Spec recognition award, Inst Elec & Electronics Engrs. *Mem:* AAAS; fel Inst Elec & Electronics Engrs; Optical Soc Am. *Res:* Optical resonators and fiberoptics; lasers; microwave antennas and antenna arrays; waveguide junctions and directional couplers; microwave measurements; monopulse, radar systems. *Mailing Add:* Sch of Eng & Appl Sci George Washington Univ Washington DC 20052

KAHNE, STEPHEN JAMES, b New York, NY, Apr 5, 37; m 70; c 2. CONTROL THEORY, SYSTEMS ENGINEERING. *Educ:* Cornell Univ, BEE, 60; Univ Ill, MS, 61, PhD(elec eng), 63. *Prof Exp:* Engr, Defense Syst Dept, Gen Elec Co, 60; res asst control systs, Coord Sci Lab, Univ Ill, 61-62, res assoc & instr elec eng, 62-63; sr engr control, Electronics Div, Westinghouse Elec Corp, 63; lectr math, Northeastern Univ, 63; asst prof elec eng, Univ Minn, Minneapolis, 65-69, assoc prof & dir, Hybrid Comput Lab, 69-76; chmn dept, 76-80, PROF SYSTS ENG, CASE WESTERN RESERVE UNIV, 76- *Concurrent Pos:* Consult, NASA Electronics Res Ctr, 64-65 & 20 various corps; ed, Trans Automatic Control, Inst Elec & Electronics Engrs, 75-78; dir, Div Elec, Comput & Systs Eng, NSF, 80-81. *Mem:* Fel Inst Elec & Electronics Engrs; fel AAAS. *Res:* Control theory, systems engineering, military command and control systems. *Mailing Add:* Dept Systs Eng Case Western Reserve Univ Cleveland OH 44106

KAHNEY, RONALD HERBERT, b Valparaiso, Ind, Mar 4, 39; m 61; c 3. CHEMICAL ENGINEERING. *Educ:* Purdue Univ, BS, 62, MS, 66, PhD(ChE), 68. *Prof Exp:* RES SPECIALIST PETROCHEMICALS, MONSANTO CO, 68- *Mem:* Am Inst Chem Engrs. *Res:* Chemical catalysis and chemical reactor design. *Mailing Add:* Monsanto Co 800 N Lindberg Blvd St Louis MO 63166

KAHNG, DAWON, b Seoul, Korea, May 4, 31; US citizen; m 56; c 5. PHYSICS, SEMICONDUCTORS. *Educ:* Univ Seoul, BSc, 55; Ohio State Univ, MSc, 56, PhD(elec eng), 59. *Prof Exp:* Res assoc elec eng, Ohio State Univ, 57-59; instr, 58-59; mem tech staff, SUPVR PHYSICS, BELL LABS, 64- *Honors & Awards:* Stuart Ballantine Medal, Franklin Inst, 75. *Mem:* Fel Inst Elec & Electronics Engrs. *Res:* Semiconductor device physics and technology in the area of impurity diffusion; surface field effect transistor; hot electron devices; Schottky barriers; thin film electroluminescence; charge coupled devices; nonvolatile semiconductor memories. *Mailing Add:* Div 11 Bell Labs Mountain Ave Murray Hill NJ 07971

KAHNG, SEUN KWON, b Seoul, Korea, Jan 16, 36; US citizen; m 70; c 2. ELECTRICAL ENGINEERING, SOLID STATE ELECTRONICS. *Educ:* Seoul Nat Univ, BSEE, 58; Univ Va, MEE, 63, PhD(elec eng), 67. *Prof Exp:* Res fel transducers, Langley Res Ctr, NASA, 67-68; from asst prof to assoc prof, 68-78, PROF ELEC ENG, UNIV OKLA, 78-, DIR ELEC ENG, 80- *Concurrent Pos:* Res fel, Langley Res Ctr, NASA, 75-76. *Mem:* Inst Elec & Electronics Engrs; Optical Soc Am. *Res:* Solid state electronic devices; piezoresistive silicon sensors; silicon-on-sapphire sensors; piezoelectric sensors. *Mailing Add:* Sch of Elec Eng & Comput Sci Col of Eng Univ of Okla Norman OK 73019

KAHRS, ROBERT F, b Lynbrook, NY, June 28, 30; m 53; c 4. VETERINARY MEDICINE, VETERINARY EPIDEMIOLOGY. *Educ:* Cornell Univ, DVM, 54, MS, 63, PhD(virol biomet), 65. *Prof Exp:* Asst vet, private practice, Interlaken, NY, 54-55; vet, Attica, NY, 55-61; res asst vet virol & biomet, 61-65, res assoc vet epidemiol & microbiol, 65-66, asst prof vet epidemiol, 66-70, assoc prof vet epidemiol, NY State Vet Col, Cornell Univ, 70-78; PROF VET EPIDEMIOL & CHMN DEPT VET PREV MED, UNIV FLA, 78- *Mem:* Am Vet Med Asn; US Animal Health Asn; Am Vet Epidemiol Soc. *Res:* Epidemiology of virus diseases of livestock. *Mailing Add:* Box J-136 Univ of Fla Gainesville FL 32610

KAIGHN, MORRIS EDWARD, b Camden, NJ, Aug 6, 22; m 62, 71. EMBRYOLOGY, VIROLOGY. *Educ:* Brooklyn Col, BS, 56; Mass Inst Technol, PhD(biol), 62. *Prof Exp:* Asst investr embryol, Carnegie Inst, 64-67; res assoc, New York Blood Ctr, 67-70, assoc investr embryol, 70-72; sr scientist cell ctr, 72-75; SR RES INVESTR, PASADENA FOUND MED RES, 75- *Concurrent Pos:* Fel virol, Univ Toronto, 62-64. *Mem:* Soc Develop Biol; Am Soc Cell Biol; Tissue Cult Asn. *Res:* Biochemistry of hatching in teleosts; purification and composition of encephalomyocarditis virus; susceptibility of differentiated embryonic cells to Rous Sarcoma virus; clonal culture of differentiated human liver cells; serum protein synthesis by cell cultures; growth control by steroids and peptide growth factors of human epithelial cells. *Mailing Add:* Pasadena Found Med Res 99 North El Molino Ave Pasadena CA 91101

KAILATH, THOMAS, b Poona, India, June 7, 35; m 62; c 3. ELECTRICAL ENGINEERING, APPLIED MATHEMATICS. *Educ:* Univ Poona, BE, 56; Mass Inst Technol, SM, 59, ScD(elec eng), 61. *Prof Exp:* Res specialist, Jet Propulsion Lab, Calif Inst Technol, 61-62; assoc prof elec eng, 63-68, dir, Info Systs Lab, 71-81, PROF ELEC ENG, STANFORD UNIV, 68-, ASSOC CHMN, 81- *Concurrent Pos:* Consult ed, Prentice-Hall, 63-, ed, Info Theory Series, 63-; vis prof, India Inst Sci, Bangalore, 69-70, Katholieke Univ Leuven, 77 & Tech Univ, Delft, 81; Guggenheim fel, 69-70. *Honors & Awards:* Churchill Col fel, Eng, 77. *Mem:* Fel Inst Elec & Electronics Engrs; Inst Math Statist. *Res:* Statistical signal processing; statistical communication, control and system theory; signal detection and estimation; operator theory and integral equations. *Mailing Add:* Dept of Elec Eng Stanford Univ Stanford CA 94305

KAIMAL, JAGADISH CHANDRAN, b Kuala Lumpur, Malaysia, Nov 18, 30; US citizen; m 57; c 3. METEOROLOGY. *Educ:* Benares Hindu Univ, BSc, 53; Univ Wash, MS, 59, PhD(meteorol), 61. *Prof Exp:* Res physicist, Air Force Cambridge Res Labs, 61-76; RES PHYSICIST, WAVE PROPAGATION LAB, ENERGY RES LAB, NAT OCEANIC & ATMOSPHERIC ADMIN, 76- *Mem:* Am Meteorol Soc. *Res:* Experimental investigations of turbulent fluctuations in the atmospheric boundary layer and the study of the fluxes of momentum and heat within this layer. *Mailing Add:* Wave Propagation Labs Nat Oceanic & Atmospheric Admin Boulder CO 80302

KAIN, RICHARD YERKES, b Chicago, Ill, Jan 20, 36; m 61, 81; c 3. ELECTRICAL ENGINEERING. *Educ:* Mass Inst Technol, SB, 57, SM, 59, ScD(elec eng), 62. *Prof Exp:* Asst elec eng, Mass Inst Technol, 57-60, from instr to asst prof, 60-66; assoc prof, 66-77, PROF ELEC ENG, UNIV MINN, MINNEAPOLIS, 77- *Concurrent Pos:* Ford fel eng, 62-64; consult, Honeywell Corp, 75- *Mem:* AAAS; Soc Indust & Appl Math; Asn Comput Mach; Inst Elec & Electronics Engrs. *Res:* Computer systems; computer architecture. *Mailing Add:* Dept of Elec Eng Univ Minn 123 Church St SE Minneapolis MN 55455

KAINEN, PAUL CHESTER, b Washington, DC, July 31, 43; m 63. MATHEMATICS. *Educ:* George Washington Univ, BA, 66; Cornell Univ, PhD(math), 70. *Prof Exp:* From asst prof to assoc prof math, Case Western Reserve Univ, 70-77; MEM TECH STAFF, BELL LABS, 77- *Concurrent Pos:* Vis asst prof opers res, Univ Pa, 71 & 72; consult, ADAR Corp, 74 & Systs Res Ctr, Case Western Reserve Univ, 74-77. AAAS; Am Math Soc; Soc Indust & Appl Math; Inst Elec & Electronic Engrs. *Res:* Behavior of large networks; computer heuristics; combinatorics; topology; information theory. *Mailing Add:* Network Configuration Planning Ctr Bell Labs Holmdel NJ 07733

KAINSKI, MERCEDES H, b Kewaunee Co, Wis, Jan 26, 23; m 64. FOOD SCIENCE, NUTRITION. *Educ:* Univ Wis, BS, 44, MS, 55, PhD(foods), 57. *Prof Exp:* Control chemist, Wilson Res Lab, Ill, 44; with res lab, Carnation Co, Wis, 45-47; teacher pub schs, Wis, 48-53; assoc prof foods & nutrit, Kans State Univ, 57-65; assoc prof home econ, Bowling Green State Univ, 65-67; PROF FOOD & NUTRIT, UNIV WIS-STOUT, 67- *Mem:* Am Home Econ Asn; Inst Food Technol; Am Dietetic Asn. *Res:* Minerals, iron and copper in pork; magnesium and fat metabolism; iron, phenols and organic acid in potatoes. *Mailing Add:* Dept of Food Sci Univ of Wis-Stout Menomonie WI 54751

KAISEL, S(TANLEY) F(RANCIS), b St Louis, Mo, Aug 2, 22; m 58; c 2. ELECTRONICS. *Educ:* Wash Univ, BS, 43; Stanford Univ, MA, 46, PhD(elec eng), 49. *Prof Exp:* Instr math, Wash Univ, 42-43; spec res assoc, Radio Res Lab, Harvard Univ, 43-45; res assoc, Stanford Univ, 46-49; res engr, Radio Corp Am Labs, 49-51; res assoc & group leader, Univ Stanford, 51-55; lectr, 53-55; mgr eng, Electron Tube Div, Litton Industs, 55-58; electronics consult engr, 58-59; founder & pres, Microwave Electronics Corp, 59-69; CONSULT, 69- *Honors & Awards:* Joint Army & Navy Cert, 48. *Mem:* Fel Inst Elec & Electronics Engrs. *Res:* Radio and radar countermeasures; radar; microwave tubes; traveling wave tubes; vacuum tube technology. *Mailing Add:* 595 Albion Way Woodside CA 94062

KAISER, ARMIN DALE, b Piqua, Ohio, Nov 10, 27; m 53; c 2. BIOCHEMISTRY, GENETICS. *Educ:* Purdue Univ, BSc, 50; Calif Inst Technol, PhD(biol), 54. *Prof Exp:* From instr to asst prof microbiol, Wash Univ, 56-59; from asst prof to assoc prof, 59-66, PROF BIOCHEM, SCH MED, STANFORD UNIV, 66- *Concurrent Pos:* Am Cancer Soc fel, 54-56; NSF fel, 64-65; mem genetics study sect, USPHS, 63-68; mem genetic biol panel, NSF, 71-73. *Honors & Awards:* Award in Molecular Biol, US Steel Found, 70; Lasker Award, 80; Waterford Biomed Sci Award, 81. *Mem:* Nat Acad Sci; Genetics Soc Am; Am Soc Biol Chemists. *Res:* Bacteriophage genetics; nucleic acid biochemistry; biochemistry of morphogenesis. *Mailing Add:* Dept of Biochem Stanford Univ Sch of Med Stanford CA 94305

KAISER, CARL, b Baltimore, Md, Feb 8, 29; m 53; c 3. MEDICINAL CHEMISTRY. *Educ:* Univ Md, BS, 51, MS, 53, PhD(pharmaceut chem), 55. *Prof Exp:* Lab asst pharmaceut chem, Univ Md, 51-53; Smith Kline & French fel, Univ Va, 55-57; sr med chemist, 57-65, med chem group leader, 65-68, sr investr, 68-72, asst dir chem, 72-79, assoc sci dir, 79-81, SR FEL, SMITH KLINE & FRENCH LABS, 81- *Mem:* Am Chem Soc; Am Pharmaceut Asn. *Res:* Design and synthesis of potential drug products, especially substances affecting the central and autonomic nervous systems, enzyme inhibitors, antimetabolites, drug metabolism and small ring compounds. *Mailing Add:* 1105 Sylvan Dr Haddon Heights NJ 08035

KAISER, CHRISTOPHER B, b Greenwich, Conn, Oct 16, 41; m 70; c 2. HISTORY & PHILOSOPHY OF SCIENCE, COMPUTER SCIENCES. *Educ:* Harvard Univ, BA, 63; Univ Colo, PhD(astrogeophys), 68; Edinburgh Univ, PhD(theology), 74. *Prof Exp:* Lectr physics, Gordon Col, 68-71 & Edinburgh Univ, 73-74; with Systs Develop, QEI Inc, Bedford, Mass, 75-76; ASST PROF, WESTERN THEOL SEM, HOLLAND, MICH, 77- *Concurrent Pos:* Mem, Gravity Res Found, 68- *Mem:* Am Asn Physics Teachers; Philos Sci Asn; Brit Soc Philos Sci; Inst Religion Age Sci; AAAS. *Res:* Theological science; history of science; history of interaction between theological beliefs and scientific progress. *Mailing Add:* Western Theol Seminary 86 E 12th St Holland MI 49423

KAISER, DAVID GILBERT, b Detroit, Mich, Aug 25, 28; m 61; c 2. PHARMACEUTICAL CHEMISTRY. *Educ:* Detroit Inst Technol, BS, 52; Purdue Univ, MS, 54, PhD(pharmaceut chem), 59. *Prof Exp:* Fel radiochem, Univ Mich, 59; chemist, 59-69, res head drug metab, 69-79, RES MGR DRUG METAB, UPJOHN CO, 79- *Mem:* AAAS; Am Chem Soc; Am Pharmaceut Asn. *Res:* Drug metabolism and analytical chemistry. *Mailing Add:* 6605 Robinswood Kalamazoo MI 49002

KAISER, EDWARD WILLIAM, JR, b Minneapolis, Minn, May 10, 42; m 68; c 1. PHYSICAL CHEMISTRY. *Educ:* Northwestern Univ, BA, 64; Harvard Univ, MA, 66, PhD(chem), 70. *Prof Exp:* NATO fel, Southampton Univ, 69-70; temp mem tech staff, Bell Labs, 70-72; assoc scientist, Xerox Corp, 72-74; sr res scientist, 74-80, PRIN RES ASSOC, FORD MOTOR CO, 80- *Mem:* Am Phys Soc; Am Chem Soc. *Res:* Chemical kinetics; combustion research; molecular spectroscopy; ion-molecule reactions. *Mailing Add:* 7 Windham Lane Dearborn MI 48120

KAISER, EDWIN MICHAEL, b Youngstown, Ohio, Oct 15, 38; m 60; c 5. ORGANIC CHEMISTRY. *Educ:* Youngstown Univ, BS, 60; Purdue Univ, PhD(org chem), 64. *Prof Exp:* Res assoc org chem, Duke Univ, 64-66; from asst prof to assoc prof, 70-74, PROF ORG CHEM, UNIV MO-COLUMBIA, 74- *Mem:* Am Chem Soc; Sigma Xi; AAAS; Am Inst Chemists. *Res:* Organometallic derivatives of methylated heterocycles; condensations and cyclizations in nonaqueous media. *Mailing Add:* 304 Chem Bldg Univ of Mo Columbia MO 65211

KAISER, EMIL THOMAS, b Budapest, Hungary, Feb 15, 38; US citizen; m 68; c 2. PHYSICAL ORGANIC CHEMISTRY, BIOORGANIC CHEMISTRY. *Educ:* Univ Chicago, BS, 56; Harvard Univ, MA, 57, PhD(org chem), 59. *Prof Exp:* NIH fel org chem, Harvard Univ, 59-60; NIH fel enzyme chem, Northwestern Univ, 60-61; asst prof chem, Wash Univ, 61-63; from asst prof to assoc prof chem, 63-70, mem adv coun col chem, 67-69, PROF CHEM & BIOCHEM, UNIV CHICAGO, 70-, LOUIS BLOCK PROF & DIR, CTR BIOORG & BIOINORG CHEM, 81- *Concurrent Pos:* Alfred P Sloan fel, 68-70; mem, Med Chem Study Sect A, NIH, 73-77; Guggenheim fel, 75; prof, Jordan Mar Sci, 76; vis comt, Dept Chem, Purdue Univ & Brookaven Nat Lab, 77-81; assoc ed, J Am Chem Soc, 72-82. *Mem:* Am Chem Soc; Am Soc Biol Chemists. *Res:* Enzyme chemistry; mechanisms of organic and biochemical reactions; chemical modification of enzymes; stereochemistry and biochemistry; electron spin resonance studies of free radicals; chemistry of peptides. *Mailing Add:* Dept of Chem Univ of Chicago Chicago IL 60637

KAISER, GEORGE C, b Bronx, NY, July 30, 28; m 53; c 3. THORACIC SURGERY. *Educ:* Lehigh Univ, AB, 49; Johns Hopkins Univ, MD, 53. *Prof Exp:* Intern surg, Johns Hopkins Hosp, Baltimore, Md, 53-54; resident, Vet Admin Hosp, Ft Howard, Md, 54; clin assoc, clin of surg, Nat Heart Inst, 54-56; resident surg, Med Ctr, Ind Univ, 56-61, from instr to asst prof, 61-63; from asst prof to assoc prof, 63-70, PROF SURG, SCH MED, ST LOUIS UNIV, 70- *Concurrent Pos:* Staff surgeon, Vet Admin Hosp, Indianapolis, Ind, 61; dir St Louis Univ surg serv, Vet Admin Hosp, 63-65. *Mem:* Soc Thoracic Surg; AMA; Am Col Surg; Int Cardiovasc Soc; Am Asn Thoracic Surg. *Res:* General and thoracic surgical problems, including research in cardiac physiology. *Mailing Add:* Dept Surg Sch Med St Louis Univ St Louis MO 63104

KAISER, GERARD ALAN, b Brooklyn, NY, Dec 9, 32; m 55; c 3. THORACIC SURGERY, CARDIOVASCULAR SURGERY. *Educ:* Princeton Univ, AB, 54; Columbia Univ, MD, 58. *Prof Exp:* Intern, Presby Hosp, New York, 58-59, asst resident gen surg, 59-62, resident, 64-65; resident thoracic surg, Vet Admin Hosp & Bellevue Hosp Ctr, New York, 66 & Presby Hosp, 67; instr surg, Columbia Univ, 67-68; asst prof, Mt Sinai Sch Med, 68-69; assoc prof, Columbia Univ, 69-71; PROF SURG & CHIEF, DIV THORACIC & CARDIOVASCULAR SURG, SCH MED, UNIV MIAMI, 71- *Concurrent Pos:* Fel, NY Tuberc & Health Asn, 66-67; Glorney-Raisbeck fel, NY Acad Med, 68-69; asst surg, Columbia Univ, 65-67; asst vis prof, Delafield Hosp, 68; asst attend surg, Columbia-Presby Med Ctr, 68, assoc attend surg, 69-71; vis asst surg, Elmhurst Hosp, 68-69 & Harlem Hosp Ctr, 69-71; asst attend surg, Mt Sinai Hosp, 68-69; consult, Vet Admin Hosp, 68-71; active attend & chief div thoracic & cardiovasc surg, Jackson Mem Hosp; Otto G Storm estab investr, Am Heart Asn, 70. *Mem:* Soc Univ Surgeons; Soc Thoracic Surgeons; Asn Acad Surg; Am Fedn Clin Res; Int Cardiovasc Soc. *Res:* Cardiovascular physiology and pharmacology, especially electrophysiology. *Mailing Add:* Div Thoracic & Cardiovasc Surg R114 Box 016960 Miami FL 33101

KAISER, IRWIN HERBERT, b New York, NY, Jan 27, 18; m 38; c 6. OBSTETRICS & GYNECOLOGY. *Educ:* Columbia Univ, AB, 38; Johns Hopkins Univ, MD, 42; Univ Minn, PhD, 53. *Prof Exp:* Assoc prof obstet & gynec, Med Sch, Univ Minn, 54-59; prof & head dept, Col Med, Univ Utah, 59-68; PROF OBSTET & GYNEC, ALBERT EINSTEIN COL MED, 68- *Mem:* Soc Gynec Invest; Am Gynec & Obstet Soc; Am Col Obstet & Gynec. *Res:* Physiology of mammalian reproduction; water, electrolyte and gas equilibria between fetal and maternal circulations during pregnancy; contractile activity of pregnant human uterus prior to labor. *Mailing Add:* Dept of Obstet & Gynec 1825 Eastchester Rd Bronx NY 10461

KAISER, IVAN IRVIN, b Stuart, Nebr, Nov 21, 38; m 66; c 1. BIOCHEMISTRY. *Educ:* Wayne State Univ, BA, 62; Iowa State Univ, PhD(biochem), 67. *Prof Exp:* From asst prof to assoc prof biochem, 67-75, prof biochem & chem, 75-78, CHMN BIOCHEM, UNIV WYO, 78- *Mem:* Am Chem Soc; Am Soc Biol Chemists; Sigma Xi. *Res:* Structure and function of ribonucleic acids; selenium biochemistry. *Mailing Add:* Dept of Biochem Univ of Wyo Box 3944 Laramie WY 82071

KAISER, JACK ALLEN CHARLES, b Chicago, Ill, Nov 15, 35; m 63; c 2. AIR-SEA INTERACTION, INSTRUMENTATION. *Educ:* Ill Inst Technol, BS, 57; Univ Chicago, PhD(geophysics), 69. *Prof Exp:* Weather forcaster, US Air Force, 58-60; res asst, Univ Chicago, 62-69, res assoc, 69-72; RES PHYSICIST, NAVAL RES LAB, 72- *Concurrent Pos:* Prin investr, Naval Res Lab, 74- *Mem:* Am Meterol Soc; Am Geophys Union; Sigma Xi. *Res:* Experiments on air-sea interaction and upper ocean dynamics, structure and irradiance distribution. *Mailing Add:* Code 4310 Naval Res Lab Washington DC 20375

KAISER, JAMES F(REDERICK), b Piqua, Ohio, Dec 10, 29; m 54; c 4. ELECTRICAL ENGINEERING. *Educ:* Univ Cincinnati, EE, 52; Mass Inst Technol, SM, 54, ScD, 59. *Prof Exp:* Asst, Servomech Lab, Mass Inst Technol, 52-55, from instr to asst prof elec eng, 55-60; MEM TECH STAFF, DIGITAL SYSTS RES DEPT, BELL TEL LABS, INC, 59- *Mem:* Fel Inst Elec & Electronics Engrs; Asn Comput Mach; Math Asn Am; Soc Indust & Appl Math; Acoust Soc Am. *Res:* Theory of control and signal processing systems; system optimization; application of digital computations to continuous systems; digital signal processing; continuous system modeling. *Mailing Add:* Bell Tel Labs Inc Murray Hill NJ 07974

KAISER, JOSEPH ANTHONY, b Baltimore, Md, Mar 22, 26; m 51; c 3. PHARMACOLOGY. *Educ:* Univ Md, BS, 50, MS, 52, PhD(pharmacol), 55. *Prof Exp:* Sr res pharmacologist, Pfizer Therapeut Inst, NJ, 55-58; exp therapeut res sect, Lederle Labs, Am Cyanamid Co, 58-63; pharmacologist, Drug Rev Br, Div Toxicol Eval, Bur Sci Standards & Eval, Food & Drug Admin, 63-64, res pharmacologist, Div Pharmacol, Bur Sci Res, 64-66; exec secy pharmacol & endocrinol fels rev sect, 66-69, from asst chief to dep chief, Career Develop Rev Br, 69-73, exec secy spec progs, 73-74, EXEC SECY PHARMACOL STUDY SECT, DIV RES GRANTS, NIH, 74- *Mem:* Am Soc Pharmacol & Exp Therapeut. *Res:* Pharmacology-toxicology; antibiotics; anticholinergics, antihistamines, antiparasiticides and anti-tubercular agents; health science administration; toxicological evaluation. *Mailing Add:* NIH Div of Res Grants 5333 Westbard Ave Bethesda MD 20016

KAISER, KLAUS L(EO) E(DUARD), b Kempten, Ger, June 17, 41; Can Citizen; m; c 3. ORGANIC CHEMISTRY, ANALYTICAL CHEMISTRY. *Educ:* Tech Univ, Munich, cand chem, 64, dipl chem, 66, Dr rer nat(chem), 68. *Prof Exp:* Fel organometallic chem, Fonds Ger Chem Indust, 68-69 & Nat Res Coun, McMaster Univ, Ont, 69-71; RES SCIENTIST, CAN CTR INLAND WATERS, ENVIRON CAN, 72-, HEAD, ORG PROP SECT, 80- *Concurrent Pos:* From alt mem to mem, Water Qual Objectives Subcomt, Int Joint Comn, 74-78; mem, Task Force Polychlorinated Biphenyls, Environ Can & NHW Can, 75-76 & Task Force Mirex, 76-77; liaison mem, Task Force Ecol Effects Non-Phosphate Detergent Builders, Int Joint Comn, 78-80. *Mem:* Chem Inst Can; Int Asn Great Lakes Res; Ger Chem Soc; Asn Chem Engrs. *Res:* Chemistry of contaminants in the biosphere, including their analysis, bioaccumulation, metabolic and photochemical transformation and their toxicity; quantitative structure-activity correlation (QSAR) of contaminants; organometallic and environmental chemistry. *Mailing Add:* Nat Water Res Inst PO Box 5050 Burlington ON L7R 4A6 Can

KAISER, MARY AGNES, b Pittston, Pa, June 11, 48; m 79. ANALYTICAL CHEMISTRY. *Educ:* Wilkes Col, BS, 70; St Joseph's Univ, Pa, MS, 72; Villanova Univ, PhD(chem), 76. *Prof Exp:* Assoc chem, Univ Ga, 76-77; res chemist, 77-80, SUPVR, E I DU PONT DE NEMOURS & CO, INC, 80- *Mem:* Sigma Xi; Am Chem Soc; fel Am Inst Chemists; Am Soc Testing & Mat. *Res:* Analytical chemistry of separations; spectroscopy; environmental chemistry. *Mailing Add:* E I du Pont de Nemours & Co Inc Exp Sta 228 Wilmington DE 19898

KAISER, MICHAEL LEROY, b Keokuk, Iowa, Dec 28, 41; m 68; c 2. RADIO ASTRONOMY. *Educ:* Univ Iowa, BA, 64; Univ Md, College Park, MS, 73. *Prof Exp:* Comput programmer astron, Nat Radio Astron Observ, 64-65; sci analyst astron celestial mech, Wolf Res & Develop Corp, 65-69; RADIO ASTRONR, GODDARD SPACE FLIGHT CTR, NASA, 69- *Mem:* Am Astron Soc; Am Geophys Union; Int Union Radio Scientists; Inst Elec & Electronics Engrs. *Res:* Planetary radio physics; magnetospheric physics. *Mailing Add:* NASA/GSFC Code 695 Greenbelt MD 20771

KAISER, PETER, b Aschaffenburg, W Ger, 1938; m 66; c 2. ELECTRICAL ENGINEERING. *Educ:* Munich Tech Univ, Diplom Ing, 63; Univ Calif, Berkeley, MS, 65, PhD(elec eng), 66. *Prof Exp:* NATO fel, 63-64; mem staff, Guided Waves Res Lab, 66-79, SUPVR, LIGHTWAVE TECH GROUP, BELL LABS, 79- *Mem:* Inst Elec & Electronics Engrs; Optical Soc Am. *Res:* Frequency independent antennas; optical communication; guided wave transmission. *Mailing Add:* Bell Labs Box 400 Holmdel NJ 07733

KAISER, QUENTIN C, b Ridgewood, NY, Sept 12, 21; m 45; c 3. SOLID STATE PHYSICS. *Educ:* Hofstra Col, BA, 49; Okla Agr & Mech Col, MS, 50. *Prof Exp:* Physicist, Res Lab, Harry Diamond Labs, 50-53, supvry electronics scientist, Develop Lab, 53-59, physicist, Microminiaturization Br, 59-61, supvr res & develop, 61-63, br chief & supvry physicist, 63-80. *Mem:* Am Phys Soc; Inst Elec & Electronics Engrs. *Res:* Dielectric measurements; proximity fuze design; solid state devices. *Mailing Add:* 4114 Byrd Ct Kensington MD 20895

KAISER, REINHOLD, b Duisburg, Ger, Nov 19, 27. MAGNETIC RESONANCE. *Educ:* Univ Gottingen, dipl physics, 53, Dr rer nat, 54. *Prof Exp:* Ger Res Coun fel, Imp Col, Univ London, 55; Can Res Coun fel, Dalhousie Univ, 56; from asst prof to assoc prof, 57-66, PROF PHYSICS, UNIV NB, 66- *Concurrent Pos:* Res fel, Harvard Univ, 64 & Shell Develop Co, Calif, 65; guest prof, Swiss Fed Inst Technol, 71-72. *Res:* Acoustics; magnetic resonance. *Mailing Add:* Dept of Physics Univ of NB Fredericton NB E3B 5A3 Can

KAISER, RICHARD EDWARD, b Chicago, Ill, Dec 20, 36; m 63; c 3. NUCLEAR ENGINEERING. *Educ:* Northwestern Univ, Evanston, BS, 59; Kans State Univ, MS, 62, PhD(nuclear eng), 68. *Prof Exp:* Mem staff reactor shielding, Atomics Int, 61-64; asst nuclear engr, 67-72, NUCLEAR ENGR, ARGONNE NAT LAB, 72-, ZPPR REACTOR MGR, 78- *Concurrent Pos:* Instr, Aerojet Nuclear Co, 68-; affiliate prof, Univ Idaho. *Mem:* Sigma Xi; Am Nuclear Soc. *Res:* Doppler effect and sodium void coefficients in fast reactors. *Mailing Add:* Argonne Nat Lab PO Box 2528 Idaho Falls ID 83401

KAISER, ROBERT, b Strasbourg, France, June 22, 34; US citizen. CHEMICAL ENGINEERING, APPLIED CHEMISTRY. *Educ:* Mass Inst Technol, SB, 56, MS, 57, ScD(chem eng), 62. *Prof Exp:* Res engr, M W Kellogg Co, 61, res chemist, Res & Develop Ctr, Pullman, Inc, NJ, 62-65, res engr, 65-66; sr staff scientist, Res & Tech Labs, Space Systs Div, Avco Corp, Lowell, 66-71, group leader, Advan Processes Dept, Systs Div, 71-74; CONSULT ENGR, 74-; PRES & FOUNDER, AGROS ASSOCS, INC, WINCHESTER, MASS, 77- *Mem:* Am Chem Soc; Am Inst Chem Engrs; Soc Civil Engrs France. *Res:* Oil/water separation; magnetic liquids; applied surface chemistry; fine powder technology; process development; technology assessment and forecasting; industrial market research. *Mailing Add:* 12 Glengarry Rd Winchester MA 01890

KAISER, ROBERT L, b Erie, Pa, Feb 9, 31; m 59; c 3. TROPICAL MEDICINE, EPIDEMIOLOGY. *Educ:* Brown Univ, AB, 53; Yale Univ, MD, 57; Univ London, DTM&H, 63. *Prof Exp:* Chief parasitic dis unit, Commun Dis Ctr, 63-67, dir malaria prog, Ctr Dis Control, USPHS, 67-73; DIR PARASITIC DIS DIV, CTR DIS CONTROL, USPHS, ATLANTA, 73- *Mem:* Am Soc Trop Med & Hyg; Royal Soc Trop Med & Hyg. *Res:* Epidemiology of parasitic diseases including malaria and schistosomiasis. *Mailing Add:* 846 Barton Woods Rd NE Atlanta GA 30307

KAISER, THOMAS BURTON, b St Louis, Mo, May 11, 40; m 67; c 1. PLASMA PHYSICS. *Educ:* St Edward's Univ, BS, 62; Univ Md, College Park, MS, 71, PhD(physics), 73. *Prof Exp:* Sr analyst programming, LTV Aerospace Corp, Mass, 66-68; res assoc space physics, Goddard Space Flight Ctr, Md, 73-75; PHYSICIST PLASMA PHYSICS, LAWRENCE LIVERMORE LAB, 76- *Concurrent Pos:* Resident res assoc, Nat Acad Sci-Nat Res Coun, 73-75. *Mem:* AAAS; Am Phys Soc; Fedn Am Scientists. *Res:* Theoretical plasma physics; computational physics. *Mailing Add:* Lawrence Livermore Lab L-630 PO Box 808 Livermore CA 94550

KAISER, WILLIAM RICHARD, b Racine, Wis, Aug 15, 37; m 70; c 2. COAL GEOLOGY, AQUEOUS GEOCHEMISTRY. *Educ:* Univ Wis-Madison, BA, 59, MS, 62; Johns Hopkins Univ, PhD(geol), 72. *Prof Exp:* Geologist micropaleont, Exxon Co, USA, 62-63, geologist petrol geol, 65-68; geologist igneous & metamorphic petrog, Ghana Geol Surv, Accra, Ghana, 63-65; RES SCIENTIST, BUR ECON GEOL, UNIV TEX, 72- *Concurrent Pos:* Lectr, Dept Geol Sci, Univ Tex, Austin, 78-; mem, Lignite Subcomt & Fossil Energy Adv Comt, Dept Energy, 78. *Res:* Depositional systems; occurrence of Gulf Coast (Texas) lignite; hydrogeologic evaluation of deep-basin lignite; underground coal gasification; low-temperature aqueous geochemistry (uranium); brive equilibria in the predication of hydrocarbon reservoir quality. *Mailing Add:* Bur of Econ Geol Univ of Tex Austin TX 78712

KAISERMAN-ABRAMOF, ITA REBECA, b Belo Horizonte, Brazil, Sept 11, 33; div; c 1. NEUROBIOLOGY, NEUROCYTOLOGY. *Educ:* Univ Minas Gerais, BS, 55, MS, 56, PhD(biol sci), 62. *Prof Exp:* Actg dept chmn biol, Univ Minas Gerais, 62-63, assoc prof cytol, histol & embryol, 65-66; teaching asst histol, Sch Med, Harvard Univ, 66-67; asst prof anat, Sch Med, Boston Univ, 67-71; ASSOC PROF ANAT, SCH MED, CASE WESTERN RESERVE UNIV, 71- *Mem:* Am Inst Biol Sci; Am Soc Cell Biol; Am Asn Anatomists. *Res:* Cytological investigations of the mammalian brain, including visual and motor cerebral cortex and cerebellum; use of electron microscopy with experimental and quantitative analysis of connectivity; anophthalmic mutant mice and mechanisms involved in epilepsy. *Mailing Add:* Dept of Anat Sch of Med Case Western Reserve Univ Cleveland OH 44106

KAIZER, HERBERT, b Boston, Mass, Sept 30, 30; m 54; c 3. ONCOLOGY, BONE MARROW TRANSPLANTATION. *Educ:* Boston Univ, AB, 51, PhD(exp psychol), 56; Stanford Univ, MD, 65. *Prof Exp:* Assoc psychologist, Int Bus Mach, Inc, 56-58; mem tech staff, Thompson, Ramo, Wooldridge, Inc, 58-59; intern & asst resident, Johns Hopkins Hosp, 65-67; fel microbiol, Johns Hopkins Univ, 67-69; sr fel pediat, Univ Tex M D Anderson Hosp & Tumor Inst, 69-70; ASST PROF PEDIAT & ONCOL, SCH MED, JOHNS HOPKINS UNIV, 70- *Mem:* AAAS; Am Soc Microbiol. *Res:* Autologous bone marrow transplantation in cancer. *Mailing Add:* Oncol Ctr Sch Med Johns Hopkins Univ Baltimore MD 21205

KAIZERMAN, SAMUEL, b Montreal, Que, Jan 15, 27; nat US; m 65; c 2. ORGANIC CHEMISTRY. *Educ:* NY Univ, AB, 46, MS, 48, PhD(chem), 52. *Prof Exp:* Res assoc chem, Univ Akron, 51-53; sr res chemist, 55-60, res group leader, 60-72, MGR RES & DEVELOP, CHEM RES DIV, AM CYANAMID CO, 72- *Mem:* Am Chem Soc. *Res:* Mechanisms of polymerization; elastomers. *Mailing Add:* Chem Res Div Am Cyanamid Co Bound Brook NJ 08805

KAJFEZ, DARKO, b Delnice, Yugoslavia, July 8, 28; m 54; c 2. ELECTRICAL ENGINEERING. *Educ:* Univ Ljubljana, EE, 53; Univ Calif, Berkeley, PhD(eng), 67. *Prof Exp:* Assoc prof elec eng, 67-70, PROF ELEC ENG & RES ENGR, UNIV MISS, 70- *Concurrent Pos:* Vis prof elec eng, Univ Ljubljana, 76-77. *Mem:* Inst Elec & Electronics Engrs; Int Union Radio Sci. *Res:* Microwave circuits and antennas. *Mailing Add:* Dept of Elec Eng Univ of Miss University MS 38677

KAJI, AKIRA, b Tokyo, Japan, Jan 13, 30; m 58; c 2. BIOCHEMISTRY. *Educ:* Univ Tokyo, BS, 53; Johns Hopkins Univ, PhD(biochem), 58. *Prof Exp:* Res assoc microbiol, Sch Med, Vanderbilt Univ, 60-61; assoc, 63, from asst prof to assoc prof, 64-72, PROF MICROBIOL, SCH MED, UNIV PA, 72- *Concurrent Pos:* Res fel ophthal, Sch Med, Johns Hopkins Univ, 58-59, res fel, McCollum Pratt Inst, 59-60; Helen Hay Whitney Found fel, 61-63; vis investr, Rockefeller Inst, 59; vis scientist, Oak Ridge Nat Lab, 62; Helen Hay Whitney estab investrship, 64-69; John Simmon Guggenheim Scholar, Imperial Cancer Res Fund Lab, London & Prof, Tokyo Univ, 69- *Res:* Sulfur metabolism; neurochemistry; mechanism of enzyme action; tumorgenesis; protein biosynthesis; nucleic acids. *Mailing Add:* Dept of Microbiol Univ of Pa Sch of Med Philadelphia PA 19174

KAJI, HIDEKO (KATAYAMA), biochemistry, pharmacology, see previous edition

KAK, AVINASH CARL, b Srinagar, Kashmir, Oct 22, 44; m 76; c 1. ELECTRICAL ENGINEERING. *Educ:* Indian Inst Technol, PhD(elec eng), 70. *Prof Exp:* Asst prof, 70-74, ASSOC PROF ELEC ENG, PURDUE UNIV, 74- *Concurrent Pos:* Consult, C T Systs Div, G D Searle Inc, 75-78 & E M I Med Systs Inc, 78-; assoc ed, Ultrasonic Imaging, 78- *Mem:* Inst Elec & Electronics Engrs; Optical Soc Am. *Res:* Computerized imaging with x-rays and ultrasound; digital image processing; digital signal processing. *Mailing Add:* Sch of Elec Eng Purdue Univ West Lafayette IN 47907

KAKAR, ANAND SWAROOP, b India, Oct 14, 37; US citizen; m 69; c 1. CONDUCTIVE COATINGS, SURFACE CHEMISTRY. *Educ:* Banaras Hindu Univ, BSc, 60; Indian Inst Technol, MTech, 64; Wayne State Univ, MS, 71, PhD(phys chem), 78. *Prof Exp:* Lectr chem eng, Indian Inst Technol, Delhi, 65-68; technician, Can Gen Elec, 68-69 & Mercury Paint Co, 71-72; mfg develop engr, Ford Motor Co, Mt Clemons, Mich, 72-74; res asst, Wayne State Univ, 74-78; staff chemist, Acheson Colloids, Mich, 78-81; DIR RES, GRAFO COLLOIDS, 81- *Mem:* Electrochem Soc; Am Inst Chem Engrs. *Res:* Heat transfer and hold-up fluidized beds; zone refining and single crystal growth; optical and electrical properties of semiconductor; photovaltaic cells; electroless deposition; size reduction; colloidal dispersion; conductive coatings; solid film lubricants; surface preparation and analysis. *Mailing Add:* PO Box 89 Emlenton PA 16373

KAKAR, RAJESH KUMAR, b New Delhi, India, Oct 2, 50; m 77. STATISTICS, DATA PROCESSING. *Educ:* Univ Delhi, BSc, 70, MS, 72; Tex Tech Univ, DBA(bus statist), 78. *Prof Exp:* Instr bus statist, Tex Tech Univ, 72-78; ASST PROF BUS STATIST, ARIZ STATE UNIV, 78- *Mem:* Am Statist Asn; Inst Mgt Sci; Am Inst Decision Sci. *Res:* Empirical bayesian estimation; assessment of subjective probabilities; forecasting; manpower models; auditing software. *Mailing Add:* Col of Bus Admin Ariz State Univ Tempe AZ 85281

KAKEHASHI, SAMUEL, b Seattle, Wash, Dec 17, 27; m 51; c 2. DENTISTRY. *Educ:* Ohio State Univ, BSc, 52, DDS, 56; Med Col Va, MSc, 61; Am Bd Periodont, dipl, 65. *Prof Exp:* Prin investr, 61-69, chief dent serv br, 69-73, CHIEF PERIODONT DIS PROG, NAT INST DENT RES, NIH, 73- *Concurrent Pos:* Pvt pract. *Mem:* Am Acad Periodont; Am Dent Asn; Int Asn Dent Res. *Res:* Periodontal healing and instrumentation studies; etiology of periodontal disease; experimental calculus formation. *Mailing Add:* 5923 Anniston Rd Bethesda MD 20034

KAKIS, FREDERIC JACOB, b Drama, Greece, Nov 1, 30; US citizen; m 52; c 4. PHYSICAL ORGANIC CHEMISTRY, AIR POLLUTION. *Educ:* City Col New York, 60; Stanford Univ, PhD(org chem), 64. *Prof Exp:* Chmn dept, 63-68, assoc prof, 66-71, chmn, Div Natural Sci, 78-80, PROF CHEM, CHAPMAN COL, 71- *Concurrent Pos:* Grants, NSF, 65, Petrol Res Fund, 65, 66, 76 & 77, Res Corp, 66, 67, 70 & Union Oil Found, 74, 75, 76 & 77; res fel, Oak Ridge Nat Lab, 66; assoc prof, Calif State Col, Long Beach, 66-67 & Calif State Univ, Fullerton, 66-70; res fel, NASA-Ames Res Ctr & Stanford Univ, 69; environmentalist, Defense Contract Admin Serv, 70; vis prof, Lab Org Synthesis, Polytech Sch, Paris, 70-71; NSF res fel, Univ Calif, Riverside; vis prof, Univ Calif, Los Angeles & Univ Calif, Riverside; Fulbright award, 80. *Honors & Awards:* Cert of Recognition, NASA, 69; Am Chem Soc plaque, 70; NSF Prof Develop Award, 77. *Mem:* AAAS; Am Chem Soc; fel Am Inst Chem; The Chem Soc; NY Acad Sci. *Res:* Study of reaction mechanisms by isotopic labelling; air pollution research; synthetic and mechanistic organic chemistry; heterogeneous catalysis and adsorption. *Mailing Add:* Dept of Chem Chapman Col Orange CA 92666

KAKO, KYOHEI JOE, b Tokyo, Japan, May 29, 28; Can citizen; m 62; c 2. BIOCHEMISTRY. *Educ:* Tokyo Jikei Univ, MD, 53. *Prof Exp:* Resident internal med, Tokyo Jikei-Kai Tokyo Hosp, 54-56; res asst med, Sch Med, Washington Univ, 56-57; res assoc, Wayne State Univ, 59-61; from asst prof to assoc prof, 64-75, PROF PHYSIOL, FAC MED, UNIV OTTAWA, 75- *Concurrent Pos:* Mo Heart Asn fel, 57-59; fel, Kanton Hosp, Univ Zurich, 61-63; Alexander von Humboldt fel, I Med Clin, Univ Munich, 63-64; med res assoc, Med Res Coun Can, 68- *Mem:* Am Physiol Soc; Can Physiol Soc; Can Cardiovasc Soc; fel Am Col Cardiol; fel Royal Col Physicians & Surgeons. *Res:* Heart muscle biochemistry; lipid and carbohydrate metabolism; cardiomyopathies. *Mailing Add:* Dept of Physiol Univ of Ottawa Fac of Med Ottawa ON K1N 9A9 Can

KAKU, MICHIO, b San Jose, Calif, Jan 24, 47. THEORETICAL HIGH ENERGY PHYSICS, NUCLEAR PHYSICS. *Educ:* Harvard Univ, BA, 68; Univ Calif, Berkeley, PhD(physics), 72. *Prof Exp:* Lectr physics, Princeton Univ, 72-73; asst prof, 73-77, ASSOC PROF PHYSICS, CITY COL NEW YORK, 77- *Mem:* Fel Am Physical Soc. *Res:* High energy and nuclear physics; unified field theories; quantum gravity and supergravity; kinetics and neutron transport theory; reactor physics. *Mailing Add:* Dept of Physics City Col of New York New York NY 10031

KAKUNAGA, TAKEO, b Keijo, Japan, Nov 8, 37; m 63. CARCINOGENESIS, CELL BIOLOGY. *Educ:* Kanazawa Univ, BA, 60; Osaka Univ, MS, 62, PhD(pharmacol), 66. *Prof Exp:* Asst prof microbiol, Dept Tumor Viruses, Inst Microbiol Dis, Osaka Univ, 66-73, assoc prof, 73-78; CHIEF ONCOL, CELL GENETICS SECT, LAB MOLECULAR CARCINOGENESIS, NAT CANCER INST, NIH, 77- *Concurrent Pos:* Adv consult, Int Agency Res Cancer, 80; mem sci adv comt, Am Cancer Soc, 81-; assoc ed, J Cancer Res, Am Asn Cancer Res, 82- *Mem:* Am Asn Cancer Res; Am Soc Cell Biol; Japan Cancer Asn. *Res:* Carcinogenesis by chemical, irradiation and viruses, using techniques of molecular biology, somatic cell genetics, cell biology and chemistry; gene structure, expression, differentiation, transformation and mutation. *Mailing Add:* Bldg 37 Rm 3E08 Nat Cancer Inst Bethesda MD 20205

KAKUTANI, SHIZUO, b Osaka, Japan, Aug 28, 11; m 52; c 1. MATHEMATICS. *Educ:* Tohoku Univ, Japan, MA, 34; Osaka Univ, PhD(math), 41. *Hon Degrees:* MA, Yale Univ, 53. *Prof Exp:* Res mem, Inst Adv Study, 40-42; asst prof, Osaka Univ, 42-48; res mem, Inst Advan Study, 48-49; from asst prof to assoc prof, 49-53, PROF MATH, YALE UNIV, 53- *Mem:* Am Math Soc; Math Soc Japan. *Res:* Functional analysis; probability and stochastic processes. *Mailing Add:* Dept of Math Yale Univ New Haven CT 06520

KALAB, BRUNO MARIE, b Vienna, Austria, Sept 19, 29; US citizen. PHYSICS, ELECTRONICS ENGINEERING. *Educ:* Univ Vienna, PhD(physics), 64. *Prof Exp:* Supvry physicist nuclear physics & nuclear instrumentation, Naval Radiol Defense Lab, San Francisco, Calif, 64-66, res physicist electronics & nuclear weapons effects, 66-68, head, Electromagnetic Effects Prog, 68-69; res electronics engr nuclear weapons effects, USA Mobility Equip Res & Develop Ctr, Ft Belvoir, Va, 69-71; PHYSICIST NUCLEAR WEAPONS EFFECTS, DEPT ARMY, HARRY DIAMOND LABS, 71- *Mem:* Am Phys Soc; Inst Elec & Electronics Engrs. *Res:* Radiation effects on electronics; nuclear instrumentation. *Mailing Add:* Dept of the Army 2800 Powder Mill Rd Adelphi MD 20783

KALAB, MILOSLAV, b Urcice, Czech, June 12, 29; m 56; c 2. BIOCHEMISTRY. *Educ:* Brno Tech Univ, BSc, 50; Slovak Tech Univ, Bratislava, MSc, 52; Slovak Acad Sci, PhD(chem), 57. *Prof Exp:* Res scientist, Chem Inst, Slovak Acad Sci, 57-58; from asst prof to assoc prof, Sch Med, Palacky Univ, Czech, 58-65, assoc prof, Dept Natural Sci, 65-66; Nat Res Coun Can fel, 66-68; RES SCIENTIST, FOOD RES INST, AGR CAN, 68- *Concurrent Pos:* Co ed, Food Microstructure. *Mem:* Am Dairy Sci Asn; Can Inst Food Sci & Technol; Microscopical Soc Can; Electron Microscopy Soc Am. *Res:* Food proteins; milk protein gelation, composition, texture; microstructure of dairy products using electron microscopy. *Mailing Add:* Food Res Inst Agr Can Ottawa ON K1A 0C6 Can

KALAFUS, RUDOLPH M, b Jackson, Mich, Dec 17, 37; m 65; c 1. ELECTRICAL ENGINEERING. *Educ:* Univ Mich, BS(elec eng) & BS(eng math), 60, MS, 63, PhD(elec eng), 66. *Prof Exp:* Asst res engr, Radiation Lab, Univ Mich, 64-67, asst res engr, Electronics Res Ctr, NASA, 67-70; ENGR ELECTRONICS, TRANSP SYSTS CTR, US DEPT TRANSP, 70- *Mem:* Inst Elec & Electronics Engrs. *Res:* Electrodynamics of moving media; fundamental limitations of antennas; mutual coupling between antennas; cylindrical phased arrays. *Mailing Add:* US Dept Transp 55 Broadway Kendall Square Cambridge MA 02142

KALANT, HAROLD, b Toronto, Ont, Nov 15, 23; m 48. PHARMACOLOGY, CELL PHYSIOLOGY. *Educ:* Univ Toronto, MD, 45, BSc, 48, PhD(path chem), 55. *Prof Exp:* Sect head, Defence Res Med Labs, Can, 56-59; assoc prof, 59-64, PROF PHARMACOL, UNIV TORONTO, 64- *Concurrent Pos:* Nat Res Coun Can fel biochem, Cambridge Univ, 55-56; asst res dir, Ont Alcoholism Res Found, 59-62, assoc res dir biol sci, 62-; mem res comt NAm Asn of Alcoholism Progs, 62-67; mem alcoholism Study sect, NIMH, Washington, DC, 70-74; res comt non-med use drugs, Dept Nat Health & Welfare, Can, 70-72; mem sci adv bd, Int Coun Alcoholism & Addictions, Lausanne, 72-; mem expert adv panel on drugs of dependence, WHO, 74-; mem, Comn Prob Drug Dependence, US, 78-; Int Gold Medal res award, Raleigh Hills Found, 81. *Honors & Awards:* Jellinek Mem Award Res on Alcoholism, 72. *Mem:* Pharmacol Soc Can; Brit Biochem Soc; fel Royal Soc Can. *Res:* Pharmacology of ethanol and other addictive drugs; cell membrane chemistry and physiology; drug-behavier interactions in drug tolerance and dependence. *Mailing Add:* Dept of Pharmacol Univ of Toronto Toronto ON M5S 1A1 Can

KALANT, NORMAN, b Toronto, Ont; m 48; c 3. ENDOCRINOLOGY, METABOLISM. *Educ:* Univ Toronto, MD, 47, BSc, 49; McGill Univ, PhD(exp med), 54. *Prof Exp:* From asst dir to assoc dir res, Hosp, 55-67, DIR, LADY DAVIS INST MED RES, JEWISH GEN HOSP, 67- *Concurrent Pos:* Asst prof, McGill Univ, 58-64, assoc prof, 64-81, prof, 81- *Mem:* Am Fedn Clin Res; Am Diabetes Asn; Can Soc Clin Invest; Can Biochem Soc; Can Diabetes Asn. *Res:* Diabetes; atherosclerosis. *Mailing Add:* Lady Davis Inst of Med Res Jewish Gen Hosp Montreal PQ H3T 1E2 Can

KALANTAR, ALFRED HUSAYN, b Chicago, Ill, Dec 13, 34; m 61; c 4. SPECTROSCOPY, PHOTOPHYSICS. *Educ:* Rutgers Univ, BSc, 56; Cornell Univ, PhD(chem), 63. *Prof Exp:* NSF res fel chem, Calif Inst Technol, 63-64; asst prof, 64-69, ASSOC PROF CHEM, UNIV ALTA, 69- *Concurrent Pos:* Adj assoc prof, State Univ NY Binghamton, 70-71. *Res:* Emission spectroscopy of luminescent organic molecules; polarization of emission studies to assign states, uncover vibronic interactions; radiative and radiationless processes, lifetimes, energy transfer effects. *Mailing Add:* Dept of Chem Univ of Alta Edmonton AB T6G 2G2 Can

KALASINSKY, VICTOR FRANK, b Columbus, Ohio, Dec 30, 49; m 74. PHYSICAL CHEMISTRY, SPECTROSCOPY. *Educ:* Mass Inst Technol, SB, 72; Univ SC, PhD(phys chem), 75. *Prof Exp:* Asst prof chem, Furman Univ, 76-77; ASST PROF CHEM, MISS STATE UNIV, 77- *Mem:* Am Chem Soc; Am Phys Soc; Soc Appl Spectros; Coblentz Soc. *Res:* Raman, infrared and microwave spectroscopy; chemical structure and conformation; intramolecular and intermolecular interactions; applications of the laboratory computer. *Mailing Add:* Dept of Chem Miss State Univ Mississippi State MS 39762

KALATHIL, JAMES SAKARIA, b Shertallai, India, Dec 4, 35; US citizen; c 2. ATMOSPHERIC PHYSICS, PHYSICS. *Educ:* Univ Madras, BS, 56; Southern Ill Univ, MS, 63; Univ Nev, PhD(atmospheric physics), 77. *Prof Exp:* Instr physics, Frostburg State Col, Md, 63-65; ASSOC PROF PHYSICS, CALIF POLYTECH STATE UNIV, SAN LUIS OBISPO, 65- *Mem:* Am Meteorol Soc; Am Asn Physics Teachers. *Res:* Cumulus cloud models; history of meteorology; effects of solar activity on weather and climate. *Mailing Add:* Dept of Physics Calif Polytech State Univ San Luis Obispo CA 93401

KALB, G WILLIAM, b Akron, Ohio, Dec 10, 43; m 65; c 2. MINERALOGY, ANALYTICAL CHEMISTRY. *Educ:* Col Wooster, BA, 65; Ohio State Univ, MS, 67, PhD(mineral), 69. *Prof Exp:* Lab mgr mineral, Geol Surv, 69-70; PRES ANAL CHEM, TRADET LABS INC, 70- *Honors & Awards:* Bituminous Coal Res Award, Am Chem Soc, 72. *Mem:* Am Chem Soc; Am Soc Testing & Mat; Geol Soc Am. *Res:* Determination of volatile trace metals in coal; development of analytical methods for the collection and measurement of volatilized mercury in high SO2 concentration gas streams. *Mailing Add:* TraDet Labs Inc Wheeling-Ohio County Airport Wheeling WV 26003

KALBACH, CONSTANCE, b Chicago, Ill, Jan 12, 44; m 75. NUCLEAR CHEMISTRY, NUCLEAR PHYSICS. *Educ:* Univ Rochester, BS, 65, PhD(nuclear chem), 70. *Prof Exp:* Vis res assoc nuclear structure res lab, Univ Rochester, & lectr chem, Nazareth Col Rochester, 70-71, fel chem, 71-73; guest researcher, Dept Physics, Tech Univ Munich, 72; sr res collabr physics, French AEC, 73-74; asst prof physics, Univ Tenn & res consult physics div, Oak Ridge Nat Lab, Union Carbide, 74-75; guest researcher, Triangle Univs Nuclear Lab, 75-81; CONSULT, 78- *Concurrent Pos:* Vis asst prof, Dept Chem, NC State Univ, 77; vis scholar, Dept Physics, Duke Univ, 81- *Mem:* Am Chem Soc; Am Phys Soc; Sigma Xi. *Res:* Mechanisms of nuclear reactions especially preequilibrium particle emission; level densities. *Mailing Add:* Triangle Univ Nuclear Lab Duke Sta Durham NC 27701

KALBACH, ROBERT MICHAEL, experimental high energy physics, cosmic ray physics, deceased

KALBERER, JOHN THEODORE, JR, b New York, NY, Mar 15, 36. PHYSIOLOGY, BIOLOGY. *Educ:* Adelphi Univ, AB, 56; Creighton Univ, MS, 57; NY Univ, PhD(biol, physiol), 66. *Prof Exp:* Res assoc path, Beth Israel Med Ctr, NY, 57-66; grants assoc, Div Res Grants, NIH, 66-67; spec asst to assoc dir extramural activities, 67-73, assoc dir prog planning, Nat Cancer Inst, 74-78, ASST DIR, OFF MED APPLN RES, OFF DIR, NIH, 79- *Concurrent Pos:* Coordr for Dis Prev & Health Prom, NIH, 78- *Mem:* Am Soc Zool; Am Asn Anat; Aerospace Med Asn; Am Acad Polit & Soc Sci; NY Acad Sci. *Res:* Decompression sickness, especially as it relates to fat embolization to the lung; role of vasoactive substances as they relate to stress conditions. *Mailing Add:* Rm 210 Bldg 1 Nat Cancer Inst Bethesda MD 20205

KALBFELL, DAVID CONRAD, b Indianapolis, Ind, Aug 20, 14; m 39; c 4. PHYSICS, ELECTRONICS. *Educ:* Univ Calif, Los Angeles, AB, 34; Univ Calif, Berkeley, MA, 36, PhD(nuclear physics), 39. *Prof Exp:* Asst, Univ Calif, 35-39, physicist, Div War Res, Off Sci Res & Develop, 41-46; physicist, Standard Oil Co, Calif, 39-41; pres, Kalbfell Labs, Inc, 46-53; PRES, KALBFELL ELECTRONIX, 53- & INSTRUMENTS INC, 61- *Concurrent Pos:* Prof exten, Univ Calif, 42-60 & San Diego State Col, 48-72; consult, Convair Div, Gen Dynamics Corp, Missile & Space Div, Lockheed Aircraft Corp, Beckman Instruments Inc, Ampex Corp & Cubic Corp, 55-58; pres, San Diego Sci Corp, 57-61. *Mem:* Fel Inst Elec & Electronics Engrs. *Res:* Electronic systems; instrumentation; magnetic amplifiers. *Mailing Add:* 941 Rosecrans St San Diego CA 92106

KALBFLEISCH, GEORGE RANDOLPH, b Long Beach, Calif, Mar 14, 31; m 54; c 4. PARTICLE PHYSICS, HIGH ENERGY PHYSICS. *Educ:* Loyola Univ, Calif, BS, 52; Univ Calif, Berkeley, PhD(physics), 61. *Prof Exp:* Qual control supvr, United Can & Glass, Hunt Foods, Inc, Calif, 52-56; anal chemist, Hales Testing Labs, 57; technician, Lawrence Radiation Lab, Univ Calif, 57-59, asst, 59-61, physicist, 61-64; assoc physicist, 64-67, physicist, Brookhaven Nat Lab, 67-76; physicist, Fermi Nat Accelerator Lab, 76-79; PROF PHYSICS, UNIV OKLA, NORMAN, 79- *Concurrent Pos:* Consult, Anamet Testing Labs, 62-64. *Res:* Neutrino interactions; muon and pion physics; photon physics; superconducting magnets; beauty and charm physics. *Mailing Add:* Dept Physics & Astron Univ Okla Norman OK 73019

KALBFLEISCH, JAMES G, b Galt, Ont, Sept 12, 40; m 63; c 3. MATHEMATICAL STATISTICS. *Educ:* Univ Toronto, BSc, 63; Univ Waterloo, MA, 64, PhD(math), 66. *Prof Exp:* Lectr math, 64-66, from asst prof to assoc prof statist, 66-71, chmn dept, 75-79, PROF STATIST, UNIV WATERLOO, 71- *Concurrent Pos:* Adj prof, York Univ, 67; Dept Univ Affairs res grant, 67-70; Nat Res Coun Can res grant, 67-; vis prof, Univ Essex, 68-69; C D Howe fel, 68-69; prof statist, Univ Man, 70-71. *Mem:* Biomet Soc; fel Int Statist Inst; Royal Statist Soc; fel Am Statist Asn. *Res:* Statistical inference; combinatorial mathematics. *Mailing Add:* Dept Statist Univ Waterloo Waterloo ON N2L 3G1 Can

KALCKAR, HERMAN MORITZ, b Copenhagen, Denmark, Mar 26, 08; nat US; m 51, 68; c 3. BIOCHEMISTRY. *Educ:* Univ Copenhagen, MD, 33, PhD(chem), 39. *Hon Degrees:* MA, Harvard Univ, 64; DSc, Washington Univ, 64; Univ Copenhagen, 79, Denmark & Chicago, 75. *Prof Exp:* Mem, on leave, res staff, Inst Cytophysiol, Denmark, 43-45, assoc prof, 46-48, res prof & head dir, 49-54; vis scientist, Nat Inst Arthritis & Metab Dis, 53-56; head sect metab enzymes, 56; prof biol, Johns Hopkins Univ, 58-61; head biochem res lab, Mass Gen Hosp, 61-74; prof, 61-74, EMER PROF BIOL CHEM, HARVARD MED SCH, 74-; DISTINGUISHED RES PROF BIOCHEM, GRAD SCH, BOSTON UNIV, 79- *Concurrent Pos:* Assoc ed, J Cellular Physiol, 76. *Mem:* Nat Acad Sci; Am Soc Biol Chem; Soc Gen Physiol; Harvey Soc; Am Acad Arts & Sci. *Res:* Biological phosphorylations; biochemical genetics in man and microorganisms with special reference to galactose metabolism. *Mailing Add:* Chem Dept Boston Univ 685 Commonwealth Ave Boston MA 02215

KALDJIAN, MOVSES J(EREMY), b Beirut, Lebanon, Dec 26, 25; US citizen; m 58; c 3. STRUCTURAL MECHANICS, CIVIL ENGINEERING. *Educ:* Am Univ, Beirut, BA, 48, BSc, 49; Univ Man, MSc, 52; Univ Mich, PhD(civil eng), 60. *Prof Exp:* Off engr, Trans-Arabian Pipeline Co, Lebanon, 49-50; civil engr, Dom Bridge Co Ltd, Can, 52-53; lectr struct, Queen's Univ, Ont, 53-54; from instr to assoc prof solid mech, 57-76, ASSOC PROF CIVIL ENG, UNIV MICH, 76- *Concurrent Pos:* Partic, Ford Found comput proj, 61 & Ford Fac Develop adv comt grant, 62; vis prof, Univ Mich-US Agency Int Develop Prog & Indian Inst Technol, Kanpur, 62-64; consult, G C Optronics & Palmer-Shile. *Mem:* Am Soc Civil Engrs. *Res:* Numerical techniques in structural mechanics including finite element methods; response of buildings and dams to earthquake forces; ship structures in ice fields and some experimentation with holography. *Mailing Add:* 2927 Sheffield Ann Arbor MI 48105

KALDOR, ANDREW, b Budapest, Hungary, Oct 11, 44; US citizen; m 67; c 2. PHYSICAL CHEMISTRY, LASER PHYSICS. *Educ:* Univ Calif, Berkeley, BS, 66; Cornell Univ, PhD(chem), 70. *Prof Exp:* Mem staff laser chem, Nat Bur Standards, 70-74; sr res chemist appl physics, 74-77, head chem physics group, 77-81, DIR CHEM PHYSICS SCI LAB, CORP RES LAB, EXXON RES & ENG CO, 81- *Concurrent Pos:* Nat Acad Sci-Nat Res Coun fel, Nat Bur Stand4rds, 70-72. *Honors & Awards:* Silver Medal, Dept Com, 73. *Mem:* AAAS; Am Chem Soc; Am Vacuum Soc. *Res:* Laser chemistry; laser isotope separation; chemical physics; reaction dynamics; molecular spectroscopy; surface chemistry. *Mailing Add:* Corp Res Lab PO Box 45 Linden NJ 07036

KALDOR, GEORGE, b Budapest, Hungary, Feb 10, 26; nat US; m 63. PHYSIOLOGY. *Educ:* Med Univ Budapest, MD, 50; Am Bd Clin Chem, dipl, 64; Am Bd Path, dipl clin path, 65, dipl chem path, 78. *Prof Exp:* Asst prof clin biochem, Med Univ Budapest, 54-56; res assoc biochem & head phys chem, Isaac Albert Res Inst, Jewish Chronic Dis Hosp, 59-65; assoc prof physiol, 65-69, prof physiol & biophys, Med Col Pa, 69-75, clin path, 70-75, CLIEF, CLIN LAB SERV, VETERANS ADMIN HOSP, ALLEN PARK, MICH, 75-; PROF PATH, WAYNE STATE UNIV, DETROIT, 75- *Concurrent Pos:* Res fel biochem, Mass Gen Hosp, 57-58 & McArdle Mem Lab, Wis, 58-59. *Mem:* Am Soc Biol Chem; Am Physiol Soc; Am Soc Exp Path; fel Am Soc Clin Pathologists; fel Royal Soc Health. *Res:* Biochemistry of muscular contraction and relaxation; computer assisted medical decision making. *Mailing Add:* Vet Admin Hosp Allen Park MI 48101

KALE, HERBERT WILLIAM, II, b Trenton, NJ, Dec 24, 31; m 61; c 3. ORNITHOLOGY, CONSERVATION. *Educ:* Rutgers Univ, BSc, 54; Univ Ga, MSc, 61, PhD(zool), 64. *Prof Exp:* Ornithologist, Encephalitis Res Ctr, Fla Div Health, 64-66; vert ecologist, Fla Med Entom Lab, 66-74; V PRES ORNITH RES, FLA AUDUBON SOC, 75- *Mem:* Am Ornith Union; Ecol Soc Am; Cooper Ornith Soc; Wilson Ornith Soc; Am Ornithologists Union. *Res:* Ecology, animal ecology, breeding biology, density and status of avian populations, territoriality and dispersal of birds; conservation of animal populations and habitats, especially colonial nesting birds, rare and endangered species. *Mailing Add:* 1101 Audubon Way Maitland FL 32751

KALELKAR, MOHAN SATISH, b Bombay, India, Apr 24, 48. PHYSICS. *Educ:* Harvard Col, BA, 68; Columbia Univ, MA, 70, PhD(physics), 75. *Prof Exp:* Res assoc physics, Columbia Univ, 75-77, asst prof, 77-78; ASST PROF PHYSICS, RUTGERS UNIV, PISCATAWAY, 78- *Mem:* Am Phys Soc; Am Inst Physics. *Res:* Experimental work in elementary particle physics; neutrino interactions and hadron-hadron collisions. *Mailing Add:* Serin Physics Lab Frelinghuysen Rd Piscataway NJ 08854

KALENDA, NORMAN WAYNE, b Grand Rapids, Mich, Nov 27, 28. ORGANIC CHEMISTRY. *Educ:* Univ Mich, BS, 51; Univ Ill, PhD(chem), 55. *Prof Exp:* Res chemist, Mellon Inst, 54-55; RES CHEMIST, EASTMAN KODAK CO, 57- *Mem:* Am Chem Soc. *Res:* Organic chemistry; photographic chemistry. *Mailing Add:* Eastman Kodak Co Kodak Park Bldg 82 Rochester NY 14601

KALENSHER, BERNARD EARL, b Beaumont, Tex, May 4, 27. APPLIED MATHEMATICS, STATISTICS. *Educ:* Univ Tex, PhD(physics), 54. *Prof Exp:* Sr res engr, Jet Propulsion Lab, Calif Inst Technol, 54-60; sr physicist, Electro-Optical Systs, Xerox Corp, 61-76; SR ANAL PHYSICIST, PHRASOR SCI, INC, 77- *Mem:* Am Inst Aeronaut & Astronaut. *Mailing Add:* Phrasor Sci Inc 1536 Highland Ave Duarte CA 91010

KALER, JAMES BAILEY, b Albany, NY, Dec 29, 38; m 60; c 4. ASTRONOMY. *Educ:* Univ Mich, Ann Arbor, AB, 60; Univ Calif, Los Angeles, PhD(astron), 64. *Prof Exp:* Asst prof, 64-68, assoc prof, 68-76, PROF ASTRON, UNIV ILL, URBANA, 76- *Mem:* AAAS; Am Astron Soc; Int Astron Union. *Res:* Planetary nebulae; nebular spectrophotometry; interstellar medium; chemical abundances. *Mailing Add:* 341 Astron Bldg Univ Ill 1011 W Springfield Urbana IL 61801

KALEY, GABOR, b Budapest, Hungary, Nov 16, 26; m 53; c 2. PHYSIOLOGY, EXPERIMENTAL PATHOLOGY. *Educ:* Columbia Univ, BS, 50; NY Univ, MS, 57, PhD(exp path), 60. *Prof Exp:* Resident asst surg, Bellevue Hosp, New York, 55-56; res asst path, NY Univ Med Ctr, 56-60, from instr to asst prof, 61-62; assoc prof, 64-70, PROF PHYSIOL, NY MED COL, 70-, CHMN DEPT, 72- *Concurrent Pos:* USPHS fel, NY Univ Med Ctr, 60-62. *Res:* Cardiovascular physiology; hypertension; juxtaglomerular cells; renal-adrenal relationships; renen-angiotens in system; erythropoietin; inflammation; microcirculation and prostaglandins; endotoxins. *Mailing Add:* Dept of Physiol NY Med Col Valhalla NY 10595

KALF, GEORGE FREDERICK, b New Britain, Conn, Dec 22, 30; m 53; c 2. BIOCHEMISTRY. *Educ:* Upsala Col, BS, 52; Pa State Univ, MS, 54; Yale Univ, PhD(biochem), 57. *Prof Exp:* Enzymologist, Chem & Physics Sect, Animal Dis & Parasite Res Div, USDA, 59; from asst prof to assoc prof biochem, NJ Col Med & Dent, 60-66; PROF BIOCHEM, JEFFERSON MED COL, THOMAS JEFFERSON UNIV, 66-, PROF PATH, 79- *Concurrent Pos:* Nat Found fel, Yale Univ, 57-59; Am Heart Asn estab investr. *Mem:* Am Soc Cell Biol; Am Soc Biol Chem; Am Asn Cancer Res; Brit Biochem Soc. *Res:* Nucleic acid biosynthesis in mitochondria; control of DNA replication in normal and neoplastic tissues; biochemical oncology; benene toxicity. *Mailing Add:* Jefferson Med Col Thomas Jefferson Univ Philadelphia PA 19107

KALFAYAN, SARKIS HAGOP, b Turkey, July 2, 16; US citizen; m 53; c 3. POLYMER CHEMISTRY. *Educ:* Am Univ, Beirut, BA, 40, MA, 42; Case Inst Technol, PhD(chem), 50. *Prof Exp:* Instr chem, Am Univ, Beirut, 42-47; from asst prof to assoc prof, Mt St Mary's Col, Calif, 51-55; fel, Univ Southern Calif, 55-56; group supvr, Prod Res Co, 56-58, chief chemist, 58-60; lab mgr, Chem-Seal Corp, 60-62; sr scientist polymer chem, 62-67, TECH GROUP SUPVR POLYMER CHEM, JET PROPULSION LAB, CALIF INST TECHNOL, 67- *Mem:* AAAS; Am Chem Soc; fel Am Inst Chem. *Res:* Polymer synthesis and electrical properties of polymers; spacecraft materials; physical testing of polymers; chemorheology of polymers. *Mailing Add:* 4834 Matley Rd La Canada CA 91011

KALFF, JACOB, b Velsen, Netherlands, Dec 20, 35; Can citizen; m 59; c 3. HYDROBIOLOGY. *Educ:* Univ Toronto, BSc, 59, MSc, 61; Ind Univ, PhD(limnol), 65. *Prof Exp:* Asst prof, 65-69, assoc prof, 70-76, PROF ECOL, MCGILL UNIV, MONTREAL, 77- *Concurrent Pos:* Vis scientist hydrobiol, Inst Nat Rech Agron, France, 72-73; consult, Ecol Adv Comt, Baie James Energy Corp, 77-; vis prof, Dept Bot, Univ Nairobi, Kenya, 79-80; dir, Limnol Res Group, Dept Biol, McGill Univ, 82- *Mem:* AAAS; Am Soc Limnol & Oceanog; Ecol Soc NAm; Int Asn Theoret & Appl Limnol. *Res:* Ecology of algae and aquatic higher plants with an emphasis on their productivity and their role in the material cycling in lakes. *Mailing Add:* Dept Biol McGill Univ 1205 Ave Docteur Penfield Montreal PQ H3A 1B1 Can

KALFOGLOU, GEORGE, b Istanbul, Turkey, June 12, 39; m 68. SURFACE CHEMISTRY. *Educ:* Robert Col, Istanbul, BS, 63; NC State Univ, PhD(chem), 68. *Prof Exp:* RES CHEMIST, RES LAB, TEXACO INC, 68- *Mem:* AAAS; Am Chem Soc; Soc Petrol Engrs. *Res:* Solution thermodynamics; colloidal chemistry; chemical treatment of water-sensitive minerals; physical and interfacial properties of surfactants; design enhanced petroleum recovery processes by utilizing proper surfactant systems; tertiary oil recovery by micellar and polymer systems and caustic floods. *Mailing Add:* 11703 Bandlon Dr Houston TX 77072

KALICKI, HENRIETTA, b Hartford, Conn, Jan 21, 18; m 50. DEVELOPMENTAL GENETICS. *Educ:* Hunter Col, BA, 39; Univ Iowa, MS, 42; St John's Univ, NY, PhD(zool), 60. *Prof Exp:* Chief bacteriologist, Schwarz Labs, NY, 44-46; instr biol, Univ Bridgeport, 46-51; asst prof, Manhattanville Col, 52-59; from asst prof to assoc prof, 60-75, PROF BIOL, ADELPHI UNIV, 75- *Concurrent Pos:* NSF, 61-75; Nat Inst Gen Med Sci grant, 62-65. *Mem:* Am Soc Zoologists; Tissue Cult Asn; fel AAAS; Am Chem Soc; Am Asn Univ Prof. *Res:* Genetic control of embryogenesis, cell differentiation and metabolism. *Mailing Add:* Dept of Biol Adelphi Univ Garden City NY 11530

KALIKSTEIN, KALMAN, b Strzemieszyce, Poland, Sept 4, 29; m 55; c 4. PHYSICS. *Educ:* Brooklyn Col, BS, 52; NY Univ, MS, 54, PhD(physics), 62. *Prof Exp:* Res physicist, Naval Appl Sci Lab, 53-64; res assoc hypervelocity impact, Fundamental Methods Assoc Inc, 64-65; asst prof, 65-71, assoc prof, 71-82, PROF PHYSICS, HUNTER COL, 82- *Mem:* Am Phys Soc. *Res:* Theoretical experimental physics and device design; electromagnetic propagation, microwave properties of ferrites and other solid devices; plasmas, nuclear and atomic physics; hypervelocity impact; photoconductivity and luminescence. *Mailing Add:* Dept of Physics Hunter Col 695 Park Ave New York NY 10021

KALIL, FORD, b Akron, Ohio, Jan 5, 25; m 50; c 3. ENGINEERING PHYSICS. *Educ:* Univ Akron, BEE, 50; Vanderbilt Univ, MS, 51, PhD(physics), 58. *Prof Exp:* Physicist, USPHS, 51-53; staff mem, Los Alamos Sci Lab, 53-55; supvr lab, Martin Co, 58-59, gen supvr test eval, 59, mgr, 59-60, design engr, 60-63; aerospace technologist, Goddard Space Flight Ctr, 63-68, sr tech asst to br head, Manned Flight Planning & Anal Div, 68-74, sr tech consult, network procedures & eval div, networks directorate, 74-78, systs mgr cosmic background explorer proj, Eng Directorate, 78-80, TECH ENGR & OPERS MGR & PRES, GODDARD SPACE FLIGHT CTR, NASA, 80- *Concurrent Pos:* Adj prof, Drexel Inst, 58-; mem, Apollo Exten Syst, Commun & Navig Traffic Control Panel, 65 & Apollo Exten Syst Working Group, NASA, 65- *Mem:* Am Inst Aeronaut & Astronaut; Am Phys Soc. *Res:* Aerospace technology; mission and systems analysis; orbital mechanics; electron and radiation physics; management. *Mailing Add:* 9108 Bridgewater St College Park MD 20740

KALIL, J(AMES), b Buffalo, NY, Oct 22, 19; m 46; c 4. CHEMICAL ENGINEERING. *Educ:* City Col New York, BChE, 41; Polytech Inst Brooklyn, MS, 50, PhD(chem eng), 51. *Prof Exp:* Chem engr, Chem Warfare Serv, 42-44; res chem engr, Los Alamos Sci Lab, 46-47; asst instr chem eng, Polytech Inst Brooklyn, 49-51; chem eng develop, 51-56, develop supvr, 56-63, res engr, E I Du Pont De Nemours & Co, Inc, 63-80. *Mem:* Am Chem Soc; Am Inst Chem Engrs. *Res:* Rheology of slurries; mass and momentum transfer in fluidized beds; synthetic elastomers; rubber chemicals. *Mailing Add:* 2424 Dorval Rd Wilmington DE 19810

KALIN, ELWOOD WALTER, b Detroit, Mich, Aug 2, 17; m 42; c 4. HORTICULTURE, FLORICULTURE. *Educ:* Mich State Col, BS, 39; Purdue Univ, MS, 42, PhD(hort, floricult), 53. *Prof Exp:* Instr hort, Purdue Univ, 40-45; asst prof floricult & greenhouse supt, Univ NH, 45-47; PROF HORT & HORTICULTURIST, WASH STATE UNIV, 47- *Honors & Awards:* Alex Laurie Award, Soc Am Florists, 80. *Mem:* Am Soc Hort Sci; Am Hort Soc; Am Chrysanthemum Soc; Wildlife Soc. *Res:* Bulb production and forcing qualities of hardy Dutch bulbs; chrysanthemum culture and breeding; Protea culture and use; mineral nutrition. *Mailing Add:* Dept of Hort Wash State Univ Pullman WA 99164

KALIN, ROBERT, b Everett, Mass, Dec 11, 21; m 62; c 4. MATHEMATICS. *Educ:* Univ Chicago, BS, 47; Harvard Univ, MAT, 48; Fla State Univ, PhD(math educ), 61. *Prof Exp:* Teacher high sch, Mass, 48-49 & pub sch, Mo, 49-52; statistician, Naval Air Tech Training Ctr, Okla, 52-53; test specialist math, Educ Testing Serv, NJ, 53-55, res assoc math educ, 55; exec asst, Comn Math Col Bd, 55-56; from instr to assoc prof, chmn math educ prog, 74-78, 56-65, PROF MATH EDUC, FLA STATE UNIV, 65- *Concurrent Pos:* Dir, NSF Acad Year Insts, 69-71. *Mem:* Nat Coun Teachers Math; Math Asn Am; Int Group Psychol Math Educ; Asn Teachers Math. *Res:* Programmed texts in advanced mathematics for intermediate grade students; television-text instructional system for elementary school teachers; analytic geometry; elementary mathematics texts for grades 1-8. *Mailing Add:* Math Educ Prog Fla State Univ Tallahassee FL 32306

KALINA, ROBERT E, b New Prague, Minn, Nov 13, 36; m 59; c 2. OPTHAMOLOGY. *Educ:* Univ Minn, BA, 57, BS, 60, MD, 60. *Prof Exp:* Intern med, Univ Ore, 60-61, resident ophthal, 61-66; fel retina, Children's Hosp, San Francisco, 66-67 & Harvard Med Sch, 67; chief, Harborview Med Ctr, 68-69; actg chmn, 70-71, PROF & CHMN OPHTHAL, UNIV WASH, SEATTLE, 70- *Concurrent Pos:* Consult, Vet Admin Hosp, 69-, Pub Health Hosp, 69- & Madigan Gen Hosp, US Army, 69-; med dir, Lions Eye Bank, 69-; assoc head, Ophthal Div, Children's Orthopedic Hosp, 75- *Mem:* Am Acad Ophthal; Am Bd Ophthal; Asn Univ Professors Ophthal; Nat Soc Prevent Blindness. *Res:* Diseases and surgery of the retina. *Mailing Add:* Dept Ophthal RJ-10 Univ Wash Seattle WA 98195

KALINOWSKI, MATHEW LAWRENCE, b Chicago, Ill, Jan 1, 15; m 46; c 2. PETROLEUM CHEMISTRY. *Educ:* Univ Chicago, BS, 37; Univ Ill, MS, 40. *Prof Exp:* Chemist, Ill State Geol Surv, 37-41 & Sherwin-Williams Co, 41-48; group leader petrol refining, Stand Oil Co, Ind, 48-66, SR PATENT ADV, AMOCO RES CTR, 66- *Mem:* Am Chem Soc. *Res:* Petroleum refining and products. *Mailing Add:* 734 S Sleight Naperville IL 60540

KALINOWSKI, WALBERT C, b Crary, NDak, Mar 4, 14. MATHEMATICS. *Educ:* St John's Univ, Minn, BA, 35; St Louis Univ, PhD(math), 48. *Prof Exp:* Instr math, 37, from instr to assoc prof, 40-53, PROF MATH, ST JOHN'S UNIV, MINN, 54- *Mem:* AAAS. *Mailing Add:* Dept of Math St John's Univ Collegeville MN 56321

KALINSKE, A(NTON) A(DAM), b Plymouth, Wis, Sept 1, 11; m 34; c 4. ENVIRONMENTAL ENGINEERING, FLUID MECHANICS. *Educ:* Univ Wis, BS, 33, MS, 35. *Prof Exp:* From instr hydraul to assoc prof mech & hydraul, Univ Iowa, 36-45; vpres & tech dir, Infilco, Inc, 45-65; dir res, Eimco Corp, 65-69; prof eng, Utah Water Res Lab, Utah State Univ, 69-71; chief sanit engr, Environ Control Dept, Kaiser Engrs, 71-72; VPRES, CAMP, DRESSER & McKEE, INC, 72- *Honors & Awards:* Hilgard Prize, Am Soc Civil Engrs, 47; Thomas R Camp Medal, Water Pollution Control Fedn, 77. *Mem:* Am Soc Civil Engrs; Am Water Works Asn; Water Pollution Control Fedn; Am Inst Chem Engrs. *Res:* Water and waste treatment; sediment transportation; fluid flow; turbulence; flow control. *Mailing Add:* Camp Dresser & McKee Inc 710 S Broadway Walnut Creek CA 94596

KALINSKY, ROBERT GEORGE, b Cleveland, Ohio, Sept 18, 45; m 71. PHYCOLOGY, ENVIRONMENTAL BIOLOGY. *Educ:* Univ Dayton, BS, 67; Ohio State Univ, MSc, 69, PhD(bot), 73. *Prof Exp:* Lectr bot, Ohio State Univ, 73-74; ASST PROF BIOL, LA STATE UNIV, SHREVEPORT, 74- *Concurrent Pos:* Biol consult, Dames & Moore Engrs, Cincinnati, 73-74. *Mem:* Sigma Xi; Phycol Soc Am; Brit Phycol Soc; Bot Soc Am. *Res:* Systematic revision of the diatom genus Nitzschia; ecological studies of the major waterways of Northwestern Louisiana. *Mailing Add:* Dept of Biol Sci La State Univ 8515 Youree Dr Shreveport LA 71115

KALISCH, GERHARD KARL, b Breslau, Ger, Dec 21, 14; nat US; m 42; c 2. MATHEMATICS. *Educ:* Univ Iowa, BA, 38, MS, 39; Univ Chicago, PhD(math), 42. *Prof Exp:* Asst, Inst Adv Study, 41-42; instr math, Univ Kans, 42-44 & Cornell Univ, 44-46; from asst prof to prof, Univ Minn, 46-65; PROF MATH, UNIV CALIF, IRVINE, 65- *Mem:* AAAS; Am Math Soc; Math Asn Am; Math Soc France. *Res:* Functional analysis; topological algebra. *Mailing Add:* Dept of Math Univ of Calif Irvina CA 92664

KALISCH, JOHN HANS, b Vienna, Austria, Sept 14, 15; Can citizen; m 62; c 1. PULP CHEMISTRY, PAPER CHEMISTRY. *Educ:* Vienna Tech Univ, dipl chem eng, 37, DSc(electrochem), 39. *Prof Exp:* Res chemist food technol, Standard Brands Ltd, 44-49 & Can Breweries Ltd, 49-51; mgr prod & process dev, Standard Prod Lab, 51-52; res engr metall, Carballoy Div, Can Gen Elec Co, 52-54; SR RES ASSOC PULP & PAPER, CAN INT PAPER RES LTD, 54- *Honors & Awards:* I H Weldon Gold Medal, Can Pulp & Paper Asn, 70. *Mem:* Chem Inst Can; Tech Asn Pulp & Paper Indust; Can Pulp & Paper Asn. *Res:* Cellulose and wood chemistry in its applications to pulp and paper technology; research and development on chemical, chemi-mechanical, mechanical and ultra high yield pulping processes. *Mailing Add:* Can Int Paper Res Ltd 179 Main St W Hawkesbury ON K6A 2K8 Can

KALISH, DAVID, b New York, NY, Aug 15, 39; div; c 1. LIGHTGUIDE GLASS TECHNOLOGY. *Educ:* Mass Inst Technol, SB, 60, SM, 64, ScD, 66. *Prof Exp:* Engr, ManLabs, Inc, 60-63; instr metall, Mass Inst Technol, 63-65; staff scientist, ManLabs, Inc, 65-68; scientist & team leader phys metall, Lockheed-Ga Co, 68-71; mem tech staff mat eng & chem, 71-73, supvr metall eng, 73-79, SUPVR LIGHTGUIDE GLASS TECHNOL, BELL TEL LABS, INC, 80- *Concurrent Pos:* Vis assoc prof, Ga Inst Technol, 70, lectr mech eng, 73-81. *Mem:* Fel Am Soc Metals; Am Inst Mining, Metall & Petrol Engrs; Am Soc Test & Mat. *Res:* Optical fibers, physical properties and fabrication; metal deformation processes; high strength steels, titanium and aluminum; superplasticity; fatigue and fracture; fabrication methods and properties of refractory materials; thermomechanical treatments of steels. *Mailing Add:* Bell Tel Labs Inc 2000 NE Expressway Norcross GA 30071

KALISH, HERBERT S(AUL), b New York, NY, Aug 11, 22; m 50; c 2. METALLURGICAL ENGINEERING. *Educ:* Univ Mo, BS, 43, MetE, 53; Univ Pa, MS, 48. *Prof Exp:* Metall observer open hearth steel, Carnegie-Ill Steel Corp, 43; res engr alloy develop, Battelle Mem Inst, 43-44, 46; asst, Thermodyn Res Lab, Univ Pa, 46-48; res metallurgist lead alloys, Elec Storage Battery Co, 48; sr engr spec prod, Sylvania Elec Prod, Inc, 48-50, engr-in-charge, Zirconium Sect, 50-52, sect head appl metall, 52-55, eng mgr metal fabrication & assembly, 55-57; eng mgr, Sylvania-Corning Nuclear Corp, 57; sect chief mat, Nuclear Fuel Res Labs, Olin Mathieson Chem Corp, 57-60, chief nuclear metall, Nuclear Fuel Res, 60-62; mgr com fuel dept, United Nuclear Corp, Conn, 62-65; asst to pres, 65-71, VPRES, ADAMAS CARBIDE CORP, 71- *Mem:* Am Soc Metals; Am Welding Soc; Sigma Xi; Am Soc Test & Mat; Am Inst Mining, Metall & Petrol Engrs. *Res:* Nuclear materials; high temperature materials; powder metallurgy, particularly alloy development; physical metallurgy; fabrication research. *Mailing Add:* Adamas Carbide Corp 141 Market St Kenilworth NJ 07033

KALISKI, MARTIN EDWARD, b New York, NY, Oct 22, 45; m 69. MICROPROCESSOR-BASED CONTROL, SYSTEMS THEORY. *Educ:* Mass Inst Technol, BS, 66 & 68, SM, 68, PhD(elec eng), 71. *Prof Exp:* Asst prof comput sci, City Col New York, 71-73; asst prof, 73-76, ASSOC PROF ELEC ENG, NORTHEASTERN UNIV, 76- *Concurrent Pos:* Fulbright scholar, France, 80-81. *Mem:* Inst Elec & Electronics Engrs. *Res:* Systems theory; industrial automation & robotics; microprocessor-based control; software engineering. *Mailing Add:* Dept of Elec Eng Northeastern Univ Boston MA 02115

KALISON, SEYMOUR LINCOLN, b New York, NY, Feb 4, 15; m 50; c 3. VETERINARY MEDICINE. *Educ:* Yale Univ, BA, 36; Mich State Univ, DVM, 40. *Prof Exp:* Assoc prof vet sci, Univ Tenn, 50-54; prof vet sci, VA Polytech Inst & State Univ, 54-78; RETIRED. *Mem:* AAAS; Am Vet Med Asn; US Animal Health Asn; Royal Soc Health. *Res:* Prevention and control of livestock diseases; bovine sterility and bovine mastitis. *Mailing Add:* 1309 Palmer Dr Blacksburg VA 24060

KALISS, NATHAN, b New York, NY, Aug 1, 07; m 28; c 3. IMMUNOLOGY. *Educ:* City Col New York, BS, 29; Columbia Univ, MA, 31, PhD(zool), 38. *Prof Exp:* Asst zool, Columbia Univ, 31-38 & Univ Pa, 39-40; asst path, Med Col, Cornell Univ, 41-43; instr zool, George Washington Univ, 46-47; Am Cancer Soc sr fel, 47-50, staff scientist cancer res, 50-59, asst dir res, 58-62 & 75-76, sr staff scientist, 59-72, EMER SR STAFF SCIENTIST, 72-, GUEST INVESTR, JACKSON LAB, 76- *Concurrent Pos:* Med statistician, US Vet Admin, 46-47; vis fel, Sloan-Kettering Inst, 48; ed, Transplantation Bull, 53-63 & Transplantation, 63-75; Guggenheim fel, 56-57; res assoc surg, Harvard Med Sch, 66-73. *Mem:* Soc Exp Biol & Med; Am Asn Cancer Res; Transplantation Soc; Reticuloendothelial Soc. *Res:* Homograft immunity; etiology of carcinogenesis; biology of cancer; immunology of tissue grafting. *Mailing Add:* Seely Rd Bar Harbor ME 04609

KALIVODA, FRANK E, JR, b Cicero, Ill, Mar 17, 30; m 57; c 3. MECHANICAL ENGINEERING. *Educ:* Ill Inst Technol, BSME, 54, MSME, 58. *Prof Exp:* Coop trainee prod, Link-Belt Corp, 49-52; asst res engr, Heat-Power Res Dept, Armour Res Found, 54-58; sr res engr, Roy C Ingersoll Res Ctr, Borg-Warner Corp, 58-65; mgr component develop, Res Div, Cummins Engine Co, 65, mgr adv fuel systs, Eng Div, 65-66, mgr thermosci, Res Div, 66-68; mgr res & develop, South Wind Div, Stewart Warner Corp, 68-70, chief engr, 70-73; mgr prod eval, 73-81, MGR ENG, COPELAND CORP, 81- *Concurrent Pos:* Instr quality control & mfg processes, Edison State Univ, 75-78. *Mem:* Am Soc Mech Engrs; Am Soc Heating, Refrig & Air-Conditioning Engrs; Sigma Xi; Am Soc Qual Control. *Res:* Development of air conditioners, heat exchangers, compressors, combustion heaters, hydraulic equipment, engine fuel injectors and pumps; research on engine heat transfer, hydrodynamic bearings; manufacturing processes; reliability engineering. *Mailing Add:* Copeland Corp Sidney OH 45365

KALKA, MORRIS, b Landsberg, Ger, May 4, 49; US citizen; m 71. MATHEMATICAL ANALYSIS. *Educ:* Yeshiva Univ, BA, 71; NY Univ, MS, 73, PhD(math), 75. *Prof Exp:* Instr math, Univ Utah, 75-77; asst prof math, Johns Hopkins Univ, 77-80; mem fac math, Tulane Univ, 80- *Mem:* Am Math Soc. *Res:* Study of holomorphic functions of several complex variables using methods of differential geometry and partial differential equations. *Mailing Add:* Tulane Univ New Orleans LA 70118

KALKHOFF, RONALD KENNETH, b Milwaukee, Wis, Dec 6, 33; m 56; c 4. ENDOCRINOLOGY, METABOLISM. *Educ:* Yale Univ, BA, 56; Washington Univ, St Louis, MD, 60. *Prof Exp:* PROF INTERNAL MED, MED COL WIS, 74-, CHIEF, ENDOCRINE-METAB SECT, 74-, PROF MED, DEPT PHARMACOL, 76- *Concurrent Pos:* Sr staff med-endocrine-metab, Froedtert Mem Lutheran Hosp, 80- *Mem:* Am Soc Clin Invest; Am Diabetes Asn; Endocrine Soc; Cent Soc Clin Res; Am Soc Pharmacol & Exp Therapeut. *Res:* Metabolic effects of insulin antagonism and deficiency as they relate to diabetes mellitus obesity and related human health disorders. *Mailing Add:* Froedtert Mem Lutheran Hosp 9200 W Wisconsin Ave Milwaukee WI 53226

KALKOFEN, ULRICH PAUL, parasitology, see previous edition

KALKOFEN, WOLFGANG, b Mainz, Ger, Nov 15, 31; US citizen; m 60; c 2. ASTROPHYSICS. *Educ:* Univ Frankfurt, BS, 56; Harvard Univ, MA, 61, PhD(physics), 63. *Prof Exp:* Engr, Raytheon Mfg Co, 57-59; PHYSICIST, SMITHSONIAN ASTROPHYS OBSERV, SMITHSONIAN INST, 63-, PHYSICIST, CTR FOR ASTROPHYS, HARVARD COL OBSERV, 74- *Concurrent Pos:* Res fel, Harvard Col Observ, 64-66; vis lectr astron, Yale Univ, 65; lectr, Harvard Univ, 65-; vis fel, Univ Heidelberg, 79-80; sr US scientist award, Alexander von Humboldt Found, 79. *Mem:* Am Astron Soc; AAAS; Int Astron Union. *Res:* Theoretical astrophysics; radiative transfer; gas dynamics. *Mailing Add:* Smithsonian Astrophys Observ 60 Garden St Cambridge MA 02138

KALKWARF, DONALD RILEY, b Portland, Ore, Aug 17, 24; m 49; c 4. BIOPHYSICAL CHEMISTRY. *Educ:* Reed Col, BA, 47; Northwestern Univ, PhD(chem), 51. *Prof Exp:* Chemist, Gen Elec Co, 51-53, sr scientist, 54-62, res specialist, 62-65; res assoc chem dept, 65-66, mgr radiation chem unit, Environ & Radio Sci Dept, 66-68, res assoc radiol sci dept, 68-78, STAFF SCIENTIST PHYS SCI DEPT, BATTELLE-NORTHWEST, 78- *Mem:* Am Chem Soc; Royal Soc Chem; Sigma Xi. *Res:* Radiation biochemistry; synthetic biomembranes; electron spin resonance spectroscopy; controlled release of pharmaceuticals; kinetics of pollutant transformation. *Mailing Add:* 329 Bldg Battelle-Northwest Richland WA 99352

KALLAHER, MICHAEL JOSEPH, b Cincinnati, Ohio, Sept 4, 40; m 63; c 5. MATHEMATICS. *Educ:* Xavier Univ Ohio, BS, 61; Syracuse Univ, MS, 63, PhD(math), 67. *Prof Exp:* Instr math, Syracuse Univ, 66-67; fel Univ Man, 67-68, asst prof, 68-69; from asst prof to assoc prof, 69-76, PROF MATH, WASH STATE UNIV, 76- *Concurrent Pos:* Fulbright-Hays fel, Fulbright Comn, 75-76. *Mem:* AAAS; Am Math Soc; Math Asn Am; Sigma Xi. *Res:* Non-associative algebras; finite geometries, particularly finite projective planes and finite affine planes. *Mailing Add:* Dept of Math Wash State Univ Pullman WA 99164

KALLAI-SANFACON, MARY-ANN, b Montreal, Que, Apr 16, 49; m 77. BIOCHEMISTRY, ENDOCRINOLOGY. *Educ:* McGill Univ, Montreal, BSc, 70; Laval Univ, Que, MSc, 73; Univ Toronto, PhD(physiol), 77. *Prof Exp:* Res fel biochem, Erindale Col, Univ Toronto, 77-78; res fel, 78-80, SR SCIENTIST, AYERST RES LAB, MONTREAL, 80- *Concurrent Pos:* Indust fel, Nat Res Coun Can, 78-80. *Mem:* Can Biochem Soc; NY Acad Sci. *Res:* Lipid metabolism; the development of hypolipidemic agents and the elucidation of their mode of action; carbohydrate metabolism; development of oral hypoglycaemic agents; hypertension; development of antihypertensive agents particularly those associated with angiotensin converting enzyme inhibition. *Mailing Add:* Ayerst Lab PO Box 6115 Montreal PQ H5B 1A9 Can

KALLAL, R(OBERT) J(OHN), b Chesterfield, Ill, Feb 1, 21; m 46; c 5. CHEMICAL ENGINEERING. *Educ:* Univ Ill, BS, 43, MS, 46; Mass Inst Technol, ScD(chem eng), 49. *Prof Exp:* Asst munitions develop, Univ Ill, 43-45; asst chem eng, Mass Inst Technol, 46-47, instr, 47; chem engr plastics develop, 49-55, asst tech supt, 55-58, sr supvr res & develop, 58-70, asst plants tech mgr, 70-74, res mgr, 74-75, PLANNING MGR, E I DU PONT DE NEMOURS & CO, INC, 75- *Mem:* AAAS; Am Chem Soc; Am Inst Chem Engrs. *Res:* Organic and inorganic chemical process development. *Mailing Add:* 518 Kerfoot Farm Rd Wilmington DE 19803

KALLAND, GENE ARNOLD, b Ashland, Wis, Dec 15, 36; div; c 2. REPRODUCTIVE ENDOCRINOLOGY. *Educ:* San Fernando Valley State Col, BA, 62; Ind Univ, PhD(zool), 66. *Prof Exp:* Assoc engr, Rocketdyne Div, NAm Aviation, Inc, 57-62; from asst prof to assoc prof, 66-76, chairperson dept, 72-75, PROF BIOL, CALIF STATE UNIV, DOMINGUEZ HILLS, 71- *Concurrent Pos:* Vis asst prof, Univ Southern Calif, 71; res assoc endocrinol, Harbor-Univ Calif, Los Angeles Med Ctr, 75-80. *Mem:* AAAS; Am Soc Zoologists; Sigma Xi. *Res:* Mammalian reproductive endocrinology; thyroid effect on fertility. *Mailing Add:* Dept Biol Calif State Univ Dominguez Hills Carson CA 90747

KALLANDER, JOHN WILLIAM, b Bessemer, Mich, June 20, 27; m 69. COMPUTER SCIENCE. *Educ:* Mich Technol Univ, BS, 48; Univ Cincinnati, MS, 50, PhD(appl sci), 52. *Prof Exp:* Develop engr analog computs, Gen Elec Co, 52; res physicist magnetic amplifiers, 53-56 & high-energy radiation effects, 56-61, proj leader, prog sect, 61-63, consult prog lang & physics to head res comput ctr, 63-64, head prog systs sect, 64-68, SUPVRY MATHEMATICIAN, US NAVAL RES LAB, 68- *Mem:* Sigma Xi; Inst Elec & Electronics Eng; Asn Comput Mach. *Res:* Digital computer systems analysis and programming; data base management analysis and programming. *Mailing Add:* 7808 Rebel Dr Annandale VA 22003

KALLELIS, THEODORE S, b Peabody, Mass, Oct 12, 12; m 47. PHARMACOGNOSY. *Educ:* Tufts Univ, BS, 35; Mass Col Pharm, BS, 52; Temple Univ, MS, 52; Univ Md, PhD, 56. *Prof Exp:* Assoc prof pharm & chmn dept, Fordham Univ, 56-65; assoc prof, 65-71, chmn dept pharmacog & toxicol, 65-69, prof, 71-80, EMER PROF PHARMACOG, TEMPLE UNIV, 80- *Mem:* Am Chem Soc; Sigma Xi; Am Pharmaceut Asn; Am Soc Pharmacog; NY Acad Sci. *Res:* Isolation of plant constituents. *Mailing Add:* Dept of Pharmacog & Toxicol Temple Univ Sch of Pharm Philadelphia PA 19140

KALLEN, FRANK CLEMENTS, b Colonie, NY, May 27, 28; m 58; c 2. VERTEBRATE ANATOMY. *Educ:* Cornell Univ, BA, 49, PhD(zool), 61. *Prof Exp:* Instr anat, Sch Med & Dent, Univ Rochester, 60-64; from asst prof to assoc prof, 64-75, PROF ANAT, STATE UNIV NY BUFFALO, 75- *Mem:* Am Asn Anat; Am Soc Mammal; Am Soc Zoologists. *Res:* Blood volume, fluid balance, hibernation, hypothermia and functional morphology in bats and other vertebrates. *Mailing Add:* Dept of Anat Farber Hall State Univ of NY Buffalo NY 14214

KALLEN, ROLAND GILBERT, b Glasgow, Scotland, July 3, 35; US citizen; m 63; c 2. MEDICINE, BIOCHEMISTRY. *Educ:* Amherst Col, AB, 56; Columbia Univ, MD, 60; Brandeis Univ, PhD(biochem), 65. *Prof Exp:* Intern, NY Univ-Bellevue Med Ctr, 60-61; asst prof, 65-71, assoc prof biochem, 71-77, PROF BIOCHEM & BIOPHYS, SCH MED, UNIV PA, 78- *Mem:* Am Chem Soc; Am Soc Biol Chem. *Res:* Biochemistry of cancer; mechanisms and regulation of enzymatic activity; mechanisms of hormone action; mechanisms and regulation of gene expression. *Mailing Add:* Dept of Biochem and Biophys Univ of Pa Sch of Med Philadelphia PA 19104

KALLEN, THOMAS WILLIAM, b Hammond, Ind, Oct 26, 38; m 58; c 2. INORGANIC CHEMISTRY. *Educ:* Beloit Col, BS, 65; Wash State Univ, PhD(chem), 68. *Prof Exp:* Res assoc chem, Georgetown Univ, 68-70; asst prof, 70-76, assoc prof, 76-80, PROF CHEM, STATE UNIV NY COL BROCKPORT, 80- *Mem:* Sigma Xi; Am Chem Soc. *Res:* Kinetics and mechanisms of substitution reactions and oxidation-reduction reactions of transition-metal complex ions; catalysis by transition-metal ions; ion-exchange chromatography. *Mailing Add:* Dept of Chem State Univ of NY Col Brockport NY 14420

KALLENBACH, ERNST ADOLF THEODOR, b Minden, Ger, Feb 21, 26; m 57; c 3. HISTOLOGY, ELECTRON MICROSCOPY. *Educ:* George Williams Col, BSc, 58; McGill Univ, MSc, 60, PhD(anat), 63. *Prof Exp:* Res assoc histol, McGill Univ, 60-63; instr anat, 63-64; asst prof, 64-67, assoc prof path, 67-77, assoc prof anat, 77-81, PROF ANAT, COL MED, UNIV FLA, 81- *Concurrent Pos:* Assoc ed, Anat Rec. *Mem:* Am Asn Anatomists; Electron Micros Soc Am. *Res:* Lymphocyte production in thymus gland; presence and arrangement of cytoplasmic fibrils within epithelial cells; formation of enamel; fine structure of enamel organ. *Mailing Add:* Dept Anat Univ of Fla Col of Med Gainesville FL 32610

KALLENBACH, NEVILLE R, b Johannesburg, SAfrica, Jan 30, 38; US citizen; m 59; c 1. BIOPHYSICAL CHEMISTRY. *Educ:* Rutgers Univ, BS, 58; Yale Univ, PhD(chem), 61. *Prof Exp:* NSF fel biophys chem, Univ Calif, San Diego, 61-62, NIH fel, 62-64; from asst prof to assoc prof, 64-71, PROF BIOL, UNIV PA, 71- *Concurrent Pos:* Guggenheim Mem Found fel, 72-73. *Mem:* Biophys Soc; Am Soc Biol Chemists. *Res:* Structure and function of nucleic acids. *Mailing Add:* Dept of Biol 223 Leidy Labs Univ of Pa Philadelphia PA 19174

KALLER, CECIL LOUIS, b Humboldt, Sask, Mar 26, 30; m 62; c 4. MATHEMATICS. *Educ:* Univ Sask, BA & BEd, 54, MA, 56; Purdue Univ, PhD(math statist), 60. *Prof Exp:* Teacher elem & high schs, Sask, 48-52; from asst prof to assoc prof math, Univ Sask, 60-65, from assoc prof to prof, Univ Regina, 65-70, chmn dept, 65-70; prof math & pres, Notre Dame Univ of Nelson, BC, 70-76; MATHEMATICIAN, OKANAGAN COL, BC, 76- *Mem:* Am Math Soc; Math Asn Am; Am Statist Asn; Biomet Soc; Sigma Xi. *Res:* Mathematical statistics and probability theory; statistical models in biological sciences. *Mailing Add:* 2056 Pandosy St Kelowna BC V1Y 1S3 Can

KALLFELZ, FRANCIS A, b Syracuse, NY, July 17, 38; m 65; c 1. NUTRITION. *Educ:* Cornell Univ, DVM, 62, PhD(phys biol), 66. *Prof Exp:* Asst prof, 66-73, ASSOC PROF CLIN NUTRIT, DEPT LARGE ANIMAL MED OBSTET & SURGERY, NY STATE COL VET MED, CORNELL UNIV, 73- *Mem:* Am Vet Med Asn; Am Inst Nutrit; Am Soc Vet Physiol & Pharmacol; Soc Nuclear Med; Am Soc Vet Nutritionists. *Res:* Alkaline earth metabolism, the role of vitamin D in calcium metabolism; applications of radioisotopes in clinical veterinary medicine; protein nutrition in calves, energy metabolism in dogs, mineral metabolism in cats; metabolic diseases. *Mailing Add:* LAMO NY State Col of Vet Med Cornell Univ Ithaca NY 14853

KALLFELZ, JOHN MICHAEL, b Atlanta, Ga, Nov 21, 34; m 59; c 3. NUCLEAR ENGINEERING. *Educ:* US Mil Acad, BS, 56; Calif Inst Technol, MS, 61; Univ Karlsruhe, Dr Ing(nuclear eng), 66. *Prof Exp:* Res engr, Atomics Int Div, NAm Aviation, Inc, 61-62; res in reactor physics, Inst Appl Nuclear Physics, Nuclear Res Ctr, Univ Karlsruhe, 63-65, scientist, 66; asst prof nuclear eng, Ga Inst Technol, 67; asst nuclear engr, Reactor Physics Div, Argonne Nat Lab, 67-69; asst prof, 69-71, assoc prof, 71-80, PROF NUCLEAR ENG, GA INST TECHNOL, 80- *Mem:* Am Nuclear Soc; Sigma Xi. *Res:* Neutron thermalization and transport theory; fast reactor physics. *Mailing Add:* Sch of Nuclear Eng Ga Inst of Technol Atlanta GA 30332

KALLIANOS, ANDREW GEORGE, b Piraeus, Greece, Sept 14, 30; nat US; m 56; c 4. ORGANIC CHEMISTRY. *Educ:* Hendrix Col, 51; Univ Okla, MS, 56, PhD(chem), 58. *Prof Exp:* Asst chem, Univ Okla, 54-58; res org chemist & supvr res, Liggett & Myers Inc, 58-80. *Mem:* Am Chem Soc; assoc mem Food & Extracts Mfrs Asn Am. *Res:* Separation and identification of naturally occurring substances; synthesis and evaluation of odorous materials and determination of their pyrolysis products. *Mailing Add:* 13439 Glendower Rd Midlothian VA 23113

KALLIANPUR, GOPINATH, b Mangalore, India, Apr 16, 25; m 53; c 1. MATHEMATICS. *Educ:* Univ Madras, BA, 45, MA, 46; Univ NC, PhD(math statist), 51. *Prof Exp:* Lectr statist, Univ Calif, 51-52; mem, Inst Advan Study, 52-53; reader statist, Indian Statist Inst, Calcutta, 53-56; vis assoc prof, Mich State Univ, 56-59; assoc prof math, Ind Univ, 59-61; prof statist, Mich State Univ, 61-63; PROF MATH & STATIST, UNIV MINN, MINNEAPOLIS, 63- *Mem:* AAAS; fel Inst Math Statist. *Res:* Probability theory; stochastic processes; statistics. *Mailing Add:* Dept of Statist Univ of Minn Minneapolis MN 55455

KALLIO, REINO EMIL, b Worcester, Mass, July 6, 19; m 42; c 3. MICROBIAL PHYSIOLOGY. *Educ:* Univ Ala, BS, 41; Univ Iowa, MS, 48, PhD(bact), 50. *Prof Exp:* Sr supvr, Trojan Powder Co, 41-44; asst, Univ Iowa, 46-48, instr microbiol, 48-50, from asst prof to prof, 50-65; DIR SCH LIFE SCI, UNIV ILL, URBANA, 65- *Concurrent Pos:* Consult, Am Petrol Inst, 70- *Mem:* Am Chem Soc; Am Soc Microbiol; Brit Soc Gen Microbiol. *Res:* Microbial hydrocarbon metabolism; fatty acids; lipids. *Mailing Add:* Dept of Microbiol Univ of Ill Urbana IL 61801

KALLIOKOSKI, JORMA OSMO KALERVO, b Harma, Finland, Nov 23, 23; nat US; m 49; c 3. ECONOMIC GEOLOGY. *Educ:* Univ Western Ont, BSc, 47; Princeton Univ, PhD(geol), 51. *Prof Exp:* Geologist, Geol Surv Can, 49-53 & Newmont Explor, Ltd, 53-56; from asst prof to assoc prof geol, Princeton Univ, 56-68; head, Geol Eng Dept, 68-81, PROF GEOL, MICH TECHNOL UNIV, 68- *Concurrent Pos:* Bus ed, Econ Geol Publ Co, 71-77. *Mem:* Geol Soc Am; Soc Econ Geol (secy, 65-67, pres elect, 79, pres, 80); Can Inst Mining & Metall; Geol Soc Finland; Am Inst Min Metall. *Res:* Relationship between structure and mineral deposits; Precambrian geology in Canada, the United States and Venezuela; uranium geology. *Mailing Add:* Dept of Geol & Geol Eng Mich Technol Univ Houghton MI 49931

KALLMAN, BURTON JAY, b New York, NY, Nov 1, 27; m 58; c 2. BIOCHEMISTRY, TOXICOLOGY. *Educ:* Bethany Col, WVa, BS, 47; Univ Southern Calif, MS, 51, PhD(biochem), 58. *Prof Exp:* Instr chem, Sch Dent, Univ Southern Calif, 52-53; res assoc, Sch Med, 53-58; fel, Attend Staff Asn, Los Angeles County Gen Hosp, 58-59; biochemist, Fish-pesticide Res Lab, US Fish & Wildlife Serv, 59-63 & Vet Admin Ctr, 63-67; biochemist, TRW Inc, 67-76; sr scientist, Sci Appln Inc, 76-80; PRIN, INTERDISCIPLINARY SCI ASSOC, INC, 80- *Concurrent Pos:* Consult, Childrens Asthma Res Inst, 62-63; Behav Health Serv, 74-76, US State Dept, 78, IWG Corp, 80-, Sci Appln Inc, 80- *Mem:* AAAS; Am Chem Soc. *Res:* Adrenocorticotropic hormone release; thyroid hormone metabolism and physiology; pesticide biochemistry and pharmacology; immunochemistry; bioconversion of energy; fate and effects of petroleum on marine ecosystems; potential health effects of shale oil industry. *Mailing Add:* 23214 Robert Rd Torrance CA 90505

KALLMAN, KLAUS D, b Berlin, Ger, July 20, 28; US citizen; m 65. GENETICS, ICHTHYOLOGY. *Educ:* Queens Col, NY, BS, 52; NY Univ, MS, 55, PhD(genetics), 59. *Prof Exp:* Res assoc, 60-62, GENETICIST, OSBORN LABS MARINE SCI, NY AQUARIUM, 63-; RES ASSOC ICHTHYOL, AM MUS NATURAL HIST, NEW YORK, 65- *Concurrent Pos:* USPHS fel, 59-61; lectr, City Col New York, 60-66. *Mem:* Genetics Soc Am; Am Soc Zool; Am Soc Ichthyol & Herpet. *Res:* Tissue transplantation; sex determination; evolution; pigment cell biology. *Mailing Add:* Osborn Labs of Marine Sci New York Aquarium Brooklyn NY 11224

KALLMAN, MARY JEANNE, b Alexandria, Va, May 27, 48; m 69. PSYCHOBIOLOGY, PSYCHOPHARMACOLOGY. *Educ:* Lynchburg Col, BS, 70; Univ Ga, MS, 74, PhD(biopsychol), 76. *Prof Exp:* Res asst psychiat, Med Ctr, Univ Miss, 73-74; fel, 76-79, res assoc, 79-80, ASST PROF PHARMACOL, MED COL VA, 80- *Concurrent Pos:* Mem adj fac, Dept Psychol, Va Commonwealth Univ, 75-76. *Mem:* AAAS; Soc Neurosci; Soc Stimulus Properties Drugs; Am Psychol Asn. *Res:* State dependency of drugs and stimulus control; central nervous system function and sites of drug action; comparative and developmental central nervous system differences; central sensory processing; psychophysiology; behavioral toxicology and teratology. *Mailing Add:* Dept of Pharmacol Med Col of Va Richmond VA 23298

KALLMAN, RALPH ARTHUR, b Holdrege, Nebr, Sept 17, 34. MATHEMATICS. *Educ:* Univ Minn, BA, 56, MA, 61, PhD(math), 65. *Prof Exp:* Asst prof math, Univ Minn, Duluth, 65-67; asst prof, 67-73, ASSOC PROF MATH, BALL STATE UNIV, 73- *Mem:* Am Math Soc; Math Asn Am; Asn Comput Mach. *Res:* Real and functional analysis; probability and statistics; computational combinatorics; computational probability and statistics. *Mailing Add:* Dept of Math Sci Ball State Univ Muncie IN 47306

KALLMAN, ROBERT FRIEND, b New York, NY, May 21, 22; m 48, 69; c 3. RADIOBIOLOGY. *Educ:* Hofstra Col, AB, 43; NY Univ, MS, 49, PhD, 52. *Prof Exp:* Instr biol, Brooklyn Col, 47-48; asst res physiologist, Univ Calif, 52-56; res assoc, 56-60, from asst prof to assoc prof, 60-72, dir radiobiol res div, 59-77, PROF RADIOL, STANFORD UNIV, 72- *Mem:* AAAS; Radiation Res Soc; Am Asn Cancer Res; Am Asn Lab Animal Sci; fel NY Acad Sci. *Res:* Radiation effects in mammals; mechanisms of biological action of radiation; experimental cancer therapy; carcinogenesis. *Mailing Add:* Dept of Radiol Stanford Univ Stanford CA 94305

KALLMAN, WILLIAM MICHAEL, b New York, NY, Mar 18, 47; m 69. PSYCHOPHYSIOLOGY. *Educ:* Lynchburg Col, BA, 69; Univ Ga, MS, 73, PhD(psychol), 75. *Prof Exp:* Asst instr psychol, Lynchburg Col, 69-70; asst prof, 75-80, dir, Psychol Serv Ctr, 78-80, ASSOC PROF PSYCHOL, VA COMMONWEALTH UNIV, 80- *Concurrent Pos:* Prog consult, Crossroads Drug Treatment Ctr, 73-74; consult, Va Dept Corrections, 75-79, Va Hosp, 79-, Va Dept Ment Health, 79-80. *Mem:* Am Psychol Asn; Asn Advan Behav Ther; Sigma Xi. *Res:* Interrelationships of the autonomic nervous system and the central nervous system functioning in psychopathology; biofeedback. *Mailing Add:* Dept of Psychol Va Commonwealth Univ Richmond VA 23220

KALLMANN, SILVE, b Ger, Feb 13, 15; nat US; m 41; c 1. ANALYTICAL CHEMISTRY. *Educ:* Real Gymnasium Bitburg, Ger, 35; Univ Cologne, 37. *Prof Exp:* Anal chemist, Dr Oppenheimer Lab, Duesseldorf, Ger, 35-37; analyst, Walker & Whyte, Inc, NY, 37-41; analyst, 41-51, res dir, 51-78, vpres, 61-78, ASN CONSULT, CHEM & CHEM ENERGY, LEDOUX & CO, INC, 78- *Mem:* Am Chem Soc; Am Soc Test & Mat; Asn Consult Chemists & Chem Eng; Inst Mining, Metall & Petrol Eng. *Res:* Analysis of metallurgical products by chemical and instrumental methods. *Mailing Add:* Ledoux & Co Inc 359 Alfred Ave Teaneck NJ 07666

KALLO, ROBERT MAX, b San Francisco, Calif, Oct 6, 23; m 47; c 2. PHYSICAL CHEMISTRY. *Educ:* Univ Calif, Berkeley, BS, 45, PhD, 50. *Prof Exp:* From instr to assoc prof, 50-60, PROF CHEM, CALIF STATE UNIV, FRESNO, 60- *Res:* Thermodynamics. *Mailing Add:* Dept of Chem Calif State Univ Fresno CA 93740

KALLOK, MICHAEL JOHN, b Gary, Ind, April 9, 48. CARDIOVASCULAR PHYSIOLOGY, PULMONARY MECHANICS. *Educ:* Univ Colo, BS, 70; Purdue Univ, MS, 74; Univ Minn, PhD(biomed eng), 78. *Prof Exp:* Design engr, Pratt & Whitney Aircraft, 70-71; instr math, Andrean High Sch, 71-72; staff eng, Chicago Metallic Corp, 72-74; res asst, Univ Minn, 74-77; res fel, Mayo Clin, 77-79; sr engr,, 79-81, SR SCIENTIST, MEDTRONIC, INC, 81- *Concurrent Pos:* Eng consult, Ind Health Eng Assocs, Inc, 76; instr physiol, Mayo Med Sch, 79. *Mem:* Am Physiol Soc; Am Soc Mech Engrs; Biomed Eng Soc; NY Acad Sci. *Res:* Pulmonary mechanics; cardiac tachyarrhythmia mechanisms; detection and therapy of ventricular tachycardia and ventricular fibrillation; applications of engineering for medicine and physiology. *Mailing Add:* 3055 Old Highway Eight PO Box 1453 Minneapolis MN 55440

KALLOS, GEORGE J, b Greece, May 21, 36; US citizen; m 63; c 2. ANALYTICAL CHEMISTRY. *Educ:* Cent Mich Univ, BS, 60; Univ Detroit, MS, 62. *Prof Exp:* Res chemist, Dow Chem Co, 63-71, sr res chemist, 71-75, sr res specialist, 75-78, ASSOC SCIENTIST CHEM, DOW CHEM USA, 78- *Concurrent Pos:* Chmn, Carcinogen Safety Monograph Rev Panel, Nat Cancer Inst, 78. *Mem:* Am Chem Soc; Sigma Xi. *Res:* Development of new analytical technology for trace analysis; application of mass spectrometry to the elucidation of organic structure; monitoring of environmental pollutants. *Mailing Add:* 20 Winfred Pl Saginaw MI 48602

KALLSEN, HENRY ALVIN, b Jasper, Minn, Mar 25, 26; m 50; c 4. ENGINEERING ECONOMY, COMPUTER SCIENCE. *Educ:* Iowa State Univ, BS, 48; Univ Wis, MS, 52, PhD, 56. *Prof Exp:* Asst engr, Wabash RR Co, 48-49; from instr to asst prof civil eng, Univ Wis, 49-59; from assoc prof to prof, La Polytech Inst, 59-64, actg head dept, 62-63; asst exec secy, Am Soc Eng Educ, 64-65; prof civil eng & asst dean eng, 65-72, PROF INDUST ENG, UNIV ALA, 72- *Concurrent Pos:* Mem adv res coun, La Hwy Dept, 62-64; consult bd eng educ, Comn Higher Educ, State of Tenn, 69. *Mem:* Sigma Xi; Am Soc Eng Educ; Am Soc Civil Engrs. *Res:* Engineering economy; geometronics; safety; computer science. *Mailing Add:* Box 6316 Univ of Ala University AL 35486

KALLUS, FRANK THEODORE, b La Grange, Tex, Aug 19, 36; wid; c 2. PHYSIOLOGY, ANESTHESIOLOGY. *Educ:* Tex A&M Univ, BS, 66; Univ Tex Southwestern Med Sch, MD, 61, PhD(physiol), 70. *Prof Exp:* Intern, Methodist Hosp Dallas, 61-62; resident, Parkland Mem Hosp, 64-66; instr physiol, Univ Tex Southwestern Med Sch, 69-70; asst prof physiol, Sch Med, La State Univ, Shreveport, 70-72; ASST PROF ANESTHESIOL & DIR ANESTHESIOL LABS, UNIV TEX SOUTHWESTERN MED SCH, DALLAS, 72- *Concurrent Pos:* Res fel, Parkland Mem Hosp, Tex, 65-66; USPHS spec fel, 66-70. *Mem:* Am Physiol Soc. *Res:* Physiology of anesthesia; potassium and sodium metabolism and fluid and electrolyte balance. *Mailing Add:* Dept of Anesthesiol Univ of Tex Southwestern Med Sch Dallas TX 75235

KALM, MAX JOHN, b Ger, Nov 27, 28; nat US; m 69; c 2. MEDICINAL CHEMISTRY. *Educ:* Univ Calif, BS, 52, PhD(chem), 54. *Prof Exp:* Res assoc chem, Univ Mich, 54-55; sr investr, G D Searle & Co, 55-65; dir sci liaison, 65-69, dir control, 69-73, qual assurance dir compliance, 73-74, dir, 74-78, V PRES, QUAL ASSURANCE, CUTTER LABS, INC, 78- *Mem:* AAAS; Am Chem Soc; Acad Pharmaceut Sci; fel Am Inst Chem. *Res:* Organic chemistry; pharmaceutical and medicinal chemistry. *Mailing Add:* Cutter Labs Inc Fourth & Parker St PO Box 1986 Berkeley CA 94701

KALMA, ARNE HAERTER, b Long Branch, NJ, May 26, 41; m 65; c 1. NUCLEAR RADIATION EFFECTS, OPTICAL SENSORS. *Educ:* Rensselaer Polytech Inst, BS, 63, MS, 65, PhD(nuclear sci eng), 68. *Prof Exp:* Res scientist physics, Univ Paris, 68-69; res scientist group leader physics, IRT Corp, 69-79; MEM STAFF, NORTHROP RES & TECH CTR, 79- *Mem:* Am Phys Soc; Optical Soc Am; Inst Elec & Electronics Engrs; Sigma Xi. *Res:* Radiation effects in materials, particularly infrared detectors, optical materials and semiconductors; design and use of radiation hard fiber optics systems; radiation testing; nuclear radiation effects; optical sensors. *Mailing Add:* Northrop Res & Tech Ctr 1 Res Park Palos Verdes Peninsula CA 90274

KALMAN, CALVIN SHEA, b Montreal, Que, Oct 29, 44; m 66; c 2. HIGH ENERGY PHYSICS. *Educ:* McGill Univ, BSc, 65; Univ Rochester, MA, 67, PhD(physics), 71. *Prof Exp:* Asst prof, Loyola Col Montreal, 68-75; ASSOC PROF PHYSICS, SIR GEORGE CAMPUS, CONCORDIA UNIV, 75- *Mem:* Am Phys Soc; Am Asn Physics Teachers; Inst Particle Physics. *Res:* Quark model phenomenology; subquark structure; computer aided instruction. *Mailing Add:* Dept of Physics Concordia Univ Montreal PQ H3G 1M8 Can

KALMAN, GABOR, b Budapest, Hungary, Dec 12, 29; c 2. PLASMA PHYSICS, THEORETICAL PHYSICS. *Educ:* Polytech Univ, Budapest, dipl, 52; Israel Inst Technol, DSc, 61. *Prof Exp:* From jr res scientist to res scientist, Cent Res Inst Physics, Budapest, Hungary, 52-56; res assoc plasma physics, Israel Inst Technol, 57-58, lectr physics, 58-61; adj prof plasma physics, Univ Paris, 61-66, dir res, 66-68; vis prof, Brandeis Univ, 66-70; RES PROF PHYSICS, BOSTON COL, 70- *Concurrent Pos:* Vis fel, Joint Lab Astrophys, 65-66; expert, Air Force Cambridge Res Lab, 67-68; vis scientist, Observatoire de Paris, Meudon, France, 73-74; Groupe de Recherche Ionospherique du CNRS, Orleans, France, 74; sr vis fel, Univ Oxford, 75; exchange prof, Univ Paris, 76; Ctr Astrophys, Harvard Univ, 73-77; res leader, Int Ctr Theoret Physics, 81. *Mem:* AAAS; Am Astron Soc; European Phys Soc; Am Phys Soc; Fr Phys Soc. *Res:* Plasma physics; controlled thermonuclear fusion; plasma response functions; strongly coupled plasmas; plasma astrophysics; models for high density; astrophysical many body systems. *Mailing Add:* Dept of Physics Boston Col Chestnut Hill MA 02167

KALMAN, RUDOLF EMIL, b Budapest, Hungary, May 19, 30; nat US; m 59; c 2. MATHEMATICS, ENGINEERING. *Educ:* Mass Inst Technol, SB, 53, SM, 54; Columbia Univ, DSci, 57. *Prof Exp:* Asst Servomechanisms Lab, Mass Inst Technol, 53-54; res engr process control res, E I du Pont de Nemours & Co, Del, 54-55; instr, Columbia Univ, 55-57; staff engr, Int Bus Mach Corp, NY, 57-58; staff mathematician, Res Inst Adv Studies, 58-62, head ctr control theory, 62-64; prof eng mech & elec eng, Stanford Univ, 64-67, prof math syst theory & opers res, 67-71; GRAD RES PROF & DIR CTR MATH SYST THEORY, UNIV FLA, 71- *Concurrent Pos:* Prof math system theory, Swiss Fed Inst Technol, Zurich, 73- *Honors & Awards:* Medal of Honor, Inst Elec & Electronics Engrs, 74; Rufus Oldenburger Medal, Am Soc Mech Eng, 76. *Mem:* Hungarian Acad Sci; Am Math Soc; Inst Elec & Electronics Engrs. *Res:* Automatic control; network and information theory; mathematical statistics; automata; nonlinear dynamic systems; calculus of variations; stochastic processes; engineering science; algebraic system theory. *Mailing Add:* Dept of Math Univ of Fla Gainesville FL 32611

KALMAN, SUMNER MYRON, b Boston, Mass, Nov 14, 18; m 52; c 1. BIOLOGICAL CHEMISTRY. *Educ:* Harvard Univ, AB, 40; Stanford Univ, MD, 51. *Prof Exp:* Intern, Mt Zion Hosp, Calif, 50-51; fel pharmacol, Stanford Univ, 51-53; NIH, Carlsberg Lab, Denmark, 53-54; physiol, Univ Copenhagen, 54; Graham fel pharmacol, Stanford Univ Sch Med, 54-59; from instr to assoc prof, 54-67, PROF PHARMACOL, SCH MED, STANFORD UNIV, 67- *Concurrent Pos:* Res Career Develop Award, Div Gen Med Sci, US Pub Health Serv, 59-69; consult, US Food & Drug Admin, 72-75; dir drug assay lab, Stanford Univ, 73- *Mem:* AAAS; Am Soc Pharmacol & Exp Therapeut; Am Soc Biol Chem; Am Fedn Clin Res; Soc Gen Physiol. *Res:* Human pharmacology; measurement of drug dosage responses in man and basis for individual differences in sensitivity; metabolic fate and elimination, especially digitalis as a model for detecting such differences. *Mailing Add:* Dept of Pharmacol Stanford Univ Sch of Med Stanford CA 94305

KALMAN, THOMAS IVAN, b Budapest, Hungary, Jan 20, 36; nat US; m 63; c 2. MOLECULAR PHARMACOLOGY, BIO-ORGANIC CHEMISTRY. *Educ:* Dipl ChE, Tech Univ Budapest, 59; State Univ NY Buffalo, PhD(biochem, pharmacol), 68. *Prof Exp:* Res chemist, Hungary, 59-62; res asst, Res Found, State Univ NY, 63-66; fel, NIH, 67-68; adj asst prof & sr res assoc health sci, 68-70, asst prof biochem pharmacol, 70-75, assoc prof med chem, 76-80, ASSOC PROF BIOCHEM PHARMACOL, STATE UNIV NY BUFFALO, 80- *Concurrent Pos:* NIH res career develop award, 71-76; vis assoc prof, Dept Pharmacol, Sch Med, Yale Univ, 75-76. *Mem:* AAAS; Am Chem Soc; NY Acad Sci; fel Am Inst Chem. *Res:* Mechanisms of enzyme and drug action; design and synthesis of selective enzyme inhibitors; biosynthesis, function, damage and repair of DNA; drug design; experimental chemotherapy; cancer research. *Mailing Add:* Dept Med Chem State Univ NY Buffalo Amherst NY 14260

KALMANSON, KENNETH, b Brooklyn, NY, Mar 26, 43; m 66; c 1. MATHEMATICS. *Educ:* Brooklyn Col, BS, 64; City Col New York, PhD(math), 70. *Prof Exp:* Teacher high schs, NY, 65-66; ASST PROF MATH, MONTCLAIR STATE COL, 70- *Mem:* Am Math Soc; Math Asn Am. *Res:* Combinatorial geometry, especially extreme Hamiltonian lines with respect to metric spaces. *Mailing Add:* Dept of Math Montclair State Col Upper Montclair NJ 07043

KALMBACH, SYNDEY HOBART, b Fond du Lac, Wis, June 8, 13; m 40; c 1. PHYSICS. *Educ:* Marquette Univ, BS, 34, MS, 39. *Prof Exp:* Asst prof physics, Elmhurst Col, 40-43 & US Naval Acad, 47-52; assoc prof, 52-62, PROF PHYSICS, NAVAL POSTGRAD SCH, 62- *Mem:* Am Phys Soc; Am Asn Physics Teachers. *Res:* Ifnrared spectroscopy; atmospheric optics. *Mailing Add:* Dept of Physics Naval Postgrad Sch Monterey CA 93940

KALME, JOHN S, b Riga, Latvia, June 20, 38; US citizen. MATHEMATICS. *Educ:* Univ Pa, BA, 61, MA, 64, PhD(math), 66. *Prof Exp:* Teaching fel math, Univ Pa, 61-64; instr, Drexel Inst, US Naval Acad, Annapolis, 65-66, asst prof, 69-73, assoc prof math, 73-79; CONSULT & COMPUT PROG, DAVID TAYLOR US NAVAL SHIP RES & DEVELOP CTR, ANNAPOLIS, 79- *Mem:* Am Math Soc. *Res:* Mathematical analysis, chiefly probability theory and integral operators; stochastic processes, time series analysis; use of time series analysis in source and path identification of structure-borne noise on ships; vibration analysis. *Mailing Add:* Dept of Math US Naval Acad Annapolis MD 21402

KALMIJN, ADRIANUS JOHANNES, b Utrecht, Neth. BIOLOGY, BIOPHYSICS. *Educ:* State Univ Utrecht, BS, 59, PhD(biol & physics), 63. *Prof Exp:* Asst prof biophys, State Univ, Utrecht, 63-70; asst scientist, Scripps Inst Oceanog, Univ Calif, San Diego, 70-74; ASSOC SCIENTIST BIOPHYS, WOODS HOLE OCEANOG INST, 74- & FAC MEM, MARINE BIOL LAB, 74- *Res:* Electric and magnetic detection in aquatic organisms; physical, neurophysiological and behavioral aspects. *Mailing Add:* Woods Hole Oceanog Inst Clark Lab Rm 411 Woods Hole MA 02543

KALMUS, GERHARD WOLFGANG, b Berlin, Ger, Dec 19, 42; m 67. DEVELOPMENTAL BIOLOGY. *Educ:* Univ Calif, Berkeley, BA, 67; Rutgers Univ, Camden, MS, 74; Rutgers Univ, New Brunswick, PhD(zool), 77. *Prof Exp:* Res asst physiol, Univ Pa, 67-68; asst proj mgr transl, Info Intersci Inc, 69-70; teacher biol, Quakertown Community High Sch, 72; res asst embryol, Temple Univ, 73; teaching asst zool, Rutgers Univ, 73-77; asst prof develop, 77-80, ASST PROF BIOL, EAST CAROLINA UNIV, 80- *Mem:* AAAS; Am Soc Zoologists; Am Inst Biol Sci; Tissue Cult Asn; Soc Develop Biol. *Res:* Transplantation immunology; chick primordial germ cells; marine invertebrate fertilization; differentiation in cell culture. *Mailing Add:* Dept of Biol ECarolina Univ Greenville NC 27834

KALMUS, HENRY P(AUL), b Vienna, Austria, Jan 9, 06; nat US; m 54; c 3. PHYSICS, ELECTRICAL ENGINEERING. *Educ:* Vienna Tech Univ, Dipl Eng, 30, Dr Tech, 60. *Prof Exp:* Researcher, Orion Radio Corp, Budapest, 30-38; develop engr, Emerson Radio Corp, NY, 38-41; res physicist, Zenith

Radio Corp, Ill, 41-48; physicist, Nat Bur Standards, US Dept Commerce, 48-53; CHIEF SCIENTIST & ASSOC DIR, HARRY DIAMOND LABS, US ARMY MATERIEL COMMAND, 53- *Concurrent Pos:* Consult, W M Welch Mfg Co, Ill, 48- *Honors & Awards:* Except Serv Award, US Dept of Commerce, 54; Except Civilian Serv Award, US Dept Army, 61; Gravity Res Found Award, 64; Prod Eng Master Designer Award, 67; Distinguished Civilian Serv Award, US Dept Defense, 70; Sperry Award, Instrument Soc Am, 70. *Mem:* Fel Inst Elec & Electronics Engrs. *Res:* Electronics, measurement techniques; mathematics. *Mailing Add:* 3000 University Terr NW Washington DC 20016

KALNAJS, AGRIS JANIS, b Riga, Latvia, May 8, 37; US citizen; m 62; c 3. ASTRONOMY. *Educ:* Mass Inst Technol, SB, 59; Harvard Univ, PhD(astron), 65. *Prof Exp:* Res fel astron, Harvard Univ, 65-70; vis lectr, Tel-Aviv Univ, 70-71; sr res fel, Royal Greenwich Observ, Eng, 71-72; sr res fel, 73-76, SR FEL, MT STROMLO OBSERV, AUSTRALIA, 76- *Mem:* Am Astron Soc; Royal Astron Soc; Int Astron Union. *Res:* Galactic dynamics; self gravitating systems. *Mailing Add:* Mt Stromlo & Siding Spring Observ Pvt Bag Woden Australia

KALNIN, ILMAR L, b Riga, Latvia, Jan 23, 26; US citizen; m 54; c 3. MATERIALS SCIENCE. *Educ:* Westminster Col, Pa, BA, 52; Ill Inst Technol, PhD(chem), 57. *Prof Exp:* Mem tech staff, Bell Tel Labs, 57-62; res scientist, Am-Standard Co, 62-66; sr res scientist, 66-67, RES ASSOC, CELANESE RES CO, 67- *Mem:* Am Chem Soc; Am Ceramic Soc; Am Soc Testing & Mat. *Res:* Fiber reinforced plastics; chemistry and physics of composites and refractories; high temperature polymers and coatings; electronic materials; carbon fibers. *Mailing Add:* 135 Haas Rd Millington NJ 07946

KALNINS, ARTURS, b Riga, Latvia, Feb 13, 31; US citizen; m 56. MECHANICS. *Educ:* Univ Mich, BS, 55, MS, 56, PhD(eng mech), 60. *Prof Exp:* Res asst eng mech, Univ Mich, 56-58; res engr appl mech, Univ Calif, Berkeley, 58-60; asst prof eng & appl sci, Yale Univ, 60-65; assoc prof mech, 65-67, PROF MECH, LEHIGH UNIV, 67- *Concurrent Pos:* Assoc ed, J Acoust Soc Am, 70-; Fulbright-Hayes fel, Univ Innsbruck, 77. *Mem:* Am Soc Mech Engrs; Acoust Soc Am. *Res:* Stress analysis, vibration and buckling of thin shells. *Mailing Add:* Dept of Mech Eng & Mech Lehigh Univ Bethlehem PA 18015

KALNITSKY, GEORGE, b Brooklyn, NY, Oct 22, 17; m 40; c 3. BIOCHEMISTRY. *Educ:* Brooklyn Col, BA, 39; Iowa State Col, PhD(physiol bact), 43. *Prof Exp:* Asst, Iowa State Col, 42-43, res assoc, 43; res assoc & instr biochem, Univ Chicago, 43-45; from instr to assoc prof, 46-57, PROF BIOCHEM, UNIV IOWA, 57- *Concurrent Pos:* Univ col med travelling fel, Oxford Univ, 56-57; Guggenheim fel, Weizmann Inst Sci, Israel, 65-66; Welcome res travel award, 80. *Mem:* Fel AAAS; Am Chem Soc; Soc Exp Biol & Med; Am Soc Biol Chemists. *Res:* Bacterial metabolism; intermediary carbohydrate metabolism; mechanism of action of enzymes; proteolytic enzymes; intracellular proteases, lung, and protease inhibitors. *Mailing Add:* Dept of Biochem Univ of Iowa Col of Med Iowa City IA 52242

KALNOKI-KIS, TIBOR, chemical engineering, see previous edition

KALOGEROPOULOS, THEODORE E, b Megalopolis, Greece, Jan 20, 31; m 54. HIGH ENERGY PHYSICS. *Educ:* Dipl physics, Nat Univ Athens, 54; dipl electronics, Radio-Eng Sch, Athens, 51; Univ Calif, Berkeley, PhD(physics), 59. *Prof Exp:* Res assoc physics, Lawrence Radiation Lab, Univ Calif, 59; instr, Columbia Univ, 59-62; from asst prof to assoc prof, 62-69, PROF PHYSICS, SYRACUSE UNIV, 69- *Concurrent Pos:* Vis physicist, Argonne Nat Lab, 65, Brookhaven Nat Lab, 67-78; vis prof, Nuclear Res Ctr Democritos, 69. *Res:* Elementary particle physics; investigations on antinucleon-nucleon interactions, using emulsions, bubble chambers, spark chambers, counters and drift chambers. *Mailing Add:* Dept of Physics Syracuse Univ Syracuse NY 13210

KALOOSTIAN, GEORGE H, b Kaisarea, Turkey, Jan 12, 12; nat US; m 35; c 2. ENTOMOLOGY. *Educ:* Fresno State Col, BA, 35; Ore State Col, MS, 39. *Prof Exp:* Res leader, Calif, 38-40, Wash, 40-48, Utah, 48-57, Ga, 57-61, RES LEADER, FRUIT & VEG INSECT RES, AGR RES SERV, USDA, CALIF, 61- *Mem:* Entom Soc Am; Am Phytopath Soc. *Res:* Life history and control of dried fruit insects; plant and insect survey methods; insects in relation to fruit tree diseases caused by virus and mycoplasmalike organisms. *Mailing Add:* Boyden Entom Lab Agr Res Serv USDA Univ of Calif Riverside CA 92502

KALOS, MALVIN HOWARD, b New York, NY, Aug 5, 28; m 49; c 2. THEORETICAL PHYSICS, COMPUTER SCIENCE. *Educ:* Queens Col, NY, BS, 48; Univ Ill, MS, 49, PhD(physics), 52. *Prof Exp:* Res asst physics, Univ Ill, 52-53 & Cornell Univ, 53-55; adv scientist, Nuclear Develop Corp, 55-64; RES PROF, COURANT INST MATH SCI, NY UNIV, 64- *Concurrent Pos:* Lectr, Univ Paris, 70-77. *Mem:* Am Phys Soc; fel NY Acad Sci; AAAS; fel Am Nuclear Soc. *Res:* Nuclear physics; statistical physics; neutron interactions; parallel computers; application of computers to physics, especially Monte Carlo methods. *Mailing Add:* Courant Inst of Math Sci NY Univ 251 Mercer St New York NY 10012

KALOTA, DENNIS JEROME, b North Tonawanda, NY, Nov 15, 45; m 67; c 2. ORGANIC CHEMISTRY. *Educ:* Niagara Univ, BS, 68; Univ Detroit, MS, 71, PhD(chem), 74. *Prof Exp:* SR CHEMIST, MONSANTO INDUST CHEM CO, 74- *Mem:* Am Chem Soc. *Res:* Process development research in the area of chlorinated aromatic hydrocarbons. *Mailing Add:* 1306 Green Mist Dr Fenton MO 63026

KALOW, WERNER, b Cottbus, Ger, Feb 15, 17; nat Can; m 46; c 2. PHARMACOLOGY. *Educ:* Univ Koenigsberg, MD, 41. *Prof Exp:* Sci asst, Univ Berlin, 47-48; sci asst, Free Univ Berlin, 49; instr, Univ Pa, 51; from lectr to assoc prof, 52-62, chmn dept, 66-77, PROF PHARMACOL, UNIV TORONTO, 62- *Concurrent Pos:* Res fel pharmacol, Univ Pa, 50; dir biol res, C H Boehringer Sohn, Ingelheim, WGer, 65-66; fel Royal Soc Can, 76- *Honors & Awards:* Upjohn Award, Pharmacol Soc Can, 81. *Mem:* Am Soc Pharmacol & Exp Therapeut; NY Acad Sci; Can Physiol Soc; Pharmacol Soc Can (secy-treas, 56-58, pres, 63-64); Ger Pharmacol Soc. *Res:* Bile secretion; serum cholinesterase; curare; local anesthetics; genetics and drug response. *Mailing Add:* Dept of Pharmacol Univ of Toronto Toronto ON M5S 1A8 Can

KALPAKJIAN, SEROPE, b Istanbul, Turkey, May 6, 28; US citizen; m 62; c 2. MECHANICAL ENGINEERING. *Educ:* Robert Col, Istanbul, BSc, 49; Harvard Univ, SM, 51; Mass Inst Technol, SM, 53. *Prof Exp:* Res engr, Mass Inst Technol, 53-54; res supvr metal forming, Cincinnati Milacron, Inc, 57-63; PROF MECH ENG, ILL INST TECHNOL, 63- *Concurrent Pos:* Consult, Ill Inst Technol Res Inst, 63-80, Continental Can Co, 69-76, Belden Corp, 79-80 & Xerox Corp, 79; assoc ed, J Appl Metalworking, 78- *Mem:* Am Soc Mech Engrs; Am Soc Metals; Sigma Xi. *Res:* Grinding, friction, wear and lubrication; machining and forming; formability of metals. *Mailing Add:* Dept of Mech & Aerospace Eng Ill Inst Technol 10 W 32nd St Chicago IL 60616

KALRA, S(URINDRA) N(ATH), b Lahore, India, May 12, 27; nat Can; m 59; c 2. COMMUNICATIONS. *Educ:* Panjab Univ, India, BS, 46; Univ Ill, MS, 47, PhD, 50. *Prof Exp:* Reader in electronics, Phys Res Lab, India, 50-52; fel, Nat Res Coun Can, 52-53, head high frequency physics lab, Div Appl Physics, 53-62; assoc prof elec eng, Univ Windsor, 62-67, dir interdisciplinary studies in commun, 65-67; assoc prof, 67-69, PROF ELEC ENG, UNIV WATERLOO, 69- *Mem:* Sr mem Inst Elec & Electronics Engrs; Brit Inst Elec Engrs. *Res:* Communication sciences; electronics; computers. *Mailing Add:* Dept Elec Eng Univ Waterloo Waterloo ON N2L 3G1 Can

KALRA, SATYA PAUL, b Mari Indus, WPakistan, Jan 1, 39; m 69; c 1. NEUROENDOCRINOLOGY, ENDOCRINOLOGY. *Educ:* Univ Delhi, BSc, 60, MSc, 62, PhD(physiol), 66. *Prof Exp:* Res asst physiol reproduction, Univ Delhi, 66-68; asst prof, 71-76, ASSOC PROF REPRODUCTIVE BIOL, COL MED, UNIV FLA, 76- *Concurrent Pos:* Ford Found fel anat, Col Med, Univ Calif, Los Angeles, 68-69 & fel physiol, Southwestern Med Sch, Univ Tex Health Sci Ctr, Dallas, 69-71; NIH grant obstet & gynec, Univ Fla, 71- *Mem:* Endocrine Soc; Am Physiol Soc; Soc Gynec Invest; Int Soc Neuroendocrinol. *Res:* Neuroendocrinology of reproduction; regulation of pituitary gonadotropin functions by gonadal steroids; monoamines and hypothalamic releasing hormones. *Mailing Add:* Dept of Obstet & Gynec Univ of Fla Gainesville FL 32610

KALRA, VIJAY KUMAR, b Multan, WPakistan, Aug 26, 42; m 71. BIOCHEMISTRY. *Educ:* Univ Delhi, BSc, 61, MSc, 63, PhD(chem), 67. *Prof Exp:* asst prof, 71-77, ASSOC PROF BIOCHEM, SCH MED, UNIV SOUTHERN CALIF, 77- *Concurrent Pos:* USDA res fel, Ctr Advan Studies Chem of Natural Prod, Univ Delhi, 67; USPHS res fel, Sch Med, Univ Southern Calif, 67-70. *Mem:* Am Chem Soc; Am Soc Biol Chem. *Res:* Structure and function of membranes; oxidative phosphorylation, mechanism of transport of amino acids in bacterial and mammalian cells; sterol metabolism in animal and human cells and relationship to atherosclerosis; structure and function of membranes of red blood cells and sickle cells. *Mailing Add:* Dept of Biochem Univ of Southern Calif Sch Med Los Angeles CA 90033

KALSBECK, JOHN EDWARD, b Grand Rapids, Mich, May 20, 27; m 59; c 3. NEUROSURGERY. *Educ:* Calvin Col, AB, 49; Univ Mich, MD, 53; Am Bd Neurol Surg, dipl, 68. *Prof Exp:* From instr to asst prof, 62-67, assoc prof, 67-80, PROF SURG NEUROSURG, IND UNIV, INDIANAPOLIS, 80- *Concurrent Pos:* NIH fel, Nat Hosp, Queen Sq, London, 60-61; consult, New Castle State Hosp, 63- *Mem:* Am Asn Neurol Surg; Cong Neurol Surg. *Mailing Add:* Dept of Surg Ind Univ Sch of Med Indianapolis IN 46202

KALSER, MARTIN, b Pittsburgh, Pa, Jan 7, 23; m 53; c 3. GASTROENTEROLOGY. *Educ:* Univ Pittsburgh, BS, 42, MD, 46; Univ Ill, MS, 51, PhD(physiol), 53; Am Bd Internal Med, dipl, 55; Am Bd Gastroenterol, dipl, 57. *Prof Exp:* From instr to assoc prof gastroenterol, Grad Sch Med, Univ Pa, 54-56; assoc prof, 59-63; PROF GASTROENTEROL & PHYSIOL, SCH MED, UNIV MIAMI, 63-, CHIEF DIV GASTROENTEROL, 61- *Concurrent Pos:* Res fel clin sci, Univ Ill, 50-53; res fel gastroenterol, Grad Sch Med, Univ Pa, 54-55; consult, Montefiore Hosp, Pittsburgh, 47-50, Vet Admin Clin, Dayton, Ohio & dean's comt, Col Med, Univ Cincinnati, 50-52, Cook County Hosp, Chicago, 52-53, Grad Hosp, Philadelphia, 54-55; mem comn enteric infections, Armed Forces Epidemiol Bd, 63-67. *Mem:* AMA; Am Gastroenterol Asn; Am Col Physicians. *Res:* Internal medicine; physiology. *Mailing Add:* Univ of Miami Sch of Med Jackson Mem Hosp Miami FL 33136

KALSER, SARAH CHINN, b Connellsville, Pa, June 11, 29; m 52. PHARMACOLOGY. *Educ:* Pa State Univ, BS, 51; Northwestern Univ, MS, 53; Univ Pittsburgh, PhD(pharmacol), 61. *Prof Exp:* Biochemist, Med Labs, US Army Chem Ctr, 53-58; res assoc pharmacol, Sch Med, Univ Pittsburgh, 58-60, from instr to asst prof, 61-68; LIVER DIS PROG DIR, NAT INST ARTHRITIS, DIABETES & DIGESTIVE & KIDNEY DIS, NIH, 68- *Mem:* AAAS; Am Gastroenterol Asn; Am Asn Study Liver Dis; Am Soc Exp Pharmacol & Therapeut. *Res:* Glutathione synthesis in trauma; atropine metabolism; drug metabolism in hypothermia and in cold acclimatization. *Mailing Add:* Nat Inst of Arthritis Metab & Digestive Dis Bethesda MD 20014

KALSNER, STANLEY, b New York, NY, Aug 21, 36; m 63; c 3. PHARMACOLOGY. *Educ:* NY Univ, AB, 58; Univ Man, PhD(pharmacol), 66. *Prof Exp:* Asst pharmacologist, Schering Corp, 62; asst prof, 67-72, assoc prof, 72-77, PROF PHARMACOL, UNIV OTTAWA, 77- *Concurrent Pos:* Fel pharmacol, Cambridge Univ, 66-67; Med Res Coun Can grant, 67-; Ont Heart Found grant, 70- *Mem:* Pharmacol Soc Can; Am Soc Pharmacol & Exp Therapeut. *Res:* Autonomic and cardiovascular pharmacology; biogenic amines; supersensitivity of autonomic effectors to drugs and denervation; receptor mechanisms; coronary artery disease; vascular smooth muscle; hypertension. *Mailing Add:* Dept of Pharmacol Univ of Ottawa Fac of Med Ottawa ON K1N 6N5 Can

KALSOW, CAROLYN MARIE, b Elgin, Ill, July 9, 43; m 81; c 5. MICROBIOLOGY, IMMUNOLOGY. *Educ:* Iowa State Univ, BS, 65; Univ Tex Med Br, MA, 67; Univ Louisville, PhD(microbiol), 70. *Prof Exp:* Instr microbiol, Univ Louisville, 70-71, lectr biol, 70-72, res assoc opthal, 71-72, instr, 72-73, asst prof, 73-79, assoc prof, 79-81; DIR CLIN OPHTHAL MICROBIOL, 74- *Concurrent Pos:* Vis asst prof med microbiol, Sfla Med Sch, 72; adj assoc prof biol, Hope Col, 81- *Mem:* Am Soc Microbiol; Asn Res Vision & Ophthal; Sigma Xi. *Res:* Ocular immunology and microbiology. *Mailing Add:* Dept Biol Hope Col Holland MI 49423

KALT, MARVIN ROBERT, b Elizabeth, NJ, Aug 25, 45; m 67. ANATOMY, CELL BIOLOGY. *Educ:* Lafayette Col, AB, 67; Case Western Reserve Univ, PhD(anat), 71. *Prof Exp:* ASST PROF ANAT, HEALTH CTR, UNIV CONN, 73- *Concurrent Pos:* NIH fel, Dept Biol, Yale Univ, 71-73. *Mem:* Am Soc Cell Biol; Am Asn Anat; Soc Develop Biol; AAAS. *Res:* Vertebrate germ cell development; vertebrate morphogenesis. *Mailing Add:* Dept of Anat Univ of Conn Health Ctr Farmington CT 06032

KALT, MELVYN BARRY, b Detroit, Mich, Aug 12, 41; m 67; c 2. ENVIRONMENTAL MANAGEMENT. *Educ:* Univ Mich, BS, 63; Wayne State Univ, PhD(anal chem), 67; Detroit Col Law, JD, 73. *Prof Exp:* Sr res chemist, M&T Chem, Inc, 67-74; asst dist coun, 74-78, actg dist coun, 78-80, SUPV GEN ATTY, US ARMY CORPS ENGRS, 80- *Mem:* Am Bar Asn; Fed Bar Asn. *Res:* Analytical absorption spectroscopy; environmental law, water quality monitoring. *Mailing Add:* 27370 Harvard Southfield MI 48076

KALTENBACH, CARL COLIN, b Buffalo, Wyo, Mar 22, 39; m 64; c 2. REPRODUCTIVE PHYSIOLOGY. *Educ:* Univ Wyo, BSc, 61; Univ Nebr, MSc, 63; Univ Ill, PhD(animal physiol), 67. *Prof Exp:* Australian Wool Bd fel, Univ Melbourne, 67-69; actg head, Div Animal Sci, 78, assoc dir res, Col Agr, 80, PROF ANIMAL PHYSIOL, UNIV WYO, 69- *Mem:* AAAS; Am Soc Animal Sci; Soc Study Fertil; Soc Study Reprod. *Res:* Luteotrophic and steroidogenotrophic properties of pituitary hormones; corpus luteum function; radioimmunoassay for protein and steroid hormones; experimental surgery; fetal growth and development. *Mailing Add:* Div of Animal Sci Univ of Wyo Box 3354 Laramie WY 82071

KALTENBACH, JANE COUFFER, b Chicago, Ill, Dec 21, 22; m 66. HISTOLOGY, ENDOCRINOLOGY. *Educ:* Beloit Col, BS, 44; Univ Wis, MA, 46; Univ Iowa, PhD, 50. *Prof Exp:* Asst zool, Univ Wis, 44-47; asst, Univ Iowa, instr, 48-50; asst & proj assoc path, Univ Wis, 50-53; Am Cancer Soc res fel, Wenner-Grens Inst, Stockholm, 53-56; asst prof zool, Nowthwestern Univ, 56-58; from asst prof to assoc prof, 58-70, PROF ZOOL, MT HOLYOKE COL, 70-, CHMN BIOL SCI, 80- *Mem:* Fel AAAS (secy, sect Biol Sci, 74-78); Am Asn Anat; Am Inst Biol Sci; Am Soc Zoologists; Sigma Xi. *Res:* Amphibian metamorphosis; local thyroxine-induced effects; histochemical patterns; circulating thyroid hromone levels. *Mailing Add:* Dept of Biol Sci Mt Holyoke Col South Hadley MA 01075

KALTENBACH, JOHN PAUL, b Rockford, Ill, Feb 28, 20; m 53; c 1. BIOCHEMISTRY. *Educ:* Beloit Col, BS, 44; Univ Iowa, MS, 48, PhD, 50. *Prof Exp:* Chief cell metab lab, Vet Admin Res Hosp, Chicago, Ill, 54-56; asst prof, 56-60, assoc prof path & biochem, 60-80, dir, Dent Sch Interview Prog, 77-79, actg dir admin, 78-79, PROF PATH, MED SCH, NORTHWESTERN UNIV, 80- *Concurrent Pos:* Brittingham fel cancer res, McArdle Mem Lab, Wis, 50-52; USPHS fel, Karolinska Inst, Stockholm, Sweden, 53-54. *Mem:* AAAS; Am Asn Cancer Res; Am Soc Exp Path; Am Soc Cell Biol; Asn Clin Sci. *Res:* Metabolism of whole cells, normal and neoplastic; metabolism of ischemic myocardium. *Mailing Add:* Dept Path Northwestern Univ Med Sch Chicago IL 60611

KALTENBORN, HOWARD SCHOLL, b Pittsburgh, Pa, Jan 21, 07; m 37; c 2. MATHEMATICS. *Educ:* Carnegie Inst Technol, BS, 28; Univ Mich, MS, 31; Univ Mich, PhD(math), 34. *Prof Exp:* Instr math, Carnegie Inst Technol, 29-32 & Univ Mich, 34-37; instr appl math, Univ Tex, 38-39; assoc prof math, La Polytech Inst, 39-43 & Univ Idaho, 45-46; prof & chmn dept, 46-72, EMER PROF MATH, MEMPHIS STATE UNIV, 72- *Mem:* Math Asn Am. *Res:* Mathematical analysis; mathematics education. *Mailing Add:* 169 S Mendenhall Rd Memphis TN 38117

KALTENBRONN, JAMES S, b New Baden, Ill, Nov 21, 34. ORGANIC CHEMISTRY. *Educ:* Univ Ill, BS, 56; Mass Inst Technol, PhD(org chem), 60. *Prof Exp:* RES CHEMIST, PARKE, DAVIS & CO, 60- *Mem:* Am Chem Soc. *Res:* Medicinal chemistry; natural products; stereochemistry. *Mailing Add:* Res Labs Parke Davis & Co Ann Arbor MI 48106

KALTER, HAROLD, b New York, NY, Feb 26, 24; m 45; c 3. GENETICS, TERATOLOGY. *Educ:* Sir George Williams Col, BA, 49; McGill Univ, MSc, 51, PhD(genetics), 53. *Prof Exp:* From asst prof to assoc prof, 58-70, PROF RES PEDIAT, COL MED, UNIV CINCINNATI, 70-; RES ASSOC, CHILDREN'S HOSP RES FOUND, 55- *Concurrent Pos:* Nat Cancer Inst fel, McGill Univ, 53-55; mem human embryol & develop study sect, NIH, 66-70; ed, Teratol, 67-76; mem Secy's Comn Pesticides, 69; adv comt, 2, 4, 5-T, Environ Protection Agency, 71; consult, comt biol effects atmospheric pollutants, Nat Res Coun Panel Vapor Phase Organic Air Pollutants from Hydrocarbon, 71; mem adv comt, Dept Safety Assessment, Merck Inst Therapeut Res, 75-80; mem panel qual criteria water reuse, Nat Acad Sci, 79-81. *Mem:* Teratology Soc; AAAS. *Res:* Experimental mammalian teratology. *Mailing Add:* Children's Hosp Res Found Elland Ave & Bethesda Cincinnati OH 45229

KALTER, SEYMOUR SANFORD, b New York, NY, Mar 19, 18; m 46; c 3. VIROLOGY. *Educ:* St Joseph's Col, Pa, BS, 40; Univ Kans, MA, 43; Syracuse Univ, PhD(med bact), 47; Am Bd Microbiol, dipl. *Prof Exp:* Asst instr bact, Univ Kans, 41-43; asst med bact, Sch Med, Univ Pa, 43-45; from instr to assoc prof microbiol, State Univ NY Upstate Med Ctr, 45-56; chief, virus diag methodology unit, Commun Dis Ctr, USPHS, Ga, 56-61; chief, Virol Sect, US Air Force Sch Aerospace Med, Brooks AFB, Tex, 61-63; chmn dept microbiol, 63-66, DIR DIV MICROBIOL & INFECTIOUS DIS, SOUTHWEST FOUND RES & EDUC, 66- *Concurrent Pos:* Bacteriologist, Syracuse Dept Health, NY, 45-56; asst prof prev med, Sch Med, Emory Univ, 56-60; lectr, Med Sch, Baylor Univ, 61-63; adj prof, Trinity Univ & Univ Tex Health Sci Ctr, San Antonio, adj prof pediat & microbiol; adj prof, Dent Sci Inst, Univ Tex Health Sci Ctr, Houston; consult, Pan Am Sanit Bur, simian viruses & poxviruses & chmn comt simian viruses, WHO; consult, Neurol Inst, Univ Cologne; consult off pesticide progs, EPA; consult virology, Univ Tex Syst Cancer Ctr, Houston; mem bd dir, Cancer Ther & Res Found, San Antonio; mem, Fedn US Culture Collections. *Mem:* Fel AAAS; Am Acad Microbiol; Soc Exp Biol & Med; Am Asn Immunol; fel Am Pub Health Asn. *Res:* Enteroviruses; respiratory viruses; oncogenic viruses; virus diagnosis; simian virology; comparative primate virology; oncogenic viruses; latent viruses. *Mailing Add:* Southwest Found for Res & Educ PO Box 28147 San Antonio TX 78284

KALTHOFF, KLAUS OTTO, b WGer, Feb 5, 41. DEVELOPMENTAL BIOLOGY. *Educ:* Univ Hamburg, BA, 64; Univ Freiburg, MA, 67, PhD(zool), 71. *Prof Exp:* Asst prof zool, Univ Freiburg, 71-76, assoc prof, 76-77; assoc prof, 78-80, PROF ZOOL, UNIV TEX, AUSTIN, 80- *Mem:* Europ Develop Biologist Orgn; Soc Develop Biol; Am Soc Photobiol; AAAS. *Res:* Role of localized cytoplasmic determinants in embryogenesis using insect (chironomid) embryos and ultra violet irradiation, centrafugation microscopy and application of molecular probes. *Mailing Add:* Dept Zool Univ Tex Austin TX 78712

KALTON, ROBERT RANKIN, b Minneapolis, Minn, Oct 28, 20; m 42; c 5. CROP BREEDING. *Educ:* Univ Minn, BS, 41, Iowa State Col, MS, 45, PhD(crop breeding), 47. *Prof Exp:* Asst crop prod, Iowa State Col, 41-42, res assoc, 46-47; jr supvr grain inspection, Grain Mkt Br, USDA, Univ Minn, 42-44, agent, Regional Soybean Lab, Ames, Iowa, 44-46; assoc agronomist, Tex Res Found, 47-50; assoc prof farm crops, Iowa State Univ, 50-57, prof, 57-60; res dir, Rudy-Patrick Seed Div, W R Grace & Co, 60-70; DIR AGRON RES, LAND O'LAKES, INC, 70- *Concurrent Pos:* Mem, Nat Coun Com Plant Breeders. *Mem:* Fel AAAS; fel Am Soc Agron; Am Genetic Assn; Crop Sci Soc Am. *Res:* Crop breeding, genetics and seed production, especially forage grasses, sorghums and soybeans. *Mailing Add:* Land O'Lakes Inc 2827 Eighth Ave S Ft Dodge IA 50501

KALTREIDER, D FRANK, b Red Lion, Pa, Nov 17, 12; m 35; c 3. OBSTETRICS. *Educ:* Johns Hopkins Univ, AB, 33; Univ Md, MD, 37. *Prof Exp:* Chief obstet, SBaltimore Gen Hosp, 45-49; chief gynec-obstet, Baltimore City Hosps, 62-75; assoc prof obstet & chief obstetrician, 49-55, PROF OBSTET & GYNEC, SCH MED, UNIV MD, BALTIMORE, 55- *Prof Exp:* Assoc prof, Johns Hopkins Univ, 71-; vis obstetrician, Hosps, Baltimore, Md. *Mem:* Am Col Obstet & Gynec. *Res:* Statistical evaluation of pregnancy. *Mailing Add:* Dept of Obstet & Gynec Sch Med Univ of Md Baltimore MD 21201

KALTSIKES, PANTOUSES JOHN, b Nigrita, Greece, Feb 19, 38; Can citizen; m 70. CYTOGENETICS, PLANT BREEDING. *Educ:* Univ Thessaloniki, BSc, 61; MSc, Univ Man, MSc, 66, PhD(plant sci), 68. *Prof Exp:* Agronomist, Hellenic Sugar Indust, 64-65; asst prof, Univ Man, 68-73, assoc prof cytogenetics, 73-77, assoc prof plant sci, 77-80; PROF PLANT BREEDING & BIOMETRY & HEAD DEPT, ATHENS AGR COL, GREECE, 80- *Concurrent Pos:* Nat Res Coun res grant, Univ Man, 68-74; vis prof, Univ Athens, Greece, 74-75; ed, Bull Genetics Soc Can, 74-; consult seed co, 80- *Mem:* Can Soc Agron; Genetics Soc Can; Crop Sci Soc Am. *Res:* Cytogenetics of synthetic amphiploids; biometrical genetics. *Mailing Add:* Athens Agr Col IERA ODOS 75 Athens Greece

KALU, DIKE NDUKWE, b Nigeria, Jan 3, 38; m 67; c 3. PHYSIOLOGY. *Educ:* Univ London, BS, 67, PhD(biochem), 71. *Prof Exp:* Sci officer, Royal Postgrad Med Sch, Univ London, 67-71; fel Sch Med, Johns Hopkins Univ, 72-75; asst prof, 75-80, ASSOC PROF PHYSIOL, UNIV TEX HEALTH SCI CTR, SAN ANTONIO, 80- *Concurrent Pos:* Fel, Inst Med Lab Sci, UK. *Mem:* Inst Med Lab Sci UK; AAAS; The Endoc Soc; Fed Am Soc Exp Biol; NY Acad Sci. *Res:* Hormonal control of calcium and skeletal metabolism and the effects of aging. *Mailing Add:* Dept of Physiol Univ of Tex Health Sci Ctr San Antonio TX 78284

KALUZIENSKI, LOUIS JOSEPH, b Union Beach, NJ, July 28, 48. X-RAY ASTRONOMY. *Educ:* Rutgers Univ, BA, 70; Univ Md, MS, 74, PhD(physics), 77. *Prof Exp:* Grad res asst x-ray astron, Goddard Space Flight Ctr, UniY Md, 74-77, res assoc, 77-78; STAFF SCIENTIST HIGH ENERGY ASTROPHYS, NASA HQ, 78- *Mem:* Am Astron Soc. *Res:* Transient x-ray sources; x-ray binaries. *Mailing Add:* Code SC-7 NASA Hq Washington DC 20546

KALVINSKAS, JOHN J(OSEPH), b Philadelphia, Pa, Jan 14, 27; m 55; c 1. CHEMICAL ENGINEERING, COAL DESULFURIZATION. *Educ:* Mass Inst Technol, BS, 51, MS, 52; Calif Inst Technol, PhD(chem eng), 59. *Prof Exp:* Res engr, Eastern Lab, E I du Pont de Nemours & Co, NJ, 52-55, 59-60; asst chem eng, Calif Inst Technol, 55-59; res specialist, Rocketdyne Div, NAm Aviation Inc, 60-61; supvr basic studies, 61-64, group scientist propellant eng, 64-68, dir environ health systs, Life Sci Opers, NAm Rockwell Corp, 68-70; pres, Resource Dynamics Corp, 70-74; proj mgr, Holmes & Narver Inc, 74; TASK MGR & GROUP SUPVR, JET PROPULSION LAB, CALIF INST TECHNOL, 74- *Concurrent Pos:* Corp res dir, Monogram Indust, Inc, 72. *Honors & Awards:* Tech Contribution, NASA, 77. *Mem:* NY Acad Sci; Am Chem Soc; Am Inst Chem Engrs; Sigma Xi; Am Water Resources Asn. *Res:* Chemical reaction kinetics; machine computation; chemical engineering process design; heat transfer; rocket propulsion; environmental engineering; coal beneficiation; bioconversion and bioenergy. *Mailing Add:* 316 Pasadena Ave South Pasadena CA 91030

KALYANARAMAN, KRISHNASWAMY, b Madras, India, June 2, 35; m 63; c 2. NEUROLOGY. *Educ:* Univ Madras, MBBS, 58, DM, 71; Univ Delhi, MD, 62. *Prof Exp:* Asst prof med, Thanjavur Med Col, Madras Univ, 62-65; asst prof neurol & hon asst, Inst Neurol, Govt Gen Hosp, Madras, 69-71; clin asst prof, 71-72, from asst prof to assoc prof neurol, Sch Med, State Univ NY Buffalo, 72-76; ASSOC PROF NEUROL, UNIV ILL COL MED PEORIA SCH MED, 76- *Concurrent Pos:* Neurologist, E J Meyer Mem Hosp, Buffalo, 71-; neurologist, Out Patient Serv, Vet Admin Hosp, Buffalo, 72-; consult neurologist, West Seneca Develop Ctr, 73-; vis lectr, Inst Neurol, Govt Gen Hosp, 75-, mem staff, St Francis Hosp Med Ctr, Methodist Med Ctr Ill & Proctor Community Hosp, Peoria, 76-; dir, Muscular Dystrophy Asn Neuromuscular Clin, Peoria Sch Med, 79- *Honors & Awards:* Citation of Merit, Muscular Dystrophy Asn Am, 69. *Mem:* Neurol Soc India; Am Acad Neurol; fel Am Col Physicians; assoc Am Asn Electromyog & Electrodiag. *Res:* Nerve and muscle involvement in systemic disorders and effects of upper motor neurone lesions on histochemical pattern of muscle. *Mailing Add:* 5522 N Briarcrest Peoria IL 61614

KALYONCU, RUSTU SUMER, b Apr 1, 43; US citizen; m 70; c 1. MATERIALS SCIENCE. *Educ:* Alfred Univ, BS, 66, MS, 67, PhD(mat), 70. *Prof Exp:* Instr, Col Ceramics, Alfred Univ, 68-70; lab chief, Yarimca Ceramic Fabrikalari, Turkey, 70-71; res scientist mat, Martin Marietta Labs, Baltimore, 71-75; PRIN SCIENTIST MAT, BATTELLE COLUMBUS LABS, 76- *Concurrent Pos:* Orgn Am States fel & vis prof & scientist, Mil Inst Eng, Brazil, 76. *Mem:* Am Ceramic Soc; Am Petrol Inst; Am Soc Mech Eng. *Res:* Cement klinker and hydration chemistry; special cements; refractories materials problems in energy conversion processes and construction materials. *Mailing Add:* Box 613 Cottondale AL 35453

KAM, GAR LAI, b Canton, China, Aug, 36; US citizen; m 69; c 1. DIGITAL SIGNAL, SPEECH ANALYSIS. *Educ:* Nat Taiwan Univ, BSEE, 61; Univ Tenn, MSEE, 66. *Prof Exp:* Sr electronics engr, Lockheed Co, Ga, 66-69; mem tech staff, Hughes Aircraft Co, 69-71; engr III, Jet Propulsion Lab, Calif Inst Technol, 71; sr engr, Martin-Marietta Aerospace Corp, 71-74; eng specialist, Singer-Kearfott Co, 74-80; PRIN ENGR, XYBION CORP, 80- *Mem:* Inst Elec & Electronics Engrs. *Res:* Developing models and algorithms of complex aerospace engineering applications and implementing these models and algoithms in comprehensive computer simulations for system performance analyses. *Mailing Add:* 38 Tarn Dr Morris Plains NJ 07950

KAM, TING KONG, b Hong Kong, July 29, 45; m 74; c 2. COMPUTER MODELING, OPERATIONS RESEARCH. *Educ:* Univ Manitoba, Can, BSc, 70; Univ Calif, Berkeley, PhD(soil physics & hydrol), 74. *Prof Exp:* Res fel, Water Eng, Univ Calif, Davis, 74-75; hydrologist, Geol Eng, Morrison Knudsen, 75-79; sr engr hydrol, Sci Applns Inc, 79-81; staff specialist, 81, CONSULT, HYDROL & GEOL, DAVY MCKEE-DAVY INC, 81- *Mem:* Am Soc Civil Engrs; Soc Petrol Engrs; Am Water Resources Asn; Sigma Xi. *Res:* Computer modeling and analyses of hydrologic and geological engineering problems. *Mailing Add:* 467 Cape Cod Dr San Leandro CA 94578

KAMACK, H(ARRY) J(OSEPH), b Conn, Dec 5, 18. CHEMICAL ENGINEERING. *Educ:* Ga Inst Technol, BS, 41; Univ Del, MS, 56. *Prof Exp:* Chem engr, Gen Chem Co, 41 & Ord Dept, US Army, 42; chem engr, E I Du Pont De Nemours & Co, Inc, 42-46, res engr, 46-54, process design engr, 54-69, sr design consult, 69-73, prin design consult, 73-78; RETIRED. *Mem:* Am Inst Chem Eng. *Res:* Chemical plant design; atomic energy design; particle size reduction and measurement. *Mailing Add:* 610 Lehigh Rd Apt 10 Newark DE 19711

KAMAL, ABDUL NAIM, b Dacca, Pakistan, Oct 28, 35; m 62; c 3. PARTICLE PHYSICS. *Educ:* Univ Dacca, BSc, 55, MSc, 56; Univ Liverpool, PhD(theoret physics), 62. *Prof Exp:* Lectr physics, Univ Dacca, 62-63; fel theoret physics, Univ Liverpool, 63 & Theoret Physics Inst, Edmonton, Alta, 63-64; from asst prof to assoc prof, 64-73, PROF PHYSICS, UNIV ALTA, 73- *Concurrent Pos:* Sr sci officer, Rutherford Lab, UK, 68-69, vis scientist, 71 & 78; vis scientist, Int Ctr Theoret Physics, Trieste, Italy, 72; vis prof, Stanford Linear Accelerator Ctr, 79. *Res:* Theoretical particle physics; weak and strong interactions. *Mailing Add:* Dept of Physics Univ of Alta Edmonton AB T6G 2J1 Can

KAMAL, ADEL S, insect physiology, insect taxonomy, see previous edition

KAMAL, MOUNIR MARK, b Beirut, Lebanon, Feb 13, 36; US citizen; m 62; c 3. ENGINEERING MECHANICS. *Educ:* Robert Col, Istanbul, BS, 56; Univ Mich, Ann Arbor, MS, 58, MS, 62, PhD(eng), 65. *Prof Exp:* Assoc sr res engr, 65-67, sr res engr, 67-68, supv res engr, 68-71, asst head dept, 71-77, HEAD DEPT ENG MECH, GEN MOTORS RES LABS, 77- *Concurrent Pos:* Mem, Univ Mich Indust Comt, 70-78. *Mem:* Sigma Xi; Soc Automotive Engrs; Am Soc Mech Engrs; Am Acad Mech. *Res:* Mechanical engineering; internal combustion engines; design, development and stress analysis of automotive components; fluid mechanics and hydrodynamic lubrication theory; vehicle crash dynamics; vehicle structural research. *Mailing Add:* Dept of Eng Mech Gen Motors Res Labs Warren MI 48090

KAMAL, MUSA RASIM, b Tulkarm, Jordan, Dec 8, 34; m 61; c 1. CHEMICAL ENGINEERING, POLYMER CHEMISTRY. *Educ:* Univ Ill, BS, 58; Carnegie Inst Technol, MS, 59, PhD(chem eng), 62. *Prof Exp:* Teacher elem sch, Kuwait, 52-54; res chem engr, Stamford Res Labs, Am Cyanamid Co, Conn, 61-65; group leader, Wallingford Develop Lab, 65-67; assoc prof, 67-73, PROF CHEM ENG, McGILL UNIV, 73- *Concurrent Pos:* Vis prof, Am Univ of Beirut, 74-75; Dir Microeconomics & Sectoral Sect, Morocco Indust Develop Plan, Dar Al-Handasah Consults, 79. *Mem:* Am Inst Chem Engrs; Am Chem Soc; Soc Plastics Engrs; Soc Rheol; NY Acad Sci. *Res:* Polymer engineering; plastics processing; injection molding; rheology; heat transfer; non-Newtonian flow; thermoset and thermoplastic processing; weatherability of plastics systems; properties of polymers; composite yarns; melt spinning; decorative laminates; industrial development planning; project evaluation and planning. *Mailing Add:* Dept of Chem Eng 3480 University St Montreal PQ H3H 2A7 Can

KAMAN, CHARLES HENRY, b Brookline, Mass, 43. COMPUTER SCIENCE. *Educ:* Harvard Col, AB, 65; Polytech Inst Brooklyn, MS, 67, PhD(syst sci), 74. *Prof Exp:* consult engr comput archit, Digital Equip Corp, Tewksbury, 69-81. *Mem:* Asn Comput Mach; Inst Elec & Electronics Engrs; Soc Indust & Appl Math; Am Math Soc; Math Asn Am. *Res:* Computer architecture; computer implementation; programming languages and semantics; computer algorithms; application of theoretical computer science to practical computer design and implementation. *Mailing Add:* 274 Dedham St Newton Highlands MA 02161

KAMAN, CHARLES HURON, b Wash, DC, June 15, 19; m 45; c 3. ENGINEERING. *Educ:* Catholic Univ, BAeroE, 40. *Prof Exp:* Aerodyn, Hamilton Standard Div, United Aircraft Corp, 40-45; PRES, KAMAN CORP, 45- *Mem:* Nat Acad Eng. *Mailing Add:* Kaman Corp Old Windsor Rd Bloomfield CT 06002

KAMAN, ROBERT LAWRENCE, b New York, NY, June 26, 41; m 67; c 2. BIOCHEMISTRY. *Educ:* Univ Pa, AB, 63; Va Polytech Inst, MS, 67, PhD(biochem), 69. *Prof Exp:* NIH fel biochem, Sch Med, Univ Mich, 69-72, res assoc, Sch Pub Health, 72-73; asst prof biochem, 73-77, ASST PROF BASIC HEALTH SCI, TEX COL OSTEOP MED, NTEX STATE UNIV, 77- *Mem:* Am Osteop Acad Sports Med; Am Col Sports Med; Am Asn Fitness Dirs. *Res:* Chemotherapy for atherosclerosis; effect of exercise on health and fitness; diet and exercise; exercise programs for firemen; exercise and alcohol rehabilitation. *Mailing Add:* Tex Col of Osteop Med Camp Bowie at Montgomery Ft Worth TX 76107

KAMATH, KRISHNA, b Shertallai, India, Aug 24, 20; m 69. PETROLEUM ENGINEERING, PHYSICAL CHEMISTRY. *Educ:* Univ Travancore, India, BSc, 41; Banaras Univ, MSc, 44; Pa State Univ, MS, 57, PhD(petrol eng), 60. *Prof Exp:* Anal chemist, Govt India, 44-46; res chemist, Alembic Chem Works, India, 47-49; prof chem, Petlad Col, India, 49-52; sr sci asst phys chem, Nat Chem Lab India, Poona, 52-54; res engr, Gulf Res & Develop Co, 59-61; asst prof petrol technol & chmn dept, Indian Sch Mines & Appl Geol, Dhanbad, 61-63; vis assoc prof petrol eng, Stanford Univ, 63-66; res engr, Continental Oil Co, Okla, 66-68 & IIT Res Inst, 69-72; environ protection engr, Ill Environ Protection Agency, 74-76; PETROL ENGR, MORGANTOWN ENERGY TECHNOL CTR, US DEPT ENERGY, 76- *Concurrent Pos:* Adj assoc prof petrol eng, WVa Univ, Morgantown, 77- *Mem:* AAAS; Am Chem Soc; Soc Petrol Engrs; Am Water Works Asn. *Res:* Preparative electrochemistry; education; surface and colloid chemistry relating to petroleum recovery and multiphase fluid flow through porous media; enhanced petroleum recovery; surface and colloid chemchemistry. *Mailing Add:* Morgantown Energy Technol Ctr PO Box 880 Morgantown WV 26505

KAMATH, SAVITRI KRISHNA, nutrition, biochemistry, see previous edition

KAMATH, VASANTH RATHNAKAR, b Mangalore, India, July 16, 44; m 74. POLYMER CHEMISTRY. *Educ:* Univ Bombay, BS, 66; Univ Akron, MS, 68, PhD(polymers), 73. *Prof Exp:* group leader, 73-77, MGR APPLNS, LUCIDOL DIV, PENNWALT CORP, 77- *Res:* Cellular plastics, rubber reinforced polymer systems, novel free radical initiators including polymeric peroxides, emulsion polymerization characteristics and polymerization processes in general including polymer-crosslinking. *Mailing Add:* Lucidol Div Pennwalt Corp 1740 Military Rd Buffalo NY 14240

KAMATH, YASHAVANTH KATAPADY, b Katapady, India, Apr 15, 38; m 72; c 1. PHYSICAL CHEMISTRY, POLYMER CHEMISTRY. *Educ:* Univ Bombay, BSc, 59 & 61, MSc, 64; Univ Conn, PhD(phys chem), 73. *Prof Exp:* Assoc lectr plastic technol, Dept Chem Technol, Univ Bombay, 63-66; fel, 72-74, staff scientist, 74-76, SR SCIENTIST, TEXTILE FINISHING, TEXTILE RES INST, 76- *Mem:* Am Chem Soc; Fiber Soc. *Res:* Surface chemical properties of human hair; effect of polymers and surfactants on the surface wettability of human hair; fractography of human hair; compressibility of fiber bundles; environmental fading of dyes in nylon; microspectrophotocetry of dyes in monofilaments; mechanisms of formaldehyde release in durable press fabric. *Mailing Add:* Textile Res Inst 601 Prospect Ave Princeton NJ 08540

KAMB, WALTER BARCLAY, b San Jose, Calif, Dec 17, 31; m 57; c 4. MINERALOGY, GLACIOLOGY. *Educ:* Calif Inst Technol, BS, 52, PhD(geol), 56. *Prof Exp:* From asst prof to assoc prof geol, 56-62, PROF GEOL & GEOPHYS, CALIF INST TECHNOL, 62-, CHMN DIV GEOL & PLANETARY SCI, 72- *Concurrent Pos:* Guggenheim Mem Found fel, 60; Sloan fel, 63. *Honors & Awards:* MSA Award, Mineral Soc Am, 68; Seligman Award, Int Glaciol Soc, 77. *Mem:* AAAS; Geol Soc Am; Am Geophys Union; Mineral Soc Am; Am Asn Petrol Geologists. *Res:* Crystallography; tectonophysics; structural geology and petrology; glaciology; mineralogy and x-ray crystallography; crystal optics. *Mailing Add:* Div of Geol & Planetary Sci Calif Inst of Technol Pasadena CA 91109

KAMBARA, GEORGE KIYOSHI, b Sacramento, Calif, Feb 23, 16; m 41; c 4. OPHTHALMOLOGY. *Educ:* Stanford Univ, AB, 37, MD, 41; Am Bd Ophthal, dipl, 47. *Prof Exp:* Asst surg, Sch Med, Stanford Univ, 41-42; instr ophthal, Med Sch, Univ Wis, 46-48; asst prof, Sch Med, Loma Linda Univ, 49-56, from assoc clin prof to clin prof, 56-59; clin prof, Univ Calif, Irvine-Calif Col Med, 66-69; CLIN PROF SURG, SCH MED, UNIV SOUTHERN CALIF, 69-; CHIEF OPHTHAL, RANCHO LOS AMIGOS HOSP, 65-; CHMN DEPT, WHITE MEM MED CTR, 65- *Concurrent Pos:* Mem attend staff, Los Angeles County Gen Hosp, 50-67, Olive View Gen Hosp, Rancho Los Amigos Hosp; chief ophthal serv, White Mem Med Ctr, 58-65. *Mem:* AMA; fel Am Col Surg; fel Am Acad Ophthal & Otolaryngol; Am Optom Asn. *Mailing Add:* 321 E Second St Los Angeles CA 90012

KAMBAYASHI, TATSUJI, b Kyoto, Japan, Nov 8, 33; m 63. ALGEBRAIC GEOMETRY. *Educ:* Univ Tokyo, ScB, 57; Northwestern Univ, PhD(math), 62. *Prof Exp:* Instr math, Brown Univ, 61-63; lectr, Ind Univ, 63-64, asst prof, 64-67; assoc prof, 67-74, PROF MATH, NORTHERN ILL UNIV, 74- *Concurrent Pos:* Mem res staff, Res Ctr Physics & Math, Pisa, Italy, 65-67; res mem, Res Inst Math Sci, Kyoto Univ, Japan, 72-73; res grant, NSF, 73- *Mem:* Am Math Soc; Math Soc Japan. *Res:* Algebraic groups. *Mailing Add:* Dept of Math Northern Ill Univ De Kalb IL 60115

KAMBER, KENNETH THOMAS, materials science, see previous edition

KAMBOUR, ROGER PEABODY, b Wilmington, Mass, Apr 1, 32; c 2. PHYSICAL CHEMISTRY, POLYMER PHYSICS. *Educ:* Amherst Col, BA, 54; Univ NH, PhD(chem), 60. *Prof Exp:* Res assoc, 60-70, mgr polymer studies unit, 70-74, RES ASSOC, GEN ELEC RES & DEVELOP CTR, 75- *Honors & Awards:* Union Carbide Chem Award, Am Chem Soc, 68. *Mem:* Fel Am Phys Soc; Am Chem Soc. *Res:* Diffusion of gases and vapors in polymers; polymer crazing and fracture; properties of block polymers; crystallization; polymer flame retardance; polymer blend thermodynamics. *Mailing Add:* Poly Properties & Reactions Br Gen Elec Co PO Box 8 Schenectady NY 12301

KAMBYSELLIS, MICHAEL PANAGIOTIS, b Antissa, Greece, Mar 1, 35. DEVELOPMENTAL GENETICS. *Educ:* Nat Univ Athens, BSc, 60; Yale Univ, MS, 65; Univ Tex, PhD(zool), 67. *Prof Exp:* Res asst genetics, Univ Tex, 65-67, res assoc, 67-68; res fel insect physiol, Harvard Univ, 68-70, lectr biol, 71; asst prof, 71-73, assoc prof develop biol, 73-80, PROF BIOL, NY UNIV, 80- *Concurrent Pos:* Vis prof, Athens Univ, Greece, 74-75. *Mem:* AAAS; Genetics Soc Am; Am Inst Biol Sci; NY Acad Sci; Soc Develop Biol. *Res:* Physiological genetics; Drosophila genetics and evolution; insect tissue transplantations; Drosophila ovarian development; insect tissue cultures; hormonal control of insect reproduction. *Mailing Add:* Dept of Biol NY Univ 952 Brown Blvd New York NY 10003

KAMDAR, MADHUSUDAN H, b Bombay, India, Mar 28, 30; m 63; c 1. MATERIALS SCIENCE & ENGINEERING. *Educ:* Univ Bombay, BSc, 53; Univ Wash, MS, 57; Mass Inst Technol, DSc(metall), 61. *Prof Exp:* Scientist, Res Inst Advan Study, 61-74; SR RES SCIENTIST, BENET WEAPONS LAB, WATERVLIET ARSENAL, 74- *Mem:* Am Soc Metals; Am Inst Mining, Metall & Petrol Engrs; Am Soc Testing & Mat. *Res:* Environmental sensitive fracture behavior of materials. *Mailing Add:* Benet Weapons Lab Mat Eng Div Watervliet Arsenal Watervliet NY 12189

KAMEGAI, MINAO, b Koshu, Korea, July 7, 32; US citizen; m 58; c 2. HYDRODYNAMICS. *Educ:* Univ Hawaii, BA, 57; Univ Chicago, MS, 60, PhD(physics), 63. *Prof Exp:* Res assoc nuclear physics, Enrico Fermi Inst, Univ Chicago, 63; physicist, Knolls Atomic Power Lab, Gen Elec Co, 63-66; SR PHYSICIST, LAWRENCE LIVERMORE LAB, 66- *Mem:* Am Phys Soc; Sigma Xi. *Res:* Theoretical and computational physics; materials science, hydrodynamics and laser optics. *Mailing Add:* Lawrence Livermore Lab PO Box 808 Livermore CA 94550

KAMEGO, ALBERT AMIL, b Detroit, Mich, June 11, 41; m 73. PHYSICAL ORGANIC CHEMISTRY. *Educ:* Wayne State Univ, BS, 64; Calif State Univ, Long Beach, MS, 68; Univ Calif, Santa Barbara, PhD(chem), 74. *Prof Exp:* Chemist paints, Ford Motor Co, 65-67; teaching asst chem, Calif State Univ, Long Beach, 67-68; from teaching asst chem to staff res assoc, Univ Calif, Santa Barbara, 68-73; fel chem, State Univ NY Buffalo, 73-75; lectr chem, Univ Mont, 75-76; instr chem, Univ Tex, Arlington, 76-77; SR RES CHEMIST, CORE LABS, INC, 77- *Mem:* Sigma Xi; Soc Petrol Engrs; AAAS; Am Chem Soc. *Mailing Add:* Core Labs Inc Dallas Stemmons Dallas TX 75247

KAMEL, HYMAN, b Philadelphia, Pa, Dec 2, 19; m 41, 68; c 2. MATHEMATICS. *Educ:* Univ Pa, AB, 41, NY Univ, MS, 44; Univ Pa, PhD(math), 52. *Prof Exp:* Instr math, Univ Pa, 50-52 & Cornell Univ, 52-54; asst prof, Rensselaer Polytech Inst, 54-61; assoc prof, Howard Univ, 61-67; PROF MATH, WIDENER COL, 67- *Mem:* Am Math Soc; Math Asn Am; Sigma Xi. *Res:* Functional analysis. *Mailing Add:* Dept of Math Widener Col Chester PA 19013

KAMEMOTO, FRED ISAMU, b Honolulu, Hawaii, Mar 8, 28; m 63; c 3. ZOOLOGY, COMPARATIVE ENDOCRINOLOGY. *Educ:* George Washington Univ, AB, 50, MS, 51; Purdue Univ, PhD(zool), 54. *Prof Exp:* Res assoc zoophysiol, Wash State Col, 57-59; asst prof zool, Univ Mo, 59-62; from asst prof to assoc prof, 62-69, PROF ZOOL, UNIV HAWAII, 69- *Mem:* AAAS; Am Soc Zoologists. *Res:* Neurosecretion and osmoregulation. *Mailing Add:* Dept of Zool Univ of Hawaii 2538 The Mall Honolulu HI 96822

KAMEMOTO, HARUYUKI, b Honolulu, Hawaii, Jan 18, 22; m 52; c 2. HORTICULTURE. *Educ:* Univ Hawaii, BS, 44, MS, 47; Cornell Univ, PhD, 50. *Prof Exp:* From asst horticulturist to assoc horticulturist, 50-58, prof hort & chmn dept, 69-75, HORTICULTURIST, UNIV HAWAII, 58- *Concurrent Pos:* Fulbright award, 56-57; consult, Food & Agr Orgn, UN, 71. *Honors & Awards:* Gold Medal, Malayan Orchid Soc, 63; Norman Jay Colman Award, 77; Orchid Soc Thailand Medal of Honor, 78. *Mem:* AAAS; Am Soc Hort Sci; Am Inst Biol Sci; Genetics Soc Am; Am Genetic Asn. *Res:* Cytogenetics and breeding of tropical ornamentals. *Mailing Add:* Dept of Hort Univ of Hawaii 3190 Maile Way Honolulu HI 96822

KAMEN, EDWARD WALTER, b Mansfield, Ohio, Oct 2, 45. ENGINEERING, MATHEMATICS. *Educ:* Ga Inst Technol, BEE, 67; Stanford Univ, MS, 69, PhD(elec eng), 71. *Prof Exp:* Engr, Argo Systs Inc, Calif, 70-71; asst prof, 71-76, ASSOC PROF ELEC ENG, GA INST TECHNOL, 76- *Concurrent Pos:* NSF res initiation grant, Ga Inst Technol, 72-74; res specialist, Inst Res Info & Automatic Control, France, 72- *Mem:* AAAS; Inst Elec & Electronics Engrs. *Res:* Mathematical system theory; network theory; receiver systems. *Mailing Add:* Sch of Elec Eng Ga Inst of Technol Atlanta GA 30332

KAMEN, MARTIN DAVID, b Toronto, Ont, Aug 27, 13; nat US; m 67; c 1. PHYSICAL BIOCHEMISTRY. *Educ:* Univ Chicago, BS, 33, PhD(phys chem), 36. *Hon Degrees:* ScD, Univ Chicago, 69; hon Dr, Univ Paris, 69; ScD, Washington Univ, 77, Univ Ill, Chicago Circle, 78, Univ Freiburg, Ger 79. *Prof Exp:* Fel nuclear chem, Radiation Lab, Univ Calif, 37-39, res assoc, 39-41; marine test engr, Kaiser Cargo, Calif, 44-45; assoc prof biochem, Wash Univ, 45-46, assoc prof chem & chemist, Mallinckrodt Inst, 45-57; prof biochem, Brandeis Univ, 57-61; prof chem, Univ Calif, San Diego, 61-74, chmn dept, 71-73; prof biol sci, 74-78, EMER PROF BIOL SCI, UNIV SOUTHERN CALIF, 78-; EMER PROF CHEM, UNIV CALIF, SAN DIEGO, 78- *Concurrent Pos:* NSF sr fel, 56; Guggenheim fel, 56 & 72. *Honors & Awards:* Award, Am Chem Soc, 63; C F Kettering Award, Am Soc Plant Physiol, 69; Merck Award, Am Soc Biol Chemists, 82. *Mem:* Nat Acad Sci; Am Chem Soc; Am Soc Biol Chemists; Am Acad Arts & Sci; fel Am Inst Chem; Am Philosoph Soc. *Res:* Application of biophysical chemical methods, including isotopic tracer methodology, to study bacterial metabolism; energy storage, especially in photosynthesis; comparative biochemical iron proteins. *Mailing Add:* Dept Chem A-002 Univ Calif-San Diego La Jolla CA 92093

KAMENETZ, HERMAN LEO, b Kovno, Russia, Sept 1, 07; US citizen; m 47. PHYSICAL MEDICINE & REHABILITATION. *Educ:* Univ Paris, BA, 44, MS, 45, MD, 52. *Prof Exp:* Intern med & surg, St Anthony's Hosp, Rockford, Ill, 53-54; resident phys med & rehab, State of Conn Vet Hosp, Rocky Hill, 54-56, Yale Univ Med Ctr, 56-57 & Ga Warm Springs Found, 58; physiatrist, Woodruff Rehab Ctr, New Haven, Conn, 58-59; chief of staff, State of Conn Vet Home & Hosp, 60-66, chief phys med & rehab, 59-75; CHIEF REHAB MED SERV, US VET ADMIN HOSP, WASHINGTON, DC, 75- *Concurrent Pos:* Physicians Recognition Awards, AMA, 70-73, 73-76, 76-79 & 79-82; asst attend physician, Med Ctr, Yale Univ, 57-60, physician, Outpatient Dept, 60-75, clin instr med, Sch Med, 58-64, asst clin prof phys med, 64-68; consult phys med, St Francis Hosp, Hartford, 64-75; Waterbury Hosp, 68-75 & Gaylord Rehab Hosp, Wallingford, 70-75; clin prof med, George Washington Univ Sch Med & Health Sci, 75-, prof lectr phys med & rehab, 76- *Honors & Awards:* Silver Award Exhibit, Am Cong Rehab Med, Montreal, 68. *Mem:* Int Soc Hist Med; Int Rehab Med Asn; Am Med Writers Asn; Am Cong Rehab Med. *Res:* Lexicography in English and French in physical medicine and rehabilitation; translation and editing. *Mailing Add:* The Chatham 4501 Arlington Blvd Arlington VA 22203

KAMENTSKY, LOUIS A, b Newark, NJ, July 28, 30; m 55; c 3. ENGINEERING PHYSICS, BIOPHYSICS. *Educ:* Newark Col Eng, BS, 52; PhD(eng physics), 56. *Prof Exp:* Res asst physics, Brookhaven Nat Lab, 51; res asst eng physics, Cornell Univ, 52-54; mem staff, Electronics Res Lab, Columbia Univ, 54-55; mem staff, Bell Tel Labs, Inc, 56-60 & Watson Lab, IBM Corp, 60-68; pres, Bio/Physics Systs, Inc, 68-76; dir res & develop, Ortho Instruments, 76-80, VPRES RES, ORTHO DIAGNOSTICS SYSTS, 80- *Concurrent Pos:* Physicist, Res Lab, US Steel Corp, 53; adj assoc prof, Dept Path, Med Ctr, NY Univ, 69-73; consult, Dept Path, Mem Hosp for Cancer, New York, 73-; sr res scientist, Res Lab Electronics, Mass Inst Technol, 80- *Mem:* AAAS; Inst Elec & Electronics Engrs; NY Acad Sci; Biophys Soc. *Res:* Information and computer theories; solid state physics; optics; pattern recognition; medical instrumentation; research administration. *Mailing Add:* Ortho Diagnostics Systs 410 University Ave Westwood MA 02090

KAMIEN, C ZELMAN, b Bialystock, Poland, Feb 24, 27; US citizen; m 55; c 2. MECHANICAL ENGINEERING. *Educ:* Purdue Univ, BS, 55, MSEng, 56, PhD(eng), 60. *Prof Exp:* Instr mech eng, Purdue Univ, 58-60; sr scientist, Res & Adv Develop Div, Avco Corp, 60-63; proj mgr thermionics, Thermo Electron Eng Corp, 63-66; assoc prof mech eng, Lowell Technol Inst, 66-81, ASSOC PROF & CHMN, MECH ENG DEPT, UNIV LOWELL, 81- *Mem:* AAAS; Am Soc Mech Engrs; Am Soc Eng Educ. *Res:* Effect of pressure and temperature on viscosity of refrigerants; effect of rain intensity on prevention of icing on transmission cables; solar thermionic power systems development. *Mailing Add:* Univ Lowell 1 University Ave Lowell MA 01854

KAMIEN, ETHEL N, b New York, NY, July 1, 30; m 55; c 2. PLANT PHYSIOLOGY, HUMAN BIOLOGY. *Educ:* Brooklyn Col, BA, 50; Univ Wis, MS, 52, PhD(bot), 54. *Prof Exp:* Asst bot, Univ Wis, 50-54; instr hort, Purdue Univ, 54-58; from instr to assoc prof, 60-66, PROF BIOL, UNIV LOWELL-SOUTH CAMPUS, 66-, CHMN DEPT BIOL & PHYS SCI, 65- *Concurrent Pos:* Coop teacher, Ed Serv, Inc, 65- *Mem:* Am Soc Plant Physiol; Am Inst Biol Sci; Nat Sci Teachers Asn; Nat Asn Biol Teachers; Sigma Xi. *Res:* Polarity of auxin transport; chemical control of plant growth; plant senescence; elementary school science and college biology curriculum development. *Mailing Add:* Dept of Biol Sci Univ of Lowell-S Campus Lowell MA 01854

KAMIL, ALAN CURTIS, b Bronx, NY, Nov 20, 41; m 63; c 2. ANIMAL BEHAVIOR, BEHAVIORAL ECOLOGY. *Educ:* Hofstra Univ, BA, 63; Univ Wis-Madison, MS, 66, PhD(psychol), 67. *Prof Exp:* Asst prof, 67-72, ASSOC PROF PSYCHOL, UNIV MASS, AMHERST, 67- *Concurrent Pos:* Vis assoc prof psychol, Univ Calif, Berkeley, 76-77; prin investr grants, NSF, 77-79 & NIH, 78-79. *Mem:* AAAS; Animal Behav Soc; Ecol Soc Am; Am Ornithologists Union. *Res:* Mechanisms of foraging behavior, especially in insectivarous and nectarivarous birds. *Mailing Add:* Dept of Psychol Univ of Mass Amherst MA 01003

KAMILLI, DIANA CHAPMAN, b New York, NY, Sept 5, 41; m 68. ARCHAEOMETRY, PETROLOGY. *Educ:* Vassar Col, BA, 63; Rutgers Univ, MS, 66, PhD(igneous petrol, metamorphic petrol), 68. *Prof Exp:* Instr geol, Vassar Col, 68; asst prof mineral, City Col New York, 68-69; asst prof geol, Wellesley Col, 69-75, chmn dept geol, 69-74; res assoc archeol mat anal, Mass Inst Technol & res fel archeol mat anal, Harvard Univ Peabody Mus, 75-77; RES ASSOC ARCHAEOL MAT ANAL, UNIV COLO MUS, 77- *Concurrent Pos:* NSF grant, Colo Plateau, 71; Fisher fel fund & fac grants, Wellesley Col, 71-72; consult, Sardis Expedition, Harvard Univ, 74-76; NSF res grant, 75; consult, Amax Molybdenum Co, 76-77 & 79-80. *Mem:* Geol Soc

Am; Mineral Soc Am; Soc Am Archaeol. *Res:* Petrology and geochemistry of granitic and metagranitic rocks, New Jersey, Ontario and Colorado; mineralogic and chemical analysis of ancient mesopotamian, north and central American ceramics; geochemistry and correlation of Ubaid, Samarran and Halaf ceramics, Mesopotamia. *Mailing Add:* 715 Coors St Golden CO 80401

KAMILLI, ROBERT JOSEPH, b Philadelphia, Pa, June 14, 47; m 69. ECONOMIC GEOLOGY. *Educ:* Rutgers Univ, BA, 69; Harvard Univ, AM, 71, PhD(geol), 76. *Prof Exp:* geologist, 76-79, asst resident geologist, 79-80, PROJ GEOLOGIST, AMAX, INC, 80-; ADJ PROF, UNIV COLO, BOULDER, 81- *Concurrent Pos:* Consult geologist, Huampar Mines, 73-76 & Buenaventura Mines, 75-76. *Mem:* Geol Soc Am; Mineral Soc Am; Am Inst Mining, Metall & Petrol Engrs; AAAS; Geochem Soc. *Res:* Investigation of the origin of vein and porphyry-type metal deposits, especially molybdenum and silver; emphasis on the geochemistry of such ore deposits. *Mailing Add:* AMAX Inc 1707 Cole Blvd Golden CO 80401

KAMIN, HENRY, b Warsaw, Poland, Oct 24, 20; US citizen; m 43. BIOCHEMISTRY. *Educ:* City Col New York, BS, 40; Duke Univ, PhD(biochem), 48. *Prof Exp:* Asst biochem, 40-43, 46-48, instr, 50-52, assoc, 52-56, from asst prof to prof, 56-65, PROF BIOCHEM, MED CTR, DUKE UNIV, 65- *Concurrent Pos:* USPHS fel, 48-50; prin scientist, radioisotope unit, Vet Admin Hosp, 53-68, chmn basic sci prog comt, 74-80; mem biochem & biophys prog eval comt, 68-71, mem basic sci merit rev bd, 73-76; Vet Admin liaison mem biochem study sect, NIH, 62-65; chmn subcomt on ammonia, Comt Med & Biol Effects of Environ Pollutants, Nat Res Coun-Nat Acad Sci, 75-78, mem food and nutrit bd, 78-81, chmn comt dietary allowances, 80-; mem adv panel, Metab Biol, NSF, 76-79. *Mem:* AAAS; Am Soc Biol Chem; Am Chem Soc; Am Inst Nutrit. *Res:* Biological oxidation; flavoprotein mechanisms; amino acid metabolism. *Mailing Add:* Dept of Biochem Duke Univ Med Ctr Durham NC 27706

KAMINER, BENJAMIN, b Slonim, Poland, May 1, 24; m 48; c 2. PHYSIOLOGY. *Educ:* Univ Witwatersrand, MB, BCh, 46; Royal Col Physicians & Surgeons, dipl child health, 50. *Prof Exp:* Intern med, surg & pediat, Johannesburg Hosp, SAfrica, 47-48; house physician & registr pediat, Edgeware Hosp, London, Eng, 49-50; res asst endocrinol, Postgrad Med Sch, Univ London, 50-51; from lectr to sr lectr physiol, Med Sch, Univ Witwatersrand, 51-59; investr muscle, Inst Muscle Res, 59-69; lectr anat, Harvard Med Sch, 69-70; PROF PHYSIOL & CHMN DEPT, SCH MED, BOSTON UNIV, 70- *Concurrent Pos:* Rockefeller Found fel, 59-60. *Mem:* Soc Gen Physiol; Biophys Soc; Am Soc Cell Biol; Am Physiol Soc; Corp Marine Biol Lab. *Res:* Physiology and biochemistry of muscle; motility in non-muscle cells. *Mailing Add:* Dept of Physiol 80 E Concord St Boston MA 02118

KAMINETZKY, HAROLD ALEXANDER, b Chicago, Ill, Sept 6, 23; m 57; c 2. OBSTETRICS & GYNECOLOGY. *Educ:* Univ Ill, BS, 48, MD, 50; Am Bd Obstet & Gynec, dipl. *Prof Exp:* From instr to prof, Col Med, Univ Ill, 54-68; PROF OBSTET & GYNEC, CHMN DEPT, COL MED & DENT NJ, NEWARK, 68- *Concurrent Pos:* Mem cancer adv comt, Chicago Bd Health. *Mem:* AMA; Am Col Obstet & Gynec; Am Col Surg. *Res:* Experimental dysplasia and carcinogenesis of the uterine cervix; maternal nutrition; vitamin profiles of mothers and newborns at partuition; nutrition during pregnancy. *Mailing Add:* 65 Bergen St Newark NJ 07107

KAMINKER, JEROME ALVIN, b Chicago, Ill, May 10, 41; m 67; c 2. TOPOLOGY, MATHEMATICAL ANALYSIS. *Educ:* Univ Calif, Berkeley, BA, 63; Univ Calif, Los Angeles, MA, 65, PhD(math), 68. *Prof Exp:* Asst prof math, Ind Univ, Bloomington, 68-73; from asst prof to assoc prof, 73-79, PROF MATH, IND UNIV-PURDUE UNIV, 79- *Mem:* Am Math Soc; Sigma Xi. *Res:* Development of relations between algebraic topology and functional analysis; application of K-theory to the theory of linear operators on Hilbert space. *Mailing Add:* Dept of Math Ind Univ-Purdue Univ Indianapolis IN 46205

KAMINOW, IVAN PAUL, b Union City, NJ, Mar 3, 30; m 52; c 3. APPLIED PHYSICS, ELECTROOPTICS. *Educ:* Union Univ NY, BS, 52; Univ Calif, Los Angeles, MS, 54; Harvard Univ, AM, 57, PhD(appl physics), 60. *Prof Exp:* Mem tech staff, Hughes Aircraft Co, 52-54; MEM TECH STAFF, BELL LABS, INC, 54- *Concurrent Pos:* Vis lectr, Princeton Univ, 68, & Univ Calif, Berkeley, 77; mem Nat Acad Sci-Nat Bur Stand eval panel, Optical Physics Div, 72-75; assoc ed, J Quantum Electronics, 77-83. *Mem:* Fel Inst Elec & Electronics Eng; fel Am Phys Soc; fel Optical Soc Am. *Res:* Microwave antennas; ferrites; high pressure physics; ferroelectrics; optical lasers and communication techniques; light modulation; Raman scattering; photopolymers; integrated optics; optical fibers; semiconductor lasers. *Mailing Add:* Bell Labs Inc Box 400 Holmdel NJ 07733

KAMINSKI, DONALD LEON, b Elba, Nebr, Nov 9, 40; m 65; c 4. SURGERY. *Educ:* Creighton Univ, BS, 62, MD, 66. *Prof Exp:* Asst prof, 71-75, assoc prof, 75-80, PROF SURG, ST LOUIS UNIV, 80- *Mem:* Am Physiol Soc; Am Gastroenterol Soc; Soc Univ Surgeons; Asn Acad Surg; Am Col Surgeons. *Res:* Gastrointestinal physiology, studying the hormonal control of hepatic bile flow. *Mailing Add:* Dept of Surg St Louis Univ 1325 S Grand Blvd St Louis MO 63104

KAMINSKI, EDWARD JOZEF, b Torun, Poland, Mar 24, 26; US citizen; m 51; c 2. BIOCHEMISTRY, TOXICOLOGY. *Educ:* Northwestern Univ, PhB, 60, PhD(chem), 64. *Prof Exp:* Res technologist, Royal Cancer Hosp, London, Eng, 51-53; res asst path, Mt Sinai Hosp, Toronto, Can, 53-56; res technologist, Dent Sch, 56-60, res assoc path, 64-67, asst prof, 67-71, assoc prof, 71-79, PROF PATH, DENT & MED SCH, NORTHWESTERN UNIV, 79- *Concurrent Pos:* Consult toxicology, 64- *Mem:* Soc Toxicol; Am Chem Soc. *Res:* Toxicology of metals and other materials used in the human body; study on the mechanism of absorption of substances from the environment. *Mailing Add:* Dept of Path Northwestern Univ Dent & Med Sch Chicago IL 60611

KAMINSKI, JAMES JOSEPH, b Buffalo, NY, June 5, 47; m 68. ORGANIC CHEMISTRY. *Educ:* State Univ NY Col Fredonia, BS, 69; Univ NH, PhD(org chem), 72. *Prof Exp:* sr res chemist, Interx Res Corp, 72-78; res chemist, 78-80, SECT LEADER, SCHERING CORP, 80- *Mem:* Am Chem Soc. *Res:* Physical-chemical approach to pharmaceutical problems; chemical modification of drug to improve drug delivery and development of soft medicinal agents. *Mailing Add:* Schering Corp 60 Orange St Bloomfield NJ 07003

KAMINSKI, JOAN MARY, b Darby, Pa, May 3, 47. ORGANIC CHEMISTRY. *Educ:* West Chester State Col, BA, 69; Drexel Univ, PhD(org chem), 75. *Prof Exp:* Asst res chemist, Univ Ill, Urbana, 67 & 69; teaching asst chem, Drexel Univ, 70-74; Nat Res Coun-Agr Res Serv res assoc org chem, 74-75, res scientist org chem, fats & proteins res found, Eastern Regional Res Ctr, Agr Res Serv, USDA, 75-77; res chemist, Mobil Res & Develop Corp, 77-80. *Mem:* Am Chem Soc; Sigma Xi; Am Oil Chemist's Soc. *Res:* Lubricants, petroleum chemistry, organic surfactants; amphoteric lime soap dispersing agents; fatty acid derivatives; lipid chemistry; gel chromatography; chemistry of the sulfur-nitrogen bond. *Mailing Add:* 3653 S Hamilton Chicago IL 60609

KAMINSKI, TONY L, b Moose Jaw, Sask, June 29, 39; m 62; c 2. AGRICULTURAL ENGINEERING. *Educ:* Univ Sask, BE, 61, MS, 63; Mich State Univ, PhD(agr eng), 65. *Prof Exp:* SR RES ENGR, ALLIS-CHALMERS, 65- *Mem:* Sigma Xi; Am Soc Agr Engrs; Am Soc Mech Engrs. *Res:* Engineering and development related to fluid flow, materials handling and power systems. *Mailing Add:* Allis Chalmers Mfg Co Res PO Box 512 Milwaukee WI 53201

KAMINSKI, ZIGMUND CHARLES, b Hartford, Conn, Jan 15, 29. MEDICAL MICROBIOLOGY, INFECTIOUS DISEASES. *Educ:* Univ Conn, BA, 52; Hahnemann Med Col, MS, 54, PhD(microbiol), 57; Am Bd Med Microbiol, dipl pub health & med microbiol, 72. *Prof Exp:* From instr to asst prof microbiol, Col Med, Seton Hall Univ, 57-65; asst prof, 68-71, ASSOC PROF MICROBIOL & PATH, COL MED NJ, 71-; DIR CLIN MICROBIOL, COLLEGE HOSP, 68- *Mem:* Am Soc Microbiol; Acad Clin Lab Physicians & Scientists; Am Venereal Dis Asn; NY Acad Sci; Asn Clin Scientists. *Res:* Non-specific urethritis; candidalbicans; morphogenesis. *Mailing Add:* Dept of Microbiol Col Med NJ Newark NJ 07103

KAMINSKY, KENNETH S, statistics, see previous edition

KAMINSKY, LAURENCE SAMUEL, b Cape Town, SAfrica, Dec 25, 40; m 66; c 2. BIOLOGICAL SCIENCES, TOXICOLOGY. *Educ:* Univ Cape Town, BS, 62, Hons, 63, PhD(chem), 66. *Prof Exp:* Res assoc biochem, Sch Med, Yale Univ, 67-68; assoc prof med biochem, Med Sch, Univ Cape Town, 68-75; prin ress scientist biochem, 75-77, DIR BIOCHEM TOXICOL, NY STATE DEPT HEALTH, 78- *Concurrent Pos:* Vis res prof biochem, State Univ NY Albany, 74; adj assoc prof, Albany Med Col, 76- *Mem:* Brit Biochem Soc; Am Soc Biol Chemists; Soc Toxicol. *Res:* Investigations into the role of of the heme proteins hepatic microsomal cytochrome P-450 in the metabolism of drugs; toxifying and detoxifying properties of cytodromes phosphorus-450. *Mailing Add:* Div of Labs & Res NY State Dept of Health Albany NY 12201

KAMINSKY, MANFRED STEPHAN, b Koenigsberg, Ger, June 4, 29; m 57; c 2. EXPERIMENTAL PHYSICS, SURFACE PHYSICS. *Educ:* Univ Rostock, Dipl, 51, Univ Marburg, Ger, PhD(physics), 57. *Prof Exp:* Asst physics, Univ Rostock, 50-52, lectr, Med Tech Sch, 52; res asst, Phys Inst, Univ Marburg, 53-57, sr asst, 57-58; res assoc, 58-59, asst physicist, 59-62, assoc physicist, 62-70, dir, Surface Sci Ctr, 74-80, SR PHYSICIST, ARGONNE NAT LAB, 70- *Concurrent Pos:* Coop US scientist, Div Int Prog, NSF, 78-83; chmn, Steering Comt Fusion Technol, Int Union Vacuum Sci, Technol & Appln, 81-83; res fel, Japanese Soc Prom Sci, 82; invited prof, Inst Energy, Univ Quebec, Montreal-Varennes, 76-; mem, Task Group Plasma-Wall Interactions, Office Fusion Energy, Dept Energy, 79- *Mem:* AAAS; fel Am Phys Soc; Am Chem Soc; Sigma Xi; sr mem Am Vacuum Soc. *Res:* Atomic and ionic impact phenomena on solids; channeling phenomena; nuclear polarization; surface science in thermonuclear research; mass spectrometry; ultrahigh vacuum technology; ionic processes in electrolytic solutions. *Mailing Add:* Argonne Nat Lab 9700 S Cass Ave Argonne IL 60439

KAMLET, MORTIMER JACOB, b New York, NY, July 2, 25; m 50; c 2. PHYSICAL ORGANIC CHEMISTRY. *Educ:* City Col New York, BS, 47; Columbia Univ, MA, 49; Univ Md, PhD, 54. *Prof Exp:* Asst chem, Kamlet Lab, 46-48; res chemist, Publicker Industs, 48-49; res chemist, Tenn Prod & Chem Co, 49-51; asst, Univ Md, 51-54; SR CHEMIST, US NAVAL SURFACE WEAPONS CTR, 54- *Concurrent Pos:* Co-founder Org Spectral Data, Inc, 57-58. *Mem:* Am Chem Soc. *Res:* High energy compounds; polynitroaliphatic chemistry; ultraviolet and infrared spectroscopy; solution kinetics and reaction mechanisms; chemistry of detonations; linear solvation energy relationships. *Mailing Add:* 12000 Old Georgetown Rd Rockville MD 20852

KAMM, DONALD E, b Rochester, NY, July 10, 29; m 56; c 4. NEPHROLOGY, PHYSIOLOGY. *Educ:* Cortland State Col, BS, 51; Albany Med Col, MD, 60. *Prof Exp:* Intern & resident med, Beth Israel Hosp, Boston, 60-62; from instr to asst prof, 66-71, ASSOC PROF MED, SCH MED & DENT, UNIV ROCHESTER, 71- *Concurrent Pos:* NIH res fel renal physiol, Sch Med, Boston Univ, 62-64; NIH fel metab, Harvard Med Sch, 64-66. *Mem:* Am Fedn Clin Res; Am Physiol Soc Nephrology; Int Soc Nephrology. *Res:* Effects of potassium balance on the regulation of urea production and renal ammonia production. *Mailing Add:* Rochester Gen Hosp 1425 Portland Ave Rochester NY 14620

KAMM, GILBERT G(EORGE), b Emington, Ill, Aug 6, 25; m 54; c 1. CHEMICAL ENGINEERING. *Educ:* Univ Ill, BS, 49. *Prof Exp:* Group leader metals, Res Div, Ill, 58-66, mgr metals sect, Res & Develop Ctr, 66-68, asst to assoc dir, Mat Sci Sect, 68-71, assoc dir, Princeton Res Ctr, 71-78, assoc dir metall, 79-81, DIR, METAL MAT TECHNOL, BARRINGTON TECH CTR, AM CAN CO, 82- *Mem:* Am Chem Soc; Electrochem Soc; Am Soc Metals. *Res:* Metal cleaning and plating; corrosion, especially electrolytic tin plate and other metals used in containers; metallurgical properties of container materials; plastic-metal composites; energy related research in pulp and paper processes. *Mailing Add:* Barrington Tech Ctr Am Can Co 433 N Northwest Hwy Barrington IL 60010

KAMM, JAMES A, b Ft Collins, Colo. ECONOMIC ENTOMOLOGY. *Educ:* Univ Wyo, BS, 61, MS, 63, PhD(entom), 67. *Prof Exp:* RES ENTOMOLOGIST, AGR RES SERV, USDA, 67- *Concurrent Pos:* Assoc prof, Ore State Univ, 70- *Mem:* Entom Soc Am; AAAS. *Res:* Grassland insects. *Mailing Add:* Agr Res Serv USDA Ore State Univ Dept of Entom Corvallis OR 97331

KAMM, JEROME J, b New York, NY, June 4, 33; m 56. BIOCHEMICAL PHARMACOLOGY. *Educ:* Brooklyn Col, BS, 54; Georgetown Univ, MS, 59, PhD(biochem), 64. *Prof Exp:* Chemist, Nat Heart Inst, 55-64; sr biochemist, Smith, Kline & French Labs, 64-67; SECT HEAD, HOFFMANN-LA ROCHE, INC, 67- *Mem:* AAAS; Am Chem Soc; Acad Pharmaceut Sci; NY Acad Sci; Am Soc Pharmacol & Exp Therapeut. *Res:* Drug metabolism and mechanisms of drug metabolism; toxicology. *Mailing Add:* Dept of Toxicology Hoffmann-La Roche Inc Nutley NJ 07110

KAMM, LEONARD MAURICE, b Vancouver, BC, Jan 6, 26; m 49; c 5. BIOCHEMISTRY, FOOD TECHNOLOGY. *Educ:* Univ BC, BSA, 49; Ore State Col, MS, 51. *Prof Exp:* Chief nutritionist feeds, Buckerfields Ltd, 53-55; inspector legis, Food & Drug Directorate, 55-57, lab supvr anal chem, 57-64, res officer protein chem, 64-74; CHIEF FOOD SCI MEAT INSPECTION, MEAT HYG DIRECTORATE, 74- *Concurrent Pos:* Can deleg, Int Standards Orgn, 78; adv Can deleg, Codex Comt Food Hyg, 78. *Mem:* Can Inst Food Sci & Technol. *Mailing Add:* Meat Hyg Directorate 580 Booth St Ottawa ON K1A 0Y9 Can

KAMM, RICHARD CONRAD, experimental pathology, see previous edition

KAMM, ROGER DALE, b Ashland, Wis, Oct 10, 50; K 74. BIOMEDICAL ENGINEERING, FLUID MECHANICS. *Educ:* Northwestern Univ, BS, 72; Mass Inst Technol, SM, 73, PhD(mech eng), 77. *Prof Exp:* Instr, 77, lectr & res assoc, 77-78, asst prof, 78-81, ASSOC PROF MECH ENG, MASS INST TECHNOL, 81- *Mem:* Sigma Xi; Am Soc Mech Engrs; Asn Res Vision & Ophthal. *Res:* Biomedical fluid mechanics, specifically physiology and pathophysiology of venous circulation, respiratory tract and eye. *Mailing Add:* Dept of Mech Eng Rm 3-258 77 Massachusetts Ave Cambridge MA 02139

KAMMANN, KARL PHILIP, JR, b St Louis, Mo, Mar 30, 36; m 60; c 4. CHEMISTRY. *Educ:* Washington Univ, AB, 57; La State Univ, MS, 60, PhD(chem), 62. *Prof Exp:* Sr res chemist, Cities Serv Co, 62-64; group leader, Emery Indust, Inc, 64-74; PROD DEVELOP MGR, KEIL CHEM DIV, FERRO CORP, 75- *Mem:* Am Chem Soc; Am Oil Chemists Soc; Am Soc Lubrication Engrs. *Res:* Sulfurization and chlorosulfurization; fats and oils, and derivatives. *Mailing Add:* Keil Chem Div Ferro Corp 3000 Sheffield Ave Hammond IN 46320

KAMMASH, TERRY, b Salt, Jordan, Jan 27, 27; nat US; m 56. NUCLEAR ENGINEERING, ENGINEERING MECHANICS. *Educ:* Pa State Univ, BS, 52, MS, 54; Univ Mich, PhD(nuclear eng), 58. *Prof Exp:* Asst aerodyn, Pa State Univ, 52-53, instr eng mech, 53-54; asst aircraft propulsion lab, Eng Res Inst, 54-55, from instr to assoc prof nuclear eng & eng mech, 55-67, prof nuclear eng, 67-77, STEPHEN S ATWOOD PROF NUCLEAR ENG & ACTG CHMN DEPT, UNIV MICH, ANN ARBOR, 77- *Concurrent Pos:* Vis scientist, Lawrence Radiation Lab, 62-63. *Mem:* Am Phys Soc; Am Nuclear Soc; Am Soc Eng Educ; Soc Eng Sci. *Res:* Magnetohydrodynamics; plasma physics; plasticity and physics of ionized gases. *Mailing Add:* Dept of Nuclear Eng Univ of Mich Ann Arbor MI 48109

KAMMEN, HAROLD OSCAR, biochemistry, see previous edition

KAMMER, ANN EMMA, b Auburn, NY, Dec 26, 35. NEUROBIOLOGY. *Educ:* State Col Teachers Albany, BS, 56; Univ NH, MS, 58; Univ Calif, Berkeley, PhD(zool), 66. *Prof Exp:* Lectr zool, Univ Calif, Davis, 65, from actg asst prof to asst prof, 65-72, ASSOC PROF ZOOL, KANS STATE UNIV, 72- *Concurrent Pos:* Vis res fel, Univ Saarland, 70 & Univ Cologne, 71. *Mem:* Am Soc Zoologists; Soc Exp Biol; Soc Neurosci; Am Physiol Soc. *Res:* Neural control of muscles; development of central nervous system and temperature regulation in insects. *Mailing Add:* Div of Biol Kans State Univ Manhattan KS 66506

KAMMERAAD, ADRIAN, b Holland, Mich, Feb 25, 12; m 48; c 3. EXPERIMENTAL BIOLOGY, RESEARCH ADMINISTRATION. *Educ:* Hope Col, AB, 33; Yale Univ, PhD(exp embryol), 40. *Prof Exp:* Asst zool, Yale Univ, 33-36; instr, Dartmouth Col, 36-38; asst anat, Sch Med, La State Univ, 38-40, instr, 40-42; sci dir, Van Patten Pharmaceut Co, 46-50; dir res & prod control, Kremers-Urban Co, 50-56; in chg pharmaceut prod develop, Dow Chem Co, 56-60, dir pharm lab, 59-60, in chg res admin, 60-62, mgr drug regulatory sect, Res Ctr, 62-77; RETIRED. *Concurrent Pos:* Instr, Sch Med, Northwestern Univ, 47-50. *Res:* Administration and supervision of drug regulatory activities. *Mailing Add:* 9115 Washington Blvd Indianapolis IN 46240

KAMMERER, WILLIAM JOHN, b Rochester, NY, Oct 8, 31; m 57; c 2. MATHEMATICS. *Educ:* Univ Rochester, BA, 54; Univ Wis, Madison, MS, 55, PhD(math), 59. *Prof Exp:* Asst prof math, Case Western Reserve Univ, 59-60; from asst prof to assoc prof, 60-71, PROF MATH, GA INST TECHNOL, 71- *Concurrent Pos:* Soc Indust & Appl Math lectr, 71-72. *Mem:* Am Math Soc; Soc Indust & Appl Math. *Res:* Numerical analysis; approximation theory and optimization. *Mailing Add:* Sch of Math Ga Inst of Technol Atlanta GA 30332

KAMMERMEIER, MARTIN A, b Cold Spring, Minn, Oct 23, 31; m 59; c 3. SPEECH PATHOLOGY. *Educ:* St Cloud State Col, BS, 58, MS, 63; Univ Minn, Minneapolis, PhD(speech path), 69. *Prof Exp:* Speech therapist, Pub Sch, 58-62; from instr to asst prof, 62-73, PROF SPEECH PATH, ST CLOUD STATE UNIV, 73-, CHMN DEPT SPEECH SCI, PATH & AUDIOL, 70- *Mem:* Am Speech & Hearing Asn. *Res:* Acoustic analysis of the voices of speakers with a variety of central nervous system disorders. *Mailing Add:* Dept Speech Sci & Path & Audiol St Cloud State Univ St Cloud MN 56301

KAMMERMEYER, KARL, b Nurnberg, Ger, June 15, 04; nat US; m 30; c 1. CHEMICAL ENGINEERING. *Educ:* Univ Mich, BSChE & BS, 29, MSE, 31, DSc(chem eng), 32. *Prof Exp:* Res assoc eng, Univ Mich, 30-32; develop engr, Standard Oil Co, Inc, 33-36; refinery chief chemist & chem engr, Pure Oil Co, Ohio, 36-39; asst prof chem eng, Drexel Inst, 39-42; dir res, Publicker Industs Inc, 42-47; mgr res & develop, Chem Div, Glenn L Martin Co, 47-49; prof chem eng & head dept, 49-73, EMER PROF CHEM ENG, UNIV IOWA, 73- *Concurrent Pos:* Sci consult, US Dept of Com, Ger, 46; consult, Robert A Taft Sanit Eng Ctr, Vet Admin Hosp, Iowa City, Bendix Corp & Monsanto Res Corp; chmn, Gordon Res Conf Separation & Purification, 57. *Mem:* AAAS; Am Chem Soc; fel Am Inst Chem Engrs; Am Soc Eng Educ. *Res:* Separation processes; membrane separations and distillation; air purification in submarines and space capsules. *Mailing Add:* Dept of Chem Eng Univ of Iowa Iowa City IA 52242

KAMMERUD, RONALD CLAIRE, b Monroe, Wis, July 10, 42; m 63; c 2. SOLAR ENERGY. *Educ:* Drexel Univ, BS, 66; Ind Univ, Bloomington, MS, 69, PhD(physics), 70. *Prof Exp:* Res assoc exp high energy physics, Ohio State Univ, 70; res assoc exp high energy physics, Fermi Nat Accelerator Lab, 73-76; SOLAR ENERGY RES PHYSICIST, LAWRENCE BERKELEY LAB, 76- *Mem:* Am Phys Soc; Int Solar Energy Soc. *Res:* Heat transfer analysis as applied to passive solar building energy analysis. *Mailing Add:* Energy & Environ Div One Cyclotron Rd Berkeley CA 94720

KAMMEYER, CARL WILLIAM, physical chemistry, see previous edition

KAMMLER, DAVID W, b Belleville, Ill, Oct 29, 40; m 65; c 2. NUMERICAL ANALYSIS, APPROXIMATION THEORY. *Educ:* Southern Ill Univ, Carbondale, BA, 62; Southern Methodist Univ, MS, 69; Univ Mich, Ann Arbor, PhD(math), 71. *Prof Exp:* Mem tech staff, Tex Instruments Inc, 65-68; from asst prof to assoc prof, 71-78, PROF MATH, SOUTHERN ILL UNIV, CARBONDALE, 78- *Concurrent Pos:* fel, Rome Air Develop Ctr, 80-81. *Mem:* Am Math Soc; Soc Indust & Appl Math; Math Asn Am; Sigma Xi. *Res:* Approximation with sums of exponentials; transient analysis; numerical analysis. *Mailing Add:* Dept of Math Southern Ill Univ Carbondale IL 62901

KAMON, ELIEZER, b Jerusalem; US citizen; m 67; c 3. ERGONOMICS, OCCUPATIONAL HEALTH. *Educ:* Israel State Col, T dipl, 52; Hebrew Univ, Jerusalem, MSc, 59, PhD(zool), 64. *Prof Exp:* Res asst occup health, Univ Pittsburgh, 66-67; res assoc, 68-73; PROF PHYSIOL, PA STATE UNIV, 74- *Concurrent Pos:* Fel ergonomics, Loughboro Univ Technolog, 65. *Mem:* Am Physiol Soc; Am Indust Hyg Asn; fel Am Col Sports Med; Ergonomics Soc; Human Factors Soc. *Res:* Human thermal physiology and man's adaptability to his working conditions as they relate to muscular strength, cardiovascular capacity and respiratory functions. *Mailing Add:* 104 Noll Lab Pa State Univ University Park PA 16802

KAMOWITZ, HERBERT M, b Brooklyn, NY, Dec 31, 31; m 55; c 3. MATHEMATICS. *Educ:* City Col New York, BS, 52; Brown Univ, ScM, 54, PhD(math), 60. *Prof Exp:* Assoc scientist math, Res & Advan Develop Div, Avco Corp, 57-60, sr scientist, 60-61, from staff scientist to sr staff scientist, 61-66; assoc prof, 66-70, PROF MATH, UNIV MASS, BOSTON, 70- *Concurrent Pos:* Vis scientist, Pure Math Dept, Weizmann Inst Sci, Rehovot, Israel, 73 & 80. *Mem:* Am Math Soc. *Res:* Functional analysis. *Mailing Add:* Dept of Math Univ of Mass Dorchester MA 02125

KAMP, DAVID ALLEN, b St Louis, Mo, Sept 26, 47; m 73. ORGANIC CHEMISTRY, POLYMER CHEMISTRY. *Educ:* Univ Calif, Los Angeles, BSc, 70; Univ Ore, PhD(chem), 76. *Prof Exp:* Assoc chem, Univ Calif, 76-77; staff org chemist, Res & Develop Ctr, Gen Elec Co, 77-80; STAFF SCIENTIST, RAYCHEM CORP, 80- *Mem:* Am Chem Soc. *Res:* Organic synthesis; non-benzenoid aromatics. *Mailing Add:* Raychem Corp 300 Constitution Dr Menlo Park CA 94025

KAMPAS, FRANK JAMES, b Buffalo, NY, Apr 24, 46. PHYSICAL CHEMISTRY, SOLID STATE PHYSICS. *Educ:* Univ Pa, BA & MS, 68; Stanford Univ, PhD(physics), 74. *Prof Exp:* Res assoc chem, Univ Wash, 74-77; res assoc, Molecular Sci Div, 77-78, asst scientist, 78-80, ASSOC SCIENTIST, MAT SCI DIV, DEPT ENERGY & ENVIRON, BROOKHAVEN NAT LAB, 80- *Mem:* Am Phys Soc. *Res:* Physics of organic molecules in the solid state and in solution; plasma chemistry as applied to thin film deposition; optical spectroscopy. *Mailing Add:* Bldg 480 Brookhaven Nat Lab Upton NY 11973

KAMPE, DENNIS JAMES, b Brooklyn, NY, July 16, 45; m 74; c 1. ELECTRON MICROSCOPY. *Educ:* State Univ NY Stony Brook, BESc, 67; Univ Va, MMSc, 69, PhD(mat sci), 72. *Prof Exp:* Staff scientist, 72-73, dept head micros & phys testing, 73-75, RES SCIENTIST, CARBON PROD DIV, UNION CARBIDE CORP, 75- *Mem:* Electron Micros Soc Am; Am Soc

Testing & Mat. *Res:* Optical and electron microscopy and physical properties determinations of carbons, graphites and fibers; structure and performance capabilities of porous air-oxygen cathodes in chlor-alkali cells. *Mailing Add:* 3100 Marda Dr Parma OH 44134

KAMPER, ROBERT ANDREW, b Surbiton, Eng, Mar 14, 33; nat US; m 55; c 3. PHYSICS. *Educ:* Oxford Univ, BA, 54, MA & DPhil(physics), 57. *Prof Exp:* Imp Chem Industs res fel, Oxford Univ, 57-61; physicist, Cent Elec Generating Bd, Eng, 61-63; physicist, Cryogenics Div, 63-74, ASSOC CHIEF, ELECTROMAGNETICS DIV, NAT BUR STAND, 74- *Concurrent Pos:* Fulbright travel grant, Univ Calif, Berkeley, 58-59. *Mem:* Sr mem Inst Elec & Electronics Engrs. *Res:* Cryoelectronics; superconductivity; electrical measurement technique; electron spin resonance. *Mailing Add:* Electromagnetics Div Nat Bur of Stand Boulder CO 80302

KAMPHOEFNER, FRED J(OHN), b San Francisco, Calif, Mar 23, 21; m 60. ELECTRONICS. *Educ:* Univ Calif, BS, 43; Stanford Univ, MA, 47, PhD, 49. *Prof Exp:* Res assoc, Radio Res Lab, Harvard Univ, 43-45 & Stanford Univ, 46-49; mgr control systs lab, 49-71, DIR, ENG SCI LAB, STANFORD RES INST, 71- *Concurrent Pos:* Res analyst, Opers Res Off, Johns Hopkins Univ, 52. *Mem:* AAAS; Sigma Xi; sr mem Inst Elec & Electronics Engrs. *Res:* Instrumentation; data systems; bioengineering. *Mailing Add:* 175 Ravenswood Ave Atherton CA 94025

KAMPHUIS, J(OHN) WILLIAM, b Vollenhove, Netherlands, Sept 9, 38; Can citizen; m 60; c 2. COASTAL & OCEANOGRAPHIC ENGINEERING. *Educ:* Queen's Univ, Ont, BSc, 61, MSc, 63, PhD(civil eng), 66; Delft Technol Univ, dipl hydraul eng, 64. *Prof Exp:* Asst res officer, Nat Res Coun Can, 65-68; from asst prof to assoc prof, 68-72, PROF CIVIL ENG, QUEEN'S UNIV, ONT, 74- *Concurrent Pos:* Lectr, Carleton Univ, 65-68; specialist consult coastal eng, 69- *Mem:* Am Soc Civil Engrs; Int Asn Hydraul Res; Int Soc Hydraul Engrs (pres, 64); Can Soc Civil Engrs. *Res:* Wave mechanics; interaction of waves and coasts; coastal sediment transport by waves and tides; model analysis; tidal propagation and numerical analysis; marina design. *Mailing Add:* Ellis Hall Queen's Univ Kingston ON K7L 3N6 Can

KAMPMEIER, JACK A, b Cedar Rapids, Iowa, June 11, 35; m 58; c 3. ORGANIC CHEMISTRY. *Educ:* Amherst Col, BA, 57; Univ Ill, PhD(org chem), 60. *Prof Exp:* From instr to assoc prof, 60-71, chmn dept, 75-79, PROF CHEM, UNIV ROCHESTER, 71- *Concurrent Pos:* NSF sci fac fel, Univ Calif, Berkeley, 71-72; NSF fel, 58-60; Fulbright-Hays, sr res fel, Univ Frenburg, 79-80; sr scientist, NATO, 79-80. *Mem:* Am Chem Soc; Sigma Xi. *Res:* Mechanistic organic chemistry; free radical reactions; organometallic reactions; photochemistry. *Mailing Add:* Dept of Chem Univ of Rochester River Sta Rochester NY 14627

KAMPRATH, EUGENE JOHN, b Seward, Nebr, Jan 9, 26; m 56; c 2. SOIL FERTILITY. *Educ:* Univ Nebr, BS, 50, MS, 52; NC State Col, PhD(soils), 55. *Prof Exp:* From asst prof to assoc prof, 55-62, prof, 62-81, WILLIAM NEAL REYNOLDS PROF SOIL SCI, NC STATE UNIV, 81- *Concurrent Pos:* Dir soil testing div, State Dept Agr, NC, 57-62; ed-in-chief, Soil Science Soc Am, 69-74. *Mem:* Fel Am Soc Agron; Soil Conserv Soc Am; Soil Sci Am. *Res:* Soil fertility; soil chemistry relationships in soils as they affect availability of nutrients to plants. *Mailing Add:* Dept of Soil Sci NC State Univ Raleigh NC 27650

KAMPSCHMIDT, RALPH FRED, b Gerald, Mo, May 6, 23; m 54; c 4. BIOCHEMISTRY. *Educ:* Univ Mo, BS, 47, MS, 49, PhD(agr chem), 51. *Prof Exp:* Instr animal husb, Univ Mo, 47-51; res chemist biochem, Armour & Co, 51-55; SECT HEAD, SAMUEL ROBERTS NOBLE FOUND, INC, 55- *Mem:* Fel AAAS; Am Asn Cancer Res; Soc Exp Biol & Med; Reticuloendothelial Soc; NY Acad Sci. *Res:* Cancer research; iron metabolism; reticuloendothelial system; endotoxin; monokines. *Mailing Add:* Samuel Roberts Noble Found Inc Rte 1 Ardmore OK 73401

KAMRA, OM PERKASH, b Lahore, India, Mar 18, 35; m 59; c 2. RADIATION GENETICS, CYTOGENETICS. *Educ:* Univ Delhi, BSc, 54; NC State Univ, MS, 56; Wash State Univ, PhD(genetics), 59; Univ Lund, dipl, 59. *Prof Exp:* Fel Swedish Agr Res Coun, 59; secy, Food & Agr Orgn-Swedish Int Training Ctr Genetics, Univ Lund, 59-60; res officer radiation genetics, Atomic Energy Estab, Trombay, India, 60-61; res assoc plant genetics, Univ Man, 61-63; assoc prof, 63-72, PROF RADIATION BIOL, DALHOUSIE UNIV, 72- *Concurrent Pos:* Fel, Swedish Agr Res Coun, 59-60; chmn biol subcomt, Atlantic Prov Inter-Univ Comt Sci, 67-68; consult, Int Atomic Energy Agency, Vienna, 69-70 & UN Develop Prog, Indonesia, 72; mem comt int exchange, Nat Res Coun, 73-76; vis prof, Belgium Nuclear Res Estab, 77, 78 & 81. *Honors & Awards:* Travel Award, Can Genetics Soc, 63. *Mem:* Sigma Xi. *Res:* Cytology; genetics; mutations; food additives; effect of laser beams on biological systems. *Mailing Add:* Lab of Radiaiton Biol Dalhousie Univ Halifax NS B3H 3J5 Can

KAMRAN, MERVYN ARTHUR, b Sialkot, Pakistan, Nov 8, 38. ENTOMOLOGY, ECOLOGY. *Educ:* Punjab Univ, Pakistan, BS, 57, MS, 59; Univ Hawaii, PhD(entom), 65. *Prof Exp:* Lectr biol, Pakistan Ed Serv, Lahore, 59-61; Pakistan AEC scholar, Cent Treaty Orgn Inst Nuclear Sci, Tehran, Iran, 61; res fel entom, Int Rice Res Inst, Philippines, 65-67; asst prof entom, Pa State Univ, 68; asst prof biol, 68-72, assoc prof, 72-79, PROF BIOL, DOWLING COL, 79- *Mem:* AAAS; Am Entom Soc; Entom Soc Am. *Res:* Ecology and biological control of insect pests; taxonomy of tachinid flies. *Mailing Add:* Dept of Biol Dowling Col Oakdale NY 11769

KAMRASS, MURRAY, b Far Rockaway, NY, Jan 24, 21; m 42; c 2. OPERATIONS RESEARCH, SYSTEMS ANALYSIS. *Educ:* Univ Mich, BS, 42; Univ Buffalo, MS, 52. *Prof Exp:* Aerodynamicist, Stinson Div, Convair, 42-44; res engr to sect head, Cornell Aeronaut Lab, Inc, 46-62; mgr adv eng planning, Curtiss Div, Curtiss Wright Corp, 62-63; TECH STAFF MEM, INST DEFENSE ANAL, 63- *Concurrent Pos:* Consult, mil agencies, 56- & State NJ, 61; mem & past pres, Wash Opers Res Coun. *Mem:* Opers Res Soc Am. *Res:* Transportation systems; urban problems; military systems. *Mailing Add:* 5311 Waneta Rd Bethesda MD 20816

KAMRIN, MICHAEL ARNOLD, b Brooklyn, NY, Aug 5, 40; m 64; c 2. SCIENCE EDUCATION, SCIENCE POLICY. *Educ:* Cornell Univ, BA, 60; Yale Univ, MS, 62, PhD(chem), 65. *Prof Exp:* Res assoc biol, Biol Div, Oak Ridge Nat Lab, 63-64, consult, 65-66; NIH trainee, Hopkins Marine Sta, Stanford Univ, 66-67; asst prof, 67-72, assoc prof, 72-79, PROF NATURAL SCI, MICH STATE UNIV, 79- *Concurrent Pos:* Vis scientist, Mich Legis Off Sci Adv, 80-81. *Mem:* AAAS; Am Chem Soc; Sigma Xi. *Res:* Primary processes in photosynthesis; science education for non-scientists; science policy. *Mailing Add:* Dept of Natural Sci Mich State Univ East Lansing MI 48824

KAMYKOWSKI, DANIEL, b Chicago, Ill, Nov 23, 45. BIOLOGICAL OCEANOGRAPHY. *Educ:* Loyola Univ, Chicago, BS, 67; Univ Calif, San Diego, PhD(oceanog), 73. *Prof Exp:* Killam res assoc oceanog, Dalhousie Univ, 73-75; asst prof bot & marine sci, Univ Tex, Austin, 75-79; ASSOC PROF MARINE, EARTH & ATMOSPHERIC SCI, NC STATE UNIV, 79- *Mem:* Am Soc Limnol & Oceanog; Phycol Soc Am. *Res:* Physiology and behavior of marine dineflagellates as they are affected by physical processes; global patterns in hydrographic factors, plant nutrients and phytoplankton species composition. *Mailing Add:* Dept Marine Earth & Atmospheric Sci PO Box 5068 NC State Univ Raleigh NC 27650

KAN, JAMES HUNG-KEI, b Hong Kong, May 12, 28. GENETICS. *Educ:* Pomona Col, BA, 50; Univ Calif, Berkeley, MS, 54; Tex A&M Univ, PhD(poultry sci), 58. *Prof Exp:* Asst poultry sci, Tex A&M Univ, 54-57; asst prof, Univ Ark, 57-62; res assoc, Univ Wis, 65; res assoc, Princeton Univ, 66-69; investr, City of Hope Nat Med Ctr, Div Biol, 69-80, INVESTR, DIV NEUROSCI, CITY OF HOPE RES INST, 82- *Concurrent Pos:* Fel biochem genetics, Mich State Univ, 62-63 & Univ Wis, 63-65. *Mem:* AAAS. *Res:* Biochemical and developmental genetics. *Mailing Add:* City of Hope Res Inst 1450 E Duarte Rd Duarte CA 91010

KAN, JOSEPH RUCE, b Shanghai, China, Feb 10, 38; US citizen; m; c 3. SPACE PLASMA PHYSICS, PLASMA PHYSICS. *Educ:* Nat Cheng-Kung Univ, Taiwan, BS, 61; Wash State Univ, MS, 66; Univ Calif, San Diego, PhD(appl physics), 69. *Prof Exp:* Fel space physics, Dartmouth Col, 69-72; asst prof, 72-76, assoc prof, 76-81, head, Space Physics & Atmospheric Sci Prog, 77-80, PROF GEOPHYSICS, GEOPHYSICS INST, UNIV ALASKA, 81- *Concurrent Pos:* Consult, Aerospace Corp, 80-81. *Mem:* AAAS; Sigma Xi; Am Phys Soc; Am Geophys Union. *Res:* Space physics. *Mailing Add:* Geophys Inst Univ of Alaska Fairbanks AK 99701

KAN, LOU SING, b Honan, China, Feb 28, 43; m 70. PHYSICAL CHEMISTRY, BIOPHYSICS. *Educ:* Nat Taiwan Univ, BS, 64; Duquesne Univ, PhD(phys chem), 70. *Prof Exp:* Asst chem, Nat Taiwan Univ, 65; asst phys chem, Duquesne Univ, 66-70, fel, 70-71; fel chem, 71-74, res assoc, 74-77, ASST PROF, DIV BIOPHYS, SCH HYG & PUB HEALTH, JOHNS HOPKINS UNIV, 77- *Concurrent Pos:* Vis fel, Mellon Inst, Carnegie-Mellon Univ, 70-71. *Mem:* Am Chem Soc; Biophys Soc; Sigma Xi. *Res:* Studies of structure and backbone conformations of oligoribonucleotides and deoxyribonucleotides; conformation of nucleic acids; modified nucleic acids. *Mailing Add:* Dept of Biochem Biophys Sch Hyg & PH Johns Hopkins Univ Baltimore MD 21205

KAN, PETER TAI YUEN, b Canton, China, Apr 12, 27; US citizen; m 51; c 2. ORGANIC CHEMISTRY. *Educ:* Gannon Col, BS, 49; Univ Mich, MS, 51; Wayne State Univ, PhD(org chem), 58. *Prof Exp:* Sr anal chemist, R P Scherer Corp, Mich, 51-55; from res chemist to sr res chemist, Wyandotte Chem Corp, 57-68, res assoc, 68-76, RES SUPVR, BASF WYANDOTTE CORP, 76- *Mem:* AAAS; Am Chem Soc; fel Am Inst Chem. *Res:* Isocyanates; isocyanurates; polyurethanes; organo-metallics; general organic synthesis. *Mailing Add:* Cent Res & Develop BASF Wyandotte Corp Wyandotte MI 48192

KAN, YUET WAI, b Hong Kong, China, June 11, 36; m 64; c 2. GENETICS, HEMATOLOGY. *Educ:* Univ Hong Kong, MB & BS, 58, DSc, 80. *Hon Degrees:* MD, Univ Cagliari, Italy, 81; DSc, Chinese Univ Hong Kong, 81. *Prof Exp:* Asst prof pediat, Harvard Med Sch, 70-72; chief, Hemat Sect, San Francisco Gen Hosp, 72-79; PROF MED, UNIV CALIF, SAN FRANCISCO, 77-, PROF BIOCHEM & BIOPHYSICS, 79- *Concurrent Pos:* Assoc prof med, Depts Med & Lab Med, Univ Calif, San Francisco, 72-77; Harvey Soc lectr, 80-81; investr, Howard Hughes Med Inst Lab, 76- *Honors & Awards:* Damashek Award, Am Soc Hemat, 79; Stratton lectr, Int Soc Hemat, 80. *Mem:* Am Soc Hemat; Am Fedn Clin Res; Am Soc Clin Invest; Asn Am Physicians; fel Royal Soc London. *Res:* Normal control of globin synthesis and genetic defects in homoglobinopathies and thalassemia. *Mailing Add:* Dept Med HSE 1504 Univ Calif San Francisco CA 74143

KANA, ALFRED JAN, b Yonkers, NY, Aug 7, 20; m 52. APPLIED STATISTICS, ANALYTICAL STATISTICS. *Educ:* Columbia Univ, AB, 42, MA, 50, PhD(statist), 68. *Prof Exp:* From asst to assoc statist, Columbia Col, Columbia Univ, 48-64; assoc prof, 65-73, PROF STATIST & QUANT ANAL, SETON HALL UNIV, 74- *Concurrent Pos:* Statist consult, Am Footwear Mfrs Asn, NY, 68-71. *Mem:* AAAS; Am Statist Asn. *Res:* Teaching methods in applied statistics; impact of imported footwear on the domestic industry; analysis of Air Force management problems. *Mailing Add:* 34 Ashton Rd Yonkers NY 10705

KANA, DANIEL D(AVID), b Cuero, Tex, Sept 22, 34; m 58; c 3. ENGINEERING MECHANICS, MECHANICAL ENGINEERING. *Educ:* Univ Tex, BS, 58, PhD(eng mech), 67; Univ NMex, MS, 61. *Prof Exp:* From res engr to sr res engr, 61-70, group leader, 70-71, MGR STRUCT DYNAMICS & ACOUST, SOUTHWEST RES INST, 71- *Mem:* fel Am Soc Mech Engrs; fel Am Inst Aeronaut & Astronaut. *Res:* Liquid and structure dynamic interaction; linear and non-linear vibrations; dynamic response and stability of structures; general structural dynamics and acoustics; environmental testing; earthquake engineering. *Mailing Add:* Southwest Res Inst PO Drawer 28510 San Antonio TX 78284

KANA'AN, ADLI SADEQ, b Nablus, Jordan, Mar 15, 31; m 64; c 2. PHYSICAL CHEMISTRY. *Educ:* Univ Baghdad, BSc, 55; Colo State Univ, MSc, 57; Univ Wis, PhD(chem), 63. *Prof Exp:* Asst chemist, Indust Res Inst, Iraq, 55-56; instr, Nablus UNRWA Sch, Jordan, 56; Inst Int Ed Smith-Mond exchange scholar, Colo State Univ, 56-57; fel, Univ Wis, 62; fel & res assoc chem, Rice Univ, 63-65; from asst prof to assoc prof, 65-77, PROF CHEM, WESTERN MICH UNIV, 77- *Mem:* Am Chem Soc. *Res:* High temperature chemistry and reactions of metastable species in electric discharges; spectroscopy of diatomic and triatomic free radicals; chemiluminescence in cross-molecular beams. *Mailing Add:* Dept of Chem Western Mich Univ Kalamazoo MI 49001

KANABROCKI, EUGENE LADISLAUS, b Chicago, Ill, Apr 18, 22; m 50; c 2. BIOCHEMISTRY. *Educ:* DePaul Univ, BS, 47; Loyola Univ Chicago, MS, 69; Nat Registry Clin Chem, cert. *Prof Exp:* Asst chief chemist, Clin Lab, Hines Vet Admin Hosp, 46-48, asst chief biochemist, 48-56, biochemist nuclear med, 56-73, CHIEF CLIN CHEMIST, FOUR HOSP COMPLEX, HINES VET ADMIN HOSP, 73- *Concurrent Pos:* Consult, 56-; res assoc, Loyola Univ Chicago; chemist, US Customs Lab, Chicago; WHO investr, Int Atomic Energy Agency. *Mem:* Am Chem Soc; Am Asn Clin Chem; Radiation Res Soc; Health Physics Soc. *Res:* Etiology of arteriosclerosis; chronobiology. *Mailing Add:* 151 Braddock Dr Melrose Park IL 60160

KANAKKANATT, ANTONY, b Cochin, India, Mar 6, 35; m 65; c 3. POLYMER CHEMISTRY. *Educ:* Univ Kerala, India, BSc, 56; Marquette Univ, MS, 60; Univ Akron, PhD, 63. *Prof Exp:* Sr res chemist, Monsanto Co, 63-65; res asst, 65-67, SR ASSOC INDEXER, CHEM ABSTRACTS SERV, 67- *Mem:* Am Chem Soc. *Res:* Catalytic isomerization; sequence distribution in polypeptides; reinforcement in elastomers. *Mailing Add:* Chem Abstracts Serv 2540 Olentangy River Rd Columbus OH 43210

KANAKKANATT, SEBASTIAN VARGHESE, b Kerala, India, Jan 20, 29; US citizen; m 58; c 1. POLYMER PHYSICS. *Educ:* Univ Madras, BSc, 50; Univ Akron, MS, 65, PhD(polymer physics), 69. *Prof Exp:* Instr chem, Univ Madras, 50-52 & Univ Addis Ababa, 52-64; asst prof, 69-72, assoc prof, 72-80, PROF GEN TECHNOL, UNIV AKRON, 80-, ASST DIR ENVIRON MGT LAB, 76- *Mem:* Am Chem Soc; Rheol Soc; Sigma Xi. *Res:* Diffusion in polymeric matrices used in the controlled release of pesticides, herbicides, fertilizers and others. *Mailing Add:* Div of Eng & Sci Univ of Akron Akron OH 44304

KANAL, LAVEEN NANIK, b Dhond, India, Sept 29, 31; m 60; c 3. COMPUTER SCIENCE, STATISTICS. *Educ:* Univ Wash, BS, 51, MS, 53; Univ Pa, PhD(elec eng), 60. *Prof Exp:* Develop engr, Can Gen Elec Co, Ont, 53-55; instr elec eng, Moore Sch Elec Eng, Univ Pa, 55-60; mgr mach intel lab, Gen Dynamics/Electronics, NY, 60-62; res mgr info sci, Philco Appl Res Lab, Philco-Ford Corp, 62-65, mgr advan eng & res activ, Commun & Electronics Div, Philco-Ford Corp, 65-69; pres, 69-70, MANAGING DIR, L N K CORP, SILVER SPRING, 70-; PROF COMPUT SCI, UNIV MD, COLLEGE PARK, 70- *Concurrent Pos:* Lectr, Wharton Grad Sch, Univ Pa, 63-64, vis assoc prof, 64-66, vis prof, 66-74; adj prof, Lehigh Univ, 65-70. *Mem:* Fel AAAS; Asn Comput Mach; Pattern Recognition Soc; Am Statist Asn; fel Inst Elec & Electronics Eng. *Res:* Information science; machine recognition of patterns; stochastic learning models; statistical classification theory and applications of artificial intelligence; pattern recognition and image processing in remote sennsing and automated digital cartography. *Mailing Add:* Comput Sci Dept Univ of Md College Park MD 20742

KANAMORI, HIROO, b Tokyo, Japan, Oct 17, 36; m 64; c 2. SEISMOLOGY, GEOPHYSICS. *Educ:* Univ Tokyo, BS, 59, MS, 61, PhD(geophys), 64. *Prof Exp:* Res fel geophys, Calif Inst Technol, 65-66; from assoc prof to prof, Univ Tokyo, 66-72; PROF GEOPHYS, CALIF INST TECHNOL, 72- *Concurrent Pos:* Vis assoc prof geophys, Mass Inst Technol, 69-70. *Mem:* Fel Am Geophys Union; Seismol Soc Am; Seismol Soc Japan. *Res:* Mechanism of earthquakes; earthquake prediction; application of seismology to earthquake engineering. *Mailing Add:* Seismol Lab Calif Inst Technol Pasadena CA 91125

KANAMUELLER, JOSEPH M, b Chicago, Ill, July 4, 38. INORGANIC CHEMISTRY. *Educ:* St Joseph's Col Ind, BS, 60; Univ Minn, PhD(inorg chem), 65. *Prof Exp:* Res assoc inorg chloramine chem, Univ Fla, 65-66; asst prof chem, 66-72, assoc prof, 72-80, PROF CHEM, WESTERN MICH UNIV, 80- *Concurrent Pos:* Vis prof inorg chem, Vienna Tech Univ, Austria, 74. *Mem:* AAAS; Am Chem Soc. *Res:* Synthetic inorganic chemistry, especially sulfur-nitrogen and phosphorus-nitrogen compounds. *Mailing Add:* Dept of Chem Western Mich Univ Kalamazoo MI 49008

KANARIK, ROSELLA, b Hungary, Feb 7, 09; US citizen; m 36; c 2. MATHEMATICS. *Educ:* Univ Pittsburgh, BA, 30, MA, 31, PhD(math), 34. *Prof Exp:* Asst math, Univ Pittsburgh, 31-33; teacher 46-53; instr, 53-56, counr, 56-62, from assoc prof to prof, 62-74, EMER PROF MATH, LOS ANGELES CITY COL, 74- *Mem:* Am Math Soc; Math Asn Am. *Res:* Differential equations; group theory. *Mailing Add:* 238 S Mansfield Ave Los Angeles CA 90036

KANAROWSKI, S(TANLEY) M(ARTIN), b Beausejour, Man, Dec 12, 12; nat US; m 36; c 3. MATERIALS ENGINEERING. *Educ:* Univ Toledo, BS, 34. *Prof Exp:* from chemist to chief chemist, Dept Liquor Control, Ohio, 36-42; consult & sr chemist, Ord Plant, Firestone Tire & Rubber Co, Nebr, 42-43, asst dir corp gen lab, Ohio, 43, chief factory prod chem engr, 43-46, res & develop compounding chem engr, 46-49; lab dir & asst res & develop mgr, Fremont Rubber Co, 49-52; res & develop chem engr, Glass Fibers Inc, 52-53; chief res & develop chemist-engr & qual control mgr, Dairypak Butler Inc, 53-60; chief chemist, Northern Region, Enforcement Div, Ohio, 60-62; res & develop chem engr, Consol Paper Co, 62-63; sewage & indust wastes chemist, City of Toledo, 63-64; proj engr & head chemist, Invests Sect, Ohio River Div Labs, Chem & Thermal Effects Br, US Army Eng Div, 64-69, PROJ LEADER & PRIN INVESTR, CONSTRUCT ENG RES LAB, ENG MAT DIV, US ARMY, 69- *Mem:* Am Chem Soc; Am Inst Chem Engrs; Am Defense Preparedness Asn. *Res:* Construction materials application research and development; sealants; waterproofing materials; reflective solar control films for windows; maple gymnasium floor finishes; rubber and synthetic rubber products; elastomers; polymers; coatings; plastics; glass fibers; resins; paperboard; compounding; quality control; laboratory and factory operations. *Mailing Add:* 2014 Trout Valley Rd Champaign IL 61820

KANASEWICH, ERNEST RAYMOND, b Eatonia, Sask, Mar 4, 31; m 69; c 2. GEOPHYSICS. *Educ:* Univ Alta, BSc, 52, MSc, 60; Univ BC, PhD(geophys), 62. *Prof Exp:* Seismologist, Tex Instruments-Geophys Serv, Inc, 53-58; fel, Univ BC, 62-63; from asst prof to assoc prof, 63-71, from asst chmn to actg chmn dept, 69-74, PROF PHYSICS, UNIV ALTA, 71- *Concurrent Pos:* Mem cubcomt glaciol, Nat Res Coun, 63-, subcomt seismol, 67-; mem adv comt explor tech, Northern Alta Inst Technol, 64- & subcomt phys methods appl to geol probs, Nat Adv Comt Res Geol Sci, 65-; vis assoc prof, Dept Earth & Planetary Sci, Calif Inst Technol, 70-71. *Mem:* Am Geophys Union; Soc Explor Geophys; Seismol Soc Am; Can Asn Physicists. *Res:* Gravity; seismology; isotope dating techniques; glaciology. *Mailing Add:* Dept of Physics Univ of Alta Edmonton AB T6G 2E1 Can

KANATZAR, CHARLES LEPLIE, b St Elmo, Ill, Apr 12, 14; m 40; c 2. ZOOLOGY. *Educ:* Eastern Ill State Teachers Col, BEduc, 35; Univ Ill, MS, 36, PhD(protozool), 40. *Prof Exp:* Asst zool, Univ Ill, 35-38; asst prof biol, 46-48, prof & head dept, 48-61, dean fac, 61-67, dean col, 67-74, EMER DEAN, MacMURRAY COL, 74- *Concurrent Pos:* Mem bd adv, Ill State Mus, 62-74, chmn, 70-74. *Mem:* Fel AAAS. *Res:* Free-living protozoa; general zoology; general education in science. *Mailing Add:* 1841 Mound Rd Jacksonville IL 62650

KANCIRUK, PAUL, b New York, NY, Oct 10, 47; m 77. BEHAVIORAL ECOLOGY, MARINE BIOLOGY. *Educ:* City Col New York, BS, 69; Fla State Univ, PhD, 76. *Prof Exp:* Fel marine biol, Nova Ocean Sci Ctr, 76-77; RES ASSOC AQUATIC ECOL, OAK RIDGE NAT LAB, 78- *Mem:* Ecol Soc Am. *Res:* Behavioral ecology of marine organisms; emphasis on migration, orientation and biorhythms; mass migration of spiny lobster. *Mailing Add:* Environ Sci Div Oak Ridge Nat Lab Oak Ridge TN 37830

KANCZAK, NORBERT M, b Buffalo, NY, Feb 12, 31; m 58; c 4. ANATOMY. *Educ:* State Univ NY Buffalo, BA, 58, PhD(anat), 64. *Prof Exp:* Sr instr anat, Sch Med, Tufts Univ, 65-66, asst prof, 66-70; ASSOC PROF ANAT, SCH DENT MED, UNIV PITTSBURGH, 70- *Concurrent Pos:* Nat Inst Arthritis & Metab Dis fel, Ohio State Univ, 63-64, Nat Cancer Inst fel, 64-65. *Res:* Morphology and physiology of transitional epithelium; oncology of transitional cell carcinoma; electron microscopic histochemistry. *Mailing Add:* 121 Shefield Lane McMurray PA 15317

KANDEL, ABRAHAM, b Tel-Aviv, Israel, Oct 6, 41; US citizen; m 66; c 3. COMPUTER SCIENCES. *Educ:* Technion-Israel Inst Technol, BSc, 66; Univ Calif, Santa Barbara, MSc, 68; Univ NMex, PhD(elec eng, comput sci), 77. *Prof Exp:* From instr to assoc prof comput sci, NMex Inst Mining & Technol, 70-78; assoc prof, 78-80, PROF COMPUT SCI, FLA STATE UNIV, 80-, DIR COMPUT SCI, DEPT MATH, 78- *Concurrent Pos:* Vis sr lectr, Ben Gurion Univ Negev & Tel-Aviv Univ, Israel, 76-77; consult, Sandia Labs, Albuquerque, NMex, 76 & TASC Corp, Mass; distinguished vis, Inst Elec & Electronics Engrs-Comput Soc, 81-82. *Mem:* Inst Elec & Electronics Engrs; Asn Comput Mach; Pattern Recognition Soc; Am Soc Eng Educ. *Res:* Fuzzy sets and systems; computer architecture; performance evaluation; pattern recognition; fault-tolerant systems; switching, microprocessors and logic design. *Mailing Add:* Dept Math & Comput Sci Fla State Univ Tallahassee FL 32306

KANDEL, ERIC RICHARD, b Vienna, Austria, Nov 7, 29; nat US; m 56; c 2. NEUROBIOLOGY, PSYCHIATRY. *Educ:* Harvard Univ, AB, 52; NY Univ, MD, 56. *Prof Exp:* Intern, Montefiore Hosp, New York, 56-57; res assoc, Lab Neurophysiol, NIH, 57-60; dir, Mass Ment Health Ctr, 60-65, res psychiat, 60-62, 63-64; from assoc prof physiol & psychiat to prof, Sch Med, NY Univ, 65-74; PROF PHYSIOL & PSYCHIAT & DIR, CTR NEUROBIOL & BEHAV, COL PHYSICIANS & SURGEONS, COLUMBIA UNIV, 74- *Concurrent Pos:* Teaching fel psychiat, Harvard Med Sch, 60-61, Milton res fel, 61-62; USPHS spec fel, Lab Gen Neurophysiol, Col of France, 62-63; res assoc psychiat, Harvard Med Sch, 63-64, instr, 64-65; chief dept neurobiol & behav, Pub Health Res Inst of the City of New York, 68-74; mem, Inst Brain Res Orgn. *Honors & Awards:* Moses Award, 59. *Mem:* Fel Nat Acad Sci (pres 80-81); fel AAAS; Am Physiol Soc; Soc Neuro Sci; Am Acad Arts & Sci. *Res:* Electrophysiology of central neurons; neurosecretion; cellular mechanisms of behavior; neuronal plasticity. *Mailing Add:* Div of Neurobiol & Behav Columbia Univ Col Phys & Surg New York NY 10032

KANDEL, RICHARD JOSHUA, b New York, NY, Apr 30, 24; m 48; c 4. PHYSICAL CHEMISTRY. *Educ:* NY Univ, BS, 46, PhD(chem), 50. *Prof Exp:* Instr gen chem, NY Univ, 49-50; mem staff phys chem, Los Alamos Sci Lab, 50-67; mem staff chem prog br, Div Res, 67-69, chief radiation, Isotope & Phys Chem Br, 69-75, chief chem & atomic physics br, div phys res, US Energy Res & Develop Admin, 75-77; CHIEF FUNDAMENTAL INTERACTIONS BR, DIV CHEM SCI, US DEPT ENERGY, 77- *Mem:* AAAS; Am Chem Soc; Am Phys Soc. *Res:* Mass spectrometry; kinetics; radiation chemistry. *Mailing Add:* Div Chem Sci US Dept of Energy Washington DC 20545

KANDINER, HAROLD J(ACK), b Detroit, Mich, Mar 23, 17; m 41; c 2. CHEMICAL ENGINEERING. *Educ:* Cooper Union, BChE, 38; Univ Mich, MS, 39. *Prof Exp:* Res chemist, Ansbacher Siegle, NY, 39; chemist in charge anal sect, US Treas Dept, Washington, DC, 39-42; chem engr, Navy Dept, 42-43, US Bur Mines, Md, 43-45 & Pa, 45-51; chem engr, Barrett Div, 51-58, dir qual control, 58-66, asst tech dir, 66-67, asst tech dir, Fabricated Prod Div, 67, SR TECH ASSOC CORP RES, ALLIED CHEM CORP, 67- *Concurrent*

Pos: Spec lectr, Univ Pittsburgh, 47-49. *Mem:* Am Chem Soc; Am Inst Chem Engrs; Air Pollution Control Asn. *Res:* Coal hydrogenation and high pressure equipment design; metallurgy of alumina; hydrocarbon phase equilibria; industrial wastes; quality control; coal conversion technology. *Mailing Add:* Allied Chem Corp PO Box 1021R Morristown NJ 07960

KANDOIAN, A(RMIG) G(HEVONT), b Van, Armenia, Nov 28, 11; nat US; m 45; c 3. ENGINEERING. *Educ:* Harvard Univ, BS, 34, MS, 35. *Hon Degrees:* DEng, Newark Col Eng, 67. *Prof Exp:* From jr engr to head dept radio commun equip, Int Tel & Tel Corp, 35-46, head radio commun lab, Fed Telecommun Labs, Inc, 46-58, vpres commun systs, Int Tel & Tel Labs, 58-59, vpres & gen mgr, 60-64, vpres eng, 64-65; vpres & gen mgr, Commun Systs Inc, Comput Sci Corp, 65-66, pres, 66-67, exec staff vpres, 67-68; vpres & dir, Scanwell Labs, Inc, 68-70; consult telecommun, US Dept Commerce, 70, dir off telecommun, 70-73; INDEPENDENT CONSULT, TELECOMMUN ENG, 73- *Concurrent Pos:* Exec secy, Cable Television Tech Adv Comt, Fed Commun Comn; mem, Panel on Telecommun Res in US, Nat Acad Eng. *Honors & Awards:* Award, Inst Elec & Electronics Engrs, 65. *Mem:* Fel Inst Elec & Electronics Engrs. *Res:* Radio aids to air navigation; instrument landing systems; radio antenna systems, particularly in the range; design of radio transmitters and receivers for the very high frequency regions; radio ranges for point to point flight of aircraft; radar components; radio communication systems; satellite communication. *Mailing Add:* 195 Orchard Pl Ridgewood NJ 07450

KANDRUP, HENRY EMIL, b Manhasset, NY, July 24, 55; m 80. GENERAL RELATIVITY, THEORETICAL ASTROPHYSICS. *Educ:* Princeton Univ, AB, 76; Univ Chicago, PhD(physics), 80. *Prof Exp:* Fel physics, Enrico Fermi Inst, Univ Chicago, 80; fel, 80-81, LECTR, DEPT PHYSICS, UNIV CALIF, SANTA BARBARA, 82- *Res:* Applications of non-equilibrium statistical mechanics in theoretical astrophysics and classical general relativity, including relativistic hydrodynamics and kinetics, stellar dynamics, and cosmology; accretion processes; black hole physics; stability analysis. *Mailing Add:* Dept Physics Univ Calif Santa Barbara CA 93106

KANDUTSCH, ANDREW AUGUST, b Kennan, Wis, Oct 10, 26; m 52; c 2. BIOCHEMISTRY. *Educ:* Ripon Col, BA, 50; Univ Wis, MS, 52, PhD(biochem), 54. *Prof Exp:* Res fel biochem, Roscoe B Jackson Mem Lab, 54-55, res assoc, 55-57, staff scientist, 57-64, asst dir res, 65-66, SR STAFF SCIENTIST, JACKSON LAB, 64- *Mem:* Am Chem Soc; Am Soc Biol Chemists. *Res:* Animal sterols and their metabolism; tissue transplantation antigens; sterol biosynthesis and its regulation; membrane structure and function; relationships between sterols, cancer and atherosclerosis. *Mailing Add:* Jackson Lab Bar Harbor ME 04609

KANE, BERNARD JAMES, b New York, NY, Sept 22, 32; m 55; c 6. ORGANIC CHEMISTRY. *Educ:* Iona Col, BS, 54; Adelphi Col, MS, 56. *Prof Exp:* Chemist, 57-62, mgr develop terpene chem, 62-71, DIR RES, GLIDDEN-DURKEE, DIV SCM CORP, 71- *Honors & Awards:* D P Joyce Award, Glidden-Durkee, Div SCM Corp, 70. *Mem:* Am Chem Soc. *Res:* Terpene chemical and organic research and development. *Mailing Add:* 333 Ocean Blvd Atlantic Beach FL 32233

KANE, CONRAD GABRIEL, b Brooklyn, NY, July 17, 09. PHYSICS. *Educ:* Manhattan Col, AB, 32; Cath Univ, PhD(physics), 39; Univ Notre Dame, MA, 52. *Prof Exp:* Teacher elem & high schs, NY, 29-36; teacher physics, De LaSalle Co, 36-39; instr, 39-41, asst prof, 41-43, head dept, 41-60, PROF PHYSICS, MANHATTAN COL, 43- *Concurrent Pos:* Dir, NSF-AEC Inst Nuclear Reactor Theory & Exp, 64-65. *Res:* Cosmic rays using nuclear emulsions. *Mailing Add:* Dept of Physics Manhattan Col Bronx NY 10471

KANE, DANIEL E(DWIN), b Iowa Park, Tex, Aug 12, 23; m 53; c 2. CHEMICAL ENGINEERING. *Educ:* Iowa State Univ, BS, 47; Lawrence Col, MS, 50, PhD(chem eng), 53. *Prof Exp:* Chem engr, Phillips Petrol Co, 47-48; sr chem engr, Fibreboard Paper Prod Corp, 53-59; res assoc res & develop, Nat Vulcanized Fibre Co, 59-66, tech mgr, NVF Co, 66-70; supvr paper/coatings, Bus Equip Div, SCM Corp, 70-73, mgr pilot prod, 73-76; group leader mfg technol, 76-80, MGR PROCESS DEVELOP, CUTTER LABS, 80- *Mem:* Tech Asn Pulp & Paper Indust; Am Chem Soc. *Res:* Kraft chemical recovery; vulcanized fibre; saturating and specialty papers; water and air pollution abatement; reprographics; coatings; hospital supplies; intravenous solutions. *Mailing Add:* Cutter Labs Div S CM Corp Berkeley CA 94302

KANE, E(NEAS) D(ILLON), b San Francisco, Calif, Jan 8, 17; m 44; c 8. ENGINEERING. *Educ:* Univ Calif, BS, 38, PhD(mech eng), 49; Kans State Col, MS, 39. *Prof Exp:* Student & design engr, Westinghouse Mfg Co, Philadelphia, 39-40; mech engr, Radiation Lab, Univ Calif, 42-43; group engr, Clinton Eng Works, Tenn Eastman Corp, Oak Ridge, 43-45; asst prof eng design, Univ Calif, 45-47, lectr, 47-48, assoc prof, 50-51, assoc prof radiation lab, 51-52; supvr process eval, Calif Res & Develop Co, 52-53; res, Calif Res Corp, 54-63, mgr prod res, Chevron Res Co, 63-64, asst secy exec comt, Standard Oil Co Calif, 64-65, vpres prod res, Chevron Res Co, 65-67, pres, 67-70, vpres res, 70-76, VPRES TECHNOL, STANDARD OIL CO CALIF, 77- *Mem:* Am Inst Chem Engrs; Am Inst Mining, Metall & Petrol Engrs; Am Soc Mech Engrs; Nat Acad of Eng. *Res:* Flow of gases at low pressures; process design and evaluation in nuclear energy and petroleum refining; oil field research. *Mailing Add:* Standard Oil Co of Calif 225 Bush St San Francisco CA 94120

KANE, EVAN O, b Kane, Pa, Dec 23, 24; m 50; c 3. SOLID STATE PHYSICS. *Educ:* Princeton Univ, AB, 48; Cornell Univ, PhD(physics), 53. *Prof Exp:* Fel, Corning Glass Works, 53-54; res assoc, Physics Res Lab, Gen Elec Co, NY, 54-59; mem tech staff, Mat Res Lab, Prod Div, Hughes Aircraft Co, 59-61; MEM TECH STAFF, BELL TEL LABS, 61- *Mem:* Fel Am Phys Soc. *Res:* Theoretical solid state physics. *Mailing Add:* Bell Tel Labs PO Box 261 Rm 1d242 Murray Hill NJ 07974

KANE, FRANCIS JOSEPH, JR, b New York, NY, Mar 29, 29; m 55; c 7. PSYCHIATRY. *Educ:* Iona Col, BS, 49; NY Med Col, MD, 53. *Prof Exp:* Intern med, Mercy Hosp, Wilkes Barre, Pa, 53-54; resident path, NY Med Col, 54-55; resident, psychiat, Inst Living, 57-60, staff psychiatrist, 60-61; from instr to prof psychiat, Sch Med, Univ NC, Chapel Hill, 61-71; clin prof, Sch Med, Tulane Univ, 71-74; PROF PSYCHIAT, BAYLOR COL MED, 74-; DEP CHIEF PSYCHIAT, METHODIST HOSP, TEX MED CTR, 74- *Concurrent Pos:* NIH career teacher award, 63-65; med dir, DePaul Hosp, 71-74. *Mem:* AAAS; AMA; Am Psychosom Soc; Am Psychiat Asn; Acad of Psychoanal. *Res:* Relationship between gonadal hormones and behavior in the normal and mentally ill. *Mailing Add:* Methodist Hosp Tex Med Ctr Houston TX 77025

KANE, GEORGE E, b York, Pa, Sept 7, 25; m 47; c 2. INDUSTRIAL ENGINEERING. *Educ:* Pa State Univ, BS, 48; Lehigh Univ, MS, 54. *Prof Exp:* Indust engr, Western Elec Co, 48-50; PROF INDUST ENG, LEHIGH UNIV, 50-, DIR MFG PROCESSES LAB, 65-, CHMN INDUST ENG DEPT, 74- *Concurrent Pos:* Consult, Army Ord Corps, Frankford Arsenal, 55-76. *Mem:* Soc Mfg Engrs; Am Inst Indust Engrs; Am Soc Mech Engrs. *Res:* Metal cutting and machinability of metals. *Mailing Add:* Dept of Indust Eng Lehigh Univ Bethlehem PA 18015

KANE, GORDON LEON, b St Paul, Minn, Jan 19, 37; m 58. HIGH ENERGY PHYSICS. *Educ:* Univ Minn, BA, 58; Univ Ill, MS, 61, PhD(physics), 63. *Prof Exp:* Res assoc physics, Johns Hopkins Univ, 63-65; asst prof, 65-75, PROF PHYSICS, UNIV MICH, ANN ARBOR, 75- *Concurrent Pos:* Guggenheim Mem Found fel, 71-72. *Mem:* Fel Am Phys Soc. *Res:* Theoretical high energy physics. *Mailing Add:* Dept of Physics Univ of Mich Ann Arbor MI 48104

KANE, GORDON PHILO, b New York, NY, Feb 21, 26; m 52; c 3. PESTICIDE FORMULATION. *Educ:* Adelphi Univ, BA, 49; Polytech Inst Brooklyn, MS, 53. *Prof Exp:* Chemist, Warner-Lambert Pharmaceut Corp, NY, 51-54; indust chemist, Barrett Div, Allied Chem Corp, 56; res dir, Valchem Div, United Merchants & Mfrs, SC, 56-62, res scientist, Res Ctr, 62-64; sr org chemist, Columbia Nitrogen Corp, 64-68; sr chemist, 68-73, group leader, 73-78, SR STAFF CHEMIST, CIBA-GEIGY CORP, 78- *Mem:* Am Chem Soc; fel Am Inst Chemists. *Res:* Pesticide formulation and process development. *Mailing Add:* Ciba-Geigy Corp PO Box 11 St Gabriel LA 70776

KANE, HARRISON, b Brooklyn, NY, Jan 2, 25; m 52; c 3. CIVIL ENGINEERING. *Educ:* City Col New York, BCE, 47; Columbia Univ, MS, 48; Univ Ill, PhD(soil mech), 61. *Prof Exp:* Design engr, Parsons, Brinckerhoff Hall & Macdonald, 48-51, 53-56; planning engr, US Dept Army, Ger, 51-53; lectr struct, City Col New York, 56; asst prof civil eng, Pa State Univ, 56-61; asst prof, Univ Ill, 61-64; from assoc prof to prof, 64-77, PROF CIVIL & MAT ENG, UNIV IOWA, 77-, CHMN, DEPT CIVIL ENG, 71- *Concurrent Pos:* NSF res grant, 67-69. *Mem:* Am Soc Civil Engrs; Am Soc Eng Educ. *Res:* Dynamic soil properties; engineering properties of loess; earth pressures on braced excavations. *Mailing Add:* Dept of Civil Eng Univ of Iowa Iowa City IA 52242

KANE, HENRY EDWARD, b New Orleans, La, Dec 18, 17; m 53; c 2. GEOLOGY. *Educ:* La State Univ, BS, 45, MS, 48; Univ Calif, Los Angeles, PhD, 65. *Prof Exp:* Geol scout, Tex Co, 44; field geologist, Miss River Comn, 45; asst, La State Univ, 46-48; subsurface geologist, Stanolind Oil & Gas Co, Standard Oil Co Ind, 48; asst, Univ Calif, Los Angeles, 49-51; geologist, Lloyd Corp Ltd, 52-56; asst prof geol, Lamar State Col Technol, 56-60 & Ft Hays Kans State Col, 60-61; from asst prof to assoc prof, 61-70, PROF GEOL, BALL STATE UNIV, 70- *Concurrent Pos:* Res grants, Shell Res & Develop Co, Shell Oil Co, 56-59, Univ Calif, Los Angeles, 64-65, Ball State Univ, 65-67, 68-69 & 70-71, Ind Acad Sci, 66 & Non-Western Studies, 67; Univ Sci Improv Prog grant, 70-71; Partic, NSF teachers cong, Univ Ore, 59, Am Univ, 61, field geol inst, Ind Univ, 60, res adv undergrad res prog, 59 & NSF geol of Gulf Coast, Rice Univ, 67. *Mem:* Fel Geol Soc Am. *Res:* Recent sedimentation, microfaunas, quaternary geomorphology and geology of the Gulf Coast and the Southern Rockies; fluviatile geomorphology; Kentucky River Basin; geology, Eastern Indiana. *Mailing Add:* Dept of Geog-Geol Ball State Univ Muncie IN 47306

KANE, HOWARD L, b Pittsburgh, Pa, Dec 11, 11; m 32; c 2. ORGANIC CHEMISTRY. *Educ:* Univ Pittsburgh, BS, 32, PhD(org chem), 36. *Prof Exp:* Chief res chemist, Nat Starch Prods, Inc, 36-42, chief chemist, Synthetics Dept, 42-46; vpres & dir res, Polymer Indust, Inc, 46-64; chmn dept sci, 64-67, chmn div basic sci, 67-75, PROF CHEM, EDISON COMMUNITY COL, 75- *Honors & Awards:* Phillips Medal, 32. *Mem:* AAAS; Am Chem Soc. *Res:* Adhesives; modifications of starch; adhesive compositions of matter. *Mailing Add:* Div of Basic Sci Edison Community Col Ft Myers FL 33901

KANE, JAMES FRANCIS, microbiology, biochemistry, see previous edition

KANE, JAMES FRANKLIN, b Benton, Ark, Jan 7, 28; m 48; c 3. INORGANIC CHEMISTRY, CHEMICAL ENGINEERING. *Educ:* Little Rock Univ, BS(chem) & BS(math), 65. *Prof Exp:* Anal supvr, 56-61, test scientist, 61-66, sr scientist, 66-74, SECT HEAD CHEM, REYNOLDS METALS CO, 74- *Mem:* Am Inst Chem Engrs. *Res:* Development of data fundamental to plant design; process optimization; quality control for the alumina industry. *Mailing Add:* Reynolds Metals Co Box 97 Bauxite AR 72011

KANE, JAMES JOSEPH, b New York, NY, Mar 4, 29; m 67. ORGANIC CHEMISTRY. *Educ:* Upsala Col, BS, 54; Ohio State Univ, PhD(org chem), 60. *Prof Exp:* Res chemist, E I du Pont de Nemours & Co, 60-64; asst prof, 64-65, coordr, 65-66, asst prof, 66-70, ASSOC PROF CHEM, WRIGHT STATE UNIV, 70- *Mem:* Am Chem Soc. *Res:* Chemistry of small and medium carbocyclic and heterocyclic systems; polymers with high thermal stability. *Mailing Add:* Dept of Chem Wright State Univ Col Glenn Hwy Dayton OH 45431

KANE, JOHN J, b Montpelier, Vt, Oct 15, 28; m 53; c 6. MECHANICAL ENGINEERING, FLUID MECHANICS. *Educ:* US Naval Acad, BS, 51; Univ Pittsburgh, MS, 59, PhD(mech eng), 61. *Prof Exp:* Sr engr, Bettis Atomic Power Lab, Westinghouse Elec Corp, 55-63; mem tech staff, Aerospace Corp, 63-66; selfemployed, 66-69; HEAD, DEPT MECH ENG, CALIF POLYTECH STATE UNIV, 69-, PROF AEORNAUT & MECH ENG, 80- *Concurrent Pos:* Adj prof, Univ Pittsburgh, 61-63; lectr, Univ Southern Calif, 64- *Mem:* Am Soc Mech Engrs; Am Soc Eng Educ. *Res:* Nuclear reactor design; reentry physics; gas dynamics. *Mailing Add:* Dept of Mech Eng Calif Polytech State Univ San Luis Obispo CA 93407

KANE, JOHN JOSEPH, b Key West, Fla, Jan 13, 15; m 39; c 1. RADIOLOGY. *Educ:* Col Charleston, BS, 35; Med Col SC, MD, 38; Am Bd Radiol, dipl, 57. *Prof Exp:* From instr to assoc prof, 57-66, prof radiol, 66-80, EMER PROF RADIOL, MED UNIV SC, 80-, RADIOLOGIST, MED UNIV HOSP, 57- *Concurrent Pos:* Consult, Mat Air Transport Serv, US AFB, Charleston, 62- *Mem:* Am Col Radiol; Radiol Soc NAm. *Res:* Cardiac radiology. *Mailing Add:* Dept of Radiol Med Univ of SC Charleston SC 29403

KANE, JOHN POWER, b West Point, NY, July 15, 32; m 66; c 3. MEDICINE, BIOCHEMISTRY. *Educ:* Ore State Univ, BS, 55; Univ Ore, MS & MD, 57; Univ Calif, San Francisco, PhD(biochem), 71. *Prof Exp:* Intern med, Santa Clara County Hosp, San Jose, 57-58; asst resident internal med, Hosps, Stanford Univ, 58-59; asst resident, Hosps, 59-60, asst prof, 71-76, ASSOC PROF MED, CARDIOVASC RES INST, UNIV CALIF, SAN FRANCISCO, 76- *Concurrent Pos:* Am Heart Asn estab investr, Cardiovasc Res Inst, Univ Calif, San Francisco, 71-76; mem coun arteriosclerosis, Am Heart Asn. *Mem:* AAAS; Am Chem Soc; Biophys Soc; Am Soc Clin Invest; Am Fedn Clin Res. *Res:* Structure and function of serum lipoproteins; lipid and carbohydrate metabolism. *Mailing Add:* Cardiovasc Res Inst Univ of Calif San Francisco CA 94122

KANE, JOHN ROBERT, b Washington, DC, May 16, 36. NUCLEAR PHYSICS. *Educ:* Loyola Col, Md, BS, 59; Carnegie-Mellon Univ, MS, 62, PhD, 64. *Prof Exp:* Res assoc, 64-68, asst prof, 68-71, ASSOC PROF NUCLEAR PHYSICS, COL WILLIAM & MARY, 71- *Mem:* Am Phys Soc. *Res:* Muonic and hadronic atom x-ray studies; muonium in vacuum measurements. *Mailing Add:* Dept of Physics Col of William & Mary Williamsburg VA 23185

KANE, JULIUS, b Vorozenh, Russia, Jan 23, 35; US citizen; m 57; c 4. ENVIRONMENTAL SYSTEMS & TECHNOLOGY. *Educ:* Brooklyn Col, BA, 54; NY Univ, PhD(math), 60. *Prof Exp:* Radiation physicist, Hosp Joint Dis, 54-55; staff consult elec eng, Dorne & Margolin, Inc, 59-60; assoc prof elec eng, Univ RI, 60-64, prof math, 64-67; res prof, Hancock Found, Univ Southern Calif, 67-68; PROF MATH ECOL, UNIV BC, 68- *Concurrent Pos:* Vis prof, Calif Inst Technol, 64-65; consult, Gorham Electronics, Inc, 61-62; Am Optical Co, 62- & Rand Corp, 65-; res geophysicist, Univ Calif, Los Angeles, 65-68; consult, Stanford Res Inst, 72- & NASA, 75- *Honors & Awards:* Award, Can Coun, 74; Award, Humanities Res Coun, 75. *Mem:* Sr mem Inst Elec & Electronics Eng; Am Math Soc; Am Phys Soc; Soc Indust & Appl Math; Sigma Xi. *Res:* Mathematical problems of geophysics and space sciences; antenna and array; vector and scalar diffraction theory; environmental systems; resource management; long range planning; policy analysis; mathematical models of intervention. *Mailing Add:* Dept of Animal Resource Ecol Univ of BC Vancouver BC V6T 1E1 Can

KANE, MARTIN FRANCIS, b Portland, Maine, Sept 9, 28; m 57; c 5. GEOPHYSICS. *Educ:* St Francis Xavier Univ, BSc, 51; St Louis Univ, PhD, 70. *Prof Exp:* Geophysicist, Regional Geophys Br, 52-63 & Astrogeol Br, 64-67, supvry geophysicist, Regional Geophys Br, 68-70, geologist-in-chg, Marine Geol Br, 70-71, CHIEF REGIONAL GEOPHYS BR, US GEOL SURV, 72- *Mem:* Geol Soc Am; Am Geophys Union; Soc Explor Geophys; Europ Asn Explor Geophys. *Res:* Regional geophysics; marine geophysics; planetary geophysics. *Mailing Add:* US Geol Surv Denver Fed Ctr Denver CO 80225

KANE, PHILIP FRANCIS, b London, Eng, Dec 1, 20; nat US; m 42; c 2. ANALYTICAL CHEMISTRY. *Educ:* Univ London, BSc, 48; FRSC. *Prof Exp:* Technician, Stand Tel & Cables Ltd, Eng, 38-48; res chemist, Laporte Chem Ltd, 48-51, chief analyst, 51-57; supvr anal chem, Chemagro Corp, Mo, 57-59; mgr cent anal chem facil, dir, Mat Characterization Lab, Tex Instruments Inc, 69-80; PROG OFFICER, NSF, 80- *Concurrent Pos:* Assoc ed, J Trace Microprobe Tech. *Mem:* Soc Appl Spectros(treas, 74, pres, 80) ; Royal Soc Chem. *Res:* Characterization of semiconductor materials; surfaces and thin films. *Mailing Add:* Div Chem NSF 1800 G St NW Washington DC 20550

KANE, ROBERT B, b Oak Park, Ill, July 27, 28; m 50; c 5. MATHEMATICS. *Educ:* Univ Ill, BS, 50, MS, 58, PhD(math educ), 60. *Prof Exp:* Teacher pub schs, Ill, 50-51; mgr trainee, Stand Oil Co, 53-55, indust engr, 55-57; res asst bur educ res, Univ Ill, 59-60; from asst prof to assoc prof, 60-69, PROF MATH & EDUC, PURDUE UNIV, 69-, DIR TEACHER EDUC, 75- *Concurrent Pos:* Consult sch dists, 61-; vis res prof, Univ Canterbury, 69. *Mem:* Math Asn Am; Nat Coun Teachers Math; Am Educ Res Asn. *Res:* Linguistic factors in learning and teaching mathematics; cognitive development and mathematics learning. *Mailing Add:* Dept of Educ Purdue Univ West Lafayette IN 47907

KANE, ROBERT EDWARD, b Erie, Pa, Mar 22, 31; m 53, 70. CELL BIOLOGY. *Educ:* Mass Inst Technol, SB, 53; Johns Hopkins Univ, PhD(develop biol), 57. *Prof Exp:* Asst prof biochem, Brandis Univ, 58-61; asst prof cytol, Dartmouth Med Sch, 61-66; assoc prof, 66-69, PROF BIOL, UNIV HAWAII, 69-, ASSOC DIR PAC BIOMED RES CTR, KEWALO LAB, 66- *Mem:* Am Soc Cell Biol; Int Soc Develop Biologists. *Res:* Cell division; cell motility; fine structure of cells; biochemistry of development. *Mailing Add:* Kewalo Lab Pac Biomed Res Ctr Univ of Hawaii Honolulu HI 96822

KANE, RONALD STEVEN, b New York, NY, Feb 11, 44; m 68; c 2. THERMAL FLUID ANALYSIS, ENERGY SYSTEMS. *Educ:* City Col New York, BS, 65, ME, 69; City Univ New York, PhD(eng), 73. *Prof Exp:* Mech engr heat transfer, Pratt & Whitney Aircraft, 65-66; proj engr mech, Esso Res & Eng, 66-70; grad asst fluid mech, City Col New York, 70-73; consult thermal sci, Polytech Design Co, 73-74; asst prof, 74-81, ASSOC PROF MECH ENG, CHMN DEPT & GRAD DIR REACTOR ADMIN, MANHATTAN COL, 81- *Concurrent Pos:* Res asst, City Col New York Res Found, 70-73; consult, Polytech Design Co, Foster Wheeler Energy Corp, 74-; reviewer, McGraw-Hill Publ Co, 76-; consult, Burns & Roe, 80- *Mem:* Am Soc Mech Engrs; Am Inst Chem Engrs; Sigma Xi; Am Soc Eng Educ. *Res:* Drag reduction in particulate suspensions; coal gasification; liquid metal heat transfer and fluid mechanics; ocean thermal energy conversion; heat pipe development; new energy resource development; advanced reactor safety. *Mailing Add:* 98 Algonquin Trail Oakland NJ 07436

KANE, STEPHEN SHIMMON, b Chicago, Ill, Nov 5, 17; m 46; c 2. CHEMISTRY. *Educ:* Univ Chicago, BS, 37, PhD(org chem), 41. *Prof Exp:* Res chemist, Phillips Petrol Co, Okla, 40-42 & Apex Smelting Co, Chicago, 42-44; instr chem, Jersey City Jr Col, 46-48, San Bernardino Valley Col, 48-50 & East Los Angeles Col, 50-59; res chemist, Zolatone Process, Inc, 59-63; instr chem, East Los Angeles Col, 63-68; asst dean instr, West Los Angeles Col, 68-75, dean student serv, 75-80; RETIRED. *Mem:* AAAS; Am Chem Soc; Soc Coating Technol. *Res:* Organic coatings; petroleum; aluminum magnesium metallurgy; organic synthesis. *Mailing Add:* 4333 Redwood Ave #5 Marina Del Rey CA 90291

KANE, THOMAS R(EIF), b Vienna, Austria, Mar 23, 24; nat US; m 51; c 2. MECHANICS, AEROSPACE ENGINEERING. *Educ:* Columbia Univ, BS, 49 & 50, MS, 52, PhD(appl mech), 53. *Prof Exp:* Res assoc, Columbia Univ, 52-53; from asst prof to assoc prof mech eng, Univ Pa, 53-60; PROF ENG MECH, STANFORD UNIV, 61- *Concurrent Pos:* Fulbright lectr, Victoria Univ Manchester, 58-59; vis prof, Fed Univ Rio de Janeiro, 71-72. *Mem:* Am Soc Mech Engrs; Am Astronaut Soc. *Res:* Dynamics; human motion; mechanics of continua. *Mailing Add:* Dept of Mech Eng Stanford Univ Stanford CA 94305

KANE, WALTER REILLY, b Ithaca, NY, Nov 3, 26; m 53; c 1. NUCLEAR PHYSICS. *Educ:* Stanford Univ, BS, 49; Univ Wash, MS, 51; Harvard Univ, PhD(physics), 59. *Prof Exp:* Physicist, Nat Bur Stand, 51-52; mem staff, Los Alamos Sci Lab, 52-54; physicist, Avco Mfg Corp, 56-57; res assoc, 58-60, from asst physicist to assoc physicist, 60-66, PHYSICIST, BROOKHAVEN NAT LAB, 66- *Mem:* Fel Am Phys Soc. *Res:* Nuclear spectroscopy; neutron physics. *Mailing Add:* Dept of Physics Brookhaven Nat Lab Upton NY 11973

KANE, WILLIAM J, b Brooklyn, NY, Feb 22, 33; m 60; c 5. ORTHOPEDIC SURGERY, PHYSIOLOGY. *Educ:* Col of the Holy Cross, AB, 54; Columbia Univ, MD, 58; Univ Minn, Minneapolis, PhD(orthop surg), 65. *Prof Exp:* From instr to assoc prof orthop surg, Univ Minn, Minneapolis, 64-71; Ryerson prof orthop surg & chmn dept, 71-78, PROF ORTHOP SURG, MED SCH, NORTHWESTERN UNIV, 78- *Honors & Awards:* Kappa Delta Award, Am Acad Orthop Surg, 66. *Mem:* Am Orthop Asn; Am Acad Orthop Surg; Scoliosis Res Soc (pres, 79-80); Int Soc Study Lumbar Spine; Am Col Surgeons. *Res:* Bone blood flow; degenerative diseases of the spine; pelvic fractures; scoliosis. *Mailing Add:* Dept Orthop Surg Northwestern Univ Med Sch Chicago IL 60611

KANE, WILLIAM PAUL, b Brooklyn, NY, Apr 29, 24. ORGANIC CHEMISTRY. *Educ:* Fordham Univ, BS, 49, MS, 50, PhD, 55. *Prof Exp:* Res chemist, Columbia Univ, 53-55; res chemist, 55-65, SR CHEMIST, E I DU PONT DE NEMOURS & CO, INC, 65- *Mem:* Am Chem Soc. *Res:* Polymer chemistry, cellophane and Mylar; applied analytical chemistry. *Mailing Add:* 720 Randolph Circle Beaumont TX 77706

KANE, WILLIAM THEODORE, b Jamaica, NY, Sept 8, 32; m 54; c 4. X-RAY DIFFRACTION, SPECTROSCOPY. *Educ:* Univ Kans, BA, 60; Univ Mo, PhD(x-ray crystallog), 66. *Prof Exp:* Crystallographer, 66-67, res crystallographer, 67-73, supvr, X-ray Anal, 73-74, RES SUPVR, CORNING GLASS WORKS, 74- *Concurrent Pos:* Treas, Nat Conf Electron Probe Anal, 69-71. *Mem:* Mineral Soc Am; Am Crystallog Asn; Microbeam Anal Soc. *Res:* Instrumental analysis of materials including electron probe, x-ray diffraction, scanning electron micorscopy, electron transmission microscopy; laboratory automation and computerization. *Mailing Add:* Corning Glass Works Sullivan Park Corning NY 14830

KANEDA, TOSHI, b Utsunomiya-shi, Japan, May 21, 25; m 59; c 2. BIOCHEMISTRY. *Prof Exp:* Tokyo Inst Technol, BEng, 50; Univ Tokyo, DSc(biochem), 62. *Prof Exp:* Fel microbiol, Prairie Regional Lab, Nat Res Coun Can, 56-58; fel biochem, Sch Med, Western Reserve Univ, 58-60; RES MICROBIOLOGIST, ALTA RES COUN, 60-, HEAD BIOL, 81- *Concurrent Pos:* Med Res Coun Can grant, 64-; hon prof med bact, Univ Alta, 75- *Mem:* Am Chem Soc; Can Biochem Soc. *Res:* Microbiology of fossil fuels; low temperature microbiology; biosynthesis and functions of iso and anteiso series of fatty acids in bacteria. *Mailing Add:* Alta Res Coun 11315-87th Ave Edmonton AB T6G 2C2 Can

KANEHIRO, YOSHINORI, b Puuloa, Hawaii, Oct 6, 19; m 47; c 2. SOIL SCIENCE. *Educ:* Univ Hawaii, BS, 42, MS, 48, PhD(soil sci), 64. *Prof Exp:* Asst soils & agr chem, 42-48, jr soil scientist, 48-57, from asst soil scientist & asst prof soil sci to assoc soil scientist & assoc prof soil sci, 57-70, SOIL SCIENTIST & PROF SOIL SCI, UNIV HAWAII, 70- *Concurrent Pos:* Tech consult, Olin Mathieson Chem Corp, 57; res soil scientist, Agr Res Serv, USDA, Ft Collins, Colo, 68-69. *Mem:* Am Soc Agron; Soil Sci Soc Am; Sigma Xi. *Res:* Nitrogen transformation in soils; minor elements, especially zinc in soils; clay mineralogy of soils. *Mailing Add:* Dept of Agron & Soil Sci Univ of Hawaii 3190 Maile Way Honolulu HI 96822

KANEKO, JIRO JERRY, b Stockton, Calif, Nov 20, 24; m 50; c 3. PHYSIOLOGY. *Educ:* Univ Calif, AB, 52, DVM, 56, PhD(comp path), 59. *Hon Degrees:* DVSc, Belgium, 80. *Prof Exp:* Asst specialist, Exp Sta, 56-59, from asst prof to assoc prof, 59-69, PROF CLIN PATH & CHMN DEPT, SCH VET MED, UNIV CALIF, DAVIS, 69- *Concurrent Pos:* Lectr, 57-59. *Mem:* Soc Exp Biol & Med; Am Physiol Soc; Am Asn Clin Chem; Am Vet Med Asn. *Res:* Biochemistry of erythrocyte and hemoglobin of animals; blood dyscrasias of animals; metabolic diseases; kinetics of erythropoiesis and granulopoiesis. *Mailing Add:* Dept Clin Path Univ Calif Sch Vet Med Davis CA 95616

KANEKO, THOMAS MOTOMI, b Tokyo, Japan, Aug 15, 14; US citizen; m 57. ORGANIC CHEMISTRY, POLYMER CHEMISTRY. *Educ:* Univ Utah, BSChE, 36, PhD(metall), 56. *Prof Exp:* Assayer, Nev Mines Div, Kennecott Copper Corp, 36-39; res chemist, Cent Res Labs, Mitsubishi Chem Industs Ltd, Japan, 39-41; res engr, Res & Planning Dept, Mitsubishi Rayon Co, Ltd, 50-52; res metallurgist, Union Carbide Nuclear Div, 56-57; res chemist, Nat Distillers & Chem Corp, 57-59; res metallurgist, 59-65, sr res chemist, 65-78, RES ASSOC, BASF WYANDOTTE CORP, 78- *Concurrent Pos:* Task force chmn, Am Soc Test & Mat, 77- *Mem:* Fel AAAS; Am Chem Soc; fel Am Inst Chem; NY Acad Sci; Weed Sci Soc Am. Res; Extractive metallurgy; reaction kinetics; colloid and surfactant chemistry; surfactant applications research in the formulating and evaluating of detergents, pesticides and metal processing compounds. *Mailing Add:* Corp Res & Develop BASF Wyandotte Corp Wyandotte MI 48192

KANE-MAGUIRE, NOEL ANDREW PATRICK, b Brisbane, Queensland, Australia, May 4, 42; m 69; c 1. INORGANIC CHEMISTRY. *Educ:* Univ Queensland, BSc, 63, Hons, 64, PhD(chem), 69. *Prof Exp:* Assoc inorg chem, Boston Univ, 68-69 & Wayne State Univ, 69-70; assoc, Carleton Univ, 70-73; asst prof, 73-76, ASSOC PROF CHEM, FURMAN UNIV, 77- *Mem:* Am Chem Soc. *Res:* Reaction mechanisms of inorganic compounds; transition metal photochemistry. *Mailing Add:* Dept of Chem Furman Univ Greenville SC 29613

KANEMASU, EDWARD TSUKASA, b Hood River, Ore, Nov 16, 40. AGRICULTURE. *Educ:* Mont State Univ, BS, 62, MS, 64; Univ Wis-Madison, PhD(soil physics), 69. *Prof Exp:* Asst prof, 69-74, assoc prof, 74-78, PROF AGRON, EVAPOTRANSPIRATION LAB, KANS STATE UNIV, 78- *Mem:* AAAS; fel Am Soc Agron; Am Meteorol Soc. *Res:* Stomatal diffusion resistance as influenced by leaf water potential and light; evapotranspiration and water use efficiency of agronomic crops. *Mailing Add:* Evapotranspiration Lab Kans State Univ Manhattan KS 66506

KANES, WILLIAM H, b New York, NY, Oct 15, 34; m 59; c 4. STRATIGRAPHY, SEDIMENTOLOGY. *Educ:* City Col New York, BS, 56; Univ WVa, MS, 58, PhD(geol), 65. *Prof Exp:* Sr res geologist, Exxon Prod Res Co, 60-66, area geologist, Exxon Stan Libya, 67-69; asst prof geol, WVa Univ, 69-70; assoc prof, 71-75, dir, Earth Sci & Resource Inst, 75, PROF GEOL, UNIV SC, 75- *Concurrent Pos:* Vis hon prof fel, Univ Wales, 77- *Mem:* Assoc mem Am Asn Petrol Geol; Soc Econ Paleontologists & Mineralogists; fel Geol Soc Am; fel AAAS; Am Geophys Union. *Res:* Stratigraphy, sedimentation and structural geology in the Appalachian Region; African and circum Mediterranean regional geology and tectonics. *Mailing Add:* Earth Sci & Resources Inst Univ of SC Columbia SC 29208

KANESHIGE, HARRY MASATO, b Aiea, Oahu, Hawaii, July 11, 29; m 63; c 2. CIVIL ENGINEERING. *Educ:* Univ Wis, BS, 51, MS, 52, PhD(civil eng), 59. *Prof Exp:* Instr civil eng, Univ Wis, 54-56, 57-58, proj assoc, 56-57; from asst prof to assoc prof, 58-77, PROF CIVIL ENG, OHIO UNIV, 77- *Mem:* AAAS; Am Soc Eng Educ; Am Soc Civil Engrs; Am Water Works Asn; Water Pollution Control Fedn. *Res:* Environmental health and sanitation; surveying and mapping; water and wastewater treatment. *Mailing Add:* Dept of Civil Eng Ohio Univ Athens OH 45701

KANESHIRO, EDNA SAYOMI, b Hilo, Hawaii, Dec 20, 37. CELL BIOLOGY, BIOCHEMISTRY. *Educ:* Syracuse Univ, BS, 57, MS, 62, PhD(zool), 68. *Prof Exp:* USPHS fel cell biol, Univ Chicago, 68-70; NSF fel biochem, Bryn Mawr Col, 70-72; asst prof, 72-78, ASSOC PROF BIOL, UNIV CINCINNATI, 78- *Concurrent Pos:* Mem corp, Marine Biol Lab, Woods Hole, 73-; sr res microbiologist, Nat Inst Allergy & Infectious Dis, 80-81. *Mem:* Am Soc Cell Biol; Soc Protozoologists; AAAS; NY Acad Sci; Sigma Xi. *Res:* Structure and function of protozoans; membrane Structure, function and biochemistry; osmoregulation in marine organisms. *Mailing Add:* Dept of Biol Sci Univ of Cincinnati Cincinnati OH 45221

KANESHIRO, KENNETH YOSHIMITSU, b Honolulu, Hawaii, Dec 15, 43; m 67; c 2. EVOLUTIONARY BIOL. *Educ:* Univ Hawaii, BA, 65, MS, 68, PhD(entom), 74. *Prof Exp:* RES ASSOC & COORDR EVOLUTIONARY BIOL, HAWAIIAN DROSOPHILA PROJ, DEPT ENTOM, UNIV HAWAII, 70- *Mem:* Entom Soc Am; Soc Study Evolution; Am Soc Naturalists. *Res:* Basic mechanisms of speciation processes in Hawaiian Drosophila; tools and techniques for the formulation of a biosystematic classification of the endemic Hawaiian Drosophilidae; sexual behavior and inferences of directions of evolution. *Mailing Add:* Dept of Entom Univ of Hawaii 3050 Maile Way Honolulu HI 96822

KANESHIRO, TSUNEO, b Maunaloa, Hawaii, Nov 3, 30; m 69; c 4. MICROBIOLOGY. *Educ:* Univ Wis, BS, 52, MS, 56; Univ Calif, Davis, PhD(microbiol), 61. *Prof Exp:* NSF fel chem, Harvard Univ, 61-62, NIH fel, 62-63; NIH fel, Sch Med, Univ Southern Calif, 63-64, res assoc agr residue, 64-65; MICROBIOLOGIST, NORTHERN REGIONAL RES LAB, USDA, 65- *Mem:* Am Soc Microbiol; AAAS; Sigma Xi. *Res:* Symbiotic nitrogen-fixation in microorganisms and non-leguminous plants to reduce the requirement for crop fertilization. *Mailing Add:* Northern Regional Res Lab US Dept of Agr Peoria IL 61604

KANEY, ANTHONY ROLLAND, b Centralia, Ill, Mar 8, 40. GENETICS. *Educ:* Wabash Col, AB, 61; Univ Ill, Urbana, PhD(microbiol), 66. *Prof Exp:* Res assoc microbiol, Univ Ill, Urbana, 66-67; asst prof biol, Univ PR, San Juan, 67-69; asst prof, 69-74, ASSOC PROF BIOL, BRYN MAWR COL, 74- *Mem:* Genetics Soc Am; Soc Protozool. *Res:* Developmental genetics of Tetrahymena pyriformis. *Mailing Add:* Dept of Biol Bryn Mawr Col Bryn Mawr PA 19010

KANFER, JULIAN NORMAN, b Brooklyn, NY, May 23, 30; m 53; c 2. BIOCHEMISTRY. *Educ:* Brooklyn Col, BS, 54; George Washington Univ, MS, 58, PhD(biochem), 61. *Prof Exp:* Lab asst biol, Brooklyn Col, 54-55; chemist, Nat Inst Neurol Dis & Blindness, 55-61, biochemist, 62-69; assoc biochemist, Mass Gen Hosp, Boston, 69-71, biochemist, 71-75; dir biochem, Eunice Kenedy Shriver Ctr, 71-75; PROF BIOCHEM, FAC MED, UNIV MAN, 75- *Dept Head,* 75- *Concurrent Pos:* NIH res fel, Harvard Med Sch, 61-62, NSF res fel, 62-63; assoc prof, Med Sch, Duke Univ, 68-69 & Harvard Med Sch; adj assoc prof Brandeis Univ; mem med adv bd, Nat Tay-Sachs Found. *Mem:* AAAS; Am Chem Soc; Am Soc Biol Chem; Am Soc Neurochem; Int Soc Neurochem. *Res:* Sphingolipid metabolism in relationship to the sphingolipidosis. *Mailing Add:* Dept of Biochem Univ of Man Winnipeg MB R3T 2N2 Can

KANG, CHIA-CHEN CHU, b China, Apr 14, 23; m 51; c 2. FUEL SCIENCE, PETROLEUM SCIENCE. *Educ:* Shanghai Univ, BS, 44; Univ Ill, MS, 49, PhD(anal chem), 51. *Prof Exp:* Res chemist, M W Kellogg Co, 51-52, supvr, 53-57, sect head, 57-67, mgr sci serv, 67-70; consult chemist, 70-74; asst to sr vpres res & develop, Hydrocarbon Res, Inc, 74-78; V PRES, CATALYSIS RES CORP, 78- *Concurrent Pos:* Consult catalysis, United Catalysts, Inc, 71- *Mem:* Am Chem Soc. *Res:* Catalysis; coal liquefaction process development; petroleum and petrochemical process development; trouble shooting for ammonia unit; chemical and instrumental analytical method development. *Mailing Add:* 301 Gallup Rd Princeton NJ 08540

KANG, CHUNGHEE KIM, food science, see previous edition

KANG, DAVID SOOSANG, b Yiryong, Korea, Nov 7, 31; US citizen; m 58; c 4. PEDIATRICS, GENETICS. *Educ:* Seoul Nat Univ, MD, 53, PhD(pharmacol), 63. *Prof Exp:* Asst prof genetics, Ill Inst Technol, 71-75; asst prof, 77-80, ASSOC PROF PEDIAT & GENETICS, COL MED, RUSH UNIV, 80- *Mem:* Am Soc Human Genetics. *Res:* Genetic and biochemical studies of genetic disease and common diseases: interrelations of basic amino acids and their metabolites in urea cycle disorder, and role of protein-bound homocystine in common diseases. *Mailing Add:* 908 Red Fox Lane Oakbrook IL 60521

KANG, IK-JU, b Korea, Nov 13, 28; m 55; c 3. ATOMIC PHYSICS. *Educ:* Yonsei Univ, Korea, BS, 55, MS, 57; Northwestern Univ, PhD(physics), 62. *Prof Exp:* Instr physics, Yonsei Univ, 55-59; res assoc, Brandeis Univ, 62-63; asst prof, Univ Mass, Amherst, 63-67; assoc prof, Carbondale, 67-69, assoc prof, Edwardsville, 69-70, PROF PHYSICS, SOUTHERN ILL UNIV, EDWARDSVILLE, 70-, CHMN, 80- *Mem:* Am Phys Soc; Am Asn Physics Teachers. *Res:* Theoretical atomic physics and scattering theory. *Mailing Add:* Dept of Physics Southern Ill Univ Edwardsville IL 62025

KANG, JUNG WONG, b Tokyo, Japan, July 25, 33; Korean citizen; m 57; c 3. ORGANIC CHEMISTRY. *Educ:* Kinki Univ, Japan, BSc, 56; Osaka Univ, MSc, 59, PhD(org chem), 62. *Prof Exp:* Instr chem, Nara Med Col, Japan, 62-63; fel org chem, Harvard Univ, 63-64; fel organometallic chem, Univ NC, 64-66; res assoc, McMaster Univ, 66-70; res scientist chem, 70-75, sr res scientist, 75-78, ASSOC SCIENTIST, FIRESTONE TIRE & RUBBER CO, 78- *Mem:* Am Chem Soc; Japanese Chem Soc; Korean Chem & Chem Eng NAm. *Res:* Polymer chemistry; organometallic chemistry. *Mailing Add:* Firestone Fire & Rubber Co 1200 Firestone Pkwy Akron OH 44317

KANG, KENNETH S, b Seoul, Korea, Nov 20, 33; US citizen; m 59; c 3. MICROBIAL PHYSIOLOGY. *Educ:* Yonsei Univ, Korea, BS, 57; Univ Del, MS, 63, PhD(microbiol), 65. *Prof Exp:* Sr res chemist, 66-68, proj leader, 68-69, sect head biochem develop, 69-78, MGR BIOCHEM RES, KELCO DIV, MERCK & CO, 78- *Concurrent Pos:* Fel, Pa State Univ, 75-76. *Mem:* AAAS; Am Chem Soc; Sigma Xi; Am Soc Microbiol. *Res:* Development, production and characterization of microbial polysaccharides for industrial applications. *Mailing Add:* 8225 Aero Dr San Diego CA 92123

KANG, KEWON, b Andong, Korea, July 3, 34; US citizen; m 60; c 2. GENETICS. *Educ:* Seoul Univ, Korea, BS, 57, MS, 60; NC State Univ, PhD(genetics), 66. *Prof Exp:* Res assoc forest genetics, Inst Genetics, Korea, 57-60; res asst genetics, NC State Univ, 61-66; fel, 66-69, asst prof, 69-75, ASSOC PROF MED GENETICS, IND UNIV, INDIANAPOLIS, 76- *Concurrent Pos:* Vis assoc prof, Seoul Univ, 77; vis researcher, Univ Hawaii, 77. *Mem:* Am Soc Human Genetics; Am Soc Oil Chemists; Am Soc Genetics; Korea Soc Scientists & Engrs. *Res:* Human quantitative genetics and computer application in medical genetics. *Mailing Add:* Dept Med Genetics Ind Univ Sch Med Indianapolis IN 46223

KANG, KI DONG, b Seoul, Korea, Dec 9, 34; m 59; c 2. ELECTRICAL ENGINEERING. *Educ:* Seoul Nat Univ, BS, 57; Ohio State Univ, MSc, 60, PhD(elec eng), 62. *Prof Exp:* Res assoc, Res Found, Ohio State Univ, 61-63; sect mgr res & develop, Motorola Semiconductor Div, 63-69; tech dir, Stewart-Warner Microcircuits, 69-80; PRES, K&K ELECTRONICS, INC, 80- *Mem:* Inst Elec & Electronics Engrs. *Res:* Semiconductor devices and integrated circuits. *Mailing Add:* K&K Electronics Inc 783 E Evelyn Ave Sunnyvale CA 94086

KANG, KYUNGSIK, b Jochiwon, Korea, July 12, 38; m 63; c 2. THEORETICAL PHYSICS. *Educ:* Seoul Nat Univ, BS, 59; Ind Univ, PhD(theoret physics), 64. *Prof Exp:* Res assoc, 64-66, from asst prof to assoc prof, 66-73, PROF PHYSICS, BROWN UNIV, 73- *Concurrent Pos:* Vis prof, Univ Paris, 72-73; vis scientist, Europ Orgn Nuclear Res, 73; vis physicist,

Fermi Nat Accelerator Lab, 74. *Mem:* Korean Phys Soc; Korean Scientists & Engrs Am (vpres, 76-77); Am Phys Soc. *Res:* Phenomenological descriptions of high energy elementary particle physics; S-matric theory; algebra of currents; multiparticle dynamics; weak interaction theory; lepton-induced reactions; gauge models. *Mailing Add:* Dept of Physics Brown Univ Providence RI 02912

KANG, PILWON, b Seoul, Korea, Feb 5, 33; US citizen; m 63; c 4. PHYSICS. *Educ:* Seoul Nat Univ, BS, 55; Vanderbilt Univ, MS, 62; Am Univ, PhD(physics), 76. *Prof Exp:* Asst prof physics & phys sci, Clarion State Col, 62-63; instr physics, Hamilton Col, 63-66; asst prof, 66-78, ASSOC PROF PHYSICS & MATH, HOOD COL, 78- *Mem:* Am Asn Physics Teachers; Am Asn Univ Prof; Korean Scientists & Engrs Asn Am. *Res:* Optics; critical point phenomena in fluid; theoretical molecular physics; elementary particle theory. *Mailing Add:* Dept of Physics Hood Col Frederick MD 21701

KANG, SUNGZONG, b Puyo, Korea, Mar 1, 37; m 65. BIOPHYSICS, BIOCHEMISTRY. *Educ:* Univ Tubingen, PhD(chem), 64. *Prof Exp:* Res assoc chem, Chem Inst, Univ Tubingen, 64-66, Univ Notre Dame, 66-67 & NY Univ, 67-68; from instr to asst prof, 68-72, ASSOC PROF, MT SINAI SCH MED, CITY UNIV NEW YORK, 72- & BRONX VET ADMIN MED CTR, 80- *Concurrent Pos:* Vis prof, Max Plank Inst Biophys Chem, Gottingen, 76-77, Max Plank Inst physiol, Dortmund, 77-78, Seoul Nat Univ, 78-79 & AID, 78-79; Fogarty sr int scholar, 76-77; Alexander von Humboldt US sr scientist fel, 77-78. *Mem:* AAAS; Am Chem Soc; NY Acad Sci; Am Soc Pharmacol & Exp Therapeut. *Res:* Stability, structure and function of biological macromolecules, membranes, proteins and nucleic acids; brain research; molecular pharmacology; quantum biochemistry. *Mailing Add:* Mt Sinai Sch Med City Univ NY Bronx Vet Admin Med Ctr New York NY 10029

KANG, T L, b Shanghai, China, Dec 12, 23; m 53; c 3. CHEMICAL ENGINEERING. *Educ:* Chekiang Univ, BS, 47; Univ Tex, MS, 58, PhD(chem eng), 60. *Prof Exp:* Res engr, B F Goodrich Res Ctr, 60-63, sr res engr, 63-65, res assoc, 65-67, sr res assoc, 67-70, sr develop scientist, Avon Lake Develop Ctr, 70-76; PROCESS SPECIALIST, MONSANTO CO, 76- *Mem:* Inst Chem Engrs. *Res:* Thermodynamics; chemical process research fluidization and applied kinetics; petroleum refinery engineering. *Mailing Add:* 18623 Prince William Lane Nassau Bay TX 77058

KANG, UAN GEN, b Chanpuk, Korea, March 2, 38; US citizen; m 68; c 2. POLYMER CHEMISTRY. *Educ:* Chanpuk Nat Univ, BS, 60; Mich State Univ, MS, 69, PhD(org chem), 72; Johns Hopkins Univ, MAS, 82. *Prof Exp:* Vis res assoc biochem, Ohio State Univ, 73-75 & org chem, 75-77; res chem, 77-81, SR RES CHEMIST POLYMER, W R GRACE WASHINGTON RES CTR, 81- *Mem:* Am Chem Soc. *Res:* Organic reaction mechanism; mechanism of enzyme action; carbine chemistry; polymer chemistry. *Mailing Add:* W R Grace Washington Res Ctr 7379 Rt 32 Columbia MD 21044

KANGAS, DONALD ARNE, b Detroit, Mich, Feb 12, 29; m 54; c 5. CHEMISTRY. *Educ:* Mich Technol Univ, BS, 50; Mich State Univ, MS, 58. *Prof Exp:* Anal chemist, R P Scherer Corp, 50-51; develop chemist, US Army-Chem Corp, 51-53; sr res specialist, 53-80, RES ASSOC POLYMER, DOW CHEM USA, 80- *Mem:* Am Chem Soc. *Res:* Hydrophobic colloids formed from vinyl monomers; kinetics of polymerization; characterization of dispersion; morphology of particles; properties of films and composites; hydrophillic polyelectrolytes from ionizable vinyl monomers; kinetics characterization and properties. *Mailing Add:* Design Latexes & Resins Res Lab 1604 Bldg Dow Chem USA Midland MI 48640

KANICK, VIRGINIA, b Coaldale, Pa, Nov 10, 25. RADIOLOGY. *Educ:* Barnard Col, AB, 47, Columbia Univ, MD, 51; Am Bd Radiol, dipl, 55. *Prof Exp:* Attend physician, 55-63, DEP DIR, DEPT RADIOL, ST LUKE'S HOSP, NEW YORK, 64-; PROF CLIN RADIOL, COLUMBIA UNIV, 75- *Concurrent Pos:* assoc prof, Columbia Univ, 74-75. *Mem:* Fel Am Col Radiol; Radiol Soc NAm; Am Roentgen Soc. *Res:* Clinical research in angiology; use of contrast media in radiology. *Mailing Add:* 560 Riverside Dr New York NY 10027

KANIECKI, THADDEUS JOHN, b Brooklyn, NY, Mar 24, 31; m 55; c 3. ORGANIC CHEMISTRY. *Educ:* NY Univ, BA, 53, MS, 55, PhD(org chem), 60. *Prof Exp:* Res assoc, Res & Develop Div, Lever Bros Co, NJ, 60-67; res supvr, Armour-Dial Inc, Chicago, 67-69, res mgr, 69-72; sect mgr, Am Cyanamid Co, 72-75; sr chemist res & develop, Stauffer Chem Co, 75-81; SR TECH SERV REP, BRENT CHEM CORP, 81- *Mem:* Am Chem Soc; Soc Cosmetic Chem. *Res:* Synthesis and applications of surface active molecules; detergents, toiletries and consumer products, both basic and applied research; preparation and uses of disinfectants, sanitizers and biocides. *Mailing Add:* 2 Van Alen Pl Pompton Plains NJ 07444

KANIG, JOSEPH LOUIS, pharmaceutics, see previous edition

KANIPE, LARRY GENE, b Charlotte, NC, Nov 9, 43. PHYSICAL CHEMISTRY, RADIOCHEMISTRY. *Educ:* Belmont Abbey Col, BS, 66; Univ Ala, PhD(chem), 74. *Prof Exp:* anal chemist, 74-79, SUPVR, WESTERN AREA RADIOL LAB, TENN VALLEY AUTHORITY, 79- *Mem:* Am Soc Qual Control; Am Chem Soc. *Res:* Analytical methodology, including chemical and spectroscopic techniques for radioactive isotopes; special applications of gamma spectroscopy and liquid scintillation; industrial hygiene chemistry. *Mailing Add:* River Oaks Bldg Tenn Valley Authority Muscle Shoals AL 35660

KANIZAY, STEPHEN PETER, b Cleveland, Ohio, Feb 3, 24; m 48; c 3. GEOLOGY. *Educ:* Miami Univ Ohio, AB, 49, MS, 50; Colo Sch Mines, DSc, 56. *Prof Exp:* From instr to asst prof geol, Colo Sch Mines, 52-58; GEOLOGIST, ENG GEOL BR, US GEOL SURV, 58- *Concurrent Pos:* Consult, 54-58. *Mem:* Am Geophys Union; Asn Eng Geol. *Res:* Engineering and structural geology; rock and soil mechanics. *Mailing Add:* 625 S Parfet Lakewood CO 80226

KANKEL, DOUGLAS RAY, b Waterbury, Conn, Jan 22, 44. DEVELOPMENTAL BIOLOGY, NEUROBIOLOGY. *Educ:* Brown Univ, PhD(biol), 70. Res fel neurobiol, Calif Inst Technol, 70-74; MEM FAC BIOL DEPT, YALE UNIV, 74- *Mailing Add:* 41 Vista Rd North Haven CT 06473

KANNAPPAN, PALANIAPPAN, b Nattarasan Kottai, India, June 28, 34; m 52; c 5. MATHEMATICS. *Educ:* Annamalai Univ, Madras, BSc(Hons), 55, MA, 57; Univ Wash, Seattle, MS & PhD(math), 64. *Prof Exp:* Lectr math, Annamalai Univ, Madras, 55-61, reader, 64-67; asst, Univ Wash, 61-64; assoc prof, 67-77, PROF MATH, UNIV WATERLOO, 77- *Concurrent Pos:* Consult, Dept Univ Affairs, Can, 68-69 & Nat Res Coun Can, 69- *Mem:* Am Math Soc; Indian Math Soc. *Res:* Functional analysis and functional equations; linear algebra and quasigroups; information theory. *Mailing Add:* Dept of Pure Math Univ of Waterloo Waterloo ON N2L 3G1 Can

KANNE, WILLIAM R(UDOLPH), JR, b Chicago, Ill, Dec 12, 40; m 79; c 3. METALLURGY, WELDING. *Educ:* Johns Hopkins Univ, BA, 62; Univ Wis, PhD(metall eng), 68. *Prof Exp:* STAFF METALLURGIST, SAVANNAH RIVER PLANT, E I DU PONT DE NEMOURS & CO, INC, 67- *Mem:* Am Soc Metals; Am Welding Soc. *Res:* Physical metallurgy, especially creep of intermetallic compounds, dislocation structures during creep, corrosion of materials by liquid tellurium and refractory metal technology; metal bonding and welding. *Mailing Add:* Savannah River Plant Aiken SC 29801

KANNEL, WILLIAM B, b Brooklyn, NY, Dec 13, 23; m 42; c 4. CARDIOVASCULAR DISEASES, INTERNAL MEDICINE. *Educ:* Ga Med Col, MD, 49; Harvard Univ, MPH, 59. *Prof Exp:* Intern & resident, USPHS Hosp, Staten Island, NY, 49-50, 53-56; clin investr heart dis epidemiol study, NIH, Framingham, Mass, 50-51; med officer, Newton Heart Prog, Mass, 51-52; assoc dir, Framingham Unit, NIH, 56-65, dir, 65-79. *Concurrent Pos:* Fel, Harvard Med Sch, 56-59; asst med, Peter Bent Brigham Hosp, 56-62; instr, Harvard Med Sch, 59-60, assoc prev med, 60-70, lectr, 70-; consult, Cushing State Hosp, 56-73 & Framingham Union Hosp, 64- *Mem:* AMA; fel Am Heart Asn; fel Am Col Physicians; fel Am Col Cardiol; fel Am Col Epidemiol. *Res:* Cardiovascular epidemiology; investigation of factors of risk and natural history of coronary heart disease, hypertension, stroke and peripheral vascular disease; preventive medicine. *Mailing Add:* Boston Univ Med Ctr 121 Bay St Boston MA 02215

KANNENBERG, LLOYD C, b Sarasota, Fla, Mar 23, 39; m 63. PHYSICS. *Educ:* Mass Inst Technol, SB, 61; Univ Fla, MS, 63; Northeastern Univ, PhD(physics), 67. *Prof Exp:* Instr physics, Lowell Technol Inst, 66-67 & Northeastern Univ, 67-68; from instr to asst prof, Lowell Technol Inst, 68-72, assoc prof physics, Lowell Technol Inst, 72-77, PROF PHYSICS, UNIV LOWELL, 77- *Concurrent Pos:* Vis res assoc, Northeastern Univ, 72- *Mem:* Am Phys Soc; NY Acad Sci; Int Soc Gen Relativity & Gravitation. *Res:* General relativity, field theory. *Mailing Add:* Dept of Physics Univ of Lowell Lowell MA 01854

KANNENBERG, LYNDON WILLIAM, b Chicago, Ill, Oct 15, 31; m 54; c 5. PLANT BREEDING. *Educ:* Mich State Univ, BSc, 57, MS, 59; Univ Calif, Davis, PhD(genetics), 64. *Prof Exp:* NIH fel, Univ Calif, Davis, 64-65; asst prof, 65-69, assoc prof, 69-77, PROF CORN BREEDING, UNIV GUELPH, 77- *Concurrent Pos:* Appointment, Nat Res Coun Can Grants Comt, 71-73. *Mem:* Am Soc Agron; Genetics Soc Can; Sigma Xi; Can Soc Agron. *Res:* Development of short season corn breeding populations. *Mailing Add:* Dept of Crop Sci Univ of Guelph Guelph ON N1G 2W1 Can

KANNEWURF, CARL RAESIDE, b Waukegan, Ill, Mar 24, 31. SOLID STATE ELECTRONICS. *Educ:* Lake Forest Col, BA, 53; Univ Ill, MS, 54; Northwestern Univ, PhD(physics), 60. *Prof Exp:* Res assoc physics, 60-62, from asst prof to assoc prof elec eng, 63-71, PROF ELEC ENG, NORTHWESTERN UNIV, EVANSTON, 71- *Mem:* Am Phys Soc; Sigma Xi; sr mem Inst Elec & Electronics Engrs. *Res:* Study of various electrical and optical phenomena in semiconductors, semimetals and metal alloys; transport phenomena and superconductivity; development of optical materials and devices. *Mailing Add:* Dept of Elec Eng Tech Inst Northwestern Univ Evanston IL 60201

KANNEY, LYNNA BABS, see Spornick, Lynna

KANNOWSKI, PAUL BRUNO, b Grand Forks, NDak, Aug 11, 27; m 53; c 2. ZOOLOGY. *Educ:* Univ NDak, BS, 49, MS, 52; Univ Mich, PhD(zool), 57. *Prof Exp:* Asst biol, Univ NDak, 50-52; instr, Bowling Green State Col, 56-57; from asst prof to assoc prof, 57-69, dir, Inst Ecol Studies, 65-81, PROF BIOL, UNIV NDAK, 69- *Concurrent Pos:* Res assoc, Harvard Univ, 66-67; NSF sr fel, 66-67; vis scientist, Smithsonian Trop Res Inst, 67, 68; entom consult, Lystads Pest Control, Inc, 68-75; ed, Prairie Naturalist, 68-; natural resources consult, US Congressman Mark Andrews, NDak, 69-70. *Mem:* Am Inst Biol Sci; Am Soc Zoologists; AAAS; Entom Soc Am; Ecol Soc Am. *Res:* Ecology; biogeography; animal behavior; myrmecology; chemical communication. *Mailing Add:* Dept Biol Univ of NDak Grand Forks ND 58202

KANO, ADELINE KYOKO, b Mitchell, Nebr, Nov 22, 27. CHEMISTRY, ACADEMIC ADMINISTRATION. *Educ:* Univ Nebr, BA, 48. *Prof Exp:* Instr chem & jr chemist, 55-60, asst chemist, 60-66, asst prof, 60-73, ADMIN ASST & FAC AFFIL, COLO STATE UNIV, 73- *Mem:* Am Chem Soc; Sigma Xi. *Res:* Factors imposed on chicks and rats, their alleviation and relation to blood and tissue content of amino acids. *Mailing Add:* Dept of Biochem Colo State Univ Ft Collins CO 80523

KANOFSKY, ALVIN SHELDON, b Philadelphia, Pa, July 5, 39; m 64; c 2. ELEMENTARY PARTICLE PHYSICS. *Educ:* Univ Pa, BA, 61, MS, 62, PhD(physics), 66. *Prof Exp:* From asst prof to assoc prof, 67-76, PROF PHYSICS, LEHIGH UNIV, 76- *Concurrent Pos:* Res collabr, Brookhaven Nat Lab. *Mem:* Am Phys Soc; Sigma Xi. *Res:* Research in eta decay; proton-proton scattering; mu magnetic moment, Glauber calculations in particles, high energy particle channeling in crystals, particle-nuclei interactions, hypernuclei, jet production, cosmic rays and instrumentation; accelerator research. *Mailing Add:* Dept of Physics Lehigh Univ Bethlehem PA 18015

KANOJIA, RAMESH MAGANLAL, b Mangrol, India, Feb 15, 33; m 67. MEDICINAL CHEMISTRY. *Educ:* Bombay Univ, BSc, 54, BScTech, 56, MScTech, 61; Univ Wis, PhD(pharmaceut chem), 66. *Prof Exp:* Instr pharmaceut chem, Bombay Univ, 58-59, hon lectr tech pharmaceut & fine chem, 59-60; res asst pharmaceut chem, Sch Pharm, Univ Wis, 61-66; assoc scientist, 66-70, scientist, 70-76, sr scientist, 77-79, RES FEL, ORTHO PHARMACEUT CORP, 80- *Honors & Awards:* Philip B Hoffman Award, Johnson & Johnson Co, 77. *Mem:* Am Chem Soc. *Res:* Isolation, characterization and synthesis of natural and synthetic organic medicinal compounds; antifertility compounds of natural and synthetic origin; synthesis of cardiovascular-active drugs. *Mailing Add:* 18 Jeffrey Court Somerville NJ 08876

KANT, FRED H(UGO), b Vienna, Austria, Jan 11, 30; nat US; m 52; c 2. CHEMICAL ENGINEERING. *Educ:* Columbia Univ, BS, 51, MS, 53, DEngSc, 57. *Prof Exp:* Sr staff adv, New Areas Staff, Esso Res & Eng Co, 54-66, dir new invests res lab, Linden, 66-69, proj mgr, Corp Res Staff, 69-72, sr staff adv, 72-75, planning mgr, Govt Res, 75-78, LAB DIR, GOVT RES, EXXON RES & ENG CO, 78- *Mem:* Am Chem Soc. *Res:* Fuels process; staff research coordination, planning and project evaluation in new areas; research administration. *Mailing Add:* 31 Rutgers Rd Cranford NJ 07016

KANT, KENNETH JAMES, b Elyria, Ohio, July 14, 35; m 58; c 4. PHYSIOLOGY, VETERINARY MEDICINE. *Educ:* Ohio State Univ, BS, 58; Univ Ill, Urbana, MS, 64, PhD(physiol), 67. *Prof Exp:* From instr to asst prof physiol, State Univ NY Buffalo, 67-74; ASSOC PROF PHYSIOL, UNIV TENN, KNOXVILLE, 74- *Mem:* Am Vet Med Asn; Am Physiol Soc; Soc Neurosci. *Res:* Neurophysiology and behavior, especially limbic structures. *Mailing Add:* Univ of Tenn Col of Nursing 1200 Volunteer Blvd Knoxville TN 37916

KANTACK, BENJAMIN H, b Greenleaf, Kans, Sept 26, 27; m 53; c 7. ENTOMOLOGY, AGRONOMY. *Educ:* Kans State Univ, BS, 51; Okla State Univ, MS, 54; Univ Nebr, PhD(entom), 63. *Prof Exp:* Trainee agron, Libby, McNiel & Libby, Hawaii, 51-52; asst entom, Okla State Univ, 52-54; instr & entomologist, Univ RI, 54-55; entomologist, USDA, Ga, 55-58; instr entom, Univ Nebr, 58-62; from asst prof to assoc prof, 62-64, PROF ENTOM, S DAK STATE UNIV, 64-, EXTEN ENTOMOLOGIST, 63- *Mem:* Entom Soc Am. *Res:* Stored grain, vegetable and field crop insects; livestock ecto parasites. *Mailing Add:* Dept of Entomol S Dak State Univ Brookings SD 57006

KANTAK, KATHLEEN MARY, b Syracuse, NY, Nov 11, 51; m 75. PSYCHOBIOLOGY. *Educ:* State Univ NY Potsdam, BA, 73; Syracuse Univ, PhD (biopsychol), 77. *Prof Exp:* Res asst prof biopsychol, Syracuse Univ, 78; res assoc behav neurochem, Univ Wis-Madison, 78-81; RES ASSOC PSYCHOL, TUFTS UNIV, 81- *Mem:* Soc Neurosci; Sigma Xi; Int Soc Res Aggression. *Res:* Neurochemical correlates of ingestive behavior, body weight regulation, and aggression in terms of how these measures are affected by age and nutritional factors. *Mailing Add:* Dept Psychol Tufts Univ Medford MA 02155

KANTER, GERALD SIDNEY, b New York, NY, Dec 7, 25; m 56; c 2. PHYSIOLOGY. *Educ:* Long Island Univ, BS, 47; Univ Rochester, PhD(physiol), 52. *Prof Exp:* Jr instr physiol, Sch Med, Univ Rochester, 52; from instr to assoc prof physiol, 52-63, lectr biochem, 53-55, asst to dean, 66-67, asst dean, 67-69, PROF PHYSIOL, ALBANY MED COL, 63-, ASSOC DEAN, 69- *Concurrent Pos:* Chief physiol br, US Army Inst Environ Med, 63-64. *Mem:* AAAS; Am Physiol Soc. *Res:* Body fluid and electrolyte regulation; kidney function; thirst; temperature regulation and environmental physiology. *Mailing Add:* Albany Med Col Albany NY 12208

KANTER, HELMUT, b Hamburg, Ger, Jan 19, 28; US citizen. ELECTRON PHYSICS. *Educ:* Univ Marburg, MS, 53, PhD(physics), 56. *Prof Exp:* Res physicist, Res Labs, Westinghouse Elec Corp, 57-64; mem tech staff, Lab Div, 64-74, MEM STAFF, ELECTRONIC RES LAB, AEROSPACE CORP, 74- *Mem:* Am Phys Soc; Ger Phys Soc. *Res:* Electron scattering; photo and secondary electron emission; electron transport; photoconductivity; imaging tubes. *Mailing Add:* Electronic Res Lab Aerospace Corp PO Box 92957 Los Angeles CA 90009

KANTER, IRA E, b Chicago, Ill, Oct, 31, 31; m 68; c 2. ENGINEERING PHYSICS. *Educ:* Ill Inst Technol, BS, 53, MS, 54. *Prof Exp:* Asst chem engr, US Army Chem Corps, 54-56; engr high temp, Flight Propulsion Lab, Gen Elec, 57-59; res staff high temp chem, Univ Wis, 60-61; sr engr nuclear reactors, Astronuclear Labs, 63-69, sr engr chem eng, 69-77, SR ENGR CHEM PHYSICS, RES & DEVELOP LABS, WESTINGHOUSE, 77- *Mem:* Am Nuclear Soc; Inst Elec & Electron Engrs. *Res:* Radio-chemical reactions for synthesis; chemical thermodynamics; inertially and magnetically confined fusion reactor blanket systems; radio-gas waste treatment and storage; glow discharge chemistry; physical chemistry. *Mailing Add:* Westinghouse Res & Develop Labs Beulah Rd Pittsburgh PA 15235

KANTER, LOUIS HAROLD, b Brooklyn, NY, Mar 17, 09. MATHEMATICS. *Educ:* Univ Mo, AB, 35; Wash Univ, MS, 38; Stanford Univ, PhD(math), 47. *Prof Exp:* Asst instr math, Wash Univ, 38-39 & Stanford Univ, 39-40; instr, Univ Wis, 43-48; asst prof, Univ Ark, 48-49; assoc prof, Miss State Col, 50-55; Clarkson Col Technol, 55-56, Drexel Inst, 56-58 & Montclair State Col, 58-60; assoc prof math, Queens Col, NY, 60-79; RETIRED. *Mem:* Math Asn Am. *Res:* Orthogonal polynomials. *Mailing Add:* Flushing NY 11367

KANTER, MANUEL ALLEN, b Boston, Mass, Jan 18, 24; div; c 4. PHYSICAL CHEMISTRY. *Educ:* Northeastern Univ, BS, 44; Ill Inst Technol, MS, 49, PhD, 55. *Prof Exp:* Assoc chemist, Argonne Nat Lab, 46-68, training coordr, Argonne Ctr Educ Affairs, 69-75, DIR INT ATOMIC ENERGY AGENCY NUCLEAR POWER TRAINING, ARGONNE DIV EDUC PROGRAMS, 75- *Mem:* AAAS; Am Nuclear Soc; Inst Nuclear Mat Mgt; Am Phys Soc; Sigma Xi. *Res:* High temperature chemistry; galvanomagnetic effects; actinide compounds; diffusion; nuclear material safeguards. *Mailing Add:* 16121 Lakeview Ave Union Pier MI 49127

KANTHA, LAKSHMI H, b Bangalore, India; m 74. OCEANIC CIRCULATION. *Educ:* Bangalore Univ, BE, 67; Indian Inst Sci, ME, 69; Mass Inst Technol, PhD(aerospace & astron), 73. *Prof Exp:* Fel, Johns Hopkins Univ, 74-75; assoc res scientist, 75-79, res scientist, 79-80; RES SCIENTIST, DYNALYSIS PRINCETON, 80- *Res:* Turbulence and wave motions in the atmosphere and the oceans; ocean circulation in the coastal regions; oceanic mixing and influence of the ice cover on polar oceans; numerical and experimental modeling of oceanic and atmospheric processes. *Mailing Add:* Dynalysis Princeton Princeton NJ 08540

KANTOR, FRED STUART, b New York, NY, July 2, 31; m 58; c 3. IMMUNOLOGY. *Educ:* Union Col NY, BS, 52; NY Univ, MD, 56; Am Bd Internal Med, dipl, 64; Am Bd Allergy, dipl, 66. *Prof Exp:* Intern, Ward Med Serv, Barnes Hosp, St Louis, Mo, 56-57; res assoc, Nat Inst Allergy & Infectious Dis, 57-59; asst res med, Grace New Haven Hosp, Sch Med, Yale Univ, 59-60; from instr to assoc prof, 62-73, PROF MED, SCH MED, YALE UNIV, 73- *Concurrent Pos:* Whitney fel, Sch Med, Yale Univ, 60-61 & NY Univ, 61-62; USPHS career develop awardee, 62-; vis scientist with Dr Gustave Nossal, Walter & Eliza Hall Inst, Melbourne, Australia, 68-69; mem coun, Am Heart Asn. *Mem:* Asn Am Physicians; Am Soc Clin Invest; Am Acad Allergy; Am Asn Immunol. *Res:* Immune response in man, including both delayed and immediate types of immunity. *Mailing Add:* Dept of Med Yale Univ Sch of Med New Haven CT 06510

KANTOR, GEORGE JOSEPH, b Titusville, Pa, Jan 24, 37; m 66; c 3. BIOPHYSICS, MOLECULAR BIOLOGY. *Educ:* Slippery Rock State Col, BS, 58; NMex Highlands Univ, MS, 62; Pa State Univ, PhD(biophys), 67. *Prof Exp:* NIH fel biophys, Pa State Univ, 67-68; fel, Biomed Res Group, Los Alamos Sci Lab, 68-70; from asst prof to assoc prof, 70-80, PROF BIOL SCI, WRIGHT STATE UNIV, 80- *Mem:* Biophys Soc; AAAS; Sigma Xi; Tissue Culture Asn; Am Soc Photobiol. *Res:* Effects of radiation on biological systems with emphasis on human cells cultured in vitro. *Mailing Add:* Dept of Biol Sci Wright State Univ Dayton OH 45431

KANTOR, HARVEY SHERWIN, b New York, NY, Apr 30, 38. INFECTIOUS DISEASES, MICROBIOLOGY. *Educ:* Washington Univ, MD, 62; Am Bd Internal Med, dipl, 68. *Prof Exp:* Asst med, Sch Med, Washington Univ, 62-63; res fel, New Eng Med Ctr Hosp, Tufts Univ, 66-69, asst, Sch Med, 66-69; res educ assoc, Vet Admin, 70-71; asst prof med & microbiol, Univ Ill Med Ctr, 71-75; ASSOC PROF MED & DIR DIV INFECTIOUS DIS, CHICAGO MED SCH, 75-; CHIEF INFECTIOUS DIS SECT, VET ADMIN HOSP, NORTH CHICAGO, 75-; ASSOC PROF PATH, CHICAGO MED SCH, 78- *Concurrent Pos:* Actg dir div infectious dis, Cook County Hosp, 72-74; consult, Highland Park Hosp, Highland Park & US Naval Hosp, Great Lakes, Ill, 75- *Mem:* Fel Am Col Physicians; Sigma Xi; fel Royal Soc Med; Am Soc Microbiol; NY Acad Sci. *Res:* Bacterial toxins and their mechanism of action; their influence on cyclic nucleotides and prostaglandin interactions. *Mailing Add:* Univ Health Sci Chicago Med Sch Dept of Med North Chicago IL 60064

KANTOR, PAUL B, b Washington, DC, Nov 27, 38; m 62; c 2. ECONOMICS OF INFORMATION. *Educ:* Columbia Univ, AB, 59; Princeton Univ, PhD(physics), 63. *Prof Exp:* Res assoc physics, Brookhaven Nat Lab, 63-65; vis asst prof, State Univ NY Stony Brook, 65-67; asst prof, Case Western Reserve Univ, 67-69, assoc prof physics, 69-74, assoc prof oper res, Libr & Info Sci, 74-77, prog dir, Complex Systs Inst, 73-74, sr res assoc, systs eng, 77-81; PRES, TANTALUS INC, 77- *Concurrent Pos:* Guest physicist, Brookhaven Nat Lab, 65-; adj assoc prof libr & info sci, Kent State Univ, 78- *Mem:* Am Phys Soc; Am Statist Asn; Am Soc Info Sci; NY Acad Sci; Am Libr Asn. *Res:* Nucleon-nucleon interactions; higher symmetry schemes; weak interactions of elementary particles; stability of complex systems; economics of information. *Mailing Add:* Dept of Systs Eng Case Western Reserve Univ Cleveland OH 44106

KANTOR, SIDNEY, b New York, NY, Feb 1, 24; m 49, 73; c 5. PARASITOLOGY, PROTOZOOLOGY. *Educ:* George Washington Univ, BA, 47, MA, 49; Univ Ill, PhD(zool), 56. *Prof Exp:* Invert zoologist, Acad Natural Sci, Pa, 51-53; asst parasitol, Col Vet Med, Univ Ill, 53-55; coop agent, USDA, Ill, 55-56; from parasitologist to group leader, 56-73, SR RES BIOLOGIST PROTOZOOL CHEMOTHER, ANIMAL SCI DEPT, AGR DIV, AM CYANAMID CO, 73- *Mem:* Am Soc Parasitol; Soc Protozool; Am Inst Biol Sci; Sigma Xi. *Res:* Parasitic chemotherapy; veterinary entomology. *Mailing Add:* Animal Sci Dept Agr Div Am Cyanamid Co PO Box 400 Princeton NJ 08540

KANTOR, SIMON WILLIAM, b Brussels, Belg, Mar 23, 25; nat US; m 70; c 5. POLYMER CHEMISTRY, ORGANIC CHEMISTRY. *Educ:* City Col New York, BS, 45; Duke Univ, PhD(org chem), 49. *Prof Exp:* Fel, Duke Univ, 49-51; res assoc, Gen Elec Co, Schenectady, NY, 51-60, sect mgr, 60-65, br mgr, 65-72; V PRES RES & DEVELOP, GAF CORP, WAYNE, 72- *Honors & Awards:* Gold Patent Medallion, Gen Elec Co, 66. *Mem:* AAAS; Am Chem Soc; Soc Chem Indust; Indust Res Inst. *Res:* Organic reactions of carbanions; organosilicon polymers; synthesis of aromatic condensation polymers. *Mailing Add:* 315 Grandview Circle Ridgewood NJ 07450

KANTOROVITZ, SHMUEL, b Casablanca, Morocco, Sept 17, 35; m 60; c 4. MATHEMATICS. *Educ:* Hebrew Univ Israel, MSc, 56; Univ Minn, Minneapolis, PhD(math), 62. *Prof Exp:* Instr math, Princeton Univ, 62-63; mem, Inst Advan Study, 63-64; asst prof, Yale Univ, 64-67; assoc prof, 67-70, PROF MATH, UNIV ILL, CHICAGO CIRCLE, 70- *Mem:* Am Math Soc. *Res:* Functional analysis. *Mailing Add:* Dept of Math Univ of Ill at Chicago Circle Chicago IL 60680

KANTOWSKI, RONALD, b Shreveport, La, Dec 18, 39; m 61; c 3. PHYSICS. *Educ:* Univ Tex, Austin, BS, 62, PhD(physics), 66. *Prof Exp:* Res scientist med, Univ Tex Med Br, Galveston, 62-73; teaching asst physics, Univ Tex, Austin, 63-66, asst prof, 66-67; res assoc, Southwest Ctr Advan Studies, 67-68; from asst prof to assoc prof, 68-81, PROF PHYSICS, UNIV OKLA, 81- *Mem:* Am Phys Soc. *Res:* Gravity theories. *Mailing Add:* Dept of Physics & Astron 440 W Brooks Norman OK 73019

KANTRO, DAVID LEON, b Chicago, Ill, Jan 6, 27; c 2. PHYSICAL CHEMISTRY, MATERIALS SCIENCE. *Educ:* Univ Ill, BS, 49; Ill Inst Technol, PhD, 53. *Prof Exp:* Asst res chemist, Armour Res Found, Ill Inst Technol, 51-52; prin res chemist, Portland Cement Asn, 52-80; DIR ADMIXTURE RES, MASTER BUILDERS, 80- *Mem:* Fel Am Ceramic Soc; Am Soc Testing & Mat; Am Concrete Inst. *Res:* Chemistry of portland cement; hydration of portland cement; admixture science and technology; x-ray diffraction quantitative analysis. *Mailing Add:* Portland Cement Asn 5420 Old Orchard Rd Skokie IL 60077

KANTROWITZ, ADRIAN, b New York, NY, Oct 4, 18; m 48; c 3. SURGERY. *Educ:* NY Univ, AB, 40; Long Island Col Med, MD, 43; Am Bd Surg, dipl. *Prof Exp:* Intern, Jewish Hosp, Brooklyn, 44; surg resident, Mt Sinai Hosp, 47; resident, Montefiore Hosp, 48-50; from asst prof to prof surg, State Univ NY Col Med, 55-70; PROF SURG, COL MED, WAYNE STATE UNIV, 70- *Concurrent Pos:* USPHS fel cardiovasc res & teaching fel physiol, Dept Physiol, Western Reserve Univ, 51-52; dir cardiovasc surg, Maimonides Med Ctr, Brooklyn, 55-64, dir surg, 64-70; chmn dept surg, Sinai Hosp, Detroit, 70- *Honors & Awards:* H L Moses Prize, Montefiore Alumnus, 49; Exhibit Prize, NY State Med Soc, 52; Theodore & Susan B Cummings Award, Am Col Cardiol, 67; Gold Plate Award, Am Acad Achievement, 66; Max Berg Award, 69. *Mem:* Fel NY Acad Sci; Am Chem Soc; Int Soc Angiol; Am Soc Artificial Internal Organs (pres, 68-69); Harvey Soc. *Res:* Cardiac pacemakers; heart transplants; human balloon pump; partial human mechanical heart. *Mailing Add:* 70 Gallogly Rd Pontiac MI 48055

KANTROWITZ, ARTHUR (ROBERT), b Bronx, NY, Oct 20, 13; m 43, 80; c 3. GAS DYNAMICS. *Educ:* Columbia Univ, BS, 34, MA, 36, PhD(physics), 47. *Hon Degrees:* DE, Mont Col Mineral Sci & Technol, 75; DSc, NJ Inst Technol, 81. *Prof Exp:* Physicist, Nat Adv Comt Aeronaut, 36-46; from assoc prof to prof aeronaut eng & eng physics, Cornell Univ, 46-56; vpres & dir, Avco Corp, 56-72, dir Avco Everett Res Lab, 55-72, sr vpres, dir & chmn, 72-78; PROF ENG, THAYER SCH ENG, DARTMOUTH COL, 78- *Concurrent Pos:* Vis lectr, Harvard Univ, 52; Fulbright scholar & Guggenheim fel, Cambridge Univ & Univ Manchester, 54; vis inst prof & fel, Sch Advan Study, Mas Inst Technol, 57; hon trustee, Univ Rochester, 71; mem adv coun, Dept Aeronaut Eng, Princeton Univ, 59-77; mem bd overseers, Thayer Sch Eng, Dartmouth Col, 75-; eng adv bd mem, Stanford Univ & Rensselaer Polytech Inst; hon prof, Huazhang Inst Technol, Wuhan, China, 80. *Honors & Awards:* Messenger lectr, Cornell Univ, 78. *Mem:* Nat Acad Sci; Nat Acad Eng; Am Phys Soc; fel Am Inst Aeronaut & Astronaut; fel Am Acad Arts & Sci. *Res:* Physical gas dynamics; magneto-hydrodynamics power; high power lasers; cardiac assist devices; strategic technology; social control of technology. *Mailing Add:* 24 Pinewood Village West Labanon MA 03784

KANTZ, PAUL THOMAS, JR, b Jacksonville, Tex, Jan 21, 41; m 62; c 2. PHYCOLOGY. *Educ:* Univ Tex, BA, 63, MA, 65, PhD(phycol), 67. *Prof Exp:* Asst prof, 67-71, assoc prof biol, 71-81, PROF BIOL, CALIF STATE UNIV, SACRAMENTO, 81- *Mem:* Phycol Soc Am; Bot Soc Am; NY Acad Sci. *Res:* Taxonomy and morphology of blue green algae. *Mailing Add:* Dept of Biol Sci Calif State Univ Sacramento CA 95819

KANTZES, JAMES (GEORGE), b Bertha, Pa, Mar 29, 24; m 54; c 3. PLANT PATHOLOGY. *Educ:* Univ Md, BS, 51, MS, 54, PhD(plant path), 57. *Prof Exp:* From instr to assoc prof, 52-69, PROF PLANT PATH, COL AGR, UNIV MD, 69- *Mem:* Am Phytopath Soc. *Res:* Agriculture; control of vegetable diseases. *Mailing Add:* Veg Res Farm Univ of Md Salisbury MD 21801

KANWAL, RAM PRAKASH, b India, July 4, 24; m 54; c 2. GENERALIZED FUNCTIONS. *Educ:* Punjab Univ, India, BA, 45, MA, 48; Ind Univ, PhD, 57. *Prof Exp:* Asst, Ministry of Agr, Govt of India, 48-50; lectr math, Daynand Anglo Vernacular Col, India, 50-51; asst prof, Birla Col, Pilani, 51-52; asst lectr, Indian Inst Technol, Kharagpur, 52-54; res assoc appl math, Ind Univ, 54-57; asst prof, Math Res Ctr, Univ Wis, 57-59; sr scientist, Oak Ridge Nat Lab, 59; assoc prof math, 59-62, PROF MATH, PA STATE UNIV, 62- *Concurrent Pos:* Vis prof, Tech Univ Denmark, 65-66 & Royal Inst Technol, Stockholm, 66. *Mem:* Soc Indust & Appl Math. *Res:* Hydrodynamics; aerodynamics; magnetohydrodynamics; elasticity; diffraction; integral and differential equations. *Mailing Add:* Dept Math Pa State Univ University Park PA 16802

KANZELMEYER, JAMES HERBERT, b Manila, Philippines, Aug 9, 26; m 49; c 9. ANALYTICAL CHEMISTRY. *Educ:* Univ Calif, AB, 47; Ore State Col, PhD(anal chem), 55. *Prof Exp:* Chemist, Beacon res labs, Tex Co, 47-49; instr chem, Ore State Col, 53-54; asst prof, NMex Highlands Univ, 54-57; anal res chemist, St Joe Zinc Co, 57-63, chief chemist smelting div, 63-80, CHIEF CHEMIST, CORP ANAL SERV, ST JOE MINERALS CORP, 80- *Concurrent Pos:* Mem, Nat Res Coun Eval Panel, Anal Chem Div, Nat Bur Standards, 75-78. *Mem:* Am Chem Soc; Am Soc Testing & Mat. *Res:* Analytical chemistry of zinc-containing materials, including chemical, optical-emission and x-ray spectrographic methods. *Mailing Add:* St Joe Minerals Corp Box A Monaca PA 15061

KANZLER, WALTER WILHELM, b Jersey City, NJ, Sept 17, 38. ANIMAL BEHAVIOR, BIOETHICS. *Educ:* Montclair State Col, BA, 60, MA, 63; Marshall Univ, MA, 64; Univ Cincinnati, PhD(ecol, behav), 72. *Prof Exp:* Instr biol, Union City High Schs, NJ, 60-65; asst prof, Trenton State Col, 65-66; from instr to asst prof, 66-76, ASSOC PROF BIOL, WAGNER COL, 76- *Concurrent Pos:* NASA fel, 69-70; NSF grant, Nat Primate Ctr, Univ Calif, Davis, 71; sr res assoc, Nat Ctr Bioethics, Drew Univ, 76; consult, Scientists Ctr Animal Welfare, 80- *Mem:* Animal Behav Soc; Sigma Xi; AAAS; Nat Wildlife Fed. *Res:* Insect, gerbil and primate behavior; history of biology and medicine; social issues in biology and medicine. *Mailing Add:* Dept of Biol Wagner Col Staten Island NY 10301

KAO, CHIEN YUAN, b Shanghai, China, Dec 20, 27; nat US; m 57; c 2. PHYSIOLOGY, PHARMACOLOGY. *Educ:* Univ Southern Calif, BA, 48; State Univ NY, MD, 52. *Prof Exp:* Intern & asst path, NY Hosp-Cornell Med Ctr, 52-53, res assoc neurol, Col Physicians & Surgeons, Columbia Univ, 53-54; instr, State Univ NY Downstate Med Ctr, 55-56; asst, Rockefeller Inst, 56-57; asst prof pharmacol, 57-69, PROF NEUROSCI, STATE UNIV NY DOWNSTATE MED CTR, 74-, PROF PHARMACOL, 80- *Concurrent Pos:* Fel physiol, State Univ NY Downstate Med Ctr, 54-55. *Mem:* Am Physiol Soc; Am Soc Pharmacol & Exp Therapeut; Soc Gen Physiol; Int Soc Toxicol. *Res:* Cellular physiology; electrical properties of cellular membrane in relation to permeability properties; nerve and muscle physiology; ions and excitation in axons and smooth muscles; tetrodotoxin, saxitoxin on ionic channels; voltage clamp studies of smooth muscles. *Mailing Add:* State Univ NY Downstate Med Ctr 450 Clarkson Ave Brooklyn NY 11203

KAO, DAVID TEH-YU, b Shanghai, China, May 1, 36; m 68; c 2. CIVIL ENGINEERING. *Educ:* Cheng Kung Univ, Taiwan, BS, 59; Duke Univ, MS, 65, PhD(civil eng), 67. *Prof Exp:* From instr to asst prof, 66-76, PROF CIVIL ENG, UNIV KY, 77- *Mem:* Am Soc Civil Engrs. *Res:* Effect of transient flow conditions on solids moving through viscous fluid; dynamic drainage of fluid under moving bodies; mechanics of gully erosion of soil due to rain fall and runoff. *Mailing Add:* Dept of Civil Eng Univ of Ky Lexington KY 40506

KAO, FA-TEN, b Hankow, China, Apr 20, 34; nat US; m 60; c 1. GENETICS. *Educ:* Nat Taiwan Univ, BS, 55; Univ Minn, St Paul, PhD(genetics), 64. *Prof Exp:* Asst prof, Univ Col Med Ctr, 67-70, assoc prof biophys, 70-81, PROF BIOCHEM BIOPHYS & GENETICS, UNIV COLO HEALTH SCI CTR, DENVER, 81- *Concurrent Pos:* Nat Cancer Inst fel biophys, Univ Colo Med Ctr, Denver, 65-67; mem & sr fel, Eleanor Roosevelt Inst Cancer Res, Denver, 65-; Int Union Against Cancer-Eleanor Roosevelt Int Cancer fel, Univ Oxford, 73-74. *Mem:* Genetics Soc Am; Am Soc Cell Biol; Am Soc Human Genetics; Am Asn Cancer Res; Tissue Cult Asn. *Res:* In vitro genetic studies of somatic mammalian cells; somatic cell and molecular genetic analysis of the human genome; mapping of human genes; recombinant DNA studies. *Mailing Add:* Eleanor Roosevelt Inst Cancer Res Univ Colo Med Ctr Denver CO 80262

KAO, FREDERICK FENGTIEN, b Peking, China, Jan 29, 19; nat US; m 49; c 1. PHYSIOLOGY. *Educ:* Yenching Univ, China, BS, 43; W China Union Univ, MD, 47; Northwestern Univ, MS. 50, PhD(physiol), 52. *Prof Exp:* Instr physiol, Northwestern Univ, 51; instr med physics, Yale Univ, 52; from instr to assoc prof, 52-65, PROF PHYSIOL, STATE UNIV NY DOWNSTATE MED CTR, 65- *Concurrent Pos:* Vis prof, Med Col, Nat Taiwan Univ, 56-57; vis scientist, Lab Physiol, Oxford Univ, 59; career scientist, Health Res Coun New York, 61-; vis lectr, Univ Hong Kong, 64; spec consult, Vet Admin Hosp, Brooklyn, NY, 65; vis prof, Inst Clin Physiol, Univ Gottingen, 65 & Hacettape Univ, Turkey, 68; vis scientist, Nobel Inst Neurophysiol, Karolinska Stockholm, Sweden, 76; hon prof, Shanghai First Med Col, Shanghai, 80- *Mem:* AAAS; Am Physiol Soc; Soc Exp Biol & Med; NY Acad Sci; Harvey Soc. *Res:* Pneumo-hemodynamics during muscular activity; cardiac output during metabolic adjustments; central and peripheral control of respiration; cardiovascular and respiratory functions during environmental stress; sensitivity of respiratory centers to analeptics; brain neurotransmitter and respiration. *Mailing Add:* Dept of Physiol State Univ NY Downstate Med Ctr Brooklyn NY 11203

KAO, JAMES T F, chemical engineering, see previous edition

KAO, KUNG-YING TANG, b Nanking, China, May 8, 17; nat US; m 43; c 4. BIOCHEMISTRY. *Educ:* Nat Kiangsu Med Col, China, MD, 40; Purdue Univ, MS, 50; Univ Md, PhD(chem), 53. *Prof Exp:* Res assoc, Johns Hopkins Univ, 52-53; instr, Univ Md, 53; dir protein lab, Miami Heart Inst, Fla, 53-56; investr, Howard Hughes Med Inst, 56-57; chief res chemist, Geriat Res Lab, Vet Admin Ctr, Martinsburg, WVa, 57-78. *Mem:* Am Chem Soc; Gerontol Soc; Soc Exp Biol & Med; Am Inst Nutrit. *Res:* Biochemical studies on aging processes, especially of the connective tissue. *Mailing Add:* Gum Spring Hollow Brunswick MD 21716

KAO, ORANDA HAI-WEN, physical chemistry, biochemistry, see previous edition

KAO, SAMUEL CHUNG-SIUNG, b Kaohsiung, Taiwan, June 12, 41; c 2. MATHEMATICAL STATISTICS, MATHEMATICS. *Educ:* Nat Taiwan Univ, BS, 64; Nat Tsing Hua Univ, MS, 66; Columbia Univ, PhD(statist), 72. *Prof Exp:* Lectr math, Nat Tsing Hua Univ, 66-67; statist assoc, Biomet Res, NY State Psychiat Inst, 71-73; asst prof statist, Univ Mass, Amherst, 73-74; STATISTICIAN, BROOKHAVEN NAT LAB, 74- *Mem:* Am Statist Asn; Inst Math Statist; Biomet Soc; Sigma Xi; NY Acad Sci. *Res:* Sequential experimentation; robust statistical procedures; applied probability. *Mailing Add:* Dept of Appl Math Brookhaven Nat Lab Upton NY 11973

KAO, SHIH-KUNG, b Foochow, China, Mar 9, 18; nat US; m 59; c 1. METEOROLOGY, AIR POLLUTION. *Educ:* Tsing Hua Univ, BS, 39; Univ Calif, Los Angeles, MA, 48, PhD(meteorol), 52. *Prof Exp:* Instr, Aeronaut Res Inst, Tsing Hua Univ, 39-46; res assoc, Johns Hopkins Univ, 53-55; vis asst prof, Univ Calif, Los Angeles, 56-57, res scientist, 57-60; PROF

ATMOSPHERIC SCI, UNIV UTAH, 60-, CHMN DEPT METEOROL, 72-, DIR, ATMOSPHERIC TURBULENCE & DIFFUSION PROJ, 61- *Concurrent Pos:* Coun mem, Univ Corp Atmospheric Res, 65-67, mem rep, 67-71, trustee, 71-74; vis scientist, Nat Ctr Atmospheric Res, 69-70; consult, NASA, 74- & Weather Modification Tech Adv Comt, State Utah, 76-; assoc ed, Plenum Publ Corp; res grants, AEC, Dept Energy, Environ Protection Agency, ERDA, NASA & NSF. *Mem:* AAAS; Am Meteorol Soc; Am Geophys Union; Meteorol Soc Japan; Royal Meteorol Soc Gt Brit. *Res:* Atmospheric diffusion; turbulence; atmospheric dynamics; atmospheric turbulence and diffusion; wave motion in rotating fluids; fluid mechanics. *Mailing Add:* Dept of Meteorol Univ of Utah Salt Lake City UT 84112

KAO, TAI-WU, b China, Jan 5, 35; m 59; c 5. COMMUNICATION. *Educ:* Nat Taiwan Univ, BS, 58; Chiao Tung Univ, MS, 61; Univ Utah, PhD(elec eng), 65. *Prof Exp:* From asst prof to assoc prof, 65-77, PROF ELEC ENG, LOYOLA MARYMOUNT UNIV, 77- *Concurrent Pos:* Consult, Teledyne Systs Control Syst, 65-68, DWP, Los Angeles, 71-72, Dept Navy, 73-74 & TRW, 75- *Mem:* Inst Elec & Electronics Engrs. *Res:* Electromagnetics and semiconductors; communication systems. *Mailing Add:* Dept Elec Eng Loyola Marymount Univ Loyola Blvd at W 80th St Los Angeles CA 90045

KAO, TIMOTHY WU, b Shanghai, China, July 20, 37; US citizen; m 65; c 2. FLUID MECHANICS, CIVIL ENGINEERING. *Educ:* Univ Hong Kong, BSc, 59; Univ Mich, MSE, 60, PhD(eng mech), 63. *Prof Exp:* Asst prof space sci, 64-66, assoc prof atmospheric sci, 66-70, PROF CIVIL ENG, CATH UNIV AM, 70-, CHMN, DEPT CIVIL ENG, 81- *Concurrent Pos:* Prin investr, NSF grants, 65- & Off Naval Res Contracts, 74-; consult, Arctec, Inc, 78- *Mem:* Am Meteorol Soc; Am Soc Civil Engrs. *Res:* Physical oceanography; air-sea interaction; mountain waves; environmental fluid mechanics. *Mailing Add:* Dept Civil Eng Cath Univ Am Washington DC 20064

KAO, YI-HAN, b Foochow, China, Jan 27, 31; m 57; c 2. PHYSICS. *Educ:* Nat Taiwan Univ, BS, 55; Okla State Univ, MS, 58; Columbia Univ, PhD(physics), 62. *Prof Exp:* Res assoc physics, Thomas J Watson Lab, Int Bus Mach Corp, 62-63; from asst prof to assoc prof, 63-71, PROF PHYSICS, STATE UNIV NY STONY BROOK, 71- *Mem:* Am Phys Soc. *Res:* Low temperature solid state physics; superconductivity; physics of thin films; transport phenomena. *Mailing Add:* Dept of Physics State Univ of NY Stony Brook NY 11790

KAO, YUEN-KOH, b Liaoning, China, Apr 3, 41; US citizen; m 66; c 2. CHEMICAL ENGINEERING, CONTROL ENGINEERING. *Educ:* Nat Taiwan Univ, BS, 64; Northwestern Univ, MS, 68, PhD(chem eng), 73. *Prof Exp:* Assoc chem eng, Rensselaer Polytech Inst, 73-75; asst prof, 75-81, ASSOC PROF CHEM ENG, UNIV CINCINNATI, 81- *Concurrent Pos:* Consult, Mound Lab, Monsanto Res Corp, 77, Columbia Gas, 76, R Katzen Asn, 80. *Mem:* Am Inst Chem Engrs; Sigma Xi; Electrochem Soc. *Res:* Process simulation and control; electrochemical engineering; boiling heat transfer; reaction engineering. *Mailing Add:* Dept of Chem Eng Univ of Cincinnati Cincinnati OH 45221

KAPADIA, ABHAYSINGH J, b Bombay, India, Mar 14, 29; m 55; c 2. PHARMACY. *Educ:* L M Col Pharm, Ahmedabad, India, 52; Univ Mich, Ann Arbor, MS, 58; Univ Tex, Austin, PhD(pharm), 63. *Prof Exp:* Res chemist, Univ Mich, 57-58; sect head anal res, Alcon Labs, 63-65; res assoc, 65-74, MGR STABILITY TESTING & PROD EVAL, A H ROBINS CO INC, 74- *Mem:* Am Pharmaceut Asn. *Res:* Analytical methods development; stability testing of pharmaceuticals; preformulation studies of pharmaceuticals; drug plastic interactions. *Mailing Add:* 2221 Walhala Dr Richmond VA 23236

KAPANY, NARINDER SINGH, b Moga, India, Oct 31, 27; nat US; m 54; c 2. PHYSICS, OPTICS. *Educ:* DAV Col, Dehra Dun, BS, 48; Imp Col, London, dipl, 52; Univ London, PhD(optics), 54. *Prof Exp:* Supvr, Ord Factory, India, 49-51; lens designer, Barr & Stroud Optical Co, Scotland, 52; res assoc physics, Imp Col, London, 54-55; res assoc, Inst Optics, Rochester, 55-57; supvr optics sect, Armour Res Found, Ill Inst Technol, 57-61; pres & dir res, Optics Technol, Inc, 61-73; CHMN BD & PRES, KAPTRON INC, 73- *Concurrent Pos:* Consult, Bausch & Lomb Optical Co, 55-57, Argus Camera Co, 55-57 & Johns Hopkins Hosp, 56-57; res assoc, Palo Alto Med Res Found, Calif, 62-; vis scholar, Stanford Univ, 73-74; regents prof, Univ Calif, Santa Cruz, 76-77, dir, Ctr Innovation & Entrepreneurial Develop, 78. *Honors & Awards:* Distinguished Achievement Award, Watumull Found, 65. *Mem:* AAAS; fel Am Phys Soc; fel Optical Soc Am; sr mem Inst Elec & Electronics Engrs; fel Brit Inst Phys. *Res:* Geometrical and physical optics; fiber optics with applications in medicine, photoelectronics, photography, high-speed photography; infrared fiber optics; laser and its applications; image evaluation and optical information processing; photoelectronics; aspherics; interference microscopy; refractometry; solar energy. *Mailing Add:* 2126 Greenways Dr Woodside CA 94061

KAPECKI, JON ALFRED, b Chicago, Ill, June 8, 42. PHYSICAL ORGANIC CHEMISTRY, PHOTOGRAPHIC SCIENCE. *Educ:* Col St Thomas, BS, 64; Univ Vienna, Dipl, 64; Univ Ill, Urbana, PhD(org chem), 69. *Prof Exp:* NIH fel chem, Cornell Univ, 68-71, fel, 71-72; sr chemist, 72-80, RES ASSOC, EASTMAN KODAK CO, 80- *Concurrent Pos:* Mem staff, X-ray Clinic, State Univ NY, Albany, 75-; lectr, Univ Rochester, 72-80, sr lectr, 80- *Mem:* Am Chem Soc; Am Crystallog Asn. *Res:* Organic cycloaddition mechanisms; solid state reactions; molecular orbital theory; x-ray crystallography; computer applications to organic chemistry; models for reactive intermediates; structure-pharmacological activity relationships; reaction mechanisms. *Mailing Add:* Eastman Kodak Co Res Labs Kodak Park Rochester NY 14650

KAPER, HANS G, b Alkmaar, Neth, June 10, 36; US citizen; m 62; c 2. APPLIED METHEMATICS, MATHEMATICAL PHYSICS. *Educ:* State Univ Groningen, Neth, MSc, 60, PhD(math), 65. *Prof Exp:* Asst prof appl math, State Univ Groningen, Neth, 65-66, assoc prof, 67-69; res assoc, Stanford Univ, 66-67; MATHEMATICIAN APPL MATH, ARGONNE NAT LAB, 69- *Concurrent Pos:* vis prof, Univ van Amsterdam, Neth, 76-77, Univ Vienna, Austria, 77; ed, Integral Equations & Operator Theory. *Mem:* Am Math Soc; Soc Indust & Appl Math; Math Soc Neth. *Res:* Applied analysis. *Mailing Add:* Argonne Nat Lab 9700 S Case Ave Argonne IL 60439

KAPER, JACOBUS M, b Madjalenka, Indonesia, Dec 9, 31; US citizen; m 55; c 1. BIOCHEMISTRY, MOLECULAR BIOLOGY. *Educ:* Univ Leiden, BS, 51, Drs, 54, PhD(biochem), 57. *Prof Exp:* Asst biochem, Univ Leiden, 54-57, sr res biochemist, 59-62; res fel, Virus Lab, Univ Calif, 57-59; biochemist, Plant Sci Res Div, 62-69, RES CHEMIST, PLANT PROTECTION INST, AGR RES SERV, USDA, 69- *Concurrent Pos:* Netherlands Orgn Pure Res fel, 57-58; USPHS trainee, 58; assoc res prof, George Washington Univ, 62-69; prin investr, NIH res grants, 62-69 & USDA res grant, 78-81. *Mem:* Royal Neth Chem Soc; Am Chem Soc; Am Soc Biol Chemists; Am Soc Microbiol; corresp mem Royal Neth Acad Sci. *Res:* Molecular organization and stabilizing interactions of viruses; structural biochemistry of proteins nucleic acids; divided genome viruses; mechanisms of viral disease regulation. *Mailing Add:* 115 Hedgewood Dr Greenbelt MD 20770

KAPETANAKOS, CHRISTOS ANASTASIOS, b Sparta, Greece, Jan 2, 36; US citizen; m 62; c 2. PLASMA PHYSICS. *Educ:* Nat Univ Greece, Bachelor, 60; Mass Inst Technol, Master, 64; Univ Md, PhD(physics), 70. *Prof Exp:* Res physicist plasma physics, Univ Tex, 70-71; SUPVRY RES PHYSICIST PLASMA PHYSICS, NAVAL RES LAB, 71-, HEAD, BEAM DYNAMICS PROG, 80- *Concurrent Pos:* Energy Res & Develop Admin grant, 75-77; Dept Energy grant, 77-80. *Honors & Awards:* Outstanding Performance Award, Naval Res Lab, 72, Res Publ Awards, 73, 76 & 79. *Mem:* Fel Am Phys Soc; Inst Elec & Electronics Engrs. *Res:* Supervise and contact research on intense, relativistic electron and ion beams and fusion reactors based on reversed magnetic field configurations. *Mailing Add:* Code 6761 Naval Res Lab Washington DC 20375

KAPIKIAN, ALBERT ZAVEN, b New York, NY, May 9, 30; m 60; c 3. EPIDEMIOLOGY, VIROLOGY. *Educ:* Queens Col, NY, BS, 52; Cornell Univ, MD, 56; Am Bd Med Microbiol, dipl, 65. *Prof Exp:* Intern, Meadowbrook Hosp, Hempstead, NY, 56-57; res epidemiologist, 57-64, actg head sect, 64-67, HEAD EPIDEMIOL SECT, LAB INFECTIOUS DIS, NAT INST ALLERGY & INFECTIOUS DIS, 67-, ASST CHIEF LAB INFECTIOUS DIS, 67- *Concurrent Pos:* Guest worker virol, Royal Postgrad Med Sch, Univ London, 70. *Honors & Awards:* Kabakjian Award, Armenian Students' Asn Am, 74; Stitt Award, Asn Mil Surgeons US, 74. *Mem:* Am Pub Health Asn; AMA; Am Epidemiol Soc; Infectious Dis Soc Am; Soc Epidemiol Res. *Res:* Epidemiologic investigations of infectious diseases; viral gastroenteritis. *Mailing Add:* 11201 Marcliff Rd Rockville MD 20852

KAPILA, ASHWANI KUMAR, b Ludhiana, India, Aug 26, 46; US citizen; m 71; c 2. ASYMPTOTICS. *Educ:* Punjabi Univ, India, BS, 68; Univ Sask, Can, MS, 70; Cornell Univ, PhD(theoret & appl mech), 75. *Prof Exp:* Instr & res assoc mech, Cornell Univ, 74-76; asst prof, 76-81, ASSOC PROF APPL MATH, RENSSELAER POLYTECH INST, 81- *Concurrent Pos:* Vis asst prof, Northwestern Univ, 78 & Math Res Ctr, Univ Wis, Madison, 79-80. *Mem:* Combustion Inst; Soc Indust & Appl Math. *Res:* Applied mathematics, especially asymptotics and perturbation theory; application to problems in mechanics, chemically reactive flows and combustion theory. *Mailing Add:* Dept Math Sci Rensselaer Polytech Inst Troy NY 12181

KAPLAN, ABNER, b New York, NY, June 21, 23; m 50; c 3. AERONAUTICS. *Educ:* Calif Inst Technol, BS, 48, MS, 49, PhD(aeronaut), 54. *Prof Exp:* Res engr, Struct Res Group, Northrop Aircraft Corp, 52-55; mem tech staff & mgr struct dept, 55-70, STAFF ENGR, TRW SYSTS GROUP, 70- *Mem:* Am Soc Mech Engrs; Am Inst Aeronaut & Astronaut. *Res:* Nonlinear buckling; thin shells; pressure vessels. *Mailing Add:* TRW 0556 1 Space Park Redondo Beach CA 90278

KAPLAN, ALAN MARC, b Brooklyn, NY, Dec 10, 40; m 72; c 1. IMMUNOLOGY. *Educ:* Tufts Univ, BS, 63; Purdue Univ, PhD(immunol), 69. *Prof Exp:* Res asst tumor immunol, Sloan-Kettering Inst, 63-65; asst prof, Med Col Va, 72-75, assoc prof surg & microbiol, 75-82, coordr, Tumor Immunol Sect, 74-82, deputy chmn, Dept Microbiol, 81-82, assoc dir res, Va Commonwealth Univ Cancer Ctr, 80-82; PROF & CHMN, DEPT MICROBIOL & IMMUNOL, SCH MED, UNIV KY, 82- *Concurrent Pos:* Can Med Res Coun fel immunol, Univ Toronto, 69-72. *Mem:* Am Soc Microbiol; NY Acad Sci; Can Soc Immunol; Am Asn Immunol; Am Asn Cancer Res. *Res:* Tumor and cellular immunology; immunologic tolerance; immunoadjuvants; immunogenetics; macrophage differentiation. *Mailing Add:* Dept Microbiol & Immunol Albert B Chandler Med Sch Univ Ky Lexington KY 40536

KAPLAN, ALBERT SYDNEY, b Philadelphia, Pa, Nov 29, 17; m 59; c 2. VIROLOGY. *Educ:* Philadelphia Col Pharm, BS, 41; Pa State Univ, MS, 49; Yale Univ, PhD, 52. *Prof Exp:* Civilian chemist, US Dept Army, 41-43, 46-47; instr prev med, Sch Med, Yale Univ, 54-55; res assoc bact, Univ Ill, 55-58; head dept microbiol, Res Labs, Albert Einstein Med Ctr, 58-72; res prof, Sch Med, Temple Univ, 65-72; PROF MICROBIOL & CHMN DEPT, SCH MED, VANDERBILT UNIV, 72- *Concurrent Pos:* Nat Found Infantile Paralysis fel, Pasteur Inst, 52-53; fel, Yale Univ, 53-54; assoc ed, Virology, 66-69, 72-75 & J Virol, 67-73; consult, Virol Study Sect, NIH, 70-73, chmn, 72-73; assoc ed, Cancer Res, 74-81; consult, Advisory Panel Virol & Microbiol, Am Cancer Soc, 78-81 & Microbiol Testing Comt, Nat Bd Med Examr, 79-83. *Mem:* AAAS; Am Asn Immunol; Am Soc Microbiol; Sigma Xi; Am Assoc Cancer Res. *Res:* Quantitative studies on animal viruses in tissue culture and biochemical virology. *Mailing Add:* Dept of Microbiol Vanderbilt Univ Sch of Med Nashville TN 37232

KAPLAN, ALEX, b New York, NY, May 22, 10; m 40; c 3. PHYSIOLOGY, CHEMISTRY. *Educ:* Univ Calif, Los Angeles, AB, 32; Univ Calif, PhD(physiol), 36. *Prof Exp:* Res assoc, Mt Zion Hosp, San Francisco, 37-39; asst physiol, Univ Calif, 39-40; asst dir, Harold Brunn Inst Cardiovasc Res, San Francisco, 40-42; chief lab, Vio-Bin Corp, 46-50; asst dir dept biochem, Michael Reese Hosp, Ill, 50-57; chief chemist, Children's Hosp, San Francisco, 57-60; assoc prof biochem, 60-69, prof biochem & lab med & dir, Chem Div, 69-80, dir, Hosp Chem Labs, 60-80, EMER PROF LAB MED, SCH MED, UNIV WASH, 80- *Mem:* AAAS; Soc Exp Biol & Med; Am Physiol Soc; Am Asn Clin Chem (pres, 71). *Res:* Lipid metabolism; clinical chemistry. *Mailing Add:* BB245 Univ Hosp SB-10 Sch Med Univ Wash Seattle WA 98195

KAPLAN, ALEXANDER E, b Kiev, USSR, June 9, 38; US citizen. OPTICS, THEORETICAL PHYSICS. *Educ:* Moscow Phys-Tech Inst, MS, 61; USSR Acad Sci, Moscow & Gorkii State Univ, PhD(physics & math), 67. *Prof Exp:* Res scientist, USSR Acad Sci, Moscow, 63-79; MEM RES STAFF, FRANCIS BITTER NAT MAGNET LAB, MASS INST TECHNOL, 79- *Concurrent Pos:* Vis scientist, Max Planck Inst, Garching, WGer & Los Alamos Lab, 81; consult, Bell Labs, 80-81; prin investr res proj, Off Sci Res, US Air Force, 80- *Mem:* Am Phys Soc; Optical Soc Am. *Res:* Quantum electronics and nonlinear optics; theory of two-level systems in a strong field; self-focusing and self-bending effects; interaction of light with nonlinear interfaces and theory of cavityless optical bistability; Sagnac effect in nonlinear ring resonators. *Mailing Add:* Francis Bitter Nat Magnet Lab Mass Inst Technol Cambridge MA 02139

KAPLAN, ALLAN STEVEN, pharmaceutics, see previous edition

KAPLAN, ANN ESTHER, b New York, NY, Dec 28, 26. BIOCHEMISTRY, BIOPHYSICS. *Educ:* Hunter Col, BA, 47; Mt Holyoke Col, MA, 49; Univ Pa, PhD(biochem), 59. *Prof Exp:* Instr neurol, Albert Einstein Col Med, 62-63; res assoc, Rockefeller Inst, 63-65; asst prof doctoral fac biochem, City Univ New York, 65-67; sr res assoc, Salk Inst Biol Studies, 67-72; biochemist, 72-77, RES BIOCHEMIST, NAT CANCER INST, 77- *Concurrent Pos:* Dazian Found fel microbiol, Sch Med, NY Univ, 59-60; NIH sr fel physiol, Albert Einstein Col Med, 60-62; comnr rep, sci manpower comn, Am Soc Exp Biol, 78-81. *Mem:* AAAS; Am Chem Soc; NY Acad Sci; Am Soc Biol Chem; Biophys Soc. *Res:* Biosynthesis of lipids in biological membranes; serum lipid factors in cell growth; oxygenase pathway in heart mitochondria; lactate dehydrogenace in central nervous system and serum in experimental allergic encephalomyelitis; modification of lactate dehydrogenace in hepatocyte lines with chemical transformation. *Mailing Add:* Bg 37-3B27 NCI-NIH Bethesda MD 20014

KAPLAN, ARNOLD, b New York, NY, Dec 20, 39; m 63; c 2. LYSOSOMOLOGY, ORGANELLE BIOGENESIS. *Educ:* City Col NY, BS, 61; George Wash Univ, MS, 63, PhD(biochem), 66; Univ Calif, PhD(biochem), 68. *Prof Exp:* Asst prof, 68-73, ASSOC PROF MICROBIOL, MED SCH, ST LOUIS UNIV, 73- *Concurrent Pos:* NIH fel, 66-68 & spec res fel, 70-72; fel, Nat Cancer Soc, 66-68; vis scientist biophysics, Weissman Inst, 72; vis assoc prof pediatrics, Wash Univ Med Sch, 76; consult, Weissman Inst, Calbiochem, Monsanto & Childrens Inst. *Mem:* Am Soc Biol Chemists. *Mailing Add:* Dept Microbiol Sch Med St Louis Univ 1402 S Grand Blvd St Louis MO 63104

KAPLAN, ARTHUR LEWIS, b Boston, Mass, Mar 13, 33; m 57; c 2. HEALTH PHYSICS, NUCLEAR ENGINEERING. *Educ:* Mass Inst Technol, BS, 54, MS, 55. *Prof Exp:* Proj engr, Aircraft Nuclear Propulsion Prog, Wright Air Develop Ctr, Ohio, 55-57; physicist, Tech Opers, Inc, 57-60; physicist & unit mgr, Gen Elec Co, 60-64; physicist & proj leader, Tech Opers Res, 64-69; tech dir, Systs Sci & Eng, Inc, 69-72; consult engr, Gen Elec Co Nuclear Fuel Dept, 72-78; mgr licensing & compliance, mfg dept, 78-81, MGR ENVIRON CONTROL, LIGHTING BUS GROUP, GEN ELEC CO, CLEVELAND, 81- *Mem:* AAAS; Am Phys Soc; Am Nuclear Soc; Health Physics Soc; Inst Nuclear Mat Mgt. *Res:* Theoretical and experimental radiation shielding; biological effects of ionizing radiation; long range environmental effects of radioactive fallout; radiation effects in electronics and materials; health physics and radiation safety; health physics, licensing and compliance in uranium fabrication plants. *Mailing Add:* 25422 Bryden Rd Beachwood OH 44122

KAPLAN, BARRY HUBERT, b Brooklyn, NY, Nov 16, 38; m 62; c 2. ONCOLOGY, BIOCHEMISTRY. *Educ:* NY Univ, BA, 58; Johns Hopkins Univ, MD, 62, PhD(physiol chem), 67. *Prof Exp:* Intern med, Johns Hopkins Hosp, Baltimore, 62-63; res assoc biochem, Nat Heart Inst, 64-66; resident med, Bronx Munic Hosp Ctr, NY, 66-67; assoc, 67-70, asst prof med, 71-75, actg dir div oncol, 74-80, ASST PROF BIOCHEM, ALBERT EINSTEIN COL MED, 73-, ASSOC PROF MED, 75-, DIR DIV ONCOL, 81- *Concurrent Pos:* USPHS fel physiol chem, Sch Med, Johns Hopkins Univ, 63-64; USPHS training grant, Albert Einstein Col Med, 67-69; attend physician, Bronx Munic Hosp Ctr, New York, 67-; Am Heart Asn estab investr, Albert Einstein Col Med, 69-74. *Mem:* AAAS; Am Soc Hemat; Harvey Soc; Am Asn Cancer Res; Am Soc Clin Oncol. *Mailing Add:* Dept of Med Albert Einstein Col of Med Bronx NY 10461

KAPLAN, BERNARD, b New York, NY, Feb 16, 21; m 54; c 3. MATHEMATICAL PHYSICS. *Educ:* City Col New York, BS, 47; Ohio State Univ, PhD(physics), 53. *Prof Exp:* Prin engr math eng anal, Aircraft Nuclear Propulsion Dept, Gen Elec Co, 53-61; assoc prof, 61-69, PROF PHYSICS, US AIR FORCE INST TECHNOL, 69- *Mem:* Am Asn Physics Teachers. *Res:* Numerical solution with digital computers of boundary value and initial value problems of engineering and applied physics, especially in heat transfer and nuclear engineering. *Mailing Add:* Dept of Physics US Air Force Inst of Technol Wright-Patterson AFB OH 45433

KAPLAN, DANIEL ELIOT, b San Mateo, Calif, Aug 17, 32; m 59; c 4. SOLID STATE PHYSICS, PLASMA PHYSICS. *Educ:* Univ Calif, AB, 53, MA, 55, PhD(physics), 58. *Prof Exp:* Res scientist, 58-67, SR STAFF SCIENTIST, LOCKHEED PALO ALTO RES LAB, 67- *Mem:* Am Phys Soc. *Res:* Paramagnetic and ferrimagnetic resonance; plasma resonance phenomena. *Mailing Add:* Dept 52-51 Bldg 202 Lockheed Palo Alto Lab Palo Alto CA 94304

KAPLAN, DAVID GILBERT, b Chicago, Ill, Nov 13, 44; m 71; c 2. PHYSICAL CHEMISTRY. *Educ:* Univ Ill, Urbana, BS, 65; Univ Southern Calif, PhD(phys chem), 72. *Prof Exp:* Fel biochem, Sch Med, Univ Calif, Los Angeles, 72-74; res coordr radiopharm, Sch Pharm, Univ Southern Calif, 75-76; UNIT HEAD GELATIN RES, BANNER GELATIN PROD CORP, 76- *Mem:* Am Chem Soc. *Res:* Studies on the viscoelastic behavior of connective tissue and lipid metabolism of biological systems. *Mailing Add:* 17211 Avenida de la Herradura Pacific Palisades CA 90272

KAPLAN, DAVID JEREMY, b Honolulu, Hawaii, Oct 8, 34; c 3. OPERATIONS RESEARCH, SYSTEMS ANALYSIS. *Educ:* State Univ Iowa, BA, 56; Univ Calif, Berkeley, MA, 58. *Prof Exp:* Mathematician, Ames Res Ctr, NASA, 58-60; mathematician syst anal, Stanford Res Inst, 60-69; OPERS RES ANALYST, NAVAL RES LAB, 69- *Mem:* Fel AAAS; Sigma Xi; Opers Res Soc Am; Math Asn Am. *Res:* Developing the symbolic framework that underlies command and control systems; data-driven language representations that form the interface between signal coordinating systems and their environment. *Mailing Add:* Code 5155 Naval Res Lab Washington DC 20375

KAPLAN, DAVID L, b New York, NY, Feb 14, 18; m 51; c 2. STATISTICS, DEMOGRAPHY. *Educ:* NY Univ, BA, 39. *Prof Exp:* Statistician pop div, US Bur Census, 40-56, census planner, 57-62, asst chief, 62-68, coordr 1970 census pop & housing, 66-73, chief demog census staff, 71-78, asst dir, 74-79, CONSULT STATISTICIAN, US BUR CENSUS, 79- *Honors & Awards:* Silver Medal, Dept Com, 52, Gold Medal, 71. *Mem:* Fel AAAS; fel Am Statist Asn; Pop Asn Am; Int Asn Surv Statisticians; Int Union Sci Study Pop. *Res:* Techniques for collecting, processing and disseminating demographic data from censuses and surveys. *Mailing Add:* 204 Belton Rd Silver Spring MD 20901

KAPLAN, DONALD ROBERT, b Chicago, Ill, Jan 17, 38; m 64; c 2. PLANT MORPHOLOGY. *Educ:* Northwestern Univ, BA, 60; Univ Calif, Berkeley, PhD(bot), 65. *Prof Exp:* Asst prof biol sci, Univ Calif, Irvine, 65-68; from asst prof to assoc prof, 68-77, PROF BOT, UNIV CALIF, BERKELEY, 77- *Concurrent Pos:* NSF fel, Royal Bot Garden, Eng, 65. *Mem:* AAAS; Bot Soc Am; Int Soc Plant Morphol; Am Soc Cell Biol; fel Linnean Soc London. *Res:* Comparative and developmental morphology of monocotyledons, especially leaf development and shoot growth; floral morphology of primitive and advanced angiosperms. *Mailing Add:* Dept of Bot Univ of Calif Berkeley CA 94720

KAPLAN, EDWARD LYNN, b Philadelphia, Pa, May 11, 20. MATHEMATICS PROGRAMMING. *Educ:* Carnegie Inst Technol, BS, 41; Princeton Univ, PhD(math), 51. *Prof Exp:* Mathematician, US Naval Ord Lab, 41-48; asst, Princeton Univ, 48-50; mem tech staff, Bell Tel Labs, 50-57; mathematician, Lawrence Radiation Lab, Univ Calif, 57-61; assoc prof, 61-64, PROF MATH, ORE STATE UNIV, 64- *Mem:* Am Math Soc; Math Prog Soc. *Res:* Random sequences; elliptic-integral tables; probability; statistics; Monte Carlo methods; computation; mathematical programming; optimization. *Mailing Add:* Dept of Math Ore State Univ Corvallis OR 97331

KAPLAN, EHUD, b Jerusalem, Israel, Dec 29, 42; m 66; c 2. NEUROPHYSIOLOGY, SENSORY PROCESS. *Educ:* Hebrew Univ, Jerusalem, Israel, BA, 67; Syracuse Univ, PhD(neurophysiol), 73. *Prof Exp:* Res asst vision, Hadassah Hosp, Jerusalem Israel, 63-65 & Syracuse Univ, 68-73; fel, 73-76, ASST PROF, ROCKEFELLER UNIV, 77- *Concurrent Pos:* Instr, Marine Biol Lab, Woods Hole, Mass, 77- *Mem:* NY Acad Sci; Asn Res Vision & Opthal; Sigma Xi. *Res:* Information processing by the brain especially in the visual system; the way photoreceptors transduce light into electrical energy. *Mailing Add:* Rockfeller Univ New York NY 10021

KAPLAN, EMANUEL, b Clearfield, Pa, Mar 12, 10; m 34; c 2. BIOCHEMISTRY. *Educ:* Johns Hopkins Univ, AB, 31, ScD(biochem), 34. *Prof Exp:* Spec asst biochem, Sch Hyg & Pub Health, Johns Hopkins Univ, 30-32, asst, 31-34; chief div chem, Bur Labs, Baltimore City Health Dept, 34-57, asst dir, 57-65; chief, Div Biochem, Bur Labs, Md State Dept Health, 65-76. *Concurrent Pos:* Instr, Sch Nursing, Sinai Hosp, 39-44. *Mem:* Am Chem Soc; fel Am Pub Health Asn; Am Asn Clin Chem. *Res:* Environmental chemistry; clinical chemistry; completely edible dentifrice. *Mailing Add:* 3 Stonehenge Circle Apt 1 Baltimore MD 21208

KAPLAN, EPHRAIM HENRY, b New York, NY, Nov 16, 18; m 52; c 3. ANALYTICAL CHEMISTRY. *Educ:* City Col New York, BS, 38; Univ Iowa, MS, 40; Univ Pittsburgh, PhD(phys chem, biochem), 45. *Prof Exp:* Asst sci aide, Eastern Regional Res Lab, Bur Agr & Indust Chem, USDA, 41-42; org chemist, Bur Mines, Pittsburgh, 42-45; res chemist, Sinclair Refining Co, Ind, 45-47; res assoc, Polytech Inst Brooklyn, 47-49; Res Corp fel enzyme chem, Inst Enzyme Res, Univ Wis, 49-50; res assoc, Med Sch, Northwestern Univ, 50-53; res chemist, Vico Prod Co, 53-56; res assoc, Inst Tuberc Res, Univ Ill, 56-57; tech dir, Hodag Chem Corp, 57-60; res chemist, Velsicol Chem Corp, Chicago, 60-69; TOXICOLOGIST & SUPVR SPEC CHEM SECT, CHICAGO BD HEALTH, 70- *Mem:* AAAS; Am Chem Soc. *Res:* Surface active chemicals; enzymes; proteins; intermediary metabolism; sorption of vapors by and permeation through polymers; organic synthesis; analysis of hydrocarbon mixtures; pesticides; instrumental, drug and clinical analysis. *Mailing Add:* 9526 Kostner Ave Skokie IL 60076

KAPLAN, ERVIN, b Independence, Iowa, June 19, 18; m 45; c 2. INTERNAL MEDICINE, NUCLEAR MEDICINE. *Educ:* Univ Ill, BS, 47, MS & MD, 49; Am Bd Internal Med, dipl; Am Bd Nuclear Med, dipl. *Prof Exp:* Intern, Mt Sinai Hosp, Chicago, 49-50; resident internal med, Vet Admin Hosp, 50-52, actg assoc dir radioisotope serv, 52-59, chief, 59-70 sr physician, 71-75; clin asst, 52-53, clin instr, 53-57, clin asst prof, 59-64, assoc prof, 64-69, PROF MED & PHYSIOL, UNIV ILL COL MED, 69-; CHIEF NUCLEAR MED SERV, VET ADMIN HOSP, 70- *Concurrent Pos:* Physician-in-charge, Radioisotope Clin & assoc attend physician, Mt Sinai Hosp, Chicago, 53-59, consult, 67-; physician-in-charge, Radioisotope Lab, Michael Reese Hosp, Chicago, 56-59; assoc attend physician, Cook County Hosp, 59-64, attend physician, 64-; consult nuclear med, Louis Weiss Mem Hosp, 70-; lectr, Chicago Med Sch, 71-78 & Stritch Sch Med, Loyola Univ; sci corresp, Revista Biol & Nuclear Med, Uruguay. *Honors & Awards:* First Prize Award, Gema Czerniak; Award Nuclear Med & Radiopharmacol, Ahavat Zion Found, Israel, 74. *Mem:* AAAS; Soc Exp Biol & Med; Soc Nuclear Med. *Res:* Application of radioisotopes in medicine and biological research. *Mailing Add:* Nuclear Med Serv Vet Admin Hosp Hines IL 60141

KAPLAN, EUGENE HERBERT, b Brooklyn, NY, June 26, 32; m 58; c 2. PARASITOLOGY, SCIENCE EDUCATION. *Educ:* Brooklyn Col, BS, 54; Hofstra Col, MS, 56; Ny Univ, PhD(sci educ), 63. *Prof Exp:* Teacher high sch, NY, 56-58; from lectr to assoc prof, 58-74, PROF BIOL, HOFSTRA UNIV, 75- *Concurrent Pos:* NSF sci fac fel, 63-64; UNESCO expert elem sci, Israel, 71-72. *Mem:* Am Soc Parasitol; Nat Asn Res Sci Teaching. *Res:* Marine ecology, especially coral reef invertebrates; effects of dredging on benthos; introductory science courses for non-science majors; measuring aspects of scientific thinking. *Mailing Add:* Dept of Biol Hofstra Univ Hempstead NY 11550

KAPLAN, FRED, b Brooklyn, NY, Sept 2, 34; m 73; c 4. ORGANIC CHEMISTRY. *Educ:* NY Univ, BA, 55; Yale Univ, PhD(chem), 60. *Prof Exp:* USPHS res fel chem, Swiss Fed Inst Technol, 59-60; univ fel, Calif Inst Technol, 60-61; from instr to assoc prof, 61-68, PROF CHEM, UNIV CINCINNATI, 68- *Mem:* AAAS; Am Chem Soc; Am Asn Univ Professors. *Res:* Applications of ion cyclotron resonance spectroscopy; gas phase ion-molecule reactions; gas phase properties of organic species; electron deficient species. *Mailing Add:* Dept of Chem Univ of Cincinnati Cincinnati OH 45221

KAPLAN, GEORGE HARRY, b Hagerstown, Md, Apr 24, 48; m 72. ASTROMETRY, RADIO INTERFEROMETRY. *Educ:* Univ Md, BS, 69, MS, 76. *Prof Exp:* ASTRONR, US NAVAL OBSERV, 71- *Mem:* AAAS; Am Astron Soc. *Res:* Radio and optical astrometry; radio interferometry; earth rotation; solar system dynamics and ephemerides. *Mailing Add:* US Naval Observ 34th St & Mass Ave NW Washington DC 20390

KAPLAN, GERALD, b Brooklyn, NY, Dec 21, 39; m 67; c 4. ANALYTICAL CHEMISTRY. *Educ:* Columbia Univ, BS, 61, MS, 63; Rutgers Univ, PhD(pharmaceut chem), 68. *Prof Exp:* Res scientist, 67-71, sr res scientist anal chem, 71-72, group leader methods develop, 72-75, asst mgr, 75-79, MGR ANAL LABS, JOHNSON & JOHNSON RES CTR, 79- *Mem:* Am Chem Soc; Sigma Xi. *Res:* Separations sciences. *Mailing Add:* Johnson & Johnson Res Ctr Rte 1 North Brunswick NJ 08902

KAPLAN, HAROLD IRWIN, b Brooklyn, NY, Oct 1, 27; m 81; c 3. PSYCHIATRY, PSYCHOANALYSIS. *Educ:* Columbia Univ, BS, 45; New York Med Col, MD, 49; Am Bd Psychiat & Neurol, dipl, 57. *Prof Exp:* Intern med, Brooklyn Jewish Hosp, 49-50; resident psychiat, Bronx Vet Admin Hosp, 50-53; resident psychiat, Mt Sinai Hosp, New York, 52-53; from instr to assoc prof psychiat, New York Med Col, 54-60, prof, 60-80; PROF PSYCHIAT, SCH MED, NY UNIV, 80- *Concurrent Pos:* Attend psychiatrist, Metrop Hosp, 54-80, Flower & Fifth Hosp, 54-80 & Bird S Coler Hosp, 54-80; attend psychiatrist, Univ Hosp & Bellevere Hosp, New York Univ Med Ctr, NY. *Mem:* Am Psychiat Asn; Am Acad Psychoanal; Am Col Physicians; NY Acad Med; Am Med Writers Asn. *Res:* Education of women physicians; psychiatric education research; psychosomatic medicine. *Mailing Add:* 50 E 78th St New York NY 10021

KAPLAN, HAROLD M, b Boston, Mass, Sept 4, 08; m 34; c 2. PHYSIOLOGY. *Educ:* Dartmouth Col, AB, 30; Harvard Univ, AM, 31, PhD(physiol), 33. *Prof Exp:* Asst instr zool, Harvard Univ, 33-34; instr physiol, Middlesex Univ, 34-37, prof, Med Sch, 37-45 & Vet Sch, 45-47; prof, Brandeis Univ, 47; assoc prof, Univ Mass, 47-49; chmn dept, 49-71, PROF PHYSIOL, SOUTHERN ILL UNIV, CARBONDALE, 49- *Concurrent Pos:* Pvt res with Dr E V Enzmann, Biol Labs, Harvard Univ, 35-37; writer, Wash Inst Med, 46- *Mem:* AAAS; Am Physiol Soc; Am Soc Zool; Electron Micros Soc Am. *Res:* Laboratory animal medicine. *Mailing Add:* Sch Med Southern Ill Univ Carbondale IL 62901

KAPLAN, HARRY ARTHUR, b Duluth, Minn, Oct 25, 11. NEUROSURGERY. *Educ:* Univ Minn, BS, 35, MD, 38. *Prof Exp:* From instr to assoc prof, Col Med, State Univ NY Downstate Med Ctr, 51-60; PROF NEUROSURG, COL MED & DENT NJ, NEWARK, 63- *Concurrent Pos:* Fel neurosurg, Long Island Col Med, 49-51. *Mem:* Am Electroencephalog Soc; Am Asn Neurol Surg; AMA; Asn Res Nervous & Ment Dis; Am Asn Neuropath. *Res:* Neurological sciences; neurovascular and trauma of the nervous system. *Mailing Add:* Div Neurosurg Col Med & Dent 100 Bergen St Newark NJ 07103

KAPLAN, HARVEY, b New York, NY, Nov 29, 24; m 47; c 3. THEORETICAL PHYSICS. *Educ:* City Col New York, BS, 48; Univ Calif, PhD(physics), 52. *Prof Exp:* Res assoc, Mass Inst Technol, 52-54; asst prof physics, Univ Buffalo, 54-59; from asst prof to assoc prof, 59-65, PROF PHYSICS, SYRACUSE UNIV, 65- *Mem:* Am Phys Soc. *Res:* Theory of solid state; electronic structure of molecules. *Mailing Add:* Dept of Physics Syracuse Univ Syracuse NY 13210

KAPLAN, HARVEY, b New York, NY, May 24, 40; Can citizen; m 66; c 2. BIOCHEMISTRY. *Educ:* Queen's Univ, Ont, BSc, 62; Univ Ottawa, PhD(kinetics), 66. *Prof Exp:* Nat Res Coun Can fel, 66-67; fel, Lab Molecular Biol, Cambridge Univ, 67-68; asst res officer biochem, Nat Res Coun Can, 68-71; ASST PROF BIOCHEM, UNIV OTTAWA, 71- *Mem:* Can Biochem Soc. *Res:* Kinetics and mechanism of enzyme action; structure and function of serine proteases; ionization constants and reactivity of functional groups in proteins. *Mailing Add:* 432 Crestview Ottawa ON K1H 5G9 Can

KAPLAN, HARVEY ROBERT, b New Brunswick, NJ, Aug 21, 41; m 64; c 2. PHARMACOLOGY. *Educ:* Philadelphia Col Pharm, BSc, 63; Univ Conn, MSc, 65, PhD(pharmacol), 66. *Prof Exp:* Assoc dir, Dept Pharmacol, 67-80, DIR CARDIOVASC SECT, WARNER-LAMBERT RES INST, 80- *Concurrent Pos:* NIH fel, Univ Pittsburgh, 66-67. *Mem:* AAAS; NY Acad Sci; Am Soc Pharmacol & Exp Therapeut. *Res:* Cardiovascular and autonomic pharmacology; cardiac arrhythmias and antiarrhythmic drugs; central cardiovascular mechanisms; evaluation and assay of synthetics as well as natural products isolated form both plant and animals. *Mailing Add:* Warner-Lambert Co 2800 Plymouth Rd Ann Arbor MI 48105

KAPLAN, HELEN SINGER, b Vienna, Austria, Feb 6, 29; US citizen; div; c 3. PSYCHIATRY, PSYCHOLOGY. *Educ:* Syracuse Univ, BFA, 49; Columbia Univ, MA, 51, PhD(psychol), 55; NY Med Col, MD, 59. *Prof Exp:* Instr physiol & pharmacol, NY Med Col, 59-62, from clin assoc to assoc, 62-65, from asst prof to assoc prof, 65-71; CLIN ASSOC PROF PSYCHIAT, COL MED, CORNELL UNIV, 71- *Concurrent Pos:* Fel psychiat, Sch Med, NY Univ, 60-61; NIMH career teacher award, NY Med Col, 64-65; assoc attend psychiatrist, New York Hosp, 71-, chief sexual prog, Payne Whitney Clin. *Mem:* Am Psychol Asn; fel Am Psychiat Asn; Psychosom Soc; Acad Psychoanal. *Res:* Psychopharmacology; psychosomatic medicine; treatment of sexual disorders; psychiatric education. *Mailing Add:* 912 Fifth Ave New York NY 10021

KAPLAN, HENRY SEYMOUR, b Chicago, Ill, Apr 24, 18; m 42; c 2. RADIOLOGY. *Educ:* Univ Chicago, BS, 38; Rush Med Col, MD, 40; Univ Minn, MS, 44. *Hon Degrees:* ScD, Univ Chicago, 69. *Prof Exp:* mem panel radiobiol, Comt Growth, Nat Res Coun, 51-55, mem comt radiol, 55-57; mem radiation study sect, NIH, 55-59, mem phys biol training grant comt, 58-59; mem panel path effects of atomic radiation, Nat Acad Sci-Nat Res Coun, 57-; mem comn res, Int Union Against Cancer, 58-62; mem nat adv cancer coun, USPHS, 59-63; lectr & mem lectr many foreign & Am Univs, insts, found, hosps & socs, 63-; mem adv comt, Argonne Cancer Res Hosp, 66; mem adv comt biol, Oak Ridge Nat Lab; panel consult cancer res, US Senate, 70; mem prog comt, Int Cancer Cong, Florence, Italy, 74; Chas B Smith Mem vis prof, Mem-Sloan-Kettering Cancer Ctr, 77; vis cancer scientist, Univ Calif Med Ctr, San Francisco, 78; vis prof, Univ Auckland, 78. *Honors & Awards:* Chevalier, French Legion of Honor; Atoms for Peace Prize, 69; Order of Merit, Repub of Italy, 69; Shahbanou Award Cancer Res, Lila Motley Cancer Found, 69; R R de Villiers Award, Leukemia Soc Am, 71; Lucy Wortham James Award, James Ewing Soc, 71; Ann Nat Award, Am Cancer Soc, 72; Prix Griffuel, Asn Cancer Res, France, 77; Gold Medal, Am Soc Therapeut Radiol, 77; Lila Gruber Cancer Res Award, Am Acad Dermatol, 78; Medal of Honor, Danish Cancer Soc, 78; Gold Medal, Asn Univ Radiologists, 79; Walker Prize, Royal Col Surgeons, Eng, 81. *Mem:* Nat Acad Sci; Am Soc Therapeut Radiol (pres, 67-68); Radiation Res Soc (pres, 56-57); Int Asn Radiation Res (pres, 74-79); Am Asn Cancer Res (pres, 66-67). *Res:* Carcinogenesis by irradiation, especially leukemia induction by x-radiation of mice; biological effects of radiation; cell culture and virology of the human malignant lymphomas; human-human hybridoma monoclonal antibodies; natural history and treatment of Hodgkin's disease; megavoltage x-ray and electron beam therapy of cancer; total lymphoid irradiation in auto-immune disease and organ transplantation. *Mailing Add:* Dept of Radiol Stanford Univ Sch of Med Palo Alto CA 94305

KAPLAN, HERMAN, b New York, NY, Aug 17, 28; m 56; c 3. PSYCHIATRY, DENTISTRY. *Educ:* NY Univ, AB, 48, DDS, 53; State Univ NY Upstate Med Ctr, MD, 63. *Prof Exp:* From asst prof to assoc prof oral surg, 64-75, ASSOC PROF MED, DEPT ORAL DIAG, SCH DENT, UNIV OF THE PAC, 75-, ADJ PROF DIAG SCI & MED, 81- *Concurrent Pos:* Consult, Cowell Hosp & Mt Zion Hosp; resident psychiat, Presby Hosp-Pac Med Ctr, 72-75; mem div behav sci, Sch Dent, Univ of the Pac; consult, WHO, 80. *Mem:* Fel Acad Dent Int; AAAS. *Res:* Rapid stick method to detect diabetes mellitus; vital dye staining technique for oral cancer; use of a thermal sensing device in assessing and modifying inflammation in tissues; use of intravenous agents in ambulatory anesthesis. *Mailing Add:* 38 Arroyo Dr Moraga CA 94556

KAPLAN, HESH J, b Brooklyn, NY, Feb 16, 33; m 62; c 4. BOTANY, ENGINEERING. *Educ:* Ga Inst Technol, BIE, 54; Claremont Grad Sch, MBE, 66; Ore State Univ, PhD(bot), 77. *Prof Exp:* Engr comput, Mergenthaler Linotype Corp, 56-57; engr spacecraft, Marshall Space Flight Ctr, NASA, 57-59; engr missiles, Gen Dynamics Corp, 59-61; mgr prod assurance aircushion ships, Aerojet Gen Corp, 61-71; instr bot, Ore State Univ, 73-77; DIR RES DECAY CONTROL, PENNWALT CORP, 78- *Concurrent Pos:* Engr, Westinghouse Elec Co, 54-56; prof, Rio Hondo Jr Col, 66-67; instr, Linn-Benton Community Col, 77-78. *Mem:* Am Soc Hort Sci; Am Inst Biol Sci; Int Chem Soc. *Res:* Efficacy of post-harvest treatments of fruits and vegetables to control decay and extend storage life; modes of action of fungicides; genetics of resistance. *Mailing Add:* Dept of Res 1713 S California Ave Monrovia CA 91016

KAPLAN, IRVING, b New York, NY, Dec 1, 12; m 45; c 3. THEORETICAL PHYSICS. *Educ:* Columbia Univ, AB, 33, AM, 34, PhD(chem), 37. *Prof Exp:* Res chemist, Michael Reese Hosp, Chicago, 37-41; theoret physicist, Div War Res, Manhattan Proj, 41-44; sr scientist & head reactor physics div, Nuclear Eng Dept, Brookhaven Nat Lab, 45-57; vis prof, 57-58, prof nuclear eng, 58-80, EMER PROF, MASS INST TECHNOL, 80-, SECY FAC, DEPT NUCLEAR ENG, 74- *Concurrent Pos:* Theoret physicist, Sam Labs,

Columbia Univ & Carbide & Carbon Chem Corp, 44-46; vis lectr, Harvard Univ, 56. *Mem:* Am Phys Soc; Am Nuclear Soc; Am Acad Arts & Sci. *Res:* Nuclear physics; nuclear reactor physics. *Mailing Add:* Dept of Nuclear Eng Mass Inst of Technol Cambridge MA 02139

KAPLAN, ISSAC R, b Baranowicze, Poland, July 10, 29; m 55; c 2. GEOCHEMISTRY. *Educ:* Univ Canterbury, BSc, 52, MSc, 53; Univ Southern Calif, PhD(biogeochem), 61. *Prof Exp:* Res officer oceanog, Commonwealth Sci & Indust Res Orgn, Australia, 53-57; res fel geochem, Calif Inst Technol, 61-62; guest lectr & Ziskind scholar microbiol & geochem, Hebrew Univ, Israel, 63-65; assoc prof geol & geophys, 65-69, PROF GEOL & GEOCHEM, UNIV CALIF, LOS ANGELES, 69- *Concurrent Pos:* Assoc ed, Geochem Soc, 66-70 & Chem Geol, 66-67; mem planetary biol subcomt, Space Sci & Appln Steering Comt, NASA, 67-; Guggenheim Mem Found fel, Mineral Res Labs, Commonwealth Sci & Indust Res Orgn, Japan, New Caledonia, NZ & Australia, 70-71; assoc ed, Marine Chem, 72- & Geochem J, 76-; mem exobiol panel, Space Sci Bd, Nat Acad Sci. prin investr lunar return mat, Apollo 11, 12, 14 & 15. *Mem:* Geochem Soc; fel Am Inst Chemists; Am Asn Petrol Geologists; AAAS. *Res:* Biogeochemistry of recent sediments; factors controlling the distribution of elements in the ocean; isotope geochemistry and organic geochemistry of terrestrial rocks and meteorites; biological fractionation of stable isotopes. *Mailing Add:* Geol Rm 5853 Slichter Hall Univ of Calif Los Angeles CA 90024

KAPLAN, JACOB GORDIN, b New York, NY, Nov 26, 22; m 49; c 2. CELL BIOLOGY, MOLECULAR BIOLOGY. *Educ:* City Col New York, BA, 43; Columbia Univ, MA, 48, PhD(gen physiol, biophys), 50. *Hon Degrees:* DSc, Concordia Univ, 78. *Prof Exp:* Instr biol, City Col New York, 46-50; from asst prof to prof physiol, Dalhousie Univ, 50-66; prof biol, Univ Ottawa, 66-81, chmn, 75-81; VPRES RES & PROF BIOCHEM, UNIV ALBERTA, 81- *Concurrent Pos:* Vis res worker, Dept Colloid Sci, Cambridge Univ, 56; Lalor Found fel, 56; NSF sr res fel, 56-57; vis res worker, Nat Inst Med Res, Mill Hill, Eng, 57, Inst Pasteur, France, 57 & Lab Genetic Physiol, Gif-sur-Yvette, 64-65; vis res worker, dept cell biochem, Inst Pasteur, Paris, 73-74; ed, Can J Biochem, 73-; pres, llth Int Cong Biochem, Toronto, 79. *Mem:* Can Biochem Soc; Am Soc Biol Chem; Can Soc Cell Biol. *Res:* Enzyme regulation and biosynthesis; molecular biology of lymphocyte activation. *Mailing Add:* Off VPres Res Univ Alberta Edmonton AB T6G 2J9 Can

KAPLAN, JAMES, b Brooklyn, NY, Mar 17, 46; m 67. MATHEMATICS. *Educ:* Brooklyn Col, BS, 66; Univ Md, PhD(math), 70. *Prof Exp:* Asst prof math, Northwestern Univ, 70-72; ASSOC PROF MATH, BOSTON UNIV, 72- *Mem:* Am Math Soc. *Res:* Ordinary and functional differential equations; oscillation in biological systems. *Mailing Add:* Dept Math Boston Univ Boston MA 02215

KAPLAN, JEROME I, b New York, NY, July 28, 26; m 65; c 1. SOLID STATE PHYSICS. *Educ:* Univ Mich, BS, 50; Univ Calif, Berkeley, PhD(physics), 54. *Prof Exp:* Res scientist, Naval Res Lab, DC, 54-59; res assoc physics, Brandeis Univ, 59-62, asst prof, 62-63; Fulbright lectr, Univ Col, Rhodesia & Nyasaland, 63-64; assoc res prof, Brown Univ, 64-67; res fel, Battelle-Columbus, 67-74; res assoc, Krannert Inst Cardiol, 74-80; PROF PHYSICS, IND UNIV-PURDUE UNIV INDIANAPOLIS, 74-; SR FEL, INDIANAPOLIS CTR ADVAN RES, 80- *Concurrent Pos:* Louis Lipsky fel physics, Weizmann Inst, 56-57; consult, Lincoln Lab, Mass Inst Technol, 61; vis scientist, Naval Res Lab, 81; consult, Hercules Chem Co. *Mem:* Am Phys Soc. *Res:* Magnetic properties of solids; nuclear and ferromagnetic wave resonance; electron, nuclear and ferromagnetic spin resonance phenomena; magnetic resonance in liquids and liquid crystals; nuclear magnetic resonance in heart muscle; solar heating design; nuclear magnetic resonance theory. *Mailing Add:* Dept of Physics Ind Univ-Purdue Univ Indianapolis IN 46205

KAPLAN, JOEL HOWARD, b New York, NY, Apr 6, 41; m 63; c 3. IMMUNOLOGY, CELL BIOLOGY. *Educ:* City Col New York, BS, 62; Johns Hopkins Univ, PhD(biochem), 67. *Prof Exp:* Nat Cancer Inst fel cancer biochem, McArdle Lab Cancer Res, 67-69; STAFF SCIENTIST MED SCI, GEN ELEC RES & DEVELOP CTR, 69- *Mem:* Am Asn Immunol; AAAS. *Res:* Invitro methods in cell-mediated immunity; electrokinetic properties of lymphocyte subpopulations; cancer-immunodiagnosis. *Mailing Add:* Gen Elec Res & Develop Ctr Bldg K-1 Schenectady NY 12301

KAPLAN, JOEL HOWARD, b Paterson, NJ, Sept 8, 38; m; c 1. CHEMICAL ENGINEERING. *Educ:* Newark Col Eng, BS, 61, MS, 62, DSc(chem eng), 66. *Prof Exp:* Res chem engr, 66-69, group leader, Process Anal Sect, 69-71, MGR SYSTS ANAL DEPT, ORG CHEM DIV, AM CYANAMID CO, BOUND BROOK, 71- *Concurrent Pos:* Adj prof chem eng, NJ Inst Technol, 78- *Mem:* Am Inst Chem Engrs; Am Chem Soc; NY Acad Sci. *Res:* Kinetics and reactor design of industrial processes; process development; application of computer control to industrial processes; research management concerned with plant and laboratory automation and development of research strategy models. *Mailing Add:* 26 Bianculli Dr South Plainfield NJ 07080

KAPLAN, JOHN ERVIN, b Chicago, Ill, Dec 4, 50; m 73; c 2. PHAGOCYTOSIS, THROMBOSIS. *Educ:* Univ Ill, BS, 72; Albany Med Col, PhD(physiol), 76. *Prof Exp:* Fel, 75-77, instr, 76-77, asst prof, 77-80, ASSOC PROF PHYSIOL, ALBANY MED COL, 80- *Concurrent Pos:* Prin investr res grants, New York Heart Asn, 77-78, NIH, 78- & Shared Instrumentation Prog, 79-; Sinsheimer Fund Scholar, 80-83. *Mem:* Sigma Xi; Reticuloendothelial Soc. *Res:* Mechanisms by which phagocytosis and opsonic factors act as physiological anti-thrombotic mechanisms, and the role of these mechanisms in sepsis, trauma, intravascular coagulation and vascular injury. *Mailing Add:* Dept Physiol Albany Med Col Albany NY 12208

KAPLAN, JOSEPH, b Tapolcza, Hungary, Sept 8, 02; nat US; m 33. PHYSICS, GEOPHYSICS. *Educ:* Johns Hopkins Univ, BSc, 24, MA, 26, PhD(physics), 27. *Hon Degrees:* ScD, Univ Notre Dame, 57, Carleton Col, 57; LHD, Hebrew Union Col, 58, Yeshiva Univ, 58. *Prof Exp:* Instr physics, Johns Hopkins Univ, 25-27; Nat Res Coun fel, Princeton Univ, 27-28; from asst prof to prof, 28-74, chmn dept meteorol, 40-44, chmn dept physics, 40-45, dir inst geophys, 46-47, EMER PROF PHYSICS, UNIV CALIF, LOS ANGELES, 74- *Concurrent Pos:* Consult, Off Sci & Tech & NSF; chmn, US Nat Comt, Int Geophys Year; mem comt space res, Int Coun Sci Unions, sci adv bd, US Air Force; Int Astron Union; Int Union Geod & Geophys, 63-; chmn sci adv group, Off Aerospace Res, 63-; mem adv coun, Atomic Energy Develop & Radiation Protection, State of Calif. *Honors & Awards:* Decoration for Exceptional Civilian Serv, War Dept, 47; Astronaut Award, Rocket Soc, Am Inst Aeronaut & Astronaut, 56; Exceptional Serv Award, US Air Force, 60; Hogkins Medal & Prize, Smithsonian Inst, 65. *Mem:* Nat Acad Sci; Am Astron Soc; fel Am Inst Aeronaut & Astronaut; Meteoritical Soc; Am Meteorol Soc. *Res:* Molecular spectroscopy; chemical aeronomy; general geophysics. *Mailing Add:* Dept of Physics Univ of Calif 405 Hilgard Ave Los Angeles CA 90024

KAPLAN, KENNETH, b New York, NY, Dec 26, 26; m 51; c 2. SHOCK WAVES, DOCUMENTARY FILMS. *Educ:* Univ Calif, BS, 49. *Prof Exp:* Res engr, Univ Calif, 49-51; engr, San Francisco Dist, US Corps Engr, 51-52, hydraul engr, Beach Erosion Bd, Washington, DC, 52-54; dep dir, Burlingame Res Ctr, 54-69, vpres planning, 69-70, vpres & dir eng res div, URS Res Co, URS Systs Corp, 70-74, ; sr assoc, 75-77, CONSULT, SCI SERV, INC, 74-, MGT SCI ASSOCS, 77- *Mem:* AAAS. *Res:* Hydrodynamics, especially shock waves and their interactions and effects; surface water waves and their generation, propagation and effects; producer of technical documentary films. *Mailing Add:* 30 White Plains Ct San Mateo CA 94402

KAPLAN, LAWRENCE, b Chicago, Ill, Apr 14, 26; m 46; c 1. BOTANY. *Educ:* Univ Iowa, BA, 49, MS, 51; Univ Chicago, PhD(bot), 56. *Prof Exp:* Assoc cur, Mus Useful Plants, Mo Bot Gardens, 55; instr biol, Wright Jr Col, 56; asst prof, Roosevelt Univ, 57-65; assoc prof, 65-68, PROF BIOL, UNIV MASS, BOSTON, 68- *Mem:* AAAS; Bot Soc Am. *Res:* Ethnobotany; systematics. *Mailing Add:* Dept of Biol Univ of Mass Boston MA 02125

KAPLAN, LAWRENCE JAY, b Newark, NJ, Mar 20, 43; m 65; c 2. BIOCHEMISTRY. *Educ:* Univ Pittsburgh, BS, 64; Purdue Univ, PhD(chem), 70. *Prof Exp:* Fel, Univ Mass, Amherst, 70-71; asst prof, 71-77, ASSOC PROF CHEM, WILLIAMS COL, 77- *Concurrent Pos:* Res scientist, Weizmann Inst, Israel, 76-77; vis assoc prof, Biochem Dept, Brandeis Univ, 80-81. *Mem:* AAAS; Am Chem Soc; Am Soc Biol Chemists. *Res:* Physical biochemistry of proteins; conformational transitions of macromolecules; structure of chromatin. *Mailing Add:* Dept of Chem Williams Col Williamstown MA 01267

KAPLAN, LEON H, physical chemistry, see previous edition

KAPLAN, LEONARD, b Brooklyn, NY, July 18, 39. ORGANIC CHEMISTRY, CATALYSIS. *Educ:* Cooper Union, BChE, 60; Univ Ill, PhD(org chem), 64. *Prof Exp:* Res assoc org chem, Columbia Univ, 64-65; instr, Univ Chicago, 65-67, asst prof, 67-74; proj scientist, 74-75, res scientist, 75-79, SR RES SCIENTIST, UNION CARBIDE CORP, 79- *Concurrent Pos:* NSF fel, 64-65; Alfred P Sloan Found fel. *Mem:* Am Chem Soc; The Chem Soc. *Res:* Homogeneous catalysis; organometallic chemistry; mechanistic and physical organic chemistry; exploratory synthesis; free radical chemistry. *Mailing Add:* Union Carbide Corp PO Box 8361 South Charleston WV 25303

KAPLAN, LEONARD LOUIS, b New York, NY, Oct 10, 28; m 68; c 2. PHARMACEUTICS. *Educ:* NY Univ, BA, 48, PhD(statist, mgt sci), 68; Ohio State Univ, BScPharm, 52; City Col New York, MBA, 63. *Prof Exp:* Res assoc pharm, Sterling-Winthrop Res Inst, 55-59; dir develop, Walker Labs Div, Richardson-Merrell, 59-63, group mgr, Vick Div Res, 63-69; dir res & develop, Health Care Div, 69-78, DIR RES & DEVELOP, ORTHO PHARM CORP, JOHNSON & JOHNSON-DOMESTIC OPER CO, 78- *Concurrent Pos:* Adj assoc prof, Brooklyn Col Pharm, 66-69 & Col Pharm Rutgers Univ, 79- *Mem:* Acad Pharmaceut Sci; Soc Cosmetic Chemists. *Res:* Pharmaceutical research specializing in areas of analgesics, oral hygiene, sports medicine, dermatology and deodorancy; contraceptives; diagnostics. *Mailing Add:* One Minuteman Ct East Brunswick NJ 08816

KAPLAN, LEWIS DAVID, b Brooklyn, NY, June 21, 17; m 42; c 1. GEOPHYSICS, METEOROLOGY. *Educ:* Brooklyn Col, BA, 39; Univ Chicago, SM, 47, PhD(meteorol), 51. *Prof Exp:* Observer, US Weather Bur, 40-45, meteorologist, 47-54; mem, Inst Advan Study, 54-56; guest, Univ London, 56-57; mem res staff, Mass Inst Technol, 57-61; staff scientist, Jet Propulsion Lab, Calif Inst Technol, 62-70; prof, 70-79, EMER PROF METEOROL, UNIV CHICAG0, 80-; PRIN SCIENTIST, ATMOSPHERIC & ENVIRON RES INC, 81- *Concurrent Pos:* Res assoc & instr, Univ NMex, 48-49; instr, Univ Chicago, 50; prof, Univ Nev, 61-64; prin experimenter, Mariner II Infrared Exp, 61-63; vis prof, Oxford Univ, 64-65, Univ Oslo, 65, Mass Inst Technol, 68 & Univ Paris, 69-70; sr staff scientist, Goddard Space Flight Ctr, NASA, 78-81. *Honors & Awards:* Except Sci Achievement Medal, NASA, 68; Second Half-Century Award, Am Meteorol Soc, 70. *Mem:* AAAS; fel Am Meteorol Soc; Am Geophys Union; Royal Meteorol Soc. *Res:* Radiative heat transfer in planetary atmospheres; analysis of infrared spectra; composition and structure of planetary atmospheres; atmospheric dynamics and energy exchange; numerical weather prediction. *Mailing Add:* Atmospheric & Environ Res Inc 840 Mem Dr Cambridge MA 02139

KAPLAN, LOUIS, microbiology, see previous edition

KAPLAN, MANUEL E, b New York, NY, Nov 6, 28; m 55; c 3. INTERNAL MEDICINE, HEMATOLOGY. *Educ:* Univ Ariz, BS, 50; Harvard Med Sch, MD, 54. *Prof Exp:* Intern med, Boston City Hosp, 54-55, from asst resident to sr resident, 55-59; res assoc, Mt Sinai Hosp, New York, 62-63, asst dir hemat, 63-65; asst prof med, Sch Med, Wash Univ, 65-69; assoc prof, 69-73, PROF MED, MED SCH, UNIV MINN, MINNEAPOLIS, 73-; CHIEF HEMAT, VET ADMIN HOSP, 69- *Concurrent Pos:* Fel hemat, Thorndike Mem Lab, Boston City Hosp, 59-62; USPHS res grants, 63-64 & 66-, career develop award, 67-69; res fel microbiol, Col Physicians & Surgeons, Columbia Univ, 63-65; chief hemat, Jewish Hosp of St Louis, 65-69. *Mem:* AAAS; Am Fedn Clin; Am Soc Clin Invest; Am Soc Hemat; NY Acad Sci. *Res:* Immunohematology; lymphocyte structure and function; hematopoiesis. *Mailing Add:* Vet Admin Hosp 54th St & 48th Ave S Minneapolis MN 55417

KAPLAN, MARK STEVEN, b New York, NY, Feb 25, 47; div; c 2. PHOTOGRAPHIC CHEMISTRY. *Educ:* Bucknell Univ, BS & MS, 67; Univ Ore, PhD(org chem), 71. *Prof Exp:* SR RES SCIENTIST GRAPHIC ARTS, EASTMAN KODAK CO, 71- *Mem:* Am Chem Soc; Soc Photog Scientists & Engrs. *Res:* Novel imaging systems for graphic arts; use of lasers in graphic arts; photoresists. *Mailing Add:* Eastman Kodak Co Res Labs B-82 Kodak Park Rochester NY 14650

KAPLAN, MARSHALL HARVEY, b Detroit, Mich, Nov 5, 39; m 61; c 2. AERONAUTICS, ASTRONAUTICS. *Educ:* Wayne State Univ, BS, 61; Mass Inst Technol, SM, 62; Stanford Univ, PhD(aeronaut, astronaut), 68. *Prof Exp:* Mem tech staff, Hughes Res Lab, Calif, 62-64; mem tech staff, Space Systs Div, Hughes Aircraft Co, 64-65; sr engr, Western Develop Labs, Philco Corp, 65-66; from asst prof to assoc prof aerospace eng, 68-78, PROF AEROSPACE ENG, PA STATE UNIV, 78- *Honors & Awards:* Outstanding Res Award, Pa State Univ, 78. *Mem:* Am Inst Aeronaut & Astronaut; Am Astronaut Soc; Am Soc Eng Educ. *Res:* Space systems synthesis and engineering; astrodynamics; propulsion; satellite dynamics and control. *Mailing Add:* Col of Eng Pa State Univ 233 Hammond Bldg University Park PA 16802

KAPLAN, MARTIN L, b New York, NY, Apr 7, 23; m 48; c 2. COMPARATIVE PHYSIOLOGY, INSECT PATHOLOGY. *Educ:* Brooklyn Col, AB, 49; NY Univ, MS, 54, PhD(exp zool), 58. *Prof Exp:* Lectr biol, Brooklyn Col, 53-56, tutor, 56-57; instr biol, Fairleigh Dickinson Univ, 57-58, asst prof anat, Sch Dent, 58-59; assoc path, St Vincent's Hosp, New York, 59-62; from asst prof to assoc prof, 62-71, asst dean sch gen studies, 70-75, PROF BIOL, QUEENS COL, NY, 71- *Concurrent Pos:* Lectr, Sch Gen Studies, Brooklyn Col, 59-62. *Mem:* AAAS; Am Soc Zool. *Res:* Histogenesis and biochemistry of melanotic tumors in Drosophila. *Mailing Add:* Dept of Biol Queens Col Flushing NY 11367

KAPLAN, MARTIN L, b New York, NY, Dec 27, 35; m 64; c 1. PHYSICAL ORGANIC CHEMISTRY. *Educ:* City Col New York, BS, 56; Fla State Univ, MS, 60; Seton Hall Univ, JD, 70. *Prof Exp:* Res technician microbiol, Columbia Univ, 56-57 & Sloan-Kettering Inst Cancer Res, 57-58; res assoc phys chem, Fla State Univ, 60; chemist, Richfield Oil Corp, 60-62; vol sci teaching, US Peace Corps, 62-64; assoc mem staff, 64-77, MEM STAFF, BELL LABS, 77- *Mem:* AAAS; Am Chem Soc; Royal Soc Chem. *Res:* Mechanisms of organic reactions; rates of conformational isomerization of organic molecules by nuclear magnetic resonance; multicharged carbonium ion species; reactions by singlet oxygen with polymers; electrical conductivity of organic molecules and polymers. *Mailing Add:* Bell Labs Murray Hill NJ 07974

KAPLAN, MARTIN MARK, b Philadelphia, Pa, June 23, 15; m 44; c 3. PUBLIC HEALTH. *Educ:* Univ Pa, VMD, 40, AB, 41, MPH, 42. *Hon Degrees:* DrMedVet, Hanover Vet Univ, 63. *Prof Exp:* Assoc prof vet prev med & pub health, Sch Vet Med, Middlesex Univ, 42-45; chief livestock sect, UN Relief & Rehab Admin, Greece, 45-47; vet consult, UN Food & Agr Orgn, 47-49; chief vet pub health sect, 49-71, spec adv res develop, 62-69, spec asst sci, 69-71, dir off res promotion & develop, Off Dir-Gen, World Health Orgn, Geneva, Switz, 71-76, DIR-GEN PUGWASH CONFS SCI & WORLD AFFAIRS, LONDON & GENEVA, 76- *Concurrent Pos:* NIH fel, 59-60. *Honors & Awards:* K F Meyer Award, 67; Schofield Mem Medal, 74; Medal of French Comt World Vet Asn, 74. *Mem:* AAAS; hon assoc Royal Col Vet Surgeons. *Res:* Animal diseases transmissible to man; food hygiene; comparative medicine; virology. *Mailing Add:* Pugwash Confs II 9 60 Great Russell St London WCI England

KAPLAN, MAURICE, b Gorzd, Lithuania, Oct 10, 07; nat US. PSYCHIATRY. *Educ:* Univ Ill, BS, 32, MD, 35, MS, 39; Am Bd Psychiat & Neurol, dipl psychiat, 48, cert, child psychiat, 59. *Prof Exp:* Asst instr psychiat, Col Med, Univ Ill, 36-39; staff psychiatrist, Inst Juv Res, Ill, 39-42; asst med dir, Am Joint Dist Comn, France, 46-47; asst dir, Children's Div, Langley Porter Clin & lectr psychiat, Clin & Sch Med, Univ Calif, 48-50, from clin instr to assoc clin prof, 50-62; assoc clin prof psychiat, Univ Ill Col Med, 62-67; CONSULT, MARY BARTELME HOME, CHICAGO, 69-; LECTR, NORTHWESTERN UNIV, 69- *Concurrent Pos:* Fel, Neuropsychiat Inst, Univ Ill, 36-39; instr, Col Med, Univ Ill, 40-42; dir, Child Guid Clin, Children's Hosp, San Francisco, Calif, 48-60; pvt pract, 49-59; consult, San Francisco Unified Sch Dist, 50-59; consult dept psychiat, US Army Letterman Gen Hosp, San Francisco, 58-59; Fulbright lectr, India, 59; dir, South Coast Child Guid Clin, 67-69. *Mem:* Am Med Asn; fel Am Psychiat Asn; fel Am Orthopsychiat Asn; Am Psychoanal Asn; Am Acad Child Psychiat. *Res:* Child psychiatry; psychoanalysis; psychotherapy. *Mailing Add:* 572 Cherokee Highland Park IL 60035

KAPLAN, MELVIN, b Brooklyn, NY, Nov 11, 27; m 53; c 4. ORGANIC CHEMISTRY. *Educ:* Brooklyn Col, BS, 50; Ohio State Univ, PhD(org chem), 54. *Prof Exp:* From proj leader to res supvr urethane applns, Indust Chem Div, 54-70, MGR TECH SERV & DEVELOP URETHANES, SPECIALTY CHEM DIV, ALLIED CHEM CORP, BUFFALO, 70- *Mem:* Am Chem Soc; Am Soc Testing & Mat; Int Isocyanate Inst; Soc Plastics Indust. *Res:* Isocyanate and urethane polymer chemistry; plastics; organic synthesis; kinetics of chemical reactions; blowing agents; plastic foams. *Mailing Add:* 292 Culpepper Rd Williamsville NY 14221

KAPLAN, MELVIN HYMAN, b Malden, Mass, Dec 23, 20. MEDICINE, IMMUNOLOGY. *Educ:* Harvard Univ, AB, 42, MD, 52. *Prof Exp:* Intern med, Boston City Hosp, 52-53; asst bact & immunol, Harvard Med Sch, 53-54; from asst prof to prof, Sch Med, Case Western Reserve Univ, 58-74; PROF MED & HEAD, DIV RHEUMATOLOGY & IMMUNOL, MED SCH, UNIV MASS, 74- *Concurrent Pos:* Res fel, House Good Samaritan, Boston, 53-54; USPHS res career award, 64-; res assoc, House Good Samaritan, Boston, 54-57; instr, Harvard Med Sch, 54-56, assoc, 57-58; estab investr, Am Heart Asn, 54-; assoc mem comn streptococcal dis, Armed Forces Epidemiol Bd, US Dept Defense, 56-; temp adv, WHO, 65-66. *Mem:* Am Soc Clin Invest; Am Soc Microbiol; Am Heart Asn; Am Asn Immunol; Am Rheumatism Asn. *Res:* Microbiology; pathogenesis of rheumatic diseases, particularly in relation to the role of immunologic mechanisms; clinical immunology and rheumatology. *Mailing Add:* Univ of Mass Med Sch 55 Lake Ave N Worcester MA 01605

KAPLAN, MICHAEL, b New York, NY, Nov 7, 37; m 68; c 2. RADIATION CHEMISTRY. *Educ:* Rensselaer Polytech Inst, BS, 59; Columbia Univ, MA, 61, PhD(electron spin resonance), 65. *Prof Exp:* MEM TECH STAFF, RCA LABS, 65- *Mem:* Am Chem Soc; Am Phys Soc; NY Acad Sci; fel Am Inst Chemists. *Res:* Electron spin resonance of organic materials; interaction of charged particles with thin films; electron-beam lithography; x-ray lithography. *Mailing Add:* RCA Corp RCA Labs David Sarnoff Res Ctr Princeton NJ 08540

KAPLAN, MILTON TEMKIN, b Russia, Apr 11, 12; nat US; m 41; c 1. MEDICAL MICROBIOLOGY. *Educ:* Univ Calif, Los Angeles, BA, 36; Univ Southern Calif, MS, 52, PhD(bact), 61. *Prof Exp:* Bacteriologist, Vet Admin Hosp, Los Angeles, 46-48; mem fac, Dept Med Microbiol, Col Osteop Physicians & Surgeons, Los Angeles, 48-64; asst prof med microbiol, Univ Calif, Irvine, 64-78; RETIRED. *Concurrent Pos:* Consult microbiologist, Los Angeles County Gen Hosp, Unit 2, 53-63. *Mem:* AAAS; Am Soc Microbiol. *Res:* Food bacteriology; bacteriological methods; toxins of staphylococci. *Mailing Add:* 464 High Dr Laguna Beach CA 92651

KAPLAN, MORTON, b Chicago, Ill, Nov 21, 33; m 57; c 2. NUCLEAR CHEMISTRY, PHYSICAL CHEMISTRY. *Educ:* Univ Chicago, AB, 54, SM, 56; Mass Inst Technol, PhD(phys chem), 60. *Prof Exp:* Res assoc chem, Mass Inst Technol, 60; res staff chem, Lawrence Radiation Lab, 60-62; from asst prof to assoc prof, Yale Univ, 62-70; assoc prof, 70, PROF CHEM, CARNEGIE-MELLON UNIV, 71- *Concurrent Pos:* Alfred P Sloan res fel, 65-69; vis scientist, Univ Oxford, 71-72. *Mem:* Am Phys Soc; Am Chem Soc; AAAS. *Res:* Nuclear reactions induced by heavy ions; Mossbauer effect; perturbed angular correlations of gamma rays; magnetic properties and chemical bonding at low temperatures; nuclear spectroscopy; low temperature nuclear orientation. *Mailing Add:* Dept of Chem Carnegie- Mellon Univ Pittsburgh PA 15213

KAPLAN, MURRAY LEE, b Jan 9, 41; m 65; c 2. NUTRITION, METABOLISM. *Educ:* Alfred Univ, NY, BA, 62; City Univ New York, PhD(biol), 72. *Prof Exp:* Lectr biol, Brooklyn Col, 66-71; res assoc nutrit, Dept Food Sci & Human Nutrit, Mich State Univ, 71-74; asst prof nutrit, Rutgers Univ, 74-80; ASSOC PROF FOOD & NUTRIT, IOWA STATE UNIV, 81- *Concurrent Pos:* NIH res fel, Dept Food Sci & Human Nutrit, Mich State Univ, 72-74. *Mem:* AAAS; Am Chem Soc; Am Soc Zoologists; Am Inst Nutrit; NY Acad Sci. *Res:* Role of early nutritional experiences on the development of regulation of carbohydrate, lipid metabolism and obesity; Adipocyte metabolism. *Mailing Add:* Dept Food & Nutrit Iowa State Univ Ames IA 50011

KAPLAN, NATHAN, b New York, NY, Aug 2, 20; m 42; c 3. ELECTROCHEMISTRY, RESEARCH ADMINISTRATION. *Educ:* City Col New York, BS, 39; George Washington Univ, MS, 54. *Prof Exp:* Instr, Air Force Tech Training Command, 42-43; asst chem, Manhattan Proj, NY, 43-45, engr, Develop Plant, Oak Ridge, Tenn, 45-46; assoc chemist, NIH, 46-51; res supvr, 51-63, chief power supply br, 63-69, chief mat br, 70-76, CHIEF MFG TECHNOL BR, HARRY DIAMOND LABS, 76- *Mem:* Am Chem Soc; Electrochem Soc. *Res:* Energy conversion systems and devices; design and production of unconventional special purpose power sources; ordnance applications of polymers; thin-film hybrid circuit technology. *Mailing Add:* 1200 Schindler Dr Silver Spring MD 20903

KAPLAN, NATHAN ORAM, b New York, NY, June 25, 17; m 46; c 1. BIOCHEMISTRY. *Educ:* Univ Calif, Los Angeles, AB, 39; Univ Calif, PhD(biochem), 43. *Prof Exp:* Asst biochem, Univ Calif, 40-42; chemist, Manhattan Proj, 42-44; instr med biochem, Col Med, Wayne Univ, 44-45; res assoc, Mass Gen Hosp, Boston, 45-49; asst prof, Col Med, Univ Ill, 49-50; from asst prof to prof biol, McCollum-Pratt Inst, Johns Hopkins Univ, 50-57; prof biochem & chmn grad dept, Brandeis Univ, 57-68; PROF CHEM, UNIV CALIF, SAN DIEGO, 68- *Concurrent Pos:* NSF traveling fel, 52; Guggenheim Mem Found fel, 64-65 & sr fel, 75-76; consult, Pabst Labs; spec consult, Nat Cancer Inst; mem adv comt metab biol, NSF. *Honors & Awards:* Eli Lilly Award, 53. *Mem:* Nat Acad Sci; Am Soc Biol Chem; Am Chem Soc; Am Soc Microbiol; Am Acad Arts & Sci. *Res:* Enzymology; relationship of vitamins to metabolism; microbial metabolism; influence of hormones on metabolism; action of antimetabolites; biochemical evolution; chemotherapy. *Mailing Add:* Dept Chem Univ Calif San Diego La Jolla CA 92093

KAPLAN, NORMAN M, b Dallas, Tex, Jan 2, 31; m 50; c 3. INTERNAL MEDICINE. *Educ:* Univ Tex, BS, 50, MD, 54; Am Bd Internal Med, dipl & cert endocrinol & metab. *Prof Exp:* Res physician, Parkland Mem Hosp, Dallas, 55-58; from instr to assoc prof, 61-70, PROF MED, UNIV TEX HEALTH SCI CTR, DALLAS, 70-, HEAD HYPERTENSION SECT, 78- *Concurrent Pos:* USPHS res fel, Clin Endocrinol Br, Nat Heart Inst, 60-61; USPHS grants, 62-70; dep vpres res progs, Am Heart Asn, 75-76; NIH acad award, 79-84. *Mem:* Am Fedn Clin Res; Endocrine Soc; Am Col Physicians; Am Soc Clin Invest; Coun High Blood Pressure Res. *Res:* Mechanisms controlling biosyntheses of adrenal cortical hormones particularly aldosterone; relationship of renin-angiotension system to hypertension; sodium restriction in treatment of hypertension. *Mailing Add:* Univ Tex Health Sci Ctr 5323 Harry Hines Blvd Dallas TX 75235

KAPLAN, PAUL, b New York, NY, Dec 6, 29; m 56; c 2. FLUID DYNAMICS, APPLIED MATHEMATICS. *Educ:* City Col New York, BS, 50; Stevens Inst Technol, MS, 51, DSc(appl mech), 55. *Prof Exp:* Physicist, Stevens Inst Technol, 50-56, res asst prof math & mech eng, 56-59, staff scientist, 56-57, head, Math Studies Div, 57-58 & Fluid Dynamics Div, 58-59; chief hydrodynamicist, TRG, Inc, 59-61; pres, Oceanics, Inc, Plainview, 61-79; PRES, HYDROMECHANICS, INC, PLAINVIEW, 79- *Concurrent Pos:* Lectr, City Col New York, 54-56; adj prof, Webb Inst Naval Archit, 63-66; consult, Edo Corp, NY, 58, Vitro Lab, Md, Westinghouse Elec Corp, Calif, Elec Boat Div, Gen Dynamics Corp, Conn, 59 & Marine Adv, Inc, 61-62. *Mem:* Soc Naval Archit & Marine Engrs; Am Inst Aeronaut & Astronaut; Marine Technol Soc; Royal Inst Naval Architects. *Res:* Hydrodynamics; wave motion; stability and control; hydroelasticity; dynamics; random vibration and motion analysis; acoustics; analog, digital and hybrid computation; oceanography; automatic control systems; structural dynamics; offshore structures. *Mailing Add:* 14 Birchwood Park Crescent Jericho NY 11753

KAPLAN, PHYLLIS DEEN, b Everett, Wash, Feb 9, 31; c 2. CHEMISTRY, BIOCHEMISTRY. *Educ:* Univ Wash, BA, 53; Brandeis Univ, MA, 56; Univ Cincinnati, PhD(chem), 66. *Prof Exp:* Spectroscopist chem, Syntex Corp, 67-68; res assoc, Med Ctr, Univ Cincinnati, 68-71, asst prof environ health, 71-77; SR RES TOXICOLOGIST, AM CYANAMID CO, 77- *Concurrent Pos:* Am Chem Soc Petroleum Res Fund grant, Univ Cincinnati, 65-66; NIOSH res grant, 71-76; lectr, Col Nursing, Univ Cincinnati, 73-74. *Mem:* AAAS; Am Chem Soc; Sigma Xi. *Res:* Metabolism, binding and structural identity of transition metal compounds in the body, with a special interest in elucidating the mechanisms determining toxicity and essentiality of metals within living systems. *Mailing Add:* Toxicol Res Dept 973 Am Cyanamid Co Pearl River NY 10965

KAPLAN, RALPH BENJAMIN, b New York, NY, Feb 20, 20; m 53; c 2. ORGANIC CHEMISTRY. *Educ:* Brooklyn Col, BA, 42; Ohio State Univ, PhD(chem), 50. *Prof Exp:* Res assoc, Res Found, Ohio State Univ, 50-51; RES CHEMIST, ORG CHEM DEPT, JACKSON LAB, E I DU PONT DE NEMOURS & CO, INC, 51- *Honors & Awards:* US Dept Navy Award, 62. *Mem:* Am Chem Soc. *Res:* Synthesis and chemistry of nitro and polynitro aliphatic compounds and anthraquinon vat dyes; properties of synthetic elastomers; petroleum chemicals; organometallic compounds; electrochemistry; patent law. *Mailing Add:* 1409 Silverside Rd Wilmington DE 19803

KAPLAN, RAPHAEL, b New York, NY, Mar 26, 36. SOLID STATE PHYSICS. *Educ:* Syracuse Univ, AB, 57; Brown Univ, PhD(physics), 63. *Prof Exp:* PHYSICIST, SEMICONDUCTORS BR, SOLID STATE DIV, US NAVAL RES LAB, 63- *Mem:* Am Phys Soc. *Res:* Spin resonance of color centers in irratiated crystals; far infrared and millimeter wave spectroscopy in semiconductors and other materials. *Mailing Add:* Code 5234 US Naval Res Lab Washington DC 20375

KAPLAN, RAYMOND, b New York, NY, Jan 26, 29; m 65; c 2. SOLID STATE PHYSICS. *Educ:* City Col New York, BS, 50; Columbia Univ, MA, 52, PhD(physics), 59. *Prof Exp:* Jr res physicist, Univ Calif, 58-59; res physicist, Airborne Instruments Lab, 60-62; asst prof physics, Adelphi Univ, 62-64; res physicist, US Rubber Co, NJ, 64-68; asst prof, Cooper Union, 68-71, assoc prof physics, 71-77; adj assoc prof physics, York Col, 77-79; asst prof physics, Maritime Col, State Univ NY, 79-80; ASST PROF PHYSICS, FORDHAM UNIV, 81- *Concurrent Pos:* Consult, Info Div, Am Inst Physics & Electronic Semiconductor Co. *Mem:* Am Phys Soc; Am Asn Physics Teachers; NY Acad Sci. *Res:* Superconductivity; cryogenics. *Mailing Add:* 2408 Hawthorn Dr Yorktown Heights NY 10598

KAPLAN, RICHARD E, b Philadelphia, Pa, July 4, 38; m 60; c 2. AEROSPACE ENGINEERING, FLUID MECHANICS. *Educ:* Mass Inst Technol, BS & MS, 61, ScD(aerospace eng), 64. *Prof Exp:* From asst prof to assoc prof, 64-73, dir systs simulation lab, 69-71, PROF AEROSPACE ENG, UNIV SOUTHERN CALIF, 73- *Concurrent Pos:* Fulbright lectr & Guggenheim fel, 71-72; Fulbright lectr, 75-76. *Mem:* Am Inst Aeronaut & Astronaut; Am Phys Soc. *Res:* Fluid dynamic stability theory and turbulence experimentation; numerical methods in fluid mechanics; digital techniques in turbulence experimentation; aerosonics and jet noise. *Mailing Add:* Dept of Aerospace Eng Univ of Southern Calif Los Angeles CA 90007

KAPLAN, RICHARD STEPHEN, b Pittsburgh, Pa, Aug 24, 45; m 70. MEDICAL ONCOLOGY. *Educ:* Univ Pittsburgh, BA, 66; Univ Miami, MD, 70; Am Bd Internal Med, dipl, 74; Am Bd Med Oncol, dipl, 75. *Prof Exp:* Clin assoc oncol, Nat Cancer Inst, 71-73; fel, Univ Miami, 74-75, asst prof oncol, 75-79; ASST PROF ONCOL & MED, UNIV MD, 79- *Concurrent Pos:* Surgeon, USPHS, 71-73; consult oncologist, Miami Vet Admin Hosp & sr staff mem, Comprehensive Cancer Ctr, Fla, 75-79; sr investr, Nat Cancer Inst, 79-81. *Mem:* Fel Am Col Physicians; Am Asn Cancer Res; Am Soc Clin Oncol; NY Acad Sci; AAAS. *Res:* Clinical and laboratory research in clinical oncology: neuro-oncology, malignant lymphomas and gastrointestinal malignancy. *Mailing Add:* Baltimore Cancer Res Ctr 22 S Greene St Baltimore MD 21201

KAPLAN, ROBERT JOEL, b New York, NY, Sept 13, 47. DERMATOLOGY. *Educ:* Franklin & Marshall Col, BA, 69; Univ Tenn, Memphis, MD, 73. *Prof Exp:* Tech asst, Englewood Hosp, 68-69; internship, Geisinger Med Ctr, Danville, Pa, 73-74; residency, 74-77, ASST PROF DERMAT, UNIV TENN, 77- *Mem:* Am Acad Dermat; AMA; Dermat Found; Soc Invest Dermat. *Res:* Clinical studies involving elevation of cyclic adenosine monophate in atopic dermatitis. *Mailing Add:* 910 Madison Suite 922 Memphis TN 38103

KAPLAN, ROBERT LEWIS, b Long Branch, NJ, Oct 5, 28; c 1. OPERATIONS RESEARCH, SYSTEMS ENGINEERING. *Educ:* US Mil Acad, BS, 53; Mass Inst Technol, MS, 60. *Prof Exp:* vpres opers res, Actuarial Res Corp, 76-80; PRES, RUMSON CORP, 80- *Concurrent Pos:* dep dir mat plans & prog & dep chief staff res, develop & aquisition, Hq, Dept Army, 63- *Mem:* Am Inst Aeronaut & Astronaut; Am Helicopter Soc; Sigma Xi. *Res:* Low speed aeronautical research c|w v-stol, helicopters, and aircushion vehicles; command and control operations research; quantitative measurement of subjective judgements. *Mailing Add:* Rumson Corp 6739 Baron Rd McLean VA 22101

KAPLAN, ROBERT S, b New York, NY, Aug 13, 40; m 67; c 2. EXTRACTIVE METALLURGY, CHEMICAL METALLURGY. *Educ:* Univ Mich, BSE, 62, MSE, 64; Carnegie-Mellon Univ, PhD(metall, mat sci), 68. *Prof Exp:* Res metallurgist, Battelle Columbus Labs, 68-71; staff metallurgist, Bur Mines, US Dept Interior, 71-76; proj mgr res recovery, Off Tech Assess, US Cong, 76; res supvr metall, Res Recovery & Nonfuel Mining, 76-78, mem staff policy rev, 78-79, MGR EXTRACTIVE NONFUEL MINERALS PROCESSES, BUR MINES, US DEPT INTERIOR, 80- *Mem:* Am Inst Mining, Metall & Petrol Engrs. *Res:* Iron-making slags; decarburization of steels; steel refining; inclusions in steels; recovery of metals from nonferrous metal scrap and wastes. *Mailing Add:* Bur of Mines 2401 East St NW Washington DC 20241

KAPLAN, RONALD M, b Los Angeles, Calif, July 15, 46; m 70. COMPUTER SCIENCE. *Educ:* Univ Calif, Berkeley, BA, 68; Harvard Univ, MA, 70, PhD(social psychol), 75. *Prof Exp:* Consult, Rand Corp, 68-72 & Info Sci Inst, Univ Southern Calif, 72-73; consult, 73-74, RES SCIENTIST PSYCHOLING, PALO ALTO RES CTR, XEROX CORP, 74- *Concurrent Pos:* Res assoc, Harvard Univ, 73-74; vis scholar cognitive sci, Mass Inst Technol, 78. *Mem:* Asn Comput Mach; Asn Comput Ling. *Res:* Computational models of human language comprehension. *Mailing Add:* Xerox Palo Alto Res Ctr 3333 Coyote Hill Rd Palo Alto CA 94304

KAPLAN, RONALD SLOAN, b New York, NY, July 12, 51. MEMBRANE BIOCHEMISTRY, BIOENERGENTICS. *Educ:* New York Univ, BA, 73, MS, 75, PhD(biol), 81. *Prof Exp:* Fel, New York Univ, 73-81; FEL PHYSIOL CHEM, JOHNS HOPKINS UNIV, 80- *Mem:* AAAS; Biophys Soc. *Res:* Mitochondrial transport systems; bioenergentics and the interactions between transporters and enzymes within membranes. *Mailing Add:* Dept Physiol Chem Johns Hopkins Univ 725 N Wolfe St Baltimore MD 21205

KAPLAN, ROY IRVING, physical inorganic chemistry, see previous edition

KAPLAN, SAM H, b Chicago, Ill, Jan 16, 15; m 41; c 2. ELECTRONICS, PHYSICAL CHEMISTRY. *Educ:* Armour Inst Technol, BS, 37. *Prof Exp:* Proj engr monochrome & color tubes, Rauland Div, 52-57, mgr advan color tube develop, 57-62, mgr color tube res, 62-80, SR TECHNOL CONSULT DISPLAY DEVICE, RES & DEVELOP, ZENITH RADIO CORP, 80- *Honors & Awards:* Vladimir K Zworykin award, Inst Elec & Electronics Engrs, 78; IR-100 Award, 70; Eugene McDonald award, Zenith Radio Corp, 70. *Mem:* Fel Inst Elec & Electronics Engrs; Electrochem Soc; Soc Info Display; Soc Motion Picture & TV Engrs. *Res:* Improving performance and reducing cost of color television display tube; improvement of brightness, contrast, and color under high ambient illumination; development of simplified means to make present very complicated tube. *Mailing Add:* 1000 Milwaukee Ave Glenview IL 60025

KAPLAN, SAMUEL, b Detroit, Mich, Sept 13, 16; m 53; c 2. MATHEMATICS. *Educ:* Univ Mich, BS, 37, MS, 38, PhD(math), 42. *Prof Exp:* Instr math, Univ Mich, 46; Rackham fel, Princeton Univ, 46-47; researcher, Inst Adv Study, 47-48, 56-57; from asst prof to prof, Wayne State Univ, 48-61; PROF MATH, PURDUE UNIV, 61- *Mem:* Am Math Soc. *Res:* Homology theory; topological groups; topological spaces; duality; functional analysis. *Mailing Add:* Div of Math Purdue Univ West Lafayette IN 47907

KAPLAN, SAMUEL, b Johannesburg, SAfrica, Mar 28, 22; nat US; m 52. CARDIOLOGY. *Educ:* Univ Witwatersrand, MD & MB, BCh, 44. *Prof Exp:* Lectr physiol, Univ Witwatersrand, 46-47; lectr internal med, 47-49; registr cardiol, Postgrad Med Sch, Univ London, 49-50; sr res assoc pediat, 51-54, asst prof, 54-61, asst prof internal med, 54-67, assoc prof pediat, 61-66, PROF PEDIAT, UNIV CINCINNATI, 66-, ASSOC PROF INTERNAL MED, 67-; DIR DIV CARDIOL, CHILDREN'S HOSP, 53- *Concurrent Pos:* Consult, NIH. *Mem:* Soc Pediat Res; Am Pediat Soc; Am Fedn Clin Res. *Res:* Hemodynamics and extracorporeal circulation. *Mailing Add:* Div Cardiol Children's Hosp Cincinnati OH 45229

KAPLAN, SANDRA SOLON, b Chicago, Ill, Sept 9, 34; m 57; c 2. INTERNAL MEDICINE, HEMATOLOGY. *Educ:* Roosevelt Univ, BS, 55; Boston Univ, MD, 59. *Prof Exp:* Res assoc, Yale Univ, 65-69; asst res prof path & med, 70-78, ASST PROF CLIN PATH, SCH MED UNIV PITTSBURGH, 78- *Concurrent Pos:* USPHS res fel hemat, Children's Hosp, San Francisco, 61-62; USPHS res training grant, Med Sch, Yale Univ, 63-64; res worker, Sir William Dunn Sch Path, Oxford Univ, 71-72; dir hemat, Magee Womens Hosp, Pittsburgh, 78- *Mem:* Am Soc Hemat. *Res:* Mechanisms of leukocyte activation associated with phagocytosis; mechanisms of bacterial killing by leukocytes. *Mailing Add:* 326 Orchard Dr Mt Lebanon PA 15228

KAPLAN, SANFORD SANDY, b New York, NY, Oct 2, 50; m 75; c 2. STRATIGRAPHY, SEDIMENTATION. *Educ:* Lafayette Col, AB, 71; Lehigh Univ, MS, 76; Univ Pittsburgh, PhD(geol), 81. *Prof Exp:* Vis lectr geol, Nathampton Co Area Community Col, 74-75; teaching asst, Lehigh Univ, 75-76; lectr gen geol, Univ Nebr-Lincoln, 77-78; vis lectr coal geol, Univ Pittsburgh, 80; geologist, Coal Prep Div, Pittsburgh Mining Technol Ctr, US Dept Energy, 79-80; GEOLOGIST, PENZOIL EXPLORATION & PROD CO, 80- *Mem:* Am Asn Petrol Geologists; Geol Soc Am; Soc Econ Paleontologists & Mineralogists; Sigma Xi; AAAS. *Res:* Interpreting ancient environments of deposition of sedimentary sequences especially those containing coal, oil and gas and deducing their tectonic setting from such evidence. *Mailing Add:* 11761 E Asbury Pl Aurora CO 80014

KAPLAN, SELIG N(EIL), b Chicago, Ill, June 30, 32; m 54; c 2. NUCLEAR PHYSICS & ENGINEERING. *Educ:* Univ Ariz, BS, 52; Univ Calif, MA, 54, PhD(physics), 57. *Prof Exp:* Physicist, Lab, 57-68, from asst prof to assoc prof nuclear eng, 65-75, PROF NUCLEAR ENG, UNIV CALIF, BERKELEY, 75-, SR PHYSICIST, LAWRENCE BERKELEY LAB, 68- *Concurrent Pos:* Lectr nuclear eng, Univ Calif, Berkeley, 62-65. *Mem:* Am Phys Soc; Am Nuclear Soc; Inst Elec & Electronics Engrs. *Res:* Nuclear instrumentation; neutronics; interaction of muons with nuclei. *Mailing Add:* Dept of Nuclear Eng Univ of Calif Berkeley CA 94720

KAPLAN, SELNA L, b Brooklyn, NY, Apr 8, 27. PEDIATRICS, ENDOCRINOLOGY. *Educ:* Brooklyn Col, BA, 48; Wash Univ, MA, 50, PhD(anat), 53, MD, 55. *Prof Exp:* Asst anat, Sch Med, Wash Univ, 51-52; instr pediat, Col Physicians & Surgeons, Columbia Univ, 61-63, assoc, 63-65, asst prof, 65-66; from asst prof to assoc prof, 66-74, PROF PEDIAT, SCH MED, UNIV CALIF, SAN FRANCISCO, 74- *Concurrent Pos:* NIH fel, 58-61, career develop award, 62-71. *Mem:* Endocrine Soc; Soc Pediat Res; NY Acad Sci; Am Pediat Soc. *Res:* Growth disorders in children; immunochemistry of pituitary human growth hormone; ontogenesis of human fetal hormones; pubertal development. *Mailing Add:* Dept of Pediat Univ of Calif Sch of Med San Francisco CA 94143

KAPLAN, SOLOMON ALEXANDER, b SAfrica, Feb 5, 24; nat US; m 57. MEDICINE. *Educ:* Univ Witwatersrand, MB & BCh, 46. *Prof Exp:* Instr pediat, Univ Cincinnati, 51-53; from asst prof to assoc prof, State Univ NY, 53-59; from assoc prof to prof, Sch Med, Univ Southern Calif, 59-68; PROF PEDIAT, MED CTR, UNIV CALIF, LOS ANGELES, 68- *Concurrent Pos:* Res fel pediat, Univ Cincinnati, 49-51. *Mem:* AAAS; Am Physiol Soc; Soc Pediat Res; Am Pediat Soc; Brit Soc Endocrinol. *Res:* Pediatrics; endocrinology; biochemistry. *Mailing Add:* Dept of Pediat Univ of Calif Med Ctr Los Angeles CA 90024

KAPLAN, STANLEY, b Canton, Ohio, Apr 28, 36; m 62; c 3. TERATOLOGY, HUMAN DEVELOPMENT. *Educ:* Univ Miami, BS & BEd, 62, PhD(teratology), 67. *Prof Exp:* Instr anat, Col Med, Univ Fla, 66-67, asst prof anat sci, 67-69; asst prof, 69-72, ASSOC PROF & VCHMN ANAT, MED COL WIS, 72- *Mem:* Am Ass Anat; Am Soc Zool; Am Inst Biol Sci; Europ Teratology Soc; Teratology Soc. *Res:* Mechanisms by which chemical and physical environmental agents produce congenital malformations. *Mailing Add:* Dept of Anat Med Col of Wis PO Box 26509 Milwaukee WI 53226

KAPLAN, STANLEY ALBERT, b New York, NY, Sept 28, 38; m 60; c 3. PHARMACEUTICS. *Educ:* Columbia Univ, BS, 59, MS, 61; Univ Calif, San Francisco, PhD(pharmaceut chem), 65. *Prof Exp:* NIH fel, Univ London, 65-66; sr biochemist, 66-71, res group chief, 71-73, asst dir, 74-76, assoc dir, Dept Biochem & Drug Metab, 76-78, DIR, DEPT PHARMACOKINETICS & BIOPHARMACEUT, HOFFMANN-LA ROCHE INC, 79- *Mem:* AAAS; NY Acad Sci; fel Am Inst Chemists; fel Acad Pharmaceut Sci; Am Soc Pharmacol & Exp Therapeut. *Res:* Physiological disposition of drugs, including biopharmaceutics, pharmacokinetics, drug bioavailability, drug metabolism, pharmacodynamics and analytical techniques. *Mailing Add:* Dept Pharmacokinetics & Biopharmaceut Hoffmann-La Roche Inc Nutley NJ 07110

KAPLAN, STANLEY BARUCH, b Memphis, Tenn, Jan 6, 31. MEDICINE, RHEUMATOLOGY. *Educ:* Univ Tenn, MD, 54. *Prof Exp:* Intern med, Jefferson Med Col, 55; from asst resident to chief resident, 58-62, from instr to assoc prof, 61-73, PROF MED & RHEUMATOL, SCH MED, UNIV TENN, MEMPHIS, 73- *Concurrent Pos:* Fel rheumatol, Sch Med, Univ Tenn, 60-62; attend physician, Vet Admin Hosp, 67- *Mem:* AMA; Am Rheumatism Asn. *Res:* Clinical investigation in rheumatic diseases. *Mailing Add:* Sect of Rheumatol Univ of Tenn Sch of Med Memphis TN 38163

KAPLAN, STANLEY MEISEL, b Cincinnati, Ohio, May 10, 22; m 50; c 3. PSYCHIATRY. *Educ:* Univ Cincinnati, BS, 43, MD, 46. *Prof Exp:* Intern med, Cincinnati Jewish Hosp, 46-47, resident, 47-48, resident psychiat, Cincinnati Gen Hosp, 49-51; from instr to assoc prof, 52-69, actg dir, 75-77, PROF PSYCHIAT, COL MED, UNIV CINCINNATI, 69- *Concurrent Pos:* Res fel, May Inst, 48-49; fel psychosom, Cincinnati Gen Hosp, 51-52; NIMH spec res fel, 54-56. *Mem:* AAAS; Am Psychosom Soc; Am Med Asn; fel Am Psychiat Asn. *Res:* Psychosomatic medicine. *Mailing Add:* Dept Psychiat Univ Cincinnati Col Med Cincinnati OH 45267

KAPLAN, STEPHEN ROBERT, b Brooklyn, NY, May 18, 37; m 61; c 3. RHEUMATOLOGY, MEDICAL EDUCATION. *Educ:* Wesleyan Univ, BA, 59; Col Med, NY Univ, MD, 63; Brown Univ, MA, 77. *Prof Exp:* Instr med, 69-70, asst prof, 70-77, ASSOC PROF RHEUMATOLOGY, PROG MED, BROWN UNIV, 77- *Concurrent Pos:* Adj prof pharmacol, Prog Med, Brown Univ, 78-, adj dean med, 82-; mem, Nat Arthritis Info Clearing House, 79- & Pharm Panel Anti-Rheumatic Drugs, 78- *Mem:* Am Fedn Clin Res; Am Rheumatism Asn; Arthritis Health Prof Asn; AAAS; Am Col Physicians. *Res:* Mechanism and use of anti-rheumatic and immunomanipulative drugs; medical education and the teaching of rheumatology. *Mailing Add:* 825 Chalkstone Ave Providence RI 02908

KAPLAN, THOMAS ABRAHAM, b Philadelphia, Pa, Feb 24, 26; m 56; c 3. SOLID STATE PHYSICS. *Educ:* Univ Pa, BS, 48, PhD(physics), 54. *Prof Exp:* Res asst physics, Willow Run Res Ctr, Univ Mich, 54-55, res assoc, Eng Res Inst, 55-56; res assoc, Pa State Univ working at Brookhaven Nat Lab, 56-59; staff mem, Lincoln Lab, Mass Inst Technol, 59-70; PROF PHYSICS, MICH STATE UNIV, 70- *Concurrent Pos:* Alexander von Humboldt sr scientist award, 81-82. *Mem:* Fel Am Phys Soc. *Res:* Quantum theory of solids; magnetism; mixed-valence. compounds. *Mailing Add:* Dept of Physics Mich State Univ East Lansing MI 48824

KAPLAN, WILFRED, b Boston, Mass, Nov 28, 15; m 38; c 2. MATHEMATICS. *Educ:* Harvard Univ, AB, 36, AM, 36, PhD(math), 39. *Prof Exp:* Instr math, Col of William & Mary, 39-40; from instr to assoc prof, 40-57, PROF MATH, UNIV MICH, ANN ARBOR, 57- *Concurrent Pos:* Res assoc, Brown Univ, 44-45; Guggenheim Found fel, 49-50. *Mem:* AAAS; Am Phys Soc; Am Math Soc; Math Asn Am; Math Soc France. *Res:* Non-linear differential equations; dynamics; Riemann surfaces; statistical mechanics. *Mailing Add:* Dept of Math Univ of Mich Ann Arbor MI 48109

KAPLAN, WILLIAM, b New York, NY, Apr 27, 22; m 53. MEDICAL MYCOLOGY. *Educ:* Cornell Univ, BS, 43, DVM, 46; Univ Minn, Minneapolis, MPH, 51. *Prof Exp:* Vet, UN Relief & Rehab Admin, 46-47; vet, USDA, 47-50; COMMISSIONED OFFICER, MYCOL DIV, CTR DIS CONTROL, USPHS, 51- *Concurrent Pos:* Adj field prof, Sch Pub Health, Univ NC, 69-; adj assoc prof, Ga State Univ, 71-; lectr, Sch Vet Med, Univ Pa, 71- *Mem:* Am Soc Microbiol; Am Pub Health Asn; Int Soc Human & Animal Mycol (vpres, 67-71); Med Mycol Soc of the Americas; Am Vet Med Asn. *Res:* Selected zoonosis, with emphasis on epidemiology; diagnostic procedures for mycotic diseases, with emphasis on immunofluorescence. *Mailing Add:* Ctr for Dis Control-Mycol Div USPHS Atlanta GA 30333

KAPLAN, WILLIAM DAVID, b New York, NY, Aug 24, 14; m 52; c 2. GENETICS. *Educ:* Brooklyn Col, BA, 36; Harvard Univ, MA, 37; Univ Calif, PhD(zool), 51. *Prof Exp:* Chief genetics sect, 53-58, chmn dept genetics, 58-62, ASST CHMN & SR RES GENETICIST, DEPT BIOL, CITY OF HOPE RES INST, 62- *Concurrent Pos:* Agr Res Coun sr res fel, Inst Animal Genetics, Univ Edinburgh, 51-53; Fulbright res scholar, Norsk Hydro's Inst Cancer Res, Oslo, Norway, 63-64; lectr, Univ Calif, 51; vis prof, Univ Calif, Los Angeles, 62-63; vis prof, Max-Planck Inst Biol Cybernet, Tübingen, Ger, 74-75. *Mem:* Genetics Soc Am; AAAS; Behav Genetics Asn; Soc Neurosci. *Res:* Mutation and biochemical genetics; Drosophila melanogaster; mammalian cytology; behavioral genetics. *Mailing Add:* Dept of Biol City Hope Res Inst Duarte CA 91010

KAPLANIS, JOHN NICHOLAS, entomology, see previous edition

KAPLAN-KOCH, DORA DEBORAH, microbiology, biochemistry, see previous edition

KAPLANSKY, IRVING, b Toronto, Ont, Mar 22, 17; m 51; c 3. MATHEMATICS. *Educ:* Univ Toronto, BA, 38, MA, 39; Harvard Univ, PhD(math), 41. *Hon Degrees:* DMath, Univ Waterloo, 68; DSc, Queens Univ, Ont, 69. *Prof Exp:* Instr math, Harvard Univ, 41-44; res mathematician, Appl Math Group, Nat Defense Res Comt, Columbia Univ, 44-45; from instr to prof, 45-69, chmn dept, 62-67, GEORGE HERBERT MEAD DISTINGUISHED SERV PROF MATH, UNIV CHICAGO, 69- *Concurrent Pos:* Guggenheim Found fel, 48-49. *Mem:* Nat Acad Sci; Am Math Soc; Math Asn Am. *Res:* Algebra. *Mailing Add:* Dept of Math Univ of Chicago Chicago IL 60637

KAPLER, JOSPEH EDWARD, b Cresco, Iowa, Mar 13, 24; m 59; c 4. BIOLOGY. *Educ:* Loras Col, BS, 48; Marquette Univ, MS, 53; Univ Wis, PhD(entom), 58. *Prof Exp:* Instr biol, Loras Col, 48-51; asst zool, Marquette Univ, 51-53, instr, 53-54; instr biol, Loras Col, 54-55; asst entom, Univ Wis, 55-57; from asst prof to assoc prof, 57-69, PROF BIOL, LORAS COL, 69- *Mem:* Entom Soc Am; AAAS. *Res:* Biology and ecology of forest insects. *Mailing Add:* Dept of Biol Loras Col Dubuque IA 52001

KAPLIT, MICHAEL, electrical engineering, solid state physics, see previous edition

KAPLON, MORTON FISCHEL, b Philadelphia, Pa, Feb 11, 21; m 46; c 3. PHYSICS. *Educ:* Lehigh Univ, BS, 41, MS, 47; Univ Rochester, PhD(physics), 51. *Prof Exp:* Res assoc physics, Univ Rochester, 51-52, from asst prof to prof, 52-71, assoc dean col arts & sci, 63-65, chmn dept physics & astron, 64-69; assoc provost, 71-75, VPRES ADMIN AFFAIRS, CITY COL NEW YORK, 75- *Concurrent Pos:* NSF sr fel, 59-60. *Mem:* AAAS; Am Phys Soc; Am Geophys Union; Ital Phys Soc; Am Astron Soc. *Res:* Cosmic ray physics; fundamental particle physics; high energy nuclear physics. *Mailing Add:* City Col of New York Admin Bldg Convent Ave at 138th St New York NY 10031

KAPLOW, ROY, b New York, NY, Aug 17, 32; m 59; c 2. INTERACTIVE COMPUTER SYSTEMS, ELECTRONIC MATERIALS. *Educ:* Mass Inst Technol, BS, 54, ScD(metall), 58. *Prof Exp:* Res asst metall, 54-58, mem res staff, 58-62, from asst prof to assoc prof, 62-72, PROF METALL, MASS INST TECHNOL, 72- *Concurrent Pos:* Ford fel, 62-64. *Mem:* AAAS; Am Soc Metals; Am Phys Soc; Asn Comput Mach. *Res:* Physics of solids and liquids; structure of alloys; x-ray diffraction; Mossbauer analyses; computer system program design; solar energy collector systems; photovoltaics. *Mailing Add:* 68 Lombard St Newton MA 02158

KAPNER, ROBERT S(IDNEY), b New York, NY, Dec 23, 27; m 55; c 2. CHEMICAL ENGINEERING, PHYSICAL CHEMISTRY. *Educ:* Polytech Inst Brooklyn, BChE, 50; Univ Cincinnati, MSc, 52; Johns Hopkins Univ, DEng, 59. *Prof Exp:* Develop engr, Cent Res Labs, Gen Foods Corp, 52-53; res & develop engr, Gen Aniline & Film Corp, 53-55; assoc prof chem eng, Rensselaer Polytech Inst, 59-68; PROF CHEM ENG & HEAD DEPT, COOPER UNION, 68- *Concurrent Pos:* Instr, McCoy Col, Johns Hopkins Univ, 56-57; consult, Chem & Metall Div, Gen Elec Co, 60- *Mem:* AAAS; Am Inst Chem Engrs; Am Chem Soc; Am Soc Eng Educ; Electrochem Soc. *Res:* Chemical engineering and kinetics; catalysis; reactor design; properties of materials. *Mailing Add:* Dept of Chem Eng Cooper Union 51 Astor Pl New York NY 10003

KAPOOR, AMRIT LAL, b Amritsar, India, Oct 15, 31; m 59; c 2. MEDICINAL CHEMISTRY, PHARMACEUTICAL CHEMISTRY. *Educ:* Punjab Univ, India, BS, 52, MS, 54; Swiss Fed Inst Technol, ScD(pharmaceut chem), 56. *Prof Exp:* Teaching fel, Sorbonne, 56-57; fel, Wayne State Univ, 57-58; sci officer, Nat Chem Labs, India, 58-59; chief chemist, Merck, Sharpe & Dohme Int, NY, 59-63; res fel chem, 63-66, PROF PHARMACEUT CHEM, COL PHARM & ALLIED HEALTH PROFESSIONS, ST JOHN'S UNIV, NY, 66- *Mem:* AAAS; Am Chem Soc; Am Pharmaceut Asn. *Res:* Natural products; synthesis of biologically active peptides and polypeptides. *Mailing Add:* Dept Pharmaceut Sci Col Pharm St John's Univ Jamaica NY 11432

KAPOOR, BRIJ M, b Chawli, India, Mar 3, 36; m 63; c 1. PLANT CYTOLOGY. *Educ:* Univ Delhi, BSc, 57, MSc, 59, PhD(cytol), 63. *Prof Exp:* Nat Res Coun Can res assoc plant biosyst, Univ Montreal, 63-65; NSF res assoc cytogenetics, Univ Colo, 65-66, vis prof biol, 66-67, asst prof, 67-68; asst prof, 68-72, chmn dept, 72-77, assoc prof, 72-80, PROF BIOL, ST MARY'S UNIV, NS, 80- *Mem:* Bot Soc Am; Genetics Soc Can; Am Inst Biol Sci; Soc Econ Bot. *Res:* Cytomorphological development of the endosperm of angiosperms; cytomorphological studies of the genus Solidago; cytogenetics of Eastern North American plants with special emphasis on compositae. *Mailing Add:* Dept of Biol St Mary's Univ Halifax NS B3H 3C3 Can

KAPOOR, INDER PRAKASH, b Multan, India, Sept 9, 37; m 70; c 2. METABOLISM, INSECT TOXICOLOGY. *Educ:* Univ Delhi, BSc, 57; Univ Ill, Urbana, PhD(entom), 70. *Prof Exp:* Tech asst entom, Ministry Food & Agr, India, 57-66; res asst, Univ Calif, Riverside, 66-68; from res asst to res assoc entom metab, Univ Ill, Urbana, 68-72; res chemist, 73-75, group leader, 76-80, MGR, PLANT INDUST DISCOVERY, AM CYANAMID CO, 80- *Mem:* Am Chem Soc. *Res:* Metabolism of pesticides in the environment and its elements. *Mailing Add:* Am Cyanamid Co PO Box 400 Princeton NJ 08540

KAPOOR, MANJU, enzymology, see previous edition

KAPOOR, NARINDER N, b Calcutta, India, Sept 4, 37; Can citizen; m 69; c 3. ZOOLOGY, PHYSIOLOGY. *Educ:* Panjab Univ, India, BSc, 60, MSc, 61; McMaster Univ, PhD(animal behav & physiol), 68. *Prof Exp:* Lectr zool, Govt Col, Panjab, India, 61-62; demonstr physiol, McMaster Univ, 63-68; lectr, Univ Waterloo, 68-69, asst prof, 69-73; asst prof, 73-76, ASSOC PROF BIOL, CONCORDIA UNIV, LOYOLA CAMPUS, 76- *Mem:* Am Soc Zool; Can Soc Zool. *Res:* Respiratory physiology and behavior of stream animals; morphology, osmoregulation, scanning electron microscopy; Plecoptera. *Mailing Add:* Dept Biol Concordia Univ 7141 Sherbrooke St W Montreal PQ H4B 1R6 Can

KAPOOR, S F, b Bombay, India, Sept 7, 34. MATHEMATICS. *Educ:* Univ Bombay, BSc, 55, MSc, 57, LLB, 63; Mich State Univ, PhD(math), 67. *Prof Exp:* Staff asst, State Bank India, 58-61; lectr math, Kirti Col, Univ Bombay, 61-63; asst, Mich State Univ, 63-67; asst prof, 67-80, ASSOC PROF MATH, WESTERN MICH UNIV, 80- *Mem:* Math Asn Am. *Res:* Topology; graph theory. *Mailing Add:* Dept of Math Western Mich Univ Kalamazoo MI 49008

KAPOS, ERVIN, b Brashov, Rumania, June 21, 31; US citizen; m 52; c 1. OPERATIONS RESEARCH, SYSTEMS ANALYSIS. *Educ:* Ind Univ, AB, 54. *Prof Exp:* Assoc math, Ind Univ, 53-58; analyst, Opers Eval Group, Mass Inst Technol, 58-59, rep to oper test & eval force, US Pac Fleet, 59-60, rep to comdr 1st Fleet, 60-61, head command & control sect, Ctr Naval Anal, Franklin Inst, 62-66, rep to comdr-in-chief, US Pac Fleet, 66-67, dir, Southeast Asia Combat Anal Div, Opers Eval Group, 67-68 & Marine Corps Anal Group, 68-69, dir opers eval group, 69-72; exec vpres & dir, Washington Opers, 72-80, PRES, KETRON, INC, 80- *Concurrent Pos:* Assoc mem, Defense Sci Bd, 74-76; panel mem marine bd, Nat Acad Sci, 78- *Mem:* Am Math Soc; Opers Res Soc Am. *Res:* Military operations research, particularly in command, control and communications; surveillance, intelligence and electronic warfare; human information processing and problem-solving. *Mailing Add:* 908 Turkey Run Rd McLean VA 22101

KAPP, LEON NEAL, molecular biology, cell biology, see previous edition

KAPP, ROBERT WESLEY, JR, b Point Pleasant, NJ. TOXICOLOGY, GENETICS. *Educ:* Syracuse Univ, AB, 67; George Washington Univ, MS, 74, PhD(genetic toxicol), 79. *Prof Exp:* Head cytogenetics, Nat Naval Med Ctr, Md, 69-72; med technician med, Group Health Asn, Washington, DC, 69-73; staff scientist toxicol, Hazleton Lab Am, Va, 73-78, sr toxicologist, 78-79; ASSOC DIR TOXICOL, EAST LAB, BIO-DYNAMICS, INC, NJ, 79- *Concurrent Pos:* Vis fac, Cancer Ctr, Med Br, Univ Tex, 78-; consult, Genetic Toxicol Ctr, 79-; mem, Dominant Lethal Comt & Sperm Anal Comt, Genetic Toxicol Prog, Environ Protection Agency, 79- *Mem:* Environ Mutagen Soc; Soc Occup & Environ Health; Genetic Toxicol Asn; Am Col Toxicol; Sigma Xi. *Res:* Development of clinical and nonclinical methodology to determine occupational carcinogenesis and mutagenesis; evaluation of general and genetic toxicological procedures for safety assessment. *Mailing Add:* Bio-dynamics Inc Mettlers Rd PO Box 43 East Millstone NJ 08873

KAPPAS, ATTALLAH, b Union City, NJ, Nov 4, 26; m 63; c 3. METABOLISM, PHARMACOLOGY. *Educ:* Columbia Univ, AB, 47; Univ Chicago, MD, 50; Am Bd Internal Med, dipl. *Prof Exp:* Intern med, Univ Serv, Kings County Hosp, New York, 50-51; med resident, Peter Bent Brigham Hosp, 54-56; assoc, Sloan-Kettering Inst, 56-57; from asst prof to assoc prof, Sch Med, Univ Chicago, 57-67; assoc prof & physician, 67-71, sr physician, 71-74, PROF ROCKELLER UNIV, 71-, PHYSICIAN-IN-CHIEF, 74-, SHERMAN FAIRCHILD PROF, 81- *Concurrent Pos:* Res fel, Sloan-Kettering Inst, 51-54; Commonwealth Fund fel, Courtauld Inst, Middlesex Hosp Med Sch, London, Eng, 61-62; John Simon Guggenheim Found fel & guest investr, Rockefeller Univ, 66-67; Vincent Astor prof clin sci, Mem Sloan-Kettering Cancer Ctr, Cornell Univ Med Col, 79-81. *Mem:* Am Soc Clin Invest; Endocrine Soc; Harvey Soc; Asn Am Physicians; Am Clin & Climat Asn. *Res:* Metabolic-genetic diseases; hormone biology; drug metabolism and disorders of porphyrin-heme synthesis. *Mailing Add:* Rockefeller Univ Hosp 1230 York Ave New York NY 10021

KAPPAUF, CHARLES HAMILTON, operations research, industrial engineering, see previous edition

KAPPE, DAVID SYME, b Philadelphia, Pa, Sept 28, 35; m 57; c 3. PHYSICAL CHEMISTRY, RADIOCHEMISTRY. *Educ:* Univ Md, College Park, BS, 59; Pa State Univ, PhD(phys chem), 65. *Prof Exp:* Phys sci aid, Metall Div, Nat Bur Standards, 58-59; chief radiation appln sect, Hittman Assocs, Inc, 66-67; RES DIR, SCI RES DIV, KAPPE ASSOCS, INC, 67- *Concurrent Pos:* Consult, Am Acad Environ Eng-Environ Protection Agency Manpower Training Proj, 71. *Mem:* AAAS; Am Chem Soc; Am Inst Physics; Am Water Works Asn; Soc Appl Spectros. *Res:* Reclamation of spent nuclear reactor fuels; measurement of thermal neutron cross sections; development and application of radionuclide-phosphor self-luminescent light sources; treatment of domestic, industrial and agricultural waste-waters. *Mailing Add:* Kappe Assoc Inc PO Box 1036 Rockville MD 20850

KAPPELMAN, ELLIS EUGENE, b Waverly, Mo, Apr 6, 38; m 60; c 2. PHYSICS, MATHEMATICS. *Educ:* Mo Valley Col, BS, 60. *Prof Exp:* ASST DIV HEAD, NAVAL WEAPONS CTR, 60- *Res:* Missile propulsion; propulsion cost prediction methodology development; weapon system systems analysis. *Mailing Add:* 619 Mary Ann Ave Ridgecrest CA 93555

KAPPENMAN, RUSSELL FRANCIS, b Lennox, SDak, Sept 2, 38; m 64; c 4. STATISTICS. *Educ:* Univ SDak, BA, 60; Univ Iowa, MS, 62; State Univ NY Buffalo, PhD(statist), 69. *Prof Exp:* asst prof statist, Pa State Univ, 69-76; MATH STATISTICIAN, NORTHWEST & ALASKA FISHERIES CTR, SEATTLE, 76- *Mem:* Am Statist Asn. *Res:* Statistical inference. *Mailing Add:* Northwest & Alaska Fisheries Ctr 2725 Montlake Blvd East Seattle WA 98112

KAPPERS, LAWRENCE ALLEN, b Hingham, Wis, May 27, 41; m 63. SOLID STATE PHYSICS. *Educ:* Cent Col, Iowa, BA, 63; Univ Mo-Columbia, MS, 66, PhD(physics), 70. *Prof Exp:* Air Force Off Sci res fel physics, Univ Minn, Minneapolis, 70-72; NSF res assoc, Okla State Univ, 72-73; asst prof physics, Univ Conn, 73-78, assoc prof, 78-80. *Mem:* Am Phys Soc; Am Chem Soc. *Res:* Electronic structure of defects in ionic crystals; optical absorption; luminescence and electron paramagnetic resonance; production and decay mechanisms of color centers, additive coloration and radiation damage. *Mailing Add:* 238 Village Hill Rd Willington CT 06279

KAPPUS, KARL DANIEL, b Cleveland, Ohio, July 2, 38. MEDICAL ENTOMOLOGY, EPIDEMIOLOGY. *Educ:* Ohio State Univ, BSc, 60, MSc, 62, PhD(entom), 64. *Prof Exp:* Res asst mosquito biol, Res Found, Ohio State Univ, 61-64; Nat Res Coun fel arborvirus infection, US Army Biol Labs, 65-66; res assoc mosquito biol, Res Found, Ohio State Univ, 66-67; res entomologist, Nat Commun Dis Ctr, 67-69, BIOLOGIST, NAT CTR DIS CONTROL, 69- *Mem:* AAAS; Wildlife Dis Asn; Entom Soc Am; Sigma Xi. *Res:* Animal photoperiodism; viral infection in arthropods; mosquito behavior; viral zoonoses; epidemiology of viral infections. *Mailing Add:* Virol Ctr for Dis Control 1600 Clifton Rd Atlanta GA 30333

KAPRAL, FRANK ALBERT, b Philadelphia, Pa, Mar 12, 28; m 51; c 3. MEDICAL MICROBIOLOGY, IMMUNOLOGY. *Educ:* Philadelphia Col Pharm & Sci, BS, 52; Univ Pa, PhD(med microbiol), 56. *Prof Exp:* Asst instr microbiol, Univ Pa, 52-56, from instr to assoc prof, 56-69, actg chmn dept, 73-78, PROF MED MICROBIOL, OHIO STATE UNIV, 69- *Concurrent Pos:* NIH grants, Ohio State Univ, 67-75, NIH training grant, 68-71; assoc microbiol, Philadelphia Gen Hosp, 62-64, chief microbiol res, 64-66, chief microbiol, 65-66; asst chief microbiol res, Vet Admin Hosp, Philadelphia, 62-66. *Mem:* AAAS; Am Soc Microbiol; Am Asn Immunol; Infectious Dis Soc; Soc Exp Biol & Med. *Res:* Pathogenesis of staphylococcal infections; bacterial host-parasite interactions; bacterial toxins; immune mechanisms. *Mailing Add:* Dept Med Microbiol & Immunol Ohio State Univ Columbus OH 43210

KAPRAL, RAYMOND EDWARD, b Swoyersville, Pa, Mar 21, 42; m 64; c 1. PHYSICAL CHEMISTRY. *Educ:* King's Col, Pa, BS, 64; Princeton Univ PhD(chem), 67. *Prof Exp:* Res assoc chem, Princeton Univ, 67 & Mass Inst Technol, 68-69; asst prof, 69-74, assoc prof, 74-80, PROF CHEM, UNIV TORONTO, 80- *Honors & Awards:* Noranda Award, Chem Inst Can, 81. *Mem:* Am Phys Soc. *Res:* Statistical mechanics; quantum mechanics; chemical kinetics. *Mailing Add:* Dept of Chem Univ of Toronto Toronto ON M5S 1A3 Can

KAPRAUN, DONALD FREDERICK, b Spring Valley, Ill, Sept 13, 45; m 75. PHYCOLOGY. *Educ:* Eastern Ill Univ, BS, 66; Univ Tex, PhD(bot), 69. *Prof Exp:* Asst prof bot, Univ Southwestern La, 69-71; assoc prof bot & phycol, 71-77, ASSOC PROF BIOL, UNIV NC, WILMINGTON, 77- *Mem:* Phycol Soc Am; Int Phycol Soc; Brit Phycol Soc. *Res:* Ecology and reproductive periodicity of benthic marine algae in North Carolina. *Mailing Add:* Dept of Biol Univ of NC Wilmington NC 28401

KAPRELIAN, EDWARD KARNIG, b Union Hill, NJ, June 20, 13; m 36; c 3. OPTICS, PHOTOGRAPHY. *Educ:* Stevens Inst Technol, ME, 34. *Prof Exp:* Patent exam, US Patent Off, 36-42; physicist, Bd Econ Warfare, 42-45; patent adv, Off Chief Signal Officer, 45-46; chief photog res br, US Army Signal Eng Lab, 46-52; dir res & eng, Kalart Co, 52-55; dir res, Kaprelian Res & Develop Co, 55-57; dept dir res, US Army Signal Res & Develop Lab, 57-62, tech dir, US Army Limited War Lab, 62-67; vpres & tech dir, Keuffel & Esser Co, Morristown, 68-73; PRES, KAPRELIAN RES & DEVELOP CO, 73- *Concurrent Pos:* Mem, Nat Acad Sci-Nat Res Coun, 52-58. *Mem:* Fel Soc Photog Sci & Eng (pres, 48-52); Optical Soc Am; Am Soc Mech Eng; Soc Motion Picture & TV Eng; sr mem Inst Elec & Electronics Engrs. *Res:* Applied physics; photographic processes and apparatus; electronics; patent law; optical instruments. *Mailing Add:* Lowery Lane Mendham NJ 07945

KAPRIELIAN, ZOHRAB A(RAKEL), b Aleppo, Syria, Sept 23, 23; nat US. ELECTRICAL ENGINEERING. *Educ:* Am Univ Beirut, BA, 42, MS, 43; Univ Calif, Berkeley, PhD(elec eng), 54. *Prof Exp:* Instr appl physics, Am Univ Beirut, 47-49; res asst elec eng, Univ Calif, Berkeley, 50-54; res fel, Calif Inst Technol, 54-56; from asst prof to assoc prof, 56-62, chmn, Elec Eng Dept, 62-70, vpres acad planning & res, 70-72, vpres acad admin res, 72-75, exec vpres, 75-81, PROF ELEC ENG, UNIV SOUTHERN CALIF, 62-, DIR, GRAD CTR ENG SCI & SEAVER SCI CTR, 63-, DEAN, SCH ENG, 69- *Mem:* Am Phys Soc; fel Inst Elec & Electronics Engrs. *Res:* Electromagnetic theory, especially antennas, microwave circuitry, artificial dielectrics and plasma physics. *Mailing Add:* SSC 510 Univ Southern Calif Los Angeles CA 90007

KAPRON, FELIX PAUL, b St Catharines, Ont, Nov 29, 40; US citizen; m 71. OPTICS, SOLID STATE PHYSICS. *Educ:* Univ Toronto, BASc, 62; Univ Waterloo, MSc, 63, PhD(physics), 67. *Prof Exp:* Physicist, Corning Glass Works, 67-72; sr scientist & mgr, Bell-Northern Res, 73-82; STAFF SCIENTIST, ELECTRO-OPTICAL PROD DIV, INT TEL & TEL, 82- *Mem:* Optical Soc Am; Soc Photo-Optical Instrumentation Engrs; Can Asn Physicists. *Res:* Fiber optical communications, fiber and cable; passive and active devices, subsystems. *Mailing Add:* Rte 2 Box GF22 Troutville VA 24175

KAPSALIS, JOHN GEORGE, b Mytilene, Greece, Jan 27, 27; US citizen; m 54; c 2. FOOD SCIENCE, BIOCHEMISTRY. *Educ:* Athens Col Agr, BS, MS, 54; Univ Fla, MAgr, 55; Tex A&M Univ, PhD(food sci), 59. *Prof Exp:* Asst prof & fel dairy tech, Ohio State Univ, 59-60; food technologist, Armed Forces Food & Container Inst, 60-62, res chemist, 62-63, chief, Food Biochem Lab, 63-74, HEAD FOOD CHEM GROUP, SCI & ADVAN TECHNOL LAB, US ARMY NATICK RES & DEVELOP LABS, 74- *Concurrent Pos:* Secy Army res & study fel, 65-66. *Honors & Awards:* US Dept Army Outstanding Performance Award & Sustained Superior Performance Award, 62-63; Scientific Dir Silver Key Award Res, US Army Natick Lab, 69. *Mem:* Am Chem Soc; Sigma Xi; fel Am Inst Chemists; NY Acad Sci. *Res:* Quality parameters of dehydrated foods; effect of water vapor equilibrium on chemical and rheological properties of foods; nondestructive methods of measurement in foods; chemical and rheological properties of lipids. *Mailing Add:* 38 Larnis Rd Framingham MA 01701

KAPUR, BHUSHAN M, b Amritsar, India, Feb 23, 38; m 68; c 2. TOXICOLOGY, CLINICAL BIOCHEMISTRY. *Educ:* Bombay Univ, BSc, 59; Univ Basel, PhD(org chem), 67; ARIC, 72, MRIC, 76, FRSC, 79. *Prof Exp:* Res assoc, Univ Basel, 67; fac pharm, Univ Toronto, 68-71; sr chemist, 71-72, DIR LABS, CLIN INST, ADDICTION RES FOUND, 72- *Concurrent Pos:* Lectr, Dept Clin Biochem, Fac Med, Univ Toronto, 74 & 76-78, asst prof, 78; instr, Toronto Inst Med Technol, 74-79. *Mem:* Swiss Chem Soc; The Chem Soc; Can Soc Clin Chem; Am Asn Clin Chem; Can Soc Sci. *Res:* Natural product chemistry; clinical biochemistry; toxicology; biochemical changes due to alcohol use. *Mailing Add:* Clin Inst Addiction Res Found 33 Russell St Toronto ON M5S 2S1 Can

KAPUR, KRISHAN KISHORE, b Jullundur, India, Mar 14, 30; US citizen; m 59; c 3. PHYSIOLOGY, PROSTHODONTICS. *Educ:* Panjab Univ, India, BSc, 48; Univ Bombay, BDS, 54; Tufts Univ, MS, 56, DMD, 58; Am Bd Prosthodont, dipl, 71. *Prof Exp:* Res assoc prosthetics, Sch Dent Med, Tufts Univ, 56-58; from instr to assoc prof, 58-62; assoc prof dent, Univ Detroit, 64-65, dir dent res, 64-67, prof oral biol & chmn dept, 65-67; assoc clin prof prosthetics, Harvard Sch Dent Med, 67-75, asst dean, Vet Admin Progs, 69-75; chief dent serv, Vet Admin Hosp, West Roxbury Mass, 71-75; CHIEF DENT SERV, VET ADMIN HOSP, SEPULVEDA, CALIF, 75-; PROF IN RESIDENCE PROSTHODONT, SCH DENT, UNIV CALIF, LOS ANGELES, 75- *Concurrent Pos:* Teaching fel, Sch Dent Med, Tufts Univ, 56-58; pvt pract, Boston, 58-63; consult, Warner-Lambert Pharmaceut Co, 65-67 & Vet Admin Oral Dis Res Prog Eval Comt, Washington, DC, 67-72; prog dir dent res, Vet Admin Outpatient Clin, Boston, 67-75, chief dent serv, 67-71 & 74-75; consult, Coun Hosp & Inst Den Serv, Am Dent Asn. *Mem:* Am Dent Asn; Int Asn Dent Res; Acad Dent Prosthetics; Fedn Int Col Dent. *Res:* Oral physiology; oral sensations; prosthodontics. *Mailing Add:* 3935 Bon Homme Rd Woodland Hills CA 91364

KAPUR, SHAKTI PRAKASH, b Ludhiana, Panjab, India, Aug 20, 32; m 66; c 2. HUMAN ANATOMY, HISTOLOGY. *Educ:* Panjab Univ, India, BSc, 53, MSc, 54; McGill Univ, PhD(zool), 64. *Prof Exp:* Lectr biol, Govt Col, Panjab, 55-61; sr teaching asst zool, McGill Univ, 61-64; exp biologist, Ayerst Drug Res Labs, Can, 64-66; asst prof zool, Panjab Univ, India, 66-71; res assoc, 71-72, asst prof, 72-78, ASSOC PROF ANAT, GEORGETOWN UNIV, 78- *Mem:* Sigma Xi; Am Asn Anatomists; Soc Exp Biol & Med; AAAS. *Res:* Electron microscopy; histochemistry of thyroid-parathyroid; endocrine mechanisms controlling calcium homeostasis; calcification in biological systems; zinc homeostasis; immunocytochemistry; radioimmunoassay. *Mailing Add:* Georgetown Univ Sch Med 27th & O Sts NW Washington DC 22207

KAPUSCINSKI, JAN, b Warsaw, Poland, June 2, 36; m 63. FLUORESCENCE SPECTROSCOPY, NUCLEIC ACIDS ASSAY. *Educ:* Polytech Univ Lodz, Poland, BS, 61, MS, 61, PhD(chem), 65. *Prof Exp:* Asst prof org chem, Polytech Univ Lodz, Poland, 61-65, assoc prof, 65-68; head lab res & develop, Pharmaceut & Cosmetic Indust, 69-78; fel, NY Univ Med Ctr, 78-79; RES ASSOC, MEM SLOAN-KETTERING CANCER CTR, 79- *Concurrent Pos:* Adj scientist phys biochem, Neucki Inst Explor Biol, Warsaw, 75-78. *Mem:* Polish Chem Soc; AAAS; NY Acad Sci. *Res:* Fluorescence methods of nucleic acids assay; the mechanisms of interactions between nucleic acids and dyes and antitumor agents; organic synthesis and molecular searousenets of phosphorousorganic and terpenoids compounds. *Mailing Add:* Mem Sloan-Kettering Cancer Ctr Walker Lab 145 Boston Post Rd Rye NY 10580

KAPUSTA, GEORGE, b Max, NDak, Nov 20, 32; m 58; c 4. AGRONOMY, WEED CONTROL. *Educ:* NDak State Univ, BS, 54; Univ Minn, MS, 57; Southern Ill Univ, PhD(bot), 75. *Prof Exp:* Agronomist, NDak State Univ, 58-64; assoc prof, 64-80, PROF AGRON, SOUTHERN ILL UNIV, 80- *Honors & Awards:* Outstanding Res & Exten Award, Land of Lincoln Soybean Asn, 78. *Mem:* Agron Soc Am; Soil Sci Soc Am; Weed Sci Soc Am; Sigma Xi. *Res:* Weed control in field and forage crops; minimum and zero-tillage; culture, especially plant density and geometry, cultivars and growth regulators; nitrification inhibition; symbiotic nitrogen fixation. *Mailing Add:* Dept of Plant & Soil Sci Southern Ill Univ Carbondale IL 62901

KAR, NIKHILES, b Bankura, WBengal, June 18, 47; m 77. SOLID STATE PHYSICS. *Educ:* Univ Calcutta, BSc, 67, MSc, 70; Univ Pa, PhD(physics), 76. *Prof Exp:* Res investr physics, Univ Pa, 77; fel physcis, Univ Md, 77-79; SR RES ASSOC, SCI RES COUN, DARESBURY LAB, ENG, 79- *Mem:* Am Phys Soc; Inst Physics (UK). *Res:* Surface physics, especially surface states and resonances in transition metals. *Mailing Add:* Dept of Physics & Astron Univ of Md College Park MD 20742

KARABATSOS, GERASIMOS J, b Chomatada, Greece, May 17, 32; US citizen; m 56; c 4. ORGANIC CHEMISTRY. *Educ:* Adelphi Col, BA, 54; Harvard Univ, PhD(org chem), 59. *Prof Exp:* From asst prof to assoc prof, 59-66, PROF CHEM, MICH STATE UNIV, 66-, CHMN DEPT, 75- *Concurrent Pos:* Sloan Found res fel, 63-66; NSF sr fel, 65-66; sci dir, Greek Atomic Energy Comn, 74-75. *Honors & Awards:* Petrol Chem Award, Am Chem Soc, 71. *Mem:* Am Chem Soc; corresp mem Acad Athens; The Chem Soc. *Res:* Carbonium ions; nuclear magnetic resonance spectroscopy; isotope effects; stereochemistry of enzymatic reactions. *Mailing Add:* Dept of Chem Mich State Univ East Lansing MI 48824

KARABLY, L(OUIS) S(TEPHEN), b Buffalo, NY, Feb 23, 16; m 42; c 5. EARTH SCIENCE. *Educ:* Univ Idaho, BS, 42; Boston Univ, MA, 53. *Prof Exp:* Instr, Air Univ, 46-48, instr & dir, Turkish Air Force Intel Sch, 49-51, dir reconnaissance & phys sci, Air Force Syst Command, 53-64; asst city engr, Hollywood, Fla, 45-46; staff engr, Electro-Optics Div, Perkin-Elmer Corp, 64-66; sr phys scientist, Sci & Technol Div, Exec Br, US Govt, Washington, DC, 66-73; CONSULT & ADV, STUDIES FOR INDUST & MUNIC, 73- *Res:* Concepts, techniques and equipment utilized in all facets of aerial and space reconnaissance and surveillance; imagery interpretation as applied to earth sciences; ocean engineering, oceanography and water resources. *Mailing Add:* PO Box 575 Melrose FL 32666

KARADBIL, LEON NATHAN, b New York, NY, Apr 2, 20; m 41; c 3. RESOURCE MANAGEMENT. *Educ:* City Col New York, BS, 40. *Prof Exp:* Asst sect chief, Census Bur, US Dept of Com, 40-42, economist & statistician, War Prod Bd, 42-45, economist, Civilian Prod Admin, 45-46, statistician, War Assets Admin, 46-48, economist, Econ Coop Admin, 48-51, indust specialist, Nat Prod Auth, Defense Prod Admin, 51-53 & Off Defense Mobilization, 53-57; consult & analyst, Opers Res Off, Johns Hopkins Univ, 57-61; opers analyst & study chmn opers res, Res Anal Corp, Va, 61-72; study chmn, Gen Res Corp, Va, 72-76; DIR, EMERGENCY PREPAREDNESS DIV, INT TRADE ADMIN, US DEPT COM, 76- *Concurrent Pos:* Consult, Opers Res Off, Johns Hopkins Univ, 57-58. *Mem:* Opers Res Soc Am. *Res:* Military operations research in logistics and costing; analysis of industrial resources. *Mailing Add:* 6909 Winterberry Lane Bethesda MD 20817

KARADI, GABOR, b Budapest, Hungary, Sept 12, 24; m 51; c 2. CIVIL ENGINEERING. *Educ:* Tech Univ Budapest, BSc, 50, MSc, 54, PhD(civil eng), 60; Hungarian Acad Sci, DSc(hydraul), 64. *Prof Exp:* Asst hydraul engr, Hungarian Dept Hydraul Eng, 50-51; sr engr, Inst Water Resources Eng, Budapest, 54-58; sr engr, Inst Hwy Eng, 58-59; sr engr, Water Resources Co, 59-60, chief develop engr, 60-63; lectr civil eng, Univ Khartoum, 63-64, sr lectr, 65-66; vis assoc prof, Northwestern Univ, Evanston, 66-67; assoc prof, 67-69, prof eng mech, 69-77, PROF CIVIL ENG & CHMN DEPT, UNIV WIS-MILWAUKEE, 77- *Concurrent Pos:* Consult, Agr Res Inst, 60-63, Inst Chem Eng, Budapest, Hungary, 61-63 & Northwestern Univ, Evanston, 67-68; mem US comn, Int Comn Irrig & Drainage, 68. *Mem:* Am Soc Civil Engrs; Am Water Resources Asn. *Res:* Hydrodynamics of groundwater flow; watershed hydrology; urban hydrology. *Mailing Add:* Dept of Civil Eng Col of Eng Univ of Wis PO Box 413 Milwaukee WI 53201

KARADY, GEORGE GYORGY, b Budapest, Hungary, Aug 17, 30; Can citizen. POWER ELECTRONICS, ELECTRICAL ENGINEERING. *Educ:* Tech Univ Budapest, Dipl Ing, 52, Dr Ing(high voltage tech), 60. *Prof Exp:* Assoc prof elec eng, Tech Univ Budapest, 52-68; invited lectr, Univ Salford, 68-69; prog mgr res, Hydro Que Inst Res, Montreal, Can, 69-77; dir energy conversion & consult engr, 77-78, CHIEF ELEC CONSULT ENGR, EBASCO SERV INC, 79- *Concurrent Pos:* Consult high voltage res, Inst Elec Energy Res, Budapest, 58-63; consult power syst anal, Elec Bd, Budapest, 63-66; vis prof, Univ Iraq, Baghdad, 66-68; invited prof, Univ Montreal, 71-77 & McGill Univ, 72-77; adj prof, Polytech Inst Brooklyn, 78- *Mem:* Fel Inst Elec & Electronics Engrs; Can Elec Asn; Conf Int Grandes Reseaux Electriques. *Res:* High voltage technic, insulation pollution and special insulators; high voltage thyristor valves and high voltage direct current technology; rectifier and inverter systems for plasma generation. *Mailing Add:* Ebasco Serv Inc Two World Trade Ctr New York NY 10048

KARADY, SANOR, b Budapest, Hungary, Aug 18, 33; US citizen; m 63; c 2. ORGANIC CHEMISTRY. *Educ:* Eotvos Lorand Univ, Lorand, Budapest, BSc, 56; Mass Inst Technol, PhD(org chem), 63. *Prof Exp:* Chemist, Pharmaceut Res Labs, Budapest, Hungary, 55-56; res chemist, 57-66, sr res chemist, 66-75, RES FEL, RES LABS, MERCK & CO, 66- *Concurrent Pos:* NIH fel, Mass Inst Technol, 63-64; NIH fel, Inst Org Chem, Gif sur Yvette, France, 64-65. *Mem:* Am Chem Soc. *Res:* Synthetic organic chemistry; natural products; pharmaceuticals; cephalosporin chemistry; heterocycles. *Mailing Add:* 348 Longview Dr Mountainside NJ 07092

KARAFIN, LESTER, b Philadelphia, Pa, Sept 26, 26; m 50; c 3. UROLOGY. *Educ:* Temple Univ, MD, 49, MSc, 56. *Prof Exp:* PROF UROL, MED COL PA, 64- *Concurrent Pos:* Consult, Vet Admin Hosp, Philadelphia, 64-; clin prof, Med Ctr, Temple Univ. *Mem:* AMA; Am Urol Asn. *Res:* Pediatric urology. *Mailing Add:* Dept of Urol Med Col of Pa Philadelphia PA 19129

KARAGIANES, MANUEL TOM, b Boise, Idaho, Sept 22, 32; m 57; c 3. EXPERIMENTAL SURGERY, BIOMATERIALS. *Educ:* Wash State Univ, BS, 61, DVM, 63. *Prof Exp:* Pvt pract, Sunset Animal Clin, Idaho, 63-67; res scientist, 67-70, res assoc, 70-78, MGR, INHALATION TECHNOL & TOXICOL, PAC NORTHWEST LABS, BATTELLE MEM INST, 78- *Mem:* Am Vet Med Asn. *Res:* Development of intravascular implant operations for bioengineering-biomaterials research; use of porous metals as bone substitutes for orthopedic and dental prostheses. *Mailing Add:* Battelle NW Battelle Blvd Richland WA 99352

KARAKASH, JOHN J, b Istanbul, Turkey, June 14, 14; nat US; m 45; c 1. ELECTRICAL ENGINEERING. *Educ:* Duke Univ, BS, 37; Univ Pa, MS, 38. *Hon Degrees:* DEng, Lehigh Univ, 71. *Prof Exp:* Instr, Univ Pa, 38-40; with Am TV Inc, Ill, 40-42; ed dir, 6th Serv Comn, Signal Corps Radar Sch, 42-44; instr & proj engr, Moore Sch Elec Eng, Univ Pa, 44-46; from asst prof to prof elec eng, 46-62, head dept, 55-68, distinguished prof elec eng, 62-81, dean eng, 66-81, DISTINGUISHED PROF EMER ELEC & COMPUTER ENG, LEHIGH UNIV, 81-, DEAN EMER, 81- *Concurrent Pos:* Consult, Bell Tel Labs, NY, 50-55; proj engr, Signal Corps, 50-54, proj dir, 54-61; mem hon adv bd, Pergamon Inst; mem, Nat Accreditation Coun Eng Cols; consult, Dept Educ, Commonwealth of PR, 72-76 & Gen State Authority, Commonwealth of Pa, 74-77. *Honors & Awards:* Hillman Award, 63; Distinguished Engr Award, Nat Soc Prof Engrs, 65; Outstanding Teaching Award, 69; Fac Distinguished Serv Award, 74. *Mem:* Fel Inst Elec & Electronics Engrs. *Res:* Electrical networks; microwaves; transmission line theory; filter networks. *Mailing Add:* 1732 Chelsea Ave Bethlehem PA 18015

KARAKASHIAN, ARAM SIMON, b Philadelphia, Pa, Nov 16, 39; m 75. THEORETICAL SOLID STATE PHYSICS. *Educ:* Temple Univ, BA, 61, MA, 63; Univ Md, PhD(physics), 70. *Prof Exp:* asst prof, 70-77, ASSOC PROF PHYSICS, UNIV LOWELL, 77- *Mem:* Am Phys Soc; Am Asn Physics Teachers. *Res:* Optical properties of metals and semiconductors; surface plasma oscillations; infrared properties of semiconductors. *Mailing Add:* Dept of Physics & Appl Physics Univ of Lowell Lowell MA 01854

KARAL, FRANK CHARLES, JR, b Philadelphia, Pa, Aug 3, 26. APPLIED MATHEMATICS. *Educ:* Univ Colo, BS, 46; Univ Tex, Austin, PhD(physics), 50. *Prof Exp:* Res physicist, Defense Res Lab, 49-50; res engr, Hughes Aircraft Co, 50-51; res physicist, Defense Res Lab, 51-52; sr res technologist, Mobil Oil Corp, 52-56; fel, 56-58, assoc res scientist, Courant Inst Math Sci, 58-61, from asst prof to assoc prof, 61-70, PROF MATH, NY UNIV, 71- *Mem:* Am Math Soc; Am Phys Soc; Am Geophys Union. *Res:* Geophysics; electromagnetic theory. *Mailing Add:* NY Univ 251 Mercer St New York NY 10012

KARAM, JIM DANIEL, b Kumasi, Ghana, Jan 31, MOLECULAR GENETICS, BIOCHEMISTRY. *Educ:* Am Univ Beirut, BS, 58; Univ NC, PhD(biochem), 65. *Prof Exp:* Res asst biochem, Am Univ Beirut, 59-60; res asst prof genetics & cell biol sect, Univ Conn, 67-68; res assoc, Sloan-Kettering Inst Cancer Res, 68-71; assoc prof, 71-80, PROF BIOCHEM, MED UNIV SC, 80- *Concurrent Pos:* USPHS fel, Cold Spring Harbor Lab Quant Biol, 65-67; USPHS res career develop award, 74- *Mem:* Genetics Soc Am; Am Soc Biol Chemists; Am Soc Microbiol. *Res:* Genetic control of DNA replication of phage T4. *Mailing Add:* Dept of Biochem Med Univ of SC Charleston SC 29403

KARAM, JOHN HARVEY, b Shreveport, La, July 20, 29; m 55; c 2. ENDOCRINOLOGY. *Educ:* St Louis Univ, BS, 49; Tulane Univ, MD, 53. *Prof Exp:* Resident physician internal med, Bronx Vet Admin Hosp, Bronx, NY, 54-56; res fel endocrinol, Hammersmith Hosp, London, Eng, 59-60; res fel, 60-63, asst prof, 63-74, ASSOC PROF INTERNAL MED, UNIV CALIF, SAN FRANCISCO, 74- *Concurrent Pos:* Fulbright vis prof, Univ Baghdad, 65-67. *Mem:* Endocrine Soc; Am Fedn Clin Res; Am Diabetes Asn. *Res:* Diabetes mellitus, particularly relating to disorders of insulin secretion; obesity and factors relating to insulin insensitivity; hypoglycemia and its management. *Mailing Add:* 69 Bemis St San Francisco CA 94131

KARAM, RATIB A(BRAHAM), b Miniara, Lebanon, Mar 8, 34; US citizen; m 60; c 1. NUCLEAR ENGINEERING, MATHEMATICS. *Educ:* Univ Fla, BChE, 58, MSE, 60, PhD(nuclear eng), 63. *Prof Exp:* Res asst nuclear field, Fla, 58-63; asst nuclear engr, Argonne Nat Lab, 63-67, assoc nuclear engr, 67-72; PROF NUCLEAR ENG, GA INST TECHNOL, 72- *Mem:* Am Nuclear Soc; Am Phys Soc. *Res:* Fast reactor physics; neutron transport; alternate fuel cycles; new breeder concepts and heterogeneity effects. *Mailing Add:* Sch of Nuclear Eng Ga Inst of Technol Atlanta GA 30332

KARAMCHETI, K(RISHNAMURTY), b India, Feb 8, 23; m 45; c 3. AERONAUTICAL ENGINEERING. *Educ:* Benares Hindu Univ, BS, 44; Indian Inst Sci, Bangalore, dipl, 46; Calif Inst Technol, MS, 52, PhD(aeronaut, physics), 56. *Prof Exp:* Lectr & asst aeronaut & appl mech, Indian Inst Sci, Bangalore, 47-48, sci officer aeronaut, 50-51; asst prof mech eng & in chg lab, Birla Eng Col, India, 48-49; res asst aeronaut, Calif Inst Technol, 51-55; res assoc & assoc prof, Eng Ctr, Univ Southern Calif, 55-58; from asst prof to assoc prof aeronaut & astronaut, 58-66, PROF AERONAUT & ASTRONAUT, STANFORD UNIV, 66- *Mem:* Assoc fel Am Inst Aeronaut & Astronaut. *Res:* Mechanics of ideal fluids; compressible fluid flows; physical gas dynamics; mechanics of high temperature and rarefied gases. *Mailing Add:* Dept of Aeronaut & Astronaut Stanford Univ Stanford CA 94305

KARAN, DANIEL MICHAEL, b Chicago, Ill, Mar, 22, 43; c 1. BIOPHYSICS. *Educ:* Univ Ill, BS, 65, MS, 67; Univ Calif, Berkeley, PhD(biophys), 77. *Prof Exp:* Physicist transmission reflectometics, IBM Corp, 65, physicist transistor design, 66; physicist nuclear devices, Lawrence Livermore Labs, Univ Calif, Berkeley, 67-69, res physiologist membrane trans, 77-81. *Res:* Red blood cell membrane transport; biological effects of high hydrostatic pressure; physical modeling of transport systems; design and development of mechanical instrumentation. *Mailing Add:* 5324 Manila Ave 6 Oakland CA 94618

KARAOGLAN, ESER IBRAHIM, b Ankara, Turkey, Nov 28, 43; m 70; c 1. NUCLEAR REACTOR & NEUTRON PHYSICS. *Educ:* Univ Ankara, BS, 68, MS, 70; Georgetown Univ, MS & PhD(nuclear physics), 76. *Prof Exp:* Res scientist reactor & neutron physics, Int Atomic Agency Turkey, 68-74; res asst nuclear physics, Georgetown Univ, 71-76; consult & prog mgr ion mass & surface anal, Commonwealth Sci Corp, 76-77; RES ASSOC DENT CARRIER PROBS, SCH DENT, GEORGETOWN UNIV, 77- *Concurrent Pos:* Consult & researcher nuclear methods & appln, Consol Controls Corp, 78- *Mem:* Sigma Xi. *Res:* Nuclear scattering, especially few nucleons at final state problems and solar neutrino problem; neutron activation analysis related to bore hole uranium and oil exploration, quality control with ion beam x-ray and neutron activation; spectroscopy. *Mailing Add:* Consol Controls Corp 7213 Lockport Pl Box 726 Springfield VA 22150

KARARA, H(OUSSAM) M, b Cairo, Egypt, Sept 5, 28; m 55; c 2. PHOTOGRAMMETRY. *Educ:* Univ Cairo, BSc, 49; Swiss Fed Inst Technol, MSc, 53, DSc(geod sci), 56. *Prof Exp:* Field civil engr, Dept Reservoirs, Pub Works Ministry, Egypt, 49-51 & La Grande Dixence, Sion, Switz, 55; sci collabr & asst photogram, Swiss Fed Inst Technol, 55-57; sci collabr, Wild-Heerbrugg Survey Instruments Co, Switz, 57; from asst prof to assoc prof civil eng, 57-66, PROF CIVIL ENG, UNIV ILL, URBANA, 66- *Concurrent Pos:* Assoc mem, Ctr Adv Study, Univ Ill, 65-66. *Honors & Awards:* Talbert Abrams Award, Am Soc Photogram, 59 & 61; Res Prize, Am Soc Civil Engrs, 64. *Mem:* Am Soc Photogram; Am Soc Civil Engrs; Am Cong Surv & Mapping; Can Inst Surv. *Res:* Photogrammetry, especially close range; surveying. *Mailing Add:* Dept of Civil Eng Univ of Ill Urbana IL 61801

KARAS, JAMES GLYNN, b Chicago, Ill, Feb 24, 33. HORTICULTURE, BIOLOGY. *Educ:* Univ Ill, BS, 56; Mich State Univ, MS, 58, PhD(hort, bot), 62. *Prof Exp:* Teaching asst hort, Mich State Univ, 56-61, res assoc biochem, hort & bot, 62-64, asst prof natural sci, 64-67; asst prof hort, NMex State Univ, 67-69; ASSOC PROF BIOL SCI, YOUNGSTOWN STATE UNIV, 69- *Mem:* Am Soc Hort Sci; Am Inst Biol Sci. *Res:* Phytovirology; plant physiology; amino acid metabolism; natural products; genetics; plant nutrition; seed germination. *Mailing Add:* Dept of Biol Sci Youngstown State Univ Youngstown OH 44503

KARAS, JOHN ATHAN, b Lebanon, Pa, Apr 7, 22; m 58; c 1. PHYSICS. *Educ:* Lehigh Univ, BS, 43, MS, 47; Lowell Tech Inst, DSc, 60. *Prof Exp:* Instr physics, Lehigh Univ, 43-44, 45-50; asst prof, Univ NH, 51-57; PRES, JONATHAN KARAS & ASSOCS, 60-; PRES, SCI HOUSE, 65- *Concurrent Pos:* Sci dir, WBZ-TV, Boston, Mass; asst, US Air Force Cambridge Res Ctr, 43-44; res proj dir, Univ NH; consult commun of sci & technol. *Mem:* AAAS; Am Phys Soc; Am Asn Physics Teachers. *Res:* Accident reconstruction; science and information films and television programs; science museum design and concepts. *Mailing Add:* Science House Manchester MA 01944

KARASAKI, SHUICHI, b Kure, Japan, Nov 27, 31; m 61; c 1. DEVELOPMENTAL BIOLOGY, CANCER. *Educ:* Nagoya Univ, Japan, BSc, 54, MSc, 56, PhD(biol), 59. *Prof Exp:* Asst prof chem, Col Gen Educ, Nagoya Univ, 59-61; vis investr, Biol Div, Oak Ridge Nat Lab, Tenn, 61-65; staff mem, Putnam Mem Hosp Inst Med Res, Bennington, Vt, 65; from assoc prof to prof anat, Univ Montreal, 68-79; mem staff, Montreal Cancer Inst, Notre Dame Hosp, 65-79; MEM STAFF, DEPT PATHOL, CHIBA CANCER CTR, RES INST, JAPAN, 79- *Concurrent Pos:* Nat Cancer Inst Can res assoc, 70- *Mem:* Soc Develop Biol; Am Soc Cell Biol; Can Soc Cell Biol; Am Asn Cancer Res; Int Soc Develop Biologists. *Res:* Subcellular analyses on neoplastic transformation of epithelial cells induced by oncogenic viruses, chemical agents and physiological stresses. *Mailing Add:* Dept Path Chiba Cancer Ctr Res Inst 666-2 Nitona-CHO Chiba 280 Japan

KARASEK, FRANCIS WARREN, b Council Bluffs, Iowa, Dec 11, 19; m 42; c 7. ANALYTICAL CHEMISTRY. *Educ:* Elmhurst Col, BS, 42; Ore State Col, PhD(chem), 52. *Prof Exp:* Sr chemist, Res & Develop Labs, Pure Oil Co, 42-48; mgr instrument develop, Phillips Petrol Co, 51-68; prof chem, Univ Waterloo, 68-80. *Mem:* Am Chem Soc; Soc Appl Spectros; Am Soc Mass Spectrometry. *Res:* Infrared spectroscopy; mass spectroscopy; chromatography; analytical instrumentation; plasma chromatography. *Mailing Add:* 4502 E Wayland Rd Phoenix AZ 85040

KARASEK, MARVIN A, b Chicago, Ill, Mar 8, 31. BIOCHEMISTRY. *Educ:* Purdue Univ, BS, 53; Univ Calif, PhD(biochem), 56. *Prof Exp:* Asst prof biochem, Tufts Univ, 57-60; asst prof, 60-68, ASSOC PROF BIOCHEM & RES DERMAT, SCH MED, STANFORD UNIV, 68- *Concurrent Pos:* Boston Med Found fel, 58-61. *Mem:* Am Chem Soc; Soc Invest Dermat; Soc Cell Biol. *Res:* Protein synthesis; nucleotide metabolism; biochemistry of virus infections; blood vessel metabolism; sebaceous gland metabolism. *Mailing Add:* Dept of Dermat Stanford Univ Sch of Med Palo Alto CA 94305

KARASZ, FRANK ERWIN, b Vienna, Austria, July 23, 33; m 58; c 2. POLYMER SCIENCE, BIOPHYSICAL CHEMISTRY. *Educ:* Univ London, BSc, 54, DSc(chem), 72; Univ Wash, PhD(phys chem), 58. *Prof Exp:* Fel, Univ Ore, 58-59; sr res fel, Basic Physics Div, Nat Phys Lab, Eng, 59-61; res chemist, Gen Elec Co, 61-67; assoc prof, 67-71, PROF POLYMER SCI & ENG, UNIV MASS, AMHERST, 71-, CO-DIR MAT RES LAB, 73- *Concurrent Pos:* Mem comt fire safety of polymeric mat, Nat Acad Sci, 74- *Honors & Awards:* Mettler Award, NAm Thermal Analysis Soc, 75. *Mem:* Am Phys Soc; Am Chem Soc. *Res:* Physical chemistry of polymers; thermodynamics and statistical thermodynamics of liquids; biological macromolecules. *Mailing Add:* Grad Res Ctr Univ of Mass Amherst MA 01002

KARATZAS, IOANNIS, b Kallithea, Greece, May 29, 51; m 75. STOCHASTIC PROCESSES & CONTROL. *Educ:* Nat Tech Univ Athens, dipl, 75; Columbia Univ, MSc, 76, PhD(math statist), 80. *Prof Exp:* Vis asst prof appl math, Brown Univ, 79-80; ASST PROF MATH STATIST, COLUMBIA UNIV, 80- *Mem:* Sigma Xi; Inst Math Statist; Inst Elec & Electronics Engrs. *Mailing Add:* Dept Math Statist 614 Math Columbia Univ New York NY 10027

KARAVOLAS, HARRY J, b Peabody, Mass, Feb 21, 36; m 62. BIOCHEMISTRY. *Educ:* Mass Col Pharm, BS, 57, MS, 59; St Louis Univ, PhD(biochem), 63. *Prof Exp:* Res fel biol chem, Harvard Med Sch, 63-66, res assoc & tutor biochem sci, Harvard Univ, 66-68; from asst prof to assoc prof, 68-75, PROF PHYSIOL CHEM & CHMN DEPT, SCH MED, UNIV WIS-MADISON, 75- *Concurrent Pos:* Nat Inst Child Health & Human Develop res career develop award, 72- *Mem:* AAAS; Am Chem Soc; Am Soc Biol Chem; Soc Neurosci; Endocrine Soc. *Res:* Mechanism of action of steroid hormones; steroid control of hypothalamic-hypophyseal-gonadal axis; steroid metabolic patterns in neural and pituitary tissues; enzymology. *Mailing Add:* Dept of Physiol Chem Univ of Wis Sch of Med Madison WI 53706

KARAYANNIS, NICHOLAS M, b Athens, Greece, May 30, 31; m 55; c 2. INORGANIC CHEMISTRY. *Educ:* Nat Tech Univ Athens, BS, 55; Univ London, PhD(chem), 60. *Prof Exp:* Sci collabr, Hellenic Nat Defense Gen Staff, 61-62 & Greek Ministry of Coord, 62-65; NIH res fel anal chem, Johns Hopkins Univ, 65-67; US Army Edgewood Arsenal res fel inorg chem, Drexel Univ, 67-70; res chemist, 70-72, sr res chemist, 72-76, RES ASSOC, AMOCO CHEM CORP, 76- *Mem:* AAAS; Am Chem Soc; NY Acad Sci; Greek Tech Chamber. *Res:* Coordination chemistry; metal complexes of neutral and acidic phosphoryl ligands and aromatic amine oxides; catalysis; catalysts for olefin polymerization; analytical chemistry, high pressure gas chromatography; organic chemistry, redox systems; bioinorganic chemistry. *Mailing Add:* Amoco Chem Corp Res & Develop PO Box 400 Naperville IL 60540

KARCHMER, JEAN HERSCHEL, b Dallas, Tex, Dec 28, 14; m; c 2. ANALYTICAL CHEMISTRY. *Educ:* Southern Methodist Univ, BS, 36. *Prof Exp:* Jr engr, Dept Agr, Tex, 38; chief chemist, Nat Chemsearch Co, 39-42; asst chemist, Tenn Valley Authority, Ala, 42-44; sr analyst & res chemist, Humble Oil & Refining Co, 44-50, sr res chemist, 50-55, res specialist, 55-63, res assoc, 63-77, CONSULT ANAL CHEM, EXXON RES & ENG CO, 78- *Mem:* Am Chem Soc. *Res:* Analytical chemistry of sulfur compounds; analysis of petroleum, coal, polymers; elemental analysis; polarography. *Mailing Add:* 3018 Castlewood Houston TX 77025

KARCZMAR, ALEXANDER GEORGE, b Warsaw, Poland, May 9, 18; nat US; m 46; c 2. PHARMACOLOGY, PHYSIOLOGY. *Educ:* Warsaw & Free Polish Univ, Med Sci, 39; Columbia Univ, MA, 41, PhD(biophysics, embryol), 46. *Prof Exp:* Res assoc, Amherst Col, 44-45; asst, Columbia Univ, 46; from instr to assoc prof pharmacol, Sch Med, Georgetown Univ, 47-54; assoc mem, Sterling-Winthrop Res Inst, 54-56; PROF PHARMACOL & THERAPEUT & CHMN DEPT, STRITCH SCH MED, LOYOLA UNIV CHICAGO, 56-, SR CO-DIR INST MIND, DRUGS & BEHAV, 65- *Concurrent Pos:* Am Philos Soc grant, NY Univ, 42-44; Guggenheim fel, 69-70; mem pharmacol A study sect, NIH, 68-72, mem multiple sclerosis study sect, 73-; hon prof, Kurume Univ, 80-; mem nat toxicol panel, Nat Res Coun, 80-; consult, US Army Res Develop Co, 80- *Mem:* AAAS; Am Soc Pharmacol & Exp Therapeut; Soc Exp Biol & Med; fel Am Col Neuropsychopharmacol; Int Brain Res Orgn. *Res:* Physiology and pharmacology of synaptic transmission; cholinesterases and anticholinesterase drugs; cholinergic system and behavior; neuropsychopharmacology. *Mailing Add:* Dept of Pharmacol Loyola Univ Stritch Sch of Med Maywood IL 60153

KARDONSKY, STANLEY, b Brooklyn, NY, Nov 21, 41; c 2. NUCLEAR CHEMISTRY, ANALYTICAL CHEMISTRY. *Educ:* Long Island Univ, BS, 63; Univ Fla, MS, 64; City Univ New York, PhD(nuclear chem), 70. *Prof Exp:* from instr to asst prof, 64-73, PROF CHEM & DIR ADMIN, LONG ISLAND UNIV, 73- *Mem:* AAAS; Am Chem Soc. *Res:* Neutron activation analysis; nuclear reactions; radiation effects on biologically active materials; mechanisms of genetic damage caused by ultraviolet radiation. *Mailing Add:* Off of Admin Brooklyn Ctr Long Island Univ Brooklyn NY 11201

KARDOS, GEZA, b Tolna, Hungary, Mar 2, 26; Can citizen; m 49; c 3. MECHANICAL ENGINEERING. *Educ:* Univ Sask, BSc, 48; McGill Univ, ME, 57, PhD(mech eng), 65. *Prof Exp:* Jr res officer fire hazards, Nat Res Coun Can, 48-50; proj engr, Tamper Ltd, 50-54; proj engr, Aviation Elec Ltd, 54-56, eng supvr, 56-62, staff engr, 65-66; site mgr, HARP, McGill Univ, 62-63; assoc prof design, McMaster Univ, 66-71; vis assoc prof, Stanford Univ, 71; PROF ENG, CARLETON UNIV, 71- *Concurrent Pos:* Assoc dir res, Ctr Appl Res & Eng Design, McMaster Univ, 67-69; vis prof, Royal Col Arts; consult, Vitro-Tech, Monterey, Mex, 80-82. *Mem:* Am Soc Mech Engrs; Am Soc Eng Educ. *Res:* Mechanical pressure elements; experimental stress analysis; high strain rates; design and computer aided design; case method of engineering teaching; metal physics; fracture mechanics; creative problem solving. *Mailing Add:* Eng Fac Carleton Univ Ottawa ON K1S 5B6 Can

KARDOS, JOHN LOUIS, b Colfax, Wash, Apr 19, 39; m 66; c 3. CHEMICAL ENGINEERING, POLYMER SCIENCE. *Educ:* Pa State Univ, BS, 61; Univ Ill, MS, 62; Case Inst Technol, PhD(polymer physics), 65. *Prof Exp:* From asst prof to assoc prof, 65-74, actg chmn, 77-78, PROF CHEM ENG, WASHINGTON UNIV, 74-, DIR, MAT RES LAB, 70-, CHMN, MAT SCI & ENG PROG, 71- *Mem:* Am Chem Soc; Soc Rheology; Am Phys Soc; Am Inst Chem Engrs; Soc Plastics Engrs. *Res:* Chemistry, physics and fabrication of composite materials; structure-property relations in reinforced plastics; polymer crystallization and morphology; materials characterization techniques. *Mailing Add:* Dept of Chem Eng Box 1198 Wash Univ St Louis MO 63130

KARDOS, LOUIS THOMAS, b Perth Amboy, NJ, Aug 15, 10; m 38, 77; c 3. SOIL CHEMISTRY. *Educ:* Rutgers Univ, BSc, 32, MSc, 34, PhD(soil chem), 37. *Prof Exp:* From instr to asst prof soils, State Col Wash, 36-43; from asst prof to assoc prof agron, Univ NH, 43-54; prof soil physics, 54-76, EMER PROF SOIL PHYSICS, PA STATE UNIV, 54-, ENVIRON SCIENTIST, INST RES ON LAND & WATER RESOURCES, 68- *Mem:* Soil Sci Soc Am; fel Am Soc Agron; fel Soil Conserv Soc Am; Int Soc Soil Sci. *Res:* Lysimeter studies; toxicity of spray residues in soils; soil structure; waste water recycling. *Mailing Add:* Land & Water Res Bldg Pa State Univ University Park PA 16802

KARDOS, OTTO, b Vienna, Austria, Feb 7, 07; nat US; m 30; c 1. CHEMISTRY. *Educ:* Univ Vienna, PhD(chem), 32. *Prof Exp:* Electrochemist, Galvapol, Vienna, 35-38; electroplating consult, France, 38-42; res electrochemist, Conmar Prod, NJ, 43-44; res electrochemist, Hanson-Van Winkle-Munning Co, 44-52, chief res electrochemist, 53-58, sr scientist, 58-64; res assoc, 64-69, sr res assoc, 69-72, CONSULT, M&T CHEM INC, 72- *Honors & Awards:* Heussner Award, Am Electroplaters Soc, 56-57, Sci Achievement Award, 73. *Mem:* Am Chem Soc; Electrochem Soc; Am Electroplaters Soc. *Res:* Electrodeposition of metals. *Mailing Add:* 96 W Pearl Hazel Park MI 48030

KARE, MORLEY RICHARD, b Winnipeg, Man, Mar 7, 22; m 51; c 2. PHYSIOLOGY, NUTRITION. *Educ:* Univ Man, BSA, 43; Univ BC, MSA, 48; Cornell Univ, PhD(zool), 52. *Prof Exp:* Asst nutrit, Univ BC, 46-48; asst zool, Cornell Univ, 49-51, from asst prof to prof physiol, 52-61; prof physiol, NC State Univ, 62-67; PROF PHYSIOL & DIR MONELL CHEM SENSES CTR, UNIV PA, 68- *Concurrent Pos:* Tanner lectr, 70; pub trustee, Nutrit Found, 74-; mem corp, Cult Inst Am, 74-; mem mus & planetarium bd, Franklin Inst, 74-; fel, Col Physicians Philadelphia, 77; mem, Sci Coun Human Nutrit Ctr on Aging, Tufts Univ, 81. *Honors & Awards:* Poultry Sci Res Award, 58; Borden Award, 62; Underwood-Prescott Award, 78. *Mem:* Am Physiol Soc; Soc Exp Biol & Med; Ecol Soc Am; Can Physiol Soc; Soc Neurosci. *Res:* Comparative aspect of the sense of taste; function of chemical senses indigestio , role of taste in nutrition. *Mailing Add:* Monell Chem Senses Ctr Univ Pa 3500 Market St Philadelphia PA 19104

KAREEM, AHSAN, b Lahore, Pakistan, Sept 29, 47. PROBABILISTIC DYNAMICS, STRUCTURAL ENGINEERING. *Educ:* WPakistan Univ Eng & Technol, BSc, 68; Univ Hawaii, Honolulu, MSc, 75; Colo State Univ, PhD(civil eng), 78. *Prof Exp:* Design engr, Harza Eng Co Int, Pakistan, 68-71; res assoc, Colo State Univ, 77-78; ASST PROF CIVIL ENG, UNIV HOUSTON, 78- *Concurrent Pos:* Gen consult, Aerovironment Inc, 79- & Northwest Hydraulic Consult Inc, 80- *Mem:* Wind Eng Res Coun; Am Soc Civil Engrs; Sigma Xi; Am Inst Aeronaut & Astronaut. *Res:* Analysis and design of civil engineering and ocean engineering structures subjected to stochastic excitation due to wind, waves and earthquakes; reliability based design and digital simulation of civil engineering systems; design of vibration mitigation devices. *Mailing Add:* Dept of Civil Eng Univ of Houston 4800 Calhoun Houston TX 77004

KAREIVA, PETER MICHAEL, b Utica, NY, Sept 20, 51. INSECT POPULATION BIOLOGY, AGRICULTURAL ECOLOGY. *Educ:* Duke Univ, BS, 73; Univ Calif, Irvine, MS, 76; Cornell Univ, PhD(ecol & evolution),81. *Prof Exp:* Lectr environ biol, Calif State Univ, Los Angeles, 76; ASST PROF THEORET ECOL & MATH MODELLING, BROWN UNIV, 81- *Mem:* Ecol Soc Am; Entom Soc Am. *Res:* Population biology of herbivorus insects; mathematical models of insect dispersal; the influence of vegetation texture on herbivore dynamics. *Mailing Add:* Div Biol Box G Brown Univ Providence RI 02912

KAREL, KARIN JOHNSON, b Portland, Ore, Aug 9, 50; m 72; c 1. ORGANOMETALLIC CHEMISTRY. *Educ:* Univ Chicago, BS, 72; Princeton Univ, MA, 74, PhD(chem), 78. *Prof Exp:* NSF fel, Univ Ill, 78-79; CHEMIST, CENT RES & DEVELOP, E I DU PONT DE NEMOURS & CO, 80- *Mem:* Am Chem Soc. *Res:* Organometallic reagents for organic synthesis; preparation and characterization of novel organometallic species. *Mailing Add:* 919A Cloister Rd Wilmington DE 19809

KAREL, LEONARD, b Baltimore, Md, Jan 23, 12; m 42; c 3. PHARMACOLOGY. *Educ:* Johns Hopkins Univ, AB, 32; Univ Md, PhD(pharmacol), 41. *Prof Exp:* Toxicologist & actg chief toxicol sect, Med Div, Chem Corps, US Army, 46-47; exec secy div res grants, NIH, 47-51, chief extramural progs, Nat Inst Allergy & Infectious Dis, 51-61; spec asst to assoc dir res, NSF, 61, assoc head sci resources planning off, 61-63, actg head, 63-64; chief bibliog serv div, Nat Libr Med, 64-66, asst toxicol, Info Prog, 68-69, spec asst to assoc dir libr opers, 66-74; RETIRED. *Concurrent Pos:* Consult chem warfare, US War Dept, 47; lectr, Sch Med, Univ Md, 47-51; mem fels speciality bd, NIH, 51-55, mem fels cent qualifications, 51-59, mem exec comt extramural res & training activ, 51-61; mem civil defense lab resources comt, Commun Dis Ctr, USPHS, 56; consult, Jewish Nat Home Asthmatic Children, 59; mem bd dirs, Common Cold Found, 56-60; consult, Pan-Am Health Orgn, WHO & interim dir regional med libr for SAm, 67-68; asst to chmn comt sci & technol info, Off Sci & Technol, Exec Off President, 68, exec secy panel info sci technol, 69-70. *Mem:* Fel AAAS; Am Soc Pharmacol & Exp Therapeut; Am Pub Health Asn. *Res:* Toxicology; chemotherapy; science resources planning; educational manpower statistics; information science; automatic data processing publications; science administration. *Mailing Add:* 7509 Westfield Dr Bethesda MD 20817

KAREL, MARCUS, b Lwow, Poland, May 17, 28; US citizen; m 58; c 4. FOOD SCIENCE. *Educ:* Boston Univ, AB, 55; Mass Inst Technol, PhD, 60. *Prof Exp:* Res assoc food tech, 57-61, asst prof, 61-64, assoc prof food eng, 64-69, dep head, Dept Nutrit & Food Sci, 74-79, PROF FOOD ENG, MASS INST TECHNOL, 69- *Concurrent Pos:* Consult var food & chem co, 60- *Honors & Awards:* William V Cruess Award, Inst Food Technol, 70; Food Eng Award, Am Soc Agr Engrs & Dairy & Food Industs Supply Asn, 78. *Mem:* Nat Acad Sci, Argentina; fel Inst Food Technol; fel Brit Inst Food Sci

& Technol; NY Acad Sci; Am Inst Chem Eng. *Res:* Food engineering; autoxidation of lipids; diffusion of gases and vapors through polymeric membranes; physicochemical properties of foods; heat and mass transfer aspects of food processing; controlled drug release. *Mailing Add:* Dept of Nutrit & Food Sci Mass Inst of Technol Cambridge MA 02139

KAREL, MARTIN LEWIS, b Baltimore, Md, Mar 15, 44; m 72; c 1. MATHEMATICS. *Educ:* Johns Hopkins Univ, BA, 66; Univ Chicago, MA, 67, PhD(math), 72. *Prof Exp:* Asst math, Inst Advan Study, Princeton Univ, 72-73, mem, 73-74; asst prof math, Univ NC, Chapel Hill, 74-80; ASST PROF, RUTGERS UNIV, CAMDEN COUNTY ARTS & SCI, 80- *Concurrent Pos:* NSF fel, 75-; res assoc, Univ Ill, Urbana-Champaign, 79. *Mem:* Am Math Soc. *Res:* Arithmetical theory of automorphic forms. *Mailing Add:* Camden County Arts & Sci Dept Math Rutgers Univ Camden NJ 08102

KARG, GERHART, b New York, NY, Jan 21, 36; m 66; c 5. PHYSICAL CHEMISTRY, COSMETIC CHEMISTRY. *Educ:* Manhattan Col, BS, 57; Polytech Inst Brooklyn, PhD(phys chem), 63. *Prof Exp:* Res chemist, M W Kellogg Co, 62-64; res chemist, Ultra Chem Co Div, Witco Chem Co, 64-69; develop chemist, 69-70, SR PHYS CHEMIST, AVON PROD, INC, 71- *Res:* Photochemistry; surface chemistry; hair properties. *Mailing Add:* Avon Prod Inc Fair & Division Sts Suffern NY 10901

KARGER, BARRY LLOYD, b Boston, Mass, Apr 2, 39; m 61; c 1. ANALYTICAL CHEMISTRY. *Educ:* Mass Inst Technol, BS, 60; Cornell Univ, PhD(anal chem), 63. *Prof Exp:* From asst prof to assoc prof, 63-72, PROF CHEM, NORTHEASTERN UNIV, 72-, DIR INST CHEM ANAL, APPL & FORENSIC SCI, 73- *Concurrent Pos:* NIH res grant, 69-; NSF res grant, 66-; Fed Water Pollution Control Admin res grant, 67-70; Off Naval Res & NIH res grants, 69-74; sci adv, Food & Drug Admin, 73-76; consult, Tech Distriments Corp, 77- *Honors & Awards:* Gulf Res Award, 71; Steven Dal Nogare Mem Award, Delaware Valley Chromatog Form, 75; Chromatography Award, Am Chem Soc, 82; Tswett Mem Medal, USSR, 80. *Mem:* AAAS; Am Chem Soc; Ny Acad Sci; Sigma Xi. *Res:* High performance liquid chromatography; biochemical applications of high performance liquid chromatography; fundamentals of biopolymer separations; solution and adsorption thermodynamics; clinical analysis; liquid chromatography and mass spectrometry; separation science. *Mailing Add:* Inst of Chem Anal Northeastern Univ Boston MA 02115

KARGL, THOMAS E, b Des Plaines, Ill, Feb 25, 32; m 57; c 8. BIOCHEMISTRY. *Educ:* St Ambrose Col, BA, 54; Purdue Univ, MS, 56, PhD(biochem), 59. *Prof Exp:* From asst prof to assoc prof, 59-70, head dept, 64-68, PROF CHEM, BELLARMINE COL, 70- *Res:* Carotenoid pigments of tomatoes; Lewis acid catalyzed reactions of methyl vinyl ketone; structure determination of complex polyenes; slow release fertilizers. *Mailing Add:* Dept Chem Div Natural Sci Bellarmine Col Louisville KY 40205

KARICKHOFF, SAMUEL WOODFORD, b Buckhannon, WVa, Oct 22, 43; m 64; c 2. PHYSICAL CHEMISTRY. *Educ:* WVa Wesleyan Col, BS, 65; Fla State Univ, PhD(phys chem), 71. *Prof Exp:* RES CHEMIST, ENVIRON RES LAB, ENVIRON PROTECTION AGENCY, 71- *Mem:* Am Chem Soc. *Res:* Fate and trasport of pollutants in the environment. *Mailing Add:* Environ Res Lab Environ Protection Agency Athens GA 30606

KARIG, DANIEL EDMUND, b Irvington, NJ, July 20, 37; m 71; c 1. GEOLOGY. *Educ:* Colo Sch Mines, GeolE, 59, MSc, 64; Scripps Inst Oceanog, PhD(earth sci), 70. *Prof Exp:* NSF grant & asst res geologist, Scripps Inst Oceanog, 70-71; asst prof geol sci, Univ Calif, Santa Barbara, 71-74; asst prof, 74-75, assoc prof, 75-80, PROF GEOL SCI, CORNELL UNIV, 80- *Mem:* Geol Soc Am; Am Geophys Union; Sigma Xi; Geol Soc Malaysia. *Res:* Marine geology and geophysics of marginal basins and island arc systems; genesis of rift zones; environmental problems in streams and small lagoons; structure and evolution of island arcs and young mountain belts. *Mailing Add:* Dept of Geol Sci Cornell Univ Ithaca NY 14853

KARIM, AZIZ, b Dar es Salaam, Tanzania, Aug 20, 39; m 64; c 2. PHARMACEUTICAL CHEMISTRY. *Educ:* Univ London, BPharm, 64, PhD(pharmaceut chem), 67. *Prof Exp:* NIH fel, Univ Wis, 67-69; sr res investr drug metab, Dept Biochem Res, 69-72, group leader, 72-74, res fel, dept drug metab, 74-79, DIR CLIN BIOAVAILABILTY & PHARMACOKINETICS, G D SEARLE & CO, 79- *Mem:* Am Chem Soc; Pharmaceut Soc Gt Brit; Am Soc Clin Pharmacol & Therapeut; Am Soc Exp Pharmacol & Therapeut; Acad Am Pharm Sci. *Res:* Drug metabolism; study of biotransformation and pharmacokinetics of drugs; isolation and structural elucidation of natural products possessing biological activities. *Mailing Add:* Dept of Drug Metab G D Searle & Co PO Box 5110 Chicago IL 60680

KARIM, GHAZI A, b Baghdad, Iraq, Jan 2, 34; m 57; c 3. ENGINEERING, COMBUSTION. *Educ:* Univ Durham, BSc, 56; Univ London, DIC & PhD(mech eng), 60. *Hon Degrees:* DSc, Univ London, 72. *Prof Exp:* Trainee prime movers, Eng Elec Co, 56-57; res asst mech eng, Imp Col, Univ London, 57-60; consult engr, Ministry of Indust Repub Iraq, 60-61; UN tech fels, 61-62; lectr mech eng, Imp Col, Univ London, 62-68, chmn combustion res group, 64-68; assoc prof, 68-69, PROF MECH ENG, UNIV CALGARY, 69- *Concurrent Pos:* Vis prof, Univ Cambridge, 72-73; consult, Can Petrol Asn, 75-76, Chevron Can Ltd, 77-78 & C N G Ltd, 80- *Honors & Awards:* Unwin Award in Mech Eng, Eng, 60. *Mem:* Soc Automotive Engrs; Combustion Inst; Brit Inst Mech Engrs. *Res:* Utilization of natural gas for power in internal combustion engines; chemical kinetics of common gaseous fuels; air pollution from combustion processes; fire and explosion research; engineering education; liquid natural gas utilization; thermodynamics; oil sands and heavy oil. *Mailing Add:* Dept of Mech Eng Univ of Calgary Calgary AB T2N 1N4 Can

KARINATTU, JOSEPH J, b Kerala, India, Aug 6, 38; US citizen; m 63; c 1. CLINICAL BIOCHEMISTRY, PATHOLOGY. *Educ:* Univ Kerala, BSc, 61; Univ Delhi, MSc, 63; St Thomas Inst, MS, 65, PhD(biochem), 67; Univ Autonoma, MD, 80. *Prof Exp:* Biochemist, Jewish Hosp, Cincinnati, 67-69; biochemist, St Therese Hosp, 69-78; PHYSICIAN-RESEARCHER, EAST CENT ILL EDUC FOUND & UNIV ILL, CHAMPAIGN, 80- *Concurrent Pos:* Biochemist consult, Our Lady of Mercy Hosp, Cincinnati, Ohio, 66-69; vis prof clin chem, Col of Lake County, Grayslake, Ill, 73- *Mem:* AMA; Am Chem Soc; fel Am Asn Clin Scientists; Am Asn Clin Chemists; NY Acad Sci. *Res:* Diagnostic methods in laboratory medicine; trace metals. *Mailing Add:* 1407 Woodridge Dr Danville IL 61832

KARIPIDES, ANASTAS, b Canton, Ohio, July 4, 37. INORGANIC CHEMISTRY, PHYSICAL CHEMISTRY. *Educ:* Oberlin Col, BA, 59; Univ Ill, MS, 61, PhD(chem), 64. *Prof Exp:* Res chemist, David Sarnoff Res Ctr, RCA Corp, NJ, 64-66; fel, Cornell Univ, 66-68; asst prof, 68-73, ASSOC PROF CHEM, MIAMI UNIV, 73- *Res:* Co-ordination chemistry; spectroscopy; crystallography. *Mailing Add:* Dept of Chem Miami Univ Oxford OH 45056

KARIYA, TAKASHI, b Belmont, Calif, June 23, 25; m 51; c 2. BIOCHEMISTRY. *Educ:* Drake Univ, BS, 52, MA, 54. *Prof Exp:* Res asst atherosclerosis res, 55-61, biochemist, 61-65, sect head, Lipid Metab Sect, Biochem Dept, Merrell-Nat Labs, Div Richardson-Merrell, Inc, 65-80, SECT HEAD, PHARMACOL DEPT, MERRELL DOW PHARMACEUT, DOW CHEM CO, 80- *Mem:* Am Chem Soc; Am Oil Chemists Soc; NY Acad Sci. *Res:* Pharmacological control of metabolism of cholesterol and other lipids in relation to the treatment of atherosclerosis; biochemical approaches to the regulation of cardiovascular function by pharmacentical agents. *Mailing Add:* Merrell Dow Pharmaceut 2110 E Galbraith Rd Cincinnati OH 45215

KARK, ROBERT ADRIAAN PIETER, b Boston, Mass, Dec 3, 40; c 3. NEUROLOGY, NEUROCHEMISTRY. *Educ:* Oxford Univ, BA, 62, MA, 67; Harvard Univ, MD, 65. *Prof Exp:* asst prof neurol, Reed Neurol Res Ctr, Neuropsychiat Inst, Sch Med, 72-80, ASSOC PROF NEURO-PSYCHIAT INST HOSP, UNIV CALIF, LOS ANGELES & DIR, ATAXIA CTR, 80- *Concurrent Pos:* Clin assoc & guest scientist neurol & neurochem, Med Neurol Br, Nat Inst Neurol Dis & Stroke, NIH, 68-71; investr, Neurobiochem Group, Ment Retardation Prog, Neuropsychiat Inst, Univ Calif, Los Angeles, 72-, assoc co-dir, Clin Neuromuscular Dis, 74-76, dir, Friedreichs Ataxia Clin, 75-; consult, Wadsworth Vet Admin Hosp, 73- & Friedreichs Ataxia Group Am, 75-; mem, Med Adv Bd, Nat Ataxia Found, 75-; mem, Med Adv Bd, Nat Ataxia Found, Western Regional Chap, 77- & Joseph's Dis Found. *Mem:* Am Acad Neurol; Am Fedn Clin Res; Am Soc Neurochem; Int Soc Neurochem. *Res:* Enzymatic defects, metabolic changes, pathophysiology and treatment of inherited forms of ataxia, mental retardation and neuromuscular disease; neurochemistry of mercurial poisoning; biochemical aspects of neuromuscular trophic effects. *Mailing Add:* Reed Neurol Res Ctr Sch of Med Univ of Calif Los Angeles CA 90024

KARKALITS, OLIN CARROLL, JR, b Pauls Valley, Okla, May 31, 16; m 61; c 2. CHEMICAL ENGINEERING. *Educ:* Rice Inst, BS, 38; Univ Mich, MS, 41, PhD(chem eng), 50. *Prof Exp:* Jr res chemist, Shell Oil Co, 37-42; instr chem eng, Univ Mich, 45-47; group leader process develop, Am Cyanamid Co, 48-56; supvr res, Petro-Tex Chem Corp, 56-63, mgr, 63-66, asst dir technol, 66-72; DEAN, COL ENG & TECHNOL, McNEESE STATE UNIV, 72- *Mem:* AAAS; Am Inst Chem Engrs; Am Soc Eng Educ; Am Asn Cost Engrs. *Res:* Catalysis; geothermal energy. *Mailing Add:* 1161 Bayouwood Dr Lake Charles LA 70605

KARKAS, JOHN D, biochemistry, see previous edition

KARKHECK, JOHN PETER, b New York, NY, Apr 26, 45; m 69; c 3. PHYSICS. *Educ:* Le Moyne Col, BS, 66; State Univ NY Buffalo, MS, 72; State Univ NY Stony Brook, PhD(physics), 78. *Prof Exp:* Physics assoc energy, Brookhaven Nat Lab, 78-79; ASST PROF PHYSICS, GEN MOTORS INST, 81- *Concurrent Pos:* Fel, State Univ NY Stony Brook, 78, res assoc, 79-81. *Mem:* Am Phys Soc. *Res:* Transport theory; energy modeling. *Mailing Add:* Sci & Math Dept Gen Motors Inst Flint MI 48502

KARKLINS, OLGERTS LONGINS, b Tukums, Latvia, Oct 3, 24; US citizen; m 56; c 1. GEOLOGY, BIOLOGY. *Educ:* Columbia Univ, BS, 57, Univ Minn, MS, 61, PhD, 66. *Prof Exp:* GEOLOGIST BIOSTRATIG PALEONT, US GEOL SURV, 63- *Concurrent Pos:* Asst prof lectr, Col Gen Studies, George Washington Univ, 69-72. *Mem:* Paleont Soc; Am Geol Inst; Geol Soc Am; AAAS; Int Bryozool Asn. *Res:* Invertebrate paleontology; biostratigraphy; use of paleobiology, stratigraphy and paleogeography of Paleozoic Ectoprocta in regional correlations. *Mailing Add:* US Geol Surv US Nat Mus E501 Washington DC 20560

KARL, CURTIS LEE, b Milwaukee, Wis, Apr 27, 40; m 63. ORGANIC CHEMISTRY, POLYMER CHEMISTRY. *Educ:* St Olaf Col, BA, 62; Mich State Univ, PhD(org chem), 67. *Prof Exp:* Res assoc, Polymer Develop Dept, Gen Mills Chem Inc, 67-80; RES ASSOC, POLYMER DEVELOP DEPT, HENKEL CORP, 80- *Mem:* Am Chem Soc. *Res:* Preparation and chemistry of synthetic water soluble polymers; polysaccharide chemistry; commercial applications of water soluble polymers; rheology of aqueous polymer solutions. *Mailing Add:* Henkel Corp 2010 E Hennepin Minneapolis MN 55413

KARL, DAVID JOSEPH, b New Haven, Conn, Nov 1, 34; m 58; c 3. PHYSICAL CHEMISTRY, MATERIALS ENGINEERING. *Educ:* Providence Col, BS, 56; Mich State Univ, PhD(chem), 60. *Prof Exp:* Asst prof chem & physics, St Francis Col, Pa, 60-61; asst prof chem, Univ Dayton, 61-66; assoc prof, 66-77, chmn dept, 69-77, PROF CHEM, WRIGHT STATE UNIV, 77- *Concurrent Pos:* VPres, Biomech Int, Inc; pres, Wright Co; consult, Southwestern Portland Cement Co & Allyn Corp. *Mem:* Am Chem Soc; Soc Mfg Engrs; Nat Asn Corrosion Engrs. *Res:* Mass spectrometry; quantum chemistry. *Mailing Add:* Dept of Chem Wright State Univ Dayton OH 45431

KARL, GABRIEL, b Cluj, Romania, Apr 30, 37; Can citizen; m 65; c 1. THEORETICAL PHYSICS. *Educ:* Univ Cluj, BA, 58; Univ Toronto, PhD(chem), 64. *Prof Exp:* Fel molecular physics, Univ Toronto, 64-66; fel high energy physics, Oxford Univ, 66-69; from asst prof to assoc prof physics, 69-75, PROF PHYSICS, UNIV GUELPH, 75- *Concurrent Pos:* Vis scientist, Europ Orgn Nuclear Res, Geneva, 74. *Mem:* Am Phys Soc; Can Asn Physicists. *Res:* High energy physics; atomic physics. *Mailing Add:* Dept of Physics Univ of Guelph Guelph ON N1G 2W1 Can

KARL, HERMAN ADOLF, b New York, NY, Mar 24, 47; m 70. MARINE GEOLOGY, SEDIMENTOLOGY. *Educ:* Colgate Univ, BS, 69; Univ Nebr, MS, 71; Univ Southern Calif, PhD(geol sci), 77. *Prof Exp:* Explor geologist petrol explor, Humble Oil & Refining Co, 71; res geologist, Esso Prod Res Co, 72; Nat Res Coun res assoc marine geol, 77, MARINE GEOLOGIST, PAC-ARCTIC BR MARINE GEOL, US GEOL SURV, 77- *Mem:* AAAS; Geol Soc Am; Soc Econ Paleontologists & Mineralogists; Int Asn Sedimentologists; Am Geophys Union. *Res:* Dynamics of depositional processes and sediment transport on continental margins. *Mailing Add:* Pac-Arctic Br of Marine Geol 345 Middlefield Menlo Park CA 94025

KARL, RICHARD C, b Albany, NY, Feb 16, 20; m 44; c 3. SURGERY. *Educ:* Columbia Univ, AB, 42; Cornell Univ, MD, 44; Am Bd Surg, dipl, 52. *Prof Exp:* Instr anat, Med Col, Cornell Univ, 46-47, asst surg, 48-51, from instr to assoc prof, 52-70; DIR SURG, DARTMOUTH-HITCHCOCK AFFIL HOSPS, 70-; PROF SURG & CHMN DEPT, DARTMOUTH MED SCH, 70- *Concurrent Pos:* From asst to assoc attend surgeon, New York Hosp, 54-70; dir second surg div, Bellevue Hosp, New York, 63-67; dir surg, North Shore Hosp, 67-70; consult, New York Vet Admin Hosp, 63-70, USPHS Hosp, Staten Island, 64-70 & Vet Admin Hosp, White River Junction, Vt, 70- *Mem:* Fel Am Col Surg. *Res:* Academic educational surgery. *Mailing Add:* Dept of Surg Dartmouth Med Sch Hanover NH 03755

KARL, ROBERT RAYMOND, JR, b Sewickley, Pa, June 15, 45. ATMOSPHERIC CHEMISTRY, PHYSICS. *Educ:* Pa State Univ, BS, 67; Cornell Univ, PhD(phys chem), 74. *Prof Exp:* Res assoc surface adsorption, Chem Dept, Pa State Univ, 66-67; res asst molecular struct, Chem Dept, Cornell Univ, 68-73, res asst chem laser, 73-74; fel spectros, State Univ NY, Binghamton, 74-76; STAFF SCIENTIST, LOS ALAMOS NAT LAB, 76- *Mem:* Am Inst Physics; Am Chem Soc. *Res:* Spectroscopy, photochemistry; remote atmospheric sensing. *Mailing Add:* Los Alamos Nat Lab MS-466 Los Alamos NM 87545

KARLANDER, EDWARD P, b Manchester, Vt, Nov 30, 31; wid; c 6. BOTANY. *Educ:* Univ Vt, BS, 60; Univ Md, MS, 62, PhD, 64. *Prof Exp:* From res asst to res assoc, 60-65, asst prof, 66-69, ASSOC PROF ALGAL PHYSIOL, UNIV MD, COLLEGE PARK, 69- *Concurrent Pos:* Prog officer NSF, 79-80; actg dir, Md Water Resources Res Ctr, 80-81. *Mem:* Am Soc Plant Physiol; Phycol Soc Am; Am Soc Limnol & Oceanog; Ecol Soc Am; Am Inst Biol Sci. *Res:* Ecological biophysics; algal physiology; responses of organisms to light; cell growth. *Mailing Add:* Dept of Bot Univ of Md College Park MD 20742

KARLE, HARRY P, b Sanger, Calif, Jan 4, 27; m 56; c 4. PLANT PATHOLOGY, VITICULTURE. *Educ:* Fresno State Col, BS, 50; Univ Calif, Davis, MS, 59, PhD(plant path), 65. *Prof Exp:* Instr, High Sch, Calif, 50-51; foreman viticulture, Fresno State Col, 51-53; lab helper plant path, Univ Calif, Davis, 54-55, lab asst, 55-58, res asst, 58-59, lab technician, 59-62; assoc prof, 62-74, PROF PLANT PATH, CALIF STATE UNIV, FRESNO, 74-, CHMN DEPT PLANT SCI, 69- *Concurrent Pos:* Consult res & study comt, Calif Raisin Adv Bd, 65- *Mem:* AAAS; Am Phytopath Soc; Am Soc Hort Sci; Am Inst Biol Sci. *Res:* Grape diseases; non-cultivation studies. *Mailing Add:* Dept of Plant Sci Calif State Univ Sch Agr & Home Econ Fresno CA 93740

KARLE, ISABELLA LUGOSKI, b Detroit, Mich, Dec 2, 21; m 42; c 3. CHEMISTRY. *Educ:* Univ Mich, BS, 41, MS, 42, PhD(phys chem), 44. *Hon Degrees:* DSc, Univ Mich, 76 & Wayne State Univ, 79. *Prof Exp:* Assoc chemist, Univ Chicago, 44; instr, Univ Mich, 44-46; physicist, 46-59, HEAD, X-RAY ANAL SECT, US NAVAL RES LAB, 59- *Concurrent Pos:* Mem, Nat Comt Crystallog, Nat Acad Sci-Nat Res Coun, 74-77; mem, Exec Comt, Am Peptide Symposium, 76-81; mem bd, Int Orgn & Progs, Nat Acad Sci, 80-; mem adv bd, Off Chem & Chem Tech, Nat Res Coun, 78-81. *Honors & Awards:* Navy Superior Civilian Serv Award, 65; Award, Sci Res Soc Am, 67; Achievement Award, Soc Women Engrs, 68; Hillebrand Award, Am Chem Soc, 69, Garvan Award, 76; Fed Woman's Award, US Govt, 73. *Mem:* Nat Acad Sci; Am Phys Soc; Biophys Soc; Am Crystallog Asn (vpres, 75, pres, 76); Am Chem Soc. *Res:* Application of electron and x-ray diffraction to structure problems; phase determination in crystallography; elucidation of molecular formulae; peptides; configurations and conformations of natural products and biologically active materials. *Mailing Add:* X-ray Anal Sect Code 6030 US Naval Res Lab Washington DC 20375

KARLE, JEAN MARIANNE, b Washington, DC, Nov 14, 50. DRUG METABOLISM. *Educ:* Univ Mich, BS, 71; Duke Univ, PhD(chem), 76. *Prof Exp:* Pub health serv fel, Nat Inst Arthritis, Diabetes, Digestive & Kidney Dis, 76-78, STAFF FEL, NAT CANCER INST, NIH, 78- *Mem:* Am Chem Soc; Am Asn Cancer Res; Int Soc Study Xenobiotics. *Res:* Biochemical basis of action of chemotherapeutic agents; biochemical processes involved in the normal growth of cells; cancer research. *Mailing Add:* Nat Inst Health Bldg 37 Rm 5A13 Bethesda MD 20205

KARLE, JEROME, b New York, NY, June 18, 18; m 42; c 3. CRYSTALLOGRAPHY. *Educ:* City Col New York, BS, 37; Harvard Univ, AM, 38; Univ Mich, MS, 42, PhD(phys chem), 43. *Prof Exp:* Lab asst, State Dept Health, NY, 39-40; res assoc, Manhattan Proj, Chicago, 43-44 & US Navy Proj, Mich, 44-46; head electron diffraction sect, 46-58, head diffraction br, 58-67, CHIEF SCIENTIST, LAB FOR STRUCT OF MATTER, US NAVAL RES LAB, 67- *Concurrent Pos:* Mem, Nat Res Coun, 54-56 & 67-; prof, Univ Md, 51-70; chmn, USA Nat Comt Crystallog, Nat Acad Sci-Nat Res Coun, 73-75; mem exec comt, Int Union Crystallog, 78-, pres, 81- *Honors & Awards:* Award, Sigma Xi, 59; Chair of Sci Award, 67; Navy Distinguished Civilian Serv Award, 68; Hillebrand Award, Am Chem Soc, 69; Robert Dexter Conrad Award, 76. *Mem:* Nat Acad Sci; Am Chem Soc; fel Am Phys Soc; Am Crystallog Asn (treas, 50-52, vpres, 71, pres, 72); Am Math Soc. *Res:* Structure of atoms, molecules, glasses, crystals and solid surfaces. *Mailing Add:* Lab Struct Matter Code 6030 US Naval Res Lab Washington DC 20375

KARLEKAR, BHALCHANDRA VASUDEO, b Baroda, India, Jan 19, 39; m 64; c 2. MECHANICAL ENGINEERING. *Educ:* Univ Baroda, BE, 58; Univ Ill, Urbana, MS, 59, PhD(mech eng), 62. *Prof Exp:* Lectr mech eng, Indian Inst Technol, 62-63; consult, Ibcon Pvt Ltd, Bombay, 63-66; PROF MECH ENG, ROCHESTER INST TECHNOL, 66- *Concurrent Pos:* Consult, Eastman Kodak Co, 66-70, A Burgart Inc, 70-71, Xerox, 74-77 & Chapin Co, 78; actg chmn, Chapin Co, 76-77; chmn energy task force, Rochester Inst Technol. *Mem:* Am Soc Mech Engrs; Am Soc Eng Educ. *Res:* Heat transfer; energy conservation. *Mailing Add:* Dept of Mech Eng Rochester Inst of Technol Rochester NY 14623

KARLER, RALPH, b Mishawaka, Ind, Nov 11, 28; m 53. PHARMACOLOGY. *Educ:* Univ Chicago, AB, 47; Ind Univ, BA, 50; Univ Calif, MS, 53, PhD(physiol), 59. *Prof Exp:* Res instr, 59-63, from asst prof to assoc prof, 63-76, PROF PHARMACOL, COL MED, UNIV UTAH, 76- *Concurrent Pos:* USPHS spec res fel, 61-62, USPHS res career develop award, 62-72. *Mem:* Am Soc Pharmacol & Exp Therapeut; assoc Am Physiol Soc; Int Soc Biochem Pharmacol. *Res:* Pharmacology of drugs affecting the nervous system and muscle; role of calcium in contraction; drug metabolism. *Mailing Add:* Dept of Pharmacol Univ of Utah Col of Med Salt Lake City UT 84112

KARLIN, ALVAN A, b Newark, NJ, May 3, 50. EVOLUTION, SYSTEMATICS. *Educ:* Rutgers Univ, AB, 72; Ind State Univ, MA, 75; Miami Univ, PhD(zool), 78. *Prof Exp:* STAFF BIOLOGIST GENETICS, TALL TIMBERS RES STA, 78- *Concurrent Pos:* Adj asst prof, Fla State Univ, 79- *Mem:* Soc Study Evolution; Soc Syst Zoologists; Am Soc Ichthyologists & Herpetologists; Soc Study Amphibians & Reptiles; Sigma Xi. *Res:* Evolutionary biology, population genetics and ecological genetics; vertebrate biology and sociobiology. *Mailing Add:* Tall Timbers Res Sta Rte 1 Box 160 Tallahassee FL 32312

KARLIN, ARTHUR, b Philadelphia, Pa, Jan 14, 36. NEUROBIOLOGY. *Educ:* Swarthmore Col, BA, 57; Rockefeller Univ, PhD(biol), 62. *Prof Exp:* From res asst to res assoc neurol, 62-64, from asst prof to assoc prof physiol, 65-74, assoc prof neurochem, 74-78, PROF BIOCHEM & NEUROL, COLUMBIA UNIV, 78- *Concurrent Pos:* New York City Health Res Coun career scientist award, Columbia Univ, 70-72; mem bd rev, Fedn Proc, 74. *Mem:* Am Soc Biol Chem; Am Soc Pharmacol & Exp Therapeut. *Res:* Molecular mechanisms of acetylcholine receptors. *Mailing Add:* Dept Neurol Col of Phys & Surg Columbia Univ 630 W 168th St New York NY 10032

KARLIN, KENNETH DANIEL, b Pasadena, Calif, Oct 30, 48. INORGANIC CHEMISTRY. *Educ:* Stanford Univ, BS, 70; Columbia Univ, PhD(inorg chem), 75. *Prof Exp:* Res assoc & NATO fel organometallic chem, Cambridge Univ, Eng, 75-77; ASST PROF INORG CHEM, STATE UNIV NY ALBANY, 77- *Concurrent Pos:* Hon US Ramsey fel, 76-77. *Mem:* Am Chem Soc; The Chem Soc. *Res:* Bioinorganic chemistry; chemistry of copper I; binuclear copper complexes; activation of molecular oxygen; models for copper metalloproteins; organometallic chemistry; reactions of Lewis acids with transition metals. *Mailing Add:* Dept of Chem State Univ of NY Albany NY 12222

KARLIN, SAMUEL, b Yonava, Poland, June 8, 23; nat US; m 47; c 3. MATHEMATICAL STATISTICS, STATISTICS. *Educ:* Ill Inst Technol, BS, 44; Princeton Univ, PhD(math), 47. *Prof Exp:* Asst prof math, Calif Inst Technol, 49-50 & 51-54, assoc prof, 54-56; vis asst prof, Princeton Univ, 50-51; prof math & statist, 56-74, prof math, 74-78, Robert Grimmitt PROF MATH, STANFORD UNIV, 78-, DEAN FAC MATH, WEIZMANN INST SCI, REHOVOT, ISRAEL, 74-, CHMN DEPT MATH, 74- *Concurrent Pos:* Consult, Rand Corp, Calif, 48-; Andrew D White Prof-at-large, Cornell Univ, 75-81; Wilkes Lectr, Princeton Univ, 77; Seymour Sherman Mem Lectr, 78. *Mem:* Nat Acad Sci; Am Math Soc; Inst Math Statist (pres-elect, 77, pres, 78-79); Am Statist Asn. *Res:* Problems in mathematics, statistics, genetics and biology. *Mailing Add:* Dept Math Stanford Univ Stanford CA 94305

KARLINER, JERROLD, b Stanislawow, Poland, Mar 5, 40; US citizen; m 63; c 2. STRUCTURE ELUCIDATION, APPLIED SPECTROSCOPY. *Educ:* City Col New York, BS, 62; Stanford Univ, PhD(org mass spectrometry), 66. *Prof Exp:* Res assoc mass spectrometry, Lederle Labs Div, Am Cyanamid Co, 66-68; group leader spectros, 68-78, DEPT HEAD, ANAL RES DEPT, CIBA-GEIGY CORP, 78- *Mem:* Am Chem Soc; Am Soc Mass Spectrometry. *Res:* Structure elucidation of organic compounds by physical methods; analysis of organic compounds by mass spectrometry, nuclear magnetic resonance, optical rotatory dispersion and circular dichroism; analytical methods development. *Mailing Add:* Anal Res Dept Ciba-Geigy Corp Ardsley NY 10502

KARLL, ROBERT E, b Davenport, Iowa, Apr 29, 24; m 46; c 3. ORGANIC CHEMISTRY. *Educ:* St Ambrose Col, BS, 45; Univ Iowa, MS, 47, PhD(org chem), 49. *Prof Exp:* Res chemist, Standard Oil Co (Ind), 49-54, group leader, 54-65, SECT LEADER, AMOCO CHEM CORP, 65- *Mem:* Am Chem Soc. *Res:* Surfactants; motor oil additives; tertiary oil chemicals. *Mailing Add:* Res & Develop Dept PO Box 400 Naperville IL 60540

KARLOF, JOHN KNOX, b Rochester, NY, Nov 9, 46; m 69; c 2. MATHEMATICS. *Educ:* State Univ NY Col Oswego, BA, 68; Univ Colo, MA, 70, PhD(math), 73. *Prof Exp:* Asst prof math, Univ Nebr at Omaha, 74-77, assoc prof, 77-80; ASSOC PROF MATH & COMPUT SCI, STATE UNIV NY STONY BROOK, 80- *Mem:* Am Math Soc; Math Asn Am. *Res:* Gaussian channel coding theory; algebraic coding theory; group theory. *Mailing Add:* Dept Appl Math State Univ NY Stony Brook NY 11794

KARLOVITZ, BELA, b Papa, Hungary, Nov 9, 04; nat US; m 29; c 3. MECHANICAL & ELECTRICAL ENGINEERING. *Educ:* Budapest Tech Univ, ME, 26; Swiss Fed Inst Technol, EE, 28. *Prof Exp:* Sect engr, Elec Power Co, Hungary, 29-38; res engr, Westinghouse Elec Corp, 38-47; sect chief, US Bur Mines, 47-53; MEM STAFF, COMBUSTION & EXPLOSIVES RES, INC, 53- *Mem:* Am Phys Soc; Combustion Inst. *Res:* Magnetohydrodynamic power generation; combustion; turbulent flames; propulsion systems; electrically augmented flames; high power dispersed electrical discharge; plasma phenomena. *Mailing Add:* 1016 Oliver Bldg Pittsburgh PA 15241

KARLOW, EDWIN ANTHONY, b Glendale, Calif, May 13, 42; m 64; c 2. PHYSICS. *Educ:* Walla Walla Col, BS, 66; Wash State Univ, MS, 68, PhD(physics), 71. *Prof Exp:* Chmn dept math & physics, Columbia Union Col, 72-78; CHMN DEPT PHYSICS, LOMA LINDA UNIV, 78- *Mem:* Am Asn Physics Teachers; Am Phys Soc; Optical Soc Am; Am Sci Affil. *Res:* Analog and digital processing of signals; radiation biophysics. *Mailing Add:* Dept of Physics Loma Linda Univ Riverside CA 92515

KARLSON, ALFRED GUSTAV, b Virginia, Minn, Apr 26, 10; m; c 5. MEDICAL MICROBIOLOGY, PATHOLOGY. *Educ:* Iowa State Univ, BS, 34, DVM, 35, MS, 38; Univ Minn, PhD(path), 42; Am Col Vet Path, dipl; Am Bd Microbiol, dipl. *Prof Exp:* Instr, Iowa State Univ, 35-38; instr, Univ Minn, 39-41, assoc exp path, Mayo Found, 46-56, assoc prof, 56-62, PROF COMP PATH, MAYO GRAD SCH MED, UNIV MINN, 62-, PROF MICROBIOL, MAYO MED SCH, 62-, CONSULT MICROBIOL, MAYO CLINIC, 53- *Concurrent Pos:* Ed, sect vet sci, Biol Abstr. *Mem:* AAAS; Am Soc Microbiol; Soc Exp Biol & Med; Am Vet Med Asn; Am Asn Path & Bact. *Res:* Tuberculosis of domestic animals; chemotherapy of experimental tuberculosis; comparative pathology; bacteriology of tuberculosis. *Mailing Add:* Mayo Clin Rochester MN 55901

KARLSON, ESKIL LEANNART, b Johnkeping, Sweden; Jan 5, 20; US citizen; m 42; c 3. BIOPHYSICS, ZOOLOGY. *Educ:* Pa State Univ, EE, 41; Univ Pittsburgh, MS, 48; Univ St Louis DSc(physics, zool), 70. *Prof Exp:* Lab leader develop radiation instrumentation, Savana River Plant, AEC, 50-55; group leader, Reactor Inst, Greenwich Plant, AMF Inc, 55-57; chief appl physics atomic bomb tests, Las Vegas Labs, EG&G, 57-61; pres gas analyzers, Precision Res, 61-67; vpres res ozone systs, Pollution Control Industs, 67-71; PRES ION EXCHANGE, LIFE SUPPORT SYSTS INC, 71- *Concurrent Pos:* Consult to reactor control, 74-77; res & develop adv ozone, Iconex, Inc, Stamford, Conn, 75-78; consult ion exchange, Facet Enterprises, Tulsa, Okla, 77-78. *Mem:* Optical Soc Am; Inst Soc Am; Health Physics Soc; Am Nuclear Soc. *Res:* Developed first digital pressure transducer, first 8 gas analyzer, first atomatic inbedable heat pump; developed first continuous separation system for oil, blood or water employing the chromatographic phenomena. *Mailing Add:* Life Support Systs Inc 4634 State St Erie PA 16509

KARLSON, KARL EUGENE, b Worcester, Mass, July 30, 20; m 47; c 6. SURGERY. *Educ:* Univ Minn, BS, 42, MB, 44, MD, 45, PhD(surg), 52; Am Bd Surg, dipl, 53; Am Bd Thoracic Surg, dipl, 56. *Prof Exp:* Intern surg, Univ Hosps, Univ Minn, 44-45, resident, 47-51; from instr to prof, Col Med, State Univ NY Downstate Med Ctr, 51-71; PROF MED SCI & SURG, BROWN UNIV, 71- *Concurrent Pos:* From asst vis surgeon to vis surgeon, Kings County Hosp, Brooklyn, 51-71; mem cent adv comt, Coun Cardiovasc Surg, Am Heart Asn, 62-; surgeon & surgeon-in-charge thoracic & cardiovasc surg, RI Hosp, Providence, 71- *Mem:* Am Asn Thoracic Surg; Int Cardiovasc Soc; Am Surg Asn; Soc Vascular Surg; Soc Univ Surg. *Res:* Heart surgery and cardiovascular physiology. *Mailing Add:* Dept of Surg Rhode Island Hosp Providence RI 02903

KARLSON, RONALD HENRY, b Coalinga, Calif, Oct 13, 47; m 77; c 1. MARINE ECOLOGY, BENTHIC ECOLOGY. *Educ:* Pomona Col, BA, 69; Duke Univ, MA, 72, PhD(zool), 75. *Prof Exp:* Fel, Johns Hopkins Univ, 76-78; ASST PROF INVERT BIOL, UNIV DEL, 78- *Mem:* Ecol Soc Am; Am Soc Zoologists; AAAS. *Res:* Ecological and evolutionary questions involving biological interactions; physical disturbance, and life history strategies of sessile colonial invertebrates. *Mailing Add:* Ecol Prog Sch Life Health & Sci Univ Del Newark DE 19711

KARLSSON, STURE KARL FREDRIK, b Sodra Vi, Sweden, Oct 11, 25; US citizen; m 49; c 2. FLUID MECHANICS. *Educ:* Johns Hopkins Univ, PhD(aeronaut), 58. *Prof Exp:* Fel aeronaut, Johns Hopkins Univ, 58-59; NATO fel, Royal Inst Technol Sweden, 59-60; from asst prof to assoc prof eng, 60-71, PROF ENG, BROWN UNIV, 71- *Mem:* Am Phys Soc. *Res:* Turbulent flows; laminar stability. *Mailing Add:* Div of Eng Brown Univ Providence RI 02912

KARLSSON, ULF LENNART, b Uppsala, Sweden, Sept 11, 35; m 60; c 3. ANATOMY, NEUROBIOLOGY. *Educ:* Karolinska Inst, Sweden, MK, 58, Doc, 66, ML, 68. *Hon Degrees:* DrMed, Royal Univ Umea, Sweden, 69. *Prof Exp:* Res zoologist, Univ Calif, Los Angeles, 61-65; teacher anat, Royal Univ Umea, Sweden, 65-69; assoc prof, 69-74, PROF ANAT & DENT, COL MED & DENT, UNIV IOWA, 74- *Mem:* AAAS; Am Asn Anatomists; Soc Neurosci; Scand Asn Electron Micros. *Res:* Structural correlates of nervous system activity. *Mailing Add:* Dept of Anat Univ of Iowa Col of Med Iowa City IA 52240

KARLSTROM, ERNEST LEONARD, b Seattle, Wash, May 18, 28; m 50; c 3. HERPETOLOGY, ECOLOGY. *Educ:* Augustana Col, AB, 49; Univ Wash, Seattle, MS, 52; Univ Calif, Berkeley, PhD(zool), 56. *Prof Exp:* Assoc zool, Univ Calif, Berkeley, 55-56; from asst prof to assoc prof biol, Augustana Col, 56-61; assoc prof, 61-64, PROF BIOL, UNIV PUGET SOUND, 64- *Concurrent Pos:* Arctic Inst NAm res grant, 59-61; NSF basic res grants, 62-64. *Mem:* Am Soc Ichthyol & Herpet; Sigma Xi; Western Soc Naturalists. *Res:* Comparative anatomy of reptiles; ecology and systematics of amphibians; basic marine ecology; radioactive tracer methods. *Mailing Add:* Dept of Biol Univ Puget Sound Tacoma WA 98416

KARLSTROM, THOR NELS VINCENT, b Seattle, Wash, Mar 10, 20; m 48; c 4. GEOLOGY. *Educ:* Augustana Col, AB, 43; Univ Chicago, PhD(geol), 53. *Prof Exp:* Assoc prof geol, Upsala Col, 46-49, dean men, 48-49; geologist, Alaska Terrain & Permafrost Sect, Mil Br, 49-65, GEOLOGIST, ASTROGEOL BR, US GEOL SURV, 65- *Concurrent Pos:* Adj prof, Dept Geol, Northern Ariz Univ, 69- *Mem:* Fel Geog Soc Am. *Res:* Structural and quaternary geology; paleoclimatology; photogrammetry; astrogeology. *Mailing Add:* 628 N Bertrand Flagstaff AZ 86001

KARMAS, ENDEL, US citizen; m 59; c 3. FOOD SCIENCE. *Educ:* Ill Inst Technol, BS, 56; Univ Chicago, MS, 58; Rutgers Univ, PhD(food sci), 68. *Prof Exp:* From asst prof to assoc prof, 69-80, PROF FOOD SCI, RUTGERS UNIV, 80- *Concurrent Pos:* Sci adv, Food & Drug Admin, US Dept Health & Human Serv, 73-80. *Mem:* Fel Inst Food Technol; Swiss Soc Food Sci & Technol; Sigma Xi. *Res:* Chemistry of food proteins, protein-water interactions, water relations in foods, and meat science and technology. *Mailing Add:* Dept of Food Sci Rutgers Univ New Brunswick NJ 08903

KARMAS, GEORGE, b Rochester, NY, Dec 18, 20; m 51. ORGANIC CHEMISTRY. *Educ:* Univ Rochester, BS, 42; NY Univ, MS, 45; Polytech Inst Brooklyn, PhD(org chem), 55. *Prof Exp:* Res chemist, Manhattan Dist Proj, Iowa State Col, 42-44; asst, 44-64, RES FEL, ORTHO PHARMACEUT CORP, RARITAN, 64- *Mem:* Am Chem Soc. *Res:* Synthetic medicinal chemistry, especially antimicrobials; heterocyclic and steroid chemistry. *Mailing Add:* 757 Cedarcrest Dr Bound Brook NJ 08805

KARMEN, ARTHUR, b New York, NY, Feb 25, 30; m 55; c 3. MEDICINE, CLINICAL PATHOLOGY. *Educ:* NY Univ, AB, 50, MD, 54. *Prof Exp:* Resident & intern med, Bellevue Hosp, New York, 54-56; res investr, Nat Heart Inst, 56-63; assoc prof radiol, radiol sci & med, Johns Hopkins Univ, 63-68; prof path & med, Sch Med & dir clin labs, Univ Hosp, NY Univ & Bellevue Hosp, 68-71; PROF & CHMN DEPT LAB MED, ALBERT EINSTEIN COL MED, 71- *Concurrent Pos:* Dir clin labs, Bronx Munic Hosp Ctr & Hosp Albert Einstein Col Med, 71- *Honors & Awards:* Sloan Award Cancer Res, 57; Van Slyke Award, Am Asn Clin Chemists, 79; Tswett Medal Chromatography, 82. *Res:* Analytical biochemistry, clinical pathology and chemistry, lipid metabolism and clinical enzymology; nuclear medicine; biochemistry. *Mailing Add:* Albert Einstein Col Med Yeshiva Univ Bronx NY 10461

KARMIS, MICHAEL E, b Athens, Greece, June 9, 48; m 72; c 3. MINING ENGINEERING. *Educ:* Univ Strathclyde, BSc, 71, PhD(rock mech), 74. *Prof Exp:* Royal Soc Brit fel rock mech, Dept Mining Eng, Univ Strathclyde, 74-75; asst prof mining eng, Nat Tech Univ Athens, Greece, 75-78; asst prof, 78-81, ASSOC PROF MINING ENG, VA POLYTECH INST & STATE UNIV, 81- *Mem:* Am Inst Mining, Metall & Petrol Engrs; Inst Mining, Metall & Petrol Engrs; Int Soc Rock Mech. *Res:* Stress analysis around mining excavations using theoretical and experimental methods; design of instrumentation for monitoring underground stresses and strains; in-situ investigations; mining subsidence; geotechnical techniques; mine design. *Mailing Add:* Dept of Mining & Minerals Eng Va Polytech Inst & State Univ Blacksburg VA 24061

KARN, JAMES FREDERICK, b Columbus, Ohio, Jan 28, 39; m 60; c 2. RANGE RUMINANT NUTRITION, FORAGE EVALUATION. *Educ:* Ohio State Univ, BS, 62, MS, 64; Univ Nebr, PhD(ruminant nutrit), 76. *Prof Exp:* Res technician, North Platte Sta, Univ Nebr, 67-76; RES ANIMAL SCIENTIST BEEF CATTLE NUTRIT, NORTHERN GREAT PLAINS RES CTR, AGR RES SERV, USDA, 76- *Mem:* Am Soc Animal Sci; Soc Range Mgt. *Res:* Improving the efficiency of producing beef cattle on rangelands; forage evaluation; clarifying the nutrient requirements of range cattle. *Mailing Add:* Northern Great Plains Res Ctr PO Box 459 Mandan ND 58554

KARN, ROBERT CAMERON, b Berwyn, Ill, Mar 12, 45; m 66; c 2. HUMAN GENETICS, BIOCHEMICAL GENETICS. *Educ:* Ind Univ, BA, 67, MA, 70, PhD(zool), 72. *Prof Exp:* Instr, 74-76, asst prof, 76-81, dir, Genotyping Labs, Dept Med Genetics, 75-81, ASSOC PROF MED GENETICS, SCH MED, IND UNIV, 81- *Concurrent Pos:* NIH fel, Sch Med, Ind Univ, 74-75, career develop award, 77- *Mem:* Sigma Xi; Genetics Soc Am; Am Soc Human Genetics; Am Inst Biol Sci. *Res:* Genetics and biochemistry of salivary proteins; evolution by gene duplication; genetics of obesity and diabetes; genetic polymorphisms. *Mailing Add:* Dept of Med Genetics 1100 W Michigan St Indianapolis IN 46223

KARNER, FRANK RICHARD, b Elmhurst, Ill, Aug 14, 34; m 58; c 5. GEOLOGY. *Educ:* Wheaton Col, BS, 57; Univ Ill, PhD(geol), 63. *Prof Exp:* From asst prof to assoc prof, 62-69, PROF GEOL, UNIV N DAK, 69- *Mem:* AAAS; Geol Soc Am; Sigma Xi. *Res:* Mineralogy and petrology of igneous, sedimentary and metamorphic rocks. *Mailing Add:* Dept of Geol Univ of NDak Grand Forks ND 58202

KARNES, CHARLES HENRY, structural mechanics, see previous edition

KARNEY, CHARLES FIELDING FINCH, b Eng, Nov 7, 51. RADIO-FREQUENCY HEATING. *Educ:* Cambridge Univ, Eng, BA, 72; Mass Inst Technol, SM, 74, PhD(elec eng & comp sci), 77. *Prof Exp:* Res assoc, Dept Elec Eng & Comp Sci, Mass Inst Technol, 77; res assoc, 77-79, RES STAFF, PLASMA PHYSICS LAB, PRINCETON UNIV, 79- *Res:* Plasma physics, especially radio-frequency heating; intrinsic stochasticity with application to plasma physics. *Mailing Add:* Plasma Physics Lab Princeton Univ PO Box 451 Princeton NJ 08544

KARNI, SHLOMO, b Lodz, Poland, June 23, 32; US citizen; m 61; c 2. ELECTRICAL ENGINEERING. *Educ:* Israel Inst Technol, BS, 56; Yale Univ, MEng, 57; Univ Ill, PhD(elec eng), 60. *Prof Exp:* Testing engr, Palestine Power Co, 55-56; asst elec eng, Yale Univ, 56-57; from instr to asst prof, Univ Ill, 57-61; from asst prof to assoc prof, 61-69, PROF ELEC ENG,

UNIV N MEX, 69-, GRAD ADV, 71- *Concurrent Pos:* Mem circuits group, Univ Ill, 60-61; consult, Los Alamos Nat Lab & Kirtland AFB; vis prof, Univ Hawaii, 68-69 & Tel Aviv Univ, 70-71. *Mem:* AAAS; fel Inst Elec & Electronics Engrs; Am Soc Eng Educ. *Res:* Network theory; system theory; power and energy modelling. *Mailing Add:* Dept of Elec Eng & Comput Sci Univ of NMex Albuquerque NM 87131

KARNOPP, BRUCE HARVEY, b Milwaukee, Wis, June 13, 38; m 63; c 3. ENGINEERING MECHANICS, APPLIED MATHEMATICS. *Educ:* Mass Inst Technol, SB, 60; Brown Univ, ScM, 63; Univ Wis, PhD(eng mech), 65. *Prof Exp:* Engr, AC Spark Plug, Gen Motors Corp, Wis, 60-61; engr, Sanders Assocs, NH, 61; instr eng mech, Univ Wis, 62-65; asst prof mech eng, Univ Toronto, 65-68; asst prof eng mech, 68-77, ASSOC PROF ENG MECH, UNIV MICH, ANN ARBOR, 77- *Mem:* Acoust Soc Am; Tensor Soc. *Res:* Variational methods in mechanics, vibrations and dynamics. *Mailing Add:* Dept Mech Eng & Appl Mech Univ of Mich Ann Arbor MI 48109

KARNOPP, DEAN CHARLES, b Milwaukee, Wis, June 12, 34; m 58; c 2. MECHANICAL ENGINEERING. *Educ:* Mass Inst Technol, BS & MS, 57, PhD(mech eng), 61. *Prof Exp:* Asst appl mech, Mass Inst Technol, 57-59, instr, 59-61, asst prof & Ford fel, 61-63; develop engr, Siemens Schuckert Res Ctr, Ger, 63-64; from asst prof to assoc prof syst dynamics & control, Mass Inst Technol, 64-69, prof syst dynamics & control, 69-80, PROF MECH ENG, UNIV CALIF, DAVIS, 80- *Concurrent Pos:* Vis prof, Univ Stuttgart, Ger, 75-76. *Honors & Awards:* Levy Medal, Franklin Inst, 69; Sr US Scientist Award, Humbolt Found, 75. *Mem:* Am Soc Mech Engrs. *Res:* Dynamic systems; random vibrations; search and optimization theory; control; computation; bond graph modeling of engineering systems. *Mailing Add:* Dept of Mech Eng Univ of Calif Davis CA 95616

KARNOSKY, DAVID FRANK, b Rhinelander, Wis, Oct 12, 49; m 70. FOREST GENETICS. *Educ:* Univ Wis-Madison, BS, 71, MS, 72, PhD(forest genetics), 75. *Prof Exp:* FOREST GENETICIST, CARY ARBORETUM, NY BOT GARDEN, 75- *Mem:* Int Soc Arboriculture; Am Phytopathological Soc; Air Pollution Control Asn; Soc Am Foresters; Int Tissue Cult Asn; tissue culture of trees; attempting interspecific hybridization of Ulmus species. *Res:* Variation in air pollution tolerance of trees; cytogenetic and tissue culture studies of elms; developing urban hardy trees. *Mailing Add:* Cary Arboretum Box AB Millbrook NY 12545

KARNOVSKY, MANFRED L, b Johannesburg, SAfrica, Dec 14, 18; nat US; m 52; c 1. BIOCHEMISTRY. *Educ:* Univ Witwatersrand, BSc, 51, hons, 42, MSc, 43; Univ Capetown, PhD(org chem), 47. *Prof Exp:* Jr lectr chem, Univ Witwatersrand, 41-42; chief chemist & inspector, Brit Ministry Aircraft Prod, SAfrica, 42-43; asst, Univ Capetown, 44-47; from res assoc to assoc, 50-51, from asst prof to prof, 52-65, chmn dept, 69-73, HAROLD T WHITE PROF BIOL CHEM, HARVARD MED SCH, 65- *Concurrent Pos:* Res fel, Univ Wis, 47-48; Lederle med fac award, 55-58. *Honors & Awards:* Glycerine Producers Asn Second Award, 53; Gold Medal, Reticuloendothelial Soc, 66. *Mem:* Am Soc Biol Chemists; fel Am Acad Arts & Sci; Histochem Soc; Am Chem Soc; Am Soc Cell Biol. *Res:* Biochemistry of phagocytosis, pinocytosis and other transport phenomena; biochemistry of sleep. *Mailing Add:* Dept of Biol Chem Harvard Med Sch Boston MA 02115

KARNOVSKY, MORRIS JOHN, b Johannesburg, SAfrica, June 28, 26; nat US; m 51; c 2. PATHOLOGY. *Educ:* Univ Witwatersrand, BSc, 46, MB, BCh, 50; Univ London, dipl clin path, 54. *Hon Degrees:* MA, Harvard Univ, 65. *Prof Exp:* House officer med & surg, Johannesburg Gen Hosp, 51; asst resident path, Beth Israel Hosp, 55-56; assoc, 61-63, from asst prof to assoc prof, 63-68, PROF PATH, HARVARD MED SCH, 68- *Concurrent Pos:* Res fel, Harvard Med Sch, 56-60; Lederle med fac award, 63-66; assoc, Peter Bent Brigham Hosp, 58-60; sci collabr, Sch Med, Univ Geneva, 61-63; mem study group path, USPHS, 65-69. *Mem:* Am Soc Cell Biol; fel Am Acad Arts & Sci; Am Soc Exp Path; Histochem Soc; Int Acad Path. *Res:* Histochemistry; electron microscopy; ultrastructural cytochemistry; cell surface topography and modulation; cell junctions; metabolism and structure of kidney; structure and function of capillaries. *Mailing Add:* Dept of Path Harvard Med Sch Boston MA 02115

KARNS, CHARLES W(ESLEY), b Waynesboro, Pa, July 15, 20; m 46; c 3. OPERATIONS ANALYSIS. *Educ:* Dickinson Col, BA, 41; Northwestern Univ, MA, 48. *Prof Exp:* Asst math, Northwestern Univ, 46-51; mem staff, Opers Eval Group, Div Sponsored Res, Mass Inst Technol, 51-53, 54-62, Opers Res Group, 53-54; mem staff opers eval group, Ctr Naval Anal, Franklin Inst, 62-63, naval warfare anal group, 63-64, opers eval group, 64-67; mem staff, Opers Eval Group, Ctr Naval Anal, Univ Rochester, 67-71; staff asst off dep dir test & eval, Off Dir Defense Res & Eng, Off Secy Defense, 71-78; STAFF SPECIALIST PROG & FINANCIAL MATTERS, OFF DIR TEST & EVAL, OFF UNDERSECY DEFENSE RES & ENG, 78- *Mem:* Opers Res Soc Am; Math Asn Am. *Res:* Military operations research. *Mailing Add:* 8629 Redwood Dr Vienna VA 22180

KARO, ARNOLD MITCHELL, b Wayne, Nebr, May 14, 28; m 66; c 2. CHEMICAL PHYSICS, SOLID STATE PHYSICS. *Educ:* Stanford Univ, BS, 49; Mass Inst Technol, PhD(chem phys), 53. *Prof Exp:* Mem staff, Lincoln Lab, Mass Inst Technol, 55-58; mem chem staff, 58-70, group leader theoret chem, 70-76, SR RES SCIENTIST, LAWRENCE LIVERMORE LAB, UNIV CALIF, 76- *Concurrent Pos:* Vis res scientist, Europ Ctr Atomic & Molecular Theory, Univ Paris, Orsay, 75. *Mem:* Fel AAAS; fel NY Acad Sci; fel Am Phys Soc; fel Am Inst Chem; Sigma Xi. *Res:* Atomic and molecular physics; theoretical solid state physics; lattice and molecular dynamics; quantum chemistry; computer characterization of the elementary excitations and the optical and defect properties of solid materials; application of computer properties of solids; application of molecular dynamics to shock and detonation phenomena in condensed matter. *Mailing Add:* Dept of Chem & Mat Sci L-324 Lawrence Livermore Lab Livermore CA 94550

KARO, DOUGLAS PAUL, b Seattle, Wash, Aug 24, 47; m 71. STATISTICAL MECHANICS, OPTICS. *Educ:* Stanford Univ, BS, 69; Mass Inst Technol, PhD(physics), 73, MS, 80. *Prof Exp:* Physicist, Harry Diamond Lab, US Army, 71; sr staff scientist physics, Avco Everett Res Lab Inc, 73-78, SR CONSULT ENGR, AVCO SYSTS DIV, 80- *Mem:* Optical Soc Am; Am Phys Soc; AAAS; Sigma Xi. *Res:* Stellar speckle interferometry; image processing; nonisoplanatic effects; turbulence; atmospheric propagation; digital data processing; lasers; isotope separation; management; low light level sensors. *Mailing Add:* Avco Systs Div 201 Lowell St Wilmington MA 01887

KARO, WOLF, b Altona-Hamburg, Ger, Apr 2, 24; nat US; m 55; c 1. INDUSTRIAL ORGANIC CHEMISTRY, ORGANIC POLYMER CHEMISTRY. *Educ:* Cornell Univ, AB, 45, PhD(org chem), 49. *Prof Exp:* Aeronaut res scientist jet fuel, Nat Adv Comt Aeronaut, 49-53; aeronaut res scientist fuel synthesis, Monomer-Polymer, Inc, 53-55; group leader contract res, Synthesis & Polymerization Sects, Borden Chem Co, 55-61, develop mgr, Monomer-Polymer & Dajac Labs, 61-68; sr sci specialist, Scott Paper Co, 68-69; new prod mgr, Sartomer Resins, Inc, 70-71; supvr qual control, Lactona Corp Div, Warner-Lambert Pharmaceut Co, 72-75; RES SUPVR, HAVEN CHEM CO, 75- *Mem:* AAAS; Am Chem Soc. *Res:* Reaction kinetics and mechanisms in organic chemistry; organic functional group synthesis; emulsion and anaerobic polymerization; adhesives; coatings; product and process development; materials for radiation-induced polymerization; anionic polymerization. *Mailing Add:* 328 Rockledge Ave Huntingdon Valley PA 19006

KAROL, FREDERICK J, b Norton, Mass, Feb 28, 33; m 58; c 3. POLYMER CHEMISTRY. *Educ:* Boston Univ, BS, 54; Mass Inst Technol, PhD(org chem), 62. *Prof Exp:* Chemist, Chem & Plastics Group, 56-59 & 62-65, proj scientist, 65-67, res scientist, 67-69, group leader chem & plastics, 69-78, RES ASSOC & GROUP SUPVR, UNION CARBIDE CORP, 78- *Mem:* Am Chem Soc. *Res:* Heterogeneous and polyolefin catalyses; mechanism of polyermization. *Mailing Add:* Hiland Dr Belle Mead NJ 08502

KAROL, J(ACOB), b Kansas City, Kans, Oct 22, 07. CIVIL ENGINEERING. *Educ:* Univ Ill, BS, 29, MS, 30, PhD(civil eng), 38. *Prof Exp:* Head stress anal unit, Curtiss-Wright Airplane Div, St Louis, 42-45; detailer & designer, Ash-Howard-Needles & Tammen, Kansas City, Mo, 30-36; detailer & designer, Howard-Needles-Tammen & Bergendoff, 38-42, design engr, 45-48, 52-63, struct design consult, 64-73; RETIRED. *Mem:* Fel Am Soc Civil Engrs. *Res:* Suspension bridge analysis; analysis of aircraft structures; partial influence line procedure for suspension bridge analysis by the deflection theory. *Mailing Add:* 769 E 70th Terr Kansas City MO 64131

KAROL, MERYL HELENE, b New York, NY; m 63; c 3. IMMUNOCHEMISTRY, TOXICOLOGY. *Educ:* Cornell Univ, BS, 61; Columbia Univ, PhD(microbiol), 67. *Prof Exp:* Fel biochem, State Univ NY Stony Brook, 67-68; res assoc epidemiol, 74-76, res asst prof toxicol, 76-78, ASSOC PROF IMMUNOTOXICOL, UNIV PITTSBURGH, 79- *Honors & Awards:* Frank R Blood, 81. *Mem:* Am Chem Soc; Am Indust Hyg Asn; AAAS; Soc Toxicol; NY Acad Sci. *Res:* Chemical and industrial allergens; lung disease; animal models for occupational disease. *Mailing Add:* Dept of Indust Environ Health Sci Univ of Pittsburgh Pittsburgh PA 15261

KAROL, PAUL JASON, b New York, NY, Mar 18, 41; m 63; c 3. NUCLEAR CHEMISTRY, PHYSICAL CHEMISTRY. *Educ:* Johns Hopkins Univ, BA, 61; Columbia Univ, MS, 62, PhD(chem), 67. *Prof Exp:* Res assoc nuclear chem, Brookhaven Nat Lab, 67-69; asst prof chem, 69-74, ASSOC PROF CHEM, CARNEGIE-MELLON UNIV, 74-, ASSOC DEAN SCI, 81- *Concurrent Pos:* Res collabr, Brookhaven Nat Lab, 69-72; consult, Westinghouse Elec Corp, 72- *Mem:* AAAS; Am Chem Soc; Am Phys Soc; NY Acad Sci; Am Nuclear Soc. *Res:* Mechanisms of high energy nuclear reactions, spallation and fission; rapid radiochemical separations; pion reactions; positronium chemistry; role of nuclear surface in nuclear reactions. *Mailing Add:* Dept of Chem 4400 Fifth Ave Pittsburgh PA 15213

KAROLY, GABRIEL, b Budapest, Hungary, May 19, 30; US citizen. CHEMICAL ENGINEERING, POLYMER CHEMISTRY. *Educ:* Budapest Tech Univ, MS, 52. *Prof Exp:* Sr engr, Esso Res & Eng Co, 56-66; res chemist, Union Carbide Corp, 66-69; RES SUPVR, M&T CHEM INC, 69- *Mem:* Am Chem Soc. *Res:* Block and graft copolymers; anionic polymerization; telechelic polymers; coordination polymerization; synthetic fibers; coatings. *Mailing Add:* 255 Baltusrol Way Springfield NJ 07081

KARON, JOHN MARSHALL, b Milwaukee, Wis, Nov 6, 41. BIOSTATISTICS. *Educ:* Carleton Col, BA, 63; Stanford Univ, MS, 65, PhD(math), 68. *Prof Exp:* Asst prof math, Syracuse Univ, 68-70; res assoc, Stanford Univ, 70-71; asst prof math, Colo Col, 71-77; fel biostatist, 77-80, RES ASSOC PROF, BIOSTATISTS, UNIV NC, 80- *Concurrent Pos:* Vis lectr, Tel Aviv Univ, 72-73. *Mem:* AAAS; Soc Indust & Appl Math; Am Statist Asn. *Res:* Evaluation of statistical methods; statistical epidemiology. *Mailing Add:* Dept of Biostatist Univ of NC Chapel Hill NC 27514

KAROSAKA, MITSURU, b Mukden, China, Mar 26, 35; US citizen; m 63; c 3. MECHANICAL ENGINEERING, APPLIED MATHEMATICS. *Educ:* Univ Tokyo, BS, 59, MS, 61; Calif Inst Technol, PhD(mech eng), 68. *Prof Exp:* Design engr, Hitachi Ltd, 61-63; grad res & teaching asst, Calif Inst Technol, 63-67; eng specialist, AiResearch Mfg Co, 67-69; fluid mech engr, Gen Elec Res & Develop Ctr, 69-77; ASSOC PROF MECH & AEROSPACE ENG, UNIV TENN SPACE INST, 77- *Concurrent Pos:* Consult, Gen Elec Co, 77- & ARO, Inc, 78- *Mem:* Assoc fel Am Inst Aeronaut & Astronaut; Am Soc Mech Engrs; Sigma Xi. *Res:* Aerothermodynamics of gas turbines; aeroacoustics; unsteady flow, aeroelasticity; nonlinear waves; two-phase flow. *Mailing Add:* Dept of Mech & Aerospace Eng Univ of Tenn Space Inst Tullahoma TN 37388

KAROW, ARMAND MONFORT, JR, b New Orleans, La, Nov 11, 41; m 64; c 2. PHARMACOLOGY, CRYOBIOLOGY. *Educ:* Duke Univ, BA, 62; Univ Miss, PhD(pharmacol), 68. *Prof Exp:* Instr nursing & pharmacol, Med Ctr, Univ Miss, 65-68; res instr, Dept Surg, 68-71, res asst prof, 71-77, asst prof, Dept Pharmacol, 68-70, assoc prof, 70-75, dir grad studies, 73-80, RES ASSOC PROF, DEPT SURG, MED COL GA, 77-, PROF, DEPT PHARMACOL, 75- *Concurrent Pos:* Officer, Xytex Corp, Augusta, Ga, 75-; res grants, NIH & USPHS; mem, Nat Endowment Humanities, 80; Fogarty sr int fel award, NIH, 81. *Mem:* Fel AAAS; Am Chem Soc; assoc mem Am Soc Clin Pathologists; Am Soc Pharmacol & Exp Therapeut. *Res:* Freezing organs and tissues; electron microscopy; molecular pharmacology; cell physiology. *Mailing Add:* Dept of Pharmacol Med Col of Ga Augusta GA 30902

KARP, ABRAHAM E, b New York, NY, Mar 11, 15; m 40; c 2. OPERATIONS RESEARCH, MATHEMATICS. *Educ:* City Col New York, BS, 36, MS, 37. *Prof Exp:* Mathematician, Aberdeen Proving Ground, Dept Army, 40-50, chief anal sect math statist, 50-55, dir anal lab, 55-62, chief gaming div, Strategy & Tactics Anal Group, 62-66; prog mgr opers res, Nat Bur Standards, 66-69; dir, Ctr Criminal Justice Opers & Mgt, Law Enforcement Assistance Admin, 69-70; dir, Tech Anal Div, Nat Bur Standards, 70-71; PVT CONSULT, SYSTS ANAL & OPERS RES, 71- *Concurrent Pos:* Mem, US Civil Serv Bd Exam, 63- & Army Math Steering Comt, 63-66. *Mem:* Opers Res Soc Am. *Res:* Operations research and systems analysis in the areas of transportation, other public systems and military defense systems. *Mailing Add:* 10308 Green Trail Dr N Boynton Beach FL 33436

KARP, ALAN H, b Syracuse, NY, Aug 6, 46; m 70. ASTROPHYSICS. *Educ:* Rensselaer Polytech Inst, BS, 68; Univ Md, College Park, PhD(astron), 74. *Prof Exp:* Fel astron, IBM Res, Yorktown Heights, NY, 74-76; asst prof physics, Dartmouth Col, 76-77; MEM STAFF PHYSICS, IBM SCI CTR, 77- *Concurrent Pos:* Consult, IBM Res, Yorktown Heights, NY, 76-77. *Mem:* Am Astron Soc. *Res:* Radiative transfer in moving stellar atmospheres; radiative transfer in planetary atmospheres containing dust. *Mailing Add:* 1382 Kingfisher Way Sunnyvale CA 94087

KARP, ARTHUR, b New York, NY, Apr 26, 28. HIGH FREQUENCY PHYSICS, MICROWAVE ELECTRONICS . *Educ:* City Col New York, BEE, 48; Mass Inst Technol, SM, 50; Cambridge Univ, PhD(elec eng), 62. *Prof Exp:* Jr engr, A Alford Consult Engrs, Mass, 48; res asst electronics, Mass Inst Technol, 48-50; res asst cent lab, Int Tel & Tel, Paris, France, 50-51, mem tech staff, Bell Tel Labs, Inc, 51-56; engr lab, Cambridge Univ, 56-59; res engr, W W Hansen Labs, Stanford, 60-64; sr res engr, SRI Int, 64-77; SR ENGR, VARIAN ASSOCS INC, 77- *Concurrent Pos:* Consult, Sylvania Elec Prod Inc, Calif, 60-62, Varian Assocs, 62-63 & Goodyear Aerospace Corp, Ariz, 63-64. *Honors & Awards:* B J Thompson Mem Prize, Inst Radio Engrs, 58. *Mem:* AAAS; Inst Elec & Electronics Engrs. *Res:* Electron devices; ultrahigh frequency, microwave and millimeter-wave techniques, components, circuits, electron tubes, bio-effects; color perception and display techniques including color encryption. *Mailing Add:* Microwave Tube Div Varian Assoc Inc Palo Alto CA 94303

KARP, HERBERT RUBIN, b Atlanta, Ga, Apr 13, 21; m 48; c 3. NEUROLOGY. *Educ:* Emory Univ, AB, 43; MD, 51; Am Bd Psychiat & Neurol, dipl, 60. *Prof Exp:* Intern & jr asst resident internal med, Grady Mem Hosp, 51-53; fel metab dis, Sch Med, Emory Univ, 53-54; resident neurol, Univ Hosp, Duke Univ, 54-56; clin & res fel, Harvard Med Sch, 56-57, res fel neuropath, 57-58; asst prof med, 58-63, PROF NEUROL, SCH MED, EMORY UNIV, 63- *Concurrent Pos:* Nat Inst Neurol Dis & Blindness spec trainee, 56-58; consult, Vet Admin Hosp, Atlanta, Ga. *Mem:* AAAS; Am Neurol Asn; fel Am Acad Neurol. *Res:* Cerebrovascular disease from the standpoint of further understanding of underlying pathophysiology as well as evaluation of current methods of therapy. *Mailing Add:* 69 Butler St SE Atlanta GA 30303

KARP, HOWARD, b Pittsburgh, Pa, Sept 26, 26; m 52; c 4. ANALYTICAL CHEMISTRY. *Educ:* Univ Pittsburgh, BS, 49. *Prof Exp:* ASSOC RES CONSULT CHEM, US STEEL CORP, 49- *Res:* Analytical chemistry as it pertains to steel chemistry. *Mailing Add:* US Steel Res Lab Monroeville PA 15146

KARP, LAURENCE EDWARD, b Paterson, NJ, Apr 26, 39; m 62; c 2. OBSTETRICS & GYNECOLOGY, MEDICAL GENETICS. *Educ:* NY Univ, MD, 63. *Prof Exp:* Instr obstet & gynec, Sch Med, Univ Tex, San Antonio, 69-70; sr fel reprod genetics, Sch Med, Univ Wash, 70-72, asst prof obstet & gynec, 72-76; assoc prof, Harbor Gen Hosp, Univ Calif, Los Angeles, 76-77; ASSOC PROF OBSTET & GYNEC, SCH MED, UNIV WASH, 77-; DIR EDUC OBSTET & GYNEC, SWED HOSP MED CTR, SEATTLE, 77- *Mem:* Fel Am Col Obstet & Gynec; AAAS; Am Soc Human Genetics. *Res:* Investigation of chromosomal anomalies in gametes and preimplantation embryos; also, advancement of procedures and techniques for prenatal diagnosis. *Mailing Add:* Dept of Obstet & Gynec RH-20 Univ of Wash Sch of Med Seattle WA 98195

KARP, RICHARD DALE, b Minneapolis, Minn, June 19, 43; m 68; c 3. IMMUNOLOGY. *Educ:* Univ Minn, BA, 65, MS, 68, PhD(microbiol), 72. *Prof Exp:* Res assoc microbiol, Univ Minn, 66-72; NIH & C D Rogers fels, Univ Calif, Los Angeles, 73-75; asst prof, 75-80, ASSOC PROF BIOL SCI, UNIV CINCINNATI, 80- *Mem:* Am Soc Microbiol; Am Soc Zoologists; Am Asn Immunologists; AAAS; NY Acad Sci. *Res:* Immune response to solid tumor growth and the nature of tumor-host interactions; phylogenetic development of the immune response. *Mailing Add:* Dept of Biol Sci Univ of Cincinnati Cincinnati OH 45221

KARP, RICHARD M, b Boston, Mass, Jan 3, 35; m 79. COMPUTER THEORY. *Educ:* Harvard Univ, AB, 55, SM, 56, PhD(appl math), 59. *Prof Exp:* Mem res staff, Watson Res Ctr, Int Bus Mach Corp, 59-68; adj assoc prof indust & mgt eng, Columbia Univ, 67-68; assoc chmn dept, 73-75, Miller res prof, 80-81, fac res lectr, 81-82, PROF COMPUT SCI, INDUST ENG & OPER RES, UNIV CALIF, BERKELEY, 68-, PROF MATH, 80- *Concurrent Pos:* Vis assoc prof elec eng, Univ Mich, 64-65; vis assoc prof, Polytechnic Inst Brooklyn, 65-68, vis prof, 68. *Honors & Awards:* Lanchester Prize, 77; Fulkerson Prize, 79. *Mem:* Nat Acad Sci; NY Acad Sci. *Res:* Construction of computational algorithms and the determination of the inherent computational complexity of problems with particular emphasis on combinatorial problems. *Mailing Add:* Comput Sci Dept Univ Calif Berkeley CA 94720

KARP, SAMUEL NOAH, b Brooklyn, NY, Feb 13, 24; m 46; c 2. APPLIED MATHEMATICS. *Educ:* Brown Univ, MSc, 45, PhD, 48. *Prof Exp:* Res assoc compressible fluids & flutter, Brown Univ, 46-48; sr res scientist, Div Electromagnetic Res, 48-55, from res asst prof to res assoc prof math, 55-61, instr, Wash Square Col, 48-55, PROF MATH, COURANT INST MATH SCI, NY UNIV AT WASH SQUARE, 61- *Concurrent Pos:* Indust consult. *Mem:* Am Math Soc. *Res:* Electromagnetic theory; diffraction; boundary value problems; ship resistance and motions; surface waves; far field expansions of radiated fields; multiple impedance; higher order eigen functions of integral equations; inverse scattering. *Mailing Add:* Dept Math Courant Inst Math Sci NY Univ Wash Sq Ctr New York NY 10003

KARP, STEWART, b New York, NY, Mar 17, 32; m 57; c 2. ANALYTICAL CHEMISTRY. *Educ:* Queens Col, NY, BS, 53; Polytech Inst Brooklyn, MS, 60, PhD(chem), 67. *Prof Exp:* Chemist, Sperry Gyroscope Co, 57-60; anal chemist, Colgate-Palmolive Co, 60-62; sr chemist, Am Cyanamid Co, 67-68; asst prof, 68-71, ASSOC PROF CHEM, C W POST COL, LONG ISLAND UNIV, 71-, CHMN, DEPT CHEM, 81- *Mem:* Am Chem Soc. *Res:* Electroanalytical chemistry, especially polarography and controlled-potential electrolysis; analytical methods. *Mailing Add:* Dept of Chem C W Post Col Long Island Univ Greenvale NY 11548

KARP, WARREN B, b Brooklyn, NY, Feb 12, 44; m 76; c 1. BIOCHEMISTRY. *Educ:* Pace Univ, BS, 65; Ohio State Univ, PhD(physiol chem), 70; Med Col Ga, DMD, 77. *Prof Exp:* Teaching asst physiol chem, Ohio State Univ, 66-68, res assoc, 68-70, res assoc pediat, 70-71; pediat res instr, Sch Med, 71-73, instr cell & molecular biol, 72-73, asst res prof pediat & asst prof cell & molecular biol, Sch Med & asst prof, Sch Grad Studies, 73-79, asst prof biochem, Sch Dent, 74-79, ASSOC RES PROF PEDIAT, SCH MED & ASSOC PROF ORAL BIOL, BIOCHEM & ORAL MED, SCH DENT, MED COL GA, 79- *Concurrent Pos:* Environ Protection Agency grant, Med Col Ga, 71-74, dir pediat res, 77-, dir clin perinatal lab, 78- *Mem:* AAAS; Sigma Xi; Am Chem Soc; NY Acad Sci; Int Dent Res Soc. *Res:* Environmental effects on human placental enzymology; human placental amino acid metabolism; the effect of bilirubin on brain metabolism; human placental lipid metabolism. *Mailing Add:* Med Col of Ga Augusta GA 30902

KARPATKIN, SIMON, b Brooklyn, NY, Sept 6, 33; m 65. BIOCHEMISTRY, PHYSIOLOGY. *Educ:* Brooklyn Col, BS, 54; NY Univ, MD, 58. *Prof Exp:* Intern med, Bellevue Hosp, NY Univ, 58-59, resident, 59-60; resident, Einstein Med Ctr, Bronx, 60-61; from instr to assoc prof, 64-74, PROF MED, SCH MED, NY UNIV, 74- *Concurrent Pos:* Fel hemat, Sch Med, Wash Univ, 61-62; fel biochem, 62-64; USPHS trainee, 61-62; Am Cancer Soc fel, 62-64; res grants, Health Res Coun City of New York, 66, Muscular Dystrophy Asn Am, 66-68, NY Heart Asn, 67-70, NIH, 70-84 & NSF, 78-82; career scientist, Health Res Coun City of New York, 66-71. *Mem:* Am Soc Hemat; Am Fedn Clin Res; Am Soc Physiol; Am Soc Clin Invest; Am Soc Biol Chem. *Res:* Regulation and organization of glycolytic enzymes in platelets; platelet biochemical interactions during hemostasis; biochemical and physiological aspects of human platelet senescence; regulation of platelet production; autoimmune platelet disorders; role of platelets in cancer. *Mailing Add:* NY Univ Sch Med 550 First Ave New York NY 10016

KARPEL, RICHARD LESLIE, b New York, NY, May 31, 44; m 68; c 1. BIOCHEMISTRY. *Educ:* Queens Col, NY, BA, 65; Brandeis Univ, PhD(chem), 70. *Prof Exp:* Res assoc, Princeton Univ, 70-71; NIH res fel, 71-72, res assoc, 72-74, NIH res fel biochem sci, 74-76; ASST PROF CHEM, UNIV MD, BALTIMORE COUNTY, 76- *Mem:* AAAS; Am Chem Soc; Sigma Xi. *Res:* Effects of proteins and small molecules on nucleic acid conformation and function; nucleic acid helix-destabilizing; metal ion probes of macromolecular structure. *Mailing Add:* Dept Chem Univ Md 5401 Wilkens Ave Catonsville MD 21228

KARPIAK, STEPHEN EDWARD, b Hartford, Conn, Aug 13, 47. NEUROSCIENCE. *Educ:* Col of the Holy Cross, BA, 69; Fordham Univ, MA, 71, PhD(exp psychol), 72. *Prof Exp:* Fel neuroimmunol, Parkinson Dis Found, Dept Neurol, Col Physicans & Surgeons & vis fel, Dept Psychiat, Columbia Univ, 72-74; SR RES SCIENTIST, DIV NEUROSCI, NY STATE PSYCHIAT INST, 74-; ASST PROF PSYCHIAT, COLUMBIA UNIV, 78- *Concurrent Pos:* Asst prof psychol, Manhattan Col, 72-78. *Mem:* Soc Neurosci; Am Psychol Asn. *Res:* Development of immunological tools for the study of brain function and pathology, specifically the use of brain antibodies to study behavior and electrophysiology; effects of exogenous administration of gangliosides on central nervous system function. *Mailing Add:* Div of Neurosci NY State Psychiat Inst New York NY 10032

KARPINSKI, ROBERT WHITCOMB, b Ann Arbor, Mich, May 17, 06. GEOLOGY. *Educ:* Univ Mich, AB, 26; Univ Nancy, Ing Geol, 27, DSc(econ geol), 31. *Prof Exp:* Chief geologist, Union Financiere Privee, Paris, 28-29; chief geologist & dir mining explor, French Indochina, 29-30; consult & geologist, US, Can & Alaska, 31-32; head dept geol & geog, Flint Jr Col, 33-34 & Ind State Univ, 34-41; econ geologist, Bd Econ Warfare, 41-42; in charge mineral sect, NAfrican Econ Bd, Morocco, 43; mineral economist, Foreign

Econ Admin, 44; sr field geologist, Standard Oil Co, NJ, 45-47; with dept geol, 48-69, EMER PROF GEOL, UNIV ILL, CHICAGO CIRCLE, 69-; INDUST CONSULT, 69- Concurrent Pos: Part-time prof, Calif State Polytech Univ, San Luis Obispo, 69-; consult, San Luis Eng Inc. Honors & Awards: Palmes Academiques, French Govt, 61. Mem: Fel Geol Soc Am; fel Am Soc Civil Engrs; Asn Eng Geologists; Int Asn Rock Mech. Mailing Add: PO Box 6252 Los Osos Br San Luis Obispo CA 93402

KARPINSKY, GEORGE EUGENE, b Landstul, WGer, May 5, 46; US citizen. CLINICAL MIRCOBIOLOGY. Educ: McGill Univ, Montreal, BSc, 68; Cornell Univ, PhD(microbiol), 78. Prof Exp: Asst microbiol, 72-77, SR MICROBIOLOGIST, NY HOSP, MED CTR, CORNELL UNIV, 69-; ASST PROF MICROBIOL, NY MED COL, 78- Mem: Am Soc Microbiol; Environ Mutagen Soc; NY Acad Sci. Res: Role of colon bacteria in colon cancer especially as regards chemical carcinogenesis; refining in vitro mutagenicity test systems to eliminate the possibility of false negatives (carcinogens). Mailing Add: Dept Microbiol NY Med Col Valhalla NY 10595

KARPLUS, MARTIN, b Vienna, Austria, Mar 15, 30; nat US; m 61; c 2. PHYSICAL CHEMISTRY. Educ: Harvard Univ, BA, 51; Calif Inst Technol, PhD(chem), 53. Prof Exp: NSF fel chem, Oxford Univ, 53-55; from instr to assoc prof phys chem, Univ Ill, 55-60; from assoc prof to prof, Columbia Univ, 60-66; prof chem, 66-79, THEODORE WILLIAM RICHARDS PROF CHEM, HARVARD UNIV, 79- Concurrent Pos: NSF sr fel, 65-66; vis prof, Univ Paris, 72-73 & 80-81, prof, 74-75. Honors & Awards: Fresenius Award, 65; Harrison Howe Award, 66. Mem: Nat Acad Sci; Am Acad Arts & Sci; Int Acad Quantum Molecular Sci; Am Phys Soc. Res: Theory of molecular structure and spectra with emphasis on biologically important molecules. Mailing Add: Dept of Chem Harvard Univ Cambridge MA 02138

KARPLUS, ROBERT, b Vienna, Austria, Feb 23, 27; nat US; m 48; c 7. EDUCATIONAL PHYSICS. Educ: Harvard Univ, SB, 45, AM, 46, PhD(chem physics), 48; Univ Gothenburg, Sweden, Sweden, PhD, 80. Prof Exp: Jewett fel, Inst Advan Study, 48-50; asst prof physics, Harvard Univ, 50-54; assoc prof, 54-58, dir sci curric improv study, 62-75, actg dir, Lawrence Hall Sci, 76-77, PROF PHYSICS, UNIV CALIF, BERKELEY, 58-, ASSOC DIR, LAWRENCE HALL SCI, 68-, DEAN, SCH EDUC, 80- Concurrent Pos: Guggenheim fel, Vienna, 60-61; Guggenheim fel, 73-74. Mem: Am Phys Soc; Nat Sci Teachers Asn; Am Asn Physics Teachers (vpres, 75, pres, 77); Nat Coun Teachers Math; Nat Asn Res Sci Teaching. Res: Analytical chemistry; infrared spectroscopy; microwave spectroscopy; molecular structure; field theories; quantum field theory of elementary particles; magnetohydrodynamics; geomagnetism; elementary education; development of reasoning; psychology of mathematics education. Mailing Add: Lawrence Hall of Sci Univ of Calif Berkeley CA 94720

KARPLUS, WALTER J, b Vienna, Austria, Apr 23, 27; nat US; m 69. COMPUTER SCIENCE. Educ: Cornell Univ, BEE, 49; Univ Calif, MS, 51; Univ Calif, Los Angeles, PhD(elec eng), 55. Prof Exp: Field party chief, Sun Oil Co, 49-50; res engr, Int Geophys Inc, 51-52; chmn, Comput Sci Dept, 71-79, PROF COMPUT, ELEC CIRCUITS & ELECTRONICS, UNIV CALIF, LOS ANGELES, 52- Concurrent Pos: Fulbright res fel, 61; Guggenheim fel, 68. Honors & Awards: Sr Sci Simulation Award, Soc Comput Simulation. Mailing Add: Dept of Comput Sci Univ of Calif 3732 Boelter Hall Los Angeles CA 90024

KARR, CLARENCE, JR, b St Louis, Mo, May 12, 23; m 47; c 4. CHEMISTRY. Educ: St Louis Univ, BS, 44; Johns Hopkins Univ, PhD(chem), 50. Prof Exp: Fel petrol chem, Mellon Inst, 50-55; supvry res chemist low temperature tar, US Bur Mines, 55-66, coal chemistry, 66-75; supvry res chemist coal liquefaction, Res & Develop Admin, 75-77, res chemist synthetic fuels, 77-80, PROJ MGR ADVAN GASIFICATION, MORGANTOWN ENERGY TECHNOL CTR, US DEPT ENERGY, 80- Concurrent Pos: Prin investr, Apollo 12, 14 & 15 Lunar Sample Prog, 69-72. Honors & Awards: Award, US Dept Interior, 65 & 66. Mem: Fel Am Inst Chem; Am Chem Soc. Res: Composition of low temperature coal tar, petroleum; organic synthesis; chromatography; infrared ultraviolet spectroscopy; air pollution; coal minerals; synthetic fuels from coal; lunar minerals; liquid fuels from coal; coal gasification. Mailing Add: US Dept of Energy PO Box 880 Morgantown WV 26505

KARR, GERALD WILLIAM, pharmacology, internal medicine, see previous edition

KARR, HUGH JAMES, b LaSalle, Ill, Jan 17, 16; m 42; c 1. NUCLEAR PHYSICS. Educ: Washington Univ, St Louis, AB, 38, MS, 40, PhD(physics), 49. Prof Exp: Physicist, Western Cartridge Co, 40-41; instr physics, Univ St Louis, 41-42; PHYSICIST, LOS ALAMOS NAT LAB, 49- Mem: Am Phys Soc. Res: Plasma, atomic weapon and reactor physics; electronics. Mailing Add: 1509 42nd Los Alamos NM 87544

KARR, JAMES PRESBY, b Nashua, NH, July 24, 41; m 62; c 2. REPRODUCTIVE PHYSIOLOGY, STEROID BIOCHEMISTRY. Educ: Univ Vt, BA, 64, MS, 66; Pa State Univ, PhD(reprod physiol), 70. Prof Exp: Res assoc reprod physiol, Pa State Univ, 70-71; asst prof animal breeding, Haille Selassie I Univ, 71-73; cancer res scientist reprod physiol, Roswell Park Mem Inst, 73-74 & 76-77; asst prof animal breeding & reprod physiol, Am Univ, Beirut, 74-75; DEP DIR SCI AFFAIRS CANCER RES, NAT PROSTATIC CANCER PROJ, 78- Mem: AAAS; Am Asn Cancer Res; NY Acad Sci. Res: Reproductive endocrinology, steroid biochemistry, plasma steroid binding proteins and hormone receptors in the normal physiology and disease states of the human prostate. Mailing Add: Nat Prostatic Cancer Proj 666 Elm St Buffalo NY 14263

KARR, JAMES RICHARD, b Shelby, Ohio, Dec 26, 43; m 63; c 2. TROPICAL BIOLOGY, ORNITHOLOGY. Educ: Iowa State Univ, BSc, 65; Univ Ill, Urbana-Champaign, MSc, 67, PhD(zool), 70. Prof Exp: Fel, Princeton Univ, 70-71 & Smithsonian Tropical Res Inst, 71-72; asst prof ecol,

Purdue Univ, 72-75; assoc prof, 75-80, PROF ECOL, UNIV ILL, URBANA-CHAMPAIGN, 80- Concurrent Pos: Mem, Evaluation Panel, Instrnl Sci Equip Prog, NSF, 75, Undergrad Res Participation, 76; consult, Orgn Am States, 80; prin investr grants, Nat Sci Found, Environ Protection Agency, Nat Geog Soc, Am Philos Soc, US Fish & Wildlife Serv, US Forest Serv & Off Water Resources Technol, 73-; affil, Ill Natural Hist Surv, 81-; ed, Tropical Ecol, 77-81 & Ecol, 81- Mem: Ecol Soc Am; fel Am Ornithologists Union; Wilson Ornithological Soc; Int Soc Tropical Ecol; fel AAAS. Res: Community ecology from both basic and applied perspectives with emphasis on studies of tropical forest birds and stream fishes, including a wide range of land use and water resource problems; improving knowledge of biological communities and to apply that knowledge to solution of selected environmental and natural resource problems. Mailing Add: Dept Ecol Ethology & Evolution Univ Ill 606 E Healey St Champaign IL 61820

KARR, PHILIP R, b Newark, NJ, June 17, 13; m 39; c 2. PHYSICS. Educ: City Col New York, BS, 33, MS, 38; George Washington Univ, MS, 46; Cath Univ Am, PhD(physics), 51. Prof Exp: Physicist, Ord Develop Div, Nat Bur Standards, 41-48, Atomic Physics Div, 48-50, Ord Develop Div, 50-53 & Diamond Ord Fuze Labs, 53-56; PHYSICIST, ELECTRONIC SYSTS DIV, TRW INC, 56- Mem: Assoc Am Phys Soc; sr mem Inst Elec & Electronics Eng. Res: Statistical communication theory; gamma ray transport theory; ordnance; proximity fuze research; electromagnetic radiation; noise theory; information theory; antimissile research; electronic counter-measures; antenna and propagation theory; infrared detection. Mailing Add: TRW Systs 1 Space Park Electronic Systs Div Redondo Beach CA 90278

KARR, REYNOLD MICHAEL, JR, b New York, NY, June 24, 42; m 76; c 2. ALLERGY, RHEUMATOLOGY. Educ: Johns Hopkins Univ, BA, 64; Univ Md, MD, 69. Prof Exp: Assoc prof med, Clin Immunol Sect, Sch Med, Tulane Univ, 76-80; ASSOC PROF MED, UNIV WASH, 80- Concurrent Pos: Vis consult, Vet Admin Hosp, New Orleans, 76-; vis physician, Charity Hosp, New Orleans, 76- Mem: Fel Am Col Physicians; Am Acad Allergy; Am Thoracic Soc; Am Rheumatism Asn. Res: Arthritis; occupational lung disease; bronchoprovocation. Mailing Add: Sch Med Univ Wash 9706 171st Ave SE Snohomish WA 98290

KARRAKER, ROBERT HARRELD, b Carbondale, Ill, May 6, 31; m 53; c 2. INORGANIC CHEMISTRY. Educ: Southern Ill Univ, BA, 53; Iowa State Univ, PhD(inorg chem), 61. Prof Exp: Chemist, Olin-Mathieson Chem Corp, NY, 53-55; asst prof chem, Memphis State Univ, 61-67; assoc prof chem, 67-80, PROF CHEM, EASTERN ILL UNIV, 80- Mem: Am Chem Soc. Res: Chemistry of rare earth elements. Mailing Add: Dept of Chem Eastern Ill Univ Charleston IL 61920

KARRAS, THOMAS WILLIAM, b Chicago, Ill, Jan 4, 36; m 60; c 2. LASERS, PLASMA PHYSICS. Educ: Univ Chicago, BS, 57; Ill Inst Technol, MS, 61; Univ Calif, Los Angeles, PhD(physics), 64. Prof Exp: Physicist elec propulsion, Rocketdyne Div, NAm Aviation, 59-61; physicist, 64-72, mgr laser & plasma ph 'sics, Space Sci Lab, 72-79, MGR LASER RES, SPACE DIV, GEN ELEC CO, KING OF PRUSSIA, PA, 79- Mem: Am Phys Soc; Am Inst Aeronautics & Astronautics; Sigma Xi. Res: Metal vapor lasers; nanosecond discharges. Mailing Add: 231 Wooded Way Berwyn PA 19312

KARREMAN, GEORGE, b Rotterdam, Holland, Nov 4, 20; US citizen; m 53; c 3. MATHEMATICAL BIOLOGY. Educ: Univ Leiden, BS, 39, MS, 41; Univ Chicago, PhD(math biol), 51. Prof Exp: Instr math & physics, Col Tech Sci, Holland, 46-48; res assoc math biol, Univ Chicago, 51-53, asst prof, 53-54; res assoc theoret biol, Int Muscle Res, Mass, 54-57; med res scientist, Eastern Pa Psychiat Inst, 57-62; assoc prof, 62-70, PROF PHYSIOL, SCH MED, UNIV PA, 70- Mem: Am Physiol Soc; Soc Math Biol (pres, 73-). Res: Physiological irritability; biological energy transfer; quantum biology; system analysis of cardiovascular, central nervous renal and endocrine systems; cooperative phenomena; threshold mechanisms; bioelectric phenomena; adsorption mechanism. Mailing Add: Bockus Res Inst Univ of Pa 19th & Lombard St Philadelphia PA 19146

KARREMAN, HERMAN FELIX, b Rotterdam, Neth, June 21, 13; US citizen; m 38, 74; c 3. APPLIED MATHEMATICS. Educ: Neth Sch Econ, Drs, 49. Prof Exp: Staff employee, Royal Packet Navig Co, Dutch E Indies, 37-47; sr officer, Cent Planning Bur, Neth, 49-54; res assoc, Nat Bur Econ Res, NY, 54-56; res assoc, Economet Res Prog, Princeton Univ, 56-63; mem math res ctr, 63-77, PROF MATH, SCH BUS, UNIV WIS-MADISON, 65-, PROF COL ENG, 68- Honors & Awards: Lanchester Prize, Opers Res Soc Am, 60. Mem: Opers Res Soc Am; Inst Math Statist; Soc Indust & Appl Math; Math Asn Am; Am Math Soc. Res: Applied probability. Mailing Add: Sch of Bus Univ of Wis Madison WI 53706

KARREN, KENNETH W, b Vernal, Utah, May 20, 32; m 53; c 5. STRUCTURAL ENGINEERING, ENGINEERING MECHANICS. Educ: Univ Utah, BS, 53, MS, 61; Cornell Univ, PhD(civil eng), 65. Prof Exp: Proj develop engr, Pipeline Div, Phillips Petrol Co, 56-57; engr & asst plant mgr, Otto Buehner & Co, 57-61; asst prof civil eng, Brigham Young Univ, 61-62; res asst, Cornell Univ, 62-65; assoc prof civil eng, Brigham Young Univ, 65-70, prof, 70-78; CONSULT ENGR, 78- Concurrent Pos: Consult, Hercules, Inc, Utah, 66-71. Mem: Am Soc Civil Engrs. Res: Effects of cold-forming on light gage steel; finite element method of analysis of problems of elasticity. Mailing Add: 3865 S Wasatch Blvd #202 Salt Lake City UT 84109

KARRER, KATHLEEN MARIE, b Grosse Pointe Farms, Mich, June 16, 49. MOLECULAR BIOLOGY, DEVELOPMENTAL BIOLOGY. Educ: Marquette Univ, BS, 71; Yale Univ, PhD(biol), 76. Prof Exp: Fel biol, Ind Univ, 76-80; ASST PROF BIOL, BRANDEIS UNIV, 80- Concurrent Pos: Jane Coffin Childs Mem Fund Med Res fel, 76-78; NIH fel, 78-79. Honors & Awards: John Spangler Nicholas Prize Exp Zool, Yale Univ, 77. Mem: AAAS; Am Soc Cell Biol; Soc Develop Biol. Res: Eukaryotic chromosome structure and function; determination of the germ line. Mailing Add: Dept Biol Brandeis Univ Waltham MA 02254

KARROW, PAUL FREDERICK, b St Thomas, Ont, Sept 14, 30; m 62; c 4. GEOLOGY. *Educ:* Queen's Univ, Ont, BSc, 54; Univ Ill, PhD(geol), 57. *Prof Exp:* Geologist, Ont Dept Mines, 57-63; prof civil eng, 63-65, assoc prof earth sci, 65-69, chmn dept, 65-70, PROF EARTH SCI, UNIV WATERLOO, 69- *Concurrent Pos:* Geologist, Ont Dept Mines, 64 & 73. *Mem:* Geol Soc Am; Soc Econ Paleont & Mineral; Geol Asn Can; Int Asn Gt Lakes; Am Asn Quaternary Environ. *Res:* Quaternary geology; glacial geology; geomorphology; urban geology; paleoecology. *Mailing Add:* Dept Earth Sci Univ Waterloo Waterloo ON N2L 3G1 Can

KARSCH, FRED JOSEPH, b New York, NY, Aug 8, 42; m 67; c 2. REPRODUCTIVE ENDOCRINOLOGY. *Educ:* Juniata Col, BS, 64; Univ Maine, MS, 66; Univ Ill, PhD(animal sci, biochem & physiol), 70. *Prof Exp:* Asst prof, 72-75, ASSOC PROF PHYSIOL, UNIV MICH, ANN ARBOR, 75- *Concurrent Pos:* Ford Found fel, Med Sch, Univ Pittsburgh, 70-71, NIH fel, 71-72. *Mem:* Endocrine Soc; Soc Study Reprod; Am Physiol Soc. *Res:* Neuroendocrine control of gonadotropin secretion; regulation of progesterone secretion by the corpus luteum; developmental endocrinology. *Mailing Add:* Reprod Endocrinol Prog Univ Mich Dept of Path Ann Arbor MI 48109

KARSON, JEFFREY ALAN, b Akron, Ohio, Nov 3, 49; m 78; c 1. STRUCTURAL GEOLOGY. *Educ:* Case Inst Technol, BS, 72; State Univ NY, Albany, MS, 75, PhD(geol), 77. *Prof Exp:* Asst instr, State Univ NY, Albany, 72-75, res asst, 75-77; fel, Erindale Col & Univ Toronto, 77-79; scholar, 79-80, ASST SCIENTIST, GEOL, WOODS HOLE OCEANOG INST, 80- *Concurrent Pos:* Vis lectr, Bridgewater State Col, Mass, 81- *Mem:* Geol Soc Am; Am Geophys Union. *Res:* Internal structure of the oceanic lithosphere via direct observation of the sea floor and structural analysis of ophiolites. *Mailing Add:* Dept Geol & Geophys Woods Hole Oceanog Inst Woods Hole MA 02543

KARSTAD, LARS, b Langenburg, Sask, Sept 22, 29; m 50; c 4. VETERINARY SCIENCE. *Educ:* Ont Vet Col, DVM, 55; Univ Wis, MS, 57, PhD(vet sci), 60. *Prof Exp:* Res asst vet sci, Univ Wis, 55-56, instr, 56-60; virologist zoonoses, Ga Dept Pub Health, 60-61; assoc prof, Ont Vet Col, Univ Guelph, 61-63, prof zoonoses & dis wildlife & head div, 64-77; MEM STAFF WILDLIFE RES, KENYA, AFRICA, 77- *Concurrent Pos:* Mem expert comt zoonoses, WHO, 62-72; ed, J Wildlife Dis, Wildlife Dis Asn, 67-74. *Honors & Awards:* Distinguished Serv Award, Wildlife Dis Asn, 71. *Mem:* Wildlife Dis Asn (pres, 63-65); Conf Res Workers Animal Dis; Can Vet Med Asn. *Res:* Wildlife disease and zoonotic infections, especially role of wildlife as reservoirs of infection for man and his domestic animals. *Mailing Add:* Vet Res Lab Kabete Kenya

KARSTEN, KENNETH STEPHEN, b Holland, Mich, July 24, 13; m 39; c 4. PLANT PHYSIOLOGY, CHEMISTRY. *Educ:* Hope Col, AB, 35; Univ Nev, MS, 37; Univ Wis, PhD(plant physiol), 39. *Prof Exp:* Chemist-analyst, Sullivan Mining Co, Idaho, 37; asst, Univ Wis, 37-39; tutor biol, Brooklyn Col, 39-41; dir org res, Niagara Sprayer & Chem Co, 41-45; insecticide chemist, Rohm and Haas Co, Pa, 45-47; dept mgr, 48-72, dir res & develop, 72-78, V PRES RES & DEVELOP, R T VANDERBILT CO, INC, 78- *Concurrent Pos:* Consult, Indust Minerals & Chemicals. *Mem:* Am Chem Soc. *Res:* Organic syntheses; insecticide and fungicide formulation and development; plant hormones; plant physiology; root activity and oxygen in relation to soil fertility; fungicides; bactericides; sap stain control chemicals; bacteriostats for soap. *Mailing Add:* 69 Ledgebrook Dr Norwalk CT 06854

KARSTENS, ANDRES INGVER, b Pendleton, Ore, Dec 17, 11; m 42. AEROSPACE MEDICINE. *Educ:* Univ Ore, BA, 38, MD & MS, 43; Am Bd Prev Med, dipl aerospace med, 56. *Prof Exp:* Res aviation med, high altitude physiol & environ physiol, Aero Med Lab, Wright-Patterson AFB, US Air Force, 46-50, commanding officer, Arctic Aero Med Lab, Ladd AFB, Alaska, 50-55, dir res, US Air Force Sch Aviation Med, Randolph AFB, Tex, 56-58, from asst chief to chief, Aerospace Med Res Lab, Wright-Patterson AFB, 58-64, dir Bioastronaut, Manned Orbiting Lab, Space & Missiles Syst Orgn, Los Angeles, 64-69, dir res & develop, Aerospace Med Div, Air Force Systs Command, Brooks AFB, Tex, 69-71; staff physician & chief flight surgeon, Med Support Serv, NASA Johnson Space Ctr, Houston, RETIRED. *Honors & Awards:* Hubertus Stughold Award Aerospace Med, 73. *Mem:* Fel AAAS; AMA; fel Aerospace Med Asn; fel Am Col Prev Med. *Res:* Autonomic control of cardiac function and intestinal motility; high altitude and environment physiology; environmental protection and life support; arctic physiology and ecology; life support in aeronautical and space flight. *Mailing Add:* RR 3 150 Prospect Ave Walla Walla WA 99362

KARTEN, HARVEY J, b New York, NY, July 13, 35; m 64; c 3. NEUROANATOMY. *Educ:* Yeshiva Col, BA, 55, Albert Einstein Col Med, MD, 59. *Prof Exp:* Intern med, Univ Utah, 59-60; resident psychiat, Univ Colo, 60-61; res assoc neurophysiol, Walter Reed Army Inst Res, 61-65; res assoc neuroanat, Mass Inst Technol, 65-73, sr res assoc, 73-74; PROF PSYCHIAT & ANAT SCI, STATE UNIV NY STONY BROOK, 74-, PROF NEUROBIOL, 79- *Concurrent Pos:* USPHS fel, Univ Colo, 60-61; NIMH career develop award, 61-65; Nat Inst Child Health & Human Develop career develop award, 65-74; res assoc, Lab Neuropsychol, Wash Sch Psychiat, 63-65. *Honors & Awards:* Herrick Award, Am Asn Anat, 68. *Mem:* Am Soc Zool; Am Asn Anat; Soc Neurosci. *Res:* Neuroanatomy. *Mailing Add:* Dept of Psychiat & Anat Sci State Univ NY Stony Brook NY 11794

KARTEN, MARVIN J, b New York, NY, Apr 26, 31; m 56; c 2. MEDICINAL CHEMISTRY. *Educ:* Brooklyn Col, BS, 54; Univ Pittsburgh, PhD(chem), 58. *Prof Exp:* Res chemist, Monsanto Chem Co, Ohio, 58-59, Mass, 59-60; sr res chemist, USV Pharmaceut Corp, 60-67, group leader, 67-70; HEALTH SCI ADMINR, NAT INST CHILD HEALTH & HUMAN DEVELOP, NIH, 71- *Mem:* Am Chem Soc; NY Acad Sci. *Res:* Medicinal chemistry; organic synthesis; synthesis and biological evaluation of new contraceptive agents. *Mailing Add:* Nat Inst of Child Health & Human Develop NIH Bethesda MD 20205

KARTHA, GOPINATH, b Alleppey, India, Jan 26, 27; m 56; c 4. PHYSICS. *Educ:* Univ Madras, MA, 48, PhD(physics), 53; Andhra Univ, India, MSc, 49. *Prof Exp:* Nuffield Found traveling fel physics, Cavendish Lab, Cambridge Univ, 55-56; fel, Nat Res Coun Can, 56-58; res assoc, Polytech Inst Brooklyn, 58-59; res assoc, 59-67, PRIN CANCER RES SCIENTIST, ROSWELL PARK MEM INST, 67- *Concurrent Pos:* USPHS res career develop award, 63-; res prof, State Univ NY, Buffalo, 66; res prof, Niagara Univ, 67. *Mem:* Am Crystallog Asn; fel, Indian Acad Sci; Sigma Xi. *Res:* X-ray crystallography; protein structure; biophysics; molecular biology. *Mailing Add:* Dept of Biophys Roswell Park Mem Inst Buffalo NY 14263

KARTHA, MUKUND K, b Pattanakad, Kerala, India, July 31, 36; US citizen; m 63; c 2. RADIOLOGY, BIOPHYSICS. *Educ:* Univ Kerala, BSc, 58; Univ Sagar, India, MSc, 61; Univ Western Ont, PhD(radiol physics), 69. *Prof Exp:* Sci officer radiol physics, India Atomic Energy Comn, 61-63; cancer res fel, Ont Cancer Found, 63-68; asst prof, 68-73, ASSOC PROF RADIOL, OHIO STATE UNIV, 73-, ASSOC PROF ALLIED MED PROF, 76- *Concurrent Pos:* Am Cancer Soc fel, Ohio State Univ, 70-71, Nat Cancer Inst fel, 74-77; co-dir, Radiation Ther Consult Prog, Cancer Res Ctr, Ohio State Univ, 73- *Mem:* Radiol Soc NAm; Radiation Res Soc; Am Asn Physicists in Med; Am Col Radiol. *Res:* Experimental and clinical research in radiation therapy; investigation of cancer treatment using radiation. *Mailing Add:* N-059 410 W Tenth Ave Columbus OH 43210

KARTZMARK, ELINOR MARY, b Selkirk, Man, May 16, 26; c 1. PHYSICAL CHEMISTRY. *Educ:* Univ Man, BSc, 49, MSc, 50, PhD(chem), 52. *Prof Exp:* Mem staff, 47-50, lectr, 51-52, asst prof, 52-58, ASSOC PROF PHYS CHEM, UNIV MAN, 58- *Mem:* Fel Chem Inst Can. *Res:* Electrolytic conductance; heterogeneous equilibria. *Mailing Add:* Dept of Chem Univ of Man Winnipeg MB R3T 2N2 Can

KARU, ALEXANDER EDWIN, b Washington, DC, July 21, 43. BIOCHEMISTRY, ANIMAL VIROLOGY. *Educ:* Johns Hopkins Univ, BES, 64, PhD(cellular & develop biol), 68. *Prof Exp:* Chief biochem lab, Letterman Army Inst Res, 68-71; Nat Cancer Inst spec fel biochem, Univ Calif, Berkeley, 71-75; ASST PROF BIOCHEM, UNIV CALIF, RIVERSIDE, 75- *Res:* Mammalian tumor virus-cell interactions; enzymology of nucleic acid metabolism in virus-infected cells; mechanisms of genetic recombination, repair and mutagenesis of DNA and RNA. *Mailing Add:* Dept of Biochem Univ of Calif Riverside CA 92521

KARUSH, FRED, b Chicago, Ill, July 12, 14; m 36; c 3. IMMUNOLOGY. *Educ:* Univ Chicago, BS, 35, PhD(chem), 38. *Prof Exp:* Res physicist, E I du Pont de Nemours & Co, Inc, NJ, 41-46; from asst prof to assoc prof immunol, Dept Pediat, 50-57, PROF IMMUNOCHEM, UNIV PA, 57-, PROF MICROBIOL, 60- *Concurrent Pos:* Rockefeller fel enzyme kinetics, Mass Inst Technol, 39-40; Harrison fel biophysics, Univ Pa, 40-41; Am Cancer Soc sr fel, Col Med, NY Univ, 47-48, Sloan-Kettering Inst Cancer Res, 49 & Col Physicians & Surgeons, Columbia Univ, 50; res career award, NIH, 62- *Mem:* Am Chem Soc; Am Soc Biol Chem; Am Asn Immunol. *Res:* Photoelectric polarimetry; enzyme kinetics; physics of pigments; protein interactions; bacterial synthesis of proteins; molecular immunology; affinity analysis of monoclonal antibodies. *Mailing Add:* Dept of Microbiol Univ of Pa Sch of Med Philadelphia PA 19174

KARUSH, WILLIAM, b Chicago, Ill, Mar 1, 17; m 39; c 2. MATHEMATICS. *Educ:* Univ Chicago, BS, 38, MS, 39, PhD(math), 42. *Prof Exp:* Mathematician, Geophys Lab, Carnegie Inst, 42-43; physicist, Metall Lab, Univ Chicago, 43-45, from instr to assoc prof math, 45-56; mem sr staff, Ramo-Wooldridge Corp, 56-57; sr opers res scientist, Syst Develop Corp, 58-62, prin scientist, 62-67; PROF MATH, CALIF STATE UNIV, NORTHRIDGE, 67- *Concurrent Pos:* Mathematician, Inst Numerical Anal, Nat Bur Standards, Univ Calif, Los Angeles, 49-52; mem tech staff, Res & Develop Labs, Hughes Aircraft Co, 53 & Ramo-Wooldridge Corp, 54-55; Ford fac fel, Univ Calif, Los Angeles, 55-56. *Mem:* Am Math Soc; Opers Res Soc Am. *Res:* Operations research; calculus of variations; applied mathematics. *Mailing Add:* Dept of Math Calif State Univ 18111 Nordoff St Northridge CA 91324

KARUZA, SARUNAS KAZYS, b Kaunas, Lithuania, Jan 19, 40; m 77; c 1. ATOMIC FREQUENCY STANDARDS, NAVIGATION SYSTEMS. *Educ:* Univ Southern Calif, BSEE, 63, MSEE, 66, PhD(elec eng), 72. *Prof Exp:* Mem tech staff, Commun Div, Hughes Aircraft Co, 63-65, Ground Systs Div, 65-66, Aeronaut Systs Div, 66-67; dir & prof staff assoc, Electronics Lab, Rancho Los Amigos Hosp, 72-80; MEM TECH STAFF, ELECTRONIC RES LABS, AEROSPACE CORP, 80- *Concurrent Pos:* Consult, Fullerton Internal Med Clin, 78; adj asst prof med & biomed eng, Univ Southern Calif, 75- *Mem:* Sigma Xi; Inst Elec & Electronics Engrs. *Res:* Precision atomic frequency standards (ceslum-rubidium) which are used in the ground power supply/Navy study of transport aircraft requirements satellites for world wide navigation; stability properties of these standards as they are influenced by their electronics and environmental factors. *Mailing Add:* Aerospace Corp PO Box 92957 Los Angeles CA 90009

KARVE, MOHAN DATTATREYA, b Kupwad, India, Aug 14, 39; m 67; c 2. INDUSTRIAL MICROBIOLOGY, MYCOLOGY. *Educ:* Univ Poona, BSc, 59, Hons, 60, MSc, 61; Ohio State Univ, PhD(mycol), 65. *Prof Exp:* Asia-Pac area rep, 65-71, GEN MGR, NORTHERN ASIA-PAC AREA, BUCKMAN LABS, INC, 71- *Mem:* Soc Indust Microbiol; Am Chem Soc; fel Am Inst Chem; Tech Asn Pulp & Paper Indust. *Res:* Microbial physiology; fungal proteins and amino acids; microbial deterioration. *Mailing Add:* 985 Iopono Loop Kailua HI 96734

KARWAN, MARK HENRY, b Cleveland, Ohio, Nov 16, 51; m 73; c 4. INTEGER PROGRAMMING, MULTICRITERIA DECISION MAKING. *Educ:* Johns Hopkins Univ, BES, 74, MSE, 75; Ga Inst Technol, PhD(opers res), 76. *Prof Exp:* Asst prof, 76-81, ASSOC PROF OPERS RES, DEPT INDUST ENG, STATE UNIV NY BUFFALO, 81- *Concurrent Pos:*

Prin investr, NSF, 78-82. *Mem:* Opers Res Soc Am; Am Inst Indust Engrs. *Res:* Surrogate duality in integer programming; multicriteria decision making; multilevel decentralized planning; redundancy in mathematical programming; industrial inspection. *Mailing Add:* 342 Bell Hall Dept Indust Eng State Univ NY Buffalo NY 14260

KARWEIK, DALE HERBERT, b Milwaukee, Wis, May 27, 48; m 70; c 2. ANALYTICAL CHEMISTRY. *Educ:* Univ Wis-Milwaukee, BS, 70; Purdue Univ, PhD(anal chem), 75. *Prof Exp:* Asst prof, Wayne State Univ, 75-80; MEM FAC, DEPT CHEM, OHIO STATE UNIV, 80- *Mem:* Am Chem Soc. *Res:* Measurement of homogeneous electron transfer rates; electrochemistry of porphyrins and related compounds with mechanistic studies. *Mailing Add:* Dept Chem Ohio State Univ Columbus OH 43210

KARY, CHRISTINA DOLORES, b Detroit, Mich, June 12, 40. BIOCHEMICAL PHARMACOLOGY, INHALATION TOXICOLOGY. *Educ:* Madonna Col, BA, 62; Univ Mo, PhD(pharmacol), 73. *Prof Exp:* Technologist inhalation toxicol, Dow Chem Co, 62-67; asst pharmacol, Univ Mo, 71-73; instr, Baylor Col Med, 73-74; USPHS fel, Inst Lipid Res, 74-77; toxicologist, Shell Oil Co, 77, sr toxicologist, 78-80, MGR, PRODUCT & PROCESS, TOXICOL DEPT, SHELL DEVELOP CO, 80- *Mem:* Am Chem Soc; Sigma Xi; Soc Toxicol. *Res:* Drug metabolism; gas chromatography-mass spectroscopy; inhalation toxicity; chemical intermediates; solvents. *Mailing Add:* Shell Oil Co One Shell Plaza PO Box 4320 Rm 1024 Houston TX 77210

KARZON, DAVID T, b New York, NY, July 8, 20; m 46; c 2. VIROLOGY, PEDIATRICS. *Educ:* Ohio State Univ, BS, 40, MS, 41; Johns Hopkins Univ, MD, 44; Am Bd Pediat, dipl; Am Bd Microbiol, dipl, 64. *Prof Exp:* Instr contagious dis, Johns Hopkins Univ Hosp, 45, 48, instr virol, Sch Med, 49-50; from asst prof to prof pediat, Sch Med, State Univ NY Buffalo, 52-68, from asst prof to prof virol, Dept Bact & Immunol, 54-68, dir virol lab, 55-68; PROF PEDIAT & CHMN DEPT, SCH MED, VANDERBILT UNIV, 68-, MED DIR, CHILDREN'S HOSP, UNIV, 72- *Concurrent Pos:* Lowell Palmer fel, 53-56; res career develop award, NIH, 62-68; Markle scholar, 56-61; spec consult, Nat Commun Dis Ctr, USPHS, Atlanta, Ga, 59-62, mem surgeon-gen spec adv comt immunization pract, 64-70; consult res reagents comt, Nat Inst Allergy & Infectious Dis, 63-67, chmn, 66-67, mem virol & rickettsiol study sect, 67-69; prog consult growth & develop sect, Nat Inst Child Health & Human Develop, 64-68; assoc ed, Am J Epidemiol, 66-78; mem biol rev steering comt, Food & Drug Admin, 72- *Mem:* Soc Pediat Res; Soc Exp Biol & Med; Fedn Am Soc Exp Biol; Am Epidemiol Soc; Infectious Dis Soc. *Res:* Animal virology; tissue culture. *Mailing Add:* Dept of Pediat Vanderbilt Univ Sch of Med Nashville TN 37232

KAS, ARNOLD, b Washington, DC, July 18, 40. MATHEMATICS. *Educ:* Johns Hopkins Univ, BA, 62; Stanford Univ, PhD(math), 66. *Prof Exp:* Instr math, Stanford Univ, 66-67; Air Force Off Sci Res fel, Math Inst, State Univ Leiden, 67-69; asst prof, Univ Calif, Berkeley, 69-73; assoc prof, 73-80, PROF MATH, ORE STATE UNIV, 80- *Res:* Complex manifolds; algebraic geometry. *Mailing Add:* Dept of Math Ore State Univ Corvallis OR 97331

KASAHARA, AKIRA, b Tokyo, Japan, Oct 11, 26; US citizen; m 52; c 2. METEOROLOGY. *Educ:* Univ Tokyo, BS, 48, MS, 50, DSc, 54. *Prof Exp:* Asst geophys inst, Univ Tokyo, 48-53, res assoc, 53-54; res assoc oceanog & meteorol, Agr & Mech Col Tex, 54-56; res assoc meteorol, Univ Chicago, 56-62; res scientist, Courant Inst Math Sci, NY Univ, 62-63; prog scientist, 63-73, SR SCIENTIST, NAT CTR ATMOSPHERIC RES, 73- *Concurrent Pos:* Affil prof dept meteorol, Tex A&M Univ, 67-70; assoc ed, J Appl Meteorol, 67-72; vis lectr, Inst Meteorol, Univ Stockholm, Sweden, 71-72; adj prof, Dept Meteorol, Univ Utah, 79- *Honors & Awards:* Award, Meteorol Soc Japan, 61. *Mem:* Am Geophys Union; Meteorol Soc Japan; fel Am Meteorol Soc. *Res:* Dynamic meteorology; development of weather prediction method with the numerical integrations of thermo-hydro-dynamical equations. *Mailing Add:* Nat Ctr for Atmospheric Res PO Box 3000 Boulder CO 80307

KASAI, PAUL HARUO, b Osaka, Japan, Jan 30, 32; m 59; c 2. PHYSICAL CHEMISTRY. *Educ:* Univ Denver, BS, 55; Univ Calif, Berkeley, PhD(chem), 59. *Prof Exp:* Mem res staff, Hitachi Cent Res Lab, Japan, 59-62; res inst, Union Carbide Corp, 62-66; assoc prof chem, Univ Calif, Santa Cruz, 66-67; mem res staff, Res Inst, Union Carbide Corp, 67-75, group leader, 75-77, sr scientist, Tarrytown Tech Ctr, 77-79; MGR TECH SUPPORT, IBM INSTRUMENTS INC, DANBURY, 79- *Mem:* Am Chem Soc. *Res:* Magnetic resonance studies of organometallic complexes, free radicals and surface states. *Mailing Add:* PO Box 332 Orchard Park Danbury CT 06810

KASAMEYER, PAUL WILLIAM, b Detroit, Mich, Sept 9, 43; m 65; c 3. GEOPHYSICS. *Educ:* Mass Inst Technol, BS, 65, PhD(geophys), 74; Yale Univ, MS, 66. *Prof Exp:* GEOPHYSICIST, LAWRENCE LIVERMORE NAT LAB, 74- *Mem:* Soc Explor Geophysicists; Sigma Xi; Am Geophys Union. *Res:* Collection and interpretation of geophysical data; thermal modeling; magnetotellurics. *Mailing Add:* PO Box 808-Mail Stop L-224 Livermore CA 94550

KASAPLIGIL, BAKI, b Istanbul, Turkey, Nov 13, 18; US citizen; m 55; c 2. BOTANY. *Educ:* Istanbul Univ, BSc, 41; Univ Calif, Berkeley, PhD(bot), 50; Univ Ankara, cert, 53. *Prof Exp:* Engr, Forest Serv Turkey, 41-42; asst botanist, Agr Col Ankara, 44-46; cur & botanist, Univ Ankara, 50-53, asst prof bot, 53-54; forest ecologist, Food & Agr Orgn, UN, 54-56; from asst prof to assoc prof, 56-66, PROF BOT, MILLS COL, 66- *Mem:* Bot Soc Am. *Res:* Floristics of the Middle East; ontogenetic studies in Lauraceae; histotaxonomy of Corylus; forest ecology of the Mediterranean region; tertiary flora of Asia Minor; systematics of Corylus and Quercus. *Mailing Add:* Dept of Bot Mills Col Oakland CA 94613

KASARDA, DONALD DAVID, b Kingston, Pa, Oct 12, 33; m 64; c 1. PROTEIN CHEMISTRY. *Educ:* King's Col, Pa, BS, 55; Boston Col, MS, 57; Princeton Univ, MA, 59, PhD(phys chem), 61. *Prof Exp:* Mem tech staff, Bell Tel Labs, NJ, 61-63; Cardiovasc Res Inst fel, Sch Med, Univ Calif, San Francisco, 63-64; res chemist, 64-72, RES LEADER, FOOD PROTEINS RES UNIT, WESTERN REGIONAL RES CTR, AGR RES SERV, USDA, 72- *Concurrent Pos:* Assoc Exp Sta, Dept Agron & Range Sci, Univ Calif, Davis, 74- *Mem:* AAAS; Am Chem Soc; Am Asn Cereal Chem. *Res:* Protein chemistry; wheat genetics. *Mailing Add:* Western Regional Res Ctr USDA Berkeley CA 94710

KASARSKIS, EDWARD JOSEPH, b Chicago, Ill, Oct 9, 46; m 69; c 3. NEUROLOGY. *Educ:* Col St Thomas, BA, 68; Univ Wis-Madison, MD, 74, PhD(biochem), 75. *Prof Exp:* Resident internal med, Univ Wis-Madison Hosp, 74-76; resident neurol, Univ Va Hosp, 76-79; asst prof neurol, Sch Med, La State Univ, 79-80; ASST PROF NEUROL, UNIV KY, 80- *Mem:* Sigma Xi; Am Acad Neurol; Soc Neurosci; Am Soc Neurochem; Int Soc Neurochem. *Res:* Role of trace metals in the function of the brain; investigate factors that modify zinc metabolism; alcohol drugs; role of trace metals in degenerative. *Mailing Add:* Dept Neurol Univ Ky Col Med 800 Rose St Lexington KY 40536

KASBEKAR, DINKAR KASHINATH, b Bombay, India, Apr 3, 32; m 61; c 1. PHYSIOLOGY, BIOCHEMISTRY. *Educ:* Univ Bombay, BSc, 52 & 54, MSc, 57; Univ Calif, PhD(biochem), 61. *Prof Exp:* Jr res biochemist, Univ Calif, San Francisco, 61-63, asst res biochemist, Cardiovasc Res Inst, 63-65; asst res physiologist, Univ Calif, Berkeley, 66-68; asst prof physiol & biophys, 69-77, ASSOC PROF PHYSIOL & BIOPHYS, SCH MED & DENT, GEORGETOWN UNIV, 77- *Concurrent Pos:* San Francisco Heart Asn fel, 64-65; prin investr, Washington Heart Asn, 70-71, NSF, 70-; vis sr fel, Nat Inst Arthritis, Metab & Digestive Dis, NIH, 81. *Mem:* Biophys Soc; Am Physiol Soc; NY Acad Sci. *Res:* Isolation and investigation of properties of enzymes from tumors; metabolic fate of drugs used in cancer chemotherapy; ion transport, zymogen secretion, specifically in the area of gastric secretion. *Mailing Add:* Dept of Physiol & Biophys Georgetown Univ Sch Med & Dent Washington DC 20007

KASCHAK, GEORGE RAYMOND, physics, electro-optics, see previous edition

KASCIC, MICHAEL JOSEPH, JR, b Jersey City, NJ, Feb 23, 41; m 62; c 2. MATHEMATICS. *Educ:* St Joseph's Col, Pa, BS, 62; NY Univ, MS, 64; Univ Calif, Los Angeles, PhD(math), 67. *Prof Exp:* Res instr math, Dartmouth Col, 67-69; asst prof, Stevens Inst Technol, 69-74; analyst, Boole & Babbage, 74-76; MATH CONSULT, CONTROL DATA CORP, 76- *Concurrent Pos:* adj prof, Univ Minn, 79- *Mem:* Sigma Xi; Am Math Soc. *Res:* Abstract functional analytic aspects of analysis, such as linear function-space treatment of partial differential operators on distribution spaces; non-Markovian queueing analysis applied to multiprogramming environments; analysis and development of algorithms for solution of partial differential equations in various computational environments, especially on vector processors. *Mailing Add:* 8308 34th Ave N New Hope MN 55427

KASCSAK, RICHARD JOHN, b Whitestone, NY, Sept 20, 47; m 72; c 2. SLOW VIRUS INFECTIONS, PERSISTENT INFECTIONS. *Educ:* St Francis Col, NY, BS, 69; Adelphi Univ, MS, 71; Cornell Univ Med Col, PhD(virol), 76. *Prof Exp:* Teaching asst, Adelphi Univ, NY, 69-71; training fel, Cornell Univ, 71-75; RES SCIENTIST, NY STATE INST BASIC RES DEVELOP DISABILITIES, 75- *Mem:* Am Soc Microbiol. *Res:* Slow viral infections of the central nervous system with emphasis on the creation of model systems relevant to human disease; viruses include lactic dehydrogenase & semliki forest virus. *Mailing Add:* Dept Virol NY State Inst Basic Res Develop Disabilities Staten Island NY 10314

KASE, KENNETH RAYMOND, b Oak Park, Ill, July 13, 38; m 62; c 2. MEDICAL PHYSICS, HEALTH PHYSICS. *Educ:* Ga Inst Technol, BS, 61; Univ Calif, Berkeley, MS, 63; Stanford Univ, PhD(biophys), 75; Am Bd Health Physics, cert, 69; Am Bd Radiol, cert, 81. *Prof Exp:* Scientist reactors environ, Lockheed Missiles & Space Co, 61-62; health physicist radiation safety, Lawrence Livermore Lab, Univ Calif, 63-67, chief radiation safety, 67-69; health physicist, Stanford Linear Accelerator, Stanford Univ, 69-73; ASST PROF & CHIEF DOSIMETRY & RADIATION SAFETY RADIOL PHYSICS, HARVARD MED SCH, 75- *Concurrent Pos:* Ed, Health Physics J, Health Physics Soc, 77-; vis prof, Lowell Univ, 78- *Honors & Awards:* Elda E Anderson Award, Health Physics Soc, 78. *Mem:* Health Physics Soc; Am Asn Physicists Med; Radiation Res Soc. *Res:* Radiation measurement and dosimetry; biological effects of radiation; application of new treatment modalities to cancer therapy. *Mailing Add:* Joint Ctr for Radiation Ther 44 Binney St Boston MA 02115

KASEL, JULIUS ALBERT, b Homestead, Pa, Dec 7, 23; m 50; c 3. MICROBIOLOGY, VIROLOGY. *Educ:* Univ Pittsburgh, BS, 49; Georgetown Univ, MS, 58, PhD(microbiol, virol), 60. *Prof Exp:* Head med virol sect, Nat Inst Allergy & Infectious Dis, 50-72; PROF MICROBIOL & IMMUNOL, BAYLOR COL MED, 72- *Res:* Virological research related to clinical medicine. *Mailing Add:* Dept of Microbiol Immunol Baylor Col of Med Houston TX 77025

KASER, J(OHN) D(ONALD), b Oak Park, Ill, Nov 21, 29; div; c 2. CHEMICAL ENGINEERING. *Educ:* Augustana Col, BA, 56; Univ Iowa, BS, 58, MS, 60, PhD(chem eng), 63. *Prof Exp:* Sr develop engr, Battelle-Northwest, 63-76; staff engr, 76-80, PRIN ENGR, ROCKWELL HANFORD OPER, 80- *Concurrent Pos:* Mem fac, Joint Ctr for Grad Study, 68-; mem steering comn on shallow land burial of radioactive waste, Dept Energy, 77-78. *Mem:* Am Inst Chem Engrs; Am Nuclear Soc. *Res:* Solidification and disposal of radioactive waste from nuclear fuel reprocessing; decontamination; solvent extraction; radioactive waste management; heat transfer. *Mailing Add:* Rockwell Hanford Oper PO Box 800 Richland WA 99352

KASETA, FRANCIS WILLIAM, b Norwood, Mass, June 6, 33; m 60; c 1. SOLID STATE PHYSICS. *Educ:* Boston Col, BS, 55; Mass Inst Technol, PhD(solid state physics), 62. *Prof Exp:* Asst prof elec eng, Mass Inst Technol, 62-64; asst prof physics, 64-67, ASSOC PROF PHYSICS, COL HOLY CROSS, 67-, CHMN DEPT PHYSICS, 80- *Concurrent Pos:* Ford Found fel, 62-64; consult, Mass Inst Technol, 64-65. *Mem:* Am Phys Soc. *Res:* Dielectric breakdown; conduction processes in semiconductors and dielectrics; electrooptics. *Mailing Add:* Dept of Physics Col of the Holy Cross Worcester MA 01610

KASHA, HENRY, b Warsaw, Poland. HIGH ENERGY PHYSICS, COSMIC RAY PHYSICS. *Educ:* Hebrew Univ, Jerusalem, MSc, 54; Israel Inst Technol, DSc(physics), 60. *Prof Exp:* Lectr physics, Israel Inst Technol, 60-63; asst physicist, Brookhaven Nat Lab, 64-66, assoc physicist, 66-70; sr res assoc, 70-73, SR RES PHYSICIST, YALE UNIV, 73- *Mem:* AAAS; Am Phys Soc. *Mailing Add:* Dept of Physics Yale Univ New Haven CT 06520

KASHA, KENNETH JOHN, b Lacombe, Alta, May 6, 33; m 58; c 2. PLANT CYTOGENETICS. *Educ:* Univ Alta, BSc, 57, MSc, 58; Univ Minn, PhD(plant genetics), 62. *Prof Exp:* Teaching asst, Univ Minn, 60-61; res officer 2, Ottawa Res Sta, Can Dept Agr, 62-64, res officer 3, 64-66, res scientist 1, 66; asst prof crop sci & crop cytogeneticist, 66-69, assoc prof crop cytogenetics, 69-74, PROF CROP CYTOGENETICS, UNIV GUELPH, 74- *Concurrent Pos:* Orgn chmn, Int Symposium Haploids in Higher Plants, Guelph, 74. *Mem:* Genetics Soc Am; Genetics Soc Can (secy, 66-69, dir, 70-72, vpres, 75, pres, 76); Am Soc Agron; Can Soc Agron; Sigma Xi. *Res:* Crop plant cytogenetics; haploidy in barley; hybrid barley; interspecific hybridization and chromosome pairing in Hordeum, Triticum and Secale; linkage and chromosome behavior studies using interchange and trisomics in barley and alfalfa; plant cell culture; male sterility. *Mailing Add:* Dept of Crop Sci Univ of Guelph Guelph ON N1G 2W1 Can

KASHA, MICHAEL, b Elizabeth, NJ, Dec 6, 20; m 47; c 1. CHEMICAL PHYSICS, SPECTROSCOPY. *Educ:* Univ Mich, BS, 43; Univ Calif, PhD(phys chem), 45. *Prof Exp:* Lab asst, Res Lab, Merck & Co, Inc, 38-41; res chemist, Plutonium Proj, Univ Calif, 44-46, univ fel & instr, 46, res assoc, 46-49; AEC fel, Univ Chicago, 49-50; Guggenheim fel & spec lectr, Univ Manchester, 50-51; chmn dept chem, Univ, 59-61, PROF CHEM, FLA STATE UNIV, 51-, DIR INST MOLECULAR BIOPHYS, 60- *Concurrent Pos:* Vis prof, Harvard Univ, 59-60; Reilly lectr, Univ Notre Dame, 59; Kettering res award, 63- *Honors & Awards:* Award, Petrol Res Fund, Am Chem Soc, 59. *Mem:* Nat Acad Sci; Am Chem Soc; Biophys Soc; Am Acad Arts & Sci. *Res:* Molecular biophysics and electronic spectroscopy; triplet states of molecules; emission spectroscopy of molecules; classification of electronic transitions; spin-intercombinations; n-pi transitions; radiationless transitions; theoretical photochemistry; molecular excitons and energy transfer; biological molecular interactions. *Mailing Add:* Inst of Molecular Biophys Fla State Univ Tallahassee FL 32306

KASHAR, LAWRENCE JOSEPH, b Brooklyn, NY, June 1, 33; m 81; c 2. METALLURGY, MATERIALS SCIENCE. *Educ:* Rensselaer Polytech Inst, BMetE, 55; Stevens Inst Technol, MS, 59; Carnegie Inst Technol, MS, 61; Carnegie-Mellon Inst, PhD(metall, mat sci), 69. *Prof Exp:* Assoc metallurgist, Amax Res & Develop Co, Inc, 55-59; res assoc, Carnegie Inst Technol, 60-64; sr res metallurgist, US Steel Appl Res Lab, 64-70; mem tech staff, B-1 Div, Rockwell Int, 71-72; staff engr, Orlando Div, Martin Marietta Corp, 73; dir metall serv, 73-79, DIR TECH SERV & VPRES, SCANNING ELECTRON ANAL LABS, INC, 79- *Concurrent Pos:* Adj lectr, Univ Southern Calif, 75-; vpres, Litigation Consults Int, 78- *Mem:* Am Soc Metals; Am Soc Testing & Mat; Inst Elec & Electronics Engrs; Sigma Xi; Int Soc Testing & Failure Anal. *Res:* Causes and prevention of failures of metal structures. *Mailing Add:* Scanning Electron Anal Lab Inc 5301 Beethoven St Los Angeles CA 90066

KASHATUS, WILLIAM C, b Nanticoke, Pa, Apr 23, 29; m 54; c 2. PATHOLOGY, HEMATOLOGY. *Educ:* Wilkes Col, BS, 51; Bucknell Univ, MS, 53; Hahnemann Med Col, MD, 59. *Prof Exp:* Instr chem, Bucknell Univ, 51-52; from instr to assoc prof path, 63-73, dir sch med technol, 64-71, PROF PATH & VCHMN DEPT, HAHNEMANN MED COL, 73-; MED DIR & V PRES LAB PROCEDURES, UPJOHN CO, 71- *Concurrent Pos:* Mary Bailey Heart Found fel, 56-58; Am Cancer Soc fel, 62-64; dir labs, Hahnemann Hosp, 64-70; mem tech adv bd, Southeast Pa Div, Am Red Cross, 68-72 & West Co, 69-71. *Honors & Awards:* Excellence in Teaching Award, Lindback Found, 69. *Mem:* AMA; fel Col Am Path; Am Soc Clin Path; Acad Clin Lab Physicians & Scientists. *Res:* Hematology, especially cancer chemotherapy; blood banking, especially immunochematology; tissue typing. *Mailing Add:* Upjohn Co Lab Procedures 1075 First Ave King of Prussia PA 19406

KASHEF, A(BDEL-AZIZ) I(SMAIL), b Cairo, Egypt, Feb 10, 19; m 48. GEOTECHNICAL ENGINEERING, GROUNDWATER SCIENCES. *Educ:* Univ Cairo, BS, 40, MS, 48; Purdue Univ, PhD(soil mech), 51. *Prof Exp:* Irrig engr, Egyptian Govt, 40-45 & 48-51; instr struct, Univ Cairo, 45-48; sr lectr, Ein Shams Univ, 51-54 & Univ Cairo, 54-56; prof, Am Univ Beirut, 56-60; vis prof soil mech & ground water, 62-67, prof, 67-80, EMER PROF CIVIL ENG, NC STATE UNIV, 80- *Concurrent Pos:* Consult soil engr, 52-; mem water-well comt, Nat Prod Coun, Govt Egypt, 53, mem, Nat Hydraul Comt, 56, mem tech comt, River Harbors Comt, 60-62; soil consult, High Aswan Dam Auth, Egypt, 54-56; dir, Consult Eng Off, Saudi Arabia, 59-60; ed, Water Resources Bull, 70-73. *Mem:* Fel Am Water Resources Asn; fel Am Soc Civil Engrs; Am Geophys Union; Int Water Resources Asn. *Res:* Water resources research, especially in ground-water field and geotechnical engineering. *Mailing Add:* Dept of Civil Eng NC State Univ Raleigh NC 27650

KASHGARIAN, MARK, b Worcester, Mass, Feb 17, 27; m 53; c 3. PREVENTIVE MEDICINE, PSYCHIATRY. *Educ:* NY Univ, AB, 48; Univ Basel, MD, 54; Univ Mich, MPH, 58. *Prof Exp:* Asst prof prev med, Univ Tenn, Memphis, 59-66, assoc prof path, 64-70, assoc prof prev med, 66-71, resident psychiat, 70-73, asst prof psychiat, Med Col, 73-76, dir forensic psychiat sect, Ment Health Ctr, 73-76; CHIEF PSYCHIAT, US ARMY HOSP, BERLIN, GER, 76- *Mem:* Am Statist Asn; Am Pub Health Asn. *Res:* Epidemiology; cancer epidemiology; glaucoma detection and screening; epidemiology of chronic disease and congenital malformations; uterine and oral cancer detection; natural history of disease; psychiatric disorders; forensic psychiatry; medical statistics. *Mailing Add:* Berlin MEDDAC Box 61 APO New York NY 09742

KASHGARIAN, MICHAEL, b New York, NY, Sept 20, 33; m 60; c 2. PATHOLOGY. *Educ:* NY Univ, BA, 54; Yale Univ, MD, 58. *Prof Exp:* Asst med, Sch Med, Wash Univ, 58-59; asst resident path, 59-61, from instr to assoc prof, 62-74, PROF PATH, YALE UNIV, 74-, VCHMN DEPT, 76- *Concurrent Pos:* Life Ins Med Res fel physiol, Univ Gottingen, 61-62; USPHS spec fel, 63-65 & res career award, 65-75; assoc pathologist, Yale New Haven Hosp, 63-66, asst attend pathologist, 66-69, attend pathologist, 69-, assoc chief pathologist, 76- *Mem:* Am Asn Path; Am Physiol Soc; Am Soc Clin Path; Am Soc Nephrology; Int Acad Path. *Res:* Pathology and physiology of the kidney. *Mailing Add:* Dept Path Sch Med Yale Univ 310 Cedar St New Haven CT 06510

KASHIN, PHILIP, b New York, NY, Oct 27, 30; m 58; c 3. NEUROPHYSIOLOGY, PHARMACOLOGY. *Educ:* Brooklyn Col, BA, 53; Columbia Univ, MA, 58; NY Univ, MS, 61; Ill Inst Technol, PhD(physiol), 70. *Prof Exp:* Teacher high sch, NY, 58-60; res asst immunochem, Hosp for Spec Surg, New York, 61-62; res asst biochem, State Univ NY Downstate Med Ctr, 62-63; asst biochemist, IIT Res Inst, 63-64, assoc biochemist, 64-69, res biochemist, 69-70; Nat Inst Neurol Dis & Stroke spec res fel neurophysiol, Univ Ore, 70-71; asst prof biol, Queens Col, NY, 71-76; sr asst dir clin res, USV Pharmaceut Corp, 76-82; CONSULT, 82- *Honors & Awards:* I R 100 Award, 67. *Mem:* AAAS; Soc Neurosci; NY Acad Sci; Am Physiol Soc. *Res:* Methods to assay mosquito repellents; mechanisms of attraction of hematophagus insects to hosts; mechanism of action of carbon dioxide with neurotransmitters in the central nervous system. *Mailing Add:* 47 Glen Cove Dr Glen Head NY 11545

KASHIWA, BRYAN ANDREW, b Oswego, NY, Feb 20, 52; m 69; c 3. NUMERICAL FLUID DYNAMICS. *Educ:* Worcester Polytech Inst, BS, 73; Univ Wash, MS, 78. *Prof Exp:* Engr, K2 Corp, 73-79; MEM STAFF, LOS ALAMOS NAT LAB, 79- *Mem:* Am Soc Mech Engrs. *Res:* Application and development of methods in numerical fluid dynamics with emphasis on multifield flows. *Mailing Add:* Gr T-3 MS-216 Los Alamos Nat Lab Los Alamos NM 87545

KASHIWA, HERBERT KORO, b Waialua, Hawaii, Nov 12, 28; m 47; c 3. ANATOMY, HISTOCHEMISTRY. *Educ:* Univ Hawaii, BS, 50; George Washington Univ, MS, 54, PhD(anat), 60. *Prof Exp:* From instr to asst prof anat, Sch Med, Univ Louisville, 59-66; asst prof, 66-71, ASSOC PROF ANAT, SCH MED, UNIV WASH, 71- *Mem:* Am Asn Anat; Histochem Soc; Biol Stain Comn. *Res:* Mineral metabolism; hormonal control of magnesium; development of the glyoxal bis method for labile calcium; role of cells as depositors of calcium during ossification, calcification and odontogenesis. *Mailing Add:* Dept of Biol Struct Univ of Wash Sch of Med Seattle WA 98195

KASHKARI, CHAMAN NATH, b Srinagar, India, Aug 27, 33; m 63; c 2. ELECTRICAL ENGINEERING. *Educ:* Univ Jammu & Kashmir, India, BA, 52; Univ Rajasthan, BS, 57; Univ Detroit, MS, 65; Univ Mich, Ann Arbor, PhD(elec eng), 69. *Prof Exp:* Asst engr, Gen Elec Co, India, 57-58, grad trainee, Eng, 58-60, plant engr, India, 61-64; teaching fel, Univ Detroit, 64-65 & Univ Mich, Ann Arbor, 66-69; asst prof elec eng, 69-75, ASSOC PROF ELEC ENG, UNIV AKRON, 75- *Concurrent Pos:* Energy consult, Govt Nepal, NSF, 75. *Mem:* Inst Elec & Electronics Engrs; Am Soc Eng Educ. *Res:* Energy planning in developing countries; solar energy; biogas plants; mini power plants; energy conservation; electric power systems engineering. *Mailing Add:* Dept of Elec Eng Univ of Akron Akron OH 44325

KASHKET, EVA RUTH, b Zagreb, Yugoslavia, Mar 1, 36; US citizen; m 57; c 2. BACTERIOLOGY, BIOCHEMISTRY. *Educ:* McGill Univ, BSc, 56, MSc, 57; Harvard Univ, PhD(med sci), 63. *Prof Exp:* Res assoc, Dept Physiol, Harvard Med Sch, 57-74; ASSOC PROF MICROBIOL, SCH MED, BOSTON UNIV, 74- *Concurrent Pos:* Fel biochem pharmacol, Sch Med Tufts Univ, 62-65. *Mem:* Am Soc Microbiol; Am Soc Biol Chem. *Res:* Oxidative phosphorylation in bacterial systems; membrane transport related to cancer; energetics of sugar ion transport and nitrogen fixation in bacteria. *Mailing Add:* Dept of Microbiol Boston Univ Sch of Med Boston MA 02118

KASHKET, SHELBY, b Montreal, Que, Feb 1, 31; m 57; c 1. BIOCHEMISTRY. *Educ:* McGill Univ, BSc, 52, MSc, 53, PhD(biochem), 56. *Prof Exp:* Res fel biochem, McGill Univ, 56-57; res fel bact, Harvard Med Sch, 57-59; asst biochemist, Mass Gen Hosp, 63-67; biochemist, USPHS, 67-70; ASST RES PROF, SCH MED, BOSTON UNIV, 67-, ASST RES PROF, SCH GRAD DENT, 71-; MEM STAFF, FORSYTH DENT CTR, 80- *Concurrent Pos:* Res fel med, Harvard Med Sch, 59-60, res assoc, 60-77, lectr, 79- *Mem:* AAAS; Int Asn Dent Res; Am Chem Soc; Am Soc Cell Biol; Sigma Xi. *Res:* Metabolic effects of fluoride and food products; interaction between bacteria and salivary proteins; biological adhesion; mucin biochemistry; oral biology; intermediary metabolism; biochemical and clinical methods. *Mailing Add:* Forsyth Dent Ctr 140 The Fenway Boston MA 02115

KASHNOW, RICHARD ALLEN, b Worcester, Mass, Mar 26, 42; m 63; c 2. PHYSICS. *Educ:* Worcester Polytech Inst, BS, 63; Tufts Univ, PhD(physics), 68. *Prof Exp:* Physicist, US Army Natick Labs, 68-70; physicist, 70-75, liaison scientist, Corp Technol Study, 75-77, mgr liaison oper, Corp Res & Develop, Major Appliance Bus Group, 78-79, mgr, Electronics Lab, 79-81, PROD GEN MGR, LIGHTING BUS GROUP, GEN ELEC CORP, 81- *Mem:* Am Phys Soc; Inst Elec & Electronics Engrs. *Res:* Liquid crystals; quantum electronics; lattice dynamics. *Mailing Add:* 3960 Beechmont Terrace Orange OH 44122

KASHY, EDWIN, b Beirut, Lebanon, July 8, 34; US citizen; m 57; c 2. EXPERIMENTAL NUCLEAR PHYSICS. *Educ:* Rice Univ, BA, 56, MA, 57, PhD(physics), 59. *Prof Exp:* NSF fel physics, Mass Inst Technol, 59-60, instr, 60-62; asst prof, Princeton Univ, 62-64; assoc prof, 64-67, PROF PHYSICS, MICH STATE UNIV, 67- *Concurrent Pos:* Guggenheim fel, Niels Bohr Inst, Copenhagen, 70-71. *Mem:* Am Phys Soc. *Res:* Experimental investigations of nuclear spectroscopy and nuclear reaction mechanisms by means of charged particle and gamma ray studies. *Mailing Add:* Cyclotron Lab Dept of Physics Mich State Univ East Lansing MI 48823

KASHYAP, MOTI LAL, b Singapore, Feb 19, 39; m 70; c 2. INTERNAL MEDICINE, LIPIDOLOGY. *Educ:* Univ Singapore, MB, BS, 64; McGill Univ, MS, 67; FRCP(C), 69. *Prof Exp:* Intern med & surg, Teaching Hosps, Univ Singapore, 64-65; fel endocrinol & metab, Royal Victoria Hosp, McGill Univ, 65-67, resident internal med, 67-69, lectr, Fac Med, 69-70; sr fel, Cardiovasc Res Inst, Sch Med, Univ Calif, San Francisco, 70-71; sr lectr med physiol, Fac Med, Univ Singapore, 71-74; asst prof, 74-76, assoc prof, 81-81, PROF MED, COL MED, UNIV CINCINNATI, 81- *Concurrent Pos:* Assoc dir Lipid Res Clin, Cincinnati, 74-; fel, Arteriosclerosis Coun, Am Heart Asn. *Mem:* Am Fedn Clin Res; Int Soc Cardiol; Can Soc Endocrinol & Metab; Cent Soc Clin Res. *Res:* Lipoprotein metabolism. *Mailing Add:* Lipid Res Ctr K Pavilion Cincinnati Gen Hosp Cincinnati OH 45267

KASHYAP, RANGASAMI LAKSMINARAYANA, b Mysore, India, Mar 28, 38. ELECTRICAL ENGINEERING. *Educ:* Univ Mysore, BSc, 58; Indian Inst Sci, Bangalore, Dipl, 61, MEng, 63; Harvard Univ, PhD(eng), 66. *Prof Exp:* Res asst control systs, Harvard Univ, 63-65, teaching fel, 64, res fel eng, 65-66; from asst prof to assoc prof elec eng, 66-74, PROF ELEC ENG, PURDUE UNIV, 74- *Concurrent Pos:* Gordon McKay fel, 62-63; consult, Gen Elec Co, Ind, 67-68. *Mem:* Fel Inst Elec & Electronics Engrs; Asn Comput Mach. *Res:* Systems science; pattern recognition; learning systems; statistical inference; image processing. *Mailing Add:* Sch of Elec Eng Purdue Univ West Lafayette IN 47907

KASHYAP, TAPESHWAR S, b Kapurthala, India, Oct 15, 29; US citizen; m 59; c 2. POPULATION GENETICS, POULTRY BREEDING. *Educ:* Punjab Agr Col, India, BSc, 50; Univ Minn, St Paul, MSc, 56, PhD(animal husb), 58. *Prof Exp:* Asst animal husb, Univ Minn, St Paul, 55-58; geneticist & head data processing dept, 59-73, DIR GENETICS DEVELOP, KIMBER FARMS INC, 73- *Concurrent Pos:* FAO consult, Poultry Proj POL/71/515, Poznan, Poland, 76-78; consult geneticist poultry res proj, Animal Sci Dept, Univ Nebr, 78-; systs consult, Bank Am, 81- *Mem:* Genetics Soc Am; Am Genetics Asn; AAAS. *Res:* Animal breeding; improving livestock performance with the aid of principles of genetics; statistical analysis of data, using modern computers, to evaluate and seek answers to various problems in poultry breeding. *Mailing Add:* 41532 Pasco Padre Pkwy Fremont CA 94538

KASIK, JOHN EDWARD, b Chicago, Ill, Aug 9, 27; m 45; c 6. MEDICINE, PHARMACOLOGY. *Educ:* Roosevelt Univ, BS, 49; Univ Chicago, MS, 53, MD, 54, PhD(pharmacol), 62; Am Bd Internal Med, dipl. *Prof Exp:* Intern, Clins Univ Chicago, 54-55, from jr asst to asst resident med, 55-56, from asst prof to assoc prof, Grad Sch Med, 59-70; assoc prof, 70-73, PROF MED, COL MED, UNIV IOWA, 73- *Concurrent Pos:* Miller fel, Univ Chicago, 57-59; Fulbright scholar, Dunn Sch, Oxford Univ, 66-67; med dir, Kirchwood Col-Vet Admin Hosp Iowa City Sch Respiratory Ther. *Mem:* Am Thoracic Soc; Am Fedn Clin Res; fel Am Col Physicians; fel Am Soc Clin Pharmacol & Therapeut; Am Acad Clin Toxicol. *Res:* Pharmacology of immunosuppressent drugs; pharmacology of antibiotics. *Mailing Add:* Dept of Internal Med Univ of Iowa Iowa City IA 52240

KASINSKY, HAROLD EDWARD, b New York, NY, Jan 20, 41; m 67; c 1. BIOCHEMISTRY, DEVELOPMENTAL BIOLOGY. *Educ:* Columbia Col, BA, 61; Univ Calif, Berkeley, PhD(biochem), 67. *Prof Exp:* NIH fel, Dept Embryol, Carnegie Inst, 67-69; asst prof, 69-81, ASSOC PROF ZOOL, UNIV BC, 81- *Concurrent Pos:* Vis asst prof, Univ Calif, Berkeley, Univ Calgary & Univ Amsterdam. *Mem:* AAAS; Am Soc Zool; Soc Develop Biol; Can Soc Cell Biol; Am Soc Cell Biol. *Res:* Biochemistry of early development; nuclear protein synthesis during spermiogenesis and early embryogenesis in amphibia; diversity of sperm histones in the vertebrates. *Mailing Add:* Dept of Zool Univ of BC Vancouver BC V6T 1E1 Can

KASK, JOHN LAURENCE, b Red Deer, Alta, Mar 21, 06; nat US; m 35; c 2. FISHERIES. *Educ:* Univ BC, BA, 28; Univ Wash, Seattle, PhD(zool), 36. *Prof Exp:* Asst, Biol Bd Can, 28; asst scientist, Int Fisheries Comn, 29-38; assoc scientist & asst dir, Int Salmon Comn, 39-43; cur aquatic biol, Calif Acad Sci, 45-48; chief biologist, Fisheries Div, Food & Agr Orgn, UN, 48-50; chief invests & asst dir, Pac Oceanic Fish Invest, Honolulu, 51; chief officer of foreign activ, US Fish & Wildlife Serv, & asst dir fish, Washington, DC, 51-53; chmn & sci adminstr, Fisheries Res Bd Can, 53-63; dir invests, Inter-Am Trop Tuna Comn, 63-71; CONSULT, FISHERIES & BIOL OCEANOG, FOOD & AGR ORGN, UN, 71-81. *Concurrent Pos:* Lectr, Univ Hawaii, 51; lectr sch fisheries, Univ Wash, 35-43; assoc, Scripps Inst Oceanog, Univ Calif, San Diego; consult, Govt of Costa Rica, 47 & US Dept State, 47-48. *Mem:* AAAS; Am Fisheries Soc; Am Soc Ichthyol & Herpet; Am Soc Limnol & Oceanog. *Res:* Population dynamics; genetics; scientific administration. *Mailing Add:* 5877 Honors Dr San Diego CA 92122

KASK, UNO, b Sadala, Estonia, Sept 16, 22; US citizen. INORGANIC CHEMISTRY. *Educ:* Univ Ga, BS, 50; Univ Minn, MA, 56; Univ Tex, PhD(inorg chem), 63. *Prof Exp:* Instr chem, Armstrong Col, 52-55 & Eureka Col, 55-56; asst prof, Valdosta State Col, 56-57, Am Int Col, 57-60, Ind State Col, 61-62 & Univ Ga, 63-66; assoc prof, 66-69, chmn dept, 70-72, PROF CHEM, TOWSON STATE UNIV, 69- *Mem:* Am Chem Soc. *Res:* Nonaqueous reactions and reaction mechanisms of transition metal compounds with liquid sulfur; science education; science writing. *Mailing Add:* Dept of Chem Towson State Univ Towson MD 21204

KASKA, HAROLD VICTOR, b Brooklyn, NY, Jan 11, 26; m 50; c 3. GEOLOGY. *Educ:* NY Univ, BA, 50; Univ Ind, MA, 52. *Prof Exp:* Paleont asst, Univ Ind, 50-52; micropaleontologist, Dominion Oil Ltd, 52-53, chief paleontologist, 53-56; explor paleontologist, Calif Explor Co, 56-57; stratig paleontologist, Compania Guatemala Calif de Petroleo, 57-62; palynologist, Calif Explor Co, 62-65; paleontologist, Chevron Explor Co, 65-67; sr paleontologist, Standard Oil Co, Calif, 68-71; STAFF PALEONTOLOGIST, CHEVRON OVERSEAS PETROL INC, 71- *Mem:* Am Asn Petrol Geol; Am Inst Prof Geol. *Res:* Palynology, Paleozoic and Mesozoic spores, dinoflagellates and acritarchs; micropaleontology, Mesozoic and Tertiary foraminifera, planktonics, tintinnids, calcareous nannoplankton; application of micropaleontology and palynology to petroleum exploration, dating, correlation and facies studies. *Mailing Add:* Chevron Overseas Petrol Inc 575 Market St San Francisco CA 94105

KASKA, WILLIAM CHARLES, b Ancon, CZ, May 13, 35; m 64; c 1. CHEMISTRY. *Educ:* Loyola Univ, Calif, BS, 57; Univ Mich, PhD(chem), 63. *Prof Exp:* Res assoc chem, Pa State Univ, 63-64; asst prof, 65-74, assoc prof, 74-79, PROF CHEM, UNIV CALIF, SANTA BARBARA, 79- *Mem:* Am Chem Soc. *Res:* Synthesis and chemistry of organometallic compounds of the transition elements. *Mailing Add:* Dept of Chem Univ of Calif Santa Barbara CA 93106

KASKAS, JAMES, b Detroit, Mich, Jan 30, 39. THEORETICAL PHYSICS. *Educ:* Wayne State Univ, BS, 60, MS, 61, PhD(physics), 64. *Prof Exp:* From instr to asst prof, 63-74, ASSOC PROF PHYSICS, DETROIT INST TECHNOL, 74- *Mem:* Am Phys Soc; Am Asn Physics Teachers. *Res:* Elementary particle theory; quantum field theory. *Mailing Add:* Dept of Physics 2727 Second Ave Detroit MI 48201

KASLER, FRANZ JOHANN, b Vienna, Austria, Jan 1, 30; m 64; c 2. ANALYTICAL CHEMISTRY. *Educ:* Univ Vienna, PhD(org microanal), 59. *Prof Exp:* Asst prof, 59-65, ASSOC PROF CHEM, UNIV MD, COLLEGE PARK, 65- *Mem:* AAAS; Am Chem Soc; Am Microchem Soc; Austrian Chem Soc. *Res:* Quantitative nuclear magnetic resonance; organic elemental analysis of classic and instrumental methods. *Mailing Add:* Dept of Chem Univ of Md College Park MD 20742

KASLICK, RALPH SIDNEY, b Brooklyn, NY, Oct 17, 35. PERIODONTICS, ORAL MEDICINE. *Educ:* Columbia Univ, AB, 56, DDS, 59. *Prof Exp:* From instr to assoc prof, 65-74, asst dean acad affairs, 72-75, actg dean, 75-76, PROF PERIODONT & ORAL MED, SCH DENT, FAIRLEIGH DICKINSON UNIV, 74-, DEAN, 76- *Concurrent Pos:* Res grants from various indust firms & founds, 65-; res consult for various indust firms, 69- *Honors & Awards:* Jour Award, Int Col Dent, 72; Medallion, Japan Stomatol Soc, 78. *Mem:* Fel Am Col Dent; Am Acad Periodont; Int Asn Dent Res; Sigma Xi; Am Asn Dent Schs. *Res:* Genetic studies of periodontal diseases in young adults; quantitative analysis of gingival fluid; clinical testing of therapeutic dentifrices, ointments and hygiene aids. *Mailing Add:* Sch of Dent Fairleigh Dickinson Univ Hackensack NJ 07601

KASLOW, CHRISTIAN EDWARD, b Mora, Minn, Mar 20, 03; m 26; c 2. ORGANIC CHEMISTRY. *Educ:* Hamline Univ, BS, 24; Univ Iowa, MS, 29; Univ Minn, PhD(org chem), 43. *Prof Exp:* Teacher pub sch, Minn, 24-30; instr chem, NDak Col, 30-41; instr, 41-46, from asst prof to assoc prof, 46-56, prof, 56-71, dir labs, 63-68, EMER PROF CHEM, IND UNIV, BLOOMINGTON, 71- *Concurrent Pos:* Civilian with Off Sci Res & Develop, 44. *Mem:* AAAS; Am Chem Soc. *Res:* Quinoline chemistry. *Mailing Add:* Dept Chem Ind Univ Bloomington IN 47401

KASLOW, DAVID EDWARD, b Bloomington, Ind, Sept 27, 42. AEROSPACE SYSTEM ENGINEERING. *Educ:* Ind Univ, Bloomington, AB, 64, MS, 66; Univ Mich, Ann Arbor, PhD(physics), 71. *Prof Exp:* Res assoc physics, Lehigh Univ, 71-73; ANALYST, VALLEY FORGE SPACE CTR, GEN ELEC CO, 73- *Mem:* Am Phys Soc. *Mailing Add:* Valley Forge Space Ctr Gen Elec Co PO Box 8048 Philadelphia PA 19101

KASLOW, HAVEN DELOSS, b Mora, Minn, Nov 30, 10; m 44. BIOCHEMISTRY. *Educ:* NDak State Col, BS, 34. *Prof Exp:* Asst chem, Iowa State Col, 36-40; res chemist, Corn Prods Ref Co, Ill, 41-44 & Gen Mills, Inc, 44-62; CONSULT TO VPRES RES, AM CANCER SOC, NEW YORK, 66- *Mem:* AAAS; Am Chem Soc; Am Inst Chem; NY Acad of Sci. *Res:* Wet and dry milling processes; morphology of corn and wheat, rheology of cereal doughs and glutens; medical and physiological chemistry; cancer research, especially clinical pathology and health sciences. *Mailing Add:* 1430 E Como Blvd St Paul MN 55117

KASMAN, SIDNEY, b Toronto, Ont, Dec 12, 27; US citizen; m 61; c 3. PHOTOGRAPHIC CHEMISTRY. *Educ:* Univ Toronto, BA, 50, MA, 51; McGill Univ, PhD(org chem), 55. *Prof Exp:* Scientist, 55-65, res group leader, 65-73, SR RES GROUP LEADER, POLAROID CORP, 73- *Mem:* Am Chem Soc; Sigma Xi; Soc Photog Sci & Eng. *Res:* Photographic research and development; design and optimization of photographic reagents; techniques, processes and equipment for their preparation, evaluation and manufacture; instrument design. *Mailing Add:* Polaroid Corp 28 Osborn St 4A Cambridge MA 02139

KASNER, FRED E, b New York, NY, July 8, 26; m 53; c 1. PHYSICAL CHEMISTRY. *Educ:* City Col New York, BS, 48; Univ Chicago, MS, 49, PhD(phys chem), 61. *Prof Exp:* From instr to asst prof natural sci, Univ Chicago, 54-59; from instr to prof chem, Fenger Jr Col, 61-70; PROF CHEM, OLIVE-HARVEY COL, 71- *Concurrent Pos:* Consult, US Air Force, 59; vis scholar, Northwestern Univ, 71; vis scientist, Afgonne Nat Lab, 79. *Mem:* Am Chem Soc; Am Soc Testing & Mat. *Res:* Laser Raman spectroscopy of aqueous solutions; thermal conductivity and its temperature coefficient; heats of dilution of aqueous solutions of strong electrolytes. *Mailing Add:* Olive-Harvey Col 10001 S Woodlawn Chicago IL 60628

KASNER, WILLIAM HENRY, b Killbuck, Ohio, Jan 27, 29; m 51; c 1. PHYSICS. *Educ:* Case Western Reserve Univ, BS, 51; Univ Pittsburgh, PhD(physics), 58. *Prof Exp:* Res assoc physics, Univ Md, 58-59, asst res prof, 59-61; FEL SCIENTIST, GAS LASERS RES & DEVELOP, WESTINGHOUSE RES & DEVELOP CTR, 61- *Mem:* Am Phys Soc. *Res:* Atomic physics, especially atomic and electronic collision phenomena; ultraviolet spectroscopy; gas discharges; optics; laser development and application. *Mailing Add:* Atomic & Molecular Sci Westinghouse Res & Develop Ctr Pittsburgh PA 15235

KASNITZ, HAROLD LOUIS, physics, see previous edition

KASOWSKI, ROBERT V, b Bremond, Tex, Feb 14, 44; m 69; c 1. SOLID STATE PHYSICS. *Educ:* Tex A&M Univ, BS, 66; Univ Chicago, PhD(physics), 69. *Prof Exp:* Physicist, E I du Pont de Nemours & Co, Inc, 69-80. *Mem:* Am Phys Soc. *Res:* Calculating the electronic properties of molecules adsorbed onto metal or semiconductor surfaces using linear combination of muffin tin orbitals method. *Mailing Add:* 2 Box 48 AB Chaddsford PA 19317

KASPAREK, STANLEY VACLAV, b Prague, Czech, Jun 11, 29. ORGANIC CHEMISTRY, MEDICINAL CHEMISTRY. *Educ:* Charles Univ, Prague, Dr rer nat, 65. *Prof Exp:* Chemist, Res Inst Pharm & Biochem, Prague, 50-59 & Czech Acad Sci, 62-65; fel & chemist, Nat Res Coun Can, 65-67; abstractor, Chem Abstracts Serv, Ohio, 68; info scientist, 68-81, TECH FEL, HOFFMANN-LA ROCHE INC, 82- *Mem:* Am Chem Soc. *Res:* Scientific information. *Mailing Add:* 3 Rockledge Pl 340 Kingsland St Cedar Grove NJ 07009

KASPER, ANDREW E, JR, b Bridgeport, Conn, Oct 29, 42; m 67; c 2. PALEOBOTANY. *Educ:* Duquesne Univ, BA, 65; Univ Conn, MS, 68, PhD(bot), 70. *Prof Exp:* Asst prof, 70-75, ASSOC PROF BOT, RUTGERS UNIV, NEWARK, 75- *Mem:* Bot Soc Am; Sigma Xi; Paleont Soc; Am Asn Stratig Palynologists. *Res:* Description and classification of Devonian age plant fossils. *Mailing Add:* Dept of Bot Rutgers Univ Newark NJ 07102

KASPER, CHARLES BOYER, b Joliet, Ill, Apr 27, 35; m 57; c 4. BIOCHEMISTRY. *Educ:* Univ Ill, BS, 58; Univ Wis, PhD(physiol chem), 62. *Prof Exp:* Asst prof biol chem, Univ Calif, Los Angeles, 64-65; asst prof, 65-71, ASSOC PROF ONCOL, McARDLE LAB, UNIV WIS-MADISON, 71- *Concurrent Pos:* NIH fels, Univ Utah, 62-63 & Univ Calif, Los Angeles, 63-64. *Mem:* Am Soc Biol Chemists. *Res:* Role of the nuclear envelope in cell function; molecular basis of enzyme induction. *Mailing Add:* McArdle Lab Univ of Wis Med Sch Madison WI 53706

KASPER, GEORGE PHILIP, chemical engineering, see previous edition

KASPER, JOHN SIMON, b Newark, NJ, May 27, 15. PHYSICAL CHEMISTRY. *Educ:* Johns Hopkins Univ, AB, 37, PhD(chem), 41. *Prof Exp:* Jr instr chem, Johns Hopkins Univ, 37-41; instr, St Louis Univ, 41-42; res chemist, Nat Defense Res Comt contract, Johns Hopkins Univ, 42-43 & Manhattan Dist Proj, SAM Labs, Columbia Univ, 43-45; res assoc, 45-58, PHYS CHEMIST, RES LAB, GEN ELEC CO, 58- *Mem:* AAAS; Am Chem Soc; Am Phys Soc; Am Crystallog Asn. *Res:* X-ray diffraction; structures of crystals; structural chemistry; fluorocarbon chemistry; gas adsorption; physical properties; aqueous solutions; neutron diffraction. *Mailing Add:* Res Lab Gen Elec Co PO Box 1088 Schenectady NY 12301

KASPER, JOSEPH EMIL, b Cedar Rapids, Iowa, May 2, 20; m 57; c 5. SCIENCE EDUCATION. *Educ:* Coe Col, BA, 51; Univ Iowa, MS, 54, PhD(physics), 58. *Prof Exp:* Asst physics, Univ Iowa, 51-57, instr, 58; asst prof, 59-63, PROF PHYSICS, COE COL, 63- *Mem:* Am Phys Soc; Am Asn Physics Teachers. *Res:* Geomagnetic theory; cosmic radiation; soft radiations in upper atmosphere; rocketry. *Mailing Add:* 3344 Carlisle St NE Cedar Rapids IA 52402

KASPER, JOSEPH F, JR, b Baltimore, Md, Dec 9, 43; m 66; c 2. NAVIGATION, APPLIED PHYSICS. *Educ:* Mass Inst Technol, BS, 64, MS, 66, DSc(instrumentation), 68. *Prof Exp:* Mgr, spec projs, 75-78, mgr, Navig Systs, 78-79, dir, Stratig Syst Div, 79-80, DIR SEA-LAUNCHED BALLISTIC MISSILE, ANAL SCI CORP, 80- *Mem:* Am Geophys Union; Inst Navig; Inst Elec & Electronics Engrs; Am Inst Aeronaut & Astronaut. *Res:* Mathematical modeling of very low frequency propagation anomalies; statistical description of geodetic phenomena; analysis of radio and inertial navigation error behavior; applied Kalman filtering. *Mailing Add:* Anal Sci Corp 6 Jacob Way Reading MA 01867

KASPERBAUER, MICHAEL J, b Manning, Iowa, Oct 8, 29; m 62; c 4. PLANT PHYSIOLOGY. *Educ:* Iowa State Univ, BS, 54, MS, 57, PhD(plant physiol), 61. *Prof Exp:* NSF fel, Univ Md, 61-62; plant physiologist pioneering res lab plant physiol, Md, 62-63, PLANT PHYSIOLOGIST, AGR RES SERV, USDA, KY, 63-; PROF AGRON, UNIV KY, 73- *Concurrent Pos:* Assoc ed, Agronomy Jour, 75- *Mem:* Am Soc Plant Physiol; Crop Sci Soc Am; Am Soc Agron; Am Soc Photobiol. *Res:* Interaction of light and temperature on plant growth, development and composition; phytochrome control of flowering; haploid and double haploid utilization in crop improvement. *Mailing Add:* Agron Dept Univ Ky Lexington KY 40546

KASPEREK, GEORGE JAMES, b Albert Lea, Minn, June 1, 44; m 66; c 2. BIOCHEMISTRY, EXERCISE. *Educ:* Mankato State Col, BA, 66; Ore State Univ, PhD(org chem), 69. *Prof Exp:* Fel bioorg, Univ Calif, Santa Barbara, 69-72; asst prof biochem, Conn Col, 72-77, assoc prof, 77-78; ASSOC PROF BIOCHEM, SCH MED, ECAROLINA UNIV, 78- *Concurrent Pos:* NIH fel, 69-71; vis prof, Sch Med, ECarolina Univ, 78-79. *Mem:* Am Chem Soc; AAAS. *Res:* Metabolism of exercise; solution kinetics; mechanisms of organic and biochemical reactions. *Mailing Add:* Dept Biochem Sch Med ECarolina Univ Greenville NC 27834

KASPROW, BARBARA ANN, b Hartford, Conn, Apr 23, 36. ANATOMY, REPRODUCTIVE BIOLOGY. *Educ:* Albertus Magnus Col, BA, 58; Loyola Univ, Ill, PhD(anat), 69. *Prof Exp:* Res asst anat & reprod biol, Sch Med, Yale Univ, 61; res assoc, NY Med Col, 61-62; from res assoc to sr res & admin assoc, Inst Study Human Reprod, Ohio, 62-67; sr res assoc, Stritch Sch Med, Loyola Univ, Chicago, 67-69, asst prof anat, 69-80. *Mem:* AAAS; Am Asn Anatomists; Histochem Soc; Am Soc Zoologists; NY Acad Sci. *Res:* Reproductive phenomena in the mammalian female; growth mechanisms, pathologic variants in reproductive organs and endocrinologic interrelationships; cytophysiology. *Mailing Add:* 1021 S Hwy 83 Elmhurst IL 60126

KASRIEL, ROBERT H, b Tampa, Fla, Oct 18, 18; m 46; c 2. MATHEMATICS. *Educ:* Univ Tampa, BS, 40; Univ Va, MA, 49, PhD(math), 53. *Prof Exp:* Coordr war-training courses, Univ Tampa, 40-42; aeronaut res scientist, Nat Adv Comt Aeronaut, 52-54; from asst prof to assoc prof, 54-62, PROF MATH, GA INST TECHNOL, 62- *Honors & Awards:* Ferst Res Award, Sigma Xi, 62. *Mem:* Am Math Soc; Math Asn Am. *Res:* Analytic topology; fixed point theorems; mapping theorems. *Mailing Add:* Sch of Math Ga Inst of Technol Atlanta GA 30322

KASS, EDWARD HAROLD, b New York, NY, Dec 20, 17; m; c 8. INFECTIOUS DISEASES. *Educ:* Univ Ky, AB, 39, MS, 41; Univ Wis, PhD(med bact), 43; Univ Calif, MD, 47. *Hon Degrees:* MA, Harvard Univ, 58; DSc, Univ Ky, 62. *Prof Exp:* Asst bact, Univ Ky, 39-40, instr, 41; asst med bact, Univ Wis, 41-43, instr, 43; immunologist phys chem, 43-44, asst path, 44-45; intern path, Boston City Hosp, 47-48; intern med serv, Harvard Univ, 48-49; instr med, 51-52, assoc, 52-55, asst prof, 55-58, assoc prof bact & immunol, 58-68, from assoc prof to prof med, 68-73, WILLIAM ELLERY CHANNING PROF MED, HARVARD MED SCH, 73-, DIR DEPT MED BACT & CHANNING LAB, 63- *Concurrent Pos:* Res fel med, Harvard Med Sch, 49-51; Nat Res Coun sr fel, 49-52; assoc physician, Thorndike Mem Lab, Boston City Hosp, 51-76; assoc vis physician, 2nd & 4th Med Serv, Harvard Univ, 52-76; vis physician, Mallory Inst Path, 58-76, assoc dir, 58-64, physician, Brigham & Women's Hosp, 76-; consult med, Beth Israel Hosp, Children's Hosp, Cambridge Hosp, Lemuel Shattuck Hosp & Chelsea Soldier's Home; fel Coun Epidemiol, Am Heart Asn; vpres, Intersci Conf Antimicrobial Agents & Chemother; ed, J Infectious Dis; mem adv comt epidemiol & biomet, Nat Heart & Lung Inst, chmn, 71-72; mem space sci bd, Nat Acad Sci-Nat Res Coun, chmn comt space med, 71-74; mem bd maternal, child & family health res, Nat Res Coun, 75-78; mem, Assembly Life Sci, Nat Res Coun, 79- *Honors & Awards:* Rosenthal Found Award, Am Col Physicians. *Mem:* Infectious Dis Soc Am (secy-treas, 62-70, pres, 70); Am Epidemiol Soc; Am Soc Clin Invest; Am Asn Immunol; Asn Am Physicians. *Res:* Infectious diseases, clinical epidemiology, internal medicine; preventive medicine. *Mailing Add:* Todd Pond Rd Lincoln MA 01773

KASS, GUSS SIGMUND, b Chicago, Ill, Oct 19, 15; m 39; c 2. COSMETIC CHEMISTRY. *Educ:* Univ Chicago, BS, 38. *Prof Exp:* Res chemist, Munic Tuberc Sanitarium, 38-39; chemist, Prod Corp Am, 39-40; res chemist, Acme Cosmetic Corp, 40-41; chief chemist, Duart Mfg Co, Ltd, Calif, 41-42 & 46-48; asst res dir, Helene Curtis Industs, Inc, 48-54; res dir & vpres, Lanolin Plus, Inc, 54-60; from tech dir to vpres & dir corp res & develop, Alberto-Culver Co, 60-74; PRES, G S KASS & ASSOCS, LTD, 74- *Concurrent Pos:* Lectr, Univ Chicago, 58; lectr, Sch Med, Univ Ill, 65- *Mem:* Am Acad Dermat; Am Chem Soc; fel Soc Cosmetic Chem; fel Am Inst Chem. *Res:* Cosmetics; toiletries; proprietary pharmaceuticals. *Mailing Add:* 8938 N Keeler Ave Skokie IL 60076

KASS, IRVING, b Topeka, Kans, July 15, 17; m 54; c 3. MEDICINE. *Educ:* Univ Kans, AB, 39, MD & MA, 44; Am Bd Internal med, dipl, 55. *Prof Exp:* Physician, Vet Admin Ctr, 51-55; asst med dir, Nat Jewish Hosp, 55-64; asst clin prof med, Sch Med, Univ Colo, 56-64; assoc med dir, Will Rogers Hosp, 64-66; from assoc prof to prof, 66-69, chief div pulmonary dis, 65-80, MARGARET & RICHARD LARSON PROF MED, COL MED, UNIV NEBR, 69-, DIR RES, PULMONARY DIV, 80- *Concurrent Pos:* Mem steering comt, AMA Guides to Eval Permanent Impairment, 80-; mem peer rev panel, Nat Inst Handicapped Res, 81; chmn pulmonary sem, IVth Cong Int Med Rehab Asn, San Juan, PR, 82. *Mem:* Fel Am Col Chest Physicians; Am Col Physicians. *Res:* Chronic obstructive pulmonary diseases; rehabilitation and natural history. *Mailing Add:* Dept of Internal Med Univ of Nebr Med Ctr Omaha NE 68105

KASS, LEON RICHARD, b Chicago, Ill, Feb 12, 39; m 61; c 2. MEDICAL ETHICS. *Educ:* Univ Chicago, BS, 58, MD, 62; Harvard Univ, PhD(biochem, molecular biol), 67. *Prof Exp:* Intern med, Beth Israel Hosp, Boston, Mass, 62-63; staff assoc molecular biol, Nat Inst Arthritis & Metab Dis, 67-69, sr staff fel, 69-70; exec secy comt life sci & social policy, Nat Acad Sci, 70-72; tutor, St John's Col, Md, 72-74; Joseph P Kennedy, Sr res prof bioethics, Kennedy Inst & assoc prof neurol & philos, Georgetown Univ, 74-76; HENRY R LUCE PROF IN THE LIB ARTS OF HUMAN BIOL, COL & COMT ON SOCIAL THOUGHT, UNIV CHICAGO, 76- *Concurrent Pos:* Guggenheim fel, 72-73; fel & mem bd dir, Inst Soc, Ethics & Life Sci, 70- *Mem:* AAAS. *Res:* Ethical and social implications of advances in biomedical science and technology; philosophy of biology and medicine; philosophy of biology and medicine. *Mailing Add:* Univ of Chicago 1116 E 59th St Chicago IL 60637

KASS, ROBERT S, b New York, NY, June 13, 46. CARDIAC ELECTROPHYSIOLOGY, MEMBRANE BIOPHYSICS. *Educ:* Univ Ill, BSc, 68; Univ Mich, MSc, 69, PhD(physics), 72. *Prof Exp:* Fel physiol, Univ Mich, 72-74; fel membrane biophysics, Marine Biol Labs, Mass, 73; fel physiol, Yale Univ, 74-77; ASST PROF PHYSIOL, UNIV ROCHESTER, 77- *Mem:* Biophys Soc. *Res:* Physiology and biophysics of excitable membranes with a particular interest in the membranes of heart muscle cells; multiple roles of calcium ions in these preparations. *Mailing Add:* Dept Physiol Univ Rochester Med Ctr Rochester NY 14642

KASS, SEYMOUR, b New York, NY, Apr 13, 26; m 55; c 2. ALGEBRA. *Educ:* Brooklyn Col, BA, 48; Stanford Univ, MS, 57; Univ Chicago, SM, 65; Ill Inst Technol, PhD(math), 66. *Prof Exp:* Mathematician, Curtiss Wright Corp, 52-55 & Stanford Res Inst, 55-57; from instr to asst prof math, Ill Inst Technol, 60-71; chmn dept, 72-75, assoc prof, 71-77, PROF MATH, BOSTON STATE COL, 77- *Concurrent Pos:* NSF res grant, 69 & 70. *Mem:* Am Math Soc; Math Asn Am; Sigma Xi. *Res:* Non-associative algebras, varieties of algebras, philosophy of science. *Mailing Add:* 118 York Terr Brookline MA 02146

KASS, STANLEY, metals, see previous edition

KASS, THOMAS LEWIS, genetics, see previous edition

KASSAKHIAN, GARABET HAROUTIOUN, b Jerusalem, Palestine, Aug 15, 44; Can citizen; m 69; c 1. ENVIRONMENTAL CHEMISTRY. *Educ:* Yerevan State Univ, Armenia, MSc, 67; Harvard Univ, AM, 70, PhD(anal chem), 75. *Prof Exp:* Asst prof chem, Univ Mass, Boston, 75-78; environ chemist, El Dorado Nuclear Ltd, Ottawa, 78-80. *Mem:* Am Chem Soc; Chem Inst Can; Am Asn Univ Prof. *Res:* Uranium mine and mill tailings; waste management; air and water pollution; radionuclides in environment; uranium and thorium health physics; electrochemistry of transition elements with multiple oxidation states. *Mailing Add:* 15 Avon Way Parlin NJ 08859

KASSAKIAN, JOHN GABRIEL, b Mar 27, 43; US citizen; c 2. POWER ENGINEERING, ELECTRICAL ENGINEERING. *Educ:* Mass Inst Technol, SB, 65, SM, 67, EE, 67, ScD(elec eng), 73. *Prof Exp:* Tech rep to Univac naval data syst, US Navy, 69-71; asst prof, 73-78, ASSOC PROF ELEC ENG, MASS INST TECHNOL, 78-, ASSOC DIR, ELEC POWER SYST ENG LAB, 79- *Concurrent Pos:* Consult, Gould Labs, Gould Inc, 75-, Rotron Div, EG&G Inc, 77-, Lutron Electronics, 78- *Mem:* Inst Elec & Electronics Engrs. *Res:* Simulation, analysis, synthesis of energy conversion systems; transient behavior of electric power transmission systems; pulsed power supplies for fusion research; asynchronous machine drives; power electronics. *Mailing Add:* Rm 10-098 Mass Inst of Technol 77 Massachusetts Ave Cambridge MA 02139

KASSAL, ROBERT JAMES, b Berwick, Pa, Oct 23, 36; m 58; c 4. ORGANIC CHEMISTRY. *Educ:* Hofstra Univ, BA, 58; Univ Fla, PhD(org chem), 64. *Prof Exp:* Chemist, Am Cyanamid Co, 58-60; res asst fluorine chem, Univ Fla, 60-63; res chemist 63-68, sr res chemist, Plastics Dept, 68-69, res supvr, 69-75, mem staff, Elastomers Dept, 75-78, RES ASSOC, POLYMER PROD DEPT, E I DU PONT DE NEMOURS & CO INC, 78- *Mem:* Soc Plastics Indust. *Res:* Fluorine chemistry; polymer preparation; fluorocarbon heterocyclic polymers; intermediates and monomer exploratory research; new product development; polymer synthesis; polymer modification; high performance composite development; novel elastomer systems. *Mailing Add:* Exp Sta Lab E I du Pont de Nemours & Co Inc Wilmington DE 19898

KASSAM, SALEEM ABDULALI, b Dar es Salaam, Tanzania, June 16, 49; m 78; c 2. SIGNAL PROCESSING, COMMUNICATION THEORY. *Educ:* Swarthmore Col, BS, 72; Princeton Univ, MSE & MA, 74, PhD(elec eng), 75. *Prof Exp:* Asst prof, 75-80, ASSOC PROF SYSTS ENG, MOORE SCH ELEC ENG, UNIV PA, 80- *Concurrent Pos:* Prin investr, Air Force Off Sci Res res grant, Univ Pa, 76-, NSF grant, 77-79, Naval Res Lab grant, 78-80 & Off Naval Res grant, 80-; consult, RCA, 80- *Mem:* Inst Elec & Electronics Engrs. *Res:* Statistical communication theory; statistical inference; signal processing. *Mailing Add:* Moore Sch of Elec Eng Univ of Pa Philadelphia PA 19104

KASSANDER, ARNO RICHARD, JR, b Carbondale, Pa, Sept 10, 20; m 43; c 1. GEOLOGY. *Educ:* Amherst Col, BA, 41; Univ Okla, MS, 43; Iowa State Col, PhD(physics), 50. *Hon Degrees:* DSc, Amherst Col, 71. *Prof Exp:* Asst geologist, Tex Co, 41; asst geophysics, Magnolia Petrol Co, 43; asst prof physics, Iowa State Col, 50-54; assoc dir, Inst Atmospheric Physics, 54-57, dir, 57-73, head dept atmospheric sci, 58-73, VPRES RES, UNIV ARIZ, 72-, PROF ATMOSPHERIC SCI, 76- *Concurrent Pos:* Dir, Water Resources Res Ctr, Univ Ariz, 64-72; mem panel environ, President's Sci Adv Comt; trustee, Ariz Sonora Desert Mus; chmn, Univ Corp Atmospheric Res, 58-68; dir, Burr Brown Res Corp, 74- *Mem:* Fel AAAS; Am Phys Soc; fel Am Meteorol Soc. *Res:* General geophysical instrumentation; recording and automatic analysis of statistical data. *Mailing Add:* 603 Admin Bldg Univ of Ariz Tucson AZ 85721

KASSCHAU, MARGARET RAMSEY, b Cambridge, Mass, Sept 9, 42; m 64; c 2. COMPARATIVE PHYSIOLOGY, CELL PHYSIOLOGY. *Educ:* Univ Rochester, AB, 64; Univ SC, MS, 70, PhD(biol), 73. *Prof Exp:* Res asst biol, Oak Ridge Nat Lab, 64-67; guest worker parasitol, NIH, 73-74; fel res physics, M D Anderson Hosp & Tumor Inst, 74-75; asst prof, 75-79, ASSOC PROF BIOL, UNIV HOUSTON, CLEAR LAKE CITY, 79- *Concurrent Pos:* Prin investr, Sea Grant Col Prog, 78-80; vis res assoc, Med Sch, Stanford Univ, 80-81. *Mem:* Am Soc Zoologists; Estuarine Res Fedn; AAAS; Soc Environ Toxicol & Chem. *Res:* Osmoregulation of marine invertebrates; aquatic toxicology of marine animals; cellular toxicology. *Mailing Add:* Sch of Sci & Technol Univ Houston at Clear Lake City Houston TX 77058

KASSIRER, JEROME PAUL, b Buffalo, NY, Dec 19, 32; c 6. NEPHROLOGY, INTERNAL MEDICINE. *Educ:* Univ Buffalo, BA, 53, MD, 57. *Prof Exp:* Asst physician, New Eng Med Ctr Hosp, Tufts Univ, 62-65; physician, 69-74, assoc physician-in-chief, 71-76, actg physician-in-chief, 76-77, instr med & nephrology, Sch Med, 62-65, from asst prof to assoc prof med, 65-74, assoc chmn, 71-76, actg chmn, 74-75 & 76-77, PROF MED, SCH MED, TUFTS UNIV, 74-, ASSOC CHMN, 77-, ASSOC PHYSICIAN-IN-CHIEF, NEW ENG MED CTR, 77- *Concurrent Pos:* Consult, Fed Trade Comn, 76-; mem med sci panel, Am Inst Biol Sci, 77-; co-ed, Kidney Int, Nephrology Forum, 78- *Res:* Renal, electrolytes and acid-base physiology; clinical nephrology; decision analysis and clinical cognition. *Mailing Add:* Dept of Med New Eng Med Ctr 171 Harrison Ave Boston MA 02111

KASSNER, JAMES EDWARD, industrial organic chemistry, see previous edition

KASSNER, JAMES LYLE, JR, b Tuscaloosa, Ala, May 1, 31; m 56; c 5. CLOUD PHYSICS. *Educ:* Univ Ala, BS, 52, MS, 53, PhD(physics), 57. *Prof Exp:* Asst physics, Univ Ala, 53-54, res assoc, 54-56; asst prof, Mo Sch Mines, 56-59; assoc prof, 59-66, PROF PHYSICS, UNIV MO-ROLLA, 66-, DIR, GRAD CTR CLOUD PHYSICS RES, 68- *Concurrent Pos:* Mem subcomt nucleation, Int Asn Meteorol & Atmospheric Physics; mem subcomn IV, Ions, Aerosols & Radioactivity, Int Comn Atmospheric Elec. *Mem:* Fel Am Phys Soc; Am Meteorol Soc; Am Geophys Union. *Res:* Atmospheric condensation; homogeneous and heterogeneous nucleation from the vapor; mobility of cluster ions; laboratory simulation of cloud formation; measurements on atmospheric particulates; nucleation of ice. *Mailing Add:* Cloud Physics Res Ctr Univ of Mo Rolla MO 65401

KASSNER, RICHARD J, b Chicago, Ill, July 1, 39; m 62; c 3. BIOCHEMISTRY. *Educ:* Purdue Univ, BS, 61; Yale Univ, MS, 63, PhD(biophys chem), 66. *Prof Exp:* NIH fel chem, Univ Calif, San Diego, 66-68; instr, 68-69; asst prof, 69-74, ASSOC PROF CHEM, UNIV ILL, CHICAGO CIRCLE, 74- *Res:* Structural basis for the properties of heme and iron-sulfur proteins; model systems for the active sites of hemeproteins; heme and chlorophyll biosynthesis. *Mailing Add:* Dept of Chem Univ of Ill at Chicago Circle Chicago IL 60680

KASSOY, DAVID R, b Brooklyn, NY, Jan 29, 38; m 64; c 2. FLUID MECHANICS, COMBUSTION. *Educ:* Polytech Inst Brooklyn, BAE, 59; Univ Mich, MSAE, 61, PhD(aerospace eng), 65. *Prof Exp:* Asst res engr, Univ Calif, San Diego, 65-67, asst prof aerospace & mech eng sci, 68-69; from asst prof to assoc prof mech eng, 69-78, PROF MECH ENG, UNIV COLO, BOULDER, 78- *Concurrent Pos:* Guggenheim fel, 73; reservoir comt, Hot Dry Rocks Prog Develop Coun, Los Alamos Geothermal Prog, 79- *Mem:* Am Phys Soc; Soc Indust & Appl Math; Am Geophys Union. *Res:* Combustion theory; porous medium flow; geothermal heat and mass transfer; perturbation methods; theoretical fluid mechanics. *Mailing Add:* Dept of Mech Eng Univ of Colo Boulder CO 80309

KASTELLA, KENNETH GEORGE, b Kalispell, Mont, May 27, 33; div; c 1. PHYSIOLOGY. *Educ:* Univ Wash, BS, 59, MS, 65, PhD(physiol), 69. *Prof Exp:* NIH training grant neurophysiol, Univ Wash, 69-70, res assoc, 70; asst prof physiol, Univ NMex, 70-76; ADJ ASSOC PROF, UNIV ALASKA, 76- *Mem:* AAAS; Inst Elec & Electronics Engrs; Biophys Soc; Am Physiol Soc. *Res:* Neurophysiology, especially central control of blood pressure; temperature regulation. *Mailing Add:* WAMI Med Educ Prog Univ of Alaska Fairbanks AK 99701

KASTEN, FREDERICK H, b New York, NY, Mar 7, 27; m 49; c 4. CELL BIOLOGY. *Educ:* Univ Houston, BA, 50; Univ Tex, MS, 51, PhD(zool), 54. *Prof Exp:* Scientist cancer res, Roswell Park Mem Inst, NY, 54-56; asst prof zool, Agr & Mech Col, Tex, 56-61; res coordr & dir ultrastruct cytochem dept, Pasadena Found Med Res, 63-70; PROF ANAT, MED CTR, LA STATE UNIV, 70- *Concurrent Pos:* NSF sr fel, Giessen, Ger, 61-62; NSF sr fel, Inst Cancer Res, Villejuif, France, 62-63, NIH spec res fel, 62-63; from adj asst prof to adj assoc prof, Univ Southern Calif, 63-70; from asst clin prof to assoc clin prof, Loma Linda Univ, 65-70; partic, W Alton Jones Cell Sci Ctr, 71; consult, Nat Heart & Lung Inst, 71- & Nat Cancer Inst, 73-; assoc coordr, La Cancer Ctr, 73-78; rev ed, In Vitro, 75-77; vis prof anat, ETenn State Univ Med Sch, 80-81. *Mem:* Histochem Soc; Am Soc Cell Biol; Am Asn Cancer Res; Ger Histochem Soc; Tissue Cult Asn. *Res:* Quantitative cytochemistry of nucleic acids; absorption curve analyses of stained cells; development of new staining techniques; electron microscopy; cytochemistry of viral infections; dye impurities; fluorescence microscopy; cancer; tissue culture. *Mailing Add:* Dept of Anat La State Univ Med Ctr New Orleans LA 70119

KASTEN, PAUL R(UDOLPH), b Jackson, Mo, Dec 10, 23; m 47; c 3. CHEMICAL ENGINEERING. *Educ:* Univ Mo Sch Mines, BS, 44, MS, 47; Univ Minn, PhD(chem eng), 50. *Prof Exp:* Staff mem, 50-55, sect chief, 55-61, assoc dept head, 61-63, guest dir, Inst Reactor Develop, WGer, 63-65, assoc dir, Molten Salt Reactor Prog, 65-70, dir, Gas Cooled Reactor & Thorium Utilization Progs & mgr, Alternate Fuel Cycle Eval, 77-79, DIR, GAS COOLED REACTOR PROGS, OAK RIDGE NAT LAB, 79- *Concurrent Pos:* Lectr, Univ Tenn, Knoxville, 53-60, prof, 65- *Mem:* Fel Am Nuclear Soc; fel AAAS; Nat Soc Prof Engrs. *Res:* Nuclear engineering. *Mailing Add:* Oak Ridge Nat Lab PO Box Y Oak Ridge TN 37830

KASTENBAUM, MARVIN AARON, mathematical statistics, see previous edition

KASTENBERG, WILLIAM EDWARD, b New York, NY, June 25, 39; m 63; c 3. NUCLEAR ENGINEERING. *Educ:* Univ Calif, Los Angeles, BS, 62, MS, 63; Univ Calif, Berkeley, PhD(eng), 66. *Prof Exp:* From asst prof eng to assoc prof eng & appl sci, 66-75, vchmn dept chem, nuclear & thermal eng, 77-78, PROF CHEM, NUCLEAR & THERMAL ENG, UNIV CALIF, LOS ANGELES, 75-, ASST DEAN GRAD STUDIES, 81- *Mem:* Fel Am Nuclear Soc. *Res:* Nuclear reactor kinetics and control; nuclear reactor safety; nuclear reactor physics; fusion technology; risk assessment. *Mailing Add:* Sch of Eng & Appl Sci Univ of Calif Los Angeles CA 90024

KASTENDIEK, JON EDWIN, b Santa Monica, Calif, Sept 15, 47. MARINE BENTHIC ECOLOGY. *Educ:* Univ Calif, Los Angeles, BA, 70, PhD(zool), 75. *Prof Exp:* ASST PROF ECOL, DEPT BIOL SCI, UNIV SOUTHERN CALIF, 76- *Mem:* Ecol Soc Am; Brit Ecol Soc; Am Soc Limnol & Oceanog; Physcol Soc Am; AAAS. *Res:* Role of competitive interactions in structuring marine algal communities; impact of thermal effluents on benthic communities; predator-prey relationships in subtidal marine invertebrate communities. *Mailing Add:* Dept Biol Sci Univ Southern Calif Los Angeles CA 90007

KASTENHOLZ, CLAUDE E(DWARD), b Milwaukee, Wis, Nov 27, 36; m 59; c 5. ELECTRICAL ENGINEERING. *Educ:* Marquette Univ, BEE, 58; Univ Southern Calif, MS, 60; Univ Wis, PhD(elec eng), 63; Pepperdine Univ, MBA, 70. *Prof Exp:* Mem tech staff, Hughes Aircraft Co, Calif, 58-60; res engr, Autonetics Div, N Am Aviation, Inc, 60-61; res asst circuit design, Univ Wis, 61-62; res specialist, Autonetics Div, N Am Rockwell Corp, 63-67; sr staff engr, 67-75, SR SCIENTIST, HUGHES AIRCRAFT CO, 75- *Mem:* Inst Elec & Electronics Engrs. *Res:* Sonar systems engineering; fire control system design; system test. *Mailing Add:* 16932 Nightingale Lane Yorba Linda CA 92686

KASTENS, KIM ANNE, b Menlo Park, Calif, May 19, 54. MARINE GEOLOGY, MARINE GEOPHYSICS. *Educ:* Yale Univ, BS, 75; Scripps Inst Oceanog, PhD(oceanog), 81. *Prof Exp:* RES ASSOC, LAMONT-DOHERTY GEOL OBSERV, COLUMBIA UNIV, 81- *Mem:* Am Geophys Union; Geol Soc Am; Sigma Xi. *Res:* Tectonic and sedimentological processes in the deep sea. *Mailing Add:* Lamont-Doherty Geol Observ Columbia Univ New York NY 10027

KASTENS, MERRITT LOUIS, b Chicago, Ill, Nov 12, 22; m 52; c 1. INDUSTRIAL CHEMISTRY. *Educ:* Roosevelt Univ, BS, 44. *Prof Exp:* Plant chemist, Int Harvester Co, 42-44; asst phys chemist, Armour Res Found, 44-45; assoc ed, Chem & Eng News, 46-52; asst to dir, Stanford Res Inst, 52-53, asst dir, 53-59; mgr mkt res, Union Carbide Int Co Div, Union Carbide Corp, 59-61, mgr proj planning & anal, 61-65; dir, Ctr Planning & Develop, Am Found Mgt Res, 66-69; consult mgt strategies, 69-77; mgr, Tech Dept, Montedison USA, 77-79; CONSULT MGT STRATEGIES, 79- *Concurrent Pos:* Active assoc, Ctr for the Future, 72-; dir, Am Sect, Fr Soc Chem Indust; ed & publ, Food Indust Futures, 72- *Honors & Awards:* Solar Pioneer, Int Solar Energy Soc. *Mem:* Am Chem Soc; Soc Chem Indust; French Soc Chem Indust; World Future Soc; NAm Soc Corp Planning. *Res:* Research administration; market research; strategic planning, technological forecasting; world food & energy interaction. *Mailing Add:* E Lake Rd RD1 Box 124 Hamilton NY 13346

KASTIN, ABBA J, b Cleveland, Ohio, Dec 24, 34. ENDOCRINOLOGY, NEUROSCIENCES. *Educ:* Harvard Col, AB, 56; Harvard Med Sch, MD, 60. *Hon Degrees:* Dr, Univ Nat Federico Villarreal, Lima, Peru, 80. *Prof Exp:* Clin assoc endocrinol, NIH, 62-64; spec fel, Sch Med, Tulane Univ, 64-65; clin investr med, Vet Admin Hosp, New Orleans, 65-68; assoc prof, 71-74, PROF MED, SCH MED, TULANE UNIV, 74-; CHIEF ENDOCRINOL, VET ADMIN HOSP, 68- *Concurrent Pos:* Vis physician, Charity Hosp New Orleans, 69-78, sr vis physician, 79-; mem med adv bd, Nat Pituitary Agency, 74-77; assoc mem grad fac, Dept Psychol, Univ New Orleans, 76-; mem res adv comt, Nat Asn Retarded Citizens, 78-79; consult, Food & Drug Admin, 79-80; ed-in-chief, Peptides, 80- *Honors & Awards:* Edward T Tyler Fertil Award, Int Fertil Soc, 75; Copernicus Medal, Poland, 79. *Mem:* Endocrine Soc; Am Physiol Soc; Soc Exp Biol & Med; Soc Neurosci; Int Soc Psychoneuroendocrinol. *Res:* Effects of naturally occurring peptides upon central nervous system; brain peptides; neuroendocrinology; hypothalamic hormones. *Mailing Add:* Vet Admin Med Ctr 1601 Perdido St New Orleans LA 70146

KASTING, ROBERT, b Edmonton, Alta, Aug 22, 23; m 47; c 4. BIOCHEMISTRY. *Educ:* Univ Alta, BSc, 46, MSc, 48; Univ Calif, PhD(comp biochem), 56. *Prof Exp:* BIOCHEMIST, ENTOM & CHEM SECT, RES STA, CAN DEPT AGR, 51- *Concurrent Pos:* Vis biochemist, Swed Inst Food Res, Goteborg, Sweden, 69-70. *Res:* Comparative biochemistry; biochemistry of growing wheat plants; biochemical resistance of plants to insects; nutrition and metabolism of amino acids for plant feeding insects. *Mailing Add:* Res Sta Can Dept Agr Lethbridge AB T1J 4C7 Can

KASTL, PETER ROBERT, b Alexandria, La, July 25, 49; m 74; c 2. OPHTHALMOLOGY, BIOCHEMISTRY. *Educ:* Centenary Col La, BS, 71; Tulane Univ, MD, 74, PhD(biochem), 78. *Prof Exp:* instr biochem, 75-81, instr ophthal, 77-81, ASST PROF BIOCHEM & OPHTHAL, TULANE UNIV, 81- *Concurrent Pos:* Fel, Nat Inst Gen Med Sci, 75-76; NIH res grant, 81-83. *Mem:* Sigma Xi; AMA; Southern Med Asn; Am Acad Ophthal. *Res:* Microsomal treatment of ingested toxins; pharmacologic prevention of cataracts; design of new types of ophthalmologic prosthetic devices; tear analysis. *Mailing Add:* Dept of Ophthal Tulane Med Ctr New Orleans LA 70112

KASTNER, MIRIAM, b Bratislava, Czech; US citizen. GEOLOGY. *Educ:* Hebrew Univ Jerusalem, Israel, BSc & MSc, 64; Harvard Univ, PhD(geol), 70. *Prof Exp:* Fel geol, Harvard Univ, 70-71, Univ Chicago, 71-72; asst prof, 72-77, ASSOC PROF GEOL, SCRIPPS INST OCEANOG, 77- *Concurrent Pos:* Assoc ed, J Sedimentary Petrology. *Honors & Awards:* Newcomb Cleveland Prize, AAAS. *Mem:* AAAS; Geochem Soc; Am Geophys Union; Electron Probe Anal Soc Am; Sigma Xi. *Res:* Origin, mineralogy and geochemistry of silicates and carbonates in marine and non-marine environments; stable isotopes for diagenesis; processes that cause metal enrichment in oceanic sediments; surface chemistry in diagenesis; hydrothermal deposits in the submarine environment. *Mailing Add:* SVH-A012 Scripps Inst of Oceanog La Jolla CA 92093

KASTNER, SIDNEY OSCAR, b Winnipeg, Man, Apr 20, 26; m 51; c 3. PHYSICS. *Educ:* McGill Univ, BSc, 50; Syracuse Univ, MS, 55, PhD(physics), 60. *Prof Exp:* Jr res officer, Nat Res Coun Can, 50-52; physicist, Gen Elec Res Lab, 55-57; PHYSICIST, GODDARD SPACE FLIGHT CTR, NASA, 59- *Mem:* AAAS; Am Phys Soc; NY Acad Sci. *Res:* Atomic physics and spectroscopy; solar physics and astrophysics. *Mailing Add:* Goddard Space Flight Ctr Code 682 Greenbelt MD 20770

KASTON, BENJAMIN JULIAN, b New York, NY, July 2, 06; m 30. BIOLOGY. *Educ:* NC State Col, BS, 30; Yale Univ, PhD(zool), 34. *Prof Exp:* Asst zool, NC State Col, 28-30, asst bot, 29-30; asst zool, Yale Univ, 30-33; asst, Conn Exp Sta, 34-38; prof biol, Brenau Col, 38-45; asst prof zool, Syracuse Univ, 45-46; assoc prof biol, Cent Conn State Col, 46-48, prof, 48-63; lectr, 64-71, prof, 71-73, EMER PROF ZOOL, SAN DIEGO STATE UNIV, 73-; EMER PROF BIOL, CENT CONN STATE COL, 63- *Mem:* AAAS; Am Soc Zoo; Am Micros Soc; Am Arachnological Soc. *Res:* Taxonomy of spiders; parasites of spiders; behavior in spiders. *Mailing Add:* Dept of Zool San Diego State Univ San Diego CA 92182

KASUBA, ROMUALDAS, US citizen. MECHANICAL ENGINEERING, APPLIED MECHANICS. *Educ:* Univ Ill, Urbana, BS, 54, MS, 57, PhD(mech eng), 62. *Prof Exp:* Res asst dynamics, mech eng dept, Univ Ill, Urbana, 58-62; head stress & dynamics group power systs div, TRW Inc, Ohio, 62-68; from assoc prof to prof mech eng, 68-78, CHAIRPERSON DEPT MECH ENG, CLEVELAND STATE UNIV, 78-, PROF MECH ENG, 81- *Concurrent Pos:* Indust consult; lectr, US & Can; consult, Indust Fasteners Inst, 70-75 & Am Nat Standards Inst, 71-74. *Mem:* Am Soc Mech Engrs. *Res:* Vibration and noise studies in industrial machines; dynamic loads in geared systems; development of optimum threaded fastener system; dynamic simulation of geared systems; dynamic simulation of machine tool structures and drives; application of finite element techniques. *Mailing Add:* Dept Mech Eng Cleveland State Univ Cleveland OH 44115

KASUBICK, ROBERT VALENTINE, organic chemistry, see previous edition

KASUPSKI, GEORGE JOSEPH, b Boston, Mass, July 26, 46; m 79; c 1. DIAGNOSTIC VIROLOGY, MOLECULAR VIROLOGY. *Educ:* McGill Univ, BSc, 69, PhD(molecular biol), 75. *Prof Exp:* Lectr genetics, Dept Biol, McGill Univ & fel virol, Dept Microbiol, Royal Victoria Hosp, 75-78; STAFF MICROBIOLOGIST VIROL, WELLESLEY HOSP, UNIV TORONTO, 78- *Concurrent Pos:* Lectr, Dept Med Microbiol, Univ Toronto, 78-81, asst prof, 81; adv, Toronto Inst Med Technol, 81, Wellesley Hosp Res Inst, 81. *Mem:* Am Soc Microbiol; Pan Am Group Rapid Viral Diag; NY Acad Sci. *Res:* Pathogenesis and diagnosis of viral infections of the lower respiratory tract in immunocompromised adults. *Mailing Add:* Dept Microbiol Wellesley Hosp 160 Wellesley St E Toronto ON M4Y 1J3 Can

KASVINSKY, PETER JOHN, b Bridgeport, Conn, Dec 7, 42; m 74. BIOCHEMISTRY, ENZYMOLOGY. *Educ:* Bucknell Univ, BSc, 64; Univ Vt, PhD(biochem), 70. *Prof Exp:* Biochemist, US Army Aeromed Res Lab, 69-72; instr biochem, Sch Med, Wayne State Univ, 72-74; sr res assoc biochem, Univ Alta, 74-79; asst, Dept Biochem, 79; ASST PROF BIOCHEM, SCH MED, MARSHALL UNIV, 79- *Concurrent Pos:* Radiol control officer, US Army Aeromed Res Lab, 70-72; adj asst prof biomed sci, WVa Univ, 80- *Mem:* Am Chem Soc; AAAS; Can Biochem Soc; NY Acad Sci; Sigma Xi. *Res:* Enzymology of covalent modification of proteins, enzyme regulation, structure function and allosteric control, especially as applied to the regulation of enzymes of glycogen metabolism. *Mailing Add:* Dept Biochem Sch Med Marshall Univ Huntington WV 25701

KATAN, THEODORE, b San Francisco, Calif, June 21, 28. ELECTROCHEMICAL SYSTEMS, PHYSICAL CHEMISTRY. *Educ:* Univ Calif, Berkeley, BS, 50; Stanford Univ, PhD(chem), 60. *Prof Exp:* Prod engr, Kaiser Aircraft Co, Mich, 51-53; sr chemist, Glenn L Martin Co, Md, 53-55; staff scientist physical chem, 60-80, SR STAFF SCIENTIST PHYS CHEM & MEM STAFF, RES LAB, LOCKHEED MISSLES & SPACE CO, INC, 80- *Mem:* Am Chem Soc; Electrochem Soc; Int Soc Electrochem. *Res:* Electrochemistry at porous electrodes; batteries, fuel cells, electrochemical systems and corrosion problems; porous electrodes. *Mailing Add:* Lockheed Missiles & Space Co Inc Dept 52-35 3251 Hanover St Palo Alto CA 94304

KATAYAMA, DANIEL HIDEO, b Honolulu, Hawaii, Sept 26, 39; m 63. MOLECULAR SPECTROSCOPY. *Educ:* Univ Hawaii, BS, 62, MS, 64; Tufts Univ, PhD(physics), 70. *Prof Exp:* Physicist aeronomy, Air Force Cambridge Res Lab, 63-66; physicist solid state physics, Gillette Co, 70-71; PHYSICIST, AIR FORCE GEOPHYS LAB, 71- *Concurrent Pos:* Vis scientist, Bell Lab, Murray Hill, NJ, 78-79 & Mass Inst Tech, Cambridge, 80-81. *Mem:* AAAS; Am Phys Soc; Optical Soc Am. *Res:* Laser induced fluorescence of molecules and ions; absorption-photoionization cross sections and spectroscopy of atmospheric gases in vacuum ultraviolet; phonon scattering in solids; elastic constants of materials. *Mailing Add:* Air Force Cambridge Res Labs (LKO) L G Hanscom Field Bedford MA 01730

KATCHEN, BERNARD, b New York, NY, May 20, 28; m 51; c 2. BIOCHEMISTRY. *Educ:* City Col New York BS, 49; Ohio State Univ, MSc, 51; NY Univ, PhD(biochem), 56. *Prof Exp:* Chemist, Clairol Inc, 54-56; sr chemist, Nat Cash Register, 56-61; PRIN SCIENTIST, SCHERING CORP, 62- *Mem:* AAAS; Am Chem Soc; NY Acad Sci. *Res:* Pharmacokinetics; drug metabolism; biopharmaceutics. *Mailing Add:* Schering Corp 86 Orange St Bloomfield NJ 07003

KATCHER, DAVID ABRAHAM, b New York, NY, Apr 28, 15; m 47; c 2. PHYSICS, OPERATIONS RESEARCH. *Educ:* Univ Wis, BA, 36. *Prof Exp:* Tech ed, Naval Ord Lab, 41-43; founding ed, Physics Today, Am Inst Physics, 47-51; assoc ed, Opers Res Off, 51-56; ed, Weapons Systs Eval Group, Inst Defense Anal, 56-60, exec secy, Jason Div, 60-66; mem sr staff, Opers Res Sect, Arthur D Little, Inc, Mass, 66-72; sr staff mem, Secretariat of Nat Adv Comt Oceans & Atmospheres, Nat Oceanic & Atmospheric Admin, 72-76; sr policy analyst, Off Sci & Technol Policy, Exec Off of the Pres, 76-77; spec asst to under secy state for security assistance, Sci & Technol, Dept State, 77-80; CONSULT, 80- *Mem:* Opers Res Soc Am (treas, 58-60); AAAS. *Mailing Add:* 5608 Warwick Pl Chevy Chase MD 20015

KATCHMAN, ARTHUR, b New York, NY, Oct 4, 24; m 60; c 2. ORGANIC CHEMISTRY. *Educ:* NY Univ, BA, 49; Polytech Inst Brooklyn, PhD(chem), 55. *Prof Exp:* Asst instr biochem, NY Med Co, 49-50, instr, 50-52, assoc, 52-54; res chemist, Hooker Chem Co, 55-56; res assoc, Polytech Inst Brooklyn, 57-58; res assoc, Gen Elec Res Lab, 59-62, mgr mat physics & chem, Capacitor Dept, 63-66, mgr polymer chem, Chem Develop Oper, 66-

68, mgr advan res, Plastics Dept, 68-70, mgr prod develop, Plastics Dept, 70-75, mgr chem develop, 76-79, mgr opers control & planning, 80-81, MGR DEPT QUALITY ASSURANCE, GEN ELEC CO, 81- *Concurrent Pos:* Hooker fel, 57-58. *Mem:* Am Chem Soc. *Res:* Mechanism and kinetics of polymerization polymer structure and properties; stereospecific polymerization. *Mailing Add:* Plastics Dept Gen Elec Co Noryl Ave Selkirk NY 12158

KATCOFF, SEYMOUR, b Chicago, Ill, Aug 19, 18; m 51; c 2. NUCLEAR CHEMISTRY, RADIOCHEMISTRY. *Educ:* Univ Chicago, BS, 40, PhD(phys chem), 44. *Prof Exp:* Assoc chemist, Metall Lab, Univ Chicago, 43-45; staff mem, Los Alamos Sci Lab, 45-48; SR CHEMIST, BROOKHAVEN NAT LAB, 48- *Concurrent Pos:* Fel, Weizmann Inst Sci, 58-59; Guggenheim fel, 67-68. *Mem:* AAAS; Am Chem Soc; Am Phys Soc. *Res:* High-energy nuclear reactions; nuclear track detectors; cross section measurements; neutron-rich isotope studies; nuclear spectroscopy. *Mailing Add:* Brookhaven Nat Lab Upton NY 11973

KATEKARU, JAMES, b Kauai, Hawaii, June 10, 35; m 64; c 2. ANALYTICAL CHEMISTRY, NUCLEAR CHEMISTRY. *Educ:* Univ Ore, BS, 56; Univ Ariz, MS, 61; Univ Cincinnati, PhD(chem), 65. *Prof Exp:* Anal chemist, Food & Drug Admin, 62-63; res chemist, Rocketdyne Div, NAm Rockwell, 65-66; index ed, Chem Abstr Serv, 66-67; res mgr, Naval Radiol Defense Lab, 67-69; from asst prof to assoc prof, 69-80, PROF CHEM, CALIF POLYTECH STATE UNIV, 80- *Concurrent Pos:* Res consult, Trapelo West Div, Lab for Electronics, 70-71. *Mem:* Am Chem Soc; Am Inst Physics. *Res:* Solvent extraction; polarography; rocket exhaust product analysis; catalysis of non-hypergollic propellant combinations; nuclear fallout phenomenology; detection and diagnosis of nuclear weapons. *Mailing Add:* Dept of Chem Calif Polytech State Univ San Luis Obispo CA 93401

KATELL, SIDNEY, b New York, NY, Feb 2, 15; m 48; c 2. CHEMICAL ENGINEERING. *Educ:* NY Univ, BChE, 41. *Prof Exp:* Design engr, US Naval Shipyard, Pa, 41-46; design engr, Dept Chem Eng, Tenn Valley Authority, 46-48; mech engr design, US Bur Mines, Mo, 48-53; sr proj engr pilot plant design, Westinghouse Elec Corp, Pa, 53-54; chief process econ eval, US Bur Mines, 54-67, chief process eval group, 67-81; res prof, Col Mineral & Energy Resources, WVa Univ, 76-81; RETIRED. *Concurrent Pos:* Vis assoc prof, WVa Univ, 69-76. *Mem:* Am Gas Asn; Am Chem Soc; Am Asn Cost Engrs (pres, 70-71); Am Inst Chem Engrs. *Res:* Evaluation of research programs through economic analysis. *Mailing Add:* 1464 Dogwood Ave Morgantown WV 26506

KATER, STANLEY B, b Cleveland, Ohio, June 12, 43; m 74; c 1. NEUROPHYSIOLOGY. *Educ:* Case Western Reserve Univ, BA, 65; Univ Va, PhD(biol), 68. *Prof Exp:* NIH fel biol, Univ Ore, 68-69; from asst prof to assoc prof, 69-79, PROF ZOOL, UNIV IOWA, 79- *Mem:* AAAS; Am Soc Zool; Soc Neurosci; NY Acad Sci; Midwest Neurobiol Soc. *Res:* Integrative mechanisms underlying behavior; developmental neurobiology; stimulus-secretion coupling. *Mailing Add:* Dept of Zool Univ of Iowa Iowa City IA 52242

KATES, JOSEF, b Vienna, Austria, May 5, 21; nat Can; m 44; c 3. SCIENCE POLICY, SYSTEMS SCIENCE. *Educ:* Univ Toronto, BA, 48, MA, 49, PhD(physics), 51. *Hon Degrees:* LLD, Concordia Univ, Can, 81. *Prof Exp:* Supvr, Imp Optical Co, 42-44; proj engr, Rogers Electronic Tubes, 44-48; res engr, Univ Toronto, 48-54; pres, KCS Ltd & Traffic Res Corp, 54-66; dep managing partner, Kates, Peat, Marwick & Co, 67-68, assoc, 69-73; PRES, JOSEF KATES ASSOCS, INC, 74- *Concurrent Pos:* Pres, Setak Comput Servs Co, 67-; pres, Teleride Corp, 78- mem, Sci Coun Can, 68-74, chmn, 75-78; consult, US AEC. *Mem:* Inst Mgt Sci; Can Oper Res Soc; fel Eng Inst Can; Sci, Eng & Technol Community Can. *Res:* Application of scientific methods, especially computers and operations research to industrial, scientific and engineering problems. *Mailing Add:* 17 Fifeshire Rd Willowdale ON M2L 2G4 Can

KATES, JOSEPH R, b Udine, Italy, Nov 14, 39; US citizen; m 66. BIOCHEMISTRY. *Educ:* Univ Pa, AB, 62; Princeton Univ, PhD(biochem), 66. *Prof Exp:* Res assoc biochem, Princeton Univ, 65-66, NIH fel virol, 66-67; from asst prof to assoc prof biochem, Univ Colo, Boulder, 67-72; prof microbiol & chmn cellular biol, State Univ NY Stony Brook, 72-79; MEM STAFF & CHMN CELLULAR BIOL, SCRIPPS CLIN & RES FOUND, LA JOLLA, CALIF, 79- *Concurrent Pos:* NSF equip grant, 66-69; NIH res grant, 68-, virol study sect, 72- *Honors & Awards:* Eli Lilly Award, 74. *Mem:* Am Soc Biol Chemists; Am Soc Microbiol. *Res:* Animal virology; biochemistry of the cellular cycle, cell differentiation and meiotic deoxyribonucleic acid replication; regulation of viral gene expression in vaccinia; structural and functional studies of viral chromosomal complexes. *Mailing Add:* Cellular Biol Dept Scripps Clin La Jolla CA 92037

KATES, KENNETH CASPER, SR, b Millville, NJ, Apr 29, 10; m; c 3. PARASITOLOGY. *Educ:* Columbia Univ, AB, 32; Duke Univ, MA, 34, PhD(zool), 37. *Prof Exp:* Asst zool, Duke Univ, 32-34; instr biol, Williamsport-Dickinson Jr Col, 35-38; from jr parasitologist to sr parasitologist, USDA, 38-60; prin parasitologist, Bur Vet Med, Food & Drug Admin, US Dept Health, Educ & Welfare, 60-66; prin res parasitologist, Animal Parasitol Inst, USDA, 66-68, zoologist, 68-75; RETIRED. *Concurrent Pos:* Prof lectr, George Washington Univ, 46-78; lectr, Univ Md, 50, 60 & 62. *Mem:* Am Soc Parasitol; Conf Res Workers Animal Dis; Am Soc Vet Parasitol; World Asn Advan Vet Parasitol. *Res:* Parasites of domestic animals. *Mailing Add:* 2601 Imperial Court Apple Greene Dunkirk MD 20754

KATES, MORRIS, b Galati, Roumania, Sept 15, 23; Can citizen; m 57. LIPID CHEMISTRY. *Educ:* Univ Toronto, BA, 45, MA, 46, PhD(biochem), 48. *Prof Exp:* Asst, Banting & Best Med Res, 48-49; Nat Res Labs fel, Nat Res Coun Can, 49-51, asst res officer, Div Appl Biol, 51-55, assoc res officer, 55-

61, sr res officer, 61-69; PROF BIOCHEM, UNIV OTTAWA, 69-, VICE-DEAN RES, 78- *Concurrent Pos:* Co-ed, Can J Biochem, 74-; staff res lectr, Univ Ottawa, 81. *Mem:* Am Chem Soc; Am Soc Biol Chem; Can Biochem Soc; Brit Biochem Soc; Royal Soc Can. *Res:* Synthesis of lecithins and related compounds; structure of the alkaloid, gelsemine; plant lecithinases and plant phospholipids; glycerides; lipases; bacterial lipids; phospholipid desaturases; biosynthesis of phospholipids. *Mailing Add:* Dept of Biochem Univ of Ottawa Ottawa ON K1N 9B4 Can

KATHAN, RALPH HERMAN, b Chicago, Ill, Feb 1, 29; m 50, 76; c 2. CLINICAL BIOCHEMISTRY. *Educ:* Univ Chicago, SB, 49; Univ Ill, MS, 59, PhD(biochem), 61. *Prof Exp:* Res asst biol chem, Univ Chicago, 48-49; biochemist res labs, Kraft Foods Div, Nat Dairy Prod Corp, 49-51; tech serv, Am Can Co, 56-57; res asst, 57-61, res assoc, 61-62, asst prof, 62-68, ASSOC PROF BIOL CHEM, COL MED, UNIV ILL, 68-; CHMN DIV BIOCHEM, COOK COUNTY HOSP, 71- *Concurrent Pos:* Consult comn influenza, Armed Forces Epidemiol Bd, 64-68. *Mem:* Nat Acad Clin Biochemists; Soc Complex Carbohydrates; Soc Exp Biol & Med; Am Soc Biol Chem; Am Asn Clin Chem. *Res:* Protein structure; mechanisms of viral infection; bacterial metabolism; carbohydrate absorption; plasma expanders; diagnostic biochemistry. *Mailing Add:* Div of Biochem Cook County Hosp 627 S Wood St Chicago IL 60612

KATHOLI, CHARLES ROBINSON, b Charleston, WVa, Jan 2, 41; m 80; c 1. BIOMATHEMATICS. *Educ:* Lehigh Univ, BA, 63; Adelphi Univ, MS, 65, PhD(math, appl anal), 70. *Prof Exp:* Asst, Adelphi Univ, 64-66; instr math, Suffolk County Community Col, 66-67; instr, Adelphi Univ, 67-70; asst prof biomath, 70-77, asst prof info sci, 73-76, ASSOC PROF BIOMATH, UNIV ALA, BIRMINGHAM, 77- *Mem:* AAAS; Soc Indust & Appl Math; NY Acad Sci; Asn Comput Mach; Acoust Soc Am. *Res:* Mathematical modelling and computer simulations in the field of cardiovascular research; computational methods for special functions. *Mailing Add:* Dept Biomath Univ Ala Univ Sta Birmingham AL 35294

KATHREN, RONALD LAURENCE, b Windsor, Ont, June 6, 37; US citizen; m 64; c 2. HEALTH PHYSICS, HISTORY OF SCIENCE. *Educ:* Univ Calif, Los Angeles, BS, 57; Univ Pittsburgh, MS, 62; Am Bd Health Physics, dipl, 66; Am Acad Environ Eng, dipl, 78. *Prof Exp:* Supvr health physicist, Mare Island Naval Shipyard, US Navy, 59-61; health physicist, Lawrence Radiation Lab, Univ Calif, 62-67; sect mgr & sr res scientist radiation dosimetry, Pac Northwest Div, Battelle Mem Inst, 67-72; corp health physicist, Portland Gen Elec Co, 72-78; STAFF SCIENTIST, PAC NORTHWEST DIV, BATTELLE MEM INST, 78- *Concurrent Pos:* Abstractor, Chem Abstr, 62-78; lectr, Joint Ctr Grad Study, Univ Wash, 71-72, affil assoc prof, 78-, coordr radiol sci, 80-; adj prof, Ore State Div Continuing Educ, 72-77; health physicist, Reed Col, 73-78; mem traineeship adv comt, US Atomic Energy Comn, 73-74; mem, Nat Adv Comt Nuclear Technicians, Tech Educ Res Ctr, 75-81; mem, Ore Radiation Adv Comt, 77-78; ed, Health Physics J, Health Physics Soc, 77-81 ; mem panel examr, Am Bd Health Physics, 77-; consult, US Nuclear Regulatory Comn, 78, US Adv Comt, 78; mem, Int Atomic Energy Agency Tech Expert, 77. *Honors & Awards:* Elda E Anderson Award, Health Physics Soc, 77. *Mem:* Health Physics Soc; Am Asn Physicists Med; AAAS; Am Nuclear Soc; Nat Soc Prof Engrs. *Res:* Applied health physics; radiological calibration and standardization; environmental radioactivity; history of radiation protection and physics; radiation monitoring instrumentation; education and training of nuclear technicians. *Mailing Add:* 137 Spring Rd PO Box 999 Richland WA 99352

KATNER, ALLEN SAMUEL, b London, Eng, Dec 26, 38; m 63; c 3. ORGANIC CHEMISTRY. *Educ:* Univ Nottingham, BSc, 61, PhD(org chem), 64. *Prof Exp:* Res assoc, Stanford Univ, 64-66; SR ORG CHEMIST, ELI LILLY & CO, 66- *Mem:* The Chem Soc; Am Chem Soc. *Res:* Heterocyclic chemistry; medicinal chemistry. *Mailing Add:* Res Labs Eli Lilly & Co 307 E McCarty St Indianapolis IN 46285

KATO, KAREN FRIEDMAN, molecular biology, see previous edition

KATO, TOSIO, b Kanuma, Japan, Aug 25, 17; m 44. MATHEMATICS. *Educ:* Univ Tokyo, BS, 41, DSc(math physics), 51. *Prof Exp:* From asst to prof physics, Univ Tokyo, 43-62; PROF MATH, UNIV CALIF, BERKELEY, 62- *Honors & Awards:* Asahi Award, 60; Norbert Wiemer Prize, 80. *Mem:* Am Math Soc; Math Soc Japan. *Res:* Functional analysis and applications; mathematical physics. *Mailing Add:* Dept of Math Univ of Calif Berkeley CA 94720

KATO, WALTER YONEO, b Chicago, Ill, Aug 19, 24; m 53. REACTOR SAFETY. *Educ:* Haverford Col, BS, 46; Univ Ill, MS, 49; Pa State Col, PhD(physics), 54. *Prof Exp:* Res assoc hydrodyn, Ord Res Lab, Sch Eng, Pa State Col, 49-52; jr res assoc neutron physics, Brookhaven Nat Lab, 52-53; asst physicist nuclear & reactor physics, Argonne Nat Lab, 53; assoc physicist, Reactor Eng Div, 53-63, assoc physicist, Reactor Physics Div, 63-68, sr physicist, 68-75, sr physicist, Appl Physics Div, 69-75, head fast reactor exps sect, 63-70, assoc chmn & sr nuclear engr, 75-80, DEP CHMN, DEPT NUCLEAR ENERGY, BROOKHAVEN NAT LAB, 80- *Concurrent Pos:* Fulbright res scholar, Japan Atomic Energy Res Inst & Univ Tokyo, 58-59; vis prof nuclear eng, Univ Mich, 74-75; consult, Off Nuclear Regulatory Res, Nuclear Regulatory Comn, 74- *Honors & Awards:* Distinguished Appointment Award, Argonne Univ Asn, 74. *Mem:* AAAS; Am Phys Soc; Am Nuclear Soc. *Res:* Hydrodynamics; cavitation studies; neutron resonance phenomenon; neutron total cross section measurements; neutron inelastic scattering studies; reactor physics; critical assembly experiments; fast reactor physics and safety; reactor safety research. *Mailing Add:* Brookhaven Nat Lab Upton NY 11973

KATOCS, ANDREW STEPHEN, JR, b Passaic, NJ, Oct 7, 44; m 67; c 2. PHARMACOLOGY, ULTRASOUND. *Educ:* Rutgers Univ, BPh & BS, 67; Marquette Univ, PhD(pharmacol), 72. *Prof Exp:* Nat Heart & Lung Inst fel & instr pharmacol, Sch Med, Ind Univ, 72-73; SR RES PHARMACOLOGIST ATHEROSCLEROSIS, LEDERLE LABS, AM CYANAMID CO, 73- *Mem:* Am Heart Asn; Am Soc Pharmacol & Exp Therapeut. *Res:* Development of animal models of atherosclerosis; evaluation of compounds for anti-atherosclerotic activity; real-time ultrasonic imaging of arterial vasculature. *Mailing Add:* Lederle Labs Middletown Rd Pearl River NY 10965

KATOH, ARTHUR, b Honolulu, Hawaii, Aug 24, 33; m 63; c 1. DEVELOPMENTAL BIOLOGY. *Educ:* Syracuse Univ, AB, 54; Univ Ill, MS, 56, PhD(zool), 60. *Prof Exp:* NSF fel, 60-61; res assoc zool, Univ Ill, 61-62; asst prof biol, Univ Toledo, 62-63; res assoc, Argonne Nat Lab, 63-66; dir oncol lab, Dept Radiother, 66-73, DIR, DIV NUCLEAR PATH & ONCOL, MERCY HOSP, 73- *Mem:* Soc Develop Biol; NY Acad Sci; Am Soc Cell Biol. *Res:* Developmental biology; cellular differentiation in amphibian and chick embryos; human tumor stem cell cloning. *Mailing Add:* Div Nuclear Path & Oncol Mercy Hosp Pittsburgh PA 15219

KATON, JOHN EDWARD, b Toledo, Ohio, Jan 5, 29; m 55; c 3. PHYSICAL CHEMISTRY. *Educ:* Bowling Green State Univ, BA, 51; Kans State Univ, MS, 55; Univ Md, PhD(chem), 58. *Prof Exp:* Sr res chemist, Monsanto Chem Co, 58-61, res group leader, Monsanto Res Corp, Ohio, 61-68; assoc prof, 68-72, PROF CHEM, MIAMI UNIV, 72- *Concurrent Pos:* Consult, US Air Force, 60-61 & 68-69; consult, NIH, 70; bd dirs, Coblentz Soc, 78-82. *Mem:* Am Chem Soc; Optical Soc Am; Soc Appl Spectros; Coblentz Soc; Soc Appl Spectros (pres, 76). *Res:* Molecular spectroscopy and structure; chemical physics; organic chemistry; hydrogen bonding; crystal structures. *Mailing Add:* Dept Chem Miami Univ Oxford OH 45056

KATONA, PETER GEZA, b Budapest, Hungary, June 25, 37; US citizen; m 66; c 2. ELECTRICAL & BIOMEDICAL ENGINEERING. *Educ:* Univ Mich, BS, 60; Mass Inst Technol, SM, 62, ScD(elec eng), 65. *Prof Exp:* From instr to asst prof elec eng, Mass Inst Technol, 63-69; assoc prof biomed eng, 69-78, PROF BIOMED ENG, CASE WESTERN RESERVE UNIV, 78-, CHMN, DEPT BIOMED ENG, 80- *Concurrent Pos:* Ford res fel, 65-67; consult, Biosysts, Inc, Mass, 65-67 & Mass Gen Hosp, Boston, 66-69; Fogarty sr int fel, 78-79. *Mem:* AAAS; Inst Elec & Electronics Engrs; Biomed Engrs Soc; Physiol Soc; Am Soc Eng Educ. *Res:* Neural control of the cardiovascular system; interaction of cardisvascular and respiratory control mechanisms; use of computers to automate laboratories and health-care procedures; automated control of physiological systems; noninvasive diagnostic techniques. *Mailing Add:* Dept of Biomed Eng Case Western Reserve Univ Cleveland OH 44106

KATSAMPES, CHRIS PETER, b Rochester, NY, Aug 23, 10; m 45; c 3. PEDIATRICS. *Educ:* Cornell Univ, BS, 31; Univ Rochester, MD, 36; Am Bd Pediat, dipl, 44. *Prof Exp:* From instr to asst prof pediat, Univ Rochester, 39-60; asst dir clin res, Warner-Lambert Res Inst, 60-72; from asst clin prof to assoc clin prof, Col Physicians & Surgeons, Columbia Univ, 61-75; dir clin invest, 72-75, CONSULT, WARNER-CHILCOTT MED DEPT, 75- *Mem:* Soc Pediat Res; Am Pediat Soc; Am Acad Pediat; Sigma Xi. *Res:* Bacteriology and serology in infectious diseases; giardiasis; rheumatic fever; vitamin A in infections; antibacterial agents; new drugs; bronchodilators. *Mailing Add:* 48 Holly Dr Short Hills NJ 07078

KATSANIS, D(AVID) J(OHN), b Philadelphia, Pa, Sept 28, 26; m 48; c 3. PHYSICS, PRODUCTION OPERATIONS MANAGEMENT. *Educ:* Temple Univ, BA, 52, MA, 54, PhD, 62, George Washington Univ, MEng, 80. *Prof Exp:* Physicist fluid dynamics, Naval Air Mat Ctr, 52-54; physicist ballistics, Frankford Arsenal, 54-57, chief, gas mech sect, 57-58, theoret ballistics sect, 58-59, systs ballistics sect, 59-63, LASH Proj, 63-65, advan concepts br, 65-66 & spec prods lab, 66-68, chief physicist, laser safety team, 68-69; chief physicist, US Army Small Arms Systs Agency, 69-73, chief, suppressive shielding, Edgewood Arsenal, 73-77, chief mech process, Chem Systs Lab, US Army Small Arms Systs Agency, Aberdeen Proving Ground, 77-81; PHYSICIST & CHIEF PRODUCIBILITY ENG BR, T&E INT, INC, BEL-AIR, 81- *Mem:* Am Phys Soc; Sigma Xi; Am Ord Asn; assoc fel Am Inst Aeronaut & Astronaut. *Res:* Weapon systems analysis; fluid dynamics; mechanics; thermodynamics; design of experiments; production technology. *Mailing Add:* Route 1 Box 780 Pylesville MD 21132

KATSANIS, ELEFTHERIOS P, b Mytilene, Greece, Sept 28, 44; US citizen; div; c 1. COLLOID CHEMISTRY, SURFACE CHEMISTRY. *Educ:* Lehigh Univ, BS, 67, MS, 70; Clarkson Col Tech, PhD, 81. *Prof Exp:* SR CHEMIST, PHILADELPHIA QUARTZ CO, 75- *Mem:* Am Chem Soc; Sigma Xi; Soc Petrol Engrs. *Res:* Preparation of hydrous metal oxide sols via precipitation techniques; zeolites; stabilization of colloidal dispersions and their application to practical systems; enhanced oil recovery; water chemistry. *Mailing Add:* PQ Corp Res & Develop Ctr PO Box 258 Lafayette Hill PA 19444

KATSAROS, CONSTANTINE, b Chicago, Ill, Mar 16, 26; m 50; c 2. PESTICIDE CHEMISTRY. *Educ:* Ill Inst Technol, BS, 49; Northwestern Univ, PhD(chem), 53. *Prof Exp:* Res chemist org res, Ringwood Chem Corp, 53-58; res supvr agr chem, Morton Chem Co, 58-66, dir agr chem res, 66-69; TECH V PRES, NOR-AM AGR PROD, INC, 69- *Mem:* Am Chem Soc; Sigma Xi. *Res:* Partial synthesis of steroids; aromatic hydrocarbon synthesis; agricultural chemicals and pesticides. *Mailing Add:* 4608 Wild Cherry Rd Crystal Lake IL 60014

KATSAROS, KRISTINA, b Gothenburg, Sweden, July 24, 38; m 59; c 2. ATMOSPHERIC PHYSICS. *Educ:* Univ Wash, BS, 60, PhD(atmospheric sci), 69. *Prof Exp:* Res asst atmospheric sci, 60 & 67-68, res assoc, 69-74, res asst prof, 74-77, RES ASSOC PROF ATMOSPHERIC SCI, UNIV WASH, 77- *Mem:* Am Geophys Union; Am Meteorol Soc; AAAS; Swed Geophys Soc. *Res:* Infrared emission from earth surfaces; turbulent fluxes; free convection; air-sea interactions. *Mailing Add:* Dept of Atmospheric Sci AK-40 Univ of Wash Seattle WA 98195

KATSH, SEYMOUR, b New York, NY, Jan 13, 18; m 46; c 3. BIOLOGY. *Educ:* NY Univ, BA, 44, MS, 48, PhD, 50. *Prof Exp:* Instr zool & physiol, Univ Mass, 49-50; vis assoc biologist, Brookhaven Nat Lab, 50-51; instr zool & physiol, Univ Mass, 51-52; res fel physiol & biochem, Calif Inst Technol, 52-55; researcher, Carnegie Inst, 55-58; from asst prof to assoc prof, 58-65, actg chmn dept, 64-67, PROF PHARMACOL, MED CTR, UNIV COLO, DENVER, 65-, ASSOC DEAN GRAD & RES AFFAIRS, 69- *Mem:* AAAS; Endocrine Soc; Am Soc Zool; Soc Exp Biol & Med; Am Physiol Soc. *Res:* Transplantation; endocrinology; pharmacology; immunology; reproduction. *Mailing Add:* Dept of Pharmacol Med Ctr Univ of Colo 4200 E Ninth Ave Denver CO 80262

KATSOYANNIS, PANAYOTIS G, b Greece, Jan 7, 24; nat US; m 55; c 2. BIOCHEMISTRY. *Educ:* Nat Univ Athens, MS, 48, PhD(chem), 52. *Prof Exp:* Res assoc, Med Col, Cornell Univ, 52-56, asst prof biochem, 56-58; assoc res prof, Sch Med, Univ Pittsburgh, 58-64; head div biochem, Med Res Ctr, Brookhaven Nat Lab, 64-68; PROF BIOCHEM & CHMN DEPT, MT SINAI SCH MED, 68- *Mem:* Am Chem Soc; Am Soc Biol Chem; NY Acad Sci; Royal Soc Chem; Brit Biochem Soc. *Res:* Biologically active polypeptides; isolation, characterization and synthesis; insulin synthesis. *Mailing Add:* Dept Biochem Mt Sinai Sch of Med New York NY 10029

KATSUMOTO, KIYOSHI, b Oakland, Calif, May 4, 36; m 68; c 2. CHEMISTRY. *Educ:* San Jose State Col, BS, 64; Univ Calif, Berkeley, PhD(chem), 68. *Prof Exp:* From res chemist to sr res chemist, 67-75, SR RES ASSOC, CHEVRON RES CO, 75- *Mem:* Am Chem Soc. *Res:* Reaction mechanisms of cyclopropane ring openings; heterogeneous catalytic oxidations of hydrocarbons. *Mailing Add:* 2615 Brooks Ave El Cerrito CA 94530

KATTAMIS, THEODOULOS ZENON, b Kythrea, Cyprus, May 7, 35; US citizen. PHYSICS, METALLURGY. *Educ:* Univ Liege, Mining Engr, 60, Geol Engr, 61, Metall Engr, 62; Mass Inst Technol, MS, 63, ScD(metall), 65. *Prof Exp:* Res assoc metall, Mass Inst Technol, 65-69; from asst prof to assoc prof, 69-75, PROF METALL, UNIV CONN, 75- *Concurrent Pos:* Grants, NASA, 72-74, NSF, 73-76 & Air Force Off Sci Res, 77- *Mem:* Am Soc Metals; Metall Soc; Am Foundrymen's Soc; Royal Belg Soc Eng & Indust. *Res:* Solidification and properties of materials, eutectics, composite materials, joining, powder metallurgy, vapor deposition, single crystal growth and materials processing; microstructures and their control. *Mailing Add:* Dept of Metall Univ of Conn Storrs CT 06268

KATTAN, ABRAHAM, b Baghdad, Iraq, Sept 21, 29; US citizen; m 59; c 2. ENGINEERING, OPERATIONS RESEARCH. *Educ:* Israel Inst Technol, BSc, 56, dipl eng, 58, MSc, 61; Case Western Reserve Univ, PhD(eng), 67. *Prof Exp:* Lab technician, Consol Refineries, Israel, 51-52; plant engr, Kadar Pottery Works, Israel, 56; res engr, Scientific, 56-62; sr engr, Shell Chem Co, 66-70, res engr, Shell Develop Co, 70-73; gen mgr trop textile enterprises, Fla, 73-76; CONSULT, 76- *Concurrent Pos:* Lectr, City Univ New York, 68-70. *Mem:* Am Chem Soc; Am Inst Chem Engrs. *Res:* Mixing and modeling of chemical reactors; statistical design and analysis; process analysis, development and design; venture analysis; resource management. *Mailing Add:* 125 N Oakhurst Beverly Hills CA 90210

KATTAN, AHMED A, b Cairo, Egypt, Mar 21, 25; nat US; m 51; c 3. HORTICULTURE, FOOD SCIENCE. *Educ:* Cairo Univ, BSc, 45; Univ Md, MS, 50, PhD(hort), 52. *Prof Exp:* Asst, Cairo Univ, 46-48, lectr, 53-54; asst veg crops, Univ Md, 51-52, res assoc, 52-53, asst prof, 54-55; from asst prof to assoc prof, 55-62, PROF HORT FOOD SCI, UNIV ARK, FAYETTEVILLE, 62-, HEAD DEPT, 68- *Honors & Awards:* Woodbury Award, Am Soc Hort Sci, 59; Gourley Award, 79. *Mem:* Fel Am Soc Hort Sci; Inst Food Technol. *Res:* Pre- and post-harvest physiology of horticultural crops; methods of quality evaluation of raw and processed fruits and vegetables; methods of handling and mechanical harvesting of fruits and vegetables. *Mailing Add:* Dept of Hort Food Sci Univ of Ark Route 11 Fayetteville AR 72701

KATTAWAR, GEORGE W, b Beaumont, Tex, Aug 10, 37; m 61; c 3. PLANETARY ATMOSPHERES, OCEAN OPTICS. *Educ:* Lamar State Col, BS, 59; Tex A&M Univ, MS, 61, PhD(physics), 64. *Prof Exp:* Theoretical physicist, Los Alamos Sci Lab, 63-64; sr res physicist, Esso Prod Res, 64-66; asst prof physics, NTex State Univ, 66-68; assoc prof, 68-73, PROF PHYSICS, TEX A&M UNIV, 73- *Mem:* Fel Optical Soc Am; Sigma Xi; Am Astron Soc. *Res:* Radiative transfer theory; atmospheric optics. *Mailing Add:* Dept of Physics Tex A&M Univ College Station TX 77843

KATTERMAN, FRANK REINALD HUGH, b Paia, Hawaii, June 28, 29; m 56; c 5. PLANT PHYSIOLOGY. *Educ:* Univ Hawaii, BA, 54; Tex A&M Univ, PhD(plant physiol), 60. *Prof Exp:* Plant physiologist, Agr Res Serv, USDA, 59-67; assoc prof plant breeding, 67-70, PROF AGRON & PLANT GENETICS, UNIV ARIZ, 70-, PLANT BREEDER, AGR EXP STA, 74- *Concurrent Pos:* Mem, Nat Cotton Coun Am. *Mem:* AAAS. *Res:* Composition and biochemistry of the nucleic acids in higher plants. *Mailing Add:* Dept of Agron & Plant Genetics Univ of Ariz Tucson AZ 85721

KATTI, SHRINIWAS KESHAV, b Bijapur, India, June 20, 36; US citizen; m 60; c 2. ANALYTICAL STATISTICS, APPLIED STATISTICS. *Educ:* Univ Delhi, BA, 56; Iowa State Univ, MA, 58, PhD(statist), 60. *Prof Exp:* From asst prof to assoc prof statist, Fla State Univ, 60-69; PROF STATIST, UNIV MO-COLUMBIA, 69- *Concurrent Pos:* US Air Force fel, Fla State Univ, 60-62, USPHS fel, 64-66 & USDA fel, 67-69; consult, Underwriter's Nat Assurance Co, 62-64 & Scot Res Lab, Perkesie, 67-70; assoc ed, Biomet Soc, 67-72; vis prof, Univ New South Wales, 71. *Mem:* Biomet Soc; fel Am Statist Asn; Am Inst Biol Sci; Am Math Soc; Inst Math Statist. *Res:* Inference; methods of tested priors; adaptive estimators. *Mailing Add:* Dept of Statist Univ of Mo Columbia MO 65201

KATTUS, ALBERT ADOLPH, JR, b Cincinnati, Ohio, Oct 8, 17; m 45; c 7. MEDICINE, CARDIOLOGY. *Educ:* Ohio Wesleyan Univ, AB, 39; Univ Rochester, MD, 43. *Prof Exp:* Intern med, Johns Hopkins Hosp, 44, asst resident, 45, fel, Pvt Outpatient Serv, 46-47; asst, Johns Hopkins Univ, 47-51; from asst prof to prof med, 51-81, CLIN PROF MED & CARDIOLOGY, SCH MED, UNIV CALIF, LOS ANGELES, 81- *Concurrent Pos:* Searle fel, Johns Hopkins Univ, 47-51; attend physician, Vet Admin Hosp, West Los Angeles, 51- *Mem:* Asn Univ Cardiologists; Am Fedn Clin Res. *Res:* Cardiac physiology; coronary heart disease. *Mailing Add:* Univ of Calif Ctr for Health Sci Los Angeles CA 90024

KATZ, ADOLPH ISIDORE, b Boston, Mass, Apr 30, 25; m 52; c 3. ENGINEERING MECHANICS, MECHANICAL ENGINEERING. *Educ:* Northeastern Univ, BS, 46; Harvard Univ, MS, 48; Rutgers Univ, PhD(eng mech), 68. *Prof Exp:* Asst prof textile eng, Lowell Tech Inst, 51-53, dir tech res, Res Found, 53-55; sr res engr, Lord Mfg Co, 55-59; dir educ & training, Princeton Comput Ctr, Electronic Assocs Inc, 59-65; instr civil eng, Rutgers Univ, 66-68, asst prof, 68-72; dir plan & res, Dept Higher Educ, NJ, 72-80; PROD MGR VIDEOTEXT, COLUMBIA BROADCASTING SYSTS, 80- *Concurrent Pos:* Consult, Lenox Hill Hosp & Electronic Assoc Inc, 66-72 & NJ State Dept Higher Educ. *Mem:* NY Acad Sci; Sigma Xi. *Res:* Analog and hybrid simulation of physical and biological systems; conceptual and mathematical models of physiological systems; continuing engineering education; institutional research in higher education. *Mailing Add:* Five Tunnell Rd Somerset NJ 08873

KATZ, ADRIAN I, b Bucharest, Romania, Aug 3, 32; m 65; c 2. INTERNAL MEDICINE, PHYSIOLOGY. *Educ:* Hebrew Univ Jerusalem, MD, 62. *Prof Exp:* House officer internal med, Belinson Med Ctr, Sch Med, Tel-Aviv Univ, 62-65; res fel med, Sch Med, Yale Univ, 65-67; res fel, Harvard Med Sch, 67-68, asst prof & attend physician, 68-71, assoc prof, 71-74, PROF MED, SCH MED, UNIV CHICAGO, 75- *Concurrent Pos:* Asst med, Peter Bent Brigham Hosp, Boston, 67-68; head sect nephrology, Univ Chicago, 73- *Mem:* Am Soc Clin Invest; Am Fedn Clin Res; Am Soc Nephrology; NY Acad Sci; fel Am Col Physicians. *Res:* Renal physiology, especially biochemical mechanisms of renal tubular sodium transport; renal handling of polypeptide hormones; kidney function in pregnancy; clinical nephrology; biochemistry. *Mailing Add:* Dept Med Box 83 Univ Chicago Chicago IL 60637

KATZ, ALAN JEFFREY, b Columbus, Ohio, Oct 2, 47; m 68; c 3. POPULATION GENETICS, BIOSTATISTICS. *Educ:* Ohio State Univ, BS, 69, MS, 70, PhD(genetics), 74. *Prof Exp:* NIH fel pop genetics, Dept Genetics & Cell Biol, Univ Minn, 74-75; asst prof, 75-80, ASSOC PROF GENETICS, DEPT BIOL SCI, ILL STATE UNIV, 80- *Mem:* Genetics Soc Am; Biomet Soc; Environ Mutagens Soc; AAAS. *Res:* The estimation of fitness components in natural populations of Drosophila and statistical aspects of experiments on environmental mutagenesis. *Mailing Add:* Dept of Biol Sci Ill State Univ Normal IL 61761

KATZ, ARNOLD MARTIN, b Chicago, Ill, July 30, 32; m 59; c 4. MEDICINE, PHYSIOLOGY. *Educ:* Univ Chicago, BA, 52; Harvard Univ, MD, 56. *Prof Exp:* Intern med, Mass Gen Hosp, 56-57; res assoc, Nat Heart Inst, 57-59; asst resident, Mass Gen Hosp, 59-60; hon registr, Inst Cardiol, London, 60-61; res fel med, Med Sch, Univ Calif, Los Angeles, 61-64; asst prof physiol, Col Physicians & Surgeons, Columbia Univ, 63-67; assoc prof med & physiol, Univ Chicago, 67-69; Philip J & Harriet L Goodhart prof med-cardiol, Mt Sinai Sch Med, 69-77; PROF MED & HEAD DIV CARDIOL, HEALTH CTR, UNIV CONN, 77- *Concurrent Pos:* Mosely traveling fel from Harvard Univ, 60-61; Am Heart Asn res fel, 61-63; estab investr, Am Heart Asn, 63-68, mem exec coun, Coun Basic Sci, 68-71; asst physician, Med Serv, Presby Hosp, 63-67; mem, Comt Myocardial Infarction, Nat Heart Inst, 66, Ad Hoc Comt Rev Proposals Myocardial Infarction Study Ctrs, 67, Heart Prog Proj B Comt, 67-69 & prog proj comt A, 80-; session chmn, Gordon Res Conf Cellular Control Cardiac Contraction, 68 & Gordon Res Conf Cardiac Muscle, 70; consult, Vet Admin, 70-; vchmn task group cardiac failure, Nat Heart, Blood, Lung & Blood Vessel Prog, NIH. *Mem:* Am Physiol Soc; Am Soc Pharmacol & Exp Therapeut; Harvey Soc; Cardiac Muscle Soc (pres, 69-71); Am Soc Biol Chemists. *Res:* Cardiology; cardiovascular physiology; muscle biochemistry. *Mailing Add:* Dept of Med Univ of Conn Health Ctr Farmington CT 06032

KATZ, DAVID HARVEY, b Richmond, Va, Feb 17, 43; m 63; c 2. MEDICINE, IMMUNOLOGY. *Educ:* Univ Va, AB, 63, Duke Univ, MD, 68. *Prof Exp:* Med house officer, Johns Hopkins Hosp, 68-69; staff assoc immunol, NIH, 69-71; from instr to assoc prof immunol & path, Harvard Med Sch, 71-76; chmn & mem immunol staff, Scripps Clin & Res Found, 76-81; CHIEF EXEC OFF & PRES, QUIDEL, 81-; PRES & DIR, MED BIOL INST, LA JOLLA, 81- *Concurrent Pos:* Mem adv comt cancer ctrs, Nat Cancer Inst, 72-74; mem allergy & immunol study sect, NIH, 77; mem human cell biol adv panel, NSF, 77-78. *Mem:* Am Asn Immunologists; Am Soc Clin Invest; AAAS; Am Asn Pathologists; Am Fedn Clin Res. *Res:* Basic immunology; allergy; tumor immunology; developmental biology. *Mailing Add:* Dept Immunol Med Biol Inst 11077 N Torrey Pines Rd La Jolla CA 92037

KATZ, DONALD L(AVERNE), b Jackson Co, Mich, Aug 1, 07; m 32; c 2. CHEMICAL ENGINEERING. *Educ:* Univ Mich, BSE, 31, MS, 32, PhD(chem eng), 33. *Prof Exp:* Res engr, Phillips Petrol Co, 33-36; from asst prof to prof chem eng, 36-66, chmn dept chem & metall eng, 51-62, A H White prof, 66-77, EMER PROF CHEM ENG, UNIV MICH, 77- *Concurrent Pos:* Consult engr, 36-; vis prof, Univ Brazil, 63. *Honors & Awards:* John F Carll Award, Am Inst Mining, Metall & Petrol Engrs; Founders Award, 64, W K Lewis Award, 67, & W H Walker Award, 68, Am Inst Chem Engrs; E V Murphree Award, Am Chem Soc, 75; Gas Indust Res Award, Am Gas Asn, 77; Lucas Medal, Soc Petrol Engrs, Am Inst Mining, Metall & Petrol Engrs, 79. *Mem:* Nat Acad Eng; Am Chem Soc; Am Gas Asn; Am Inst Mining, Metall & Petrol Engrs; Am Inst Chem Engrs (vpres, 58, pres, 59). *Res:* Physical properties of hydrocarbons; heat transfer; oil and gas reservoirs; underground storage of fluids. *Mailing Add:* Dept of Chem Eng Univ of Mich 2028 E Eng Bldg Ann Arbor MI 48109

KATZ, EDWARD, b New York, NY, Aug 10, 23; m 51; c 1. MICROBIOLOGY, BIOCHEMISTRY. *Educ:* NY Univ, BA, 47; Rutgers Univ, PhD(microbiol), 51. *Prof Exp:* Asst supvr antibiotics, Heyden Chem Corp, 48; asst prof microbiol, Univ NH, 51-54 & Rutgers Univ, 54-60; Nat Heart Inst sr res fel biochem, 60-62; assoc prof, 62-69, PROF MICROBIOL, SCHS MED & DENT, GEORGETOWN UNIV, 69- *Concurrent Pos:* Am Med Asn Educ & Res Found grant, 63; Nat Cancer Inst res grant, 63-; consult, Nat Heart Inst, 63-65, Civil Div, US Justice Dept, Schering-Plough Corp & Schwarz BioRes Corp; vchmn & chmn div appl & environ microbiol, Am Soc Microbiol. *Mem:* Am Soc Microbiol; Am Soc Biol Chemists. *Res:* Antibiotics; biosynthesis of peptide antibiotics; tryptophan metabolism; imino acid biosynthesis. *Mailing Add:* Georgetown Univ Schs Med & Dent 3900 Reservoir Rd Washington DC 20007

KATZ, ELI JOEL, b Brooklyn, NY, Jan 12, 37; m 57; c 3. PHYSICAL OCEANOGRAPHY. *Educ:* Polytech Inst Brooklyn, BSME, 57; Pa State Univ, MS, 59; Johns Hopkins Univ, PhD(fluid mech), 62. *Prof Exp:* Res assoc mech, Johns Hopkins Univ, 62-63; vis lectr meteorol, Hebrew Univ Jersualem, 63-65; res specialist acoustics, Gen Dynamics Corp, 65-66; asst scientist, Woods Hole Oceanog Inst, 66-69, assoc scientist phys oceanog, 70-78; sr lectr mech, Tel Aviv Univ, 69-70; SR RES ASSOC, LAMONT-DOHERTY GEOL OBSERV, 79- *Res:* Ocean dynamics and ocean role in world climate. *Mailing Add:* Lamont-Doherty Geol Observ Columbia Univ Palisades NY 10964

KATZ, ERNST, b Maehr-Ostrau, Austria, July 23, 13; m 39; c 1. SOLID STATE PHYSICS. *Educ:* Univ Utrecht, BS, 33, MS, 37, PhD(physics), 41. *Prof Exp:* Asst physics, Univ Utrecht, 38-47, Rockefeller Biophys Res Group, 37-41; with Neth Instrument & Elec Apparatus Co, 41-45, dir res, 45-47; from asst prof to assoc prof, 47-59, prof, 59-80, EMER PROF PHYSICS, UNIV MICH, ANN ARBOR, 80- *Mem:* Fel Am Phys Soc. *Res:* Ionic solids; crystallization; magneto-resistance; general solid state problems. *Mailing Add:* Dept of Physics Univ of Mich Ann Arbor MI 48109

KATZ, EUGENE RICHARD, b Brooklyn, NY, Apr 10, 42; m 69; c 2. GENETICS. *Educ:* Univ Wis, Madison, BS, 62; Univ Cambridge, Eng, PhD(molecular genetics), 69. *Prof Exp:* Asst prof, Dept Biol, 70-75, assoc prof, Dept Biol, 75-80, ASSOC PROF GENETICS, DEPT MICROBIOL, STATE UNIV NY AT STONY BROOK, 80- *Concurrent Pos:* Vis scientist, Mass Inst Technol, 70; dir, Grad Prog Cellular & Develop Biol, State Univ NY at Stony Brook, 75-80, Grad Prog Genetics, 80-; vis prof, Univ Nijmegen, Netherlands, 77-78. *Res:* Genetic control of development using the cellular slime mold; Dictyostelium discoideum as a model system; formal genetics and biochemical analysis of mutants affecting development. *Mailing Add:* Dept Microbiol Grad Biol Bldg Sch Med State Univ New York Stony Brook NY 11794

KATZ, FRANK FRED, b Philadelphia, Pa, July 19, 27; m 55; c 2. PARASITOLOGY. *Educ:* Philadelphia Col Pharm, BS, 51; Tulane Univ, MS, 53; Univ Pa, PhD(parasitol), 56. *Prof Exp:* Asst zool, Philadelphia Col Pharm, 51; asst instr parasitol, Univ Pa, 54-55; jr res assoc biol, Brookhaven Nat Lab, 55-56; sr parasitologist, Eaton Labs, Norwich Pharmacal Co, 56-57; asst prof microbiol, Jefferson Med Col, 57-62; from asst prof to assoc prof, 62-70, actg chmn dept, 71-72, PROF BIOL, SETON HALL UNIV, 70-, CHMN DEPT BIOL, 72- *Mem:* AAAS; Am Soc Parasitol; Am Soc Trop Med & Hyg; Soc Protozool; Micros Soc Am. *Res:* Helminthology; protozoology; experimental parasitology; biology of Strongyloides, Trichinella, Hymenolepis, Tribolium, Plasmodium and trypanosomes. *Mailing Add:* Dept of Biol Seton Hall Univ South Orange NJ 07079

KATZ, FRED H, b Essen, Ger, Apr 7, 30; US citizen; m 60; c 3. INTERNAL MEDICINE, ENDOCRINOLOGY. *Educ:* Columbia Univ, AB, 52, MD, 56; Am Bd Internal Med, dipl, 64. *Prof Exp:* Asst prof med, Sch Med, Univ Chicago, 63-66; assoc prof med & chief endocrinol, Stritch Sch Med, Loyola Univ, 66-69; assoc prof, 69-75, head div endocrinol, 72-76, PROF MED, UNIV COLO, 75-, CLIN PROF MED, 76- *Concurrent Pos:* Nat Found fel, Presby Hosp, New York, 59-60, Nat Inst Arthritis & Metab Dis trainee, 60-61; chief endocrinol, Vet Admin Hosp, Denver, 69-76; mem med adv bd, Coun High Blood Pressure, Cent Soc Clin Res. *Mem:* Endocrine Soc; Soc Exp Biol & Med; fel Am Col Physicians. *Res:* Steroid hormone metabolism, physiology and pharmacology. *Mailing Add:* Rose Med Ctr 4545 E Ninth Ave Denver CO 80220

KATZ, GARY VICTOR, b New York, NY, July 12, 43; m 67; c 1. INHALATION TOXICOLOGY, INDUSTRIAL HYGIENE. *Educ:* City Col New York, BS, 65; NY Univ, MS, 68, PhD(biol & environ health sci), 75. *Prof Exp:* Asst res scientist inhalation toxicol & chem carcinogenesis, Dept Environ Med, NY Univ Med Ctr, 69-75, assoc res scientist, 75-77; TOXICOLOGIST INHALATION TOXICOL, EASTMAN KODAK CO, 77- *Concurrent Pos:* Adj asst prof environ med, Dept Environ Med, NY Univ Med Ctr, 77- *Mem:* Am Indust Hygiene Asn. *Res:* Chemical carcinogenesis; neurotoxicology. *Mailing Add:* Toxicol Sect B-320 Eastman Kodak Co Rochester NY 14650

KATZ, GEORGE MAXIM, b Mar 26, 22; US citizen; m 49; c 2. ENGINEERING, NEUROPHYSIOLOGY. *Educ:* City Col New York, BEE, 42; Polytech Inst Brooklyn, MEE, 57; Columbia Univ, EE, 61, PhD(physiol), 67. *Prof Exp:* Engr, Gen Elec Co, NY, 42-47; lectr elec eng, City Col New York, 47-50; sr engr, Advan Develop Lab, Allen B Dumont Co, NJ, 50-51; res assoc surg, 52-61, SR RES ASSOC & ASST PROF NEUROL, COL PHYSICIANS & SURGEONS, COLUMBIA UNIV, 62- *Concurrent Pos:* Consult, St Vincent's Hosp & Med Ctr, New York, 68- *Mem:* Biophys Soc. *Res:* Methodology and instrumentation for conducting research; mathematical analysis of data. *Mailing Add:* Col of Physicians & Surgeons Columbia Univ New York NY 10032

KATZ, GERALD, b Brooklyn, NY; m 58; c 3. SOLID STATE SCIENCE, X-RAY CRYSTALLOGRAPHY. *Educ:* Brooklyn Col, BA, 44; Pa State Univ, PhD(solid state sci), 65. *Prof Exp:* Physicist weapons res, US Army Chem Warfare Serv, 48-49; physicist solid state mat res, US Signal Corps Res & Develop Labs, US Electronics Command, 49-58; res fel struct of metals & alloys, Israel Inst Technol, 58-59; staff mem x-ray crystallog res uranium & intermetallic compounds, Dept Metall, Israel AEC, 59-61; from res asst to res assoc solid state mat res, Mat Res Lab, Pa State Univ, 61-66; staff scientist crystal films & epitaxy, IBM Watson Res Ctr, 66-68; dir x-ray lab, Inst Res & Develop, Israel Mining Industs Ltd, 68-73; res assoc solid state mat res, Dept Mat Eng, Israel Inst Technol, 73-79; SR RES LECTR, DEPT INORG CHEM, HEBREW UNIV, JERULSALEM, 79- *Mem:* Am Crystallog Asn; Israel Soc Crystal Growth & Thin Films; Am Asn Crystal Growth. *Res:* Synthesis and/or crystal growth of inorganic materials, metals, intermetallic compounds including thin films; their structural characterization by x-ray crystallography and their associated magnetic, electrical, optical properties; solid state reaction mechanisms; topotaxy. *Mailing Add:* Dept Inorg Chem Hebrew Univ Jerusalem Givat Ram Israel

KATZ, HAROLD W(ILLIAM), b New York, NY, June 4, 23; m 45; c 2. ELECTRICAL ENGINEERING. *Educ:* Rensselaer Polytech Inst, BSEE, 43; Univ Ill, PhD(elec eng), 52. *Prof Exp:* Instr elec eng, Univ Ill, 46-52; engr, Gen Elec Co, 52-55; consult engr, 55-58, mgr adv components & networks, Electronic Lab, 58-64; dir res, Res Lab, Tecumseh Prod Co, 64-67; dir electronic components, KMS Industs Inc, 67-69; pres, Vicom Industs Inc, 69-70, vpres, Vicom Mfg Co, 70-72; vpres corp develop, Interactive Systs Inc, 72-79, mgr mkt develop, 79-81; VPRES BROADBAND COMMUN, STEM TELECOMMUN, 81- *Res:* Broadband coaxial cable communications. *Mailing Add:* 10 Waters Edge Rye NY 10580

KATZ, HERBERT M(ARVIN), b Brooklyn, NY, Apr 4, 26; m 54; c 2. CHEMICAL ENGINEERING. *Educ:* City Col New York, BChE, 49; Univ Cincinnati, MS, 50, PhD(chem eng), 54. *Prof Exp:* Asst chem engr, Argonne Nat Lab, 54-56; staff engr, Eng Ctr, Univ Columbia, 56-57; chem engr, Brookhaven Nat Lab, 57-67; chem engr, Res Div, W R Grace & Co, 67-68; chmn dept, 68-73, PROF CHEM ENG, HOWARD UNIV, 73- *Concurrent Pos:* Consult, Nuclear Safety Asn & Brookhaven Nat Lab. *Mem:* Sigma Xi; Am Inst Chem Engrs. *Res:* Chemical reprocessing of nuclear reactor fuels; treatment of radioactive wastes; fluidized bed technology. *Mailing Add:* Dept of Chem Eng Howard Univ Washington DC 20001

KATZ, IRA, b New York, NY, Nov 10, 33; m 55; c 3. FOOD SCIENCE. *Educ:* Univ Ga, BSA, 57; Univ Md, MS, 59, PhD, 62. *Prof Exp:* Res asst lipid chem, Univ Md, 61-62, res assoc, 62-65, asst prof, 65-67; proj leader, 67-71, groupleader, 71-73, dir, 73-80, VPRES & DIR, RES & DEVELOP, INT FLAVORS & FRAGRANCES, INC, 80- *Mem:* AAAS; Am Dairy Sci Asn; Am Oil Chem Soc; Am Chem Soc; Inst Food Technologists. *Res:* Flavor of food and fragrance systems. *Mailing Add:* Int Flavors & Fragrances Inc 1515 Hwy 36 Union Beach NJ 07735

KATZ, IRA, b Brooklyn, NY, July 15, 45; m 65; c 2. PLASMA PHYSICS. *Educ:* Case Inst Technol, BS, 67; Univ Chicago, PhD(chem physics), 71. *Prof Exp:* Res assoc chem physics, Univ Ill, 71-72; STAFF SCIENTIST PHYSICS, SYST SCI & SOFTWARE, 72- *Res:* Numerical simulation of magnetospheric spacecraft charging; modeling of heavy ion impurity radiation losses from controlled thermonuclear reaction type plasmas. *Mailing Add:* PO Box 1620 La Jolla CA 92038

KATZ, IRVING, b Brooklyn, NY, Oct 25, 33; m 57; c 3. MATHEMATICS. *Educ:* Brooklyn Col, BS, 56; Ohio State Univ, MA, 58; Univ Md, PhD(math), 64. *Prof Exp:* Mathematician, Nat Security Agency, 58-59 & Opers Res Inc, 59-60; from instr to assoc prof, Am Univ, 61-66; from asst prof to assoc prof, 66-77, PROF MATH, GEORGE WASHINGTON UNIV, 77- *Mem:* Am Math Soc; Math Asn Am. *Res:* Matrix theory. *Mailing Add:* Dept of Math George Washington Univ Washington DC 20006

KATZ, IRWIN ALAN, b Malden, Mass, Feb 13, 40; m 64; c 4. PHARMACEUTICS, PHARMACY. *Educ:* Boston Univ, AB, 61; Mass Col Pharm, BS, 68, MS, 69, PhD(pharm), 71. *Prof Exp:* Res investr formulation design, E R Squibb & Sons Inc, 71-73; hosp pharmacist, JFK Med Ctr, 74-75; RES INVESTR LIQUID FORMULATION DEVELOP, E R SQUIBB & SONS INC, 73- *Concurrent Pos:* Retail pharmacist, Wash Park Pharm, Newtonville, Mass, 68-71; hosp pharmacist, Boston Lying In Hosp, 70-71 & Raritan Valley Hosp, 75- *Mem:* Am Pharmaceut Asn; Acad Pharmceut Sci. *Res:* Parenteral research and development; lyophilization; parenteral particulate matter monitoring; pharmaceutical formulation design; physical pharmacy and biopharmaceutics. *Mailing Add:* 3 Noel Lane East Brunswick NJ 08816

KATZ, ISRAEL, b New York, NY, Nov 30, 17; m 42; c 3. MECHANICAL ENGINEERING, ENGINEERING MANAGEMENT. *Educ:* Northeastern Univ, BS, 41; Mass Inst Technol, cert naval archit, 42; Cornell Univ, MME, 44. *Prof Exp:* Test engr, Gen Elec Co, 38-41, engr in chg submarine propulsion mach, US Navy Diesel Eng Lab, Cornell Univ, 42-45, asst prof, Grad Sch Aeronaut Eng, 45-48, assoc prof mech eng, 48-56; mgr liaison & consult eng, Adv Electronics Ctr, Gen Elec Co, 56-63; dean ctr continuing educ, 63-67, PROF ENG TECHNOL, NORTHEASTERN UNIV, 67- *Concurrent Pos:* Consult engr, 63-; mem, Comt Yield Electronic Mat & Devices, Nat Mat Adv Bd, Nat Acad Sci, 71-72, Comt Mat Sci Res & Coord, 72-73, eng consult, 74-; consult proj proc, Mass Inst Technol, 76-; adv continuing educ, NSF, 77-; mem bd dirs, Mass Eng Coun, 77- & chmn, 81-83. *Honors & Awards:* Pioneer Award, Am Soc Eng Educ, 78. *Mem:* Am Soc Eng Educ; Inst Elec & Electronics Engrs; AAAS; Sigma Xi. *Res:* Engineering thermodynamics; electromechanical systems; aerospace technology; continuing education of scientists and engineers. *Mailing Add:* 40 Auburn St Brookline MA 02146

KATZ, ISRAEL NORMAN, b New York, NY, Apr 14, 32; m 57; c 2. MATHEMATICS, STATISTICS. *Educ:* Yeshiva Univ, BA & MS, 52; Mass Inst Technol, PhD(math), 59. *Prof Exp:* Asst math, Yeshiva Univ, 52-54; asst, Mass Inst Technol, 55-58, res asst, 58-59; sr staff scientist, Res & Adv Develop Div, Avco Corp, 59-63, chief math anal sect, 63-65, mgr math dept, 66-67; assoc prof appl math & comput sci, 67-74, PROF APPL MATH & SYSTS SCI, WASH UNIV, 74- *Concurrent Pos:* Lectr, Math Asn Am; vis consult, Soc Indust & Appl Math. *Mem:* Opers Res Soc Am; Am Math Soc; Math Asn Am; Soc Indust & Appl Math. *Res:* Applied math; numerical analysis; facility location; finite elements; biomathematics; ordinary and partial differential equations; algorithms for paralell computation. *Mailing Add:* Dept Systs Sci & Math Wash Univ Box 1040 St Louis MO 63130

KATZ, J LAWRENCE, b Brooklyn, NY, Dec 18, 27; m 50; c 3. BIOPHYSICS, BIOMEDICAL ENGINEERING. *Educ:* Polytech Inst Brooklyn, BS, 50, MS, 51, PhD(physics), 57. *Prof Exp:* Instr math, Polytech Inst Brooklyn, 52-56; asst prof, 56-61, assoc prof, 61-67, PROF PHYSICS, RENSSELAER POLYTECH INST, 67-, PROF BIOPHYS & BIOMED ENG, 73-, DIR, CTR BIOMED ENG, 74- *Concurrent Pos:* Consult, Ernest F Fullam, Inc, NY, 58-; NSF sci fac fel & hon res asst crystallog, Univ Col, London, 59-60; consult, Bio-Anal Labs, Inc, 61-, mem bd dirs, 69-; mem eng in biol & med training comt, NIH, 68-71; vis prof biomed eng & oral biol, Sch Eng & Sch Med, Univ Miami, 69-70; mem equip & mat for med radiation appln & chmn subcomt diag radiol, Am Nat Standards Inst, 69-74; consult & site vis, Nat Inst Dent Res & Nat Inst Gen Med Sci; partic vis sci prog physics, Am Asn Physics Teachers-Am Inst Physics, 70-71; lectr conf, Nat Acad Sci-Nat Res Coun, 70 & 71; prof surg, Albany Med Col, 75-; Jerome Fischbach travel grant, Rensselaer Polytech Inst, 76; consult, Orthop Panel, Food & Drug Admin, 76-; Guggenheim fel, Harvard Univ, 78, vis lectr orthopaedics, Sch Med, 78; vis biophysicist, Orthopaedics Res Lab, Children's Hosp, Boston, 78; mem nat bd & NY state bd, Am Dem Action; E Leon Watkins vis prof, Wichita State Univ, Kans, 78; vis prof biophys & biomed eng, Inst de Fisica e Quimica de Sao Carlos, Univ de Sao Paulo, Brasil, 78; mem, Coun Alliance Eng Med & Biol, 78-81; consult, Johnson & Johnson Orthorp Div, 79-; mem, Sci Rev & Eval Bd for Rehab Eng Res & Develop, Vet Admin, 81-83. *Honors & Awards:* 3rd Annual Award for Outstanding Contributions to Tech Lit Biomat, Soc Biomat & Clemson Univ, 75. *Mem:* Am Crystallog Asn; Am Phys Soc; Int Asn Dent; Sigma Xi; Soc Biomat (pres, 78-79). *Res:* Biomechanics of calcified and connective tissues; electromechanical properties of bone and bone remodeling; rehabilitation engineering; scanning electron microscopy; X-ray diffraction and ultrasonic studies of bone and teeth; biomedical materials. *Mailing Add:* Ctr for Biomed Eng Rensselaer Polytech Inst Troy NY 12181

KATZ, JACK, b New York, NY, Mar 25, 34; m 56; c 2. AUDIOLOGY. *Educ:* Brooklyn Col, BA, 56; Syracuse Univ, 57; Univ Pittsburgh, PhD(audiol), 61. *Prof Exp:* Therapist speech & hearing, Bd Educ, Cayuga County, NY, 57-58; res audiologist, Univ Pittsburgh, 60-61; asst prof audiol, Northern Ill Univ, 61-62; asst prof speech path & audiol, Tulane Univ, 62-65; dir audiol lab, Menorah Med Ctr, Kansas City, 65-74; clin prof, 74-76, PROF COMMUN DISORDERS & SCI, STATE UNIV NY, BUFFALO, 76- *Concurrent Pos:* Consult audiol, Univ Pittsburgh, 61-62, Menorah Med Ctr, 74- & Roswell Park Mem Inst, Buffalo, NY, 79-; assoc clin prof, Univ Mo-Kansas City, 70-74 & Univ Kans, 71-74; Fulbright lectr, Ankara, Turkey, 72-73; mem spec med staff, Chedoke-McMaster Hosps, Hamilton, Ont, 81- *Mem:* Fel Am Speech & Hearing Asn; Acoust Soc Am. *Res:* Evaluation of central auditory integrity, binaural hearing, low level adaptation and auditory perception. *Mailing Add:* Dept Commun Disorders & Sci State Univ NY Buffalo NY 14226

KATZ, JACOB FEUER, b Hungary, June 1, 11; US citizen; m 37; c 3. ORTHOPEDIC SURGERY. *Educ:* NY Univ, BS, 32, MD, 35. *Prof Exp:* Intern, Nathan Littauer Hosp, 35-36; resident orthop surg, Vet Admin Hosp, Ft Howard, Md, 46-47 & Mt Sinai Hosp, New York, 47-49; from assoc clin prof to assoc prof, 66-68, prof clin orthop, 68-81, EMER PROF CLIN ORTHOP, MT SINAI SCH MED, 81- *Concurrent Pos:* Chief orthop, Blythedale Childrens Hosp, Valhalla, NY, 56-; orthop consult, Hebrew Home for Aged, Riverdale & Bur Handicapped Children, New York, 60- & Med Control Bd, Health Ins Plan Greater NY, 71- *Mem:* Am Acad Orthop Surgeons; Orthop Res Soc; Am Col Surgeons; AMA. *Res:* Clinical research in perthes disease in children; laboratory studies in disorders of epiphyseal growth. *Mailing Add:* Mt Sinai Sch of Med 1 E 100th St New York NY 10029

KATZ, JAY, b Zwickau, Ger, Oct 20, 22; nat US; m 52; c 3. PSYCHIATRY. *Educ:* Univ Vt, BA, 44; Harvard Univ, MD, 49; Am Bd Psychiat & Neurol, dipl. *Prof Exp:* Intern, Mt Sinai Hosp, New York, 49-50; asst resident psychiat, State Univ NY & Northport Vet Admin Hosp, Long Island, 50-51; asst resident psychiat, Sch Med, 53-54, chief resident outpatient clin, 54-55, from instr to asst prof psychiat, 55-58, asst prof psychiat & law, 58-60, assoc prof law & assoc clin prof psychiat, 60-67, ADJ PROF LAW & PSYCHIAT, YALE UNIV, 67-; TRAINING & SUPV PSYCHOANALYST, WESTERN NEW ENG INST PSYCHOANAL, 72- *Concurrent Pos:* Asst investr, USPHS res grant hypnotic dreams, 53-56; attend psychiatrist, Yale-New Haven Med Ctr, 57-; chmn adv comt ment health, Woodbridge Bd Educ, Conn, 64-68; staff psychoanalyst, Psychoanal Clin, Western New Eng Inst Psychoanal, 66-69, trustee, 68-71; fel, Ctr Advan Psychoanal Studies, 67-; fel, Morse Col, Yale Univ, 68- *Honors & Awards:* Isaac Ray Award, Am Psychiat Asn, 75. *Mem:* Inst of Med of Nat Acad Sci; fel Am Psychiat Asn; Am Orthopsychiat Asn; Am Col Psychiatry; Am Psychoanal Asn. *Mailing Add:* Dept of Psychiat Yale Univ New Haven CT 06520

KATZ, JONATHAN ISAAC, b New York, NY, Jan 5, 51. ASTROPHYSICS. *Educ:* Cornell Univ, AB, 70, MA, 71, PhD(astron), 73. *Prof Exp:* Mem staff astrophysics, Inst Advan Study, 73-76; assoc prof astron & geophysics, Univ Calif, Los Angeles, 76-81; ASSOC PROF PHYSICS, WASHINGTON UNIV, MO, 81- *Concurrent Pos:* Consult, Lawrence Livermore Lab, 73-, SRI Int, 74- & NASA, Jet Propulsion Lab; Sloan Found fel, 77-79. *Mem:* Am Phys Soc; Am Astron Soc. *Res:* Theoretical high energy astrophysics. *Mailing Add:* Dept Physics Washington Univ St Louis MO 63130

KATZ, JOSEPH, b Vilno, Lithuania, Jan 15; US citizen; m; c 5. BIOCHEMISTRY. *Educ:* Univ Calif, Berkeley, BS, 43, PhD, 49. *Prof Exp:* Asst res physiologist, Univ Calif, Berkeley, 53-55; from res assoc to sr res assoc, Inst Med Res, Cedars of Lebanon Hosp, 55-70, SR RES SCIENTIST, MED RES INST, CEDARS-SINAI MED CTR, 70- *Concurrent Pos:* Res fel biochem, Univ Calif, Berkeley, 49-51, fel physiol, 51-53; advan res fel, Cedars-Sinai Med Ctr, 59-61; estab investr, Am Heart Asn, 61-66; adj prof, Univ Southern Calif, 69- *Mem:* Am Chem Soc; Am Soc Biol Chemists; Am Nutrit Soc; Am Physiol Soc; Brit Biochem Soc. *Res:* Carbohydrate metabolism determination of pathways of glucose utilization; the interrelationship between lipogenesis and glucose utilization; plasma protein metabolism. *Mailing Add:* Cedars-Sinai Med Ctr 8700 Beverly Blvd Los Angeles CA 90048

KATZ, JOSEPH J, b Detroit, Mich, Apr 19, 12; m 44; c 4. PHYSICAL CHEMISTRY. *Educ:* Wayne State Univ, BS, 32; Univ Chicago, PhD(chem), 42. *Prof Exp:* Chemist, Univ Chicago, 42-43, chemist metall lab, 43-46; SR CHEMIST, ARGONNE NAT LAB, 46- *Concurrent Pos:* Guggenheim fel, 57-58; Am ed, J Inorg & Nuclear Chem; ed-in-chief, Inorg & Nuclear Chem Letters, 55-81. *Honors & Awards:* Nuclear Appln Award, Am Chem Soc, 61, Midwest Award, 69; Medal Distinguished Serv, Univ Chicago, 75. *Mem:* Nat Acad Sci; AAAS; Am Chem Soc. *Res:* Chemistry of uranium and transuranium elements; deterium isotope studies; chlorophyll chemistry; photosynthesis; solar energy. *Mailing Add:* Argonne Nat Lab 9700 S Cass Ave Argonne IL 60439

KATZ, JOSEPH L, b Colon, Panama, Aug 4, 38; US citizen; m 65; c 2. CHEMICAL PHYSICS, CHEMICAL ENGINEERING. *Educ:* Univ Chicago, BS, 60, PhD(phys chem), 63. *Prof Exp:* Asst prof phys chem, Univ Copenhagen, 63-64; mem tech staff, N Am Rockwell Sci Ctr, 64-70; prof chem eng, Clarkson Col Technol, 70-79; PROF CHEM ENG, JOHNS HOPKINS UNIV, 79-, DEPT CHMN & DIR, ENERGY RES INST, 81- *Concurrent Pos:* Guggenheim fel, 76-77. *Honors & Awards:* John W Graham Prize, 75. *Mem:* AAAS; Am Phys Soc; Am Chem Soc; Am Inst Chem Engrs; Sigma Xi. *Res:* Nucleation; equations of state; thermal conductivity. *Mailing Add:* Dept Chem Eng Johns Hopkins Univ Baltimore MD 21218

KATZ, KURT, b Kassel, Ger, Aug 1, 32; US citizen; m 56; c 3. NUCLEAR & CHEMICAL ENGINEERING. *Educ:* Polytech Inst Brooklyn, BChE, 54; NY Univ, MChE, 55. *Prof Exp:* Design engr, Bettis Atomic Power Lab, Westinghouse Elec Corp, 55-59, sr engr, res labs, 59-61, fel eng anal, 61-65, mgr mkt planning & new prod develop, Atomic Equip Div, 65-68, mgr, water waste treatment dept, 68-70, gen mgr, Water Qual Control Div, 70-73; PRES WATER/FLUIDS GROUP, PEABODY INT CORP, 73-, VPRES & DIR, 74- *Mem:* Am Chem Soc. *Mailing Add:* Peabody Int Corp 722 Post Rd Darien CT 06820

KATZ, LEON, b Poland, Aug 9, 09; Can citizen; m 41; c 4. SCIENCE POLICY. *Educ:* Queen's Univ, Ont, BSc, 34, MSc, 37; Calif Inst Technol, PhD(physics), 42. *Prof Exp:* Res lead acid batteries, Monarch Battery Co, Ont, 31-33, plant foreman, 34-36; res engr, Westinghouse Elec Corp, 42-46; assoc prof physics, Univ Sask, 46-52, prof, 52-75, head dept, 65-75, dir accelerator lab, 61-75; dir, Sci Policy Secretariat, Govt Sask, 75-80; RETIRED. *Concurrent Pos:* Mem, Sci Coun Can, 66-72. *Honors & Awards:* Officer, Order of Can, 74. *Mem:* Fel Am Phys Soc; Can Asn Physicist (past pres); fel Royal Soc Can. *Res:* Thermodynamics; radar; ratio of specific heats of gases; nuclear physics. *Mailing Add:* Univ Saskatoon Saskatoon SK S7N 0W0 Can

KATZ, LEON, b Springfield, Mass, Aug 27, 21; m 47; c 3. ORGANIC CHEMISTRY. *Educ:* Trinity Col, Conn, BS, 44; Univ Ill, PhD(org chem), 47. *Prof Exp:* Chemist, Am Cyanamid Co, 47-49; mgr org chem, Schenley Labs, 49-53; res chemist, Gen Aniline & Film Corp, NY, 53-55, sect mgr dyes & pigments, 55-58, prod mgr pigments, 58-59, tech dir, 59-62, dir res, Dyestuff & Chem Div, 62-65, corp dir res, 65-66, vpres, 66-69; exec vpres, Rockwood Industs, Conn, 69-71; vpres corp develop, Polychrome Corp, Yonkers, NY, 71-73; V PRES RES & DEVELOP & PACKAGING, AM CAN CO, GREENWICH, CONN, 73- *Mem:* AAAS; Indust Res Inst; Am Chem Soc; NY Acad Sci; Am Inst Chem. *Res:* Alkaloids; pharmaceuticals; dyestuffs; pigments; reprographics; photography; specialty chemicals packaging. *Mailing Add:* 195 Dogwood Ct Stamford CT 06903

KATZ, LEWIS, b Fond du Lac, Wis, Mar 19, 23; m 48; c 2. PHYSICAL CHEMISTRY. *Educ:* Univ Minn, BChem, 46, PhD(phys chem), 51. *Prof Exp:* Asst chem, Univ Minn, 46-50; res fel, Calif Inst Technol, 51-52; instr phys chem, 52-55, from asst prof to assoc prof, 55-64, PROF PHYS CHEM, UNIV CONN, 64- *Concurrent Pos:* NSF sci fac fel, Cambridge Univ, 61-62; guest scientist, Weizmann Inst, Univ Leyden & Univ Stockholm, 69. *Mem:* Am Chem Soc; Am Crystallog Asn. *Res:* X-ray diffraction by crystals. *Mailing Add:* Dept of Chem Univ of Conn Storrs CT 06268

KATZ, LEWIS E, b Philadelphia, Pa, July 9, 40; m 69; c 1. PHYSICAL METALLURGY, MATERIALS SCIENCE. *Educ:* Drexel Inst, BS, 63; Univ Pa, MS, 64, PhD(mat sci), 67. *Prof Exp:* Fel diffusion, Lawrence Radiation Lab, Univ Calif, 67-69; mem tech staff, 69-80, SUPVR, BELL LABS, 80- *Mem:* Electrochem Soc. *Res:* Radiation damage; phase transformations; diffusion; electron microscopy; x-ray analysis; crystal growth; semiconductor development. *Mailing Add:* 1142 N 27 Allentown PA 18104

KATZ, LOUIS, b New York, NY, Aug 3, 32; m 68; c 1. MOLECULAR BIOLOGY, COMPUTER SCIENCE. *Educ:* City Col New York, BS, 53; Univ Wis, MS, 55, PhD(physics), 59. *Prof Exp:* Physicist, Union Carbide Metals Co, 58-60, res physicist, Visking Co Div, Union Carbide Corp, 60-61; res assoc biol, Mass Inst Technol, 61-64; res assoc biochem, Albert Einstein Col Med, 64-65 & Mass Inst Technol, 65-68; SR RES ASSOC & DIR COMPUT GRAPHICS FACIL, DEPT BIOL SCI, COL PHYSICIANS & SURGEONS, COLUMBIA UNIV, 68- *Mem:* Biophys Soc; Asn Comput Mach. *Res:* Small angle x-ray scattering; molecular biophysics; interactive computer graphics; macromolecular structure. *Mailing Add:* Col of Physicians & Surgeons 630 W 168th St New York NY 10032

KATZ, LUDWIG, b Bad Hersfeld, Ger, Apr 27, 24; US citizen; m 63; c 2. SPACE PHYSICS, MAGNETOSPHERIC PHYSICS. *Educ:* Temple Univ, AB, 45, MA, 47. *Prof Exp:* Part-time instr physics, Temple Univ, 45-47; res physicist, Air Force Cambridge Res Labs, 50-71; nuclear physicist, Joint Continental Defense Syst Integration Staff, 71-72; supvry physicist, Air Force Cambridge Res Labs, 72-76; SR SCIENTIST, VISIDYNE, INC, 76- *Mem:* Am Phys Soc; Am Geophys Union; Sigma Xi. *Res:* Solar-Terrestrial relations; trapped radiation; geomagnetism; space plasmas; near earth particulate environment; spacecraft charging. *Mailing Add:* Visidyne Inc 19 Third Ave Burlington MA 01803

KATZ, MANFRED, b Ger, Feb 16, 29; nat US; m 53; c 3. POLYMER CHEMISTRY, TEXTILE CHEMISTRY. *Educ:* Okla State Univ, BS, 50, MS, 51; Univ Del, PhD, 61. *Prof Exp:* Res supvr, 51-67, tech supvr, 67-71, RES ASSOC, E I DU PONT DE NEMOURS & CO, INC, 71- *Mem:* AAAS; Am Chem Soc; Sci Res Soc Am. *Res:* Condensation polymers; synthetic fibers; non-woven fabrics; composites. *Mailing Add:* 310 Brockton Rd Sharpley Wilmington DE 19803

KATZ, MARTIN, b New York, NY, May 16, 27; m 47; c 2. PHARMACEUTICS. *Educ:* St John's Univ, NY, BS, 47; Columbia Univ, MS, 48, MA, 52; Philadelphia Col Pharm, DSc, 54. *Prof Exp:* Instr pharm, Columbia Univ, 48-52; group leader, Pharmaceut Res & Develop, Chas Pfizer & Co, Inc, 53-55; group leader cosmetics, Revlon, Inc, 55-57, Thayer Labs Div, 57-60; Middle Atlantic Dir, R A Gosselin & Co, Boston, 50-60; dir pharmaceut res & develop, Syntex Labs, 60-64, vpres, Syntex Res & dir, Inst Pharmaceut Sci, 64-77, dir, Prof Prod Group & sr vpres, Syntex Res, 77-81, SR VPRES RES & DEVELOP & INT MKT, SYNTEX BEAUTY CARE INC, 81- *Honors & Awards:* Ebert Award, Am Pharmaceut Asn, 54; IFF Award, Soc Cosmetic Chem, 72. *Mem:* Am Chem Soc; Am Pharmaceut Asn; Acad Pharmaceut Sci; Soc Cosmetic Chem. *Res:* Pharmaceutical and cosmetic development; sublingual absorption; percutaneous absorption. *Mailing Add:* Syntex Beauty Care Inc 3401 Hillview Ave Palo Alto CA 94304

KATZ, MARVIN L(AVERNE), b Tulsa, Okla, Dec 12, 35; m 55; c 3. CHEMICAL ENGINEERING. *Educ:* Univ Mich, BS, 56, MS, 58, PhD(chem eng), 60. *Prof Exp:* Res engr, Sinclair Res Inc, 60-64, adminr sci comput, 64-69; mgr admin dept, 69-72, mgr, Res & Develop Dept, NAm Producing Div, 72-78, VPRES & DEVELOP DEPT, ARCO OIL-GAS CO DIV, ATLANTIC RICHFIELD CO, 79- *Concurrent Pos:* Chmn, technol task group, Nat Petrol Coun Comt on enhanced recovery techniques for oil & gas in the US, 76. *Mem:* Soc Petrol Engrs (pres, 80); Am Inst Chem Engrs. *Res:* Fluid flow through porous media; heat transfer; computer science. *Mailing Add:* Arco Oil & Gas Co PO Box 2819 Dallas TX 75221

KATZ, MAURICE JOSEPH, b Brooklyn, NY, May 17, 37. ENERGY, WEAPONS EFFECTS. *Educ:* Columbia Univ, AB, 58, MA, 61, PhD(physics), 65. *Prof Exp:* Res physicist, IBM Forschungs Lab, Zurich, Switz, 61-63; appointee physics div, Los Alamos Sci Lab, Univ Calif, 65-67, staff mem, 67-70, prog mgr, 70-72, group leader, 72-73, asst div leader, Energy & Controlled Thermonuclear Res Divisions, 73-74; tech asst to dir, Controlled Thermonuclear Res Div, US Energy Res & Develop Admin, 75-76, spec asst to asst adminr, Solar, Geothermal & Advan Energy Systs, 76-77, asst dir electrochem systs, Div Energy Storage Systs, 77-79, dir, Div Distributed Solar Technol, 79-80, off dir solar power appln, 80, DEP DIR, DIV SOLAR ELEC TECHNOL, ENERGY RES & DEVELOP ADMIN, US DEPT ENERGY, 81- *Mem:* Am Phys Soc; Sigma Xi. *Res:* Physics of the solid and liquid states; neutron scattering; structure of liquids; x-ray effects in materials and structures, controlled thermonuclear research, advanced energy systems; energy storage systems; photovoltaic, wind, and ocean thermal energy systems. *Mailing Add:* Off Solar Elec Technol Dept Energy 1000 Independence Ave Washington DC 20585

KATZ, MAX, b Seattle, Wash, Mar 27, 19; m 46; c 4. FISHERIES. *Educ:* Univ Wash, Seattle, BS, 39, MS, 42, PhD(fisheries biol), 49. *Prof Exp:* Fisheries biologist, State Dept Fisheries, Wash, 40-42; asst, Inst Paper Chem, Wis, 46-47; from fisheries res biologist to pollution biologist, USPHS, Cincinnati, 49-53, Corvallis, 53-60; actg assoc prof fisheries, Univ Wash, 60-66, res prof, 66-73, dir water resources info ctr, 71-73; res dir, Seattle Marine Labs, Inc, res dir, Parametrix, Inc, 74-76; PRES, ENVIRON INFO SERV, INC, 76-; AFFIL PROF FISHERIES, UNIV WASH, 73- *Concurrent Pos:* Hon assoc prof, Dept Fish & Game Mgt, Ore State Col, 54-60; consult, Calif Water Pollution Control Bd, 58, Rayonier, Inc, Wash, 59, Northwest Pulp & Paper Asn, 61, off resource develop, USPHS, 62-64, Simpson Timber Co, Wash, 63, Libby, McNeil & Libby, Ill, 63-65, Health Plating Co, Wash, 64-65 & various other companies. *Mem:* Am Fisheries Soc; Am Soc Ichthyol & Herpet; Am Inst Fishery Res Biol; Water Pollution Control Fedn; Marine Biol Asn UK. *Res:* Water quality requirements of fish; fish toxicology; biological effects of water pollution; blood parasites of fish; hematology of fish; fish diseases. *Mailing Add:* 3455 72nd Pl Southeast Mercer Island WA 98040

KATZ, MICHAEL, b Lwow, Poland, Feb 13, 28; nat US. PEDIATRICS, VIROLOGY. *Educ:* Univ Pa, AB, 49; State Univ NY, MD, 56; Columbia Univ, MS, 63. *Prof Exp:* Instr biol, Queen's Col, NY, 51-52; intern, Med Ctr, Univ Calif, Los Angeles, 56-57; resident pediat, Babies Hosp, New York, 60-62; instr, Col Physicians & Surgeons, Columbia Univ, 64-65; assoc, Sch Med, Univ Pa, 65-66, asst prof, 66-70; prof pediat, 71-77, PROF TROP MED, COL PHYSICIANS & SURGEONS, COLUMBIA UNIV, 70-, REUBEN S CARPENTER PROF PEDIAT & CHMN DEPT, 77- *Concurrent Pos:* Hon lectr, Makerere Univ, Uganda & hon pediat specialist, Mulago Hosp, Kampala, Uganda, 63-64; consult Peace Corps vols, Princeton Univ, 64; assoc vis pediatrician, Harlem Hosp Ctr, New York, & asst pediatrician, Babies Hosp, 64-65, assoc mem, Wistar Inst, Philadelphia, 65-70; assoc physician, Children's Hosp Philadelphia, 66-70; attend pediatrician, Presby Hosp, 70-77, dir pediat serv, 77-; mem, Subcomt Interactions Nutrit & Infections, Nat Acad Sci, 71-74, chmn, 74-75, consult, 75- *Mem:* Inst Med-Nat Acad Sci; Am Soc Trop Med & Hyg; NY Acad Sci; Am Pediat Soc; Soc Pediat Res. *Res:* Relationship of malnutrition to infection; antibody production and other host defense responses in protein deficiency; etiology of diarrhea; rubella and vaccine production; nature of slow virus infections. *Mailing Add:* Dept of Pediat Columbia Univ New York NY 10032

KATZ, MORRIS, b Kiev, Russia, Apr 6, 01; nat Can; m 46; c 4. CHEMICAL ENGINEERING, CHEMISTRY. *Educ:* McGill Univ, BSc, 26, MSc, 27, PhD, 29. *Hon Degrees:* DSc, McGill Univ, 71, York Univ, 81. *Prof Exp:* Demonstr chem, McGill Univ, 26-29; chemist, assoc comt trail smelter smoke, Nat Res Coun Can, 29-31, asst res chemist, Div Chem, 31-37, assoc res chemist, 37-47; res scientist, Res Chem Lab, Defence Res Bd Can 48-55; consult atmospheric pollution, Dept Nat Health & Welfare Can, 56-65, dir environ assessment, 59-65; prof atmospheric sanit, Syracuse Univ, 65-69; prof, 69-80, EMER PROF CHEM, YORK UNIV, 80- *Concurrent Pos:* Officer in chg, Trail Smelter Smoke Invests, Nat Res Coun Can, 34-37; instr, Sch Grad Studies, Syracuse Univ; chmn Can sect, Tech Adv Bd Air Pollution, Int Joint Comn, 49-65; consult, WHO expert adv panel air pollution, 63-; ed, Intersoc Comt, 69- *Honors & Awards:* Coronation Medal, 38; Plummer Medal, Eng Inst Can, 56; Chambers Award, Air Pollution Control Asn, 65; R S Jane Mem Award, Can Soc Chem Engrs, 69; M D Thomas Gold Medal Award, Am Soc Testing & Mat, 81. *Mem:* Am Chem Soc; Am Soc Testing & Mat; Air Pollution Control Asn; fel Chem Inst Can; Eng Inst Can; Can Soc Chem Engrs. *Res:* Polymerization reactions and high polymers; synthetic rubber; effects of sulphur dioxide on vegetation; catalytic oxidation of carbon monoxide; heterogeneous catalysis; effects of air pollutants on plants and health; methods of analysis and instrumentation; polynuclear aromatic hydrocarbons in urban air pollution; photochemical reactions of air pollutants. *Mailing Add:* Dept Chem T-115 Steacie Sci Bldg York Univ 4700 Keele St Toronto ON M3J 2R3 Can

KATZ, MORRIS HOWARD, b Milwaukee, Wis, Jan 12, 20; m 54; c 2. FOOD SCIENCE, BIOCHEMISTRY. *Educ:* Univ Wis, BS, 43. *Prof Exp:* Chemist, Nat Syrup Prod Co, 46-47; chief chemist, Martin Food Prod, Inc, 47-49; asst res dir, Orange Crush Co, 49-52; mfg dir, B A Railton Co, 52-53; flavor res chemist, Fries & Fries, Inc, 53-58; sr chemist, Pillsbury Co, 58-59, head flavor sect, 59-61, sr scientist, 61-68, res assoc res labs, 68-80; PRES, M H KATZ CONSULT INC, 80- *Concurrent Pos:* Guest lectr, Ill Inst Technol, 66 & 70; lectr flavor technol, Ctr Prof Advan, 74 & 76, Univ Minn, 76, Int Microwave Power Inst, 77 & Am Asn Cereal Chemists, 79. *Mem:* Am Chem Soc; Inst Food Technol; Soc Flavor Chemists. *Res:* Flavor chemistry; food texture, ingredient systems and processes; flavor and food products development. *Mailing Add:* 2700 S Yosemite Ave Minneapolis MN 55416

KATZ, MORTON, b New York, NY, Apr 25, 34; m 61; c 3. ORGANIC CHEMISTRY, POLYMER CHEMISTRY. *Educ:* State Univ NY Albany, BS, 56, MS, 61; Wayne State Univ, PhD(org chem), 68. *Prof Exp:* Teacher high sch, 56-58; technician, Gen Elec Res Lab, 59-61; res chemist, Buffalo, 67-70, RES CHEMIST, PLASTIC PROD DEPT, E I DU PONT DE NEMOURS & CO, INC, 70- *Mem:* Am Chem Soc. *Res:* Chemistry of bicyclic and tricyclic molecules; high temperature polymers; market research. *Mailing Add:* Plastic Prod Dept E I du Pont de Nemours & Co Inc Circleville OH 43113

KATZ, MURRAY ALAN, b Albuquerque, NMex, June 15, 41; m 64; c 2. NEPHROLOGY, CARDIOVASCULAR DISEASES. *Educ:* Johns Hopkins Univ, BA, 63, MD, 66. *Prof Exp:* Intern med, Osler Ward Serv, Johns Hopkins Univ Hosp, 66-67, resident, 67-68; fel nephrol, Univ Tex Southwestern Med Br, 68-70; asst prof, Sch Med, Temple Univ, 71-74, actg chief nephrol, 73-74; asst prof nephrol, 74-76, assoc prof, 76-81, PROF, SCH MED, UNIV ARIZ, 81- *Concurrent Pos:* Res develop award, Pub Health Serv, 71-76; clin investr award, Vet Admin, 76; staff physician med, Vet Admin Hosp, Tucson, 74- *Mem:* Am Soc Nephrol; Int Soc Nephrol; Am Fedn Clin Res; AAAS; Microcirculatory Soc. *Res:* General microcirculatory physiology and pathophysiology; control of microcirculatory dynamics, hypertension, capillaropathies, vasculitis. *Mailing Add:* 1501 N Campbell Tucson AZ 85724

KATZ, NORMAN L, b Boston, Mass. PHARMACOLOGY. *Educ:* Mass Col Pharm, BS, 63; Albany Med Col, Union Univ, PhD(pharmacol), 69. *Prof Exp:* Fel neurophysiol, State Univ NY Albany, 69-72; asst prof, 72-81, ASSOC PROF PHARMACOL, UNIV ILL MED CTR, 81- *Mem:* Soc Neurosci; Am Col Clin Pharmacol. *Res:* Examination of the molecular mechanisms involved when a nerve impulse arrives at the region of the neuromuscular junction and the nerve axon releases a chemical transmitter from its terminals. *Mailing Add:* Univ of Ill Med Ctr Col of Pharm 833 S Wood St Chicago IL 60680

KATZ, O(WEN) M(ARVIN), physical metallurgy, see previous edition

KATZ, RALPH VERNE, b Jersey City, NJ, Mar 10, 44; m 68; c 1. EPIDEMIOLOGY, HEALTH ECOLOGY. *Educ:* Trinity Col, Conn, BS, 65; Tufts Univ, DMD, 69; Univ Minn, MPH, 71, PhD(epidemiol), 76. *Prof Exp:* Chief, Div Prev Dent, Inst Dent Res, US Army, Washington, DC, 74-76; dir dent serv, Phys Med & Rehab Unit, 72-74, ASSOC PROF, DEPT HEALTH ECOL, SCH DENT, UNIV MINN, 76- *Concurrent Pos:* Assoc prof, Prog Dent Public Health, Sch Public Health, Univ Minn, 76-, Dept Epidemiol, Grad Sch, 78-, dir & prin investr, Cardiol Training Prog, 80-, dir grad studies, Oral Health Serv Older Adults, 81- *Honors & Awards:* Hatton award, 77. *Mem:* Am Public Health Asn; Int Asn Dent Res; Soc Epidemiol Res; Am Asn Dent Sch; Sigma Xi. *Res:* Epidimiology of root caries and coronal caries; clinical trials of preventive agents for dental caries. *Mailing Add:* Dept Health Ecol Sch Dent Univ Minn Minneapolis MN 55455

KATZ, RICHARD WHITMORE, b Williamsburg, Va, Sept 12, 48. STATISTICS, ATMOSPHERIC SCIENCE. *Educ:* Univ Va, BA, 70; Pa State Univ, PhD(statist), 74. *Prof Exp:* Statistician climatic & environ assessment, Environ Data Serv, Nat Oceanic & Atmospheric Admin, 74-75; scientist & statistician environ & societal impacts, Nat Ctr Atmospheric Res, 75-79; ASST PROF, DEPT ATMOSPHERIC SCI, ORE STATE UNIV, 79- *Concurrent Pos:* Fel, Nat Ctr Atmospheric Res, 75-76; consult, NASA, 77; adj prof, Dept Econ, Univ Colo, 77-79; prin investr, NSF grant, 80-; consult, Lawrence Livermore Nat Lab, 81. *Honors & Awards:* Spec Achievement Award, Environ Data Serv, 75. *Mem:* Am Statist Asn; Inst Math Statist; AAAS; Am Meteorol Soc. *Res:* Meteorological statistics; probabilistic models for hydrological variables; applied probability theory; climatic impacts. *Mailing Add:* Dept Atmospheric Sci Ore State Univ Corvallis OR 97331

KATZ, ROBERT, b New York, NY, July 17, 17; m 43; c 2. PHYSICS. *Educ:* Brooklyn Col, AB, 37; Columbia Univ, AM, 38; Univ Ill, PhD(physics), 49. *Prof Exp:* Radiologist, US Army Air Force, Wright Field, 39-43, physicist, 43-46; from asst prof to assoc prof, 49-56, prof, 56-66; vchmn dept, 68-73, PROF PHYSICS, UNIV NEBR, LINCOLN, 66- *Mem:* AAAS; fel Am Phys Soc; Health Physics Soc; Radiation Res Soc; Soc Photog Scientists & Engrs. *Res:* Radiography; precipitation static radio interference; cereal technology; nuclear physics; structure of particle tracks; theory of RBE. *Mailing Add:* 5850 Sunrise Rd Lincoln NE 68510

KATZ, ROBERT, b Walsenburg, Colo, Jan 14, 28; c 2. MECHANICAL & NUCLEAR ENGINEERING. *Educ:* Univ Colo, BS, 48; Calif Inst Technol, MS, 54, PhD(mech eng), 58. *Prof Exp:* Design engr, Colo Fuel & Iron Corp, 49-50; develop engr, Jet Propulsion Lab, Calif Inst Technol, 54, res asst turbomach, inst, 55-58; staff mem, 58-64, dep div head eng anal, 64-68, sect leader steam generator res, 68-71, SR TECH ADV ENG RES & DEVELOP, GEN ATOMIC CO, 71- *Mem:* Am Soc Mech Engrs; Am Inst Aeronaut & Astronaut. *Res:* Nuclear reactor heat transfer and fluid mechanics; nuclear reactor safety analysis; fluid mechanics of axial turbomachinery; heat transfer in solar and fusion power plants. *Mailing Add:* Gen Atomic Co PO Box 81608 San Diego CA 92138

KATZ, ROBERT SANFORD, b Chicago, Ill, Jan 26, 48; m 70; c 2. HUMAN NUTRITION. *Educ:* Univ Ill, Urbana, BS, 70, MS, 73, PhD(nutrit), 75. *Prof Exp:* Group leader nutrit, Quaker Oats Co, 75-76; ASST DIR NUTRIT, NAT DAIRY COUN, 76- *Mem:* Am Inst Nutrit; Am Soc Animal Sci. *Mailing Add:* Nat Dairy Coun 6300 N River Rd Rosemont IL 60018

KATZ, RONALD LEWIS, b New York, NY, Apr 22, 32; m 54; c 3. ANESTHESIOLOGY. *Educ:* Univ Wis, BA, 48; Boston Univ, MD, 52; Am Bd Anesthesiol, dipl, 62; FRCPS, 81. *Prof Exp:* Intern, Staten Island Pub Health Serv, NY, 56-57; resident anesthesiol, Columbia-Presby Med Ctr Hosp, 57-59; instr, Col Physicians & Surgeons, Columbia Univ, 60-61, assoc, 61-62, from asst prof to prof, 62-73; PROF ANESTHESIOL & CHMN DEPT, MED SCH, UNIV CALIF, LOS ANGELES, 73- *Concurrent Pos:* Fel pharmacol, Col Physicians & Surgeons, Columbia Univ, 59-60; Guggenheim fel, 68-69; consult, Coun Drugs, AMA, 62-; consult anesthesiol res grant comt, NIH, 65-, mem anesthesiol res training grant comt, 70-; vis prof, Royal Postgrad Med Sch, Univ London, 68-69. *Mem:* Am Soc Anesthesiol; fel Am Col Anesthesiol; Am Soc Pharmacol & Exp Therapeut; Am Physiol Soc. *Res:* Physiology; pharmacology; respiratory neurophysiology and neuropharmacology; cardiovascular physiology and pharmacology; neuromuscular transmission. *Mailing Add:* Dept of Anesthesiol Univ of Calif Sch of Med Los Angeles CA 90024

KATZ, SAM, b Seattle, Wash, May 5, 21; m 52; c 2. BIOCHEMISTRY. *Educ:* Univ Wash, BS, 43; Northwestern Univ, PhD(chem), 50. *Prof Exp:* Res assoc chem, Sch Med, Univ Va, 52-53; res assoc, Sharp & Dohme, Inc, 53-54; instr path, Sch Med, Univ Pittsburgh, 54-56; chemist, Upjohn Co, 56-58; asst prof, Albert Einstein Col Med, 58-60; chemist radiation biol, Naval Med Res Inst, 60-65; from asst prof to assoc prof, 65-76, PROF BIOCHEM, SCH MED, UNIV W VA, 76- *Concurrent Pos:* US Qm Corps spec fel, 46-48; USPHS grant, Carlsberg Lab, Copenhagen, 50-52. *Mem:* AAAS; Am Chem Soc; Biophys Soc. *Res:* Thermodynamics study of forces stabilizing protein structure; dilatometric and zone-electrophoretic investigation of protein perturbants systems; kinetics and mechanisms of enzymatic processes; protein and steroid conformational studies. *Mailing Add:* Dept Biochem WVa Med Ctr Morgantown WV 26506

KATZ, SAMUEL, b Berlin, Ger, Feb 13, 23; nat US; m 53; c 3. GEOPHYSICS. *Educ:* Univ Mich, BS, 43; Columbia Univ, AM, 47, PhD, 55. *Prof Exp:* Mem staff, Radiation Lab, Mass Inst Technol, 43-46; asst, Lamont Geol Observ, Columbia Univ, 48-53; physicist, Stanford Res Inst, 53-56, sr physicist, 56-57; assoc prof, 57-61, chmn dept, 63-68, PROF GEOPHYS, RENSSELAER POLYTECH INST, 61- *Honors & Awards:* Kunz Prize, NY Acad Sci, 53. *Mem:* AAAS; Soc Explor Geophys; Am Geophys Union; Seismol Soc Am. *Res:* Marine sciences; seismology; underwater sound propagation; high pressure; ultrasonics. *Mailing Add:* Dept of Geol Rensselaer Polytech Inst Troy NY 12181

KATZ, SAMUEL LAWRENCE, b Manchester, NH, May 29, 27; div; c 7. VIROLOGY, PEDIATRICS. *Educ:* Dartmouth Col AB, 48; Harvard Univ, MD, 52. *Prof Exp:* Intern, Med Serv, Beth Israel Hosp, Boston, Mass, 52-53; jr asst resident, Children's Hosp Med Ctr, 53-54, resident, 55; asst resident, Children's Med Serv, Mass Gen Hosp, 54-55; exchange registr from Children's Hosp Med Ctr to pediat unit, St Mary's Hosp Med Sch, London, 56; instr pediat, Harvard Med Sch, 58-59, assoc, 59-63, tutor med sci, 61-63, asst prof pediat, 63-68; PROF PEDIAT & CHMN DEPT, SCH MED, DUKE UNIV, 68- *Concurrent Pos:* Nat Found Infantile Paralysis res fel pediat, Res Div Infectious Dis, Children's Hosp Med Ctr & Harvard Med Sch, 56-58; Nat Inst Allergy & Infectious Dis career develop award, 65-68; pediatrician-in-chief, Beth Israel Hosp, 58-61; assoc physician, Children's Med Ctr, 58-63, res assoc, Res Div Infectious Dis, 58-68, chief newborn div, 61-68, sr assoc med, 63-68; consult coun drugs, AMA, 63-65; mem, Vaccine Develop Bd, Nat Inst Allergy & Infectious Dis, 67-71, Armed Forces Epidemiol Bd, Comn Immunization, 69-73, Gen Clin Res Ctr Comt, NIH, 71-74 & Nat Adv Coun Child Health & Human Develop, 74-77; pres, Asn Med Sch & chmn pediat dept, 77-79. *Mem:* Inst Med-Nat Acad Sci; Infectious Dis Soc Am; Am Epidemiol Soc; Am Pediat Soc; Am Soc Clin Invest. *Res:* Tissue culture studies of measles virus variants; development of live attenuated measles virus vaccine; central nervous system viral infections. *Mailing Add:* Dept of Pediat Duke Univ Sch of Med Durham NC 27710

KATZ, SHELDON LANE, b Philadelphia, Pa, Oct 6, 48; m 73; c 1. PHYSICS. *Educ:* Temple Univ, BA, 69, MA, 73, PhD(physics), 77. *Prof Exp:* Lab instr physics, Temple Univ, Philadelphia, 69-74, res asst, 74-77; vis lectr, 77-78, ASST PROF PHYSICS, LAFAYETTE COL, 78- *Mem:* Am Phys Soc. *Res:* Dynamics of first and second order phase transitions; renormalization group; Monte Carlo simulations. *Mailing Add:* Dept of Physics Lafayette Col Easton PA 18042

KATZ, SIDNEY, b Winnipeg, Man, Aug 17, 09; m 37; c 2. PHYSICAL CHEMISTRY. *Educ:* Univ Man, BSc, 34, MSc, 35; McGill Univ, PhD(phys chem), 37. *Prof Exp:* Royal Soc Can traveling fel, London, 37-38; res chemist, British Thompson-Houston Co, Eng, 38-39, Pfanstiehl Chem Co, Ill, 40-41 & Goldsmith Bros, Chicago, 41-44; res assoc, Manhattan proj, 44-45; assoc prof chem, Inst Gas Technol, 45-52; res phys chemist, Ill Inst Technol Res Inst, 52-58, sci adv, 58-69, SR SCI ADV, IIT RES INST, 69- *Concurrent Pos:* Lectr eng, Sci & Mgt War Training, Ill Inst Technol, 42-45. *Mem:* Am Chem Soc. *Res:* Light scattering; kinetics of gaseous reactions; kinetics and thermodynamics; spectroscopy; aerosol technology. *Mailing Add:* IIT Res Inst 10 W 35th St Chicago IL 60616

KATZ, SIDNEY, b Chicago, Ill, Mar 1, 16; m 43; c 2. CHEMISTRY. *Educ:* Kalamazoo Col, BA, 37; Mich State Univ, MS, 46, PhD, 49. *Prof Exp:* Chemist, Oak Ridge Gaseous Diffusion Plant, 49-62; chemist, Oak Ridge Nat Lab, 62-81; CONSULT, 81- *Honors & Awards:* Jour Award, Soc Appl Spectros, 61. *Mem:* Am Chem Soc; Sigma Xi. *Res:* High resolution liquid chromatography; analysis of body fluids; ultrasensitive methods for determination of stable organic compounds in polluted waters; sensitive detectors for liquid chromatographs; coal liquefaction; catalytic oxygen-hydrogen combination. *Mailing Add:* 110 Wendover Circle Oak Ridge TN 37830

KATZ, SIDNEY, b Brooklyn, NY, Dec 23, 30; m 57. PHYSIOLOGY, NEUROPHYSIOLOGY. *Educ:* NY Univ, BA, 57, MS, 59, PhD(physiol), 63. *Prof Exp:* Teaching asst neuroanat, Sch Med, NY Univ, 61-62, instr physiol, Col Dent, 62-63; asst prof, 65-71, assoc prof, 71-77, PROF PHYSIOL, MED UNIV SC, 77- *Concurrent Pos:* Nat Heart Inst fel, 63-65. *Mem:* Am Physiol Soc; Soc Neurosci. *Res:* Central control of respiration and circulation; modulation of medullary neuron discharge patterns; ionic permeabiltiy of muscle studies with electrophysiological methods; electrophysiology of spinal cord injury. *Mailing Add:* Dept of Physiol Med Univ of SC Charleston SC 29401

KATZ, SIDNEY, b Cleveland, Ohio, Feb 4, 24; m 46; c 4. PREVENTIVE MEDICINE. *Educ:* Case Western Reserve Univ, BS, 45, MD, 48. *Prof Exp:* Intern & resident med, Univ Hosps Cleveland, 48-50; fel path, Sch Med, Case Western Reserve Univ, 50; physician med, US Army Reserves, 50-52; mem fac internal med & prev med, Sch Med, Case Western Reserve Univ, 52-71, prof & assoc dir prev med, 71; dir, Off Health Serv, Educ & Res, 71-77, PROF MED, COL HUMAN MED, MICH STATE UNIV, 71-, PROF COMMUNITY HEALTH SCI & CHMN DEPT, 78- *Mem:* Inst Med-Nat Acad Sci; Asn Teachers Prev Med; Int Epidemiol Asn; Geront Soc. *Res:* Health services research; gerontology; clinical epidemiology. *Mailing Add:* Dept of Community Health Sci Mich State Univ East Lansing MI 48824

KATZ, SIDNEY A, b Camden, NJ, June 4, 35; m 57; c 2. RADIOCHEMISTRY, ANALYTICAL CHEMISTRY. *Educ:* Rutgers Univ, AB, 58; Univ Pa, PhD(chem), 62. *Prof Exp:* Chemist, R H Hollingshead Corp, 53-58; asst instr chem, Univ Pa, 58-60; instr, 60-62, from asst prof to assoc prof, 62-71, PROF CHEM, RUTGERS UNIV, 71- *Concurrent Pos:* Res chemist, E I du Pont de Nemours & Co, Inc, 66; res assoc, Univ Pa Hosp, 60-70; prof, Temple Univ, 66-70; vis prof, The Univ, Reading, Berkshire, UK, 73; NATO sr fel sci, NSF, 73; consult, ACCU Test & Consult Lab, 74-75, John G Reutter & Assocs, 74-75, Rossnagel & Assocs, 77-78 & Jack McCormick & Assocs, 78; vis prof, Trace Anal Res Ctr, Dalhousie Univ, 77. *Mem:* AAAS; Am Chem Soc; Am Nuclear Soc. *Res:* Environmental and biochemical effects of trace elements. *Mailing Add:* Dept Chem Rutgers Univ Camden NJ 08102

KATZ, SIDNEY MARCO, b Baltimore, Md, July 12, 22; m 44; c 3. DATA PROCESSING, COMPUTER SCIENCES. *Educ:* Johns Hopkins Univ, BE, 43; Princeton Univ, AM, 48, PhD(phys chem), 49. *Prof Exp:* Res chemist, Jackson Lab, E I du Pont de Nemours & Co, 49-51, reactor physicist, Atomic Energy Div, 49-54, res supvr, 54-61, sr physicist, 61-63; vis assoc prof bus admin, Univ SC, 63-64; sr engr, Sperry Gyroscope Co, 64-65; supvr data collection & anal, Goddard Space Flight Ctr, NASA, Md, 65-69; mem tech staff, Sci Data Systs, Inc, 69; mgr data processing systs, Xerox Data Systs, 69-75, mgr spec systs group, 75-76; comput specialist, 76-78, unit chief, Tech Specif Develop Unit, 78-81, SUPVRY COMPUT SCIENTIST, DEFENSE INTEL AGENCY, FED BUR INVEST, 81- *Concurrent Pos:* Fel, Textile Res Inst; prof lectr, Am Univ, 73-74. *Mem:* Asn Comput Mach. *Res:* Electronic computing; programming analysis; administration. *Mailing Add:* 914 Brentwood Lane Silver Spring MD 20902

KATZ, SOL, b New York, NY, Mar 29, 13; m 46; c 3. MEDICINE. *Educ:* City Col New York, BS, 35; Georgetown Univ, MD, 39; Am Bd Internal Med, dipl, 48. *Hon Degrees:* DSc, Sch Med, Georgetown Univ, 79. *Prof Exp:* Adj clin prof, 45-58, assoc prof, 58-65, dir pulmonary dis, 70-78, PROF MED & KOBER LECTR, GEORGETOWN UNIV, 65-, PROF PULMONARY MED, 78- *Concurrent Pos:* Adj clin prof, George Washington Univ, 50-58, prof lectr, 58-; chief med serv, Vet Admin Hosp, DC, 59-70; clin prof med, Sch Med, Howard Univ, 67-; consult, NIH, 58-, Children's Hosp, Walter Reed Army Hosp & Bethesda Naval Hosp; vis consult, Cardiothoracic Inst, Brompton Hosp, London, 74-75. *Mem:* Am Thoracic Soc; Am Col Physicians; Am Col Chest Physicians; Am Fedn Clin Res; Brit Thoracic Asn. *Res:* Pulmonary diseases. *Mailing Add:* Pulmonary Div Georgetown Univ Hosp Washington DC 20007

KATZ, THOMAS JOSEPH, b Prague, Czech, Mar 21, 36; US citizen; m 63; c 1. ORGANIC CHEMISTRY, ORGANOMETALLIC CHEMISTRY. *Educ:* Univ Wis, BA, 56; Harvard Univ, MA, 57, PhD(chem), 59. *Prof Exp:* Instr, 59-61, from asst prof to assoc prof, 61-68, PROF CHEM, COLUMBIA UNIV, 68- *Concurrent Pos:* Sloan fel, 62-66; Guggenheim fel, 67-68. *Mem:* Am Chem Soc. *Res:* Non-benzenoid aromatic compounds; organometallic compounds; organic synthesis; catalysis by metals. *Mailing Add:* Dept of Chem Columbia Univ New York NY 10027

KATZ, WILLIAM J(ACOB), b Chicago, Ill, Jan 19, 25; m 48; c 3. SANITARY & CHEMICAL ENGINEERING. *Educ:* Univ Ill, BS, 48; Univ Wis, MS, 49, PhD(chem eng), 53. *Prof Exp:* Proj assoc indust waste & treatment, Univ Wis, 49-52; dir sanit & indust wastes res & consult, Envirex Inc Div, Rexnord Inc, 53-63, tech dir & mgr water treatment & water pollution control res, 63-70, mgr, Ecol Div, Rex Chainbelt Inc Div, 70-75, vpres res & develop, Envirex Inc, 76-77; dir tech serv, Milwaukee Metrop Sewerage Dist, 77-81; PRES, ENVIRON PLANNING & SCI DIV, CAMP DRESSER & MCKEE INC, 81- *Concurrent Pos:* Vis prof civil eng, Univ Wis, 65- *Honors & Awards:* Eddy Medal, Water Pollution Control Fedn, 55, Gascoigne Medal. *Mem:* Water Pollution Control Fedn. *Res:* Water and industrial waste treatment; packing plant; mechanism of activated sludge; foundries; refineries. *Mailing Add:* 220 W Cherokee Milwaukee WI 53217

KATZ, YAIR, b Tel Aviv, Israel, Dec 22, 43; m 68; c 2. COMPARATIVE ENDOCRINOLOGY. *Educ:* Hebrew Univ Jerusalem, BSc, 66, MSc, 68, PhD(physiol), 74. *Prof Exp:* Fel endocrinol, Univ Western Ont, 74-76, lectr physiol, 76-77; ASST MEM ENDOCRINOL, MONELL CHEM SENSES CTR, UNIV PA, 77- *Mem:* Endocrine Soc; Soc Study Reproduction. *Res:* Steroid metabolism in gonads; gonadotropic hormones steroidogenic activities; role of olfactory communicants in control of reproduction. *Mailing Add:* 3209 Pearl Philadelphia PA 19104

KATZ, YALE H, b Milwaukee, Wis, Mar 15, 20; m 45; c 2. METEOROLOGY. *Educ:* Univ Wis, BS, 47, MS, 48; Pa State Col, MS, 51. *Prof Exp:* Asst, Univ Wis, 47-48; meteorologist, US Air Force Air Weather Serv, 51, asst to chief, Data Integration Br, 51-52, specialist climatic res, 52-54, tech consult, 54-56; res assoc, Phys Res Labs, Univ Boston, 56-57; sr staff meteorologist, Itek Corp, 58-60; phys scientist, Rand Corp, Calif, 60-67; sr staff mem, TRW Systs Group, Redondo Beach, 67-73, sr systs engr, 73-76; dir, Appl Res Assocs, 76-77; tech dir, Soc Photo-Optical Instrumentation Engrs, 77-81; DIR, INST FOR TECHNOL COMMUNICATION, 82- *Concurrent Pos:* Partner & assoc, Appl Res Assocs, 54-60; lectr, Air Force Sr Technol Specialist Sch, Mather AFB, 56; ed, J Soc Photo-Optical Instrumentation Engrs, 70-72, assoc ed, Optical Eng, 72-78. *Mem:* Am Meteorol Soc; Am Geophys Union; fel Soc Photo-Optical Instrument Engrs (vpres, 71-75, gov, 70-71 & 75); Coun Eng Sci Soc Execs; NAm Infrared Thermographic Asn. *Res:* Development and direction of educational and training programs for medical, legal and industrial professionals; technology transfer; applied optical and electro-optical engineering; environmental engineering; utilization of solar energy; atmospheric pollution; statistical meteorology and climatology; utilization of solar energy; environmental engineering. *Mailing Add:* 2800 Woodridge Dr Bellingham WA 98226

KATZBERG, ALLAN ALFRED, b Can, July 6, 13; nat US; m 48; c 4. ANATOMY. *Educ:* Univ Man, BSc, 43; Inst Divi Thomae, MS, 49; Univ Okla, PhD(med sci), 56. *Prof Exp:* Instr histol & embryol, Sch Med, Univ Okla, 49-51, from instr to asst prof anat, 51-59; res assoc prof & head cellular biol sect, Aerospace Med Ctr, US Air Force, Brooks AFB, Tex, 59-63, dep chief, Astrobiol Div, 60-63; assoc prof physiol, Med Sch, Univ Sask, 63-64; head anat div, Southwest Found for Res & Educ, 64-65, chmn dept, 65-68; assoc prof biol, Western Ill Univ, 68-69; assoc prof anat, 69-77, PROF ANAT, MED CTR, IND UNIV-PURDUE UNIV, INDIANAPOLIS, 77- *Concurrent Pos:* Consult, Arctic Aeromed Lab, US Air Force, 61 & Fed Aviation Admin-US Air Force 6571st Aeromed Res Lab, Holloman AFB, 67; actg chmn dept anat, Ind Univ-Purdue Univ, Indianapolis, 70-71. *Honors & Awards:* Eli Lilly Award, 72. *Mem:* AAAS; Am Asn Anat; hon mem Mex Soc Anat; fel Royal Micros Soc; Int Primatol Soc. *Res:* Aging processes; tissue culture; regeneration; aerospace medicine; primate histology. *Mailing Add:* Dept of Anat Ind Univ-Purdue Univ Med Ctr Indianapolis IN 46202

KATZEN, ELLIOTT D(EXTER), b Baltimore, Md, Apr 30, 20; m 44, 80; c 6. AERONAUTICS. *Educ:* Univ Md, BS, 43; Univ Minn, MS, 47. *Prof Exp:* Res scientist-proj engr, Ames Res Ctr, NASA, 49-58, res scientist-sect head, 58-59, res scientist-asst br chief, 59-68, chief hypersonic aerodyn br, 68-71, tech asst to dir astronaut, 71-75; CONSULT, 75- *Mem:* Assoc fel Am Inst Aeronaut & Astronaut. *Res:* Supersonic and hypersonic aircraft and missile aerodynamics, performance, stability and control; atmosphere-entry trajectories and aerodynamics, heat transfer and mass transfer. *Mailing Add:* 455 Ferne Ave Palo Alto CA 94306

KATZEN, HOWARD M, b Baltimore, Md, May 2, 29; m 60; c 3. BIOCHEMISTRY. *Educ:* Johns Hopkins Univ, BS, 56; George Washington Univ, MS, 58, PhD(enzym), 62. *Prof Exp:* Biochemist, Nat Inst Arthritis & Metab Dis, 54-62; instr pediat, Sch Med, Johns Hopkins Univ & asst dir pediat res, Sinai Hosp Baltimore, Inc, 63-65; sr res biochemist, 65-75, RES ASST DIR, MERCK INST THERAPEUT RES, RAHWAY, 75- *Concurrent Pos:* Am Cancer Soc res fel enzym, Mass Inst Technol, 62-63; vis scientist, Nat Inst Arthritis & Metab Dis, 65; guest scientist, Imp Col, Univ London, 69. *Mem:* AAAS; Am Chem Soc; Am Diabetes Asn; Am Soc Biol Chem; Am Inst Chem. *Res:* Glycogen structure and metabolism; insulin metabolism and disulfide biosynthesis; methionine biosynthesis; folate-vitamin B-twelve regulations; isoenzymes; insulin action; coenzymes; enzyme regulation; membrane receptors. *Mailing Add:* 109 Meadowbrook Rd North Plainfield NJ 07062

KATZENBERGER, EDWARD F(REDERICK), aeronautical engineering, see previous edition

KATZENELLENBOGEN, BENITA SCHULMAN, b Brooklyn, NY, Apr 11, 45; m 67; c 2. REPRODUCTIVE ENDOCRINOLOGY. *Educ:* Brooklyn Col, BA, 65; Harvard Univ, MA, 66, PhD(biol), 70. *Prof Exp:* NIH res fel endocrinol, Dept Physiol & Biophys, Univ Ill, Urbana, 70-71, asst prof physiol, 71-76, ASSOC PROF PHYSIOL, SCH BASIC MED SCI, UNIV ILL COL MED & DEPT PHYSIOL & BIOPHYS, UNIV ILL, URBANA, 76- *Concurrent Pos:* Vis prof, Dept Biochem & Biophys, Univ Calif, San Francisco, 77-78. *Mem:* Am Physiol Soc; Endocrine Soc. *Res:* Regulation of the growth and function of reproductive tissues and tumors by reproductive hormones and antihormones. *Mailing Add:* Dept of Physiol & Biophys Univ of Ill 524 Burrill Hall Urbana IL 61801

KATZENELLENBOGEN, JOHN ALBERT, b Poughkeepsie, NY, May 10, 44; m 67. BIO-ORGANIC CHEMISTRY, SYNTHETIC ORGANIC CHEMISTRY. Educ: Harvard Univ, BA, 66, MA, 67, PhD(chem), 69. Prof Exp: From asst prof to assoc prof, 69-79, PROF CHEM, UNIV ILL, URBANA, 79- Concurrent Pos: Sloan fel, 74-76; Guggenheim fel, 77-78. Honors & Awards: Teacher Scholar Award, Camille & Henry Dreyfus Found, 74-79. Mem: AAAS; Am Chem Soc; NY Acad Sci; Am Soc Biol Chemists; Royal Soc Chem. Res: New synthetic methods; organometallic chemistry; natural product synthesis; mechanism of hormone action; affinity labeling; tumor localizing agents; radiopharmaceutical development. Mailing Add: Sch Chem Sci Univ Ill 1609 W California St Urbana IL 61801

KATZENSTEIN, JACK, physics, see previous edition

KATZIN, GERALD HOWARD, b Winston-Salem, NC, Aug 2, 32; m 58; c 2. PHYSICS. Educ: NC State Univ, BS, 54, MS, 56, PhD(relativity), 63. Prof Exp: Assoc nuclear reactor theory, Astra, Inc, Conn, 57-58; asst prof, 63-67, assoc prof, 67-76, PROF PHYSICS, NC STATE UNIV, 76- Concurrent Pos: NSF grant, 67. Mem: Am Phys Soc. Res: General relativity; theoretical mechanics; classical electrodynamics; Riemannian geometry and tensor analysis; study of the relations between symmetries and conservation laws; differential geometry. Mailing Add: Dept of Physics NC State Univ Raleigh NC 27650

KATZIN, LEONARD ISAAC, b Eau Claire, Wis, Jan 18, 15; m 38; c 4. PHYSICAL INORGANIC CHEMISTRY. Educ: Univ Calif, Los Angeles, AB, 35; Univ Calif, PhD(phys chem biol), 38. Prof Exp: Asst zool, Univ Calif, 35-37, fel, 38-40; jr biologist, USPHS, 40-41, asst biologist, 41-42; fel radiol, Sch Med & Dent, Univ Rochester, 42-43; res assoc, Metall Lab, Univ Chicago, 43-46; sr chemist, Argonne Nat Lab, 46-78. Concurrent Pos: Vis prof, Univ Chicago, 56-57; exchange fel, Atomic Energy Res Estab, Harwell, Eng, 58-59; asst prof, Univ Ill, 61; vis prof inorg chem, Hebrew Univ Jerusalem, 69-70 & Inst Chem, Tel Aviv Univ, 69-70. Mem: AAAS; Am Phys Soc; Am Chem Soc; Sigma Xi. Res: Nuclear chemistry; heavy element chemistry; optical rotation; coordination chemistry; nuclear waste management. Mailing Add: 428 Hudson Lane Port Hueneme CA 93041

KATZMAN, PHILIP AARON, b Omaha, Nebr, May 18, 06; m 33; c 2. BIOCHEMISTRY. Educ: Kalamazoo Col, AB, 27; St Louis Univ, PhD(biochem), 32. Prof Exp: Res instr, 32-36, sr instr, 36-41, from asst prof to prof, 41-74, EMER PROF BIOCHEM, MED SCH, ST LOUIS UNIV, 74- Concurrent Pos: US Pharmacopoeia Comt, 40-50; lectr, Univ Kans, 52; Merck Sharpe & Dohme vis prof, Univ SDak, 63. Mem: AAAS; Am Soc Biol Chem; Am Chem Soc; Endocrine Soc; Soc Study Reproduction. Res: Chorionic gonadotropin; reproduction; antihormones; antibiotics; hydrolysis of conjugated steroids; biological properties of estrogens; molecular action of ovarian hormones. Mailing Add: Dept Biochem St Louis Univ Med Sch St Louis MO 63104

KATZMAN, ROBERT, b Denver, Colo, Nov 29, 25; m 47; c 2. NEUROLOGY. Educ: Univ Chicago, BS, 49, MS, 51; Harvard Med Sch, MD, 53; Am Bd Psychiat & Neurol, dipl & cert neurol, 59. Prof Exp: Intern, Harvard Med Serv, Boston City Hosp, 53-54; asst resident neurol, Neurol Inst, Columbia Presby Hosp, 54-56, chief resident neurologist, 56-57; instr, 57-58, assoc, 58-60, from asst prof to assoc prof, 60-64, chmn dept, 64-81, PROF NEUROL, ALBERT EINSTEIN COL MED, 64-, DIR, HOSP, 74- Concurrent Pos: Nat Mult Sclerosis Soc fel, 57-59; USPHS sr fel neurophysiol, 61-62, USPHS career res develop award, 62-66; asst neurol, Columbia Univ, 56-57; guest scholar, Polytech Inst Brooklyn, 60-61; consult, Jewish Bd Guardians, 61-65; attend neurologist, Bronx Munic Hosp, 64-, dir neurol serv, 70-; mem res rev panel, Nat Mult Sclerosis Soc, 64-70; asst examr, Am Bd Psychiat & Neurol, 63-70; mem neurol prog, Proj A Comn, Nat Inst Neurol & Commun Disorders & Strokes, 69-73, chmn neurol disorders prog proj rev comt, 72-73, Aging Rev Comt, NIH, 76-81, chmn Aging Rev Comt, 80-81. Honors & Awards: S Weir Mitchell Award, Am Acad Neurol, 60; Ann Prize, Am Asn Neuropathologists, 62. Mem: AAAS; fel Am Acad Neurol; Am Asn Neuropathologists; Int Soc Neurochem; Soc Neurosci. Mailing Add: Dept of Neurol Albert Einstein Col of Med New York NY 10461

KATZMANN, FRED L, b Magdeburg, Ger, Apr 10, 29; US citizen; m 55; c 3. ELECTRONICS. Educ: City Col New York, BEE, 52; Stevens Inst Technol, MSc, 62. Prof Exp: Res eng, Allen B DuMont Labs Div, Fairchild Camera & Instrument Corp, 52-59, eng mgr, Corp, 59-65; dir electronic instruments dept, Electronic Prod & Controls Div, Monsanto Co, 66-69, dir & gen mgr, 69-70; vpres mkt, Electronic Prods Div, Singer Co, 70-71; PRES, BALLANTINE LABS, INC, 71- Mem: Inst Elec & Electronics Engrs; Precision Measurement Asn; Int Standards Asn; Instrument Soc Am. Res: Electronic instrumentation, particularly oscilloscopes, voltmeters and digital frequency counters, ultra fast transient recording instrumentation systems and alternating current. Mailing Add: Ballantine Labs Box 97 Boonton NJ 07005

KATZOFF, SAMUEL, b Baltimore, Md, Aug 3, 09. AERODYNAMICS. Educ: Johns Hopkins Univ, BS, 29, PhD(chem), 34. Prof Exp: Lab technician, Rockefeller Inst, 29-30; res chemist, Baltimore Paint & Color Works, 34-53; Jones fel biophys, Cold Spring Harbor, 35-36; physicist, Nat Adv Comt Aeronaut, 36-58, res scientist, NASA, 58-60, asst chief, Appl Mat & Physics Div, 60-64, sr staff scientist, Langley Res Ctr, 64-69, CHIEF SCIENTIST, LANGLEY RES CTR, NASA, 69- Concurrent Pos: Ed, Proc Symposium on Thermal Radiation of Solids, 64 & Remote Measurement of Pollution, 71. Mem: AAAS; assoc fel Am Inst Aeronaut & Astronaut. Res: X-ray crystallography; x-ray studies of the molecular arrangements in liquids; colloids; general aerodynamics; stability; electrical analogies; wind-tunnel interference; cascades; helicopters; space sciences; thermal control of spacecraft. Mailing Add: 285-G Clemwood Pkwy Hampton VA 23669

KATZPER, MEYER, b Ramat-Gan, Israel, July 31, 36; US citizen; m 73. BIOPHYSICS, COMPUTER SCIENCE. Educ: Yeshiva Univ, BA, 57; NY Univ, MS, 62, PhD(physics), 67. Prof Exp: Asst prof physics, Long Island Univ, 66-67; sr res scientist biophysics, Nat Biomed Res Found, 67-70; asst prof comput sci, State Univ NY Plattsburgh, 70-74; tech assoc software, Ocean Data Systs, Inc, 74-76; INDEPENDENT CONSULT PHYSICS INFO SCI, 76- Concurrent Pos: Instr, Washington Lehrhaus, 75-76; asst prof lectr, Dept Physiol, George Wash Univ Med Sch, 76-78, assoc prof lectr, 78- Mem: Am Asn Physics Teachers; AAAS; Asn Comput Mach; Inst Elec & Electronics Engrs; Simulation Coun. Res: Modeling and simulation of biophysical, physiological, environmental and social processes. Mailing Add: 2 Locks Pond Ct Rockville MD 20854

KATZUNG, BERTRAM GEORGE, b Floral Park, NY, June 11, 32; m 57; c 2. PHARMACOLOGY. Educ: Syracuse Univ, BA, 53; State Univ NY, MD, 57; Univ Calif, PhD, 62. Prof Exp: Lectr, 60-62, from asst prof to assoc prof, 62-71, chmn dept, 67-79, PROF PHARMACOL, MED CTR, UNIV CALIF, SAN FRANCISCO, 71-, CO-VCHMN DEPT, 67-, ACTING CHMN, 80- Honors & Awards: Markle Scholar, 66-71. Mem: AAAS; Soc Pharmacol & Exp Therapeut; Biophys Soc. Res: Cardiovascular pharmacology; electrophysiology. Mailing Add: 65 Knoll Rd San Rafael CA 94901

KAUDER, OTTO SAMUEL, b Vienna, Austria, Nov 26, 26; US citizen; m 56; c 2. ORGANIC CHEMISTRY. Educ: City Col New York, BS, 46; Polytech Inst Brooklyn, MS, 49; Oxford Univ, DPhil(org chem), 52. Prof Exp: Chemist, Polychem Labs, NY, 46-48; chemist plastics additives, 52-59, res group leader, 59-68, patent liaison & toxicol supvr, 62-68, VPRES RES & DEVELOP, ARGUS CHEM CORP, 68- Mem: Am Chem Soc. Res: Time-dependent properties of organic compounds and effect of additives and contaminants thereon; synthesis of organic compounds containing phosphorus, cadmium, tin and antimony. Mailing Add: 633 Court St Brooklyn NY 11231

KAUER, JAMES CHARLES, b Cleveland, Ohio, Jan 17, 27; m 54; c 5. ORGANIC CHEMISTRY. Educ: Case Western Reserve Univ, BS, 51; Univ Ill, PhD(chem), 55. Prof Exp: RES CHEMIST, CENT RES DEPT, EXP STA, E I DU PONT DE NEMOURS & CO, INC, 55- Mem: Am Chem Soc; Sci Res Soc Am; The Chem Soc. Res: Organic synthesis; heterocycles; peptides; antiviral agents; neurotransmitter analogs. Mailing Add: Cent Res Dept E I du Pont de Nemours & Co Inc Wilmington DE 19898

KAUER, JOHN STUART, b New York, NY, Dec 26, 43; c 2. SENSORY PHYSIOLOGY. Educ: Clark Univ, BA, 67, MA, 69; Univ Pa, PhD(anat), 73. Prof Exp: Fel neurophysiol, 73-75, res assoc & dir lab studies, 76-78, ASST PROF, SECT NEUROSURG, SCH MED, YALE UNIV, 78- Mem: Soc Neurosci; Am Asn Anatomists. Res: Central synaptic organization of the olfactory and other sensory systems; anatomy and physiology of spinal cord trauma; animal model for the study of tinnitus. Mailing Add: Sect of Neurosurg Sch of Med Yale Univ New Haven CT 06510

KAUFERT, FRANK HENRY, b Princeton, Minn, Dec 2, 05; m 38; c 1. FOREST PRODUCTS. Educ: Univ Minn, BS, 28, MS, 30, PhD(forestry & plant path), 35. Prof Exp: Field asst, US Forest Serv, 29 & 31; instr forestry, Univ Minn, 32-37; technologist, Div Pest Control Res, Exp Sta, E I du Pont de Nemours & Co, 37-40; assoc prof forestry, Univ Minn, 40-42; technologist, Forest Prods Lab, US Forest Serv, 42-45; prof forestry & dir sch, 45-70, dean, 70-74, EMER DEAN COL FORESTRY, UNIV MINN, ST PAUL, 74- Concurrent Pos: Dir Soc Am Foresters forestry res proj, 53; asst adminr, Coop State Res Serv, USDA, DC, 63-64; mem, Bd Agr & Renewable Resources, Nat Res Coun- Nat Acad Sci, 75- Mem: Fel Soc Am Foresters; Forest Prod Res Soc (pres, 57-58); assoc Am Wood Preservers Asn; Forest Hist Soc (pres, 54-55 & 63-65). Res: Wood technology and preservation; forest management. Mailing Add: 223 Kaufer Lab Dept Forest Prod Col of Forestry Univ of Minn St Paul MN 55108

KAUFERT, JOSEPH MOSSMAN, b Minneapolis, Minn, Feb 10, 43; m 70; c 1. MEDICAL ANTHROPOLOGY. Educ: Univ Minn, BA, 66; Northwestern Univ, MA, 68, PhD(polit sci, anthrop), 73. Prof Exp: Asst prof health admin, Baylor Univ, 71-72; asst prof med sociol & social psychiat, Med Sch, Univ Tex, San Antonio, 72-74; head soc sci sect, St Thomas Hosp Med Sch, Univ London, 74-76; ASSOC PROF MED ANTHROP, DEPT SOCIAL & PREV MED, FAC MED, UNIV MAN, 76- Concurrent Pos: Leverhulme fel, Univ Birmingham, 73-74; consult, Welsh Off, Brit Health & Social Serv, UK, 74-76, Nat Haemophilia Soc UK, 74-76 & Ment Health Man, 77-78; adj prof, Dept Anthrop, Univ Man, 77- Honors & Awards: Keith L Were Award, Nat Media Develop Trust, 72. Mem: Soc Social Med; fel Soc Appl Anthrop; Brit Sociol Asn; Soc Med Anthrop. Res: Social epidemiology; medical sociology; illness behavior; the sociology of disability; social gerontology. Mailing Add: Dept of Social & Prev Med Fac of Med Univ of Man Winnipeg MB R3T 2N2 Can

KAUFFELD, NORBERT M, b Trivandrum, Kerala, India, Jan 30, 23; US citizen; m 45; c 5. ENTOMOLOGY, APICULTURE. Educ: Kans State Univ, BS & MS, 49, PhD(entom), 67. Prof Exp: Rancher, 49-58; instr high sch, Kans, 58-62; instr apicult, Kans State Univ, 62-66; res entomologist, Univ Wis, 66-67, invest leader, Bee Breeding Invest, La State Univ, Baton Rouge, 67-74, RES ENTOMOLOGIST, BEE RES LAB, AGR RES SERV, TUCSON, ARIZ, 74- Concurrent Pos: Apiarist entom div, Kans State Bd Agr, 61-63. Mem: AAAS; Entom Soc Am; Bee Res Asn. Res: Pollination of crops, honey bee behavior, nutrition and the interrelationship between them. Mailing Add: Bee Res Lab 2000 E Allen Rd Tucson AZ 85719

KAUFFMAN, ELLWOOD, b Philadelphia, Pa, Mar 18, 28; m 50; c 4. MATHEMATICS. Educ: Temple Univ, AB, 52. Prof Exp: Sr analyst, Remington Rand, Inc, NY, 52-55; comput applns officer, Chesapeake & Ohio Rwy Co, Va, 55-57; sr programmer digital comput, Elec Assocs, Inc, 57-58; comput consult, 58-59; pres, Appl Data Res, Inc, 59-63 & Comput Mgt Corp, 63-65; tech dir, Mgt Info Systs, Inc, 65-69; exec vpres, Mainstem, Inc, 65-78;

EXEC VPRES, K-SQUARED SYSTS, INC, 78- *Mem:* Opers Res Soc Am. *Res:* Utility concept of computer problem solving; application of digital computing systems to the solutions of commercial and scientific problems; automatic programming procedures for digital computers. *Mailing Add:* K-Squared Systs 1101 State Rd Bldg G Princeton NJ 08540

KAUFFMAN, ERLE GALEN, b Washington, DC, Feb 9, 33; m 56; c 3. PALEOBIOLOGY, PALEOECOLOGY. *Educ:* Univ Mich, BS, 55, MS, 56, PhD(geol, paleont, stratig), 61. *Hon Degrees:* MS, Oxford Univ, 70. *Prof Exp:* Asst cur, 60-61, assoc cur, 61-67, CUR DEPT PALEOBIOL, US NAT MUS, SMITHSONIAN INST, 67- *Concurrent Pos:* Lectr, George Washington Univ, 63-64, adj prof, 65-; NSF res grant, 63-71; Am Geol Inst vis lectr, 65-66; Smithsonian Res Found grants, 65-; Paleont Soc rep, Comt Earth Sci, Nat Res Coun-Nat Acad Sci, 65-71; vis prof, Oxford Univ, 70-71, Univ Tübingen, 74 & Univ Colo, 76-78; res assoc, Mus Paleontol, Univ Mich, 75-; adj prof, Univ Colo, 76- *Mem:* AAAS; Brit Palaeont Asn; Malacol Soc London; Int Palaeont Union; Paleont Soc. *Res:* Systematics, evolution and paleoecology of Mesozoic-Cenozoic Mollusca; ecology of Recent Mollusca; Mesozoic-Cenozoic stratigraphy, biostratigraphy and sedimentation. *Mailing Add:* US Nat Mus Dept Paleobiol E206 Tenth & Constitution Ave NW Washington DC 20560

KAUFFMAN, FREDERICK C, b Chicago, Ill, July 9, 36; m 61; c 2. BIOCHEMISTRY, PHARMACOLOGY. *Educ:* Knox Col, Ill, BA, 58; Univ Ill, Chicago, PhD(pharmacol), 65. *Prof Exp:* Asst prof & assoc pharmacol, State Univ NY, Buffalo, 67-74; assoc prof, 74-78, PROF PHARMACOL, SCH MED, UNIV MD, BALTIMORE, 78- *Concurrent Pos:* USPHS fel pharmacol, Wash Univ, 65-67. *Mem:* AAAS; Am Chem Soc; Soc Neurosci; Am Soc Pharmacol & Exp Therapeut; Am Soc Neurochem. *Res:* Biochemical pharmacology; neurochemistry. *Mailing Add:* Dept of Pharmacol Univ of Md Sch of Med Baltimore MD 21201

KAUFFMAN, GEORGE BERNARD, b Philadelphia, Pa, Sept 4, 30; m 52, 69; c 5. INORGANIC CHEMISTRY, HISTORY OF SCIENCE. *Educ:* Univ Pa, BA, 51; Univ Fla, PhD(chem), 56. *Prof Exp:* Asst chem, Univ Fla, 51-55; instr, Univ Tex, 55-56; from asst prof to assoc prof, 56-66, PROF CHEM, CALIF STATE UNIV, FRESNO, 66- *Concurrent Pos:* Res corp grant, 55, 57, 59 & 69; NSF res grants, 60 & 67-69, Zurich, 63 & Berkeley, 76-77; NSF undergrad res partic dir, 72; Am Chem Soc Petrol Res Fund grant, 62 & 65; Am Philos Soc grant, 63 & 69; tour speaker, Am Chem Soc, 71; fel, John Simon Guggenheim Mem Found, 72, grant, 75; contributing ed, J Col Sci Teaching, 73-; co-ed, Topics Hist Chem, Lectures on Tape Series, Am Chem Soc, 75-78, ed, 78-81; vis scholar, Univ Calif, Berkeley, 76 & Univ Puget Sound, 78. *Honors & Awards:* Lev Aleksandrovich Chugaev Jubilee Dipl & Bronze Medal, USSR Acad Sci, 76; Dexter Award in the Hist of Chem, 78. *Mem:* AAAS; Am Chem Soc (chmn div hist chem, 69); Hist Sci Soc; Soc Study Alchemy & Chem. *Res:* Inorganic synthesis; stereochemistry; coordination compounds; chromatography separations; ion exchange; platinum metals; lanthanides; chemical education; unusual oxidation states; history of chemistry; biographies of chemists; translations of classics of chemistry. *Mailing Add:* Dept of Chem Calif State Univ Fresno CA 93740

KAUFFMAN, GLENN MONROE, b Goshen, Ind, Apr 8, 38. PHYSICAL ORGANIC CHEMISTRY. *Educ:* Goshen Col, BA, 61; Univ Pa, PhD(org chem), 66. *Prof Exp:* PROF CHEM, EASTERN MENNONITE COL, 65-, CHMN DEPT, 66- *Concurrent Pos:* Acad exten grant, Univ Fla & Eastern Mennonite Col, 68-70; Res Corp res grant, Eastern Mennonite Col, 68-69; res fel, Univ Fla, 75-76. *Mem:* AAAS; Am Chem Soc. *Res:* Conformational analysis of cyclopentane compounds; mechanisms of epoxidation reactions and ring-opening reaction of epoxides; hydrogen-deuterium exchange of pyridine-N-oxides. *Mailing Add:* Dept of Chem Eastern Mennonite Col Harrisonburg VA 22801

KAUFFMAN, HAROLD, b West Liberty, Ohio, Apr 23, 39; m 61; c 3. PHYTOPATHOLOGY, AGRONOMY. *Educ:* Goshen Col, BS, 61; Mich State Univ, PhD(plant path), 67. *Prof Exp:* plant pathologist, Int Rice Res Inst, 67-81, joint coordr, Int Rice Testing Prog, 75-81; DIR, INT SOYBEAN PROG, UNIV ILL, URBANA, 81- *Mem:* Am Phytopath Soc. *Res:* International agriculture; bacterial diseases of rice plants; crop improvement. *Mailing Add:* Int Soybean Prog 113 Mumford Hall Univ Ill Urbana IL 61801

KAUFFMAN, JAMES FRANK, b St Joseph, Mo, Jan 29, 37; m 64; c 2. ELECTRICAL ENGINEERING. *Educ:* Univ Mo-Rolla, BS, 60; Univ Ill, Urbana, MS, 64; NC State Univ, PhD(elec eng), 70. *Prof Exp:* Engr airborne radar, Westinghouse Elec Corp, 60-62; res asst lens antennas, Antenna lab, Univ Ill, Urbana, 64-65; sr engr, Electronics Res Lab, Corning Glass Works, 67-70; asst prof elec eng, 70-76, ASSOC PROF ELEC ENG, NC STATE UNIV, 76- *Mem:* Inst Elec & Electronics Engrs. *Res:* Electromagnetics, especially antennas and microwave transmission. *Mailing Add:* Dept of Elec Eng PO Box 5275 NC State Univ Raleigh NC 27650

KAUFFMAN, JOEL MERVIN, b Philadelphia, Pa, Jan 3, 37; m 66. ORGANIC CHEMISTRY. *Educ:* Philadelphia Col Pharm, BS, 58; Mass Inst Technol, PhD(org chem), 63. *Prof Exp:* Chemist, Reaction Motors Div, Thiokol Chem Corp, 63-64; USPHS fel antiradiation drugs, Mass Col Pharm, 64-66; res chemist, ICI Am Inc, Mass, 66-69; res & develop dir, Pilot Chem Div, New Eng Nuclear Corp, Watertown, 69-76; res assoc, Mass Col Pharm, 77-79; ASST PROF CHEM, PHILADELPHIA COL PHARM & SCI, 79- *Concurrent Pos:* Consult, Mass Div, Am Automobile Asn, 64-; consult liquid scintillation counting, 76- & laser dyes, 82- *Mem:* Am Chem Soc. *Res:* Synthesis of fluors, fluorescent dyes, laser dyes, scintillators, antiallergenic drugs, antimalarials, anticancer drugs and other medicinal chemicals; laser dyes; scintillators; blocked amino acids; heterocyclics; vinyl monomers; photochemical reactions; terpenes; peptides; boron cage compounds; antiradiation-anticancer drugs; radiation sensitizers; plasticizers; fatty acid derivatives; formulation of liquid scintillators, solubilizers, decontaminants. *Mailing Add:* Philadelphia Col Pharm & Sci 43 St & Woodland Ave Philadelphia PA 19104

KAUFFMAN, JOHN W, b Washington, DC, Mar 28, 25; m 59; c 1. BIOPHYSICS. *Educ:* George Washington Univ, BS, 47; Univ Md, MS, 49; Univ Ill, PhD, 55. *Prof Exp:* Res physicist, US Naval Res Lab, 48-50; asst, Univ Ill, 50-55; PROF MAT SCI & ENG & BIOL SCI, NORTHWESTERN UNIV, 55- *Res:* Biomaterials. *Mailing Add:* Dept of Mat Sci Technol Inst Northwestern Univ Evanston IL 60201

KAUFFMAN, LEON A, b Philadelphia, Pa, July 26, 34; m 69; c 2. PULMONARY DISEASES, INTERNAL MEDICINE. *Educ:* Temple Univ, AB, 57, MD, 61; Am Bd Internal Med, dipl, 73, cert pulmonary med, 78. *Prof Exp:* Resident path, SDiv, Einstein Med Ctr, Philadelphia, 62-63; resident internal med, Hahnemann Med Col & Hosp, 63-65, instr med, 66-68, sr instr & dir pulmonary function lab, 68-70, asst dir pulmonary dis div & dir respiratory intensive care unit, 69-73, asst prof med, 70-77; med dir sect respiratory ther, St Agnes Hosp, 73-78; ASSOC PROF MED, HAHNEMANN MED COL & HOSP, 77-; CHMN, DIV PULMONARY MED, METROP HOSP, PHILADELPHIA, 73- *Concurrent Pos:* Pa Thoracic Soc fel pulmonary physiol & clin chest dis, 65-66; clin asst pulmonary med, Hahnemann Div, Philadelphia Gen Hosp, Pa, 66-78; mem ad hoc comt to evaluate med care in state tuberc hosp syst, Pa, 67; mem fel & res comt, Pa Thoracic Soc, 68-74; pulmonary consult, Shock & Trauma Unit, Hahnemann Med Col & Hosp, 70-; attend pulmonary med, St Agnes Hosp, 73- *Mem:* AAAS; AMA; Am Thoracic Soc; fel Am Col Chest Physicians; An Med Instrumentation. *Res:* Respiratory intensive care and respiratory failure in man; design of systems for delivery of care and treatment of repiratory failure; respiratory therapy; clinical pulmonary physiology. *Mailing Add:* 1900 Spruce St Philadelphia PA 19103

KAUFFMAN, MARVIN EARL, b Lancaster, Pa, Aug 31, 33; m 53; c 7. GEOLOGY. *Educ:* Franklin & Marshall Col, BS, 55; Northwestern Univ, MS, 57; Princeton Univ, PhD, 60. *Prof Exp:* Asst geologist, Alaskan Br, US Geol Surv, 53; asst geologist, Bethlehem Steel Co, 53-55; PROF GEOL, FRANKLIN & MARSHALL COL, 59- *Concurrent Pos:* NSF sci fel, State Univ Utrecht, 65-66; consult geologist various co; pres, Yellowstone-Bighorn Res Asn. *Mem:* Nat Asn Geol Teachers; Int Asn Sedimentologists; Soc Econ Paleontologists & Mineralogists; Geol Soc Am. *Res:* Structure and stratigraphy of the Garnet Range and Marine Jurassic of western Montana; stratigraphy of southeastern Pennsylvania. *Mailing Add:* Dept of Geol Franklin & Marshall Col Lancaster PA 17604

KAUFFMAN, ROBERT GILLER, b St Joseph, Mo, Dec 29, 32; m 55; c 2. MEAT SCIENCE. *Educ:* Iowa State Univ, BS, 54; Univ Wis, MS, 58, PhD(animal sci), 61. *Prof Exp:* Asst prof animal sci, Univ Ill, 61-66; prof animal sci, 66-81, PROF MEAT & ANIMAL SCI, UNIV WIS-MADISON, 81- *Mem:* Am Soc Animal Sci; Am Meat Sci Asn; Inst Food Technol. *Res:* Lipid transport in striated muscle; composition of meat animals and carcasses. *Mailing Add:* Dept of Meat & Animal Sci Univ of Wis Madison WI 53706

KAUFFMAN, SHIRLEY LOUISE, b Grand Junction, Colo, Sept 10, 24. PATHOLOGY. *Educ:* Univ Chicago, BS, 46, MS, 48; Univ Kans, MD, 55. *Prof Exp:* Asst path, Med Col, Cornell Univ, 55-57; Nat Cancer Inst trainee path, Francis Delafield Hosp, 57-59; instr, Albert Einstein Col Med, 59-60; fel, 60, from asst prof to assoc prof, 61-70, PROF PATH, STATE UNIV NY DOWNSTATE MED CTR, 70- *Concurrent Pos:* Provisional asst pathologist, NY Hosp, 55-57; vis prof, Dept Anat, Univ Berne, 69, Path Inst Rikshospitalet, Oslo, Norway, 76- & Inst Cancer Res Royal Marsden, Sutton Surrey, UK, 77. *Mem:* Am Soc Exp Path; NY Acad Sci; Int Soc Stereology; Am Asn Path & Bact. *Res:* Mammalian embryogenesis; lung morphometry; cell differentiation and proliferation; neoplasia. *Mailing Add:* Dept of Path State Univ NY Downstate Med Ctr Brooklyn NY 11203

KAUFFMAN, STUART ALAN, b Sacramento, Calif, Sept 28, 39; m 67; c 1. MEDICINE, THEORETICAL BIOLOGY. *Educ:* Dartmouth Col, BA, 61; Oxford Univ, BA, 63; Univ Calif, San Francisco, MD, 68. *Prof Exp:* Vis scientist, Mass Inst Technol, 67-68; intern, Cincinnati Gen Hosp, 68-69; asst prof theoret biol, Univ Chicago, 69-73, asst prof med, 70-73; res assoc, Lab Theoret Biol, Nat Cancer Inst, 73-75; assoc prof biochem-biol, 75-81, ASSOC PROF BIOCHEM & BIOPHYS, UNIV PA, 81- *Concurrent Pos:* Fel genetics, Univ Cincinnati, 68-69. *Honors & Awards:* Norbert Wiener Gold Medal, Am Soc Cybernet, 70. *Mem:* Philos Sci Asn. *Res:* Theory of organization of eukaryotic gene regulation networks; control of DNA synthesis. *Mailing Add:* Dept of Biochem Univ of Pa Philadelphia PA 19104

KAUFFMANN, STEVEN KENNETH, b Canton, Ohio, Oct 22, 44; m 68; c 1. NUCLEAR & PARTICLE PHYSICS. *Educ:* Calif Inst Technol, BS, 65, PhD(physics, math), 73. *Prof Exp:* Res assoc physics, Univ Utah, 73; res fel, Calif Inst Technol, 73-74 & Univ Cape Town, 76-77; physicist, Lawrence Berkeley Lab, 77-80; CONTRACT RES OFFICER, UNIV CAPE TOWN, SAFRICA, 80- *Res:* Collisions of relativistic heavy ions; collisions of low energy heavy ions; quantum field theories. *Mailing Add:* Physics Dept Univ Cape Town Pvt Bag Rondebosch C P 7700 Repub SAfrica

KAUFMAN, ALBERT IRVING, b New York, NY, July 22, 38; m 62. MEDICAL PHYSIOLOGY, NEUROPHYSIOLOGY. *Educ:* Cooper Union, BEE, 61; Drexel Inst Technol, MS, 62; Temple Univ, PhD(physiol), 68. *Prof Exp:* Instr, 66-69, asst prof, 69-80, ASSOC PROF PHYSIOL, STATE UNIV NY DOWNSTATE MED CTR, 80- *Concurrent Pos:* Vis prof, Tokyo Metrop Inst Geront, 75-76. *Res:* Neurophysiology of autonomic nervous system. *Mailing Add:* 2609 Ave S Brooklyn NY 11229

KAUFMAN, ALLAN N, b Chicago, Ill, July 21, 27; m 57; c 2. PLASMA PHYSICS. *Educ:* Univ Chicago, PhD(physics), 53. *Prof Exp:* Assoc prof, 65-67, PROF PHYSICS, UNIV CALIF, BERKELEY, 67-, STAFF PHYSICIST, LAWRENCE BERKELEY LAB, 53- *Concurrent Pos:* Consult, Convair, 58-59; sr fel, Goddard Space Flight Ctr, 67. *Mem:* Fel Am Phys Soc. *Res:* Meson theory; hydrodynamics; many-body problem; statistical mechanics. *Mailing Add:* Dept of Physics Univ of Calif Berkeley CA 94720

KAUFMAN, ALVIN B(ERYL), b Jacksonville, Fla, Oct 9, 17; m 48; c 2. ELECTRICAL ENGINEERING. *Educ:* Los Angeles City Col, AA, 38. *Prof Exp:* Res analyst, Douglas Aircraft Co, Calif, 39-52; group engr, Northrop Aircraft Corp, 52-55; chief develop engr, Arnoux Corp, 55-58; head, mat & devices res sect, Res & Anal Dept, Litton Industs, 58-65, mem tech staff, Litton Systs Div, 65-70; sr mil systs engr, Lockheed Aircraft Corp, 70-74; proj engr, Inet Div, Teledyne Corp, 74-78; mem tech staff, Hughes Aircraft Co, 78-81; WRITING, CONSULT & LECTR, 81- *Res:* Development of instrumentation equipment and systems; development and test of night vision systems, radar and uninterruptible power supply systems; technical writing; nuclear effects on guidance and control systems. *Mailing Add:* 22420 Philiprimm St Woodland Hills CA 91367

KAUFMAN, ARNOLD, b Nuremberg, Ger, Dec 23, 28; US citizen; m 52; c 3. RESEARCH ADMINISTRATION, BIOCHEMICAL ENGINEERING. *Educ:* Columbia Univ, BS, 50, MA, 60. *Prof Exp:* Chem engr, Merck Sharp & Dohme Res Lab, 50-58, group leader chem eng res & develop, 58-62, res assoc, 62-64, sect mgr, 64-66, sr res fel, 66-69, mgr eng develop & process automation, 69-71, assoc dir chem eng res & develop, 71-77, dir, chem eng res & develop, 77-81, SR DIR RES PLANNING & ANAL, MERCK SHARP & DOHME RES LABS, MERCK & CO, INC, RAHWAY, 81- *Mem:* Am Inst Chem Engrs; Am Chem Soc. *Res:* Processes to manufacture organic chemical and naturally derived products for pharmaceutical use; biological development; heterogeneous catalysis; separations techniques; solids processing; process control using digital computers; fermentation technology; production of vaccines; planning and analysis of research and development activities; chemical engineering. *Mailing Add:* PO Box 2000 Rahway NJ 07065

KAUFMAN, BERNARD, b Chicago, Ill, Aug 17, 32; m 56; c 2. BIOCHEMISTRY. *Educ:* Univ Ill, BSc, 54, MSc, 56; Ind Univ, PhD(microbiol), 61. *Prof Exp:* Asst microbiol, Univ Ill, 54-56; asst, Ind Univ, 56-61; Arthritis & Rheumatism Found fel, Univ Mich, Ann Arbor, 61-64, lectr bot, 64-66; asst prof biochem, Johns Hopkins Univ, 66-68; ASSOC PROF BIOCHEM, MED CTR, DUKE UNIV, 68- *Mem:* AAAS; Am Soc Microbiol. *Res:* Elucidation of the reactions concerned in the synthesis of brain gangliosides; relationship of axonal gangliosides to myelination; chemistry and biosynthesis of cell surface glycolipids and glycoproteins. *Mailing Add:* Dept of Biochem Duke Univ Med Ctr Durham NC 27710

KAUFMAN, BERNARD TOBIAS, biochemistry, see previous edition

KAUFMAN, BORIS, b New York, NY, Jan 10, 26; m 49; c 1. MECHANICAL ENGINEERING. *Educ:* Univ Cincinnati, BS, 50, MechEng, 60; Ill Inst Technol, MS, 52. *Prof Exp:* Asst engr, Armour Res Found, Ill Inst Technol, 50-53, design engr, US Air Conditioning Corp, Ohio, 53-57, chief engr, 57-59; asst prof mech eng, Univ Idaho, 59-61; from asst prof to assoc prof, 61-69, PROF MECH ENG, CALIF STATE UNIV, SACRAMENTO, 69- *Concurrent Pos:* Co-dir, Bio-Eng Sect, Cardio-Pulmonary Div, Sutter Hosps Med Res Found, Sacramento, 62- *Mem:* Am Soc Heating, Refrig & Air-Conditioning Engrs. *Res:* Air conditioning theory and design; bio-engineering aspects of prosthetic heart devices. *Mailing Add:* Sch of Eng 6000 J St Sacramento CA 95819

KAUFMAN, C(HARLES) W(ESLEY), b Thomas, WVa, Nov 26, 11; m 35; c 1. CHEMICAL ENGINEERING. *Educ:* Washington & Lee Univ, BS, 33; Univ Ariz, MS, 63, PhD, 67. *Prof Exp:* Chemist, Nat Fruit Prod Corp, 33-34; chem engr, Nat Canners Asn, 35-39; lab mgr food technol, Gen Foods Corp, 39-43, dir res, 44-48, vpres, 48-50, dir, 49-50; dir res, Kraft Foods Corp, 50-51, vpres res & develop, 51-57; dir, Nat Dairy Prod Corp, 58-61; vpres, Foremost Dairies, 61-62; assoc prof dairy sci, Univ Ariz, 64-67; vpres res & develop, Mars, Inc, 67-70; CONSULT, CJC CONSULT, 70- *Concurrent Pos:* Consult, Off Qm Gen, US Army, 40-44; lectr NY Univ, 47; vpres, Res & Develop Assoc Food & Container Inst, 50-52; mem bd trustees, Shimer Col, 58-63; vpres admin, Pima Community Col, Tucson, 70-71. *Mem:* Inst Food Technol; hon mem Packaging Inst (pres, 59-60); fel Am Inst Chemists. *Res:* Food technology and engineering; colloid chemistry; research administration. *Mailing Add:* 2601 Camino Valle Verde Tucson AZ 85715

KAUFMAN, CHARLES, b Brooklyn, NY, June 4, 37. THEORETICAL PHYSICS. *Educ:* Univ Wis, BS, 56; Pa State Univ, MS, 59, PhD(physics), 63. *Prof Exp:* Instr physics, Pa State Univ, 63-64; asst prof, 64-73, ASSOC PROF PHYSICS, UNIV RI, 73- *Concurrent Pos:* Physicist, US Naval Underwater Systs Ctr, 69-71; guest lectr, Univ Vienna, 71-72; consult, Raytheon Corp, 78- *Mem:* Am Phys Soc; Acoust Soc Am; NY Acad Sci; Am Asn Univ Professors. *Res:* Electrodynamics; quantum field theory; atomic and elementary particle physics; turbulence theory; underwater acoustics. *Mailing Add:* Dept of Physics Univ of RI Kingston RI 02881

KAUFMAN, CLEMENS MARCUS, b Moundridge, Kans, Aug 27, 09; m 41; c 3. SILVICULTURE, FOREST ECOLOGY. *Educ:* Bethel Col, Kans, AB, 36; Univ Minn, MS, 38, PhD(forestry), 43. *Prof Exp:* Asst, Div Forestry, Univ Minn, 39, asst forester, Agr Exten Serv, 40-42, asst, Cloquet Forest Exp Sta, 42-43; from asst res prof to assoc res prof forestry, NC State Col, 43-48, prof forest mgt, 48-51; dir sch forestry, 51-62, prof, 62-76, EMER PROF FORESTRY, UNIV FLA, 76- *Mem:* Soc Am Foresters; Ecol Soc Am. *Res:* Physiological ecology; growth of slash pine. *Mailing Add:* 13026 NW 49th Ave Gainesville FL 32601

KAUFMAN, DANIEL, b Washington, DC, Mar 8, 20; m 43; c 5. ORGANIC CHEMISTRY. *Educ:* Univ Md, MS, 41. *Prof Exp:* Asst, Univ Md, 41-42; chemist, US Bur Mines, Utah, 42-44, NC, 46-47; chemist, Manhattan Proj, Los Alamos, NMex, 44-46; res chemist, Nat Lead Co, 47-59; supvr inorg res, Res Div, Wyandotte Chem Corp, 59-68; res assoc, Kerr Mfg Co Div, Ritter Pfaudler Corp, 68-69, dir res & develop, Kerr Mfg Co Div, Sybron Corp, 69-71, vpres res & develop, 71-75; RES DIR, KAUFMAN DEVELOP CO, 75- *Concurrent Pos:* Mem nat adv bd biomat res, Clemson Univ; US mem, Fedn Dentaire Int Comn, 75-77. *Mem:* Am Chem Soc; Int Asn Dent Res; AAAS. *Res:* Hydrogenation and hydrogenolysis of furfural; production of elemental boron; hydrometallurgy of manganese ores; titanium chemistry; cyclopentadienyl metal compounds; catalysis and olefin polymerization; metallurgical chemistry; dental materials. *Mailing Add:* 1921 Sorrel St Camarillo CA 93010

KAUFMAN, DAVID GORDON, b Jersey City, NJ, May 28, 43; m 66; c 1. PATHOLOGY, BIOCHEMISTRY. *Educ:* Reed Col, BA, 66; Wash Univ, MD, 68, PhD(exp path), 73. *Prof Exp:* Intern path, Barnes Hosp, Wash Univ, 68-69, resident, 69-70; res assoc carcinogenesis, Nat Cancer Inst, 70-73, res scientist, 73-75; assoc prof, 75-80, PROF MATH, UNIV NC, 80- *Concurrent Pos:* Mem, Path B Study Sect, NIH, 77-79, Chem Path Study Sect, 79-; mem prototype explicit anal pesticides comt, Nat Acad Sci, 78-80; res career develop award, Nat Cancer Inst, 78. *Mem:* Am Asn Cancer Res; Am Asn Pathologists; Am Soc Cell Biol; Am Col Toxicol; NY Acad Sci. *Res:* Chemical carcinogenesis; eukaryotic DNA replication and repair; cell biology of respiratory tract and female genital tract tissues. *Mailing Add:* Dept of Path Sch of Med Univ of NC Chapel Hill NC 27514

KAUFMAN, DON ALLEN, b Wahoo, Nebr, Aug 4, 40; m 63; c 1. ORGANIC CHEMISTRY. *Educ:* Univ Nebr, BS, 61; Univ Colo, MBS, 65; Colo State Univ, PhD(chem), 69. *Prof Exp:* Instr gen sci, Omaha Pub Schs, Nebr, 61-63; instr chem, Chandler High Sch, Ariz, 63-64; PROF ORG CHEM, KEARNEY STATE COL, 69- *Concurrent Pos:* NSF fac prof develop grant, Univ Nebr-Lincoln, 77-78. *Mem:* Am Chem Soc. *Res:* Use of crown ethers in organic synthesis; stability of vinyl cations; pH of precipitation; synthesis and reactions of Bunte salts. *Mailing Add:* Dept of Chem Kearney State Col Kearney NE 68847

KAUFMAN, DONALD DEVERE, b Wooster, Ohio, Dec 2, 33; m 57. SOIL MICROBIOLOGY, AGRICULTURAL CHEMISTRY. *Educ:* Kent State Univ, BA, 55, MA, 58; Ohio State Univ, PhD(plant path), 62. *Prof Exp:* Res technician, Plant Path, Ohio Agr Exp Sta, 56-57, res asst, 58-62; soil microbiologist pesticides, Plant Indust Sta, 62-73, SOIL MICROBIOLOGIST, AGR ENVIRON QUAL INST, BELTSVILLE AGR RES CTR W, SCI & EDUC ADMIN-AGR RES, USDA, 73- *Concurrent Pos:* Fulbright lectr soil microbiol, Khonkaen Univ, Thailand, 67-68. *Mem:* AAAS; Am Phytopath Soc; Am Soc Microbiol; Am Chem Soc; Weed Sci Soc Am. *Res:* Microbial decomposition of pesticides; effects of pesticides on soil microorganisms; soil microbiology of root diseases. *Mailing Add:* Agr Environ Qual Inst USDA Beltsville Agr Res Ctr West Beltsville MD 20705

KAUFMAN, DONALD WAYNE, b Abilene, Tex, June 7, 43; m 67; c 1. MAMMALIAN ECOLOGY, EVOLUTIONARY BIOLOGY. *Educ:* Ft Hays Kans State Col, BS, 65, MS, 67; Univ Ga, PhD(zool), 72. *Prof Exp:* Fel genetics, Univ Tex, 71-73; vis scientist, Savannah River Ecology Lab, Aiken, SC, 73-74; asst prof zool, Univ Ark, 74-75; asst prof biol, State Univ NY Binghamton, 75-77; dir pop biol & physiol ecol prog, NSF, 77-80; ASST PROF BIOL, KANS STATE UNIV, 80- *Concurrent Pos:* Mem rev panel, Environ Protection Agency, 81- *Mem:* Am Soc Mammalogists; Ecol Soc Am; AAAS; Soc Study Evolution; Am Inst Biol Scientists. *Res:* Ecology of rodents, evolutionary ecology, ecological genetics; grassland ecology. *Mailing Add:* Div Biol Kans State Univ Manhattan KS 66506

KAUFMAN, EDWARD GODFREY, b New York, NY, June 8, 19; m 38; c 3. DENTISTRY. *Educ:* NY Univ, DDS, 43. *Prof Exp:* From instr to assoc prof prosthodont, 46-66, asst dean, 69-71, PROF PROSTHODONT, COL DENT, NY UNIV, 67-, ASSOC DEAN, 72-, CHMN DEPT, 74- *Concurrent Pos:* Gordon Res Found grant, 57-60; NIH grant base metal alloys, 61-; Williams Ref Corp grant, 64-; pvt pract, 46-; res assoc, Mat Res Lab, Murry & Leone Guggenheim Inst Dent Res, 56-; consult dent asst training prog, NIH, 60-, co-prin investr, NIH Grant, 66-71; consult outpatient clin USPHS, 66- *Mem:* AAAS; Am Dent Asn; Am Soc Metals; Am Ceramic Soc; Sigma Xi. *Res:* Clinical and laboratory research in fields of dental materials, stress analysis and applied technology. *Mailing Add:* 18 W Woods Rd Great Neck NY 11020

KAUFMAN, ERNEST D, b Cologne, Ger, Sept 21, 31; US citizen; m 59; c 3. PHYSICAL CHEMISTRY. *Educ:* Ill Inst Technol, BS, 53; Loyola Univ, Ill, MS, 58, PhD(phys chem), 62. *Prof Exp:* Res chemist, Dearborn Chem Co, Ill, 53-57; sr engr, Cook Elec Co, 57-61; lectr phys sci, Roosevelt Univ, 61-62; from asst prof to assoc prof chem, St Mary's Col, Minn, 62-69; res chemist, Am Cyanamid Co, 69-74, proj leader, 74-77, proj mgr, 77-78, dir, Bradford Tech Ctr, Cyanamid Int, UK, 78-80, TECH DIR, CYANAMID BV, NETH, 80- *Concurrent Pos:* Lectr phys chem, Mundelein Col, 61-62; Fulbright lectr, Univ Ceylon, 66-67. *Mem:* Am Chem Soc; Am Mgt Asn; Indian Chem Soc. *Res:* Polymerization kinetics; process development; sodium atom reactions; protein conformation; rotation of collagen model compounds; polymer-cellulose interactions. *Mailing Add:* Cyanamid BV PO Box 1523 3000 BM Rotterdam Netherlands

KAUFMAN, FRANK B, b June 23, 43; US citizen. PHYSICAL CHEMISTRY, ORGANIC CHEMISTRY. *Educ:* Univ Rochester, BS, 65; Johns Hopkins Univ, PhD(chem), 71. *Prof Exp:* NIH fel phys chem, Royal Inst Great Brit, 70-72; vis prof, Univ Ill, 72-73; MEM RES STAFF PHYS CHEM, T J WATSON RES CTR, IBM CORP, 73- *Mem:* Am Chem Soc; NY Acad Sci. *Res:* Design, synthesis and properties of new monomeric and polymeric materials with novel electronic properties. *Mailing Add:* T J Watson Res Ctr IBM Corp Yorktown Heights NY 10598

KAUFMAN, FREDERICK, b Vienna, Austria, Sept 13, 19; nat US; m 51; c 1. PHYSICAL CHEMISTRY. *Educ:* Johns Hopkins Univ, PhD(chem), 48. *Prof Exp:* Supvry chemist, chief phys chem sect & chem phys br, US Army Ballistic Res Labs, Aberdeen Proving Ground, Md, 48-64; chmn dept chem, 77-80, PROF CHEM, UNIV PITTSBURGH, 64-, DIR SPACE RES DEVELOP CTR, 75-, VPRES COMBUSTION INST, 78- *Concurrent Pos:* Lectr, McCoy Col, Johns Hopkins Univ, 48-64; Rockefeller pub serv award, Cambridge, Eng, 55-56. *Honors & Awards:* Kent Award, 58; US Army Res & Develop

Achievement Award, 62; Pittsburgh Award, Am Chem Soc, 77. *Mem:* Nat Acad Sci; Am Phys Soc; Faraday Soc; Combustion Inst; Am Chem Soc. *Res:* High temperature gas kinetics; combustion science; atom and free radical reactions; upper atmosphere processes. *Mailing Add:* 5854 Aylesboro Ave Pittsburgh PA 15217

KAUFMAN, HAROLD ALEXANDER, b Brooklyn, NY, Jan 27, 33; m 56; c 2. ORGANIC CHEMISTRY. *Educ:* Brooklyn Col, BS, 55; Univ Pittsburgh, PhD(chem), 61. *Prof Exp:* Instr chem, Brooklyn Col, 55; res chemist, AMP, Inc, 55-56; mgr pesticides synthesis, screening & develop, Mobil Chem Co, 61-76; V PRES RES & DEVELOP, J T BAKER CHEM CO, 76- *Mem:* Am Chem Soc; The Chem Soc; Weed Sci Soc Am; Entom Soc Am; AAAS. *Mailing Add:* J T Baker Chem Co 222 Red School Lane Phillipsburg NJ 08865

KAUFMAN, HAROLD RICHARD, b Audubon, Iowa, Nov 24, 26; m 48; c 4. PLASMA PHYSICS, MECHANICAL ENGINEERING. *Educ:* Northwestern Univ, BS, 51; Colo State Univ, PhD(mech eng), 71. *Prof Exp:* Res engr, Nat Adv Comt Aeronaut, 51-57, sect head aircraft propulsion res, 57-58, res engr, NASA, 58-60, sect head, Space Propulsion Res, 60-64, br chief, 64-67, asst div chief, 67-74; prof mech eng & physics, 74-81, PROF PHYSICS & CHMN DEPT, COLO STATE UNIV, 81-, CHMN PHYSICS, 79- *Honors & Awards:* James H Wyld Award, Am Inst Aeronaut & Astronaut, 69; Medal Except Sci Achievement, NASA, 71. *Mem:* Assoc fel Am Inst Aeronaut & Astronaut; Am Phys Soc; Am Vacuum Soc. *Res:* Electric space propulsion; ion beams and ion sources. *Mailing Add:* Dept of Physics Colo State Univ Ft Collins CO 80523

KAUFMAN, HERBERT EDWARD, b New York, NY, Sept 28, 31; c 3. OPHTHALMOLOGY. *Educ:* Princeton Univ, AB, 52; Harvard Med Sch, MD, 56; Am Bd Ophthal, dipl, 63. *Prof Exp:* Head & lectr ophthal, Uveitis Lab, Mass Eye & Ear Infirmary, 59-62; prof ophthal & pharmacol & chmn Ophthal, Col Med, Univ Fla, 62-77; PROF OPHTHAL & PHARMACOL & HEAD OPHTHAL, LA STATE UNIV MED CTR, NEW ORLEANS, 78- *Concurrent Pos:* Dir outpatient clins, Univ Fla; dir, Eye Bank Asn Am; ed-in-chief, Invest Ophthal; ed, Am J Ophthal & Chemotherapy, Metabolic Ophthal & Ann Ophthal; med dir, Eye & Ear Inst La, 79- *Honors & Awards:* Knapp Award, AMA, 63; Albion O Bernstein Award, NY State Med Soc, 63; Lions Int Humanitarian Award, 68; Conrad Berens Award, 75; Jackson Mem lectr, 79; Pocklington lectr, 79; Proactor lectr, 81. *Mem:* AAAS; AMA; Asn Res Vision & Ophthal (secy-treas, 64-73, pres, 75); Am Asn Immunol; Am Fedn Clin Res. *Mailing Add:* Dept Pharmacol & Ophthal La State Univ Med Ctr New Orleans LA 70112

KAUFMAN, HERBERT S, b Salina, Kans, Apr 30, 35; m 63; c 3. MEDICINE, ALLERGY. *Educ:* Univ Kans, BA, 57; Baylor Univ, MD, 61; Am Bd Pediat, dipl & cert pediat allergy, 66. *Prof Exp:* Intern pediat, St Louis Childrens Hosp, Mo, 61-62, resident, 62-63; resident, Tex Childrens Hosp, 63-64; NIH fel allergy & immunol, 64-66, CLIN INSTR DERMAT, MED CTR, UNIV CALIF, SAN FRANCISCO, 66- *Concurrent Pos:* Res grant, Univ Calif, San Francisco, 66-; comt mem & course chmn, Continuing Educ Dept, Pac Presby Med Ctr, 66-, dir pediat allergy clin, 66-68; consult, Dept Rehab, State of Calif & Letterman Gen Hosp, 66-; chief allergy & immunol clin, Dept Pediat, Children's Hosp San Francisco, 68-71. *Mem:* AMA; Am Acad Allergy; Am Col Allergists; Brit Soc Allergy; Brit Soc Immunol. *Res:* Immunoglobin defects in allergic individuals; complement levels in allergic disease; organic components of mental illness. *Mailing Add:* 2352 Post #303 San Francisco CA 94115

KAUFMAN, HERMAN S, b New York, NY, Mar 31, 22; m 43; c 3. POLYMER SCIENCE, SCIENCE EDUCATION. *Educ:* Brooklyn Col, BA, 42; Polytech Inst Brooklyn, MS, 45, PhD(phys chem), 47. *Prof Exp:* Jr chemist radar lab, Sig Corps, US Army, NJ, 42; res chemist, Manhattan Proj, Columbia Univ, 43-45; res chemist, Carbide & Carbon Chem Co, 45; instr phys chem, Polytech Inst Brooklyn, 45-49; supvr polymer properties group, M W Kellogg Co, 49-57; asst tech dir, Jersey City Div, Minn Mining & Mfg Co, 57-59; tech asst to res mgr, Cent Res Lab, Allied Chem Corp, 59-61, corp coordr polymer res, 61-64, dir res planning, 64-68; assoc prof chem, Yeshiva Univ, 68-70; prof chem & dir sch theoret & appl sci, 70-77, EXEC DIR RES & DEVELOP, RAMAPO COL NJ, 77- *Concurrent Pos:* Am Chem Soc fel, 47-49; adj prof, Polytech Inst Brooklyn, 49-63; lectr, Fairleigh Dickinson Univ, 63-67; res dir, Plastics Inst Am, 65-70, bd chmn, 69-70; tech consult, UN Indust Orgn, 68; ed, Int J Polymeric Mat, 71- *Mem:* Distinguished mem Soc Plastics Eng; Am Chem Soc; Am Phys Soc. *Res:* Polymer structure and properties; polymer structure and properties and biomedical application of polymers. *Mailing Add:* Off of Res & Develop Ramapo Col Mahwah NJ 07430

KAUFMAN, HOWARD NORMAN, b Boston, Mass, Jan 2, 26; m 47; c 3. MECHANICAL ENGINEERING, TRIBOLOGY. *Educ:* Northeastern Univ, BS, 45; Carnegie-Mellon Univ, MS, 52. *Prof Exp:* RES FEL ENGR MECH ENG & TRIBOLOGY, WESTINGHOUSE RES LABS, WESTINGHOUSE ELEC CORP, 47- *Concurrent Pos:* Instr mech eng, Carnegie-Mellon Univ, 52-56 & Allegheny County Community Col, 66-69. *Honors & Awards:* Walter D Hodson Award, Am Soc Lubrication Engrs, 55. *Mem:* Am Soc Lubrication Engrs. *Res:* Research and development in the field of friction, wear, and lubrication mechanics encompassing the theory, test, and application of journal and thrust bearings, rolling contact bearings and seals. *Mailing Add:* Westinghouse Res Labs 1310 Beulah Rd Pittsburgh PA 15235

KAUFMAN, HYMAN, b Lachine, Que, Feb 2, 20; m 59. MATHEMATICS. *Educ:* McGill Univ, BSc, 41, MSc, 45, PhD(physics), 48. *Prof Exp:* Lectr math, McGill Univ, 41-48; fel & asst instr elec eng, Yale Univ, 48-49; geophysicist, Continental Oil Co, 49-51; engr, Lab, Fox Electronics, Inc, 51-52; prof math, McGill Univ, 52-80. *Mem:* Soc Indust & Appl Math; Soc Explor Geophys; Asn Comput Mach; Math Asn Am; Inst Elec & Electronics Engrs. *Res:* Applied mathematics in engineering. *Mailing Add:* 400 Stewart Apt 2211 Ottawa ON K1N 6L2 Can

KAUFMAN, IRVING, b Geinsheim, Ger, Jan 11, 25; US citizen; m 50; c 3. ELECTRICAL ENGINEERING. *Educ:* Vanderbilt Univ, BE, 45; Univ Ill, MS, 49, PhD(elec eng), 57. *Prof Exp:* Engr, RCA Victor, 45-48; asst elec eng, Univ Ill, 48-49, instr, 49-53, res assoc, 53-56; mem tech staff, Ramo-Wooldridge & Space Tech Labs, TRW, Inc, 57-64, head microwave res, 61-64; dir, Solid State Res Lab, 68-78, PROF ENG, ARIZ STATE UNIV, 65- *Concurrent Pos:* Fulbright sr res fel, Italy, 64-65; collaborating scientist, Consiglio Nazionale delle Ricerche, Florence, 73-74; liaison scientist, Off Naval Res, London, 78-80. *Mem:* Fel Inst Elec & Electronics Engrs; Am Inst Physics; Sigma Xi. *Res:* Microwave electronics; electronic and optical device research; displays; non-destructive evaluation. *Mailing Add:* Dept of Eng Sci Ariz State Univ Tempe AZ 85281

KAUFMAN, IRVING CHARLES, psychiatry, see previous edition

KAUFMAN, JANICE NORTON, b Denver, Colo, June 22, 23. PSYCHIATRY. *Educ:* Univ Utah, BA, 48, MD, 51; Am Bd Psychiat & Neurol, dipl, 58. *Prof Exp:* Intern med, Strong Mem Hosp, Rochester, NY, 51-52, resident psychiat, 52-55; from instr to assoc prof, Univ Colo Med Ctr, Denver, 55-72; dir, 69-72, MEM FAC, DENVER ISNT PSYCHOANAL, 72-; PROF PSYCHIAT, UNIV COLO MED CTR, DENVER, 72- *Concurrent Pos:* USPHS career teacher fel, 56-58; mem fac, Chicago Inst Psychoanal, 63- *Mem:* Fel Am Psychiat Asn; Am Psychoanal Asn. *Res:* Practice and teaching of psychoanalysis and psychiatry. *Mailing Add:* Dept of Psychiat Univ of Colo Med Ctr Denver CO 80220

KAUFMAN, JAY VICTOR RICHARD, b Camphill, Pa, June 9, 17; m 44; c 3. INORGANIC CHEMISTRY, EXPLOSIVES. *Educ:* Dickinson Col, BS, 40; Mass Inst Technol, PhD(chem), 44. *Prof Exp:* Res chemist, Rohm and Haas Co, Pa, 44-46; res chemist, Johns-Manville Corp, 46-49; res chemist, Picatinny Arsenal, NJ, 49-62; chief scientist, US Army Munitions Command, Dover, 62-69; dep dir res, develop & eng, US Army Materiel Command, Washington, DC, 69-74; CONSULT SCIENTIST, 75-; RES PROF, GEORGE WASHINGTON UNIV, 76- *Mem:* Am Chem Soc; Am Phys Soc; Am Geophys Union; NY Acad Sci. *Res:* Radioisotopes; ultra-high speed photography; solid state chemistry; radiation damage. *Mailing Add:* RFD Eaglenest Highfields Washington Depot CT 06794

KAUFMAN, JOSEPH J, b New Haven, Conn, Feb 10, 21; m 42; c 2. UROLOGY, SURGERY. *Educ:* Univ Calif, Los Angeles, BA, 42; Univ Calif, San Francisco, MD, 45; Univ Guadalajara, Mex, MD Hons, 80. *Prof Exp:* From asst prof to prof surg & urol, 66-76, CHIEF, DIV UROL, SCH MED, UNIV CALIF, LOS ANGELES, 70- *Concurrent Pos:* Hon mem fac, Sch Med, Univ Chile, 66. *Mem:* Am Urol Asn; Int Soc Urol; Soc Clin Urol; Soc Univ Urol; Am Asn Genito-Urinary Surg. *Res:* Renovascular hypertension; kidney transplantation; urological oncology. *Mailing Add:* Dept of Surg Univ of Calif Sch of Med Los Angeles CA 90024

KAUFMAN, JOYCE J, b New York, NY, June 21, 29; m 48; c 1. QUANTUM CHEMISTRY, PSYCHOPHARMACOLOGY. *Educ:* Johns Hopkins Univ, BS, 49, MA, 59, PhD(chem, chem physics), 60; Sorbonne Univ, Dr es sci(theoret physics), 63. *Prof Exp:* Chemist, US Army Chem Ctr, Md, 49-52; res asst, Johns Hopkins Univ, 52-60; scientist, Res Inst Advan Studies, 60-62, head quantum chem group, 62-69; ASSOC PROF ANESTHESIOL, SCH MED & PRIN RES SCIENTIST CHEM, JOHNS HOPKINS UNIV, 69- *Concurrent Pos:* Vis staff mem, Ctr Appl Quantum Mech, France, 62; Soroptimist fel int study, 62; mem heavy ion sources comt, Nat Acad Sci, 73-75; US deleg, Int Atomic Energy Symp, Vienna, Austria, 64. *Honors & Awards:* Gold Medal, Martin Co, 64, 65 & 66; Dame Chevalier, Nat Ctr Sci Res, France, 69; Garvan Medal, Am Chem Soc, 74; Lucy Pickett Award, 75. *Mem:* Am Chem Soc; fel Am Phys Soc; fel Am Inst Chem; Int Soc Quantum Biol. *Res:* Physicochemistry and theory of drugs which affect the central nervous system; computer systems, experimental chemical physics; chemical effects of nuclear transformation; isotopic exchange reactions of boron hydrides. *Mailing Add:* Dept of Chem Johns Hopkins Univ Baltimore MD 21218

KAUFMAN, KARL LINCOLN, b Attica, Ohio, Aug 18, 11; m 36; c 3. PHARMACY, MEDICINAL CHEMISTRY. *Educ:* Ohio State Univ, BSc, 33; Purdue Univ, PhD(pharm), 36. *Prof Exp:* Spec investr revision comt, US Pharmacopoeia, 36; from instr to asst prof pharm, Wash State Univ, 36-40; prof pharm & pharm chem & head dept, Med Col, Va, 40-49; exec officer & prof, Butler Univ, 49-52, dean col pharm, 52-76; STATE PHARM DIR, IND DEPT MENT HEALTH, 76- *Concurrent Pos:* Indust consult, 41-; consult, Vet Admin, 60- *Mem:* Assoc Am Chem Soc; Am Pharmaceut Asn; Am Heart Asn (past pres); Int Asn Torch Clubs (past int pres); Sigma Xi. *Res:* Drug deterioration; drug analysis; professional ethics; product development and quality control; drug abuse and control. *Mailing Add:* 101 Pharmacy Bldg Butler Univ Indianapolis IN 46208

KAUFMAN, KURT DUNN, b Rochester, NY, Oct 23, 29; m 72; c 3. ORGANIC CHEMISTRY. *Educ:* Wabash Col, AB, 51; Oxford Univ, DPhil(org chem), 54. *Prof Exp:* From instr to prof chem, Kalamazoo Col, 56-80, chmn sci div, 70-73, chmn dept chem, 70-73. *Concurrent Pos:* NSF res grant, Kalamazoo Col, 58-61, fac fel, 62-63; res grant, Upjohn Co, 58-63; consult, Kalamazoo Spice Extraction Co, 63-65 & 73-80 & Paul B Elder Co, Ohio, 63-67 & 77-80. *Mem:* Am Chem Soc. *Res:* Synthesis of oxygen heterocyclic compounds; synthesis of compounds affecting skin pigmentation; synthesis of food additives. *Mailing Add:* Kalamazoo Col Kalamazoo MI 49007

KAUFMAN, LARRY, b Brooklyn, NY, June 6, 31; m 55; c 3. THERMODYNAMICS, MATERIALS SCIENCE. *Educ:* Polytech Inst Brooklyn, BMetE, 52; Mass Inst Technol, ScD(metall), 55. *Prof Exp:* Mem res staff, Lincoln Lab, Mass Inst Technol, 55-58; sr metallurgist, Mfg Labs, Inc, 58-63, dir res, 63-76, V PRES, MANLABS INC, 76- *Concurrent Pos:* Ed-in-chief, Calphad, 77- *Honors & Awards:* Rossiter Raymond Award, Am Inst Mining, Metall & Petrol Engrs, 64. *Mem:* Am Soc Metals; Am Inst Mining, Metall & Petrol Engrs. *Res:* Kinetics; phase equilibria; high pressure and temperature; transformations; computer calculation of phase diagrams. *Mailing Add:* Manlabs Inc 21 Erie St Cambridge MA 02139

KAUFMAN, LEO, b New York, NY, Jan 20, 30; m 52; c 3. MEDICAL MYCOLOGY. *Educ:* Brooklyn Col, BS, 52; Univ Ky, MS, 55, PhD(bact), 59. *Prof Exp:* Instr bact, Univ Ky, 58-59; microbiologist med res, 59-62, in charge fungus serol lab, Mycol Unit, 63-67, CHIEF FUNGUS IMMUNOL BR, MYCOL DIV, CTR DIS CONTROL, USPHS, 67- *Concurrent Pos:* Dir, Nat Ctr Fungal Serol; mem fac, Univ NC, Sch Pub Health & Ga State Univ. *Honors & Awards:* Kimble Methodology Res Award, 74. *Mem:* Am Asn Immunol; Am Thoracic Soc; Am Soc Microbiol; Int Soc Human & Animal Mycol; Sigma Xi. *Res:* Immunological procedures for diagnosis of systemic fungus infections and for identification of fungal pathogens. *Mailing Add:* Ctr for Dis Control Mystic Dis Div Bldg 5 B-13 Atlanta GA 30333

KAUFMAN, LINDA, b Fall River, Mass, Mar 20, 47; m 81. NUMERICAL ANALYSIS, COMPUTER SCIENCE. *Educ:* Brown Univ, ScB, 69; Stanford Univ, MS, 71, PhD(comput sci), 73. *Prof Exp:* Asst prof comput sci, Univ Colo, Boulder, 73-76; MEM STAFF, BELL LABS, 76- *Concurrent Pos:* Vis lectr comput sci, Univ Aarhus, 73-74; prin investr, NSF Grant, 76- *Mem:* Asn Comput Mach; Soc Indust & Appl Math. *Res:* Development of algorithms in numerical linear algebra and function minimization. *Mailing Add:* Bell Labs 600 Mountain Ave Murray Hill NJ 07974

KAUFMAN, LOUIS G(RAVERAET), II, b New York, NY, Jan 3, 31. AERODYNAMICS, APPLIED MECHANICS. *Educ:* Mass Inst Technol, BS, 53; Polytech Inst Brooklyn, MS, 54, PhD(appl mech), 58. *Prof Exp:* Res engr aerodyn, 54-57, res scientist, 59-69, STAFF SCIENTIST AERODYN, RES DEPT, GRUMMAN AEROSPACE CORP, 69- *Mem:* Fel Am Inst Aeronaut & Astronaut. *Res:* Theoretical and experimental research in hypersonic aerodynamics, including pressure estimation techniques, real gas and separated flow effects, controls and flow stability analyses. *Mailing Add:* Res Dept Plant 35 Grumman Aircraft Eng Corp Bethpage NY 11714

KAUFMAN, MARTIN HENRY, b New York, NY, Feb 5, 26; m 53; c 3. POLYMER CHEMISTRY. *Educ:* Univ Calif, Los Angeles, BS, 49; Polytech Inst Brooklyn, PhD(polymer chem), 52. *Prof Exp:* Res assoc, Polymer Res Inst, Polytech Inst Brooklyn, 52-53; chemist, Colloid Sect, Res Dept, US Naval Ord Test Sta, 53-54, head, Polymer Phys Properties Sect, 54-57, head, Polymer Res Sect, Explosive & Pyrotechnic Div, Propulsion Develop Dept, 57-60, head, Hybrid Propellant Task Group, 61-63, head, Solid Propellant Br, Propulsion Develop Dept, 63-66, mem combustion res comt, 64-65, HEAD, MAT BR, NAVAL WEAPONS CTR, 66- *Concurrent Pos:* Naval Ord Test Sta adv res fel, Inst Chem, Univ Naples & Inst Chem Indust, Milan Polytech Inst, 65-66. *Honors & Awards:* William B McLean Medal, 71. *Mem:* Am Chem Soc; Sigma Xi. *Res:* Propellants; explosives; pyrotechnics; polymer science; materials; combustion; elastomers; castable resins; igniters; adhesives; propellant engineering. *Mailing Add:* Code 4541 Nat Weapons Ctr China Lake CA 93555

KAUFMAN, MAVIS ANDERSON, b Yonkers, NY, July 14, 19. NEUROPATHOLOGY. *Educ:* Radcliffe Col, AB, 41; NY Med Col, MD, 44. *Prof Exp:* Intern med & surg, Flower & Fifth Ave Hosp, 44-45; resident path, NY Postgrad Hosp, 45-46, resident med & surg, Northern Westchester Hosp, 46-47; resident internal med, Aultman Hosp, Canton, Ohio, 47-48; resident psychiat, Kings County Hosp, NY, 48-50; resident path, Vet Admin Hosp, 50-53; instr, 53-55, assoc, 55-56, asst prof, 56-69, ASSOC PROF NEUROPATH, COL PHYSICIANS & SURGEONS, COLUMBIA UNIV, 69- *Concurrent Pos:* Assoc res scientist, NY State Psychiat Inst, 56- *Mem:* Am Asn Neuropath. *Res:* Surgical and autopsy specimens of central nervous system; demyelinating and degenerative diseases; effects of psychopharmacologic agents; effects of aging. *Mailing Add:* Dept of Neuropath NY State Psychiat Inst 722 W 168 St New York NY 10032

KAUFMAN, MYRON JAY, b New York, NY, Mar 24, 37; m 67. PHYSICAL CHEMISTRY. *Educ:* Rensselaer Polytech Inst, BS, 58; Harvard Univ, MS, 63, PhD(chem physics), 65. *Prof Exp:* Trainee, Gen Elec Co, 58-59; res fel chem, Harvard Univ, 64-66; asst prof, Princeton Univ, 66-72; assoc prof, 72-78, PROF CHEM, EMORY UNIV, 78- *Mem:* Am Phys Soc; Am Chem Soc. *Res:* Chemical kinetics; plasma chemistry; molecular beams; atmospheric chemistry. *Mailing Add:* Dept of Chem Emory Univ Atlanta GA 30322

KAUFMAN, NATHAN, b Lachine, Que, Aug 3, 15; m 46; c 5. PATHOLOGY. *Educ:* McGill Univ, BSc, 37, MD & CM, 41; Am Bd Path, dipl, 50. *Prof Exp:* Intern, Royal Victoria Hosp, Montreal, 41-42; resident path, Jewish Gen Hosp, 46-47; asst resident, Cleveland City Hosp, 47-48; from instr to assoc prof, Med Sch, Western Reserve Univ, 48-60; prof, Sch Med, Duke Univ, 60-67; prof & head dept, 67-79, EMER PROF PATH, QUEEN'S UNIV, ONT, 81-; SECY-TREAS, US-CAN DIV, INT ACAD PATH, 79- *Concurrent Pos:* Asst pathologist, Cleveland Metrop Gen Hosp, 48-52, pathologist in chg, 52-60; pathologist-in-chief, Kingston Gen Hosp, 67-79; mem grants comt path & morphol, Med Res Coun, 68-74, chmn, 71-74, mem coun, 71-77, exec, 71-74; consult, Lennox & Addington County Gen Hosp, Napanee, Ont & Hotel Dieu Hosp, 69-79 & Ont Cancer Treatment & Res Found, Kingston Clin, 71-79; mem grants panel, Nat Cancer Inst Can, 70-74; ed, Lab Invest, 72-75. *Mem:* Int Acad Path (vpres, 72-74, pres-elect, 74-76, pres, 76-78); Can Asn Path; Am Asn Path; Soc Exp Biol & Med; Int Acad Path-US-Can Div (pres, 73-74, secy-treas, 79-). *Mailing Add:* US-Can Div Int Acad Path 1003 Chafee Ave Augusta GA 30904

KAUFMAN, PAUL LEON, b New York, NY, Sept 16, 43; m 70; c 1. OPHTHALMOLOGY, GLAUCOMA. *Educ:* New York Univ, MD, 67. *Prof Exp:* Staff assoc, Nat Cancer Inst, 68-70; resident ophthal, Washington Univ, 70-73; res fel, Univ Uppsala, Sweden, 73-75; asst prof, 75-80, ASSOC PROF OPHTHAL, UNIV WIS-MADISON, 80- *Concurrent Pos:* Mem, Glaucoma Prog Planning Panel, Nat Adv Eye Coun, Nat Eye Inst, NIH, 80-82, Special Study Sects & Site Visit Teams, 80-82; prin investr, Nat Eye Inst Res Groups, 79-82; consult, Retinal & Choroidal Dis Prog Planning Panel, Nat Adv Eye Coun, NIH, 77. *Mem:* Asn Res Vision & Ophthal; Am Acad Ophtal. *Res:* Anatomy, physiology, and pharmacology of aqueous human formation and drainage, as related to pathophysiology and treatment of glaucoma. *Mailing Add:* Animal Sci Ctr Univ Wis 600 Highland Ave Madison WI 53792

KAUFMAN, PETER BISHOP, b San Francisco, Calif, Feb 25, 28; m 58; c 2. PLANT PHYSIOLOGY, PLANT MORPHOLOGY. *Educ:* Cornell Univ, BS, 49; Univ Calif, PhD(bot), 54. *Prof Exp:* Res technician hort, Cornell Univ, 45-49; res technician, Shell Develop Co, 49; res technician & asst bot, Univ Calif, 49-54; Muellhaupt scholar, Ohio State Univ, 54; res assoc, 56-57, from instr to assoc prof bot, 56-73, cur, Bot Gardens, 57-73, PROF BOT, UNIV MICH, ANN ARBOR, 73- *Concurrent Pos:* NSF grants, 59-61, 75 & 80-83; grants, Inst Plant Physiol, Univ Lund, 64-66, Am Cancer Soc, 68-71, Inst Environ Qual, Univ Mich, 71-72 & NASA, 79-80, 80-81 & 81-82; vis prof cell, molecular & develop biol, Univ Colo, Boulder, 74 & Nagoya Univ, Japan, 81; vis scientist, Int Rice Res Inst, Los Banos, Philippines, 81 & US Dept Agr, Beltsville, Md, 81. *Mem:* Am Soc Plant Physiol; Soc Develop Biol; Bot Soc Am; Int Soc Plant Morphol; Scand Soc Plant Physiol. *Res:* Scanning electron microscopy, electron microprobe analysis and neutron activation analysis as related to silicification mechanisms in rice, oats, sugarcane and other grasses; studies on hormonal interactions and primary mode of action of gibberellin hormone regulation of stem elongation in grasses; regulation, especially by auxin, of the negative gravitropic response in grasses following lodging. *Mailing Add:* Dept of Bot Univ of Mich Ann Arbor MI 48104

KAUFMAN, PRISCILLA C, b Shanghai, China, Oct 5, 30; US citizen; m 60; c 2. ORGANIC CHEMISTRY, RADIATION CHEMISTRY. *Educ:* MacMurray Col, BA, 53; Univ Chicago, PhD(chem), 58. *Prof Exp:* Res assoc chem, Brookhaven Nat Lab, 58-60, assoc chemist, 60-62; res chemist, Atlas Chem Indust, NJ, 63-66; vis asst prof chem, Elmhurst Col, 67. lectr, Rosary Col, 67-71; lectr, 71-77, INSTR CHEM, COL DUPAGE, 77- *Mem:* Am Chem Soc. *Res:* Radiolysis of organic compounds; radiation induced polymerizations. *Mailing Add:* Col of Dupage Glen Ellyn IL 60137

KAUFMAN, RAYMOND, b Aug 30, 17; US citizen; m 42; c 3. EXPERIMENTAL PHYSICS. *Educ:* City Col New York, BS, 42, MS, 46; NY Univ, PhD(physics), 50. *Prof Exp:* Asst physicist labs, US Signal Corps, 42-43; tutor physics, City Col New York, 43-44, 47-49; asst physicist, Farrand Optical Co, Inc, 44-47, physicist, 49-58; dir res, 58-76, PRES & CHIEF EXEC OFFICER, DEL ELECTRONICS CORP, MT VERNON, 76- *Concurrent Pos:* Assoc prof, City Col NY. *Mem:* Am Phys Soc; Am Asn Physics Teachers. *Res:* Ionization potentials of molecules; electron optics; mass spectroscopy; ultrahigh vacuum techniques; infrared; high voltage phenomena. *Mailing Add:* 3755 Henry Hudson Pkwy Riverdale NY 10463

KAUFMAN, RAYMOND H, b Brooklyn, NY, Nov 24, 25; m 46; c 4. OBSTETRICS & GYNECOLOGY. *Educ:* Univ Md, MD, 48; Am Bd Obstet & Gynec, dipl. *Prof Exp:* Resident obstet & gynec, Beth Israel Hosp, New York, 48-53; from asst prof to assoc prof obstet, gynec & path, 58-73, actg chmn dept obstet & gynec, 68-72, PROF PATH, OBSTET & GYNEC, & ERNST W BERTNER CHMN OBSTET & GYNEC, BAYLOR MED COL, 73- *Concurrent Pos:* Fel path, Methodist Hosp, Houston, 55-58. *Mem:* Am Col Obstet & Gynec; fel Am Col Surg. *Res:* Gynecologic pathology; cytopathology. *Mailing Add:* Baylor Col of Med Tex Med Ctr Houston TX 77030

KAUFMAN, ROGER E(MANUEL), mechanical engineering, see previous edition

KAUFMAN, SAMUEL, b Toledo, Ohio, Jan 29, 13; m 41. PHYSICAL CHEMISTRY. *Educ:* Univ Toledo, BEd, 37, BSc, 40, MSc, 47. *Prof Exp:* Control & prod supvr ceramics, Save Elec Corp, 37-38; control analyst, US Gypsum Co, 41; chemist, Engr Corps, US Army, 41-45; chemist, Nat Bur Standards, 45-48; chemist, 48-75, CONSULT, US NAVAL RES LAB, 76- *Concurrent Pos:* Instr, Montgomery Jr Col, 46-47. *Mem:* Am Chem Soc (secy-treas, Colloid Div, 61-64); Sigma Xi. *Res:* Isopycnic ultracentrifugation; lubricant additives; water pollution abatement; micelle formation and solubilization; reactions of amines in nonaqueous media; analysis of fluorine-bearing silicates; concrete curing agents; nonaqueous titrations; carbon fiber composites. *Mailing Add:* 919 Hyde Rd Silver Spring MD 20902

KAUFMAN, SAMUEL, b Pottsville, Pa, Feb 3, 17; m 66. INFORMATION SCIENCE. *Educ:* Pa State Col, BS, 42; Univ Mich, MS, 46, PhD(org chem), 51. *Prof Exp:* Tech trainee, US Rubber Co, 42-43; asst, Off Sci Res & Develop Proj, Univ Pa, 43-45; res chemist, Monsanto Chem Co, 51-58; appl sci rep, Int Bus Mach Corp, 58-59, sr systs programmer, 59-60, proj coordr, 60-61, staff programmer, 61-63, ADV PROGRAMMER, IBM CORP, 63- *Mem:* Am Chem Soc; Am Soc Info Sci; NY Acad Sci; Asn Sci Info Dissemination Ctr (vpres, 73-75). *Res:* Design of systems for textual data capture, storage and retrieval; synthesis of substituted cyclohexenones; colorimetric analytical methods; organic phosphorus chemistry; isocyanate syntheses; scientific applications of computing; information retrieval; computer languages; systems design and programming; design of library processing systems. *Mailing Add:* IBM Tech Info Retrieval Ctr Armonk NY 10504

KAUFMAN, SEYMOUR, b NY, Mar 13, 24; m 48; c 3. BIOCHEMISTRY. *Educ:* Univ Ill, BS, 45, MS, 46; Duke Univ, PhD(biochem), 49. *Prof Exp:* Res fel, Sch Med, NY Univ, 49, from instr to asst prof, 50-53; chief sect cellular regulatory mechanisms, 54-68, CHIEF LAB NEUROCHEM, NIMH, 68- *Concurrent Pos:* NSF travel award, Int Cong Biochem, Paris, 52. *Mem:* Am Soc Biol Chemists; Am Chem Soc; Harvey Soc. *Res:* Mechanism of action of enzymes; intermediary carbohydrate metabolism; intermediary metabolism of amino acids. *Mailing Add:* NIMH 36/3D-30 Bethesda MD 20205

KAUFMAN, SHELDON BERNARD, b Los Angeles, Calif, June 7, 29; m 60; c 2. NUCLEAR CHEMISTRY. *Educ:* Univ Chicago, MS, 51, PhD, 53. *Prof Exp:* Res assoc chem, Columbia Univ, 55-57; from instr to asst prof, Princeton Univ, 57-66; assoc chemist, 66-73, CHEMIST, ARGONNE NAT LAB, 73- *Mem:* Am Phys Soc; AAAS; Am Chem Soc. *Res:* Radiochemical studies of low and high energy nuclear reactions; hot-atom chemistry; tracer applications to inorganic chemistry; high-energy nuclear reactions; nuclear fission; pi-meson reactions; reactions of complex nuclei with energetic protons, pi mesons, and heavy ions; nuclear fission. *Mailing Add:* 910 W Elm St Wheaton IL 60187

KAUFMAN, SIDNEY, b Passaic, NJ, Aug 10, 08; m 36; c 2. CRUSTAL STUDIES, GEOTHERMAL STUDIES. *Educ:* Cornell Univ, AB, 30, PhD(physics, math), 35. *Prof Exp:* Asst physics, Cornell Univ, 30-33, Coffin Found fel, 35; geophysicist, Shell Oil Co, 36-41, sr physicist, Shell Develop Co, 46-58, head geophys instrumentation dept, 58-61, sr res assoc, 61-65, asst to vpres, 65-74; PROF GEOPHYSICS, CORNELL UNIV, 74- *Concurrent Pos:* Prin physicist, Naval Res Labs, 46; consult, Adv Res Projs Agency, US Dept Defense, 61-73; mem geophys adv panel, Air Force Off Sci Res, 61-74, chmn, 64-66; mem comt seismol, Nat Acad Sci-Nat Res Coun, 66-71, 74-77; consult, Energy Res & Develop Admin, 75-; dir, Geothermal Resources Coun, 73-77. *Mem:* Soc Explor Geophys; Seismol Soc Am; Am Geophys Union; Sigma Xi; Europ Asn Explor Geophysicists. *Res:* Geophysical exploration; deep crustal seismic profiling; geothermal resource assessment. *Mailing Add:* Dept Geol Sci Cornell Univ Ithaca NY 14853

KAUFMAN, SOL, b New York, NY, Mar 2, 28; m 54; c 5. OPERATIONS RESEARCH. *Educ:* Wash Univ, AB, 51; Cornell Univ, PhD(math), 65. *Prof Exp:* Physicist, Nat Bur Standards, 51-52; systs analyst & asst head opers res dept, Cornell Aeronaut Lab/Calspan Corp, 53-62 & 65-73; coordr res & eval, Niagara Falls Community Ment Health Ctr, 73-74; cancer control network coordr, State Univ NY Buffalo, 74-79; MEM STAFF, FALCON RES & DEVELOP CO, 79- *Concurrent Pos:* Lectr indust eng & social & preventive med, State Univ NY Buffalo, 70- *Mem:* Math Asn Am; Soc Automotive Engrs; Opers Res Soc Am. *Res:* Statistical analysis of automotive exhaust emissions and fuel economy; cancer epidemiology and outcome analysis; higher educational systems planning; public systems research; statistical communication theory. *Mailing Add:* 1201 Stolle Rd Elma NY 14059

KAUFMAN, STANLEY, b New York, NY, Oct 30, 41; m 64; c 2. MATERIALS SCIENCE. *Educ:* City Col New York, BS, 63; Brown Univ, PhD(chem), 70. *Prof Exp:* Res scientist, Uniroyal Res Ctr, 68-70; mem tech staff, 70-77, SUPVR, METALL & FIRE-RESISTANT PLASTICS GROUP, BELL LABS, 77- *Honors & Awards:* Akzo Chemie Award, UK, 80. *Mem:* Am Phys Soc; Am Soc Testing & Mat. *Res:* Materials for communications use. *Mailing Add:* Bell Labs 2000 Northeast Expressway Norcross GA 30071

KAUFMAN, STEPHEN J, b New York, NY, Jan 3, 43; div; c 2. CELL BIOLOGY, DEVELOPMENTAL BIOLOGY. *Educ:* State Univ NY, Binghamton, BA, 64, MA, 66; Univ Colo, PhD(microbiol), 71. *Prof Exp:* Fel molecular biol, Mass Inst Technol, 71-74; asst prof microbiol, 74-81, asst prof cell biol, 77-81, ASSOC PROF MICROBIOL & CELL BIOL, UNIV ILL, 81- *Concurrent Pos:* Jane Coffin Childs Found fel, 71-73; Muscular Dystrophy Asn fel, 73-74; prin investr, 75-78; prin investr, Basil O'Connor Grant, 75-78; consult, Nat Birth Defect Found, 78-81; prin investr, NIH grant, 79- *Mem:* AAAS; Soc Develop Biol; Am Soc Cell Biol; Am Soc Microbiol. *Res:* Muscle differentiation; development of specialized cells; cell fusion; transformation; effect of viruses on development. *Mailing Add:* Dept of Microbiol 131 Burrill Hall Urbana IL 61801

KAUFMAN, SYDNEY MORTON, metallurgy, physical chemistry, see previous edition

KAUFMAN, THOMAS CHARLES, b Chicago, Ill, July 28, 44; m 67; c 1. GENETICS. *Educ:* San Fernando Valley State Col, BA, 67; Univ Tex, Austin, MA, 69, PhD(genetics), 71. *Prof Exp:* Nat Res Coun Can res assoc zool, Univ BC, 71-73; lectr, 73-74; asst prof zool, 75-81, ASSOC PROF BIOL, IND UNIV, BLOOMINGTON, 81- *Mem:* AAAS; Genetics Soc Am. *Res:* Mutagenesis; genetic fine structure in eucaryotic organisms; cytology of dipterin polytene salivary gland chromosomes; position effect variegation and developmental genetics of drosophila; genetics and control of redundant genes. *Mailing Add:* Dept of Zool Ind Univ Bloomington IL 47401

KAUFMAN, VICTOR, b New York, NY, Sept 27, 25; m 49; c 4. ATOMIC PHYSICS. *Educ:* Kans State Univ, BS, 49, MS, 50; Purdue Univ, PhD(physics), 59. *Prof Exp:* Instr physics, Univ NDak, 50-55; res assoc, Purdue Univ, 59-60; PHYSICIST, NAT BUR STANDARDS, 60- *Mem:* Fel Optical Soc Am. *Res:* Atomic emission spectroscopy; interferometry; wavelength standards by precision measurement and by calculation from atomic energy levels; laser absorption spectroscopy. *Mailing Add:* Spectros Sect Bldg 221 Rm A167 Nat Bur Standards Washington DC 20234

KAUFMAN, WILLIAM CARL, JR, b Appleton, Minn, Jan 21, 23; m 46; c 2. HUMAN PHYSIOLOGY, BIOPHYSICS. *Educ:* Univ Minn, BA, 48; Univ Ill, MS, 53; Univ Wash, PhD(physiol), 61. *Prof Exp:* Instr aviation physiol, Wright-Patterson AFB, 50-51, proj officer altitude suits, Aeromed Lab, 53-56, res biologist thermal environ, Aerospace Med Res Labs, 58-66, chief physiol br, Aeromed Res Lab, Holloman AFB, 66-68; Nat Inst Med Res spec res fel, Hampstead Labs, London, Eng, 68-69; prof human adaptability & chmn dept, 69-78, chmn res coun, 78-81, PROF HUMAN BIOL, UNIV WIS-GREEN BAY, 78- *Concurrent Pos:* Asst prof prev med, Ohio State Univ, 62-67; mem nuclear weapons effects res comt, Defense Atomic Support Agency, 65-68. *Mem:* AAAS; Aerospace Med Asn; Am Physiol Soc. *Res:* Temperature regulation and peripheral circulation; thermal and space environments; respiration; evaluation and development of cold weather protective equipment. *Mailing Add:* Col of Human Biol Univ of Wis Green Bay WI 54302

KAUFMAN, WILLIAM M(ORRIS), b Pittsburgh, Pa, Dec 31, 31; m 53; c 3. ELECTRICAL ENGINEERING. *Educ:* Carnegie Inst Technol, BS & MS, 53, PhD(elec eng), 55. *Prof Exp:* Instr, Carnegie Inst Technol, 53-54, res engr, 54-55; engr, Westinghouse Elec Corp, 55-57, res mathematician, 57-59, supvry engr, 59-62; dir res, Gen Instrument Corp, 62-65; consult engr, Gen Elec Co, 65-66; mgr, Med Eng Dept, Hittman Assocs, Inc, 66-71; V PRES ENG, ENSCO, INC, 71- *Mem:* Inst Elec & Electronics Engrs. *Res:* The application of solid state materials to electronic and electromechanical systems; artificial organs; medical instrumentation; data acquisition and processing; transportation safety research; railroad track geometry automated inspection. *Mailing Add:* ENSCO Inc 5400 Port Royal Rd Springfield VA 22151

KAUFMANN, ALVERN WALTER, b Cleveland, Ohio, Feb 21, 24; m 46; c 3. MATHEMATICS. *Educ:* Greenville Col, BA, 47; Ohio State Univ, MA, 48, PhD, 60. *Prof Exp:* Instr math, Aurora Col, 48-50; instr math & physics, Cent Col, Kans, 50-52; teacher, Pub Sch, Ohio, 52-54; asst instr math, Ohio State Univ, 54-57; assoc prof math & physics, Roberts Wesleyan Col, 57-65, prof math, 65-81, acad dean, 74-81; PROF MATH, MT VERNON NAZARENE COL, OHIO, 81- *Mem:* Math Asn Am; Am Sci Affil; Nat Coun Teachers Math. *Res:* Meaning and definition in mathematics. *Mailing Add:* Mt Vernon Nazarene Col Mt Vernon OH 43050

KAUFMANN, ANTHONY J, b Millen, Ga, Aug 19, 36; m 66. MICROBIOLOGY, BIOCHEMISTRY. *Educ:* Univ Ga, BS, 59, MS, 61; La State Univ, PhD(microbiol), 67. *Prof Exp:* Med microbiologist, Nat Communicable Dis Ctr, 62-63; fel microbiol, La State Univ, 63-67; assoc prof health sci, ETenn State Univ, 67-69; assoc prof, 69-74, PROF BIOL, ST MARY'S UNIV, SAN ANTONIO, 74- *Concurrent Pos:* Res assoc, La State Univ, 67; consult, Southwest Res Found & Inst, San Antonio, 71- *Mem:* AAAS; Am Soc Microbiol; Am Inst Biol Sci. *Res:* Microorganisms capable of degrading certain solid waste products such as cellulose, paper products and certain plastics. *Mailing Add:* 2700 Cincinnati Ave San Antonio TX 78284

KAUFMANN, ARNOLD FRANCIS, b Dubuque, Iowa, Feb 24, 36; div; c 3. EPIDEMIOLOGY. *Educ:* Iowa State Univ, DVM, 60; Univ Minn, MS, 68; Am Col Vet Path, dipl. *Prof Exp:* Vet, 62-63; vet epidemiologist, Ctr, 63-67, vet pathologist, 68-70, CHIEF BACT ZOONOSES BR, CTR DIS CONTROL, 71- *Mem:* Am Vet Med Asn; Am Asn Lab Animal Sci; US Animal Health Asn; Am Col Vet Pathologists. *Res:* Pathology and epidemiology of infectious diseases; diseases of non-human primates. *Mailing Add:* Bact Zoonoses Br Ctr Dis Control Atlanta GA 30333

KAUFMANN, BERWIND NORMAN, b Philadelphia, Pa, Mar 26, 25; m 50; c 4. MEDICAL GENETICS, ENVIRONMENTAL MEDICINE. *Educ:* Univ Pa, BA, 46, MD, 56; Johns Hopkins Univ, MA, 49; Univ Miss, cert, 54. *Prof Exp:* Instr biol, Univ Miss, 48-51; instr Hofstra Col, 51-52; intern, Philadelphia Gen Hosp, 56-57; physician, Whitesburg Mem Hosp, Ky, 57-58; assoc prof physiol & biophys, Med Ctr, Univ Miss, 48-60, assoc prof prev med, 62-63; prof anat & chmn dept, Hahnemann Med Col, 63-74; RETIRED. *Concurrent Pos:* USPHS spec res fel med genetics, Sch Med, Johns Hopkins Univ, 61-62; vis prof genetics, Univ SAla Med Sch, 76-; chief, Outpatient & Admitting Sect, Biloxi, Miss, VDMC, 78- *Mailing Add:* Biloxi Vet Admin Med Ctr Biloxi MS 39531

KAUFMANN, ELTON NEIL, b Cleveland, Ohio, Mar 18, 43. PHYSICS, MATERIALS SCIENCE. *Educ:* Rensselaer Polytech Inst, BS, 64; Calif Inst Technol, PhD(physics), 69. *Prof Exp:* MEM TECH STAFF, BELL TELEPHONE LABS, 68-; PHYSICIST, LAWRENCE LIVERMORE NAT LAB, 81- *Concurrent Pos:* Ed, Hyperfine Interactions, 80- *Mem:* Am Phys Soc. *Res:* Hyperfine interactions using nuclear spectroscopic methods; particle-solid interactions including ion-beam channeling and ion-implantation; directed energy beam materials modification. *Mailing Add:* Lawrence Livermore Nat Lab PO Box 808 L-217 Livermore CA 94550

KAUFMANN, ESTEBAN, b Szeged, Hungary, Aug 28, 16; nat Mex; m 47; c 4. ORGANIC CHEMISTRY. *Educ:* Swiss Fed Inst Technol, Chem Engr, 38, DrTech Sci & PhD, 41. *Prof Exp:* Res dir, Lab Vieta-Plasencia, Cuba, 45-47; res dir, 47-49, prod mgr, 49-56, dir opers, 56-60, VPRES SYNTEX, S A, MEX, 60- *Mem:* AAAS; Am Chem Soc; NY Acad Sci; Swiss Chem Soc; Mex Chem Soc. *Res:* Steroid chemistry. *Mailing Add:* Syntex S A PO Box 10063 Mexico DF Mexico

KAUFMANN, GERALD WAYNE, b Dubuque, Iowa, Sept 18, 40; m 66; c 3. ANIMAL BEHAVIOR, ECOLOGY. *Educ:* Loras Col, BS, 62; Iowa State Univ, MS, 64; Univ Minn, Minneapolis, PhD(biol), 71. *Prof Exp:* From instr to assoc prof, 64-79, PROF BIOL, LORAS COL, 79- *Mem:* Am Ornith Union; Wilson Ornith Soc. *Res:* Marsh ecology; behavior of soras and Virginia rails; behavior of Weddell seals. *Mailing Add:* Dept of Biol Loras Col Dubuque IA 52001

KAUFMANN, JOHN HENRY, b Baltimore, Md, Jan 7, 34; m 59; c 3. VERTEBRATE ZOOLOGY. *Educ:* Cornell Univ, BS, 56; Univ Calif, Berkeley, PhD(vert zool), 61. *Prof Exp:* Biologist animal ecol, Nat Inst Neurol Dis & Blindness, 61-63; from asst prof to assoc prof zool, 63-74, PROF ZOOL, UNIV FLA, 74- *Mem:* Am Soc Mammal; Ecol Soc Am. *Res:* Social behavior and ecology of Procyonidae, Mustelidae, Primates and Macropodidae, including home range and movements, food habits and activity cycles. *Mailing Add:* Dept of Zool Univ of Fla Gainesville FL 32611

KAUFMANN, JOHN SIMPSON, b Raleigh, NC, Apr 18, 31; m 59; c 3. CLINICAL PHARMACOLOGY, INTERNAL MEDICINE. *Educ:* Wake Forest Univ, BS, 53, MD, 56, PhD(pharmacol), 68; Am Bd Internal Med, dipl, 64. *Prof Exp:* Instr med, 62-64, instr pharmacol & assoc med, 64-70, asst prof, 70-75, ASSOC PROF MED & PHARMACOL, BOWMAN GRAY SCH MED, WAKE FOREST UNIV, 75- *Concurrent Pos:* USPHS spec fel, & vis asst prof, Vanderbilt Univ, 68-70. *Mem:* AAAS. *Res:* Interaction of drugs in man; mechanisms of action of antihypertensive agents; platelet amine uptake and aggregation; actions of hematologic and oncolytic agents; neuronal amine uptake and psychoactive drugs. *Mailing Add:* Dept of Med & Pharmacol Bowman Gray Sch of Med Winston-Salem NC 27103

KAUFMANN, KENNETH JAMES, b New York, NY, May 2, 47. INSTRUMENTATION. *Educ:* City Col New York, BS, 68; Mass Inst Technol, PhD(chem), 73. *Prof Exp:* Fel chem, Calif Inst Technol, 73-74; Bell Tel Labs, 74-75; asst prof chem, Univ Ill, Urbana, 76-80; MEM STAFF, WORTHINGTON GROUP, MCGRAW EDISON CO, 80- *Mem:* Am Phys Soc; Am Chem Soc; Sigma Xi. *Res:* Picosecond kinetics of biological and chemical reaction. *Mailing Add:* McGraw Edison Co Worthington Group 270 Sheffield Mountainside NJ 07092

KAUFMANN, MAURICE JOHN, b Hopedale, Ill, Nov 11, 29. PLANT PATHOLOGY. *Educ:* Bluffton Col, BS, 52; Univ Ill, MS, 55, PhD(plant path, bot), 57. *Prof Exp:* Plant pathologist, Agr Res Serv, USDA, Wis, 57-63; mem fac biol, 63-70, assoc prof, 70-71, PROF BIOL, BLUFFTON COL, 71- *Mem:* Am Phytopath Soc. *Res:* Diseases of soybeans and forage grasses. *Mailing Add:* Dept of Biol Bluffton Col Bluffton OH 45817

KAUFMANN, MERRILL R, b Paxton, Ill, June 17, 41; m 62; c 2. PLANT PHYSIOLOGY, PHYSIOLOGICAL ECOLOGY. *Educ:* Univ Ill, BS, 63; Duke Univ, MF, 65, PhD(forestry), 67. *Prof Exp:* Asst prof plant physiol & asst plant physiologist, Univ Calif, Riverside, 67-73, assoc prof plant physiol & assoc plant physiologist, 73-77; PRIN PLANT PHYSIOLOGIST, ROCKY MOUNTAIN FOREST & RANGE EXP STA, US FOREST SERV, USDA, 77- *Mem:* AAAS; Am Soc Plant Physiologists. *Res:* Plant water relations; development of water stress and factors controlling water flow through the soil-plant-atmosphere continuum; water potential and leaf conductance methodology; stomatal response to environment. *Mailing Add:* Rocky Mountain Forest & Range 240 W Prospect St Ft Collins CO 80526

KAUFMANN, PETER JOHN, b Amsterdam, Holland, Oct 30, 35; US citizen; m 63; c 2. COSMETIC CHEMISTRY. *Educ:* Univ Ill, Urbana, BS, 59. *Prof Exp:* Chief chemist, Dr P Fahrney & Sons, Chicago, 63-65; res chemist cosmetics, Alberto-Culver Co, Ill, 65-67; lab dir, Marcelle Cosmetics Div, Borden, Inc, 67-70; DIR PROD DEVELOP, MAX FACTOR & CO, 70- *Mem:* Am Chem Soc; Soc Cosmetic Chemists. *Res:* Emulsion technology; formulation, development and manufacture of makeup and skin care products; efficacy and safety of cosmetics. *Mailing Add:* Max Factor & Co Res Lab 1655 N McCadden Pl Hollywood CA 90028

KAUFMANN, RICHARD L, b Honolulu, Hawaii, June 11, 35; m 63; c 2. PHYSICS. *Educ:* Calif Inst Technol, BS, 57; Yale Univ, MS, 58, PhD(chem), 60. *Prof Exp:* From asst prof to assoc prof, 63-73, PROF PHYSICS, UNIV NH, 73- *Res:* Space physics. *Mailing Add:* Dept of Physics DeMeritt Hall Univ of NH Durham NH 03824

KAUFMANN, ROBERT FRANK, b Valley Stream, NY, June 23, 40; m 64; c 3. GEOLOGY, HYDROGEOLOGY. *Educ:* Villanova Univ, BS, 62; Ohio State Univ, MS, 64; Univ Wis-Madison, MS, 69, PhD(geol), 70. *Prof Exp:* Assoc res prof hydrol, Desert Res Inst, Univ Nev Syst, 70-74; hydrogeologist, Off Radiation Progs, US Environ Protection Agency, 74-80; PRIN GEOLOGIST, CONVERSE CONSULT INC, 80- *Mem:* Am Geophys Union; Am Water Resources Asn; Sigma Xi; Nat Water Well Asn. *Res:* Hydrogeology of solid and liquid waste disposal; ground water management; ground water quality. *Mailing Add:* Converse Consult Inc 4055 S Spencer St Suite 120 Las Vegas NV 89109

KAUFMANN, THOMAS G(ERALD), b Szombathely; Hungary, Jan 10, 38; US citizen; m 60; c 2. CHEMICAL ENGINEERING. *Educ:* Columbia Univ, BS, 60, MS, 62, PhD(chem eng), 65. *Prof Exp:* Teaching asst thermodyn, Columbia Univ, 60-62; engr, Esso Res & Eng Co, Florham Park, 64-74, dir process develop, Exxon Res & Develop Labs, 75-77, mgr process eng, 77-79, MGR, CORP BUS SERV, EXXON RES & ENG CO, 79- *Concurrent Pos:* USPHS res asst, 64-65. *Mem:* Am Inst Chem Engrs; Am Chem Soc. *Res:* Thermodynamics; irreversible thermodynamics; membrane transport; gaseous diffusion; fractionation; tower internals; computer systems; catalytic cracking; fluid/solid systems; heavy crude upgrading; flexicoking; hydrodesulfurization; fluid coking; hydrofining; environmental control; energy conservation. *Mailing Add:* 11 E Cheryl Rd Pine Brook NJ 07058

KAUFMANN, WILLIAM B, b San Francisco, Calif. ELEMENTARY PARTICLE PHYSICS. *Educ:* Univ Calif, Berkeley, PhD(physics), 68. *Prof Exp:* Asst prof, 69-75, ASSOC PROF PHYSICS, ARIZ STATE UNIV, 75- *Mem:* Am Phys Soc; AAAS. *Mailing Add:* Dept of Physics Ariz State Univ Tempe AZ 85281

KAUFMANN, WILLIAM KARL, b Richland, Wash, Aug 13, 51. MOLECULAR BIOLOGY. *Educ:* Yale Univ, BS, 73; Univ NC, PhD(path), 79. *Prof Exp:* Fel biol, 79-82, ASST RES BIOLOGIST, LAB RADIOL & ENVIRON HEALTH, UNIV CALIF, SAN FRANCISCO, 82- *Mem:* AAAS; Sigma Xi. *Res:* Mechanisms of DNA replication and repair and their importance in carcinogenesis. *Mailing Add:* 1880 Fell St #1 San Francisco CA 94117

KAUGERTS, JURIS E, b Riga, Latvia, Sept 24, 40; US citizen; m 69; c 2. LOW TEMPERATURE PHYSICS. *Educ:* Stevens Inst Technol, BS, 62, MS, 64, PhD(physics), 72. *Prof Exp:* Presidential intern superconductivity, Lawrence Berkeley Lab, Univ Calif, 72-73; res assoc, Plasma Physics Lab, Princeton Univ, 73-75; asst physicist superconductivity, 75-77, ASSOC PHYSICIST SUPERCONDUCTIVITY, BROOKHAVEN NAT LAB, 77- *Mem:* Am Phys Soc. *Res:* Superconducting accelerator magnet research, design and development. *Mailing Add:* Accelerator Dept Brookhaven Nat Lab Upton NY 11973

KAUKER, MICHAEL LAJOS, b Szerecseny, Hungary, Jan 24, 35; US citizen; m 61; c 4. PHARMACOLOGY. *Educ:* Univ Ala, Birmingham, PhD(pharmacol), 67. *Prof Exp:* Asst prof, 69-72, ASSOC PROF PHARMACOL, CTR HEALTH SCI, UNIV TENN, MEMPHIS, 72- *Concurrent Pos:* NIH fel, Univ NC, Chapel Hill, 67-69. *Mem:* Am Soc Pharmacol & Exp Therapeut; Soc Exp Biol & Med; Am Soc Nephrology. *Res:* Electrolyte and water metabolism; renal micropuncture; mechanism of action of antidiuretic hormone; renal effects of diuretic drugs; regulation of body fluid compartments. *Mailing Add:* Dept of Pharmacol Univ of Tenn Ctr for Health Sci Memphis TN 38163

KAUL, PUSHKAR NATH, b Srinagar, India, June 29, 33; m 61; c 4. PHARMACOLOGY, CLINICAL PHARMACOLOGY. *Educ:* Banaras Hindu Univ, BPharm, 54, MPharm, 55; Univ Calif, San Francisco, PhD(pharmacol, pharmaceut chem), 60. *Prof Exp:* Asst prof pharmaceut, Birla Inst Technol, India, 55-57; asst pharmaceut chem, Med Ctr, Univ Calif, San Francisco, 57-58, asst pharmacol, 58-60; res assoc pharmacol & vis scientist, Med Sch, Univ Melbourne, 60-61; chief res pharmacol, Antibiotics Res Ctr, India, 61-65; group leader, Farbwerke Hoechst, Ger, 65-68; assoc prof pharmacol, res med & res pediat, Univ Okla 68-75, prof pharmacol, 75-77, prof pharmacodyn & toxicol, 77-81; PROF & CHMN PHARMACOL & ASST TO PRES, RES & SPEC PROGS, SCH MED, MOREHOUSE UNIV, 81- *Concurrent Pos:* Lectr, Univ Poona, 62-63; dir marine pharmacol & adj prof pediat & res med, Univ Okla; dir drug metab, Cent State Hosp, Norman; chmn, Nat Task Force Marine Biomed. *Honors & Awards:* Aruna & Malaviya Prizes, 54; Lunsford Richardson Pharm Award, 60; Ebert Prize Cert, 62; Univ Okla Alumni Res Award, 69-& 70. *Mem:* Assoc fel Royal Australian Chem Inst; Am Soc Pharmacol & Exp Therapeut; Int Soc Biochem Pharmacol; Acad Pharmaceut Sci. *Res:* Biotransformation of drugs; mechanism of drug action; screening of pharmacologically active substances from the sea; antibiotics; psychotropic drugs. *Mailing Add:* Morehouse Sch Med 830 Wesview Dr, SW Atlanta GA 30314

KAUL, ROBERT BRUCE, b Faribault, Minn, Jan 28, 35. BOTANY. *Educ:* Univ Minn, 57, PhD(bot), 64. *Prof Exp:* Asst bot, Univ Minn, 57-60, instr, 61-62; from asst prof to assoc prof, 64-72, PROF BOT, UNIV NEBR, LINCOLN, 72- *Mem:* Bot Soc Am; Am Soc Plant Taxon; Soc Syst Zool; Am Inst Biol Sci. *Res:* Morphology and life history strategies of angiosperms, aquatic plants and Fagaceae. *Mailing Add:* Sch of Life Sci Univ of Nebr Lincoln NE 68588

KAUL, RUDOLF, crop physiology, see previous edition

KAUL, S K, b Lucknow, India, Dec 25, 36; m 63. PURE MATHEMATICS. *Educ:* Univ Lucknow, BSc, 54, MSc, 55; Univ Delhi, PhD(math), 59. *Prof Exp:* Instr math, Hampton Inst, 58-59; instr math, Univ Rochester, 59-60, univ fel, 60-61; instr math, Univ Utah, 62; from asst prof to assoc prof, 63-71, PROF MATH, UNIV REGINA, 71- *Mem:* Am Math Soc; Can Math Cong. *Res:* Topology. *Mailing Add:* Dept Math Univ Regina Regina SK S4S 0A2 Can

KAULA, WILLIAM MASON, b Sydney, Australia, May 19, 26; US citizen; m 49; c 4. GEOPHYSICS. *Educ:* US Mil Acad, BS, 48; Ohio State Univ, MS, 53. *Hon Degrees:* DSc, Ohio State Univ, 75. *Prof Exp:* Geodesist, Army Map Serv, Washington DC, 57-58, chief geod res & anal div, 58-60; geophysicist geod, celestial mech & planetary interiors, Goddard Space Flight Ctr, NASA, Md, 60-63; PROF GEOPHYS, INST GEOPHYS & PLANETARY PHYSICS, UNIV CALIF, LOS ANGELES, 63- *Mem:* Fel Am Geophys Union; Am Astron Soc; Geol Soc Am; Seismol Soc Am. *Res:* Statistical and harmonic analysis of geophysical data; gravitational fields of the earth and moon; origin and evolution of the earth, moon and planets. *Mailing Add:* Dept of Earth & Space Sci Univ of Calif Los Angeles CA 90024

KAUNE, WILLIAM TYLER, b Everett, Wash, Aug 31, 40; m 72; c 2. BIOENGINEERING. *Educ:* Univ Wash, BS, 66; Stanford Univ, PhD(physics), 73. *Prof Exp:* Res asst high energy physics, Stanford Linear Accelerator Ctr, 68-72; res assoc, Univ Wash, 72-73; asst prof physics, Loyola Marymount Univ, 73-75; sr res engr, 75-80, STAFF ENGR BIOENG, PAC NORTHWEST DIV, BATTELLE MEM INST, 80- *Mem:* Bioelectromagnetics Soc; Inst Elec & Electronics Engrs. *Res:* Biological effects of electromagnetic radiation; exposure systems and dosimetry. *Mailing Add:* Battelle Northwest Battelle Blvd Richland WA 99352

KAUNITZ, HANS, b Vienna, Austria, Oct 20, 05; US citizen; m 43. NUTRITION. *Educ:* Vienna Univ, MD, 30. *Prof Exp:* Attending physician & head clin lab, Dept Med, Sch Med, Univ Vienna, 35-38; assoc prof med & head clin lab, Univ Philippines, 38-40; clin prof path, Columbia Univ, 41-73. *Concurrent Pos:* NIH grants, 55-73; consult several food firms, 53-78; consult geront, Rutgers Univ, 78. *Honors & Awards:* Achievement award, Am Oil Chem Soc, 70; Presidential Merit Medal Philippines, 73; Big Sign Honor, Repub Austria, 73; Alton E Bailey Award, Am Oil Chem Soc, 81. *Mem:* Sigma Xi; Am Soc Exp Path; Harvey Soc; Am Oil Chem Soc; Am Inst Nutrit. *Res:* Biological effect of edible fats, especially medium chain triglycerides; function of cholesterol in arteriosclerosis; biological effects of sodium chloride; philosophy of science. *Mailing Add:* 152 E 94th St New York NY 10028

KAUP, DAVID JAMES, b Marionville, Mo, Apr 8, 39. INTEGRABLE SYSTEMS, NONLINEAR STUDIES. *Educ:* Univ Okla, BS, 60, MS, 62; Univ Md, PhD(physics), 67. *Prof Exp:* Asst prof physics, 67-74, res asst prof, 74-75, res assoc prof, 75-76, assoc prof, 76-78, PROF PHYSICS, CLARKSON COL TECHNOL, 78- *Mem:* Am Phys Soc; Sigma Xi. *Res:* Interacting physical models of physical systems for making predictions as to what will happen in the physical system. *Mailing Add:* Dept Physics Clarkson Col Technol Potsdam NY 13676

KAUP, EDGAR GEORGE, b Irvington, NJ, Oct 5, 27; m 53; c 2. CHEMICAL ENGINEERING. *Educ:* Lehigh Univ, BS, 50; Neward Col Eng, BS, 58, MS, 63. *Prof Exp:* Phys chemist, Hoffmann-La Roche, NJ, 52-54; spectroscopist, Air Reduction Lab, 54-55, res chem engr, 55-62; develop engr, Celanese Plastic Co, 62-65; sr chem engr, 65-69, resident eng mgr, 69-76, SR CHEM ENGR, BURNS & ROE, INC, BURNS & ROE CONSTRUCT CORP DIV, CONTRACTOR TO OFF SALINE WATER, US DEPT INTERIOR, 76- *Mem:* Am Chem Soc; Am Inst Chem Engrs; Am Soc Test & Mat. *Res:* Desalting and water pollution abatement; reverse osmosis evaluations and applications; water and waste treatment by ion exchange and evaporative methods. *Mailing Add:* Burns & Roe Inc 8 Essex Rd Essex Fells NJ 07021

KAUPP, VERNE H, b Denver, Colo, Apr 15, 40; m 66; c 2. ELECTRICAL ENGINEERING. *Educ:* Univ Md, BS, 71. *Prof Exp:* Engr microwave sensor, Martin Marietta Corp, 71-75; eng consult microwave sensor, Earth Resources Technol, 75; sr res engr microwave remote sensing, Ctr for Res, Inc, 75-80; ASST PROF ELEC ENG, UNIV ARK, 80- *Concurrent Pos:* Consult, Systs Technol/Appl Res Corp, 77- *Mem:* Inst Elec & Electronics Engrs. *Res:* Microwave remote sensing. *Mailing Add:* Univ Ark Dept Elec Eng Fayetteville AR 72701

KAUPPILA, RAYMOND WILLIAM, b Iron Mountain, Mich, Feb 17, 29; m 52; c 4. MECHANICAL ENGINEERING, ENGINEERING MECHANICS. *Educ:* Univ Mich, BS(mech eng) & BS(eng math), 51; Mich Col Mining & Technol, MS, 60; Univ Mich, PhD, 68. *Prof Exp:* Maintenance, develop & inspection engr, Standard Oil Div, Am Oil Co, Ind, 51-55; plant engr, Cliffs Dow Chem Co, Mich, 55-57; assoc prof mech eng, 57-61, ASSOC PROF MECH ENG, MICH TECHNOL UNIV, 64- *Mem:* Am Soc Eng Educ; Am Soc Mech Engrs. *Res:* Machine design; dynamics and vibrations of machinery; stress analysis; thermal stresses; plasticity in forming operations. *Mailing Add:* Dept of Mech Eng-Eng Mech Mich Technol Univ Houghton MI 49931

KAUPPILA, WALTER ERIC, b Hancock, Mich, Sept 11, 42; m 66; c 2. ATOMIC PHYSICS. *Educ:* Mich Technol Univ, BS, 64; Univ Pittsburgh, PhD(physics), 69. *Prof Exp:* Res assoc, Joint Inst Lab Astrophys, Univ Colo, 69-71; asst prof physics, Univ Mo, Rolla, 71-72; asst prof, 72-77, ASSOC PROF PHYSICS, WAYNE STATE UNIV, 77- *Mem:* Am Phys Soc. *Res:* Experimental studies of elastic and inelastic scattering for positrons, electrons and ions colliding with ions, atoms and molecules. *Mailing Add:* Dept of Physics Wayne State Univ Detroit MI 48202

KAUS, PETER EDWARD, b Vienna, Austria, Oct 9, 24; nat US; m 50; c 3. THEORETICAL PHYSICS. *Educ:* Univ Calif, Los Angeles, BS, 47, MA, 52, PhD, 55. *Prof Exp:* Asst physics, Univ Calif, Los Angeles, 51-53; res physicist, Labs, Radio Corp Am, NJ, 54-58; asst prof physics, Univ Southern Calif, 58-62; assoc prof, 62-67, PROF PHYSICS, UNIV CALIF, RIVERSIDE, 67- *Concurrent Pos:* Consult, Hughes Aircraft Co, 58-59 & Jet Propulsion Lab, Pasadena, 59-61; trustee, Aspen Ctr Physics, 64-, vpres, 70-; Fulbright res scholar, Denmark, 65-66. *Mem:* Fel Am Phys Soc. *Res:* Field theory; elementary particle theory; biophysics. *Mailing Add:* Dept of Physics Univ of Calif Riverside CA 92521

KAUSHIK, NARINDER KUMAR, Can citizen. ECOLOGY. *Educ:* Univ Delhi, India, BS, 54, MS, 56; Univ Waterloo, MS, 66, PhD(biol), 69. *Prof Exp:* Asst fisheries, Delhi Admin, India, 57-60; res & sr res asst sanit biol, Cent Pub Health Eng Res Inst, 61-64; fel ecol, Univ Toronto, 69-71; asst prof biol, Univ Waterloo, 71-72; asst prof, 73-77, ASSOC PROF ENVIRON BIOL, UNIV GUELPH, 77- *Mem:* Am Soc Limnol & Oceanog; NAm Benthol Soc; Can Soc Zoologists; Int Soc Theoret & Appl Limnol; Sigma Xi. *Res:* Role of autumn shed leaves in secondary production in streams; nitrogen transport and transformations in streams. *Mailing Add:* Dept Environ Biol Univ Guelph Guelph ON N1G 2W1 Can

KAUTTER, DONALD ALBERT, b Stroudsburg, Pa, Dec 17, 29; m 68; c 2. MICROBIOLOGY. *Educ:* Juniata Col, BS, 51; Univ Richmond, MS, 53. *Prof Exp:* Microbiologist, US Army, Fort Detrick, 54-60; microbiologist, 60-68, SUPVRY MICROBIOLOGIST, MICROBIOL DIV, FOOD & DRUG ADMIN, 68-, ASST CHIEF FOOD MICROBIOL, 69- *Mem:* Am Soc Microbiol; Inst Food Technol; Sigma Xi. *Res:* Food microbiology; pathogenic anaerobes that are associated with foods, especially Clostridium botulism and Clostridium perfringens; the detection, identification, isolation and characterization of these microorganisms. *Mailing Add:* Food & Drug Admin 200 C St SW Washington DC 20204

KAUTZ, WILLIAM H(ALL), b Seattle, Wash, Feb 9, 24; div; c 4. COMPUTER ARCHITECTURE, TRANSPERSONAL PSYCHOLOGY. *Educ:* Mass Inst Technol, BS, 48, MS, 49, ScD(elec eng), 51. *Prof Exp:* Asst, res lab, electronics, Mass Inst Technol, 49-51; STAFF SCIENTIST, SRI INT, 51-, DIR, RES CTR APPL INTUITION, 79- *Mem:* Fel Inst Elec & Electronics Engrs; Am Transpersonal Psychol; Am Geophys Union; AAAS; Sigma Xi. *Res:* Basic and applied research in the information sciences; application of computer science in biology, seismology and the social sciences; mathematics of digital systems; enhancement of intuition and its application in science and technology. *Mailing Add:* 61 Renato Ct #8 Redwood City CA 94061

KAUZLARICH, JAMES J(OSEPH), b Des Moines, Iowa, Sept, 27, 27; m 52; c 4. MECHANICAL ENGINEERING, TRIBOLOGY. *Educ:* Univ Iowa, BS, 50; Columbia Univ, MS, 52; Northwestern Univ, PhD(mech eng), 58. *Prof Exp:* Lab asst, Columbia Univ, 50-52; develop engr, Gen Elec Co, NY, 52-54; instr mech eng, Northwestern Univ, 54-57; from asst prof to assoc prof, Worcester Polytech Inst, 58-61; assoc prof, Univ Wash, Seattle, 61-63; chmn dept, 63-75, PROF MECH ENG, UNIV VA, 63- *Concurrent Pos:* Vis res, Cambridge Univ, 70-71. *Mem:* Am Soc Eng Educ; fel Am Soc Mech Engrs; Am Soc Lubrication Engrs. *Res:* Thermodynamics; fluid mechanics; heat transfer; lubrication. *Mailing Add:* Dept of Mech Eng Univ of Va Charlottesville VA 22902

KAUZMANN, WALTER (JOSEPH), b Mt Vernon, NY, Aug 18, 16; m 51; c 3. PHYSICAL CHEMISTRY, PROTEIN CHEMISTRY. *Educ:* Cornell Univ, BA, 37; Princeton Univ, PhD(phys chem), 40. *Prof Exp:* Fel, Westinghouse Elec & Mfg Co, 40-42; chemist, Nat Defense Res Comt Contract, Pa, 42-43; engr, Manhattan Dist Proj, Los Alamos, 44-46; from asst to assoc prof chem, Princeton Univ, 46-63, chmn dept, 64-68, David B Jones prof chem, 63-82, chmn, Dept Biochem Sci, 80-82. *Concurrent Pos:* Guggenheim fel, 57 & 74-75; vis prof, Univ Ibadan, 75. *Mem:* Nat Acad Sci; Am Geophys Union; Am Acad Arts & Sci; Am Chem Soc; Am Phys Soc. *Res:* Physical chemistry of proteins; theory of water; properties of matter at high pressures; geochemistry. *Mailing Add:* Frick Chem Lab Princeton Univ Princeton NJ 08540

KAVALER, FREDERIC, b New York, NY, Feb 2, 26; m 55; c 2. PHYSIOLOGY. *Educ:* Columbia Univ, AB, 47; Johns Hopkins Univ, MD, 51. *Prof Exp:* Intern med, Maimonides Hosp, Brooklyn, 51-52; resident, Goldwater Mem Hosp, NY, 52-54; NY Heart Asn fel, 54-55; fel physiol, Col Med, Cornell Univ, 55-56; instr physiol, 56-57; from instr to assoc prof, 58-65, PROF PHYSIOL, STATE UNIV NY DOWNSTATE MED CTR, 65- *Mem:* Am Physiol Soc. *Res:* Electrophysiology of the heart; cardiac physiology. *Mailing Add:* 425 Riverside Dr New York NY 10025

KAVALJIAN, LEE GREGORY, b Chicago, Ill, Feb 6, 26. PLANT MORPHOLOGY. *Educ:* Univ Chicago, PhB, 47, BS, 48, PhD(bot), 51. *Prof Exp:* Res assoc bot, Brooklyn Bot Garden, NY, 51-52; vis res assoc, Brookhaven Nat Lab, NY, 52; asst to chief chemist, Modern Agr Crop Serv, Calif, 53; Ford Found teaching intern natural sci, Univ Chicago, 53-54, instr, 54; from instr to assoc prof biol sci, 54-64, PROF BIOL SCI, CALIF STATE UNIV, SACRAMENTO, 64- *Mem:* Bot Soc Am; Soc Econ Bot. *Res:* Plant tissue cultures; floral morphology; cytochemistry; ethnobotany. *Mailing Add:* 150 Breckenwood Way Sacramento CA 95825

KAVAN, EVA MARY, b Prague, Czech; nat US. ANESTHESIOLOGY. *Educ:* Charles Univ, Prague, MD, 45. *Prof Exp:* Asst resident internal med, Tuberc Sanatorium for Children, Czech, 45-47 & Charles Univ Prague, 47-49; asst resident anesthesiol, Presby Hosp, NY, 49-51; intern, St Louis City Hosp, Mo, 51-52; resident anesthesiol, Francis Delafield Hosp, New York, 52-53; instr surg & anesthesia, Med Sch, Northwestern Univ, 54-56; asst prof, Med Sch, Univ Calif, Los Angeles, 56-64, lectr, 64-65; assoc prof anesthesiol, Univ Wash, 67-68; sr anesthesiologist, City of Hope Med Ctr, Duarte, Calif, 69-71; assoc res pharmacologist, Univ Calif, Irvine, 71-75, consult, Physiol Res Lab, 75-80. *Concurrent Pos:* NIH res fel neurophysiol, Lab Electrophysiol, Inst Marey, Univ Paris, 65-67; staff anesthesiologist, VA Hosp, Sepulveda, Calif, 77-82. *Mem:* Int Anesthesia Res Soc; Can Anaesthetists Soc; Am Soc Anesthesiologists; Asn Anesthesiol Great Brit & Northern Ireland. *Res:* Anesthesia for open heart surgery; neurophysiology in relationship to anesthesiology; computing electroencephalogram in anesthesia. *Mailing Add:* 4700 Natick Ave #108 Sherman Oaks CA 91403

KAVANAGH, RALPH WILLIAM, b Seattle, Wash, July 15, 24; m 48; c 5. NUCLEAR PHYSICS. *Educ:* Reed Col, BA, 50; Univ Ore, MA, 52; Calif Inst Technol, PhD, 56. *Prof Exp:* From res fel to sr res fel, 56-60, from asst prof to assoc prof, 60-70, PROF PHYSICS, KELLOGG LAB, CALIF INST TECHNOL, 70- *Mem:* Am Phys Soc. *Res:* Spectroscopy of light nuclei using electrostatic accelerators. *Mailing Add:* 450 S Bonita Ave Pasadena CA 91107

KAVANAGH, ROBERT JOHN, b Whitchurch, Hants, Eng, Oct 7, 31; m 56; c 2. ELECTRICAL ENGINEERING, CONTROL SYSTEMS. *Educ:* Univ NB, BSc, 53; Univ Toronto, MASc, 54, PhD(elec eng), 57. *Prof Exp:* Lectr elec eng, Univ Toronto, 57-59, asst prof, 60-62; assoc prof, 62-68, assoc dean, 69-71; PROF ELEC ENG, UNIV NB, 68-, DEAN GRAD STUDIES, 71- *Concurrent Pos:* Nat Res Coun Can fel, Imp Col, Univ London, 59-60; guest worker, Control Eng Div, Warren Spring Lab, Eng, 68-69. *Mem:* Inst Elec & Electronics Engrs; assoc mem Inst Elec Engrs; fel NY Acad Sci. *Res:* Analysis and synthesis of systems including multivariable control systems, nonlinear systems and random signal processors; properties of pseudo-random binary sequences. *Mailing Add:* Sch of Grad Studies & Res Univ of NB PO Box 4400 Fredericton NB E3B 5A3 Can

KAVANAGH, THOMAS MURRAY, b Elrose, Sask, Can, Apr 21, 32; US citizen; div; c 3. NUCLEAR PHYSICS, ATOMIC PHYSICS. *Educ:* Univ Sask, BA, 53, MA, 55; McGill Univ, PhD(physics), 60. *Prof Exp:* Physicist, Suffield Exp Sta, Defence Res Bd, Can, 55-56; res physicist nuclear res, Atomic Energy Res Estab, UK Atomic Energy Authority, 56-57; lectr physics, McGill Univ, 60-62, asst prof, 62-64; res physicist, Nuclear-Chicago Corp, 64-66; PHYSICIST, PHYSICS RES & RES ADMIN, LAWRENCE LIVERMORE NAT LAB, UNIV CALIF, 66- *Mem:* Fel Am Phys Soc; Can Asn Physicists; Sigma Xi; AAAS. *Res:* Photonuclear physics; neutron physics; proton induced nuclear reactions; bio-medical instrumentation; nuclear explosives design; heavy element production in nuclear explosives; nuclear weapons diagnostics; seismology of underground nuclear explosions; atomic collisions physics; nuclear non-proliferation analysis; international science policy. *Mailing Add:* Lawrence Livermore Lab Livermore CA 94550

KAVANAU, JULIAN LEE, b Detroit, Mich, Jan 21, 22. ETHOLOGY. *Educ:* Univ Mich, BS, 43; Univ Calif, MS & PhD(zool), 52. *Prof Exp:* Asst physics, Univ Mich, 41-43; physicist, Univ Calif, 43; mem res staff physics, Calif Inst Technol, 43-45; asst math, Univ Calif, Los Angeles, 46-47; asst zool, Univ Calif, 49-51; USPHS fel, Wenner-Gren Inst, Stockholm, Sweden, 52-54; res assoc develop biol, Rockefeller Inst, 55-57; from asst prof to assoc prof biol, 57-67, PROF BIOL, UNIV CALIF, LOS ANGELES, 67- *Mem:* AAAS; Am Soc Zool; Ecol Soc Am; Animal Behav Soc; Am Soc Mammal. *Res:* Instrumentation for behavior research; influences of environmental variables on mammalian activity; symmetry of curves and figures. *Mailing Add:* Dept of Biol Univ of Calif Los Angeles CA 90024

KAVANAUGH, DAVID HENRY, b San Francisco, Calif, Apr 7, 45; m 65; c 5. SYSTEMATIC ENTOMOLOGY, BIOGEOGRAPHY. *Educ:* San Jose State Univ, BA, 67; Univ Colo, Denver, MA, 70; Univ Alta, PhD(entom), 78. *Prof Exp:* Asst cur entom, 74-78, ASSOC CUR ENTOM, CALIF ACAD SCI, 78-, CHMN DEPT, 79- *Concurrent Pos:* Nat Res Coun Can fel, 72-74. *Mem:* Soc Syst Zool; Entom Soc Am; Coleopterists Soc. *Res:* Classification, phylogeny, zoogeography and natural history of ground beetles; biogeography and evolution of high altitude biota, especially the coleoptera faunas of western North America; theory and practice of systematic zoology. *Mailing Add:* Dept of Entom Calif Acad of Sci San Francisco CA 94118

KAVARNOS, GEORGE JAMES, b New London, Conn. CLINICAL CHEMISTRY. *Educ:* Clark Univ, BA, 64; Univ RI, PhD(org chem), 68; Dipl, Am Bd Clin Chem. *Prof Exp:* NIH fel, Columbia Univ, 68-71; chief chemist, New London, 71-74, ASSOC DIR & CLIN CHEMIST, CYTO MED LAB, INC, NORWICH, 74- *Concurrent Pos:* Vpres, Bio-Anal Labs, 73-; adj prof chem, Univ RI, 78- *Mem:* Am Chem Soc; Am Asn Clin Chemists; NY Acad Sci. *Res:* Photochemistry; clinical chemistry; molecular orbital calculations of biochemical and toxicological molecules important in disease processes. *Mailing Add:* 121 Riverview Ave New London CT 06320

KAVENOFF, RUTH, b New York, NY, Aug 11, 44. BIOPHYSICAL CHEMISTRY, VIROLOGY. *Educ:* Reed Col, BA, 67; Albert Einstein Col Med, PhD(cell biol), 71. *Prof Exp:* UN Int Agency Res Cancer-WHO fel virol, Univ Auckland, NZ, 72-73; fel phys chem, 71-72 & 73-79, res assoc virol, 79-80, RES ASSOC BIOL, UNIV CALIF, SAN DIEGO, 80- *Concurrent Pos:* Anna Fuller Found fel, 74-75; NIH fel, 75-78. *Res:* Chromosome structure; nucleic acids. *Mailing Add:* 106 11th Del Mar CA 92014

KAVESH, SHELDON, b New York, NY, Jan 15, 33; m 57; c 2. CHEMICAL ENGINEERING. *Educ:* Mass Inst Technol, BSChE, 57; Polytech Inst Brooklyn, MChE, 60; Univ Del, PhD(chem eng), 68. *Prof Exp:* Res engr, Celanese Corp Am, 57-60, Foster Grant Co, Inc, 60-62 & Avisun Corp, 62-65; proj leader polymers, Films Packaging Div, Union Carbide Corp, 68-70; res assoc, 70-80, SR RES ASSOC, ALLIED CHEM CORP, MORRISTOWN, 80- *Mem:* Am Inst Chem Engrs; Am Phys Soc; Am Chem Soc. *Res:* Polymer physics; transport phenomena; materials science. *Mailing Add:* 16 N Pond Rd Whippany NJ 07981

KAWAHARA, FRED KATSUMI, b Penngrove, Calif, Feb 26, 21; m 52; c 3. ENVIRONMENTAL POLLUTION. *Educ:* Univ Tex, BS, 44; Univ Wis, MS, 46, PhD(chem), 48. *Prof Exp:* Assoc chemist, USDA, 48-51; fel org chem, Univ Chicago, 51-53; sr res scientist, Standard Oil Co, Ind, 53-65; org chemist, Anal Qual Control Lab, 68-71, spec consult, Method Develop & Qual Assurance Lab, 72-74, SPEC CONSULT OIL IDENTIFICATION, ANAL QUAL CONTROL LAB, ENVIRON PROTECTION AGENCY, 71- *Honors & Awards:* Group Superior Serv Award, Bur Agr & Indust Chem, USDA, 52. *Mem:* Fel Am Inst Chem; Am Chem Soc. *Res:* Synthetic fuels, coal liquefaction; Lubricants; phosphorus; fluorocarbons; gasoline additives; waxes; carcinogens; chromatography; infrared, ultraviolet, synthesis, identification; insecticides; greases; phenols; mercaptans; oil pollution; soy bean oil flavor reversion; aromatic amines; peroxides. *Mailing Add:* Environ Monitor & Support Lab 26 W St Clair Cincinnati OH 45268

KAWAI, MASATAKA, 4, b Gifu, Japan, June 13, 43; m 69; c 2. ELECTRICAL ENGINEERING, COMPUTER CONTROLLED EXPERIMENTS. *Educ:* Tokyo Univ, BSc, 66; Princeton Univ, PhD(biol), 71. *Prof Exp:* Res assoc, 71-78, ASST PROF MUSCLE PHYSIOL, DEPT NEUROL, COLUMBIA UNIV, 78- *Concurrent Pos:* Prin investr cross-bridge kinetics res, Dept Neurol, Columbia Univ, 76- *Mem:* Biophys Soc; Gen Physiol Soc. *Res:* Cross-bridge kinetics in chemically skinned muscle fibers by use of sinnsoidal analysis which changes the length and detects concomitant amplitude and phase shift in tension. *Mailing Add:* P&S 4-408 Columbia Univ 630 W-168th St New York NY 10032

KAWALEK, JOSEPH CASIMIR, JR, b Stockton, Calif, Dec 21, 45; m 72; c 1. BIOCHEMISTRY, BIOCHEMICAL PHARMACOLOGY. *Educ:* St Francis Col, BS, 67; Univ Pittsburgh, PhD(biochem), 74. *Prof Exp:* Res asst biochem, Univ Pittsburgh, 70-73; res assoc, Hoffmann-La Roche, Inc, 74-75; staff scientist chem carcinogen, Frederick Cancer Res Ctr, Litton Bionetics, Inc, 76-80; RES CHEMIST, DIV VET MED RES, BUR VET MED, FOOD & DRUG ADMIN, 80- *Mem:* Am Chem Soc; AAAS; Am Inst Biol Sci; Sigma Xi; NY Acad Sci. *Res:* Role of cytochrome P-450 in the activitation of carcinogens to reactive metabolites. *Mailing Add:* 617 Biggs Ave Frederick MD 21701

KAWAMURA, KAZUHIKO, b Nagoya, Japan, Feb 4, 39; m 71. LONG-RANGE PLANNING, TECHNOLOGY ASSESSMENT. *Educ:* Waseda Univ, Japan, BEng, 63; Univ Calif, Berkeley, MS, 66; Univ Mich, Ann Arbor, PhD(elec eng), 72. *Prof Exp:* Lectr elec eng, Univ Mich-Dearborn, 72-73; res specialist exp vehicles, Ford Motor Co, 73; prin researcher tech assessment, Columbus Div, Battelle Mem Inst, 73-81; ASSOC PROF TECHNOL & PUB POLICY, VANDERBILT UNIV, 81- *Concurrent Pos:* Sr res fel, Japan Soc Prom Sci, 80; vis prof, Kyoto Univ, Japan, 80-81; consult, Saudi Arabian Nat Ctr Sci & Technol, 81-; orgn coordr, Int Asn Impact Assessment, 81- *Mem:* Inst Elec & Electronics Engrs; AAAS. *Res:* Futures research; long-range planning; policy analysis; simulation and modeling; structural modeling. *Mailing Add:* Vanderbilt Univ PO Box 1674 Sta B Nashville TN 37235

KAWASAKI, EDWIN POPE, b Sikeston, Mo, Jan 25, 26; m 48; c 2. CHEMICAL ENGINEERING, PHYSICAL CHEMISTRY. *Educ:* Case Inst Technol, BS, 54, MS, 58, PhD(chem eng), 60. *Prof Exp:* Res engr, res ctr, 54-58, supvr chem processing, 58-63, div head surface chem, 63-73, div head processing, 73-75, ASST DIR RES, REPUB STEEL RES CTR, 75- *Mem:* Nat Asn Corrosion Engrs. *Res:* Corrosion of ferrous metals; chemical processing; environmental control; iron and steel making. *Mailing Add:* 6801 Brecksville Rd Repub Steel Res Ctr Independence OH 44131

KAWASE, MAKOTO, b Japan, May 20, 26; m 54; c 3. PLANT PHYSIOLOGY, HORTICULTURE. *Educ:* Univ Tokyo, BS, 51; Univ Minn, MS, 58; Cornell Univ, PhD(plant physiol), 60. *Prof Exp:* Fel, Purdue Univ, 60-62; res officer plant physiol, Can Dept Agr, 62-66; assoc prof hort, 66-70, PROF HORT, OHIO AGR & RES & DEVELOP CTR, 70- *Concurrent Pos:* NATO vis prof, Pisa Univ, Italy, 74. *Honors & Awards:* Alex Laurie Award, Am Soc Hort Sci, 62 & 67. *Mem:* Am Soc Plant Physiol; AAAS; Am Soc Hort Sci; Bot Soc Am; Scand Soc Plant Physiol. *Res:* Dormancy of seeds, tuber and buds; rooting of cuttings; physiology of flooded plants; evaluation of woody ornamentals. *Mailing Add:* Ohio Agr Res & Develop Ctr Wooster OH 44691

KAWATA, KAZUYOSHI, b Portland, Ore, Jan 2, 24; m 49; c 3. SANITARY ENGINEERING, ENVIRONMENTAL HEALTH. *Educ:* Ore State Col, BS, 49; Univ Minn, MS, 50; Univ Calif, Berkeley, MPH, 58; Johns Hopkins Univ, DrPH(sanit eng), 65. *Prof Exp:* Civil-sanit engr, Bd Missions, Methodist Church, 50-66; asst prof, 66-69, assoc prof, 70-80, PROF ENVIRON HEALTH ENG & PROF INT HEALTH, JOHNS HOPKINS UNIV, 80- *Concurrent Pos:* Consult, WHO, Bangladesh, 73 & Philippines, 75, consult & lectr, Egypt, 76; expert health sci, AID, 76-78, consult, 79-81. *Mem:* Am Soc Civil Engrs; Am Pub Health Asn; Am Water Works Asn;

Water Pollution Control Fedn; Am Acad Environ Engrs. *Res:* Water and waste-water treatment processes; disinfection kinetics; tropical environmental health. *Mailing Add:* Dept of Environ Health 615 N Wolfe St Baltimore MD 21205

KAWATRA, MAHENDRA P, b Wazirabad, India, June 22, 35; US citizen; m 62; c 3. PHYSICS. *Educ:* Univ Delhi, BSc, 55, MSc, 57, PhD(physics), 62. *Prof Exp:* Lectr physics, Univ Delhi, 57-63; Smith-Mundt scholar & Fulbright grant, Mass Inst Technol, 63-64; assoc res scientist, Courant Inst Math Sci, NY Univ, 64-66; asst prof, Fordham Univ, 66-71; PROF PHYSICS, MEDGAR EVERS COL, CITY UNIV NEW YORK, 71-, DIR EDUC & COMPUT TECHNOL, 80- *Concurrent Pos:* Res assoc, Univ Ill, 64. *Mem:* Am Phys Soc. *Res:* Quantum-statistical mechanics; many-body problem; liquid helium; thin film and theory of superconductivity; low-temperature physics. *Mailing Add:* 10 Seagull Ln Port Washington NY 11050

KAWIN, BERGENE, b Rock Springs, Wyo, Apr 20, 19; m 50; c 2. PHYSIOLOGY. *Educ:* Univ Calif, BS, 40, PhD(mammal physiol), 50. *Prof Exp:* Physiologist, Crocker Radiation Lab, Univ Calif, 46-50; assoc prof agr chem, Mich State Col, 50-54; biologist, Gen Elec Co, 54-59; radiobiologist, Boeing Co, 59-60; res chemist, US Vet Admin Hosp, Ft Howard, 60-65 & DC, 65-69; PHARMACOLOGIST, DIV ONCOL & RADIOPHARM, BUR DRUGS, US FOOD & DRUG ADMIN, ROCKVILLE, 69- *Mem:* Am Physiol Soc. *Res:* Evaluation and regulation of radiopharmaceuticals; fission product metabolism; radioisotope techniques. *Mailing Add:* 807 Hillsboro Dr Silver Spring MD 20902

KAY, ALVIN JOHN, b Luling, Tex, June 10, 38; m 67; c 4. MATHEMATICAL ANALYSIS. *Educ:* Southwest Tex State Univ, BS, 61, MA, 65; Univ Houston, PhD(math), 75. *Prof Exp:* Teacher math, Woodsboro High Sch, 61-64; asst, Southwest Tex State Univ, 64-65; instr, San Jacinto Col, 65-69; asst, Univ Houston, 69-70; instr, 70-75, asst prof, 75-78, ASSOC PROF MATH, TEX A&I UNIV, 78- *Mem:* Am Math Soc. *Res:* Integral equations and product integral. *Mailing Add:* Dept of Math Tex A&I Univ Kingsville TX 78363

KAY, BONNIE JEAN, b Chicago, Ill, Nov 13, 41. HEALTH SYSTEMS PLANNING, POLICY ANALYSIS. *Educ:* Oberlin Col, AB, 63; Univ Chicago, MS, 66; Northwestern Univ, PhD(urban systs eng), 75. *Prof Exp:* Instr chem, US Peace Corps, 63-65, Ministry Educ, Ghana, 67-68 & Chicago City Col, 68-70; chemist, US Customs Lab, 70-72; asst prof health systs, GA Inst Technol, 75-80; ASST PROF, SCH PUB HEALTH, UNIV MICH, 80- *Mem:* Am Pub Health Asn; Am Health Planning Asn; Sigma Xi; Am Asn Pub Opinion Res. *Res:* Evaluation research of programs and public policy related to population, emergency medical systems, and other forms of health delivery systems. *Mailing Add:* Dept Health Planning & Admin Sch Pub Health Univ Mich Ann Arbor MI 48109

KAY, CALVIN FREDERICK, b Iowa City, Iowa, Feb 1, 12; m 37; c 2. MEDICAL EDUCATION. *Educ:* Univ Iowa, BA, 32; Univ Pa, MD, 35. *Prof Exp:* Intern, Univ Pa Hosp, 35-37; asst med, Johns Hopkins Univ, 37-40; assoc, 40-46, from asst prof to prof med, 61-71, PROF CLIN MED, SCH MED, UNIV PA, 71- *Concurrent Pos:* Archbold fel, Johns Hopkins Univ, 37-40; chief cardiac sect, Univ Pa Hosp, 53-71; mem cardiovasc study sect, NIH, 56-59, cardiovasc training comt, 59-62 & cardiovasc prog projs comt, 63-66; vis prof med, Thomas Jefferson Univ, 79-81; ed, Med Knowledge Self Assessment Prog, Am Col Physicians, 81- *Mem:* Am Soc Clin Invest; Am Clin & Climat Asn; Am Heart Asn; Asn Am Physicians; fel Am Col Physicians (dep exec vpres, 71-79). *Res:* Cardiovascular dynamics; electrocardiographic theory; nephritis; mechanism of nephritis; clinical observations on cardiovascular diseases. *Mailing Add:* 4200 Pine St Philadelphia PA 19104

KAY, CAROL ANN, insect ecology, see previous edition

KAY, CYRIL MAX, b Calgary, Alta, Oct 3, 31; m 53; c 2. BIOCHEMISTRY. *Educ:* McGill Univ, BSc, 52; Harvard Univ, PhD(biochem), 56. *Prof Exp:* Fel, Life Ins Med Res Fund, Cambridge Univ, 56-57; res phys biochemist, Eli Lilly & Co, 57-58; from asst prof to assoc prof, 58-67, PROF BIOCHEM, UNIV ALTA, 67- *Concurrent Pos:* Med Res Coun Can vis prof, Weizmann Inst Sci, Rehovot, Israel, 69-70; co-dir, Med Res Coun Group Protein Structure & Function Function, Univ Alta, 74- *Honors & Awards:* Ayerst Award Biochem, 70. *Mem:* Fel NY Acad Sci; fel Royal Soc Can; Brit Biochem Soc; Am Soc Biol Chem; Can Biochem Soc. *Res:* Protein physical chemistry; hydrodynamic and optical properties of macromolecules; correlation of physico-chemical properties with biological function for muscle proteins. *Mailing Add:* Dept of Biochem Univ of Alta Edmonton AB T6G 2E8 Can

KAY, DAVID CLIFFORD, b Oklahoma City, Okla, July 26, 33; m 55, 78; c 3. COMBINATORICS, FINITE MATHEMATICS. *Educ:* Otterbein Col, BS, 55; Univ Pittsburgh, MS, 59; Mich State Univ, PhD(math), 63. *Prof Exp:* Asst prof math, Univ Wyo, 63-66; from asst prof to assoc prof, 66-80, PROF MATH, UNIV OKLA, 80- *Concurrent Pos:* Res Coun award, Univ Wyo, 65; dir, Reg NSF Conf, Convexity, Nat Sci Found, 71. *Mem:* Sigma Xi; Am Math Soc; Math Asn Am. *Res:* Problems regarding curve-curvature in metric spaces; axiomatic convexity, matroids and geometric problems in topological linear spaces. *Mailing Add:* Dept of Math 601 Elm Rm 423 Norman OK 73019

KAY, DAVID CYRIL, b Sault Ste Marie, Mich, Sept 5, 32; m 61; c 4. PSYCHIATRY, PSYCHOPHARMACOLOGY. *Educ:* Wheaton Col, Ill, BS, 54; Univ Ill, Chicago, MD, 58; Am Bd Psychiat & Neurol, dipl, 69. *Prof Exp:* Intern, Presby-St Luke's Hosp, Chicago, 58-59; staff physician, USPHS Hosp, Ft Worth, Tex, 59-61; res psychiatrist, Ill State Psychiat Inst, 61-64; chief exp psychiat unit, Addiction Res Ctr, Nat Inst Drug Abuse, 66-69, chief exp psychiat sect, 69-80; DIR DRUG ABUSE PROG, HOUSTON VET ADMIN HOSP, 80-; ASSOC PROF PSYCHIAT & PHARMACOL & MED DIR, SLEEP DISORDERS CTR, BAYLOR COL MED, 80- *Concurrent*

Pos: USPHS Ment health career develop fel, 61-66; fel, Addiction Res Ctr, Nat Inst Ment Health, 64-66; vis lectr, Asbury Theol Sem, 64-66; clin assoc prof, Med Ctr, Univ Ky. *Mem:* Am Soc Pharmacol & Exp Therapeut; Int Brain Res Orgn; Sigma Xi; Am Psychiat Asn; AMA. *Res:* Behavioral and physiological investigation of psychoactive drugs and individuals who abuse them; interaction of sleep with drugs and sexual function. *Mailing Add:* Dept Psychiat Baylor Col Med Houston TX 77030

KAY, EDWARD LEO, b Cleveland, Ohio, Sept 23, 24; m 55; c 4. ORGANIC CHEMISTRY. *Educ:* Case Western Reserve Univ, BS, 47, MS, 53, PhD(org chem), 55. *Prof Exp:* Res scientist org chem, Texaco Inc, 55-60; RES ASSOC ORG CHEM, FIRESTONE TIRE & RUBBER CO, 60- *Mem:* Am Chem Soc. *Res:* Organic chemicals synthesis; organic chemical process development; oxidation studies; vulcanization accelerators; adhesion studies; vapor phase oxidation of hydrocarbons; scrap rubber disposal processes; fire and smoke suppressants; guayule natural rubber processing. *Mailing Add:* 79 S Tamarack Akron OH 44319

KAY, ELIZABETH ALISON, b Kauai, Hawaii, Sept 27, 28. BIOLOGY. *Educ:* Mills Col, BA, 50; Cambridge Univ, BA, 52, MA, 56; Univ Hawaii, PhD, 57. *Prof Exp:* From asst prof to assoc prof sci, 57-66, assoc dean, Grad Div, 75-79, PROF ZOOL, UNIV HAWAII, MANOA, 70-; HON ASSOC MALACOL, B P BISHOP MUS, 58- *Mem:* Fel AAAS; Soc Syst Zool; Marine Biol Asn UK; Challenger Soc; Malacol Soc Australia. *Res:* Functional morphology of marine gastropods; marine ecology. *Mailing Add:* Dept of Gen Sci Univ of Hawaii Manoa Honolulu HI 96822

KAY, ERIC, b Heidelberg, Ger, Nov 23, 26; nat US; m 53; c 3. INORGANIC CHEMISTRY, PHYSICAL CHEMISTRY. *Educ:* Univ Calif, BS, 53; Univ Wash, Seattle, PhD(chem), 58. *Prof Exp:* Res chemist, Best Co, Oakland, Calif, 48-52 & Lawrence Radiation Lab, Univ Calif, 52-54; asst phys chem, Univ Wash, Seattle, 54-55; staff res chemist, 58-65, HEAD MAT SCI DEPT, RES LAB, IBM CORP, 65- *Concurrent Pos:* Vis prof, Univ Calif, Berkeley, 68-69; mem, tech rev panel, Nat Bur Standards, 76-79 & rev comt, Argonne Univ Asn Chem Div, Argonne Nat Lab, 81- *Mem:* Am Vacuum Soc; Am Phys Soc; Sigma Xi. *Res:* High temperature chemistry; electron microscopy and diffraction; ion impact phenomena on condensed phases; plasma chemistry; surface phenomena; chemistry and physics of thin films. *Mailing Add:* IBM San Jose Res Lab 5600 Cottle Rd San Jose CA 95193

KAY, ERNEST ROBERT MACKENZIE, b Hamilton, Ont, Aug 19, 25. BIOCHEMISTRY. *Educ:* McMaster Univ, BA, 47, MA, 49; Univ Rochester, PhD, 53. *Prof Exp:* Asst zool, McMaster Univ, 47-48; lectr biol, Acadia Univ, 48-49; res assoc, Glasgow Univ, 53-55; asst prof biochem, Dalhousie Univ, 56-58; from asst to assoc prof, Sch Med & Dent, Univ Rochester, 59-66; ASSOC PROF BIOCHEM, FAC MED, UNIV TORONTO, 66- *Concurrent Pos:* Brit Empire Cancer Campaign Exchange fel, 53-55; prof biol, Acadia Univ, 56-57; vis investr, Rockefeller Inst, 56. *Mem:* AAAS; Am Soc Biol Chem; Chem Inst Can; Brit Biochem Soc. *Res:* Cancer biochemistry; cytochemistry; nucleic acids; nucleoproteins. *Mailing Add:* Dept Biochem Fac Med Univ Toronto Toronto ON M5S 1A3 Can

KAY, FENTON RAY, b Pacoima, Calif, Oct 10, 42; m 71; c 1. PHYSIOLOGICAL ECOLOGY, VERTEBRATE ZOOLOGY. *Educ:* Nev Southern Univ, BS, 67; Univ Nev, Las Vegas, MS, 69; NMex State Univ, PhD(biol), 75. *Prof Exp:* Res asst, Desert Res Inst, Univ Nev, Las Vegas, 70, US Int Biol Prog, Desert Biome, Dept Biol, NMex State Univ, 70-74; NIH trainee, Dept Physiol, Col Med, Univ Fla, 74-76; asst prof biol, Calif State Univ, Los Angeles, 76-78; sr ecologist, HDR Ecosci, 78-80. *Mem:* AAAS; Ecol Soc Am; Am Soc Zoologists; Am Soc Mammalogists; Herpetologists League. *Res:* Respiratory and metabolic responses of rodents to carbon dioxide; thermal biology of desert animals; desert animal community composition. *Mailing Add:* 4100 Cholla Road Las Cruces NM 88001

KAY, IRVIN (WILLIAM), b Savannah, Ga, Apr 19, 24; m 54; c 2. APPLIED MATHEMATICS. *Educ:* NY Univ, BA, 48, MS, 49, PhD(math), 53. *Prof Exp:* Res assoc math, NY Univ, 52-58, from asst prof to assoc prof, 59-62; sr res mathematician, Conductron Corp, 62-64, dept head advan systs, 64-68, dir independent res & develop, 68-71; prof elec eng, Wayne State Univ, 71-73; STAFF MEM, INST DEFENSE ANAL, 73- *Mem:* Am Math Soc; Am Phys Soc. *Res:* Electromagnetic theory; systems analysis. *Mailing Add:* 400 Army Navy Dr Arlington VA 22202

KAY, JACK GARVIN, b Scott City, Kans, July 11, 30; m 52; c 2. PHYSICAL CHEMISTRY. *Educ:* Univ Kans, AB, 52, PhD(phys chem), 60. *Prof Exp:* From instr to asst prof inorg chem, Univ Ill, Urbana, 59-66; prof chem, Univ Toledo, 66-69, chmn dept, 66-68; PROF CHEM & HEAD DEPT, DREXEL UNIV, 69- *Concurrent Pos:* Consult, Chemotronics, Inc, Avco, Inc, Charlestown Twp, Chester County, Pa & Alex C Fergusson Co. *Mem:* AAAS; Am Chem Soc; Am Phys Soc; Faraday Soc; fel Am Inst Chem. *Res:* Electronic spectroscopy of gaseous diatomic molecules; spin-orbit coupling; flash heating and kinetic spectroscopy; flash photolysis; high temperature chemistry; solar furnaces; radiation chemistry; hot atom chemistry in inorganic crystals; nuclear and radiochemistry. *Mailing Add:* Dept of Chem Drexel Univ Philadelphia PA 19104

KAY, MICHAEL AARON, b San Francisco, Calif, May 7, 43; m 76; c 2. RADIOANALYTICAL CHEMISTRY, RADIATION DETECTION. *Educ:* Univ Calif, Berkeley, BS, 65; Mass Inst Technol, ScD(nuclear chem), 70. *Prof Exp:* Radiochemist, US Naval Radiol Defense Lab, Calif, 65; sr chemist, Res Reactor Facility, Univ Mo, Columbia, 70-75, sr res scientist, 75-78; mem fac, Univ Mo-Columbia, 75-78; sr scientist, Rockwell Hanford Opers, Wash, 78-80; ASSOC PROF CHEM & DIR REED REACTOR FACIL, REED COL, 80- *Concurrent Pos:* Consult forensic probs, 81- *Mem:* AAAS; Am Nuclear Soc; Am Chem Soc. *Res:* Neutron activation analysis; trace elements in the environment; environmental radiation monitoring; radioisotope production. *Mailing Add:* Dept Chem Reed Col 3203 SE Woodstock Blvd Portland OR 97202

KAY, MORTIMER ISAIA, b Bronx, NY, Aug 27, 30; m 64. CRYSTALLOGRAPHY. *Educ:* Brooklyn Col, BA, 52; Purdue Univ, MS, 53; Univ Conn, PhD(phys chem), 58. *Prof Exp:* Asst chem, Purdue Univ, 52-53; asst, Univ Conn, 53-57; res assoc, Pa State Univ, 57-59; fel, Royal Norweg Coun Sci & Indust Res, 59-60; res scientist, NASA, 60-61; res assoc prof, Ga Inst Technol, 62-64; sr scientist & head neutron diffraction prog, PR Nuclear Ctr, 64-77, head, Mats Sci Div, PR Ctr Energy & Environ Res, 76-79; head sea water-surfactant project, ocean thermal energy conversion, 79-80, PHYS SCIENTIST, US DEPT ENERGY, 81- *Concurrent Pos:* Vis assoc physicist, Brookhaven Nat Lab, 57-59. *Mem:* AAAS; Am Chem Soc; Am Phys Soc; Am Crystallog Asn. *Res:* Molecular and crystal structure; diffraction studies of ferroelectric transitions; ocean thermal energy; pyroelectric energy conversion; surface chemistry; atomic energy. *Mailing Add:* 70 Oak Shade Rd Gaithersburg MD 20878

KAY, PETER STEVEN, b Milwaukee, Wis, Sept 24, 37; m 71. CLINICAL CHEMISTRY, INSTRUMENTATION. *Educ:* Cornell Univ, AB, 59; Purdue Univ, PhD(org chem), 66. *Prof Exp:* Tech asst coal chem, US Steel Res Ctr, 59-60; teaching asst chem, Purdue Univ, 60-62; res chemist, Textile Fibers Dept, 66-69, col rels rep, Employee Rels Dept, 69-70; res chemist, Textile Fibers Dept, 70-72, mkt rep, 72-73, dist mgr, 73-76, nat sales mgr, Sci Instruments, Inst Prod, 76-77, mgr thermal anal, 77-79, mgr liquid chromatography, 79-80, NAT SALES MGR, ELECTRONIC DIV, E I DU PONT DE NEMOURS & CO INC, 80- *Mem:* AAAS; Am Chem Soc; Sigma Xi. *Res:* Kinetics and product distributions in solvolyses of allylic halides and esters; polyamide fiber research, primarily fundamental work directed towards development of new biocomponent fibers; process and product development of polyamide textile fibers; marketing and technical development of clinical laboratory automated analyzers. *Mailing Add:* 6 Bristol Knoll Rd Newark DE 19711

KAY, ROBERT EUGENE, b Missoula, Mont, Dec 23, 25; m 51; c 3. BIOCHEMISTRY, INFRARED DETECTORS. *Educ:* Univ Calif, Los Angeles, BS, 48, PhD(bot sci), 52. *Prof Exp:* Asst bot, Univ Calif, Los Angeles, 51-52; supvry chemist, US Naval Radiol Defense Lab, 54-61; mgr, Biosci Dept, 61-80, PRIN STAFF SCIENTIST, ELECTROOPTICAL IMAGING SYSTS, AERONUTRONIC DIV, FORD AEROSPACE & COMMUNS, 61- *Res:* Radiobiology; lipid metabolism; isolated perfused organs; adaptive enzyme systems; olfactory transduction in insects; model membrane systems; interactions of dyes with biological macromolecules; immobilized enzymes; organic semiconductors; infrared detectors; missile/vehicle integration; missile systs mgt; high temperature batteries. *Mailing Add:* 1515 Warwick Ln Newport Beach CA 92660

KAY, ROBERT LEO, b Hamilton, Ont, Dec 13, 24; m 52; c 3. PHYSICAL CHEMISTRY. *Educ:* Univ Toronto, MA, 50, PhD(phys chem), 52. *Prof Exp:* Merck fel, Rockefeller Inst, 52, res asst, 53-56; asst prof chem, Brown Univ, 56-63; sr fel, Mellon Inst, 63-67, actg dir, Ctr Spec Studies, Univ, 73-74, PROF CHEM, CARNEGIE-MELLON UNIV, 67-, HEAD DEPT, 74- *Concurrent Pos:* Ed, Jour Solution Chem, 71- *Mem:* AAAS; Am Chem Soc; Biophys Soc. *Res:* Transport properties of electrolyte solutions; structure of liquids; electrophoresis; solutions at high pressure. *Mailing Add:* Dept of Chem 4400 Fifth Ave Pittsburgh PA 15213

KAY, ROBERT WOODBURY, b New York, NY, Jan 14, 43; m 75; c 2. GEOCHEMISTRY. *Educ:* Brown Univ, AB, 64; Columbia Univ, PhD(geol), 70. *Prof Exp:* Asst prof geol, Columbia Univ, 70-75; asst res geophysicist, Univ Calif, Los Angeles, 75-76; asst prof, 76-81, ASSOC PROF GEOL, CORNELL UNIV, 81- *Mem:* Fel Geol Soc Am; Am Geophys Union; Geochem Soc. *Res:* Geochemistry of rare earth elements in volcanic rocks; regional geology of the Aleutian Islands, Alaska; chemistry of the lower crust. *Mailing Add:* Dept Geol Sci Cornell Univ Ithaca NY 14853

KAY, RUTH MCPHERSON, b Seaforth, Ont, Mar 26, 49. NUTRITIONAL BIOCHEMISTRY. *Educ:* Univ Toronto, BSc, 71; Univ London, MSc, 73, PhD(nutrit biochem), 76. *Prof Exp:* Asst prof appl human nutrit, Dept Family Studies, Univ Guelph, 76-77; asst prof, Dept Nutrit, 78-80, ASST PROF RES, DEPT SURG, UNIV TORONTO, 77- *Concurrent Pos:* Fel, Ont Ministry Health, Can, 77-79; Med Res Coun Can grant, 78- *Honors & Awards:* Nutrit Award, Van den Bergh & Jurgens, UK, 73. *Mem:* Nutrit Soc Can; Am Soc Parenteral & Enteral Nutrit; Am Heart Asn. *Res:* Nutritional modification of cholesterol metabolism; dietary fibre and its effect on plasma lipids, steroid turnover, bile composition and glucose metabolism. *Mailing Add:* Lab 1224 Toronto Western Hosp 399 Bathurst St Toronto ON M5T 2S8 Can

KAY, SAUL, b New York, NY, Feb 13, 14; m 40; c 1. SURGICAL PATHOLOGY. *Educ:* NY Univ, BA, 36, MD, 39; Am Bd Path, dipl & cert path anat & clin path. *Prof Exp:* Resident path, Fordham Hosp, 41-42 & NY Postgrad Hosp, 46-48; resident surg path, Presby Med Ctr, Columbia Univ, 48-50; assoc prof, 50-52, PROF SURG PATH, MED COL VA, 52- *Mem:* Am Asn Path & Bact; fel Am Col Path; fel Am Soc Clin Path; Am Soc Cytol; Int Acad Path. *Res:* Granulomas and oncology. *Mailing Add:* 322 Charmain Rd Richmond VA 23226

KAY, SUZANNE MAHLBURG, b Rockford, Ill, May 30, 47; m 75; c 2. PETROLOGY, MINERALOGY. *Educ:* Univ Ill, Urbana, BS, 69, MS, 72; Brown Univ, PhD(geol), 75. *Prof Exp:* Fel geol, Univ Calif, Los Angeles, 75-76; RES ASSOC GEOL, CORNELL UNIV, ITHACA, NY, 76- *Mem:* Geol Soc Am; Mineral Soc Am; Am Geophys Union; Sigma Xi. *Res:* Study of natural and experimentally produced intergrowths in ternary and plagioclase feldspars, genesis of plutonic rocks in island arcs, particularly in the Aleutian Islands, Alaska; study of lower crustal xenoliths. *Mailing Add:* Dept Geol Sci Cornell Univ Ithaca NY 14853

KAY, WEBSTER BICE, b Hammond, Ind, Dec 8, 00; m 39; c 2. CHEMICAL ENGINEERING, PHYSICAL CHEMISTRY. *Educ:* Ohio State Univ, BChE, 22; Univ Chicago, PhD(phys chem), 26. *Prof Exp:* Res engr phys properties, Standard Oil Co, Ind, 26-47; prof thermodyn, 47-71, EMER PROF PHYS PROPERTIES, DEPT CHEM ENG, OHIO STATE UNIV, 71- *Concurrent Pos:* Dir & prin investr grants, Am Chem Soc Res Fund, 54-58, NSF, 57-71 & Am Petrol Inst, 65-71. *Mem:* Am Chem Soc; Am Inst Chem Engrs; AAAS. *Res:* Phase behavior of mixtures at high temperature and pressure; thermodynamic properties of pure compounds and mixtures; critical properties of vapor-liquid mixtures. *Mailing Add:* Dept of Chem Eng 140 W 19th Ave Columbus OH 43214

KAYA, AZMI, b Acik, Turkey, Feb 1, 33; m 64; c 1. SYSTEMS ENGINEERING. *Educ:* Tech Col Men, Ankara, Dipl, 52; Univ Wis, Madison, MS, 62; Univ Minn, Minneapolis, MS & PhD, 70. *Prof Exp:* Control engr, Honeywell, Inc, 62-68; teaching assoc, Univ Minn, Minneapolis, 70; asst prof mech eng, 70-75, ASSOC PROF MECH ENG, UNIV AKRON, 75- *Concurrent Pos:* NSF res grant, Univ Akron, 71-72; NATO vis expert, 74. *Mem:* Am Soc Mech Engrs; Sigma Xi; Inst Elec & Electronics Engrs; Am Soc Eng Educ; Tech Asn Pulp & Paper Indust. *Res:* Modeling, control and optimization of large scale systems; control theory applications; energy management systems. *Mailing Add:* Dept of Mech Eng Univ of Akron Akron OH 44325

KAYA, HARRY KAZUYOSHI, b Honolulu, Hawaii, Nov 20, 40; m 64. INSECT PATHOLOGY. *Educ:* Univ Hawaii, BS, 62, MS, 66; Univ Calif, Berkeley, PhD(insect path), 70. *Prof Exp:* Asst entomologist, Conn Agr Exp Sta, 71-76; mem staff 76-80, ASSOC PROF, DIV NEMAT, UNIV CALIF, DAVIS, 80- *Mem:* AAAS; Soc Invert Path; Entom Soc Am; Int Orgn Biol Control; Soc Hemat. *Res:* Pathogens of forest defoliation insects; biological control of insects; epizootiology in insect populations; use of microorganisms to control insects; use of nematodes to control insects. *Mailing Add:* Div of Nemat Univ of Calif Davis CA 95616

KAYANI, JOSEPH THOMAS, b Kuravilangad, India, Mar 8, 45; US citizen; m 69; c 2. APPLIED MECHANICS, STRESS ANALYSIS. *Educ:* Univ Kerala, India, BSc, 67; Polytech Inst Brooklyn, MS, 71; Polytech Inst NY, PhD(mech eng), 75. *Prof Exp:* Engr supvr construct, Telecommun Dept, Govt India, 67-69; mech engr, Acoustics & Vibrations Lab, Souncoat Co, Inc, Brooklyn, 72-74, stress analysis, Nuclear Power Servs, Inc, New York, 74-75, Burns & Roe, Inc, 75-78; PRIN ENGR APPL MECH, EBASCO SERV, INC, 78- *Concurrent Pos:* Res asst, Polytech Inst Brooklyn, 73-75; res fel, Polytech Inst New York, 75- *Mem:* Am Soc Mech Engrs; Am Acad Mech. *Res:* Stress and vibration analysis of pressure vessels and piping; nonlinear random vibrations; acoustics and noise control of machines and structural components. *Mailing Add:* 300 Ellen Pl Jericho NY 11753

KAYDEN, HERBERT J, medicine, see previous edition

KAYE, ALBERT L(OUIS), b New York, NY, Mar 16, 09; m 34; c 3. ELECTROCHEMICAL ENGINEERING. *Educ:* Mass Inst Technol, SB, 31, MS, 32, ScD(electrochem), 34. *Prof Exp:* Asst chem, Calif Inst Technol, 32-33; res assoc, Div Indust Coop, Mass Inst Technol, 34-37, secy comt corrosion metals, 35-37; metallurgist, Carnegie-Ill Steel Corp, Chicago, 37-41, mgr alloy bur, Metall Div, Chicago Dist, 41-44, metall engr, Pittsburgh, 44-45; vpres & gen mgr, Beckman Supply Co, 45-67; from assoc prof to prof metall eng technol, 67-74, EMER PROF METALL ENG TECHNOL, PURDUE UNIV, CALUMET CAMPUS, 74-, SPEC ASST TO CHANCELLOR, 76- *Mem:* AAAS; Am Soc Testing & Mat; Am Soc Metals; Am Inst Mining, Metall & Petrol Engrs. *Res:* Development of alloy steels for automotive, aircraft and high temperature uses; electrochemistry of the alkaline-earth metals. *Mailing Add:* 6618 Forest Ave Hammond IN 46324

KAYE, ALVIN MAURICE, b New York, NY, Sept 18, 30; m 58. REPRODUCTIVE ENDOCRINOLOGY, DEVELOPMENTAL BIOLOGY. *Educ:* Columbia Univ, AB, 51, AM, 55; Univ Pa, PhD, 56. *Prof Exp:* Asst cytol, Columbia Univ, 51-52; asst cell physiol, Univ Pa, 53-55; mem res staff biochem cancer, 56-68, sr scientist biodynamics, 68-77, ASSOC PROF, HORMONE RES, SCIENTIST BIODYNAMICS, WEIZMANN INST SCI, 77- *Concurrent Pos:* Corresp ed, J Steroid Biochem. *Mem:* Israel Chem Soc; Biochem Soc Israel; Am Soc Cell Biol; Israel Endocrine Soc; Endocrine Soc. *Res:* Enzymic modification of nucleic acids and proteins; hormonal induction of protein synthesis; enzyme catabolism; mechanism of carcinogenesis by ethyl carbamate; mechanism of action of estrogens. *Mailing Add:* Dept Hormone Res Weizmann Inst Sci 76100 Rehovoth Israel

KAYE, BRIAN H, b Hull, Eng, July 8, 32; m 57; c 2. PHYSICS. *Educ:* Univ Hull, BSc, 53, MSc, 55; Univ London, PhD(physics), 62. *Prof Exp:* Sci officer, Brit Atomic Weapons Res Estab, 55-59; lectr physics, Univ Nottingham, 59-62; res officer, Welwyn Res Asn, 62-63; sr physicist, IIT Res Inst, 63-68; PROF PHYSICS & DIR INST FINE PARTICLES RES, LAURENTIAN UNIV, 68- *Concurrent Pos:* Consult, Brit Atomic Energy Authority, 61-63; managing dir, Brian Kaye Assocs Ltd; educ & res consult. *Mem:* Am Soc Testing & Mat. *Res:* Particle size analysis of powders; physical and chemical properties of powder systems and aerosols. *Mailing Add:* Inst for Fine Particles Res Laurentian Univ Sudbury ON P3E 2C6 Can

KAYE, CARMEN JIMENEZ, b Loiza, PR, Apr 18, 18; m 51; c 2. MEDICINE. *Educ:* Univ PR, San Juan, BS, 38; Univ Mich, Ann Arbor, MPH, 45; Med Col Va, MD, 52. *Prof Exp:* Physician outpatient dept, Med Col Va Hosp, 55-60; clin investr drug res, A H Robins Inc, Va, 60-62; DIR GERIAT PROG, PSYCHIAT HOSP, PR DEPT HEALTH, 63- *Concurrent Pos:* Mem bd dirs, Bd Serv Sr Citizens Inc, 66-; instr, Sch Pub Health, Univ PR, 69- *Mem:* Fel Am Geriat Soc; Geront Soc; PR Med Asn. *Res:* Process of aging. *Mailing Add:* Dept of Health Geriat Prog Psychiat Hosp Rio Piedras PR 00927

KAYE, DONALD, b New York, NY, Aug 12, 31; m 55; c 4. MEDICINE. *Educ:* Yale Univ, AB, 53; NY Univ, MD, 57; Am Bd Internal Med, dipl, 64, cert infectious dis, 74. *Prof Exp:* From asst prof to assoc prof med, Cornell Univ, 63-69; PROF MED & CHMN DEPT, MED COL PA & CHIEF MED, HOSP, 69- *Concurrent Pos:* NIH fel, Cornell Univ Med Col, 60-62, spec fel, 62-63, NY Health Res Coun career scientist award, 66-69; from asst attend physician to assoc attend physician, NY Hosp, 63-69. *Honors & Awards:* Lindback Award. *Mem:* Asn Am Physicians; Asn Profs Med; Infectious Dis Soc Am; fel Am Col Physicians; Am Soc Clin Invest. *Res:* Research in infectious diseases with special interest in pathogenesis of bacterial infections and host defense mechanisms against bacterial infection. *Mailing Add:* Med Col of Pa 3300 Henry Ave Philadelphia PA 19129

KAYE, GEORGE THOMAS, b Lorain, Ohio, Dec 11, 44; m 67; c 2. OCEANOGRAPHY. *Educ:* US Naval Acad, BS, 66; Univ Mich, MS, 72, PhD(oceanog), 74. *Prof Exp:* Asst res oceanogr, Sea Grant Prog, Univ Mich, 71-74; asst res oceanogr, Marine Phys Lab, Scripps Inst Oceanog, Univ Calif, San Diego, 74-78; BR HEAD, NAVAL OCEAN SYSTS CTR, SAN DIEGO, 79- *Mem:* Acoust Soc Am. *Res:* High-frequency sound scattering from biota and water density structures; theoretical acoustics; upper-ocean measurements with drifting arrays; acoustic noise generation by storms; modal decomposition of internal waves. *Mailing Add:* 6414 Corsica Way San Diego CA 92111

KAYE, GORDON I, b New York, NY, Aug 13, 35; m 56; c 2. ANATOMY, PATHOLOGY. *Educ:* Columbia Col, AB, 55; Columbia Univ, AM, 57, PhD(anat), 61. *Prof Exp:* Res assoc anat, Columbia Univ, 61-63, assoc surg path, 63-66, from asst prof to assoc prof , 66-76; PROF & CHMN DEPT ANAT, ALBANY MED COL, 76-, ASSOC PROF SURG PATHOL, 81- *Concurrent Pos:* Career scientist, Health Res Coun New York, 63-72; dir, F H Cabot Lab Electron Micros, Columbia Univ, 63-76; consult, NY Vet Admin Hosp, 65-; metab & digestive dis res career award, Nat Inst Arthritis, 72-76; consult surg, 76-78; affil alt surgeon, Albany Med Ctr Hosp, 78- *Honors & Awards:* Charles Huebschman Prize, Columbia Univ, 54. *Mem:* Am Soc Cell Biol; Am Asn Anat; Asn Anat Chmn (pres, 80-81); Sigma Xi. *Res:* Electron microscopy; fluid transport; gastrointestinal tissue differentiation; structure and function; corneal morphophysiology; electron microscopy of soft tissue tumors. *Mailing Add:* Dept of Anat Albany Med Col Albany NY 10032

KAYE, HOWARD, b New York, NY, Dec 9, 38; m 66; c 2. POLYMER CHEMISTRY, INDUSTRIAL CHEMISTRY. *Educ:* Polytech Inst Brooklyn, BS, 60, PhD(polymer chem), 65. *Prof Exp:* NIH fel, Cambridge Univ, 65-67; asst prof chem, Tex A&M Univ, 67-73; pres, Howard Kaye & Assoc, 73-80; DIR, POLYHEDRON LABS, 80- *Concurrent Pos:* Consult chem indust. *Mem:* Fel Am Inst Chemists; Am Chem Soc; Soc Plastic Engrs; Royal Soc Chem. *Res:* Synthesis and properties of macromolecules; new syntheses for the manufacture of industrially important materials and chemicals; process and product improvement research; characterization of high polymers; automatic chemical analysis. *Mailing Add:* PO Box 11669 Houston TX 77093

KAYE, IRVING ALLAN, b Brooklyn, NY, May 23, 16. ORGANIC CHEMISTRY. *Educ:* City Col New York, AB, 35; NY Univ, MS, 39; Mich State Col, PhD(org chem), 42. *Prof Exp:* Anal chemist, Pediat Res Lab, Brooklyn Jewish Hosp, 35-39; Rockefeller Found fel & res assoc, Northwestern Univ, 41-42; instr chem, City Col New York, 43-44; from instr to assoc prof, 45-65, PROF CHEM, BROOKLYN COL, 65- *Concurrent Pos:* Res chemist, Endo Prod, Inc, 42-45; res assoc, Polytech Inst Brooklyn, 43-44; USPHS spec fel, Harvard Univ, 53-55; mem staff, Weizmann Inst, 62-63; consult, CPC, Inc, 66-72. *Mem:* Am Chem Soc; Royal Chem Soc. *Res:* Synthetic organic chemistry. *Mailing Add:* Dept of Chem Brooklyn Col Brooklyn NY 11210

KAYE, JAMES HERBERT, b Seattle, Wash, Sept 3, 37; m 65; c 3. RADIOCHEMISTRY. *Educ:* Univ Wash, BS, 58; Carnegie Inst Technol, MS, 61, PhD(nuclear chem), 63. *Prof Exp:* RES SCIENTIST RADIOCHEM, PAC NORTHWEST LABS, BATTELLE MEM INST, 63- *Mem:* Am Chem Soc; Am Nuclear Soc; AAAS. *Res:* Development of highly sensitive instrumentation and techniques for measurement of trace substances in the environment. *Mailing Add:* Battelle Pac Northwest Labs 320 Bldg 300 Area Richland WA 99352

KAYE, JEROME SIDNEY, b Hartford, Conn, June 15, 30; m 55. CELL BIOLOGY. *Educ:* Columbia Univ, AB, 52, MA, 54, PhD, 57. *Prof Exp:* Instr zool, Univ Calif, Los Angeles, 57-59; from asst prof to assoc prof biol, 59-75, PROF BIOL, UNIV ROCHESTER, 75- *Concurrent Pos:* Lalor Found fel, 58. *Mem:* Am Soc Cell Biol; Electron Micros Soc Am. *Res:* Fine structure and basic protein composition of chromatin in somatic and developing sperm cell nuclei. *Mailing Add:* Dept of Biol Univ of Rochester Rochester NY 14627

KAYE, JOHN, b Herkimer, NY, July 1, 15; m 49; c 1. ENGINEERING, MANAGEMENT SCIENCE. *Educ:* Calif Inst Technol, BS, 39, MS, 48. *Prof Exp:* Student engr, Ingersoll-Rand Co, 39-40; jr engr, Hughes Aircraft Co, 40-41; aeronaut engr, War Prod Bd, 41-43; mech engr, Pan Am-Grace Airways, Inc, 43-45 & Hydrodyn Lab, Calif Inst Technol, 45-50; from asst prof to assoc prof mech eng, 50-57, assoc prof eng admin, 57-62, assoc prof eng & appl sci, 62-68, PROF ENG & APPL SCI, GEORGE WASHINGTON UNIV, 68- *Concurrent Pos:* Expert eng economy, UNESCO, Lima, Peru, 66-68. *Mem:* Am Soc Mech Engrs; Am Soc Eng Educ; Opers Res Soc Am; Inst Mgt Sci. *Res:* Engineering administration methods; structured analysis; management problems. *Mailing Add:* Sch Eng & Appl Sci George Washington Univ Washington DC 20052

KAYE, MICHAEL PETER, b Chicago, Ill, Feb 10, 35; m 60; c 5. PHYSIOLOGY, SURGERY. *Educ:* Loyola Univ, Chicago, MS & MD, 59. *Prof Exp:* Clin assoc physiol, Stritch Sch Med, Loyola Univ, 61-62, from asst prof to assoc prof surg & physiol, 67-71; sci dir artificial heart prog,

Res Inst, Ill Inst Technol, 71-74; assoc prof, 74-79, PROF SURG, MAYO MED SCH, UNIV MINN, 79-, DIR CARDIOVASC RES, MAYO CLIN, 74- *Concurrent Pos:* Assoc thoracic & cardiovasc, Cook County Hosp, Chicago, 67-74; adj assoc prof physiol, Loyola Univ, 71-74. *Mem:* Am Asn Thoracic Surg; Am Col Surg; Am Col Cardiol; Int Can Cardiac Transplantation; Am Physiol Soc. *Res:* Cardiovascular surgery and physiology; neural control of the heart. *Mailing Add:* 1704 Teton Lane NE Rochester MN 55901

KAYE, NANCY WEBER, b Englewood, NJ, Sept 14, 29; m 56; c 2. EMBRYOLOGY, ENDOCRINOLOGY. *Educ:* Swarthmore Col, BA, 51; Hunter Col, MEd, 54; Columbia Univ, MA, 58, PhD(zool), 60. *Prof Exp:* Res worker, Col Physicians & Surgeons, Columbia Univ, 62-76; RES ASSOC, ALBANY MED COL, 76- *Concurrent Pos:* Fel neuroanat, Columbia Univ, 60-61. *Mem:* Sigma Xi; AAAS; Am Asn Anat. *Res:* Thyroid and neuro-endocrine developmental relationships; corneal fine structure and physiology. *Mailing Add:* Albany Med Col Albany NY 12208

KAYE, ROBERT, b New York, NY, July 17, 17; m 42; c 3. PEDIATRICS. *Educ:* Johns Hopkins Univ, AB, 39, MD, 43. *Prof Exp:* From intern to chief resident pediat, Johns Hopkins Hosp, 43-45; instr, Med Sch, Johns Hopkins Univ, 45; assoc physiol, Sch Pub Health, Harvard Univ, 46-47; instr pediat, Sch Med, Univ Pa, 48-50, assoc, 50-51, from asst prof to prof, 51-73; PROF PEDIAT & CHMN DEPT, HAHNEMANN MED COL & HOSP, 73- *Concurrent Pos:* Asst, Harvard Med Sch, 46-47; asst physician, Children's Hosp, 48-51, sr physician, 51-, dir clins & clin teaching, 52-57, dep physician-in-chief, 64; asst chmn dept, Sch Med, Univ Pa, 64-73; chmn, Nat Med Adv Bd, Juvenile Diabetes Found, 73-76. *Mem:* AAAS; Am Pediat Soc; Soc Pediat Res; AMA; Am Diabetes Asn. *Res:* Nutrition and metabolism. *Mailing Add:* 230 N Broad St Philadelphia PA 19102

KAYE, SAMUEL, b Canton, Ohio, Dec 18, 17; m 41; c 4. ORGANIC CHEMISTRY. *Educ:* Mt Union Col, BS, 40; Ohio State Univ, MS, 41, PhD(chem), 48. *Prof Exp:* Anal chemist, Repub Steel Corp, 41; inspector powder & explosives, Ind Ord Works, 42; aeronaut res scientist chem, Nat Adv Comt Aeronaut, 48-56; tech specialist, Aerojet Gen Corp, 56-57; STAFF SCIENTIST, SPACE SCI DEPT, GEN DYNAMICS/CONVAIR, 57- *Mem:* AAAS; Am Chem Soc; Am Inst Aeronaut & Astronaut; fel Am Inst Chem; Combustion Inst. *Res:* Pollution detection; materials sciences; space manufacturing. *Mailing Add:* 5626 Albalone Pl La Jolla CA 92037

KAYE, SAUL, b Montreal, Que, May 23, 20; m 41; c 2. MICROBIOLOGY. *Educ:* Brooklyn Col, BA, 41; Univ Chicago, MS, 69. *Prof Exp:* Chemist, Biol Labs, Chem Corps, US Army, 43-48; res assoc med, Univ Chicago, 48-50; chief decontamination br, Chem Corps, US Army, Ft Detrick, 50-56; res dir, Sterilants Ben Venue Labs, 56-58; res dir, US Movidyn Co, 58-61; PRES, KAYE RES INC, 61- *Mem:* AAAS; Am Chem Soc; Am Soc Microbiol; Sigma Xi; Soc Indust Microbiol. *Res:* Disinfection and sterilization, basic principles; methods of application; development of new methods and devices. *Mailing Add:* Kaye Res Inc 838 Mich Ave Evanston IL 60202

KAYE, SIDNEY, b Brooklyn, NY, Mar 10, 12; m 51; c 2. TOXICOLOGY. *Educ:* NY Univ, BS, 35, MSc, 39; Med Col Va, PhD(pharmacol), 56; Am Bd Clin Chem, dipl, 52; Nat Registry Clin Chem, cert, 68. *Prof Exp:* Lab asst chem, NY Univ, 31-35, teaching fel, 35-38; res asst toxicol lab, City Off Chief Med Exam, New York, 38-41; instr path, Sch Med, Wash Univ, 46-47; toxicologist & dir toxicol labs, Off Chief Med Exam, Va, 47-62, dir, Richmond Poison Control Ctr, 58-62; PROF TOXICOL, PHARMACOL & LEGAL MED, SCH MED, UNIV PR, SAN JUAN, 62-, ASSOC DIR, INST LEGAL MED, 62- *Concurrent Pos:* Toxicologist & assoc dir, Sci Crime Detection Lab, St Louis Police Dept, 46-47; from asst prof to assoc prof, Med Col Va, 47-62; mem subcomt alcohol & drugs, Nat Safety Coun, 52-; lectr, Armed Forces Inst Path, 58-62 & 71; coordr poison control ctrs, Community PR, 64-; consult toxicologist, Vet Admin Hosp, Richmond, US Army Hosp, San Juan, 64-70, Vet Admin Hosp, San Juan, 69-, US Air Force Hosp, 71- & US Navy Hosp, 71-; emer consult toxicol, Dept of US Army, 70-; exec res liaison officer, Defense Civil Prep Agency, Dept of Defense, 73- *Mem:* Assoc fel Am Soc Clin Path; Asn Mil Surg US; Soc Toxicol; Pan Am Med Asn; Sigma Xi. *Res:* Analytical method for detection of lead poisoning; identification of seminal stains; diagnosis of poisoning; alcohol and its effects on man. *Mailing Add:* Univ of PR Sch of Med San Juan PR 00936

KAYE, STEPHEN VINCENT, b Rahway, NJ, Sept 17, 35; m 59; c 3. HEALTH PHYSICS, RADIOECOLOGY. *Educ:* Rutgers Univ, BS, 57; NC State Univ, MS, 59; Univ Rochester, PhD(radiation biol), 66. *Prof Exp:* Res staff health physics & radioecol, Ecol Div & Health Physics Div, 60-72, proj supvr environ impacts, Environ Sci Div, 73-75, sect head radiol assessments, 75-77, DIV DIR HEALTH & SAFETY RES, OAK RIDGE NAT LAB, 77- *Concurrent Pos:* Adv health physics fel, Univ Rochester, 63-66; mem nuclear fuel subgroup, Comt Nuclear & Alternative Energy Systs, Nat Res Coun, 76-; chmn radiol data working group, US Dept Energy Reactor Safety Data Coord Group, 76- *Mem:* Health Physics Soc; Soc Risk Analysis; Am Nuclear Soc; Sigma Xi; AAAS. *Res:* Transport of radionuclides in the environment and estimation of dose to man from ingestion or external exposure; assessments and comparisons of health and environmental issues related to all energy technologies. *Mailing Add:* Health & Safety Res Div Oak Ridge Nat Lab PO Box X Oak Ridge TN 37830

KAYE, W(ARREN) H(ARDING), b Lawrence, Mass, Mar 4, 21; m 42; c 4. CHEMICAL ENGINEERING. *Educ:* Mass Inst Technol, SB, 42. *Prof Exp:* Metals res, Univ Vt, 46-49; process develop engr extractive metall, Saratoga Labs, Inc, NY, 49-50; proj leader electrochem res, Olin Industs, Inc, 50-55, sect chief metals-glass res, 55-57, corp long range planning res & develop, 58-65, sr proj engr chem group, 66-68, proj mgr chem, 70-79; TECH CONSULT, 79- *Mem:* Am Chem Soc. *Res:* Extractive metallurgy; electrochemical development; pyrometallurgy; crystallization; chemical process development; project engineering; project management. *Mailing Add:* Old Trolley Rd Guilford CT 06437

KAYE, WILBUR (IRVING), b Pelham Manor, NY, Jan 28, 22; m 44; c 2. CHEMISTRY, INSTRUMENTATION. *Educ:* Stetson Univ, BS, 42; Univ Ill, PhD(chem), 45. *Prof Exp:* Asst chem, Univ Ill, 42-44; sr res chemist, Tenn Eastman Corp, 45-55; dir res, Sci Instruments Div, Fullerton, 56-68, dir sci res, Corp Res Activity, 68-73, sr scientist, 73-80, PRIN STAFF SCIENTIST, BECKMAN INSTRUMENTS INC, IRVINE, 80- *Mem:* Am Chem Soc; Optical Soc Am; Soc Appl Spectros. *Res:* Infrared and ultraviolet spectroscopy; chromatography; instrument development. *Mailing Add:* 3607 Surfview Lane Corona del Mar CA 92625

KAYEL, ROBERT GEORGE, computer science, see previous edition

KAYES, STEPHEN GEOFFREY, b Madison, Wis, May 1, 46. IMMUNOPARASITOLOGY. *Educ:* Univ Wis-Madison, BS, 71; Tulane Univ, MS, 73; Univ Iowa, PhD(anat), 77. *Prof Exp:* Fel immunol, Sch Med, Vanderbilt Univ, 77-81; ASST PROF NEUROANAT, DEPT ANAT & ASST PROF PARASITOL, DEPT MICROBIOL, UNIV SOUTH ALA, 81- *Concurrent Pos:* Res assoc, Vet Admin Med Ctr, 77-81. *Mem:* Am Soc Trop Med & Hyg; Am Soc Parasitologists; AAAS. *Res:* Immunologic basis of the host-parasite relationship by correlation of the host's immune status with the pathology elicited by the parasite. *Mailing Add:* Dept Anat Univ SAla Mobile AL 36688

KAYHART, MARION, b Butler, NJ, Sept 14, 26. GENETICS. *Educ:* Drew Univ, BA, 47; Univ Pa, MA, 49, PhD(zool), 54. *Prof Exp:* From instr to asst prof biol, Roanoke Col, 49-52; from asst prof to assoc prof, 54-57, PROF BIOL & CHMN DEPT, CEDAR CREST COL, 57- *Mem:* AAAS; Genetics Soc Am; Nat Asn Biol Teachers. *Res:* Radiation genetics. *Mailing Add:* Dept of Biol Cedar Crest Col Allentown PA 18104

KAYHOE, DONALD ELLSWORTH, b Washington, DC, Sept 13, 20; m 52; c 5. MEDICINE. *Educ:* George Washington Univ, AB, 47, MD, 50. *Prof Exp:* Asst physiol, Med Sch, George Washington Univ, 41-42; intern, Del Hosp, Wilmington, 50-51; asst resident med, George Washington Univ Hosp, 51-52; physician, Med Br, US Dept State, 52-53; med officer, US Marine Hosp, USPHS, 54-55, clin assoc, Nat Inst Allergy & Infectious Dis, 55-57, clin investr, 57-58; sr asst resident med, Med Ctr, Georgetown Univ, 58-59; sr investr, Nat Inst Allergy & Infectious Dis, 59-61, head med groups sect, Clin Br Collab Res, Nat Cancer Inst, 61-66, HEAD TRANSPLANTATION IMMUNOL BR, NAT INST ALLERGY & INFECTIOUS DIS, 66- *Concurrent Pos:* Lectr, George Washington Univ, 58-; instr, Georgetown Univ. *Mem:* Transplantation Soc; Am Soc Clin Histocompatability Testing; AMA. *Res:* Clinical tropical medicine; transplantation-immunology. *Mailing Add:* 9440 Culver Kensington MD 20795

KAYLL, ALBERT JAMES, b Vancouver, BC, Jan 21, 35; m 62; c 2. FORESTRY. *Educ:* Univ BC, BSF, 59; Duke Univ, MF, 60; Aberdeen Univ, PhD(fire ecol), 64. *Prof Exp:* Res scientist fire ecol, Can Dept Forestry, 60-68; asst prof fire ecol, Univ NB, 68-71, actg chmn, Dept Forest Resources, 75-76, assoc prof fire ecol, 71-77, co-dir, Fire Sci Ctr, 70-78, prof fire ecol & chmn, Dept Forest Resources, 77-80; PROF & DIR, SCH FORESTRY, LAKEHEAD UNIV, 81- *Concurrent Pos:* Mem fire mgt working group, NAm Forestry Comn, Food & Agr Orgn, UN, 73-75. *Mem:* Soc Am Foresters; Can Inst Forestry; Asn Univ Forestry Schs Can. *Res:* Ecological and physiological effects of fire on forest vegetation. *Mailing Add:* Sch Forestry Lakehead Univ Thunder Bay ON P7B 3R7 Can

KAYLOR, HOYT MCCOY, b Alexander City, Ala, Aug 17, 23; m 57; c 2. PHYSICS. *Educ:* Birmingham-Southern Col, BS, 43; Univ Tenn, MS, 49, PhD(physics), 53. *Prof Exp:* Assoc prof, 52-58, prof physics, 58-51, PROF PHYSICS & MATH, BIRMINGHAM-SOUTHERN COL, 81- *Mem:* Fel AAAS; Am Phys Soc; Optical Soc Am; Am Asn Physics Teachers. *Res:* High dispersion infrared spectroscopy; physical properties of optical materials. *Mailing Add:* Dept Phys Birmingham-Southern Col 800 8th Ave Birmingham AL 35204

KAYNE, FREDRICK JAY, b Washington, DC, Jan 19, 41; m 65; c 1. BIOCHEMISTRY. *Educ:* Ill Inst Technol, BS, 62; Mich State Univ, PhD(biochem), 66. *Prof Exp:* NATO fel, Max Planck Inst Phys Chem, 67; res assoc phys chem, 67-69; asst prof phys biochem, Johnson Res Found, 69-74, assoc prof biochem & biophys, Univ Pa, 74-77; ASSOC PROF PATH & LAB MED, HAHNEMANN MED COL, 77- *Mem:* AAAS; Am Asn Clin Chemists; Am Soc Biol Chemists. *Res:* Enzyme mechanisms; chemical relaxation; rapid kinetics; monovalent cation effects on enzymes. *Mailing Add:* Dept of Path 230 N Broad St Philadelphia PA 19102

KAYNE, HERBERT LAWRENCE, b Chicago, Ill, Sept 22, 34; m 62; c 2. PHYSIOLOGY. *Educ:* Univ Ill, BS, 55, MS, 58, PhD(physiol), 62. *Prof Exp:* From instr to asst prof, 62-69, ASSOC PROF PHYSIOL, SCH MED, BOSTON UNIV, 69- *Mem:* Am Physiol Soc; Biomet Soc. *Res:* Biostatistics. *Mailing Add:* Dept of Physiol Boston Univ Sch of Med Boston MA 02118

KAYNE, MARLENE STEINMETZ, b Bronx, NY, July 6, 41; m 65. BIOCHEMISTRY, MOLECULAR BIOLOGY. *Educ:* St John's Univ, BS, 62; Mich State Univ, PhD(biochem), 66. *Prof Exp:* Fel immunol, Max Planck Inst Exp Med, 67-69; res assoc enzym, Dept Biophysics, Univ Pa, 70-74 & Dept Biol, 74-77; ASST PROF MOLECULAR BIOL & CHMN DEPT BIOL, TRENTON STATE COL, 77- *Concurrent Pos:* Ger Res Asn fel, 67-69; NSF res grants, 76-77 & 78- *Res:* Purification and characterization of procaryotic enzymes required in protein biosynthesis. *Mailing Add:* Dept of Biol Trenton State Col Trenton NJ 08625

KAYS, M ALLAN, b Princeton, Ind, May 13, 34; m 55; c 3. GEOLOGY, PETROLOGY. *Educ:* Southern Ill Univ, BA, 56; Univ Wash, St Louis, MA, 58, PhD(geol), 61. *Prof Exp:* Asst prof, 61-66, assoc prof, 66-80, PROF GEOL, UNIV ORE, 80- *Concurrent Pos:* Vis geologist, Precambrian Geol Div, Dept Mineral Resources, Prov Sask, Can, 70-71. *Mem:* Am Geophys Union; Geol Soc Am. *Res:* Petrology of xenoliths and their fused products in margins of basic intrusions; petrology and structural relations of Archaean supracrustal metamorphic and plutonic rocks, East Greenland; petrology of migmatized gneisses of Canada, Finland and East Greenland; metamorphism and structure of convergent plate marginal sequences in cordillera of western North America. *Mailing Add:* Dept of Geol Univ of Ore Eugene OR 97403

KAYS, STANLEY J, b Stillwater, Okla, Feb 3, 45. HORTICULTURE, VEGETABLE CROP PHYSIOLOGY. *Educ:* Okla State Univ, BS, 68; Mich State Univ, MS, 69, PhD(hort), 71. *Prof Exp:* Researcher plant biol, Dept Biol, Tex A&M Univ, 71; researcher, Sch Plant Biol, Univ Col Northern Wales, UK, 71-72; asst prof veg crops, Dept Hort, Univ Ga, Tifton, 73-75; assoc prof, Dept Hort Food Sci, Univ Ark, 76-77; ASSOC PROF VEG CROPS & POST-HARVEST, DEPT HORT, UNIV GA, 77- *Concurrent Pos:* Grants, Nat Pecan Shellers, 76, Gilroy Foods Inc, 78, Woolfolk Chem Works Inc, 78 & Sci Educ Adm, USDA, 81. *Mem:* Am Soc Hort Sci; Am Soc Plant Physiol. *Res:* Developmental and post-harvest physiology of vegetable crops. *Mailing Add:* Dept of Hort Univ of Ga Athens GA 30602

KAYS, WILLIAM MORROW, b Norfolk, Va, July 29, 20; m 47; c 4. MECHANICAL ENGINEERING. *Educ:* Stanford Univ, AB, 42, MS, 47, PhD(mech eng), 51. *Prof Exp:* Res assoc, 47-51, from asst prof to assoc prof, 51-57, head dept, 61-72, PROF MECH ENG, STANFORD UNIV, 57-, DEAN ENG, 72- *Concurrent Pos:* Fulbright lectr, Imp Col London, 59-60, NSF sr fel, 66-67. *Honors & Awards:* Mem Award, Am Soc Mech Engrs, 65. *Mem:* Fel Am Soc Mech Engrs; Nat Acad Eng. *Res:* Heat transfer to fluids, especially turbulent boundary layers. *Mailing Add:* Sch of Eng Stanford Univ Stanford CA 94305

KAYSER, BORIS JULES, b New York, NY, June 2, 38; m 60. THEORETICAL ELEMENTARY PARTICLE PHYSICS. *Educ:* Princeton Univ, AB, 60; Calif Inst Technol, PhD(physics), 64. *Prof Exp:* Res assoc physics, Univ Calif, Berkeley, 64-66; asst prof, State Univ NY Stony Brook, 66-69; asst prof, Northwestern Univ, Evanston, 69-74; assoc prog dir theoret physics, 72-75, PROG DIR THEORET PHYSICS, NSF, 75- *Mem:* Am Phys Soc. *Res:* Weak interactions; electron-position collisions; nuetrino oscillations and massive neutrinos. *Mailing Add:* Div of Physics Nat Sci Found Washington DC 20550

KAYSER, FRANCIS X, b Toledo, Ohio, Feb 10, 27; m 52; c 5. METALLURGICAL ENGINEERING. *Educ:* Univ Notre Dame, BS, 48; Mass Inst Technol, MS, 50, DSc(metall), 63. *Prof Exp:* Metallurgist, Unitcast Corp, Ohio, 48-49; res metallurgist, Res Labs Div, Gen Motors Corp, Mich, 50-55; res metallurgist, sci labs, Ford Motor Co, 55-57; asst prof phys metall, 63-70, ASSOC METALLURGIST, INST ATOMIC RES, AMES LAB, 63-; assoc prof, 70-75, PROF METALL, IOWA STATE UNIV, 75- *Concurrent Pos:* Consult, Northern Natural Gas Co, 77- *Mem:* Am Soc Metals; Sigma Xi; Am Inst Mining, Metall & Petrol Engrs. *Res:* Nature of solid solutions; vibration spectra; diffraction; phase transformations in solids; elastic and plastic behavior of metallic and non-metallic materials. *Mailing Add:* Ames Lab DOE Iowa State Univ Ames IA 50011

KAYSER, RICHARD FRANCIS, b Toledo, Ohio, Feb 24, 25; m 50; c 9. TECHNICAL MANAGEMENT. *Educ:* Univ Cincinnati, PhD(chem eng), 52. *Prof Exp:* Engr, Linde Div, 52-65, prod mgr, Silicones Div, 65-72, opers mgr, 72-74, dir, Res & Develop, Chem & Plastics Div, 74-80, VPRES TECHNOL, ETHYLENE OXIDE/GLYCOL DIV, UNION CARBIDE CORP, 80- *Res:* Silicones processes; low pressure oxo process and oxo alcohols; new ethylene oxide catalyst developments. *Mailing Add:* Union Carbide Corp PO Box 8361 South Charleston WV 25303

KAYSER, ROBERT HELMUT, b Orange, NJ, Aug 21, 48; m 72; c 1. BIO-ORGANIC CHEMISTRY. *Educ:* Stevens Inst Technol, BS, 70; Georgetown Univ, PhD(org chem), 75. *Prof Exp:* Res asst org chem, Georgetown Univ, 74; res assoc bio-org chem, Univ Md, Baltimore County, 74-80; MEM STAFF US ENVIRON PROTECTION AGENCY, WASHINGTON, DC, 80- *Mem:* Am Chem Soc. *Res:* Designing model systems in an attempt to mimic various enzymatic processes and elucidate enzymatic mechanisms. *Mailing Add:* 4th & M St SW US Environ Protection Agency TS-777 Washington DC 20460

KAZAKIA, JACOB YAKOVOS, b Istanbul, Turkey, Feb 27, 45; m 72; c 1. APPLIED MECHANICS. *Educ:* Istanbul Tech Univ, MS, 68; Lehigh Univ, PhD(appl mech), 72. *Prof Exp:* Res assoc, 72-74, asst prof, 74-79, ASSOC PROF, CTR APPLN MATH, LEHIGH UNIV, 79- *Mem:* Am Acad Mech. *Res:* Nonlinear wave propagation in fluids; nonlinear waves in solids; viscoelastic fluid flows; stability of liquid filled shells; run-up and spin-up problems. *Mailing Add:* Ctr for Appln of Math Lehigh Univ 4 W Fourth St Bethlehem PA 18015

KAZAKS, PETER ALEXANDER, b Riga, Latvia, Feb 22, 40; US citizen; m 68; c 4. THEORETICAL NUCLEAR PHYSICS. *Educ:* McGill Univ, BSc, 62; Yale Univ, MS, 63; Univ Calif, Davis, PhD(physics), 68. *Prof Exp:* Res assoc, Ohio Univ, 68-70; asst prof physics, St Lawrence Univ, 70-73; asst prof, 73-75, ASSOC PROF PHYSICS & CHMN, DIV NATURAL SCI, NEW COL, UNIV SOUTH FLA, 75- *Concurrent Pos:* NSF res partic, Univ Fla, 71; NSF grant, St Lawrence Univ, 71-72; Res Corp grant, 75. *Mem:* Am Phys Soc. *Res:* Three-body models of nuclear reactions; electron-atom collision collisions; pion-nucleus scattering. *Mailing Add:* Dept of Physics New Col of Univ of SFla Sarasota FL 33579

KAZAL, LOUIS ANTHONY, b Newark, NJ, July 2, 12; m 42; c 4. BIOCHEMISTRY, HEMATOLOGY. *Educ:* Seton Hall Col, BS, 35; Rutgers Univ, PhD(biochem, physiol), 40. *Prof Exp:* Asst physiol & biochem, Rutgers Univ, 37-40; res biochemist, Merck Sharp & Dohme, Inc, 40-50, dir biol develop, 50-54, mgr tech info, 54-55, tech asst to med dir, 55-56; head sect blood plasma fractionation, Cardeza Found, 56-60, from asst prof to prof physiol, 57-78, assoc prof med & assoc dir Cardeza Found Hemat Res, 60-78, HON PROF PHYSIOL & HON ASSOC PROF MED, JEFFERSON MED

COL, 78- *Honors & Awards:* Co-recipient Rorer Award, Am J Gastroenterol, 66. *Mem:* Am Chem Soc; Soc Exp Biol & Med; Am Soc Biol Chem; NY Acad Sci; Int Soc Thrombosis & Homeostasis. *Res:* Blood coagulation; proteins; blood group specific substances; ion-exchange resins; erythropoietin inhibitors; lipids; trypsin inhibitor; isolation and crystalization of pancreatic secretory trypsin inhibitor. *Mailing Add:* 18215 Organ Pipe Dr Sun City AZ 85373

KAZAN, BENJAMIN, b New York, NY, May 8, 17; div; c 1. PHYSICS. *Educ:* Calif Inst Technol, BS, 38; Columbia Univ, MA, 40; Munich Tech Univ, Dr rer nat, 61. *Prof Exp:* Radio engr, Signal Corps Eng Labs, 40-44, chief spec purpose tube sect, 44-50; physicist, RCA Labs, 50-58; head solid-state display sect, Res Labs, Hughes Aircraft Co, 58-61; chief scientist aerospace electronics div, Electro-Optical Systs, Inc, 61-68; mgr explor display dept, Thomas J Watson Res Ctr, IBM Corp, 68-74; HEAD, DISPLAY GROUP, XEROX CORP, 74- *Concurrent Pos:* Ed, Advan in Image Pickup & Display; assoc ed, Inst Elec & Electronics Engrs, Trans on Electron Devices; consult adv group electron devices, Defense Dept, 73- *Honors & Awards:* Silver Medal, Am Roentgen Ray Soc, 57; Coolidge Award, Gen Elec Co, 58. *Mem:* Sigma Xi; Am Phys Soc; Inst Elec & Electronics Engrs; Soc Info Display. *Res:* Electronic image storage; image pickup and display devices; display devices; solid-state image devices. *Mailing Add:* Palo Alto Res Ctr Xerox Corp 3333 Coyote Hill Rd Palo Alto CA 94304

KAZANJIAN, ARMEN ROUPEN, b New Haven, Conn, Feb 13, 28; m 62; c 3. PHYSICAL CHEMISTRY. *Educ:* Northeastern Univ, BS, 51; Univ Calif, Los Angeles, PhD(phys chem), 65. *Prof Exp:* Chemist, Raw Mat Develop Lab, AEC, 51-56; res chemist, Rocketdyne Div, NAm Aviation, Inc, 56-60; res chemist, Rocket Power Inc, 66; res chemist, Rocky Flats Div, Dow Chem Co, 66-75; RES CHEMIST, ROCKY FLATS DIV, ROCKWELL INT, 75- *Mem:* AAAS; Radiation Res Soc; Sigma Xi; Nuclear Soc Am. *Res:* Chemical effects of nuclear transformations; radiation chemistry. *Mailing Add:* 4543 Eldorado Springs Dr Boulder CO 80303

KAZARIAN, LEON EDWARD, b Norwalk, Conn. BIOMECHANICS. *Educ:* Northrop Inst Technol, BSAAE, 66; Karolinska Inst, Sweden, Dr Ing(orthop biomech), 72. *Prof Exp:* RES SCIENTIST BIOMECH, AEROSPACE MED RES LABS, WRIGHT PATTERSON AFB, 67- *Mem:* Orthop Res Soc; Aerospace Med Asn. *Res:* Hard and soft tissue mechanics as related to dynamic environments. *Mailing Add:* Aeroapce Med Res Labs Wright Patterson AFB OH 45433

KAZARINOFF, MICHAEL N, b Ann Arbor, Mich, Mar 24, 49; m 70; c 2. BIOCHEMISTRY. *Educ:* Yale Univ, BS, 70; Cornell Univ, PhD(biochem), 75. *Prof Exp:* Fel biochem, Univ Calif, Berkeley, 75-76; fel microbiol, Univ Tex, Austin, 76-78; ASST PROF NUTRIT BIOCHEM, CORNELL UNIV, 78- *Mem:* Am Chem Soc; AAAS. *Res:* Enzymology; protein-coenzyme interactions; protein turnover; coenzyme mechanisms; purification and properties of enzymes of vitamin metabolism. *Mailing Add:* Div of Nutrit Scis Cornell Univ Ithaca NY 14853

KAZARINOFF, NICHOLAS D, b Ann Arbor, Mich, Aug 12, 29; m 48; c 6. MATHEMATICS. *Educ:* Univ Mich, BS, 50, MS, 51; Univ Wis, PhD, 54. *Prof Exp:* Asst math, Univ Wis, 51-53; from instr to asst prof, Purdue Univ, 53-56; from asst prof to prof, Univ Mich, 56-71, consult elec eng, Radiation Lab, 58-65; Martin prof math, 72-77, chmn dept, 71-75, PROF MATH, STATE UNIV NY BUFFALO, 71- *Concurrent Pos:* Res assoc, Univ Wis, 54; exchange prof, Steklov Math Inst, Moscow, 60-61 & 65, vis Ctr Nat Res Prof, Trento, Italy, 78, 80. *Mem:* Soc Indust & Appl Math; Am Math Soc; Math Asn Am. *Res:* Ordinary and partial differential equations and applications; geometry; inequalities; scattering and diffraction problems. *Mailing Add:* SUNY Buffalo Dept Math 4246 Ridge Lea Rd Amherst NY 14226

KAZDA, LOUIS F(RANK), b Dayton, Ohio, Sept 21, 16; m 40; c 3. ELECTRICAL ENGINEERING. *Educ:* Univ Cincinnati, EE, 40, MSE, 43; Syracuse Univ, PhD(elec eng), 62. *Prof Exp:* Res & develop engr elec eng, Bendix Aviation Corp, 43-46; from instr to assoc prof, 47-60, prof elec eng, 60-81, PROF ELEC & COMPUT ENG, UNIV MICH, ANN ARBOR, 81- *Concurrent Pos:* Consult, Cook Res Labs, 51-53, Willow Run Labs, Mich, 54-, US Air Force, 57-59, Maxitrol Corp, 58-68, Clark Equipment Co, 60-62, Ford Motor Co, 62 & Conduction Corp, 63. *Mem:* AAAS; fel Inst Elec & Electronics Engrs. *Res:* Feedback control systems of linear, nonlinear or adaptive type; inertial navigation systems; application of system engineering techniques to societal problems. *Mailing Add:* Dept of Elec & Comput Eng Univ of Mich Ann Arbor MI 48104

KAZDAN, JERRY LAWRENCE, b Detroit, Mich, Oct 31, 37; m 71. GEOMETRY, MATHEMATICAL ANALYSIS. *Educ:* Rensselaer Polytech Inst, BS, 59; NY Univ, MS, 61, PhD(math), 63. *Prof Exp:* Instr math, NY Univ, 63; Benjamin Peirce instr, Harvard Univ, 63-66; from asst prof to assoc prof, 66-74, PROF MATH, UNIV PA, 74- *Concurrent Pos:* Vis assoc prof, Harvard Univ, 71-72; vis prof, Univ Calif, Berkeley, 74-76. *Mem:* Am Math Soc; Math Asn Am. *Res:* Partial differential equations; differential geometry. *Mailing Add:* Dept of Math E1 Univ of Pa Philadelphia PA 19104

KAZEMI, HOSSEIN, b Iran, Mar 11, 38; m 64; c 3. PETROLEUM ENGINEERING. *Educ:* Univ Tex, BS, 61, PhD(petrol eng), 63. *Prof Exp:* Sr res scientist, reservoir eng, Tulas Res Ctr, Sinclair Oil & Gas Co, 63-69, res scientist, Atlantic Richfield Co, 69; sr res scientist & res proj dir, 69-80, MGR ENG DEPT, DENVER RES CTR, MARATHON OIL CO, 80- *Concurrent Pos:* Lectr math, Univ Tulsa, 67-69; adj assoc prof petroleum eng, Colo Sch Mines, 81- *Mem:* Soc Petrol Engrs; Am Inst Mining, Metall & Petrol Engrs; Sigma Xi. *Res:* Solution mining; pressure transient testing of oil and gas wells; reservoir simulation; enhanced oil recovery. *Mailing Add:* Marathon Oil Co Denver Res Ctr PO Box 269 Littleton CO 80160

KAZES, EMIL, b Istanbul, Turkey, June 13, 26; nat US; m 54; c 3. THEORETICAL PHYSICS. *Educ:* Univ Wis, BS, 49, MS, 50; Univ Chicago, PhD(physics), 56. *Prof Exp:* Proj assoc physics, Univ Wis, 57-59; from asst prof to assoc prof, 59-66, PROF PHYSICS, PA STATE UNIV, 66- *Mem:* Fel Am Phys Soc. *Res:* Electrodynamics; general relativity; soluble field theories; elementary particle theory; pion nucleon interaction, current algebra. *Mailing Add:* Dept of Physics Pa State Univ University Park PA 16802

KAZI, A HALIM, physics, nuclear engineering, see previous edition

KAZMAIER, HAROLD EUGENE, b Bowling Green, Ohio, Feb 17, 24; m 49; c 3. ENVIRONMENTAL SCIENCES, ENVIRONMENTAL MANAGEMENT. *Educ:* Ohio State Univ, BS, 49, MS, 51, PhD(bot), 60. *Prof Exp:* Asst plant path, Agr Exp Sta, Ohio State Univ, 50-52; sr res plant pathologist, Battelle-Columbus, 52-72; CHIEF TECH ASSISTANCE, PESTICIDE BR, US ENVIRON PROTECTION AGENCY, 72- *Mem:* Am Phytopath Soc; Soc Nematol. *Res:* Pesticides; plant pest control; registration support data. *Mailing Add:* US Environ Protection Agency Pesticide Br Kennedy Fed Bldg Boston MA 02203

KAZMANN, RAPHAEL GABRIEL, b Brooklyn, NY, Oct 16, 16; m 42; c 3. HYDROLOGY, HYDROLOGIC ENGINEERING. *Educ:* Carnegie-Mellon Univ, BS, 39. *Prof Exp:* Hydraul engr ground water, US Geol Surv, Washington, DC, 40-45; chief hydraul engr ground water explor, Ranney Method Water Supplies, Inc, Columbus, Ohio, 46-50; consult engr ground water, 50-63; PROF CIVIL ENG, LA STATE UNIV, 63- *Mem:* Am Soc Civil Engrs; Soc Mining Engrs; Nat Water Well Asn; Am Water Works Asn; Am Geophys Union. *Res:* Cyclic storage of fresh water in saline aquifers; storage and retrieval of heated and superheated water in saline aquifers; miscible displacement processes and their application to solution mining and deepwell disposal of wastes; monitoring of leachates from landfills; geomorphology and national water policy. *Mailing Add:* Dept of Civil Eng CEBA Bldg La State Univ Baton Rouge LA 70803

KAZMERSKI, LAWRENCE L, b Chicago, Ill, June 9, 45; m 68; c 2. PHOTOVOLTAICS, SURFACE SCIENCE. *Educ:* Univ Notre Dame, BSEE, 67, MSEE, 68, PhD(elec eng), 70. *Prof Exp:* Res fel, Am Eng Coun, Notre Dame Radiation Lab, 71; asst prof teaching res, Univ Maine, Orono, 71-74, assoc prof, 74-77; sr scientist, 77-79, PRIN SCIENITIST, SOLAR ENERGY RES INST, 79-, BR CHIEF, 80- *Concurrent Pos:* Adj prof, Univ Colo, 79-, Colo Sch Mines, 80-; ed, J Solar Cells, 79-, Polycrystelline & Amorphous Thin Films & Devices, 80; chmn, Nat Am Vacuum Soc Symposium, 82. *Honors & Awards:* Peter Mark Mem Award, Am Vacuum Soc, 80. *Mem:* Am Vacuum Soc; Inst Elec & Electronics Engrs; Am Phys Soc; Electrochem Soc; Sigma Xi. *Res:* Photovoltaic devices and solid-state physics, with emphasis on the correlation of compositional/chemical properties and electrical characteristics of interfaces in solar cells and other semiconductor devices. *Mailing Add:* Solar Energy Res Inst 1617 Cole Blvd Golden CO 80401

KAZNOFF, ALEXIS I(VAN), b Harbin, China, Oct 22, 33; US citizen. MATERIALS SCIENCE, CHEMICAL ENGINEERING. *Educ:* Univ Calif, Berkeley, BS, 55, PhD(phys metall), 61; Calif Inst Technol, MS, 56. *Prof Exp:* Scientist mat sci, 60-64, mgr ceramics & electronic mat, 64-66, mat sci & develop, nucleonics lab, 66-69, metall & ceramics lab, nuclear technol & appln oper, 69-73 & consult engr, prod & qual assurance oper, 73-75, MGR PROD ASSURANCE, PROD & QUAL ASSURANCE OPER, NUCLEAR ENERGY BUS GROUP, GEN ELEC CO, 75- *Mem:* Am Soc Metals; Am Ceramic Soc; Am Chem Soc; Am Welding Soc; Am Mgt Asn. *Res:* Nuclear fuel technology; structural materials for nuclear plants; nuclear materials; structural materials and processing. *Mailing Add:* Gen Elec Co 175 Curtner Ave M/C 152 San Jose CA 95125

KE, PAUL JENN, b Ahwei Prov, China, Jan 16, 34; Can citizen; m 61; c 2. ANALYTICAL BIOCHEMISTRY, FOOD TECHNOLOGY. *Educ:* Nat Cheng-Kung Univ, Taiwan, BEng, 59; Nat Taiwan Univ, MSc, 63; Mem Univ Nfld, MSc, 66; Univ Windsor, PhD(anal biochem), 72. *Prof Exp:* Res & develop chem engr, Taiwan Sugar Res Inst, Taiwan, 59-61; instr, Nat Taiwan Univ, 62-64; anal chemist, Fish Res Bd Can, 66-69; RES SCIENTIST, HALIFAX LAB, FISHERIES & OCEANS CAN, 72- *Concurrent Pos:* Assoc prof, Tech Col NS, 79- *Mem:* Chem Inst Can; Can Soc Chem Engrs; Inst Food Technologists; Can Inst Food Sci & Technol; Am Oil Chemists Soc. *Res:* Biochemical study on kinetics of lipid oxidation and various rancidity reactions; methodological studies for determination of biochemical parameters and contaminates in various fishery products and waters; quality science studies for sea foods; preservation biochemistry investigation; fish engineering sciences. *Mailing Add:* Fisheries & Oceans Can Halifax Lab PO Box 550 Halifax NS B3J 2S7 Can

KEAHEY, KENNETH KARL, b Covington, Okla, Sept 17, 23; m 56; c 3. VETERINARY PATHOLOGY. *Educ:* Okla State Univ, BS, 48, DVM, 54; Mich State Univ, PhD(vet path), 63. *Prof Exp:* Adv vet med, Imp Ethiopian Col Agr & Mech Arts, 54-56, head dept animal sci, 56-57, dean, 57-58, actg pres, 58-60; NIH fel, 60-63, from asst prof to assoc prof, 63-69, PROF VET PATH, MICH STATE UNIV, 69-, DIR ANAL HEALTH DIAG LAB, 77- *Mem:* AAAS; Am Vet Med Asn. *Res:* Infectious diseases and nutritional deficiencies in swine. *Mailing Add:* Dept of Path Mich State Univ East Lansing MI 48824

KEAIRNS, DALE LEE, b Vincennes, Ind, Nov 20, 40; m 67; c 1. CHEMICAL ENGINEERING, RESEARCH ADMINISTRATION. *Educ:* Okla State Univ, BS, 62; Carnegie Inst Technol, MS, 64, PhD(chem eng), 67. *Prof Exp:* Assoc develop engr, Oak Ridge Nat Lab, 62 & Gaseous Diffusion Plant, Tenn, 63; sr engr, Res & Develop Ctr, 67-73, mgr fluidized bed eng, 73-78, MGR FOSSIL FUEL & FLUIDIZED BED PROCESSING, WESTINGHOUSE RES & DEVELOP CTR, WESTINGHOUSE ELEC CORP, 78- *Concurrent Pos:* Chmn, First Int Fluidization Conf, Eng Found, 75, co-chmn, 78; mem, Fossil Fuel Adv Comt, Oak Ridge Nat Lab, 79, 80 & 81. *Mem:* Am Inst Chem Engrs; Am Chem Soc; AAAS. *Res:* Hydrodynamic, heat transfer and reaction rate studies on fluidized bed systems; pilot plant engineering and design; gasification and fluidized bed combustion systems development. *Mailing Add:* Westinghouse Res & Develop Ctr Beulah Rd Pittsburgh PA 15235

KEALY, THOMAS JOSEPH, b New York, NY, Dec 22, 27; m 53; c 9. ORGANIC CHEMISTRY. *Educ:* Manhattan Col, BS, 50; Duquesne Univ, MS, 52; Carnegie Inst Technol, PhD(chem), 55. *Prof Exp:* Res chemist, Cent Res Dept, 55-61, RES CHEMIST, ELASTOMER CHEM DEPT, E I DU PONT DE NEMOURS & CO, INC, 61- *Mem:* AAAS; Am Chem Soc. *Res:* Coordination catalysis; polymer synthesis and evaluation; organic synthesis. *Mailing Add:* 23 N Cliffe Dr Wilmington DE 19809

KEAMMERER, WARREN ROY, b Gary, Ind, Nov 25, 46; m 70. PLANT ECOLOGY. *Educ:* Capital Univ, BS, 68; NDak State Univ, PhD(bot), 72. *Prof Exp:* Lectr biol, Capital Univ, 71-72; fel ecol, Univ Colo, 72-73; ECOL CONSULT, STOECKER-KEAMMERER & ASSOCS, 73- *Concurrent Pos:* Consult, C-b Shale Oil Proj, Atlantic Richfield Co Coal Oper & Flatiron Co, 74- & CH2M Hill, 74-75. *Mem:* Ecol Soc Am; Brit Ecol Soc; Sigma Xi; Wilderness Soc. *Res:* Preparation of baseline plant ecological reports designed to provide necessary data for impact analyses; study areas are located in eastern Wyoming and western Colorado. *Mailing Add:* 5858 Woodbourne Hollow Rd Boulder CO 80301

KEAN, BENJAMIN HARRISON, b Chicago, Ill, Dec 2, 12; m 48. TROPICAL MEDICINE. *Educ:* Univ Calif, AB 33; Columbia Univ, MD, 37; Am Bd Path, dipl, 45; Am Bd Microbiol, dipl, 63. *Prof Exp:* From intern to resident, Gorgas Hosp, CZ, 37-39, sr pathologist, 40-45; asst prof path, Postgrad Med Sch, NY Univ, 46-52; from asst prof to assoc prof trop med, 52-65, PROF TROP MED, MED COL, CORNELL UNIV,65-, PROF PUB HEALTH, 72- *Concurrent Pos:* Attend pathologist, Col Med, NY Univ-Bellevue Med Ctr, 46-52; attend physician & parasitologist, New York Hosp, 52-, dir parasitol lab, 52-; attend physician, Doctors Hosp, 52-; asst prof parasitol pub health & prev med, Med Col, Cornell Univ, 54-65. *Mem:* Am Soc Trop Med & Hyg; Am Soc Clin Path; fel AMA. *Res:* Medical parasitology. *Mailing Add:* Cornell Univ Med Col 1300 York Ave New York NY 10021

KEAN, CHESTER EUGENE, b Chicago, Ill, Oct 16, 25; m 49; c 4. FOOD CHEMISTRY. *Educ:* Univ Ill, BS, 48; Ore State Col, MS, 50; Univ Calif, PhD(agr chem), 54. *Prof Exp:* Asst chem, Ore State Col, 48-50; food technologist, Univ Calif, 50-53; assoc technologist, Calif & Hawaiian Sugar Refining Corp, 53-58, technologist, 58-61, new prod technologist, 61-66, sr technologist, 66-78, CHIEF CHEMIST PROD DEVELOP, C&H SUGAR CO, CROCKETT, 78- *Mem:* Am Chem Soc; Inst Food Technologists; Am Soc Enol. *Res:* Copper clouding in wines; fungal amylases in butanol acetone fermentation; organic acids in wine; method for determining the sub-sieve particle size distribution of pulverized sugar; carbohydrate chemistry; product development based on sugar properties. *Mailing Add:* 667 Byrdee Way Lafayette CA 94549

KEAN, EDWARD LOUIS, b Philadelphia, Pa, Oct 19, 25; m 62; c 4. BIOCHEMISTRY. *Educ:* Univ Pa, BA, 49, PhD(biochem), 61; Drexel Inst Technol, MS, 56. *Prof Exp:* Chemist, Sharp & Dohme Inc, 49-52 & Smith Kline & French Labs, 52-56; asst instr biochem, Univ Pa, 56-57; res assoc, Univ Mich, 61-64; sr cancer res scientist, Roswell Park Mem Inst, NY, 64-65; from sr instr to assoc prof, 65-79, PROF OPHTHAL & BIOCHEM, SCH MED, CASE WESTERN RESERVE UNIV, 79- *Concurrent Pos:* Arthritis & Rheumatism Found fel, 61-64; Nat Inst Neurol Dis & Stroke & Nat Eye Inst res grants, 68-; mem, Marine Biol Lab Corp; exchange scientist, Japan, 81. *Mem:* Am Chem Soc; Am Soc Biol Chem; Asn Res Vision & Ophthal. *Res:* Biosynsthesis, subcellular location and degradation of cytosine monophosphate-sialic acid; glycolipid sulfation and vitamin A deficiency; biosynthesis and enzymatic degradation of rhodopsin; multiple forms of bovine and bacterio-rhodopsins; dolichol pathway and rhodopsin glycosylation; regulation of the dolichol pathway; role of carbohydrates in phagocytosis. *Mailing Add:* Dept of Ophthal Case Western Reserve Univ Cleveland OH 44106

KEANA, JOHN F W, b St Joseph, Mich, Sept 14, 39; m 66; c 2. ORGANIC CHEMISTRY. *Educ:* Kalamazoo Col, BA, 61; Stanford Univ, PhD(chem), 65. *Prof Exp:* NSF fel, Columbia Univ, 64-65; from asst prof to assoc prof, 65-77, PROF CHEM, UNIV ORE, 77- *Mem:* Am Chem Soc. *Res:* Biological membranes; new synthetic reactions; preparation and properties of unusual organic molecules; chemistry and biophysics of nitroxide free radical spin-labels; neurochemistry. *Mailing Add:* Dept of Chem Univ of Ore Eugene OR 97403

KEANE, DAVID DONAGH, chemistry, see previous edition

KEANE, JOHN FRANCIS, JR, b Milford, Mass, Feb 3, 22; m 48; c 2. BIOPHYSICS, PHYSIOLOGY. *Educ:* Boston Col, BS, 43; Fordham Univ, MS, 49; Univ St Louis, PhD(biol chem), 54. *Prof Exp:* Asst biol, Fordham Univ, 48-49 & Cytochem Sect, Sloan-Kettering Inst, 49-50; asst biol, Biophys Inst, Univ St Louis, 50-54, res assoc, 54-56; from instr to asst prof, 55-68, ASSOC PROF PHYSICS, ST LOUIS COL PHARM, 68- *Mem:* AAAS; NY Acad Sci. *Res:* Physical properties and chemical constitution of crystalline inclusions in giant Amoebae; ultraviolet microspectrography of normal and malignant, desquammated and cultured cells; protective and other action of chemical agents of biological and physical systems subjected to subfreezing temperatures; studies of the action of amides. *Mailing Add:* Dept of Physics St Louis Col of Pharm St Louis MO 63110

KEANE, KENNETH WILLIAM, b Newark, NJ, Aug 27, 21; m 50; c 3. NUTRITION, BIOCHEMISTRY. *Educ:* Murray State Col, BS, 44; Univ Ill, MS, 51, PhD(nutrit biochem), 53. *Prof Exp:* Chemist, Nutrit Res, Raritan Labs, 46-48 & Lederle Labs, Am Cyanamid Co, 48-50; sr res radiochemist, Int Minerals & Chem Corp, 53-56; head, Div Nutrit Res, Campbell Soup Co,

56-71; DIR NUTRIT RES, CHAMPION VALLEY FARMS, MOORESTOWN, 71- *Concurrent Pos:* Assoc prof biochemistry, Camden County Col, 74- *Mem:* AAAS; Am Chem Soc; Asn Vitamin Chem; Animal Nutrit Res Coun; Am Inst Nutrit. *Res:* New growth factors and intermediary metabolism; nutritional biochemistry. *Mailing Add:* 300 Sheffield Rd Cherry Hill NJ 08034

KEAR, BERNARD HENRY, materials & technology, see previous edition

KEAR, EDWARD B, JR, b Yonkers, NY, Mar 23, 32; m 54; c 3. MECHANICAL ENGINEERING, SYSTEMS ANALYSIS. *Educ:* Clarkson Tech Univ, BME, 54; Cornell Univ, MS, 56, PhD, 69. *Prof Exp:* From asst prof to assoc prof control systs anal, 58-76, ASSOC PROF MECH & INDUST ENG, CLARKSON COL TECHNOL, 76-, EXEC OFFICER, MECH ENG DEPT, 71- *Mem:* Am Soc Eng Educ. *Res:* Control systems analysis; variation of hand-eye coordination with age. *Mailing Add:* Dept of Mech Eng Clarkson Col of Technol Potsdam NY 13676

KEARLEY, FRANCIS JOSEPH, JR, b Mobile, Ala, July 7, 21; m 54. ORGANIC CHEMISTRY. *Educ:* Spring Hill Col, BS, 42; Vanderbilt Univ, MS, 44, PhD(org chem), 50. *Prof Exp:* Assoc prof, 53-66, PROF CHEM & CHMN DEPT, SPRING HILL COL, 66- *Mailing Add:* Dept of Chem Spring Hill Col Mobile AL 36608

KEARNEY, EDNA BEATRICE, b Nottingham, Eng, Sept 27, 19; US citizen; div; c 1. BIOCHEMSITRY, MICROBIOLOGY. *Educ:* Univ Mich, BS, 41, MS, 42; Univ Wis, PhD(med bact), 47. *Prof Exp:* Asst bact, Univ Mich, 41-44 & Univ Mich Hosp, 44-45; asst med bact, Univ Wis, 45-47, res assoc, 47; sr res fel biochem, Nat Cancer Inst, Western Reserve Univ, 47-49; Guggenheim fel, Univ Paris & Cambridge Univ, 51-52 & Enzyme Inst, Univ Wis, 52-54; mem dept biochem, Edsel B Ford Inst Med Res, Henry Ford Hosp, 54-65; res chemist, Vet Admin Hosp, Madison, Wis, 65-67; assoc res pharmacologist, Med Ctr, Univ Calif, San Francisco, 67-69; res chemist, 70-81, RES CAREER SCIENTIST, VET ADMIN MED CTR, SAN FRANCISCO, 81- *Mem:* Am Soc Biol Chem. *Res:* Enzyme chemistry; intermediary metabolism. *Mailing Add:* Vet Admin Med Ctr 151S 4150 Clement St San Francisco CA 94121

KEARNEY, JOSEPH W(ILLIAM), b Denver, Colo, Apr 6, 22. SYSTEM ENGINEERING, MICROWAVE ENGINEERING. *Educ:* Univ Colo, BS, 43. *Prof Exp:* Spec res assoc, Radio Res Lab, Harvard Univ, 43-45; engr, Airborne Instruments Lab, Div Cutler-Hammer, Inc, 46-53, asst supvr engr, 53-55, sect head, 55-58, dept head, 58-62, dept div dir, 62-64, dir new progs, 64-65, div dir, 65-67, vpres, 67-79; DIR BUS DEVELOP, INSTRUMENTS & SYSTS OPER, EATON CORP, 79- *Concurrent Pos:* Chmn reconnaissance panel, electronic warfare adv group, US Air Force, 59-60. *Mem:* AAAS; fel Inst Elec & Electronics Engrs; Am Inst Aeronaut & Astronaut. *Res:* Electronic warfare systems for the military services and electronic systems for space exploration. *Mailing Add:* Eaton Corp Suite 231 4640 Admiralty Way Marina del Rey CA 90291

KEARNEY, PHILIP C, b Baltimore, Md, Dec 31, 32; m 55; c 2. BIOCHEMISTRY, AGRICULTURE. *Educ:* Univ Md, BS, 55, MS, 57; Cornell Univ, PhD(agr), 60. *Prof Exp:* NSF fel biochem, 60-62; BIOCHEMIST PESTICIDES, AGR RES CTR-WEST, USDA, 62-, CHIEF PESTICIDE DEGRADATION LAB, 72- *Concurrent Pos:* Unit leader, Pesticide Degradation Lab, 65-72. *Honors & Awards:* Int Award Res Pesticide Chem, Am Chem Soc, 81. *Mem:* Am Chem Soc; Int Union Pure & Appl Chem; AAAS; Weed Sci Soc Am; Asn Off Anal Chemists. *Res:* Pesticides; metabolism of organic pesticides by soil microorganisms; enzymology of pesticides. *Mailing Add:* Bldg 050 Agr Res Ctr-West USDA Beltsville MD 20705

KEARNEY, PHILIP DANIEL, b Detroit, Mich, Nov 21, 33; m 58; c 4. PHYSICS. *Educ:* Univ Mich, BS, 58, MS, 60, PhD(physics), 64. *Prof Exp:* Asst prof, 64-74, ASSOC PROF PHYSICS, COLO STATE UNIV, 74-; CONSULT, ARGONNE NAT LAB, 81- *Concurrent Pos:* Sabbatical leave, Solar Particle Physics, Los Alamos Sci Lab, 71-72, Environ Radiation Measurements, Argonne Nat Lab, 80-81. *Mem:* Am Phys Soc; Health Physics Soc. *Res:* Environmental radiation measurements. *Mailing Add:* Dept of Physics Colo State Univ Ft Collins CO 80523

KEARNEY, ROBERT JAMES, b Manchester, NH, Oct 5, 35; m 61; c 4. SOLID STATE PHYSICS. *Educ:* Univ NH, BS, 57, MS, 59; Iowa State Univ, PhD(physics), 64. *Prof Exp:* Asst physics, Ames Lab, AEC, 60-64; from asst prof to assoc prof, 64-73, PROF PHYSICS, UNIV IDAHO, 73- *Concurrent Pos:* Vis prof, Univ Milano, Italy, 72-73. *Mem:* AAAS; Am Asn Physics Teachers; Am Phys Soc. *Res:* Electronic structure of metals and semi-conductors; optical spectroscopy of molecules. *Mailing Add:* Dept of Physics Univ of Idaho Moscow ID 83844

KEARNS, DAVID R, b Urbana, Ill, Mar 20, 35; m 58; c 3. PHYSICAL CHEMISTRY. *Educ:* Univ Ill, BS, 56; Univ Calif, Berkeley, PhD(phys chem), 60. *Prof Exp:* Fel theoret chem, Univ Chicago, 60-61; Inst, Mass Inst Technol, 61-62; from asst prof to prof phys chem, Univ Calif, Riverside, 62-75; PROF CHEM, UNIV CALIF, SAN DIEGO, 75- *Concurrent Pos:* A P Sloan fel, 65-67; lectr comt biophys, Harvard Med Sch, 65; Guggenheim fel, 69-70. *Honors & Awards:* Calif Sect Award, Am Chem Soc, 73. *Mem:* Am Chem Soc; Am Photobiol Soc; Biophys Soc. *Res:* Physical biochemistry; spectroscopy. *Mailing Add:* Dept of Chem Univ of Calif San Diego La Jolla CA 92093

KEARNS, DONALD ALLEN, b New Bedford, Mass, Sept 10, 23; m 47; c 7. MATHEMATICS. *Educ:* Boston Univ, AB, 47, PhD(math), 55; Brown Univ, MA, 50. *Prof Exp:* From instr to asst prof math, Merrimack Col, 48-53; asst prof math, Univ Maine, 53-58; PROF MATH, MERRIMACK COL, 58- *Mem:* Am Math Soc; Math Asn Am. *Res:* Differential equations. *Mailing Add:* Dept of Math Merrimack Col North Andover MA 01845

KEARNS, JOHN L(ELAND), b Ottawa, Ont, May 3, 23; m 55; c 3. INDUSTRIAL ENGINEERING. *Educ:* Univ Toronto, BASc, 45; Iowa State Univ, PhD(chem eng), 54; Youngstown State Univ, MBA, 79. *Prof Exp:* Res scientist, Indust Rayon Corp, 54-56; mgr dept process eng, Catalytic Construct Can, Ltd, 56-58; Abitibi prof eng sci, Univ Western Ont, 59-65, head dept chem eng, 58-65; mgr dept process eng, Lord Mfg Co, Pa, 65-66, mfg eng dept, 66-70; dir opers, Robintech Inc, 70; assoc prof, 71-79, PROF INDUST ENG, YOUNGSTOWN STATE UNIV, 79- *Mem:* Am Inst Chem Engrs; Am Inst Indust Engrs. *Res:* Pollution control; manufacturing systems and management; organization and personnel utilization; facilities economics and design. *Mailing Add:* Dept of Indust Eng Youngstown State Univ Youngstown OH 44503

KEARNS, LANCE EDWARD, b Greensburg, Pa, May 22, 49; m 71; c 2. GEOLOGY, MINERALOGY. *Educ:* Waynesburg Col, BS, 71; Univ Del, MS, 73, PhD(mineral), 77. *Prof Exp:* ASST PROF GEOL, JAMES MADISON UNIV, 76- *Mem:* Am Mineral Soc. *Res:* Mineral chemistry, especially fluorine effects in high temperature metacarbonates. *Mailing Add:* Dept of Geol James Madison Univ Harrisonburg VA 22807

KEARNS, THOMAS J, b Evanston, Ill, June 1, 40; m 63; c 3. ALGEBRA. *Educ:* Univ Santa Clara, BS, 62; Univ Ill, MS, 64, PhD(math), 68. *Prof Exp:* From instr to asst prof math, Univ Del, 67-75; asst prof, 75-77, ASSOC PROF MATH, NORTHERN KY UNIV, 77-, CHAIRPERSON DEPT, 81- *Mem:* Am Math Soc; Math Asn Am. *Res:* Representation theory for Lie algebras of classical type. *Mailing Add:* Dept of Math Northern Ky Univ Highland Heights KY 41076

KEARNS, THOMAS P, b Louisville, Ky, Apr 2, 22; m 44; c 2. OPHTHALMOLOGY. *Educ:* Univ Louisville, AB, 44, MD, 46; Univ Minn, MS, 52. *Prof Exp:* From asst prof to assoc prof, 53-77, MEM FAC OPHTHAL, MAYO MED SCH UNIV MINN, 77- *Concurrent Pos:* Consult, Mayo Clin, 53- *Res:* Diseases of the brain and eye. *Mailing Add:* Dept of Ophthal Mayo Clin 200 E First St SW Rochester MN 55901

KEARSLEY, ELLIOT ARMSTRONG, b Springfield, Mass, Jan 15, 27; m 57, 64; c 2. RHEOLOGY, CONTINUUM MECHANICS. *Educ:* Harvard Univ, AB, 49, MA, 50; Brown Univ, PhD(physics), 55. *Prof Exp:* Physicist, Res Lab, Bendix Aviation Corp, Mich, 53-55; physicist, Nat Acad Sci-Nat Res Coun, 55-76; sr liaison scientist, Off Naval Res, Tokyo, 76-78; PHYSICIST POLYMERS DIV, NAT BUR STANDARDS, 78- *Mem:* Fel Am Phys Soc; Soc Rheol. *Mailing Add:* Polymers Div Nat Bur Standards Washington DC 20234

KEASLING, HUGH HILARY, b Wilmington, Ill, Sept 19, 22; m 46; c 4. PHARMACOLOGY. *Educ:* Univ Iowa, BS, 40, MS, 49, PhD(pharmacol), 50. *Prof Exp:* Asst, Col Pharm, Univ Iowa, 48-49, asst pharmacol, Col Med, 49-50, instr, 50-51, assoc, 51-52, from asst prof to prof, 52-61; sect head cent nerv syst pharmacol, Upjohn Co, 60-67; DIR HEALTH & NUTRIT, BIOL SCI RES CTR, SHELL DEVELOP CO, 67- *Concurrent Pos:* Col Med Cent Sci traveling fel, Univ Ill, 53. *Mem:* AAAS; Am Soc Pharmacol & Exp Therapeut; NY Acad Sci; Am Soc Animal Sci; Soc Exp Biol & Med. *Res:* Structure-activity relationship and central nervous system pharmacology. *Mailing Add:* 2402 Dorrington Ct Modesto CA 95350

KEAST, DAVID N(ORRIS), b Pittsburgh, Pa, Jan 8, 31; m 55; c 4. ENVIRONMENTAL NOISE, EMERGENCY WORKING. *Educ:* Amherst Col, BA, 54; Mass Inst Technol, BS & MS, 54. *Prof Exp:* Engr acoust, Bolt Beranek & Newman, Inc, Los Angeles, 54-57, sr engr, 57-60, consult acoust & instrumentation, Calif, 60-64, supvr consult, 64-66, vpres data equip div, 66-71; vpres develop, MFE Corp, Wilmington, 71-73; MGR, ENVIRON DEPT, BOLT BERANEK & NEWMAN, 73- *Mem:* Acoust Soc Am; sr mem Inst Elec & Electronics Engrs; Inst Noise Control Engrs; Air Pollution Control Asn. *Res:* Acoustic-meteorological interactions and processing techniques for high-frequency dynamic data; effects of sound on the human environment; community noise and emergency working. *Mailing Add:* 657 Westford Rd Carlisle MA 01741

KEAST, F(RANCIS) H(ENRY), b Barrow-in-Furness, Eng, Oct 14, 20; m 52; c 2. AERODYNAMICS. *Educ:* Cambridge Univ, BA, 42, MA, 46. *Prof Exp:* From jr engr to projs engr, Power Jets Ltd, Eng, 42-46; sect head aerodyn, Orenda Engines Ltd, Div A V Roe Can, Ltd, 46-47, chief aerodynamicist, 47-48, chief exp engr, 48-52, asst chief engr, 52-54, dep chief engr, 54-57, chief engr, 57-59, tech dir, 59, aeronaut group, 59-62; dir res, Hawker Siddeley Can Ltd, 62-67; prin engr, Ont Res Found, 67-76; CONSULT, 77- *Concurrent Pos:* Chmn, Adv Comt Gas Dynamic Res, Defence Res Bd Can, 52-62. *Mem:* Fel Can Aeronaut & Space Inst; assoc fel Royal Aeronaut Soc; Brit Inst Mech Engrs. *Res:* Aerothermodynamics; heat transfer; energy. *Mailing Add:* RR 2 Brampton ON L6V 1A1 Can

KEAST, JAMES ALLEN, vertebrate ecology, see previous edition

KEASTER, ARMON JOSEPH, b Lilbourn, Mo, Mar 12, 33; m 56; c 2. ENTOMOLOGY. *Educ:* Univ Mo, BS, 59, MS, 61, PhD(entom), 65. *Prof Exp:* From instr to assoc prof, 70-76, PROF ENTOM, UNIV MO-COLUMBIA, 76- *Res:* Biology and control of insect pests attacking corn and other field crops; bionomics and management of soil arthropod pests. *Mailing Add:* Dept of Entom Univ of Mo Columbia MO 65211

KEAT, PAUL POWELL, b Elizabeth, NJ, Nov 29, 23; m 52; c 3. CERAMICS, PHYSICAL CHEMISTRY. *Educ:* Rutgers Univ, BSc, 47, MSc, 50, PhD(ceramics), 56. *Prof Exp:* Asst, 53-58, sr res engr, 58-63, RES ASSOC, NORTON CO, 63- *Res:* Design of ultrahigh pressure equipment; synthesis at ultrahigh pressure; hydrothermal synthesis; abrasive bond development. *Mailing Add:* Res & Develop Norton Co New Bond St Worcester MA 01606

KEATING, BARBARA HELEN, b Brooksville, Fla, Dec 25, 50. PALEOMAGNETISM, ARCHAEOLOGY. *Educ:* Fla State Univ, BA, 71; Univ Tex, Dallas, MS, 75, PhD(geosci), 76. *Prof Exp:* RESEARCHER GEOPHYSICS, UNIV HAWAII, 76-, PROF OCEANOG, 81- *Mem:* Geol Soc Am; Am Geophys Union; Int Asn Geomagnetism & Aeronomy; Soc Econ Paleontologist & Mineralogist. *Res:* Paleomagnetism and marine geology of the Pacific Ocean basin. *Mailing Add:* Hawaii Inst Geophysics Univ Hawaii 2525 Correa Rd Honolulu HI 96822

KEATING, EUGENE KNEELAND, b Liberal, Kans, Feb 15, 28; m 51; c 2. AGRICULTURAL BIOCHEMISTRY, NUTRITION. *Educ:* Kans State Univ, BS, 53, MS, 54; Univ Ariz, PhD(ruminant nutrit), 64. *Prof Exp:* Instr animal sci, Midwestern Univ, 57-59, farm mgr, 57-59, asst farm mgr, 59-60, from asst prof to assoc prof, 64-71, chmn dept animal sci, 71-78, PROF RUMINANT NUTRIT, CALIF STATE POLYTECH UNIV, POMONA, 78- *Mem:* Am Soc Animal Sci; Brit Soc Animal Prod; Am Soc Lab Animal Sci; fel Am Inst Chem. *Res:* Ruminant nutrition, particularly in cattle. *Mailing Add:* Dept of Animal Sci Calif State Polytech Univ Pomona CA 91768

KEATING, JAMES T, b Oak Park, Ill, Jan 21, 41; m 70; c 3. ORGANIC CHEMISTRY, POLYMER CHEMISTRY. *Educ:* St Mary's Col, Minn, BA, 62; Pa State Univ, PhD(chem), 68. *Prof Exp:* Res chemist, Plastic Prod & Resins Dept, Exp Sta, Wilmington, Del, 68-76, sr chemist, Seneca, 76-81, SR CHEMIST, E I DU PONT DE NEMOURS & CO, INC, WILMINGTON, DEL, 81- *Concurrent Pos:* NSF fel, 62-66. *Mem:* Am Chem Soc. *Res:* Carbene chemistry; aliphatic carbonium ion reactions; fluorinated free radicals; electrochemistry; Friedel-Crafts-type polymerizations; organic and inorganic coatings; emulsion polymerization; occupational safety and health. *Mailing Add:* 1709 Gunning Dr Forest Hills Park Wilmington DE 19803

KEATING, JOHN JOSEPH, b Montrose, SDak, Jan 17, 38; m 61; c 4. NUCLEAR REACTOR FUELS. *Educ:* SDak State Col, BS, 60; Iowa State Univ, MS, 66, PhD(nuclear eng), 68. *Prof Exp:* Nuclear engr, Idaho Opers Off, US Atomic Energy Comn, 68-73, reactor fuels engr, Div Reactor Develop & Technol, 73-74, asst dir engr technol & fuels, Fast Flux Test Fac Proj Off, US Atomic Energy Comn, US Energy Res & Develop Agency, 74-78; dir, Reactor Technol Div, Fast Flux Test Fac Proj Off, 78-81, DIR, FUELS SUPPLY DIV, RICHLAND OPERS OFF, US DEPT ENERGY, 81- *Mem:* Am Nuclear Soc. *Res:* Development and production of core components for liquid metal fast breeder reactors; core components include fuel, blanket, absorber and reflector assemblies. *Mailing Add:* 2611 Harris Ave Richland WA 99352

KEATING, KENNETH L(EE), b Chicago, Ill, May 19, 23; m 47; c 2. METALLURGY. *Educ:* Mass Inst Technol, SB, 47; Univ Mo, MS, 50; Stanford Univ, PhD(metall), 54. *Prof Exp:* Metallurgist, Titanium Div, Nat Lead Co, 47-48; asst metall, Univ Mo, 48-49, instr, 49-50; instr, Stanford Univ, 51-54; metallurgist, Bell Tel Labs, Inc, 54-55; metallurgist, Semiconductor Prod Div, Motorola, Inc, Ariz, 55-61; assoc prof metall eng, 61-67, PROF METALL ENG, UNIV ARIZ, 67- *Mem:* Am Soc Metals; Electrochem Soc; Am Inst Mining, Metall & Petrol Engrs; Am Ceramic Soc; Nat Asn Corrosion Engrs. *Res:* Corrosion of metals; phase relations between materials; solid state metallurgy. *Mailing Add:* Col of Mines Univ of Ariz Tucson AZ 85721

KEATING, PATRICK NORMAN, b Newcastle, UK, Feb 18, 39; m 61; c 2. APPLIED PHYSICS. *Educ:* Univ Nottingham, BSc, 59, MSc, 61; Univ Mich, PhD(physics), 69. *Prof Exp:* Physicist, Assoc Elec Industs, UK, 60-63; physicist, Tyco Labs, Inc, Waltham, Mass, 63-65; proj physicist, 65-70, head laser optics & acoustics dept, 70-74, dir, Appl Physics Dept, Bendix Res Lab, 74-79, ASSOC DIR RES, BENDIX ADVAN TECHNOL CTR, 80- *Mem:* Am Mgt Asn; Am Phys Soc. *Res:* Acoustics, underwater acoustics, and acoustic signal processing; sensors; optics; lattice dynamics; solid state physics. *Mailing Add:* Bendix Advan Technol Ctr 9140 Old Annapolis Rd Columbia MD 21045

KEATING, RICHARD CLARK, b St Paul, Minn, Aug 6, 37; m 61; c 2. SYSTEMATIC BOTANY. *Educ:* Colgate Univ, AB, 59; Univ Cincinnati, MS, 62, PhD(bot), 65. *Prof Exp:* Asst prof biol, Wis State Univ, Platteville, 64-65; vis asst prof bot, Univ Cincinnati, 65-66; from asst prof to assoc prof, 66-75, PROF BIOL, SOUTHERN ILL UNIV, EDWARDSVILLE, 75- *Concurrent Pos:* Res assoc, Mo Bot Garden, St Louis, 69-; dir, Trop Biol Prog, Assoc Univs Int Educ, 70; res assoc, Marie Selby Bot Garden, Sarasota, 74- *Mem:* AAAS; Bot Soc Am; Int Asn Wood Anatomists; Int Asn Plant Taxon; Int Aroid Soc. *Res:* Anatomical investigations on the evolution and classification of vascular plants. *Mailing Add:* Dept of Biol Southern Ill Univ Edwardsville IL 62026

KEATING, ROBERT JOSEPH, b Forest Hills, NY, Oct 24, 44. REPRODUCTIVE ENDOCRINOLOGY, NUTRITION. *Educ:* Univ St Thomas, BA, 69; Univ Houston, MS, 72, PhD(reprod physiol), 75. *Prof Exp:* Supvr &coordr bacterial monitoring prog respiratory ther, Methodist Hosp, Houston, 67-73; res asst reprod physiol, Univ Houston, 73-75; fel reprod endocrin, Univ Tex Med Sch, 75-78; SR SUBJ SPECIALIST ONCOL, M D ANDERSON HOSP & TUMOR INST, UNIV TEX SYST CANCER CTR, 78-, ASST PROF BIOL, 81- *Concurrent Pos:* Teaching asst biol, Univ Houston, 69-72; mem, Study Group Prostatic Cancer, M D Anderson Hosp & Tumor Inst. *Mem:* AAAS; Soc Study Reprod; Andrology Soc; Endocrine Soc. *Res:* In vivo dynamics of circulatory hormones; total parenteral nutrition; oncology (clinical); computerized data storage and retrieval. *Mailing Add:* CIDAC Prog for Diagnosis & Therap 6723 Bertner Ave Houston TX 77030

KEATON, CLARK M, b LaGrande, Ore, Feb 24, 10; m 38; c 2. PHYSICAL CHEMISTRY. *Educ:* Univ Kans, BS, 31; Univ Idaho, MS, 36; State Col Wash, PhD(soil chem), 38. *Prof Exp:* Asst, State Col Wash, 36-40; res chemist, Grange Powder Co, 40-42; res chemist, Rayonier, Inc, 42-43; res chemist, Am Marietta Col, 43-62; res dir, Atwood Adhesives Inc, 62-75; RETIRED. *Res:* Phenol-formaldehyde resins; sulfite waste liquor; oxidation-reduction potentials and acid determination of soils; liquid industrial adhesives. *Mailing Add:* 2637 30th W Seattle WA 98199

KEATON, MICHAEL JOHN, b Alton, Ill, April 30, 45; m 81. CHEMICAL ENGINEERING. *Educ:* Univ Calif, Berkeley, BS, 66, MS, 67; Princeton Univ, PhD(chem eng), 70. *Prof Exp:* Vpres, Energy & Environ Eng, 70-72, exec vpres, Teknekron Industs, 72-74; PRES & CHMN BD, TERA CORP, 74-, CHIEF EXEC OFFICER, 82- *Res:* Integrated line of proprietary computer systems including hardware and software, automated document storage and retrieval systems, and related computer-aided engineering services, principally for the energy industry--fuel exploration, production, processing and transportation. *Mailing Add:* Tera Corp 2150 Shattuck Ave Berkeley CA 94704

KEATON, PAUL W, JR, b Roanoke, Va, Oct 1, 35; m 57; c 3. NUCLEAR PHYSICS. *Educ:* Emory & Henry Col, BS, 57; Johns Hopkins Univ, PhD(physics), 63. *Prof Exp:* Res assoc nuclear physics, Johns Hopkins Univ, 63-65; staff mem, Physics Div, 65-73, leader, Electron Div, 73-79, asst to the dir, 79-80, STRATEGIC PLANNING & POLICY ANALYSIS, LOS ALAMOS NAT LAB, 80- *Concurrent Pos:* Vis scientist, Ctr Europ Nuclear Res, Geneva, Switz, 72-73. *Mem:* Fel Am Phys Soc; sr mem Inst Elec & Electronic Eng. *Res:* Experimental research with charged particle polarization, Mossbauer effect, direct reactions, electronics and fast neutron cross sections. *Mailing Add:* 137 Piedra Loop Los Alamos NM 87544

KEATS, ARTHUR STANLEY, b New Brunswick, NJ, May 31, 23; m 46; c 4. PHARMACOLOGY. *Educ:* Rutgers Univ, BS, 43; Univ Pa, MD, 46. *Prof Exp:* Asst instr, Sch Med, Univ Pa, 46; asst anesthetist, Mass Gen Hosp, 51; anesthesiologist, Schwesternhaus von Roten Kreuz, Switz, 52-53; anesthesiologist, Mary Imogene Bassett Hosp, 53-55; prof anesthesiol & chmn dept, Baylor Col Med, 55-74, clin prof, 74-75; CLIN PROF ANESTHESIOL, UNIV TEX HEALTH SCI CTR HOUSTON, 78-; CHIEF ANESTHESIA, DIV CARDIOVASC ANESTHESIA, TEX HEART INST, 74- *Concurrent Pos:* Assoc anesthesiol, Col Physicians & Surgeons, Columbia Univ, 53-55; dir anesthesiol, Ben Taub Gen Hosp, 55- *Mem:* AAAS; Am Soc Pharmacol & Exp Therapeut; Am Soc Anesthesiol. *Res:* Opiates; analgesics. *Mailing Add:* Div Cardiovasc Anesthesia Tex Heart Inst Houston TX 77025

KEATS, JOHN BERT, b New York, NY, Sept 14, 36; m 68; c 2. INDUSTRIAL ENGINEERING, STATISTICS. *Educ:* Lehigh Univ, BS, 59; Fla State Univ, MS, 64, PhD(educ res), 70. *Prof Exp:* Indust engr, US Steel Corp, Ill, 59-61; asst prof indust eng, La Tech Univ, 64-66; assoc, Advan Proj Dept, Syst Develop Corp, Calif, 68; assoc prof, La Tech Univ, 69-80; MEM FAC, SCH INDUST ENG & MGT, OKLA STATE UNIV, 80- *Concurrent Pos:* Consult, Southern Regional Off, Col Entrance Exam Bd, Ga, 70- *Mem:* Sr mem Am Inst Indust Engrs; Am Statist Asn; Am Educ Res Asn. *Res:* Educational and operations research; computer assisted instruction. *Mailing Add:* Sch Indust Eng & Mgt Okla State Univ Stillwater OK 74074

KEATS, THEODORE ELIOT, b New Brunswick, NJ, June 26, 24; m 49; c 2. RADIOLOGY. *Educ:* Rutgers Univ, BS, 45; Univ Pa, MD, 47; Am Bd Radiol, dipl. *Prof Exp:* Intern, Hosp Univ Pa, 47-48; resident radiol, Univ Mich Hosp, 48-51; from instr to asst prof, Sch Med, Univ Calif, 53-56; from assoc prof to prof, Sch Med, Univ Mo, 56-63; vis prof, Karolinska Inst, Sweden, 63-64; PROF RADIOL & CHMN DEPT, UNIV HOSP, UNIV VA, 64- *Concurrent Pos:* Trustee, Am Bd Radiol, 73- *Mem:* Radiol Soc NAm; Roentgen Ray Soc; AMA; Am Col Radiol; Asn Univ Radiol. *Res:* Pediatric and cardiovascular radiology. *Mailing Add:* Dept of Radiol Univ of Va Hosp Charlottesville VA 22901

KEAVENEY, WILLIAM PATRICK, b New York, Dec 25, 36; m 61; c 5. ORGANIC CHEMISTRY. *Educ:* Manhattan Col, BS, 58; Fordham Univ, PhD(org chem), 64. *Prof Exp:* RES ASSOC, INMONT CORP, CLIFTON, 62- *Mem:* Am Chem Soc. *Res:* Pyrodoxine determination; synthesis of dichloro-diphenyl-trichlorethane analogs; norbornylene polymerization; ozonolysis; radiation curing; polymer chemistry. *Mailing Add:* 1255 Broad St Inmont Corp-Res Labs Clifton NJ 07015

KEAY, LEONARD, b Crayford, Eng, Nov 26, 32; nat US; m 54; c 3. BIOCHEMISTRY, MICROBIOLOGY. *Educ:* Univ London, BSc, 53, PhD(chem), 55, MSc, 56. *Prof Exp:* Hon asst biochem, Univ Col, Univ London, 56-58; hon fel, Sch Advan Study & res fel enzymol, Mass Inst Technol, 58-60; res biochemist, Monsanto Co, 60-71; res biochemist, Sch Med, Washington Univ, 71-74, dir, Basic Cancer Res Ctr, 71-80; MEM STAFF, MCDONNELL DOUGLAS ASTRONAUT CO, 80- *Concurrent Pos:* Salters Inst Indust Chem res fel, Univ Col, Univ London, 56-58. *Mem:* Am Chem Soc; Tissue Cult Asn. *Res:* Organo phosphorus chemistry and biochemistry; enzymology; applied biochemistry and microbiology; animal cell culture; tissue culture; fermentation technology. *Mailing Add:* McDonnell Douglas Astronaut Co PO Box 516 St Louis MO 63166

KEBABIAN, JOHN WILLIS, b New York, NY, Sept 20, 46; m 75; c 2. ENDOCRINOLOGY. *Educ:* Yale Univ, BS, 68, MPhil, 70, PhD(pharm), 73. *Prof Exp:* Res fel, Dept Pharmacol, Yale Univ, 72-74; res assoc, Clin Sci Lab, NIMH, 74-76; SECT CHIEF RES, EXP THERAPEUT, NAT INST NEUROL & COMMUN DIS STROKE, 76- *Mem:* Am Soc Biol Chemists. *Res:* Dopamine receptors in brain and pituitary gland. *Mailing Add:* Nat Inst Health Bldg 10 Rm 6D 16 Bethesda MD 20205

KEBARLE, PAUL, b Sofia, Bulgaria, Sept 21, 26; m 55; c 1. PHYSICAL CHEMISTRY. *Educ:* Swiss Fed Inst Technol, Dipl Ing Chem, 52; Univ BC, PhD, 55. *Prof Exp:* Nat Res Coun Can fel, 55-58; from asst prof to assoc prof, 58-68, PROF CHEM, UNIV ALTA, 68- *Mem:* Fel Royal Soc Can. *Res:* Application of mass spectrometry to reaction kinetics in the gas phase; ion-molecule interactions at high pressure; ionic solvation and ionic reactivity in the gas phase; ion-molecule equilibria. *Mailing Add:* Dept of Chem Univ of Alta Edmonton AB T6G 2E8 Can

KEBLAWI, FEISAL SAID, b Acre, Palestine, July 11, 35; US citizen; m 73; c 4. COMMUNICATIONS SYSTEMS ENGINEERING. *Educ:* Am Univ Beirut, BS, 57; NC State Univ, MS, 62, PhD(elec eng), 65. *Prof Exp:* Mem tech staff satellite systs eng, RCA Corp, 65-68; mem tech staff systs eng, Mitre Corp, 68-81. *Concurrent Pos:* US deleg, US/USSR Working Group on Air Traffic Control, Moscow, 78; cong fel, Inst Elec & Electronic Engrs, 81-82; staff asst defense, Senator Thurmond, 81- *Mem:* Sr mem Inst Elec & Electronics Engrs; Am Inst Aeronaut & Astronaut; Planetary Soc. *Res:* Satellite communications deep space and tactical systems; communications systems; air traffic control; advanced automation; control systems engineering; stabilization of heat transfer process in nuclear reactors; legislation in civil defense; researcher of major foreign policy and armed sales issues. *Mailing Add:* Mitre Corp Westgate Res Park McLean VA 22102

KEBLER, RICHARD WILLIAM, b Owosso, Mich, Nov 25, 20; m 50; c 4. APPLIED PHYSICS. *Educ:* Univ Mich, BSE, 42, MS, 47, PhD(physics), 54. *Prof Exp:* Res assoc, Eng Res Inst, Univ Mich, 42; res physicist, Linde Co Div, Union Carbide Corp, 53-55, develop supvr, 56-59; res physicist, Gen Motors Res Lab, 59; group leader, Union Carbide Res Inst, 60-66, mgr mat res & develop, Space Sci & Eng Lab, 66-68, sr res assoc, Linde Co Div, 68-70, PROG MGR COMPOSITES, LINDE CO DIV, UNION CARBIDE CORP, 70- *Mem:* Am Phys Soc; Optical Soc Am; Am Ceramic Soc; Metall Soc. *Res:* Spectro-chemical analysis; extreme ultraviolet spectroscopy; crystal growth; refractory and composite materials; turbine engine compressors. *Mailing Add:* Union Carbide Corp 1500 Polco St Indianapolis IN 46224

KECECIOGLU, D(IMITRI) B(ASIL), b Istanbul, Turkey, Dec 26, 22; nat US; m 51; c 2. MECHANICS. *Educ:* Robert Col, Istanbul, BS, 42; Purdue Univ, MS, 48, PhD(eng mech), 53. *Prof Exp:* Instr mech, Purdue Univ, 47, asst metal cutting, 49-52, asst instr eng drawing & descriptive geom, 50-52, asst instr mach tool lab, 51; eng scientist-in-chg mech lab, Res Labs, Allis-Chalmers Mfg Co, 52-57, asst to dir mech eng industs group, 57-63, dir reliability & corp consult, 60-63; PROF AEROSPACE & MECH ENG, UNIV ARIZ, 63-, PROF, RELIABILITY ENG PROG, 69- *Concurrent Pos:* Fulbright scholar, Greece, 71-72; dir, Reliability Eng & Mgt Insts; consult reliability & maintainability eng, indust & govt. *Honors & Awards:* Ralph Teetor Award, Soc Automotive Engrs, 77; Allen Chop Award, 81. *Mem:* AAAS; Am Soc Mech Engrs; Am Soc Eng Educ; Soc Exp Stress Anal; Inst Elec & Electronics Engrs. *Res:* System effectiveness, reliability, maintainability; quality control; statistics; probability; design; production engineering; design by reliability; tooling engineering; applied mathematics. *Mailing Add:* Dept of Aerospace & Mech Eng Univ of Ariz Tucson AZ 85721

KECK, DONALD BRUCE, physics, see previous edition

KECK, JAMES COLLYER, b New York, NY, June 11, 24; m 47; c 2. PHYSICS. *Educ:* Cornell Univ, BA, 47, PhD, 51. *Prof Exp:* Res assoc physics, Cornell Univ, 51-52; res fel, Calif Inst Technol, 52-55; prin scientist, Avco-Everett Res Lab, Mass, 55-65, dep dir, 60-64; FORD PROF MECH ENG, MASS INST TECHNOL, 65- *Mem:* Am Phys Soc; AAAS; Sigma Xi; fel Am Acad Arts & Sci; Combustion Inst. *Res:* Atomic and molecular kinetics; high temperature gas dynamics; combustion; nonequilibrium thermodynamics; high energy nuclear physics. *Mailing Add:* Mass Inst of Technol 3-342 77 Massachusetts Ave Cambridge MA 02139

KECK, KONRAD, b Vienna, Austria, Mar 13, 28; nat US; m 57; c 2. BIOLOGY. *Educ:* Univ Vienna, PhD(biol, chem), 52. *Prof Exp:* Instr physiol chem, Med Sch, Univ Vienna, 53-54; Int Co-op Admin fel, Univ Wis, 54-56; res assoc, Max Planck Inst Marine Biol, Ger, 56-57; res assoc, New Eng Med Ctr, 57-58; res assoc chem, Ind Univ, 58-59; asst prof biol, Johns Hopkins Univ, 59-64; assoc prof zool, 64-68, PROF CELL DEVELOP BIOL, UNIV ARIZ, 68- *Res:* Nucleocytoplasmic interactions in microorganisms, structure and function of nucleic acids in viral reproduction. *Mailing Add:* Dept of Cell Develop Biol Univ of Ariz Tucson AZ 85721

KECK, MAX HANS, b Konstanz, Ger, May 7, 19; US citizen; m 49; c 2. POLYMER CHEMISTRY. *Educ:* Col Wooster, BA, 41; Univ Akron, MSc, 45. *Prof Exp:* Sr res chemist polyester chem, 42-67, RES SCIENTIST, FIBER TECH CTR, GOODYEAR TIRE & RUBBER CO, 67- *Mem:* Am Chem Soc. *Res:* Linear polyester research, preparation of new linear polyesters and new monomers; catalysis studies; dyeable and specialty polyester fibers; cross-linkable polyesters for coatings. *Mailing Add:* Fiber & Polymer Prod Res Div Goodyear Tire & Rubber Co Akron OH 44316

KECK, MAX JOHANN, b Feb 22, 39; US citizen. VISUAL PSYCHOPHYSICS. *Educ:* Mass Inst Technol, BS, 61; Purdue Univ, MS, 64, PhD(physics), 68. *Prof Exp:* From asst prof to assoc prof, 68-78, PROF PHYSICS, JOHN CARROLL UNIV, 78- *Concurrent Pos:* Adj staff mem ophthalmol, Cleveland Clin Found, Ohio, 78-; prin investr res grant, Nat Eye Inst, NIH, 79- *Mem:* Am Phys Soc; Asn Res Vision & Ophthal. *Res:* Binocular vision; spatial vision; amblyopia and strabismus. *Mailing Add:* Dept of Physics John Carroll Univ Cleveland OH 44118

KECK, ROBERT WILLIAM, b Manchester, Iowa, Jan 2, 41; m 64; c 2. PLANT PHYSIOLOGY. *Educ:* Univ Iowa, BS, 62, MS, 64; Ohio State Univ, PhD(plant physiol), 68. *Prof Exp:* Researcher photosynthesis, Charles F Kettering Res Lab, 68-70; researcher hort, Univ Ill, 70-71, researcher bot, 71-72, lectr bot, 72; asst prof biol, 72-78, ASSOC PROF BIOL, IND UNIV-PURDUE UNIV, 78- *Mem:* Am Soc Plant Physiologists; Crop Sci Soc Am. *Res:* Photosynthesis, membrane physiology. *Mailing Add:* Dept of Biol 1201 E 38th St Indianapolis IN 46205

KECK, WINFIELD, b Clifton Heights, Pa, Sept 15, 17; m 44; c 4. PHYSICS. *Educ:* Amherst Col, AB, 37; Univ Pa, MA, 38; Brown Univ, PhD(physics), 49. *Prof Exp:* Instr math, Franklin & Marshall Col, 39-40; instr physics, Muhlenberg Col, 41-46; instr, Brown Univ, 46-48; from asst prof to assoc prof, 49-61, PROF PHYSICS, LAFAYETTE COL, 61-, CHMN DEPT, 60- *Concurrent Pos:* Vis assoc prof, Brown Univ, 58-59. *Mem:* Math Asn Am; Am Asn Physics Teachers. *Res:* Acoustic wave propagation. *Mailing Add:* Dept of Physics Lafayette Col Easton PA 18042

KEDDY, JAMES RICHARD, b Boston, Mass, Oct 18, 36; m 61; c 3. COMPUTER SCIENCES. *Educ:* Colby Col, BA, 58. *Prof Exp:* Mem staff air defense, Syst Develop Corp, 60-62, sect mgr satellite control, 63-67; sect mgr oper systs, Sci Data Systs, 68-71, mem advan design staf, Xerox Data Systs, 72-73, prin engr off systs, Xerox Corp, 74-80; PROJ LEADER, TERADATA CORP, 80- *Res:* Word processing systems; information storage and retrieval; operating systems; database management systems; communications. *Mailing Add:* 16331 Serenade Lane Huntington Beach CA 92647

KEDER, WILBERT EUGENE, b Columbus, Nebr, July 29, 28; m 51; c 4. PHYSICAL INORGANIC CHEMISTRY. *Educ:* Doane Col, BA, 50; Univ Pittsburgh, PhD(chem), 56. *Prof Exp:* Asst, Univ Pittsburgh, 50-56; res chemist, Hanford Labs, Gen Elec Co, 56-64; sr res scientist, Pac Northwest Labs, Battelle-Northwest, 65-68; adj assoc prof, Wash State Univ, 68-69; res assoc, Battelle-Northwest, 69-71; asst prof, 71-77, ASSOC PROF CHEM, UNIV PITTSBURGH, BRADFORD, 77-, DIR PETROL TECHNOL PROG, 75- *Mem:* Am Chem Soc; Soc Petrol Engrs. *Res:* Solution chemistry; solvent extraction; chemistry of the actinide elements; petroleum technology; environmental effect of energy utilization. *Mailing Add:* Dept Chem Univ Pittsburgh Bradford PA 16701

KEDZIE, ROBERT WALTER, b Milwaukee, Wis, Sept 16, 32; m 56; c 4. SOLID STATE PHYSICS. *Educ:* Marquette Univ, BS, 54; Univ Calif, MA, 56, PhD(physics), 59. *Prof Exp:* Asst neutron diffraction, Oak Ridge Nat Lab, 54; instr physics, Univ Calif, Berkeley, 54-56; res physicist, Exp Sta, E I du Pont de Nemours & Co, 59-61; staff physicist, Sperry Rand Res Ctr, 61-68; mgr spectrometer eng, Magnion Div, Ventron Instrument Corp, 68-69; assoc prof physics, Univ Detroit, 69-79, chmn dept, 75-79; SR STAFF PHYSICIST, HUGHES AIRCRAFT CO, 79- *Concurrent Pos:* Asst, Los Alamos Sci Lab, 55. *Mem:* Am Phys Soc. *Res:* Electron and nuclear magnetic resonance; electric and magnetic phenomena in polymers, defect soild state, magneto-acoustic and photochromic phenomena. *Mailing Add:* Space Comn Group Hughes Aircraft Co El Segundo CA 90245

KEE, DAVID THOMAS, b Escanaba, Mich, July 25, 29; m 62; c 2. ORNITHOLOGY. *Educ:* Northern Mich Univ, AB, 58; Univ Ark, MS, 60; Mich State Univ, PhD(ornith), 64. *Prof Exp:* Asst prof, 64-67, ASSOC PROF ZOOL, NORTHEAST LA STATE UNIV, 67- *Mem:* Cooper Ornith Soc; Am Ornith Union; Wildlife Soc; Am Soc Mammal. *Res:* Taxonomy and distribution of Louisiana birds and mammals; pesticide studies, birds and mammals. *Mailing Add:* Dept of Biol Northeast La State Univ Monroe LA 71201

KEE, ROBERT M(UNSON), b Brooklyn, NY, Mar 18, 20. AERONAUTICAL ENGINEERING. *Educ:* Princeton Univ, BS, 42. *Prof Exp:* From develop engr to supvr blade sect, Sikorsky Aircraft Div, United Technol Corp, 42-66, chief test br, 66-69 & test resources, test eng, 69-75, chief rotor eng commercial helicopters, 75-77; RETIRED. *Honors & Awards:* George Mead Silver Medal, 65. *Mem:* Assoc fel Am Inst Aeronaut & Astronaut. *Res:* Helicopter development and design. *Mailing Add:* 1700 Broadbridge Ave Apt A-47 Stratford CT 06497

KEECH, GERALD (LESTER), computer science, see previous edition

KEEDY, CURTIS RUSSELL, b Selma, Calif, Sept 14, 38; m 76; c 2. PHYSICAL CHEMISTRY, RADIOCHEMISTRY. *Educ:* Occidental Col, BA, 60; Univ Wis, PhD(phys chem), 65. *Prof Exp:* Resident res assoc nuclear chem, Chem Eng Div, Argonne Nat Lab, 64-66; asst prof chem, Reed Col, 66-70, reactor supvr, 68-72; asst prof, 72-75, ASSOC PROF CHEM, LEWIS & CLARK COL, 75- *Concurrent Pos:* Vis lectr, Lewis & Clark Col, 71-72. *Mem:* Am Chem Soc; Am Nuclear Soc. *Res:* Nuclear chemistry; neutron activation analysis as applied to geochemical systems and environmental areas. *Mailing Add:* Dept of Chem Lewis & Clark Col Portland OR 97219

KEEDY, HUGH F(ORREST), b Berkeley Springs, WVa, Sept 22, 26; m 48; c 2. ENGINEERING MECHANICS. *Educ:* George Peabody Col, BS, 51, MA, 52; Univ Mich, MSE, 62, PhD, 67. *Prof Exp:* Asst prof appl math, 51-68, assoc prof eng sci, 68-74, assoc dean instr, 69-71, PROF ENG SCI, VANDERBILT UNIV, 74- *Concurrent Pos:* Consult various industs, 54-; asst, Univ Mich, 62-63, instr, 63-65; tech ed & writer, Lawrence Livermore Nat Lab, 80-81. *Mem:* Am Soc Eng Educ; Soc Tech Commun. *Res:* Fluid mechanics; engineering education; technical communication. *Mailing Add:* Box 1686 Vanderbilt Univ Nashville TN 37235

KEEDY, MERVIN LAVERNE, b Bushnell, Nebr, Aug 2, 20; m 41; c 2. MATHEMATICS. *Educ:* Univ Chicago, BS, 46; Univ Nebr, MA, 50, PhD, 57. *Prof Exp:* Teacher, Pub Sch, Idaho, 47-49; asst math, Univ Nebr, 49-50; supvr lab sch, Nebr State Teachers Col, Peru, 50; asst prof physics, NDak State Col, 51-53; instr math, Univ Nebr, 53-55, instr physics, 55-56, counr sci tech improv prog, 56-57; assoc dir math prog, Univ Md, 57-60; supvr math & sci, Jr High Sch, 60-61; PROF MATH, PURDUE UNIV, WEST LAFAYETTE, 61- *Concurrent Pos:* Ground & flight instr, Rodman Aircraft Co, 48-49. *Mem:* Am Math Soc; Math Asn Am. *Res:* Mathematics education. *Mailing Add:* Dept of Math Sch of Sci Purdue Univ West Lafayette IN 47907

KEEFE, DENIS, b Dublin, Ireland, Feb 28, 30; m 53; c 3. HIGH ENERGY PHYSICS, ACCELERATOR PHYSICS. *Educ:* Nat Univ Ireland, BSc, 51, MSc, 53; Bristol Univ, PhD(physics), 55. *Prof Exp:* Lectr physics, Univ Col, Dublin, 55-59; PHYSICS GROUP LEADER, LAWRENCE BERKELEY LAB, UNIV CALIF, 59- *Concurrent Pos:* Vis res physicist, Plasma Physics Lab, Princeton Univ, 75-76. *Mem:* Am Phys Soc; Royal Irish Acad. *Res:* Elementary particle physics; high-energy collision phenomena; high-energy proton and ion accelerators; high-current and collective acceleration; heavy ion fusion. *Mailing Add:* Lawrence Berkeley Lab Univ of Calif Berkeley CA 94720

KEEFE, JOHN RICHARD, b Sandusky, Ohio, Jan 31, 35; m 59; c 2. DEVELOPMENTAL BIOLOGY, CELL BIOLOGY. *Educ:* John Carroll Univ, BS, 60, MS, 65; Case Western Reserve Univ, PhD(anat), 69. *Prof Exp:* Res assoc, Basic Res Div, Cleveland Psychiat Inst, Ohio, 61-65; from instr to asst prof anat, Med Sch, Univ Va, 69-75; assoc prof anat, Med Sch, Univ Louisville, 75-77; assoc prof, 77-81, ASST PROF ANAT, DEVELOP BIOL CTR, CASE WESTERN RESERVE UNIV, 81- *Concurrent Pos:* NIH grant, Univ Va, 69-71; Nat Eye Inst grant, 71-75 & 75-79; NASA contractor, 74-81. *Mem:* Am Soc Cell Biol; Soc Develop Biol; Asn Res Vision & Ophthal; NY Acad Sci; Am Asn Anat. *Res:* Cytological studies of retinal and vestibular development and regeneration in amphibian, avian and mammalion species utilizing autoradiography, electron microscopy and cytochemistry. *Mailing Add:* Dept of Anat Case Western Reserve Univ Cleveland OH 44106

KEEFE, THOMAS J, b Algona, Iowa, Dec 4, 37; m 65; c 4. VETERINARY MEDICINE. *Educ:* Univ Mo, BS & DVM, 63. *Prof Exp:* Pvt vet pract, 66-67; livestock consult, Livestock Servs, Ralston Purina, 67-69; mgr clin res, Bristol Labs, 69-74; DIR VET MED, BEECHAM LABS, 74- *Mem:* Am Vet Med Asn; Am Asn Swine Practitioners (pres, 71); Am Asn Bovine Practitioners; fel Am Col Pharmacol & Therapeut; Indust Vet Asn. *Res:* Pharmacology; pathology; diagnostic medicine. *Mailing Add:* 68 Country Club Estates Bristol TN 37620

KEEFE, THOMAS LEEVEN, b Columbia, SC, Jan 22, 37; m 64. BOTANY, BIOLOGY. *Educ:* Univ SC, BS, 59, MS, 61; Univ Ga, PhD(bot), 67. *Prof Exp:* Asst prof biol, Newberry Col, 62; ASST PROF BIOL, EASTERN KY UNIV, 66- *Mem:* Am Forestry Asn; Am Inst Biol Sci. *Res:* Shoot development in forest trees; radiation inducted mutations in insects. *Mailing Add:* Dept of Biol Sci Eastern Ky Univ Richmond KY 40475

KEEFE, WILLIAM EDWARD, b Norfolk, Va, Feb 23, 23; m 46; c 2. BIOPHYSICS, CRYSTALLOGRAPHY. *Educ:* Va Polytech Inst, BS, 59, MS, 64; Med Col Va, PhD(biophys), 67. *Prof Exp:* Asst prof biophys, 66-76, asst prof, 76-81, ASSOC PROF MICROBIOL, MED COL VA, VA COMMONWEALTH UNIV, 81- *Mem:* Am Crystallog Asn; Am Inst Physics; Am Phys Soc; Sigma Xi; Int Solar Energy Soc. *Res:* Formation of kidney stone nuclei; interaction of fast neutrons with biological materials; determination of molecular structure of biologically important compounds; computer programming to solve crystal structures; model building of proteins. *Mailing Add:* Health Sci Div Med Col of Va Va Commonwealth Univ Richmond VA 23298

KEEFER, DENNIS RALPH, b Winter Haven, Fla, Sept 22, 38; m 57; c 3. AEROSPACE ENGINEERING, LASER PROPULSION. *Educ:* Univ Fla, BES, 62, MSE, 63, PhD(aerospace eng), 67. *Prof Exp:* Asst prof, 67-76, assoc prof aerospace eng, Univ Fla, 76-78; PROF ENG SCI & MECH, UNIV TENN, 78- *Mem:* Am Phys Soc. *Res:* Electrodeless arcs and discharges; gas lasers; plasma specroscopy. *Mailing Add:* Univ Tenn Space Inst Tullahoma TN 37388

KEEFER, DONALD WALKER, b Idaho Falls, Idaho, Nov 7, 31; m 54; c 2. METALLURGY. *Educ:* Univ Idaho, BS, 54; Univ Ill, MS, 57, PhD(metall), 61. *Prof Exp:* Mem tech staff, Atomics Int, 61-77; mgr, Off Res Mgt, Fuels & Mat Div, 77-81, MGR MAT SCI BR, MAT TECH DIV, EG&G IDAHO INC, 81- *Mem:* Am Asn Advan Sci; Am Soc Metals. *Res:* Studies of point defects in metals and alloys by means of anelastic techniques; studies of void formation in irradiated reactor cladding materials; environmental effects on materials. *Mailing Add:* 1852 Malibu Dr Idaho Falls ID 83401

KEEFER, LARRY KAY, b Akron, Ohio, Oct 28, 39; m 62; c 2. ORGANIC CHEMISTRY, CANCER. *Educ:* Oberlin Col, BA, 61; Univ NH, PhD(org chem), 65. *Prof Exp:* Asst prof oncol, Inst Med Res, Chicago Med Sch, 65-68; asst prof biochem, Col Med, Univ Nebr, 68-71; HEAD, ANAL CHEM SECT, LAB CARCINOGEN METAB, NAT CANCER INST, 71- *Mem:* Am Chem Soc; AAAS. *Res:* Organic, analytical and biological chemistry of nitrosamines and other chemical carcinogens; analyzes results of this research for possible implications in cancer cause and prevention. *Mailing Add:* Nat Cancer Inst Bldg 37 Rm 1E22 Bethesda MD 20205

KEEFER, RAYMOND MARSH, b Twin Falls, Idaho, Apr 29, 13; m 43; c 3. PHYSICAL CHEMISTRY. *Educ:* Univ Calif, BS, 34, PhD(chem), 40. *Prof Exp:* From asst to assoc, 36-41, from instr to assoc prof, 41-56, chmn dept, 62-74, prof, 56-81, EMER PROF CHEM, UNIV CALIF, DAVIS, 81- *Mem:* Am Chem Soc. *Res:* Molecular complexes; electrophilic aromatic halogenation; participation by ortho substituents in reactions at aromatic side chains; medium effects on nucleophilic solvolytic displacement reactions. *Mailing Add:* Dept of Chem Univ of Calif Davis CA 95616

KEEFER, ROBERT FARIS, b Wheeling, WVa, May 27, 30; m 57; c 4. SOIL SCIENCE. *Educ:* Cornell Univ, BS, 52; Ohio State Univ, MS, 61, PhD(agron), 63. *Prof Exp:* Res agronomist, Hercules Powder Co, 63-65; from asst prof to assoc prof soil sci, 65-74, Dept Health, Educ & Welfare grant, 66-70, assoc prof & assoc agronomist, 74-76, PROF AGRON & AGRONOMIST, WVA UNIV, 76- *Mem:* Am Soc Agron; Soil Sci Soc Am; Int Soil Sci Soc. *Res:* Soil organic matter; soil fertility, particularly micronutrient nutrition. *Mailing Add:* Plant Sci Div WVa Univ Morgantown WV 26506

KEEFER, WILLIAM RICHARD, b Fayette, Ohio, June 7, 24; m 45; c 2. GEOLOGY. *Educ:* Univ Wyo, BA, 48, MA, 52, PhD, 57. *Prof Exp:* geologist, US Geol Surv, Denver, 48-81; EXPLOR ADV, MITCHELL ENERGY CORP, 81- *Mem:* Geol Soc Am; Am Asn Petrol Geologists. *Res:* Regional stratigraphy and structure, especially in sedimentary rocks. *Mailing Add:* Mitchell Energy Corp 1670 Broadway Ste 3200 Lakewood CO 80202

KEEFFE, JAMES RICHARD, b Visalia, Calif, Nov 13, 37; m 61; c 1. ORGANIC CHEMISTRY. *Educ:* Univ Calif, Santa Barbara, BA, 59; Univ Wash, Seattle, PhD(chem), 64. *Prof Exp:* NIH res fel, 64-65; from asst prof to assoc prof, 65-74, PROF CHEM, SAN FRANCISCO STATE UNIV, 74- *Concurrent Pos:* Res grants, Petrol Res Fund, 65-66 & Res Corp, 66-68. *Res:* Kinetic hydrogen isotope effects; acid-base catalysis; organic reaction mechanisms. *Mailing Add:* 377 Monticello San Francisco CA 94132

KEEGSTRA, KENNETH G, b Grand Rapids, Mich, Aug 10, 45; m 65; c 3. BIOMEMBRANES, PLANT-PATHOGEN INTERACTIONS. *Educ:* Hope Col, BA, 67; Univ Colo, PhD(biochem), 71. *Prof Exp:* Fel biochem, Mass Inst Technol, 71-73; asst prof microbiol, State Univ NY, 73-77; asst prof, 77-79, ASSOC PROF PLANT PHYSIOL, UNIV WIS-MADISON, 79- *Honors & Awards:* George Olmsted Award, Am Paper Inst, 73. *Mem:* Am Soc Plant Physiologists. *Res:* Natural role of plant lectins; structure, function and biogenesis of plastid envelope membranes. *Mailing Add:* Dept of Bot Birge Hall Univ of Wis Madison WI 53706

KEEHN, PHILIP MOSES, b Brooklyn, NY, Mar 22, 43; m. ORGANIC CHEMISTRY, PHYSICAL-ORGANIC CHEMISTRY. *Educ:* Yeshiva Col, BA, 64; Yale Univ, MA, 67, PhD(chem), 69. *Prof Exp:* NIH res fel chem, Harvard Univ, 69-71; asst prof, 71-78, Wolfson Professorship, 79-80, ASSOC PROF CHEM, BRANDEIS UNIV, 78- *Concurrent Pos:* Consult, Am Optical Corp, 76- *Mem:* Am Chem Soc. *Res:* Synthesis of strained rings and theoretically interesting molecules; synthetic methods; application of nuclear magnetic resonance spectroscopy to organic systems; photooxidation; thermal chemistry; pure and applied laser chemistry of organic systems. *Mailing Add:* Dept of Chem Brandeis Univ Waltham MA 02154

KEEHN, ROBERT JOHN, b Rochester, NY, Jan 1, 22; m 46; c 5. MEDICAL STATISTICS. *Educ:* Hartwick Col, BS, 47; Johns Hopkins Univ, MSHyg, 53. *Prof Exp:* Statistician, NY State Dept of Health, 48-53; dir bur vital statist, Conn State Dept Health, 53-58; PROF ASSOC MED, FOLLOW-UP AGENCY, NAT ACAD SCI-NAT RES COUN, 58- *Concurrent Pos:* Statistician, Atomic Bomb Casualty Comn, 63-66 & 71-73. *Mem:* Am Pub Health Asn; Royal Soc Health; Soc Epidemiol Res; Soc Clin Trials. *Res:* Medical etiology; natural history and epidemiology of human diseases; cancer therapy trials; effects in humans of exposure to atomic bomb radiation. *Mailing Add:* Nat Acad of Sci-Nat Res Coun 2101 Constitution Ave NW Washington DC 20418

KEELE, BERNARD B, JR, biochemistry, microbiology, see previous edition

KEELE, DOMAN KENT, b Burnet, Tex, July 13, 23; m 53; c 2. PEDIATRICS, ENDOCRINOLOGY. *Educ:* Univ Tex, BA, 49, MD, 53; Am Bd Pediat, dipl, 62. *Prof Exp:* Intern pediat, Univ Minn Hosps, 53-54; resident, Children's Med Ctr, 54-56; assoc prof, Med Ctr, Univ Okla, 58-63; clin assoc prof, 63-67, ASSOC PROF PEDIAT, UNIV TEX HEALTH SCI CTR & DIR, UNIV AFFIL CTR, 67- *Concurrent Pos:* Res fel, Children's Hosp, Pittsburgh, Pa, 56-58; clin dir, Denton State Sch, 63-67. *Mem:* Endocrine Soc; Am Diabetes Asn; Am Acad Ment Retardation; Am Asn Ment Deficiency. *Mailing Add:* Dept of Pediat Univ Tex Health Sci Ctr Dallas TX 75235

KEELER, CLYDE EDGAR, b Marion, Ohio, Apr 11, 00; m 39; c 1. ZOOLOGY. *Educ:* Denison Univ, BS, 23, MS, 25; Harvard Univ, MA, 25, ScD(genetics), 26. *Hon Degrees:* DS, Denison Univ, 72. *Prof Exp:* Asst zool, Harvard Univ, 24-25, instr opthal res, Howe Lab, Harvard Med Sch, 27-39; fel, Wistar Inst, 39-42, curator animal colony, 40-42; mem staff, Edgewood Sch, 42-43; instr biol, Woman's Col, Univ NC, 43-44; prof & head dept, Wesleyan Col, 44-45; prof, Ga State Col Women, 45-61; dir res dept, Cent State Hosp, 61-75, head genetics lab, 61-76, consult genetics, 80-, mem res comt, 61- *Concurrent Pos:* Asst, Radcliffe Col, 28-30; Sheldon fel, Paris & Berlin, 26-27, Turkey, 30; Milton fel, China & Japan, 36; Bache Fund, 37-38; Guggenheim Mem Found fel, Europe, 38; Rockefeller Found grant-in-aid, 47-54; Southern Fund fel, 55-56. *Honors & Awards:* Prize, Souhteastern Asn Biol, 47, 52. *Mem:* Zool Soc France; Am Genetic Asn. *Res:* Medical genetics; mammalian heredity; vertebrate eye defects; effect of coat color genes on morphology and behavior in mammals; rodless retina, an ophthalmic mutation in the house mouse; Cuna Indian culture and moonchildren; albinism in man; pre-Columbus cultures in America. *Mailing Add:* 130 N Tattnall St Milledgeville GA 31061

KEELER, EMMETT BROWN, b West Point, NY, Sept 28, 41. SYSTEMS ANALYSIS. *Educ:* Oberlin Col, BA, 62; Harvard Univ, MA, 67, PhD(math), 69. *Prof Exp:* MEM STAFF, RAND CORP, 68- *Concurrent Pos:* Vis assoc prof econ, Univ Chicago, 73; vis res assoc, Sch Pub Health, Harvard Univ, 74-75 & 82. *Mem:* Am Math Soc. *Res:* Utility theory; game theory; health economics; operations research; medical decision-making. *Mailing Add:* Rand Corp 1700 Main St Santa Monica CA 90406

KEELER, JOHN S(COTT), b Toronto, Ont, Can, Aug 12, 29; m 51; c 3. ELECTRICAL ENGINEERING. *Educ:* Univ Toronto, BASc, 51, MASc, 63. *Prof Exp:* Res officer, Nat Res Coun Can, 51-55; chief engr, Hallman Organs, Ont, 55-59; from lectr to asst prof, 60-64, ASSOC PROF ELEC ENG, UNIV WATERLOO, 64- *Mem:* Sr mem Inst Elec & Electronics Engrs; Audio Eng Soc. *Res:* Numerical analysis and synthesis of sound particularly noise and music; effects of noise on man; acoustical instrumentation; environmental noise. *Mailing Add:* Dept Elec Eng Univ Waterloo Waterloo ON N2L 3G1 Can

KEELER, MARTIN HARVEY, b New York, NY, June 16, 27; m 53; c 3. MEDICINE. *Educ:* NY Univ, BA, 49; NY Med Col, MD, 53; Am Bd Psychiat & Neurol, dipl, 59. *Prof Exp:* Intern, State Univ NY Upstate Med Ctr, 53-54; from asst resident to resident psychiat, Sch Med, Univ NC, Chapel Hill, 54-57, from instr to assoc prof, 57-69; prof, NY Med Col, 69-70; prof psychiat, Med Univ, SC, 70-77; DIR ALCOHOLIC TREAT PROG HOUSTON, VA HOSP, 77-; PROF PSYCHIAT, BAYLOR COL MED, 77- *Concurrent Pos:* Res grants, 61 & 62- *Mem:* AMA; Am Psychoanalytic Asn;

Am Med Soc Alcoholism; Am Psychiat Asn. *Res:* Defining of the psychological abnormalities in schizophrenia as specific to the individual or to the disease process and the pharmacological manipulation of these differences in schizophrenic and normal populations. *Mailing Add:* 5230 Ariel Houston TX 77096

KEELER, RALPH, b Norwich, Eng, Jan 11, 30; m 56; c 2. PHYSIOLOGY. *Educ:* Univ Birmingham, BSc, 53, PhD(physiol), 56. *Prof Exp:* Asst lectr physiol, Univ Birmingham, 55-56; lectr, Univ Ibadan, 56-59; lectr, Univ Newcastle, 59-66; from asst prof to assoc prof, 66-74, PROF PHYSIOL, UNIV BC, 74- *Mem:* Can Physiol Soc; Brit Physiol Soc. *Res:* Pathophysiology of renal function; control of sodium excretion. *Mailing Add:* 4159 Nanaimo Vancouver BC V5N 5H6 Can

KEELER, RICHARD FAIRBANKS, b Provo, Utah, Jan 24, 30; m 52; c 5. NATURAL PRODUCTS CHEMISTRY. *Educ:* Brigham Young Univ, BS, 54; Ohio State Univ, MS, 55, PhD(biochem), 57. *Prof Exp:* Asst biochemist, Mont State Col, 57-61; res chemist biochem, Nat Animal Dis Lab, 61-65; RES CHEMIST BIOCHEM, USDA, UTAH STATE UNIV, 65- *Honors & Awards:* Superior Serv Award, USDA, 75. *Mem:* Am Chem Soc; Soc Exp Biol & Med; AAAS; Teratology Soc. *Res:* Molybdenum-tungsten metabolism; silicon-mucoprotein interaction in urolithiasis; muscular dystrophy; cytochemistry of Listeria and Vibrio; products of Nocardia; steroidal, quinolizidine and piperidine alkaloid chemistry and metabolic effects; chemistry of poisonous and teratogenic plants. *Mailing Add:* USDA 1150 E 14th N Logan UT 84321

KEELER, ROBERT ADOLPH, b New York, NY, Feb 4, 20; m 49; c 2. PHYSICAL INORGANIC CHEMISTRY. *Educ:* Queens Col, NY, BS, 42. *Prof Exp:* Chief chemist, NY Testing Labs, 42-45 & Pub Serv Testing Labs, 45; supvr anal chem, Allied Chem & Dye Corp, 45-50; group leader nuclear chem, Vitro Labs Div, Vitro Corp, 50-63; proj supvr propellant chem, Reaction Motors Div, Thiokol Chem Corp, 63-68; SR RES CHEMIST, RADIATION SAFETY OFF, ALLIED CHEM, DIV ALLIED CORP, 68- *Concurrent Pos:* Mem, Air Pollution Control Bd, Newark, NJ, 59-69. *Mem:* AAAS; Am Chem Soc. *Res:* Abatement of industrial atmospheric pollutants and recovery as useful materials. *Mailing Add:* 301 Oakridge Dr Camillus NY 13031

KEELER, ROGER NORRIS, b Houston, Tex, Aug 12, 30; m 57; c 4. HIGH PRESSURE PHYSICS. *Educ:* Rice Univ, BA, 51, BS, 52; Univ Colo, MS, 58; Univ Calif, Berkeley, PhD(chem eng), 63. *Prof Exp:* Engr, Maintenance Eng Corp, Tex, 52; cryogenic eng lab, Nat Bur Standards, Colo, 58-59 & Aerojet-Gen Corp, Calif, 59; physicist, Lawrence Livermore Lab, 63-68, dep proj leader, 68-69, div leader, 69-71, dep head physics dept, 71-72, head physics dept, 72-75; dir Navy Technol, Dept Navy, Washington, DC, 75-78; STAFF OF ASSOC DIR PHYSICS, LAWRENCE LIVERMORE LAB, 78- *Concurrent Pos:* Consult, Nat Bur Standards, Colo, 59-62 & Air Force, 78-; lectr, Univ Calif, Davis, 67-76, Nat Univ Mex, 68 & Univ Calif, Berkeley, 69; mem bd dir, Sci Appln Inc, 71; consult dir, Defense Advan Res Proj Agency, 78-; adj prof physics & chem, US Naval Postgrad Sch, 78- *Honors & Awards:* Commendation, Secy Navy, 70. *Mem:* Fel Am Phys Soc; fel Am Inst Chem; Sigma Xi. *Res:* High pressure properties; turbulence; geophysics. *Mailing Add:* PO Box 637 Diablo CA 94528

KEELEY, DEAN FRANCIS, b Chicago, Ill, Nov 16, 26; m 51; c 1. INORGANIC CHEMISTRY, RADIOCHEMISTRY. *Educ:* Univ Ill, BS, 52; Fla State Univ, PhD(chem), 57. *Prof Exp:* From asst prof to assoc prof, 57-77, PROF CHEM, UNIV SOUTHWESTERN LA, 77- *Mem:* Am Chem Soc. *Res:* Isotopic exchange reactions. *Mailing Add:* PO Box 44250 Univ of Southwestern La Sta Lafayette LA 70504

KEELEY, FRED W, b Winnipeg, Man, Mar 21, 44; m 66; c 3. BIOCHEMISTRY. *Educ:* Univ Man, BSc, 65, PhD(pharmacol), 70. *Prof Exp:* Med Res Coun Can fels, Agr Res Coun, Langford, Eng, 70-72 & Res Inst, Hosp Sick Children, Toronto, 72-73; SCIENTIST, RES INST, HOSP SICK CHILDREN, TORONTO, 73- *Concurrent Pos:* Med Res Coun Can scholarship, Res Inst, Hosp Sick Children, 73-; asst prof biochem, Univ Toronto, 75- *Mem:* Can Biochem Soc; NY Acad Sci. *Res:* Biosynthesis of elastin; calcification of aortic tissue in atherosclerosis. *Mailing Add:* 405 Sutherland Dr Toronto ON M4G 1K2 Can

KEELEY, JOHN L, b Streator, Ill, Apr 12, 04; m 37; c 3. SURGERY. *Educ:* Loyola Univ, Ill, BS, 27, MD, 29. *Prof Exp:* Instr surg, Med Sch, Univ Wis & Wis Gen Hosp, 35-36; Arthur Tracy Cabot fel, Harvard Med Sch-Peter Bent Brigham Hosp, 36-38, Harvey Cushing & Univ res fels, 37-38; from instr to asst prof, Sch Med, La State Univ, 39-41; from asst clin prof to assoc clin prof, 41-54, asst, Dept Chem, 54-58, chmn dept, 58-69, PROF SURG, STRITCH SCH MED, LOYOLA UNIV CHICAGO, 54- *Mem:* Int Soc Surg; Am Surg Asn; fel Am Col Surgeons; Am Asn Thoracic Surg; Soc Vascular Surg; Am Col Chest Physicians; Am Heart Asn. *Mailing Add:* Dept of Surg Stritch Sch Med Loyola Univ Med Ctr Maywood IL 60153

KEELEY, JON E, b Chula Vista, Calif, Aug 11, 49; m 73. POPULATION ECOLOGY. *Educ:* San Diego State Univ, BS, 71, MS, 73; Univ Ga, PhD(bot), 77. *Prof Exp:* Lectr bot, Univ Ga, 76-77; ASST PROF BIOL, OCCIDENTAL COL, 77- *Mem:* Ecol Soc Am; Soc Study Evolution; Bot Soc Am; Am Soc Plant Physiologists; Am Soc Naturalists. *Res:* Aquatic plant photosynthesis; reproductive biology and demography of plants; physiological ecology of flood-tolerance in plants. *Mailing Add:* Dept of Biol Occidental Col Los Angeles CA 90041

KEELEY, LARRY LEE, b South Bend, Ind, Jan 3, 39; m 59; c 5. INSECT PHYSIOLOGY. *Educ:* Univ Notre Dame, BS, 62; Purdue Univ, PhD(entom), 66. *Prof Exp:* From asst prof to assoc prof, 66-77, PROF ENTOM, TEX A&M UNIV, 77- *Concurrent Pos:* NSF grants, 74-76, 76-78 & 81-83; NIH grant, 78-81. *Mem:* AAAS; Entom Soc Am; Am Soc Zool; Sigma Xi. *Res:* Hormonal regulation of metabolism; neuroendocrine regulation of mitochondrial development and functions. *Mailing Add:* Dept of Entom Tex A&M Univ College Station TX 77843

KEELEY, STERLING CARTER, b San Francisco, Calif, Oct 23, 48; m 73. SYSTEMATIC BOTANY, ECOLOGY. *Educ:* Stanford Univ, AB, 70; San Diego State Univ, MS, 73; Univ Ga, PhD(bot), 77. *Prof Exp:* Res asst ecol, Int Biol Prog Struct Ecosysts, 70-73; lectr bot, Calif State Univ, Long Beach, 78-79; ASST PROF BIOL, WHITTIER COL, 79- *Concurrent Pos:* NSF dissertation improv grant, 74-77; consult flora, Southern Calif Ocean Studies Consortium of Calif State Univ & Cols, 78-; res assoc, Los Angeles County Mus Natural Hist, 78-; consult salt marsh veg, Port of Los Angeles, 79-81. *Mem:* Soc Study Evolution; Am Soc Plant Taxonomists; Am Bot Soc; AAAS; Sigma Xi. *Res:* Systematics and biogeography of neotropical species of the genus Vernonia, Compositae; ecology and reproductive biology of mediterranean climate plants in relation to fire. *Mailing Add:* Dept Biol Whittier Col Whittier CA 90608

KEELING, BOBBIE LEE, b Durant, Okla, Apr 22, 31; m 57; c 2. PLANT PATHOLOGY. *Educ:* Southeastern State Col, BS, 56; Okla State Univ, MS, 59; Univ Minn, Minneapolis, PhD(plant path), 66. *Prof Exp:* RES PLANT PATHOLOGIST, DELTA BR EXP STA, USDA, 66- *Mem:* Am Phytopath Soc. *Res:* Diseases of soybeans with emphasis on pathogenic variation, nature of host resistance and host-parasite interaction. *Mailing Add:* USDA Delta Br Exp Sta Stoneville MS 38776

KEELING, CHARLES DAVID, b Scranton, Pa, Apr 20, 28; m 54; c 5. PHYSICAL CHEMISTRY, MARINE GEOCHEMISTRY. *Educ:* Univ Ill, BA, 48; Northwestern Univ, PhD(chem), 53. *Prof Exp:* Fel geochem, Calif Inst Technol, 53-56; asst res chemist, 56-60, from assoc res chemist to assoc prof, 60-68, PROF OCEANOG, SCRIPPS INST OCEANOG, UNIV CALIF, SAN DIEGO, 68- *Concurrent Pos:* Guest prof oceanog, Univ Heidelberg, 69-70; mem, comn atmospheric chem & global pollution, Int Asn Meteorol & Atmospheric Physics, 67-; mem, Panel on Energy & Climate of US, Nat Acad Sci, 74-77; mem, Interim Sci Directorate Carbon Dioxide Res Prog, US Dept Energy, 77-80; guest prof, Physikaliches Inst, Univ Bern, Switz, 79-80. *Honors & Awards:* Second Half Century Award, Am Meteorol Soc, 80. *Mem:* AAAS; Am Geophys Union. *Res:* Marine chemistry; geochemistry of carbon and oxygen; atmospheric chemistry; influence of atmospheric carbon dioxide on carbon cycle and on world climate. *Mailing Add:* Scripps Inst of Oceanog La Jolla CA 92093

KEELING, RICHARD PAIRE, b Crawfordsville, Ind, Sept 17, 31; m 52; c 2. MYCOLOGY. *Educ:* Wabash Col, AB, 57; Purdue Univ, MS, 60, PhD(bot), 63. *Prof Exp:* Asst prof microbiol, 63-70, assoc prof biol, 70-74, PROF BIOL, EMPORIA KANS STATE COL, 74- *Mem:* AAAS; Mycol Soc Am; Am Soc Microbiol; Soc Indust Microbiol; Japanese Mycol Soc. *Res:* Fungus physiology; metabolism. *Mailing Add:* 1219 Frontier Way Emporia KS 66801

KEELING, ROLLAND OTIS, JR, b Hillsboro, Ind, Aug 13, 25; m 46; c 2. PHYSICS. *Educ:* Wabash Col, AB, 50; Pa State Univ, MS, 52, PhD(physics), 54. *Prof Exp:* Instr physics, Pa State Univ, 53-54; physicist, Gulf Res & Develop Co, Pa, 54-61; PROF PHYSICS, MICH TECHNOL UNIV, 61-, DEPT HEAD, 80- *Mem:* AAAS; Am Phys Soc; Am Asn Physics Teachers; Am Crystallog Asn. *Res:* X-ray diffraction; crystallography; x-ray spectroscopy; magnetic structures. *Mailing Add:* Dept of Physics Mich Technol Univ Houghton MI 49931

KEELY, WILLIAM MARTIN, b Louisville, Ky, Nov 10, 24; m 58; c 5. PHYSICAL CHEMISTRY. *Educ:* Univ Louisville, BA, 45; Ind Univ, MA, 46; Univ Ky, PhD(phys chem), 49. *Prof Exp:* Asst chem, Ind Univ, 45-46; chemist, Girdler Chem, Inc, 49-51, group leader, 51-55, supvr phys measurements, 55-78; MGR ANAL, UNITED CATALYSTS, INC, 78- *Concurrent Pos:* instr, Univ Louisville, 61-75; dir catalyst selection & evaluation, Ctr Prof Advan, 72- *Mem:* Am Chem Soc. *Res:* Catalysts; solid state reactions; x-ray diffraction; surface area and pore volume; thermogravimetric analysis; differential thermal analysis; magnetic inductance investigations and microscopic studies; fats and oils; selective hydrogenations; chemisorption and physical adsorption investigations; reformer; water gas shift; dehydrogenation, hydrogenation; zeolites. *Mailing Add:* United Catalysts Inc 1227 S 12th Louisville KY 40210

KEEM, JOHN EDWARD, b Buffalo, NY, May 31, 48; m 70. SOLID STATE PHYSICS. *Educ:* Syracuse Univ, BS, 70; Purdue Univ, PhD(physics), 76. *Prof Exp:* Fel, Dept Physics, Purdue Univ, 76-77; mem staff, Dept Physics, Gen Motors Res Lab, 77-80; WITH ENERGY CONVERSION DEVICES, 80- *Res:* Conduction mechanisms in transition metal oxides; experimental and theoretical work on nickel oxide and vanadium sesquioxide; magnetism and magnetoelastic phenomena in Rare Earth intermetallic compounds. *Mailing Add:* Energy Conversion Devices 1657 W Maple Rd Troy MI 48084

KEEN, CHARLOTTE ELIZABETH, b Halifax, NS, June 22, 43; m 63. MARINE GEOPHYSICS. *Educ:* Dalhousie Univ, BSc, 64, MSc, 66; Cambridge Univ, PhD(geophys), 70. *Prof Exp:* RES SCIENTIST MARINE GEOPHYS, ATLANTIC GEOSCI CENTRE, BEDFORD INST, 70- *Concurrent Pos:* Mem working group 8 of inter-union comn on geodynamics, Int Union Geod & Geophys & Int Union Geol Sci, 72-; chmn study group NW Atlantic Continental Margin, Inter-Union Comn Geodynamics; assoc ed, Can J of Earth Sci; chmn, Can Nat Lithosphere Comn, 81- *Mem:* Geol Asn Can; Royal Soc Can; Am Geophys Union. *Res:* Surface wave propagation in Canadian shield and along mid ocean ridges; plate tectonics of Baffin Bay region; continental-oceanic transition in the North West Atlantic; application of Backus-Gilbert inversion to upper mantle properties at ocean-continent transition; subsidence and thermal history continental margins. *Mailing Add:* Atlantic Geosci Centre Bedford Inst Dartmouth NS B2Y 4A2 Can

KEEN, DOROTHY JEAN, b Lancaster, Pa, June 19, 22. PHYSICAL OCEANOGRAPHY. *Educ:* Swarthmore Col, BA, 44. *Prof Exp:* Res asst chem & phys oceanog, Woods Hole Oceanog Inst, 44-53; phys oceanogr mil appln, Hydrographic Off, US Naval Oceanog Off, 53-58, oceanogr ocean prediction, 58-66, head systs anal group, Ocean Prediction, 66-71, sci staff asst, Ocean Sci Dept, Plans & Requirements Off, 71-78; PHYS SCI

ADMINR, NAVAL OCEAN RES & DEVELOP ACTIV, 78- *Mem:* AAAS; Marine Tech Soc; Am Geophys Union. *Res:* Military oceanography, plans and analysis; ocean prediction; fleet environmental support programs; effects on acoustic systems and tactics; ocean and estuarine dynamics; chemical analyses of sea water. *Mailing Add:* Naval Ocean Res & Develop Activ NSTL Station MS 39529

KEEN, LINDA, b New York, NY, Aug 9, 40; c 2. MATHEMATICS. *Educ:* City Col NY, BS, 60; NY Univ, MS, 62, PhD(math), 64. *Prof Exp:* NSF fel math, Inst Advan Study, 64-65; asst prof, Hunter Col, 65-67; from asst prof to assoc prof, 67-74, PROF MATH, CUNY, LEHMAN COL, GRAD CTR, 74- *Concurrent Pos:* NSF partial res grant, 66-68; vis prof, Col, 80-81. *Mem:* Am Math Soc; Asn Women Math. *Res:* Complex analysis; Riemann surfaces, discontinuous groups; Teichmüller spaces. *Mailing Add:* Dept Math Herbert H Lehman Col Bedford Park Blvd W Bronx NY 10468

KEEN, MICHAEL J, b Seaford, Eng, Jan 1, 35; m 76. GEOPHYSICS, OCEANOGRAPHY. *Educ:* Oxford Univ, BA, 57; Cambridge Univ, PhD(geophys), 61. *Prof Exp:* From asst prof to assoc prof geophys & oceanog, Dalhousie Univ, 61-69, asst dean arts & sci, 73-75, prof geophys & oceanog & chmn dept, 69-73 & 75-77; DIR, ATLANTIC GEOSCI CTR, GEOL SURV CAN, BEDFORD INST OCEANOG, 77- *Mem:* Am Geophys Union; Geol Asn Can (pres, 74-75); Royal Soc Can; Can Geophys Union (pres, 81-83). *Res:* Seismic studies of Eastern Canadian seaboard; magnetic properties of sediments; geophysical and geologic studies of Eastern and Arctic Canadian seaboard and of mid-Atlantic ridge. *Mailing Add:* Bedford Inst of Oceanog Geol Surv Can Dartmouth NS B2T 4A2 Can

KEEN, (ANGELINE) MYRA, b Colorado Springs, Colo, May 23, 05. INVERTEBRATE PALEONTOLOGY. *Educ:* Colo Col, AB, 30; Stanford Univ, MA, 31; Univ Calif, PhD(psychol), 34. *Prof Exp:* Res assoc geol, 34-36, curator paleont, 36-70, from asst prof to prof, 54-70, EMER PROF PALEONT, STANFORD UNIV, 70- *Concurrent Pos:* Guggenheim fel, 64-65. *Mem:* Fel Geol Soc Am; fel Paleont Soc; Am Malacol Union (vpres, 47, pres, 48; Western Soc Malacol (vpres, 69, pres, 70). *Res:* Molluscan systematics, especially Pelecypoda; tertiary and recent molluscan faunas. *Mailing Add:* Dept of Geol Stanford Univ Stanford CA 94305

KEEN, NOEL THOMAS, b Marshalltown, Iowa, Aug 13, 40; m 64. PLANT PATHOLOGY. *Educ:* Iowa State Univ, BS, 63, MS, 65; Univ Wis, Madison, PhD(plant path), 68. *Prof Exp:* PROF PLANT PATH, UNIV CALIF, RIVERSIDE, 68- *Mem:* AAAS; Am Phytopath Soc; Am Chem Soc; Am Soc Plant Physiologists; Int Soc Plant Path. *Res:* Mechanisms of pathogenesis by plant parasitic microorganisms; mechanisms of disease resistance. *Mailing Add:* Dept of Plant Path Univ of Calif Riverside CA 92521

KEEN, RAY ALBERT, b Valley Falls, Kans, Oct 9, 15; m 43; c 4. ORNAMENTAL HORTICULTURE. *Educ:* Kans State Col, BS, 42; Ohio State Univ, MSc, 47, PhD, 56. *Prof Exp:* From asst prof to assoc prof, 47-62, prof, 62-81, EMER PROF HORT, KANS STATE UNIV, 81-, RES HORTICULTURIST, AGR EXP STA, 72- *Mem:* Am Soc Hort Sci; Am Soc Agron. *Res:* Turf grass genetics; shade trees; woody ornamentals; propagation; soils and mineral nutrition. *Mailing Add:* Dept of Hort Kans State Univ Manhattan KS 66506

KEEN, ROBERT ERIC, b Oakland, Calif, May 29, 44; m 72; c 2. LIMNOLOGY, POPULATION ECOLOGY. *Educ:* Kans State Univ, BS, 65; Mich State Univ, MS, 67, PhD(zool), 71. *Prof Exp:* Asst prof zool, Univ Vt, 71-76; vis asst prof biol, Kans State Univ, 76-77; vis asst prof zool, Ind Univ, 77; ASST PROF BIOL, MICH TECHNOL UNIV, 77- *Concurrent Pos:* Fel, Philadelphia Acad Natural Sci, 70-71; partic, Advan Inst Statist Ecol, Pa State Univ, 72; staff consult, Nat Comn Water Qual, 75; consult, Vt Inst Water Resources Res, 76-77. *Mem:* Am Soc Limnol & Oceanog; Ecol Soc Am; Int Soc Limnol; Soc Pop Ecol. *Res:* Ecology of littoral Cladocera; population ecology of zooplankton; limnology of Lake Superior. *Mailing Add:* Dept of Biol Sci Mich Technol Univ Houghton MI 49931

KEEN, VERYL F, b Stilwell, Okla, Jan 14, 23; m 59; c 2. BIOLOGY. *Educ:* Northeastern State Col, BS, 50; Okla State Univ, MS, 54; Univ Colo, MA, 62, PhD(zool), 65. *Prof Exp:* Teacher, Maramec Sch, Okla, 50-52, supt schs, 52-57; instr biol, Univ Colo, 59-60, vis lectr, 65-66; assoc prof, Northeastern Mo State Col, 63-65; asst prof & coordr, 66-71, PROF BIOL & CHMN DEPT, ADAMS STATE COL, 71- *Mem:* AAAS; Am Soc Mammal; Nat Asn Biol Teachers. *Res:* Small mammal population ecology; rodent botflies of Colorado; ecology of small mammals of San Luis Valley in Colorado. *Mailing Add:* Dept of Biol Adams State Col Alamosa CO 81101

KEEN, WILLIAM HUBERT, b Jewell Ridge, Va, Sept 2, 44; m 68. ECOLOGY, ZOOLOGY. *Educ:* Pikeville Col, BA, 67; Eastern Ky Univ, MS, 71; Kent State Univ, PhD(ecol), 75. *Prof Exp:* Teacher biol & sci, Buchanan County Pub Sch, Grundy, Va, 67-68; coordr interdisciplinary field studies, Pikeville Col, Ky, 68-69; teacher biol & sci, Jefferson County Pub Sch, Louisville, Ky, 69-70; instr, Kent State Univ, Ohio, 75-76; asst prof biol, 76-80, ASSOC PROF BIOL, STATE UNIV NY CORTLAND, 80- *Concurrent Pos:* Lectr, Cuyahoga Community Col, Cleveland, Ohio, 75-76. *Mem:* Sigma Xi; AAAS; Ecol Soc Am; Soc Study Amphibians & Reptiles; Am Soc Ichthyologists & Herpetologists. *Res:* Population ecology of lower vertebrates; thermoregulation in amphibians; functions of fish schooling; interspecific interactions. *Mailing Add:* Dept Biol Sci State Univ NY Cortland NY 13045

KEENAN, ARTHUR GEORGE, b Finland, June 12, 20; nat US; m 46. PHYSICAL CHEMISTRY. *Educ:* Univ Toronto, BA, 41, MA, 42, PhD(phys chem), 44. *Prof Exp:* Res chemist, Can Industs, Ltd, 44-47, Nat Res Labs, Can, 47-49; asst prof phys chem, Cornell Univ, 49-51, Champlain Col, State Univ NY, 51-52 & Ill Inst Technol, 52-57; assoc prof, 57-63, PROF CHEM, UNIV MIAMI, 63- *Res:* Transference numbers of electrolytes; physical adsorption of gases; electrochemistry in fused salts; mechanisms of thermal decompositions. *Mailing Add:* Dept of Chem Univ of Miami Coral Gables FL 33124

KEENAN, CHARLES WILLIAM, b Ft Worth, Tex, Apr 10, 22; m 45; c 2. INORGANIC CHEMISTRY. *Educ:* Centenary Col, BS, 43; Univ Tex, PhD(chem), 49. *Prof Exp:* Chemist, La Ord Plant, 42-43; asst, Univ Tex, 43-44, instr, 46-49; chemist, Naval Ord Plant, 44-46; from asst prof to assoc prof, 49-58, assoc dean liberal arts, 73-78, PROF CHEM, UNIV TENN, KNOXVILLE, 58- *Concurrent Pos:* NSF sci fac fels, Cambridge Univ, 57-58, 64-65. *Mem:* AAAS; Am Chem Soc; Hist Sci Soc; Am Asn Univ Profs; Sigma Xi. *Res:* Reactions in non-aqueous solvents. *Mailing Add:* Dept of Chem Univ of Tenn Knoxville TN 37916

KEENAN, EDWARD JAMES, b Shelton, Wash, Sept 6, 48. PHARMACOLOGY, ENDOCRINOLOGY. *Educ:* Creighton Univ, BS, 70, MS, 72; WVa Univ, PhD(pharmacol), 75. *Prof Exp:* Res assoc, 75-76, ASST PROF SURG, UNIV ORE HEALTH SCI CTR, 76-, ASST PROF PHARMACOL, 78- *Concurrent Pos:* Dir, Clin Res Ctr Lab & Hormone Res Lab, Univ Ore Health Sci Ctr, 76-, instr pharmacol, 77-78. *Mem:* Am Soc Andrology; AAAS; Sigma Xi. *Res:* Significance of steroid hormones in cancer of the breast and prostate gland; mechanism of steroid hormone action; role of prolactin in male accessory sex organ function. *Mailing Add:* Univ of Ore Health Sci Ctr 3181 SW Sam Jackson Park Rd Portland OR 97201

KEENAN, EDWARD MILTON, b East Orange, NJ, Jan 27, 38. MATHEMATICS. *Educ:* Mass Inst Technol, SB, 60, PhD(math), 65. *Prof Exp:* From asst prof to assoc prof, 65-72, PROF MATH, FAIRLEIGH DICKINSON UNIV, 72- *Mem:* Am Math Soc; Soc Indust & Appl Math. *Res:* Algebra. *Mailing Add:* Dept of Math Fairleigh Dickinson Univ Madison NJ 07940

KEENAN, JOSEPH ALOYSIUS, b Washington, DC, Aug 5, 38; m 68; c 2. NUCLEAR CHEMISTRY. *Educ:* Spring Hill Col, BS, 64; Clark Univ, PhD(nuclear chem), 71. *Prof Exp:* mem res staff, 69-80, SR MEM TECH STAFF, NUCLEAR CHEM LAB, TEX INSTRUMENTS INC, 80- *Mem:* Am Chem Soc; Soc Appl Spectros. *Res:* Instrumental neutron activation analysis, radiotracer techniques and x-ray fluorescence analysis in materials characterization; design and building of mini computer systems for manufacturing and laboratory automation. *Mailing Add:* Tex Instruments Inc PO Box 225936 Mail Sta 147 Dallas TX 75265

KEENAN, KATHLEEN MARGARET, b St Paul, Minn, May 24, 34. BIOSTATISTICS. *Educ:* St Catherine Col, BA, 56; Univ Minn, MS, 58, PhD(biostatist), 64. *Prof Exp:* Asst prof, 64-68, from asst prof to assoc prof, Sch Dent, 68-77, ASSOC PROF HUMAN & ORAL GENETICS, UNIV MINN, 77- *Mem:* AAAS; Am Statist Asn; Biom Soc; fel Am Pub Health Asn; Am Soc Human Genetics. *Res:* Statistical problems in standardization of a method for microbial surface sampling. *Mailing Add:* Dept of Human & Oral Genetics Univ of Minn 515 Delaware St SE Minneapolis MN 55455

KEENAN, PHILIP CHILDS, b Bellevue, Pa, Mar 31, 08. ASTRONOMY. *Educ:* Univ Ariz, BS, 29, MS, 30; Univ Chicago, PhD(astrophysics), 32. *Hon Degrees:* Dr, Cath Univ Cordoba, 71. *Prof Exp:* Asst astron, Yerkes Observ, Univ Chicago, 29-35, instr, 36-42; instr Perkins Observ, Ohio State Univ & Ohio Wesleyan Univ, 35-36; physicist, Bur Ord, US Dept Navy, 42-46; from asst prof to prof, 46-76, actg dir, 57-59, EMER PROF ASTRON, PERKINS OBSERV, OHIO STATE UNIV, 76- *Mem:* fel Royal Astron Soc. *Res:* Stellar spectroscopy; spectral classification; history of astronomy. *Mailing Add:* Perkins Observ Delaware OH 43015

KEENAN, ROBERT GREGORY, b St Albans, Vt, Dec 19, 15; m 44; c 3. ENVIRONMENTAL CHEMISTRY. *Educ:* Catholic Univ, BS, 37; Univ Md, MS, 52. *Prof Exp:* Lab helper chem, Div Occup Health, USPHS, 38-40, from jr chemist to assoc chemist, 40-45, sr asst scientist, 45-49, scientist, 49-53, chief phys anal unit, 53-56, asst chief anal serv, 56-60, chief, 60-69, dep chief res & med affairs, 66-67, assoc chief div occup health, 67-69; vpres & dir lab serv, George D Clayton & Assocs, 69-76; RETIRED. *Concurrent Pos:* Guest worker, Anal Chem Div, Radiochem Anal Sect, Nat Bur Standards, 63-64. *Mem:* Am Chem Soc; Am Indust Hyg Asn; Am Soc Testing & Mat. *Res:* Spectrography; determination of cobalt in dust samples; determination of iron in welding fume samples; quantitative analytical methods in emission spectroscopy; activation analysis; atomic absorption; beryllium in air; biological materials and ores; analytical techniques for industrial hygiene; author or coauthor of over 75 scientific publications. *Mailing Add:* 122 Country Club Dr E South Burlington VT 05401

KEENAN, ROBERT KENNETH, b Pueblo, Colo, Nov 29, 38; m 60; c 2. ELECTRONIC ENGINEERING. *Educ:* Univ Calif, Los Angeles, BSc, 62; Calif Inst Technol, MSEE, 63; Monash Univ, Australia, PhD(elec eng), 67. *Prof Exp:* Staff engr, Commun Div, Hughes Aircraft Co, 62-64; lectr elec eng, Monash Univ, 64-67; eng specialist, Electronics Div, Gen Dynamics Corp, 67-68; mgr res & adv develop, Electronic Commun Inc, Nat Cash Register Co, 68-71; mem tech staff, Mitre Corp, 71-75; mem tech staff, Aerospace Corp, 75-77; dir systs sci, BDM Corp, 77-78; sr prof eng, TRW Inc, 78-81; PRES, KEENAN CORP, 81- *Mem:* Inst Elec & Electronics Engrs; Am Inst Aeronaut & Astronaut. *Res:* Communications and communications electronics, particularly signal processing theory and practice. *Mailing Add:* 421 Mill St SE Vienna VA 22180

KEENAN, THOMAS AQUINAS, b Rochester, NY, Mar 8, 27; m 48; c 3. COMPUTER SCIENCE. *Educ:* Univ Rochester, BS, 47; Purdue Univ, MS, 50, PhD(physics), 55. *Prof Exp:* Instr physics, Purdue Univ, 50-55; dir comput ctr, Rochester Univ, 56-66, chmn prog appl math, 58-66, asst prof physics, 57-62; dir systs planning, Interuniv, Commun Coun, 66-68, exec dir educ info network, 68-69; PROG DIR SOFTWARE SYSTS SCI, NSF, 69- *Concurrent Pos:* Exec dir, comt on uses of comput, Nat Acad Sci-Nat Res Coun, 62-63; consult, Sch Math Study Group, 65-66. *Mem:* AAAS; Asn Comput Mach; Inst Elec & Electronics Engrs. *Res:* Computation; formal languages; symbol manipulation; information retrieval; data structure; phase transitions; combinatorial mathematics. *Mailing Add:* NSF Washington DC 20550

KEENAN, THOMAS K, b Ft Dodge, Iowa, Oct 8, 24; m 52; c 4. INORGANIC CHEMISTRY. *Educ:* SDak Sch Mines & Technol, BS, 48; Univ NMex, MS, 50, PhD(chem), 54. *Prof Exp:* Asst, Univ NMex, 49-53; mem staff, 54-75, group leader waste mgt, 75-81, ASST TO DEP ASSOC DIR, LOS ALAMOS NAT LAB, 81- *Mem:* Am Nuclear Soc. *Mailing Add:* Los Alamos Sci Lab PO Box 1663 MS-671 Los Alamos NM 87545

KEENAN, THOMAS WILLIAM, b Johnstown, Pa, May 12, 42; m 64; c 3. FOOD SCIENCE. *Educ:* Pa State Univ, BS, 64; Ore State Univ, MS, 65, PhD(food sci), 67. *Prof Exp:* Assoc prof food sci, 67-73, PROF ANIMAL SCI, PURDUE UNIV, 73-, ASST DEAN GRAD SCH, 77- *Mem:* Am Chem Soc; Am Dairy Sci Asn; Inst Food Technol. *Res:* Membrane function; microbial biochemistry; lipid metabolism. *Mailing Add:* Dept of Animal Sci Purdue Univ West Lafayette IN 49707

KEENE, HARRIS J, b Brooklyn, NY, Apr 13, 31; m 56; c 3. ORAL PATHOLOGY. *Educ:* Univ Md, DDS, 55. *Prof Exp:* Res officer dent, US Navy, 60-77, dir, Naval Dent Res Inst, 68-77; MEM STAFF, UNIV TEX DENT BR, DENT SCI INST, 77- *Mem:* Fel AAAS; Am Dent Asn; Am Asn Phys Anthrop; Int Asn Dent Res. *Res:* Epidemiology of oral diseases; dental oncology; dental anthropology; paleopathology; oral physiology. *Mailing Add:* Univ Tex Dental Br Dent Sci Inst Houston TX 77025

KEENE, JAMES H, b Epps, La, May 8, 30; m 58; c 2. POULTRY NUTRITION. *Educ:* Univ Ark, BS, 57; La State Univ, MS, 59, PhD(poultry nutrit), 62. *Prof Exp:* Nutritionist, George B Matthews & Sons Inc, 62-64; from asst prof to assoc prof, 64-70, PROF POULTRY & DAIRYING, ARK STATE UNIV, 70- *Mem:* Poultry Sci Asn. *Res:* Poultry production and physiology. *Mailing Add:* Dept of Poultry & Dairying Ark State Univ State University AR 72467

KEENE, OWEN DAVID, b New Eagle, Pa, Apr 28, 34; m 57; c 1. POULTRY NUTRITION. *Educ:* Pa State Univ, BS, 55; Univ Md, MS, 59, PhD(poultry nutrit), 63. *Prof Exp:* Sr biochemist, Abbott Labs, 63-69; asst prof, 69-75, ASSOC PROF POULTRY SCI EXTEN, PA STATE UNIV, 75- *Mem:* Poultry Sci Asn; World Poultry Sci Asn. *Res:* Product development relating to the nutrition of poultry. *Mailing Add:* 212 Animal Industries Bldg Pa State Univ University Park PA 16802

KEENE, WAYNE HARTUNG, b Boothbay Harbor, Maine, Apr 29, 37; m 57; c 2. PHYSICS, LASER RADAR. *Educ:* Univ Maine, BS, 58, MS, 61; Worcester Polytech Inst, PhD(physics), 64. *Prof Exp:* Physicist elec boat div, Gen Dynamics Corp, Conn, 58-59; sr engr, Defense & Space Ctr, Westinghouse Elec Corp, Md, 64-65; sr engr, 65-67, prin engr, 67-69, sect mgr, 69-79, CONSULT SCIENTIST, ELECTROOPTICS DEPT, EQUIP DIV, RAYTHEON CO, 79- *Mem:* Optical Soc Am. *Res:* Time-resolved spectroscopy of neodymium glass laser emission; laser dynamics; x-ray crystallography; design and development of laser scanners, imagers, modulators, coherent optics and doppler laser radar systems. *Mailing Add:* Electro-Optics Dept Equip Div Raytheon Co Sudbury MA 01776

KEENE, WILLIS RIGGS, b Woodbine, Ga, Jan 30, 32; m; c 4. INTERNAL MEDICINE, HEMATOLOGY. *Educ:* Emory Univ, BA, 53; Johns Hopkins Univ, MD, 57. *Prof Exp:* From intern to resident, Johns Hopkins Hosp, 57-59; with Nat Cancer Inst, 59-60 & USPHS Hosp, Boston, 60-61; fel med, Harvard Univ, 61-63, instr, 63-64; staff physician, Dept Internal Med, Lahey Clin, 64-68; prof med, Col Med, Univ Fla, 71-75, assoc chmn dept internal med, 74-75; CLIN PRACTICE, 75- *Mem:* Am Col Physicians; Am Soc Hemat. *Res:* Blood platelet physiology; iron metabolism. *Mailing Add:* 1001 N Third St Folkston GA 31537

KEENER, CARL SAMUEL, b Columbia, Pa, Apr 12, 31; m 55; c 3. BOTANY. *Educ:* Eastern Mennonite Col, AB, 57; Univ Pa, MS, 60; NC State Univ, PhD(bot), 66. *Prof Exp:* Asst prof biol, Eastern Mennonite Col, 60-63; asst prof, 66-71, ASSOC PROF BOT, PA STATE UNIV, 71- *Honors & Awards:* Jesse M Greeman Award, 68. *Mem:* AAAS; Bot Soc Am; Am Soc Plant Taxon; Int Asn Plant Taxon; Int Orgn Biosyst. *Res:* Biosystematics of Carex; evolutionary patterns in the shale barren endemics of eastern US; floristics of Pennsylvania; Ranunculaceae of North America. *Mailing Add:* 306 Buckhout Lab Pa State Univ University Park PA 16802

KEENER, E(VERETT) L(EE), b Grafton, WVa, Jan 30, 22; m 42. ELECTRICAL ENGINEERING. *Educ:* Univ WVa, BSEE, 44; Purdue Univ, MSEE, 49. *Prof Exp:* Test engr, Gen Elec Co, 44; from instr to asst prof elec eng, Univ WVa, 46-55; instr, Purdue Univ, 47-48; sr res engr, analog & hybrid comput, 55-66, ASSOC RES CONSULT, RES CTR, US STEEL CORP, 66- *Mem:* Sr mem Inst Elec & Electronics Engrs. *Res:* Instrumentation, control and electrical analogs for steel industry processes. *Mailing Add:* US Steel Corp Appl Res Lab Jamison Lane Monroeville PA 15146

KEENER, HAROLD MARION, b Ashland, Ohio, July 28, 43. AGRICULTURAL ENGINEERING. *Educ:* Ohio State Univ, BS, 67, MS, 68, PhD(agr eng), 73. *Prof Exp:* Inst, 68-73, asst prof, 74-80, ASSOC PROF AGR ENG, OHIO AGR RES & DEVELOP CTR, 80- *Mem:* Am Soc Agr Engrs. *Res:* Dairy housing and mechanization systems, concentrating on labor efficiencies and feeding systems; analysis of total energy consumption in crop production systems and livestock enterprises; solar grain drying. *Mailing Add:* Dept of Agr Eng Ohio Agr Res & Develop Ctr Wooster OH 44691

KEENER, HARRY ALLAN, b Greensboro, Pa, Dec 22, 13; m 41; c 2. ANIMAL NUTRITION. *Educ:* Pa State Univ, BS, 36, PhD(animal nutrit, dairy husb), 41; WVa Univ, MS, 38. *Prof Exp:* Asst dairy husb, WVa Univ, 36-38 & Pa State Univ, 38-41; from instr to asst prof animal & dairy husb, 41-45, assoc prof dairy husb, 45-50, prof animal sci, 50-78, dir agr exp sta, 58-78, dean, Col Life Sci & Agr, 61-78, EMER PROF ANIMAL SCI & EMER DEAN, COL LIFE SCI & AGR, UNIV NH, 78- *Mem:* Am Soc Animal Sci; Dairy Sci Asn; NY Acad Sci. *Res:* Trace elements; cobalt; vitamin D; nitrogen and energy metabolism. *Mailing Add:* PO Box 165 Durham NH 03824

KEENER, MARVIN STANFORD, b Birmingham, Ala, Oct 25, 43; m 65; c 2. MATHEMATICAL ANALYSIS. *Educ:* Birmingham-Southern Col, BS, 65; Univ Mo-Columbia, MA, 67, PhD(math), 70. *Prof Exp:* From asst prof to assoc prof, 70-79, PROF MATH, OKLA STATE UNIV, 79- *Mem:* Am Math Soc; Sigma Xi; Soc Indust & Appl Math; Math Asn Am. *Res:* Ordinary differential equations. *Mailing Add:* Dept Math Okla State Univ Stillwater OK 74074

KEENEY, ARTHUR HAIL, b Louisville, Ky, Jan 20, 20; m 42; c 3. OPHTHALMOLOGY. *Educ:* Col William & Mary, BS, 41; Univ Louisville, MD, 44; Univ Pa, MS, 52, DSc(med), 55; Am Bd Ophthal, dipl, 51. *Prof Exp:* Res surgeon, Wills Eye Hosp, Philadelphia, Pa, 49-51; dir res, Sect Ophthal, Sch Med, Univ Louisville, 52-59, from asst prof to assoc prof ophthal, 59-65; prof & chmn dept, Sch Med, Temple Univ, 66-74; dean, 73-80, EMER DEAN & DISTINGUISHED PROF OPHTHAL, SCH MED, UNIV LOUISVILLE, 80- *Concurrent Pos:* Area consult, US Vet Admin, 54-; Alvaro lectr to SAm, 60; consult ed, Am J Ophthal; mem sci adv comt, Nat Coun Combat Blindness; chmn Z80 comt on ophthalmol standards, Am Nat Standard Inst; ophthalmologist-in-chief, Wills Eye Hosp & Res Inst, 65-73; mem Nat Adv Coun to US Secy Transportation, 67-71; pres, Int Cong Ultrasound in Ophthal, 68; chmn med adv bd, Nat Aid Visually Handicapped, 70-80; mem grants adv coun, The Seeing Eye, 68-71; vchmn, Residency Rev Comt Ophthal, 69-73. *Mem:* Fel Am Ophthal Soc; AMA; fel Am Asn Hist Med; fel Am Acad Ophthal & Otolaryngol; Am Asn Automotive Med (pres, 67). *Res:* Newcastle virus disease; ocular injuries; ultrasounds; diabetic retinopathy; safety lens materials; macular disease; dyslexia; strabismus. *Mailing Add:* Sch of Med PO Box 35260 Louisville KY 40232

KEENEY, CLIFFORD EMERSON, b Springfield, Mass, June 28, 21; m 50; c 2. PHYSIOLOGY. *Educ:* Springfield Col, BS, 48, MEd, 49; Rutgers Univ, MS, 51; NY UNiv, PhD(phys ed), 59. *Prof Exp:* Teacher high sch, Mass, 49-50; instr biol, Springfield Col, 51-52; biologist, Lederle Labs Div, Am Cyanamid Co, NY, 52-55; asst prof physiol, 55-57, from asst prof to assoc prof biol, 57-65, dir div arts & sci, 62-64, PROF BIOL, SPRINGFIELD COL, 65- *Concurrent Pos:* NSF sci fac fel, 64-65. *Mem:* AAAS; Nat Asn Biol Teachers; fel Am Col Sports Med; NY Acad Sci. *Res:* Cytological changes induced by exercise. *Mailing Add:* Dept of Biol Springfield Col Springfield MA 01109

KEENEY, DENNIS RAYMOND, b Osceola, Iowa, July 2, 37; m 59; c 2. SOIL FERTILITY, BIOCHEMISTRY. *Educ:* Iowa State Univ, BS, 59, PhD(soil fertil), 65; Univ Wis, MS, 61. *Prof Exp:* Fel soil biochem, Iowa State Univ, 65-66; from asst prof to assoc prof, 66-74, PROF SOILS, UNIV WIS, 74-, CHMN SOILS, 79- *Concurrent Pos:* Romnes grad sch fel, Univ Wis Grad Sch, 75. *Mem:* Fel Am Soc Agron; Soil Sci Soc Am; Soil Conserv Soc Am; AAAS. *Res:* Development of methodology for determination and isotope-ratio analysis of nitrogen in soils; elucidation of nitrogen transformation in soils; characterization of the forms and amounts of nitrogen in soils, sediments and waters; land application of solid and liquid municipal and industrial wastes. *Mailing Add:* Soil Sci Dept Univ Wis 1525 Observatory Dr Madison WI 53706

KEENEY, JOE, b Arkansas City, Kans, Dec 19, 33; m 58; c 4. ENERGY CONVERSION, COSMOLOGY. *Educ:* Univ Okla, BS, 56; NMex Inst Min & Tech, MS, 64, PhD(geophys), 68. *Prof Exp:* Physicist, Geophys Lab, Superior Oil Co, 67-80; SR GEOPHYSICIST, GEOSOURCE, INC, HOUSTON TX, 81- *Mem:* Int Solar Energy Soc; AAAS; Soc Exp Geophysicists. *Res:* Physics of thunderstorms; properties of gases; exploration geophysics; solar energy conversion and storage; experimental cosmology. *Mailing Add:* 10202 Huntington Dale Dr Houston TX 77099

KEENEY, MARK, b Sharon, Pa, May 18, 21; m 51. DAIRY SCIENCE. *Educ:* Pa State Univ, BS, 42, PhD(dairy husb), 50; Ohio State Univ, MS, 47. *Prof Exp:* Chemist, Borden Co, 43-44; asst, Pa State Univ, 48-50; asst prof dairy mfg, 50-54, from assoc prof to prof dairy sci, 54-74, prof chem & dairy sci, 74-81, PROF BIOCHEM & CHMN DEPT, UNIV MD, COLLEGE PARK, 81- *Mem:* Am Dairy Sci Asn; Am Soc Biol Chemists; NY Acad Sci. *Res:* Food chemistry; lipid metabolism; characterization and metabolism of rumen microbial lipids and of oxygenated fatty acids in animals. *Mailing Add:* Dept of Chem Univ of Md College Park MD 20742

KEENEY, NORWOOD HENRY, JR, b Hartford, Conn, July 10, 24; m 46; c 1. CHEMICAL ENGINEERING, PULP AND PAPER-FOREST PRODUCTS. *Educ:* Trinity Col, Conn, BS, 48; Univ Maine, Orono, MS, 50; Victoria Univ, Manchester, PhD, 62. *Prof Exp:* Paper chemist, Fram Corp, 50-53; from asst prof to assoc prof, 53-64, PROF CHEM ENG, UNIV LOWELL, 64-, CHMN DEPT, 76- *Mem:* Am Inst Chem Engrs; Tech Asn Pulp & Paper Indust; Sigma Xi; Soc Prof Engrs. *Res:* Chemical engineering applications to pulp and paper industry; porous media; filtration of compressibles; zeta potentials; stress-strain properties of fibers and fibrous structures. *Mailing Add:* Dept of Chem Eng One University Ave Lowell MA 01800

KEENEY, PHILIP G, b Caldwell, NJ, Feb 28, 25; m 57; c 1. FOOD SCIENCE. *Educ:* Univ Nebr, BSc, 49; Ohio State Univ, MSc, 53; Pa State Univ, PhD(dairy sci), 55. *Prof Exp:* Asst prof dairy sci, 55-63, assoc prof, 63-68, PROF FOOD SCI, PA STATE UNIV, 68- *Mem:* Fel AAAS; Am Chem Soc; Am Dairy Sci Asn; Inst Food Technol. *Res:* Food technology and chemistry; ice cream; chocolate products. *Mailing Add:* Borland Lab Pa State Univ University Park PA 16802

KEENEY, RALPH LYONS, b Lewistown, Mont, Jan 29, 44. OPERATIONS RESEARCH. *Educ:* Univ Calif, Los Angeles, BS, 66; Mass Inst Technol, MS, 67, EE, 68, PhD(opers res), 69. *Prof Exp:* Engr, Bell Tel Labs, 66-69; asst prof civil eng & staff mem, Opers Res Ctr, Mass Inst Technol, 69-72, assoc prof mgt & opers res, 72-74; res scholar, Int Inst Appl Systs Anal, Laxenburg, Austria, 74-76; HEAD DECISION ANAL, WOODWARD-CYCLE CONSULTS, 76-, VPRES, 80- *Concurrent Pos:* Consult, New York City-Rand Inst, 69-72. *Mem:* Opers Res Soc Am; Inst Mgt Sci. *Res:* Public systems; decision analysis; probabilistic models. *Mailing Add:* Woodward-Clyde Consults Suite 700 San Francisco CA 94111

KEENLEYSIDE, MILES HUGH ALSTON, b Ottawa, Ont, Apr 8, 29; m 51; c 2. ETHOLOGY. *Educ:* Univ BC, BA, 52, MA, 53; Univ Groningen, PhD(zool), 55. *Prof Exp:* Asst scientist fisheries biol, Biol Sta, Fisheries Res Bd Can, 55-57, assoc scientist, 57-61; from asst prof to assoc prof, 61-72, PROF ZOOL, UNIV WESTERN ONT, 72- *Mem:* Can Soc Zoologists; Animal Behav Soc. *Res:* Social and reproductive behavior of fishes; parent-young interactions; social organization, breeding systems and ecology; reproductive isolation. *Mailing Add:* Dept Zool Univ Western Ont London ON N6A 5B7 Can

KEENLYNE, KENT DOUGLAS, b Durand, Wis, May 28, 41; m 64; c 2. WILDLIFE ECOLOGY, GEOLOGY. *Educ:* Univ Wis-River Falls, BS, 64; Univ Minn, MS, 68, MAPA, 71, PhD(wildlife ecol), 76. *Prof Exp:* Wildlife biologist river basin studies, US Fish & Wildlife Serv, Minneapolis, Minn, 70-72; coordr interagency coord, Upper Miss River Conserv Comt, 72-74; herpetologist herpetol studies & res, Fla Game & Fresh Water Fish Comn, 75-76; fish & wildlife biologist ecol serv & proj planning, Rock Island, Ill, 76, coal coordr mineral develop, Casper, Wyo, 76-77, SUPVR ADMIN, US FISH & WILDLIFE SERV, 77- *Concurrent Pos:* Big game biologist, Minn Dept Natural Resources, 78; Interior Coal rep, Interior Task Force Strip Mine Legis Coal Develop, 78. *Honors & Awards:* Spec Achievement Award, US Fish & Wildlife Serv, 76. *Mem:* Am Fisheries Soc; Wildlife Soc; Soc Study Amphibians & Reptiles. *Res:* Whitetailed deer reproduction; natural history and populations of turtles; reproduction and life history of rattlesnakes; alligator attacks; physiology of whitetailed deer; telemetry studies on whitetailed deer. *Mailing Add:* US Fish & Wildlife Serv PO Box 250 Pierre SD 57501

KEENMON, KENDALL ANDREWS, b Detroit, Mich, Sept 13, 20; m 42; c 4. PETROLEUM GEOLOGY. *Educ:* Univ Mich, BS, 47, MS, 48, PhD(geol), 50. *Prof Exp:* Div geologist, Shell Oil Co, 50-60, sr geologist, 60-61, sr res geologist, Shell Develop Co, 61-67, sr geologist, Shell Oil Co, 67-69 & Shell Develop Co, 69-72, sr geologist, Int Region, 72-77, STAFF GEOLOGIST, SHELL OIL CO, INT REGION, 78- *Mem:* Geol Soc Am; Am Asn Petrol Geol. *Res:* Structural geology; stratigraphy. *Mailing Add:* 5158 Imogene St Houston TX 77096

KEENY, SPURGEON MILTON, JR, b New York, NY, Oct 24, 24; m 52; c 3. PHYSICS. *Educ:* Columbia Univ, BA, 44, MA, 46. *Prof Exp:* Asst physics, Columbia Univ, 44-46; intel analyst, Directorate of Intel Hq, US Air Force, 50-52, chief spec weapons sect, 52-55; mem staff, Panel Peaceful Uses Atomic Energy, 55-56; chief atomic energy div, Off Asst Secy Defense Res & Eng, 56-57; mem, Gaither Security Resources Panel, 57; tech asst, President's Sci Adv, 58-69; sr staff mem, Nat Security Coun, 63-69; asst dir sci & technol, US Arms Control & Disarmament Agency, 69-73; dir policy & prog develop, Mitre Corp, 73-77; dep dir, US Arms Control & Disarmament Agency, 77-81; SCHOLAR-IN-RESIDENCE, NAT ACAD SCI, 81- *Concurrent Pos:* Mem US del, Geneva Conf Experts Nuclear Test Detection, 58, Conf Discontinuance Nuclear Weapon Tests, 58-60,, Am Phys Soc Study Group Light-Water Reactor Safety, 74-75; dep chmn, Nat Acad Sci, Comt on Environ Decision Making, 74; chmn, Ford-Mitre Nuclear Energy Policy Study, 75-77; mem comt int security & arms control, Nat Acad Sci, 81-; head US deleg, US/Soviet Theater Nuclear Force Talks, 80. *Honors & Awards:* Rockefeller Pub Serv Award, 70. *Mem:* Fel Am Acad Arts & Sci; Coun Foreign Relations; Am Phys Soc. *Res:* Arms control and disarmament; defense policy; military and civilian applications of atomic energy; energy and environmental policy. *Mailing Add:* 3600 Albemarle St NW Washington DC 20008

KEEPIN, GEORGE ROBERT, JR, b Oak Park, Ill, Dec 5, 23; m 48; c 5. NUCLEAR PHYSICS, INSTRUMENTATION. *Educ:* Univ Chicago, PhB, 45; Mass Inst Technol, BS & MS, 47; Northwestern Univ, PhD(physics), 49. *Prof Exp:* Consult, Argonne Nat Lab, 48-49; AEC fel radiation lab, Univ Calif, 50; consult, Los Alamos Sci Lab, 52-62; head physics sect, Int Atomic Energy Agency, Vienna, 63-65; group leader nuclear assay res, 66-75, NUCLEAR SAFEGUARDS PROG DIR, LOS ALAMOS SCI LAB, 75- & ASSOC DIV LEADER, NUCLEAR SAFEGUARDS, REACTOR SAFETY & TECHNOL DIV, 75- *Concurrent Pos:* Deleg, Atoms for Peace Conf, Geneva, 55, 64 & 71; tech adv, Int Atomic Energy Agency, Geneva, 64; nat prog chmn, Inst Nuclear Mat Mgt, 77-78. *Honors & Awards:* Am Nuclear Soc Award, 73. *Mem:* NY Acad Sci; fel Am Phys Soc; fel Am Nuclear Soc. *Res:* Fission physics; reactor dynamics; pulsed neutron research, nuclear safeguards research and development; development of non-destructive assay techniques for domestic and international inspection and safeguards of fissionable materials; development and implementation of nondestructive assay technology for stringent nuclear safeguards on both the national and international level. *Mailing Add:* Los Alamos Sci Lab Los Alamos NM 87544

KEEPING, ELEANOR SILVER (DOWDING), b London, Eng, Oct 29, 01; m 33; c 1. MYCOLOGY. *Educ:* Univ Man, PhD(bot), 30, PhD(mycol). *Prof Exp:* Lectr bot, Univ Alta, 23; RES WORKER MYCOL, NAT RES COUN CAN, 46- *Concurrent Pos:* Nat Res Coun Can med res grants, 35-50. *Mem:* Mycol Soc Am; Can Soc Microbiol; Genetics Soc Can; Brit Mycol Soc. *Res:* Pure mycology; medical mycology; cytology; ecology; evolution. *Mailing Add:* Dept of Genetics Univ of Alta Edmonton AB I6G 2E8 Can

KEEPLER, MANUEL, b Atlanta, Ga, Nov 4, 44; m 66; c 1. EVOLUTIONS. *Educ:* Morehouse Col, BS, 65; Columbis Univ, MA, 67; Univ NMex, PhD(math), 73. *Prof Exp:* Asst prof math, Va State Univ, 70-71; assoc prof & chmn, Laugston Univ, 71-73; assoc prof, 73-80, PROF MATH & COMPUT SCI, SC STATE COL, 80-, CHMN DEPT, 81- *Concurrent Pos:* Vis prof, Dilliard Univ, 76; fel comput, Lawrence Livermore Lab, 77, comput sci, Langley REs Ctr, 81. *Mem:* Am Math Soc; Am Statist Asn; Inst Math Statist; Math Asn Am; NY Acad Sci. *Res:* Random evolutions on Marlsov processes; various stochastic processes connected with the theory of random evolutions. *Mailing Add:* Box 1656 SC State Col Orangeburg SC 29117

KEER, LEON M, b Los Angeles, Calif, Sept 13, 34; m 56; c 4. CIVIL ENGINEERING, ENGINEERING MECHANICS. *Educ:* Calif Inst Technol, BS, 56, MS, 58; Univ Minn, PhD(eng mech), 62. *Prof Exp:* Mem tech staff, Hughes Aircraft Co, 56-59; NATO fel eng mech, Newcastle, 62-63; preceptor, Columbia Univ, 63-64; from asst prof to assoc prof, 64-70, PROF CIVIL ENG, NORTHWESTERN UNIV, 70- *Concurrent Pos:* Guggenheim sr vis fel, Dept Math, Univ Glasgow, 72-73. *Mem:* Am Soc Mech Engrs; Acoust Soc Am; Am Soc Civil Engrs; Am Acad Mech (secy, 81-85). *Res:* Contact stress and fracture problems in the mathematical theory of elasticity; wave propagation. *Mailing Add:* Dept of Civil Eng Northwestern Univ Evanston IL 60201

KEESE, CHARLES RICHARD, b Cooperstown, NY, Mar 4, 44; m 67; c 2. MOLECULAR BIOLOGY, CELL BIOLOGY. *Educ:* State Univ NY, Albany, BS, 67; Rensselaer Polytech Inst, PhD(biol), 71. *Prof Exp:* Asst prof physics, 71-73, assoc prof, 74-79, PROF BIOL, STATE UNIV NY, COBLESKILL, 79- *Concurrent Pos:* NSF fel sci fac prof develop award, Gen Elec Corp Res & Develop, 77-78, consult, 78-80; assoc investr, Nat Found Cancer Res, 81-82. *Mem:* Sigma Xi; Am Soc Microbiol; AAAS. *Res:* Behavior of cells in culture; properties of proteins on surfaces; mechanisms of tumor promotion and carcinogenesis. *Mailing Add:* Stony Brook Rd Schoharie NY 12157

KEESEE, JOHN WILLIAM, b Elaine, Ark, Sept 11, 13; m 45. MATHEMATICS. *Educ:* Ark Agr & Mech Col, BS, 35; Tulane Univ, PhD(math), 50. *Prof Exp:* From asst prof to assoc prof, 50-65, PROF MATH, UNIV ARK, FAYETTEVILLE, 65- *Mem:* AAAS; Am Math Soc; Math Asn Am. *Res:* Algebraic topology. *Mailing Add:* Dept of Math Univ of Ark Fayetteville AR 72701

KEESEY, ULKER TULUNAY, b Ankara, Turkey, Oct 18, 32; m 59. PSYCHOPHYSICS. *Educ:* Mt Holyoke Col, BA, 55; Brown Univ, MA, 57, PhD(psychol), 59. *Prof Exp:* Res psychologist, Brown Univ, 59-60 & Univ Calif, Los Angeles, 60-62; instr ophthal, 63-65, from asst prof to assoc prof, 65-75, PROF OPHTHAL, SCH MED, UNIV WIS-MADISON, 75- *Concurrent Pos:* NIH res grant, 63-64; mem comt vision, Nat Res Coun. *Mem:* Optical Soc Am; Asn Res Vision & Ophthal. *Res:* Sensory psychophysics; physiology of vision. *Mailing Add:* Dept of Ophthal Sch of Med Univ of Wis Madison WI 53706

KEESLING, JAMES EDGAR, b Indianapolis, Ind, June 26, 42; m 63; c 4. TOPOLOGY, APPLIED MATHEMATICS. *Educ:* Univ Miami, Fla, BSIE, 64, MS, 66, PhD(math), 68. *Prof Exp:* Teaching asst, Univ Miami, Fla, 64-65; from asst prof to assoc prof, 67-75, PROF MATH, UNIV FLA, 75- *Mem:* AAAS; Am Math Soc; Math Asn Am; Soc Indust & Appl Math. *Res:* Topology. *Mailing Add:* Dept of Math Univ of Fla Gainesville FL 32611

KEESOM, PIETER HENDRIK, b Leiden, Netherlands, Feb 10, 17; m 46; c 4. PHYSICS. *Educ:* Univ Leiden, PhD(physics), 48. *Prof Exp:* Asst, Kamerlingh Onnes Lab, Univ Leiden, 39-46; physicist, State Mines of Netherlands, 46-48; vis prof, 48-50, from asst prof to assoc prof, 50-57, PROF PHYSICS, PURDUE UNIV, 57- *Concurrent Pos:* Guggenheim fel, 60-61. *Mem:* Am Phys Soc; Netherlands Phys Soc. *Res:* Low temperatures; specific heat of elements. *Mailing Add:* Dept of Physics Purdue Univ Lafayette IN 47907

KEETON, WILLIAM TINSLEY, animal behavior, deceased

KEETON-WILLIAMS, JAMES G, b Atascedero, Calif, Nov 4, 44; m 66, 77. COMPUTER SCIENCES. *Educ:* Carleton Col, BA 66; Univ Calif, Berkeley, PhD(math), 73. *Prof Exp:* Asst prof math, Bowling Green State Univ, 72-75, assoc prof, 75-76; MEM TECH STAFF, MITRE, 79- *Mem:* Am Math Soc; Asn Comput Sci. *Res:* Program verification; software development methodology; computer security. *Mailing Add:* Mitre Corp Box 208 Bedford MA 01730

KEETTEL, WILLIAM CHARLES, b Lyons, Nebr, Apr 30, 11; m 40; c 1. OBSTETRICS & GYNECOLOGY. *Educ:* Univ Nebr, AB, 32, BS & MD, 36; Am Bd Obstet & Gynec, dipl, 42. *Prof Exp:* Obstet consult, Sch Med, Univ Wis, 40-43; from asst prof to assoc prof, 46-53, head dept, 59-77, PROF OBSTET & GYNEC, COL MED, UNIV IOWA, 53- *Concurrent Pos:* Examr, Am Bd Obstet & Gynec. *Mem:* Soc Gynec Invest; Am Asn Obstet & Gynec; Am Gynec Soc; Am Col Obstet & Gynec; Am Col Surg. *Res:* Cancer; endocrinology. *Mailing Add:* Dept of Obstet & Gynec Univ of Iowa Col of Med Iowa City IA 52241

KEEVERT, JOHN EDWARD, JR, b Columbus, Ohio, Mar 2, 44. PHOTOGRAPHIC CHEMISTRY. *Educ:* Northwestern Univ, BS, 67; Stanford Univ, MS, 69. *Prof Exp:* SR RES CHEMIST, RES LABS, EASTMAN KODAK CO, 69- *Mem:* Soc Photog Scientists & Engrs. *Res:* Image forming mechanisms and electrical properties of silver halides and other novel recording media. *Mailing Add:* Res Labs Eastman Kodak Co Rochester NY 14650

KEEVIL, NORMAN BELL, b Saskatoon, Sask, Oct 24, 10; m 38; c 5. CHEMISTRY, PHYSICS. *Educ:* Univ Sask, BSc, 30, MSc, 32; Harvard Univ, PhD, 37. *Prof Exp:* Demonstr chem, Univ Sask, 30-33; asst phys chem, Harvard Univ, 33-37, res assoc geophys, 37-38, geol, Mass Inst Technol, 38-39 & geophys, Univ Toronto, 39-43, asst prof, 43-46; pres, Mining Geophys Corp, Ltd, 46-63; PRES, TECK CORP LTD, 63- *Concurrent Pos:* Pres, Copperfields Mining Corp, Ltd, 64- *Mem:* AAAS; fel Geol Soc Am; Am Inst Mining, Metall & Petrol Engrs; Soc Expl Geophysics; Geol Soc Can. *Res:* Hydrothermal reactions and vapor pressures; electrochemical and equilibrium data; radioactive tracers; age and heat production of rocks; diffusion; viscosity; gas analysis; mass spectrometry; geological mapping; aeromagnetics; distribution of uranium and thorium in rocks; geophysical exploration. *Mailing Add:* Teck Corp Ltd 1199 West Hastings St Vancouver BC V6E 2K5 Can

KEEVIL, THOMAS ALAN, b Long Branch, NJ, Feb 11, 47; m 69; c 1. ORGANIC CHEMISTRY, BIOCHEMISTRY. *Educ:* Bucknell Univ, BS, 68; Univ Calif, PhD(chem), 72. *Prof Exp:* Res assoc biochem, Med Sch, Univ Ore, 72-74; asst prof, 74-78, ASSOC PROF CHEM, SOUTHERN ORE STATE COL, 78- *Res:* Oxidase mechanisms. *Mailing Add:* Dept of Chem Southern Ore State Col Ashland OR 97520

KEFALIDES, NICHOLAS ALEXANDER, b Alexandroupolis, Greece, Jan 17, 27; US citizen; m 49; c 3. BIOLOGICAL CHEMISTRY, INTERNAL MEDICINE. *Educ:* Augustana Col, Ill, AB, 51; Univ Ill, BS, 54, MD & MS, 56, PhD(biochem), 65. *Prof Exp:* Intern med, Res & Educ Hosps, Univ Ill, 56-57; dir res proj in burns, USPHS, Peru, 57-60; resident internal med, Res & Educ Hosps, Univ Ill, 60-63, instr, Col Med, 64-65; from asst prof to assoc prof, La Rabida Inst & Dept Med, Univ Chicago, 65-70; assoc prof, 70-74, PROF MED, UNIV PA, 74-, PROF BIOCHEM & BIOPHYS, 75- *Concurrent Pos:* USPHS fel, 62-64; assoc attend physician, Cook County Hosp, Chicago, Ill, 62-65; chief infectious dis sect, Vet Admin Hosp, Hines, 64-65; dir, Connective Tissue Res Inst, Univ Pa, 75- *Honors & Awards:* Borden Award, 56. *Mem:* Int Soc Nephrology; Am Chem Soc; Am Soc Exp Path; Am Soc Clin Invest; Am Soc Biol Chem. *Res:* Infection and immunity in burns; infectious diseases; chemistry of glycoproteins and basement membranes. *Mailing Add:* University City Sci Ctr 3624 Market St Philadelphia PA 19104

KEFFER, CHARLES JOSEPH, b Philadelphia, Pa, Aug 7, 41; m 66; c 4. SOLID STATE PHYSICS, CRYSTALLOGRAPHY. *Educ:* Univ Scranton, BS, 63; Harvard Univ, AM, 64, PhD(solid state physics), 69. *Prof Exp:* From instr to asst prof physics, Univ Scranton, 69-73; dean, 73-77, PROVOST, COL ST THOMAS, 77- *Mem:* Am Phys Soc; Am Asn Physics Teachers. *Res:* Crystal structure analysis-powder and single crystal; structure related properties in solid state physics; x-ray diffraction techniques; low temperature physics. *Mailing Add:* Col of St Thomas 2115 Summit Ave St Paul MN 55105

KEFFER, FREDERIC, b Anaconda, Mont, May 23, 19; m 49; c 2. SOLID STATE PHYSICS. *Educ:* State Col Wash, BS, 45; Univ Calif, PhD(physics), 52. *Prof Exp:* Res assoc physics, Univ Calif, 52; from asst prof to assoc prof, 52-59, chmn dept, 63-69, PROF PHYSICS, UNIV PITTSBURGH, 59- *Concurrent Pos:* Res physicist, Westinghouse Res Labs, 52-55; vis prof, Univ Calif, 59-60. *Mem:* AAAS; Am Phys Soc. *Res:* Magnetism; theory of solids. *Mailing Add:* Dept of Physics & Astron Univ of Pittsburgh Pittsburgh PA 15260

KEFFER, JAMES F, b Toronto, Ont, Dec 15, 33; m 55; c 2. MECHANICAL ENGINEERING. *Educ:* Univ Toronto, BASc, 56, MASc, 58, PhD(mech eng), 62. *Prof Exp:* Nat Res Coun Can fel physics, Cambridge Univ, 62-64; from asst prof to assoc prof, 64-73, PROF MECH ENG, UNIV TORONTO, 73- *Concurrent Pos:* Consult, Pulp & Paper Res Co Can, 65-; vis prof, Inst Mechnique Statisque Turbulence, Marseille, France, 73-74. *Res:* Fluid mechanics; heat and mass transfer; fluid mechanics of pulp and paper; turbulent flows. *Mailing Add:* Dept of Mech Eng Univ of Toronto Toronto ON M5S 1A1 Can

KEFFER, THOMAS, b Berkeley, Calif, June 2, 52. PHYSICAL OCEANOGRAPHY. *Educ:* Cornell Univ, BA, 74; Ore State Univ, PhD(oceanog), 81. *Prof Exp:* FEL, WOODS HOLE OCEANOG INST, 80- *Mem:* Am Geophys Union; Am Meteorol Soc. *Res:* Physics of large-scale ocean circulation; tracer dispersion; heat flux and climate. *Mailing Add:* Physical Oceanog Dept Woods Hole Oceanog Inst Woods Hole MA 02543

KEFFORD, NOEL PRICE, b Melbourne, Victoria, Australia, Feb 5, 27; m 50; c 3. PLANT PHYSIOLOGY. *Educ:* Univ Melbourne, BSc, 48, MSc, 50; Univ London, PhD(bot, plant physiol), 54. *Prof Exp:* Res officer, Australian Paper Mfrs, Ltd, 50-51; res officer div plant indust, Commonwealth Sci & Indust Res Orgn, 54-59, sr res officer, 59-64, prin res officer, 64-65; PROF BOT & CHMN DEPT, UNIV HAWAII, 65- *Concurrent Pos:* Fulbright sr res fel & res assoc biol, Yale Univ, 62-63; res assoc, Univ Calif, Santa Cruz, 71; actg assoc dir, Hawaii Agr Exp Sta, 76- *Mem:* Am Soc Plant Physiol; Brit Soc Exp Biol; Australian Soc Plant Physiol. *Res:* Plant growth and development; hormonal regulation; research management and administration. *Mailing Add:* Dept of Bot 3190 Maile Way Univ of Hawaii Honolulu HI 96822

KEGEL, GUNTER HEINRICH REINHARD, b Herborn, Ger, June 16, 29; m 57; c 2. NUCLEAR PHYSICS. *Educ:* Rio de Janeiro, BS, 51; Mass Inst Technol, PhD(physics), 61. *Prof Exp:* Engr, Nat Inst Technol, Brazil, 51-56; prof physics, Cath Univ, Rio de Janeiro, 61-64; prof physics, 64-66, prof nuclear eng, 66-71, chmn dept physics & appl physics, 71-81, PROF PHYSICS, UNIV LOWELL, 71- *Concurrent Pos:* Prof, Rio de Janeiro, 52-56 & 61-64; res asst, Lab Nuclear Sci, Mass Inst Technol, 58-61; consult, Millipore Corp, Bedford, Mass, 69- *Mem:* Brazilian Acad Sci; Am Phys Soc; Electrochem Soc; Am Nuclear Soc; Inst Elec & Electronics Engrs. *Res:* Nuclear spectroscopy; environmental radiation; proton induced x-ray emission (PIXE); neutron physics; neutron radiation damage. *Mailing Add:* Dept of Physics & Appl Physics Univ of Lowell Lowell MA 01854

KEGELES, GERSON, b New Haven, Conn, Apr 23, 17; m 44; c 5. BIOPHYSICAL CHEMISTRY. *Educ:* Yale Univ, BS, 37, PhD(phys chem), 40. *Prof Exp:* Fel, Yale Univ, 40-41; fel, Univ Wis, 45-47; phys chemist, Nat Cancer Inst, 47-51; from assoc prof to prof chem, Clark Univ, 51-68; PROF SECT BIOCHEM & BIOPHYS, UNIV CONN, 68- *Mem:* Am Chem Soc; Biophys Soc; Am Soc Biol Chem; Am Acad Arts & Sci. *Res:* Ultracentrifugation; countercurrent distribution; equilibria and kinetics of reversible protein subunit interactions; diffusion. *Mailing Add:* Sect of Biochem & Biophys Univ of Conn Storrs CT 06268

KEGELES, LAWRENCE STEVEN, b Madison, Wis, Feb 9, 47. THEORETICAL ASTROPHYSICS. *Educ:* Princeton Univ, AB, 69; Univ Pa, PhD(physics), 74. *Prof Exp:* Res assoc physics, Univ Pa & Naval Res Lab, 74-76 & Univ Alta, 76-78; res assoc physics, Stevens Inst Technol, 78-80; MEM TECH STAFF, BELL LABS, 81- *Mem:* Sigma Xi; NY Acad Sci. *Res:* Perturbations of spacetimes; pulsar magnetospheres; nonspherical gravitational collapse; equations of motion and radiation damping. *Mailing Add:* Bell Labs 600 Mountain Ave Murray Hill NJ 07974

KEGELMAN, MATTHEW ROLAND, b New York, NY, June 24, 28; m 53; c 10. ELECTROCHEMISTRY. *Educ:* Fordham Univ, BS, 48, MS, 49, PhD(org chem), 53. *Prof Exp:* From res chemist to sr res chemist, 53-71, RES ASSOC PETROCHEM DEPT, E I DU PONT DE NEMOURS & CO, 71- *Concurrent Pos:* Prin investr, Dielectric Gases Proj, Elec Power Res Inst. *Mem:* AAAS; Am Chem Soc. *Res:* Heterocyclics; pinacol rearrangement; petroleum chemicals; dielectric fluids; high-energy batteries; electro-organic synthesis; polymer intermediates. *Mailing Add:* 204 N Pembrey Dr Graylyn Crest Pembrey DE 19803

KEGGI, JANIS JOHN, b Riga, Latvia, Aug 24, 32; US citizen; m 57; c 3. SCIENCE EDUCATION, ORGANIC CHEMISTRY. *Educ:* Brooklyn Col, BS, 54; Yale Univ, MS, 58, PhD(org chem), 62. *Prof Exp:* Res chemist, Am Cyanamid Co, 61-66; sr staff assoc continuing educ, Sun Oil Co, 66-70, training mgr org develop, Am Hoechst Corp, 70-71; consult training & org develop, 71-76; dir mgt progs, Indust Labor Rels Sch, Cornell Univ, 73-76; dir continuing educ, Inst Paper Chem, 76-80; training consult, Kimberly Clark, Mex, 81-82. *Concurrent Pos:* Lectr chem, Hunter Col, 65-66. *Mem:* Am Chem Soc; Am Soc Eng Educ; Sigma Xi; Tech Asn Pulp & Paper Indust. *Res:* Natural products; catalysis; reactions at interfaces; interaction of personal, technological and organizational value systems. *Mailing Add:* 10 S Meadows Dr Appleton WI 54911

KEHEW, ALAN EVERETT, b Pittsburgh, Pa, Sept 17, 47; m 74; c 2. GEOMORPHOLOGY, GLACIOLOGY. *Educ:* Bucknell Univ, BS, 69; Montana State Univ, MS, 71; Univ Idano, PhD(geol), 77. *Prof Exp:* Geologist, NDak Geol Surv, 77-80; ASST PROF GEOL, UNIV NDAK, 80- *Mem:* Geol Soc Am; Nat Water Well Asn; Sigma Xi; Am Inst Mech Engrs. *Res:* Geomorphology and paleohydrology of proglacial lake spillways; groundwater contamination by waste disposal; engineering geology of north central North Dakota. *Mailing Add:* Dept Geol Univ NDak Grand Forks ND 58202

KEHL, THEODORE H, b Racine, Wis, Apr 1, 33; m 54; c 2. COMPUTER SCIENCE, BIOPHYSICS. *Educ:* Univ Wis, BS, 56, MS, 58, PhD(zool), 61. *Prof Exp:* Wis Alumni Res Found res assoc, Univ Wis, 56-61, NIH fel, 61; NIH fel, Sch Med, 61-63; from instr to assoc prof physiol & biophys, 63-73, assoc prof, 73-77, PROF PHYSIOL, BIOPHYS & COMPUTER SCI, SCH MED, UNIV WASH, 77- *Mem:* AAAS; Asn Comput Mach. *Res:* Implementation of computer science to quantitative physiology and biophysics. *Mailing Add:* Dept of Physiol & Biophys Univ of Wash Sch of Med Seattle WA 98195

KEHL, WILLIAM BRUNNER, b Pittsburgh, Pa, Apr 8, 19; m 44; c 2. COMPUTER SCIENCE. *Educ:* Harvard Univ, SB, 40, AM, 42 & 48. *Prof Exp:* Instr math, Ga Inst Tech, 43-46; instr, Mass Inst Technol, 48-54, head anal group, Instrumentation Lab, 54-56; prof comput sci & dir comput & data processing ctr, Univ Pittsburgh, 56-66; assoc prof elec eng & assoc dir comput ctr, Mass Inst Technol, 66-67; DIR ACADEMIC COMPUTING, UNIV CALIF, LOS ANGELES, 67- *Concurrent Pos:* Consult, US Air Force, 57-59 & comt use of comput, Nat Acad Sci; consult, Nat Sci Found & NIH; mem sci adv bd, Regional Indust Develop Corp. *Mem:* Asn Comput Mach. *Res:* Computers; applied mathematics. *Mailing Add:* Off of Acad Comput C0012 Univ of Calif Los Angeles CA 90024

KEHLENBECK, MANFRED MAX, b Bremen, Ger, Jan 16, 37; US citizen; m 68. STRUCTURAL GEOLOGY, METAMORPHIC GEOLOGY. *Educ:* Hofstra Univ, BA, 59; Syracuse Univ, MA, 64; Queen's Univ, PhD(geol), 71. *Prof Exp:* Vis asst prof geol, Univ NB, 69-70; asst prof, 71-76, ASSOC PROF GEOL & CHMN DEPT, LAKEHEAD UNIV, 76- *Concurrent Pos:* Nat Res Coun Can grant, 72- *Mem:* Am Geol Inst; Geol Asn Can. *Res:* Structural evolution of Archean gneissic terrains; polyphase folding in volcano sedimentary belts in northwestern Ontario. *Mailing Add:* Dept of Geol Lakehead Univ Thunder Bay ON P7B 5E1 Can

KEHLER, PHILIP LEROY, b Lyons, NY, June 15, 36; m 65; c 2. STRATIGRAPHY, SEDIMENTOLOGY. *Educ:* Purdue Univ, BS, 59, MS, 61; Southern Methodist Univ, PhD(geol), 70. *Prof Exp:* Asst, Southern Methodist Univ, 65-69; asst prof geol, ETex State Univ, 69-73, fac res grant, 71-72; ASSOC PROF EARTH SCI, UNIV ARK AT LITTLE ROCK, 73- *Concurrent Pos:* NSF student originated studies grant, 75. *Res:* Regional studies of Jurassic and Cretaceous rocks in western North America; stratigraphic relationships associated with widespread unconformities within these rocks. *Mailing Add:* Dept of Earth Sci Univ of Ark 33rd & University Ave Little Rock AR 72204

KEHN, DONALD M(OREHEAD), b Maquoketa, Iowa, Aug 5, 23; m 49; c 2. CHEMICAL ENGINEERING. *Educ:* Univ Iowa, BS, 44; Rice Inst, MS, 50. *Prof Exp:* Res engr, Phillips Petrol Co, 46-48; sr res engr crude oil, Prod Res Div, Humble Oil & Refining Co, 49-64; res specialist, Esso Prod Res Co, 64-71, SR RES SPECIALIST, EXXON PROD RES CO, 71- *Mem:* Am Soc Petrol Engrs; Am Inst Mining, Metall & Petrol Engrs. *Res:* Crude oil production research, particularly phase behavior of naturally occurring hydrocarbon systems; thermal recovery methods; well stimulation. *Mailing Add:* Exxon Prod Res Co Box 2189 Houston TX 77001

KEHOE, BRANDT, b Cleveland, Ohio, Nov 20, 33; m 61; c 2. PHYSICS. *Educ:* Cornell Univ, BA, 56; Univ Wis, MS, 59, PhD(physics), 63. *Prof Exp:* Res asst physics, Los Alamos Sci Lab, 56-57; from asst prof to assoc prof, Univ Md, 62-72; PROF PHYSICS, CALIF STATE UNIV, FRESNO, 72-, DEAN SCH NATURAL SCI, 72- *Mem:* Am Asn Physics Teachers; AAAS. *Res:* High energy physics; weak interactions rare decay modes and low energy K-N and high energy P-P interactions. *Mailing Add:* Sch of Natural Sci Calif State Univ Fresno CA 93740

KEHOE, LAWRENCE JOSEPH, b Rock Island, Ill, Nov 17, 40; m 66; c 2. ORGANIC CHEMISTRY. *Educ:* St Ambrose Col, AB, 62; Univ Iowa, MA, 64, PhD(org chem), 67. *Prof Exp:* Sr res chemist, 66-78, PROD MGR, ETHYL CORP, 78- *Mem:* Am Chem Soc; Am Soc Enologists. *Res:* Pharmaceutical intermediates. *Mailing Add:* Ethyl Corp Ind Chem Div 451 Florida Blvd Baton Rouge LA 70801

KEHOE, THOMAS J, b Bisbee, Ariz, June 16, 19; m 50; c 6. ANALYTICAL CHEMISTRY, INORGANIC CHEMISTRY. *Educ:* Loyola Univ, BS, 41. *Prof Exp:* Res chemist, Am Potash & Chem Co, 42-48, lab supvr, 48-50; consult waste treatment, Pomeroy & Assocs, 50-54; appln engr, 54-61, MGR APPLN ENG, BECKMAN INSTRUMENTS, INC, 61- *Mem:* Fel Instrument Soc Am (pres, 69-70); Am Inst Chem; Am Chem Soc; Am Inst Chem Eng. *Res:* Process analytical instrumentation; industrial waste treatment; phase rule studies in inorganic chemistry of Searles Lake brine. *Mailing Add:* Beckman Instruments Inc 2500 Harbor Blvd Fullerton CA 92634

KEHR, CLIFTON LEROY, b Brodbeck, Pa, May 25, 26; m 48; c 3. ORGANIC CHEMISTRY, POLYMER CHEMISTRY. *Educ:* Gettysburg Col, AB, 49; Univ Del, MS, 50, PhD(org chem), 52. *Prof Exp:* Res asst synthetic org chem, Forrestal Res Ctr, Princeton Univ, 52-53; res chemist, org chem dept, E I du Pont de Nemours & Co, 53-57, elastomers chem dept, 57-59; RES CHEMIST, RES & DEVELOP DIV, WASH RES CTR, W R GRACE & CO, 59-, RES DIR, 69- *Mem:* Am Chem Soc. *Res:* Mechanisms of organic reactions; polyurethanes; elastomers; polyolefins; isocyanate chemistry; polymers from chloroprene and related monomers; foam technology; radiation curable polymers; water based coatings. *Mailing Add:* 1216 Ednor Rd Silver Spring MD 20904

KEHR, PAUL FREDERICK, analytical chemistry, see previous edition

KEHR, WILLIAM R, b Blue Earth, Minn, July 1, 21; m 46; c 3. AGRONOMY. *Educ:* Univ Minn, BS, 43, PhD(plant genetics), 49; Kans State Univ, MS, 47. *Prof Exp:* Plant breeder, Delmonte Foods, Ill, 49-53; RES AGRONOMIST, Sci & Educ Admin-Agr Res, USDA, 53- *Mem:* AAAS; Am Soc Agron; Crop Sci Soc Am. *Res:* Genetics and breeding of field corn, oats, sweet corn, pop corn, pumpkins and alfalfa. *Mailing Add:* 332 Keim Hall Univ of Nebr Lincoln NE 68583

KEHRER, JAMES PAUL, b Watertown, Wis, Aug 25, 51; m 77; c 1. PULMONARY TOXICOLOGY. *Educ:* Purdue Univ, BS, 74; Univ Iowa, PhD(pharm), 78. *Prof Exp:* Investr, Biol Div, Oak Ridge Nat Lab, 78-80; ASST PROF PHARMACOL & TOXICOL, COL PHARM, UNIV TEX, AUSTIN, 80- *Concurrent Pos:* Consult, Radian Corp, 82- *Mem:* Soc Toxicol; AAAS. *Res:* Collagen synthesis and degradation during the development of pulmonary fibrosis after acute lung damage; effects of corticosteroids on pulmonary repair processes. *Mailing Add:* Div Pharmacol & Toxicol Univ Tex Austin TX 78712

KEHRES, PAUL W(ILLIAM), b Milwaukee, Wis, Dec 14, 22; m 50; c 2. ANALYTICAL CHEMISTRY, MATERIALS TESTING. *Educ:* Univ Wis, BS, 47; Marquette Univ, MS, 48. *Prof Exp:* Res assoc chem, Ames Lab, AEC, 48-51; instr, Iowa State Univ, 50-51; intermediate scientist, Atomic Power Div, Westinghouse Elec Corp, 51-52; asst dir anal res, A O Smith Corp, 52-62, supvr chem processes, 62-66, mgr, 66-68, asst mgr, 68-76, PROJ COORDR PLASTICS RES & DEVELOP, A O SMITH CORP, 76- *Concurrent Pos:* Chief chemist, Glendale Crime Lab, 66-, dir, 76- *Mem:* Am Chem Soc; Soc Appl Spectros; Am Acad Forensic Sci; Int Narcotic Enforcement Officers Asn. *Res:* X-ray and optical emission spectroscopy; mass spectro- metry; x-ray diffraction; infrared and ultraviolet spectrophotometry and radioisotopes; paints and other coatings; mastic and tape sealers; fiberglass reinforced plastics; drug analysis. *Mailing Add:* A O Smith PO Box 584 Milwaukee WI 53201

KEICHER, WILLIAM EUGENE, b Pittsburgh, Pa, Dec 28, 47; m 72; c 2. ELECTRO-OPTICAL SYSTEMS, MILLIMETER WAVE SYSTEMS. *Educ:* Carnegie-Mellon Univ, BS, 69, MS, 70, PhD(elec eng), 74. *Prof Exp:* Elec engr, Manned Spacecraft Ctr, NASA, 69; tech asst, Kodak Res Labs, 70; sr elec engr, CBS Labs, 73-75; MEM TECH STAFF, LINCOLN LAB, MASS INST TECHNOL, 75- *Mem:* Sr mem Inst Elec & Electronic Engrs; Optical Soc Am. *Res:* Laser radar systems; infrared detection systems; millimeter wave radar and communication systems. *Mailing Add:* 6 Winn Valley Dr Burlington MA 01803

KEIDEL, FREDERICK ANDREW, b New Brunswick, NJ, Feb 4, 26. PHYSICAL CHEMISTRY. *Educ:* Rutgers Univ, BS, 46; Cornell Univ, PhD(phys chem), 51. *Prof Exp:* Res engr phys chem, 51-56; res proj engr, 56-60, sr res phys chemist, 61-80, RES ASSOC, E I DU PONT DE NEMOURS & CO INC, 80- *Honors & Awards:* Longstreth Medal, Franklin Inst, 60. *Mem:* Am Chem Soc; Electrochem Soc; Sigma Xi; Mineral Soc Am; Am Inst Chemists. *Res:* Electron diffraction; electrochemical processes; chemical physics of surfaces; mineralogy. *Mailing Add:* E I du Pont de Nemours & Co Inc 1007 Market St Wilmington DE 19898

KEIDERLING, TIMOTHY ALLEN, b Waterloo, Iowa, June 22, 47; m 76. SPECTROSCOPY, OPTICAL ACTIVITY. *Educ:* Loras Col, BS, 69; Princeton Univ, MA, 71, PhD(phys chem), 74. *Prof Exp:* Res assoc optical activity, Univ Southern Calif, 73-76; asst prof chem, 76-81, ASSOC PROF CHEM, UNIV ILL, CHICAGO CIRCLE, 81- *Mem:* Am Chem Soc; Am Phys Soc. *Res:* Experimental studies of electronic structure of transition metal systems and vibrational optical activity; vibrational optical activity studies of small chiral molecules for theoretical modeling, biological systems and instrument development. *Mailing Add:* Dept of Chem Univ of Ill at Chicago Circle Box 4348 Chicago IL 60680

KEIFFER, DAVID GOFORTH, b New Orleans, La, July 24, 31; m 56; c 6. PHYSICS. *Educ:* Loyola Univ, La, BS, 52; Univ Notre Dame, MS, 54, PhD(physics), 56. *Prof Exp:* Asst prof physics, Canisius Col, 56-64; ASSOC PROF PHYSICS, LOYOLA UNIV, LA, 64-, CHMN DEPT, 73- *Mem:* Am Phys Soc. *Res:* Radiation damage in glass. *Mailing Add:* Dept of Physics Loyola Univ New Orleans LA 70118

KEIGHER, WILLIAM FRANCIS, b Montclair, NJ, Oct 28, 45; m 68; c 3. ALGEBRA. *Educ:* Montclair State Col, BA, 67; Univ Ill, AM, 69, PhD(math), 73. *Prof Exp:* Lectr math, Southern Ill Univ, Carbondale, 73-74; asst prof mat, Univ Tenn, Knoxville, 74-78; ASST PROF MATH, RUTGERS UNIV, 78- *Mem:* Am Math Soc; Math Asn Am. *Res:* Category theory and its applications to differential algebra. *Mailing Add:* Dept of Math Rutgers Univ Newark NJ 07102

KEIGHIN, CHARLES WILLIAM, b Pontiac, Ill, Aug 29, 32; m 60; c 3. GEOCHEMISTRY, ECONOMIC GEOLOGY. *Educ:* Oberlin Col, BA, 54; Univ Colo, MS, 60, PhD(geol), 66. *Prof Exp:* Res mineralogist, Cerro de Pasco Corp, La Oroya, Peru, SAm, 60-62, geologist, 62-63; asst prof geol, Northern Ill Univ, 66-72; vis asst prof geol & mineral, Ohio State Univ, 72-73; asst prof geosci, Northeastern La Univ, 73-74; GEOLOGIST, US GEOL SURV, DENVER, 74- *Mem:* Am Asn Petrol Geologists; Soc Econ Paleontologists & Mineralogists; Soc Petrol Engrs; Can Soc Petrol Geologists. *Res:* Trace element migration; diagenesis of clastic rocks; inorganic geochemistry; oil shale resource evaluation. *Mailing Add:* US Geol Surv Denver Fed Ctr Box 25046 MS 921 Denver CO 80225

KEIGLER, JOHN EDWARD, b Baltimore, Md, July 10, 29; m 55; c 6. AEROSPACE ENGINEERING, ELECTRICAL ENGINEERING. *Educ:* Johns Hopkins Univ, BE, 50, MS, 51; Stanford Univ, PhD(elec eng), 58. *Prof Exp:* Aeronaut res scientist, Ames Res Lab, NASA, 56; res assoc commun theory, Stanford Electronics Labs, 56-58; systs engr space electronics, 58-63, mgr spacecraft systs eng, 63-69, mgr systs eng, 69-73, MGR COMMUN SATELLITE SYSTS, RCA ASTRO ELECTRONICS, 73- *Mem:* Inst Elec & Electronics Engrs; Am Geophys Union; assoc fel Am Inst Aeronaut & Astronaut. *Res:* Communication and information theory; video systems; spacecraft systems design, attitude control and stabilization; satellite telecommunications systems. *Mailing Add:* RCA Astro Electronics PO Box 800 Princeton NJ 08540

KEIHM, STEPHEN JOSEPH, planetary physics, applied mathematics, see previous edition

KEIHN, FREDERICK GEORGE, b Scranton, Pa, Aug 29, 23; m 48; c 4. SOLID STATE CHEMISTRY. *Educ:* Randolph Macon Col, BS, 47; Lehigh Univ, MS, 49; Syracuse Univ, PhD(chem), 53. *Prof Exp:* Asst electrochem, Lehigh Univ, 48-49; asst chem, Syracuse Univ, 49-51; inorg chemist electronics lab, Gen Elec Co, 52-57; res chemist ceramics lab, Corning Glass Works, 57-59; mem staff, Union Carbide Res Inst, NY, 59-65; assoc prof chem, Presby Col, SC, 65-67; PROF CHEM, BRIDGEWATER COL, 67- *Mem:* AAAS; Am Chem Soc; Am Crystallog Asn. *Res:* Double crystal x-ray diffractometry high temperature phase and mechanical properties studies; physical science curriculum development; applied ecology. *Mailing Add:* Dept of Chem Bridgewater Col Bridgewater VA 22801

KEIL, DAVID JOHN, b Elmhurst, Ill, Dec 13, 46. PLANT TAXONOMY. *Educ:* Ariz State Univ, BS, 68, MS, 70; Ohio State Univ, PhD(bot), 73. *Prof Exp:* Vis asst prof biol, Grand Valley State Col, 73-74; asst prof, Franklin Col, 75; lectr, 76-78, asst prof, 78-80, PROF BIOL, CALIF POLYTECH STATE UNIV, 80- *Concurrent Pos:* Vis assoc prof bot, Ohio State Univ, 80. *Mem:* Bot Soc Am; Am Soc Plant Taxon; Int Asn Plant Taxon; Torrey Bot Club; Asn Trop Biol. *Res:* Cytology and systematics of compositae; cytology, taxonomy, evolution and biogeography of genus Pectis. *Mailing Add:* Dept of Biol Sci Calif Polytech State Univ San Luis Obispo CA 93407

KEIL, JULIAN EUGENE, b Charleston, SC, Oct 30, 26; m 48; c 3. EPIDEMIOLOGY. *Educ:* Clemson Univ, BS, 49, MS, 68; Univ NC, Chapel Hill, PhD(epidemiol), 75. *Prof Exp:* Entomologist, W R Grace & Co, 49-55, pesticide dept mgr, 56-67; field studies supvr, 67-68, instr, 68-69, assoc, 70-72, asst prof prev med, 73-77, ASSOC PROF EPIDEMIOL, SCH PUB HEALTH, UNIV SC, 77- *Concurrent Pos:* Coun epidemiol, Am Heart Asn. *Mem:* Am Pub Health Asn; AAAS; Entom Soc Am; Asn Teachers Prev Med. *Res:* Cardiovascular epidemiology with emphasis on hypertension; the environmental epidemiology of pesticides and metals. *Mailing Add:* Dept Epidemiol & Biostatist Univ SC Columbia SC 29208

KEIL, KLAUS, b Hamburg, Ger, Nov 15, 34; US citizen; m 61; c 2. METEORITICS, PETROLOGY. *Educ:* Univ Jena, MSc, 58; Univ Mainz, PhD(mineral, meteoritics), 61. *Prof Exp:* Res assoc & instr mineral & meteoritics, Mineral Inst, Univ Jena, 58-60; res assoc, meteoritics & cosmochem, Max Planck Inst Chem, 61 & Univ Calif, San Diego, 61-63; Nat Acad Sci-Nat Res Coun resident res assoc, Space Sci Div, Ames Res Ctr, NASA, 63-64, staff res scientist, 64-68; lectr, Dept Geol, San Jose State Col, 66-67; PROF GEOL & DIR, INST METEORITICS, UNIV N MEX, 68- *Concurrent Pos:* Mem, Nat Steering Comt, 66-; prin investr, Electron Microprobe Study of Returned Lunar Sample, NASA, 67-68, mem planetology adv subcomt, space sci & applns steering comt, 68; US rep, Comt Cosmic Mineral, Int Mineral Asn, 67-70, secy, 70-; rep, Comt Meteorites, Int Union Geol Sci, 68-; John Wesley Powell invited lectr, Ariz Acad Sci, 71; invited speaker, Int Geol Cong, 72; mem lunar sci review bd, 71-73; mem & chmn, US Nat Comt Geochem, Nat Acad Sci, 71-75; assoc ed, Chem Geol, 73-; mem geophys res bd, Nat Acad Sci, 74-75; mem & chmn, Lunar Sample Anal Planning Team, 74-78 & chmn facil subcomt, 75-76; distinguished vis prof, Inst Earth Sci, Univ Sao Paulo, Brazil, 74, 76, 77 & 78; mem, Viking Mars Flight Team, 76-; vis assoc geochem, Div Geol Planet Sci, Calif Inst Technol, 76-77; honorary res assoc, Dept Mineral Sci, Am Mus Natural Hist, 77-; mem, Lunar & Planet, Sci Coun, 77-; mem, Antarctic Meteorite Working Group, NSF, 78-; dir, Caswell Silver Found, Univ NMex, 80-; distinguished vis scientist, Jet Propulsion Lab, Pasadena, 81; ann res lectr, Univ NMex, 81. *Honors & Awards:* Apollo Achievement Award, NASA, 70; George P Merrill Award, Nat Acad Sci, 70; NASA Except Sci Achievement Medal, 77. *Mem:* Fel AAAS; Geol Soc Brazil; Ger Mineral Soc; Electron Probe Anal Soc Am (pres-elect, 71, pres, 72); Int Asn Geochem & Cosmochem (secy, 72-76). *Res:* Lunar geology; chemistry, geology and mineralogy of extraterrestrial materials, such as meteorites, cosmic dust and lunar surface; application of electron microprobe, laser microprobe and ion microprobe to study of rocks and minerals; geology of mars. *Mailing Add:* Dept of Geol & Inst of Meteoritics Univ of NMex Albuquerque NM 87131

KEIL, LANNY CHARLES, b Elgin, Nebr, Apr 16, 36; m 66; c 3. PHYSIOLOGY, ENDOCRINOLOGY. *Educ:* Creighton Univ, BS, 63, MS, 66; Univ Calif, Davis, PhD(physiol), 73. *Prof Exp:* Res scientist, Physiol Br, 67-72, RES SCIENTIST ENDOCRINOL, BIOMED RES DIV, AMES RES CTR NASA, 72- *Mem:* Edocrine Soc; AAAS; Am Physiol Soc. *Res:* Hormonal control of water and electrolyte metabolism; gravitational biology; acceleration stress physiology. *Mailing Add:* Biomed Res Div Ames Res Ctr NASA Moffett Field CA 94035

KEIL, ROBERT GERALD, b New Rochelle, NY, May 7, 41; m 64; c 2. PHYSICAL CHEMISTRY. *Educ:* Villanova Univ, BS, 63; Temple Univ, PhD(phys chem), 67. *Prof Exp:* Res chemist, Org Chem Dept, E I du Pont de Nemours & Co, Inc, 67-69; asst prof 69-77, ASSOC PROF CHEM, UNIV DAYTON, 77- *Mem:* Electrochem Soc; Am Chem Soc. *Res:* Anodic oxide films; kinetic study of film growth; polarography of complexes in aqueous and nonaqueous solutions; general physical chemistry problems. *Mailing Add:* Dept of Chem Univ of Dayton Dayton OH 45469

KEIL, STEPHEN LESLEY, b Billings, Mont, Feb 21, 47; m 71. SOLAR PHYSICS. *Educ:* Univ Calif, Berkeley, AB, 69; Boston Univ, AM, 71, PhD(physics & astron), 75. *Prof Exp:* Nat Acad Sci-Nat Res Coun res fel, Air Force Geophys Lab, 78-80, RES ASSOC SOLAR PHYSICS, AIR FORCE CAMBRIDGE RES LAB, SACRAMENTO PEAK OBSERV, 75-, SOLAR PHYSICIST, AIR FORCE GEOPHYS LAB, SACRAMENTO PEAK OBSERV, 80- *Concurrent Pos:* Res fel appl math, Univ Sydney, Australia, 76-77. *Mem:* Am Astron Soc. *Res:* Solar atmospheric inhomogenonities; multidimensional stellar atmospheres; high resolution solar observations; mathematical models of solar atmospheric structure. *Mailing Add:* Sacramento Peak Observ Sunspot NM 88349

KEIL, THOMAS H, b Philadelphia, Pa, July 24, 39; m 64. SOLID STATE PHYSICS. *Educ:* Calif Inst Technol, BS, 61; Univ Rochester, PhD(optics), 65. *Prof Exp:* Sloan fel solid state physics, Princeton Univ, 65-66, Sloan vis lectr, 66-67; asst prof, 67-72, assoc prof & chmn dept physics, 72-78, PROF PHYSICS, WORCESTER POLYTECH INST, 78- *Mem:* Am Phys Soc. *Res:* Solid state theory; optics. *Mailing Add:* Dept of Physics Worcester Polytech Inst Worcester MA 01609

KEILIN, BERTRAM, b New York, NY, Oct 18, 22; m 54; c 3. WATER CHEMISTRY. *Educ:* NY Univ, BA, 42; Calif Inst Technol, MS, 45, PhD(phys chem), 50. *Prof Exp:* Res engr radar labs, US Sig Corps, 42-43; res chemist, Aridye Corp, 43-44; res chemist, Nat Defense Res Comt, 45-47 & Douglas Aircraft Co, 48-50; fel & res assoc, Univ Southern Calif, 50-51; sr res engr, Jet Propulsion Lab, Calif Inst Technol, 51-53; res chemist, Olin Mathieson Chem Corp, 53-56; mgr water resources dept, Chem & Struct Prod Div, Aerojet-Gen Corp Div, Gen Tire & Rubber Co, 56-66; vpres process develop, Amicon Corp, 66-68; dir environ sci dept, Tyco Labs, Inc, 68-69; mgr filter div, Bohna Eng & Res, Inc, 69-71; exec dir, Pac Water Conditioning Asn, 71-80; PRES, ENVIRONMANAGEMENT SERV CO, 80- *Mem:* AAAS; Am Chem Soc; Am Water Works Asn; Water Pollution Control Fedn. *Res:* Ion exchange, water softening; molecular structure; electron diffraction; polarography; boron hydrides; rocket propulsion; adsorption; hydraulic fluids; membrane technology; water desalting. *Mailing Add:* 18 Springwater Irvine CA 92714

KEILSON, JULIAN, b Brooklyn, NY, Nov 19, 24; m 54; c 2. MATHEMATICAL STATISTICS, OPERATIONS RESEARCH. *Educ:* Brooklyn Col, BS, 47; Harvard Univ, PhD(physics), 50. *Prof Exp:* Res fel electronics, Harvard Univ, 50-52; mem staff, Lincoln Lab, Mass Inst Technol, 52-56; staff consult & sr eng specialist, Gen Tel & Electronics Labs, Inc, 56-62, sr scientist, 62-66; PROF STATIST, UNIV ROCHESTER, 66- *Concurrent Pos:* Lectr, Boston Univ, 56-; res fel, Univ Birmingham, 63; dir , Ctr Syst Sci; ed, Stochastic Processes and Their Appln, 72- *Mem:* Am Phys Soc; sr mem Inst Elec & Electronics Eng; fel Inst Math Statist; fel Royal Statist Soc; fel Int Statist Inst. *Res:* Semiconductor diffusion; electronic noise; Brownian motion; information theory; stochastic processes; electromagnetic propagation; probability theory; queuing theory; reliability theory. *Mailing Add:* Dept of Statistics Univ of Rochester Rochester NY 14627

KEILY, HUBERT JOSEPH, b Worcester, Mass, Jan 29, 21; m 45, 71; c 2. ANALYTICAL CHEMISTRY. *Educ:* Niagra Univ, BS, 49; Union Col, MS, 51; Mass Inst Technol, PhD(anal chem), 56. *Prof Exp:* Lab asst, Res Lab, Linde Co, 40-43; asst, Union Col, 49-51; asst, Mass Inst Technol, 51-55; anal chemist, Gen Elec Co, 56-58; sect chief anal methods, Res Ctr, Lever Bros Co, 58-64; DEPT HEAD ANAL CHEM, MERRELL DOW PHARMACEUT INC, 64- *Concurrent Pos:* Adj asst prof pharmaceut chem, Col Pharm, Univ Cincinnati, 82- *Mem:* Am Chem Soc; fel Am Inst Chem; Acad Pharmaceut Sci. *Res:* Pharmaceutical analysis; evaluations of drug purity and stability; thermal methods; applied statistics. *Mailing Add:* 2210 Victory Pkwy Cincinnati OH 45206

KEIM, BARBARA HOWELL, b Detroit, Mich, Mar 9, 46; m 75; c 1. ECOLOGICAL GENETICS. *Educ:* Univ NC, Greensboro, BA, 67; Rutgers Univ, MS, 69; Univ Va, PhD(genetics), 76. *Prof Exp:* Asst ed biol, Biol Sci Info Serv, Philadelphia, 69-70; instr, Dept Biol, Wheaton Col, Norton, Mass, 75-76; asst prof, Dept Biol, Bradley Univ, 76-77, asst prof, Dept Nursing, 77-78, prof, Dept Biol, 79-80; ASST PROF BIOL, EUREKA COL, ILL, 80- *Mem:* Am Soc Human Genetics. *Res:* Disruptive selection; speciation; polymorphisms. *Mailing Add:* Math & Sci Div Eureka Col Eureka IL 61530

KEIM, CHRISTOPHER PETER, b Tecumseh, Nebr, Apr 6, 06; m 29; c 2. CHEMISTRY. *Educ:* Nebr Wesleyan Univ, AB, 27; Univ Nebr, MSc, 32, PhD(chem), 40. *Hon Degrees:* DSc, Nebr Wesleyan Univ, 59. *Prof Exp:* Head dept phys sci, York Col, 33-37; instr chem, Univ Tulsa, 40-41; res engr, Sylvania Corp, Mass, 41-42; res chemist & fel, Mellon Inst, 42-44; res physicist & adminr, Tenn Eastman Corp, 44-47; dir stable isotope res & prod div, Oak Ridge Nat Lab, 47-57, tech info div, 57-71; CONSULT, ROANE STATE COMMUNITY COL, 71- *Concurrent Pos:* Consult, Roane-Anderson Economic Coun, 74-, consult, Hiwassee Col, 78- *Mem:* Fel AAAS; Am Chem Soc; fel Am Phys Soc; Sigma Xi. *Res:* Isotope separations and properties; properties; monomolecular surface films; electrical discharge in gases; surface chemistry; spreading of organic liquids and mixtures on water in the presence of monomolecular surface films; technical information. *Mailing Add:* 102 Orchard Lane Oak Ridge TN 37830

KEIM, GERALD INMAN, b Mt Berry, Ga, Oct 28, 10; m 43; c 1. PAPER CHEMISTRY. *Educ:* Univ Ga, BS, 32; MS, 35; Polytech Inst Brooklyn, PhD(chem), 44. *Prof Exp:* Instr, Univ Ga, 32-35; anal chemist, Warner-Quinlan Ref Co, NJ, 35-36; anal chemist, Colgate-Palmolive-Peet Co, 36-39, res chemist, 39-43; res chemist, Nat Defense Res Comt contract, 43-44; from res chemist to sr res chemist, Hercules Powder Co, 44-64, res assoc, Res Ctr, Hercules Inc, 64-75; RETIRED. *Mem:* Am Chem Soc; Tech Asn Pulp & Paper Indust. *Res:* C2 C3 elastomers; sterioregular olefin polymers; wet strength resins for paper; special sizes for paper; synthetic detergents; heterocyclic nitrogen compounds; functional and decorative coatings. *Mailing Add:* RD2 Box 85 West Grove PA 19390

KEIM, LON WILLIAM, b Washington, DC, June 1, 43. PULMONARY DISEASE. *Educ:* Med Col Va, BS, 66, MD, 70. *Prof Exp:* Intern med, Univ Kans Med Ctr, Kansas City, 70-71; resident, Med Col Va, 71-73; fel, Col Med, Univ Iowa, 73-75, assoc pulmonary dis, 75-76; ASST PROF INTERNAL MED, UNIV NEBR, 76-; MEM MED STAFF, BISHOP CLARKSON MEM HOSP, 76- *Mem:* Fel Am Col Physicians; fel Am Col Chest Physicians; Am Thoracic Soc. *Res:* Pulmonary vasculitides, Wegeners Granulomatosis; pulmonary granulamotous disease, tuberculosis and atypical mycobacteria; pulmonary diagnostic techniques, fiberoptic bronchoscopy. *Mailing Add:* Respiratory Ther 42nd & Dewey Omaha NE 68105

KEIM, WAYNE FRANKLIN, b Ithaca, NY, May 14, 23; m 47; c 3. CROP BREEDING. *Educ:* Univ Nebr, BS, 47; Cornell Univ, MS, 49, PhD(plant breeding), 52. *Prof Exp:* From instr to asst prof bot, Iowa State Col, 52-56; from asst prof to prof agron, Purdue Univ, 56-75; HEAD DEPT AGRON, COLO STATE UNIV, 75- *Concurrent Pos:* NSF sci fac fel, Inst Genetics, Univ Lund, 62-63. *Honors & Awards:* Agron Educ Award, Am Soc Agron, 71. *Mem:* Fel AAAS; fel Am Soc Agron; Genetics Soc Am; Am Genetic Asn. *Res:* Legume genetics; breeding. *Mailing Add:* Dept of Agron Colo State Univ Ft Collins CO 80523

KEINATH, GERALD E, b Grand Rapids, Mich, May 1, 24; m 56; c 3. MECHANICAL ENGINEERING. *Educ:* Northwestern Univ, BSME, 49. *Prof Exp:* Engr in training, Chicago & Northwestern RR, 46-49; res engr, Battelle Mem Inst, Ohio, 49-52, bus mgr Europ opers, Frankfurt & Geneva, 52-58, asst supvr contract prep, Ohio, 58-63; vpres, NStar Res & Develop Inst, 63-72; PRES, NOVUS INC, 72- *Mem:* Am Soc Mech Engrs; Am Soc Automotive Engrs. *Res:* Product development; glass repair; research management. *Mailing Add:* Novus Inc 5301 Edina Industrial Blvd Minneapolis MN 55436

KEINATH, THOMAS M, b Frankenmuth, Mich, Jan 5, 41; m 63. ENVIRONMENTAL ENGINEERING. *Educ:* Univ Mich, Ann Arbor, BSE, 63, MSE, 64, PhD(water resources eng), 68. *Prof Exp:* Inst Sci & Technol fel, Univ Mich, 68-69; PROF ENVIRON SYSTS ENG & HEAD DEPT, CLEMSON UNIV, 69- *Concurrent Pos:* Consult, Waverly Assocs, 68-69, Westvaco Inc, 70-, Gaston Co, Dyeing Mach Co, 71-, Eng Sci, Inc, 74- & UNESCO, 80; expert sci adv, Environ Protection Agency, 75-76. *Mem:* Am Chem Soc; Am Inst Chem Engrs; Am Water Works Asn; Am Soc Civil Engrs; Asn Environ Eng Prof. *Res:* Physiochemical processes of water and waterwaste treatment; automation and control of water and wastewater treatment systems. *Mailing Add:* Dept of Environ Systs Eng Clemson Univ Clemson SC 29631

KEIPER, RONALD R, b Allentown, Pa, Sept 21, 41; m 64; c 2. ANIMAL BEHAVIOR. *Educ:* Muhlenberg Col, BS, 63; Univ Mass, MS, 66, PhD(zool), 68. *Prof Exp:* Asst prof zool & biol, 68-73, ASSOC PROF ZOOL, PA STATE UNIV, 73- *Concurrent Pos:* Theodore Roosevelt Mem Fund-Am Mus Natural Hist grant, 68-69; Frank M Chapman Mem Fund-Am Mus Natural Hist grant, 68-70; Nat Park Serv study grants. *Mem:* Animal Behavior Soc; Lepidopterists Soc. *Res:* Causes and functions of the abnormal stereotyped behaviors shown by caged birds; effects of early experience on bird behavior; natural behavior of cyptic moths; studying the behavior, ecology and social organization of feral ponies. *Mailing Add:* Dept of Biol Pa State Univ Mont Alto PA 17237

KEIRANS, JAMES EDWARD, b Worcester, Mass, Apr 4, 35; m 63; c 2. MEDICAL ENTOMOLOGY, PARASITOLOGY. *Educ:* Boston Univ, AB, 60, AM, 63; Univ NH, PhD(zool), 66. *Prof Exp:* Res asst parasitol, Boston Univ, 60-63; res asst entom, Univ NH, 65-66; res entomologist, Commun Dis Ctr, USPHS, 66-69; RES ENTOMOLOGIST, NIH, 69- *Concurrent Pos:* Res entomologist, Brit Mus Nat Hist, 77-78. *Mem:* Soc Syst Zool; Entom Soc Am; Acarological Soc Am. *Res:* Arthropods of public health significance; Ixodoidea taxonomy. *Mailing Add:* USPHS Rocky Mountain Lab Hamilton MT 59840

KEIRNS, JAMES JEFFERY, b New Haven, Conn, July 1, 47; m 67; c 3. BIOCHEMISTRY. *Educ:* Rice Univ, BA, 68; Yale Univ, MPhil, 70, PhD(molecular biophys & biochem), 72. *Prof Exp:* Jane Coffin Childs Mem Fund Med Res fel biochem, Dept Path, Sch Med, Yale Univ, 72-75; sr res biochemist & proj leader allergy res, Lederle Labs Div, Am Cyanamid Co,

75-79; HEAD, DEPT BIOCHEM, BOEHRINGER INGELHEIM LTD, 79- *Mem:* Am Chem Soc; AAAS; NY Acad Sci. *Res:* Biochemical aspects of metabolic and immunological disease; endocrine physiology and disease; cyclic nucleotides; mechanism of enzyme reactions; inflammation; immediate hypersensitivity; harmacokinetics and drug metabolism. *Mailing Add:* Boehringer Ingelheim Ltd 90 E Ridge Rd Ridgefield CT 06877

KEIRNS, MARY HULL, b Jacksonville, Fla, Mar 16, 47; m 67; c 3. CHEMISTRY, AUTOMOTIVE ENGINEERING. *Educ:* Yale Univ, MPhil, 71, PhD(chem), 75. *Prof Exp:* RES CHEMIST, EXXON RES & ENG CO, 74- *Mem:* Am Chem Soc; Soc Automotive Engrs. *Res:* Pollution control systems and fuel economy; aviation fuel quality and handling. *Mailing Add:* RD3 Sherwood Mill Rd Brewster NY 10509

KEIRS, RUSSELL JOHN, b Springfield, Ill, Aug 27, 15; m 41; c 1. ANALYTICAL CHEMISTRY. *Educ:* Univ Ill, BS, 37, MS, 38, PhD, 41. *Prof Exp:* Chemist, Continental Can Co, 41-42; assoc prof chem, Fla State Univ, 50-65, assoc dean, Grad Sch & dir res, 62-69, prof, 65-81; RETIRED. *Mem:* Am Chem Soc. *Res:* Molecular phosphorescence analysis at low temperatures; instrumental analysis. *Mailing Add:* Dept of Chem Fla State Univ Tallahassee FL 32306

KEIRSTEAD, KARL FREEMAN, b Natal, Union SAfrica, Apr 8, 09; Can citizen; m 37; c 2. WOOD CHEMISTRY, SURFACE CHEMISTRY. *Educ:* Mt Allison Univ, BA, 35; Columbia Univ, MA, 39; Laval Univ, DSc, 49. *Prof Exp:* Sci officer, Can Armament Res & Develop Estab, Defense Res Bd Can, 49-54; chief chemist lignin chem, Lignosol Chem, 54-60, tech dir, 60-70, tech & res dir, 70-74; tech consult, pulp & paper group, 74-77, CONSULT, 77-; RES ASSOC, ROYAL MIL COL CAN, 77- *Mem:* Fel Chem Inst Can. *Res:* Reduction of aromatic nitro compounds; parachor of azo and azoxy compounds; properties of lignosulphonates; commercial preparation of drilling fluids and dispersants from lignosulphonates; stability of gelled slurry explosives; surface chemistry of soluble lignins; water-reducing and air-entraining agents for concrete. *Mailing Add:* 247 Chelsea Rd Kingston ON K7M 3Z3 Can

KEISCH, BERNARD, b Brooklyn, NY, Aug 1, 32; m 54; c 3. RADIOCHEMISTRY. *Educ:* Rensselaer Polytech Inst, BS, 53; Wash Univ, St Louis, PhD(chem), 57. *Prof Exp:* Res chemist, Idaho Chem Processing Plant, Phillips Petrol Co, 57-59, mat testing reactor, 59-62; sr scientist, Nuclear Sci & Eng Corp, 62-66; from fel to sr fel, Carnegie-Mellon Univ, 66-74, sr fel, Carnegie-Mellon Inst Res, 74-78; CHEMIST, BROOKHAVEN NAT LAB, 78- *Mem:* Sigma Xi; AAAS; Am Chem Soc. *Res:* Nuclear applications in art and archaeology; activation analysis; isotope mass spectrometry; carbon-14 dating; Mossbauer effect; nuclear safeguards. *Mailing Add:* Bldg 197 Brookhaven Nat Lab Upton NY 11973

KEISER, BERNHARD E(DWARD), b Richmond Heights, Mo, Nov 14, 28; m 55; c 5. TELECOMUNICATIONS ENGINEERING, ELECTRICAL ENGINEERING. *Educ:* Washington Univ, St Louis, BS, 50, MS, 51, DSc(elec eng), 53. *Prof Exp:* Proj engr, White-Rodgers Elec Co, Mo, 53-56, Petrolite Corp, 56-57 & Mo Res Labs, 57-59; group leader new commun systs, RCA Corp, 59-64, mgr plans & prog sect, Kennedy Space Ctr Commun Proj, RCA Serv Co, Fla, 64-67, admin advan tech planning, RCA Missile & Surface Radar Div, NJ, 67-69; vpres systs res & eng, Page Commun Engrs, Va, 69-70; dir advan systs electronics & commun, Atlantic Res Corp, Alexandria, 71-75; dir analysis, Fairchild Space & Electronics Co, 75-77; PRES, KEISER ENG, INC, 75- *Mem:* Fel Inst Elec & Electronics Engrs; Armed Forces Commun-Electronics Asn. *Res:* Telecommunications; electronic systems; engineering management and consulting. *Mailing Add:* 2046 Carrhill Rd Vienna VA 22180

KEISER, EDMUND DAVIS, JR, b Appalachia, Va, Feb, 18, 34; div; c 2. VERTEBRATE ZOOLOGY, WILDLIFE ECOLOGY. *Educ:* Southern Ill Univ, BA, 56, MS, 61; La State Univ, PhD(vert zool), 67. *Prof Exp:* Teacher high sch, Ill, 56-57, pub schs, 57; sci instr & dist coordr, Dist 70, Freeburg, 58-62; instr zool & anat, La Salle-Peru-Oglesby Jr Col, 62-64; teaching asst zool, La State Univ, 64-66; dir, Nat Sci Found Coop Col-Sch Sci Prog biol, physics & chem, 69-70; from asst prof to prof comp anat & syst zool, Univ Southwestern La, 66-76; assoc prof, 76-77, PROF & CHMN DEPT BIOL, UNIV MISS, 77- *Concurrent Pos:* Teaching asst, Southern Ill Univ, 61; sci ed consult, Southwestern La Parish Schs, 66-71; exec coun, La Acad Sci, 72-74; res assoc, Gulf South Res Inst, Baton Rouge, 72-75; consult & proj dir, US Fish & Wildlife Serv, Atchafalaya Basin Surv, 73-76; dir, Lafayette Natural Hist Mus, 73; consult, La Chenier Plain Study, US Fish & Wildlife Serv, 78; comnr, Miss Dept Wildlife Conserv, 78-79, 80-84, Miss Wildlife Heritage Comt, 80-84; mem, Governor's Select Comt Radioactive Waste & Waste Depository, 79. *Mem:* Am Soc Ichthyol & Herpet; Inst Caribbean Sci; Sigma Xi; Soc Study Amphibians & Reptiles; Herpetologist League. *Res:* Systematics, ecology and developmental morphology of vertebrates, especially amphibians and reptiles of the United States and the Neotropics; wetlands ecology and management. *Mailing Add:* Dept of Biol Univ of Miss University MS 38677

KEISER, GEORGE MCCURRACH, b Plainfield, NJ, July 21, 47. GRAVITATIONAL & ATOMIC PHYSICS. *Educ:* Middlebury Col, AB, 69; Duke Univ, PhD(physics), 76. *Prof Exp:* Res assoc, Joint Inst Lab Astrophys, 76-77; Nat Res Coun fel, Nat Bur Standards, 77-80; MEM FAC, DEPT PHYSICS, STANFORD UNIV, 80- *Concurrent Pos:* Lectr, Univ Colo, 77-78. *Mem:* Am Phys Soc. *Res:* High precision measurements in gravitational and atomic physics. *Mailing Add:* Dept Physics Stanford Univ Stanford CA 94305

KEISER, JEFFREY E, b Kalamazoo, Mich, Feb 25, 41. ORGANIC CHEMISTRY. *Educ:* Kalamazoo Col, AB, 62; Wayne State Univ, PhD(org chem), 66. *Prof Exp:* Asst prof, 66-71, ASSOC PROF CHEM, COE COL, 71-, CHMN CHEM DEPT, 76- *Mem:* Am Chem Soc; Brit Chem Soc. *Res:* Organic analytical chemistry. *Mailing Add:* Dept of Chem Coe Col Cedar Rapids IA 52402

KEISLER, HOWARD JEROME, b Seattle, Wash, Dec 3, 36; m 59; c 3. MATHEMATICAL LOGIC. *Educ:* Calif Inst Technol, BS, 59; Univ Calif, Berkeley, PhD(math), 61. *Prof Exp:* Mathematician, Commun Res Div, Inst Defense Anal, 61-62; from asst prof to assoc prof, 62-67, PROF MATH, UNIV WIS, MADISON, 67- *Concurrent Pos:* Vis res assoc, Princeton Univ, 61-62; Alfred P Sloan fel, 66-69; vis prof, Univ Calif, Los Angeles, 67-68; John S Guggenheim fel, 76-77. *Mem:* Am Math Soc; Asn Symbolic Logic (vpres, 77-80). *Res:* Model theory; set theory; applications of model theory to probability theory and mathematical economics. *Mailing Add:* Dept Math Univ Wis Madison WI 53706

KEISLER, JAMES EDWIN, b Spartanburg, SC, Aug 20, 29; m 50; c 3. MATHEMATICS. *Educ:* Midland Col, BS, 49; Univ Mich, MA, 54, PhD(math), 59. *Prof Exp:* Teacher high sch, Nebr, 49-51; from asst prof to assoc prof, 59-73, PROF MATH, LA STATE UNIV, BATON ROUGE, 73- *Mem:* Am Math Soc; Math Asn Am. *Res:* Point-set topology; fixed point problems and characterizations of spaces. *Mailing Add:* Dept of Math La State Univ Baton Rouge LA 70803

KEISTER, DONALD LEE, b Beckley, WVa, Dec 10, 33; m 62; c 3. MICROBIAL BIOCHEMISTRY. *Educ:* WVa Wesleyan Col, BS, 54; Univ Md, MS, 56, PhD, 59. *Prof Exp:* Fel, McCollum-Pratt Inst, Johns Hopkins Univ, 58-61; fel, Res Inst Adv Study, Md, 61-62; SR INVESTR, CHARLES F KETTERING RES LAB, 62-; ASST PROF BIOCHEM, ANTIOCH COL, 62- *Concurrent Pos:* Nat Found fel, 58-60; chmn, Gordon Res Conf Photosynthesis, 69; grad fac, Wright State Univ, 80- *Mem:* Am Soc Biol Chemists; Am Soc Plant Physiol; NY Acad Sci; Am Soc Microbiol. *Res:* Mechanisms of pyridine nucleotide reduction in photosynthetic organisms; structure and function in photosynthetic organelles; control mechanisms in nitrogen fixation; symbiotic nitrogen fixation in legumes; author or co-author of over 50 publications. *Mailing Add:* Charles F Kettering Res Lab Yellow Springs OH 45387

KEISTER, JEROME BAIRD, b Baton Rouge, La, Mar 28, 53. INORGANIC CHEMISTRY, ORGANOMETALLIC CHEMISTRY. *Educ:* La State Univ, Baton Rouge, BS, 73; Univ Ill, Urbana-Champaign, PhD(chem), 78. *Prof Exp:* res chemist organometallic catalysis, Corp Pioneering Res, Exxon Res & Eng Co, 77-80; ASST PROF INORG CHEM, DEPT CHEM, STATE UNIV NY, BUFFALO, 80- *Mem:* Am Chem Soc. *Res:* Homogeneous catalysis, organometallic chemistry; metal cluster chemistry. *Mailing Add:* 107 Creekside Dr Tonawanda NY 14150

KEISTER, THOMAS DWIGHT, forestry, experimental statistics, see previous edition

KEITEL, GLENN H(OWARD), b Chicago, Ill, Feb 16, 30; m 53; c 2. ELECTRICAL ENGINEERING, OFFICE AUTOMATION. *Educ:* Wash Univ, BS, 52, MS, 54; Stanford Univ, PhD(elec eng), 55. *Prof Exp:* Fulbright fel, Cavendish Lab, Cambridge Univ, 55-56; engr advan studies, Microwave Lab, Gen Elec Co, 56-59; eng dept mgr, Western Develop Lab, Philco Corp, Calif, 59-62; assoc prof elec eng, San Jose State Col, 62-66, prof & chmn dept, 66-69; prof elec eng & chmn elec eng curric, Drexel Univ, 69-71; prof elec eng & dean eng, Bucknell Univ, 71-79; dir eng & technol planning, CPT Corp, 80-81; PRES, OFF AUTOMATION CONSULT, INC, 81- *Concurrent Pos:* Electronics liaison scientist, Off Naval Res, Br Off, London, 63-64; consult, Stanford Res Inst, 62-63 & 64-69 & Western Develop Labs, Philco Corp, 62-63; adv scientist, Lockheed Missiles & Space Co, 65-69. *Mem:* Am Mgt Asn. *Res:* Functional and engineering design, selection and implementation of office automation systems, with training and applications development. *Mailing Add:* 14960 Ironwood Ct Eden Prairie MN 55344

KEITER, RICHARD LEE, b Winchester, Va, Jan 10, 39; m 66; c 2. INORGANIC CHEMISTRY. *Educ:* Sheperd Col, BS, 61; WVa Univ, MS, 64; Univ Md, PhD(inorg chem), 67. *Prof Exp:* Assoc inorg chem, Iowa State Univ, 67-69; assoc prof, 69-80, PROF INORG CHEM, EASTERN ILL UNIV, 80- *Concurrent Pos:* Vis prof, Univ Exeter, Eng, 75 & Univ Ill, 80. *Mem:* Am Chem Soc; AAAS. *Res:* Phosphorous-31 nuclear magnetic resonance spectroscopy; coordination chemistry of trivalent phosphorous ligands; inorganic zwitterions; transition metal carbonyls; polydentate phosphorus ligand control; synthetic inorganic and organometallic chemistry. *Mailing Add:* Dept of Chem Eastern Ill Univ Charleston IL 61920

KEITH, BRIAN DUNCAN, sedimentary petrology, see previous edition

KEITH, CHARLES HERBERT, b Deerfield, Mass, Feb 2, 26; m 48; c 4. PHYSICAL CHEMISTRY. *Educ:* Williams Col, BA, 46; Brown Univ, PhD(chem), 52. *Prof Exp:* Res assoc phys chem, Oceanog Inst, Woods Hole, 51-54; res chemist, Liggett & Myers Tobacco Co, 54-64; group leader, 64-66, res assoc, 66-68, SR RES ASSOC, PHYS CHEM, CELANESE FIBERS CO, 68- *Mem:* AAAS; Am Chem Soc. *Res:* Nonaqueous solutions of long chain electrolytes; aerosols; combustion; pyrolysis; filtration; gas analysis. *Mailing Add:* 2301 Overhill Rd Charlotte NC 28211

KEITH, DAVID ALEXANDER, b Chelmsford, Essex, Eng, Aug 28, 44; m 76; c 2. BIOLOGICAL CHEMISTRY. *Educ:* Univ London, BDS, 66; FDSRCS(Eng), 70. *Prof Exp:* Lectr oral surg, Hosp Dent Sch, Kings Col, London, 71-73; res fel, Mass Gen Hosp, Boston, 73-74; res fel, 75-77, ASST PROF ORAL SURG, HARVARD SCH DENT MED, 78- *Concurrent Pos:* Res assoc orthop surg, Children's Hosp Med Ctr, 77-, consult dent dept, 78-; clin assoc oral surg, Mass Gen Hosp, 78- *Honors & Awards:* Malleson Prize Dent Student Res, Guy's Hosp Dent Sch, London, 66; Brit Asn Oral Surgeons Award, 73. *Mem:* Brit Dent Asn; Brit Asn Oral Surgeons; Int Asn Dent Res; Am Dent Asn; Int Asn Oral Surgeons. *Res:* Biochemistry of elastin; biochemistry of craniofacial development. *Mailing Add:* G1221 Orthop Res 320 Longwood Ave Boston MA 02115

KEITH, DAVID LEE, b Mankato, Minn, Dec 7, 40; m 61; c 4. ENTOMOLOGY. *Educ:* Gustavus Adolphus Col, BSc, 62; Univ Minn, MSc, 65; Univ Nebr, Lincoln, PhD(entom), 71. *Prof Exp:* EXTEN ENTOMOLOGIST, UNIV NEBR, LINCOLN, 67- *Mem:* Sigma Xi; Entom Soc Am. *Res:* Biology, ecology and control of cutworms; development of integrated pest management projects on Nebraska field crops. *Mailing Add:* Dept of Entom Univ of Nebr Lincoln NE 68503

KEITH, DENNIS DALTON, b Hartford, Conn, July 11, 43; c 2. ORGANIC SYNTHESIS, ANTIBIOTICS. *Educ:* Bates Col, BS, 65; Yale Univ, MS, 67, MPh, 69, PhD(org chem), 69. *Prof Exp:* NIH fel, Harvard Univ, 69-71; sr res chemist, 71-76, res fel, 76-81, RES GROUP CHIEF, HOFFMANN-LA ROCHE INC, 81- *Mem:* Am Chem Soc; Am Soc Microbiol; Sigma Xi. *Res:* Synthesis of natural products; heterocyclic chemistry; synthetic methods. *Mailing Add:* 8 Mendl Terr Montclair NJ 07042

KEITH, DONALD EDWARDS, b Ft Worth, Tex, Oct 7, 38; m 59. INVERTEBRATE ECOLOGY. *Educ:* Tex Christian Univ, BA, 62, MS, 64; Univ Southern Calif, PhD(biol), 68. *Prof Exp:* NSF res grant, summer 61; asst prof biol, Tex Christian Univ, 68-75, dir environ sci prog, 69-71; asst prof, 75-79, ASSOC PROF, TARLETON STATE UNIV, 79- *Concurrent Pos:* Consult, US Army Corps Engrs, Lake Proctor, 76- *Mem:* AAAS; Sigma Xi. *Res:* Benthic ecology; substrate selection, feeding and functional digestive tract morphology of Caprellid amphipods; amphipod phylogeny; effects of industrial effluents on benthic invertebrate communities; corals of the Swan Islands, Honduras; brachyuran crabs of West Indies. *Mailing Add:* Dept of Biol Sci Tarleton State Univ Stephenville TX 76402

KEITH, EADEN FRANCIS, pharmacology, biochemistry, see previous edition

KEITH, ERNEST ALEXANDER, b Fayetteville, Tenn, Dec 19, 51; m 72. RUMINANT NUTRITION. *Educ:* Univ Ark, BS, 73, MS, 74; Purdue Univ, PhD(ruminant nutrit), 78. *Prof Exp:* ASST PROF DAIRY NUTRIT, DEPT DAIRY SCI, LA STATE UNIV, 78- *Mem:* Sigma Xi; Am Dairy Sci Asn; Am Soc Animal Sci; Am Forage & Grassland Coun. *Res:* Forage nutrition of dairy cattle. *Mailing Add:* Dept of Dairy Sci La State Univ Baton Rouge LA 70803

KEITH, FREDERICK W(ALTER), JR, b Chicago, Ill, Jan 20, 21; m 43; c 1. CHEMICAL ENGINEERING. *Educ:* Yale Univ, BS, 42; Univ Pa, PhD(chem eng), 51. *Prof Exp:* Chem engr process develop, E I du Pont de Nemours & Co, 42-44; chem engr res & develop, Sharples Res Lab, 44-48; asst instr, Univ Pa, 49; chem engr process develop, Pennwalt Chem Equip Div, Sharples Corp, 50-71, dir environ technol, Sharples Div, Pennwalt Corp, Warminster, 71-79; CONSULT, 79- *Mem:* Am Chem Soc; Am Inst Chem Engrs; Water Pollution Control Fedn. *Res:* Development and evaluation of centrifuges; waste and sewage process development; separations in synfuel processing. *Mailing Add:* 454 Conshohocken State Rd Gladwyne PA 19035

KEITH, HARVEY DOUGLAS, b Belfast, Ireland, Mar 10, 27; US citizen; m 53; c 2. EXPERIMENTAL PHYSICS. *Educ:* Queen's Univ, Belfast, BS, 48; Bristol Univ, PhD(physics), 51. *Prof Exp:* Lectr physics, Bristol Univ, 52-57; res physicist, Am Viscose Corp, Pa, 57-59, leader phys sect, 59-60; MEM TECH STAFF, BELL LABS, MURRAY HILL, 60-, HEAD, ORG MAT RES DEPT, 65- *Concurrent Pos:* Lectr, St Joseph's Col, Pa, 58-60. *Honors & Awards:* High Polymer Physics Prize, Am Phys Soc, 73. *Mem:* Fel Am Phys Soc; fel AAAS. *Res:* Solid state physics; crystallography; optics; high polymers. *Mailing Add:* Rm 1A215 Bell Labs PO Box 261 Summit NJ 07901

KEITH, JAMES OLIVER, b Pasadena, Calif, Mar 20, 32; m 50; c 5. WILDLIFE ECOLOGY. *Educ:* Univ Calif, Berkeley, AB, 53; Univ Ariz, MS, 56; Ohio State Univ, PhD(ecol), 78. *Prof Exp:* Wildlife res biologist, Rocky Mt Forest & Range Exp Sta, US Forest Serv, 56-61; wildlife res biologist, Denver Wildlife Res Ctr, 61-76, chief, 69-73, wildlife res biologist environ contaminants, Patuxent Wildlife Res Ctr, 76-81, WILDLIFE RES BIOLGIST, INT PROG, DENVER WILDLIFE RES CTR, US FISH & WILDLIFE SERV, 81- *Concurrent Pos:* Res assoc, Agr Exp Sta, Univ Calif, 61-65. *Mem:* AAAS; Ecol Soc Am; Wildlife Soc; Am Ornith Union. *Res:* Ecological effects of land management practices; influence of logging, grazing, agriculture and pesticides on wildlife and their habitats. *Mailing Add:* Wildlife Res Ctr Bldg 16 Denver Fed Ctr Denver CO 80225

KEITH, JERRY M, b Salt Lake City, Utah, Oct 22, 40. ENZYMOLOGY, VIROLOGY. *Educ:* Univ Calif, Berkeley, BA, 73, PhD(comparative biochem), 76. *Prof Exp:* Staff fel, Lab Biol Viruses, Nat Inst Allergy & Infectious Dis, NIH, 76-78; ASST PROF BIOCHEM, COL DENT, NY UNIV, 78- *Concurrent Pos:* Adj asst prof biol doctoral fac, City Univ New York, 81-; prin investr, gen med-biochem, NIH, 81-84. *Mem:* Sigma Xi; AAAS; Am Soc Microbiol; Am Soc Virol. *Res:* Structure and function of biologically active nucleic acids and proteins, with a particular interest in the isolation and characerization of the enzymes related to the synthesis, processing and post-transcriptional modification of mRNA's. *Mailing Add:* New York Univ Col Dent 345 E 24th St New York NY 10010

KEITH, LAWRENCE H, b Morris, Ill, Apr 5, 38; m 69. POLLUTION CHEMISTRY. *Educ:* Stetson Univ, BS, 60; Clemson Univ, MS, 63; Univ Ga, PhD(natural prod chem), 66. *Prof Exp:* Res chemist, Environ Protection Agency, 66-77; head, Org Chem Dept, 77-78, mgr, Anal Chem Div, 79-81, CHEM DEVELOP COORDR, RADIAN CORP, 81- *Concurrent Pos:* Pres, KCP, 73-; vchmn, Gordon Res Conf Environ Sci & Water, 78. 73-; mem comt mil environ res & subcomt indust hyg, Nat Res Coun, 81. *Honors & Awards:* Chemist of the Year, Am Chem Soc, 75. *Mem:* Am Chem Soc; Sigma Xi. *Res:* Chemical changes produced by pollution treatment; nuclear magnetic resonance of pesticides; mass spectrometry; identification of organic chemical pollutants; computerized GC-MS analysis of pollutants; industrial pollutants; global geographic distribution of organic chemical pollutants. *Mailing Add:* Radian Corp PO Box 9948 Austin TX 78766

KEITH, LLOYD BURROWS, b Victoria, BC, Nov 29, 31; m 54; c 4. WILDLIFE MANAGEMENT. *Educ:* Univ Alta, BSc, 53, MSc, 55; Univ Wis, PhD(wildlife mgt), 59. *Prof Exp:* Asst forestry & wildlife mgt, 55-59, fel, 59-60, from instr to assoc prof, 60-70, PROF WILDLIFE ECOL, UNIV WIS-MADISON, 70- *Mem:* Wildlife Soc; Am Soc Mammal; Ecol Soc Am. *Res:* Natural regulation of animal populations; ten-year cycle of northern furbearers and grouse. *Mailing Add:* Dept of Wildlife Ecol Univ of Wis Russell Labs Madison WI 58706

KEITH, MACKENZIE LAWRENCE, b Edmonton, Alta, Oct 12, 12; nat US; m 40; c 5. GEOCHEMISTRY. *Educ:* Univ Alta, BSc, 34; Queen's Univ, Can, MSc, 36; Mass Inst Technol, PhD(geol), 39. *Prof Exp:* Field geologist, Ventures, Ltd, 37, Geol Surv Can, 38 & US Smelting, Ref & Mining Co, 39-40; asst prof geol, Queen's Univ, Can, 40-47; petrologist, Geophys Lab, Carnegie Inst, 47-50; PROF GEOCHEM, PA STATE UNIV, 50- *Concurrent Pos:* Field geologist, McIntyre Mines, Ont, 41, Aluminum Co Can, Montreal, 42-43 & Ont Dept Mines, Toronto, 45-47. *Mem:* Fel Geol Soc Am; Mineral Soc Am; Geochem Soc; Geol Asn Can. *Res:* Petrology of alkaline rocks; staining methods for silicate minerals; mineral deposits; silicate chemistry, including system MgO-Cr2O3-SiO2; element distribution; geochemical prospecting; isotope ratios in limestone and fossils; high-low quartz inversion as a geological thermometer; geochemistry of sedimentary rocks; trace element and isotopic criteria for differentiating marine and fresh water sediments; global tectonics; evidence against plate tectonics. *Mailing Add:* Dept of Geosci Pa State Univ 309 Deike Bldg University Park PA 16802

KEITH, NANCY KAY, b St Louis, Mo, Jan 23, 52; m 72. MATHEMATICAL PROGRAMMING, STATISTICS. *Educ:* Univ Ark, BS, 73, MBA, 74; Purdue Univ, PhD(mgt sci), 78. *Prof Exp:* Asst prof mgt sci, Purdue Univ, 78-79; ASST PROF EXP STATIST, LA STATE UNIV, 79- *Mem:* Inst Mgt Sci; Am Inst Decision Sci. *Res:* Multivariate statistics; decision theory. *Mailing Add:* Dept of Exp Statist La State Univ Baton Rouge LA 70803

KEITH, PAULA MYERS, b Wheeling, WVa, Jan 13, 50; m 73. MICROBIOLOGY, BACTERIAL PHYSIOLOGY. *Educ:* W Liberty State Col, AB, 71; WVa Univ, MS, 73; Va Polytech Inst, PhD(microbiol), 78. *Prof Exp:* Clin microbiologist, Pub Health Sect, WVa State Ref Lab, 73-75; res asst bact, Va Polytech Inst, 75-76, res assoc, 75-77; RES MICROBIOLOGIST, IMC CORP, 79- *Concurrent Pos:* Consult, WHO, 79. *Mem:* Am Soc Microbiol; Sigma Xi; Soc Indust Microbiol. *Res:* Microbial control agents of insects; secondary metabolism in spore-forming bacteria including toxin biosynthesis and biochemistry; ultra structure of spore-forming bacteria; fermentation microbiology; bacterial and fungal physiology; industrial microbiology; animal growth promotants and vaccines. *Mailing Add:* IMC Corp 1331S 1st St Terre Haute IN 47808

KEITH, TERRY EUGENE CLARK, b Redlands, Calif, Jan 28, 40; m 66; c 2. HYDROTHERMAL ALTERATION, MINERALOGY. *Educ:* Univ Ariz, BS, 62; Univ Ore, MS, 64. *Prof Exp:* GEOLOGIST, US GEOL SURV, 64- *Res:* Hydrothermal and fumarolic alteration mineralogy in Yellowstone National Park, the Pacific Northwest Cascade Range, and Alaskan volcanoes; field distribution and petrography of ultramafic rocks in the Yukon-Tanana Upland, Alaska. *Mailing Add:* Br of Field Geochem & Petrol 345 Middlefield Rd Menlo Park CA 94025

KEITH, THEO GORDON, JR, b Cleveland, Ohio, July 2, 29; m 60; c 2. THERMAL SCIENCES, NUMERICAL ANALYSIS. *Educ:* Fen Col, BME, 64; Univ Md, MSME, 68, PhD(mech eng). *Prof Exp:* Mech engr, Nat Standards Reference Data Ctr, Annapolis, Md, 64-71; PROF & CHMN MECH ENG, UNIV TOLEDO, 71- *Concurrent Pos:* Prin investr pumping ring seal grant, Lewis Res Ctr, NASA, 77-81 & wing energy grant, 79-, co-prin investr deicing grant, 80- *Mem:* Am Soc Mech Engrs; Am Soc Eng Educ; Am Inst Aeronaut & Astronaut; Soc Automotive Engrs; Sigma Xi. *Mailing Add:* Dept Mech Eng Univ Toledo 2801 W Bancroft St Toledo OH 43606

KEITH, WARREN GRAY, b Anamosa, Iowa, Sept 16, 08; m 37; c 2. CIVIL ENGINEERING, ENGINEERING EDUCATION. *Educ:* Iowa State Col, BS, 34; Univ Mo, MS, 48. *Prof Exp:* Asst county hwy engr, Lyon Co, Minn, 27-34; area engr admin & construct, Fed Emergency Relief Admin & Works Progress Admin, 34-37; county hwy engr, Chisago Co, 37-41; asst prof drawing, surv & structures, Univ Ala, 41-44; sr stress analyst aircraft structures, Goodyear Aircraft Corp, Ohio, 44-45; assoc prof structures, 45-51, prof civil eng, 51-66, head dept, 66-70, prof civil eng & structures, 70-72, dir eng technol progs, 72-74, EMER PROF CIVIL ENG, UNIV ALA, TUSCALOOSA, 74- *Mem:* Am Soc Civil Engrs; Nat Soc Prof Engrs. *Mailing Add:* 1611 27th Ave East Tuscaloosa AL 35401

KEITT, GEORGE WANNAMAKER, JR, b Madison, Wis, Sept 11, 28; m 57; c 4. PLANT PHYSIOLOGY. *Educ:* Harvard Univ, AB, 50; Univ Wis, MS, 52, PhD(bot), 57. *Prof Exp:* Res assoc, Ford Agr Plant Nutrit Proj, Mich, 57-59; asst prof bot, Fla State Univ, 59-67; sr fel, Mackinac Col, 67-70; res dept, Brooklyn Botanic Garden, 70-75, chmn, 70-74; PLANT PHYSIOLOGIST BENEFITS & FIELD STUDIES DIV, PESTICIDE PROG, ENVIRON PROTECTION AGENCY, 75- *Concurrent Pos:* Vis investr, Princeton Univ, 70. *Mem:* NY Acad Sci; Sigma Xi; Bot Soc Am; Am Inst Biol Sci; Soc Develop Biol. *Res:* Chemical control of plant growth and differentiation. *Mailing Add:* Plant Sci Br BFSD TS-768 EPA 401 M St SW Washington DC 20460

KEIZER, CLIFFORD RICHARD, b Hudsonville, Mich, Mar 19, 18; m 43; c 2. PHYSICAL CHEMISTRY. *Educ:* Hope Col, AB, 39; Univ Ill, MS, 41, PhD(phys chem), 43. *Prof Exp:* Jr res physicist, Monsanto Chem Co, 43-44; instr chem, Univ Ill, 44-46; from instr to asst prof chem, Western Reserve Univ, 46-48; prof chem & chmn div nat sci, Cent Col Iowa, 48-57; prof chem, Ky Contract Team to Univ Indonesia, 57-62, from actg chief to chief, 58-62; prof chem, Lindenwood Col, 62-64; head dept, 64-70, actg dean col, 66-67 & 74-75, actg vpres acad affairs, 76-77, PROF CHEM, NMEX INST MINING & TECHNOL, 64- *Mem:* Am Chem Soc. *Res:* Electrochemistry. *Mailing Add:* Dept of Chem NMex Inst Mining & Technol Socorro NM 87801

KEIZER, EUGENE O(RVILLE), b LeMars, Iowa, Sept 13, 18; m 41; c 2. VIDEO SYSTEMS, COLOR TELEVISION. *Educ:* Iowa State Col, BS, 40. *Prof Exp:* Asst, Exp Sta, Iowa State Col, 37-40; res engr, RCA Labs, 40-64, head TV res group, Systs Res Lab, 64-67, head video systs res group, Consumer Electronics Res Lab, 67-77, head microtopographics res, 77-78, head video recording res, Commun Res Labs, 78-79, staff scientist RCA selecta-vision video disc oper, 79-80, STAFF SCIENTIST, VIDEO DISC SYSTS RES LAB, RCA CORP, 80- *Concurrent Pos:* Instr war training prog, Rutgers Univ, 41-45. *Honors & Awards:* David Sarnoff Award, RCA Corp, 77 & 81; Edvard Rhein Award, 80. *Mem:* Inst Elec & Electronics Engrs. *Res:* Television; radar; microwave; radio frequency receivers and radio frequency circuits; color television; information storage and retrieval; video disc systems. *Mailing Add:* Video Disc Systs Res Lab RCA Labs David Sarnoff Res Ctr Princeton NJ 08540

KEIZER, JOEL EDWARD, b North Bend, Ore, Aug 31, 42; m 64; c 2. PHYSICAL CHEMISTRY, STATISTICAL PHYSICS. *Educ:* Reed Col, BA, 64; Univ Ore, PhD(chem physics), 69. *Prof Exp:* Actg instr, Univ Calif, Santa Cruz, 69, asst prof, Davis, 71-75, assoc prof, 75-78, PROF CHEM, UNIV CALIF, DAVIS, 78- *Concurrent Pos:* Vis scientist, NIH, 78-79; assoc ed, Accounts Chem Res, 78- *Mem:* Fel Battelle Mem Inst, 69-71; AAAS. *Res:* Molecular origins and nature of macroscopic dynamic phenomena in chemical and physical systems; Nonlinear, nonequilibrium thermodynamics; fluctuations and stochastic processes. *Mailing Add:* Dept of Chem Univ of Calif Davis CA 95616

KELBER, CHARLES NORMAN, physics, see previous edition

KELBER, JEFFRY ALAN, b Philadelphia, Pa, Dec 17, 52. SURFACE CHEMISTRY. *Educ:* Calif Inst Technol, BS, 75; Univ Ill, Urbana-Champaign, PHD(inorg chem), 79. *Prof Exp:* MEM TECH STAFF, SANDIA NAT LABS, 79- *Mem:* Am Vacuum Soc; Am Chem Soc. *Res:* Photoelectron spectroscopy of organic systems; auger lineshape analysis; electron and photon stimulated desorption. *Mailing Add:* Org 5811 Sandia Nat Labs Albuquerque NM 87112

KELCH, WALTER L, b Dayton, Ohio, Oct 27, 48; m 70. ASTROPHYSICS. *Educ:* Miami Univ, AB, 70; Ind Univ, MA, 73, PhD(astrophys), 75. *Prof Exp:* Instr astron, Kean Col, NJ, 75-76; res assoc, Joint Inst Lab Astrophys, Univ Colo, 76-78; ANALYST, CENT INTEL AGENCY, LANGLEY, VA, 78- *Mem:* Am Astron Soc. *Res:* Spectral line formation in stellar atmospheres; solar and stellar atmosphere models; radiative transport. *Mailing Add:* 2103 Sugarloaf Ct Herndon VA 22070

KELCHNER, BURTON L(EWIS), b Bethlehem, Pa, Nov 15, 21; m 44; c 3. CHEMICAL ENGINEERING. *Educ:* Moravian Col, BS, 43; Va Polytech Inst, BS, 44. *Prof Exp:* Sect leader, Los Alamos Sci Lab, 46-51; supt dept, Rocky Flats Div, Dow Chem Co, 52-65, mfg tech mgr, 65-68, sr res engr, facilities eng, 68-70, proj mgr, 70-75; mgr nuclear waste processing, 75-79, PROJ MGR, LONG-RANGE ROCKY FLATS UTILIZATION STUDY, ROCKWELL INT CORP, 79- *Mem:* Am Inst Chem Engrs; Am Nuclear Soc. *Res:* Nuclear waste processing; uranium and plutonium processing. *Mailing Add:* 10790 W 36th Ave Wheat Ridge CO 80033

KELE, ROGER ALAN, b Waterbury, Conn, Jan 24, 43; m 72; c 2. INDUSTRIAL MICROBIOLOGY. *Educ:* Clark Univ, BA, 64; Harvard Univ, MA, 66; Univ Wis, PhD(bact), 70. *Prof Exp:* RES MICROBIOLOGIST, LEDERLE LABS DIV, AM CYANAMID CO, 70- *Mem:* Am Soc Microbiol; Soc Indust Microbiol. *Res:* Strain improvement work on the tetracycline antibiotics. *Mailing Add:* Lederle Labs Pearl River NY 10965

KELEHER, JAMES J, b Winnipeg, Man, Feb 9, 26; m 53; c 3. ENVIRONMENTAL SCIENCES. *Educ:* Univ Man, BA, 48; Univ Toronto, MA, 50. *Prof Exp:* Biologist, Fisheries Res Bd Can, 50-68; chief fisheries biologist, Man Dept Mines & Natural Resources, 68-69, chief, Fisheries Opers, 70-71, SPEC ASST, MAN DEPT CONSUMER, CORP AFFAIRS & ENVIRON, 72- *Concurrent Pos:* Exec secy, Man Environ Coun, 73- *Mem:* Am Fisheries Soc; Am Inst Fishery Res Biol. *Res:* Environmental management. *Mailing Add:* 10 Baldry Bay Winnipeg MB R3T 3C4 Can

KELEMEN, CHARLES F, b Mt Vernon, NY, Jan 7, 43; m 75. MATHEMATICS. *Educ:* Valparaiso Univ, BA, 64; Pa State Univ, MA, 66, PhD(math), 69. *Prof Exp:* Asst prof math, Ithaca Col, 69-73, assoc prof, 73-80; ASSOC PROF COMPUT SCI, LEMOYNE COL, 80- *Concurrent Pos:* Res assoc, Dept Comput Sci, Cornell Univ, 75-76, vis assoc prof, 77-81; NSF grant, 77-81. *Mem:* Inst Elec & Electronics Engrs; Math Asn Am; Am Math Soc; Asn Comput Mach; Soc Indust & Appl Math. *Res:* Computational complexity; analysis of algorithms. *Mailing Add:* Comput Sci Dept Le Moyne Col Syracuse NY 13214

KELEMEN, DENIS GEORGE, b Budapest, Hungary, June 18, 25; nat US; m 51; c 1. PHYSICAL CHEMISTRY. *Educ:* Princeton Univ, PhD(chem), 51. *Prof Exp:* Ed asst tables of chem kinetics, Nat Res Coun, 48-50; res chemist, 50-57, res supvr, 57-68, res mgr electronic prod div, Photoprod Dept, 68-70, planning mgr, Photoprod Dept, 70-72, prod mgr, 72-78, develop mgr, Electronic Prod Div, Photoprod Dept, 78-80, PRIN CONSULT, CENT RES & DEVELOP DEPT, E I DU PONT DE NEMOURS & CO, INC, 80- *Mem:* Am Chem Soc. *Res:* Physical chemistry of solids. *Mailing Add:* Electron Prod Div Photoprod Dept E I du Pont de Nemours & Co Wilmington DE 19898

KELIHER, THOMAS FRANCIS, b Washington, DC, Jan 4, 09. MEDICINE. *Educ:* Georgetown Univ, BSM, 32, MD, 34; FACP. *Hon Degrees:* DSc, Georgetown Univ, 78. *Prof Exp:* Instr med, 37-45, assoc prof clin med, 45-57, from assoc prof to prof med, 57-77, dir referral clin, Med Ctr, 65-77, EMER PROF MED, GEORGETOWN UNIV, 77- *Concurrent Pos:* Consult, US Air Force, 49-69. *Mem:* AAAS; Am Col Physicians; AMA; Int Col Physicians. *Mailing Add:* Georgetown Univ Med Ctr Washington DC 20007

KELISKY, RICHARD PAUL, b St Louis, Mo, Nov 27, 29; m 60; c 1. MATHEMATICS, DATA PROCESSING. *Educ:* Tex Tech Col, BS, 51; Univ Tex, MA, 53, PhD(math), 57. *Prof Exp:* Asst appl math, Univ Tex, 52-55, lectr, 55-57, asst prof, 57-58; RES MATHEMATICIAN, THOMAS J WATSON RES CTR, IBM CORP, 58-, DIR COMPUT SYSTS DEPT, 71- *Concurrent Pos:* Adj prof, Grad Div, City Univ NY, 65-72. *Mem:* Am Math Soc; Math Asn Am; Asn Comput Mach. *Res:* Theory of numbers; numerical analysis; computing center management. *Mailing Add:* Thomas J Watson Res Ctr IBM Corp PO Box 218 Yorktown Heights NY 10598

KELKER, DOUGLAS, b Logan, Utah, Mar 23, 40; m 75; c 2. STATISTICS. *Educ:* Hiram Col, BA, 61; Univ Ore, MA, 63, PhD(math), 68. *Prof Exp:* Asst prof probability & statist, Mich State Univ, 68; asst prof math, Wash State Univ, 68-73; vis asst prof, 73-76, asst prof math, 76-81, ASSOC PROF STATIST, UNIV ALTA, 81- *Mem:* Inst Math Statist; Am Statist Asn; Can Statist Soc. *Res:* Characterization Theorems; infinite divisibility; distributions on the unit sphere applied to geological data. *Mailing Add:* Dept Statist Appl Prob Univ Alta Edmonton AB T6G 2G1 Can

KELL, GEORGE SINCLAIR, b Churchill, Ont, Sept 6, 30; m 60; c 3. CHEMICAL PHYSICS. *Educ:* Univ Toronto, BA, 55, MA, 56, PhD(phys chem), 58. *Prof Exp:* Asst res officer, 58-64, assoc res officer, 65-72, SR RES OFFICER, DIV CHEM, NAT RES COUN CAN, 72- *Concurrent Pos:* Lectr, Carleton Univ, 60-61; proj officer, Indust Prog Off, Nat Res Coun Can, 77-78. *Mem:* Can Asn Physicists; AAAS; Am Chem Soc; Am Phys Soc; Chem Inst Can. *Res:* Thermodynamics of fluids; properties of water; experimental error. *Mailing Add:* Div of Chem Nat Res Coun Ottawa ON K1A 0R9 Can

KELL, ROBERT M, b Piqua, Ohio, Nov 27, 22; m 49; c 3. CHEMICAL ENGINEERING. *Educ:* Ohio State Univ, BChE, 47, MSc, 48. *Prof Exp:* Jr chem engr, Olin Corp, 48-52; res chemist, Battelle Mem Inst, 52-62, sr res chemist, 62-68; res chemist, 68-79, SR RES ASSOC, FRANKLIN CHEM INDUSTS, 79- *Mem:* Am Chem Soc. *Res:* Adhesives; physical chemistry of polymers; plastics applications; vinyl polymerization. *Mailing Add:* Franklin Chem Industs 2020 Bruck St Columbus OH 43207

KELLAND, DAVID ROSS, b East Orange, NJ, July 29, 35; m 56; c 3. PHYSICS. *Educ:* Montclair State Col, BA, 57, MA, 60. *Prof Exp:* Teacher high sch, NJ, 57-60; instr physics, Simmons Col, 61-63; asst prof, Emmanuel Col, Mass, 63-67; staff mem, 67-77, asst group leader, 77-78, co-group leader, 78-80, GROUP LEADER, FRANCIS BITTER NAT MAGNET LAB, MASS INST TECHNOL 80- *Mem:* Am Phys Soc; Inst Elec & Electronics Engrs. *Res:* Applied magnetism and low temperature physics. *Mailing Add:* Francis Bitter Nat Magnet Lab Mass Inst Technol Cambridge MA 02139

KELLAR, KENNETH JON, b Baltimore, Md, Feb 13, 45; m 72; c 2. NEUROPHARMACOLOGY, MOLECULAR PHARMACOLOGY. *Educ:* Johns Hopkins Univ, BS, 66; Ohio State Univ, PhD(pharmacol), 74. *Prof Exp:* asst prof, 76-81, ASSOC PROF PHARMACOL, SCH MED, GEORGETOWN UNIV, 81- *Mem:* Soc Neurosci; Am Soc Pharmacol Exp Therapeut. *Res:* Regulation of neurotransmission. *Mailing Add:* Dept Pharmacol Sch Med Georgetown Univ Washington DC 20007

KELLAWAY, PETER, b Johannesburg, SAfrica, Oct 20, 20; nat US; m 58; c 5. NEUROPHYSIOLOGY. *Educ:* Occidental Col, BA, 41, MA, 42; McGill Univ, PhD(physiol), 47. *Hon Degrees:* MD, Gothenburg Univ, Sweden, 77. *Prof Exp:* Demonstr physiol, McGill Univ, 44-46, lectr, 46-47, asst prof, 47-48; from assoc prof to prof physiol, 48-77, PROF NEUROL, BAYLOR COL MED, 77-, CHIEF SECT NEUROPHYSIOL, 48- *Concurrent Pos:* Dir, Blue Bird Children's Epilepsy Clin, 49-60; dir dept electroencephalog, Methodist Hosp, 49-71, chief & sr attend, Neurophysiol Serv, 71-; consult, US Vet Admin Hosp, 49-75, Hermann Hosp, 55-73 & St Luke's Hosp, 71-; ed, Electroencephalog J, 68-71, consult ed, 72-75; dir, EEG Lab, Ben Taub Gen Hosp, 65-; chief Neurophysiol Serv, Dept Med, Tex Children's Hosp, 72- & St Luke's Hosp, 73-; dir, Epilepsy Res Ctr, Baylor Col Med & Methodist Hosp, 75- *Honors & Awards:* Sir William Osler Medal, Am Asn Hist Med, 46. *Mem:* Am Physiol Soc; Am Electroencephalog Soc (treas, 56-58, pres elect, 62-63, pres, 63-64); Soc Neurosci; Am Neurol Asn; Int League Against Epilepsy (secy-treas, 55-58, pres, 60). *Res:* Genesis and ontogenesis of electrical activity of the brain and of the epileptic process; epilepsy. *Mailing Add:* Dept of Neurol Sect Neurophysiol Baylor Col of Med Houston TX 77030

KELLEHER, JAMES JOSEPH, b Hudson, Mass, Sept, 12, 38; m 63; c 4. IMMUNOLOGY, MEDICAL MICROBIOLOGY. *Educ:* Boston Col, BS, 60, MS, 63; Rutgers Univ, PhD(microbiol), 68. *Prof Exp:* Instr microbiol, Rutgers Univ, 66-67; res asst, Woods Hole Oceanog Inst, 67-68; asst prof, 68-73, ASSOC PROF MICROBIOL, SCH MED, UNIV NDAK, 73- *Concurrent Pos:* Fel, Woods Hole Oceanog Inst, 67-68; consult diag virol, 72- *Mem:* AAAS; Am Soc Microbiol; Sigma Xi. *Res:* Nutrition, viral infection and immune response; clinical diagnosis of viral infections; herpes virus latency in cell culture and animal model systems; virus transmission by the water route. *Mailing Add:* Dept of Microbiol Univ of NDak Grand Forks ND 58201

KELLEHER, MATTHEW D(ENNIS), b Flushing, NY, Feb 1, 39; m 69. MECHANICAL ENGINEERING. *Educ:* Univ Notre Dame, BS, 61, MS, 63; PhD(mech eng), 66. *Prof Exp:* Asst prof mech eng, Univ Notre Dame, 65-66; Ford Found fel eng, Dartmouth Col, 66-67; asst prof mech eng, 67-72, ASSOC PROF MECH ENG, NAVAL POSTGRAD SCH, 72- *Mem:* Am Soc Mech Engrs. *Res:* Heat transfer and fluid mechanics, specifically convection and radiation; heat pipes. *Mailing Add:* Dept of Mech Eng Naval Postgrad Sch Code 69 Kk Monterey CA 93940

KELLEHER, PHILIP CONBOY, b New Rochelle, NY, July 23, 28; m 55; c 3. BIOCHEMISTRY, INTERNAL MEDICINE. Educ: Georgetown Univ, BS, 50, MD, 54. Prof Exp: Resident physician, State Univ NY Upstate Med Ctr, 55-58; res fel biochem, Harvard Med Sch, 60-63; from instr to asst prof, 63-68, ASSOC PROF MED, COL MED, UNIV VT, 69- Concurrent Pos: Tutor, Harvard Med Sch, 62-63; clin fel med, Mass Gen Hosp, 61-63. Mem: AAAS; AMA; Am Fedn Clin Res; Int Soc Co-develop Mental Biol & Med. Res: Serum protein metabolism; glycoproteins; specific fetal serum proteins; carcinoembryonic antigens; collagen metabolism. Mailing Add: Dept Med Col Med Univ Vt Burlington VT 05405

KELLEHER, RAYMOND JOSEPH, JR, b Fall River, Mass, Sept 27, 39; m 64; c 3. GENETICS, BIOCHEMISTRY. Educ: Col of the Holy Cross, AB, 61; Boston Col, MS, 64; Univ NC, Chapel Hill, PhD(genetics), 69. Prof Exp: NIH fel genetics & biochem, 69-73, res assoc, 73-75, sr res assoc, Salk Inst Biol Studies, 75-76; res fel, Univ Calif, San Diego, 76-77; ASST PROF, STATE UNIV NY, BUFFALO, 77- Mem: AAAS; Genetics Soc Am. Res: Somatic cell genetics; molecular endocrinology; eukaryotic gene regulation. Mailing Add: 97 Jeanmoor Dr Tonawanda NY 14150

KELLEHER, ROGER THOMSON, b New Haven, Conn, Dec 28, 26; m 52; c 3. PHARMACOLOGY. Educ: Univ Conn, BA, 50; NY Univ, MA, 53, PhD(exp psychol), 55. Prof Exp: Asst psychol, NY Univ, 52-55; asst exp psychol, Yerkes Labs Primate Biol, 55-56, res assoc, 56-57; sr pharmacologist, Smith Kline & French Labs, NJ, 57-61; from asst prof to assoc prof pharmacol, 61-72, PROF PSYCHOBIOL, HARVARD MED SCH, 72- Concurrent Pos: Specific field ed, J Am Soc Pharmacol & Exp Therapeut. Mem: AAAS; Am Soc Pharmacol & Exp Therapeut. Res: Behavioral pharmacology; behavioral physiology; effects of drugs on cardiovascular regulation. Mailing Add: Lab Psychobiol Harvard Med Sch Boston MA 02115

KELLEHER, WILLIAM JOSEPH, b Hartford, Conn, July 18, 29. BIOCHEMISTRY, PHARMACOGNOSY. Educ: Univ Conn, BS, 51, MS, 53; Univ Wis, PhD(biochem), 60. Prof Exp: Asst pharm, Univ Conn, 51-53; asst biochem, Univ Wis, 56-60; from asst prof to assoc prof, 60-70, chmn med chem & pharmacog sect, 71-76, asst dean, 76-81, PROF PHARMACOG, SCH PHARM, UNIV CONN, 60- Concurrent Pos: Mem, Nat Formulary Adv Panel Pharmacog, 64-71; guest prof, Univ Freiburg, 70-71 & 77-78; assoc ed, Lloydia, 71-76. Mem: Am Chem Soc; Am Soc Pharmacog; Brit Biochem Soc. Res: Microbiol chemistry and the production and biosynthesis of alkaloids and other medicinal products by fermentation processes. Mailing Add: Univ of Conn Sch of Pharm Storrs CT 06268

KELLER, ALLEN S, b New Haven, Conn, Jan 24, 29; m 58; c 6. STRATIGRAPHY, STRUCTURAL GEOLOGY. Educ: Univ Utah, BS, 51, MS, 52; Columbia Univ, PhD(geol), 63. Prof Exp: Instr geol, Univ Pa, 60-63; from asst prof to prof geol, Western Ill Univ, 63-80; SR EXPLOR GEOLOGIST, PHILLIPS PETROL CO, 80- Concurrent Pos: Consult, Amoco Res Ctr, 74-77. Mem: Geol Soc Am; Am Asn Petrol Geologists. Res: Geology of southeastern Idaho and Serrania del Interior, Venezuela; fractured petroleum reservoirs. Mailing Add: Phillips Petrol Co 7800 E Dorado Place Englewood CO 80111

KELLER, ARTHUR CHARLES, b New York, Aug 18, 01; m 28; c 1. ELECTRICAL ENGINEERING. Educ: Cooper Union, BS, 23, EE, 24; Yale Univ, MS, 25. Prof Exp: Lab asst, Bell Tel Labs, 17-23, mem tech staff, 23-42, spec apparatus engr, 42-46, switching apparatus engr, 46-49, dir switching apparatus develop, 49-55, 56-58, dir components, 55-56, dir switching systs develop, 58-61, dir switching apparatus lab, 61-66; RES & DEVELOP CONSULT, A C KELLER CO, 66- Concurrent Pos: Consult, Munitions Bd, 51-53, consult res & develop, Dept Defense, 55-61; mem bd dirs, Waukesha Motor Co, 63-; dir, Fifth Dimension, Inc, NJ, 67- Honors & Awards: US Navy Bur Ships & Bur Ord Awards; Emile Berliner Award, Audio Eng Soc, 62. Mem: Fel Inst Elec & Electronics Engrs; fel Acoust Soc; Am Soc Motion Picture & TV Engrs; Am Phys Soc. Res: Design, development and preparation for manufacture of electromechanical apparatus; sound recording; sonar; electrical measurements; telephone apparatus, radio frequency heating, telephone signaling and switching systems. Mailing Add: 125 White Plains Rd Bronxville NY 10708

KELLER, BARRY LEE, b Chicago, Ill, Nov 15, 37; m 62; c 2. WILDLIFE ECOLOGY. Educ: Western Mich Univ, BA, 61, MA, 62; Ind Univ, PhD(ecol), 68. Prof Exp: Fel ecol, Ind Univ, 68-69; assoc prof biol, Keen State Col, 69-70; asst prof, 70-75, assoc prof, 75-80, PROF POP ECOL, IDAHO STATE UNIV, 80- Concurrent Pos: Cur mammals, Idaho Mus Natural Hist, 79- Mem: Am Soc Mammalogists; Brit Ecol Soc; Ecol Soc Am; Soc Pop Ecol; Wildlife Soc. Res: Wildlife ecology, with emphasis on population ecology of non-game species; ecology of desert mammals, with emphasis on small mammals residing on radioactive waste disposal sites; powerline corridor analyses. Mailing Add: Dept Biol Idaho State Univ Pocatello ID 83209

KELLER, BERNARD GERARD, JR, b New Orleans, La, Dec 18, 36. PHARMACY. Educ: Loyola Univ, BS, 59; Univ Miss, MS, 64, PhD(pharm admin), 66. Prof Exp: Asst prof pharm & pharm admin, Southern Col Pharm, 65-67, assoc prof pharm admin, 67-69; asst dean clin progs, 72-81, PROF PHARMACEUT & CHMN DEPT, SCH PHARM, SOUTHWESTERN OKLA STATE UNIV, 69-, CHMN, DIV PHARMACEUT & PHARM ADMIN, 70-, DEAN, 81- Mem: Am Pharmaceut Asn; Am Soc Hosp Pharmacists; Am Col Apothecaries; Nat Asn Retail Druggists. Res: Pharmacy administration; motivation research; the pharmacist's relationship to the terminal patient; medical ethics. Mailing Add: PO Box 60304 Oklahoma City OK 73146

KELLER, CHARLES A(LBERT), b Columbus, Ohio, June 30, 19; m 41; c 2. CHEMICAL ENGINEERING. Educ: Ohio State Univ, BChE, 41. Prof Exp: Analyst, E I du Pont de Nemours & Co, Va, 41; asst declassification officer, US AEC, 46-47, declassification officer & actg asst chief declassification br,

47-48, chief, 48-50, chem engr, Oak Ridge Prod Div, 50-52, asst chief opers div, Portsmouth Area, 52-55, dep dir, Prod Div, 55-57, dir, 57-75, asst mgr opers, 75-79, asst mgr mfg & support, 79-81, TECH ADV TO MGR, OAK RIDGE OPERS OFF, US DEPT ENERGY, 81- Mem: Am Inst Chem Engrs; fel Am Inst Chem. Res: Absorption of volatile hydrocarbons from air mixtures; absorption and desorption of a volatile nontoxic, noninflammable organic solvent from an air-gas mixture. Mailing Add: 106 Norwood Lane Oak Ridge TN 37830

KELLER, DOLORES ELAINE, b New York, NY, Oct 29, 26; m 46; c 3. REPRODUCTIVE PHYSIOLOGY, MICROBIOLOGY. Educ: Long Island Univ, BS, 45; NY Univ, MA, 47, PhD(sex educ), 56; Univ Hawaii, cert, 64; Univ Calif, Berkeley, cert, 66. Prof Exp: Teacher biol & chmn dept, NY Pub Sch, 49-52; instr biol, French & lang & asst dean women, Long Island Univ, 52-56; from instr to assoc prof & chmn, Dept Sci, Fairleigh Dickinson Univ, 56-65; chmn dept biol, 65-68, PROF BIOL & DIR ALLIED HEALTH PROGS, PACE UNIV, 65-, DIR, NSF INSERV INST CELL PHYSIOL & GENETICS, WESTCHESTER CAMPUS, 66- Concurrent Pos: US deleg, Int Oceanog Conf, 59; NSF grants, 63-; res assoc, Haskins Labs, Carnegie Found, 63-; consult, Rennselaer Polytech Prog Intgerdisciplinary Col Sci, Charles Kettering Found, 64-; curriculum chmn, Bergen County Community Col, 64-; NSF-AEC grant marine & radiation biol, Univ Hawaii, 64-; res assoc, Lamont Geol Lab, Columbia Univ, 67-; NSF partic, Conf Primate Behav, Univ Calif, Davis, 71; spec consult, UN Comt Human Environ, 71-72; clin asst prof biol in psychiat, Dept Psychiat, Med Col, Cornell Univ, 74-; sr therapist, Payne Whitney Sexual Disorder Clin & pvt pract marriage counr sexual dysfunction, NJ, 74- Mem: Fel AAAS; Nat Sci Teachers Asn; Soc Protozool; Int Soc Clin & Exp Hypnosis; Am Asn Sex Educ Counrs. Res: Protozoology; fresh water and marine microbiology; science curriculum and education; sex education; human sexuality. Mailing Add: Dept of Biol Pace Univ Pleasantville NY 10570

KELLER, DONALD V, b Centralia, Wash, Aug 17, 30; m 59; c 2. EXPERIMENTAL PHYSICS. Educ: Harvard Univ, AB, 52; Univ Calif, Berkeley, PhD(physics), 57. Prof Exp: Chief shock dynamics, Boeing Co, 57-62; chief tech exp physics, Northrop Corp, Calif, 62-66; mem tech staff, Defense Res Corp, 66-69; pres, Effects Technol, Inc, 69-71; PRES, KTECH CORP, 71- Mem: Am Phys Soc. Res: High energy nuclear physics; shock hydrodynamics; laser physics; dynamic mechanic and thermal properties of materials. Mailing Add: Ktech Corp 911 Pennsylvania NE Albuquerque NM 87110

KELLER, DOUGLAS VERN, JR, b Syracuse, NY, Feb 8, 28; m; c 4. PHYSICAL CHEMISTRY. Educ: Univ Buffalo, BA, 55; Syracuse Univ, PhD(chem), 58. Prof Exp: Asst prof metall, Mont Sch Mines, 58-59; from asst prof to assoc prof metall eng, 59-69, prof mat sci, Syracuse Univ, 69-78; VPRES TECHNOL, OTISCA INDUSTS LTD, 78- Concurrent Pos: Chmn bd dirs, Otisca Industs Ltd, NY, 73-; adj prof mat sci, Syracuse Univ, 78- Mem: Am Chem Soc; Am Phys Soc; Am Soc Metals. Res: Physical chemistry of surfaces; coal physical chemistry and fuels benification. Mailing Add: Otisca Industs Ltd 501 Butternut St PO Box 127 Syracuse NY 13208

KELLER, EDWARD ANTHONY, b Los Angeles, Calif, June 6, 42; m 66; c 2. GEOMORPHOLOGY. Educ: Calif State Univ, Fresno, BS, 65, BA, 68; Univ Calif, Davis, MS, 69; Purdue Univ, PhD(geol), 73. Prof Exp: Asst prof geol, Calif State Univ, Fresno, 69-70; instr, Purdue Univ, 70-73, res asst, 71-73; asst prof, Univ NC, Charlotte, 73-76; ASST PROF ENVIRON STUDIES & GEOL SCI, UNIV CALIF, SANTA BARBARA, 76- Mem: Geol Soc Am; Sigma Xi. Res: Fluvial processes in geomorphology; environmental aspects of channelization; landscape aesthetics. Mailing Add: Dept of Environ Studies & Geol Sci Univ of Calif Santa Barbara CA 93106

KELLER, EDWARD CLARENCE, JR, b Freehold, NJ, Oct 8, 32; m 50; c 2. ECOLOGY, BIOSTATISTICS. Educ: Pa State Univ, BSc, 56, MSc, 59, PhD(genetics), 61. Hon Degrees: ScD, Salem Col, 78. Prof Exp: Asst genetics, Pa State Univ, 56-61; NIH trainee, Med Sch, Univ NC, 61-62, res assoc, 62, NIH fel, 62-64; asst prof zool, Univ Md, Col Park, 64-67; mgr biostatist, NUS Corp, 66-68; chmn dept, 68-74, PROF BIOL, WVA UNIV, 68- Concurrent Pos: Staff biologist, Comn Undergrad Educ Biol Sci, 65-66; pres, WVa Acad Sci, 75-76; vpres, Ecometrics Corp, 73-79; secy, Found Sci & the Handicapped, 77- Mem: AAAS; Soc Study Evolution; Biomet Soc; Ecol Soc Am; Am Statist Asn. Res: Aquatic ecology; quantitative inheritance of biochemical traits in Drosophila; vibration stress in organisms; ecosystem analysis and simulation; ecological data handling techniques; handicapped in science; genetics. Mailing Add: Dept of Biol WVa Univ Morgantown WV 26506

KELLER, EDWARD LEE, b Glade Springs, Va, Nov 23, 41; m 68. APPLIED MATHEMATICS. Educ: Duke Univ, BS, 64; Univ Mich, Ann Arbor, MA, 66, PhD(math), 69. Prof Exp: Res asst, Univ Mich, Ann Arbor, 64-68; asst prof, 69-73, assoc prof, 73-80, PROF MATH, CALIF STATE UNIV, HAYWARD, 80- Mem: Am Math Soc; Math Asn Am; Soc Indust & Appl Math. Res: Mathematical programming, particularly quadratic programming; matrix theory; mathematics of population. Mailing Add: Dept of Math Calif State Univ Hayward CA 94542

KELLER, EDWARD LOWELL, b Rapid City, SDak, Mar 6, 39; m 65; c 3. BIOMEDICAL ENGINEERING, NEUROBIOLOGY. Educ: US Naval Acad, BS, 61; Johns Hopkins Univ, PhD(biomed eng), 71. Prof Exp: Asst prof, 71-76, assoc prof, 76-79, PROF ELEC ENG, UNIV CALIF, BERKELEY, 79- Concurrent Pos: Dir, Smith-Kettlewell Ctr for Vision Res & sr scientist, Smith-Kettlewell Inst Visual Sci, 80. Mem: AAAS; Asn Res Vision & Ophthal; Inst Elec & Electronic Engrs; Soc Neurosci. Res: Neurophysiological studies of the central organization of the primate oculomotor system; mathematical modelling of neuromuscular control systems. Mailing Add: Dept Elec Eng & Comput Sci Univ Calif Berkeley CA 94720

KELLER, ELDON LEWIS, b Tiffin, Ohio, Dec 25, 34; m 61; c 1. NUCLEAR PHYSICS, RESEARCH ADMINISTRATION. *Educ:* Heidelberg Col, BS, 56; Univ Pittsburgh, MS, 60. *Prof Exp:* From assoc scientist to sr scientist, 60-69, res prog adminr, 69-74, ASST TO RES DIR, WESTINGHOUSE RES & DEVELOP CTR, 74- *Mem:* Am Phys Soc; Am Nuclear Soc. *Res:* Low-temperature radiation effects in superconductors; gamma-ray imaging using image intensifiers; semiconductor gamma-ray monitor; thickness gauging; gamma-ray spectrometry. *Mailing Add:* Westinghouse Res & Develop Ctr Pittsburgh PA 15235

KELLER, ELIZABETH BEACH, b Diongloh, China, Dec 28, 17; US citizen; m 41. BIOCHEMISTRY. *Educ:* Univ Chicago, BS, 40; George Washington Univ, MS, 45; Cornell Univ, PhD(biochem), 48. *Prof Exp:* Asst, Med Col, Cornell Univ, 46-48; Atomic Energy Comn fel, Col Med, Ohio State Univ, 48-49; Huntington Mem Lab, Mass Gen Hosp, 49-50, res fel, Harvard Univ, 50-52, res assoc, 52-58, USPHS spec fel & res fel, 58-60; res assoc, Mass Inst Technol, 60-62; res specialist, 62-65, asst prof, 65-71, ASSOC PROF BIOCHEM, CORNELL UNIV, 71- *Mem:* Am Soc Biol Chem. *Res:* Mechanism of the biosynthesis and functions of nucleic acids. *Mailing Add:* Dept of Biochem Wing Hall Cornell Univ Ithaca NY 14850

KELLER, EVELYN FOX, b New York, NY, Mar 20, 36; c 2. MATHEMATICAL BIOLOGY. *Educ:* Brandeis Univ, BA, 57; Harvard Univ, PhD(physics), 63. *Prof Exp:* Instr, NY Univ, 62-63, asst res scientist, 63-66, from asst prof to assoc prof, Grad Sch Med Sci, Cornell Univ, 66-72; ASSOC PROF, STATE UNIV NY, PURCHASE, 72- *Concurrent Pos:* Mem, Ctr for Policy Res, 76- *Mem:* AAAS. *Res:* Mathematical models of chemotaxis and pattern formation; psychological basis of scientific beliefs. *Mailing Add:* Dept of Nat Sci State Univ of NY Purchase NY 10577

KELLER, FREDERICK ALBERT, JR, b New York, NY; m 66. BIOCHEMISTRY, BIOCHEMICAL ENGINEERING. *Educ:* Stevens Inst Technol, BE, 61; Rutgers Univ, New Brunswick, MS, 67, PhD(microbial biochem & eng), 68. *Prof Exp:* Chemist polymerization develop lab, Hercules Inc, 61-62; USPHS fel, 68-70; biochem engr, Biol & Med Sci Lab, Gen Elec Co, 70-75; sr biochem engr, Union Carbide Corp, 75-79; SECT LEADER, CPC INT, 79- *Mem:* AAAS; Am Inst Chem Engrs; Am Chem Soc; Am Soc Microbiol; Soc Indust Microbiol. *Res:* Biosynthesis, physiology, bioregulation and biodegradation of structural and storage macromolecules, especially cellulo-lignins, starch, chitin, glycogen; enzymic kinetics; adsorption processes; regenerable raw materials; SCP; chemicals by fermentation; microbial process development. *Mailing Add:* CPC Int Moffett Tech Ctr PO Box 345 Summit-Argo IL 60501

KELLER, FREDERICK JACOB, b Huntington, WVa, May 10, 34; m 54; c 4. EXPERIMENTAL SOLID STATE PHYSICS. *Educ:* Marshall Univ, BS, 60; Univ Tenn, MS, 62, PhD(physics), 66. *Prof Exp:* Teaching asst physics, Univ Tenn, 63-64; physicist, Oak Ridge Nat Lab, 66; from asst prof to assoc prof, 66-77, PROF PHYSICS, CLEMSON UNIV, 77- *Mem:* Am Phys Soc. *Res:* Color centers in alkali halides. *Mailing Add:* Dept of Physics & Astron Clemson Univ Clemson SC 29631

KELLER, GEOFFREY, b New York, NY, June 12, 18; m 50; c 2. ASTRONOMY. *Educ:* Swarthmore Col, BS, 38; Columbia Univ, PhD(astron), 48. *Prof Exp:* Asst physics, Columbia Univ, 38-41; assoc physicist, Bur Ord, US Dept Navy, 41-45; from instr to prof physics & astron, Ohio State Univ, 48-59, dir Perkins Observ, 53-59; prog dir astron, NSF, 59-61, div dir math & phys sci, 61-66, dep planning dir, 66-68; dean col math & phys sci, 68-71, PROF ASTRON, OHIO STATE UNIV, 72- *Concurrent Pos:* Instr, Ohio Wesleyan Univ, 48-49. *Mem:* Am Astron Soc. *Res:* Internal constitution of stars; fluid turbulence. *Mailing Add:* Dept of Astron Ohio State Univ Columbus OH 43210

KELLER, GEORGE EARL, b Baton Rouge, La, Nov 6, 40; m 64. NUCLEAR PHYSICS. *Educ:* La State Univ, BS, 62, PhD(physics), 69. *Prof Exp:* ASST PROF PHYSICS, W GA COL, 69- *Mem:* Am Phys Soc; Am Asn Physics Teachers; Am Inst Physics. *Res:* Gamma ray spectroscopy; determination of the properties of the excited states of the doubly even deformed nuclei. *Mailing Add:* Dept of Physics West Ga Col Carrollton GA 30117

KELLER, GEORGE H, b Hartford, Conn, Sept 9, 31; m 55; c 2. MARINE GEOLOGY. *Educ:* Univ Conn, AB, 54; Univ Utah, MS, 56; Univ Ill, PhD(marine geol), 66. *Prof Exp:* Geologist, Stand Oil Co Tex, 57-59; geol oceanogr, US Naval Oceanog Off, DC, 59-67; res oceanogr, Inst Oceanog, Md, 67-69, res oceanogr, Atlantic Oceanog Labs, Nat Oceanic & Atmospheric Admin, Fla, 69-75; ASSOC DEAN, SCH OCEANOG, ORE STATE UNIV, 75- *Concurrent Pos:* Mem Mid-Atlantic Ridge explor, Nat Oceanic & Atmospheric Admin & others, 74-77. *Mem:* Geol Soc Am; Int Asn Sedimentol; Am Geophys Union. *Res:* Marine geology and oceanography of the Malacca Strait, Malaysia; marine geotechniques, study of the mass physical and engineering properties of deep sea sediments. *Mailing Add:* Sch Oceanog Ore State Univ Corvallis OR 97331

KELLER, GEORGE RANDY, JR, b Muskogee, Okla, Apr 17, 46; m 67; c 1. SEISMOLOGY. *Educ:* Tex Tech Univ, BS, 68, MS, 69, PhD(geophys), 73. *Prof Exp:* Instr geophys, Tex Tech Univ, 70-71; res asst prof, Univ Utah, 72-73; asst prof, Univ Ky, 73-76; asst prof, 76-78, ASSOC PROF GEOPHYS, UNIV TEX, EL PASO, 78-, DIR SEISMIC OBSERV, 76- *Mem:* Am Geophys Union; Am Asn Petrol Geologists; Geol Soc Am; Seismol Soc Am; Soc Explor Geophysicist. *Res:* Solid earth geophysics (seismology, gravity and geomagnetism); specifically the crustal structure and tectonics of North America. *Mailing Add:* Dept of Geol Sci Univ Tex El Paso TX 79968

KELLER, GERTA, b Liechtenstein, Fla, Mar 7, 45. PALEONCEANOGRAPHY, PALEONTOLOGY. *Educ:* Stanford Univ, PhD(geol), 78. *Prof Exp:* Geologist, Stanford Univ, 78-80; Nat Res Coun fel, 80-81, GEOLOGIST RES, US GEOL SURV, 81- *Concurrent Pos:* Res assoc, Stanford Univ, 80- *Mem:* Geol Soc Am; NAm Micropaleontol Soc; Soc Econ Paleontologists & Mineralogists; Schweizeizische Geologishe Ges. *Res:* Biostratigraphic, paleoclimatic and paleooceanographic interpretations based on faunal analyses of planktic foraminifers in the world ocean and land sections; stratigraphy-sedimentation; paleontology; paleoceanography; paleoclimatology. *Mailing Add:* MS 99 Paleont & Sedimentation Br 345 Middlefield Rd Menlo Park CA 94025

KELLER, HAROLD WILLARD, b Newton, Kans, Dec 10, 37; m 65; c 2. MYCOLOGY. *Educ:* Kans Wesleyan Col, BA, 60; Univ Kans, MA, 63; Univ Iowa, PhD(bot), 71. *Prof Exp:* Fel bot, Grad Sch, Univ Fla, 71-72; asst prof biol, 72-78, asst dir, 78-80, ASSOC DIR, UNIV RES SERV & ADJ ASSOC PROF, DEPT MICROBIOL & IMMUNOL, WRIGHT STATE UNIV, 80- *Concurrent Pos:* Conf partic, Comn Undergrad Educ Biol Sci, 70; NSF grants, 75-78. *Mem:* Asn Southeastern Biologists; Mycol Soc Am; Sigma Xi; NAm Mycol Soc. *Res:* Taxonomic, monographic and floristic studies of the corticolous myxomycetes. *Mailing Add:* Univ Res Serv Wright State Univ Dayton OH 45435

KELLER, HARRY BERT, III, b Ft Wayne, Ind, June 4, 24; m 51; c 3. PHYSICS. *Educ:* Univ Mich, BSE, 48, PhD(physics), 51. *Prof Exp:* Supvr magnet testing group, Lawrence Radiation Lab, Univ Calif, 51-53 & diag photography group, 54-56, test group dir, 57-58, dept head oper safety, 59-64, supvr plowshare environ eval, 64-65; ASSOC PROF PHYSICS, ST OLAF COL, 65- *Mem:* Am Phys Soc. *Res:* Magnetic measurements; beta ray spectroscopy; sweeping image cameras; radioactivity measurements. *Mailing Add:* Dept of Physics St Olaf Col Northfield MN 55057

KELLER, HERBERT BISHOP, b Paterson, NJ, June 19, 25; m 53; c 2. APPLIED MATHEMATICS, NUMERICAL ANALYSIS. *Educ:* Ga Inst Technol, BEE, 45; NY Univ, MA, 48, PhD(math), 54. *Prof Exp:* Instr physics & math, Ga Inst Technol, 46-47; res scientist, Div Electromagnetic Res, Inst Math Sci, NY Univ, 48-53, lectr math, Wash Sq Col, 57-59, assoc prof, Univ, 59-61, prof appl math, Courant Inst Math Sci, 61-67, assoc dir, AEC Comput & Appl Math Ctr, 64-67; PROF APPL MATH, CALIF INST TECHNOL, 67- *Concurrent Pos:* Head dept math, Sarah Lawrence Col, 51-53; assoc ed, J Appl Math, Soc Indust & Appl Math, 61-66, ed, J Numerical Anal, 64-71; ed, Monogr Ser, Asn Comput Mach, 63-65; vis prof, Calif Inst Technol, 65-66; mem math div, Nat Res Coun, 69-72; mem coun, Conf Bd Math Sci, 71-73; assoc ed, J Comput & Systs Sci, 71-74, ed, 74-; consult, var indust & govt concerns. *Mem:* Soc Indust & Appl Math (pres, 75-76); Asn Comput Mach; Am Math Soc; Math Asn Am; fel Am Acad Arts & Sci. *Res:* Numerical analysis; fluid mechanics; nuclear and chemical reactors; applied mechanics; computing machinery; bifurcation theory. *Mailing Add:* Dept of Appl Math Calif Inst of Technol Pasadena CA 91125

KELLER, JAMES LLOYD, b Kittanning, Pa, June 21, 18; m 41, 60; c 4. ALCOHOL FUELS, ALTERNATIVE FUELS. *Educ:* Pa State Col, BS, 39; Emory Univ, MS, 40; Univ Calif, Los Angeles, PhD(phys org chem), 48. *Prof Exp:* Chemist, Magnolia Petrol Co, 40 & Koppers Co, 41-42; lab dept head synthetic rubber, US Rubber Co, 42-45; sr res assoc, 48-80, STAFF CONSULT, SCI & TECHNOL DIV, UNION OIL CO, 80- *Mem:* Am Chem Soc; Soc Automotive Engrs; Am Petrol Inst. *Res:* Petroleum product development and application; alternative fuels evaluation. *Mailing Add:* 1425 Longview Dr Fullerton CA 92631

KELLER, JEFFREY THOMAS, b Cincinnati, Ohio, Oct 17, 46; m 76. NEUROANATOMY. *Educ:* Univ Cincinnati, BA, 69, MS, 72, PhD(anat), 75. *Prof Exp:* Asst biol, Univ Cincinnati, 69-71, asst anat, Col Med, 71-75; DIR NEUROANAT RES, MAYFIELD NEUROL INST, 75- *Concurrent Pos:* Adj asst prof anat, Col Med, Univ Cincinnati, 75-79, adj assoc prof, 79- *Mem:* Sigma Xi; fel Am Heart Asn; Am Asn Anatomists; Soc Neurosci. *Res:* Post-operative cicatrix and the spinal dura; spinal dura repair; basal ganglia; trigeminal system. *Mailing Add:* Inst Med Res Christ Hosp 2141 Auburn Ave Cincinnati OH 45219

KELLER, JOHN GEORGE, toxicology, physiology, see previous edition

KELLER, JOHN RANDALL, b Ogdensburg, NY, Dec 14, 25; m 60. MICROBIOLOGY. *Educ:* Cornell Univ, BS, 47, PhD, 52. *Prof Exp:* Asst prof plant path, Univ Md, 52-54; teacher pub schs, 55-59; res assoc phys chem, Clarkson Col Technol, 59-60; from asst prof to assoc prof microbiol 60-64, ASSOC PROF BIOL, SETON HALL UNIV, 64- *Concurrent Pos:* Res assoc phys chem, Clarkson Tech, 59- *Honors & Awards:* Vaughn Award, Am Soc Hort Sci, 52. *Mem:* Mycol Soc; Am Soc Microbiol. *Res:* Microbiology; plasmids; cyclic adenosine monophosphate. *Mailing Add:* Dept of Biol Seton Hall Univ South Orange NJ 07079

KELLER, JOSEPH BISHOP, b Paterson, NJ, July 31, 23; m 63; c 2. MATHEMATICS. *Educ:* NY Univ, BA, 43, MS, 46, PhD(math), 48. *Prof Exp:* Instr physics, Princeton Univ, 43-44; asst, Div War Res, Columbia Univ, 44-45; mathematician, Inst Math & Mech, 45-52; asst, Washington Sq Col, 46-47; asst prof, NY Univ, 48-52, assoc res prof, 52-56, prof, 56-79, chmn dept, 67-73, dir, Div Electromagnetic res, Courant Inst Math Sci, 66-79; PROF MATH, STANFORD UNIV, 79- *Concurrent Pos:* Lectr, Grad Sch, Stevens Inst Technol, 48; head math br, Off Naval Res, 53-54; vis prof, Stanford Univ, 69-70, 76-78; res assoc, Woods Hole Oceanog Inst, 69-; vis scholar, Calif Inst Technol, 73-74; consult, var indust & govt concerns. *Mem:* Nat Acad Sci; Am Phys Soc; Am Math Soc; Soc Indust & Appl Math (vpres, 78-79); Am Acad Arts & Sci. *Res:* Applied mathematics; acoustics; electromagnetic theory; fluid dynamics; geometrical optics. *Mailing Add:* 820 Sonoma Terrace Stanford CA 94305

KELLER, JOSEPH EDWARD, JR, b La Crosse, Wis, Mar 31, 36. APPLIED MECHANICS, MECHANICAL ENGINEERING. *Educ:* Swarthmore Col, BS, 58; Univ Kans, MS, 60, PhD(eng mech), 64. *Prof Exp:* Engr, 64-74, dep leader, Weapons Prog, 74, dep div leader, 74-78, DIV LEADER, LAWRENCE LIVERMORE NAT LAB, 78- *Mem:* Am Soc Mech Engrs; Sigma Xi; AAAS. *Res:* Development and implementation of numerical techniques. *Mailing Add:* Lawrence Livermore Nat Lab PO Box 808 L-471 Livermore CA 94550

KELLER, JOSEPH HERBERT, b Bristol, Va, Sept 25, 46; m 69. PHYSICAL CHEMISTRY. *Educ:* King Col, BS, 68; Univ Ill, Urbana, MS, 70, PhD(phys chem), 74. *Prof Exp:* Res assoc & NSF fel chem, Univ Tenn, Knoxville, 73-75; res assoc catalysis, Oxy-Catalyst, Inc, 75-77, sr res assoc, 77-80, MGR, CATALYST DEPT, MET-PRO CORP, 80- *Mem:* Am Chem Soc; Sigma Xi; Catalysis Club; Org Reactions Catalysis Soc. *Res:* Heterogeneous catalysis; kinetic isotope effects of hydrogen and carbon; vapor pressure isotope effects; surface and media effect on reaction rates. *Mailing Add:* 522 N Maryland Ave West Chester PA 19380

KELLER, KENNETH F, b Louisville, Ky, July 3, 21; m 46; c 7. MICROBIOLOGY. *Educ:* Univ Louisville, BA, 43, MS, 57, PhD(microbiol), 65. *Prof Exp:* Instr, 61-66, asst prof, 66-80, ASSOC PROF MICROBIOL, SCH MED, UNIV LOUISVILLE, 80-, ASSOC PROF PATH, 74- *Concurrent Pos:* Consult, Gen Elec Co, 60-63 & Stand Oil Co Ky, 63. *Mem:* Am Soc Microbiol. *Res:* Biological and antigenic properties of the inclusion conjunctivitis agent; adrenergic receptors of mouse adipose tissue; use of lectins in diagnostic microbiology. *Mailing Add:* Dept of Microbiol Sch of Med Univ of Louisville Louisville KY 40208

KELLER, KENNETH FRANK, b Salt Lake City, Utah, July 22, 19; m 42; c 2. GEOLOGY. *Educ:* Univ Utah, BS, 41, MS, 42. *Prof Exp:* Geologist, 46-51, dist geologist, 51-60, dist explor supt, 60-61, div explor mgr, 61-66, mgr explor res, 66-68, explor mgr int div, 68-72, pres Mobil Producing, North West Europe, 72-75, VPRES EXPLOR, NORTH AM DIV, MOBIL OIL CORP, 75-, PRES MOBIL EXPLOR & PROD SOUTHEAST, INC, 80- *Mem:* AAAS; Geol Soc London; Am Asn Petrol Geologists; Geol Soc Am; Soc Explor Geophysicists. *Res:* Petroleum exploration involving structure and sedimentary geology; seismic, gravity and magnetic geophysics; geochemistry and petroleum economics. *Mailing Add:* Mobil Oil Corp 150 E 42nd St New York NY 10017

KELLER, KENNETH H(ARRISON), b New York, NY, Oct 19, 34; m 57; c 2. CHEMICAL & BIOMEDICAL ENGINEERING. *Educ:* Columbia Univ, BA, 56, BS, 57; Johns Hopkins Univ, MSE, 63, PhD(chem eng), 64. *Prof Exp:* Engr, Div Reactor Develop, AEC, Washington, DC, 57-61; from asst prof to assoc prof chem eng, 64-71, actg dean grad sch, 74-75, PROF CHEM ENG, UNIV MINN, MINNEAPOLIS, 71-, HEAD DEPT CHEM ENG & MAT SCI, 78- *Concurrent Pos:* NIH spec fel, 72-73; mem surg & bioeng study sect, NIH, 76-80; Sigma Xi nat lectr, 78-79. *Mem:* Am Inst Chem Engrs; Am Soc Artificial Internal Organs. *Res:* Transport phenomena in biological systems; artificial internal organ development. *Mailing Add:* 8209 York Ave S Minneapolis MN 55431

KELLER, KENNETH RAYMOND, b Minn, Nov 21, 13; m 43; c 2. PLANT BREEDING. *Educ:* Iowa State Col, PhD, 48. *Prof Exp:* Asst prof farm crops, Iowa State Col, 48; agronomist, USDA, Agr Exp Sta, Ore State Col, 48-54, agr administr, Tobacco & Spec Crops, Md, 54-57, asst dir in chg tobacco res, USDA, 57-76, ASSOC DEAN & DIR AGR EXP STA, NC STATE UNIV, 76-, PROF CROP SCI, 57- *Res:* Statistics. *Mailing Add:* 100B Patterson Hall NC State Univ Raleigh NC 27650

KELLER, LELAND EDWARD, b Carnegie, Okla, Jan 21, 23; m 49; c 3. ANATOMY. *Educ:* Univ Wichita, BA, 50; Univ Kans, PhD(anat), 58. *Prof Exp:* From asst prof to prof anat & physiol, 57-74, PROF BIOL, PITTSBURG STATE UNIV, 74- *Res:* Histology; physiology; history and use of old medical quack devices. *Mailing Add:* Dept of Biol Pittsburg State Univ Pittsburg KS 66762

KELLER, MARGARET ANNE, b Boston, Mass, May 29, 47; m 71; c 1. INFECTIOUS DISEASES. *Educ:* Mass Inst Technol, SB, 68; Albert Einstein Col Med, MD, 72. *Prof Exp:* From intern to resident pediat, Med Ctr, Univ Calif, San Diego, 72-75, chief resident, 75, fel infectious dis, Dept Pediat, 75-76; fel immunol & infectious dis, Dept Pediat, 76-78, ASST PROF PEDIAT, HARBOR-UNIV CALIF LOS ANGELES MED CTR, 78- *Mem:* Fel Am Acad Pediat; Am Fedn Clin Res; Soc Pediat Res; Am Phys Soc; Am Soc Microbiol. *Res:* Immunology of human brest milk. *Mailing Add:* 7018 Crest Rd Rancho Palo Verdes CA 90274

KELLER, MARION WILES, b Dayton, Ohio, June 21, 05; m 27, 54; c 1. MATHEMATICS. *Educ:* Ohio Wesleyan Univ, AB, 26; Ind Univ, MA, 29, PhD(anal), 32. *Prof Exp:* Teacher, Ohio Pub Schs, 26-27; head dept math, Kans Wesleyan Univ, 27-28; asst, Ind Univ, 28-29, instr, 29-30, asst, 30-31; teacher, Ohio Pub Schs, 33-36; from instr to prof, 36-71, asst head dept, 60-71, EMER PROF MATH, PURDUE UNIV, 71- *Mem:* Am Math Soc; Am Soc Eng Educ; Math Asn Am. *Res:* Student errors; placement; testing; angular velocity between the foci in Keplerian elliptic motion. *Mailing Add:* Div of Math Sci Purdue Univ Lafayette IN 47907

KELLER, MARTIN DAVID, b New York, NY, Apr 7, 23; m 53; c 3. EPIDEMIOLOGY. *Educ:* Yeshiva Univ, AB, 44; NY Univ, MS, 46, PhD(biol), 53; Cornell Univ, MD, 52; Columbia Univ, MPH, 58. *Prof Exp:* Intern pediat, New York Hosp-Cornell Med Ctr, 52-53; med resident internal med, Vet Admin Hosp, New York, 55-56; resident med serv, Columbia Univ, 57; actg dir chronic dis div, Ohio Dept Health, 57-58, dir res training, 58-60; dir clin serv, Beth Israel Hosp, Boston, Mass, 60-62; assoc prof prev med, 62-66, head div epidemiol & biomet, 66-67, ASST PROF MED, OHIO STATE UNIV, 62-, PROF PREV MED, 66-, HEAD DIV COMMUNITY HEALTH, 67- *Concurrent Pos:* Lectr, Harvard Med Sch, 60-62; consult, Ohio Dept Health, 64- *Mem:* Am Pub Health Asn; Am Col Prev Med; NY Acad Sci. *Res:* Environmental and host factors affecting distribution of human disease entities. *Mailing Add:* Dept of Prev Med Ohio State Univ Columbus OH 43210

KELLER, OSWALD LEWIN, b New York, NY, May 24, 30; m 53; c 4. PHYSICAL CHEMISTRY, RESEARCH ADMINISTRATION. *Educ:* Univ of the South, BS, 51; Mass Inst Technol, PhD(phys chem), 59. *Prof Exp:* USPHS res fel, 59-60; chemist, 60-67, dir transuranium res lab, 67-74, DIR

CHEM DIV, OAK RIDGE NAT LAB, 74- *Concurrent Pos:* Mem nuclear physics panel, Physics Surv Comt, Nat Acad Sci, 69-72. *Mem:* Fel AAAS; Am Chem Soc; Am Phys Soc; Sigma Xi. *Res:* Physical chemistry of proteins; chemistry of transuranium elements; molecular spectroscopy; preparation and characterization of compounds; heavy ion reactions; coal chemistry; administration of nuclear and non-nuclear energy research. *Mailing Add:* Oak Ridge Nat Lab PO Box X Oak Ridge TN 37830

KELLER, PATRICIA J, b Detroit, Mich, Nov 16, 23. BIOCHEMISTRY. *Educ:* Univ Detroit, BS, 45; Wash Univ, PhD(biochem), 53. *Prof Exp:* Res assoc biochem, Sch Med, 55-56, instr, 56-57, res asst prof, 57-62, assoc prof, Sch Dent, 62-67, assoc dean, Grad Sch, 74-77, PROF ORAL BIOL, SCH DENT, UNIV WASH, 67-, CHMN ORAL BIOL, 79- *Concurrent Pos:* USPHS fels, Wash Univ, 53-54 & Univ Wash, 54-55; vis fel, Inst Marine Biochem, Aberdeen, Scotland, 78-79. *Mem:* AAAS; Am Soc Biol Chem; Am Soc Cell Biol; Am Chem Soc; Int Asn Dent Res. *Res:* Structure, function and biosynthesis of enzyme proteins. *Mailing Add:* Dept of Oral Biol Univ of Wash Sch of Dent Seattle WA 98195

KELLER, PHILIP CHARLES, b San Francisco, Calif, Mar 10, 39; m 65. INORGANIC CHEMISTRY. *Educ:* Univ Calif, Berkeley, BA, 61; Ind Univ, PhD(boron chem), 66. *Prof Exp:* From asst prof to assoc prof, 66-75, PROF CHEM, UNIV ARIZ, 75- *Mem:* Am Chem Soc; The Chem Soc. *Res:* Boron hydride chemistry; chemistry of Group III elements. *Mailing Add:* Dept of Chem Univ of Ariz Tucson AZ 85721

KELLER, PHILIP JOSEPH, b New Brunswick, NJ, Sept 21, 41; m 63. PHYSICAL CHEMISTRY. *Educ:* Temple Univ, AB, 64, PhD(phys chem), 70. *Prof Exp:* Sr anal chemist, Merck Sharp & Dohme Res Labs, Pa, 64-66; res chemist, 69-72, develop rep, 71-72, prod technologist, 73-74, mkt res specialist, 75, planning specialist, Indust Chems Dept, 75-76, purchasing agent, 76-79, SR PURCHASING AGENT, ENERGY & MAT DEPT, E I DU PONT DE NEMOURS & CO, INC, 79- *Concurrent Pos:* Adj asst prof, Temple Univ, 69-70. *Mem:* AAAS; Am Chem Soc. *Res:* Waste water chemistry; fused salts; electrochemistry; polyelectrolytes; surface chemistry. *Mailing Add:* E I du Pont de Nemours & Co Energy & Mat Dept Wilmington DE 19898

KELLER, RAYMOND E, b Cape Girardeau, Mo, May 25, 45; div; c 1. DEVELOPMENTAL BIOLOGY, CELL BIOLOGY. *Educ:* Southeast Mo State Univ, BS, 67; Univ Ill, Urbana, MS, 69, PhD(develop), 75. *Prof Exp:* Assoc, Lab of Prof J P Trinkaus, Dept Biol, Yale Univ, 75-76, Am Cancer Soc fel, 76-77; vis scientist, Ind Univ, 77-80; ASST PROF, DEPT ZOOL, UNIV CALIF, BERKELEY, 80- *Res:* Analysis of the mechanisms of metazoan morphogenetic cell movements. *Mailing Add:* Dept Zool Univ Calif Berkeley CA 94720

KELLER, REED THEODORE, b Aberdeen, SDak, May 26, 38; m 59; c 3. GASTROENTEROLOGY, INTERNAL MEDICINE. *Educ:* Univ NDak, BA, 60, BS, 61; Harvard Med Sch, MD, 63; cert, Am Bd Internal Med, 66 & 77; cert, Am Bd Gastroenterol, 75. *Prof Exp:* From intern to resident med, Univ Hosp, Cleveland, 63-66, chief resident, 67-68; asst prof, Med Sch, Case Western Reserve Univ, 70-73; PROF MED & CHMN DEPT, SCH MED, UNIV NDAK, 73-, CHIEF MED, MED CTR REHAB HOSP, 74- *Concurrent Pos:* Fel gastroenterol, Vet Admin Hosp, Cleveland, 66-67, Vet Admin grant, 72-73; grant, Univ NDak, 73-; vis prof med, Univ Guadalajara, 74; chief med, Fargo Vet Admin Hosp, 74-, consult gastroenterol, 74-75 & 76- *Honors & Awards:* Physicians Recognition Award, AMA, 77. *Mem:* Am Soc Gastrointestinal Endoscopy; Soc Exp Biol & Med; AMA; fel Am Col Gastroenterol; fel Am Col Physicians. *Res:* Use of acrylic polymers to control gastrointestinal hemorrhage. *Mailing Add:* Dept of Med Univ of NDak Sch of Med Grand Forks ND 58201

KELLER, RICHARD ALAN, b Pittsburgh, Pa, Nov 28, 34; m 56; c 3. CHEMICAL PHYSICS. *Educ:* Allegheny Col, BS, 56; Univ Calif, Berkeley, PhD(phys chem), 61. *Prof Exp:* Asst prof chem, Univ Ore, 59-63; staff mem, Div Phys DIV PHYS Chem, Nat Bur Standards, 63-76; STAFF MEM CHEM, LOS ALAMOS NAT LABS, 76- *Mem:* Am Chem Soc; Am Phys Soc. *Res:* Laser induced chemistry; laser induced isotope enrichment; laser based analytical techniques. *Mailing Add:* Los Alamos Nat Lab MS 732 Los Alamos NM 87545

KELLER, ROBERT, b Vienna, Austria, Aug 3, 26; nat US; m 54. MICROBIOLOGY. *Educ:* Univ Denver, AB, 50; Univ Pa, MS, 51, PhD(microbiol), 53; Am Bd Med Microbiol, dipl. *Prof Exp:* Asst bact, Sch Dent, Univ Pa, 52-53; res assoc, Univ Tex, 53-54; from instr to asst prof microbiol, Sch Med, Univ Mo, 54-58; asst dir, 58-62, ASSOC DIR DEPT MICROBIOL, MICHAEL REESE HOSP & MED CTR, 62- *Mem:* AAAS; Am Asn Immunologists; Am Soc Microbiol; Tissue Cult Asn. *Res:* Immune response to viral infections; cytomegalovirus. *Mailing Add:* Dept of Microbiol Michael Reese Hosp Med Ctr Chicago IL 60616

KELLER, ROBERT B, b Wichita, Kans, Nov 8, 24; m 52; c 2. MECHANICAL ENGINEERING. *Educ:* Univ Wichita, BS, 48; Univ Mich, MS, 51, PhD(mech eng), 62. *Prof Exp:* Res engr, N Am Aviation, Inc, 51-54; supvr turbine engines, Allison Div, Gen Motors Corp, 54-59; ASSOC PROF MECH ENG, UNIV MICH, ANN ARBOR, 62- *Concurrent Pos:* Consult, Chem & Indust Corp, Ford Motor Co, Babcock & Wilcox & Clark Equip Co. *Mem:* AAAS; Am Soc Mech Engrs; Am Inst Aeronaut & Astronaut; Soc Automotive Engrs. *Res:* Rocket propulsion systems; gas turbine technology; fluid control systems. *Mailing Add:* 1603 E Stadium Ann Arbor MI 48104

KELLER, ROBERT ELLIS, b Marshalltown, Iowa, Jan 10, 23; m 46; c 2. ANALYTICAL CHEMISTRY. *Educ:* Univ Iowa, BA, 47, MS, 49, PhD(anal chem), 51. *Prof Exp:* Res chemist anal chem, Smith, Kline & French Labs, 50-52; res chemist, 52-54, proj leader, 54-55, from group leader to sr res group leader, 55-67, sect mgr, 67-69, MGR APPL SCI, MONSANTO CO, 69- *Mem:* Am Chem Soc; Soc Appl Spectros. *Res:* Spectroscopy. *Mailing Add:* 10142 Glenfield Terr St Louis MO 63126

KELLER, ROBERT MARION, b St Louis, Mo, June 12, 44; m 67. COMPUTER SCIENCE, ELECTRICAL ENGINEERING. *Educ:* Wash Univ, BS, 66, MS, 68; Univ Calif, Berkeley, PhD(elec eng, comput sci), 70. *Prof Exp:* Asst prof elec eng, Princeton Univ, 70-76; assoc prof, 76-81, PROF COMPUT SCI, UNIV UTAH, 81- *Mem:* Asn Comput Mach; Inst Elec & Electronics Engrs. *Res:* Computer system organization; theories of computation; parallel and asychronous computation; functional programming languages. *Mailing Add:* Dept of Comput Sci 3160 MEB Univ of Utah Salt Lake City UT 84112

KELLER, ROGER F, JR, b Manchester, NH, July 24, 22; m 48; c 3. ZOOLOGY. *Educ:* Univ NH, BS, 48; Mich State Univ, PhD(zool), 53. *Prof Exp:* Instr zool, Mich State Univ, 52-54; assoc prof & head dept, 54-66, PROF BIOL, UNIV AKRON, 66-; chmn Div Nat Sci & Allied Health Prog, 77-82; RETIRED. *Mem:* AAAS; Am Soc Human Genetics; Am Genetic Asn; Am Inst Biol Sci; Am Eugenics Soc. *Mailing Add:* Dept Biol Univ Akron Akron OH 44325

KELLER, ROY ALAN, b Davenport, Iowa, Feb 5, 28; m 52; c 4. ANALYTICAL CHEMISTRY. *Educ:* Univ Ariz, BSc, 50, MS, 52; Univ Utah, PhD(chem), 57. *Prof Exp:* Instr chem, Univ Ariz, 51-53, from asst prof to assoc prof, 56-68; chmn dept, 68-74, PROF CHEM, STATE UNIV NY COL FREDONIA, 68- *Concurrent Pos:* Petrol Res Fund Int Award, Free Univ Brussels, 62-63; ed, J Chromatog Sci. *Mem:* AAAS; Am Chem Soc. *Res:* Chromatography. *Mailing Add:* Dept of Chem State Univ of NY Col Fredonia NY 14063

KELLER, ROY FRED, b Cape Girardeau, Mo, Apr 3, 27; m 49; c 2. MATHEMATICS, COMPUTER SCIENCE. *Educ:* Southeast Mo State Univ, BS, 50; Univ Mo, AM, 58, PhD(math), 62. *Prof Exp:* Instr math, Univ Mo-Columbia, 56-57, actg dir comput res ctr, 59-62, asst prof math & dir comput ctr, 62-67; assoc prof math & comput sci, Iowa State Univ, 67-71, prof, 71-81; PROF COMPUT SCI & CHMN DEPT, UNIV NEBR, 81- *Mem:* Asn Comput Mach; Inst Elec & Electronics Engrs; Asn Educ Data Systs. *Res:* Iterative methods for solving systems of equations; programming and programming languages. *Mailing Add:* Dept of Comput Sci Univ Nebr Lincoln NE 68588

KELLER, SEYMOUR PAUL, b New York, NY, July 5, 22; m 49; c 4. SOLID STATE PHYSICS. *Educ:* Univ Chicago, BS, 47, MS, 48, PhD(chem, physics), 51. *Prof Exp:* Du Pont fel chem, Univ Wis, 51-52; res assoc, Columbia Univ, 52-53; staff mem, 53-63, mgr solid state physics & chem, 62-64, dir tech planning res, 64-66, dir phys sci dept, 66-72, CONSULT TO DIR RES, THOMAS J WATSON RES CTR, IBM CORP, 72- *Mem:* Fel Am Phys Soc. *Res:* Optical and electrical properties of dielectric and semiconducting solids; luminescent materials; paramagnetic resonance of solids; wave function calculations. *Mailing Add:* Thomas J Watson Res Ctr PO Box 218 Yorktown Heights NY 10598

KELLER, STANLEY E, b Medford, Mass, Sept 9, 21; m 45; c 4. DENTISTRY. *Educ:* Tufts Univ, DMD, 44; Univ Ala, MS, 62. *Prof Exp:* Instr dent, Sch Dent Med, Tufts Univ, 47-48; assoc prof, 57-61, chmn div restorative & prosthetic dent, 61-62, chmn, Dept Oral Diag, 62-74, PROF DENT, SCH DENT, UNIV ALA, BIRMINGHAM, 61-, DIR CLINS, 62- *Concurrent Pos:* Consult, Vet Admin Hosp, Birmingham, 67- *Mem:* Am Asn Dent Schs; Int Asn Dent Res; Sigma Xi; Am Dent Asn; fel Am Col Dentists. *Res:* Studies of the affect and removal of dental plaque. *Mailing Add:* Univ of Ala Sch of Dent Birmingham AL 35294

KELLER, STEPHEN JAY, b Philadelphia, Pa, July 30, 40; m 62; c 2. MOLECULAR BIOLOGY, BIOCHEMISTRY. *Educ:* Univ Pa, AB, 63; State Univ NY Stony Brook, PhD(biol), 70. *Prof Exp:* NSF fel, 69-71; asst prof, 69-75, ASSOC PROF BIOL, UNIV CINCINNATI, 75- *Concurrent Pos:* Am Cancer Soc grant, 69-71; NSF grants, 70-78; vis assoc prof microbiol, State Univ NY, Stony Brook, 78-79. *Res:* Molecular biology of development and differentiation of animal cell cultures and viruses. *Mailing Add:* Dept of Biol Univ of Cincinnati Cincinnati OH 45201

KELLER, TEDDY MONROE, b Parrottsville, Tenn, Nov 20, 44. POLYMER CHEMISTRY, ORGANIC CHEMISTRY. *Educ:* E Tenn State Univ, BS, 66; Univ SC, PhD(org chem), 72. *Prof Exp:* Chief chemist leather, A C Lawrence Leather Co, 74-75; RES CHEMIST POLYMER CHEM, NAVAL RES LAB, 77- *Concurrent Pos:* Fel, Univ Fla, 72-74. *Mem:* Am Chem Soc. *Res:* Monomer synthesis, polymerization, and unusual polymer properties such as exceptional thermal and oxidative stability of polyphthalocyanines and polyimides; electrical conductivity of infinite network, fully conjugated polymers. *Mailing Add:* Naval Res Lab Code 6120 4555 Overlook Ave SW Washington DC 20375

KELLER, WALDO FRANK, b Hicksville, Ohio, Apr 13, 29; m 58; c 2. VETERINARY SURGERY. *Educ:* Ohio State Univ, DVM, 53; Mich State Univ, MS, 61; Am Col Vet Ophthal, dipl. *Prof Exp:* Instr, 53-55 & 57-61, univ clin res grant, 61-65, from asst prof to assoc prof, 61-70, PROF VET SURG & MED, MICH STATE UNIV, 70-, CHMN DEPT SMALL ANIMAL SURG & MED, 68-, ASSOC DEAN, 79- *Concurrent Pos:* Trainee, Div Ophthal, Sch Med, Stanford Univ, 65-66. *Mem:* Am Asn Vet Clinicians; Am Soc Vet Ophthal. *Res:* Veterinary ophthalmology; growth of cornea in tissue culture and pathology of eye tissues in evaluating surgical techniques. *Mailing Add:* Vet Clin Ctr Mich State Univ East Lansing MI 48824

KELLER, WALTER DAVID, b North Kansas City, Mo, Mar 13, 00; m 36; c 2. GEOLOGY, CERAMICS. *Educ:* Univ Mo, AB, 25, AM, 26, BS, 30, PhD(geol), 33; Harvard Univ, AM, 32. *Prof Exp:* Instr, Univ Mo, 26-29; ceramic technologist, A P Green Fire Brick Co, 29-31; from asst prof to assoc prof, 32-43, prof, 43-70, chmn dept, 42-45, EMER PROF GEOL, UNIV MO-COLUMBIA, 70- *Concurrent Pos:* Chmn clay minerals comt, Nat Res Coun-Nat Acad Sci, 57-60; distinguished prof geol, Univ Mo; vis prof, Univ SFla, 70-73. *Honors & Awards:* Neil A Miner Award, Nat Asn Geol Teachers, 67; Hardinge Award, Am Inst Mining, Metall & Petrol Engrs, 79; William H Twenhofel Award, Soc Econ Paleontologists & Mineralogists. *Mem:* Fel AAAS; Am Ceramic Soc; fel Geol Soc Am; fel Mineral Soc Am; Soc Econ Paleont & Mineral. *Res:* Clay mineralogy; fire clay; sedimentary petrology; optical mineralogy; mineral and rock soil amendments; lunar sample research. *Mailing Add:* 305 Geol Bldg Univ of Mo Columbia MO 65201

KELLER, WAYNE HICKS, b Henderson, Ky, July 8, 99; m 40. PHYSICAL CHEMISTRY. *Educ:* Georgetown Col, AB, 21; Univ Ky, MS, 32; Cornell Univ, PhD(phys chem), 37. *Prof Exp:* Instr chem, Univ Ky, 27-38; assoc prof, Morehead State Col, 38-42; res assoc phys chem, Manhattan Proj, Iowa State Col, 42-45; asst tech dir, Uranium Proj Contracts, Mallinckrodt Chem Works, 45-52; head chem dept, Nat Res Corp, Norton Co, 52-64; prof chem, Parsons Col, 64-68; vis prof, Western Ky Univ, 68-70; prof physics & chem, Union Univ, Tenn, 70-74; RETIRED. *Concurrent Pos:* Fulbright lectr chem, Tunghai Univ, 66-67. *Mem:* Am Chem Soc. *Res:* Chemical metallurgy of uranium, rare earths, titanium, zirconium, tantalum and other nonferrous metals; vacuum melting of nonferrous metals and alloys. *Mailing Add:* Apt 28-C 1315 Morreene Rd Durham NC 27705

KELLER, WILLIAM EDWARD, b Cleveland, Ohio, Mar 11, 25; m 47, 61; c 4. QUANTUM PHYSICS. *Educ:* Harvard Univ, AB, 45, AM, 47, PhD(chem), 48. *Prof Exp:* Assoc supvr mil sponsored res, Res Found, Ohio State Univ, 48-50; mem staff, 50-70, GROUP LEADER CRYOGENICS, LOS ALAMOS SCI LAB, 70- *Mem:* Am Chem Soc; fel Am Phys Soc; fel Am Inst Chemists. *Res:* Infrared spectroscopy; low temperature physics; liquid helium hydrodynamics; applications of superconductivity to electric power systems. *Mailing Add:* Group P-10 Los Alamos Nat Lab PO Box 1663 MS764 Los Alamos NM 87545

KELLER, WILLIAM JOHN, b Meridian, Miss, Sept 26, 20; m 46; c 2. ORGANIC CHEMISTRY. *Educ:* Miss State Col, BS, 43; Mass Inst Technol, PhD(org chem), 51. *Prof Exp:* Chemist org res, E I du Pont de Nemours & Co, Inc, 51-79; RETIRED. *Mem:* AAAS; Am Chem Soc. *Res:* Synthetic rubber; noble metal catalysis. *Mailing Add:* Rte 4 Box 2176 Branson MO 65616

KELLERHALS, GLEN E, b Vinton, Iowa, Sept 29, 45; m 73; c 2. PHYSICAL CHEMISTRY. *Educ:* Upper Iowa Col, BS, 67; Okla State Univ, PhD(chem), 74, Tulsa Univ, MBA, 80. *Prof Exp:* Res chemist, 74-77, group leader, 77-80, strategic planner, 80-81, SPECIAL PROJECTS ENGR, CITIES SERV CO, 81- *Mem:* Am Chem Soc; Soc Petrol Engrs; Am Petrol Inst. *Res:* Enhanced oil recovery. *Mailing Add:* 4304 Valley Dr Midland TX 79703

KELLERMAN, KARL F(REDERIC), b Washington, DC, May 11, 08; m 34; c 1. ENGINEERING. *Educ:* Cornell Univ, EE, 29. *Prof Exp:* Commun engr, NY Tel Co, 29-36; head electronics coord br, Bur Aeronaut, US Dept Navy, Washington, DC, 42-46; engr, Aircraft Radio Corp, 46-47; exec dir comt guided missiles; Res & Develop Bd, 47-49; engr, Brush Develop Co, 49-53; pres, Educ Labs, Kellerman & Co, 53-55; asst vpres eng, Bendix Corp, 55-62; pres, Microwave Devices, Inc, 62-64; sci adv, US Air Forces Systs Command, 64-73; pres, Low Country Guild, Inc, 73-78; PRES, KELLERMAN & ASSOCS, 78- *Mem:* AAAS; Inst Elec & Electronics Engrs; Sigma Xi. *Res:* Communication and navigation equipment; guided missiles; space systems; electronic measuring equipment. *Mailing Add:* 18 S Beach Lane Hilton Head Island SC 29928

KELLERMAN, MARTIN, b New York, NY, Feb 11, 32; m 63; c 2. PHYSICAL CHEMISTRY. *Educ:* Polytech Inst Brooklyn, BS, 53; Univ Wash, PhD(chem), 66. *Prof Exp:* Anal chemist, Continental Baking Co, 58-61; NIH res traineeship, Univ Calif, San Diego, 66-68; ASSOC PROF CHEM, CALIF POLYTECH STATE UNIV, SAN LUIS OBISPO, 68- *Mem:* AAAS. *Res:* X-ray crystal structure analysis; structure of metal chelate compounds; circular dichroism studies on structure of molecules of biological interest. *Mailing Add:* Dept of Chem Calif Polytech State Univ San Luis Obispo CA 93407

KELLERMAN, RICHARD, surface chemistry, see previous edition

KELLERMANN, KENNETH IRWIN, b New York, NY, July 1, 37; m 67; c 1. RADIO ASTRONOMY. *Educ:* Mass Inst Technol, SB, 59; Calif Inst Technol, PhD(physics & astron), 63. *Prof Exp:* Res scientist, Radiophys Lab, Commonwealth Sci & Indust Res Orgn, 63-65; from asst scientist to assoc scientist, 65-69, scientist, 69-77, asst dir, 77, SR SCIENTIST, NAT RADIO ASTRON OBSERV, 78- *Concurrent Pos:* NSF fel, 65-66; lectr, Leiden Univ, 67; res assoc, Calif Inst Technol, 69; adj prof, Univ Ariz, 70-73; dir, Max Planck Inst fur Radio Astronomie, 77-79. *Honors & Awards:* Calif Inst Technol-Eastman Kodak Corp Eastman Kodak Prize, 63; Rumford Prize, Am Acad Arts & Sci, 70; Helen B Warner Prize, Am Astron Soc, 71; B A Gould Prize, Nat Acad Sci, 73. *Mem:* Nat Acad Sci; Am Astron Soc; Am Acad Arts & Sci; Int Astron Union; Int Radio Sci Union. *Res:* Extragalactic radio sources; galaxies; quasars; cosmology; planetary radio astronomy. *Mailing Add:* Nat Radio Astron Observ PO Box 2 Green Bank WV 24944

KELLERS, CHARLES FREDERICK, b Montclair, NJ, Sept 12, 30; m 58; c 2. PHYSICS. *Educ:* Swarthmore Col, BA, 53; Duke Univ, PhD(physics), 60. *Prof Exp:* Engr, Gen Elec Co, 53-55; res assoc, Duke Univ, 60; asst prof physics, Wells Col, 61-65; sr res assoc, Cornell Univ, 65-68; assoc prof, 68-70, chmn dept, 71-80, PROF PHYSICS, CALIF STATE UNIV, SAN BERNARDINO, 70- *Mailing Add:* Dept of Physics Calif State Univ San Bernardino CA 92407

KELLERSTRASS, ERNST JUNIOR, b Peoria, Ill, Jan 9, 33; m 54; c 5. CIVIL ENGINEERING, GEOPHYSICS. *Educ:* Bradley Univ, BSCE, 54; St Louis Univ, MS, 62; George Washington Univ, MS, 67. *Prof Exp:* Engr, US Army Corps Engrs, 54, US Air Force, 54-, aeronaut meteorologist, 55-57, analyst & forecaster, Weather Cent Japan, 57-60, asst staff meteorologist for environ eng, 62-64, geophysicist, Electronic Syst Div, 64-66, geophysicist VELA prog, 67-71, chief planning remote piloted vehicle syst prog off, Aeronaut Systs Div, 71-74, staff scientist, Advan Res Br, Foreign Technol Div, Wright-Patterson AFB, 74-79; Instr Univ Dayton, 79-80; civil engr, Sanitary Landfills, Bowse Morner Testing Lab, 80-81, CIVIL ENGR ENVIRON, SYSTECH CORP, 81- *Mem:* Am Meteorol Soc; Am Geophys Union; Am Soc Civil Eng; Sigma Xi. *Res:* Meteorology--forecasting and environmental engineering; management of research in meteorological sensors, environmental effects, electric systems survivability-vulnerability, seismological instrumentation-field experiments and aeronautical systems; research and development management; geotechnical engineering; hydrology; environmental engineering. *Mailing Add:* 2547 Sugarloaf Ct Xenia OH 45385

KELLETT, CLAUD MARVIN, b Memphis, Tenn, Sept 5, 28; m 48; c 4. SOLID STATE PHYSICS. *Educ:* Ga Inst Technol, BEE, 50; Purdue Univ, MS, 57. *Prof Exp:* Res test engr, Allison Div, Gen Motors Corp, 50-54; sr engr, Tex Instruments, Inc, 56-62; develop engr, Semiconductor Div, Raytheon Co, 62-63; prod eng supvr, Sperry Semiconductor Div, Sperry Rand Corp, 63-64; prod supvr transistor mfg, Crystalonics, Inc, 64-65; sr res physicist, Ion Physics Corp, 65-66; physicist, Electronics Res Ctr, NASA, 66-70; sr res scientist, Tyco Corp Technol Ctr, 71; PROG MGT OFFICER, NSF, 72- *Res:* Electrical measurements, especially Hall and photoelectromagnetic effects of semiconductor materials; modification of electrical properties of semiconductor materials by ion implantation. *Mailing Add:* NSF Div of Astron Sci 1800 G St NW Washington DC 20550

KELLETT, JAMES CLARENCE, JR, b Spartanburg, SC, Oct 14, 35; m 57; c 3. SCIENCE ADMINISTRATION, ACADEMIC DEVELOPMENT. *Educ:* Univ SC, BS, 57; Purdue Univ, MS, 59, PhD(med chem), 61. *Prof Exp:* Asst prof chem, Div Health Affairs, Univ NC, 61-65; from asst prog dir to prog dir sci educ, NSF, 65-72; staff scientist, Ill Legis Coun, 73-74; proj mgr sci educ, NSF, 74-75, mgr comprehensive assistance to undergrad sci educ prog, 75-76; asst dir educ & training progs, Div Univ & Manpower Develop Progs, Energy Res & Develop Admin, 76-77; DIR, EDUC DIV, US DEPT ENERGY, 77- *Concurrent Pos:* Assoc prof, Sangamon State Univ, 73-74. *Mem:* AAAS; Am Soc Environ Educ; Fedn Am Scientists. *Res:* Application of science to public policy decision making; improvingrole of academic science in policy-making ; development of education programs for meeting national science and energy needs. *Mailing Add:* US Dept Energy Washington DC 20545

KELLEY, ALBERT J(OSEPH), b Boston, Mass, July 27, 24; m 45; c 3. SYSTEMS ENGINEERING, INSTRUMENTATION. *Educ:* US Naval Acad, BS, 45; Mass Inst Technol, BS, 48, ScD(instrumentation), 56. *Prof Exp:* Asst head, Air-to-Air Missile Br, Navy Bur Aeronaut, Washington, DC, 56-57 & Guided Missile Guid Br, 57-58, proj mgr, Eagle Missile Syst, 58-60; proj mgr, Navy Bur Weapons, 60; prog mgr, Agena Launch Vehicle, NASA, Washington, DC, 60-61, dir electronics & control, 61-64, mgr electronics res task group, 63-64, dep dir, Electronics Res Ctr, Cambridge, 64-67, consult, 67-70; dean sch mgt, Boston Col, 67-77; PRES, ARTHUR D LITTLE PROG SYSTS MGT CO, 77- *Concurrent Pos:* dir, LFE Corp, 70- & State St Bank & Trust Co, 75-; chmn bd econ adv, Mass, 70-75; consult, Dept Transp, 71-77; mem bd vis, US Defense Systs Mgt Col, 74-78; mem, Space Appln Bd, Nat Acad Eng, 77-; dir, Mass Bus Develop Corp, 78- *Honors & Awards:* Except Serv Medal, NASA, 67; Meritorious Serv Award, Armed Forces Comn & Electronics Asn, 67. *Mem:* Assoc fel Am Inst Aeronaut & Astronaut; fel Inst Elec & Electronics Engrs; Int Acad Astronaut. *Res:* Guided missiles and space vehicles; aircraft flight guidance and control; control systems engineering and management; electronics; technical and engineering management; project management. *Mailing Add:* Arthur D Little Prog Systs Mgt Co Acorn Park Cambridge MA 02140

KELLEY, ALEC ERVIN, b Pharr, Tex, Oct 28, 23; m 70. ORGANIC CHEMISTRY. *Educ:* Univ Tex, BS, 44; Purdue Univ, MS, 49, PhD, 56. *Prof Exp:* Asst chem, Univ Tex, 43-44; asst, Metall Lab, Univ Chicago, 44-45, jr chemist, 45-46; asst chem, Purdue Univ, 47-49, res fel, 49-52; from instr to assoc prof, 52-70, PROF CHEM, UNIV ARIZ, 70-, ASST DEPT HEAD, 68- *Mem:* Am Chem Soc; Royal Soc Chem. *Res:* Organic fluorine compounds; diazonium salts; kinetics and mechanisms of organic reactions. *Mailing Add:* Dept of Chem Univ of Ariz Tucson AZ 85721

KELLEY, ALLEN FREDERICK, JR, b Franklin, NH, July 1, 33. MATHEMATICS, FORESTRY. *Educ:* Mont State Univ, BS, 55; Univ Calif, Berkeley, PhD(math), 63. *Prof Exp:* Instr math, Univ Calif, Berkeley, 63-64; partic, Exchange Prog, US Nat Acad Sci-USSR Acad Sci, 64-65; mem fac, Inst Advan Study, 65-66; asst prof, 66-69, ASSOC PROF MATH, UNIV CALIF, SANTA CRUZ, 69- *Mem:* Soc Am Foresters; Am Math Soc. *Res:* Differential equations and celestial mechanics; wood technology and engineering. *Mailing Add:* Dept of Math Univ of Calif Santa Cruz CA 95064

KELLEY, ARNOLD E, b Menomonie, Wis, Mar 31, 17; m 58; c 2. CHEMICAL ENGINEERING. *Educ:* Univ Minn, BS, 40. *Prof Exp:* Asst engr, Union Oil Co, Calif, 41-43, engr, 43-50, res supvr, 50-51, chief process engr, 51-58, mgr res, 58-66, assoc dir, Res, Eng & Develop Div, 66-78,, VPRES ENG & DEVELOP, UNION RES CTR, UNION OIL CO, CALIF, 79- *Concurrent Pos:* Chmn oil shale task group, Nat Petrol Coun Comt. *Mem:* Am Inst Chem Engrs. *Res:* Development of processes used in the chemical and petroleum industries. *Mailing Add:* 1219 E Fairway Dr Orange CA 92666

KELLEY, C(LAIR) STUART, solid state physics, see previous edition

KELLEY, CHARLES JOSEPH, b Akron, Ohio, Feb 2, 43; c 2. ORGANIC CHEMISTRY. *Educ:* St Joseph's Col, Ind, BA, 64; Ind Univ, Bloomington, PhD(org chem), 70. *Prof Exp:* Res assoc org synthesis, Ind Univ, 70-75; asst prof chem, Ball State Univ, 75-76; res assoc natural prod, Northeastern Univ, 76-77; ASST PROF CHEM, MASS COL PHARM, 77- *Mem:* Am Chem Soc; Sigma Xi; AAAS. *Res:* Chemical synthesis or isolation from plant sources of potential pharmaceutical agents. *Mailing Add:* Dept of Chem 179 Longwood Ave Boston MA 02115

KELLEY, CHARLES THOMAS, JR, b Boston, Mass, Feb 9, 40; m 64; c 3. SYSTEMS ANALYSIS, PHYSICS. *Educ:* Univ Notre Dame, BS, 61; Univ Mass, MS, 63; Ind Univ, PhD(nuclear physics), 67. *Prof Exp:* Res asst nuclear physics, Cyclotron Lab, Ind Univ, 65-67; physicist, Anal Serv Inc, Falls Church, Va, 67-71; analyst, Washington Defense Res Div, Washington, DC, 71-73, phys scientist, 73-77, dir, Ground Warfare Prog, 77-79, SR PHYS SCIENTIST, RAND CORP, 79- *Mem:* Am Phys Soc; Opers Res Soc Am. *Res:* Weapon systems analysis; operations research; nuclear physics. *Mailing Add:* 909 Glenhaven Dr Pacific Palisades CA 90272

KELLEY, DANA ROBINEAU, b New York, NY, Nov 14, 27; m 50; c 2. EXPLORATION GEOLOGY. *Educ:* Amherst Col, BA, 50, MA, 52; Columbia Univ, PhD(mineral), 57. *Prof Exp:* Field geologist vertebrate paleontol, Col Mus, Amherst Col & Harvard Univ, 51; area geologist econ geol, AEC, 52-54; geologist petrol, Texaco, Inc, 57-62, dist geologist, 62-65; geologist, Pa Geol Surv, 65-68, chief oil & gas div, 68-71; chief geologist, Troy Enterprises, Inc, Pa, 71-73; MANAGING DIR, NATURAL RESOURCES DEVELOP DIV, UGI DEVELOP CO, 73- *Concurrent Pos:* Consult, Tex-Zinc Minerals Co, 59. *Mem:* Asn Prof Geol Scientists; Geol Soc Am; Soc Vert Paleont; Mineral Soc Am. *Res:* Vertebrate paleontology; clay mineralogy; geology of sedimentary uranium deposits; regional stratigraphy as applied to petroleum geology; sedimentary petrology. *Mailing Add:* 837 Somerville Dr Pittsburgh PA 15243

KELLEY, DONALD CLIFFORD, b St John, Kans, June 23, 13; m 36; c 2. VETERINARY MEDICINE. *Educ:* Kans State Univ, DVM, 35, MS, 52; Am Bd Vet Pub Health, dipl. *Prof Exp:* Assoc prof vet pub health, 58-69, prof infectious dis, 69-78, PROF EMER, COL VET MED, KANS STATE UNIV, 78- *Concurrent Pos:* Secy-treas, Am Bd Vet Pub Health, 63-66, pres, 66-; fels, 63- & 66- *Mem:* Am Vet Med Asn; Conf Pub Health Vets; Asn Mil Surgeons US; Am Col Vet Toxicologists; Med Mycol Soc Am. *Res:* Mycology and epidemiology as related to zoonotic diseases. *Mailing Add:* Dept of Infectious Diseases Kans State Univ Col of Vet Med Manhattan KS 66502

KELLEY, FENTON CROSLAND, b Chicago, Ill, Aug 24, 26. MAMMALIAN PHYSIOLOGY, ENVIRONMENTAL PHYSIOLOGY. *Educ:* Univ NMex, BSc, 51, MSc, 54; Univ Calif, Berkeley, PhD(physiol), 67. *Prof Exp:* Fisheries biologist, Calif State Dept Fish & Game, 54-57; res assoc physiol, Inst Environ Stress, Univ Calif, Santa Barbara, 57-58, lectr, Dept Phys Educ & Ergonomics, 58-59; asst prof, 69-76, ASSOC PROF ZOOL, BOISE STATE UNIV, 76- *Concurrent Pos:* Consult, US Corps of Engrs, 73-; consult fisheries, Stearns, Rogers, Inc, Denver, 75- & City of Boise, 80, 81 & 82. *Mem:* Am Fisheries Soc; Sigma Xi. *Res:* Fresh water fisheries biology; aquatic ecology; various aspects of adaptation to environmental extremes in mammals; anatomy; physiological effects of selective pesticides; aquaculture and invertebrates. *Mailing Add:* Dept of Biol Boise State Univ Boise ID 83725

KELLEY, FRANK NICHOLAS, b Akron, Ohio, Jan 19, 35; m 60; c 3. ADVANCED NON-METALLIC MATERIALS, SOLID ROCKET PROPELLANTS. *Educ:* Univ Akron, BS, 58, MS, 59, PhD(polymer chem), 61. *Prof Exp:* Res chemist, Air Force Rocket Propulsion Lab, 64-66, br chief solid rockets, 66-70, chief advan plans, 70-71, chief scientist, 71-73; chief scientist, Dept Defense, Wright-Patterson AFB, 73-76, dir, Air Force Mat Lab, 76-78; DIR & PROF, INST POLYMER SCI, UNIV AKRON, 78- *Concurrent Pos:* Chmn, Interagency Working Group Mech Behav, 63-65; consult, NSF, 79- & Dept Energy Progs, Jet Propulsion Lab, Midwest Res Inst, Solar Energy Res Inst, 79- *Honors & Awards:* Rubber Age Award; Outstanding Tech Contrib Award, Am Ins Aeronaut & Astronaut. *Mem:* Assoc fel Am Inst Aeronaut & Astronaut; Am Chem Soc. *Res:* Polymer physics; structure-property relationships of elastomers; mechanical properties of solid propellants. *Mailing Add:* Inst Polymer Sci Univ Akron Akron OH 44325

KELLEY, GEORGE GREENE, b Philadelphia, Pa, Nov 6, 18; m 47; c 4. BIOLOGICAL CHEMISTRY. *Educ:* Fla State Univ, BS, 50, MS, 51, PhD(biochem, food, nutrit), 56. *Prof Exp:* Tech res asst chem, Fla State Univ, 52-54; asst prof, Univ Mo, 56-57; instr pharmacol, Howard Col, 58-61; assoc prof chem, 63-67, chmn div sci & math, 64-73, PROF CHEM, JACKSONVILLE UNIV, 67- *Concurrent Pos:* Sr biochemist, Southern Res Inst, 57-62; instr, Exten Ctr, Univ Ala, 59-62, guest lectr, Med & Dent Schs, 61. *Mem:* AAAS; Am Chem Soc; Am Soc Limnol & Oceanog; NY Acad Sci; fel Am Inst Chemists. *Res:* Study of the life cycle, the propagation and large scale cultivation of three species of the large fresh water shrimp, genus Macrobrachium. *Mailing Add:* Dept of Chem Jacksonville Univ Jacksonville FL 32211

KELLEY, GEORGE W, JR, b Winfield, Kans, Dec 5, 21; m 42; c 3. ZOOLOGY. *Educ:* Univ Nebr, BS, 48, PhD(zool), 53; Univ Ky, MS, 50. *Prof Exp:* Asst parasitologist, Univ Ky, 48-50; parasitologist, State Dept Health, Nebr, 50-53; from asst prof to assoc prof parasitol, Univ Nebr, 53-64; tech sales assoc, Eli Lilly Int Corp, 64-67; chmn dept, 67-74, PROF BIOL, YOUNGSTOWN STATE UNIV, 67- *Concurrent Pos:* Consult-evaluator, NCen Asn Sch, 72- *Mem:* AAAS; Am Soc Parasitol; Am Inst Biol Sci. *Res:* Epidemiology of parasites of domestic animals. *Mailing Add:* Dept of Biol Sci Youngstown State Univ Youngstown OH 44503

KELLEY, HENRY J, b New York, NY, Feb 8, 26; m 58; c 2. AEROSPACE ENGINEERING, MATHEMATICS. *Educ:* NY Univ, BAeroE, 48, MS, 51, ScD(aeronaut eng), 58. *Prof Exp:* Res engr, Grumman Aircraft Eng Corp, 48-63; vpres, Analytical Mech Assocs, Inc, Jericho, 63-78; PROF AEROSPACE ENG, VA POLYTECH INST & STATE UNIV, 78- *Honors & Awards:* Mech & Control of Flight Award, Am Inst Aeronaut & Astronaut, 73; Pendray Award, Am Inst Aeronaut & Astronaut, 79. *Mem:* Fel Am Inst Aeronaut & Astronaut; Soc Indust & Appl Math; Inst Elec & Electronics Engrs; Am Astronaut Soc. *Res:* Flight mechanics; guidance theory; optimization techniques. *Mailing Add:* 29 High Meadow Dr Blacksburg VA 24060

KELLEY, JAMES CHARLES, b Los Angeles, Calif, Oct 5, 40; m 63. OCEANOGRAPHY. *Educ:* Pomona Col, BA, 63; Univ Wyo, PhD(geol), 66. *Prof Exp:* Asst prof oceanog, Univ Wash, 66-72, assoc prof oceanog, biomath & geol sci, 72-75; DEAN SCI, SAN FRANCISCO STATE UNIV, 75- *Concurrent Pos:* Fulbright prof, Univ Athens, 71. *Mem:* AAAS; Am Geophys Union; Biomet Soc. *Res:* Coastal upwelling; structural petrology; statistics; computer science. *Mailing Add:* Sch of Natural Sci 1600 Holloway Ave San Francisco CA 94132

KELLEY, JAMES DURRETT, b Louisville, Ky, June 10, 29. ORNAMENTAL HORTICULTURE. *Educ:* Univ Ky, BS, 52; Iowa State Col, MS, 54; Mich State Univ, PhD, 57. *Prof Exp:* Res asst, Iowa State Col, 52-54 & Mich State Univ, 54-57; from asst prof to assoc prof hort, Univ Ky, 57-67; ASSOC PROF HORT, IOWA STATE UNIV, 67- *Mem:* Am Soc Hort Sci; Am Asn Bot Gardens & Arboretums; Int Plant Propagators' Soc. *Res:* Plant nutrition and marketing of nursery crops. *Mailing Add:* Dept of Hort Iowa State Univ Ames IA 50010

KELLEY, JAMES LEROY, b San Diego, Calif, Nov 12, 43; m 67; c 3. MEDICINAL CHEMISTRY. *Educ:* Fresno State Col, BS, 67; Univ Calif, Santa Barbara, PhD(chem), 70. *Prof Exp:* RES SCIENTIST CHEM, BURROUGHS WELLCOME & CO, 70- *Mem:* Am Chem Soc. *Res:* Chemistry on purine, pyrimidine and imidazole heterocycles and antiviral agents; design and synthesis of enzyme inhibitors. *Mailing Add:* Wellcome Res Labs 3030 Cornwallis Rd Research Triangle Park NC 27709

KELLEY, JAY HILARY, b Greensburg, Pa, Mar 9, 20; m 49; c 9. MINING ENGINEERING, COMPUTER SCIENCE. *Educ:* Pa State Univ, BS, 42, MS, 47, PhD(mining eng), 52. *Prof Exp:* Res asst mining, Pa State Univ, 46-49, instr, 49-52; sr res & develop engr, Joy Mfg Co, Pa, 52-57; sr engr, Westinghouse Elec Corp, 57-62; tech specialist, Off Sci & Technol, Exec Off President, Washington, DC, 62-65; prof info sci & assoc dir bur info sci res, Rutgers Univ, 65-66; mgr comput asst instr, Philco-Ford Corp, Pa, 66-69; PRES, KELASTIC MINE BEAM CO, GREENSBURG, 69-; DISTINGUISHED PROF, COL MINERAL & ENERGY RESOURCES, W VA UNIV, 78- *Concurrent Pos:* Engr, Mammoth Coal & Coke Co, 46-54; dir, Leonard Express, Inc, 54-; exec secy panel sci info, President's Sci Adv Comt, 62-63, asst exec secy panel drug info, 64-66; exec secy comt sci & technol info, Fed Coun Sci & Technol, 62-65; trustee, Engrs Index, Inc, 67-, dir, 69-78, pres, 76-78; dean sch mines, WVa Univ, 70-78; chmn, Coal Mining Sect, Nat Safety Coun, Chicago, 79-80, chmn-elect, 78-79; chmn, WVa Mine Inspectors Exam Bd. *Mem:* AAAS; Inst Elec & Electronics Engrs; Opers Res Soc Am; Am Soc Info Sci; Am Inst Mining, Metall & Petrol Engrs. *Res:* Mineral science policy; mineral resource science; entropic systems; mineral education administration; mine roof control; mine machinery development. *Mailing Add:* Maplewood Terr Greensburg PA 15601

KELLEY, JIM LEE, b Ada, Okla, Oct 20, 47; m 68; c 2. BIOCHEMISTRY, CHEMISTRY. *Educ:* Bethany Nazarene Col, BS, 69; Univ Okla, PhD(biochem), 73. *Prof Exp:* Fel, 73-76, STAFF SCIENTIST MED RES, OKLA MED RES FOUND, 76- *Concurrent Pos:* Grants, Am Heart Asn, Okla Affil, Inc, 76-77 & 77-78 & HEW Pub Health Serv, 78- *Mem:* AAAS; Sigma Xi. *Res:* Chemistry and structure of plasma lipoproteins as related to atherosclerosis. *Mailing Add:* Lab of Lipid & Lipoprotein Studies 825 NE 13th St Oklahoma City OK 73104

KELLEY, JOHN DANIEL, b Chicago, Ill, July 30, 37; m 60; c 2. CHEMICAL PHYSICS. *Educ:* St Louis Univ, BS, 59; Georgetown Univ, PhD(phys chem), 64. *Prof Exp:* Res assoc theoret chem, Georgetown Univ, 63-64; res fel, Brookhaven Nat Lab, 64-67; res scientist, 67-70, assoc scientist, 70-73, SR SCIENTIST, McDONNELL DOUGLAS RES LABS, 73- *Mem:* AAAS; Am Chem Soc. *Res:* Theoretical and experimental reaction kinetics; molecular quantum mechanics; inter-molecular energy transfer processes. *Mailing Add:* McDonnell Douglas Res Labs PO Box 516 St Louis MO 63166

KELLEY, JOHN ERNEST, b Milwaukee, Wis, June 27, 19; m 50; c 4. MATHEMATICS. *Educ:* Univ Wis, BS, 41; Marquette Univ, MS, 48; Univ Mich, PhD(math), 60. *Prof Exp:* Instr math, Univ Miami, 49-51; analyst, US Dept Defense, 53-54; from instr to asst prof math & chmn dept, Marquette Univ, 54-64; chmn dept, 66-69, ASSOC PROF MATH, UNIV S FLA, 64- *Mem:* Math Asn Am; Nat Coun Teachers of Math. *Res:* Mathematical logic. *Mailing Add:* Dept of Math Univ of S Fla St Petersburg FL 33701

KELLEY, JOHN FRANCIS, JR, b Boston, Mass, July 10, 20; m 52; c 2. BIOCHEMISTRY, ACADEMIC ADMINISTRATON. *Educ:* Boston Col, BS, 46, MS, 47; Georgetown Univ, PhD(chem), 52. *Prof Exp:* Asst chem, Boston Col, 46-47; from instr to assoc prof, 47-58, PROF CHEM, US NAVAL ACAD, 58-, ASST DEAN ACAD AFFAIRS, 68- *Mem:* Am Chem Soc. *Res:* Organic iodine compounds; radioisotopes; identification of organic compounds; radiochemistry. *Mailing Add:* Off of Acad Dean US Naval Acad Annapolis MD 21402

KELLEY, JOHN FREDRIC, b Gay, WVa, Sept 17, 31; m 60; c 3. PSYCHIATRY. *Educ:* Marietta Col, AB, 54; McGill Univ, MD, 58; Am Bd Psychiat & Neurol, cert psychiat, 66, cert child psychiat, 71. *Prof Exp:* Resident psychiat, Health Ctr, Ohio State Univ, 59-62; staff psychiatrist, Patuxent Inst, Md, 64-66; fel child psychiat, Worcester Youth Guid Ctr, Mass, 66-68; assoc prof, 68-74, PROF BEHAV MED, PSYCHIAT & PEDIAT, MED SCH, WVA UNIV, 74-, DIR CHILD PSYCHIAT PROG, MED CTR, 68- *Mem:* Am Psychiat Asn; AMA; Am Acad Child Psychiat. *Res:* Child psychiatry. *Mailing Add:* Dept of Behav Med & Psychiat WVa Univ Med Ctr Morgantown WV 26506

KELLEY, JOHN JOSEPH, II, b Philadelphia, Pa, Jan 4, 33; m 70. OCEANOGRAPHY, METEOROLOGY. *Educ:* Pa State Univ, BS, 58; Univ Nagoya, Japan, PhD(oceanog), 71. *Prof Exp:* Sr scientist meteorol, Univ Wash, 60-68; oceanogr, 68-73, asst prof oceanog, Univ Alaska, 73-77, dir, Naval Arctic Res Lab, 77-80, ASSOC PROF MARINE SCI, UNIV ALASKA, 80- *Concurrent Pos:* Prog mgr, NSF Off Polar Prog, 74-76; chmn, Sci Adv Comt, Northslope Borough/Alaska Eskimo Whaling Comn, 80- *Mem:* Am Geophys Union; Am Soc Limnol & Oceanog; Am Polar Soc; Arctic Inst NAm. *Res:* Exchange processes; polar ecosystems; coastal upwelling phenomena; air-sea exchange processes. *Mailing Add:* Naval Arctic Res Lab Barrow AK 99723

KELLEY, JOHN LE ROY, b Kans, Dec 6, 16; m 63; c 3. MATHEMATICS. *Educ:* Univ Calif, Los Angeles, AB, 36, MA, 37; Univ Va, PhD(math), 40. *Prof Exp:* Asst prof math, Univ Notre Dame, 40-42; mathematician, Ballistic Res Lab, Aberdeen Proving Grounds, 42-45; asst prof math, Univ Chicago, 45-47; assoc prof, Univ Calif, 47-50; vis assoc prof, Tulane Univ, 50-52 & Univ Kans, 52-53; chmn dept, 57-60, 75-78, PROF MATH, UNIV CALIF, BERKELEY, 53- *Concurrent Pos:* Fel, Inst Advan Study, 45-46; NSF fel, 53-54; Fulbright res prof, Cambridge Univ, 57-58; Am-Kanpar Prog lectr, Indian Inst Technol, Kanpar, 64-65; nat teacher, Continental Classroom, NBC, 60. *Mem:* Am Math Soc; Nat Coun Teachers Math; US Comn Math Instrs; Math Asn Am. *Res:* Topology; functional analysis. *Mailing Add:* Dept of Math Univ of Calif Berkeley CA 94720

KELLEY, JOHN MICHAEL, b Lynchburg, Va, Feb 28, 48; m 70; c 1. MICROBIOLOGY, TOXICOLOGY. *Educ:* Va Polytech Inst & State Univ, BS, 70; Univ Va, MS, 72, PhD(microbiol), 75. *Prof Exp:* Fel virol, Duke Univ, 74-76; prin investr virol, Meloy Labs Inc, 76-79; SR SCIENTIST & PROJ MGR, JRB ASSOC, 79- *Concurrent Pos:* NIH fel, NIH grant Neurosciences, 75-76. *Mem:* Am Soc Microbiologists. *Res:* Chief fields of interest are type and group specific radioimmunoassays for type-D retroviruses, and indentification and localization of tumor specific or viral antigens within tumor tissue by immunoperoxidase staining. *Mailing Add:* 8400 Westpark Dr JRB Assoc Inc McLean VA 22102

KELLEY, JOHN PAUL, b Milwaukee, Wis, Dec 15, 25; m 48; c 3. HEALTH PHYSICS, RADIOLOGICAL PHYSICS. *Educ:* Rensselaer Polytech Inst, BEE, 47. *Prof Exp:* Test engr, Apparatus Dept, Gen Elec Co, 47-48 & X-ray Dept, 48-49, qual engr, Lamp Dept, 49-50, asst to tech adv, X-ray Dept, Radiation Physics Lab, 50-55, radiation physics engr, 55-62, dir lab, 62-64, appln engr, Advan Tech Proj, 64-66; assoc prof elec eng, 66-71, asst dir, X-ray Sci Lab, 66-76, ASSOC PROF RADIOL PHYSICS, ORE STATE UNIV, 71-, RADIATION SAFETY OFFICER, 76- *Mem:* AAAS; Health Physics Soc; Am Asn Physicists in Med; Inst Elec & Electronics Engrs; Radiol Soc NAm. *Res:* Radiological instrumentation; radiation protection and instruction. *Mailing Add:* Radiation Safety Office Ore State Univ Corvallis OR 97331

KELLEY, JOSEPH MATTHEW, JR, b Baltimore, Md, Dec 10, 29; m 55; c 3. POLYMER CHEMISTRY. *Educ:* Loyola Col, Md, BS, 50; Fordham Univ, MS, 52, PhD(chem), 56; NY Univ, BSChE, 66. *Prof Exp:* Res chemist, Chem Res Div, Esso Res & Eng Co, NJ, 55-57, proj leader polyolefins, 57-61; supvr polyolefins res, Rexall Chem Co, Paramus, 61-63, mgr develop res, Dart Industs Chem Group, 63-65, mgr polymer res, 65-66, asst dir styrenic polymer develop, 66-67, dir, ABS res & develop, 67-69, dir mkt admin rexene polymers, 69-70, vpres res & develop, 70-79; VPRES RES & DEVELOP, EL PASO POLYOLEFINS CO, 79- *Mem:* Am Chem Soc; Sigma Xi. *Res:* Polymerization of olefins; stabilization of polymers; organic synthesis; enzyme chemistry; heterogeneous catalysis; styrene type polymers. *Mailing Add:* 1321 E Broad St Westfield NJ 07090

KELLEY, KEITH WAYNE, b Bloomington, Ill, Nov 5, 47; m 78. ENVIRONMENTAL PHYSIOLOGY. *Educ:* Ill State Univ, BS, 69; Univ Ill, MS, 73, PhD(animal sci), 76. *Prof Exp:* asst prof, 76-81, ASSOC PROF ANIMAL SCI, WASH STATE UNIV, 81- *Concurrent Pos:* mem grad fac, Wash State Univ, 78. *Mem:* Am Soc Animal Sci; Soc Exp Biol & Med; Coun Agr Sci & Technol; AAAS. *Res:* Influence of psychosocial and thermal stressors on physiological systems which regulate antibody and cell mediated immune events in mammals and birds; effect of thermal stressors on humoral and cellular immune systems of food animals. *Mailing Add:* Dept of Animal Sci Wash State Univ Pullman WA 99164

KELLEY, LEON A, b Madison, Wis, June 28, 23; m 45; c 4. BIOCHEMISTRY. *Educ:* Univ Wis, BS, 48, MS, 49, PhD(agr chem), 51. *Prof Exp:* Asst prof agr chem, Univ Calif, Davis, 53-54; from asst prof to assoc prof, 54-63, PROF CHEM, SAN JOSE STATE UNIV, 63- *Mem:* Am Chem Soc; Am Dairy Sci Asn. *Res:* Dairy chemistry; factors affecting rennet coagulation; rancidity in milk; development of instant milk products. *Mailing Add:* Dept Chem San Jose State Univ 125 S Seventh St San Jose CA 95112

KELLEY, MAURICE JOSEPH, b Danielson, Conn, Aug 6, 16; m 45. ORGANIC CHEMISTRY. *Educ:* La Salle Col, AB, 36; Fordham Univ, MS, 41; Univ Pa, PhD(org chem), 42; NY Univ, MBA, 65. *Prof Exp:* Res chemist, Nopco Chem Co, 36-44, chief chemist chg sales develop lab, 44-48, dir indust develop lab, 48-53, dir indust specialties lab, 53-58, dir proj coord dept, 58-61; dir res labs, Diversey Corp, Ill, 61-65; dir electrostatics res, 66-69, dir res, 69-75, ASST VPRES & DIR RES, PHILIP A HUNT CHEM CORP, 75- *Mem:* AAAS; Am Chem Soc; Chem Mkt Res Asn; Soc Photog Scientists & Engrs; fel Am Inst Chemists. *Res:* Management of research and development; surface active agents; nitrogen compounds oil and fat derivatives; emulsion polymers; plastics; metallic soaps; synthetic detergents; bactericides; metal processing chemicals; photographic and graphic arts chemicals. *Mailing Add:* Philip A Hunt Chem Corp Palisades Park NJ 07650

KELLEY, MAURICE LESLIE, JR, b Indianapolis, Ind, June 29, 24. MEDICINE. *Educ:* Univ Rochester, MD, 49. *Prof Exp:* From instr to assoc prof med, Univ Rochester, 55-67; assoc prof, 67-74, PROF CLIN MED, DARTMOUTH MED SCH, 74-; STAFF MEM MARY HITCHCOCK MEM HOSP CLIN, 67- *Concurrent Pos:* Fel, Mayo Clin, 57-59; from asst physician to assoc physician, Strong Mem Hosp, 55-59, sr assoc physician, 63-; consult, Vet Admin Hosp, Canandaigua, NY, Genesee Hosp & Rochester Gen Hosp. *Mem:* AMA; Am Gastroenterol Asn; Am Fedn Clin Res; Am Col Physicians; Am Physiol Soc. *Res:* Gastroenterology; pancreatic small bowel motility of the gastrointestinal tract. *Mailing Add:* 15 Ledge Rd Hanover NH 03755

KELLEY, MYRON TRUMAN, b Allerton, Iowa, Mar 9, 12; m 37. ANALYTICAL CHEMISTRY. *Educ:* Univ Nebr, BSc, 32, MSc, 33; Iowa State Univ, PhD(phys chem), 37. *Prof Exp:* Asst chief anal chemist, Queeny Plant Monsanto Chem Co, Mo, 37-41, chief anal chemist, 41-45; asst sect chief chem process develop sect, Clinton Lab, 45-48; dir anal chem div, 48-72, CONSULT, OAK RIDGE NAT LAB, 73-; CONSULT, HARSHAW CHEMICAL CO, 81- *Mem:* AAAS; Am Nuclear Soc; Am Chem Soc; Sigma Xi. *Res:* Analytical instrumentation; instrumental methods of analysis, especially applications of small computers; analysis of highly radioactive materials. *Mailing Add:* Oak Ridge Nat Lab PO Box X Oak Ridge TN 37830

KELLEY, PATRICIA HAGELIN, b Cleveland, Ohio, Dec 8, 53; m 77. INVERTEBRATE PALEONTOLOGY, EVOLUTIONARY PALEONTOLOGY. *Educ:* Col Wooster, BA, 75; Harvard Univ, AM, 77, PhD(geol), 79. *Prof Exp:* Instr, New England Col, 79; ASST PROF GEOL, UNIV MISS, 79- *Mem:* Paleont Soc; Geol Soc Am; AAAS; Sigma Xi. *Res:* Evolutionary patterns, including modes and rates of evolution; origin of macroevolutionary trends, particularly as exhibited by Miocene molluscs; gastropod predation; sexual dimorphism; biometric analysis. *Mailing Add:* Dept Geol & Geol Eng Univ Miss University MS 38677

KELLEY, PHILIP CARLOS, polymer chemistry, see previous edition

KELLEY, RALPH EDWARD, b Greenville, SC, Mar 6, 30; m 68; c 3. ATOMIC PHYSICS, MOLECULAR PHYSICS. *Educ:* Furman Univ, BA, 51, BS, 55; Univ Va, MS, 57, PhD(physics), 60. *Prof Exp:* Sr scientist theoret anal, Res Labs Eng Sci, Univ Va, 60-66; PROG MGR PHYSICS DIRECTORATE, OFF SCI RES, US AIR FORCE, 66- *Mem:* Am Phys Soc; Sigma Xi. *Res:* Annihilation radiation of positrons in crystals; polarization effects in scattering. *Mailing Add:* 7551 Marshall Dr Annandale VA 22003

KELLEY, RAYMOND H, b Roscoe, Mont, July 10, 22; m 51; c 1. NUCLEAR PHYSICS. *Educ:* Mont State Col, BS, 50; Ohio State Univ, MS, 55, PhD(nuclear physics), 63. *Prof Exp:* Instr electronics, Ellington AFB, Tex, US Air Force, 51-54, nuclear res officer, Modern Physics Br, Wright-Patterson AFB, Ohio, 55 & Aeronaut Res Lab, 57-60, staff scientist, Brookhaven Nat Lab, 55-57, from instr to assoc prof physics, US Air Force Acad, 62-69; part-time instr math, 69-71, assoc prof physics & math, 71-75, PROF PHYSICS & MATH, SOUTHWESTERN ORE COMMUNITY COL, 75- *Mem:* Am Phys Soc; Am Asn Physics Teachers. *Res:* Helium filled scintillation detectors; radiation damage to semiconductor materials; particle accelerators; gamma ray spectroscopy. *Mailing Add:* Phys Sci Div Southwestern Ore Community Col Coos Bay OR 97420

KELLEY, RICHARD NORMAN, b Rochester, NY, Nov 20, 40; m 63; c 2. POLYMER SCIENCE, CHEMICAL ENGINEERING. *Educ:* Pa State Univ, BS, 62, MS, 65; Rensselaer Polytech Inst, PhD(chem eng), 69. *Prof Exp:* Engr, Carothers Res Lab, E I du Pont de Nemours & Co, 63-64; sr develop engr, Roll Coating Div, Eastman Kodak Co, 69-75, sr develop chemist, Synthetic Chem Div, 75-76, tech assoc, 77-78, supvr chem develop, Synthetic Polymer Develop, Synthetic Chem Div, 78-81, TECH ASSOC, MFT TECHNOL DIV, EASTMAN KODAK CO, 81- *Mem:* AAAS. *Res:* Polymeric structure-property relationships; polymer synthesis; scaleup of polymerization reactions; polymerization modelling; applications of polymers in photographic systems. *Mailing Add:* 19 Park Circle Dr Fairport NY 14450

KELLEY, ROBERT LEE, b East St Louis, Ill, Mar 20, 37. MATHEMATICAL PHYSICS. *Educ:* Univ Ill, Urbana, BS, 58; Univ Miami, MS, 60; Univ Mich, PhD(math), 66. *Prof Exp:* From instr to asst prof, 64-72, ASSOC PROF MATH, UNIV MIAMI, 72- *Mem:* Am Math Soc; Math Asn Am; AAAS; Sigma Xi; Soc Indust & Appl Math. *Res:* Mathematical physics; functional analysis; mathematical biology; theory of algorithms. *Mailing Add:* Dept Math Univ Miami PO Box 9085 Coral Gables FL 33124

KELLEY, ROBERT OTIS, b Santa Monica, Calif, Apr 30, 44; m 65; c 2. DEVELOPMENTAL BIOLOGY, CELL BIOLOGY. *Educ:* Abilene Christian Col, BS, 65; Univ Calif, Berkeley, MA, 66, PhD(zool), 69. *Prof Exp:* Assoc zool, Univ Calif, Berkeley, 67-68, actg asst prof, 69; from instr to assoc prof, 69-79, PROF ANAT, SCH MED, UNIV NMEX, 79-, CHMN DEPT, 81- *Concurrent Pos:* NIH grant, 70-, res career develop award, NIH, 72; res fel, Hubrecht Lab, Utrecht, Neth, 72-73. *Mem:* Soc Develop biol; Am Soc Cell Biologists; Am Asn Anat; Electron Micros Soc Am; Biophys Soc. *Res:* Fine structural associations between interacting cell layers during early amphibian development; ultrastructure and cell biology of vertebrate limb mesenchyme and associated limb morphogenesis; biology of the aging cell surface; organization of the cytoskeleton imaging cells. *Mailing Add:* Dept of Anat Univ NMex Sch of Med Albuquerque NM 87131

KELLEY, RUSSELL VICTOR, b Norfolk, Va, Dec 21, 34; m 56; c 3. BIOLOGY, SCIENCE EDUCATION. *Educ:* Va State Col, BS, 57; NY Univ, MA, 64; Purdue Univ, PhD(biol sci), 72. *Prof Exp:* Teacher chem & biol, Baltimore Pub Schs, 60-62; teacher biol, Plainview, Long Island Pub Schs, 62-66; ASSOC PROF BIOL SCI, MORGAN STATE UNIV, 66- *Concurrent Pos:* Consult, NASA, 67 & 68; lectr contemp biol, Towson State Univ, 72 & 75; lectr zool & biol, Community Col Baltimore, 74-; consult sci, Md State Dept Educ Bicentennial Comt, 76 & Sci Curric Adv Comt, Div Instr & Curric, Baltimore City Pub Sch Syst, 78-; chmn bd adv, Math Eng Sci Achievement, 77- *Mem:* Nat Sci Teachers Asn; AAAS. *Res:* Instructional strategies in science teaching and population genetics. *Mailing Add:* 3400 Olympia Ave Baltimore MD 21233

KELLEY, THOMAS F, b Melrose, Mass, Mar 23, 32; m 56; c 3. BIOMEDICAL ENGINEERING, CLINICAL CHEMISTRY. *Educ:* Boston Univ, AB, 54, MA, 55; Brown Univ, PhD(biol), 59. *Prof Exp:* Sr res assoc, Bio-Res Inst, Inc, 58-68; prog mgr, 68-80, DIR APPL RES, INSTRUMENTATION LAB, INC, 80- *Mem:* Am Asn Clin Chemists; Am Soc Clin Path. *Res:* Development of hospital, medical and laboratory instrumentation. *Mailing Add:* Instrumentation Lab Inc 113 Hartwell Ave Lexington MA 02173

KELLEY, THOMAS NEIL, b Toledo, Ohio, Feb 1, 29; m 55; c 3. PROCESS METALLURGY. *Educ:* Purdue Univ, BS, 51; Univ Pittsburgh, MS, 61. *Prof Exp:* Res metallurgist, NAm Aircraft Corp, Columbus, Ohio, 54-55; process develop supvr, Universal-Cyclops Div, Cyclops Steel Corp, 55-62; wrought alloy mgr, Austenal Div, Howmet Corp, 62-67; CHIEF METALLURGIST, STELLITE DIV, CABOT CORP, 67- *Mem:* Am Inst Mining, Metall & Petrol Engrs, Fel Am Soc Metals. *Res:* Wrought special purpose steel and nickel or cobalt base alloy mill process development; statistical process and product control. *Mailing Add:* Stellite Res & Develop Dept Cabot Corp 1020 W Park Ave Kokomo IN 46901

KELLEY, VINCENT CHARLES, b Tyler, Minn, Jan 23, 16; m 42; c 7. PEDIATRICS. *Educ:* Univ NDak, BA, 34, MS, 35; Univ Minn, BS, 36, PhD(biochem), 42, BS, 44, MB, 45, MD, 46. *Prof Exp:* Asst chem, Univ NDak, 34-35; asst biochem, Univ Minn, 40-41; asst prof org chem, Col St Thomas, 42-43; chief dept biophys, US Air Force Sch Aerospace Med, 46-47, res med, 47-48; instr pediat, Univ Minn, 49-50; from asst prof to assoc prof, Univ Utah, 50-58; PROF PEDIAT, SCH MED, UNIV WASH, 58- *Concurrent Pos:* Swift fel pediat, Univ Minn, 48-50. *Mem:* AAAS; Am Chem Soc; Am Pediat Soc; Soc Pediat Res; Soc Exp Biol & Med. *Res:* Starch chemistry; renal and liver function; deceleration injuries; aviation medicine; protein chemistry; physiochemical studies of electrodialyzed starches; pituitary-adrenal function; endocrinology. *Mailing Add:* Dept of Pediat Univ of Wash Seattle WA 98195

KELLEY, VINCENT COOPER, b Seattle, Wash, July 6, 04; m 29, 46; c 4. ECONOMIC GEOLOGY. *Educ:* Univ Calif, Los Angeles, AB, 31; Calif Inst Technol, MS, 32, PhD(geol), 37. *Prof Exp:* From instr to prof & chmn dept, 37-70, EMER PROF GEOL, UNIV NMEX, 70-, INDUST CONSULT, 70- *Concurrent Pos:* Geologist, US Geol Surv, 38-70; consult, AEC, 53-55 & NSF, 64-65; adj prof geol, Tex Tech Univ, 71-73; consult, Los Alamos Sci Lab, 76- *Mem:* Fel Geol Soc Am; Soc Econ Geologists; Am Asn Petrol Geologists; Am Inst Mining, Metall & Petrol Engrs. *Res:* Tectonics; mineral deposits; structural and engineering geology. *Mailing Add:* Dept of Geol Univ of NMex Albuquerque NM 87131

KELLEY, VIRGINIA CRAWFORD, microbiology, see previous edition

KELLEY, WILLIAM NIMMONS, b Atlanta, Ga, June 23, 39; m 59; c 4. INTERNAL MEDICINE, RHEUMATOLOGY. *Educ:* Emory Univ, MD, 63. *Prof Exp:* Intern med, Parkland Mem Hosp, 63-64, resident, 64-65; clin assoc, Nat Inst Arthritis & Metab Dis, 65-67; sr resident med, Mass Gen Hosp, 67-68; from asst prof to prof med, Med Ctr, Duke Univ, 68-75; PROF & CHMN DEPT INTERNAL MED & PROF BIOCHEM, MED SCH, UNIV MICH, 75- *Concurrent Pos:* Mosby scholar award, 63-; Am Col Physicians Mead-Johnson scholar, 67-68; teaching fel med, Harvard Med Sch, 67-68; Am Rheumatism Asn clin scholar, 69-72; res career develop award, 72-75; Macy Fac scholar, Oxford Univ, 74-75; from asst prof to assoc prof biochem, Med Ctr, Duke Univ, 69-75, chief div rheumatic & genetic dis, 70-75. *Honors & Awards:* John D Lane Award, USPHS, 69; Geigy Int Prize Rheumatology, 69; Heinz Karger Prize, 73. *Mem:* AAAS; Am Fedn Clin Res (pres-elect, 78-79, pres, 79-80); Am Rheumatism Asn; Am Soc Biol Chemists; Am Soc Clin Invest. *Res:* Human biochemical genetics; rheumatology. *Mailing Add:* Dept of Internal Med Univ of Mich Med Sch Ann Arbor MI 48104

KELLEY, WILLIAM RUSSELL, b Universal, Pa, Feb 3, 14; m 42; c 5. BOTANY. *Educ:* Pa State Teachers Col, Indiana, BS, 39; Univ Pittsburgh, MLitt, 48; Cornell Univ, MS, 49, PhD(bot), 51. *Prof Exp:* Pub sch teacher, Pa, 39-41 & 45-48; asst bot, Cornell Univ, 49-51; from asst prof to assoc prof, Univ SC, 51-59; from assoc prof to prof bot, 61-77, PROF BIOL, SHIPPENSBURG STATE COL, 77- *Mem:* Bot Soc Am; Ecol Soc Am; Am Inst Biol Sci. *Mailing Add:* Dept of Biol Shippensburg State Col Shippensburg PA 17257

KELLEY, WILLIAM SHELDON, b Washington, Pa, Nov 30, 41; m 68; c 1. MOLECULAR BIOLOGY. *Educ:* Haverford Col, BA, 63; Mass Inst Technol, MS, 65; Tufts Univ, PhD(microbiol), 68. *Prof Exp:* USPHS fel biol sci, Edinburgh Univ, 68-70; univ fel, Brandeis Univ, 70-71; ASSOC PROF BIOL SCI, MELLON INST SCI, CARNEGIE-MELLON UNIV, 71- *Mem:* AAAS; Am Soc Microbiol. *Res:* Nucleic acid metabolism; genetics and enzymology of DNA replication in Escherichia coli; role of DNA polymerase in bacterial plasmid replication. *Mailing Add:* Dept of Biol Sci Mellon Inst Sci Carnegie-Mellon Univ Pittsburgh PA 15213

KELLGREN, JOHN, b New York, NY, Dec 26, 40; m 71; c 2. ORGANIC CHEMISTRY, RUBBER CHEMISTRY. *Educ:* Rutgers Univ, BS, 62; Columbia Univ, PhD(org chem), 66; Univ New Haven, MBA, 77. *Prof Exp:* Res chemist, Uniroyal Res Ctr, 67-75, tech supt, 76-79, RES SCIENTIST INDUST PROD, UNIROYAL INC, 79- *Mem:* Am Inst Chemists; The Chem Soc. *Res:* Free radical reactions; polyurethane chemistry; oxidation of organic compounds; aging; vulcanization. *Mailing Add:* Uniroyal Inc Oxford Mgt & Res Ctr Middlebury CT 06749

KELLIHER, GERALD JAMES, b Taunton, Mass, May 31, 42; m 65; c 2. PHARMACOLOGY. *Educ:* Univ RI, BS, 65; Duquesne Univ, MS, 67; Univ Pittsburgh, PhD(pharmacol), 69. *Prof Exp:* From asst prof to prof pharmacol, 70-78, ASSOC PROF MED, MED COL PA, 75- *Concurrent Pos:* Fel pharmacol, Sch Med, Univ Pittsburgh, 69-70; Southeast Pa Heart Asn, Del Heart Asn, Heart & Lung Found, Ayerst Co & Shering Co grants, Med Col Pa, 71-81; Whitehall Found grants, 71-77; Nat Heart & Lung Inst grants, 71-75 & 73-77, 76-80; Nat Inst Age grant, 76-80; Nat Inst Child Health & Human Develop grant, 72-76; consult, Vet Admin, 78-80; educ consult, Smith Kline Corp. *Mem:* Am Soc Pharmacol & Exp Therapeut; assoc fel Am Col Cardiol; Geront Soc; fel Am Col Clin Pharmacol; Am Fedn Clin Res. *Res:* Cardiovascular and autonomic pharmacology with emphasis on the mechanisms and treatment of cardiac arrhythmias and hypertension. *Mailing Add:* Dept of Pharmacol Med Col of Pa Philadelphia PA 19129

KELLING, CLAYTON LYNN, b Killdeer, NDak, Mar 26, 46; m 74. VETERINARY VIROLOGY. *Educ:* NDak State Univ, BS, 68, MS, 71, PhD(pharm chem), 75. *Prof Exp:* TECHNICIAN VET VIROL, DEPT VET SCI, NDAK STATE UNIV, 68- *Mem:* Am Soc Microbiol; Sigma Xi. *Res:* Veterinary microbiology concerned with respiratory and reproductive diseases of animals; antiviral agents; virological diagnostic techniques. *Mailing Add:* Dept of Vet Sci NDak State Univ Fargo ND 58102

KELLISON, ROBERT CLAY, b Marlinton, WVa, Nov 20, 31; m 65; c 2. FOREST GENETICS. *Educ:* WVa Univ, BSF, 59; NC State Univ, MS, 66, PhD(forest genetics), 70. *Prof Exp:* Forest supt, WVa Univ, 59-61; liaison geneticist, 63-67, assoc dir coop prog, 66-77, DIR HARDWOOD COOP, NC STATE UNIV, 77- *Concurrent Pos:* Fel, Am-Scand Found, 65; panel expert, Food & Agr Orgn-Int Breeding Prog for Preserv Forest Gene Resources, 68; scientist, NZ Forest Serv, 73-74. *Res:* Selection and breeding of forest trees for improved volume yields, quality, adaptability and resistance to frost, drought and environmental pollution; preservation of forest gene resources. *Mailing Add:* 1019 Biltmore Hall NC State Univ Raleigh NC 27650

KELLMAN, MARTIN C, physical geography, see previous edition

KELLMAN, RAYMOND, b Staten Island, NY, Feb 27, 42; m 78; c 2. POLYMER CHEMISTRY, ORGANIC CHEMISTRY. *Educ:* St Peter's Col, NJ, BS, 63; Univ Colo, Boulder, PhD(org chem), 68. *Prof Exp:* Res assoc chem, Univ Wis, Madison, 67-69; res chemist, Uniroyal Inc, 69-72; res assoc, 72-75, lectr chem, Univ Ariz, 75-77; ASST PROF POLYMER CHEM, UNIV TEX, 77- *Mem:* AAAS; Am Chem Soc. *Res:* Synthesis of new monomers; new methods of condensation polymerization; synthesis of thermally stable and conductive polymers; physical organic chemistry. *Mailing Add:* Div Earth & Phys Sci Univ Tex San Antonio TX 78285

KELLMAN, SIMON, b Brooklyn, NY, July 26, 34; m 59; c 2. REACTOR PHYSICS. *Educ:* Carnegie Inst Technol, BS, 55, MS, 58, PhD(physics), 61. *Prof Exp:* Sr physicist, Lawrence Radiation Lab, Univ Calif, Livermore, 61-64 & United Nuclear Corp, 64-69; fel scientist, 69-72, mgr math & programming, 72-76, acting mgr methods develop, 76-78, MGR, SAFEGUARDS RELIABILITY & APPLN, PWR SYSTS DIV, WESTINGHOUSE ELEC CORP, MONROEVILLE NUCLEAR CTR, 78- *Mem:* Am Nuclear Soc. *Res:* Depletion calculations; nuclear safety analysis; Monte Carlo techniques in neutron transport. *Mailing Add:* Westinghouse PWR Systs Div Monroeville Nuclear Ctr Box 355 Pittsburgh PA 15230

KELLN, ELMER, b Sask, Can, Nov 6, 26; m 51; c 3. ORAL PATHOLOGY, CANCER. *Educ:* Univ Nebr, BSc & DDS, 49; Univ Minn, MSD(path), 60. *Prof Exp:* Assoc prof path, Sch Med, WVa Univ, 60-66; prof oral med, Univ, 66-71, PROF ORAL MED, GRAD SCH & ASSOC DEAN SCH DENT, LOMA LINDA UNIV, 71- *Concurrent Pos:* Grants wound healing, 60-63 & age studies, 61-; cancer coordr, Sch Dent, WVa Univ & mem tumor bd, WVa Univ Hosp, 63-66. *Mem:* Fel Am Acad Oral Path; Am Dent Asn; Int Asn Dent Res. *Res:* Cancer behavior; disease processes of oral diseases, particularly wound healing, cancer treatment and behavior, and vascular degeneration. *Mailing Add:* Sch of Dent Loma Linda Univ Loma Linda CA 92354

KELLNER, AARON, b New York, NY, Sept 24, 14; m 42; c 3. PATHOLOGY. *Educ:* Yeshiva Univ, BA, 34; Columbia Univ, MS, 36; Univ Chicago, MD, 39. *Prof Exp:* Res assoc exp cardiovasc path, 47-50, from asst prof to assoc prof path, 50-68, PROF PATH, MED COL, CORNELL UNIV, 68-; DIR NEW YORK BLOOD CTR, 64- *Concurrent Pos:* Life Ins Res Fund fel, 47-48; dir cent labs, NY Hosp, 48-64; mem coun arteriosclerosis, Am Heart Asn. *Mem:* Soc Study Blood (pres, 53); Am Soc Exp Path; Am Asn Path & Bact; Am Asn Blood Banks (pres, 54); Am Heart Asn (pres, 60). *Res:* Experimental cardiovascular pathology and arteriosclerosis. *Mailing Add:* 40 E 83rd St New York NY 10028

KELLNER, HENRY L(OUIS), b Philadelphia, Pa, Sept 18, 05; m 35; c 2. CHEMICAL ENGINEERING. *Educ:* Pa State Col, BS, 26; Yale Univ, PhD(chem eng), 30. *Prof Exp:* Res chemist, Scovill Mfg Co, 27-29; chem engr, Doherty Res Co, 30-33 & Eastern Eng Co, 33-35; from chem engr to secy & tech dir, 35-56, vpres, 56-68, tech dir, 56-70, exec vpres, 68-76, pres, 76-78, MGR FOREIGN OPERS, LEA MFG CO, 70-, VCHMN, 78- *Mem:* Am Chem Soc; Am Electroplaters Soc. *Res:* Buffing and polishing compositions; chemical and electroplating processes. *Mailing Add:* Lea Mfg Co 237 E Aurora St Waterbury CT 06720

KELLNER, JORDAN DAVID, b New York, NY, Aug 25, 38; m 60; c 2. PHYSICAL CHEMISTRY. *Educ:* City Col New York, BS; NY Univ, MS, 62, PhD(phys chem), 64; Rensselaer Polytech Inst, MS, 72. *Prof Exp:* Jr chemist, Kings County Hosp, 58-59; res asst biochem res, St Catherine's Hosp, 59-61; res asst phys chem, NY Univ, 61-64; sr chemist, Atomics Int Div, NAm Aviation, 64-68; res scientist, Hamilton Standard Div, United Technologies Corp, 68-71; sr res scientist, 71-78, supvr chem processes, Res Ctr, 78-80, supvr, 80-81; RES ASSOC, KENDALL RES LAB, 81- *Concurrent Pos:* Adj prof chem, Univ Hartford, 80-81. *Mem:* Sigma Xi; Am Chem Soc; Nat Asn Corrosion Engrs. *Res:* Transport processes in fused salts and metal-metal salt mixtures; Soret effect and viscosity; electrodeposition of semi-metals and their compounds from fused fluorides; electrochemical techniques of corrosion measurement. *Mailing Add:* 38 Grove St Wayland MA 01778

KELLNER, STEPHAN MARIA EDUARD, b Friedberg, Ger, Feb 1, 33; US citizen; m 60; c 12. PHYSICAL CHEMISTRY. *Educ:* Univ Rochester, BS, 55, PhD(phys chem), 60. *Prof Exp:* From asst prof to assoc prof, 59-69, chmn dept, 71-75, PROF CHEM, ST MICHAEL'S COL, VT, 69- *Mem:* Am Chem Soc. *Res:* Rates and mechanisms of homogeneous gas phase reactions. *Mailing Add:* Dept of Chem St Michael's Col Winooski VT 05404

KELLOGG, CHARLES EDWIN, soil science, deceased

KELLOGG, CHARLES NATHANIEL, b Albuquerque, NMex, June 29, 38; m 57; c 3. MATHEMATICS. *Educ:* NMex Inst Mining & Technol, BS, 60; La State Univ, PhD(math), 64. *Prof Exp:* Teaching asst math, La State Univ, 63-64; asst prof, Univ Ky, 64-70; ASSOC PROF MATH, TEX TECH UNIV, 70- *Mem:* Am Math Soc; Math Asn Am. *Res:* Harmonic analysis; theory of multiplier operators; Banach algebras. *Mailing Add:* Dept of Math Tex Tech Univ Lubbock TX 79409

KELLOGG, CRAIG KENT, b Westfield, Mass, Dec 3, 37; m 60; c 3. ORGANIC CHEMISTRY. *Educ:* Ga Inst Technol, BS, 59, PhD(org chem), 63. *Prof Exp:* Res chemist, E I du Pont de Nemours & Co, Inc, 63-66; asst prof, 66-70, ASSOC PROF CHEM, GA SOUTHERN COL, 70- *Mem:* Am Chem Soc. *Res:* Natural products. *Mailing Add:* Dept of Chem Ga Southern Col Statesboro GA 30458

KELLOGG, DAVID WAYNE, b Seymour, Mo, Aug 19, 41; m 64; c 4. NUTRITION, ANIMAL SCIENCE. *Educ:* Univ Mo-Columbia, BS, 63, MS, 64; Univ Nebr-Lincoln, PhD(nutrit), 68. *Prof Exp:* From asst prof to prof dairy sci, NMex State Univ, 67-81; HEAD, DEPT ANIMAL SCI, UNIV ARK, FAYETTEVILLE, 81- *Mem:* Am Dairy Sci Asn; Am Soc Animal Sci; Am Forage & Grassland Coun; Sigma Xi. *Res:* Etiology of induced bovine ketosis; nutritive value of alfalfa varieties; mineral nutrition; improvement of forage digestion by ruminants. *Mailing Add:* Dept Animal Sci Univ Ark Fayetteville AR 72701

KELLOGG, DOUGLAS SHELDON, JR, b Washington, DC, May 22, 26; m 54; c 3. MEDICAL MICROBIOLOGY. *Educ:* Univ Ill, BS, 50; Univ Tex, MS, 54, PhD(bact), 57. *Prof Exp:* Res scientist biochem, Univ Tex, 56-57, res assoc cytol, M D Anderson Hosp & Tumor Inst, 57-60; RES SUPVRY MICROBIOLOGIST, VENEREAL DISEASE RES BR, CTR FOR DISEASE CONTROL, USPHS, 60- *Mem:* Am Soc Microbiol; Sigma Xi; Am Venereal Disease Asn. *Res:* Immunology; biochemical genetics; host-parasite interrelationships. *Mailing Add:* Ctr for Disease Control USPHS Atlanta GA 30333

KELLOGG, EDWIN M, b New York, NY, Feb 3, 39; m 60, 74; c 3. ELECTRON & ION BEAM SYSTEMS, LITHOGRAPHY REGISTRATION. *Educ:* Rensselaer Polytech Inst, BS, 60; Univ Pa, MS, 63, PhD(physics), 66. *Prof Exp:* Physicist, Radiation Dynamics, Inc, 61-62; sr scientist, Am Sci & Eng, Inc, Mass, 65-69, sr staff scientist, 69-73, mem, Inst Advan Study, 73; astrophysicist, Smithsonian Astrophys Observ, 73-79; proj mgr, Micro-Bit Div, Control Data Corp, Mass, 80, software mgr, 81-82; STAFF SCIENTIST, ION BEAM TECHNOL, INC, 82- *Concurrent Pos:* Lectr astron, Harvard Univ, 73- *Honors & Awards:* Newton Lacey Pierce Prize, Am Astron Soc, 74. *Mem:* Fel Am Phys Soc; Am Astron Soc; Am Vacuum Soc; Electron Micros Soc Am. *Res:* Extragalactic and galactic research. *Mailing Add:* Ion Beam Technol Inc 123 Brimbal Ave Beverly MA 01915

KELLOGG, HERBERT H(UMPHREY), b New York, NY, Feb 24, 20; m; c 4. EXTRACTIVE METALLURGY. *Educ:* Columbia Univ, BS, 41, MS, 43. *Prof Exp:* Jr engr, Dorr Co, Conn, 41; asst mineral dressing, Columbia Univ, 41-42; instr, Pa State Col, 42-44; assoc prof mineral preparation, 44-46; assoc prof extractive metall, 46-56, prof, 56-68, STANLEY-THOMPSON PROF CHEM METALL, COLUMBIA UNIV, 68- *Concurrent Pos:* Chmn titanium adv comt, Off Defense Mobilization, 54-58; consult, Int Nickel Co & Am Smelting & Refining Co, 59- *Honors & Awards:* James Douglas Gold Medal, Am Inst Mining, Metall & Petrol Engrs, 73. *Mem:* Nat Acad Eng; Am Chem Soc; Am Inst Mining, Metall & Petrol Engrs; fel Inst Mining & Metall, London. *Res:* Thermodynamics and kinetics of metallurgical reactions; high-temperature chemistry; equilibria in the systems Cu-S-O, Ni-Fe-S; slag chemistry; computer modeling of metallurgical processes. *Mailing Add:* Henry Krumb Sch of Mines Columbia Univ New York NY 10027

KELLOGG, LILLIAN MARIE, b Detroit, Mich, Mar 6, 39. SOLID STATE CHEMISTRY. *Educ:* Ariz State Univ, BS, 61; Wayne State Univ, PhD(phys chem), 67. *Prof Exp:* Assoc scientist chem, Aeroneutronic Div, Ford Motor Co, 61-62; RES ASSOC RES LABS, EASTMAN KODAK CO, 68- *Concurrent Pos:* Adj fac, Rochester Inst Technol, 70-75. *Mem:* AAAS; Am Chem Soc; Am Phys Soc; Soc Photog Scientists & Engrs; NY Acad Sci. *Res:* Solid state chemistry; light interactions in solids; photoconductivity, photochemical and photographic studies. *Mailing Add:* Res Lab B-81 Eastman Kodak Co Kodak Park Rochester NY 14650

KELLOGG, PAUL JESSE, b Tacoma, Wash, Nov 6, 27; m 69; c 4. PLASMA PHYSICS. *Educ:* Mass Inst Technol, BS, 50; Cornell Univ, PhD(theoret physics), 55. *Prof Exp:* Nat Res Coun fel, Naval Res Lab, 55-56; res assoc, 56-57, from asst prof to assoc prof, 57-64, PROF PHYSICS, UNIV MINN, MINNEAPOLIS, 64- *Concurrent Pos:* Guggenheim Mem Found fel, 62-63; NATO fel; fel, Minna-James-Heineman Stiftung, 73. *Mem:* Fel Am Phys Soc. *Res:* Plasma physics as applied to the earth's upper atmosphere and the interplanetary medium; beam-plasma interaction, waves in plasma. *Mailing Add:* Sch of Physics & Astron Univ of Minn Minneapolis MN 55455

KELLOGG, RALPH HENDERSON, b New London, Conn, June 7, 20. PHYSIOLOGY. *Educ:* Univ Rochester, BA, 40, MD, 43; Harvard Med Sch, PhD(physiol), 53. *Prof Exp:* Intern med, Cleveland Univ Hosps, 44; investr physiol, Naval Med Res Inst, 46; instr, Harvard Med Sch, 47-53; asst prof, Sch Med, 53-59, assoc prof, 59-65, actg chmn dept, 66-70, PROF PHYSIOL, UNIV CALIF, SAN FRANCISCO, 65- *Concurrent Pos:* Sr res fel, Sch Pub Health, Harvard Univ, 62-63; mem physiol study sect, NIH, 66-70; physiol test comt, Nat Bd Med Examrs, 66-73 & chmn, 69-73; vis fel, Corpus Christi Col, Oxford Univ, 70-71; vis scientist, Lab Physiol Respiratory, Cent Nat Res Sci, Strausbourg, France, 77. *Mem:* AAAS; Am Physiol Soc; Am Asn Hist Med; History Sci Soc. *Res:* Isotonic and osmotic diuresis in rats; respiration at altitude; history of physiology. *Mailing Add:* Dept of Physiol Univ of Calif San Francisco CA 94143

KELLOGG, RICHARD MORRISON, b Los Angeles, Calif, Dec 24, 39; m 67; c 2. ORGANIC CHEMISTRY. *Educ:* Kans State Teachers Col, AB, 61; Univ Kans, PhD(org chem), 65. *Prof Exp:* Res fel chem, Univ Kans, 65; res fel, 65-70, assoc prof, 70-75, PROF CHEM, STATE UNIV GRONINGEN, 75- *Mem:* Am Chem Soc. *Res:* Synthetic organic chemistry; photochemistry; bio-organic chemistry; synthesis of unusual organic molecules and models for mechanisms of enzymic reactions. *Mailing Add:* Dept of Org Chem State Univ of Groningen Nijenborgh Groningen 9747 AG Netherlands

KELLOGG, ROYAL BRUCE, b Chicago, Ill, Dec 28, 30; m 56; c 3. APPLIED MATHEMATICS. *Educ:* Mass Inst Technol, BS, 52; Univ Chicago, MS, 53, PhD(math), 59. *Prof Exp:* Mathematician, Combustion Eng, Inc, 58-61; mathematician, Westinghouse Elec Corp, 61-66; from assoc prof to prof math, 66-74, res prof, Inst Fluid Dynamics & Applied Math, 74-80, RES PROF MATH & INST PHYS SCI & TECHNOL, UNIV MD, COLLEGE PARK, 80- *Mem:* Am Math Soc; Soc Indust & Appl Math. *Res:* Numerical analysis. *Mailing Add:* Inst Fluid Dynamics & Appl Math Univ of Md College Park MD 20740

KELLOGG, SPENCER, II, b Buffalo, NY, Dec 9, 13; m 38; c 5. AERONAUTICAL ENGINEERING. *Educ:* Cornell Univ, ME, 37; Polytech Inst Brooklyn, MSEE, 67. *Prof Exp:* Field serv engr, Sperry Gyroscope Co, 37-39, flight test engr, 39-40, from gyropilot engr to dept head, 40-50, dept head flight instrument eng, 50-59, asst chief engr, Aeronaut Equip Div, 59-67; INDEPENDENT AVIATION CONSULT, 67- *Res:* Gyropilot and gyroscopic flight instruments; altitude control for aircraft; turn error control of gyroscopes; erection mechanism for gyroscopes; flight directors. *Mailing Add:* Terminal Bldg MacArthur Airport Ronkonkoma NY 11779

KELLOGG, THOMAS FLOYD, b Aurora, Ill, Apr 7, 34; c 2. BIOCHEMISTRY. *Educ:* Iowa State Univ, BS, 59, MS, 60; Univ Wis-Madison, PhD(biochem), 64. *Prof Exp:* Res asst biochem, Univ Wis, 60-64; fel microbiol, Lobund Lab, Univ Notre Dame, 64-65, res scientist, 65-68, asst prof, 68-70; assoc prof, 70-78, PROF BIOCHEM, MISS STATE UNIV, 78-, DIR RADIOISOTOPE CTR, 77- *Concurrent Pos:* NIH Spec Res fel, 67-68. *Mem:* Am Chem Soc; Am Physiol Soc; Asn Gnotobiotics (vpres & pres-elect, 81-82). *Res:* Cholesterol and bile acid metabolism; lipid metabolism intestinal microflora effects on metabolism; liquid scintillation counting. *Mailing Add:* Dept Biochem Miss State Univ PO Drawer BB Mississippi State MS 39762

KELLOGG, WILLIAM WELCH, b New York Mills, NY, Feb 14, 17; m 42; c 5. METEOROLOGY. *Educ:* Yale Univ, AB, 39; Univ Calif, Los Angeles, MS, 42, PhD(meteorol), 49. *Prof Exp:* Teacher prep sch, Mass, 39-40; asst optics lab, Univ Calif, Los Angeles, 40-41, instr meteorol, 42-43, res asst, 47-48, res assoc, Inst Geophys, 48-49, asst prof, 49-52; phys scientist & dept head, Rand Corp, Calif, 47-64; assoc dir, 64-73, SR SCIENTIST NAT CTR ATMOSPHERIC RES, 73- *Concurrent Pos:* Mem, Upper Atmosphere Comt, Nat Adv Comt Aeronaut, 53-55; mem, Comt Meteorol Aspects Effects Atomic Radiation, Nat Acad Sci, 56-64, Space Sci Bd, 59-66, Comt Atmospheric Sci, 63-67, Spec Comt Int Years Quiet Sun, 63-66 & Polar Res Bd, 75-78; Rocket & Satellite Res Panel, 57-; chmn int comn meteorol upper atmosphere, Int Union Geod & Geophys, 60-75; mem tech panel, Earth Satellite Prog, Int Geophys Year, 57-58; consult & mem sci adv bd, US Air Force, 57-65, mem sci adv group, Off Aerospace Res, 65-70; chmn meteorol satellite comt, Adv Res Projs Agency, 58-59; mem planetary atmospheres subcomt, NASA, 61-65; chmn working group upper atmosphere, World Meteorol Orgn, 61-65; mem consult group potentially harmful effects of space exp, Comt Space Res, 62-68; mem tech adv bd, US Dept Com, 62-64; mem adv group supporting tech oper meteorol satellites, NASA-US Weather Bur, 64-75; mem panel on environ, President's Sci Adv Comt, 68-70; chmn meteorol adv comt, Environ Protection Agency, 70-74. *Mem:* AAAS; fel Am Geophys Union; Sigma Xi; fel Am Meteorol Soc (pres, 73-74); Fedn Am Scientists. *Res:* Physics of the atmosphere; turbulence and structure of the upper atmosphere; scientific uses of rockets, satellites and space probes; atmospheres of Mars and Venus; causes of climate change. *Mailing Add:* Nat Ctr for Atmospheric Res Boulder CO 80307

KELLOGG, WILLIS CARL, b Cleveland, Ohio, May 28, 32; m 61; c 3. STATISTICAL COMMUNICATION, NUMERICAL ANALYSIS. *Educ:* Yale Univ, BS, 54; Harvard Univ, MA, 55, PhD(appl physics), 66. *Prof Exp:* Staff engr, Lincoln Lab, Mass Inst Technol, 66-68; assoc prof systs eng, Boston Univ, 68-71; staff engr, Lincoln Lab, Mass Inst Technol, 72-80; ENGR, RAYTHEON CO, 80- *Concurrent Pos:* Consult, Electronics Res Ctr, NASA, 68-70 & Solar-Environ Sci, Inc, 71- *Mem:* AAAS; Inst Elec & Electronics Engrs. *Res:* Digital signal processing, spectral analysis; matrix analysis. *Mailing Add:* Raytheon Co Boston Post Rd Wayland MA 01778

KELLOW, WILLIAM FRANCIS, b Geneva, NY, Mar 14, 22; m 51; c 5. MEDICINE. *Educ:* Univ Notre Dame, BS, 45; Georgetown Univ, MD, 46; Am Bd Internal Med, dipl, 54, 74; Am Bd Pulmonary Dis, dipl, 57. *Hon Degrees:* DSc, St Joseph's Col, Pa, 67, Georgetown Univ, 79; LHD, Hahnemann Med Col, 78. *Prof Exp:* Intern, DC Gen Hosp, 46-47, asst resident med, 47-48, asst resident surg, Georgetown Univ Hosp, 48-49; asst resident med, DC Gen Hosp, 49-50, chief resident pulmonary dis, 50-51; asst to chief med, West Side Vet Admin Hosp, Chicago, Ill, 53-55; asst prof med & asst dean, Col Med, Univ Ill, 55-59, assoc prof & assoc dean, 59-61; prof & dean, Hahnemann Med Col, 61-67; dean, 67-82, PROF MED & VPRES, JEFFERSON MED COL, 67-, EMER DEAN, 82- *Honors & Awards:* Centennial Sci Award, Univ Notre Dame, 65; Schaffrey Award, St Joseph's Col, 78. *Mem:* Am Thoracic Soc; AMA; Am Fedn Clin Res; Am Col Physicians. *Res:* Pulmonary and renal diseases. *Mailing Add:* Jefferson Med Col 1025 Walnut St Philadelphia PA 19107

KELLS, LYMAN FRANCIS, b Seattle, Wash, May 19, 17; div; c 2. ASTRONOMY, CHEMISTRY. *Educ:* Univ Wash, BS, 38, PhD(phys chem), 44. *Prof Exp:* Teaching fel, Univ Wash, 38-44; res scientist, Manhattan Proj, Kellex Corp, Carbide & Carbon Corp & Columbia Univ, 44-46; res chemist, Standard Oil Develop Co, 46-48; mem fac, Hunter Col, 48-49; asst prof, Iona

Col, 49-51; res chemist, Gen Chem Div, Allied Chem Corp, 51-61; spec lectr, Newark Col Eng, 61; assoc prof chem, East Tenn State Univ, 62-64; prof chem, Westmar Col, 64-74; RES, 74- *Mem:* Am Chem Soc; Am Astron Soc. *Res:* Reaction kinetics and mechanisms, catalysis and molecular structure; non-ideal behavior in solutions and gases; light, variable stars, gravity, energy, atomic structure and relativity; individual psychology, interpersonal relationships and education; physics. *Mailing Add:* 4246 S 146 Seattle WA 98168

KELLS, MILTON CARLISLE, b Seattle, Wash, May 7, 20; m 49; c 3. PHYSICAL CHEMISTRY. *Educ:* Univ Wash, BS, 42; Mass Inst Technol, PhD(chem), 48. *Prof Exp:* Res scientist, Gaseous Diffusion Studies, Manhattan Proj, Kellex Corp, 44-46; Atomic Energy Process Develop, 48-51; contract adminr, Res Div, AEC, 51-54; atomic energy process develop, Sylvania Elec Co, 54-56; head detonations sect, Stanford Res Inst, 56-61; scientist, Ames Res Ctr, NASA, 61-66; PROF PHYS SCI, CALIFORNIA STATE COL, PA, 66- *Mem:* AAAS; Am Chem Soc; Sigma Xi. *Res:* Vacuum ultraviolet spectroscopy. *Mailing Add:* Dept of Phys Sci California State Col California PA 15419

KELLS, WILLIAM PAUL, particle physics, see previous edition

KELLY, AMY SCHICK, b Rochester, NY, Nov 11, 40; m 71; c 2. NEUROBIOLOGY, NEUROPHYSIOLOGY. *Educ:* Mt Holyoke Col, AB, 62; Brown Univ, MSc, 64, PhD(psychol), 67. *Prof Exp:* Fel psychol, Northeastern Univ, 67-68, asst prof, 68-71; fel neurobiol, Univ Calif, Berkeley, 72-74; fel neurobiol, Med Ctr, Stanford Univ, 74-78; ASST PROF PHYSIOL, UNIV CALIF, SAN FRANCISCO, 78- *Concurrent Pos:* Fel, Northeastern Univ, 67-68; spec res fel, Med Sch, Stanford Univ, 74-77. *Mem:* Soc Neurosci; Asn Res Vision & Ophthal; AAAS. *Res:* Organization of the mammalian central visual system; development of the central visual pathways and visual centers; plasticity of central connections in the mammalian visual system. *Mailing Add:* Dept of Physiol Univ of Calif San Francisco CA 94143

KELLY, BEATRICE L, b Baltimore, Md, Jan 4, 20. MICROBIAL GENETICS. *Educ:* Univ Calif, Berkeley, BA, 41; Univ Calif, Los Angeles, MA, 51; Univ Southern Calif, PhD(bact), 58. *Prof Exp:* Res assoc bact metab, Univ Southern Calif, 58-59; NIH res fel bact genetics, Sch Med, Univ Southern Calif & Karolinska Inst, Sweden, 59-62; asst prof bact, Univ Southern Calif, 62-67; from asst prof to assoc prof, 67-73, PROF MICROBIOL, SAN DIEGO STATE UNIV, 73- *Mem:* AAAS; Am Soc Microbiol. *Res:* Bacterial genetics; bacteriophage. *Mailing Add:* Dept of Microbiol San Diego State Univ San Diego CA 92182

KELLY, BERNARD WAYNE, b Corning, NY, Oct 7, 18; m 45; c 3. AGRICULTURAL ECONOMICS. *Educ:* Pa State Univ, BS, 49, MS, 50. *Prof Exp:* Instr & asst county agt, Agr Exten, Univ Md, 50-53, asst prof & county agt, 54-56; from asst prof to assoc prof, 56-73, PROF FARM MGT EXTEN, PA STATE UNIV, UNIVERSITY PARK, 73- *Mem:* Am Agr Econ Asn; Am Soc Farm Mgrs & Rural Appraisors. *Res:* Cost of production; fruits and vegetables crops; taxation, insurance, investments and credits. *Mailing Add:* Dept of Farm Mgt Exten Pa State Univ University Park PA 16802

KELLY, CLARK ANDREW, b Rocky Ford, Colo, Sept 14, 25; m 54; c 1. ANALYTICAL CHEMISTRY, PHARMACEUTICAL CHEMISTRY. *Educ:* Univ Colo, BS, 46; Temple Univ, MS, 51; Univ Minn, PhD(anal pharm chem), 58. *Prof Exp:* Res asst, 46-48 & summers 51-54, res assoc, 56-63, res chemist, 63-68, SR RES CHEMIST & GROUP LEADER, STERLING-WINTHROP RES INST, RENSSELAER, 68- *Mem:* Am Chem Soc; Am Pharmaceut Asn; fel Acad Pharmaceut Sci; NY Acad Sci; Sigma Xi. *Res:* Polarography of organic compounds; ion exchange separations of organic compounds; colorimetric and spectrophotometric studies. *Mailing Add:* 22 Huntersfield Rd Delmar NY 12054

KELLY, CONRAD MICHAEL, b Bradford, Pa, Nov 26, 44; m 66; c 1. CHEMICAL ENGINEERING. *Educ:* Mich State Univ, BS, 66, MS, 67, PhD(chem eng), 70. *Prof Exp:* Asst prof, 69-75, assoc prof, 75-80, PROF CHEM ENG, VILLANOVA UNIV, 80-; ASSOC PROF, AIR PROD & CHEM INC, 80- *Mem:* Am Inst Chem Engrs; Am Soc Eng Educ. *Res:* Molecular diffusion; air and water pollution abatement; mathematical modeling. *Mailing Add:* Dept of Chem Eng Villanova Univ Villanova PA 19085

KELLY, DENNIS D, b New York, NY, June 18, 38. NEUROPSYCHOLOGY. *Educ:* Fordham Univ, BA, 60; Columbia Univ, MA, 62, PhD(psychol), 66. *Prof Exp:* Res psychologist, Walter Reed Army Inst Res, 64-67; prin investr neuropsychol, Inst Behav Res, Silver Spring, Md, 67-68; assoc res scientist, 68-76, asst prof, 71-81, ASSOC PROF MED PSYCHOL, COLUMBIA UNIV, 81-, RES SCIENTIST BEHAV PHYSIOL, NY STATE PSYCHIAT INST, 76- *Concurrent Pos:* Lectr, Univ Col, Univ Md, 67-68; adj asst prof psychol, Columbia Univ, 68-70. *Mem:* Asn Res Nervous & Mental Dis; Am Psychol Asn; Int Asn Study Pain; Soc Neurosci; fel NY Acad Sci. *Res:* Biology of emotional and aggressive behaviors; pain perception; conditioning and learning. *Mailing Add:* NY State Psychiat Inst 722 W 168th St New York NY 10032

KELLY, DONALD C, b Poland, Ohio, Aug 18, 33; m 55; c 4. THEORETICAL PHYSICS. *Educ:* Miami Univ, Ohio, AB, 55, MA, 56; Yale Univ, PhD(physics), 59. *Prof Exp:* Res assoc physics, Yale Lab Marine Physics, 59-60; from asst prof to assoc prof, 60-69, PROF PHYSICS, MIAMI UNIV, OHIO, 69- *Concurrent Pos:* Nat Acad Sci sr res assoc, Inst Space Studies, 70-71. *Mem:* Am Phys Soc; Am Asn Physics Teachers. *Res:* Classical and quantum kinetic theory; scattering theory; theoretical plasma physics. *Mailing Add:* Dept of Physics Miami Univ Oxford OH 45056

KELLY, DONALD HORTON, b Erie, Pa, May 6, 23; m 50; c 1. VISION. *Educ:* Univ Rochester, BS, 44; Univ Calif, Los Angeles, PhD(eng), 60. *Prof Exp:* Engr, Mitchell Camera Corp, 44; photog res engr, Technicolor Corp, 46-52, sr staff mem res, 53-61; sr staff mem optics res div, Itek Corp, Mass, 61-63, mgr info systs dept, Vidya Div, Calif, 63-66; STAFF SCIENTIST, VISUAL SCI PROG, SRI INT, 66- *Concurrent Pos:* Mem comt vision, Armed Forces-Nat Res Coun, 62-; vis prof & NIH spec fel, Ctr Visual Sci, Univ Rochester, 71-72; mem visual sci B study sect, NIH, 73-77. *Mem:* AAAS; fel Optical Soc Am; Asn Res Vision & Ophthal. *Res:* Vision research; visual instruments; spatio-temporal interactions in the visual process; stabilized retinal images and automated psychophysical techniques. *Mailing Add:* Visual Sci Prog SRI Int Menlo Park CA 94025

KELLY, DOROTHY HELEN, b Fitchburg, Mass, July 29, 44. PEDIATRICS. *Educ:* Fitchburg State Col, BSN, 66; Wayne State Univ, BS, 68, MD, 72. *Prof Exp:* Intern, Dept Pediat, Mass Gen Hosp, 72-73, resident, 73-75; instr pediat, 75-81, ASST PROF PEDIAT, HARVARD MED SCH, 81- *Concurrent Pos:* Fel pediat pulmonary med, Mass Gen Hosp, 76-79, co-dir, Pediat Pulmonary Lab, 77, asst pediatrician, 79; consult, Sudden Infant Death Syndrome Proj, Bur Commun Health Serv, Dept Health, Educ & Welfare, 79-80; chmn, Apnea Adv Comt, Nat Sudden Infant Death Syndrome Found, 79-81, mem, Sci Rev Comt, 81. *Mem:* Fel Am Acad Pediat; Asn Psychophysiol Study; Int Pediat Soc; Am Med Women's Asn; Am Thoracic Soc. *Res:* Control of ventilation; Sudden Infant Death Syndrome; sleep apnea. *Mailing Add:* 39 Drummer Rd Acton MA 01720

KELLY, DOUGLAS ELLIOTT, b Cheyenne, Wyo, Nov 13, 32; m 54; c 4. DEVELOPMENTAL ANATOMY, MICROSCOPIC ANATOMY. *Educ:* Colo State Univ, BS, 54; Stanford Univ, PhD(biol sci), 58. *Prof Exp:* From instr to asst prof biol, Univ Colo, 58-63; from asst prof to assoc prof biol struct, Sch Med, Univ Wash, 63-70; prof & chmn dept, Sch Med, Univ Miami, 70-74; PROF ANAT & CHMN DEPT, SCH MED, UNIV SOUTHERN CALIF, 74- *Concurrent Pos:* USPHS res fel, Zool Lab, State Univ Utrecht, 59-60; NSF res grants, Univ Colo, 60-63, Univ Wash, 63-70, Univ Miami, 70-74, & Univ Southern Calif, 77-; Univ Colo fac res fel, Univ Wash, 62-63; mem anat comt, Nat Bd Med Exam, 70-74; NIH Human Embryol & Develop Study Sect, 78-82; mem admin bd, Coun Acad Sci, 82-84. *Mem:* Am Asn Anat; Soc Develop Biol; Am Soc Zool; Am Soc Cell Biol. *Res:* Electron microscopy; development and ultrastructure of junctional complexes; ultrastructure of muscle and eye. *Mailing Add:* Dept of Anat Sch of Med Univ of Southern Calif Los Angeles CA 90033

KELLY, EDGAR PRESTON, JR, b Beaumont, Tex, Aug 5, 33; m 54; c 3. MATHEMATICS. *Educ:* Stephen F Austin State Col, BS, 55; Fla State Univ, MS, 56; Okla State Univ, PhD(math), 60. *Prof Exp:* Mathematician comput ctr, Socony Mobil Oil Co, 56-57; asst prof math, Stephen F Austin State Col, 60-62; prof & dir comput ctr & dean basic col, Univ Southern Miss, 62-64, chmn dept math, 64-67; prof math, 67-80, PROF MATH & STATIST, LA TECH UNIV, 80- *Mem:* Am Math Soc; Math Asn Am. *Res:* Infinite series and summability methods. *Mailing Add:* Dept of Math La Tech Univ Ruston LA 71270

KELLY, EDWARD JOSEPH, b Baltimore, Md, Mar 4, 34; m 67; c 2. PHYSICAL CHEMISTRY. *Educ:* Johns Hopkins Univ, BES, 56, MAT, 62, MS, 68; Purdue Univ, MS, 67, PhD(chem, physics), 72. *Prof Exp:* Engr, Bendix Radio Corp, 60-61; teacher, Mt St Joseph High Sch, Md, 62-65; asst prof math & physics, Mt Marty Col, 72-75; asst prof, 75-80, ASSOC PROF CHEM, MARIAN COL, 80- *Mem:* AAAS; Am Chem Soc; Am Asn Physics Teachers; Sigma Xi. *Res:* Exploring alternatives in science teaching; quantum mechanics of small molecules. *Mailing Add:* Dept of Chem Marian Col Indianapolis IN 46222

KELLY, EDWARD M, b Northumberland, Pa, Sept 6, 14; m 41; c 2. PHYSICS. *Educ:* Pa State Univ, BS, 43, MS, 45; Brown Univ, PhD, 50. *Prof Exp:* Asst prof physics, Univ Maine, 48-50; res specialist, NAm Aviation Inc, 50-53; ord physicist, Res & Develop Lab, Rheem Mfg Co, 53-57; actg chmn dept, 70-74, PROF PHYSICS, CALIF STATE POLYTECH COL, KELLOGG-VOORHIS, 57- *Concurrent Pos:* Consult, Aerojet-Gen Corp, Gen Tire & Rubber Co, 58- *Res:* Theoretical hydrodynamics; high explosives; ordnance. *Mailing Add:* Dept of Physics Calif State Polytech Univ Pomona CA 91768

KELLY, ERNEST L, b DuBois, Pa, Jan 6, 50; m 69; c 3. PHYSICAL PHARMACY, ANALYTICAL METHODS DEVELOPMENT. *Educ:* Millersville State Col, BA, 71; Villanova Univ, MS, 74, PhD(phys chem), 77. *Prof Exp:* Res asst, McNeil Labs, 72-74; res chemist, Merck Sharp & Dohme Res Labs, 74-79; sr anal chem, Mallory Battery Co Can Ltd, 64-69; SECT HEAD, WM H RORER, INC, 79- *Mem:* Am Chem Soc; Am Pharmaceut Asn; Acad Pharmaceut Sci. *Res:* Development of analytical and microscopic methods for the analysis of pharmaceutical drug substances and raw materials; evaluation of physical chemical properties of pharmaceutical drug substances in relationship to the formulation and stability of the drug. *Mailing Add:* 821 Eldridge Rd Fairless Hills PA 19030

KELLY, FLOYD W, JR, b Greeley, Colo, Dec 30, 41; m 65. ORGANIC CHEMISTRY. *Educ:* Colo State Univ, BS, 63; Univ Ore, MS, 65; Univ Idaho, PhD(org chem), 68. *Prof Exp:* Fel chem, Utah State Univ, 68-69; INSTR CHEM, CASPER COL, 69- *Mem:* Am Chem Soc. *Res:* Organic synthesis; organic photochemistry; gas phase homolyses. *Mailing Add:* Dept of Chem Casper Col Casper WY 82601

KELLY, FRANCIS JOHN, b Sydney, Australia, May 5, 35. PHYSICAL CHEMISTRY, SCIENCE POLICY. *Educ:* Univ Sydney, BSc, 56; Univ New England, Australia, PhD(phys chem), 61. *Prof Exp:* Demonstr chem, Univ New England, Australia, 57-60; Fulbright travel grant & res assoc chem, USDA, Rensselaer Polytech Inst, 60-63; dir phys & chem res, Mallory Battery Co Can Ltd, 64-69; sci adv, Sci Coun Can, 70-75; SR ADV CORP DEVELOP, ELDORADO NUCLEAR LTD, 75- *Concurrent Pos:* Consult, Sci Coun Can, 75- *Mem:* Fel Can Inst Chem; assoc Royal Australian Chem Inst; Can Res Mgt Asn; Electrochem Soc. *Res:* Demographic policy; energy systems; nuclear fuel cycle; diffusion in multicomponent systems; physicochemical properties of molten salts; non-aqueous electrolyte solutions; electrode processes; powder metallurgy; scientific manpower; industrial innovation. *Mailing Add:* River Rd Manstick ON K1M 1P7 Can

KELLY, FREDERICK MILES, b Chengtu, China, Oct 28, 16; m 47; c 2. PHYSICS. *Educ:* Univ Toronto, BA, 39, MA, 40, PhD(physics), 49. *Prof Exp:* Meteorologist, Meteorol Serv Can, 40-46; res fel physics, Univ Toronto, 49-50, res fel, Oxford Univ, 50-51; asst, Nat Res Coun Can, 51-53; PROF PHYSICS, UNIV MAN, 53- *Mem:* Can Asn Physicists. *Res:* Life time of atomic energy levels. *Mailing Add:* Dept of Physics Univ of Man Winnipeg MB R3T 2N2 Can

KELLY, GEORGE EUGENE, b Brooklyn, NY, Mar 28, 44; m 70; c 2. MECHANICAL ENGINEERING, STATISTICAL MECHANICS. *Educ:* State Univ NY, Stony Brook, BES, 65; Northwestern Univ, PhD(mech eng), 70. *Prof Exp:* Assoc statist mech, Nat Res Coun, 70-72, MECH ENGR, NAT BUR STANDARDS, 72- *Honors & Awards:* Silver Medal, Dept Commerce, 78. *Mem:* Am Phys Soc; Am Soc Heating, Refrig & Air-Conditioning Engrs. *Res:* Theoretical, laboratory and field research on the performance of heating and cooling equipment and control systems in buildings and residences; thermodynamics, fluid mechanics, heat transfer and methods of numerical and analytical analysis. *Mailing Add:* Mech Systs Group Nat Bur of Standards Washington DC 20234

KELLY, HENRY CHARLES, b Boston, Mass, July 10, 45; m 69. PHYSICS, SCIENCE POLICY. *Educ:* Cornell Univ, BA, 67; Harvard Univ, PhD(physics), 72. *Prof Exp:* Physicist, US Arms Control & Disarmament Agency, 71-74; tech adv to off, Off Technol Assessment, 75-78, dir technol & int rels, 78-79; assoc dir, Solar Energy Res Inst, 79-81; SR ASSOC, OFF TECHNOL ASSESSMENT, 81- *Concurrent Pos:* AAAS Cong Sci fel, 74-75. *Res:* Theory and application of light scattering techniques, particularly those involving photon correlation phenomenon; photovoltaic and other solar energy equipment; energy conservation technologies; international relations. *Mailing Add:* Off of Technol Assessment Cong of the US Washington DC 20510

KELLY, HENRY CURTIS, b Providence, RI, May 17, 30; m 56; c 3. INORGANIC CHEMISTRY. *Educ:* Bates Col, BS, 51; Brown Univ, PhD(chem), 62. *Prof Exp:* Anal chemist, Metal Hydrides Inc, 51-52, res chemist, 52-58, sr res chemist, 62-64; from asst to instr chem, Brown Univ, 58-62; from asst prof to assoc prof, 64-74, hons prof, 75, PROF CHEM, TEX CHRISTIAN UNIV, 74- *Mem:* AAAS; Am Chem Soc; The Chem Soc; Sigma Xi. *Res:* Chemistry of boron and silicon hydrides; boron-nitrogen compounds; kinetics and mechanisms of hydride reactions in solution; amineborane solvolysis and oxidation; kinetics of peroxidatic activity of metal-porphyrins and enzymes. *Mailing Add:* Dept of Chem Tex Christian Univ Ft Worth TX 76129

KELLY, HERBERT BARRETT, b Chicago, Ill, Dec 10, 28; m 59; c 2. ENVIRONMENTAL PHYSIOLOGY, NEUROPHYSIOLOGY. *Educ:* Loyola Univ, La, BS, 51; Tulane Univ, PhD(physiol), 64. *Prof Exp:* Instr physiol, Tulane Univ, 59-61; res physiologist, Naval Missile Ctr, Calif, 61-62; res specialist, Space Div, NAm Rockwell, 62-68; sr engr-scientist, Advan Marine Technol Div, Litton Indust, 68-69; SR STAFF SCIENTIST LIFE SCI, McDONNELL DOUGLAS ASTRONAUTICS, HUNTINGTON BEACH, 69- *Res:* Centrifugal reflex facilitation and inhibition of brainstem reticular formation; cross-adaptation studies of altitude acclimatization and thermal, hypoxic, hpercapnic, exercise and decompression tolerances; effects of prolonged rotation on human physiology and performance; design of zero-gravity holding facilities for biological specimens for use in space research. *Mailing Add:* 2511 Mammoth Circle El Toro CA 92630

KELLY, HOWARD GARFIELD, b Kingston, Ont, Aug 16, 17; m 41; c 2. INTERNAL MEDICINE. *Educ:* Queen's Univ, Ont, MD, CM, 40; FRCPS(C). *Prof Exp:* Asst therapeut, Univ Toronto, 47-48; from asst prof to assoc prof med, 49-66, PROF MED, FAC MED, QUEEN'S UNIV, ONT, 66- *Concurrent Pos:* Fel med, Univ Toronto, 46-47; Nuffield fel, Post-Grad Med Sch, Univ London, 48-49; Nat Res Coun Can fel, 49-50; attend physician, Kingston Gen Hosp; consult, Hotel Dieu Hosp, Armed Forces Hosp & Dept Vet Affairs; dir continuing educ & assoc dean clin affairs to vprin health sci, Fac Med, Queen's Univ, Ont, 73. *Mem:* Fel Am Col Cardiol; Am Heart Asn; Am Rheumatism Asn; fel Am Col Physicians; Can Rheumatism Asn (past pres). *Res:* Rheumatic diseases. *Mailing Add:* Fac of Med Queen's Univ Kingston ON K7L 3N6 Can

KELLY, HUGH P, b Boston, Mass, Sept 3, 31; m 55; c 6. PHYSICS. *Educ:* Harvard Univ, AB, 53; Univ Calif, Los Angeles, MS, 54; Univ Calif, Berkeley, PhD(physics), 63. *Prof Exp:* Physicist, Univ Calif, Berkeley, 62-63; res physicist, Univ Calif, San Diego, 63-64, res asst prof, 64-65; from asst prof to assoc prof & assoc dean, 65-70, prof, 70-77, COMMONWEALTH PROF PHYSICS, UNIV VA, 77- *Concurrent Pos:* Lectr, Univ Calif, San Diego, 65. *Mem:* Fel Am Phys Soc. *Res:* Theoretical physics, particularly many-body and atomic physics. *Mailing Add:* Dept Physics Univ Va Charlottesville VA 22903

KELLY, JAMES FRANCIS, b New Bedford, Mass, Nov 4, 48; m 71. INVERTEBRATE PATHOLOGY, MARINE SCIENCE. *Educ:* Stonehill Col, BS, 70; St Lawrence Univ, MS, 72; Univ Miami, PhD(marine sci), 75. *Prof Exp:* ASST RES SCIENTIST INVERTEBRATE PATH, DEPT ENTOM & NEMATOL, INST FOOD & AGR SCI, UNIV FLA, 75- *Concurrent Pos:* Res assoc, Insects Affecting Man Lab, Sci & Educ Admin-USDA, 75- *Mem:* AAAS; Soc Invertebrate Path. *Res:* Use of pathogens in biological control of medically important insects; protozoan diseases of aquatic and marine Crustacea. *Mailing Add:* Dept of Entom & Nematol Univ of Fla Gainesville FL 32611

KELLY, JAMES L(ESLIE), b New Orleans, La, Dec 20, 32; m 56; c 4. CHEMICAL & NUCLEAR ENGINEERING. *Educ:* Tulane Univ, BS, 54; La State Univ, MS, 60, PhD(chem eng), 62. *Prof Exp:* Process engr, Kaiser Aluminum & Chem Corp, 56-57 & Ormet Corp, 57-59; develop engr, Oak Ridge Nat Labs, 62-64; assoc prof, 64-72, PROF NUCLEAR ENG, SCH ENG & APPL SCI, UNIV VA, 72- *Mem:* Am Chem Soc; Am Inst Chem Engrs; Am Nuclear Soc. *Res:* Radiation processing; reactor materials; nuclear chemical engineering; radioactive waste disposal. *Mailing Add:* Rte 1 Box 295 Keswick VA 22947

KELLY, JEFFREY JOHN, b Portland, Ore, Nov 2, 42; m 66; c 3. BIOCHEMISTRY, CHEMISTRY. *Educ:* Harvey Mudd Col, BS, 64; Univ Calif, Berkeley, PhD(chem), 68. *Prof Exp:* Asst prof chem, Reed Col, 68-72; FAC MEM, DEPT CHEM, EVERGREEN STATE COL, 72- *Concurrent Pos:* Vis prof chem, Harvey Mudd Col, 80-81. *Mem:* AAAS; Sigma Xi. *Res:* Physical and chemical processes of photosynthesis; spectroscopy of biological systems. *Mailing Add:* Dept of Chem Evergreen State Col Olympia WA 98505

KELLY, JOHN, JR, b Preston, Idaho, Aug 8, 24; m 48; c 4. PHYSICAL CHEMISTRY. *Educ:* Idaho State Col, BS, 49; Univ Chicago, MS, 50; Stanford Univ, PhD(phys chem), 54. *Prof Exp:* Sr res technologist, 54-62, RES ASSOC, FIELD RES LAB, MOBIL RES & DEVELOP CORP, 62- *Mem:* Am Chem Soc; Sigma Xi; Soc Petrol Engrs. *Res:* Liquid ammonia chemistry; structure and analysis by x-ray diffraction; oxidative and thermal stability of oil well drilling fluid additives; stabilization of earth formations while drilling wells; kinetics of reactions of clays with organic compounds. *Mailing Add:* 2605 Keystone Dr Arlington TX 76011

KELLY, JOHN BECKWITH, b New York, NY, Aug 30, 21. MATHEMATICS. *Educ:* Columbia Univ, AB, 42; Mass Inst Technol, PhD, 48. *Prof Exp:* Instr math, Univ Wis, 48-50; mem, Inst Advan Study, 50-51; from instr to assoc prof, Mich State Univ, 51-62; assoc prof, 62-66, PROF MATH, ARIZ STATE UNIV, TEMPE, 66- *Res:* Number theory; graph theory; combinatorial analysis. *Mailing Add:* Dept of Math Ariz State Univ Tempe AZ 85281

KELLY, JOHN FRANCIS, b Chicago, Ill, Nov 28, 31; m 59; c 9. HORTICULTURE, OLERICULTURE. *Educ:* Mich State Univ, BS, 53, MS, 57; Univ Wis, PhD(hort, plant physiol), 60. *Prof Exp:* Agr res asst, Campbell Soup Co, 52-53; asst, Mich State Univ, 56 & Univ Wis, 57-59; asst prof veg crops & soils, Southern Ill Univ, 59-62; soils technologist, Campbell Soup Co, 62-64; dir pioneer plant res, 65-66, vpres pioneer res, Campbell Inst Agr Res, 66-72; prof veg crops & chmn dept, Univ Fla, 72-78; PROF HORT & CHMN DEPT, MICH STATE UNIV, 78- *Mem:* Fel AAAS; fel Am Soc Hort Sci; Am Hort Soc. *Res:* Culture, physiology, nutrition and chemical composition of vegetable crops; quality of food crops. *Mailing Add:* Dept of Hort Mich State Univ East Lansing MI 48824

KELLY, JOHN HENRY, b Tonawanda, NY, Sept 26, 52. DIFFRACTION, NON-LINEAR PROPAGATION. *Educ:* Univ Buffalo, BS, 74; Univ Rochester, MS, 76, PhD(optics), 80. *Prof Exp:* RES ASSOC, LAB LASER ENERGETICS, 80- *Mem:* Inst Elec & Electronics Engrs; Optical Soc Am. *Res:* Diffraction and the propagation of light in large laser systems; resonant energy transfer in both crystalline and amorphous materials. *Mailing Add:* Lab Laser Energetics 250 E River Rd Rochester NY 14620

KELLY, JOHN J, b Wilkes Barre, Pa, May 30, 19; m 47; c 5. INTERNAL MEDICINE, CARDIOLOGY. *Educ:* Univ Scranton, BS, 41; Univ Rochester, MD, 48. *Prof Exp:* Intern med, Strong Mem Hosp, 48-49, asst resident, 49-50; instr, Sch Med & Dent, Univ Rochester, 51-52; asst prof, State Univ NY Downstate Med Ctr, 52-59; dir med educ, Mercy Hosp, San Diego, 59-63; assoc clin prof, 63-72, CLIN PROF MED, UNIV CALIF, SAN FRANCISCO, 72- *Concurrent Pos:* Fel med, Stanford Univ, 50-51; co-dir, cardiopulmonary lab, Pac Med Ctr, 63-, chief med, 65-73. *Mem:* Am Fedn Clin Res; fel Am Col Physicians; NY Acad Med; fel Am Col Cardiol. *Mailing Add:* PO Box 7999 Pac Med Ctr San Francisco CA 94120

KELLY, JOHN MARTIN, b Chelsea, Mass, Oct 1, 14; m 38; c 4. PETROLEUM ENGINEERING, GEOLOGY. *Educ:* NMex Sch Mines, BS, 36, Petrol E, 39. *Hon Degrees:* DSc, NMex Sch Mines, 63. *Prof Exp:* Mining engr, Rosedale Gold Mines, 36; mine chemist, Am Metal Co, 36-37; petrol engr, Lea Co Opers Co, 37-41; NMex state geologist & coordr NMex mines, War Prod Bd, 41-45; pres, Elk Oil Co, 45-61; asst Secy Interior for mineral resources, 61-65, petrol consult, 65-75; REGENT, NMEX INST MINING & TECHNOL, 75- *Concurrent Pos:* Mem, Nat Coun Petrol Regulatory Authorities, Petrol Admin War, 41-45; consult & mineral adv, NMex State Land Off, 45-61; US deleg energy & petrol comts, Orgn Econ Coop & Develop, Paris, 61-65 & mem adv comt to US deleg to petrol comt, 65-; US deleg petrol planning comt, NATO, Paris, 61-65; chmn, US deleg, Petrol Con, Econ Comn, Asia & Far East, Tehran 62 & Tokyo, 65; mem, Nat Petrol Coun, 65- *Honors & Awards:* Distinguished Serv Honor Award, US Dept Interior, 66. *Mem:* Fel AAAS; Am Inst Mining, Metall & Petrol Engrs; Am Asn Petrol Geol; fel Geol Soc Am; Mining & Metall Soc Am. *Res:* Energy resources of the United States. *Mailing Add:* PO Box 310 Roswell NM 88201

KELLY, JOHN RUSSELL, b Nashua, NH, Jan 25, 52. OCEANOGRAPHY. *Educ:* Univ NH, BA, 74; Univ RI, PhD(oceanog), 82. *Prof Exp:* Res asst, Grad Sch Oceanog, Univ RI, 75-81; RES ASSOC, ECOSYSTS RES CTR, CORNELL UNIV, 81- *Mem:* Am Soc Limnol & Oceanog. *Res:* Elemental cycling in marine, aquatic and terrestrial systems. *Mailing Add:* Ecosysts Res Ctr 141 Biol Sci Bldg Cornell Univ Ithaca NY 14853

KELLY, JOHN V, b London, Ont, Aug 21, 26; nat US. OBSTETRICS, GYNECOLOGY. *Educ:* Wayne State Univ, BS, 48, MD, 51; Am Bd Obstet & Gynec, dipl, 61. *Prof Exp:* Intern, Metrop Hosp, NY Med Col, 51-52, resident obstet & gynec, 52-55; from instr to asst prof, Sch Med, Univ Calif, Los Angeles, 57-64; med missionary, St Luke's Hosp, Anua, ENigeria, 64-66; prof obstet & gynec, Sch Med, Univ Pa, 67-75; CHMN DEPT OBSTET & GYNEC, MARICOPA COUNTY HOSP, PHOENIX, 75- *Concurrent Pos:* Res fel, Harvard Med Sch, 55; Graves fel, Free Hosp Women, Brookline, Mass, 55; Fulbright fel, Stockholm, Sweden, 56; adj prof obstet & gynec, Sch Med, Univ Ariz, 75- *Mem:* Am Fertil Soc; Am Med Asn; Am Fedn Clin Res. *Res:* Dynamics of uterine muscle contraction. *Mailing Add:* Dept of Obstet & Gynec 2601 E Roosevelt Phoenix AZ 85008

KELLY, KENNETH WILLIAM, b New York, NY. ORGANIC CHEMISTRY. *Educ:* St John's Univ, NY, BS, 61, MS, 63; Rutgers Univ, PhD(chem), 69. *Prof Exp:* Chemist synthesis, Merck & Co, Rahway, NJ, 63-69; DIR RES, KAY-FRIES, INC, 69- *Mem:* Am Chem Soc. *Res:* Organic synthesis; organic analysis. *Mailing Add:* 123 Shetland Dr New York NY 10956

KELLY, KERRY JAMES, b Dodgeville, Wis, Nov 16, 52; m 77; c 2. NEUTRON ACTIVATION ANALYSIS, X-RAY FLUORESCENCE. *Educ:* Univ Wis-Madison, BS, 74. *Prof Exp:* From chemist to sr res chemist, 74-81, PROJ LEADER RES & DEVELOP, MICH DIV, DOW CHEM CO, 81- *Res:* Developing methodology, instrumentation and software for neutron activation analysis and x-ray fluorescence spectroscopy and applying this technology to on-line process monitors. *Mailing Add:* 7577 E Beal City Rd Mt Pleasant MI 48858

KELLY, KEVIN ANTHONY, b United Kingdom, March 29, 45; US citizen; m 81. SCIENCE & PUBLIC POLICY. *Educ:* Notre Dame Univ, BS, 67; Yale Univ, MS, 68; Ohio State Univ, PhD(nuclear eng), 76. *Prof Exp:* Sr res assoc, Mech Eng Dept, Ohio State Univ, 76-77; ASSOC DIR RES, NAT REGULATORY RES INST, 77- *Concurrent Pos:* Adj asst prof nuclear eng, Ohio State Univ, 77. *Mem:* Am Nuclear Soc. *Res:* Regulation of electric and gas utilities-the economic, technological and sociological impacts of regulation. *Mailing Add:* Nat Regulatory Res Inst 2130 Neil Ave Columbus OH 43210

KELLY, LEROY MILTON, b Leominster, Mass, May 8, 14; m 44; c 2. MATHEMATICS. *Educ:* Northeastern Univ, BSCE, 38; Boston Univ, MA, 40; Univ Mo, PhD(math), 48. *Prof Exp:* Instr math, Univ Mo, 45-48; from asst prof to assoc prof, 48-58, PROF MATH, MICH STATE UNIV, 58- *Mem:* Am Math Soc; Math Asn Am. *Res:* Metric geometry; topology; lattice theory. *Mailing Add:* Dept of Math Mich State Univ East Lansing MI 48824

KELLY, LEWIS ANDREW, b Butler, Pa, Mar 30, 43; m 66; c 3. HORMONE ACTION, CANCER. *Educ:* Muskingum Col, BS, 65; Univ Pittsburgh, PhD(biochem), 70. *Prof Exp:* Res assoc, Naval Air Develop Ctr, 69-70; res assoc, 70-71, res instr, 71-73, instr, 73-74, ASST PROF MED BIOCHEM, MED SCH, UNIV MASS, 74- *Concurrent Pos:* Co-prin investr, Nat Inst Drug Abuse, 75-78; prin investr, Am Lung Asn, 79-81, Nat Inst Aging, 79-82; assoc dir, Nat Bladder Cancer Proj, 81- *Mem:* Tissue Culture Asn; NY Acad Sci; AAAS. *Res:* Regulation of cell function: mechanisms, relationship to cellular growth status, and modulation by extrinsic nutritional, hormonal, and pharmacological factors. *Mailing Add:* Dept Biochem Med Sch Univ Mass 55 Lake Ave N Worcester MA 01605

KELLY, LOLA SZANTO, b Vienna, Austria, Nov 5, 24; nat US; div; c 2. BIOPHYSICS. *Educ:* Univ Calif, BA, 45, PhD(biophys), 49. *Prof Exp:* Res assoc med, physics & biophys, Donner Lab, Med Physics Div, Univ Calif, 54-78; RETIRED. *Mem:* Radiation Res Soc Am; Am Physiol Soc; Am Asn Cancer Res; Reticuloendothelial Soc. *Res:* Nucleic acid metabolism; biological effects of radiation; physiology of reticuloendothelial system and leukocytes; leukemogenesis. *Mailing Add:* 524 Grizzley Peak Blvd Berkeley CA 94708

KELLY, MAHLON GEORGE, JR, b Plymouth, NH Mar 24, 39; m 70. AQUATIC ECOLOGY, BIOLOGICAL OCEANOGRAPHY. *Educ:* Harvard Univ, AB, 60, PhD(biol), 68; Univ NH, MS, 62. *Prof Exp:* Sci staff, R/V Anton Bruun Nat Sci Found, 62-63; res asst biol, Woods Hole Oceanog Inst, 63 & Harvard Univ, 64-67; staff oceanogr, Mass Inst Technol, 68; vis asst prof environ biol, Univ Miami, 68-69; asst prof biol, NY Univ, 69-70; asst prof, 70-75, ASSOC PROF ENVIRON SCI, UNIV VA, 75- *Concurrent Pos:* Vis scientist, Scottish Marine Biol Lab, 76; vis scientist, Danish Fresh Water Lab, 78, 80. *Mem:* AAAS; Am Soc Limnol & Oceanog; Ecol Soc Am; Sigma Xi. *Res:* Phytoplankton productivity and eutrophication; marine bioluminescence; aerial photography of benthic communities; taxonomy of dinoflagellates; limnology. *Mailing Add:* Dept Environ Sci Clark Hall Univ Va Charlottesville VA 22903

KELLY, MARTIN JOSEPH, b New York, NY, Sept 27, 24. PHYSICS. *Educ:* St John's Univ, NY, BS, 49; NY Univ, PhD, 58. *Prof Exp:* Physicist, Naval Mat Lab, 51-53; assoc, Nucleonics, Inc, 54-59; assoc, Tech Res Group, Inc, 59; mem fac, Manhattan Col, 59-64; chmn dept, 64-74, PROF PHYSICS, C W POST COL, LONG ISLAND UNIV, 64- *Mem:* Am Phys Soc. *Res:* Neutron physics; reactors; shielding. *Mailing Add:* Dept of Physics C W Post Col Greenvale NY 11548

KELLY, MICHAEL JAMES, laser physics, see previous edition

KELLY, MICHAEL THOMAS, b Indianapolis, Ind, Mar 8, 43; m 65; c 4. CLINICAL MICROBIOLOGY, IMMUNOLOGY. *Educ:* Purdue Univ, BS, 65; Ind Univ, PhD(microbiol), 69, MD, 73. *Prof Exp:* Fel, Sch Med, Ind Univ, 69-71, res assoc infectious dis, 71-73; intern path, Scg Med, Univ Minn, 73-74; comn officer res, Rocky Mountain Lab, NIH, USPHS, 74-76; asst prof path, Sch Med, Univ Utah, 76-78; ASSOC PROF PATH, UNIV TEX MED BR, GALVESTON, 78- *Mem:* AAAS; Reticuloendothelial Soc; Am Asn Immunologists; Am Soc Microbiol; Am Fedn Clin Res. *Res:* Host-parasite relationships; modulation of macrophage function by microbial agents; immunopotentiation by microbial agents; mechanism of macrophage activation; clinical microbiology; antimicrobial susceptibility testing; marine microbiology. *Mailing Add:* Dept of Path Med Br Univ Tex Galveston TX 77550

KELLY, MIKE, b Pineville, Mo, June 27, 32; m 57; c 3. POULTRY NUTRITION. *Educ:* Univ Mo, BS, 55, AM, 56; Univ Ill, PhD(animal sci), 66. *Prof Exp:* Supvr nutrit lab, Hales & Hunter Co, 57-61, supvr qual control, 61-62, mgr growing opers, 62-63; res asst animal sci, Univ Ill, 63-66, res assoc, 66; exten specialist & asst prof poultry nutrit, Va Polytech Inst & State Univ, 66-72; dir res & qual control, 72-74, DIR NUTRIT, JIM DANDY CO, 74- *Mem:* Poultry Sci Asn; Am Soc Animal Sci. *Res:* Availability of amino acids in proteins; nutrient requirements of turkeys. *Mailing Add:* 3325 Monte D'Oro Dr Birmingham AL 35216

KELLY, MINTON J, b Liberty, Mo, Feb 14, 21; m 49; c 3. HIGH TEMPERATURE CHEMISTRY. *Educ:* Tex A&M Univ, BS, 47, MS, 50, PhD(phys chem), 56. *Prof Exp:* Field party chief oceanog res found, Tex A&M Univ, 47-48, consult instrumentation, 50-54, teaching fel chem univ, 54-55; develop engr instrumentation & controls div, Oak Ridge Nat Lab, 55-59, group leader reactor chem div, 59-62; group supvr instrumentation, Aerospace Div, Boeing Co, 62-63; chemist, Reactor Chem Div, 63-74, RES ASSOC, CHEM TECHNOL DIV, OAK RIDGE NAT LAB, 74- *Concurrent Pos:* Engr, Arabian-Am Oil Co, 48-49. *Mem:* AAAS; Sigma Xi; fel Am Inst Chemists. *Res:* Instrumental measurements under nuclear conditions. *Mailing Add:* 114 Lewis Lane Oak Ridge TN 37830

KELLY, PATRICK CLARKE, b Edmonton, Alta, Feb 18, 42; c 2. ANALYTICAL CHEMISTRY. *Educ:* Univ Alta, BSc, 64; PhD(chem), 70. *Prof Exp:* Vpres anal chem, Dean & Kelly Anal Chem Ltd, 70-71; fel, Dept Chem, Univ Alta, 71-72; asst prof, Dept Chem, Univ Ga, 72-73; SCIENTIST ANAL CHEM, RES CTR, CAN PACKERS, 73- *Concurrent Pos:* Chmn TC34/SC6, Can Adv Comt, Int Orgn Stand, 76- *Mem:* Chem Inst Can; Asn Off Anal Chemists. *Res:* The analysis of food, feed and drugs; special interest in instrumental analysis, automation, and the application of probability and statistical communications theory to the extraction of information from instrumentation. *Mailing Add:* Res Ctr Can Packers 2211 W St Clair Ave Toronto ON M6N 1K4 Can

KELLY, PATRICK JOSEPH, b Minneapolis, Minn, Feb 12, 26; m 50; c 8. ORTHOPEDIC SURGERY. *Educ:* St Lawrence Univ, BS, 45; St Louis Univ, MD, 49; Univ Minn, MS, 58. *Prof Exp:* Consult, Mayo Clin, 57- *Concurrent Pos:* Am Orthop Asn Traveling Fel; pres, Bd Trustees, Orthopaedic Res & Educ Found. *Mem:* Am Col Surg; Am Acad Orthop Surg; Am Orthop Asn; Orthop Res Soc (past pres); Am Physiol Soc. *Res:* Circulation and physiology of bone; bone metabolism. *Mailing Add:* Mayo Clin 200 First St SW Rochester MN 55901

KELLY, PAUL ALAN, b Washington, DC, June 3, 43; m 69; c 1. MEDICAL RESEARCH. *Educ:* Western Mich Univ, BS, 66, MS, 68; Univ Wis, PhD(endocrinol & reprod physiol), 72. *Prof Exp:* Fel endocrinol, McGill Univ, 72-74; fel, 74-75, asst prof, 75-80, ASSOC PROF PHYSIOL, LAVAL UNIV, 80- *Concurrent Pos:* Sr mem, Med Res Coun Group Molecular Endocrinol, 75-; Med Res Coun Can scholar, 75- *Mem:* Endocrine Soc; Am Physiol Soc; Can Soc Clin Invest; Int Soc Neuroendocrinol; Can Soc Endocrinol & Metab. *Res:* Endocrine control of mammary carcinoma; neuroendocrine regulation of pituitary hormone secretion; control of polypeptide and steroid hormone receptors in target tissues. *Mailing Add:* MRC Group Molec Endocrinol CHUL 2705 Boul Laurier Quebec PQ B1V 4G2 Can

KELLY, PAUL J, b Riverside, Calif, June 26, 16; m 46; c 2. MATHEMATICS. *Educ:* Univ Calif, Los Angeles, AB, 37, MA, 39; Univ Wis, PhD(math), 42. *Prof Exp:* Instr math, Univ Southern Calif, 46-49; from asst prof to assoc prof, 49-59, PROF MATH, UNIV CALIF, SANTA BARBARA, 59- *Res:* Metric geometry. *Mailing Add:* Dept of Math Univ of Calif Santa Barbara CA 93106

KELLY, PAUL JAMES, b Montreal, Que, July 19, 34; m 60; c 5. PHYSICS. *Educ:* Sir George Williams Univ, BSc, 60; Carleton Univ, MSc, 62, PhD(physics), 65. *Prof Exp:* From asst res officer to assoc res officer, 65-76, SR RES OFFICER PHYSICS, NAT RES COUN, 76- *Concurrent Pos:* Asst invest officer, Energy Res & Develop Admin consult grant, Wash State Univ, 75-77; Air Force consult grant, Wash State Univ, 78- *Res:* Thermally stimulated processes; interaction of high-intensity laser pulses with solids. *Mailing Add:* 310 Smyth Rd Ottawa ON K1H 5A3 Can

KELLY, PAUL SHERWOOD, b Erie, Pa, Dec 22, 27; m 56; c 3. ATOMIC PHYSICS, QUANTUM MECHANICS. *Educ:* Haverford Col, AB, 49; Yale Univ, MS, 50; Univ Calif, Los Angeles, PhD(physics), 61. *Prof Exp:* Physicist, US Naval Ord Lab, Md, 50-51; electronic scientist, Nat Bur Standards, Calif, 51-53; res scientist, Lockheed Missiles & Space Co, Palo Alto, 60-68; PROF PHYSICS, HUMBOLDT STATE UNIV, 68- *Mem:* Am Phys Soc; Sigma Xi. *Res:* Calculation of atomic wave functions and related atomic parameters; nuclear structure calculations. *Mailing Add:* Dept of Physics Humboldt State Univ Arcata CA 95521

KELLY, PETER MICHAEL, b New York, NY, July 6, 22; m 46; c 3. PHYSICS, ELECTRICAL ENGINEERING. *Educ:* Union Col, NY, BS, 50; Calif Inst Technol, MS, 52, PhD(physics) & PhD(elec eng), 60. *Prof Exp:* Design engr, jet propulsion lab, Calif Inst Technol, 51-52; proj engr, electronics div, Century Metalcraft Co, 53-54; mem tech staff, Hughes Aircraft Co, 54-56; from design engr to prin scientist, aeronutronic div, Ford Motor Co, 56-61; mgr elec dept, Astropower, Douglas Aircraft Co, 61-62; from assoc dir res to chief engr, Systs Tech Ctr, Philco-Ford, 62-69; pres & chmn bd, Kelly Sci Corp, 69-80; PROF ELEC ENG & DIR, TELECOMMUN CTR, GEORGE WASHINGTON UNIV, WASHINGTON, DC, 80- *Concurrent Pos:* Consult, Nat Sci Found, 60-61; consult, President's Crime Comn, 66 & President's Commun Task Force, 68. *Mem:* AAAS; Asn Comput Mach. *Res:* Radar; network synthesis; data processing. *Mailing Add:* 3431 N Emerson St Arlington VA 22207

KELLY, RAYMOND CRAIN, b Portland, Ore, Sept 4, 45; m 68; c 1. TOXICOLOGY. *Educ:* Wash State Univ, BS, 67; Univ Ore, PhD(chem), 75. *Prof Exp:* Develop chemist, Sacred Heart Gen Hosp, 69-71; assoc toxicologist, Cuyahoga County Coroners Off, Ohio, 75-77; head toxicol & statist, Lab Procedures, Upjohn Co, 77-78; ASST DIR, DEPT TOXICOL & EMERGENCY SERV, BIO-SCI LAB, VAN NUYS, CALIF, 78- *Concurrent Pos:* Nat Res Serv fel, Nat Inst Drug Abuse, NIH, 76. *Mem:* Am Chem Soc; Am Acad Forensic Sci; Am Asn Clin Chem; AAAS. *Res:* Devising of novel methods for the analysis of drugs in biological fluids, characterization of drug metabolites, mechanisms of drug toxicity and monitoring of therapeutic drug concentrations in man. *Mailing Add:* Bio-Sci Lab 7600 Tyrone St Van Nuys CA 91405

KELLY, RAYMOND LEROY, b Rockford, Ill, Feb 2, 21; m 43; c 2. ATOMIC SPECTROSCOPY. *Educ:* Univ Wis, PhD(physics), 51. *Prof Exp:* Asst, Univ Wis, 47-51; res physicist, Stanford Res Inst, 51-60; assoc prof, 60-68, PROF PHYSICS, NAVAL POSTGRAD SCH, 68- *Concurrent Pos:* Mem comt line spectra elements, Nat Res Coun, 71-78. *Mem:* Am Phys Soc; fel Optical Soc Am; Am Asn Physics Teachers. *Res:* Infrared; spectroscopy of the ultraviolet. *Mailing Add:* Dept Physics & Chem Naval Postgrad Sch Monterey CA 93940

KELLY, REGIS BAKER, b Edinburgh, Scotland, May 26, 40; m 71; c 2. NEUROBIOLOGY. *Educ:* Univ Edinburgh, BSc, 61, dipl, 62; Calif Inst Technol, PhD(biophys), 67. *Prof Exp:* Instr neurobiol, Harvard Med Sch, 69-71; asst prof biochem & biophys, 71-74, assoc prof, 74-78, PROF BIOCHEM & BIOPHYS, UNIV CALIF, SAN FRANCISCO, 78- *Concurrent Pos:* Helen Hay Whitney Found fel, Sch Med, Stanford Univ, 67-69 & Harvard Med Sch, 69-70; Multiple Sclerosis fel, 70-71. *Mem:* Soc Neurosci; Am Soc Biol Chem. *Res:* Replication of bacterial nucleic acids; biochemistry of nervous system; synaptic transmission. *Mailing Add:* Dept of Biochem & Biophys Univ of Calif Med Ctr San Francisco CA 94143

KELLY, RICHARD DELMER, b Kingston, NY, Aug 24, 35; m 54; c 4. BIOLOGY, SCIENCE EDUCATION. *Educ:* State Univ NY Albany, BS, 55, MS, 56; Syracuse Univ, EdD(biol, sci educ), 65. *Prof Exp:* High sch teacher, NY, 56-63; PROF BIOL, STATE UNIV NY ALBANY, 63- *Concurrent Pos:* Consult, NY State Educ Dept, 60- & NSF Summer Progs, 60-65; vis fel, Col Educ, Kingston Upon Hull, Eng, 73-74 & Rosentiel Inst, Univ Miami, 82. *Mem:* AAAS; Am Inst Biol Sci. *Res:* Instructional technology; television, audio-tutorial; cetaceans and whaling history. *Mailing Add:* Dept of Biol State Univ of NY Albany NY 12222

KELLY, RICHARD W(ALTER), b Iowa City, Iowa, Sept 6, 35; m 64. ELECTRICAL ENGINEERING. *Educ:* Univ Iowa, BSEE, 58, MS, 62, PhD(elec eng), 65. *Prof Exp:* From instr to asst prof elec eng, Univ Iowa, 58-65; assoc prof, 65-70, PROF ELEC ENG, ARIZ STATE UNIV, 70-, CHMN, 80- *Concurrent Pos:* Sr Fulbright-Hays lectureship, Trinity Col, Dublin, 72-73. *Mem:* Inst Elec & Electronics Engrs; Am Soc Eng Educ. *Res:* Application of modern signal theory; detection and estimation theory. *Mailing Add:* Dept of Elec Eng Ariz State Univ Tempe AZ 85281

KELLY, ROBERT CHARLES, b St Joseph, Mich, Nov 28, 39; m 60; c 2. ORGANIC CHEMISTRY. *Educ:* Kalamazoo Col, BA, 61; Harvard Univ, MA, 63, PhD(chem), 66. *Prof Exp:* RES ASSOC ORG CHEM, UPJOHN CO, 65- *Mem:* Am Chem Soc. *Res:* Organic synthesis and structure determination, particularly of cyclic hydrocarbons; terpenes and oxygen heterocycles; natural products chemistry; prostaglandins. *Mailing Add:* Exp Chem Res Upjohn Co Kalamazoo MI 49001

KELLY, ROBERT EDWARD, anatomy, cytology, see previous edition

KELLY, ROBERT EDWARD, b Abington, Pa, Oct 20, 34; m 64; c 2. FLUID MECHANICS, HEAT TRANSFER. *Educ:* Franklin & Marshall Col, BA, 57; Rensselaer Polytech Inst, BS, 57; Mass Inst Technol, AE, 59, ScD(aeronaut eng), 64. *Prof Exp:* Guest scientist, Nat Phys Lab, UK, 60-61, UK Civil Serv sr res fel fluid mech, 64-66; res asst aeronaut eng, Mass Inst Technol, 61-64; asst res geophysicist, Inst Geophys & Planetary Physics, Univ Clif, San Diego, 66-67; from asst prof to assoc prof, 67-75, PROF ENG, UNIV CALIF, LOS ANGELES, 75- *Concurrent Pos:* Sci Res Coun sr vis fel, Dept Math, Imp Col, London, 73-74; consult, Hughes Aircraft Co, 76-81. *Mem:* Am Phys Soc; Am Acad Mech; Soc Indust & Appl Math; Am Soc Mech Engrs. *Res:* Viscous flow; boundary layer theory; hydrodynamic stability; fluid wave motion; stratified and rotating flow phenomena; thermal convection. *Mailing Add:* Dept of Mech & Structures Boelter Hall 5731 Univ of Calif Los Angeles CA 90024

KELLY, ROBERT EMMETT, b Cape Girardeau, Mo, Nov 26, 29; m 62; c 3. PHYSICS. *Educ:* Southeast Mo State Univ, BS, 50; Univ Mo-Rolla, MS, 52; Univ Conn, PhD(physics), 59. *Prof Exp:* PROF PHYSICS, UNIV MISS, 59- *Concurrent Pos:* Consult, Boeing Co, 54, E I du Pont de Nemours & Co, Inc, 57 & Am Optical Co, 59; Richland fac fel, Hanford Lab, 65; vis investr oceanog, Woods Hole Oceanog Inst, 67; prof, NMex Highlands Univ, 68; physicist, Gen Elec Co, 52 & Marshall Space Flight Ctr, NASA, 70 & 71; consult, Los Alamos Sci Lab, 75-82 & Lawrence Livermore Lab, 75-79; vis scientist, Ctr d'Etudes Bruyeres-le-kChatel, Serv Physique Nucleaire, France, 81 & 82. *Mem:* Am Geophys Union; Acoust Soc Am. *Res:* Electromagnetic theory; physical optics; atmospheric and mathematical physics; mathematical approach to transient radiation damage in optical fibers; energy deposition and profiles of particle beams, plus topics in musical acoustics. *Mailing Add:* Dept of Physics Univ of Miss University MS 38677

KELLY, ROBERT FRANK, b Fond du Lac, Wis, May 21, 19; m 44; c 6. BIOCHEMISTRY, ANIMAL HUSBANDRY. *Educ:* Univ Wis, BS, 48, MS, 53, PhD(biochem, animal husb), 55. *Prof Exp:* Pub sch instr, Wis, 48-51; asst, Univ Wis, 51-55; assoc prof, 55-58, PROF FOOD SCI & TECHNOL, VA POLYTECH INST & STATE UNIV, 58- *Mem:* Fel AAAS; Am Meat Sci Asn; Am Soc Animal Sci; Am Inst Food Technologists; NY Acad Sci. *Res:* Food science and nutrition. *Mailing Add:* Dept of Food Sci & Technol Va Polytech Inst & State Univ Blacksburg VA 24061

KELLY, ROBERT JAMES, b New York, NY, Dec 2, 23; m 52; c 7. ORGANIC CHEMISTRY. *Educ:* Trinity Col, BS, 43; NY Univ, MS, 47, PhD(chem), 52. *Prof Exp:* Asst, NY Univ, 46-51; res chemist, 51-62, sr res scientist, 62-65, mgr new fiber res & develop, Uniroyal Fiber & Textile Div, 65-69, mgr tire cord res & develop, 69-76, TECH DIR UNIROYAL FIBER & TEXTILE DIV, 76- *Mem:* Am Chem Soc. *Res:* Synthetic rubber and fibers. *Mailing Add:* Res & Develop Dept Uniroyal Fiber & Textile Div Winnsboro SC 29180

KELLY, ROBERT LINCOLN, b Honolulu, Hawaii, Oct 29, 39; m 65; c 1. ELEMENTARY PARTICLE PHYSICS. *Educ:* Univ Calif, Riverside, BA, 61; Univ Calif, Berkeley, PhD(physics), 66. *Prof Exp:* Nat Res Coun-Nat Acad Sci fel physics, Nat Bur Stand, 66-68; asst prof, Univ Md, Baltimore County, 68-69; res fel, Univ Mich, Ann Arbor, 69-70; res physicist, Carnegie-Mellon Univ, 70-72; PHYSICIST, LAWRENCE BERKELEY LAB, UNIV CALIF, BERKELEY, 72- *Res:* Phenomenology of high energy and hadronic interactions; partial wave analysis. *Mailing Add:* Lawrence Berkeley Lab Univ of Calif Berkeley CA 94720

KELLY, ROBERT P, b Dover, NJ, Mar 17, 38; m 63. CELL PHYSIOLOGY. *Educ:* Fairleigh Dickinson Univ, BS, 62; Fordham Univ, MS, 65, PhD(biol), 66. *Prof Exp:* From instr to asst prof, 64-70, assoc prof, 70-80, PROF BIOL & CHMN DEPT & COORDR PROG BIOL CHEM, ST PETER'S COL, NJ, 80- *Concurrent Pos:* Fac res grant, St Peter's Col, NJ, 64-65 & 67. *Res:* Insect and cell physiology with emphasis on nutrition and enzyme chemistry. *Mailing Add:* Dept of Biol St Peter's Col Jersey City NJ 07306

KELLY, ROBERT WITHERS, b Stanford, Ky, Oct 20, 26; m 48; c 2. ZOOLOGY, ECOLOGY. *Educ:* Centre Col, BA, 49; Univ Ore, MS, 50; Univ Mo, PhD(zool), 56. *Prof Exp:* Head sci dept, Campbellsville Jr Col, 51-53; assoc prof biol, Southeastern La Col, 56-63 & Ariz State Col, 63-64; PROF BIOL, FURMAN UNIV, 64-, CHMN DEPT, 74- *Mem:* Am Soc Zool. *Res:* Invertebrate ecology, especially freshwater forms. *Mailing Add:* Dept of Biol Furman Univ Greenville SC 29613

KELLY, RONALD BURGER, b Fairvale, NB, May 26, 20; m 45. ORGANIC CHEMISTRY. *Educ:* Univ NB, MSc, 51, PhD(chem), 53. *Prof Exp:* Beaverbrook overseas scholar, Univ London, 53-54; Nat Res Coun Can fel, Queen's Univ, Ont, 54-55; sr res chemist, Merck & Co, Ltd, Can, 55-58; res assoc chem, Upjohn Co, 58-67; PROF CHEM, UNIV NB, 67-, CHMN DIV SCI & MATH, 73- *Mem:* AAAS; Am Chem Soc; Royal Soc Chem; fel Chem Inst Can; NY Acad Sci. *Res:* Structure determination of organic molecules; synthesis of natural products. *Mailing Add:* Dept of Chem Univ of NB St John NB E2L 4L5 Can

KELLY, SALLY MARIE, b Bridgeport, Conn. BIOCHEMICAL MEDICAL GENETICS. *Educ:* Conn Col, AB, 43; Univ Wis, MA, 44, PhD(bot), 46; NY Univ, MD, 63; Am Bd Path, dipl, 71. *Prof Exp:* Instr, Simmons Col, 47-48; asst prof plant sci, Vassar Col, 48-51; sr res scientist, Div Labs & Res, 51-64, assoc res scientist, 64-67, RES PHYSICIAN BIRTH DEFECTS INST, NY STATE DEPT HEALTH, 67- *Concurrent Pos:* Fel, Brooklyn Bot Garden, 45-47; fel, Harvard Univ, 47-48; Brown-Hazen Fund fel, 58-59 & 60-63; res assoc prof pediat, Albany Med Col, 68- *Mem:* Soc Exp Biol & Med; Am Soc Human Genetics. *Res:* Cell physiology; enteroviruses; biochemical medical genetics. *Mailing Add:* Div Labs & Res NY State Dept of Health Albany NY 12201

KELLY, SIDNEY J(OHN), b Brooklyn, NY, Apr 15, 24; m 51; c 4. ENGINEERING. *Educ:* Polytech Inst Brooklyn, BMechEng, 45; Bucknell Univ, MS, 51; Hofstra Univ, MS, 59; Columbia Univ, dipl, 63. *Prof Exp:* Instr eng, Bucknell Univ, 45-51; head dept diesel technol, State Univ NY Agr & Tech Col, Alfred, 51-56; asst prof eng, Hofstra Univ, 56-61; dean tech col, 63-77, MEM FAC ENG TECHNOL, FRANKLIN UNIV, 77- *Concurrent Pos:* Kellogg Community Col scholar, Columbia Univ, 61-63. *Mem:* Inst Elec & Electronics Engrs; Am Soc Mech Engrs; Am Soc Eng Educ. *Res:* Mechanical power; machine design; engineering economy; industrial management; engineering administration. *Mailing Add:* Col of Sci & Eng Technol Franklin Univ 201 S Grant Ave Columbus OH 43215

KELLY, SUSAN JEAN, b Cincinnati, Ohio, Oct 2, 47; m 70; c 1. ENZYMOLOGY, BIOCHEMICAL ENGINEERING. *Educ:* Col Mt St Joseph, AB, 69; Purdue Univ, PhD(biochem), 74. *Prof Exp:* Res assoc enzyme eng, Dept Biochem, Purdue Univ, 74-80. *Mem:* Sigma Xi. *Res:* Enzyme-catalyzed synthesis of sucrose and other economically important physiological compounds; enzymic mechanism of phosphatases; phosphonate analogs of phosphatase substrates; relationship of phosphatases to developmental changes and to cancer. *Mailing Add:* 110 Monterey Lane Purdue Univ Durham NC 27713

KELLY, THADDEUS ELLIOTT, b New York, NY, Oct 7, 37; m 60; c 3. MEDICAL GENETICS. *Educ:* Davidson Col, BS, 59; Med Col SC, MD, 63; Johns Hopkins Univ, PhD(genetics), 75. *Prof Exp:* Asst prof med & pediat, Sch Med, Johns Hopkins Univ, 73-75; assoc prof, 75-80, PROF PEDIAT, UNIV VA, 80- *Concurrent Pos:* Dir, Div Med Genetics, Univ Va, 75-, assoc dir, Clin Res Ctr, 76-81; chmn, Genetics Adv Comt, State Va, 79- *Mem:* Soc Pediat Res; Am Pediat Soc; Am Soc Human Genetics; Am Fedn Clin Res; Clin Genetics & Birth Defects Soc. *Res:* Biochemical genetic analysis of genetic heterogenity; genetic disorders in large family studies. *Mailing Add:* Univ Hosp Univ Va Box 386 Charlottesville VA 22908

KELLY, THOMAS JOSEPH, b Brooklyn, NY. AEROSPACE ENGINEERING, MECHANICAL ENGINEERING. *Educ:* Cornell Univ, BME, 51; Columbia Univ, MSME, 56; Mass Inst Technol, MS in IM, 70. *Prof Exp:* Propulsion engr, Rigel Missile prog, Grumman Aerospace Corp, 51-53, group leader jet air induction, 53-56; performance engr, Wright Patterson AFB, 56-58; group leader rocket propulsion, Lockheed Aircraft Corp, 58-59; asst chief propulsion, Grumman Aerospace Corp, 59-60, eng proj leader Apollo & Lunar Module studies & proposals, 60-62, proj engr, eng mgr & dep prog mgr, Lunar Module Prog, 62-70, dep dir space shuttle prog, 70-72, dir space progs, 72-76, vpres eng, 76-81, VPRES TECH OPERS, GRUMMAN AEROSPACE CORP, 81- *Concurrent Pos:* Mem NASA panel on space vehicles, Res & Technol Adv Coun, 75-77; mem aeronaut & space eng bd ad hoc comt on technol large space syst, Nat Res Coun, 78. *Honors & Awards:* Cert Appreciation, NASA, 69, Distinguished Pub Serv Medal, 73; Spacecraft Design Award, 73, fel, Am Inst Aeronaut & Astronaut. *Mem:* Am Inst Aeronaut & Astronaut; Am Soc Mech Engrs. *Res:* Development of manned spacecraft; engineering effort of Project Apollo Lunar Module; development and production engineering of a variety of military aircraft. *Mailing Add:* Grumman Aerospace Corp S Oyster Bay Rd Bethpage NY 11714

KELLY, THOMAS MICHAEL, b Watertown, NY, May 16, 41; m 62; c 3. PHYSICS, SOLID STATE SCIENCE. *Educ:* Le Moyne Col, NY, BS, 62; Wayne State Univ, PhD(physics), 66. *Prof Exp:* AEC res assoc positron annihilation, New Eng Inst Med Res, 66-68; sr res physicist, 68-74, RES ASSOC, EASTMAN KODAK RES LABS, 74- *Mem:* Am Phys Soc; Inst Elec & Electronics Engrs. *Res:* Physics of solid state imaging; design and fabrication. *Mailing Add:* Eastman Kodak Co Res Labs Rochester NY 14650

KELLY, THOMAS ROSS, b New York, NY, Apr 26, 42; m 66; c 2. ORGANIC CHEMISTRY. *Educ:* Col of the Holy Cross, BS, 64; Univ Calif, Berkeley, PhD(org chem), 68. *Prof Exp:* Asst prof, 69-74, assoc prof, 74-80, PROF CHEM, BOSTON COL, 80- *Res:* Organic synthesis; natural products. *Mailing Add:* Dept of Chem Boston Col Chestnut Hill MA 02167

KELLY, WALTER JAMES, b Cleveland, Ohio, Feb 25, 41; m 71. ORGANIC CHEMISTRY, POLYMER CHEMISTRY. *Educ:* Case Inst Technol, BS, 63, Case Western Reserve Univ, PhD(phys org chem), 70. *Prof Exp:* Sr res chemist, Polymer Res, Goodyear Tire & Rubber Co, 69-78; staff scientist, Polymer Technol, 78-80, proj engr, 80-81, PROJ MGR, FOIL DIV, GOULD INC, 81- *Mem:* Am Chem Soc; Electrochemical Soc. *Res:* Dynamic properties of elastomers; structure-property correlations; polymer rheology and processing; crosslinking mechanisms; post polymerization reactions; adhesion, polymer modification electrodeposition. *Mailing Add:* Gould Inc Gould Labs 540 E 105th St Cleveland OH 44109

KELLY, WILLIAM ALBERT, b Cincinnati, Ohio, July 16, 27; m 52; c 2. NEUROSURGERY. *Educ:* Ohio Wesleyan Univ, BA, 50; Univ Cincinnati, MD, 54. *Prof Exp:* Res fel neurosurg, Univ Chicago Clins, 56-57; resident, 57-59, chief resident & clin asst, 60-61, from instr to assoc prof, 61-77, PROF NEUROSURG, UNIV WASH, 77- *Concurrent Pos:* Res fel, Univ Wash, 59-60. *Mem:* Am Asn Neurol Surg. *Res:* Cerebral circulation and allied clinical research; medical education on student and resident level. *Mailing Add:* Dept of Neurol Surg Univ of Wash Sch of Med R1-20 Seattle WA 98195

KELLY, WILLIAM ALVA, b Cullman, Ala, Feb 24, 37; div; c 5. VETERINARY PATHOLOGY. *Educ:* Auburn Univ, DVM, 62; Purdue Univ, PhD(vet path), 71. *Prof Exp:* Vet, pvt pract, 62-66; instr vet path, Purdue Univ, 66-70; VET PATHOLOGIST, MEAD JOHNSON & CO, 70- *Mem:* Am Col Vet Pathologists; Int Acad Path. *Res:* Experimental toxicologic pathology; pathology of laboratory animals; nutritionally-induced pathology; chemical carcinogenesis. *Mailing Add:* Mead Johnson & Co Evansville IN 47721

KELLY, WILLIAM CARY, b Memphis, Tenn, June 14, 19; m 42; c 4. VEGETABLE CROPS. *Educ:* Univ Tenn, BS, 40; Ohio State Univ, MS, 41; Cornell Univ, PhD(veg crops), 45. *Prof Exp:* Asst, Ohio State Univ, 40-41 & Cornell Univ, 42-45; assoc agronomist, Plant Soil & Nutrit Lab, USDA, 45-46, horticulturist, 46-52; assoc prof, 52-55, PROF, DEPT VEG CROPS, CORNELL UNIV, 55- *Concurrent Pos:* Vis prof, Univ Philippines, 59-60. *Mem:* Fel AAAS; Am Soc Hort Sci; fel Am Soc Plant Physiol. *Res:* Plant growth and development; yield and composition of vegetables as influenced by environment and mineral nutrition. *Mailing Add:* Dept of Veg Crops Cornell Univ Ithaca NY 14853

KELLY, WILLIAM CLARK, b Braddock, Pa, Mar 18, 22; m 47; c 2. PHYSICS. *Educ:* Univ Pittsburgh, BS, 43, MS, 46, PhD(physics), 51. *Prof Exp:* From asst to assoc prof physics, Univ Pittsburgh, 46-58; dir dept educ & manpower, Am Inst Physics, 58-65; fel officer, Nat Acad Sci-Nat Res Coun, 65-67, dir off sci personnel, 67-74; EXEC DIR COMN HUMAN RESOURCES, NAT RES COUN, 74- *Concurrent Pos:* Ford fac fel, 54-55; mem subcomt prof sci & technol manpower, Dept Labor, 71-72; secy comn physics educ, Int Union Pure & Appl Physics, 66-72, chmn, 72-75; mem coun on teaching sci, Int Coun Sci Unions, 75-78. *Mem:* AAAS; Am Phys Soc; Am Asn Physics Teachers. *Res:* Measurement of spectral emissivities of metals; beta and gamma ray spectroscopy; improvements in the teaching of science; manpower studies; human-resource supply and demand, especially in science and engineering. *Mailing Add:* Nat Res Coun 2101 Constitution Ave NW Washington DC 20418

KELLY, WILLIAM CROWLEY, b Philadelphia, Pa, May 10, 29; m 59. ECONOMIC GEOLOGY. *Educ:* Columbia Univ, AB, 51, MA, 53, PhD(geol), 54. *Prof Exp:* Asst econ geol, Columbia Univ, 51-53; instr geol, Hunter Col, 54; opers analyst, Opers Res Off, Johns Hopkins Univ, 54-56; from instr to assoc prof geol, 56-67, prof geol & mineral, 67-80, PROF & CHMN GEOL SCI, UNIV MICH, ANN ARBOR, 80- *Concurrent Pos:* Ed, Geochem News, 61-63. *Mem:* Geol Soc Am; Geochem Soc; Mineral Soc Am; Soc Econ Geol; Geol Soc France. *Res:* Chemical weathering; telluride ore deposits; oxidation of lead-zinc ores; mineralogy of iron oxides; ore microscopy. *Mailing Add:* Dept of Geol Univ of Mich Ann Arbor MI 48103

KELLY, WILLIAM DANIEL, b St Paul, Minn, Oct 28, 22; m 51; c 6. SURGERY. *Educ:* Univ Minn, BS, 43, MB, 45, MD, 46, PhD(surg), 55; Am Bd Surg, dipl, 55; Am Bd Thoracic Surg, dipl, 59. *Prof Exp:* From instr to assoc prof, 53-61, prof surg, 61-80, mem surg staff, 62-80, CLIN PROF SURG, UNIV HOSPS, 80- *Concurrent Pos:* Dir exp surg lab, Vet Admin Hosp, Minneapolis, 59-60, chief surg, 60-62. *Mem:* AAAS; Soc Exp Biol & Med; Soc Univ Surgeons; AMA; NY Acad Sci. *Res:* Homotransplantation; cardiovascular physiology and surgery. *Mailing Add:* Dept of Surg Univ of Minn Minneapolis MN 55455

KELLY, WILLIAM H, b Rich Hill, Mo, July 2, 26; m 50; c 3. EXPERIMENTAL NUCLEAR PHYSICS, PHYSICS PEDAGOGY. *Educ:* Graceland Col, AA, 48; Univ Mich, BSE, 50, MS, 51, PhD(physics), 55. *Prof Exp:* Asst physics, Eng Res Inst, Univ Mich, 51-54; from asst prof to prof physics, Mich State Univ, 55-79, from assoc chmn to chmn dept, 68-79; PROF PHYSICS, MONT STATE UNIV, 79-, DEAN COL LETTERS & SCI, 79- *Concurrent Pos:* Physicist, Naval Res Lab, 56, Lawrence Radiation Lab, Univ Calif, 61-62, 67-68 & Oak Ridge Nat Lab, 64; mem bd trustees, Graceland Col, 78-84; mem, Spec Adv Comt on medium energy electron accelerator fac, Argonne Univ Asn, 81- *Mem:* AAAS; fel Am Phys Soc; Am Asn Physics Teachers (vpres, 79, pres elect, 80, pres, 81); Am Soc Eng Educ. *Res:* Nuclear spectroscopy; nuclear structure; gamma ray spectroscopy; physics pedagogy. *Mailing Add:* Col Letters & Sci Mont State Univ Bozeman MT 59717

KELLY, WILLIAM ROBERT, b Norfolk, Va, July 24, 44; m 69. GEOCHEMISTRY, ANALYTICAL CHEMISTRY. *Educ:* Old Dominion Col, BS, 68; Ariz State Univ, PhD(geochem), 74. *Prof Exp:* Fel geol, Ariz State Univ, 74-75; vis assoc geochem, Calif Inst Technol, 75-77, res fel, 77-79; RES CHEMIST ANAL CHEM, NAT BUR STANDARDS, 79- *Mem:* Am Chem Soc; Meteoritical Soc; Geochem Soc; Sigma Xi. *Res:* Cosmochemistry; thermal ionization mass spectrometry. *Mailing Add:* Ctr Anal Chem Nat Bur of Standards Washington DC 20234

KELLY-FRY, ELIZABETH, b New York, NY, Sept 6, 25. BIOACOUSTICS, MEDICAL ULTRASOUND. *Educ:* Hunter Col, BS, 42; Howard Univ, ScM, 53; Sarasota Univ, EdD, 75. *Prof Exp:* Head biophys sect & asst head physiol br, 50-54; res assoc biophys res lab, Col Eng, Univ Ill, 54-64; assoc dir res, Intersci Res Inst, 64-67; vpres, 68-71; assoc prof surg, 72-80, ASSOC PROF RADIOL, SCH MED, IND UNIV, INDIANAPOLIS, 80- *Concurrent Pos:* Consult, Bur Radiol Health, 79-81; mem, NIH Diag Res Adv Comt, 80-81; assoc ed, J Clin Ultrasound, 75-79. *Mem:* Am Phys Soc; Acoust Soc Am; Biophys Soc; fel Am Inst Ultrasound Med; NY Acad Sci. *Res:* Ultrasound in biological and medical research. *Mailing Add:* Dept Radiol Ind Univ Sch of Med Indianapolis IN 46202

KELMAN, ARTHUR, b Providence, RI, Dec 11, 18; m 49; c 1. PHYTOPATHOLOGY. *Educ:* Univ RI, BS, 41; NC State Univ, MS, 46, PhD(plant path), 49. *Hon Degrees:* DSc, Univ RI, 77. *Prof Exp:* From instr to prof plant path, NC State Univ, 48-62, Reynolds Distinguished prof, 62-65; prof & chmn dept, 65-75, L R JONES DISTINGUISHED PROF PLANT PATH, UNIV WIS-MADISON, 75-, PROF BACTERIOL, 78- *Concurrent Pos:* Vis investr, Rockefeller Inst, 53-54; vis lectr, Am Inst Biol Sci, 58-60; NSF sr fel, Cambridge Univ, 71-72; mem US nat comt, Int Union Biol Sci. *Honors & Awards:* Fel Award, Am Phytopath Soc, 69. *Mem:* Nat Acad Sci; Am Acad Arts & Sci; Am Inst Biol Scientists; Soc Gen Microbiol; Int Soc Plant Path (vpres, 68-73, pres, 73-78). *Res:* Physiology of parasitism; bacterial diseases of plants. *Mailing Add:* Dept of Plant Path 1630 Linden Dr Univ Wis Madison WI 53706

KELMAN, BRUCE JERRY, b Chicago, Ill, July 1, 47; m 72. PERINATAL BIOLOGY, ENVIRONMENTAL SCIENCES. *Educ:* Univ Ill, BS, 69, MS, 71, PhD(vet med sci), 75; Am Bd Toxicol, cert, 80. *Prof Exp:* Res asst physiol, Univ Ill, 69-74; res assoc toxicol, Comp Animal Res Lab, Oak Ridge, Tenn, 74-76, asst prof prenatal toxicol, 76-79; sr res scientist develop toxicol, 79-80, assoc mgr, 80-81, MGR, DEVELOP TOXICOL SECT, PAC NORTHWEST LABS, BATELLE MEM INST, RICHLAND, WASH, 81- *Mem:* Soc Toxicol; Soc Exp Biol & Med; Teratology Soc; Am Soc Pharmacol & Exp Therapeut; Am Physiol Soc. *Res:* Developmental effects, including teratology, of toxic materials; perinatal toxicology of heavy metals, including plutonium, and polynuclear aromatic hydrocarbons; transplacental movements of developmental toxicants; effects of magnetic fields on living organisms. *Mailing Add:* Pac Northwest Labs Batelle Mem Inst PO Box 999 Richland WA 99352

KELMAN, L(EROY) R, b Minneapolis, Minn, Aug 16, 19; m 42; c 3. ENGINEERING. *Educ:* Univ Minn, BS, 42. *Prof Exp:* Metallurgist, Caterpillar Tractor Co, 42-44; group leader, Metall Div, Argonne Nat Lab, 47-66, mgr fuels & mat sect, Liquid Metal Fast Breeder Reactor Prog Off, 66-70, prog planner, Mat Sci Div, 70-73, proj leader & prog coordr, Safety of Light Water Reactor Fuels, 75-78 SR METALLURGIST, ARGONNE NAT LAB, 59- *Mem:* Am Nuclear Soc; Am Soc Metals; Am Inst Mining, Metall & Petrol Engrs; Sigma Xi. *Res:* Metallurgy of materials for nuclear reactors; fuel and structural materials and liquid metal coolants; behavior of nuclear fuels under transient and hypothetical accident conditions; fuels and structural materials for nuclear reactors; materials behavior in liquid metal coolants. *Mailing Add:* Argonne Nat Lab 9700 S Cass Ave Argonne IL 60440

KELMAN, ROBERT BERNARD, b Ansonia, Conn, Aug 12, 30; m 57; c 2. MATHEMATICS, COMPUTER SCIENCE. *Educ:* Univ Calif, Berkeley, AB, 53, MA, 55, PhD(math), 58. *Prof Exp:* Comput engr, NAm Aviation, Inc, 55-56; instr, Univ Ill, 57-58; mathematician, Int Bus Mach Corp, 58-61; mgr biomath res, Univac Div, Sperry Rand Corp, 61-63; res asst prof math, Univ Md, 63-66; assoc prof math, Colo State Univ, 66-68; assoc prof prev med, Univ Colo Med Ctr, 67-72, prof, 72-80; PROF COMPUT SCI, COLO STATE UNIV, 72- *Concurrent Pos:* Lectr, Howard Univ, 61-65; consult, Exec Off President Eisenhower, 60-61. *Mem:* Fel AAAS; Am Math Soc; Math Asn Am; Soc Indust & Appl Math; Am Soc Nephrology. *Res:* Differential equations; theoretical renal physiology; computer modeling. *Mailing Add:* Dept of Comput Sci Colo State Univ Ft Collins CO 80523

KELMERS, ANDREW DONALD, b New York, NY, Mar 24, 29; m 52; c 4. INORGANIC CHEMISTRY. *Educ:* Antioch Col, BS, 52; Ohio State Univ, MS, 54. *Prof Exp:* Chemist, Oak Ridge Nat Lab, 54-57 & Union Carbide Nuclear Co, NY, 57-62; res scientist, Astropower Inc Div, Douglas Aircraft Co, Inc, Calif, 62-63; group leader, 63-78, PROG MGR PROCESS CHEM, OAK RIDGE NAT LAB, 79- *Mem:* AAAS; Am Chem Soc; Am Soc Biol Chemists. *Res:* Program planning and coordination; nuclear fuel cycle process

research and development; solvent extraction, transition element and nitrogen-compound chemistry as well as uranium and plutonium behavior; resource recovery and extrusive metallurgy. *Mailing Add:* Chem Technol Div Oak Ridge Nat Lab PO Box X Oak Ridge TN 37830

KELNER, ALBERT, b Philadelphia, Pa, Sept 7, 12; m 46; c 3. BIOLOGY. *Educ:* Univ Pa, BA, 40, PhD(biol), 43; NC State Col, MSc, 42. *Prof Exp:* William Pepper Lab Clin Med fel, Sch Med, Univ Pa, 43-46; bacteriologist, Biol Lab Cold Spring Harbor, NY, 46-49; USPHS fel, Harvard Univ, 49-51; from asst prof to assoc prof, 51-61, prof, 61-81, ABRAHAM S & GERTURDE BURG EMER PROF BIOL, BRANDEIS UNIV, 81- *Mem:* AAAS; Am Soc Microbiol; Am Soc Photobiol. *Res:* Microbiology; microbiological genetics; photobiology; genetics; DNA repair, especially photoreactivation, genetic and evolutionary aspects; science education for non-scientists, especially humanistic biology. *Mailing Add:* Dept of Biol Brandeis Univ Waltham MA 02154

KELNHOFER, WILLIAM JOSEPH, b Manitowoc, Wis, Nov 24, 30. MECHANICAL ENGINEERING, FLUID MECHANICS. *Educ:* Marquette Univ, BME, 56; Catholic Univ, MME, 60, DEng, 66. *Prof Exp:* Proj engr, US Navy Bur Ships, 56-59; from instr to assoc prof, 60-73, ORD PROF MECH ENG, CATH UNIV AM, 73- *Concurrent Pos:* Prin investr, US Navy contract, 62-; assoc, US Army contract, 63-; prin investr, Off Naval Res contract, 66; res prof, Max Planck Inst, Goettingen, 66-67 & Munich Tech Univ, 69-70; prin investr, Nat Bur Standards contracts, 74-76. *Mem:* Am Soc Mech Engrs; Nat Soc Prof Engrs; Am Soc Heating, Refrig & Air Conditioning Engrs; Sigma Xi. *Res:* Heat transfer; boundary layer theory; thermal systems; energy conservation. *Mailing Add:* Dept of Mech Eng Cath Univ of Am Washington DC 20064

KELSAY, JUNE LAVELLE, b Jacksboro, Tex, June 29, 25. NUTRITION. *Educ:* NTex State Univ, BS, 46, MA, 47; Univ Wis, PhD(foods & nutrit), 67. *Prof Exp:* Instr nutrit, NTex State Univ, 47-50; technician nutrit res, Tex Agr Exp Sta, 51-52; nutrit specialist, 54-62, RES NUTRITIONIST, AGR RES SERV, USDA, 67- *Mem:* Am Inst Nutrit; Am Soc Clin Nutrit. *Res:* Preadolescent children; folic and pantothenic acid; vitamin B-6 deficiency in man; effect of protein level; forms of vitamin B-6; excretion of niacin metabolites; nutritional status; carbohydrate response in human subjects; effects of fiber in human subjects; mineral balances. *Mailing Add:* Beltsville Human Nutrit Res Ctr Agr Res Serv USDA Beltsville MD 20705

KELSER, GEORGE ARCHIBALD, b College Park, Md, Feb 9, 25; m 50; c 2. INTERNAL MEDICINE. *Educ:* Harvard Univ, BS, 46; George Washington Univ, MD, 49; Am Bd Intern Med, dipl, 57; Am Bd Cardiovasc Dis, dipl, 60. *Prof Exp:* Intern med, George Washington Univ Hosp, 49-50; resident, DC Gen Hosp, 50-51; resident, Duke Hosp, 53-54; fel, 54-55; from instr to assoc prof, 55-70, prof, 70-80, CLIN PROF MED, SCH MED, GEORGE WASHINGTON UNIV, 80- *Concurrent Pos:* Attend physician, Mt Alto Vet Admin Hosp, 55 & DC Gen Hosp, 55-; consult, Mt Alto Vet Admin Hosp, 55-60, St Elizabeth's Hosp, 59-63 & Vet Admin Hosp, Martinsburg, WVa, 59-65; Am Heart Asn Coun Clin Cardiol fel, 63; assoc chmn dept med & dir div cardiol, Med Ctr, George Washington Univ. *Mem:* Am Soc Internal Med; Am Heart Asn; Am Col Physicians; Am Col Chest Physicians; Am Fedn Clin Res. *Res:* Cardiovascular diseases. *Mailing Add:* George Washington Univ Clin Rm 528 2150 Pennsylvania Ave NW Washington DC 20037

KELSEY, CHARLES ANDREW, b Norfolk, Nebr, July 9, 35; m 60; c 4. MEDICAL PHYSICS. *Educ:* St Edward's Col, BS, 57; Univ Notre Dame, PhD(physics), 62; Am Bd Radiol, dipl. *Prof Exp:* Res assoc physics, Univ Notre Dame, 62; res assoc, Univ Wis-Madison, 62-63, from instr to asst prof physics, 63-65, from asst prof to prof radiol, 65-75; chief biomed physics, 75-80, PROF RADIOL, UNIV NMEX, 75- *Mem:* AAAS; Am Phys Soc; Am Acad Phys Med & Rehab; Am Inst Ultrasonics in Med; Radiol Soc NAm. *Res:* Application of physics technology to medical problems. *Mailing Add:* Dept of Radiol Univ of NMex Albuquerque NM 87131

KELSEY, EUGENE LLOYD, b Ponca City, Okla, May 10, 32; m 73; c 2. ELECTRICAL ENGINEERING, AERO-SPACE ENGINEERING. *Educ:* Okla State Univ, BSEE, 58; Va Polytech Inst, MSEE, 66. *Prof Exp:* Jr engr guidance, Autonetics-NAm Aviation, 56-57; test engr B-58 radar guidance, Gen Dynamics, Fort Worth, 58-62; aerospace technologist, 62-72, ENG SUPVR SYSTS DEVELOP-ELEC FLIGHT SYSTS, NASA, 72- *Concurrent Pos:* Adj instr math, Christopher Newport Col, 76-79. *Mem:* Soc Automotive Engrs-Aerospace. *Res:* Design, development and analysis of aerospace stabilization control and pointing systems for aircraft, satellite and research projects; unique requirements-unique solutions. *Mailing Add:* Langley Res Ctr NASA Hampton VA 23665

KELSEY, FRANCES OLDHAM, b Cobble Hill, BC, Can, July 24, 14; nat US; m 43; c 2. PHARMACOLOGY. *Educ:* McGill Univ, BSc, 34, MSc, 35; Univ Chicago, PhD(pharmacol), 38, MD, 50. *Hon Degrees:* DSc, Hood Col, 62, Univ NB, 64, Western Col Women, 64, Middlebury Col, 66, Wilson Col, 67, St Mary's Col, 69 & Drexel Univ, 73. *Prof Exp:* Asst prof pharmacol, Univ Chicago, 46; assoc prof med, Sch Med, Univ SDak, 54-57; pvt pract, 57-60; DIR DIV SCI INVEST, OFF SCI EVAL, BUR DRUGS, FOOD & DRUG ADMIN, DEPT HEALTH, EDUC & WELFARE, 60- *Concurrent Pos:* Lederle award, 54-57. *Honors & Awards:* President's Award Distinguished Fed Civilian Serv, 62. *Mem:* Am Soc Pharmacol & Exp Therapeut; Soc Exp Biol & Med; Teratology Soc; Am Med Women's Asn; Am Med Writers' Asn. *Res:* Posterior pituitary; chemotherapy of malaria; radioisotpes. *Mailing Add:* Div Sci Invest Food & Drug Admin Dept of Health Educ & Welfare Rockville MD 20852

KELSEY, JENNIFER LOUISE, b Montclair, NJ, Aug 27, 42. EPIDEMIOLOGY. *Educ:* Smith Col, BA, 64; Yale Univ, MPH, 66, MPhil, 68, PhD(chronic dis, epidemiol), 69. *Prof Exp:* Asst prof, 69-75, ASSOC PROF EPIDEMIOL, SCH MED, YALE UNIV, 75- *Mem:* Int Epidemiol

Asn; Soc Epidemiol Res; Am Epidemiol Soc; Am Col Epidemiol. *Res:* Epidemiology of chronic diseases, especially those of the musculo-skeletal system; herniated lumbar intervertebral discs; epidemiology of cancers of the female reproductive system. *Mailing Add:* Dept of Epidemiol & Pub Health Yale Univ Sch of Med New Haven CT 06510

KELSEY, JOHN EDWARD, b Beloit, Wis, Oct 28, 42; m 65; c 3. SCIENTIFIC INFORMATION, ENVIRONMENTAL HEALTH. *Educ:* Univ Wis, BS, 65, PhD(pharm chem), 69. *Prof Exp:* Nat Cancer Inst overseas fel, 68-70; res chemist, 70-74, sr res chemist, 75-78, dir occup health, 78-80, DIR TECH SERV DIV, BURROUGHS WELLCOME, CO, 81- *Mem:* Am Chem Soc; Drug Info Asn. *Res:* Management of science information, clinical data processing, radiation, health and safety, and facilities services departments in the paramaceutical research development and manufacturing industry. *Mailing Add:* Tech Serv Div Burroughs-Wellcome Co Research Triangle Park NC 27709

KELSEY, LEWIS PRESTON, b Kuling, China, July 1, 14; m 44; c 1. ENTOMOLOGY. *Educ:* Cornell Univ, BS, 38, MS, 52, PhD(entom), 54. *Prof Exp:* Jr soil surveyor, Soil Conserv Serv, USDA, 38-41, soil scientist, 45-46; instr fruit growing, NY State Inst Agr, 46-51; asst prof entom & asst res prof, 55-70, assoc prof, 70-80, EMER PROF ENTOM & APPL ECOL, EXP STA, UNIV DEL, 80- *Mem:* Entom Soc Am; Am Entom Soc (pres, 75-). *Res:* Insect pests of fruit trees and ornamentals; insect morphology; taxonomy of Scenopinidae of the world; population dynamics and control of European cornborer on field corn. *Mailing Add:* Dept Entom & Appl Ecol Univ Del Newark DE 19711

KELSEY, MORRIS IRWIN, b Easton, Pa, Aug 14, 39; m 64; c 2. BIOCHEMISTRY. *Educ:* Lehigh Univ, BA, 61; Univ Mass, MS, 64; Univ Pittsburgh, PhD(biochem), 69. *Prof Exp:* Chemist starch chem, Nat Starch & Chem Corp, 63-65; asst prof biochem, Mo Inst Psychiat , 71-73; sr scientist, Frederick Cancer Res Ctr, 73-75; sect head chem carcinogenesis prog, 75-80, ASST SCI COORDR ENVIRON CANCER, NAT CANCER INST, 80- *Concurrent Pos:* Fel biochem, St Louis Univ, 69-71; adj asst prof, Univ Mo, 72-73; adj assoc prof agr biochem, WVa Univ, 77-79. *Mem:* Am Chem Soc; AAAS; NY Acad Sci; Sigma Xi; Am Soc Biol Chemists. *Res:* Biotransformation of neutral sterols and bile acids by enterohepatic enzyme systems; effects of metabolism of endogenous steroid metabolites on the metabolic activation of chemical carcinogens. *Mailing Add:* Nat Cancer Inst Landow Bldg Rm 8C25 Bethesda MD 20014

KELSEY, RICK GUY, b Libby, Mont, Aug 14, 48; div; c 4. PLANT CHEMISTRY, BIOMASS UTILIZATION. *Educ:* Univ Mont, BS, 70, PhD(forestry), 74. *Prof Exp:* res asst prof, 80-81, RES ASSOC PROF, DEPT CHEM, UNIV MONT, 81-, RES ASSOC PLANT CHEM, WOOD CHEM LAB, 74- *Mem:* NAm Phytochem Soc; Sigma Xi. *Res:* Isolation and identification of plant natural products, their use in systematics, their biochemistry, their function in the plant and their potential use to man. *Mailing Add:* Wood Chem Lab Dept of Chem Univ of Mont Missoula MT 59801

KELSEY, RONALD A(LBERT), b Oakville, Conn, Mar 29, 23; m 47; c 3. CIVIL ENGINEERING. *Educ:* Polytech Inst Brooklyn, BS, 49; Carnegie Inst Technol, MS, 52. *Prof Exp:* Res engr, Alcoa Res Labs, Aluminum Co Am, 49-55; nuclear engr, Electric Boat Div & Gen Atomic Div, Gen Dynamics Corp, 55-60; res engr, 60-70, eng assoc, 70-74, SECT HEAD, ALCOA LABS, ALUMINUM CO AM, 74- *Concurrent Pos:* Chmn, Aluminum Alloys Comn, Welding Res Coun, 68-; mem, Joint USA/USSR Comn on Properties of Welds for Low Temp Appln, 75-; chmn, Int Comn Fatigue Data Exchange & Eval, 80-; mem, Tech Adv Comn Metals Prop Coun, 80- *Mem:* Soc Exp Stress Anal; fel Am Soc Metals; Am Welding Soc. *Res:* Deformation and fracture mechanics of materials and structures; development of metal deformation process. *Mailing Add:* Alcoa Labs Alcoa Tech Ctr Alcoa Center PA 15069

KELSEY, RUBEN CLIFFORD, b Park Falls, Wis, May 26, 23; m 60; c 2. COMPARATIVE ENDOCRINOLOGY. *Educ:* Univ Wis, PhB, 49, MS, 50, PhD(zool), 59. *Prof Exp:* Sr res scientist biochem, Smith, Kline & French Labs, 59-63; asst prof biol sci, Drexel Inst Technol, 63-68; head dept, 68-74, PROF BIOL, EAST STROUDSBURG STATE COL, 68-, HEAD DEPT, 81- *Mem:* AAAS; Am Soc Zool; Am Inst Biol Sci. *Res:* Physiology of mammalian reproduction; function. *Mailing Add:* Dept Biol EStroudsburg State Col East Stroudsburg PA 18301

KELSH, DENNIS J, b Valley City, NDak, Dec 24, 36; m 61; c 3. PHYSICAL CHEMISTRY. *Educ:* St John's Univ, Minn, BA & BS, 58; Iowa State Univ, PhD(phys chem), 62. *Prof Exp:* From instr to assoc prof, 62-72, chmn dept, 68-74 & 81-84, PROF CHEM, GONZAGA UNIV, 72- *Concurrent Pos:* Res chemist, Spokane Mining Res Ctr, US Bur Mines, 65-; assoc res scientist, NY Univ, 66-67; Am Coun Educ fel acad admin & spec asst to dean grad sch, Wash State Univ, 74-75. *Mem:* Am Chem Soc. *Res:* Electrical properties of surfaces; adsorption from solution; solid-liquid separations by electrokinetics. *Mailing Add:* Dept of Chem Gonzaga Univ Spokane WA 99258

KELSO, ALBERT FREDERICK, b Ft Wayne, Ind, Nov 19, 17; m 43; c 3. PHYSIOLOGY. *Educ:* George Williams Col, BA, 43, MS, 46; Loyola Univ, PhD, 59. *Hon Degrees:* DSc, Kirksville Col Osteop & Surg, 70. *Prof Exp:* Instr physiol, George Williams Col, 46-47; from instr to assoc prof, 46-59, actg chmn dept, 54-59, PROF PHYSIOL, CHICAGO COL OSTEOP MED, 59-, CHMN DEPT, 58-, DIR RES AFFAIRS, 76- *Concurrent Pos:* Consult, Nat Bd Osteopath Exam, 65-78; res consult, Am Acad Osteop; educ consult, Am Osteopath Asn. *Mem:* AAAS; Am Physiol Soc; Soc Exp Biol & Med; Am Heart Asn; Inst Elec & Electronics Eng. *Res:* Sensorimotor performance; circulation; tissue respiration. *Mailing Add:* Dept of Physiol Chicago Col of Osteop Chicago IL 60615

KELSO, ALEC JOHN (JACK), b Chicago, Ill, Dec 5, 30; m 51; c 2. PHYSICAL ANTHROPOLOGY. *Educ:* Northern Ill Univ, BS, 52; Univ Mich, MA, 54, PhD, 58. *Prof Exp:* From instr to assoc prof anthrop, 58-75, chmn dept, 63-68 & 71-81, dir, Semester at Sea Prog, 78-79, PROF ANTHROP, UNIV COLO, BOULDER, 75- *Concurrent Pos:* Consult, Coun Grad Schs US, 64-78; mem training comt, Nat Inst Child Health & Human Develop, 64-66; NIH spec fel, Univ Hawaii, 65-66; vchancellor acad affairs, Univ Colo, Colorado Springs, 75-77. *Mem:* Am Anthrop Asn (exec bd, 74-77); Am Asn Phys Anthropologists vpres, 72-74). *Res:* Selection and blood groups; human sexuality. *Mailing Add:* Dept of Anthrop Univ of Colo Boulder CO 80303

KELSO, DONALD PRESTON, b Pulaski, Va, Aug 12, 40; m 63; c 2. MARINE ECOLOGY. *Educ:* Univ Tenn, Knoxville, BS, 62; Univ Fla, MS, 65; Univ Hawaii, PhD(zool), 70. *Prof Exp:* Asst prof, 70-77, ASSOC PROF BIOL, GEORGE MASON UNIV, 77- *Mem:* Am Inst Biol Sci; Am Soc Zool; Ecol Soc Am. *Res:* Inshore marine ecology; evolution of echinoderms; reproductive cycles of tropical animals. *Mailing Add:* Dept Biol George Mason Univ Fairfax VA 22030

KELSO, EDWARD ALBERT, b Galveston, Tex, Sept 17, 14; m 44; c 2. PETROLEUM CHEMISTRY. *Educ:* Univ Tex, BA, 36, MA, 38, PhD(phys chem), 41. *Prof Exp:* Tutor chem, Univ Tex, 36-38, instr, 38-39, res assoc res inst, 40-41; chem engr, Tech Serv Div, Humble Oil & Refining Co, Exxon Chem Co, 41-45, res chemist, Res & Develop Div, 45-49, sr res chemist, 49-52, res specialist, 52-59, sr res specialist, 59-64, res assoc, Esso Res & Eng Co, 64-76, res assoc, 76-79; CONSULT, 79- *Mem:* Am Chem Soc. *Res:* High pressure thermodynamics; hydrocarbon isomerization and conversions; relationships of some isomeric hexanes. *Mailing Add:* 302 Lakewood Dr Baytown TX 77520

KELSO, FRED J, b Portland, Maine, Jan 1, 21; m 42; c 4. CHEMICAL ENGINEERING. *Educ:* Univ Maine, BS, 42. *Prof Exp:* Engr, Eastman Kodak Co, 42-43 & 46-48; process engr, 55-60, res engr, 61-64, res supvr, 64-69, res mgr, 70-77, SR RES ASST, FMC CORP, 78- *Mem:* Am Inst Chem Eng. *Res:* Inorganic chemical technology; pilot plant design and operation; chemical economics. *Mailing Add:* FMC Corp PO Box 8 Princeton NJ 08540

KELSO, JOHN MORRIS, b Punxsutawney, Pa, Mar 12, 22; m 45; c 1. RADIO PHYSICS. *Educ:* Gettysburg Col, AB, 43; Pa State Univ, MS, 45, PhD(physics), 49. *Prof Exp:* Instr physics, Pa State Univ, 43-45, asst, 45-48, eng res assoc, 48-49, from asst prof to assoc prof eng res, 49-54; eval specialist, The Martin Co, 54-55; mem tech staff, Ramo-Wooldridge, Inc, 55-58 & Space Tech Labs, 58-62; dir res, Electro-Physics Labs, ACF Indust, Inc, 62-66; dir res, ITT Electro-Physics Lab, Inc, 66-68, vpres & dir res, 68-75; consult, Off Telecommun Policy, Exec Off of the President, 76-78; CHIEF SCIENTIST, SIGNAL ANAL CTR, HONEYWELL, INC, ANNAPOLIS, MD, 78- *Concurrent Pos:* Vis observer, Chalmers Univ Technol, Sweden, 51-52; mem, Arecibo Eval Panel, 67-69; mem comn III & US del numerous Gen Assemblies, Int Union Radio Sci; mem, US Nat Comt, 73-78, chmn, Comn G, Int Union Radio Sci, 73-75. *Mem:* Am Geophys Union; Am Phys Soc; fel Inst Elec & Electronics Eng. *Res:* Radio wave propagation; ionospheric physics; space vehicle instrumentation; systems engineering; operational evaluation of weapon systems; space physics; electricity and magnetism. *Mailing Add:* 2596 Timber Cove Annapolis MD 21401

KELTIE, RICHARD FRANCIS, b Alexandria, Va, Aug 1, 51; m 73. STRUCTURAL DYNAMICS. *Educ:* NC State Univ, BS, 73, MS, 75, PhD(mech eng), 78. *Prof Exp:* Engr, Appl Physics Lab, Johns Hopkins Univ, 78-81; ASST PROF MECH ENG, NC STATE UNIV, 81- *Mem:* Acoust Soc Am; Am Soc Mech Engrs. *Res:* Mechanical design; structural dynamics; forced acoustics radiation from large structures. *Mailing Add:* NC State Univ PO Box 5246 Raleigh NC 27650

KELTING, RALPH WALTER, b Bridgeport, Nebr, Sept 27, 18; wid; c 2. PLANT ECOLOGY. *Educ:* Southwestern Inst Technol, BA, 41; Univ Okla, MS, 48, PhD(plant sci), 51. *Prof Exp:* Instr plant sci, Univ Okla, 51-53; from asst prof to assoc prof bot, Univ Tulsa, 53-61; chief, Pine Hills Field Sta, Southern Ill Univ, 61-62; PROF BOT, PITTSBURG STATE UNIV, PITTSBURG, KANS, 62- *Mem:* Ecol Soc Am (treas, 63-66). *Res:* Grassland ecology; plant taxonomy. *Mailing Add:* Dept of Biol Pittsburg State Univ Pittsburg KS 66762

KELTON, DIANE ELIZABETH, b Holden, Mass, Dec 4, 24. GENETICS, CANCER. *Educ:* Univ Mass, BS, 45, PhD(zool), 61. *Prof Exp:* Res asst genetics, Jackson Lab, 47-50, sr res asst, 50-53; res asst cancer res, Univ Mass, Amherst, 53-56, histol, 56-58 & genetics, 58-61, res assoc genetics & neuropath, 61-74; STAFF SCIENTIST, MASON RES INST, 74- *Mem:* AAAS; Am Inst Biol Sci; Am Genetic Asn; Genetics Soc Am; Environ Mutagen Soc. *Res:* Genetics; tumor biology; cancer chemotherapy. *Mailing Add:* EG&G Mason Res Inst 57 Union St Worcester MA 01608

KELTON, FRANK CALEB, b Berkeley, Calif, Sept 1, 15; m 45, 59; c 4. PETROLEUM ENGINEERING. *Educ:* Univ Ariz, BS, 36; Johns Hopkins Univ, PhD(phys chem), 41. *Prof Exp:* Res engr, 40-45, mgr eng & res, 45-55, spec probs consult, 55-59, SR PROJ ENGR, CORE LABS, INC, 59- *Mem:* Am Inst Mining, Metall & Petrol Engrs. *Res:* Catalysis; oil well core analysis; multiphase fluid flow through porous media; electrical model studies of petroleum reservoirs; petroleum reservoir engineering; secondary recovery; pressure maintenance; electronic data processing. *Mailing Add:* 4161 Wilada Dallas TX 75220

KELTON, WILLIAM HENRY, microbiology, see previous edition

KELTS, LARRY JIM, b Westfield, Pa, Aug 13, 37; m 67; c 2. MARINE BIOLOGY, ENTOMOLOGY. *Educ:* Cornell Univ, BS, 59; Southeastern Mass Univ, MS, 71; Univ NH, PhD(zool), 77. *Prof Exp:* Res asst marine biol, Marine Lab, Duke Univ, 60-61; res asst plant path, Agr Exp Sta, Cornell Univ,

64-69; ASST PROF MARINE BIOL & ECOL, DEPT BIOL, MERRIMACK COL, 77- *Mem:* Am Inst Biol Sci; Ecol Soc Am; Nat Wildlife Fedn. *Res:* Faunal and floral community structure and composition in stressed aquatic environments, such as salt-marsh pannes, supratidal rock pools, mixohaline and oligohaline lotic systems, bogs, temporary woodland pools and creek beds; salt-marsh dragonfly ecology. *Mailing Add:* Dept of Biol Merrimack Col North Andover MA 01845

KELTY, MICHAEL PATRICK, physiology, ecology, see previous edition

KEMBLE, EDWIN CRAWFORD, b Delaware, Ohio, Jan 28, 89; m 20, 78; c 2. PHYSICS. *Educ:* Case Inst, SB, 11; Harvard Univ, AM, 14, PhD(physics), 17. *Hon Degrees:* ScD, Case Inst Technol, 31; EdD, RI Col Ed, 57. *Prof Exp:* Asst instr physics, Carnegie Inst Technol, 11-12, instr, 12-13; eng physicist, Curtiss Aeroplane Co, 17-18; instr physics, Williams Col, Mass, 19; from instr to prof, 19-57, chmn dept, 40-45, EMER PROF PHYSICS, HARVARD UNIV, 57- *Concurrent Pos:* Guggenheim fel, Univ Munich & Univ Gottingen, 27; chmn physics sect, Nat Acad Sci, 45-48; dir, Harvard Acad Year Inst High Sch Teachers, NSF, 57-60; mem exec comt, Div Phys Sci, Nat Res Coun. *Honors & Awards:* Oersted Medal, Am Asn Physics Teachers, 69. *Mem:* Nat Acad Sci; AAAS; fel Am Phys Soc; Am Asn Physics Teachers; Am Acad Arts & Sci. *Res:* Band spectra; fundamentals of quantum theory; statistical mechanics. *Mailing Add:* 8 Ash St Place Cambridge MA 02138

KEMENY, GABOR, b Budapest, Hungary, Feb 6, 33; US citizen; m 58; c 2. THEORETICAL PHYSICS. *Educ:* Eotvos Lorand Univ, Budapest, dipl, 56; NY Univ, PhD(physics), 62. *Prof Exp:* Assoc scientist, Cent Res Inst Physics, Hungarian Acad Sci, 55-56; assoc scientist, Res Dept, Lamp Div, Westinghouse Elec Corp, 57-61; res scientist, Am-Standard, 61-62; res scientist, Ledgemont Lab, Kennecott Copper Corp, 63-68; assoc prof elec eng, 68-70, assoc prof metall, mech & mat sci, 68-74, assoc prof biophys, 70-74, PROF BIOPHYS, MICH STATE UNIV, 74- *Concurrent Pos:* Sr vis, Cavendish Lab, Cambridge Univ, 66. *Mem:* AAAS; Am Phys Soc. *Res:* Quantum mechanics and electronics; many-body problem; solid state and mathematical physics; electrical conductivity in biomacromolecules; protein denaturation; microwave interactions with biological systems. *Mailing Add:* Dept of Biophys Mich State Univ East Lansing MI 48824

KEMENY, J LORANT, b Abony, Hungary, May 28, 13; US citizen; m 50; c 1. VETERINARY MICROBIOLOGY. *Educ:* Royal Hungarian Vet Col, dipl, 36, DVM, 39. *Prof Exp:* Head antisera prod dept, Phylaxia State Serum Inst, Budapest, 39-56; res fel virol, Rockefeller Found, 57-58; asst dir vet biol, Colo Serum Co, 58-63; RES VET, NAT ANIMAL DIS CTR, USDA, 63- *Mem:* Am Vet Med Asn. *Res:* Virology and immunology; production, control testing and research of new veterinary biologicals; isolation and adaptation of new animal viruses to tissue culture systems; characterization of viruses. *Mailing Add:* Nat Animal Dis Ctr USDA PO Box 70 Ames IA 50010

KEMIC, STEPHEN BRUCE, b Boston, Mass, Dec 31, 46. ASTROPHYSICS. *Educ:* Univ NC, BS, 68; Univ Colo, MS, 70, PhD(astrophys), 73. *Prof Exp:* STAFF MEM PHYSICS, LOS ALAMOS NAT LAB, 74- *Mem:* Am Astron Soc; Am Asn Physics Teachers. *Res:* Spectroscopy of magnetic white dwarfs; laser fusion. *Mailing Add:* Los Alamos Nat Lab Mail Stop 220 Los Alamos NM 87545

KEMME, HERBERT RUDOLPH, chemical engineering, see previous edition

KEMMERLY, JACK E(LLSWORTH), b Marion, Ohio, Aug 19, 24; m 45; c 5. SYSTEMS ENGINEERING. *Educ:* Cath Univ Am, BEE, 50; Univ Denver, MS, 52; Purdue Univ, PhD(elec eng), 58. *Prof Exp:* Asst res eng electronics, Denver Res Inst, Colo, 51-53; instr elec eng, Purdue Univ, 53-58; sr proj engr electronics, AC Spark Plug Div, Gen Motors Corp, 58-59; asst prof elec eng, Purdue Univ, 59-61; prin engr, Aeronutronic Div, Philco Corp, 61-68; sr staff engr, Ground Systs Group, Hughes Aircraft Co, 68; assoc prof, 68-70, chmn elec eng fac, 72-77, chmn div eng, 77-79, PROF ENG, CALIF STATE UNIV, FULLERTON, 70-79, 81. *Concurrent Pos:* Consult, AC Spark Plug Div, Gen Motors Corp; lectr, Univ Calif, Los Angeles; vis prof eng, Fort Lewis Col, Durango Colo, 80-81. *Mem:* Inst Elec & Electronics Engrs; Am Soc Eng Educ. *Res:* Systems analysis; applied probability; noise and circuit theory. *Mailing Add:* Div of Eng Calif State Univ Fullerton CA 92631

KEMMET, WILFRED J, b Rogers, Minn, Apr 3, 15; m 42; c 4. DENTISTRY. *Educ:* Marquette Univ, DDS, 39. *Prof Exp:* From instr to assoc prof, 40-64, prof, 64-81, ADJ PROF DENT, SCH DENT, MARQUETTE UNIV, 81- *Concurrent Pos:* Pres, Odontol Acad, 75-; spec lectr oper dent, Marquette Univ. *Mem:* Am Endodontic Soc; Am Acad Orthod for the Gen Practitioner; Am Acad Oper Dent; Am Acad Occlusodontia; Odontological Soc. *Res:* Gold occlusal topography; ceramic porcelain. *Mailing Add:* Dept Oper Dent Sch Dent Marquette Univ Milwaukee WI 53233

KEMNITZ, JOSEPH WILLIAM, b Baltimore, Md, Mar 15, 47. PHYSIOLOGICAL PSYCHOLOGY. *Educ:* Univ Wis, BA, 69, MS, 74, PhD(physiol psychol), 76. *Prof Exp:* Proj specialist psychol, Univ Wis, 69-71; teaching & res asst, 71-76; res assoc, 77-79, ASST SCIENTIST PSYCHOL, WIS REGIONAL PRIMATE RES CTR, UNIV WIS, 79- *Concurrent Pos:* Mem task force animal models in diabetes res, NIH, 80-81; vis scientist, Div Endocrinol, Med Ctr, Univ Calif, Los Angeles, 81. *Mem:* Soc Neurosci; Am Soc Primatologists; Int Primatological Asn; AAAS; Animal Behav Soc. *Res:* Regulation of energy balance, emphasizing obesity, diabetes, and the condition of pregnancy and the influences of ovarian hormones, particularly in Rhesus monkeys. *Mailing Add:* Wis Regional Primate Res Ctr Univ Wis 1223 Capitol Ct Madison WI 53715

KEMP, ALBERT RAYMOND, b Potomac, Ill, Mar 13, 21; m 75; c 2. FOOD SCIENCE. *Educ:* Univ Ill, BS, 42, MS, 47; Univ Wis, PhD(dairy chem), 50. *Prof Exp:* Lab res technician, Dean Milk Co, 47-48, dairy res chemist, 50-67; VPRES RES, CREST FOODS CO, 67- *Mem:* Am Chem Soc; Am Dairy Sci Asn; Inst Food Technol; Am Asn Cereal Chem. *Res:* Electrophoresis to separate serum protein fractions of milk; chromatography of fatty acids and the lipolytic degradation of milk fat; preparation of a powdered skim milk additive. *Mailing Add:* Crest Foods Co Ashton IL 61006

KEMP, ANTHONY LIONEL, geology, biochemistry, see previous edition

KEMP, ARNE K, b Kajaani, Finland, Mar 5, 18; US citizen; m 43; c 2. FOREST PRODUCTS. *Educ:* Univ Georgia, BSF, 48; Duke Univ, MF, 49; Univ Minn, PhD(wood tech), 57. *Prof Exp:* Instr wood tech, Sch Forestry, Univ Minn, 49-53; assoc prof, La State Univ, 53-55; head dept forestry, Stephen F Austin State Col, 55-63; chief div forest prod utilization & mkt & eng res, Lake State Forest Exp Sta, 63-65; asst dir forest prod utilization & mkt, Eng & Genetics Res, 65-73, ASST DIR RES, N CENT FOREST EXP STA, US FOREST SERV, 73- *Concurrent Pos:* NSF grant, 62. *Mem:* Forest Prod Res Soc; Soc Wood Sci & Technol; Int Union Forest Res Orgns. *Res:* Wood seasoning, preservation and anatomy; wood liquid relationships; forest products marketing. *Mailing Add:* 1729 Maple Lane St Paul MN 55113

KEMP, DANIEL SCHAEFFER, b Portland, Ore, Oct 20, 36. ORGANIC CHEMISTRY. *Educ:* Reed Col, BA, 58; Harvard Univ, PhD(org chem), 64. *Prof Exp:* From asst prof to assoc prof, 64-72, PROF CHEM, MASS INST TECHNOL, 72- *Concurrent Pos:* A P Sloan Found fel, 68-70; vis asst prof, Univ Calif, San Diego, 69; Camile & Henry Dreyfus fel, 70. *Mem:* Am Chem Soc. *Res:* Peptide chemistry. *Mailing Add:* Dept Chem 18-027 Mass Inst Technol Cambridge MA 02139

KEMP, EMORY LELAND, b Chicago, Ill, Oct 1, 31; m 58; c 3. STRUCTURAL ENGINEERING. *Educ:* Univ Ill, BSc, 52, PhD(theoret & appl mech), 62; Univ London, DIC, 55, MSc, 58. *Prof Exp:* Asst engr, Ill State Water Surv, 52; struct engr, consult firms, London, 56-59; instr theoret & appl mech, Univ Ill, 59-62; assoc prof, 62-65, chmn dept 67-74, PROF CIVIL ENG, W VA UNIV, 65-, PROF HIST SCI & TECHNOL, 77- *Mem:* Fel Am Coun Learned Socs; fel Am Soc Civil Engrs; Fel Brit Inst Civil Engrs; Fel Am Concrete Inst; Brit Inst Struct Engrs. *Res:* History of technology; industrial archeology; structural engineering. *Mailing Add:* Dept Hist Sci & Technol WVa Univ Morgantown WV 26506

KEMP, GAVIN ARTHUR, b Olds, Alta, Mar 18, 26; m 51; c 3. HORTICULTURE, PLANT BREEDING. *Educ:* Univ Alta, BSc, 51; Univ Minn, PhD(plant breeding), 60. RES SCIENTIST, AGR RES STA, CAN DEPT AGR, 51- *Mem:* Am Soc Hort Sci; Int Soc Hort Sci; Agr Inst Can; Can Soc Hort Sci. *Res:* Breeding and genetics of tomatoes, particularly low temperature growth responses; development of green shell beans; physiology and breeding of field beans for low temperature tolerance during early seedling growth and in nitrogen fixation. *Mailing Add:* Can Agr Res Sta Lethbridge AB T1J 4B1 Can

KEMP, GORDON ARTHUR, b Newark, NJ, Dec 12, 32; m 58; c 3. MICROBIOLOGY, RESEARCH ADMINISTRATION. *Educ:* Lehigh Univ, AB, 54; Rutgers Univ, PhD(microbiol), 61. *Prof Exp:* Res scientist microbiol, 61-64; group leader chemother, 64-70, mgr chemother res, 70-73, mgr animal indust res, 73-76, DIR ANIMAL INDUST RES & DEVELOP, AM CYANAMID CO, 76- *Mem:* Fel AAAS; Am Soc Microbiol. *Res:* Pathogenesis of disease; prophylaxis and therapy of experimental infections; veterinary microbiology and immunology; protozoal and helminth infections of domestic animals; non-medical uses of antibiotics. *Mailing Add:* 73 Broadripple Dr Princeton NJ 08540

KEMP, GRAHAM ELMORE, b Alta, Can, Jan 8, 27; US citizen; m 48. VETERINARY PUBLIC HEALTH. *Educ:* Univ Toronto, DVM, 51; Univ Calif, Berkeley, MPH, 58. *Prof Exp:* Mem staff, Div Livestock Indust, Univ Ill, 51-52; pvt pract, Ill, 52-57; mem staff, Epidemiol Bur Commun Dis, Div Prev Med Serv, Calif State Dept Pub Health, 58-64; staff mem, Rockefeller Found, Virus Res Lab, Fac Med, Univ Ibadan, 64-72; chief virol unit, San Juan Trop Dis Labs, PR, 73-75, DIR, BUR LABS, VECTOR-BORNE DIS DIV, COMMUN DIS CTR, USPHS, 75- *Concurrent Pos:* Lectr, Sch Pub Health, Univ Calif, Berkeley & Sch Vet Med, Univ Calif, Davis, 57-64; consult zoonoses, State of Calif, 58-64; hon sr scientist, PR Nuclear Ctr, 73-74; mem animal res comt, San Juan Vet Admin Hosp, 73-74. *Mem:* Am Vet Med Asn; Am Pub Health Asn; Conf Pub Health Vets; Am Soc Trop Med & Hyg. *Res:* Arbovirus; food-borne disease and zoonoses. *Mailing Add:* Bur Labs CDC Vector-Borne Dis Div USPHS PO Box 2087 Ft Collins CO 80522

KEMP, HAROLD STEEN, b Ishpeming, Mich, May 19, 17; m 44; c 4. CHEMICAL ENGINEERING. *Educ:* Univ Minn, BChE, 39; Univ Mich, MS, 40, PhD(chem eng), 44. *Prof Exp:* Asst, Univ Mich, 40-41; res chem engr, 43-53, res proj supvr, 53-55, res supvr, 55-60, consult supvr, 60-62, CONSULT MGR, E I DU PONT DE NEMOURS & CO, INC, 62- *Concurrent Pos:* Chmn, Admin Comn Design Inst Emergency Relief Systs, 76-; adj prof chem eng, Univ Del, 78- *Honors & Awards:* Founders Award, Am Inst Chem Engrs, 77. *Mem:* Fel Am Inst Chem Engrs. *Res:* Thermal properties of hydrocarbon systems; liquid flow across distillation column plates; factors influencing distillation column plate efficiency; heat transfer; fluid flow. *Mailing Add:* Eng Dept E I du Pont de Nemours & Co Inc Wilmington DE 19898

KEMP, JAMES CHALMERS, b Detroit, Mich, Feb 9, 27; m 51; c 2. ASTROPHYSICS. *Educ:* Univ Calif, Berkeley, AB, 55, PhD(eng physics), 60. *Prof Exp:* Jr res physicist, Univ Calif, Berkeley, 60-61; from asst prof to assoc prof, 61-71, PROF PHYSICS, UNIV ORE, 71- *Concurrent Pos:* Vis prof, Inst Astron, Honolulu, 71-72; NSF & Res Corp grants, 71- *Res:* Optical properties; polarization studies on magnetic stars and planets. *Mailing Add:* Dept of Physics Univ of Ore Eugene OR 97403

KEMP, JAMES DILLON, b Pickett, Ky, Feb 6, 23; m 47; c 2. ANIMAL SCIENCE. *Educ:* Univ Ky, BS, 48, MS, 49; Univ Ill, PhD(animal sci), 52. *Prof Exp:* Asst animal sci, Univ Ill, 49-52; from asst prof to assoc prof animal husb, 52-59, PROF ANIMAL SCI, UNIV KY, 59- *Concurrent Pos:* Fulbright res scholar, NZ, 64. *Honors & Awards:* Res Award, Am Soc Animal Sci, 71, Signal Serv Award, 77. *Mem:* Am Soc Animal Sci; fel Inst Food Technologists; Sigma Xi; Am Meat Sci Asn (pres, 75-76). *Res:* Meats teaching and research; composition and processing characteristics of red meats. *Mailing Add:* Dept of Animal Sci Univ of Ky Lexington KY 40546

KEMP, JOHN DANIEL, b Minneapolis, Minn, Jan 20, 40; m 75; c 3. BIOCHEMISTRY. *Educ:* Univ Calif, Los Angeles, BS, 62, PhD(biochem), 65. *Prof Exp:* NIH fel biochem, Univ Wash, 65-67, res assoc, 67-68; asst prof, 68-72, assoc prof, 72-77, PROF PLANT PATH, UNIV WIS-MADISON, 77-; RES CHEMIST, USDA, 68- *Mem:* Am Soc Plant Physiologists; Sigma Xi. *Res:* Molecular mechanisms of normal and abnormal plant growth and development; plant genetic engineering by novel approaches. *Mailing Add:* Dept Plant Path Univ Wis Madison WI 53706

KEMP, JOHN WILMER, b Midvale, Utah, July 28, 20; m 52; c 2. PHYSIOLOGICAL CHEMISTRY, PHARMACOLOGY. *Educ:* Westminster Col, AB, 50; Univ Calif, PhD(physiol chem), 57. *Prof Exp:* Res pharmacologist metab of heroin, Sch Med, Univ Calif, 57-59; ASSOC PROF PHARMACOL, COL MED, UNIV UTAH, 59- *Res:* Biochemistry and pharmacology of the central nervous system; nucleic acids; membrane transport; neuronal excitability; anticonvulsants. *Mailing Add:* Dept of Pharmacol Univ of Utah Col of Med Salt Lake City UT 84132

KEMP, KENNETH COURTNEY, b Chicago, Ill, Aug 7, 25. PHYSICAL ORGANIC CHEMISTRY. *Educ:* Northwestern Univ, BS, 50; Ill Inst Technol, PhD(chem), 56. *Prof Exp:* Asst chem, Ill Inst Technol, 50-55; from instr to assoc prof, 55-74, PROF CHEM, UNIV NEV, 74-, V CHMN DEPT, 76- *Mem:* Am Chem Soc; Chem Soc London. *Res:* Organic mechanisms; neighboring group reactions. *Mailing Add:* Dept of Chem Univ of Nev Reno NV 89507

KEMP, KENNETH E, b Detroit, Mich, Aug 24, 41; m 64, 78; c 2. STATISTICS. *Educ:* Mich State Univ, BS, 63, MS, 65, PhD(animal husb), 67. *Prof Exp:* Sr statist programmer, Biomet Serv, Agr Res Serv, USDA, 67-68; asst prof, 68-71, assoc prof, 71-79, PROF STATIST, KANS STATE UNIV, 79- *Mem:* Biomet Soc; Am Statist Asn. *Res:* Algorithms and techniques for statistical analysis on the digital computer. *Mailing Add:* Dept of Statist Kans State Univ Manhattan KS 66506

KEMP, L(EBBEUS) C(OURTRIGHT), JR, b Houston, Tex, Oct 8, 07; m 36; c 2. CHEMICAL ENGINEERING. *Educ:* Rice Inst, BS, 29. *Prof Exp:* Res chemist, Texaco, Inc, Tex, 29-33, res supvr, 33-38, asst chief chemist, 38-40, asst supt res labs, NY, 40-41, dir res, 41-53, asst to vpres, 53-54, asst to sr vpres, 54-55, gen mgr petrochem, 55-57, vpres petrochem, 57-59, vpres res & technol, 59-68, vpres spec assignments, 68-71; vpres, Texaco, Inc, Houston Area, 71-72; RETIRED. *Concurrent Pos:* Mem indust adv comt, US Bur Mines, 44; trustee, United Eng Trustees, 58-60; consult, 71- *Mem:* AAAS; Am Chem Soc; Am Inst Aeronaut & Astronaut; Soc Chem Indust; fel Am Inst Chem Engrs. *Res:* Petroleum refining including work on both product and process development; alkylation of isobutane with olefins; hydrocarbon synthesis from carbon monoxide and hydrogen; petrochemicals; synthetic liquid and gaseous fuels. *Mailing Add:* 12318 Huntingwick Dr Houston TX 77024

KEMP, LOUIS FRANKLIN, JR, b New York, NY, Mar 19, 40; m 64; c 2. MATHEMATICS. *Educ:* Princeton Univ, BS, 62; Polytech Inst NY, MS, 65, PhD(math), 67. *Prof Exp:* Engr, Grumman Aircraft Corp, 62-63; asst prof math, Polytech Inst NY, 67-69; STAFF RES SCIENTIST, AMOCO PROD CO, 69- *Mem:* Soc Indust & Appl Math; Math Asn Am. *Res:* Numerical analysis; engineering statistics. *Mailing Add:* 5334 S 74th E Ave Tulsa OK 74145

KEMP, MARWIN K, b Strong, Ark, Nov 23, 42; m 61; c 2. PHYSICAL CHEMISTRY, GEOCHEMISTRY. *Educ:* Univ Ark, BS, 64; Univ Ill, MS, 65, PhD(phys chem), 68. *Prof Exp:* Asst prof, 68-71, ASSOC PROF PHYS CHEM, UNIV TULSA, 71- *Mem:* Am Chem Soc; AAAS; Nat Sci Teachers Asn. *Res:* Natural gas equilibrium in underground reservoirs; computer assisted instruction; thermodynamics; coal liquefaction. *Mailing Add:* Dept of Chem Univ of Tulsa Tulsa OK 74104

KEMP, NELSON HARVEY, b New York, NY, Aug 15, 27; m 75; c 3. FLUID MECHANICS, HEAT TRANSFER. *Educ:* Ohio State Univ, BAeroE, 49; Cornell Univ, MAeroE, 51, PhD(aeronaut eng), 53. *Prof Exp:* Group leader eng, United Aircraft Res Labs, 53-56; res scientist aerospace, Avco Everett Res Lab, 56-68; scientist, Wolf Res & Develop Corp, 68-69; res scientist aerospace, Avco Systs Div, 69-73, res scientist aerospace, Avco Everett Res Lab, Avco Corp, 73-75; RES SCIENTIST AEROSPACE, PHYS SCI INC, 75- *Concurrent Pos:* Vis assoc prof, Mass Inst Technol, 63-64. *Mem:* Fel Am Inst Aeronaut & Astronaut; Am Phys Soc; Sigma Xi. *Res:* Laser-material interaction; laser propulsion; non-steady aerodynamics; re-entry physics. *Mailing Add:* Phys Sci Inc 30 Com Way Woburn MA 01801

KEMP, NORMAN EVERETT, b Otisfield, Maine, June 20, 16; m 42. DEVELOPMENTAL BIOLOGY. *Educ:* Bates Col, BS, 37; Univ Calif, PhD(zool), 41. *Prof Exp:* Asst zool, Univ Calif, 37-41; instr, Wayne Univ, 46-47; from instr to assoc prof, 47-61, PROF ZOOL, UNIV MICH, ANN ARBOR, 61- *Concurrent Pos:* Res assoc, Argonne Nat Lab, 54 & 55; vis investr, Rockefeller Inst, 58; vis colleague, Univ Hawaii, 65, 72; vis investr, Lab, Marine Biol Asn UK, Plymouth, Eng, 79. *Mem:* Am Soc Zool; Am Asn Anat; Electron Micros Soc Am; Am Soc Cell Biol; Soc Develop Biol. *Res:* Electron microscopy of differentiating cells; fertilization of amphibian eggs; differentiation of digestive tract and skin; calcification of bones, scales and teeth; fibrillogenesis of collagen; regeneration of fish fins. *Mailing Add:* Div Biol Sci Univ Mich Ann Arbor MI 48109

KEMP, PAUL RAYMOND, b Denver, Colo, Mar 14, 49; m 77. PLANT ECOLOGY, PLANT WATER RELATIONS. *Educ:* Colo State Univ, BS, 71, MS, 73; Wash State Univ, PhD(bot), 77. *Prof Exp:* RES ASSOC PLANT PHYSIOL, N MEX STATE UNIV, 77- *Concurrent Pos:* Lectr, NMex State Univ, 80-81. *Mem:* Sigma Xi; Ecol Soc Am; Am Soc Plant Physiologists. *Res:* Physiological plant ecology; niche relationships; populational differentiation; photosynthetic adaptations; stress physiology. *Mailing Add:* Dept of Biol NMex State Univ Las Cruces NM 88003

KEMP, ROBERT GRANT, b Massillon, Ohio, Feb 12, 37; m 67. BIOCHEMISTRY. *Educ:* Col Wooster, BA, 59, Yale Univ, PhD(biochem), 64. *Prof Exp:* Res assoc biochem, Univ Wash, 64-66; from asst prof to prof biochem, Med Col Wis, 66-76; PROF & CHMN BIOCHEM, UNIV HEALTH SCI, CHICAGO MED SCH, 76- *Concurrent Pos:* Estab investr, Am Heart Asn, 68-73. *Mem:* AAAS; Am Chem Soc; Am Soc Biol Chem. *Res:* Control of carbohydrate metabolism; structure-activity relationships of enzymes. *Mailing Add:* Dept Biochem 3333 Green Bay Rd North Chicago IL 60064

KEMP, ROBERT RICHARD DINGLE, b Toronto, Ont, June 30, 32; m 54. MATHEMATICS. *Educ:* McMaster Univ, BA, 53; Mass Inst Technol, PhD(math), 56. *Prof Exp:* Lectr math, Mass Inst Technol, 56-57; mem, Inst Adv Study, 57-58; from asst prof to assoc prof, 58-68, PROF MATH, QUEEN'S UNIV, ONT, 68-, CHMN GRAD STUDIES 76- *Mem:* Can Math Cong. *Res:* Differential equations; especially spectral theory of ordinary differential operations. *Mailing Add:* Dept of Math Queen's Univ Kingston ON K7L 3N6 Can

KEMP, THOMAS ROGERS, b Lebanon, Ky, May 13, 42; m 80. STRUCTURAL ORGANIC CHEMISTRY. *Educ:* Univ Ky, BS, 64, PhD(org chem), 70. *Prof Exp:* Asst prof, Dept Food Sci & Nutrit, 70, ASSOC PROF CHEM, DEPT HORT, UNIV KY, 70- *Mem:* Am Chem Soc. *Res:* Isolation, purification and structure determination of natural products including cytokinins and other modified nucleosides occurring in transfer RNA. *Mailing Add:* 868 Laurel Hill Rd Lexington KY 40504

KEMP, WALTER MICHAEL, b Big Spring, Tex, Aug 26, 44; div; c 2. IMMUNOBIOLOGY, PARASITOLOGY. *Educ:* Abilene Christian Col, BSE, 66; Tulane Univ, PhD(biol), 70. *Prof Exp:* Cell biol trainee biol, Tulane Univ, 68-70; asst prof, Abilene Christian Col, 70-75; asst prof, 75-78, ASSOC PROF BIOL, TEX A&M UNIV, 78- *Concurrent Pos:* Res Corp res grant, 70-71; res assoc immunol, Southwest Found Res & Educ, 70-73 & Univ Ga, 74; NIH grants, 72-75 & 78-83; Clark Found grants, 76-78 & 78-82; mem, Study Sect Trop Med Parasitol, NIH, 81-85. *Mem:* AAAS; Am Soc Parasitologists; Am Soc Trop Med & Hyg; Am Asn Immunologists. *Res:* Immune responses to parasites, particularly schistosomes and trypanosomes; host-parasite antigen sharing and parasite immune escape mechanisms. *Mailing Add:* Dept of Biol Tex A&M Univ College Station TX 77843

KEMP, WILLIAM MICHAEL, b Washington, DC, May 16, 47. ECOLOGY. *Educ:* Ga Inst Technol, BA, 69, MA, 71; Univ Fla, PhD(environ sci), 76. *Prof Exp:* Environ engr eval, US Environ Protection Agency, 71-72; SYSTS ECOLOGIST ENVIRON RES, CTR ENVIRON & ESTUARINE STUDIES, UNIV MD, 77- *Mem:* Ecol Soc Am; Am Soc Limnol & Oceanog; AAAS; Sigma Xi. *Res:* Ecosystem modeling; productivity and nutrient dynamics of estuaries; structure of ecological trophic webs; economics and energetics of environment. *Mailing Add:* Horn Pt Environ Labs PO Box 775 Cambridge MD 21613

KEMPE, CHARLES HENRY, b Breslau, Ger, Apr 6, 22; nat US; m 49; c 5. PEDIATRICS. *Educ:* Univ Calif, AB, 42, MD, 45. *Prof Exp:* Intern pediat, Univ Calif, 45-46, from instr to asst prof, 49-56; asst, Sch Med, Yale Univ, 48-49; PROF PEDIAT & MICROBIOL & CHMN DEPT PEDIAT, UNIV COLO MED CTR, DENVER, 56- *Concurrent Pos:* Fleischner Fund fel, Childrens Hosp, 46; lectr, Univ Calif, 49-50; consult to Surgeon Gen, US Dept Defense, 50-; consult, WHO, Geneva, 53-; Communicable Dis Ctr, NIH, Ga, 58 & Nat Soc Prevention of Cruelty to Children, London, 69-70; mem smallpox comt, Comn Immunization, Armed Forces Epidemiol Bd, 53-; Fulbright prof, Inst Superiore Sanita, Italy, 55-56; vis prof, Pasteur Inst, Paris, 63-64; head, Battered Children Team, Univ Colo, Denver, dir, Nat Ctr for Prevention & Treat of Child Abuse & Neglect, Dept Pediat, Med Ctr. *Honors & Awards:* Mead Johnson Award, Am Acad Pediat, 59. *Mem:* Inst Med-Nat Acad Sci; Am Pediat Soc; Am Soc Pediat Res; Am Pub Health Asn; Am Asn Immunol. *Res:* Virology, particularly pathogenesis and immunologic response of patients suffering from smallpox and complications of smallpox vaccination. *Mailing Add:* Dept of Pediat Univ of Colo Med Ctr Denver CO 80262

KEMPE, LLOYD L(UTE), b Pueblo, Colo, Nov 26, 11; m; c 1. CHEMICAL ENGINEERING. *Educ:* Univ Minn, BChE, 32, MS, 38, PhD(chem eng), 48. *Prof Exp:* Asst, Div Soils, Univ Minn, 34-35, res assoc, 40-41, asst chem eng, 46-48; asst sanit engr, State Dept Health, Minn, 35-40; instr bact, Univ Mich, 48-49, asst prof, 49-50; asst prof food tech, Univ Ill, 50-52; from asst prof to prof chem eng & bact, 52-60, prof chem eng & sanit eng, 60-63, prof, 63-81, prof microbiol, Med Sch, 67-81, EMER PROF CHEM ENG, UNIV MICH, ANN ARBOR, 63- *Concurrent Pos:* Consult engr; mem comt microbiol, Adv Bd Qm Res & Develop, Nat Acad Sci-Nat Res Coun; mem comt irradiation preservation of foods, US AEC, Am Inst Biol Sci; mem comt botulism hazards, US Food & Drug Admin. *Mem:* AAAS; Am Chem Soc; Am Soc Microbiol; Am Inst Chem Engrs; Inst Food Technol. *Res:* Biochemical engineering; irradiation processing of foods; botulism hazards in foods; industrial waste treatment. *Mailing Add:* Dept of Chem Eng Univ of Mich Ann Arbor MI 48104

KEMPE, LUDWIG GEORGE, b Brandenburg, Ger, Oct 16, 15; US citizen; m 55. NEUROSURGERY, NEUROANATOMY. *Educ:* Univ Berne, MD, 42. *Prof Exp:* Assoc clin prof neurosurg, George Washington Univ, 60-73; PROF NEUROSURG & ANAT, MED UNIV SC, 73- *Concurrent Pos:* Mem adv bd, Coun Neurosurg, 68- *Mem:* Am Asn Neurol Surgeons; Cong Neurol Surgeons; Soc Neurol Surgeons; Am Asn Anatomists; Am Col Surgeons. *Res:* Mesoscopic neuroanatomy. *Mailing Add:* 25 Rutledge Ave Charleston SC 29401

KEMPEN, RENE RICHARD, b Kankakee, Ill, Mar 24, 28; m 69; c 1. PHARMACOLOGY. *Educ:* St Joseph's Col, Ind, BS, 50; Loyola Univ Chicago, MS, 55, PhD(pharmacol), 62. *Prof Exp:* Chemist, Chicago Biol Res Lab, 54-55; lab instr pharmacol, Stritch Sch Med, Loyola Univ Chicago, 56-59; instr, Col Med, Baylor Univ, 61-63; ASST PROF, SCH MED, UNIV TEX MED BR GALVESTON, 63-, ASSOC DIR TOXICOL LAB, 73-, ASST PROF, SCH ALLIED HEALTH, 76- *Concurrent Pos:* Instr, St Anne's Hosp Sch Nursing, 55-57, Loyola Univ Sch Nursing, 56 & St Elizabeth's Hosp Sch Nursing, 57. *Mem:* AAAS; Am Asn Lab Animal Sci; Am Heart Asn. *Res:* Action of drugs on cardiac electrophysiological parameters; muscle contraction; toxicology; effect of drugs on endocrine pancrease. *Mailing Add:* Dept of Pharmacol Univ of Tex Med Br Galveston TX 77550

KEMPER, GENE ALLEN, b Drake, NDak, Apr 12, 33; m 69. NUMERICAL ANALYSIS, PERFORMANCE ANALYSIS. *Educ:* Univ NDak, BS, 56, MS, 59; Iowa State Univ, PhD(appl math), 65. *Prof Exp:* Instr math, Univ NDak, 56-59; exten lectr math, Univ Wash, Seattle, 60-61 & 65-66; mathematician, Boeing Co, 60-61, sr res specialist & vis staff mem, Boeing Sci Res Labs, 65-66; instr math, Iowa State Univ, 61-65; assoc prof, 66-72, sr consult, Comput Ctr, 69-79, dir, Inst Comput Use Educ, 74-81, assoc dir, Comput Ctr, 79-81, PROF MATH, UNIV NDAK, 72-, ASST VPRES ACAD AFFAIRS, 81- *Concurrent Pos:* NSF Col Sci Improv Prog grant, Univ NDak, 68-71. *Mem:* Soc Indust & Appl Math; Asn Comput Mach. *Res:* Numerical solution of functional differential equations and integral equations; mathematical modeling of biological systems. *Mailing Add:* Acad Affairs Univ of NDak Grand Forks ND 58202

KEMPER, JOHN D(USTIN), b Portland, Ore, May 29, 24; m 47; c 1. MECHANICAL ENGINEERING. *Educ:* Univ Calif, Los Angeles, BS, 49, MS, 59; Univ Colo, PhD(struct mech), 69. *Prof Exp:* Engr, Telecomput Corp, Calif, 49-50, proj engr, 50-52, chief mech engr, 52-55; chief mech engr, H A Wagner Co, 55-56; asst to vpres eng, Marchant Calculators, Inc, 56-58, chief engr, Marchant Div, Smith-Corona Marchant Inc, 58-59, vpres eng, 59-62; assoc prof, 62-67, PROF ENG, UNIV CALIF, DAVIS, 67-, DEAN, COL ENG, 69- *Mem:* AAAS; Nat Soc Prof Engrs; Am Soc Mech Engrs; Am Soc Eng Educ. *Res:* Mechanical vibrations; mechanical design; structural mechanics. *Mailing Add:* Col Eng Univ Calif Davis CA 95616

KEMPER, JOST HANSJOSEF KARLFRIED, b Düsseldorf, Ger, Mar 14, 34; m 61; c 2. MOLECULAR BIOLOGY. *Educ:* Univ Cologne, Staatsexamen, 61, PhD(genetics, biol math), 64. *Prof Exp:* NATO fel, Cold Spring Harbor Lab Quant Biol, 64; USPHS-NY Univ trainee genetics, Pub Health Res Inst City New York, 67-70; asst prof, 70-76, ASSOC PROF BIOL, UNIV TEX, DALLAS, 76- *Res:* Suppression; recombination; gene expression and regulation. *Mailing Add:* Dept of Biol Univ of Tex at Dallas Box 688 Richardson TX 75080

KEMPER, KIRBY WAYNE, b New York, NY, Apr 13, 40; m 64; c 3. NUCLEAR PHYSICS. *Educ:* Va Polytech Inst, BS, 62; Ind Univ, MS, 64, PhD(physics), 68. *Prof Exp:* Res assoc nuclear physics, 68-71, asst prof, 71-75, assoc prof physics, 75-79, PROF, FLA STATE UNIV, 79- *Mem:* Sigma Xi; Am Phys Soc. *Res:* Selective population of states with heavy ions; use of time-of-flight systems to measure nuclear exotic reactions. *Mailing Add:* Dept of Physics Fla State Univ Tallahassee FL 32306

KEMPER, ROBERT SCHOOLEY, JR, b Oakland, Calif, Feb 20, 27; m 49; c 4. MECHANICAL & METALLURGICAL ENGINEERING. *Educ:* Ore State Col, BS, 51, MS, 52. *Prof Exp:* Tech specialist, Hanford Atomic Prods Oper, Gen Elec Co, 52-64; res assoc, 65-66, unit mgr, 66-69, MGR MAT DEVELOP, PAC NORTHWEST LABS, BATTELLE MEM INST, 69- *Mem:* Am Soc Metals; Soc Mfg Engrs; Am Defense Preparedness Asn; AAAS; Am Soc Testing & Mat. *Res:* Irradiation damage in fuel and structural materials; metallic fabrication development. *Mailing Add:* 1623 Alder Richland WA 99352

KEMPER, WILLIAM ALEXANDER, b Baltimore, Md, Jan 1, 11; m 56, 73. ENVIRONMENTAL CHEMISTRY, BALLISTICS. *Educ:* Johns Hopkins Univ, PhD(phys chem), 34. *Prof Exp:* Chemist, Res Dept, Baltimore Gas & Elec Co, 34-43; physicist, US Naval Weapons Lab, 46-72; sci adv, Comdr Cruiser Destroyer Forces Atlantic Fleet, 72-73; sr ballistician, Navy Surface Weapons Ctr-Dahlgren Lab, 73-75; asst prof physics, Metropolitan State Col, 76-77; HONORARIUM PHYSICS, UNIV COLO, DENVER, 77- *Concurrent Pos:* Chmn, Blue Ribbon Panels, Picatinny Arsenal, US Army, 74-; consult, 75- *Honors & Awards:* Meritorious Civilian Serv Award, US Navy, 75. *Mem:* AAAS; Am Phys Soc. *Res:* Ballistics; fire control. *Mailing Add:* 7363 W 26th Place Denver CO 80215

KEMPER, WILLIAM DORAL, agronomy, see previous edition

KEMPERMAN, JOHANNES HENRICUS BERNARDUS, b Amsterdam, Netherlands, July 16, 24; m 53; c 5. MATHEMATICS. *Educ:* Univ Amsterdam, BS, 45, MS, 48, PhD(math), 50. *Prof Exp:* Res assoc appl math, Math Ctr, Amsterdam, 48-51; from asst prof to prof math, Purdue Univ, 51-61; prof, 61-69, FAYERWEATHER PROF MATH, UNIV ROCHESTER, 69- *Concurrent Pos:* On leave, Univ Amsterdam, 58-59 & 72-73, Univ Wis, 60-61, & Stanford Univ, 66-67 & Univ Tex, Austin, 77-78; corres, Royal Netherlands Acad Sci. *Mem:* Inst Elec & Electronics Engrs; Am Math Soc; Am Statist Asn; fel Inst Math Statist; Dutch Math Soc. *Res:* Analysis; probability; statistics. *Mailing Add:* Dept of Math Univ of Rochester Rochester NY 14627

KEMPH, JOHN PATTERSON, b Lima, Ohio, Dec 17, 19; m 43; c 4. PSYCHIATRY, PHYSIOLOGY. *Educ:* Ohio Northern Univ, AB, 47; Ohio State Univ, BSc, 47, MSc, 48, MD, 53; Am Bd Psychiat & Neurol, dipl psychiat, 61, dipl child psychiat, 62. *Prof Exp:* Res asst, Res Found, Ohio State Univ, 47-48, res assoc, 51-55; resident psychiat, Univ Mich, 55-56, jr clin instr, 56-57; dir, Ohio Northwest Guid Ctr, 57-60; from instr to assoc prof psychiat, Univ Mich, 60-68; prof psychiat & dir child & adolescent psychiat, State Univ NY Downstate Med Ctr, 68-72; prof psychiat & chmn dept, 72-74, VPRES ACAD AFFAIRS, DEAN MED FAC & PROF PSYCHIAT, MED COL OHIO, 74- *Concurrent Pos:* Res fel, Ohio State Univ, 48-51; fel child psychiat, Med Ctr, Univ Mich, Ann Arbor, 60-61; intern, Mt Carmel Hosp, Columbus, Ohio, 53-54; resident psychiat, Columbus State Hosp, 54-55; mem active staff, Mem Hosp, Lima, Ohio, 57-60; vice chief staff psychiat, St Rita's Hosp, 58-60; instr child psychiat, Med Ctr, Univ Mich, Ann Arbor, 60-61, infections control officer, 61-68, lectr human growth & behav, Sch Social Work & lectr psychosom med, Univ Hosp, 62-68, mem clin serv comt, 63-68; dir in-patient serv & coord res, Children's Psychiat Hosp, 61-65, clin dir, 65-68; consult, Cent Mich Coun Continuing Psychiat Educ, 64-68; chmn clin serv comt, Children's Psychiat Hosp, 65-68. *Mem:* Fel Am Psychiat Asn; AMA; Am Orthopsychiat Asn; Am Asn Ment Deficiency; Am Psychosom Soc. *Res:* Child psychiatry; applied cardiovascular and respiratory physiology; study of physiological and psychological correlates of behavior. *Mailing Add:* Off Dean Med Fac Med Col Ohio CS 10008 Toledo OH 43699

KEMPLE, MARVIN DAVID, b Indianapolis, Ind, Sept 2, 42; m 64; c 2. MAGNETIC RESONANCE. *Educ:* Purdue Univ, BS, 64; Univ Ill, Urbana-Champaign, MS, 65, PhD(physics), 71. *Prof Exp:* Enrico Fermi fel chem & physics, Enrico Fermi Inst, Univ Chicago, 71-72, res assoc, Dept Chem, 72-76; Nat Res Coun res assoc, Nat Bur Standards, 76-77; ASST PROF PHYSICS, IND UNIV-PURDUE UNIV, INDIANAPOLIS, 77- *Mem:* Am Phys Soc; AAAS; Sigma Xi. *Res:* Application of electron paramagnetic resonance and electron nuclear double resonance to the study of ions and molecules in ionic crystals, organic crystals, protein crystals, and intact, live biological systems. *Mailing Add:* Dept of Physics 1201 E 38th St Indianapolis IN 46205

KEMPNER, ELLIS STANLEY, b New York, NY, Mar 20, 32; m 61; c 3. BIOPHYSICS. *Educ:* Brooklyn Col, BS, 53; Yale Univ, MS, 55, PhD(biophys), 59. *Prof Exp:* Asst scientist bionucleonics, 58-61, PHYSICIST, NAT INST ARTHRITIS, DIABETES & DIGESTIVE & KIDNEY DIS, NIH, 61- *Concurrent Pos:* Lectr, Univ Calif, Davis, 68-69. *Mem:* Biophys Soc. *Res:* Radiation effects on macromolecules; macromolecular synthesis; growth under extreme conditions; cellular organization. *Mailing Add:* Nat Inst Arthritis & Metab Dis NIH Bethesda MD 20014

KEMPNER, JOSEPH, b Brooklyn, NY, Apr 25, 23; m 47; c 2. APPLIED MECHANICS, AEROSPACE ENGINEERING. *Educ:* Polytech Inst Brooklyn, BAeroE, 43, MAeroE, 47, PhD(appl mech), 50. *Prof Exp:* Aeronaut engr struct res, Nat Adv Comt Aeronaut, 43-47; from res asst to res assoc appl mech, 47-50, from instr to assoc prof, 50-57, head dept aerospace & appl mech, 66-76, PROF APPL MECH, POLYTECH INST NY, 57- *Concurrent Pos:* Prin investr, Off Naval Res & Air Force Off Sci Res grants & contracts, 58-77; consult, US Navy, 70-; mem adv group, Ship Res Comt, Maritime Transp Res Bd, Nat Acad Sci, 73-76; mem comt basic res, Adv Army Res Off, 73-76. *Honors & Awards:* Citation Distinguished Res, Sigma Xi, 73; Laskowitz Gold Medal Res Aerospace Eng, NY Acad Sci, 73. *Mem:* Assoc fel Am Inst Aeronaut & Astronaut; Am Soc Mech Eng; fel Am Acad Mech; fel NY Acad Sci. *Res:* Structural research related to aerospace vehicles, submersible vessels and pressure vessels; statics and dynamics of plates and shells, including large deformation and elevated temperature effects; applied mechanics. *Mailing Add:* 1163 E 13th St Brooklyn NY 11230

KEMPNER, WALTER, b Berlin, Ger, Jan 25, 03; nat US. INTERNAL MEDICINE, CELL PHYSIOLOGY. *Educ:* Univ Heidelberg, MD, 26. *Prof Exp:* Res asst, Kaiser Wilhelm Inst, 27-28; asst physician, Univ Berlin, 28-33; res assoc, Kaiser Wilhelm Inst, 33-34; from assoc med & physiol to assoc prof med, 34-52, Walter Kempner Prof Med, 72, PROF MED, MED CTR, DUKE UNIV, 52- *Honors & Awards:* Ciba Award, Am Heart Asn, 75. *Mem:* Am Physiol Soc; AMA. *Res:* Cellular respiration and fermentation; pathological physiology; dietary treatment of heart, kidney disease, hypertension and arteriosclerotic vascular disease, vascular retinopathy, diabetes mellitus and obesity. *Mailing Add:* Box 3099 Duke Univ Med Ctr Durham NC 27710

KEMPSON, STEPHEN ALLAN, b Walsall, Eng, July 2, 48; m 73; c 2. ANIMAL PHYSIOLOGY. *Educ:* Lancaster Univ, UK, BA, 70; Warwick Univ, MSc, 71; London Univ, PhD(biochem), 75. *Prof Exp:* Fel biochem, Univ Rochester, 75-77; fel physiol, Mayo Clinic, 77-80, asst prof physiol, Mayo Med Sch, 79-80; ASST PROF MED, UNIV PITTSBURGH, 80- *Concurrent Pos:* Prin investr, Pittsburgh Health Res & Serv Found grant, 81-82. *Mem:* Am Physiol Soc; Endocrine Soc; Am Soc Nephrol; Am Fedn Clin Res. *Res:* Cellular mechanism of phosphate transport in the kidney, and regulation of the process by hormone and diet. *Mailing Add:* 1191 Scaife Hall Sch Med Univ Pittsburgh Pittsburgh PA 15261

KEMPTER, CHARLES PRENTISS, b Burlington, Vt, Feb 12, 25; m 77; c 3. CHEMISTRY, MATERIALS SCIENCE. *Educ:* Stanford Univ, BS, 49, MS, 50, PhD(chem), 56. *Prof Exp:* Asst phys sci, Stanford Univ, 49-50; phys chemist, Dow Chem Co, 50-53; staff mem, Los Alamos Sci Lab, Univ Calif, 56-71; sci consult, 71-73; tech dir, Kempter-Rossman Int, 73-75, SCI ADV, 75- *Concurrent Pos:* Vis scientist, Inst Phys Chem, Vienna, 63-64; thesis adv, Los Alamos Grad Ctr, Univ NMex, 59-71. *Mem:* Fel & hon fel Am Inst Chemists; Am Chem Soc; AAAS; Sigma Xi; Int Plansee Soc Powder Metall. *Res:* Physical and biophysical chemistry; solid state science. *Mailing Add:* 333 Solana Hills Dr Solana Beach CA 92075

KEMPTHORNE, OSCAR, b Cornwall, Eng, Jan 31, 19; nat US; m 49; c 3. STATISTICS, MATHEMATICAL BIOLOGY. *Educ:* Cambridge Univ, BA, 40, MA, 43, ScD, 60. *Prof Exp:* Statistician, Rothamsted Exp Sta, Eng, 41-46; assoc prof statist, 47-51, PROF STATIST, IOWA STATE UNIV, 51-, DISTINGUISHED PROF SCI & HUMANITIES, 64- *Mem:* Int Statist Inst; fel Am Statist Asn; fel Inst Math Statist; fel Royal Statist Soc; Biomet Soc (past pres). *Res:* Design of experiments; statistical inference; biological statistics. *Mailing Add:* Statist Lab Snedecor Hall Iowa State Univ Ames IA 50011

KEMPTON, ALAN GEORGE, b Toronto, Ont, Aug 21, 32; m 55; c 2. MICROBIOLOGY. *Educ:* Univ Toronto, BSA, 54, MSA, 56; Mich State Univ, PhD(microbiol), 58. *Prof Exp:* Res officer, Can Agr Exp Farm, Sask, 58-60; res chemist, US Army Natick Labs, Mass, 60-64; group leader food bact, Can Packers Ltd, Ont, 64-66; asst prof, 66-68, assoc chmn dept, 70-76, ASSOC PROF BIOL, UNIV WATERLOO, 68- *Mem:* Fel AAAS; Soc Indust Microbiol; Can Soc Microbiol. *Res:* Microbiological deterioration of materiel, foodstuff and sewage. *Mailing Add:* Dept of Biol Univ of Waterloo Waterloo ON N2L 3G1 Can

KEMPTON, JOHN PAUL, b Buffalo, NY, Aug 14, 32; m 54; c 2. GROUNDWATER GEOLOGY. *Educ:* Denison Univ, BS, 54; Ohio State Univ, MA, 56; Univ Ill, PhD, 62. *Prof Exp:* Asst, Ohio State Univ, 54-56; geologist, Ohio Div Water, 55-56; from asst geologist to assoc geologist, 56-71, GEOLOGIST, HYDROGEOL & GEOPHYS SECT, ILL GEOL SURV, 71- *Concurrent Pos:* Vis prof, Northern Ill Univ, 73. *Mem:* AAAS; Geol Soc Am; Asn Eng Geologists. *Res:* Glacial, environmental and ground-water geology. *Mailing Add:* Natural Resources Bldg Ill Geol Surv Champaign IL 61820

KENAGA, CLARE BURTON, b Cadillac, Mich, Jan 9, 27; m 52; c 4. PLANT PATHOLOGY. *Educ:* Western Mich Col, BS, 50; Univ Mich, MS, 52; Mich State Univ, PhD(plant path), 57. *Prof Exp:* Plant pathologist, Morton Chem Co, 57-66; vis assoc prof, 66-67, assoc prof, 67-77, prof plant path, 77-81, EDUC ADMIN, PURDUE UNIV, 81- *Concurrent Pos:* Indust consult; mem, Coun Agr Sci & Technol. *Mem:* Fel Nat Asn Cols & Teachers Agr; Am Phytopath Soc; Soc Nematol. *Res:* Mechanisms of action of fungicides and soil fumigants; teaching. *Mailing Add:* Dept of Bot & Plant Path Purdue Univ West Lafayette IN 47906

KENAGA, DUANE LEROY, b Midland, Mich, Mar 9, 20; m 44; c 4. WOOD TECHNOLOGY, PULP & PAPER TECHNOLOGY. *Educ:* Univ Mich, BSChe, 43, MWT, 48. *Prof Exp:* Asst, Univ Mich, 47-48; wood technologist, Wood & Paper Sect, Southern Res Inst, 48-51; wood technologist, biochem res lab, 51-65, sr res wood chemist, 65-69, res specialist, 69-78, RES ASSOC, DESIGNED PROD DEPT, DOW CHEM CO, 78- *Mem:* Forest Prod Res Soc; Soc Wood Sci & Tech; Tech Asn Pulp & Paper Indust. *Res:* Chemical utilization of wood; chemical modification of wood to promote dimensional stability; paper and fiber treatments; wet end additives in paper systems, including bulking aids, retention aids and high filler sheets. *Mailing Add:* 4622 Chatham Court Midland MI 48640

KENAGA, EUGENE ELLIS, b Midland, Mich, July 15, 17; m 40, 79; c 3. ECOLOGY, ETOMOLOGY. *Educ:* Univ Mich, BS, 39; Univ Kans, MA, 40; Tokyo Univ Agr & Technol, PhD, 77. *Prof Exp:* Entomologist insecticides, 40-44 & 46-55, group leader entom res, 55-65, ASSOC SCIENTIST, DOW CHEM CO, 60- *Concurrent Pos:* Asst instr, Univ Kans, 39-40; mem, Nat Acad Sci Flying Pesticide Tour, 64; pesticide wildlife consult, Nat Agr Chem Asn, 64-78; assoc mem terminal pesticide residue comn, Int Union Pure & Appl Chem, 66-71; mem, Gov Comt Pesticides, 67; participant, US-Japan Seminar Pesticides, 71 & US-USSR Environ Protection Agency, Seminar Pesticide, 76; pesticide wildlife consult, WHO, 71, US Environ Protection Agency, 73-74, Nat Res Coun Can, 73-78, NATO, 74 & Am Inst Biol Sci, 76-77. *Mem:* Entom Soc Am; Am Soc Testing & Mat; emer mem Soc Environ Toxicol & Chem; Am Chem Soc; Am Ornith Union. *Res:* Insect taxonomy, insecticides and fumigant; bird migration, ecology and conservation; environmental impact of chemicals, toxicology, chemistry. *Mailing Add:* 1281 N Wagner Rd Essexville MI 48732

KENAGY, GEORGE JAMES, b Los Angeles, Calif, July 9, 45; m 69; c 2. ECOLOGY, PHYSIOLOGY. *Educ:* Pomona Col, BA, 67; Univ Calif, Los Angeles, PhD(zool), 72. *Prof Exp:* Fel & res biologist, Max Planck Inst Behav Physiol, Ger, 72-73; res biologist, Univ Calif, Los Angeles, 74; res biologist, Scripps Inst Oceanog, Univ Calif, San Diego, 74-76; asst prof, 76-81, ASSOC PROF, DEPT ZOOL, UNIV WASH, 81- *Mem:* AAAS; Ecol Soc Am; Animal Behav Soc; Am Soc Mammalogists; Am Ornithologists Union. *Res:* Daily and seasonal rhythms of animals; reproductive ecology and physiology of small mammals; environmental physiology. *Mailing Add:* Dept of Zool Univ of Wash Seattle WA 98195

KENAHAN, CHARLES BORROMEO, b Sugar Notch, Pa, Jan 29, 29; m 48; c 2. METALLURGY. *Educ:* Kings Col, Pa, BS, 50. *Prof Exp:* Res metallurgist, 53-66, chief div solid wastes recycling, 66-72, res dir, Avondale Metall Res Ctr, 73-79, DEP DIR MINERALS RES, BUR MINES, WASHINGTON, DC, 79- *Honors & Awards:* John J Haney, Am Plating Soc, 62; Silver Medal Meritorious Serv, US Dept Interior, 75. *Mem:* Am Plating Soc; Electrochem Soc; Am Chem Soc; Am Inst Mining, Metall & Petrol Engrs. *Res:* Chemistry; minerals processing; recycling; secondary metals; corrosion. *Mailing Add:* Bur Mines 2401 E St NW Washington DC 20241

KENAN, RICHARD P, b Waycross, Ga, Dec 25, 31; m 68; c 3. THEORETICAL PHYSICS, SOLID STATE PHYSICS. *Educ:* Ga Inst Technol, BA, 55; Ohio State Univ, PhD(physics), 62. *Prof Exp:* Res physicist, 62-63, sr physicist, 63-69, fel, 69-75, PRIN RES SCIENTIST, BATTELLE MEM INST, 75- *Mem:* AAAS; Am Phys Soc; Am Asn Physics Teachers; Soc Phot-Optical Inst Engrs. *Res:* Physics; solid state; theory of magnetism; band structure; integrated optics; optical processing. *Mailing Add:* Dept of Physics Battelle Mem Inst 505 King Ave Columbus OH 43201

KENAT, THOMAS ARTHUR, b Cleveland, Ohio, Aug 6, 42; m 64; c 2. CHEMICAL ENGINEERING, POLYMER SCIENCE. *Educ:* Carnegie-Mellon Univ, BS, 64, MS, 65, PhD(chem eng), 68. *Prof Exp:* Res engr, Chemstrand Res Ctr, Inc, NC, 68-69; res engr, 69-74, sr res & develop engr, 74-80, SR ENG SCIENTIST, B F GOODRICH CO, 81- *Mem:* Am Inst Chem Engrs; Am Chem Soc; Nat Asn Corrosion Engrs. *Res:* Dynamics and control of polymerization reactions; design and development of chemical reaction systems; processing of polymer composites; corrosion testing to select materials of construction for chemical process applications; design and development of chemical process concepts. *Mailing Add:* B F Goodrich Chem Group 6100 Oak Tree Blvd Cleveland OH 44131

KENDALL, BRUCE REGINALD FRANCIS, b Guildford, Western Australia, July 23, 34; m 56; c 3. SPACE PHYSICS. *Prof Exp:* Univ Western Australia, BSc, 54, PhD(physics), 60. *Prof Exp:* Res fel, Nat Res Coun Can, 59-60, asst res officer, 60-61; sr res scientist, Nuclide Corp, 61-62, dir new prod develop, 62-64; assoc prof, 64-69, PROF PHYSICS, PA STATE UNIV, 69- *Concurrent Pos:* Consult, 64- *Mem:* Am Phys Soc; Am Soc Mass Spectrometry; Am Vacuum Soc; Brit Inst Physics. *Res:* Electron, vacuum and ionosphere physics; mass spectrometry. *Mailing Add:* Dept of Physics Pa State Univ University Park PA 16802

KENDALL, BURTON NATHANIEL, b San Francisco, Calif, Dec 15, 40; m 63, 79; c 2. COMPUTER SCIENCE, SYSTEMS SCIENCE. *Educ:* Stanford Univ, BS, 62; Brown Univ, PhD(physics), 69. *Prof Exp:* Res aide microwave design, Stanford Univ, 59-62; res asst physics, Brown Univ, 62-69; lectr, Univ Calif, Santa Barbara, 69-71, asst prof, 71-73; sr res scientist, Systs Control, Inc, 73-78; sr staff scientist, 78-80, PRIN SCIENTIST, MEASUREX CORP, 80- *Concurrent Pos:* Consult, Libr Automation, 79- *Mem:* AAAS; Am Phys Soc. *Res:* Computer hardware and software design; electronics and microwave design; large scale systems design and modelling. *Mailing Add:* Measurex Corp 1 Results Way Cupertino CA 95014

KENDALL, DAVID NELSON, b Gardner, Mass, Oct 20, 16; m 42; c 3. PHYSICAL CHEMISTRY, SPECTROSCOPY. *Educ:* Wesleyan Univ, BA, 38, MA, 39; Johns Hopkins Univ, PhD(chem, physics), 43. *Prof Exp:* Res phys chemist, Titanium Div, Nat Lead Co, NJ, 43-44; res chem physicist, Calco Chem Div, Am Cyanamid Co, 44-46, head infrared spectros labs, 46-53; CONSULT CHEMIST & SPECTROSCOPIST & INFRARED SPECIALIST, KENDALL INFRARED LABS, 53- *Concurrent Pos:* Asst ed, Appl Spectros, Soc Appl Spectros, 51-55; ed, Your Consult, Newslett Asn Consult Chemists & Chem Engrs, Inc, 74- *Honors & Awards:* Gold Medal, Soc Appl Spectros, 73. *Mem:* Am Chem Soc; Soc Appl Spectros (pres, 55-56); Coblentz Soc; Asn Consult Chemists & Chem Eng (pres, 64-66); fel Am Inst Chem. *Res:* Colloid chemistry; x-ray crystallography; pigment particle size determination; colored oil smokes; lightfastness of dyes and pigments; infrared, Raman, visual and ultraviolet spectroscopy; analytical chemistry. *Mailing Add:* 1030 Sherman Ave Plainfield NJ 07063

KENDALL, H(AROLD) B(ENNE), b Midland, Mich, Apr 27, 23; m 48; c 4. CHEMICAL ENGINEERING. *Educ:* Grove City Col, BS, 48; Case Inst Technol, MS, 50, PhD(chem eng), 56. *Prof Exp:* Instr chem & metall eng, Univ Mich, 50-51; instr chem & chem eng, Case Inst Technol, 51-55, asst prof chem eng, 55-60; chmn dept, 61-67, PROF CHEM ENG, OHIO UNIV, 60- *Mem:* Am Chem Soc; Am Inst Chem; Soc Hist Technol; Am Soc Eng Educ; Am Inst Chem Engrs. *Res:* Reaction kinetics in flow reactors; catalytic processing; heterogeneous catalysis; history of technology. *Mailing Add:* Dept Chem Eng Ohio Univ Athens OH 45701

KENDALL, HARRY WHITE, b Sopchoppy, Fla, Oct 9, 24; m 50; c 3. PHYSICS. *Educ:* Tusculum Col, BA, 48; Fla State Univ, MS, 50; Univ Fla, PhD(electronics, physics), 61. *Prof Exp:* Instr physics, Chipola Jr Col, 50-51; asst prof, Emory & Henry Col, 51-54, assoc prof & head dept, 57-59; teaching asst, Univ Fla, 54-57, NSF fac fel, 59-60; assoc prof & chmn dept, 60-63, PROF PHYSICS, UNIV S FLA, 63-, ACTG CHMN DEPT, 78- *Mem:* Am Phys Soc; Am Asn Physics Teachers; Sigma Xi. *Res:* Electrical breakdown of gases. *Mailing Add:* Dept of Physics Univ of SFla Tampa FL 33620

KENDALL, HENRY WAY, b Boston, Mass, Dec 9, 26. PHYSICS. *Educ:* Amherst Col, BA, 50; Mass Inst Technol, PhD(nuclear physics), 55. *Hon Degrees:* DSc, Amherst Col, 75. *Prof Exp:* NSF fel, Mass Inst Technol, 54-56; res assoc, High Energy Lab, Stanford Univ, 56-57; lectr physics, 57-58, asst prof, 58-61; from asst prof to assoc prof, 61-67, PROF PHYSICS, MASS INST TECHNOL, 67- *Mem:* Am Phys Soc. *Res:* Nuclear structure; high energy electron scattering; meson and neutrino physics. *Mailing Add:* Dept of Physics Mass Inst Technol Cambridge MA 02139

KENDALL, JAMES TYLDESLEY, b New York, NY, Dec 14, 16; m 50; c 3. PHYSICS, PHYSICAL CHEMISTRY. *Educ:* Cambridge Univ, BA, 39, MA, 42; Univ London, PhD(physics), 53. *Prof Exp:* Scientist, Assoc Elec Industs, Ltd, 39-53; mgr semiconductor res, Plessey Co, Ltd, 53-57; gen mgr, Tex Instruments, Ltd, 57-61; managing dir, Microwave Assocs, Ltd, 61-62; gen mgr, SGS-Fairchild Ltd, 62-64; managing dir, Edwards High Vacuum Int Ltd, 64-65; mgr phys res, Nat Cash Register Co, 66-68, gen mgr integrated circuits, 69-71, ASST TO GEN MGR, MICROELECTRONICS DIV, NCR CORP, 71- *Mem:* Sr mem Inst Elec & Electronics Engrs; fel Royal Soc Edinburgh. *Res:* Semiconductor research, particularly electronic properties of silicon carbide and gray tin; metal-oxide-silicon integrated circuits. *Mailing Add:* NCR Microelectronics Div 2850 El Paso St N Colorado Springs CO 80907

KENDALL, JOHN HUGH, b Mt Pleasant, Tex, Sept 30, 42; m 65; c 2. FOOD SCIENCE, CEREAL CHEMISTRY. *Educ:* La State Univ, BS, 64, MS, 69, PhD(food sci), 73. *Prof Exp:* Qual control rep, Borden Inc, 71-73; SR FOOD TECHNOLOGIST, RIVIANA FOODS INC, 73- *Concurrent Pos:* Adj asst prof, Univ Houston, 75- *Mem:* Inst Food Technologists; Am Asn Cereal Chemists; Int Asn Milk Food & Environ Sanitarians; Am Soc Microbiol. *Res:* Rice processing and by-product utilization. *Mailing Add:* Riviana Foods Inc PO Box 2636 Houston TX 77001

KENDALL, JOHN WALKER, JR, b Bellingham, Wash, Mar 19, 29; m 54; c 3. ENDOCRINOLOGY. *Educ:* Yale Univ, BA, 52; Univ Wash, MD, 56. *Prof Exp:* Instr med, Sch Med, Vanderbilt Univ, 59-60; from asst prof to assoc prof, 62-71; prof med & head, Div Metab, Med Sch, 71-80, PROF MED & ASST DEAN RES, UNIV ORE, 80- *Concurrent Pos:* USPHS trainee, 59-62; assoc chief of staff for res, Vet Admin Hosp, Portland, 71-; chmn pro tem dept med, Med Sch, Univ Ore, 75-76; mem, Vet Admin Res Adv Comt. *Mem:* Asn Am Physicians; Endocrine Soc; Am Soc Clin Invest; Am Fedn Clin Res; Soc Exp Biol & Med. *Res:* Neural control of pituitary function. *Mailing Add:* Vet Admin Med Ctr Portland OR 97201

KENDALL, MICHAEL WELT, b Glendale, Ariz, Jan 30, 43; m 65; c 1. GROSS ANATOMY, MICROSCOPIC ANATOMY. *Educ:* Univ Northern Iowa, BA, 65; Univ Louisville, MS, 69, PhD(anat), 72. *Prof Exp:* Asst prof anat, Med Ctr, Univ Miss, 72-74; asst prof, 74-77, chmn dept, 75-77, ASSOC PROF ANAT, SCH MED SCI, UNIV NEV, RENO, 77- *Concurrent Pos:* Pesticide consult, Dept Agr, Univ Nev, 75-76; consult gross anat, Int Cong Col Physicians & Surgeons, 76- *Mem:* AAAS; Am Asn Anatomists; Am Heart Asn. *Res:* Ultrastructural descriptive analysis of carcinogenesis induced by aflatoxin-B, in rat liver; ultrastructural hepatotoxic effects of mirex in rats; scanning electron microscopy of human knee joints. *Mailing Add:* Dept of Anat Univ Nev Sch Med Sci Reno NV 89557

KENDALL, NORMAN, b Philadelphia, Pa, May 7, 12; m 44; c 2. PEDIATRICS. *Educ:* Temple Univ, MD, 36, MS, 41. *Prof Exp:* Intern, Hosp, Temple Univ, 38, resident, 41, instr pediat, Sch Med, 41-47, from asst prof to assoc prof, 47-67, prof pediat, 67-79; CONSULT, NJ DEPT HEALTH, 79-82. *Concurrent Pos:* Attend pediatrician, St Christopher's Hosp for Children; chmn dept neonatology, Temple Univ Hosp. *Mem:* AMA; Am Acad Pediat; Am Fedn Clin Res; Am Pub Health Asn. *Res:* Newborn infants. *Mailing Add:* 1611 E Park Towne Philadelphia PA 19130

KENDALL, PERRY E(UGENE), b Paoli, Ind, July 27, 21; m 42; c 3. ELECTRICAL ENGINEERING. *Educ:* Purdue Univ, BS, 48, MS, 49, PhD(elec eng), 53. *Prof Exp:* Instr elec eng, Purdue Univ, 47-52; sr engr, res in servomechanisms, Cook Res Lab, 52-54; res proj engr, Capehart-Farnsworth Co Div, Int Tel & Tel Corp, 54-56, sr engr, Farnsworth Electronics Co, 56-58, head systs anal & design labs, 58-60, lab dir guidance & control lab, Astrionics Ctr, ITT Fed Labs, 60-63; mgr res & develop, Fed Systs Div, Indust Nucleonics Corp, 63-66; mgr guid & control, Missile Div, NAm Aviation Corp, 66-70; mgr advan develop, Indust Systs Res & Develop, Indust Nucleonics Corp, 70-74; mem sr tech staff, TRW Defense & Space Systs Group, 74-79, proj engr, 79-81; RETIRED. *Res:* Servomechanisms and electronics; circuits for photoemissive electron tubes and infrared cells; guidance for guided missiles and space vehicles; application of digital computers for process control; high energy laser systems. *Mailing Add:* RR 4 Box 42-A Mitchell IN 47446

KENDALL, ROBERT MCCUTCHEON, b Pasadena, Calif, Dec 29, 31; m 57; c 4. CHEMICAL ENGINEERING. *Educ:* Stanford Univ, BS, 52, MS, 53; Mass Inst Technol, ScD, 59. *Prof Exp:* Thermodyn specialist, Calif Adv Propulsion Systs Oper, 56-60; sect mgr, Vidya Inc, 60-65; vpres & div mgr, Aerotherm Corp, 65-76, SR VPRES, CHIEF SCIENTIST & MGR COMBUSTION TECHNOL, AEROTHERM DIV, ACUREX CORP, 76- *Concurrent Pos:* Lectr, exten, Univ Calif, 59-62 & Stanford Univ, 63-64; consult prof, Stanford Univ, 78- *Mem:* Am Inst Chem Engrs; Am Inst Aeronaut & Astronaut; Combustion Inst. *Res:* Application of advanced experimental and computational techniques to the study of problems of mass, energy and momemtum exchange in combusting or chemically active fluid dynamic systems. *Mailing Add:* Acurex Corp 485 Clyde Ave Mt View CA 94042

KENDALL, WILLIAM ANDERSON, b Fitchburg, Mass, Sept 24, 24; m 52; c 3. PLANT PHYSIOLOGY. *Educ:* Univ Maine, BS, 49; Ohio State Univ, PhD(bot), 54. *Prof Exp:* Asst, Ohio State Univ, 49-54; PLANT PHYSIOLOGIST, AGR RES SERV, USDA, 54- *Prof Exp:* Adj prof, Univ Ky, 54-70 & Pa State Univ, 70- *Mem:* Am Soc Agron; Am Soc Plant Physiol; Am Soc Animal Sci. *Res:* Interactions of genotypes and environments on growth and development of forage crops. *Mailing Add:* US Regional Pasture Res Lab University Park PA 16802

KENDE, ANDREW S, b Budapest, Hungary, July 17, 32; nat US; m 54; c 1. ORGANIC CHEMISTRY. *Educ:* Univ Chicago, BA, 50; Harvard Univ, MA, 54, PhD, 57. *Prof Exp:* Res chemist, Lederle Labs, Am Cyanamid Co, 57-62, res assoc, 63-67, res fel, 67-68; prof chem, 68-81, CHARLES F HOUGHTON PROF CHEM, UNIV ROCHESTER, 81-, CHMN, 79- *Concurrent Pos:* Vis prof, Mich State Univ, 68; consult, Lederle Labs, 68- & Dow Chem Co, 74-; vis prof, Univ Geneve, 74; consult, Med Chem Study Sect, NIH, 72-76, chmn, 74-76; Guggenheim fel, 78-79. *Mem:* Am Chem Soc; The Chem Soc. *Res:* Thermal and photochemical rearrangements, total synthesis of alkaloids and antibiotics, synthetic methods, chemistry of polyhaloaromatic environmental contaminants; chemical carcinogenesis. *Mailing Add:* Dept of Chem Univ of Rochester Rochester NY 14627

KENDE, HANS JANOS, b Szekesfehervar, Hungary, Jan 18, 37; US citizen; m 60; c 3. PLANT PHYSIOLOGY. *Educ:* Univ Zurich, PhD(bot), 60. *Prof Exp:* Res fel plant physiol, Nat Res Coun Can, 60-61; res fel, Div Biol, Calif Inst Technol, 61-63; plant physiologist, Negev Inst Arid Zone Res, Israel, 63-65; assoc prof, 65-69, PROF BOT & PLANT PATH, DOE PLANT RES LAB, MICH STATE UNIV, 69- *Concurrent Pos:* Guggenheim Mem Found fel & vis prof, Swiss Fed Inst Technol, 72-73; mem, Adv Panel Develop Biol, NSF, 74-78; vis prof, Swiss Fed Inst Technol, 79-80. *Mem:* AAAS; Am Soc Plant Physiol; Soc Develop Biol. *Res:* Function, chemistry and action mechanism of plant growth regulators. *Mailing Add:* Dept of Energy Plant Res Lab Mich State Univ East Lansing MI 48824

KENDEIGH, SAMUEL CHARLES, b Amherst, Ohio, Dec 18, 04; m 30; c 2. ECOLOGY ORNITHOLOGY. *Educ:* Oberlin Col, AB, 26, AM, 27; Univ Ill, PhD, 30. *Prof Exp:* Res assoc, Baldwin Bird Res Lab, Cleveland, 25-39; instr biol, Adelbert Col & Mather Col, Western Reserve, 30-36; from asst prof to prof, 36-73, EMER PROF ZOOL, UNIV ILL, URBANA-CHAMPAIGN, 73- *Concurrent Pos:* Collabr, US Fish & Wildlife Serv, 45; US & Soviet Acad Sci cult exchange fel, USSR, 66. *Honors & Awards:* Brewster Award, Am Ornith Union, 51. *Mem:* AAAS; Ecol Soc Am (pres, 51); Am Soc Zool; Am Soc Mammal; Wilson Ornith Soc (pres, 43-45). *Res:* Ecological energetics of birds; breeding bird populations in relation to vegetation; regulation of yearly abundance of animals. *Mailing Add:* Dept of Ecol Ethol & Evolution Univ of Ill Champaign IL 61820

KENDER, DONALD NICHOLAS, b Passaic, NJ, Aug 30, 48; m 71. ANALYTICAL CHEMISTRY. *Educ:* Ohio State Univ, BA, 70; Georgetown Univ, PhD(chem), 75. *Prof Exp:* Chemist & Nat Res Coun assoc, Naval Surface Weapons Ctr, 75-76; SR SCIENTIST CHEM, CIBA-GEIGY CORP, 76- *Mem:* Am Chem Soc; Soc Appl Spectros; Sigma Xi. *Res:* Isolation, identification and physical organic chemistry of pharmaceuticals. *Mailing Add:* Anal R&D Ciba-Geigy Pharmaceut Old Mill Rd Suffern NY 10901

KENDER, WALTER JOHN, b Camden, NJ, Dec 20, 35; m 57; c 1. POMOLOGY. *Educ:* Del Valley Col, BS, 57; Rutgers Univ, MS, 59, PhD(plant nutrit), 62. *Prof Exp:* From asst prof to assoc prof hort, Univ Maine, Orono, 62-69; assoc prof, 69-75, PROF POMOL & HEAD DEPT, CORNELL UNIV, 75-, HEAD DEPT POMOL & VITICULT, NY AGR EXP STA, 72- *Concurrent Pos:* Assoc ed, Am Soc Hort Sci, 72-76. *Mem:* Am Pomol Soc; NY Acad Sci. *Res:* Physiology and culture of fruit crops; air pollution effects on agricultural crops; emphasis on impacts of fossil fuel effluents and acid rain on fruit crop productivity and economic assessment; viticulture; growth regulators. *Mailing Add:* Dept of Pomol & Viticult NY State Agr Exp Sta Cornell Univ Geneva NY 14456

KENDIG, B(ENJAMIN) F(RANKLIN), JR, aeronautical engineering, see previous edition

KENDIG, EDWIN LAWRENCE, JR, b Victoria, Va, Nov 12, 11; m 41; c 2. PEDIATRICS RESPIRATORY DISORDERS. *Educ:* Hampden-Sydney Col, BA, 32, BS, 33; Univ Va, MD, 36. *Hon Degrees:* DSc, Hampden-Sydney Col, 71. *Prof Exp:* Assoc prof, 58-61, PROF PEDIAT, MED COL VA, VA COMMONWEALTH UNIV, 61-, DIR CHILD CHEST CLIN, COL HOSP, 58- *Concurrent Pos:* Instr, Johns Hopkins Hosp, 44; mem comt med educ & founding mem sect dis in childhood, Am Thoracic Soc; mem bd visitors, Univ Va; mem Va steering com, White House Conf, 60; chmn, Richmond City Bd Health. *Honors & Awards:* Award of Recognition, Am Acad Pediat. *Res:* Pediatrics; sarcoidosis; unclassified mycobacteria. *Mailing Add:* Med Col of Va Dept of Pediat Va Commonwealth Univ Richmond VA 23219

KENDIG, JOAN JOHNSTON, b Derby, Conn, May 1, 39; m 64; c 2. NEUROBIOLOGY. *Educ:* Smith Col, BA, 60; Stanford Univ, PhD(biol sci), 66. *Prof Exp:* NSF fel neurophysiol, Univ Calif, Berkeley, 65-67; res assoc, 67-71, asst prof, 71-77, ASSOC PROF OF BIOL IN ANESTHESIA, SCH MED, STANFORD UNIV, 77- *Concurrent Pos:* Mellon fel, Stanford Univ, 76. *Mem:* Am Soc Pharmacol & Exp Therapeut; Undersea Med Soc; Biophys Soc; Soc Neurosci. *Res:* Neuropharmacology of anesthetic and analgesic drugs; cellular effects of anesthetic agents; effects of hyperbaric pressures on excitable cells. *Mailing Add:* Dept of Anesthesia Sch of Med Stanford Univ Stanford CA 94305

KENDIG, MARTIN WILLIAM, b Danville, Pa, Oct 20, 45; m 69; c 2. PHYSICAL CHEMISTRY, CORROSION SCIENCE. *Educ:* Franklin & Marshall Col, AB, 67; Brown Univ, PhD(phys chem), 74. *Prof Exp:* Res assoc, Ctr Surface & Coatings Res, Lehigh Univ, 73-76; asst chemist, 76-78, assoc chemist corrosion sci, Brookhaven Nat Lab, 78-80; MEM TECH STAFF, ROCKWELL INT SCI CTR, 80- *Mem:* Electrochem Soc; Am Chem Soc; Sigma Xi. *Res:* Kinetics of hydrogen exchange at metal and metal alloy surfaces as related to the hydrogen embrittlement of steel; electrochemistry of metals in water under high temperature and pressure; the chemistry and physics of localized corrosion and corrosion protection; corrosion monitoring; polymer coatings. *Mailing Add:* Rockwell Int Sci Ctr Thousand Oaks CA 91360

KENDRICK, AARON BAKER, b McCalla, Ala, July 18, 05; m 37; c 3. PHYSIOLOGICAL CHEMISTRY. *Educ:* Howard Col, AB, 27; Univ Chicago, PhD(biochem), 33. *Prof Exp:* Asst, Dept Physiol Chem, Univ Chicago, 31-34; asst, Univ Ill Med Ctr, 34-35, instr, 35-37, assoc, 37-43, from asst prof to assoc prof internal med, 43-73, emer assoc prof, 73; RETIRED. *Res:* Compounds of hemoglobin; liver and kidney function; plasma substitutes; determination of carbohydrates, amino acids and lipides; electrolyte metabolism; purines; gout; D-ribose in gouty man. *Mailing Add:* Route 1 Box 9B McCalla AL 35111

KENDRICK, BRYCE, b Liverpool, Eng, Dec 3, 33; m 57. MYCOLOGY. *Educ:* Univ Liverpool, BSc, 55, PhD(mycol), 58, DSc, 80. *Prof Exp:* Fel taxonomic mycol, Nat Res Coun Can, 58-59; mycologist, Plant Res Inst, Res Br, Can Dept Agr, 59-65; from asst prof to assoc prof, 65-71, PROF BIOL, UNIV WATERLOO, 71- *Concurrent Pos:* Chmn, Plant Biol Grant Selection Comt, Nat Sci & Eng Res Coun, Can, 79; Guggenheim fel, 79-80. *Mem:* Mycol Soc Am; Brit Mycol Soc; Can Bot Asn; fel Royal Soc Can. *Res:* Computer simulations; systematics of hyphomycetes; development ecology and karyology of microfungi. *Mailing Add:* Dept of Biol Univ of Waterloo Waterloo ON N2L 3G1 Can

KENDRICK, FRANCIS JOSEPH, b St Petersburg, Fla, Oct 19, 26; m 53; c 2. PATHOLOGY, DENTISTRY. *Educ:* Northwestern Univ, DDS, 52, PhD(path), 63. *Prof Exp:* Intern dent, USPHS Hosp, Seattle, 52-53; pvt practr, 53-55; instr dent, Northwestern Univ, 55-56; res assoc teratology, Nat Inst Dent Res, 60-63, pathologist, Nat Inst Child Health & Human Develop,

63-69, asst to chief gen res support br, 69-70, spec asst prog planning & eval, 70-74, actg dir gen res support prog, Div Res Resources, 74-75, dir, Biomed Res Support Prog, 75-80, ASST DIR MANPOWER & RESOURCE DEVELOP, DIV RES RESOURCES, NIH, 81- *Mem:* AAAS; Teratology Soc; fel Am Acad Oral Path; Int Asn Dent. *Res:* NY Acad Sci. Res: experimental carcinogenesis and teratology; oral and general pathology. *Mailing Add:* Nat Inst Health Bldg 31 Rm 5B05 Bethesda MD 20014

KENDRICK, HUGH, b Ewell, Eng, Jan 25, 40; m 63; c 2. NUCLEAR ENGINEERING, SOLID STATE PHYSICS. *Educ:* Univ London, BSc, 61; Calif Inst Technol, MS, 62; Univ Mich, PhD(nuclear eng), 68. *Prof Exp:* Teaching res asst mech eng, Calif Inst Technol, 61-62; scientist, Vickers Res Ltd, 62-63; sr physicist, Radiation Transport Group, Gulf Radiation Technol, 68-72; dep mgr, Div Environ & Safety, Sci Applns, Inc, 72-75, mgr, Div Safeguards & Nuclear Fuels, 75-77; spec asst, Off Fuel Cycle Eval, US Dept Energy, 77-79, dir, Off Plans & Anal, 79-81; VPRES, SCI APPLICATIONS INC, 81- *Mem:* Am Phys Soc; Inst Nuclear Mat Mgt; Am Nuclear Soc. *Res:* Investigation of magnetic materials through neutron diffraction; pulsed neutron investigation of radiation transport in shields; spectroscopy and unfolding techniques; nuclear materials assay; assessment of proliferation risks of nuclear technology; nuclear safeguards system effectiveness evaluation; environmental economic safety assessment of technology. *Mailing Add:* Sci Applications Inc 1710 Goodridge Dr McLean VA 22102

KENDRICK, JAMES BLAIR, JR, b Lafayette, Ind, Oct 21, 20; m 42; c 2. PLANT PATHOLOGY. *Educ:* Univ Calif, Berkeley, BA, 42; Univ Wis, PhD(plant path), 47. *Prof Exp:* Jr plant pathologist, Univ Calif, Riverside, 47-49, from asst plant pathologist to assoc plant pathologist, 49-61, prof plant path, 61-68, chmn dept, 63-68, asst to chancellor, 59-60; vpres agr sci, 68-77, dir Agr Exp Sta, 73-80, dir Coop Exten, 75-80, VPRES AGR & UNIV SERV, SYSTEMWIDE ADMIN, UNIV CALIF, BERKELEY, 77- *Concurrent Pos:* NSF sr fel, 61-62; mem, Calif State Bd Food & Agr, 68- & US Forest Serv Adv Comt, Region V, 70-75; chmn div agr, Nat Asn State Univs & Land Grant Cols, 73, mem exec comt, 74-76, 79; mem, Agr Res Policy Adv Comt, 74-76, Gov Bd, Agr Res Inst, 74-76 ; chmn adv panel, Off Technol Assessment, US Congress, 81- *Mem:* Fel AAAS; Am Phytopath Soc; Sigma Xi. *Res:* Soil fungicides; biology of root decaying organisms; diseases of vegetables. *Mailing Add:* Systemwide Admin 317 Univ Hall Univ Calif Berkeley CA 94720

KENDRICK, JOHN EDSEL, b Scott City, Kans, Dec 23, 28; m 54; c 3. PHYSIOLOGY. *Educ:* Univ Kans, AB, 52, PhD(physiol), 57. *Prof Exp:* From instr to asst prof, 57-67, ASSOC PROF PHYSIOL, SCH MED, UNIV WIS-MADISON, 67- *Mem:* Am Physiol Soc. *Res:* Cardiovascular physiology. *Mailing Add:* Dept of Physiol Sch Med Univ of Wis Madison WI 53706

KENDRICK, JOHN WESLEY, theriogenology, deceased

KENDRICK, LAWRENCE W, JR, b Underwood, Ala, Sept 16, 25; m 48; c 2. ORGANIC CHEMISTRY, SYNTHETIC FIBER TECHNOLOGY. *Educ:* Howard Col, BS, 53; Univ Fla, PhD(pharmaceut chem), 57. *Prof Exp:* Res chemist, Dacron Res Lab, Textile Fibers Dept, 57-65, res chemist, 65-75, SR RES CHEMIST, TEXTILE RES LAB, E I DU PONT DE NEMOURS & CO, INC, 75- *Res:* Organic reaction mechanisms; high polymer chemistry. *Mailing Add:* Textile Res Lab Chestnut Run E I du Pont de Nemours & Co Inc Wilmington DE 19898

KENDZIORSKI, FRANCIS RICHARD, b Alpena, Mich, Apr 2, 31; m 64; c 2. NUCLEAR PHYSICS. *Educ:* Univ Detroit, BS, 53; Cornell Univ, PhD(physics), 61. *Prof Exp:* Asst prof physics, Univ Detroit, 61-63; asst prof, Univ Dayton, 63-67; assoc prof, 67-77, PROF PHYSICS, WESTERN CONN STATE COL, 77-, CHMN DEPT PHYSICS & ASTRON, 78- *Mem:* AAAS; Am Phys Soc; Am Asn Physics Teachers. *Res:* Low energy studies of nuclear structure in intermediate weight nuclei; extensive cosmic ray air showers; elementary education. *Mailing Add:* Dept of Physics Western Conn State Col Danbury CT 06810

KENEALY, MICHAEL DOUGLAS, b Council Bluffs, Iowa, May 7, 47; m 69; c 2. ANIMAL NUTRITION, PHYSIOLOGY. *Educ:* Iowa State Univ, BS, 69, PhD(animal nutrit & physiol), 74. *Prof Exp:* Nutritionist, Dr Macdonalds Feed Co, 74-75; asst prof, 75-79, ASSOC PROF ANIMAL SCI, IOWA STATE UNIV, 79- *Mem:* Sigma Xi; Am Dairy Sci Asn; Am Soc Animal Sci. *Mailing Add:* Iowa State Univ 123 Kildee Hall Ames IA 50011

KENEALY, PATRICK FRANCIS, b Chicago, Ill, Aug 4, 39; m 60; c 3. NUCLEAR PHYSICS. *Educ:* Loyola Univ, Ill, BS, 61; Univ Notre Dame, PhD(physics), 67. *Prof Exp:* Asst prof, 67-74, ASSOC PROF PHYSICS, WAYNE STATE UNIV, 74- *Concurrent Pos:* Vis assoc prof, Stanford Univ, 76-77; NSF fac fel sci, 76-77. *Mem:* AAAS; Am Phys Soc; Am Asn Physics Teachers. *Res:* Experimental nuclear structure spectroscopy, involving determination of nuclear decay schemes, spin, parities and lifetimes of nuclear levels; study of solid state and nuclearr parameters of interest using the Mossbauer effect; x-ray absorption fine structure measurements on biological samples; use of computers in teaching physics; cognitive studies of learning patterns in introductory physics. *Mailing Add:* Dept of Physics Col Liberal Arts Wayne State Univ Detroit MI 48202

KENEFICK, ROBERT ARTHUR, b Syracuse, NY, Mar 9, 37; m 60; c 3. NUCLEAR PHYSICS. *Educ:* Mass Inst Technol, BS, 59; Fla State Univ, PhD(physics), 62. *Prof Exp:* Res assoc nuclear physics, Univ Colo, 62-63, asst prof, 63-64; asst prof, Univ Mich, 64-65; from asst prof to assoc prof, 65-74, PROF NUCLEAR PHYSICS, TEX A&M UNIV, 74-, MEM CYCLOTRON INST, 65- *Mem:* Am Phys Soc. *Res:* Nuclear reactions and nuclear structure; high-energy atomic collisions; particle detectors; ion sources. *Mailing Add:* Dept of Physics Tex A&M Univ College Station TX 77843

KENELLY, JOHN WILLIS, JR, b Bogalusa, La, Nov 22, 35; m 56; c 2. MATHEMATICS. *Educ:* Southeastern La Col, BS, 57; Univ Miss, MS, 57; Univ Fla, PhD(math), 61. *Prof Exp:* Instr math, Univ Fla, 59-61; asst prof, Univ Southwestern La, 61-63; assoc prof, Clemson Univ, 63-68; prof & chmn dept, La State Univ, 68-69; head dept, 69-77, PROF MATH SCI, CLEMSON UNIV, 69- *Concurrent Pos:* Consult, Addison-Wesley Publ Co & Houghton Mifflin Publ; chief reader, Advan Placement Prog Math, Educ Testing Serv, 75-79; vis lectr & curriculum consult, Math Asn Am, 70- *Mem:* Am Math Soc; Math Asn Am. *Res:* Geometry; convexity; operations research. *Mailing Add:* 327 Woodland Way Clemson SC 29631

KENESHEA, FRANCIS JOSEPH, b Providence, RI, June 25, 21; m 44; c 2. PHYSICAL CHEMISTRY. *Educ:* RI State Col, BS, 43, MS, 48; Univ NMex, PhD(chem), 51. *Prof Exp:* Instr chem, RI State Col, 46-47; asst, Cornell Univ, 47-48; sr res engr, NAm Aviation, Inc, 51-55; sr chemist, Stanford Res Inst, 55-71; consult engr, 74-80, SR CONSULT, QUADREX CORP, 80- *Concurrent Pos:* Sr res assoc, Ore State Univ, 63-64. *Mem:* AAAS; Am Nuclear Soc; Am Chem Soc; Sigma Xi. *Res:* Thermodynamics of vaporization; chemical diffusion; chemistry of molten salts and metal-salt solutions; nuclear and radiochemistry; nuclear technology. *Mailing Add:* 20 Bear Paw Portola Valley CA 94025

KENG, PETER C, b Kinagsu, China, Aug 12, 46; m 72; c 2. CELL SEPARATION. *Educ:* Tunghai Univ, BS, 68; Colo State Univ, PhD(radiation biol), 78. *Prof Exp:* RES ASST PROF, DEPT RADIATION ONCOL, UNIV ROCHESTER, 80-, ASST PROF, DEPT RADIATION BIOL & BIOPHYSICS & DIR RES, CELL SEPARATION FACIL, 81- *Mem:* Radiation Res Soc; Anal Cytometry. *Res:* Separation of cell subpopulations from solid tumors, bone marrow and tissue culture cells into various host cells; neoplastic cells and cells at different stages of the cell cycle to study the DNA damage of these cells. *Mailing Add:* Cancer Ctr Univ Rochester Box 704 Rochester NY 14642

KENIG, MARVIN JERRY, b Philadelphia, Pa, Sept 20, 36; m 59; c 2. APPLIED MECHANICS, MATERIALS SCIENCE. *Educ:* Drexel Univ, BSME, 59, MSME, 63; Princeton Univ, MA, 63, PhD(eng), 65. *Prof Exp:* From instr to asst prof mech eng, 60-69, from asst dean to assoc dean grad sch, 71-74, ASSOC PROF MECH ENG, 69-, ASST TO PRES, DREXEL UNIV, 74- *Concurrent Pos:* Consult, J P Oat & Sons, Inc, 68- & US Army Frankford Arsenal, 70-75. *Mem:* Am Soc Mech Engrs; Am Acad Mech; Am Soc Eng Educators; Am Defense Preparedness Asn; AAAS. *Res:* Effect Portevin-Le Chatalier phenomenon on plastic potential theory of yielding; implications with respect to propagation of small stress increments; creep; fatigue; quantum mechanics modeling of dislocation motion. *Mailing Add:* Off of Pres Drexel Univ Philadelphia PA 19104

KENK, ROMAN, b Ljubljana, Yugoslavia, Nov 25, 98; nat US; m 33; c 1. INVERTEBRATE ZOOLOGY. *Educ:* Graz Univ, PhD(zool), 21. *Prof Exp:* Asst zool, Univ Ljubljana, 21-26, docent, 26-37, extraordinary prof, 37-38; from assoc prof to prof biol, Univ PR, 38-48; subj cataloger, Sci & Tech Proj, Libr of Cong, 48-49, bibliographer & sci specialist, Tech Info Div, 49-56, supvr biol sci unit, Bibliog Sect, Sci & Tech Div, 56-60, asst head, Bibliog Sect, 60-63, supvry biol scientist, 63-65; RES ASSOC, SMITHSONIAN INST, 65- *Concurrent Pos:* Rockefeller Found fel, Univ Va, 31-32; exchange cur, Mus Zool, Univ Mich, 40-41; sr scientist, George Washington Univ, 66-70. *Mem:* AAAS; Am Soc Zool; Am Micros Soc. *Res:* Morphology, ecology, taxonomy and physiology of freshwater Triclads; ecology of cave animals; freshwater biology; scientific bibliography. *Mailing Add:* Nat Mus Natural Hist Smithsonian Inst Washington DC 20560

KENK, VIDA CARMEN, b San Juan, PR, Dec 24, 39; m 74; c 2. INVERTEBRATE ZOOLOGY. *Educ:* Col William & Mary, BS, 61; Radcliffe Col, AM, 62; Harvard Univ, PhD(biol), 67. *Prof Exp:* Asst prof, 66-70, assoc prof, 70-77, PROF BIOL, SAN JOSE STATE UNIV, 77- *Mem:* AAAS; Am Malacol Union; Western Soc Malacologists (pres, 80). *Res:* Systematics, ecology and functional anatomy of bivalve molluscs. *Mailing Add:* 18596 Paseo Pueblo Saratoga CA 95070

KENKARE, DIVAKER B, b Goa, India, May 25, 36; US citizen; m 66; c 1. BIOLOGICAL CHEMISTRY, PHYSICAL CHEMISTRY. *Educ:* Univ Poona, BSc, 59; Sardar Patel Univ, India, MSc, 61; Ohio State Univ, MSc, 63, PhD(food chem), 66. *Prof Exp:* Res assoc protein chem, Univ Ill, Urbana, 66-68; res chemist, 68-71, sr res chemist, 71-78, RES ASSOC, COLGATE PALMOLIVE RES CTR, PISCATAWAY, 78- *Mem:* Am Chem Soc. *Res:* Changes of protein at elevated temperatures; characterization, physical chemical behavior, and modification of proteins. *Mailing Add:* 1149 Clinton Terr South Plainfield NJ 07080

KENKNIGHT, GLENN, b Canby, Ore, Nov 26, 10; m 40; c 2. PLANT PATHOLOGY. *Educ:* Carleton Col, BA, 34; Mich State Col, MS, 37, PhD(bot, plant path), 39. *Prof Exp:* Asst plant path, Univ Minn, 35; asst, Exp Sta, Mich State Col, 35-39; plant pathologist, Exp Sta, Agr & Mech Col Tex, 40-42; assoc plant pathologist, Exp Sta, Univ Idaho, 42-45; assoc plant pathologist, Calif Dept Agr, Indio, 45-48; plant pathologist, Hort Field Lab, USDA, 48-62, res plant pathologist, Pecan Field Lab, 62-73; CONSULT, 73- *Mem:* Am Phytopath Soc. *Res:* Soil actinomyces in relation to potato scab; fungicidal action of mercury compounds; breeding vegetable crops for disease resistance; virus diseases of stone fruits; witches' broom disease of trees; pecan diseases. *Mailing Add:* 9517 Palmetto Lane Shreveport LA 71108

KENKRE, VASUDEV MANGESH, b Panjim, India, Sept 21, 46; m 69; c 2. THEORETICAL SOLID STATE PHYSICS, STATISTICAL MECHANICS. *Educ:* Indian Inst Technol, Bombay, BTech, 68; State Univ NY Stony Brook, MA, 71, PhD(physics), 71. *Prof Exp:* Instr physics, State Univ NY Stony Brook, 71-72; res assoc, 72-74, asst prof physics, 74-79, ASSOC PROF PHYSICS, UNIV ROCHESTER, 79-, FEL, INST FUNDAMENTAL STUDIES, 72- *Res:* Transport and response theories, master equations, random walks; charge, excitation and energy transfer in organic and amorphous solids; interaction of light with matter; polaron and exciton motion; size quantization effect. *Mailing Add:* Inst Fundament Studies Dept of Physics Univ Rochester Rochester NY 14627

KENLEY, RICHARD ALAN, b Chicago, Ill, Jan 17, 47; m 73. ORGANIC CHEMISTRY. *Educ:* Univ Ill, Champaign, BS, 69; Univ Calif, San Diego, PhD(org chem), 73. *Prof Exp:* PHYS ORG CHEM, SRI INT, 75- *Mem:* Am Chem Soc. *Res:* Free radical reactions in gas and solution phase. *Mailing Add:* SRI Int 333 Ravenswood Ave Menlo Park CA 94025

KENNA, BERNARD THOMAS, b Hays, Kans, Jan 4, 35; m 60; c 2. NUCLEAR CHEMISTRY, GEOCHEMISTRY. *Educ:* Ariz State Col, BS, 56; Univ Miss, MS, 58; Univ Ark, PhD(nuclear chem), 61. *Prof Exp:* Res asst radiochem, Univ Ark, 59-61; nuclear chemist in-charge radiochem & activation anal lab, 61-81, PROJ MGR, ENVIRON RES, SANDIA NAT LAB, 81- *Concurrent Pos:* Assoc prof, Univ NMex, 67-79. *Mem:* AAAS; Am Chem Soc; Am Nuclear Soc. *Res:* Theoretical and practical application of nuclear and radiochemistry to analytical chemistry; ion exchange; inorganic coordination chemistry; nuclear geochemistry; environmental research (atmosphere and water). *Mailing Add:* Sandia Nat Lab Org 4544 Albuquerque NM 87185

KENNAMER, JAMES EARL, b Fairfield, Ala, Aug 6, 42; m 67; c 1. WILDLIFE ECOLOGY. *Educ:* Auburn Univ, BS, 64; Miss State Univ, MS, 67, PhD(wildlife mgt), 70. *Prof Exp:* Instr wildlife mgt, Miss State Univ, 69-70; asst prof wildlife ecol, Auburn Univ, 70-77, assoc prof, 77-80; DIR RES, NAT WILD TURKEY FEDN, 80- *Mem:* Wildlife Soc; Sigma Xi. *Res:* Wild turkey ecology and physiology; Canada goose, white-tailed deer and fallow deer ecology and physiology. *Mailing Add:* Nat Wild Turkey Fedn PO Box 467 Edgefield SC 29824

KENNARD, KENNETH CLAYTON, b Battle Creek, Mich, Dec 18, 26; m 49; c 3. ORGANIC CHEMISTY, BIOCHEMISTY. *Educ:* Univ Notre Dame, BS, 49; Univ Nebr, MS, 52, PhD(org chem), 54; Mass Inst Technol, SM, 64. *Prof Exp:* Res chemist, 54-65, asst div head, Emulsion Res Div, 65-69, staff asst to dir res, 69-75, DIR BIOSCI DIV, KODAK RES LABS, 75- *Mem:* Am Chem Soc; Am Asn Clin Chemists; AAAS. *Res:* Organic chemistry of phosphorous and sulfur compounds; preparation and properties of light sensitive materials. *Mailing Add:* Biosci Div Res Labs Eastman Kodak Co Rochester NY 14650

KENNARD, ROBERT WAKELY, b Newark, Del, Jan 27, 23; m 41; c 1. MATHEMATICAL STATISTICS. *Educ:* Univ Del, BS, 49, MS, 52; Carnegie Inst Technol, PhD(math), 55. *Prof Exp:* MGR SYSTS ENG, E I DU PONT DE NEMOURS & CO, INC, 55- *Concurrent Pos:* Assoc prof, Univ Del, 56-63, prof, 63- *Mem:* Asn Comput Mach; Math Asn Am; fel Am Statist Asn; Inst Math Statist. *Res:* Statistical data analysis and design of experiments with emphasis on computer methods. *Mailing Add:* 35 Georgian Circle Newark DE 19711

KENNARD, WILLIAM CRAWFORD, b Centreville, Md, Nov 29, 21; m 43; c 3. PLANT PHYSIOLOGY, HORTICULTURE. *Educ:* Univ Del, BS, 43; Pa State Univ, MS, 48, PhD(plant physiol, soils), 56; Oak Ridge Inst Nuclear Studies, cert, 60. *Prof Exp:* Res fel pomol, Pa State Univ, 46-48, instr, 48-52; horticulturist, Mayaguez Inst Trop Agr, Mayaguez, PR, 52-57; prin horticulturist & res adminr, US Off Exp Sta, Washington, DC, 57-62; prof hort & assoc dir res admin, 62-74, dir inst water resources, 65-74, PROF PLANT PHYSIOL, UNIV CONN, 62- *Concurrent Pos:* Vis prof, Univ PR, 56; actg dir, Inst Water Resources, Univ Conn, 64-65; assoc seminars, Columbia Univ, 69- *Mem:* Fel AAAS; Am Inst Biol Sci; Am Soc Hort Sci. *Res:* Physiology and culture of temperate zone fruit crops; physiology of flowering; growth and development of tropical plants, including fruits, drug crops, insecticidal crops and bamboo; remote sensing of the environment. *Mailing Add:* Natural Resources Conserv Dept Univ of Conn Storrs CT 06268

KENNAUGH, EDWARD, b New York, NY, Oct 3, 22; m 51. ELECTRICAL ENGINEERING, PHYSICS. *Educ:* Ohio State Univ, BEE, 47, MSc, 52, PhD(elec eng), 59. *Prof Exp:* Res assoc electromagnetics, Antenna Lab, Ohio State Univ, 48-54, assoc supvr, 54-70, dir, Electrosci Lab, 70-74, from asst prof to assoc prof, 61-65, PROF ELEC ENG, OHIO STATE UNIV, 65- *Concurrent Pos:* Mem comn B, Int Union Radio Sci; US aerospace panel study group, Adv Group Aeronaut Res & Develop. *Mem:* Inst Elec & Electronics Engrs. *Res:* Radar reflectivity theory and measurement techniques; electromagnetic theory; polarization properties of radar targets; transient electromagnetic scattering phenomena; impulse response of distributed constant linear systems; antenna synthesis and near-field phenomena. *Mailing Add:* Dept of Elec Eng Ohio State Univ 2015 Neil Ave Columbus OH 43210

KENNEDY, ALBERT JOSEPH, b Spring Valley, Ill, July 2, 43; m; c 3. RADIOCHEMISTRY, CORROSION. *Educ:* Univ Ill, Champaign, BS, 66; Purdue Univ, PhD(nuclear chem), 72. *Prof Exp:* Fel nuclear chem, Lawrence Berkeley Lab, 72-73; sr res chemist, Babcock & Wilcox Co, 73-78; prin chemist, 78-80, SR PRIN CHEMIST, COMMONWEALTH EDISON, 80- *Mem:* Am Chem Soc; Am Nuclear Soc. *Res:* Corrosion chemistry; corrosion product deposition; activation analysis, radiochemistry, quality control and nuclear fuel evaluation. *Mailing Add:* Commonwealth Edison Co 1319 S 1st Ave Maywood IL 60153

KENNEDY, ANDREW JOHN, b Budapest, Hungary, May 16, 35; US citizen; m 58; c 2. SOLID STATE PHYSICS, PHYSICAL ELECTRONICS. *Educ:* Wash State Univ, BS, 61; Univ Wash, MS, 64. *Prof Exp:* Assoc res engr A, Boeing Co, 61-64; RES PHYSICIST, NIGHT VISION & ELECTRO-OPTICS LAB, 64- *Mem:* Inst Elec & Electronics Engrs; Am Inst Physics. *Res:* Solid state infrared detector physics and technology, intensified charge coupled devices. *Mailing Add:* 9516 Mount Vernon Landing Alexandria VA 23309

KENNEDY, ANN RANDTKE, b Rochester, NY, Dec 24, 46; m 73; c 2. CARCINOGENESIS. *Educ:* Vassar Col, AB, 69; Harvard Univ, SM, 71, SD, 73. *Prof Exp:* Res assoc, 73-75, asst prof, 76-80, ASSOC PROF RADIOBIOL, HARVARD UNIV, 80- *Concurrent Pos:* Comt mem, Nat Coun Radiation Protection Public Educ, 80-; mem, chem pathol study sect, consult, workshops & prin investr grants, NIH, 81-85. *Mem:* Am Asn Cancer Res & Radiation Res; Sigma Xi. *Res:* Radiobiology; mechanism of carcinogenesis with the ultimate aim of preventing cancer in human populations. *Mailing Add:* Dept Physiol Harvard Sch Public Health 665 Huntington Ave Boston MA 02115

KENNEDY, ANTHONY JOHN, b Brooklyn, NY, Dec 1, 52; m 60; c 6. STOCHOSTIC PROCESSES. *Educ:* Univ Notre Dame, BS, 54; Carnegie Inst Technol, MS, 56, PhD(physics), 62. *Prof Exp:* Scientist, Nuclear Div, Martin Marietta Corp, 60-65 & Space Div, Chrysler Corp, 65-70; consult, Boland & Boyce, Inc, 70-74; scientist, Space Sci Lab, Gen Elec Co, 74-77; PRIN SCIENTIST, XYBION CORP, 77- *Res:* Design of signal processing systems for the detection of signals in ocean noise; computer systems for processing oceanographic information. *Mailing Add:* Xybion Corp 7 Ridgedale Ave Ceder Knolls NJ 07927

KENNEDY, BARBARA MAE, b Plainview, Minn, Dec 5, 11; m 53; c 2. NUTRITION. *Educ:* Univ Minn, BA, 33, MS, 37; Univ Calif, PhD(animal nutrit), 45. *Prof Exp:* Asst clin biochem, Mayo Clin, 34-40 & hosp, Duke, 40; asst, 40-44, instr home econ, 44-47, asst prof, 47-65, from jr biochemist to asst biochemist, Exp Sta, 44-65, assoc prof, 65-81, assoc biochemist, Exp Sta, 65-80, EMER PROF NUTRIT SCI, UNIV CALIF, BERKELEY, 80- *Mem:* AAAS; Am Chem Soc; Am Asn Cereal Chem; Inst Food Technol; Am Inst Nutrit. *Res:* Food chemistry; nutrition; biochemistry; nature of the anemia of cholesterol-fed guinea pigs; cereal chemistry; protein quality. *Mailing Add:* Dept of Nutrit Sci Univ of Calif Berkeley CA 94720

KENNEDY, BILL WADE, b Dallas, Tex, Mar 21, 29; m 51; c 4. PLANT PATHOLOGY. *Educ:* Southeastern State Col, BS, 51; Okla State Univ, MS, 55; Univ Minn, PhD(plant path), 61. *Prof Exp:* Asst plant path, Okla State Univ, 51-52 & 54-55; sr technician, Univ Calif, 55-58; res asst, 58-59, res fel, 59-60, res assoc, 61-63, from asst prof to assoc prof, 63-72, PROF PLANT PATH, UNIV MINN, 72- *Concurrent Pos:* Res grants, Grad Sch, 64-66; Coop, US Regional Soybean Lab, Ill, 64-; USDA grant, 67; leaves for advan study, Univ Calif, Berkeley, 67, Eng, 71 & Italy, 78; sr ed, Phytopath, 73-76. *Mem:* Am Phytopath Soc; Am Inst Biol Sci; Am Soybean Asn. *Res:* Chemical control of cotton seedling blight; root-rot studies; physiology of reproduction in Phytophthora, identity and epidemiology of bacterial blight on strawberry; seed pathology; ecology of bacteria associated with soybean. *Mailing Add:* Dept of Plant Path Univ of Minn St Paul MN 55101

KENNEDY, BYRL JAMES, b Plainview, Minn, June 24, 21; m 50; c 4. INTERNAL MEDICINE. *Educ:* Univ Minn, BA & BS, 43, BM, 45, MD, 46; McGill Univ, MSc, 51; Am Bd Internal Med, dipl, Am Bd Med Oncol, cert, 79. *Prof Exp:* Intern & asst resident med, Mass Gen Hosp, 45-46; resident, Mass Gen Hosp & Harvard Univ, 51-52; from asst prof to assoc prof, Med Ctr, 52-67, PROF MED, HEALTH SCI CTR & DIR, SECT ONCOL, DEPT MED, SCH MED, UNIV MINN, MINNEAPOLIS, 70-, MASONIC PROF ONCOL, 70- *Concurrent Pos:* Fel, Mass Gen Hosp & Harvard Univ, 47-49; fel, Med Sch, McGill Univ, 49-50; fel, Med Sch, Cornell Univ, 50-51. *Mem:* AAAS; Endocrine Soc; Am Asn Cancer Res; AMA; Am Fedn Clin Res. *Res:* Medical oncology. *Mailing Add:* Dept of Med Univ of Minn Health Sci Ctr Minneapolis MN 55455

KENNEDY, CHANDLER JAMES, lasers, see previous edition

KENNEDY, CHARLES, b Buffalo, NY, Aug 27, 20; m 46; c 3. PEDIATRIC NEUROLOGY. *Educ:* Princeton Univ, AB, 42; Univ Rochester, MD, 45. *Prof Exp:* Instr path, Sch Med, Yale Univ, 45-46; resident pediat, Children's Hosp, Buffalo, 48-51; resident neurol, Hosp Univ Pa, 53-54; asst neurologist, Children's Hosp, Philadelphia, 56-58; neurologist, 58-67; from asst prof to assoc prof neurol in pediat, Sch Med, Univ Pa, 58-70; PROF PEDIAT, SCH MED, GEORGETOWN UNIV, 71- *Concurrent Pos:* Fel physiol, Grad Sch Med, Univ Pa, 51-53; vis fel, Neurol Inst, Columbia-Presby Med Ctr, 57-58; guest worker, Lab Cerebral Metab, NIMH, 68-; vis prof, Stanford Univ, 69; sr res scientist, NIMH, 79- *Mem:* AAAS; Soc Pediat Res; Am Neurol Asn; Am Pediat Soc; Soc Neurosci. *Res:* Cerebral circulation; developmental neurology; energy metabolism of developing brain. *Mailing Add:* Dept of Pediat 3800 Reservoir Rd Washington DC 20007

KENNEDY, DONALD, b New York, NY, Aug 18, 31; m 53; c 3. PHYSIOLOGY, ZOOLOGY. *Educ:* Harvard Univ, AB, 52, AM, 54, PhD, 56. *Prof Exp:* From asst prof to assoc prof zool, Syracuse Univ, 56-60; asst prof, 60-62, assoc, 62-65, chmn dept, 65-72, prof zool, Stanford Univ, 65-77; comnr, Food & Drug Admin, 77-79; vpres & provost, 79-80, PRES, STANFORD UNIV, 80- *Mem:* Nat Acad Sci; Nat Inst Med; Am Soc Zool; Soc Gen Physiol; fel Am Acad Arts & Sci. *Res:* Comparative physiology of sense organs, especially visual systems; central nervous system of Crustacea. *Mailing Add:* 623 Mirada Ave Stanford CA 94305

KENNEDY, DUNCAN TILLY, b Brooklyn, NY, May 13, 30; m 55; c 3. NEUROPHYSIOLOGY, NEUROANATOMY. *Educ:* Columbia Univ, BSc, 55; Stanford Univ, AM, 64; Wayne State Univ, PhD(anat), 66. *Prof Exp:* Phys therapist, King's Daughters Hosp, Ashland, Ky, 55-57; phys therapist, Marmet Hosp, WVa, 58-60; instr phys ther, Stanford Univ, 62; from instr to asst prof anat, Wayne State Univ, 66-75, instr neuroanat & neurophys, Div Phys & Occup Ther, 64-75; asst prof, 75-78, ASSOC PROF PHYSIOL & HEALTH SCI, BALL STATE UNIV, 78- *Concurrent Pos:* NIH spec fel, Lab Neurophysiol, Univ Wis, 70-72; fac res awards, Wayne State Univ, 74 & Ball State Univ, 75; instr, Sch Nursing, Moorhead State Col, 55-57; lectr, Mich Phys Ther Continuing Educ Prog, 74-75. *Mem:* AAAS; Soc Neurosci; Sigma Xi. *Res:* Neurophysiology and neuroanatomy of sensory motor systems; electrophysiology of the central auditory systems; biomechanics and kinesiology. *Mailing Add:* Ctr for Med Educ Ball State Univ Muncie IN 47306

KENNEDY, E A, JR, biological oceanography, geology, see previous edition

KENNEDY, EDWARD EARL, b Evansville, Ind, Jan 7, 25; m 50; c 2. ANALYTICAL CHEMISTRY. *Educ:* Purdue Univ, BS, 45; Ind Univ, MA, 48. *Prof Exp:* Anal chemist, Eli Lilly & Co, 45-46; instr, Ind Univ, 47-48; anal chemist, 48-50, head, Dept Assay Methods Develop, 50-52, Anal Res & Develop, 52-56 & Anal Develop & Spec Servs, 56-59, mgr anal control res & develop, 59-62, asst dir anal res & develop, 62-66, dir corp qual assurance, 66-69 & dir, Park Fletcher Plant, 69-70, dir biochem mfg, 70-80, DIR BIOSYNTHETIC OPER, ELI LILLY & CO, 80- *Mem:* AAAS; Am Pharmaceut Asn; Am Soc Qual Control; Am Chem Soc. *Res:* Instrumentation of analytical chemistry, particularly field of spectrophotometry. *Mailing Add:* 5420 Roxbury Rd Indianapolis IN 46226

KENNEDY, EDWARD FRANCIS, b Chicago, Ill, Jan 2, 32; m 56; c 6. NUCLEAR PHYSICS. *Educ:* Loyola Univ, Ill, BS, 54; Univ Notre Dame, PhD(nuclear physics), 60. *Prof Exp:* Technician, Argonne Nat Lab, 52-54; asst physics, Univ Notre Dame, 54-58, res assoc, 58-60; from asst prof to assoc prof physics, 60-70, actg chmn dept, 63-64, chmn dept, 64-76, PROF PHYSICS, COL OF THE HOLY CROSS, 70- *Concurrent Pos:* Consult, Air Force Cambridge Res Labs, 62-; vis scientist, Cavendish Lab, Cambridge, 68-69; vis assoc, Calif Inst Technol, 75-76, 77 & 78. *Mem:* Am Phys Soc; Am Asn Physics Teachers; Sigma Xi. *Res:* Ion channeling in crystals; surface physics; nuclear fluorescence; radiation damage. *Mailing Add:* 21 Hazelwood Rd Worcester MA 01609

KENNEDY, EDWARD STEWART, b San Angel, DF, Mex, Jan 3, 12; US citizen; m 51; c 3. MATHEMATICS. *Educ:* Lafayette Col, BSEE, 32; Lehigh Univ, AM, 37, PhD(math), 39. *Prof Exp:* Instr math, Alborz Col, Iran, 32-36; instr, Univ Ala, 39-41; asst mil attache, Am Embassy, Iran, 42-45; adj prof, 46-51, from assoc prof to prof math, 51-77, EMER PROF MATH, AM UNIV BEIRUT, 77- *Concurrent Pos:* Rockefeller fel, Brown Univ & Inst Advan Study, 49-50, vis prof, 53-54, 57-58, 61-62, 65-66, 69-70 & 73-74; Fulbright lectr, Univ Tehran, 51-52; res prof, Inst Hist Arabic Sci, Univ Aleppo, 78- *Mem:* Am Math Soc; Hist Sci Soc; Am Oriental Soc; Math Asn Am. *Res:* History of Islamic exact sciences. *Mailing Add:* Inst for Hist of Arabic Sci Univ of Aleppo Aleppo Syria

KENNEDY, EDWIN RUSSELL, b Los Angeles, Calif, Nov 4, 11; m 36; c 5. ENVIRONMENTAL CHEMISTRY. *Educ:* Calif Inst Technol, BS, 33, MS, 34, PhD(chem), 36. *Prof Exp:* Technologist, Shell Oil Co, 36-42; group leader res, 46-48, res coordr, 48-56, sr technologist, Shell Chem Co, 56-62; engr mat res, New York Port Authority, 62-77. *Mem:* Am Chem Soc; Am Inst Aeronaut & Astronaut; Am Ord Asn; Nat Asn Corrosion Eng. *Res:* Air pollution; corrosion; protective coatings; petrochemicals; rocket propellants; metallurgy; petroleum technology. *Mailing Add:* 240 Forest Ave Rye NY 10580

KENNEDY, ELDREDGE JOHNSON, b Fayetteville, Tenn, Sept 19, 35; m 61; c 3. SOLID STATE ELECTRONICS, ELECTRICAL ENGINEERING. *Educ:* Univ Tenn, BS, 58, MS, 59, PhD(eng sci), 67. *Prof Exp:* Coop student, Arnold Eng Develop Ctr, ARO Inc, Tenn, 53-57; asst elec eng, Univ Tenn, 58-59, instr, 59-63, res engr, Exp Sta, 60-63; design engr, Instrumentation & Controls Div, Oak Ridge Nat Lab, 63-70; assoc prof, 69-75, PROF ELEC ENG, UNIV TENN, KNOXVILLE, 75- *Concurrent Pos:* Ford Found assoc prof, 68-69; consult, Oak Ridge Nat Lab, 70- *Mem:* Inst Elec & Electronics Engrs; Sigma Xi; Int Soc Hybrid Microelectronics. *Res:* Electronic solid state circuit design; low-current meaurements; hybrid thick-film integrated circuits; high-speed pulse amplifiers, low-noise electronics. *Mailing Add:* Dept of Elec Eng Ferris Hall Univ of Tenn Knoxville TN 37916

KENNEDY, ELHART JAMES, b Lincoln, Nebr, Feb 15, 23; m 48; c 2. AGRICULTURAL MICROBIOLOGY, BOTANY. *Educ:* Colo Agr & Mech Col, BS, 50; Cornell Univ, PhD(veg crops), 53. *Prof Exp:* Dir res agr, Spud Chips, Inc, Colo, 53-59; chmn div sci & math, 68-81, PROF BIOL, N PARK COL, 59-, DIR CONTINUING EDUC, 81- *Concurrent Pos:* Mem prod & tech div, Nat Potato Chip Inst, chmn potato div, 55-57; agr consult, Envirodyne, Inc, 74- *Mem:* AAAS; Am Sci Affiliation; Am Soc Microbiol; Am Inst Biol Sci. *Res:* Physiology of the potato, including tuberization, pathology and irradiation effects of clostridium botulinum; microbiology of surface waters. *Mailing Add:* Dept of Biol NPark Col 5125 N Spaulding Ave Chicago IL 60625

KENNEDY, EUGENE P, b Chicago, Ill, Sept 4, 19; m; c 3. BIOCHEMISTRY. *Educ:* Univ Chicago, PhD(biochem), 49. *Hon Degrees:* MA, Harvard Univ, 60; DSc, Univ Chicago, 77. *Prof Exp:* From asst prof to prof, Dept Biochem & Ben May Lab, Univ Chicago, 51-60; HAMILTON KUHN PROF BIOL HARVARD MED SCH, 60- *Concurrent Pos:* Am Cancer Soc fel, Univ Calif, 49-50; Am Chem Soc res award, 55; NSF fel, 59-60. *Honors & Awards:* Paul Lewis Award, Am Chem Soc, 58; Lipid Res Award, Am Oil Chem Soc, 70; Gairdner Found Award, 76. *Mem:* Nat Acad Sci; Am Acad Arts & Sci; Am Chem Soc; Am Soc Biol Chemists (pres, 70-71). *Res:* Metabolism and function of lipids; membrane function. *Mailing Add:* Dept of Biol Chem Harvard Med Sch Boston MA 02115

KENNEDY, EUGENE RICHARD, b Scranton, Pa, July 3, 19; m 45; c 3. BACTERIOLOGY. *Educ:* Univ Scranton, BS, 41; Cath Univ Am, MS, 43; Brown Univ, PhD, 49; Am Bd Med Microbiol, dipl, 64. *Prof Exp:* Asst bact, Cath Univ Am, 41-43; instr, Brown Univ, 46-48; from instr to assoc prof, 49-66, PROF BACT & IMMUNOL, CATH UNIV AM, 66-, DEAN SCH ARTS & SCI, 73- *Concurrent Pos:* Serologist, US Army Med Ctr, DC, 42; instr, RI Hosp, 46-48; bacteriologist, US Food & Drug Admin, 49; consult bacteriologist, Providence Hosp, DC, 54-58, staff microbiologist, 58-77, consult microbiologist, 81- *Mem:* AAAS; Am Soc Microbiol; Sigma Xi. *Res:* Vi antigen; quantitative dye adsorption; quantitative gram reaction; staphylococcus autogenous vaccine; in vivo and in vitro staphylococci. *Mailing Add:* Sch Arts & Sci Cath Univ of Am Washington DC 20064

KENNEDY, FLYNT, b Chillicothe, Tex, May 25, 31; m 57; c 1. ORGANIC CHEMISTRY. *Educ:* Tex Christian Univ, BA, 52; Rice Univ, PhD(org chem), 56. *Prof Exp:* Res Corp fel, Calif Inst Technol, 56-57; res chemist, 57-60, sr res chemist, 60-61, res group leader, 61-64, supv res scientist, 64-69, MGR, CHEM RES DIV, CONTINENTAL OIL CO, 69- *Mem:* Am Chem Soc. *Res:* Investigation of reactions of organometallic compounds; synthesis of three and four membered compounds; upgrading of hydrocarbons; chemicals from coal, polyvinyl chloride and polyalejins. *Mailing Add:* 1605 Holbrook Ponca City OK 74601

KENNEDY, FRANK METLER, b Woodstock, Ont, Dec 6, 16; nat US; m 42; c 4. CHEMISTRY. *Educ:* Univ Toronto, BA, 41; Columbia Univ, dipl, 57. *Prof Exp:* Chemist, Res Lab, Mining & Smelting Div, Int Nickel Co Can, Ltd, 41-42, chemist platinum metals, Nickel Refining Div, 42-45; res engr, Zinc Smelting Div, St Joseph Lead Co, Pa, 46, asst dir res, 46-60, mgt engr, 60-65; ECONOMIST, TENN VALLEY AUTHORITY, 67- *Mem:* Am Chem Soc; Am Inst Chem Engrs; NY Acad Sci. *Res:* Relationships among fertilizer use, agricultural production, food and population; sulfur dioxide recovery. *Mailing Add:* Div of Chem Develop Tenn Valley Authority Muscle Shoals AL 35660

KENNEDY, FREDERICK JAMES, b Lowell, Mass, Mar 20, 37; m 67; c 3. THEORETICAL PHYSICS. *Educ:* Lowell Tech Inst, BS, 60; Univ Del, MS, 65, PhD(physics), 67. *Prof Exp:* Asst prof physics, Univ Bridgeport, 67-68; fel, Theoret Physics Inst, Univ Alta, 68-73; SCI LIBRN, MACDONALD SCI LIBR, DALHOUSIE UNIV, 73- *Res:* Classical mechanics and electrodynamics. *Mailing Add:* Macdonald Sci Libr Dalhousie Univ Halifax NS B3H 3J5 Can

KENNEDY, GEORGE ARLIE, b Chicago, Ill, Jan 11, 40; m 72. VETERINARY PATHOLOGY. *Educ:* Univ NMex, BS, 62; Wast State Univ, DVM, 67; Kans State Univ, PhD(path), 75. *Prof Exp:* Res pathologist, US Army Med Res & Nutrit Lab, 67-70; instr vet path, Dept Path, Col Vet Med, 70-75, ASST PROF, VET DIAG LAB, KANS STATE UNIV, 72- *Concurrent Pos:* Clinician, Kans State Univ Vet Teaching Hosp, 70-72. *Mem:* Am Vet Med Asn; Am Col Vet Path; Comp Gastroenterol Soc; Sigma Xi. *Res:* Transmission and scanning electron microscipic study of swine enteric diseases, particularly swine dysentery and diseases of the large intestine. *Mailing Add:* Vet Diag Lab Vet Med Ctr Kans State Univ Manhattan KS 66506

KENNEDY, GEORGE CLAYTON, b Dillon, Mont, Sept 22, 19; m 51; c 3. GEOPHYSICS. *Educ:* Harvard Univ, BA, 40, MA, 41, PhD(geol), 46. *Prof Exp:* Geologist, Alaskan Br, US Geol Surv, 42-45; physicist, US Naval Res Lab, 45; jr fel, Harvard Univ, 46-49, asst prof geol, 49-53; prof geol, Univ Calif, Los Angeles, 53-75, prof geol & geochem, 69-80. *Mem:* Fel Mineral Soc Am; fel Geol Soc Am; Soc Econ Geol; Am Acad Arts & Sci. *Res:* Volcanology; solubility in gas phase; melting relations in silicate systems; physics of high pressures. *Mailing Add:* 949 W Adams Blvd Los Angeles CA 90007

KENNEDY, GEORGE GRADY, b Amityville, NY, Mar 23, 48; m 73; c 2. ECONOMIC ENTOMOLOGY. *Educ:* Ore State Univ, BS, 70; Cornell Univ, PhD(entom), 74. *Prof Exp:* Asst prof entom, Univ Calif, Riverside, 74-75; asst prof, 76-79, ASSOC PROF ENTOM, NC STATE UNIV, 79- *Mem:* Entom Soc Am; Am Inst Biol Sci. *Res:* Pest management; host-plant resistance to insects; aphid biology. *Mailing Add:* Dept of Entom NC State Univ Raleigh NC 27607

KENNEDY, GEORGE HUNT, b Seattle, Wash, Apr 24, 36; m 61; c 2. SURFACE CHEMISTRY. *Educ:* Univ Ore, BS, 59; Ore State Univ, MS, 62, PhD(phys chem), 66. *Prof Exp:* Res chemist, Chevron Res Corp Div, Chevron Oil Co, 61-62; asst prof, 65-71, assoc prof, 71-76, PROF CHEM, COLO SCH MINES, 77-, HEAD DEPT CHEM & GEOCHEM, 76- *Mem:* Am Chem Soc. *Res:* Physical adsorption of gases on solid adsorbents; gas chromatography; sorption of vapors on liquid coated adsorbents. *Mailing Add:* Dept of Chem Colo Sch of Mines Golden CO 80401

KENNEDY, GLENN F, b Harrisburg, Pa, June 16, 20; m 43; c 1. CHEMICAL ENGINEERING. *Educ:* Drexel Inst, BS, 42. *Prof Exp:* From jr engr to supt, Air Reduction Chem Co, 46-53; sect head eng res, Gen Foods Corp, 53-55; dir, Bound Brook Labs, Air Reduction Chem Co, 55-64, mgr tech planning, 64-67, asst to group vpres, 67-71; asst to vpres prod, West Chem Prod, Inc, 71-77; ENGR, BURRY BISCUIT, DIV QUAKER OATS, 77- *Mem:* Am Inst Chem Eng. *Res:* Food products; monomers; polymers; organic chemicals; industrial maintenance products. *Mailing Add:* Burry Biscuit 963 Newark Ave Elizabeth NJ 07207

KENNEDY, HARVEY EDWARD, b Goldsboro, NC, Oct 2, 28; m 51; c 2. MICROBIOLOGY, INFORMATION SCIENCE. *Educ:* Atlantic Christian Col, BA, 48; NC State Univ, MS, 52, PhD(bact), 54. *Prof Exp:* Assoc res bacteriologist, NC Sanatorium Syst, Med Ctr, Univ NC, 54-57, sr res scientist, 57-59; asst prof & res assoc dairy bact, Ohio State Univ, 59-61; dir dairy prod res, Johnson & Johnson, 61-65, dir prod develop, Vetco Div, 65-67; asst dir-dir sci affairs, 67-75, exec dir, 75-79, PRES, BIOSCI INFO SERV, 80- *Concurrent Pos:* USPHS res grants, 54-58 & 59-61; pres, Nat Fedn Abstracting & Indexing Serv, 74-75; exec comt aeronaut bd, Int Coun Sci Unions, 80- *Mem:* AAAS; Am Soc Microbiol; Am Inst Biol Sci; Am Soc Info Sci; Coun Biol Ed (secy, 73-74). *Res:* Information science and communications applied to biological and biomedical research literature; bacterial nutrition and metabolism; virulence of pathogens; antimicrobial agents; pharmaceutical and agricultural product development. *Mailing Add:* BioSciences Info Serv 2100 Arch St Philadelphia PA 19103

KENNEDY, HARVEY ELLIS, JR, b Pearl River, La, Jan 14, 33; m 55; c 2. FOREST SOILS. *Educ:* La State Univ, BS, 63, MF, 64, PhD(forestry, forest soils), 69. *Prof Exp:* RES FORESTER, FOREST SERV, USDA, 66- *Mem:* Soc Am Foresters; Am Soc Agron; Sigma Xi. *Res:* Determine methods to effectively establish plantations of priority southern hardwoods and the effects of various cultural treatments upon soil, water and nutrient availability, plant uptake and nutrient cycling. *Mailing Add:* US Forest Serv PO Box 227 Stoneville MS 38776

KENNEDY, HUBERT COLLINGS, b Pierce, Fla, Mar 6, 31. HISTORY OF SCIENCE. *Educ:* Univ Fla, BS, 52; Univ Mich, MS, 57; St Louis Univ, PhD(math), 61. *Prof Exp:* From asst prof to assoc prof, 61-70, PROF MATH, PROVIDENCE COL, 70- *Concurrent Pos:* Fulbright-Hays res scholar, Univ Turin, 66-67 & Univ Konstanz, 74-75. *Mem:* Math Asn Am; Can Soc Hist & Philos Math. *Res:* History of mathematics; biography of Giuseppe Peano. *Mailing Add:* Dept of Math Providence Col Providence RI 02918

KENNEDY, J(OHN), R(OBERT), b Frederick, Md, Mar 25, 25; m 45; c 4. ENGINEERING. *Educ:* Purdue Univ, BS, 49. *Prof Exp:* Aeronaut engr, Chem Corps, Ft Detrick, Md, 49-50, physicist, 50-51, biol test engr, 51-55, mech engr, 55-58; gen engr, Nat Animal Disease Ctr, USDA, 58-60, chief, eng & plant mgr, 58-79, supvry gen engr, 60-79; CONSULT ENGR, 79- *Mem:* Am Inst Plant Engrs. *Res:* Maintenance engineering; design of laboratory facilities. *Mailing Add:* 510 Nicholas St Vincennes IN 47591

KENNEDY, JAMES A, b Rochester, Minn, July 3, 35; m 65. ENZYMOLOGY. *Educ:* Univ Notre Dame, BS, 57; St Louis Univ, MD, 61. *Prof Exp:* NIH fel med, Med Sch, Univ Kans, 63-65; assoc internal med, Col Physicians & Surgeons, Columbia Univ, 68-71, asst prof, 71-73; assoc prof, 73-81, PROF MED, UNIV KANS MED CTR, 81- *Concurrent Pos:* Asst vis physician, Francis Delafield Hosp, NY, 68-73; staff physician, Kansas City Vet Admin Hosp, 73-81, chief med serv, 81- *Mem:* Am Soc Biol Chemists. *Res:* Urea cycle; superoxide; regulation of pyrimidine biosynthesis in mammals; electron transport. *Mailing Add:* Dept of Med Vet Admin Hosp 4801 Linwood Blvd Kansas City MO 64128

KENNEDY, JAMES CECIL, b Toronto, Ont, Mar 14, 35; m 66; c 7. CELL BIOLOGY, IMMUNOLOGY. *Educ:* Univ Toronto, BA, 57, MD, 61, PhD(biophys), 66. *Prof Exp:* Intern, Wellesley Hosp, Toronto, 61; asst prof, 69-73, assoc prof path, 73-77, ASSOC PROF RADIATION ONCOL, QUEEN'S UNIV, ONT, 77- *Concurrent Pos:* Res fel, Nat Cancer Inst Can, 66-68, res scholar, 69-71, res assoc, 72-77; res assoc, Ont Cancer Treat & Res Found, 77- *Honors & Awards:* Starr Medal, Univ Toronto, 66. *Mem:* Am Sci Affil; Can Soc Immunologists; Can Oncology Soc. *Res:* Tumor-host relationships; radiation biology; photoradiation therapy for cancer. *Mailing Add:* Dept of Radiation Oncol Queen's Univ Kingston ON K7L 2V7 Can

KENNEDY, JAMES E(DWARD), b Latrobe, Pa, Nov 24, 35; m 57; c 3. EXPLOSIVES, SHOCKWAVE PHYSICS. *Educ:* Ill Inst Technol, BS, 57, MS, 60, PhD(chem eng), 70. *Prof Exp:* Res engr explosives, IIT Res Inst, Ill, 59-68; tech staff mem, 68-80, SUPERVISOR, DETONATING COMPONENTS DIV, SANDIA NAT LABS, 80- *Mem:* Combustion Inst. *Res:* Initiation of detonation in solid explosives by shock waves; output from explosives; explosive devices. *Mailing Add:* Sandia Nat Labs Div 2513 PO Box 5800 Albuquerque NM 87185

KENNEDY, JAMES M, b Ottawa, Ont, Apr 25, 28; m 50. COMPUTER SCIENCE, ADMINISTRATION. *Educ:* Univ Toronto, BA, 49, MA, 50; Princeton Univ, PhD(physics), 53. *Prof Exp:* Res officer, Theoret Physics Br, Atomic Energy Can Ltd, 52-66, supvr, Comput Ctr, 56-66; dir, Comput Ctr, 66-80, VPRES, UNIV BC, 80- *Mem:* Can Math Soc; Can Info Processing Soc (pres, 71-72); Can Asn Physicists. *Res:* Numerical and non-numerical computer methods. *Mailing Add:* Vpres Univ Serv Pres Off #107 6328 Mem Rd Vancouver BC V6T 2B3 Can

KENNEDY, JAMES VERN, b Jessup, Pa, May 4, 34; m 62; c 2. CHEMISTRY, RESEARCH ADMINISTRATION. *Educ:* Pa State Univ, BS, 55; Univ Pittsburgh, PhD(chem), 72. *Prof Exp:* Res assoc phys chem, Mellon Inst, 55-63; technologist, Baroid Div, Nat Lead Co, 63-69, sect leader catalysis res, 70, supvr catalysis labs, 70-71, tech mgr mineral synthesis dept, NL Industs, Inc, 71-73, catalyst prod mgr, Baroid Div, 72-73; group leader petrol prod res, Engelhard Minerals & Chem Corp, 73-74, mgr prod res, Minerals & Chem Div, 74-78, dir res-existing bus, 78, dir res-new bus, 79-80; DIR CATALYSIS RES, CHEMICALS & MINERALS DIV, GULF SCI & TECHNOL CO, 80- *Mem:* Am Chem Soc; fel Am Inst Chem; Catalysis Soc; Clay Minerals Soc. *Res:* Catalysis by layer-lattice silicates; alteration and synthesis of clay minerals; infrared characterization of synthetic clays; applications of minerals; new product development in catalyst, ceramic, industrial and paper products. *Mailing Add:* Gulf Sci & Technol Co Gulf Oil Corp PO Drawer 2038 Pittsburgh PA 15230

KENNEDY, JERRY DEAN, b Oklahoma City, Okla, June 23, 34; m 57; c 2. PHYSICS. *Educ:* Univ Okla, BS, 56; Univ Calif, Berkeley, MA, 59; Lehigh Univ, PhD(physics), 63. *Prof Exp:* Adv study scientist, Lockheed Missile & Space Co, 56-59; engr, Autonetics Div, NAm Aviation, Inc, 59; mem tech staff physics, 63-69, supvr test exp div, 69-71, supvr exp planning div, 71-73, MGR ENG SCI DEPT, SANDIA LABS, 73- *Mem:* Am Phys Soc. *Res:* Dynamic high pressure solid state physics in semiconductors; shock wave phenomena in solids. *Mailing Add:* Labs Orgn 1730 Sandia Labs PO Box 5800 Albuquerque NM 87115

KENNEDY, JESSE WARD, b Amherst, Mass, Dec 24, 33; c 3. MEDICINE, CARDIOLOGY. *Educ:* Bowdoin Col, AB, 55; Univ Rochester, MD, 59. *Prof Exp:* Intern mixed med, Univ Wash, 59-60, asst resident med, 60-62; sr surgeon, USPHS, Peace Corps, India, 62-63, chief outpatient clin, USPHS Hosp, New Orleans, 63-64; from instr to assoc prof, 66-76, PROF MED, UNIV WASH, 76-; CHIEF CARDIOL, VET ADMIN HOSP, 67- *Concurrent Pos:* Sr fel cardiol, Univ Wash, 64-66. *Mem:* Am Fedn Clin Res; Am Heart Asn. *Res:* Angiocardiography for the measurement of left ventricular volumes and left ventricular mass. *Mailing Add:* Dept Med Univ Wash Sch Med Seattle WA 98195

KENNEDY, JOHN B, b Baghdad, Iraq, Jan 7, 32; m 57; c 3. ENGINEERING MECHANICS. *Educ:* Univ Wales, BSc, 55; Univ Toronto, PhD(civil eng), 61. *Prof Exp:* Asst engr, Develop Bd Iraq, 55-57; res asst skewed bridges, Univ Toronto, 57-61; asst prof civil eng, Univ Sask, 61-63; assoc prof, 63-66, PROF CIVIL ENG & HEAD DEPT, UNIV WINDSOR, 66- *Mem:* Am Soc Civil Engrs; Am Concrete Inst; Am Soc Eng Educ; Eng Inst Can. *Res:* Structural mechanics; large and small deflection of skewed slab structures; cylindrical shells of sandwich construction; analysis of transmission towers; stresses around holes in angles. *Mailing Add:* Dept of Civil Eng Univ of Windsor Windsor ON N9B 3P4 Can

KENNEDY, JOHN EDWARD, b Kemptville, Ont, Sept 12, 16; m 41; c 3. PHYSICS, ASTRONOMY. *Educ:* Queen's Univ, Ont, BA, 37; McGill Univ, MSc, 42. *Prof Exp:* Jr res physicist, Physics Div, Nat Res Coun Can, 41-45; from asst prof to prof physics, Univ NB, 45-56; sci serv officer, Defence Res Med Labs, Defence Res Bd, 56-65, head physics group, 61-65; assoc prof, 65-69, asst head dept, 66-67, asst dean, Col Arts & Sci, 67-81, PROF PHYSICS, UNIV SASK, 69- *Concurrent Pos:* Consult physicist, NB Dept Health, 50-52; mem, Comn 41, Hist of Astron, Comn 46, Teaching Astron, Int Astron Union, 70-; Can Coun leave fel, 73-74. *Honors & Awards:* Centennial Medal, 68; Can Silver Jubilee Medal, 78; Serv Award, Royal Astron Soc Can. *Mem:* Royal Astron Soc Can (nat secy, 58-64, 2nd vpres, 64-66, 1st vpres, 66-68, pres, 68-70); Can Astron Soc; Fel Royal Astron Soc. *Res:* Spectroscopy; stellar physics; physics of clothing and footwear; history of early Canadian astronomy; history of early interest in solar-terrestrial interactions. *Mailing Add:* 323 Lake Crescent Saskatoon SK S7H 3A1 Can

KENNEDY, JOHN ELMO, JR, b Louisville, Ky, June 21, 32; div; c 4. ORGANIC CHEMISTRY, BIOLOGICAL CHEMISTRY. *Educ:* Univ Louisville, BS, 59, PhD(org chem), 63. *Prof Exp:* Lab technician anal chem, Schenley Distillers, Inc, 55-56; chemist, Ky Color & Chem Co, 56-59; chemist, Dept Exp Med, Sch Med, Univ Louisville, 59-61; res chemist, 63-64, group leader org chem, 64-67, sr group leader biol chem, 67-70, res area supvr, Brown & Williamson Tobacco Corp, 70-76; instr org chem, Univ Louisville, 76-77; PRIVATE CONSULT, 77- *Mem:* AAAS; fel Am Inst Chem; NY Acad Sci; Am Chem Soc; Phytochem Soc NAm. *Res:* Biological chemistry; pharmacology; natural products; synthesis; steroids; alkaloids; alicyclics; biosynthetic routes; reaction mechanisms; psychopharmacology; information science; science writing. *Mailing Add:* 3201 Leith Lane #803 Louisville KY 40218

KENNEDY, JOHN FISHER, b Farmington, NMex, Dec 17, 33; m 59; c 4. CIVIL ENGINEERING, FLUID MECHANICS. *Educ:* Univ Notre Dame, BS, 55; Calif Inst Technol, S, 56, PhD(hydraul, fluid mech), 60. *Prof Exp:* Res fel civil eng, Calif Inst Technol, 60-61; asst prof hydraul, Mass Inst Technol, 61-64, assoc prof, civil eng, 64-66; chmn dept, 74-76, prof, 66-81, CARVER DISTINGUISHED PROF, UNIV IOWA, 81-, DIR INST HYDRAUL RES, 66- *Concurrent Pos:* Consult engr, 61-; mem, Corps Engrs, Hydraulic Consult Bd. *Honors & Awards:* J C Stevens Award, Am Soc Civil Engrs, 62, W L Huber Award, 65; Hilgard Prize, 74 & 78. *Mem:* Nat Acad Eng; Am Soc Mech Engrs; Am Soc Eng Educ; Am Soc Civil Engrs; Int Asn Hydraul Res (pres, 80). *Res:* Flow in alluvial channels, including sediment transport, channel roughness and the mechanics of ripples and dunes; turbulence, especially turbulent wakes; waterhammer in centrifugal pump systems; ice processes in rivers and oceans; thermal pollution of rivers; cooling towers. *Mailing Add:* Inst of Hydraul Res Univ of Iowa Iowa City IA 52242

KENNEDY, JOHN HARVEY, b Oak Park, Ill, Apr 24, 33; m 56, 70; c 5. ELECTROCHEMISTRY, ANALYTICAL CHEMISTRY. *Educ:* Univ Calif, Los Angeles, BS, 54; Harvard Univ, PhD(anal chem), 57. *Prof Exp:* Res chemist, E I du Pont de Nemours & Co, Del, 57-61; asst prof, Univ Calif, Santa Barbara, 61-63; assoc prof, Boston Col, 63-64; head inorg chem, Gen Motors Defense Res Labs, 64-67; asst prof, 67-71, assoc prof, 71-76, PROF CHEM, UNIV CALIF, SANTA BARBARA, 76- *Concurrent Pos:* Tech adv, Bissett-Berman Corp, 67-71. *Mem:* Am Chem Soc; Electrochem Soc. *Res:* Solid electrolytes; fused salts; electrochemistry; instrumental methods of analysis. *Mailing Add:* Dept of Chem Univ of Calif Santa Barbara CA 93106

KENNEDY, JOHN HINES, b Washington, DC, Nov 1, 25; m 47, 72; c 8. THORACIC SURGERY, CARDIOVASCULAR SURGERY. *Educ:* Harvard Med Sch, MD, 49; Am Bd Surg, dipl, 57; Am Bd Thoracic Surg, dipl, 60. *Prof Exp:* Intern, Mass Gen Hosp, 49-50, asst resident, 50-51 & 53-54, resident, 54-55; sr registr thoracic unit, Frenchay Hosp, Bristol, Eng, 59-60; asst prof thoracic surg, Sch Med, Case Western Reserve Univ, 62-69; prof surg, Baylor Col Med, 69-76, dir Taub Labs Mech Circulatory Support, 70-76, mem, Admis Comt, 71-76; adj prof, Biomed Eng, Rice Univ, 75-76; fac mem, Dept Macro Molecular Sci, Case Western Reserve Univ, 76-77; CONSULT SURGEON, MED SCH, MIDDLESEX HOSP, WEMBLEY HOSP, LONDON, 78- *Concurrent Pos:* USPHS grant, Baylor Col Med, 69-72; clin asst, Bristol Royal Infirm, Bristol Univ, 59-60; dir, Div Thoracic Surg, Cleveland Metrop Gen Hosp, 62-69; res assoc, Eng Design Ctr, Case Western Reserve Univ, 66-69; dir, Circulatory Assistance Proj Group, Artificial Heart-Myocardial Infarction Prog, NIH contract, Case Western Reserve Univ, 67-69 & Baylor Med Col, 69-71; mem, Tech Adv Group, Artificial Heart-Myocardial Infarction Prog, Nat Heart & Lung Inst, 68, consult site visitor prog proj grants, 70-, prin investr grant, 70-; mem, Coun Cardiovasc Surg, Am Heart Asn, 68-70; adj prof, Rice Univ, 69-75; vis prof, Dept Macromolecular Sci, Case Western Reserve Univ, 75-76; consult, President's Panel Biomed Res, 75-; med dir, Moat House Hosp, London, 80- *Mem:* Am Asn Thoracic Surg; Soc Thoracic Surgeons; Western Surg Asn; fel Am Col Surg; Royal Soc Med. *Mailing Add:* 152 Harley St London England

KENNEDY, JOHN ROBERT, JR, b Cleveland, Ohio, July 17, 37; m 60; c 2. CYTOLOGY. *Educ:* Univ Mich, BS, 59, MS, 61; Univ Iowa, PhD(zool), 64. *Prof Exp:* From instr to asst prof anat, Bowman Gray Sch Med, 64-69; assoc prof, 69-77, PROF ZOOL, UNIV TENN, KNOXVILLE, 77- *Mem:* Soc Protozool; Am Soc Cell Biol; Electron Micros Soc Am; Am Asn Anatomists. *Res:* Cytology and cytodifferentiation in protozoa; effect of various physiological factors on tracheal tell fine structure; ciliary cell physiology and effects of respiratory on ciliary ultrastructure & function. *Mailing Add:* Dept of Zool Univ of Tenn Knoxville TN 37916

KENNEDY, JOSEPH PATRICK, b Houston, Tex, Mar 9, 32. ANATOMY, ECOLOGY. *Educ:* Univ St Thomas, Tex, BA, 54; Univ Tex, MA, 55, PhD(zool), 58. *Prof Exp:* Chmn dept biol, Univ St Thomas, Tex, 58-60; from asst prof to assoc prof, 60-68, prof animal ecol & chmn dept, Grad Sch Biomed Sci, 69-77, prof anat, Univ Tex Health Sci Ctr at Houston Med Sch, 76-77, PROF ANAT, UNIV TEX DENT BR, HOUSTON, 68- *Concurrent Pos:* Vis prof, Mt Lake Biol Sta, Univ Va, 62, Terra Alta Biol Sta, WVa Univ, 68; lectr, Univ Tex, Houston, 63; ed, J Herpet, 68-79; chmn, Adv Comt, Univ Tex Environ Sci Park, 69-71, dir, 71-76; prof ecol, M D Anderson Hosp & Tumor Inst, 69-76; mem exec comt & bd trustees, Armand Bayou Nature Ctr, Inc, 74-77. *Mem:* Fel AAAS; Am Soc Ichthyol & Herpet; Soc Study Amphibians & Reptiles; Brit Herpet Soc; fel Herpetologists' League. *Res:* Ecology, evolution and behavior. *Mailing Add:* Dept of Anat Dental Br PO Box 20068 Houston TX 77025

KENNEDY, JOSEPH PAUL, b Budapest, Hungary, May 18, 28; US citizen; m 57; c 3. POLYMER CHEMISTRY. *Educ:* Univ Vienna, PhD(chem), 55; Rutgers Univ, MBA, 61. *Prof Exp:* Fel biochem, Sorbonne, 55-56; res assoc, McGill Univ, 56-57; res chemist, Celanese Corp Am, 57-59; res chemist, Easso Res & Eng Co, 59-62, sr res chemist, 62-65, res assoc, 65-69, sr res assoc, 69-70; DISTINGUISHED PROF POLYMER SCI & CHEM, UNIV AKRON & RES ASSOC INST POLYMER SCI, 70- *Mem:* Am Chem Soc. *Res:* Cationic polymerizations; carbenium ion chemistry; polymer synthesis; polymerization mechanisms; elastomer chemistry, particularly butyl rubber and polyisobutylene; blocks and grafts; terminally functional liquids; derivatization of polymers. *Mailing Add:* Inst of Polymer Sci Univ of Akron Akron OH 44325

KENNEDY, KATHERINE ASH, b Bryn Mawr, Pa, Mar 24, 50. TOXICOLOGY, CANCER CHEMOTHERAPY. *Educ:* Vanderbilt Univ, BA, 73; Univ Iowa, PhD(pharmacol), 77. *Prof Exp:* Fel, Sch Med, Yale Univ, 78-81; ASST PROF PHARMACOL, SCH MED, GEORGE WASHINGTON UNIV, 81- *Mem:* AAAS; Am Asn Cancer Res. *Res:* Role of biotransformation for drug activity and toxicity; mechanisms for antitumor agents in normally aerated and hypozic cells; mechanisms of drug induced cytotoxicity. *Mailing Add:* Dept Pharmacol Sch Med George Washington Univ 2300 Eye St NW Washington DC 20037

KENNEDY, KENNETH ADRIAN RAINE, b Oakland, Calif, June 26, 30; m 61, 69. PHYSICAL ANTHROPOLOGY, ARCHAEOLOGY. *Educ:* Univ Calif, Berkeley, BA, 53, MA, 54, PhD(anthrop), 62. *Prof Exp:* Actg instr phys anthrop, Univ Calif, Berkeley, 62-63; vis prof, Deccan Col Post-Grad & Res Inst, 63-64; asst prof anthrop, 64-68, assoc prof, 68-81, assoc prof div biol sci, 69-81, PROF ECOL DIV BIOL SCI, ANTHROPOLOGY & ASIAN STUDIES, CORNELL UNIV, 81- *Concurrent Pos:* NSF fels, Deccan Col Post-Grad & Res Inst, Univ Poona, India, 63-64 & 71, 80-81, Univ Calif, Berkeley, 68-69 & Cornell Univ, 72; Cornell Univ fac res grant, Brit Mus Natural Hist, London, 65-66; vis prof, Univ Ariz, 79. *Mem:* AAAS; fel Am Anthrop Asn; Am Asn Phys Anthrop; fel Royal Anthrop Inst Gt Brit; Int Asn Human Biol. *Res:* Human evolution in South Asia, particularly the hominid osteological fossil record; history of biological sciences, especially human evolution and physical anthropology; palaeodemography of South Asia; forensic anthropology. *Mailing Add:* Dept of Anthrop 225 McGraw Hall Cornell Univ Ithaca NY 14853

KENNEDY, LARRY ZANE, optical physics, see previous edition

KENNEDY, LAWRENCE A, b Detroit, Mich, May 31, 37; m 57; c 6. FLUID MECHANICS, COMBUSTION. *Educ:* Univ Detroit, BS, 60; Northwestern Univ, MS, 62, PhD(mech eng), 64. *Prof Exp:* Res engr, Mech Res & Develop Div, Gen Am Transp Corp, Ill, 63-64; dir aerospace eng, 69-71, PROF MECH ENG, STATE UNIV NY BUFFALO, 64- *Concurrent Pos:* NSF sci fac fel, 68-69, NATO sr fel sci, 71-72; consult, Cornell Aero Labs, 66-71, Adv Group Aerospace Res & Develop, NATO, 71, MGB Res Corp, 76- & Air Preheater Div, Combustion Eng Corp, 78- *Mem:* Combustion Inst; assoc fel Am Inst Aeronaut & Astronaut; Am Phys Soc; Am Soc Mech Engrs. *Res:* High temperature gas dynamics; chemical reacting flow; magnetohydrodynamics and combustion; radiative transfer; combustion generated pollutants. *Mailing Add:* Fac of Eng & Appl Sci State Univ of NY at Buffalo Amherst NY 14260

KENNEDY, LORENE LOUISE, b Edmonton, Alta, Mar 31, 21. BOTANY. *Educ:* Univ Alta, BSc, 41, MSc, 43; Univ Iowa, PhD(bot), 57. *Prof Exp:* From lectr to assoc prof, 46-65, PROF BOT, UNIV ALTA, 65- *Mem:* Bot Soc Am; Mycol Soc Am; Can Bot Asn; Brit Mycol Soc. *Res:* Mycology; developmental, taxonomic and ecological studies of Polyporales. *Mailing Add:* Dept Bot Univ Alta Edmonton AB J6Q 2E8 Can

KENNEDY, LYNN WATSON, b Orange, Calif, Jan 3, 35; m 57; c 2. DATA PROCESSING. *Educ:* Pomona Col, BA, 56; Univ Calif, Berkeley, MA, 58; Lehigh Univ, PhD(physics), 69. *Prof Exp:* Mem tech staff, Lockheed Missile & Space Div, 56-59, Sandia Labs, 66-73; sr data analyst, 73-75, MGR FIELD TEST PROGS, GEN ELEC TEMPO, 75- *Mailing Add:* Gen Elec Tempo 7800 Marble NE 5 Albuquerque NM 87110

KENNEDY, MALDON KEITH, b Little Rock, Ark, July 26, 47. ENTOMOLOGY. *Educ:* Hendrix Col, BA, 69; Cornell Univ, MS, 71, PhD(insect ecol), 76. *Prof Exp:* ASST PROF ENTOM, MICH STATE UNIV, 75- *Mem:* Entom Soc Am; Ecol Soc Am; Acarological Soc Am. *Res:* Biology of the Sciaridae Diptera, especially those of economic importance. *Mailing Add:* Dept of Entom Mich State Univ East Lansing MI 48824

KENNEDY, MARGARET WIENER, b Arlington, Mass, Dec 16, 29; m 64. TOXICOLOGY, ENDOCRINOLOGY. *Educ:* Jackson Col, BS, 50; Boston Univ, MA, 54; Albany Med Col, PhD(toxicol), 72. *Prof Exp:* Res asst biochem, Schering Corp, 54-57; res asst endocrinol, Children's Mem Hosp, Chicago, 57-58; res assoc, Dept Obstet & Gyncol, Univ Chicago Clin, 59-63; res asst prof, Dept Obstet & Gyncol, Albany Med Col, 63-68, res asst prof toxicol, Inst Exp Path & Toxicol, 68-76; res scientist toxicol, Health Res Inc, NY State Dept Health, 77-80. *Concurrent Pos:* Res assoc, NIH res grant, 64-67 & 72-76, prin investr, 72-75; prin investr, USAEC contract, 67-70. *Mem:* Endocrine Soc. *Res:* Invitro metabolism of individual polychlorinated biphenyls; control of placental hormone synthesis. *Mailing Add:* 7 N Lyons Ave Menands NY 12204

KENNEDY, MAURICE VENSON, b Pontotoc, Miss, Nov 23, 25; m 48; c 2. BIOCHEMISTRY. *Educ:* Miss State Univ, BS, 49, MS, 54, PhD(biochem), 67. *Prof Exp:* Dir microbiol & chem, Miss Dept Agr Lab, 49-62; instr microbiol, 62-66, ASSOC PROF BIOCHEM, MISS STATE UNIV, 66- *Concurrent Pos:* Consult, NATO Sponsored Symp Pesticides, Lethbridge, Can, 70. *Mem:* AAAS; Am Chem Soc; Am Soc Microbiol. *Res:* Biochemical mechanisms of toxic substances, metabolic pathways in food poisoning microorganisms, production of useful substances from animal waste, and degradation and disposal of waste pesticides. *Mailing Add:* Dept of Biochem PO Box BB Miss State Univ Mississippi State MS 39762

KENNEDY, MICHAEL CRAIG, b Buffalo, NY, Dec 5, 46; m 67; c 3. NEUROBIOLOGY. *Educ:* Rice Univ BA, 68; Univ Rochester, MS, 71, PhD(biol, neurobiol), 74. *Prof Exp:* Fel comp neuroanat, NY Univ Med Ctr, 74-76; asst prof biol, NY Univ, 76-81; ASSOC PROF ANAT, HAHNEMANN MED COL, 81- *Mem:* AAAS; Am Asn Anatomists; Soc Neurosci. *Res:* Investigations of the anatomy and physiology of neural pathways in nonmammalian vertebrates; neural substrates of auditory communication in the Tokay Gecko, Gekko gecko; developmental neurobiology of the reptilian auditory system; the visual system in the sea lamprey, Petromyzon marinus. *Mailing Add:* Dept Anat MS 408 Hahnemann Med Col 230 N Broad St Philadelphia PA 19102

KENNEDY, MICHAEL JOHN, b London, Eng, Jan 21, 40; m 66; c 3. STRUCTURAL GEOLOGY, TECTONICS. *Educ:* Univ Dublin, BS, 63, MA & PhD(struct geol), 66. *Prof Exp:* Nat Res Coun Can fel, Geol Surv Can, 66-67; from asst prof to assoc prof, 67-74, prof geol, Mem Univ Newf, 74-76; prof & chmn, Dept Geol Sci, Brock Univ, 76-80; PROF & HEAD DEPT GEOL, UNIV COL, DUBLIN, 80- *Concurrent Pos:* Co-chmn, Int Geodynamics Working Group 9, Appalachian-Caledonian Group, 72-80. *Honors & Awards:* Young 75- Award, Atlantic Provinces Inter-Univ Comt on the Sciences, 73. *Mem:* Fel Geol Asn Can; fel Geol Soc London; fel Geol Soc Am. *Res:* Structural geology of metamorphic rocks, particularly Caledonian and Appalachian systems; petrofabrics and the relationship of deformation with metamorphism; metamorphic complexes of Appalachians and Caledonides; structural development of south east Ireland. *Mailing Add:* Dept of Geol Univ Col Belfield Dublin 4 Ireland

KENNEDY, MICHAEL LYNN, b Scotts Hill, Tenn, Jan 31, 42. VERTEBRATE ZOOLOGY. *Educ:* Memphis State Univ, BS, 66, MS, 68; Univ Okla, PhD(vert zool), 75. *Prof Exp:* Asst vert zool, Univ Okla, 69-74; asst prof, 74-80, ASSOC PROF BIOL, MEMPHIS STATE UNIV, 80- *Mem:* Am Soc Mammalogists; Soc Syst Zool; Am Ornithologists Union. *Res:* Mammalian systematics; geographic variation studies with small mammals. *Mailing Add:* Dept of Biol Memphis State Univ Memphis TN 38152

KENNEDY, PATRICK JAMES, b Louisville, Ky, Sept 8, 45. METEOROLOGY. *Educ:* Univ Notre Dame, BS, 67; Univ Colo, MS, 70. *Prof Exp:* RES SCIENTIST METEOROL, NAT CTR ATMOSPHERIC RES, 70- *Concurrent Pos:* Sci lectr, Boulder Valley Sch Dist, 70- *Res:* Mesoscale meteorology, including jet stream structure, cyclogenesis, fronts, and windstorms; aircraft observations of weather systems. *Mailing Add:* Nat Ctr Atmospheric Res Boulder CO 80307

KENNEDY, PETER CARLETON, b Berkeley, Calif, June 19, 23; m 46; c 4. VETERINARY PATHOLOGY. *Educ:* Kans State Univ, DVM, 49; Cornell Univ, PhD(vet path), 54. *Prof Exp:* Intern, Angell Mem Animal Hosp, Mass, 50; asst large animal surg, Cornell Univ, 51, asst path, 52-53; from lectr to assoc prof, 54-65, PROF VET PATH, UNIV CALIF, DAVIS, 65-, LECTR PATH, MED SCH, 57-, PATHOLOGIST, EXP STA, 70- *Mem:* Am Col Vet Path. *Res:* Pathology of infectious diseases and endocrinopathies of domestic animals. *Mailing Add:* Sch of Vet Med Univ of Calif Davis CA 95616

KENNEDY, RICHARD J, b Norristown, Pa, Aug 19, 31; m 52; c 3. ORGANIC CHEMISTRY. *Educ:* Ursinus Col, BS, 53; Purdue Univ, MS, 56, PhD(chem), 58. *Prof Exp:* Asst, Valley Forge Heart Res Inst, 52-53; res chemist, Electrochem Div, Res Dept, E I du Pont de Nemours & Co, 58-67; dir prod develop, Hilton-Davis Chem Co Div, Sterling Drug Co, 67-81; SR CHEMIST, FUNDIMENSIONS, DIV GEN MILLS, 81- *Mem:* Am Chem Soc; Soc Plastic Engrs. *Res:* Synthesis of organic fluorinated acids and esters; reformatsky and related organometallic syntheses; free radical additions to olefins; adhesives; coatings. *Mailing Add:* 51041 W Village St #202 New Baltimore MI 48047

KENNEDY, ROBERT ALAN, b Benson, Minn, Sept 29, 46; m 68. PLANT PHYSIOLOGY. *Educ:* Univ Minn, BS, 68; Univ Calif, PhD(bot), 74. *Prof Exp:* Asst prof bot, Univ Iowa, 74-80; MEM FAC, HORT DEPT, WASHINGTON STATE UNIV, 80- *Concurrent Pos:* Sigma Xi res grant, 74; NSF grant, 75. *Mem:* AAAS; Am Soc Plant Physiologists; Bot Soc Am; Sigma Xi. *Res:* Physiology of plants with the C4 pathway of photosynthesis, particularly the effects of anatomy, age and waterstress on operation of the C4 pathway. *Mailing Add:* Hort Dept Washington State Univ Pullman WA 99163

KENNEDY, ROBERT E, b Santa Monica, Calif, June 5, 39; m 61; c 3. THEORETICAL PHYSICS, PHYSICAL OCEANOGRAPHY. *Educ:* Loyola Univ, BS, 61; Univ Notre Dame, PhD(physics), 66. *Prof Exp:* Res asst, Univ Notre Dame, 63-66; asst prof, 66-72, ASSOC PROF PHYSICS & CHMN DEPT, CREIGHTON UNIV, 73- *Mem:* Am Inst Physics; Am Phys Soc; Am Asn Physics Teachers; Nat Oceanog Asn. *Res:* Theoretical investigation of physical oceanography, especially the problem of Arctic ice formation and methods to modify it. *Mailing Add:* Dept of Physics Creighton Univ 2500 California St Omaha NE 68178

KENNEDY, ROBERT KENNETH, b Webster, SDak, Sept 7, 42; m 64; c 2. PLANT ECOLOGY. *Educ:* SDak State Univ, BS, 67; Iowa State Univ, MS, 69; Univ Okla, PhD(ecol), 73. *Prof Exp:* Consult ecologist, Sargent & Lundy, 73-76; consult ecologist, Tex Instruments Inc, 76-77, mgr land & human resources, Ecol Serv, 77-78, mgr utility serv, Ecol Serv, 78-79, western region mgr, Ecol Serv, 79-81; MGR, DENVER REGIONAL CTR, NORMANDEAU ASSOCS INC, 81- *Mem:* Ecol Soc Am; Sigma Xi. *Res:* Grassland dynamics; phytosociology; remote sensing. *Mailing Add:* 7246 S Newport Way Englewood CO 80112

KENNEDY, ROBERT MICHAEL, b Scranton, Pa, July 6, 15; m 42; c 3. ORGANIC CHEMISTRY. *Educ:* Univ Scranton, BS, 37; Pa State Col, MS, 38, PhD(phys chem), 41. *Prof Exp:* Res chemist, 41-53, mgr basic res div, 53-56, assoc dir res & develop div, 56-59, dir, 59-70, DIR APPL RES DEPT, RES & DEVELOP DIV, SUN OIL CO, 70- *Mem:* Indust Res Inst; Am Chem Soc; Am Petrol Inst. *Res:* Catalysts; distillation; alkylation; thermodynamic properties of organic compounds; combustion phenomena. *Mailing Add:* 167 Saddle Dr Furlong PA 18925

KENNEDY, ROBERT SPAYDE, b Augusta, Kans, Dec 9, 33; m 55; c 3. ELECTRICAL ENGINEERING, COMMUNICATIONS. *Educ:* Univ Kans, BS, 55; Mass Inst Technol, SM, 59, ScD(info theory), 63. *Prof Exp:* Nuclear engr, Naval Reactors Br, US Atomic Energy Comn, 55-57; Ford Found grad fel, 59-60; staff mem, Lincoln Lab, 63-64, from asst prof to assoc prof elec eng, 64-76, PROF ELEC ENG, MASS INST TECHNOL, 76- *Concurrent Pos:* Ford fel, Mass Inst Technol, 64-65. *Mem:* Inst Elec & Electronics Engrs; Optical Soc Am. *Res:* Application of statistical concepts to the problem of extracting information from a corrupted received replica of a transmitted message. *Mailing Add:* Dept of Elec Eng Mass Inst of Technol Cambridge MA 02139

KENNEDY, ROBERT WILLIAM, b Syracuse, NY, Sept 13, 31; m 56; c 3. WOOD SCIENCE, TECHNOLOGY. *Educ:* State Univ NY, BS, 53; Univ BC, MF, 55; Yale Univ, PhD(wood tech), 62. *Prof Exp:* Instr wood tech, Univ BC, 55-56 & 57-61; from asst prof to assoc prof, Univ Toronto, 62-66; head wood biol sect, Western Forest Prod Lab, 66-69, prog mgr, Protection & Prod Div, 69-71, from assoc dir to dir, 71-79, PROF WOOD SCI & INDUST, UNIV BC, 79- *Concurrent Pos:* Consult, Forestry & Forest Prod Div, Food & Agr Orgn, UN, 64. *Mem:* Forest Prod Res Soc; fel Int Acad Wood Sci; Soc Wood Sci & Technol; Can Inst Forestry. *Res:* Physiology of wood formation; wood structure and properties at micro level; wood utilization. *Mailing Add:* Fac Forestry Univ BC Vancouver BC V6T 1W5 Can

KENNEDY, ROBERT WILSON, b Tampa, Fla, Sept 9, 27; m 49; c 1. ORGANIC CHEMISTRY. *Educ:* Emory Univ, AB, 53, MS, 54, PhD(chem), 56. *Prof Exp:* Develop res chemist, 56-58, sr chemist, 59-72, dept supt, Intermediates Dept, 72-73, asst div supt, Polymers Div, 73-74, asst to the works mgr, 74, proj mgr, New Prod Div, 74-79, PROJ MGR, ORG CHEM DIV, TENN EASTMAN CO, 79- *Mem:* Am Chem Soc; Sigma Xi. *Res:* Developmental research in industrial organic chemistry; mechanisms of organic reactions; naturally occurring organic compounds, particularly pine resin acids; new products marketing aspects; new products development. *Mailing Add:* Tenn Eastman Co Kingsport TN 37662

KENNEDY, RUSSELL JORDAN, b Dunrobin, Ont, Nov 23, 17; m 46; c 4. CIVIL ENGINEERING, HYDRAULICS. *Educ:* Queen's Univ, Ont, BSc, 41; Univ Iowa, MS, 49. *Prof Exp:* Lectr, 46-48, from asst prof to assoc prof, 49-59, assoc dean sch grad studies, 68-70, vprin admin, 70-76, PROF CIVIL ENG, QUEEN'S UNIV, ONT, 59-, CHMN, DONALD GORDON CTR CONTINUING EDUC, 79- *Concurrent Pos:* Consult, Ont Paper Co, 48-51, Pulp & Paper Res Inst Can, 51-64, Dept Energy, Mines & Resources, 68-71, Irving Pulp & Paper Ltd, St John, NB, 79- & North West Hydraul Consults, Vancouver, BC, 79- *Honors & Awards:* Angus Medal, Eng Inst Can, 58. *Mem:* Eng Inst Can; Int Asn Hydraul Res. *Res:* Ice control; improvement of design criteria for air bubbler systems. *Mailing Add:* Ellis Hall Queen's Univ Kingston ON K7L 3N6 Can

KENNEDY, SUZANNE, b Nashville, Tenn, May 21, 53. VETERINARY MEDICINE. *Educ:* Mich State Univ, BS & DVM, 76. *Prof Exp:* Vet intern zoo animal med & surg, Nat Zool Park, Smithsonian Inst, 76-78; ASST PROF, DEPT ENVIRON PRACT & ZOO ANIMAL MED, COL VET MED, UNIV TENN, 78- *Concurrent Pos:* Vet, Knoxville Zool Park, 78- *Mem:* Am Asn Zoo Vet; Am Vet Med Asn. *Res:* Clinically related research as it applies to problems encountered in zoological specimens, particularly with infectious diseases like tuberculosis and aspergillosis. *Mailing Add:* Col of Vet Med Univ of Tenn Knoxville TN 37901

KENNEDY, THELMA TEMY, b Chicago, Ill, Oct 18, 25. NEUROPHYSIOLOGY. *Educ:* Univ Chicago, PhB & BS, 47, MS, 49, PhD(biopsychol), 55. *Prof Exp:* Asst neurosurg, Univ Chicago, 51-56; from instr to assoc prof, 58-72, assoc dean grad sch, 69-72, PROF PHYSIOL, UNIV WASH, 72- *Concurrent Pos:* USPHS fel neurophysiol, Univ Wash, 56-58. *Mem:* AAAS; Psychonomic Soc; Soc Neurosci; Am Physiol Soc. *Res:* Cerebral cortex organization; unit activity; motor systems; sensory physiology. *Mailing Add:* Dept of Physiol & Biophys SJ-40 Univ of Wash Seattle WA 98105

KENNEDY, THOMAS JAMES, JR, b Washington, DC, June 24, 20; m 50; c 5. PHYSIOLOGY, NEPHROLOGY. *Educ:* Cath Univ, BS, 40; Johns Hopkins Univ, MD, 43; Am Bd Internal Med, dipl, 56. *Prof Exp:* Asst med, Col Med, NY Univ, 45-47; asst, Col Physicians & Surgeons, Columbia Univ, 47-50; investr, Lab Kidney & Electrolyte Physiol, Nat Heart Inst, 50-60, mem staff, Off of Dir, NIH, 60-65, chief, Div Res Facil & Resources, 65-68, assoc dir prog planning & eval, 68-74; exec dir, assembly life sci, Nat Acad Sci-Nat Res Coun, 74-76; DIR, DEPT PLANNING & POLICY DEVELOP, ASN AM MED COL, 76- *Concurrent Pos:* Res assoc, Sch Med, George Washington Univ, 51-65. *Mem:* Am Physiol Soc; Am Fedn Clin Res. *Res:* Renal physiology, especially mechanisms for excretion of electrolytes; electrolyte physiology; clinical disorders of renal and electrolyte physiology; administration of research. *Mailing Add:* Asn of Am Med Col 1 Dupont Circle NW Suite 200 Washington DC 20036

KENNEDY, THOMAS WILLIAM, b Danville, Ill, Jan 7, 38; m 61; c 2. CIVIL ENGINEERING. *Educ:* Univ Ill, BS, 60, MS, 62, PhD(civil eng), 65. *Prof Exp:* From asst to instr civil eng, Univ Ill, 62-65; from asst prof to assoc prof, 65-74, dir, Coun Advan Transp Studies, 75-78, asst vpres res, 78-79, PROF CIVIL ENG, UNIV TEX, AUSTIN, 74-, ASSOC DEAN ENG RES PLANNING, 79- *Concurrent Pos:* Hwy Res Bd, Nat Acad Sci-Nat Res Coun, 65- *Mem:* Am Soc Civil Engrs; Am Concrete Inst; Am Soc Testing & Mat. *Res:* Materials; pavements; transportation; civil engineering. *Mailing Add:* Off Dean Eng Rm 10 338 ECJ Univ of Tex Austin TX 78712

KENNEDY, VANCE CLIFFORD, b Big Run, Pa, May 18, 23; m 48; c 4. GEOCHEMISTRY, HYDROLOGY. *Educ:* Pa State Univ, BS, 48, MS, 49; Univ Colo, PhD(geol), 61. *Prof Exp:* Geologist geochem, 49-52 & 55-60, RES GEOLOGIST GEOCHEM & HYDROL, US GEOL SURV, 60- *Mem:* AAAS; Geol Soc Am; Geochem Soc; Clay Minerals Soc. *Res:* Geochemical prospecting; uranium geology and geochemistry; transport of stream sediment; effects of stream sediment on the chemistry of water. *Mailing Add:* US Geol Surv 345 Middlefield Rd Menlo Park CA 94025

KENNEDY, VERNE, engineering, deceased

KENNEDY, W KEITH, JR, b Phoenix, Ariz, Sept 19, 43; m 65; c 2. ELECTRICAL ENGINEERING, SOLID STATE PHYSICS. *Educ:* Cornell Univ, BEE & MS, 65, PhD(elec eng), 68. *Prof Exp:* Mem tech staff, 68-69, mgr, Solid State Res & Develop Sect, 69-80, VPRES DEVICES GROUP, WATKINS-JOHNSON CO, 80- *Mem:* Inst Elec & Electronics Engrs. *Res:* Microwave power generation and amplication with semiconductor devices; microwave integrated circuits; microwave systems. *Mailing Add:* Watkins-Johnson Co 3333 Hillview Ave Palo Alto CA 94304

KENNEDY, WILBERT KEITH, b Vancouver, Wash, Jan 4, 19; m 41; c 2. AGRONOMY. *Educ:* State Col Wash, BS, 40; Cornell Univ, MSA, 41, PhD(agron), 47. *Prof Exp:* Asst, Cornell Univ, 40-42 & 46-47; asst prof & asst agronomist to assoc prof & assoc agronomist, exp sta, State Col, Wash, 47-49; assoc dir, Res & Agr Exp Sta, Col Agr, 59, dir, 59-65, assoc dean col, 65-67, vprovost univ, 67-72, dean col, 72-78, PROF AGRON, NY STATE COL AGR & LIFE SCI, CORNELL UNIV, 49-, PROVOST UNIV, 78- *Concurrent Pos:* Fulbright res scholar & Guggenheim fel, 56-57. *Honors & Awards:* NY Farmers Award, 57; Merit Cert Award, Am Grassland Coun, 64. *Mem:* Fel AAAS; fel Am Soc Agron. *Res:* Chemistry; botany; factors influencing yield and nutritive value of farm crops; grazing management practices and their relationship to the behavior and grazing habits of cattle; measuring, harvesting and storage losses in hay and silage; accumulation of nitrates in forage plants; nitrate toxicity. *Mailing Add:* 300 Day Hall Cornell Univ Ithaca NY 14853

KENNEDY, WILLIAM ALEXANDER, b Merlin, Ont, Can, Sept 28, 15; m 42; c 5. FISH BIOLOGY. *Educ:* Univ Toronto, BA, 37, PhD(ichthyol), 41. *Prof Exp:* Asst, Ont Fish Res Labs, 36-41; from asst scientist to dir, Cent Fish Res Sta, 45-56, dir biol sta, 57-66, res scientist, Fisheries Res Bd Can, Nanaimo Biol Sta, 66-76; CONSULT, 77- *Concurrent Pos:* War res, Nat Res Coun Can, 41-45. *Res:* Fish farming and related fields. *Mailing Add:* 1011 Beach Dr Nanaimo BC V9S 2Y4 Can

KENNEDY, WILLIAM DEMPSEY, physical chemistry, deceased

KENNEDY, WILLIAM ROBERT, b Chicago, Ill, Nov 2, 27; m 57; c 5. NEUROLOGY. *Educ:* Univ Ill, BS, 51; Univ Wis, MS, 52; Marquette Univ, MD, 58. *Prof Exp:* From asst prof to assoc prof, 64-71, PROF NEUROL, MED CTR, UNIV MINN, MINNEAPOLIS, 71- *Concurrent Pos:* Fel internal med, Mayo Clin, 59-60, fel neurol, 60-64. *Mem:* Am Acad Neurol; Am Neurol Asn; Am Electroencephalog Soc; Am Asn Electromyog & Electrodiag (past pres). *Res:* Clinical-pathological-physiological research on neuromuscular disorders; structure and function of human muscle spindles. *Mailing Add:* Box 187 Univ of Minn Hosp Minneapolis MN 55455

KENNEKE, ALBERT PATRICK, b Brooklyn, NY, Dec 13, 34; m 57; c 4. HEALTH PHYSICS. *Educ:* St Joseph's Col, Pa, BS, 56; Univ Rochester, MS, 57; Univ Mich, MPH, 59. *Prof Exp:* Health physicist radiation protection, Univ Mich, 57-58, USPHS trainee, 58-60; res asst med physics, Sloan-Kettering Inst, NY, 61; dep radiation safety officer, Mem Sloan-Kettering Cancer Ctr, New York, 61-62; health physicist, 62-69, site analyst, 69-72, siting tech coordr, 72-75, sr policy analyst, 75-76, ASST DIR TECH POLICY EVAL, NUCLEAR REGULATORY COMN, 76- *Mem:* Health Physics Soc; Am Nuclear Soc. *Res:* Applied health physics; development of radiation protection standards; nuclear power plant siting; nuclear regulatory policy analysis. *Mailing Add:* Nuclear Regulatory Comn 1717 H St NW Washington DC 20555

KENNEL, CHARLES FREDERICK, b Cambridge, Mass, Aug 20, 39; m 64; c 2. PLASMA PHYSICS, SPACE PHYSICS. *Educ:* Harvard Univ, AB, 59; Princeton Univ, PhD(astrophys sci), 64. *Prof Exp:* Asst res scientist, Avco-Everett Res Lab, 60-61; staff mem, 64-65, prin res scientist, 66-67; vis scientist, Int Centre Theoret Physics, Trieste, 65-66; assoc prof, 67-71, PROF PHYSICS, UNIV CALIF, LOS ANGELES, 71-, MEM, INST GEOPHYS & PLANETARY PHYSICS, 72- *Concurrent Pos:* NSF fel, 65-66; consult, TRW Systs Group, Calif, 67-; Alfred P Sloan Found fac fel, 68-70; vis prof, Ctr Phys Theory, Polytech Sch, Paris, 74-75; mem sci adv group, NASA, 71-72; mem physics res eval group, Air Force Off Sci Res, 70-78; mem, Space Sci Bd, Nat Acad Sci-Nat Res Coun, 77-80, chmn, Comt Space Physics, 77-80. *Mem:* Fel Am Geophys Union; fel Am Phys Soc; Int Union Radio Sci; Am Astron Soc. *Res:* Plasma turbulence theory; solar system and astrophysical plasma physics. *Mailing Add:* Dept of Physics Univ of Calif Los Angeles CA 90024

KENNEL, JOHN MAURICE, b Sioux City, Iowa, Oct 7, 27; m 52; c 4. APPLIED PHYSICS. Educ: Miami Univ, AB, 48; Univ Tex, PhD(physics), 55. Prof Exp: Physicist, US Naval Ord Lab, Md, 49-51; res engr, NAm Aviation, Inc, 51-52, res specialist inertial navig, Autonetics Div, 55-58, supvr phys res, 58-60, group leader eng proposals, 60-62, sr scientist, 62-67, res prog mgr, NAm Rockwell Microelectronics Co, 67-70, mgr microelectronic process develop, Products Div, 70-75, MEM TECH STAFF, AUTONETICS DIV, ROCKWELL INT CORP, 75- Mem: AAAS; Am Phys Soc. Res: Inertial navigation and guidance; scientific instruments and measurements; microelectronic processes; liquid crystal displays. Mailing Add: 11591 Surburnas Way Santa Ana CA 92705

KENNEL, STEPHEN JOHN, b Peoria, Ill, Jan 15, 45; m 66; c 3. TUMOR IMMUNOLOGY. Educ: Univ Ill, BS, 67; Univ Calif, San Diego, MS, 68, PhD(chem), 71. Prof Exp: USPHS Grad fel trainee fel, 67-71; res fel, Dept Exp Path, Scripps Clin & Res Found, 71-73, res asst, 73-74, res assoc, Dept Immunopath, 74-76; staff mem, 76-81, SR STAFF SCIENTIST, BIOL DIV, OAK RIDGE NAT LAB, 81- Mem: Am Asn Cancer Res. Res: Antibody directed specific chemotherapy and specific immunotherapy of malignancies; analysis of cell surface proteins; leukemia virus proteins and radioimmunoassay. Mailing Add: Div of Biol PO Box Y Oak Ridge TN 37830

KENNEL, WILLIAM E(LMER), b St Louis, Mo, Aug 11, 17; m 39; c 2. CHEMICAL ENGINEERING. Educ: Univ Ill, BS, 40; Mass Inst Technol, MS, 47, DSc(chem eng), 49. Prof Exp: Chem engr, A E Staley Mfg Co, 39-41; chem engr, Standard Oil Co, Ind, 48-51, res group leader, 51-52, res sect leader, 52-57; mgr tech develop, 57-60, dir chem res, 60-61, vpres res & develop & dir, 61-67, vpres plastics, 68-70, group vpres & dir, 70-72, vpres mkt & dir, 72-75, EXEC V PRES & DIR, AMOCO CHEM CORP, 75- Mem: Am Chem Soc; Am Inst Chem Engrs. Res: Technical development of petrochemicals. Mailing Add: 1318 Melbrook Dr Munster IN 46321

KENNELL, DAVID EPPERSON, b Syracuse, NY, May 23, 32; m; c 3. MOLECULAR BIOLOGY. Educ: Univ Calif, Berkeley, AB, 54, PhD(biophysics), 59. Prof Exp: Res engr mineral tech, Univ Calif, Berkeley, 56-57; res fel bact & immunol, Harvard Med Sch, 59-60; res assoc, Mass Inst Technol, 60-61; from instr to assoc prof, 61-73, PROF MICROBIOL, SCH MED, WASH UNIV, 73- Concurrent Pos: Nat Cancer Inst fel, 57-61; NIH res career develop award, 69-74; mem, Microbial Physiol Study Sect, NIH, 81- Mem: Am Soc Microbiol; Am Soc Biol Chem; Biophys Soc; Am Soc Cell Biol; Am Asn Univ Professors. Res: Ribonucleic acid metabolism in bacteria and regulation of energy metabolism in cultured mammalian cells. Mailing Add: 1332 Purdue Ave University City MO 63130

KENNELL, JOHN HAWKS, b Reading, Pa, Jan 9, 22; m 49; c 3. PEDIATRICS, BEHAVIORAL SCIENCE. Educ: Univ Rochester, BS, 44, MD, 46. Prof Exp: Intern pediat, Children's Hosp, Boston, 46-47; asst resident, Children's Hosp Med Ctr, 49-50, chief resident med out-patient dept, 50, dir depat, 52, chief med resident, 51; dir, Family Clin, 52-60, dir, Pediat Clin, 60-70, sr instr, 52-55, from asst prof to assoc prof, 55-73, PROF PEDIAT, CASE WESTERN RESERVE UNIV, 73-, ASSOC PEDIATRICIAN, 56- Concurrent Pos: Nat Inst Child Health & Human Develop spec res fel, Univ London, 66-67; consult, Headstart, 68-; dir, Neonatal Nurseries, Univ Hosp, Cleveland, 52-67. Honors & Awards: George Armstrong Award, Ambulatory Pediat Asn. Mem: Am Acad Pediat; Am Pediat Soc; Asn Child Care Hosps (vpres, 73-75); Soc Res Child Develop; Ambulatory Pediat Asn (pres, 70). Res: Child development; medical education; social and psychological factors in medicine; effects of mother-infant separation on maternal attachment; effects of perinatal death on parents; effect of supportive companion during labor and delivery; medical and ambulatory care. Mailing Add: Dept of Pediat Case Western Reserve Univ Cleveland OH 44106

KENNELLEY, JAMES A, b Rochester, NY, Aug 23, 28; m 55; c 3. PHYSICAL CHEMISTRY, METALLURGY. Educ: Col Wooster, BA, 45; Mich State Univ, PhD(chem), 55. Prof Exp: Res chemist uranium, Mallinckrodt, Inc, 55-57, group leader res, 57-59, mgr res, 59-62, tech dir div, 62-65; asst to pres, Que Iron & Titanium Corp, 65-73, vpres, 73-75, group vpres, 75-78; PRES, DIRECT REDUCTION CORP, 78- Mem: Am Chem Soc; Am Soc Metals; Am Inst Mining, Metall & Petrol Engrs. Res: Rare earths; uranium chemistry & metallurgy; titanium; raw materials; ilmenite smelting; titanium dioxide pigments; direct reduction of iron ore. Mailing Add: Direct Reduction Corp 230 Park Ave New York NY 10169

KENNELLY, BRUCE, b Covington, Ky, Dec 18, 23; m 48; c 2. BIOCHEMISTRY. Educ: Univ Ky, BS, 44; Purdue Univ, MS, 46; Cornell Univ, PhD(biochem, nutrit), 52. Prof Exp: Chemist, Agr Exp Sta, Purdue Univ, 44-47; head dept chem, 67-74, PROF PHYS SCI, CALIF POLYTECH STATE UNIV, 47-, PROF CHEM, 67-, PRES CALIF INST NUTRIT, 77- Mem: AAAS; Am Chem Soc; Am Oil Chem Soc. Res: Lipogenesis; fat oxidation; intermediary metabolism; vitamins; enzymes; hormones; food analysis; nutrition; food formulation. Mailing Add: Dept Chem Calif Polytech State Univ San Luis Obispo CA 93407

KENNELLY, JAMES J, reproductive physiology, see previous edition

KENNELLY, MARY MARINA, b Chicago, Ill, Nov 12, 19. INORGANIC CHEMISTRY, ORGANIC CHEMISTRY. Educ: Mundelein Col, BS, 42; Univ Notre Dame, MS, 50, PhD(chem), 59. Prof Exp: Asst prof, 50-57, chmn dept, 59-69, PROF CHEM, MUNDELEIN COL, 59- Concurrent Pos: NSF sci fac summer fels, London, 60, Fla State, 61 & Seattle, 62. Mem: AAAS; Am Chem Soc; Nat Sci Teachers Asn; Sigma Xi. Res: Coordination chemistry; infrared studies of metal complexes of amino acids. Mailing Add: Dept of Chem 6363 Sheridan Rd Chicago IL 60626

KENNER, CHARLES THOMAS, b Waxahachie, Tex, Oct 20, 10; m 42; c 1. ANALYTICAL CHEMISTRY. Educ: Trinity Univ, BS, 32; Univ Tenn, MS, 35; Univ Tex, PhD(phys chem), 39. Prof Exp: Instr gen chem, Univ Tex, 35-38; asst prof chem, The Citadel, 38-42; chief chemist & metallurgist, Thor Corp, 46; dir res & control labs, Cent Testing Co, Chicago, 47; from asst prof to prof, 48-76, EMER PROF CHEM, SOUTHERN METHODIST UNIV, 76- Concurrent Pos: Consult, Food & Drug Admin, 67-76 & RSR Corp, 70-; vis prof, NTex State Univ, 78 & 81. Mem: Am Chem Soc; Soc Appl Spectros. Res: Ion exchange separations; chelometry; spectrophotometric methods; trace metal analysis; pharmaceutical analysis. Mailing Add: 7210 Clemson Dr Dallas TX 75214

KENNER, MORTON ROY, b Rochester, NY, June 10, 25; m 54; c 2. MATHEMATICS. Educ: Univ Rochester, AB, 49; Univ Minn, MA, 51; PhD(math, math ed), 58. Prof Exp: From asst prof to assoc prof math, Southern Ill Univ, 52-67; prof math & chmn dept, Stephens Col, 67-70; PROF MATH & CHMN DEPT, NORTHWEST MO STATE UNIV, 70-, CHMN DIV MATH & COMPUT SCI, 78- Concurrent Pos: Dir develop proj sec math, Southern Ill Univ, 58-67; consult, Opers Res Group, Ohio State Univ, 60-; dir Nairobi Math Ctr, Kenya, 64 & 65. Mem: Hist Sci Soc; Math Asn Am. Res: Foundations of mathematics; systems models; mathematical education; history of mathematics. Mailing Add: Div of Math & Comput Sci Northwest Mo State Univ Maryville MO 64468

KENNERLY, GEORGE WARREN, b Boston, Mass, Mar 11, 22; m 49; c 2. INDUSTRIAL CHEMISTRY. Educ: Harvard Univ, BS, 44, MA, 47, PhD, 49. Prof Exp: Res chemist, 49-54, group leader, 54-59, mgr, 59-68, DIR, AM CYANAMID CO, 68- Mem: AAAS; Am Chem Soc. Res: Auto-oxidation; peroxide chemistry; photochemistry; electrochemistry; luminescence; reaction kinetics. Mailing Add: Am Cyanamid Co 1937 W Main St Stamford CT 06904

KENNERLY, THOMAS EVERTON, JR, zoology, ecology, deceased

KENNET, HAIM, b Jerusalem, Israel, Apr 20, 35; US citizen. AERONAUTICS, ASTRONAUTICS. Educ: Mass Inst Technol, SB & SM, 57, ScD(aeronaut & astronaut), 61. Prof Exp: Res engr gas dynamics, Aero-Space Div, 61-63, sr group engr aerothermodyn, 63-65, sr supvr Mars Explor, 65-67, systs eng mgr, Space Div, 67-69, PROJ MGR SPACE EXPLOR SYSTS, AEROSPACE GROUP, BOEING CO, 69- Mem: Am Inst Aeronaut & Astronaut. Res: Flight mechanics, flight control, propulsion and thermal control aspects of unmanned space probes. Mailing Add: Boeing Aerospace Co Boeing Co PO Box 3996 Seattle WA 98124

KENNETT, JAMES PETER, b Wellington, NZ, Sept 3, 40; m 64; c 2. MICROPALEONTOLOGY, PALEOECOLOGY. Educ: New Zealand Univ, BSc, 62; Victoria Univ, Hons, 63, PhD(geol), 65, DSc, 76. Prof Exp: Sci officer, NZ Oceanog Inst, 65-66; NSF fel micropaleont, Allan Hancock Found, Univ Southern Calif, 66-68; asst prof, Fla State Univ, 68-70; assoc prof, 70-74, PROF, GRAD SCH OCEANOG, UNIV RI, 74- Concurrent Pos: Mem adv comt, Antarctic Deep-Sea Drilling. Honors & Awards: McKay Hammer Award, Geol Soc NZ, 68. Mem: AAAS; Geol Soc Am; Am Asn Petrol Geol; Soc Econ Paleont & Mineral; Int Quaternary Asn. Res: Marine geology; foraminiferal ecology and paleoecology; stratigraphic paleontology and stratigraphy of the Cenozoic; geology of the Antarctic continent. Mailing Add: Grad Sch of Oceanog Univ of RI Kingston RI 02881

KENNETT, ROGER H, b Lakewood, NJ, Dec 27, 40; m 66; c 3. GENETICS. Educ: Eastern Col, AB, 64; Princeton Univ, PhD(biochem sci), 70. Prof Exp: Demonstr, Genetics Lab, Oxford Univ, 72-73; res officer, 73-76; asst prof, 76-80, ASSOC PROF HUMAN GENETICS, SCH MED, UNIV PA, 80-, DIR, HUMAN GENETICS CELL CTR, 73- Mem: Am Soc Human Genetics; AAAS; Am Asn Immunologists. Res: Use of combination of immunological, biochemical and molecular genetic techniques to study molecular changes related to oncogenesis, and the molecular bases of human genetic diseases. Mailing Add: Dept Human Genetics Sch Med Univ Pa Philadelphia PA 19104

KENNETT, TERENCE JAMES, b Toronto, Ont, Aug 8, 27; m 49; c 2. NUCLEAR PHYSICS. Educ: McMaster Univ, BSc, 53, MSc, 54, PhD(physics), 56. Prof Exp: Fel physics, McMaster Univ, 56-57; assoc physicist, Argonne Nat Lab, 57-59; from asst prof to assoc prof, 59-66, PROF ENG PHYSICS & PHYSICS, MCMASTER UNIV, 66- Mem: Am Phys Soc. Res: Neutron physics; decay scheme studies; neutron capture gamma rays; instrumentation and detector development. Mailing Add: Dept Physics McMaster Univ Hamilton ON L8S 4K1 Can

KENNEY, DONALD J, b Chicago, Ill, Aug 26, 25; m 48; c 7. PHYSICAL CHEMISTRY. Educ: Loyola Univ, Ill, BS, 49; Iowa State Univ, PhD(phys chem), 53. Prof Exp: Res engr, Steel Div, Ford Motor Co, 53-54; PROF CHEM, UNIV DETROIT, 54- Concurrent Pos: Dir govt projs, 54-65. Mem: Am Chem Soc. Res: Iron complexes; metallurgy. Mailing Add: Dept of Chem Univ of Detroit Detroit MI 48221

KENNEY, FRANCIS T, b Springfield, Mass, Mar 16, 28; m 51; c 2. BIOCHEMISTRY. Educ: St Michael's Col, BS, 50; Univ Notre Dame, MS, 53; Johns Hopkins Univ, PhD(biochem), 57. Prof Exp: Instr biol, St Michael's Col, 50-51; res assoc pediat, Med Col, Cornell Univ, 57-59; from biochemist to sr biochemist, 59-69, sci dir, Carcinogenesis Prog, 69-75, SR STAFF SCIENTIST, OAK RIDGE NAT LAB, 75- Mem: AAAS; Am Soc Biol Chemists; Am Chem Soc. Res: Mammalian biochemistry; regulation. Mailing Add: Oak Ridge Nat Lab Biol Div PO Box Y Oak Ridge TN 37830

KENNEY, GARY DALE, b Akron, Ohio, Dec 17, 49; m 71. INDUSTRIAL HYGIENE, LOSS PREVENTION. Educ: Univ Arkon, BS, 71; Univ Cincinnati, MS & PhD(indust hyg), 75. Prof Exp: Indust hygienist, Firestone Tire & Rubber Co, 71-72; indust hygienist, Bell Tel Labs, Inc, 75-77; supvr indust hygiene, 77-80, SUPVR & SPECIALIST, LOSS PREVENTION, ARABIAN AM OIL CO, 80- Mem: Am Indust Hyg Asn; Am Soc Safety Engrs. Mailing Add: Aramco PO Box 5691 Dhahran Saudi Arabia

KENNEY, JAMES FRANCIS, b Buffalo, NY, Sept 3, 26; m 57; c 3. GEOPHYSICS. *Educ:* Union Col, NY, BS, 51; Univ NMex, MS, 53, PhD(physics), 57. *Prof Exp:* Res assoc physics, Univ NMex, 57-58, instr, 59-60; res fel, Univ NMex & Lab Cosmic Physics, La Paz, 58-59; staff mem geoastrophys res, Boeing Sci Res Lab, 60-69, head geoastrophys dept, 69-70, head environ sci dept, 70-73, mgr laser & environ sci lab, 73-75, resources develop mgr, 75-76, mgr, Radiation Physics, 76-79, CHIEF SCIENTIST, BOEING AEROSPACE CO, 79- *Mem:* Am Inst Aeronaut & Astronaut; AAAS; Am Geophys Union. *Res:* Cosmic rays; ionospheric properties and radio propagation; nuclear, space and solar physics; magnetic fields and micropulsations; environmental science, urban studies; remote sensing, laser physics; military sciences; radiation physics; countermeasures. *Mailing Add:* Boeing Aerospace Co Box 3999 MS-42-33 Seattle WA 98124

KENNEY, JAMES FRANKLIN, b Richmond, Va, Aug 4, 34; m 58; c 3. POLYMER CHEMISTRY. *Educ:* Howard Univ, BS, 56, MS, 58; Univ Akron, PhD(polymer chem), 64. *Prof Exp:* Res chemist, US Air Force Mat Lab, 58-61; res fel, Inst Rubber Res, Akron, 61-64; res chemist, Chemstrand Res Ctr, Inc, 64-68; res assoc plastics div, Allied Chem Corp, 68-71; res assoc, M&T Chem, Inc, 71-78; sr proj leader, 78-79, MGR POLYMERS & MAT SCI, JOHNSON & JOHNSON PRODS INC, 79- *Mem:* Am Chem Soc. *Res:* Synthesis, structure, property and performance of polymers; emulsion, condensation and addition polymerization; graft and block copolymers; polyblends; impact modification; processing characteristics of polymers; economic and technical evaluation of research; developing catalysts for polyesters and polyurethanes; emulsion and hot melt adhesives. *Mailing Add:* 5 Highfield Circle Mendham NJ 07945

KENNEY, JOHN T, b Providence, RI, Jan 30, 39; m 64; c 1. PHYSICAL CHEMISTRY. *Educ:* Providence Col, BS, 60; Catholic Univ, PhD(chem), 67. *Prof Exp:* Air pollution chemist, DC Health Dept, 63-65; fel chem, Catholic Univ, 67-68; sr res chemist, 68-70, RES LEADER, WESTERN ELEC CO, 70- *Mem:* Am Chem Soc. *Res:* Surface chemistry. *Mailing Add:* Western Elec Co PO Box 900 Princeton NJ 08540

KENNEY, MALCOLM EDWARD, b Berkeley, Calif, Oct 7, 28; m 51. ORGANOSILICON CHEMISTRY. *Educ:* Univ Redlands, BS, 50; Cornell Univ, PhD(chem), 54. *Prof Exp:* Asst, Cornell Univ, 50-52, fel, 54; from instr to assoc prof, 56-66, CASE WESTERN RESERVE UNIV, 66- *Concurrent Pos:* John Teagle prof fel, 64-66. *Mem:* Am Chem Soc. *Res:* Metal complexes and inorganic polymers. *Mailing Add:* Dept of Chem Case West Reserve Univ 2040 Adelbert Rd Cleveland OH 44106

KENNEY, MARGARET JUNE, b Boston, Mass, June 7, 35. MATHEMATICS. *Educ:* Boston Col, Chestnut Hill, BS, 57, MA, 59; Boston Univ, PhD(math), 77. *Prof Exp:* Instr, 59-63, lectr, 63-70, asst prof, 70-79, ASSOC PROF MATH, BOSTON COL, 79- *Concurrent Pos:* Asst dir, Math Inst, Boston Col, 57- *Mem:* Nat Coun Teachers Math; Math Asn Am; Am Math Soc; Nat Coun Supvrs Math; Asn Women Math. *Res:* Mathematics education at the pre-college level; problem solving; number theoretic applications of mathematics to art. *Mailing Add:* Math Inst Boston Col Chestnut Hill MA 02167

KENNEY, MARY ALICE, b Lubbock, Tex, May 16, 38. NUTRITION. *Educ:* Tex Tech Univ, BS, 58; Iowa State Univ, MS, 60, PhD(nutrit), 63. *Prof Exp:* Instr nutrit, Purdue Univ, 60-61; from asst prof to assoc prof, Iowa State Univ, 63-73; prof food & nutrit, Tex Tech Univ, 73-78; PROF FOOD, NUTRIT & INST ADMIN, OKLA STATE UNIV, 78- *Mem:* AAAS; Am Inst Nutrit; NY Acad Sci. *Res:* Immunoglobulins levels; assessment of nutritional status; magnesium nutrition; metabolic effects in offspring of malnourished rats. *Mailing Add:* Dept Food Nutrit & Inst Admin 403 HEW Okla State Univ Stillwater OK 74074

KENNEY, MICHAEL, US citizen. CLINICAL PATHOLOGY, PARASITOLOGY. *Educ:* Univ Geneva, BMedSc, 28, MD, 30; Sch Trop Med Brussels, DTM, 31. *Prof Exp:* Res physician path & trop med, Belg Colonial Govt, 33-39; res asst, Loyola Univ Chicago, 40-43; chief med serv & lab hosp, Berbice Co Ltd, Am Cyanamid Co, Brit Guiana, 43-48; chief microbiologist, Vet Admin Hosp, Bronx, 49-54; clin assoc prof, 54-68, prof, 68-74, EMER PROF PATH, STATE UNIV NY DOWNSTATE MED CTR, 74- *Concurrent Pos:* Chief clin path, Vet Admin Hosp, New York, 54-70; chief trop dis serv, Inst Path, Kings County Hosp Ctr, 68-74, consult, 74- *Honors & Awards:* Serv Star, Belg Govt, 36, Knight of the Royal Order of the Lion, 40. *Mem:* Fel Col Am Path; fel Am Soc Clin Path; Am Soc Microbiol; Am Soc Trop Med & Hyg; Am Pub Health Asn. *Res:* Immuno-parasitology; diagnostic parasitology. *Mailing Add:* State Univ NY Inst Path Brooklyn NY 11203

KENNEY, NANCY JANE, b Wilkes-Barre, Pa. PSYCHOBIOLOGY, BEHAVIORAL ENDOCRINOLOGY. *Educ:* Wilkes Col, BA, 70; Univ Va, MA, 72, PhD(psychol), 74. *Prof Exp:* Fel neurol sci, Univ Pa, 74-76; ASST PROF PSYCHOL, UNIV WASH, 76-, ASST PROF WOMEN STUDIES, 80- *Concurrent Pos:* NIH res fel, Nat Inst Child Health & Human Develop, 74-76; prin investr, Nat Inst Arthritis, Metab & Digestive Dis, 78-84. *Mem:* Soc Neurosci; Am Psychol Asn; AAAS. *Res:* Neuroendocrine control of body water, especially central interactions between angiotension II and prostaglandin E in controlling thirst and blood pressure; role of gonadal hormones and neuropeptides in controlling body weight and food intake. *Mailing Add:* Dept of Psychol Univ of Wash Seattle WA 98195

KENNEY, RICHARD ALEC, b Coventry, Eng, Oct 4, 24; m 59; c 1. MEDICAL PHYSIOLOGY. *Educ:* Univ Birmingham, BSc, 45, PhD(physiol), 47. *Prof Exp:* Lectr physiol, Univ Leeds, 47-51; sr sci officer, Colonial Res Serv, Nigeria, 51-54; prof physiol, Univ Rangoon, 55-58, Univ N Sumatra, 58-60 & Univ Singapore, 60-65; reader, Univ Melbourne, 65-68; PROF PHYSIOL, MED CTR, GEORGE WASHINGTON UNIV, 68- *Mem:* Brit Physiol Soc; Brit Renal Asn; Am Physiol Soc; Int Soc Nephrology. *Res:* Renal, climatic and cardio-vascular physiology. *Mailing Add:* Dept of Physiol George Washington Univ Med Ctr Washington DC 20037

KENNEY, ROBERT WARNER, b Portland, Ore, Nov 9, 22; m 50; c 2. HIGH ENERGY PHYSICS, PARTICLE PHYSICS. *Educ:* Univ Calif, Los Angeles, BA, 44; Calif Inst Technol, BS, 47; Univ Calif, PhD(physics), 52. *Prof Exp:* Mem staff, Los Alamos Sci Lab, 52-53; SR STAFF PHYSICIST, LAWRENCE BERKELEY LAB, UNIV CALIF, BERKELEY, 53- *Concurrent Pos:* Lectr, Univ Calif, Berkeley; consult, Marquardt Corp; NASA. *Mem:* Am Phys Soc; AAAS. *Res:* High energy particle physics; electromagnetic interactions at high energies; particle accelerators; pion nuclear interaction; weak interaction and symmetry principles. *Mailing Add:* Lawrence Berkeley Lab Univ of Calif Berkeley CA 94720

KENNEY, T CAMERON, b Montreal, Que, Mar 26, 31; m 60; c 4. CIVIL & GEOTECHNICAL ENGINEERING. *Educ:* McGill Univ, BEng, 53; Univ London, DIC, 54, MSc, 56, PhD(civil eng), 67. *Prof Exp:* Geotech engr, Acres Ltd, Niagara Falls, Ont, 56-61; res engr, Norweg Geotech Inst, Oslo, 61; assoc prof civil eng, Univ Toronto, 67-68, chmn dept, 68-74, prof civil eng, 68-80; RETIRED. *Concurrent Pos:* First Bjerrum Mem lectr, Norweg Geotech Inst; engr consult, 68- *Honors & Awards:* Walter L Huber Prize, Am Soc Civil Engrs, 67. *Res:* Engineering properties of natural soils; landslides; engineering geology. *Mailing Add:* Dept of Civil Eng Univ of Toronto Toronto ON M5S 2R8 Can

KENNEY, VINCENT PAUL, b New York, NY, Sept 15, 27; m 54; c 4. PHYSICS. *Educ:* Iona Col, AB, 48; Fordham Univ, MS, 50, PhD(physics), 56. *Prof Exp:* Predoctoral res assoc, Brookhaven Nat Lab, 53-55; asst prof physics, Univ Ky, 55-60, assoc prof, 60-63; assoc prof, 63-66, PROF PHYSICS, UNIV NOTRE DAME, 66- *Concurrent Pos:* Vis physicist, Brookhaven Nat Lab, 57-; Oak Ridge Inst Nuclear Studies, 58-64; European Organization for Nuclear Res (CERN), 61-62; Argonne Nat Lab, 65-; Fermi Nat Accelerator Lab, 71-; fel, Max Planck Inst Physics & Astrophysics, Munich, 61-62, 72. *Mem:* Fel Am Phys Soc; AAAS; Sigma Xi. *Res:* High energy particle physics; energy studies. *Mailing Add:* Dept of Physics Univ of Notre Dame Notre Dame IN 46556

KENNEY, WILLIAM CLARK, b Grand Forks, NDak, Feb 25, 40. BIOCHEMISTRY. *Educ:* Carleton Col, BA, 62; Univ Calif, Berkeley, PhD(biochem), 67. *Prof Exp:* Teaching & res asst, Univ Calif, 63-67; asst & assoc res biochemist, 70-79, RES CHEMIST, VET ADMIN MED CTR, SAN FRANCISCO, 79- *Concurrent Pos:* Adj assoc prof med, Univ Calif, San Fransisco, 79-; res award alcoholism, Vet Admin, 79- *Mem:* Am Soc Biol Chemists; AAAS; Am Chem Soc; NY Acad Sci; Res Soc Alcoholism. *Res:* Enzymology; protein biochemistry and biophysics; molecular biology; structure and function of enzymes; biological oxidations. *Mailing Add:* Liver Studies Unit (151 K) Vet Admin 4150 Clement St Med Ctr San Francisco CA 94121

KENNEY-WALLACE, GERALDINE ANNE, b London, Eng, Mar 29, 43. CHEMICAL PHYSICS, CHEMICAL DYNAMICS OPTICS. *Educ:* Royal Inst Chem, ARIC, 65; Univ BC, MS, 68, PhD(chem), 70. *Prof Exp:* Res assoc biophys, Oxford Univ, 64-66; fel chem, Univ BC, 70-71; assoc, Radiation Lab, Univ Notre Dame, 71-72; from instr to asst prof, Yale Univ, 72-74; asst prof chem, 74-78, assoc prof, 78-80, PROF CHEM & PHYSICS, UNIV TORONTO, 80- *Concurrent Pos:* Vis scientist chem, Argonne Nat Lab, 73-; Alfred P Sloan fel, 77-79; Killam Res fel, 79-81. *Honors & Awards:* Corday-Morgan Medal, UK, 79. *Mem:* The Chem Soc; Am Chem Soc; Am Phys Soc; Sigma Xi; Optical Soc Am. *Res:* Molecular photophysics, energy transfer and molecular dynamics studied via picosecond laser spectroscopy; electronic and molecular structure of electrons in fluids; laser-induced electron transfer; picosecond studies of non linear optics. *Mailing Add:* Dept of Chem Univ of Toronto Toronto ON M5S 1A1 Can

KENNICK, WALTER HERBERT, b Hampton, Va, Aug 23, 20; m 43; c 3. MEAT SCIENCE. *Educ:* Clemson Col, BS, 48; Ore State Col, MS, 58, PhD(animal husb, meats), 59. *Prof Exp:* Res fel, 56-59, asst prof, 59-70, ASSOC PROF ANIMAL HUSB, ORE STATE UNIV, 70- *Concurrent Pos:* Res scientist, The Agricultural Inst, 73; Fulbright-Hays, Animal Prod Res Ctr, Dublin, Ireland, 74. *Mem:* AAAS; Am Soc Animal Sci; Am Meat Sci Asn; Inst Food Technol. *Res:* Quantitative yield of lean tissue from meat animals, methods of evaluating quality and quantity of such tissue and factors contributing to their variation; post slaughter treatments to improve eating quality. *Mailing Add:* Clark Lab Ore State Univ Corvallis OR 97331

KENNICOTT, PHILIP RAY, b Gooding, Idaho, Apr 8, 32; m 53; c 4. PHYSICAL CHEMISTRY. *Educ:* Univ Utah, BS, 53; Calif Inst Technol, PhD(phys chem), 62. *Prof Exp:* Phys chemist, 61-77, INFO SCIENTIST, GEN ELEC RES & DEVELOP CTR, 77- *Mem:* AAAS; Asn Comput Mach. *Res:* Infrared spectroscopy; x-ray diffraction of powders; spark source mass spectrography; laboratory automation; computer-aided design; geometric modeling. *Mailing Add:* Gen Elec Res & Develop Ctr 37-549 Schenectady NY 12345

KENNINGTON, GARTH STANFORD, b Afton, Wyo, Apr 19, 15; m 43. ANIMAL ECOLOGY, ANIMAL PHYSIOLOGY. *Educ:* Univ Wyo, BS, 40; Univ Chicago, MS, 48, PhD(zool), 52. *Prof Exp:* Instr biol, George Williams Col, 47-48; instr, Roosevelt Col, 48-49; from asst prof to assoc prof zool, Lawrence Col, 52-60; assoc prof zool, Univ Wyo, 60-62, prof, 62-81, prof physiol, 74-81; RETIRED. *Concurrent Pos:* Consult, Kimberly-Clark Corp, 58-; NSF fel, Donner Lab, Univ Calif, 59-60; Fulbright lectr, Aligarh Muslim Univ, India, 63-64; Assoc Rocky Mt Univs fac grant, Nat Reactor Testing Sta, Idaho Falls, Idaho, 65-67; Oak Ridge Assoc Univs res grant, Environ Sci Div, Oak Ridge Nat Lab, 72-73. *Mem:* Fel AAAS; Am Soc Zool; Ecol Soc Am. *Res:* Ecology and physiology of the high arid plains; assessment of effects of mining and milling on biological communities in Wyoming. *Mailing Add:* 1404 Bridger Laramie WY 82070

KENNINGTON, MACK HUMPHERYS, b Kamas, Utah, Apr 6, 23. ANIMAL HUSBANDRY. *Educ:* Univ Idaho, BS, 46; Purdue Univ, MS, 56, PhD(animal nutrit), 58. *Prof Exp:* County exten agent, Exten Serv, Univ Idaho, 48-54; from asst prof to assoc prof, 58-68, PROF ANIMAL SCI, CALIF STATE POLYTECH UNIV, POMONA, 69- *Concurrent Pos:* Vis prof animal sci, Cornell Univ, 66-67. *Mem:* Am Soc Animal Sci; Poultry Sci Asn; Can Soc Animal Prod; Am Dairy Sci Asn; Brit Soc Animal Prod. *Res:* Animal production and nutrition; growth and reproduction of beef cattle, dairy cattle and swine. *Mailing Add:* Dept of Animal Sci Calif State Polytech Univ Pomona CA 91768

KENNISON, HUGH FOSTER, b Providence, RI, May 10, 16; m 41; c 2. CIVIL ENGINEERING. *Educ:* Mass Inst Technol, BSCE, 39. *Prof Exp:* Engr, Lock Joint Pipe Co, NJ, 39-47, chief engr, 47-57, vpres, Interpace Corp, 57-65, vpres & gen mgr pipe div, 65-67, pres & chief exec officer, 67-73; PRES, KENNISON ASSOCS, 73- *Concurrent Pos:* Mem bd dir, Lock Joint/Interpace, 58-75; dir, Arvin Industs, 72- *Mem:* Am Soc Civil Engrs; Am Water Works Asn; Am Concrete Inst; Nat Asn Corrosion Engrs. *Res:* Cement; concrete; admixtures; ferrous corrosion; coatings; thermoset and thermoplastic resins; ceramics; glazes; refractories and composite structures. *Mailing Add:* 111 Avon Dr Essex Fells NJ 07021

KENNISON, JOHN FREDERICK, b New York, NY, Oct 7, 38; m 64; c 2. MATHEMATICS. *Educ:* Queens Col, NY, BS, 59; Harvard Univ, AM, 60, PhD(topology), 63. *Prof Exp:* PROF MATH, CLARK UNIV, 63- *Mem:* Am Math Soc. *Res:* Category theory. *Mailing Add:* Dept of Math Clark Univ Worcester MA 01610

KENNISON, R(ALPH) GREGORY, (JR), b Gardiner, Maine, Apr 18, 24; m 47; c 2. NUCLEAR ENGINEERING. *Educ:* Rensselaer Polytech Inst, BME, 45, MME, 50. *Prof Exp:* Engr reactor design, 48-53, engr power plant design, 53-55, supv engr, 55-59, mgr mech design submarine adv reactor proj, 59-62, mgr test DIG proj, 62-63, CONSULT ENGR, KNOLLS ATOMIC POWER LAB, GEN ELEC CO, 63- *Res:* Nuclear power plant design; fluid dynamics; fluid-structure interactions; flow induced noise. *Mailing Add:* 861 Barton Pl Schenectady NY 12309

KENNY, ALEXANDER DONOVAN, b London, Eng, Mar 4, 25; nat US; m 50; c 4. PHARMACOLOGY, ENDOCRINOLOGY. *Educ:* Imp Col, London, BSc, 45; Inst Divi Thomae, MS, 49, PhD(biochem), 50. *Prof Exp:* Sr chemist, Metab Labs, Univ Col Hosp, London, 50-51; chief chem lab, Mass Gen Hosp, 52; asst dent sci, Sch Dent Med, Harvard Univ, 52-53, instr, 53-55; assoc pharmacol, Harvard Med Sch, 55-59; from assoc prof to prof, Med Ctr, WVa Univ, 59-67; prof, Sch Med, & investr, Space Sci Res Ctr, Univ Mo-Columbia, 67-71, prof biochem, 71-74, investr, Dalton Res Ctr, 67-74; prof pharmacol med br, Univ Tex, 74-75; PROF & CHMN PHARMACOL & THERAPEUT, SCH MED, TEX TECH UNIV, 76- *Concurrent Pos:* US Pub Health Serv Spec fel, Royal Postgrad Med Sch, London, 67-68; chmn, NIH Special Study Section, 75; actg dir, Tarbox Parkinson's Dis Inst, 76-78, dir, 78- *Mem:* Endocrine Soc; Biophys Soc; Am Soc Pharmacol & Exp Therapeut; Am Chem Soc; Brit Biochem Soc. *Res:* Calcium and bone metabolism; vitamin D; parathyroid hormone; calcitonin; hormone assay. *Mailing Add:* Dept of Pharmacol & Therapeut Texas Tech Univ Sch of Med Lubbock TX 79430

KENNY, DAVID HERMAN, b Lake Linden, Mich, Oct 6, 27. ORGANIC CHEMISTRY. *Educ:* Cornell Univ, AB, 49; Univ Mich, MS, 55, PhD, 59. *Prof Exp:* Asst prof chem, Eastern Michigan Univ, 58-60; Smith-Mundt lectr, Baghdad, 60-62; chmn, Org Chem Dept, 74-81, ASSOC PROF CHEM, MICH TECHNOL UNIV, 62- *Mem:* AAAS; Am Chem Soc. *Res:* Organic nitrogen chemistry. *Mailing Add:* Dept of Chem & Chem Eng Mich Technol Univ Houghton MI 49931

KENNY, GEORGE EDWARD, b Dickinson, NDak, Sept 23, 30; m 58; c 6. MICROBIOLOGY. *Educ:* Fordham Univ, BS, 52; Univ NDak, MS, 57; Univ Minn, Minneapolis, PhD(microbiol), 61. *Prof Exp:* Res instr prev med, 61-63, from asst prof to assoc prof, 63-71, PROF & CHMN DEPT PATHOBIOL, UNIV WASH, 71- *Honors & Awards:* Kimble Methodology Award, Am Pub Health Asn, 71. *Mem:* Am Soc Microbiol; Soc Exp Biol & Med; Am Asn Immunol; Infectious Dis Soc Am; Int Orgn Mycoplasmology. *Res:* Antigenic analysis of microorganisms; host-parasite relationships of animals cells and microorganisms; biology of the mycoplasmatales. *Mailing Add:* Dept of Pathobiol SC-38 Univ of Washington Seattle WA 98195

KENNY, MICHAEL THOMAS, b San Francisco, Calif, Oct 3, 38; m 63; c 1. IMMUNOLOGY. *Educ:* Univ San Francisco, BS, 60; Univ Del, PhD(microbiol), 64. *Prof Exp:* Sr virologist, Biohazards Dept, Pitman-Moore Div, 66-67, res virologist, Dow Human Health Res & Develop Labs, 67-71, sr res virologist, Dept Infectious Dis, 71-74, sr res immunologist, Dow Diag Res & Devlop, 74-78, clinical res assoc, Med Dept, 78-81, RES ASSOC, PHARMACOL DEPT, DOW CHEM CO, 74- *Res:* Invertebrate microbiology and invertebrate tissue culture; diagnostic virology; radioimmunoassay; laboratory safety; viral immunology; virus vaccine development; antibiotics and anti-viral compounds. *Mailing Add:* Health & Consumer Prod Dept Dow Chem Co PO Box 68511 Indianapolis IN 46268

KENSHALO, DANIEL RALPH, b West Frankfort, Ill, July 27, 22; m 70; c 4. PSYCHOPHYSIOLOGY. *Educ:* Wash Univ, BA, 47, PhD(exp psychol), 53. *Prof Exp:* Instr psychol, Wash Univ, St Louis, 48-49; actg asst prof, 50-53, asst prof, 53-55, assoc prof, 55-59, PROF PSYCHOL, FLA STATE UNIV, 59- *Concurrent Pos:* Vis prof physiol, Univ Marburg, Ger, 69 & Univ Claude Bernard, France, 73; distinguished prof, 74-75. *Mem:* Soc Neurosci; Fel Am Psychol Asn; Fel AAAS; Fel NY Acad Sci; Am Physiol Soc. *Res:* Psychophysical and electrophysiological investigation of the skin senses. *Mailing Add:* Dept of Psychol Fla State Univ Tallahassee FL 32306

KENSLER, CHARLES JOSEPH, b New York, NY, Jan 21, 15; m 44; c 2. PHARMACOLOGY, BIOCHEMISTRY. *Educ:* Columbia Univ, AB, 37, MA, 38; Cornell Univ, PhD(pharmacol), 48. *Prof Exp:* Chem asst, Rockefeller Inst, 38-39; res assoc biochem, Mem Hosp, NY, 39-43, researcher, Off Sci Res & Develop, 42-43; from instr to assoc prof, Med Col, Cornell Univ, 43-53; head biol labs, Arthur D Little, Inc, 54-57; prof pharmacol & exp therapeut & chmn dept, 57-60, PROF PHARMACOL, SCH MED, BOSTON UNIV, 60-; PRES & CHIEF EXEC OFFICER, ARTHUR D LITTLE, INC, 73- *Concurrent Pos:* Traveling fel, Oxford Univ, 49-50; Sloan scholar, 51-54; lectr, Harvard Med Sch, 54-57; mem drug evaluation panel & chmn pharmacol comt, Cancer Chemother Nat Serv Ctr, 57-61; mem sub-comt carcinogenesis, Nat Acad Sci-Nat Res Coun, 57-; consult, Nat Cancer Inst, 62-70 & Food & Drug Admin, 57, 60 & 71-; vis prof, Mass Inst Technol, 72-; trustee, Gordon Res Conf Coun, 77-, chmn, 79-80; pres, Mass Health Res Inst, 77-80, dir, 60- *Mem:* Soc Exp Biol & Med; Am Asn Cancer Res; Am Soc Pharmacol & Exp Therapeut; Harvey Soc; NY Acad Sci. *Res:* Nutrition and cancer; tissue metabolism; mode of action of carcinogenic agents; activity and mode of action of cancer chemotherapeutic agents; biochemical aspects of pharmacology; industrial toxicology. *Mailing Add:* Arthur D Little Inc 25 Acorn Park Cambridge MA 02140

KENSON, ROBERT EARL, b Stoneham, Mass, Apr 15, 39; m 68. PHYSICAL CHEMISTRY. *Educ:* Boston Univ, AB, 61; Purdue Univ, PhD(phys chem), 65. *Prof Exp:* Sr res chemist, Olin Mathieson Chem Corp, 65-69 & Engelhard Minerals & Chem Corp, Newark, 69-74; sr proj scientist, TRC, The Res Corp New Eng, 74-78; MGR ENGINEERED SYSTS DIV, OXY-CATALYST INC, 78- *Mem:* Am Chem Soc; Am Inst Chem Eng; Catalysis Soc; Air Pollution Control Asn; Am Mgt Asn. *Res:* Catalysis; kinetics of gas and solution reactions; petroleum chemistry and petrochemicals; energy systems; environmental control. *Mailing Add:* 1125 E Cardinal Dr West Chester PA 19380

KENT, ALLEN, b New York, NY, Oct 24, 21; m 43; c 4. INFORMATION SCIENCE. *Educ:* City Col New York, BS, 42. *Prof Exp:* Res assoc info sci, Mass Inst Technol, 51-53; prin doc engr, Battelle Mem Inst, 53-55; assoc dir & prof ctr for doc & commun res, Western Reserve Univ, 55-63; DIR, OFF COMMUN PROGS, UNIV PITTSBURGH, 63-, CHMN, INTERDISCIPLINARY DEPT INFO SCI, 68-, DISTINGUISHED SERV PROF, 76- *Concurrent Pos:* Consult, Diebold, Inc, 62-72; consult info sci ment retardation, Spec Asst to Presidents Kennedy & Johnson, 63-64; coun mem, Ctr Res Libr, 66-; chmn nat adv comt, Nat Inst Neurol Dis & Stroke, 67-70; chmn bd trustees, Educ Commun, 71-74; mem bd dirs & exec comt, Marcell Dekker Inc, 79- *Honors & Awards:* Info Technol Merit Award, Eastman Kodak Co, 68; Award of Merit, Am Soc Info Sci, 77. *Mem:* Am Soc Info Sci; fel AAAS; Asn Comput Mach; Am Libr Asn. *Res:* Quantitative studies of information transfer; modelling and simulation of library networks. *Mailing Add:* Rm 801 LIS Bldg Univ of Pittsburgh Pittsburgh PA 15260

KENT, BARBARA, b Decatur, Ill, July 29, 40. PHYSIOLOGY, SURGERY. *Educ:* Emory Univ, BA, 62, MS, 64, PhD(physiol), 70. *Prof Exp:* Teaching asst physiol, Emory Univ, 62-66, instr, 66-70; RES PHYSIOLOGIST, BRONX VET ADMIN HOSP, 70-, DIR, SURG RES, 72- *Concurrent Pos:* Investr, Mt Desert Island Biol Lab, 68-; res assoc prof surg, Mt Sinai Sch Med, NY, 71-, assoc prof physiol, 78; vis scientist, Jackson Lab, 82. *Mem:* Am Physiol Soc; NY Acad Sci. *Res:* Cardiovascular control systems; patho physiology of respiration; comparative cardiovascular physiology; aging. *Mailing Add:* Dept of Surg 130 W Kingsbridge Rd Bronx NY 10468

KENT, CLAUDIA, b South Bend, Ind, Oct 6, 45. BIOCHEMISTRY. *Educ:* St Mary's Col, Ind, BS, 67; Johns Hopkins Univ, PhD(biochem), 72. *Prof Exp:* Am Cancer Soc fel biochem, Dept Biol Chem, Sch Med, Wash Univ, 72-75; NIH fel, 74-75; asst prof 75-80, ASSOC PROF BIOCHEM, PURDUE UNIV, 80- *Mem:* Am Soc Biol Chemists; Am Soc Cell Biol. *Res:* Regulation of phospholipid metabolism; muscle differentiation. *Mailing Add:* Dept Biochem Purdue Univ West Lafayette IN 47907

KENT, CLEMENT F, b Charleston, SC, Mar 15, 27; m 48; c 3. THEORETICAL COMPUTER SCIENCE, LOGIC. *Educ:* Ga Inst Technol, BS, 48, MS, 50; Mass Inst Technol, PhD(math), 60. *Prof Exp:* Instr physics, Ga Inst Technol, 48-50; sci staff mem, Opers Eval Group, Mass Inst Technol, 51-62; from asst prof to assoc prof math, Case Western Reserve Univ, 62-68; chmn dept math, 68-72 & 76-79, PROF MATH SCI, LAKEHEAD UNIV, 68- *Concurrent Pos:* Vis prof, Univ Bristol, 72-73, Univ Laval, 79-80. *Mem:* Math Asn Am; Am Math Soc; Asn Symbolic Logic; Can Math Cong; Asn Comput Mach. *Res:* Mathematical logic; operations research; proof theory; recursive functions; constructive analysis; theoretical computer science. *Mailing Add:* Dept of Math Lakehead Univ Thunder Bay ON P7B 5E1 Can

KENT, CLIFFORD EUGENE, b Butler Co, Kans, Oct 11, 20; m 42; c 3. CHEMICAL ENGINEERING, ELECTROCHEMISTRY. *Educ:* Purdue Univ, BSChE, 42. *Prof Exp:* Pilot plant supvr, Merck & Co, NJ, 42-45; develop engr, Western Prod, Inc, 45-46; develop engr, Gen Elec Co, 46-49, design engr, 49-52, prog planning supvr, 52-56, mgr proj eng, 56-61, prog mgr advan fuel cell technol, 61-65, prog mgr electrochem eng, 65-67, MGR CHEM SYSTS DESIGN, NUCLEAR ENERGY DIV, GEN ELEC CO, 67- *Mem:* Am Inst Chem Engrs; Am Chem Soc; Am Nuclear Soc; Electrochem Soc. *Res:* Fuel cells; radiochemical plants; equipment design; chemical and gas processes; nuclear plant effluent control; water treatment. *Mailing Add:* Nuclear Energy Div Gen Elec Co 175 Curtner Ave San Jose CA 95125

KENT, DEANE FREDERICK, b Boston, Mass; m 38; c 1. GEOLOGY. *Educ:* Middlebury Col, AB, 39; Northwestern Univ, MS, 42, ScD, 62. *Prof Exp:* Asst, Northwestern Univ, 40-42; asst geologist, State Geol Surv, Ill, 42; from jr geologist to assoc geologist, US Geol Surv, Washington, DC, 43-48, geologist, Colo, 49-51; resident geologist, Am Smelting & Ref Co, Ariz, 51, geologist chg, 52-54, Explor Supvr Eastern US Div, 55-67; pres, Deane F Kent & Assocs, Inc, 68-77; CHMN BD, KENWILL, INC, 78- *Mem:* AAAS;

fel Geol Soc Am; Am Inst Mining, Metall & Petrol Eng; Geochem Soc; fel Soc Econ Geol. *Res:* Mining geology; mine water problems; metallic and non-metallic deposits; coal; structural geology; mineral economics. *Mailing Add:* Kenwill Inc Box 432 505 E Broadway Maryville TN 37801

KENT, DONALD WETHERALD, JR, b Philadelphia, Pa, June 26, 26; m 58; c 3. PHYSICS. *Educ:* Yale Univ, BSc, 49; Temple Univ, PhD(physics), 60. *Prof Exp:* Researcher cosmic radiation, H H Wills Lab, Eng, 49-52; RES PHYSICIST, BARTOL RES FOUND, FRANKLIN INST, 52- *Mem:* Am Phys Soc; Am Geophys Union. *Res:* Cosmic ray physics. *Mailing Add:* Bartol Res Found Univ of Del Newark DE 19711

KENT, DOUGLAS CHARLES, b Hastings, Nebr, Sept 26, 39; m 62; c 2. GEOLOGY. *Educ:* Univ Nebr, BSc, 61, MSc, 63; Iowa State Univ, PhD(water resources, geol), 69. *Prof Exp:* Prod geologist, Gulf Oil Corp, 64-66; instr, Iowa State Univ, 67-68, res assoc, 68-69; asst prof geol, 69-72, ASSOC PROF GEOL, OKLA STATE UNIV, 72- *Concurrent Pos:* Groundwater consult, 71- *Mem:* Geol Soc Am; Am Geophys Union; Am Water Resources Asn; Nat Water Well Asn; Sigma Xi. *Res:* Application of remote sensing to groundwater exploration and water resources; geochemistry of aquifers; application of mathematical modeling to groundwater management; stratigraphy; groundwater geology; applied geophysics and water resources. *Mailing Add:* Dept of Geol Okla State Univ Stillwater OK 74074

KENT, EARLE LEWIS, b Adrian, Tex, May 22, 10; m 35; c 2. ACOUSTICS, DATA PROCESSING. *Educ:* Kans State Univ, BS, 35, MS, 36; Univ Mich, Ann Arbor, PhD(elec eng), 52. *Prof Exp:* Instr elec eng, Armour Inst Technol, 36-40; res engr acoust, C G Conn, Ltd, Elkhart, Ind, 40-41, dir res, develop & design, 41-70; syst analyst & comput programmer data processing, Oaklawn Psychiat Ctr, 70-75; CONSULT ENGR, 75- *Mem:* Fel Acoust Soc Am; fel Audio Eng Soc; sr mem Inst Elec & Electronics Engrs; Catgut Acoust Soc. *Res:* Acoustics of wind musical instruments; acoustics of pianos; electronic organ technology. *Mailing Add:* 2510 Riverview Place Elkhart IN 46516

KENT, FRANK WILLIAM, b Franklin, Ind, May 17, 32; m 54; c 4. ORGANIC CHEMISTRY. *Educ:* Franklin Col, AB, 54; Univ Rochester, PhD(org chem), 58. *Prof Exp:* Res chemist, Esso Res & Eng Co, 58-59; RES CHEMIST, EASTMAN KODAK CO, 59- *Res:* Color photographic systems. *Mailing Add:* Res Labs Eastman Kodak Co 343 State St Rochester NY 14650

KENT, GEOFFREY, b Amsterdam, Holland, Jan 30, 14; nat US; m 44; c 4. PATHOLOGY. *Educ:* Univ Amsterdam, MD, 39; Univ Manchester, MSc, 44; Northwestern Univ, PhD(path), 57. *Prof Exp:* Chief asst hemat, Res Dept, Manchester Royal Infirmary, 40-43, asst dir, 43-44; pathologist, London Hosp, 47-50; sr pathologist, Cook County Hosp, Chicago, 53-56, assoc dir path, 56-57; from asst prof to assoc prof, 60-69, PROF PATH, MED SCH, NORTHWESTERN UNIV, 69-; CHIEF PATH, NORTHWESTERN MEM HOSP, 72- *Concurrent Pos:* Chief pathologist, WSuburban Hosp, 58-69; chmn dept path, Chicago Wesley Mem Hosp, 69-72. *Mem:* AAAS; Am Soc Exp Path; Am Asn Pathologists; Col Am Path; Am Soc Cell Biol. *Res:* Iron metabolism; liver disease. *Mailing Add:* Northwestern Univ 303 Chicago Ave Chicago IL 60611

KENT, GEORGE CANTINE, JR, b Kingston, NY, July 25, 14; m 37; c 1. VERTEBRATE MORPHOLOGY, ENDOCRINOLOGY. *Educ:* Maryville Col, AB, 37; Vanderbilt Univ, MA, 38, PhD(zool), 42. *Prof Exp:* From instr to prof comp anat, 42-67, chmn dept zool, 60-63, ALUMNI PROF ZOOL, LA STATE UNIV, 67- *Concurrent Pos:* Consult, Consult Bur, Comn Undergrad Educ in Biol Sci; vchmn, Ctr Res in Col Instruct in Sci & Math, Tallahassee, 66-67. *Mem:* Am Soc Zool; Soc Exp Biol & Med; Endocrine Soc; Sigma Xi. *Res:* Physiology of reproduction; comparative anatomy. *Mailing Add:* 482 Stanford Ave Baton Rouge LA 70808

KENT, GORDON, b Pittsfield, Mass, Oct 1, 20; m 57; c 1. ELECTRICAL ENGINEERING. *Educ:* Univ Wis, BS, 47; Stanford Univ, MS, 49, PhD(elec eng), 52. *Prof Exp:* Res engr comput design, Inst Adv Study, 51-53; res fel electronics, Gordon McKay Lab, Harvard Univ, 53-57; assoc prof elec eng, 57-63, PROF ELEC ENG, SYRACUSE UNIV, 63- *Mem:* Am Phys Soc; Inst Elec & Electronics Engrs. *Mailing Add:* Dept of Elec Eng Syracuse Univ Syracuse NY 13210

KENT, HARRY ALVIN, JR, b San Francisco, Calif, Apr 8, 27; m 49. REPRODUCTIVE PHYSIOLOGY. *Educ:* Univ Mass, BS, 51, MS, 53; Univ Ore, PhD(zool), 56. *Prof Exp:* From instr to asst prof zool, Univ Ga, 56-65, assoc prof, 65-76; assoc res prof, 76-78, RES PROF, RUTGERS UNIV, 78- *Concurrent Pos:* Porter fel, 59, Nat Insts Health spec fel, 66-67. *Mem:* AAAS; Am Soc Zool; Soc Study Reproduction; Europ Soc Comp Endocrinol; Sigma Xi. *Res:* Cause and effect of polyvular follicles and polynuclear ova in mammalia; glycostatic factor from the fallopian tube of hamsters; contraceptive tetrapeptide from 2-4 cell embryos in mammals; tetrapeptide enhancing ovulation. *Mailing Add:* 13 Deborah Dr Piscataway NJ 08854

KENT, HARRY CHRISTISON, b Los Angeles, Calif, May 20, 30; m 56; c 2. GEOLOGY. *Educ:* Colo Sch Mines, Geol E, 52; Stanford Univ, MS, 53; Univ Colo, PhD(geol), 65. *Prof Exp:* Geologist, Calif Co, Fla & La, 53-56; from instr to assoc prof, 56-69, prof & head dept geol, 69-75, PROF GEOL, COLO SCH MINES, 75-, DIR, POTENTIAL GAS AGENCY, 76- *Mem:* Am Asn Petrol Geol; Geol Soc Am; Soc Econ Paleont & Mineral. *Res:* Gas and oil resources; micropaleontology; marine geology. *Mailing Add:* Potential Gas Agency Colo Sch of Mines Golden CO 80401

KENT, HENRY PETER, b Berlin, Ger, Apr 30, 15; m 41; c 2. RADIOLOGY. *Educ:* Cambridge Univ, BA, 37, MA, 41, MB, ChB, 42; Conjoint Bd, London, Eng, DMRD, 48; Royal Col Physicians & Surgeons, Can, cert diag radiol, 53, fel, 72. *Prof Exp:* Consult diag radiol, Hackney Hosp, London, 50-52; radiologist, Med Arts Clin, Regina, 53-63; head dept, 63-82, admin med advr,

77-80, PROF DIAG RADIOL, UNIV HOSP, UNIV SASK, 63- *Concurrent Pos:* Consult, St Paul's Hosp, Saskatoon, 63- & City Hosp, 63-; actg head x-ray dept, Plains Health Ctr, Regina, 74. *Mem:* Am Col Radiol; fel Am Col Radiol; fel Royal Soc Med; Can Asn Radiol; Can Asn Gastroenterol. *Res:* Diagnostic and gastrointestinal radiology. *Mailing Add:* Dept of Radiol Univ Sask Hosp Saskatoon SK S7N 0W0 Can

KENT, J(AMES) A(LBERT), chemical & nuclear engineering, see previous edition

KENT, JAMES RONALD FRASER, b Halifax, NS, Feb 29, 12; nat US. MATHEMATICAL ANALYSIS. *Educ:* Queen's Univ, Ont, BA, 33, MA, 34; Univ Ill, PhD(math), 47. *Prof Exp:* Asst math, Syracuse Univ, 34-35 & Univ Ill, 35-39; instr, Univ Ark, 39-42; asst prof math, Univ BC, 46-48; assoc prof in charge dept math, Triple Cities Col, Syracuse, 48-50; assoc prof, 50-56, chmn dept, 50-64, prof, 56-79, EMER PROF MATH, STATE UNIV NY BINGHAMTON, 79- *Mem:* Am Math Soc; Math Asn Am; Can Math Soc; Sigma Xi. *Res:* Differential equations. *Mailing Add:* 2 Martha Rd Binghamton NY 13903

KENT, JAMES WOODWARD, b Phila, Pa, Nov 23, 19; m 44; c 2. PHYSICAL CHEMISTRY. *Educ:* Carnegie Inst Technol, BS, 40; Univ Calif, PhD(chem), 43. *Prof Exp:* Asst chem, Univ Calif, 40-43; res chemist, Calif Res Co, 43-50, tech asst to pres & supvr, Nuclear Res, 50-54, res assoc, 54-55, financial analyst, 55-59, mgr anal div comptroller staff, 59-61, asst vpres, Standard Oil of Calif, 62, exec vpres, Calif Chem Co, 63, pres, Ortho Div, 63-66, PRES, CHEVRON CHEM CO DIV, STANDARD OIL CALIF, 66-, CHIEF EXEC OFFICER, 79-, VPRES, STANDARD OIL CALIF, 81- *Concurrent Pos:* Pres & dir, Chevron Chem Co & dir, Chevron Res Co. *Res:* Infrared and ultraviolet spectroscopy; nuclear chemistry; radiotracer and agricultural chemical research. *Mailing Add:* Chevron Chem Co 575 Market St San Francisco CA 94105

KENT, JOHN FRANKLIN, b Franklin, Ind, Apr 30, 21; m 42; c 3. ZOOLOGY. *Educ:* Franklin Col, AB, 41; Cornell Univ, PhD(zool), 49. *Prof Exp:* Asst zool, Cornell Univ, 41-42 & 45-49; from instr to asst prof anat, Univ Mich, 49-57; LUCRETIA L ALLYN PROF ZOOL, CONN COL, 57- *Mem:* AAAS; Am Asn Anat. *Res:* Hematology; ultrastructure; irradiation biology. *Mailing Add:* Dept of Zool Conn Col New London CT 06320

KENT, JOSEPH C(HAN), b Victoria, BC, Jan 16, 22; nat US; m 52; c 3. CIVIL ENGINEERING. *Educ:* Univ BC, BS, 45; Stanford Univ, MS, 48; Univ Calif, PhD(fluid mech), 52. *Prof Exp:* Hydrographic surveyor, Dept Mines & Resources, Can, 45-47; asst civil eng, Univ Calif, 49-52; from instr to asst prof, 52-61, ASSOC PROF CIVIL ENG, UNIV WASH, 61- *Mem:* Am Soc Eng Educ. *Res:* Fluid mechanics specializing in waves; drag of submerged bodies and fluid flow. *Mailing Add:* Dept of Civil Eng Univ of Wash Seattle WA 98195

KENT, JOSEPH FRANCIS, b Richmond, Va, Feb 13, 44; m 66. TOPOLOGY. *Educ:* Univ Va, BA, 66, MA, 67, PhD(math), 70. *Prof Exp:* Asst prof math, Univ Fla, 70-73; asst prof, 73-80, ASSOC PROF MATH, UNIV RICHMOND, 80- *Mem:* Am Math Soc; Math Asn Am; Sigma Xi. *Res:* Topological dynamics and the study of ergodic flows; differentiability of norms on Banach spaces. *Mailing Add:* Dept of Math Univ of Richmond Richmond VA 23173

KENT, LOIS SCHOONOVER, b Marietta, Ohio, Dec 1, 12; m 43; c 1. GEOLOGY, PALEONTOLOGY. *Educ:* Oberlin Col, AB, 34; Cornell Univ, AM, 36; Bryn Mawr Col, PhD, 40. *Prof Exp:* Demonstr geol, Bryn Mawr Col, 36-40; jr geologist, Sect Metalliferous Deposits, US Geol Surv, 41-43, asst geologist, 43-45; ed asst, Geol Soc Am, 46; instr geol, Univ Ill, 54-55; asst geologist, 56-59, ASSOC GEOLOGIST, ILL STATE GEOL SURV, 59-, CUR, 56- *Mem:* Paleont Res Inst; Paleont Soc; Geol Soc Am; Soc Econ Paleont & Mineral. *Res:* Miocene mollusks of Maryland; Pennsylvanian fossils of Illinois. *Mailing Add:* Ill State Geol Surv 615 E Peabody Dr Champaign IL 61820

KENT, RAYMOND D, b Red Lodge, Mont, Dec 21, 42. COMMUNICATIVE DISORDERS, SPEECH DEVELOPMENT. *Educ:* Univ Mont, BA, 65; Univ Iowa, MA, 69, PhD(speech path), 70. *Prof Exp:* Fel, Res Lab Electronics, Mass Inst Technol, 70-71; prof commun disorders, Univ Wis-Madison, 71-79; SR RES ASSOC, BOYS TOWN INST COMMUN DISORDERS IN CHILDREN, 79- *Concurrent Pos:* Ed, J Speech & Hearing Res, 77-81; prin investr, NIH grants, 73-; mem, Ad Hoc Adv Comt Commun Disorders Prog, Nat Inst Neurol & Commun Disorders & Stroke, 81- *Mem:* Am Speech-Language-Hearing Asn; Am Asn Phonetic Sci; Acoust Soc Am; Sigma Xi; NY Acad Sci. *Res:* Production and perception of speech, especially to speech development in children, neurologic speech and language disorders, and theories of speech production. *Mailing Add:* Boys Town Inst Commun Disorders in Children 555 N 30th St Omaha NE 68131

KENT, RONALD ALLAN, b New York, NY, Feb 23, 35; m 60; c 2. CATALYSIS, INORGANIC CHEMISTRY. *Educ:* Cornell Univ, AB, 54. *Prof Exp:* Develop chemist catalytic chlorination, Gen Chem Res Lab, Allied Chem, 55-57; res assoc inorg sulfur & nitrogen, Dept Chem, Univ Pa, 57-68; res chemist platinum metal catalysis, Matthey Bishop Inc, 68-71; prin chemist heterogeneous catalysis, Dart Industs, 71-75, sr res assoc catalysis, 75-78, dir systs technol res & appl catalytic chem, 78-81, DIR TECH & DEVELOP, DART INDUSTS, 81- *Concurrent Pos:* Instr chem, Spring Garden Inst Technol, 60-61; chief chemist, Chem Info & Doc Serv, Univ Pa, 65-67. *Mem:* Am Chem Soc (secy treas, inorg sect, 70); NY Acad Sci; AAAS; Com Develop Asn; Catalysis Soc NAm. *Res:* Hydrogenation and isomerization catalysis; polymerization catalysis; oxide catalyst processes; ozone preparation and utilization; sulfur dioxide control; noble metal utilization and recovery; secondary copper recovery processes; polyolefins. *Mailing Add:* 322 Duncaster Houston TX 77079

KENT, ROSEMARY (CHRISTINE) MAY, b Bartlesville, Okla, Jan 26, 13; m 37. PUBLIC HEALTH EDUCATION. Educ: Agnes Scott Col, AB, 33; Emory Univ, MA, 34; Univ NC, MPH, 46, PhD(pub health), 49. Prof Exp: Sec teacher, Tenn, 35-40; health educ coordr, 40-43; health consult, Winston-Salem City Pub Schs, 43-45; educ dir, Am Cancer Soc, NC Div, Inc, 47-51; assoc prof, 51-72, EMER ASSOC PROF PUB HEALTH EDUC, SCH PUB HEALTH, UNIV NC, CHAPEL HILL, 72-; EMER PROF HEALTH EDUC, UNIV TENN, KNOXVILLE, 76- Concurrent Pos: Consult, US Off Educ, 42, Univ Hawaii, 68 & Indian Health Serv, USPHS, 69; fac travel fel, WHO, Western Pac & SE Asia, 56. Mem: fel Am Pub Health Asn; charter fel Soc Pub Health Educators. Res: Teacher readiness for roles in family life education; sex education; surveys of handicapped; program and technique evaluation; research on profession of public health education, particularly method of career tracing; design and development of instruments for accumulation of data on health attitudes, interests and problems of community groups. Mailing Add: Holly High Farm Rte 1 Box 299 Pittsboro NC 27312

KENT, SAMUEL SHERRILL, JR, biochemistry, plant physiology, see previous edition

KENT, SIDNEY PAGE, b Cordova, Ala, July 6, 26; m 52; c 2. PATHOLOGY. Educ: Ala Polytech Inst, BS, 46; Med Col Ala, MD, 50. Prof Exp: Fel path, 51-53, from instr to assoc prof, 53-63, PROF PATH, MED CTR, UNIV ALA, BIRMINGHAM, 63- Mem: Histochem Soc; Am Soc Exp Path; AMA; Col Am Path; Int Acad Path. Res: Histochemistry; radiobiology; immunopathology; comparative immunology. Mailing Add: Dept of Path Univ of Ala Med Ctr Birmingham AL 35294

KENT, STEPHEN BRIAN HENRY, b Wellington, NZ, Dec 12, 45; c 2. BIOLOGICAL CHEMISTRY. Educ: Victoria Univ, Wellington, BSc, 68; Massey Univ, NZ, MSc, 70; Univ Calif, Berkeley, PhD(org chem), 75. Prof Exp: Res assoc biochem, Rockefeller Univ, 74-77, asst prof, 77-80; SR SCIENTIST, MOLECULAR GENETICS, INC, 80- Mem: NY Acad Sci; Am Chem Soc; Harvey Soc. Res: Development of methodology in protein chemistry and its application to biological proglems involving the relationship of protein structure to function. Mailing Add: Molecular Genetics Inc 10320 Bren Rd E Minnetonka MN 55343

KENT, THOMAS HUGH, b Iowa City, Iowa, Aug 17, 34; m 57; c 3. PATHOLOGY. Educ: Univ Iowa, BA, 56, MD, 59; Am Bd Path, dipl, 65. Prof Exp: Intern, Methodist Hosp, Indianapolis, 59-60; resident path, Univ Iowa, 60-64; assoc pathologist, Walter Reed Army Inst Res, 64-66; from asst prof to assoc prof, 66-72, PROF PATH, COL MED, UNIV IOWA, 72- Mem: AMA; Col Am Path; Am Asn Pathologists & Bacteriologists; Am Soc Clin Path. Res: Gastroenterology. Mailing Add: 133 Med Labs Univ of Iowa Col of Med Iowa City IA 52240

KENTFIELD, JOHN ALAN CHARLES, b Hitchin, Eng, Mar 4, 30; m 66. MECHANICAL ENGINEERING. Educ: Univ Southampton, BSc, 59; Univ London, DIC & PhD(mech eng), 63. Prof Exp: Trainee, C V A Kearney & Trecker Ltd, Eng, 50-52; asst tester, Ricardo & Co Ltd, 52-56; asst lectr res & educ, Imp Col, Univ London, 62-63; proj engr, Curtiss-Wright Corp, 63-66; lectr res & educ, Imp Col, Univ London, 66-70; assoc prof, 70-79, PROF ENG, UNIV CALGARY, 81- Concurrent Pos: Nat Res Coun grant, Univ Calgary, 71-72 & operating grant, 77 & 80. Mem: Am Inst Aeronaut & Astronaut; Am Soc Mech Engrs; Brit Inst Mech Engrs. Res: Non-steady flow of compressible fluid and the application of non-steady flow phenomena in engineering equipment, such as pressure exchangers and pulsating combustors; wind-turbines and wind-energy systems. Mailing Add: Fac of Eng Univ of Calgary Calgary AB T2N 1N4 Can

KENTZER, CZESLAW P(AWEL), b Poland, June 29, 25; nat US; m 58; c 3. GAS DYNAMICS, COMPUTATIONAL FLUID MECHANICS. Educ: San Diego State Col, BS, 52; Purdue Univ, MS, 54, PhD(aerospace eng), 58. Prof Exp: Asst prof, 58-60, ASSOC PROF AERODYN, PURDUE UNIV, 60- Concurrent Pos: Consult, Missiles & Space Systs Div, Douglas Aircraft Corp. Mem: Am Math Soc; Am Acad Mech. Res: Fluid mechanics; transonic aerodynamics; acoustics; nonlinear waves; turbulence theories; computational fluid mechanics; geophysical fluid mechanics. Mailing Add: Sch of Aeronaut & Astronaut Grissom Hall Purdue Univ West Lafayette IN 47907

KENWORTHY, ALVIN LAWRENCE, b Shiatook, Okla, Sept 6, 15; m 37; c 2. HORTICULTURE. Educ: Okla State Univ, BS, 37; Kansas State Univ, MS, 39; Wash State Univ, PhD(hort), 48. Prof Exp: Asst prof hort, Univ Fla, 43-44; assoc prof hort, Univ Del, 44-48; assoc prof, Mich State Univ, 48-52, prof, 52-80. Mem: Am Soc Hort Sci. Res: Nutrient element requirements of fruit trees; nutrient element interrelationships and balance; spectrographic plant analysis; soil management; irrigation and growth chemicals. Mailing Add: 4647 N Meridian Williamston MI 48895

KENYON, ALAN J, b Whitehall, Wis, Sept 10, 29; m 54; c 3. BIOCHEMISTRY, IMMUNOLOGY. Educ: Univ Minn, BS, 54, DVM, 57, PhD(bact & biochem), 61. Prof Exp: From assoc prof to prof biochem, Univ Conn, 61-73; prof biol, Med Sch, Cornell Univ, 73-80; MEM, WALKER LAB, SLOAN-KETTERING INST CANCER RES, 73- Concurrent Pos: NIH res grants, 63- & career develop award, 65-75; consult, Manned Spacecraft Ctr, Apollo Prog, NASA, 68-, Path Dept, Hartford Hosp, 70- & Res Inst, Ill Inst Technol, 71-; sabbatical leave pediat & path, Sch Med, Univ Minn, Minneapolis, 71-72. Mem: AAAS; NY Acad Sci; Am Soc Exp Path; Reticuloendothelial Soc; Am Asn Lab Animal Sci. Res: Immunochemistry as applied to lymphoproliferative diseases and neoplasias of man and animals; comparative biochemistry of Mustelidae; diseases of marine mammals; immunological deficiency. Mailing Add: Walker Lab Sloan-Kettering Inst Cancer Res Rye NY 10580

KENYON, ALLEN STEWART, b Constance, Ky, Mar 6, 16; m 42; c 4. POLYMER SCIENCE. Educ: Univ Ky, BS, 38, MS, 39; Columbia Univ, PhD(phys chem), 47. Prof Exp: Asst phys chem, Univ Ky, 38-39, instr chem, 39-40; asst, Columbia Univ, 40-42; res chemist, 47-58, group leader, 58-69, sr res specialist, 69-80, FEL, MONSANTO CO, 80- Concurrent Pos: Asst, Nat Defense Res Comt Proj, Columbia Univ, 41-42. Mem: Am Chem Soc. Res: Mechanical properties; light scattering on high polymers; nondispersed sulfur sols; higher order Tyndall spectra; physical chemistry, structure and property relations of polymers; polymer characterization; chemistry of interfaces in composite materials. Mailing Add: Monsanto Co 800 N Lindbergh Blvd St Louis MO 63166

KENYON, GEORGE LOMMEL, b Wilmington, Del, Aug 29, 39; m 81; c 1. BIOCHEMISTRY. Educ: Bucknell Univ, BS, 61; Harvard Univ, MA, 63, PhD(org chem), 65. Prof Exp: Fel biochem, Mass Inst Technol, 65-66; asst prof chem, Univ Calif, Berkeley, 66-72; asst prof pharm chem, 72-74, assoc prof, 74-77, PROF PHARM CHEM & BIOCHEM, UNIV CALIF, SAN FRANCISCO, 77- Mem: AAAS; Am Chem Soc; Am Soc Biol Chemists; NY Acad Sci. Res: Enzyme mechanisms; organophosphorus chemistry; bioorganic chemistry of nucleotides; application of nuclear magnetic resonance spectroscopy to biological problems; design of reagents for protein modification; design of specific enzyme inhibitors. Mailing Add: Dept Pharmaceut Chem Univ Calif San Francisco CA 94143

KENYON, HEWITT, b Marysville, Calif, Aug 31, 20; m 47, m 61; c 5. MATHEMATICS. Educ: Univ Calif, BS, 42, PhD(math), 54. Prof Exp: From instr to asst prof math, Univ Rochester, 52-61; from asst prof to assoc prof, 61-67, chmn dept, 67-71, PROF MATH, GEORGE WASHINGTON UNIV, 67- Concurrent Pos: Vis assoc prof, Univ Calif, Berkeley, 66-67. Mem: Am Math Soc; Math Asn Am. Res: Convergence in topology; differentiation of set functions. Mailing Add: 1611 Kennedy Pl NW Washington DC 20052

KENYON, KERN ELLSWORTH, b Kansas City, Mo, May 24, 38; m 66; c 2. PHYSICAL OCEANOGRAPHY. Educ: Mass Inst Technol, BS & MS, 61; Scripps Inst Oceanog, PhD(oceanog), 66. Prof Exp: Asst prof, Grad Sch Oceanog, Univ RI, 67-73; ASST RES OCEANOGR, SCRIPPS INST OCEANOG, 73- Mem: Am Geophys Union; AAAS; Oceanog Soc Japan. Res: Large-scale ocean circulation and air sea interaction; wave-wave and wave-current interactions. Mailing Add: Scripps Inst Oceanog Univ of Calif La Jolla CA 92093

KENYON, RICHARD A(LBERT), b Syracuse, NY, Apr 8, 33; m 54; c 3. MECHANICAL ENGINEERING, THERMODYNAMICS. Educ: Clarkson Col Technol, BME, 54; Cornell Univ, MS, 56; Syracuse Univ, PhD(mech eng), 65. Prof Exp: Instr mech eng, Cornell Univ, 54-56; asst prof, Clarkson Col Technol, 56-62, assoc prof, 62-70, assoc dean grad sch & assoc dir, Div Res, 66-68, chmn dept & exec officer, 68-70; head dept mech eng, 70-72, PROF MECH ENG, ROCHESTER INST TECHNOL, 70-, DEAN COL ENG, 71- Mem: Fel Am Soc Mech Engrs (vpres, 78-82); Am Soc Eng Educ; Nat Soc Prof Engrs; Sigma Xi. Res: Technology transfer from the academic and private sectors to local government; solid waste engineering and resource recovery. Mailing Add: Col of Eng One Lomb Memorial Dr Rochester NY 14623

KENYON, RICHARD H, b Blakely, Pa, Nov 22, 42; m 68. VIROLOGY, IMMUNOLOGY. Educ: Bucknell Univ, BS, 64; Pa State Univ, MS, 66, PhD(microbiol), 68. Prof Exp: Virologist-immunologist, US Army Biol Labs, Ft Detrick, 69-71, Virol Lab, US Army Med Res Inst Infectious Dis, 71, rickettsiologist-immunologist, Virol Lab, 71-77, ASST CHIEF, RICKETTSIOLOGY DIV, US ARMY MED RES INST INFECTIOUS DIS, 78-, VIROL DIV, 80- Res: Vaccine development; Rocky Mountain spotted fever; Rickettsiae; Junn virus; Argentine hemorrliagic fever. Mailing Add: Rickettsiology Div US Army Med Res Inst Infect Dis Frederick MD 21701

KENYON, RICHARD R(EID), b Middletown, Ohio, Oct 6, 28. ELECTRICAL ENGINEERING, COMPUTER SCIENCE. Educ: Purdue Univ, BS, 50, MS, 51, PhD(elec eng), 61. Prof Exp: Mem tech staff, Bell Tel Labs, NJ, 51-55; res asst comput sci, Purdue Univ, 55-58, instr, 58-61, asst prof, 61-65; consult comput sci, 65-80, LEAD ENGR, MCDONNELL DOUGLAS ASTRONAUTICS CO, 80- Mem: Asn Comput Mach; Inst Elec & Electronics Engrs. Res: Circuit theory; numerical methods of approximation; computer architecture, programming languages. Mailing Add: McDonnell Douglas Astronautics Co 5301 Bolsa Ave Huntington Beach CA 92647

KENYON, VAN LESLIE, JR, b Hillsboro, NC, Nov 2, 10; m 34; c 4. MECHANICAL ENGINEERING. Educ: Univ NC, BS, 32; Univ Del, MEE, 51. Prof Exp: Asst to supt power plant, Prox Mfg Co, NC, 33-36; engr in charge utilities, Woman's Col NC, 36-42; asst prof mech eng, Univ Vt, 43-44; utility engr, Propellor Div, Beaver Plant, Curtiss-Wright Co, 44-45; from asst prof to prof mech eng, 45-76, actg chmn dept eng, 53-55 & 64-66, EMER PROF MECH ENG, DUKE UNIV, 76- Mem: Am Soc Mech Engrs; Am Soc Eng Educ; AAAS. Res: Heat transfer; thermodynamics; nuclear engineering. Mailing Add: 122 E Tryon St Hillsborough NC 27278

KEOGH, FRANK RICHARD, b London, Eng, Apr 1, 23; m 46; c 6. MATHEMATICS. Educ: Univ Manchester, BSc, 50; Cambridge Univ, PhD(math), 54, ScD(math), 63. Prof Exp: Lectr math, Univ Col Swansea, Wales, 53-63; prof, Univ London, 63-65; PROF MATH, UNIV KY, 65- Mem: Am Math Soc; fel Brit Inst Math & Appln; London Math Soc. Res: Functions of a complex variable; Fourier series; summability. Mailing Add: Dept of Math Univ of Ky Off Tower Lexington KY 40506

KEOGH, JOSEPH LLOYD, agronomy, soils, see previous edition

KEOGH, MICHAEL JOHN, b Bronx, NY, May 26, 37; m 75; c 3. ORGANIC CHEMISTRY, POLYMER CHEMISTRY. *Educ:* Manhattan Col, BS, 59; Purdue Univ, PhD(org chem), 63. *Prof Exp:* Chemist, 63-67, proj scientist, 67-70, res scientist, 70-78, SR RES SCIENTIST, POLYOLEFINS DIV, UNION CARBIDE CORP, 78- *Mem:* Am Chem Soc; Fire Retardant Chem Asn. *Res:* Synthetic, organic and polymer chemistry; fluorocarbons; condensation monomer synthesis; organometallic and anionic polymerization systems; epoxide and other thermosetting polymerization systems; polymers engineered for pollution control; wire and cable technology. *Mailing Add:* Res & Develop Dept Union Carbide Corp River Rd Bound Brook NJ 08805

KEOGH, RICHARD NEIL, b Nashua, NH, Apr 21, 40. CELL BIOLOGY. *Educ:* Tufts Univ, BS, 62; Brown Univ, PhD(biol), 67. *Prof Exp:* From asst prof to assoc prof, 67-77, PROF BIOL, RI COL, 77- *Mem:* AAAS; Am Asn Biol Teachers; Am Inst Biol Sci. *Res:* Mammalian pigment cell biology; teaching of biology via television; multimedia methods of instruction. *Mailing Add:* Dept of Biol RI Col 600 Mount Pleasant Providence RI 02908

KEOSIAN, JOHN, b Erzinjan, Armenia, Mar 28, 06; nat US; m 32; c 1. EXOBIOLOGY. *Educ:* NY Univ, BS, 27, PhD(physiol), 36. *Prof Exp:* Asst biol, Wash Sq Col, NY Univ, 27-33; instr, Newark State Col, 33-37; from asst prof to prof, 37-71, dir cadet nurse training, 42-44, gas reconnaissance off, NY, 43-46, chmn dept biol, 54-57, dir div natural sci, 57-64, EMER PROF BIOL, RUTGERS UNIV, 71- *Concurrent Pos:* Consult, Nat Defense Educ Act symp on life, Merced, 65; Fulbright fel, Nuclear Res Ctr Demokritos, US Educ Found, Greece, 69-71; corp mem, Marine Biol Lab, Woods Hole Oceanog Inst, 48-80, life mem, 80- *Mem:* Fel NY Acad Sci; Am Astron Soc. *Res:* Function of chick mesonephros in tissue culture; biochemical genetics; induced mutation; origin of life; biological effects of radiation. *Mailing Add:* Marine Biol Lab PO Box 193 Woods Hole MA 02543

KEOUGH, ALLEN HENRY, b Chelsea, Mass, Apr 24, 29; m 52; c 6. ORGANIC CHEMISTRY. *Educ:* Univ Mass, BS, 50; Univ NH, MS, 52; Mass Inst Technol, PhD(org chem), 56. *Prof Exp:* Res chemist, Johnson & Johnson, 55-58; sr res engr, Explor Res Div, Norton Co, Worcester, 58-62, res assoc, 62, asst dir res & develop, 62-63; res assoc, Nat Res Corp, 63-66, asst dir res, 66-68; pres, Chem-Tech Assocs, Inc, Mass, 68-71; sect head, Res Div, 71-74, sect head advan develop div, Dennison Mfg Co, 74-78; pres, Design Cote Co, 78-81; TECH DIR, METALL PRODS DIV, KING-SEELEY THERMOS CO, 81- *Mem:* AAAS; Am Chem Soc; Asn Finishing Processes Soc Mfg Engrs. *Res:* Synthetic organic chemistry; organometallic compounds; heterogeneous catalysis surface active agents; polymer chemistry; radiation curing printing inks and coatings. *Mailing Add:* 53 Patricia Rd Sudbury MA 01776

KEOUGH, KEVIN MICHAEL WILLIAM, b St George's, Nfld, Aug 2, 43; m 67; c 2. BIOCHEMISTRY. *Educ:* Univ Toronto, BSc, 65, MSc, 67, PhD(biochem), 71. *Prof Exp:* Muscular Dystrophy Asn Can fel phys biochem, Univ Sheffield, 71-72; asst prof, 72-76, ASSOC PROF BIOCHEM, MEM UNIV NFLD, 76-, ASSOC PROF PEDIAT, 80- *Mem:* Can Lung Asn; Biochem Soc. *Res:* Molecular organization in membranes and lung surfactant. *Mailing Add:* Dept of Biochem Mem Univ of Nfld St John's NF A1B 3X9 Can

KEOWN, ERNEST RAY, b Thurber, Tex, Mar 17, 21; m 43; c 2. APPLIED MATHEMATICS. *Educ:* Univ Tex, BS, 46; Mass Inst Technol, PhD(math), 50; Univ Ark, JD, 81. *Prof Exp:* Sr aerophysics engr, Consol Vultee Aircraft Co, 51-52; asst prof math, Tex A&M, 52-57; comput specialist, Douglas Aircraft Co, 57-59; tech specialist, Aerojet Gen Corp Div, Gen Tire & Rubber Co, 59-60; prof math, Tex A&M Univ, 60-67; PROF MATH, UNIV ARK, FAYETTEVILLE, 67- *Concurrent Pos:* Consult, Atomic Energy Comn, Standard Oil Co, Tex & Magnolia Petrol Co; mem solid state & molecular theory group, Mass Inst Technol, 63-64. *Mem:* Am Math Soc. *Res:* Group representation theory; applications of group representation theory in physics; numerical analysis; computers and law. *Mailing Add:* Dept Math SE 301 Univ Ark Fayetteville AR 72701

KEOWN, KENNETH K, b Independence, Mo, May 25, 17; m 41; c 2. ANESTHESIOLOGY. *Educ:* Hahnemann Med Col, MD, 41. *Prof Exp:* Intern, Huron Rd Hosp, Cleveland, 41-42; resident, Hahnemann Hosp, 46-48; asst anesthesiol, Hahnemann Med Col, 48-50, from asst prof to assoc prof, 50-57; med dir, Med Ctr, 69-75, PROF ANESTHESIOL, SCH MED, UNIV MO-COLUMBIA, 57- *Concurrent Pos:* Consult, Ft Leonard Wood Army Hosp. *Mem:* Am Soc Anesthesiol (1st vpres, 59-60); AMA; Am Col Anesthesiol (vchmn, 59-60); Int Anesthesia Res Soc; Sigma Xi. *Res:* Anesthesia for cardiac surgery. *Mailing Add:* Med Ctr Univ of Mo Columbia MO 65201

KEOWN, ROBERT WILLIAM, b Louisville, Ky, Apr 23, 29; m 49; c 3. ORGANIC CHEMISTRY, POLYMER CHEMISTRY. *Educ:* Univ Louisville, BS, 51, MS, 52, PhD(chem), 54. *Prof Exp:* Res chemist, 54-71, tech assoc, 71-74, supvr, Adhesives & Fluids Div, 74-81, RES ASSOC, E I DU PONT DE NEMOURS & CO, INC, 81- *Mem:* Am Chem Soc; AAAS; Adhesion Soc. *Res:* Polymer chemistry. *Mailing Add:* Polymer Prods Dept E I du Pont de Nemours & Co Wilmington DE 19898

KEPECS, JOSEPH GOODMAN, b Philadelphia, Pa, Oct 8, 12; m 2. PSYCHIATRY, PSYCHOANALYSIS. *Educ:* Univ Chicago, BS, 35, MD, 37; Chicago Inst Psychoanal, cert, 49. *Prof Exp:* Pvt practr, 46-65; PROF PSYCHIAT, MED SCH, UNIV WIS-MADISON, 65- *Concurrent Pos:* Vis lectr, Univ Cincinnati, 1; lectr, Chicago Inst Psychoanal, 57-60; prof lectr, Univ Chicago, 60-65; consult, Univ Wis, 60-65. *Mem:* Am Psychiat Asn; Am Psychoanal Asn; Am Psychosom Soc. *Res:* Applications of psychiatry to medicine; sociological studies of changes in therapists and patients; psychiatry in developing countries. *Mailing Add:* Dept of Psychiat Med Sch Univ of Wis-Madison Madison WI 53706

KEPES, JOHN J, b Budapest, Hungary, Mar 31, 28; US citizen; m 50; c 1. PATHOLOGY, NEUROPATHOLOGY. *Educ:* Univ Budapest, MD, 52. *Prof Exp:* Pathologist-in-chief, Nat Inst Neurosurg, Hungary, 54-56; from asst prof to assoc prof, 60-68, PROF PATH, UNIV KANS MED CTR, KANSAS CITY, 68- *Concurrent Pos:* Spec fel neuropath, Mayo Found, Univ Minn, 57-58; consult, Vet Admin Hosp, Kansas City, 60-; vis prof, Neurol Inst, Univ Vienna, 68-69. *Mem:* Am Acad Neurol; Am Asn Neuropathol (vpres, 78-79); Am Asn Neurol Surgeons. *Res:* Histological differential diagnosis of brain tumors; electron microscopic studies of meningiomas; spinal cord circulation; primary malignant lymphomas of central nervous system; histiocytosis and xanthosarcomas of central nervous system; pathogenesis of central pontine myelinolysis; etiology and pathogenesis of the Arnold-Chiari malformation. *Mailing Add:* Dept of Path Univ of Kans Med Ctr Kansas City KS 66103

KEPES, JOSEPH JOHN, b Cleveland, Ohio, Jan 25, 31; m 54; c 6. NUCLEAR & REACTOR PHYSICS. *Educ:* Case Inst Technol, BS, 53; Univ Notre Dame, PhD(nuclear physics), 58. *Prof Exp:* Sr scientist, Bettis Atomic Power Lab, 57-62; assoc prof, 62-71, chmn dept, 62-75, PROF PHYSICS, UNIV DAYTON, 71- *Mem:* Am Phys Soc; Am Asn Physics Teachers. *Res:* Electron-electron scattering at low energies; resonance escape probabilities in natural uranium plates. *Mailing Add:* Dept of Physics Univ of Dayton Dayton OH 45469

KEPHART, ROBERT DAVID, b Phillipsburg, Pa, Nov 27, 49; m 71. HIGH ENERGY PHYSICS, CRYOGENICS. *Educ:* Va Polytech Inst & State Univ, BS, 71; State Univ NY, Stony Brook, MS, 73, PhD(physics), 75. *Prof Exp:* Res asst physics, Dept Physics, Va Polytech Inst & State Univ, 69-71; res asst, Dept Physics, State Univ NY, Stony Brook, 71-75, fel, 75-77; STAFF PHYSICIST, FERMI NAT ACCELERATOR LAB, 77- *Concurrent Pos:* Proj mgr, Chicago Cyclotron Super Conducting Magnet Proj & leader, Fermilab Superconducting Analysis Magnetic Goup. *Mem:* Am Phys Soc. *Res:* Detector development; liquid argon calorimetry; super conducting magnet design and research and development; high purity gas systems; dimuon high energy physics; engineering physics. *Mailing Add:* Res Servs/Cryogenics Group PO Box 500 Batavia IL 60510

KEPLER, CAROL R, b Berea, Ohio, Oct 21, 37; m 59. LIPID CHEMISTRY. *Educ:* Oberlin Col, AB, 59; Univ NC, PhD(zool), 65. *Prof Exp:* Asst prof nutrit, NC State Univ, 65-66, asst prof biochem, 66-81; ASST PROF, MEREDITH COL, 81- *Concurrent Pos:* Nat Inst Health fel, 65-66. *Mem:* Sigma Xi; Am Soc Zoologists. *Res:* Rumen bacteria; hydrogenation and isomerization of unsaturated fatty acids; specificity of triglyceride synthesis. *Mailing Add:* Dept of Biochem NC State Univ Raleigh NC 27607

KEPLER, HAROLD B(ENTON), b Dayton, Ohio, Jan 3, 22; m 46; c 2. MECHANICAL ENGINEERING. *Educ:* Sinclair Col, AEA, 53, BBA, 56; Xavier Univ, Ohio, MBA, 58. *Prof Exp:* Eng draftsman, Eng Div, Wright Field, Ohio, 40-42, design checker, Aircraft Lab, Wright-Patterson AFB, 46-47; prod designer, Ohmer Corp, 47-48; from instr to assoc prof mech eng, 48-77, EMER PROF, US AIR FORCE INST TECHNOL, 77- *Concurrent Pos:* Lectr, Sinclair Col, Ohio, 60- *Mem:* Am Soc Eng Educ. *Res:* Engineering graphics; mechanisms and reliability engineering. *Mailing Add:* 90 Sheldon Dr Centerville OH 45459

KEPLER, RAYMOND GLEN, b Long Beach, Calif, Sept 10, 28; m 53; c 4. EXPERIMENTAL SOLID STATE PHYSICS. *Educ:* Stanford Univ, BS, 50; Univ Calif, MS, 55, PhD(physics), 57. *Prof Exp:* Res physicist, Cent Res Dept, E I du Pont de Nemours & Co, 57-64; div supvr, Sandia Corp, 64-69, DEPT MGR, SANDIA NAT LABS, 69- *Mem:* AAAS; Am Phys Soc; Am Phys Cos Comn Educ. *Res:* Photoconductivity; conductivity; excitons and other solid state properties, primarily of organic solids; piezoelectricity, pyroelectricity and ferroelectricity in polymers. *Mailing Add:* 9004 Bellehaven Ave NE Albuquerque NM 87112

KEPLINGER, MORENO LAVON, b Ulysses, Kans, May 25, 29; m 50; c 3. TOXICOLOGY. *Educ:* Univ Kans, BS, 51, MS, 52; Northwestern Univ, PhD(pharmacol), 56; Am Bd Toxicol, dipl, 80. *Prof Exp:* Res instr pharmacol, Univ Miami, 56-59, asst prof, 59-60; toxicologist, Hercules Powder Co, 60-64; pharmacol, Univ Miami, 64-68; asst dir, Indust Bio-Test Labs, Inc, 68-70; mgr toxicol, 70-77; CONSULT TOXICOL, 78- *Mem:* Europ Soc Toxicol; Soc Toxicol; Am Soc Pharmacol & Exp Therapeut; Am Indust Hyg Asn. *Res:* Experimental and industrial toxicology; pharmacology. *Mailing Add:* 221 Park Lane Deerfield IL 60015

KEPLINGER, ORIN CLAWSON, b Carlinville, Ill, Oct 7, 18; m 39; c 3. POLYMER CHEMISTRY, EXPLOSIVES. *Educ:* Southern Ill Univ, BEd, 40; Univ Ill, MS, 48, PhD(chem), 49. *Prof Exp:* From jr chemist to chemist explosives, Western Cartridge Co, 40-44; spec asst, Univ Ill, 46-49; sr res chemist, Polymers, Gen Tire & Rubber Co, 49-59; chem supvr, Sherwin-Williams Co, 59-64; dir varnish resin lab, 64-66, dir prod develop, 66-75, dir resin technol, 75-78; tech dir, Chem Coatings Div, Valspar, 79-81; RETIRED. *Concurrent Pos:* Pres, Paint Res Inst, 75-81. *Mem:* Am Chem Soc; Fedn Soc Coatings Technol; Soc Chem & Indust, London. *Res:* Explosives process development; synthetic rubber and plastics preparation; resins and polymers for coatings; paint formulation. *Mailing Add:* 103 Tulsa Dr Rogers AR 72756

KEPNER, RICHARD EDWIN, b Los Angeles, Calif, July 27, 16; m 46; c 2. ORGANIC CHEMISTRY. *Educ:* Univ Calif, BS, 38; Univ Calif, Los Angeles, MA, 42, PhD(org chem), 46. *Prof Exp:* Lab asst soil chem, Univ Calif, Los Angeles, 40-41, asst chem, 43-46; from instr to assoc prof, 46-60, PROF CHEM, UNIV CALIF, DAVIS, 60- *Mem:* Am Chem Soc; Am Soc Enol; Phytochem Soc NAm. *Res:* Isolation and identification of natural glycosides; odor and flavor constituents of fruits and wines; grape pigments; volatile plant terpenes. *Mailing Add:* Dept of Chem Univ of Calif Davis CA 95616

KEPPEL, CHARLES ROBERT, inorganic chemistry, see previous edition

KEPPELER, RICHARD ALBERT, b Williams Co, Ohio, Dec 5, 16; m 43; c 2. FOOD SCIENCE. *Educ:* Mich State Univ, BS, 56, MS, 57, PhD(agr eng), 62. *Prof Exp:* Plant supt, Fairmont Foods Co, 48-52; mem fac, Mich State Univ, 52-62; assoc prof, 62-80, PROF AGR ENG & FOOD PROCESSING, PA STATE UNIV, 80- *Mem:* Am Soc Agr Eng; Am Soc Eng Educ; Inst Food Technologists. *Res:* Heat transfer; food process engineering. *Mailing Add:* Dept of Agr Eng Pa State Univ University Park PA 16802

KEPPER, JOHN C, b Baltimore, Md, Nov 7, 32; m 60; c 2. SEDIMENTARY PETROLOGY, STRATIGRAPHY. *Educ:* Franklin & Marshall Col, BS, 55; Univ Wash, MS, 60, PhD(geol), 69. *Prof Exp:* Instr geol, Cabrillo Col, 61-67; asst prof geol, State Univ NY Col Oneonta, 69-73; ASSOC PROF GEOL, UNIV NEV, LAS VEGAS, 73- *Mem:* Soc Econ Paleont & Mineral; Am Asn Petrol Geol; Geol Soc Am. *Res:* Sedimentary petrology, especially carbonate petrology; regional stratigraphy of the Cambrian rocks in the Great Basin Region. *Mailing Add:* Dept of Geosci Univ of Nev Las Vegas NV 89557

KEPPLE, PAUL C, b San Luis Potosi, Mex, Feb 6, 36; US citizen; m 62; c 2. PHYSICS. *Educ:* Univ Okla, BS, 58, MS, 61; NMex State Univ, PhD(physics), 66. *Prof Exp:* Res assoc plasma physics, Univ Md, 66-69; RES PHYSICIST, NAVAL RES LAB, 69- *Mem:* Am Phys Soc. *Res:* Plasma physics; atomic physics. *Mailing Add:* Naval Res Lab 4555 Overlook Ave SW Washington DC 20375

KEPPLER, WILLIAM J, b Teaneck, NJ, Jan 20, 37; m 60; c 1. GENETICS, EVOLUTION. *Educ:* Univ Miami, Fla, BS, 59; Univ Ill, MS, 61, PhD(genetics), 65. *Prof Exp:* From asst prof to prof zool, Eastern Ill Univ, 65-76, asst provost, 73-76; DEAN ARTS & SCI, BOISE STATE UNIV, 77- *Res:* Cytochemistry of chromosomes. *Mailing Add:* Sch of Arts & Sci Boise State Univ Boise ID 83725

KEPPNER, EDWIN JAMES, parasitology, ecology, see previous edition

KEPRON, WAYNE, b Winnipeg, Man, Mar 31, 42; m 66; c 3. IMMUNOLOGY, PHYSIOLOGY. *Educ:* Univ Man, BSc & MD, 67. *Prof Exp:* ASST PROF INTERNAL MED, FAC MED, UNIV MAN, 75-, ASST PROF IMMUNOL, 78- *Concurrent Pos:* Attend physician, Respiratory Centre, Health Sci Ctr & consult physician, Dept Vet Affairs, Deer Lodge Hosp, 75-; assoc investr med res coun group for allergy res, Dept Immunol, Univ Man, 78- *Mem:* Am Acad Allergy; Am Thoracic Soc; Can Lung Asn. *Res:* Studies in the pathogenesis of Ige, Ige mediated asthma with specific reference to the role of local immune mechanisims in the lung; the modification of Ige metabolism with tolerogenic conjugates. *Mailing Add:* 668 Bannatyne Ave Winnipeg MB R3E 0V8 Can

KER, JOHN WILLIAM, b Chilliwack, BC, Aug 27, 15; m 43; c 3. FORESTRY. *Educ:* Univ BC, BASc, 41; Yale Univ, MF, 51, DF(forestry), 57. *Hon Degrees:* DSc, Univ BC, 71. *Prof Exp:* Forest ranger, BC Forest Serv, 41-45, asst forester, 45-48; asst prof forest mensuration, Univ BC, 48-53, assoc prof forest mensuration & econ, 53-61; PROF FOREST MENSURATION & ECON & DEAN FAC FORESTRY, UNIV NB, 61- *Concurrent Pos:* Consult, H G Acres & Agr Rehab & Develop Act, 64-65, Atlantic Develop Bd, 66-68, Royal Comn Econ State & Prospects of Nfld & Labrador, 66-67, Prov NB Land Compensation Bd, 70-71, Int Bank Reconstruct & Develop, 72-73, & Can Coun Rural Develop, 72-73; expert univ educ, Can Int Develop Agency, 73-74; Can deleg, Food & Agr Orgn, Adv Comt Forestry Educ, 75-78; chmn, Forest Mgt Task Force, NB Dept Natural Resources, 78-81; mem, Natural Sci & Eng Res Coun Can, 80-83. *Mem:* Can Forestry Asn (vpres, 72-73); Can Inst Forestry (pres, 72-73). *Res:* Forest economics and valuation; forest measurements and biometry; university-level forestry education in both Canada and developing countries. *Mailing Add:* Fac of Forestry Univ of NB PO Box 4400 Fredericton NB E3B 5A3 Can

KERAMIDAS, VASSILIS GEORGE, b Moudros, Greece, June 27, 38; US citizen; m 67; c 2. APPLIED PHYSICS, MATERIALS SCIENCE. *Educ:* Rockford Col, BA, 60; Univ Ill, BS, 62; John Carroll Univ, MS, 69; Pa State Univ, PhD(solid state sci), 73. *Prof Exp:* Res staff mem cadmium sulfide solar cells, Crystal Solid State Div, Harshaw Chem Co, 63-67; mem tech staff optoelectronic mat & devices, 73-80, SUPVR SPECIAL III-V SEMICONDUCTOR MAT FOR FIELD EFFECT TRANSISTORS & HIGH SPEED DEVICES, BELL LABS, 80- *Mem:* Electrochem Soc; AAAS. *Res:* Compound semiconductor light emitting sources and detectors for lightwave communications through optical fibers; compound semiconductor materials for optoelectronics; field effect transistors; high speed devices. *Mailing Add:* Bell Labs Rm 7A 411 600 Mountain Ave Murray Hill NJ 07974

KERBECEK, ARTHUR J(OSEPH), JR, b New York, NY, May 29, 26. CHEMICAL ENGINEERING. *Educ:* Columbia Univ, BS, 47, MS, 48, PhD(chem eng), 51. *Prof Exp:* Res engr, Titanium Metal Div, E I du Pont de Nemours & Co, Del, 52; chief metallurgist, Terrebonne Titanium Co, Can, 52-53; res engr, Ord & Inorg Chem Div, Food Mach & Chem Corp, 53-58; engr, Res Dept, Bethlehem Steel Corp, Pa, 58-68; INDUST CONSULT, 68- *Mem:* Am Chem Soc; Electrochem Soc; Am Inst Chem Engrs. *Res:* Chemical process technology; production metallurgy; corrosion; electrochemistry. *Mailing Add:* 53 Grove St Glenwood Landing Long Island NY 11547

KERBEL, ROBERT STEPHEN, b Toronto, Ont, Apr 5, 45; m 70; c 1. CANCER. *Educ:* Univ Toronto, BS, 68; Queen's Univ, Ont, PhD(microbiol & immunol), 72. *Prof Exp:* Res fel Nat Cancer Inst Can, Chester Beatty Res Inst, London, 72-74; asst prof, 75-80, ASSOC PROF, DEPT PATH, QUEEN'S UNIV, 80- *Concurrent Pos:* King George V Silver Jubilee Cancer Res fel, Nat Cancer Inst Can, 73-74, res scholar, 75-81, res assoc, 81-; mem, Grants Panel B, Nat Cancer Inst Can, 77-81; mem study sect B, NIH, 81-82; assoc ed, Inv & Metastasis, Cancer Metastasis Reviews, 81- *Honors & Awards:* Wild Leitz Jr Sci Award, Expl Path, 80. *Mem:* Brit Soc Immunol; Can Soc Immunol; Am Asn Immunologists; Can Assoc Pathol. *Res:* Cancer; tumor biology; immunology; cell biology of cancer metastasis studied using membrane mutant tumor sublines; tumor progression and heterogeneity; membrane biology of activated lymphocyte and macrophage cell populations. *Mailing Add:* Dept Path Botterell Hall Queens Univ Kingston ON K7L 3N6 Can

KERBER, ERICH RUDOLPH, b Langham, Sask, Apr 2, 26; m 56; c 2. CYTOGENETICS. *Educ:* Univ Sask, BSA, 50, MSc, 53; Univ Alta, PhD(cytogenetics), 58. *Prof Exp:* Res officer, plant breeding, 56-60, WHEAT CYTOGENETICIST, RES STA, CAN DEPT AGR, 60- *Mem:* AAAS; Genetics Soc Can; Am Soc Agron; Am Soc Crop Sci. *Res:* Plant cytology and genetics. *Mailing Add:* 195 Dafoe Rd Winnipeg MB R3T 0T1 Can

KERBER, RICHARD E, b New York, NY, May 10, 39; c 2. CARDIOVASCULAR DISEASES. *Educ:* Columbia Univ, AB, 60; NY Univ, MD, 64. *Prof Exp:* From asst prof to assoc prof, 71-78, PROF INT MED, COL MED, UNIV IOWA, 78- *Mem:* Am Heart Asn; fel Am Col Cardiol; Am Physiol Soc. *Res:* Echocardiography; stress electrocardiography; defibrillation and cardioversion; cardiovascular pharmacology. *Mailing Add:* Dept of Int Med Univ of Iowa Hosps Iowa City IA 52242

KERBER, ROBERT CHARLES, b Hartford, Conn, Nov 29, 38. ORGANIC CHEMISTRY. *Educ:* Mass Inst Technol, SB, 60; Purdue Univ, PhD(org chem), 65. *Prof Exp:* Fel org chem, Purdue Univ, 65; asst prof, 65-72, ASSOC PROF CHEM, STATE UNIV NY STONY BROOK, 72- *Concurrent Pos:* Fel, Humboldt Found, W Germany, 73-74. *Mem:* AAAS; Am Chem Soc; The Chem Soc; NY Acad Sci. *Res:* Organo transition metal chemisty; small-ring heterocycles; organic nitrogen compounds. *Mailing Add:* Dept of Chem State Univ of NY Stony Brook NY 11794

KERBER, RONALD LEE, b Lafayette, Ind, July 2, 43; m 63. MECHANICAL ENGINEERING, ELECTRICAL ENGINEERING. *Educ:* Purdue Univ, BS, 65; Calif Inst Technol, MS, 66, PhD(eng sci), 70. *Prof Exp:* From asst prof to assoc prof mech eng, 69-78, assoc dir, Div Eng, 78-80, PROF MECH & ELEC ENG, MICH STATE UNIV, 78-, ASSOC DEAN ENG & DIR, DIV ENG RES, 80- *Concurrent Pos:* Mem tech staff, Aerospace Corp, 70-72. *Mem:* Am Soc Mech Engrs; Inst Elec & Electronics Engrs. *Res:* Theory of phase transitions and liquids, gas-surface interaction, chemical and molecular lasers. *Mailing Add:* Div of Eng Res Mich State Univ East Lansing MI 48824

KERBY, GRACE PARDRIDGE, b Syracuse, NY, June 24, 12. MEDICINE. *Educ:* Fla State Univ, BS, 33; Duke Univ, MD, 46. *Prof Exp:* From assoc prof to prof, 57-76, EMER PROF MED, SCH MED, DUKE UNIV, 76- *Mem:* Soc Exp Biol & Med; Am Soc Clin Invest; AMA; Am Rheumatism Asn; Am Fedn Clin Res. *Res:* Internal medicine; connective tissue metabolism and diseases. *Mailing Add:* PO Box 8714 Forest Hills Sta Durham NC 27707

KERBY, HOYLE RAY, b Sweetwater, Tex, Aug 9, 32; m 50; c 4. ELECTRICAL ENGINEERING. *Educ:* Tex Tech Col, BSEE, 57; Stanford Univ, MS, 60. *Prof Exp:* Res staff mem, Res Lab, Int Bus Mach Corp, 57-64, develop engr, Systs Develop Lab, 64-67, mgr, Lab Tech Opers, 67-70, mgr prod components & technol, 71-74, mgr, Explor Storage Develop, IBM Corp, San Jose, 75-80. *Mem:* Inst Elec & Electronics Engrs. *Res:* Magnetic recording technology; speech synthesis and recognition; information storage and retrieval. *Mailing Add:* IBM Corp G09/142 5600 Cottle Rd San Jose CA 95193

KERCE, ROBERT H, b Bartow, Fla, Nov 29, 25; m 46; c 3. MATHEMATICS. *Educ:* Ga Inst Tech, BME, 46; Vanderbilt Univ, MS, 57; George Peabody Col, PhD(math), 65. *Prof Exp:* From instr to assoc prof, 46-66, PROF MATH, DAVID LIPSCOMB COL, 66-, CHMN DEPT, 65- *Mem:* Math Asn Am; Nat Coun Teachers Math. *Mailing Add:* Dept of Math David Lipscomb Col Nashville TN 37203

KERCHER, CONRAD J, b Yakima, Wash, June 17, 26; m 46; c 4. ANIMAL NUTRITION. *Educ:* Mont State Col, BS, 50; Cornell Univ, MS, 52, PhD(animal nutrit), 54. *Prof Exp:* Assoc animal nutrit, Cornell Univ, 50-54; ANIMAL NUTRITIONIST, UNIV WYO, 54- *Mem:* AAAS; Am Soc Animal Sci; Am Dairy Sci Asn. *Res:* Mineral nutrition of ruminants; forage harvesting systems; warm-up programs for calves; alternate crops for ruminants. *Mailing Add:* Col of Agr Univ of Wyo Laramie WY 82071

KERCHEVAL, JAMES WILLIAM, b Rowan, Iowa, Oct 7, 06; m 29. ORGANIC CHEMISTRY. *Educ:* Iowa State Teachers Col, BA, 29; Univ Iowa, MS, 34, PhD(org chem), 39. *Prof Exp:* Teacher pub sch, Iowa, 25-27; asst, Univ Iowa, 37-39; from asst prof to prof chem, Mich State Norm Col, 39-49; from assoc prof to prof, 49-72, EMER PROF CHEM, UNIV NORTHERN IOWA, 72- *Concurrent Pos:* Res & develop chemist, US Rubber Co, 42. *Mem:* Am Chem Soc. *Res:* Carbohydrates present in hydrolysis products of starch; separation and identification of disaccharides; ester synthesis. *Mailing Add:* 2115 Washington Cedar Falls IA 50613

KERCHNER, HAROLD RICHARD, b Lewistown, Pa, Mar 5, 46; m 68; c 2. EXPERIMENTAL SOLID STATE PHYSICS. *Educ:* Harvard Univ, AB, 68; Univ Ill, MS, 72, PhD(physics), 74. *Prof Exp:* RES ASSOC SOLID STATE PHYSICS, OAK RIDGE NAT LAB, NUCLEAR DIV, UNION CARBIDE CORP, 74- *Mem:* Am Phys Soc. *Res:* Type II superconductivity. *Mailing Add:* Solid State Div Oak Ridge Nat Lab PO Box X Oak Ridge TN 37830

KERDESKY, FRANCIS A J, b Wilkes-Barre, Pa, Mar 10, 53. CHEMISTRY. *Educ:* Wilkes Col, BS, 75; Univ Pa, PhD(org chem), 79. *Prof Exp:* Res assoc, Mass Inst Technol, 80-81; SR RES CHEMIST, ABBOTT LABS, NORTH CHICAGO, 81- *Mem:* Am Chem Soc; Sigma Xi. *Res:* Design and synthesis of antiarthritic drugs. *Mailing Add:* Abbott Labs Dept 466 14th St & Sheridan Rd North Chicago IL 60064

KEREIAKES, JAMES GUS, b Columbus, Ohio, Aug 15, 24; m 50; c 4. PHYSICS. *Educ:* Western Ky State Col, BS, 45; Univ Cincinnati, MS, 47, PhD(physics), 50; Am Bd Radiol, dipl radiol physics, 60. *Prof Exp:* Res physicist, Environ Med Br, Med Res Lab, US Army, Ky, 50-53, supvy physicist, Radiobiol Dept, 53-57, dep dir, 57-59; from asst prof to assoc prof, 59-68, PROF RADIOL, COL MED, UNIV CINCINNATI, 68- *Honors & Awards:* Coolidge Award, Am Asn Physicists in Med, 81. *Mem:* AAAS; Am

Phys Soc; Biophys Soc; Radiation Res Soc; Am Asn Physicists in Med (pres, 69-70). *Res:* Radiation physics and biology; radiopharmaceutical dosimetry. *Mailing Add:* Dept of Radiol Univ of Cincinnati Col of Med Cincinnati OH 45267

KEREKES, RICHARD JOSEPH, b Welland, Ont, July 9, 40; m 78. FLUID MECHANICS, SUSPENSIONS. *Educ:* Univ Toronto, BASc, 63, MASc, 65; McGill Univ, PhD(chem eng), 70. *Prof Exp:* Scientist, 71-77, SECT HEAD, PULP & PAPER RES INST CAN, 77- *Concurrent Pos:* Hon prof pup & paper technol, Univ BC, 78- *Mem:* Can Soc Chem Eng; Can Pulp & Paper Asn. *Res:* Fluid mechanics of floculation and mixing in pulp suspensions. *Mailing Add:* Chem Eng Bldg Univ BC Vancouver BC V6T 1W5 Can

KERELUK, KARL, microbiology, public health, see previous edition

KEREN, JOSEPH, b Czech, Feb 28, 30; m 64. PHYSICS. *Educ:* Univ Melbourne, BSc, 54, MSc, 56; Columbia Univ, PhD(physics), 63. *Prof Exp:* Instr physics, Agr & Mech Col Tex, 56-57; res assoc, Australian Nat Univ, 63-64; asst prof, 65-69, ASSOC PROF PHYSICS, NORTHWESTERN UNIV, 69- *Mem:* Am Phys Soc. *Res:* Theoretical investigations of charge transfer reactions in helium-helium scattering; experimental work in elementary particles. *Mailing Add:* Dept Physics Northwestern Univ Evanston IL 60201

KERESZTES-NAGY, STEVEN, physical chemistry, biochemistry, see previous edition

KERKA, WILLIAM (FRANK), b Cleveland, Ohio, Apr 5, 21; m 53; c 1. MECHANICAL ENGINEERING. *Educ:* Fenn Col, BS, 48; Case Inst Technol, MS, 52. *Prof Exp:* Instr graphics, Case Inst Technol, 51-52; instr mech eng, Ore State Col, 52-54; res engr res lab, Am Soc Heating, Refrig & Air-Conditioning Engrs, 54-61; assoc dean eng, 61-77, ASSOC PROF MECH ENG, CLEVELAND STATE UNIV, 77- *Res:* Odor control and acoustics as related to air conditioning. *Mailing Add:* Dept of Mech Eng Cleveland State Univ Cleveland OH 44115

KERKAY, JULIUS, b Sopron, Hungary, Apr 27, 34; US citizen; m 60; c 2. CLINICAL CHEMISTRY. *Educ:* Veszprem Tech Univ, BS, 55, MS, 56; Univ Louisville, PhD(biochem), 69; Am Bd Clin Chem, dipl. *Prof Exp:* Chief chem engr, Alcohol Factory Gyor, Hungary, 56; technician, Alloys & Chem Mfg Co, Ohio, 57-58; asst in res, Cleveland Clin Found, 58-59; chief anal sect, US Army Res Inst Environ Med, 62-64; dir lab, Euclid Clin Found, 68-70; asst prof, 70-74, assoc prof & dir clin chem, 74-81, PROF CHEM & BIOL, CLEVELAND STATE UNIV, 81- *Concurrent Pos:* Adj prof, Cleveland State Univ, 68-70; speaker, Health Careers Info, Cleveland Hosp Coun, 69-; adj consult, Cleveland Clin Found, 70-; mem, Nat Registry Clin Chem; consult, Diamond Shamrock Health Sci Labs, 74-76. sci vpres, Euclid Clin Res Found, 69-; affil staff, St Luke's Hosp Cleveland, 77- *Mem:* AAAS; fel Am Asn Clin Chem; fel Am Inst Chem; NY Acad Sci; Am Chem Soc. *Res:* Phospholipid purification; protein electrophoresis; protein and steroid hormone interactions; serum constituents of mothers of mongoloid children; clinical chemistry methodology, computerization in clinical chemistry; changes in body fluid constituents of hemodialysis patients; development of radiobioassays for vitamins and isoenzymes. *Mailing Add:* Dept of Chem Cleveland State Univ Cleveland OH 14415

KERKER, MILTON, b Utica, NY, Sept 25, 20; m 46; c 4. PHYSICAL CHEMISTRY. *Educ:* Columbia Univ, AB, 41, MA, 47, PhD(chem), 49. *Hon Degrees:* DSc, Lehigh Univ, 75. *Prof Exp:* Asst chem, Columbia Univ, 46-49; from instr to prof, 49-60, chmn dept, 60-64, dean sch sci, 64-66, dean sch arts & sci, 66-74, THOMAS S CLARKSON PROF, CLARKSON COL TECHNOL, 74-, DEAN SCH SCI, 81- *Concurrent Pos:* Ed-in-chief, J Colloid & Interface Sci, 65-; fel, Ford Found, 52-53; Unilever prof, Univ Bristol, 67-68; chmn, Nat Acad Sci-Nat Res Coun comt colloids & surface chem, 70-74; vis prof, Hebrew Univ & Technion, 74-75; titular mem & secy comn on colloids & surfaces, Int Union Pure & Appl Chem, 78- *Honors & Awards:* Kendall Award, Am Chem Soc, 71. *Mem:* Am Chem Soc; Hist Sci Soc; fel Optical Soc Am. *Res:* Light scattering; aerosols; history of science. *Mailing Add:* Sch of Arts & Sci Clarkson Col of Technol Potsdam NY 13676

KERKMAN, DANIEL JOSEPH, b Milwaukee, Wis, Sept 17, 51; m 73; c 2. CHEMISTRY. *Educ:* Johns Hopkins Univ, MA, 76; Mass Inst Technol, PhD(chem), 79. *Prof Exp:* Assoc fel, Mass Inst Technol, 79-80; MED CHEMIST, ABBOTT LABS, 80- *Mem:* Am Chem Soc. *Res:* Medicinal chemistry. *Mailing Add:* Abbott Labs D-466 North Chicago IL 60064

KERKMAN, RUSSEL JOHN, b Burlington, Wis, Aug 11, 48; m 71. ELECTRICAL ENGINEERING. *Educ:* Purdue Univ, BS, 71, MS, 73, PhD(elec eng), 76. *Prof Exp:* Elec engr mach anal, Gen Elec Co, 76-80; SR PROJ ENGR, ALLEN-BRADLEY CO, 80- *Mem:* Inst Elec & Electronics Engrs. *Res:* Electric machine design and analysis; power systems; control systems; solid state power conditioning. *Mailing Add:* Allen-Bradley Co 1201 S 2nd St Milwaukee WI 53204

KERLAN, JOEL THOMAS, b Minneapolis, Minn, Feb 23, 40. ENDOCRINOLOGY. *Educ:* Col St Thomas, Minn, BS, 52; Univ Utah, MS, 65; Univ Mich, Ann Arbor, PhD(zool), 72. *Prof Exp:* Instr, 70-71, asst prof, 71-81, ASSOC PROF BIOL, HOBART & WILLIAM SMITH COLS, 81- *Concurrent Pos:* Vis prof, Dept Obstet & Gynec, Univ Mich, 75. *Mem:* Sigma Xi; Am Soc Zoologists. *Res:* Regulation and biosynthesis of sex steroid hormones in vertebrate testes. *Mailing Add:* Dept of Biol Hobart & William Smith Cols Geneva NY 14456

KERLEE, DONALD D, b Ryderwood, Wash, Dec 22, 26; m 50; c 4. NUCLEAR PHYSICS, MANAGEMENT INFORMATION. *Educ:* Seattle Pac Col, BS, 51; Univ Wash, PhD(physics), 56. *Prof Exp:* Res instr physics, Univ Wash, 56; from asst prof to prof, Seattle Pac Col, 56-69, chmn dept, 62-69; dir inst res, 59-69; acad vpres, Roberts Wesleyan Col, 69-74; vpres admin,

74-76, dir res, 76-79, DIR PLANNING RES, SEATTLE PAC COL, 79- *Concurrent Pos:* Sci fac fel, Univ Manchester, 63-64; Am Inst Physics & Am Asn Physics Teachers Regional Counsr, Washington State, 65-69. *Mem:* AAAS; Am Asn Physics Teachers; Am Phys Soc. *Res:* Heavy ion, nuclear and cosmic ray physics; institutional planning; forecasting models. *Mailing Add:* Seattle Pac Col Seattle WA 98119

KERLEY, ELLIS R, b Covington, Ky, Sept 1, 24; m 55; c 3. PHYSICAL ANTHROPOLOGY, FORENSIC SCIENCE. *Educ:* Univ Ky, BS, 50; Univ Mich, MS, 56, PhD(anthrop), 62. *Prof Exp:* Staff anthropologist, Bowman Gray Sch Med, 50-53; phys anthropologist, US Army Graves Registrn, 54-55; Armed Forces Inst Path, 57-66; from assoc prof to prof, Univ Kans, 66-71; chmn dept, 74-78, PROF & DIR ANTHROP, UNIV MD, COLLEGE PARK, 72- *Concurrent Pos:* Vis assoc prof, Univ Ky, 65-66; pres, Am Bd Forensic Anthrop, 77-; pres, Forensic Sci Found, 78. *Honors & Awards:* Award of Merit, Am Acad Forensic Sci, 75. *Mem:* Fel AAAS; fel Am Anthrop Asn; Am Asn Phys Anthrop; fel Am Acad Forensic Sci (vpres, 74); Sigma Xi. *Res:* Skeletal identification and anatomy; bone age changes; human genetics; paleopathology; growth; constitutional and population variation; evolution; primate studies. *Mailing Add:* Dept of Anthrop Univ of Md College Park MD 20742

KERLEY, GERALD IRWIN, b Houston, Tex, Mar 23, 41; m 67; c 3. PHYSICAL CHEMISTRY. *Educ:* Ohio Univ, BS, 63; Univ Ill, PhD(chem physics), 66. *Prof Exp:* Fel chem, Univ Ill, 66-67; STAFF MEM PHYS CHEM, LOS ALAMOS NAT LAB, UNIV CALIF, 69- *Mem:* Am Phys Soc. *Res:* Theory and calculation of equations of state of gases, liquids, and solids; statistical mechanics; theory of electrons in condensed matter. *Mailing Add:* Los Alamos Nat Lab Los Alamos NM 87545

KERLEY, MICHAEL A, b Crockett, Tex, Apr 17, 41; m 64; c 2. ANATOMY. *Educ:* Stephen F Austin State Col, BS, 64; Tex A&M Univ, MS, 69, PhD(zool), 71. *Prof Exp:* ASST PROF BIOL, SOUTHWESTERN OKLA STATE UNIV, 71- *Concurrent Pos:* Fel, Univ Conn Health Ctr, 75-77. *Mem:* Am Asn Anatomists; Am Soc Zoologists. *Res:* Embryonic development of mammalian dentitions. *Mailing Add:* Dept of Biol Sci Southwestern Okla State Univ Weatherford OK 73096

KERLEY, TROY LAMAR, b Allen, Okla, Aug 20, 29; m 50; c 1. PHARMACOLOGY. *Educ:* Univ Okla, BS, 53, MS, 55; Purdue Univ, PhD(pharmacol), 58. *Prof Exp:* Asst pharm, Purdue Univ, 55-56; pharmacologist, Res Dept, Pitman-Moore Div, Dow Chem Co, 57-64; head biomed res dept, 64-66; dir biol sci res, Riker Labs, Calif, 66-71; dir biol res, 71-73, tech dir, Riker Labs Res & Develop, 73-80, DIR INT NEW BUSINESS DEVELOP, RIKER LABS INT, 3M CO, 81- *Mem:* AAAS; Sigma Xi; Am Pharmaceut Asn; Am Found Pharmaceut Educ; Am Soc Pharmacol & Exp Therapeut. *Res:* Pharmacologic aspects of the blood-brain barrier; neuromuscular pharmacology; pharmacology and physiology of tremor and rigidity syndromes; asthmatic pharmacology. *Mailing Add:* Riker Labs Int 3M Ctr Bldg Old Hudson Rd 225-5S St Paul MN 55144

KERLICK, GEORGE DAVID, b Sharon, Pa, June 24, 49. THEORETICAL PHYSICS. *Educ:* Rensselaer Polytech Inst, BS, 70; Princeton Univ, MA, 72, PhD(physics), 75. *Prof Exp:* Res assoc physics, Mont State Univ, 75; res fel physics, Alexander von Humboldt Found, Univ Cologne, 75-76 & Max-Planck-Inst, Munich, 76-77; vis asst prof math, Ore State Univ, 77-78; adj asst prof physics, Univ San Francisco, 78-79; RES SCIENTIST, COMPUT FLUID DYNAMICS DEPT, NIELSEN ENG & RES INC, 79- *Mem:* Am Phys Soc; Am Math Soc; Am Inst Aeronaut & Astronaut; Sigma Xi. *Res:* Mathematics applied to numerical models of fluid flow, especially transonic flows, perturbation theory, strained coordinate techniques, numerical mesh generation for finite difference calculations. *Mailing Add:* Nielsen Eng & Res Inc 510 Clyde Ave Mountain View CA 94043

KERLIN, THOMAS W, b Charlotte, NC, Apr 7, 36; m 54; c 3. NUCLEAR ENGINEERING. *Educ:* Univ SC, BSChE, 58; Univ Tenn, MS, 59, PhD(eng sci), 65. *Prof Exp:* Res engr, Atomics Int Div, NAm Aviation, 59-61 & Oak Ridge Nat Lab, 61-66; assoc prof, 66-76, PROF NUCLEAR ENG, UNIV TENN, KNOXVILLE, 76- *Concurrent Pos:* Consult, Oak Ridge Nat Lab, 66- *Mem:* Am Nuclear Soc. *Res:* Dynamics and stability of nuclear power reactors and other process systems; optimal design of nuclear power plants. *Mailing Add:* Dept of Nuclear Eng Univ of Tenn Knoxville TN 37916

KERMAN, ARTHUR KENT, b Montreal, Que, Can, May 3, 29; m 52; c 5. THEORETICAL PHYSICS. *Educ:* McGill Univ, BSc, 50; Mass Inst Technol, PhD, 53. *Prof Exp:* Res fel theoret physics, Nat Res Coun, Calif Inst Technol, 53-54; res fel, Nat Res Coun Can, Inst Theoret Physics, Copenhagen, 54-55, mem res staff, 55-56; from asst prof to assoc prof, 56-64, PROF PHYSICS, MASS INST TECHNOL, 64-, DIR, CTR THEORET PHYSICS, 76- *Concurrent Pos:* Consult, Shell Develop Co div, Shell Oil Co, 53-58, Argonne Nat Lab, 61-, Brookhaven Nat Lab, 65-81, Lawrence Berkeley Lab, 75-, Lawrence Livermore Lab, 64-, Los Alamos Sci Lab, 61-, Nat Bureau Standards, 80-81 & Oak Ridge Nat Lab, 79-; exchange prof, Guggenheim mem fel, Paris, 61-62; consult, Educ Serv, Inc, Brookhaven Nat Lab, Los Alamos Sci Lab & Lawrence Berkeley Lab; mem Nat Acad Sci panels on nuclear data, heavy ion physics & physics surv comt; adj prof, Brooklyn Col, City Univ NY, 71-76 & Argonne Nat Lab; assoc prof, Unitersite Paris-Sud, Institut de Physique Nucleaire, 80- *Mem:* Am Phys Soc; Am Acad Arts & Sci; NY Acad Sci. *Res:* Theoretical nuclear physics. *Mailing Add:* Dept of Physics Mass Inst of Technol Cambridge MA 02139

KERMICLE, JERRY LEE, b Dundas, Ill, Mar 8, 36; m 57; c 5. GENETICS. *Educ:* Univ Ill, BS, 57; Univ Wis, MS, 59, PhD(genetics), 63. *Prof Exp:* Fel genetics & biochem, 63, asst prof, 63-71, assoc prof, 71-77, PROF GENETICS, UNIV WIS-MADISON, 77- *Mem:* AAAS; Genetics Soc Am. *Res:* Maize genetics, cytogenetics and development; analysis of spontaneous mutation, paramutation and complex loci. *Mailing Add:* Lab of Genetics Univ of Wis Madison WI 53706

KERMISCH, DORIAN, b Bucharest, Romania, Nov 13, 31; m 62; c 2. OPTICS, ELECTROMAGNETICS. *Educ:* Israel Inst Technol, BSc, 55; Polytech Inst Brooklyn, MS, 64, PhD(elec eng), 68. *Prof Exp:* Elec engr, Israeli Ministry Defense, 60-62; res fel, Polytech Inst Brooklyn, 62-66; lectr, City Col New York, 67-68; SR SCIENTIST OPTICS, XEROX CORP, 68- *Mem:* Optical Soc Am. *Res:* Theoretical investigations of blazed holograms, volume holograms and phase imaging; optical and computer image processing. *Mailing Add:* 329 Village Green Dr Penfield NY 14526

KERN, BERNARD DONALD, b New Castle, Ind, Oct 31, 19; m 46; c 3. NUCLEAR PHYSICS. *Educ:* Univ Ind, BS, 42, MS, 47, PhD(physics), 49. *Prof Exp:* Jr physicist radar, Signal Corps, US Army, 42-43; asst nuclear physics, Metall Lab, Chicago, 43; physics, Ind Univ, 46-49; sr physicist, Nuclear Physics, Oak Ridge Nat Lab, 49-50; from asst prof to assoc prof, 50-58, chmn dept physics & astron, 67-69, PROF PHYSICS, UNIV KY, 58- *Concurrent Pos:* Vis physicist, US Naval Radiol Defense Lab, 57-58; prof, Univ Ky overseas prog, Bandung Tech Inst, 61-62. *Honors & Awards:* Alumni Research Award, Univ Ky, 59. *Mem:* Am Phys Soc; Am Asn Physics Teachers. *Res:* Nuclear energy level studies with Van de Graaff accelerator; beta and gamma-ray spectroscopy; heavy ion induced reactions. *Mailing Add:* Dept of Physics & Astron Univ of Ky Lexington KY 40506

KERN, CHARLES WILLIAM, b Middletown, Ohio, July 13, 35. THEORETICAL CHEMISTRY. *Educ:* Carnegie Inst Technol, BS, 57; Univ Minn, PhD(chem), 61. *Prof Exp:* Fel theoret chem, Dept Chem & IBM Watson Lab, Columbia Univ, 61-64; asst prof chem, State Univ NY Stony Brook, 64-66; res scientist, 66-72, mgr chem phys sect, Battelle Mem Inst, 72-76, dir Battelle Inst Prog, 74-76; prof chem, Ohio State Univ, 76-80; PROG OFFICER, NSF, 78- *Concurrent Pos:* Adj assoc prof, Ohio State Univ, 66-71, adj prof, 71-76, acad vchmn, Dept Chem, 72-73. *Mem:* Am Phys Soc; Am Chem Soc; Sigma Xi. *Res:* Theoretical chemistry; theory of molecular structure and spectra. *Mailing Add:* Chem Div NSF Washington DC 20550

KERN, CLIFFORD DALTON, b Oakland, Calif, Jan 6, 28; m 51; c 3. METEOROLOGY. *Educ:* Univ Calif, Berkeley, AB, 52; Univ Calif, Los Angeles, MA, 58; Univ Wash, Seattle, PhD(atmospheric sci), 65. *Prof Exp:* US Air Force, 52-72, weather officer, 52-58, adv weather officer, Cambridge Res Lab & Electronics Systs Div, 58-65, tech serv officer, Southeast Asia, 65-67, adv weather officer, Satellite Control Facil, Calif, 67-69, chief spec proj br, Air Force Global Weather Ctr, Offutt Air Force Base, Nebr, 69-70 & develop activities in sci & numerical area, 70-71, staff meteorologist, Space & Missile Systs Orgn, 71-72; res supvr, Environ Transp Div, Savannah River Lab, E I du Pont de Nemours & Co, Inc, 72-78; staff engr & group leader, Atmospheric Effects Group, 78-80, SR STAFF ENGR & GROUP LEADER, PROPAGATION SCIENCES, LOCKHEED MISSILES & SPACE C0, 80- *Mem:* AAAS; Am Meteorol Soc; Am Geophys Union; Sigma Xi. *Res:* Infrared emission of the earth and its cloud fields as seen by weather satellites; satellites considering solar interactions with the earth, its upper atmosphere and geomagnetic field; propagation of electromagnetic radiation through the atmosphere and ionosphere. *Mailing Add:* Lockheed Missiles & Space Co PO Box 504 Sunnyvale CA 95086

KERN, CLIFFORD H, III, b New Orleans, La, Aug 30, 48; m 72; c 1. DEVELOPMENTAL GENETICS. *Educ:* Washington & Lee Univ, BS, 70; Ind Univ, MA, 72, PhD(zool), 79. *Prof Exp:* Instr genetics & biochem, DePauw Univ, 76-79, asst prof, 79-81; PROG COORDR, DIABETES UNIV, LA DEPT HEALTH & HUMAN RESOURCES, 81- *Concurrent Pos:* Vis asst prof, Ind Univ, Bloomington, 80 & 81; lectr, Ind Univ & Purdue Univ, 81. *Mem:* Soc Develop Biol; Genetics Soc Am; Sigma Xi; Am Diabetes Asn. *Res:* Diabetes; genetics and development of female-sterile mutants in Drosophila. *Mailing Add:* Chronic Dis Sect La Dept Health & Human Resources PO Box 60630 New Orleans LA 70160

KERN, DENNIS MATTHEW, b Ft Smith, Ark, Dec 19, 48; m 71; c 2. STATISTICS, COMPUTER SCIENCE. *Educ:* St Mary's Univ, Tex, BS, 70, MS, 72; Tex Tech Univ, PhD(statist), 76. *Prof Exp:* Res assoc data anal, Johnson Space Ctr, Nat Res Coun, 76-78; ASST PROF, DEPT STATIST & COMPUT SCI, UNIV GA, 78- *Concurrent Pos:* Consult, TBL Consult Inc. *Mem:* Am Statist Asn; Inst Math Statist; Asn Comput Mach. *Res:* Analysis of satellite data from agricultural regions; linear models; unique minimum variance unbiased estimation; software development. *Mailing Add:* Dept of Statist & Comput Sci Univ of Ga Athens GA 30602

KERN, EARL R, b Auburn, Wyo, May 22, 40; m 62; c 2. MEDICAL MICROBIOLOGY. *Educ:* Univ Utah, BS, 66, MS, 70, PhD(microbiol), 73. *Prof Exp:* Microbiologist, Dugway Proving Ground, Dept Army, 66-68; instr microbiol, 73-76, res instr, Dept Pediat, 74-76, res asst prof, Dept Microbiol, 76-78, res asst prof, Dept Pediat, 76-80, RES ASSOC PROF MICROBIOL, COL MED, UNIV UTAH, 80- *Mem:* Am Soc Microbiol; Soc Exp Biol Med; Sigma Xi; Am Asn Cancer Res. *Res:* Pathogenesis, chemotherapy and host resistance in experimental viral infections; cancer chemotherapy; immunomodulation of host resistance; herpesvirus infections. *Mailing Add:* Dept of Pediat Col of Med Univ of Utah Salt Lake City UT 84132

KERN, FRED, JR, b Montgomery, Ala, Sept 9, 18; m 42; c 3. INTERNAL MEDICINE, GASTROENTEROLOGY. *Educ:* Univ Ala, BA, 39; Columbia Univ, MD, 43; Am Bd Internal Med, dipl. *Prof Exp:* Asst, Sch Med, Emory Univ, 43, asst path, 44; asst med, Med Col, Cornell Univ, 47-48, instr, 51; from asst prof to assoc prof, 52-65, PROF MED & HEAD DIV GASTROENTEROL, UNIV COLO MED CTR, DENVER, 65- *Concurrent Pos:* Res fel med, Med Col, Cornell Univ, 47-49, Ledyard Jr fel, 49-50; intern, Grady Hosp, Atlanta, 43, asst resident, 44; asst resident, NY Hosp, 47-48, provisional asst outpatients, 47 & 49; physician, Colo Gen Hosp, 52; assoc attend physician, Div Internal Med, Denver Gen Hosp, 52, chief div prev med & pub health, 52, dir gen med clin, 51-59; chmn, Am Bd Gastroenterol, 69-72; mem, Nat Arthritis, Metab & Digestive Dis Adv Coun, NIH, 78-81; pres, Digestive Dis Info Ctr, 78-80; mem, Sci Adv Bd, Nat Found Ileitis-Colitis, chmn, Grants Review Comt, 78-81. *Mem:* AAAS; Am Inst Nutrit; Am Gastroenterol Asn (vpres, 73-74, pres-elect, 74-75, pres, 75-76); hon mem Gastroenterol Soc Australia; Asn Am Physicians; fel Am Col Physicians. *Res:* Medical education and gastroenterology; bile acid metabolism; intestinal absorption. *Mailing Add:* Div of Gastroenterol Univ of Colo Med Ctr Denver CO 80262

KERN, HAROLD L, b Holyoke, Mass, July 31, 21; m 49, 58; c 3. BIOCHEMISTRY. *Educ:* Univ Mich, BS, 42; Johns Hopkins Univ, ScD(hyg), 53. *Prof Exp:* Tech compounder, Hewitt Rubber Corp, NY, 42-44; anal chemist, Strong Steel Foundry, 46-47; asst ophthal res, Howe Lab Ophthal, 52-55, instr, 55-60; instr, Univ Buffalo, 60-62; asst prof, 63-71, ASSOC PROF OPHTHAL, ALBERT EINSTEIN COL MED, 71- *Mem:* Asn Res Vision & Ophthal. *Res:* Mechanism of transport of organic solutes in lens; isolation and characterization of lenticular transport proteins. *Mailing Add:* Dept of Ophthal Albert Einstein Col of Med Bronx NY 10461

KERN, JEROME, b New York, NY, Nov 2, 27; m 52; c 3. VIROLOGY. *Educ:* Brooklyn Col, BSc, 50; Ohio State Univ, MSc, 54; George Washington Univ, PhD(virol), 62. *Prof Exp:* Asst bact, Ohio State Univ, 51-54; res assoc, Smithsonian Inst, 54-56; bacteriologist, US Dept Interior, 56-57; bacteriologist, Walter Reed Army Inst Res, 57-58; bacteriologist, Nat Inst Allergy & Infectious Dis, 58-65; res microbiologist, Nat Cancer Inst, 65-66; sr scientist, Flow Labs, Inc, 66-76; RES ASSOC, AM TYPE CULT COLLECTION, 76- *Mem:* AAAS; Am Soc Microbiol. *Res:* serological methods of virus identification; immunological relationships between human and animal viruses; virus purification. *Mailing Add:* 12301 Parklawn Dr Rockville MD 20852

KERN, JOHN MILTON, b Abington, Pa, Sept 17, 48; m 80; c 3. TECHNICAL MANAGEMENT. *Educ:* Univ Del, BSME, 71, BA, 71; Cornell Univ, MS, 73. *Prof Exp:* Teaching asst, Cornell Univ, 71-73; jr proj engr, Morse Chain Div, 73-75, proj engr, 75-77, sr proj engr, 77-79, MGR RES & DEVELOP, TRANSMISSION COMPUT GROUP, BORG WARNER CORP, 79- *Res:* Mechanical power transmission development. *Mailing Add:* 23 Bush Lane Ithaca NY 14850

KERN, JOHN PHILIP, b Springfield, Mass, Jan 3, 39; m 69. INVERTEBRATE PALEONTOLOGY. *Educ:* Univ Calif, Los Angeles, AB, 63, PhD(geol), 68. *Prof Exp:* From asst prof to assoc prof, 68-77, PROF GEOL, SAN DIEGO STATE UNIV, 77- *Mem:* Paleont Soc; Paleont Res Inst. *Res:* Paleoenvironmental studies of late Cenozoic marine invertebrates; trace fossils. *Mailing Add:* Dept of Geol San Diego State Univ San Diego CA 92182

KERN, JOHN W, b Mansfield, Ohio, Dec 16, 30; m 62. GEOPHYSICS. *Educ:* Univ Calif, Berkeley, BS, 56, MA, 58, PhD(geophys), 60. *Prof Exp:* Phys scientist, Rand Corp, Calif, 60-64; asst prof physics, Univ Houston, 64-66, assoc prof, 66-71, prof physics, 71-74; sr res specialist, Exxon Prod Res Co, Houston, 75-81; CHIEF LOG ANALYST, DRESSER PETROL ENG SERV, HOUSTON, 81- *Concurrent Pos:* Mem comn 4, Int Sci Radio Union, 62; mem working group data anal, comn II, Int Union Geod & Geophys, 63-; consult phys scientist, Rand Corp, 64-; adj prof physics, Univ Houston, 75-78. *Mem:* Soc Explor Geophys; Am Geophys Union; Soc Prof Well Log Analysts. *Res:* Rock magnetism; geomagnetism; auroral and magnetospheric physics; magnetohydrodynamics; magneto-gas dynamics; solar and planetary physics; well log analysis; well log methods development. *Mailing Add:* 3405 Amherst Houston TX 77005

KERN, JOSEPH HERSCHEL, b Chillicothe, Ohio, Jan 31, 20; m 46; c 1. PHARMACY ADMINISTRATION. *Educ:* Ohio State Univ, BSc, 49, MSc, 51, PhD(pharm), 54. *Prof Exp:* Asst pharm, Col Pharm, Ohio State Univ, 49-50, instr, 50-55; asst prof, Col Pharm, Univ Fla, 55-58; assoc prof, 58-62, PROF PHARM ADMIN, SCH PHARM, NORTHEAST LA UNIV, 62- *Mem:* Am Heart Asn. *Res:* Pharmacy law; retail pharmacy management; drug marketing. *Mailing Add:* Sch of Pharm Northeast La Univ Monroe LA 71209

KERN, MICHAEL DON, b Los Angeles, Calif, Nov 25, 38; m 61; c 3. AVIAN PHYSIOLOGY. *Educ:* Whittier Col, BA, 62; Wash State Univ, MS, 65, PhD(zoophysiol), 70. *Prof Exp:* USPHS trainee avian reprod physiol, Cornell Univ, 69-71; asst prof chordate morphogenesis, Fordham Univ, 71-75; asst prof animal physiol, 76-81, ASST PROF BIOL, COL WOOSTER, 81- *Mem:* AAAS, Cooper Ornith Soc; Ecol Soc Am; Am Ornithologists Union. *Res:* Photoperiodism in birds; annual cycles of birds; avian reproductive physiology, particularly incubation, nest construction, and nesting energetics. *Mailing Add:* Dept of Biol Col of Wooster Wooster OH 44691

KERN, MILTON, b Brooklyn, NY, Jan 12, 25; m 50; c 3. BIOCHEMISTRY. *Educ:* Brooklyn Col, BS, 49; Yale Univ, PhD(microbiol), 54. *Prof Exp:* Fel biochem, Am Cancer Soc, McCollum-Pratt Inst, Johns Hopkins Univ, 54-56; instr microbiol & med, Sch Med, Wash Univ, 56-59, asst prof med, 59-63, RES CHEMIST, LAB BIOCHEM, NAT INST ARTHRITIS, METAB & DIGESTIVE DISORDERS, NIH, 63- *Mem:* Am Soc Microbiol; Am Asn Immunol; Am Soc Biol Chemists. *Res:* Synthesis and secretion of immunoglobulins. *Mailing Add:* Biochem & Metab Lab Bldg 10 Rm 9B11 Bethesda MD 20014

KERN, RALPH DONALD, JR, b New Orleans, La, Aug 8, 35; m 61; c 3. PHYSICAL CHEMISTRY. *Educ:* Univ Tex, Austin, BS, 57 & 60, PhD(chem), 65. *Prof Exp:* Res fel, Harvard Univ, 65-67; from asst prof to assoc prof, 67-77, PROF CHEM, UNIV NEW ORLEANS, LAKEFRONT, 77-, CHMN, 80- *Mem:* Am Chem Soc; Am Phys Soc; Combustion Inst. *Res:* Rates of gas phase reactions in shock tubes monitored by infrared emission and time-of-flight mass spectrometry. *Mailing Add:* Dept of Chem Univ New Orleans Lakefront New Orleans LA 70122

KERN, ROLAND JAMES, b Bay City, Mich, Oct 29, 25; m 53; c 2. CHEMISTRY. *Educ:* Univ Mich, BS, 48; Northwestern Univ, PhD(chem), 52. *Prof Exp:* RES CHEMIST, MONSANTO CO, 52- *Concurrent Pos:* Fac, Univ Col, Wash Univ. *Mem:* Am Chem Soc. *Res:* Polymerization; polymer technology. *Mailing Add:* Monsanto Co 800 N Lindberg Blvd St Louis MO 63166

KERN, ROY FREDRICK, b Lewiston, Minn, Oct 25, 18; m 44; c 3. METALLURGY, MECHANICAL ENGINEERING. *Educ:* Macalester Col, BS, 39; Marquette Univ, BS, 43. *Prof Exp:* Chief metallurgist, Allis-Chalmers Mfg Co, 43-62; plant mgr, Knoxville Iron Co, 63-65; proj engr, Caterpillar Tractor Co, 65-71; OWNER, KERN ENG CO, 71- *Mem:* Am Soc Metals. *Res:* Development of boron and alloy boron steels, heat treating of steel parts, designing for heat treatment, selection of steel for heat treated parts; exculusive method developed for buying steels: cost reduction-works better-costs less; gear problems; gears of all kinds and sizes. *Mailing Add:* Kern Eng Co 818 E Euclid Peoria IL 61614

KERN, WERNER, b Basel, Switzerland, Mar 18, 25; US citizen; m 55; c 3. SOLID STATE CHEMISTRY, CHEMICAL VAPOR DEPOSTION. *Educ:* Univ Basel, Cert chem, 44; Polyglot Sch Lang, Switz, dipl lang, 47; Rutgers Univ, AB, 55. *Prof Exp:* Jr chemist, Hoffmann-LaRoche, Ltd, Switzerland, 42-48, anal res chemist, NJ, 48-55, Dept Radioisotope Biochem, 55-57; chief chemist & radiol safety officer, Nuclear Corp Am, 58-59; engr & div health physicist, Electronics Component & Devices Div, Somerville, 59-64, MEM TECH STAFF, DAVID SARNOFF RES CTR, RCA CORP, 64- *Concurrent Pos:* Safety coun rep, RCA Labs, RCA Corp, 70-; chem vapor deposition course lectr, Am Vac Soc, 81- *Honors & Awards:* T C Callinan Award, Electrochem Soc Inc, 72. *Mem:* Am Chem Soc; Electrochem Soc; Sigma Xi; Am Vac Soc. *Res:* Semiconductor device process research; chemical vapor deposition processes; semiconductor device passivation technology; chemical etching methods for microelectronic device materials; process control method development; radioactive tracer applications; solar cell research. *Mailing Add:* Integrated Circuit Technol Ctr David Sarnoff Res Ctr RCA Corp Princeton NJ 08540

KERN, WOLFHARD, b Berlin, Ger, Feb 18, 27; m 52; c 3. HIGH ENERGY PHYSICS. *Educ:* Univ Frankfurt, BS, 48, MS, 51; Univ Bonn, PhD(physics), 58. *Prof Exp:* Asst prof physics, Univ Bonn, 58-60; res assoc, Deutsches Elektronen-Synchrotron, 60-63, scientist, 65-67; res assoc physics, Mass Inst Tech, 63-64; assoc prof, 64-65, PROF PHYSICS, SOUTHEASTERN MASS UNIV, 67- *Concurrent Pos:* Vis scientist, Max-Planck Inst, 75-76. *Mem:* Am Phys Soc; Am Asn Physics Teachers. *Res:* Experimental high energy physics. *Mailing Add:* Dept of Physics Southeastern Mass Univ North Dartmouth MA 02747

KERNAGHAN, ROY PETER, b Schenectady, NY, Mar 26, 33; m 56. BIOLOGY, GENETICS. *Educ:* Dartmouth Univ, BA, 55, MA, 57; Univ Conn, PhD(genetics), 63. *Prof Exp:* NIH trainee electron micros, Col Physicians & Surgeons, Columbia Univ, 63-65; asst prof biol sci, State Univ NY Stony Brook, 65-74; PROF BIOL & CHMN DEPT, SALISBURY STATE COL, 74- *Mem:* Genetics Soc Am; Am Soc Cell Biol. *Res:* Developmental genetics. *Mailing Add:* Dept of Biol Salisbury State Col Salisbury MD 21801

KERNAN, ANNE, b Dublin, Ireland, Jan 15, 33; US citizen. PHYSICS. *Educ:* Univ Col, Dublin, BSc, 53, PhD(physics), 57. *Prof Exp:* Asst lectr physics, Univ Col, Dublin, 58-62; res physicist, Lawrence Berkeley Lab, 62-66 & Stanford Linear Accelerator Ctr, Stanford Univ, 66-67; assoc prof, 67-70, PROF PHYSICS, UNIV CALIF, RIVERSIDE, 70- *Concurrent Pos:* Orgn Europ Econ Coop sr vis fel, 61; Soroptimist Found fel, 62-63; consult, adv comt physics, NSF, 78- *Mem:* AAAS; Am Phys Soc. *Res:* Experimental high energy physics. *Mailing Add:* Dept of Physics Univ of Calif Riverside CA 92521

KERNAN, WILLIAM J, JR, b Baltimore, Md, Oct 18, 33; m 56; c 3. PHYSICS. *Educ:* Loyola Col, Md, BS, 55; Univ Chicago, MS, 56, PhD(physics), 60. *Prof Exp:* Asst physicist, Argonne Nat Lab, 60-61; asst prof physics, NY Univ, 61-63; assoc prof, 63-66, PROF PHYSICS, IOWA STATE UNIV, 66-; SR PHYSICIST, AMES LAB, 66- *Concurrent Pos:* Guest staff mem, Brookhaven Nat Lab, 60-65; physicist, Ames Lab, 63-66; prog dir high energy physics, Ames Labs, ERDA, 75-78, assoc dir opers, Dept of Energy, 78- *Mem:* Fel Am Phys Soc. *Res:* Properties and interactions of elementary particles. *Mailing Add:* 116 Off & Lab Ames Lab Iowa State Univ Ames IA 50011

KERNBERG, OTTO F, b Vienna, Austria, Sept 10, 28; US citizen; c 3. PSYCHIATRY. *Educ:* Univ Chile, BS, 47, MD, 53. *Prof Exp:* Intern, Hosp J J Aquirre, Santiago, Chile, 53; resident psychiat, Psychiat Clin, Univ Chile, 54-57, staff mem, Dept Psychiat, 57-61, asst prof psychiat, 58-59; staff psychiatrist, C F Menninger Mem Hosp, Topeka, Kans, 61-62; staff psychiatrist, Res Dept, Menninger Found, 62-67, chief investr, Psychother Res Proj, 67-69; dir, C F Menninger Mem Hosp, 69-73; dir gen clin serv, NY State Psychiat Inst, 73-76; prof clin psychiat, Col Physicians & Surgeons, Columbia Univ, 73-76; TRAINING & SUPV ANALYST, COLUMBIA UNIV CTR FOR PSYCHOANAL TRAINING & RES, 74-; PROF PSYCHIAT, CORNELL UNIV MED COL, 76-; MED DIR, NY HOSP-CORNELL UNIV MED CTR, WESTCHESTER DIV, 76- *Concurrent Pos:* Prof psychopath, Sch Social Work, Nat Health Serv, Santiago, 57-59, prof ment health, 58-59; prof ment health & prof psychol diag, Sch Psychol, Cath Univ Chile, 58-61; Rockefeller Found fel psychiat, Henry Phipps Clin, Johns Hopkins Hosp, Baltimore, 59-60; consult, Topeka State Hosp, Kans, 64-68; fac mem, Menninger Sch Psychiat & Topeka Inst Psychoanal, 64-73; resident psychiat, C F Menninger Mem Hosp, Topeka, 65-68, consult, 68-69; training analyst, Topeka Inst Psychoanal, 66-73, treas, 68-73; staff psychiatrist, Adult Outpatient Serv, Menninger Found, 68-69; assoc clin prof psychiat, Univ Kans Med Ctr, Kansas City, Kans, 71-73; mem staff, A K Rice Inst, Group Rels Conf, Washington Sch Psychiat, 72-75; vis prof, Menninger Sch Psychiat & Mass Gen Hosp, Harvard Med Sch, 74-75 & Albert Einstein Col Med, 77-; attend psychiatrist, Serv Psychiat, Presby Hosp, New York, 74-76; asst ed, J Am Psychoanal Asn, 74-77, assoc ed, 77-; fac mem, New York Psychoanal Inst, 74-81. *Honors & Awards:* Heinz Hartman Award, 72; Edward A Strecker Award, 75. *Mem:* Fel Am Psychiat Asn; AMA; fel Am Col Physicians; Sigma Xi; fel NY Acad Med. *Mailing Add:* 21 Bloomingdale Rd White Plains NY 10625

KERNELL, ROBERT LEE, b Greer, SC, Mar 24, 29; m 59; c 2. NUCLEAR PHYSICS. *Educ:* Wofford Col, AB, 50; Univ SC, MS, 58; Univ Tenn, PhD(physics), 68. *Prof Exp:* Asst prof physics, Col William & Mary, 58-62; assoc prof, 67-79, PROF PHYSICS, OLD DOMINION UNIV, 79- *Mem:* Am Phys Soc; Am Asn Physics Teachers; NY Acad Sci; Sigma Xi. *Res:* Nuclear structure physics; radiation effects induced by charged particles. *Mailing Add:* Dept of Physics Old Dominion Univ Norfolk VA 23508

KERNER, EDWARD HASKELL, b New York, NY, Apr 22, 24; m 48; c 3. THEORETICAL PHYSICS, THEORETICAL BIOLOGY. *Educ:* Columbia Col, AB, 43; Cornell Univ, PhD(physics), 50. *Prof Exp:* Instr physics, Princeton Univ, 43-44; physicist, Manhattan eng dist, 44-45; asst prof physics, Wayne State Univ, 49-51; res assoc, Iowa State Univ, 51-53; from asst prof to assoc prof, Univ Buffalo, 53-62; PROF PHYSICS, UNIV DEL, 62- *Mem:* Fel Am Phys Soc; Soc Math Biol. *Res:* Relativistic particle dynamics; projective relativity; atomic and molecular collision theory; band structure of random lattices; theory of biological population fluctuations and of biochemical kinetics; non-linear dynamics. *Mailing Add:* Dept of Physics Univ of Del Newark DE 19711

KERNEY, PETER JOSEPH, b Philadelphia, Pa, Apr 7, 40; m 68; c 3. MECHANICAL ENGINEERING. *Educ:* Univ Notre Dame, BS, 62, MS, 64; Pa State Univ, PhD(mech eng), 70. *Prof Exp:* Instr mech eng, Tri-State Col, 65-66 & Pa State Univ, 66-70; asst prof, Lafayette Col, 70-72; res staff engr, Draper Lab, Mass Inst Technol, 72-77; MGR ADVAN TECHNOL, CTI-CRYOGENICS, 77- *Concurrent Pos:* Res asst, Ord Res Lab, 68-70; consult, US Army Frankford Arsenal, 71; vis lectr mech eng, Tufts Univ, 77- *Mem:* Am Soc Mech Engrs; assoc mem Am Soc Eng Educ; Am Soc Heating, Refrig & Air Conditioning Engrs; Sigma Xi. *Res:* Two phase flow and turbulent jet mixing; jet penetration characteristics of a submerged steam jet; energy and momentum characteristics of liquid bath downstream of steam jet; convection and cryogenic heat transfer. *Mailing Add:* CTI-Cryogenics 266 Second Ave Waltham MA 02154

KERNIS, MARTEN MURRAY, b Chicago, Ill, Sept 21, 41. ANATOMY, TERATOLOGY. *Educ:* Roosevelt Univ, BS, 63; Univ Fla, PhD(anat sci), 68. *Prof Exp:* from asst prof to assoc prof anat, Sch Basic Med Sci, 68-76, from asst prof to assoc prof anat in obstet & gynec, Abraham Lincoln Sch Med, 68-76, from asst dean to assoc dean, Sch Basic Med Sci, 72-76; assoc prof anat, Jefferson Med Col & dean, Col Allied Health Sci, Thomas Jefferson Univ, 76-78; ASSOC PROF ANAT, SCH BASIC MED SCI & DEP EXEC DEAN, COL MED, UNIV ILL, 78- *Mem:* AAAS; Teratology Soc. *Res:* Transport across the placenta during normal and abnormal embryogenesis; effects of teratogens on function; distribution of teratogens; mechanism of malformations. *Mailing Add:* Univ Ill Col Med 131 CMW 1853 W Polk St Chicago IL 60612

KERNKAMP, MILTON F, b Washington Co, Minn, Sept 16, 11; m. PLANT PATHOLOGY. *Educ:* Univ Minn, BS, 34, MS, 38, PhD(plant path), 41. *Prof Exp:* Asst pathologist, Agr & Mech Col, Tex, 35; asst, Univ Minn, 35-36, instr, 36-41; asst pathologist, USDA, Miss, 41-46; from asst prof to assoc prof, 46-56, asst dir agr exp sta, 56-61, head dept plant path, 61-72, prof plant path, 72-77, PROF EMER, UNIV MINN, ST PAUL, 77- *Mem:* AAAS; Am Soc Agron; Am Phytopath Soc; Indian Phytopath Soc. *Res:* Genetics and variability of smut fungi; diseases of forage legumes and grasses; diseases of wild rice. *Mailing Add:* 9431 Hutton Dr Sun City AZ 85351

KERNS, DAVID MARLOW, b Minneapolis, Minn, Oct 7, 13. ELECTROMAGNETICS. *Educ:* Univ Minn, BEE, 35; Cath Univ Am, PhD(physics), 51. *Prof Exp:* Asst, Univ Minn, 35-39; chief elec unit, Aerial Camera Lab, Air Mat Command, US Air Force, Ohio, 40-42; from proj leader to asst div chief, Radio Standards Lab & Electromagnetic Fields Div, 46-71, SR RES SCIENTIST, ELECTROMAGNETIC FIELDS DIV, NAT BUR STANDARDS, 71- *Concurrent Pos:* Adj prof, Univ Colo, 61-; mem US comn, Int Sci Radio Union, 58- *Honors & Awards:* Silver Medal, US Dept Com, 60, Gold Medal, 73; Harry Diamond Award, Inst Elec & Electronic Engrs, 78. *Res:* Electromagnetic theory of wave guides and wave guide junctions; scattering-matrix theory of antennas and antenna-antenna interactions. *Mailing Add:* Electromagnetics Div Nat Bur of Standards Boulder CO 80302

KERPER, MATTHEW J(ULIUS), b St Louis, Mo, Apr 9, 22; m 48; c 1. CERAMICS. *Educ:* Univ Mo, BS, 43, MS, 47; George Washington Univ, MS, 59; Am Univ, MPA. *Prof Exp:* Ceramic engr, Laclede Christy Co, Mo, 47-52, Nat Bur Standards, 52-66, Off Aerospace Res, 66-70 & Air Force Systs Command, 70-72; CERAMIC ENGR, AIR FORCE OFF SCI RES, 72- *Mem:* AAAS; Am Ceramic Soc; Am Inst Ceramic Engrs; Sigma Xi; Am Soc Pub Admin. *Res:* Physical properties of ceramics and glass at elevated temperatures; science administration. *Mailing Add:* 4620 North Park Ave Apt 1509E Chevy Chase MD 20015

KERR, ANDREW, JR, b Wilkinsburg, Pa, Dec 30, 14; c 3. MEDICINE. *Educ:* Colgate Univ, AB, 37; Harvard Univ, MD, 41. *Prof Exp:* Instr med, Tulane Univ, 49-50; from instr to asst prof, La State Univ, 51-55; assoc Col Med, State Univ NY Upstate Med Ctr, 55-60; assoc prof clin med, Med Col Ga, 60-61, clin prof med, 61; asst prof clin med, Sch Med & Dent, Univ Rochester, 61-67; dir, Cardiopulmonary Lab, Vet Admin Hosp, 61-67, chief med, 64-67; PROF MED, NORTHEAST OHIO COL MED, 78- *Concurrent Pos:* Fel med, Tulane Univ, 48-49; asst chief med, Vet Admin Hosp, Syracuse, NY, 55-60, chief, Augusta, Ga, 60-61; chmn Dept Med, Akron City Hosp, 67-76, Div Cardiol, 76- *Mem:* Am Fedn Clin Res. *Res:* Cardiovascular diseases. *Mailing Add:* Dept of Med Akron City Hosp Akron OH 44309

KERR, ANTHONY ROBERT, b Farnborough, Eng, Aug 30, 41; Australian citizen; m 74. MICROWAVE ELECTRONICS, RADIO ASTRONOMY. *Educ:* Univ Melbourne, BE, 63, MESc, 67, PhD(elec eng), 69. *Prof Exp:* Res scientist radio astron, Div Radiophys, Commonwealth Sci & Indust Res Orgn, Sydney, Australia, 69-71; electronics engr millimeter-wave electronics, Nat

Radio Astron Observ, Charlottesville, Va, 71-74; PHYSICIST MILLIMETER-WAVE ELECTRONICS, GODDARD INST SPACE STUDIES, NASA, 74- *Honors & Awards:* The Microwave Prize, Inst Elec & Electronics Engrs, 78. *Mem:* Sr mem Inst Elec & Electronics Engrs; Int Union Radio Sci; Astron Soc Australia. *Res:* Development of low-noise receivers at millimeter and submillimeter wavelengths, and their application in radio astronomy, atmospheric physics, and space communications. *Mailing Add:* Goddard Inst for Space Studies 2880 Broadway New York NY 10025

KERR, ARNOLD D, b Suwalki, Poland, Mar 9, 28; US citizen; m 66; c 2. ENGINEERING MECHANICS, RAILROAD ENGINEERING. *Educ:* Munich, Dipl Ing, 52; Northwestern Univ, MS, 56, PhD(theoret & appl mech), 58. *Prof Exp:* Engr design & anal, Hazelet & Erdal, Consult Engrs, 55; asst res scientist mech solids, Courant Inst Math & Sci, New York Univ, 58-59, asst prof aeronaut, 59-61, assoc prof aeronaut & astronaut, 61-66, prof, 66-73, dir, Lab Mech Solids, 67-73; vis prof civil eng, Princeton Univ, 73-78; PROF CIVIL ENG, UNIV DEL, 78- *Concurrent Pos:* Consult to US govt agencies & indust, 59-; pres, Inst Railroad Eng, 80- *Mem:* Am Soc Mech Engrs; Am Railway Eng Asn. *Res:* Structural mechanics; continuously supported structures; dynamics and stability of structures; bearing capacity and dynamics of floating ice covers; railroad track analyses and technology. *Mailing Add:* Dept Civil Eng Univ Del Newark DE 19711

KERR, CARL E, b Corsicana, Tex, Sept 16, 26; m 50; c 1. MATHEMATICS. *Educ:* La Salle Col, BA, 50; Univ Del, MA, 53; Lehigh Univ, PhD(math), 59. *Prof Exp:* Asst prof math, Lafayette Col, 53-59; asst prof, Dickinson Col, 59-69; prof math, 69-76, PROF MATH & COMPUT SCI, SHIPPENSBURG STATE COL, 76- *Concurrent Pos:* Mathematician, Frankford Arsenal, 52-54; mathematician, Convair Div, Gen Dynamics Corp, 56. *Mem:* Am Math Soc; Math Asn Am. *Res:* Linear spaces; summability. *Mailing Add:* Dept of Math Shippensburg State Col Shippensburg PA 17257

KERR, DONALD L(AURENS), b Putnam, Conn, June 28, 43; m 66; c 1. CHEMICAL ENGINEERING. *Educ:* Worcester Polytech Inst, BS, 65; Univ Del, MChE, 68, PhD(chem eng, phys chem), 70. *Prof Exp:* Sr chemist, Photog Eng Lab, 69-75, RES ASSOC PHOTOG PROCESSES LAB, RES LABS, EASTMAN KODAK CO, 75- *Mem:* Am Inst Chem Engrs. *Res:* Mass tranfer; chemical kinetics; drying; photographic processing. *Mailing Add:* Photog Processes Lab Res Labs Eastman Kodak Co Rochester NY 14650

KERR, DONALD M, JR, research administration, geophysics, see previous edition

KERR, DONALD PHILIP, b Winnipeg, Man, Oct 22, 38; m 62; c 2. ATOMIC PHYSICS, MOLECULAR PHYSICS. *Educ:* Univ Man, BSc, 60, MSc, 61, PhD(physics), 65. *Prof Exp:* Nat Res Coun Can fel, Univ Giessen, 65-67; res assoc, Harvard Univ, 67-69; asst prof physics, Univ Winnipeg, 69-74, assoc prof, 74-79. *Mem:* Can Asn Physicists. *Res:* Positron annihilation in organic liquids and solids; high resolution mass spectrometry; heavy ion scattering. *Mailing Add:* 19 Grover Hills St Boniface Winnipeg MB R2J 3C2 Can

KERR, DONALD R, b Chicago, Ill, Mar 12, 38; m 60; c 1. MATHEMATICS. *Educ:* Univ Ariz, BS, 60, MS, 62; Lehigh Univ, PhD(math), 67. *Prof Exp:* Instr math, Lafayette Col, 63-67; asst prof, State Univ NY Albany, 67-69; vis prof math, 69-71, assoc prof educ & asst dir math educ develop ctr, 71-78, ACAD OFFICER & BASIC SKILLS COORDR MATH, IND UNIV, BLOOMINGTON, 78- *Mem:* Am Math Soc; Math Asn Am; Nat Coun Teachers Math. *Res:* Elementary education in mathematics and the mathematics training of elementary teachers; problem solving of children, grades 4, 5, 6; basic skills in mathematics for college students. *Mailing Add:* Dept Math Indiana Univ Bloomington IN 47401

KERR, DOUGLAS S, b Wash, DC, Nov 19, 40; m 68. COMPUTER SCIENCES. *Educ:* Yale Univ, BA, 62; Purdue Univ, MS, 64, PhD(computer sci), 67. *Prof Exp:* Asst prof, 67-71, ASSOC PROF, COMPUT & INFO SCI, OHIO STATE UNIV, 71- *Mem:* Am Math Soc; Asn Comput Mach; Math Asn Am; Soc Indust & Appl Math. *Res:* Programming; numerical solution of ordinary differential equations; numerical linear algebra; data base systems; numerical analysis. *Mailing Add:* Dept of Comput & Info Sci 2036 Neil Ave Columbus OH 43210

KERR, EDWIN ROBERT, b Leetonia, Ohio, Mar 15, 22; m 46; c 4. PHYSICAL CHEMISTRY. *Educ:* Univ Mich, BSE, 42; Wayne State Univ, PhD(chem), 53. *Prof Exp:* Org chemist, Ethyl Corp, 47-50; res chemist, 53-65, group leader, 65-74, RES ASSOC, BEACON RES LABS, TEXACO, INC, 75- *Mem:* AAAS; Am Chem Soc; Am Inst Chem Eng. *Res:* Petrochemicals; hydrocarbon chemistry; application of chemical and physical techniques to petroleum processing; catalysis. *Mailing Add:* Beacon Res Labs Texaco Inc PO Box 509 Beacon NY 12508

KERR, ERIC DONALD, b Gipsy, Mo, Feb 21, 30; m 71. PHYTOPATHOLOGY. *Educ:* Univ Mo, Columbia, BS, 51, MS, 60; Univ Nebr, Lincoln, PhD(plant path), 67. *Prof Exp:* Res plant pathologist, Agr Res Serv, 67; EXTEN PLANT PATHOLOGIST, PANHANDLE STA, UNIV NEBR, 67- *Mem:* Soc Nematol; Am Phytopath Soc. *Res:* Effects of nematodes on growth and yield of wheat; effects of stalk rot on yield of corn; dry bean yield losses caused by white mold; effects of phorate on growth and yield of wheat. *Mailing Add:* 2460 Valencia Gering NE 69341

KERR, ERNEST ANDREW, b Guelph, Ont, Aug 24, 17; m 45; c 3. PLANT BREEDING. *Educ:* McMaster Univ, BA, 40; McGill Univ, MSc, 41; Univ Wis, PhD(genetics, plant path), 44. *Prof Exp:* Asst, Hort Exp Sta, Ont Dept Agr & Food, 44-52, res assoc, 52-54, chief res scientist, Plant Breeding, 54-70, res coordr prod systs, Hort Res Inst Ont, 70-72, RES SCIENTIST, ONT MINISTRY AGR & FOOD, 72- *Concurrent Pos:* Mem comn protected cultivation, Int Soc Hort Sci. *Mem:* Am Soc Hort Sci; Genetics Soc Can; fel Agr Inst Can; Can Soc Hort Sci; Int Soc Hort Sci. *Res:* Horticultural plant breeding, particularly tomatoes and sweet corn; disease resistance; genetics and earliness in tomatoes. *Mailing Add:* Hort Exp Sta PO Box 587 Simcoe ON N3Y 4N5 Can

KERR, FRANK JOHN, b St Albans, Eng, Jan 8, 18; m 66; c 3. RADIO ASTRONOMY. *Educ:* Univ Melbourne, BSc, 38, MSc, 40, DSc(astron), 62; Harvard Univ, MA, 51. *Prof Exp:* Res officer radiophysics, Div Radiophysics, Commonwealth Sci & Indust Res Orgn, Australia, 40-45, sr res officer radio astron, 45-55, prin res officer, 60-68; vis prof, 66-68, dir astron prog, 73-78, PROF ASTRON, UNIV MD, COLLEGE PARK, 68-, PROVOST, DIV MATH & PHYS SCI & ENG, 79- *Concurrent Pos:* Res scholar, Harvard Univ, 51-52; vis scientist, Leiden Univ, 57-58; fel, Guggenheim Found, 75. *Mem:* Int Astron Union; Am Astron Soc; Royal Astron Soc; Astron Soc Australia; Australian Inst Physics. *Res:* Galactic structure; tropospheric radio propagation; moon radar; radio studies of Galaxy and Magellanic Clouds. *Mailing Add:* Math & Phys Sci & Eng Div Univ of Md College Park MD 20742

KERR, FREDERICK WILLIAM LAWSON, b Buenos Aires, Arg, Mar 25, 23; US citzen; m 53; c 1. NEUROSURGERY, NEUROANATOMY. *Educ:* Univ Buenos Aires, MD, 49. *Prof Exp:* Instr neurosurg, Sch Med, Washington Univ, 56-58; instr & clin asst prof, State Univ NY Upstate Med Ctr, 58-59; asst prof neurosurg, 61-66, from asst prof to assoc prof neuroanat, 64-73, assoc prof neurol surg, 66-70, PROF NEUROL SURG, MAYO GRAD SCH MED, UNIV MINN, 70-, NEUROANAT, 73- *Concurrent Pos:* Fel neurosurg, Sch Med, Washington Univ, 52-56; USPHS grants, 61-64 & 63-66; actg chief neurol surg, Vet Admin Hosp, Syracuse, 58-59; consult, Mayo Clin & Allied Hosps, 61- *Mem:* Am Asn Anatomists; fel Am Col Surg; Am Asn Neurol Surg; AMA; Am Neurol Asn. *Res:* Anatomy and physiology of the brain stem and spinal cord; central pathways of the autonomic nervous system; pain, central mechanisms; mechanisms of narcotic addiction and tolerance; plasticity in the central nervous system; author or coauthor of over 90 publications. *Mailing Add:* Sect of Neuro Surg Mayo Clin Rochester MN 55901

KERR, GEORGE R, b Winnipeg, Man, May 15, 30; m 54; c 6. PUBLIC HEALTH NUTRITION, PEDIATRICS. *Educ:* Dalhousie Univ, MD & CM, 55. *Prof Exp:* Intern med & surg, Victoria Gen Hosp, Halifax, NS, 54-55; gen pract, 55-56; resident pediat & orthop, Gen Hosp, St Johns, Nfld, 56-57; asst resident pediat, Vancouver Gen Hosp, BC, 57-58, asst resident med, 59; instr, Univ BC, 61-62; asst prof pediat, Med Sch, Univ Ore, 62-63; from asst prof to assoc prof, Sch Med, Univ Wis-Madison, 63-71; assoc prof nutrit, Sch Pub Health, Harvard Univ, 71-77; PROF NUTRIT, SCH PUB HEALTH, UNIV TEX, 77- *Concurrent Pos:* Res fel, Vancouver Gen Hosp, BC, 59; R Samuel McLaughlin traveling fel, 59-60; res fel pediat endocrinol & metab, Med Sch, Univ Ore, 59-61; Queen Elizabeth II Can res fel, 60-61; asst dir, Ore Regional Primate Res Ctr, 62-63; res assoc, Joseph P Kennedy, Jr Mem Lab & Wis Regional Primate Res Ctr, 63-71; dir, Human Nutrit Ctr, Univ Tex, Health Sci Ctr, 77- *Res:* Public health nutrition program needs and effectiveness, nutrition and child development. *Mailing Add:* Sch of Pub Health Univ of Tex Houston TX 77025

KERR, GEORGE THOMSON, b Baltimore, Md, May 7, 23; m 50; c 3. SURFACE CHEMISTRY. *Educ:* Pa State Univ, BS, 45, MS, 46, PhD(chem), 52. *Prof Exp:* Instr chem, Pa State Univ, 49-50; asst prof, Lebanon Valley Col, 50-52; res supvr, Res Div, AMP, Inc, 52-56; sr res chemist, Socony Mobil Labs, 56-62, res assoc, 62-75, SR RES ASSOC, CENT RES DIV LAB, MOBIL RES & DEVELOP CORP, 75- *Concurrent Pos:* Mem comt zeolite nomenclature, Int Union Pure & Appl Chem; mem organizing comt, Fourth Int Conf Molecular Sieves, 77. *Mem:* Int Zeolite Asn; Am Chem Soc; Int Zeolite Asn (pres, 80-83). *Res:* Synthesis and physical properties of high molecular weight hydrocarbons; kinetics of acid attack of clay minerals; synthesis and properties of crystalline zeolites. *Mailing Add:* Mobil Res & Develop Corp Cent Res Div Lab PO Box 1025 Princeton NJ 08540

KERR, HAROLD DELBERT, b Clarkton, Mo, Jan 3, 33; m 51; c 2. WEED SCIENCE. *Educ:* Univ Mo, BSc, 55, MS, 57; Wash State Univ, PhD(agron), 63. *Prof Exp:* Res agronomist, Univ Mo, Agr Res Serv, USDA, 55-57 & Wash State Univ, 58-62; res agronomist, Plant Indust Sta, Md, 62-67; asst prof weed sci, 67-71, ASSOC PROF AGRON, UNIV MO, 71- *Mem:* Weed Sci Soc Am; Am Soc Agron; Crop Sci Soc Am. *Res:* Botany of weeds and ecology of control in agronomic crops. *Mailing Add:* Dept of Agron Univ of Mo Delta Ctr Portageville MO 63873

KERR, HUGH BARKLEY, b Maryville, Tenn, July 22, 22; m 51; c 2. MECHANICAL ENGINEERING. *Educ:* Univ Tenn, BS, 47, MS, 51. *Prof Exp:* Mech engr res & develop, Combustion Eng Co, 47-48; instr mech eng, Clemson Col, 48-51; asst prof, Univ Ala, 51-54; gen engr, Mine Detection Lab, US Navy, Fla, 54-55; assoc prof mech eng, Univ Miss, 55-61 & Tex Western Col, 61-62; ASSOC PROF ENG SCI & DIR, D W MATTSON COMPUT CTR, TENN TECHNOL UNIV, 62- *Concurrent Pos:* Mech engr, Int Harvester Co, 57; plant engr, Western Elec Co, 59. *Mem:* Am Soc Eng Educ. *Res:* Heat power; refrigeration and air conditioning; photoelastic stress analysis; data processing; computer sciences. *Mailing Add:* D W Mattson Comput Ctr PO Box 5071 TTU Cookeville TN 38501

KERR, JAMES S(ANFORD) S(TEPHENSON), b Vancouver, BC, Mar 9, 26; nat US; m 49; c 2. ELECTRICAL ENGINEERING, ELECTROMAGNETISM. *Educ:* Univ BC, BASc, 48; Univ Ill, MS, 49, PhD, 51. *Prof Exp:* Eng analyst elec eng, Gen Elec Co, NY, 51-56; mgr guid, tracking & eval dept, TRW Space Technol Labs, 56-65, asst lab dir antisubmarine warfare, 65-66, asst mgr, Guid & Control Opers, TRW Systs Group, 66-67, sr staff engr to gen mgr electronics systs div, 67-71, sr staff engr, Ballistic Missile Defense Prog Off, Redondo Beach, 71-76, sr staff engr spec proj, TRW Defense & Space Systs Group, 76-80, SR STAFF ENGR, SPACE COMMUN DIV, TRW ELECTRONICS SYSTS GROUP, 80- *Mem:* AAAS; sr mem Inst Elec & Electronics Engrs. *Res:* Analysis and design of space communications systems; analysis of advanced radar systems and data therefrom; management of radio guidance system and radio guidance equation development for space programs such as Mercury, Ranger and Mariner. *Mailing Add:* 16620 Linda Terr Pacific Palisades CA 90272

KERR, JAMES WILLIAM, b Coleman, Alta, Jan 24, 36; m 65. GEOLOGY. *Educ:* Univ Alta, BSc, 56; Columbia Univ, PhD(geol), 60. *Prof Exp:* Lectr geol, Queen's Univ, Ont, 59-61; RES GEOLOGIST, INST SEDIMENTARY & PETROL GEOL, GEOL SURV CAN, 61- *Honors & Awards:* Medal of Merit, Can Soc Petrol Geologists, 65. *Mem:* Geol Asn Can; Can Soc Petrol Geologists. *Res:* Arctic geological research; stratigraphy, structural geology, continental drift and tectonics. *Mailing Add:* 320 39th Ave SW Calgary AB T2S 0W7 Can

KERR, JOHN M(ARTIN), b Normal, Ill, Jan 31, 34; m 56; c 4. CERAMIC & CHEMICAL ENGINEERING. *Educ:* Univ Ill, BS, 56. *Prof Exp:* Metallurgist, Oak Ridge Nat Lab, 56-61; sr engr, 61-66, supvr nuclear ceramics, 66-71, mgr ceramics sect, 71-74, MGR NUCLEAR FUEL CYCLE SECT, BABCOCK & WILCOX CO, 74- *Mem:* Fel Am Ceramic Soc; Am Soc Testing & Mat. *Res:* Ceramic bodies for waste disposal; ceramic fuel-metal compatibility studies; ceramic fuels development and development of fuels fabrication methods; nuclear ceramics; nuclear fuel cycle studies. *Mailing Add:* 1425 Brookville Lane Lynchburg VA 24502

KERR, JOHN POLK, b Little Rock, Ark, July 14, 31; m 56; c 4. ZOOLOGY, AQUATIC BIOLOGY. *Educ:* Rutgers Univ, BA, 56; Univ Calif, MS, 57; Univ Mich, PhD(zool), 62. *Prof Exp:* Asst biol, Rutgers Univ, 55-56; researcher animal behavior, Ciba Pharmaceut Co, 57-58; teaching asst zool, Univ Mich, 58-59; instr biol, Adrian Col, 61-62; res assoc fisheries, Univ Mich, 62-63; asst prof zool, Univ Ga, 63-69; assoc prof biol & marine sci, Univ WFla, 69-73; vpres & sr ecol consult, Baseline, Inc, 73-76, gen mgr & pres, 76-78; HEAD, NEW SOUTH ECOSYSTEMS, INC, 78- *Concurrent Pos:* Rackham fel fisheries, Univ Mich, 62-63; vis asst prof, Ore Inst Marine Biol, Univ Ore, 65; partic, Electronics for Scientists Prof, Univ Ill, 68; faculty fel, Systs Design Prog, NASA & Am Soc Eng Educ, Auburn Univ, 70. *Mem:* Am Soc Zool; Ecol Soc Am; Am Fisheries Soc; Am Soc Ichthyol & Herpet; Am Soc Limnol & Oceanog. *Res:* Aquatic ecology; biology of vertebrates, especially fishes; ichthyology and herpetology; fisheries; marine and freshwater ecosystems, especially rivers, estuaries, wetlands, and lakes; animal behavior, especially under field conditions. *Mailing Add:* 4770 Velasquez St R4 Pensacola FL 32504

KERR, KENTON E, US citizen. PHYSIOLOGICAL OPTICS. *Educ:* Univ Calif, Berkeley, BS, 58, MOpt, 59, PhD(physiol optics), 69. *Prof Exp:* Pvt pract, Oakland, Calif, 59-64; clin instr, Col Optom, Ohio State Univ, 60-66, from instr to asst prof, 66-70; assoc prof physiol optics, Univ Ala, Birmingham, 70-72; asst prof, 72-77, ASSOC CLIN PROF OPTOM, UNIV CALIF, BERKELEY, 77- *Mem:* Fel Am Acad Optom. *Res:* Device for measuring the curvature for contact lenses. *Mailing Add:* Dept of Optom Univ of Calif Berkeley CA 94720

KERR, KIRKLYN M, b Green Bank, WVa, May 1, 36; m 57; c 3. VETERINARY PATHOLOGY. *Educ:* Univ WVa, BS, 61, MS, 66; Ohio State Univ, DVM, 61; Tex A&M Univ, PhD(vet path), 70; Am Col Vet Path, dipl, 68. *Prof Exp:* Vet practitioner, North Side Vet Clin, Carlisle, Pa, 61-62; res assoc vet microbiol & path, Univ WVa, 62-65; from instr to assoc prof vet path, Col Vet Med, Tex A&M Univ, 65-72; assoc prof vet pathobiol & dir div appl path, Col Vet Med, Ohio State Univ, 72-78; ASST DEAN FOR RES & ADVAN STUDIES, SCH VET MED & HEAD VET SCI, LA STATE UNIV, 78- *Mem:* Am Vet Med Asn; Int Acad Path. *Res:* Veterinary pathology; mycoplasmatacea; cancer research in animals. *Mailing Add:* La State Univ Baton Rouge LA 70803

KERR, MARILYN SUE, b Sumner, Ill. DEVELOPMENTAL BIOLOGY. *Educ:* Gettysburg Col, BA, 59; Duke Univ, MA, 61, PhD(zool), 66. *Prof Exp:* USPHS fel vitellogenesis, Biol Div, Oak Ridge Nat Lab, 66-69, Nat Inst Child Health & Human Develop trainee biophys, 69-70; ASST PROF BIOL, SYRACUSE UNIV, 70- *Mem:* Am Soc Zoologists; Soc Develop Biol; AAAS; Sigma Xi. *Res:* Vitellogenesis and limb regeneration correlated with studies of hemocyte origin, differentiation and functions in arthropods; hemocyanin synthesis, its isolation and characterization. *Mailing Add:* Biol Res Labs 130 College Pl Syracuse NY 13210

KERR, NORMAN STORY, b St Louis, Mo, Aug 6, 33; m 65; c 2. DEVELOPMENTAL BIOLOGY. *Educ:* Oberlin Col, AB, 54; Northwestern Univ, MS, 55, PhD(biol), 58. *Prof Exp:* Asst biol, Northwestern Univ, 54-56; from instr to assoc prof, 58-71, asst dean, 66-68, prof zool, 71-76, assoc dean col biol sci, 69-78, PROF GENETICS & CELL BIOL, UNIV MINN, MINNEAPOLIS, 76- . *Mem:* Fel AAAS; Am Soc Zool; Am Soc Cell Biol; Soc Protozool. *Res:* Morphogenesis and genetics of the true slime molds; computer assisted instruction. *Mailing Add:* Dept of Genetics & Cell Biol Univ of Minn St Paul MN 55108

KERR, RALPH OLIVER, b Oakland City, Ind, May 14, 26; m 46; c 4. ORGANIC CHEMISTRY. *Educ:* Ind Univ, AB, 49; Univ Ill, MS, 50, PhD(chem), 53. *Prof Exp:* Asst inorg chem, Univ Ill, 49-53; chemist org develop, Columbia Southern Chem Corp, 53-56; res assoc, Petro-Tex Chem Corp, 56-76; OWNER, INDIAN HILL PROD, 76- *Mem:* Am Chem Soc. *Res:* Reductions of hindered ketones; organic oxidations; heterogeneous oxidation catalysts; maleic catalyst development. *Mailing Add:* Indian Hill Prods 6700 S Victor Pike Bloomington IN 47401

KERR, RICHARD JOHN, organic chemistry, see previous edition

KERR, SANDRIA NEIDUS, b Youngstown, Ohio, Oct 1, 40; m 63; c 2. COMPUTER BASED INSTRUCTION. *Educ:* Col Wooster, BA, 62; Bryn Mawr Col, MA, 64; Cornell Univ, PhD(math), 71. *Prof Exp:* Asst prof, 71-74, ASSOC PROF MATH, WINSTON-SALEM UNIV, 74- *Mem:* Am Math Soc. *Res:* Analysis on infinite-dimensional manifolds; multivariable calculus studies involving placement of students in math courses, experimentation with computer based instruction. *Mailing Add:* 1938 Fac Dr Winston-Salem NC 27106

KERR, STEPHEN ROY, ecology, see previous edition

KERR, STRATTON H, b Springfield, Mass, May 17, 24; m 48; c 2. ENTOMOLOGY. *Educ:* Univ Mass, BS, 49; Cornell Univ, PhD(entom), 53. *Prof Exp:* From asst entomologist to assoc entomologist, 53-68, ENTOMOLOGIST, UNIV FLA, 68- *Mem:* AAAS; Entom Soc Am. *Res:* Insects of turfgrass, arthropod resistance to insecticides; applied entomology. *Mailing Add:* Dept of Entomol Univ of Fla Gainesville FL 32611

KERR, SYLVIA JEAN, b St Louis, Mo, July 2, 41. BIOCHEMISTRY. *Educ:* Smith Col, AB, 62; Columbia Univ, PhD, 67. *Prof Exp:* Asst prof surg, 70-75, ASSOC PROF BIOCHEM, UNIV COLO MED CTR, DENVER, 76- *Concurrent Pos:* Nat Cancer Inst career develop award, 71- *Mem:* Am Chem Soc; Am Soc Biol Chemists. *Res:* Biochemical control mechanisms; transfer RNA metabolism. *Mailing Add:* Dept of Biochem Univ of Colo Med Ctr Denver CO 80262

KERR, SYLVIA JOANN, b Detroit, Mich, June 19, 41; m 65; c 2. DEVELOPMENTAL BIOLOGY, MICROBIOLOGY. *Educ:* Carleton Col, BA, 63; Univ Minn, Minneapolis, MS, 66, PhD(zool), 68. *Prof Exp:* Asst prof biol, Augsburg Col, 68-71; res fel pharmacog, Univ Minn, 72, med fel cell biol, 74-75; asst prof biol, Anoka-Ramsey Community Col, Augsburg Col & Hamline Univ, 72-74; ASST PROF BIOL, HAMLINE UNIV, 76- *Res:* Environmental control of gene expression in cell differentiation with emphasis on the role of cell membranes and membrane receptors. *Mailing Add:* Dept of Biol Hamline Univ Snelling & Hewitt St Paul MN 55104

KERR, THEODORE WILLIAM, JR, b Patterson, NJ, Nov 20, 12; m 38. ENTOMOLOGY. *Educ:* Mass State Col, BS, 36; Cornell Univ, PhD(econ entomol), 41. *Prof Exp:* Field asst, NY Exp Sta, Geneva, 35-36; asst entomologist, Cornell Univ, 37-42; sr res entomologist, US Rubber Co, 42-46; from asst res prof entomol to res prof entomol & plant path, 46-77, EMER RES PROF PLANT PATH & ENTOMOL, UNIV RI, 77- *Mem:* Entomol Soc Am. *Res:* Biology and control of insects attacking trees, shrubs and turf. *Mailing Add:* 18 Clarke Lane Kingston RI 02881

KERR, THOMAS JAMES, b Muskogee, Okla, Oct 7, 27; m 51; c 7. MICROBIOLOGY. *Educ:* Okla A&M Univ, BS, 50; Okla State Univ, MS, 63; Univ Ga, PhD(microbiol), 76. *Prof Exp:* Asst to dir biol res, US Biol Warfare Ctr, Frederick, Md, 58-60, dep dir med res, 63-64; proj officer, US Army Test & Eval Command, Aberdeen, Md, 67-70; res asst microbiol, 71-76, DIR LAB STUDIES, UNIV GA, 76- *Mem:* Am Soc Microbiol. *Res:* Biological inhibition of fusarium moniliforme various subglutinans; the casual agent of pine pitch canker; production of single cell protein from agricultural waste products. *Mailing Add:* Dept of Microbiol Univ of Ga Athens GA 30602

KERR, WARWICK ESTEVAM, b Santana de Parnaiba, Brazil, Sept 9, 22; m 56; c 7. GENETICS. *Educ:* Univ Sao Paulo, MSc, 48, PhD(genetics), 50. *Prof Exp:* Biologist genetics, Grad Sch Agr, Univ Sao Paulo, 46-48, from asst prof to assoc prof, 48-58; prof biol, Col Sci UNESP-Rio-Claro, 59-64; prof genetics, Col Med, Univ Sao Paulo, 64-75; dir, Nat Res Inst Amazon, 75-79; PROF BIOL, UNIV FED MARANHAO, SAO LUIS, 81- *Concurrent Pos:* Rockefeller Found fel, 51-52; Brazilian Nat Res Coun grants, USDA, 61-66; State of Sao Paulo Res Found grants, 65-67. *Mem:* Soc Study Evolution; Brazilian Genetics Soc (pres, 64-66); Brazilian Soc Advan Sci (pres, 69-73). *Res:* Bee genetics; cytology and evolution; plant breeding. *Mailing Add:* Nat Inst Res of Amazon Caixolastal 478 Manaus Am Brazil

KERR, WENDLE LOUIS, b Harlan, Iowa, Dec 16, 17; m 43; c 2. PHARMACY. *Educ:* Univ Iowa, BS, 41, MS, 50. *Prof Exp:* From instr to asst prof, 47-61, ASSOC PROF PHARM, COL PHARM, UNIV IOWA, 61-, COORDR PHARM EXTEN SERV, 66- *Concurrent Pos:* Sta pharmacist, Univ Iowa, 46-61 & dir pharmaceut procurement, 61-66. *Mem:* Am Soc Hosp Pharmacists; Am Pharmaceut Asn; Teachers Pharm Admin & Continuing Educ; Sigma XI. *Res:* Improved formulations for the oral administration of drugs; administrative pharmacy; hospital pharmacy. *Mailing Add:* Col of Pharm Univ of Iowa Iowa City IA 52240

KERR, WILLIAM, b Sawyer, Kans, Aug 19, 19; m 45; c 3. REACTOR SAFETY, REACTOR SHIELDING. *Educ:* Univ Tenn, BS, 42, MS, 47; Univ Mich, PhD(elec eng), 54. *Prof Exp:* Asst prof elec eng, Univ Tenn, 47-48; asst prof elec eng, 53-56, assoc prof nuclear eng, 56-58, chmn dept nuclear eng, 61-74, from assoc dir to actg dir, Mich Mem Phoenix Proj, 60-65, PROF NUCLEAR ENG, UNIV MICH, ANN ARBOR, 58-, DIR, MICH MEM PHOENIX PROJ, 65-, DIR OFF ENERGY RES, 77- *Concurrent Pos:* Proj supvr nuclear energy proj, USAID, 56-65; consult, Atomic Power Develop Assocs, 54-59, Union Carbide Nuclear Corp, 54 & USAID, 56-65; pres bd dir, Assoc Midwest Univs, 65; mem adv comt reactor safeguards, US Nuclear Regulatory Comn, 72-; mem gov task force on nuclear waste disposal, State of Mich, 76- *Honors & Awards:* Arthur Holly Compton Award, Am Nuclear Soc, 74. *Mem:* Fel Am Nuclear Soc; sr mem Inst Elec & Electronics Engrs; Am Soc Eng Educ; Sigma Xi. *Res:* Application of telemetering to power systems; autoradiography; nuclear reactor system dynamics; reactor control; reactor shielding; reactor safety analysis. *Mailing Add:* 3034 Phoenix Mem Lab North Campus Univ of Mich Ann Arbor MI 48109

KERREBROCK, JACK LEO, b Los Angeles, Calif, Feb 6, 28; m 53; c 3. AERONAUTICS, ASTRONAUTICS. *Educ:* Ore State Col, BS, 50; Yale Univ, MS, 51; Calif Inst Technol, PhD(mech eng), 56. *Prof Exp:* Res engr, Oak Ridge Nat Lab, 56-58; sr res fel, Calif Inst Technol, 58-60; from asst prof to prof, 60-75, dir, Space Propulsion Lab, 62-76 & Gas Turbine Lab, 68-78, head dept, 78-81, RICHARD COCKBURN MACLAURIN PROF AERONAUT & ASTRONAUT, MASS INST TECHNOL, 75- *Concurrent Pos:* Chmn, Sci & Technol Adv Group, USAF Sci Adv Bd; mem Nat Res Coun Aeronaut & Space Eng Bd; mem Am Soc Mech Engrs Turbomach Comt; NASA Adv Bd Aircraft Fuel Conserv Technol; assoc adminr, Off Aeronaut & Space Technol, NASA, 81-; hon prof, Beijing Inst Aeronaut & Astronaut, China, 80. *Honors & Awards:* Dryden lectr, Am Inst Aeronaut & Astronaut, 80. *Mem:* Nat Acad Eng; fel Am Inst Aeronaut & Astronaut; fel

Explorers Club; Am Phys Soc; sr mem Am Astronaut Soc. *Res:* Aircraft propulsion; space propulsion and power generation systems; magnetohydrodynamics; nuclear rockets. *Mailing Add:* Dept of Aeronaut & Astronaut Rm 33-207 Mass Inst of Technol Cambridge MA 02139

KERRI, KENNETH D, b Napa, Calif, Apr 25, 34; m 58; c 2. CIVIL & SANITARY ENGINEERING. *Educ:* Ore State Univ, BS, 56, PhD(civil eng), 66; Univ Calif, Berkeley, MS, 59. *Prof Exp:* Assoc prof, 59-68, PROF CIVIL ENG, CALIF STATE UNIV, SACRAMENTO, 68- *Concurrent Pos:* Fac res award, Calif State Univ, Sacramento, 69; pres, Nat Environ Training Asn, 79-80. *Honors & Awards:* Collection Syst Award, Water Pollution Control Fedn, 77. *Mem:* Water Pollution Control Fedn; Am Soc Civil Engrs; Am Water Works Asn; Am Soc Eng Educ. *Res:* Water quality economics; training manuals for operators of water and wastewater facilities. *Mailing Add:* Dept of Civil Eng Calif State Univ 6000 J St Sacramento CA 95819

KERRICK, DERRILL M, b Santa Cruz, Calif, Dec 27, 40; m 61; c 2. PETROLOGY, GEOCHEMISTRY. *Educ:* San Jose State Col, BS, 63; Univ Calif, Berkeley, PhD(geol), 68. *Prof Exp:* Lectr geol, Victoria Univ Manchester, 67-69; asst prof, 69-73, assoc prof, 73-79, PROF PETROL, PA STATE UNIV, 79- *Concurrent Pos:* Assoc ed, Geochimica et Cosmochimica Acta. *Mem:* Mineral Soc Am. *Res:* Laboratory and field investigations of metamorphic reactions and stability relations of metamorphic assemblages. *Mailing Add:* Col of Earth & Mineral Sci Pa State Univ University Park PA 16802

KERRIDGE, KENNETH A, b London, Eng, Mar 26, 28. MEDICINAL CHEMISTRY, ORGANIC CHEMISTRY. *Educ:* Univ London, BPharm, 51, PhD(med chem), 55. *Prof Exp:* Res chemist, Smith & Nephew Res Ltd, 55-57; res chemist, Parke, Davis & Co, Eng, 57-60; sr org chemist, Arthur D Little, Inc, 60-61; sr res chemist, Armour Pharmaceut Co, 61-71; HEAD LIT SERV, BRISTOL LABS, 71- *Concurrent Pos:* Fel, Sch Pharm, Univ Md, 60. *Mem:* Am Chem Soc; Royal Inst Chem; fel The Chem Soc; fel Pharmaceut Soc Gt Brit. *Res:* Synthetic antibacterials, antitubercular, antifungal and antitumour agents; central nervous system stimulants and depressants; cardiovascular agents. *Mailing Add:* Bristol Labs PO Box 657 Syracuse NY 13201

KERRIGAN, GERALD AUSTIN, b New York, NY, Sept 4, 20; m 47; c 4. PEDIATRICS. *Educ:* Harvard Univ, BS, 43; Harvard Med Sch, MD, 46. *Prof Exp:* Intern, Children's Hosp, Mass, 46-47; house officer, Mass Gen Hosp, 49-50, asst resident, 50-51, chief resident pediat, 51-52; instr, Harvard Med Sch, 54-56; from asst prof to assoc prof, 56-64, dean, 65-77, PROF PEDIAT, MED COL WIS, 65- *Concurrent Pos:* Teaching & res fel, Harvard Med Sch & Mass Gen Hosp, 52-54; vpres med affairs, Baystate Med Ctr, 78- *Mem:* Soc Pediat Res; Am Pediat Soc. *Res:* Water and electrolyte metabolism. *Mailing Add:* Med Col Wis Milwaukee WI 53233

KERSCHNER, JEAN, b Baltimore, Md, May 31, 22. GENETICS. *Educ:* Hood Col, AB, 43; Univ Pa, PhD(zool), 50. *Prof Exp:* Chemist, E I du Pont de Nemours & Co, 43-45; lab asst, Univ Pa, 45-46; asst prof biol, Elmira Col, 50-51; histologist, Army Chem Ctr, 51-52; from asst prof to assoc prof, 52-68, PROF BIOL, WESTERN MD COL, 68- *Concurrent Pos:* Fac fel, NSF, Columbia Univ, 60-61. *Mem:* Genetics Soc Am; Sigma Xi. *Res:* X-ray induced mutations in Drosophila. *Mailing Add:* Dept of Biol Western Md Col Westminster MD 21157

KERSEY, ROBERT LEE, JR, b Richmond, Va, Nov 6, 22; m 43. ANALYTICAL CHEMISTRY. *Educ:* Univ Richmond, BS, 48. *Prof Exp:* Asst proj chemist, Standard Oil Co, Ind, 48-53; chemist, 53-65, spec asst to dir res, 65-70, mgr prod develop, 70-75, dir res, 75-78, VPRES, LIGGETT & MYERS TOBACCO CO, 78-, CHIEF RES OFFICER, 81- *Mem:* Am Chem Soc; Inst Food Technol. *Res:* Tobacco and tobacco products research and development. *Mailing Add:* Res Dept Liggett & Myers Inc West Main St Durham NC 27702

KERSHAW, DAVID STANLEY, b Missoula, Mont, May 20, 43; m 66; c 3. THEORETICAL PHYSICS, COMPUTER SCIENCE. *Educ:* Harvard Univ, BA, 65; Univ Calif, Berkeley, PhD(physics), 70. *Prof Exp:* Fel theoret partical physics, Stanford Linear Accelerator Ctr, 70-72 & Dept Physics & Astron, Univ Md, College Park, 72-74; PHYSICIST LASER FUSION, LAWRENCE LIVERMORE LAB, UNIV CALIF, 74- *Mem:* Am Phys Soc. *Res:* Computer simulation of the physics of laser fusion. *Mailing Add:* Lawrence Livermore Lab PO Box 5508 Livermore CA 94550

KERSHAW, KENNETH ANDREW, b Morecambe, Eng, Sept 5, 30; m 67; c 3. PLANT ECOLOGY, LICHENOLOGY. *Educ:* Manchester Univ, BS, 52; Univ Wales, PhD(ecol), 57, DSc, 68. *Prof Exp:* Lectr, Imp Col, Univ London, 57-63; sr lectr, Secondment to Ahmadu Bell Univ, N Nigeria, 63-65; lectr, Imp Col, Univ London, 65-68; PROF BIOL, McMASTER UNIV, 69- *Mem:* Brit Ecol Soc; Brit Lichen Soc; Can Bot Soc; fel Royal Soc Can. *Res:* Ecology of northern plant systems with special emphasis on the interaction of microclimate and plant physiology; lichen physiology. *Mailing Add:* Dept of Biol McMaster Univ 1280 Main St W Hamilton ON L8S 4L8 Can

KERSHENSTEIN, JOHN CHARLES, b New York, NY, Sept 23, 41; m 68; c 1. PHYSICS, ELECTROOPTICS. *Educ:* Georgetown Univ, BS, 64, MS, 67, PhD(physics), 69. *Prof Exp:* Fel physics, 68-69, RES PHYSICIST, US NAVAL RES LAB, 69- *Mailing Add:* 11842 Clara Way Fairfax Station VA 22039

KERSHENSTEIN, KAREN WEIS, physics, see previous edition

KERSHNER, CARL JOHN, b Lima, Ohio, Dec 15, 34; m 58; c 2. PHYSICAL CHEMISTRY, RADIOCHEMISTRY. *Educ:* Capital Univ,BS, 56; Univ Ohio, PhD(inorg chem), 61. *Prof Exp:* Sr res chemist, 61-64, group leader radiochem res, 64-66, sect mgr, 66-68, sr res specialist, 68-70, sci fel, Mound Lab, 70-79, SR SCI FEL, MONSANTO RES CORP, 79- *Concurrent Pos:* Adj prof, Ohio State Univ, 80-81. *Mem:* Am Inst Physics; Am Chem Soc; The Chem Soc; Sigma Xi. *Res:* High temperature radiochemical research; syntheses and physical property determinations; isotope separation; radioactive waste and emission control; laser photochemistry. *Mailing Add:* Mound Lab Monsanto Res Corp Miamisburg OH 45342

KERST, AL FRED, b Greeley, Colo, June 3, 40; m 62; c 3. ORGANIC CHEMISTRY, PHYSICAL CHEMISTRY. *Educ:* Colo State Univ, BS, 62, MS, 63; Harvard Univ, PhD(chem), 67. *Prof Exp:* Sr chemist, Monsanto Co, 67-68; mgr, Gates Rubber Co, 69-71; vpres res & develop, Mich Chem Corp, 71-76, Velsicol Chem Corp, 76-77; VPRES RES & DEVELOP, CALGON CORP, 77- *Concurrent Pos:* Eval Panel, Nat Bur Standards Ctr Fire Res, 76-79. *Mem:* Am Chem Soc. *Res:* Chemistry of phosphorus compounds, flame retardants, polymers; agriculture pesticides and industrial biocides. *Mailing Add:* Calgon Corp Box 1346 Pittsburgh PA 15230

KERST, DONALD WILLIAM, b Galena, Ill, Nov 1, 11; m 40; c 2. PLASMA PHYSICS. *Educ:* Univ Wis, BA, 34, PhD(physics), 37. *Hon Degrees:* ScD, Univ Wis, 61; ScD, Lawrence Col, 42; Dr, Univ Sao Paulo, 53. *Prof Exp:* X-ray tube developer, Gen Elec X-ray Corp, 37-38; from instr to prof physics, Univ Ill, 38-57; tech dir, Midwestern Univ Res Asn, 53-57; thermonuclear proj, John Jay Hopkins Lab Pure & Appl Sci, Gen Atomic Div, Gen Dynamics Corp, 57-62; PROF PHYSICS, UNIV WIS, MADISON, 62- *Concurrent Pos:* Physicist, Res Lab, Gen Elec Co, 40-41 & Manhattan Dist, Los Alamos Sci Lab, Calif, 43-45. *Honors & Awards:* Comstock Prize, Nat Acad Sci, 43; Scott Award, Franklin Inst, 47. *Mem:* Nat Acad Sci; AAAS; fel Am Phys Soc. *Res:* Nuclear physics; enriched chain reactor; electrostatic accelerator; betatron and thermonuclear research; x-ray tubes and radiography; fixed field alternating gradient accelerator developments. *Mailing Add:* Dept of Physics Univ of Wis Madison WI 53706

KERSTEN, MILES S(TOKES), b St Paul, Minn, Aug 12, 13; m 38; c 2. ENGINEERING. *Educ:* Univ Minn, BCE, 34, MS, 36, PhD(hwys, soils), 45. *Prof Exp:* Soils engr, State Hwy Dept, Minn, 36-37; instr hwys & soils, Univ Minn, 37-44; spec investr, Hwy Res Bd, Washington, DC, 44-45; from asst prof to prof, 45-78, EMER PROF SOIL MECH, HWYS & SOILS, UNIV MINN, MINNEAPOLIS, 78- *Mem:* Am Soc Civil Eng; Am Soc Eng Educ; Nat Asn Prof Engrs. *Res:* Thermal conductivity of soil; soil stabilization; subgrade moisture conditions and their role in flexible pavement design; airport engineering; general civil engineering; surveying and mapping. *Mailing Add:* 179 Exp Eng Bldg Univ Minn Minneapolis MN 55455

KERSTEN, ROBERT D(ONAVON), b Carlinville, Ill, Jan 30, 27; m 50; c 2. ENGINEERING & FLUID MECHANICS. *Educ:* Okla State Univ, BS, 49, MS, 56; Northwestern Univ, PhD(fluid mech), 61. *Prof Exp:* Hydraulic engr, US Dept Interior, 49-53; res assoc civil eng, Okla State Univ, 53-56, asst prof, 56; res engr, Jersey Prod Res Co, Standard Oil NJ, 56-57; from asst prof to assoc prof eng, Ariz State Univ, 57-60, prof civil eng & chmn, 60-68; dir univ res, 68-69, DEAN, COL ENG, UNIV CENT FLA, 68- *Concurrent Pos:* Mem, NASA-NSF Conf Lunar Explor, 62, Flight Safety Found, 62, Col Bus Exchange Prog Found Econ Ed, 63 & NASA-Cambridge Conf Explor Mars & Venus, 65; vis scholar, Stanford Univ, 66; actg dir, Fla Solar Energy Ctr, 75; chmn bd trustees, Inst Cert Eng Technicians, 78-80. *Mem:* AAAS; Soc Eng Educ; Am Soc Civil Engrs; Nat Soc Prof Engrs; Sigma Xi. *Res:* Fluid mechanics, including fluid turbulence, turbulent diffusion, non-Newtonian flow, two phase flow; water resources engineering; applied mathematics. *Mailing Add:* Col Eng Univ Cent Fla PO Box 25000 Orlando FL 32816

KERSTETTER, JAMES DAVID, b Darby, Pa, Dec 27, 41; m 77; c 2. ALCOHOL FUELS, TRANSPORTATION. *Educ:* Drexel Inst Technol, BS, 64; Yale Univ, MS, 68. MPhil & PhD(chem physics), 69. *Prof Exp:* 77; sr scientist, Mont Energy & MHD Res & Develop Inst, 77-80; PROG MGR, CALIF ENERGY COMN, 80- *Mem:* Am Chem Soc; Am Soc Heating, Refrig & Air-Conditioning Engrs; AAAS; Int Solar Energy Soc; Am Phys Soc. *Res:* Ion-molecule reaction dynamics in chemical accelerator; high resolution mass spectrometry; computer models; solar energy application; biomass conversions; net energy analysis and technological assessment; alcohol fuel technologies. *Mailing Add:* Calif Energy Comn 1111 Howe Ave MS 68 Sacramento CA 95825

KERSTETTER, REX E, b Ashland, Kans, Nov 22, 38; m 60; c 2. PLANT PHYSIOLOGY. *Educ:* Ft Hays Kans State Col, BS, 60, MS, 63; Fla State Univ, PhD(plant physiol), 67. *Prof Exp:* Instr biol, Fla State Univ, 67; from asst prof to assoc prof, 67-80, PROF BIOL, FURMAN UNIV, 80- *Mem:* AAAS; Am Soc Plant Physiologists; Bot Soc Am; Sigma Xi. *Res:* Plant hormone physiology; plant tissue culture; peroxidase isoenzymes. *Mailing Add:* Dept of Biol Furman Univ Greenville SC 29613

KERSTETTER, THEODORE HARVEY, b Milwaukee, Wis, Dec 16, 30; m 61; c 2. ANIMAL PHYSIOLOGY. *Educ:* Univ Nev, Reno, BS, 59; Wash State Univ, MS, 62, PhD(zoo physiol), 69. *Prof Exp:* Instr biol, Peninsula Col, 63-64; NIH fel, Wash State Univ, 69-70; asst prof, 70-74, assoc prof, 74-81, PROF ZOOL, HUMBOLDT STATE UNIV, 81-, DIR MARINE LAB & SEA GRANT PROG, 74- *Mem:* AAAS; Am Fisheries Soc; Am Soc Zoologists. *Res:* Water and ion balance in lower vertebrates; mechanisms of ion transport through epithelia; fish physiology. *Mailing Add:* 734 Shirley Arcata CA 95521

KERSTING, EDWIN JOSEPH, b Ottawa, Ohio, Nov 4, 19; m 46; c 2. VETERINARY MEDICINE. *Educ:* Ohio State Univ, DVM, 52; Univ Conn, MS, 64. *Prof Exp:* Pvt pract, 52-61; res asst, 61-62, assoc prof animal diseases, 62-65, asst dean col agr & natural resources & dir, Ratcliffe Hicks Sch Agr, 65-66, PROF ANIMAL DISEASES, DEAN COL AGR & NATURAL RESOURCES, DIR, STORRS AGR EXP STA & DIR, COOP EXTEN SERV, UNIV CONN, 66-, TITLE XII OFFICER, 77- *Concurrent Pos:* Consult staff, Hartford Hosp, 63-; mem adv coun, Col Vet Med, Cornell Univ, 78. *Mem:* Am Vet Med Asn; AAAS; Royal Soc Health; NY Acad Sci; Sigma Xi. *Res:* Clinical veterinary medicine. *Mailing Add:* Off of the Dean Univ Conn Col Agr & Natural Resources Storrs CT 06268

KERSTING, RAYMOND JAMES, polymer chemistry, see previous edition

KERTAMUS, NORBERT JOHN, b Murray City, Utah, Oct 12, 32; m 56; c 3. FUEL & CHEMICAL ENGINEERING. *Educ:* Univ Utah, BS, 60, PhD(fuels eng), 64. *Prof Exp:* Res engr, Phillips Petrol Co, 64-66; sr res chemist nuclear fuels, Idaho Nuclear Co, 66-70; res specialist chem & combustion, Babcock & Wilcox Co, 70-75; sr process engr, C F Braun Engrs, 75-79; SR RES SCIENTIST, SOUTHERN CALIF EDISON, 79- *Mem:* Am Chem Soc; Am Inst Chem Engrs. *Res:* Conversion of coal to gases and/or liquids; hydrogen processing and catalysis; combustion and air pollution control, both sulfur and nitrogen oxides; reprocessing graphite containing nuclear fuels. *Mailing Add:* Southern Calif Edison PO Box 800 Walnut Grove CA 91770

KERTESZ, ANDREW (ENDRE), b Budapest, Hungary, Oct 10, 38; US citizen; m 63; c 2. VISION, BIOMEDICAL ENGINEERING. *Educ:* McGill Univ, BEng, 63; Northwestern Univ, Evanston, MS, 66, PhD(bioeng), 69. *Prof Exp:* Design engr, Can Marconi Co, 63-64; asst prof elec eng, Univ Pittsburgh, 69-72; PROF ELEC ENG & PSYCHOL, NORTHWESTERN UNIV, EVANSTON, 72- *Concurrent Pos:* Sr res fel appl sci, Calif Inst Technol & prin investr, USPHS res grant, 70-; NIH res career award, 74; clin assoc ophthal, Evanston Hosp, 77. *Mem:* Inst Elec & Electronics Engrs; Asn Res Vision & Ophthal; Biomed Eng Soc; Optical Soc Am; Nat Eyetracking Study Group (pres, 77-). *Res:* Human binocular information processing; binocular vision. *Mailing Add:* Biomed Eng Ctr Technol Inst Northwestern Univ Evanston IL 60201

KERTESZ, JEAN CONSTANCE, b New York, NY, Sept 3, 43. PHARMACEUTICAL CHEMISTRY. *Educ:* Northwestern Univ, BA, 63; Univ Southern Calif, PhD(pharmaceut chem), 70. *Prof Exp:* Res asst biochem, Sch Med, 65-66, res assoc biomed chem, 68-77, ASST RES PROF, SCH PHARM, UNIV SOUTHERN CALIF, 77- *Mem:* Am Chem Soc; Intra-Sci Res Found; Int Soc Magnetic Resonance. *Res:* Free radical intermediates in biological systems; utilization of electron spin resonance techniques for biomedical applications; molecular mechanisms of radiation damage; protection processes; carcinogenesis. *Mailing Add:* Univ of Southern Calif Sch of Pharm Los Angeles CA 90033

KERTH, LEROY THOMAS, b Visalia, Calif, Nov 23, 28; m 50; c 3. PHYSICS. *Educ:* Univ Calif, AB, 50, PhD, 57. *Prof Exp:* Asst, 50-57, res physicist, 57-65, assoc dean col lett & sci, 66-70, PROF PHYSICS, LAWRENCE BERKELEY LAB, UNIV CALIF, 65- *Mem:* Am Phys Soc. *Res:* High energy physics; K meson-nucleon interaction; nucleon-nucleon interactions; weak interactions. *Mailing Add:* Dept of Physics Lawrence Berkeley Lab Berkeley CA 94720

KERTZ, ALOIS FRANCIS, b Bloomsdale, Mo, Sept 15, 45; m 69; c 3. ANIMAL NUTRITION. *Educ:* Univ Mo-Columbia, BS, 67, MS, 68; Cornell Univ, PhD(animal nutrit), 74. *Prof Exp:* Nutrit officer, US Army Natick Labs, 68-69; food supply & mgt officer, US Army Depot, Sattahip, Thailand, 69-70; res asst animal nutrit, Cornell Univ, 70-73; res nutritionist, 73-75, MGR RES, DAIRY RES DEPT, RALSTON PURINA CO, 75- *Mem:* Am Dairy Sci Asn; Am Soc Animal Sci; AAAS; Nutrit Today Soc; Am Inst Nutrit. *Res:* Efficiency of nitrogen and energy utilization by calves and dairy cattle; evaluation and utilization of common feedstuffs and other by-products. *Mailing Add:* Ralston Purina Co Checkerboard Sq St Louis MO 63188

KERTZ, GEORGE J, b Bloomsdale, Mo, Dec 10, 33; m 68. MATHEMATICS. *Educ:* Cardinal Glennon Col, BA, 55; St Louis Univ, MA, 63, PhD(math), 66. *Prof Exp:* Mem staff, Int Bus Mach Corp, 58-60; asst prof, 66-71, ASSOC PROF MATH, UNIV TOLEDO, 71- *Mem:* Am Math Soc; Math Asn Am. *Res:* Complex analysis. *Mailing Add:* Dept of Math Univ of Toledo Toledo OH 43606

KERVER, JOHN K(INGSLEY), b Cleveland, Ohio, Apr 30, 23; m 45; c 3. PETROLEUM ENGINEERING. *Educ:* Univ Notre Dame, BS, 48, MS, 49. *Prof Exp:* Res engr, Humble Oil & Refining Co, 49-60, res specialist, 60-64; SR RES SPECIALIST, EXXON PROD RES CO, 64- *Mem:* Am Inst Petrol Engrs; Am Chem Soc; Am Petrol Inst; Nat Asn Corrosion Engrs. *Res:* Oil and gas production research; reservoir engineering; core analysis; surface chemistry; electric well logging; sand consolidation, corrosion; corrosion inhibitors; fluid flow; scale control. *Mailing Add:* Exxon Prod Res Co PO Box 2189 Houston TX 77001

KERWAR, SURESH, b Madras, India, May 9, 37; US citizen; m 64; c 2. MOLECULAR BIOLOGY. *Educ:* Univ Madras, BS, 56; Univ Nagpur, MS, 58; Ore State Univ, PhD(microbiol), 64. *Prof Exp:* Res assoc biochem, Scripps Clin & Res Found, 63-67; fel, Brandeis Univ, 67-69; res assoc, Roche Inst Molecular Biol, NJ, 69-71, asst mem staff, 71-75; sr scientist, Div Metab Dis, Ciba-Geigy Inc, 75-77; GROUP LEADER, CONNECTIVE TISSUES RES SECT, LEDERLE LABS, 77- *Concurrent Pos:* Am Soc Biol Chemists travel grant, 73 & 76. *Mem:* Am Soc Biol Chemists. *Res:* Protein synthesis; regulation of connective tissue metabolism; animal models of joint diseases. *Mailing Add:* Lederle Labs Pearl River NY 10965

KERWIN, EDWARD MICHAEL, JR, b Oak Park, Ill, Apr 20, 27; m 53; c 9. ACOUSTICS. *Educ:* Mass Inst Technol, SB & SM, 50, ScD(elec eng, acoustics), 54. *Prof Exp:* Consult acoustics, Bolt Beranek & Newman, Inc, 50-54; asst elec eng, Mass Inst Technol, 50-54; consult acoustics, 54-67, sr consult, INC, 67- *Concurrent Pos:* Assoc staff, Peter Bent Brigham Hosp, Boston, 72-74. *Mem:* Fel Acoust Soc Am; Soc Indust & Appl Math; sr mem Inst Elec & Electronics Eng. *Res:* Underwater sound; noise and vibration control; vibration damping; sound radiation and transmission. *Mailing Add:* Bolt Beranek & Newman 50 Moulton St Cambridge MA 02138

KERWIN, JAMES FRANCIS, b Hancock, NY, Oct 28, 19; m 55; c 4. MEDICINAL CHEMISTRY. *Educ:* Univ Notre Dame, BS, 41, PhD(org chem), 44. *Prof Exp:* Res asst, Comt Med Res Contract, Univ Notre Dame, 44-45; sr chemist, 46-57, group leader, 57-61, sect head, 61-68, DIR CHEM, SMITH, KLINE & FRENCH LABS, 68- *Mem:* Am Chem Soc. *Res:*

Medicinal chemistry of chloroethylamines; preparation and reduction of acetylenic hydrocarbons; preparation of some derivatives of quinoline carboxylic acids; thyromimetic agents; steroids. *Mailing Add:* Smith Kline & French Labs 1500 Spring Garden St Philadelphia PA 19101

KERWIN, JOHN LARKIN, b Quebec, Que, June 22, 24; m 50; c 8. PHYSICS. *Educ:* St Francis Xavier Univ, BSc, 44; Mass Inst Technol, MSc, 46; Laval Univ, DSc, 49. *Hon Degrees:* LLD, St Francis Xavier Univ, 70; DSc, Univ BC, 73; DLaw, Univ Toronto, 73; DSc, McGill Univ, 74; DSc, Mem Univ & DCL, Bishop's Univ, 78; DSc, Univ Ottawa, 81. *Prof Exp:* Lectr, 46, from asst prof to prof, 48-56, chmn dept, 61-67, vdean fac sci, 67-68, acad vrector, 69-72, rector, 72-77, PROF PHYSICS, LAVAL UNIV, 56- *Concurrent Pos:* Mem, Defence Res Bd Can, 71-77; mem standing comt int rels, Nat Res Coun Can, 72-80; secy-gen, Int Union Pure & Appl Physics; mem bd dirs, Can-France-Hawaii Telescope Corp, Nat Res Coun Can, 73-78; pres, Asn Univs & Cols Can, 74; mem adv coun, Order of Can, 75; pres, Nat Coun Can, 80- *Honors & Awards:* Gov Gen Medal, 44; Laureate of Lit & Sci Competition of Prov of Que, 51; Pariseau Medal, Fr-Can Asn Advan Sci, 65; Centenary Medal, 67; Gold Medal, Can Asn Physicists, 69; Comdr, Equestrian Order, Holy Sepulchre of Jerusalem, 74. *Mem:* Am Phys Soc; Can Asn Physicists (vpres, 53, pres, 54); Fr-Can Asn Advan Sci; fel Royal Soc Can (pres, 76); Nat Sci & Eng Coun Can (vpres, 78-80). *Res:* Mass spectrometry; atomic and molecular structure. *Mailing Add:* 2166 Parc Bourbonniere Sillery PQ G1T 1B4 Can

KERWIN, JOSEPH PETER, aerospace medicine, see previous edition

KERWIN, RICHARD MARTIN, b West Chester, Pa, Apr 5, 22; m 57; c 3. BACTERIOLOGY. *Educ:* Dartmouth Col, AB, 47; Univ NH, MS, 49; Pa State Univ, PhD(bact), 56. *Prof Exp:* Sr res scientist bact, Wyeth Labs Div, Am Home Prod Corp, 52-75; CONSULT, 75- *Mem:* Am Chem Soc; Am Soc Microbiologists; Soc Indust Microbiologists; Sigma Xi. *Res:* Antibiotics; screening new antibiotics; bacterial fermentation products; microbiological production of enzymes and steroids; anti-cancer research. *Mailing Add:* Box 117 Old Harrisville Rd Hancock NH 03449

KERWIN, ROBERT EUGENE, b Wollaston, Mass, Dec 6, 32; m 59; c 2. PHOTOCHEMISTRY. *Educ:* Boston Col, BS, 54; Mass Inst Technol, MS, 58; Univ Pittsburgh, PhD(chem), 67. *Prof Exp:* Jr fel polymer sci, Mellon Inst, 58-64; MEM TECH STAFF, BELL TEL LABS, INC, 64- *Mem:* Am Inst Chemists; Soc Photog Scientists & Engrs. *Res:* Water structure; electrochemistry; photolithography; semiconductor processing; quality control; quality assurance. *Mailing Add:* Bell Tel Labs Inc Whippany NJ 07981

KERWIN, WILLIAM J(AMES), b Portage, Wis, Sept 27, 22; m 47; c 3. ELECTRICAL ENGINEERING, PHYSICS. *Educ:* Univ Redlands, BS, 48; Stanford Univ, MS, 54, PhD(elec eng), 67. *Prof Exp:* Aeronaut res scientist, Nat Adv Comt Aeronaut & NASA, Ames Res Ctr, 48-62; head electronics dept, Stanford Linear Accelerator Ctr, 62; chief space tech br, Ames Res Ctr, NASA, 62-64, chief electronics res br, 64-69; PROF ELEC ENG, UNIV ARIZ, 69- *Concurrent Pos:* Lectr, Stanford Univ, 56-61 & 68; asst prof, San Jose State Col, 63-68; NASA res awards, 70 & 75. *Mem:* Sr mem Inst Elec & Electronics Engrs. *Res:* Network and circuit theory, especially synthesis of active resistance-capacitance networks. *Mailing Add:* 1981 Shalimar Way Tucson AZ 85704

KERZMAN, NORBERTO LUIS MARIA, b Buenos Aires, Arg, Feb 1, 43. ANALYSIS, FUNCTIONAL ANALYSIS. *Educ:* Univ Buenos Aires, Lic, 66; NY Univ, PhD(math), 70. *Prof Exp:* Asst prof math, Princeton Univ, 70-73; asst prof math, Mass Inst Technol, 73-76, assoc prof, 76-79; ASSOC PROF MATH, UNIV NC, CHAPEL HILL, 79- *Concurrent Pos:* Vis mem staff, Göttingen, Münster, Florence, Paris & Marseille; Sloan fel, 73-75. *Mem:* Am Math Soc. *Res:* Complex analysis in particular several complex variables, involving mathods of partial differential equations and singular integrals. *Mailing Add:* Dept Math Univ NC Chapel Hill NC 27514

KESARWANI, ROOP NARAIN, b Kanpur, India, July 6, 32; Can citizen; m 57; c 2. MATHEMATICS. *Educ:* Univ Lucknow, BSc, 52, Hons, 53, MSc, 54, PhD(math), 57. *Prof Exp:* Asst prof math, Univ Lucknow, 54-58; assoc prof, G S Tech Inst, Indore, 58-59; lectr, Punjab Univ, India, 59-61; asst prof, Washington Univ, 61-62; assoc prof, Wayne State Univ, 62-64; assoc prof, 64-70, PROF MATH, UNIV OTTAWA, ONT, 70- *Honors & Awards:* Swami Rama Tirtha Gold Medal & Debi Satdi Misra Gold Medal, Univ Lucknow, 54. *Mem:* Am Math Soc; Math Asn Am; Indian Math Soc; Can Math Soc; Soc Indust & Appl Math. *Res:* Theory of functions of a complex variable; special functions and applications to theoretical physics; integral transforms and equations; quantum mechanics. *Mailing Add:* 1964 Camborne Crescent Ottawa ON K1H 7B7 Can

KESHAVAN, KRISHNASWAMIENGAR, b Hassan, India, June 5, 29; m 57; c 3. CIVIL ENGINEERING, ENVIRONMENTAL ENGINEERING. *Educ:* Univ Mysore, BSc, 50, BE, 55; Univ Iowa, MS, 60; Cornell Univ, PhD(sanit eng), 63. *Prof Exp:* Sect officer, Cent Pub Works Dept, Govt of India, 55-58; asst civil eng, Cornell Univ, 60-63; assoc prof, Univ Maine, Orono, 63-67; assoc prof, 67-76, PROF CIVIL ENG & HEAD DEPT, WORCESTER POLYTECH INST, 76- *Concurrent Pos:* Water Resources Ctr res grant, Univ Maine, Orono, 65-67; Off Water Resources Res grant thermal pollution & NSF grant & chlorination, 71; co-dir, Environ Systs Study Prog, Sloan fel; sr adv, UNESCO, 75-76, consult, 76- *Mem:* Am Soc Civil Engrs; Am Soc Eng Educ; Water Pollution Control Fedn; Am Water Works Asn. *Res:* Kinetics of biological treatment of organic liquid wastes; nitrification of natural bodies of water and its effect on oxygen utilization; combined effects of thermal and organic pollution; hazardous chlorinated compounds due to chlorination. *Mailing Add:* Dept of Civil Eng Worcester Polytech Inst Worcester MA 01609

KESHAVIAH, PRAKASH RAMNATHPUR, b Bangalore, India, Feb 15, 45; c 2. ARTIFICIAL ORGANS, END-STAGE RENAL DISEASE. *Educ:* Indian Inst Technol, Madras, BTech, 67; Univ Minn, MS, 70, PhD(mech eng), 74, MS, 80. *Prof Exp:* Process Planning Engr, Larsen & Toubro Ltd, India, 67-68; res asst, Dept Mech Eng, Univ Minn, 68-73; BIOMED ENGR, REGIONAL KIDNEY DIS CTR, 73-, MGR BIOENG, 76- *Concurrent Pos:* Consult & mem, Artificial Kidney-Chronic Uremia Adv Comt, Nat Inst Arthritis, Metab & Digestive Dis, 78-79; prin investr, Dept Health Educ & Welfare, Food & Drug Admin, 77-81; res assoc, Dept Med, Hennepin County Med Ctr & Univ Minn, 77-81, sr res assoc, 81- *Mem:* Am Soc Artificial Internal Organs; Int Soc Artificial Organs. *Res:* Basic physiology, kinetic modeling and engineering design aspects of therapies for end-state renal disease and kinetic modeling of biological systems. *Mailing Add:* Regional Kidney Dis Prog 701 Park Ave Minneapolis MN 55415

KESHOCK, EDWARD G, b Campbell, Ohio, Mar 2, 35; m 59; c 3. MECHANICAL ENGINEERING. *Educ:* Univ Detroit, BME, 58; Okla State Univ, MS, 66, PhD(mech eng), 68. *Prof Exp:* Res engr, Lewis Res Ctr, NASA, 58-64; res asst film boiling heat transfer, Okla State Univ, 64-67; asst prof mech eng, Cleveland State Univ, 67-69; assoc prof thermal eng, Old Dominion Univ, 69-77; assoc prof, 77-81, PROF MECH & AEROSPACE ENG, UNIV TENN, 81- *Concurrent Pos:* Vis scientist, Nat Sci Coun, Repub China & Nat Tsing Hua Univ, Taiwan, 74-75. *Mem:* Am Soc Mech Engrs; Am Soc Eng Educ; Am Inst Chem Engrs. *Res:* Boiling heat transfer and two-phase flow; condensation heat transfer; thermophysical properties. *Mailing Add:* Dept of Mech & Aerospace Eng Univ of Tenn Knoxville TN 37916

KESIK, ANDRZEJ B, b Warsaw, Poland, Oct 27, 30; m 64; c 2. PHYSICAL GEOGRAPHY, REMOTE SENSING. *Educ:* Marie Curie-Sklodowska Univ, MSc, 51, PhD(geog), 59; Int Training Centre Aerial Surv, Holland, dipl geomorphol, 63. *Prof Exp:* Sr asst phys geog, Marie Curie-Sklodowska Univ, 55-60, lectr, 60-64; lectr cartog & photo interpretation, 64-70; vis prof photo interpretation, 70-71, assoc prof photo interpretation, 71-81, PROF GEOG, UNIV WATERLOO, 76- *Concurrent Pos:* Govt training grant, Univ Amsterdam, 63; nat reporter, Comn VII, Int Soc Photogram, 68-70; Brit Coun scholar, 70. *Mem:* Can Inst Surveying; Am Soc Photogram; Can Asn Geogr; Am Asn Geogr. *Res:* Physical elements of the environment; application of remote sensing techniques to the land evaluation; geomorphological mapping. *Mailing Add:* Dept of Geog Univ of Waterloo Waterloo ON N2L 3G1 Can

KESKKULA, HENNO, b Tartu, Estonia, Mar 25, 26; nat US; m 52; c 2. CHEMISTRY. *Educ:* Davis & Elkins Col, BS, 49; Univ Cincinnati, MS, 51, PhD(org chem), 53. *Prof Exp:* Chemist, 53-56, group leader, 56-68, ASSOC SCIENTIST, DOW CHEM CO, 68- *Concurrent Pos:* Sr vis res fel, Queen Mary Col, Univ London, 69-70. *Mem:* Am Chem Soc; Sigma Xi. *Res:* Elastomers; polymer chemistry; mechanical behavior of polymers; heterogeneous polymer systems. *Mailing Add:* 4503 James Dr Midland MI 48640

KESLER, CLYDE E(RVIN), b Condit, Ill, May 7, 22; m 47; c 2. CONCRETE. *Educ:* Univ Ill, BS, 43, MS, 46. *Prof Exp:* Jr eng aide, Ill Cent RR, 46-47; res assoc theoret & appl mech, 47-48, from instr to assoc prof, 48-57, PROF THEORET & APPL MECH, UNIV ILL, URBANA, 57-, PROF CIVIL ENG, 63- *Concurrent Pos:* Mem, Hwy Res Bd. *Honors & Awards:* Thompson Award, Am Soc Testing & Mat, 58; Lindau Award, Am Concrete Inst, 71. *Mem:* Nat Acad Eng; Am Soc Testing & Mat; fel Am Soc Civil Engrs; hon mem Am Concrete Inst (pres, 67-68); Am Soc Eng Educ. *Res:* Plain and reinforced concrete. *Mailing Add:* Dept Civil Eng 208 N Romine St Univ of Ill at Urbana-Champaign Urbana IL 61801

KESLER, DARREL J, b Portland, Ind, Sept 21, 49; m 73; c 2. REPRODUTION, LACTATION. *Educ:* Purdue Univ, BS, 71, MS, 74; Univ Mo, PhD(reprod physiol), 77. *Prof Exp:* Teaching asst acad coun & admin, Deans Off, Sch Agr, Purdue Univ, 71-74; res asst reprod & lactation physiol, Dept Dairy Husb, Univ Mo, 74-77; asst prof, 77-81, ASSOC PROF REPROD & LACTATION PHYSIOL, DEPT ANIMAL SCI, UNIV ILL, URBANA, 81-, SECY, DEPT ANIMAL SCI, 78- *Mem:* AAAS; Am Soc Animal Sci; Am Dairy Sci Asn; Soc Study Reprod; Sigma Xi. *Res:* Methods to improve reproductive efficiency and to study hypothalmic, pituitary, ovarian and uterine interactions in farm animals during the postpartum period. *Mailing Add:* 101 Animal Genetics Lab 1301 W Lorado Taft Dr Urbana IL 61801

KESLER, EARL MARSHALL, b Dunmore, WVa, Dec 3, 20; m 45; c 3. DAIRY SCIENCE. *Educ:* WVa Univ, BS, 43; Pa State Univ, MS, 48, PhD, 51. *Prof Exp:* From instr to assoc prof, 48-64, PROF DAIRY SCI, PA STATE UNIV, UNIVERSITY PARK, 64- *Mem:* AAAS; Am Soc Animal Sci; Am Dairy Sci Asn. *Res:* Dairy cattle nutrition, physiology of digestion; calf nutrition rumen metabolism and intermediary metabolism of the bovine; forage production; physiology of milk secretion; management of cows. *Mailing Add:* 205 Borland Lab Pa State Univ University Park PA 16802

KESLER, G(EORGE) H(ENRY), b West Terre Haute, Ind, Oct 29, 20; m 42; c 2. CHEMICAL ENGINEERING. *Educ:* Rose Polytech Inst, BS, 42; Mass Inst Technol, MS, 49, ScD, 52. *Prof Exp:* Chem engr distillation, Tex Co, 42-48; asst chem engr, Mass Inst Technol, 49-51; prin chem engr, Battelle Mem Inst, 51-55, asst div chief, 55-59; assoc dir res, Nat Stell Corp, 59-65; dept mgr, Mat Lab Dept, McDonnell Aircraft Co, St Louis, 65-77; ENG CONSULT, 77- *Mem:* Am Chem Soc; Asn Iron & Steel Eng; Am Inst Chem Engrs; Am Inst Mining, Metall & Petrol Engrs; Am Soc Metals. *Res:* Mass transport in spray-laden turbulent air streams; titanium production; laboratory distillation column evaluation; heat and mass transfer; steelmaking fundamentals; materials testing. *Mailing Add:* 2758 S Olympia Circle Evergreen CO 80439

KESLER, MICHAEL G, chemical engineering, computer applications, see previous edition

KESLER, OREN BYRL, b Crawford Co, Ill, Aug 28, 39; m 67; c 1. ELECTRICAL ENGINEERING, APPLIED ELECTROMAGNETIC THEORY. *Educ:* Univ Ill, BS, 61, MS, 62, PhD(elec eng), 65; Univ Wis, MA, 68. *Prof Exp:* Asst prof elec eng, Univ Tex, Austin, 65-72; mem tech staff, 72-81, SR MEM TECH STAFF, ANTENNA & MICROWAVE LAB, EQUIP GROUP, TEX INSTRUMENTS, INC, 81- *Concurrent Pos:* NSF sci fac fel, 70-71. *Mem:* Sr mem Inst Elec & Electronics Engrs. *Res:* Electromagnetic field; antennas; microwaves; radar; information processing; mathematical and computational techniques for engineering analysis. *Mailing Add:* 316 S Lois Lane Richardson TX 75081

KESLER, STEPHEN EDWARD, b Washington, DC, Oct 5, 40; m 65; c 2. ECONOMIC GEOLOGY, EXPLORATION GEOCHEMISTRY. *Educ:* Univ NC, BS, 62; Stanford Univ, PhD(geol), 66. *Prof Exp:* Asst prof geol, La State Univ, Baton Rouge, 66-70; asst prof, 70-71, assoc prof geol, Univ Toronto, 71-77; PROF GEOL, UNIV MICH, 77- *Mem:* Geol Soc Am; Am Inst Mining, Metall & Petrol Engrs; Asn Explor Geochemists; Soc Econ Geologists. *Res:* Tectonic and petrologic framework of ore deposition; exploration geochemistry; geology of Central America, Mexico and West Indies. *Mailing Add:* Dept of Geol Univ of Mich Ann Arbor MI 48109

KESLING, ROBERT VERNON, b Cass Co, Ind, Sept 11, 17; m 42; c 3. PALEONTOLOGY. *Educ:* DePauw Univ, AB, 39; Univ Ill, MS, 41, PhD(geol), 49. *Prof Exp:* From asst prof to assoc prof geol, 49-59, assoc cur micropaleont, Mus Paleont, 49-58, dir, 66-74, PROF GEOL, UNIV MICH, ANN ARBOR, 59-, CUR, MUS PALEONT, 58- *Concurrent Pos:* Ed, J Paleont, 58-64. *Mem:* Paleont Soc; Sigma Xi; AAAS. *Res:* Living and fossil Ostracoda; middle Devonian stratigraphy; Paleozoic echinoderms. *Mailing Add:* Mus of Paleont Ann Arbor MI 48104

KESMODEL, LARRY LEE, b Fort Worth, Tex, Mar 5, 47; m 70; c 3. SOLID STATE PHYSICS, SURFACE SCIENCE. *Educ:* Calif Inst Technol, BS, 69; Univ Tex, Austin, PhD(physics), 74. *Prof Exp:* Fel phys chem, Univ Calif, Berkeley, 73-75, staff scientist surface physics, Mat & Molecular Res Div, Lawrence Berkeley Lab, 75-78; ASST PROF PHYSICS, IND UNIV, BLOOMINGTON, 78- *Mem:* Am Phys Soc. *Res:* Experimental studies of solid surfaces and chemisorption; low-energy electron diffraction; high-resolution electron energy loss spectroscopy. *Mailing Add:* Dept of Physics Ind Univ Bloomington IN 47401

KESNER, LEO, b New York, NY, Feb 22, 31; m 54; c 3. BIOCHEMISTRY, ANALYTICAL CHEMISTRY. *Educ:* City Col New York, BS, 54; State Univ NY, PhD(biochem), 61. *Prof Exp:* Sr technician biophys, Sloan-Kettering Inst, 54; jr biochemist, 54-56, asst, 56-60, from instr to asst prof, 61-69, ASSOC PROF BIOCHEM, STATE UNIV NY DOWNSTATE MED CTR, 69- *Mem:* AAAS; Am Asn Clin Chem; Am Chem Soc; NY Acad Sci; Am Soc Biol Chemists. *Res:* Relationship of acid-base balance to intermediary metabolism; metabolic differences between normal and tumor tissue; design of analytical techniques in biochemistry; protein chemistry; inborn errors of metabolism; membrane phospholipids. *Mailing Add:* Dept of Biochem State Univ NY Downstate Med Ctr Brooklyn NY 11203

KESNER, MICHAEL H, b Pawtucket, RI, Nov 30, 45; m 69; c 1. SYSTEMATICS, MAMMALOGY. *Educ:* Northwestern Univ, BA, 69, MS, 72; Univ Mass, PhD(zool), 76. *Prof Exp:* ASSOC PROF HUMAN ANAT & COMP ANAT, IND UNIV PA, 76- *Concurrent Pos:* Grant in aid, Sigma Xi, 76, Theodore Roosevelt Grant, Am Mus Natural Hist, 76 & Univ Res Grant, Ind Univ Pa, 77, 78 & 81. *Mem:* Am Soc Mammalogists; Soc Syst Zool. *Res:* Mammalian (Rodent) functional morphology and systematics primarily of the subfamily microtinae; biogeography and systematics of insular populations of the genus Microtus from off the coast of Northeastern North America. *Mailing Add:* Biol Dept Ind Univ Pa Indiana PA 15705

KESNER, RAYMOND PIERRE, b Oran, Algeria, Dec 19, 40; US citizen; m 65; c 2. PHYSIOLOGICAL PSYCHOLOGY, NEUROSCIENCE. *Educ:* Wayne State Univ, BS, 62; Univ Ill, MS, 64, PhD(psychol), 65. *Prof Exp:* Fel physiol, Ctr Brain Res, Rochester, NY, 65-67; from asst prof to assoc prof, 67-75, PROF PSYCHOL, UNIV UTAH, 75- *Concurrent Pos:* Fel, Ctr Advan Study Behav Sci, 71-72. *Mem:* Soc Neurosci; Psychonomic Soc. *Res:* Neurobiological mechanisms of memory. *Mailing Add:* Dept of Psychol Univ of Utah Salt Lake City UT 84112

KESSEL, BRINA, b Ithaca, NY, Nov 20, 25; wid. ORNITHOLOGY, VERTEBRATE ZOOLOGY. *Educ:* Cornell Univ, BS, 47, PhD(ornith), 51; Univ Wis, MS, 49. *Prof Exp:* Asst ornith & conserv, Cornell Univ, 47-48 & 49-51; asst prof biol sci, 51-54, assoc prof zool, 54-59, head dept biol sci, 57-66, dean col biol sci & renewable resources, 61-72, PROF ZOOL, UNIV ALASKA, FAIRBANKS, 59- *Concurrent Pos:* Proj dir, Univ Alaska Ecol Invests, AEC Proj Chariot, 59-63; cur terrestrial vertebrate mus collections, Univ Mus, 72-, admin assoc acad progs, Off of Chancellor, Univ Alaska, 73- *Mem:* Fel AAAS; Wilson Ornith Soc; Cooper Ornith Soc; fel Am Ornithologists Union. *Res:* European starling in North America; biology, ecology, behavior and biogeography of Alaskan birds. *Mailing Add:* Univ Museum Univ of Alaska Fairbanks AK 99701

KESSEL, DAVID HARRY, b Monroe, Mich, Jan 8, 31. BIOCHEMISTRY. *Educ:* Mass Inst Technol, BS, 52; Univ Mich, MS, 54, PhD(biochem), 59. *Prof Exp:* Res assoc, Children's Cancer Res Found & asst path, Harvard Med Sch, 65-68; from asst prof to assoc prof pharmacol, Sch Med, Univ Rochester, 69-73; PROF PHARMACOL & ONCOL, SCH MED, WAYNE STATE UNIV, 74- *Concurrent Pos:* NIH fel, Harvard Univ, 59-63; res scientist, Mich Cancer Found, 74. *Mem:* AAAS; Biochem Soc; Am Asn Cancer Res; Am Soc Pharmacol & Exp Therapeut; Am Soc Biol Chemists. *Res:* Development of anti-tumor agents; mode of action of anti-neoplastic drugs. *Mailing Add:* Oncol Dept Harper Hosp Detroit MI 48201

KESSEL, EDWARD LUTHER, b Osborne, Kans, Apr 27, 04; m 35; c 2. ZOOLOGY. *Educ:* Univ Calif, BS, 25, MS, 28, PhD(entom), 36. *Prof Exp:* Instr zool & entom, Marquette Univ, 28-30; from asst prof to prof & chmn dept, 30-75, EMER PROF BIOL, UNIV SAN FRANCISCO, 75- *Concurrent Pos:* Ed, Wasmann J Biol, 39-; asst cur diptera, Calif Acad Sci, 45-50, assoc cur insects, 50-75, cur emer, 75- *Mem:* Fel AAAS; Soc Syst Zool. *Res:* Entomology; embryology of fleas; biosystematics of Platypezidae. *Mailing Add:* 13505 SE River Rd Portland OR 97222

KESSEL, QUENTIN CATTELL, b Boston, Mass, Aug 15, 38; m 60; c 2. EXPERIMENTAL ATOMIC PHYSICS. *Educ:* Yale Univ, BS, 60; Univ Mich, MS, 62; Univ Conn, PhD(physics), 66. *Prof Exp:* Res asst physics, Univ Conn, 62-65, res assoc, 65-66; physicist, Robert J Van de Graaff Lab, High Voltage Eng Corp, 66-70; guest scientist, Inst Physics, Aarhus Univ, 70-71; asst prof, 71-73, assoc prof, 73-78, PROF PHYSICS, UNIV CONN, 78- *Concurrent Pos:* Guest prof, Univ Freiburg, Ger, 77-78. *Mem:* AAAS; fel Am Phys Soc; Europe Phys Soc. *Res:* Interaction of accelerated ions and molecules with matter. *Mailing Add:* 97 Codfish Falls Rd Storrs CT 06268

KESSEL, RICHARD GLEN, b Fairfield, Iowa, July 19, 31. ZOOLOGY, ANATOMY. *Educ:* Parsons Col, BS, 53; Univ Iowa, MS, 56, PhD(zool), 59. *Prof Exp:* Marine Biol Lab, summer 57; from instr to asst prof anat, Bowman Gray Sch Med, 59-61; from asst prof to assoc prof, 61-68, PROF ZOOL, UNIV IOWA, 68- *Concurrent Pos:* NIH fel, 60-61; Nat Inst Gen Med Sci res grant, 60-65, career develop award, 64-69; Nat Inst Child Health & Human Develop res grant, 64-69; prog dir, NIH Training grant develop biol, 66-78; NSF res grant, 68-71; assoc ed, J Exp Zool, 78- *Mem:* AAAS; Am Asn Anat; Soc Develop Biologists; Am Soc Cell Biologists; Am Soc Zoologists. *Res:* Electron microscopic, autoradiographic and cytochemical studies on oocyte growth and differentiation; origin, structure and function of cell organelles; mechanisms of secretion; scanning electron microscopy of tissues and organs. *Mailing Add:* Dept of Zool Univ of Iowa Iowa City IA 52242

KESSEL, ROSSLYN WILLIAM IAN, b London, Eng, May 5, 29; m 53; c 2. IMMUNOLOGY, MICROBIOLOGY. *Educ:* Univ London, MB & BS, 56; Rutgers Univ, PhD(microbiol), 60. *Prof Exp:* Res assoc microbiol, Rutgers Univ, 60-61, asst prof, 62-65; asst prof, Univ Mass, Amherst, 65-67; assoc prof, 67-75, PROF MICROBIOL, UNIV MD SCH MED, BALTIMORE CITY, 75- *Concurrent Pos:* NSF res fel, Post-Grad Med Sch, Univ Milan, 61-62. *Mem:* AAAS; Am Soc Microbiol; Am Soc Naturalists; Reticuloendothelial Soc; Am Soc Cell Biol. *Res:* Cellular immunology; organization of biomedical knowledge; curricular organization; information transfer; pathogenesis of silicosis and other pneumoconioses; intracellular parasitism. *Mailing Add:* Dept of Microbiol Univ of Md Sch of Med Baltimore MD 21201

KESSEL, WILLIAM GEORGE, b Terre Haute, Ind, Feb 25, 11; m 36; c 2. ORGANIC CHEMISTRY. *Educ:* Franklin Col, AB, 32; Ind State Teachers Col, MA, 33; Purdue Univ, MS, 46; Ind Univ, EdD, 60. *Prof Exp:* Org lab asst, Commercial Solvents Corp, 34-36; pub sch teacher, Ind, 37-46; from asst prof to prof, 46-77, treas, 60-66, chmn elect, 67, EMER PROF CHEM, IND STATE UNIV, TERRE HAUTE, 77- CHMN DIV CHEM EDUC, 68- *Concurrent Pos:* Chemist, J W Davis, 41-45. *Mem:* Am Chem Soc (secy, 47); Fel Am Inst Chemists. *Res:* Efficiency of rectifying columns; hydroponics for tomatoes and cucumbers; home economics chemistry; high school chemistry curricula. *Mailing Add:* 1637 S Fifth St Terre Haute IN 47802

KESSELL, STEPHEN ROBERT, b Lewiston, Maine, May 22, 49. PLANT ECOLOGY, RESOURCE MANAGEMENT. *Educ:* Amherst Col, BA, 72; Cornell Univ, MS, 77. *Prof Exp:* Res asst plant ecol, Cornell Univ, 72-74; fire ecologist, Glacier Nat Park, Nat Park Serv, 74-76; RES SUPVR, COOP RES AGREEMENTS, USDA FOREST SERV, 76- *Concurrent Pos:* Coop biologist, Glacier Nat Park, Nat Park Serv, 72-74, consult resource modeling, 75-77; consult, Can Forest Serv, Northern Forest Res Ctr, Edmonton, 77-, div plant indust, Canberra, Australia, 77- & Nat Parks & Wildlife Serv New South Wales, Sydney, Australia, 77-; vis fel, Res Sch Biol Sci, Australian Nat Univ, 78-; invited fac, USDA Forest Serv, Nat Interagency Tranining Ctr, Marana, Ariz, 78- pres, Gradient Modeling, Inc, 75- *Mem:* Sigma Xi; Ecol Soc Am; Am Inst Biol Sci; AAAS. *Res:* Development and implementation of computer-based resource management and forest fire simulation models; gradient analysis and gradient modeling; habitat and niche relations of vascular plants; species diversity. *Mailing Add:* Gradient Modeling Inc Box 2666 Missoula MT 59806

KESSELRING, JOHN PAUL, b Detroit, Mich, Mar 26, 40; m 66; c 2. COMBUSTION, FLUID DYNAMICS. *Educ:* Univ Mich, BS, 61; Stanford Univ, MS, 62, PhD(aeronaut & astronaut sci), 68. *Prof Exp:* Res engr, Rocketdyne Div, N Am Aviation, Inc, 62-63, mem tech staff, N Am Rockwell Corp, 67-69; asst prof mech & aerospace eng, Univ Tenn, Knoxville, 69-74; mgr catalytic combustion progs, 74-80, ASSOC MGR COMBUSTION TECHNOL, ACUREX CORP, 81- *Concurrent Pos:* Instr aeronaut & astronaut, Stanford Univ, 77. *Mem:* Am Inst Aeronaut & Astronaut; Combustion Inst; Am Soc Mech Engrs. *Res:* Propulsion; liquid rocket performance; catalytic combustion research; control of nitrogen oxide emissions by combustion modification. *Mailing Add:* Acurex Corp 485 Clyde Ave Mountain View CA 94042

KESSIN, RICHARD HARRY, b Bayonne, NJ, Feb 24, 44; c 2. DEVELOPMENTAL GENETICS. *Educ:* Yale Univ, BA, 66; Brandeis Univ, PhD(biol), 71. *Prof Exp:* asst prof, 74-80, assoc prof biol, Harvard Univ, 80- *Mem:* Genetics Soc Am. *Res:* Development and regulation of gene expression. *Mailing Add:* Biol Labs Harvard Univ 16 Divinity Ave Cambridge MA 02138

KESSINGER, WALTER PAUL, JR, b Corsicana, Tex, July 9, 30; m 62; c 3. MICROPALEONTOLOGY. *Educ:* Tex Technol Col, BS, 51, MS, 53; La State Univ, PhD(geol), 74. *Prof Exp:* Asst prof, 53-54, ASSOC PROF & HEAD DEPT GEOL, UNIV SOUTHWESTERN LA, 56- *Mem:* Geol Soc Am; Am Asn Petrol Geologists; Paleont Soc; Soc Econ Paleontologists & Mineralogists; Nat Asn Geol Teachers. *Res:* Ostracoda of the Comanche Series of north Texas. *Mailing Add:* PO Box 40109 Univ Southwestern La Lafayette LA 70504

KESSLER, ALEXANDER, b Vienna, Austria, Mar 19, 31; US citizen; m 53; c 4. MEDICINE, PUBLIC HEALTH. *Educ:* NY Univ, BA, 51; Columbia Univ, MD, 55; Rockefeller Univ, PhD(pop biol), 66. *Prof Exp:* Res physician, Albert Einstein Med Ctr, New York, 56-57 & Georgetown Univ Hosp, 60-61; DIR SPEC PROG RES HUMAN REPRODUCTION, WHO, GENEVA, 66- *Res:* International public health; family planning; reproductive biology and contraceptive technology; research administration. *Mailing Add:* Spec Prog of Res in Human Reprod 20 Ave Appia Geneva Switzerland

KESSLER, BERNARD V, b Brooklyn, NY, June 27, 28; m 57; c 2. INFRARED, LASERS. *Educ:* NY Univ, BA, 59; Cath Univ Am, MS, 69, PhD(physics), 72. *Prof Exp:* RES PHYSICIST, ELECTRO-OPTICS BR, NAVAL SURFACE WEAPONS CTR, 59- *Mem:* Optical Soc Am; Am Phys Soc; Am Asn Physics Teachers. *Res:* Optics; laser mode studies; ultra low temperature thermodynamics of paramagnetic materials; adaptive optics for coherent optical systems; laser speckle phenomena; communication theory; infrared search and surveillance. *Mailing Add:* R42 Electro-Optics Br Naval Surface Weapons Ctr Silver Spring MD 20910

KESSLER, DAN, b Vienna, Austria, May 23, 24; m 53; c 3. HIGH ENERGY PHYSICS. *Educ:* Hebrew Univ, Israel, MSc, 50; Sorbonne, DesSc(physics), 54. *Prof Exp:* Res physicist, Nat Ctr Sci Res, Fr Res Coun, 51-58; sr physicist, Israel Atomic Energy Comn, 58-64; res assoc high energy physics, Univ Chicago, 64-67; PROF PHYSICS, CARLETON UNIV, 67- *Concurrent Pos:* Assoc prof, Tel-Aviv Univ, 62-64. *Mem:* Am Phys Soc; Can Asn Physicists. *Res:* Electromagnetic and nuclear interactions of cosmis-ray muons; interactions of K-mesons; mesic atoms; production of heavy mesons in P-P collisions. *Mailing Add:* Dept Physics Carleton Univ Ottawa ON K1S 5B6 Can

KESSLER, DAVID PHILLIP, b Anderson, Ind, Nov 1, 34; m 57; c 4. CHEMICAL ENGINEERING, BIOENGINEERING. *Educ:* Purdue Univ, BS, 56; Univ Mich, MS, 59, PhD(chem eng), 62. *Prof Exp:* Mem res staff, Delco Remy Div, Gen Motors Corp, 52, 53, 55 & Dow Chem Co, 56-58; group leader explor develop, Procter & Gamble Co, 62-64; from asst prof to assoc prof chem eng, 64-75, asst provost, 76-80, PROF CHEM ENG, PURDUE UNIV, 73- *Concurrent Pos:* Mem res staff, Humble Oil & Ref Co, 65 & Phillips Petrol Co, 66; consult, Great Lakes Chem Corp, 67, Midwest Appl Sci & D&M Corp, 68, Am Oil Co, Melnor Corp, Am Filters & Araneida Corp, 69, Roper Corp, 70, Westinghouse Corp, 71 & Exxon Corp, 80; mediator/fact finder, Ind Educ Employ Rels Bd, 74- *Mem:* Am Inst Chem Engrs; AAAS; Am Mgt Asn; Soc Prof Dispute Resolution. *Res:* Multiphase flow; transport properties in disperse media. *Mailing Add:* Dept of Chem Eng Purdue Univ Lafayette IN 47907

KESSLER, DIETRICH, b Hamilton, NY, May 28, 36; m 61; c 2. CELL BIOLOGY. *Educ:* Swarthmore Col, BA, 58; Univ Wis, MS, 60, PhD(zool), 64. *Prof Exp:* From asst prof to assoc prof, 64-77, PROF, DEPT BIOL, HAVERFORD COL, 77- *Concurrent Pos:* Am Cancer Soc fel, Brandeis Univ, 66-67; NSF sci fac fel, Swiss Inst Exp Cancer Res, Lausanne, 71-72. *Mem:* AAAS; Am Soc Cell Biologists; Am Soc Zoologists. *Res:* Molecular mechanism of amoeboid movement in Physarum polycephalum by examination of ultrastructural, immunological and biochemical properties of cytoplasmic actomyosin filaments, and by examination of intracellular ion movements. *Mailing Add:* Dept of Biol Haverford Col Haverford PA 19041

KESSLER, EDWIN, III, b New York, NY, Dec 2, 28; m 50; c 2. METEOROLOGY. *Educ:* Columbia Univ, AB, 50; Mass Inst Technol, SM, 52, ScD(meteorol), 57. *Prof Exp:* Chief synoptic sect, Weather Radar Br, Air Force Cambridge Res Ctr, 54-61; dir atmospheric physics div, Travelers Res Ctr, 61-64; DIR, NAT SEVERE STORMS LAB, US WEATHER BUR, 64- *Concurrent Pos:* Adj prof, Univ Okla, 64-; vis prof, Mass Inst Technol, 75-76; vis lectr, McGill Univ, 80. *Mem:* Fel AAAS; Am Geophys Union; fel Am Meteorol Soc; Royal Meteorol Soc; Sigma Xi. *Res:* Synthesis of varied observations and theory to improve understanding of meteorological phenomena and to develop and apply technology in the public interest. *Mailing Add:* Nat Severe Storms Lab 1313 Halley Cirlce Norman OK 73069

KESSLER, ERNEST GEORGE, JR, b Hanover, Pa, Sept 12, 40; m 62; c 4. OPTICAL PHYSICS, ATOMIC SPECTROSCOPY. *Educ:* Shippensburg State Col, BS, 62; Univ Wis-Madison, MS, 64, PhD(physics), 69. *Prof Exp:* Nat Res Coun-Nat Bur Standards res assoc spectros, 69-71, PHYSICIST, CTR ABSOLUTE PHYS QUANTITIES, NAT BUR STANDARDS, 71- *Mem:* Am Phys Soc. *Res:* High resolution studies of the ionized helium spectrum; determination of the Rydberg constant from wavelength measurements on ionized helium; precise x-ray and r-ray wavelength measurements. *Mailing Add:* Ctr for Absolute Phys Quantities Nat Bur of Standards Washington DC 20234

KESSLER, FREDERICK MELVYN, b Brooklyn, NY, May 15, 32; m 54; c 3. ENGINEERING ACOUSTICS, ELECTROMECHANICAL ENGINEERING. *Educ:* City Col NY, BME, 54; Rutgers Univ, MS, 67, PhD(elec eng), 71. *Prof Exp:* Jr test engr, Curtiss-Wright Corp, 54-55; sr proj mgr acoust, David Taylor Model Basin, Washington, DC, 59-61; sr develop engr eng acoust, Ingersoll-Rand Co, 61-68; fac mem elec eng, Rutgers Univ, 68-71; vpres eng acoust, Lewis S Goodfriend & Assoc, 71-73; partner, 73-80, MANAGING PARTNER ENG ACOUST, DAMES & MOORE, 80- *Concurrent Pos:* Adj prof, Dept Mech Eng, Stevens Inst Technol, Hoboken, NJ, 78- *Mem:* Acoust Soc Am; Inst Elec & Electronics Engrs; Inst Noise Control Eng. *Res:* Optimization muffler design parameters using conjugate gradient search techniques. *Mailing Add:* Dames & Moore 6 Commerce Dr Cranford NJ 07016

KESSLER, GEORGE MORTON, b Philadelphia, Pa, July 26, 17; m 43; c 2. HORTICULTURE. *Educ:* Pa State Univ, BS, 46, MS, 47; Mich State Col, PhD(hort), 53. *Prof Exp:* From instr to asst prof, 47-71, ASSOC PROF HORT, MICH STATE UNIV, 71- *Concurrent Pos:* Ed, Fruit Varieties & Hort Digest, Am Pomol Soc, 53-72. *Mem:* Am Soc Hort Sci; Am Pomol Soc (secy-treas, 57-64, pres, 67-68). *Res:* Teaching and evaluating of fruit varieties. *Mailing Add:* Dept of Hort Mich State Univ East Lansing MI 48824

KESSLER, GEORGE WILLIAM, b St Louis, Mo, Mar 1, 08; m 51; c 2. MECHANICAL ENGINEERING. *Educ:* Univ Ill, BS, 30. *Prof Exp:* Apprentice engr, Babcock & Wilcox Co, 30-31, sales engr, 31-32, anal engr, 32-33, proposition & contract engr, 33-38, eng group leader, 38-46, head marine design & estimating, 46, appln engr, 46-51, asst mgr proposition dept, 51-53, asst chief engr, 53-54, chief engr, 54-61, vpres eng, 61-73; CONSULT, 73- *Concurrent Pos:* Mem, Shipbuilders Coun Am, 48-; Metals Properties Coun, Eng Found, 65- & Welding Res Coun, 68- *Honors & Awards:* Joseph H Linard Award, Soc Naval Archit & Marine Engrs, 48. *Mem:* Nat Acad Eng; fel Am Soc Mech Engrs; Am Soc Naval Engrs; Soc Naval Archit & Marine Engrs. *Res:* Steam boiler design; engineering functions related to fossil fuel boiler equipment. *Mailing Add:* 720 Williams Dr Winter Park FL 32789

KESSLER, GERALD, b New York, NY, Mar 27, 30; m 52; c 4. BIOCHEMISTRY. *Educ:* City Col New York, BS, 50; Univ Md, MS, 52, PhD(biochem), 54. *Prof Exp:* Clin biochemist, Albert Einstein Med Ctr, 54-57; biochemist, Technicon Instruments Corp, NY, 57-61; head clin ctr core lab, Montefiore Hosp, NY, 61-64; chief automation div, Bio-Sci Labs, Los Angeles, 65-67; DIR DIV BIOCHEM, JEWISH HOSP OF ST LOUIS, 67- *Concurrent Pos:* Assoc scientist, Dept Biochem, Sloan-Kettering Inst Cancer Res, 59-61; consult automation res prog, Vet Admin Hosp, Bronx, NY, 63-64; assoc prof, Sch Med, Washington Univ, 67- *Mem:* AAAS; Am Chem Soc; Am Asn Clin Chem; NY Acad Sci. *Res:* Clinical biochemistry; methodological instrumentation research as applied to automation of analytical procedures. *Mailing Add:* Jewish Hosp 216 S Kingshighway St Louis MO 63110

KESSLER, HENRY A, b Vienna, Austria, Sept 12, 36; US citizen; m 61; c 1. PHARMACY. *Educ:* Long Island Univ, BS, 58; Columbia Univ, MS, 60; Purdue Univ, PhD(pharm), 64. *Prof Exp:* Pharmacist, Richardson-Merrill, Inc, 60-61; res assoc prod develop, Lever Bros Co, 64-66; scientist, 67-68, sr scientist & group leader phys pharm, Warner-Lambert Res Inst, 67-77; mgr prod develop, Lactona Corp Subsid, Warner-Lambert Co, 77-80; PRES, SUSSEX COUNTY DRUG CO, 81- *Mem:* Am Chem Soc; Am Pharmaceut Asn; Acad Pharmaceut Sci. *Res:* Physical and industrial pharmacy; pharmaceutical product development; application of physical chemistry to pharmaceutical problems; instrumentation; dental products research development. *Mailing Add:* 11 Picardy Rd Succasunna NJ 07876

KESSLER, IRVING ISAR, b Chelsea, Mass, Mar 22, 31. PREVENTIVE MEDICINE, EPIDEMIOLOGY. *Educ:* NY Univ, AB, 52; Harvard Univ, MA, 55, DrPH, 69; Stanford Univ, MD, 60; Columbia Univ, MPH, 62; Am Bd Prev Med, dipl. *Prof Exp:* Instr environ med, State Univ NY, 64-66; asst prof chronic dis, Johns Hopkins Univ, 66-69, assoc prof epidemiol, 70-72, prof, 73-78; assoc prof prev med, 70-78, CHMN EPIDEMIOL & PREV MED, UNIV MD, 78- *Concurrent Pos:* Fac res award, Am Cancer Soc, 72-77; med dir res, USPHS; mem exec comn, Gov Coun Toxic Substances, Md. *Mem:* AAAS; Am Epidemiol Soc; Am Asn Cancer Res; Am Pub Health Asn; Asn Teachers Prev Med. *Res:* Epidemiological research in cancer, Diabetes Mellitus, birth defects and Parkinson's disease; epidemiological principles; community studies of health; gerontology; environmental and occupational health; health regulation. *Mailing Add:* Dept Epidemiol & Prev Med Sch Med Univ Md Baltimore MD 21201

KESSLER, IRVING JACK, b Brooklyn, NY, May 14, 40; c 2. MATHEMATICS. *Educ:* Brooklyn Col, BA, 62; Univ Wis, MS, 63, PhD(math), 66. *Prof Exp:* Asst prof math, Univ Mich, 66-68; from asst prof to assoc prof, Southern Ill Univ, 68-78, prof math, 78-80 ; RES STAFF MATH, INST DEFENSE ANAL, 77- *Concurrent Pos:* Res staff math, Inst Defense Anal, 74-75 & 77- *Mem:* Am Math Soc; Math Asn Am. *Res:* Combinatorial mathematics; number theory; applying mathematics to problems in speech recognition. *Mailing Add:* Inst for Defense Anal Thanet Rd Princeton NJ 08540

KESSLER, JOHN OTTO, b Vienna, Austria, Nov 26, 28; nat US; m 50; c 2. PHYSICS. *Educ:* Columbia Univ, AB, 49, MS, 50, PhD(physics), 53. *Prof Exp:* Asst physics, Columbia Univ, 48-52; physicist labs, Radio Corp Am, 52-62 & Princeton Univ, 63-65; mgr grad recruiting, RCA Corp, 65-66; PROF PHYSICS, UNIV ARIZ, 66- *Concurrent Pos:* Vis prof physics, Univ Leeds, 72-73 & Technische Hogeschoole, Delft, Neth, 79. *Mem:* Fel AAAS; Am Phys Soc. *Res:* Thermodynamics, water purification, liquid crystals; biophysics; plant physiology. *Mailing Add:* Dept of Physics Univ of Ariz Tucson AZ 85721

KESSLER, KARL GUNTHER, b Hamburg, Ger, Aug 21, 19; nat US; m 44; c 2. ATOMIC PHYSICS. *Educ:* Univ Mich, AB, 41, MS, 42, PhD(physics), 47. *Prof Exp:* Instr physics, Univ Mich, 41-48, res physicist, 43-48; physicist, 48-62, chief atomic physics div, 62-70, chief optical physics div, 70-78, DIR CTR ABSOLUTE PHYS QUANTITIES, NAT BUR STANDARDS, 78- *Mem:* AAAS; fel Am Phys Soc; fel Optical Soc Am; Am Astron Soc. *Res:* Atomic spectra and beams; hyperfine structure; analysis of spectra; atomic beams and standard wavelengths; interferometry. *Mailing Add:* Nat Bur of Standards Washington DC 20234

KESSLER, KENNETH J, JR, b Wheeling, WVa, Mar 15, 33; m 54; c 4. PLANT PATHOLOGY. *Educ:* WVa Univ, BS, 55, MS, 57, PhD(plant path), 60. *Prof Exp:* PLANT PATHOLOGIST, NORTH CENT FOREST EXP STA, US FOREST SERV, 59- *Mem:* Am Phytopath Soc; Mycol Soc Am. *Res:* Hardwood tree diseases. *Mailing Add:* N Cent Forest Exp Sta Southern Ill Univ Carbondale IL 62901

KESSLER, LAWRENCE W, b Chicago, Ill, Sept 26, 42; m 64; c 4. ULTRASOUND, BIOENGINEERING. *Educ:* Purdue Univ, BS, 64; Univ Ill, Urbana-Champaign, MS, 65, PhD(elec eng), 68. *Prof Exp:* Mem res staff acoust visualization, Zenith Radio Corp, 68-74; PRES ACOUST MICROS, SONOSCAN, INC, 74- *Concurrent Pos:* Mem adv panel, Tech Electronic Prod Radiation Safety Standards Comt, Dept Health, Educ & Welfare, 72-75; nat lectr, Inst Elec & Electronics Engrs, 81-82. *Mem:* Sr mem Inst Elec & Electronics Engrs; Am Inst Ultrasound Med; Acoust Soc Am; Am Soc Nondestructive Testing. *Res:* Acoustic microscopy and ultrasonic visualization applications in life and materials sciences; quality assurance inspection equipment; biomedical engineering; laser scanning systems. *Mailing Add:* Sonoscan Inc 530 E Green St Bensenville IL 60106

KESSLER, MICHAEL J, biochemistry, see previous edition

KESSLER, NATHAN, b St Louis, Mo, Aug 19, 23; m 47; c 3. CHEMICAL ENGINEERING. *Educ:* Washington Univ, BSChE & MS, 44. *Prof Exp:* Chem engr, 44-51, tech supvr, Ohio, 51-53, sr chem eng, Ill, 53-57, chief chem engr, 57-60, dir process eng, 60-61, plant supt, 61-62, gen supt, 62-67, MEM BD DIRS & TECH GROUP VPRES, A E STALEY MFG CO, ILL, 67- *Concurrent Pos:* Mem eng adv bd, Rice Univ, 71; mem bd dirs, Wastech, Inc, Tex, 70-76. *Mem:* Am Inst Chem Engrs; Am Oil Chem Soc; Water Pollution Control Fedn; Air Pollution Control Asn; Am Asn Energy Engrs. *Res:* Engineering, research and development; food processes. *Mailing Add:* 49 Allen Bend Dr Decatur IL 62521

KESSLER, RICHARD HOWARD, b Paterson, NJ, Dec 15, 23; m 44; c 3. MEDICINE, PHYSIOLOGY. *Educ:* Rutgers Univ, BSc, 48; NY Univ, MD, 52. *Prof Exp:* Asst chem, Rutgers Univ, 47-48; asst med, NY Univ, 52-55; from instr to assoc prof physiol, Cornell Univ, 55-68; prof med, Med Sch, Northwestern Univ, Chicago, 68-78, assoc dean Med Sch, 70-78; PROF MED, PRITZKER SCH MED, UNIV CHICAGO, 78-; SR VPRES, MICHAEL REESE HOSP & MED CTR, 78- *Concurrent Pos:* Life inst med res fel, 55-56; Hofheimer Found fel, 57-62; mem, Sect Renal Dis, Coun Circulation, Am Heart Asn; mem, Health Econ Adv Comt, Nat Bur Econ Res; consult, Educ Serv, Vet Admin; vpres, Kidney Found Ill; comnr, Health & Hosps Gov Comn Cook County; fel, Hastings Inst Soc, Ethics & Life Sci; comnr, Chicago Health Syst Agency. *Mem:* AAAS; Harvey Soc; Soc Exp Biol & Med; Am Physiol Soc; fel Am Col Physicians. *Res:* Cardiovascular and renal physiology; fluid balance; electrolyte transport; diuretics; renal disease; hypertension. *Mailing Add:* Dept Acad Affairs Michael Reese Hosp & Med Ctr Chicago IL 60616

KESSLER, SEYMOUR, b New York, NY, Sept 3, 28; m 53; c 2. GENETICS. *Educ:* City Col New York, BS, 60; Columbia Univ, MA, 62, PhD(zool), 65; PhD(soc-clin psychol). *Prof Exp:* Fel psychiat, 65-67, asst prof, 67-73, sr scientist, 73-74; adj prof psychiat, Sch Med, Stanford Univ, 74-75; DIR & SR LECTR, UNIV CALIF, BERKELEY, 75- *Mem:* AAAS; Behav Genetics Asn; Am Soc Human Genetics. *Res:* Behavior and psychiatric genetics; genetic counseling. *Mailing Add:* Genetic Counseling Univ of Calif Berkeley CA 94720

KESSLER, THOMAS J, b Neptune, NJ, Nov 13, 38; m 62; c 3. GAS DYNAMICS, SYSTEMS DESIGN. *Educ:* Rutgers Univ, BS, 61, PhD(separated flow), 66; NY Univ, MME, 63. *Prof Exp:* Mem tech staff mech develop, Bell Tel Labs, Inc, 61-63; res asst mech eng, Rutgers Univ, 63-64, res asst gas dynamics, 66; mem tech staff, Bell Tel Labs, Inc, Whippany, 66-69, supvr, 69-75; AREA MGR, XEROX CORP, 75- *Mem:* Am Soc Mech Engrs; Am Soc Eng Educ. *Res:* Separated flows; cooling electronic equipment; xerographic process and design. *Mailing Add:* 30 Harwood Lane East Rochester NY 14445

KESSLER, WAYNE VINCENT, b Milo, Iowa, Jan 10, 33; m 53; c 2. BIONUCLEONICS. *Educ:* NDak State Univ, BS, 55, MS, 56; Purdue Univ, PhD(pharmaceut chem), 59. *Prof Exp:* Asst pharmaceut chem, Purdue Univ, 56-57; asst prof, NDak State Univ, 59-60; from asst prof to assoc prof, 60-68, PROF BIONUCLEONICS, PURDUE UNIV, WEST LAFAYETTE, 68- *Concurrent Pos:* Lederle pharm fac award, 62; vis scientist, Am Asn Cols Pharm, 64-70; assoc prof, Sch Med, Ind Univ, 70-73. *Mem:* AAAS; Am Pharmaceut Asn; Am Chem Soc. *Res:* Medicinal chemistry; radioisotope tracer techniques; body composition studies; nuclear instrumentation. *Mailing Add:* Dept of Bionucleonics Purdue Univ West Lafayette IN 47907

KESSLER, WILLIAM J(OSEPH), b Roebling, NY, Feb 28, 17; m; c 4. COMMUNICATIONS ENGINEERING. *Prof Exp:* Lab instr elec eng, Univ Fla, 43-45, asst prof, 45-67, asst res engr, 45-53; OWNER, W J KESSLER ASSOCS, 67- *Concurrent Pos:* Microwave, TV & commun consult. *Honors & Awards:* Cert Off Sci & Res & Develop & Ord Develop Award, 45. *Res:* Thunderstorm electricity; propagation of low frequency electromagnetic radiations; special instrumentation for radio location of thunder-storms for meteorological forecasting purposes. *Mailing Add:* 1554 N W 21st Ave Gainesville FL 32605

KESSLIN, GEORGE, b New York, NY, Mar 5, 19; m 40; c 2. ORGANIC CHEMISTRY. *Educ:* City Col New York, BS, 39; Polytech Inst Brooklyn, MS, 59, PhD(chem), 61. *Prof Exp:* Res chemist, 40-59, RES DIR ORG CHEM SYNTHESIS, KAY-FRIES CHEM, INC, 59- *Mem:* Am Chem Soc; Royal Soc Chem. *Res:* Organic chemical synthesis of heterocyclics; ortho esters; pharmaceutical intermediates; crop protection chemicals. *Mailing Add:* Kay-Fries Chem Inc Stony Point NY 10980

KESSNER, DAVID MORTON, b New York, NY, Aug 23, 32; m 59; c 2. INTERNAL MEDICINE. *Educ:* Univ Ariz, BS, 54; Washington Univ, MD, 58; Am Bd Internal Med, dipl, 67. *Prof Exp:* Intern med, Mary Imogene Bassett Hosp, 58-59, asst resident internal med, 59-60; jr attend physician, Med Clin, Univ Ill, 61-62; second year resident internal med, Sch Med, Yale Univ, 64-65, from instr to asst prof med & epidemiol, 65-69; study dir & res assoc, Inst Med, Nat Acad Sci, 69-73; dir, Health Serv Res Off & assoc prof community med & int health, Georgetown Univ, 73-75; PROF & V CHMN COMMUNITY & FAMILY MED, UNIV MASS MED CTR, 75- *Concurrent Pos:* Fel prev med, Sch Med, Univ Ill, 60-62; fel med, Sch Med, Yale Univ, 62-64; Nat Inst Arthritis & Metab Dis fel, 63-64; attend physician, Metab Sect, Yale-New Haven Hosp, 65-69, assoc physician, Dept Med, 66-69, consult internist, Yale Psychiat Inst, 67-69; asst clin prof, Sch Med, George Washington Univ, 70-73, attend physician, Hosp, 70- *Mem:* Am Fedn Clin Res; Am Pub Health Asn; Int Epidemiol Asn; fel Am Col Physicians. *Res:* Chronic disease epidemiology; the use of epidemiology in health services research. *Mailing Add:* Dept of Comm & Family Med Univ of Mass Med Ctr Worcester MA 01605

KESTEN, ARTHUR S(IDNEY), b New York, NY, Sept 10, 34; m 56; c 2. CHEMICAL ENGINEERING. *Educ:* NY Univ, BS, 55; Univ Pittsburgh, MS, 58, PhD(chem eng), 61. *Prof Exp:* Assoc engr res & develop, Bettis Atomic Power Lab, Westinghouse Elec Corp, 55-57, engr, 57-61, sr engr, 61-63; res engr, 63-65, sr res engr, 65-68, supvr kinetics & heat transfer, 68-72, prin scientist kinetics & environ sci, 72-76, mgr combustion sci, 76-77, mgr energy res, 77-81, ASST DIR RES POWER INDUST SYSTS TECHNOL, UNITED TECHNOL RES CTR, 81- *Concurrent Pos:* Adj asst prof, Rensselaer Polytech Inst, 65-69, dj assoc prof, 69- *Mem:* Fel Am Inst Chem Engrs; Sigma Xi. *Res:* Combustion; chemical reactor analysis; transport processes. *Mailing Add:* 17 Morning Crest Dr West Hartford CT 06117

KESTENBAUM, RICHARD CHARLES, b New York, NY, Apr 3, 31; m 54; c 3. BACTERIOLOGY. *Educ:* City Col New York, BS, 52; Rutgers Univ, MS, 54, PhD(bact), 59. *Prof Exp:* Asst bact, Rutgers Univ, 52-54 & 56-59; bacteriologist, 59-61, sr res microbiologist, 61-63, sect head microbiol, 63-66, sect head oral res, 66-69 & 71-75, sect head oral prod, 69-71, sr sect head oral prod & appl res, 77-78, mgr oral prod, 78-81, ASSOC DIR PERSONAL CARE PROD, COLGATE-PALMOLIVE CO, PISCATAWAY, 81- *Mem:* Am Soc Microbiol; Int Asn Dent Res. *Res:* Dental medicine; bacterial metabolism; microbial quality control; antimicrobial agents; oral and clinical research; oral products. *Mailing Add:* 18 Bradford Rd East Brunswick NJ 08816

KESTENBAUM, RICHARD STEVEN, b New York, NY, Mar 20, 42; m 70; c 1. NEUROPSYCHOPHARMACOLOGY, PSYCHOTHERAPY. *Educ:* NY Univ, BA, 63, PhD(psychol), 68. *Prof Exp:* Res fel psychol, NIMH, 66-68; asst prof, State Univ NY Stony Brook, 68-73; assoc dir res, Dept Phychiat, NY Med Col, 74-79; ASSOC PROF PSYCHOL & CLIN SUPVR, TEACHER'S COL, COLUMBIA UNIV, 80- *Concurrent Pos:* Fel, Nat Inst Psychother, 74-79. *Honors & Awards:* Creative Talent Award, Am Inst Res, 70. *Mem:* AAAS; Am Psychol Asn; NY Acad Sci. *Res:* Neural coding of pain and neuropsychopharmacology of pain perception; neuropsychopharmacology of opiates and implications for treatment; neuropsychopharmacology of cocaine in man; psychotherapy outcome evaluation. *Mailing Add:* 142 West End Ave New York NY 10023

KESTER, ANDREW STEPHEN, b Abington, Pa, Sept 1, 32; m 60; c 2. BACTERIOLOGY. *Educ:* Pa State Univ, BS, 54; Univ Tex, PhD(bact), 61. *Prof Exp:* Res microbiologist, Miles Chem Co, Ind, 61-67; asst prof, 67-74, ASSOC PROF BIOL, NTEX STATE UNIV, 74- *Mem:* Am Soc Microbiol; Am Chem Soc. *Res:* Microbial oxidation of hydrocarbons; industrial microbiology. *Mailing Add:* Dept of Biol Sci NTex State Univ Denton TX 76203

KESTER, DALE EMMERT, b Audubon, Iowa, July 28, 22; m 46; c 2. POMOLOGY. *Educ:* Iowa State Col, BS, 47; Univ Calif, MS, 49, PhD(plant physiol), 51. *Prof Exp:* Res asst, 48-50, jr specialist, 51, instr pomol, 51-53, lectr, 53, from asst prof to assoc prof, 54-69, from jr pomologist to assoc pomologist, 51-69, PROF POMOL, UNIV CALIF, DAVIS & POMOLOGIST, EXP STA, 69- *Honors & Awards:* Stark Award, Am Soc Hort Sci, 80. *Mem:* AAAS; fel Am Soc Hort Sci; Int Plant Propagators Soc; Genetics Soc Am; Int Asn Plant Tissue Cult. *Res:* Plant breeding, almonds, rootstocks; tissue and embryo culture of prunus species; plant propagation; somatic variation. *Mailing Add:* Dept of Pomol Univ of Calif Davis CA 95616

KESTER, DANA R, b Los Angeles, Calif, Jan 26, 43; m 63; c 1. CHEMICAL OCEANOGRAPHY, PHYSICAL CHEMISTRY. *Educ:* Univ Wash, BS, 64; Ore State Univ, MS, 66, PhD(oceanog), 69. *Prof Exp:* From asst prof to assoc prof, 69-76, PROF OCEANOG, UNIV RI, 76- *Concurrent Pos:* Ed, Marine Chem, 73-78, J Marine Res, 73- *Mem:* Am Geophys Union; Sigma Xi. *Res:* Physical chemistry of seawater; effects of temperature and pressure on ionic equilibria; transition metal marine chemistry; oceanic chemical distributions; waste disposal in the ocean. *Mailing Add:* Grad Sch of Oceanog Univ of RI Kingston RI 02881

KESTER, DENNIS EARL, b Eureka, Kans, Aug 21, 47; m 68; c 1. ORGANIC POLYMER CHEMISTRY. *Educ:* Col Emporia, BS, 69; Univ Ark, PhD(org chem), 75. *Prof Exp:* Res scientist polymers & coatings, 74-80, SUPVR ORGANIC RES & DIR PROD DEVELOP, AM CAN CO, 80- *Mem:* Am Chem Soc. *Res:* Polymer characterization and polymer synthesis; anionic, condensation and free radical polymerizations for the preparation of materials for specific coatings applications; radiation curable resins and coatings, adhesion. *Mailing Add:* 1915 Marathon Ave Neenah WI 54956

KESTEVEN, MICHAEL, b Sydney, Australia, July 30, 40. ASTRONOMY. *Educ:* Univ Sydney, BSc, 63, PhD(astron), 68. *Prof Exp:* ASST PROF PHYSICS, QUEEN'S UNIV, ONT, 68- *Mem:* Am Astron Soc; fel Royal Astron Soc; found fel Astron Soc Australia. *Res:* Radio astronomy. *Mailing Add:* Dept of Physics Stirling Hall Queen's Univ Kingston ON K7L 3N6 Can

KESTIGIAN, MICHAEL, b Charlton Depot, Mass, Sept 1, 28; m 49; c 2. INORGANIC CHEMISTRY. *Educ:* Univ Mass, BS, 52; Univ Conn, PhD(inorg chem), 56. *Prof Exp:* Lab asst chem, Univ Mass, 51-52; asst, Univ Conn, 52-55; res chemist, E I du Pont de Nemours & Co, 56-58; mem tech staff, RCA Labs, 58-62, sr staff scientist, Sperry Rand Res Ctr, Mass, 62-68; group leader, Off Aerospace Res, Air Force Cambridge Res Lab, 68-69; dept head, 69-71, MGR ELECTRONIC MAT DEPT, SPERRY RAND RES CTR, 71- *Mem:* Am Chem Soc; fel Am Ceramic Soc; Electrochem Soc; fel Am Inst Chem. *Res:* Single crystal growth; preparative chemical reactions; crystal growth mechanisms; ultra high vacuum techniques; x-ray diffraction; measurement of dielectric and optical properties of materials; magnetic materials; liquid-phase eptaxy; magneto-optic thin films; penetration phosphors; wear, corrosion and lubrication research. *Mailing Add:* Mat Dept Sperry Res Ctr Sudbury MA 01776

KESTIN, J(OSEPH), b Warsaw, Poland, Sept 18, 13; m 49; c 1. MECHANICAL ENGINEERING, THERMODYNAMICS. *Educ:* Univ Warsaw, dipl, 37; Imp Col, dipl & Univ London, PhD(thermodyn), 45. *Hon Degrees:* MA, Brown Univ, 57; DSc, Univ London, 66. *Prof Exp:* From sr lectr to prof mech eng & head dept, Polish Univ Col, London, Eng, 44-52; PROF ENG, BROWN UNIV, 52-, DIR CTR ENERGY STUDIES, 76- *Concurrent Pos:* US deleg, Int Conf Steam Properties, 54, 56, 63, 68, 74 & 79 & Int Comn Steam Properties, 54-; tech ed, J Appl Mech, Am Soc Mech Engrs, 56-71; assoc prof, Univ Paris, 66; adv to chancellor, Univ Tehran, 68; chmn working group, Int Asn Properties Steam, pres, 74-76; consult, Nat Bur Standards; assoc prof, Univ Claude Bernard, Lyon II, 74; chmn, Nat Acad Sci/Nat Res Coun Eval Panel Off Standard Ref Data Nat Bur Standards, 74-80, mem eval panel, Nat Measurement Lab, 78-; mem numerical data adv bd, Nat Acad Sci, 76-; consult, Off Naval Res, RAND Corp. *Honors & Awards:* Prize, Brit Inst Mech Engrs, 49; Centennial Medal, Am Soc Mech Engrs, 80; James Harry Potter Gold Medal, 81. *Mem:* Am Soc Mech Engrs; Brit Inst Mech Engrs; Ges Physikalische Chem. *Res:* Measurement of thermodynamic and transport properties; classical, irreversible, and statistical thermodynamics; heat transfer; boundary layers; thermodynamics of stress and strain; geothermal energy-conversion systems. *Mailing Add:* Div of Eng Brown Univ Providence RI 02912

KESTING, ROBERT E, b Jamaica, NY, Feb 8, 33; m 59; c 4. POLYMER CHEMISTRY. *Educ:* Manhattan Col, BS, 56; State Univ NY Col Forestry, Syracuse, MS, 59, PhD(chem), 61. *Prof Exp:* Res chemist, Heberlein & Co AG, Switz, 60-62 & Von Karman Ctr, Aerojet-Gen Corp Div, Gen Tire & Rubber Co, Calif, 62-65; sr scientist, Philco-Ford, 65-67; consult, 67-69; vpres polymer opers, Chem Systs, Inc, Santa Anna, 69-76, vpres, Irvine, 76-79; vpres, 79-81, PRES, PURPORE INC, DIV GELMAN SCI, 92- *Res:* Graft copolymerization on polymer substrates; structure and function of reverse osmosis membranes; new theory for the lyotropic swelling of polar polymers; developed Kesting process for the fabrication of wet-dry reversible reverse osmosis membranes; synthetic polymeric membranes. *Mailing Add:* 4625 Green Tree Lane Irvine CA 92715

KESTNER, DANIEL WILLIAM, JR, b New Kensington, Pa, July 7, 38; m 66; c 2. MINERALS PROCESSING. *Educ:* Pa State Univ, BS, 60, MS, 62. *Prof Exp:* Res engr, 62-77, sr supporting engr, 77-80, sr consult, 80-81, TECH MGR DEVELOP ENGR MINERALS, DRAVO CORP, 81- *Mem:* Am Inst Mining, Metall & Petrol Engrs; Can Inst Mining & Metall. *Res:* Grinding, beneficiation and agglomeration of ores and minerals; stabilization of sludge from fine coal processing and from sulfur dioxide scrubbing on power plants; processing of coal-oil-mixtures. *Mailing Add:* One Oliver Plaza Dravo Corp Pittsburgh PA 15222

KESTNER, MARK OTTO, b Berea, Ohio, Dec 10, 47; m 71; c 1. INORGANIC CHEMISTRY. *Educ:* Carnegie-Mellon Univ, BS, 69; Northwestern Univ, MS, 70, PhD(chem), 74. *Prof Exp:* Res chemist, Borg-Warner Corp, 74-78; group leader, 78-80, MGR, PROD DEVELOP, APOLLO CHEM CORP, 80- *Mem:* Am Chem Soc; NY Acad Sci; Sigma Xi. *Res:* Handling, storage and combustion of coal and other fossil fuel; air pollution control and chemical treatments for control of particulate and gaseous emissions; solid waste disposal. *Mailing Add:* Apollo Chem Corp 35 S Jefferson Rd Whippany NJ 07981

KESTNER, MELVIN MICHAEL, b Wooster, Ohio, Oct 20, 45; m 71. ORGANIC CHEMISTRY. *Educ:* Heidelberg Col, BS, 67; Purdue Univ, PhD(org chem), 73. *Prof Exp:* SR CHEMIST ORG CHEM, EASTMAN KODAK CO, 73- *Mem:* Am Chem Soc. *Res:* Synthesis of compounds used in photographic products. *Mailing Add:* 343 State St Rochester NY 14650

KESTNER, NEIL R, b Milwaukee, Wis, Dec 11, 37. CHEMICAL PHYSICS. *Educ:* Univ Wis-Milwaukee, BS, 60; Yale Univ, MS, 62, PhD(theoret chem), 64. *Prof Exp:* Res assoc, Inst Study Metals, Univ Chicago, 63-64; asst prof chem, Stanford Univ, 64-66; assoc prof, 66-72, chmn freshman chem, 73-76, chmn dept, 76-81, PROF CHEM, LA STATE UNIV, BATON ROUGE, 72- *Concurrent Pos:* Vis prof, Tel-Aviv Univ, 72; res collabr, Brookhaven Nat Lab, 81. *Mem:* Am Chem Soc; Am Phys Soc; Sigma Xi; AAAS. *Res:* Quantum chemistry; intermolecular forces; electrons in disordered media; electron transfer reactions. *Mailing Add:* Dept of Chem La State Univ Baton Rouge LA 70803

KETCHAM, ALFRED SCHUTT, b Newark, NY, Oct 7, 24; m 46; c 6. SURGERY. *Educ:* Hobart Col, BS, 45; Univ Rochester, MD, 49; Am Bd Surg, dipl, 59. *Hon Degrees:* DSc, Hobart Col, 70. *Prof Exp:* Intern surg, US Naval Med Ctr, Bethesda, 49-50; resident, USPHS Hosps, San Francisco, 50-52, Seattle, 52-55; chief, Dept Surg, Nat Cancer Inst, 62-74, assoc sci dir clin res, Gen Labs & Clins & clin dir, Inst, 71-74; PROF SURG & CHIEF DIV ONCOL, SCH MED, UNIV MIAMI, 74- *Honors & Awards:* Meritorious Serv Medal, USPHS. *Mem:* Fel Am Col Surg; Am Asn Cancer Res; Am Radium Soc; Soc Head & Neck Surgeons; Am Surg Asn. *Res:* Cancer surgery; experimental metastases; clinical and laboratory investigation. *Mailing Add:* Dept Surg Sch Med Univ Miami Miami FL 33152

KETCHAM, BRUCE V(ALENTINE), b Wilmington, Del, Mar 17, 18; m 44. AEROSPACE ENGINEERING. *Educ:* Yale Univ, BME, 40; Univ Okla, MAE, 56. *Prof Exp:* Designer aero engines, Pratt & Whitney Aircraft Div, United Aircraft Corp, 40-47; chmn sch aero eng, Univ Okla, 53-63, dir aero res, 57-64, mem fac, 47-64; head dept aerospace eng, 64-67, dir res & develop, 66-67, PROF MECH & AEROSPACE ENG, UNIV TULSA, 64-, DIR SOLAR ENERGY PROJS, 76- *Concurrent Pos:* Consult, Aero Design & Eng Co, 56-58 & Todd Eng Co, 61- *Mem:* Am Soc Eng Educ; Am Inst Aeronaut & Astronaut. *Res:* Space engineering; rocket propulsion; gas turbine. *Mailing Add:* Dept of Mech Eng Univ of Tulsa Tulsa OK 74104

KETCHAM, ROGER, b Berea, Ohio, Sept 2, 26; m 50; c 4. ORGANIC CHEMISTRY. *Educ:* Antioch Col, BS, 51; Cornell Univ, PhD(chem), 56. *Prof Exp:* From instr to assoc prof, 56-69, PROF CHEM & PHARMACEUT CHEM, SCH PHARM, UNIV CALIF, SAN FRANCISCO, 69- *Concurrent Pos:* Mem, Orgn Am States Professorship, Monterrey Inst Technol & Higher Educ, 64-65; vis prof, Univ Hamburg, Ger, 79-80. *Mem:* Am Chem Soc; Am Pharmaceut Asn; The Chem Soc; Sigma Xi. *Res:* Three-membered rings; nitrogen heterocycles; reaction mechanisms; organo-sulfur chemistry. *Mailing Add:* Dept of Pharm Chem Univ of Calif San Francisco CA 94143

KETCHEL, MELVIN M, b Pontiac, Mich, June 1, 22; m 58; c 3. REPRODUCTIVE PHYSIOLOGY. *Educ:* Olivet Col, AB, 48; Western Reserve Univ, MS, 49; Harvard Univ, PhD(biol), 54. *Prof Exp:* Res asst biophys chem, Harvard Univ, 54-55; res assoc cytol, Protein Found Labs, 55-56; res assoc surg, Harvard Med Sch, 56-59; staff scientist physiol, Worcester Found Exp Biol, 59-63, sr scientist, 63-65; from assoc prof to prof, Sch Med, Tufts Univ, 65-72; dir, Oak Ridge Pop Res Inst, 72-75; scientist, Human Reprod Unit, WHO, 75-77; owner, The Shelter Co, 77-81; CONSULT, DIV RES GRANTS, NIH, 81- *Concurrent Pos:* NSF sr fel, 71-72; prof zool, Univ Tenn, 74-75. *Mem:* AAAS; Am Physiol Soc; Transplantation Soc; Soc Study Reproduction; Brit Soc Study Fertil. *Res:* Hormonal aspects of pregnancy and pseudopregnancy; immunological aspects of the relationships between the fetus and its mother. *Mailing Add:* Div Res Grants Westwood Bldg NIH Bethesda MD 20205

KETCHEN, EUGENE EARL, b Miami, Fla, May 3, 21; m 51; c 3. PHYSICAL CHEMISTRY. *Educ:* Univ Miami, BS, 43; Univ Pittsburgh, PhD(phys chem), 50. *Prof Exp:* Asst, Univ Pittsburgh, 46-50; asst prof chem, Washington & Jefferson Col, 50-51; chemist, Isotope Div, 51-74, INDUST HYG CHEMIST, OAK RIDGE NAT LAB, 74- *Mem:* Am Chem Soc; Am Indust Hyg Asn; Am Acad Indust Hyg. *Res:* Radio-isotopes; industrial hygiene chemistry; industrial toxicology. *Mailing Add:* Oak Ridge Nat Lab X 10 Area Oak Ridge TN 37830

KETCHEN, MARK B, b St Stephens, Can, Sept 15, 48. CRYOGENIC DIGITAL DEVICES. *Educ:* Mass Inst Technol, BS, 70; Univ Calif, Berkeley, MA, 71, PhD(physics), 77. *Prof Exp:* Officer, Physics Thermodynamics Reactor Oper, US Naval Nuclear Power Prog, 72-76; RES STAFF MEM & MGR, THOMAS J WATSON RES CTR, IBM, 77- *Mem:* Am Phys Soc; Inst Elec & Electronics Engrs. *Res:* Electrical design and evaluation of superconducting quantum interference devices for digital and analog applications; logic and power circuits for an ultra-high-speed cryogenic computer. *Mailing Add:* IBM T J Watson Res Ctr PO Box 218 Yorktown Heights NY 10598

KETCHIE, DELMER O, b Salisbury, NC, July 7, 32; m 59; c 2. PLANT PHYSIOLOGY, BIOCHEMISTRY. *Educ:* Wash State Univ, BS, 59; Univ Idaho, MS, 61; Cornell Univ, PhD(pomol), 65. *Prof Exp:* Plant physiologist, Date & Citrus Sta, USDA, Calif, 65-67; from asst horticulturist to assoc horticulturist, 67-80, HORTICULTURIST, TREE FRUIT RES CTR, WASH STATE UNIV, 80- *Honors & Awards:* Stark Award, 73. *Mem:* Am Soc Hort Hort Sci; Soc Cryobiol; Int Soc Hort Sci. *Res:* Winter hardiness of deciduous fruit trees, including biochemical and physical aspects; rest dormancy of deciduous fruit trees. *Mailing Add:* Tree Fruit Res Ctr Wash State Univ Wenatchee WA 98801

KETCHLEDGE, EDWIN HERBERT, b Trenton, NJ, Dec 29, 24; m 46; c 3. FOREST ECOLOGY, BRYOLOGY. *Educ:* Syracuse Univ, BS, 49, MS, 50; Stanford Univ, PhD(biol), 57. *Prof Exp:* Asst bot, Stanford Univ, 51-54; instr, Univ Mass, 54-55; from asst prof to prof, 55-74, DISTINGUISHED TEACHING PROF FOREST BOT, STATE UNIV NY COL ENVIRON SCI & FORESTRY, 74- *Concurrent Pos:* Forest mgr & dir, Cranberry Lake Biol Sta, NY. *Mem:* AAAS; Am Bryol & Lichenological Soc; Ecol Soc Am; Soc Am Foresters; Brit Bryol Soc. *Res:* Ecological impact of recreationists on the natural environment of the Adirondacks high-peak region; ecology of Bryophytes of New York State. *Mailing Add:* Dept Environ & Forest Biol State Univ NY Syracuse NY 13210

KETCHLEDGE, RAYMOND WAIBEL, b Harrisburg, Pa, Dec 8, 19; m 70; c 6. COMMUNICATIONS, ELECTRONICS. *Educ:* Mass Inst Technol, BS, 41, MS, 42. *Prof Exp:* Mem tech staff, Bell Tel Labs, 42-82, exec dir electronic switching div, 66-75, exec dir ocean systs div, 75-82; RETIRED. *Honors & Awards:* Alexander Graham Bell Medal, Inst Elec & Electronics Engrs, 76. *Mem:* Nat Acad Eng; fel Inst Elec & Electronics Engrs. *Res:* Oceanographic research. *Mailing Add:* Bell Tel Labs Whippany Rd Whippany NJ 07981

KETCHMAN, JEFFREY, b New York, NY, Nov 23, 42; m 62; c 2. MECHANICAL ENGINEERING. *Educ:* City Col New York, BSME, 64; Ohio State Univ, MSME, 67; Columbia Univ, DrEngSci, 72. *Prof Exp:* Proj task leader, Battelle Mem Inst, 64-67; mem tech staff, Bell Labs, 67-76; DIR, ENG & ANAL CTR, AMF, INC, 76- *Mem:* AAAS; NY Acad Sci; Asn Res Dirs. *Res:* Optimizing radioisotope thermoelectric generators; design and development of touch sonar systems. *Mailing Add:* 14 Caccamo Lane West Port CT 06880

KETCHUM, BOSTWICK HAWLEY, b Cleveland, Ohio, Jan 21, 12; m 36; c 3. ECOLOGY, BIOLOGICAL OCEANOGRAPHY. *Educ:* St Stephens Col, AB, 34; Harvard Univ, PhD(biol), 38. *Hon Degrees:* ScD, Bard Col, 64 & Clarkson Col Technol, 70, Lowell Technol Inst, 73. *Prof Exp:* Asst biol, Labs, Harvard Univ, 38-39; instr, Long Island Univ, 39-40; assoc marine biol, 40-45, marine microbiologist, 45-53, in-chg marine ecol course, Marine Biol Lab, 52-

57, sr biologist, Inst, 53-54, sr oceanogr, 54-64, ASSOC DIR, WOODS HOLE OCEANOG INST, 62-, SR SCIENTIST, 64- *Concurrent Pos:* Lectr, Harvard Univ, 60-68, assoc mem dept biol, 68-71; NSF res grants, Off Naval Res, AEC, 64; sect head ecol & syst biol, NSF, 68-69; trustee, Inst of Ecol, 70-73; mem ecol adv comt, Environ Protection Agency, 74-76; consult, Arthur D Little, Mass, 75- *Honors & Awards:* David B Stone Award, New Eng Aquarium, Boston, 72. *Mem:* AAAS; Ecol Soc Am (pres, 65-66); Am Soc Limnol & Oceanog (secy-treas, 53-58, vpres, 58-59, pres, 59-60). *Res:* Physiology of algae; action of anti-fouling paints; viability and dispersal of pollution bacteria in the sea; circulation in estuaries; global marine pollution. *Mailing Add:* Woods Hole Oceanog Inst Box 32 Woods Hole MA 02543

KETCHUM, GARDNER M(ASON), b Philadelphia, Pa, Oct 20, 19; m 49; c 1. MECHANICAL ENGINEERING. *Educ:* Mass Inst Technol, SB, 41, SM, 44, ScD(mech eng), 49. *Prof Exp:* Instr mech eng, Mass Inst Technol, 41-48; engr gen eng lab, Gen Elec Co, 48-53; assoc prof mech eng, 53-56, chmn dept, 62-74, PROF MECH ENG, UNION COL, NY, 56- *Mem:* Sigma Xi; fel Am Soc Mech Engrs; Am Soc Eng Educ. *Res:* Fluid mechanics; heat transfer; thermodynamics; technology-society interactions, particularly urban and environmental. *Mailing Add:* Dept Mech Eng Union Col Schenectady NY 12308

KETCHUM, PAUL ABBOTT, b Hyannis, Mass, Aug 11, 42; m 63; c 2. MICROBIAL PHYSIOLOGY. *Educ:* Bates Col, BS, 64; Univ Mass, PhD(microbiol), 69. *Prof Exp:* NIH fel biochem, Johns Hopkins Univ, 68-70; asst prof, 70-77, NSF grant, 71-77, ASSOC PROF BIO SCI, OAKLAND UNIV, 77- *Mem:* AAAS; Am Soc Microbiol. *Res:* Inorganic nitrogen metabolism; biochemistry of nitrate reductase; role of molybdenum in inorganic nitrogen metabolism. *Mailing Add:* Dept of Biol Sci Oakland Univ Rochester MI 48063

KETELLAPPER, HENDRIK JAN, b Ridderkerk, Neth, Dec 23, 25; nat US; m 51; c 3. PLANT PHYSIOLOGY. *Educ:* Univ Utrecht, BSc, 47, MSc, 51, PhD(plant physiol), 53. *Prof Exp:* Instr gen bot, Univ Utrecht, 48-51; res officer, Div Plant Indust, Commonwealth Sci & Indust Res Orgn, Canberra, Australia, 54-57; res fel biol, Calif Inst Technol, 57-64; lectr, 64-65, assoc prof, 65-69, PROF BOT, UNIV CALIF, DAVIS, 69-, ASSOC DEAN COL LETT & SCI, 67- *Concurrent Pos:* Nat Acad Sci exchange scientist, USSR, 63. *Mem:* AAAS; Bot Soc Am; Am Soc Plant Physiol; NY Acad Sci; Royal Neth Bot Soc. *Res:* Climate and plant growth and development; algal physiology; physiological ecology. *Mailing Add:* Dept of Bot Univ of Calif Davis CA 95616

KETHLEY, JOHN BRYAN, b Passaic, NJ, Oct 18, 42; m 68. ENTOMOLOGY. *Educ:* Univ Ga, BS, 64, PhD(entom), 69. *Prof Exp:* NIH trainee acarol lab, Ohio State Univ, 69-70; asst cur insects, 70-75, HEAD DIV, FIELD MUS NATURAL HIST, 74-, ASSOC CUR, 75- *Concurrent Pos:* Lectr comt evolutionary biol, Univ Chicago, 71-72, 74; instr biol sci, Northwestern Univ, 73- *Mem:* Acarological Soc Am; Entom Soc Am; AAAS; Am Inst Biol Sci; Sigma Xi. *Res:* Acarine systematics; methodologies in cladistics and phylogenetics; population ecology; functional morphology. *Mailing Add:* Div of Insects Field Mus of Natural Hist Chicago IL 60605

KETHLEY, THOMAS WILLIAM, b Crystal Springs, Miss, Apr 3, 13; m 37; c 3. BIOLOGY. *Educ:* Emory Univ, AB, 34, MS, 35. *Prof Exp:* Drug & insecticide chemist, State Chemist's Off, Ga, 37-41; mineral chemist, State Div Mines, 41; toxicologist, Med Div, US Army, Edgewood Arsenal, Md, 41-46; from res asst prof to res assoc prof, Eng Exp Sta, Ga Inst Technol, 46-60, head bio-eng br, 60-77, res prof appl biol, 60-81, prof biol, 74-81, EMER PROF BIOL, GA INST TECHNOL, 81- *Concurrent Pos:* Res biologist, Ga Inst Technol, 51-60; consult, Commun Dis Ctr, 54-55 & 57-58; consult, Chem Corps, US Army, 58- *Mem:* AAAS; Am Pub Health Asn; Am Soc Microbiol; NY Acad Sci. *Res:* Effect of ice formation on living cells; thermal properties of frozen tissues; preservation of foods by freezing; instrumental methods of analysis; gas and aerosol chamber techniques; aerobiology; water content of bacterial aerosols; aerial disinfectants. *Mailing Add:* Sch of Biol Ga Inst of Technol Atlanta GA 30332

KETLEY, ARTHUR DONALD, b London, Eng, Dec 27, 30. PHOTOCHEMISTRY, POLYMER CHEMISTRY. *Educ:* Univ London, BSc, 51, PhD(chem), 53. *Prof Exp:* Res assoc chem, Mass Inst Technol, 53-55; lectr, Univ Sydney, 56-57; res fel, Ga Inst Technol, 57-58; chemist, Esso Res & Eng Co, 58-59; chemist, 59-73, mgr mat develop photopolymer systs, 73-79, DIR, TECHNOL PROD RES, W R GRACE & CO, 79- *Concurrent Pos:* Chief ed, J Radiation Chem. *Mem:* Am Chem Soc; Int Am Photochem Soc. *Res:* Mechanisms of organic reactions; organometallic chemistry; photochemistry; development and applications of photopolymerizable materials. *Mailing Add:* Photopolymer Res W R Grace & Co 7379 Rte 32 Columbia MD 21044

KETLEY, JEANNE NELSON, b New York, NY, Apr 18, 38. ENZYMOLOGY, DRUG METABOLISM. *Educ:* Queens Col, NY, BS, 62; Cornell Univ, MS, 67; Johns Hopkins Univ, PhD(biochem), 73. *Prof Exp:* Res assoc biochem, Cornell Univ, 67, res asst enzym & biochem, Med Col, 68-69; vis scientist develop biol, Nat Inst Dent Res, 73-74, staff fel enzyme biochem, lab biochem & metab, Nat Inst Arthritis, Metab & Digestive Dis, NIH, 74-76, sr staff fel, Nat Inst Aging, 76-77; chemist, Bur Foods, Food & Drug Admin, 77-79; EXEC SECY, PHYSICAL BIOCHEM STUDY SECTION, NIH, 79- *Concurrent Pos:* Muscular Dystrophy Asn Am fel, 73-74. *Mem:* AAAS; Am Chem Soc; Biophys Soc; Soc Exp Biol & Med. *Res:* Drug metabolism; mammalian biochemical processes at the molecular level; changes in biological structure and function of proteins due to natural and induced causes. *Mailing Add:* Phys Biochem Study Sect Div Res Grants NIH Westwood Bldg Rm 218 Bethesda MD 20205

KETRING, DAROLD L, b Van Nuys, Calif, Mar 14, 30; m 50; c 2. PLANT PHYSIOLOGY, BIOCHEMISTRY. *Educ:* Univ Calif, Los Angeles, BS, 63, PhD(plant sci), 67. *Prof Exp:* PLANT PHYSIOLOGIST, USDA, 67- *Mem:* Am Soc Plant Physiologists; Am Soc Agron; Am Peanut Res & Educ Asn; Plant Growth Regulator Soc Am. *Res:* Relation of ethylene and other plant hormones to plant growth, development, senescence and accompanying biochemistry; effect of environmental stress on plant growth and development. *Mailing Add:* Agron Dept Okla State Univ Stillwater OK 74074

KETTEL, LOUIS JOHN, b Chicago, Ill, Nov 4, 29; m 51; c 3. PULMONARY PHYSIOLOGY, MEDICAL EDUCATION. *Educ:* Purdue Univ, BS, 51; Northwestern Univ, MD, 54, MS, 58; Am Bd Internal Med, dipl, 61; Am Bd Pulmonary Dis, dipl, 65. *Prof Exp:* Chief pulmonary dis sect, Vet Admin Res Hosp, Chicago, 62-68 & Tucson, 68-72; assoc dean Col Med, 74-77, assoc prof, 68-73, PROF MED, SCH MED, UNIV ARIZ, 73-, DEAN COL MED, 77- *Concurrent Pos:* USPHS fel, Northwestern Univ, 56-57, USPHS trainee, 60-62; asst prof, Northwestern Univ, 66-68; asst chief med serv, Vet Admin Hosp, Tucson, 72-74. *Mem:* AAAS; Am Fedn Clin Res; fel Am Col Physicians; Am Med Asn; Am Thoracic Soc. *Res:* Health care delivery using allied health professionals; evaluation of techniques in medical education. *Mailing Add:* Col Med Univ Ariz Health Sci Ctr Tucson AZ 85724

KETTELKAMP, BEN H, b Pana, Ill, June 25, 01; m 27; c 1. PHYSIOLOGY. *Educ:* Univ Kans, AB, 25, AM, 26; Univ Pittsburgh, PhD(physiol), 31. *Prof Exp:* Prof & head dept, 35-67, EMER PROF BIOL, UNIV WIS-RIVER FALLS, 67-; ENVIRON DIR, BELWIN FOUND, 70- *Mem:* AAAS. *Res:* Physiology of reproduction; mammalian ova; physiology of prostate gland. *Mailing Add:* Belwin Found 9200 Wayzata Blvd Minneapolis MN 55426

KETTELKAMP, DONALD B, b Anamosa, Iowa, Jan 21, 30; m 54; c 4. ORTHOPEDIC SURGERY. *Educ:* Cornell Col, BA, 52; Univ Iowa, MD, 55, MS, 60. *Prof Exp:* From asst prof to assoc prof orthop surg, Albany Med Col, 64-68; assoc prof, Univ Iowa, 68-71; prof & chmn dept, Med Ctr, Univ Ark, Little Rock, 71-74; PROF ORTHOP SURG & CHMN DEPT, IND UNIV MED CTR, INDIANAPOLIS, 74- *Concurrent Pos:* Consult, Vet Admin Hosp, Little Rock, 71-74. *Mem:* Fel Am Acad Orthop Surg; Orthop Res Soc; fel Am Col Surg; Am Orthop Asn; Am Med Asn. *Res:* Knee and hand reconstruction and biomechanics. *Mailing Add:* Ind Sch of Med 1100 W Michigan St Indianapolis IN 46202

KETTENRING, JON ROBERTS, b Seattle, Wash, June 9, 38; m 69; c 2. APPLIED STATISTICS, MATHEMATICAL STATISTICS. *Educ:* Stanford Univ, BS, 61, MS, 62; Univ NC, PhD(statist), 69. *Prof Exp:* MEM TECH STAFF STATIST, BELL LABS, 69- *Concurrent Pos:* Vis assoc prof biostatist, Univ Wash, 75-76. *Mem:* Fel Am Statist Asn; Inst Math Statist. *Res:* Multivariate statistics; methods for data analysis; robust methods; cluster analysis. *Mailing Add:* Bell Labs 600 Mountain Ave Murray Hill NJ 07974

KETTER, ROBERT L(EWIS), b Welch, WVa, Dec 7, 28; m 48; c 4. CIVIL ENGINEERING. *Educ:* Univ Mo, BS, 50; Lehigh Univ, MS, 52, PhD(civil eng), 56. *Hon Degrees:* DSc, Kyungpook Nat Univ, Korea, 73; DEng, Lehigh Univ. *Prof Exp:* Asst civil eng, Lehigh Univ, 50-52, res instr, 52-56, res asst prof civil eng & eng mech, 56-58; prof civil eng & head dept, 58-64, actg dean grad sch, 64-65, dean grad sch, 65-66, vpres facilities planning, 66-69, PRES, STATE UNIV NY, BUFFALO, 70- *Concurrent Pos:* Mem, Welding Res Coun, Eng Found, 56-70, chmn tech comts, Struct Stability Res Coun, 70-; US deleg, Int Inst Welding, 59, off expert rep, US, Comn X; mem bd dirs, Roswell Park Mem Inst; mem bd trustees, Univs Res Asn, 77-, chmn, Coun Pres, 81-82; mem bd dirs, Sierra Res Corp, 78- *Honors & Awards:* Adams Mem Award, Am Welding Soc, 68. *Mem:* Int Asn Bridge & Struct Engrs; Am Soc Civil Engrs; Am Welding Soc. *Res:* Stability; nonlinear mechanics; structural analysis; material properties; brittle fracture mechanics. *Mailing Add:* Off of the Pres Capen Hall Amherst NY 14260

KETTERER, CHARLES CLIFFORD, b Louisville, Ky, Oct 4, 25; m 53; c 7. ORGANIC CHEMISTRY. *Educ:* Univ Louisville, BS, 49, MS, 51, PhD(chem), 54. *Prof Exp:* Chemist, Girdler Corp, Ky, 51-52; sr res chemist, 54-71, RES ASSOC, TEXTILE FIBERS DEPT, E I DU PONT DE NEMOURS & CO, INC, 71- *Mem:* Am Chem Soc. *Res:* Textile fibers. *Mailing Add:* Textile Fibers Dept E I du Pont de Nemours & Co Inc Waynesboro VA 22980

KETTERER, JOHN JOSEPH, b Philadelphia, Pa, Mar 12, 21; m 46; c 2. ZOOLOGY. *Educ:* Dickinson Col, BS, 43; NY Univ, PhD(biol), 53. *Prof Exp:* Asst biol, NY Univ, 46-52, instr, 52-53; from asst prof to prof, 53-73, head dept, 59-73, W P PRESSLY PROF BIOL, MONMOUTH COL, 73- *Mem:* AAAS; Soc Protozool; Am Soc Zool. *Res:* Invertebrate zoology with special reference to protozoa. *Mailing Add:* Dept of Biol Monmouth Col Monmouth IL 61462

KETTERER, PAUL ANTHONY, b Warwick, NY, Aug 2, 41; m 62; c 2. ORGANIC CHEMISTRY. *Educ:* Syracuse Univ, AB, 64; Seton Hall Univ, MS, 73. *Prof Exp:* Chemist, Polaks Frutal Works Inc, 64-68; sr chemist, 68-73, group leader anal chem, 74-75, LAB MGR POLYMER CHARACTERIZATION & ANAL, TENNECO CHEM INC, PISCATAWAY, 76- *Mem:* Am Chem Soc; Soc Appl Spectros; Coblentz Soc; Sigma Xi. *Res:* Polymer characterization and analysis, determination of structure-property relationships of vinyl polymers and additives; development of analytical methods for trace analysis of air and water pollutants; organotin chemistry. *Mailing Add:* 312 Market St Middlesex NJ 08846

KETTERING, JAMES DAVID, b Pekin, Ill, Mar 27, 42; m 63; c 3. MEDICAL MICROBIOLOGY. *Educ:* Andrews Univ, BA, 64; Loma Linda Univ, MS, 68, PhD(microbiol), 74. *Prof Exp:* Microbiologist, Indust Bio-Test Labs, 64-66, Abott Labs Inc, 66; instr, 72-74, asst prof, 74-80, ASSOC PROF MICROBIOL, SCH MED, LOMA LINDA UNIV, 80- *Concurrent Pos:* Fel med microbiol, Calif State Dept Health, Berkeley, 75-77. *Mem:* Am Soc Microbiol; Sigma Xi. *Res:* Enzymology of bacteriophage-infected bacteria; diagnostic virology-clinical; tumor immunology; dental immunology. *Mailing Add:* 11980 Canary Ct Grand Terrace CA 92324

KETTERINGHAM, JOHN M, b Bournemouth, Eng, Mar 9, 40; m 64. PHYSICAL CHEMISTRY. *Educ:* Oxford Univ, BA, 61, MA & DPhil(chem), 64. *Prof Exp:* Mgr chem systs sect, 64-77, VPRES ARTHUR D LITTLE, INC, 77- *Mem:* AAAS; Am Soc Artificial Internal Organs. *Res:* Membrane technology. *Mailing Add:* Concord Rd Lincoln MA 01773

KETTERSON, JOHN BOYD, b Orange, NJ, Oct 2, 34; m 61; c 3. PHYSICS. *Educ:* Univ Chicago, BS, 57, MS, 59, PhD(physics), 62. *Prof Exp:* Assoc physicist, Argonne Nat Lab, Ill, 62-72; sr physicist, 74; PROF PHYSICS, NORTHWESTERN UNIV, 74-; CONSULT, ARGONNE NAT LAB, 74- *Mem:* Fel Am Phys Soc. *Res:* Electronic properties of metals and Fermi surfaces; properties of monomolecular films; low and ultra low temperature technique; physics of liquid crystals; properties of composition modulated structures; properties of liquid and solid helium. *Mailing Add:* Dept Phys & Astron Northwestern Univ Evanston IL 60201

KETTMAN, JOHN RUTHERFORD, JR, b Niles, Calif, Nov 29, 39; m 68; c 2. IMMUNOLOGY. *Educ:* Univ Calif, Berkeley, BA, 61; Ore State Univ, PhD(biochem), 68. *Prof Exp:* Asst chem, Ore State Univ, 61-62, biochem, 62-64; asst res biologist, Univ Calif, San Diego, 69-72; asst prof, 73-75, assoc prof, 75-80, PROF MICROBIOL, SOUTHWESTERN MED SCH, UNIV TEX HEALTH SCI CTR, DALLAS, 80- *Concurrent Pos:* NIH trainee immunochem, Kaiser Res Found, San Francisco, 67-69; mem immunol sci study group, 80-83. *Mem:* Am Chem Soc; Am Asn Immunologists; Am Soc Zoologists. *Res:* Cellular immunology; cell cooperation in the immune response; biology of lymphoid systems. *Mailing Add:* Southwestern Med Sch Univ of Tex Health Sci Ct Dallas TX 75235

KETTNER, DAVID MORGAN, electrical engineering, see previous edition

KETY, SEYMOUR SOLOMON, b Philadelphia, Pa, Aug 25, 15; m 40; c 2. PHYSIOLOGY, PSYCHOBIOLOGY. *Educ:* Univ Pa, AB, 36, MD, 40. *Hon Degrees:* ScD, Univ Pa, 65, Loyola Univ, 69; MD, Univ Copenhagen, 79, Univ Ill, 81. *Prof Exp:* Nat Res Coun fel, Harvard Med Sch, 42-43; instr pharmacol, Sch Med, Univ Pa, 43-44, assoc, 44-46, asst prof, 46-48, prof clin physiol, Grad Sch Med, 48-61; sci dir, NIMH & Nat Inst Neurol Dis & Blindness, 51-56, chief lab clin sci, NIMH, 56-67; dir psychiat res lab, Mass Gen Hosp, 67-77; PROF PSYCHIAT, HARVARD MED SCH, 67-; DIR PSYCHIAT RES LABS, MAILMAN RES CTR, McLEAN HOSP, 77- *Concurrent Pos:* Numerous hon lectureships, 51-; mem adv bd ment health res, Ford Found, 55-57; mem sci adv bd, Scottish Rite Found Res Schizophrenia, 57-, chmn, 71-; chmn biosci adv comt, NASA, 59-60; ed-in-chief, J Psychiat Res, 59-; mem, President's Panel Ment Retardation, 61-62; Henry Phipps prof, Johns Hopkins Univ & psychiatrist-in-chief, Hosp, 61-62; assoc, Neurosci Res Found, 62-; vis prof, Col France, 66-67; mem vis comt biol, Calif Inst Technol, 72-; mem bd trustees, Rockefeller Univ, 77- *Honors & Awards:* Theobald Smith Award, AAAS, 49; Max Weinstein Award, United Cerebral Palsy Res Found, 54; Distinguished Serv Award, Dept Health, Educ & Welfare, 58; McAlpin Medal & Res Achievement Award, Nat Asn Ment Health, 72; Paul Hoch Award, Am Psychopath Asn, 73; Kovalenko Award, Nat Acad Sci, 73; Menninger Award, Am Col Physicians, 76; Fromm-Reichmann Award, Am Acad Psychoanal, 78; Passano Award, 80; FFRP Award Psychiatric Res, 80; Res Award Asn Res Nerv & Ment Dis, 80. *Mem:* Nat Acad Sci; Psychiat Res Soc; Am Physiol Soc; Asn Res Nerv & Ment Dis (pres, 65); Am Psychopath Asn (pres, 65). *Res:* Lead citrate complex and therapy of lead poisoning; circulation and metabolism of the human brain; theory of capillary-tissue exchange of non-metabolized diffusible substances; psychiatric genetics; biological aspects of mental illness. *Mailing Add:* Dept of Psychiatry Harvard Univ Cambridge MA 02138

KETZLACH, NORMAN, b Seattle, Wash, Sept 8, 21; m 50; c 3. CHEMICAL ENGINEERING. *Educ:* Univ Wash, BS, 43, MS, 44. *Prof Exp:* Chem engr, Manganese Prod, Inc, 44-46, chief chemist, 46-51; chem engr, Gen Elec Co, 51-55, nuclear safety specialist, 55-59; sr engr res, fuels & mat dept, Atomics Int Div, NAm Aviation, Inc, 59-60, criticality safeguards adv, 60-71, mgr criticality & nuclear mat safeguards, NAm Rockwell Corp, 71-73; SR SCIENTIST, US NUCLEAR REGULATORY COMN, 73- *Mem:* Am Nuclear Soc; Am Inst Chem Engrs. *Res:* Nuclear safety in the storage, handling and processing of fissionable materials; nuclear materials safeguards and accountability. *Mailing Add:* 900 Kersey Rd Silver Springs MD 20902

KEUDELL, KENNETH CARSON, b Oklahoma City, Okla, May 3, 41; m 67; c 2. MICROBIOLOGY. *Educ:* Okla State Univ, BS, 63, MS, 67; Univ Mo, PhD(microbiol), 69. *Prof Exp:* Fel microbiol, Albert Einstein Col Med, 69-71; asst prof, Sch Dent Med, Washington Univ, 71-78; ASSOC PROF MICROBIOL, WESTERN ILL UNIV, 78- *Concurrent Pos:* Nat Inst Dent Res res grant, 74-76. *Mem:* Am Soc Microbiol; Sigma Xi. *Res:* Medical microbiology, with emphasis on anaerobic microorganisms. *Mailing Add:* Dept of Biol Sci Western Ill Univ Macomb IL 61455

KEULKS, GEORGE WILLIAM, b East St Louis, Ill, Apr 2, 38; m 60; c 4. PHYSICAL CHEMISTRY. *Educ:* Washington Univ, AB, 60; Univ Ark, MS, 62; Northwestern Univ, PhD(chem), 64. *Prof Exp:* Res chemist, Gulf Res & Develop Co, 64-65; res assoc, Johns Hopkins Univ, 65-66; from asst prof to assoc prof chem, 66-74, assoc dean natural sci, 74-75, actg dean grad sch, 75-77, PROF CHEM, UNIV WIS-MILWAUKEE, 74-, DEAN GRAD SCH, 77- *Concurrent Pos:* Consult, Monsanto Polymers & Petrochem Co, 74-, Nelson Industs, Inc, 74, Celanese, 77- & Atlantic Richfield Co, 80- *Mem:* AAAS; Am Chem Soc; Catalysis Soc NAm. *Res:* Heterogeneous catalysis; catalytic kinetics; synthesis of new catalysts; mechanisms of catalytic oxidation; physical characteristics of catalysis. *Mailing Add:* Dept of Chem Univ of Wis Milwaukee WI 53201

KEUPER, JEROME PENN, b Ft Thomas, Ky, Jan 12, 21; m 48; c 2. PHYSICS. *Educ:* Mass Inst Technol, BS, 48; Stanford Univ, MS, 49; Univ Va, PhD, 52. *Prof Exp:* Res assoc, Carnegie Inst Technol, 49-50; sr res physicist, Remington Arms Co, Inc, 52-58; sr scientist, RCA Missile Test Proj, 58-60, mgr syst anal, 60-62; PRES, FLA INST TECHNOL, 58- *Concurrent Pos:* Chmn math dept, Bridgeport Eng Inst, 54-58. *Mem:* Am Soc Eng Educ; Opers Res Soc Am; Asn Comput Mach. *Res:* Solid state, radiation and nuclear physics; computing machines; operations research; ballistics; error analysis; space technology. *Mailing Add:* Off of the Pres Fla Inst of Technol PO Box 1150 Melbourne FL 32901

KEUSCH, GERALD TILDEN, b New York, NY, Apr 3, 38; m 62; c 2. INFECTIOUS DISEASES. *Educ:* Columbia Col, AB, 58; Harvard Univ, MD, 63. *Prof Exp:* Instr, Tufts-New Eng Med Ctr, 69-70; from asst prof to prof med, Mt Sinai Sch Med, 70-78; PROF MED, TUFTS-NEW ENG MED CTR, 78- *Concurrent Pos:* Mem subcomt interactions nutrit & infection, Nat Acad Sci, 71-, chmn, 76-; mem comt int nutrit progs, 75- & comn int rels, 76- *Honors & Awards:* Squibb Award, Infectious Dis Soc Am, 81. *Mem:* AAAS; Am Soc Microbiol; Am Fedn Clin Res; Infectious Dis Soc Am; NY Acad Sci. *Res:* Pathogenesis of bacterial infections, particularly bacillary dysentery and vaccine development; effect of malnutrition on the immune response and host defenses. *Mailing Add:* Tufts-New Eng Med Ctr 171 Harrison Ave Boston MA 02111

KEVAN, DOUGLAS KEITH MCEWAN, b Helsinki, Finland, Oct 31, 20; Can citizen; m 43; c 3. ENTOMOLOGY. *Educ:* Univ Edinburgh, BSc Hons, 41; Imp Col Trop Agr, Trinidad, BWI, AICTA, 43; Univ Nottingham, PhD, 56. *Prof Exp:* Brit Colonial Off cadet entom, Imp Col Trop Agr, 41-43; entomologist, Kenya Dept Agr, EAfrica, 43-48; head agr zool sect, Univ Nottingham, 48-58; prof entom & chmn dept entom & plant path, Macdonald Col, 58-64, chmn dept entom, 64-72, chmn, Lyman Entom Mus, 60-72, DIR, LYMAN ENTOM MUS & RES LAB, MCGILL UNIV, 72- *Concurrent Pos:* Agr sr entomologist, Uganda, 45; Tech adv locust control, E Ethiopia & Somalilands, 46-47. *Mem:* Fel Royal Soc Edinburgh; Am Entom Soc; fel Entom Soc Can (pres, 72-73); Entom Soc Am; fel Royal Entom Soc London. *Res:* Taxonomy and distribution of orthopteroid insects, especially Pyrgomorphidae; biology and ecology of soil fauna, especially microarthropods; insect poetry and ethnoentomology. *Mailing Add:* Lyman Entom Mus & Res Lab Macdonald Campus McGill Univ Ste Anne de Bellevue PQ H0A 1C0 Can

KEVAN, LARRY, b Kansas City, Mo, Dec 12, 38. PHYSICAL CHEMISTRY. *Educ:* Univ Kans, BS, 60; Univ Calif, Los Angeles, PhD(chem), 63. *Prof Exp:* Vis res assoc chem, Univ Newcastle, 63; instr, Univ Chicago, 63-65; from asst prof to assoc prof, Univ Kans, 65-69; prof chem, Wayne State Univ, 69-; CULLEN PROF CHEM, UNIV HOUSTON, 80- *Concurrent Pos:* Exchange fel, Czech, 69; vis scientist, Danish Atomic Energy Lab, 70; Guggenheim fel, 70-71; vis prof, Univ Utah, 71, Univ Nagoya, Japan, 76, Univ Paris, 77 & Armed Forces Tech Univ, Munich, 79; exchange fel to USSR, Nat Acad Sci, 74, 75 & 77; vis scientist, Japan Soc Promotion Sci, 76; vis comt chem, Brookhaven Nat Lab, 74-78; chmn, Gordon Conf Radiation Chem, 75. *Mem:* AAAS; Am Chem Soc; fel Am Phys Soc; The Chem Soc; NY Acad Sci. *Res:* Electron magnetic resonance and relaxation; electron spin echo spectrometry; photoredox reactions in micelles and vesicles; irons and radicals on oxide surfaces; peroxy and nitroxide radical probes of molecular motion; ion solution geometry; electron localization and solution; radiation-produced intermediates. *Mailing Add:* Dept Chem Univ Houston Houston TX 77004

KEVANE, CLEMENT JOSEPH, b Rembrandt, Iowa, May 17, 22; m 53; c 9. PHYSICS. *Educ:* Iowa State Col, BS, 48, PhD(physics), 53. *Prof Exp:* Physicist, Motorola, Inc, 53-56; assoc prof, 56-63, PROF PHYSICS, ARIZ STATE UNIV, 63- *Mem:* Am Phys Soc. *Res:* Physics of solid state, semiconductor properties; conduction of heat and electricity in refractory oxides. *Mailing Add:* Dept of Physics Ariz State Univ Tempe AZ 85281

KEVERN, NILES RUSSELL, b Elizabeth, Ill, May 15, 31; m 55; c 3. AQUATIC BIOLOGY, ECOLOGY. *Educ:* Univ Mont, BS, 58; Mich State Univ, MS, 61, PhD(limnol), 63. *Prof Exp:* Limnologist, Oak Ridge Nat Lab, Union Carbide Corp, 63-66; from asst prof to assoc prof, 66-69, PROF FISHERIES & WILDLIFE, & CHMN DEPT, MICH STATE UNIV, 69- *Concurrent Pos:* Asst dir, Inst Water Res, Mich State Univ, 67-69. *Mem:* Am Fisheries Soc; Am Soc Limnol & Oceanog; AAAS. *Res:* Aquatic ecology, particularly bioenergetics and mineral cycling of flowing water ecosystems; radiation ecology. *Mailing Add:* Dept of Fisheries & Wildlife Mich State Univ Nat Resources Bldg East Lansing MI 48824

KEVILL, DENNIS NEIL, b Walton-le-Dale, Eng, May 27, 35. PHYSICAL ORGANIC CHEMISTRY. *Educ:* Univ Col London, BSc, 56, PhD(chem), 60. *Prof Exp:* Asst lectr chem, Univ Col London, 59-60; res assoc, Univ Nebr, 60-63; from asst prof to assoc prof, 63-70, PROF CHEM, NORTHERN ILL UNIV, 70- *Concurrent Pos:* Petrol Res Fund grants, 63-64 & 65-70; consult, Carus Chem Co, Inc, 65-68; NSF grants, 67-71 & 74-75; NIH grant, 75-76; hon res fel, Univ Col London, 75-76. *Mem:* Am Chem Soc; The Chem Soc. *Res:* Organic reaction mechanisms; nucleophilicity; reaction mechanisms in solvents of low polarity; elimination reactions; electrophilic assistance to nucleophilic substitutions; perchlorate esters; adamantane derivatives. *Mailing Add:* Dept of Chem Northern Ill Univ DeKalb IL 60115

KEVORKIAN, JIRAIR, b Jerusalem, Palestine, May 14, 33; US citizen; m 80. APPLIED MATHEMATICS. *Educ:* Ga Inst Technol, BS, 55, MS, 56; Calif Inst Technol, PhD(aeronaut, math), 61. *Prof Exp:* Aerodynamicist, Gen Dynamics/Convair, 56-57; res fel aeronaut, Calif Inst Technol, 61-64; from asst prof to assoc prof, 64-71, PROF AERONAUT & ASTRONAUT & APPL MATH, UNIV WASH, 71- *Concurrent Pos:* Vis prof, Univ Paris, 71-72; Fulbright-Hays Award, Coun Int Exchange of Scholars, 75. *Mem:* Soc Indust & Appl Math. *Res:* Development and application of perturbation techniques. *Mailing Add:* 206 Guggenheim Hall FS-10 Univ of Wash Seattle WA 98195

KEWISH, RALPH WALLACE, b Bridgeport, Ala, Apr 28, 10; m 32, 68; c 2. CHEMISTRY. *Educ:* Ohio State Univ, AB, 31, MSc, 34, PhD(phys chem), 35. *Prof Exp:* Res chemist, Lowe Bros Co, Ohio, 35-42 & 46; with Los Alamos Sci Lab, 47-55; with Kaiser Aluminum & Chem Corp, 55-63; with Sherwin-Williams Co, 64-65; with Princeville Canning Co, 66-69; with Silliman Inst, Inc, 70-72; chemist, Mat Testing Lab, La Dept Hwys, 72-75; CHEMIST, HOLRITE, INC, 75- *Mem:* Sigma Xi. *Res:* Paints and their rheological properties; activity of driers; vapor pressure of organic compounds; chemistry of uranium; kinetics of gas-solid reactions; precipitation, granulometry and purity of alumina. *Mailing Add:* 8255 Queenswood Ct Baton Rouge LA 70806

KEY, ANTHONY W, b Edinburgh, Scotland, Mar 3, 39; m 63; c 2. PARTICLE PHYSICS. *Educ:* Aberdeen Univ, MA, 60; Oxford Univ, DPhil(physics), 64. *Prof Exp:* Lectr physics, Univ Natal, 64-66; mem coun, Can Inst Particle Physics, 73-75; fel, 66-68, asst prof, 68-73, ASSOC PROF PHYSICS, UNIV TORONTO, 73- *Mem:* Can Asn Physicists; Brit Inst Physics. *Res:* Experimental particle physics; high energy physics using the techniques of bubble or spark chambers. *Mailing Add:* Dept of Physics Univ of Toronto Toronto ON M5S 1A1 Can

KEY, CHARLES R, b Oklahoma City, Okla, Aug 4, 34; m 58; c 3. PATHOLOGY. *Educ:* Okla State Univ, BS, 56; Univ Okla, MD, 59, MS, 62, PhD(med sci), 66; Am Bd Path, dipl, 64. *Prof Exp:* Intern path, Med Ctr, Univ Okla, 59-60, resident, 60-64; pathologist, Div Air Pollution, USPHS, Ohio, 64-66; pathologist, Atomic Bomb Casualty Comn, Hiroshima, Japan, 66-69; asst prof, 69-73, ASSOC PROF PATH, SCH MED, UNIV NMEX, 73- *Concurrent Pos:* Med dir, NMex Tumor Registry, 69- *Mem:* Col Am Path; Asn Clin Scientists; Int Acad Path; Am Asn Pathologists & Bacteriologists; Int Soc Stereology. *Res:* Use of quantitative methods in morphology; pathology of radiation injury; epidemiological pathology of cancer; tumor registry. *Mailing Add:* Dept of Path Univ of NMex Med Sch Albuquerque NM 87131

KEY, JOE LYNN, b Troy, Tenn, Sept 10, 33; m 56; c 2. PLANT PHYSIOLOGY. *Educ:* Univ Tenn, BS, 55; Univ Ill, MS, 57, PhD(plant physiol), 59. *Prof Exp:* Asst agron, Univ Ill, 55-59, fel biochem, 59-60; NSF fel, Univ Calif, Davis, 60, asst prof, 60-62; from assoc prof to prof, plant physiol, Purdue Univ, 62-69; RES PROF BOT, UNIV GA, 69- *Concurrent Pos:* Dir, Competitive Grants Prog, Sci & Educ Admin, USDA, 78-79. *Res:* Biochemistry of auxin action; nucleic acid metabolism; developmental regulation in plants; RNA metabolism; control of protein synthesis; stress-regulated RNA and protein synthesis. *Mailing Add:* Dept of Bot Univ of Ga Athens GA 30601

KEY, MORRIS DALE, b Hobbs, NMex, May 31, 39; m 70; c 1. ENVIRONMENTAL CHEMISTRY, ANALYTICAL CHEMISTRY. *Educ:* Midwestern State Univ, BS, 64; Univ Tex, Dallas, PhD(environ geochem), 76. *Prof Exp:* Sales engr, Drew Chem Corp, 65-66; sales rep, Beckman Instruments, Inc, 66-67; co-founder, Anal Consult, Inc, 67-71; PRES, KEY LABS, INC, 71- *Concurrent Pos:* Consult several co, 70- *Mem:* Am Chem Soc; Am Inst Chemists; Am Soc Metals; Am Soc Testing & Mat; Asn Consult Chemists & Chem Engrs. *Res:* Heavy metal mobilities in sediments and water; precious metal recovery systems. *Mailing Add:* Key Labs Inc 2636 Walnut Hill Lane Suite 275 Dallas TX 75229

KEYES, EVERETT A, b Duncan, Okla, May 28, 03; m 38; c 3. ANIMAL HUSBANDRY. *Educ:* Mont State Col, BS, 35; Univ Vt, MS, 37; Pa State Col, PhD(nutrit), 48. *Prof Exp:* Asst nutrit, Univ Vt, 37-40; from asst to instr dairy husb, Pa State Col, 40-45; from assoc prof to prof, 45-70, EMER PROF DAIRY SCI, MONT STATE UNIV, 70- *Concurrent Pos:* Prof, Rafi Ahmed Kidwai, Agr Inst, India, 58-60. *Mem:* AAAS; Am Soc Animal Sci; Am Dairy Sci Asn. *Res:* Vitamins A and D in the nutrition of dairy calves; forages and their handling in the nutrition of dairy animals; milk secretion and mastitis control; artificial insemination and reproduction. *Mailing Add:* 1010 E Babcock Bozeman MT 59715

KEYES, J(OHN) J(UDSON), JR, chemical engineering, see previous edition

KEYES, JACK LYNN, b St Johns, Mich, Nov 15, 41; m 68; c 2. PHYSIOLOGY. *Educ:* Linfield Col, BA, 63; Univ Ore Med Sch, PhD(physiol), 70. *Prof Exp:* Instr physiol, Med Col, Cornell Univ, 70-71; asst prof, 71-77, ASSOC PROF PHYSIOL, MED SCH, ORE HEALTH SCI UNIV, 78- *Mem:* Assoc Am Physiol Soc; NY Acad Sci. *Res:* Renal physiology, acid-base regulation during development and adult life. *Mailing Add:* Dept of Physiol Univ of Ore Med Sch Portland OR 97201

KEYES, PAUL HOLT, b Hartford, Conn, Oct 23, 43; m 68; c 1. LIQUID CRYSTALS, PHASE TRANSITIONS. *Educ:* Rensselaer Polytech Inst, BS, 65; Univ MD, PhD (physics), 72. *Prof Exp:* Fel physics, Univ Del, 72-75, asst prof physics, Univ Mass, Boston, 75-79; ASST PROF, BARTOL RES FOUND, UNIV DEL, 79- *Mem:* Am Phys Soc; Sigma Xi. *Res:* Critical phenomena; liquid crystals; phase transitions. *Mailing Add:* Bartol Res Found Univ Del Newark DE 19711

KEYES, PAUL LANDIS, b Thomasville, NC, July 7, 38; m 66; c 2. REPRODUCTIVE ENDOCRINOLOGY, PHYSIOLOGY. *Educ:* NC State Univ, BS, 60, MS, 62; Univ Ill, PhD(animal sci, physiol), 66. *Prof Exp:* Res asst prof, Dept Obstet & Gynec, Albany Med Col, 68-72; from asst prof path to assoc prof path, 72-80, asst prof physiol, 74-80, ASSOC PROF PHYSIOL, UNIV MICH, ANN ARBOR, 81- *Concurrent Pos:* NIH fel, Med Sch, Harvard Univ, 66-68; ed, Endocrinol, 79-82; mem rev comt, Clin C Fel, NIH, 79- *Mem:* Endocrine Soc; Soc Study Reproduction; Am Physiol Soc. *Res:* Endocrinology of the ovary in pregnancy; action of estrogen on the corpus luteum. *Mailing Add:* Ctr Human Growth & Develop M2251 Med Sci I Univ Mich Ann Arbor MI 48109

KEYES, ROBERT WILLIAM, b Chicago, Ill, Dec 2, 21. PHYSICS. *Educ:* Univ Chicago, BS, 42, MS, 49, PhD(physics), 53. *Prof Exp:* Jr physicist, Argonne Nat Lab, 46-50; res physicist, Res Lab, Westinghouse Elec Corp, 53-56, adv physicist, 57-60, consult physicist, 60; PHYSICIST, IBM CORP, 60- *Concurrent Pos:* Corresp, Comments on Solid State Physics, 70-; consult, Nat Acad Sci Physics Surv Comt, 70-72. *Mem:* Nat Acad Eng; Am Phys Soc; fel Inst Elec & Electronics Engrs. *Res:* Solid state physics and its applications to electronics. *Mailing Add:* IBM Corp Res Lab PO Box 218 Yorktown Heights NY 10598

KEYES, THOMAS FRANCIS, b New Haven, Conn, Sept 21, 45; m 68. THEORETICAL CHEMISTRY. *Educ:* Yale Univ, BS, 67; Univ Calif, Los Angeles, PhD(chem), 71. *Prof Exp:* NSF fel chem, Mass Inst Technol, 71-74; asst prof, 74-81, ASSOC PROF CHEM, YALE UNIV, 81- *Res:* Statistical mechanics, emphasizing theory of light scattering, dynamics of fluctuations in fluids and kinetic theory. *Mailing Add:* Sterling Chem Lab 225 Prospect St New Haven CT 06520

KEYL, ALEXANDER CHARLES, b Cleveland, Ohio, July 10, 12. PHARMACOLOGY. *Educ:* Case Inst Technol, BS, 34; Northwestern Univ, MS, 51, PhD(pharmacol), 53. *Prof Exp:* Res dir, F A Stresen-Reuter, Ill, 48-50; from instr to assoc prof pharmacol, Med Sch, Northwestern Univ, 53-65; actg chief, Pharmacol Lab, 65-66, chief, 66-80, CONSULT RES PHARMACOLOGIST, RUSSELL RES CTR, WESTERN REGIONAL LAB, USDA, 80- *Concurrent Pos:* Consult, Sherwin-Williams Co, Ohio, 53-; USPHS sr res fel, 59-64. *Mem:* AAAS; Soc Exp Biol & Med; Am Soc Pharmacol & Exp Therapeut; Am Chem Soc. *Res:* Mechanism of action of the cardiac glycosides; chemical pharmacology; biological effects of aflatoxins and other mycotoxins. *Mailing Add:* 4275 Old Lexington Rd Athens GA 30605

KEYL, MILTON JACK, b Decatur, Ill, Mar 5, 24; m 48; c 2. PHYSIOLOGY. *Educ:* Univ Cincinnati, BS, 47, MS, 48, PhD(physiol), 57. *Prof Exp:* Asst pharmacologist res, Wm S Merrell Co, 48-52; from asst prof to assoc prof, 57-66, PROF PHYSIOL, MED CTR, UNIV OKLA, 66- *Mem:* Soc Exp Biol & Med; Am Physiol Soc; Am Soc Nephrology; Int Soc Lymphology. *Res:* Renal excretion of organic acids and bases; physiology and pharmacology of choline esters and inorganic ion metabolism; lymphatics. *Mailing Add:* Dept Physiol Univ Okla Med Ctr Box 26901 Oklahoma City OK 73190

KEYNES, HARVEY BAYARD, b Philadelphia, Pa, Dec 27, 40; m 64. MATHEMATICS. *Educ:* Univ Pa, BA, 62, MA, 63; Wesleyan Univ, PhD(math), 66. *Prof Exp:* Asst prof math, Univ Calif, Santa Barbara, 66-68; vis asst prof, 68-69, from asst prof to assoc prof, 69-78, PROF MATH, UNIV MINN, MINNEAPOLIS, 78-, ASSOC HEAD MATH, 79- *Concurrent Pos:* Trainee math, US Naval Air Develop Ctr, Pa, summers 58-62; NSF grants, summers, 67-; HEW grant, 73-75. *Mem:* AAAS; Am Math Soc; Fedn Am Scientists. *Res:* Topological dynamics; dynamical systems; ergodic theory. *Mailing Add:* Dept of Math Univ of Minn Minneapolis MN 55455

KEYS, ANCEL (BENJAMIN), b Colorado Springs, Colo, Jan 26, 04; m 39; c 3. PHYSIOLOGY, NUTRITION. *Educ:* Univ Calif, BA, 25, MS, 29, PhD(biol), 30; Cambridge Univ, PhD(physiol), 38. *Prof Exp:* Asst, Scripps Inst, Univ Calif, 27-30; Nat Res Coun fel, Copenhagen Univ, 30-31; Nat Res Coun fel, Cambridge Univ, 31-32, lectr & demonstr physiol, 32-33; instr biochem sci, Harvard Univ, 33-36; asst prof biochem, Mayo Found, 36-37, from assoc prof to prof physiol, 37-46, prof physiol hyg, 46-75, dir lab physiol hyg, 39-75, EMER PROF PHYSIOL HYG, UNIV MINN, MINNEAPOLIS, 75- *Concurrent Pos:* Res assoc, Oceanog Int, Woods Hole, 33-34; mgr, Int High Altitude Exped, Chile, 35; sr Fulbright fel, Oxford Univ, 51-52; USPHS spec fel, 63-64; consult, UN, WHO, Food & Agr Orgn & UNESCO, 50- *Mem:* AAAS; Am Physiol Soc; Am Inst Nutrit; Am Soc Clin Nutrit; Int Soc Cardiol. *Res:* Epidemiology; cardiology. *Mailing Add:* Lab of Physiol Hyg Univ of Minn Minneapolis MN 55455

KEYS, CHARLES EVEREL, b Wis, May 10, 21; m 43; c 3. VERTEBRATE EMBRYOLOGY. *Educ:* Greenville Col, AB, 43; Univ Kans, PhD(zool), 52. *Prof Exp:* Asst zool, Greenville Col, 42-43; asst, Atomic Energy Proj, Univ Kans, 50-51; from asst prof to prof biol, Asbury Col, 51-56; assoc prof & chmn div sci & math, Wesleyan Col, NY, 56-60; prof biol, Asbury Col, 60-64 & Florence State Col, 64-68; prof & chmn dept, Seattle Pac Col, 68-71; PROF BIOL, UNIV N ALA, 71- *Concurrent Pos:* Asst, Univ Kans, 51-56; vis prof, Malone Col, 62; chairperson, Health Professions Adv Comt & coordr gen biol, Univ NAla. *Mem:* Sigma Xi. *Res:* Comparative development of rodents; gametogenesis and early development of fish. *Mailing Add:* Dept of Biol Univ NAla Florence AL 35630

KEYS, JOHN DAVID, b Toronto, Ont, Sept 30, 22; m 45; c 2. PHYSICS. *Educ:* McGill Univ, BSc, 47, MSc, 48, PhD(nuclear physics), 51. *Prof Exp:* From asst prof to prof physics, Can Serv Col, Royal Roads, 51-58, head dept, 57-58; sr sci off, Dept Energy, Mines & Resources, Ont, 58-67, head mineral physics sect, 63-67, chief hydrol sci div, Inland Waters Br, 67-70; sci adv, Treasury Bd Secretariat, 70-71; asst vpres, Nat Res Coun Can, 71-73, vpres, 73-76; asst dep minister, Sci & Technol Sector, Dept Energy, 76-81; CONSULT, 81- *Mem:* AAAS; Am Phys Soc; Can Asn Physicists; Royal Astron Soc. *Res:* Application of radiotracers to industrial problems associated with mining; solid state physics studies applied to minerals and semiconductors. *Mailing Add:* 22 Oaklands Ave Toronto ON M4V 2E5 Can

KEYS, LLOYD KENNETH, b Cincinnati, Ohio, Nov 6, 39; m 61. SOLID STATE PHYSICS. *Educ:* Univ Cincinnati, BS, 61; Pa State Univ, PhD(solid state sci), 65. *Prof Exp:* AEC fel, Mat Res Lab, Pa State Univ, 65-66; prin engr, Nuclear Systs Progs, Gen Elec Co, Ohio, 66-69; chem engr, Magnavox Co, 69-71, mgr advan microelectronic develop lab, 71-74; mgr advan microelectronics eng, Bell Northern Res Labs, 74-76; MGR MFG TECHNOL, NORTHERN TELECOMMUN LTD, 76- *Mem:* AAAS; NY Acad Sci; sr mem Inst Elec & Electronics Eng; Int Soc Hybrid Microelectronics. *Res:* Magnetic properties of solids; analytical-physical chemical instrumental analysis; neutron damage to materials; thin-film deposition; thick film screen printing; hybrid microelectronics; stripline printed circuit boards; micromin. *Mailing Add:* Northern Telecommun Ltd PO Box 3116 Sta C Ottawa ON K1Y 4J4 Can

KEYS, RICHARD TAYLOR, b Salina, Kans, Feb 11, 31; m 55. PHYSICAL CHEMISTRY. *Educ:* Harvard Univ, AB, 53; Iowa State Col, PhD(chem), 58. *Prof Exp:* Asst chem, Iowa State Col, 53-58; res fel, Calif Inst Technol, 58-59; from asst prof to assoc prof, 59-72, PROF CHEM, CALIF STATE UNIV, LOS ANGELES, 72- *Concurrent Pos:* NIH spec fel, Univ Calif, Riverside, 66-67; vis prof, Nat Univ Mex, 75-76. *Mem:* Am Chem Soc; Am Phys Soc. *Res:* Chemistry of free radicals; magnetic resonance. *Mailing Add:* Dept of Chem Calif State Univ Los Angeles CA 90032

KEYS, THOMAS EDWARD, b Greenville, Miss, Dec 2, 08; m 34; c 2. HISTORY OF MEDICINE. *Educ:* Beloit Col, AB, 31; Univ Chicago, MA, 34. *Hon Degrees:* ScD, Beloit Col, 72. *Prof Exp:* Order asst, Newberry Libr, Univ Chicago, 31-32; libr asst, Mayo Clin Libr, 34-35, ref librn, 35-42, librn, 46-69, sr libr consult & emer chmn, Mayo Found, 69-72, from asst prof to assoc prof hist med, Mayo Grad Sch Med, Univ Minn, 56-69, prof, 69-72, EMER PROF HIST MED, MAYO GRAD SCH MED, UNIV MINN & MAYO FOUND & MED LIBR CONSULT, MAYO CLIN LIBR, 73- *Concurrent Pos:* Hon consult, Army Med Libr, 46-50; mem, Bd Regents, Nat Libr Med, 59-62; spec lectr, Int Cong, Med Libr, Amsterdam, 69 & Int Cong Hist Med, London, 72; vis lectr, Univ Iceland Sch Med, 77, Univ Tra Wetwatersrant, Johannesburg, SAfrica & Capetown Univ, 79. *Honors & Awards:* George Dock Mem lectr, Univ Calif, 66. *Mem:* Hon mem Med Libr Asn (pres, 57-58); Am Asn Hist Med; Am Soc Anesthesiol. *Res:* History of anesthesia, cardiology, medical education and medical librarianship. *Mailing Add:* 1224 S Peninsula Dr Apt 108 Daytona Beach FL 32018

KEYSER, DAVID RICHARD, b Ft Wayne, Ind, Dec 5, 41; m 65; c 2. MECHANICAL ENGINEERING, APPLIED MATHEMATICS. *Educ:* Swarthmore Col, BS, 63; Univ Pa, MS, 65. *Prof Exp:* Res engr fluid dynamics & flow measurement, Naval Boiler & Turbine Lab, 65-68; res engr flow & temperature measurement, Naval Ship Eng Ctr, Philadelphia, 68-72, sr proj engr fluid dynamics & control systs, 72-81; AEROSPACE ENGR, NAVAL AIR DEVELOP CTR, WARMINSTER, PA, 81- *Concurrent Pos:* Mem, Govt Fluidics Coord Group, 72- *Mem:* Am Soc Mech Engrs. *Res:* Flight controls and flying qualities; advanced actuation systems; unsteady flow measurements; new methods of flow measurement. *Mailing Add:* 1358 Chinquapin Rd Churchville PA 18966

KEYSER, N(AAMAN) H(ENRY), b Philadelphia, Pa, Dec 5, 18; m 42; c 4. METALLURGY. *Educ:* Antioch Col, BS, 41; Ohio State Univ, MS, 43. *Prof Exp:* Res engr process metall, Battelle Mem Inst, 41-47; asst group leader fabrication group, Los Alamos Sci Lab, Univ Calif, 47-48; asst chief process metall, Battelle Mem Inst, 48-62; DIR RES, INTERLAKE INC, 62- *Concurrent Pos:* Consult, 80- *Mem:* Am Soc Metals; Am Foundrymen's Soc (secy, 48-60); Am Inst Mining, Metall & Petrol Engrs. *Res:* Economic studies and new processes for metals and inorganic chemicals using elevated temperatures produced by electric and blast furnaces; making, forming and treating of steel and steel products. *Mailing Add:* 122 W Walnut Hinsdale IL 60521

KEYSER, PAUL, b Camden, NJ, Feb 9, 42. MICROBIOLOGY. *Educ:* Univ Miami, BS, 71, MS, 74, PhD(microbiol), 76. *Prof Exp:* RES ASSOC, INT PAPER CO, 78- *Concurrent Pos:* Waksman fel, Am Soc Microbiol Found, 73, 74 & 75; res assoc, USDA Forest Prod Lab, Madison, Wis, 76-77 & Dept Bact, Univ Wis, 76-77. *Mem:* Am Soc Microbiol; Soc Gen Microbiol; Soc Indust Microbiol. *Res:* Microbial physiology and enzymology involving the dissimilation of natural and synthetic aromatic compounds and polymers. *Mailing Add:* Corp Res Ctr Int Paper Co PO Box 797 Tuxedo Park NY 10987

KEYSER, PETER D, b Columbus, Ohio, Oct 26, 45; m 69; c 1. MEDICAL MICROBIOLOGY. *Educ:* Ohio State Univ, BS, 68, MS, 70, PhD(microbiol), 72. *Prof Exp:* Res fel microbiol, Univ Ky & Fla State Univ, 72-73; asst prof microbiol, 73-81, ASST PROF MICROBIOL & IMMUNOL, TEX COL OSTEOP MED, NORTH TEX STATE UNIV HEALTH SCI CTR, 81-, ADJ PROF BIOL SCI, 75- *Mem:* Sigma Xi; Am Soc Microbiol. *Res:* Role of lipases in pathogenicity of gram negative organisms, particularly those species isolated from burn wound sepsis. *Mailing Add:* 2309 Bowling Green Denton TX 76201

KEYSER, WILLIAM LACY, b Ardmore, Pa, Nov 18, 38; m 65; c 2. FOOD SCIENCE. *Educ:* Del Valley Col, BS, 61; Cornell Univ, MS, 64, PhD(dairy chem), 69. *Prof Exp:* Proj leader process develop, Kellogg Co, 67-69; group leader, 69-71, sr group leader, 71-74, sect mgr, 74-75, MGR FOOD RES, JOHN STUART LABS, QUAKER OATS CO, 75- *Concurrent Pos:* Alt counr, Chicago Sect, Inst Food Technologists, 76-79. *Mem:* AAAS; Am Dairy Sci Asn; Inst Food Technologists. *Res:* Mechanism of the Whiteside Test for detecting mastitis in cows; changes in casein bound water during Rennet curd syneresis; development and scale up of highly nutritious new food products and application of new technology to established products. *Mailing Add:* Quaker Oats Co 617 W Main St Barrington IL 60010

KEYT, DONALD E, b Indianapolis, Ind, Oct 30, 27; m 53; c 3. MECHANICAL ENGINEERING. *Educ:* Purdue Univ, BS, 50; Mass Inst Technol, MS, 53. *Prof Exp:* Design & res engr, Arthur D Little, Inc, 52-62; asst prof mech eng, Towne Sch Civil & Mech Eng, Univ Pa, 62-69; PROF & CHMN DEPT MECH ENG, SPRING GARDEN COL, 69- *Concurrent Pos:* Design consult, High Field Magnet Lab, Univ Pa, 63, lectr, 69-; design engr, HEFLEX Proj, Space Lab I, 78- *Mem:* Am Soc Eng Educ; Am Soc Mech Engrs; Instrument Soc Am. *Res:* Ultrahigh field electromagnet design, development and research; numerical solution of engineering problems; compressor design and development; instrumentation and control applied to systems; machine design. *Mailing Add:* 1196 Skippack Rd Harleysville PA 19438

KEYWORTH, DONALD ARTHUR, b Flint, Mich, Apr 21, 30. ANALYTICAL CHEMISTRY. *Educ:* Univ Mich, BS, 51; Mich State Univ, MS, 54; Wayne State Univ, PhD(chem), 58. *Prof Exp:* Chief anal controls, Lapaco Chem Co, Mich, 51-52; anal chemist, Ethyl Corp, Mich, 54 & Wyandotte Chem Co, 58-60; asst res dir, Universal Oil Prod Co, 60-67, vpres & tech dir, Sci & Educ Serv, 67-68; mgr res, Tenneco Chem, Tenneco Inc, 68-80; MGR RES, PETRO-TEX CHEM CORP, 80- *Concurrent Pos:* Instr, Wayne State Univ, 57-60. *Honors & Awards:* Res Award, Sigma Xi, 68. *Mem:* Am Soc Testing & Mat; Am Chem Soc; Soc Appl Spectros; NY Acad Sci. *Res:* Industrial research; methods and techniques of analysis of indutrial products, acetylenics synthesis and manufacturing; industrial utilization of pi-complexes; chemical technician training. *Mailing Add:* 5324 Dora Houston TX 77005

KEYWORTH, GEORGE A, II, b Boston, Mass, Nov 30, 39; m 62; c 2. EXPERIMENTAL NUCLEAR PHYSICS. *Educ:* Yale Univ, BS, 63; Duke Univ, PhD(physics), 68. *Prof Exp:* Res assoc, Duke Univ, 68; staff mem, Los Alamos Sci Lab, 68-74, group leader, 74-78, alt physics div leader & physics div leader, 78-81, laser fusion div leader, 80-81; DIR, OFF SCI & TECHNOL POLICY & SCI ADV TO PRESIDENT, 81- *Mem:* AAAS; Am Phys Soc; Sigma Xi. *Res:* Nuclear structure problems; isobaric analogue states; polarization experiments; fission physics; neutron physics; fusion physics; science policy. *Mailing Add:* Sci Adv to Pres The White House Washington DC 20500

KEYZER, HENDRIK, b Djakarta, Indonesia, Dec 7, 31; m 54; c 7. PHYSICAL CHEMISTRY, SOLID STATE CHEMISTRY. *Educ:* Univ NSW, BS, 63, PhD(chem), 66. *Prof Exp:* Res chemist, Mus Appl Arts & Sci, 62-63; lectr, Sydney Tech Col, 64-66; univ fel & NIH fel, 67, res grant, 67-68, from asst prof to assoc prof, 67-79, PROF CHEM, CALIF STATE UNIV, LOS ANGELES, 79- *Concurrent Pos:* NIMH res grant, 68-69 & 71-72; consult, Jet Propulsion Lab, 68-; reader, Victoria Univ, Wellington, 72-73; Health & Human Welfare, res grant, 76-80. *Honors & Awards:* NASA Award, 71. *Mem:* Am Chem Soc; Australian & NZ Asn Advan Sci; fel NZ Inst Chem. *Res:* Physical-organic chemistry of natural compounds and compounds of biological importance; psychotropic drugs; polymer chemistry; electrochemistry; micro-analysis. *Mailing Add:* Dept of Chem Calif State Univ Los Angeles CA 90032

KEZDI, PAUL, b Hungary, Nov 13, 14; nat US; m 43, 65; c 3. CARDIOLOGY. *Educ:* Pazmany Peter Univ, Budapest, MD, 42; Am Bd Internal Med, dipl, 61. *Prof Exp:* Dir heart sta, Wesley Mem Hosp, Chicago, Ill, 54-65; dir prof med, Wright State Univ, 75-77; dir res, 65-67, DIR, COX HEART INST, 67-; ASSOC DEAN RES AFFAIRS, WRIGHT STATE UNIV SCH MED, 77- *Concurrent Pos:* Am Heart Asn fel clin cardiol; assoc prof, Sch Med, Northwestern Univ, 62; mem, Med Adv Bd, Coun High Blood Pressue Res, Am Heart Asn, 63; prof med, Ind Univ, 65-72; clin prof, Ohio State Univ, 65-75. *Mem:* Fel Am Col Chest Physicians; fel Am Col Cardiol; Am Physiol Soc; Am Fedn Clin Res; Am Heart Asn. *Res:* Cardiac physiology; coronary artery disease; hypertension. *Mailing Add:* Cox Heart Inst 3525 Southern Blvd Dayton OH 45429

KEZDY, FERENC J, b Budapest, Hungary, July 28, 29; m 58; c 3. BIOCHEMISTRY. *Educ:* Univ Louvain, DrSci(phys org chem), 57. *Prof Exp:* Asst phys & org chem, Univ Louvain, 57-61; assoc biochem, Northwestern Univ, 61-65; from asst prof to assoc prof, 66-71, PROF BIOCHEM, UNIV CHICAGO, 71- *Honors & Awards:* Stas-Spring Prize, Belg Royal Acad Sci, 58; Woutes Prize, Chem Soc Belg, 60. *Mem:* Am Chem Soc; Am Assoc Adv Sci; Chem Soc Fr; Soc African Insect Scientists. *Res:* Physical organic chemistry; surface biochemistry; enzymology. *Mailing Add:* Dept of Biochem Univ of Chicago Chicago IL 60637

KEZIOS, STOTHE PETER, b Chicago, Ill, Apr 8, 21; m 52; c 1. THERMODYNAMICS. *Educ:* Ill Inst Technol, BS, 42, MS, 48, PhD(mech eng), 55. *Prof Exp:* Asst instr mech eng, Ill Inst Technol, 42-44, instr, 46-47, res engr, 47-49, from asst prof to prof, 49-67, dir heat transfer lab, 55-68; PROF MECH ENG & DIR, SCH MECH ENG, GA INST TECHNOL, 67- *Concurrent Pos:* Consult govt & indust, 48-; vchmn, Nat Heat Transfer Conf, 58; consult ed, J Heat Transfer, 58-63, tech ed, 63-; secy, Int Heat Transfer Conf, 61-62, adv orgn comt, 66; Am Soc Mech Eng rep, Comt Int Rels, Eng, Joint Coun, 62-; mem sci adv panel, Eng Sect, NSF, 63-66. *Honors & Awards:* Ralph Coates Roe award, Am Soc Eng Educ, 77. *Mem:* Am Soc Mech Engrs (secy, 53-57, vpres, 73-77, pres, 77-78); Am Soc Eng Educ; Am Inst Chem Engrs; Sigma Xi. *Res:* Heat transfer; analogy between heat and mass transfer; forced convection heat transfer, especially with free jets; boiling in forced convection flow. *Mailing Add:* 1060 Winding Creek Trail NW Atlanta GA 30328

KEZLAN, THOMAS PHILLIP, b Omaha, Nebr, Aug 6, 35. MATHEMATICS. *Educ:* Univ Omaha, 57; Univ Kans, MA, 59, PhD(math), 64. *Prof Exp:* Asst prof math, Univ Mo, Kansas City, 63-64; asst prof, Univ Tex, Austin, 64-68; ASSOC PROF MATH, UNIV MO-KANSAS CITY, 68- *Mem:* Math Asn Am; Am Math Soc. *Res:* Theory of rings. *Mailing Add:* Dept of Math Univ of Mo Kansas City MO 64110

KHABBAZ, SAMIR ANTON, b Tel Aviv, Palestine, Mar 31, 32; US citizen; m 59; c 3. MATHEMATICS. *Educ:* Bethel Col, BA, 54; Univ Kans, MA, 56, PhD, 60. *Prof Exp:* Instr math, Univ Mass, 60; asst prof, Lehigh Univ, 60-62; Off Naval Res res fel, Yale Univ, 62-63; univ res fel, 63-64; assoc prof, 64-68, PROF MATH, LEHIGH UNIV, 66- *Mem:* Am Math Soc. *Res:* Algebra and topology. *Mailing Add:* Dept of Math Lehigh Univ Bethlehem PA 18015

KHACHADURIAN, AVEDIS K, b Aleppo, Syria, Jan 6, 26; m 61; c 2. MEDICINE. *Educ:* Am Univ Beirut, BA, 49, MD, 53. *Prof Exp:* Resident internal med, Am Univ Beirut, 53-56, fel biochem, 56-57, from asst prof to prof biochem & internal med, Sch Med, 59-71; lectr pediat, Northwestern Univ, Chicago, 65-66, prof, 71-73; dir, Clin Res Ctr, Children's Mem Hosp, 71-73; PROF MED, COL MED & DENT NJ-RUTGERS MED SCH, 73-,

CHIEF DIV ENDOCRINE & METAB DIS, 73- *Concurrent Pos:* Res fel, New Eng Deaconess Hosp & Joslin Clin, Mass, 57-59; mem, Gulbenkian Found & Int Conf Biochem Lipids. *Mem:* Am Diabetes Asn; Endocrine Soc; Am Fedn Clin Res; Am Heart Asn; NY Acad Sci. *Res:* Adipose tissue metabolism; inborn errors of metabolism and hyperlipidemias. *Mailing Add:* Dept of Med Col Med & Dent of NJ Rutgers Med Sch PO Box 101 Piscataway NJ 08854

KHACHATURIAN, NARBEY, b Teheran, Iran, Jan 12, 24; nat US; m 52; c 4. CIVIL ENGINEERING, STRUCTURAL ENGINEERING. *Educ:* Univ Ill, BS, 47, MS, 48, PhD(eng), 52. *Prof Exp:* From instr to assoc prof, 49-60, PROF CIVIL ENG, UNIV ILL, URBANA, 60- *Concurrent Pos:* NSF sr fel, Univ Calif, Los Angeles, 63-64; chmn, Ill Struct Engr Examining Comt, 71. *Mem:* Fel Am Soc Civil Engrs; Am Soc Eng Educ; Am Concrete Inst; Nat Soc Prof Engrs; Sigma Xi. *Res:* Experimental and analytical structural engineering, especially reinforced and prestressed concrete; structural optimization; structural concrete. *Mailing Add:* 3129 Civil Eng Bldg Univ of Ill Urbana IL 61801

KHACHATURIAN, ZAVEN SETRAK, b Allepo, Syria, Apr 15, 37; US citizen; m 63; c 1. NEUROSCIENCE. *Educ:* Yale Univ, BA, 61; Case Western Reserve Univ, PhD(neurobiol), 67. *Prof Exp:* Fel neurophysiol, Col Physicians & Surgeons, Columbia Univ, 67-69; asst prof develop neurobiol, Div Child Psychiatry, Med Sch, Univ Pittsburgh, 69-72, prog dir neurophysiol, Dept Psychiatry, 72-77; grants assoc, Div Res Grants, NIH, 77-78; prog dir, Neurosci Aging, Nat Inst Aging, NIH, 78-79; health policy coordr, Off Secy, Dept Health, Educ & Welfare, 79-80; spec asst dir, 80-81, CHIEF, PHYSIOL AGING BR, NAT INST AGING, NIH, 81- *Mem:* Soc Neurosci. *Res:* Role of thalamic nuclei in gating sensory information particularly auditory and visual stimuli; neuroscience of aging; neural plasticity; science policy. *Mailing Add:* Nat Inst Aging Bldg 31-C NIH Bethesda MD 20205

KHADJAVI, ABBAS, b Tehran, Iran, Feb 12, 38; US citizen; m 67; c 1. ATOMIC PHYSICS, OPTICS. *Educ:* Univ Wis-Madison, BA, 61; Columbia Univ, MA, 64, PhD(physics), 67. *Prof Exp:* Asst physics, Columbia Univ, 63-65 & IBM Watson Lab, 65-67; sr scientist, Westinghouse Res Labs, 67-69; fel chem, Columbia Univ, 69-70; asst prof, 70-76, ASSOC PROF PHYSICS, FAIRFIELD UNIV, 76- *Mem:* Am Phys Soc. *Res:* Interaction of radiation and matter; coherence effects in atomic and molecular fluorescence; plasma physics; laser technology and application of lasers to molecular spectroscopy; interferometry. *Mailing Add:* 2576 Redding Rd Fairfield CT 06430

KHAIRALLAH, EDWARD A, b Beirut, Lebanon, Jan 9, 36; US citizen; m 62; c 2. ENDOCRINOLOGY, NUTRITIONAL BIOCHEMISTRY. *Educ:* Am Univ, Beirut, BSc, 56; Harvard Univ, MA, 59; Mass Inst Technol, PhD(nutrit, biochem), 64. *Prof Exp:* Instr physiol chem, Mass Inst Technol, 64-66; NIH res fel, McArdle Labs, Univ Wis, 66-67; asst prof biochem, 67-69, assoc prof biochem & biophysics, 69-74, prof biochem & biophysics, 74-81, PROF BIOL, UNIV CONN, 81- *Mem:* AAAS; Am Inst Nutrit; Endocrine Soc; NY Acad Sci; Am Soc Biol Chem. *Res:* Hormonal and dietary regulation of protein synthesis and degradation in mammalian cells; amino acid compartmentation; translational mechanisms regulating gluconeogenic and amino acid catabolizing enzymes. *Mailing Add:* Dept of Biol Sci Box 125 Univ of Conn Storrs CT 06268

KHAIRALLAH, PHILIP ASAD, b New York, NY, Feb 3, 28. PHYSIOLOGY, PHARMACOLOGY. *Educ:* Am Univ Beirut, BA, 47; Columbia Univ, MD, 51. *Prof Exp:* Am Heart Asn estab investr, Found, 58-63, mem staff, Res Div, 63-70, SCI DIR, RES DIV & HEAD DEPT CARDIOVASC RES, CLEVELAND CLIN FOUND, 70- *Concurrent Pos:* Am Heart Asn fel, Duke Univ, 51-53, Cleveland Clin Found, 56-57 & Am Univ Beirut, 57-58; adj prof, John Carroll Univ & Cleveland State Univ; mem, Coun High Blood Pressure Res, Am Heart Asn. *Mem:* Am Soc Pharmacol & Exp Therapeut; Am Physiol Soc; Am Soc Nephrology; AMA. *Res:* Cardiovascular research in biochemistry, physiology and pharmacology; cardiac and blood vessel contraction; medical ethics. *Mailing Add:* Cleveland Clin Found 9500 Euclid Ave Cleveland OH 44106

KHALAF, KAMEL T, b Mosul, Iraq, 1922; m 58; c 3. ZOOLOGY, MEDICAL ENTOMOLOGY. *Educ:* Univ Baghdad, BS, 44; Univ Okla, MS, 50, PhD(zool), 52. *Prof Exp:* Instr high teachers col, Univ Baghdad, 53-56, from asst prof to prof, 56-62, res prof, Iraq Natural Hist Inst, 62-63; from asst prof to assoc prof, 63-69, PROF ENTOM, LOYOLA UNIV, LA, 69- *Concurrent Pos:* NIH res grant, 65-68; Edward G Schlieder Educ Found res grant, 69-71. *Res:* Surveys of biting gnats; biology of puss caterpillar and its parasites; animal surveys; micromorphology of Anthropods Integument. *Mailing Add:* Dept of Biol Sci Loyola Univ New Orleans LA 70118

KHALAFALLA, SANAA E, b Mit Yaish, Egypt, July 1, 24; US citizen; m 56; c 2. PHYSICAL CHEMISTRY, CHEMICAL METALLURGY. *Educ:* Cairo Univ, BSc, 44; Univ Minn, Minneapolis, MS, 49, PhD(phys chem), 53. *Prof Exp:* Demonstr chem fac sci, Cairo Univ, 44-48, from asst prof to assoc prof phys chem, 53-61; Hill Family Found res fel & res assoc, Univ Minn, 61-64; proj leader, 64-66, RES SUPVR, TWIN CITIES METALL RES CTR, BUR MINES, US DEPT INTERIOR, 66- *Concurrent Pos:* Vis prof, Bristol Univ, 60-61. *Honors & Awards:* Spec Act of Serv Award, Twin Cities Metall Res Ctr, US Bur Mines, 66. *Mem:* Am Inst Mining, Metall & Petrol Engrs; Am Inst Elec & Electronics Engrs. *Res:* Process and extractive metallurgy; kinetics and mechanisms of metallurgical reactions; electrochemistry and polarography; catalytic reactions; magneto chemistry; plasma chemistry; leaching processes; asbestos fibers; mine wastes; magnetic fluids; water conservation; minerals and mining. *Mailing Add:* Twin Cities Res Ctr Bur of Mines PO Box 1660 Twin Cities MN 55111

KHALED, MOHAMMED ABU, b Murshidabad, India, Nov 1, 42; Bangladesh citizen; m 76. BIOPHYSICS, PHYSICAL CHEMISTRY. *Educ:* Univ Calcutta, BSc, 61; Aligarh Muslim Univ, India, MSc, 64; Univ London, PhD(biophys, chem), 75. *Prof Exp:* Lectr chem, Polytech Inst, Chittagong, Bangladesh, 64-65; lectr, Cadet Col, Rajshahi, Bangladesh, 66-71; fel, 75-77, instr, 77-78, ASST PROF BIOCHEM, UNIV ALA, 78- *Mem:* Sigma Xi. *Res:* Spectroscopic approach in determining biomolecular conformations and structure-function relationships. *Mailing Add:* Dept of Biochem Univ of Ala Birmingham Med Ctr Birmingham AL 35294

KHALIFAH, RAJA GABRIEL, b Tripoli, Lebanon, May 5, 42; m 71. CHEMISTRY, BIOCHEMISTRY. *Educ:* Am Univ Beirut, BS, 62; Princeton Univ, PhD(phys chem), 69. *Prof Exp:* Res assoc biochem, Harvard Univ, 68-70; res assoc pharmacol, Sch Med, Stanford Univ, 70-73; asst prof chem, Univ Va, 73-80; MEM STAFF, VET ADMIN MED CTR, 80- *Mem:* Am Chem Soc; Am Soc Biol Chemists. *Res:* Biophysical chemistry; kinetics and thermodynamics of protein conformation changes; enzyme kinetics and mechanism; chemical modification of active sites; nuclear magnetic resonance applications to proteins and enzymes. *Mailing Add:* Vet Admin Med Ctr 4801 Linwood Blvd Kansas City MO 64128

KHALIL, HATEM MOHAMED, b Cairo, Egypt, July 2, 35. COMPUTER SCIENCE. *Educ:* Victoria Univ Manchester, BSc, 62; Rice Univ, MS, 64; Univ Del, PhD(comput sci), 69; London, FBCS, 72. *Prof Exp:* Analyst eng mech, Brown & Root, Inc, Tex, 64-65, consult, Marine Eng Div, 65-66; comput programmer analyst, 66-69, from asst prof to assoc prof comput sci, 69-75, chmn comput sci, 78-81, PROF COMPUT SCI, UNIV DEL, 75- *Concurrent Pos:* Univ Del Res Found grants, Univ Del, 71-73; consult, Am Univ Cairo, 74-; vis prof, Cairo Univ, 75. *Mem:* AAAS; Asn Comput Mach; Brit Comput Soc. *Res:* Computer systems and computer science education. *Mailing Add:* Dept of Comput & Info Sci Univ of Del Newark DE 19711

KHALIL, M ASLAM KHAN, b Jhansi, India, Jan 7, 50; Pakistan citizen; m 73. ATMOSPHERIC CHEMISTRY. *Educ:* Univ Minn, BPhys, BA(math) & BA(psychol), 70; Va Polytech Inst & State Univ, MS, 72; Univ Tex, Austin, PhD(physics), 76; Ore Grad Ctr, MS & PhD(environ sci), 79. *Prof Exp:* Teach asst physics, Va Polytech Inst & State Univ, 70-71; teaching asst physics & math, Univ Tex, Austin, 71-73, res scientist asst physics, 73-76; res asst, 77-79, sr res assoc, 79-80, ASST PROF ENVIRON SCI, ORE GRAD CTR, 78- *Concurrent Pos:* Instr physics, Pac Univ, 77-78; NSF & NASA co-prin investr, 80-; consult & owner, Andarz Co, 81- *Res:* Cycles of natural and man-made gases in the earth's atmosphere; elementary particles with spin (theoretical physics); author or co-author of more than 30 publications. *Mailing Add:* Dept Environ Sci Ore Grad Ctr 19600 NW Walker Rd Beaverton OR 97006

KHALIL, MOHAMED THANAA, b Al-Kosair, Egypt, Feb 8, 33; m 60; c 2. BIOPHYSICS, MATHEMATICS. *Educ:* Cairo Univ, BSc, 53; Univ Pittsburgh, BS, 74, PhD(biophys), 66; Univ Alexandria, MSc, 61. *Prof Exp:* Instr & res asst physics, Univ Alexandria, 53-61; res assoc biophys, Univ Pittsburgh, 61-66, res prof biophys & microbiol, 66-71; from asst prof to prof phys sci, 69-74, dean int students, 74-77, PROF NATURAL SCI & ENG TECHNOL, POINT PARK COL, 74- *Mem:* AAAS; Biophys Soc; NY Acad Sci; Am Chem Soc; Am Inst Physics. *Res:* Effect of laser beam on the system of polymerization of virus protein; thermodynamics of the reconstitution of virus particles in deuterim; structure and function of tobacco mosaic virus interferon and plant viruses. *Mailing Add:* Dept of Natural Sci & Eng Technol Point Park Col Pittsburgh PA 15222

KHALIL, MUHAMMAD AHSAN KHAN, b Shahjahanpur, India, July 5, 18; Can Citizen; m 42; c 3. QUANTITATIVE GENETICS, BIOMETRICS. *Educ:* Muslim Univ, Aligarh, India, BSc, 37, MSc, 39; Indian Forest Col & Res Inst, Dehradun, AIFC, 42; Univ Minn, St Paul, PhD(forest genetics), 67. *Prof Exp:* Asst conservator forests, United Prov Forest Serv, Lucknow, India, 42-45, dep conservator forests, 45-50 & Gov Pakistan, Karachi, 51-53; prof forestry, Pakistan Forest Inst, Peshawar, 53-56, cent silviculturist, 56-58, dir, 58-60; dir, Pakistan Forest Res Inst, Chittagong, 60-63; res assoc, Univ Minn, St Paul, 67-69; asst prof, Lakehead Univ, 69-71; RES SCIENTIST GENETICS, NFLD FOREST RES CTR, CAN FORESTRY SERV, ENVIRON CAN, 71- *Concurrent Pos:* Ed, Pakistan J Forestry, 58-60. *Mem:* Soc Am Foresters; Am Inst Biol Sci; Can Inst Forestry; Sigma Xi; Can Tree Improvement Asn. *Res:* Study of variation patterns and genetic parameters of Picea glauca, P mariana, P rubens and P sitchensis; clonal trials of hybrids of Populus species to determine suitability for different environments; forest biomass for energy. *Mailing Add:* Nfld Forest Res Centre Can Forestry Serv Box 6028 St John's NT A1A 2M2 Can

KHALIL, SHOUKRY KHALIL WAHBA, b Cairo, Egypt, Dec 7, 30; US citizen; m 64. PHARMACOGNOSY. *Educ:* Cairo Univ, BPharm & Pharm Chem, 53, MPharm, 56, PhD(pharmacog), 60. *Prof Exp:* From instr to assoc prof pharmacog, Cairo Univ, 54-68; from asst prof to assoc prof, 68-75, PROF PHARMACOG, N DAK STATE UNIV, 75- *Concurrent Pos:* Egyptian govt fel, Univ Mich, Ann Arbor, 62-63. *Mem:* Am Pharmaceut Asn; Am Soc Pharmacog; Soc Cosmetic Chemists. *Res:* Plant chemistry; analysis of medicinal plants. *Mailing Add:* 1801 11th Ave N Fargo ND 58102

KHALILI, ALI A, b Ardebil, Iran, Feb 9, 32; US citizen; m 62; c 2. REHABILITATION MEDICINE. *Educ:* Tehran Univ, MD, 57. *Prof Exp:* Instr phys med & rehab, State Univ NY Downstate Med Ctr, 62-65; asst prof, Med Ctr, 65-68, dir residency prog phys med & rehab, 67-69, ASSOC PROF PHYS MED & REHAB, McGAW MED CTR, NORTHWESTERN UNIV, 68-; DIR REHAB MED, GRANT HOSP, CHICAGO, 68-, CHMN, DEPT REHAB MED, 77- *Concurrent Pos:* Dir, Neuromuscular Diag & Res Dept, Rehab Inst Chicago, 68-70; consult psychiatrist, Mem Hosp DuPage County, 68- & Rehab Inst Chicago, 70-; chmn, Comt Allied Health Professions, Grant Hosp, Chicago, 73-75; chmn med pract comt, Am Acad Phys Med & Rehab, 79-80. *Mem:* AMA; Am Acad Phys Med & Rehab; Am Cong Rehab Med; Am Asn Electromyography & Electrodiag. *Res:* Spasticity and peripheral phenol nerve block (clinical, physiological and histological aspects, including electromyographic changes); radio-linked bladder stimulation in neurogenic bladder; burn rehabilitation; sensory input discrimination in normal and hemiplegic subjects. *Mailing Add:* Dept of Rehab Med Grant Hosp of Chicago Chicago IL 60614

KHAMIS, HARRY JOSEPH, b San Jose, Calif, Dec 20, 51. LOG-LINEAR MODEL THEORY. *Educ:* Santa Clara Univ, BS, 74; Va Tech, MS, 76, PhD(statist), 80. *Prof Exp:* ASST PROF MATH & STATIST, WRIGHT STATE UNIV, 80- *Mem:* Am Statist Asn; Biometric Soc. *Res:* Loglinear model analysis and applications to genetic data; goodness-of-fit tests. *Mailing Add:* 2170 Rockdell Dr Apt 15 Fairborn OH 45324

KHAN, ABDUL JAMIL, b Allahabad, India, May 5, 40; m 68; c 2. PEDIATRICS, MEDICINE. *Educ:* Univ Allahabad, BSc, 57; Univ Lucknow, MB & BS, 62; Agra Univ, DCH, 64; Panjab Univ, India, MD(pediat), 67. *Prof Exp:* Intern, King George Med Col, Univ Lucknow, 62-63; physician med & pediat, Northern Railway Hosp, India, 64-65; teaching fel pediat, Inst Post-Grad Med, Panjab Univ, India, 66-67; registr pediat Med Col, Aligarh Muslim Univ, India, 68-69; resident, Kings County, State Univ Hosp, Brooklyn, 69-70; fel, 71-73, CHIEF DIV PEDIAT NEPHROLOGY, JEWISH HOSP MED CTR, BROOKLYN, 73- *Concurrent Pos:* From instr to asst prof clin pediat, State Univ NY Downstate Med Ctr, 73-78, assoc prof, 78-; attending, Kings County, State Univ Hosp & Greenpoint Hosp, Brooklyn, 73-; consult pediat infectious dis, Jewish Hosp Med Ctr, 73- *Mem:* Am Fedn Clin Res; Soc Pediat Res; Am Soc Pediat Nephrology; Soc Exp Biol & Med; fel Am Acad Pediat. *Res:* White blood cell functions including Chemotaxis; studies on efficacy and pharmacokinetics of newer antibiotics; renal diseases in infants and children. *Mailing Add:* Jewish Hosp & Med Ctr 555 Prospect Pl Brooklyn NY 11238

KHAN, ABDUL WAHEED, b Lahore, WPakistan, Apr 16, 28; Can citizen; m 60; c 2. BIOCHEMISTRY, MICROBIOLOGY. *Educ:* Univ Panjab, Pakistan, MSc, 52, PhD(biochem), 56; Manchester Col Sci & Technol, Eng, PhD(microbiol), 58. *Prof Exp:* Res fel biochem, Univ Panjab, Pakistan, 52-54, lectr org chem, 54-55; res fel microbiol, Manchester Col Sci & Technol, Eng, 55-58; fel biophys, Div Biosci, 58-60, from asst res officer to assoc res officer, 60-72, SR RES OFFICER, DIV BIOSCI, NAT RES COUN CAN, 72- *Mem:* Inst Food Technologists; Can Biochem Soc; Can Soc Microbiol; fel Royal Soc Chem. *Res:* Conversion of biomass to fuels and chemical feed stock; anaerobic degradation of cellulose; methanogensis; meat biochemistry; effect of freezing and storage on muscle proteins; biosynthesis of cellulose; studies in bacterial cell wall components; microbiological synthesis of fat from carbohydrates; nutritive values of foods and dietary standards. *Mailing Add:* Div of Biol Sci Nat Res Coun Ottawa ON K1A 0R6 Can

KHAN, AKHTAR SALAMAT, b Aligarh, India, June 8, 44; m 72; c 2. SOLID MECHANICS, MECHANICAL ENGINEERING. *Educ:* Aligarh Muslim Univ, India, BS, 61, BS, 65; Johns Hopkins Univ, PhD(solid mech), 72. *Prof Exp:* Lectr mech eng, Aligarh Muslim Univ, India, 65-67; from res asst to res assoc mech, Johns Hopkins Univ, 67- 73; staff engr stress anal, Arthur McKee, Cleveland, 73-74; sr staff engr, Bechtel Power Corp, 74-78; asst prof, 78-81, ASSOC PROF AEROSPACE, MECH & NUCLEAR ENG, UNIV OKLA, 81- *Mem:* Am Soc Mech Engrs; Am Acad Mech; Soc Exp Stress Anal; Soc Natural Philos. *Res:* Dynamic and quasi-static behavior of metallic solids; finite amplitude wave propagation in solids; use of finite element techniques to study stresses in shell-to-shell intersections; fracture mechanics. *Mailing Add:* Dept Eng Univ Okla Norman OK 73019

KHAN, AMANULLAH RASHID, b Bhavnagar, India, Mar 1, 27; US citizen; m 52; c 2. CHEMICAL ENGINEERING. *Educ:* Univ Bombay, BS, 47; Ill Inst Technol, MS, 51. *Prof Exp:* Develop engr, Dry Freeze Corp, 51-52; res engr, Inst Gas Technol, Ill Inst Technol, 52-53; fel, French Petrol Inst, 53-54; supvr refinery processing, Attock Oil Co, 54-61; opers engr, Universal Oil Prod Co, 61-62; mgr gas opers res, 62-70, PRES, GAS DEVELOP CORP, INST GAS TECHNOL, ILL INST TECHNOL, 70- *Mem:* Am Chem Soc; Am Inst Chem Engrs; Am Gas Asn. *Res:* Liquefaction, storage and utilization of liquefied natural gas; gas distribution and transmission research; hydrocarbon processing. *Mailing Add:* Gas Develop Corp Inc 10 W 35th St Chicago IL 60616

KHAN, ANWAR AHMAD, b Monghyr, India, Oct 16, 34; m 67; c 2. PLANT PHYSIOLOGY, PLANT BIOCHEMISTRY. *Educ:* Univ Karachi, BS, 56, MS, 57; Univ Chicago, PhD(bot), 63. *Prof Exp:* Demonstr bot, Univ Karachi, 57-58; demonstr & lectr, Univ Sind, Pakistan, 58-60; res asst, Univ Chicago, 60-63; res assoc biochem, Mich State Univ, 63-65; from asst prof to assoc prof, 65-80, PROF SEED PHYSIOL, NY STATE AGR EXP STA, CORNELL UNIV, 80- *Concurrent Pos:* Am Seed Res Found res grants, 67-69 & 70-76; NSF traveling res fel, Univ Liege, Univ Ghent & Univ Clermont-Ferrand, 71-72; Herman Frasch Found grant agr chem, 72-76; Centre Nat de la Recherche res grant, Univ Clermont-Ferrand, France, 72; sr res fel, Agr Univ, Wageningen, Neth, 78; mem, UN Develop Prog, Pakistan, 81. *Mem:* AAAS; Am Soc Plant Physiologists; Scand Soc Plant Physiologists; Am Soc Hort Sci; Int Plant Growth Substances Asn. *Res:* Seed physiology and biochemistry; molecular biology; growth regulators. *Mailing Add:* Dept of Seed & Vegetable Sci NY State Agr Exp Sta Geneva NY 14456

KHAN, ATA M, b Khan, W Pakistan, Dec 15, 41; m 69. TRANSPORTATION & TRAFFIC ENGINEERING. *Educ:* Am Univ Beirut, BEng, 63, MEng, 65; Univ Waterloo, PhD(transp planning), 70. *Prof Exp:* Asst civil eng, Am Univ Beirut, 63-65; engr, Trans Arabian Pipeline Co, 64; transp engr, De Leuw, Cather & Co, Chicago, 65-67; teaching asst transp eng, Univ Waterloo, 67-69; asst prof, 69-77, ASSOC PROF ENG, CARLETON UNIV, 77- *Concurrent Pos:* Individual supporting mem, Hwy Res Bd, Nat Res Coun-Nat Acad Sci, 68-; spec consult, N D Lea & Assocs, 71; Nat Res Coun Can fel, 68-69. *Mem:* Assoc mem Am Soc Civil Engrs; jr mem Inst Traffic Eng. *Res:* Development of transport planning methodology for the evaluation of policy and investment alternatives and for the analysis of transport subsidy policy in Canada. *Mailing Add:* 145 Owl Dr Ottawa ON K1V 9J5 Can

KHAN, AUSAT ALI, b India, Mar 3, 39; m 65; c 2. ORGANIC CHEMISTRY, POLYMER CHEMISTRY. *Educ:* Aligarh Muslim Univ India, BSc, 57, MSc, 59; Nat Univ of the South, Arg, PhD(org chem), 62. *Prof Exp:* Asst prof org chem, Nat Univ Cordoba, 62-64; fel, Univ Del, 64-66; RES ASSOC, E I DU PONT DE NEMOURS & CO, INC, 66- *Mem:* NY Acad Sci; Am Chem Soc. *Res:* Fluorocarbon polymers and monomers; hydrocarbon rubbers; emulsion polymerization and colloidal stability of lattices. *Mailing Add:* Polymer Prod Dept E I du Pont de Nemours & Co Inc Wilmington DE 19898

KHAN, FAIZ MOHAMMAD, b Multan, Pakistan, Nov 1, 38; m 66; c 3. BIOPHYSICS, RADIOLOGICAL PHYSICS. *Educ:* Emerson Col, Multan, Pakistan, BSc, 57; Govt Col Lahore, MSc, 59; Univ Minn, Minneapolis, PhD(biophys), 69. *Prof Exp:* Health physicist, Radiother Inst, Mayo Hosp, Lahore, Pakistan, 60-63; instr radiol, 68-69, from asst prof to assoc prof, 69-79, PROF THERAPEUT RADIOL, UNIV MINN, MINNEAPOLIS, 79-, HEAD SECT RADIATION PHYSICS, 74- *Concurrent Pos:* Consult physicist, Vet Admin Hosp, Minneapolis, 71- *Mem:* Am Asn Physicists Med; Sigma Xi. *Res:* Radiation dosimetry and treatment techniques in radiation therapy; application of computers in radiotherapy; biological effects of radiation. *Mailing Add:* Dept of Therapeut Radiol Univ of Minn Hosps Minneapolis MN 55455

KHAN, FAZLUR R, b Dacca, Bangladesh, Apr 3, 29; nat US; m 59; c 1. STRUCTURAL ENGINEERING. *Educ:* Univ Dacca, BS, 50; Univ Ill, Struct Engr & MSSE, 52, MS & PhD, 55. *Hon Degrees:* ScD, Northwestern Univ, 73; DTech Sci, Swiss Fed Inst Technol, Zurich, 80; DEng, Lehigh Univ, 80. *Prof Exp:* Lectr, Univ Dacca, 50-52; proj engr, 55-57, sr proj engr, 60-65, assoc partner, 66-70, GEN PARTNER, SKIDMORE, OWINGS & MERRILL, 70- *Concurrent Pos:* Exec engr, Karachi Develop Authority, Pakistan, 58-60; adj prof archit, Ill Inst Technol, 66-; chmn, Int Coun on Tall Bldgs & Urban Habitat; designer struct syst for many high rise bldgs in cities worldwide. *Honors & Awards:* Middlebrooks Award, Am Soc Civil Engrs, 72; Oscar Faber Medal, Inst Struct Engrs, London, 73; J Lloyd Kimbrough Medal, Am Inst Steel Construct, 73; Alfred E Lindau Award, Am Concrete Inst, 73; Ernest E Howard Award, 77; G Brooks Earnest Award, Am Soc Civil Engrs, 79. *Mem:* Nat Acad Eng; Int Asn Bridge & Struct Engrs; fel Am Concrete Inst; Am Welding Soc; fel Am Soc Civil Engrs. *Mailing Add:* Skidmore Owings & Merrill 30 W Monroe St Chicago IL 60603

KHAN, JAMIL AKBER, b Hyderabad, Pakistan, Mar 17, 52. ORGANOMETALLIC CHEMISTRY. *Educ:* Univ Sind, Pakistan, BSc, 71, MSc, 73; Univ London, Eng, PhD(org chem), 79. *Prof Exp:* Chemist qual control, Eastman Chem Co, 73-74; lectr chem, D J Sci Col, Pakistan, 74-76; demonstr chem, Univ Col London, Eng, 76-79; res assoc chem, Duke Univ, 79-81; RES CHEMIST, UNIROYAL INC, 81- *Concurrent Pos:* Secy gen, Inst Pub Affairs, Pakistan, 75-78; joint secy, Sind Lectr Asn, 76-77. *Mem:* Am Chem Soc; Royal Soc Chem; Sigma Xi. *Res:* Synthesis and development of activators and catalysts, which can be used in polymerization, autoxidation of unsaturated fatty acids; synthesis of antioxidants, which can be used to inhibit the autoxidation of phospholipid biomembranes. *Mailing Add:* Uniroyal Inc World Headquarter Middlebury CT 06749

KHAN, JHAN M, b Tulare, Calif, Nov 8, 34; m 59; c 2. ATOMIC PHYSICS, SURFACE PHYSICS. *Educ:* Univ Calif, Berkeley, BA, 55, PhD(physics), 62. *Prof Exp:* Res physicist, Lawrence Livermore Nat Lab, 62-80; VPRES, DELPHIC ENG, INC, 80-, PRES, DELPHIC DEVELOP, INC, 81- *Mem:* Am Phys Soc; Am Vacuum Soc. *Res:* Surface and thin film phenomena; nucleation and growth studies; mechanical and optical properties; electron and ion interactions with surfaces; scanning high energy electron diffraction. *Mailing Add:* 1504 Franklin St Suite 303 Oakland CA 94612

KHAN, MAHMOOD AHMED, b Hyderabad, India, Sept 16, 45; m 75. FOOD SCIENCE, NUTRITION. *Educ:* Osmania Univ, BS, 66; Andhra Pradesh Agr Univ, BS, 69; La State Univ, MS, 72, PhD(food sci), 75. *Prof Exp:* Res asst food sci, La State Univ, 71-75; asst prof foods & nutrit, Albright Col, 75-78; ASST PROF FOODS & NUTRIT, UNIV ILL, URBANA, 78- *Mem:* Inst Food Technologists; Am Dietetic Asn; Coun Hotel, Restaurant & Inst Educ; Nat Restaurant Asn. *Res:* Food quality in food service systems; concepts of nutrition and obesity; nutritional evaluation of food processing; international food patterns; food habits; food service consultant. *Mailing Add:* Dept Foods & Nutrit Univ Ill 905 S Goodwin Urbana IL 61801

KHAN, MOHAMED SHAHEED, b Bloomfield, Guyana, Dec 29, 33; US citizen; m 58; c 3. PLANT PATHOLOGY, AGRICULTURE. *Educ:* Eastern Caribbean Inst, Trinidad, diplom, 57; Iowa State Univ, BSc, 64, MSc, 66, PhD(plant path & hort), 68. *Prof Exp:* Agr ext agent agr educ, Govt Brit Guyana, 57-60; agr res asst, McGill Univ, 60-63; res asst, Iowa State Univ, 63-68; plant pathologist res, Ministry Agr Govt Guyana, 69-71; assoc prof biol & physical sci, Morris Col SC, 72; PLANT PATHOLOGIST & PESTICIDE COORDR PATH, ENTOM PESTICIDES, UNIV DC & USDA, 72- *Concurrent Pos:* Teacher hort & landscaping, Spingarn-Phelp's Voc Sch, Washington, DC, 73-77; teacher pesticide applicators, DC Coop Ext Serv, Washington, DC, 73-; coordr training, EPA grant, 74-; consult res agronomist, JWK Int Corp, USAID, Govt Chad, Africa, 78- *Mem:* Am Phytopath Soc; Am Hort Soc; Am Entom Soc; Am Chem Soc; Am Soc Plant Physiologists. *Res:* Mycorrhizal associates of Juglans Nigra with special emphasis on nitrogen and phosphorous uptake; pesticide screening; chemical and biological control of pests; environmental preservation. *Mailing Add:* Univ DC & USDA 1331 H St NW Washington DC 20005

KHAN, MOHAMMAD ASAD, b Pakistan. GEODESY, RESEARCH ADMINISTRATION. *Educ:* Univ Panjab, WPakistan, BSc, 57, MSc, 63; Univ Hawaii, PhD(geophys), 67. *Prof Exp:* Forecaster, Pakistan Meteorol Dept, 58-63; lectr geophys, Univ Panjab, WPakistan, 63-64; PROF GEOPHYS & GEOD, UNIV HAWAII & GEOPHYSICIST & GEODESIST, HAWAII INST GEOPHYS, 67- *Concurrent Pos:* Sr resident assoc, Nat Acad Sci, Goddard Space Flight Ctr, NASA, 72-74; sr scientist, Comput Sci Corp, 74-76, sr consult, 76-; adv resource surv, Gov of Pakistan, 74-76; mem, Hawaii State Environ Coun, 79-, chmn, Environ Coun Exec Comn, 79- & vchmn, Environ Coun, 81- *Mem:* Am Geophys Union; Am Geol Inst; Pakistan Asn Advan Sci. *Res:* Satellite altimetry; earth density modelling; geophysical, geodetic and geodynamical applications of satellites; plate tectonics; gravity and isostasy; resource surveys and management; research and academic administration; geodesy; geodynamics; core-mantle boundary problems; technology transfer; technical management. *Mailing Add:* Hawaii Inst of Geophys Univ of Hawaii Honolulu HI 96822

KHAN, MOHAMMAD IQBAL, b Karachi, Pakistan, Dec 27, 50; m 80; c 1. ENDOCRINOLOGY, REPRODUCTIVE PHYSIOLOGY. *Educ:* Univ Karachi, Pakistan, BSc Hons, 70, MSc, 71; Univ Goteborg, Swed, 80. *Prof Exp:* Fel endocrinol, Dept Physiol, Univ Goteborg, Swed, 80 & Dept Animal Sci, Univ Ill, Urbana-Champaign, 80-81; RES ASSOC ENDOCRINOL, DEPT PHYSIOL & BIOPHYSICS, MED CTR, UNIV ILL, CHICAGO, 81- *Concurrent Pos:* Asst lectr, Dept Physiol, Sch Med, Univ Goteborg, Swed, 76-79. *Mem:* Soc Study Reprod; Scand Soc Physiologists; Swed Med Asn. *Res:* Mechanism of action of gonadotropins in the maintenance and function of the corpus luteum as well as the role of prostaglandins in the regression of the corpus luteum. *Mailing Add:* Dept Physiol & Biophysics Univ Ill Med Ctr 901 S Wolcott St Chicago IL 60680

KHAN, MOHAMMED ABDUL QUDDUS, b India, Mar 10, 39; m 74. ENVIRONMENTAL TOXICOLOGY, INSECT TOXICOLOGY. *Educ:* Univ Karachi, BSc, 57, MSc, 59; Univ Western Ont, PhD(zool), 64. *Prof Exp:* Fel entom, NC State Univ, 65-67, Ore State Univ, 67-68 & Rutgers Univ, 68-69; assoc prof, 69-74, PROF BIOL, UNIV ILL, CHICAGO CIRCLE, 74- *Concurrent Pos:* Vis prof, Univ Wis, 70; consult Velsicol Chem Corp, Chicago, 75, NSF, 77-78 & Environ Protection Agency, 80; vis scientist, Nat Inst Environ Health Sci, NIH, 75-76; vis chemist, US Environ Protection Agency, Corvallis, 80. *Mem:* AAAS; Entom Soc Am; Am Chem Soc; Genetics Soc Am; Soc Environ Toxic Chem. *Res:* Metabolism of insecticides; drugs and lipids in insects, crustacea, fish, birds and mammals; biochemistry and genetics of insecticide resistance; environmental toxicology; metabolism of xenobiotics including pesticides in fish, birds, mammals, crustacea; biological concentration of pesticides by foodchains; invitro detoxication and mechanisms; induction of drug metabolizing enzymes. *Mailing Add:* Dept of Biol Sci Box 4348 Univ of Ill at Chicago Circle Chicago IL 60680

KHAN, MOHAMMED NASRULLAH, b Hyderabad, India, Oct 11, 33; m; c 2. PHYSIOLOGY, VETERINARY SCIENCE. *Educ:* Osmania Univ, India, BVSc, 55; La State Univ, Baton Rouge, MS, 63, PhD(environ physiol), 70. *Prof Exp:* Vet, Govts Hyderabad & Andhra Pradesh, India, 55-58; asst lectr anat, State Vet Sch, Hyderabad, India, 58-61; res asst, La State Univ, Baton Rouge, 61-63, res asst, 67-70; asst prof biol, City Cols Chicago, Mayfair Col & Southwest Col, 70-72; instr anat & physiol & microbial, Schs Nursing, Michael Reese Hosp & Med Ctr, Chicago, 73-74; instr anat, physiol & microbiol, South Chicago Community Hosp Schs Nursing & Radiol, 72-77; ASSOC PROF ANAT, PHYSIOL, MICROBIOL & CHEM, LITTLE COMPANY MARY HOSP SCH NURSING, 75-; ASST PROF BIOL, TRUMAN COL, 77- *Concurrent Pos:* NEH Nizam fel; Ford Found res scholar. *Res:* Physiology as related to nutritional endocrinology and/or toxicological aspects. *Mailing Add:* 2904 W Greenleaf Ave Chicago IL 60645

KHAN, MUSHTAQ AHMAD, b Lyallpur, Pakistan, Dec 12, 39; US citizen; m 59; c 4. PERINATAL TOXICOLOGY, ENDOCRINOLOGY. *Educ:* Univ Punjab, Pakistan, BSc, 60; Mont State Univ, MS, 62; Wash State Univ, PhD(vet sci & physiol), 68. *Prof Exp:* Chemist steroid biochem, Syntex Res Ctr, Calif, 64-65; asst prof vet physiol, Univ Agr, Pakistan, 65-72; res assoc pediat, Med Sch, Univ Md, Baltimore, 72-74, asst prof, 74-78, asst prof path, 77-78; physiologist food additives, Div Toxicol, 78-80, res physiologist perinatal toxicol, Metab Br, 80-81, SUPVRY RES PHYSIOLOGIST & HEAD, PERINATAL TOXICOL, BUR FOODS, FOOD & DRUG ADMIN, 81- *Concurrent Pos:* Prin investr, Sch Med, Univ Md, Baltimore, 72-78; adj asst prof, Univ RI, 80- *Mem:* Am Physiol Soc; Am Inst Nutrit; Am Col Toxicol; Am Soc Vet Physiologists & Pharmacologists; World Asn Physiol, Pharmacol & Biochem. *Res:* Endocrine and nutritional factors in obesity and atherosc-lerosis; perinatal toxicology; perinatal nutrition and delayed effects-imprinting; cholesterol metabolism; age and sex related changes in metabolic responses. *Mailing Add:* Food & Drug Admin Bur Foods Rte 2 Box 277 Laurel MD 20708

KHAN, NASIM A, b Benaress, India, June 1, 38; US citizen; m 77. GENE REGULATION, MITOCHONDRIAL GENETICS. *Educ:* Univ Dacca, BSc, 58, MSc, 60; City Univ New York, PhD(genetics), 67. *Prof Exp:* Lectr bot, Univ Decca, 61-62; fel gen biol, 62-64, lectr gen biol, 64-68, instr, Genetics Lab, 68-69, asst prof, 70-75, ASSOC PROF GENETICS, BROOKLYN COL, CITY UNIV NEW YORK, 76- *Mem:* Sigma Xi. *Res:* Construction of yeast strains exhibiting elevated levels of ethanol production using genetic selection procedures and certain recombinant DNA technique; interaction of nuclear and cytoplasmic genes in the utilization of fermentive sugars in yeast. *Mailing Add:* Dept Biol Brooklyn Col City Univ New York Brooklyn NY 11210

KHAN, PAUL, b Vienna, Austria, Nov 4, 23; nat US; m 50. FOOD SCIENCE. *Educ:* NY Univ, BA, 48; Univ Chicago, MS, 49. *Prof Exp:* Asst microbiol, Squibb Inst Med Res, Olin Mathieson Chem Co, 49-53; chief microbiologist, Food & Drug Res Lab, 53-55; dir frozen food prod lab, DCA Food Industs, Inc, 55-60, mgr cent res labs, 60-62; mgr res admin, Continental Baking Co, 62-71; dir food protection, 71-80, VPRES QUAL & FOOD PROTECTION, ITT CONTINENTAL BAKING CO, INC, 80- *Concurrent Pos:* Mem, Tech Comt Food Protection-Grocery Mfg; indust liaison panel, Food Protection Comt, Nat Acad Sci-Nat Res Coun. *Mem:* Am Chem Soc; Am Asn Cereal Chemists; Inst Food Technologists; Asn Food & Drug Officials; Soc Chem Indust. *Res:* Food preservation, technology, poisoning and protection; laboratory management; regulatory compliance; quality assurance. *Mailing Add:* ITT Continental Baking Co Inc PO Box 731 Rye NY 10580

KHAN, RASUL AZIM, b Port Mourant, Guyana, Oct 31, 34; Can citizen; m 66; c 3. PARASITOLOGY. *Educ:* Univ Toronto, Can, BSA, 64, MSc, 66, PhD(parasitol), 69. *Prof Exp:* Asst prof, 69-74, ASSOC PROF BIOL, MEM UNIV NFLD, 74- *Concurrent Pos:* Res scientist, Marine Sci Res Lab, 72- *Mem:* Am Soc Parasitilogists; Am Soc Protozoologists; Can Soc Zoologists. *Res:* Studies on the effects of parasites and pollutants as causative agents of disease in commercial fish in Eastern Canada. *Mailing Add:* Marine Sci Res Lab Mem Univ Nfld St Johns NF A1C 5S7 Can

KHAN, SALEEM AHMAD, b Varanasi, India, Sept 4, 50. DNA REPLICATION, PLASMIDS. *Educ:* Aligarh Muslim Univ, India, BSc, 68, MSc, 70; Indian Inst Sci, PhD(biochem), 75. *Prof Exp:* Asst res scientist biochem, Sch Med, NY Univ, 75-77; fel, 77-80, ASSOC BIOCHEM, PUB HEALTH RES INST, NY, 80- *Concurrent Pos:* Res asst prof, Sch Med, NY Univ, 80- *Res:* Control of plasmid DNA replication in staphylococcus auurens; mechanism of initiation, elongation and termination of DNA replication; genetic engineering gene expression. *Mailing Add:* Dept Plasmid Biol Pub Health Res Inst 455 First Ave New York NY 10016

KHAN, SEKENDER ALI, b Bogra, Bangladesh, Feb 1, 33; m 63; c 2. PLANT PATHOLOGY. *Educ:* Univ Dacca, BArg, 53, MAgr, 54; La State Univ, PhD(plant path), 59. *Prof Exp:* Sect officer, EPakistan Indust Develop Corp, 55-57; asst cane develop officer, M/S Carew & Co, 57; prof biol, Tex Col, 59-63, chmn sci & math, 60-63; actg chmn dept, 64-65, PROF BIOL, ELIZABETH CITY STATE UNIV, 64-, CHMN DEPT, 65- *Mem:* AAAS; Bot Soc Am; Bangladesh Bot Soc. *Res:* Plant hormones; plant alkaloids extraction of active chemicals from Vitex negundo L; science education; tropical vegetable plants. *Mailing Add:* Dept of Biol Elizabeth City State Univ Elizabeth City NC 27909

KHAN, SHAHAMAT ULLAH, b Rampur, India, Apr 25, 37; Can citizen; m 63; c 2. AGRICULTURAL CHEMISTRY. *Educ:* Agra Univ, BSc, 57; Aligarh Muslim Univ, India, MSc, 59; Univ Alta, MSc, 63, PhD(soil chem), 67. *Prof Exp:* Res asst soil chem, Univ Alta, 63-64; RES SCIENTIST ORG MATTER, CAN DEPT AGR, 68- *Mem:* Soil Sci Soc Am; Am Soc Agron; Chem Inst Can; Int Soc Soil Sci. *Res:* Chemistry and reactions of organic matter in soils and waters; soil and water pollution; pesticides in soils and waters. *Mailing Add:* 12 Lynhaven Circle Nepean ON K2E 5K2 Can

KHAN, SHAKIL AHMAD, b Bareilly, India; US citizen; m 74. PHYSICAL CHEMISTRY. *Educ:* Univ Karachi, Pakistan, BS, 67, MS, 68; Univ Islamabad, MPhil, 69; Northwestern Univ, Evanston, Ill, PhD(phys org chem), 74. *Prof Exp:* Fel molecular orbital theory, Univ SC, 74; asst prof spectros quantum chem, Univ Islamabad, Pakistan, 74-77; fel, Fla State Univ, 77-78, RES SPECIALIST NUCLEAR MAGNETIC RENOSANCE SPECTROS & ANAL, MOBAY CHEM CORP, 78- *Mem:* Am Chem Soc; Soc Plastic Industs. *Res:* Use of nuclear magnetic renosance spectroscopy to study polymers especially polyurethanes, polycarbonates, acrylonitrile-butadiene-styrene, etc. *Mailing Add:* Mobay Chem Corp Penn Lincoln Pkwy W Pittsburgh PA 15205

KHAN, SHARIF AHMAD, b Sathla, India, July 1, 38; US citizen; m 63; c 3. EXPERIMENTAL SOLID STATE PHYSICS. *Educ:* Agra Univ, India, BS, 55; Aligarh Muslim Univ, India, MS, 57; La State Univ, Baton Rouge, PhD(physics), 67. *Prof Exp:* Asst prof physics, Aligarh Muslim Univ, 57-63; fel, La State Univ, Baton Rouge, 67-70; prof physics, 70-80, PROF COMP SCI, MISS VALLEY STATE UNIV, 80- *Mem:* Am Phys Soc. *Res:* Electroreflectance, Faraday rotation and Hall effect of narrow gap semiconductor materials; oscillatory Knight shift in single crystals of pure metals. *Mailing Add:* Dept of Physics Box 173 Miss Valley State Univ Itta Bena MS 38941

KHAN, SULTANA, b Dacca, Bangladesh, Dec 13, 47; m 74. SOLID STATE PHYSICS. *Educ:* Univ Dacca, BSc, 70, MSc, 72; Univ Grenoble, Doc(solid state physics), 77. *Prof Exp:* ASST PROF PHYSICS, ELIZABETH CITY STATE UNIV, 78- *Mem:* Bangladesh Phys Soc; Am Phys Soc. *Res:* Metal-insulator transitions under different physical conditions. *Mailing Add:* Elizabeth City State Univ PO Box 187 Elizabeth City NC 27909

KHANDELWAL, RAMJI LAL, b Dausa, India, June 2, 44; m 62; c 3. BIOCHEMISTRY. *Educ:* Univ Udaipur, India, BSc, 63; Punjab, Agr Univ, India, MSc, 66; Univ Man, PhD(biochem), 72. *Prof Exp:* Demonstr agr, Univ Udaipur, India, 63-64; res asst agr, Govt Rajasthan, India, 66-68; teaching asst biochem, Univ Man, 69-70, res asst biochem, 72-73; res biochem, Univ Calif, Davis, 73-75; asst prof oral biol, Univ Man, 75-80; ASSOC PROF BIOCHEM, UNIV SASK, 80- *Concurrent Pos:* Med Res Coun Can scholar, 75-80. *Mem:* Can Biochem Soc; Am Soc Biol Chemists. *Res:* Role of insulin and cyclic adenosine monophosphate in the regulation of glycogen metabolism in mammalian systems; regulation of protein dephosphorylation in biological systems. *Mailing Add:* Dept Biochem Univ Sask Saskatoon SK S7N 0W0 Can

KHANG, SOON-JAI, b Seoul, Korea, Feb 26, 44; m 73; c 2. CHEMICAL ENGINEERING. *Educ:* Yonsei Univ, Korea, BE, 66; Ore State Univ, MS, 72, PhD(chem eng), 75. *Prof Exp:* Instr chem eng, Ore State Univ, 74-75; asst prof, 75-79, ASSOC PROF CHEM ENG, UNIV CINCINNATI, 80- *Concurrent Pos:* Consult, Procter & Gamble Co, 78-80, Amoco Oil, 80- & Exxon, 81- *Mem:* Am Inst Chem Engrs; Sigma Xi. *Res:* Chemical reaction engineering, including residence time distribution, mixing and catalyst deactivation; energy conversion and coal gasification; application of statistical methods for process control; mathematical modeling. *Mailing Add:* Dept of Chem & Nuclear Eng Univ of Cincinnati Cincinnati OH 45221

KHANNA, FAQIR CHAND, b Lyallpur, India, Jan 23, 35; m 66. NUCLEAR PHYSICS. *Educ:* Univ Panjab, India, BSc, 55, MSc, 56; Fla State Univ, PhD(physics), 62. *Prof Exp:* Lectr physics, Univ Panjab, India, 56-58; fel, Univ Iowa, 61-63 & Rice Univ, 63-65; Nat Res Coun Can fel, 66-67, assoc res physicist, 67-77, SR RES PHYSICIST, ATOMIC ENERGY COMN LABS, 77- *Res:* Nuclear physics, especially low and high energy physics; low energy physics study of the few nucleon problem, particularly the three nucleon system; many body problem with emphasis on nuclear physics and solid state physics; quantum liquids and solids; effective operators. *Mailing Add:* Atomic Energy Comn Lab Chalk River ON K0J 1J0 Can

KHANNA, JATINDER MOHAN, b Amritsar, India, Apr 15, 36; m 66; c 2. BIOCHEMICAL PHARMACOLOGY. *Educ:* Punjab Univ, India, BSc, 58, MSc, 60; Univ Conn, PhD(pharmacol), 64. *Prof Exp:* Res fel pharmacol, 64-65, lectr, 65-66, from asst prof to assoc prof, 66-77, PROF PHARMACOL, FAC MED, UNIV TORONTO, 77- *Concurrent Pos:* scientist IV, Alcohol & Drug Addiction Res Found, 69-, head, Behav Pharmacol & Drug Anal Sect. *Mem:* AAAS; Soc Neurosci; Can Pharmacol Soc; Am Soc Pharmacol & Exp Therapeut; Res Soc Am. *Res:* Biochemical and behavioral mechanisms of alcohol and drug addiction. *Mailing Add:* Dept Pharmacol Univ Toronto Toronto ON M5S 1A1 Can

KHANNA, KRISHAN L, b Amritsar, India, Nov 19, 33; m 63; c 2. PHYTOCHEMISTRY, PHARMACEUTICAL CHEMISTRY. *Educ:* Univ Panjab, India, BPharm, 57, MPharm, 59; Univ Conn, PhD(pharm sci), 63. *Prof Exp:* Lectr pharmacog, Univ Panjab, India, 59-60; asst instr org chem, Univ Conn, 62-63, instr, 63-64; lectr pharmacog, Univ Panjab, India, 64-68; res assoc, Col Pharm, Univ Mich, Ann Arbor, 68-70, NIH fel toxicol, 70-71, res assoc indust toxicol, 71-74; ASSOC PROF, COL PHARM & PHARMACAL SCI, HOWARD UNIV, 74- *Mem:* AAAS; Royal Soc Chem; NY Acad Sci; Am Asn Cols Pharm. *Res:* Toxicology; drug metabolism; metabolism of foreign compounds. *Mailing Add:* 4208 Downing St Annandale VA 22003

KHANNA, PYARE LAL, b Lahore, Mar 28, 45; Indian citizen; m 73; c 2. BIO-ORGANIC CHEMISTRY, SYNTHETIC CHEMISTRY. *Educ:* Univ Delhi, BSc, 65, MSc, 67, PhD(chem), 70. *Prof Exp:* Res assoc natural prod, Indian Nat Sci Acad, 70-71; asst prof chem, Ramjas Col, Univ Delhi, 71-74; res assoc, Columbia Univ, 74-77; res group leader, 77-80, MGR RES, SYVA RES INST, 80- *Mem:* Am Chem Soc. *Res:* Natural products isolation and synthesis; steroids; small ring compounds; fluorescent dyes; protein modifications; development of new drug assay techniques. *Mailing Add:* Syva Res Inst 900 Arastradero Palo Alto CA 94304

KHANNA, RAVI, b Kapurthala, India, Sept 27, 44; m 74. POLYMER CHEMISTRY, CHEMICAL ENGINEERING. *Educ:* Indian Inst Technol, Kanpur, BTech, 67; Mass Inst Technol, SM, 68. *Prof Exp:* Res chemist, 68-72, sr res chemist polymer chem, 72-76, res assoc, 76-77, lab head, 77-81, TECH ASST TO DIR RES, EASTMAN KODAK CO RES LABS, 81- *Mem:* Am Chem Soc; Am Inst Chem Engrs. *Res:* Investigation of the mechanism and kinetics of batch and continuous free radical polymerization. *Mailing Add:* Eastman Kodak Co Res Labs B82 1660 Lake Ave Rochester NY 14650

KHANNA, SARDARI LAL, b Amritsar, India, Apr 15, 37; m 63; c 2. PHYSICS. *Educ:* Panjab Univ India, BA, 56; Univ Saugar, MSc, 59, PhD(physics), 63. *Prof Exp:* Lectr physics, DAV Col, Amritsar, India, 59-60; lectr, Panjab Univ, 62-64; from asst prof to assoc prof, York Jr Col, Pa, 65-68; sci pool off, Panjab Univ, 68-69; assoc prof, 70-78, PROF PHYSICS, YORK COL, PA, 78- *Mem:* Am Phys Soc; Am Asn Physics Teachers. *Res:* Electrets; solid state physics; study of dielectrics subjected to electric and magnetic fields. *Mailing Add:* Dept of Physics York Col of Pa York PA 17405

KHANNA, SHADI LALL, b Lahore, India, Jan 27, 33; m 60; c 2. DENTISTRY. *Educ:* Univ Punjab, India, BA, 53, BDS, 57; Univ Rochester, MS, 64; Univ Man, DMD, 66. *Prof Exp:* Demonstr dent, Punjab Govt Dent Col, India, 59-61; Nat Res Coun res fel, 66-67; ASST PROF DENT, UNIV BC, 67- *Mem:* Fel AAAS; Can Dent Asn; Int Asn Dent Res. *Res:* Dental plaque; enamel solubility; saliva. *Mailing Add:* Fac of Dent Univ of BC Vancouver BC V6T 1W5 Can

KHANNA, SHYAM MOHAN, b Agra, India, May 10, 32; m 59; c 2. AUDIOLOGY, PHYSIOLOGY. *Educ:* Univ Lucknow, BS, 51; St Xavier's Col, India, DRE, 54; City Univ New York, PhD(hearing), 70. *Prof Exp:* Develop engr instrumentation, Pye Ltd, Eng, 54-55; design engr commun, Can Westinghouse Ltd, Ont, 55-58; sr engr avionics, Int Tel & Tel Labs, 58-61; adv engr commun, IBM Corp, 61-64; res assoc hearing, 64-70, asst prof otolaryngol, 70-71, ASSOC PROF OTOLARYNGOL, COL PHYSICIANS & SURGEONS, COLUMBIA UNIV, 71- *Concurrent Pos:* NIH res grants, 64-, prin investr, 79- *Mem:* Sr mem Inst Elec & Electronics Engrs; fel Acoust Soc Am; Sigma Xi; Asn Res Otolaryngol. *Res:* Physics of hearing; mechanics of the middle and inner ear; transducer action and coding in the peripheral auditory system. *Mailing Add:* Col of Physicians & Surgeons 630 W 16B St New York NY 10032

KHANNA, SOM NATH, b Lyal Pur, W Panjab, India, May 30, 32; m 59; c 2. POLYMER CHEMISTRY. *Educ:* Panjab Univ, India, BSc, 53 & 55, MSc, 56; Univ Calcutta, PhD(polymer chem), 59. *Prof Exp:* NSF fel, Col Forestry, Syracuse Univ, 60-62; Nat Res Coun Can fel chem, Univ Ottawa, 62-64 & McGill Univ, 64-65; CHEMIST POLYMERS, RES LABS, UNIROYAL LTD, 65- *Mem:* Chem Inst Can. *Res:* Research and development in the area of application of polymeric materials in automotives and construction. *Mailing Add:* 68 Balmoral Dr Guelph ON N1E 3N7 Can

KHARAKA, YOUSIF KHOSHU, b Mosul, Iraq, May 15, 41; c 2. GEOCHEMISTRY, HYDROGEOLOGY. *Educ:* King's Col, Univ London, BSc, 63; Univ Calif, Berkeley, PhD(geol), 71. *Prof Exp:* Asst geologist explor & res dept, Ministry of Oil, Baghdad, Iraq, 63-67; asst res geologist, Univ Calif. Berkeley, 71-75; HYDROLOGIST WATER RESOURCES DIV, US GEOL SURV, 75- *Concurrent Pos:* Asst geol, Univ Baghdad, 63-64; consult explor, Mining & Metals Div, Union Carbide Corp, 74-75. *Mem:* Int Asn Geochem & Cosmochem; Geochem Soc; Am Asn Petrol Geologists; Am Geophys Union; Geol Soc Am. *Res:* Geochemistry of sediments, sedimentary rocks and their associated fluids; computer modelling of water-rock interactions; membrane properties of fine grained sediments; stable isotopes. *Mailing Add:* US Geol Surv 345 Middlefield Rd Menlo Park CA 94025

KHARASCH, NORMAN, b Poland, Sept 11, 14; nat US. CHEMISTRY. *Educ:* Univ Chicago, BS, 37, MS, 38; Northwestern Univ, PhD(chem), 44. *Prof Exp:* Instr chem, Chicago Jr Col, 38-39, Ill Inst Technol, 39-43 & N⁰rthwestern Univ, 44-46; from asst prof to prof chem, 46-66, PROF BIOMED CHEM, UNIV SOUTHERN CALIF, 66- *Concurrent Pos:* Sci dir, Intra-Sci Found, Los Angeles, 66- *Mem:* Am Chem Soc. *Res:* Organic sulfur compounds; mechanisms of organic reactions; chemistry of prostaglandins and related substances; free radical reactions. *Mailing Add:* Dept of Biomedicinal Chem Univ of Southern Calif Los Angeles CA 90033

KHARE, BISHUN NARAIN, b Varanasi, India, June 27, 33; m 62; c 2. PHYSICS, PHYSICAL CHEMISTRY. *Educ:* Banaras Hindu Univ, BSc, 53, MSc, 55; Syracuse Univ, PhD(physics), 61. *Prof Exp:* Res assoc, Univ Toronto, 61-62 & State Univ NY Stony Brook, 62-64; assoc res scientist, Ont Res Found, Can, 64-66; physicist, Smithsonian Astrophys Observ, Mass, 66-68; SR RES PHYSICIST, CTR RADIOPHYSICS & SPACE RES, CORNELL UNIV, 68- *Concurrent Pos:* Assoc, Harvard Observ, 66-68. *Mem:* AAAS; Am Phys Soc; Am Astron Soc; Int Soc Study Origin of Life; Astron Soc India. *Res:* Interdisciplinary research; molecular structure and spectroscopy; synthesis of organic compounds in primitive terrestrial and contemporary planetary atmospheres by photochemical reaction; hydrogen bonding; planetary simulation studies of Mars and Venus; interstellar photochemistry. *Mailing Add:* 306 Space Sci Ctr for Radiophys & Space Res Cornell Univ Ithaca NY 14850

KHARE, MOHAN, b Varanasi, India, May 15, 42. PHYSICAL CHEMISTRY, ENVIRONMENTAL CHEMISTRY. *Educ:* Banaras Hindu Univ, BSc, 61, MSc, 63 & PhD(chem), 67. *Prof Exp:* Lectr chem, Banaras Hindu Univ, 67; res assoc & fel, Univ Md, 68-69 & Radiation Ctr, Ore State Univ, 69-70; res assoc, Cornell Univ, 70-80; WITH I T ENVISCIENCE INC, 80- *Mem:* Am Chem Soc. *Res:* Radiochemical separation of isotopes; kinetics of annealing of radiation damage; energy transfer in solids; photolysis and radiolysis of aqueous systems and interstellar molecules; water pollution characterization and environmental research; analytical methods development for trace and toxic materials, organic and inorganic, in diverse matrices. *Mailing Add:* I T Enviscience Inc 9041 Executive Park Dr Knoxville TN 37919

KHASAWNEH, FAYEZ ESSA, b Eidun, Jordan, Sept 18, 38; m 68. SOIL CHEMISTRY, AGRONOMY. *Educ:* Am Univ, Beirut, BSc, 59; Auburn Univ, MSc, 63, PhD(soil & phys chem), 65. *Prof Exp:* Res fel soil chem, Purdue Univ, 65-67; RES SOIL SCIENTIST, NAT FERTILIZER DEVELOP CTR, TENN VALLEY AUTHORITY, 67- *Mem:* Am Soc Agron; Soil Sci Soc Am; Brit Soc Soil Sci. *Res:* Reactions of fertilizer salts with soil; mobility of plant nutrients in soil; transport mechanisms of ions in soil to plant roots; diffusive and viscous transport; phosphate rock for direct application; fertilizer practices for soils with high residual levels of phosphates. *Mailing Add:* Agr Res Br Tenn Valley Authority Muscle Shoals AL 35660

KHATIB-RAHBAR, MOHSEN, b Rafsandjan, Iran, Feb 21, 54. CHEMICAL ENGINEERING, NUCLEAR ENGINEERING. *Educ:* Univ Minn, BChemEng, 74; Cornell Univ, PhD(nuclear eng), 78. *Prof Exp:* MEM SCI STAFF, BROOKHAVEN NAT LAB, 78- *Mem:* Assoc mem Am Inst Chem Engrs; Am Nuclear Soc. *Res:* Nuclear reactor dynamics and safety; heat transfer; fluid dynamics; numerical methods. *Mailing Add:* Bldg 130 Dept of Nuclear Energy Brookhaven Nat Lab Upton NY 11973

KHATRA, BALWANT SINGH, b Nabha, India, Feb 2, 45; US citizen; m 68; c 2. BIOCHEMISTRY. *Educ:* Punjab Univ, BSc Hons, 65, MSc, 67; Univ Leeds, PhD(biochem), 72. *Prof Exp:* Res fel, Clin Res Facil, Emory Univ, 72-75; res assoc, 75-78, ASST PROF, DEPT PHYSIOL, VANDERBILT UNIV, 78- *Res:* Phosphoprotein phosphatases: isolation, characterization and their role in the regulation of glycogen metabolism. *Mailing Add:* Dept Physiol Vanderbilt Univ Nashville TN 37232

KHATRI, HIRALAL C, b Navsari, India, Feb 6, 36; m 65; c 1. MECHANICAL ENGINEERING. *Educ:* Imp Col Eng, Addis Ababa, Ethiopia, BS, 58; Purdue Univ, MS, 63, PhD(mech eng), 66. *Prof Exp:* Engr, Imp Hwy Authority, Ethiopia, 58-61; asst prof elec eng, Mont State Univ, 65-67; assoc prof mech eng, Cath Univ Am, 67-71; mech engr, 71-80, PHYS SCIENTIST, HARRY DIAMOND LABS, 80- *Concurrent Pos:* NSF res grant, 66-68. *Mem:* Assoc mem Am Soc Mech Engrs; Inst Elec & Electronics Engrs. *Res:* Automatic control systems; optimal filter, identification and control of distributed systems; stability and sensitivity of distributed parameter systems; radar systems and signal processing. *Mailing Add:* Harry Diamond Labs 2800 Powder Mill Rd Adelphi MD 20783

KHATTAB, GHAZI M A, b Baghdad, Iraq, Nov 20, 30; c 1. POLYMER CHEMIST. *Educ:* Univ Baghad, BS, 53; Univ Ill, Urbana, MS, 58; Polytech Inst Brooklyn, PhD(polymer chem), 65. *Prof Exp:* Sr res chemist res & develop, Allied Chem Corp, 65-71; prog mgr, BiomedSci, 72-73; res assoc, GAF Corp, 73-75; sr res chemist res & develop, Allied Chem Corp, 76-80; TECH DIR RES & DEVELOP, WELLMAN, INC, 81- *Mem:* Am Chem Soc; Soc Plastics Engrs; Sigma Xi. *Res:* New polymeric materials; engineering plastics including fluoropolymers; polyamides; polyesters and polysulfones. *Mailing Add:* PO Box 188 Johnsonville SC 29555

KHATTAK, CHANDRA PRAKASH, b Rawalpindi, Pakistan, May 19, 44; m 70. SOLID STATE PHYSICS, MATERIALS SCIENCE. *Educ:* Indian Inst Technol, Bombay, BTech, 65; State Univ NY Stony Brook, MS, 71, PhD(mat sci), 73. *Prof Exp:* Jr sci officer magnetism, DMR Lab, Hyderabad, India, 65-68; asst mat sci, State Univ NY Stony Brook, 68-73; res assoc solid state physics, Brookhaven Nat Lab, 74-75, asst physicist, 75-77; dir res & develop, 77-80, VPRES TECHNOL, CRYSTAL SYSTS INC, 80- *Honors & Awards:* IR-100 Award, 79. *Mem:* Am Ceramic Soc; Am Phys Soc; Am Asn Crystal Growth; Electrochemical Soc. *Res:* Directional solidification of large diameter sapphire for optical application, silicon single crystals for photovoltaic applications and laser crystals by heat exchanger method; low-cost slicing of silicon by multi-ware fixed abrasive slicing technique; characterization and evaluation of silicon material for solar cells; thermodynamic evaluation of vacuum processing of silicon. *Mailing Add:* Crystal Systs Inc Shetland Indust Park 35 Congress St Salem MA 01970

KHAWAJA, IKRAM ULLAH, b Delhi, India, Dec 25, 42; m 68. ECONOMIC GEOLOGY. *Educ:* Univ Karachi, BS, 62, MS, 63; Southern Ill Univ, MS, 68; Ind Univ, Bloomington, PhD(geol), 69. *Prof Exp:* From asst prof to assoc prof, 68-81, PROF GEOL, YOUNGSTOWN STATE UNIV, 81- *Mem:* Geol Soc Am; Sigma Xi. *Res:* Coal geology; petrology; sulphides in coal. *Mailing Add:* Dept of Geol Youngstown State Univ Youngstown OH 44503

KHAYAT, ALI, b Tehran, Iran, Feb 2, 38; US citizen; m 66; c 2. AGRICULTURAL CHEMISTRY, FOOD SCIENCE. *Educ:* Univ Tehran, BS, 61; Univ Calif, Davis, MS, 64, PhD(agr chem), 68. *Prof Exp:* Res asst biochem, Univ Calif, Davis, 64-68; asst prof, Med Sch, Pahlavi Univ, Iran, 68-70; res biochemist, 70-72, assoc scientist, 72-77, SR SCIENTIST RES DEPT, VAN CAMP DIV, RALSTON PURINA CO, 77- *Mem:* Am Chem Soc; Sigma Xi; Inst Food Technologists. *Res:* Chemical modification of heme-proteins as related to the color of heme-pigments; flavor chemistry of canned sea food as investigated by gas chromatography-mass spectrometry system; spoilage studies and identification of developed components in tuna fish; corrosion studies of food containers. *Mailing Add:* Van Camp Sea Food 4245 Sorrento Valley Blvd San Diego CA 92121

KHAZAN, NAIM, b Baghdad, Iraq, Feb 15, 21; US citizen; m 52; c 2. PHARMACOLOGY. *Educ:* Col Pharm & Chem, Baghdad, PhC, 43; Hebrew Univ Jerusalem, PhD(pharmacol), 60. *Prof Exp:* Res assoc cent nerv syst pharmacol, Upjohn Co, 63-64; lectr, Hadassah Med Sch & Sch Pharm, Hebrew Univ, Jerusalem, 64, sr lectr, 66; asst prof, Med Sch, Univ Ore, 66-67; assoc prof, Columbia Univ, 67-68; assoc prof pharmacol, Mt Sinai Sch Med, 68-72; head dept pharmacol, Merrell Nat Labs, Cincinnati & assoc clin prof, Col Med, Univ Cincinnati, 72-74; prof pharmacol & toxicol, 74-80, EMERSON PROF PHARMACOL, SCH PHARM, UNIV MD, BALTIMORE, 80-, CHMN, DEPT PHARMACOL & TOXICOL & DIR, GRAD PROG PHARMACOL, 74- *Concurrent Pos:* Mem, Grad Coun, Univ Md, Baltimore City, 78- USPHS int fel, 68; NIMH grants, 67, 68-72 & 72-75; Nat Inst Drug Abuse grants, 75-78. *Mem:* Am Pharmaceut Asn; Am Soc Pharmacol & Exp Therapeut; NY Acad Sci; Soc Exp Biol & Med; Soc Neurosci. *Res:* Electroencephalographic and behavioral studies of experimental drug dependence on narcotics; electroencephalographic effects of cannabinoids; pharmacology of rapid eye movement sleep; opioid multiple receptors and electroencephalograph power spectra. *Mailing Add:* Dept Pharmacol & Toxicol Univ of Md Sch of Pharm Baltimore MD 21201

KHERA, KUNDAN SINGH, b Wadala Khurd, India, May 12, 22; Can citizen. TOXICOLOGY, TERATOLOGY. *Educ:* Punjab Univ, BSc, 44, DVM & BVSc, 52, MVSc & MSc, 56; Univ Paris, DSc, 58. *Prof Exp:* Dis invest officer, Vet Dept, Punjab Govt, India, 58-61; prof vet path, Vet Col, Punjab Univ & Govt Punjab, 61-64; SECT HEAD TERATOLOGY, HEALTH PROTECTION BR, NAT HEALTH & WELFARE, CAN, 64- *Concurrent Pos:* Fel, Col Med, Baylor Univ, 62-63. *Mem:* Soc Toxicol; Teratology Soc; Europe Teratology Soc. *Res:* Study of food additives and environmental contaminants on embryonic, postnatal and reproductive phases of mammalian development to determine admissible levels for humans. *Mailing Add:* Health Protection Br Nat Health & Welfare Ottawa ON K1A 0L2 Can

KHO, BOEN TONG, b Tegal, Indonesia, Dec 3, 19; US citizen; m 60; c 4. ANALYTICAL CHEMISTRY. *Educ:* Univ Utrecht, BS, 42; State Univ Leiden, Drs, 47, apotheker, 49; Philadelphia Col Pharm, MS, 52; Univ Wis, PhD(pharm), 57. *Prof Exp:* Res chemist, Cent Res Labs, Gen Aniline & Film Co, Pa, 57-60; head methods develop, Merck Sharp & Dohme, 60-64; head anal res, Toms River Res Lab, Ciba Chem & Dye Co, 64-67; mgr anal res, Ciba-Agrochem Co, 67-68; asst dir anal res & develop, 68-71, DIR ANAL RES & DEVELOP, AYERST LABS, INC, 71- *Mem:* Am Chem Soc; Am Pharmaceut Asn; NY Acad Sci. *Mailing Add:* Ayerst Labs Inc Maple St Rouses Point NY 12979

KHODADAD, JENA KHADEM, b Tehran, Iran; US citizen; c 3. ULTRASTRUCTURE, MEMBRANES. *Educ:* Mt Union Col, BS, 60; Northwestern Univ, MS, 71, PhD(biol sci), 75. *Prof Exp:* Fel membrane, 77-78, instr cell biol, Dept Path, 78-79, ASST PROF, DEPT ANAT & PATH, MED COL, RUSH UNIV, 79- *Mem:* Am Soc Cell Biol; Am Asn Anatomists; AAAS. *Res:* Membrane research; biological membranes and the correlationship of ultrastructure with biochemical studies; red blood cell is the model membrane system used. *Mailing Add:* Dept Anat Med Col Rush Univ 600 S Paulina Chicago IL 60612

KHOO, TENG LEK, b Penang, Malaysia, June 1, 43; m 72; c 2. NUCLEAR PHYSICS. *Educ:* Dalhousie Univ, BSc, 65, MSc, 67; McMaster Univ, PhD(physics), 72. *Prof Exp:* Res assoc nuclear physics, Mich State Univ, 72-74, asst prof, 74-77; asst physicist, 77-79, PHYSICIST NUCLEAR PHYSICS, ARGONNE NAT LAB, 79- *Mem:* Am Phys Soc. *Res:* Experimental nuclear structure physics, especially properties of deformed nuclei, effective nucleon interaction and nuclei at high angular momentum. *Mailing Add:* Div of Physics Argonne Nat Lab 9700 S Cass Ave Argonne IL 60439

KHOOBIAR, SARGIS, b Kermansha, Iran, Jan 5, 30; US citizen; m 71; c 1. PETROLEUM CHEMISTRY, CHEMICAL ENGINEERING. *Educ:* Abadan Inst Technol, Iran, BS, 54; Ill Inst Technol, MS, 57, PhD(chem eng), 60. *Prof Exp:* From res engr to sr res engr, Esso Res & Eng Co, Linden, NJ, 59-63; res assoc catalytic chem, 63-71, DIR CATALYTIC RES, HALCON INT, INC, NEW YORK, 71- *Mailing Add:* Halcon Int Inc 2 Park Ave New York NY 10016

KHOOBYARIAN, NEWTON, b Tabriz, Iran, Oct 20, 24; US citizen; m 55; c 2. VIROLOGY. *Educ:* Lafayette Col, AB, 49; Univ Ill, MS, 50; Univ Wis, PhD(med microbiol), 54; Am Bd Microbiol, dipl. *Prof Exp:* Asst biol sci, Univ Ill, 49-50; asst med microbiol, Univ Wis, 50-54; res fel microbiol, Sch Med, Ind Univ, 54-55, res assoc, 55-56, instr pediat, 56-60; from asst prof to assoc prof, 60-72, PROF MICROBIOL, COL MED, UNIV ILL MED CTR, CHICAGO, 72-, ACTG HEAD, DEPT MICROBIOL & IMMUNOL, 80- *Concurrent Pos:* Consult, Miles Labs, Inc, 70- *Mem:* AAAS; Am Soc Microbiol. *Res:* Mammalian cell-virus relationship; viral genetics; biology of adenovirus proteins; chemical carcinogen-virus interactions. *Mailing Add:* Dept Microbiol Univ Ill Med Ctr 835 S Wolcott Chicago IL 60680

KHORANA, BRIJ MOHAN, b Multan, India, Apr 11, 39; m 67; c 2. PHYSICS. *Educ:* Univ Delhi, BSc, 58, MSc, 60; Indian Inst Technol, Kharagpur, MTech, 61; Univ Chicago, MS, 64; Case Western Reserve Univ, PhD(physics), 68. *Prof Exp:* Res assoc physics, James Franck Inst, Univ Chicago, 67-68 & Univ Rochester, 68-70; asst prof physics, Univ Notre Dame, 70-77; ASSOC PROF PHYSICS, ROSE-HULMAN INST TECHNOL, 77-, HEAD DIV PHYSICS, 81- *Mem:* Am Phys Soc. *Res:* Low temperature physics; macroscopic quantum properties of superfluid helium and superconductors; biomedical physics. *Mailing Add:* Div Physics Elec Eng & Comput Sci Rose-Hulman Inst of Technol Terre Haute IN 47803

KHORANA, HAR GOBIND, b Raipur, India, Jan 9, 22; m 52; c 3. ORGANIC CHEMISTRY. *Educ:* Punjab Univ, India, BSc, 43, MSc, 45; Univ Liverpool, PhD, 48. *Hon Degrees:* DSc, Univ Chicago, 67; Univ Liverpool, 71; JD, Simon Fraser Univ, 69. *Prof Exp:* Govt India fel, with Prof V Prelog, Swiss Fed Inst Technol, 48-49; Nuffield fel, with Prof Sir Alexander Todd, Cambridge Univ, 50-52; head org chem group, BC Res Coun & res prof fac grad studies, Univ BC, 52-59; prof & group leader, Inst Enzyme Res, Univ Wis, Madison, 60-62, prof, 62-71, Conrad A Elvejhem Prof life sci, 64-71; ALFRED P SLOAN PROF BIOL & CHEM, MASS INST TECHNOL, 71- *Concurrent Pos:* Vis prof, Rockefeller Inst, 58- *Honors & Awards:* Nobel Prize in Med, 68; Merck Award, Chem Inst Can, 58; Gold Medal, Prof Inst Can Pub Serv, 60; Dannie Heinneman Prize, 67; Lasker Found Award, 68; Louisa Gross Horwitz Prize, 68. *Mem:* Nat Acad Sci; AAAS; Am Chem Soc; Am Soc Biol Chem; The Chem Soc. *Res:* Peptides and proteins; chemistry of phosphate esters of biological interest; nucleic acids; chemical synthesis and structure; enzymes of nucleic acid metabolism; viruses and chemical genetics. *Mailing Add:* Dept of Biol & Chem Mass Inst of Technol Cambridge MA 02139

KHOSHNEVISAN, MOHSEN MONTE, b Mashad, Iran. ELECTROOPTICS, NONLINEAR OPTICS. *Educ:* Calif State Univ, San Jose, BS & BA, 68; Mich State Univ, MS, 71, PhD(physics), 73. *Prof Exp:* Asst prof physics, Arya-Mehr Univ Technol, Iran, 73-77; vis asst prof, Mich State Univ, Lansing, 77-78; MEM TECH STAFF, ELECTRO-OPTICS DEPT, SCI CTR, ROCKWELL INT, 78- *Mem:* Am Phys Soc; Optical Soc Am; Soc Photo-Instrumentation Engrs. *Mailing Add:* Rockwell Int Sci Ctr 1049 Camino Dos Rios Thousand Oaks CA 91360

KHOSLA, RAJINDER PAUL, b Phillaur, India, July 25, 33; m 66; c 3. SOLID STATE PHYSICS. *Educ:* Univ Delhi, BSc, 53; Benaras Hindu Univ, MSc, 55; Purdue Univ, PhD(physics), 66. *Prof Exp:* Lectr physics, Govt Col, Narnaul, India, 55-56; sci asst, Nat Phys Lab India, New Delhi, 56-59; teaching & res asst, Purdue Univ, 59-66; sr physicist, 66-70, res assoc, 71-76, group leader device technol, Solid State Lab, 75-76, actg lab head, 76, lab head, 76-79, SR RES LAB HEAD, SOLID STATE LAB, EASTMAN KODAK CO, 79- *Concurrent Pos:* Lectr, Eve Sch, Univ Rochester, 72-74; vis scholar, Dept Elec Eng & Comput Sci, Univ Calif, Santa Barbara, 74-75. *Mem:* AAAS; Am Phys Soc; sr mem Inst Elec & Electronics Engrs. *Res:* Transport and photoconductive properties of semiconductors and solid state devices. *Mailing Add:* Res Labs Eastman Kodak Co Rochester NY 14650

KHOURY, GEORGE, b Pittsburgh, Pa, Aug 7, 43; m 67; c 2. MOLECULAR BIOLOGY, ANATOMY. *Educ:* Princeton Univ, AB, 65; Harvard Med Sch, MD, 69. *Prof Exp:* Res assoc, Nat Inst Alergy & Infectious Dis, 70-75; SECT HEAD & LAB CHIEF, NAT CANCER INST, 75- *Concurrent Pos:* Asst ed, J Virol, 74- & assoc ed, Cell, 77- *Honors & Awards:* Arthur S Fleming Award, US Govt, 80. *Mem:* Am Soc Microbiol; Am Soc Virol. *Res:* Determination factors which regulate gene expression; small DNA tumor viruses or recombinant DNA molecules; regulation of transcription; analysis of the histocompatability antigens. *Mailing Add:* Nat Inst Health Bldg 41 Suite 200 Bethesda MD 20205

KHUDAIRI, ABDUL KARIM, plant physiology, see previous edition

KHULLAR, SUBHASH C, b Pakpatan, India, Apr 12, 45; m 70; c 2. CARDIOLOGY. *Educ:* Punjab Univ, India, MB & BS, 67; Am Bd Internal Med, dipl, 73, dipl cardiovasc dis, 77; Am Bd Nuclear Med, dipl, 75. *Prof Exp:* Sr resident med, Med Col Ohio, 71-72; clin instr fel cardiol, Ohio State Univ, 73-74; res assoc cardiovasc nuclear med, Univ Calif, San Diego, 74-75; asst prof med & radiol, Med Col Ohio, 75-78; CHIEF CARDIOL & DIR CARDIOVASC NUCLEAR MED, DETROIT GEN HOSP, 78-; ASSOC PROF MED & RADIOL, WAYNE STATE UNIV, 78- *Concurrent Pos:* Dir cardiovasc nuclear med, Med Col Hosp, Toledo, 75-78; consult cardiologist, Harper Gen Hosp, Detroit, 78- *Mem:* AAAS; Am Col Physicians; Am Col Nuclear Physicians; Am Col Int Physicians; Am Col Cardiol. *Res:* Cardiovascular diseases; nuclear cardiology. *Mailing Add:* Chief of Cardiol 1326 St Antoine Detroit MI 48207

KHURANA, SURJIT SINGH, b Tandlianwala, Pakistan, June 15, 31; m 62; c 3. MATHEMATICS. *Educ:* Panjab Univ, India, BA, 53, MA, 55; Univ Ill, Urbana, PhD(math), 68. *Prof Exp:* Lectr math, Camp Col, Panjab Univ, India, 56-59 & Post-Grad Inst, Univ Delhi, 59-64; asst prof, 68-74, assoc prof, 74-79, PROF MATH, UNIV IOWA, 79- *Mem:* Am Math Soc. *Res:* Measure theory; functional analysis; general topology; probability theory; topological vector spaces. *Mailing Add:* Dept of Math Univ of Iowa Iowa City IA 52242

KHURI, NICOLA NAJIB, b Beirut, Lebanon, May 27, 33; US citizen; m 55; c 2. THEORETICAL PHYSICS. *Educ:* Am Univ, Beirut, BA, 52; Princeton Univ, PhD(physics), 57. *Prof Exp:* Asst prof physics, Am Univ, Beirut, 57-58; mem Inst Adv Study, 59-60; assoc prof physics, Am Univ, Beirut, 61-62; mem Inst Adv Study, 62-63; vis assoc prof, Columbia Univ, 63-64; assoc prof, 64-68, PROF PHYSICS, ROCKEFELLER UNIV, 68- *Concurrent Pos:* Brookhaven Nat Lab, 63-73; trustee, Am Univ Beirut, 69-; trustee, Brearley Sch, 70-79. *Mem:* Fel Am Phys Soc. *Res:* Quantum field theory; scattering theory; theory of dispersion relations and their applications; high energy particle physics. *Mailing Add:* Dept Theoret Physics Rockefeller Univ New York NY 10021

KHUSH, GURDEV S, b Rurki, India, Aug 22, 35; m 61; c 4. PLANT BREEDING. *Educ:* Punjab Univ, India, BSc, 55; Univ Calif, Davis, PhD(genetics), 60. *Prof Exp:* Asst genetics, Univ Calif, Davis, 57-61, jr res geneticist, 61-62, asst res geneticist, 62-67; plant breeder, 67-72, HEAD VARIETAL IMPROV DEPT, INT RICE RES INST, 72- *Concurrent Pos:* Vis prof, Colo State Univ, 75-76. *Honors & Awards:* Borlong Award, 77. *Mem:* Indian Nat Sci Acad; Genetics Soc Am; Bot Soc Am; NY Acad Sci. *Res:* Cytogenetic studies of genus Secale and origin of cultivated rye and genus Lycopersicon particularly gene location, chromosome mapping and centromere location in the cultivated tomato; rice genetics and breeding. *Mailing Add:* Int Rice Res Inst PO Box 933 Manila Philippines

KHWAJA, TASNEEM AFZAL, b Pakistan, Apr 20, 36; m 65; c 2. CANCER, CHEMOTHERAPY. *Educ:* Univ Panjab, WPakistan, BSc, 55, MSc, 57; Cambridge Univ, MA, 61, PhD(synthetic nucleic acid chem), 64. *Prof Exp:* NIH res assoc grant, Univ Utah, 65-66; NIH proj assoc grant, McArdle Lab Cancer Res, Univ Wis-Madison, 66-68; res asst, Max Planck Inst Exp Med, Ger, 69-70; head dept cancer chemother, ICN Nucleic Acid Res Inst, 70-73; asst prof, 73-75, ASSOC PROF PATH, SCH MED, UNIV SOUTHERN CALIF, 76-, SR RES SCIENTIST & DIR ANIMAL TUMOR RESOURCE FACIL & PHARMACOANALYTIC FACIL, LOS ANGELES COUNTY-UNIV SOUTHERN CALIF CANCER CTR, 73- *Mem:* Am Asn Cancer Res; fel Royal Chem Soc; Am Chem Soc. *Res:* Synthesis of nucleoside antimetabolites as antitumor agents; biochemical mechanisms of drug action; use of animal tumor models. *Mailing Add:* LAC/USC Cancer Ctr 1720 Zonal Ave Los Angeles CA 90033

KIANG, CHIA SZU, b Shanghai, China, Sept 9, 41; US citizen; m 68; c 2. ATMOSPHERIC SCIENCES, PHYSICS. *Educ:* Nat Taiwan Univ, BS, 62; Ga Inst Technol, MS, 64, PhD(physics), 70. *Prof Exp:* Assoc prof physics, Clark Col, 67-74; res scientist, Nat Ctr Atmospheric Res, 74-76, aerosol proj leader, 76-78; PROF GEOPHYS SCI, GA INST TECHNOL, 78- *Concurrent Pos:* Sr res assoc, Atmospheric Sci Res Ctr, State Univ NY Albany, 71-; adj prof, Dept Chem, Atlanta Univ, 74-76 & Dept Atmospheric Sci, Colo State Univ, 74-78; adj prof physics, Ga Inst Technol, 76-77. *Mem:* Am Chem Soc; Am Physics Soc; Am Meteorol Soc; Am Asn Advan Sci. *Res:* Nucleation; aerosol physics; aerosol chemistry; atmospheric chemistry; surface science; phase transition; critical phenomena; statistical physics; planetary atmosphere; environmental science and planning; natural phenomena. *Mailing Add:* Sch of Geophys Sci Ga Inst of Technol Atlanta GA 30332

KIANG, DAVID TEH-MING, b Chekiang, China, Nov 13, 35; m 68; c 3. INTERNAL MEDICINE, ONCOLOGY. *Educ:* Nat Defense Med Ctr Taiwan, MB, 60; Columbia Univ, MS, 64; Univ Minn, PhD, 73. *Prof Exp:* Intern med, Beekman-Downtown Hosp, NY, 64-65, resident, 65-66; resident, Francis Delafield Hosp, 66-68; USPHS fel oncol, 68-70, instr, 70-73, asst prof, 73-81, ASSOC PROF MED, MED SCH, UNIV MINN, MINNEAPOLIS, 81- *Mem:* Soc Exp Biol & Med; Am Fedn Clin Res; Am Asn Cancer Res; Am Soc Clin Oncol. *Res:* Treatment of mammary cancer. *Mailing Add:* Dept of Med Med Sch Univ Minn Minneapolis MN 55455

KIANG, NELSON YUAN-SHENG, b Shanghai, China, July 6, 29; m 57; c 2. NEUROPHYSIOLOGY. *Educ:* Univ Chicago, PhB, 47, PhD(biopsychol), 55. *Hon Degrees:* MD, Univ Geneva, Switzerland, 81. *Prof Exp:* Res asst otol, 57-62, DIR EATON PEABODY LAB, MASS EYE & EAR INFIRMARY, 62-; STAFF MEM, RES LAB ELECTRONICS, MASS INST TECHNOL, 55-, LECTR ELEC ENG, 68-; NEUROPHYSIOLOGIST, NEUROL SERV, MASS GEN HOSP, 77- *Concurrent Pos:* Res asst otol, Harvard Med Sch, 57-61, res asst otolaryngol, 61-69, sr res assoc otolaryngol & physiol, 69-; mem, Commun Sci Study Sect, Div Res Grants, NIH, 68-72; mem, Comt Hearing Bioacoust & Biomech, Nat Acad Sci-Nat Res Coun. *Honors & Awards:* Beltone Award, 68. *Mem:* AAAS; Soc Neurosci; Am Physiol Soc; Acoust Soc Am; Am Otol Soc. *Res:* Physiology of auditory and other sensory systems; relation of brain to behavior. *Mailing Add:* Eaton Peabody Lab Mass Eye & Ear Infirmary Boston MA 02114

KIANG, ROBERT L(I-HSIEN), b Chungking, China, Nov 30, 39; US citizen; m 64; c 1. MECHANICAL ENGINEERING, FLUID MECHANICS. *Educ:* Nat Taiwan Univ, BS, 61; Stanford Univ, MS, 64, PhD(aeronaut eng), 70. *Prof Exp:* Res engr, Stanford Res Inst, 63-71, SR RES ENGR, SRI INT, 71- *Mem:* Am Soc Mech Engrs; Am Nuclear Soc. *Res:* Fluid dynamics; dynamic modeling; nuclear safety; heat transfer; noise and vibration; friction and lubrication. *Mailing Add:* SRI Int 333 Ravenswood Ave Menlo Park CA 94025

KIANG, YUN-TZU, b Taiwan, Feb 1, 32; US citizen; m 57; c 3. POPULATION GENETICS, PLANT BREEDING. *Educ:* Taiwan Normal Univ, BS, 56; Ohio State Univ, MA, 62; Univ Calif, Berkeley, PhD(genetics), 70. *Prof Exp:* Res asst genetics, Univ Calif, Berkeley, 67-68, teaching asst, 68-69, teaching assoc, 69-70; asst prof, 70-75, ASSOC PROF PLANT SCI & GENETICS, UNIV NH, 75- *Concurrent Pos:* Vis prof, Taiwan Normal Univ, 78; vis scientist, Academia Sinica, 78. *Mem:* AAAS; Genetics Soc Am; Am Genetic Asn; Soc Study Evolution; Sigma Xi. *Res:* Genetics and evolution of economic and natural plant populations. *Mailing Add:* Dept of Plant Sci Univ of NH Durham NH 03824

KIBBEE, GARY W(ILLARD), mechanical engineering, see previous edition

KIBBEL, WILLIAM H, JR, b Buffalo, NY, Aug 31, 23; m 49; c 2. CHEMICAL ENGINEERING, INORGANIC CHEMISTRY. *Educ:* Case Inst Technol, BS, 44, MS, 48. *Prof Exp:* Chem eng reactor design, Buffalo Electro Chem Co, 47-52; sales mgr peroxy chem, Becco Sales Corp, 52-57, mgr mkt res, Becco Chem Div, 57-58; mgr indust appln develop, 58-77, MGR TECH SERV, FMC CORP, 77- *Mem:* Sigma Xi; Am Inst Chem Engrs; Tech Asn Pulp & Paper Indust; Am Asn Textile Chemists & Colorists. *Res:* Pulp and paper; textiles; pollution control; metal surface treatments. *Mailing Add:* FMC Corp PO Box 8 Princeton NJ 08540

KIBBEY, DONALD EUGENE, b Junction City, Kans, Feb 19, 12; m 38; c 3. MATHEMATICS. *Educ:* Univ Ill, AB, 35, AM, 36, PhD(math), 42. *Prof Exp:* Asst math, Univ Ill, 36-39; instr, Univ Kansas City, 39-42 & Mich State Col, 42; sr instr, US Mil Acad, 42-46; from asst prof to prof math, 46-77, chmn dept, 52-71, vpres res & grad affairs, 71-77, EMER PROF MATH, SYRACUSE UNIV, 78- *Mem:* Am Math Soc; Math Asn Am. *Res:* Ranges of analytical functions; boundary values of analytic functions. *Mailing Add:* 200 Carnegie Bldg Syracuse Univ Syracuse NY 13210

KIBBY, CHARLES LEONARD, b Wenatchee, Wash, Jan 2, 38; m 70; c 1. CHEMICAL KINETICS, SURFACE CHEMISTRY. *Educ:* Reed Col, BA, 59; Purdue Univ, PhD, 64. *Prof Exp:* Fel chem, Harvard Univ, 63-65; res assoc, Brookhaven Nat Lab, 65-67; fel catalysis, Mellon Inst Sci, Carnegie-Mellon Univ, 67-69; res chemist, 70-75, res chemist, Pittsburgh Energy Res Ctr, 76-77, sr res chemist, 77-80, RES ASSOC, GULF RES & DEVELOP CO, PITTSBURGH, 81- *Concurrent Pos:* Vis scientist catalysis, Inst Org Chem, Moscow, USSR, 74. *Mem:* Am Chem Soc; AAAS; Catalysis Soc. *Res:* Characterization of heterogeneous catalysts for hydrocarbon processing and synthetic fuels and chemicals production, by chemical and physical methods; design and testing of new catalysts for synthesis gas conversion. *Mailing Add:* 4 Boxwood Dr Gibsonia PA 15044

KIBBY, HAROLD V, b San Diego, Calif. AQUATIC BIOLOGY. *Educ:* Wash State Univ, BS, 64; Ore State Univ, MS, 66; Univ London, PhD(zool), 69. *Prof Exp:* Asst prof biol, State Univ NY Brockport, 70-72; RES BIOLOGIST, US ENVIRON PROTECTION AGENCY, 72- *Concurrent Pos:* Fel, Univ Toronto, 69-70; consult, US Environ Protection Agency, 71-72. *Mem:* Am Soc Limnol & Oceanog; AAAS; Brit Freshwater Biol Asn. *Res:* Wetlands ecology; limnology. *Mailing Add:* US Environ Protection Agency 200 SW 35th St Corvallis OR 97330

KIBENS, VALDIS, b Riga, Latvia, Oct 22, 36; US citizen; m 58; c 2. AEROACOUSTICS, TURBULENCE. *Educ:* Yale Univ, BE, 57; Johns Hopkins Univ, PhD(mech), 68. *Prof Exp:* Res engr, Gen Dynamics Corp, Conn, 57-60; asst prof aerospace eng, Univ Mich, Ann Arbor, 68-74; SR SCIENTIST AEROACOUST, RES LABS, MCDONNELL DOUGLAS CORP, 74- *Concurrent Pos:* Consult & vis res scientist, Res Labs, Gen Motors Corp, Mich, 73. *Mem:* Am Phys Soc; assoc fel Am Inst Aeronaut & Astronaut. *Res:* Control of the development of turbulent structures in flow fields as the basis for technological devices to reduce aerodynamic noise, enhance mixing, and control buffeting. *Mailing Add:* 471 Maymont Ballwin MO 63011

KIBLER, KENNETH G, b Peoria, Ill, Apr 15, 40; m 61; c 2. GEOPHYSICS, ENVIRONMENTAL SCIENCE. *Educ:* Univ Iowa, MS, 64, PhD(nuclear physics), 66. *Prof Exp:* Res asst nuclear physics, Univ Iowa, 62-66; res assoc, Case Western Reserve Univ, 66-69; SR RES SCIENTIST, GEN DYNAMICS-CONVAIR AEROSPACE, 69- *Concurrent Pos:* Asst prof, Tex Wesleyan Col, 69- *Mem:* AAAS; Am Phys Soc; Am Geophys Union. *Res:* Heavy-ion nuclear reactions; gravity measurement; remote sensing of earth resources; enhancement techniques for aerial or orbital images; physics of materials. *Mailing Add:* 7005 Valholla Ft Worth TX 76116

KIBLER, RUTHANN, b Mansfield, Ohio, Dec 1, 42. IMMUNOLOGY, VIROLOGY. *Educ:* Marietta Col, BS, 64; Purdue Univ, MS, 67; Univ Calif, Berkeley, PhD(immunol), 73. *Prof Exp:* res scientist immmunol, Dept Microbiol, 76-79, ASST PROF, DEPT MOLECULAR & MED MICROBIOL, COL MED, UNIV ARIZ, 80- *Concurrent Pos:* mem staff, Calif State Dept Health Serv, Berkeley, 79-80. *Mem:* Am Soc Microbiol; Reticuloendothelial Soc; Sigma Xi; Am Asn Immunologists. *Mailing Add:* Dept Molecular & Med Microbiol Col Med Univ Ariz Tucson AZ 85724

KIBRICK, SIDNEY, b Boston, Mass, Apr 2, 16; m 49; c 2. PEDIATRICS. *Educ:* Harvard Univ, AB, 38; Mass Inst Technol, PhD(bact), 43; Boston Univ, MD, 46; Am Bd Pediat, dipl, 53; Am Bd Microbiol, dipl, 65. *Prof Exp:* Res assoc bact, Sch Med, Univ Boston, 43-44; intern med, Mass Mem Hosps,

Boston, 46-47; jr asst resident med, Children's Hosp Med Ctr, 50-52; asst pediat, Harvard Med Sch, 52-53, instr, 53-56, res assoc, 56-57, assoc, 57-60, asst clin prof, 60-61; assoc prof microbiol, 61-67, chief sect virol, Univ Hosp, 61-68, ASSOC PROF MED, SCH MED, BOSTON UNIV, 61-, PROF MICROBIOL, 67-, PROF PEDIAT, 72- *Concurrent Pos:* USPHS res fel, Children's Hosp Med Ctr, Boston, 49-50, res assoc, 52-62, from asst physician to assoc physician, 52-61, consult, 61-; lectr microbiol, Sch Med, Boston Univ, 53-61; lectr pediat, Harvard Med Sch, 61-65; vis physician, Boston City Hosp & Boston Univ Hosp, 61- *Mem:* Soc Pediat Res; Infectious Dis Soc Am; Am Pediat Soc; Am Soc Microbiol; Nat Found Infectious Dis. *Res:* Virology; infectious diseases. *Mailing Add:* Boston Univ Med Ctr 80 E Concord St Boston MA 02118

KICE, JOHN LORD, b Colorado Springs, Colo, Feb 18, 30; m 53; c 2. ORGANIC CHEMISTRY. *Educ:* Harvard Univ, AB, 50, MA, 53, PhD(chem), 54. *Prof Exp:* Sr chemist, Rohm and Haas Co, 53-56; from asst prof to assoc prof org chem, Univ SC, 56-60; from assoc prof to prof, Ore State Univ, 60-70; prof & chmn dept, Univ Vt, 70-75; chmn dept, 75-81, PROF CHEM, TEX TECH UNIV, 75- *Concurrent Pos:* Sloan Found fel, 57-61; NIH spec fel, 68-69. *Mem:* Am Chem Soc. *Res:* Organic reaction mechanisms; free radical reactions; organic sulfur chemistry; organic selenium chemistry. *Mailing Add:* Dept of Chem Tex Tech Univ Lubbock TX 79409

KICHER, THOMAS PATRICK, b Johnsonburg, Pa, Oct 20, 37; m 62; c 3. ENGINEERING MECHANICS. *Educ:* Case West Reserve Univ, BS, 59, MS, 62, PhD(eng mech), 64. *Prof Exp:* Res engr, Aeronca Mfg Co, 59; res asst, Case Western Reserve Univ, 59-64; design engr, Douglas Aircraft Co, Inc, Calif, 64-65; asst prof eng, 65-68, assoc prof, 68-81, PROF MECH ENG, CASE WESTERN RESERVE UNIV, 81-, ASSOC DEAN SCI & ENGR, 76- *Concurrent Pos:* Consult, 65- *Mem:* Am Inst Aeronaut & Astronaut; Am Soc Mech Engrs; NY Acad Sci. *Res:* Computer methods of optimum design; basic phenomena of buckling of elastic systems; analysis and testing of composite materials; analysis and testing of plates and shells. *Mailing Add:* Dept of Civil Eng Case Western Reserve Univ Cleveland OH 44106

KICLITER, ERNEST EARL, JR, b Ft Pierce, Fla, June 19, 45; m 67. NEUROANATOMY, COLOR VISION. *Educ:* Univ Fla, BA, 68; State Univ NY Upstate Med Ctr, PhD(anat), 73. *Prof Exp:* Asst prof neuroanat, Col Med, Sch Basic Med Sci & asst prof physiol, Col Lib Arts & Sci, Univ Ill, Urbana-Champaign, 74-77; ASSOC PROF ANAT, SCH MED, UNIV PR, 77- *Concurrent Pos:* NIH fel neurol surg, Sch Med, Univ Va, 72-74; vis prof, Univ Med Sch, Pecs, Hungary, 76. *Mem:* AAAS; Soc Neurosci; Asn Res Vision & Ophthal; Am Asn Anatomists; Cajal Club. *Res:* Comparative studies of structure and function in vertebrate visual systems; color vision and neuronal plasticity in visual systems. *Mailing Add:* Lab Neurobiol Univ PR Blvd del Valle 201 San Juan PR 00901

KICSKA, PAUL A, b New York, NY, Nov 23, 32; m 60; c 3. PHYSICS. *Educ:* Muhlenberg Col, BS, 58; Lehigh Univ, MS, 60, PhD(physics), 65. *Prof Exp:* Instr math, Lafayette Col, 58-60; engr, Bell Tel Labs, 60-61; instr physics, Lafayette Col, 61-63; engr, Gen Elec Co, 66-67; PROF PHYSICS, EAST STROUDSBURG STATE COL, 67- *Concurrent Pos:* Chief consult, Tech Consult Serv, 67- *Mem:* Am Phys Soc; Sigma Xi; Soc Physics Students; AAAS; Nat Fluid Power Asn. *Res:* Analytic description of vehicle collisions; accident reconstruction. *Mailing Add:* Dept of Physics East Stroudsburg State Col East Stroudsburg PA 18301

KIDD, BERNARD SEAN LANGFORD, b Belfast, Northern Ireland, July 7, 31; m 58; c 4. CARDIOVASCULAR PHYSIOLOGY. *Educ:* Queen's Univ Belfast, MB, BCh & BAO, 54, MD, 57. *Prof Exp:* Asst lectr physiol, Queen's Univ Belfast, 55-57; tutor & registr, Royal Victoria Hosp, Belfast, 57-60; physician & assoc scientist, Hosp for Sick Children, 61-67; assoc prof pediat physiol, Univ Toronto, 61-75; dep dir, 73-75, HARRIET LANE HOME PROF PEDIAT CARDIOL & DIR DIV, SCH MED, JOHNS HOPKINS UNIV, 75- *Concurrent Pos:* Physician & assoc scientist, Hosp Sick Children, 67-75. *Mem:* Am Pediat Soc; Can Soc Clin Invest; Am Col Cardiol; Am Heart Asn; Soc Pediat Res. *Res:* Circulatory physiology, hemodynamics in congenital heart disease. *Mailing Add:* Helen B Taussig Children's Cardiac Ctr Johns Hopkins Univ Hosp Baltimore MD 21205

KIDD, DAVID EUGENE, b Evanston, Ill, Apr 13, 30; m 55; c 1. PHYCOLOGY. *Educ:* Ariz State Col, BS, 51; Northwestern Univ, MS, 52; Univ NH, MST, 60; Mich State Univ, PhD(bot), 63. *Prof Exp:* Sci teacher high sch, Ariz, 54-55; prof chem, Lindsey Wilson Col, 55-56; sci teacher high sch, Ariz, 56-60; asst prof natural sci, Mich State Univ, 60-67; assoc prof, 67-73, PROF BIOL, UNIV NMEX, 73- *Concurrent Pos:* Grants, Am Philos Soc, 64-66; Sigma Xi, 65-66; NSF Undergrad Equip, 69-71; Water Resources Inst, 69-72; NSF, 71-77. *Mem:* Am Micros Soc; Am Chem Soc; Nat Sci Teachers Asn. *Res:* taxonomy and ecology of algae in polluted ranch ponds in northern Arizona; carbon-14 primary productivity and population dynamics of phytoplankton in Elephant Butte Reservoir and Lake Powell; nutrient loading models and their modification as applied to Southwestern reservoirs. *Mailing Add:* Dept of Biol Univ of NMex Albuquerque NM 87106

KIDD, DEREK JOHN, b London, Eng, July 5, 22; Can citizen; m 52. HUMAN PHYSIOLOGY. *Educ:* Univ London, MB, BS, 52; MRCS & LRCP, 52. *Prof Exp:* Officer in chg, Personnel Res Unit, Royal Can Navy, 61-66, cmndg officer, Oper Med Estab, Can Forces Inst Environ Med, Toronto, 66-71, command surgeon, Maritime Forces Pac HQ, 71-78; RETIRED. *Concurrent Pos:* Mem, Adv Bd, Nat Asn Underwater Instrs; mem, Adv Bd, Can Asn Underwater Couns. *Mem:* Royal Soc Med; NY Acad Sci; Undersea Med Soc. *Res:* Human physiology in military environments, especially arctic and tropic climates and waters; physiology of diving and submarine escape with special reference to decompression sickness and its prevention. *Mailing Add:* 1025 Moss Victoria BC V8V 4P2 Can

KIDD, FRANK ALAN, b Dodge City, Kans, July 24, 52; m 73. PLANT PHYSIOLOGY. *Educ:* Ore State Univ, BS, 74; Colo State Univ, MS, 76, PhD(tree physiol), 82. *Prof Exp:* Teaching asst forestry, Ore State Univ, 73-74; teaching asst forest biomet, econ & physiol, Colo State Univ, 74-81, res asst forest tree physiol, 74-80, instr forest ecol, 80-81; RES FORESTER, POTLATCH CORP, 81- *Concurrent Pos:* Consult, Repub Nat Bank, Dallas, Tex, 76-82; contributing researcher, Lightwood Res Coord Coun, US Forest Serv, 76-78. *Mem:* AAAS; Soc Am Foresters; Am Forestry Asn. *Res:* Forest tree physiology; mycorrhizal relationships; physiological consequences of silvicultural treatment of conifers. *Mailing Add:* Forestry Res Potlatch Corp PO Box 1016 Lewiston ID 83501

KIDD, GEORGE JOSEPH, JR, b Grand Rapids, Mich, May 6, 34; m 56; c 3. MECHANICAL ENGINEERING. *Educ:* Northwestern Univ, BS, 56, MS, 57; Univ Tenn, PhD(eng sci), 66. *Prof Exp:* Assoc engr, Y-12 Plant, 57-58, res staff mem reactor develop, Oak Ridge Nat Lab, 58-68, develop engr, 68-77, DEPT SUPVR, OAK RIDGE GASEOUS DIFFUSION PLANT, UNION CARBIDE CORP, 77- *Mem:* Am Soc Mech Engrs; Am Inst Chem Engrs; Nat Soc Prof Engrs. *Res:* Heat transfer; fluid mechanics. *Mailing Add:* 120 Windham Rd Oak Ridge TN 37830

KIDD, HAROLD J, b Billings, Okla, Jan 30, 24; m 55; c 2. CYTOGENETICS, PLANT MORPHOLOGY. *Educ:* Okla State Univ, BS, 49, MS, 51; Washington Univ, PhD(bot), 56. *Prof Exp:* Instr bot, Okla State Univ, 51-53; BR PLANT MGR, PLANT BREEDING, PIONEER HI-BRED INT, INC, 55- *Mem:* Am Genetics Asn. *Res:* Cultivated sorghum; plant breeding; morphology. *Mailing Add:* PO Box 1506 Plainview TX 79072

KIDD, KENNETH KAY, b Bakersfield, Calif, Sept 5, 41; m 64. POPULATION GENETICS, BEHAVIORAL GENETICS. *Educ:* Univ Southern Calif, AB, 65; Univ Wis, MS, 67, PhD(genetics), 69. *Prof Exp:* Res assoc genetics, Sch Med, Stanford Univ, 71-72; asst prof anthrop genetics, Sch Med, Washington Univ, 72-73; asst prof, 73-78, assoc prof human genetics, 78-81, ASSOC PROF HUMAN GENETICS & PSYCHIAT, SCH MED, YALE UNIV, 81- *Concurrent Pos:* NIH fel, Univ Pavia, 69-71 & Sch Med, Stanford Univ, 71. *Mem:* Genetics Soc Am; Soc Study Evolution; Am Soc Human Genetics; Am Asn Phys Anthrop; Behav Genetics Asn. *Res:* Genetics of human behavioral disorders; genetic relationships of human populations. *Mailing Add:* Dept of Human Genetics Yale Univ Sch of Med New Haven CT 06510

KIDD, RICHARD WAYNE, b Westminster, Md, June 16, 47; m 69; c 1. PHYSICAL CHEMISTRY. *Educ:* Western Md Col, BA, 69; Univ Ill, MS, 71, PhD(chem), 75. *Prof Exp:* Teaching & res asst, Univ Ill, Urbana, 69-75, res assoc chem, 75-77; res scientist, Mat Technol Sect, 77-80, PRIN RES SCIENTIST, CERAMICS & MAT PROCESSING SECT, COLUMBUS LAB, BATTELLE MEM INST, 80- *Mem:* Am Chem Soc; Sigma Xi. *Res:* Mathematical modeling and experimental determination of isotope effects in chemical reactions; mechanisms of reactions; chemical vapor deposition of coatings to enhance the properties of the substrate material. *Mailing Add:* Sect 777 Battelle's Columbus Lab 505 King Ave Columbus OH 43201

KIDD, ROBERT GARTH, b Stockton-on-Tees, Eng, July 19, 36; Can citizen; m 59; c 3. INORGANIC CHEMISTRY. *Educ:* Univ Man, BSc, 58, MSc, 60; Univ London, PhD(chem), 62. *Prof Exp:* Asst prof, 63-69, ASSOC PROF CHEM, UNIV WESTERN ONT, 69-, ASST DEAN GRAD STUDIES, 70- *Mem:* Chem Inst Can; Am Chem Soc. *Res:* Nature of bonding in transition metal complexes; nuclear magnetic resonance spectroscopy of inorganic compounds. *Mailing Add:* Dept Chem Univ Western Ont London ON N6A5B7 Can

KIDD, WILLIAM SPENCER FRANCIS, b Shawford, Eng, Feb 23, 47; UK citizen. GEOLOGY. *Educ:* Univ Cambridge, Eng, BA, 69, PhD(geol), 74. *Prof Exp:* Vis lectr geol, Erindale Col, Univ Toronto, 72-73; lectr, 74, asst prof, 75-81, ASSOC PROF GEOL, STATE UNIV NY, ALBANY, 81- *Mem:* Am Geophys Union; Geol Soc Am. *Res:* Structural geology; tectonics; Applachian geology; orogenic belts; Tibet. *Mailing Add:* Dept Geol Sci State Univ NY 1400 Washington Ave Albany NY 12222

KIDDER, ERNEST H(IGLEY), b Amiret, Minn, July 14, 12; m 46; c 2. ENGINEERING. *Educ:* Univ Minn, BAgrEng, 35; Univ Ill, MSCE, 47; US Naval Acad, CMet, 45. *Prof Exp:* Jr soil conservationist, Soil Conserv Serv, USDA, Minn, 35-39; jr hydraul engr, Univ Ill, 39-41, asst hydraul engr, 41-43, assoc hydraul engr, 46-48; proj supvr, Auburn, Ala, 48-49; from assoc prof to prof agr eng, 50-79, EMER PROF AGR ENG, MICH STATE UNIV, 79- *Honors & Awards:* Hancor Award, Am Soc Agr Engrs, 71. *Mem:* Fel Am Soc Agr Engrs. *Res:* Hydraulic, hydrologic, meteorologic, soil physical and agronomic phases of soil and water conservation. *Mailing Add:* 1709 Cahill Dr East Lansing MI 48823

KIDDER, GEORGE WALLACE, b Oregon City, Ore, Dec 29, 02; m 30; c 3. BIOLOGY, BIOCHEMISTRY. *Educ:* Univ Ore, AB, 26; Univ Calif, MA, 29; Columbia Univ, PhD(zool), 32. *Hon Degrees:* MA, Amherst Col, 49; ScD, Wesleyan Univ, 50. *Prof Exp:* Teacher pub sch, Ore, 26-28; instr biol, City Col New York, 29-37; asst prof, Brown Univ, 37-46; assoc prof, 46-49, Stone Prof, 49-70, EMER PROF BIOL, AMHERST COL, 70- *Concurrent Pos:* Mem corp, Marine Biol Lab, Woods Hole, 43-47; chmn vitamins & metab, Gordon Res Confs, 57; mem, Training Grant Comt, NIH, 60-64; vis prof biochem, Univ Calif, Santa Cruz, 68. *Mem:* AAAS; fel Am Acad Microbiol; Am Soc Zoologists; fel Am Acad Arts & Sci; fel Am Soc Protozoologists. *Res:* Life histories of protozoan parasites; protozoan cytology and physiology; biochemistry of microorganisms; vitamins and amino acids; purine and pyrimidine metabolism in Trypanosomid flagellates; metabolism; nutrition; chemotherapy of cancer. *Mailing Add:* Biol Lab Amherst Col Amherst MA 01002

KIDDER, GEORGE WALLACE, III, b New York, NY, Sept 24, 34; m 57; c 2. PHYSIOLOGY, BIOPHYSICS. *Educ:* Amherst Col, AB, 56; Univ Pa, PhD(bot), 61. *Prof Exp:* Res fel, Johnson Found, Univ Pa, 61-62; res fel biophys labs, Harvard Med Sch, 62-64; asst prof biol, Wesleyan Univ, 64-73; assoc prof, 73-78, PROF PHYSIOL, UNIV MD SCH DENT, 78- *Concurrent Pos:* USPHS fel, Harvard Univ, 64. *Mem:* AAAS; Am Physiol Soc; Biophys Soc. *Res:* Gastric acid secretion; electrophysiology; active transport of ions in relation to aerobic metabolism. *Mailing Add:* Dept of Physiol Univ of Md Sch of Dent Baltimore MD 21201

KIDDER, GERALD, b Leonville, La, Jan 2, 40; m 66; c 3. SOIL SCIENCE. *Educ:* Univ Southwestern La, BS, 61; Univ Ill, MS, 64; Okla State Univ, PhD(soil sci), 69. *Prof Exp:* Lab asst soil nitrogen, Univ Ill, 63-64; vol, Papal Vol Latin Am, US Cath Bishop's Conf, 64-66; res agronomist, Standard Fruit Co, Castle & Cooke, Inc, 69-72, mgr agr serv, 72-75; asst prof agron, 75-80, ASSOC PROF SOIL SCI, INST FOOD & AGR SCI, UNIV FLA, 80- *Mem:* Am Soc Agron; Int Soc Soil Sci; Soil Sci Soc Am; Am Soc Sugarcane Technologists. *Res:* Sugarcane, banana and pineapple production problems, particularly nutrition, irrigation, drainage, pest control, cultural practices, genetic improvement and harvesting; soil test interpretations and crop fertilization recommendations. *Mailing Add:* G-159 McCarty Hall Univ Fla Gainesville FL 32611

KIDDER, GERALD MARSHALL, b Harlingen, Tex, Dec 26, 44. DEVELOPMENTAL CELL BIOLOGY, DEVELOPMENTAL GENETICS. *Educ:* Hiram Col, BA, 66; Yale Univ, PhD(biol), 71. *Prof Exp:* Fel res assoc biol sci, Reed Col, Ore, 71-72; asst prof, 72-78, ASSOC PROF ZOOL, UNIV WESTERN ONT, 78- *Concurrent Pos:* Res scientist, Alpha Helix Exped, Honduras Reef, 77; vis res assoc radiobiol, Med Sch, Univ Calif, San Francisco, 79-80. *Mem:* AAAS; Am Soc Cell Biol; Can Soc Cell Biol; Am Soc Zoologists; Soc Develop Biol. *Res:* Developmental genetics of the early embryo: gennetic control of morphogenesis and the early events of cell differentiation and the control of gene expression in early development. *Mailing Add:* Dept Zool Cell Sci Lab Univ Western Ont London ON N6A 5B7 Can

KIDDER, HAROLD EDWARD, b Crowley, Colo, Mar 12, 22. PHYSIOLOGY. *Educ:* Colo Agr & Mech Col, BS, 50; Univ Wis, MS, 51, PhD, 54. *Prof Exp:* Asst genetics, Univ Wis, 50-51, instr, 51-54; asst prof animal husb, 54-57, assoc prof & assoc husbandman, 57-60, PROF ANIMAL VET SCI & ANIMAL HUSBANDMAN, WVA UNIV, 60- *Mem:* Am Soc Animal Sci; Sigma Xi. *Res:* Physiology of reproduction; animal breeding. *Mailing Add:* Dept of Animal Sci WVa Univ Morgantown WV 26506

KIDDER, JOHN NEWELL, b Boston, Mass, Apr 30, 32; m 60; c 3. PHYSICS, PHYSIOLOGICAL OPTICS. *Educ:* Calif Inst Technol, BS, 54; Duke Univ, PhD(physics), 60. *Prof Exp:* Res assoc physics, Yale Univ, 60-62; from asst prof to assoc prof, 62-74, PROF PHYSICS, DARTMOUTH COL, 74- *Mem:* Am Phys Soc; Am Asn Physics Teachers; Optical Soc Am; Inter-Soc Col Coun; Asn Res Vision & Ophthal. *Res:* Color science; vision; models of visual response. *Mailing Add:* 42 Rip Rd Hanover NH 03755

KIDDER, RAY EDWARD, b New York, NY, Nov 12, 23; m 47; c 3. APPLIED MATHEMATICS, PHYSICS. *Educ:* Ohio State Univ, PhD(physics), 50. *Prof Exp:* Sr physicist, Calif Res Corp, 50-56; ASSOC DIV LEADER, THEORET DIV, LAWRENCE LIVERMORE LAB, UNIV CALIF, 56- *Mem:* Fel Am Phys Soc. *Res:* Thermonuclear physics; astrophysics; quantum electronics. *Mailing Add:* 637 E Angela St Pleasanton CA 94566

KIDDY, CHARLES AUGUSTUS, b Boston, Mass, Apr 14, 31; m 51; c 5. ANIMAL SCIENCE. *Educ:* Univ Mass, BS, 51; Univ Wis, MS, 55, PhD, 58. *Prof Exp:* Instr genetics, Univ Wis, 55-58; res animal scientist, Dairy Cattle Res Br, Animal Sci Res Div, USDA, 58-72, res animal scientist, Reproduction Lab, Animal Physiol & Genetics Inst, USDA, 72-79, NAT RES PROJ LEADER DAIRY PROD, AGR RES SERV, USDA, 79- *Mem:* Am Soc Animal Sci; Am Dairy Sci Asn; AAAS. *Res:* Physiology of reproduction in farm animals; dairy cattle genetics. *Mailing Add:* Nat Prog Staff ARS USDA Agr Res Ctr W Bldg 005 Beltsville MD 20705

KIDNAY, ARTHUR J, b Milwaukee, Wis, Apr 4, 34; m 60; c 3. CHEMICAL ENGINEERING, PHYSICAL CHEMISTRY. *Educ:* Colo Sch Mines, BS, 56, DSc(chem eng), 68; Univ Colo, MS, 61. *Prof Exp:* Proj engr, Monsanto Chem Co, Mass, 56-58; res engr, Cryogenics Div, Nat Bur Standards, Colo, 59-68; from asst prof to assoc prof, 68-76, PROF CHEM & PETROL REFINING ENG, COLO SCH MINES, 77- *Mem:* Am Inst Chem Engrs. *Res:* Solid-vapor and liquid vapor equilibria at cryogenic temperatures; physical adsorption at cryogenic temperatures. *Mailing Add:* Dept of Eng Colo Sch of Mines Golden CO 80401

KIDSON, EVAN JOSEPH, geology, palynology, see previous edition

KIDWELL, ALBERT LAWS, b Auxvasse, Mo, Jan 1, 19; m 43; c 4. PETROLEUM GEOLOGY. *Educ:* Mo Sch Mines, BS, 40; Washington Univ, MS, 42; Univ Chicago, PhD(geol), 49. *Prof Exp:* Photogrammetric engr, US Coast & Geod Surv, 42-44; geologist, Mo Geol Surv, 44-47; res geologist, Carter Oil Co, 50-58; sect head, Jersey Prod Res Co, 58-65; res assoc, Esso Prod Res Co, 65-73, SR RES ASSOC, EXXON PROD RES CO, 73- *Mem:* Geol Soc Am; Mineral Soc Am; Am Asn Petrol Geol; Soc Econ Geol. *Res:* Igneous and economic geology. *Mailing Add:* 14403 Carolcrest Dr Houston TX 77079

KIDWELL, MARGARET GALE, b Askham, Eng, Aug 17, 33; m 61; c 2. GENETICS. *Educ:* Nottingham Univ, BSc, 53; Iowa State Univ, MS, 62; Brown Univ, PhD(genetics), 73. *Prof Exp:* Adv officer agr, Ministry Agr, London, 55-60; assoc res, 66-70, res fel, 73-74, res assoc, 74-75, instr, 75-77, asst prof, 77-80, ASSOC PROF RES BIOL, BROWN UNIV, 80- *Mem:* Am Genetic Asn; Am Soc Naturalists; Genetics Soc Am; Soc Study Evolution. *Res:* Drosophila genetics and evolution; recombination mutator mechanisms; modes of reproductive isolation. *Mailing Add:* Div of Biol & Med Sci Brown Univ Providence RI 02912

KIDWELL, ROBERT E(DWARD), JR, b Washington, DC, Mar 17, 23; m 55; c 6. ENGINEERING. *Educ:* Cath Univ, BEE, 49. *Prof Exp:* Aeronaut res engr, Naval Res Labs, 49-59; head temperature control sect, 59-67, ASST HEAD THERMOPHYS BR, GODDARD SPACE FLIGHT CTR, NASA, 67- *Mem:* Am Inst Aeronaut & Astronaut. *Res:* Spacecraft temperature control; heat transfer analysis by digital computer; thermophysical properties of spacecraft materials. *Mailing Add:* Code 762 NASA Goddard Space Flight Ctr Greenbelt MD 20771

KIDWELL, ROGER LYNN, b Nevada City, Calif, Feb 24, 38; m 61; c 1. SYNTHETIC ORGANIC CHEMISTRY. *Educ:* Chapman Col, BS, 62; Univ Southern Calif, PhD(org chem), 66. *Prof Exp:* Res chemist, 66-71, res specialist, 71-73, RES GROUP LEADER SURFACTANTS, MONSANTO CO, 73- *Mem:* Am Chem Soc; Sigma Xi. *Res:* Synthesis and process development for new surface active agents. *Mailing Add:* Monsanto Co 800 N Lindbergh Blvd St Louis MO 63166

KIDWELL, WILLIAM ROBERT, b La Follette, Tenn, Sept 2, 36; m 55; c 2. CELL BIOLOGY, BIOCHEMISTRY. *Educ:* Berea Col, BA, 63; Wash Univ, PhD(biochem), 67. *Prof Exp:* Staff fel, 69-73, res biologist growth regulation, 73-75, CHIEF, CELL CYCLE REGULATION SECT, NAT CANCER INST, 75- *Concurrent Pos:* Proj officer, Breast Cancer Task Force, Nat Cancer Inst, 74- *Mem:* AAAS; Am Asn Cancer Res; Am Soc Cell Biologists. *Res:* Cell cycle regulation; rate limiting steps of the division cycle and the effect of hormones on these processes; extracellular matrix and its role in growth regulation. *Mailing Add:* Bldg 10 Rm 5B39 Nat Cancer Inst Bethesda MD 20014

KIEBLER, JOHN W(ILLIAM), b Hershey, Pa, Apr 1, 28; m 55; c 3. ELECTRONICS. *Educ:* Lafayette Col, BS, 50. *Prof Exp:* Electronic scientist, Nat Bur Standards, 51-52; proj engr, Off Chief Ord, 52-53; assoc engr, Appl Physics Lab, Johns Hopkins Univ, 53-58, engr, 58-59, engr, Emerson Res Labs, 59-60; head, Network Implementation Br, 60-65, actg chief, Proj Opers Support Div, 65-66, asst chief, 66-70, proj mgr, Satellite Tracking & Data Acquisition, 70-73, SR ENGR, COMMUN DIV & SR COMMUN ENGR, HQ, GODDARD SPACE FLIGHT CTR, NASA, 79- *Concurrent Pos:* mem, US Deleg World Admin Radio Conf, 79 & Nat Acad Sci Comt Radio Frequencies. *Mem:* Inst Elec & Electronics Engrs. *Res:* Communications systems; remote sensing. *Mailing Add:* 14520 Dowling Dr Burtonsville MD 20866

KIEBURTZ, R(OBERT) BRUCE, b Seattle, Wash, Mar 22, 31; m 54; c 2. ELECTRICAL ENGINEERING. *Educ:* Univ Wash, BSEE, 52, MSEE, 63, PhD(elec eng), 66. *Prof Exp:* Proj engr, Gen Elec Co, 54-57; res engr, Boeing Co, 57-65, supvr, 66-67; mem tech staff, Bell Tel Labs, 67-77, ASST ENG MGR, NETWORK PLANNING & BUS SERV, AM TEL & TEL CO, 77- *Mem:* AAAS; sr mem Inst Elec & Electronics Engrs; NY Acad Sci. *Res:* Ballistic missile defense; balanced magnetic circuits for logic and memory; digital processing of signals, including digital filtering. *Mailing Add:* Am Tel & Tel Co Basking Ridge NJ 07920

KIEBURTZ, RICHARD B(RUCE), b Spokane, Wash, Nov 28, 33; m 59; c 2. COMPUTER SCIENCE. *Educ:* Univ Wash, BSEE, 55, MSEE, 57, PhD(elec eng), 61. *Prof Exp:* Actg instr elec eng, Univ Wash, 57-60; from asst prof to assoc prof, NY Univ, 61-64; assoc prof elec sci, State Univ NY Stony Brook, 64-67, prof comput sci, 68-81, chmn dept, 70-75; PROF & CHMN DEPT COMPUT SCI & ENGR, OREGON GRAD CTR, 81- *Concurrent Pos:* Consult, CBS Labs, Conn, 62-63 & Rome Air Develop Ctr, US Air Force, 63-68; NSF sci fac fel, 68-69. *Mem:* AAAS; Inst Elec & Electronics Engrs; Asn Comput Mach. *Res:* programming languages; distributed computing. *Mailing Add:* Dept Comput Sci & Engr Oregon Grad Ctr Beaverton OR 97006

KIECKHEFER, ROBERT WILLIAM, b Milwaukee, Wis, Mar 13, 33; m 69; c 3. INSECT ECOLOGY. *Educ:* Univ Wis, BS, 55, PhD(entom), 62; Univ Minn, MS, 58. *Prof Exp:* RES ENTOMOLOGIST, NORTHERN GRAIN INSECTS RES LAB, USDA, 63- *Mem:* Entom Soc Am; Ecol Soc Am; Int Orgn Biol Control. *Res:* Aphid biology and ecology; ecology and biological control of cereal insects. *Mailing Add:* Northern Grain Insects Res RR 3 Brookings SD 57006

KIEFER, BARRY IRWIN, b Bayonne, NJ, May 16, 33; m 60. DEVELOPMENTAL BIOLOGY. *Educ:* Univ Denver, BS, 60; Univ Calif, Berkeley, PhD(zool), 65. *Prof Exp:* From asst prof to assoc prof, 65-77, PROF BIOL, WESLEYAN UNIV, 77- *Mem:* Am Soc Cell Biol. *Res:* Genetic regulation of spermiogenesis in Drosophila. *Mailing Add:* Dept of Biol Wesleyan Univ Middletown CT 06457

KIEFER, DAVID JOHN, b Sewickley, Pa, Oct 1, 38; m 62. MICROBIOLOGY, IMMUNOLOGY. *Educ:* Univ Pittsburgh, BS, 68; Univ Miami, PhD(microbiol), 77. *Prof Exp:* Res technician immunol, Sch Med, Univ Miami, 68-77; staff immunologist, 78-80, SR STAFF IMMUNOLOGIST, CORDIS LABS, INC, 80- *Mem:* Am Soc Microbiol. *Res:* Pregnancy associated plasma proteins; immunology of pregnancy; immunosuppressive properties of pregnancy serum; enzyme-labeled immunoassays for the detection and quantitation of humoral constituents. *Mailing Add:* Cordis Labs Inc 2140 N Miami Ave Miami FL 33127

KIEFER, EDGAR FRANCIS, b Tsingtoa, China, Sept 9, 34; US citizen; m 57, 74; c 6. ORGANIC CHEMISTRY. *Educ:* Stanford Univ, BS, 57; Calif Inst Technol, PhD(chem), 60. *Prof Exp:* Asst chem, Calif Inst Technol, 57-58; res assoc, Univ Ill, 60-61; res chemist, Chevron Res Corp, 61-62; from asst prof to assoc prof, 62-72, PROF CHEM, UNIV HAWAII, 72- *Concurrent Pos:* NSF sci fac fel, Stanford Univ, 68-69; vis scientist, Mass Inst Technol, 78. *Mem:* Am Chem Soc. *Res:* Physical organic and bioorganic chemistry; stereochemistry. *Mailing Add:* Dept of Chem Univ of Hawaii Honolulu HI 96822

KIEFER, HAROLD MILTON, b Detroit, Mich, Mar 9, 33; m 66; c 1. THEORETICAL PHYSICS. *Educ:* Wayne State Univ, PhD(physics), 69. *Prof Exp:* Personnel exam, City of Detroit, 58-62; asst prof, 69-81, ASSOC PROF PHYSICS, NORFOLK STATE COL, 81- *Mem:* Am Phys Soc. *Res:* Applications of group theory to coulomb potential problems. *Mailing Add:* Dept of Physics Norfolk State Col Norfolk VA 23504

KIEFER, HELEN CHILTON, biochemistry, enzymology, see previous edition

KIEFER, JACK C, mathematical statistics, deceased

KIEFER, JOHN DAVID, b Evansville, Ind, Jan 2, 40; m 64; c 5. GEOLOGIC HAZARDS, ENERGY RESOURCES. *Educ:* St Josephs Col, BA, 61; Univ Ill, MS, 65, PhD(eng geol), 70. *Prof Exp:* Instr geol, Univ Ill, 65-67; assoc prof, Eastern Ky Univ, 67-71; head, Eng Geol Div, Geotech Eng Assocs, 71-78; eng geologist, Geol Surv Ala, 78-79, head, Water Resources Div, 79; HEAD, WATER RESOURCES SECT, KY GEOL SURV, 79-, ASST STATE GEOLOGIST, 81- *Mem:* Geol Soc Am; Am Asn Petrol Geologists; Soc Econ Paleontologists & Mineralogists; AAAS. *Res:* Engineering geology and hydrogeology. *Mailing Add:* 311 Breckinridge Hall Ky Geol Surv Univ Ky Lexington KY 40506

KIEFER, JOHN HAROLD, b New Ulm, Minn, Aug 27, 32; m 61; c 1. PHYSICAL CHEMISTRY. *Educ:* Univ Minn, BS, 54; Cornell Univ, PhD(phys chem), 61. *Prof Exp:* Fel, Cornell Univ, 59-60; res staff mem, Los Alamos Sci Lab, Univ Calif, 61-67; assoc prof, 67-72, PROF ENERGY ENG & CHEM, UNIV ILL, CHICAGO CIRCLE, 72- *Concurrent Pos:* Consult, Los Alamos Nat Lab, 67- *Mem:* Combustion Inst. *Res:* Shock tube studies of kinetics; energy transfer in high temperature gases; laser induced chemistry. *Mailing Add:* Dept of Energy Eng Univ of Ill at Chicago Circle Chicago IL 60680

KIEFER, JOSEPH HENRY, b Chicago, Ill, Aug 20, 10; m 45; c 3. UROLOGY. *Educ:* Northwestern Univ, BS, 31, BM, 34, MD, 35. *Prof Exp:* From instr to asst prof surg, 37-45, assoc prof in chg div urol, 45-60, PROF UROL, UNIV ILL COL MED, 60-, SR CONSULT, UNIV HOSP, 71- *Mem:* AAAS; Am Asn Hist Med; Am Asn Genito-Urinary Surg; fel Am Col Surg; Int Soc Urol. *Res:* Congenital sexual anomalies; history of urology. *Mailing Add:* Univ of Ill Hosp Div of Urol PO Box 6998 Chicago IL 60680

KIEFER, MICHAEL P, b San Antonio, Tex, Jan 12, 46; m 74; c 1. RECOMBINANT DNA. *Educ:* WTex State Univ, BS, 71, MS, 72; Stanton Univ, PhD(biol), 75. *Prof Exp:* Res mgr, Duncan Investments, 68-72; PRES, MPK OMEGA CO, 72- *Honors & Awards:* Einstein Award, World Biol Soc, 78; Darwin Award, World Biol Soc, 82. *Mem:* Am Biol Asn. *Res:* Aquatography; hypnosis; genetics. *Mailing Add:* 3615 Carson Amarillo TX 79109

KIEFER, RALPH W, b Somerville, NJ, Nov 28, 34; m 59; c 2. CIVIL ENGINEERING. *Educ:* Cornell Univ, BCE, 56, MS, 60, PhD(civil eng), 64. *Prof Exp:* Asst hwy engr, NJ State Hwy Dept, 58; asst civil eng, Cornell Univ, 58-62; from asst prof to assoc prof, 62-70, PROF CIVIL ENG, UNIV WIS-MADISON, 71-, ENG DIR, ENVIRON REMOTE SENSING CTR, 81- *Concurrent Pos:* Vis prof, Univ Hawaii, 70-71. *Mem:* Am Soc Civil Engrs; Am Soc Photogram. *Res:* Remote sensing of the environment; engineering applications of airphoto interpretation. *Mailing Add:* 1210 Eng Bldg Univ of Wis Madison WI 53706

KIEFER, RICHARD L, b Columbia, Pa, Dec 14, 37; m 62; c 2. NUCLEAR CHEMISTRY. *Educ:* Drew Univ, AB, 59; Univ Calif, Berkeley, PhD(nuclear chem), 64. *Prof Exp:* Res assoc, Brookhaven Nat Lab, 63-65; asst prof, 65-68, assoc prof, 68-81, PROF CHEM, COL WILLIAM & MARY, 81- *Mem:* Am Chem Soc; Am Phys Soc. *Res:* Nuclear reactions induced by both high-energy and low-energy projectiles; studies of nuclear reaction mechanisms. *Mailing Add:* Dept of Chem Col of William & Mary Williamsburg VA 23185

KIEFF, ELLIOTT DAN, b Philadelphia, Pa, Feb 2, 43; m 65; c 2. INFECTIOUS DISEASES, VIROLOGY. *Educ:* Univ Pa, AB, 63; Johns Hopkins Univ, MD, 66; Univ Chicago, PhD(virol), 71. *Prof Exp:* Intern, Hosp, 66-67, from jr asst resident to sr asst resident, 67-69, resident, 69-70, asst prof, 70-74, assoc prof, 74-78, PROF, SCH MED, UNIV CHICAGO, 79-CHIEF SECT INFECTIOUS DIS, 71- *Concurrent Pos:* Mem, Comt Virol, Univ Chicago, 70-; fac res award, Am Cancer Soc; Carl Hartford vis prof, Washington Univ. *Mem:* Infectious Dis Soc Am; Am Soc Clin Invest; Am Asn Cancer Res; Am Soc Microbiol. *Res:* Molecular biology of animal viruses, particularly herpes viruses. *Mailing Add:* 910 E 58th St Univ Chicago Chicago IL 60637

KIEFFER, HUGH HARTMAN, b Norwich, Conn, Oct 31, 39; m 66; c 1. PLANETARY SCIENCE. *Educ:* Calif Inst Technol, BS, 61, PhD(planetary sci), 68. *Prof Exp:* Res fel planetary sci, Calif Inst Technol, 68-69; asst prof, 69-75, assoc prof planetary sci, Univ Calif, Los Angeles, 75-78; RES GEOPHYSICIST, BR ASTROGEOL STUDIES, GEOL DIV, US GEOL SURV, 78- *Concurrent Pos:* Adj prof planetary sci, Univ Calif, Los Angeles, 78-81. *Honors & Awards:* Sci Achievement Medal, NASA, 77. *Mem:* AAAS; Am Astron Soc; Am Meteorol Soc; Am Optical Soc; Am Geophys Union. *Res:* Planetary atmospheres and surfaces; spectra of the moon and planets; atmospheric condensation processes; infrared observations and thermal models; thermal infrared and radar observations of volcanos. *Mailing Add:* Astrogeol 2255 N Gemini Dr Flagstaff AZ 86001

KIEFFER, LEE JOSEPH, b Dubuque, Iowa, July 6, 31; m 59; c 5. ATOMIC PHYSICS. *Educ:* Iowa State Univ, BS, 53; St Louis Univ, MS, 55, PhD(physics), 58. *Prof Exp:* Resident res assoc, Argonne Nat Lab, 57-58, temp mem staff, 58-59; physicist, Aeronutronic Div, Ford Motor Co, 59-60; PHYSICIST, NAT BUR STANDARDS, 60- *Concurrent Pos:* Lectr & fel, Joint Inst Lab Astrophys, Univ Colo, Boulder, 64- *Honors & Awards:* Gold

Medal Award, US Dept Com, 70. *Mem:* Fel Am Phys Soc. *Res:* Molecular pressure broadening; hyperfine structure and nuclear moments; electron and atomic cross-section; critical evaluation of atomic data. *Mailing Add:* Physics B362 Nat Bur Standards Washington DC 20234

KIEFFER, NAT, b Montgomery, La, July 13, 30; m 51; c 3. GENETICS. *Educ:* Univ Southwestern La, BS, 52; La State Univ, MS, 56; Okla State Univ, PhD(animal breeding), 59. *Prof Exp:* Animal geneticist, Range Livestock Exp Sta, USDA, 59-62, supt beef cattle res, 62-64; res assoc & fel molecular biol, Univ Calif, Berkeley, 64-65; asst prof, 65-69, assoc prof mammalian cytogenetics, 69-77, PROF GENETICS, ANIMAL & PLANT SCI, TEX A&M UNIV, 77- *Mem:* Genetics Soc Am; Am Soc Animal Sci. *Res:* Population genetics; beef cattle breeding; molecular biology, gene action in bacteria on molecular level; mammalian cytogenetics, beef cattle. *Mailing Add:* Dept of Animal Sci & Plant Sci Tex A&M Univ College Station TX 77843

KIEFFER, STEPHEN A, b Minneapolis, Minn, Dec 20, 35; m 58; c 4. RADIOLOGY. *Educ:* Univ Minn, BA, 56, BS, 57, MD, 59. *Prof Exp:* From instr to prof radiol, Univ Minn, 66-74; PROF RADIOL & CHMN DEPT, STATE UNIV NY UPSTATE MED CTR, 74- *Concurrent Pos:* Nat Heart Inst cardiovasc trainee, Univ Minn, 61-62 & 64-65, Nat Inst Neurol Dis & Blindness fel neuroradiol, 66, James Picker Found scholar radiol res, 66-68; chief radiol, Minneapolis Vet Admin Hosp, 68-74. *Honors & Awards:* Outstanding Paper Award, Am Soc Neuroradiol, 70. *Mem:* Am Col Radiol; Am Soc Neuroradiol (pres, 78-79); Radiol Soc NAm; Am Roentgen Ray Soc. *Res:* Neuroradiology; myelography; cerebrospinal fluid circulation. *Mailing Add:* Dept of Radiol State Univ NY Upstate Med Ctr Syracuse NY 13210

KIEFFER, SUSAN WERNER, b Warren, Pa, Nov 17, 42; m 66; c 1. VOLCANOLOGY, MINERAL PHYSICS. *Educ:* Allegheny Col, BSc, 64; Calif Inst Technol, MSc, 67, PhD(planetary sci), 71. *Prof Exp:* Res geophysicist, Univ Calif, Los Angeles, 71-73, asst prof, 73-78, assoc prof geol, 78-79; GEOLOGIST, US GEOL SURV, 78- *Concurrent Pos:* Alfred P Sloan res fel, 77-79. *Honors & Awards:* Mineral Soc Am Award, 80; W H Mendenhall lectr, US Geol Surv, 80. *Mem:* Geol Soc Am; Am Geophys Union; Meteoritical Soc. *Res:* Geological physics; high pressure geophysics and impact processes; shock metamorphism of natural materials; thermodynamic properties of minerals; mechanisms of geyser and volcano eruptions. *Mailing Add:* US Geol Surv 2255 N Gemini Dr Flagstaff AZ 86001

KIEFFER, WILLIAM FRANKLIN, b Trenton, NJ, Mar 16, 15; m 40; c 2. PHYSICAL CHEMISTRY. *Educ:* Col Wooster, BA, 36; Ohio State Univ, MSc, 38; Brown Univ, PhD(photochem), 40. *Prof Exp:* Asst chem, Ohio State Univ, 36-38 & Brown Univ, 38-39; instr, Col Wooster, 40-42; from instr to asst prof, Western Reserve Univ, 42-46; prof, 46-80, EMER PROF CHEM, COL WOOSTER, 80- *Concurrent Pos:* Res partic, Chem Div, Oak Ridge Nat Lab, 51-52; ed J Chem Educ, Am Chem Soc, 55-67; NSF fac fel, Mass Inst Technol, 63-64; vis scholar, Stanford Univ, 69-70 & Univ Calif, Santa Cruz, 74-75, vis prof, US Naval Acad, 81. *Honors & Awards:* Award Chem Educ, Mfg Chem Asn, 65 & Am Chem Soc, 68. *Mem:* AAAS; Am Chem Soc; Am Inst Chemists; NY Acad Sci. *Res:* Photochemistry; radiation chemistry; chemical education. *Mailing Add:* 1873 Golden Rain Rd 3 Walnut Creek CA 94595

KIEFT, JOHN A, b Oak Park, Ill, Feb 27, 41; m 65. PHYSICAL CHEMISTRY, INORGANIC CHEMISTRY. *Educ:* Hope Col, BA, 63; Ill Inst Technol, PhD(chem), 68. *Prof Exp:* Chemist, Shell Chem Co, 67-70; res chemist anal chem, 70-71, supvr prod develop, 72-74, sect mgr, 74-76, sr sect mgr anal, 76-79, DEPT MGR RES SERV, WESTERN RES LAB, STAUFFER CHEM CO, 79- *Mem:* Am Chem Soc. *Res:* New product development; analytical chemistry; agricultural chemicals; research administration. *Mailing Add:* Stauffer Chem Co 1200 S 47th St Richmond CA 94804

KIEFT, LESTER, b Grand Haven, Mich, Sept 18, 12; m 41; c 3. ANALYTICAL CHEMISTRY. *Educ:* Hope Col, AB, 34; Pa State Col, MS, 36, PhD(anal chem), 39. *Prof Exp:* Asst, Pa State Col, 34-37; asst prof chem, Pa State Jr Col, 37-42; asst prof, 42-44, head dept, 44-70, secy fac, 68-80, PROF CHEM, BUCKNELL UNIV, 44- *Mem:* AAAS; Am Chem Soc; Nat Sci Teachers Asn. *Res:* Analytical properties of salts of the iodometallic acids. *Mailing Add:* Dept of Chem Bucknell Univ Lewisburg PA 17837

KIEFT, RICHARD LEONARD, b Lewisburg, Pa, Apr 27, 45. INORGANIC CHEMISTRY, ANALYTICAL CHEMISTRY. *Educ:* Dickinson Col, BS, 67; Univ Ill, Urbana, PhD(inorg chem), 73. *Prof Exp:* Teaching res assoc chem, Tulane Univ, 73-75; asst prof, 75-81, ASSOC PROF CHEM, MONMOUTH COL, ILL, 82- *Mem:* Am Chem Soc; Sigma Xi. *Res:* Synthesis and identification of organometallic compounds which have potential biological importance. *Mailing Add:* 520 E First Ave Monmouth IL 61462

KIEHL, JEFFREY THEODORE, b Harrisburg, Pa, June 10, 52; m 80. RADIATIVE TRANSFER, CLIMATE MODELING. *Educ:* Elizabethtown Col, BS, 74; Ind Univ, MS, 77; State Univ NY, Albany, PhD(atmospheric sci), 81. *Prof Exp:* VIS SCIENTIST ATMOSPHERIC SCI, NAT CTR ATMOSPHERIC RES, 81- *Res:* Electromagnetic scattering from spherical and non-spherical particles; two-dimensional radiative-convective climate model; infrared transfer in the atmosphere with applications to the carbon dioxide climate problems. *Mailing Add:* Nat Ctr Atmospheric Res PO Box 3000 Boulder CO 80307

KIEHL, RICHARD ARTHUR, b Akron, Ohio, Feb 14, 48. PHYSICAL ELECTRONICS. *Educ:* Purdue Univ, BS & MS, 70; PhD(elec eng), 74. *Prof Exp:* Asst elec eng, Sch Elec Eng, Purdue Univ, 71-74; mem tech staff, Div Solid-State Device Physics Res, Sandia Labs, 74-80; MEM TECH STAFF, EXPLOR HIGH-SPEED DEVICE GROUP, BELL LABS, 80- *Mem:* Inst Elec & Electronics Engrs. *Res:* Microwave and optical active semiconductor devices; high-speed logic devices in compound semiconductors. *Mailing Add:* 600 Mountain Ave 7B-416 Murray Hill NJ 07974

KIEHLMANN, EBERHARD, b Grosshartmannsdorf, Ger, Feb 9, 37. ORGANIC CHEMISTRY. *Educ:* Univ Tübingen, Vordiplom, 59; Univ Md, College Park, PhD(org chem), 64. *Prof Exp:* Res fel, Univ Calif, Berkeley, 64-65 & Dartmouth Col, 65-66; asst prof, 66-72, ASSOC PROF CHEM, SIMON FRASER UNIV, 72- *Mem:* Am Chem Soc; Ger Soc Chem; Chem Inst Can. *Res:* Synthesis of isoflavanoids. *Mailing Add:* Dept Chem Simon Fraser Univ Burnaby BC V5A 1S6 Can

KIEHN, ROBERT MITCHELL, b Oak Park, Ill, Dec 29, 29; m 58. PHYSICS. *Educ:* Mass Inst Technol, BS, 50, PhD, 54. *Prof Exp:* Staff physicist, Los Alamos Sci Lab, 54-62; assoc prof, 62-72, PROF PHYSICS, UNIV HOUSTON, 72- *Mem:* Am Phys Soc; Am Nuclear Soc. *Res:* Neutron reactor physics; hydrodynamics; thermodynamics. *Mailing Add:* Dept of Physics Univ of Houston Houston TX 77004

KIEL, JOHNATHAN LLOYD, b Houston, Tex, Sept 4, 49; m 73; c 2. BIOCHEMICAL IMMUNOLOGY, BACTERIOLOGY. *Educ:* Tex A&M Univ, BS, 73, DVM, 74, Health Sci Ctr, PhD(microbiol & biochem), 81. *Prof Exp:* Instr vet microbiol, Sch Vet Med, Tex A&M Univ, 74-75; vet, Vet Pub Health, Grissom AFB, Ind, 75-77, RES IMMUNOL, PHYSICS BBR, RADIATION SCI DIV, US AIR FORCE SCH AEROSPACE MED, BROOKS AFB, TEX, 81- *Mem:* Am Vet Med Asn. *Res:* Oxidative metabolism of the various cells of the immune system and how it influences the immune response and cytotoxic mechanisms; influence of radiofrequency radiation on this metabolism. *Mailing Add:* 5814 Fort Stanwix San Antonio TX 78233

KIEL, OTIS GERALD, b Wichita Falls, Tex, Feb 10, 31; m 53; c 3. ENGINEERING SCIENCES, MATHEMATICS. *Educ:* NTex State Univ, BS, 49; Univ Okla, BS, 56, MS, 57, PhD(eng sci), 63. *Prof Exp:* sect supvr, Continental Oil Co, 59-80, CHIEF RESERVOIR ENGR, CONOCO, INC, 80- *Honors & Awards:* C K Ferguson Award, Am Inst Mining, Metall & Petrol Engrs, 63. *Mem:* Am Inst Mining, Metall & Petrol Engrs; Soc Petrol Engrs. *Res:* Reservoir mechanics, mathematical modeling; reserve determination enhanced recovery projects. *Mailing Add:* 807 Soboda Ct Houston TX 77079

KIELKOPF, JOHN F, b Louisville, Ky, Aug 1, 45; m 70. ATOMIC SPECTROSCOPY, ASTROPHYSICS. *Educ:* Univ Louisville, BS & MS, 66; Johns Hopkins Univ, PhD(physics), 69. *Prof Exp:* Asst prof, 69-74, assoc prof, 74-77, PROF PHYSICS, UNIV LOUISVILLE, 77- *Concurrent Pos:* Assoc res scientist, Johns Hopkins Univ, 74; vis scientist, Argonne Nat Lab, 74-75; astronomer, Observatory Paris, Meudon, 79-80; scientist in residence, Argonne Nat Lab, 81. *Mem:* Am Phys Soc; Optical Soc Am; Am Astron Soc. *Res:* Optical interferometry; high resolution atomic spectroscopy; spectra of ionized rare earths; shift and shape of atomic spectral lines; stellar spectroscopy; interatomic forces. *Mailing Add:* Dept of Physics Univ of Louisville Louisville KY 40208

KIELY, DONALD EDWARD, b Waterbury, Conn, Jan 5, 38; m 63; c 3. SYNTHETIC ORGANIC CHEMISTRY. *Educ:* Fairfield Univ, BS, 60; Univ Conn, PhD(org chem), 65. *Prof Exp:* Vis asst prof org chem, Wofford Col, 65-66; staff fel, Nat Inst Arthritis & Metab Dis, 66-68; from asst prof to assoc prof, 68-77, PROF CHEM, UNIV ALA, BIRMINGHAM, 77- *Concurrent Pos:* Vis fel, Res Sch Chem, Australian Nat Univ, 74; resident prof, Staley Mfg Co, 81-82; ed, J Carbohydrate Chem, 81- *Mem:* Am Chem Soc; Sigma Xi. *Res:* Synthesis of biologically interesting carbohydrates, cyclitols and other carbocyclic compounds; chemical studies related to cyclitol biosynthesis; synthetic carbohydrate chemistry; industrially related carbohydrate chemistry. *Mailing Add:* Dept of Chem Univ Col Univ of Ala Birmingham AL 35294

KIELY, JOHN ROCHE, b Berkeley, Calif, Nov 8, 06; m 40; c 5. CIVIL ENGINEERING. *Educ:* Univ Wash, BSCE, 31. *Prof Exp:* Construct engr, Rainier Pulp & Paper Co, 24-31, supt, 31-36; resident engr, Rayonier, Inc, 37-40, asst gen supt, 40-42; mgr outfitting, subassembly & transport, Calif Shipbuilding Corp, 42-45; proj mgr, Bechtel Bros McCone Co, 45-48, mgr, Bechtel Corp, 48-51, vpres, 51-54, sr vpres, 57-67, exec vpres, 67-71, dir, 54-74, EXEC CONSULT, BECHTEL CORP, 74- *Mem:* Nat Acad Eng; fel Am Inst Mech Engrs; Am Soc Civil Engrs; Am Soc Mech Eng; Sigma Xi. *Mailing Add:* Bechtel Corp 50 Beale St PO Box 3965 San Francisco CA 94119

KIELY, JOHN STEVEN, b Missoula, Mont, Oct 11, 51; m 74. PHARMACOLOGY. *Educ:* Mont State Univ, BSc, 74; NDak State Univ, PhD(organ chem), 79. *Prof Exp:* Assoc res fel, Lawrence Berkeley Lab, Univ Calif, 79-81; scientist, 81, SR SCIENTIST, PARKE DAVIS/WARNER LAMBERT PHARMACEUT RES, WARNER LAMBERT CO, 81- *Mem:* Am Chem Soc; Sigma Xi; AAAS. *Res:* Synthesis of physiologically active lipids and phospholipid; design and synthesis of ovally active antihypertensive agents. *Mailing Add:* Parke Davis/Warner Lambert Pharmaceut Res PO Box 1047 2800 Plymouth Rd Ann Arbor MI 48106

KIELY, LAWRENCE J, b Truxton, NY, Feb 26, 22; m 51; c 9. ANATOMY, PHYSIOLOGY. *Educ:* Niagara Univ, BS, 43, MA, 47; Columbia Univ, MA, 49, EdD(biol), 51. *Prof Exp:* From instr to assoc prof biol, 49-60, prof sci educ, 60-74, PROF BIOL, NIAGARA UNIV, 60- *Concurrent Pos:* Lectr, Rosary Hill Col, 55-, grant exp psychol, 64-65; res grant human physiol, Williams Col, 65; res grant marine biol & trop ecol, Univ PR, 67; res grant sci educ, Ithaca Col, 68; res grant hist biol, Ohio State Univ, 69. *Mem:* AAAS; Am Physiol Soc; Nat Sci Teachers Asn; Nat Asn Biol Teachers. *Res:* Human anatomy, physiology and biology; science education. *Mailing Add:* Dept of Biol Niagara University NY 14109

KIELY, MICHAEL LAWRENCE, b Springfield, Ill, June 17, 38; m 67; c 2. ANATOMY. *Educ:* Lewis Col, BS, 60; Loyola Univ Ill, MS, 64, PhD(anat), 67. *Prof Exp:* Res assoc, Stritch Sch Med, 67, asst prof, 67-76, ASSOC PROF ANAT, SCH DENT, LOYOLA UNIV, CHICAGO, 76- *Mem:* Am Asn Anatomists; Int Asn Dent Res; Am Asn Dent Res. *Res:* Gross and oral anatomy; influence of endocrines and magnesium deficiency on the tissues of the rat incisor, especially mitotic activity related to eruption rates. *Mailing Add:* 607 Arrowhead Carol Stream IL 60187

KIENHOLZ, ELDON W, b Moscow, Idaho, May 27, 28; m 50; c 4. ANIMAL NUTRITION. *Educ:* Manchester Col, BS, 50; Wash State Univ, BS, 52, MS, 59; Univ Wis, PhD(biochem), 62. *Prof Exp:* Instr high sch, Wash, 52-54 & 55-57; asst poultry nutrit, Wash State Univ, 57-59; res asst poultry biochem, Univ Wis, 59-61, proj asst biochem, 61-62; from asst prof to assoc prof, 62-69, prof poultry nutrit, 69-81, PROF DEPT ANIMAL SCI, COLO STATE UNIV, 81- *Concurrent Pos:* Nutritionist, Human Nutrit Div, USDA, Beltsville, Md, 69-70; vis prof, Dept Animal Sci, Univ Ill, 76-77. *Mem:* Poultry Sci Asn. *Res:* Mineral nutrition and metabolism; processing of legume seeds; value of foodstuffs for poultry; pollution and animal wastes. *Mailing Add:* Dept of Animal Sci Colo State Univ Ft Collins CO 80521

KIENTZ, MARVIN L, b Clovis, Calif, Jan 28, 36; m 59; c 2. BIOCHEMISTRY. *Educ:* Fresno State Col, BA, 58, MA, 61; Western Ont Univ, PhD(biochem), 66. *Prof Exp:* Teacher high sch, 59-63; res biochemist, Med Ctr, Univ Calif, San Francisco, 66-67; assoc prof, 67-74, PROF CHEM, SONOMA STATE UNIV, 74- *Concurrent Pos:* Inst dir, Nat Sci Found, 71-73. *Mem:* Am Chem Soc. *Res:* Determination of the structure of proteins; protein polymorphism. *Mailing Add:* Dept of Chem Sonoma State Univ Rohnert Park CA 94928

KIER, ANN B, b Littlefield, Tex, June 26, 49; m 79. PATHOLOGY, ANIMAL MEDICINE. *Educ:* Univ Tex, Austin, BA, 71; Tex A&M Univ, BS, 73, DVM,74; Univ Mo, Columbia, PhD(path), 79; Am Col Lab Animal Med, dipl. *Prof Exp:* NIH fel, Lab Animal Med & Comparative Path, 76-79, ASST PROF PATH, UNIV MO-COLUMBIA, 79- *Concurrent Pos:* Dir, Histopath Lab, Vet Med Diag Lab, 80- *Mem:* Am Vet Med Asn; Am Asn Vet Med Col; Am Asn Lab Animal Sci. *Res:* Immunpathology, histopathology and oncogenicity of tumors; neutrophil and macrophage chemotaxis; development of a colony of coagulation factor XII deficient domestic cats; genetics; neutrophil and macrophage chemotaxis. *Mailing Add:* Dept Vet Path Col Vet Med Univ Mo Columbia MO 65211

KIER, LAWRENCE CHARLES, toxicology, forensic science, see previous edition

KIER, LEMONT BURWELL, b Cleveland, Ohio, Sept 13, 30; m 53; c 5. MEDICINAL CHEMISTRY. *Educ:* Ohio State Univ, BS, 54, PhD(med chem), 58. *Prof Exp:* Asst prof pharmaceut chem, Univ Fla, 59-63; assoc prof, Ohio State Univ, 63-66; sr med chemist, Columbus Labs, Battelle Mem Inst, 66-69, assoc fel med chem, 69-72; prof chem, Mass Col Pharm, 72-77; PROF & CHMN, DEPT PHARMACEUT CHEM, MED COL VA-VA COMMONWEALTH UNIV, 77- *Concurrent Pos:* Adj prof, Univ Mich, 69-72; chmn dept chem, Mass Col Pharm, 72-74. *Mem:* Am Pharmaceut Asn; Am Chem Soc; fel Acad Pharmaceut Sci. *Res:* Theoretical approaches to drug structure activity relationships. *Mailing Add:* 1604 Willingham Dr Richmond VA 23233

KIER, PORTER MARTIN, b Pittsburgh, Pa, Oct 22, 27; m 50; c 2. INVERTEBRATE PALEONTOLOGY. *Educ:* Univ Mich, BS, 50, MS, 51; Cambridge Univ, PhD, 54. *Hon Degrees:* ScD, Cambridge Univ, 74. *Prof Exp:* Asst prof, Univ Houston, 56-57; assoc cur, Smithsonian Inst, 57-67, cur & chmn dept paleobiol, 67-73, dir, Nat Mus Natural Hist, 73-80. *Concurrent Pos:* Guggenheim fel, 68; ed, J Paleont, Paleont Soc. *Mem:* Geol Soc Am; Paleont Soc. *Res:* Fossils and living echinoids. *Mailing Add:* Nat Mus Natural Hist Smithsonian Inst Washington DC 20560

KIERBOW, JULIE VAN NOTE PARKER, b Fayetteville, Tenn, Feb 13, 25; m 65. PHYSICAL CHEMISTRY, RADIOCHEMISTRY. *Educ:* Ohio State Univ, BS, 45; Univ Hawaii, MS, 48; Univ Colo, PhD(chem), 57. *Prof Exp:* Asst chem, Ohio State Univ, 44-45; res engr, Battelle Mem Inst, 45-46 & 48-50; asst, Univ Hawaii, 46-48; phys chemist, Redstone Arsenal Res Div, Rohm & Haas Co, 51-54; asst chem, Univ Colo, 54-56; from asst prof to assoc prof, 57-67, PROF CHEM, CALIF STATE UNIV, LONG BEACH, 67- *Mem:* AAAS; Am Chem Soc. *Res:* Scintillation properties of solutions, particularly as related to structure of metal-organic compounds; use of radiotracers in development of analytical techniques. *Mailing Add:* Dept of Chem Calif State Univ Long Beach CA 90840

KIERNAN, JOHN ALAN, b Kidderminstar, Eng, 1942; m 67; c 5. NEUROHISTOLOGY. *Educ:* Univ Birmingham, BSc, 63, MB & ChB, 66, PhD(neuroanat), 69. *Hon Degrees:* DSc, Univ Birmingham, 79. *Prof Exp:* House surgeon, East Birmingham Hosp, 66-67, res fel, Dept Anat, 67-69; fel med, Sidney Sussex Col, 69-72; asst prof, 72-75, assoc prof, 75-81, PROF, DEPT ANAT, UNIV WESTERN ONT, 81- *Concurrent Pos:* House physician, Worcester Royal Infirmary, 67; sr res fel, Sidney Sussex Col, Univ Cambridge, 69-71, dir studies med, 70-72; univ demonstr, 71-72. *Mem:* Anat Soc Brit; Bot Soc Brit Isles; Histochem Soc. *Res:* Reactions of nervous tissue to injury; histology and histochemistry; neuroanatomy. *Mailing Add:* Dept Anat Univ Western Ont London ON N6A 5C1 Can

KIERSCH, GEORGE ALFRED, b Lodi, Calif, Apr 15, 18; m 42; c 4. GEOLOGY. *Educ:* Colo Sch Mines, GE, 42; Univ Ariz, PhD(geol), 47. *Prof Exp:* Geologist, 79 Mining Co, Ariz, 46-47; instr, Mont Sch Mines, 47; geologist eng geol, Corps Engrs, 48; geologist, Folsom Dam Proj, 49-50; supv geologist, Int Boundary & Water Comn, 50-51; asst prof geol, Univ Ariz, 51-55; asst chief explor, Southern Pac Co, 56-60; chmn dept, 65-71, prof, 61-78, EMER PROF GEOL SCI, CORNELL UNIV, 78- *Concurrent Pos:* Consult eng geologist, 53-; dir mineral resources surv, Navajo-Hopi Indian Reservations, 53-56; NSF sr fel, Tech Univ Vienna, 63-64. *Honors & Awards:* Holdredge Award, Asn Eng Geol, 65. *Mem:* Fel Geol Soc Am; Soc Econ Geol; fel Am Soc Civil Eng; Asn Eng Geologists; Int Asn Eng Geologists. *Res:* Engineering geology; nonmetallic mineral deposits; environmental geology; geomechanics; forensic geology; application of geology to planning, design and operation engineering works. *Mailing Add:* Dept Geol Sci Cornell Univ Ithaca NY 14850

KIERSTEAD, HENRY ANDREW, b Pittsfield, Mass, June 5, 22; div; c 3. THERMODYNAMICS. *Educ:* Princeton Univ, AB, 43, MA, 45, PhD(chem), 46. *Prof Exp:* Asst, Rubber Reserve Bd, Princeton, 43; chemist, Argonne Nat Lab, 46-47, Inst Nuclear Studies fel, 47-48, AEC fel, Inst Nuclear Studies, 48-49; asst prof chem, Brown Univ, 49-52; CHEMIST, ARGONNE NAT LAB, 52- *Mem:* Am Phys Soc. *Res:* Phase transformations; critical phenomena; metallic hydrides. *Mailing Add:* Argonne Nat Lab 9700 S Cass Ave Argonne IL 60439

KIERSTEAD, RICHARD WIGHTMAN, b Fredericton, NB, Feb 17, 27; m 51, 64; c 3. ORGANIC CHEMISTRY. *Educ:* Univ NB, BSc, 48, MSc, 50; Univ London, PhD(org chem), 52. *Prof Exp:* Res assoc, Univ Toronto, 52-53 & Univ Calif, Los Angeles, 53-54; res chemist, E I du Pont de Nemours & Co, 54-55 & Harvard Univ, 55-56; sr res chemist, 56-63, group chief, 63-69, sect chief, 69-77, DIR MED CHEM, HOFFMANN-LA ROCHE, INC, 78- *Mem:* Am Chem Soc. *Res:* Synthesis of medicinal compounds. *Mailing Add:* 30 Willowbrook Dr North Caldwell NJ 07110

KIES, CONSTANCE, b Blue River, Wis, Dec 13, 34. NUTRITION. *Educ:* Wis State Univ, Platteville, BS, 55; Univ Wis, MS, 60, PhD(nutrit), 63. *Prof Exp:* Teacher high sch, Wis, 55-58; res asst human nutrit, Univ Wis, 60-63; from asst prof to assoc prof, 63-68, PROF HUMAN NUTRIT, UNIV NEBR, 68-, CHAIRPERSON DEPT, 81- *Concurrent Pos:* Univ res coun animal facility res grant, Univ Nebr, 65; NIH res grant, 64-69. *Honors & Awards:* Borden Award, Am Home Econ Asn, 73. *Mem:* Inst Food Technologists; Am Home Econ Asn; Am Dietetic Asn; Am Chem Soc; Am Inst Nutrit. *Res:* Human nutrition; protein and amino acid requirements of adult humans as determined in nitrogen balance studies; cereal proteins; dietary factors as related to blood lipid components; fibre-mineral interrelationships. *Mailing Add:* Dept of Food & Nutrit Univ of Nebr Lincoln NE 68503

KIES, MARIAN WOOD, b Centralia, Ill, June 10, 15; m 35; c 3. BIOCHEMISTRY, NEUROCHEMISTRY. *Educ:* Univ Ill, BS, 36; George Washington Univ, MA, 38, PhD(biochem), 44. *Prof Exp:* Asst, Med Sch, George Washington Univ, 36-38, instr biochem, 43-44; jr chemist, Bur Home Econ, USDA, Washington, DC, 38-39, jr chemist, Bur Agr & Indust Chem, 39-43, enzyme chemist, Calif, 44-47; biochemist, Oak Ridge Nat Lab, 47-48; biochemist, Div Biol Active Compounds, Bur Agr & Indust Chem, USDA, Md, 48-52; biochemist, NSF, 52-53; biochemist, 53-57, chief sect biochem, Lab Clin Sci, 57-68, CHIEF SECT MYELIN CHEM, LAB CEREBRAL METAB, NIMH, 68- *Mem:* Am Chem Soc; Am Soc Biol Chemists; Am Asn Immunol; Am Asn Neuropath; Am Soc Neurochem. *Res:* Etiology of allergic demyelinating diseases; function, structure and biological activity of myelin basic proteins; immunological studies on the nervous system. *Mailing Add:* 5407 Surrey St Washington DC 20815

KIESCHNICK, W(ILLIAM) F(REDERICK), JR, b Dallas, Tex, Jan 5, 23; m 48; c 2. CHEMICAL ENGINEERING. *Educ:* Rice Univ, BS, 47. *Prof Exp:* From jr engr to theoret oil reservoir engr, Atlantic Refining Co, 47-48, admin asst, Res Dept Admin, 48-49, sr chem engr, 49-51, supv engr, 51-54, head res sect, 54-59, asst to gen mgr explor, 59-61, mgr explor prod dist, 61-63, div mgr dists, 63-66, vpres & mgr cent region, Tex, 66-69, vpres synthetic crude & mineral opers, 69-70, vpres chem opers, 70-72, vpres & head corp planning, 72-73, exec vpres, 73-79, vchmn, 79, PRES IN CHARGE OF DOWNSTREAM DIV & MEM BD DIRS, ATLANTIC RICHFIELD CO, 73- *Mem:* Am Inst Mining, Metall & Petrol Engrs; Am Inst Chem Engrs; Am Asn Petrol Geologists; Am Petrol Inst. *Mailing Add:* Atlantic Richfield Co PO Box 2679 Los Angeles CA 90051

KIESEWETTER, WILLIAM BURNS, b Noble, Pa, Oct 5, 15; m 42; c 3. MEDICINE. *Educ:* Davidson Col, BA, 38; Univ Pa, MD, 42. *Prof Exp:* SURGEON-IN-CHIEF, CHILDREN'S HOSP, 55-; PROF PEDIAT SURG, SCH MED, UNIV PITTSBURGH, 59- *Mem:* Soc Univ Surgeons; Am Col Surg; Int Soc Surg; Am Surg Asn; Brit Asn Pediatric Surg. *Res:* Newborn surgery and particularly the metabolic and endocrine response of infant to surgery. *Mailing Add:* Children's Hosp 125 De Sota St Pittsburgh PA 15213

KIESLING, ERNST W(ILLIE), b Eola, Tex, Apr 8, 34; m 56; c 3. STRUCTURAL MECHANICS. *Educ:* Tex Tech Col, BS, 55; Mich State Univ, MS, 58, PhD(appl mech), 66. *Prof Exp:* From instr to asst prof civil eng, Tex Tech Col, 56-63; sr res engr, Struct Res Dept, Southwest Res Inst, 66-69; PROF CIVIL ENG & CHMN DEPT, TEX TECH UNIV, 69- *Mem:* Am Soc Eng Educ; Am Soc Civil Engrs; Nat Soc Prof Engrs. *Mailing Add:* Dept of Civil Eng Tex Tech Univ Lubbock TX 79409

KIESLING, RICHARD LORIN, b Rockford, Ill, Nov 20, 22; m 47; c 4. PLANT PATHOLOGY. *Educ:* Univ Wis, BS, 49, MS, 51, PhD(plant path), 52. *Prof Exp:* From asst prof to assoc prof plant path, Mich State Univ, 52-60; PROF PLANT PATH & HEAD DEPT, NDAK STATE UNIV, 60- *Concurrent Pos:* Chmn, Nat Barley Improv Comt, 79-80. *Mem:* Am Phytopath Soc; Am Inst Biol Sci. *Res:* Nature of disease resistance; smut fungi and pathological histology; genetics of barley disease resistance. *Mailing Add:* Dept Plant Path NDak State Univ Box 5012 Fargo ND 58105

KIESS, EDWARD MARION, b Washington, DC, Mar 10, 33; m 59; c 3. PHYSICS. *Educ:* Mass Inst Technol, 55; Pa State Univ, MS, 62, PhD(physics), 65. *Prof Exp:* Asst prof physics, Lycoming Col, 65; physicist, Battelle Mem Inst, 65-67; ASSOC PROF PHYSICS, HAMPDEN-SYDNEY COL, 68-, COTRELL GRANT, 71- *Mem:* Optical Soc Am. *Res:* Brillouin scattering; Fourier spectroscopy. *Mailing Add:* Dept of Physics Hampden-Sydney Col Hampden-Sydney VA 23943

KIESS, NORMAN HALVOR, b Washington, DC, Apr 6, 30. MOLECULAR SPECTROSCOPY, SPECTROSCOPY SOLIDS. *Educ:* Swarthmore Col, BA, 52; Univ Md, MS, 55; Johns Hopkins Univ, PhD(physics), 63, La Salle Exten Univ, dipl bus law, 74. *Prof Exp:* Physicist, Nat Bur Standards, 52-63; assoc prof physics, Stephen F Austin State Col, 63-66; assoc prof, Univ Southern Miss, 66-69. *Res:* Spectroscopy of lanthanide salt crystals; crystal growth; flame spectroscopy. *Mailing Add:* 2928 Brandywine St NW Washington DC 20008

KIESSLING, GEORGE ANTHONY, b New York, NY, Dec 2, 20; m 51; c 6. ELECTRICAL ENGINEERING. *Educ:* Manhattan Col, BSEE, 51; Stevens Inst Technol, MSIE, 53. *Prof Exp:* Mem tech staff, Physics Lab, Sylvania Electronics Prod, Inc, 51-54; adminr eng financial planning, 54-55, mgr eng stand & serv, 56-61, staff engr, 61, mgr prod admin, 62-63, mgr prod eng prof develop, 63-69, dir prof eng serv, 69-70, DIR PROD SAFETY PLANS & PROGS, RCA CORP, 70- *Mem:* Inst Elec & Electronics Engrs. *Res:* Product safety programs, including policy, management, systems, audit, standards, legislation and regulations; product ionizing and nonionizing radiation safety; laser safety including standards, legislation and regulations. *Mailing Add:* RCA Corp Cherry Hill Offices Bldg 202-2 Camden NJ 08101

KIESSLING, OSCAR EDWARD, b Jefferson, Wis, Apr 15, 01; m 28; c 5. MINERALOGY. *Educ:* Univ Wis, BA, 23, MA, 25; Brookings Inst, PhD(mineral econ), 27. *Prof Exp:* Mineral economist, US Bur Mines, 27-30, econ analyst, 30, chief economist, Div Mineral Statist, 30-35, Div Mineral Prod & Econs, 35-39, chg mineral technol & output studies in coop with Works Prog Admin-Nat Res Proj, 36-39; chief mineral industs, US Bur Census, 39-41, chief basic mat, 42; secy, Mach & Allied Prod Inst, 43-47; spec indust adv, US Tariff Comn, 47-71; CONSULT & AUTHOR RESOURCE MGT, 71- *Concurrent Pos:* Mem, Harris Mem Found Round Table Conf Population Probs, 29; lectr, Am Univ, 30-31, 34-35 & 37-38; ed, Minerals Yearbook, 32-36; mem, Cent Statist Bd, US Dept Interior, 33-; spec consult, Off Prod Mgt, 41. *Res:* Mineral economics and resources; economics of capital goods industries; cooperative development of oil pools. *Mailing Add:* 7048 Haycock Rd Falls Church VA 22043

KIEVAL, HARRY SEARS, b Brooklyn, NY, Nov 17, 13. MATHEMATICS. *Educ:* Cornell Univ, AB, 36, Univ Cincinnati, AM, 39, PhD(math), 43. *Prof Exp:* Instr math, Ind Tech Col, 41-42; instr, NC State Col, 42-43; instr, Univ Rochester, 43-45; instr, Brooklyn Col, 46-51; instr, Polytech Inst Brooklyn, 52-54; mathematician, Control Instrument Co, 55-58; engr, Radio Corp Am, 58-59; assoc prof math, State Univ NY Col New Paltz, 59-66; prof, 66-81, EMER PROF MATH, HUMBOLDT STATE COL, 81- *Concurrent Pos:* Mem staff, Polytech Inst Brooklyn, 54-59. *Mem:* Am Math Soc; Math Asn Am. *Mailing Add:* Dept of Math Humboldt State Col Arcata CA 95521

KIEWIET DE JONGE, JOOST H A, b Leiden, Netherlands, Sept 4, 19; m 54; c 1. ASTRONOMY. *Educ:* Harvard Univ, PhD(astron), 54. *Prof Exp:* Instr, 50-54, asst prof, 54-65, ASSOC PROF ASTRON, UNIV PITTSBURGH, 66-, ACTG CHMN, 70-75. *Concurrent Pos:* Lectr, Chatham Col, 56-70; consult, J W Fecker Div, Am Optical, 60-70; actg dir, Allegheny Observ, 70-77, mem staff, 77- *Mem:* Am Astron Soc. *Res:* Astronomical navigation; stellar statistics; celestial mechanics; astronomical instrumentation. *Mailing Add:* Allegheny Observ Observ Sta Pittsburgh PA 15214

KIEWIT, DAVID ARNOLD, b Cincinnati, Ohio, Feb 25, 40; m 63; c 2. APPLIED PHYSICS, MATERIALS SCIENCE. *Educ:* Northwestern Univ, Evanston, BA, 62, PhD(mat sci), 68. *Prof Exp:* Mem tech staff, Hughes Res Labs, Hughes Aircraft Co, 67-73; mgr device develop, Gould Lab, Elec & Electronic Res, Gould Inc, 73-81; DIR ENG & ADVAN DEVELOP, A C NIELSEN CO, 81- *Honors & Awards:* Div Invention Awards, Hughes Aircraft Co, 70-73; Sci Achievement Award, Gould Inc, 78. *Mem:* Am Phys Soc; Inst Elec & Electronics Engrs. *Res:* Development of intelligent instrumentation systems for statistical measurements; application of pattern recognition and signal analysis methodologies to instrument development. *Mailing Add:* 375 Patricia A C Nielsen Co Dunedin FL 33528

KIFER, EDWARD W, b Penn, Pa, Oct 31, 38; m 63; c 1. INORGANIC CHEMISTRY, PHYSICAL CHEMISTRY. *Educ:* Ind State Col, BSEd, 60; George Washington Univ, MS, 65; Carnegie-Mellon Univ, PhD(inorg chem), 69. *Prof Exp:* Teacher, Norwin Sch Syst, Pa, 60-63; asst chem, George Washington Univ, 63-65; asst res scientist phys chem, Res Dept, Koppers Co, Inc, 65-68, sr res scientist, 68-69, res group mgr physics & phys chem, 69-75, sr res group mgr physics & phys chem, Res Dept, 75-80, MGR RES, PHENOLIC PROD DEPT, KOPPERS CO INC, 80- *Mem:* AAAS; Am Chem Soc; fel Am Inst Chemists. *Res:* Synthesis and characterization of compounds of the group IV elements, especially silicon hydrides; inorganic coordination polymer behavior; fire retardant systems for wood and plastics. *Mailing Add:* Res Dept Koppers Co, Inc Monroeville PA 15146

KIFER, PAUL EDGAR, b Grove City, Pa, Aug 16, 24; m 50; c 3. FOOD SCIENCE. *Educ:* Mich State Univ, BS, 50, MS, 53, PhD(animal nutrit), 56. *Prof Exp:* Asst prof poultry, Univ Ga, 56-57; asst mgr poultry res div, Ralston Purina Co, 57-59, mgr, Spec Chows Res Div, 59-64, dir, Pet Food Res & Develop, 64-67, asst to vpres corp res, 67-69, asst dir corp res, 69-73; HEAD DEPT FOOD SCI & TECHNOL, ORE STATE UNIV, 73- *Mem:* AAAS; Poultry Sci Asn; Inst Food Technologists; Am Inst Nutrit; NY Acad Sci. *Res:* Nutrition as related to food science, food safety. *Mailing Add:* Dept of Food Sci & Technol Ore State Univ Corvallis OR 97331

KIFFNEY, GUSTIN THOMAS, JR, b New York, NY, May 17, 30; m 54; c 5. OPHTHALMOLOGY. *Educ:* Col Holy Cross, AB, 51; Albany Med Col, MD, 55; Am Bd Ophthal, dipl, 63. *Prof Exp:* Clin instr surg, 59-61, asst prof, 61-64, assoc prof, 64-81, CLIN ASSOC PROF OPHTHAL, SCH MED, UNIV NC, CHAPEL HILL, 81- *Concurrent Pos:* Asst attend surgeon, NC Mem Hosp, 61-64, assoc attend surgeon, 64-; attend surgeon ophthal, Watts Hosp, Durham, NC, 61- *Mem:* AMA; Am Acad Ophthal & Otolaryngol. *Res:* Experimental and clinical ocular pathology. *Mailing Add:* Dept of Ophthal Univ of NC Sch of Med Chapel Hill NC 27515

KIGER, EUGENE OLIVER, b Winston-Salem, NC, Nov 21, 24; m 50; c 3. ELECTRICAL & NUCLEAR ENGINEERING. *Educ:* NC State Col, BS, 50, MS, 51. *Prof Exp:* Physicist, Argonne Nat Lab, 51-52, process engr, Atomic Energy Div, Del, 52-53, process supvr, Savannah River Plant, 53-55, sr supvr, 55-60, res supvr, Savannah River Lab, 61-62, sr res supvr, 63-64, chief tech supvr, Savannah River Plant, 65-75, asst dept supt, Chem Separations Plant, 76-77, dept supt, Reactor Dept, Savannah River Plant, 77-78, DEPT SUPT, CHEM SEPARATIONS PLANT, E I DU PONT DE NEMOURS & CO, INC, 79- *Mem:* Am Nuclear Soc. *Res:* Design and operation of large nuclear reactors; fuel development and testing for power reactors; reactor instrumentation; operation and management of nuclear materials production plants. *Mailing Add:* Savannah River Plant 703-A E I du Pont de Nemours & Co Aiken SC 29801

KIGER, JOHN ANDREW, JR, b Dayton, Ohio, Feb 6, 41. GENETICS, BIOPHYSICS. *Educ:* Calif Inst Technol, BS, 63, PhD(biophys), 68. *Prof Exp:* Instr biol, Mass Inst Technol, 68-69; asst prof biochem, Ore State Univ, 69-73; asst prof, 73-76, ASSOC PROF GENETICS, UNIV CALIF, DAVIS, 76- *Concurrent Pos:* Am Cancer Soc fel, 69. *Mem:* AAAS; Genetics Soc Am; Soc Developmental Biol; Soc Study Evolution. *Res:* Biochemical and developmental genetics of Drosophila. *Mailing Add:* Dept of Genetics Univ of Calif Davis CA 95616

KIGER, ROBERT WILLIAM, b Washington, DC, Oct 4, 40; m 68; c 2. SYSTEMATIC BOTANY, HISTORY OF BIOLOGY. *Educ:* Tulane Univ, BA, 66; Univ Md, MA, 71, PhD(bot), 72. *Prof Exp:* Teacher elem schs, Montgomery County, Md, 66-67; res botanist, Smithsonian Inst, 72-73; dir develop, Sea Kal Develop Cor, 73-74; asst dir & sr res scientist, 74-77, DIR & PRIN RES SCIENTIST, HUNT INST BOT DOC, CARNEGIE-MELLON UNIV, 77- *Concurrent Pos:* Res assoc, bot dept, Carnegie Mus Nat Hist, 78-; adj prof hist sci, Dept Hist Philos, Carnegie-Mellon Univ, 79- *Mem:* Linnean Soc London; Bot Soc Am; Am Soc Plant Taxonomists; Soc Study Evolution; Int Asn Plant Taxon. *Res:* Floristic and monographic study of various New World angiosperms, especially Flacourtiaceae and Talinum; history, philosophy and theory of biological systematics; evolutionary philosophy, especially in relation to theory of evolutionary mechanism and change, and to systematics. *Mailing Add:* Hunt Inst Carnegie-Mellon Univ Pittsburgh PA 15213

KIGGINS, EDWARD M, b Stamford, Conn, Mar 26, 29; m 58; c 2. MICROBIOLOGY. *Educ:* Univ Conn, AB, 52, MS, 54, PhD(microbiol), 58. *Prof Exp:* Asst animal dis, Univ Conn, 52-57; mem staff microbiol, Abbott Labs, 58-60, group leader, 61-66, sect heaad, 66-67, mgr animal heaalth res, Amdal Co Div, 67-70, dir res & devlop, Agr & Vet Prod Div, 70-75, dir & prod develop, Rhodia, Hess & Clark Div, 75-80; WITH DIAMOND SHAMROCK CORP, 80- *Mem:* AAAS; Am Soc Microbiol; US Animal Health Asn; Sigma Xi; NY Acad Sci. *Res:* Veterinary microbiology. *Mailing Add:* Diamond Shamrock Corp PO Box 348 Painesville OH 44077

KIHARA, HAYATO, b Oakland, Calif, Feb 28, 22; m 50; c 2. BIOCHEMISTRY, BIOCHEMICAL GENETICS. *Educ:* Univ Tex, BS, 44; Univ Wis, MS, 51, PhD(biochem), 52. *Prof Exp:* Chemist, 406th Med Gen Lab, Japan, 46-48; asst biochem, Univ Wis, 48-51; res scientist, Biochem Inst, Univ Tex, 51-56; asst res biochemist, Univ Calif, 56-60; res specialist, Sonoma State Hosp, Eldridge, Calif, 60-63; chief res biochemist, Pac State Hosp, 63-73; assoc res biochemist, 73-75, CHIEF, BIOCHEM LAB, MAT & MECH RES CTR, UNIV CALIF, LOS ANGELES-LANTERMAN STATE HOSP, 73-, PROF BIOCHEM, UNIV, 75- *Concurrent Pos:* Vis prof, Sch Med, Nikon Univ, Tokyo, 80. *Mem:* Am Chem Soc; Am Soc Biol Chem; Am Soc Human Genetics; Am Asn Ment Defective. *Res:* Biochemistry of inborn errors of metabolism; tissue culture; enzyme purification; diagnosis of genetic disorders; heterozygote identification; prenatal diagnosis. *Mailing Add:* Mat & Mech Res Ctr Group Lanterman State Hosp Univ Calif Los Angeles Pomona CA 91769

KIHN, HARRY, b Tarnow, Austria, Jan 24, 12; nat US; m 37; c 2. ELECTRONICS. *Educ:* Cooper Union, BSEE, 34; Univ Pa, MSEE, 52. *Prof Exp:* Res engr, Hygrade Sylvania Corp, 35-37; chief engr, Polytherm, Inc, 37-38; res engr, Ferris Instrument Co, 38-39; res engr, RCA Corp, Camden, 39-42 & Princeton, NJ, 42-58, group head space systs res, 58-60, staff engr to vpres res & eng, 60-70, staff tech adv corp licensing, 71-75, sr tech adv patent opers, 75-77; PRES, KIHN ASSOCS, 77- *Concurrent Pos:* Mem mat adv bd, Nat Acad Sci-Nat Res Coun, 60- *Mem:* AAAS; Sigma Xi; fel Inst Elec & Electronics Engrs; NY Acad Sci; Am Defense Preparedness Asn. *Res:* Electronics and systems research; television communication theory and devices; electromagnetics; radar; infrared; space physics and instrumentation; solid state circuits and devices; integrated circuits; computer design; information processing systems; medical electronics; nuclear energy and waste isolation; industrial electronics. *Mailing Add:* Kihn Assocs 30 Green Ave Lawrenceville NJ 08648

KIILSGAARD, THOR H, b Honeyville, Utah, June 10, 19; m 46; c 3. ECONOMIC GEOLOGY. *Educ:* Univ Idaho, BS, 42; Univ Calif, MA, 49. *Prof Exp:* Jr geologist, State Bur Mines & Geol, Idaho, 46-47, asst geologist, 48-49, assoc geologist, 49-51; proj geologist, US Geol Surv, 51-54, staff asst, 54-59, commodity geologist, 59-69, chief br resources res, 63-69, dep asst chief geologist, 69-72, chief, US Geol Surv-Saudi Arabia prog, 72-76, GEOLOGIST-IN-CHG, US GEOL SURV OFF, WASH, 76- *Concurrent Pos:* Int Coop Admin consult, Peru, 58-59 & Bolivia, 59-60; US Geol Surv adv, Iran, 63, Sudan, 77 & Yemen, 79. *Mem:* Soc Econ Geol; Geol Soc Am; Am Inst Mining, Metall & Petrol Engrs. *Mailing Add:* US Geol Surv 656 US Court House Spokane WA 99201

KIJEWSKI, LOUIS JOSEPH, b Philadelphia, Pa, Mar 20, 36; m 75. THEORETICAL PHYSICS. *Educ:* LaSalle Col, BA, 58; Columbia Univ, MA, 61; NY Univ, PhD(physics), 67. *Prof Exp:* Asst physics, Columbia Univ, 58-61; physicist, RCA Corp, Moorestown & Princeton, 61-64; res asst atomic physics, NY Univ, 64-67, assoc res scientist, 67-68; PROF PHYSICS, MONMOUTH COL, NJ, 68- *Mem:* Am Phys Soc; Math Asn Am. *Res:* Calculations for the energy of atomic systems using density matrices. *Mailing Add:* Dept of Physics Monmouth Col West Long Branch NJ 07764

KIKER, WILLIAM EDWARD, medical physics, radiological health, see previous edition

KIKTA, EDWARD JOSEPH, JR, b Buffalo, NY, June 11, 48. ANALYTICAL CHEMISTRY, CHROMATOGRAPHY. *Educ:* State Univ NY, Buffalo, BA, 70, PhD(anal chem), 78; Canisius Col, MS, 72. *Prof Exp:* Anal res chemist & lab supvr, 76-80, MGR ANAL SERV, AGR CHEM GROUP, FMC CORP, 80- *Honors & Awards:* Chromatography Award, Am Chem Soc, 81. *Mem:* Am Chem Soc; Am Inst Chemists; AAAS; Am Soc Testing & Mat; NY Acad Sci. *Res:* Chromographic methods and systems development; application of hplc to high resolution and high sensitivity analysis; optimization of hplc and gc systems; new hplc bonded phases. *Mailing Add:* FMC Corp 100 Niagara St Middleport NY 14105

KIKUCHI, CHIHIRO, b Seattle, Wash, Sept 26, 14; m 46; c 3. PHYSICS, NUCLEAR ENGINEERING. *Educ:* Univ Wash, BS, 39, PhD(physics), 44; Univ Cincinnati, MS, 43. *Prof Exp:* Instr physics, Haverford Col, 43-44; from instr to assoc prof, Mich State Col, 44-53; res physicist, Naval Res Lab, 53-55; res physicist & head, Solid State Physics Lab, Willow Run Labs, 55-59, PROF NUCLEAR ENG, UNIV MICH, ANN ARBOR, 59- *Concurrent Pos:* Vis physicist, Brookhaven Nat Lab, 51-52, consult, 50, 53-55; consult, Naval Res Lab, 51-53; consult, Int Atomic Energy Agency, spec consult, Tsing Hua, China, 64; vis prof, Kyoto Univ, Japan, 69-70; int collabr, Inst Energia Atomica, Sao Paulo, Brazil, 76-77. *Mem:* Fel Am Phys Soc; Am Asn Physics Teachers; Am Nuclear Soc. *Res:* Quantum electrodynamics; electron-spin resonance; ruby maser; photoconductivity; radiation damage; lasers; nuclear plant safety. *Mailing Add:* Dept of Nuclear Eng Univ of Mich Ann Arbor MI 48109

KIKUCHI, RYOICHI, b Osaka, Japan, Dec 25, 19; US citizen; m 43; c 2. STATISTICAL MECHANICS. *Educ:* Univ Tokyo, BS, 42, PhD(physics), 51. *Prof Exp:* Res assoc physics, Univ Tokyo, 45-50; res assoc, Div Indust Coop, Mass Inst Technol, 51-53; asst prof, Inst Study Metals, Univ Chicago, 53-55; res physicist, Armour Res Found, Ill Inst Technol, 55-56; assoc prof, Wayne State Univ, 56-58; mem tech staff, 58-59, sr staff physicist, 59-63, SR SCIENTIST, HUGHES RES LABS, 63- *Concurrent Pos:* Consult, Lawrence Radiation Lab, Univ Calif, 63-67; adj prof, Univ Calif, Los Angeles, 75-; vis prof, Purdue Univ, 77-, Delft Tech Univ, Netherlands, 80 & 81. *Mem:* Am Phys Soc; Phys Soc Japan. *Res:* Statistical mechanics of cooperative phenomena, equilibrium, and irreversible solid state physics; physical metallurgy. *Mailing Add:* Hughes Res Labs 3011 Malibu Canyon Rd Malibu CA 90265

KIKUCHI, TOM T, b Osaka, Japan, Feb 4, 25; US citizen; m 57; c 1. LASERS, QUANTUM MECHANICS. *Educ:* Univ Chicago, BS, 50; Ill Inst Technol, MS, 53, PhD(physics), 59. *Prof Exp:* Asst physics, Ill Inst Technol, 51-53, res physicist, Armour Res Found, 53-61; STAFF SCIENTIST, DELCO ELECTRONICS, GEN MOTORS CORP, 61- *Mem:* Am Phys Soc. *Res:* Inertial guidance systems; computers and electrooptics; pollution instrumentations; gaseous and reentry physics; vacuum ultraviolet spectroscopy; quantum mechanics of gaseous and solid state lasers; experimental and theoretical studies in electron paramagnetic resonance. *Mailing Add:* Delco Electronics Gen Motors Corp Goleta CA 93017

KIKUDOME, GARY YOSHINORI, b Hakalau, Hawaii, Jan 2, 25. CYTOGENETICS. *Educ:* Univ Mich, BS, 49, MS, 50; Univ Ill, PhD(bot), 59. *Prof Exp:* Asst bot, Univ Hawaii, 50-52 & Univ Ill, 54-56; biologist maize cytogenetics, Oak Ridge Nat Lab, 58-59; asst prof, 59-68, ASSOC PROF MAIZE CYTOGENETICS, UNIV MO-COLUMBIA, 68- *Mem:* Genetics Soc Am; Am Genetics Asn. *Res:* Cytogenetics of maize. *Mailing Add:* Div of Biol Sci Univ of Mo-Columbia Columbia MO 65211

KILAMBI, RAJ VARAD, b India, Feb 1, 33; m 57; c 3. FISHERIES, ZOOLOGY. *Educ:* Univ Wash, PhD(fisheries), 65. *Prof Exp:* from asst prof to assoc prof, 66-71, PROF ZOOL, UNIV ARK, FAYETTEVILLE, 77- *Mem:* Am Fisheries Soc. *Res:* Fish biology and population dynamics; reservoir fisheries. *Mailing Add:* Dept of Zool Univ of Ark Fayetteville AR 72701

KILB, RALPH WOLFGANG, b Chicago, Ill, Feb 7, 31; m 59; c 2. PLASMA PHYSICS, IONOSPHERIC PHYSICS. *Educ:* Univ Nebr, BS, 52; Harvard Univ, MA, 53, PhD(chem), 56. *Prof Exp:* Asst chem, Harvard Univ, 53; phys chemist, Res Labs, Gen Elec Co, 56-60, physicist, 60-69, Tech Mil Planning Opers, 69-71; physicist, 71-73, PLASMA PHYSICS GROUP LEADER, MISSION RES CORP, 73- *Mem:* Am Chem Soc; Am Phys Soc; Am Geophys Union; NY Acad Sci. *Res:* Microwave spectroscopy of gases; properties and structure of high polymers; thermonuclear fusion; atmospheric physics; nuclear burst effects at high altitudes; magnetohydrodynamic code simulation. *Mailing Add:* Mission Res Corp PO Drawer 719 Santa Barbara CA 93102

KILBOURN, JOAN PRISCILLA PAYNE, b Juneau, Alaska, June 15, 36; m 61. MEDICAL MICROBIOLOGY. *Educ:* Univ Ore, BS, 58, MS, 60; Ore State Univ, PhD(microbiol), 63. *Prof Exp:* Instr bact, Univ Ore, 63-66, pediat, Med Sch, 66-68; tutor sci & math, Portland Community Col, 68-71; microbiologist, Clin Path Lab, Vet Admin Hosp, 71-74; assoc dir, ICN Med Labs, 74-76; instr, Clackamas Community Col, 78; CONSULT MICROBIOLOGIST, 78- *Concurrent Pos:* Am Cancer Soc res grant, 63-65; consult, Choice, Books for Col Libraries, 64-; tutor, Portland Community Col, 71-; instr, Med Sch, Univ Ore, 73-74; instr, Portland State Univ Cont Educ Div, 77. *Mem:* AAAS; Am Soc Clin Pathologists; Am Soc Microbiol. *Res:* Use of a radiation resistant microorganism as a protectant and therapeutic agent from the lethal effects of irradiation; automation of clinical medical microbiology; bacterial flora of chronic lung diseases. *Mailing Add:* 3178 SW Fairmount Blvd Portland OR 97201

KILBOURNE, EDWIN DENNIS, b Buffalo, NY, July 10, 20; m 52; c 4. MICROBIOLOGY, VIROLOGY. *Educ:* Cornell Univ, AB, 42, MD, 44. *Prof Exp:* Intern med, New York Hosp, 44-45, asst resident, 45-46; asst resident physician, Hosp Rockefeller Inst, 48-51; assoc prof med & dir, Div Infectious Dis, Tulane Univ, 51-55; assoc prof pub health, Med Col, Cornell Univ, 55-61, prof, 61-69, dir, Div Virus Res, 55-69; PROF MICROBIOL & CHMN DEPT, MT SINAI SCH MED, 69- *Concurrent Pos:* NIH res career award, 61-68; asst, Rockefeller Inst, 48-51; mem, Comn Influenza, US Armed Forces Epidemiol Bd, 59-71; mem, Infectious Dis Adv Comt Nat Inst Allergy & Infectious Dis, 69-73, chmn subcomt influenza, 71-74; NIH Virol Task Force chmn, & mem, Adv Comt Immunization Practices, CDC, 76- *Mem:* Am Soc Clin Invest; Am Acad Microbiol; Asn Am Physicians; Am Asn Immunologists; Am Epidemiol Soc. *Res:* Influenza virus genetics; host determinants of viral virulence; viral genetics and immunology; experimental epidemiology; vaccines. *Mailing Add:* Dept of Microbiol Mt Sinai Sch of Med New York NY 10029

KILBUCK, JOHN HENRY, b Ottawa, Kans, Dec 26, 20; m 48; c 4. FOOD TECHNOLOGY. *Educ:* Ore State Col, BS, 43; Univ Calif, MS, 48. *Prof Exp:* Assoc food technol, Agr Exp Sta, Univ Calif, 48-51; tech dir, Dried Fruit Asn, Calif, 53-55; food technologist, Stange Co, 55-64, div mgr, 64-71, vpres res & develop, 71-75, div mgr, 75-81, WESTERN OPERS MGR, STANGE FLAVOR DIV, MCCORMICK & CO, INC, 81- *Mem:* AAAS; Inst Food Technologists. *Res:* Spices; food seasonings; food colors; hydrolyzed vegetable proteins; liquid smokes. *Mailing Add:* Stange Flavor Div McCormick & Co Inc PO Box 3687 Hayward CA 94540

KILBURN, KAYE HATCH, b Logan, Utah, Sept 20, 31; m 54; c 3. INTERNAL MEDICINE. *Educ:* Univ Utah, BS, 51, MD, 54. *Prof Exp:* Intern med, Univ Hosps, Cleveland, 54-55; resident, Univ Utah Hosps, 55-57; asst prof med, Washington Univ, 61-62; from assoc prof to prof, Med Ctr, Duke Univ, 62-73, asst prof anat, 68-73, dir, Div Environ Med, 70-73; prof med, assoc prof anat & dir, Div Pulmonary & Environ Med, Med Ctr, Univ Mo-Columbia, 73-77; PROF MED & COMMUNITY MED, MT SINAI SCH MED, CITY UNIV NEW YORK, 77- *Concurrent Pos:* Fel cardiopulmonary physiol, Duke Univ, 57-58; Am Trudeau Soc fel, 58; USPHS fel cardiol, Brompton Hosp, Univ London, 60-61; Nat Heart Inst res grant & USPHS training grants, 62-; chief med serv, Durham Vet Admin Hosp, 63-68; consult, Vet Admin Hosps, Durham, Fayetteville & Oteen, 68- *Mem:* AAAS; Am Fedn Clin Res; Am Thoracic Soc; Am Heart Asn; AMA. *Res:* Pulmonary structure and function, particularly pulmonary circulation; early detection of dysfunction; respiratory failure causing cerebral and circulatory dysfunction; pulmonary responses to environmental and occupational agents; alveolar surfactant; structure and function of cilia, mechanism of inflammation; proteolytic enzymes and antienzymes; mediators of leukocyte response; experimental pathology of lung. *Mailing Add:* Div of Pulmonary & Environ Med City Univ New York New York NY 10029

KILBY, JACK ST CLAIR, b Jefferson City, Mo, Nov 8, 23; m 48; c 2. ELECTRICAL ENGINEERING. *Educ:* Univ Ill, BS, 47; Univ Wis, MS, 50. *Prof Exp:* Engr, Globe-Union, Inc, Wis, 47-58; from engr to asst vpres, Tex Instruments Inc, 58-70; CONSULT, 70- *Concurrent Pos:* Distinguished prof, Tex A&M Univ, 77- *Honors & Awards:* Sarnoff Award, Inst Elec & Electronics Engrs, 66 & Brunetti Award, 80; Ballantine Medal, Franklin Inst, 66; Hall Minuteman Trophy, Order of Daedalians, 66; Nat Medal Sci, 70; Zworykwin Medal, Nat Acad Eng, 75. *Mem:* Nat Acad Eng; fel Inst Elec & Electronics Engrs. *Res:* Monolithic integrated circuits. *Mailing Add:* 5924 Royal Lane Suite 150 Dallas TX 75230

KILDAL, HELGE, b Oslo, Norway, June 23, 42; US citizen; m 67; c 2. APPLIED PHYSICS. *Educ:* Norweg Inst Technol, sivil 67; Stanford Univ, 69, PhD(appl physics), 72. *Prof Exp:* Res asst appl physics, Stanford Univ, 72-74; mem staff, Lincoln Lab, Mass Inst Technol, 74-80; MEM STAFF, FORSVARETS FORSKNINGS INST, 80- *Mem:* Optical Soc Am; Inst Elec & Electronics Engrs. *Res:* Development and applications of infrared nonlinear materials; optically pumped vibrational energy transfer lasers; absolute frequency calibration in the infrared; third harmonic generation in molecules. *Mailing Add:* Forsvarets Forsknings Inst PO Box 25 2007 Kjeller Norway

KILDAY, WARREN D, b Westminster, Calif, July 10, 29; m 58; c 3. ORGANIC CHEMISTRY. *Educ:* Fresno State Col, BA, 59; Wash State Univ, PhD(org chem), 64. *Prof Exp:* Asst prof org chem, 63-67, assoc prof chem, 67-74, PROF CHEM, PEPPERDINE UNIV, 74- *Mem:* Am Chem Soc. *Res:* Papain catalyzed reactions of acylated amino acids. *Mailing Add:* Dept of Chem Pepperdine Univ Malibu CA 90265

KILDSIG, DANE OLIN, b Oshkosh, Wis, Aug 3, 35; m 58; c 2. PHYSICAL PHARMACY. *Educ:* Univ Wis, Madison, BS, 57, PhD(phys pharm), 65. *Prof Exp:* Res scientist, Wyeth Labs, 65-66; from asst prof to assoc prof, 66-75, prof phys pharm, 75-81, PROF INDUST & PHYS PHARM, PURDUE UNIV, 81-, ASSOC HEAD DEPT, 81- *Mem:* Acad Pharmaceut Sci. *Res:* Mechanism of dissolution of solids and drug binding to protein. *Mailing Add:* Sch of Pharm Purdue Univ Lafayette IN 47907

KILEN, THOMAS CLARENCE, b Jackson, Minn, Jan 24, 33; m 65. PLANT GENETICS. *Educ:* Univ Wis, BS, 63, MS, 66, PhD(agron, genetics), 68. *Prof Exp:* PLANT RES GENETICIST, AGR RES SERV, USDA, 67- *Mem:* Am Soc Agron; Crop Sci Soc Am. *Res:* Inheritance of disease resistance in soybeans; inheritance of characters modifying plant type and their effect upon seed yield; genetics of resistance to foliar feeding insects of soybeans. *Mailing Add:* PO Box 196 Agr Res Serv USDA Stoneville MS 38776

KILEY, CHARLES WALTER, b Staten Island, NY, Feb 25, 44; m 70; c 2. ICHTHYOLOGY. *Educ:* Wagner Col, BS, 66; NY Univ, MS, 69, PhD(biol, ichthyol), 73, DDS, 80. *Prof Exp:* Instr biol, 69-74, ASST PROF BIOL, WAGNER COL, 74-, CHMN DEPT, 75- *Concurrent Pos:* Adj asst prof, Staten Island Community Col, 74-75, St John's Univ, 76- & Int Med Educ, 76- *Mem:* Am Inst Biol Sci; AAAS; Am Fisheries Soc; Am Soc Ichthyologists & Herpetologists; NY Acad Sci. *Res:* Histology and ultrastructure of immunocompetent organs in fishes; field collection and identification of fishes. *Mailing Add:* 445 Hoyt Ave Staten Island NY 10301

KILEY, JOHN EDMUND, b New York, NY, Mar 22, 20; m 45; c 5. MEDICINE. *Educ:* Rennselaer Polytech Inst, BS, 42; Harvard Med Sch, MD, 45. *Prof Exp:* From instr to assoc prof, 52-62, prof, Albany Med Col, 62-78; PROF MED NEPHROLOGY, UNIV MISS MED CTR, 78- *Concurrent Pos:* Fel physiol, Albany Med Col, 48-49. *Mem:* Fel Am Col Physicians; Am Fedn Clin Res. *Res:* Extracorporeal vividialysis and renal disease. *Mailing Add:* Dept Med Clin Sci Bldg 2500 N State St Jackson MS 39216

KILEY, LEO AUSTIN, b Boston, Mass, May 22, 18; m 44; c 2. NUCLEAR CHEMISTRY. *Educ:* Mass Inst Technol, SB, 39; Ohio State Univ, PhD(chem), 52. *Hon Degrees:* LLD, NMex State Univ, 67. *Prof Exp:* Dep dir, Atomic Warfare Directorate, Air Force Cambridge Res Ctr, 53-54, dep chief biophys div, Spec Weapons Ctr, 55-56, chief, 57-58, tech dir, Weapons Effects Tests, Field Command, Defense Atomic Support Agency, 59-60, dir, 60-63, vcomdr, Air Force Cambridge Res Labs, 63-64, comdr, 64-65, Air Force Missile Develop Ctr, 65-68, Off Aerospace Res, 68-69; gen mgr, Neutron Devices Dept, Gen Elec Co, 69-78; MGR CORP PLANNING, LOS ALAMOS TECH ASSOC INC, 79- *Res:* Environmental and physical sciences. *Mailing Add:* PO Box 1122 Santa Fe NM 87501

KILGORE, BRUCE MOODY, b Los Angeles, Calif, Mar 26, 30; m 52; c 2. FOREST ECOLOGY, FIRE ECOLOGY. *Educ:* Univ Calif, Berkeley, AB, 52, PhD(zool), 68; Univ Okla, MA, 54. *Prof Exp:* Info asst, Nature Conserv, DC, 56-57; ed, Nat Parks Mag, Nat Parks Asn, 57-60; managing ed, Sierra Club Pub & ed, Sierra Club Bull, Sierra Club, Calif, 60-65; teaching asst zool, Univ Calif, Berkeley, 63-68; res biologist, Off Chief Scientist, Nat Park Serv, 68-72, assoc regional dir prof serv, Western Region, 72-81; RES PROJ LEADER, NORTHERN FOREST FIRE LAB, INTERMOUNTAIN FOREST & RANGE EXP STA, US FOREST SERV, MONTANA, 81- *Mem:* Ecol Soc Am; Wildlife Soc; Soc Am Foresters. *Res:* Fire ecology of giant sequoia-mixed conifer forests; crown fire potential; fire history frequency; impact of prescribed burning of vegetation and fuel conditions, and breeding bird populations; red fir forests. *Mailing Add:* US Forest Serv Northern Forest Fire Lab Drawer G Missoula MT 59806

KILGORE, DELBERT LYLE, JR, b Hutchinson, Kans, Sept 28, 42; m 66; c 1. ENVIRONMENTAL PHYSIOLOGY. *Educ:* Univ Kans, BA, 64, MA, 67, PhD(physiol, cell biol), 72. *Prof Exp:* Res assoc physiol, Duke Univ, 71-73; asst prof, 73-76, ASSOC PROF ZOOL, UNIV MONT, 76- *Mem:* AAAS; Am Physiol Soc; Am Soc Zoologists. *Res:* Physiological adaptations of vertebrates to extreme environments; physiology of temperature regulation, respiration, acid-base balance and water balance. *Mailing Add:* Dept of Zool Univ of Mont Missoula MT 59812

KILGORE, LOIS TAYLOR, b Feb 9, 22; US citizen; m 44; c 2. NUTRITION. *Educ:* Miss State Univ, BS, 55, MS, 63, PhD(physiol), 68. *Prof Exp:* Med technologist, Vicksburg Hosp, 43-44 & Scales Clin, 44-46; med technologist with Dr Hunt Cleveland, 46-48; jr chemist, Petrol Prod Lab, Motor Vehicle Controller, 53-55; asst home economist, 55-69, PROF HOME ECON, MISS STATE UNIV, 69- *Mem:* AAAS; Home Econ Asn Am; Am Soc Clin Pathologists; Am Inst Nutrit; Am Dietetic Asn. *Res:* Nutrition of pre-school children; interrelationships of nutrients; international nutrition. *Mailing Add:* Dept of Home Econ PO Drawer HE Miss State Univ Mississippi State MS 39762

KILGORE, ROBERT L, b Childress, Tex, Nov 24, 24; m 47; c 3. VETERINARY MEDICINE. *Educ:* Tex A&M Univ, DVM, 50. *Prof Exp:* Mgr clin res, Ralston Purina Co, 50-60; mgr diagnostic lab, Tex Agr Exp Sta, 60-61; field vet, Merck, Sharp & Dohme Res Labs, 63-80, DIR, MERCK FARMS, INC, 80- *Res:* Coccidiosis, enterhepatitis and other diseases of poultry; parasitology in cattle. *Mailing Add:* 907 Arlington Terr Fayetteville AR 72701

KILGORE, WENDELL WARREN, b Greenfield, Mo, June 21, 29; m 52; c 3. TOXICOLOGY. *Educ:* Univ Calif, AB, 51, PhD(microbiol), 59. *Prof Exp:* Asst microbiol, Univ Calif, 55-58, microbiologist, 58-59; microbiologist, Stanford Res Inst, 59-60; chmn dept, 70-77, dir food protection & toxicol ctr, 70-78, PROF ENVIRON TOXICOL, UNIV CALIF, DAVIS, 60-, PROF COMMUNITY HEALTH, SCH MED, 78- *Mem:* AAAS; Am Soc Microbiol; Am Chem Soc; Soc Toxicol. *Res:* Environmental toxicology; toxicology of pesticides; analysis and detection of pesticides; effect of pesticides on human health; mechanism of action of insect sterilants. *Mailing Add:* Dept of Environ Toxicol Univ of Calif Davis CA 95616

KILGOUR, GORDON LESLIE, b Vancouver, BC, Apr 24, 29; m 49; c 2. BIOCHEMISTRY. *Educ:* Univ BC, BA, 51, MSc, 53; Univ Wash, PhD(biochem), 56. *Prof Exp:* Jr res biochemist, Univ Calif, Berkeley, 56-57; asst prof biochem, Mich State Univ, 57-63; from assoc prof to prof, San Fernando Valley State Col, 63-68; head dept chem, 68-74, PROF CHEM, PORTLAND STATE COL, 68- *Mem:* Am Chem Soc. *Res:* Oxidative enzymes and coenzymes; chemistry and biochemistry of phosphorylated carbohydrate compounds. *Mailing Add:* Dept of Chem PO Box 751 Portland State Col Portland OR 97207

KILHAM, LAWRENCE, b Brookline, Mass, Aug 10, 10; m 41; c 5. VIROLOGY. *Educ:* Harvard Univ, AB, 32, MA, 35, MD, 40. *Prof Exp:* Intern med, Lakeside Hosp, Cleveland, 40-41; physician, Harvard-Am Red Cross Hosp, Eng, 41-42; asst Med, Harvard Med Sch, 46-47, instr epidemiol, Sch Pub Health, Harvard Univ, 48-49; sr surgeon, Lab Infectious Dis, NIH, 49-61; PROF MICROBIOL, DARTMOUTH MED SCH, 61- *Mem:* AAAS; Soc Exp Biol & Med; fel Am Pub Health Asn; Am Ornith Union. *Res:* Virus diseases; mumps; Newcastle disease; canine distemper; virus fibromas of squirrels and cottontails; K-virus; Kilham rat viruses. *Mailing Add:* Dept of Microbiol Dartmouth Med Sch Hanover NH 03755

KILHAM, PETER, b Salisbury, Eng, June 26, 43; US citizen; m 67. LIMNOLOGY, GEOCHEMISTRY. *Educ:* Dartmouth Col, AB, 65; Duke Univ, PhD(zool), 72. *Prof Exp:* Vis investr biol, Woods Hole Oceanog Inst, 72; asst prof zool, 72-77, ASSOC PROF BIOL, UNIV MICH, ANN ARBOR, 77- *Mem:* Sigma Xi; Am Soc Limnol & Oceanog; Ecol Soc Am; Phycol Soc Am; Int Asn Great Lakes Res. *Res:* Population dynamics, ecological physiology and competition in planktonic diatoms; biogeochemistry of African lakes and rivers; paleolimnology of Lake Ohrid, Yugoslavia; nutrient cycling, primary productivity and physical mixing processes in lakes. *Mailing Add:* Div of Biol Sci Nat Sci Bldg Univ of Mich Ann Arbor MI 48109

KILHAM, SUSAN SOLTAU, b Duluth, Minn, Jan 22, 43; m 67. ECOLOGY, AQUATIC BIOLOGY. *Educ:* Eckerd Col, BS, 65; Duke Univ, PhD(zool), 71. *Prof Exp:* Res assoc microbiol, Duke Univ, 70-72; guest investr oceanog, Woods Hole Oceanog Inst, 72 & 79-80; lectr, 73, asst res scientist natural resources, 73-75, asst res scientist, 75-78, ASSOC RES SCIENTIST BIOL, UNIV MICH, ANN ARBOR, 79- *Concurrent Pos:* NSF oceanog trainee, 67-70; scholar, Univ Mich, 75-76. *Mem:* Am Soc Limnol & Oceanog; Phycol Soc Am; AAAS; Int Soc Limnol; Int Asn Great Lakes Res. *Res:* Aquatic ecology; freshwater phytoplankton; algal physiology and ecology; population dynamics and competition. *Mailing Add:* Div of Biol Sci Univ of Mich Ann Arbor MI 48109

KILINC, ATTILA ISHAK, b Mersin, Turkey, Feb 15, 36; m 61; c 1. GEOCHEMISTRY. *Educ:* Istanbul Univ, BS, 60; Pa State Univ, MSc, 66, PhD(geol), 69. *Prof Exp:* Res asst geochem, Pa State Univ, 64-68; res assoc, Stanford Univ, 68-70; asst prof, 70-74, assoc prof, 74-79, PROF GEOL, UNIV CINCINNATI, 79-, HEAD DEPT, 75- *Concurrent Pos:* Asst head dept geog, Univ Cincinnati, 72-75. *Mem:* Geol Soc Am; Am Geophys Union. *Res:* Geochemistry of hydrothermal systems at high temperatures and pressures. *Mailing Add:* Dept of Geol Old Tech Bldg Univ of Cincinnati Cincinnati OH 45221

KILKSON, HENN, b Tartu, Estonia, Dec 30, 30; nat US; m 63; c 2. CHEMICAL ENGINEERING, PHYSICAL CHEMISTRY. *Educ:* Univ Colo, BS, 52, MS, 54; Cornell Univ, PhD(chem eng), 57. *Prof Exp:* Res engr, Eastern Lab, 57-59, res engr, Eng Res Lab, 60-65, sr res engr, Eng Tech Lab, 65-66, res assoc, 66-72, RES FEL, E I DU PONT DE NEMOURS & CO, 72- *Mem:* Am Chem Soc; Am Inst Chem Engrs; NY Acad Sci. *Res:* Mathematical aspects of polymerizations; chemical kinetics; chemical reactor design and stability. *Mailing Add:* 5 Birch Knoll Rd Northminster Wilmington DE 19810

KILKSON, REIN, b Tartu, Estonia, Aug 1, 27; nat US. BIOPHYSICS. *Educ:* Yale Univ, BS, 53, MS, 54, PhD(physics), 56. *Prof Exp:* Mem tech staff, Bell Tel Labs, Inc, 56-58; asst prof physics, Wayne State Univ, 58-59 & biophysics, Yale Univ, 59-66; guest researcher, Dept Med Physics, Karolinska Inst, Stockholm, 64-70; vis prof chem & physics, 70-72, prof physics, 72-76, PROF PHYSICS & MICROBIOL, UNIV ARIZ, 76- *Mem:* AAAS; Biophys Soc; Am Soc Microbiol; Sigma Xi; Am Phys Soc. *Res:* Molecular biophysics; virus structure; macromolecular arrangements in cell organelles; molecular regulation; molecular evolution; theoretical biology and biophysics; biological systems; light scattering and nerve conduction. *Mailing Add:* Dept of Physics Univ of Ariz Tucson AZ 85721

KILLAM, ELEANOR, b Whitefield, NH, May 18, 33. MATHEMATICS. *Educ:* Univ NH, BS, 55, MS, 56; Yale Univ, PhD(math), 61. *Prof Exp:* ASST PROF MATH, UNIV MASS, AMHERST, 60- *Mem:* Am Math Soc; Math Asn Am. *Res:* Banach algebras; locally m-convex algebras. *Mailing Add:* Dept of Math Univ of Mass Amherst MA 01003

KILLAM, ELLEN EVA KING, b New York, NY, Nov 16, 21; m 55; c 3. PHARMACOLOGY, NEUROPHARMACOLOGY. *Educ:* Sarah Lawrence Col, AB, 42; Mt Holyoke Col, AM, 44; Univ Ill, PhD, 53. *Prof Exp:* Instr, Sarah Lawrence Col, 44-46; instr biol, Albertus Magnus Col, 46-47; asst therapeut, Col Med, NY Univ, 47-48; pharmacologist & toxicologist, Med Sch, Univ Ill, 52-53; res pharmacologist, Univ Calif, Los Angeles, 53-59; res assoc pharmacol, Sch Med, Stanford Univ, 59-68; prof in residence, 68-78, PROF PHARMACOL, SCH MED, UNIV CALIF, DAVIS, 78- *Concurrent Pos:* Ed-in-chief, J Pharmacol & Exp Therapeut, 78- *Honors & Awards:* Abel Award, 54. *Mem:* Am Soc Pharmacol & Exp Therapeut; Am Col Neuropsychopharmacol; Soc Exp Biol & Med; Am Epilepsy Soc. *Res:* Neuropharmacology, especially central nervous system; influence of drugs on epilepsy; eletrophysiological correlations of behavior and influence of drugs thereon. *Mailing Add:* Dept Pharmacol Sch Med Univ Calif Davis CA 95616

KILLAM, KEITH FENTON, JR, b Hollywood, Fla, Mar 2, 27; m 55; c 3. PHARMACOLOGY. *Educ:* Tufts Col, BS, 48; Univ Ill, MS, 53, PhD(pharm), 54. *Prof Exp:* Res pharmacologist, Smith Kline & French Labs, 48-50 & 54-55; NIH sr res fel, Univ Calif, Los Angeles, 55-59; prof pharmacol, Sch Med, Stanford Univ, 59-68; chmn dept, 68-75, PROF PHARMACOL, SCH MED, UNIV CALIF, DAVIS, 68-, CHAIRPERSON DEPT, 81- *Concurrent Pos:* Res fel neurophys, Mass Gen Hosp, 58; mem psychopharmacol study sect, NIH, 58-62; mem, Int Brain Res Orgn. *Mem:* AAAS; Am Soc Pharmacol & Exp Therapeut; Am Col Neuropsychopharmacol. *Res:* Neuropharmacology; physiological mechanisms in brain; correlation between brain electrical activity and behavior and effects of psychotropic agents. *Mailing Add:* Dept of Pharmacol Univ of Calif Sch Med Davis CA 95616

KILLE, JOHN WILLIAM, developmental biology, reproductive physiology, see previous edition

KILLEBREW, FLAVIUS CHARLES, b Canadian, Tex, Apr 2, 49; m 78; c 1. MAMMALOGY. *Educ:* WTex State Univ, BS, 70, MS, 72; PhD(zool), 76. *Prof Exp:* Instr zool, Univ Ark, 72-76; ASST PROF BIOL, WTEX STATE UNIV, 76- *Concurrent Pos:* Res asst grant, Killgore Comt, 71-72, res prof grant, 76-77; res asst grant-in-aid, Sigma Xi, 71-72; res asst, Univ Ark Mus, 74-76; res prof grant, US Dept Interior, 78-79. *Mem:* Sigma Xi (vpres, 77-78, pres, 78-79); Soc Study Amphibians & Reptiles; Herpetologists League; Am Soc Ichthyologists & Herpetologists. *Res:* Systematics and ecology of reptiles. *Mailing Add:* Dept of Biol WTex State Univ Canyon TX 79016

KILLEEN, JOHN, b Guam, July 28, 25; m 50; c 6. PLASMA PHYSICS, MAGNETOHYDRODYNAMICS. *Educ:* Univ Calif, AB, 49, MA, 51, PhD(math), 55. *Prof Exp:* Mathematician, Radiation Lab, Univ Calif, 50-55, Bell Tel Labs, Inc, 55 & Inst Math Sci, NY Univ, 56; mathematician, Math Radiation Lab, 57-68, PROF APPL SCI, LAWRENCE LIVERMORE LAB, UNIV CALIF, 68-, DIR, NAT MAGNETIC FUSION ENERGY COMPUT CTR, 74- *Concurrent Pos:* Ed, J Comput Physics, 68- *Mem:* Am Math Soc; Am Phys Soc. *Res:* Mathematical physics; computation; computer applications to controlled thermonuclear research. *Mailing Add:* Dept of Appl Sci Lawrence Livermore Lab Univ Calif Livermore CA 94550

KILLELEA, JOSEPH R(ICHARD), b New York, NY, July 14, 17; m 50; c 1. NUCLEAR ENGINEERING. *Educ:* Manhattan Col, BS, 40; NY Univ, PhD(chem), 49. *Prof Exp:* Instr chem, Manhattan Col, 40-44; prof, Iona Col, 48-52; sr engr, Westinghouse Elec Corp, 52-53; group leader, Mineral Beneficiation Lab, Columbia Univ, 53-54, tech dir, 54-58; eng mgr, Indust Reactor Labs, Inc, NJ, 58-63; DIR NUCLEAR SCI & ENG CTR, UNIV LOWELL, 63-, PROF CHEM, 78- *Concurrent Pos:* Res assoc, Fordham Univ, 51-52. *Mem:* Am Chem Soc; Am Nuclear Soc. *Res:* Organic chemistry; ceramics. *Mailing Add:* 25 Berkeley Dr Chelmsford MA 01824

KILLGOAR, PAUL CHARLES, JR, b Boston, Mass, Aug 3, 46; m 69; c 2. ELASTOMERS. *Educ:* State Col, Bridgewater, BA, 68; Mich State Univ, PhD(chem), 72. *Prof Exp:* Scientist, Cabot Corp, 68; res assoc, Mich State Univ, 72; SCIENTIST, FORD MOTOR CO, 72- *Mem:* Am Chem Soc; Sigma Xi. *Res:* Physical properties of elastomers; dynamic mechanical and fatigue properties. *Mailing Add:* 15455 Ashurst St Livonia MI 48154

KILLGORE, CHARLES A, b Lisbon, La, Aug 19, 34; m 54; c 3. CHEMICAL ENGINEERING, NUCLEAR PHYSICS. *Educ:* La Polytech Inst, BS, 56, MS, 63. *Prof Exp:* Chem engr, Am Oil Co, Ark, 56; chemist, Claiborne Gasoline Co, La, 59; from instr to prof chem eng, La Tech Univ, 59-76, dir nuclear ctr, 63-76, assoc dean eng & dir eng res, 72-76; PRES, KILLGORE'S, INC, RADIATION & ENG CONSULTS, 76- *Concurrent Pos:* NSF sci fac fel. *Honors & Awards:* Award, Am Soc Eng Educ, 70. *Mem:* Am Inst Chem Engrs; Am Soc Eng Educ; Am Nuclear Soc; Health Physics Soc; Am Asn Physicists Med. *Res:* Industrial applications of radioactive isotopes. *Mailing Add:* Killgore's Inc 506 Hundred Oaks Dr Ruston LA 71270

KILLIAN, CARL STANLEY, b Cleveland, Ohio, Apr 13, 33. CHEMICAL PATHOLOGY, DIAGNOSTIC IMMUNOLOGY. *Educ:* Daemen Col, BS, 73; State Univ NY, Buffalo, MA, 77, PhD(chem path), 81. *Prof Exp:* Res technologist, Corning Glass Works, NY, 59-61; technologist, Hemat, Blood Banking & Urinalysis, 62-64, sr technologist, Clin Chem, 64-76, CANCER RES SCIENTIST, DIAG IMMUNOL RES & BIOCHEM, ROSWELL PARK MEM INST, BUFFALO, NY, 76- *Concurrent Pos:* lectr, Div Grad Sch, Roswell Park Mem Inst, State Univ NY, Buffalo, 77- *Res:* Methods of detection and application of biologic tumor markers in prostate cancer; author or co-author of over 30 publications. *Mailing Add:* Diag Immunol Res & Biochem Roswell Mem Inst 666 Elm St Buffalo NY 14263

KILLIAN, FREDERICK LUTHER, b Lancaster, Pa, May 31, 42; m 63; c 2. POLYMER CHEMISTRY. *Educ:* Franklin & Marshall Col, AB, 63; Northwestern Univ, Ill, PhD(org chem), 67. *Prof Exp:* Res chemist, 67-72, SR RES CHEMIST, E I DU PONT DE NEMOURS & CO, Inc, 72- *Mem:* Am Chem Soc. *Res:* Physical-organic chemistry; reaction mechanisms; polymer synthesis and conversion to synthetic fibers; fiber structure; organic polymer chemistry. *Mailing Add:* 1138 Elderon Dr Wilmington DE 19808

KILLIAN, GARY JOSEPH, b Rockville Centre, NY, Dec 6, 45; m 65; c 3. REPRODUCTIVE PHYSIOLOGY. *Educ:* Kans State Univ, BS, 67, MS, 69; Pa State Univ, PhD(reprod biol), 73. *Prof Exp:* Asst prof anat physiol, Dept Biol, Pa State Univ, 73-74, from res asst to res assoc, 72-75, asst prof reprod physiol, Dept Dairy & Animal Sci, 75-76; asst prof, 76-79, ASSOC PROF REPROD PHYSIOL, DEPT BIOL SCI, KENT STATE UNIV, 79- *Mem:* Soc Study Reprod; AAAS. *Res:* Male reproductive physiology, endocrine regulation and effects of contraceptives on epididymal physiology and sperm maturation; biology of spermatozoa and sperm capacitation. *Mailing Add:* Dept of Biol Sci Kent State Univ Kent OH 44242

KILLIAN, JAMES R(HYNE), JR, b Blacksburg, SC, July 24, 04; m 29; c 2. ENGINEERING. *Educ:* Mass Inst Technol, BS, 26. *Hon Degrees:* 39 degrees from var schs & univs. *Prof Exp:* Asst managing ed, Tech Rev, Mass Inst Technol, 26-27, managing ed, 27-30, exec asst to pres, 39-43, exec vpres, 43-45, vpres, 45-48, pres, 48-59, chmn corp, 59-71; RETIRED. *Concurrent Pos:* Pres bd trustees, Atoms for Peace Awards Inc, 55-58, 59-; trustee, Alfred P Sloan Found, 54-77, Inst Defense Anal, 56-69, chmn, 56-57, 59-61, Mellon Inst, 60-67, Educ Develop Ctr, 67-69, Mitre Corp & others; mem of var govt comts. *Honors & Awards:* Vannevar Bush Award, Nat Sci Bd, 80. *Mem:* Nat Acad Eng; fel Am Acad Arts & Sci; hon mem Am Soc Eng Educ. *Mailing Add:* Mass Inst Technol Rm 9-235 77 Mass Ave Cambridge MA 02139

KILLICK, KATHLEEN ANN, b Chicago, Ill, Jan 22, 42. MICROBIAL BIOCHEMISTRY. *Educ:* Ill Inst Technol, BS, 64, MS, 66, PhD(biochem), 69. *Prof Exp:* AEC res assoc biochem, Argonne Nat Lab, 69-70; NIH trainee develop biol, 70-72, NIH spec fel, 72-74, STAFF SCIENTIST DEVELOP BIOL, BOSTON BIOMED RES INST, 74- *Concurrent Pos:* Instr develop biol, Harvard Univ, 75-77. *Mem:* AAAS; Am Soc Microbiol; Am Chem Soc; Am Soc Biol Chemists; Sigma Xi. *Res:* Biochemical basis of cellular differentiation in the slime mold, Dictyostelium discoideum. *Mailing Add:* Boston Biomed Res Inst 20 Staniford St Boston MA 02114

KILLINGBECK, STANLEY, b Blackburn, Eng, May 20, 29; US citizen. PHYSICAL CHEMISTRY. *Educ:* Blackburn Tech Col, BS, 51; Cornell Univ, MS, 56, PhD(chem), Univ Kans, 64. *Prof Exp:* Lab asst, Walpamur Paint Co, Eng, 46-52; asst tech off, Imp Chem Indust, Eng, 52-54; asst prof, 63-71, ASSOC PROF CHEM, CENT MO STATE COL, 71- *Res:* Analytical chemistry. *Mailing Add:* Dept of Chem Cent Mo State Col Warrensburg MO 64093

KILLINGER, DENNIS K, b Boone, Iowa, Sept 23, 45; m 69; c 1. LASER REMOTE SENSING, QUANTUM OPTICS. *Educ:* Univ Iowa, BA, 67; DePauw Univ, MA, 69; Univ Mich, PhD(physics), 78. *Prof Exp:* Res physicist, Naval Avionics Fac, 68-74; res assoc, physics, Univ Mich, 74-78; mem quantum electronics staff, 79-81, PROG MGR, LASER REMOTE SENSING, LINCOLN LAB, MASS INST TECHNOL, 81- *Mem:* Am Phys Soc; Optical Soc Am. *Res:* Physics of new optical and laser sources, quantum electornics and non-linear optical techniques with applications toward laser remote sensing. *Mailing Add:* Lincoln Lab Rm C-128 Mass Inst Technol Lexington MA 02173

KILLINGER, JOANNE MARIE, biochemical pharmacology, see previous edition

KILLINGLEY, JOHN STANLEY, b Birmingham, Eng, July 22, 35; m 67. MARINE CHEMISTRY, GEOCHEMISTRY. *Educ:* London Univ, BSc, 58; Univ Mo, MS, 71; Univ Hawaii, PhD(chem), 75. *Prof Exp:* Chemist petrochem, Shell, UK, 60-62; chemist uranium mining, Territory Enterprises, Australia, 62-65; chemist forest prod, NZ Forest Prod, 65-66; chief chemist petrochem, Valley Nitrogen, Calif, 66-69; fel, 75-76, ASSOC SPECIALIST MARINE GEOCHEM, SCRIPPS INST OCEANOG, 76- *Mem:* Sigma Xi; AAAS. *Res:* Stable isotope geochemistry in marine systems, particularly the study of deep sea calcareous deposits and near shore mollusca. *Mailing Add:* Scripps Inst of Oceanog La Jolla CA 92093

KILLINGSWORTH, LAWRENCE MADISON, b Cuthbert, Ga, Mar 9, 46; m 66; c 1. CLINICAL CHEMISTRY, PATHOLOGY. *Educ:* Emory Univ, BS, 68; Univ Fla, PhD(path, clin chem), 73. *Prof Exp:* Asst prof med & path, Sch Med, Univ NC, Chapel Hill, 73-77, assoc dir clin chem, NC Mem Hosp, 73-77, assoc dir, Radioassay Lab, 74-76; DIR CLIN CHEM & IMMUNOL LABS, SACRED HEART MED CTR, 77- *Mem:* Am Asn Clin Chem; Asn Clin Scientists. *Res:* Application of light-scattering techniques to the measurement of immunochemical reactions; application of immunochemical techniques to the clinical chemistry laboratory; study of protein physiology in health and disease. *Mailing Add:* Clin Chem & Immunol Labs West 101 Eighth Ave Spokane WA 99204

KILLINGSWORTH, R(OY) W(ILLIAM), b Headland, Ala, Apr 8, 25; m 50; c 2. CIVIL ENGINEERING, ENGINEERING MECHANICS. *Educ:* Univ Ala, BS, 48, MS, 56. *Prof Exp:* Asst col eng, Univ Ala, 48-49; field engr, Pressure Concrete Co, 49-50, vpres, 50-52; asst to dean col eng, 52-56, from asst prof to prof eng, 56-67, from asst dean to assoc dean col eng, 63-70, PROF CIVIL ENG, UNIV ALA, 67-, DIR PHYS PLANNING & FACIL, 70- *Concurrent Pos:* Gen contractor, Ala, 48-49; consult, US Army, 63- *Mem:* AAAS; Am Soc Civil Engrs; Am Soc Eng Educ; Nat Soc Prof Engrs. *Res:* Properties of materials; soil mechanics; hydrology. *Mailing Add:* 731 Capstone Ct Tuscaloosa AL 35401

KILLION, JERALD JAY, b Wichita, Kans, Oct 4, 42; c 2. IMMUNOBIOLOGY, CANCER. *Educ:* Wichita State Univ, BS, 70, MS, 71; Univ Okla, PhD(biophys), 73. *Prof Exp:* Instr biophys, 73-74, asst prof, Dept Radiol Sci, Health Sci Ctr, Univ Okla, 74-78; mem fac, 78-81, ASSOC PROF DEPT PHYSIOL, ORAL ROBERTS UNIV SCH MED, 81- *Concurrent Pos:* Affil instr, Cancer Res Prog, Okla Med Res Found, 73-74, staff scientist, 74-75, asst mem, 75- *Mem:* Sigma Xi; Am Asn Cancer Res; Am Soc Cell Biol; Biophys Soc; Tissue Cult Asn. *Res:* Membrane properties of tumor cells and tumor cell subpopulations; the influence of biological and biochemical properties of tumor on the tumor-host relationship; antigenic topography of tumor cell membranes. *Mailing Add:* Dept of Physiol 7777 S Lewis Ave Tulsa OK 74171

KILLION, LAWRENCE EUGENE, b Ross, Tex, Mar 28, 24; m 48; c 2. LASERS, COMPUTER SCIENCE. *Educ:* Baylor Univ, BA, 44; Univ Ind, MS, 48; Washington Univ, PhD(physics), 55. *Prof Exp:* Asst dir, Blast & Shock Prog, Defense Atomic Support Agency, US Dept Defense, 51-52, Nuclear Prog, 55-56, tech asst to dir defense weapons effects tests, 56-58; chief, Nuclear Qual Assurance Agency, Albuquerque Opers Off, US AEC, 58-64, sci adv electronics, US Army Electronics Proving Ground, 64-65, chief scientist, 65-67, dep asst controller info systs, US AEC, DC, 67-69, spec asst to asst gen mgr, div mil appln, 69-73, dep asst dir res & develop, 73-74; dep asst dir laser & isotope separation technol, 74-75, actg asst dir laser & isotope separation technol, Div Mil Appln, Energy Res & Develop Admin, 75-77; DIR, LASER FUSION DIV, DEPT ENERGY, 77- *Mem:* Am Phys Soc; sr mem, Inst Elec & Electronics Engrs; Am Statist Asn. *Res:* Computer controls and computation; communications electronics; laser technology for laser fusion and laser isotope separation; electron and ion beam technology and application to fusion. *Mailing Add:* Off of Laser Fusion Dept of Energy Washington DC 20545

KILLIP, THOMAS, III, b Rochester, NY, June 18, 27; m 50; c 4. INTERNAL MEDICINE, CARDIOLOGY. *Educ:* Swarthmore Col, AB, 48; Cornell Univ, MD, 52. *Prof Exp:* Intern med, Strong Mem Hosp, NY, 52-53; asst resident, NY Hosp-Cornell Med Ctr, 53-55, resident, 57-58, from instr to assoc prof med, Med Col, Cornell Univ, 57-68, Roland Harriman prof, 68-74; prof med & assoc dean, Med Col, Northwestern Univ, Chicago, 74-79; PROF CLIN MED, UNIV MICH, 80-; CHMN DEPT MED, HENRY FORD HOSP, DETROIT, 80- *Concurrent Pos:* Am Heart Asn res fel, 55-57; Markle scholar, 58-63; asst, Med Col, Cornell Univ, 54-57; mem, Subspeciality Bd cardiovasc Dis, Am Bd Internal Med; fel Coun Clin Cardiol, Am Heart Asn; attend physician, NY Hosp, 68-74; Chmn, Dept Med,

Evanston Hosp, 74-79. *Mem:* AAAS; Am Heart Asn; Am Fedn Clin Res; Harvey Soc; fel Am Col Physicians. *Res:* Physiology and diseases of cardiovascular system. *Mailing Add:* Henry Ford Hosp 2799 W Grand Blvd Detroit MI 48202

KILLPATRICK, JOSEPH E, b Hillsboro, Ill, Feb 15, 33; m 55; c 3. ELECTRICAL ENGINEERING, PHYSICS. *Educ:* Univ Ill, BS, 55. *Prof Exp:* Res engr, Aero Res, 55-59, sr res engr, MPG Res, 59-62, supvr optics, 62-67, sect head electro-optics, Systs & Res Ctr, 67-69, mem staff, Aeronaut Div, 69-74, RES MGR, SYSTS & RES CTR, HONEYWELL INC, 74- *Mem:* Optical Soc Am; Inst Elec & Electronics Engrs. *Res:* Electronic devices and circuitry; optical scanning and detection systems; horizon scanners; sun seekers; lasers; laser devices and systems; laser gyro; frequency stability and precision control of lasers. *Mailing Add:* 2901 32nd Ave NE Minneapolis MN 55418

KILMAN, JAMES WILLIAM, b Terre Haute, Ind, Jan 22, 31; m 68; c 3. CARDIOVASCULAR SURGERY, THORACIC SURGERY. *Educ:* Ind State Univ, BS, 56; Ind Univ, Indianapolis, MD, 60; Am Bd Surg, dipl 67; Am Bd Thoracic Surg, dipl, 67. *Prof Exp:* Intern, Med Ctr, Ind Univ, Indianapolis, 60-61, resident, 61-66; from asst prof to assoc prof, 66-73, PROF SURG & DIR THORACIC SURG DIV, MED COL, OHIO STATE UNIV, 73- *Concurrent Pos:* USPHS fel cardiovasc surg, Med Ctr, Ind Univ, Indianapolis, 63-64; consult, Vet Admin Hosp, Dayton, Ohio, 66-; attend surgeon, Ohio State Univ & Children's Hosp, Columbus, 66- *Mem:* Am Col Surg; Am Acad Pediat; Am Col Chest Physicians; Am Col Cardiol; Am Surg Asn. *Res:* Infant cardiopulmonary bypass and peripheral blood flow. *Mailing Add:* Dept Surg Ohio State Univ Col Med Columbus OH 43210

KILMER, EARL EUGENE, b Martinsburg, WVa, July 30, 28; m 52; c 3. CHEMISTRY. *Educ:* WVa Univ, BS, 54. *Prof Exp:* Res chemist, 54-73, CONSULT EXPLOSIVES, NAVAL SURFACE WEAPONS CTR, 73- *Res:* Explosive train design; heat resistant explosives; application of explosives to modern weaponry, aerospace and modern aircraft. *Mailing Add:* 7411 Baylor Ave College Park MD 20740

KILP, GERALD R, b Carrollton, Mo, Sept 16, 31; m 56; c 3. PHYSICAL METALLURGY. *Educ:* Mo Valley Col, BS, 52; Iowa State Univ, PhD(metall), 57. *Prof Exp:* Asst metall, Ames Lab, AEC, 52-57; sr engr, Atomic Power Dept, 57-62, supvry engr, Astro-Nuclear Lab, 62-68, MGR FUEL ENG, WESTINGHOUSE NUCLEAR CORE OPERS, WESTINGHOUSE ELEC CORP, 68- *Mem:* Am Soc Metals. *Res:* Thermoelectric and thermionic materials; graphite nuclear reactor fuels. *Mailing Add:* 890 Fredericka Dr Bethel Park PA 15102

KILP, TOOMAS, b Charleroi, Belgium, Oct 24, 48; Can citizen. PHOTOPHYSICS, PHOTOCHEMISTRY. *Educ:* Univ Toronto, BSc, 74, MSc, 75, PhD(chem), 79. *Prof Exp:* Chemist, Inmont Can Ltd, 70-72; chemist, Lumonics Res Ltd, 78-79; ASST PROF, UNIV NOTRE DAME, 79- *Mem:* Chem Inst Can; AAAS; Sigma Xi. *Res:* Polymer photochemistry; photophysics including degradation; polymerization; photoconductivity; intramolecular energy migration; excited state complex formation. *Mailing Add:* Radiation Lab Univ Notre Dame Notre Dame IN 46556

KILPATRICK, CHARLES WILLIAM, b Wichita Falls, Tex, June 10, 44; m 66; c 3. EVOLUTION, BIOCHEMICAL SYSTEMALLES. *Educ:* Midwestern Univ, BS, 68, MS, 69; NTex State Univ, PhD(zool), 73. *Prof Exp:* Instr human biol, Midwestern Univ, 69-70; vis asst prof, Dept Biol, St Lawrence Univ, 73-74; asst prof, 74-80, ASSOC PROF EVOLUTION, DEPT ZOOL, UNIV VT, 80- *Concurrent Pos:* Vis prof, Dept Zool, Univ Fla, 80-81; res assoc, Fla State Mus, Univ Fla, 80-81. *Mem:* Am Soc Mammalogists; Soc Study Evolution; Soc Syst Zoologists; Am Genetic Asn; Soc Study Amphibians & Reptiles. *Res:* Genetic changes and evolutionary processes associated with speciation; effects of isolation on the genetic structure of populations; evolutionary relationships based upon analysis of morphology, biochemistry and kanyology of vertebrates. *Mailing Add:* Dept Zool Univ Vt Burlington VT 05405

KILPATRICK, EARL BUDDY, b Burkburnett, Tex, June 21, 20; m 56; c 6. FISH BIOLOGY. *Educ:* Univ Okla, BS, 42, MS, 49, PhD(zool), 59. *Prof Exp:* Asst zool, Univ Okla, 46-49; from asst prof to assoc prof, 49-62, PROF & HEAD DEPT BIOL, SOUTHEASTERN OKLA STATE UNIV, 62- *Concurrent Pos:* Dir, NSF res partic prog, 59-60. *Mem:* AAAS. *Res:* Cytology, seasonal gonadal cycles of the fresh-water fishes. *Mailing Add:* Dept of Biol Southeastern Okla State Univ Durant OK 74701

KILPATRICK, JOHN EDGAR, b Monroe, La, Jan 3, 20; m 46; c 3. CHEMISTRY. *Educ:* Stephen F Austin State Univ, BA, 40; Univ Kans, MA, 42; Univ Calif, PhD(chem), 45. *Prof Exp:* Asst instr chem, Univ Kans, 40-42; asst, Univ Calif, 42-44; res assoc, Am Petrol Inst Proj, Nat Bur Stand, Washington, DC, 44-47; from asst prof to assoc prof, 47-53, PROF CHEM, RICE UNIV, 53- *Concurrent Pos:* Consult, Los Alamos Sci Lab, Calif, 48-; Guggenheim fel, 57- *Mem:* Am Chem Soc; Am Phys Soc. *Res:* Low temperature calorimetry; statistical thermodynamics; quantum mechanics; equation of state of gases. *Mailing Add:* Dept of Chem Rice Univ Houston TX 77001

KILPATRICK, KERRY EDWARDS, b Baltimore, Md, Mar 17, 39; m 65; c 2. INDUSTRIAL ENGINEERING, OPERATIONS RESEARCH. *Educ:* Univ Mich, Ann Arbor, BSE(mech eng) & BSE(eng math), 61, MS, 67, PhD(indust eng), 70; Harvard Univ, MBA, 63. *Prof Exp:* Methods engr, Buick Motor Div, Gen Motors Corp, 63-65; res asst indust eng, Univ Mich, Ann Arbor, 67-70; PROF INDUST & SYSTS ENG, UNIV FLA, 70-, PROF HEALTH & HOSP ADMIN, COL BUS ADMIN, 71-, PROF COMMUNITY HEALTH & FAMILY MED, 72-, DIR, HEALTH SYSTS RES DIV, J HILLIS MILLER HEALTH CTR, 72-, DIR, CTR HEALTH POLICY RES, 81- *Concurrent Pos:* Consult, World Health Orgn & Vet Admin, 77- *Mem:* Inst Mgt Sci; Opers Res Soc Am; Am Inst Indust Engrs.

Res: Industrial and systems engineering, analysis of production and health service systems; analysis of extended function auxiliaries in health care delivery systems; evaluation of international health services delivery programs. *Mailing Add:* Health Systs Res Div Box J-177 Univ of Fla Gainesville FL 32610

KILPATRICK, R A, plant pathology, see previous edition

KILPATRICK, S JAMES, JR, b Belfast, Northern Ireland, Apr 24, 31; nat US; m 56; c 2. BIOSTATISTICS. *Educ:* Queen's Univ Belfast, BSc, 54, MSc, 57, PhD(demog), 60. *Prof Exp:* Asst lectr med statist, Queen's Univ Belfast, 54-58, lectr, 58-61; lectr, Aberdeen Univ, 61-65, NIH fel statist, 62-63; PROF BIOSTATIST, MED COL VA, 65-, PROF FAMILY PRACT, 79- *Concurrent Pos:* NIH fel statist, Iowa State Univ, 60-61; mem, Working Comt Drug Monitoring, Aberdeen Univ, 63-65; mem, Va Health Interview Coun, 77-79; chmn, Va Health Statist Adv Coun, 78- *Mem:* Biomet Soc; Int Epidemiol Asn; hon res fel Royal Col Gen Practrs. *Res:* Demography; population studies; operations research in health care systems; statistics of epidemiological studies. *Mailing Add:* Dept Biostatist Med Col Va Box 460 Richmond VA 23298

KILPATRICK, WALLACE DORMAN, b Worcester, Mass, Aug 31, 20. MATHEMATICS. *Educ:* Clark Univ, BA, 42; Fla Atlantic Univ, MS, 70; Univ Fla, PhD, 75. *Prof Exp:* Instr math, Worcester Polytech Inst, 46-47; physicist, Lawrence Radiation Lab, 48-60; scientist, Electro-Optical Systs, Inc, Calif, 60-66; sr res physicist, Franklin GNO Corp, Fla, 66-71; researcher, Univ Fla, 71-75; assoc prof math & chmn dept, Palm Beach Atlantic Col, 75-81; LECTR MATH & PHYSICS, EASTERN DIV, OVERSEAS PROG, UNIV MD, 81- *Mem:* Am Phys Soc; Am Math Soc; Am Inst Aeronaut & Astronaut; Am Vacuum Soc; Inst Elec & Electronics Engrs. *Res:* Negative ions; ion-molecule reactions; high voltage breakdown; ion sources. *Mailing Add:* 753 Anchorage Dr North Palm Beach FL 33408

KILPPER, ROBERT WILLIAM, b Houston, Tex, Oct 21, 38; m 60; c 3. TOXICOLOGY, BIOMATHEMATICS. *Educ:* Univ Houston, BS, 61, MS, 63, PhD(biophys), 67. *Prof Exp:* Asst prof biomath, radiation biol & biophys, Sch Med & Dent, Univ Rochester, 67-75, assoc prof, 75-81; TOXICOLOGIST, XEROX CORP, 81- *Mem:* Soc Toxicol. *Res:* Mathematical model analysis of physiological systems, especially the mechanical behavior of some mammalian lung models and the compartmental distribution of various compounds. *Mailing Add:* 144 Branford Rd Rochester NY 14618

KILSHEIMER, JOHN ROBERT, b Mt Vernon, NY, Sept 21, 23; m 46; c 6. AGRICULTURAL CHEMISTRY. *Educ:* Col Holy Cross, BS, 44; Fordham Univ, MS, 48; Syracuse Univ, PhD(chem), 51. *Prof Exp:* Instr chem, Fordham prep sch, 46-47; asst, Syracuse Univ, 47-48; res chemist, Polymer Div, Union Carbide Chem Co, 50-54, org-agr, 54-61; supvr agr chem, Mobil Chem Co, 61-63, mgr org chem, 63-66; sr staff adv agr prods, Esso Res & Eng Co, 66-67, head pesticides res & develop, 67-71; vpres res & develop, 71-80, SR VPRES RES & DEVELOP, O M SCOTT & SONS CO, 80- *Concurrent Pos:* Mem bd dirs, Nat Agr Chem Asn, 72-81, Fertilizer Inst, 77-80. *Mem:* Am Chem Soc; Nat Agr Chem Asn; Fertil Inst. *Res:* Pesticides; fertilizers; oxidation reactions; synthetic organics; vinyl polymers; turf research. *Mailing Add:* 2955 Pickwick Dr Upper Arlington OH 43221

KILSHEIMER, SIDNEY ARTHUR, b New Rochelle, NY, Oct 19, 30; m 72. ORGANIC CHEMISTRY. *Educ:* Wagner Col, BS, 52; NC State Col, MS, 54; Purdue Univ, PhD(chem), 59. *Prof Exp:* Asst chem, NC State Col, 52-54; asst, Purdue Univ, 54-56, instr, 56-58; from asst prof to assoc prof, 58-72, PROF CHEM, BUTLER UNIV, 72- *Mem:* Fel AAAS; Am Chem Soc; fel The Chem Soc; fel Am Inst Chemists. *Res:* Chemical reductions; natural products. *Mailing Add:* Dept of Chem Butler Univ Indianapolis IN 46208

KIM, AGNES KYUNG-HEE, b Seoul, Korea, May 17, 37; US citizen; m 65; c 3. CLINICAL PATHOLOGY, HEMATOLOGY. *Educ:* Yonsei Univ, BS, 58, MD, 62. *Prof Exp:* Asst pathologist, St Barnabas Med Col, 69-70, Lenox Hill Hosp, 71; assoc pathologist, Vet Admin Hosp, WRoxbury, Mass, 71-73; ASSOC PATHOLOGIST, NEW ENG DEACONESS HOSP & NEW ENG BAPTIST HOSP, 73- *Mem:* Fel Col Am Pathologists; Am Soc Clin Pathologists. *Mailing Add:* New Eng Deaconess Hosp 185 Pilgrim Rd Boston MA 02215

KIM, BORIS FINCANNON, b Commerce, Ga, Nov 19, 38; m 62; c 2. MOLECULAR SPECTROSCOPY, LASERS. *Educ:* Johns Hopkins Univ, BES, 60, PhD(physics), 67. *Prof Exp:* SR STAFF PHYSICIST, JOHNS HOPKINS UNIV APPL PHYSICS LAB, 69- *Concurrent Pos:* Instr physics, Evening Col, Johns Hopkins Univ, 70-; prin investr, Dept Health, Educ & Welfare Res Grant, 75- *Mem:* Am Phys Soc. *Res:* High resolution, low temperature optical spectroscopy, and electron spin resonance studies of the class of porphyrin compounds. *Mailing Add:* Johns Hopkins Univ Appl Phys Lab Johns Hopkins Rd Laurel MD 20810

KIM, BYUNG C, b Pyongyang, Korea, Nov 2, 34; US citizen; m 60; c 5. CHEMICAL ENGINEERING, MATHEMATICS. *Educ:* Ripon Col, AB, 58; Mass Inst Technol, BS, 58, MS, 61. *Prof Exp:* Prin chem engr, 61-66, sr chem engr, 66-79, ASSOC SECT MGR, COLUMBUS DIV, BATTELLE MEM INST, 79- *Mem:* Am Inst Chem Engrs; Sigma Xi. *Res:* Fluidized bed combustion; biomass gasification; process modeling and simulation; microencapsulation; waste treatment and disposal; pollution control; coal gasification. *Mailing Add:* Columbus Div Battelle Mem Inst 505 King Ave Columbus OH 43201

KIM, BYUNG KYU, b Kyung-Nam, Korea, Apr 19, 31; US citizen; m 58; c 3. HEMATOLOGY. *Educ:* Yonsei Univ, Seoul, MD, 58. *Prof Exp:* Intern & resident internal med, Severnace Hosp, Yonsei Univ, 59-64; res assoc pharmacol, Up State Med Ctr, State Univ NY, 64-65; res assoc biochem & pharmacol, Brown Univ, 65-67; res assoc, Div Hemat, Mem Hosp, 67-72;

instr, 72-75, asst prof, 75-82, ASSOC PROF MED, BROWN UNIV, 82- *Concurrent Pos:* Lectr, Med Technol Sch, Yonsei Univ, 60-64; sr investr, Div Hemat, Mem Hosp, 72-; consult, Sect Biol, Yorktown Heights Lab, IBM, 81- *Mem:* Am Asn Blood Bank; NY Acad Sci; Soc Cryobiol; Int Soc Blood Transfusion; Int Soc Thermbosis & Hemostasis. *Res:* Biochemistry, pathophysiology and preservation of human blood platelets. *Mailing Add:* 8 Morpheus Dr Cumberland RI 02864

KIM, BYUNG SUK, b Korea, Mar 20, 42; US citizen; m 67; c 2. IMMUNOLOGY. *Educ:* Seoul Nat Univ, BS, 67; Va State Col, MS, 69; Univ Ill, PhD(microbiol), 73. *Prof Exp:* Res assoc radiation biol, Atomic Energy Res Inst, Korea, 67-68; sr res technician genetics, Univ Chicago, 69-70; sr staff assoc immunol, Columbia Univ, 73-74; res asst prof immunol, UniV Chicago, 74-76; asst prof, 76-81, ASSOC PROF IMMUNOL, NORTHWESTERN UNIV, CHICAGO, 81- *Mem:* Am Soc Microbiol; Am Asn Immunologists; Sigma Xi. *Res:* Regulation of immunoglobulin synthesis by anti-antibodies; factors controlling tumor immunity; tumor immunity to hybridomas. *Mailing Add:* Dept of Microbiol & Immunol Med Sch Northwestern Univ Chicago IL 60611

KIM, CARL STEPHEN, b Los Angeles, Calif, Sept 12, 43; m 70; c 2. BIOPHYSICS, COMPUTER SCIENCE GENERAL. *Educ:* Calif State Univ, Fresno, BS, 66; Univ Calif, Davis, PhD(biophysics), 72. *Prof Exp:* Res assoc chem, Cornell Univ, 72-74; jr res scientist biophys, Roswell Park Mem Inst, 74; sr res scientist biophys, 74-77, chief biomet lab, Toxicol Ctr, Div Labs & Res, 77-79, dir, Toxicol Inst, 79-81, DIR COMPUT SYST MGT & DATA PROCESSING, NY STATE DEPT HEALTH, 81- *Concurrent Pos:* NIH fel, 74; adj asst prof physics, State Univ NY Albany, 75- *Res:* Risk assessment, molecular toxicology; elucidation of structure and function of biologically important molecules by x-ray diffraction and molecular orbital theory. *Mailing Add:* NY State Dept Health Empire State Plaza Tower Albany NY 12237

KIM, CHARLES WESLEY, b Nashville, Tenn, Mar 20, 26; m 56; c 1. IMMUNOLOGY, PARASITOLOGY. *Educ:* Univ Calif, BA, 49; Univ NC, MSPH, 52, PhD(parasitol, bact), 56. *Prof Exp:* Instr microbiol, NY Med Col, 56-59, asst prof, 59-64; assoc scientist, 65-68, scientist, 68-70, RES COLLABR, MED DEPT, BROOKHAVEN NAT LAB, 70-; ASSOC PROF MICROBIOL, HEALTH SCI CTR, STATE UNIV NY STONY BROOK, 70-, ASSOC VPROVOST, GRAD SCH, 81- *Concurrent Pos:* La State Univ Inter-Am fel, Cent Am, 58; USPHS fel, Argonne Nat Lab & Univ Chicago, 64-65; assoc dean, Sch Basic Health Sci, Health Sci Ctr, State Univ NY Stony Brook, 72-74; assoc dean, Grad Sch, State Univ NY Stony Brook, 74-81. *Mem:* AAAS; Am Soc Microbiol; Am Soc Trop Med & Hyg; fel Royal Soc Trop Med & Hyg; Sigma Xi. *Res:* Immune response to parasites. *Mailing Add:* Grad Sch State Univ of NY Stony Brook NY 11794

KIM, CHUNG SUL (SUE), b Seoul, Korea, Dec 21, 32; US citizen; m 57; c 2. ORGANIC POLYMER CHEMISTRY, PROPELLANT CHEMISTRY. *Educ:* Univ Ill, BS, 55; Cornell Univ, PhD(org chem), 60. *Prof Exp:* Proj leader polymer chem, Standard Oil Ohio, 59-62; res chemist, Ga Pac Corp, 63-65; sr chem specialist, Aerojet Solid Propulsion Co, 66-73; asst prof, 73-80, ASSOC PROF CHEM, CALIF STATE UNIV, SACRAMENTO, 80- *Concurrent Pos:* Fel biochem, Univ Calif, Davis, 65-66; consult, Aerojet Solid Propulsion Co, 74-76. *Mem:* Am Chem Soc; Soc Advan Mat & Process Eng. *Res:* Dicarbollyl metal complexes; polynitro compounds; chemistry and behavior of polymers in composite; propellant binders; polymer synthesis. *Mailing Add:* Dept of Chem Calif State Univ Sacramento CA 95819

KIM, CHUNG W, b Hiroshima, Japan, Jan 8, 34; m 60; c 1. THEORETICAL HIGH ENERGY PHYSICS, THEORETICAL NUCLEAR PHYSICS. *Educ:* Seoul Nat Univ, BS, 58; Univ Ind, PhD(physics), 63. *Prof Exp:* Res assoc physics, Univ Pa, 63-66; from asst prof to assoc prof, 66-73, PROF PHYSICS, JOHNS HOPKINS UNIV, 73- *Mem:* Am Phys Soc. *Res:* Nuclear and elementary particle physics. *Mailing Add:* Dept of Physics Johns Hopkins Univ Baltimore MD 21218

KIM, DAE MANN, b Seoul, Korea, Apr 22, 38; m 67; c 1. ATOMIC PHYSICS, QUANTUM ELECTRONICS. *Educ:* Seoul Nat Univ, BS, 60; Yale Univ, MS, 65, PhD(physics), 67. *Prof Exp:* Res assoc physics, Mass Inst Technol, 67-69, instr, 69-70; asst prof elec eng, 70-74, ASSOC PROF ELEC ENG, RICE UNIV, 74- *Mem:* Am Phys Soc. *Res:* Modelocked laser pulses and their detection processes; photorefractive phase holography, dye lasers, light scattering study. *Mailing Add:* Dept of Elec Eng Rice Univ Houston TX 77001

KIM, DANIEL Y, geophysics, physics, see previous edition

KIM, DONG YUN, b Korea, May 6, 29; Can citizen; m 62; c 3. ELEMENTARY PARTICLE PHYSICS. *Educ:* Univ Seoul, Korea, BSc, 53; Aachen Tech Univ, Ger, PhD(theoret physics), 62. *Prof Exp:* Fel, Radiation Lab, New York Univ, 62-63; asst prof physics, Dept Physics, Mont State Univ, 63-65; ASSOC PROF PHYSICS, DEPT PHYSICS, UNIV REGINA, SASK, 65- *Concurrent Pos:* Vis scientist at var orgn including: Int Ctr Theoret Physics, Trieste, Italy; Inst Theoret Physics, Univ Heidelberg, Ger; Theory Group, Stanford Univ; Theory Group, Fermi Nat Lab; Dept Appl Math & Theoret Physics, Univ Cambridge, Eng & Bohr Inst, Denmark, 71-79. *Mem:* Can Asn Physicists; Am Phys Soc. *Res:* Theoretical nuclear and elementary particle physics. *Mailing Add:* Dept Physics & Astron Univ Regina Regina SK S4S 0A7 Can

KIM, GIHO, b Seoul, Korea, May 15, 37; m 68; c 2. CLINICAL BIOCHEMISTRY. *Educ:* Simpson Col, BA, 63, Iowa State Univ, MS, 69, PhD(biochem), 71. *Prof Exp:* Res assoc biochem, Iowa State Univ, 71-72; RES ASSOC MED RES, DOWNSTATE MED CTR, 73- *Concurrent Pos:* Clin instr, Downstate Med Ctr, 76- *Mem:* Am Chem Soc. *Res:* Biochemical and effect of environmental pollutants on intestinal transport. *Mailing Add:* 81 Morewood Oaks Port Washington NY 11050

KIM, HAN JOONG, b Seoul, Korea, Nov 3, 37; m 62; c 2. METALLURGY, CERAMICS ENGINEERING. *Educ:* Seoul Nat Univ, BS, 60; San Jose State Col, MS, 66; Lehigh Univ, PhD(metall), 69. *Prof Exp:* Mem tech staff electronic mat, GTE Labs, Inc, 69-76, MGR RES & DEVELOP, GIBSON ELEC, SUBSID GTE, 76- *Mem:* Am Ceramic Soc; Am Soc Metals; Am Inst Mining, Metall & Petrol Engrs. *Res:* Oxidation of metals; glass-metal sealing; crystal growth; electrical contact materials. *Mailing Add:* Gibson Elec-GTE One Contact Pl Delmont PA 15626

KIM, HAN-SEOB, b Seoul, Korea, Sept 5, 34; m 63; c 2. PATHOLOGY. *Educ:* Seoul Nat Univ, MS, 59, PhD(biochem), 68. *Prof Exp:* Asst biochem, Col Med, Seoul Nat Univ, 63-67, instr, 67-69, asst prof, 69; instr, 71-73, ASST PROF PATH, BAYLOR COL OF MED, 73- *Mem:* Am Soc Pathologists; Int Acad Path; Col Am Pathologists; AMA; AAAS. *Res:* Anatomic pathology relating to cardiac pathology; lipid chemistry relating to atherosclerosis. *Mailing Add:* Dept Path 1200 Moursund Ave Baylor Col Med Houston TX 77030

KIM, HARRY HI-SOO, b Taegu, Korea, Jan 23, 22; US citizen; m 47; c 3. PATHOLOGY. *Educ:* Yonsei Univ, Korea, MD, 45; Univ Pa, MSc, 59. *Prof Exp:* Res asst path, Children's Hosp, Philadelphia, Pa, 57-58; res assoc, Sch Med, Univ Wash & Children's Orthop Hosp, Philadelphia, Pa, 57-58; res assoc, Sch Med, Univ Wash & Children's Orthop Hosp, 58-59, clin instr, 60-61; asst prof, 61-67, ASSOC PROF PATH, NY MED COL, 67-, ASSOC PATHOLOGIST, FLOWER & FIFTH AVE HOSPS, 68- *Concurrent Pos:* Fel, Grad Sch Med, Univ Pa, 56-58; assoc pathologist, Metrop Hosp, NY, 60-67; pathologist, NIH maternal & child health prog, NY Med Col Unit, 61-67, consult pathologist, 67- *Mem:* Int Acad Path; fel Am Soc Clin Path; fel Am Col Path. *Res:* Pediatric-pathology; genetics. *Mailing Add:* 531 Eastgate Rd Ho Ho Kus NJ 07423

KIM, HEE JOONG, b Seoul, Korea, Feb 10, 34; US citizen; m 63; c 2. NUCLEAR PHYSICS. *Educ:* Case Inst Technol, MS, 59, PhD(physics), 62. *Prof Exp:* PHYSICIST, PHYSICS DIV, OAK RIDGE NAT LAB, 62- *Mem:* Am Phys Soc. *Res:* Experimental nuclear physics. *Mailing Add:* Physics Div Oak Ridge Nat Lab PO Box X Oak Ridge TN 37830

KIM, HYEONG LAK, b Korea, Jan 18, 33; nat US; m 67; c 5. NATURAL PRODUCTS CHEMISTRY. *Educ:* Seoul Nat Univ, BS, 56; St Louis Univ, MS, 68; Tex A&M Univ, PhD(biochem), 70. *Prof Exp:* RES CHEMIST, TEX AGR EXP STA, TEX A&M UNIV, 69-, MEM GRAD FAC, DEPT VET PHYSIOL & PHARMACOL, 75-, ASST PROF, 79- *Mem:* Am Chem Soc; AAAS; NY Acad Sci. *Res:* Chemical constituents of poisonous plants; naturally occurring toxicants in food chain. *Mailing Add:* 4002 Oaklawn Bryan TX 77801

KIM, HYONG KAP, b Chungup, Korea, May 29, 30; m 63; c 3. ELECTRICAL ENGINEERING. *Educ:* Chunpuk Nat Univ, Korea, BS, 55; Univ Pa, MS, 60, PhD(elec eng), 64. *Prof Exp:* Lectr elec eng, Chunpuk Nat Univ, Korea, 55-58; res engr, Gen Elec Co, Pa, 60-61; instr elec eng, Univ Pa, 61-64, fel, 64-65; from asst prof to assoc prof, 65-73, PROF ELEC ENG, UNIV MAN, 73- *Mem:* Sr mem Inst Elec & Electronics Engrs. *Res:* Electric network analysis and synthesis. *Mailing Add:* Dept Elec Eng Univ Man Winnipeg MB R3T 2N2 Can

KIM, HYUN DJU, b Ham Buk, Korea, Jan 4, 37; US citizen; m 69; c 2. PHYSIOLOGY, BIOCHEMISTRY. *Educ:* Duke Univ, AB, 62, PhD(physiol), 68. *Prof Exp:* Muscular Dystrophy Asn of Am fel physiol, Univ Calif, Los Angeles, 69-71; Alexander von Humboldt fel, Div Med Physiol, Aachen Tech Univ, 71-72; assoc prof physiol, Univ Ariz, 72-80; PROF PHARMACOL & PHYSIOL, UNIV ALA, BIRMINGHAM, 80- *Mem:* Biophys Soc; Am Soc Cell Biol; Am Physiol Soc. *Res:* Membrane transport and energy metabolism in red blood cells; protein metabolism in muscle development. *Mailing Add:* Med Ctr Univ Ala Birmingham AL 35294

KIM, HYUNYONG, b Pusan, Korea, Oct 21, 33; m 64. PHYSICAL CHEMISTRY, QUANTUM CHEMISTRY. *Educ:* Evansville Col, BA, 60; Univ Calif, Berkeley, PhD(chem), 64. *Prof Exp:* Asst prof chem, Miami Univ, 65-66; vis scientist, Argonne Nat Lab, 66-67; ASSOC PROF CHEM, UNIV MO-COLUMBIA, 67- *Mem:* Am Phys Soc. *Res:* Microwave and infrared spectroscopy. *Mailing Add:* Dept of Chem Univ of Mo Columbia MO 65201

KIM, JAE HO, b Taegu, Korea, Dec 17, 35; US citizen; m 63; c 2. RADIOBIOLOGY, RADIOTHERAPY. *Educ:* Kyung-Pook Nat Univ, Korea, MD, 59; Univ Iowa, PhD(radiobiol), 63. *Prof Exp:* Res assoc, Sloan-Kettering Inst Cancer Res, 63-68, asst prof biophys, Sloan-Kettering Div, Cornell Univ, 67-68; intern med, Montefiore Hosp, Bronx, 68-69; resident radiother, Mem Hosp, New York, 69-72; ASSOC MEM, SLOAN-KETTERING INST, 72-; from asst prof to assoc prof radiol, 72-79, ASSOC PROF BIOPHYS, MED COL, CORNELL UNIV, 72-, PROF RADIOL, 80- *Concurrent Pos:* Asst attend, Mem Hosp, 72-75, assoc attend, 75-77, attend, 78- *Mem:* AMA; NY Acad Sci; Radiation Res Soc; Am Asn Cancer Res; Am Radium Soc. *Res:* Cellular radio and chemo-biology; metabolic studies occurring during the cell cycle of mammalian cells in vitro; effects of ionizing radiation, metabolic inhibitors, hyperthermia on nucleic acid metabolism and cell viability in various tumors in culture. *Mailing Add:* Mem Hosp 444 E 68th St New York NY 10021

KIM, JAI BIN, b Seoul, Korea, May 17, 34; m 60; c 4. CIVIL ENGINEERING. *Educ:* Ore State Univ, BS, 59, MS, 60; Univ Md, PhD(civil eng), 65. *Prof Exp:* Chief hwy res engr, DC Dept Transp, 64-66; from asst prof to assoc prof civil eng, 66-77, PROF CIVIL ENG & CHMN DEPT, BUCKNELL UNIV, 77- *Concurrent Pos:* Res engr, Nat Bur Standards, 76-77. *Mem:* Am Soc Testing & Mat; Am Concrete Inst; Am Soc Civil Engrs; Sigma Xi. *Res:* Structural mechanics; engineering analysis; foundation engineering; nonlinear structural analysis; pile foundations; shallow excavations; pile caps. *Mailing Add:* Dept of Civil Eng Bucknell Univ Lewisburg PA 17837

KIM, JAI SOO, b Korea, Nov 1, 25; nat US; m 52; c 4. ATMOSPHERIC PHYSICS. *Educ:* Seoul Nat Univ, BSc, 49; Univ Sask, MSc, 57, PhD(physics), 58. *Prof Exp:* Instr physics, Tonga Col, Pusan, 52-53; instr, Sung Kyun Kwan Univ, Korea, 53-54; asst prof, Clarkson Tech, 58-59; from asst prof to prof, Univ Idaho, 59-67; chmn dept, 69-76, PROF ATMOSPHERIC SCI & PHYSICS, STATE UNIV NY ALBANY, 67- *Concurrent Pos:* Rep, Univ Corp Atmospheric Res, State Univ NY Albany, 71-76; consult, US Army Res Off, 78-80, Battelle Mem Inst, 77-80, NY State Environ Conserv Dept & Environ One Corp, 76-; investr grants, NSF, Air for Off Sci & Res, US Army Res Off, Environ Protection Agency & NY State Environ Conserv Dept. *Mem:* Am Asn Physics Teachers; Am Geophys Union. *Res:* Upper atmospheric physics; solar-terrestrial relations; plasma physics; magneto-hydrodynamics. *Mailing Add:* Dept of Atmospheric Sci State Univ of NY Albany NY 12222

KIM, JEAN BARTHOLOMEW, b Philadelphia, Pa, Oct 12, 40; m 65; c 2. ORGANIC CHEMISTRY. *Educ:* Eastern Baptist Col, BA, 61; Bryn Mawr Col, PhD(chem), 68. *Prof Exp:* Asst prof chem, Haverford Col, 67-68; res assoc chem, Drexel Univ, 68-70; PROF CHEM & HEAD DEPT, EASTERN COL, 70-, VPRES & ACAD DEAN, 80- *Mem:* AAAS; Am Chem Soc; Sigma Xi; Nat Sci Teachers Asn. *Res:* Electrophilic substitution on electronic properties of porphin derivatives. *Mailing Add:* Dept of Chem Eastern Col St Davids PA 19087

KIM, JIN BAI, b Sangju, Korea, June 23, 21; m 45; c 1. ALGEBRA. *Educ:* Yonsei Univ, Korea, BS, 50; Univ Chicago, MS, 56; Va Polytech Inst, PhD(math), 66. *Prof Exp:* From instr to asst prof math, Yonsei Univ, Korea, 49-61; asst prof, Mich State Univ, 65-67; asst prof, 67-71, assoc prof, 71-76, PROF MATH, WVA UNIV, 76- *Mem:* Am Math Soc; Math Asn Am. *Res:* Algebraic semigroups; linear algebra; matrices; tensors and differential manifolds. *Mailing Add:* Dept of Math WVa Univ Morgantown WV 26505

KIM, JINCHOON, b Choon-Chun, Korea, Mar 5, 43; US citizen; m 70; c 1. PLASMA PHYSICS. *Educ:* Seoul Nat Univ, BS, 65; Univ Calif, Berkeley, MS, 68, PhD(plasma physics), 71. *Prof Exp:* Physicist, Cyclotron Corp, 71-74; physicist, Oak Ridge Nat Lab, 74-80; STAFF SCIENTIST, GEN ATOMIC CO, 80- *Mem:* Am Phys Soc; Am Vacumm Soc; Korean Nuclear Soc. *Res:* Physics of energetic neutral beam generation and its interaction with magnetically-confined plasmas; particle accelerators; plasma diagnostics. *Mailing Add:* 12920 Sundance Ave San Diego CA 92129

KIM, JOHN K, b Seoul, Korea, Oct 26, 37; US citizen; m 61; c 2. ELECTRICAL ENG, MATERIAL SCIENCE. *Educ:* Ohio Univ, BS, 63; Ohio State Univ, MS, 63, PhD(elec eng), 67. *Prof Exp:* Mem tech staff electronics, Lincoln Lab, Mass Inst Technol, 66-67; sr engr solid state, Semiconductor Group, Motorola, 67-68; head sect semiconductor eng, Micro State, 68-70, head dept semiconductor res & develop, Raytheon Co, 70-75; PRES, SUPERTEK CO, 75- *Mem:* Sigma Xi; Inst Elec & Electronics Engrs; Korean Sci Eng Asn. *Res:* Analysis and development of solid state devices for high efficiency and high power generation of microwave energy. *Mailing Add:* Supertek Co 2320 Cotner Ave Los Angeles CA 90064

KIM, JONATHAN JANG-HO, b Kwang-Ju, Korea, June 11, 32; m 58; c 1. METALLURGICAL ENGINEERING. *Educ:* Seoul Nat Univ, BS, 55; Carnegie Inst Technol, MS, 61; Univ Okla, PhD(metall eng), 66. *Prof Exp:* Res engr, Sci Res Lab, Ministry of Nat Defense, Korea, 55-59; design engr, Lummus Co, 65-67; sr proj engr, Ledgemont Lab, Kennecott Copper Corp, 67-75; staff metall engr, Lexington Develop Ctr, 75-80; MGR, PROCESS RES, CORBORUNDUM CO, STANDARD INDUST PROD CO, 80- *Mem:* Am Inst Mining, Metall & Petrol Engrs; Am Ceramic Soc. *Res:* Smelting and refining of nonferrous metals; extractive metallurgy; ceramic manufacturing processes via fusion and sintering; ceramic grains synthesis. *Mailing Add:* 79 Brandywine Dr Williamsville NY 14221

KIM, JUHEE, b Osan, Korea, Sept 13, 35; m 68; c 2. MICROBIOLOGY. *Educ:* Seoul Nat Univ, BS, 58; Cornell Univ, MS, 62, PhD(food sci & microbiol), 66. *Prof Exp:* Researcher food & nutrit, Sci Res Inst, Ministry Defense, Seoul, Korea, 58-59; from asst prof to assoc prof, 66-75, PROF MICROBIOL, CALIF STATE UNIV, LONG BEACH, 75- *Concurrent Pos:* Vis investr, Scripps Inst Oceanog, 70-71 & Wood Hole Oceanog Inst, 73; environ specialist, Southern Calif Coastal Water Res Proj, 74. *Mem:* AAAS; Am Soc Microbiol; Am Chem Soc; NY Acad Sci. *Res:* Food and industrial microbiology; public health. *Mailing Add:* Dept Microbiol Calif State Univ Long Beach CA 90840

KIM, KE CHUNG, b Seoul, Korea, Mar 7, 34; m 64; c 2. SYSTEMATIC ENTOMOLOGY, MEDICAL ENTOMOLOGY. *Educ:* Seoul Nat Univ, BS, 56; Univ Mont, MA, 59; Univ Minn, PhD(entom), 64. *Prof Exp:* Res fel entom, Univ Minn, 64-67, res assoc, 67-68; from asst prof to assoc prof, 68-79, PROF ENTOM, PA STATE UNIV, UNIVERSITY PARK, 79- *Concurrent Pos:* Consult, Smithsonian Inst, 64-67; Nat Inst Allergy & Infectious Dis res grants, 64-; Fulbright lectr/researcher, 75; vis scientist, Atomic Energy Res Inst, Seoul, 75-76; vis prof, Seoul Nat Univ, 75-76 & Univ Heidelberg, 76; rep-at-large, Asn Systs Collections, 79-81. *Mem:* AAAS; Entom Soc Am; Soc Syst Zool. *Res:* Biosystematics of the dipterous family Sphaeroceridae; systematics and ecology of sucking lice; ecology of ectoparasites-mammalian host relationships; evolution of lice on marine carnivores. *Mailing Add:* Frost Entom Mus Pa State Univ University Park PA 16802

KIM, KENNETH, b Honolulu, Hawaii, Dec 24, 31. MICROBIOLOGY. *Educ:* Univ Hawaii, BA, 53; Wash Univ, MS, 60, PhD(microbiol), 64. *Prof Exp:* Instr prev med, Univ Wash, 64-71; asst prof, 71-80, ASSOC PROF CLIN PATH, BACT DIV, MED SCH, UNIV ORE, 80- *Mem:* Am Soc Microbiol; NY Acad Sci. *Res:* Relationship of diphtheria toxin to the diphtheria phage-bacterium relationship and the mode of action of toxin on cultured cells; biology of Rubella virus. *Mailing Add:* Dept of Clin Path Bacteriol Div Univ of Ore Med Sch Portland OR 97201

KIM, KEUN YOUNG, b Kaesong, Korea, May 29, 28; US citizen; m 58; c 2. CHEMICAL ENGINEERING, INORGANIC CHEMISTRY. *Educ:* Seoul Nat Univ, BS, 51; Univ Wis, MS, 56, PhD(chem eng), 59. *Prof Exp:* Res investr, Inst Sci Res & Technol, Korea, 50-53; res chem engr, 62-66, res specialist, 66-70, FEL, DEPT RES & DEVELOP, DETERGENT & PHOSPHATE DIV, MONSANTO INDUST CHEM CO, 70- *Mem:* Am Inst Chem Engrs; Am Chem Soc. *Res:* Phosphates product and process research; calcium phosphates, particularly dentifrices. *Mailing Add:* Detergent & Phosphate Div 800 N Lindburg Blvd St Louis MO 63166

KIM, KI HANG, b Munduk, Pyongando, Korea, Aug 5, 36; US citizen; m 63; c 2. MATHEMATICS. *Educ:* Univ Southern Miss, BS, 60, MS, 61; George Washington Univ, MP, 70, PhD(math), 71. *Prof Exp:* Instr math, Univ Hartford, 61-66; lectr, George Washington Univ, 66-68; assoc prof, St Mary's Col, Md, 68-70; assoc prof, Pembroke State Univ, 70-73; vis prof math, Portugal Inst Physics & Math, 73-74; PROF MATH, ALA STATE UNIV, 74- *Concurrent Pos:* Managing ed, Int J Math Social Sci. *Mem:* Am Math Soc. *Res:* Applied mathematics; finite mathematics; other mathematics. *Mailing Add:* Box 69 Ala State Univ Montgomery AL 36195

KIM, KI HONG, b Seoul, Korea; US citizen; m 68; c 2. ANALYTICAL CHEMISTRY. *Educ:* Ohio State Univ, BS, 59; Ohio Univ, MS, 62; George Washington Univ, MPH, 73, PhD(chem), 76. *Prof Exp:* Res assoc biochem, Med Ctr, Univ Ky, 63-66; res assoc biochem, Wayne State Univ, 66-67, proj leader, 73-78, MGR METAL SYSTS, EMCON DIV, ILL TOOL WORKS INC, SAN DIEGO, 78- *Mem:* Am Chem Soc; Soc Appl Spectros; Am Ceramic Soc. *Res:* Spectrophotometric and photopolarographic studies of organo-metallic compounds; research and development of precious metal powder and electrode ink systems for ceramic chip capacitor. *Mailing Add:* 17011 Cloudcroft Dr Poway CA 92064

KIM, KI-HAN, b Seoul, Korea, June 20, 32; US citizen; m 58; c 2. BIOCHEMISTRY. *Educ:* Univ Calif, Berkeley, BA, 57; Wayne State Univ, PhD(chem), 61. *Prof Exp:* Res assoc biochem, Wayne State Univ, 61-65 & Univ Wis-Madison, 65-67; from asst prof to assoc prof, 67-73, PROF BIOCHEM, PURDUE UNIV, 73- *Mem:* AAAS; Am Soc Biol Chem. *Res:* Mechanism of hormone action; biochemical basis of cellular differentiation. *Mailing Add:* Dept of Biochem Purdue Univ West Lafayette IN 47907

KIM, KI-HYON, b Ui ju City, Korea, Apr 20, 33; m 65; c 3. MEDICAL PHYSICS, NUCLEAR MEDICINE. *Educ:* Seoul Nat Univ, BSc, 56; Univ Vienna, PhD(nuclear physics), 63. *Prof Exp:* Res off, Atomic Energy Res Inst, Seoul, 63-66; assoc prof nuclear physics, 68-72, PROF APPL PHYSICS, NC CENT UNIV, 72- *Concurrent Pos:* Resident res assoc, NASA-Langley Res Ctr, 66-68; lectr-consult, 68-; consult, Oak Ridge Assoc Univs, 71- *Mem:* Am Phys Soc; Korean Phys Soc; Am Asn Physicists in Med; Soc Nuclear Med; Korean Scientists & Engrs Am. *Res:* Nuclear spectrometry; high-flux pulsed neutron sources; biomedical applications of nuclear electronics; organ visualization by means of radiopharmaceuticals and computer based scanning. *Mailing Add:* 3604 Mossdale Ave Durham NC 27707

KIM, KIL CHOL, b Hyokyong Hampook, Korea, Apr 22, 19; US citizen; m 65; c 4. ANESTHESIOLOGY, PHARMACOLOGY. *Educ:* Kyung-Pook Nat Univ, Korea, MD, 44; Loyola Univ, PhD(pharm), 62. *Prof Exp:* Intern med, Edgewater Hosp, 56-57; resident, Univ Chicago Clin, 57-58; resident, Cook County Hosp, 58-59; resident, Michael Reese Hosp, 59-60; sr investr pharm, Loyola Univ, 61-66; physician, Galesbury Res Hosp, 59-60; resident med, Albert Einstein Col Med, 68-69; ASST PROF MED, MED CTR, IND UNIV, INDIANAPOLIS, 69- *Mem:* AMA; assoc Am Soc Anesthesiol; Soc Neurosci. *Res:* Mechanism of contractility depression of cardiac muscle by anesthetics through interaction; investigation of drugs which reduce sleeping time of several anesthetics. *Mailing Add:* Dept of Anesthesiol Ind Univ Sch of Med Indianapolis IN 46202

KIM, KI-SOO, b Korea, Nov 6, 42; m 70; c 3. POLYMER CHEMISTRY. *Educ:* Seoul Nat Univ, BS, 65; City Univ NY, PhD(chem), 72. *Prof Exp:* Res asst chem, Atomic Energy Res Inst Korea, 66-68; assoc, Res Inst, City Univ New York, 72-74; SR RES CHEMIST, EASTERN RES CTR, STAUFFER CHEM CO, 74- *Mem:* Am Chem Soc; Korean Chem Soc. *Res:* New condensation and vinyl polymerization; synthesis of phosphorus and sulfur-containing polymers; engineering plastics; conductive polymers. *Mailing Add:* Eastern Res Ctr Stauffer Chem Co Dobbs Ferry NY 10522

KIM, KWANG SHIN, b Seoul, Korea, Nov 15, 37; m 65; c 2. MEDICAL MICROBIOLOGY, HORTICULTURE. *Educ:* Seoul Nat Univ, BS, 59; Rutgers Univ, New Brunswick, MS, 63, PhD(hort), 67. *Prof Exp:* Res asst hort, Rutgers Univ, New Brunswick, 65-66, res assoc, 66-67; from asst res scientist to assoc res scientist microbiol, 67-71, asst prof, 71-75, ASSOC PROF MICROBIOL, SCH MED, MED CTR, NY UNIV, 75- *Mem:* AAAS; Am Soc Microbiol; Sigma Xi. *Res:* Ultrastructure and cytochemistry of bacteria and mammalian cells; plant breeding and embryology. *Mailing Add:* Dept of Microbiol NY Univ Sch of Med New York NY 10016

KIM, KYEKYOON, b Seoul, Korea, Oct 5, 41; US citizen; m 69; c 2. APPLIED PHYSICS. *Educ:* Seoul Nat Univ, BS, 66; Cornell Univ, MS, 68, PhD(appl physics), 71. *Prof Exp:* Res asst nuclear sci & appl physics, Cornell Univ, 66-71, fel appl physics, 71-72; fel phys chem, 72-74; fel elec eng, 74-76, asst prof, 76-81, ASSOC PROF ELEC & NUCLEAR ENG, UNIV ILL, URBANA, 81- *Concurrent Pos:* Consult, Y-Div, Lawrence Livermore Lab, 78-, NASA, 80- & Environ Protection Res Inst, 81- *Mem:* Am Phys Soc; Inst Elec & Electronics Engrs; Am Vacuum Soc. *Res:* Fusion technology; plasma engineering; cryogenic laser fusion targets; electrohydrodynamics; monodispersed micro-particle generation from insulators; polymers and metals. *Mailing Add:* 155 EEB Dept of Elec Eng Univ of Ill Urbana IL 61801

KIM, KYUNG JIN, b Busan, SKorea, Sept 20, 45; US citizen; m 72; c 2. PHYSICS, MATERIAL SCIENCE. *Educ:* Korea Univ, BS, 67; Fairleigh Dickinson Univ, MS, 72; Rensselaer Polytech Inst, PhD(physics), 75. *Prof Exp:* Fel mat sci & eng, Northwestern Univ, 75-77; res scientist, 77-80, SR RES SCIENTIST POLYMER PHYSICS, FIRESTONE RES, FIRESTONE TIRE & RUBBER CO, 80- *Mem:* Metall Soc; Am Asn Physics Teachers; Sigma Xi; Adhesion Soc; Electron Micros Soc Am. *Res:* Mossbauer study on microcrystalline structure of glass containing iron oxides; effect of microstructure on mechanical properties of low carbon steels; rubber to metal adhesion and related surface/interface studies using ESCA/AES; polymer morphology by transmission electron microscope, scanning electron microscope and optical microscopy. *Mailing Add:* Cent Res Lab 1200 Firestone Pkwy Akron OH 44317

KIM, LEO, b Reedley, Calif, Oct 3, 42; m 63. ORGANIC CHEMISTRY, ORGANOMETALLIC CHEMISTRY. *Educ:* Fresno State Col, BS, 64; Univ Kans, PhD(org chem), 67. *Prof Exp:* NIH fel, Mass Inst Technol, 67-68; chemist, Calif, 68-74, staff res chemist, 74-78, dept head, organic chem, 80, mgr biol chem, 81, RES & DEV DIR, SHELL DEVELOP CO, 81- *Concurrent Pos:* spec assignment bio technol, Shell Res, Kent Eng. *Mem:* Am Inst Chemists. *Res:* Biochemistry; research administration; organic reaction mechanisms; oxidation reactions; catalytic reactions of organic and organometallic compounds; enzyme modeling; free radical reactions. *Mailing Add:* Shell Oil Co 901 Grayson Berkeley CA 94710

KIM, MOON W, b Seoul, Korea. MATHEMATICAL ANALYSIS. *Educ:* Univ NH, BA, 64; Polytech Inst Brooklyn, MS, 68, PhD(math), 69. *Prof Exp:* Teaching fel math, Polytech Inst Brooklyn, 66-67, instr, 67-69; ASSOC PROF, SETON HALL UNIV, 69- *Mem:* Am Math Soc; Math Asn Am. *Res:* Functional analysis; fixed points theorems in non-linear analysis; analytic sets in Banach spaces. *Mailing Add:* Dept of Math Seton Hall Univ South Orange NJ 07079

KIM, MYUNGHWAN, b Seoul, Korea, Feb 8, 32; US citizen; m 59; c 2. ELECTRICAL ENGINEERING. *Educ:* Univ Ala, BS, 58; Yale Univ, MEng, 59, PhD(elec eng), 62. *Prof Exp:* Elec engr, Tenn Valley Authority, 58-59; from asst prof to assoc prof elec eng, 62-76, PROF ELEC ENG, CORNELL UNIV, 76- *Concurrent Pos:* NSF res grants, 65-67, 72-74 & 82-84; Nat Res Coun assoc, Jet Propulsion Lab, Calif Inst Technol, 68-69, vis assoc biol, 69; NIH spec res fel, 68-70, res grant, 75-78; Res Corp grant, 71-72. *Mem:* Inst Elec & Electronics Engrs; NY Acad Sci. *Res:* Automatic control and computer systems; bioengineering; neurobiology and systems. *Mailing Add:* Dept of Elec Eng Col of Eng Cornell Univ Ithaca NY 14850

KIM, PAIK KEE, b Korea, Nov 10, 44; m 68; c 3. MANIFOLDS, TRANSFORMATON GROUP. *Educ:* Seoul Nat Univ, BA, 68; Mich State Univ, MA, 70, PhD(math), 73. *Prof Exp:* Asst prof math, Univ RI, 75-76 & Univ Kans, 76-78; Asst prof, 78-81, ASSOC PROF MATH, IOWA STATE UNIV, 81- *Mem:* Am Math Soc. *Res:* Geometric topology with emphasis on topology of manifolds; three-manifold group theory; involutions and finite group actions. *Mailing Add:* Dept Math Iowa State Univ Ames IA 50011

KIM, RHYN H(YUN), b Seoul, Korea, Feb 4, 36; m 66; c 2. MECHANICAL & CHEMICAL ENGINEERING. *Educ:* Seoul Nat Univ, BSME, 58; Mich State Univ, MS, 61, PhD(mech eng), 65. *Prof Exp:* Assoc prof mech eng, Univ NC, Charlotte, 65-76; staff engr, Off Air Qual Planning & Standards, Environ Protection Agency, 76-77, mech engr, Indust Environ Res Lab, Off Res & Develop, 77-78; PROF, COL ENG, UNIV NC, CHARLOTTE, 78- *Concurrent Pos:* Consult, Indust Environ Res Lab, Off Res & Develop, Environ Protection Agency, 78-; consult, Duke Power Co, NC. *Mem:* Am Soc Mech Engrs; Am Soc Heating, Refrig & Air-Conditioning Engrs. *Res:* Burning rate study of fuel combustions in a spherical autoclave; stability of transient heat conduction in solid structures; combustion, energy conservation and utilization; environmental emission controls; mass transfer in porous media; thermal system optimization and simulations; computer aided heat exchanger design. *Mailing Add:* 2726 Wamath Dr Charlotte NC 28210

KIM, RYUNG-SOON (SONG), b Jeonju, Korea, Nov 24, 38; Can citizen; m 63; c 3. PHARMACOLOGY, MEDICINAL CHEMISTRY. *Educ:* Seoul Nat Univ, BSc, 61; Duquesne Univ, MSc, 63; Univ Man, PhD(chem), 76. *Prof Exp:* Teaching asst pharm, Duquesne Univ, 61-63; res asst biochem, Hahnemann Med Col, 63-64; lab instr pharm chem, 71-75, RES STAFF PHARMACOL, UNIV MAN, 76- *Concurrent Pos:* Res fel, Can Heart Found, 76-79. *Mem:* Pharmacol Soc Can. *Res:* Cardiovascular pharmacology; endogenous ligands and modulators of the digitalis receptor; chemical and biological characterization of endogenous ionophores; drug-receptor interactions. *Mailing Add:* 79 Morningside Dr Winnipeg MB R3T 4A2 Can

KIM, SANG HYUNG, b Kyunggi, Korea, Oct 18, 42; m 68; c 2. PHYSICAL CHEMISTRY, ELECTROCHEMISTRY. *Educ:* Seoul Nat Univ, BS, 64; Univ Utah, PhD(phys chem), 71. *Prof Exp:* Asst teaching & res, Seoul Nat Univ, 66-67; res asst, Univ Utah, 67-70; fel electrochem, Univ Pa, 70-71; fel membrane biophys, Northwestern Univ, 71-74; SR RES CHEMIST RES DEVELOP, RES LABS, EASTMAN KODAK CO, 74- *Mem:* Am Chem Soc. *Res:* Ion-selective electrodes; solution and interfacial electrochemistry; membrane biophysics; electrochemistry applied to biological and medical sciences; emulsion and polymer coatings; photographic sciences. *Mailing Add:* Res Labs Eastman Kodak Co Rochester NY 14650

KIM, SANG-CHUL, b Korea, Jan 17, 24; nat US; m 56; c 2. ELECTRICAL ENGINEERING. *Educ:* Northeastern Univ, BS, 51; Harvard Univ, SM, 52, SD(appl physics), 56. *Prof Exp:* Asst physics, Harvard Univ, 53-55; elec engr, 55-65, RES PHYSICIST, LIGHTING RES LAB, GEN ELEC CO, 65- *Res:* Computer controlled ELH projection lamp alignment system, spectroradiometer system, and deposition of optical interference filter; selective reflector lamp system; double arc lamp and the system; electric power system; computer science technology; water diffusion through quartz; determination of the distribution of particle size; sequential flash lamp system. *Mailing Add:* Lighting Res Lab Gen Elec Co Nela Park Cleveland OH 44112

KIM, SANGDUK, b Seoul, Korea, June 15, 30; US citizen; m 59; c 3. BIOCHEMISTRY. *Educ:* Seoul Women's Med Col, MD, 53; Univ Wis, PhD(biochem), 59. *Prof Exp:* Res assoc physiol chem, Univ Wis, 59-61; res assoc biochem, Univ Ottawa, 62-65; res assoc biochem, 65-78, ASSOC PROF BIOCHEM, FELS RES INST, SCH MED, TEMPLE UNIV, 78- *Res:* Biochemistry of protein methylation; enzymatic modification of protein molecule, particularly methylation. *Mailing Add:* Fels Res Inst Temple Univ Sch of Med Philadelphia PA 19140

KIM, SEUNG U, b Osaka, Japan, Oct 28, 36; US Citizen; m 62; c 2. NEUROPATHOLOGY, NEUROBIOLOGY. *Educ:* Univ Seoul, Korea, MD, 60; Kyoto Univ, Japan, PhD(neurobiol), 65. *Prof Exp:* Multiple Sclerosis Soc fel, Col Physicians & Surgeons, Columbia Univ, 66-69; assoc prof neurobiol, Univ Sask, Saskatoon, 70-72; asst prof neuropath, 72-75, assoc prof neuropath, 75-81, PROF NEUROL, UNIV PA, 81- *Mem:* Tissue Cult Asn; Am Asn Neuropathologists; Histochem Soc; Soc Neurosci; Am Soc Cell Biol. *Res:* Experimental neurology; neural tissue culture. *Mailing Add:* Div of Neuropath Univ of Pa Sch of Med Philadelphia PA 19104

KIM, SHOON KYUNG, b Ham Hun, Korea, Feb 29, 20; m 49; c 3. THEORETICAL CHEMISTRY. *Educ:* Osaka Univ, BS, 44; Yale Univ, PhD(phys chem), 56. *Prof Exp:* Res chemist, Inst Chem, Kyoto Univ, 44-46; instr chem, Seoul Nat Univ, 46-47, from instr to prof phys chem, 49-62; res chemist, Cent Indust Res Inst, 47-49; vis prof phys chem, Brown Univ, 62-66; prof, Univ Louisville, 66-69; PROF CHEM, TEMPLE UNIV, 69- *Honors & Awards:* Korean Nat Sci Award, 61. *Mem:* Korean Chem Soc (secy gen, 60-61); Am Chem Soc; Am Phys Soc; Am Vacuum Soc. *Res:* Statistical mechanical theory of classical and quantal systems; chemical kinetics. *Mailing Add:* Dept of Chem Temple Univ Philadelphia PA 19122

KIM, SOO MYUNG, b Chaeryung, Korea, Oct 24, 36; m 70; c 2. SOLID STATE PHYSICS. *Educ:* Seoul Nat Univ, BS, 59; Univ NC, Chapel Hill, PhD(physics), 68. *Prof Exp:* Res assoc physics, Univ NC, Chapel Hill, 67-68; fel dept physics, Univ Guelph, 68-70; Nat Res Coun fel neutron physics br, 70-72, ASSOC RES OFFICER, ATOMIC ENERGY CAN LTD, CHALK RIVER, 72- *Mem:* Am Phys Soc; Can Asn Physicists; Korean Scientists & Engrs Am. *Res:* Positron annihilation in metals; defects in metals. *Mailing Add:* Neutron & Solid State Physics Br Atomic Energy of Can Ltd Chalk River ON K0J 1J0 Can

KIM, SOON SAM, b Seoul, Korea, Jan 3, 45; US citizen; m 70. ELECTRON SPIN RESONANCE, NUCLEAR MAGNETIC RESONANCE. *Educ:* Seoul Nat Univ, BS, 67; Univ Chicago, PhD(phys chem), 74. *Prof Exp:* Fel phys chem, Wash Univ, 74-79; RES CHEMIST PHYS CHEM, OCCIDENTAL PETROL CORP, 79- *Mem:* Am Chem Soc. *Res:* Application of magnetic resonance, electron spin resonance, for the study of chemical kinetics, optical spin polarization, and molecular structure determination. *Mailing Add:* 2100 SE Main St PO Box 19601 Irvine CA 92713

KIM, SOON-KYU, b Hadong, Korea, Oct 3, 32; m 59; c 3. MATHEMATICS. *Educ:* Seoul Nat Univ, BS, 57, MS, 59; Univ Mich, PhD(math), 67. *Prof Exp:* Instr math, Seoul Univ & Kunkook Univ, 59-62; instr, Univ Ill, Urbana, 66-69; asst prof, 69-72, ASSOC PROF MATH, UNIV CONN, 72- *Concurrent Pos:* Vis assoc prof, Mich State Univ, 75-76. *Mem:* Am Math Soc; Math Asn Am; Korean Math Soc; Korean Scientists & Engrs Asn Am. *Res:* Fiberings and transformation groups. *Mailing Add:* Dept of Math Univ of Conn Storrs CT 06268

KIM, SUNG KYU, b Chulla Namdo, Korea, Jan 12, 39; m 68; c 2. THEORETICAL PHYSICS. *Educ:* Davidson Col, BS, 60; Duke Univ, AM, 64, PhD(physics), 65. *Prof Exp:* Asst prof, 65-70, assoc prof, 71-75, PROF PHYSICS, MACALESTER COL, 75- *Concurrent Pos:* Master teacher, Twin City Inst Talented Youth, 68-69; asst prof, Univ Calif, Irvine, 70-71; vis scholar, Fermi Inst, Univ Chicago, 80-81. *Mem:* Am Phys Soc; Soc Hist Sci; Am Asn Physics Teachers. *Res:* Weak interactions; elementary particles; history of science. *Mailing Add:* 3134 N Victoria St St Paul MN 55112

KIM, SUNG WAN, b Pusan, Korea, Aug 21, 40; m 66; c 1. BIOMATERIALS, PHARMACEUTICS. *Educ:* Seoul Nat Univ, BS, 63, MS, 65; Univ Utah, PhD, 69. *Prof Exp:* Res asst, Seoul Nat Univ, 63-65; res asst chem, 66-69, fel, 69, res assoc mat sci, 69-70, asst res prof mat sci & eng, 70-73, from asst prof to assoc prof pharmaceut, 73-80, PROF PHARMACEUT, COL PHARM, UNIV UTAH, 80- *Concurrent Pos:* NIH res career develop award, 77-81. *Mem:* AAAS; Am Chem Soc; Korean Chem Soc; Am Soc Artificial Internal Organs; Am Pharm Asn. *Res:* Blood compatible polymers; membrane diffusion; interface induced thrombosis; polymeric drug delivery system. *Mailing Add:* Col of Pharm Skaggs Hall 206 Univ of Utah Salt Lake City UT 84117

KIM, SUNG-HOU, b Taegu, Korea, Dec 12, 37; US citizen; m 68; c 2. BIOPHYSICAL CHEMISTRY, STRUCTURAL MOLECULAR BIOLOGY. *Educ:* Seoul Nat Univ, Korea, BS, 60, MS, 62; Univ Pittsburgh, PhD(phys chem), 66. *Prof Exp:* Res assoc biol, Mass Inst Tech, 66-70, sr res scientist, 70-72; asst prof biochem, Sch Med, Duke Univ, 72-73, assoc prof, 73-78; PROF BIOPHYS CHEM, UNIV CALIF, BERKELEY, 78- *Concurrent Pos:* NIH consult, 76-80; fulbright fel, Fulbright Found, 62; Lansdowne scholar, Univ Victoria, Can, 80. *Mem:* Am Soc Biol Chemists; Am Crystallog Asn; Am Chem Soc; AAAS; Korean Scientists & Engrs Am. *Res:* Structure and function of DNA, RNA and proteins. *Mailing Add:* Dept Chem Univ Calif Berkeley CA 94720

KIM, SUN-KEE, b Seoul, Korea, Dec 11, 37; US citizen; m 63; c 2. CELL BIOLOGY, ANATOMY. *Educ:* Yon-sei Univ, Korea, BS, 60; Univ Rochester, MS, 64, PhD(biol), 70. *Prof Exp:* Asst cancer res scientist endocrinol, Rosewell Park Mem Inst, Buffalo, 64-65; RES BIOLOGIST, VET ADMIN MED CTR, 68-, COORDR ELECTRON MICROSCOPY, RES SERV, 73- *Concurrent Pos:* Co-dir, Advan Spec Training Dent Res, Vet

Admin Med Ctr, 70-75; res assoc anat, Sch Med, Univ Mich, 70-74, asst prof, 74-81, assoc prof, 81-; proj dir aging studies salivary gland, Nat Inst Aging, NIH, 78. *Mem:* Am Soc Cell Biol; Am Asn Anatomists; Int Asn Dent Res; AAAS; Sigma Xi. *Res:* Age-related changes in secretory function of exocrine glands; ultrastructure and protein synthesis in secretory cells of the salivary gland. *Mailing Add:* Res Serv 2215 Fuller Rd Ann Arbor MI 48105

KIM, TAI KYUNG, b Pyungyang, Korea, June 19, 27; m 59; c 2. PHYSICAL CHEMISTRY. *Educ:* Seoul Nat Univ, BSE, 51; Adrian Col, BS, 55; Univ Detroit, MS, 60; Duquesne Univ, PhD(phys chem), 63. *Prof Exp:* Res chemist, 63-77, ENG SPECIALIST, CHEM & METALL DIV, G T E SYLVANIA INC, 77- *Mem:* Am Chem Soc. *Res:* Metal complexation; solvent extraction; radiochemistry; molybdenum and tungsten chemistry. *Mailing Add:* RD 1 Hillcrest Towanda PA 18848

KIM, THOMAS JOON-MOCK, b Seoul, Korea, Oct 13, 36; US citizen; m 67; c 2. MECHANICAL ENGINEERING, APPLIED MECHANICS. *Educ:* Seoul Nat Univ, BS, 59; Villanova Univ, MS, 64; Univ Ill, PhD(mech), 67. *Prof Exp:* Instr mech, Univ Ill, 65-67; asst prof math, Villanova Univ, 67-68; from asst prof to assoc prof, 68-79, PROF & CHMN MECH ENG, UNIV RI, 79- *Concurrent Pos:* Consult, US Naval Underwater Systs Ctr, 77- *Mem:* Am Soc Mech Engrs; Am Ceramic Soc. *Res:* Solid mechanics, especially elasticity, plates and shells; ceramic processing; dynamic face seals; thermal stress analysis; ceramic processing. *Mailing Add:* Dept of Mech Eng Univ of RI Kingston RI 02881

KIM, WAN H(EE), b Osan, Korea, May 24, 26; US citizen; m 60; c 2. ELECTRICAL ENGINEERING. *Educ:* Seoul Nat Univ, BE, 50; Univ Utah, MS, 54, PhD(elec eng), 56. *Prof Exp:* Teacher pub sch, Korea, 47-50; asst elec eng, Univ Ill, 55-56; assoc engr res ctr, IBM Corp, 56-57; from asst prof to prof elec eng, Columbia Univ, 57-78, NSF res grants, 58-78; prin adv, Elec Res & Test Lab, Telecommun Res Inst, Korea Inst Electronics Technol, 78-81; PRES, WHK ENG CORP, 82- *Concurrent Pos:* Guggenheim Found fel, 63-64; chmn, Faculties Assoc Consult, Inc, NY, 63-; mem US nat comt, Comn 6, Int Sci Radio Union, 65-; spec adv prom electronics industs, Korean Govt, 68-; vis scientist, Japan, US-Japan Scientists Coop Prog, 70-71; organizer & chmn, Seoul Int Conf, Elec & Electronics Engrs, 70; chmn & chief exec officer, Komkor of Am, Inc, NY & mem bd, Korea Keyboard Corp, Seoul, Korea, 70- *Mem:* Fel Inst Elec & Electronics Engrs; Am Math Soc; Tensor Soc. *Res:* Network theory; information theory; network and systems analysis and design, particularly application of graph theory to engineering problems and theory of coding. *Mailing Add:* WHK Eng Corp CPO Box 1422 Seoul Korea

KIM, WON KYUM, b Kapsan, Korea, May 7, 29; m 59; c 3. MOLECULAR BIOLOGY, PLANT BIOCHEMISTRY. *Educ:* Seoul Nat Univ, BSc, 53, MSc, 55; Univ NC, PhD(plant physiol), 61. *Prof Exp:* Lectr, Seoul Nat Univ, 55-57; Can Nat Res Coun fel plant develop, 61-63; res assoc, Univ Toronto, 63-65; RES SCIENTIST, RES STA, AGR CAN, 65- *Concurrent Pos:* Adj prof, Univ Man, 72- *Mem:* Can Soc Plant Physiologists; Am Soc Plant Physiologists; Sigma Xi. *Res:* Molecular biology of cereal diseases; determining the molecular basis of host-parasite specificity and the mechanisms of resistance of cereal crops against pathogens. *Mailing Add:* Res Br Res Sta 195 Dafoe Rd Winnipeg MB R3T 2M9 Can

KIM, WOO JONG, b Seoul, Korea, Jan 15, 37. MATHEMATICS. *Educ:* Seoul Nat Univ, BS, 58; Okla State Univ, MS, 60; Carnegie-Mellon Univ, MS & PhD(chem eng), 64, PhD(math), 68. *Prof Exp:* Asst prof, 68-69, ASSOC PROF APPL MATH, STATE UNIV NY STONY BROOK, 70- *Mem:* Am Math Soc; Math Asn Am. *Res:* Disconjugacy, oscillation and asymptotic behavior of ordinary differential equations. *Mailing Add:* Dept of Appl Math & Statist State Univ of NY Stony Brook NY 11790

KIM, YEE SIK, b Seoul, Korea, Apr 15, 28; US citizen; m 50; c 4. BIOCHEMISTRY, PHARMACOLOGY. *Educ:* Kans State Univ, BS, 57, MS, 60; St Louis Univ, PhD(pharmacol), 65. *Prof Exp:* Instr chem, Kans State Univ, 60; res chemist, Union Starch & Refining Co, Ill, 60-63; asst prof, 66-70, assoc prof, 70-76, PROF PHARMACOL, ST LOUIS UNIV, 76- *Concurrent Pos:* USPHS fel biochem, State Univ NY Buffalo, 65-66; Gen res support grant & Cancer Inst res grant, 66-; USPHS res grant, 67- *Mem:* AAAS; Am Soc Pharmacol & Exp Therapeut; Am Chem Soc; NY Acad Sci. *Res:* Molecular mechanism of hormone action; enzyme reaction mechanisms; metabolisms of macromolecules; diabetic pregnancy. *Mailing Add:* Dept of Pharmacol St Louis Univ Sch of Med St Louis MO 63104

KIM, YEONG ELL, b SKorea; US citizen; m 61; c 2. THEORETICAL NUCLEAR PHYSICS. *Educ:* Lincoln Mem Univ, BS, 59; Univ Calif, Berkeley, PhD, 63. *Prof Exp:* Fel physics, Bell Tel Labs Inc, 63-65, Oak Ridge Nat Lab, 65-67; asst prof, 67-73, assoc prof, 73-77, PROF PHYSICS, PURDUE UNIV, 77- *Concurrent Pos:* Proj dir, Purdue Nuclear Theory Group, 71-; vis staff mem, Los Alamos Nat Lab, Univ Calif, 73-74, consult, 74-; Humboldt vis prof, Univ Mainz West Ger, 77-78; chmn, Gordon Res Conf, 77; vis prof, Seoul Nat Univ, 79 & 80. *Mem:* Korean Scientists & Engrs Asn Am; fel Korean Phys Soc; fel Am Phys Soc. *Res:* Quantum theory of scattering; theory of the three-nucleon systems; intermediate energy physics; theories of meson-exchange currents; parity violations in nuclear physics; photonuclear reactions; nuclear structure and reactions. *Mailing Add:* Dept of Physics Purdue Univ West Lafayette IN 47907

KIM, YONG IL, b Seoul, Korea, June 5, 45; m 75; c 2. NEUROMUSCULAR DISEASE, BIOELECTRIC PHENOMENA. *Educ:* Seoul Nat Univ, BS, 68; Cornell Univ, MS, 73, PhD(biomed eng), 77. *Prof Exp:* Systs analyst trainee, Korea Comput Ctr, 68; systs engr, Gadelius & Co, Ltd, 68-70; instr bioeng & elec systs, Cornell Univ, 77; res assoc, Dept Neurol, 77-79, ASST PROF BIOMED ENG & NEUROL, SCH MED, UNIV VA, 79- *Mem:* Inst Elec & Electronics Engrs; Biomed Eng Soc; AAAS; Soc Neurosci; Korean Scientists & Engrs Am. *Res:* Electrophysiology of disorders of neuromuscular transmission; bioelectric signal processing and analysis. *Mailing Add:* Dept Neurol & Biomed Eng Box 394 Sch Med Univ Va Charlottesville VA 22908

KIM, YONG WOOK, b Seoul, Korea, Sept 30, 38; nat US; m 66; c 1. ATOMIC PHYSICS, STATISTICAL PHYSICS. *Educ:* Seoul Nat Univ, BS, 60, MS, 62; Univ Mich, PhD(physics), 68. *Prof Exp:* Asst prof, 68-73, assoc prof, 73-77, PROF PHYSICS, LEHIGH UNIV, 77- *Mem:* Am Phys Soc. *Res:* Autocorrelations in molecular and Brownian fluctuation; atomic physics of very dense plasmas; kinetics of high density gas lasers. *Mailing Add:* Dept of Physics Lehigh Univ Bethlehem PA 18015

KIM, YONG-KI, b Seoul, Korea, Feb 20, 32; m 63; c 2. ATOMIC PHYSICS. *Educ:* Seoul Nat Univ, BS, 57; Univ Del, MS, 61; Univ Chicago, PhD(physics), 66. *Prof Exp:* Instr physics, Korean Air Force Acad, 57-59; res assoc, 66-68, asst physicist, 68-70, assoc physicist, 70-79, SR PHYSICIST, ARGONNE NAT LAB, 79- *Concurrent Pos:* Lectr, Univ Chicago, 67-68. *Mem:* Am Phys Soc; Korean Phys Soc. *Res:* Atomic structure theory; atomic collision theory; radiation physics. *Mailing Add:* Argonne Nat Lab 9700 S Cass Ave Argonne IL 60439

KIM, YOON BERM, b Soon Chun, Korea, Apr 25, 29; m 59; c 3. IMMUNOLOGY. *Educ:* Seoul Nat Univ, MD, 58; Univ Minn, PhD(microbiol), 65. *Prof Exp:* Intern med, Univ Hosp, Seoul Nat Univ, 58-59; from asst teaching & res to assoc teaching & res, 60-64, from instr to assoc prof microbiol, Med Sch, Univ Minn, Minneapolis, 65-73; HEAD, LAB ONTOGENY IMMUNE SYSTEM, SLOAN-KETTERING INST CANCER RES, NY, 73-; PROF BIOL & IMMUNOL, GRAD SCH MED SCI, CORNELL UNIV, 73-, CHMN, IMMUNOL UNIT, 80- *Concurrent Pos:* Res fel, 60-64; USPHS career develop res award, 68-73. *Mem:* Asn Gnotobiotics (pres, 79-80); Am Asn Immunol; Am Soc Microbiol; Reticuloendothelial Soc; Am Asn Path. *Res:* Immunobiology and immunochemistry; ontogeny of the immune system; mechanism of the immune response, regulation of the immune system; tumor immunity; immunochemistry and biology of bacterial toxins and host-parasite relationships; gnotobiology. *Mailing Add:* Sloan-Kettering Inst for Can Res 145 Boston Post Rd Rye NY 10580

KIM, YOUNG BAE, b Korea, Oct 23, 22; m 51; c 3. PHYSICS. *Educ:* Univ Wash, BS, 50; Princeton Univ, PhD(physics), 54. *Prof Exp:* Asst, Princeton Univ, 51-53; res assoc, Univ Ind, 54-55; assoc prof, Univ Wash, 56-61; mem tech staff, Bell Tel Labs, Murray Hill, NJ, 61-68; prof physics & elec eng, 69-75, CHMN ELEC ENG & PROF PHYSICS, UNIV SOUTHERN CALIF, 75- *Concurrent Pos:* Guggenheim fel, Tokyo Univ, 66-67; invited prof, Korea Advan Inst Sci, Seoul, 73-74. *Mem:* Fel Am Phys Soc. *Res:* Superconductivity, superconducting magnets and technology, solid state and low temperature physics; high energy physics, energy resources management. *Mailing Add:* Dept of Physics Univ of Southern Calif Los Angeles CA 90007

KIM, YOUNG C, b Seoul, Korea, May 25, 36; US citizen; m 65; c 3. CIVIL ENGINEERING. *Educ:* Univ Southern Calif, BS, 58, PhD(civil eng), 64; Calif Inst Technol, MS, 59. *Prof Exp:* Civil engr, Daniel, Mann, Johnson & Mendenhall, 59-61; lectr civil eng, Univ Southern Calif, 61-64; from asst prof to assoc prof, 65-73, chmn dept, 76-79, PROF CIVIL ENG, CALIF STATE UNIV, LOS ANGELES, 73-, ACTG ASSOC DEAN, SCH ENG, 78- *Concurrent Pos:* Sr lectr, Univ Southern Calif, 65-70; Res Corp res grants, 64 & 67, travel grant, 68; NSF res grant, 65; resident consult, US Naval Civil Eng Lab, 67 & 69; resident consult, Sci Eng Assocs, 67-, sr res engr, 69; vis scholar, Univ Calif, Berkeley, 71; NATO sr fel sci, Delft Technol Univ, Neth, 75; vis scientist, US-Japan Coop Sci Prog, Osaka City Univ, 76; prin investr, NSF, Res Corp & Defense Atomic Support Agency, 65-; reviewer, Sci Develop Countries Prog, NSF, 80; mem bd gov, Southern Calif Ocean Studies Consortium, 78. *Mem:* AAAS; Am Soc Civil Engrs; Int Asn Hydraul Res; Am Soc Eng Educ; Sigma Xi. *Res:* Underwater explosions; wave forces; interaction of structures and sea waves; hydraulic model studies; oil slick transport on coastal waters; wave energy absorption in coastal structures; extraction of energy from the sea; author of numerous publications. *Mailing Add:* Dept of Civil Eng Calif State Univ Los Angeles CA 90032

KIM, YOUNG DUC, b Korea, Oct 28, 32; m 65; c 1. ELECTRICAL ENGINEERING. *Educ:* Newark Col Eng, MSEE, 63, ScD, 68. *Prof Exp:* RES ELECTRONIC ENGR, US NAVAL AMMUNITION DEPOT, 68- *Mem:* Inst Elec & Electronics Engrs. *Res:* Investigation of noise spectral density observed in solid state devices. *Mailing Add:* Naval Weapons Support Ctr Crane IN 47522

KIM, YOUNG NOK, b Seoul, Korea, Jan 30, 21; m 60; c 3. THEORETICAL PHYSICS. *Educ:* Seoul Nat Univ, BS, 47, MS, 49; Univ Birmingham, PhD(math physics), 57. *Prof Exp:* Res grants, Inst Theoret Physics, Copenhagen, Denmark, 56-58, Heidelberg, Ger, 58, Edmonton, Can, 62-63, Inst Henri Poincare, Paris, France, 58-59 & Univ Wash, 60-62; prof physics, Mem Univ, 63-64; PROF PHYSICS, TEX TECH UNIV, 64- *Mem:* Am Phys Soc; Italian Phys Soc. *Res:* Nuclear structure; collision; mesonic atoms. *Mailing Add:* Dept of Physics Tex Tech Univ Lubbock TX 79409

KIM, YOUNG SHIK, b Seoul, Korea, Feb 5, 33; US citizen; m; c 2. MEDICINE. *Educ:* Stanford Univ, AB, 56; Cornell Univ, MD, 60. *Prof Exp:* Instr med, Med Col, Cornell Univ, 64-65; res assoc path, Stanford Univ, 65-66; asst prof biochem, New York Med Col, 67-68; from asst prof to assoc prof med, 68-76, PROF MED, UNIV CALIF, SAN FRANCISCO, 76- *Concurrent Pos:* Am Cancer Soc res scholar, 65-68; mem gen med study sect A, NIH, 76-79. *Mem:* Am Asn Cancer Res; Am Soc Clin Invest; Am Gastroenterol Asn; Biochem Soc; Asn Am Physicians. *Res:* Glycoprotein and glycolipid chemistry, immunochemistry and metabolism of the gastrointestinal tract. *Mailing Add:* 4150 Clement St Vet Admin Med Ctr San Francisco CA 94121

KIM, YOUNG TAI, b Seoul, Korea, Nov 10, 30; m 55; c 3. BIOCHEMISTRY, IMMUNOLOGY. *Educ:* Seoul Nat Univ, BS, 53, MS, 57; Univ Calif, Los Angeles, PhD(plant biochem), 63. *Prof Exp:* Asst prof biochem, Kyung Hee Univ, Korea, 57-60; res assoc bot, Univ Calif, Los Angeles, 63-64; biochem specialist, Growth Sci Ctr, Int Minerals & Chem Corp, 65-70; asst prof, 70-80,

ASSOC PROF MED, MED COL, CORNELL UNIV, 80- *Mem:* AAAS; Am Chem Soc; Am Inst Chemists; NY Acad Sci; Am Asn Immunologists. *Res:* Virology; molecular biology; relationship between immunological response and genetics; autounmune; immune response in aging. *Mailing Add:* 34-11 149th Place Flushing NY 11354

KIM, YUNGKI, b Korea, Dec 11, 35; US citizen; m 61; c 2. ORGANIC CHEMISTRY, POLYMER CHEMISTRY. *Educ:* Tex Christian Univ, BA, 59; Univ Colo, Boulder, MS, 61; Ariz State Univ, PhD(org chem), 65. *Prof Exp:* Fac res assoc chem, Ariz State Univ, 64-65; res chemist, 65-68, sr res chemist, 68-70, RES GROUP LEADER, SILICONE POLYMERS & INTERMEDIATES, DOW CORNING CORP, 70- *Mem:* Am Chem Soc; Sigma Xi. *Res:* Synthetic organic and polymer chemistry; silicone fluorosilicone and hybrid of silicone and organic/fluoro-organic leading to sealants, rubbers and resins. *Mailing Add:* Res Dept Dow Corning Corp Box 66 Midland MI 48640

KIM, ZAEZEUNG, b Hamhung, Korea, Feb 21, 28; US citizen; m 61; c 2. IMMUNOLOGY, ALLERGY. *Educ:* Seoul Nat Univ, MD, 60; Univ Cologne, PhD(immunol), 68. *Prof Exp:* Resident physician, Seoul Nat Univ Hosp, 61-63; resident physician, Heidelberg Univ Hosp, 63-64; res fel immunol, Max Planck Inst, 65-67; clin fel hematol, Univ Tex M D Anderson Hosp, 67-68; resident physician allergy-immunol, Temple Univ Hosp, 68-69; fel allergy-immunol, Col Med, Ohio State Univ, 69-71; instr med, 72-75, asst prof, 75-78, assoc prof med, 78-80, CLIN ASSOC PROF, DEPT MED ALLERGY SECT, MED COL WIS, 80- *Concurrent Pos:* Travel grants, AAAS, 67 & Am Acad Allergy, 70. *Mem:* AAAS; Am Acad Allergy; AMA. *Res:* Modification (change) of cellular antigenicity by enzyme treatment. *Mailing Add:* 4521 N Wildwood Ave Milwaukee WI 53211

KIMBALL, ALLYN WINTHROP, b Buffalo, NY, Oct 2, 21; m 44; c 2. BIOSTATISTICS. *Educ:* Univ Buffalo, BS, 43; NC State Univ, PhD(statist), 50. *Prof Exp:* Exp statistician aerospace med, US Air Force Sch Aviation Med, 48-50; chief statist sect, Math Panel, Oak Ridge Nat Lab, 50-60; PROF BIOSTATIST, SCH HYG & PUB HEALTH, JOHNS HOPKINS UNIV, 60- *Concurrent Pos:* Chmn dept biostatist, Johns Hopkins Univ, 60-66, prof, Sch Med, 60-, chmn dept statist, 62-66, prof, Fac Arts & Sci, 62-, dean fac arts & sci, 66-70. *Mem:* AAAS; Biomet Soc (treas, 55-60); Am Statist Asn; Inst Math Statist; Am Math Soc. *Res:* Statistics and mathematics applied to biology and medicine. *Mailing Add:* Sch of Hyg & Pub Health Johns Hopkins Univ Baltimore MD 21205

KIMBALL, AUBREY PIERCE, b Lufkin, Tex, Oct 20, 26; m 53; c 1. DRUG METABOLISM, ENZYMOLOGY. *Educ:* Univ Houston, BS, 58, PhD(chem), 62. *Prof Exp:* Serologist, Houston Med Group, 48-50; res technician, Baylor Col Med, 52-54; fel, Stanford Res Inst, 61-62, biochemist, 62-67; from assoc prof to prof, Dept Biochem & Biophys, Univ Houston, 67-81, planning dir, Cancer Prog, 76-80. *Concurrent Pos:* Dir, Southwest Sci Forum, 76-81, vpres, 79-80, pres, 80-81. *Mem:* AAAS; Am Chem Soc; Soc Exp Biol & Med; Am Asn Cancer Res; Am Soc Biol Chemists. *Res:* Design, synthesis and mechanism studies of carcinostatic drugs; biochemical evolution; enzyme affinity labeling. *Mailing Add:* Dept Biophys & Biochem Sci Univ of Houston Houston TX 77004

KIMBALL, BRUCE ARNOLD, b Aitkin, Minn, Sept 27, 41; m 66; c 3. SOIL PHYSICS, MICROMETEOROLOGY. *Educ:* Univ Minn, St Paul, BS, 63; Iowa State Univ, MS, 65; Cornell Univ, PhD(soil physics), 70. *Prof Exp:* SOIL SCIENTIST, US WATER CONSERV LAB, USDA, 70- *Mem:* Am Soc Agron; Soil Sci Soc Am; Am Soc Agr Eng; Int Solar Energy Soc. *Res:* Evaporation and transpiration; soil air movement; energy relationships of greenhouses. *Mailing Add:* 3335 N Rose Circle Dr Phoenix AZ 85018

KIMBALL, CHARLES NEWTON, b Boston, Mass, Apr 21, 11; m 51; c 2. ELECTRICAL ENGINEERING. *Educ:* Northeastern Univ, BEE, 31; Harvard Univ, MS, 32, ScD(elec eng), 34. *Hon Degrees:* DEng, Northeastern Univ, 55; ScD, Park Col, 58; LittD, Westminster Col, 78. *Prof Exp:* Res engr, Radio Corp Am, NY, 34-41; vpres & dir, Aircraft Acessories Corp, 41-47; tech dir, Res Labs Div, Bendix Aviation Corp, Mich, 48-50; pres, 50-75, chmn bd trustees, 75-79, EMER PRES, MIDWEST RES INST, 79- *Concurrent Pos:* Instr grad sch, NY Univ, 40-41; dir, Trans-World Airlines, Inc; trustee, US Comt Econ Develop, Hallmark Found & Menninger Found; chmn adv coun, Off Technol Assessment, US Cong, 79. *Mem:* Fel Inst Elec & Electronics Engrs; Sigma Xi. *Res:* Vacuum tube and circuit design; measurement and control of industrial processes; technology, transfer and assessment applications of technology to regional development. *Mailing Add:* Midwest Res Inst 425 Volker Blvd Kansas City MO 64110

KIMBALL, CHASE PATTERSON, b Ware, Mass, July 21, 32; m 58; c 4. PSYCHIATRY, INTERNAL MEDICINE. *Educ:* Brown Univ, AB, 54; State Univ NY, MD, 59. *Prof Exp:* Intern med, Univ Vt Hosps, 59-60, resident, 63-65; resident psychiat, New York Hosp, 60-61; instr psychiat med, Univ Rochester, 65-67; asst prof psychiat & med, Yale Univ, 67-72; PROF PSYCHIAT & MED & BEHAV SCI, PRITZKER SCH MED, UNIV CHICAGO, 72- *Concurrent Pos:* NIMH fel psychosom med, Univ Rochester, 65-67; lectr, Conn Acad Gen Pract, Conn Psychiat Asn, 67-; Am Heart Asn res grant, 68-71; consult, USPHS, 69-; chmn comt community health affairs & hosps, dir psychiat curric & chmn social med, Univ Chicago, 72-; lectr, Sch Med, Yale Univ, 72-; dir progs intercult med, Yale Univ & Univ Chicago, 72-; vpres, Int Col Psychosomatic Med, 77-79, pres-elect, 79- *Mem:* Am Psychosom Soc; Am Psychiat Soc; Am Heart Asn; NY Acad Sci; Soc Health & Human Values. *Res:* Investigation of psychosocial factors associated with illness and the adaptation of individuals to illness; medical education as a humanizing experience. *Mailing Add:* Pritzker Sch of Med Univ of Chicago Chicago IL 60637

KIMBALL, CLYDE WILLIAM, b Laurium, Mich, Apr 20, 28; m 52; c 2. SOLID STATE PHYSICS. *Educ:* Mich Tech Univ, BS, 50, MS, 52; St Louis Univ, PhD(physics), 59. *Prof Exp:* Asst physicist, Argonne Nat Lab, 50-53, res assoc, 57-59; res physicist solid state physics, Autonetics Div, NAm Aviation, Inc, 59-60; mem res staff res opers, Aeronutronics Div, Ford Motor Co, Calif, 60-62; assoc physicist, Solid State Div, Argonne Nat Lab, 62-64; assoc prof physics, Northern Ill Univ, 64-68; prog dir low temperature physics, Div Mat Res, NSF, 77-78; PROF PHYSICS, NORTHERN ILL UNIV, 68- *Concurrent Pos:* Consult, Argonne Nat Lab, 64- *Mem:* AAAS; fel Am Phys Soc; Sigma Xi; Am Asn Physics Teachers. *Res:* Experimental reactor physics; photodisintegration cross sections; neutron cross sections and nuclear reactions; magnetic and electronic properties of metals and alloys; Mossbauer effect; superconductivity; amorphous solids; lattice properties. *Mailing Add:* Dept of Physics Northern Ill Univ De Kalb IL 60115

KIMBALL, FRANCES ADRIENNE, b Oakland, Calif, May 2, 39. REPRODUCTIVE ENDOCRINOLOGY. *Educ:* Univ Calif, Berkeley, BA, 61; Calif State Univ, Chico, MA, 70; Cornell Univ, PhD(physiol), 73. *Prof Exp:* Res asst endocrinol, Reed Col, 61-68; res technician, Med Sch, Univ Calif, San Francisco, 68; instr biol, Calif State Univ, Chico, 68-70; USPHS fel, Cornell Univ, 70-73; scientist, 74-75, res scientist II, 75-80, SR RES SCIENTIST III REPRODUCTIVE ENDOCRINOL, FERTILITY RES, UPJOHN CO, 80- *Concurrent Pos:* NIH fel, Upjohn Co, 73-74. *Mem:* Am Soc Zoologists; Soc Study Reproduction. *Res:* Mechanism of hormone action in the uterus and corpus luteum; action of prostaglandins in uterine contractility. *Mailing Add:* Fertility Res Upjohn Co 301 Henrietta St Kalamazoo MI 49001

KIMBALL, GRACE CAROLINE, b Rochester, NY, Apr 24, 11. BACTERIOLOGY. *Educ:* Univ Rochester, AB, 32; Cornell Univ, PhD(bact), 37. *Prof Exp:* Res instr histopath, Dept Animal Nutrit, Cornell Univ, 37-40; jr bacteriologist, State Lab, NY, 40-42; res instr histopath, Dept Physiol, Albany Med Col, Union Univ, NY, 42-43; bacteriologist, Ellis Hosp, 43-44; from instr to assoc prof biol, Evansville Col, 44-51; res assoc oral path, Western Reserve Univ, 51-55; asst prof biol, Univ Akron, 55-63; asst prof biol, Wilkes Col, 63-70, assoc prof, 70-80. *Concurrent Pos:* Bacteriologist, Boehne Tuberc Hosp, Ind, 45 & St Mary's Hosp, 46-51. *Mem:* AAAS; Am Soc Microbiol; Hist Sci Soc. *Res:* Physiology of bacteria; history of science. *Mailing Add:* 113 Acad Wilkes-Barre PA 18702

KIMBALL, KENNETH DAVID, b Manchester, NH, Mar 22, 47; m 69. LIMNOLOGY, AQUATIC MACROPHYTES. *Educ:* Cornell Univ, BS, 69; Univ Mass, MS, 72; Univ NH, PhD(bot), 81. *Prof Exp:* Teaching asst zool, Univ Mass, 69-72; aquatic biologist, Smithsonian Inst & Peace Corps Environ Prog, Iran, 72-74; ecol consult, Biospheric Consult Int Inc, 74-76; res asst, Univ NH, 76-80; NSF resident scientist, Lakes Region Planning Comn, 80-81; RES ASSOC, ECOSYSTS RES CTR, CORNELL UNIV, 81- *Concurrent Pos:* Dir & lectr, Environ Sci Prog, Brewster Acad, 76-81. *Mem:* AAAS; Am soc Limnol & Oceanog; Sigma Xi. *Res:* Littoral zone ecology including, mineral ecology of submersed macrophytes and competitive interactions for nutrients between macrophytes, phytoplankton and sediments; water quality criteria. *Mailing Add:* Ecosysts Res Ctr 468 Hollister Hall Cornell Univ Ithaca NY 14853

KIMBALL, PAUL CLARK, b New London, Conn, Jan 26, 46; div. MOLECULAR GENETICS, VIROLOGY. *Educ:* Mass Inst Technol, BS, 68; Univ Calif, Berkeley, PhD(molecular biol), 72. *Prof Exp:* Instr microbiol, Univ Ill Med Ctr, 72-73; sr scientist tumor virol, Meloy Labs, Inc, 73-75; asst prof microbiol, Ohio State Univ & molecular virologist, Cancer Res Ctr, 75-81; PRIN RES SCIENTIST, COLUMBUS LABS, BATTELLE MEM INST, 81- *Mem:* AAAS; Am Soc Microbiol. *Res:* Use of recombinant DNA technology to determine genetic bases of chemical and viral carcinogenesis; genetic engineering for microbial production of biologicals with medical/veterinary/industrial import; use of microcomputers in biotechnology research. *Mailing Add:* Dept Biol Sci Columbus Labs Battelle Mem Inst Columbus OH 43201

KIMBALL, RALPH B, b Ann Arbor, Mich, July 18, 44; m 72; c 2. COMPUTER SCIENCE. *Educ:* Stanford Univ, MS, 67, PhD(elec eng), 73. *Prof Exp:* Res scientist man-machine syst, Xerox Palo Alto Res Ctr, 72-76, consult develop staff, Xerox Systs Develop Div, 76-79, mgr customer prog lang develop, 79-81, MGR APPLICATIONS MKT, XEROX OFF PROD DIV, 81- *Mem:* Inst Elec & Electronics Engrs; Asn Comput Mach. *Res:* Evaluation of man-machine interactions, particularly as applied to the information processing requirements of organizations. *Mailing Add:* Xerox Palo Alto Res Ctr 3333 Coyote Hill Rd Palo Alto CA 94304

KIMBALL, RICHARD FULLER, b Baltimore, Md, Feb 1, 15; m 40; c 2. BIOLOGY. *Educ:* Johns Hopkins Univ, AB, 35, PhD(zool), 38. *Prof Exp:* Sterling fel, Yale Univ, 38-39; instr biol, Johns Hopkins Univ, 39-43, asst prof, 43-47; sr biologist, 47-67 & 69-76, dir biol div, 67-69, sr biologist, 69-76, assoc sect head, 76-80, CONSULT, OAK RIDGE NAT LAB, 80- *Concurrent Pos:* Guggenheim fel, Karolinska Inst, Sweden, 57-58; on leave, Biol Br, Div Biol & Med, AEC, 71-72; res fel, Union Carbide Corp, 79; mem, Nat Adv Environ Health Sci Coun, 80- *Mem:* AAAS; Genetics Soc Am; Radiation Res Soc; Am Soc Cell Biology; Environ Mutagen Soc. *Res:* Mutation genetics; induced mutation processes in bacteria. *Mailing Add:* Biol Div Oak Ridge Nat Lab PO Box Y Oak Ridge TN 37830

KIMBARK, EDWARD W(ILSON), b Chicago, Ill, Sept 21, 02; m 30, 77. ELECTRICAL ENGINEERING, ENGINEERING EDUCATION. *Educ:* Northwestern Univ, BS, 24, EE, 25; Mass Inst Technol, SM, 33, ScD, 37. *Prof Exp:* Asst & instr elec eng, Mass Inst Technol, 33-37; vis assoc prof elec commun, Radar Sch, 42-44; asst prof elec eng, Polytech Inst Brooklyn, 37-39; from asst prof to prof, Northwestern Univ, 39-42, 44-50; prof electronics, Inst Aeronaut Tech, Sao Jose dos Campos, Brazil, 50-55; dean sch eng, Seattle Univ, 55-62; consult, Syst Eng Br, 56-62, head systs anal unit, 62-76, CONSULT ENGR, US BONNEVILLE POWER ADMIN, 76- *Concurrent*

Pos: Mem, Int Conf Large Elec Systs & Conf Int des Grands Reseaux Electrique a Haute Tension. *Honors & Awards:* Distinguished Serv Award, US Dept Interior, 74. *Mem:* Fel Inst Elec & Electronics Engrs. *Res:* Electric power systems; including transmission and stability; engineering education. *Mailing Add:* Bonneville Power Admin PO Box 3621 Portland OR 97208

KIMBEL, PHILIP, b Philadelphia, Pa, Mar 23, 25; m 53; c 3. MEDICINE, PULMONARY DISEASES. *Educ:* Temple Univ, MD, 53; Am Bd Internal Med, dipl, 61. *Prof Exp:* Resident internal med, 54-56, head pulmonary dis sect, 61-79, DIR PULMONARY FUNCTION LAB, ALBERT EINSTEIN MED CTR, 58- *Concurrent Pos:* USPHS res fel physiol & pharmacol, Grad Sch Med, Univ Pa, 56-57; res assoc, Gerontol Res Inst, Pa, 58-64; res assoc, Inst Cancer Res & Grad Sch Med, Univ Pa, 59-61; clin instr, Sch Med, Temple Univ, 59-64, assoc, 64-67, assoc prof, 67-71, prof, 71-79, clin prof med & chmn dept med, Grad Hosp, Sch Med, Univ Pa, 80- *Mem:* AAAS; fel Am Col Chest Physicians; fel Am Col Physicians; Am Thoracic Soc; Am Fedn Clin Res. *Res:* Pulmonary physiology and circulation; internal medicine; lung mechanics; rehabilitation in emphysema; experimental emphysema. *Mailing Add:* Albert Einstein Med Ctr York & Tabor Rds Philadelphia PA 19141

KIMBER, GORDON, b Manchester, Eng, July 21, 32; m 57; c 1. CYTOGENETICS. *Educ:* Univ London, BSc, 54; Univ Manchester, PhD(genetics), 61. *Prof Exp:* Res asst genetics, Univ Manchester, 54-58; sci officer, Plant Breeding Inst, 58-63, sr sci off, 63-67; assoc prof, 67-72, PROF AGRON, UNIV MO-COLUMBIA, 72- *Concurrent Pos:* Kellog Found fel, 63-64; Int Atomic Energy Agency expert, Indian Agr Res Inst, New Delhi, 70-71. *Mem:* Genetics Soc Am; Brit Genetical Soc. *Res:* Wheat cytogenetics. *Mailing Add:* Dept of Agron 220 Curtis Hall Univ of Mo-Columbia Columbia MO 65201

KIMBERG, DANIEL VICTOR, internal medicine, gastroenterology, see previous edition

KIMBERLING, WILLIAM J, b Logansport, Ind, Oct 16, 40; m 62; c 6. GENE LINKAGE, COMMUNICATION DISORDERS. *Educ:* Ind Univ Sch Med, PhD(med genetics), 67. *Prof Exp:* Fel, Med Sch, Univ Ore, 67-71, instr med genetics, 71-72; asst prof, Med Sch, Univ Colo, 72-79; ASSOC PROF MED GENETICS, MED SCH, CREIGHTON UNIV, 79- *Concurrent Pos:* Res assoc, Boys Town Inst Hered Commun Dis, 79- *Mem:* AAAS; Am Soc Human Genetics. *Res:* Gene linkage and localization in humans. *Mailing Add:* Boys Town Inst Heredity Commun Dis 555 N 30th St Omaha NE 68131

KIMBLE, GERALD WAYNE, b Bakersfield, Calif, Apr 24, 28; m 48, 65. NUMERICAL ANALYSIS. *Educ:* Univ Calif, Berkeley, AB, 49, Univ Calif, Los Angeles, MA, 58, PhD(math), 62. *Prof Exp:* Mathematician, Nat Bur Standards Inst Numerical Anal, Univ Calif, Los Angeles, 49-51; engr, Hughes Aircraft Co, 55-58; res assoc numerical anal, Univ Calif, Los Angeles, 59-61; asst prof math, Calif State Col, Long Beach, 61-63; assoc prof math & dir comput ctr, Univ Mont, 63; mathematician, TRW, Inc, Calif, 63-67; assoc prof, 67-75, PROF MATH, UNIV NEV, RENO, 75- *Mem:* Am Math Soc; Math Asn Am; Asn Comput Mach. *Res:* Calculus of variations; computer science. *Mailing Add:* Dept of Math Univ of Nev Reno NV 89557

KIMBLE, GLENN CURRY, b Norfolk, Nebr, June 6, 15; m 40; c 2. CHEMISTRY. *Educ:* Iowa State Col, BS, 37; Lawrence Col, MS, 39, PhD(paper & pulp chem), 41. *Prof Exp:* Res chemist, Nekoosa Edwards Paper Co, Wis, 38, Detroit Sulfite Pulp & Paper Co, 39, NW Paper Co, Minn, 40 & Gardner-Richardson Co, Ohio, 41-44; res supvr, Develop Insulation Bd, Minn & Ont Paper Co, Minn, 44-48; supt mill tech dept, Union Bag-Camp Paper Corp, 48-52, asst tech dir, 52-56, tech dir, Savannah Plant, 56-62, tech dir unbleached paper & board div, 62-68, dir air & water conserv, 68-75, MGR AIR & WATER RESOURCES, UNION CAMP CORP, 75- *Mem:* Tech Asn Pulp & Paper Indust. *Res:* Pulp and paper chemistry; development, process engineering and quality control for manufacture of pulp and paper. *Mailing Add:* 5714 Colonial Dr Savannah GA 31406

KIMBLE, HARRY JEFFREY, b Floydada, Tex, Apr 23, 49. PHYSICS. *Educ:* Abilene Christian Univ, BS, 71; Univ Rochester, MA, 73, PhD(physics), 78. *Prof Exp:* assoc sr res physicist, Gen Motors Res Labs, 77-79; ASST PROF PHYSICS, UNIV TEX, AUSTIN, 79- *Mem:* Am Phys Soc; Optical Soc Am. *Res:* Quantum optics; theory of coherence; atomic physics; infrared spectroscopy; semiconductor diode lasers; laser intracavity absorption spectroscopy; optoacoustic spectroscopy; theory of resonance fluorescence; photostatistics. *Mailing Add:* Dept of Physics Univ Tex Austin TX 78712

KIMBLER, OSCAR K(AVANAH), b Marengo Co, Ala, Aug 22, 21; m 45; c 2. PETROLEUM ENGINEERING. *Educ:* Vanderbilt Univ, BE, 48, MSChE, 49; Univ Tex, PhD(petrol eng), 64. *Prof Exp:* Sr res engr, Atlantic Ref Co, 55-62; from assoc to prof petrol eng, 64-77, CAMPANILE PROF PETROL ENG, LA STATE UNIV, BATON ROUGE, 77- *Mem:* Am Inst Mining, Metall & Petrol Engrs. *Res:* Fluid flow in porous media; petroleum reservoir engineering; enhanced oil recovery. *Mailing Add:* Dept of Petrol Eng La State Univ Baton Rouge LA 70803

KIMBLIN, CLIVE WILLIAM, b Stockport, Eng, Dec 25, 38; US Citizen; m 68; c 3. ARC & INTERRUPTION PHYSICS. *Educ:* Univ Liverpool, BSc, 60, PhD(elec eng), 64, Univ Pittsburgh, MSIE, 76. *Prof Exp:* Res engr arc physics, 64-65, sr engr, 65-74, fel engr, 74-75, MANAGER POWER INTERRUPTION RES, WESTINGHOUSE RES & DEVELOP CTR, 75- *Mem:* Am Phys Soc; sr mem Inst Elec & Electronic Engrs. *Res:* Physics of arcing and interruption in vacuum and air with particular reference to electrode mechanisms, properties of the inter-electrode metallic plasma and development of high power switching devices. *Mailing Add:* Westinghouse Res & Develop Ctr 1310 Beulah Rd Pittsburgh PA 15235

KIMBRELL, JACK T(HEODORE), b Peoria, Ill, Apr 23, 21; m 48; c 4. MECHANICAL ENGINEERING. *Educ:* Purdue Univ, BS, 43; Univ Mo-Columbia, MS, 47. *Prof Exp:* Prod engr, Eversharp Corp, 43-44; asst prof mech eng, Univ Mo, 47-51; sr res engr, Midwest Res Inst, 51-54; dean col eng, 69-70, chmn dept mech eng, 70-77, PROF MECH ENG, WASH STATE UNIV, 54-, ALCOA PROF, 66- *Mem:* Am Soc Eng Educ; Am Soc Mech Engrs. *Res:* Machinery design with emphasis on the kinematic synthesis of mechanisms. *Mailing Add:* Dept of Mech Eng Wash State Univ Pullman WA 99164

KIMBROUGH, EMMETT A(LEXANDER), JR, b Elizabeth, Miss, Oct 26, 21; m 45; c 2. AGRICULTURAL ENGINEERING. *Educ:* Miss State Univ, BS, 47; Agr & Mech Col, Tex, MS, 53. *Prof Exp:* Assoc agr engr, Agr Exp Sta & assoc prof agr eng, Miss State Univ, 48-59; agr eng consult, Agr & Mech Col, Tex Foreign Prog, Pakistan, 59; ASSOC AGR ENGR, MISS AGR & FORESTRY EXP STA, 59- *Concurrent Pos:* Consult, IRI Res Inst-AID Contract, Brazil, 66. *Mem:* Am Soc Agr Engrs. *Res:* Agricultural machinery and irrigation. *Mailing Add:* Dept of Agr & Biol Eng Box 5465 Mississippi State MS 39762

KIMBROUGH, EVERETT LAMAR, agronomy, see previous edition

KIMBROUGH, JAMES W, b Eupora, Miss, Nov 7, 34; m 61; c 3. MYCOLOGY. *Educ:* Miss State Univ, BS, 57, MS, 60; Cornell Univ, PhD(mycol), 64. *Prof Exp:* Asst bacteriologist, Vet Sci Dept, Miss State Univ, 60-61; instr bot, 61-62; teaching asst mycol, Cornell Univ, 62-64; asst prof, 64-71, assoc prof, 71-76, PROF BOT, UNIV FLA, 76- *Concurrent Pos:* Assoc chmn dept bot, Univ Fla, 74-75. *Mem:* Mycol Soc Am (secy-treas, 74-77, vpres, 77-78, pres elect, 78-79, pres, 79-80); Bot Soc Am; Int Asn Plant Taxon; Brit Mycol Soc. *Res:* Developmental and taxonomic studies in the powdery mildews; morphological, developmental and taxonomic studies of operculate Discomycetes; fungi as biocontrol agents of termites. *Mailing Add:* Dept of Bot Univ of Fla Gainesville FL 32611

KIMBROUGH, RENATE DORA, b Hannover, Ger, Jan 14, 33; US citizen; m 56; c 3. PATHOLOGY. *Educ:* Univ Gottingen, MD, 57. *Prof Exp:* Intern, Evanston Hosp, Ill, 58-59; resident path, St Joseph's Infirmary, Atlanta, Ga, 60-62; res pathologist, Pesticide Prog, Toxicol Lab, Nat Commun Dis Ctr, 62-69; pathologist, Atlanta Toxicol Br, US Food & Drug Admin, 68-70 & Environ Protection Agency, 70-73; RES MED OFFICER, TOXICOL BR, CTR DIS CONTROL, DHEW, USPHS, 73- *Concurrent Pos:* Consult, St Joseph's Infirmary, 62-74. *Mem:* Am Soc Clin Path; Sigma Xi; Soc Toxicol. *Res:* Effect of pesticides, chlorinated biphenyls and chlorinated phenols on animals and man; toxicology; metabolism and ultrastructure; investigation of poisoning episodes. *Mailing Add:* Toxicol Br Ctr for Dis Control Atlanta GA 30333

KIMBROUGH, THEO DANIEL, JR, b Lafayette, Ala, Sept 17, 33; m 65; c 2. PHYSIOLOGY, BIOCHEMISTRY. *Educ:* Univ Ala, BS, 55, MA, 59; Auburn Univ, PhD(zool), 65. *Prof Exp:* Teaching asst zool, Auburn Univ, 62-63, NIH fel physiol, 63-64; asst prof biol, Birmingham-Southern Col, 64-67; asst prof, 67-74, ASSOC PROF BIOL, VA COMMONWEALTH UNIV, 74- *Mem:* AAAS; fel Am Inst Chem; Soc Indust Microbiol. *Res:* Physiology of intestinal serotonin; animal physiology; histology. *Mailing Add:* Dept of Biol 901 W Franklin St Va Commonwealth Univ Richmond VA 23284

KIME, JOSEPH MARTIN, b Akron, Ohio, Feb 16, 17; m 41; c 3. PHYSICS. *Educ:* Univ Akron, BS, 38. *Prof Exp:* Physicist, B F Goodrich Co, 39-41 & 45-60, sect leader, New Prod Dept, 60-62, tech mgr, Bldg Prod Dept, 62-64, mgr prod res, 65-78, dir, Int Tech Admin, 78-81. *Mem:* Am Phys Soc; Acoust Soc Am; Inst Elec & Electronics Engrs. *Res:* Underwater acoustics; application of plastics in the building industry; electrical, mechanical and acoustic properties of high polymers. *Mailing Add:* 346 Sand Run Rd Akron OH 44313

KIMEL, JACOB DANIEL, JR, b Winston-Salem, NC, Aug 11, 37; m 65; c 4. PARTICLE PHYSICS, THEORETICAL PHYSICS. *Educ:* Univ NC, Chapel Hill, BS, 59; Univ Wis-Madison, MS, 60, PhD(physics), 66. *Prof Exp:* Res assoc physics, Univ Wis-Madison, 66; res assoc, 66-67, asst prof, 67-73, ASSOC PROF PHYSICS, FLA STATE UNIV, 73- *Mem:* Sigma Xi; Am Phys Soc. *Res:* Theoretical physics with emphasis on studies of elementary particle properties and intearctions. *Mailing Add:* Dept of Physics Fla State Univ Tallahassee FL 32306

KIMEL, WILLIAM R(OBERT), b Cunningham, Kans, May 2, 22; m 52. MECHANICAL & NUCLEAR ENGINEERING. *Educ:* Kans State Univ, BS, 44, MS, 49; Univ Wis, PhD(mech), 56. *Prof Exp:* Design engr, Goodyear Tire & Rubber Co, Ohio, 44-46; from instr to assoc prof mech, Kans State Univ, 46-55; mech engr, US Forest Prod Lab, Univ Wis, 55-56; assoc prof mech eng, Kans State Univ, 56-58, prof nuclear eng & head dept, 58-68; PROF NUCLEAR ENG, DIR ENG EXP STA & DEAN COL ENG, UNIV MO-COLUMBIA, 68- *Concurrent Pos:* Consult, Argonne Nat Lab, 58-; mem, Assoc Midwest Univ Nuclear Eng Educ Comt, 59-68, chmn, 67; mem, Kans Gov Atomic Energy Adv Coun, 61-68, chmn, 66-68; chmn, Nuclear Eng Educ Conf Comt, Assoc Midwest Univ-Argonne Nat Lab, 61, Argonaut Prog Eval & Rev Comt, 65-67; Fac Study Conf Comt, 66 & Long Range Planning Comt, Assoc Midwest Univ-Nuclear Eng Educ Conf, 66-68; Atomic Energy Comn observer, UN Atomics for Peace Conf, 64; mem, Adv Comt to Off Civil Defense, 64-70, chmn, 69-70; consult, Div Nuclear Educ & Training, Atomic Energy Comn & mem fel rev panel, HEW, 66-68; mem, Argonne Univs Asn Nuclear Educ Comt, 68- *Mem:* AAAS; Fel Am Nuclear Soc (pres, 78-79); Am Soc Eng Educ; Nat Soc Prof Engrs; fel Am Soc Mech Engrs. *Res:* Engineering mechanics composite structures; neutron activation analysis. *Mailing Add:* Col Eng Univ Mo Columbia MO 65211

KIMELBERG, HAROLD KEITH, b Hertford, Eng, Dec 5, 41; m 66; c 2. NEUROBIOLOGY, CELL CULTURE. *Educ:* Univ London, BS, 63; State Univ NY Buffalo, PhD(biochem), 68. *Prof Exp:* Fel, Johnson Res Found, Univ Pa, 68-69; NIH fel, Roswell Park Mem Inst, 69-70, sr cancer res scientist, 70-74; asst res prof, Roswell Park Div, State Univ NY Grad Sch, 72-74; res assoc prof neurosurg, 74-80, ASSOC PROF BIOCHEM, ALBANY MED COL, UNION UNIV, 74-, RES PROF NEUROSURG & PROF ANATOMY, 80- *Concurrent Pos:* Adj assoc prof biol, State Univ NY, Albany, 78- *Mem:* Am Soc Biol Chemists; Am Soc Neurochem; Biophys Soc; Soc Neurosci. *Res:* Ion transport, electrical properties, transmitter responsiveness and enzyme properties of astroglial cells, especially using cultured cells as models; properties of membranes and membrane enzymes; properties of liposomes. *Mailing Add:* Neurosurg & Dept Biochem Albany Med Col Albany NY 12208

KIMELDORF, DONALD JEROME, b Salt Lake City, Utah, Jan 9, 20; m 43; c 3. RADIATION BIOLOGY, GERONTOLOGY. *Educ:* Reed Col, BA, 42; Univ Ore, MA, 44; Univ Calif, Los Angeles, PhD(physiol), 47. *Prof Exp:* Biol aide aquatic physiol, US Army Engrs, Ore, 42; asst biol, Univ Ore, 42-43, instr, 48; asst, Univ Calif, Los Angeles, 44-46, fel, 47-48; res assoc, Naval Radiol Defense Lab, 48-51, head physiol-psychol br, 51-67; PROF RADIATION BIOL, ORE STATE UNIV, 67- *Concurrent Pos:* Mem US del, UN Sci Comt on effects atomic radiations, 67-69; Am Inst Biol Sci vis lectr radiation biol, 67-70; mem, Ed Bd, Radiation Res, 64-67, 74-77; mem Radiation Adv Comt, Oregon Health Div, 77-81. *Mem:* Fel AAAS; Radiation Res Soc; fel Geront Soc; Am Physiol Soc; Am Soc Photobiol. *Res:* Radiation effects on receptor systems, neuroregulatory processes and behavior; persistent and late effects on growth, metabolism and morphology; analysis of aging processes and life span determinants. *Mailing Add:* Radiation Ctr Ore State Univ Corvallis OR 97331

KIMELDORF, GEORGE S, b New York, NY, Sept 3, 40; m 64; c 2. STATISTICS, MATHEMATICS. *Educ:* Univ Rochester, AB, 60; Univ Mich, MA, 61, PhD(math), 65. *Prof Exp:* From asst prof to assoc prof math, Calif State Univ, Hayward, 65-69; from asst prof to assoc prof statist, Fla State Univ, 69-75; assoc prof, 75-76, PROF MATH SCI, UNIV TEX, DALLAS, 76- *Concurrent Pos:* Vis asst prof, Math Res Ctr, Univ Wis, 67-68, vis assoc prof, 68-69. *Mem:* Inst Math Statist; Am Statist Asn. *Res:* Mathematical statistics; probability; operations research. *Mailing Add:* Math Sci Univ of Tex Dallas PO Box 688 Richardson TX 75080

KIMERLING, LIONEL COOPER, b Birmingham, Ala, Dec 2, 43; m 66; c 2. SOLID STATE SCIENCE, PHYSICS. *Educ:* Mass Inst Technol, SB, 65, PhD(mat sci), 69. *Prof Exp:* Res asst, Dept Metall & Mat Sci, Mass Inst Technol, 65-69; res physicist, Air Force Cambridge Res Labs, US Air Force, 69-72; mem tech staff, 72-81, HEAD, MAT PHYSICS RES DEPT, BELL LABS, 81- *Concurrent Pos:* Vis fel, Inst Study Defects Solids, 75-; adj prof phys, Lehigh Univ, 77-; lectr, Welsh Found, 79. *Mem:* AAAS; Am Inst Mining, Metall & Petrol Engrs; Am Phys Soc; Electrochem Soc. *Res:* Defects in solids: structure, electrical properties and chemical reactions; elemental and III-V semiconductor systems. *Mailing Add:* Bell Labs 600 Mountain Ave Murray Hill NJ 07974

KIMES, THOMAS FREDRIC, b Phoenixville, Pa, July 24, 28; m 52, 74; c 2. NUMERICAL ANALYSIS; MATHEMATICAL ANALYSIS. *Educ:* Ursinus Col, BS, 49; Univ Tex, MA, 56; Carnegie Inst Technol, PhD, 62. *Prof Exp:* Asst math, Univ Tex, 54-56; asst, Carnegie Inst Technol, 56-58, proj mathematician, 58-59; mathematician, Bettis Atomic Power Lab, Westinghouse Elec Corp, 59-60, sr mathematician, 60-62; dir interactive comput serv, 73-76, from asst prof to prof math, 62-76, chmn dept, 62-73, CHADWICK PROF MATH, AUSTIN COL, 76- *Concurrent Pos:* Vis prof math, Furness Col, Univ Lancaster, 70; vis scholar, Cambridge Univ, 80. *Mem:* Am Math Soc; Math Asn Am; Prehistoric Soc UK. *Res:* Ordinary and partial differential equations. *Mailing Add:* 2501 Turtle Creek Dr Sherman TX 75090

KIMLER, BRUCE FRANKLIN, b St Paul, Minn, Sept 23, 48; m 75; c 2. RADIATION BIOLOGY, CELL BIOLOGY. *Educ:* Univ Tex, Austin, BA, 70, MA, 71, PhD(radiation biol), 73. *Prof Exp:* Appointee radiation biol, Argonne Nat Lab, 73-75; fel, Thomas Jefferson Univ Hosp, 75-77; asst prof, 77-80, ASSOC PROF RADIATION THER, UNIV KANS MED CTR, KANSAS CITY, 80- *Concurrent Pos:* Assoc scientist, Mid-Am Cancer Ctr Prog, 77-; adj prof, Dept Radiation Biophys, Univ Kans, 77- *Mem:* Radiation Res Soc; Am Asn Cancer Res; Cell Kinetics Soc (secy, 81-83); Am Soc Therapeut Radiologists; Biophys Soc. *Res:* Preclinical experimental radiation oncology; modification of radiation induced mammalian cell lethality and division delay by cancer chemotherapeutic agents, hypoxic cell radiosensitizers, hyperthermia and other combined modalities. *Mailing Add:* Dept of Radiation Ther Univ of Kans Med Ctr Kansas City KS 66103

KIMLIN, MARY JAYNE, b Cresson, Pa, July 4, 24. ANALYTICAL CHEMISTRY, PHYSICAL CHEMISTRY. *Educ:* St Francis Col, Pa, BS, 48; Pa State Univ, MS, 58, PhD(anal chem), 69. *Prof Exp:* Lab asst chem, Kinetic Div, E I du Pont de Nemours & Co, 44-46; from instr to assoc prof, 48-70, PROF CHEM, ST FRANCIS COL, PA, 70- *Mem:* Sigma Xi; AAAS; Am Chem Soc. *Res:* Polarographic study of correlations between ionic diffusion coefficients and ionic strength; polarography in fused salts; polarography of copper hydroxo complexes. *Mailing Add:* Dept of Chem St Francis Col Loretto PA 15940

KIMME, ERNEST GODFREY, b Long Beach, Calif, June 7, 29; m 52; c 3. MATHEMATICS, ENGINEERING. *Educ:* Pomona Col, BA, 52; Univ Minn, MA, 54, PhD(math), 56. *Prof Exp:* Instr math, Ore State Col, 55-57; mem tech staff, Bell Tel Labs, 57-63, supvr, 63-65; head appl sci dept, Collins Radio Co, 65-67, asst to vpres, 67-72; res engr, Northrop Electronics, 72-74; prin engr, Interstate Electronics, 74-79; DIR SPEC COMMUN PROG, GOULD DEFENSE ELEC & NAT-STANDARD CO, 79- *Concurrent Pos:* Vpres & dir, A S Johnston Drilling Co, 68-; prin assoc, Ameta Consult

Technologists, Anaheim, Calif, 78- *Mem:* AAAS; Soc Indust & Appl Math. *Res:* Analysis, particularly probability theory, mathematical statistics, information theory and operations research; communications sciences; quantitative management theory; experimental design. *Mailing Add:* 301 Starfire Anaheim CA 92807

KIMMEL, BRUCE LEE, b Poplar Bluff, Mo, Nov 6, 45; m 67; c 1. LIMNOLOGY, ECOLOGY. *Educ:* Baylor Univ, BS, 67, MS, 69; Univ Calif, Davis, PhD(ecol), 77. *Prof Exp:* Proj officer oceanic biol, Ocean Sci & Technol Group, Off Naval Res, 70-71; instr chem, Div Math Sci, US Naval Acad, 71-72; ASST PROF ZOOL & ASST DIR BIOL STA, UNIV OKLA, 77- *Concurrent Pos:* Prin investr res grant, Okla Water Resources Inst, Off Water Res & Technol, Dept Interior, 78- *Mem:* Am Soc Limnol & Oceanog; Int Asn Theoret & Appl Limnol; Ecol Soc Am; Am Inst Biol Sci; AAAS. *Res:* Biological productivity and foodweb interactions in lakes and reservoirs; energy flow and nutrient cycling in aquatic systems. *Mailing Add:* Biol Sta Dept of Zool Univ of Okla Norman OK 73019

KIMMEL, CAROLE ANNE, b Lexington, Ky, Apr 26, 44; m 70; c 1. TERATOLOGY. *Educ:* Georgetown Col, BS, 66; Univ Cincinnati, PhD(anat), 70. *Prof Exp:* Fel toxicol, Col Med, Univ Cincinnati, 70-72; sect head teratology, Environ Protection Agency, 72; instr anat, Sch Med, Harvard Univ, 72-73; sr staff fel teratology, Nat Inst Environ Health Sci, 73-77, RES PHARMACOLOGIST, DIV TERATOGENESIS RES, NAT CTR TOXICOL RES, NIH, 77-, CHIEF, PERINATAL & POSTNATAL EVAL BR, 79- *Concurrent Pos:* Consult, Environ Protection Agency, 72-73; adj asst prof, Sch Med, Univ NC, 75-76; prog mgr, Reproductive & Develop Toxicol, Nat Toxicol Prog, 79- *Mem:* Soc Toxicol; Behav Teratology Soc; Teratology Soc; Europ Teratology Soc; Am Asn Anatomists. *Res:* The effects of developmental exposures to drugs and environmental agents on the behavior and function of offspring; test methodology in teratology; extrapolation of animal data for human risk assessment. *Mailing Add:* Div of Teratogenesis Res Nat Ctr for Toxicol Res Jefferson AR 72079

KIMMEL, CHARLES BROWN, b New Orleans, La, May 3, 40; m 62; c 1. DEVELOPMENTAL BIOLOGY. *Educ:* Swarthmore Col, BA, 62; Johns Hopkins Univ, PhD(biol), 66. *Prof Exp:* NIH fel immunol, Salk Inst Biol Studies, 66-68; asst prof biol, 69-75, ASSOC PROF BIOL, UNIV ORE, 75- *Mem:* AAAS; Acad Sci; Soc Develop Biol; Soc Neurosci. *Res:* Experimental neurogenesis; vertebrate neural development. *Mailing Add:* Dept of Biol Univ of Ore Eugene OR 94703

KIMMEL, DONALD LORAINE, JR, b Swedesboro, NJ, Apr 15, 35; m 60; c 5. DEVELOPMENTAL BIOLOGY. *Educ:* Swarthmore Col, BA, 56; Temple Univ, MD, 60, MSc, 62; Johns Hopkins Univ, PhD(developgenetics), 64. *Prof Exp:* Asst prof, Div Med Sci, Brown Univ, 64-71; assoc prof & chmn dept, 71-78, PROF BIOL, DAVIDSON COL, 78- *Concurrent Pos:* Res fel, Calif Inst Technol, 70-71; corp mem, Bermuda Biol Sta; res scientist, Div Res NC Dept Mental Health, 78-79. *Mem:* AAAS; Am Soc Zool; Soc Develop Biol; Am Soc Cell Biol; Soc Neurosci. *Res:* Web building behavior, neural control of web building and web geometry during development of orb weaving spiders. *Mailing Add:* Dept of Biol Davidson Col Davidson NC 28036

KIMMEL, ELIAS, b New York, NY, Mar 7, 24; m 45; c 2. PHYSICAL CHEMISTRY. *Educ:* Univ Long Island, BS, 48; Polytech Inst Brooklyn, PhD(chem), 53. *Prof Exp:* Res chemist, Gen Chem Div, Allied Chem Corp, 52-54; consult chemist, Foster D Snell, Inc, 54-57; DIR RES & DEVELOP, TEMPIL DIV, BIG THREE INDUSTS, INC, 57- *Res:* Temperature measurement; phase-rule studies of inorganic and organic systems; surface phenomena as applied to dispersion; corrosion prevention; lubrication; properties and utilization of polymeric materials. *Mailing Add:* Res & Develop Tempil Div Big Three Industs Inc Hamilton Blvd South Plainfield NJ 07080

KIMMEL, GARY LEWIS, b Dayton, Ohio, Nov 20, 45; m 70. BIOCHEMICAL TERATOLOGY. *Educ:* Miami Univ, AB, 67; Univ Cincinnati, MS, 69, PhD(physiol), 72. *Prof Exp:* Fel steroid biochem, Worcester Found Exp Biol, 72-73; reprod biologist, Res Triangle Inst, 73-75; RES PHYSIOLOGIST, NAT CTR TOXICOL RES, 75- *Mem:* Soc Study Reprod; NY Acad Sci. *Res:* The relationship of biochemical events and developmental alterations, specifically at the cellular and subcellular level. *Mailing Add:* Nat Ctr Toxicol Res Jefferson AR 72079

KIMMEL, HOWARD S, b Brooklyn, NY, Feb 2, 38; m 64; c 1. PHYSICAL CHEMISTRY. *Educ:* Brooklyn Col, BS, 59; WVa Univ, 61; City Univ New York, PhD(phys chem), 67. *Prof Exp:* Res assoc chem, Isaac Albert Res Inst, Jewish Chronic Dis Hosp, Brooklyn, NY, 62-63; asst prof, 66-70, assoc prof, 70-80, PROF CHEM & ASSOC CHMN DEPT, NEWARK COL ENG, 80- *Mem:* Am Chem Soc. *Res:* Vibrational spectra of inorganic coordination compounds, tin compounds, olefinic compounds, monosubstituted benzene derivatives and biochemicals; kinetics studies using infrared spectroscopy. *Mailing Add:* Chem Div Newark Col of Eng Newark NJ 07102

KIMMEL, JOE ROBERT, b DuQuoin, Ill, May 3, 22; m 47; c 4. BIOCHEMISTRY, MEDICINE. *Educ:* DePauw Univ, AB, 44; Johns Hopkins Univ, MD, 47; Univ Utah, PhD(biochem), 54. *Prof Exp:* Intern, Salt Lake Gen Hosp, 47-49; from res instr to assoc res prof biochem, Col Med, Univ Utah, 54-60, assoc prof, 60-64; PROF BIOCHEM & MED, UNIV KANS, 64- *Concurrent Pos:* USPHS fel, 60-64. *Mem:* Endocrine Soc; Am Soc Biol Chemists. *Res:* Protein chemistry; proteolytic enzymes; insulin and other pancreatic hormones. *Mailing Add:* Univ of Kans Med Ctr Rainbow Blvd at 39th Kansas City KS 66103

KIMMEL, ROBERT MICHAEL, b Beverly, Mass, Feb 6, 43; m 65; c 3. MATERIALS ENGINEERING, POLYMER PHYSICS. *Educ:* Mass Inst Technol, BS, 64, MS, 65, Mat Engr, 67, ScD(mat eng), 68. *Prof Exp:* Res chemist, Celanese Res Co, 68-71, sr res chemist, 71-73, group leader, Celanese Plastics Co, 73-75, prod supvr, 76-79; INDUST MGR, AM

HOECHST CORP, 80- *Mem:* Am Phys Soc; Fiber Soc. *Res:* Fiber physics; physics of acrylic polymers; formation structure and properties of graphite fibers; effects of high pressure on materials; nature of the glassy state; structure properties of oriented films. *Mailing Add:* Am Hoechst Corp Box 1400 Greer SC 29652

KIMMEL, WILLIAM GRIFFITHS, b Scranton, Pa, Aug 27, 45; m 69; c 2. WATER POLLUTION BIOLOGY. *Educ:* Wilkes Col, BA, 67; Pa State Univ, MS, 70, PhD(zool), 72. *Prof Exp:* asst prof, 76-79, ASSOC PROF BIOL & ENVIRON SCI, CALIF STATE COL, 79- *Mem:* Sigma Xi; Am Fisheries Soc. *Res:* Responses of stream ecosystems to environmental stresses; aquatic macroinvertebrates and fishes as indicators of water quality. *Mailing Add:* 25 Esther St Charleroi PA 15022

KIMMERLE, FRANK, b Tuebingen, Ger, Mar 27, 40; Can citizen; m 63; c 3. ELECTROCHEMISTRY. *Educ:* Univ Toronto, BS, 63, MS, 64, PhD(electrochem), 67. *Prof Exp:* NATO fel, Free Univ Brussels, 67-68; asst prof chem, 68-71, ASSOC PROF CHEM, UNIV SHERBROOKE, 71- *Concurrent Pos:* Can Res Coun fel, 67. *Mem:* Electrochem Soc. *Res:* Thermodynamics and kinetics of adsorption and reaction of organic compounds at the electrode-electrolyte interface; electro-organic synthesis; non-aqueous battery systems. *Mailing Add:* 460 Bioschatel Sherbrooke PQ J1J 2R6 Can

KIMMEY, JAMES WILLIAM, b St Johns, Ore, Jan 24, 07; m 32; c 2. FOREST PATHOLOGY. *Educ:* Ore State Col, BSF, 31, MS, 32; Yale Univ, PhD(forestry), 40. *Prof Exp:* Field asst, US Forest Serv, 27; field asst div forest path, Bur Plant Indust, Agr Res Admin, USDA, 28-35, asst pathologist, 35-42, assoc pathologist, Bur Plant Indust, Soils & Agr Eng, Agr Res Admin, 42-47, pathologist, 47-53; pathologist, US Forest Serv, 53-56, sr pathologist, 56-57, chief div forest dis res, Intermountain Forest & Range Exp Sta, 57-63, proj leader, 63-65; CONSULTANT, 65- *Mem:* Fel AAAS; Soc Am Foresters; Am Phytopath Soc; Am Forestry Asn; Arctic Inst NAm. *Res:* White pine blister rust in western United States and Canada; decay of wood in use; deterioration of fire-killed timber in Pacific Coast States; decay and other cull in timber stands of California and Alaska; forest disease survey in California and Alaska; dwarf mistletoes. *Mailing Add:* PO Box 19 Westport WA 98595

KIMMICH, GEORGE ARTHUR, b Cortland, NY, Dec 8, 41; m 63; c 2. BIOCHEMISTRY. *Educ:* Cornell Univ, BS, 63; Univ Wis-Madison, MS, 65; Univ Pa, PhD(biochem), 68. *Prof Exp:* Nat Inst Dent Res fel biophys, 68-70, asst prof, 70-75, ASSOC PROF RADIATION BIOL & BIOPHYS, SCH MED & DENT, UNIV ROCHESTER, 75- *Concurrent Pos:* NIH grant, 71-; NIH Res Career Develop Award, 72-77; vis lectr biochem, Univ Manchester Inst Sci & Technol, Manchester, England, 75-76. *Mem:* Am Soc Biol Chemists; Am Physiol Soc. *Res:* Mitochondrial ion transport; metabolic regulation; sodium-dependent transport systems for sugars and amino acids. *Mailing Add:* Dept of Radiation Biol & Biophys Univ Rochester Sch Med & Dent Rochester NY 14642

KIMMINS, JAMES PETER HAMISH, b Jerusalem, Israel, July 31, 42; m 64; c 2. FOREST ECOLOGY, ENVIRONMENTAL SCIENCES. *Educ:* Univ Wales, BSc, 64; Univ Calif, MSc, 66; Yale Univ, MPhil, 68, PhD(ecol), 70. *Prof Exp:* Asst prof forest ecol, 69-74, ASSOC PROF FOREST ECOL, FAC FORESTRY, UNIV BC, 74- *Concurrent Pos:* Mem, BC Govt Ecol Reserves Comt, 69-; consult, Environ Res Consults, 71-; chmn nat forest ecol working group, Can Inst Forestry, 74-76; Killam fel, Can Coun, 75-76; vis scientist, Kyoto, Japan, 82. *Mem:* Commonwealth Forestry Asn; Can Inst Forestry. *Res:* Nutrient cycling in forest ecosystems; biogeochemistry of forest land management; effects of herbicides, whole-tree logging and slashburning on system watershed nutrient budgets; forcyte, an ecologically-based forest management computer simulation model. *Mailing Add:* Fac of Forestry Univ of BC Vancouver BC V6T 1E1 Can

KIMMINS, WARWICK CHARLES, b London, Eng, July 20, 41; m 64. PLANT PHYSIOLOGY, PLANT VIROLOGY. *Educ:* Univ London, BSc, 62, PhD(plant physiol), 65. *Prof Exp:* From asst prof to assoc prof biol, 65-74, PROF BIOL, DALHOUSIE UNIV, 74- *Concurrent Pos:* Consult res dept, Encyclop Britannica, 62-65; asst lectr, S E Essex Col Technol, Eng, 63-64. *Mem:* Soc Exp Biol & Med; Brit Asn Appl Biol; Can Soc Plant Physiol. *Res:* Plant viruses; host resistance mechanisms; cell wall composition and synthesis. *Mailing Add:* Dept of Biol Dalhousie Univ Halifax NS B3H 3J5 Can

KIMOTO, WALTER IWAO, b Honolulu, Hawaii, Mar 25, 32. FOOD CHEMISTRY. *Educ:* Univ Hawaii, BA, 54; Univ Wis, PhD(org chem), 61. *Prof Exp:* Res chemist, Am Oil Co, 61-63; res chemist, Beltsville, 63-71, RES CHEMIST, EASTERN REGIONAL RES CTR, SCI & EDUC ADMIN-AGR RES, USDA, 71- *Mem:* Am Chem Soc; Am Oil Chemists' Soc; Inst Food Technologists. *Res:* Flavor and aroma of cured meat products. *Mailing Add:* 757 E Main St Apt F 305 Lansdale PA 19446

KIMPEL, JAMES FROOME, b Cincinnati, Ohio, Apr 18, 42; m 64; c 2. METEOROLOGY. *Educ:* Denison Univ, BS, 64; Univ Wis-Madison, MS, 70, PhD(meteor), 73. *Prof Exp:* Weather officer meteorol, US Air Force, 64-68; res asst, Univ Wis-Madison, 68-73; asst prof, 73-81, assoc dean eng, Col Eng, 78-81, PROF METEOROL, UNIV OKLA, 79-, DIR, SCH METEOROL, 81- *Concurrent Pos:* Prin investr, Nat Oceanic & Atmospheric Admin, NSF, 74- *Mem:* Am Meteorol Soc; Nat Weather Asn; Japan Meteorol Soc; Sigma Xi. *Mailing Add:* Sch Meteorol Univ Okla Norman OK 73019

KIMSEY, JERRY BRUCE, fish biology, deceased

KIMSEY, LYNN SIRI, b Oakland, Calif, Feb 1, 53; m 76. SYSTEMATICS, FUNCTIONAL MORPHOLOGY. *Educ:* Univ Calif, Davis, BS, 75, PhD(entomol), 79. *Prof Exp:* Res fel, Univ Calif, Davis, 79-80 & Smithsonian Trop Res Inst, Panama, 81-82; LECTR, DEPT ENTOM, UNIV CALIF,

DAVIS, 82- *Mem:* AAAS; Sigma Xi. *Res:* Taxomony, behavior and physiology of a variety of insects, especially the hymenopteran families Chrysididae, Pompilidae, Apidae and Sphecidae; feeding energetics and male behavior of orchid bees and the ecology of neotropical sawflies. *Mailing Add:* Dept Entomol Univ Calif Davis CA 95616

KIMSEY, PAUL BRUCE, b Sacramento, Calif, Mar 5, 53; m 77; c 1. VETERINARY MICROBIOLOGY. *Educ:* Univ Calif, Davis, BA, 75, MA, 77, PhD(comput pathol), 82. *Prof Exp:* SCI RES ASSOC-4, DEPT REPRODUCTION, SCH VET MED, UNIV CALIF, DAVIS, 77- *Mem:* Am Soc Microbiologists; Am Asn Vet Lab Diagnosticians; AAAS; Wildlife Dis Asn; US Animal Health Asn. *Res:* Diagnostic and investigative medical microbiology; diseases of reproduction in veterinary medicine, including Campylobacteriosis, Trichomoniasis, Epizootic Bovine abortion, Leptospirosis, Infectious Bovine Rhinotracheitis and Chlamydia. *Mailing Add:* 903 Arnold St Davis CA 95616

KIMURA, DANIEL KEIZO, b Sidney, Nebr, Aug 29, 45. BIOMATHEMATICS, STATISTICS. *Educ:* Univ Wash, BS, 67, PhD(biomath), 72. *Prof Exp:* Qual control engr statist, Boeing Co, 67-68; FISHERIES BIOMETRICIAN, WASH STATE DEPT FISHERIES, 74- *Mem:* Biomet Soc; Am Statist Asn. *Res:* Statistical methods and mathematical modeling which are applicable to fisheries science. *Mailing Add:* Wash State Dept Fisheries Univ of Wash Seattle WA 98195

KIMURA, EUGENE TATSURU, b Sheridan, Wyo, Sept 19, 22; m 50; c 3. PHARMACOLOGY, TOXICOLOGY. *Educ:* Univ Nebr, BS, 44, MS, 46; Univ Chicago, PhD(pharmacol), 48. *Prof Exp:* Lab instr inorg chem & microbiol, Sch Nursing, St Elizabeth Hosp, Nebr, 45-46; res pharmacologist, Nepera Chem Co, NY, 49-55; res pharmacologist, 55-60, group leader, 60-62, sect head, 62-71, mgr patonomic pharmacol, Sci Div, 71-72, mgr corp res develop dept, Corp Res & Exp Ther, 72-76, SR TOXICOLOGIST, ABBOTT LABS, 76- *Concurrent Pos:* Fel pharmacol, Univ Chicago, 48-49; asst, Univ Nebr, 44-46. *Mem:* Am Soc Pharmacol & Exp Therapeut; Am Pharmaceut Asn; NY Acad Sci; Soc Exp Biol & Med; Soc Toxicol. *Res:* Pharmacology and toxicology of antihistamines and antiserotonins; bronchial asthma and allergy; drugs affecting ciliary motility; antiheparin agents; analeptics; antispasmodics; blood coagulants; anti-inflammatory compounds; toxicology and carcinogenicity of experimental drugs. *Mailing Add:* Toxicol Dept D-468 Abbott Labs North Chicago IL 60064

KIMURA, JAMES HIROSHI, b Kona, Hawaii, Oct 29, 44; m 75; c 2. BIOCHEMISTRY. *Educ:* Univ Hawaii, BS, 71; Case Western Reserve Univ, PhD(develop biol), 76. *Prof Exp:* Fel, Nat Inst Dent Res, NIH, 76-78, staff fel, 78-80, sr staff fel, 80-81; ASST PROF BIOCHEM, DEPT ORTHOD SURG, RUSH PRESBY ST LUKE'S MED CTR, 81-, ASST PROF, DEPT BIOCHEM, 81- *Mem:* Orthopaedic Res Soc. *Res:* Biochemistry of proteoglycans and mechanisms for the control of their synthesis; organization in cartilage. *Mailing Add:* Rush Presby St Luke's Med Ctr 1753 W Congress Pkwy Chicago IL 60612

KIMURA, KAZUO KAY, b Sheridan, Wyo, Sept 16, 20; m 52; c 4. CLINICAL PHARMACOLOGY, PEDIATRIC TOXICOLOGY. *Educ:* Univ Wash, BS, 42; Univ Nebr, MS, 44; Univ Ill, PhD(pharmacol), 49; St Louis Univ, MD, 53; Am Bd Med Toxicol, dipl, 75. *Prof Exp:* Asst physiol & pharmacol, Univ Nebr, 43-44, instr, 44-45; asst pharmacol, Univ Ill, 45-46; from instr to asst prof, St Louis Univ, 49-54; intern, Children's Med Serv, Mass Gen Hosp, 54-55, asst resident, 55-56; from sr resident to chief resident pediat, Raymond Blank Mem Hosp Children, Des Moines, Iowa, 56-57; chief exp med br, Chem Res & Develop Labs, Army Chem Ctr, Md, 57-61; asst chief clin res div, 58-61, chief, 62; chief pharmacologist & mgr pharmacol sect, Atlas Chem Industs, Inc, 62-63, corp med dir & dir biomed res dept, 63-70; med dir & dir med res dept, ICI Am, Inc, Del, 70-73; vpres & res dir, Hazleton Labs Am, Inc, 73-75; exec vpres & med dir, Mediserve Int, Inc, 75-77; prof pharmacol & med, Sch Med, Wright State Univ, 77-80; ASSOC CHIEF STAFF RES, MED CTR, VET ADMIN, DAYTON, 80- *Concurrent Pos:* Teaching fel pediat, Harvard Med Sch, 55-56; founder & 1st dir, Iowa State Poison Info Ctr, 56-57; pvt pract, Md, 58-62; prof lectr, Univ Md, 60-62; consult pediat, Wilmington Med Ctr Hosps, 69-73; consult med, Vet Admin Hosp, 78-80; mem active staff, Childrens Med Ctr; med dir, Western Ohio Regional Drug & Poison Info Syst, Childrens Med Ctr, 80- *Honors & Awards:* Borden Award, 53; Fac Medal, Univ Wash. *Mem:* Fel AAAS; fel Am Col Clin Pharmacol; fel Royal Soc Med; fel Am Col Physicians; Am Soc Pharmacol & Exp Therapeut. *Res:* Striated muscle paralyzing drugs; cardiac glycosides; medical toxicology; biochemophology of muscle paralyzants; dietary fiber and refined sugars; psychopharmacology; clinical pharmacology; poison control. *Mailing Add:* Vet Admin Med Ctr Mail Code 151 Dayton OH 45435

KIMURA, NAOKI, b Wakayama City, Japan, May 20, 22; m 47; c 3. MATHEMATICS. *Educ:* Osaka Univ, DSc, 44; Tulane Univ, PhD, 57. *Prof Exp:* Lectr math, Tokyo Inst Technol, Japan, 49-55; asst prof, Univ Wash, 58-60 & Univ Sask, 60-62; assoc prof, Univ Okla, 62-65; PROF MATH, UNIV ARK, FAYETTEVILLE, 65- *Mem:* Am Math Soc; Can Math Cong; Math Soc Japan; London Math Soc; Swed Math Soc. *Res:* Functional analysis and general algebra. *Mailing Add:* Dept of Math Univ of Ark Fayetteville AR 72701

KIMURA, TOKUJI, b Osaka, Japan, Nov 14, 25; m 51; c 2. ENZYMOLOGY, BIOPHYSICS. *Educ:* Osaka Univ, BS, 50, PhD(chem), 60. *Prof Exp:* Prof chem, St Paul's Univ, Tokyo, 65-68; PROF CHEM, WAYNE STATE UNIV, 68- *Concurrent Pos:* NIH res grant, 65. *Mem:* Am Soc Biol Chemists; Am Soc Chem. *Res:* Adrenal cortex mitochondrial steroid hydroxylases. *Mailing Add:* Dept of Chem Rm 435 Wayne State Univ Detroit MI 48202

KINARD, FRANK EFIRD, b Newberry, SC, Jan 15, 24; m 52; c 2. NUCLEAR SCIENCE. *Educ:* Newberry Col, BS, 46, AB, 47; Univ NC, MS, 50, PhD(physics), 54. *Prof Exp:* Instr physics, Univ NC, 49-52; physicist tech div, Savannah River Lab, E I du Pont de Nemours & Co, 53-63, head univ rels off, 63-67; exec dir, 67-68, ASST DIR, SC COMN HIGHER EDUC, 68- *Mem:* Am Phys Soc; Am Nuclear Soc. *Res:* Experimental nuclear physics; anti-neutrino experiments; reactor physics; higher education. *Mailing Add:* SC Comn Higher Educ 1429 Senate St Columbia SC 29201

KINARD, FREDRICK WILLIAM, b Leesville, SC, Oct 14, 06; m 29; c 2. PHYSIOLOGY, PHYSIOLOGICAL CHEMISTRY. *Educ:* Clemson Col, BS, 27; Univ Va, MS, 32, PhD(biochem), 33; Univ Tenn, MD, 45. *Prof Exp:* Asst chem, Med Col SC, 27-30; instr biochem, Univ Va, 30-33; from instr to assoc prof, 33-53, actg dir dept physiol, 44-46, chmn grad study comt, 49-65, prof, 53-78, dean, Col Grad Studies, 65-78, PROF EMER PHYSIOL, MED UNIV SC, 78- *Mem:* AAAS; Am Soc Zool; Am Physiol Soc; Soc Exp Biol & Med. *Res:* Creatine-creatinine metabolism; phosphatase; hemopoietine; ethanol metabolism. *Mailing Add:* The Cresent 2 Johnson Rd Charleston SC 29407

KINARIWALA, BHARAT K, b Ahmedabad, India, Oct 14, 26; US citizen; m 53; c 2. ALGORITHMS, DATABASE SYSTEMS. *Educ:* Benares Hindu Univ, BS, 51; Univ Calif, Berkeley, MS, 54, PhD(elec eng), 57. *Prof Exp:* Actg asst prof elec eng, Univ Calif, Berkeley, 56-57; mem tech staff, Bell Tel Labs, 57-66; chmn, Dept Elec Eng, 69-75 & 78-81, PROF ELEC ENG, UNIV HAWAII, 66- *Concurrent Pos:* Comput consult, Marchant, Inc, 56-57; prog chmn, Hawaiian Int Conf Systs Sci, 67; Inst Educ Exchange Serv deleg, Popov Soc Meeting, USSR, 67, prog chmn, Int Symp Circuit Theory, 68. *Mem:* Fel Inst Elec & Electronics Engrs. *Res:* System and computer sciences. *Mailing Add:* Dept of Elec Eng Univ of Hawaii 2540 Dole St Honolulu HI 96822

KINASEWITZ, GARY THEODORE, b New York, NY, Aug 17, 46. PULMONARY DISEASE, PULMONARY CIRCULATION. *Educ:* Boston Col, BS, 68, MEd, 69; Wayne State Univ, MD, 73. *Prof Exp:* Resident med, Univ Pa Hosp, 73-76; fel pulmonary dis, Dept Med, Cardiovasc Pulmonary Div, Univ Pa, 76-78, res assoc med, 78-79, asst prof med, 79-80; ASST PROF MED, LA STATE UNIV MED CTR, SHREVEPORT, 80- *Concurrent Pos:* Counr cardiopulmonary dis, Am Heart Asn. *Mem:* Am Thoracic Soc; Am Col Chest Physicians; Am Fedn Clin Res. *Res:* Quantitative analysis of fluid exchanges across the pulmonary capillaries of the visceral pleura; role of abnormal pulmonary vasomotor reactivity in the genesis of pulmonary hypertension; cardio pulmonary adjustments to exercise in patients with lung disease. *Mailing Add:* Dept Med La State Univ Med Ctr PO Box 33932 Shreveport LA 71130

KINBACHER, EDWARD JOHN, b Brooklyn, NY, Nov 19, 27; m 55; c 3. PLANT PHYSIOLOGY. *Educ:* Cornell Univ, BS, 49; Purdue Univ, MS, 51; Univ Calif, PhD(plant physiol), 55. *Prof Exp:* Asst, Purdue Univ, 49-51 & Univ Calif, 51-55; assoc prof plant breeding & agron, Cornell Univ, 55-63; assoc prof hort, 63-71, PROF HORT, UNIV NEBR, LINCOLN, 71- *Concurrent Pos:* Plant physiologist crops res div, Agr Res Serv, USDA, 55-62. *Mem:* Am Soc Plant Physiol; Am Soc Agron. *Res:* Heat, drought and cold resistance of horticultural crops and specifically turfgrasses. *Mailing Add:* Dept of Hort Univ of Nebr Lincoln NE 68583

KINCADE, PAUL W, b Moorhead, Miss, Oct 10, 44; m; C 1. IMMUNOLOGY. *Educ:* Miss State Univ, BS, 66, MS, 68; Univ Ala, PhD(microbiol & immunol), 71. *Prof Exp:* Res asst, Lobund Lab, Univ Notre Dame, 68-69; fel, Univ Ala, 71-72, Walter & Eliza Hall Inst, Melbourne, 72-74; assoc, 74-79, ASSOC MEM, SLOAN-KETTERING INST, 79-; ASSOC PROF, GRAD SCH MED SCI, CORNELL UNIV, 80- *Concurrent Pos:* Asst prof, Grad Sch Med Sci, Cornell Univ, 76-80; assoc ed, J Immunol, 79- *Mem:* Am Asn Immunologists; Am Asn Pathologists. *Res:* Humoral immune system with particular emphasis on relationships between stem cells and B lymphocytes and utilizing normal and genetically defective animal models. *Mailing Add:* Sloan-Kettering Inst 145 Boston Post Rd Rye NY 10580

KINCADE, ROBERT TYRUS, b Indianola, Miss, May 16, 41; m 68; c 3. ENTOMOLOGY, WEED SCIENCE. *Educ:* Miss State Univ, BS, 63, MS, 66, PhD(entom), 70. *Prof Exp:* Field res specialist weed control, 69-75, supvr herbicides, fungicides & insecticides, 75-77, FIELD RES SPECIALIST, BIOL RES INSECTICIDES, HERBICIDES, FUNGICIDES, CHEVRON CHEM CO, 77- *Mem:* Sigma Xi. *Res:* Development of herbicides, fungicides and insecticides for agricultural use. *Mailing Add:* Box 5008 Chevron Chem Co Greenville MS 38701

KINCAID, JAMES ROBERT, b Covington, Ky, Feb 11, 45; m 68; c 1. ANALYTICAL CHEMISTRY, BIOPHYSICAL CHEMISTRY. *Educ:* Xavier Univ, Ohio, BS, 70; Marquette Univ, PhD(chem), 74. *Prof Exp:* Vis fel chem, Princeton Univ, 74-78; ASST PROF CHEM, UNIV KY, 78- *Concurrent Pos:* Nat res serv award, NIH, 75-77 & Nat Cancer Inst, 77-78. *Mem:* Am Chem Soc. *Res:* Applications of Raman spectroscopy to biologically significant systems; structure and function relationships in heme proteins; role of trace metals in biochemistry and medicine. *Mailing Add:* Dept of Chem Univ of Ky Lexington KY 40506

KINCAID, RONALD LEE, b St Joseph, Mo, Oct 29, 50; m 70; c 3. ANIMAL NUTRITION, BIOCHEMISTRY. *Educ:* Univ Mo, BS, 71, MS, 73; Univ Ga, PhD(animal nutrit), 76. *Prof Exp:* Lectr animal nutrit, Lincoln Col, Univ Canterbury, 76-77; ASST PROF ANIMAL NUTRIT, WASH STATE UNIV, 77- *Mem:* Am Dairy Sci Asn; Am Soc Animal Sci; New Zealand Soc Animal Prod; Coun Agr Sci Technol. *Res:* Mineral metabolism in animals; phyto estrogens; dairy cattle nutrition. *Mailing Add:* Dept Animal Sci Wash State Univ Pullman WA 99164

KINCAID, STEVEN ALAN, b Indianapolis, Ind, July 6, 43; m 77; c 2. ANATOMY. *Educ:* Purdue Univ, BS, 65, DVM, 69, MS, 71, PhD(anat), 77. *Prof Exp:* Veterinarian, South Bend, Ind, 72-73; asst prof anat, Univ Tenn, 77-81; ASSOC PROF ANAT, PURDUE UNIV, 82- *Concurrent Pos:* Seeing Eye Found, Inc grant, 69-71; NIH fel, 71-72. *Mem:* Sigma Xi; Am Asn Vet Anatomists; Am Vet Med Asn; Am Soc Animal Sci. *Res:* Pathobiology of articular cartilage; comparative arthrology; copper metabolism. *Mailing Add:* Dept Animal Sci Purdue Univ West Lafayette IN 47907

KINCAID, THOMAS GARDINER, b Hamilton, Ont, Sept 18, 37; m 62; c 3. NONDESTRUCTIVE EVALUATION. *Educ:* Queens Univ Kingston, BSc, 59; Mass Inst Technol, SM, 61, PhD(elec eng), 65. *Prof Exp:* SYSTS ENGR, GEN ELEC CO, 65- *Mem:* Inst Elec & Electronics Engrs; Am Soc Nondestructive Testing. *Res:* Investigation of methods of evaluating materials for structural defects, including ultrasonic and electromagnetic techniques and x-ray. *Mailing Add:* 16 Sandstone Dr Burnt Mills NY 12027

KINCAID, WILFRED MACDONALD, b Cornhill, Scotland, Sept 13, 18; US citizen; m 52; c 3. MATHEMATICS. *Educ:* Univ Calif, AB, 40; Brown Univ, PhD(appl math), 46. *Prof Exp:* Instr math & eng, Brown Univ, 43-44; physicist, Nat Adv Comt Aeronaut, Langley Field, 44-46; instr math, 46-51, res mathematician, Vision Res Lab, 50-58, lectr math, 58-60, from asst prof to assoc prof, 60-71, PROF MATH, UNIV MICH, ANN ARBOR, 71- *Mem:* AAAS; Am Statist Asn; Am Math Soc; Math Asn Am; Asn Res Vision & Ophthal. *Res:* Numerical analysis; statistics; vision; psychophysics. *Mailing Add:* Dept Math Univ Mich Ann Arbor MI 48109

KINCANNON, DONNY FRANK, b Olustee, Okla, Jan 17, 33; m 57; c 2. BIOENVIRONMENTAL ENGINEERING. *Educ:* Okla State Univ, BS, 59, MS, 60, PhD(bioeng), 66. *Prof Exp:* Sanit engr, Tex State Dept Health, 60-61; instr civil eng, Arlington State Col, 61-63; asst prof, Univ Mo-Rolla, 65-66; from asst prof to assoc prof, 66-80, PROF CIVIL ENG, OKLA STATE UNIV, 80- *Mem:* Am Soc Civil Engrs; Am Soc Eng Educ; Water Pollution Control Fedn. *Res:* Water pollution control; biological treatment; industrial wastes; solid wastes. *Mailing Add:* Sch of Civil Eng Okla State Univ Stillwater OK 74074

KINCH, DONALD M(ILES), b Lexington, Nebr, Apr 13, 13; m 41; c 1. AGRICULTURAL ENGINEERING. *Educ:* Univ Nebr, BSc, 38; Univ Minn, MS, 40; Mich State Univ, PhD(agr eng), 53. *Prof Exp:* Asst agr eng, Univ Minn, 38-40; design engr, Oliver Tractor Corp, 40-45 & Climax Eng Co, 45-46; asst prof agr eng, Iowa State Univ, 46-47 & Purdue Univ, 47-50; asst, Mich State Univ, 50-53; agr engr & prof agr, 53-76, EMER PROF AGR, UNIV HAWAII, 76- *Concurrent Pos:* Fulbright res fel, Brazil, 62. *Mem:* AAAS; Am Soc Agr Engrs; Nat Soc Prof Engrs. *Res:* On-the-farm processing of food and fiber products with development of processing machinery and equipment for farm use. *Mailing Add:* Dept of Agr Eng Univ of Hawaii Honolulu HI 96822

KIND, CHARLES ALBERT, b Philadelphia, Pa, Apr 17, 17; m 44. BIOCHEMISTRY. *Educ:* Lafayette Col, BS, 39, Yale Univ, PhD(chem), 42. *Prof Exp:* Res chemist, Nat Defense Res Comt, Yale Univ, 42; from instr to asst prof chem, Univ Conn, 42-57, from assoc prof to prof zool, 57-67, asst dean, 63-67, prof biol & assoc dean Col Lib Arts & Sci, 67-77. *Concurrent Pos:* Lalor fel, Marine Biol Lab, Woods Hole, Mass, 49-50; Am Philos Soc fel, Bermuda Biol Sta, 51; mem corp, Marine Biol Lab, Woods Hole & Bermuda Biol Sta; actg dean, Col Lib Arts & Sci, Univ Conn, 70-71. *Mem:* AAAS; Am Chem Soc; Am Inst Chemists. *Res:* Lipids of marine invertebrate animals; sterols of vegetable oils; phosphatases. *Mailing Add:* Biol Sci Group Univ Conn Storrs CT 06268

KIND, LEON SAUL, b Boston, Mass, Dec 26, 22. MICROBIOLOGY. *Educ:* Harvard Univ, AB, 47; Yale Univ, PhD(microbiol), 51. *Prof Exp:* From asst prof to assoc prof, Med Col SC, 51-58; asst prof, Sch Med, Univ Calif, San Francisco, 58-70; assoc prof, 70-78, PROF MICROBIOL, DALHOUSIE UNIV, 78- *Concurrent Pos:* Res grants, NIH, 53- *Mem:* Soc Exp Biol & Med; Am Soc Immunol. *Res:* Immunology; experimental allergy; sensitivity of pertussis inoculated mice to histamine; anaphylaxis. *Mailing Add:* Dept of Microbiol Fac of Med Dalhousie Univ Halifax NS B3H 4H6 Can

KIND, PHYLLIS DAWN, b Sidney, Mont, July 31, 33. IMMUNOLOGY. *Educ:* Univ Mont, BA, 55; Univ Mich, MS, 56, PhD(bact), 60. *Prof Exp:* Fel dermat, Univ Mich, 60-63; from instr to asst prof path, Univ Colo, 63-71; res microbiologist, Nat Cancer Inst, 71-74; assoc prof microbiol, 74-79, PROF MICROBIOL & MED, GEORGE WASHINGTON UNIV, 79-, ASSOC DIR, TISSUE TYPING LAB, 78- *Mem:* AAAS; Am Asn Immunol; Am Soc Microbiol; Soc Exp Biol & Med; Sigma Xi. *Res:* Regulation of antibody synthesis. *Mailing Add:* Dept of Microbiol George Washington Univ Med Ctr Washington DC 20037

KINDEL, JOSEPH MARTIN, b Barberton, Ohio, Mar 10, 43; c 2. PLASMA PHYSICS. *Educ:* Univ Akron, BS, 65; Univ Calif, Los Angeles, MS, 66, PhD(physics), 70. *Prof Exp:* Res assoc plasma physics, Princeton Univ, 70-71; mem staff controlled thermonuclear res group, Physics Div, 71-72 & laser theory group, Theoret Div, 72-75, assoc group leader laser theory, Laser Div, 75-78, head, Plasma Theory Sect, 78-79, assoc group leader, 79-80, GROUP LEADER INERTIAL FUSION & PLASMA THEORY, APPL THEORET PHYSICS DIV, LOS ALAMOS NAT LAB, 80- *Res:* Space plasma physics; radio frequency heating of plasmas; nonlinear theory; controlled thermonuclear fusion; laser plasma interaction; plasma simulation studies; hydrodynamics of laser fusion. *Mailing Add:* Los Alamos Nat Lab Appl Theoret Physics Div MS 531 Los Alamos NM 87545

KINDEL, PAUL KURT, b Milwaukee, Wis, Sept 6, 34; m 61; c 3. BIOCHEMISTRY. *Educ:* Univ Wis, BS, 56; Cornell Univ, PhD(biochem), 61. *Prof Exp:* NIH fel, Max Planck Inst Cell Chem, Munich, 61-63; from asst prof to assoc prof biochem, 63-77, PROF BIOCHEM, MICH STATE UNIV, 77- *Mem:* AAAS; Am Chem Soc; Am Soc Plant Physiol. *Res:* Enzymology and hormonal regulation of plant cell wall development; isolation and chemical characterization of polysaccharides; carbohydrate chemistry. *Mailing Add:* Dept of Biochem Mich State Univ East Lansing MI 48824

KINDER, THOMAS HARTLEY, b Riverside, Calif, Sept 6, 43; m 70. PHYSICAL OCEANOGRAPHY. *Educ:* US Naval Acad, BS, 65; Univ Wash, MS, 74, PhD(phys oceanog), 76. *Prof Exp:* Res asst, Dept Oceanog, Univ Wash, 71-76, res assoc, 76-78; OCEANOGRAPHER, NAVAL OCEAN RES & DEVELOP ACTIVITY, 78- *Mem:* Am Geophys Union; Am

Meteorol Soc; AAAS. *Res:* Measurements of mesoscale features on shelves and in semi-enclosed seas (Bering, Caribbean, Mediterranean), especially fronts and eddies formed by flows exiting straits. *Mailing Add:* Naval Ocean Res & Develop Activity Code 331 NSTL Station MS 39529

KINDERLEHRER, DAVID (SAMUEL), b Allentown Pa, Oct 23, 41. MATHEMATICS. *Educ:* Mass Inst Technol, SB, 63; Univ Calif, Berkeley, PhD(math), 68. *Prof Exp:* From instr to asst prof, 68-75, PROF MATH, UNIV MINN, MINNEAPOLIS, 75- *Concurrent Pos:* Ital Govt res bursary math, Scuola Normale Superiore di Pisa, 71-72. *Res:* Partial differential equations; minimal surfaces; variational inequalities. *Mailing Add:* Sch of Math Univ of Minn Minneapolis MN 55455

KINDERMAN, EDWIN MAX, b Cincinnati, Ohio, Aug 21, 16; m 42; c 4. NUCLEAR CHEMISTRY. *Educ:* Oberlin Col, AB, 37; Univ Notre Dame, MS, 38, PhD(phys chem), 41. *Prof Exp:* Instr chem, Univ Portland, 41-43; chemist, Radiation Lab, Univ Calif, 43-45; from asst prof to assoc prof chem, Univ Portland, 45-49; chemist, Gen Elec Co, Wash, 49-56; sr physicist, 56-57, mgr, Nuclear Physics Dept, 57-68, dir, Appl Physics Lab, 68-71, Stanford Res Inst, 71-73; sr scientist, 73-75, mgr mkt Europe, 75-77, mgr nuclear & utility systs, Stanford Res Inst, 77-80, MGR ENERGY PLANNING, STANFORD RES INST INT, 80- *Concurrent Pos:* Chemist, Columbia Steel Casting Co, Ore, 43; res chemist, Res & Develop Div, H J Kaiser Co, Calif, 43; mem, Inst Nuclear Mat Mgt, Atomic Indust Forum. *Mem:* Am Chem Soc; Am Soc Int Law, panel on nuclear energy & world order; Am Phys Soc; Am Nuclear Soc; Sigma Xi. *Res:* Nuclear and analytical chemistry of uranium and transuranic elements; radiation chemistry and radiation damage effect; nuclear materials management; energy economics and planning; nuclear energy and weapons proliferation. *Mailing Add:* Stanford Res Inst Int 333 Ravenswood Ave Menlo Park CA 94025

KINDIG, NEAL B(ERT), b Medicine Lodge, Kans, July 26, 28; m 60; c 2. ELECTRONICS, PULMONARY PHYSIOLOGY. *Educ:* US Mil Acad, BS, 50; Univ Colo, MS, 57; Stanford Univ, PhD(elec eng), 64. *Prof Exp:* From instr to assoc prof, 56-79, PROF ELEC ENG, UNIV COLO, BOULDER, 79- *Concurrent Pos:* Univ Colo Coun Res & Creative Work fac fel, Univ Southampton; consult, Pulmonary Function Lab, Fitzsimons Army Med Ctr, Denver, Colo, 74-; treas, Rocky Mountain Bioeng Symp, 76-; North Found fel, Webb-Waring Lung Inst, Colo Health Sci Ctr, Denver, 77-79; prof anesthesiol, Colo Health Sci Ctr, 81-82. *Mem:* Inst Elec & Electronics Engrs; Am Phys Soc; Biomed Eng Soc. *Res:* Modelling, simulation of and instrumentation associated with lung physiology; gas exchange; chemical equilibrium and kinetics; gas transport by blood. *Mailing Add:* Dept of Elec Eng Univ of Colo Boulder CO 80302

KINDLE, EARL CLIFTON, b Memphis, Tenn, Mar 21, 19; m 42; c 3. METEOROLOGY. *Educ:* St Louis Univ, BS, 51; Univ Chicago, MS, 53; Univ Stockholm, Fil Lic, 60. *Prof Exp:* Pres, Weathercasts, Inc, Mo, 40-48; instr meteorol, Parks Col Aeronaut Technol, 48-51; proj dir geophys div, Res Triangle Inst, 65-67; dir res Navy Weather Res Facil, 67-71; asst dean, sch sci, 71-74, chmn dept, 74-77, prof physics & geophys sci, 71-80, EMINENT PROF GEOPHYS SCI & SMITH FOUND PROF OCEANOG, OLD DOMINION UNIV, 80- . *Concurrent Pos:* US Air Force grant, 65-67; adj assoc prof, Duke Univ, 67; US Navy grant, 71-73; consult, US Navy Air Systs Command, 71 & US Air Force Systs Command, 72. *Mem:* Am Meteorol Soc. *Res:* Development of techniques for applying theoretical meteorology to applied problems to develop a fuller understanding of the physical mesoscale process. *Mailing Add:* Sch of Sci Old Dom Univ Box 6173 Norfolk VA 23508

KINDLE, EDWARD DARWIN, geology, see previous edition

KINDLER, SHARON DEAN, b Omaha, Nebr, Apr 27, 30; m 64; c 2. ENTOMOLOGY. *Educ:* Univ Nebr, BSc, 59, PhD(entom), 67. *Prof Exp:* RES ENTOMOLOGIST, AGR RES SERV, USDA, UNIV NEBR, 64- *Mem:* Entom Soc Am. *Res:* Biology, ecology and control of sorghum and grass insects; plant resistance to sorghum and grass insects. *Mailing Add:* Forage-Insect Lab E Campus Univ of Nebr Lincoln NE 68583

KINDQUIST, ERIC B(IRGER) T(AGE), b Stockholm, Sweden, July 10, 18; nat US; m 49, 55; c 1. CHEMICAL ENGINEERING. *Educ:* Pratt Inst Technol, BChE, 39. *Prof Exp:* Jr metallurgist, Int Nickel Co, NJ, 39-41; res engr, Radio Corp Am, 41-42 & Battelle Mem Inst, 42-45; chief metallurgist, Eastwood Nealley Corp, 45-49, supt wire mill, 49-54; vpres & gen mgr, Garfield Wire Div, Overlakes Corp, 54-55, pres, Everite Co, Inc, 55-57; pres, Manor Plastics Labs, Inc, 57-65; dir res & develop, Coin Int, NY, 65-69; consult engr, 69-71; vpres, Tecmar, NJ, 72-80; RETIRED. *Concurrent Pos:* Mem bd dirs, Hercer Corp, 79- *Mem:* Am Soc Testing & Mat; Am Inst Mining, Metall & Petrol Engrs; Am Soc Metals. *Res:* Powder metallurgy; metallurgy of cast iron, brass, bronze and miscellaneous copper-rich alloys; wire enameling and coating; vinyl plastisols and powder; textile bonding and laminating; acrylic specialty purpose adhesives; manufacturing of specialty adhesives for textile industry; contract textile printing, thermal process. *Mailing Add:* Rollinghill Rd Skillman NJ 08558

KINDSVATER, HOWARD MAXWELL, b Wichita, Kans, Feb 14, 13; m 34; c 3. CHEMISTRY. *Educ:* Kans State Col, BS, 35; Univ Iowa, MS, 36, PhD(phys chem), 38. *Prof Exp:* Res chemist, Armour Res Found, 38-39; lacquer chemist, Reliance Varnish Co, Ky, 39-40; res chemist, Joseph E Seagram & Sons, 40-42; res chemist, Aerojet Gen Corp Div, Gen Tire & Rubber Co, 45-53, sr chemist, 53-55; prin engr, Lockheed Missile & Space Co, 55-71, systs engr, 71-76; consult, McGraw-Hill, 63-79; RETIRED. *Mem:* Am Chem Soc; Am Inst Aeronaut & Astronaut; Combustion Inst; Sigma Xi. *Res:* Propulsion engineering and development. *Mailing Add:* PO Box 880 Altaville CA 95221

KINDT, GLENN W, b Alpena, Mich, Sept 10, 30; m 60; c 4. NEUROSURGERY. *Educ:* Mich State Univ, BS, 51; Pa State Univ, BS, 52; Univ Mich, MD, 59. *Prof Exp:* Intern med, Univ Mich Hosp, 59-60, resident surg, 60-61, resident neurosurg, 62-65; resident, Harvard Med Sch & Peter Bent Brigham Hosp, Boston, 61-62; instr, Med Col SC, 65-66, assoc, 66-67; asst prof, Univ Calif, 67-69; from asst prof to assoc prof neurosurg, Univ Mich Med Ctr, Ann Arbor, 69-80; MEM STAFF, DIV NEUROSURG, UNIV COLO MED CTR, 80- *Concurrent Pos:* Chief investr, US Vet Admin res grant, 66-; co-investr, NIH res grant, 67- *Mem:* AMA; Cong Neurol Surg. *Res:* Regional hypothermia and vascular insufficiency of the brain; intracerebral hematomas. *Mailing Add:* Dept Neurosurg Univ Colo Med Ctr Denver CO 80220

KINDT, THOMAS JAMES, b Cincinnati, Ohio, May 18, 39; m 64; c 2. BIOCHEMISTRY, IMMUNOGENETICS. *Educ:* Thomas More Col, AB, 63; Univ Ill, Urbana, PhD(biochem), 67. *Prof Exp:* NIH fel biol, City of Hope Med Ctr, 67-69, asst res scientist, 69-70; fel, Rockefeller Univ, 70-71, asst prof, 71-73, assoc prof biol, 73-77; CHIEF LAB IMMUNOGENETICS, NAT INST ALLERGY & INFECTIOUS DIS, NIH, 77- *Concurrent Pos:* Adj assoc prof med, Cornell Univ Med Col, 73-77; assoc ed, J Immunol, 73-; adv ed, J Exp Med, 77- & Immunochem, 77-; adj prof micro & pediatrics, Sch Med & Dent, Georgetown Univ, 81- *Mem:* Am Heart Asn; Harvey Soc; Sigma Xi; Am Asn Immunol; Am Soc Biol Chemists. *Res:* Genetic determinants on immunoglobulins and histocompatibility antigens; protein and polysaccharide structure. *Mailing Add:* Nat Inst Health Bldg 8 Rm 100 Bethesda MD 20205

KINERSLY, THORN, b The Dalles, Ore, Sept 15, 23; m 54; c 3. DENTISTRY, DENTAL RESEARCH. *Educ:* Univ Ore, DMD, 48. *Prof Exp:* Pvt pract, 48-49; intern children's dent, Forsyth Dent Infirmary, 49-50; asst resident, Sch Med, Yale Univ & Grace-New Haven Community Hosp, 50; res fel dent, Sch Med, Yale Univ, 52-56; pvt pract, 56-64; res assoc, 64, asst prof, 64-67, ASSOC PROF DENT, DENT SCH, UNIV ORE HEALTH SCI CTR, 67- *Concurrent Pos:* Lectr, Forsyth Dent Infirmary, 52-56; res fel, Nobel Inst, 54; abstractor, Oral Res Abstr, 66-; prin investr, Educ & Res Found Prosthodontics, 69; consult on-site invest res appl, Dent Sect, NIH, 70. *Mem:* Fel AAAS; Soc Exp Biol & Med; Int Asn Dent Res; Am Dent Asn. *Res:* Paper electrophoresis of saliva and salivary glands for identification of enzymes, blood group factors and anti-bacterial factors; track radioautography of teeth with Ca-45 isotopes; lasers and their relation to dentistry. *Mailing Add:* Dept of Dent Dent Sch Univ Ore Health Sci Ctr Portland OR 97201

KING, ALBERT IGNATIUS, b Tokyo, Japan, June 12, 34; US citizen; m 60; c 2. BIOENGINEERING. *Educ:* Univ Hong Kong, BSc, 55; Wayne State Univ, MS, 60, PhD(eng mech), 66. *Prof Exp:* Demonstr civil eng, Hong Kong, 55-58; asst & instr eng mech, Wayne State Univ, 58-60; from instr to assoc prof, 60-76, PROF BIOENG, WAYNE STATE UNIV, 76-, ASSOC NEUROSURG, SCH MED, 71- *Honors & Awards:* NIH career develop award; Charles Russ Richards Mem Award, Am Soc Mech Engrs, 80. *Mem:* Am Soc Eng Educ; Am Soc Mech Engrs; Am Acad Orthop Surg. *Res:* Human response to acceleration and vibration, automotive and aircraft safety; biomechanics of the spine; mathematical modelling of impact events. *Mailing Add:* Dept of Mech Eng Wayne State Univ Detroit MI 48202

KING, ALEXANDER HARVEY, b London, Eng, July 1, 54; m 77. ELECTRON MICROSCOPY, CRYSTALLOGRAPHY. *Educ:* Univ Sheffield, BMet, 75; Univ Oxford, DPhil(metall), 79. *Prof Exp:* Harwell fel, Dept Metall & Sci Mat, Univ Oxford, 79 & Dept Mat Sci & Eng, Mass Inst Technol, 79-81; ASST PROF, DEPT MAT SCI & ENG, STATE UNIV NY, STONYBROOK, 81- *Mem:* Inst Metall; Am Inst Mining, Metall & Petrol Engrs; Electron Microscope Soc Am. *Res:* Crystal lattice defects, particularly grain boundaries; electron microscopy, electron and x-ray diffraction. *Mailing Add:* Dept Mat Sci & Eng State Univ NY Stonybrook NY 11794

KING, ALFRED DOUGLAS, JR, b Portland, Ore, May 11, 33; m 59; c 2. FOOD MICROBIOLOGY. *Educ:* Wash State Univ, BS, 55, PhD(food sci), 65; Univ Calif, Davis, MS, 61. *Prof Exp:* Food technologist, Nalley's Inc, 57-59; assoc chemist, 61-63, chemist, 63-65, microbiologist, 65-72, res leader microbiol, 73-77, RES MICROBIOLOGIST, WESTERN REGIONAL RES LAB, USDA, 78- *Concurrent Pos:* Vis scientist CSIRO Div Food Res, Sydney, Australia, 77-78. *Mem:* Inst Food Technologists; Am Soc Microbiol. *Res:* Microbial physiology; food sanitation and public health; wine flavor; human and microbial nutrition; food mycology. *Mailing Add:* Western Regional Res Lab USDA 800 Buchanan St Albany CA 94710

KING, ALLEN LEWIS, b Rochester, NY, Mar 27, 10; m 37; c 3. PHYSICS. *Educ:* Univ Rochester, BA, 32, MA, 33, PhD(physics), 37. *Hon Degrees:* MA, Dartmouth Col, 48. *Prof Exp:* Instr physics, Univ Rochester, 36-37 & Rensselaer Polytech Inst, 37-42; from instr to prof, 42-75, EMER PROF PHYSICS, DARTMOUTH COL, 75- *Concurrent Pos:* Consult, Behr-Manning Corp, NY, 41-42 & 48-57. *Mem:* AAAS; Am Phys Soc; Biophys Soc; Am Asn Physics Teachers; Optical Soc Am. *Res:* Mechanical and hydrodynamical processes in biological systems; optical measurements; thermophysics; history of physics. *Mailing Add:* Dept of Physics & Astron Dartmouth Col Hanover NH 03755

KING, AMY P, b Douglas, Wyo, Dec 30, 28; m 49. MATHEMATICS. *Educ:* Univ Mo, BS, 49; Wichita State Univ, MA, 60; Univ Ky, PhD, 70. *Prof Exp:* Teacher pub schs, Goddard, Kans, 56-58; teaching fel, Wichita State Univ, 58-60, instr, 60-62; asst instr, Univ Kans, 62-65; instr math, Washburn Univ, 66-67; teaching asst, Univ Ky, 67-70; asst prof, 70-72, assoc prof, 72-79, PROF MATH, EASTERN KY UNIV, 79- *Mem:* Am Math Soc; Math Asn Am; Nat Coun Teachers Math. *Res:* Complex variables; mathematics education. *Mailing Add:* 1228 Tates Creek Rd Lexington KY 40502

KING, ARTHUR BRUCE, b Akron, Ohio, Apr 16, 31; m 53; c 4. PHYSICAL CHEMISTRY. Educ: Duke Univ, BS, 52; Cornell Univ, PhD(phys chem), 57. Prof Exp: Fel, Nat Res Coun Can, 56-58; phys chemist, Stanford Res Inst, 59-62; res chemist, 62-64, supvr chem physics sect, 64-66, dir phys sci div, 66-70, dir planning & econ div, 70-76, mgr energy & mat res, 76-80, MGR MAT & MINERALS RES, GULF RES & DEVELOP CO, 80- Mem: NAm Soc Corp Planning. Res: Electron impact processes and mass spectral fragmentation patterns; gas phase kinetics and photochemistry; reactions involving non-thermal energy distribution; atomic reactions on solid surfaces. Mailing Add: Energy & Mat Res Gulf Res & Devel Co PO Box 2038 Pittsburgh PA 15230

KING, ARTHUR FRANCIS, b St John's, Nfld, Feb 11, 37; m 63; c 2. GEOLOGY. Educ: Mem Univ, BSc, 61, MSc, 63; Univ Reading, PhD(geol), 67. Prof Exp: Asst prof, 67-74, ASSOC PROF GEOL, MEM UNIV NFLD, 74- Res: Stratigraphy and structure of Flysch like upper Carboniferous rocks in North Cornwall, England; Hadrynian and lower Cambrian clastic sequences in Newfoundland and Labrador. Mailing Add: Dept of Geol Mem Univ St John's NF A1C 5S7 Can

KING, B(ERNARD) G(EORGE), b Kitchener, Ont, Can, Dec 22, 22; nat US; m 49; c 3. ELECTRICAL ENGINEERING. Educ: Univ Southern Calif, BE, 44; Univ Wis, MS, 51, PhD(elec eng), 55. Prof Exp: Instr elec eng, Univ Southern Calif, 44-48 & Univ Wis, 48-55; mem tech staff, Bell Tel Labs, Inc, 55-81. Concurrent Pos: ed, Bell Syst Tech J, 81. Res: Electromagnetic theory; pulse code modulation; microwave radio. Mailing Add: 5 Monmouth Ave Rumson NJ 07760

KING, BARRY FREDERICK, b Perham, Minn, Sept 22, 42. MICROSCOPIC ANATOMY, CYTOLOGY. Educ: Univ Minn, BA, 65; Univ Nev, MS, 67; Wash Univ, PhD(anat), 70. Prof Exp: Asst prof anat, Med Sch, Washington Univ, 71-77; ASSOC PROF ANAT, MED SCH, UNIV CALIF, DAVIS, 78- Concurrent Pos: USPHS fel anat, Univ Wis-Madison, 70-71. Mem: AAAS; Am Asn Anat; Perinatal Res Soc; Am Soc Cell Biol. Res: Functional histology and cytology of the female reproductive system, especially the functional morphology of the placenta and fetal membranes. Mailing Add: Dept of Human Anat Sch of Med Univ of Calif Davis CA 95616

KING, BENTON DAVIS, b Hackensack, NJ, Oct 20, 19; m 45; c 2. MEDICINE. Educ: Haverford Col, BS, 41; Univ Pa, MD, 44; Am Bd Anesthesiol, dipl, 50. Prof Exp: Assoc surg, Sch Med, Univ Pa, 48-52, res assoc, Grad Sch Med, 49-52; assoc prof anesthesiol, Col Med, State Univ NY Downstate Med Ctr, 54-57, prof & chmn dept, Sch Med, State Univ NY Buffalo, 57-69, chmn dept, 69-80, PROF ANESTHESIOL, STATE UNIV NY DOWNSTATE MED CTR, 69- Concurrent Pos: Head dept anesthesiol, Meyer Mem Hosp, Buffalo, 57-69, Children's Hosp, 64-69, Kings County & State Univ Hosps, 69-; consult, Vet Admin Hosp, Brooklyn, NY. Mem: Am Soc Anesthesiol; Asn Univ Anesthetists. Mailing Add: Dept of Anesthesiol State Univ NY Downstate Med Ctr Brooklyn NY 11203

KING, BETTY LOUISE JOSEPHSON, b Atlanta, Ga, Nov 26, 43; m 77; c 1. BIOLOGY, MOLECULAR GENETICS. Educ: Brandeis Univ, BA, 65; Harvard Univ, PhD(microbiol, molecular genetics), 72. Prof Exp: Asst prof biol, Bard Col, 72-75; asst prof biol, Skidmore Col, 76-77; ASSOC PROF BIOL, NORTHERN VA COMMUNITY COL, 78- Mem: AAAS. Res: Genetics of primary and secondary metabolism; chemical communication; biochemistry and ecology of alkaloids. Mailing Add: Dept of Biol 8333 Little River Turnpike Annandale VA 22003

KING, BLAKE, b Atlanta, Ga, Feb 4, 21; m 48; c 2. MECHANICAL ENGINEERING, PHYSICAL METALLURGY. Educ: Univ Fla, BME, 48; Calif Inst Technol, MSME, 49. Prof Exp: Asst prof mech eng, Univ Miami, 49-51, 53-54; sr engr, Design Integration Dept, Martin Co, Md, 54-56, unit supvr, Nuclear Div, 56-58; assoc prof mech eng, 58-67, PROF MECH ENG, UNIV MIAMI, 67- Mem: Am Soc Metals; Metall Soc; Am Soc Mech Engrs. Res: Dispersion-strengthened high temperature alloys; creative mechanical design. Mailing Add: Dept of Mech Eng Univ of Miami Coral Gables FL 33124

KING, C(ARY) JUDSON, b Ft Monmouth, NJ, Sept 27, 34; m 57; c 3. SEPERATION PROCESSES. Educ: Yale Univ, BE, 56; Mass Inst Technol, SM, 58, ScD(chem eng), 60. Prof Exp: Asst prof chem eng, Mass Inst Technol, 59-63; from asst prof to assoc prof, 63-69, vchmn dept, 67-72, chmn dept, 72-81, PROF CHEM ENG, UNIV CALIF, BERKELEY, 69-, DEAN COL CHEM, 81- Concurrent Pos: Dir Bayway Sta, Sch Chem Eng Pract, Mass Inst Technol, 59-61; consult, Procter & Gamble Co, 65- & Cutter Labs, Inc, Berkeley, Calif, 78- Honors & Awards: 25th Ann Inst Lectr, 73; Food, Pharmaceut & Bioeng Div Award, 75; William H Walker Award, 76, Am Inst Chem Engrs; George Westinghouse Award, 78, Am Soc Eng Educ. Mem: Nat Acad Eng; Am Chem Soc; Am Inst Food Technol; Am Inst Chem Engrs. Res: Synthesis and analysis of chemical processes; drying and concentration of foods; separation processes; water pollution abatement. Mailing Add: 7 Kensington Ct Kensington CA 94707

KING, CALVIN ELIJAH, b Chicago, Ill, June 5, 28. MATHEMATICS. Educ: Morehouse Col, AB, 49; Atlanta Univ, MA, 50; Ohio State Univ, PhD(math educ), 59. Prof Exp: Instr math, Jackson Col, 53-55; asst instr, Ohio State Univ, 55-58; head dept physics & math, 74-79, PROF MATH, TENN STATE UNIV, 58- Concurrent Pos: Specialist math & head dept, Fed Adv Teachers Col, Nigeria, 62-64. Res: Methods of teaching remedial mathematics; teaching elementary mathematics by television; the relation of modern mathematics to traditional mathematics. Mailing Add: Dept of Math Tenn State Univ Nashville TN 37203

KING, CARL D(ILLON), JR, b Dayton, Ohio, Mar 14, 31; m 51, 76; c 7. CHEMICAL ENGINEERING, TECHNICAL MANAGEMENT. Educ: Univ Dayton, BChE, 52. Prof Exp: Res chem engr, Monsanto Chem Co, 52-57, group leader process res, 57-63, sr res chem engr, Monsanto Res Corp,

63-65, mgr contractor rels, 65-77, planning specialist, 77-79, SR PROD ENGR, MONSANTO RES CORP, 79- Res: High temperature; high pressure; cryogenics; vacuum; process research; project management. Mailing Add: Monsanto Res Corp Miamisburg OH 45342

KING, CHARLES C, b Kittanning, Pa, Jan 12, 33; m 56; c 5. ECOLOGY, BOTANY. Educ: Marietta Col, BS, 54; Ohio State Univ, MSc, 56, PhD(entom), 61. Prof Exp: Res technician MSc, 56, PhD(entom), 61. Prof Exp: Res technician entom, Ohio Agr Res & Develop, 56-61; from asst prof to prof biol, Malone Col, 61-72; EXEC DIR, OHIO BIOL SURV, 72- Concurrent Pos: Consult radiation biol, Univ Wash, 62; consult dept bot, Okla State Univ, 63; consult dept geol, Univ Calgary, 68; coordr geobot conf, Malone Col, 70. Honors & Awards: Ohio Conserv Cong Citation of Merit, 65; Stark Wilderness Ctr Citation of Appreciation, 71; Ohio Conserv Achievement Award, Ohio Dept Natural Resources, 78. Mem: Am Quaternary Asn; Am Inst Biol Sci; Ecol Soc Am. Res: Effects of herbicides and fungicides on honeybees, metabolism of 2, 4-D in blackjack oak; effects of 2, 4-D on nectar secretion; peat bog palynology; environmental analysis; distribution and ecology of prairies in central Ohio. Mailing Add: Ohio Biol Surv 484 W 12th Ave Columbus OH 43210

KING, CHARLES EVERETT, b Oak Park, Ill, May 8, 34; c 2. POPULATION BIOLOGY. Educ: Emory Univ, AB, 58; Fla State Univ, MS, 60; Univ Wash, PhD(zool), 65. Prof Exp: Res assoc zool, Col Fisheries, Univ Wash, 65; instr biol, Yale Univ, 65-66; asst prof zool, Univ Ill, Urbana, 66-68; asst prof biol, Yale Univ, 68-72; from assoc prof to prof biol, Univ SFla, 72-77; PROF ZOOL & CHMN DEPT, ORE STATE UNIV, 77- Mem: AAAS; Ecol Soc Am; Am Soc Naturalists; Genetics Soc Am; Soc Study Evolution. Res: Laboratory and field investigation of population dynamics and community structure; interaction of genetical and ecological phenomena within populations; relation of life history characteristics to ecological adaptation; evolution of senescence. Mailing Add: Dept of Zool Ore State Univ Corvallis OR 97331

KING, CHARLES GLEN, b Entiat, Wash, Oct 22, 96; m 19; c 3. BIOCHEMISTRY. Educ: State Col Wash, BS, 18, ScD, 50; Univ Pittsburgh, MS, 20, PhD(chem), 23, ScD, 50; Drexel Inst, DSc, 56. Prof Exp: Asst, Exp Sta, State Col Wash, 18, by-prod specialist, 19; from instr to prof chem, Univ Pittsburgh, 19-43; vis prof, 42-46, assoc dir, Inst Nutrit Sci, 63-66, prof, 46-62, lectr, 67-73, EMER PROF CHEM, COLUMBIA UNIV, 62- Concurrent Pos: Spec consult, USPHS, 40-62; mem food & nutrit bd, Nat Res Coun, 40-69; mem adv comt, Williams-Waterman Fund, 45-55, policy comt res & mkt, USDA, 49-58 & sci adv bd, Robert A Welch Found, 56-64; sci dir, Nutrit Found, Inc, 42-56, exec dir, 56-61, pres, 61-63, trustee, 63-; spec consult, UNICEF, 55-66; expert adv panel nutrit, WHO, 60-66; consult, Surgeon Gen, US Dept Army, Rockefeller Found, 63-66; pres, Int Cong Nutrit, 60 & Int Union Nutrit Sci, 66-69, mem coun, 70-73; mem bd dirs & tech adv bd, Milbank Mem Fund, 63-70; mem nat adv coun, Food & Drug Admin, 64-68; mem, Int Comt Int Biol Prog, 67; mem exec comt, Coun Sci Unions, 69-70. Honors & Awards: Scott Medal, Philadelphia City Trusts; Pittsburgh Award, Am Chem Soc, 43 & Charles F Spencer Award, 55; Nicholas Appert Medal, Inst Food Technol, 55; Czech Acad Sci Gold Medal Award, 69. Mem: Nat Acad Sci; Am Soc Biol Chemists (secy, 38-41, pres-elect, 53, pres, 54); fel Am Pub Health Asn (treas, 52-60, pres, 62); Am Inst Nutrit (vpres, 47, pres, 49); Am Chem Soc. Res: Fats; enzymes; vitamin C; aviation feeding; nutrition. Mailing Add: 192 Kendal at Longwood Kennett Square PA 19348

KING, CHARLES MILLER, b West Salem, Ill, Oct 2, 32; m 54; c 2. BIOCHEMISTRY, ONCOLOGY. Educ: Univ Ill, Urbana, BA, 54; Univ Minn, Minneapolis, PhD(biochem), 62. Prof Exp: Res assoc, Michael Reese Hosp & Med Ctr, 65-68, from asst dir to actg dir div cancer res, 68-75; asst prof med, Pritzker Sch Med, Univ Chicago, 73-75; expert, Nat Cancer Inst, Nat Ctr Toxicol Res, 75-77; assoc prof biochem, Univ Ark for Med Sci, 75-77; CHMN DEPT CHEM CARCINOGENESIS, MICH CANCER FOUND, 77-; DIR ENVIRON CARCINOGENESIS PROG, COMPREHENSIVE CANCER CTR, METROP DETROIT, 77- Concurrent Pos: Res fel oncol, Med Sch, Univ Minn, Minneapolis, 62-63; Am Cancer Soc fel, Neth Cancer Inst, 63-65; mem, Nat Bladder Cancer Proj, Nat Cancer Inst, 73-78; mem, Amines Comt, Nat Res Coun, Nat Acad Sci, 79-80; mem, Chem Path Study Sect, NIH, 79-83. Mem: Am Asn Cancer Res; Am Chem Soc; Am Soc Biol Chem. Res: Mechanism of action of chemical carcinogens; metabolism in covalent interaction with protein and nucleic acid. Mailing Add: Mich Cancer Found 110 E Warren Detroit MI 48201

KING, CHARLES O(RRIN), b Rochester, NY, Jan 9, 16; m 43; c 3. CHEMICAL ENGINEERING. Educ: Univ Rochester, BS, 37; Univ Mich, MS, 39, ScD(chem eng), 43. Prof Exp: Asst chem eng, Univ Mich, 39-41; res engr, 43-48, process develop supvr, Tenn, 48-52, asst to tech mgr, 52-56, planning engr, 56-60, process supvr, 60-61, sr engr, 61-67, ASST TO TECH DIR, TEXTILE FIBERS DEPT, E I DU PONT DE NEMOURS & CO, INC, 67- Mem: Am Chem Soc; Am Inst Chem Engrs; Am Inst Chem; Sigma Xi. Res: Solvent extraction; polyamide textile fibers. Mailing Add: Textile Fibers Dept E I du Pont de Nemours & Co Inc Wilmington DE 19898

KING, CHARLES W(ILLIS), b Clarion Co, Pa, Nov 17, 35; m 54; c 2. MATHEMATICS, ELECTRICAL ENGINEERING. Educ: Wash Col, BS, 57; Univ Pittsburgh, 57-61. Prof Exp: Jr engr, Westinghouse Elec Corp, 57-58, engr, 58-62; asst dir elec utility appIns, C-E-I-R, Inc, 62-63; mgr elec utility serv, 63-67, instr power systs anal, Inst Advan Technol Div, 64-67; pres, Comput & Utility Serv, Inc, 67-68; pres, Utility Consult Serv Co, 68-76; CONTROL ENGR, NE UTILITIES SERV CO, 76- Mem: Inst Elec & Electronics Engrs. Res: Application of scientific computers to solving of scientific problems for electric utility industry. Mailing Add: NE Utilities Serv Co PO Box 270 Hartford CT 06101

KING, CHI-YU, b Nanking, China, Aug 14, 34; m 62; c 3. GEOPHYSICS. *Educ:* Univ Taiwan, BEE, 56; Duke Univ, MS, 61; Cornell Univ, PhD(appl physics), 65. *Prof Exp:* Res fel geophys, Calif Inst Technol, 65-66; asst res geophysicist, Univ Calif, Los Angeles, 66-68; geophysicist, US Geol Surv, 68-70; geophysicist, US Earthquake Mechanism Lab, Nat Oceanic & Atmospheric Admin, 70-73; GEOPHYSICIST, US GEOL SURV, 73- *Mem:* AAAS; Am Geophys Union; Seismol Soc Am. *Res:* Earthquake source mechanisms and prediction; fracture of solids; heat transfer; geomagnetism; geophysical fracture phenomena. *Mailing Add:* US Geol Surv 345 Middlefield Rd Menlo Park CA 94025

KING, CRESTON ALEXANDER, JR, b San Antonio, Tex, July 9, 35; m 62; c 3. LOW TEMPERATURE PHYSICS. *Educ:* Rice Univ, AB, 58, MA, 63, PhD(physics), 65; Duke Univ, MA, 62. *Prof Exp:* Asst physics, Rice Univ, 62-64; asst prof, 66-73, ASSOC PROF PHYSICS, LOYOLA UNIV, LA, 73-, CHMN DEPT, 80- *Mem:* Am Phys Soc; Am Asn Physics Teachers. *Res:* Superconductivity; solid state physics. *Mailing Add:* Dept of Physics Loyola Univ 6363 St Charles Ave New Orleans LA 70118

KING, DAN OSCAR, b Lakeland, Fla, Oct 27, 44; m 67; c 1. PLANT PHYSIOLOGY, PLANT TISSUE CULTURE. *Educ:* Univ S Fla, BA, 68; Ind Univ, MA, 71, PhD(plant physiol), 74. *Prof Exp:* Fel photobiol, Brandeis Univ, 74-77; ASST PROF BIOL, LYCOMING COL, 77- *Mem:* Am Soc Plant Physiologists. *Res:* Photosynthesis; genetic improvement of crop plants; hydrogen metabolism in photosynthetic organisms. *Mailing Add:* Dept of Biol Lycoming Col Williamsport PA 17701

KING, DANNIE HILLEARY, b Clifton Forge, Va, Apr 1, 42; m 67; c 1. MICROBIOLOGY, MEDICAL ADMINISTRATION. *Educ:* Davidson Col, BS, 64; WVa Univ, MS, 67; NC State Univ, PhD(microbiol), 73. *Prof Exp:* Instr biol & microbiol, Appalachian State Univ, 67-70; CLIN RES SCIENTIST CLIN MED, BURROUGHS WELLCOME CO, 73-, SECT HEAD, MED VIROLOGY, 76- *Concurrent Pos:* Res assoc urol, Sch Med, Duke Univ, 74-; adj asst prof microbiol, NC State Univ, 74- *Mem:* Am Soc Microbiol; NY Acad Sci. *Res:* Lipid metabolism of microorganisms; efficacy and safety evaluations of antibacterial and antiviral new drugs. *Mailing Add:* Burroughs Wellcome Co 3030 Cornwallis Rd Res Triangle Park NC 27709

KING, DARRELL LEE, b Hall, Mont, Jan 10, 37; m 62; c 3. LIMNOLOGY. *Educ:* Mont State Col, BS, 59; Mich State Univ, MS, 62, PhD(limnol), 64. *Prof Exp:* From asst prof to prof civil eng, Univ Mo-Columbia, 64-74; PROF FISHERIES & WILDLIFE & INST WATER RES, MICH STATE UNIV, 74-, ACTG DIR, INST, 78- *Concurrent Pos:* Consult, Ralston Purina, 64-65 & 72-73, St Louis County Water Co, 67-69 & 73-74, Campbell Soup Co, 70-71, Harland Bartholomew & Assocs, 73-74 & A P Green Refractories Co, 75. *Mem:* AAAS; Am Soc Limnol & Oceanog; Am Fisheries Soc; Water Pollution Control Fedn. *Res:* Interrelationships between physical, chemical and biological factors with specific reference to detailing interacting mechanisms which govern aquatic ecosystems. *Mailing Add:* Inst of Water Res Mich State Univ East Lansing MI 48824

KING, DAVID BEEMAN, b Ware, Mass, Mar 12, 37; m 61; c 2. BIOLOGY. *Educ:* Univ Mass, BS, 59, MA, 61; Ind Univ, PhD(zool), 65. *Prof Exp:* Asst prof, 65-70, assoc prof, 70-80, PROF BIOL, FRANKLIN & MARSHALL COL, 81- *Concurrent Pos:* Nat Inst Arthritis & Metab Dis res grant, 66- *Mem:* AAAS; Am Soc Zoologists. *Res:* Comparative endocrinology; role of the pituitary in the growth of chickens; thyroidal influence on muscle growth and development. *Mailing Add:* Dept of Biol Franklin & Marshall Col Lancaster PA 17603

KING, DAVID SOLOMON, b Wooster, Ohio, Jan 25, 36; m 56; c 2. ASTROPHYSICS. *Educ:* Manchester Col, BA, 60; Ind Univ, MA, 64, PhD(astrophys), 67. *Prof Exp:* From asst prof to assoc prof, 65-77, PROF ASTRON, UNIV NMEX, 77- *Concurrent Pos:* NSF res grant stellar pulsation theory, 66-77. *Mem:* Am Astron Soc. *Res:* Stellar interiors; theory of pulsating variable stars; nonlinear self-excited radial oscillations in stellar envelopes. *Mailing Add:* Dept of Physics & Astron Univ of NMex Albuquerque NM 87106

KING, DAVID THANE, b Wellington, NZ, Jan 16, 23; nat US; m 50; c 4. PHYSICS. *Educ:* Univ NZ, BSc, 44, MSc, 47; Bristol Univ, PhD(physics), 51. *Prof Exp:* Physicist, US Naval Res Lab, 51-55; from asst prof to assoc prof, 55-61, PROF PHYSICS, UNIV TENN, KNOXVILLE, 61- *Concurrent Pos:* Mem user's group zero gradient synchrotron Argonne Nat Lab, 62-; consult, Oak Ridge Nat Lab, 65- *Mem:* Am Phys Soc; Italian Phys Soc. *Res:* High energy physics. *Mailing Add:* Dept of Physics-Astron Univ of Tenn Knoxville TN 37916

KING, DELBERT LEO, b Kansas City, Mo, Jan 7, 34; m 57; c 7. PHYSICAL CHEMISTRY. *Educ:* Ariz State Col, BS, 56; Univ Nebr, MS, 59, PhD, 68. *Prof Exp:* Asst prof chem, Sterling Col, 59-62; asst prof, Nebr Wesleyan Univ, 62-65; assoc prof, 65-72, chmn natural sci div, 70-76, PROF CHEM, DOANE COL, 72-, DIR COMPUT CTR, 76- *Mem:* Digital Equip Comput Users Soc. *Res:* Solution colorimetry. *Mailing Add:* Dept of Chem Doane Col Crete NE 68333

KING, DONALD D(EWOLF), b Rochester, NY, Aug 7, 19; m 44; c 4. ELECTRONICS. *Educ:* Harvard Univ, AB, 42, AM, 44, PhD(physics), 46. *Prof Exp:* Res fel appl physics, Harvard Univ, 46-47, asst prof, 47-48; res scientist physics, Johns Hopkins Univ, 48-54, assoc dir radiation lab, 54-55, dir, 55-56; vpres res, Electronic Commun Inc, 56-64; dir electronics res lab, Aerospace Corp, 64-67; vpres & dir, 67-68, PRES, PHILIPS LABS DIV, N AM PHILIPS CORP, 69- *Concurrent Pos:* Consult, Sci Adv Bd, US Air Force, 55-56; consult, Eng Res & Develop Labs, US Army, 55-59, consult, Ballistic Res Labs, 64-68; mem sci adv panel electronics, Dept Defense, 55-61. *Mem:* Fel AAAS; Am Phys Soc; fel Inst Elec & Electronics Engrs; NY Acad Sci. *Res:* Antennas; microwave and millimeter wave techniques; military electronic systems; research management. *Mailing Add:* Philips Lab Div NAm Philips Corp Briarcliff Manor NY 10510

KING, DONALD L, b Magna, Utah, Jan 21, 25; m 48; c 4. MECHANICAL ENGINEERING. *Educ:* Univ Utah, BS, 48, cert, 57. *Prof Exp:* Trainee, Westinghouse Elec Corp, 48-49; design engr, New Holland Mach Co, 49-51; design engr, Eimco Corp, 51-58, chief engr, Process Engrs Div, 58-67, eng mgr, Processing Mach Div, 67-77; mgr cent eng, Envirotech Corp, 77-79, MGR DEVELOP ENG, PROCESS MACH DIV, EIMCO, 79- *Mem:* Fel Am Soc Mech Eng; Am Inst Mining, Metall & Petrol Engrs. *Res:* Liquid solids separation equipment. *Mailing Add:* Process Mach Div Eimco 669 W Second St S Salt Lake City UT 84110

KING, DONALD M, b Seattle, Wash, June 5, 35; m 65; c 1. ANALYTICAL CHEMISTRY. *Educ:* Wash State Univ, BS, 57; Calif Inst Technol, PhD(chem), 63. *Prof Exp:* Asst prof chem, Calif State Col Los Angeles, 61-63; Welsh fel, Univ Tex, 63-64; chemist, Org Chem Div, E I du Pont de Nemours & Co, 64-66; asst prof, 66-69, ASSOC PROF CHEM, WESTERN WASH STATE COL, 69-, CHMN DEPT, 74- *Concurrent Pos:* NSF res grant, 68-70. *Mem:* Am Chem Soc. *Res:* Application of electroanalytical techniques to the study of reaction kinetics and mechanisms. *Mailing Add:* Dept of Chem Western Wash State Col Bellingham WA 98225

KING, DONALD WEST, JR, b Cochranton, Pa, June 30, 27; m 52; c 3. PATHOLOGY. *Educ:* Syracuse Univ, MD, 49. *Prof Exp:* Resident & instr path, Col Physicians & Surgeons, Columbia Univ, 49-52; prof & chmn dept, Univ Colo, Denver, 61-67; DELAFIELD PROF PATH & CHMN DEPT, COL PHYSICIANS & SURGEONS, COLUMBIA UNIV, 67- *Concurrent Pos:* USPHS fel, Univ Chicago, 54-55 & Carlsberg Lab, 55-56. *Mem:* Am Soc Exp Path; Soc Cell Biol; Human Genetics Soc; Am Asn Path & Bact. *Res:* Cell injury; membrane transport. *Mailing Add:* Col of Physicians & Surgeons Columbia Univ New York NY 10032

KING, DOROTHY WEI (CHENG), b Hankow, China, Mar 3, 14; nat US; m 40, 61. NUTRITION, PHYSIOLOGY. *Educ:* Yenching Univ, China, BS, 36; Mt Holyoke Col, MA, 48; Iowa State Univ, PhD(animal nutrit), 54. *Prof Exp:* Asst biol, Yenching Univ, China, 36-37; teacher, China, 38-45; instr, Nat Med Col, Shanghai, 45-46; asst zool, Iowa State Univ, 50-51; from instr to asst prof histol, Univ Iowa, 54-67; vis prof, 67-70, PROF ZOOL, NAT TAIWAN UNIV, 70- *Concurrent Pos:* Sr lectr biol, Chung Chi Col, Hong Kong, 61-62. *Mem:* AAAS; Am Asn Anatomists; Am Soc Zoologists; Am Soc Animal Sci; Am Inst Nutrit. *Res:* Effects of mitomycin C, monosodium glutamate, antihistaminic drugs and heavy metals on chick embryos. *Mailing Add:* Dept of Zool Nat Taiwan Univ Taipei 117 China, Republic of

KING, EDGAR PEARCE, b Oklahoma City, Okla, Nov 4, 22; m 60; c 3. MATHEMATICAL STATISTICS. *Educ:* Carnegie Inst Technol, BS, 48, MS, 49, DSc(math), 51. *Prof Exp:* Instr math, Carnegie Inst Technol, 49-51; math statistician, Nat Bur Standards, 51-53; staff res statistician, 53-55, dept head opers res, 55-59, head statist res, 59-64, asst dir, Sci Serv Div, 64-67, dir, 67-69, dir corp qual assurance, 69-71, corp planning adv corp opers planning, 71-78, SCI ADV, SCI INFO SERV, ELI LILLY & CO, 78- *Mem:* Opers Res Soc Am; Am Soc Qual Control; Am Statist Asn; Inst Math Statist; Int Statist Inst. *Res:* Statistical design of experiments. *Mailing Add:* Eli Lilly & Co 307 E McCarty St Indianapolis IN 46206

KING, EDWARD FRAZIER, b Lake Providence, La, Dec 3, 35; m 66; c 3. INORGANIC CHEMISTRY. *Educ:* Gregorian Univ, BA, 58; Loyola Univ, BS, 65; La State Univ, New Orleans, PhD(chem), 69. *Prof Exp:* Instr, Tex Woman's Univ, 68-79, asst prof chem, 70-75; INSTR CHEM & PHYSICS, CENT TEX COL, 75- *Mem:* Am Chem Soc. *Res:* Complexes of the first row transition metals, particularly their preparation and visible infrared spectra; halogen complexes of vanadium and copper. *Mailing Add:* Dept of Chem Cent Tex Col Killeen TX 76541

KING, EDWARD LOUIS, b Grand Forks, NDak, Mar 15, 20; m 52; c 2. INORGANIC CHEMISTRY. *Educ:* Univ Calif, BS, 43, PhD(chem), 45. *Prof Exp:* Asst chem, Univ Calif, 42-44; asst chem, Manhattan Dist Proj, 44-45, res assoc, 45-46, du Pont fel & lectr chem. Harvard Univ, 46-47, instr, 47-48; from asst prof to prof, Univ Wis, 48-63; chmn dept, 70-72, PROF CHEM, UNIV COLO, BOULDER, 63- *Concurrent Pos:* Civilian with Off Sci Res & Develop, 44; Guggenheim fel, Calif Inst Technol, 57-58; ed, Inorg Chem, Am Chem Soc, 64-68. *Mem:* Am Chem Soc; Royal Soc Chem. *Res:* Chemistry of chromium and other transition metals in solution; ion solvation in mixed solvents; mechanisms of reactions in solution. *Mailing Add:* Dept of Chem Univ of Colo Boulder CO 80309

KING, EDWARD P(ETER), b Deer Creek, Ill, May 29, 05; m 28; c 2. CHEMICAL ENGINEERING. *Educ:* Eureka Col, BS, 26; Univ Ill, MS, 27, PhD(chem eng), 30. *Prof Exp:* Instr chem, Univ Ill, 26-28; sr engr, Atlantic Ref Co, 29-35; resident chemist, Pure Oil Co, Chicago, 36-48, tech foreman, 48-53, tech supt, 53-56, oper asst, 56-60, asst mgr opers-ref, 60-65, mgr ref qual control, 65-70; CONSULT LUBRICATING OIL REF OPERS, 70- *Mem:* AAAS. *Res:* Partial oxidation in liquid phase; solvent extraction of hydrocarbons; phase equilibria in hydrocarbon systems under high pressure; technical aspects of lubricating oil manufacturing operations; refinery simulation and linear programming applications; manufacturing quality control. *Mailing Add:* 107 E South St Cambridge IL 61238

KING, EDWIN WALLACE, b Melrose, Mass, Oct 15, 18; m 51; c 2. ENTOMOLOGY. *Educ:* Univ Mass, BS, 41; Va Polytech Inst, MS, 47; Univ Ill, PhD(entom), 51. *Prof Exp:* Res assoc entom, Univ Wis, 51-53; asst prof biol, Cornell Col, 53-57; asst entomologist & asst prof entom & zool, Clemson Univ, 57-58, assoc entomologist & assoc prof, 58-67, prof entom & zool, 67-82; RETIRED. *Concurrent Pos:* Fel biomath, NC State Univ, 67-68. *Mem:* Entom Soc Am. *Res:* Insect physical ecology; mathematics of insect population behavior and responses to weather; production of insects as food. *Mailing Add:* 105 Poole Lane Clemson Univ Clemson SC 29631

KING, EILEEN BRENNEMAN, b Albany, Ore, May 13, 24; m 48; c 4. PATHOLOGY, CYTOLOGY. *Educ:* Univ Ore, BA, 46, MD, 50; Am Bd Path, cert anat path, 55. *Prof Exp:* Lectr cytol, 55-59, from instr to asst clin prof, 55-69, assoc clin prof, 69-79, CLIN PROF PATH, SCH MED, UNIV CALIF, SAN FRANCISCO, 79-, PATHOLOGIST IN CHG CYTOL LAB & TRAINING PROG, 60- *Concurrent Pos:* Pathologist in chg, Pulmonary Cytol Lab, San Francisco Gen Hosp, 55-61; pathologist & dir labs, Mary's Help Hosp, 55-66; consult, San Francisco Gen Hosp, 59-61, US Naval Hosp, Oakland, 62- & US Vet Hosp, San Francisco, 66- *Mem:* Fel Col Am Path; Am Soc Cytol (pres, 78); fel Int Acad Cytol; Soc Anal Cytol. *Res:* Evaluation of cytochemical probes for potential markers of dysplasia and carcinoma in situ of uterine cervix and cancer precursors in urinary bladder; pulmonary cytology survey study for early diagnosis of lung cancer; cytologic, histologic and histochemical methods for evaluation of radiation host response in carcinoma of the cervix; histologic and cytologic studies of breast cancer and its precursors. *Mailing Add:* Univ of Calif Med Ctr San Francisco CA 94143

KING, ELBERT AUBREY, JR, b Austin, Tex, Nov 12, 35; m 57; c 2. PLANETOLOGY, SPACE GEOLOGY. *Educ:* Univ Tex, BS, 57, MA, 61; Harvard Univ, PhD(geol), 65. *Prof Exp:* Geologist, Geol & Geochem Br, Manned Spacecraft Ctr, NASA, 63-67, cur, Lunar Receiving Lab, 67-69; chmn dept, 69-74, PROF GEOL, UNIV HOUSTON, 69- *Mem:* Fel Meteoritical Soc. *Res:* Meteorites, planetary surfaces; geochemistry; mineralogy of pegmatites, petrography and composition of tektites; zoned ultramafic intrusive rocks; lunar samples. *Mailing Add:* Dept of Geol Univ of Houston Houston TX 77004

KING, ELIZABETH NORFLEET, b Concord, NC, May 22, 25. CELL PHYSIOLOGY. *Educ:* Randolph-Macon Woman's Col, AB, 46; Wellesley Col, MA, 51; Duke Univ, PhD(cell physiol), 63. *Prof Exp:* Instr zool, Wellesley Col, 51-53; instr biol, Woman's Col, NC, 53-56 & Bucknell Univ, 60-61; instr physiol, Vassar Col, 61-63, asst prof biol, 63-69; ASSOC PROF BIOL, WINTHROP COL, 69- *Mem:* AAAS; Am Soc Zoologists. *Res:* Cellular physiology; separation of cellular organelles. *Mailing Add:* Dept of Biol Winthrop Col Rock Hill SC 29733

KING, ELIZABETH RAYMOND, b Halifax, NS, Dec 5, 23; US citizen. GEOPHYSICS. *Educ:* Smith Col, AB, 47. *Prof Exp:* Geologist, 48-51, geophysicist, 51-74, RES GEOPHYSICIST, US GEOL SURV, 74- *Mem:* AAAS; Soc Explor Geophys; Am Geophys Union; fel Geol Soc Am. *Res:* Airborne magnetometer surveys; analysis of magnetic and gravity anomalies by modeling techniques; geologic interpretation of data from geophysical studies of continents and oceans. *Mailing Add:* US Geol Surv MS 927 Reston VA 22092

KING, ELLIS GRAY, b Vancouver, BC, Apr 27, 10; nat US; m 36; c 1. ORGANIC CHEMISTRY. *Educ:* Univ BC, BA, 30, MA, 32; McGill Univ, PhD(chem), 34. *Prof Exp:* Chemist, Res Lab, Can Fishing Co, 30; asst chem, Univ BC, 30-32; res chemist, Celanese Corp Am, 34-37; indust fel, Mellon Inst, 37-41, sr indust fel, 41-44, sr fel, Nat Res Coun, 44-46; group leader, Rayonier, Inc, 46-48; asst tech dir, Puget Sound Pulp & Timber Co, 49-52, res dir, 52-63; RES DIR, BELLINGHAM SOUND DIV, GA-PAC CORP, 63- *Concurrent Pos:* Teacher, Univ Tutorial Sch, 31. *Mem:* Am Chem Soc; Tech Asn Pulp & Paper Indust; Forest Prod Res Soc; Am Mgt Asn. *Res:* Pulp and cellulose utilization; resins and plastics; cork; building materials; elastomers; structure and utilization of lignin; product development. *Mailing Add:* PO Box 805 Bellingham WA 98225

KING, EMMA JOYCE, physical chemistry, agricultural chemistry, see previous edition

KING, FRANKLIN G, JR, b Mahonoy City, Pa, Sept 23, 39; m 59; c 1. CHEMICAL ENGINEERING, BIOCHEMICAL ENGINEERING. *Educ:* Pa State Univ, BS, 61; Kans State Univ, MS, 62; Stevens Inst Technol, DSc(chem eng), 66; Howard Univ, MEd, 76. *Prof Exp:* Res engr, Uniroyal Res Ctr, 62-65; process engr, Am Cyanamid Co, 65-66; asst prof chem eng, Lafayette Col, 66-72; ASSOC PROF CHEM ENG, HOWARD UNIV, 72- *Concurrent Pos:* Consult, Maxwell House Div, Gen Foods Corp, 67-72 & NIH, 77- *Mem:* Am Inst Chem Eng; Am Soc Eng Educ. *Res:* Modeling, simulation and control of chemical processes; development of physiological pharmacokinetic models; biochemical engineering including waste treatment and fermentation; application of instruction technology to education of minority engineering students. *Mailing Add:* Dept of Chem Eng Howard Univ Washington DC 20059

KING, FREDERICK ALEXANDER, b Paterson, NJ, Oct 3, 25; c 2. NEUROSCIENCE. *Educ:* Stanford Univ, AB, 53; Johns Hopkins Univ, MA, 55, PhD(psychol, med sci), 56. *Prof Exp:* Instr psychol, Johns Hopkins Univ, 55-56; from instr to asst prof psychiat, Col Med, Ohio State Univ, 56-59; from asst prof to prof psychol & neurosurg, Col Med, Univ Fla, 59-69, prof neurosci & chmn dept, 69-78, dir ctr neurobiol sci, 68-78; PROF ANAT & ASSOC DEAN, SCH MED & DIR, YERKES REGIONAL PRIMATE RES CTR, EMORY UNIV, 78- *Concurrent Pos:* NIMH grant, 57-60, div biol sci training grant, 65-, Nat Inst Neurol Dis & Stroke grant, 59-71, NIMH fel & vis prof, Inst Physiol, Univ Pisa, 61-62; vis scientist, Am Psychol Asn-NSF prog, 62-67 & neuroanat prog, NIH, 63-70; scientist co-dir, Ctr Neurobiol Sci, Univ Fla, 64-68; consult, Battelle Mem Inst, 56-59 & res mem psychobiol adv panel, Biol & Med Sci Div, NSF, 63-67; mem adv comt, Primate Res Ctr, NIH, 69-73; mem ed adv bd, Behav Biol, 71-; ed, Physiol & Animal Psychol, 71- & J Suppl Abstr Serv; chmn comt commun & coord, Biol Sci Training Prog, NIMH, 72-78, mem & chmn res scientist develop rev comt, 74-78; mem bd sci adv, Yerkes Regional Primate Res Ctr, 74-78; mem Nat Res Coun-Nat Acad Sci brain sci comt, 74-; chmn & mem comt educ, Soc Neurosci, 74-77. *Mem:* Fel AAAS; fel Am Psychol Asn; Am Physiol Soc; Soc Neurosci; Int Neuropsychol Soc (secy-treas, 69-73). *Res:* Effects of subcortical brain lesions on motivated behavior and learning in animals; analysis of cortical functions in infrahuman primates by use of ablation and brain stimulation techniques; electrophysiological and conditioning analysis of recovery of function in the isolated forebrain. *Mailing Add:* Yerkes Primate Ctr Emory Univ Atlanta GA 30322

KING, FREDERICK JESSOP, b Niagara Falls, NY, July 4, 28; m 56; c 3. FOOD SCIENCE. *Educ:* Cornell Univ, BS, 51, MFS, 52; Mass Inst Technol, PhD, 60. *Prof Exp:* BIOCHEMIST, NORTHEAST UTILIZATION RES CTR, NAT MARINE FISHERIES SERV, NAT OCEANIC & ATMOSPHERIC ADMIN, 60- *Mem:* Am Chem Soc; Inst Food Technologists; fel Am Inst Chemists. *Res:* Denaturation of fish proteins; irradiation preservation of fish; flavor chemistry of fish; nutritive value; fishery technology; process and product improvements; quality assurance. *Mailing Add:* Northeast Utilization Res Ctr Nat Marine Fisheries Serv Gloucester MA 01930

KING, GAYLE NATHANIEL, b Paulding, Ohio, July 17, 48; m 71; c 2. PHYSICAL CHEMISTRY. *Educ:* Heidelberg Col, BS, 70; Univ Pac, PhD(phys chem), 77. *Prof Exp:* Instr statist, US Air Force, 70-74; asst prof chem, Rose Hulman Inst Technol, 77-81; CHIEF CHEMIST, BITUMINOUS MAT CO, 81- *Concurrent Pos:* Consult, Bituminous Mat Inc, 78- *Mem:* Am Chem Soc; Sigma Xi. *Res:* Liquid viscosity equations of state; asphalt and oil emulsions. *Mailing Add:* 349 Bluebird Dr Terre Haute IN 47803

KING, GENERAL TYE, b King, Ky, Apr 7, 20; m 40. MEAT SCIENCE. *Educ:* Union Col, Ky, BS, 48; Univ Ky, BS, 50, MS, 51; Tex A&M Univ, PhD(meats), 58. *Prof Exp:* Asst animal husbandman, SDak State Col, 51-53; from instr to asst prof meats, 53-60, assoc prof meats, 60-69, assoc prof animal sci, 69-76, PROF ANIMAL SCI, TEX A&M UNIV, 76-, ASST HEAD DEPT, 69- *Mem:* Am Meat Sci Asn; Am Soc Animal Sci; Inst Food Technol. *Res:* Animal science; nutrition. *Mailing Add:* Dept of Animal Sci Tex A&M Univ College Station TX 77843

KING, GEORGE, III, b Tampa, Fla, Nov 12, 46; m 68; c 2. EXPERIMENTAL NUCLEAR PHYSICS. *Educ:* Talladega Col, BA, 68; Stanford Univ, MS, 74, PhD(nuclear physics), 77. *Prof Exp:* Instr physics, Albany State Col, 69-71 & Col Notre Dame, 72-73; res asst nuclear physics, Stanford Univ, 73-77; res assoc nuclear physics, Lawrence Berkeley Lab, 77-79; MEM PROF STAFF, NUCLEAR DEPT, SCHLUMBERGER DOLL RES, 79- *Concurrent Pos:* Xerox Corp fel, 74-77. *Mem:* Am Phys Soc. *Res:* Giant resonance excitation for light nuclei; relativistic heavy ion central collisions. *Mailing Add:* Schlumberger Doll Res Nuclear Dept Old Quarry Rd PO Box 307 Ridgefield CT 06877

KING, GERALD WILFRID, b Eng, Jan 22, 28; m 54; c 4. CHEMICAL PHYSICS. *Educ:* Univ London, BSc, 49, PhD(chem), 52, DSc, 70. *Prof Exp:* Asst lectr, Univ Col, London, 54-56, lectr, 56-57; from asst prof to assoc prof chem, 57-64, PROF CHEM, McMASTER UNIV, 64- *Concurrent Pos:* Hon res assoc, Univ Col, London, 65; Ed, Can J Chem, 74-79; chmn, Dept Chem, McMaster Univ, 79- *Mem:* Fel Chem Inst Can; Optical Soc Am; fel Royal Soc Chem; fel Royal Soc Can. *Res:* Electronic states and structures of molecules; multi-photon laser spectroscopy; optical-optical double resonance; high resolution electronic molecular spectroscopy. *Mailing Add:* Dept Chem McMaster Univ Hamilton ON L8S 4M1 Can

KING, GORDON JAMES, b Toronto, Ont, June 8, 32; m 57; c 2. REPRODUCTIVE PHYSIOLOGY, ENDOCRINOLOGY. *Educ:* Univ Toronto, DVM, 59; Univ Guelph, MS, 66, PhD(reprod physiol), 68. *Prof Exp:* Pvt pract vet med, 59-60; field veterinarian, Hamilton Dist Cattle Breeding Asn, 60-62, tech mgr, 62-65; asst prof, 68-70, assoc prof, 70-75, PROF ANIMAL SCI, UNIV GUELPH, 75- *Concurrent Pos:* Can Dept Agr res grant, 76-78; Nat Res Coun Can res grant, 76- *Mem:* Am Soc Animal Sci; Soc Study Reprod; Soc Study Fertil. *Res:* Endocrinology and microscopy of early gestation; control of reproductive function in the female. *Mailing Add:* Dept of Animal & Poultry Sci Univ of Guelph Guelph ON N1G 2W1 Can

KING, H(ENRY) E(UGENE), b Wilmington, Va, Sept 24, 22; m 48; c 2. PSYCHOLOGY. *Educ:* Univ Richmond, BA, 42; Columbia Univ, MA, 43, PhD, 48. *Prof Exp:* Asst psychologist, NY State Psychiat Inst, 42-43 & 46-48; sr res scientist, NY State Brain Res Proj, 48-49; assoc prof psychiat & neurol, Sch Med, Tulane Univ, 49-60; prof psychol, Sch Med & Chief Serv, Western Psychiat Inst, Univ Pittsburgh, 60-80; PROF PSYCHOL, WASHINGTON & LEE UNIV, 80- *Concurrent Pos:* Lectr, Columbia Univ, 46-49; vis scientist, Charity Hosp, New Orleans, 49-60. *Mem:* Fel AAAS; Am Physiol Soc; Soc Exp Biol & Med; fel Am Psychol Asn; Am Psychopath Asn. *Res:* Psychophysiology; experimental psychopathology; motor response systems; central nervous system stimulation and ablation. *Mailing Add:* Washington & Lee Univ Lexington VA 24450

KING, HAROLD, b Bedford, Ind, Aug 12, 22; m 52; c 2. SURGERY. *Educ:* Yale Univ, MD, 46. *Prof Exp:* From instr to assoc prof, 55-64, PROF SURG, MED CTR, IND UNIV, INDIANAPOLIS, 64-, DIR DIV THORACIC & CARDIOVASC SURG, 72- *Concurrent Pos:* Mem staff, Vet Admin Hosp & Indianapolis Gen Hosp. *Mem:* Soc Vascular Surg; Soc Univ Surg; Am Col Surg; Soc Thoracic Surg; Am Surg Asn. *Res:* Cardiovascular surgery. *Mailing Add:* Ind Univ Med Ctr Indianapolis IN 46223

KING, HARRISS THORNTON, b Ames, Iowa, June 15, 47; m 76. NUCLEAR PHYSICS. *Educ:* Iowa State Univ, BS, 69; Stanford Univ, MS, 70, PhD(physics), 75. *Prof Exp:* Res assoc physics, Rutgers Univ, 74-77; asst prof physics, Stanford Univ, 77-80; MEM STAFF, MEASUREX CORP, 80- *Mem:* Sigma Xi; Am Phys Soc. *Res:* Hyperfine interactions; nuclear electromagnetic moments; polarization phenomena. *Mailing Add:* Measurex Corp 1 Results Way Cupertino CA 95014

KING, HARRY J, b Saskatoon, Sask, May 2, 34; nat US; m 57; c 4. PLASMA PHYSICS, ELECTRICAL ENGINEERING. *Educ:* Univ Sask, BS, 56, MS, 57; McMaster Univ, PhD(nuclear & atomic physics), 60. *Prof Exp:* Sr physicist ion propulsion, Ion Physics Corp, Burlington, 60-63; sr mem tech staff, 63-72, asst dept mgr ion & plasma sources, 72-74, assoc dept mgr power utility switches, 74-78, dept mgr high voltage devices, 78-81, PROJ MGR, ELECTRON BEAM LITHOGRAPHY, HUGHES RES LABS, 81- *Mem:*

Inst Elec & Electronics Engrs. *Res:* Ion and neutral beams and sources; ion propulsion; high power switches for power utilities and fusion apparatus; electron beams. *Mailing Add:* Hughes Res Labs 3011 Malibu Canyon Rd Malibu CA 90265

KING, HARTLEY H(UGHES), b Fresno, Calif, Apr 21, 36; m 62; c 2. AERONAUTICAL SCIENCES, MECHANICAL ENGINEERING. *Educ:* Univ Calif, Berkeley, BS, 57, MS, 59, PhD(mech eng), 63. *Prof Exp:* Sr engr, Electrooptical Systs, 62-65; sr res engr, AC Electronics Defense Res Labs, Gen Motors Corp, 65-68; sr res engr, Gen Res Corp, 68-75; SR RES ENGR, EFFECTS TECHNOL, INC, 75- *Mem:* Am Inst Aeronaut & Astronaut; Inst Elec & Electronics Engrs. *Res:* Compressible fluid mechanics; wakes and separated flows; re-entry aerodynamics; flight mechanics. *Mailing Add:* 212 Canon Dr Santa Barbara CA 93105

KING, HENRY LEE, b Muleshoe, Tex, Apr 12, 21; m 48; c 4. ORGANIC CHEMISTRY, POLYMER CHEMISTRY. *Educ:* Tex Tech Col, BS, 52, MS, 54. *Prof Exp:* Res chemist, 54-65, sr res chemist, 65-70, res specialist, 70-76, SR RES SPECIALIST, CHEMSTRAND RES CTR, INC, MONSANTO CO, 76- *Mem:* Am Chem Soc. *Res:* Synthetic polymers and fibers; polymer processes; polymer modification for specific end uses; intermediate synthesis; condensation polymers, especially polyesters. *Mailing Add:* 102 Rogue Ct Cary NC 27511

KING, HERMAN (LEE), b Grand Ledge, Mich, Feb 24, 15; m 39; c 2. ACADEMIC ADMINISTRATION. *Educ:* Mich State Univ, BS, 39; Pa State Univ, MS, 41, PhD(biochem), 42. *Prof Exp:* Res fel, Reilly Tar & Chem Corp, Ind, 39-42; instr agr & biol chem, Pa State Univ, 43; orchard mgr, Mich, 44; exten entomologist, Mich State Univ, 45-46, from asst prof to assoc prof entom, 46-59, prof & asst dean, Col Arts & Sci, 59-62, dir, Div Biol Sci, 60-62, asst dean, Col Natural Sci, 62-63, asst provost, 63-74, dir acad serv, 74-81; RETIRED. *Mem:* Entom Soc Am; Am Inst Biol Sci. *Res:* University administration. *Mailing Add:* 1342 Marble Elans East Lansing MI 48912

KING, HOWARD E, b Seattle, Wash, Oct 16, 24; m 50; c 5. ELECTRICAL ENGINEERING. *Educ:* Wash Univ, BS, 46; Univ Ill, MS, 55. *Prof Exp:* Engr, RCA Victor Div, NJ, 46-52 & Andrew Corp, Ill, 52-53; res asst electromagnetics, Univ Ill, Urbana, 53-55; mem tech staff, Ramo-Wooldridge Corp, Calif, 55-58 & Space Tech Labs Inc, 58-61; mem tech staff, 61-62, mgr electromagnetics sect, 62-70, HEAD, ANTENNAS & PROPAGATION DEPT, AEROSPACE CORP, 70- *Concurrent Pos:* Lectr, Univ Calif, Los Angeles, 62-64. *Mem:* Inst Elec & Electronics Eng. *Res:* Frequency modulation and television transmitters, antennas and diplexers; antennas for aircraft, reentry vehicles, spacecraft and ground installations; millimeter wavelength research in antennas and components; radar cross section measurements and analysis. *Mailing Add:* 2350 E El Segundo Blvd Aerospace Corp El Segundo CA 90245

KING, HUBERT WYLAM, b Cardiff, Wales, Jan 20, 30; m 57; c 4. MATERIALS SCIENCE, PHYSICS. *Educ:* Univ Birmingham, BSc, 54, PhD(metall), 56. *Prof Exp:* Fel metall, Univ Birmingham, 56-58; USAEC grant metal physics, Mellon Inst, 59-62; lectr phys metall, Imp Col, Univ London, 62-65, sr lectr, 65-67; vis prof metall, Univ Calif, Berkeley, 67; reader phys metall, Imp Col, Univ London, 67-70; PROF ENG PHYSICS, DALHOUSIE UNIV, 71- *Concurrent Pos:* UK Atomic Energy Authority & Sci Res Coun grant, Imp Col, Univ London, 62-70; co-ed comn struct reports, Int Union Crystallog, 66-; consult, USAEC, 67-69; Nat Res Coun Can grant, Dalhousie Univ, 71- *Mem:* Fel Brit Inst Metall; fel Brit Inst Physics; Am Inst Mining, Metall & Petrol Engrs. *Res:* Structure and stability of alloy phases; effect of phase transformations on superconducting magnetic and ferroelectric properties. *Mailing Add:* 6120 Oakland Rd Halifax NS B3H 3J5 Can

KING, IVAN ROBERT, b Far Rockaway, NY, June 25, 27; c 4. ASTRONOMY. *Educ:* Hamilton Col, AB, 46; Harvard Univ, AM, 47, PhD(astron), 52. *Prof Exp:* Instr astron, Harvard Univ, 51-52; methods analyst, US Dept of Defense, 54-56; from asst prof to assoc prof astron, Univ Ill, 56-64; assoc prof, 64-66, PROF ASTRON, UNIV CALIF, BERKELEY, 66- *Mem:* Am Astron Soc (pres, 78-80); Int Astron Union; Am Acad Arts & Sci. *Res:* Structure of stellar systems. *Mailing Add:* Dept of Astron Univ of Calif Berkeley CA 94720

KING, J(OHN) C(HARLES) ALWYN H(ALLOWES), b Calgary, Alta, Can, May 13, 20; US citizen; m 52; c 1. MATERIALS SCIENCE, RESOURCE ECONOMICS. *Educ:* McGill Univ, BEng, 48; Columbia Univ, MS, 58; Stuttgart Tech Univ, Dr rer nat(metal physics), 60; Babson Col, MBA, 73. *Prof Exp:* Res assoc, Max Planck Inst, Stuttgart & inst metal physics, Gottingen, 58-60; staff metallurgist, Arthur D Little Inc, 60-66; group leader, Div Brunswick Corp, 66-73; RES ANAL, STRATEGIC STUDIES INST, US ARMY WAR COL, 73- *Concurrent Pos:* Fel, Inter-Univ Sem Armed Forces & Soc, 75- *Mem:* Am Soc Metals; Am Security Coun. *Res:* Influence of microstructure on physical and mechanical properties of crystalline solids; development of materials, systems and processes for environmental control; analysis of strategic and economic impact of critical resource shortages. *Mailing Add:* Box 350 US Army War Col Carlisle PA 17013

KING, JACK LESTER, b Oakland, Calif, Mar 9, 34; m 69; c 8. GENETICS. *Educ:* Univ Calif, Berkeley, AB, 59, MA, 62, PhD(zool), 63. *Prof Exp:* Nat Inst Arthritis & Metab Dis fel pop genetics, Donner Lab, 63-69, ASSOC PROF BIOL, UNIV CALIF, SANTA BARBARA, 69- *Concurrent Pos:* Ed, J Molecular Evolution, 71- *Res:* Population genetics; molecular evolution. *Mailing Add:* Dept of Biol Sci Univ of Calif Santa Barbara CA 93106

KING, JAMES, JR, b Columbus, Ga, Apr 23, 33; m 56; c 2. PHYSICAL CHEMISTRY, PHYSICS. *Educ:* Morehouse Col, BS, 53; Calif Inst Technol, MS, 55, PhD(chem, physics), 58. *Prof Exp:* Res engr electrochem, Jet Propulsion Lab, Calif Inst Technol, 56; sr res engr thermal properties,

Atomics Int Div, NAm Aviation, Inc, 58-60; sr scientist, Electro-Optical Systs, Inc, 60-61; sr scientist, Jet Propulsion Lab, Calif Inst Technol, 61-69, sect mgr physics, 69-74; dir, Space Shuttle Environ Effects, Space Shuttle Prog, NASA, Washington, DC, 74-75; dir, Upper Atmospheric Sci Prog, 75-76; mgr, User Prog Develop Off, Jet Propulsion Lab, Calif Inst Technol, 76-78; mgr space physics, 79-80, MGR SPACE SCI & APPLN, JET PROPULSION LAB, CALIF INST TECHNOL, 81- *Mem:* Am Chem Soc; Am Phys Soc; Sigma Xi; AAAS; Am Geophys Union. *Res:* Nuclear and electron resonance; radiation chemistry. *Mailing Add:* PO Box 1008 La Canada CA 91011

KING, JAMES C, b Petaluma, Calif, Jan 18, 32; div; c 3. PHARMACY. *Educ:* Univ NMex, BS, 53; Univ Tex, MS, 58, PhD(pharm), 62. *Prof Exp:* Asst pharm, Univ Tex, 57-58, lectr, 59-60, asst, 60-61, spec instr, 61-62; from asst prof to prof pharm, 62-76, dir clin pharm, 71-76, PROF CLIN PHARM, UNIV PAC, 76- *Concurrent Pos:* Consult, US Army Surgeon Gen, 72- & Vet Admin Hosp, San Diego & Palo Alto, 73-80. *Mem:* Am Pharmaceut Asn; Am Soc Hosp Pharmacists. *Res:* Development of and medicament release from dermatologic medications; incompatibilities of parenteral admixtures. *Mailing Add:* Sch of Pharm Univ of the Pac Stockton CA 95211

KING, JAMES CLAUDE, b St Joseph, Mo, Oct 2, 24; m 49; c 4. LOW TEMPERATURE PHYSICS, SOLID STATE PHYSICS. *Educ:* Amherst Col, BA, 49; Yale Univ, MS, 50, PhD(physics), 53. *Prof Exp:* Instr physics, Yale Univ, 50, asst, 50-53; mem tech staff, Bell Tel Labs, Inc, 53-65; mgr radiation physics dept, 65-68, dir appl res, 68-71, assoc dir chem physics components, 71-75, dir electrochem components & measurement systs, 75-77, DIR WEAPONS ELEC SUBSYSTS, SANDIA LABS, 77- *Honors & Awards:* C B Sawyer Award, Sawyer Res Prod, Inc, 73. *Mem:* Am Phys Soc. *Res:* Solid state physics; acoustic wave interactions with lattice defects; effects of radiation on the acoustic properties of alpha-quartz. *Mailing Add:* Sandia Labs Orgn 2300 Albuquerque NM 87115

KING, JAMES CLEMENT, b Three Rivers, Mich, Feb 4, 04; m 32; c 4. GENETICS. *Educ:* Northwestern Univ, BS, 26; Univ Chicago, MA, 28, PhD(polit sci), 33. *Prof Exp:* Vconsul, Foreign Serv, US Govt, 27-28; instr polit sci, Western Reserve Univ, 34-35; instr politics, Princeton Univ, 35-37; exec secy, Inst Int Studies, Yale Univ, 37-38; asst prof int rels, Syracuse Univ, 40-41; independent res, 41-48; res assoc genetics, Biol Lab, Long Island Biol Asn, 49-52, staff geneticist, 52-58, res investr, Columbia Univ, 58-62; asst prof med, 62-68, ASSOC PROF MICROBIOL, SCH MED, NY UNIV, 68- *Mem:* AAAS; Am Soc Naturalists; Genetics Soc Am; Soc Study Evolution. *Res:* Population and developmental genetics; evolution. *Mailing Add:* Dept of Microbiol NY Univ Med Ctr New York NY 10016

KING, JAMES DOUGLAS, b Welland, Ont, May 28, 34; m 58. NUCLEAR PHYSICS. *Educ:* Univ Toronto, BA, 56; Univ Sask, PhD(nuclear physics), 60. *Prof Exp:* Fel, McMaster Univ, 60-61; asst prof physics, Univ Sask, 61-64; asst prof, 65-67, assoc dean & registr, Scarborough Col, 71-74, assoc dean, 75-76, assoc prof, 67-80, PROF PHYSICS, UNIV TORONTO, 80- *Mem:* Am Asn Physics Teachers; Can Asn Physicists; Am Phys Soc; Am Astron Soc. *Res:* nucleosynthesis; nuclear reactions; stellar reaction rates. *Mailing Add:* Scarborough Col Univ Toronto 1265 Military Trail West Hill ON M1C 1A4 Can

KING, JAMES EDWARD, b Escanaba, Mich, July 23, 40; m 73; c 1. PALYNOLOGY. *Educ:* Alma Col, BS, 62; Univ NMex, MS, 64; Univ Ariz, PhD(geosci), 72. *Prof Exp:* Res assoc geochronol, Univ Ariz, 71-72; CUR PALEOBOT, ILL STATE MUS, SPRINGFIELD, 72-, HEAD SCI SECT, 78- *Concurrent Pos:* NSF res grants, 72, 74, 76 & 81; adj assoc prof geol, Univ Ill-Urbana, 78- *Mem:* AAAS; Am Quaternary Asn (treas); Am Asn Stratigraphic Palynologists; Ecol Soc Am; Sigma Xi. *Res:* Quaternary palynology, biogeography and paleoenvironments of North America; the ecology and extinction of the Pleistocene megafauna and the interaction of early man to his environments. *Mailing Add:* Head Sci Sect Ill State Mus Springfield IL 62706

KING, JAMES FREDERICK, b Moncton, NB, Apr 6, 34; m 65; c 3. ORGANIC CHEMISTRY. *Educ:* Univ NB, BSc, 54, PhD(org chem), 57. *Prof Exp:* Beaverbrook overseas scholar, Imp Col, London, 57-58; res fel chem, Harvard Univ, 58-59; from asst prof to assoc prof, 59-67, PROF CHEM, UNIV WESTERN ONT, 67- *Concurrent Pos:* Alfred P Sloan res fel, 66-68. *Honors & Awards:* Merck, Sharp & Dohme Lectr Award, 76. *Mem:* Am Chem Soc; Chem Inst Can; Royal Soc Chem. *Res:* Organic sulfur chemistry; reaction mechanisms; stereochemistry. *Mailing Add:* Dept of Chem Univ of Western Ont London ON N6A 5B7 Can

KING, JAMES P, b Kiangsu, China, Nov 11, 33; m 61. PHYSICAL INORGANIC CHEMISTRY. *Educ:* Newberry Col, BS, 53; Loyola Univ, Ill, MS, 56; Purdue Univ, PhD(chem), 60. *Prof Exp:* PROJ LEADER, PENNWALT CHEM CORP, 59- *Mem:* Am Chem Soc; Am Soc Lubrication Eng. *Res:* Lubrication products on high temperature application; Thermochemistry of rhenium compounds; heats of formation of various rhenium compounds determined by solution calorimetry and electrochemical cell measurements; synthesis and characterization of coordination compounds and inorganic polymers. *Mailing Add:* 904 Breezewood Lane Lansdale PA 19446

KING, JAMES REBER, b Joliet, Ill, June 30, 27; m 54. CHEMISTRY. *Educ:* Ripon Col, AB, 51. *Prof Exp:* Chemist, 51-55, res chemist, 55-65, sr res chemist, 65-71, RES ASSOC, EASTMAN KODAK CO, 71- *Mem:* Soc Photog Sci & Eng. *Res:* Photographic chemistry; processing chemistry for black and white photographic silver systems, particularly single solution and rapid processing. *Mailing Add:* Eastman Kodak Co Res Labs Rochester NY 14650

KING / 327

KING, JAMES ROGER, b San Jose, Calif, Mar 12, 27; m 50; c 3. PHYSIOLOGICAL ECOLOGY. *Educ:* San Jose State Col, AB, 50; Wash State Univ, MS, 53, PhD(zool), 57. *Prof Exp:* Actg instr zoophysiol, Wash State Univ, 56-57; asst prof exp biol, Univ Utah, 57-60; from asst prof to assoc prof zoophysiol, 60-67, chmn dept zool, 72-78, PROF ZOOPHYSIOL, WASH STATE UNIV, 67- *Concurrent Pos:* NIH res career develop award, 63-67; Guggenheim Found fel, 69; mem adv panel environ biol, NSF, 73-76; Maytag vis prof zool, Ariz State Univ, 79. *Honors & Awards:* Brewster Medal, Am Ornithologists Union, 74. *Mem:* Am Soc Zool; Cooper Ornith Soc; Am Ornith Union; Am Physiol Soc; Am Soc Naturalists. *Res:* Avian physiology and ecology; physiology of cyclic phenomena in vertebrates; vertebrate physiology. *Mailing Add:* Dept of Zool Wash State Univ Pullman WA 99164

KING, JAMES S, b Painesville, Ohio, Nov 19, 38; m 61; c 2. NEUROANATOMY. *Educ:* Taylor Univ, BS, 60; Ohio State Univ, MSc, 62, PhD(anat), 65. *Prof Exp:* From instr to assoc prof anat, 65-75, PROF ANAT, OHIO STATE UNIV, 75-, DIR, SPINAL CORD INJURY RES CTR, 77- *Concurrent Pos:* NIH gen res grant, 65-67; res fel neuroanat & electron micros, Wayne State Univ, 67-68; US Pub Health Serv grant, 69-81. *Honors & Awards:* Sigma Xi Res Award, Sigma Xi Chap, Ohio State Univ, 73. *Mem:* Am Asn Anat; Soc Neurosci; Sigma Xi; AAAS. *Res:* Synaptic organization and development of precerebellar nuclei. *Mailing Add:* Dept of Anat 1645 Neil Ave Ohio State Univ Columbus OH 43210

KING, JANET CARLSON, b Red Oak, Iowa, Oct 3, 41; m 67; c 2. NUTRITION. *Educ:* Iowa State Univ, BS, 63; Univ Calif, Berkeley, PhD(nutrit), 72. *Prof Exp:* Dietitian, Fitzsimons Gen Hosp, Denver, 64-67; fel, 72, asst prof, 72-76, ASSOC PROF NUTRIT, UNIV CALIF, BERKELEY, 76- *Concurrent Pos:* Mem, Comt Nutrit Mother & Preschool Child, Nat Acad Sci, Nat Res Coun, 74-80; consult, NIH, 79-80, mem, Nutrit Study Sec, 81- *Mem:* AAAS; Am Dietetic Asn; Sigma Xi; Soc Nutrit Educ; Am Inst Nutrit. *Res:* Study of the nutritional requirements for protein, energy, and trace elements in nonpregnant and pregnant women, lactating women, women using oral contraceptives and adolescent women. *Mailing Add:* Dept of Nutrit Sci Univ of Calif Berkeley CA 94720

KING, JERRY PORTER, b Dyersburg, Tenn, July 9, 35; m 62; c 2. MATHEMATICS. *Educ:* Univ Ky, BSEE, 58, MS, 59, PhD(math), 62. *Prof Exp:* From asst prof to assoc prof math, 62-68, PROF MATH & DEAN GRAD SCH, LEHIGH UNIV, 68- *Mem:* Math Asn Am; Am Math Soc. *Res:* Complex variables, summability. *Mailing Add:* Dept Math Lehigh Univ Bethlehem PA 18015

KING, JOE MACK, b Conroe, Tex, July 25, 44; m 67; c 1. PHYCOLOGY. *Educ:* Sam Houston State Univ, BS, 67, MA, 68; Univ Tex, Austin, PhD(bot), 71. *Prof Exp:* Res scientist aquatic ecol, Univ Tex, Austin, 68-70; asst prof biol, Univ Wis-La Crosse, 71-73; res assoc aquatic ecol, Rice Univ, 73-78; asst prof biol, 78-80, ASSOC PROF BIOL, MURRAY STATE UNIV, 80- *Concurrent Pos:* Consult, Exxon Corp, Baytown, Tex, 73-74. *Mem:* Am Soc Limnol & Oceanog; Phycol Soc Am; Int Phycol Soc; Am Inst Biol Sci. *Res:* Phytoplankton ecology; impact of nutrient enrichment on aquatic ecosystems. *Mailing Add:* Dept of Biol Sci Murray State Univ Murray KY 42071

KING, JOHN, b Darlington, Eng, Nov 4, 38; m 62; c 3. PLANT PHYSIOLOGY. *Educ:* Univ Durham, BSc, 60; Univ Man, MSc, 62, PhD(bot), 66. *Prof Exp:* Asst prof biol, Bishops Univ, 64-67; from asst prof to assoc prof, 67-77, PROF BIOL, UNIV SASK, 77- *Concurrent Pos:* Nat Res Coun Can res grant-in-aid, 64-; fel, Univ Man, 66. *Mem:* Am Soc Plant Physiol; Can Soc Plant Physiol; Int Asn Plant Tissue Culture. *Res:* Nitrogen metabolism of plant cells in tissue culture. *Mailing Add:* Dept of Biol Univ of Sask Saskatoon SK S7N 0W0 Can

KING, JOHN A(LBERT), b Columbus, Ind, Sept 6, 16; m 41; c 4. RESEARCH ADMINISTRATION. *Educ:* Ind Univ, AB, 38; Univ Minn, MS, 40, PhD(org chem), 42. *Prof Exp:* Asst chem, Ind Univ, 37-38 & Univ Minn, 38-41; Merck fel, 42-43; sr chemist, Winthrop Chem Co Div, Sterling Drug, 43-46; dir chem res, Warner Lambert Pharmaceut Co, NJ, 46-57; dir res & gen mgr res div, Armour & Co, 57-60; mgr res & develop agr div, 60-69, assoc dir agr & pharmaceut res, 70-77, DIR LICENSING AGR PROD, AM CYANAMID CO, 78- *Concurrent Pos:* Civilian with Off Sci Res & Develop, 44. *Mem:* AAAS (vpres & chmn chem sect, 59-60); Am Chem Soc; fel Inst Chem; Sigma Xi; Soc Chem Indust. *Res:* Synthesized pharmacologically active organic compounds; mechanisms of chemical reactions; coordination of chemical research with evaluation of compounds produced; research management; research development and commercialization of pharmaceutical, nutritional and industrial chemical products; licensing of pharmaceutical and agricultural products. *Mailing Add:* 90 Battle Rd Princeton NJ 08540

KING, JOHN ARTHUR, b Detroit, Mich, June 22, 21; m 49; c 2. ZOOLOGY. *Educ:* Univ Mich, AB, 43, MS, 48, PhD, 51. *Prof Exp:* Asst genetics, Univ Mich, 47-51; USPHS fel, Jackson Mem Lab, 51-53, staff scientist, 53-60; Nat Acad Sci-Nat Res Coun fel, 60-61; assoc prof zool, 61-64, PROF ZOOL, MICH STATE UNIV, 64- *Concurrent Pos:* Develop res career award, USPHS, 64-70. *Mem:* AAAS; Am Soc Mammal; Am Soc Zool; Am Soc Naturalists; Animal Behavior Soc (secy, 62-65, pres, 70). *Res:* Sociobiology; mammalian behavior; effects of early experience; behavioral evolution. *Mailing Add:* Dept of Zool Mich State Univ East Lansing MI 48823

KING, JOHN EDWARD, b Columbus, Ohio, Nov 16, 39. ANATOMY, HISTOLOGY. *Educ:* Ohio State Univ, BA, 61, PhD(anat), 65. *Prof Exp:* From instr to assoc prof anat, 65-73, ASSOC PROF PHYSIOL OPTICS, COL OPTOM, OHIO STATE UNIV, 73- *Mem:* AAAS. *Res:* Hematology. *Mailing Add:* Col of Optom Ohio State Univ Columbus OH 43210

KING, JOHN GORDON, b London, Eng, Aug 13, 25; nat US; m 49; c 8. ATOMIC PHYSICS. *Educ:* Mass Inst Technol, SB, 50, PhD(physics), 53. *Hon Degrees:* ScD, Univ Hartford, 72. *Prof Exp:* From instr to prof physics, 53-74, FRANCIS L FRIEDMAN PROF PHYSICS, MASS INST TECHNOL, 74- *Honors & Awards:* Millikan Award, 65; Harbison Award, 71. *Mem:* Am Phys Soc; Am Asn Physics Teachers. *Res:* Atomic beam studies of low temperature systems; molecular microscopy. *Mailing Add:* Dept of Physics Mass Inst Technol Cambridge MA 02139

KING, JOHN MCKAIN, b Boston, Mass, Jan 16, 27; m 47; c 1. VETERINARY PATHOLOGY, WILDLIFE DISEASES. *Educ:* Okla Agr & Mech Col, DVM, 55; Cornell Univ, PhD(path), 63. *Prof Exp:* Instr vet path, Cornell Univ, 59-60; asst prof, Wash State Univ, 60-62; fel path, Mellon Inst, 62-69; assoc prof, 69-80, PROF VET PATH, NY STATE COL, CORNELL UNIV, 80- *Concurrent Pos:* USPHS res fel, 60; consult, Animal Med Ctr, NY, 62- *Mem:* Am Vet Med Asn; Am Col Vet Path; Brit Vet Asn. *Res:* Veterinary pathology, especially lung and liver diseases; wildlife pathology, both gross and micropathology. *Mailing Add:* Dept of Vet Path NY State Vet Col Cornell Univ Ithaca NY 14853

KING, JOHN MATHEWS, b New York, NY, Oct 25, 39; m 62; c 2. ORGANIC CHEMISTRY. *Educ:* Cornell Univ, AB, 61; Univ Wis, MS, 63, PhD, 65. *Prof Exp:* NSF fel, Calif Inst Technol, 65-66; univ fel, 66 & 67; sr res assoc, 67-82, MGR, LUBRICATING OIL ADDITIVES DIV, CHEVRON RES CO, STANDARD OIL CO CALIF, 82- *Mem:* Am Chem Soc. *Res:* Synthesis of organic peroxides; organic photochemistry; radiation chemistry of organic compounds; lube oil additives. *Mailing Add:* 1194 Idylberry Rd San Rafael CA 94903

KING, JOHN PAUL, b Zena, Okla, Nov 23, 38; m 61; c 3. SOLID STATE PHYSICS. *Educ:* Cent State Col, Okla, BS, 61; Okla State Univ, PhD(solid state physics), 66. *Prof Exp:* Eng sci specialist, Missiles & Space Div, LTV Aerospace Corp, 66-68; from asst prof to assoc prof, PROF PHYSICS, CENT STATE UNIV, OKLA, 77- *Mem:* Am Phys Soc. *Res:* Effects of light illumination on the electron spin resonance of diamonds. *Mailing Add:* Dept of Physics Cent State Univ Edmond OK 73034

KING, JOHN STUART, b Buffalo, NY, Nov 12, 27. GEOLOGY. *Educ:* Univ Buffalo, BA, 55, MA, 57; Univ Wyo, PhD(geol), 63. *Prof Exp:* Res engr petrography, Res Div, Carborundum Co, 57-60; asst prof geol, 63-66, actg chmn dept, 66-67, chmn, 67-71, assoc prof, 66-77, PROF GEOL, STATE UNIV NY BUFFALO, 77- *Concurrent Pos:* Consult electro minerals div, Carborundum Co, 64-66. *Mem:* Geol Soc Am; Mineral Soc Am; Am Asn Petrol Geologists. *Res:* Igneous and metamorphic petrology and structures; structural geology; field interpretations; planetology and analog studies. *Mailing Add:* Dept Geol Sci State Univ NY 4240 Ridge Lea Rd Amherst NY 14226

KING, JOHN SWINTON, b Detroit, Mich, Oct 31, 20; m 43; c 3. PHYSICS. *Educ:* Univ Mich, PhD(nuclear physics). *Prof Exp:* Asst, Appl Physics Lab, Johns Hopkins Univ, 42-45; res assoc reactor physics, Knolls Atomic Power Lab, Gen Elec Co, 53-56, mgr submarine adv reactor physics sub-sect, 56-59; assoc prof, 59-62, PROF NUCLEAR ENG, UNIV MICH, ANN ARBOR, 62-, CHMN DEPT, 74- *Mem:* Am Nuclear Soc; Am Phys Soc. *Res:* Neutron physics as applied to reactor design and neutron optics. *Mailing Add:* Dept of Nuclear Eng Univ of Mich Ann Arbor MI 48109

KING, JOHN WILLIAM, b Butler, Ind, Mar 31, 38; div; c 3. AGRONOMY, CROP SCIENCE. *Educ:* Purdue Univ, BS, 63; Univ RI, MS, 66; Mich State Univ, PhD(crop sci), 70. *Prof Exp:* Machinist, Gen Elec Co, Ind, 56-60; ASSOC PROF AGRON, UNIV ARK, FAYETTEVILLE, 70- *Mem:* Am Soc Agron; Crop Sci Soc Am. *Res:* Turf grass soils fertilization, species and variety adaptation, cultural systems, weed control and irrigation management. *Mailing Add:* Dept of Agron Univ of Ark Fayetteville AR 72701

KING, JONATHAN ALAN, b Brooklyn, NY, Aug 20, 41. MOLECULAR BIOLOGY, DEVELOPMENTAL GENETICS. *Educ:* Yale Univ, BS, 62; Calif Inst Technol, PhD(genetics), 67. *Prof Exp:* Assoc scientist microbial ecol, Jet Propulsion Lab, Calif Inst Technol, 67-68; fel molecular biol, Purdue Univ, 68-69; fel struct biol, Lab Molecular Biol, Brit Med Res Coun, 69-70; from asst prof to assoc prof, 70-78, PROF MOLECULAR GENETICS, MASS INST TECHNOL, 78- & DIR BIOL ELECTRON MICROSCOPE FACIL, 70- *Concurrent Pos:* Childs Mem Fund Med Res res fel, 68-70; ed bd, J Virology, 78-; consult, sci & technol, World Coun Churches. *Mem:* Genetics Soc Am; Am Soc Microbiol; Biophysical Soc. *Res:* Genetic control of morphogenesis; virus assembly; molecular toxicology; protein folding. *Mailing Add:* Dept of Biol Mass Inst of Technol Cambridge MA 02139

KING, JONATHAN STANTON, b Bristol, Tenn, Oct 30, 22; m 51; c 2. BIOCHEMISTRY. *Educ:* Univ Chicago, BS, 47; Univ Tenn, PhD(biochem), 54. *Prof Exp:* Control chemist, S E Massengill Co, 47; res chemist, 48-51, res biochemist, 54-56; res assoc, Bowman Gray Sch Med, Wake Forest Univ, 56-59, instr biochem & Whitney fel, 59-62, res asst prof, 62-65, res assoc prof, 65-70; exec dir, Am Asn Clin Chem, 71-73, EXEC ED, CLIN CHEM, 69- *Concurrent Pos:* NIH res career develop award, 65-70; guest investr, Rockefeller Univ, 68-69. *Mem:* Am Asn Clin Chem; Coun Biol Ed. *Res:* Salicylate effect on pituitary-adrenal axis; function of adrenal ascorbic acid; enzyme adsorption by microcryst sulfas; colorimetric alkaloid estimation; metabolism of trimethylchromone; biochemistry of renal calculi; urinary macromolecular constituents; factors affecting calcium excretion; ninhydrin-positive substances in urine; taurine excretion in mongolism. *Mailing Add:* Am Asn Clin Chem Box 5218 Winston-Salem NC 27103

KING, JOSEPH HERBERT, b Malden, Mass, Nov 16, 39; m 65; c 2. SPACE PHYSICS. *Educ:* Boston Col, PhD(physics), 66. *Prof Exp:* Lectr physics, Regis Col, Mass, 63-64; staff scientist, Aerospace Corp, 65-67; Nat Acad Sci assoc fel, 67-69; PHYSICIST, GODDARD SPACE FLIGHT CTR, NASA, 69- *Concurrent Pos:* Proj scientist, Interplanetary Monitoring Probe Satellite,

NASA, 74- *Mem:* Am Geophys Union. *Res:* Spacecraft plasma and field data concerning the mass and energy coupling between the solar wind and the earth's magnetosphere. *Mailing Add:* Code 692 Goddard Space Flight Ctr NASA Greenbelt MD 20771

KING, KATHERINE CHUNG-HO, b Peiping, China, Aug 27, 37; US citizen. PEDIATRICS, METABOLISM. *Educ:* Meredith Col, AB, 57; Bowman Gray Sch Med, MD, 62; Am Bd Pediat, dipl, 68, dipl, Neonatal & Perinatal Med, 77. *Prof Exp:* From intern pediat to resident pediat metab, Cleveland Metrop Gen Hosp, 62-66, actg dir, Newborn Serv, 74-75; asst prof, 71-76, ASSOC PROF PEDIAT, SCH MED, 76-, ASSOC PROF NEONATOLOGY, DEPT OF REPRODUCTIVE BIOL, CASE WESTERN RESERVE UNIV, 78- ASST PEDIATRICIAN, CLEVELAND METROP GEN HOSP & CO-DIR, PERINATAL CLIN RES CTR, 69- DIR NEWBORN SERV, 81- *Concurrent Pos:* USPHS trainee, 66-68; Cleveland Diabetes Found grant, Cleveland Metrop Gen Hosp, 69-70; sr instr, Case Western Reserve Univ, 69-71. *Mem:* Am Fedn Clin Res; Am Acad Pediat; fel Am Col Nutrit. *Res:* Carbohydrate metabolism of human fetus and neonate. *Mailing Add:* Dept of Pediat Cleveland Metrop Gen Hosp Cleveland OH 44109

KING, KENDALL WILLARD, b Pittsburgh, Pa, Feb 20, 26; div; c 2. NUTRITION. *Educ:* Va Polytech Inst, BS, 49, MS, 50; Univ Wis, PhD(biochem), 53. *Prof Exp:* From asst prof bact & biochem to prof biochem, Va Polytech Inst, 53-68, head dept biochem & nutrit, 67-68; asst vpres, 68-77, VPRES GRANTS, RES CORP, NY, 77- *Concurrent Pos:* Res assoc, Inst Nutrit Sci, Columbia Univ, 59-60; mem, US comt, Int Union Nutrit Sci, Nat Acad Sci-Nat Res Coun, 75-81; Comt Blindness Prev, Helen Keller Int. *Mem:* AAAS; Am Chem Soc; Am Inst Nutrit; Am Soc Biol Chemists; Am Asn Cereal Chemists. *Res:* Evaluation of cost-effectiveness of applied nutrition programs. *Mailing Add:* Res Corp 405 Lexington Ave New York NY 10017

KING, KENNETH, JR, b Philadelphia, Pa, Dec 27, 30; m 61; c 2. BIOGEOCHEMISTRY. *Educ:* Mass Inst Technol, SB, 52, SM, 60; Columbia Univ, PhD(geol), 72. *Prof Exp:* Indust res & develop, Merck & Co, 55-64, dir res planning, 65-67; res asst, Columbia Univ, 67-72; RES ASSOC BIOGEOCHEM, LAMONT-DOHERTY GEOL OBSERV, COLUMBIA UNIV, 72- *Concurrent Pos:* Fel, Carnegie Inst Wash, 72-74. *Mem:* Sigma Xi; AAAS; Am Chem Soc; Geol Soc Am; Geochem Soc. *Res:* Proteins of modern and fossil mineralized tissues; amino acid racemization; mechanism of biomineralization. *Mailing Add:* Lamont-Doherty Geol Observ Columbia Univ Palisades NY 10964

KING, L D PERCIVAL, b Williamstown, Mass, Dec 29, 06; m 37, 70 & 79; c 2. PHYSICS. *Educ:* Univ Rochester, BS, 30; Univ Wis, PhD(exp nuclear physics), 37. *Prof Exp:* Asst physics, Univ Rochester, 30-31 & Mass Inst Technol, 31-33; asst, Univ Wis, 35-37; instr, Purdue Univ, 37-42, fel, Off Sci Res & Develop contract, 42-43; group leader, Manhattan Dist & AEC Projs, Los Alamos Sci Lab, 43-57; tech dir, US Atoms for Peace Conf, Atomic Energy Comn, Geneva, 57-58; asst div leader, Reactor Div, Los Alamos Sci Lab, 59, chmn, Rover Flight Safety Off, 60-69, res adv, 69-73; consult, 73-78; RETIRED. *Mem:* Fel AAAS; fel Am Phys Soc; fel Am Nuclear Soc. *Res:* Nuclear physics; artificial radioactivity; nuclear structure; design and construction of homogenous and fast nuclear research and test reactors; solution to flight safety problems in nuclear rocket reactors. *Mailing Add:* Rte 4 Box 16-B Santa Fe NM 87501

KING, L(EE) ELLIS, b Jamestown, NC, Aug 21, 39; m 60. TRANSPORTATION ENGINEERING, ERGONOMICS. *Educ:* NC State Univ, BS, 61; Univ Calif, Berkeley, DrEng, 67. *Prof Exp:* Assoc prof, WVa Univ, 72-73 & Univ Colo, Denver Ctr, 73-75; prof, Wayne State Univ, 75-76; CHMN & PROF, DEPT URBAN & ENVIRON ENG, UNIV NC, CHARLOTTE, 76- *Concurrent Pos:* Consult, various pvt & pub agencies. *Honors & Awards:* Walter L Huber Civil Engr Res Prize, Am Soc Civil Engrs, 73. *Mem:* Am Soc Civil Engrs; Inst Traffic Eng; Transp Res Bd; Int Comn Illum; Am Soc Eng Educ. *Res:* Traffic engineering problems; transportation planning; driver, vehicle and roadway interaction; driver behavior; reduced visibility performance; roadway lighting; roadway signing; pedestrian behavior; traffic signals. *Mailing Add:* Dept of Urban & Environ Eng Univ of NC Charlotte NC 28223

KING, LAFAYETTE CARROLL, b Marysvale, Utah, Sept 9, 14; m 37; c 5. ORGANIC CHEMISTRY. *Educ:* Utah State Col, BS, 36; Mich State Col, MS, 38, PhD(chem), 42. *Prof Exp:* Asst biol chem, Mich State Col, 36-42; res assoc, 42, from instr to assoc prof chem, 42-55, PROF CHEM, NORTHWESTERN UNIV, 55- *Concurrent Pos:* Indust consult, Food Chem, 50-; US-Japan Conf Chem Educ, Japan, 64, Berkeley, 68 & First Int Am Conf Chem Educ, Buenos Aires, 65; chmn adv coun col chem, 66-; chmn org comt, Indo-US Binat Conf Chem Educ, 69. *Honors & Awards:* Chem Educ Award, Am Chem Soc, 69. *Mem:* Fel AAAS; Am Chem Soc; Oil Chem Soc; Sci Teachers Asn; The Chem Soc. *Res:* Synthesis of quaternary salts, thiazoles and selenazoles; structures of sterols; mechanism of organic reactions. *Mailing Add:* Dept of Chem Northwestern Univ Evanston IL 60201

KING, LARRY DEAN, b Atlanta, Ga, Mar 10, 39; div; c 2. SOIL SCIENCE. *Educ:* Ga Inst Technol, BS, 62; Univ Ga, MS, 68, PhD(agron), 71. *Prof Exp:* Aircraft engr comput prog, Lockheed Aircraft, 62-65; fel soil sci, Univ Guelph, Ont, 71-72; agronomist agr develop, Tenn Valley Authority, 73-74; ASST PROF SOIL SCI, NC STATE UNIV, 74- *Mem:* Am Soc Agron; Soil Conserv Soc Am. *Res:* Land application of municipal and industrial wastes. *Mailing Add:* Dept of Soil Sci NC State Univ Raleigh NC 27650

KING, LARRY GENE, b Prosser, Wash, June 24, 36; m 56; c 4. AGRICULTURAL & IRRIGATION ENGINEERING. *Educ:* Wash State Univ, BS, 58; Colo State Univ, MS, 61, PhD(civil eng), 65. *Prof Exp:* Asst civil eng, Colo State Univ, 58-62, jr agr engr, 62; res engr hydrol, Gen Elec Co, 62-65; res scientist, Pac Northwest Labs, Battelle Mem Inst, 65, sr res engr, 65-68, res assoc, 68-69; assoc prof agr & irrig eng, Utah State Univ, 69-74; PROF AGR ENG, WASH STATE UNIV, 74-, CHEM DEPT, 79- *Mem:* Am Soc Agron; Soil Sci Soc Am; Am Soc Civil Engrs; Am Soc Agr Engrs. *Res:* Irrigation; drainage; groundwater; wells; water quality; hydraulics; hydrology; fluid flow through porous media. *Mailing Add:* Dept of Agr Eng Wash State Univ Pullman WA 99164

KING, LARRY MICHAEL, b Brooklyn, NY, Nov 29, 42; m 68. MATHEMATICS. *Educ:* Brooklyn Col, BS, 63; Univ Md, College Park, MA, 66, PhD(math), 68. *Prof Exp:* Asst prof math, Univ Mass, Amherst, 68-74; ASST PROF MATH, UNIV MICH, FLINT, 74- *Mem:* Am Math Soc; Math Asn Am. *Res:* Slices in transformation groups; topological dynamics and dynamical systems; R-isomorphisms of transformation groups; actions of non-compact semigroups. *Mailing Add:* Dept of Math Univ of Mich Flint MI 48503

KING, LAURENCE FREDERICK, b Toronto, Ont, Jan 22, 13; m 41; c 2. PETROLEUM CHEMISTRY. *Educ:* Univ Toronto, BA, 34, MA, 35. *Prof Exp:* Lab asst, Dom Tar & Chem Co, Toronto, 29-30; lab asst org chem & res chemist, Univ Toronto, 34-37, Eli Lilly Co res fel cancer res, Banting & Best Inst Med Res, 38-40; chemist, Tech Serv Dept, 40-43, chemist tech & res dept, 43-52, res chemist, Res Dept, 52-65, sr res chemist, Res Dept, Imp Oil Ltd, 65-76. *Honors & Awards:* Chem Inst Can Award, 62. *Res:* Alcoholysis of esters; carcinogens, estrogens; compounded mineral oils; lubricating greases; urea extraction and desulfurization; hyrofining, hyrogenation; petroleum solvents, alkyd resins; residual up-grading; polymers; polyvinyl chloride; industrial chemicals; patents. *Mailing Add:* 843 St Clair Pkwy Mooretown ON N0N 1M0 Can

KING, LAURENCE ROBERT, b Boston, Mass, Aug 14, 45. AQUATIC ECOLOGY, MARINE RESOURCE MANAGEMENT. *Educ:* Cornell Univ, BS, 67, MS, 69; Iowa State Univ, PhD(fishery biol), 76. *Prof Exp:* Res biologist power plant biol, Ichthyol Assoc Inc, 69-70, sr res biologist, 70-71; scientist & prog mgr power plant biol & admin, Ecol Analysts Inc, 76-81; SCIENTIST & PROG COORDR, LIVING MARINE RESOURCES & ADMIN, ATLANTIC STATES MARINE FISHERIES COMN, 81- *Mem:* Am Fisheries Soc; Sigma Xi. *Res:* Fisheries management studies to optimize utilization while maintaining healthy population stock size levels of important living marine resources of the Atlantic coast. *Mailing Add:* Atlantic States Marine Fisheries Comn 1717 Mass Ave NW Washington DC 20036

KING, LAWRENCE J, b Richmond, Ind, Feb 10, 15; m 51 & 62; c 2. PLANT PHYSIOLOGY. *Educ:* Earlham Col, AB, 38; Univ Chicago, MS, 42, PhD(plant hormones), 52. *Prof Exp:* Instr biol, Earlham Col, 38-40; asst bot, Univ Chicago, 40-42; asst, Soil Conserv Serv, Ohio, 42-44; asst hort, Ohio Agr Exp Sta, 44-46; sr res fel plant physiol, Boyce Thompson Inst, 46-59; from asst prof to assoc prof bot & pharmacog, Philadelphia Col Pharm, 60-65; prof, 65-81, EMER PROF BIOL, STATE UNIV NY COL GENESEO, 81- *Concurrent Pos:* Res partic dept physiol & biophys, Univ Ill, 65; State Univ NY Res Found fac fel & grants, 68 & 70-71; sabbatical leave, Univ Calif, Davis, 72; founder & ed, Plant Lore, 77- *Mem:* Weed Sci Soc Am; Soc Econ Botanists; Bot Soc Am. *Res:* Plant growth regulators; biochemistry of differentiation; biocrystallography; herbicides; weed biology and control; ethnobotany; history of science; processing, storage and retrieval of science literature. *Mailing Add:* Dept of Biol Col Arts & Sci State Univ of NY Col Geneseo NY 14454

KING, LESTER SNOW, b Cambridge, Mass, Apr 18, 08; m 31; c 2. PATHOLOGY. *Educ:* Harvard Univ, AB, 27, MD, 32. *Prof Exp:* Asst path, Rockefeller Inst, Princeton Univ, 37-40; asst & instr, Sch Med, Yale Univ, 40-42; from clin asst prof to clin prof, Col Med, Univ Ill, 46-64; sr ed, 63-73, contrib ed, JAMA, 73-78. *Concurrent Pos:* Res fel anat, Harvard Med Sch, 33-35; Moseley travelling fel, Inst Cancer, Madrid & Nat Hosp, London, 35-36; Nat Cancer Inst res grant, 47-49; pathologist, Fairfield State Hosp, Conn, 40-42 & Ill Masonic Hosp, 46-62; lectr path, Col Med, Univ Ill, 64-71; Boerhaave lectr, Leiden, 64; lectr, Univ Chicago, 65-; mem hist life sci study sect, NIH, 63-68, chmn, 64-66; ed, Clio Medica, 74-76; Garrison lectr, Am Asn Hist Med, 75. *Honors & Awards:* Boerhaave Medal, Leiden, 64; Welch Medal, Am Asn Hist Med, 77. *Mem:* Am Asn Hist Med (pres, 74-76). *Res:* Anatomy of the nervous system; neuropathology; cancer; virus diseases; blood brain barrier; medical history. *Mailing Add:* 360 Wellington Ave Chicago IL 60657

KING, LEWIS H, b Lockeport, NS, Nov 10, 24; m 55; c 6. MARINE GEOLOGY. *Educ:* Acadia Univ, BSc, 49;Mass Inst Technol, PhD(geol), 55. *Prof Exp:* Geologist, Geol Surv Can, NS, 54-56; geochemist, Mines Br. Dept Mines & Tech Surv, Ont, 56-63; GEOLOGIST, BEDFORD INST, DEPT ENERGY, MINES & RESOURCES. 63- *Concurrent Pos:* Part-time mem fac, Dalhousie Univ, 68- *Mem:* AAAS; fel Geol Soc Am; fel Geol Asn Can. *Res:* Geological mapping of the sea floor across the Scotian Shelf, eastern Gulf of Maine and the Grand Banks. *Mailing Add:* Bedford Inst Dartmouth NS B2Y 4A2 Can

KING, LLOYD ELIJAH, JR, b Mayfield, Ky, Sept 10, 39; m 68; c 3. DERMATOLOGY, ANATOMY. *Educ:* Vanderbilt Univ, BA, 61; Univ Tenn, Memphis, MD, 67, PhD(anat), 70. *Prof Exp:* Intern med, City of Memphis Hosps, 69-70; instr anat, Med Units, Univ Tenn, Memphis, 70-74, instr med, 73-76, asst prof dermat, 75-77; ASSOC PROF MED & CHIEF DERMAT, VANDERBILT UNIV, 77- *Concurrent Pos:* NIH fel anat, Med Units, Univ Tenn, Memphis, 68-69; Vet Admin trainee dermat, Vet Admin Hosp, Memphis, 72-74, Vet Admin res & educ associateship, 75-; NIH spec fel, St Jude Children's Res Hosp, 74-76; resident internal med, City of Memphis Hosps, 70-71, resident dermat, 71-74; clin investr, Vet Admin Hosp, Nashville, Tenn, 77-80. *Mem:* AAAS; Am Acad Dermat; fel Am Col Physicians; Am Fedn Clin Res; AMA. *Res:* Cyclic nucleotides; cell membranes; growth factors. *Mailing Add:* Vet Admin Hosp Dermat Sect 1310 24th Ave S Nashville TN 37203

KING, LOUIS DELWIN, b Walhalla, SC, July 31, 17. PHARMACY. *Educ:* Univ SC, BS, 49; Univ Fla, MS, 51, PhD, 53. *Prof Exp:* Pharmacist, Bells Drug Store, 49-50; asst col pharm, Univ Fla, 51; from asst prof to assoc prof pharm, 53-61, asst dean, 57-66, PROF PHARM, COL PHARM, RUTGERS UNIV, 61-, ASSOC DEAN, 66- *Mem:* Am Pharmaceut Asn. *Res:* Pharmaceutical manufacturing processes and equipment. *Mailing Add:* Col of Pharm Rutgers Univ Univ Heights Campus New Brunswick NJ 08903

KING, LOWELL ALVIN, b Spencer, Iowa, June 16, 32; m 54; c 3. PHYSICAL CHEMISTRY. *Educ:* Iowa State Univ, BS, 53, PhD(inorg chem), 63; Washington Univ, AM, 55. *Prof Exp:* Group leader, Materiel Lab, 56-59, instr chem, US Air Force Acad, 59-61, res assoc, Ames Lab, Iowa State Univ, 61-63, asst prof chem, US Air Force Acad, 63, assoc prof, 63-64, res assoc, F J Seiler Lab, Off Aerospace Res, 64-65, assoc prof chem, 65-71, prof chem, US Air Force Acad, 71-80, CONSULT, F J SEILER LAB, AIR FORCE SYSTS COMMAND, US AIR FORCE, 81- *Concurrent Pos:* Dir chem div, F J Seiler Lab, Off Aerospace Res, 66-68, dir chem div, F J Seiler Lab, Air Force Systs Command, 74-75, sr scientist, 75-80; prof phys sci, Europ Christian Col, Vienna, Austria, 81- *Honors & Awards:* Air Force Res & Develop Award, 70. *Mem:* Electrochemical Soc; Am Chem Soc. *Res:* Electrochemistry; molten salt chemistry; measurement of physical and electrochemical properties of molten salt mixtures containing complex halo-anions. *Mailing Add:* FJSRL/NC US Air Force Academy CO 80840

KING, LOWELL RESTELL, b Salem, Ohio, Feb 28, 32; m 60. UROLOGY. *Educ:* Johns Hopkins Univ, BA, 52, MD, 56. *Prof Exp:* Intern, Johns Hopkins Hosp, 56-57, resident, 57-61; asst prof urol, Med Sch, Johns Hopkins Univ, 63, from asst prof to assoc prof, Northwestern Univ, 63-68; prof, Univ Ill, 68-70; chmn, Div Urol, 70-77, SURGEON-IN-CHIEF, CHILDREN'S MEM HOSP, 74-; PROF UROL, NORTHWESTERN UNIV, 70- *Concurrent Pos:* Am Cancer Soc fel, 58-59; chmn dept urol, Presby-St Luke's Hosp, 68-70; mem, Am Bd Urol, 75- *Mem:* Am Urol Asn; fel Am Acad Pediat; fel Am Col Surgeons; Soc Pediat Urol; Am Urol Asn. *Res:* Pediatric urology. *Mailing Add:* Children's Mem Hosp 2300 Children's Plaza Chicago IL 60614

KING, LUCY JANE, b Vandalia, Ill, Dec, 23, 32. PSYCHIATRY. *Educ:* Wash Univ, AB, 54, MD, 58; Am Bd Psychiat & Neurol, dipl psychiat, 66. *Prof Exp:* Intern, Butterworth Hosp, Grand Rapids, Mich, 58-59; asst resident psychiat, Renard Hosp, St Louis, Mo, 59-62, chief resident, 62-63; from instr to assoc prof, Sch Med, Wash Univ, 70-74; PROF PSYCHIAT & PHARMACOL, MED COL VA, VA COMMONWEALTH UNIV, 74- *Concurrent Pos:* NIMH res career develop awards neuropharmacol, 63-73. *Mem:* AAAS; fel Am Psychiat Asn; Psychiat Res Soc. *Res:* Clinical and social psychiatry; neuropharmacology. *Mailing Add:* Dept of Psychiat & Pharmacol Med Col of Va Sta Richmond VA 23298

KING, LUNSFORD RICHARDSON, b Greensboro, NC, July 22, 37; m 61; c 2. MATHEMATICS. *Educ:* Davidson Col, BS, 59; Duke Univ, PhD(math), 63. *Prof Exp:* Res instr math, Univ Va, 63-64; from asst prof to assoc prof, 64-80, PROF MATH, DAVIDSON COL, 80- *Concurrent Pos:* Vis scholar, Dartmouth Col, 74-75. *Mem:* Math Asn Am; Am Math Soc. *Mailing Add:* PO Box 27 Davidson NC 28036

KING, MARVIN, b New York, NY, Apr 23, 40; m 61; c 1. OPTICAL SYSTEMS, ELECTRONIC SYSTEMS. *Educ:* City Col New York, BEE, 61; Polytech Inst Brooklyn, MSEE, 63; Columbia Univ, EngScD, 66. *Prof Exp:* Jr elec engr, ITT Fed Labs, 62-63, electrophysicist, 63-64; res asst, Electronics Res Labs, Columbia, 64-66, res engr, 66-67, sr res engr, 67-68; asst head electrooptics lab, 68-69, mgr optics lab, 69-76, RES DIR, RIVERSIDE RES INST, 77-, EXEC DIR PROG DEVELOP, 81- *Concurrent Pos:* Consult, US Army Electronics Command, Ft Monmouth, NJ, 67-68, Adv Optics Ctr, Radiation, Inc, Mich, 69 & spec study sect on optics, NIH, 70; lectr, Columbia Col Sci Honors Prog, 66-73; adj assoc prof, City Col New York, 72-74. *Mem:* Inst Elec & Electronics Eng; Optical Soc Am; Sigma Xi; Am Inst Physics. *Res:* Signal processing for radar and communications systems utilizing holography, photographic film, physical optics and ultrasonics; atmospheric optics; optical oceanography; infrared holography; laser radar; laser signatures; infrared acquisition and tracking systems; image processing. *Mailing Add:* Riverside Res Inst 330 W 42nd St New York NY 10036

KING, MARY MARGARET, b Oklahoma City, Okla, May 26, 46. DRUG METABOLISM, NUTRITION. *Educ:* Cent State Univ, BS, 69; Univ Okla, PhD(med physiol & biophys), 75. *Prof Exp:* Instr physiol, Cent State Univ, 69; instr, Okla City Pub Schs, 69-71; fel, 75-76, res assoc biomembrane res, 76-77, staff scientist, 77-80, ASST MEM, OKLA MED RES FOUND, 80- *Concurrent Pos:* Young Investr Award, NIH/Nat Inst Environ Health Sci, 78-81. *Mem:* Biophys Soc; Am Asn Cancer Res; Tissue Cult Asn; Sigma Xi; Soc Exp Biol Med. *Res:* Chemical carcinogens and dietary fat-antioxidant interactions as relates to mammary cancer; carcinogenesis; chemical carcinogens; dietary parameters; hormonal interactions in mammary gland, especially relating to the drug metabolizing system. *Mailing Add:* Okla Med Res Found-Biomembr Res 825 NE 13th St Oklahoma City OK 73104

KING, MARY-CLAIRE, b Evanston, Ill, Feb 27, 46; m 73; c 1. EPIDEMIOLOGY, HUMAN GENETICS. *Educ:* Carleton Col, BA, 66; Univ Calif, Berkeley, PhD(genetics), 73. *Prof Exp:* Asst prof, 76-80, ASSOC PROF EPIDEMIOLOGY, UNIV CALIF, BERKELEY, 80- *Concurrent Pos:* Vis prof, Univ Chile, Santiago, 73; asst prof genetics, Univ Calif, San Francisco, 74-80, assoc prof epidemiol, 80-; prin investr, genetic epidemiol of breast cancer in families, NIH grant, 79- *Mem:* Am Soc Human Genetics; Soc Epidemiol Res; Am Epidemiol Soc. *Res:* Genetics and epidemiology of breast cancer and other common chronic diseases, pedigree analysis, human and primate molecular evolution. *Mailing Add:* Sch of Pub Health Univ of Calif Berkeley CA 94720

KING, MERRILL KENNETH, b Claymont, Del, Nov 15, 38; m 64; c 2. COMBUSTION SCIENCE. *Educ:* Carnegie Inst Technol, BS, 60, MS, 62, PhD(chem eng), 65. *Prof Exp:* Sr res engr, 64-67, head, Thermodyn & Combustion Sect, Atlantic Res Corp Div, Susquehanna Corp, 67-72, staff scientist, 72-73, head, Energy & Pollution Technol Sect, 73-74, chief kinetics & combustion group, 74-76, CHIEF SCIENTIST RES & TECHNOL, ATLANTIC RES CORP, 76- *Mem:* Am Inst Chem Engrs; Am Inst Aeronaut & Astronaut; Combustion Inst. *Res:* Solid propellant combustion; metals combustion; graphite oxidation and erosion; air-breathing propulsion; chemical thermodynamics; chemical kinetics; vortex flow; combustion instability. *Mailing Add:* 4634 Tara Dr Fairfax VA 22032

KING, MICHAEL CHARLES, b New York, NY, June 16, 40; m 62; c 3. PHOTOLITHOGRAPHY, INTEGRATED CIRCUITS. *Educ:* Carnegie-Mellon Univ, BS, 62, MS, 64, PhD(physics), 67. *Prof Exp:* Mem tech staff, Bell Labs, 67-76; mgr eng, Qualitron Corp, 76-77; TECH DIR, MICROLITHOGRAPHY DIV, PERKIN-ELMER CORP, 77- *Mem:* Optical Soc Am; Am Phys Soc; Electrochem Soc; Sigma Xi. *Res:* Application of photolithographic technology for the fabrication of integrated circuits; holography for 3-dimensuonal imaging applications; 10 publications. *Mailing Add:* Perkin-Elmer Corp MS-245 Main Ave Norwalk CT 06856

KING, MICHAEL DUMONT, b Kansas City, Mo, Oct 20, 49; m 72; c 2. ATMOSPHERIC RADIATION, REMOTE SENSING. *Educ:* Colo Col, BA, 71; Univ Ariz, MS, 73, PhD(atmospheric sci), 77. *Prof Exp:* Res asst, Univ Ariz, 71-77; ATMOSPHERIC SCIENTIST, GODDARD SPACE FLIGHT CTR, NASA, 78- *Mem:* Am Meterol Soc; Am Geophys Union; AAAS. *Res:* Multiple light scattering and radiative transfer in cloud free and cloudy atmospheres; application of inversion methods to determination of aerosol size distributions; effect of clouds and aerosols on earth's radiation budget. *Mailing Add:* 12700 Summerwood Dr Silver Spring MD 20904

KING, MICHAEL M, b Chicago, Ill, May 10, 44; m 70. ORGANIC CHEMISTRY. *Educ:* Ill Inst Technol, BS, 66; Harvard Univ, AM, 67, PhD(org chem), 70. *Prof Exp:* Asst prof chem, NY Univ, 70-73; asst prof, 73-78, ASSOC PROF CHEM, GEORGE WASHINGTON UNIV, 78- *Mem:* Am Chem Soc; Sigma Xi. *Res:* Pyrroles and porphyrins; heterocycles, organofluorides, heteronuclear magnetic spectroscopy, enzyme model systems. *Mailing Add:* Dept of Chem George Washington Univ Washington DC 20052

KING, MICHAEL STUART, b Brackley, Eng, June 2, 31; m 62; c 3. GEOLOGICAL ENGINEERING, APPLIED GEOPHYSICS. *Educ:* Univ Glasgow, BSc, 53; Univ Calif, Berkeley, MS, 61, PhD(eng sci), 64. *Prof Exp:* Design engr, John Brown & Co, Scotland, 52-54; field engr, Iraq Petrol Co, Kirkuk, 54-59; teaching asst mineral technol, Univ Calif, Berkeley, 59-64, lectr, 64-65; sr sci officer, Geotech Div, Ministry of Technol, Eng, 65-66; prof geol sci, Univ Sask, 66-81; STAFF SCIENTIST, LAWRENCE BERKELEY LAB, UNIV CALIF, BERKELEY, 81- *Concurrent Pos:* Mem Can Nat Comt Rock Mech. *Mem:* Assoc mem Am Geophys Union; Soc Explor Geophys; Am Inst Mining, Metall & Petrol Engrs; Brit Inst Mech Engrs; Can Inst Mining & Metall. *Res:* Geological sciences; application of ultrasonics in geology; rock mechanics; fluid flow in porous media. *Mailing Add:* Earth Sci Div Lawrence Berkeley Lab Univ Calif Berkeley CA 94720

KING, MORRIS KENTON, b Oklahoma City, Okla, Nov 13, 24; m 53; c 5. INTERNAL MEDICINE. *Educ:* Univ Okla, BA, 47; Vanderbilt Univ, MD, 51. *Prof Exp:* Intern med, Barnes Hosp, St Louis, Mo, 51-52, from asst resident to resident, 52-55; asst resident, Vanderbilt Hosp, Nashville, Tenn, 53-54; instr microbiol, Sch Med, Johns Hopkins Univ, 56-57; from instr to assoc prof, 57-67, assoc dean, 62-65, PROF PREV MED, SCH MED, WASH UNIV, 67-, DEAN, 65- *Concurrent Pos:* Fel microbiol, Sch Hyg & Pub Health, Johns Hopkins Univ, 55-56. *Res:* Pathogenesis of fever; infectious diseases. *Mailing Add:* Deans Off Wash Univ Sch of Med St Louis MO 63110

KING, NELSON BYRON, b Williamsburg, Ohio, Aug 14, 14; m 38; c 2. VETERINARY MICROBIOLOGY. *Educ:* Ohio State Univ, BSc, 41, DVM, 48, MSc, 50, PhD, 57; Am Col Vet Microbiologists, dipl. *Prof Exp:* Res engr chem, Battelle Mem Inst, 44-48; instr animal dis, Dept Vet Sci, Ohio Exp Sta & Ohio State Univ, 48-57, from assoc prof to prof, 58-64; agr officer, Food & Agr Orgn, UN, 57-58, chief sect vet educ & res, Animal Health Br, 61-62; prin vet, Coop State Res Serv, USDA, 64-68; asst dean, Sch Vet Med, Auburn Univ, 68-72, assoc dean, 72-80. *Mem:* Am Vet Med Asn; Conf Res Workers Animal Dis; Am Asn Vet Med Cols. *Res:* Brucellosis in cattle; respiratory disease complex in animals; animal disease. *Mailing Add:* 850 Cary Dr Auburn AL 36830

KING, NICHOLAS S P, b Lafayette, Ind, Dec 3, 40; m 66; c 2. NUCLEAR STRUCTURE. *Educ:* Dartmouth Col, BA, 62; Univ NMex, MS, 64; Univ Colo, PhD(physics), 70. *Prof Exp:* Res physicist, Univ Calif, Davis, 71-77; staff physicist, 78-80, ASSOC GROUP LEADER, LOS ALAMOS NAT LAB, 81- *Mem:* Am Phys Soc. *Res:* Investigation of the reaction mechanisms of nuclear particles with nuclei and the resultant excitation modes of the nucleus; determination of plasma properties via measurements of emitted radiation. *Mailing Add:* Los Alamos Nat Lab MS 406 P-15 Los Alamos NM 87545

KING, NORVAL WILLIAM, JR, b Salisbury, Md, Apr 29, 38; m 64; c 2. VETERINARY PATHOLOGY, COMPARATIVE PATHOLOGY. *Educ:* Univ Ga, DVM, 62. *Prof Exp:* Res fel, 65-67, res assoc, 68-72, prin assoc, 72-76, ASSOC PROF COMPARATIVE PATH, HARVARD MED SCH, 76-, ASSOC DIR, NEW ENGLAND REGIONAL PRIMATE RES CTR, 80- *Concurrent Pos:* Lectr, Sch Med & Vet Med, Tufts Univ, 79-; consult, Pathobiol Inc, 74-; dir, Health Training grant, vet & comparative path, NIH, 75-; Res Award, Am Asn Lab Animal Sci, 69. *Mem:* Int Acad Path; Am Asn Pathologists; Am Col Vet Pathologists; Am Vet Med Asn; New England Soc Pathologists. *Res:* Ultrastructure of viruses and viral iduced lesions; pathology of the reproductive tract; animal models for human diseases. *Mailing Add:* New England Regional Primate Res Ctr Harvard Med Sch One Pine Hill Dr Southborough MA 01772

KING, NYDIA MARGARITA, b Ponce, PR, Jan 7, 25; US citizen. PHYTOCHEMISTRY. *Educ:* Univ PR, BS, 49; Univ Wis, MS, 50, PhD(pharm chem), 54. *Prof Exp:* From instr to assoc prof pharm, Univ PR, 50-67, prof, 67-80; RETIRED. *Concurrent Pos:* Spec fel, Nat Libr Med, Bethesda, Md, 65-66. *Mem:* Am Pharmaceut Asn; Am Inst Hist Pharm; Phytochem Soc NAm; Soc Econ Bot; Am Soc Pharmacog. *Res:* Chemical investigation of plants used medicinally in Puerto Rico. *Mailing Add:* Col of Pharm GPO Box 5067 Rio Piedras PR 00936

KING, ORDIE HERBERT, JR, oral pathology, see previous edition

KING, PAUL HAMILTON, sanitary engineering, see previous edition

KING, PAUL HARVEY, b Ft Wayne, Ind, Sept 4, 41; m 67, 78; c 3. BIOMEDICAL ENGINEERING, MECHANICAL ENGINEERING. *Educ:* Case Inst Technol, BS, 63, MS, 65; Vanderbilt Univ, PhD(mech eng), 68. *Prof Exp:* Res asst eng, Case Inst Technol, 63-65; asst prof eng, Vanderbilt Univ, 68-72, actg chmn dept biomed eng, 71-72, assoc prof biomed & mech eng 72- & prog dir biomed eng, 72-75, chmn biomed eng, 75-77, asst prof, Ortho & Rehab, 73-81. *Concurrent Pos:* Sr teaching fel mech eng, Vanderbilt Univ, 65-68; researcher, Oak Ridge Assoc Univ, Med & Health Sci Div, Radiopharmaceut Develop Group, 78-79. *Mem:* Sigma Xi; Asn Advan Med Instrumentation. *Res:* Orthopedics research; computer analysis of electro-cardiograms; radioisotope scanning systems; biomedical data analysis; modelling and research; positron emission tomography. *Mailing Add:* Box 1631 Sta B Nashville TN 37235

KING, PERRY, JR, b West Frankfort, Ill, Sept 17, 28; m 54; c 3. RADIOCHEMISTRY. *Educ:* Univ Ill, BS, 50; Washington Univ, PhD(chem), 60. *Prof Exp:* Chemist, Mallinckrodt Chem Works, 50-53 & 60-64, sect leader, 64-71, mgr, Process Develop Radiopharmaceut, 71-72, asst dir radiopharmaceut res & develop, 73-76, DIR QUAL ASSURANCE CHEMICALS, MALLINCKRODT, INC, 76- *Mem:* Am Chem Soc; Soc Nuclear Med. *Res:* Radiopharmaceuticals; applications of raiochemical techniques to poblems in inorganic chemistry; analytical chemistry; in vivo imaging agents. *Mailing Add:* PO Box 5439 Mallinckrodt Inc St Louis MO 63147

KING, PETER FOSTER, b New York, NY, Oct 7, 29; m 54; c 3. PHYSICAL CHEMSTRY. *Educ:* Ind Univ, BS, 51, MA, 52; Mass Inst Technol, DSc, 57. *Prof Exp:* Res & develop engr, Dow Chem Co, 57-65; chemist, 65-67, group leader, 67-80, SR RES CHEMIST, RES & DEVELOP, HOOKER CHEM & PLASTICS CORP, PARKER DIV, 80- *Mem:* Electrochem Soc; Am Chem Soc; Nat Asn Corrosion Eng. *Res:* Corrosion; electrohemistry. *Mailing Add:* 26500 Orchard Lake Rd Farmington MI 48018

KING, PETER RAMSAY, b Blackpool, UK, Nov 22, 43; m 70; c 1. COMPUTER SCIENCE. *Educ:* Univ Nottingham, BSc, 65, PhD(comput sci), 69. *Prof Exp:* Lectr math & comput sci, Univ Nottingham, 67-69; asst prof, 69-77, assoc prof, 77-80, PROF COMPUT SCI, UNIV MAN, 80- *Concurrent Pos:* Nat Res Coun Can grants, 69-72. *Mem:* Asn Comput Mach; Brit Comput Soc; Brit Inst Math & Appln. *Res:* Compiler construction for high level languages, especially Algol 68; spline interpolation; interactive problem solving. *Mailing Add:* Dept of Comput Sci Univ of Manitoba Winnipeg MB R3T 2N2 Can

KING, R MAURICE, JR, b Wilmington, NC, Jan 15, 35; wid; c 1. MATHEMATICS, STATISTICS. *Educ:* Univ NC, BS, 56. *Prof Exp:* Engr, E I du Pont de Nemours & Co, 57-59; res statistician, Cent Res Div, Am Cyanamid Co, 59-66, group leader comput, 66-71; prin mem tech staff, Eastern Technol Ctr, 71-76, prin & consult mem tech staff, Xerox Bus Systs Planning Univ, 76-78, mgr, Washington Off, Advan Systs Div, 78-80, mgr appln develop, Xerox electro-optical systs, 80-81, PLANNING MGR, PRINTING SYSTS DIV, XEROX CORP, 81- *Mem:* Am Statist Asn. *Res:* Development of computer systems for automation of the office. *Mailing Add:* Xerox Corp 880 Apollo St El Segundo CA 90245

KING, RAY J(OHN), b Montrose, Colo, Jan 1, 33; m 64; c 2. ELECTRICAL ENGINEERING. *Educ:* Ind Inst Technol, BS, 56 & 57; Univ Colo, Boulder, MS, 60, PhD(elec eng), 65. *Prof Exp:* Asst prof electronic eng, Ind Inst Technol, 60-61, asst prof elec eng & assoc chmn dept, 61-62; res assoc, Univ Colo, Boulder, 62-65; assoc prof elec eng, Univ Wis-Madison, 65-69, prof, 69-82; SR ELEC ENGR, LAWRENCE LIVERMORE LABS, 82- *Concurrent Pos:* Res assoc, Univ Colo, Boulder, 60, vis lectr, 64-65; res assoc, Univ Ill, Urbana, 65; mem US nat comt, Int Sci Radio Union, Comns B & F, 67-; Fulbright guest prof, Tech Univ Denmark, 73-74; prin investr, NSF, Oper Nonradar Directed Flights, Air Force Off Sci Res grants. *Mem:* Univ Prof Acad Order; Inst Elec & Electronics Engrs; Am Soc Eng Educ. *Res:* Electromagnetic wave propagation over nonuniform surfaces; microwave surface and leaky wave antennas; microwave instrumentation and measurement systems; microwave nondestructive testing; very low and extremely low frequency antennas. *Mailing Add:* Dept of Elec & Comput Eng Univ of Wis Madison WI 53706

KING, RAYMOND LEROY, b Burbank, Calif, Oct 4, 22; m 47; c 6. FOOD SCIENCE. *Educ:* Univ Calif, AB, 55, PhD(agr chem), 58. *Prof Exp:* Asst dairy prod, Univ Calif, 55-57, jr specialist, 57-58; asst prof dairy technol, 58-62, assoc prof food sci, 62-66, PROF FOOD SCI, UNIV MD, COLLEGE PARK, 66-, COORDR & CHMN FOOD SCI PROG, 73- *Concurrent Pos:* Consult ice cream prod, Chile, 62; consult pesticide residues in milk, 60-61; consult milk packaging, 62. *Mem:* AAAS; Am Chem Soc; Am Dairy Sci Asn; Inst Food Technol. *Res:* Mechanism of lipid oxidation in milk; characterization of milk fat globule membrane; distribution and movement of pesticides in dairy cows; food chemistry. *Mailing Add:* Dept of Dairy Sci Univ of Md College Park MD 20740

KING, REATHA CLARK, b Pavo, Ga, Apr 11, 38; m 61; c 2. INORGANIC CHEMISTRY, PHYSICAL CHEMISTRY. *Educ:* Clark Col, BS, 58; Univ Chicago, MS, 60, PhD(chem), 63; Columbia Univ, MBA, 77. *Prof Exp:* Chemist, Nat Bur Standards, 63-68; asst prof chem, 68-70, assoc prof chem & assoc dean div natural sci & math, 70-74, prof chem & assoc dean acad affairs, York Col, NY, 74-77; PRES, METROP STATE UNIV, ST PAUL, 77- *Mem:* AAAS; Am Chem Soc; Nat Orgn Prof Advan Black Chemists & Black Engrs; Sigma Xi. *Res:* Experimental study on thermochemical properties of alloys using tin solution calorimetry; heats of formation of refractory compounds; fluorine flame calorimetry at room temperature. *Mailing Add:* Metrop State Univ 121 Metro Square Bldg St Paul MN 55101

KING, RICHARD ALLEN, b Fresno, Calif, Mar 20, 39; m 63; c 2. MEDICINE, GENETICS. *Educ:* Pa State Univ, AB, 61; Jefferson Med Col, MD, 65; Univ Minn, PhD(genetics), 75. *Prof Exp:* Intern med, Univ Minn, 65-66, resident, 66-69; USPHS surgeon, Atomic Bomb Casualty Comn, Hiroshima, Japan, 69-71; from instr to asst prof med, 71-77, ASSOC PROF MED, UNIV MINN, MINNEAPOLIS, 77- *Mem:* Am Soc Human Genetics; Int Pigment Cell Soc. *Res:* Pigment metabolism and human pigment defects; genetics of common adult diseases including diabetes mellitus, arthritis and lung diseases. *Mailing Add:* Box 272 MAYO Univ Hosp Minneapolis MN 55455

KING, RICHARD AUSTIN, b Philadelphia, Pa, Mar 26, 29; m 56; c 3. PSYCHOPHYSIOLOGY, NEUROBIOLOGY. *Educ:* Univ Cincinnati, AB, 54, MA, 55; Duke Univ, PhD(psychol), 59. *Prof Exp:* From instr to asst prof psychol, Univ NC, Chapel Hill, 58-63; fel physiol, Univ Wash, 63-65; assoc prof, 65-71, PROF PSYCHOL, UNIV NC, CHAPEL HILL, 71-, ASSOC PROF PHYSIOL, 68-, ASSOC DIR NEUROBIOL, 73- *Concurrent Pos:* Vis prof psychol, Brown Univ, 71. *Mem:* Am Psychol Asn; Soc Neurosci. *Res:* Neuropeptides and behavior; biology of memory. *Mailing Add:* Dept of Psychol Univ of NC Chapel Hill NC 27514

KING, RICHARD FREDERICK, b Chicago, Ill, Apr 28, 24; m 50; c 5. APPLIED MATHEMATICS. *Educ:* Cornell Col, AB, 48; Univ Iowa, MS, 49; Univ Ill, PhD(math), 55. *Prof Exp:* Asst mathematician, Argonne Nat Lab, 55-56; computer scientist, Midwestern Univs Res Asn, 56-57; head prog develop sect, Appl Math Div, 57-61, assoc mathematician, 57-71, asst dir div, 61-70, MATHEMATICIAN, ENERGY & ENVIRON SYSTS DIV, ARGONNE NAT LAB, 71- *Concurrent Pos:* Vis prof, Univ Dundee, 69-70. *Mem:* Am Math Soc; Asn Comput Mach; Soc Indust & Appl Math. *Res:* Numerical solution of ordinary differential equations; function approximation and error analysis; solution of nonlinear equations. *Mailing Add:* Energy & Environ Systs Div Argonne Nat Lab 9700 S Cass Ave Argonne IL 60439

KING, RICHARD JOE, b Kansas City, Mo, Aug 30, 37; m 63; c 2. ANIMAL PHYSIOLOGY. *Educ:* Univ Mo-Columbia, BA, 59; Univ Calif, Berkeley, PhD(biophysics), 70. *Prof Exp:* Asst res biophysicist, Univ Calif, San Francisco, 71-74; asst prof, 74-75, assoc prof, 75-80, PROF PHYSIOL, UNIV TEX HEALTH SCI CTR, SAN ANTONIO, 80- *Concurrent Pos:* Consult, Review Comt, NIH, 75-76, 78-79 & 80-81. *Mem:* Am Physiol Soc. *Res:* Composition and properties of pulmonary surfactant; metabolism and isolation of its associated apoproteins; interaction of lipids and proteins in pulmonary surfactant; correlation of structure function relationships. *Mailing Add:* Univ Tex Health Sci Ctr 7703 Floyd Curl Dr San Antonio TX 78284

KING, RICHARD WARREN, b Philadelphia, Pa, Mar 25, 25; m 47; c 4. ANALYTICAL CHEMISTRY, PHYSICAL CHEMISTRY. *Educ:* Kenyon Col, AB, 47; Univ Del, MS, 59. *Prof Exp:* Res chemist, Res & Develop Dept, 47-59, sect chief, Anal Sect, 60-69, MGR RES SERV, RES & DEVELOP DEPT, SUN OIL CO, 69- *Mem:* Am Chem Soc; fel Am Soc Testing & Mat. *Res:* Catalytic reactions of hydrocarbons; application of physical separation techniques to the study of high-boiling fractions from petroleum; gas chromatography of petroleum fractions. *Mailing Add:* Sun Oil Co Box 1135 Marcus Hook PA 19061

KING, ROBBINS SYDNEY, b San Diego, Calif, Apr 23, 22; m 47; c 4. EMBRYOLOGY. *Educ:* Stanford Univ, AB, 47, PhD(biol), 54. *Prof Exp:* Res assoc, Hopkins Marine Sta, Stanford Univ, 52-54, asst prof biol, Univ, 55; instr, Menlo Col, 54-55; asst prof, Wabash Col, 55-56; asst prof biol, 56-65, chmn dept, 65-69, PROF BIOL SCI, CALIF STATE UNIV, CHICO, 65- *Mem:* AAAS; Am Soc Mammal; Nat Sci Teachers Asn. *Res:* Experimental embryology; regeneration. *Mailing Add:* Dept of Biol Sci Calif State Univ Chico CA 95929

KING, ROBERT (BAINTON), b Pittsburgh, Pa, Aug 26, 22; m 51; c 3. SURGERY. *Educ:* Rochester Univ, MD, 46; Am Bd Neurol Surg, dipl, 54. *Prof Exp:* Asst neuroanat, Med Sch, Wash Univ, 48; asst chief, Walter Reed Army Hosp, 49-51; from instr to asst prof neurosurg, Med Sch, Wash Univ, 51-57; PROF NEUROSURG, COL MED, STATE UNIV NY UPSTATE MED CTR, 57-, CHMN DEPT, 66- *Concurrent Pos:* Markle scholar, 51-56; attend surg, Crouse-Irving Mem Hosp, 57 & State Univ Hosp, Syracuse, 65-; consult, Vet Admin Hosp, 57 & Syracuse Psychiat Hosp, 57. *Mem:* Neurosurg Soc Am; Am Asn Neurol Surg; Am Col Surgeons; Am Acad Neurol Surg; Soc Neurol Surg. *Res:* Neurosurgery; neurophysiology. *Mailing Add:* 155 Elizabeth Blackwell State Univ NY Upstate Med Ctr Syracuse NY 13210

KING, ROBERT BRUCE, b Rochester, NH, Feb 27, 38; m 60; c 2. INORGANIC CHEMISTRY. *Educ:* Oberlin Col, BA, 57; Harvard Univ, PhD(inorg chem), 61. *Prof Exp:* Res chemist, Explosives Dept, E I du Pont de Nemours, Del, 61-62; res fel, Mellon Inst, 62-64, sr res fel, 64-66; res assoc prof chem, 66-68, res prof, 68-73, REGENTS' PROF CHEM, UNIV GA, 73-, ACTG HEAD CHEM, 80- *Concurrent Pos:* Ed, Organometallic Syntheses, 63-; tech adv, Pressure Chem Co, Pa, 64-75; ed, J Organometallic Chem, 64-; Sloan Found fel, 67-69; fel, Japan Soc Promotion Sci, 81; consult, Los Alamos Nat Lab, 79- *Honors & Awards:* Am Chem Soc Award, 71. *Mem:* Am Chem Soc; Chem Soc London. *Res:* Synthetic and spectroscopic studies on organo-metallic compounds of transition metals; molecular catalysis; proganophosphoms chemistry; chemical applications of graph theory and group theory. *Mailing Add:* Dept of Chem Univ of Ga Athens GA 30602

KING, ROBERT CHARLES, b New York, NY, June 3, 28; m 79; c 1. GENETICS. *Educ:* Yale Univ, BS, 48, PhD(zool), 52. *Prof Exp:* Scientist, Brookhaven Nat Lab, 51-56; from asst prof to assoc prof biol sci, 56-63, PROF BIOL SCI, NORTHWESTERN UNIV, 64- *Concurrent Pos:* NSF sr fels, Univ Edinburgh, 58, div entom, Commonwealth Sci & Indust Res Orgn, Canberra, Australia, 63 & sericulture exp sta, Tokyo, 70; Seoul Nat Univ, Seoul, Korea, 78 & Han Yang Univ, 79; vis investr & fel, Rockefeller Inst, 59. *Mem:* Fel AAAS; Genetics Soc Am; Am Soc Zool; Entom Soc Am; Am Soc Cell Biol (treas, 72, 73 & 74). *Res:* Developmental genetics; genetic control of oogenesis in Drosophila. *Mailing Add:* Dept Ecol & Evolutionary Biol Hogan Hall 5-130 Northwestern Univ Evanston IL 60201

KING, ROBERT E(RIC), systems engineering, electrical engineering, see previous edition

KING, ROBERT EDWARD, b Zanesville, Ohio, Dec 27, 23; m 50; c 5. BIOLOGICAL CHEMISTRY, PHARMACEUTICAL CHEMISTRY. *Educ:* Ohio State Univ, BSc, 44; Univ Minn, PhD(pharmaceut chem), 48. *Prof Exp:* Res assoc, Merck Sharp & Dohme Res Labs, 48-61; PROF INDUST PHARM, PHILADELPHIA COL PHARM, 61- *Concurrent Pos:* Ed, J Parenteral Drug Asn, 64-78. *Mem:* Am Pharmaceut Asn; Parenteral Drug Asn. *Res:* Pharmaceutical dosage forms. *Mailing Add:* Peters Corner RD 2 Doylestown PA 18901

KING, ROBERT EVANS, b Ann Arbor, Mich, Sept 20, 06; m 34; c 2. GEOLOGY. *Educ:* Univ Iowa, BA, 26; Yale Univ, PhD(geol), 29. *Prof Exp:* Researcher, State Bur Econ Geol, Tex, 25-28; geologist, Texas Co, Colombia, SAm, 29-31; researcher, Mex, 31-33; geologist, Magnolia Petrol Co, Tex, 33-34; field geologist, Socony-Vacuum Oil Co, NY, 34-36; subsurface geologist, Shell Oil Co, Tex, 37-42; field geologist, Superior Oil Co, Calif, 43-45; sr geologist, Texas Co, La, 45-47, staff geologist, NY, 47-52; supv geologist, Am Overseas Petrol, Ltd, 52-58, chief explor geologist, 58-68; indust liaison rep, Woods Hole Oceanog Inst, 69-70; pres, Comoro Explor, Ltd, NY, 70-75; CONSULT & AUTH, 75- *Mem:* Fel Paleont Soc; Soc Econ Paleontologists & Mineralogists; fel Geol Soc Am (treas, 63-71); hon mem Am Asn Petrol Geologists (secy-treas, 62-64). *Res:* Regional geology; stratigraphy; petroleum geology. *Mailing Add:* 132 Castile Venice FL 33595

KING, ROBERT LEE, neurophysiology, see previous edition

KING, ROBERT WILLIAM, b Wesson, Miss, Nov 18, 29; m 59; c 2. MATHEMATICS. *Educ:* Univ Southern Miss, BS, 51, MA, 56; Fla State Univ, MS, 65, PhD(math, educ), 67. *Prof Exp:* Instr math, Copiah-Lincoln Jr Col, 56-57; asst prof, Miss Col, 59-64; asst prof, 67-69, ASSOC PROF MATH, UNIV SOUTHERN MISS, 69- *Mem:* Math Asn Am; Nat Coun Teachers Math. *Res:* Use of various modifications of programed instruction to investigate the effects of selected social and psychological factors in the teaching and learning of mathematics. *Mailing Add:* Dept Math Univ of Southern Miss Box 8447 Southern Sta Hattiesburg MS 39401

KING, ROBERT WILSON, JR, b Fayetteville, NC, Feb 8, 47; m 70. GEODESY. *Educ:* Davidson Col, BS, 70; NC State Univ, BS, 70; Mass Inst Technol, PhD(instrumentation), 75. *Prof Exp:* Res geodesist, Terrestrial Sci Div, Air Force Geophysics Lab, 74-77; RES ASSOC, DEPT EARTH & PLANETARY SCI, MASS INST TECHNOL, 77- *Mem:* Am Geophys Union; Am Astron Soc; AAAS. *Res:* Use of precise extraterrestrial measurement techniques to monitor earth rotation, polar motion and continental drift. *Mailing Add:* 6 Summit Rd Lexington MA 02173

KING, ROGER HATTON, b Barry, Wales, Dec 16, 41; m 65; c 2. PEDOLOGY, PHYSICAL GEOGRAPHY. *Educ:* Univ Wales, BSc, 63; Univ Aberdeen, MSc, 65; Univ Sask, PhD(geog), 69. *Prof Exp:* Tutor geog, Univ Wales, 69-70; asst prof, 70-76, ASSOC PROF GEOG, UNIV WESTERN ONT, 76- *Mem:* Inst Brit Geogr; Can Soc Soil Sci; Int Soc Soil Sci; Int Quarternary Asn; Am Asn Geogr. *Res:* Persistence of chemical residues in archaeological soils and sediments; impact of environmental stress on soil development in arctic and alpine areas; palaeoenvironmental reconstruction in the Canadian Cordillera. *Mailing Add:* Dept of Geog Univ of Western Ont London ON N6A 5B8 Can

KING, RONOLD (WYETH PERCIVAL), b Williamstown, Mass, Sept 19, 05; m 37; c 1. PHYSICS, ELECTRICAL ENGINEERING. *Educ:* Univ Rochester, AB, 27, SM, 29; Univ Wis, PhD(electrodyn), 32. *Hon Degrees:* AM, Harvard Univ, 42. *Prof Exp:* Asst physics, Univ Rochester, 28-29; asst physics, Univ Wis, 32-33, asst elec eng, 33-34, Alumni Res Found fel, 34; instr physics, Lafayette Col, 34-35, asst prof, 35-37; Guggenheim Mem Found fel, Berlin & Munich, 37-38; fac instr physics & commun eng, 38-39, from asst prof to prof appl physics, 39-72, EMER PROF APPL PHYSICS, HARVARD UNIV, 72- *Concurrent Pos:* Guggenheim Mem Found fel, 58; mem comn 6, Int Sci Radio Union; consult, Raytheon Co, 74-75. *Honors & Awards:* Distinguished Serv Award, Sch Eng, Univ Wis, 73. *Mem:* AAAS; fel Inst Elec & Electronics Eng; fel Am Phys Soc; fel Am Acad Arts & Sci; cor mem Bavarian Acad Sci. *Res:* Electromagnetic theory, radiation and antennas; transmission-line theory; microwave circuits; insulated antennas, crossed antennas, antennas in dessipative media near surface; subsurface communication. *Mailing Add:* 92 Hillcrest Pkwy Winchester MA 01890

KING, ROY WARBRICK, b Liverpool, Eng, July 4, 33; m 70. MASS SPECTROMETRY, NUCLEAR MAGNETIC RESONANCE. *Educ:* Cambridge Univ, BA, 54, MA & PhD(org chem), 58. *Prof Exp:* Norman fel org chem, Hickrill Chem Res Found, NY, 58; univ fel, Iowa State Univ, 58-60, supvr instrument serv, 60-66, asst prof chem, 66-69; RES ASSOC CHEM, UNIV FLA, 69- *Mem:* Am Chem Soc; Am Soc Mass Spectrom; Sigma Xi; The Chem Soc. *Res:* Organic structure determination; organic analysis; applications of physical methods to organic chemistry. *Mailing Add:* Dept of Chem Univ of Fla Gainesville FL 32611

KING, S(ANFORD) MACCALLUM, b St Catherines, Ont, May 21, 26; US citizen; m 50; c 4. SOIL FERTILITY, AGRONOMY. *Educ:* Ont Agr Col, BSA, 48; Purdue Univ, MS, 50; Univ Wis, PhD(soil fertil), 56, Keller Grad Inst Mgt, MBA, 81. *Prof Exp:* Soil scientist, Stand Fruit & Steamship Co, 51-53; proj asst soil fertil, Univ Wis, 53-56; res asst, prof & sta supt agron, Mich State Univ, 56-61; mkt & tech serv specialist fertilizer, Int Minerals & Chem Corp, 62-70; dir agr, Develop & Resources Corp, 71-73; V PRES, TARALAN CORP, 73- *Concurrent Pos:* Agr proj develop & mkt tasks 17 countries, Potash Corp, Saskatchewan; Consult, 80- *Mem:* Am Soc Agron; Agr Inst Can; Coun Agr Sci & Technol; Soil Sci Soc Am. *Res:* Crop nutrition; crop management and production. *Mailing Add:* 615 W Park Ave Wheaton IL 60187

KING, STANLEY SHIH-TUNG, b Liau-Ning, China, Nov 12, 34; m 66; c 3. PHYSICAL CHEMISTRY, MOLECULAR SPECTROSCOPY. *Educ:* Taiwan Normal Univ, BS, 57; Drexel Univ, MS, 62; Univ Minn, Minneapolis, PhD(phys chem), 66. *Prof Exp:* res specialist, 66-80, RES LEADER, DOW CHEM USA, 80- *Mem:* Am Chem Soc. *Res:* Vibrational spectroscopy; low temperature matrix isolation study; microsample analysis by vibrational spectroscopy; polymer analysis; chromatographic analysis; electromicroscopy; catalyst analysis; analytical chemistry. *Mailing Add:* 1311 Kirkland Dr Midland MI 48640

KING, STEVEN CLARENCE, b Plainfield, NH, Dec 12, 21; m 78; c 2. ANIMAL GENETICS. *Educ:* Univ NH, BS, 47; Cornell Univ, MS, 51, PhD(genetics), 53. *Prof Exp:* Asst animal genetics, Cornell Univ, 49-53, asst prof animal genetics & poultry husb, 53-55, assoc prof, 55-56; assoc prof poultry sci, Univ & geneticist & nat coordr poultry res br, Animal Hub Res Div, Agr Res Serv, USDA, Purdue Univ, 56-59; geneticist, Mt Hope Poultry Farm, Inc, NY, 59-60; chief poultry res br, Agr Res Serv, 60-63, asst dir animal husb res div, 63-64, staff scientist, Res Prog Develop & Eval Staff, 64-66, asst dir animal husb res div, 66-68, res prog develop & eval staff, 68-70, dep adminr livestock res, 70-72, dep adminr Northeast Region, 72-78, REGIONAL ADMINR, SCI & EDUC-AGR RES SERV, USDA, 78- *Mem:* Fel AAAS; Poultry Sci Asn; World Poultry Sci Asn. *Res:* Population genetics; applied statistics; research administration. *Mailing Add:* Sci & Educ Admin Beltsville MD 20705

KING, T(HOMAS) B(URNESS), b Scotland, Apr 27, 23; nat US; m 50; c 4. METALLURGY. *Educ:* Univ Glasgow, BSc, 45, PhD(metall), 50. *Prof Exp:* Asst lectr metall, Univ Strathclyde, 46-48, lectr, 48-53; from asst prof to assoc prof, 53-61, head dept metall, 62-72, PROF METALL, MASS INST TECHNOL, 61- *Mem:* AAAS; fel Am Acad Arts & Sci; fel Am Inst Mining, Metall & Petrol Engrs. *Res:* Metallurgical thermodynamics and kinetics. *Mailing Add:* Dept Mat Sci & Eng Mass Inst Technol Cambridge MA 02139

KING, TE PIAO, b Shanghai, China, Aug 21, 30. ORGANIC CHEMISTRY. *Educ:* Univ Calif, AB, 50, MS, 51; Univ Mich, PhD, 53. *Prof Exp:* Res assoc biochem, 53-57, asst prof, 57-63, ASSOC PROF BIOCHEM, ROCKEFELLER UNIV, 63- *Mem:* Am Soc Biol Chemists. Am Acad Allergy. *Res:* Peptides; proteins. *Mailing Add:* Rockefeller Univ New York NY 10021

KING, THEODORE MATTHEW, b Quincy, Ill, Feb 13, 31; m 54; c 2. OBSTETRICS & GYNECOLOGY, PHYSIOLOGY. *Educ:* Quincy Col, BS, 50; Univ Ill, Urbana, MS, 52, MD, 59; Mich State Univ, PhD(physiol), 59. *Prof Exp:* Lab asst physiol, Univ Ill, 55-59; intern surg, Presby Hosp, New York, 59-60; from resident to chief resident obstet & gynec, Sloane Hosp Women, 60-65; asst prof physiol, obstet & gynec, Sch Med, Univ Mo, 65-68, assoc prof, 68; prof & chmn dept, Albany Med Col, 68-71; PROF OBSTET & GYNEC & DIR DEPT, SCH MED, JOHNS HOPKINS UNIV, 71- *Concurrent Pos:* Macy fel, Sloane Hosp Women, 60-64; Macy fac fel obstet, 66-67; Nat Inst Child Health & Human Develop fel, 65-68. *Res:* Study of uterine contractile protein; influence of enzyme induction on animal reproduction. *Mailing Add:* Dept of Obstet & Gynec Johns Hopkins Hosp Baltimore MD 21205

KING, THEODORE OSCAR, b Portsmouth, Ohio, May 29, 22; m 52; c 2. TOXICOLOGY, PHARMACOLOGY. *Educ:* Univ Mich, BS, 43; Georgetown Univ, PhD(pharmacol), 49; Univ Wyo, LLB, 60. *Prof Exp:* Pharmaceut control chemist, Wm R Warner & Co, NY, 43-45; anal chemist, Res Div, Colgate-Palmolive-Peet Co, NJ, 46; from assoc prof to prof pharmacol, Col Pharm, Univ Wyo, 49-58; dir div pharmacol, Ortho Res Found, NJ, 59-65; vpres & dir res, Bio/Dynamics, Inc, 65-71; dir, 71-76, SR DIR SAFETY EVAL, PFIZER, INC, 76- *Concurrent Pos:* WHO pub health fel, UK, 51; Fulbright res fel, State Univ Ghent, 55-56; sr pharmacologist, Johnson & Johnson Res Found, NJ, 57-59; lectr, Rutgers Univ, 58-65; assoc res prof, Col Pharmacol, Univ Conn, 80- *Mem:* Soc Toxicol; Am Soc Pharmacol & Exp Ther; Am Chem Soc; NY Acad Sci; Soc Study Reprod. *Res:* Drug safety evaluation; physiology of reproduction; endocrine pharmacology. *Mailing Add:* Pfizer Inc Groton CT 06340

KING, THOMAS B, b Glen Campbell, Pa, Jan 13, 26; m 48; c 4. ANIMAL SCIENCE. *Educ:* Pa State Univ, BS, 49, MS, 50; Univ Ill, PhD(animal sci), 63. *Prof Exp:* Instr animal husb, State Univ NY Agr & Tech Inst Alfred, 50-51; livestock exten specialist, 51-65, head dept animal sci, 65-71, ASSOC DIR, PA AGR & HOME ECON EXTEN SERV, PA STATE UNIV, 71- *Concurrent Pos:* Mem, Pa Conserv Comn, 74-; bd mem, Pa State Planning Bd, State Farm Show Comn, Nat 4-H Coun & Pa Land Use Coalition, 77- *Mem:* Am Soc Animal Sci (pres, 76-77). *Res:* Livestock production and management; horsemanship; ruminant nutrition. *Mailing Add:* Agr Admin Bldg Pa State Univ University Park PA 16802

KING, THOMAS CREIGHTON, b Salt Lake City, Utah, Apr 10, 28; m 52; c 4. MEDICINE, THORACIC SURGERY. *Educ:* Univ Utah, BS, 50, MD, 54; Univ Mo, Kansas City, MA, 63. *Prof Exp:* From asst resident to chief resident, Univ Utah Hosps, 55-59; assoc, Univ Kans, 60, asst prof med sch, 60-64; assoc prof surg & psychol & chief training, Ctr Study Med Educ, Univ

Ill Med Ctr, 64-66; assoc prof surg, Med Sch, Univ Utah, 66-68, prof, 68-73, assoc dean med sch, 66-68, acad vpres, 68-69, provost, 69-73; PROF SURG, COLUMBIA-PRESBY MED CTR, 73- *Concurrent Pos:* Fel surg, Univ Utah Hosps, 54 & 60; intern, Columbia-Presby Med Ctr, 54-55; staff surgeon, Kansas City Vet Admin Hosp, 60-64, assoc chief staff & dir res, 62-64; staff surgeon, Med Ctr, Univ Utah, 66-73; chief thoracic surg, Salt Lake City Vet Admin Hosp, 68-73; attend surg, Harlen Hosp Ctr, 73-80, Presbyterian Hosp, NY. *Mem:* AAAS; Am Fedn Clin Res; Asn Am Med Cols; Soc Univ Surg; Am Asn Thoracic Surg. *Res:* Medical education and teacher training; surgical nutrition and metabolism; skin degerming and infection control; surgical intensive care. *Mailing Add:* Dept Surg Columbia-Presby Med Ctr New York NY 10032

KING, THOMAS JOHN, b Albany, NY, Apr 2, 41; m 64; c 4. REACTOR PHYSICS, ELECTRICAL ENGINEERING. *Educ:* Manhattan Col, BEE, 63; Rensselaer Polytech Inst, MS, PhD(nuclear eng & sci). *Prof Exp:* Engr systs design, 67-68, PRIN ENGR EXP PHYSICS, KNOLLS ATOMIC POWER LAB, 67- *Mailing Add:* Knolls Atomic Power Lab Schenectady NY 12301

KING, THOMAS K C, b Shanghai, China, June 1, 34; US citizen; c 2. PULMONARY PHYSIOLOGY, PULMONARY DISEASES. *Educ:* Univ Edinburgh, MB, ChB, 59, MD, 63; Royal Col Physicians, MRCP, 62, FRCP, 80. *Prof Exp:* Eli Lilly Int fel, Bellevue Hosp, Columbia Univ, 65-66, Polachek Found Cardiopulmonary Lab fel, 66-67; lectr med, Sch Med, Univ Hong Kong, 67-70; asst prof med, 70-73, ASSOC PROF MED, COL MED, CORNELL UNIV, 73-, CLIN ASSOC PROF PHYSIOL, 75- *Honors & Awards:* Pulmonary Acad Award, Nat Heart & Lung Inst, 72. *Mem:* Med Res Soc, UK; Am Fedn Clin Res; Am Physiol Soc; Am Thoracic Soc; Am Col Chest Physicians. *Res:* The mechanism and quantitation of impaired blood gas exchange in the lungs in disease. *Mailing Add:* Col of Med Cornell Univ 1300 York Ave New York NY 10021

KING, THOMAS MORGAN, b Morristown, Tenn, Aug 28, 40; m 62; c 2. PHYSICAL INORGANIC CHEMISTRY. *Educ:* Carson-Newman Col, BS, 62; Univ Tenn, PhD(chem), 66. *Prof Exp:* Res chemist, Monsanto Co, 66-68, sr res chemist, 68-69, res specialist, 69, res group leader inorg res & develop div, 69-72, com develop mgr, 72-76, com dir sorbates, 77-80, DIR PLANNING & CONTROLS SPECIALTY CHEM, MONSANTO INDUST CHEM CO, 77-, DIR RESULTS MGT & PERSONNEL PLANNING, 80- *Mem:* Am Chem Soc. *Res:* Coordination chemistry of Co-II and Ni-II compounds; basic and applied research on phosphonate compounds; precipitation inhibition and corrosion inhibition. *Mailing Add:* 639 Lampadaire St Louis MO 63141

KING, TSOO E, b Soochow, China, Jan 14, 23; nat US; m 55. BIOCHEMISTRY. *Educ:* Nat Cent Univ, China, BS, 36; Ore State Col, MS, 48, PhD, 49. *Prof Exp:* Asst biochem, Ore State Univ, 47-49, res assoc, 50-51, from asst prof to prof, 51-68, asst dir sci res inst, 62-68; chmn dept, 69-72, PROF CHEM, STATE UNIV NY ALBANY, 68-, DIR, BIOENERGETIC LAB, 74- *Concurrent Pos:* NSF sr fel, Molteno Inst, Cambridge Univ, 57-58, Guggenheim fel. *Honors & Awards:* Gov Northwest Scientist Award, 65. *Mem:* Am Chem Soc; Am Soc Microbiol; Am Soc Biol Chemists; Brit Biochem Soc; Royal Soc Chem. *Res:* Enzymes and metabolism; electron transfer in biological systems. *Mailing Add:* Dept of Chem State Univ of NY Albany NY 12222

KING, WALTER BERNARD, b Ewing, Ill, Dec 3, 00; m 36; c 4. INORGANIC CHEMISTRY. *Educ:* Univ Ill, BS, 23; Iowa State Col, MS, 24, PhD(inorg chem), 30. *Prof Exp:* From asst prof to prof, 31-71, EMER PROF CHEM, IOWA STATE UNIV, 71- *Mem:* Am Chem Soc. *Mailing Add:* 2103 Country Club Blvd Ames IA 50010

KING, WILLIAM CONNOR, b Newark, Ohio, Mar 10, 27; m 50; c 2. RADAR SYSTEMS, COMMUNICATION SYSTEMS. *Educ:* Denison Univ, BA, 49; Duke Univ, PhD(physics), 53. *Prof Exp:* Asst physics, Duke Univ, 49-53, res assoc, 53; res assoc radiation lab, Johns Hopkins Univ, 53-56; commun physicist, Space Sci Lab, Missile & Space Div, Gen Elec Co, 56-62, mgr space systs anal proj, 62-64, commun eng spacecraft dept, Pa, 64-67, data systs, 67-70; mgr hard point demonstration array radar prog, RCA Corp, 71-74, leader tradex programming, Missile & Surface Radar Div, 74-77; mgr, Wayland Software Eng Dept, 78-80, SR STAFF, SOFTWARE SYSTS LAB, RAYTHEON CORP, 81- *Mem:* Am Phys Soc; Asn Comput Mach; sr mem Inst Elec & Electronics Eng; Am Inst Aeronaut & Astronaut. *Res:* Microwave spectroscopy and wave propagation in ionized media; design and development of real-time computer programs for radar, missile and communication systems; communications applications of computers. *Mailing Add:* Raytheon Co Software Systs Lab Boston Post Rd Wayland MA 01778

KING, WILLIAM EMMETT, JR, b Pittsburgh, Pa, July 27, 43. CHEMICAL ENGINEERING. *Educ:* Univ Pittsburgh, BS, 65; Carnegie-Mellon Univ, MS, 68; Univ Pa, PhD(chem eng), 76. *Prof Exp:* Chem engr, Esso Res & Eng Co, 66-68; engr mathematician, Cities Serv Res & Develop Co, 68-70; asst prof chem eng, Univ Md, 75-81; SR RES ENGR, GULF RES & DEVELOP CO, 81- *Mem:* Am Inst Chem Engrs; Am Chem Soc. *Res:* Fluid-solid reactions; applied mathematics; coal conversion technology; synthetic fuels. *Mailing Add:* 4987 Meadowridge Lane Gibsonia PA 15044

KING, WILLIAM MATTERN, b Cando, NDak, Mar 12, 30; c 1. APPLIED CHEMISTRY. *Educ:* NDak State Univ, BS, 57, MS, 58. *Prof Exp:* Chemist polymers, Hooker Chem Corp, 58-60; mgr develop membranes, Envirogenics Systs Co, 60-78; MGR DEVELOP MEMBRANES, SPECTRUM SEPARATIONS, INC, 79- *Mem:* Am Chem Soc. *Res:* Asymmetric membranes for the separation of gases and organic liquids as well as the desalination of water by reverse osmosis. *Mailing Add:* 547 Temple Hills Dr Laguna Beach CA 92651

KING, WILLIAM ROBERT, JR, b Los Angeles, Calif, Aug 25, 24; m 50; c 3. CHEMICAL METALLURGY. *Educ:* Calif Inst Technol, BS, 47; Univ Calif, Los Angeles, PhD(chem), 52. *Prof Exp:* Asst chem, Univ Calif, Los Angeles, 47-50; res chemist, Filtrol Corp, 52-54 & Sierra Talc & Clay Co, 54-55; sect head, 55-77, SR STAFF RES CHEMIST, KAISER ALUMINUM & CHEM CORP, 77- *Mem:* AAAS; Am Chem Soc. *Res:* Physical and inorganic chemistry; radiochemistry; molten salts; natural iron and aluminum minerals. *Mailing Add:* Kaiser Aluminum & Chem Corp PO Box 877 Pleasanton CA 94566

KING, WILLIAM STANELY, b Monroe, La, June 16, 35; m 58; c 2. APPLIED PHYSICS, ENGINEERING. *Educ:* Univ Calif, Berkeley, BSME, 57; Univ Calif, Los Angeles, MS, 60, PhD(appl math, physics), 66. *Prof Exp:* Res engr, Rocket Div, Rockwell Int Corp, 57-61; staff scientist, Aerospace Corp, 61-72; SR RES SCIENTIST, RAND CORP, 72- *Concurrent Pos:* Instr math, Santa Monica Col, 73-; instr eng, Univ Calif, Los Angeles, 77-; Aerospace Corp adv study grant. *Mem:* Assoc fel Am Inst Aeronaut & Astronaut; Sigma Xi. *Res:* Fluid dynamics; numerical analysis; electromagnetic theory; laser physics; applied mathematics. *Mailing Add:* Rand Corp 1700 Main St Santa Monica CA 90406

KING, WILLIAM TRAVERS, physical chemistry, see previous edition

KING, WILLIS KWONGTSU, b Shanghai, China, Sept 23, 36; m 70. COMPUTER SCIENCE, ELECTRICAL ENGINEERING. *Educ:* Darmstadt Tech Univ, Dipl Ing, 63; Univ Pa, PhD(elec eng), 69. *Prof Exp:* Res engr comput design, IBM Labs, 63-65; asst prof comput sci, 69-73, ASSOC PROF COMPUT SCI, UNIV HOUSTON, 73-, CHMN DEPT COMPUT SCI, 79- *Mem:* Asn Comput Mach; Sigma Xi; Inst Elec & Electronics Engrs. *Res:* Computer architecture; logic design; microprogramming. *Mailing Add:* Dept Comput Sci 3801 Cullen Blvd Houston TX 77004

KING, WILTON W(AYT), b Richmond, Va, Aug 11, 37; m 58; c 4. ENGINEERING MECHANICS. *Educ:* Univ Va, BME, 59, MME, 61; Va Polytech Inst, PhD(eng mech), 65. *Prof Exp:* Instr eng mech, Va Polytech Inst, 61-64; from asst prof to assoc prof, 64-77, PROF ENG MECH, GA INST TECHNOL, 77- *Mem:* Am Soc Mech Engrs. *Res:* Vibrations; fracture mechanics. *Mailing Add:* Sch of Eng Sci & Mech Ga Inst Technol Atlanta GA 30332

KINGDON, HENRY SHANNON, b Puunene, Hawaii, July 2, 34; m 57; c 3. BIOCHEMISTRY, HEMATOLOGY. *Educ:* Oberlin Col, AB, 56; Western Reserve Univ, MD & PhD(biochem), 63. *Prof Exp:* Intern & resident internal med, Univ Wash, 63-65; clin assoc, Nat Heart Inst, 65-67; from asst prof to assoc prof med & biochem, Univ Chicago, 67-73; prof med & biochem, Univ NC, Chapel Hill, 73-81; MED DIR, HYLAND THERAPEUT, GLENDALE, CALIF, 81- *Mem:* Am Chem Soc; Am Fedn Clin Res; Int Soc Thrombosis & Haemostasis; Am Soc Hemat; Am Soc Biol Chem. *Res:* Hematology; enzymology of blood coagulation; regulation of nitrogen metabolism in microorganisms; primary structure of regulatory and coagulation enzymes. *Mailing Add:* Hyland Therapeut 444 W Glenoaks Blvd Glendale CA 91202

KINGERY, BERNARD TROY, b Metter, Ga, July 16, 20; m 59; c 2. PHYSICS. *Educ:* Ga Southern Col, BS, 48; Columbia Univ, MA, 49. *Prof Exp:* Instr physics, Orange County Community Col, 50-52; supvr physics courses, Div Technol, Newark Col Eng; ASST PROF PHYSICS, NJ INST TECHNOL, 52- *Concurrent Pos:* Instr teaching of sci, Teachers Col, Columbia Univ, 57-58. *Mem:* AAAS; Am Soc Eng Educ; Am Asn Physics Teachers; Nat Sci Teachers Asn. *Res:* Science teacher education. *Mailing Add:* Dept of Physics NJ Inst of Technol 323 High St Newark NJ 07102

KINGERY, W(ILLIAM) D(AVID), b New York, NY, July 7, 26; div; c 4. CERAMICS, MATERIALS SCIENCE. *Educ:* Mass Inst Technol, SB, 48, ScD(ceramics), 50. *Prof Exp:* Res assoc, 49-50, from asst prof to assoc prof, 50-63, PROF CERAMICS, MASS INST TECHNOL, 63- *Concurrent Pos:* Foreign collabr, Comn Atomic Energy, France, 64-65. *Honors & Awards:* Purdy Award, Am Ceramics Soc, 54, Jeppson Gold Medal, 59, Sosman Lectr, 74, F H Norton Award, 77. *Mem:* Nat Acad Eng; Am Chem Soc; Am Ceramic Soc; AAAS. *Res:* Archaeological ceramics. *Mailing Add:* Mass Inst Technol Rm 13-4090 Cambridge MA 02139

KINGMAN, HARRY ELLIS, JR, b Ft Collins, Colo, Sept 4, 11; m 36; c 1. VETERINARY MEDICINE. *Educ:* Colo State Univ, DVM, 33. *Prof Exp:* Jr veterinarian, US Bur Animal Indust, 33-39; chief veterinarian, Wilson & Co, Inc, Ill, 39-53; asst exec secy, Am Vet Med Asn, 53-58, exec secy, 58-66; exec dir, Nat Soc Med Res, 66-78; RETIRED. *Concurrent Pos:* Mem, Nat Adv Food & Drug Coun, 65-69. *Mem:* Am Vet Med Asn (treas, 52-58). *Res:* Public health; food hygiene; physiology of reproduction of cattle. *Mailing Add:* 1707 Essex Dr Ft Collins CO 80526

KINGREA, C(HARLES) L(EO), b Barren Springs, Va, Aug 17, 23; m 46; c 3. CHEMICAL ENGINEERING, PROGRAM MANAGEMENT. *Educ:* Va Polytech Inst, BS, 43, MS, 51, PhD(chem eng), 53. *Prof Exp:* Owner-mgr, Kingrea Milling Co, Va, 46-53; process design engr, 53-56, asst supt mfg tech serv, 56-58, econ anal engr, 58, proj mgr, 58-60, head eng & math sci, 60-63, head spec process design assignment, La, 63-68, gen supt alcohol opers, Tex, 68-71, gen supt opers, 71-80, MGR, TECH PLANNING & PROJ COORDR, ETHYL CORP, 80- *Concurrent Pos:* Prod engr, Dallas Chem Procurement Dist, 43-44, property disposal officer, 44-46. *Mem:* Am Inst Chem Engrs. *Res:* Mass transfer operations, particularly thermal diffusion; chemical process design; chemical project management. *Mailing Add:* Ethyl Corp Chem Group 451 Florida Blvd Baton Rouge LA 70801

KINGSBURY, CHARLES ALVIN, b Louisville, Ky, Jan 12, 35; m 58; c 5. ORGANIC CHEMISTRY. *Educ:* Iowa State Col, BS, 56; Univ Calif, Los Angeles, PhD(org chem), 60. *Prof Exp:* NSF fel, Harvard Univ, 62-63; instr org chem, Iowa State Univ, 63-67; asst prof, 67-68, assoc prof, 68-72, PROF ORG CHEM, UNIV NEBR, LINCOLN, 72- *Mem:* Royal Soc Chem; Am Chem Soc. *Res:* Stereochemistry; reaction mechanisms. *Mailing Add:* Hamilton Hall Univ of Nebr Lincoln NE 68588

KINGSBURY, DAVID THOMAS, b Seattle, Wash, Oct 24, 40; div. VIROLOGY, MICROBIOLOGY. *Educ:* Univ Wash, BS, 62, MS, 64; Univ Calif, San Diego, PhD(biol), 71. *Prof Exp:* Microbiologist, Naval Med Res Inst, 64-67; res fel microbiol, Am Inst Biol Sci, 67-68; from asst prof to assoc prof microbiol, Univ Calif, Irvine, 72-81; PROF MED MICROBIOL & VIROL, UNIV CALIF, BERKELEY, 81-; DIR, NAVAL BIOSCI LAB, OAKLAND, 81- *Concurrent Pos:* Am Cancer Soc Dernham fel oncol, Univ Calif, San Diego, 71-72 & 77 & Nat Inst Health, 78-79; vis scientist, Scripps Clin & Res Found, La Jolla, Calif, 73- *Mem:* AAAS; Am Soc Microbiol. *Res:* Oncogenic viruses; viral genetics; biochemistry of virus replication; techniques in diagnostic virology and microbiology; biochemistry and genetics of the unconventional viruses. *Mailing Add:* Naval Biosci Lab Naval Supply Ctr Oakland CA 94625

KINGSBURY, DAVID WILSON, b Jersey City, NJ, Apr 2, 33; m 57; c 7. VIROLOGY, BIOCHEMISTRY. *Educ:* Manhattan Col, BS, 55; Yale Univ, MD, 59. *Prof Exp:* Intern path, Yale Univ, 59-60, asst resident, 60-61; from res fel to mem, 63-69, MEM DIV VIROL, ST JUDE HOSP, MEMPHIS, 69-, ADJ PROF MICROBIOL, UNIV TENN, MEMPHIS, 72- *Concurrent Pos:* USPHS res fel, Yale Univ, 61-63, St Jude Hosp, Memphis, 63-64, career develop award, 64-73. *Mem:* Am Asn Immunol; Sigma Xi; Am Soc Microbiol; Soc Gen Microbiol UK. *Res:* Negative strand RNA viruses. *Mailing Add:* Div of Virol St Jude Children's Res Hosp Memphis TN 38101

KINGSBURY, HERBERT B, b Pittsburgh, Pa, Feb 15, 34; m 56; c 3. SOLID MECHANICS, BIOMECHANICS. *Educ:* Univ Conn, BS, 58; Univ Pa, MS, 61, PhD(eng mech), 64. *Prof Exp:* Scientist, Dyna/Struct Inc, 61-64; engr, Missile & Space Div, Gen Elec Corp, 64-66; asst prof aerospace eng, Pa State Univ, 66-67; asst prof, 67-73, assoc prof aerospace eng, 73-80, PROF MECH & AEROSPACE ENG, UNIV DEL, 80- *Concurrent Pos:* Eng consult, Scott Paper Co, 70-; adj assoc prof, Sch Vet Med, Univ Pa, 78- *Mem:* Am Soc Mech Engrs; Am Soc Biomech; Int Soc Biomech; Nat Soc Prof Engrs. *Res:* Structural mechanics; mechanics of biological structures; mechanics of porous deformable solids and structural dynamics. *Mailing Add:* Dept of Mech & Aerospace Eng Univ of Del Newark DE 19711

KINGSBURY, ROBERT FREEMAN, b Ithaca, NY, June 26, 12; m 33; c 4. ATOMIC SPECTROSCOPY. *Educ:* Bowdoin Col, BS, 34; Cornell Univ, MS, 39; Univ Pa, PhD(physics), 56. *Prof Exp:* Teacher pub schs, NY; instr sci, Mass State Teachers Col, Westfield, 42-43; instr physics, Bowdoin Col, 43, Bates Col, 44 & Univ Maine, 44-47; from instr to assoc prof, Trinity Col, Conn, 50-64; prof, 64-77, EMER PROF PHYSICS, BATES COL, 77- *Mem:* AAAS; Am Phys Soc; Am Asn Physics Teachers; Am Optical Soc. *Res:* Atomic spectra. *Mailing Add:* 65 Vale St Lewiston ME 04240

KINGSBURY, WILLIAM DENNIS, b Buffalo, NY, Nov 21, 41; m 67; c 3. ORGANIC CHEMISTRY, MEDICINAL CHEMISTRY. *Educ:* State Univ NY Buffalo, BA, 65; Wayne State Univ, PhD(chem), 70. *Prof Exp:* Chemist, Electro Refractories & Abrasives, 61-62; instr chem, Wayne State Univ, 65-67; SR CHEMIST, SMITH KLINE & FRENCH LABS, 71- *Concurrent Pos:* NIH fel, Univ Kans, 70-71. *Mem:* Am Chem Soc. *Res:* Anthelmintics; animal nutrition; heterocyclic chemistry; organo sulfur chemistry; immunochemistry; bacterial chemotherapy. *Mailing Add:* 551 Saratoga Rd King of Prussia PA 19406

KINGSLAKE, RUDOLF, b London, Eng, Aug 28, 03; nat US; m 29; c 1. OPTICS. *Educ:* Univ London, BSc, 24, Imp Col, MSc & dipl, 26, DSc, 50. *Prof Exp:* Optical designer, Sir Howard Grubb, Parsons & Co, Eng, 27-28; res engr, Int Standard Elec Corp, London, 28-29; from asst prof to assoc prof geomet optics, 29-59, PART-TIME PROF OPTICS, INST OF OPTICS, UNIV ROCHESTER, 59- *Concurrent Pos:* Exchange prof, Imp Col, Univ London, 36-37; optical designer, Eastman Kodak Co, 37-39, head optical design dept, 39-68. *Honors & Awards:* Ives Medal, Optical Soc Am, 73; Gold Medal, Soc Photo-optical Instrumentation Engrs, 80. *Mem:* Fel Optical Soc Am (vpres, 45-47, pres, 47-49); fel Soc Motion Picture & TV Engrs; fel Soc Photog Scientists & Engrs; fel Soc Photo-Optical Instrumentation Engrs. *Res:* Design of lenses and optical systems; measurement of aberrations; effect of aberrations on optical images; applied optics. *Mailing Add:* 56 Westland Ave Rochester NY 14618

KINGSLAND, GRAYDON CHAPMAN, b Burlington, Vt, Aug 28, 28; m 50; c 4. PLANT PATHOLOGY. *Educ:* Univ Vt, BA, 52; Univ NH, MS, 55; Pa State Univ, PhD(plant path), 58. *Prof Exp:* Res technician, Conn Tobacco Lab, 52-53; assoc pathologist, United Fruit Co, Honduras, 58-60; asst prof bot & asst pathologist, 60-67, ASSOC PROF PLANT PATH & PHYSIOL, CLEMSON UNIV, 67- *Mem:* Am Phytopath Soc; Sierra Club; Wilderness Soc; Nat Audubon Soc; Sigma Xi. *Res:* Diseases of cereal grains; ecology of microflora of rhizospheres and seeds of cereal grains; chemical control of cereal grains diseases; teaching introductory and graduate phytopathology; tropical agriculture. *Mailing Add:* Dept of Plant Path & Physiol Clemson Univ Clemson SC 29631

KINGSLEY, HENRY A(DELBERT), b Wakefield, RI, May 5, 21; m 43; c 2. CHEMICAL ENGINEERING, PROCESS ENGINEERING. *Educ:* Univ RI, BS, 43; Yale Univ, DEng, 49. *Prof Exp:* Engr, Shell Develop Co, Calif, 49-59, supvr process eng, 59-63, dept head licensing & design eng, 64-65, dir res & develop lab, Indust Chem Div, Shell Chem Co, Tex, 65-67, mgr proj develop, Plastics & Resins Div, NY, 67-70, mgr chem & chem eng dept, Explor & Prod Res Ctr, Shell Develop Co, 70-72, mgr chem process eng, 72-74, MGR SUPPORT PROCESS ENG, SHELL OIL CO, 74- *Mem:* Am Inst Chem Engrs; Am Chem Soc. *Mailing Add:* Shell Oil Co PO Box 3105 Houston TX 77001

KINGSLEY, JACK DEAN, b Wonewoc, Wis, Aug 10, 34; m 62; c 3. SOLID STATE PHYSICS. *Educ:* Univ Wis, BSEE, 56, MSEE, 57; Univ Ill, MS, 58, PhD(physics), 60. *Prof Exp:* Physicist, Gen Elec Res & Develop Ctr, 60-71, mgr light emitting diode array prog, 71-72, mgr optoelectronics br, 72-81, MGR ELECTRONIC MAT BR, GEN ELEC RES & DEVELOP CTR, 81- *Mem:* Am Phys Soc; Electrochem Soc. *Res:* Optical spectroscopy of solids; quantum electronics; luminescence; point defects in solids; imaging and display devices. *Mailing Add:* Gen Elec Res & Develop Ctr PO Box 8 Schenectady NY 12301

KINGSOLVER, CHARLES H, b Peru, Nebr, Aug 31, 14; m 41; c 4. PLANT PATHOLOGY. *Educ:* Nebr State Teachers Col, Peru, AB, 35; Iowa State Univ, MS, 39, PhD(plant path), 43. *Prof Exp:* Asst prof bot, Univ Mo, 46-51; sect chief, Biol Br, Chem Corps, Biol Warfare Labs, Md, 51-55, chief biol br II, 55-57; agr adminr, Mkt Qual Res Div, Agr Mkt Serv, USDA, 57-62; chief biol br, Crops Div, US Army Biol Labs, 62-68, chief plant path div, 68-71; dir, Plant Dis Res Lab, Northeast Region, Sci & Educ Admin-Agr Res, USDA, 71-79; CONSULT PLANT DISEASE RES, 79- *Concurrent Pos:* Adj prof plant path, Pa State Univ, 72- *Mem:* AAAS; Am Inst Biol Sci; Sigma Xi; Am Phytopath Soc. *Res:* Plant disease epidemiology; quantitation of disease increase and spread; predictive systems; threat potential of foreign plant disease. *Mailing Add:* PO Box 216 Braddock Heights MD 21714

KINGSOLVER, JOHN MARK, b Selma, Ind, Mar 20, 25; m 48; c 2. ENTOMOLOGY. *Educ:* Purdue Univ, BS, 51; Univ Ill, MS, 56, PhD(entom), 61. *Prof Exp:* Res asst entom, Univ Ill, 54-61; res assoc, Ill Natural Hist Surv, 61-62; RES ENTOMOLOGIST, SYST ENTOM LAB, USDA, 62- *Mem:* Entom Soc Am; Am Entom Soc; Asn Trop Biol; Sigma Xi. *Res:* Taxonomy of seed-beetles (Bruchidae) of Western Hemisphere. *Mailing Add:* Syst Entom Lab USDA c/o Us Nat Mus Washington DC 20560

KINGSTON, CHARLES RICHARD, b San Diego, Calif, Apr 11, 31; m 69; c 1. FORENSIC SCIENCE. *Educ:* Univ Calif, Berkeley, BS, 59, MCriminol, 61, Dr Criminol, 64. *Prof Exp:* Lab technician, Criminalistics Lab, Sch Criminol, Univ Calif, Berkeley, 58-63, res criminalist, 63-64, asst res criminalist, 64-65; consult, NY State Identification & Intel Syst, 65-66, chief criminalistics res bur, 66-68; PROF CRIMINALISTICS, JOHN JAY COL, CITY UNIV NEW YORK, 68- *Mem:* Am Chem Soc; Am Statist Asn; Am Acad Forensic Sci. *Res:* Application of probability and statistics in criminalistics; computer applications in criminology and criminalistics. *Mailing Add:* Dept Sci City Univ New York John Jay Col Criminal Justice New York NY 10019

KINGSTON, DAVID GEORGE IAN, b London, Eng, Nov 9, 38; m 66; c 2. NATURAL PRODUCTS CHEMISTRY. *Educ:* Cambridge Univ, BA, 60, PhD(org chem), 63; dipl theol, Univ London, 62. *Prof Exp:* Res fel chem, Queens' Col, Cambridge Univ, 62-66, NATO fel, 64-66; asst prof chem, State Univ NY Albany, 66-71; assoc prof, 71-77, PROF CHEM, VA POLYTECH INST & STATE UNIV, 77- *Concurrent Pos:* Res assoc, Mass Inst Technol, 63-64. *Mem:* Am Chem Soc; Royal Soc Chem; Am Soc Mass Spectroscopy; Am Soc Pharmacog. *Res:* Natural products chemistry; structure and synthesis of biologically active natural products; organic structure determination by spectroscopic methods; biosynthesis of antibiotics. *Mailing Add:* Dept Chem Va Polytech Inst & State Univ Blacksburg VA 24061

KINGSTON, DAVID LYMAN, b Lansing, Mich, June 26, 30; m 54; c 3. SOLID STATE PHYSICS. *Educ:* Mich State Univ, BS, 53, MS, 55. *Prof Exp:* Res physicist, Aerospace Res Labs, 55-75, RES PHYSICIST SOLID STATE PHYSICS, AIR FORCE AVIONICS LAB, WRIGHT-PATTERSON AIR FORCE BASE, OHIO, 75- *Mem:* Am Phys Soc. *Res:* Conducting research on the characterization of III-V compound semiconductors such as GaAs and InP using the techniques of luminescence topography and x-ray photoemission spectroscopy. *Mailing Add:* 10 E Routzong Dr Fairborn OH 45324

KINGSTON, JOHN MAURICE, b Joliet, Ill, May 25, 14; m 37; c 2. MATHEMATICS. *Educ:* Univ Western Ont, BA, 35; Univ Toronto, MA, 36, PhD(theory, abstract groups), 39. *Prof Exp:* Lectr math, Univ BC, 39-40; assoc, 40-43, from instr to asst prof, 43-59, ASSOC PROF MATH, UNIV WASH, 59-, EXEC SECY DEPT, 52- *Concurrent Pos:* Fel, NSF, 59-60. *Mem:* Nat Coun Teachers Math; Math Asn Am. *Res:* Abstract group theory. *Mailing Add:* Dept of Math Univ of Wash Seattle WA 98195

KINGSTON, NEWTON, b Akron, Ohio, June 6, 25; m 52; c 3. ZOOLOGY, PARASITOLOGY. *Educ:* Wayne State Univ, BA, 54, MSc, 56; Univ Toronto, PhD(zool), 62. *Prof Exp:* Asst prof biol, Detroit Inst Technol, 59-62 & Geneva Col, 62-64; NIH fel, Nat Univ Mexico, 64-65; assoc prof, Geneva Col, 65-68; assoc prof, 68-76, PROF PARASITOL, UNIV WYO, 76- *Mem:* Am Soc Parasitol; Am Micros Soc; Soc Protozoologists; Wildlife Dis Asn. *Res:* Morphology of the nervous system of trematodes; life history studies of monogenetic and digenetic trematodes, cestodes; systematics of spinturnicid mites from bats; protozoan parasites domestic and wild ungulate raptors. *Mailing Add:* Div of Microbiol & Vet Med Univ Wyo Box 3354 Univ Sta Laramie WY 82071

KINGSTON, ROBERT HILDRETH, b Somerville, Mass, Feb 13, 28; m 52; c 4. SOLID STATE DEVICES, OPTICS. *Educ:* Mass Inst Technol, BS, 48, MS, 48, PhD(physics), 51. *Prof Exp:* Mem staff transistor res & develop, Bell Labs, 51-52; mem solid state physics group, 52-61, leader optics & infrared group, 61-69, head optics div, 69-72, leader infrared radar group, 72-77, SR STAFF, LINCOLN LAB, MASS INST TECHNOL, 77- *Concurrent Pos:* Consult, US Dept Defense, 62-; vis assoc prof, Stanford Univ, 64-65; ed, J Quantum Electronics, Inst Elec & Electronics Engrs, 65-70. *Mem:* Fel Am Phys Soc; fel Optical Soc Am; fel Inst Elec & Electronics Engrs. *Res:* Physical principles of semiconductor devices; physics of semiconductor surfaces; magnetic resonance; solid state maser, parametric amplifiers; optical masers; non-linear optics; tuneable semiconductor lasers; infrared detectors. *Mailing Add:* 4 Field Rd Lexington MA 02173

KINKEL, ARLYN WALTER, b Fond du Lac, Wis, Oct 15, 29; m 55; c 3. PHARMACY. *Educ:* Univ Wis, BS, 52, MS, 57, PhD(pharm), 58. *Prof Exp:* Assoc res pharmacist, 58-62, from res pharmacist to sr res pharmacist, 62-70, sect dir pharmaceut res & develop, 70-80, DIR CLIN PHARMACOKINETICS, PHARMACOKINETIC/DRUG METAB, PHARMACOL DEPT, RES DIV, WARNER-LAMBERT/PARKE-DAVIS, 81- *Mem:* Am Pharmaceut Asn; fel Acad Pharmaceut Sci. *Res:* Biopharmaceutics; assay of blood levels and drugs; pharmacokinetics. *Mailing Add:* Pharmaceut Res Div Warner-Lambert/Parke-Davis Ann Arbor MI 48106

KINLOCH, BOHUN BAKER, JR, b Charleston, SC, July 21, 34; m 61, 69; c 4. GENETICS, PLANT PATHOLOGY. *Educ:* Univ Va, BA, 56; NC State Univ, BS, 62, MS, 65, PhD(genetics), 68. *Prof Exp:* Res asst forest genetics & path, NC State Univ, 62-68; GENETICIST, PAC SOUTHWEST FOREST & RANGE EXP STA, US FOREST SERV, 68- *Mem:* Am Phytopath Soc. *Res:* Genetics of disease resistance in forest trees. *Mailing Add:* 1425 Greenwood Terrace Berkeley CA 94708

KINLOCH, ROBERT ARMSTRONG, b Dumbarton, Scotland, Feb 15, 39; m 63; c 3. NEMATOLOGY. *Educ:* Glasgow Univ, BSc, 63; Univ Calif, Davis, PhD(entom, nematol), 68. *Prof Exp:* Assoc nematologist, 68-80, ASSOC PROF AGRON, AGR EXP STA, UNIV FLA, 80- *Mem:* Soc Nematol; Orgn Trop Am Nematol. *Res:* Biology and host-parasite relationships of plant parasitic nematodes; economic control of plant parasitic nematodes affecting agronomic crops. *Mailing Add:* Agr Res Ctr Univ of Fla Jay FL 32565

KINMAN, MURRAY LUTHER, b Clinton, Mo, July 25, 20; m 39; c 1. AGRONOMY. *Educ:* Kans State Col, BS, 42; Iowa State Col, MS, 44, PhD(plant breeding), 50. *Prof Exp:* From res asst to res assoc, Iowa State Col, 42-44; from asst agronomist to assoc agronomist, Tex Res Found, 44-50; prof agron, Tex A&M Univ, 51-73, prof genetics, 58-73, res agronomist, Dept Soil & Crop Sci, Agr Res Serv, USDA, 50-73; RETIRED. *Concurrent Pos:* Consult agronomist, Kinman Agr Consult Serv, 73- *Honors & Awards:* V S Pustovoit Award, Int Sunflower Asn, 80. *Mem:* Am Soc Agron; Crop Sci Soc Am. *Res:* Improvement and culture of industrial crops, especially sunflower and guar; plant breeding methods. *Mailing Add:* Rte 5 Box 876 College Station TX 77840

KINMAN, RILEY NELSON, b Dry Ridge, Ky, Jan 25, 36; m 57; c 2. CIVIL & SANITARY ENGINEERING. *Educ:* Univ Ky, BS, 59; Univ Cincinnati, MS, 62; Univ Fla, PhD(sanit eng), 65. *Prof Exp:* Engr-in-training, Water Dept, City of Dayton, Ohio, 59-61, 62; res assoc chem & sanit sci, Univ Fla, 65-66; asst chief demonstration grants br, Fed Water Pollution Control Admin, 66-67, chief, 67-68; assoc prof civil eng, 68-73, PROF CIVIL ENG, UNIV CINCINNATI, 73-; PRES, PRISTINE, INC, 74- *Mem:* Am Soc Civil Engrs; Water Pollution Control Fedn; Am Water Works Asn; Am Chem Soc. *Res:* Treatment and ultimate disposal of hazardous wastes; research and development for control of water pollution, especially the physical, chemical, biological, physiological, economic and political aspects of water pollution. *Mailing Add:* Dept of Civil & Environ Eng Location 71 Univ of Cincinnati Cincinnati OH 45221

KINMAN, THOMAS DAVID, b Rugby, Eng, Aug 10, 28; m 63; c 2. ASTRONOMY. *Educ:* Oxford Univ, BA, 49, MA & DPhil(astron), 53. *Prof Exp:* Dept demonstr, Univ Observ, Oxford Univ, 49-53; sci officer physics, Admirality Res Lab, Teddington, 53-54; Radcliffe travelling fel astron, Univ Observ, Oxford Univ, 54-56 & Radcliffe Observ, Pretoria, 56-59; sr sci officer, Royal Observ, Cape Town, 59-60; from asst astronr to astronr, Lick Observ, Univ Calif, Santa Cruz, 60-69; ASTRONR, KITT PEAK NAT OBSERV, 69- *Concurrent Pos:* Mem comn, Int Astron Union, 58. *Mem:* Fel Royal Astron Soc. *Res:* Large scale structure of our own and other galaxies, particularly constitution and dynamics of older stars and star clusters; quasistellar objects. *Mailing Add:* Kitt Peak Nat Observ PO Box 26732 Tucson AZ 85726

KINN, DONALD NORMAN, b Chicago, Ill. ENTOMOLOGY, ACAROLOGY. *Educ:* Lawrence Col, BS, 56; Univ Wyo, MS, 62; Univ Calif, Berkeley, PhD(entom), 69. *Prof Exp:* Assoc specialist, Div Biol Control, Univ Calif, 69-70, asst res entom, 71-73; RES ENTOMOLOGIST ACAROL, SOUTHERN FOREST EXP STA, 75- *Mem:* Entom Soc Am; Entom Soc Can; Int Orgn Biol Control; Acarol Soc Am. *Res:* Natural control of forest insects, especially bark beetles, by mites and nematodes. *Mailing Add:* Southern Forest Exp Sta 2500 Shreveport Hwy Pineville LA 71360

KINNAIRD, RICHARD FARRELL, b Des Moines, Iowa, Oct 21, 12; m 44; c 2. ENGINEERING. *Educ:* Millsaps Col, BS, 34; Univ Chicago, MS, 36. *Prof Exp:* Asst, Dearborn Observ, Northwestern Univ, 36-39; optical engr, Bell & Howell Co, Chicago, 39-40; optical engr, 40-63, SR STAFF ENGR, PERKIN-ELMER CORP, 63- *Mem:* Am Phys Soc; Optical Soc Am. *Res:* Design and theory of optical instruments. *Mailing Add:* 69 Peaceable Hill Rd Ridgefield CT 06877

KINNAMON, KENNETH ELLIS, b Denison, Tex, May 28, 34; m 57; c 3. PHYSIOLOGY, RADIOBIOLOGY. *Educ:* Okla State Univ, BS, 56; Tex A&M Univ, DVM, 59; Univ Rochester, MS, 61; Univ Tenn, PhD(physiol), 71. *Prof Exp:* Res investr radiation chem, Walter Reed Army Inst Res, 59-60, chief radioisotope lab, Army Nutrit Lab, Fitzsimons Gen Hosp, Colo, 61-65, chief dept surveillance inspection, Med Dept, US Army Vet Sch, 65-68, res investr biol, 71-75; assoc prof physiol & asst dean instrnl & res support, 75-80, PROF PHYSIOL & ASSOC DEAN OPERS, UNIFORMED SERV UNIV HEALTH SCI, 80- *Mem:* Radiation Res Soc; Am Physiol Soc; Health Physics Soc; Am Vet Med Asn; Soc Exp Hemat. *Res:* Mineral metabolism; physiology of wound healing; bone marrow transplantation; secondary disease; immunology; cancer therapy; chemical radiation therapy; radiation injury therapy. *Mailing Add:* Uniformed Serv Univ Health Sci 4301 Jones Bridge Rd Bethesda MD 20014

KINNARD, MATTHEW ANDERSON, b Nashville, Tenn, April 12, 36; m 62; c 2. NEUROPHYSIOLOGY, HERBICIDES. *Educ:* Tenn State Univ, BS, 57, MA, 60; Georgetown Univ, PhD(physiol), 70. *Prof Exp:* Biologist virol res, Walter Reed Army Med Ctr, 60-62; biologist brain res, NIH, 63-67; asst prof physiol, DC Teachers Col, 70-71; grants assoc res admin, NIH, 71-72, scientist, 72-79; ADMIN HEALTH SCI SPECIALIST, CENT OFF, VET ADMIN, 79- *Concurrent Pos:* Lectr, Univ DC, 71-79; consult, Nat Inst Ment Health, 68-70, Physiol Dept, Howard Univ, 79-80, DC Licensure Comn, 81-; physiologist, Civil Serv Bd Examiners, 76- *Mem:* AAAS; Am Physiol Asn; Orgn Black Scientists; Int Asn Dent Res. *Res:* Herbicides (agent orange and agent blue) used in Vietnam; biological effects of ionizing radiation. *Mailing Add:* 12903 Chathlake Lane Silver Spring MD 20904

KINNARD, WILLIAM J, JR, b Wilmington, Del, Apr 18, 32; m 59. PHARMACOLOGY. *Educ:* Univ Pittsburgh, BS, 53, MS, 55; Purdue Univ, PhD(pharmacol), 57. *Prof Exp:* From asst prof to prof pharmacol, Univ Pittsburgh, 58-68; actg dean, 74-76, DEAN GRAD SCH, UNIV MD, BALTIMORE, 76-, PROF PHARMACOL & DEAN SCH PHARM, 68- *Concurrent Pos:* Chmn bd trustees, US Pharmacopoeial Conv, 74- *Honors & Awards:* Honor Achievement Award, Angiol Res Found, 65. *Mem:* Nat Acad Sci; fel AAAS; Am Soc Pharmacol & Exp Therapeut; Am Pharmaceut Asn; fel Am Col Clin Pharmacol; fel Acad Pharmaceut Sci. *Res:* General pharmacological screening, especially cardiovascular and neuropharmacology testing methods; health care systems and education. *Mailing Add:* Univ of Md Sch of Pharm Baltimore MD 21201

KINNAVY, M(ARTIN) G(ERALD), b Chicago, Ill, Nov 20, 21; m 56; c 5. MECHANICAL ENGINEERING, MECHANICS. *Educ:* Ill Inst Technol, BS, 43, MS, 52. *Prof Exp:* Proj engr, Fisher Body Detroit Div, Gen Motors Corp, 43-44; asst engr, Armour Res Found, Ill Inst Technol, 48-49, assoc engr, Ill Inst Technol Res Inst, 49-50, res engr, 50-52, supvr mechanisms anal & vibration eng, 52-59; assoc dir adv res dept, Sunbeam Corp, 59-60; assoc dir eng res dept, Continental Can Co, Inc, Ill, 60-65; dir eng, Herr Equip Corp, Ohio, 65-68, vpres, 68-70; dir, 70-76, VPRES ENG, HERR-VOSS CORP, 76- *Mem:* Am Soc Mech Engrs. *Res:* Dynamic behavior of mechanisms, linkages and structures; vibration analysis of artillery weapons; dynamics of space vehicles; methods of cam synthesis; mill equipment; tension leveling. *Mailing Add:* Herr-Voss Corp Callery PA 16024

KINNEL, ROBIN BRYAN, b Milwaukee, Wis, Jan 18, 37; m 60; c 2. ORGANIC CHEMISTRY. *Educ:* Harvard Univ, AB, 59; Mass Inst Technol, PhD(org chem), 65. *Prof Exp:* Asst chem, Hercules Powder Co, Del, 56-57; jr chemist, Merck, Sharp & Dohme, NJ, 59-60; res assoc org chem, Stanford Univ, 64-66; asst prof, 66-72, assoc prof, 72-78, assoc dean, 73-76, PROF ORG CHEM, HAMILTON COL, 76- *Concurrent Pos:* Res assoc, Cornell Univ, 76-77, Univ Hawaii, 81-82; premed adv, 72-80, Univ Wis-Madison, vis prof, 79. *Mem:* Sigma Xi; AAAS; Am Chem Soc. *Res:* Organic reaction mechanisms; medium ring chemistry; chemistry of marine natural products. *Mailing Add:* Dept of Chem Hamilton Col Clinton NY 13323

KINNEN, EDWIN, b Buffalo, NY, Mar 9, 25; m 52; c 4. ELECTRICAL ENGINEERING. *Educ:* Univ Buffalo, BS, 49; Yale Univ, ME, 50; Purdue Univ, PhD(elec eng), 58. *Prof Exp:* Res engr, Res Lab, Westinghouse Elec Corp, 50-55; asst prof elec eng, Purdue Univ, 58-59 & Univ Minn, 59-63; assoc prof, 63-77, PROF ELEC ENG, UNIV ROCHESTER, 77- *Mem:* AAAS; Inst Elec & Electronics Engrs. *Res:* System dynamics; biological controls; dynamics of blood flow; V integrated circuits. *Mailing Add:* Dept of Elec Eng Univ of Rochester Rochester NY 14627

KINNERSLEY, WILLIAM MORRIS, b Baltimore, Md, Jan 3, 44; m 66. THEORETICAL PHYSICS. *Educ:* Rensselaer Polytech Inst, BS, 64; Calif Inst Technol, PhD(theoret physics), 69. *Prof Exp:* Fac assoc physics, Univ Tex, Austin, 68-70; Nat Acad Sci resident res assoc, Wright Patterson AFB, Ohio, 70-71; asst prof, 71-75, ASSOC PROF PHYSICS, MONT STATE UNIV, 75- *Concurrent Pos:* Vis asst prof appl math, Calif Inst Technol, 73-74. *Res:* General relativity and gravitational radiation theory. *Mailing Add:* Dept of Physics Mont State Univ Bozeman MT 59717

KINNEY, DOUGLAS MERRILL, b Los Angeles, Calif, Feb 24, 17; m 42; c 3. GEOLOGY. *Educ:* Occidental Col, BA, 37; Yale Univ, MS, 42, PhD(geol), 51. *Prof Exp:* Geologist, Union Oil Co, Calif, 37-40; asst, Yale Univ, 40-42; geologist, 42-56, GEOL MAP ED, US GEOL SURV, 56- *Concurrent Pos:* Vpres, NAm Comn Geol Map of World, 66- *Mem:* Geol Soc Am; Am Asn Petrol Geol. *Res:* Stratigraphy and structure of Batesville District, Uinta Mountains, North Park, Colorado; geologic mapping standards and symbols. *Mailing Add:* Geol Surv Assoc Inc 5221 Baltimore Ave Bethesda MD 20816

KINNEY, EDWARD COYLE, JR, b Massillon, Ohio, Sept 27, 17; m 42. FISH BIOLOGY. *Educ:* Ohio State Univ, BSc, 41 & 46, MS, 48, PhD(hydrobiol), 54. *Prof Exp:* Asst to dir F T Stone Inst Hydrobiol, Ohio State Univ, 48-52; fisheries biologist, State Game & Fish Comn, Ga, 54-56; asst chief fish mgt, WVa Conserv Comn, 56-57, chief, 57-62; staff specialist, Bur Sport Fisheries & Wildlife, US Fish & Wildlife Serv, 62-68, chief br fishery mgt, 68-69 & br coop fishery units, 69-74, Great Lakes coordr, 74-78; RETIRED. *Honors & Awards:* Meritorius Serv Medal, US Army, 74. *Mem:* Am Fisheries Soc; Sigma Xi. *Res:* Life history studies of fresh water fishes; sampling methods for sampling fish populations. *Mailing Add:* 807 17th St SW Massillon OH 44646

KINNEY, GILBERT FORD, b Judsonia, Ark, Dec 29, 07; m 34; c 2. PHYSICAL CHEMISTRY, EXPLOSIONS. *Educ:* Ark Col, AB, 28; Univ Tenn, MS, 30; NY Univ, PhD(phys chem), 35. *Prof Exp:* Radio engr, Radio Sta WNBZ, NY, 30-32; res chemist, Titanium Pigment Co, 35; instr chem, Pratt Inst, 35-39, head instr, 39-42; radiologist, US Navy Bikini, 46; assoc prof thermodyn & phys chem, 46-50, prof chem eng, 50-71, chmn dept mat sci & chem, 60-69, EMER PROF CHEM ENG, NAVAL POSTGRAD SCH, 71- *Concurrent Pos:* Consult, Naval Weapons Ctr, China Lake, CA & Anamet Labs, Berkeley, CA, 71- *Honors & Awards:* Distinguished Prof Medallion,

Naval Postgrad Sch, 67. *Mem:* Am Chem Soc; Am Soc Eng Educ. *Res:* Explosive shocks; electroplating; chemical engineering thermodynamics; applications of thermodynamics to chemical equilibria problems; plastics. *Mailing Add:* Dept of Physics & Chem Naval Postgrad Sch Monterey CA 93940

KINNEY, JOHN MARTIN, b Evanston, Ill, May 24, 21; m 44; c 3. SURGERY. *Educ:* Denison Univ, AB, 43; Harvard Univ, MD, 46; Am Bd Surg, dipl; Am Bd Nutrit, dipl. *Prof Exp:* Surg intern, Peter Bent Brigham Hosp, 46-47; AEC-Nat Res Coun fel, Med Sch, Univ Colo, 49-52; from asst resident surgeon to chief resident surgeon, Peter Bent Brigham Hosp, 52-57, jr assoc surgeon, 58-63; assoc prof, 63-67, PROF SURG, COL PHYSICIANS & SURGEONS, COLUMBIA UNIV, 67-; DIR SURG METAB, PRESBY HOSP, 63- *Concurrent Pos:* Mead Johnson scholar, Am Col Surgeons, 56-59; Henry E Warren fel surg, Harvard Med Sch, 58-60 & 62-63; assoc attend surgeon, Presby Hosp, 63-67, attend surgeon, 67-; New York Health Res Coun career scientist award, 65; mem adv comt metabolism in trauma, US Army Med Res & Develop Command, 67; mem adv panel to comt on interplay of eng with biol & med, Nat Acad Eng, 68; chmn comt on shock, Comn Emergency Med Serv, Nat Res Coun, 69. *Mem:* Am Burn Asn; Am Asn Surg Trauma; Soc Univ Surg; fel Am Col Surgeons; Am Surg Asn. *Res:* Metabolic response to injury, burns, shock and peritonitis; gas exchange; calorimetry; energy balance; intensive care; patient monitoring; surgical nutrition. *Mailing Add:* 630 W 168th St New York NY 10032

KINNEY, LARRY LEE, b Salem, Iowa, Oct 26, 41; m 62; c 2. ELECTRICAL ENGINEERING. *Educ:* Univ Iowa, BS, 64, MS, 65, PhD(elec eng), 68. *Prof Exp:* Asst prof elec eng, Univ Iowa, 68; asst prof, 68-73, ASSOC PROF ELEC ENG, UNIV MINN, MINNEAPOLIS, 73- *Mem:* Inst Elec & Electronics Engrs; Asn Comput Mach. *Res:* Switching theory; computer systems. *Mailing Add:* Dept of Elec Eng Univ of Minn Minneapolis MN 55455

KINNEY, MICHAEL J, b Chicago, Ill, July 9, 37; m 71; c 2. INTERNAL MEDICINE, NEPHROLOGY. *Educ:* Univ Chicago, BS, 59, MD, 63. *Prof Exp:* Assoc chief, Renal Div Nephrol, US Pub Health Serv Hosp, 69-78; asst prof, State Univ NY Downstate Med Ctr, 77-78; assoc prof med & chief nephrology sect, Sch Med, Marshall Univ, 78-80; MED DIR, NEPHROL RES & EDUC FOUND, 80- *Mem:* Fel Am Col Physicians; fel Am Col Clin Pharmacol; Am Soc Nephrology; Soc Exp Biol & Med; Am Physiol Soc. *Res:* Hypertension; nuclear medicine. *Mailing Add:* Sch of Med Marshall Univ 1801 Sixth Ave Huntington WV 25701

KINNEY, RALPH A, b Frostproof, Fla, Nov 7, 30; m 60; c 3. ELECTRICAL ENGINEERING. *Educ:* Univ Fla, BEE, 56, MSE, 58, PhD(elec eng), 67. *Prof Exp:* Res asst elec eng, Univ Fla, 57-60; scientist, Northrop Space Labs, Calif, 60-62; asst res elec eng & aerospace, Univ Fla, 64-67; assoc prof elec eng, 67-76, PROF ELEC ENG, LA STATE UNIV, BATON ROUGE, 76- *Mem:* Inst Elec & Electronics Engrs. *Res:* Wave phenomena in homogeneous media; induction heating; computer applications; field theory. *Mailing Add:* Dept of Elec Eng La State Univ Baton Rouge LA 70803

KINNEY, ROBERT BRUCE, b Joplin, Mo, July 20, 37; m 61; c 3. MECHANICAL ENGINEERING. *Educ:* Univ Calif, Berkeley, BS, 59, MS, 61; Univ Minn, Minneapolis, PhD(mech eng), 65. *Prof Exp:* Sr res engr, United Aircraft Res Labs, 65-68; assoc prof aerospace & mech eng, 68-78, PROF AEROSPACE & MECH ENG, UNIV ARIZ, 78- *Concurrent Pos:* Alexander von Humboldt Found vis scientist, Ger, 76. *Mem:* AAAS; Am Inst Aeronaut & Astronaut; Am Soc Mech Engrs. *Res:* Energy transport in gases and liquids; dynamics of fluid flow, including unsteady viscous aerodynamics; fluid flow analogies and experimental methods. *Mailing Add:* Dept of Aerospace & Mech Eng Univ of Ariz Tucson AZ 85721

KINNEY, TERRY B, JR, b Norfolk, Mass, Sept 12, 25; m 46; c 2. POPULATION GENETICS, RESEARCH ADMINISTRATION. *Educ:* Univ Mass, BS, 55, MS, 56; Univ Minn, PhD, 63. *Prof Exp:* Res asst poultry, Univ Mass, 55-56; geneticist, Hubbard Farms Inc, NH, 56-57; instr poultry, Univ Minn, 57-62; biometrician, USDA, Md, 63-65, res geneticist, Ind, 65-69; asst dir, Animal Sci Res Div, 69-72, assoc dep adminr, NCent Region, 72-74, asst adminr livestock vet sci, 74-78, assoc adminr, 78-80, ADMINR, SCI & EDUC ADMIN-AGR RES, USDA, 80- *Mem:* Poultry Sci Asn. *Res:* Statistics; population genetic studies; administration of research relating to livestock and veterinary sciences. *Mailing Add:* Agr Res Serv USDA Rm 302 Admin Bldg Washington DC 20250

KINNIE, IRVIN GRAY, b Orlando, Fla, Apr 28, 32; m 68. RESEARCH MANAGEMENT, INFORMATION SCIENCE. *Educ:* US Mil Acad, BS, 53; Univ Ariz, MS, 60. *Prof Exp:* Res officer, E W Div, Army Proving Ground, Ariz, 56-58, area signal officer, Longlines Signal Battalion Pusan, Korea, 60-61, asst prof eng & info sci, US Mil Acad, 61-65, EDP specialist info sci, Allied Mil Commun Electronics Agency, Paris, 65-67, standards specialist, Mallard Proj, Ft Monmouth, NJ, 67-68, chief plans & opers, US Army Regional Commun Group, Saigon, 68-69, chief info sci, US Army Res & Develop Group, London, 69-73, dep dir res & develop, US Army Comput Systs Command, 73-74; syst analyst & engr tech planning, 74-76, engr software res, 76-77, engr mkt develop, 77-78, engr solar eng, 78-80, engr command, control & commun archit, 80-81, ENGR ELECTRONIC DATA PROCESSING SYSTS DESIGN, COMMAND & SPACE SYSTS, FED SYSTS DIV, IBM CORP, 81- *Mem:* Asn Comput Mach; Inst Elec & Electronics Engrs; Armed Forces Comn Electronics Asn. *Res:* Communications; electronics and information sciences; software engineering; computer systems. *Mailing Add:* 18100 Frederick Pike Gaithersburg MD 20877

KINNISON, GERALD L, b San Diego, Calif, July 16, 31; m 50; c 4. PHYSICS. *Educ:* Univ Calif, Los Angeles, BS, 58, MS, 60, PhD, 63. *Prof Exp:* PHYSICIST, PASSIVE SONAR DESIGN, US NAVAL OCEAN SYSTEMS CTR, 63- *Concurrent Pos:* Fel NSF, Univ London, 63-64. *Res:* Energy transfer through air and fibers of porous materials yielding acoustical transmission loss; adaptive beamforming; directionality of ocean ambient noise. *Mailing Add:* 970 Tarento Dr San Diego CA 92106

KINO, AKIKO, b Osaka, Japan, Sept 1, 34; m 69; c 1. MATHEMATICAL LOGIC. *Educ:* Tokyo Univ Educ, BS, 57, MS, 59, PhD(math), 62. *Prof Exp:* Asst math, Tokyo Univ Educ, 61-63; instr, Meiji Gakuin Univ, Japan, 63-66; asst prof, 66-67, ASSOC PROF MATH, STATE UNIV NY BUFFALO, 67- *Concurrent Pos:* Mem tech staff, Hughes Aircraft Co, 64-66. *Mem:* Asn Symbolic Logic; Math Soc Japan. *Res:* Proof theory; ordinals; feasible mathematics. *Mailing Add:* Dept of Math State Univ NY 106 Diefendorf Hall Buffalo NY 14214

KINO, GORDON STANLEY, b Melbourne, Australia, June 15, 28; m 57; c 1. ELECTRICAL ENGINEERING, SOLID STATE PHYSICS. *Educ:* Univ London, BSc, 48, MSc, 50; Stanford Univ, PhD(elec eng), 55. *Prof Exp:* Jr scientist, Mullard Radio Valve Co, Eng, 47-51; res asst, Electronics Res Lab, Stanford Univ, 51-55, res assoc, Microwave Lab, 55; mem tech staff, Bell Tel Labs, NJ, 55-57; res assoc, 57-70, PROF ELEC ENG, STANFORD UNIV, 70- *Concurrent Pos:* Consult, Varian, Tex Instruments, Lockheed Aircraft Corp & Advan Res Projs Agency, 57-; Guggenheim fel, 67-68. *Mem:* Fel Inst Elec & Electronics Engrs; Am Phys Soc; Nat Acad Eng. *Res:* Electromagnetic theory; design of electron and ion guns; wave propagation in plasmas; microwave tubes; microwave acoustics; acoustic imaging; non-destructive testing; waves in solids. *Mailing Add:* Ginzton Lab Stanford Univ Stanford CA 94305

KINOSHITA, FLORENCE KEIKO, b Salem, Ore, Aug 6, 41. TOXICOLOGY, PHARMACOLOGY. *Educ:* Univ Chicago, BS, 63, MS, 66, PhD(pharmacol), 69; Am Bd Toxicol, dipl. *Prof Exp:* From instr to asst prof pharmacol, Univ Chicago, 69-73; toxicologist, Indust Bio-Test Labs, Inc, 73-74, tech mgr toxicol, 74-77; SR TOXICOLOGIST, HERCULES, INC, 78- *Concurrent Pos:* Mem, Toxicol Study Sect, NIH, 79- *Mem:* AAAS; Soc Toxicol; Am Indust Hyg Asn; Soc Exp Biol & Med; NY Acad Sci. *Res:* Interactions of drugs, pesticides and chemicals as inducers of hepatic microsomal enzyme systems; effects of organophosphorus compounds on cholinestrase and aliesterases; development of hepatic microsomal enzymes in fetal and neonatal animals. *Mailing Add:* Med Dept Hercules Inc 910 Market St Wilmington DE 19899

KINOSHITA, JIN HAROLD, b San Francisco, Calif, July 21, 22; m 48. BIOLOGICAL CHEMISTRY. *Educ:* Columbia Univ, AB, 44; Harvard Univ, PhD, 52. *Hon Degrees:* ScD, Bard Col, 67. *Prof Exp:* Asst chem, Bard Col, 44-46; from instr to asst prof biochem, Harvard Med Sch, 52-64, from assoc prof to prof biochem ophthal, 64-73; chief, Lab Vision Res, 71-81, SCI DIR, NAT EYE INST, 81- *Concurrent Pos:* Biochemist, Mass Eye & Ear Infirmary, 55-73; Friedenwald mem lectr, 65; mem visual sci study sect, NIH, 65-69. *Honors & Awards:* Proctor Medal, Asn Res Vision & Ophthal, 74. *Mem:* AAAS; Am Chem Soc; Am Soc Biol Chemists; Asn Res Vision & Ophthal. *Res:* Chemistry and metabolism of ocular tissues. *Mailing Add:* Nat Eye Inst 9000 Rockville Pike Bethesda MD 20014

KINOSHITA, KIMIO, b Vancouver, BC, Aug 5, 42; m 65; c 2. ELECTROCHEMISTRY. *Educ:* Univ Alta, BSc, 64; Univ Calif, Berkeley, PhD(chem), 69. *Prof Exp:* Sr res assoc phys chem, Mat Eng Res Lab, Pratt & Whitney Aircraft, 69-76; mem staff, Chem Eng Div, Argonne Nat Lab, 76-79; MEM STAFF, SRI INT, 79- *Mem:* Am Chem Soc; Electrochem Soc; Am Carbon Soc. *Res:* Corrosion; electrochemistry; carbon chemistry; catalysis. *Mailing Add:* 20644 Nancy Ct Cupertino CA 95014

KINOSHITA, SHIN'ICHI, b Osaka, Japan, June 5, 25; m 54; c 4. TOPOLOGY. *Educ:* Osaka Univ, BS, 48, PhD(math), 58. *Prof Exp:* Lectr math, North Col, Osaka Univ, 58-59; vis mem, Inst Advan Study, 59-61; res assoc, Princeton Univ, 61-62; asst prof, Univ Sask, 62-64; assoc prof, 64-69, PROF MATH, FLA STATE UNIV, 69- *Mem:* Am Math Soc; Math Soc Japan. *Res:* Topological transformations; knot theory and fundamental group phenomena. *Mailing Add:* Dept Math & Comput Sci Fla State Univ Tallahassee FL 32306

KINOSHITA, TOICHIRO, b Tokyo, Japan, Jan 23, 25; nat US; m 51; c 3. THEORETICAL HIGH ENERGY PHYSICS. *Educ:* Univ Tokyo, BS, 47, PhD(physics), 52. *Prof Exp:* Mem, Inst Adv Study, Princeton, NJ, 52-54; fel theoret physics, Columbia Univ, 54-55; res assoc, 55-58, from asst prof to assoc prof, 58-64, PROF THEORET PHYSICS, CORNELL UNIV, 64- *Concurrent Pos:* Ford fel, European Orgn Nuclear Res, Geneva Switz, 62-63; Guggenheim Found fel, 73-74. *Mem:* Fel Am Phys Soc. *Res:* Quantum field theory; quantum theory of atoms; elementary particles; symmetry law. *Mailing Add:* Lab of Nuclear Studies Cornell Univ Ithaca NY 14853

KINRA, VIKRAM KUMAR, b Lyallpur, India, Apr 3, 46; m 76. ENGINEERING MECHANICS, MATERIALS SCIENCE. *Educ:* Indian Inst Technol, Kanpur, BTech, 67; Utah State Univ, MSc, 68; Brown Univ, PhD(eng mech), 75. *Prof Exp:* Struct eng stress anal, Northrop Corp, Hawthorne, 68-70; proj eng mech eng, Ostgaard & Assocs, Inc, Gardena, 70-71; asst & res assoc, Brown Univ, 71-75; ASST PROF MECH ENG, UNIV COLO, BOULDER, 75- *Concurrent Pos:* Prin investr & proj dir, NSF grants, Univ Colo, Boulder, 76-78 & 78-81; consult, Willow Water Dist, Denver, 76-77, Ponderosa Asn, Louisville, 80 & Corning Glass, NY, 80. *Mem:* Soc Exp Stress Anal; Am Acad Mech; Am Soc Eng Educ; Am Soc Mech Engrs; Sigma Xi. *Res:* Experimental fracture mechanics, especially dynamic crack propagation; wave propagation; photoelasticity; nondestructive testing and evaluation; composite materials; ultrasonics. *Mailing Add:* Dept of Mech Eng Box 427 Univ of Colo Boulder CO 80309

KINSBOURNE, MARCEL, b Vienna, Austria, Nov 3, 31; m 65; c 4. PEDIATRIC NEUROLOGY, EXPERIMENTAL PSYCHOLOGY. *Educ:* Oxford Univ, BA, 52, MD, 55, MA, 56, DM(neuropsychol), 63. *Prof Exp:* Lectr psychol, Oxford Univ, 64-67; assoc prof pediat & neurol & lectr psychol, Med Ctr, Duke Univ, 67-74; sr staff physician, Hosp Sick Children, Toronto, 74-80; prof psychol, Univ Waterloo, 74-79; prof pediat, 74-80, PROF PSYCHOL, UNIV TORONTO, 75-; DIR, BEHAV NEUROL DEPT, EUNICE KENNEDY SHRIVER CTR, 80- *Concurrent Pos:* Fel, New Col,

Oxford Univ, 65-67; J Arthur Lectureship evol brain, 74. *Honors & Awards:* Queen Square Prize neurol, 61. *Mem:* Fel Am Psychol Asn; Am Neurol Asn; fel Geront Soc; Int Neuropsychology Soc; Psychonomic Soc. *Res:* Human neuropsychology; developmental psychology; visual information processing; age-related changes in behavior. *Mailing Add:* Eunice Kennedy Shriver Ctr 555 University Ave Waltham MA 02254 Can

KINSBRON, ELIEZER, b Affula, Israel, July 4, 45; m 66; c 2. MATERIALS SCIENCE, SOLID STATE PHYSICS. *Educ:* Technion-Israel Inst Technol, BSc, 70, MSc, 73, PhD(mat sci), 77. *Prof Exp:* Fel reliability, 77-78, MEM STAFF MOBILE TELEPHONE SERV, VERY LARGE-SCALE INTEGRATION TECHNOL, BELL LABS, 78- *Mem:* Inst Elec & Electronics Engrs. *Res:* Semiconductor processing; oxidation; diffusion and photolitography; reliability and failure analysis of electronics materials and integrated circuits. *Mailing Add:* Bell Labs 600 Mountain Ave Murray Hill NJ 07974

KINSEL, NORMA ANN, b Boston, Mass, Feb 26, 29. MICROBIOLOGY. *Educ:* Univ Va, BS, 49; Pittsburgh Univ, MS, 52, PhD(bact), 59. *Prof Exp:* Asst yeast chem fel, Mellon Inst, 52-53, asst microbiol & micros sect, 53-56, assoc microbiologist, 56-62, fel petrol, 63-69; res biologist, Gulf Res & Develop Co, 69-73; SR MICROBIOLOGIST, ELI LILLY & CO, 74- *Concurrent Pos:* USPHS res fel, Rutgers Univ, 62-63. *Mem:* AAAS; Am Soc Microbiol; Soc Indust Microbiol. *Res:* Autotrophic iron and sulfur bacteria; petroleum microbiology; antibiotic fermentation technology. *Mailing Add:* Antibiotic Fermentation Technol Dept Eli Lilly & Co 307 E McCarty St Indianapolis IN 46285

KINSEL, TRACY STEWART, b Waterloo, Iowa, Nov 16, 30; m 53; c 4. COMPUTERS, QUANTUM ELECTRONICS. *Educ:* Univ Chicago, BA, 52, MS, 55; Rutgers Univ, PhD(physics), 63. *Prof Exp:* Engr, Semiconductor & Mat Div, Radio Corp Am, 57-63; mem tech staff, 63-79, SUPVR, BELL LABS, 79- *Mem:* Am Phys Soc. *Res:* Second kind superconductors; optical communications; minicomputers; microcomputers; magnetic tape recorders. *Mailing Add:* Bell Labs Dept 52212 Whippany NJ 07981

KINSELLA, JOHN EDWARD, b Wexford, Ireland, Feb 22, 38; m 65; c 2. FOOD CHEMISTRY, BIOCHEMISTRY. *Educ:* Nat Univ Ireland, BS, 61; Pa State Univ, MS, 65, PhD(food sci), 67. *Prof Exp:* Teacher zool, Latin & chem, CKC Onitsha, Nigeria, 61-63; asst prof food sci, 67-73, assoc prof, 73-77, PROF FOOD SCI/CHEM & CHMN DEPT FOOD SCI, CORNELL UNIV, 77-, DIR, INST FOOD SCI, 80-, LIBERTY HYDE BAILEY PROF FOOD SCI, 81- *Honors & Awards:* Borden Award for Res, 76. *Mem:* Am Inst Nutrit; AAAS; Am Chem Soc; Am Dairy Sci Asn; Inst Food Technol. *Res:* Essential fatty acids and prostaglandins; flavor chemistry of foods; lipid enzymology and metabolism in tissue cultures; nutrients in foods; functional properties of food proteins; protein modification; food protein from vegetables and yeast. *Mailing Add:* Dept of Food Sci Cornell Univ Ithaca NY 14850

KINSELLA, JOHN J, b Seneca Falls, NY, Oct 15, 26; m 49; c 8. PHYSICS. *Educ:* Univ Tex, BA, 49; Syracuse Univ, MS, 53. *Prof Exp:* Res physicist, Consol Vacuum Corp Div, Bell & Howell, 51-56; from physicist to sr physicist, Xerox Corp, 56-59, scientist, 59-62, res mgr, 62-65, mgr photoreceptor technol, 65-68, mgr xerographic consumables mfg, 68-70, mgr advan mfg eng, 70-73, mfg prog mgt, 73-78, mem res & eng tech staff, Corp Planning Consumables & Supplies, 78-81. *Mem:* Am Vacuum Soc; Inst Elec & Electronics Engrs; Optical Soc Am; Soc Photog Sci & Eng. *Res:* Vacuum pump and gauge design development; thin film microcircuit, resistors and capacitors; evaporated silver bromide research; xerographic photoconductors. *Mailing Add:* Xerox Corp 2846 St Paul Blvd Rochester NY 14617

KINSELLA, RALPH A, JR, b St Louis, Mo, June 4, 19; m; c 8. INTERNAL MEDICINE. *Educ:* St Louis Univ, AB, 39, MD, 43. *Prof Exp:* From instr to assoc prof, 48-70, PROF INTERNAL MED, SCH MED, ST LOUIS UNIV, 70-; physician & chief unit 2, Med Serv, 57-80, MED DIR, ST LOUIS CITY HOSP, 80- *Concurrent Pos:* Neilson fel, St Louis Univ, 47-48, Markle scholar, 48-53. *Mem:* AAAS; Endocrine Soc; NY Acad Sci; fel Am Col Physicians; Soc Exp Biol & Med. *Res:* Steroid hormone metabolism; endocrinology. *Mailing Add:* St Louis City Hosp 1515 Lafayette Ave St Louis MO 63104

KINSER, DONALD LEROY, b Loudon, Tenn, Sept 28, 41; m 61; c 2. MATERIALS SCIENCE, ENGINEERING. *Educ:* Univ Fla, BS, 64, PhD(mat sci), 68. *Prof Exp:* From asst prof to assoc prof ceramic eng, 68-75, PROF MAT SCI, VANDERBILT UNIV, 75- *Mem:* Am Ceramic Soc; Am Soc Metals; Am Inst Mining, Metall & Petrol Engrs; Electrochem Soc; Brit Soc Glass Technol. *Res:* Electrical behavior of two-phase alkali-silicate glasses; semiconducting glasses; mechanical properties of glasses; electrical behavior of glasses; radiation damage and mechanical properties of materials. *Mailing Add:* Dept Mat Eng Box 1689B Vanderbilt Univ Nashville TN 37235

KINSEY, BERNARD BRUNO, b London, Eng, June 15, 10; m; c 3. PHYSICS. *Educ:* Cambridge Univ, BA, 32, PhD, 37. *Prof Exp:* Lectr physics, Univ Liverpool, 36-39; with Telecommun Res Estab, UK, 39-42; res physicist, Atomic Energy Can, 44-54; guest scientist, Univ Calif, 54-55; res physicist, Atomic Energy Res Estab, Eng, 55-58; PROF PHYSICS, UNIV TEX, AUSTIN, 58- *Mem:* Fel Am Phys Soc; fel Royal Soc Can. *Res:* Nuclear physics. *Mailing Add:* Dept of Physics Univ of Tex Austin TX 78712

KINSEY, DAVID WEBSTER, b Warsaw, Ind, Mar 11, 39; m 61; c 2. MATHEMATICS. *Educ:* Manchester Col, BA, 61; Univ Ariz, MS, 64; Ind Univ, PhD(math), 72. *Prof Exp:* Instr math, Carthage Col, 63-64 & Millikin Univ, 64-68; ASSOC PROF MATH, IND STATE UNIV, EVANSVILLE, 72- *Mem:* Math Asn Am; Nat Coun Teachers Math; Am Math Soc. *Mailing Add:* Ind State Univ 8600 University Blvd Evansville IN 47712

KINSEY, JAMES HUMPHREYS, b Xenia, Ohio, June 6, 32; m 57; c 2. APPLIED PHYSICS. *Educ:* Princeton Univ, AB, 60; Univ Md, College Park, PhD(physics), 70. *Prof Exp:* Aerospace technologist, NASA, 68-71; mem res staff x-ray diffraction, Princeton Univ, 71-73, lectr, 73-74; consult, Control Data Corp, 74-76; ASSOC CONSULT, MAYO CLIN, 76-, ASST PROF BIOPHYS, 79- *Mem:* AAAS; Am Phys Soc; Am Astron Soc; Am Geophys Union; Sigma Xi. *Res:* Optical aurora; low energy cosmic rays and energetic solar particles; x-ray diffraction studies of large biological molecules; computer analysis of radiographs; x-ray and optical detector systems for biomedical imaging, computer tomography; photo therapy of cancer. *Mailing Add:* Dept Phys & Biophysics Mayo Clinic 200 First St SW Rochester MN 55901

KINSEY, JAMES LLOYD, b Paris, Tex, Oct 15, 34; m 62; c 3. PHYSICAL CHEMISTRY. *Educ:* Rice Univ, BA, 56, PhD(chem), 59. *Prof Exp:* NSF fel, Univ Uppsala, 59-60; Miller res fel, Univ Calif, Berkeley, 60-62; from asst prof to assoc prof, 62-74, chmn dept, 77-82, PROF CHEM, MASS INST TECHNOL, 74- *Concurrent Pos:* Alfred P Sloan res fel, 63-67; Guggenheim fel, 69-70; vis assoc prof, Univ Wis, 69-70; consult, Los Alamos Nat Lab, 74-; mem, Comt Chem Sci, Nat Acad Sci-Nat Res Coun, 80, co-chm, 81-; mem, adv comt, Army Res Off-Nat Res Coun, 81-; assoc ed, J Chem Physics, 81-84. *Mem:* AAAS; Am Chem Soc; fel Am Phys Soc. *Res:* Molecular beams; intermolecular forces; chemical kinetics; scattering theory; spectroscopy; lasers. *Mailing Add:* Dept of Chem Rm 6-229 Mass Inst of Technol Cambridge MA 02139

KINSEY, JANICE DURR, see Grebe, Janice Durr

KINSEY, JOHN AARON, JR, b Panama City, Fla, Mar 12, 39; m 62. GENETICS. *Educ:* Fla State Univ, BS, 61; Univ Tex, PhD(zool), 65. *Prof Exp:* NIH res fel genetics, Univ Wash, 65-67; asst prof, 67-80, ASSOC PROF MICROBIOL, MED CTR, UNIV KANS, 80- *Mem:* Genetics Soc Am. *Res:* Biochemical aspects of Neurospora genetics. *Mailing Add:* Dept of Microbiol Univ of Kans Med Ctr Kansas City KS 66103

KINSEY, KENNETH F, b Providence, RI, Sept 14, 33. PHYSICS. *Educ:* Brown Univ, AB, 55; Univ Rochester, PhD(physics), 61. *Prof Exp:* Asst prof, Univ Rochester, 64-66; ASSOC PROF PHYSICS, STATE UNIV NY COL GENESEO, 66- *Mem:* Am Phys Soc. *Res:* Medium energy particle physics. *Mailing Add:* Dept of Physics State Univ of NY Col Geneseo NY 14454

KINSEY, PHILIP A, b Warsaw, Ind, Feb 10, 31; m 54; c 3. PHYSICAL CHEMISTRY. *Educ:* Manchester Col, AB, 53; Purdue Univ, PhD(chem), 57. *Prof Exp:* PROF CHEM, UNIV EVANSVILLE, 56- *Concurrent Pos:* Sabbatical, Univ Calif, Santa Barbara, 69-70, Univ Ill, Urbana, 80-81. *Mem:* Am Chem Soc. *Res:* Uses of computers in chemical education. *Mailing Add:* Dept Chem Univ Evansville Evansville IN 47702

KINSINGER, FLOYD ELTON, b Ness City, Kans, Jan 17, 25; m 50; c 2. RANGE ECOLOGY. *Educ:* Ft Hays Kans State Col, BS, 52, MS, 53; Utah State Univ, PhD(range mgt), 57. *Prof Exp:* Asst range mgt, Utah State Univ, 53-55; asst prof & asst plant ecologist, Agr Exp Sta, Univ Nev, 55-60; from asst prof to assoc prof bot, Ft Hays Kans State Col, 60-63; range scientist, Bur Land Mgt, Washington, DC, 63-69, range staff leader, Denver Serv Ctr, 69-79; exec secy, Soc Range Mgt, 79-82; MEM FAC, UTAH STATE UNIV, 82- *Mem:* Soc Range Mgt. *Res:* Development and testing of methods and techniques for evaluation of rangeland. *Mailing Add:* 5724 S Lowell Blvd Denver CO 80236

KINSINGER, JACK BURL, b Akron, Ohio, June 23, 25; m 46; c 2. PHYSICAL CHEMISTRY. *Educ:* Hiram Col, BA, 48; Cornell Univ, MSc, 51; Univ Pa, PhD(phys chem), 58. *Prof Exp:* Group leader polymer chem, Rohm & Haas Co, 51-56; from asst prof to assoc prof phys chem, Mich State Univ, 57-66, prof chem, 66-75, from assoc chmn to chmn dept chem, 65-75; dir chem div, NSF, 75-77; ASST V PRES RES, MICH STATE UNIV, 77-, ASSOC PROVOST, 77- *Concurrent Pos:* Consult, Union Carbide Chem Co, 58-80. *Mem:* AAAS; Am Chem Soc; Am Phys Soc; NY Acad Sci. *Res:* Micro-structure of polymers; laser light scattering spectroscopy. *Mailing Add:* Provost Off Mich State Univ East Lansing MI 48824

KINSINGER, RICHARD ESTYN, b Wilmington, Del, July 23, 42; m 64; c 2. PLASMA TECHNOLOGY, ARC TECHNOLOGY. *Educ:* Cornell Univ, BEngPhys, 64, MEng, 65, PhD(aerospace eng), 69. *Prof Exp:* Res physicist, 68-76, mgr arc interruption res, 76-81, MGR PLASMA TECHNOL PROGS, RES & DEVELOP CTR, GEN ELEC CO, 81- *Mem:* AAAS; Am Phys Soc. *Res:* Theory of collisionless plasma disturbances; arc plasma physics and interruption technology; laser produced plasmas; research and develop programs on plasma process technology and arcing devices. *Mailing Add:* Gen Elec Res & Develop Ctr PO Box 8 Schenectady NY 12301

KINSKY, STEPHEN CHARLES, b Berlin, Ger, Feb 9, 32; nat US; m 59; c 2. BIOCHEMISTRY. *Educ:* Univ Chicago, AB, 51; Johns Hopkins Univ, PhD(biochem), 57. *Prof Exp:* From instr to prof, Sch Med, Washington Univ, 59-78; PROF BIOCHEM, NAT JEWISH HOSP, 78- *Concurrent Pos:* USPHS fel, 57-59, res career develop awards, 64-70. *Mem:* Am Soc Biol Chem; Am Asn Immunol. *Res:* Membrane biochemistry; immunology. *Mailing Add:* Nat Jewish Hosp Res Ctr 3800 E Colfax Ave Denver CO 80206

KINSLAND, GARY LYNN, b Eugene, Ore, June 10, 47; m 69; c 1. GEOPHYSICS, MINERALOGY. *Educ:* Univ Rochester, BS, 69, MS, 71, PhD(geol), 74. *Prof Exp:* Res asst geol, Univ Rochester, 74-76; vis asst prof, Ariz State Univ, 76-77; asst prof, 77-80, ASSOC PROF GEOL, UNIV SOUTHWESTERN LA, 80- *Concurrent Pos:* Prin investr, Dept of Energy geopressure-geothermal energy grant, 78-79, high resolution 3-d seismic surv over geopressured reservoir, 82. *Mem:* Sigma Xi; Am Geophys Union; Soc Explor Geophysicists. *Res:* High pressure-high temperature simulation and study of earth mantle properties; geopressure-geothermal energy prospects; high pressure materials science; high-resolution 3-d seismic surveys. *Mailing Add:* Dept of Geol PO Box 44530 Lafayette LA 70504

KINSMAN, DONALD MARKHAM, b Framingham, Mass, May 20, 23; m 49; c 3. ANIMAL SCIENCE, MEAT SCIENCE. *Educ:* Univ Mass, BS, 49; Univ NH, MS, 51; Okla State Univ, PhD, 64. *Prof Exp:* Instr animal sci, Univ NH, 49-51 & Univ Vt, 51-52; farm mgr, Univ Mass, 52-56; from asst prof to assoc prof, 56-70, PROF ANIMAL SCI, UNIV CONN, 70- *Concurrent Pos:* Pres, New England Livestock Conserv, Inc, 66-78. *Honors & Awards:* Signal Serv Award, Am Meat Sci Asn, 75; Distinguished Serv Award, Am Soc Animal Sci, 78. *Mem:* Am Soc Animal Sci; Am Meat Sci Asn (pres, 78-79); Coun Agr Sci & Technol. *Res:* Humane slaughter, employing reduced stress methods; evaluation and quality of meat and meat products. *Mailing Add:* Dept of Animal Indust Univ of Conn Storrs CT 06268

KINSMAN, DONALD VINCENT, b Toledo, Ohio, July 16, 43; m 69; c 2. ORGANIC CHEMISTRY. *Educ:* Univ Cincinnati, BS, 65; Pa State Univ, PhD(chem), 69. *Prof Exp:* Develop chemist household prod, Lever Bros, 69-71; group leader develop, 71-74; group leader, 74-79, MGR FATTY ACID RES, APPLN RES, EMERY INDUSTS, 79- *Mem:* Am Chem Soc; Am Oil Chemists Soc. *Res:* Develop and administration of applications for fatty, dibasic and polybasic acids. *Mailing Add:* Emery Industs Res 4900 Este Ave Cincinnati OH 45232

KINSMAN, KENNETH ROMWALL, physical metallurgy, electron microscopy, see previous edition

KINSON, GORDON A, b Wood End, Eng, Sept 21, 35; m 60; c 1. PHYSIOLOGY, ENDOCRINOLOGY. *Educ:* Univ Aston, BS, 57; Col Advan Technol, Birmingham, ARIC, 61; Univ Ala, Birmingham, MS, 62; Univ Birmingham, PhD(endocrinol), 67. *Prof Exp:* Res asst endocrinol, Univ Ala, Birmingham, 59-63; sr res assoc, Med Sch, Birmingham Univ, 64-68; from asst prof to assoc prof, 68-79, PROF PHYSIOL, FAC MED, UNIV OTTAWA, 79- *Mem:* Brit Soc Endocrinol; assoc Royal Inst Chem; Can Physiol Soc; Am Physiol Soc. *Res:* Extrahepatic metabolism of androgen hormones; steroid hormone production by seminiferous tubules of the testis; chronic consequences of vasectomy; reninangiotensin and other factors influencing adrenocortical hormone secretion; pineal gland-adrenocortical hormone relationships; role of the pineal gland and indoles in testicular function and androgen biosynthesis; actions of anabolic androgens and estrogens. *Mailing Add:* Dept of Physiol Univ of Ottawa Fac of Med Ottawa ON K1H 5T1 Can

KINSTLE, JAMES FRANCIS, b Lima, Ohio, Nov 23, 38. POLYMER CHEMISTRY. *Educ:* Bowling Green State Univ, BS, 66, MA, 67; Univ Akron, PhD(polymer sci), 70. *Prof Exp:* Res & develop polymers, Wyandotte Chem Corp, 60-63; res & develop chemist, Allied Mat Corp, 63-65; sr res scientist, Ford Motor Co Sci Res Labs, 70-72; asst prof, 72-78, ASSOC PROF CHEM, UNIV TENN, KNOXVILLE, 78- *Concurrent Pos:* Ed-in-chief, J Radiation Curing, Technol Mkt Corp, 74-79; consult, 73- *Mem:* Am Chem Soc. *Res:* Polymer synthesis and characterization; homogeneous and surface reactions on polymers; electroactive polymers; radiation chemistry in polymer sciences; polymer reuse and disposal. *Mailing Add:* Dept of Chem Univ of Tenn Knoxville TN 37996

KINSTLE, THOMAS HERBERT, b Lima, Ohio, Dec 18, 36; m 58. ORGANIC CHEMISTRY. *Educ:* Bowling Green State Univ, BA, 58; Univ Ill, PhD(org chem), 63. *Prof Exp:* Res assoc org chem, Univ Ill, 63-64; from instr to asst prof org chem, Iowa State Univ, 64-70; assoc prof org chem, 70-74, PROF CHEM, BOWLING GREEN STATE UNIV, 74- *Concurrent Pos:* Am Chem Soc-Petrol Res Found grant, 64-; Res Corp grant, 65- *Mem:* Am Chem Soc; Am Acad Arts & Sci. *Res:* Applications of mass spectrometry to organic chemical problems; synthesis and reactions of strained ring systems; structure determination; synthesis and biosynthesis of natural products. *Mailing Add:* Dept of Chem Bowling Green State Univ Bowling Green OH 43402

KINTER, LEWIS BOADRMAN, b Exeter, NH, Aug 15, 50; m 73; c 2. VASOPRESSIN, WHOLE ANIMAL MODELS. *Educ:* Union Col, BS, 73; Harvard Univ, PhD(physiol), 78. *Prof Exp:* Fel physiol, Med Sch, Harvard Univ, 78-79, instr, 79-81; SCIENTIST, SMITH KLINE & FRENCH LABS, 81- *Mem:* Am Physiol Soc; Am Soc Nephrol; NY Acad Sci. *Res:* Homeostatic mechanisms involved in control of renal function and body fluid volume and body fluid composition. *Mailing Add:* F-63 Smith Kline & French Labs Bos 7929 1500 Spring Garden St Philadelphia PA 19101

KINTER, WILLIAM BOARDMAN, physiology, see previous edition

KINTNER, PAUL M(ARVIN), electrical engineering, see previous edition

KINTNER, ROBERT ROY, b Weeping Water, Nebr, Apr 3, 28; m 52; c 3. ORGANIC CHEMISTRY. *Educ:* Iowa State Univ, BS, 53; Univ Wash, PhD(org chem), 57. *Prof Exp:* From asst prof to assoc prof, 57-65, chmn dept, 60-65 & 66-69, PROF CHEM, AUGUSTANA COL SDAK, 65-, CHMN DEPT, 77- *Concurrent Pos:* Petrol res fund adv sci award, Univ Washington, Seattle, 64-65; NSF fac fel, Univ Calif, Santa Cruz, 71-72; vis prof chem, Univ Nebr, Lincoln, 80-81; prin investr, Sioux Falls Refuse Derived Fuel Proj, 78-80. *Mem:* AAAS; Am Chem Soc; Am Soc Testing & Mat. *Res:* Physical-organic chemistry, especially in reaction mechanisms; structure. *Mailing Add:* Dept of Chem Augustana Col Sioux Falls SD 57102

KINYON, BRICE W(HITMAN), b South Bend, Ind, May 1, 11; m 35; c 2. MECHANICAL ENGINEERING. *Educ:* Purdue Univ, BSME, 33; Oak Ridge Sch Reactor Technol, cert, 55. *Prof Exp:* Engr prod, Armstrong Cork Co, 35-37 & Hamilton Watch Co, 37-38; prod & design engr, Radio Corp Am, 38-44 & Elec Storage Battery Co, 44-47; sr design engr reactor design, Oak Ridge Nat Lab, 47-62; ANAL ENGR, THERMAL STRESS CONSULT, COMBUSTION ENG, INC, 62- *Mem:* Am Nuclear Soc; Sigma Xi; Am Soc Mech Engrs; Nat Soc Prof Engrs. *Res:* Fluid flow and heat transfer for power reactors and components. *Mailing Add:* 1312 N Shady Circle Chattanooga TN 37405

KINZEL, AUGUSTUS B(RAUN), b New York, NY, July 26, 1900; m 45; c 6. METALLURGY, ENGINEERING. *Educ:* Columbia Univ, AB, 19; Mass Inst Technol, BS, 21, DMetEng, 22; Univ Nancy, DSc, 33. *Hon Degrees:* Dr, Univ Nancy, 63; DEng, NY Univ, 55; Rensselaer Polytech Inst & Worcester Polytech Inst, 65 & Univ Mich, 67; DSc, Clarkson Col Technol, 57, Northwestern Univ, 69 & Polytech Inst NY, 81; LLD, Queen's Univ, 66. *Prof Exp:* Metallurgist, Labs, Gen Elec Co, Mass, 19-20, 22-23 & Henry Disston & Consults, Pa, 23-26; from metallurgist to vpres, Union Carbide & Carbon Res Labs, Inc Div, NY, 26-48, vpres, Electro Metall Co Div, 44-54, dir, Haynes Stellite Co Div, 47-49, pres, Union Carbide & Carbon Res Labs, Inc Div, 48-65, dir res, vpres, Union Carbide Corp, 55-65; pres & chief exec officer, Salk Inst Biol Studies, Calif, 65-67. *Concurrent Pos:* Instr & lectr, Temple Univ, 25-26; guest lectr, Int Cong Acetylene & Welding, Rome, Italy, 34, London, 36 & Soviet Metall Cong, Moscow, 36; chief consult metall, Manhattan Dist, Atomic Energy Comn, 43-45; chmn, Welding Res Coun, 52-55; chmn, Naval Res Adv Comt, 51-78; mem adv panel gen sci, Off Secy Defense, 54-57; hon mem, Engrs Joint Coun, vpres, 59, pres, 60; hon mem, MIT Corp, 56-61 & Permanent Int Comn Acetylene, 65-; trustee, Mitre Corp, 63-69 & Am Optical Co, 63-71; vchmn bd dirs, NY State Sci & Technol Found, 65; dir, Menasco Mfg Co, 67; chmn exec comt, Syst Develop Corp, 67-71; regents lectr, Univ Calif, San Diego, 69; trustee, Sprague Elec Co, 76; dir, Kalvar Corp, 76; chief consult, Argonne Nat Lab & Oak Ridge Lab; consult, Knolls Lab, Gen Elec Co; mem eng adv comt, Brookhaven Nat Lab; mem adv panel, Defense Sci Bd; mem spec adv comt, US Dept Com; chmn div eng & indust res, Nat Acad Sci; hon mem, Europsace; trustee, Syst Develop Found, Gen Am Investors Co Inc, Beckman Instruments, Inc & Calif Inst Technol; chmn gov bd, Courant Inst Math Sci, NY Univ; dir, Riverside Res Inst & Int Inst Med Electronics. *Honors & Awards:* Miller Medal, Am Welding Soc, 47; Distinguished Serv Award, Am Soc Metals, 48; Metal Progress Hall of Fame, 53-76; Morehead Medal, Indust Res Inst, 60; Douglas Gold Medal, Am Inst Mining, Metall & Petrol Engrs, 60. *Mem:* Nat Acad Sci; Nat Acad Eng (founding pres, 65-); fel NY Acad Sci; fel Am Inst Chem; Benjamin Franklin fel Royal Soc Arts. *Res:* Atomic energy; chemicals; plastics. *Mailing Add:* 1738 Castellana Rd La Jolla CA 92037

KINZEL, JERRY J, b Avon, Ohio, Apr 24, 52; m 81. MICROBIAL PHYSIOLOGY, INTERMEDIATE METABOLISM. *Educ:* Cleveland State Univ, BS, 76; Miami Univ, MS, 78, PhD(microbiol), 81. *Prof Exp:* SR ASSOC RES SCIENTIST, INT MINERALS & CHEM CORP, 81- *Mem:* Sigma Xi; Am Soc Microbiol. *Res:* Microbial physiology with special emphasis on genetics and enzymology. *Mailing Add:* Int Minerals & Chem Corp Box 207 Terre Haute IN 47808

KINZER, EARL T, JR, b Beckley, WVa, Apr 7, 31; m 57; c 2. THEORETICAL PHYSICS, SOLID STATE PHYSICS. *Educ:* Auburn Univ, BEP, 58, MS, 60; Univ Va, PhD(physics), 62. *Prof Exp:* From asst prof to assoc prof physics, Univ Ala, Tuscaloosa, 61-67; ASSOC PROF PHYSICS, AUBURN UNIV, 67- *Res:* Theory of the exchange of energy between gas particles and solids; operational solution of partial difference equations. *Mailing Add:* Dept of Physics Auburn Univ Auburn AL 36830

KINZER, H GRANT, b Grandfield, Okla, July 22, 37; m 57; c 2. ENTOMOLOGY. *Educ:* Okla State Univ, BS, 59, MS, 60, PhD(entom), 62. *Prof Exp:* From asst prof to assoc prof entom, 64-76, PROF ENTOM, N MEX STATE UNIV, 76- *Mem:* Entom Soc Am; Am Registery Prof Entomologists; Can Entom Soc; Am Mosquito Control Asn. *Res:* Biology, physiology and control of livestock insects; biology and physiology of bark beetles. *Mailing Add:* Dept of Entom & Plant Path NMex State Univ Las Cruces NM 88003

KINZER, ROBERT LEE, b Grandfield, Okla, June 23, 41; m 67; c 2. ASTROPHYSICS, ELEMENTARY PARTICLE PHYSICS. *Educ:* Univ Okla, BS, 62, MS, 66, PhD(elem particle physics), 67. *Prof Exp:* Nat Acad Sci resident res fel cosmic ray physics, 67-69, RES PHYSICIST, US NAVAL RES LAB, 69- *Res:* Cosmic ray physics; experimental elementary particle physics; experimental gamma-ray astronomy and x-ray astronomy. *Mailing Add:* Code 7128.3 Naval Res Lab Washington DC 20375

KINZEY, BERTRAM Y(ORK), JR, b Rutland, Mass, Sept 25, 21; m 44; c 2. ARCHITECTURAL ACOUSTICS. *Educ:* Va Polytech Inst, BS, 42, MS, 43. *Prof Exp:* Naval architect, Norfolk Navy Yard, 43-45; archit draftsman & struct engr, Baskervill & Son, Va, 45-47; from asst prof to assoc prof archit eng, Va Polytech Inst, 47-59; assoc prof archit, 59-65, PROF ARCHIT, UNIV FLA, 65- *Concurrent Pos:* Mem comt archit & acoust, Am Guild Organists, 52-56; mem comn archit, Nat Coun Churches, 54-, chmn joint comt church archit & music, 56-; consult archit acoust, 60- *Mem:* Acoust Soc Am; Am Inst Archit; Am Soc Heating, Refrig & Air-Conditioning Engrs. *Res:* Heating, lighting, acoustics and sanitation; tests on wood box columns to determine formulas for design; thermal performance of ventilated building skins. *Mailing Add:* Dept of Archit Univ of Fla Gainesville FL 32611

KINZEY, WARREN GLENFORD, b Orange, NJ, Oct 31, 35; m 57; c 3. ANATOMY, PHYSICAL ANTHROPOLOGY. *Educ:* Univ Minn, BA, 56, MA, 58; Univ Calif, Berkeley, PhD(anat), 64. *Prof Exp:* Asst prof zool, Univ Calif, Davis, 63-67; asst prof anat, Sch Med, 67-68; planning officer regional med progs, 67-68; ASSOC PROF ANTHROP, CITY COL NEW YORK, 70- *Concurrent Pos:* Asst res anatomist, Nat Ctr Primate Biol, 64-65; Wenner-Gren Found Anthrop Res Conf grant, 65; Nat Inst Child Health & Human Develop res grant, 65-67; Wenner-Gren res grant, Belg, 71; Explor Club res grant, Peru, 74; Earthwatch res grants, Peru, 75, 76, 77 & 80. *Mem:* Fel AAAS; Am Asn Phys Anthrop; Am Asn Anat; Am Soc Mammal; Int Primatol Soc. *Res:* Comparative morphology and evolution of primates; dental anthropology; new world primates; primate ecology. *Mailing Add:* Dept of Anthrop City Col of New York New York NY 10031

KINZIE, JEANNIE JONES, b Gt Falls, Mont, Mar 14, 40; m 65; c 1. RADIOTHERAPY. *Educ:* Mont State Univ, BS, 61; Washington Univ, MD, 65. *Prof Exp:* Intern surg, Univ NC, 65-66; resident therapeut radiol, Washington Univ, 68-71, instr radiol, 71-73; asst prof, Med Col Wis, 73-74; asst prof radiol, Univ Chicago, 75-78, assoc prof, 78-80; ASSOC PROF RADIATION ONCOL, WAYNE STATE UNIV, 80- *Concurrent Pos:* Am Cancer Soc advan clin fel, 71-74; consult radiol, Homer G Phillips Hosp, St Louis, 71-73, Vet Hosp, Wood, Wis & West Allis Mem Hosps, 73-74. *Mem:* Am Col Radiol; AMA; Am Soc Therapeut Radiologists; Am Soc Clin Oncol; AAAS. *Res:* Patterns of care in Hodgkins disease; pediatric cancer treatment; combination treatment of head and neck cancer. *Mailing Add:* 436 Lakeland Grosse Pointe MI 48230

KINZIE, ROBERT ALLEN, III, b Santa Cruz, Calif, June 7, 41. ZOOLOGY. *Educ:* Univ Hawaii, MS, 66; Yale Univ, PhD(biol), 70. *Prof Exp:* Fel, Univ Ga, 70-71; asst prof zool, 71-79, ASSOC PROF ZOOL, UNIV HAWAII, 75- *Concurrent Pos:* Consult, Upjohn Drug Co, 70- *Mem:* Ecol Soc Am; Soc Study Evolution; Soc Syst Zool; Am Soc Limnol & Oceanog. *Res:* Coral reef ecology; symbiosis. *Mailing Add:* Dept of Zool Univ of Hawaii Honolulu HI 96822

KINZLY, ROBERT EDWARD, b North Tonawanda, NY, July 4, 39; m 63; c 2. ELECTROOPTICS, OPTICAL ENGINEERING. *Educ:* Univ Buffalo, BA, 61; Cornell Univ, MS, 64. *Prof Exp:* Physicist, Cornell Aeronaut Lab, Inc, 63-67, sect head optical sci, Calspan Corp, 67-75; PRES, SCIPAR, INC, 75- *Concurrent Pos:* Mem, Am Stand Inst working group microdensity. *Mem:* Optical Soc Am; Soc Phys Optics. *Res:* Statistical data analyses; image evaluation; atmospheric optics; remote sensing; visual perception; planetology; computer science; electro-optical warfare; optical countermeasures; target acquisition; image processing. *Mailing Add:* SCIPAR,Inc PO Box 185 Buffalo NY 14221

KIOVSKY, JOSEPH RICHARD, catalysis, process development, see previous edition

KIPKIE, GEORGE FREDERICK, b Pembroke, Ont, Sept 12, 15; m 43; c 2. PATHOLOGY. *Educ:* Queen's Univ, Ont, MDCM, 39; McGill Univ, MSc, 48; Royal Col Physicians & Surgeons Can, dipl, 46. *Prof Exp:* Intern, Regina Gen Hosp, Sask, 39-40, resident path, 40-42; resident, Regina Gray Nun's Hosp, 42-43, asst pathologist, 43-44, dir labs, 45-46; actg dir tumor teaching prog, Duke Univ, 50; assoc prof, 50-66, prof, 66-81, EMER PROF PATH, QUEEN'S UNIV, ONT, 81- *Concurrent Pos:* Fel path, Duke Univ, 48-50; dir labs, Kingston Gen Hosp, 50-81. *Mem:* Can Asn Path; Can Med Asn. *Res:* Tumor pathology and arteritis. *Mailing Add:* Dept of Path Queen's Univ Kingston ON K7L 3N6 Can

KIPLING, ARLIN LLOYD, b Melfort, Sask, Dec 15, 36; m 63; c 3. SOLID STATE PHYSICS. *Educ:* Univ Sask, BEng, 58; McGill Univ, MSc, 61; Univ Exeter, PhD(physics), 67. *Prof Exp:* Engr, Northern Elec Co, Que, 58-59; physicist, Noranda Res Ctr, 63-64; PROF PHYSICS, CONCORDIA UNIV, 67- *Mem:* Can Asn Physicists. *Res:* Semiconductors at low temperatures. *Mailing Add:* Dept of Physics Concordia Univ Montreal PQ H4B 1R6 Can

KIPLINGER, GLENN FRANCIS, b Indianapolis, Ind, Sept 29, 30; m 53; c 4. PHARMACOLOGY. *Educ:* Butler Univ, BS, 53; Univ Mich, PhD(pharmacol), 59; Univ Tex, MD, 67. *Prof Exp:* Teaching asst, Univ Mich, 54-58; instr pharmacol, Boston Univ, 58-60, asst prof, 60-62; asst prof, Univ Tex Med Br Galveston, 62-67; clin pharmacologist, Lilly Lab Clin Res, Marion County Gen Hosp, 67-70, chief clin pharmacol serv, 70-71, asst dir, 71-72, dir toxicol, Lilly Res Labs, 72-73, exec dir, Lilly Res Labs, 73-75, vpres, Lilly Res Labs, 74-77; mgr dir, Lilly Res Ctr, Windlesham, Eng, 77-80; VPRES RES & DEVELOP ORTHO, PHARMACEUT CORP, RARITAN, NJ, 80- *Concurrent Pos:* Clin assoc prof pharmacol & toxicol, Med Sch, Ind Univ-Purdue Univ, Indianapolis, 70- *Mem:* Am Soc Pharmacol & Exp Therapeut; Am Soc Clin Pharmacol & Therapeut; NY Acad Sci. *Res:* Experimental design; narcotic analgesics; clinical psychopharmacology; pharmacology of cannabis. *Mailing Add:* Ortho Pharmaceut Corp Rt 202 Raritan NJ 08869

KIPNIS, DAVID MORRIS, b Baltimore, Md, May 23, 27; m 53; c 3. INTERNAL MEDICINE, ENDOCRINOLOGY. *Educ:* Johns Hopkins Univ, AB, 45, MA, 49; Univ Md, MD, 51. *Prof Exp:* Intern med, Johns Hopkins Hosp, 51-52; from jr asst resident to sr asst resident, Duke Univ Hosp, 52-54; chief resident, Univ Md Hosp, 54-55; asst prof biochem in med, 57-62, from assoc prof to prof med, 62-73, BUSCH PROF MED & CHMN DEPT, SCH MED, WASH UNIV, 73-, DIR CLIN RES CTR, 60- *Concurrent Pos:* Am Col Physicians fel biochem, Sch Med, Wash Univ, 55-56; Markle scholar, 56-61; mem sci adv bd, US Air Force; mem endocrinol study sect, NIH; mem, Nat Pituitary Agency; mem & chmn, Nat Diabetes Adv Bd, 77- *Honors & Awards:* Oppenheimer Award, Endocrine Soc. *Mem:* Inst Med-Nat Acad Sci; Am Soc Clin Invest; Asn Am Physicians; Endocrine Soc; Biochem Soc. *Res:* Hormonal control of carbohydrate and protein metabolism. *Mailing Add:* Dept of Med Wash Univ Sch of Med St Louis MO 63110

KIPP, EGBERT MASON, b Angola, Port WAfrica, Nov 27, 14; m 35; c 3. PHYSICAL CHEMISTRY. *Educ:* Iowa Wesleyan Col, BS, 34; Boston Univ, AM, 35; Pa State Univ, PhD(phys chem), 39. *Hon Degrees:* DSc, Iowa Wesleyan Col, 61. *Prof Exp:* Asst chem, Pa State Univ, 35-39; res chemist, Aluminum Co Am, 39-44, asst chief phys chem div, 44-47, exec secy oils & lubricants comt, 46-57, chief lubricants div, 47-57; dir res & develop, Foote Mineral Co, 57-59; asst to mgr prod develop, Sun Oil Co, 59-60, mgr basic res, 60-61, assoc dir res & develop, 62-70; INDEPENDENT CONSULT TECH MGT, 70- *Concurrent Pos:* Consult, chem & metals indust, 71-; eval agent, Off Energy related Inventions, Nat Bur standards. *Mem:* Am Chem Soc; fel Am Soc Lubrication Eng (pres, 46); fel Am Inst Chem. *Res:* Lubrication engineering sciences; research and development management and organization; energy, market and commercial development; air, soil and water conservation; technology audits. *Mailing Add:* Suite A Sta Sq Two Paoli PA 19301

KIPP, HAROLD LYMAN, b Graig, Nebr, Feb 19, 03; m 28; c 6. MECHANICAL ENGINEERING. *Educ:* Univ Nebr, BSc, 31, MSc, 34. *Prof Exp:* Instr heat power, Univ Kans, 36-37; instr, Sch Mines, Univ SDak, 37-38; from assoc prof to prof, Tex Tech Col, 38-47; prof, 47-73, asst chmn dept mech eng, 66-73, EMER PROF HEAT POWER, UNIV KANS, 73- *Mem:* Am Soc Mech Engrs; Am Soc Eng Educ. *Res:* Thermodynamics; heat power; heat transfer. *Mailing Add:* Dept of Mech Eng Univ of Kans Lawrence KS 66044

KIPP, RAYMOND J, b Ossian, Iowa, Dec 7, 22; m 49; c 2. SANITARY ENGINEERING. *Educ:* Marquette Univ, BS, 51; Univ Wis, MS, 57, PhD(sanit eng, bact), 65. *Prof Exp:* Asst prof civil eng, 60-68, ASSOC PROF CIVIL ENG, MARQUETTE UNIV, 68-, CHMN DEPT, 65-, DEAN COL ENG, 71- *Concurrent Pos:* Chmn, Milwaukee Metrop Sewerage Dist, 78-79. *Mem:* Water Pollution Control Fedn; Am Acad Environ Engrs; Am Soc Civil Engrs; Nat Soc Prof Engrs; Am Soc Eng Educ. *Res:* Activated sludge process for sewage treatment, including bacteriology of the sludge flocs; industrial wastes. *Mailing Add:* 1515 W Wisconsin Ave Milwaukee WI 53233

KIPPAX, DONALD, b Pawtucket, RI, Dec 4, 30; m 53; c 1. CHEMISTRY AND CHEMICAL ENGINEERING. *Educ:* Univ NH, BS, 52 & 55. *Prof Exp:* Chem engr, Explosive Dept, E I du Pont de Nemours & Co, 55-58, sr chem engr, 58-59 & Elec Boat Div, Gen Dynamics Corp, 59-60, process engr, Semiconductor Div, Raytheon Co, 60-63; develop engr, Gen Elec Co, 63-65, prof engr, 65-67; plant mgr, Collagen Corp, 67-71; prod mgr coatings, Pervel Indust, 71-73; TECH MGR AUTO PARTS, DAVIDSON RUBBER CO, 73- *Mem:* Am Chem Soc; Am Inst Chem Eng; Soc Plastics Engrs. *Res:* Process and project development; organic and organometallic materials; polymers; monomers. *Mailing Add:* Davidson Rubber Indust Park Dover NH 03820

KIPPENBERGER, DONALD JUSTIN, b St Louis, Mo, Feb 25, 47; m 73; c 2. PHYSICAL CHEMISTRY. *Educ:* Univ St Thomas, BS & BA, 70; Sam Houston State Univ, MS, 72; Tex A&M Univ, PhD(chem), 82. *Prof Exp:* Chemist path residents, Gorgas Army Hosp, 77-80 & Tex A&M Univ, 80-82; CHEMIST OFF CHEM READINESS, EDGEWOOD ARSENAL, 82- *Concurrent Pos:* Lectr, Fayetteville Univ, 74-77; consult chem, Commander XVIII Airborne Corp, 74-77 & Gov, Canal Zone, 77-80; co-investr, Heart Enzyme Group, Walter Reed Army Inst, 76-77; asst prof, Canal Zone Col, 77-80. *Mem:* Am Inst Chemists. *Res:* Membrane memitic chemistry: characterization of polymeric vesicles utilizing proton and carbon nuclear magnetic resonance, fluorescense and absorption techniques; surface chemistry: characterization of catalytically active inorganic complexes in zeolites and ambevlytes using electron spin resonance techniques. *Mailing Add:* 2512 Allen Forest Bryan TX 77801

KIPPENHAN, C(HARLES) J(ACOB), b Middle Amana, Iowa, Nov 8, 19; m 41; c 2. MECHANICAL ENGINEERING. *Educ:* Univ Iowa, BSME, 40, MSME, 46, PhD(mech eng), 48. *Prof Exp:* Jr mech engr, Stanley Eng Co, 40; instr mech eng, Univ Iowa, 41-42; from asst prof to assoc prof, Washington Univ, 48-54, prof & head dept, 54-63; chmn dept, 63-73, PROF MECH ENG, UNIV WASH, 63-, ADJ PROF ARCHIT, 73- *Concurrent Pos:* Mech eng consult. *Mem:* Am Soc Heating, Refrigerating & Airconditioning Engrs; Am Soc Mech Engrs; Am Soc Eng Educ. *Res:* Building energy systems analysis, simulation; energy conservation and management; convective and radiation heat transfer; thermal properties; transient techniques. *Mailing Add:* Dept of Mech Eng Univ of Wash Seattle WA 98195

KIPPS, THOMAS CHARLES, b Eureka, Utah, Feb 28, 23; m 48; c 4. MATHEMATICS. *Educ:* Univ Calif, Berkeley, AB, 49, MA, 50, PhD(math), 57. *Prof Exp:* Instr math & physics, Univ Santa Clara, 53-55; asst math, Univ Calif, Berkeley, 55-56; from instr to assoc prof, 56-67, chmn dept, 69, PROF MATH, CALIF STATE UNIV, FRESNO, 67- *Mem:* Am Math Soc; Math Asn Am. *Res:* Double integral problems in the calculus of variations; methods of linear algebra in numerical analysis. *Mailing Add:* Dept of Math Calif State Univ Fresno CA 93740

KIPROV, DOBRI D, b Sofia, Bulgaria, May 1, 49; US citizen; m 73; c 1. IMMUNOLOGY. *Educ:* Med Acad, Bulgaria, MD, 74. *Prof Exp:* Instr pathol, Sackler Sch Med, Israel, 74-77; resident, Mt Sinai Hosp, Case Western Reserve Univ, 77-79; clin res fel, Mass Gen Hosp, Harvard Med Sch, 79-81; clin res fel, 81-82, DIR, PLASMAPHERESIS, DEPT CELLULAR IMMUNOL, CHILDREN'S HOSP, UNIV CALIF, SAN FRANCISCO, 82- *Mem:* AMA; Am Soc Clin Pathol; Am Col Pathologists. *Res:* Basic immunologic defects in autoimmune diseases, including renal diseases; evaluation of lymphocyte subsets from peripheral blood and tissues using moncolonal antibodies; effect of plasmapheresis, lymphocytapheresis and immunosuppressive therapy on the immunologic system of patients with autoimmune diseases; clinical correlation with immunologic assays. *Mailing Add:* Children's Hosp 3700 Calif St San Francisco CA 94118

KIRBER, MARIA WIENER, b Prague, Czech, Feb 19, 17; nat US; m 43; c 2. MICROBIOLOGY, VIROLOGY. *Educ:* Univ Prague, MUC, 38; Univ Pa, MS, 41, PhD(bact), 42; Am Bd Microbiol, dipl. *Hon Degrees:* ScD, Med Col Pa, 73. *Prof Exp:* Asst bact, 41-43, from instr to assoc prof, 43-61, prof virol, 61-72, prof microbiol, 62-72, EMER PROF VIROL & MICROBIOL, MED COL PA, 72- *Concurrent Pos:* Nat Coun Combat Blindness grant, Med Col Pa, 58-59, 62-63 & 66-67 & Nat Soc Prev Blindness grant, 68-70; mem res staff, Children's Hosp, Philadelphia, 51-52. *Honors & Awards:* Christian R & Mary E Lindback Award, 71. *Mem:* Fel Am Acad Microbiol; Am Soc Microbiol; NY Acad Sci. *Res:* Antigenic structure of hemolytic streptococci; complement fixing antigens of influenza viruses; mouse brain tissue culture; experimental viral infections and auto-immune reactions of the eye; experimental mycobacterial eye infection. *Mailing Add:* 9 Waterman Ave Philadelphia PA 19118

KIRBY, ALBERT CHARLES, b Baton Rouge, La, Mar 31, 41; m 61; c 3. PHYSIOLOGY. *Educ:* La State Univ, Baton Rouge, BS, 62, MS, 63; Univ Ill, Urbana, PhD(physiol), 67. *Prof Exp:* NIH sr fel physiol, Univ Wash, 67-69; asst prof, 69-75, ASSOC PROF PHYSIOL, CASE WESTERN RESERVE UNIV, 75- *Concurrent Pos:* NIH res grants, Case Western Reserve Univ, 69- *Mem:* Soc Gen Physiol; Biophys Soc; Am Physiol Soc. *Res:* Excitation-contraction coupling and contractile proteins in denervated mammalian muscle. *Mailing Add:* Dept of Physiol Case Western Reserve Univ Cleveland OH 44106

KIRBY, ANDREW FULLER, b Washington, DC, Feb 15, 55; m 81. ELECTRONIC SPECTROSCOPY, COORDINATION CHEMISTRY. *Educ:* Col Holy Cross, AB, 77; Duke Univ, PhD(phys chem), 81. *Prof Exp:* Technician, Wyo Mineral Corp, Westinghouse, 76; teaching asst, Phys Chem Lab, Holy Cross Col, 76-77; res asst, Duke Univ, 79-80, instr chem, 78-81; ASSOC INSTR, UNIV VA, 81- *Mem:* Am Chem Soc; Sigma Xi. *Res:* Detailed electronic and molecular structures of rare earth elements and compounds; intensities of electronic transitions occuring in crystalline lanthanide complexes. *Mailing Add:* Dept Chem Univ Va Charlottesville VA 22901

KIRBY, BRUCE JOHN, b Toronto, Ont, Nov 19, 28; m 58; c 2. APPLIED MATHEMATICS. *Educ:* Univ Toronto, BA, 50, MA, 51; Univ London, PhD, 67. *Prof Exp:* Teaching fel math, Univ Toronto, 51-53; lectr, Univ Liverpool, 53-54; lectr, 54-60, from asst prof to assoc prof, 60-69, PROF MATH, QUEEN'S UNIV, ONT, 69- *Mem:* Soc Indust & Appl Math. *Res:* Mathematics of control theory. *Mailing Add:* Dept Math Queen's Univ Kingston ON K7L 3N6 Can

KIRBY, CONRAD JOSEPH, JR, b Opelousas, La, Aug 2, 41; m 68; c 2. ECOLOGY. *Educ:* Univ Southwestern La, BS, 64; La State Univ, MS, 67, PhD(marine sci), 71. *Prof Exp:* Asst prof biol, Univ Southeastern La, 67-72; res ecologist, 72-74, SUPVRY ECOLOGIST, WATERWAYS EXP STA, 74- *Mem:* Ecol Soc Am; Am Soc Limnol & Oceanog; Nat Estuarine Res Fedn; Gulf Estuarine Res Fedn. *Res:* Impacts and mitigation of construction activities in wetlands; development and management of wetlands and other ecosystems. *Mailing Add:* Waterways Exp Sta YR PO Box 631 Vicksburg MS 39180

KIRBY, EDWARD PAUL, b Ithaca, NY, Sept 28, 41; m 66. BIOCHEMISTRY, HEMATOLOGY. *Educ:* Univ Rochester, BS, 63; Case Western Reserve Univ, PhD(biochem), 68. *Prof Exp:* NSF resident res associateship, Naval Med Res Inst, Bethesda, Md, 68-70; NIH fel, Univ Wash, 70-71; asst prof, 71-77, ASSOC PROF BIOCHEM, TEMPLE UNIV, 77- *Concurrent Pos:* Mem coun thrombosis, Am Heart Asn; Res career develop award, 76-80. *Mem:* Am Soc Biol Chemists; AAAS; NY Acad Sci. *Res:* Blood coagulation; protein chemistry; structure and function of the Antihemophilic factor and Hageman factor. *Mailing Add:* Dept of Biochem Temple Univ Health Sci Ctr Philadelphia PA 19140

KIRBY, HILLIARD WALKER, b Asheville, NC, June 12, 49; m 81. INTEGRATED PEST MANAGEMENT. *Educ:* Univ NC, BS, 71; NC State Univ, MS, 74, PhD(plant path), 81. *Prof Exp:* Agr exten agent, NC Agr Exten Serv, 74-78; ASST PROF PLANT PATH, COL AGR, UNIV ILL, 81- *Mem:* Am Phytopath Soc. *Res:* Effects of conservation tillage on plant disease development. *Mailing Add:* Dept Plant Path N-519 Turner Hall Univ Ill 1102 S Goodwin St Urbana IL 61801

KIRBY, JAMES RAY, b Goldsboro, NC, Oct 22, 33; m 62; c 1. ANALYTICAL CHEMISTRY. *Educ:* E Carolina Col, AB & BS, 55; Duke Univ, MA, 57, PhD(chem, physics), 60. *Prof Exp:* From res chemist to sr res chemist, 60-68, res specialist, 68-73, SR RES SPECIALIST, MONSANTO CO, 73- *Mem:* Am Chem Soc. *Res:* Chelate chemistry; polymer characterization. *Mailing Add:* Monsanto Co Box 12274 Research Triangle Park NC 27709

KIRBY, JON ALLAN, b San Antonio, Tex, May 31, 48; m 70; c 1. FLIGHT SOFTWARE. *Educ:* Ottawa Univ, BS, 70; Univ Calif, Berkeley, MA, 72, PhD(physics), 81. *Prof Exp:* Mem tech staff software design anal, 79-81, sect head software systs anal, 81-82, SECT HEAD & STAFF ENGR, DEFENCE SYST GROUP, SATELLITE DIV, TRW, INC, 82- *Mem:* Am Phys Soc. *Res:* Missile and satellite software performance analysis and design improvement especially guidance and navigation performance. *Mailing Add:* 16271 Honolulu Lane Huntington Beach CA 92647

KIRBY, KAREN MARIE, b Rockville Centre, NY, July 9, 50; m 74. STATISTICS, POPULATION GENETICS. *Educ:* Brown Univ, ScB & MS, 72; Princeton Univ, MA, 74, PhD(statist), 75. *Prof Exp:* Asst prof math, Univ Md, College Park, 75-77; ASST PROF MATH & STATIST, CENT CONN STATE COL, 77- *Mem:* Am Statist Asn. *Res:* Population genetics. *Mailing Add:* Dept Math & Statist Cent Conn State Col New Britain CT 06050

KIRBY, KENNETH WILLIAM, b Mankato, Minn, July 1, 23; m 47; c 2. BIOCHEMISTRY. *Educ:* Gustavus Adolphus Col, BA, 45; Purdue Univ, MS, 56, PhD(biochem), 58. *Prof Exp:* Jr chemist, Green Giant Co, 45-50, lab mgr, 50-53; asst, Purdue Univ, 56-58; res chemist, Penick & Ford, Ltd, Inc, & R J Reynolds Tobacco Co, 65-69; asst to tech dir, Penick & Ford, 69-77; RES SCIENTIST, DEPT PREV MED & ENVIRON HEALTH, UNIV IOWA, 77-, PROJ DIR, EFFECT OF PESTICIDES ON HUMAN HEALTH, INST AGR MED, 77- *Mem:* Am Chem Soc. *Res:* Derivafication of natural products. *Mailing Add:* Inst of Agr Med Univ of Iowa Oakdale IA 52319

KIRBY, MARGARET LOEWY, b Ft Smith, Ark, June 5, 46; m 71; c 2. ANATOMY, PHARMACOLOGY. *Educ:* Manhattanville Col, AB, 68; Univ Ark, PhD(anat), 72. *Prof Exp:* Teaching asst anat, Univ Ark, 69-71; asst prof gross anat, State Col Ark, 72-74; asst prof gross anat, 77-80, ASSOC PROF ANAT, MED COL GA, 80- *Concurrent Pos:* Prin investr, Ga Heart Asn, 78-79, Nat Inst Drug Abuse, 79-81 & NIH, 81-84. *Mem:* Am Asn Anatomists; Sigma Xi; Soc Neurosci; Int Soc Develop Neurosci. *Res:* Effects of neurotransmitters on embryonic development; effects of opioids on fetal development. *Mailing Add:* Dept of Anat Med Col of Ga Augusta GA 30901

KIRBY, MAURICE J(OSEPH), b Cedar Rapids, Iowa, Jan 19, 16; m 45; c 3. SYSTEMS & ELECTRICAL ENGINEERING. *Educ:* Iowa State Univ, BS, 37; Carnegie Inst Technol, MS, 47, DSc(elec eng), 48. *Prof Exp:* Engr, Gen Elec Co, 37-40; from asst engr to sr engr, US Navy Bur Ord, 40-46; engr, Sperry Gyroscope Co, 48-51, eng sect head, 51-60, res sect head, 60-63, sr res sect head, 63-73, SR RES SECT HEAD, SPERRY SYSTS MGT DIV, SPERRY CORP, 73- *Mem:* Inst Elec & Electronics Engrs; NY Acad Sci; sr mem Soc Logistics Engrs; Nat Soc Prof Engrs. *Res:* Electromagnetic fields; feedback control; navigation and guidance; reliability, maintainability and logistics; system integration; simulators and training systems. *Mailing Add:* 181 Tullamore Rd Garden City NY 11530

KIRBY, PAUL EDWARD, b Washington, DC, Mar 12, 49; m 71; c 1. CELL BIOLOGY. *Educ:* Mt St Mary's Col, Md, BS, 71; Cath Univ Am, MS, 74, PhD(cell biol), 78. *Prof Exp:* res scientist in vitro mutagenesis, 78-80, CHIEF, MAMMALIAN MUTAGENESIS SECT, EG&G MASON RES INST, 80- *Concurrent Pos:* Prin investr, Nat Cancer Inst; consult, 80- *Mem:* AAAS; Environ Mutagen Soc; Tissue Cult Asn; Genetic Toxicol Asn. *Res:* In vitro carcinogenesis and mutagenesis in mammalian cells, especially the L5178Y mouse lymphoma mutagenesis assay as a tool for the screening of compounds for mutagenic potential. *Mailing Add:* EG&G Mason Res Inst 1530 E Jefferson St Rockville MD 20852

KIRBY, RALPH C(LOUDSBERRY), b Washington, DC, July 21, 25; m 50; c 1. EXTRACTIVE METALLURGY, MINERAL ENGINEERING. *Educ:* Cath Univ Am, BChE, 50. *Prof Exp:* Chem engr, Metall Res Ctr, 50-54, metall engr, 55-58, proj leader, 59-65, staff metallurgist, Div Metall, 66-70, sr staff metallurgist, 71-72, chief, Div Metall, 72-76, asst dir metall, 76-79, DIR, MIN RESOURCES TECHNOL, US BUR MINES, 79- *Concurrent Pos:* Bd dirs, Metall Soc, 76- *Honors & Awards:* Gold Medal, Am Inst Chem, 50; Invention Award, US Bur Mines, 62; Spec Serv Award, 68 & 75; Meritorious Serv Award, US Dept Interior, 78. *Mem:* Am Inst Mining, Metall & Petrol Engrs; Am Inst Chem Engrs; AAAS; Am Soc Metals. *Res:* Metallurgical research; research and development management. *Mailing Add:* 116 Southwood Ave Silver Spring MD 20901

KIRBY, RICHARD C(YRIL), b Galesburg, Ill, Nov 22, 22; m 44; c 7. ELECTRICAL ENGINEERING. *Educ:* Univ Minn, BEE, 51. *Prof Exp:* Telegrapher, West Union Tel Co, Minn, 40-42; asst chief engr radio broadcast, KFEQ Inc, Mo, 46-48; res worker & proj leader radio propagation studies, Nat Bur Standards, 48-55, chief, Ionospheric Res Sect, 55-57, asst chief, Radio Propagation Physics Div, 57-59, chief radio commun & systs div, Cent Radio Propagation Lab, 59-65; dir, Ionospheric Telecommun Lab, Inst Telecommun Sci & Aeronomy, US Dept Commerce, 65-68, dir, Inst Telecommun Sci, US Dept Commerce, 68-71, assoc dir Off Telecommun, 71-74; DIR, INT RADIO CONSULT COMT, GENEVA, SWITZ, 74- *Concurrent Pos:* Asst, Univ Minn, 41-42; mem, Interdept Radio Adv Comt, Exec Off President, 59-60; US Dept Commerce fel sci & technol, 65-66; chmn, Comt Fixed Systs, US Int Consult Radio Comt. *Honors & Awards:* Exceptional serv gold medal, US Dept Commerce, 56 & 68. *Mem:* AAAS; Sigma Xi; fel Inst Elec & Electronics Engrs; Int Union Radio Sci. *Res:* Telecommunications; radio wave propagation; antennas; information transmission; ionospheric studies. *Mailing Add:* PO Box 813 Boulder CO 80306

KIRBY, ROBERT EMMET, b Stowe Twp, Pa, Feb 27, 21; m 44; c 4. ANALYTICAL CHEMISTRY. *Educ:* Univ Pittsburgh, BS, 49; Carnegie Inst Technol, MS, 52; Univ Ariz, PhD(anal chem), 61. *Prof Exp:* Res chemist, Shell Chem Co, 52-57; salesman, Wm C Buchanan Co, 57-58; instr, Tex Col Arts & Indust, 58-59; sr res chemist, Colgate-Palmolive Co, 62-63; asst prof, 63-70, ASSOC PROF CHEM, QUEENS COL, NY, 70- *Mem:* Am Chem Soc; The Chem Soc. *Res:* Electroanalytical methods; chelate chemistry; photoelectron spectroscopy. *Mailing Add:* Dept of Chem Queens Col Flushing NY 11367

KIRBY, ROBION C, b Chicago, Ill, Feb 25, 38; div; c 2. MATHEMATICS. *Educ:* Univ Chicago, BS, 59, MS, 60, PhD(math), 65. *Prof Exp:* Asst prof math, Univ Calif, Los Angeles, 65-69; PROF MATH, UNIV CALIF, BERKELEY, 71- *Honors & Awards:* Veblen Prize Geom, 71. *Mem:* Am Math Soc. *Res:* Topology, specifically topology of manifolds, differential and combinatorial topology. *Mailing Add:* Dept of Math Univ of Calif Berkeley CA 94720

KIRBY, ROGER D, b Lansing, Mich, June 1, 42; m 64; c 1. PHYSICS. *Educ:* Mich State Univ, BS, 64; Cornell Univ, PhD(physics), 69. *Prof Exp:* Res assoc physics, Cornell Univ, 68-69 & Univ Ill, 69-71; asst prof, 71-74, ASSOC PROF PHYSICS, UNIV NEBR, LINCOLN, 74- *Mem:* Am Phys Soc. *Res:* Lattice dynamics; Raman scattering from solids; far infrared optical properties of solids. *Mailing Add:* Behlen Lab of Physics Univ of Nebr Lincoln NE 68588

KIRBY, WILLIAM M M, b Springfield, SDak, Nov 21, 14; m 44. MEDICINE. *Educ:* Trinity Col, Conn, BS, 36; Cornell Univ, MD, 40. *Prof Exp:* Intern med, NY Hosp, 40-41; from asst resident to resident, Stanford Univ Hosps, 41-44, head chest dept & instr med, Sch Med, 47-49; assoc prof, 49-55, PROF MED, SCH MED, UNIV WASH, 55- *Concurrent Pos:* Vis investr, Rockefeller Inst, 47. *Mem:* Am Soc Clin Invest (secy, 51-54); Am Thoracic Soc; Am Fedn Clin Res. *Res:* Clinical infectious diseases. *Mailing Add:* Dept Med Sch Med Univ Wash Seattle WA 98195

KIRCH, LAWRENCE S, b Philadelphia, Pa, Dec 7, 32; m 55; c 3. ORGANIC CHEMISTRY. *Educ:* Temple Univ, AB, 55; Univ Cincinnati, MS, 57, PhD(chem), 58. *Prof Exp:* Sr res chemist, 58-73, proj leader, 73-81, SECTION MGR, ROHM & HAAS CO, 81- *Mem:* Am Chem Soc. *Res:* Organic reactions at high pressures; catalysis; reaction kinetics and mechanisms; organometallic compounds; coordination chemistry; reactions of acetylenes and of carbon monoxide; oxidation of organic compounds; chlorination, sulfonation and dehydrogenation of organic compounds; development of new chemical processes and optimization of existing processes. *Mailing Add:* 871 Oriole Lane Huntingdon Valley PA 19006

KIRCH, MURRAY R, b Philadelphia, Pa, Oct 11, 40; m 65; c 2. NUMERICAL ANALYSIS, MATHEMATICS OF GAMBLING. *Educ:* Temple Univ, AB, 62; Lehigh Univ, MS, 64, PhD(math), 68. *Prof Exp:* Instr math, Lehigh Univ, 65-68; asst prof, State Univ NY Buffalo, 68-72; ASSOC PROF MATH, STOCKTON STATE COL, 72- *Mem:* Am Math Soc; Math Asn Am; Soc Indust & Appl Math; Am Statist Asn. *Res:* Point-set topology; functional analysis; numerical methods for nonlinear systems; mathematical analysis of gambling and risk taking. *Mailing Add:* Fac of Natural Sci & Math Stockton State Col Pomona NJ 08240

KIRCH, WILLIAM, b Cincinnati, Ohio, May 20, 27; m 56; c 2. CHEMICAL ENGINEERING, TECHNICAL MANAGEMENT. *Educ:* Univ Cincinnati, ChE, 52. *Prof Exp:* Res engr, Am Synthetic Rubber Corp, 52-53, sr proj leader, 53-57; group leader, US Indust Chem Co Div, Nat Distillers & Chem Corp, 57-59, sr res supvr, 59-64; asst mgr, Polyolefins Develop, 64-66, mgr, 66-68; MGR TECH SECT, CHEMPLEX CO, 68- *Mem:* Am Inst Chem Engrs. *Res:* Processes and products of polyolefins. *Mailing Add:* Chemplex Co PO Box 819 Clinton IA 52732

KIRCHBERGER, MADELEINE, b Buffalo, NY. PHYSIOLOGY. *Educ:* Hunter Col, BA, 60; Columbia Univ, MA, 62, PhD(cell physiol), 66. *Prof Exp:* Res fel med, Mass Gen Hosp & Sch Med, Harvard Univ, 66-69; instr physiol, 70-71, assoc, 71-74, asst prof, 74-78, ASSOC PROF PHYSIOL, BIOPHYS & MED, MT SINAI SCH MED, 78- *Mem:* Am Physiol Soc; Biophys Soc; Am Soc Biol Chem; Int Soc Heart Res. *Res:* Regulation of cardiac contractility by catecholamines; calcium transport in biological membranes. *Mailing Add:* Mt Sinai Sch Med Fifth Ave & 100 St New York NY 10029

KIRCHER, CHARLES E(DMUND), JR, b El Paso, Tex, 08; m 41; c 6. CHEMICAL ENGINEERING. *Educ:* Calif Inst Technol, BS, 31, MS, 33; Iowa State Col, PhD(chem eng), 40. *Prof Exp:* Prod chemist, E I du Pont de Nemours & Co, Calif, 33-36, res chemist, NY, 36-37, chem engr, 39-40, process supvr, 40-43, spec asst develop div, Del, 45-47; asst, Iowa State Col, 37-39; sect leader, Manhattan Dist Proj, Chicago, 43-44 & Hanford Eng Works, Wash, 44-45; prof chem eng & head dept, Rose Polytech Inst, 47-52; res engr, Detrex Corp, 52-55, mgr res, Detrex Chem Industs, 55-70; CONSULT, 70- *Mem:* AAAS; fel Am Inst Chemists; Am Soc Testing & Mat. *Res:* Production, stabilization and use of chlorinated hydrocarbon solvents; patents on chlorinated products and processes; air pollution control. *Mailing Add:* 11409 Duluth Ave Youngtown AZ 85363

KIRCHER, HENRY WINFRIED, b Frankfurt am Main, Ger, Apr 7, 25; nat US; m 50; c 5. ORGANIC CHEMISTRY. *Educ:* Northwestern Univ, BS, 49; Univ Chicago, PhD(chem), 53. *Prof Exp:* Res chemist, Olympic Res Div, Rayonier, Inc, Wash, 53-58; from asst prof to assoc prof agr biochem, 58-66, prof biochem, 66-76, PROF NUTRIT & FOOD SCI, UNIV ARIZ, 76-, RES PROF BIOCHEM, AGR RES STA, 76- *Concurrent Pos:* Vis scientist, USDA, La, 65-66. *Mem:* AAAS; Am Chem Soc; Am Oil Chemists' Soc. *Res:* Carbohydrates; lipids; sterols. *Mailing Add:* Agr Exp Sta Univ of Ariz Tucson AZ 85721

KIRCHER, JOHN FREDERICK, b Athens, Ohio, Jan 31, 29; m 51; c 4. PHYSICAL CHEMISTRY. *Educ:* Ohio Univ, BS, 50, MS, 51; Syracuse Univ, PhD(chem), 56. *Prof Exp:* Design & develop engr, Radio Corp Am, 55-57; proj leader, 57-60, assoc div chief chem physics res, 60-65, fel chem physics res, 65-70, div chief chem physics res, 70-73, sr chemist, Dept Physics, 73-76, sr chemist, Energy & Environ Technol Dept, 76-78, prog mgr, 78-80, WASTE PACKAGE DEPT MGR, OFF NUCLEAR WASTE ISOLATION, COLUMBUS DIV, BATTELLE MEM INST, 80- *Mem:* AAAS; Am Chem Soc; fel Am Inst Chem; Sigma Xi. *Res:* Radiation chemistry of inorganic gas phase reactions; polymers and other organic systems; radiation dosimetry; surface chemistry; vacuum techniques; gas kinetics and electrical discharges; flames. *Mailing Add:* Battelle Mgt Div/ONWI 505 King Ave Columbus OH 43201

KIRCHER, MORTON S(UMMER), b Rome, NY, May 3, 17; m 42; c 3. CHEMICAL ENGINEERING, ELECTROCHEMICAL ENGINEERING. *Educ:* Univ Rochester, BS, 38. *Prof Exp:* Chem engr, Hooker Chem Corp, NY, 38-51, res supvr, 51-58, mgr electrochem & inorg res, 58-59, sr engr electrochem develop, 59-61; gen mgr, Dryden Chem Ltd, 61-71, pres, 67-71; INDUST CONSULT ELECTROCHEM, MORTON S KIRCHER, 71- *Concurrent Pos:* Civilian, Off Sci Res & Develop, AEC; gen mgr, BC Chem Ltd, 65-71. *Mem:* Electrochem Soc; Am Chem Soc; Am Inst Chem Eng. *Res:* Electrochemistry of caustic-chlorine cells, fluorine cells, chlorate, perchlorate and chloralkali cells including diaphragm type; development of membrane diaphragm, cells. *Mailing Add:* 1111 Granada St Clearwater FL 33515

KIRCHGESSNER, JOSEPH L, b Wheeling, WVa, June 23, 32; m 56; c 3. PHYSICS, ELECTRICAL ENGINEERING. *Educ:* Le Moyne Col, NY, BS, 54; Cornell Univ, MS, 56. *Prof Exp:* Mem prof tech staff, Princeton Penn Accelerator, 56-65, sr tech staff, 65-70, div head, 68-70; ACCELERATOR PHYSICIST, CORNELL ELECTRON SYNCHROTRON, 70- *Concurrent Pos:* Del, Int Accelerator Conf, Italy, 65, Mass, 67 & USSR, 69; mem prog comn, US Nat Particle Accelerator Conf, 66 & 67; consult, Princeton Penn Accelerator, 71. *Mem:* Am Phys Soc. *Res:* Accelerator design and development. *Mailing Add:* Wilson Lab Cornell Univ Ithaca NY 14853

KIRCHHEIMER, WALDEMAR FRANZ, b Schneidemuhl, Ger, Jan 11, 13; nat US; m 45. MICROBIOLOGY. *Educ:* Univ Giessen, MD, 37; Univ Wash, PhD, 49. *Prof Exp:* Res physician, King County Tuberc Hosp, Seattle, Wash, 42-46; res assoc tuberc, Univ Wash, 46-47, instr microbiol, Sch Med, 48-49; from asst prof to assoc prof bact, Med Sch, Northwestern Univ, 49-56; dep safety dir & med bacteriologist, Ft Detrick, Md, 56-61; mem res staff, Inst Allergy & Infectious Dis, 61-62; chief microbiol sect, 62-64, lab br, 65-67 & lab res dept, 67-71, CHIEF LAB RES BR, US PUB HEALTH SERV HOSP, 71- *Concurrent Pos:* Clin prof bact trop dis & med parasitol, La State Univ Med Ctr, New Orleans. *Mem:* Am Soc Microbiol. *Res:* Immunology; mechanism of tuberculin-type sensitivity; medical bacteriology; cell culture of leprosy bacillus; animal transmission of leprosy. *Mailing Add:* US Pub Health Serv Hosp Carville LA 70721

KIRCHHOFF, WILLIAM HAYES, b Chicago, Ill, Nov 27, 36; m 58; c 4. PHYSICAL CHEMISTRY. *Educ:* Univ Ill, BS, 58; Harvard Univ, MA, 61, PhD(chem physics), 63. *Prof Exp:* NATO fel phys chem, Inorg Chem Lab, Oxford Univ, 62-63; Nat Res Coun res assoc chem physics, 64-66, physicist, 66-72, phys sci adminr off air & water measurement, 72-78, dep dir, Ctr Thermodynamics & Molecular Sci, 78-80, CHIEF, OFF ENVIRON MEASUREMENTS, NAT BUR STANDARDS, 80- *Mem:* AAAS; Am Phys Soc; Am Chem Soc; Am Soc Testing & Mat. *Res:* Quantum chemistry; microwave spectroscopy; molecular structure. *Mailing Add:* Nat Bur of Stand Washington DC 20234

KIRCHMAYER, LEON K, b Milwaukee, Wis, July 24, 24; m 50; c 2. ELECTRICAL POWER ENGINEERING. *Educ:* Marquette Univ, BS, 45; Univ Wis, MS, 47, PhD, 50. *Prof Exp:* Mgr power syst oper invests, 56-58, mgr syst generation anal eng, 58-63, mgr syst planning & control, 63-77, MGR ADVAN SYST TECHNOL & PLANNING, GEN ELEC CO, 77- *Concurrent Pos:* Dir ESIN, SAm consult firm; mem, Int Conf Large High Tension Elec Systs. *Mem:* Nat Acad Eng; fel Am Soc Mech Engrs; fel Inst Elec & Electronics Engrs; Opers Res Soc Am; Nat Soc Prof Engrs. *Res:* Computer applications; system technology; power generation. *Mailing Add:* Gen Elec Co 2-602 Schenectady NY 12345

KIRCHMEIER, ROBERT LYNN, b Portland, Ore, Apr 25, 42; m 70; c 1. FLUORINE CHEMISTRY, ANALYTICAL CHEMISTRY. *Educ:* Univ Mont, BS, 68; Univ Idaho, PhD(chem), 75. *Prof Exp:* Chemist, USAEC, 68-71 & Univ Idaho, 71-75; CHEMIST, PFIZER, INC, 75- *Mem:* Sigma Xi; Am Chem Soc. *Res:* Development of modern techniques for application to pharmaceutical and related product analysis. *Mailing Add:* Pfizer Inc Qual Control Eastern Point Rd Groton CT 06340

KIRCHMEYER, FREDERICK JOSEPH, b St Louis, Mo, Mar 27, 15; m 40; c 3. PHARMACY. *Educ:* St Louis Col Pharm, BS, 38. *Prof Exp:* Instr pharm, St Louis Col Pharm, 38-39; asst pharmaceut res, Abbott Labs, 39-46, head, 46-54, dir new prod coord, 54-57, dir new prod & mem bd dirs, 57-61, vpres com develop, 61, mem opers comt & vpres prod planning & develop, 61-64, vpres allied opers, 64-68, vpres agr prod, 68-70, vpres res & develop, Consumer Prods Div, 70-77; CONSULT PHARMACEUT, 77- *Concurrent Pos:* Mem bd, Wiekman Pharmaceut. *Mem:* AAAS; Am Chem Soc; Am Pharmaceut Asn. *Res:* Pharmaceutical forms of new drugs; product development; water soluble form of vitamin K; solubilization of riboflavin with veratryl alcohol; compounds of nitride acetyl sulfonamides and vasoconstrictor amines. *Mailing Add:* 6510 Burning Tree Dr Seminole FL 33542

KIRCHNER, FREDERICK KARL, b New YOrk, NY, May 10, 11; m 38; c 1. ORGANIC CHEMISTRY, INFORMATION SCIENCE. *Educ:* Maryville Col, AB, 34; Univ Tenn, MS, 35; Ohio State Univ, PhD(org chem), 38. *Prof Exp:* Asst prof chem, Bridgewater Col, 38-43; res chemist, Winthrop Chem Co, NY, 43-45, sr res chemist & group leader, Sterling-Winthrop Res Inst, 45-66, dir coord, 66-76; RETIRED. *Mem:* Am Chem Soc; fel NY Acad Sci; fel Am Inst Chem; Nat Micrographics Asn. *Res:* Synthesis of pharmaceuticals; scientific information research. *Mailing Add:* 1714 Glen Echo Rd Nashville TN 37215

KIRCHNER, FREDERICK ROY, b Chicago, Ill, Mar 31, 47; m 68; c 3. FOSSIL FUEL TOXICOLOGY, AEROSOC PHYSICS. *Educ:* Loras Col, BS, 73; Univ Iowa, MS, 75, PhD(radiation biol), 79. *Prof Exp:* Fel inhalation toxicol, 78-80, ASST SCIENTIST MAMMALIAN TOXICOL, ARGONNE NAT LAB, 80- *Mem:* Sigma Xi; Radiation Res Soc; Aerosol Res Soc. *Res:* Toxicological effects of emerging fossil fuel technologies on in-vivo and in-vitro mammalian systems. *Mailing Add:* Div Biol & Med Res Argonne Nat Lab 9700 S Cass Ave Argonne IL 60439

KIRCHNER, H(ENRY) P(AUL), b Buffalo, NY, Sept 9, 23; m 50; c 3. CERAMICS. *Educ:* Cornell Univ, BME, 47; Pa State Univ, PhD(ceramics), 55. *Prof Exp:* Prod engr, Carborundum Co, 47-51; proj engr, Corning Glass Works, 54-57; prin ceramic engr, Aeronaut Lab, Cornell Univ, 57-60, asst dept head, Mat Dept, 60-63; tech dir, Linden Labs, Inc, 63-66, vpres, 66-68; PRES, CERAMIC FINISHING CO, 68- *Mem:* Fel Am Ceramic Soc; Nat Inst Ceramic Engrs. *Res:* Physical and chemical properties of ceramic materials, especially refractories, abrasives and dielectrics; processes to improve strength; fractography; failure analysis; fracture mechanics. *Mailing Add:* Box 498 State College PA 16801

KIRCHNER, JAMES GARY, b Detroit, Mich, Sept 11, 38. PETROLOGY, GEOLOGY. *Educ:* Wayne State Univ, BS, 60, MS, 62; Univ Iowa, PhD(geol), 71. *Prof Exp:* Geologist petrol, Gulf Oil Corp, 62-66; ASSOC PROF GEOL, ILL STATE UNIV, 69- *Mem:* Geol Soc Am; AAAS; Nat Asn Geol Teachers; Sigma Xi. *Res:* Igneous geology of the northern Black Hills in South Dakota. *Mailing Add:* Dept of Geog & Geol Ill State Univ Normal IL 61761

KIRCHNER, JOHN ALBERT, b Waynesboro, Pa, Mar 27, 15; m 47; c 5. OTOLARYNGOLOGY. *Educ:* Univ Va, MD, 40. *Prof Exp:* Instr otolaryngol, Johns Hopkins Hosp, 48-49, resident, 49; from asst prof to assoc prof, 51-62, PROF OTOLARYNGOL, SCH MED, YALE UNIV, 62- *Concurrent Pos:* Commonwealth Fund fel otolaryngol, Royal Col Surg, 63-64; jr attend otolaryngologist, Deaconess, Christ & Good Samaritan Hosps, 49-50; assoc surgeon, Grace-New Haven Community Hosp, 51-; mem otolaryngol post-grad training comt, NIH, 56-59. *Honors & Awards:* Mosher Award, 58; Casselbery Award, Am Laryngol Asn, 66 & Newcomb Award, 69; Semon lectr, Univ London, 81. *Mem:* Am Laryngol Asn (pres, 79); Am Laryngol, Rhinol & Otol Soc (pres, 81-82); Am Acad Ophthal & Otolaryngol; fel Am Col Surg; Am Soc Head & Neck Surg (pres, 76). *Res:* Physiology of the larynx and pharynx. *Mailing Add:* Yale-New Haven Med Ctr 333 Cedar St New Haven CT 06510

KIRCHNER, RICHARD MARTIN, b San Francisco, Calif, Dec 1, 41. INORGANIC CHEMISTRY, STRUCTURAL CHEMISTRY. *Educ:* Univ Calif, Berkeley, AB, 64; Calif State Univ, San Jose, MS, 66; Univ Wash, PhD(chem), 71. *Prof Exp:* Fel chem, Northwestern Univ, 71-73; asst prof, 73-80, ASSOC PROF CHEM & CHMN, MANHATTAN COL, 80- *Concurrent Pos:* Consult, Tarrytown Tech Ctr, Union Carbide Corp, 74-; res collabr chem, Brookhaven Nat Lab, 75- *Mem:* Am Crystallog Asn; Am Chem Soc; Am Phys Soc; Sigma Xi; NY Acad Sci. *Res:* Preparation and characterization of transition metal complexes with unusual ligands; x-ray crystallography. *Mailing Add:* Dept of Chem Manhattan Col Bronx NY 10471

KIRCHNER, ROBERT P, b Orange, NJ, Jan 21, 39; m 62; c 2. MECHANICAL ENGINEERING. *Educ:* Newark Col Eng, BS, 62, MS, 64; Rutgers Univ, PhD(mech eng), 68. *Prof Exp:* From asst instr to asst prof mech eng, Newark Col Eng, 62-76; PROF MECH ENG, NJ INST TECHNOL, 76- *Mem:* Am Soc Mech Engrs; Am Soc Eng Educ. *Res:* Thermodynamics; fluid mechanics; heat transfer. *Mailing Add:* Dept of Mech Eng 325 High St Newark NJ 07103

KIRCHOFF, WILLIAM F, b New Rochelle, NY, Apr 28, 29; m 54; c 4. MICROBIOLOGY. *Educ:* Fordham Univ, BS, 51; Purdue Univ, MS, 57, PhD(microbiol), 59; Seton Hall Univ, JD, 72. *Prof Exp:* Sr microbiologist, Nuodex Prod Co Div, Tenneco Corp, 59-60; res microbiologist biochem res & develop, Chas Pfizer & Co, 60-65; tech coordr drug regulatory affairs, Hoffmann-La Roche, Inc, 65-72; dir res, Drug Regulatory Affairs, Sandoz Inc, 72-74; asst dir, Short Term Res & Develop, 74-77, consult, 77-79; SR ATTY, WARNER-LAMBERT CO, 79- *Mem:* Am Soc Microbiol; NY Acad Sci; Sigma Xi; Am Bar Asn. *Res:* Microbiol fermentation; antibiotics; enzymes. *Mailing Add:* 284 Roseland Ave Essex Fells NJ 07021

KIRDANI, RASHAD Y, b Cairo, Egypt, Oct 20, 29; US citizen; m 58; c 1. ORGANIC CHEMISTRY, BIOCHEMISTRY. *Educ:* Cairo Univ, BSc, 50, MSc, 55; Univ Buffalo, PhD(org chem), 61. *Prof Exp:* Trainee steroid training prog, Worcester Found Exp Biol & Clark Univ, 60-61; res assoc steroid chem, Worcester Found Exp Biol, 61-62; staff scientist steroid chem & biochem, 62-65; PRIN CANCER RES SCIENTIST, ROSWELL PARK MEM INST, 65-; ASST RES PROF CHEM, STATE UNIV NY BUFFALO, 72- *Mem:* AAAS; Endocrine Soc; NY Acad Sci; Sigma Xi. *Res:* Chemistry and biochemistry of steroid hormones. *Mailing Add:* Roswell Park Mem Inst 666 Elm St Buffalo NY 14203

KIRK, ALEXANDER DAVID, b London, Eng, Apr 17, 34; m 63; c 3. PHYSICAL CHEMISTRY. *Educ:* Univ Edinburgh, BSc, 56, PhD(chem), 59. *Prof Exp:* Res fel chem, Univ BC, 59-61; from asst prof to assoc prof, 61-71, chmn dept, 74-79, PROF CHEM, UNIV VICTORIA, BC, 71- *Concurrent Pos:* Humbolt fel, 68-69; vis prof, Univ Sussex, Sch Molecular Sci, 75-76. *Mem:* fel Chem Inst Can; Can Asn University Teachers. *Res:* Photochemistry; inorganic photochemistry and luminescence; photochemistry and luminescence of coordination compounds. *Mailing Add:* Dept of Chem Univ of Victoria Victoria BC V8W 2Y2 Can

KIRK, BEN TRUETT, b Natchitoches, La, Oct 1, 42; m 66. PLANT PATHOLOGY. *Educ:* La Polytech Inst, BS, 64; La State Univ, MS, 66, PhD(plant path), 68. *Prof Exp:* Asst prof, 68-73, ASSOC PROF BOT, SOUTHEASTERN LA UNIV, 73- *Mem:* Am Phytopath Soc. *Res:* Fungal ultrastructure; systemic fungicides. *Mailing Add:* Dept of Biol Southeastern La Univ Hammond LA 70401

KIRK, BILLY EDWARD, b Robinson, Ill, May 5, 27; div; c 2. VIROLOGY. *Educ:* Univ Ill, BS, 49; Ohio State Univ, MSc, 55, PhD(microbiol), 57. *Prof Exp:* Sr bacteriologist, Eli Lilly & Co, Ind, 57-62; instr, Univ Mich, 62-64; asst prof, 64-73, ASSOC PROF MICROBIOL, WVA UNIV, 73- *Mem:* AAAS; Am Soc Microbiol; Brit Soc Gen Microbiol; Tissue Culture Asn. *Res:* Virology; biology and pathogenic role of defective viruses; virus persistence. *Mailing Add:* Dept of Microbiol WVa Univ Med Ctr Morgantown WV 26506

KIRK, DALE E(ARL), b Payette, Idaho, July 2, 18; m 39; c 5. AGRICULTURAL ENGINEERING. *Educ:* Ore State Univ, BS, 42; Mich State Univ, MS, 54. *Prof Exp:* Asst, Agr Eng, 41-42, asst agr engr, 42-44 & 46-54, assoc prof agr eng, 54-63, actg head dept, 70-71, PROF AGR ENG & AGR ENGR, ORE STATE UNIV, 63-, ACTG DEPT HEAD, 80- *Mem:* Am Soc Agr Engrs. *Res:* Food engineering; processing and handling agricultural products. *Mailing Add:* Dept of Agr Eng Ore State Univ Corvallis OR 97331

KIRK, DANIEL EDDINS, b Rocky Mount, NC, Feb 19, 24; m 46; c 4. BIOLOGY. *Educ:* Furman Univ, BS, 48; Univ NC, MA, 50; Emory Univ, PhD, 57. *Prof Exp:* Asst prof biol, Furman Univ, 50-57; PROF BIOL, CATAWBA COL, 57- *Mem:* Am Soc Parasitol; Am Micros Soc. *Res:* Helminthology; reptilian blood flukes. *Mailing Add:* Dept of Biol Catawba Col Salisbury NC 28144

KIRK, DAVID BLACKBURN, b Lock Haven, Pa, Nov 18, 21; m 44; c 2. MATHEMATICS. *Educ:* Haverford Col, BS, 43; Univ Pa, MA, 48. *Prof Exp:* Instr statist, Univ Pa, 47-48; methods analyst electronics comt, Mutual Benefit Life Ins Co, NJ, 48-56; sr res mathematician, Res Div, Curtiss-Wright Corp, Pa, 56-59; res mathematician, Willow Run Labs, Univ Mich, 59-66; head statist & res prog, Data Processing Div, Educ Testing Serv, Princeton NJ, 66-67, opers res scientist, 67-74; dir statist serv, Univ City Sci Ctr, 74-77; supvry comput specialist regional off, 77-78, DIR MGT INFO DIV, REGION III, HUD, 78- *Concurrent Pos:* Part-time teaching comput sci & numerical anal, Rutgers Univ, 69-70 & quant methods & statist, Rider Col, 70-74. *Mem:* Am Math Soc; Math Asn Am; Am Statist Asn; Asn Comput Mach; Sigma Xi. *Res:* Application of digital computers to mathematical, engineering and statistical research problems. *Mailing Add:* 1914 Yardley Rd Morrisville PA 19067

KIRK, DAVID CLARK, JR, b Newark, NJ, May 19, 24; m 53; c 3. PHYSICAL CHEMISTRY. *Educ:* Lehigh Univ, BS, 44; Polytech Inst Brooklyn, MS, 51; Univ Iowa, PhD(chem), 53; Furman Univ, MBA, 79. *Prof Exp:* Chem engr, Am Dyewood Co, 46-48; chemist, Merck & Co, 48-50; res chemist, Hercules Powder Co, 53-59; dir fundamental res, Ecusta Paper Div, Olin Corp, 59-69, dir res & Develop, 69-76; TECH DIR, ALLIED PAPER DIV, SCM CORP, 76- *Mem:* Am Chem Soc; Sigma Xi; Am Tech Asn Pulp & Paper Indust. *Res:* Organic chemistry; kinetics, photo and surface chemistry of protective coatings; elastomers and papers. *Mailing Add:* PO Box 2528 Kalamazoo MI 49003

KIRK, DAVID LIVINGSTONE, b Clinton, Mass, Mar 19, 34; m 58; c 1. DEVELOPMENTAL BIOLOGY. *Educ:* Northeastern Univ, AB, 56; Univ Wis, MS, 58, PhD(biochem), 60. *Prof Exp:* Res technician, Lovett Mem Lab, Mass Gen Hosp, Boston, 52-56; res asst biochem, Univ Wis, 56-60; sr res chemist, Biol Res Labs, Colgate-Palmolive Co, 60-62; res assoc develop biol, Univ Chicago, 62-65, asst prof, 65-69; ASSOC PROF BIOL, WASH UNIV, 69- *Mem:* AAAS; Am Chem Soc; Soc Develop Biol; Soc Cell Biol. *Res:* Developmental biochemistry and genetics; analysis of genetic, cytological and molecular basis of cell determination and cytodifferentiation in simple eukaryotes. *Mailing Add:* Dept of Biol Wash Univ St Louis MO 63130

KIRK, DONALD EVAN, b Baltimore, Md, Apr 4, 37; m 62; c 2. ELECTRICAL ENGINEERING. *Educ:* Worcester Polytech Inst, BS, 59; Naval Postgrad Sch, MS, 61; Univ Ill, PhD(elec eng), 65. *Prof Exp:* Instr elec eng, Naval Postgrad Sch, 59-62; teaching asst, Univ Ill, 62-63, instr, 63-64; from asst prof to assoc prof, 65-76, PROF ELEC ENG, NAVAL POSTGRAD SCH, 76-, CHMN DEPT, 76- *Mem:* Inst Elec & Electronics Engrs; Am Soc Eng Educ. *Res:* Theory and application of optimal estimation and control of systems. *Mailing Add:* Dept of Elec Eng Naval Postgrad Sch Monterey CA 93940

KIRK, DONALD WAYNE, b Carleton Place, Ont, Aug 18, 34; m 58; c 3. CIVIL ENGINEERING. *Educ:* Queen's Univ, BSc, 56, MSc, 65, PhD(struct eng), 69. *Prof Exp:* From lectr to assoc prof, 62-75, PROF STRUCT, ROYAL MIL COL CAN, 75-, HEAD DEPT CIVIL ENG, 77- *Honors & Awards:* Duggan Medal, Eng Inst Can, 65. *Mem:* Am Concrete Inst; Eng Inst Can; Am Soc Eng Educ. *Res:* Ultimate strength of reinforced concrete slab and girder systems; analysis and design of beams containing web openings; slab column connections. *Mailing Add:* Dept of Civil Eng Royal Mil Col of Can Kingston ON K7L 2W3 Can

KIRK, IVAN WAYNE, b Lark, Tex, Jan 25, 37; m 60; c 2. COTTON PRODUCTION. *Educ:* Tex Tech Univ, BS, 59; Clemson Univ, MS, 61; Auburn Univ PhD(agr eng), 68. *Prof Exp:* Res agr engr, Agr Res Serv, USDA, Lubbock, 60-65, Auburn, 65-67, Lubbock, 67-71; lab dir, Agr Res Serv, USDA, NMex, 71-77; assoc dir, 77-80, ACTG CTR DIR, SOUTHERN REGIONAL RES CTR, AGR RES SERV, USDA, 80- *Concurrent Pos:* Instr & asst prof, Dept Agr Engr, Tex Tech Univ, 63-65. *Mem:* Am Peanut Res & Educ Soc; AAAS; Am Soc Agr Engrs. *Res:* New and improved methods, and machinery for cotton production, harvesting, and ginning. *Mailing Add:* PO Box 19687 New Orleans LA 70179

KIRK, JAMES CURTIS, b Hubbard, Tex, May 10, 21; m 44; c 5. ORGANIC CHEMISTRY. *Educ:* Baylor Univ, BS, 44; Ohio State Univ, PhD(chem), 49. *Prof Exp:* Analyst, Pan Am Ref Corp, 44-46; asst chem, Ohio State Univ, 46-49; from assoc res chemist to sr res chemist, Continental Oil Co, 49-53, res group leader, 53-55, supvry res chemist, 55-57; dir res, Petrol Chem, Inc, 57-60; dir, Petrochem Res Div, Res & Develop Dept, 60-66, dir, Environ Conserv, Res & Eng Dept, 66-67, gen mgr, 67-75, VPRES RES & DEVELOP DEPT, CONOCO INC, 75- *Mem:* Am Chem Soc; Soc Petrol Engrs. *Res:* Hydrocarbon oxidation; lubricating oil additives; surface active agents; reaction mechanisms; polymerication; research administration. *Mailing Add:* R&D Dept Conoco Inc PO Drawer 1267 Ponca City OK 74603

KIRK, JOE ECKLEY, JR, b Houston, Tex, May 17, 39; m 67. MATHEMATICS. *Educ:* Sam Houston State Univ, BA, 60; Univ Tex, Austin, MA, 62, PhD(math), 67. *Prof Exp:* Opers res analyst, US Arms Control & Disarmament Agency, 67-69; asst prof math, Univ Wyo, 69-74; asst prof math, Univ Tenn, Chattanooga, 74-76, assoc prof, 76-80; ASSOC PROF MATH, SAM HOUSTON STATE UNIV, 80- *Mem:* Asn Comput Mach; Am Math Soc; Math Asn Am. *Res:* Complex analysis; function theory. *Mailing Add:* Dept Math Sam Houston State Univ Huntsville TX 77341

KIRK, JOHN GALLATIN, b Wilmington, Ohio, Oct 21, 38. SOLAR PHYSICS, AEROSPACE SCIENCES. *Educ:* Amherst Col, AB, 60; Univ Mich, AM, 62, PhD(astron), 66. *Prof Exp:* Jr astronr, Kitt Peak Nat Observ, 66-69; asst prof astron, Univ Toledo, 69-74; staff scientist, Comput Sci Corp, 74-79; sr analyst, Electronics Div, Gen Dynamics Corp, 79-80, MEM PROF STAFF, GEODYNAMICS CORP, 80- *Mem:* Am Astron Soc; Sigma Xi; Sci Res Soc. *Res:* Physics of the solar atmosphere. *Mailing Add:* 55 Hitchcock Way Suite 209 Geodynamics Corp Santa Barbara CA 93105

KIRK, MARILYN CHALOUPKA, b Bridgeport, Nebr, May 8, 27; m 58; c 1. DEVELOPMENTAL BIOLOGY. *Educ:* Univ Nebr, BS, 48; Univ Wis, MS, 54, PhD(nutrit, biochem), 56. *Prof Exp:* Asst nutrit, Univ Nebr, 48-52; asst prof foods & nutrit, Sch Home Econ, Univ Wis, 56-60; res assoc, Am Meat Inst Found, Ill, 63-64; res assoc, Dept Biol, Univ Chicago, 65-69; RES ASSOC, DEPT BIOL, WASH UNIV, 69- *Res:* Biochemical studies of development and cytodifferentiation in simple eukaryotes. *Mailing Add:* Dept of Biol Wash Univ St Louis MO 63130

KIRK, PAUL WHEELER, JR, b Jacksonville, Fla, Feb 23, 31; m 58; c 2. MYCOLOGY. *Educ:* Univ Richmond, BS, 57, MS, 61; Duke Univ, PhD(bot), 66. *Prof Exp:* Asst prof biol, Western Carolina Col, 65-66; asst prof bot, Va Polytech Inst, 66-70; assoc prof biol, 71-77, asst dean sci & health professions, 73-78, PROF BIOL, OLD DOMINION UNIV, 77-, . *Mem:* Mycol Soc Am; Sigma Xi. *Res:* Marine ascomycetes and deuteromycetes. *Mailing Add:* Dept of Biol Sci Old Dominion Univ Norfolk VA 23508

KIRK, R(OBERT) S(TEWART), b Chicago, Ill, Nov 2, 22; m 58; c 2. CHEMICAL ENGINEERING. *Educ:* Ill Inst Technol, BS & MS, 43; Univ Wis, PhD(chem eng), 48. *Prof Exp:* Asst prof chem eng, Univ Wis, 48-55; res engr, Calif Res Corp, 55-58, group supvr thermal recovery, 58-64, sr res engr, Chevron Res Co, Standard Oil Co Calif, 64-66; ASSOC PROF CHEM ENG, UNIV MASS, AMHERST, 66- *Mem:* Am Chem Soc; Am Inst Chem Engrs; Am Inst Mining, Metall & Petrol Engrs. *Res:* Process design and evaluation; chemical kinetics and reactor design; thermal methods of secondary recovery of crude oil. *Mailing Add:* Dept of Chem Eng Univ of Mass Amherst MA 01003

KIRK, ROBERT WARREN, b Stamford, Conn, May 20, 22; m 49; c 3. VETERINARY MEDICINE. *Educ:* Univ Conn, BS, 43; Cornell Univ, DVM, 46; Am Col Vet Internal Med, dipl & cert internal med & dermat. *Prof Exp:* Pvt pract, 46-50; from asst prof to assoc prof, 52-74, chmn dept small animal med & surg & dir small animal hosp, 69-77, PROF MED, STATE UNIV NY VET COL, CORNELL UNIV, 74- *Concurrent Pos:* Fel, Sch Med, Univ Colo, 60-61; NSF sci fac fel, Sch Med Stanford Univ, 67-69; mem grants adv bd, Seeing Eye Found, NY, 70-73; Evelyn Williams fel & vis scholar, Univ Sydney, Australia, 74; pres, Am Col Vet Internal Med, 74-76; vis prof, Sch Med Stanford Univ, 75; chmn bd regents, Am Col Vet Internal Med; trustee, Seeing Eye Found, 77- *Honors & Awards:* Fido Award, Am Animal Hosp Asn, 64; Gaines Medal, 67. *Mem:* Am Vet Med Asn. *Res:* Clinical medicine and dermatology therapeutics. *Mailing Add:* State Univ of NY Col of Vet Med Cornell Univ Ithaca NY 14853

KIRK, THOMAS BERNARD WALTER, b Denver, Colo, June 13, 40; m 74; c 2. HIGH ENERGY PHYSICS. *Educ:* Univ Colo, Boulder, BS, 62; Univ Wash, MS, 64, PhD(physics), 67. *Prof Exp:* Fel physics, Harvard Univ, 67-69, from asst prof to assoc prof, 69-73; assoc prof physics, Univ Ill, Urbana, 73-76; head neutrino dept, 76-81, TEV II PROJ MGR, DEP RES DIV HEAD, FERMI NAT ACCELERATOR LAB, 81- *Concurrent Pos:* Mem prog adv comt, Fermilab, 70-72. *Mem:* Am Phys Soc. *Res:* Experimental investigation of fundamental particle processes in strong, electromagnetic and weak interactions at high energies. *Mailing Add:* Neutrino Dept PO Box 500 Batavia IL 60510

KIRK, VERNON MILES, b Bellefonte, Pa, Feb 24, 22; m 43; c 3. ECONOMIC ENTOMOLOGY. *Educ:* Dickinson Col, BS, 47; Cornell Univ, PhD(entom), 51. *Prof Exp:* Prof entom, Pee Dee Exp Sta, Clemson Univ, 51-65; RES ENTOMOLOGIST, NORTHERN GRAIN INSECTS RES LAB, USDA, 65- *Mem:* Entom Soc Am. *Res:* Life history and control research on insects affecting corn and small grains, with emphasis on naturally occurring predators of soil insect pests of corn; site requirements for oviposition by western and northern corn rootworms. *Mailing Add:* 1633 Elmwood Dr Brookings SD 57006

KIRK, WILEY PRICE, b Joplin, Mo, July 24, 42; m 64; c 2. LOW TEMPERATURE PHYSICS. *Educ:* Wash Univ, BA, 64; State Univ NY Stony Brook, MS, 67, PhD(physics), 70. *Prof Exp:* Jr res assoc physics, Brookhaven Nat Lab, 67-69; instr, State Univ NY Stony Brook, 69-70; fel, Univ Fla, 70-71, interim asst prof, 71-73, asst prof, 73-75; asst prof, 75-78, ASSOC PROF PHYSICS, TEX A&M UNIV, 78- *Concurrent Pos:* Tech collabr, Brookhaven Nat Lab, 69-70; consult, Sci Instruments, Inc, 70-75. *Mem:* AAAS; Am Phys Soc; Sigma Xi. *Res:* Thermodynamic, magnetic and nuclear magnetic resonance properties of materials, particularly quantum crystals of helium; methods of low temperature thermometry; cryogenic and superconducting devices; low temperature thermoelectric studies; millikelvin-thermocouple-thermometry; superconducting quantum interference detector and pulsed nuclear magnetic resonance techniques. *Mailing Add:* Dept of Physics Tex A&M Univ College Station TX 77843

KIRK, WILLIAM ARTHUR, b Montour Falls, NY, Oct 3, 36; m 59; c 3. MATHEMATICS. *Educ:* DePauw Univ, AB, 58; Univ Mo, MA, 60, PhD(math), 62. *Prof Exp:* Asst prof math, Univ Calif, Riverside, 62-67; assoc prof, 67-70, PROF MATH, UNIV IOWA, 70- *Mem:* Am Math Soc; Math Asn Am. *Res:* Metric and geodesic geometry; functional analysis. *Mailing Add:* Dept of Math Univ of Iowa Iowa City IA 52240

KIRK, WILLIAM LEROY, b Charleston, Miss, Aug 29, 30; m 53; c 3. NUCLEAR ENGINEERING. *Educ:* US Naval Acad, BS, 52; Air Force Inst Technol, MS, 57. *Prof Exp:* Staff mem, Nuclear Rocket Div, 61-67, asst div leader, 67-73, assoc div leader energy technol, 77-78, alt div leader, 78-81, PRIN ASST DIV LEADER, ENERGY DIV, LOS ALAMOS NAT LAB, 81- *Mem:* Am Nuclear Soc. *Res:* Energy research and development, including nuclear safeguards and safety, nuclear system development and other energy systems. *Mailing Add:* Energy Div Los Alamos Nat Lab MS-561 PO Box 1663 Los Alamos NM 87545

KIRKALDY, J(OHN) S(AMUEL), b Victoria, BC, May 13, 26; m 52; c 3. PHYSICAL METALLURGY. *Educ:* Univ BC, BASc, 49, MASc, 51; McGill Univ, PhD(physics), 53. *Prof Exp:* Res assoc physics, McGill Univ, 53-54, asst prof metall eng, 54-57; from asst prof to assoc prof metall, 57-63, chmn dept, 62-66, PROF METALL, McMASTER UNIV, 63-, STEEL CO CAN CHAIR METALL, 66- *Mem:* Am Soc Metals; Am Inst Mining, Metall & Petrol Engrs; Can Asn Physicists; Can Inst Mining & Metall. *Res:* Application of thermodynamics of irreversible processes to metallurgy. *Mailing Add:* Dept of Metall & Mat Sci McMaster Univ Hamilton ON L8S 4L8 Can

KIRKBRIDE, CLYDE ARNOLD, b Los Angeles, Calif, Mar 14, 24; m 44; c 5. VETERINARY BACTERIOLOGY. *Educ:* Okla State Univ, DVM, 53; SDak State Univ, MS, 70. *Prof Exp:* Vet practr, 53-63; asst prof vet med, Col Vet Med, Kans State Univ, 63-67; from instr to asst prof, 67-74, ASSOC PROF VET MED, ANIMAL DIS RES & DIAG LAB, SDAK STATE UNIV, 74- *Concurrent Pos:* Vet investr officer, NZ Ministry Agr & Fisheries, 74-75; pres, Am Leptospirosis Res Conf, 81. *Mem:* Am Vet Med Asn; Am Asn Vet Lab Diagnosticians; US Animal Health Asn. *Res:* Water intoxication in cattle; relationship of milking machine function to mastitis in cattle; diseases affecting reproduction in animals; fetal serology in diagnosis of bovine abortion; swine tuberculosis; diagnosis of leptospirosis. *Mailing Add:* 2015 Iowa St Brookings SD 57006

KIRKBRIDE, JOSEPH HAROLD, JR, b St Louis, Mo, Feb 4, 43; m 75. TAXONOMIC BOTANY. *Educ:* St Louis Univ, BA, 66, MS(R), 68; City Univ New York, PhD(biol), 75. *Prof Exp:* Assoc cur bot, Smithsonian Inst, 75-79; ASSOC PROF, UNIV BRASILIA, 79- *Mem:* Am Asn Plant Taxonomists; Int Asn Plant Taxon; Soc Syst Zool; Asn Trop Biol; Sigma Xi. *Res:* Complete taxonomic revision of the neotropical Rubiaceae. *Mailing Add:* Univ Brasilia Brasilia #70919 Brazil

KIRKBRIDE, L(OUIS) D(ALE), b Morris, Ill, Oct 18, 32; m 57; c 3. MEDICAL INSTRUMENTATION. *Educ:* Carnegie Inst Technol, BS, 54, MS & PhD(metall), 57. *Prof Exp:* Develop engr nuclear mat, Knolls Atomic Power Lab, Gen Elec Co, 57-60, mgr core mat develop, 60-61; group leader power reactor mat, Los Alamos Sci Lab, 61-66; proj analyst, Gen Elec Res & Develop Ctr, Schenectady, 66-68, mgr clin equip develop, Med Develop Oper, 68-70, mgr bus develop & strategic planning, Med Systs Bus Div, Gen Elec Co, 70-71, mgr nuclear diag, Med Systs Div, 71-74; gen mgr, Diag Div, J T Baker, 74-81; VPRES & GEN MGR, LAB PROD DIV, LITTON BIONETICS, 81- *Mem:* Am Nuclear Soc; Instrument Soc Am; fel Am Inst Chemists. *Res:* Semiconductor materials; radioimmunoassay; clinical chemistry; hematology; immunology. *Mailing Add:* Litton Bionetics 5516 Nicholson Lane Kensington MD 20795

KIRKEMO, HAROLD, b Birney, Mont, Oct 16, 15; m 41; c 2. GEOLOGY. *Educ:* Univ Wash, BS, 38; Indust Col Armed Forces, dipl, 63. *Prof Exp:* Mine geologist, Anaconda Copper Mining Co, Mont, 41-45; explor geologist, Thailand, 46-47, Pac Northwest & BC, 47-52; geologist defense minerals explor prog, US Geol Surv, 52-53, chief, Colo Plateau Uranium Explor Prog, 54-56; geologist minerals resources sect & resources res br, DC, 56-69, chief officer minerals explor, 69-79; RETIRED. *Mem:* AAAS; Soc Econ Geologists; Am Inst Mining, Metall & Petrol Eng; Geol Soc Am. *Res:* Economic, mining and structural geology. *Mailing Add:* 638 Duquesna Dr Sun City Center FL 33570

KIRKENDALL, THOMAS DODGE, b Columbus, Ohio, Sept 8, 37; m 61; c 3. ANALYTICAL CHEMISTRY, SPECTROSCOPY. *Educ:* Colby Col, BA, 61. *Prof Exp:* Asst physics, Middlebury Col, 61-62; res scientist, Machlett Labs, Raytheon Co, 62-69; tech staff mem, 69-81, MGR, DEPT ANAL CHEM & FAILURE ANAL, COMSAT LABS, COMMUN SATELLITE CORP, 81- *Honors & Awards:* NASA ATS-6 Propagation Exp Award, Commun Satellite Corp, 74 & Centimeter Wave Beacon Award, 76. *Mem:* Soc Appl Spectros (treas, 74-76); Microbeam Anal Soc. *Res:* Physics and failure mechanisms of solid state devices; energy conversion and storage; surface analysis and characterization. *Mailing Add:* Dept Anal Chem & Failure Anal COMSAT Labs Clarksburg MD 20871

KIRKENDALL, WALTER MURRAY, b Louisville, Ky, Mar 31, 17; m 48; c 10. INTERNAL MEDICINE. *Educ:* Univ Louisville, MD, 41. *Prof Exp:* Asst anat, Univ Louisville, 38-39; from asst to assoc internal med, Univ Iowa, 49-51, asst prof, 51-52, clin assoc prof, 52-58, from assoc prof to prof, 58-71; chmn dept, 72-76, PROF MED, UNIV TEX MED SCH, HOUSTON, 72-, DIR HYPERTENSION DIV, 76- *Concurrent Pos:* Chief med serv, Vet Admin Hosp, Iowa City, 52-58; dir cardiovasc res lab, Univ Iowa, 58-70, dir renal-hypertension-electrolyte div, 58-71; Louis Mark lectr, Am Col Chest Physicians, 63. *Mem:* AAAS; AMA; Am Heart Asn; Am Soc Internal Med; Am Soc Nephrology. *Res:* Clinical investigation of kidney disease and hypertension. *Mailing Add:* 5203 Del Monte Dr Houston TX 77056

KIRKHAM, FREDERIC THEODORE, b McAllen, Tex, Feb 21, 22; m 49; c 2. MEDICINE. *Educ:* Cornell Univ, MD, 47. *Prof Exp:* From instr to clin assoc prof, 50-73, CLIN PROF MED, MED COL, CORNELL UNIV, 73-, CLIN ASSOC PROF PUBLIC HEALTH, 80-; MED DIR, TIME, INC, 66- *Concurrent Pos:* Mem clin staff, Nat Heart Inst, 51-55; from asst attend physician to assoc attend physician, 59-73, attend physician, New York Hosp, 73- *Mem:* NY Acad Med; Am Heart Asn; Am Col Physicians. *Res:* Internal medicine; cardiology; electrocardiography. *Mailing Add:* TIME Inc Time & Life Bldg New York NY 10020

KIRKHAM, M B, b Cedar Rapids, Iowa. PLANT PHYSIOLOGY. *Educ:* Wellesley Col, BA; Univ Wis-Madison, MS; PhD(bot). *Prof Exp:* NSF fel, Inst Environ Studies, Univ Wis-Madison; plant physiologist, US Environ Protection Agency, Ohio; plant physiologist, Univ Mass, Amherst; crop physiologist, Okla State Univ, Stillwater; PLANT PHYSIOLOGIST, KANS STATE UNIV, MANHATTAN, 80- *Honors & Awards:* Mary White Peterson Prize, Wellesley Col. *Mem:* Am Soc Plant Physiol; Am Meteorol Soc; Soil Sci Soc Am; AAAS; Int Soc Hort Sci. *Res:* Plant-soil-water relationships; effect on plants of sludge spread on agricultural land, particularly reference to uptake of trace elements in sludge; wheat physiology. *Mailing Add:* Evapotranspiration Lab Kans State Univ Manhattan KS 66506

KIRKHAM, WAYNE WOLPERT, b Elizabeth, Ind, July 20, 18; m 42; c 1. VETERINARY SCIENCE, MICROBIOLOGY. *Educ:* Tex A&M Univ, DVM, 41, MS, 55; Iowa State Univ, PhD(microbiol), 62. *Prof Exp:* Asst prof poultry res, Tex A&M Univ, 52-55; assoc prof poultry & swine res, Kans State Univ, 55-56; assoc prof microbiol, Iowa State Univ, 56-62; bacteriologist, Diag Lab, Fla State Dept Agr, 62-63; assoc virologist, Univ Fla, 63-68; head animal dis diag lab, 68-72, PROF VET MICROBIOL, PURDUE UNIV, 68- *Mem:* Am Vet Med Asn; US Animal Health Asn; Am Asn Equine Practitioners; Am Asn Avian Path. *Res:* Veterinary microbiol, virology and equine blood protozoa. *Mailing Add:* Dept of Vet Microbiol Path Purdue Univ West Lafayette IN 47907

KIRKHAM, WILLIAM R, b Olive Branch, Ill, Aug 5, 25; m 52; c 5. PATHOLOGY, BIOCHEMISTRY. *Educ:* Univ Mo, AB, 48, MA, 50, PhD(biochem), 52; Univ Okla, MD, 60; Am Bd Path, dipl, 65. *Prof Exp:* Asst prof biochem, Okla State Univ, 54-56; intern, USPHS Hosp, NY, 60-61; resident, NIH, Md, 61-65, asst chief chem, 65-66; assoc dir, Inst Lab Med, Perth Amboy Gen Hosp, 66-70; pathologist, S Community Hosp, Oklahoma City, 70-71; chief path res unit, 73-77, CHIEF AVIATION TOXICOL LAB,

CIVIL AEROMED INST, FED AVIATION AGENCY, 78-; ASSOC PROF PARASITOL & LAB PRACT, MED SCH, UNIV OKLA, OKLAHOMA CITY, 71- *Mem:* Col Am Path; Am Soc Clin Path. *Res:* Chemistry of chromosomes and cell nucleus; hormone effects on mammary growth; agricultural chemical analyses; radiation effects on salivary glands; blood culture techniques; automation and computerization of clinical laboratories; multiphasic health screening; devices for cytologic detection of cancer; pathology of aircraft accidents. *Mailing Add:* 1201 SW 93rd St Oklahoma City OK 73109

KIRKIEN-RZESZOTARSKI, ALICIA M, b Lodz, Poland; m 73. PHYSICAL CHEMISTRY. *Educ:* Polish Univ Col, London, MChEng, 51; Univ London, PhD(phys org chem), 55. *Prof Exp:* From asst prof to assoc prof phys chem, Univ Col West Indies, 56-61; assoc prof, Univ West Indies, 61-65; assoc prof, 65-69, PROF PHYS CHEM, TRINITY COL DC, 69- *Concurrent Pos:* Hon res fel, Univ Col, Univ London, 71-72. *Mem:* The Chem Soc; fel Royal Inst Chem; Am Chem Soc. *Res:* Physical organic chemistry; kinetics of reactions in solutions and in the gas-phase kinetic isotope effects; organic mass spectrometry, effect of chemical structure on ionization potentials; fragmentation patterns. *Mailing Add:* 4607 Brandywine St NW Washington DC 20016

KIRKLAND, GORDON LAIDLAW, JR, b Troy, NY, June 4, 43; m 66; c 1. MAMMALOGY, VERTEBRATE ECOLOGY. *Educ:* Cornell Univ, BS, 65; Mich State Univ, MS, 68, PhD(ornith), 69. *Prof Exp:* Asst prof 69-73, assoc prof, 73-78, PROF ZOOL, SHIPPENSBURG STATE COL, 78- CUR, VERT MUS, 71- *Concurrent Pos:* Res collabr, Dept Vertebrate Zool, Smithsonian Inst, 78-; res assoc, Sect Mammals, Carnegie Mus, 73- *Mem:* Am Soc Mammal (secy-treas, 80-); Wildlife Soc; Am Ornith Union; Soc Syst Zoologists; Ecol Soc Am. *Res:* Mammalian ecology, systematics, and natural history; boreal and sub-boreal ecology; ecology of vertebrates on disturbed ecosystems; mammalian zoogeography. *Mailing Add:* Vert Mus Box F-207 Shippensburg State Col Shippensburg PA 17257

KIRKLAND, JERRY J, b Elk City, Okla, May 18, 36; m 57; c 4. MICROBIOLOGY. *Educ:* Northwestern State Col, Okla, BS, 58; Okla State Univ, MS, 61, PhD(microbiol), 64. *Prof Exp:* RES ORAL MICROBIOLOGIST, PROCTER & GAMBLE CO, 64- *Mem:* Am Soc Microbiol. *Res:* Inducible enzyme formation in microorganisms and their role in dental plaque; microbiology of skin; etiology of acne. *Mailing Add:* 727 Daphne Ct Cincinnati OH 45240

KIRKLAND, JOSEPH JACK, b Winter Garden, Fla, May 24, 25; m 49; c 3. ANALYTICAL CHEMISTRY. *Educ:* Emory Univ, AB, 48, MS, 49; Univ Va, PhD(chem), 53. *Prof Exp:* Chemist, Exp Sta, Hercules Powder Co, 49-51; from res chemist to sr res chemist, 53-61, res assoc, 61-69, RES FEL, E I DU PONT DE NEMOURS & CO, 69- *Honors & Awards:* Chromatography Award, Am Chem Soc, 72; Stephen Dal Nogare Award in Chromatography, Chromatography Forum, 73. *Mem:* Am Chem Soc. *Res:* Gas and liquid chromatography; field flow fractionation. *Mailing Add:* Cent R&D Dept Exp Sta Bldg 228 E I Du Pont De Nemours & Co Wilmington DE 19898

KIRKLAND, RICHARD HORACE, b Richmond, Va, Mar 22, 24; m 46; c 2. MEDICINE. *Educ:* Med Col Va, MD, 48. *Prof Exp:* From assoc to assoc prof, 53-69, PROF MED, MED COL VA, 69- *Mem:* Am Col Physicians. *Res:* Endocrinology. *Mailing Add:* Dept of Med Med Col of Va Richmond VA 23298

KIRKLAND, WALTER DEAN, b Louisville, Ohio, Mar 1, 32; m 54; c 2. PHARMACY, CHEMISTRY. *Educ:* Ohio State Univ, BS, 55, MS, 56; Univ Fla, PhD(pharm), 58. *Prof Exp:* Asst prof, Univ Fla, 58-59; res pharmacist, Abbott Labs, 59-64; res pharmacist, 64-72, sr res coordr, 72-76, PHARMACEUT RES & DEVELOP MGR, CUTTER LABS, 76- *Mem:* Am Pharmaceut Asn; Parenteral Drug Asn. *Res:* Pharmaceutical research and development. *Mailing Add:* Cutter Labs Fourth & Parker St Berkeley CA 94710

KIRKLIN, JOHN W, b Muncie, Ind, Aug 5, 17; m; c 3. CARDIOVASCULAR SURGERY. *Educ:* Univ Minn, BA, 38, Harvard Univ, MD, 42; Am Bd Surg, dipl, 50; Am Bd Thoracic Surg, dipl, 50. *Hon Degrees:* DMed, Univ Munich, 61; DSc, Hamline Univ, 66. *Prof Exp:* Surgeon, Mayo Clin, 50-66, from instr to assoc prof surg, Mayo Grad Sch Med, Univ Minn, 51-60, prof, Mayo Clin, 60-66, chmn dept, Mayo Clin & Grad Sch Med, 64-66; PROF SURG & CHMN DEPT, MED COL, UNIV ALA, BIRMINGHAM & SURGEON-IN-CHIEF, HOSPS & CLINS, 66- *Concurrent Pos:* Mem bd gov, Mayo Clin, 65-66; mem surg study sect B, NIH, 64-67 & chmn Sect A, 68-70, mem comt standardization of classification congenital heart dis, 67, mem adv comt artificial heart-myocardial infarction prog, 67-69 & adv comt crippled children serv regional prog; chmn ad hoc comt to consider appln for subspec bd pediat surg, Am Bd Surg, 66-73. *Mem:* Nat Acad Sci; Am Col Surgeons; Am Surg Asn; Am Asn Thoracic Surg; Am Col Cardiol. *Mailing Add:* Dept of Surg Univ of Ala Med Ctr Birmingham AL 35294

KIRKLIN, PERRY WILLIAM, b Ellwood City, Pa, Feb 28, 35; m 56; c 3. PETROLEUM CHEMISTRY. *Educ:* Westminster Col, BS, 57; Univ Minn, Minneapolis, PhD(phys chem), 64. *Prof Exp:* Group leader anal res, Rohm and Haas Co, Pa, 64-70; ASSOC CHEM & PROJ LEADER, AVIATION FUELS RES, MOBIL RES & DEVELOP CORP, PAULSBORO, NJ, 70- *Mem:* Am Chem Soc; Soc Automotive Engrs; Catalysis Soc. *Res:* Electron nuclear double resonance studies of hole center in magnesium oxide single crystals; catalyst characterization, especially metal function of catalysts using x-ray and chemisorption techniques; exploratory process research; aviation fuels. *Mailing Add:* 1860 Hillside Rd Southampton PA 18966

KIRKMAN, HENRY NEIL, JR, b Jacksonville, Fla, Sept 14, 27; m 50; c 4. MEDICINE, PEDIATRICS. *Educ:* Ga Inst Technol, BS, 47; Emory Univ, MS, 50; Johns Hopkins Univ, MD, 52; Am Bd Pediat, dipl, 60. *Prof Exp:* Intern pediat, Johns Hopkins Hosp, 52-53; intern, Vanderbilt Univ Hosp, 55-56, asst resident, Sch Med, 56-57; res investr, Nat Inst Arthritis & Metab Dis, 58-59; asst prof pediat, Sch Med, Univ Okla, 59-65; PROF PEDIAT, SCH MED, UNIV NC, CHAPEL HILL, 65- *Concurrent Pos:* Nat Inst Arthritis & Metab Dis fel metab enzymes, 57-58; Markle scholar, 61. *Honors & Awards:* Mead Johnson Award, 67. *Mem:* Am Pediat Soc; Am Soc Biol Chem. *Res:* Metabolic and enzymatic disturbances in children; mathematical genetics; human biochemical genetics. *Mailing Add:* Dept of Pediat Univ of NC Sch of Med Chapel Hill NC 27515

KIRKPATRICK, C(HARLES) V(ERNE), b Jacksonville, Tex, Sept 27, 16; m 41; c 2. ENGINEERING. *Educ:* Agr & Mech Col, Tex, BS, 40; Univ Houston, ML, 52. *Hon Degrees:* PhD, China Acad, Taiwan, 70. *Prof Exp:* Chmn, Petrol Eng, 47-77, actg dean, Cullen Col Eng, 63-65, assoc dean, 62-63, dean, 65-77, prof, 53-81, EMER PROF PETROL ENG, UNIV HOUSTON, 81- *Concurrent Pos:* Consult, Humble Oil & Refining Co, 58- *Mem:* Am Soc Petrol Engrs; Am Soc Eng Educ; Nat Soc Prof Engrs; Am Inst Mining, Metall & Petrol Engrs. *Res:* Single and multi-phase flow of fluids in vertical conduits; hydrocarbon processing and recovery techniques; nuclear logging development. *Mailing Add:* Cullen Col of Eng Univ of Houston Houston TX 77004

KIRKPATRICK, CHARLES HARVEY, b Topeka, Kans, Nov 5, 31; m 59; c 3. ALLERGY, IMMUNOLOGY. *Educ:* Univ Kans, BA, 54, MD, 58. *Prof Exp:* Asst med, Med Ctr, Univ Colo, 62-63, instr, 63-65; asst prof, Med Ctr, Univ Kans, 65-68, assoc prof, 68; sr investr & head sect allergy & hypersensitivity, Lab Clin Invest, Nat Inst Allergy & Infectious Dis, 68-79; DIR, DIV CLINICAL IMMUNOL, DEPT MED, NAT JEWISH HOSP, 79-; PROF, UNIV COLO, 79- *Concurrent Pos:* Fel allergy & immunol, Univ Colo, 62-65. *Mem:* AAAS; Am Acad Allergy; Am Soc Clin Invest; Am Asn Immunol; Transplantation Soc. *Res:* Mechanisms of cellular immunity and the role of cellular immunity to resistance to infectious diseases and neoplasia; methods of correcting diseases associated with abnormal cellular immunity. *Mailing Add:* Nat Jewish Hosp Dept Med 3800 E Colfax Ave Denver CO 80206

KIRKPATRICK, CHARLES MILTON, b Greensburg, Ind, Jan 1, 15; m 39; c 2. WILDLIFE ECOLOGY. *Educ:* Purdue Univ, BS, 38; Univ Wis, MA, 40, PhD(zool), 43. *Prof Exp:* Asst zool, Univ Wis, 38-41; from instr to assoc prof, 41-60, PROF WILDLIFE MGT, AGR EXP STA, PURDUE UNIV, 60- *Concurrent Pos:* Ed, J Wildlife Mgt, Wildlife Soc, 59-62. *Mem:* Wilson Ornith Soc; Am Soc Mammal. *Res:* Wildlife physiology and ecology. *Mailing Add:* Agr Exp Sta Purdue Univ West Lafayette IN 47907

KIRKPATRICK, CONILEE GAY, b St Louis, Mo, Aug 18, 48; m 76. EXPERIMENTAL SOLID STATE PHYSICS, ELECTRICAL ENGINEERING. *Educ:* Washington Univ, BS, 69, AM, 70; Univ Ill, Urbana, PhD(elec eng), 74. *Prof Exp:* Res asst elec eng, Coord Sci Lab, Univ Ill, 71-74; staff physicist elec eng, Gen Elec Res & Develop Ctr, 74-79; mem tech staff, Sci Ctr, 79, proj leader ion implantation, 79-80, MGR, MAT TECHNOL SECT, MICROELECTRONICS RES & DEVELOP CTR, ROCKWELL INT, 80- *Concurrent Pos:* Consult, Electronics Div, Electrochem Soc. *Mem:* Sr mem Inst Elec & Electronics Engrs; sr mem Soc Women Engrs; Am Phys Soc. *Res:* Ion implantation; growth of compound semiconductors; processing of compound semiconductors; radiation effects in solids; semiconductors; memory, display, integrated circuit devices. *Mailing Add:* 1049 Camino Dos Rios Thousand Oaks CA 91360

KIRKPATRICK, DIANA (RORABAUGH) M, b Washington, DC, Mar 24, 44. PHYSICAL CHEMISTRY. *Educ:* George Washington Univ, BS, 67, PhD(phys chem), 72. *Prof Exp:* Forensic scientist chem, Bur Alcohol, Tobacco & Firearms, 72, res analyst, 73-74; res analyst, Consumer Prod Safety Comn, 74-77; PROJ LEADER THERMAL INSULATION & LAB ACCREDITATION, NAT BUR STANDARDS, 77- *Mem:* Am Chem Soc; Am Soc Testing & Mat; Sigma Xi. *Res:* Testing of thermal insulation materials; maintenance of minimum standards for testing laboratories; testing of carpet; testing of solid fuel burning room heaters; testing programs. *Mailing Add:* 24408 Kakae Dr Damascus MD 20872

KIRKPATRICK, E(DWARD) T(HOMSON), b Cranbrook, BC, Jan 15, 25; m 48; c 4. MECHANICAL ENGINEERING. *Educ:* Univ BC, BASc, 47; Carnegie Inst Technol, MS, 56, PhD, 58. *Prof Exp:* Test engr, Gen Elec Co, Can, 47; sales engr, F D Bolton, Ltd, 47-51, dist mgr, 51-53, sales mgr, 53-54; from instr to asst prof mech eng, Carnegie Inst Technol, 54-58; asst prof, Univ Pittsburgh, 58-59; prof & chmn dept, Univ Toledo, 59-64; dean, Col Appl Sci, Rochester Inst Technol, 64-71; PRES, WENTWORTH INST TECHNOL, 71- *Mem:* Am Soc Eng Educ; Am Soc Mech Engrs. *Res:* Conduction heat transfer; numerical analysis and digital computer technology. *Mailing Add:* Wentworth Inst Technol 550 Huntington Ave Boston MA 02115

KIRKPATRICK, EDWARD SCOTT, b Wilmington, Del, Dec 12, 41; m 74. SOLID STATE PHYSICS. *Educ:* Princeton Univ, AB, 63; Harvard Univ, PhD(physics), 69. *Prof Exp:* Res assoc physics, James Franck Inst, Univ Chicago, 69-71; STAFF MEM, RES DIV, IBM CORP, 71- *Concurrent Pos:* Consult, Lincoln Labs, Mass Inst Technol, 65-66, Argonne Nat Labs, AEC, 69-71; vis assoc prof, State Univ NY, Stony Brook, 77; exchange prof, Ecole Normale Superieure, Paris France, 78- *Mem:* Fel Am Phys Soc. *Res:* Magnetic order and excitations in disordered materials, transport in low-mobility materials. *Mailing Add:* IBM Res Ctr Yorktown Heights NY 10598

KIRKPATRICK, JAMES W, b Monmouth, Ill, Jan 9, 36; m 55; c 3. TECHNICAL TRAINING. *Educ:* Western Ill Univ, BS, 58, MSEduc, 60; Univ Ill, PhD(anal chem), 70. *Prof Exp:* Teacher high schs, Ill, 58-65; asst, Univ Ill, 65-69, from asst prof to assoc prof chem, Western Ill Univ, 69-78; mem staff, Inst Gas Technol, 78-79; MEM STAFF, VARIAN ASSOCS,

PALO ALTO, 79- *Concurrent Pos:* Mem, Region 5 Lab, Environ Protection Agency, 76-78. *Mem:* AAAS; Am Chem Soc; Am Soc Training & Develop. *Res:* Quantitative determination of nitrogen isotope ratios; spectrometric determination of nitrogen content; spectrometric analysis of nonmetals. *Mailing Add:* 642 Bryson Ave Palo Alto CA 94306

KIRKPATRICK, JAY FRANKLIN, b Quakertown, Pa, Feb 24, 40; m 66. ANIMAL PHYSIOLOGY. *Educ:* East Stroudsburg State Col, BS, 62, MS, 64; Cornell Univ, PhD(physiol), 71. *Prof Exp:* Teacher biol, Quakertown High Sch, Pa, 62-63 & Pennsburg High Sch, Yardley, Pa, 64-65; asst prof & chmn dept, Bucks County Community Col, 65-67; assoc prof animal physiol, 70-76, DEAN, SCH LIB ARTS, EASTERN MONT COL, 76- *Concurrent Pos:* Fel, Col Vet Med, Univ Pa, 73. *Mem:* Soc Study Reproduction. *Res:* Comparative mammalian reproduction, especially species indigenous to hostile environments, such as the pika and wild horses; chemical fertility control in wild and feral species. *Mailing Add:* Sch Lib Arts Eastern Mont Col Billings MT 59101

KIRKPATRICK, JOEL BRIAN, b Odessa, Tex, Feb 19, 36; m 59; c 4. NEUROPATHOLOGY. *Educ:* Rice Univ, BA, 58; Wash Univ, MD, 62. *Prof Exp:* Instr path, Wash Univ, 65-67; asst prof pharmacol, Rutgers Univ, New Brunswick, 68-70; assoc prof path, Univ Ariz, 70-72; assoc prof path & neurol, Univ Tex Health Sci Ctr, Dallas, 72-78, prof, 78-80; PROF PATH, BAYLOR COL MED, 81- *Concurrent Pos:* Am Cancer Soc fel, 64-65; NIH spec fel, 67-68; Nat Inst Neurol Dis & Stroke grant, 70; with Vet Admin, NIH, 71- *Mem:* Soc Neurosci; Am Asn Neuropath; Am Asn Pathologists; Geront Soc. *Res:* Molecular mechanisms in normal and abnormal nervous system functions; electronmicroscopy of chromatolysis, peripheral nerve and skeletal muscle; quantitative analysis of cerebral cortex; trauma. *Mailing Add:* Methodist Hosp MS 205 6565 Fannin Houston TX 77030

KIRKPATRICK, JOEL LEE, b Abilene, Tex, June 21, 36; m 57; c 2. ORGANIC CHEMISTRY, PESTICIDE CHEMISTRY. *Educ:* Abilene Christian Col, BS, 58, MS, 60; Univ Ill, PhD(org chem), 69. *Prof Exp:* Med chemist, Smith Kline & French Labs, 61-65; sr res chemist, Gulf Oil Chem Co, 69-79; res assoc, Mobil Chem Co, 79-81; SR SCIENTIST, VELSICOL CHEM CORP, 81- *Mem:* AAAS; Am Chem Soc. *Res:* Synthetic organic chemistry; nitrogen containing heterocycles; structure activity relationships, particularly pesticides; pheromones insect growth regulants; organophosphorus chemistry. *Mailing Add:* 341 East Ohio St Chicago IL 60611

KIRKPATRICK, LARRY DALE, b Lewiston, Idaho, Feb 11, 41; div; c 3. PHYSICS, PHYSICS EDUCATION. *Educ:* Wash State Univ, BS, 63, Mass Inst Technol, PhD(physics), 68. *Prof Exp:* Res assoc physics, Mass Inst Technol, 68-69; asst prof, Univ Wash, 69-74; asst prof, 74-78, ASSOC PROF PHYSICS, MONT STATE UNIV, 78- *Mem:* Am Asn Physics Teachers; Nat Sci Teachers Asn. *Res:* Experimental high energy physics. *Mailing Add:* Dept of Physics Mont State Univ Bozeman MT 59717

KIRKPATRICK, RALPH DONALD, b Jonesboro, Ind, Feb 10, 30; m; c 4. WILDLIFE ECOLOGY. *Educ:* Ball State Univ, BS, 53; Univ Ariz, MS, 57; Okla State Univ, PhD(zool), 64. *Prof Exp:* Game biologist, State Dept Conserv, Ind, 54-55, game res biologist, 56-59; asst prof biol, Taylor Univ, 59-60; res cur div birds, Smithsonian Inst, 64-65; asst prof zool, Ind Univ, 65-67; from asst prof to assoc prof, 67-73, PROF BIOL, BALL STATE UNIV, 73- *Concurrent Pos:* Consult, Pac Proj div birds, Smithsonian Inst, 65-, Aquatic Control, Inc, Seymour, Ind, 71- & Upper Wabash Resource Ctr, Huntington Col, Huntington, Ind, 75- *Mem:* Wildlife Soc; Am Soc Mammal; Soc Range Mgt; Am Ornith Union. *Res:* Ecology of game species introduced to Indiana, including Japanese Quail and the San Juan rabbit; population dynamics of mammals, including rodents on coral atolls. *Mailing Add:* Dept of Biol Ball State Univ Muncie IN 47306

KIRKPATRICK, ROBERT JAMES, b Schenectady, NY, Dec 31, 46; m 68; c 2. GEOLOGY, PETROLOGY. *Educ:* Cornell Univ, AB, 68; Univ Ill, PhD(geol), 72. *Prof Exp:* Sr res geologist, Exxon Prod Res Co, 72-73; res fel geophys, Harvard Univ, 73-76; asst res scientist, Deep Sea Drilling Proj, Scripps Inst Oceanog, Univ Calif, San Diego, 76-78; asst prof, 78-80, ASSOC PROF GEOL, UNIV ILL, URBANA, 80- *Mem:* Am Geophys Union; fel Am Mineral Soc. *Res:* Igneous petrology; processes of crystallization of igneous rocks, crystal growth from the melt, rates and mechanisms of geologic processes; origin of the oceanic crust. *Mailing Add:* Dept Geol Univ Ill 254 Natural Hist Bldg 1301 W Green St Urbana IL 61801

KIRKPATRICK, ROY LEE, b Fairview, WVa, Apr 16, 40; m 61; c 2. REPRODUCTIVE PHYSIOLOGY. *Educ:* WVa Univ, BS, 62; Univ Wis, MS, 64, PhD(reproductive physiol, endocrinol), 66. *Prof Exp:* Res asst reproductive physiol, Univ Wis, 62-64, instr, 64-66; asst prof wildlife physiol, Va Polytech Inst & State Univ, 66-69; asst prof animal sci, Univ Wis, 69-71; asst prof, 72-74, assoc prof, 75-77, PROF WILDLIFE SCI, VA POLYTECH INST & STATE UNIV, 77- *Mem:* Wildlife Soc; Am Soc Mammal; Wildlife Dis Asn. *Res:* Environmental influences on reproduction and mortality of wildlife, particularly effects of nutrition. *Mailing Add:* Dept of Fisheries & Wildlife Va Polytech Inst & State Univ Blacksburg VA 24061

KIRKSEY, AVANELLE, b Mulberry, Ark, Mar 23, 26. NUTRITION, BIOCHEMISTRY. *Educ:* Univ Ark, BS, 47; Univ Tenn, MS, 50; Pa State Univ, PhD(nutrit), 61. *Prof Exp:* Assoc prof home econ, Ark Polytech Col, 50-55; res asst nutrit, Pa State Univ, 56-59; assoc prof, 61-70, PROF NUTRIT, PURDUE UNIV, 70- *Honors & Awards:* Borden Award. *Mem:* Am Inst Nutrit. *Res:* Vitamin B-6 metabolism; nutrition in pregnancy and development. *Mailing Add:* Dept of Foods & Nutrit Purdue Univ West Lafayette IN 47907

KIRKSEY, DONNY FRANK, b Aberdeen, Miss, Apr 13, 48; m 70. PHARMACOLOGY. *Educ:* Delta State Univ, BS, 70; Univ Miss, PhD(pharmacol), 76. *Prof Exp:* Fel, Duke Univ, 76-78; ASST PROF BIOMED SCI, OHIO UNIV, 78- *Concurrent Pos:* Neurosci fel, NIMH, 76-78; grant, NC Heart Asn, 77-78; NIH fel, Nat Inst Drug Abuse, 78. *Mem:* Sigma Xi. *Res:* Investigations of pre/postsynaptic neuronal mechanisms in the central monoaminergic systems and pharmacological manipulation of those systems by drugs of abuse. *Mailing Add:* Col of Osteop Med Ohio Univ Athens OH 45701

KIRKSEY, HOWARD GRADEN, JR, b Memphis, Tenn, June 19, 40; m; c 3. SCIENCE EDUCATION. *Educ:* Mid Tenn State Univ, BS, 61; Auburn Univ, PhD(phys chem), 66. *Prof Exp:* assoc prof, 65-80, PROF CHEM, MEMPHIS STATE UNIV, 80- *Concurrent Pos:* Staff scientist phys sci group, Boston Univ, 70-72. *Mem:* AAAS; Am Chem Soc. *Res:* Chemical education, especially development of text and laboratory teaching materials. *Mailing Add:* Dept Chem Memphis State Univ Memphis TN 38152

KIRKWOOD, CHARLES EDWARD, JR, b Richmond, Va, Oct 10, 13; m 42; c 2. MATHEMATICAL SCIENCES. *Educ:* Lynchburg Col, AB, 35; Univ Ga, MS, 37. *Prof Exp:* Teacher pub sch, Ga, 36-37; from instr to asst prof math, Clemson Univ, 37-48, assoc prof math sci, 48-79; RETIRED. *Concurrent Pos:* Asst prof elec eng, Comput Ctr, Clemson Univ, 51-52, comput analyst, 64-70, mgr prog, 70-75; vis assoc prof comput sci & math sci, Clemson Univ, 79- *Res:* Dielectric properties of ceramic materials; electrical properties of cotton; thermoconductivity of felts. *Mailing Add:* Dept Comput Sci Clemson Univ Clemson SC 29631

KIRKWOOD, JAMES BENJAMINE, b Beulah, Ky, Jan 22, 24; m 53. ZOOLOGY, RADIATION BIOLOGY. *Educ:* West Ky State Col, 48; Univ Louisville, MS, 52, PhD(zool), 62. *Prof Exp:* Proj leader fishery biol, Ky Dept Fish & Wildlife Resources, 52-57; US Bur Com Fisheries, 57-60, prog supvr invert biol, 62-64, prog leader, 64-68; tech coordr bio-environ studies, Battelle-Columbus, 68-73, mgr, W F Clapp Labs, 73-75; COASTAL ECOSYSTS ACTIV LEADER, US FISH & WILDLIFE SERV, REGION 4, 75- *Mem:* AAAS; Am Fisheries Soc; Sigma Xi; Nat Shellfish Asn; Int Acad Fishery Scientists. *Res:* Ecology and ichthyology of Kentucky teleost fishes; life history and ecology of Pacific salmon; biology and population dynamics of shellfish species in Gulf of Alaska and Bering Sea. *Mailing Add:* 3803 W Nancy Creek Ct Atlanta GA 30319

KIRKWOOD, SAMUEL, b Edmonton, Alta, June 14, 20; US citizen; m 47; c 3. BIOCHEMISTRY. *Educ:* Univ Alta, BS, 42; Univ Wis, MS, 44, PhD(biochem), 47. *Prof Exp:* Biochemist, Camp Detrick, Md, 47; asst res officer, Nat Res Coun Can, 48; from assoc prof to prof chem, McMaster Univ, 50-56; assoc prof, 56-62, PROF BIOCHEM, COL BIOL SCI, UNIV MINN, ST PAUL, 62- *Res:* Intermediary metabolism; route of synthesis of thyroxin; enzymology of carbohydrates. *Mailing Add:* Dept of Biochem Col Biol Sci Univ of Minn St Paul MN 55101

KIRMSE, DALE WILLIAM, b Alva, Okla, July 9, 38; m 62; c 4. CHEMICAL ENGINEERING. *Educ:* Okla State Univ, BS, 60; Iowa State Univ, MS, 63, PhD(chem eng), 64. *Prof Exp:* Res assoc chem eng, Univ Fla, 64-65, asst prof, 65-67; mgr asst, Parma Tech Ctr, Union Carbide Corp, 67-69; asst prof, 69-80, ASSOC PROF CHEM ENG, UNIV FLA, 80- *Mem:* AAAS; Am Inst Chem Engrs; Am Chem Soc. *Res:* Transport phenomena, turbulent diffusion, thermal battery heat transfer, mass separation processes; mathematical modeling and computer methods; stochastic systems and Monte Carlo techniques; chemical kinetics and reactor design. *Mailing Add:* Dept of Chem Eng Univ of Fla Gainesville FL 32601

KIRMSER, P(HILIP) G(EORGE), b St Paul, Minn, Dec 17, 19; m 42; c 2. APPLIED MATHEMATICS, ENGINEERING. *Educ:* Univ Minn, BChE, 39, MS, 44, PhD, 58. *Prof Exp:* Instr, Kans State Col, 42-44; mech engr, US Naval Ord Lab, 46-48; instr, Univ Minn, 49-54; assoc prof appl mech, 54-58, head dept, 62, PROF APPL MECH, KANS STATE UNIV, 58- *Concurrent Pos:* Consult, Phillips Petrol Co, Bayer & McElrath & Boeing Co. *Mem:* Am Math Soc; Math Asn Am; Soc Indust & Appl Math; Neth Royal Inst Eng. *Res:* Partial differential equations of engineering dealing with heat flow, vibrations and stresses; dynamics and motion of artificial satellites; analog computers; simulation; approximation; automatic controls; industrial processes; analysis of data. *Mailing Add:* Dept of Appl Mech Kans State Univ Manhattan KS 66502

KIRPEKAR, SADASHIV M, Indian citizen. PHARMACOLOGY. *Educ:* Univ Bombay, BSc, 49; Glasgow Univ, PhD(pharmacol), 59. *Prof Exp:* Instr pharmacol, State Univ NY, 61-62; Med Res Coun scholar physiol, Glasgow Univ, 62-65; asst prof, 65-68, assoc prof, 68-74, PROF PHARMACOL, STATE UNIV NY DOWNSTATE MED CTR, 74- *Concurrent Pos:* USPHS fel, State Univ NY, 59-62. *Mem:* Am Soc Pharmacol. *Res:* Autonomic pharmacology; release and inactivation of adrenergic transmitter from peripheral organs. *Mailing Add:* Dept Pharmacol State Univ NY Downstate Med Ctr Brooklyn NY 11203

KIRSCH, DONALD R, b Newark, NJ, Apr 28, 50; m 74. MOLECULAR BIOLOGY. *Educ:* Rutgers Col, BA, 72; Princeton Univ, MA, 74, PhD(biol), 78. *Prof Exp:* Instr pharmacol, Rutgers Med Sch, 78-81; RES INVESTR MOLECULAR BIOL, SQUIBB INST MED RES, 81- *Concurrent Pos:* Adj asst prof, Rutgers Med Sch, 82- *Mem:* Genetics Soc Am; Am Soc Cell Biol. *Res:* Genome organization and gene expression in lower eucaryotes. *Mailing Add:* Squibb Inst Med Res PO Box 4000 Princeton NJ 08540

KIRSCH, EDWIN JOSEPH, b Hoboken, NJ, Aug 25, 24; m 45; c 3. MICROBIOLOGY. *Educ:* Mich State Univ, BS, 49; Purdue Univ, MS, 55, PhD(microbiol), 58. *Prof Exp:* Biologist, Lederle Labs, Am Cyanamid Corp, 50-53, sr res scientist, 57-63; assoc prof sanit eng microbiol, 63-70, PROF ENVIRON ENG, PURDUE UNIV, 70- *Mem:* Am Soc Microbiol; Soc Indust Microbiol; Water Pollution Control Fedn. *Res:* Microbiology of wastewater purification; microbial interactions; environmental microbiology; biodegradation. *Mailing Add:* Dept Environ Eng Sch Civil Eng Purdue Univ West Lafayette IN 47907

KIRSCH, FRANCIS WILLIAM, b Wheeling, WVa, Aug 27, 25; m 61; c 2. CHEMISTRY. *Educ:* Univ Del, BChE, 45, MChE, 47; Univ Pa, PhD(chem), 52. *Prof Exp:* Instr inorg qual anal, Univ Pa, 46-50; assoc res chemist, Houdry Process Corp, 50-59, proj dir, 59-64; proj dir, Sun Oil Co, 64-67, res assoc, Explor Res Div, 67-72; DIR, CTR ENERGY MGT & ECON DEVELOP, UNIV CITY SCI CTR, PHILADELPHIA, 73- *Concurrent Pos:* Consult, Gov Energy Coun Pa, 79-, Pa Pub Util Comn, 77-78, World Bank, 80 & NMex State Govt. *Honors & Awards:* Distinguished Serv Award, Am Chem Soc, 73. *Mem:* AAAS; Am Chem Soc. *Res:* Catalysis, heterogeneous and homogeneous; basic and process research and development: petroleum, chemicals, edible oils; industrial energy conservation; offshore oil and gas production; science policy; economic analysis and evaluation of manufacturing processes. *Mailing Add:* 512 Arbordale Rd Wayne PA 19087

KIRSCH, JACK FREDERICK, b Detroit, Mich, Aug 14, 34; m 62; c 2. BIOCHEMISTRY. *Educ:* Univ Mich, BS, 56; Rockefeller Inst, PhD(biochem, cytol), 61. *Prof Exp:* Jane Coffin Childs fel biochem, Brandeis Univ, 61-63; Helen Hay Whitney fel biophys, Weizmann Inst, 63-64; from asst prof to assoc prof, 64-74, PROF BIOCHEM, UNIV CALIF, BERKELEY, 74- *Concurrent Pos:* Guggenheim fel, Max Planck Inst Biophys Chem, 71-72; vis prof, Univ Basel, 79-80. *Mem:* Am Chem Soc; Fedn Am Socs Exp Biol; The Chem Soc. *Res:* Mechanism of enzyme action; mechanisms of organic reactions; structure reactivity relationships. *Mailing Add:* Dept of Biochem Univ of Calif Berkeley CA 94720

KIRSCH, JOSEPH LAWRENCE, JR, b Indianapolis, Ind, Aug 20, 42; m 65; c 2. PHYSICAL CHEMISTRY. *Educ:* Butler Univ, BS, 64; Univ Ill, MS, 66, PhD(phys chem), 68. *Prof Exp:* Asst prof inorg chem, Fairleigh Dickinson Univ, 68-70; asst prof, 70-74, assoc prof, 74-81, PROF PHYS CHEM, BUTLER UNIV, 81- *Mem:* Am Chem Soc; Royal Soc Chem; Sigma Xi. *Res:* Study of chemical bonding in molecules through the use of chemical spectroscopy. *Mailing Add:* Dept of Chem Butler Univ Indianapolis IN 46208

KIRSCH, LAWRENCE EDWARD, b Newark, NJ, Feb 24, 38. PHYSICS, COMPUTER SCIENCE. *Educ:* Columbia Univ, AB, 60; Rutgers Univ, MS, 62, PhD(physics), 65. *Prof Exp:* Res assoc physics, Nevis Labs, Columbia Univ, 64-66; asst prof, 66-72, ASSOC PROF PHYSICS, BRANDEIS UNIV, 72-, DIR COMPUT CTR, 70- *Mem:* Am Phys Soc; Inst Elec & Electronics Engrs; Asn Comput Mach. *Res:* High energy and particle physics. *Mailing Add:* Dept of Physics Brandeis Univ Waltham MA 02154

KIRSCH, MILTON, b Montreal, Que, Jan 16, 23; nat US; m 47; c 3. CHEMISTRY, ENVIRONMENTAL SYSTEMS. *Educ:* McGill Univ, BSc, 42, PhD(chem), 45. *Prof Exp:* Res assoc rubber chem, McGill Univ, 45; asst prof chem, Univ Man, 46-49 & Univ BC, 49-56; sr res chemist, E I du Pont de Nemours & Co, 57-63; mem tech staff, Rocketdyne Div, 63-78, SR STAFF SCIENTIST, ENVIRON MONITORING & SERV CTR, ROCKWELL INST, 78- *Mem:* Am Chem Soc; fel Am Inst Chem. *Res:* Detonation velocity; cross-section for absorption of thermal neutrons; radioactive tracers; chemical oceanography; colloid and surface chemistry; propellants; rheology; environmental chemistry; wastewater treatment; environmental technology. *Mailing Add:* 20414 Haynes St Canoga Park CA 91306

KIRSCH, NATHAN CARL, b New Brunswick, NJ, Oct 27, 18; m 46; c 2. PHARMACEUTICAL CHEMISTRY. *Educ:* Rutgers Univ, BS, 40; Univ Ill, MS, 41. *Prof Exp:* Supvr res & develop projs, 42-51, actg mgr, Pharmaceut Develop Dept, 51-53, mgr, Sterile Prods Dept, 53-68, mgr pharmaceut prod, 68-73, dir domestic mfg, 73-75, V PRES QUAL CONTROL, 75- *Mem:* AAAS; Am Chem Soc; Am Pharmaceut Asn; Pharmaceut Fedn; Royal Soc Health. *Res:* Pharmaceuticals under aseptic conditions; new methods of sterilization, especially high energy electrons and cobalt 60 in radiation sterilization; ethylene oxide and B propiolactone in gaseous sterilization. *Mailing Add:* Schering Corp 1011 Morris Ave Union NJ 07083

KIRSCH, WARREN BERNARD, inorganic chemistry, see previous edition

KIRSCH, WOLFF M, b St Louis, Mo, Mar 2, 31; m 55; c 4. NEUROSURGERY, BIOCHEMISTRY. *Educ:* Wash Univ, BA, 51, MD, 55. *Prof Exp:* Intern med, NC Mem Hosp, Univ NC, 55-56; asst resident gen surg, Barnes Hosp, Wash Univ, 59-60 & neurosurg, 61-62, chief resident & instr, 64; asst prof, 65-68, ASSOC PROF NEUROSURG, MED SCH, UNIV COLO, DENVER, 68-, CHMN DIV & DIR & CHMN TRAINING PROG, 71- *Concurrent Pos:* Fel neurol med, NC Mem Hosp, Univ NC, 56-57; fel neuroanat, Sch Med, Wash Univ, 60, res fel neuro-pharmacol, 63 & 65; attend, Vet Admin Hosp, Denver, 65-; consult, Fitzsimons Gen Hosp, Aurora, Colo, 69- *Mem:* Am Acad Neurol; Asn Acad Surg; Am Asn Neurol Surg; Int Soc Neurochem; Am Col Surg. *Res:* Experimental biology of brain tumors. *Mailing Add:* Div of Neurosurg Univ of Colo Med Sch Denver CO 80220

KIRSCHBAUM, H(ERBERT) S(PENCER), b Cleveland, Ohio, Feb 6, 20; m 46; c 4. ELECTRICAL ENGINEERING. *Educ:* Cooper Union, BS, 42; Univ Pittsburgh, MS, 46; Carnegie Inst Technol, PhD(elec eng), 53. *Prof Exp:* Engr, Westinghouse Elec Corp, 42-46; assoc prof elec eng, Ohio State Univ, 47-57; div consult, Systs Div, Battelle Mem Inst, 57-59, dept consult eng physics, 59-69; MGR SYSTS ENG, INFO SYSTS LAB, WESTINGHOUSE ELEC CO, 69- *Mem:* Inst Elec & Electronics Engrs. *Res:* Systems engineering; control systems; process control. *Mailing Add:* Westinghouse Elec Corp Bulah Rd Pittsburgh PA 15219

KIRSCHBAUM, JOEL BRUCE, b Palo Alto, Calif, Aug 29, 45; m 74. MOLECULAR BIOLOGY, GENETICS. *Educ:* Pomona Col, BA, 67; Harvard Univ, PhD(molecular biol), 72. *Prof Exp:* Fel molecular biol, H H Whitney Found, 73-75; sr researcher, Univ Geneva, 75-77; instr neuropath, Harvard Med Sch, 77-81; ACTG SUPVR, GENETIC ENG DIV, STAUFFER CHEM CO, 81- *Concurrent Pos:* Teaching fel, Harvard Univ, 69; asst instr bact genetics, Cold Spring Harbor Lab, 71; res assoc, Children's Hosp Med Ctr, 77-81; res fel, Med Found Inc, 78-80; prin investr, Am Cancer Soc, 79-81. *Mem:* AAAS. *Res:* Molecular basis for the control of gene expression; biochemistry. *Mailing Add:* Stauffer Chem Co Western Res Ctr 1200 S 47th St Richmond CA 94804

KIRSCHBAUM, JOEL JEROME, b New York, NY, Nov 23, 35; m 60; c 2. BIOCHEMISTRY, ANALYTICAL CHEMISTRY. *Educ:* City Col New York, BS, 57; Rutgers Univ, PhD(biochem), 63. *Prof Exp:* RES FEL & SR RES SCIENTIST, ANAL RES & DEVELOP DIV, SQUIBB INST MED RES, 64- *Concurrent Pos:* Mem grants comt, Am Found Scholarly Res & mem, Directorate of Inst Motivated Behav, Belle Mead, NJ; instr advan molecular genetics, Europ Molecular Biol Orgn, Univ Geneva, Switz, 76. *Mem:* Am Chem Soc; Am Soc Biol Chemists; Am Pharm Asn. *Res:* Association and dissociation of proteins, enzymes and antibiotics; lycanthropy; high pressure liquid chromatography. *Mailing Add:* Anal Res & Develop Div Squibb Inst for Med Res New Brunswick NJ 08903

KIRSCHBAUM, THOMAS H, b Minneapolis, Minn, Apr 22, 29; c 2. OBSTETRICS & GYNECOLOGY. *Educ:* Univ Minn, BA, 50, MS, 51, MD, 53. *Prof Exp:* Resident physician obstet & gynec, Univ Minn Hosps, 56-59; asst prof, Col Med, Univ Utah, 59-64; assoc prof, Med Ctr, Univ Calif, Los Angeles, 64-71; PROF OBSTET, GYNEC & REPRODUCTIVE BIOL & CHMN DEPT, COL HUMAN MED, MICH STATE UNIV, 71- *Concurrent Pos:* Consult, Rand Corp, Calif, 64-71. *Mem:* AAAS; Perinatal Res Soc; Soc Gynec Invest; Am Gynec & Obstet Soc; Cent Asn Obstetricians & Gynecologists. *Res:* Fetal physiology and maternal-fetal interrelationships. *Mailing Add:* Dept Obstet & Gynec B316 Clin Serv Bldg Mich State Univ Col Human Med East Lansing MI 48823

KIRSCHENBAUM, DONALD (MONROE), b Brooklyn, NY, June 14, 27; m 51; c 2. BIOCHEMISTRY. *Educ:* City Col New York, BS, 50; Columbia Univ, AM, 52, PhD(chem), 56. *Prof Exp:* Lectr chem, City Col New York, 53-56; from instr to asst prof, 56-63, ASSOC PROF BIOCHEM, STATE UNIV NY DOWNSTATE MED CTR, 63- *Concurrent Pos:* Fac exchange scholar, State Univ NY, 75. *Mem:* Am Chem Soc; Am Soc Biol Chem; Harvey Soc; Royal Soc Chem. *Res:* Data compilation in the biological sciences; protein biochemistry; protein modification: structure function relationship; prosthesis preparation. *Mailing Add:* Dept of Biochem State Univ NY Downstate Med Ctr Brooklyn NY 11203

KIRSCHMAN, JOHN C, b Emmaus, Pa, Jan 30, 28; m 50; c 3. BIOCHEMISTRY. *Educ:* Muhlenberg Col, BS, 48; Okla State Univ, MS, 55; Vanderbilt Univ, PhD(biochem), 60. *Prof Exp:* Anal chemist, New Brunswick Lab, US AEC, 49-50; sr res biochemist, Atlas Chem Industs, Inc, 60-61, supvr biochem, 61-67; MGR REGULATORY SCI, GEN FOODS CORP, 67- *Mem:* Am Chem Soc; Soc Toxicol. *Res:* Clinical chemistry; biochemical toxicology and pharmacology; lipid metabolism; food additive toxicology. *Mailing Add:* Gen Foods Corp Tech Ctr 250 North St White Plains NY 10625

KIRSCHNER, LEONARD BURTON, b Chicago, Ill, Nov 12, 23; m 50; c 4. PHYSIOLOGY. *Educ:* Univ Ill, BS, 44, MS, 47; Univ Wis, PhD(physiol), 51. *Prof Exp:* Nat Found Infantile Paralysis res fel, Copenhagen Univ, 51-53; from instr to assoc prof, 53-65, PROF ZOOL, WASH STATE UNIV, 65- *Mem:* Am Physiol Soc; Soc Gen Physiol; Am Soc Zoologists. *Res:* Active transport of solutes and water; invertebrate excretory organs. *Mailing Add:* Dept of Zool Wash State Univ Pullman WA 99164

KIRSCHNER, MARC WALLACE, b Chicago, Ill, Feb 28, 45; m 68; c 3. BIOCHEMISTRY, CELL BIOLOGY. *Educ:* Northwestern Univ, BA, 66; Univ Calif, Berkeley, PhD(biochem), 71. *Prof Exp:* NSF fel develop biol, Univ Calif, Berkeley, 71-72; asst prof, Princeton Univ, 72-77, prof biochem, 77-78; PROF BIOCHEM, UNIV CALIF, SAN FRANCISCO, 78- *Concurrent Pos:* NIH res career develop award, 75-80. *Mem:* Am Soc Biol Chemists; Am Soc Cell Biol. *Res:* Mechanism of microtubule assembly, regulation of mitosis and regulation of cell division in amphibian eggs; biophysical studies of macromolecules. *Mailing Add:* Univ Calif Sch Med San Francisco CA 94143

KIRSCHNER, MARVIN ABRAHAM, b Brooklyn, NY, Mar 5, 35; m 57; c 3. INTERNAL MEDICINE, ENDOCRINOLOGY. *Educ:* Albert Einstein Col Med, MD, 59. *Prof Exp:* Med intern, Bronx Munic Hosp Ctr, 59-60, asst resident, 60-61, resident med, 64-65; clin assoc endocrinol, Endocrine Br, Nat Cancer Inst, 61-64, fel reproductive endocrinol, Karolinska Inst, Stockholm, 65-66; sr investr, Endocrinol Br, 66-69; dir med, Newark Beth Israel Med Ctr, 69; assoc prof, 69-72, PROF MED, NJ MED SCH, 73- *Concurrent Pos:* Consult, Res Comt, East Orange Vet Admin Hosp, 71-; mem, Breast Cancer Task Force-Epidemiol, Nat Cancer Inst, 74-78, prog proj comt, 80- *Mem:* Am Fedn Clin Res; Endocrine Soc; Am Asn Cancer Res. *Res:* Androgen and estrogen metabolism; hirsutism; endocrine tumors; breast cancer; obesity management. *Mailing Add:* Dept of Med Newark Beth Israel Med Ctr Newark NJ 07112

KIRSCHNER, ROBERT HOWARD, b Philadelphia, Pa, Oct 30, 40; m 65; c 3. FORENSIC PATHOLOGY. *Educ:* Washington & Jefferson Col, BA, 62; Jefferson Med Col, MD, 66. *Prof Exp:* Instr path, Univ Chicago, 69-71; asst chief path dept, USPHS Hosp, 71-73; asst prof path, 73-78, Ben Horwich scholar med sci, 75-78, ASSOC PROF PATH, UNIV CHICAGO, 78-; DEP MED EXAMR, COOK CO, 78- *Concurrent Pos:* Am Cancer Soc clin fel path, Univ Chicago, 69-70; med adv comt, Lincoln Park Zoo, Chicago. *Mem:* AAAS; Am Soc Cell Biol; Sigma Xi; Am Acad Forensic Sci; NY Acad Sci. *Res:* Sudden cardiac death; comparative pathology of wild animals in captivity. *Mailing Add:* Fishbein Inst Forensic Med 1828 W Polk St Chicago IL 60612

KIRSCHNER, STANLEY, b Brooklyn, NY, Dec 17, 27; m 50; c 2. INORGANIC CHEMISTRY. *Educ:* Brooklyn Col, BS, 50; Harvard Univ, MS, 52; Univ Ill, PhD(chem), 54. *Prof Exp:* Res chemist inorg chem, Monsanto Chem Co, 51; from asst prof to assoc prof, 54-60, vchmn dept, 61-64, actg chmn, 64-65, PROF CHEM, WAYNE STATE UNIV, 60- *Concurrent Pos:* Res fels, Res Corp, 55-57, Chattanooga Med Co, 56, NSF, 58, 65-67, 73-77, sr fel, NSF, 63-64 & Ford Found, 69; Nat Insts Health grant, 62-65; Fulbright scholar, 63-64; perm secy, Int Conf Coord Chem; vis prof Univ London, 63-64, Univ Sao Paulo, Brazil, 69, Polytech Univ Timisoara,

Romania, 73, Univ Florence, Italy, 76, Tohoku Univ, Sendai, Japan, & Inst Chem, Cluj, Romania, 78. *Honors & Awards:* Fac Res Award, Sigma Xi, 74; Heyrovsky Medal, Czech Acad Sci, 78. *Mem:* AAAS; Am Chem Soc; fel NY Acad Sci; The Chem Soc; Brazilian Acad Sci. *Res:* Structure and stereochemistry of organosilicon and complex inorganic compounds; rotatory dispersion and circular dichroism of asymmetric coordination compounds; physiologically important complex inorganic compounds and their biological activity; application of computer techniques to the storage and retrieval of chemical literature references. *Mailing Add:* Dept of Chem Wayne State Univ Detroit MI 48202

KIRSCHSTEIN, RUTH LILLIAN, b Brooklyn, NY, Oct 12, 26; m 50; c 1. PATHOLOGY. *Educ:* Long Island Univ, AB, 47; Tulane Univ, MD, 51. *Prof Exp:* Pathologist, Div Biologics Stand, NIH, 57-60, chief sect path, Lab Viral Immunol, 60-62, asst chief, Lab Viral Immunol, 62-65, chief lab path, 65-72, asst dir, Div Biologics Stand, 71-72, dep dir, Bur Biologics, Food & Drug Admin, 72-73, dep assoc comnr sci, 73-74, DIR, NAT INST GEN MED SCI, NIH, 74- *Concurrent Pos:* Mem, WHO Expert Comt Poliomyelitis, 65 & 69. *Mem:* Am Asn Immunologists; Am Asn Pathologists; Am Soc Microbiol. *Res:* Pathology and pathogenesis of viral diseases; poliomyelitis, carcinogenesis; oncogenic viruses; viral vaccines; scientific peer review; scientific research administration. *Mailing Add:* Nat Inst of Gen Med Sci NIH Bethesda MD 20014

KIRSHENBAUM, ABRAHAM DAVID, b New York, NY, July 8, 19; m 43; c 2. PHYSICAL INORGANIC CHEMISTRY, EXPLOSIVES. *Educ:* City Col New York, BS, 41; Polytech Inst Brooklyn, MS, 45. *Prof Exp:* Res scientist, S A M Labs, Columbia Univ, 41-46; res chemist, Houdry Process Corp, Pa, 46-48 & Stand Oil Develop Co, 48-49; res supvr, Res Inst, Temple Univ, 49-68; RES CHEMIST & PROJ LEADER, ARRADCOM, 68- *Mem:* Am Chem Soc; Combusion Inst; Sci Res Soc Am; Sigma Xi; NAm Thermal Anal Soc. *Res:* Exchange reactions; lubrication oil additives; catalysis; inorganic fluorine chemistry; high vacuum techniques; gaseous burning velocity, calorimetric studies; high temperature physical measurements; rare gas chemistry; pyrotechnics and delays; propellants and explosives. *Mailing Add:* DRDAR-TST-S ARRADCOM Bldg 12 Dover NJ 07801

KIRSHENBAUM, GERALD STEVEN, b New York, NY, Dec 6, 44; c 3. POLYMER CHEMISTRY, PLASTICS RESEARCH. *Educ:* Case Inst Technol, BS, 66; Polytech Inst Brooklyn, MS, 70, PhD(polymer chem), 71. *Prof Exp:* Res chemist, Celanese Plastics Co, 71-74; sr res chemist, Soltex Polymer Corp, 74-75; sr chemist, Union Carbide Corp, Bound Brook, 76-78; DEVELOP ASSOC, CELANESE PLASTICS & SPECIALTIES CO, 78- *Concurrent Pos:* Asst ed, Polymer News, 72-75, ed, 75- *Mem:* Am Chem Soc; Soc Plastics Engrs. *Res:* Polyolefins; high-density polyethylene; polyethylene catalysis; polyethylene terephthalate for container application and plastics for packaging. *Mailing Add:* 10 Bryon Lane Fanwood NJ 07023

KIRSHENBAUM, ISIDOR, b New York, NY, June 22, 17; m 47; c 4. CHEMISTRY. *Educ:* City Col New York, BS, 38; Columbia Univ, MA, 39, PhD(chem), 42. *Prof Exp:* Asst instr phys chem, Columbia Univ, 40-42, res scientist, 42-45; res assoc, 45-68, sr res assoc, 68-77, SCI ADV, EXXON RES & ENG CO, 77- *Concurrent Pos:* Consult, AEC, 47-55. *Mem:* AAAS; Am Chem Soc; fel Am Inst Chem. *Res:* Oxidation reactions; patents and research analysis; polymer properties; petrochemical petroleum processes; heterogeneous catalysis; separation and physical properties of isotopes. *Mailing Add:* 436 Otisio Dr Westfield NJ 07090

KIRSHNER, HOWARD STEPHEN, b Bryn Mawr, Pa, July 11, 46; m 69; c 2. NEUROLOGY. *Educ:* Williams Col, BA, 68; Harvard Med Sch, MD, 72. *Prof Exp:* Intern med, Mass Gen Hosp, 72-73; staff assoc lab perinatal physiol, Nat Inst Neurol & Commun Dis, 73-75; resident & clin instr, Mass Gen Hosp, 75-78; ASST PROF NEUROL, SCH MED, VANDERBILT UNIV, 78- *Concurrent Pos:* Consult, Nashville Gen Hosp, 78- & Mid Tenn Ment Health Inst, 78- *Mem:* Am Acad Neurol. *Res:* Aphasia; higher cortical functions; cerebrovascular disease. *Mailing Add:* Dept Neurol Vanderbilt Univ Sch of Med Nashville TN 37240

KIRSHNER, NORMAN, b Wilkes-Barre, Pa, Sept 21, 23; m 61; c 3. BIOCHEMISTRY. *Educ:* Univ Scranton, BS, 47; Pa State Univ, MS, 51, PhD(biochem), 52. *Prof Exp:* Res asst physiol, Univ Rochester, 52-54; res asst, Yale Univ, 54; res asst, 55-57, assoc biochem, 56-59, from asst prof to assoc prof, 59-70, chmn dept pharmacol, 77, PROF BIOCHEM, DUKE UNIV, 70- *Concurrent Pos:* USPHS sr res fel, 59-62, career develop award, 62-; mem, NINCDS Prog Proj Rev Comt, 75-79, Coun Sci Adv, Roche Inst Molecular Biol, 79; ed, Molecular Pharmacol, 77. *Mem:* Am Soc Biol Chem; Am Soc Pharmacol & Exp Therapeut; Am Soc Neurochem. *Res:* Metabolism of Catecholamines; mechanism of storage and release of neurotransmitters. *Mailing Add:* Dept of Pharmacol Duke Univ Med Ctr Durham NC 27710

KIRSHNER, ROBERT PAUL, b Long Branch, NJ, Aug 15, 49; m 70; c 2. ASTRONOMY. *Educ:* Harvard Col, AB, 70; Calif Inst Technol, PhD(astron), 75. *Prof Exp:* Res assoc astron, Kitt Peak Nat Observ, 74-76; asst prof, 76-80, ASSOC PROF ASTRON & DIR, MCGRAW-HILL OBSERV, UNIV MICH, 80- *Mem:* Am Astron Soc; Int Astron Union. *Res:* Extragalactic supernovae and galactic supernova remnants; dynamics and luminosity of galaxies. *Mailing Add:* Dept of Astron Univ Mich Ann Arbor MI 48109

KIRSNER, JOSEPH BARNETT, b Boston, Mass, Sept 21, 09; m 34; c 1. INTERNAL MEDICINE, GASTROENTEROLOGY. *Educ:* Tufts Col, MD, 33; Univ Chicago, PhD(biol sci) & Am Bd Internal Med, dipl, 42. *Prof Exp:* From asst prof to prof med, 35-74, dean med affairs & chief staff, Univ Hosp, 71-76, LOUIS BLOCK DISTINGUISHED SERV PROF MED, UNIV CHICAGO, 74- *Concurrent Pos:* Mem nat adv coun, Nat Inst Arthritis & Metab Dis; chmn, Adv Group, Nat Comn Digestive Dis, 78; assoc ed, Advances Internal Med, 70- *Mem:* Am Soc Clin Invest; Am Soc Gastrointestinal Endoscopy (secy-treas, Gastroscopic Soc, 42-48, pres, 49-50); fel AMA; Am Gastroenterol Asn (treas & pres, 65-66); Am Col Physicians. *Res:* Gastroenterology, especially peptic ulcer, cancer, inflammatory diseases including regional enteritis and ulcerative colitis; protein metabolism; hepatic disease; immunological mechanisms in gastrointestinal disease. *Mailing Add:* Dept of Med Univ of Chicago Chicago IL 60637

KIRST, HERBERT ANDREW, b St Paul, Minn, Sept 22, 44. ORGANIC CHEMISTRY. *Educ:* Univ Minn, BS, 66; Harvard Univ, PhD(org chem), 71. *Prof Exp:* Fel org chem, Calif Inst Technol, 71-73; sr chemist, 73-77, RES SCIENTIST, ELI LILLY & CO, 77- *Mem:* Am Chem Soc. *Res:* Structure determination and chemical modification of new antibiotics and other fermentation products. *Mailing Add:* Dept M539 Fermentation Prod Lilly Res Lab Indianapolis IN 46285

KIRSTEN, EDWARD BRUCE, b New York, NY, Jan 28, 42; m 63; c 2. NEUROPHARMACOLOGY, CELL PHYSIOLOGY. *Educ:* Fairleigh Dickinson Univ, BS, 62; NY Univ, MS, 66; City Univ New York, PhD(biol), 69. *Prof Exp:* Assoc, Col Physicians & Surgeons, Columbia Univ, 71-72, asst prof pharmacol, 72-77; DIR CLIN PHARMACOL, KNOLL PHARMACEUT CO, 77- *Concurrent Pos:* NIH fel pharmacol, Col Physicians & Surgeons, Columbia Univ, 69-71, res career develop award, 72-77. *Mem:* AAAS; assoc Am Physiol Soc; Am Soc Pharmacol & Exp Therapeut; Soc Neurosci. *Res:* Vestibular neuropharmacology; antiarrhythmic drugs; muscle physiology. *Mailing Add:* Knoll Pharmaceut Co Whippany NJ 07981

KIRSTEN, WERNER H, b Leipzig, Ger, Oct 29, 25; US citizen; m 60; c 3. PATHOLOGY. *Educ:* Univ Frankfurt, MD, 54. *Prof Exp:* Asst path, Path Inst, Frankfurt, 53-55; intern med, Englewood Hosp, 55-56; resident path, 56-59, from instr to assoc prof, 59-66, assoc prof pediat, 66-68, PROF PATH & PEDIAT, UNIV CHICAGO, 68-, CHMN DEPT PATH, 72- *Concurrent Pos:* USPHS career develop award, 60-68. *Mem:* AAAS; Am Asn Path & Bact; Am Soc Exp Path; Am Asn Cancer Res. *Res:* Experimental pathology; cancer research; oncogenic virus, especially leukemia. *Mailing Add:* Dept of Path Univ of Chicago Chicago IL 60637

KIRSTEUER, ERNST, b Vienna, Austria, Sept 28, 33; m 58. INVERTEBRATE ZOOLOGY. *Educ:* Univ Vienna, PhD(zool), 61. *Prof Exp:* Govt res fel, Austrian Dept Educ, 61-62; prof marine biol, Inst Oceanog, Univ Oriente, Cumana, Venezuela, 63-65; from asst cur to assoc cur, 65-75, CUR, AM MUS NATURAL HIST, 75-, CHMN, DEPT INVERT, 77- *Concurrent Pos:* Mem Int Oceanog Found. *Mem:* Am Soc Zoologists; Soc Syst Zoologists. *Res:* Systematics, anatomy and ecology of Nemertina, Gnathostomulida and Archiannelida. *Mailing Add:* Dept of Invert Am Mus Nat Hist Cent Pk W-79 St New York NY 10024

KIRTLEY, MARY ELIZABETH, b Mansfield, Ohio, Aug 27, 35. BIOCHEMISTRY. *Educ:* Univ Chicago, BA, 56; Smith Col, MA, 58; Western Reserve Univ, PhD(biochem), 64. *Prof Exp:* Lab instr chem, Smith Col, 58-59; res assoc biochem, Brookhaven Nat Lab, 64-65; res assoc, Univ Calif, Berkeley, 65-66; from asst prof to assoc prof, 66-74, PROF BIOL CHEM, SCH MED, UNIV MD, BALTIMORE, 74- *Mem:* Am Chem Soc; Am Soc Biol Chem; Biophys Soc. *Res:* Enzyme mechanisms; intermediary metabolism; biochemical regulation; enzyme structure and function; enzyme-membrane interactions. *Mailing Add:* Dept of Biol Chem Univ of Md Sch of Med Baltimore MD 21201

KIRTLEY, THOMAS L(LOYD), b Salmon, Idaho, Nov 16, 18; m 43; c 2. CHEMICAL ENGINEERING. *Educ:* San Jose State Col, AB(chem) & AB(physics & math), 40; Calif Inst Technol, MS, 42. *Prof Exp:* Tech shift supvr, Ammonia Prod, Hercules Powder Co, 42-44, shift supvr, Rocket Powder Prod, 44-45, serv supvr, Chem Cotton Prod, 45-56, asst chief chemist, 56-60, chem supvr, 60-65, chem cotton tech coordr, 65-69, chem cotton supt, 69-75, supt eng develop, 75-77, SUPT ENVIRON ENG, HERCULES INC, 77- *Mem:* Am Chem Soc. *Res:* Cellulose chemistry; chemical cotton; cellulose ethers. *Mailing Add:* Hercules Inc PO Box 271 Hopewell VA 23860

KIRTLEY, WILLIAM RAYMOND, b Crawfordsville, Ind, May 30, 14; m 40; c 2. CLINICAL MEDICINE. *Educ:* Wabash Col, AB, 36; Northwestern Univ, MB, 40, MD, 41. *Prof Exp:* Staff physician, Eli Lilly & Co, 47-56, physician in chg, Diabetes Res Lab Clin Res, 53-70, sr physician, 56-61, head, Clin Med Dept, 61-65, asst dir, Clin Res Div, 63-65, dir, Med Res Div, 65-72, dir, Lilly Lab Clin Res, 72-78; assoc prof med, Sch Med, Ind Univ, 73-78; RETIRED. *Concurrent Pos:* Assoc med, Wishard Mem Hosp, 49-, chief, Diabetes Clin, 53-70; assoc med, Sch Med, Ind Univ, 52-61, asst prof, 61-73; abstr ed, Diabetes, Am Diabetes Asn, 50-68. *Honors & Awards:* Banting Medal, Am Diabetes Asn, 71. *Mem:* Am Soc Clin Pharmacol & Therapeut; Endocrine Soc; AMA; Am Diabetes Asn. *Res:* Insulin modifications; metabolism; diabetes mellitus; glucagon. *Mailing Add:* 40 N Port Royal Dr Hilton Head SC 29928

KIRTMAN, BERNARD, b New York, NY, Mar 30, 35; m 58; c 2. PHYSICAL CHEMISTRY. *Educ:* Harvard Univ, PhD(phys chem), 61. *Prof Exp:* Fel chem, Univ Wash, 60-62; asst prof chem, Univ Calif, Berkeley, 62-65, from asst prof to assoc prof chem, Univ Calif, Santa Barbara, 65-74, PROF THEORET PHYS CHEM, UNIV CALIF, SANTA BARBARA, 74- *Res:* Theoretical chemistry; application of quantum mechanics to electronic structure of atoms and molecules, intermolecular interactions and molecular dynamics. *Mailing Add:* Dept of Chem Univ of Calif Santa Barbara CA 93106

KIRWAN, ALBERT DENNIS, JR, b Louisville, Ky, Nov 29, 33; m 56; c 3. PHYSICAL OCEANOGRAPHY. *Educ:* Princeton Univ, AB, 56; Tex A&M Univ, PhD(phys oceanog), 64. *Prof Exp:* Res asst oceanog, Tex A&M Univ, 59-64; from asst prof to assoc prof, NY Univ, 64-70; prog dir phys oceanog, Off Naval Res, 70-72; SR RES SCIENTIST, TEX A&M UNIV, 72- *Mem:* AAAS; Am Meteorol Soc; Am Geophys Union. *Res:* Air-sea interaction, general circulation of oceans; physics of fluids; engineering science. *Mailing Add:* 11519 Timerwild Woodlands TX 77380

KIRWAN, DONALD FRAZIER, b Oklahoma City, Okla, Nov 9, 37; m 59; c 5. ENERGY, ENERGY EDUCATION. *Educ:* Univ Mo-Columbia, BS, 63, MS, 64, PhD(physics), 69. *Prof Exp:* From instr to asst prof, 67-74, dir, Off Energy Educ, 79, ASSOC PROF PHYSICS, UNIV RI, 74- *Concurrent Pos:* Consult, Fed Emergency Mgt Agency, 80- *Mem:* AAAS; Am Phys Soc; Am Asn Physics Teachers; Nat Sci Teachers Asn; Int Solar Energy Soc. *Res:* Fundamental interactions; few-nucleon systematics; excitation mechanisms of the nucleus; pedagogy; curriculum development. *Mailing Add:* Dept of Physics Univ of RI Kingston RI 02881

KIRWAN, WILLIAM ENGLISH, b Louisville, Ky, Apr 14, 38; m 60; c 2. MATHEMATICAL ANALYSIS. *Educ:* Univ Ky, BA, 60; Rutgers Univ, MS, 62, PhD(math), 64. *Prof Exp:* Instr math, Rutgers Univ, 63-64; from asst prof to assoc prof, 64-72, chmn dept, 77-81, PROF MATH, UNIV MD, COLLEGE PARK, 72-, VCHANCELLOR ACAD AFFAIRS, 81- *Concurrent Pos:* Vis lectr, Royal Holloway Col, Univ London, 66-67; prog dir, NSF, 75-76. *Mem:* Math Asn Am; Am Math Soc; London Math Soc; Sigma Xi. *Res:* Functions of one complex variable, particularly extremal properties of conformal and quasiconformal mappings of the unit disc. *Mailing Add:* Off VChancellor Acad Affairs Univ of Md College Park MD 20742

KIRWIN, GERALD JAMES, b Lowell, Mass, Feb 11, 29; m 55; c 2. ELECTRICAL ENGINEERING, APPLIED MATHEMATICS. *Educ:* Northeast Univ, BSEE, 52; Mass Inst Technol, MSEE, 55; Syracuse Univ, PhD(elec eng), 68. *Prof Exp:* Mem tech staff, Bell Tel Labs, 55-56; assoc prof elec eng, Merrimack Col, 56-64; instr, Syracuse Univ, 64-68; prof, Univ Maine, Portland-Gorham, 68-77; PROF ELEC ENG, SCH ENG, UNIV NEW HAVEN, 77- *Mem:* Inst Elec & Electronic Engrs. *Res:* Nonlinear systems; circuit theory and design; optimal network design, electrical engineering education. *Mailing Add:* Univ of New Haven PO Box 1306 New Haven CT 06516

KIRZ, JANOS, b Budapest, Hungary, Aug 11, 37; US citizen; m 64; c 1. EXPERIMENTAL HIGH ENERGY PHYSICS, OPTICAL PHYSICS. *Educ:* Univ Calif, Berkeley, BA, 59, PhD(physics), 63. *Prof Exp:* Nat Acad Sci-Nat Res Coun fel physics, Saclay Nuclear Res Ctr, France, 63-64; physicist, Lawrence Radiation Lab, Univ Calif, 64-68; assoc prof, 68-72, PROF PHYSICS, STATE UNIV NY STONY BROOK, 72- *Concurrent Pos:* Lectr, Univ Calif, Berkeley, 67; Sloan Found fel, 70-72; visitor, Lab Molecular Biophysics, Oxford Univ, 72-73. *Mem:* AAAS; Am Phys Soc. *Res:* Experimental particle physics; x-ray microscopy. *Mailing Add:* Dept of Physics State Univ of NY Stony Brook NY 11794

KISCHER, CLAYTON WARD, b Des Moines, Iowa, Mar 2, 30; m 64; c 2. EMBRYOLOGY, CELL BIOLOGY. *Educ:* Univ Omaha, BS, 53; Iowa State Univ, MS, 60, PhD(embryol), 62. *Prof Exp:* Cytologist, Col Med, Univ Nebr, 53-56; teacher high sch, Nebr, 56-58; asst prof zool, Ill State Univ, 62-63; resident res assoc biol & med, Argonne Nat Lab, 63; asst prof zool, Iowa State Univ, 63-64; chief sect electron micros, Southwest Found Res & Educ, 66-67; asst prof, 67-70, assoc prof, Univ Tex Med Br; vis prof surg biol, 76-77, ASSOC PROF ANAT, UNIV ARIZ COL MED, 77- *Concurrent Pos:* Fel biochem, Univ Tex M D Anderson Hosp, 64-66; res consult to chief staff, Shriners Burns Inst, Galveston, 70-73. *Mem:* AAAS; Soc Develop Biol; Am Soc Cell Biol; Electron Micros Soc Am. *Res:* Induction organogenesis; ultrastructural changes during morphogenesis; nuclear proteins and embryogenesis; tissue culture; electron microscopy; microelectrophoresis; hypertrophic scarring, inflammation, prostaglandins and fibronectin. *Mailing Add:* Dept of Anat Univ of Ariz Col Med Tucson AZ 85724

KISEL, RICHARD ANDREW, b Cleveland, Ohio, Mar 6, 36; m 58; c 2. CHEMICAL ENGINEERING. *Educ:* Case Western Reserve Univ, BS, 58; Xavier Univ, MBA, 69. *Prof Exp:* Asst prod engr, Pfizer, Inc, 58-60; pilot plant engr, Rohm and Haas Co, 60-63; sr process engr, Monsanto Co, 63-69; sect leader, US Indust Chem Co, 69-72; group leader, 72-73, MGR RES, GAF CORP, 74- *Mem:* Am Inst Chem Engrs. *Res:* Solution and suspension polymerization of styrene/acrylonitrite; Ziegler catalyst in suspension polymerization of ethylene; processing of organic chemicals and surfactants; inorganic pigmented silicate films for manufacture of artificially colored rooting granulars. *Mailing Add:* GAF Corp 34 Charles St PO Box 1418 Hagerstown MD 21740

KISER, DONALD LEE, b Keokuk, Iowa, Jan 2, 33; m 53; c 3. ANALYTICAL CHEMISTRY. *Educ:* Iowa State Univ, BS, 59; Ind State Univ, MS, 61; Univ Iowa, PhD(anal chem), 64. *Prof Exp:* Anal chemist, Com Solvents Corp, Ind, 59-61; sr anal chemist, 64-73, MGR ANAL DEVELOP, GRAIN PROCESSING CORP, 73- *Mem:* Am Chem Soc; Coblentz Soc; Am Asn Cereal Chemists. *Res:* Automated methods of analysis; protein and amino acid analysis; alcohol congeners by gas chromatography; carbohydrate molecular weight profiles by liquid chromatography. *Mailing Add:* Grain Processing Corp Box 349 1600 Ore Ave Muscatine IA 52761

KISER, KENNETH M(AYNARD), b Detroit, Mich, Nov 28, 29; m 54; c 5. CHEMICAL ENGINEERING. *Educ:* Lawrence Inst Technol, BS, 51; Univ Cincinnati, MS, 52; Johns Hopkins Univ, DS(chem eng), 56. *Prof Exp:* Asst, Univ Cincinnati, 51-52; res assoc, Inst Coop Res, Johns Hopkins Univ, 52-56; res assoc, Chem Dept, Res Lab, Gen Elec Co, 56-64; adj staff, Rensselaer Polytech Inst, 62-64; asst prof, 64-66, assoc prof, 66-80, PROF CHEM ENG, STATE UNIV NY BUFFALO, 80-, ASSOC DEAN ENG, 78- *Concurrent Pos:* Consult. *Mem:* Am Inst Chem Engrs; Am Soc Eng Educ; Sigma Xi. *Res:* Turbulent transport; non-Newtonian fluids; fluid mechanics in the human body; air and water pollution. *Mailing Add:* Dept of Chem Eng 307 Furnas Hall State Univ NY Buffalo NY 14260

KISER, LOLA FRANCES, b Selmer, Tenn, Dec 6, 30. MATHEMATICS. *Educ:* Memphis State Univ, BS, 52; Univ Ga, MA, 54; Univ Ala, Tuscaloosa, PhD(math), 71. *Prof Exp:* Instr math, Univ Ga, 54-55; from asst prof to assoc prof, 55-71, PROF MATH, BIRMINGHAM-SOUTHERN COL, 71- *Mem:* Math Asn Am. *Res:* Complex analysis; differential equations. *Mailing Add:* Dept Math Box A-32 Birmingham-Southern Col Birmingham AL 35254

KISER, ROBERT WAYNE, b Rock Island, Ill, Apr 26, 32; m 54; c 3. INORGANIC CHEMISTRY. *Educ:* St Ambrose Col, BA, 53; Purdue Univ, MS, 55, PhD, 58. *Prof Exp:* From asst prof to prof inorg chem, Kans State Univ, 57-67; chmn chem dept, 68-72, PROF CHEM & DIR MASS SPECTROMETRY CTR, UNIV KY, 67- *Mem:* Am Soc Mass Spectrometry; Mass Spectros Soc Japan; Am Chem Soc; Am Phys Soc; The Chem Soc. *Res:* Exited states of negative ions; energetics and thermochemistry of ionic species; artificial intelligence in mass spectrometry; mass spectrometry and molecular structures. *Mailing Add:* Dept of Chem Univ of Ky Lexington KY 40506

KISH, VALERIE MAYO, b Paintsville, Ky, Nov 28, 44. CELL BIOLOGY. *Educ:* Univ Ky, BS, 65; Ind Univ, MA, 66; Univ Mich, PhD(cell biol), 73. *Prof Exp:* Res asst, Inst Cancer Res, Philadelphia, 66-69; res assoc, Worcester Found Exp Biol, Shrewsbury, 73-76; ASST PROF BIOL, HOBART & WILLIAM SMITH COLS, 76- *Mem:* Am Soc Cell Biol; Soc Develop Biol; Sigma Xi. *Res:* Interaction of proteins with RNA in eukaryotic cells and the role these interactions play in the regulation of gene expression. *Mailing Add:* Dept of Biol Hobart & William Smith Cols Geneva NY 14456

KISHEL, CHESTER JOSEPH, b Cleveland, Ohio, Oct 12, 15; m 39; c 3. INDUSTRIAL & HUMAN FACTORS ENGINEERING. *Educ:* Fenn Col, BSME, 44, BSIE, 47; Case Inst Technol, MSIE, 54, PhD(eng admin), 59. *Prof Exp:* Asst chief prod eng, Iron Fireman Mfg Co, 43-45; prod mgr, A W Hecker Co, 45-46; vpres mfg, Kramic Corp, 46-48; from asst prof to assoc prof mech eng, Fenn Col, 48-57; spec lectr eng admin, Case Inst Technol, 57-59; assoc prof & dir comput ctr, Fenn Col, 59-62; contract prof comput indust eng, Mich State Univ/USAID, Polytech Sch, Sao Paulo, Brazil, 62-64; prof mech & indust eng, 65-70, dir comput ctr, 65-66, prof indust eng & actg chmn dept, 70-71, SR PROF INDUST ENG, CLEVELAND STATE UNIV, 71- *Concurrent Pos:* Polio Found grant, Highland View Hosp, 60-61. *Mem:* Am Inst Indust Engrs; Soc Mfg Eng; Asn Comput Mach; Am Arbit Asn. *Res:* Neuroanatomy and neurophysiology in desision making aspects of organization theory; electromyographical study-hypotheses of muscular control of human hand languages and techniques of digital computing; numerical controls. *Mailing Add:* Col of Eng Cleveland State Univ Cleveland OH 44115

KISHIMOTO, YASUO, b Osaka-Shi, Japan, Apr 11, 25; m 49; c 4. BIOLOGICAL CHEMISTRY, NEUROCHEMISTRY. *Educ:* Kyoto Univ, BS, 48, PhD(pharmaceut chem), 56. *Prof Exp:* Res chemist, Osaka Gas Co, 48-50; lectr pharm, Kyushu Univ, 50-54; res asst biochem, Med Sch, Northwestern Univ, 57-59; from asst to assoc res biochemist, Ment Health Res Inst, Univ Mich, Ann Arbor, 62-67; mem staff, Div Chem Res, G D Searle & Co, Ill, 67-69; asst biochemist, 69-70, assoc biochemist neurol serv, Mass Gen Hosp, 70-76; assoc prof, 76-80, PROF NEUROL, SCH MED, JOHNS HOPKINS UNIV, 80-; DIR BIOCHEM RES, JOHN F KENNEDY INST, 76- *Concurrent Pos:* Asst prof, Shizuoka Col Pharm 54-61; sr investr, Eunice Kennedy Shriver Ctr Ment Retardation, 69-76; assoc neurol, Harvard Med Sch, 69-76; assoc prof neurol, Johns Hopkins Univ Sch Med, 76-80. *Mem:* Am Soc Biol Chemists; Int Soc Neurochem; AAAS; Am Soc Neurochem. *Res:* Structures and metabolism of brain lipids; myelination, demyelination. *Mailing Add:* John F Kennedy Inst 707 N Broadway Baltimore MD 21205

KISILEVSKY, ROBERT, b Montreal, Can, Dec 19, 37; m 67; c 3. BIOCHEMISTRY, PATHOLOGY. *Educ:* McGill Univ, BSc, 58, MD, CM, 62; Univ Pittsburgh, PhD(biochem), 69; FRCP(C), 72; Am Bd Path, dipl, 72. *Prof Exp:* Asst prof path, Queen's Univ, 70-74, assoc prof, 74-79, PROF PATH, 79- *Concurrent Pos:* Asst pathologist, Kingston Gen Hosp, 70-; asst prof biochem, 71-74, assoc prof, 74-; mem, Grant Comt, Med Res Coun, 74-77, sci officer, 77- *Mem:* Int Acad Path; Am Asn Pathologists; Can Asn Pathologists; Can Biochem Soc. *Res:* Disturbances of the protein synthesizing apparatus of cells during induced injury, includes alterations in the structure and function of ribosomes, mRNA and associated protein factors; pathogenetic mechanisms of Amyloidosis. *Mailing Add:* Dept Path Queen's Univ Kingston ON K7L 3N6 Can

KISKIS, JOSEPH EDWARD, JR, b Lynwood, Calif, Oct 2, 47. THEORETICAL PHYSICS. *Educ:* Univ Calif, Davis, BS, 69; Stanford Univ, MS, 71, PhD(physics), 74. *Prof Exp:* Fel, Mass Inst Technol, 74-76 & Los Alamos Sci Lab, 76-77; mem, Inst Adv Study, 77-78; Oppenheimer fel, Los Alamos Nat Lab, 78-80; ASSOC PROF RESIDENCE, UNIV CALIF, DAVIS, 80- *Res:* High energy physics; quantum field theory. *Mailing Add:* Dept Physics Univ Calif Davis CA 95616

KISKIS, RONALD CLEMENTS, organic chemistry, see previous edition

KISLINGER, MARK BRECHER, elementary particle physics, see previous edition

KISLIUK, PAUL, b Philadelphia, Pa, Feb 22, 22; m 50; c 4. PHYSICS. *Educ:* Queen's Col, NY, BA, 43; Columbia Univ, MS, 47, PhD(physics), 52. *Prof Exp:* Mem tech staff, Bell Tel Labs, 52-62; dept head, 62-66, SR SCIENTIST, AEROSPACE CORP, 66- *Mem:* Am Phys Soc; Inst Elec & Electronics Eng. *Res:* Microwave spectroscopy; contact physics; surface physics; lasers; solid state spectroscopy. *Mailing Add:* Aerospace Corp PO Box 929957 Los Angeles CA 90009

KISLIUK, ROY LOUIS, b Philadelphia, Pa, Aug 4, 28; m 54; c 2. BIOCHEMISTRY. *Educ:* Queen's Col, NY, BS, 50; Yale Univ, MS, 52; Western Reserve Univ, PhD(biochem), 56. *Prof Exp:* Vis scientist, Nat Inst Arthritis & Metab Dis, 58-60; from asst prof to assoc prof pharmacol, 60-71, assoc prof biochem, 71-72, PROF BIOCHEM, SCH MED, TUFTS UNIV, 72- *Concurrent Pos:* Nat Found Infantile Paralysis fel biochem, Oxford Univ, 56-58. *Mem:* Am Soc Biol Chem; Am Chem Soc; Am Soc Pharmacol & Exp Therapeut; Am Soc Microbiol; Am Soc Cancer Res. *Res:* Folate enzymes, coenzymes and analogs. *Mailing Add:* Dept of Pharmacol & Biochem Tufts Univ Sch of Med Boston MA 02111

KISMAN, KENNETH EDWIN, b Sudbury, Ont, Nov 18, 46; m 70. BIOPHYSICS, ULTRASOUND. *Educ:* Queens Univ, BS, 68; Univ Toronto, MS, 70, PhD(molecular physics), 74. *Prof Exp:* res officer hyperbaric biophys, Defence & Civil Inst Environ Med, Can, 74-80. *Mem:* Can Asn Physicists; Undersea Med Soc. *Res:* Investigation of bubble formation in divers and animals during decompression involving the development and application of ultrasonic monitoring techniques; studies in bubble physics. *Mailing Add:* 2673 Lake Shore Blvd West Toronto ON M8V 1G6 Can

KISPERT, LOWELL DONALD, b Faribault, Minn, June 9, 40. CHEMICAL PHYSICS, RADIATION CHEMISTRY. *Educ:* St Olaf Col, BA, 62; Mich State Univ, PhD(chem), 66. *Prof Exp:* Fel electron spin resonance, Varian Assocs, Calif, 66-67; radiation chem, Mellon Inst, 68; from asst prof to assoc prof, 68-77, PROF CHEM, UNIV ALA, 77- *Mem:* Am Chem Soc; Am Phys Soc; Sigma Xi. *Res:* Free radicals as produced in irradiated organic single crystals by electron spin resonance; electron nuclear double resonance and electron-electron double resonance of paramagnetic single crystals, anions and biradicals; radiation chemistry and crystallography. *Mailing Add:* Chem Dept Univ of Ala Tuscaloosa AL 35486

KISS, KLARA, b Budapest, Hungary, Aug 28, 30; m 51; c 2. PHYSICAL CHEMISTRY, POLYMER CHEMISTRY. *Educ:* Budapest Tech Univ, dipl Chemiker, 54. *Prof Exp:* Jr chemist, Res Ctr Org & Polymer Chem, Budapest, 49-51; res chemist, Res Ctr Telecommun, 55-56; res & develop chemist, Filmfabrik AGFA, EGer, 56; res chemist, Dom Dyeing & Printing Co, Can, 57-59; sr res assoc phys chem & polymer sci, Horizons, Inc, Ohio, 61-65; res assoc electron micros, Case Western Reserve Univ, 65-67; res chemist, GAF Corp, 67-70; RES ASSOC, STAUFFER CHEM CO, 70- *Mem:* Soc Appl Spectros; Asn Hungarian Chemists; Ger Chem Soc; Am Crystallog Asn; Microbeam Analysis Soc. *Res:* Kinetics of redox bulk polymerization of acrylates; photopolymerization; controlled, ultrafine particle size ferroelectrics; epitaxial crystallization of polymers; identification of wairakite single crystals by electron diffraction; microbeam analysis. *Mailing Add:* Stauffer Chem Co Res Ctr Livingstone Ave Dobbs Ferry NY 10522

KISSA, ERIK, b Abja, Estonia, Apr 7, 23; nat US; m 52; c 2. COLLOID CHEMISTRY, TEXTILE CHEMISTRY. *Educ:* Karlsruhe Tech Univ, dipl, 51; Univ Del, PhD(chem), 56. *Prof Exp:* Anal chemist, 51-56, res chemist, 56-67, sr res chemist, 67-74, RES ASSOC, CHEM & PIGMENTS DEPT, E I DU PONT DE NEMOURS & CO, INC, 74- *Concurrent Pos:* UN Indust Develop Orgn consult, Atira Textile Res Inst, Ahmedabad, India, 78 & 79. *Mem:* AAAS; Am Chem Soc; fel Am Inst Chem; Int Asn Colloid & Interface Scientists. *Res:* Colloid and surface chemistry; association colloids; dispersions; emulsions; detergency; dyes; textile chemicals; physical chemistry of dyeing; polymers; analytical chemistry; organic microanalyses; physical organic chemistry; complexes; electrical properties of organic compounds; surface chemistry of textile fibers. *Mailing Add:* 1436 Fresno Rd Green Acres Wilmington DE 19803

KISSANE, JOHN M, b Oxford, Ohio, Mar 30, 28; m 51; c 5. MEDICINE. *Educ:* Univ Rochester, AB, 48; Wash Univ, MD, 52. *Prof Exp:* Asst path, 52-53, from instr to assoc prof, 53-68, PROF PATH & PROF PATH IN PEDIAT, SCH MED, WASH UNIV, 68- *Concurrent Pos:* Intern, Barnes Hosp, 52-53, chief resident, 53-54, asst pathologist, Barnes & Assoc Hosps, 58-; Nat Found Infantile Paralysis res fel, Sch Med, Wash Univ, 54-55 & 57-58, med alumni scholar, 70-71; mem sect renal dis, Coun Circulation, Am Heart Asn. *Mem:* AMA; Am Asn Path & Bact; Am Soc Exp Path; Histochem Soc; Int Acad Path. *Res:* Pathology; pediatric pathology; quantitative histochemistry of nervous system; kidney. *Mailing Add:* Dept of Path Wash Univ Sch of Med St Louis MO 63110

KISSEL, CHARLES LOUIS, b Chicago, Ill, Aug 5, 47; m 70; c 2. INDUSTRIAL ORGANIC CHEMISTRY. *Educ:* Univ Calif, Irvine, BA, 69; Univ Calif, Santa Barbara, PhD(chem), 73. *Prof Exp:* GROUP LEADER CHEM RES, MAGNA CORP, 73- *Mem:* Am Chem Soc; Sigma Xi. *Res:* Treating mechanisms and synthesis of industrial biocides, corrosion inhibitors, scale inhibitors, emulsion breakers and water clarifiers, as well as specialty chemicals; special emphasis on acrolein chemistry. *Mailing Add:* Magna Corp 11808 S Bloomfield Ave Santa Fe Springs CA 90670

KISSEL, DAVID E, b Vanderburg Co, Ind, Aug 10, 43; m 66; c 2. SOIL CHEMISTRY, SOIL FERTILITY. *Educ:* Purdue Univ, BS, 65; Univ Ky, MS, 67, PhD(soil acidity), 69. *Prof Exp:* From asst prof to assoc prof soil chem, Tex A&M Univ, 69-77, assoc prof & asst dir for res, Blackland Res Ctr, 77-78; PROF AGRON, KANS STATE UNIV, 78- *Concurrent Pos:* Assoc ed, J Environ Quality, 75-78. *Mem:* Am Soc Agron; Soil Sci Soc Am. *Res:* Plant nutrition; soil acidity; movement of water and nitrate in soils; nitrogen and phosphorus fertilizer use efficiency; ammonia volatilization. *Mailing Add:* Dept Agron Throckmorton Hall Kans State Univ Manhattan KS 66506

KISSEL, JOHN WALTER, b St Louis, Mo, Dec 12, 25; m 53; c 4. PHARMACOLOGY. *Educ:* Wash Univ, AB, 48; St Louis Col Pharm, BS, 51; St Louis Univ, MS, 55; Univ Mich, PhD(pharmacol), 58. *Prof Exp:* Asst prof pharmacog & pharmacol, Col Pharm, Univ Fla, 56-57; assoc sr pharmacologist, Mead Johnson & Co, 57-59, group leader cent nervous syst pharmacol, 59-62, sect leader, 62-69; from pharmacologist to sr pharmacologist, 69-71, mgr drug eval, 71-73, clin res assoc med res dept, Cyanamid Int, 73-75; CLIN RES ASSOC, CLIN RES DEPT, LEDERLE LABS, 75- *Mem:* Fel AAAS; Am Soc Pharmacol & Exp Therapeut; NY Acad Sci; Am Soc Clin Pharmacol Therapeut; Drug Info Asn. *Res:* Central nervous system pharmacology, especially opiate tolerance and addiction; spinal cord reflexes; muscle relaxants; effect of drugs on behavior; clinical evaluation of psychotherapeutic agents. *Mailing Add:* Clin Res Dept Lederle Labs Pearl River NY 10965

KISSEL, THOMAS ROBERT, b Chicago, Ill, Sept 26, 47; m 72. ANALYTICAL CHEMISTRY, CLINICAL ANALYSIS. *Educ:* Univ Notre Dame, BS, 69; Univ Wis, PhD(anal chem), 74. *Prof Exp:* RES CHEMIST, EASTMAN KODAK CO, 74- *Mem:* Sigma Xi; Electrophoresis Soc. *Res:* Electrochemistry, specifically ion selective electrodes. *Mailing Add:* Eastman Kodak Co 343 State St Rochester NY 14650

KISSEL, WILLIAM JOHN, b New York, NY, Mar 12, 41; m 66; c 2. POLYMER CHEMISTRY. *Educ:* City Col New York, BS, 62; State Univ NY Buffalo, PhD(org chem), 68. *Prof Exp:* RES CHEMIST, AMOCO CHEMS CORP, 67- *Mem:* Am Chem Soc. *Res:* Polymer crystallization and morphology; thermal analysis of polymers. *Mailing Add:* 1355 Old Dominion Rd Naperville IL 60540

KISSELL, KENNETH EUGENE, b Columbiana, Ohio, June 28, 28; m 53; c 2. ASTRONOMY, SPACE PHYSICS. *Educ:* Ohio State Univ, BSc, 49, MSc, 58, PhD, 69. *Prof Exp:* Res assoc rocket res lab, Res Found, Ohio State Univ, 48-51; instrumentation physicist, Propulsion Br, Flight Res Lab, Wright-Patterson AFB, 51-57, physicist, Appl Math Lab, Aeronaut Res Lab, 58-59, chief, Gen Physics Res Lab, Aerospace Res Labs, Off Aerospace Res, 59-61, physicist, 61-66, dir, 66-72, br chief, Surveillance Br, Air Force Avionics Lab, 72-75, sr scientist, Reconnaissance & Weapon Delivery Div, Air Force Avionics Lab, 76-80; STAFF SCIENTIST, LASER SYSTS ANAL, ROCKETDYNE DIV, ROCKWELL INT, 80- *Concurrent Pos:* Photog specialist, US Air Force Geod Eclipse Exped, Okak Islands, Labrador, 54; Georgetown Univ Eclipse Exped, Brit Somaliland, 55; ed measurement applns, Trans, Instrument Soc Am, 62-68; experimenter, Nat Geog Soc-Douglas Aircraft Airborne Eclipse Exped, Can, 63; NASA Int Years of Quiet Sun Airborne Solar Eclipse Exped, SPac, 65; experimenter, NASA Airborne Solar Eclipse Exped, Brazil, 66; US Air Force-Ital Solar Eclipse Expeds, Fla, 70, Que, 72 & Sahara, 73; vis prof, Arcetri Astrophys Observ, Italy, 69; lectr, Wright State Univ, 70-71; assoc dir, Aerospace Instrumentation Div ISA, 78-; instr physics, Sinclair Community Col, 80; vis astronomer, Kitt Peak Nat Observ, 81. *Mem:* Am Astron Soc; Am Phys Soc; sr mem Instrument Soc Am; Int Astron Union; fel Royal Astron Soc. *Res:* Rocket exhaust temperature measurement; ultra-high-speed photography; satellite photometry; photoelectric imaging devices; stellar spectroscopy in near infrared; solar eclipse observation; optical scattering; super luminous stars; Cepheid variables; laser systems. *Mailing Add:* 2202 N Malton Ave Simi Valley CA 93063

KISSEN, ABBOTT THEODORE, b New York, NY, Nov 24, 22; m 46; c 2. PHYSIOLOGY. *Educ:* Brooklyn Col, BA, 50; Ohio State Univ, MA, 52, PhD(zool), 56. *Prof Exp:* Res assoc physiol, Ohio State Univ, 57-59, asst prof, 59-61; RES PHYSIOLOGIST, AEROSPACE MED RES LAB, WRIGHT-PATTERSON AFB, 61- *Concurrent Pos:* Am Heart Asn fel, 57-58. *Mem:* Aerospace Med Asn; Am Physiol Soc. *Res:* Physiological effects of acceleration stresses encountered or anticipated in aerospace flight. *Mailing Add:* Aerospace Med Res Lab MEB Wright-Patterson AFB OH 45433

KISSICK, NORMAN LENNOX, b Toronto, Ont, Sept 5, 22; m 49; c 3. FOREST MANAGEMENT. *Educ:* Univ Toronto, BScF, 48; Yale Univ, MF, 51. *Prof Exp:* Forester res & mgt, Marathon Corp Can, 48-56; asst prof forestry & mgr univ forest, Univ Toronto, 56-61; PROF FORESTRY, UNIV NB, 61- *Mem:* Can Inst Forestry; Soc Am Foresters. *Res:* Forest management and land use planning; forest recreation. *Mailing Add:* Fac of Forestry Univ of NB Fredericton NB E3B 5A3 Can

KISSIN, BENJAMIN, b Philadelphia, Pa, July 17, 17; m 50; c 1. INTERNAL MEDICINE. *Educ:* Columbia Univ, BS, 38; Long Island Col Med, MD, 41; Am Bd Internal Med, dipl, 51. *Prof Exp:* Assoc prof, 60-68, dir div alcoholism & drug dependence, 70-81, PROF PSYCHIAT, STATE UNIV NY DOWNSTATE MED CTR, 68- *Concurrent Pos:* Dir alcohol clin, Kings County Hosp, 56-67, attend physician, 67-; dir psychosom clin & assoc physician med, Jewish Hosp, Brooklyn, 56-71, consult physician, 71-81. *Mem:* Am Psychosom Soc; Am Heart Asn; AMA; fel Am Col Physicians; NY Acad Sci. *Res:* Psychosomatic medicine, especially alcoholism; autonomic nervous system and the endocrines. *Mailing Add:* 450 Clarkson Ave State Univ NY Downstate Med Ctr Brooklyn NY 11203

KISSIN, G(ERALD) H(ARVEY), b New York, NY, May 7, 14; m 41; c 4. ELECTROCHEMISTRY, METALLURGY. *Educ:* City Col New York, BS, 35; Univ Mich, MS, 36, PhD(phys chem), 44. *Prof Exp:* Asst phys chem, Univ Mich, 35-37, asst electrochem, 37-39, asst metall, Sch Dent, 39-41; res assoc chem, Nat Defense Res Comt contract, Cornell Univ, 42; res engr, Am Smelting & Refining Co, NJ, 42-46; res asst prof chem eng, Ga Inst Technol, 46-48, res assoc prof, 48-49; chem eng consult, 49-50; head, Finishing & Electrochem Appln Br, Dept Metall Res, Kaiser Aluminum & Chem Corp, 50-62, tech asst to dir, 62-65, tech mgr, 65-68, mgr fabrication & appln res dept, Aluminum Div, 68-72, mgr appln res dept, Metals Div, Kaiser Aluminum & Chem Corp, 72-79; CONSULT METALL ENGR, 79- *Concurrent Pos:* US delegate, Ont Sci Orgn. *Mem:* Fel AAAS; Am Chem Soc; Electrochem Soc; Am Soc Metals; Am Electroplaters' Soc. *Res:* Raman spectroscopy; electrode potential phenomena; electrodeposition; dry battery technology; non-ferrous process metallurgy; electrolytic capacitors; finishing of aluminum; primary fabrication processes; corrosion. *Mailing Add:* PO Box 8606 Spokane WA 99203

KISSIN, STEPHEN ALEXANDER, b Ithaca, NY, Apr 11, 42; m 71; c 2. MINERALOGY, ECONOMIC GEOLOGY. *Educ:* Univ Wash, BS, 64; Pa State Univ, MS, 68; Univ Toronto, PhD(geol), 74. *Prof Exp:* Aerospace scientist, Goddard Space Flight Ctr, NASA, 67-68; engr, Siemens AG, WGer, 69; asst prof, 75-79, ASSOC PROF GEOL, LAKEHEAD UNIV, 79- *Concurrent Pos:* Nat Res Coun fel, Dept Energy, Mines & Resources, Ottawa, 74-75; vis res prof geol & chem, Ariz State Univ, 81-82; assoc, Comt Meteorites, Nat Sci & Eng Res Coun Can, 81- *Mem:* Geol Asn Can; Mineral Asn Can; Mineral Soc Am; AAAS; Meteoritical Soc. *Res:* Mineralogy and crystal chemistry of sulfides; genesis of ore deposits. *Mailing Add:* Dept of Geol Lakehead Univ Thunder Bay ON P7B 5E1 Can

KISSINGER, DAVID GEORGE, b Reading, Pa, July 26, 33; m 55; c 2. EPIDEMIOLOGY. *Educ:* Columbia Union Col, BA, 54; Univ Md, MS, 55, PhD(entom), 57; Univ Calif, MPH, 58. *Prof Exp:* Asst entom, Univ Md, 55-57; prof biol & head dept, Oakwood Col, 58-60; prof biol & head dept, Atlantic Union Col, 60-72; PROF EPIDEMIOL, LOMA LINDA UNIV, 72- *Concurrent Pos:* NIH fel, 74-76. *Mem:* Sigma Xi; Asn Comput Mach; AAAS. *Res:* Epidemiology of environmental determinants of cancer. *Mailing Add:* 11516 La Verne Ave Riverside CA 92505

KISSINGER, HOMER EVERETT, b Ottawa, Kans, Aug 29, 23; m 48; c 4. METAL PHYSICS. *Educ:* Kans State Col, BS, 49, MS, 50. *Prof Exp:* Phys sci aide, Nat Bur Standards, 48, physicist, 50-60; asst physics, Kans State Col, 49-50; sr scientist, Gen Elec Co, 60-65; sr res scientist, Pac Northwest Labs, Battelle Mem Inst, 65-71, SR RES SCIENTIST, BATTELLE-NORTHWEST, 71- *Mem:* Am Crystallog Asn; Sigma Xi. *Res:* Crystallography of radiation damage, phase transformations and x-ray diffraction methods; production and interaction of irradiation-induced point defects in metals. *Mailing Add:* 1733 Horn Ave Richland WA 99352

KISSINGER, JOHN CALVIN, b Shamokin, Pa, June 8, 25; m 50; c 2. MICROBIOLOGY. *Educ:* Bucknell Univ, BS, 49, MS, 50. *Prof Exp:* Chemist, Campbell Soup Co, 50-51; asst mgr biol standards, Sharp & Dohme, 53-55; supvr fermentation, Grain Processing Corp, 55-56; RES MICROBIOLOGIST, EASTERN REGIONAL RES CTR, USDA, 57- *Concurrent Pos:* Assoc, Nat Maple Syrup Coun, 67-75. *Honors & Awards:* Medal, Fedn Sewage & Indust Wastes Asn, 57. *Mem:* Fel Asn Off Anal Chem; Int Asn Milk, Food & Environ Sanit. *Res:* Industrial waste treatment; food microbiology; meat and meat products; maple products. *Mailing Add:* Meat Lab Eastern Regional Lab USDA 600 E Mermaid Lane Philadelphia PA 19118

KISSINGER, PAUL BERTRAM, b New York, NY, Mar 30, 30; m 57; c 2. MAGNETIC RESONANCE. *Educ:* Albright Col, BS, 52; Northwestern Univ, MS, 54; Rutgers Univ, PhD(physics), 61. *Prof Exp:* Physicist, Gen Elec Co, 56; instr physics, Rutgers Univ, 59-60; from asst prof to assoc prof, 60-70, assoc dir, Development Acad Progs, 73-74, PROF PHYSICS, DEPAUW UNIV, 70-, CHMN DEPT PHYSICS & ASTRON, 81- *Concurrent Pos:* Vis lectr, Univ Colo, 64; vis investr, Woods Hole Oceanog Inst, 67-68; NSF lectr, Munich, Ger, 68-69 & Lima, Peru, 70; physicist, Biol Warfare Labs, 54-56, res, 56-62; consult, Dept Defense Schs Europe, 77- *Mem:* AAAS; Am Asn Physics Teachers; Am Phys Soc; Sigma Xi. *Res:* Electron spin resonance; relaxation mechanisms. *Mailing Add:* Dept Physics DePauw Univ Greencastle IN 46135

KISSINGER, PETER THOMAS, b Staten Island, NY, Dec 19, 44; m 78; c 1. CHEMISTRY. *Educ:* Union Col, BS, 66; Univ NC, PhD(chem), 70. *Prof Exp:* Res assoc chem, Univ Kans, 70-72; asst prof chem, Mich State Univ, 72-75; asst prof, 75-76, assoc prof, 77-82, PROF CHEM, PURDUE UNIV, 82- *Concurrent Pos:* Pres, Bioanal Systs Inc, 74- *Mem:* Am Chem Soc; Am Asn Clin Chemists; AAAS; Am Asn Mass Spectrometry. *Res:* Trace organic analysis using chromatographic and electrochemical techniques; metabolic pathways of aromatic compounds; neurochemistry; organic redox reactions; chemical instrumentation. *Mailing Add:* Dept Chem Purdue Univ West Lafayette IN 47907

KISSLING, DON LESTER, b St Louis, Mo, Jan 29, 34; m 59; c 2. PALEOECOLOGY, SEDIMENTOLOGY. *Educ:* Mo Sch Mines, BS, 58; Univ Wis, MS, 60; Ind Univ, PhD(geol), 67. *Prof Exp:* Res geologist, Superior Oil Co, 60-62; from instr to assoc prof paleont, 65-74, ASSOC PROF GEOL, STATE UNIV NY BINGHAMTON, 74- *Mem:* Geol Soc Am; Soc Econ Paleontologists & Mineralogists; Paleont Soc. *Res:* Paleoecology of Paleozoic corals and biohermal fossil assemblages; ecology of modern corals; Paleozoic sedimentary environments and recent carbonate sediments. *Mailing Add:* Dept of Geol State Univ of NY Binghamton NY 13901

KISSLINGER, CARL, b St Louis, Mo, Aug 30, 26; m 48; c 5. GEOPHYSICS. *Educ:* St Louis Univ, BS, 47, MS, 49, PhD(geophys), 52. *Prof Exp:* From instr to prof geophys & geophys eng, St Louis Univ, 49-72, chmn dept earth & atmospheric sci, 63-72; dir, Coop Inst Res Environ Sci, 72-79, PROF GEOL SCI, UNIV COLO, BOULDER, 72- *Concurrent Pos:* UNESCO expert in seismol & chief tech adv, Int Inst Seismol & Earthquake Eng, Tokyo, 66-67; consult, US Dept Energy, 69-; chmn comt seismol, Nat Acad Sci-Nat Res Coun, 70-72, mem US Geodynamics Comt, 75-78; mem earth sci adv panel, NSF, 71-74; mem, US nat comt, Int Union Geod & Geophys, 74-, mem bur, 75-; mem earthquake hazards reduction adv group, Off Sci Technol Policy, 77-78; mem earthquake studies adv panel, US Geol Surv, 77-, chmn, 81-; mem comt scholarly communication with People's Repub China, Nat Acad Sci, 78-; Alexander von Humboldt Found US sr scientist award, 79. *Mem:* Fel AAAS; Soc Explor Geophys; Seismol Soc Am (pres, 72-73); fel Am Geophys Union (foreign secy, 74-); fel Geol Soc Am. *Res:* Generation of seismic waves by explosions and earthquakes; propagation of elastic waves in layered systems; earthquake prediction. *Mailing Add:* Coop Inst for Res in Environ Sci Univ of Colo Boulder CO 80302

KISSLINGER, FRED, b St Louis, Mo, Nov 19, 19; m 45; c 3. METALLURGICAL ENGINEERING. *Educ:* Mo Sch Mines, BS, 42; Univ Cincinnati, MS, 45, PhD(metall eng), 47. *Prof Exp:* From instr to assoc prof metall eng, Ill Inst Technol, 47-64; assoc prof, 64-69, PROF METALL ENG, UNIV MO-ROLLA, 69-; PARTNER, ASKELAND, KISSLINGER & WOLF, METALL ENG CONSULTS, 73- *Mem:* Am Soc Metals; Am Inst Mining, Metall & Petrol Engrs. *Res:* Thermodynamics; heat treating. *Mailing Add:* Dept of Metall Eng Univ of Mo Rolla MO 65401

KISSLINGER, LEONARD SOL, b St Louis, Mo, Aug 15, 30; m 56. THEORETICAL PHYSICS. *Educ:* St Louis Univ, BS, 51; Ind Univ, MS, 52, PhD(physics), 56. *Prof Exp:* From instr to prof physics, Case Western Reserve Univ, 56-68; PROF PHYSICS, CARNEGIE-MELLON UNIV, 68- *Concurrent Pos:* Res Corp fel, Bohr Inst, Copenhagen, Denmark, 58-59; res assoc, Mass Inst Technol, 66-67; vis staff mem, Los Alamos Sci Lab, 69- *Mem:* Am Phys Soc. *Res:* Nuclear models and structure; many-body problem; particle physics. *Mailing Add:* Dept of Physics Carnegie-Mellon Univ Pittsburgh PA 15213

KISSMAN, HENRY MARCEL, b Graz, Austria, Sept 9, 22; nat US; m 56; c 2. ORGANIC CHEMISTRY, COMPUTER SCIENCES. *Educ:* Sterling Col, BS, 44; Univ Cincinnati, MS, 48; Univ Rochester, PhD(org chem), 50. *Prof Exp:* Sr asst scientist org chem, NIH, 50-52; res chemist, Lederle Labs Div, Am Cyanamid Co, 52-62, dept head tech info, 62-67; dir sci info facility, US Food & Drug Admin, DC, 67-70; ASSOC DIR SPECIALIZED INFO SERVS, US NAT LIBR MED, 70- *Concurrent Pos:* Chmn comt study environ qual info progs in fed govt, Off Sci & Technol; mem adv bd, Chem Abstr Serv, 74-77; chmn, Toxicol Info Subcomt, US Dept Health, Educ & Welfare, 73- *Honors & Awards:* Super Serv Award, US Dept Health, Educ & Welfare, 73. *Mem:* AAAS; Am Chem Soc; Am Soc Info Sci; Soc Toxicol; Drug Info Asn. *Res:* Ethylenimine chemistry; amino acids; carbohydrates; nucleosides; steroids; tetracyclines; chemical documentation. *Mailing Add:* Specialized Info Serv Nat Libr Med 8600 Rockville Pike Bethesda MD 20209

KISSMEYER-NIELSEN, ERIK, b Silkeborg, Denmark, Oct 22, 22; m 62; c 2. FOOD SCIENCE, BOTANY. *Educ:* Royal Vet & Agr Col, Copenhagen, BS, 48; Cornell Univ, MS, 60; Univ Wis, PhD(food sci), 64. *Prof Exp:* Trainee food technol, Am Scand Soc, 48-50; inspector, R T French Co, NY, 50-53; asst mgr, Grimstrup Coop Starch & Dehydration Plant, Denmark, 53-58; asst food sci, Cornell Univ, 58-60 & Univ Wis, 60-63; asst prof biochem & food sci, Univ Del, 63-66; INT ADV, AGR & FOOD INDUST, 66- *Concurrent Pos:* Agr & food indust adv, UN Indust Develop Orgn & World Bank, 70-73; regional agr & food indust adv, UN Econ Comn for Africa, 73-75. *Mem:* Fel AAAS; Inst Food Technologists; Am Inst Biol Sci; Am Chem Soc; Am Potato Asn. *Mailing Add:* 65 Crabtree Rd Concord MA 01742

KIST, JOSEPH EDMUND, b Buffalo, NY, Aug 11, 29; m 69; c 1. MATHEMATICS. *Educ:* Univ Buffalo, BA, 52; Purdue Univ, MS, 54, PhD(math), 57. *Prof Exp:* Instr math, Purdue Univ, 57; asst prof, Wayne State Univ, 57-59 & Pa State Univ, 59-62; vis assoc prof, Purdue Univ, 62-63; assoc prof, Pa State Univ, 63-66; assoc prof, 66-67, PROF MATH, N MEX STATE UNIV, 67- *Mem:* Fel AAAS; Am Math Soc; Math Asn Am. *Res:* Functional analysis; lattices; semigroups. *Mailing Add:* Dept of Math NMex State Univ Las Cruces NM 88003

KISTER, JAMES MILTON, b Cleveland, Ohio, June 29, 30; m 56, 78; c 1. MATHEMATICS. *Educ:* Wooster Col, AB, 52; Univ Wis, AM, 56, PhD, 59. *Prof Exp:* Res asst, Los Alamos Sci Lab, 53-55; instr, 59-60, asst prof, 61-62, assoc prof, 64-66, chmn dept, 71-73, PROF MATH, UNIV MICH, ANN ARBOR, 66- *Concurrent Pos:* Fel, Off Naval Res, Va, 60-61; mem, Inst Advan Study, 62-64; vis prof, Univ Calif, Los Angeles, 67; vis fel, Clare Hall, Cambridge Univ, Eng, 70; vis mem, Institut des Hautes Etudes, France, 74; vis fel Wolfson Col, Oxford Univ, Eng, 77; ed, Duke Math J, 72-75; ed, Mich Math J, 76-78, managing ed, 77-78. *Mem:* Am Math Soc. *Res:* Topology; isotopies; transformation groups; manifolds. *Mailing Add:* Dept of Math Univ of Mich Ann Arbor MI 48104

KISTIAKOWSKY, GEORGE BOGDAN, b Kiev, Russia, Nov 18, 00; nat US; m 26, 45; c 1. PHYSICAL CHEMISTRY. *Educ:* Univ Berlin, DrPhil(chem), 25. *Hon Degrees:* DSc, Harvard Univ, 55, Williams Col, 58, Oxford Univ, 59, Univ Pa, 60, Univ Rochester, 60, Carnegie Inst Technol, 61, Princeton Univ, 62, Case Western Reserve Univ, 62, Columbia Univ, 67. *Prof Exp:* Int Ed Bd fel phys chem, Princeton Univ, 26-28, res assoc, 28-30; from asst prof to assoc prof, 30-37, prof, 37-71, EMER PROF CHEM, HARVARD UNIV, 71- *Concurrent Pos:* Spec asst sci & technol to President, DC, 59-61. *Honors & Awards:* Medal for Merit, 46; King's Medal for Serv, 47; Nichols Medal, Am Chem Soc, 47, Gibbs Medal, 60, Parsons Award, 61, Marshall Award, 63, Richards Medal & Debye Award, 68, Priestley Medal, 72; Priestley Award, Dickinson Col, 58; Medal of Freedom, 61; Ledlie Prize, Harvard Univ, 61; Lewis Medal, 62; Nat Medal Sci, 65; Franklin Medal, Franklin Inst, 72. *Mem:* Nat Acad Sci (vpres, 65-71); Am Chem Soc; Am Phys Soc; Am Philos Soc; hon fel Royal Soc Chem. *Res:* Chemical kinetics; thermodynamics of organic molecules; molecular spectroscopy; shock and detonation waves. *Mailing Add:* 12 Oxford St Cambridge MA 02138

KISTIAKOWSKY, VERA, b Princeton, NJ, Sept 9, 28; div; c 2. ELEMENTARY PARTICLE PHYSICS. *Educ:* Mt Holyoke Col, AB, 48; Univ Calif, PhD(chem), 52. *Hon Degrees:* DSc, Mt Holyoke Col, 78. *Prof Exp:* Scientist, US Naval Radiol Defense Lab, 52-53; Berliner fel physics, Radiation Lab, Univ Calif, 53-54; res assoc, Columbia Univ, 54-57, instr, 57-59; from asst prof to adj assoc prof, Brandeis Univ, 59-65; scientist, Lab Nuclear Sci, 65-69, sr res scientist dept physics, 69-72, PROF PHYSICS, MASS INST TECHNOL, 72- *Mem:* AAAS; fel Am Phys Soc; Asn Women Sci (pres, 82-84). *Res:* Experimental high energy elementary particle physics. *Mailing Add:* 411 575 Technol Sq Mass Inst Technol Cambridge MA 02139

KISTLER, ALAN L(EE), b Laramie, Wyo, Nov 26, 28; m 55; c 3. FLUID DYNAMICS. *Educ:* Johns Hopkins Univ, BE, 50, MS, 52, PhD(aeronaut), 55. *Prof Exp:* Res group supvr, Jet Propulsion Lab, Calif Inst Technol, 57-61; assoc prof, Yale Univ, 61-65; fluid physics sect mgr, Jet Propulsion Lab, Calif Inst Technol, 65-69; PROF MECH ENG & ASTRONAUT, TECHNOL INST, NORTHWESTERN UNIV, EVANSTON, 69- *Mem:* Am Phys Soc; Am Soc Mech Engrs; AAAS. *Res:* Diffusion in turbulent flow fields; turbulence in compressible media; mechanics of wakes and separated flows. *Mailing Add:* Dept Mech & Nuclear Eng Northwestern Univ Evanston IL 60201

KISTLER, RONALD WAYNE, b Chicago, Ill, May 18, 31; m 57; c 2. GEOLOGY. *Educ:* Johns Hopkins Univ, BA, 53; Univ Calif, Berkeley, PhD(geol), 60. *Prof Exp:* GEOLOGIST, US GEOL SURV, 60- *Concurrent Pos:* Vis prof, Northwestern Univ, 71. *Mem:* AAAS; Geol Soc Am; Am Geophys Union. *Res:* Structural geology; geochronology. *Mailing Add:* US Geol Surv 345 Middlefield Rd Menlo Park CA 94025

KISTLER, WILSON STEPHEN, JR, b Newport News, Va, Mar 1, 42. BIOCHEMISTRY, REPRODUCTIVE BIOLOGY. *Educ:* Princeton Univ, AB, 64; Harvard Univ, PhD(biochem), 70. *Prof Exp:* Res assoc, Dept Microbiol & Molecular Genetics, Sch Med, Harvard Univ, 70-71, Ben May Lab Cancer Res, Univ Chicago, 71-75; asst prof, 75-80, ASSOC PROF CHEM, UNIV SC, 80- *Mem:* Am Soc Biol Chemists; Am Chem Soc. *Res:* Study of changes in basic nuclear proteins accompanying mammalian spermatogenesis and the regulation of protein synthesis by androgenic steroid hormones. *Mailing Add:* Dept of Chem Univ of SC Columbia SC 29208

KISTNER, CLIFFORD RICHARD, b Cincinnati, Ohio, Dec 16, 36; m 61. INORGANIC CHEMISTRY. *Educ:* Carthage Col, AB, 59; Univ Iowa, MS, 62, PhD(chem), 63. *Prof Exp:* Instr chem, Univ Iowa, 63, asst prof, 63-64; from asst prof to assoc prof, 64-68, PROF CHEM & CHMN DEPT, UNIV WIS-LA CROSSE, 68- *Mem:* AAAS; Am Chem Soc. *Res:* Inorganic coordination chemistry. *Mailing Add:* Dept of Chem Univ of Wis La Crosse WI 54601

KISTNER, DAVID HAROLD, b Cincinnati, Ohio, July 30, 31; m 57; c 2. ENTOMOLOGY. *Educ:* Univ Chicago, AB, 52, SB, 56, PhD(zool), 57. *Prof Exp:* Asst termites, Univ Chicago, 53-54, asst comp anat, 55, field zoologist comp anat & arthropods, 56-57; instr biol, Univ Rochester, 57-59; instr, 59-60, from asst prof to assoc prof, 60-67, PROF BIOL, CALIF STATE UNIV, CHICO, 67- *Concurrent Pos:* NSF grants, 58-59, 60-71 & 72-83; Guggenheim Mem Found fel, 65-66; hon res assoc, Div Insects, Field Mus Natural Hist, Chicago, 67 & Atlantica Ecol Res Sta, Rhodesia; dir, Shinner Inst Study Interrelated Insects, 68-72. *Mem:* AAAS; Entom Soc Am; Soc Study Evolution; Soc Syst Zool; Am Soc Zool. *Res:* Systematics, evolution; zoogeography and behavior of myrmecophilous and termitophilous insects; systematics of Staphylinidae. *Mailing Add:* Dept of Biol (515) Calif State Univ Chico CA 95929

KISTNER, OTTMAR CASPER, b New York, NY, Mar 22, 30; m 59; c 3. NUCLEAR PHYSICS. *Educ:* Polytech Inst Brooklyn, BS, 52; Columbia Univ, PhD(physics), 59. *Prof Exp:* Asst physicist, 59-63, assoc physicist, 63-66, PHYSICIST, BROOKHAVEN NAT LAB, 66- *Concurrent Pos:* Guest physicist, Max Planck Inst Nuclear Physics, 69-70, Weizmann Inst Sci, 80. *Mem:* Sigma Xi; fel Am Phys Soc. *Res:* Experimental nuclear physics; nuclear structure and hyperfine interactions by beta and gamma ray spectroscopy; on line spectroscopy with heavy ion reactions; Mossbauer effect. *Mailing Add:* Physics Dept Brookhaven Nat Lab Upton NY 11973

KISVARSANYI, EVA BOGNAR, b Budapest, Hungary; US citizen. GEOLOGY, PETROLOGY. *Educ:* Univ Mo-Rolla, BS, 58, MS, 60. *Prof Exp:* RES GEOLOGIST, MO DEPT NATURAL RESOURCES, GEOL SURV, 59- *Concurrent Pos:* Mem, Working Group Precambrian Correlation Cent Interior Region US, Int Union Geol Sci, 76- *Mem:* Mineral Soc Am; Geol Soc Am. *Res:* Precambrian geology of the St Francois Mountains and vicinity in southeast Missouri; geology and structure of buried Precambrian basement, midcontinent region; mineral resources of Missouri. *Mailing Add:* Mo Dept of Natural Resources PO Box 250 Rolla MO 65401

KISVARSANYI, GEZA, b Tokay, Hungary, Feb 23, 26; US citizen; m 56; c 1. ECONOMIC GEOLOGY. *Educ:* Eotvos Lorand, Budapest, MS, 52; Univ Mo, Rolla, PhD(geol), 66. *Prof Exp:* Asst prof geol, Eotvos Lorand, Budapest, 52-55; chief geologist, Ore Mining & Develop Co, Hungary, 55-56; explor geologist, Bear Creek Mining Co Div, Kennecott Copper Corp, 57-62; instr, 62-66, asst prof, 66-68, assoc prof, 68-81, PROF GEOL, UNIV MO, ROLLA, 81- *Mem:* Geol Soc Am; Soc Econ Geol; Am Inst Mining, Metall & Petrol Eng; Soc Geol Appl to Mineral Deposits. *Res:* Hydrothermal ore deposits; Mississippi Valley-type lead-zinc deposits; iron-titanium ore deposits; astrogeology; geotectonics of the midcontinent; remote sensing, radar, landsat, of geologic structures, precious and base metal deposits, prophyry copper and molybdenum deposits. *Mailing Add:* Dept Geol & Geophys Univ Mo Rolla MO 65401

KISZENICK, WALTER, b New York, NY, Apr 1, 18; m 43; c 2. PHYSICS, ELECTRICAL ENGINEERING. *Educ:* Brooklyn Col, BA, 39; Polytech Inst Brooklyn, MS, 47, PhD(physics), 54. *Prof Exp:* Jr metallurgist, NY Naval Shipyard, 41-43; jr scientist, Los Alamos Sci Lab, 44-46; res asst phosphors, Polytech Inst Brooklyn, 46-52; physicist, Freed Radio Co, 52-53; from instr to asst prof physics, 53-64, ASSOC PROF PHYSICS & NUCLEAR ENG, POLYTECH INST NY, 62- *Mem:* Am Phys Soc; Electron Micros Soc Am. *Res:* Dielectric properties of phosphors; physical properties of ice. *Mailing Add:* Dept of Physics Polytech Inst of NY Brooklyn NY 11201

KISZKISS, DAVID F, immunology, see previous edition

KIT, SAUL, b Passaic, NJ, Nov 25, 20; m 45; c 3. BIOCHEMISTRY, CANCER. *Educ:* Univ Calif, AB, 48, PhD(biochem), 51. *Prof Exp:* Nat Cancer Inst fel biochem, Chicago, 51-52, Nat Found Infantile Paralysis fel, 52; res biochemist, Univ Tex M D Anderson Hosp & Tumor Inst, 53-55; asst prof biochem, Col Med, Baylor Univ, 56-57; from asst prof to assoc prof, Post-Grad Sch Med, Univ Tex, 57-61; vis prof virol, 62, PROF BIOCHEM & HEAD DIV BIOCHEM VIROL, BAYLOR COL MED, 62- *Concurrent Pos:* Assoc biochemist, Univ Tex M D Anderson Hosp & Tumor Inst, 57-60, biochemist & chief Sect Nucleoprotein Metab, 61-62; Nat Inst Arthritis & Infectious Dis res cancer award, 63-; mem cancer virol panel, USPHS, 61-62, consult, 71-; chairperson, Pathobiol Chem Study Sect, NIH, 75-79. *Mem:* Am Soc Biol Chemists; Am Soc Cell Biol (treas, 65-67, pres, 71); Am Chem Soc; Am Asn Cancer Res; Am Soc Microbiol. *Res:* Molecular biology; biochemical virology; biochemistry of cancer; nucleic acids. *Mailing Add:* Div of Biochem Virol Baylor Col of Med Houston TX 77030

KITA, DONALD ALBERT, b Fish Creek, Wis, Aug 16, 24. BIOCHEMISTRY. *Educ:* Univ Wis, BS, 44, MS, 50, PhD(biochem), 51. *Prof Exp:* Anal chemist, Gen Chem Co, 48; res biochemist, Chas Pfizer & Co, Inc, 51-71, sr biochemist, 71-73, SR RES INVESTR, PFIZER INC, 73-, RES ADV, 79- *Mem:* Am Chem Soc; Soc Indust Microbiol. *Res:* Fermentation research of steroids, amino and organic acids; clinical chemistry; diagnostics. *Mailing Add:* Pfizer Inc Groton CT 06340

KITABCHI, ABBAS E, b Tehran, Iran, Aug 28, 33; US citizen; m 57; c 3. BIOCHEMISTRY, ENDOCRINOLOGY. *Educ:* Cornell Col, BA, 54; Univ Okla, MS, 56, PhD(med sci), 58, MD, 65. *Prof Exp:* Res assoc biochem, Okla Med Res Found, 60-61, biochemist, 61-65, sr investr, 65-66; instr med, Univ Wash, 66-68; from asst prof to assoc prof med, 68-73, assoc prof biochem, 68-73, PROF MED & BIOCHEM, UNIV TENN CTR FOR HEALTH SCI, 73-, CHIEF DIV ENDOCRINOL & METAB & DIR CLIN RES CTR, 73- *Concurrent Pos:* Fel biochem, Okla Med Res Found, 58-60; NIH spec fel endocrinol, Univ Wash, 66-68; assoc chief staff res & chief endocrinol & metab labs, Vet Admin Hosp, 68-73, assoc chief metab, Med Serv, 73- *Mem:* Fel Am Col Physicians; Am Chem Soc; Am Fedn Clin Res; Am Diabetes Asn; Endocrine Soc. *Res:* Mechanism of action of adrenocorticotropic hormones, glucocorticoids and insulin at molecular level. *Mailing Add:* Univ of Tenn Ctr Health Sci 951 Court Ave Memphis TN 38163

KITAI, REUVEN, b Johannesburg, SAfrica, Oct 4, 24; m 52; c 3. ELECTRICAL ENGINEERING. *Educ:* Univ Witwatersrand, BSc, 44, MSc, 48, DSc(elec eng), 62. *Prof Exp:* Lectr elec eng, Univ Witwatersrand, 47-55, sr lectr, 55-64; assoc prof, 65-66, PROF ELEC ENG, McMASTER UNIV, 66- *Concurrent Pos:* Vis lectr, Eng Labs, Cambridge Univ, 53-54 & Dept Elec Eng, Imp Col, Univ London, 61-62; vis res officer, Standard Telecommun Labs, Ltd, Eng, 61 & Brown Boveri Co, Switz, 77. *Mem:* Sr mem Inst Elec & Electronics Engrs; fel Brit Inst Elec Engrs. *Res:* Instrumentation. *Mailing Add:* Dept of Elec Eng McMaster Univ Hamilton ON L8S 4L8 Can

KITAIGORODSKII, SERGEI ALEXANDER, b Moscow, USSR, Sept 13, 34; m 69; c 2. PHYSICAL OCEANOGRAPHY. *Educ:* Inst Physics Atmosphere Acad Sci, USSR, PhD(geophysics), 60; Inst Oceanology Acad Sci, DSc, 68. *Prof Exp:* Head lab res, Inst Oceanog Acad Sci, USSR, 68-78; LECTR, INST PHYS OCEANOG UNIV COPENHAGEN, 79-; PROF OCEANOG, DEPT EARTH & PLANETARY SCI, JOHNS HOPKINS UNIV, 80- *Res:* Oceanic turbulence and its modelling; physics of air-sea interaction; wave motions in the ocean; geophysical fluid dynamics. *Mailing Add:* Dept Earth & Planetary Sci Johns Hopkins Univ Baltimore MD 21218

KITAY, JULIAN ISRAEL, b Kearny, NJ, Aug 29, 27; m 73; c 2. INTERNAL MEDICINE, PHYSIOLOGY. *Educ:* Princeton Univ, AB, 49; Harvard Med Sch, MD, 54. *Prof Exp:* Intern med, Grace-New Haven Hosp, Conn, 54-55; asst resident, Beth Israel Hosp, Mass, 55-56; instr, Col Physicians & Surgeons, Columbia Univ, 58-59; from asst prof to assoc prof internal med, 59-70, from asst prof to assoc prof physiol, 61-70, prof internal med & physiol, Sch Med, Univ VA, 70-78; ASSOC DEAN FOR CURRICULAR AFFAIRS & PROF INTERNAL MED, PHYSIOL & BIOPHYSICS, UNIV TEX MED BR, GALVESTON, TEX, 78- *Concurrent Pos:* Commonwealth Fund fel, Col Physicians & Surgeons, Columbia Univ, 56-58; USPHS res career develop award, 61-70; asst physician, Med Serv, Presby Hosp, NY, 58-59; attend physician, Univ Hosp, Univ Va, 59-78, head div endocrinol & metab, Dept Internal Med, 70-78; mem neuroendocrinol panel, Int Brain Res Orgn. *Mem:* Endocrine Soc; Am Fedn Clin Res; Am Soc Clin Invest; Am Physiol Soc; Soc Exp Biol & Med. *Res:* Endocrine physiology; clinical aspects of endocrine disease. *Mailing Add:* Off Dean Med Univ of Tex Med Br Galveston TX 77550

KITAZAWA, GEORGE, b San Jose, Calif, May 2, 17; m 43; c 3. CHEMISTRY, WOOD SCIENCE. *Educ:* Univ Calif, BS, 40; State Univ NY, MS, 44, PhD(wood technol), 47. *Prof Exp:* Technician, Guayule Rubber Res, War Relocation Auth, Calif, 42-43; indust res fel, State Univ NY Col Forestry, Syracuse, 44-47; res wood technologist, Casein Co Am, NY, 47; wood technologist, Timber Eng Co, 47-50; res assoc, State Univ NY Col Forestry, Syracuse, 50-53; res physicist, Gillette Safety Razor Co, 53-56; group leader, Cent Res Lab, Borden Chem Co, Philadelphia, 56-57, asst lab head, 57-59, lab head, 59-73; mgr res dept, Wood Sci Group, 73-78, mgr forest prod group, forest prod res sect, 78-80, CONSULT & TECH INTERPRETER, KOPPERS CO, 80- *Concurrent Pos:* Tech liasion hydrostatic pipe tester & coke oven mach for steel indust. *Mem:* AAAS; Am Chem Soc; Soc Wood Sci & Technol; Forest Prod Res Soc; Soc Am Foresters. *Res:* Wood preservatives and fire retardants; polymer characterization; analytical chemistry; adhesives; instrumentation; sonic and ultrasonic non-destructive testing; surface chemistry and physics; wood physics; steel industry machinery. *Mailing Add:* 926 Harvard Rd Monroeville PA 15146

KITCHELL, JAMES FREDERICK, b Gary, Ind, July 20, 42; m 77; c 2. AQUATIC ECOLOGY, BIOENERGETICS. *Educ:* Ball State Teachers Col, BS, 64; Univ Colo, PhD(biol), 70. *Prof Exp:* Proj assoc ecol, Inst Environ Studies, 70-72, asst scientist, 72-74, asst prof zool, 74-77, ASSOC PROF ZOOL, UNIV WIS-MADISON, 77- *Concurrent Pos:* Scientist, Smithsonian Inst Proj, Skadar Lake, Yugoslavia, 72-77; vis scientist, Nat Marine Fisheries Serv, Honolulu, 73-78. *Mem:* Am Fisheries Soc; Ecol Soc Am; Int Soc Limnol; AAAS; Am Inst Biol Sci. *Res:* Application of ecosystem models; predator-prey interactions; trophic ecology. *Mailing Add:* Lab of Limnol Univ of Wis Madison WI 53706

KITCHELL, JENNIFER ANN, b Zanesville, Ohio, May 25, 45. PALEOBIOLOGY, EVOLUTIONARY THEORY. *Educ:* Univ Wis, BS, 68, MS, 71, PhD(geol), 78. *Prof Exp:* res assoc, 78-80, ASST SCIENTIST GEOL & ZOOL, UNIV WIS-MADISON, 80- *Mem:* Sigma Xi; Soc Econ Paleontologists & Mineralogists; Soc Oceanog & Limnol; Paleont Soc; Geol Soc Am. *Res:* Paleobiology; coevolution; taxonomic diversification; predator-prey interactions; siliceous sedimentation; paleolimnological studies of predator-prey interactions. *Mailing Add:* Dept of Geol & Geophys Univ of Wis Madison WI 53706

KITCHELL, RALPH LLOYD, b Waukee, Iowa, July 9, 19; m 47; c 3. VETERINARY ANATOMY. *Educ:* Iowa State Univ, DVM, 43; Univ Minn, PhD(human anat), 51. *Prof Exp:* Instr vet bact, Kans State Col, 43; instr vet med, Univ Minn, St Paul, 47-51, from assoc prof to prof vet anat, 51-64, head dept, 51-64; dean vet med, Kans State Univ, 64-66; prof vet anat, Iowa State Univ, 66-72, dean col vet med & dir vet med res inst, 66-71; PROF VET ANAT, SCH VET MED, UNIV CALIF, DAVIS, 72- *Concurrent Pos:* USPHS res fel, Sweden & Eng, 57-58; vis prof, Sch Vet Med, Univ Calif, Davis, 71-72; res fel & vis prof, Royal Vet Col, Edinburgh, Scotland, 76. *Mem:* Am Asn Anatomists; Am Vet Med Asn; Am Asn Vet Anat (secy, 51, pres, 54). *Res:* Veterinary neuroanatomy; sexual and fetal physiology; somatosensory physiology. *Mailing Add:* Dept of Anat Univ of Calif Sch of Vet Med Davis CA 95616

KITCHEN, HYRAM, b Oakland, Calif, Sept 24, 32; m 58; c 2. BIOCHEMISTRY, HEMATOLOGY. *Educ:* Univ Calif, Davis, BS, 54, DVM, 56; Univ Fla, PhD(biochem), 65. *Prof Exp:* Res large animal med & surg, Univ Calif, Davis, 56-57; private practice, Alta View Animal Hosp, Los Altos, Calif, 57-58; NIH fel cardiol, Col Med, Univ Fla, 63-65, instr biochem & med, 65-66, asst prof, 66-69; assoc prof biochem & asst dir ctr lab animal resources, Mich State Univ, 69-73, prof biochem & assoc dir ctr lab animal resources, 73-75, dir res comp med, 69-75, actg dir ctr lab animal resources, 74-75; head dept environ pract, 75-79, PROF, COL VET MED, UNIV TENN, 75-, DEAN, 79- *Concurrent Pos:* NIH career develop award, 66-71; mem exec comt sci adv coun, NIH Animal Resources, Inst Lab Animal Resources. *Mem:* AAAS; Conf Res Workers Animal Dis; Wildlife Dis Asn; Am Vet Med Asn; Am Soc Biol Chem. *Res:* Comparative structure of animal hemoglobins; control of biosynthesis of hemoglobins; comparative hematology and medicine. *Mailing Add:* Col of Vet Med Univ of Tenn Knoxville TN 37916

KITCHEN, JOSEPH HENRY, b Eureka, Nev, Oct 22, 35; c 2. WATERSHED MANAGEMENT. *Educ:* Ariz State Univ, BS, 64; Univ Ariz, MS, 66, PhD(watershed mgt), 71. *Prof Exp:* Res assoc, Dept Watershed Mgt, Univ Ariz, 64-71; hydrologist, Lockheed Electronics Co, 71-73; hydrologist, US Army Tropic Test Ctr, 73-75; opers res analyst, US Army Communications Command, 75-77; HYDROL ENGR, BUR RECLAMATION, BOULDER CITY, NEV, 77- *Res:* Techniques using gamma radiation in jungle vegetation measurements; modeling parts of the Colorado River and Lake Mead in the Lower Colorado River Basin; modeled Army tactical communications systems to satisfy wartime requirements in the 1980-1990 time frame; integration of a solar powerplant with the federal hydroelectric system in the southwest. *Mailing Add:* 396 El Camino Way Boulder City NV 89005

KITCHEN, LELAND JOSEPH, b Sentinel Butte, NDak, Feb 12, 17; m 43; c 3. CHEMISTRY. *Educ:* Univ Fla, BS, 39, PhD(chem), 43. *Prof Exp:* Asst chem, Univ Fla, 39-43; res chemist, Nelio Resin Processing Corp, Fla, 40-42; org res chemist, Firestone Tire & Rubber Co, 43-52, res admin asst, 52-61; chem indust specialist, 61-64, investment officer, 64-66, second vpres, 66-73, tech dir, 73-76, VPRES & TECH DIR, CHASE MANHATTEN BANK, 76- *Mem:* AAAS; Am Chem Soc; Am Soc Microbiol; Inst Chartered Financial Anal. *Res:* Chemistry of piperazine, amino alcohols, and terpenes; nondiscoloring antioxidants for rubber; synthetic rubber monomers. *Mailing Add:* 180 Woodland Ave Summit NJ 07901

KITCHEN, SUMNER WENDELL, b Somerville, Mass, Sept 17, 21. NUCLEAR SCIENCE, NUCLEAR ENGINEERING. *Educ:* Oberlin Col, BA, 43; NY Univ, PhD(physics), 51. *Prof Exp:* Physicist physics of metals, Frankford Arsenal, 43-46; instr physics, NY Univ, 46-50; group leader accelerator design, E O Lawrence Radiation Lab, 50-54; res assoc reactors physics, 54-56, mgr, 56-78, SR PHYSICIST REACTOR PHYSICS, KNOLLS ATOMIC POWER LAB, 78- *Concurrent Pos:* Consult, Res & Develop Coun, Dept Defense, 48-49. *Mem:* Am Phys Soc; Am Nuclear Soc; NY Acad Sci. *Res:* Reactor and criticality safety; reactor physics; gas discharges; accelerators. *Mailing Add:* Knolls Atomic Power Lab PO Box 1072 Schenectady NY 12301

KITCHENS, CLARENCE WESLEY, JR, b Panama City, Fla, Nov 8, 43; m 66; c 2. ENGINEERING MECHANICS, APPLIED MATHEMATICS. *Educ:* Va Polytech Inst & State Univ, BS, 66, MS, 68; NC State Univ, PhD(eng mech), 70. *Prof Exp:* Eng asst, Atlantic Res Corp, Va, 62-65; res engr, Aberdeen Res & Develop Ctr, 70-72, aerospace engr, 72-77, asst to dir, 77-78, leader fluid dynamics anal team, 78-80, CHIEF, BLAST DYNAMICS BR, US ARMY BALLISTIC RES LAB, 80- *Concurrent Pos:* Fel US Army Ballistic Res Lab. *Mem:* Assoc fel Am Inst Aeronaut & Astronaut. *Res:* Numerical computations in gas dynamics; experimental techniques in fluid dynamics; numerical analysis; computer applications in engineering; blast loading and response; flight mechanics. *Mailing Add:* Blast Dynamics Br Ballistic Res Lab Aberdeen Proving Ground MD 21005

KITCHENS, THOMAS ADREN, b Amarillo, Tex, Oct 31, 35; m 76; c 2. CONDENSED MATTER PHYSICS. *Educ:* Rice Inst, BA, 58; Rice Univ, MA, 60, PhD(physics), 63. *Prof Exp:* Staff mem physics, Los Alamos Sci Lab, 63-65; physicist, Brookhaven Nat Lab, 65-75; liaison physicist, Off Naval Res, London, 75-76; alternate group leader, Los Alamos Sci Lab, 76-80, group leader physics, 78-80; staff assoc, Div Mat Res, NSF, 80-82; STAFF MEM PHYSICS, LOS ALAMOS NAT LAB, 82- *Concurrent Pos:* Sci Res Coun Great Brit sr res fel, Univ Sussex, 70-71. *Mem:* Fel Inst Physics UK; fel Am Inst Physics; Asn Comput Mach; AAAS. *Res:* Low and ultralow temperature physics and condensed matter research utilizing neutron and light scattering. *Mailing Add:* Physics Dept Los Alamos Nat Lab Los Alamos NM 87545

KITCHIN, IRWIN CLARK, b Scotland Neck, NC, Sept 6, 11. EMBRYOLOGY. *Educ:* Wake Forest Col, BS, 41; Univ Freiburg, PhD, 35. *Prof Exp:* Seessel res fel, Yale Univ, 35-36; instr biol, Rice Univ, 36-39; from asst prof to assoc prof zool, Univ NC, 39-42; assoc prof biol, Univ Ga, 46-51; chmn dept, 51-73, prof, 51-81, EMER PROF BIOL, UNIV MISS, 81- *Res:* Artificial development of duplicitas cruciata in amphibians; embryonic functions of notochord; gastrulation in turtles; effects of contiguous tissues on development of isolated explants of central nervous system in amphibians. *Mailing Add:* Dept of Biol Univ of Miss University MS 38677

KITCHIN, JOHN FRANCIS, b Greenwood, Miss, May 6, 53. RELIABILITY & LIFE TESTING. *Educ:* Univ Southern Miss, BS, 76; Fla State Univ, MS, 78, PhD(statist), 80. *Prof Exp:* Asst prof statist, Purdue Univ, 80-81; MEM TECH STAFF, BELL LABS, 81- *Mem:* Am Statist Asn; Inst Math Statist. *Res:* Development and comparison of statistical estimators of lifelength, particularly when the life data are obtained under censoring or from repaired items. *Mailing Add:* Bell Labs WB 1H-214 Crawfords Corner Rd Holmdel NJ 07733

KITE, FRANCIS ERVIN, b Galesburg, Ill, Dec 8, 18; m 42; c 2. CEREAL CHEMISTRY. *Educ:* Knox Col, AB, 40; Univ Iowa, MS, 42, PhD(phys chem), 48. *Prof Exp:* Res chemist, Corn Prods Co, 48-71; SR RES CHEMIST, CPC INT, INC, 71- *Mem:* Am Chem Soc; Am Asn Cereal Chemists. *Res:* Raman spectroscopy; molecular structure; chemistry of corn sugar and its derivatives; starch and starch derivatives. *Mailing Add:* Moffett Tech Ctr CPC Int Inc Box 345 Argo IL 60501

KITE, JOSEPH HIRAM, JR, b Decatur, Ga, Nov 11, 26; m 70. IMMUNOLOGY, BACTERIOLOGY. *Educ:* Emory Univ, AB, 48; Univ Tenn, MS, 54; Univ Mich, PhD(bact), 59. *Prof Exp:* Res assoc, 58-59, from instr to assoc prof, 59-72, PROF MICROBIOL, SCH MED, STATE UNIV NY BUFFALO, 72- *Concurrent Pos:* Am Heart Asn adv res fel, 63-67. *Mem:* AAAS; Am Soc Microbiol; Tissue Cult Asn; Am Asn Immunol; NY Acad Sci. *Res:* Autoimmune thyroiditis, cell-mediated immune reactions, pathogenesis of Mycoplasma. *Mailing Add:* Dept of Microbiol State Univ NY Sch of Med Buffalo NY 14214

KITOS, PAUL ALAN, b Saskatoon, Sask, May 31, 27; m 52; c 7. BIOCHEMISTRY. *Educ:* Univ BC, BSA, 50, MSA, 52; Ore State Univ, PhD(chem), 56. *Prof Exp:* Chemist, E I du Pont de Nemours & Co, 56-59; asst prof biochem, 59-62, asst prof comp biochem & physiol, 62-64, assoc prof, 64-69, actg chmn dept, 69-71, PROF BIOCHEM, UNIV KANS, 69- *Concurrent Pos:* NIH fel, Dept Microbiol, Harvard Med Sch, 71-72; sr scientist, Mid Am Cancer Ctr, 75- *Honors & Awards:* Amoco Award, Amoco Found, 74- *Mem:* AAAS; Am Chem Soc; Tissue Cult Asn; Am Soc Biol Chem. *Res:* Intermediary metabolism in plant, animal and bacterial cells. *Mailing Add:* Dept of Biochem Univ of Kans Lawrence KS 66045

KITSON, JOHN AIDAN, b Victoria, BC, Feb 14, 27; m 54; c 2. FOOD SCIENCE. *Educ:* Univ BC, BA, 49; Ore State Univ, MSc, 54. *Prof Exp:* Food technologist, Sun Rype Prod Ltd, BC, 49-50; food technologist prod & process develop, Can Dept Agr, 50-64; food technologist & vis scientist, Eng & Develop Lab, USDA, Calif, 64-65; food technologist prod & process develop, Can Dept Agr, 65-71, head, Food Processing Sect, 71-80, ASSOC DIR, RES STA, AGR CAN, 80- *Honors & Awards:* Prix Industs Award, 68 & 70; W J Eva Award for Indust Serv, 77. *Mem:* Inst Food Technologists; Can Inst Food Technologists; fel Inst Food Sci & Technol (UK). *Res:* Research and development of processes, products and equipment for fruit and vegetable processing industry. *Mailing Add:* Res Sta Agr Can Summerland BC V0H 1Z0 Can

KITSON, ROBERT EDWARD, b Ashtabula, Ohio, Aug 9, 18; m 42; c 2. POLYMER CHEMISTRY. *Educ:* Mt Union Col, BS, 40; Purdue Univ, MS, 42, PhD(anal chem), 44. *Prof Exp:* Res chemist, Rayon Tech Div, 43-44, Ammonia Chem Div, 43-52 & Dacron Res Div, 52-64, SUPVR, DACRON TEXTILE RES DIV, E I DU PONT DE NEMOURS & CO, INC, 65- *Mem:* Am Chem Soc. *Res:* Texturing of textile fibers; physical chemistry of high polymers. *Mailing Add:* Textile Res Lab E I du Pont de Nemours & Co Inc Wilmington DE 19899

KITTAKA, ROBERT SHINNOSUKE, b Los Angeles, Calif, Sept 23, 34; m 62; c 3. FOOD SCIENCE, MICROBIOLOGY. *Educ:* Univ Ill, BS, 57, MS, 59, PhD(food sci), 64. *Prof Exp:* Microbiologist, Swift & Co, 64-69; mgr microbiol, 69-71, MICROBIOL & QUAL ASSURANCE DIR, FOOD RES, CENT SOYA CO, INC, 71- *Mem:* Inst Food Technol; Am Soc Microbiol; Asn Milk, Food & Environ Sanitarians; Soc Indust Microbiol; Brit Soc Appl Bact. *Res:* Food microbiology; public health and spoilage microbiology as related to food products and processes; development, implementation and auditing of quality assurance programs in food processing systems to assure compliance with governmental regulations and corporate standards for cost efficient operations. *Mailing Add:* Food Res Res & Eng Ctr 1300 Ft Wayne Nat Bank Bldg Ft Wayne IN 46802

KITTEL, CHARLES, b New York, NY, July 18, 16; m 38; c 3. PHYSICS. *Educ:* Cambridge Univ, BA, 38; Univ Wis, PhD(physics), 41. *Prof Exp:* Physicist, Naval Ord Lab, Washington, DC, 40-42; opers analyst, US Fleet, 43-45; res assoc physics, Mass Inst Technol, 45-46; res physicist, Bell Tel Labs, 47-50; vis assoc prof, 50, prof, 51-78, EMER PROF PHYSICS, UNIV CALIF, BERKELEY, 79- *Concurrent Pos:* Guggenheim fel, 46, 57 & 64. *Honors & Awards:* Buckley Prize, 57; Oersted Medal, 79. *Mem:* Nat Acad Sci; Am Acad Arts & Sci. *Res:* Solid state physics; theory of ferromagnetism; mathematical physics. *Mailing Add:* Dept of Physics Univ of Calif Berkeley CA 94720

KITTEL, J HOWARD, b Ritzville, Wash, Oct 9, 19; m 43; c 4. NUCLEAR WASTE MANAGEMENT, NUCLEAR REACTOR MATERIALS. *Educ:* Wash State Univ, BS, 43. *Prof Exp:* Aeronaut res scientist, Nat Aeronaut & Space Agency, 43-51; metal engr, 51-61, mgr adv fuels, 74-79, SR METALLURGIST, ARGONNE NAT LAB, 61-, MGR NUCLEAR WASTE RES & DEVELOP, 79- *Concurrent Pos:* Mem, Mat Adv Bd, Nat Acad Sci, 56-58; US delegate, UN Geneva Conf, 58-64. *Mem:* Fel Am Nuclear Soc; Sigma Xi; Scientists & Engrs Secure Energy. *Res:* Management of research and development programs on nuclear waste management. *Mailing Add:* Off Waste Mgt Prog Argonne Nat Lab 9700 S Cass Ave Argonne IL 60439

KITTEL, PETER, b Mt Vernon Dist, Va, Mar 23, 45; m 72; c 1. PHYSICS, CRYOGENICS. *Educ:* Univ Calif, Berkeley, BS, 67; Univ Calif, San Diego, MS, 69; Univ Oxford, Eng, DPhil(physics), 74. *Prof Exp:* Res assoc & adj asst prof physics, Univ Ore, 74-78; res assoc radiol, Stanford Univ, 78; Nat Res Coun Assoc Cryog, 78-80, RES SCIENTIST & TEAM LEADER, AMES RES CTR, NASA, 80- *Mem:* Am Phys Soc; AAAS. *Res:* Low temperature physics; far infrared spectroscopy; stocastic processes and applications of cryogenics in space. *Mailing Add:* MS 244-7 NASA-Ames Res Ctr Moffett Field CA 94035

KITTELBERGER, JOHN STEPHEN, b Palmerton, Pa, Mar 14, 39; m 63. PHYSICAL CHEMISTRY. *Educ:* Hamilton Col, AB, 61; Princeton Univ, AM, 63, PhD(phys chem), 66. *Prof Exp:* Instr chem, Princeton Univ, 65-66; res assoc, Mass Inst Technol, 66-68; asst prof, Amherst Col, 68-73; scientist, 73-81, PROJ MGR, XEROX CORP, 81- *Mem:* Am Phys Soc; Am Chem Soc. *Res:* Structural and dynamic chemistry; surface science; reprographic science; materials science. *Mailing Add:* Xerox Corp 800 Philips Rd Webster NY 14580

KITTELSON, DAVID BURNELLE, b Pelican Rapids, Minn, Mar 12, 42; m 70. MECHANICAL & CHEMICAL ENGINEERING. *Educ:* Univ Minn, Minneapolis, BSc, 64, MSc, 66; Cambridge Univ, PhD(chem eng), 72. *Prof Exp:* asst prof, 70-76, assoc prof, 76-80, PROF MECH ENG, UNIV MINN, 80- *Honors & Awards:* Teeter Award, Soc Automotive Engrs, 73, Arch T Colwell Merit Award, 78. *Mem:* AAAS; Am Chem Soc; Am Soc Mech Engrs; Soc Automotive Engrs. *Res:* Combustion generated aerosols; diesel engine combustion and emissions. *Mailing Add:* Dept of Mech Eng Univ of Minn Minneapolis MN 55455

KITTILA, ALLAN B, physical chemistry, see previous edition

KITTILA, RICHARD SULO, b Ely, Minn, July 12, 17; m 49. ORGANIC CHEMISTRY. *Educ:* Univ Minn, BChem, 41; Duke Univ, MA, 44, PhD(chem), 49. *Prof Exp:* Jr chemist, Shell Develop Co, 41-42; SR RES CHEMIST, BIOCHEM DEPT, E I DU PONT DE NEMOURS & CO, INC, 49- *Mem:* Am Chem Soc. *Res:* Organic synthesis; agricultural chemicals; dimethylformamide; agricultural chemical formulations. *Mailing Add:* Biochem Dept DuPont Exp Sta E I du Pont de Nemours & Co Inc Wilmington DE 19898

KITTILSON, HAROLD LEE, genetics, botany, see previous edition

KITTING, CHRISTOPHER LEE, b Monroe, Mich, May 23, 53. ECOLOGY OF MARINE POPULATIONS. *Educ:* Univ Calif, Irvine, BS, 74; Stanford Univ, PhD(biol sci), 79. *Prof Exp:* Res assoc, Stanford Med Sch, Hopkins Marine Sta, 78-79; res biologist, Marine Sci Inst, Univ Calif, Santa Barbara, 79; ASST PROF MARINE STUDIES & ZOOL, PORT ARANSAS MARINE LAB, UNIV TEX, AUSTIN, 79- *Concurrent Pos:* Vis teaching asst, WI Lab, Fairleigh Dickinson Univ, 75, vis investr, 76; teaching asst, Dept Biol Sci, Hopkins Marine Sta, Stanford Univ, 77, fel, 74-79. *Mem:* Western Soc Naturalists; Ecol Soc Am; Am Soc Limnol & Oceanog; Sigma Xi; NY Acad Sci. *Res:* Advancing ecological theory using specialized natural history studies, especially marine invertebrates, algae, foraging and competition; field experiments using close-up listening and visual records of activities on semi-isolated surfaces of shallow rocks, pilings, oyster reefs and seagrass blades. *Mailing Add:* Marine Sci Inst Univ Tex Austin Port Aransas Marine Lab Port Aransas TX 78373

KITTINGER, GEORGE WILLIAM, b Toledo, Ohio, Dec 10, 21; m 47. BIOCHEMISTRY. *Educ:* Northwestern Univ, BS, 48, MS, 50; Univ Ore, PhD(biochem), 53. *Prof Exp:* Instr chem, Univ Ore, 53-56; res chemist, Procter & Gamble Co, 56-58; sr biochemist, May Inst Med Res, 58-64; assoc prof biochem, Med Sch, Univ Ore, 65-67; scientist, Ore Regional Primate Res Ctr, 65-79; prof biochem, Med Sch, Univ Ore, 67-79; RETIRED. *Concurrent Pos:* Fel chem, Univ Ore, 53-56; asst prof, Col Med, Univ Cincinnati, 59-64. *Mem:* Am Chem Soc; Endocrine Soc; Soc Exp Biol & Med. *Res:* Corticosteroid biosynthesis and metabolism; mechanism of action of steroid hormones; maternal-fetal-endocrine relationships. *Mailing Add:* 2865 123rd Ave SW Beaverton OR 97005

KITTLE, CHARLES FREDERICK, b Athens, Ohio, Oct 24, 21; m 45; c 4. SURGERY. *Educ:* Ohio Univ, BA, 42; Univ Chicago, MD, 45; Univ Kans, MS, 50; Am Bd Surg, dipl; Am Bd Thoracic Surg, dipl. *Prof Exp:* Chief lab serv, Brentwood Vet Admin Hosp, Los Angeles, 47-48; from instr to assoc prof surg, Sch Med, Univ Kans, 50-66; prof surg & chief sect throacic & cardiovasc surg, Univ Chicago, 66-73; PROF SURG & HEAD SECT THORACIC SURG, RUSH MED COL, 73- *Concurrent Pos:* Consult, Oak Ridge Inst Nuclear Studies, 50-57 & Vet Admin Hosps, Kans & Mo, 53-66; Am Cancer Soc Clin fel, 50-52; Murdock fel, 51; Markle scholar, 53-58; mem, Bd Thoracic Surg, 66-77. *Mem:* Am Col Cardiol; Am Col Surgeons; Soc Thoracic Surgeons; Am Asn Thoracic Surgeons; Int Cardiovasc Soc (secy, 65-71). *Res:* Cardiovascular hemodynamics; extracorporeal circulation; clinical trials. *Mailing Add:* 1725 W Harrison St Chicago IL 60612

KITTLE, PAUL ALVIN, physical chemistry, organic chemistry, see previous edition

KITTO, GEORGE BARRIE, b Wellington, NZ, July 31, 37; m 62; c 3. BIOCHEMISTRY. *Educ:* Victoria Univ, BSc, 61, MSc, 62; Brandeis Univ, PhD(biochem), 66. *Prof Exp:* Biochemist, Wellington Pub Hosp, 60-61; asst prof, 66-71, PROF CHEM, UNIV TEX, AUSTIN, 71-; RES SCIENTIST, CLAYTON FOUND BIOCHEM INST, 66- *Mem:* AAAS; Am Chem Soc; Royal Soc Chem; assoc mem NZ Inst Chem; Royal Soc NZ; Australian Biochem Soc. *Res:* Enzyme structure and taxonomy; evolution of protein structure; multiple molecular forms of enzymes; immobilized enzymes. *Mailing Add:* Dept of Chem Univ of Tex Austin TX 78712

KITTREDGE, CLIFFORD PROCTOR, b Lowell, Mass, June 30, 06; m 29; c 2. ENGINEERING. *Educ:* Mass Inst Technol, BS, 29; Tech Hochsch, Munich, DrTechWissen(fluid mech), 32. *Prof Exp:* Asst mech eng, Mass Inst Technol, 29-30, instr, 32-33; instr power eng, Thayer Sch Civil Eng, Dartmouth Col, 33-34; engr, Freeman Trust Estate, Providence, 34-36; asst prof theoret & appl mech, Univ Ill, 36-41; develop engr, Underwater Sound Lab, Div War Res, Columbia Univ, 41-45; assoc prof mech eng, 45-71, EMER ASSOC PROF MECH ENG, PRINCETON UNIV, 71- *Mem:* Am Soc Mech Engrs. *Res:* General fluid mechanics; hydraulic machinery. *Mailing Add:* 763 Princeton-Kingston Rd Princeton NJ 08540

KITTRELL, FLEMMIE P, nutrition, deceased

KITTRELL, JAMES RAYMOND, b Arkansas City, Kans, Oct 28, 40; m 60; c 2. CHEMICAL ENGINEERING. *Educ:* Okla State Univ, BS, 62; Univ Wis, MS, 63, PhD(chem eng), 66. *Prof Exp:* From res engr to sr res engr, Chevron Res Co, 66-69; oper asst, Standard Oil Co Calif, 69-70; PROF CHEM ENG, UNIV MASS, AMHERST, 70- *Concurrent Pos:* NSF fel & instr, Univ Wis, 66. *Mem:* Am Inst Chem Engrs; Am Chem Soc. *Res:* Petroleum refining; energy economics; reactor design and analysis; catalyst deactivation; modeling of reaction and diffusion; bioengineering. *Mailing Add:* Dept of Chem Eng Univ of Mass Amherst MA 01003

KITTRICK, JAMES ALLEN, b Milwaukee, Wis, Aug 4, 29; m 53; c 2. SOIL MINERALOGY. *Educ:* Univ Wis, BS, 51, MS, 53, PhD, 55. *Prof Exp:* From asst prof to assoc prof, 55-67, PROF SOILS, WASH STATE UNIV, 67- *Mem:* Fel Am Soc Agron; Mineral Soc Am. *Mailing Add:* Dept Agron & Soils Wash State Univ Pullman WA 99164

KITTS, DAVID BURLINGAME, b Oswego, NY, Oct 27, 23; m 45; c 2. VERTEBRATE PALEONTOLOGY, GEOLOGY. *Educ:* Univ Pa, AB, 49; Columbia Univ, PhD(zool), 53. *Prof Exp:* Instr biol, Amherst Col, 53-54; from asst prof to assoc prof geol, Univ Okla, 54-62, assoc prof geol & hist sci, 62-66, David Ross Boyd prof geol & hist sci, 66-80, head cur, Dept Geol, Stoval Mus, 68-80. *Concurrent Pos:* Vis fel, Princeton Univ, 64-65. *Mem:* Soc Vert Paleontologists; Philos Sci Asn. *Res:* Historical geology; Cenozoic mammals and stratigraphy; philosophy of geology and evolutionary theory. *Mailing Add:* 518 Macy Norman OK 73069

KITTSLEY, SCOTT LOREN, b Port Washington, Wis, Feb 17, 21; m 46. PHYSICAL CHEMISTRY. *Educ:* Univ Wis, BS, 42; Case Western Reserve Univ, MS, 44, PhD(phys chem), 45. *Prof Exp:* Asst chem, Case Western Reserve Univ, 42-45; from instr to prof chem, Marquette Univ, 45-81, chmn dept, 57-62. *Mem:* Fel AAAS; Am Chem Soc; fel Am Inst Chem. *Res:* Chemical thermodynamics; solutions of nonelectrolytes. *Mailing Add:* Dept of Chem Marquette Univ Milwaukee WI 53233

KITZ, RICHARD J, b Oshkosh, Wis, Mar 25, 29; m 54; c 1. ANESTHESIOLOGY, ENZYMOLOGY. *Educ:* Marquette Univ, BS, 51, MD, 54; Harvard Univ, MA, 69; Am Bd Anesthesiol, dipl, 62. *Prof Exp:* Surg intern, Columbia-Presby Med Ctr, 54-55; surg resident, 57-58; resident anesthesiol, 58-60, instr, 60-61, from asst prof to assoc prof anesthesiol, 62-69; prof, 69-70, HENRY ISAIAH DORR PROF ANESTHESIA, HARVARD MED SCH, 70- *Concurrent Pos:* NIH spec res fel, Columbia-Presby Med Ctr, 61-62; NIH spec res fel, Karolinska Inst, Stockholm, 68; anesthetist-in-chief, Mass Gen Hosp, 69-; consult, Air Force Surg Gen, 70-80. *Mem:* Fel Am Col Anesthesiol; AMA; Am Soc Anesthesiol. *Res:* Basic sciences as related to anesthesiology with emphasis on uptake and distribution of anesthetic agents and enzymology. *Mailing Add:* Dept of Anesthesia Mass Gen Hosp Boston MA 02114

KITZES, ARNOLD S(TANLEY), b Boston, Mass, Sept 21, 17; m 42; c 2. NUCLEAR ENGINEERING, CHEMICAL ENGINEERING. *Educ:* City Col New York, BChE, 39; Univ Minn, MChE, 41, PhD(chem eng), 47. *Prof Exp:* Instr chem eng, Univ Minn, 41-42, res assoc, 45-47, chief chemist, Sangamon Ord, Ill, 42-45; group leader, Oak Ridge Nat Lab, 48-57; mgr test eng, Atomic Power Div, 57-72, ADV ENGR, NUCLEAR SERV DIV, WESTINGHOUSE ELEC CORP, 72- *Mem:* Am Soc Mech Engrs; Sigma Xi; AAAS. *Res:* Reactor technology; environment; spray drying and explosives; design of high pressure equipment; heat transfer; fluid flow; waste management; decontamination; technical administration. *Mailing Add:* Westinghouse Elec Corp Nuclear Serv Div PO Box 2728 Pittsburgh PA 15230

KITZES, GEORGE, b Denver, Colo, May 28, 19; m 42; c 3. BIOCHEMISTRY, PHARMACOLOGY. *Educ:* City Col New York, BS, 41; Univ Wis, MS, 42, PhD(chem), 44. *Prof Exp:* Res biochemist, White Labs, NJ, 44-49 & Vet Admin, 49-51; res biochemist indust toxicol, US Dept Air Force, 51-57, asst chief, Physiol Br, Aeromed Lab, 57-60, chief, Physiol Div, Aerospace Med Res Labs, Aero-Med Div, Wright-Patterson AFB, Ohio, 60-66; health sci adminr & gastroenterol prog dir, Extramural Prog, Nat Inst Arthritis, Metab & Digestive Dis, 66-81; CONSULT, 81- *Mem:* AAAS; Am Gastroenterol Asn; Am Asn Study Liver Dis. *Res:* Gastrointestinal physiology and biochemistry; nutrition; aviation physiology and toxicology; aero-space life support sciences. *Mailing Add:* 10201 Grosvenor Pl Rockville MD 20852

KITZES, LEONARD MARTIN, b New York, NY, Apr 10, 41; m 67; c 2. NEUROPHYSIOLOGY. *Educ:* Univ Calif, Los Angeles, BA, 62; Univ Calif, Irvine, PhD(psychobiol), 70. *Prof Exp:* Fel neurophysiol, Univ Wis, 70-73, res assoc, 73-74; res neurophysiologist neurol, 74-77, ASST PROF NEURPHYSIOL, DEPT ANAT, UNIV CALIF, IRVINE, 77- *Concurrent Pos:* Nat Inst Neurol Dis & Stroke res grant, 78. *Res:* Auditory neurophysiology with primary interests in responses of single inferior colliculus neurons to binaural stimulation and functional and structural development of the brainstem audiroty system. *Mailing Add:* Dept of Anat Univ of Calif Irvine CA 92717

KITZKE, EUGENE DAVID, b Milwaukee, Wis, Sept 2, 23; m 46; c 4. ENVIRONMENTAL HEALTH, TECHNICAL MANAGEMENT. *Educ:* Marquette Univ, BS, 45, MS, 47. *Prof Exp:* Instr biol, Marquette Univ, 46-47; from asst prof to assoc prof, St Thomas Aquinas Col, Grand Rapids, Mich, 47-51; res mgr biol, S C Johnson & Son, Inc, 57-76, vpres, Corp Res & Develop, 76-81; PRES, OAK CRETE BLOCK CORP, 82- *Concurrent Pos:* Instr microbiol, St Mary's Nursing Sch, Grand Rapids, Mich, 47-51; asst clin prof environ med, Dept Environ Med, Med Col Wis, 73- *Mem:* AAAS; Am Inst Biol Sci; Mycol Soc Am; Am Genetic Asn. *Res:* Aspects, theory and practice of creative technical management. *Mailing Add:* S C Johnson & Son Inc Racine WI 53403

KITZMILLER, JAMES BLAINE, b Toledo, Ohio, June 30, 18. GENETICS, MEDICAL ENTOMOLOGY. *Educ:* De Sales Col, BS, 39; Univ Mich, MS, 41, PhD(genetics), 48. *Prof Exp:* Entomologist, Toledo Mus Sci, 39-41; asst zool, Univ Mich, 41-42; from instr to prof, 48-74, EMER PROF ZOOL, UNIV ILL, URBANA, 74- *Concurrent Pos:* Fulbright fel, Univ Pavia, Italy, 53; NIH fel, Univ Cagliari, Italy & Johannes Gutenberg Univ, Ger, 65-66; consult, WHO & Pan Am Health Orgn, 53-, NIH, 58- *Mem:* AAAS; Genetics Soc Am; Soc Study Evolution; Am Entom Soc; Am Mosquito Control Asn. *Res:* Genetics and cytogenetics of mosquitoes, especially Anophelines; evolutionary cytogenetics, polymorphism and cytotaxonomy. *Mailing Add:* Fla Med Entom Lab Box 520 Vero Beach FL 32960

KIUSALAAS, JAAN, b Tartu, Estonia, June 23, 31; m 59; c 3. MECHANICS. *Educ:* Univ Adelaide, BE, 56; Northwestern Univ, MS, 59, PhD(mech), 62. *Prof Exp:* Plant design engr, Chrysler Australia Ltd, 56-57, prod design & test engr, 57-58, prod develop engr, Eng Div, Chrysler Corp, 59-60; res fel, Mat Res Ctr, Northwestern Univ, 62-63; from asst prof to assoc prof, 63-74, PROF ENG MECH, PA STATE UNIV, 74- *Concurrent Pos:* Sr resident res assoc, Marshall Space Flight Ctr, NASA, 71-72. *Mem:* Am Soc Mech Engrs; Am Acad Mech. *Res:* Finite elements; optimal structural design; structural stability. *Mailing Add:* 230 Hammond Bldg Pa State Univ University Park PA 16802

KIVEL, BENNETT, b Brooklyn, NY, Apr 29, 28; m 56; c 2. THEORETICAL PHYSICS. *Educ:* Univ Fla, BS, 49, MS, 50; Yale Univ, PhD, 54. *Prof Exp:* Mem staff theoret physics, Los Alamos Sci Lab, Calif, 51-55; prin res scientist, Avco-Everett Res Lab, 55-79; RETIRED. *Concurrent Pos:* Vis lectr, Mass Inst Technol, 69-70; ed, J Quan Spectros & Radiative Transfer, 64-80. *Mem:* Fel Am Phys Soc; assoc fel Am Inst Aeronaut & Astronaut. *Res:* Theory of atomic and molecular radiation; electronic and ionic impact phenomena; statistical mechanics; transport properties. *Mailing Add:* 146 Woodcrest Dr Melrose MA 02176

KIVELSON, DANIEL, b New York, NY, July 11, 29; m 49; c 2. CHEMICAL PHYSICS. *Educ:* Harvard Univ, AB, 49, MA, 50, PhD(chem physics), 53. *Prof Exp:* Instr physics, Mass Inst Technol, 53-55; from asst prof chem to assoc prof, 55-63, chmn dept, 75-78, PROF CHEM, UNIV CALIF, LOS ANGELES, 63- *Concurrent Pos:* Guggenheim fel, 59; Res Corp spec grant, 59; Sloan fel, 61-65; NSF sr fel, 65-66; consult, NAm Sci Ctr, 63-64; Advan Res Projs Agency, 65-66 & NSF, 76-77; assoc ed, J Chem Phys, 68-71 & Molecular Physics, 75- *Mem:* Am Phys Soc; Am Chem Soc. *Res:* Microwave spectroscopy; molecular structure; nuclear magnetic resonance; electron spin resonance; light scattering; theory of liquids; study of bilayers. *Mailing Add:* Dept of Chem Univ of Calif Los Angeles CA 90024

KIVELSON, MARGARET GALLAND, b New York, NY, Oct 21, 28; m 49; c 2. SPACE PHYSICS. *Educ:* Radcliffe Col, AB, 50, AM, 51, PhD(physics), 57. *Prof Exp:* Adj asst prof physics, 67-72, adj assoc prof, 72-73, assoc prof in residence, 75-77, prof geophys & space physics in residence, 77-80, PROF, UNIV CALIF, LOS ANGELES, 80-, RES GEOPHYSICIST, INST GEOPHYS & PLANETARY PHYSICS, 67- *Concurrent Pos:* Consult, Rand Corp, 55-71; scholar, Radcliffe Inst Independent Study, 65-66; fel, John Simon Guggenheim Mem Found, 73-74. *Mem:* AAAS; Am Geophys Union; Am Phys Soc. *Res:* Magnetospheric physics; plasma physics; particles and fields in the magnetospheres of Earth and Jupiter; interplanetary magnetic fields. *Mailing Add:* Inst of Geophys & Planetary Physics Univ of Calif Los Angeles CA 90024

KIVENSON, GILBERT, b Pittsburgh, Pa, Dec 5, 20. ENGINEERING INSTRUMENTATION. *Educ:* Carnegie Inst Technol, BS, 42; Univ Pittsburgh, MS, 47. *Prof Exp:* Rubber Reserve Co fel anal distillation, Mellon Inst, 47-50, develop engr, 50-51; chem engr, US Steel Co, 51-53; consult instrumentation, 53-55; chem engr, Atomic Power Dept, Westinghouse Elec Corp, 55-62, sr engr, Res & Develop Ctr, 62-68; sr engr, Electro-Optical Systs Div, Xerox Corp, 68-70; sr engr, Liquid Metals Eng Ctr, Atomics Int, Chatsworth, 71-73; sr engr, C F Braun Co, Calif, 73-75; CONSULT, 75- *Concurrent Pos:* Lectr, Pa Technol Inst & Northrop Inst Technol. *Mem:* Am Chem Soc. *Res:* Electronic instruments; stroboscopes; control systems; transducers; process control instrumentation. *Mailing Add:* 22030 Wyandotte St Canoga Park CA 91303

KIVER, EUGENE P, b Cleveland, Ohio, Feb 26, 37; m 64; c 3. GEOMORPHOLOGY. *Educ:* Case Western Reserve Univ, BA, 64; Univ Wyo, PhD(glacial geol, geomorphol), 68. *Prof Exp:* Chmn dept, 71-74, from asst prof to assoc prof, 71-77, PROF GEOL, EASTERN WASH UNIV, 77- *Mem:* AAAS; Geol Soc Am; Nat Speleol Soc; Am Quaternary Asn. *Res:* Pleistocene and neoglacial history of alpine regions of western US; general geomorphology; volcanism in the Cascade Mountains; geology of the national parks; quaternary geology of NE Washington. *Mailing Add:* Dept of Geol Eastern Wash Univ Cheney WA 99004

KIVIAT, FRED E, b New York, NY, May 16, 40. PHYSICAL CHEMISTRY. *Educ:* City Col, New York, BS, 62; Univ Pittsburgh, PhD(chem), 68, MS, 78. *Prof Exp:* SR RES CHEMIST, GULF RES & DEVELOP CO, 68- *Res:* determination of properties of heterogeneous catalysts via spectroscopic techniques; mathematical modelling of physio-chemical processes; process development. *Mailing Add:* Gulf Res & Develop Co PO Box 2038 Pittsburgh PA 15230

KIVILAAN, ALEKSANDER, b Jaarja, Estonia, July 20, 06; nat US; m 35; c 3. PLANT PHYSIOLOGY. *Educ:* Univ Tartu, Estonia, BS, 32, MS, 35; Univ Berlin, dipl, 38; Mich State Univ, PhD(plant path, bot), 57. *Prof Exp:* Asst plant path, Univ Tartu, Estonia, 32-36, res instr pomol, 39-44; lectr dendrol, Baltic Univ, Ger, 48-50; plant propagator, Mt Arbor Nurseries, Iowa, 50-53; asst plant path, 54-56, res instr plant physiol, 57, asst prof, 58-60, assoc prof, 60-78, EMER ASSOC PROF PLANT PHYSIOL, MICH STATE UNIV, 78- *Mem:* Am Phytopath Soc; Am Soc Plant Physiol. *Res:* Physiology of fungi, parasitism, plant growth and plant cell wall. *Mailing Add:* 1167 Marigold Ave East Lansing MI 48823

KIVIOJA, LASSI A, b Finland, Mar 29, 27; US citizen; m 64; c 2. GEODESY. *Educ:* Univ Helsinki, BS, 51, MS, 52; Ohio State Univ, PhD, 63. *Prof Exp:* Res asst, Int Isostatic Inst, Helsinki, Finland, 49-52; res assoc geod gravity, Ohio State Univ Res Found, 55-63; asst prof geod, 64-67, ASSOC PROF CIVIL ENG, PURDUE UNIV, 68- *Concurrent Pos:* Instr, Dept Geod Sci, Ohio State Univ, 59-62; geodesist, US Coast & Geod Surv, 70-71; res scientist, Defense Mapping Agency, 79-80. *Mem:* Am Geophys Union; Am Cong Surv & Mapping. *Res:* Gravity anomalies isostasy; geodetic and astro-geodetic instruments; geodetic lines on the ellipsoid; the vertical mirror and its applications; mean sea level; mercury leveling instruments; hydrostatic leveling on land; precise astro-azimuths by mercury leveling of a theodolite. *Mailing Add:* Sch of Civil Eng Purdue Univ West Lafayette IN 47907

KIVISILD, H(ANS) R(OBERT), b Tartu, Estonia, July 19, 22; m 47; c 4. CIVIL ENGINEERING. *Educ:* Royal Inst Technol, Sweden, CE, 46, DEng(hydraul eng), 54. *Prof Exp:* Engr, City of Stockholm, Sweden, 46-48 & VBB, 48-50; with Found Co Can, Ltd, Montreal, 50-53; designing engr, Found Can Eng Corp Ltd, Montreal, 54-56, dist engr, Vancouver, 57-63, chief hydraul engr, Toronto, 64-65, chief civil engr, 65-70, dir res & develop, 70-73, vpres, 73-75; vpres & mgr, 75-81, DIR, WESTERN OPERS, CALGARY, FENCO CONSULTS LTD, 77-; VPRES, LAVALIN INC, 82- *Concurrent Pos:* Consult, Belg Govt, 56, Tech Assistance Opers, UN, 61, Spec Fund, 63, Food & Agr Orgn, 64; mem snow & ice subcomt, Nat Res Coun Can, 65-75, mem cold regions res comt, 77-79. *Honors & Awards:* Eng Medal, Asn Prof Engrs Ont, 76; Queen Elizabeth II Silver Jubilee Medal, 77. *Mem:* Can Soc Civil Eng; Int Asn Hydraul Res; Marine Technol Soc; Asn Sci, Eng & Technol Community Can; fel Eng Inst Can. *Res:* Oceanography and hydraulics of ice-covered waters; arctic development. *Mailing Add:* 1420 Premier Way SW Calgary AB T2T 1L9 Can

KIVLIGHN, HERBERT DANIEL, JR, b Mineola, NY, Apr 10, 31; m 54; c 3. PHYSICAL CHEMISTRY, INORGANIC CHEMISTRY. *Educ:* Hofstra Col, BA, 54; Pa State Univ, PhD(phys chem), 58. *Prof Exp:* Res chemist, Corning Glass Works, 57-58, res supvr, 58-61; res scientist, Am Stand Res Labs, 61-63; res scientist, 63-69, STAFF SCIENTIST, GRUMMAN AEROSPACE CORP, 69- *Mem:* AAAS; fel Am Inst Chemists; Am Ceramic Soc; Am Chem Soc. *Res:* Photochromic glass response under high excitation intensities; effect on the kinetics of darkening and fading. *Mailing Add:* Res Dept Grumman Aerospace Corp Bethpage NY 11714

KIVNICK, ARNOLD, b Philadelphia, Pa, June 30, 23; m 46; c 3. CHEMICAL ENGINEERING, APPLIED MATH. *Educ:* Univ Pa, BS, 43, PhD(chem eng), 51. *Prof Exp:* Asst, SAM Labs, Columbia Univ, 43-44; jr chem engr, Tenn Eastman Co, 44-46; res assoc chem eng, Univ Ill, 50-52; sr chem engr, Tech Div, Pennsalt Chem Corp, 52-60, group leader, 60-68, mgr process develop dept, 68-72; LIAISON ENGR, CENT ENG DEPT, PENNWALT CORP, 72- *Concurrent Pos:* adj prof chem eng, Univ Pa, 80- *Mem:* Am Inst Chem Engrs. *Res:* Process development; applied statistics; cost estimation; process economics. *Mailing Add:* 308 Glenway Rd Philadelphia PA 19118

KIYASU, JOHN YUTAKA, b San Francisco, Calif, Dec 25, 27; m 54; c 4. BIOCHEMISTRY. *Educ:* Univ Calif, Berkeley, BA, 50, MA, 51, PhD(physiol), 55. *Prof Exp:* Fel biochem, Univ Chicago, 56-57, instr & res assoc, 57-60; asst prof biochem & asst res prof psychiat, Sch Med & Dent, Univ Rochester, 60-63; from asst prof to assoc prof chem, Adelphi Univ, 63-70; ASSOC CLIN PROF PATH, COL PHYSICIANS & SURGEONS, COLUMBIA UNIV, 72-; DIR DIV BIOCHEM & ASST DIR LAB, DEPT PATH, ROOSEVELT HOSP, 70- *Concurrent Pos:* USPHS fel, 55-57; NIH grant, Adelphi Univ; res biochemist & mem staff, Dept Path & Labs, Div Biochem, Meadowbrook Hosp, East Meadow, NY, 67-69, dir lab systs, 69-70. *Mem:* Am Oil Chem Soc; Am Chem Soc; fel Am Inst Chem; NY Acad Sci; Am Asn Clin Chem. *Res:* Biosynthesis of phospholipids and liponucleotides; lipid enzymology and control mechanisms. *Mailing Add:* Dept of Path Roosevelt Hosp New York NY 10019

KIZER, DONALD EARL, b Benton Co, Iowa, Oct 12, 21; m 42; c 6. BIOCHEMISTRY. *Educ:* Upper Iowa Univ, BS, 47; Purdue Univ, MS, 50; Univ NC, PhD(bact), 54. *Prof Exp:* Asst dairy, Purdue Univ, 48-50; asst animal indust, Univ NC, 52-54; res assoc, 54-60, HEAD BIOCHEM PHARMACOL SECT, BIOMED DIV, SAMUEL ROBERTS NOBLE FOUND, INC, 60- *Mem:* AAAS; Am Chem Soc; Am Soc Microbiol; Soc Exp Biol & Med; Am Asn Cancer Res. *Res:* Biochemistry of carcinogenesis; biochemical changes in pre-cancerous tissues. *Mailing Add:* Biomed Div Samuel Roberts Noble Found Inc Ardmore OK 73401

KIZER, JOHN STEPHEN, b Charleston, WVa, Jan 8, 45; m 70; c 3. NEUROENDOCRINOLOGY. *Educ:* Princeton Univ, AB, 66; Duke Univ, MD, 70. *Prof Exp:* Intern med, Johns Hopkins Hosp, Baltimore, 70-71, resident, 71-72; res assoc neuroendocrinol, Lab Clin Sci, Nat Inst Ment Health, 72-75; asst prof, 75-80, ASSOC PROF MED & PHARMACOL, SCH MED, UNIV NC, CHAPEL HILL, 80- *Res:* Investigation of neurotransmitters, neural pathways and relationship of these to regulation of anterior pituitary function. *Mailing Add:* Biol Sci Res Ctr Sch of Med Univ of NC Chapel Hill NC 27514

KJAR, HAROLD ANTHONY, b Lexington, Nebr, June 13, 20; m 44; c 4. VETERINARY SURGERY. *Educ:* Iowa State Univ, DVM, 43. *Prof Exp:* Pvt pract, Nebr, 44-68; ASSOC PROF LARGE ANIMAL MED & SURG, AUBURN UNIV, 68- *Concurrent Pos:* Ala Exten Vet, 78. *Mem:* Am Vet Med Asn; Am Asn Swine Practr. *Res:* Swine diseases and surgery; reproductive problems of swine caused by beta-hemolytic streptococci; effectiveness of low level antibiotics in pig creep feed. *Mailing Add:* Exten Hall Auburn Univ Auburn AL 36830

KJAR, RAYMOND ARTHUR, b Farnam, Nebr, Feb 27, 38; m 67; c 1. ELECTRONIC ENGINEERING. *Educ:* Univ Nebr, BSEE, 60; Iowa State Univ, MS, 62, PhD, 64. *Prof Exp:* Res engr, Naval Res Lab, Off Naval Res, 64-68; mem res staff, Autonetics Div, NAm Rockwell Corp, 68-76; SUPVR,

IC TECH ELECTRONICS DIV, 76-; MGR SOS PROD, ROCKWELL INT, 80- Mem: Inst Elec & Electronics Engrs. Res: Semiconductor devices; integrated circuits; radiation effects; semiconductor surfaces. Mailing Add: Rockwell Int 3370 Miraloma Ave Anaheim CA 92803

KJELDAAS, TERJE, JR, b Oslo, Norway, Oct 24, 24; US citizen; m 50; c 2. THEORETICAL PHYSICS. Educ: Polytech Inst Brooklyn, BS, 48; Columbia Univ, AM, 49; Univ Pittsburgh, PhD, 59. Prof Exp: Res engr, Res Labs, Westinghouse Elec Corp, 49-59; from asst prof to assoc prof, 59-63, head dept, 77-80, PROF PHYSICS, POLYTECH INST NY, 63- Concurrent Pos: Consult, indust labs. Mem: Am Phys Soc. Res: Solid state theory; atomic-molecule-electron interactions. Mailing Add: Dept of Physics Polytech Inst of NY Brooklyn NY 11201

KJELDGAARD, EDWIN ANDREAS, b Brush, Colo, Sept 14, 39; m 65; c 2. APPLIED CHEMISTRY, METROLOGY. Educ: St Olaf Col, BA, 61; Univ Colo, PhD(chem), 66. Prof Exp: Staff mem, 66-70, DIV SUPVR, SANDIA LABS, 70- Mem: Am Chem Soc. Res: Organic fluorine chemistry; fluorinated cyclobutenes; explosive chemistry; coordination compounds. Mailing Add: 2532 Harold Pl NE Albuquerque NM 87106

KJELDSEN, CHRIS KELVIN, b Stockton, Calif, Apr 26, 39; m 62; c 1. PHYCOLOGY. Educ: Univ of the Pac, BA, 60, MS, 62; Ore State Univ, PhD(bot), 66. Prof Exp: Instr bot, Ore State Univ, 62-66; asst prof biol, 66-70, assoc prof, 70-73, chmn dept, 72-75, PROF BIOL, SONOMA STATE COL, 73- Concurrent Pos: Sabbatical leave, Univ NWales, 76; IPA assignment, US Dept Energy, Educ Progs, Washington, DC, 78-79. Honors & Awards: Mosser Award, Ore State Univ, 66. Mem: Sigma Xi (vpres, 67). Res: Marine algae; physiological ecology and taxonomy. Mailing Add: Dept of Biol Sonoma State Col 1801 E Cotati Ave Rohnert Park CA 94928

KJELGAARD, WILLIAM L, b Lindley, NY, Aug 27, 20; m 50; c 5. AGRICULTURAL ENGINEERING. Educ: Pa State Univ, BS, 50, MS, 53. Prof Exp: Instr agr eng, WVa Univ, 51-52; from instr to asst prof, 52-60, ASSOC PROF AGR ENG, PA STATE UNIV, 60- Mem: Am Soc Agr Engrs. Res: Mechanization and processing of forage crops. Mailing Add: Dept of Agr Eng Pa State Univ University Park PA 16802

KJELSBERG, MARCUS OLAF, b Mayville, NDak, Dec 27, 32; m 62; c 2. BIOSTATISTICS. Educ: Concordia Col, Moorhead, Minn, BA, 52; Univ Minn, MA, 55, PhD(biostatist), 62. Prof Exp: Instr biostatist, Sch Med, Tulane Univ, 57-60; asst prof biostatist & res assoc epidemiol, Sch Pub Health, Univ Mich, Ann Arbor, 61-66; assoc prof, 66-75, PROF BIOMET, SCH PUB HEALTH, UNIV MINN, MINNEAPOLIS, 75-, DEPT HEAD, BIOMET & HEALTH INFO SYSTS, 80- Concurrent Pos: Mem, US Nat Comt Vital & Health Statist, 73-77. Mem: Am Pub Health Asn; Am Statist Asn; Am Heart Asn; Biometric Soc; Pop Asn Am. Res: Statistical epidemiology; health statistics; clinical trials methodology. Mailing Add: Sch of Public Health Univ of Minn Minneapolis MN 55455

KJELSON, MARTIN ANTON, III, ecology, fish biology, see previous edition

KJONAAS, RICHARD A, b Minot, NDak, Mar 20, 49; m 79; c 2. ORGANIC CHEMISTRY. Educ: Valley City State Col, BS, 71; Purdue Univ, PhD(chem), 78. Prof Exp: Fel, Ohio State Univ, 78-79; ASST PROF ORG CHEM, FT HAYS STATE UNIV, 79- Mem: Am Chem Soc; Sigma Xi. Res: Organic synthesis via transition metals. Mailing Add: Dept Chem Ft Hays State Univ 600 Park St Hays KS 67601

KLAAS, ERWIN EUGENE, b Batchtown, Ill, Aug 23, 35; m 69; c 3. WILDLIFE BIOLOGY. Educ: Univ Mo, BS, 56; Univ Kans, MA, 63, PhD(zool), 70. Prof Exp: From asst prof to assoc prof biol, Rockhurst Col, 65-71; RES BIOLOGIST, US FISH & WILDLIFE SERV, 71-; PROF WILDLIFE BIOL, IOWA STATE UNIV, 80- Mem: AAAS; Am Ornith Union; Cooper Ornith Soc; Wilson Ornith Soc; Wildlife Soc. Res: Population ecology of birds; effects of environmental pollution on wild bird populations; management of habitat for optimal utilization by game and non-game species. Mailing Add: Iowa Coop Wildlife Res Unit Iowa State Univ Ames IA 50011

KLAAS, NICHOLAS PAUL, b Kieler, Wis, June 25, 25; m 49; c 4. FUEL TECHNOLOGY, PETROLEUM ENGINEERING. Educ: Loras Col, BA, 45; Univ Notre Dame, PhD(org chem), 48. Prof Exp: Chemist, Rohm and Haas Co, 48, actg prod mgr, 49-51; tech asst to sales develop mgr, Minn Mining & Mfg Co, 52, mkt specialist, 52-53, mgr oil indust prod, 53-59, mgr res & develop, 60-65; exec vpres, Wyomissing Corp, Reading, 65-71, dir, 68-71, chief operating officer, 70-71; vpres com develop, GAF Corp, 71-74, group vpres chem group, 74-77; gen mgr spec chem div, Ga-Pac Corp, 77; exec vpres, 77-79, GEN MGR, J T BAKER CHEM CO, 77-, PRES, 79- Mem: AAAS; Am Chem Soc; NY Acad Sci; Soc Chem Indust. Res: Organic chemical intermediates and polymers; chemicals derived from acetylene; surfactants; dyes; pigments; carbonyl iron powders; textile auxiliaries; filters; agricultural chemicals; laboratory chemicals; herbicides; roofing granules; quarry products; photographic products; building products. Mailing Add: 410 Gravel Hill Rd Smoke Rise Kinnelon NJ 07405

KLAAS, ROSALIND AMELIA, b Maple Park, Ill, May 8, 05; m 34; c 2. BIOCHEMISTRY. Educ: Univ Ariz, BS, 26, MS, 27; Univ Chicago, PhD(chem), 32. Prof Exp: Instr chem, Univ Ariz, 27-29; asst, Univ Chicago, 32-37; biochemist, Munic Tuberc Sanitarium, 37-57; from asst prof to assoc prof, 57-73, EMER ASSOC PROF CHEM, UNIV ILL, CHICAGO CIRCLE, 73- Concurrent Pos: Lectr hort, Wright Col, Chicago, 72-74 & Triton Col, River Grove, Ill, 74-79; consult, Argonne Nat Lab, 65-81 & Ladd Arboretum, Evanston, Ill, 74-81; consult hort, 73- Mem: AAAS; Am Chem Soc; fel Am Inst Chem; Sigma Xi. Res: Carbohydrates; bacterial metabolism; silicosis; electrophoresis; chromatography. Mailing Add: 462 W Harrison St Claremont GA 91711

KLAASEN, GENE ALLEN, b Holland, Mich, Feb 3, 41; m 63; c 3. MATHEMATICS. Educ: Hope Col, BA, 63; Univ Nebr, Lincoln, MA, 65, PhD(math), 68. Prof Exp: Asst prof math, Univ Nebr, Lincoln, 68-69; asst prof, 69-74, ASSOC PROF MATH, UNIV TENN, KNOXVILLE, 74- Mem: Am Math Soc; Math Asn Am. Res: Boundary value problems for ordinary differential equations. Mailing Add: Dept of Math Univ of Tenn Knoxville TN 37916

KLAASSEN, CURTIS DEAN, b Ft Dodge, Iowa, Nov 23, 42; m 64; c 2. PHARMACOLOGY, TOXICOLOGY. Educ: Wartburg Col, BA, 64; Univ Iowa, MS, 66, PhD(pharmacol), 68. Prof Exp: From instr to assoc prof, 68-77, PROF PHARMACOL & TOXICOL, UNIV KANS, 77- Mem: Soc Toxicol; Am Soc Pharmacol & Exp Therapeut. Res: Biliary excretion of drugs and toxicants. Mailing Add: Dept of Pharmacol Univ of Kans Med Ctr Kansas City KS 66103

KLAASSEN, DWIGHT HOMER, b Weatherford, Okla, Aug 15, 36; m 57; c 3. BIOCHEMISTRY. Educ: Tabor Col, BA, 58; Kans State Univ, MS, 61, PhD(biochem), 65. Prof Exp: Asst inst biochem, Kans State Univ, 63-64; assoc prof, 64-67, PROF CHEM, UNIV WIS-PLATTEVILLE, 67- Concurrent Pos: Coordr Coop Educ & Internships, 77-; Assoc Dean, Student Affairs, 81- Mem: Am Sci Affil; Sigma Xi; Coop Educ Asn. Res: Binding of sulfur-containing azo dyes related to dimethylaminoazobenzene to rat liver proteins; comparative study of mitochondrial proteins involving amino acid composition and solubility. Mailing Add: Dept Chem Univ Wis Platteville WI 53818

KLAASSEN, HAROLD EUGENE, b Hillsboro, Kans, Apr 18, 35; m 56; c 2. ECOLOGY, FISH BIOLOGY. Educ: Tabor Col, BA, 57; Kans State Univ, MS, 59; Univ Wash, Seattle, PhD(aquatic ecol), 67. Prof Exp: Fishery biologist, Univ Wash, Seattle, 59; ASSOC PROF BIOL, KANS STATE UNIV, 67- Mem: Am Fisheries Soc; Sigma Xi. Res: Fisheries management; fish distribution and production; aquaculture. Mailing Add: Div of Biol Kans State Univ Manhattan KS 66506

KLABUNDE, KENNETH JOHN, b Madison, Wis, May 30, 43; m 67; c 2. ORGANIC CHEMISTRY, INORGANIC CHEMISTRY. Educ: Augustana Col, BA, 65; Univ Iowa, PhD(org chem), 69. Prof Exp: Res assoc org chem, Pa State Univ, 69-70; asst prof org chem, Univ NDak, 70-74, assoc prof, 74-76, prof, 77-79; PROF CHEM & HEAD DEPT, KANS STATE UNIV, 79- Concurrent Pos: Grants, Res Corp, 70-72, Univ NDak, 70-71 & 71-72, Petrol Res Fund, 71-74 & 79-81; grants from NSF, 72-81, US Dept Energy, 74-80 & Indust, 79-81. Honors & Awards: Excellence in Res, Univ Iowa, 69. Mem: Am Chem Soc; Sigma Xi. Res: Organic-Inorganic: reactive intermediates such as metal atom chemistry, carbonmonosulfide chemistry, gas phase cations and radicals; coal conversion and catalysis studies; use of metal vapors and other reactive species as synthetic reagents. Mailing Add: Dept of Chem Kans State Univ Manhattan KS 66506

KLABUNDE, RICHARD EDWIN, b Pasadena, Calif, Oct 7, 48; m 68; c 4. CARDIOVASCULAR PHYSIOLOGY, MICROCIRCULATION. Educ: Pepperdine Univ, BS, 70; Univ Ariz, PhD(physiol), 75. Prof Exp: Am Heart Asn fel physiol, Univ Ariz, 75-76; fel, Nat Heart Lung & Blood Inst, Univ Calif, San Diego, 76, asst res physiologist, Pharmacol Div, 77-78; ASST PROF, DEPT PHYSIOL, WVA UNIV MED CTR, 78- Mem: Am Physiol Soc; Microcirculatory Soc. Res: Mechanisms of blood flow regulation, particularly in skeletal muscle during exercise and following short periods of ischemia; metabolism of adenosine as it relates to blood flow regulation is being studied in skeltal muscle and blood. Mailing Add: Dept Physiol WVa Univ Med Ctr Morgantown WV 26506

KLACSMANN, JOHN ANTHONY, b West New York, NJ, Oct 6, 21; m 44; c 3. ORGANIC CHEMISTRY. Educ: Yale Univ, BS, 42, MS, 44, PhD(org chem), 47. Prof Exp: Lab instr, Yale Univ, 42-44 & 46-47; dept supvr, Carbide & Carbon Chems Corp, Tenn, 44-46; res chemist, Fabrics & Finishes Dept, Newburgh Lab, E I du Pont de Nemours & Co, Inc, 47-49, supvr, 49-53, res mgr, 53-56, res mgr, Marshall Lab, 56-58, lab dir, Exp Sta, Del, 58-59, asst dir res, Fabrics & Finishes Dept, Res Div, 60-64, asst dir mkt, Automative & Indust Prods, 64-66, gen sales mgr consumer prods, 66-67, dir mkt, Consumer Prod Div, 67-69, dir, Finishes Mkt Div, Fabrics & Finishes Dept, 69-71, dir, Finishes Div, 71-73, vpres & gen mgr, Fabrics & Finishes Dept, 73-75, vpres & gen mgr, Int Dept, 75-78; RETIRED. Mem: Am Chem Soc. Res: Finishes; coated fabrics; polymers. Mailing Add: 62 Village Walk Dr Sawgrass Ponte Vedra Beach FL 32082

KLAFTER, RICHARD D(AVID), b New York, NY, Aug 5, 36; m 59; c 2. CONTROLS, ROBOTICS. Educ: Mass Inst Technol, SB, 58; Columbia Univ, MSEE, 59, EE, 63; City Univ New York, PhD(optimal control), 69. Prof Exp: Lectr elec eng, City Col New York, 59-64 & 65-67; asst prof, 67-74, ASSOC PROF ELEC ENG, DREXEL UNIV, 74- Concurrent Pos: Assoc proj dir, NASA-Am Soc Eng Educ, 71; proj dir cardiac pacemakers, NSF, 73-75. Mem: Sigma Xi; Inst Elec & Electronics Engrs. Res: Control theory, vision systems and other robotic sensors; optimal control applied to cardiac and brain pacemakers. Mailing Add: Dept of Elec Eng Drexel Univ 32nd & Chestnut Philadelphia PA 19104

KLAGER, KARL, b Vienna, Austria, May 15, 08; nat US; m 38; c 1. ORGANIC CHEMISTRY. Educ: Univ Vienna, PhD(chem), 34. Prof Exp: Instr, Univ Vienna, 32-34; asst prod engr, Neuman Bros, Roumania, 34-36; res chemist, Chinoin, AG, Hungary, 36-38 & I G Farben, Ger, 39-48; res & develop chemist, Off Naval Res, 49; mgr solid propellant develop, Aerojet-Gen Corp, 50-67, res & tech opers, 67-69, asst gen mgr, Solid Rocket Div, 69-71, vpres-dir opers, Aerojet Solid Propulsion Co, 71-73, TECH CONSULT, AEROJET-GEN CORP, 73- Concurrent Pos: Tech consult, Essex Chem Corp, 73-77. Honors & Awards: Distinguished Pub Serv Award, US Navy, 58; James H Wyld Propulsion Award, Am Inst Aeronaut & Astronaut, 72; Chem Pioneer Award, Am Inst Chemists, 78. Mem: Fel Am Inst Aeronaut & Astronaut; fel Am Inst Chemists; Am Chem Soc; Sigma Xi.

Res: Acetylene derivatives; hydrogenation; cyclooctatetraene; organic preparative and catalytic chemistry; rocket fuels; chemical rocket propellants; synthesis and composition; manufacturing methods; combustion properties; safety characteristics. *Mailing Add:* 4110 Riding Club Lane Sacramento CA 95825

KLAHR, CARL NATHAN, b Pittsburgh, Pa, July 3, 27; m 53; c 3. APPLIED PHYSICS. *Educ:* Carnegie Inst Technol, BS & MS, 48, MS & DSc(physics), 50. *Prof Exp:* Physicist, Res Labs, Westinghouse Elec Corp, 50-52; physicist & proj mgr, Nuclear Develop Corp Am, 52-57; proj mgr & sr physicist, Tech Res Group, Inc, 57-61; sr assoc, 61-67, PRES, FUNDAMENTAL METHODS ASSOCS, INC, 67- *Concurrent Pos:* Lectr, Columbia Univ, 53-58. *Mem:* Am Phys Soc; Am Nuclear Soc; Opers Res Soc Am; Inst Mgt Sci; Inst Elec & Electronics Eng. *Res:* Hypervelocity physics; space vehicle technology; semiconductor device design and technology; solid state physics; operations research; electromagnetic radiation and quantum electronics. *Mailing Add:* Fundamental Methods Assoc Inc 678 Cedar Lawn Ave Lawrence NY 11559

KLAHR, PHILIP, b Mar 7, 46; US citizen. COMPUTER SCIENCE. *Educ:* Univ Mich, BS, 67; Univ Wis, MS, 69, PhD(comput sci), 75. *Prof Exp:* Sr analyst, Syst Develop Corp, 72-78; COMPUT SCIENTIST, RAND CORP, 78- *Mem:* Asn Comput Mach; Spec Interest Group Artificial Intelligence; Cognitive Sci Soc; Am Asn Artificial Intel. *Res:* Artificial intelligence research in knowledge-based systems; rule-based modeling, simulation, languages; explanation techniques, man-machine interfaces,; deductive question-answering, problem solving, learning, planning; abstraction, data-base management and cognitive modeling. *Mailing Add:* Rand Corp 1700 Main St Santa Monica CA 90406

KLAHR, SAULO, b Santander, Colombia, June 8, 35; US citizen; m 65; c 2. NEPHROLOGY. *Educ:* Col de Santa Librada, BS, 54; Nat Univ Colombia, MD, 59. *Prof Exp:* USPHS trainee, 61-63, from instr to assoc prof, 63-72, PROF MED & DIR RENAL DIV, SCH MED, WASHINGTON UNIV, 72- *Concurrent Pos:* Asst physician, Barnes Hosp, St Louis, Mo, 66-72, assoc physician, 72-75, physician, 75-; established investr, Am Heart Asn, 68-73; mem adv comt, Artificial Kidney, Chronic Uremia Prog, Nat Inst Arthritis & Metab Dis, 70-78; chmn med adv bd & mem bd dirs; Kidney Found Eastern Mo & Metro East, 73-74; mem fel comt, Nat Kidney Found, 77-81 & chmn, 80-81; assoc ed, J Clin Invest, 77-82. *Mem:* NY Acad Sci; Am Physiol Soc; Biophys Soc; Am Soc Clin Invest; Asn Am Physicians. *Res:* Hormonal control of ion transport across isolated membranes; studies on the functional and metabolic alterations produced by kidney disease; intermediary metabolism of the kidney. *Mailing Add:* Sch of Med Renal Div 4550 Scott Ave St Louis MO 63110

KLAIBER, FRED WAYNE, b Lafayette, Ind, Oct 7, 40; m 64; c 2. STRUCTURAL ENGINEERING. *Educ:* Purdue Univ, BSCE, 62, MSCE, 64, PhD(struct eng), 68. *Prof Exp:* Res engr, Caterpillar Tractor Co, 68; assoc prof, 68-80, PROF CIVIL ENG, IOWA STATE UNIV, 68- *Mem:* Am Soc Civil Engrs; Am Railway Eng Asn; Am Concrete Inst. *Res:* Engineering mechanics; prestressed folded plate theory; durability study of bridges and bridge slabs. *Mailing Add:* Dept of Civil Eng Iowa State Univ Ames IA 50011

KLAIBER, GEORGE STANLEY, b Toledo, Ohio, Nov 20, 16; m 44; c 2. PHYSICS. *Educ:* Univ Buffalo, BA, 38; Univ Ill, MA, 41, PhD(physics), 43. *Prof Exp:* Asst physics, Univ Buffalo, 38-39; from asst to instr, Univ Ill, 39-44; res physicist, Gen Elec Co, 44-47; from asst prof to assoc prof physics, Univ Buffalo, 47-60; consult physicist, Wurlitzer Co, 60-67; INDEPENDENT CONSULT PHYSICIST, 67- *Mem:* Am Phys Soc. *Res:* Acoustics and vibrations. *Mailing Add:* 2504 Colvin Blvd Tonawanda NY 14150

KLAINER, ALBERT S, b Chelsea, Mass, Oct 29, 35; m 57; c 3. INTERNAL MEDICINE, INFECTIOUS DISEASES. *Educ:* Mass Inst Technol, BSc, 57; Tufts Univ, MD, 61. *Prof Exp:* Assoc prof med, Col Med, Ohio State Univ, 71-72; prof med & infectious dis, Sch Med, WVa Univ, 72-75; PROF MED, MED SCH, RUTGERS UNIV, 75-; CHMN DEPT MED, MORRISTOWN MEM HOSP, 75-; PROF CLIN MED, COL PHYSICIANS & SURGEONS, COLUMBIA UNIV, 80- *Concurrent Pos:* Grant infectious dis & internal med, New Eng Med Ctr Hosps, 63-64 & 65-66. *Honors & Awards:* Hull Award, AMA, 71, Morrissey Award, 72 & Bronze Medal, 72. *Mem:* Infectious Dis Soc Am; fel Am Col Physicians; Am Fedn Clin Res. *Res:* Scanning electron microscopy; infectious diseases and antibiotic pharmacology. *Mailing Add:* Dept of Med Morristown Mem Hosp Morristown NJ 07960

KLAINER, STANLEY M, b Chelsea, Mass, Apr 11, 30; m 52; c 4. INSTRUMENTATION, PHYSICAL CHEMISTRY. *Educ:* Clark Univ, BA, 52, MA, 55, PhD, 59. *Prof Exp:* Res coordr qual control, Martin Div, Martin Marietta Corp, 57-59; chemist, Res Labs, Bendix Corp, 59-60; sr chemist, Nat Res Corp, 60-61; sr chemist, Tracerlab Div, Lab for Electronics, Inc, 61-63, spec projs mgr instruments, 63-64, from res & develop mgr to res mgr, 64-67; staff chemist, Block Eng, Inc, 67-70, mgr anal systs dept, 70-77; tech consult laser spectroscopy, 78; DEP GROUP LEADER GEOSCI, LAWRENCE BERKELEY LAB, 78-, GROUP LEADER EARTH CHEM, 81- *Mem:* Am Chem Soc; NY Acad Sci; Soc Appl Spectros; fel Am Inst Chemists. *Res:* Development of microwave spectrometers and nuclear instruments; analysis of trace atmospheric constituents, ablation, encapsulation, special quality control analytical techniques and ultracentrifugation; interferometry; Raman, remote Raman, micro Raman and infrared spectroscopy; nuclear quadrupole resonance; micro particle analysis; chemical transport in natural systems. *Mailing Add:* 20 Belinda Ct San Ramon CA 94583

KLAMKIN, MURRAY S, b Brooklyn, NY, Mar 5, 21. MATHEMATICS. *Educ:* Cooper Union, BChE, 42; Polytech Inst Brooklyn, MS, 47. *Prof Exp:* From instr to assoc prof math, Polytech Inst Brooklyn, 48-56; prin staff mathematician, Res & Adv Develop Div, Avco Corp, 56-62; prof interdisciplinary studies & res in eng, State Univ NY, Buffalo, 62-64; vis prof math, Univ Minn, 64-65; prin res scientist, Sci Lab, Ford Motor Co, 65-75; prof appl math, Univ Waterloo, 74-76; PROF & CHMN DEPT MATH, UNIV ALTA, 76- *Concurrent Pos:* Problem ed, Soc Indust & Appl Math Review, 59-; Nat High Sch Math Contest Comt, 72-; mem, Can Olympiad Comt, 74-; coach, US Int Math Olympiad Team, 75- *Mem:* AAAS; Am Math Soc; Math Asn Am; Soc Indust & Appl Math. *Res:* Applied mathematics; geometry; heat conduction and radiation. *Mailing Add:* Dept of Math Univ of Alta Edmonton AB T6G 2G1 Can

KLAMUT, CARL J, b Maspeth, NY, Oct 26, 26; m 53; c 3. METALLURGY. *Educ:* NY Univ, BSME, 51. *Prof Exp:* Asst metallurgist, 51-61, METALLURGIST, BROOKHAVEN NAT LAB, 61- *Mem:* Am Soc Metals; Am Soc Testing & Mat. *Res:* Liquid metal corrosion; materials development and evaluation; superconducting materials. *Mailing Add:* Dept Energy & Environ Brookhaven Nat Lab Upton NY 11973

KLAND, MATHILDE JUNE, b Chicago, Ill, June 7, 16; m 50; c 2. ENVIRONMENTAL CHEMISTRY, FOSSIL FUEL CHEMISTRY. *Educ:* Univ Chicago, BS, 39; Northwestern Univ, PhD(org chem), 48. *Prof Exp:* Sr chemist, Distillation Prods, Inc, NY, 39-41; sr chemist, Revere & La Ord Divs, 41-43; asst prof chem, Goucher Col, 48-49; E I du Pont fel, Ohio State Univ, 49-51; res assoc, Boston Univ, 51-52; writer & abstractor, 52-54 & 56-58; res assoc, Med Sch, Tufts Univ, 54-56; STAFF SCIENTIST, LAWRENCE BERKELEY LAB, UNIV CALIF, 58- *Concurrent Pos:* fel, Ohio State Univ, 49-51. *Mem:* AAAS; Am Chem Soc. *Res:* Reactions of styrene oxide; structure of styrene oxide dimers; molecular structure and spectra of organic compounds; abnormal bimolecular reactions of furfuryl chloride; grignard reactions; radiation chemistry of peptides; water pollution monitoring of bio-parameters and organics; toxic effects of pollutants, food additives and drugs; use of structure-toxicity/carcinogenicity relationships in prediction of health effects; fossil fuel chemistry. *Mailing Add:* 3678 Hastings Ct Lafayette CA 94549

KLANDERMAN, BRUCE HOLMES, b Grand Rapids, Mich, Feb 27, 38; m 60; c 3. ORGANIC CHEMISTRY. *Educ:* Calvin Col, AB, 59; Univ Ill, MS, 61, PhD(org chem), 63. *Prof Exp:* Res chemist, 63-64, sr res chemist, 64-68, res assoc, 68-74, tech assoc, Synthetic Chem Div, 75, dept head, 76-77, govt regulations coordr, Gen Mgt, 78-80, DIR, ENVIRON TECH SERV, KODAK PARK DIV, EASTMAN KODAK CO, 81- *Mem:* Soc Photog Scientists & Engrs; Am Chem Soc. *Res:* Benzyne chemistry; liquid crystals; organic semiconductors; aliphatic diazonium chemistry; anthracene and triptycene chemistry. *Mailing Add:* Environ Tech Serv Kodak Park Div Eastman Kodak Co Rochester NY 14650

KLANFER, KARL, b Vienna, Austria, Oct 10, 04; m 46; c 1. CHEMICAL ENGINEERING. *Educ:* Inst Technol, Vienna, Austria, ChemE, 27. *Prof Exp:* Chief chemist, Wiener Leather Indust, Vienna, Austria, 27-34; supt, E Traub Co, Prague, Czech, 35-39; res chemist, Beardmore & Co Ltd, Acton, Ont, Can, 40-46; res dir, Cortume Carioca, Brazil, 46-50; res dir, AR Clarke & Co Ltd, Toronto, Can, 50-56; tech dir, A C Lawrence Leather Co, Peabody, 56-61; CONSULT CHEM ENG, 61- *Concurrent Pos:* Lectr, Univ Vienna, 30-34. *Mem:* Sr mem Am Chem Soc; Am Leather Chem Asn; fel Chem Inst Can; Royal Soc Chem. *Res:* Chemistry and technology of leather and tanning; author or coauthor of 40 publications. *Mailing Add:* 18 Colgate Rd Marblehead MA 01945

KLANICA, ANDREW JOSEPH, b West Leechburg, Pa, Mar 21, 20; m 45; c 5. INDUSTRIAL CHEMISTRY. *Educ:* Univ Pittsburgh, BS, 49. *Prof Exp:* Res chemist, Am Cyanamid Corp, 50-53; group leader, High Energy Fuels Div, Olin Mathieson Chem Corp, 53-60, sr res chemist, 60-73, RES ASSOC, OLIN CORP, 73- *Mem:* Am Chem Soc. *Res:* Fluorine chemistry; fertilizer technology; process development; industrial chemicals. *Mailing Add:* Olin Corp 120 Long Ridge Rd Stamford CT 06904

KLAPMAN, SOLOMON JOEL, b Chicago, Ill, Apr 25, 12; m 37; c 2. MATHEMATICAL PHYSICS. *Educ:* Univ Chicago, BS, 32, PhD(physics), 40; Univ Mich, MS, 35. *Prof Exp:* Math physicist, Jensen Mfg Co, Ill, 37-40; physicist, Frankford Arsenal, Pa, 40-41, Utah Radio Prods Co, Ill, 41-46, Indust Res Prods Co, 47-49, E I Guthman & Co, 49-50 & Admiral Corp, 51-52; sr electronics engr, Chicago Midway Labs, 52-55 & Lockheed Missile Systs, 55-56; sr scientist, Hughes Aircraft Co, Culver City, 56-73; ADJ PROF CIVIL ENG, UNIV SOUTHERN CALIF, 73- *Concurrent Pos:* Instr evening div, Ill Inst Technol, 42-50; lectr, Roosevelt Col, 50-, Mt St Mary Col, 63-64 & Immaculate Heart Col, 64-65. *Mem:* Am Phys Soc; Acoust Soc Am; Am Asn Physics Teachers. *Res:* Acoustics; magnetism; infrared. *Mailing Add:* 7842 E Lakeview Trail Orange CA 92669

KLAPPER, CLARENCE EDWARD, b Schenectady, NY, Dec 13, 08; m 46. EMBRYOLOGY. *Educ:* Union Col, NY, AB, 32; Cornell Univ, MA, 33, PhD(histol, embryol), 38. *Prof Exp:* Asst histol & embryol, Cornell Univ, 32-37; from instr to asst prof biol, Hobart Col, 37-43; from instr to asst prof anat, Sch Med, La State Univ, 43-46; asst prof, Med Col Ala, 46-51; assoc prof, Univ Ala, Birmingham, 51-58, prof anat, Med Col & Sch Dent, 58-79; RETIRED. *Concurrent Pos:* Technician, Biol Surv, State Conserv Dept, NY, 34 & 39. *Mem:* AAAS; Am Asn Anat; Asn Am Med Cols; Int Asn Dent Res. *Res:* Embryology of pharyngeal derivatives; sex hormone effect on thymus and lymph nodes; experimental dental caries in Syrian hamster; structure, development and function of salivary glands. *Mailing Add:* 1619 Lakewood Dr University Sta Birmingham AL 35216

KLAPPER, GILBERT, b Wichita, Kans, Sept 29, 34; m 59; c 3. PALEONTOLOGY. *Educ:* Stanford Univ, BS, 56; Univ Kans, MS, 58; Univ Iowa, PhD(geol), 62. *Prof Exp:* Paleontologist, Shell Oil Co, La, 58-59; NSF fel & res assoc, Ill State Geol Surv, 62-63; res paleontologist, Res Ctr, Pan Am Petrol Corp, 63-68; assoc prof, 68-73, PROF GEOL, UNIV IOWA, 73- *Concurrent Pos:* Vis prof, Ore State Univ, 78. *Mem:* Paleont Res Inst; Paleont Soc; Soc Econ Paleont & Mineral; Brit Paleont Asn; Ger Paleont Soc. *Res:* Micropaleontology, especially research in conodonts; biostratigraphy, Silurian, Devonian and Mississippian. *Mailing Add:* Dept of Geol Univ of Iowa Iowa City IA 52242

KLAPPER, JACOB, b Ulanow, Poland, Sept 17, 30; US citizen; m 58; c 2. COMMUNICATIONS SYSTEMS. *Educ:* City Col New York, BEE, 56; Columbia Univ, MS, 58; NY Univ, EngScD, 65. *Prof Exp:* Elec engr, Columbia Broadcasting Syst, 52-56; lectr elec eng, City Col New York, 56-59; proj engr, Fed Sci Corp, 59-60; sr mem tech staff, Adv Commun Labs, Radio Corp Am, 60-65, sr proj mem tech staff, 65-67; from assoc prof to prof elec eng, Newark Col Eng, 67-71; PROF, NJ INST TECHNOL, NEWARK, 71- *Mem:* Sr mem Inst Elec & Electronics Eng; Aerospace & Electron Systs Soc. *Res:* Electrical communication; systems and techniques with emphasis on phase-locked loops and FM systems. *Mailing Add:* NJ Inst of Technol 323 High St Newark NJ 07102

KLAPPER, MARGARET STRANGE, b New Orleans, La, May 23, 14; m 46. INTERNAL MEDICINE. *Educ:* Tulane Univ, BS, 35, MD, 39; Am Bd Internal Med, dipl, 46. *Prof Exp:* Intern & resident internal med, Charity Hosp, New Orleans, La, 39-41; physician & instr hyg, Univ SC, 41-42; asst med, Tulane Univ, 42-44, instr internal med, Sch Med, 44-46; instr med, 46-48, asst prof internal med, 48-61, assoc prof med, 61-66, asst dean students, 62-67, asst prof clin dent, Sch Dent, 48-59, assoc prof clin dent, Sch Dent, 59-80, prof med, 66-80, EMER PROF MED, SCH MED, UNIV ALA, 80- *Concurrent Pos:* Dir, Div Continuing Med Educ, Univ Ala, 62-75. *Mem:* AMA; fel Am Col Physicians. *Res:* Investigation of drugs in therapy of hypertension and congestive heart failure. *Mailing Add:* Univ of Ala Med Ctr University Sta Birmingham AL 35294

KLAPPER, MICHAEL H, b Berlin, Ger, June 10, 37; US citizen; m 60; c 2. BIOCHEMISTRY. *Educ:* Harvard Univ, AB, 58; Univ Rochester, MS, 59; Univ Calif, PhD(biochem), 64. *Prof Exp:* Fel chem, Northwestern Univ, 64-66; asst prof, 66-73, ASSOC PROF CHEM, OHIO STATE UNIV, 73- *Mem:* Biophys Soc; Am Soc Biol Chemists. *Res:* Physical biochemistry of enzyme structure; theoretical and experimental studies of enzyme catalysis; sexual attraction in lower plants; physical, chemical and metabolic studies on effects of sexual attractants. *Mailing Add:* 1641 Essex Rd Columbus OH 43221

KLAPPROTH, WILLIAM JACOB, JR, b Springfield, Ohio, Aug 2, 20; m 45; c 2. POLYMER CHEMISTRY. *Educ:* Wittenberg Col, AB, 42; Univ Chicago, MS & PhD(org chem), 49. *Prof Exp:* Res chemist, Stamford Res Labs, Am Cyanamid Co, 49-54, group leader, Warners Plant, 54-57, group leader catalytic & gen process improv, Bridgeville Plant, 57-59, mgr acids & miscellaneous chems develop, 59-63; tech dir, Bridgeville Plant, Koppers Co, Inc, 63-67, sr proj scientist, Monroeville Res Ctr, Arco Polymers Inc, 67-70, sr group mgr, 70-78, prin scientist, Arco Chem Co, 79-81; CONSULT, 81- *Mem:* Am Chem Soc. *Res:* Research and development in polymers, especially polystyrene, high pressure polyethylene and related copolymers. *Mailing Add:* 3576 Logans Ferry Rd Murrysville PA 15668

KLARER, DAVID MATTHEW, Springfield, Ohio. LIMINOLOGY. *Educ:* Duke Univ, BA, 70; Univ Alta, MSc, 73; Glasgow Univ, UK, PhD(zool), 78. *Prof Exp:* Fel paleolimnol, Dept Bot, Univ Alta, 76-78; SANCTUARY ECOLOGIST LIMNOL, DIV NAT AREAS & PRESERVES, OHIO DEPT NATURAL RESOURCES, 79- *Mem:* Am Soc Limnol & Oceanog; Phycol Soc Am; Brit Phycol Asn; Int Asn Appl & Thoeret Limnol; Brit Freshwater Biol Asn. *Mailing Add:* Old Woman Creek Nat Estuarine Sanctuary 2005 Cleveland Rd E Huron OH 44839

KLARFELD, JOSEPH, b Poland, Dec 22, 35. THEORETICAL PHYSICS. *Educ:* Israel Inst Technol, BSc, 59, MSc, 62; Yeshiva Univ, PhD(physics), 69. *Prof Exp:* Instr physics, Israel Inst Technol, 58-61; res assoc, Israel Atomic Energy Comn, 61-63; asst prof, 69-73, asst chmn dept, 69-76, dep chmn dept, 76-78, ASSOC PROF PHYSICS, QUEENS COL, NEW YORK, 74-; ASSOC PROF, GRAD CTR, CITY UNIV NY, 80- *Concurrent Pos:* Vis assoc prof, Tel Aviv Univ, 78-79; res fel, City Univ New York, 78-79. *Mem:* Asn Math Physics; Sigma Xi; Am Phys Soc; NY Acad Sci; Int Soc Gen Relativity & Gravitation. *Res:* Quantization of general relativity; foundations of quantum field theory; relativistic astrophysics. *Mailing Add:* Dept of Physics Queens Col of City Univ Flushing NY 11367

KLARMAN, KARL J(OSEPH), b Scotia, NY, Mar 18, 22; m; c 2. ELECTRICAL ENGINEERING. *Educ:* Union Col, BS, 44; Columbia Univ, MS, 47. *Prof Exp:* Jr engr, Carl L Norden, Inc, 44; lectr elec eng, Union Univ, NY, 45-46; proj engr, Avion Instrument Corp, 46-47; proj engr, Eclipse-Pioneer Div, Bendix Aviation Corp, 47-51; plant mgr, Electro Tec Corp, 51-53, dir eng, 53-55, vpres, 55-57; sect head, Sanders Assocs, 57-59; chief prod engr, Precision Prod Dept, Northrop, 59-61; eng scientist, Defense Electronic Prod Div, Radio Corp Am, 61-74, eng scientist, Govt & Com Div, RCA Corp, 71-74; CONSULT, 74- *Mem:* Sigma Xi; Nat Soc Prof Engrs; Inst Elec & Electronics Engrs. *Res:* Gyroscopic instruments, design, development and production; design, development, test and production of inertial and other electro-mechanical instruments and systems. *Mailing Add:* 20 Kipling St Nashua NH 03062

KLARMAN, WILLIAM L, phytopathology, see previous edition

KLARMANN, JOSEPH, b Berlin, Ger, Jan 16, 28; m 57; c 2. PHYSICS. *Educ:* Hebrew Univ, Israel, MSc, 54; Univ Rochester, PhD(physics), 58. *Prof Exp:* Res assoc & instr, Univ Rochester, 57-58, instr, 58-61; from asst prof to assoc prof, 61-74, PROF PHYSICS, WASH UNIV, 74- *Mem:* Int Astron Union; AAAS; Am Asn Physics Teachers. *Res:* Cosmic ray astrophysics. *Mailing Add:* Dept of Physics Wash Univ St Louis MO 63130

KLASNER, JOHN SAMUEL, b Flint, Mich, June 22, 35; m 64; c 4. STRUCTURAL GEOLOGY, APPLIED GEOPHYSICS. *Educ:* Mich State Univ, BS, 57, MS, 64; Mich Technol Univ, PhD(geol), 72. *Prof Exp:* Geophys engr, Geophys Serv Inc, 57-62; geophysicist, Standard Oil Co Calif, 64-69; from asst prof to assoc prof geol, 72-79, chmn dept, 74-78, PROF GEOL, WESTERN ILL UNIV, 80-; GEOLOGIST ECON GEOL, US GEOL SURV, 72- *Mem:* AAAS; Sigma Xi; Geol Soc Am; Soc Explor Geophysicists; Geol Asn Can. *Res:* Economic geology, Northern Michigan; Precambrian geology, Northern Michigan; structural geology, tectonics; geophysical archeology; regional geophysics North and South Dakota. *Mailing Add:* Dept Geol Western Ill Univ Macomb IL 61455

KLASS, ALAN ARNOLD, b Russia, Aug 13, 07; nat; m 39; c 2. ANATOMY, SURGERY. *Educ:* Univ Man, BA, 27, MD, 32; FRCS(E), 37; FRCS(C), 43. *Hon Degrees:* LLD, Univ Man, 74. *Prof Exp:* Asst prof anat & assoc prof surg, 37-68, ASST PROF SURG & ASSOC PROF ANAT, UNIV MAN, 68- *Concurrent Pos:* Assoc surgeon, Winnipeg Gen Hosp, 38- & Misericordia Gen Hosp, 38-; pres, Medico-Legal Soc Man, 63-65; chmn, Govt Comt Cent Drug Purchasing & Distrib. *Mem:* Can Surg Soc (past secy); Can Fedn Biol Soc; Can Asn Anat; Medico-Legal Soc (pres). *Res:* Pilo-nidal sinus; acute mesenteric occlusion; fatigue fractures tibia; engineering and scientific principles; professionalism and professional integrity. *Mailing Add:* Mall Med Bldg Osborne St N Winnipeg MB R3C 1V8 Can

KLASS, DONALD LEROY, b Waukegan, Ill, July 23, 26; m; c 3. ORGANIC CHEMISTRY. *Educ:* Univ Ill, BS, 51; Harvard Univ, AM, 52, PhD(org chem), 55. *Prof Exp:* Res chemist, Standard Oil Co, Ind, 54-55 & Am Can Co, 56-59; dir process & prod res div, Pure Oil Co, Ill, 59-65; asst dir basic res, 65-69, asst res dir, 69-76, dir basic res, 76-77, dir eng & sci res, 77-79, asst vpres, 79-80, VPRES EDUC, INST GAS TECHNOL, ILL INST TECHNOL, 80- *Concurrent Pos:* consult energy & chem prod. *Honors & Awards:* Richard A Glenn Award, 76. *Mem:* Am Chem Soc; Am Asn Univ Prof; Am Inst Chem Eng; Am Gas Asn. *Res:* Research and education administration; gas processing; petrochemicals; refining; catalysis; fermentation; waste treatment; pollution control; gasification-liquefaction of wastes, biomass & fossil fuels; energy supplies. *Mailing Add:* 25543 W Scott Rd Barrington IL 60010

KLASSEN, DAVID MORRIS, b Clovis, NMex, June 15, 39; m 65; c 2. INORGANIC CHEMISTRY, SPECTROSCOPY. *Educ:* Univ Tex, El Paso, BS, 61; Univ NMex, PhD(phys chem), 67. *Prof Exp:* Teaching asst, Univ NMex, 61-62; NATO res fel, Inst Phys Chem, Frankfurt, WGer, 66-67; res assoc, Univ NC, Chapel Hill, 67-69; from asst prof to assoc prof, 69-77, PROF CHEM, McMURRY COL, 77- *Mem:* Am Chem Soc; Sigma Xi; Sci Res Soc Am. *Res:* Synthesis, bonding and electronic structure of transition-metal complexes; luminescence of ruthenium and osmium complexes. *Mailing Add:* Dept of Chem McMurry Col Abilene TX 79697

KLASSEN, J(OHN), b Waterloo, Ont, Jan 9, 28; m 50; c 4. CHEMICAL ENGINEERING. *Educ:* Queen's Univ, Ont, BSc, 48, MSc, 49; Univ Wis, PhD(chem eng), 54. *Prof Exp:* Jr res officer, chem eng, Nat Res Coun Can, 49-53, asst res officer, 53-55; res engr, 55-57, res supvr, 57-59, tech supt, 59-62, tech mgr, 62-66, asst works mgr, 66-69, mgr, Cent Res Lab, Maitland, 69-71, tech mgr, 71-75, SR ENG SPECIALIST, DU PONT CAN, 75- *Mem:* Can Soc Chem Engrs; fel Chem Inst Can. *Res:* Commercial processing of industrial chemicals. *Mailing Add:* DuPont Can Inc 555 Dorchester Blvd W Montreal PQ H3C 2V1 Can

KLASSEN, NORMAN VICTOR, b Winnipeg, Man, Nov 6, 33; m 61; c 3. PHYSICAL CHEMISTRY. *Educ:* McGill Univ, BSc, 54, PhD(chem), 57; Univ Col, London, PhD(chem), 61. *Prof Exp:* Fel, Nat Res Coun Can, 61-63; fel phys chem, Mellon Inst, 63-66; MEM RES STAFF, PHYSICS DIV, NAT RES COUN CAN, 66- *Mem:* Royal Soc Chem; Chem Inst Can. *Res:* Radiation chemistry; pulse radiolysis. *Mailing Add:* Physics Div Nat Res Coun of Can M-35 Ottawa ON K1A 0R6 Can

KLASSEN, RUDOLPH WALDEMAR, b Hanna, Alta, Sept 30, 28; m 67; c 4. GEOLOGY. *Educ:* Univ Alta, BSc, 59, MSc, 60; Univ Sask, PhD(geol), 65. *Prof Exp:* RES SCIENTIST QUATERNARY GEOLOGY, GEOL SURV CAN, 65- *Mem:* Geol Asn Can; Am Quaternary Asn. *Res:* Quaternary stratigraphy and geomorphology. *Mailing Add:* Geol Surv of Can 3303 33rd St NW Calgary AB T2L 2A7 Can

KLASSEN, WALDEMAR, b Vauxhall, Alta, Dec 28, 35; US citizen; m 64; c 1. ENTOMOLOGY, GENETICS. *Educ:* Univ Alta, BSc, 57, MSc, 59; Univ Western Ont, PhD(zool), 63. *Prof Exp:* USPHS res assoc zool, Univ Ill, 63-65; res geneticist, Metab & Radiation Res Lab, Entom Res Div, 65-67, leader insect physiol & metab sect, 67-70, asst to dep adminr plant sci & entom, 70-72, STAFF SCIENTIST PEST MGT, AGR RES SERV, USDA, 72- *Honors & Awards:* Dipl & Medal, Int Cong Plant Protection, 75. *Mem:* AAAS; Entom Soc Am; Am Chem Soc; Genetics Soc Can. *Res:* Dispersal of mosquitoes; inheritance of resistance to insecticides in mosquitoes; cytogenetics of mosquitoes; chemosterilization of insects; program planning in entomological research; insect population dynamics. *Mailing Add:* USDA Rm 338 Bldg 005 Agr Res Ctr-W Beltsville MD 20705

KLATSKIN, GERALD, b New York, NY, May 14, 10; m 49; c 3. INTERNAL MEDICINE. *Educ:* Cornell Univ, AB, 29, MD, 33. *Hon Degrees:* MA, Yale Univ, 57. *Prof Exp:* Instr med, Univ Rochester, 36-37; instr, 37-42, from asst clin prof to assoc prof, 46-57, David Paige Smith prof, 57-78, EMER DAVID PAIGE SMITH PROF MED, SCH MED, YALE UNIV, 78-, STAFF MEM, DEPT PATHOL, 78- *Concurrent Pos:* Commonwealth Fund res fel, Copenhagen, 64-65; consult, Vet Hosp, West Haven, Conn, 46-; assoc physician, Yale-New Haven Med Ctr, 48- *Honors & Awards:* Blake Award, Yale Univ, 52. *Mem:* Soc Exp Biol & Med; Asn Am Physicians; master Am Col Physicians; Am Fedn Clin Res. *Res:* Liver diseases. *Mailing Add:* Dept of Path Yale Univ Sch of Med New Haven CT 06510

KLATT, ARTHUR RAYMOND, b Hamilton, Tex, June 10, 43; m 64; c 3. PLANT BREEDING. *Educ:* Tex Tech Univ, BS, 66; Colo State Univ, MS, 68, PhD(plant breeding & genetics), 69. *Prof Exp:* Plant breeder, 69-80, ASSOC DIR, WHEAT PROG, INT MAIZE & WHEAT IMPROV CTR, 80- *Mem:* Am Soc Agron; Crop Sci Soc Am; Am Genetic Asn; AAAS. *Res:* Genetics and environmental factors affecting drought tolerance; genetics and environmental influence on dormancy, vernalization and winterhardiness; incorporation of horizontal resistance; breeding adapted high yielding winter and spring wheat varieties. *Mailing Add:* Int Maize & Wheat Improv Ctr Apartado Postal 6-641 06600 Mexico DF Mexico

KLATT, GARY BRANDT, b Milwaukee, Wis, Nov 22, 39; m 64; c 2. MATHEMATICS. *Educ:* Case Western Reserve Univ, BS, 61; Univ Wis, MS, 62, PhD(math), 69. *Prof Exp:* Instr math, Marquette Univ, 64-65; from asst prof to assoc prof, 67-75, PROF MATH, UNIV WIS-WHITEWATER, 75- *Mem:* Math Asn Am; Nat Coun Teachers Math. *Res:* Theory of rings and modules. *Mailing Add:* Dept of Math Univ of Wis Whitewater WI 53190

KLATT, LEON NICHOLAS, b Underhill, Wis, Aug 28, 40; m 61; c 2. ELECTROANALYTICAL CHEMISTRY, CHEMICAL INSTRUMENTATION. *Educ:* Wis State Univ-Oshkosh, BS, 62; Univ Wis, Madison, PhD(anal chem), 67. *Prof Exp:* Chemist, Dow Chem Co, Mich, 62-63; asst, Univ Wis, Madison, 63-66; asst prof chem, Southern Ill Univ, 67-69 & Univ Ga, 69-74; RES STAFF MEM, OAK RIDGE NAT LAB, 74- *Mem:* Am Chem Soc; Sigma Xi. *Res:* Instrumentation for remote analyses; trace analysis and characterization of environmental samples; study of homogeous and heterogenous electron transfer reactions; application of small computers to analytical problems; liquid chromatography instrumentation and applications. *Mailing Add:* Oak Ridge Nat Lab PO Box X Oak Ridge TN 37830

KLATTE, EUGENE, b Indianapolis, Ind, Mar 19, 28; m 50; c 4. RADIOLOGY. *Educ:* Ind Univ, AB, 49, MD, 52. *Prof Exp:* Resident radiol, Univ Calif, 55-57; from instr to assoc prof, Sch Med, Ind Univ, 58-62; prof & chmn dept, Sch Med, Vanderbilt Univ, 62-71; prof, 71-80, DISTINGUISHED PROF & CHMN DEPT, SCH MED, IND UNIV, INDIANAPOLIS, 80- *Concurrent Pos:* Picker res scholar, Sch Med, Ind Univ, 57-58; consult, Vet Admin Hosp, Nashville, Tenn, 62-71; clin prof, Meharry Med Col, 64-71. *Mem:* Am Col Radiol; Asn Univ Radiol; Radiol Soc NAm; Soc Pediat Radiol; AMA. *Res:* Diagnostic radiology, especially cardiovascular radiology. *Mailing Add:* Dept of Radiol Ind Univ Med Ctr Indianapolis IN 46202

KLATZO, IGOR, b St Petersburg, Russia, Oct 9, 16; nat US; m 57; c 2. MEDICINE. *Educ:* Univ Freiburg, MD, 47; McGill Univ, MSc, 51. *Prof Exp:* Asst to Prof O Vogt, Brain Res Inst, Ger, 46-48; demonstr neuropath, Montreal Neurol Inst, 48-51; prosecutor & lectr path, Path Inst, McGill Univ, 53-54; chief clin neuropath, Surg Neurol Br, 56-68, CHIEF LAB NEUROPATH & NEUROANAT SCI, NAT INST NEUROL DIS & STROKE, 68- *Concurrent Pos:* Victor Mem scholar, 51-52; Douglas fel path, Path Inst, McGill Univ, 51-52; teaching fel, 52-53; Blari Mem fel, US, Mex & Europe, 54-56. *Mem:* Am Asn Neuropath. *Res:* Neuropathology; experimental neurology. *Mailing Add:* Lab Neuropath & Neuroanat Sci Commun Dis & Stroke Bethesda MD 20014

KLAUBER, MELVILLE ROBERTS, b San Diego, Calif, Aug 9, 33; m 53; c 6. STATISTICS. *Educ:* Stanford Univ, AB, 54, MS, 56, PhD(statist), 64. *Prof Exp:* From assoc prof to prof family & community med & chief, Div Biostatist, Col Med, Univ Utah, 67-78. *Concurrent Pos:* Adj assoc prof math, Univ Utah, 72-76, adj prof math, 76-78; prin statistician, Sch Med, Univ Calif, La Jolla, 78-81, adj prof community & family med, 81- *Mem:* AAAS; Inst Math Statist; Am Statist Asn; Biomet Soc. *Res:* Biostatistics; statistical methods for the medical sciences, especially epidemiology. *Mailing Add:* Dept Family & Community Med Univ Calif Sch Med T-002 La Jolla CA 92093

KLAUBERT, DIETER HEINZ, b Ger, Dec 15, 44; Can citizen; m 69; c 2. MEDICINAL CHEMISTRY. *Educ:* Univ Alta, BSc, 67; Mass Inst Technol, PhD(org chem), 71. *Prof Exp:* Fel org chem, Univ Calif, Berkeley, 71-73; RES CHEMIST, WYETH LABS INC, AM HOME PROD CORP, 73- *Mem:* Am Chem Soc; The Chem Soc. *Res:* Synthesis of novel compounds of pharmaceutical interest. *Mailing Add:* Wyeth Labs Inc PO Box 8299 Philadelphia PA 19101

KLAUDER, JOHN RIDER, b Reading, Pa, Jan 24, 32; m 53; c 4. THEORETICAL PHYSICS. *Educ:* Univ Calif, Berkeley, BS, 53; Stevens Inst Technol, MS, 56; Princeton Univ, MA, 57, PhD(physics), 59. *Prof Exp:* Head theoret physics dept, 66-67 & 69-71, head solid state spectros dept, 71-76, MEM TECH STAFF, BELL TEL LABS, 53- *Concurrent Pos:* Vis assoc prof, Univ Bern, 61-62; adj prof, Rutgers Univ, 65; prof, Syracuse Univ, 67-68. *Mem:* Fel Am Phys Soc. *Res:* Solid state physics; relativity; quantum field theory. *Mailing Add:* Bell Labs Murray Hill NJ 07971

KLAUS, E(LMER) ERWIN, b Neffsville, Pa, Apr 19, 21; m 45; c 2. CHEMICAL ENGINEERING, TRIBOLOGY. *Educ:* Franklin & Marshall Col, BS, 43; Pa State Univ, MS, 46, PhD(chem), 52. *Prof Exp:* Res asst, 43-47, instr petrol chem, 47-52, asst prof, 52-56, assoc res prof, 56-65, PROF CHEM ENG, PA STATE UNIV, 65- *Concurrent Pos:* Consult, US Dept Defense, 55; mem mechanisms comt, Off Naval Res Mech Failures Prevention Group; coun mem, Nat Bur Standards Mech Failures Prev Group, 70-, coun chmn, 76-80; assoc ed, J Lubrication Technol, 74-80; mem nat res coun comt, US Army Basic Res, 77-80; Fenske fac fel chem eng, 79- *Honors & Awards:* Outstanding Achievement Res, Pa State Eng Asn, 72; Nat Award, Am Soc Lubrication Engrs, 76; Capt Alfred E Hunt Award, Am Soc Lubrication Engrs, 80. *Mem:* Am Chem Soc; fel Am Soc Lubrication Engrs; fel Am Inst Chem; Am Inst Chem Engrs; Am Soc Mech Engrs. *Res:* Boundary lubrication; metal corrosion; petroleum refining; physical and chemical properties of lubricants; use of surfactants and polymers in enhanced oil recovery; surface chemical effects. *Mailing Add:* Dept of Chem Eng 198 Fenske Lab Pa State Univ University Park PA 16802

KLAUS, EWALD FRED, JR, b Needville, Tex, Oct 22, 28; m 64. ZOOLOGY, ENTOMOLOGY. *Educ:* Univ Tex, BA, 52, MA, 58; Tex A&M Univ, PhD(entom), 65. *Prof Exp:* From asst prof to assoc prof, 64-74, PROF BIOL, ETEX STATE UNIV, 74- *Concurrent Pos:* Fac res grant, 67-68, NSF fel, Col Sci Improv Prog, 71-72. *Res:* Biology and taxonomy of mosquitoes; genetics of insecticide resistance in cotton insects; insecticide residue studies. *Mailing Add:* Dept of Biol ETex State Univ Commerce TX 75428

KLAUS, RONALD LOUIS, b Brooklyn, NY, Apr 23, 40; m 68; c 1. CHEMICAL ENGINEERING. *Educ:* Rensselaer Polytech Inst, BChE, 60, PhD(chem eng), 67. *Prof Exp:* Res engr combustion, Jet Propulsion Lab, 63-65 & 68-70; ASST PROF CHEM ENG, UNIV PA, 70- *Concurrent Pos:* Resident res assoc fel, Jet Propulsion Lab, 68-70. *Mem:* Am Inst Chem Engrs. *Res:* Computer-aided design in chemical engineering; thermodynamics of liquid mixtures; computer-based estimation of thermodynamic properties; numerical methods; design and implementation of computer-based problem-oriented languages for engineering. *Mailing Add:* 607 S 48th St Philadelphia PA 18143

KLAUS, SIDNEY N, b Detroit, Mich, June 29, 31; m 59; c 2. DERMATOLOGY. *Educ:* Univ Mich, BA, 53, MD, 57. *Prof Exp:* From asst prof to assoc prof, 65-74, PROF DERMAT, SCH MED, YALE UNIV, 74- *Mem:* Tissue Cult Asn; Soc Invest Dermat. *Res:* Pigment cell biology. *Mailing Add:* Dept of Internal Med Yale Univ Sch of Med New Haven CT 06510

KLAUSMEIER, ROBERT EDWARD, b Evansville, Ind, June 6, 26; m 51; c 4. MICROBIOLOGY, CHEMISTRY. *Educ:* Univ Ind, AB, 51, MA, 53; La State Univ, PhD(bact), 58. *Prof Exp:* Asst bact, Univ Ind, 51-53; res bacteriologist, Army Chem Corps, Ft Detrick, Md, 53-55; asst prof bact, Southwestern La Inst, 55-57; asst, La State Univ, 57-58; microbiologist, 58-80, CHEMIST, WEAPONS QUAL ENG CTR, NAVAL WEAPONS SUPPORT CTR, 80- *Mem:* AAAS; Am Soc Microbiol; Soc Indust Microbiol. *Res:* Microbial deterioration of materials, particularly explosives and synthetic polymers; microbial physiology; enzymology; economcially effective demilitarization of ammunition. *Mailing Add:* Weapons Qual Eng Ctr Naval Weapons Support Ctr Crane IN 47522

KLAUSTERMEYER, WILLIAM BERNER, b San Pedro, Calif, Nov 30, 39; m 62; c 3. ALLERGY, IMMUNOLOGY. *Educ:* Univ Calif, Los Angeles, BA, 62; Univ Cincinnati, MD, 66. *Prof Exp:* Intern, Wadsworth Vet Admin Hosp, 66-67, resident, 67-68, fel pulmonary, 68-69; fel allergy & immunol, Nat Jewish Hosp, 69-70; allergist, US Air Force Med Ctr, Wright Patterson Air Force Base, 70-72; CHIEF ALLERGY & IMMUNOL, WADSWORTH VET ADMIN HOSP, LOS ANGELES, 72-; ASSOC PROF MED & CONSULT ALLERGY & RESPIRATORY DIS, UNIV CALIF, LOS ANGELES, 72- *Mem:* Fel Am Acad Allergy; Am Thoracic Soc; fel Am Col Allergy; Am Fedn Clin Res. *Res:* Respiratory mechanics and immunologic aspects of allergic and respiratory disease; nasal and bronchial provocation testing. *Mailing Add:* Dept Med Univ Calif Los Angeles Med Ctr Los Angeles CA 90024

KLAVAN, BENNETT, dentistry, periodontology, see previous edition

KLAVANO, PAUL ARTHUR, b Valley, Wash, Nov 30, 19; m 45; c 4. PHARMACOLOGY. *Educ:* State Col Wash, BS, 41, DVM, 44. *Prof Exp:* Instr vet anat, 44-45, instr vet physiol & pharmacol, 45-48, from asst prof to assoc prof, 48-62, chmn dept, 52-72, PROF VET PHARMACOL, WASH STATE UNIV, 62- *Concurrent Pos:* Chemist, Wash Horse Racing Comn, 42-46. *Mem:* Am Col Vet Pharmacol & Therapeut; Am Soc Vet Physiol & Pharmacol (secy, 53-54, pres, 64-65); NY Acad Sci; Am Soc Vet Anesthesiol. *Res:* Anesthesia of domestic animals. *Mailing Add:* Col of Vet Med Wash State Univ Pullman WA 99164

KLAVERKAMP, JOHN FREDERICK, b Sauk Rapids, Minn, Aug 6, 41; m 65; c 4. PHARMACOLOGY, TOXICOLOGY. *Educ:* Univ Minn, BS, 64; Univ Wash, MS, 70, PhD(pharmacol), 72. *Prof Exp:* Res scientist, 73-77, res mgr, 77-78, RES SCIENTIST, FISHERIES & MARINE SERV, FRESHWATER INST, 78- *Concurrent Pos:* Fel, Wash State Univ, Toxicol Lab, 72-73; adj prof, Dept Zool, Univ Man, 77- *Res:* Acidification of freshwater; biochemical mechanisms of tolerance in fish; cadmium toxicology; cardiovascular-respiratory physiology of fish; embryology of fish; heavy metal toxicology; mercury toxicology; selenium toxicology; organophosphate insecticides. *Mailing Add:* Freshwater Inst 501 University Crescent Winnipeg MB R3T 2N6 Can

KLAVINS, JANIS VILBERTS, b Latvia, May 6, 21; nat US; m 50; c 3. MEDICINE. *Educ:* Am Bd Path, cert anat path, 57, cert clin path, 59; Am Bd Nutrit, cert, 68. *Prof Exp:* Demonstr path, Sch Med, Western Reserve Univ, 54-55, from instr to sr instr, 55-60, asst prof, 60; from assoc prof to prof, Med Ctr, Duke Univ, 60-65, dir sch cytotech, 63-65; clin prof path, State Univ NY Downstate Med Ctr, 65-71; prof path, State Univ NY Stony Brook, 71-77; DIR DEPT PATH, LONG ISLAND JEWISH MED CTR/QUEENS HOSP CTR, 70-; CHMN DEPT PATH, CATH MED CTR, 77- *Concurrent Pos:* Asst pathologist, Marymount Hosp, Garfield Heights, Ohio, 55-57; cytologist-in-chg, Cleveland Metrop Gen Hosp, 55-60, assoc pathologist, 58-60; chief lab serv, Vet Admin Hosp, Durham, NC, 61-63; pathologist-in-chief, Brooklyn-Cumberland Med Ctr, 65-70; adj prof biol, Fac Grad Arts, Long Island Univ, 68-; clin prof path, Col Physicians & Surgeons, Columbia Univ, 69-; prof lectr, State Univ NY Downstate Med Ctr, 71- *Mem:* AAAS; Am Soc Cytol; Am Asn Path & Bact; Col Am Path; Am Soc Exp Path. *Res:* Iron metabolism; pathology of iron excess; effects of antimetabolites, particularly entionine; embryonic and specific proteins in malignant neoplasms; pathology of amino acid excess. *Mailing Add:* 5 Broadmoor Rd Scarsdale NY 10583

KLAWE, WITOLD L, b Piotrkow Trybunalski, Poland, June 9, 23; US citizen; m 55; c 1. FISH BIOLOGY. *Educ:* Univ Toronto, BA, 53, MA, 55. *Prof Exp:* Jr scientist, 55-56, scientist, 56-61, SR SCIENTIST, INTER-AM TROP TUNA COMN, SCRIPPS INST OCEANOG, 61- *Concurrent Pos:* Mem working groups, Expert Panel Facilitation Tuna Res, Food & Agr Orgn, UN, 65, consult, Food & Agr Orgn, UN & SPacific Comn. *Mem:* Am Inst Fishery Res Biol; AAAS. *Res:* Early life history of scombroid fishes; general marine biology; fishery oceanography; statistics on global catches of tunas. *Mailing Add:* Inter-Am Trop Tuna Comn Scripps Inst of Oceanog La Jolla CA 92093

KLAY, ROBERT FRANK, b Ft Benton, Mont, Jan 2, 30; m 59; c 3. ANIMAL NUTRITION. *Educ:* Mont State Univ, BS, 52; Wash State Univ, MS, 58; Univ Minn, Minneapolis, PhD(nutrit), 64. *Prof Exp:* Asst animal sci, Wash State Univ, 56-58, asst prof, 61-64; res fel animal genetics, Commonwealth Sci & Indust Res Orgn, Australia, 58-59; res asst animal nutrit, Univ Minn, Minneapolis, 59-61; NUTRITIONIST, MOORMAN MFG CO, 64- *Mem:* Am Soc Animal Sci. *Res:* Protein and amino acid digestion and availability; ruminant and nonruminant nutrition. *Mailing Add:* Moorman Mfg Co Res Dept Quincy IL 62301

KLAYMAN, DANIEL LESLIE, b New York, NY, Feb 28, 29; m 58; c 2. MEDICINAL CHEMISTRY, ORGANIC CHEMISTRY. *Educ:* Columbia Univ, BS, 50; Rutgers Univ, MS, 52 & 54, PhD(org chem), 56. *Prof Exp:* Fulbright grant chem, Sch Trop Med, Calcutta, 56-57; asst prof chem, Hofstra Col, 58-59; res chemist med chem, Dept Radiobiol, 59-63, res chemist med chem, Div Med Chem, 63-78, RES CHEMIST MED CHEM, DIV EXP THERAPEUT, WALTER REED ARMY INST RES, 78- *Concurrent Pos:* Partic, US-Soviet Health Exchange, Moscow, 69; lectr, US-India Exchange Scientists, 72. *Mem:* Am Chem Soc. *Res:* Isolation and structural investigation of alkaloids; organic sulfur, selenium and nitrogen chemistry; synthesis of antiradiation, antimalarial, antibacterial and antiviral compounds. *Mailing Add:* Div of Exp Therapeut Walter Reed Army Inst of Res Washington DC 20012

KLEBANOFF, P(HILIP) S(AMUEL), b New York, NY, July 21, 18; m 50; c 3. FLUID MECHANICS. *Educ:* Brooklyn Col, BA, 39, Dr Eng, Hokkaidd Univ, Japan, 79. *Prof Exp:* Asst phys aide, 41-42, jr physicist, 42-44, from asst physicist to physicist, 44-57, aeronaut res engr, 57-61, physicist, 61-69, chief aerodynamics sect & asst chief fluid mech, Mech Div, 69-75, chief, Fluid Mech Sect, Mech Div, 75-78, SR SCIENTIST, NAT BUR STANDARDS, 78- *Concurrent Pos:* Mem, US Nat Comt Theoret & Appl Mech, 70-74, hydromechanics comt, Naval Sea Systs Command, 74-, boundary layer transition study group, 70- *Honors & Awards:* Naval Ord Develop Award; Gold Medal, US Dept of Com, 75; Fluid Dynamics Prize, Am Phys Soc, 81. *Mem:* Nat Acad Eng; fel Am Inst Aeronaut & Astronaut; AAAS; fel Am Phys Soc. *Res:* Flow instability; magnetohydrodynamics; anemometry; turbulence; boundary layers. *Mailing Add:* Fluid Eng Div Nat Bur Standards Washington DC 20234

KLEBANOFF, SEYMOUR J, b Toronto, Ont, Feb 3, 27; m 51; c 2. INFECTIOUS DISEASES, BIOCHEMISTRY. *Educ:* Univ Toronto, MD, 51; Univ London, PhD(biochem), 54. *Prof Exp:* Intern, Toronto Gen Hosp, 51-52; lectr path chem, Univ Toronto, 54-57; guest investr & asst physician, Rockefeller Inst, 57-59, res assoc, 59, asst prof, assoc physician & radiation protection officer, 59-62; assoc prof, 62-68, PROF MED, SCH MED, UNIV WASH, 68- *Concurrent Pos:* NIH res career develop award, 64-68. *Mem:* Am Soc Clin Invest; Infectious Dis Soc Am; Asn Am Physicians; Am Soc Biol Chem; Endocrine Soc. *Res:* Role of granulocytes in host defense; role of enzyme peroxidase in biological processes; microbicidal activity of peroxidases. *Mailing Add:* Dept of Med Univ of Wash Sch of Med Seattle WA 98195

KLEBE, ROBERT JOHN, b Philadelphia, Pa, Oct 26, 43. HUMAN GENETICS, BIOCHEMISTRY. *Educ:* Johns Hopkins Univ, BA, 65; Yale Univ, PhD(biol), 70. *Prof Exp:* From asst prof to assoc prof human genetics, Grad Sch Biomed Sci, Univ Tex Med Br, Galveston, 76-81; ASSOC PROF ANAT, GRAD SCH BIOMED SCI, UNIV TEX HEALTH SCI CTR, 81- *Concurrent Pos:* Jane Coffin Child Mem Fund fel, Salk Inst, 70-72; NIH grant, 73- *Mem:* Am Soc Human Genetics; Am Soc Cell Biol. *Res:* Somatic cell genetics; biochemistry of cell adhesion; developmental genetics. *Mailing Add:* Dept Anat Univ Tex Health Sci Ctr San Antonio TX 78284

KLEBER, EUGENE VICTOR, b Cleveland, Ohio, July 7, 20; m 42, 64, 78; c 5. CHEMISTRY. *Educ:* Univ Calif, Los Angeles, AB, 40, MA, 41; Univ Wis, PhD(chem), 43. *Prof Exp:* Res chemist, Sharples Chem, Inc, Mich, 43-45, Golden Bear Oil Co, Calif, 45-46 & Lockheed Aircraft Corp, 46-47; pres, Res Chem, Inc, 47-59, gen mgr res chem div, Nuclear Corp Am, 59-62; staff asst, Atomics Int Div, Rockwell Int Corp, 62-78; PHYS SCIENTIST, FED ENERGY REGULATORY COMN, DEPT ENERGY, 78- *Concurrent Pos:* Res chemist, Coast Paint & Chem Co, 47 & Lockheed Aircraft Corp, 51-56. *Mem:* Am Chem Soc. *Res:* Nuclear fuels and materials; organic synthesis; fine chemical manufacturing; production and use of purified rare earth oxides and metals; energy and environmental programs. *Mailing Add:* 12225 Cedar Hill Dr Silver Spring MD 20904

KLEBER, HERBERT DAVID, b Pittsburgh, Pa, June 19, 34; m 56; c 3. PSYCHIATRY. *Educ:* Dartmouth Col, BA, 56; Jefferson Med Col, MD, 60. *Prof Exp:* Resident psychiat, Sch Med, Yale Univ, 61-64; chief receiving serv, USPHS Hosp, Lexington, Ky, 64-66; from asst prof to assoc prof psychiat, 66-75, PROF PSYCHIAT, SCH MED, YALE UNIV, 75-; DIR DRUG DEPENDENCE UNIT, CONN MENT HEALTH CTR, 68- *Concurrent Pos:* Consult, Nat Inst Drug Abuse, 71- & Nat Acad Sci, 73-; fund prize res psychiat, Am Psychiat Asn, 81. *Honors & Awards:* Gold Medal, Am Psychiat Asn, 75. *Mem:* Fel Am Psychiat Asn. *Res:* Treatment of drug dependence; etiological aspects of drug abuse. *Mailing Add:* Conn Ment Health Ctr 34 Park St New Haven CT 06508

KLEBER, JOHN WILLIAM, b Warsaw, Ill, Jan 1, 23; m 45; c 5. BIOPHARMACEUTICS. *Educ:* Duquesne Univ, BS, 43; Univ Minn, PhD(pharmaceut chem), 49. *Prof Exp:* Asst prof pharm, Univ Buffalo, 49-52, assoc prof, 52-60; sr biologist, Eli Lilly & Co, 60-70, sr anal chemist, 70-75, sr formulations chemist, 75-81; RETIRED. *Concurrent Pos:* USPHS trainee grant steroid biochem, Univ Utah, 59-60. *Mem:* Am Chem Soc. *Res:* Development of animal health care products. *Mailing Add:* 5335 Ashbourne Lane Indianapolis IN 46226

KLEBESADEL, RAY WILLIAM, b Shawano, Wis, Nov 18, 32; m 59; c 4. GAMMA-RAY BURST ASTRONOMY. *Educ:* Univ Wis, BA, 59, MS, 60. *Prof Exp:* MEM STAFF SPACE SCI, LOS ALAMOS NAT LAB, 60- *Mem:* Am Astron Soc. *Res:* Space Science; cosmic gamma-ray bursts. *Mailing Add:* Los Alamos Nat Lab ESS-9 MS436 Los Alamos NM 87545

KLECKA, MIROSLAV EZIDOR, b Yoakum, Tex, Nov 9, 21; m 45. CHEMICAL ENGINEERING. *Educ:* Univ Tex, BS, 43, MS, 46, PhD(chem eng), 48. *Prof Exp:* Res asst chem eng, Univ Tex, 45-46, res assoc, 46, instr, 46-47; sr res engr, Shell Oil Co, 47-66, staff res engr, 66-77, STAFF RES ENGR, SHELL DEVELOP CO, HOUSTON, 77- *Mem:* Am Inst Chem Engrs. *Res:* Petroleum refining design and evaluation; phase equilibria and separation processes; operations research and computer calculations systems design; process control systems. *Mailing Add:* Shell Develop Co PO Box 1380 Houston TX 77001

KLECKNER, ALBERT LOUIS, b Allentown, Pa, Oct 23, 09; m 43; c 2. VETERINARY MICROBIOLOGY. *Educ:* Franklin & Marshall Col, BS, 31; Univ Pa, MS, 32, PhD(bact), 35, DVM, 53; Am Bd Clin Microbiologists, dipl, 64; Am Col Vet Microbiologists, dipl, 66. *Prof Exp:* Instr bact, Univ Pa, 32-36, res assoc milk hyg, 37-43; instr bact, Kans State Col, 36-37; res bacteriologist, Biol Div, Pitman-Moore Co, Ind, 43-44, res bacteriologist, Pharmaceut Div, 44-47 & tech serv sales dept, 48-49; head dept microbiol & prev med, 49-66, dir vet res, 50-64, assoc dir, Inst Comp Med, 65-67, assoc dean, Sch Vet Med, 67-69, asst vpres instr, 69-73, prof microbiol, 49-77, EMER PROF MICROBIOL & PREV MED, SCH VET MED, UNIV GA, 77- *Concurrent Pos:* Collab, Animal Dis & Parasite Res Div, Agr Res Serv, 54-64; rep mem, Am Vet Med Asn, 64-70. *Mem:* Fel Am Acad Microbiol; Am Soc Microbiol; Am Vet Med Asn; Conf Res Workers Animal Dis (pres, 73); Am Col Vet Microbiologists. *Res:* Poultry diseases; virology; mycoplasma. *Mailing Add:* 530 Riverhill Dr Athens GA 30606

KLEE, GERALD D'ARCY, b New York, NY, Jan 29, 27; m 50; c 5. PSYCHIATRY, MEDICINE. *Educ:* Harvard Med Sch, MD, 52; Am Bd Psychiat & Neurol, dipl, 59. *Prof Exp:* Sr asst surgeon, USPHS, 53-54; res assoc psychiat, Sch Med, Univ Md, 56-58, from asst prof to assoc prof, 58-67, dir div outpatient psychiat, Psychiat Inst, 58-67; prof psychiat, Sch Med, Temple Univ, 67-70; LECTR PSYCHIAT, SCH MED, JOHNS HOPKINS UNIV, 76- *Concurrent Pos:* Consult, Md Drug Abuse Authority, 71-72; Baltimore County Health Dept, Bur Ment Health, 71-73; pvt pract, psychiat, 71- *Mem:* AMA; fel Am Psychiat Asn. *Res:* Psychopharmacology; psychotherapy; community psychiatry. *Mailing Add:* 28 Allegheny Ave Towson MD 21204

KLEE, LUCILLE HOLLJES, b Baltimore, Md, Dec 8, 24; m 59; c 2. BIOCHEMISTRY. *Educ:* Bryn Mawr Col, AB, 46, AM, 47, PhD(chem), 51. *Prof Exp:* Instr, Barnard Col, Columbia Univ, 51-56, class adv, 54-56; res chemist, Toni Co, Div Gillette Co, 56-57; res assoc, Brandeis Univ, 57-59, lectr chem, 58-69; sci coord, Douglas County Bd Educ, 69-70; assoc prof chem, Lowell State Col, 70-71; assoc prof chem, 71-74, assoc prof, 74-78, PROF SCI EDUC, W GA COL, 78- *Mem:* AAAS; Nat Sci Teachers Asn; Am Chem Soc. *Res:* Biochemical mechanisms; science education. *Mailing Add:* Sch of Educ WGa Col Carrollton GA 30117

KLEE, VICTOR LA RUE, JR, b San Francisco, Calif, Sept 18, 25; m 45; c 4. MATHEMATICS. *Educ:* Pomona Col, BA, 45, Univ Va, PhD(math), 49. *Hon Degrees:* DSc, Pomona Col, 65. *Prof Exp:* Instr math, Univ Va, 47-48, asst prof, 49-53; from asst prof to assoc prof, 53-57, PROF MATH, UNIV WASH, 57-, PROF APPL MATH, 76- *Concurrent Pos:* Nat Res Coun fel, Inst Advan Study, 51-52; vis assoc prof, Univ Calif, Los Angeles, 55-56 & Univ Western Australia, 79; Sloan res fel, Univ Wash, 56-58 & 60-61; NSF sr fel, Copenhagen Univ, 58-59, Sloan res fel, 59-60; consult, Boeing Sci Res Labs, 63-69, Rand Corp, 66-69, Holt, Rinehart & Winston, 66-76, E I du Pont de Nemours & Co, Inc, 68-72, IBM Corp, 72 & W H Freeman, 76-; Sigma Xi nat lectr, 69; vis prof, Univ Colo, 71; adj prof comput sci, Univ Wash, 74-; vis prof, Univ Victoria, 75; fel, Ctr Advan Study Behav Sci, 75-76; trustee, Conf Bd Math Sci, 72-73; Guggenheim fel & Von Humboldt awardee, Univ Erlangen, Nurnberg, 80-81. *Honors & Awards:* Pres & Visitor's Res Prize, Univ Va, 52; L R Ford Award, 72; C B Allendoerfer Award, Math Asn Am, 80. *Mem:* Fel AAAS; Am Math Soc (assoc secy, 55-58); Math Asn Am (1st vpres, 68-69, pres-elect, 70, pres, 71-72); Soc Indust & Appl Math; Opers Res Soc Am. *Res:* Convex sets; mathematical programming; combinatorial mathematics; design and analysis of algorithms; functional analysis; point-set topology. *Mailing Add:* Dept of Math Univ of Wash Seattle WA 98105

KLEEMAN, CHARLES RICHARD, b Los Angeles, Calif, Aug 19, 23; m 45; c 3. PHYSIOLOGY, METABOLISM. *Educ:* Univ Calif, BS, 44, MD, 47. *Prof Exp:* Rotating internship, San Francisco City Hosp, 47-48; asst resident path, Mallory Inst, Boston City Hosp, 48-49; from intermediate resident to sr resident med, Newington Vet Admin Hosp, 49-51; from instr to asst prof med, Metab Sect, Sch Med, Yale Univ, 53-56; from assoc clin prof to assoc prof, Sch Med, Univ Calif, Los Angeles, 56-64, prof, Sch Med & dir div med, Cedars-Sinai Med Ctr, 64-74; prof med & chief dept, Hadassah Med Sch, Hebrew Univ, Israel, 74-75; prof med & chief div nephrology, 75-77, EMER PROF MED & EMER CHIEF DIV NEPHROLOGY, SCH MED, UNIV CALIF, LOS ANGELES, 77-, DIR CTR HEALTH ENHANCEMENT EDUC & RES, CTR HEALTH SCI, 77- *Concurrent Pos:* Fel metab, Newington Vet Admin Hosp, 50-51; Upjohn-Endocrine Soc scholar, Univ Col, Univ London, 60-61; chief metab sect, Vet Admin Hosp, Los Angeles, 56-60, consult, 62-; dir div med, Mt Sinai Hosp, Los Angeles, 61-; mem, Exec Comt, Renal Coun, Am Heart Asn; mem sci adv bd, Nat Kidney Dis Found; vis prof, Univ Queensland, 66; consult artificial kidney, Chronic Uremia Prog & Kidney Dis Control Prog, NIH, 67-; vis prof, Beilinson Hosp, Tel-Aviv Univ & Med Sch, Hadassah-Hebrew Univ, 68; vis prof, St Francis Hosp, Honolulu, 69; chmn internal med sect, Nat Bd Med Exam, 71. *Mem:* Inst Med-Nat Acad Sci; AMA; Am Physiol Soc; Am Soc Clin Invest; Endocrine Soc. *Res:* Renal physiology; electrolyte and water metabolism; nephrology. *Mailing Add:* Dept of Med Univ of Calif Sch of Med Los Angeles CA 90024

KLEEN, HAROLD J, b Nebr, July 2, 11; m 34; c 2. GEOLOGY. *Educ:* Univ Nebr, BSc, 33. *Prof Exp:* Geologist, Skelly Oil Co, 37-44, dist geologist, Okla, 44-49; div mgr, Cent US, Kerr-McGee Oil Industs, Inc, 49-53, chief geologist, 53-58, explor mgr, 58-61, geol adv to pres, 61-67, mgr mineral explor, 67-68, explor asst to chief exec off, Kerr-McGee Corp, 68-69, vpres minerals explor, 69-74; CONSULT, 74- *Mem:* Am Inst Prof Geol; Soc Mining Engrs. *Res:* Investment economics. *Mailing Add:* 6229 Smith Blvd Oklahoma City OK 73112

KLEENE, STEPHEN COLE, b Hartford, Conn, Jan 5, 09; m; c 4. MATHEMATICAL LOGIC. *Educ:* Amherst Col, AB, 30; Princeton Univ, PhD(math), 34. *Hon Degrees:* ScD, Amherst Col, 70. *Prof Exp:* Instr math, Princeton Unv, 30-31, asst, 34-35; from instr to asst prof, Univ Wis, 35-41; assoc prof, Amherst Col, 41-42; from assoc prof to prof math, 46-64, chmn dept, 57-58 & 60-62, numerical analyst, 62-63, dean, Col Letters & Sci, 69-74, Cyrus C MacDuffee prof math, 64-74, Cyrus C MacDuffee prof math & comput sci, 74-79, EMER PROF MATH & COMPUT SCI & EMER DEAN LETT & SCI, UNIV WIS-MADISON, 79- *Concurrent Pos:* Mem, Inst Advan Study, 39-40 & 65-66; Guggenheim fel, 49-50; vis prof, Princeton Univ, 56-57; mem math div, Nat Res Coun, 57-58, chmn designate div math sci, 69-72; NSF grant, Univ Marburg, 58-59; pres, Int Union Hist & Philos Sci, 61, pres div logic, methodology & philos sci, 60-62; actg dir math res ctr, US Army, 66-67. *Mem:* Nat Acad Sci; Am Math Soc; Asn Symbolic Logic (vpres, 41-42 & 47-49, pres, 56-58); Am Acad Arts & Sci. *Res:* Recursive functions. *Mailing Add:* 725 Van Vleck Hall Univ of Wis 480 Lincoln Dr Madison WI 53706

KLEESATTEL, CLAUS, b Düsseldorf, Ger, Aug 10, 17; US citizen; m 59. PHYSICS, ELECTRICAL ENGINEERING. *Educ:* Chemnitz Tech Acad, EE, 39; Darmstadt Tech Univ, dipl, 44, Dr rer nat(physics), 46. *Prof Exp:* Asst microwave res, Inst Exp Physics, Darmstadt Tech Univ, 44-46; mfr, Ultrason Argentina SA, 48-53; asst dir res, Cavitron Ultrasonics, Inc, NY, 53-60; CONSULT PHYSICIST, 60- *Mem:* Acoust Soc Am; Am Soc Test & Mat. *Res:* Vibration and sound; acoustical instrumentation; materials inspection instruments. *Mailing Add:* Apartado 4969 1000 San Jose Costa Rica

KLEESE, ROGER ALLEN, plant genetics, see previous edition

KLEHR, EDWIN HENRY, b Shakopee, Minn, Nov 26, 32; m 57; c 6. ENVIRONMENTAL CHEMISTRY, WATER CHEMISTRY. *Educ:* St John's Univ, Minn, BA, 54; Iowa State Univ, PhD(chem), 59. *Prof Exp:* Asst prof chem, Sienna Col, 60-61; assoc prof, 61-65, PROF ENVIRON SCI, UNIV OKLA, 65- *Concurrent Pos:* Consult, Okla Master Conservancy Dist, 63, Okla City Pub Sch Syst, 64-65 & US Army Corps Engrs, 73-78; Fed Water Qual Asn spec res fel, 70-71; Int Res & Exchange Bd res fel, 73-74. *Mem:* Am Chem Soc. *Res:* Nuclear measurement techniques; modeling of chemical environment. *Mailing Add:* 306 Chautauqua Norman OK 73069

KLEI, HERBERT EDWARD, JR, b Detroit, Mich, May 5, 35; m 59; c 5. CHEMICAL ENGINEERING. *Educ:* Mass Inst Technol, BS, 57; Univ Mich, MS, 58 & 59; Univ Conn, PhD(chem eng), 65. *Prof Exp:* Res engr, Chas Pfizer & Co, 59-63; instr, 64-65, from asst prof to assoc prof, 65-78, PROF CHEM ENG, SCH ENG, UNIV CONN, 78- *Concurrent Pos:* Fed Water Pollution Control Admin study grant, 67-70. *Honors & Awards:* Ralph Teetor Award, Soc Automotive Engrs, 78. *Mem:* Am Inst Chem Eng; Am Chem Soc; Catalysis Soc. *Res:* Water pollution control, including biological kinetics and reactor design, membrane polarization and process control. *Mailing Add:* Dept of Chem Eng Univ of Conn Sch of Eng Storrs CT 06268

KLEI, THOMAS RAY, b Detroit, Mich, Dec 11, 42; m 65; c 1. PARASITOLOGY, IMMUNOLOGY. *Educ:* Northern Mich Univ, BS, 65; Wayne State Univ, PhD(biol & parasitol), 71. *Prof Exp:* NIH fel parasitol, Sch Vet Med, Univ Ga, 71-73; asst prof biol & zool, Millersville State Col, 73-75; asst prof parasitol, 75-77, ASSOC PROF PARASITOL, SCH VET MED, LA STATE UNIV, 77- *Concurrent Pos:* Prin investr, WHO & USDA Coop States Res Study grants, 77- *Mem:* Am Soc Parasitologists; Am Soc Trop Med & Hyg; Soc Protozoologists; Royal Soc Trop Med & Hyg; Wildlife Dis Asn. *Res:* Immunologic and pathologic responses of vertebrate hosts to parasitic animals; parasitic diseases of wildlife. *Mailing Add:* Dept of Vet Microbiol & Parasitol La State Univ Baton Rouge LA 70803

KLEIBACKER, WILSON MCALARNEY, b Pittsburgh, Pa, Nov 23, 09; m 38; c 3. ORGANIC CHEMISTRY. *Educ:* Williams Col, AB, 31; Univ Pittsburgh, PhD(org chem), 38. *Prof Exp:* Teacher & head sci dept, Oakland City Col, 38-39; chemist, Am Cyanamid & Chem Corp, Pa, 39-41; asst prof chem, The Citadel, 41-42; instr, Univ Del, 42-45; chemist, United Shoe Machinery Corp, 45-51 & Clark Lab, Kendall Co, 51-60; prof chem & head dept, Yankton Col, 60-68; assoc prof, 68-73, PROF CHEM, UNIV WIS-STOUT, 73- *Mem:* Am Chem Soc. *Mailing Add:* Dept of Chem Univ of Wis-Stout Menomonie WI 54751

KLEIER, DANIEL ANTHONY, b Louisville, Ky, Aug 19, 45; m 68; c 1. PHYSICAL CHEMISTRY, THEORETICAL CHEMISTRY. *Educ:* Bellarmine Col, Ky, BA, 67; Univ Notre Dame, PhD(chem), 71. *Prof Exp:* Woodrow Wilson teaching intern & asst prof chem, Va State Col, 70-72; res fel, Harvard Univ, 72-75; asst prof chem, Williams Col, 75-81; CHEMIST, SHELL DEVELOP CO, 81- *Concurrent Pos:* NSF fel, Harvard Univ, 72-73, Am Cancer Soc fel, 74-75; vis staff mem, Los Alamos Nat Lab, 78- *Mem:* Am Chem Soc. *Res:* Theoretical investigations of chemical bonding and potential energy surfaces; nuclear magnetic resonance studies of stereodynamic processes. *Mailing Add:* Biol Sci Res Ctr Shell Develop Co Modesto CA 95352

KLEIMAN, DEVRA GAIL, b New York, NY, Nov 15, 42; m 71; c 2. ETHOLOGY, REPRODUCTIVE BIOLOGY. *Educ:* Univ Chicago, BS, 64; Univ Col, Univ London, PhD(zool), 69. *Prof Exp:* Res asst biopsychol, Univ Chicago, 64-65; res asst reproductive biol, Wellcome Inst Comp Physiol, Zool Soc London, 65-69; NIH fel develop, Inst Animal Behav, Rutgers Univ, 69-71; reproduction zoologist, 72-79, HEAD ZOOL RES, NAT ZOOL PARK, SMITHSONIAN INST, 79- *Concurrent Pos:* Adj asst prof psychol, Rutgers Univ, 70-71; res assoc, Smtihsonian Inst, 70-72; adj assoc prof, George Washington Univ, 73-76 & Univ Md, 79-; adj prof, George Mason Univ, 80- *Mem:* Animal Behav Soc (secy, 77-81 & pres, 81-82); Am Asn Zool Parks & Aquariums; Am Soc Mammalogists; Sigma Xi; Am Inst Biol Sci. *Res:* Social behavior and social organization of mammals; mammalian reproductive physiology. *Mailing Add:* Zool Res Nat Zool Park Smithsonian Inst Washington DC 20008

KLEIMAN, HERBERT, b New York, NY, Oct 1, 33; m 60; c 1. PHYSICS. *Educ:* Mass Inst Technol, BS, 54; Purdue Univ, MS, 57, PhD(physics), 61. *Prof Exp:* NSF fel physics, Univ Calif, Berkeley, 61-63, asst prof, 63-66; MEM STAFF, LINCOLN LAB, MASS INST TECHNOL, 66- *Res:* High resolution spectroscopy; atomic structure and atomic spectra; quantum optics and photon correlation studies; physical optics. *Mailing Add:* 16 Reed Lane Bedford MA 01730

KLEIMAN, HOWARD, b New York, NY, Apr 15, 29; m 56; c 3. ALGEBRA, NUMBER THEORY. *Educ:* NY Univ, BA, 50, MS, 61; Columbia Univ, MA, 54; King's Col, Univ London, PhD(math), 69. *Prof Exp:* Teacher, New York City Bd Educ, 55-56 & Bur Educ Physically Handicapped, 56-67; from asst prof to assoc prof, 67-78, PROF MATH, QUEENSBOROUGH COMMUNITY COL, 78- *Mem:* London Math Soc; Am Math Soc; Math Asn Am. *Res:* Discovery of necessary and sufficient conditions for a planar graph to have a hamilton line; method of h-admissible permutations for obtaining Hamilton dicircuits and circuits in digraphs and graphs. *Mailing Add:* 188-83 85th Rd Holliswood NY 11423

KLEIMAN, MORTON, b Kansas City, Mo, Mar 8, 16; m 40; c 2. ORGANIC CHEMISTRY. *Educ:* Univ Mich, BS, 37, MS, 38; Univ Chicago, PhD, 42. *Prof Exp:* Coman fel, Univ Chicago, 42-43; res chemist, Velsicol Corp, 43-46, head org res dept, 46-51, dir res, 51-53; pres & tech dir, Chemley Prods co, 53-82; PRES & TECH DIR, M KLEIMAN ASSOCS, 53- *Mem:* Am Chem Soc. *Res:* Syntheses of various medicinals; insecticides and fungicides; reactions such as liquid ammonia, Grignard, elimination, carboxylation, chlorination, Diels-Alder and redistribution; structure proofs; ionic and free radical mechanisms; synthetic resins; organo-metallics; industrial organic chemicals. *Mailing Add:* 2827 W Catalpa Ave Chicago IL 60625

KLEIN, ABEL, b Rio de Janeiro, Brazil, Jan 16, 45; div. MATHEMATICAL PHYSICS. *Educ:* Univ Brazil, BS, 67; Inst Pure & Appl Math, MS, 68; Mass Inst Technol, PhD(math), 71. *Prof Exp:* Instr math, Inst Pure & Appl Math, 67; teaching asst, Mass Inst Technol, 68-71; actg asst prof, Univ Calif, Los Angeles, 71-72; instr, Princeton Univ, 72-74; from asst prof to assoc prof, 74-82, PROF MATH, UNIV CALIF, IRVINE, 82- *Mem:* Am Math Soc; Int Asn Math Physics. *Res:* Mathematics of quantum field theory; mathematical physics; functional analysis. *Mailing Add:* Dept of Math Univ of Calif Irvine CA 92717

KLEIN, ABRAHAM, b Brooklyn, NY, Jan 10, 27; m 50; c 2. THEORETICAL PHYSICS. *Educ:* Brooklyn Col, BA, 47; Harvard Univ, MA, 48, PhD(physics), 50. *Prof Exp:* Asst physics, Harvard Univ, 47-49, instr, 50-52; assoc prof, 55-58, PROF PHYSICS, UNIV PA, 58- *Concurrent Pos:* NSF sr fel, 61-62; Alfred P Sloan Found fel, 61-63; vis prof, Univ Paris, 61-62, Princeton Univ, 69-70 & Univ Tsukuba, Japan, 81; consult, Res Inst Advan Study, Martin Marietta, 59 & Gen Dynamics-Convair, 60; Guggenheim fel, 75; vis scientist, Ctr Theoret Physics, Mass Inst Technol, 75-76. *Mem:* AAAS; fel Am Phys Soc. *Res:* Quantum electrodynamics; meson theory of nuclear forces; theory of scattering; many body problem; quantum field theory; theory of nuclear structure. *Mailing Add:* Dept of Physics Univ of Pa Philadelphia PA 19104

KLEIN, ALAN F(RANK), b Brooklyn, NY, Jan 24, 38; m 60; c 2. ENGINEERING PHYSICS, AERONAUTICS. *Educ:* Cornell Univ, BEP, 60, MAeroE, 61; Calif Inst Technol, PhD(aeronaut), 67. *Prof Exp:* Mem tech staff, Aerospace Corp, 61-66; staff scientist, Physics Int Co, 66-68, mgr vulnerability dept, 68-69, mgr nuclear radiation effects dept, 69-70, dir appl sci div, 70-76; SR V PRES, SYSTS, SCI & SOFTWARE, SAN FRANCISCO DIV, 76- *Mem:* Am Phys Soc. *Res:* Shock wave physics; high temperature gas dynamics; stress waves in solids; plasma physics; magnetofluidynamics. *Mailing Add:* Systems, Sci & Software PO Box 4803 Hayward CA 94540

KLEIN, ALBERT JONATHAN, b Dayton, Ohio, Nov 16, 44; m 65; c 3. TOPOLOGY. *Educ:* Ohio State Univ, BSc, 66, MS, 67, PhD(math), 69. *Prof Exp:* Asst prof, 69-74, assoc prof math, 74-80, ASSOC PROF MATH & COMPUT SCI, YOUNGSTOWN STATE UNIV, 80- *Mem:* Math Asn Am; Am Math Soc. *Res:* Fuzzy topology; uniform ideas in fuzzy sets. *Mailing Add:* Dept of Math Youngstown State Univ Youngstown OH 44555

KLEIN, ALBERT WILLIAM, b Pittsburgh, Pa, Jan 18, 42; m 61; c 3. ANATOMY, PATHOLOGY. *Educ:* Washington & Jefferson Col, BA, 64; Duke Univ, PhD(anat), 72. *Prof Exp:* Res physiologist exp path, US Army Res Inst Environ Med, 69-72; asst prof anat, Univ Md, Baltimore City, 72-78; ASST PROF ANAT & GROSS ANAT, EASTERN VA MED SCH, 78- *Concurrent Pos:* Bressler Reserve grant, Univ Md, Baltimore, 73-74; consult, Greenbrier Col Osteop Med, 74; guest scientist, Geront Res Ctr, Baltimore City Hosps, 74-78; develop res award, Eastern Va Med Sch, 78-79. *Mem:* Soc Cryobiol; Am Asn Anat. *Res:* Prenatal physiology; aging in central nervous system; freeze thaw injury; neurological geriatrics. *Mailing Add:* Dept of Anat Sci Box 1980 Norfolk VA 23501

KLEIN, ANDREW, b Budapest, Hungary, July 21, 36; m 59; c 2. POLYMER CHEMISTRY, ENGINEERING. *Educ:* City Col New York, BS, 61; Stevens Inst Technol, MS, 65; NC State Univ, PhD(chem eng), 72. *Prof Exp:* Res chemist, Alexander Labs, Nat Starch & Chem Corp, 61-67, res supvr phys chem polymers, 67-80; MEM STAFF, MONSANTO AGR PROD CO, 80- *Mem:* Am Chem Soc. *Res:* Colloid and surface chemical aspects of heterogeneous polymerization; kinetics and engineering; surface chemical aspects of coatings; coagulation kinetics and flocculation. *Mailing Add:* Monsanto Agr Prod Co Mail Zone T4E St Louis MO 63166

KLEIN, ATTILA OTTO, b Subotica, Yugoslavia, July 10, 30; nat US; m 52; c 3. PLANT PHYSIOLOGY. *Educ:* Brooklyn Col, BA, 53; Ind Univ, PhD(plant physiol), 59. *Prof Exp:* USPHS fel biochem, Yale Univ, 59-61; asst biochemist, Conn Agr Exp Sta, 61-62; asst prof, 62-67, chmn dept, 68-70, ASSOC PROF BIOL, BRANDEIS UNIV, 67- *Res:* Cellular and plant physiology; developmental biochemistry of leaves; light-induced metabolic oscillations. *Mailing Add:* Dept of Biol Brandeis Univ Waltham MA 02154

KLEIN, AUGUST S, b Newton, Mass, Aug 31, 24; m 67; c 3. PHYSICS, CHEMISTRY. *Educ:* Williams Col, BA, 48; Harvard Univ, MS, 50. *Prof Exp:* Physicist, Atomic Power Div, Westinghouse, 50-58; west coast mgr, High Voltage Eng Corp, 59-64; gen mgr, spec prod div, Tech Measurement Corp, 64-67; PRES, NUCLEAR EQUIP CORP, 67- *Mem:* Electron Micros Soc Am; Am Inst Mining Engrs. *Res:* Energy dispersive x-ray fluorescent analysis; x-ray crystallography. *Mailing Add:* 160 La Questa Way Woodside CA 94062

KLEIN, BARBARA P, b New York, NY, Dec 30, 36; m 56; c 2. FOOD CHEMISTRY. *Educ:* Cornell Univ, BS, 57, MS, 59; Univ Ill, PhD(foods & nutrit), 74. *Prof Exp:* Res asst food chem, Col Home Econ, Cornell Univ, 57-58; res asst, 66-68, teaching asst, 69-72, asst prof, 74-80, ASSOC PROF FOODS & NUTRIT, SCH HUMAN RESOURCES & FAMILY STUDIES, UNIV ILL, URBANA, 80- *Mem:* Inst Food Technologists; Am Home Econ Asn; Am Chem Soc; Am Dietetics Asn; Am Asn Cereal Chemists. *Res:* Relationship of lipid oxidizing systems in vegetables to food quality; use of soybeans and soy products for human consumption; nutrient content of fresh and processed foods. *Mailing Add:* Univ Ill 905 S Goodwin Urbana IL 61801

KLEIN, BENJAMIN GARRETT, b Durham, NC, Jan 24, 42; m 71; c 2. MATHEMATICAL ANALYSIS. *Educ:* Univ Rochester, BA, 63; Yale Univ, MA, 65, PhD(Ergodic theory), 68. *Prof Exp:* Lectr math, NY Univ, 67-68, asst prof, 69-71; asst prof, 71-76, ASSOC PROF MATH, DAVIDSON COL, 76- *Mem:* Am Math Soc; Math Asn Am. *Res:* Ergodic theory; topological dynamics; numerical analysis. *Mailing Add:* Dept of Math Davidson Col Davidson NC 28036

KLEIN, BERNARD, b New York, NY, Sept 16, 14; m 42; c 2. ORGANIC CHEMISTRY. *Educ:* Brooklyn Col, BS, 34; Polytech Inst Brooklyn, PhD(chem), 50. *Prof Exp:* Chemist, Bethel Hosp, NY, 36-41; biochemist, Jewish Sanitarium & Hosp Chronic Dis, 41-42; res chemist, Warner Inst, NY, 46-48 & Harlem Hosp Cancer Found, 48; biochemist, US Vet Admin Hosp, Bronx, 48-67; biochemist, Res Div, Hoffmann-La Roche, Inc, 67, group chief clin chem, 67-71, asst dir, Dept Diag Res, 71-80; PROF, DEPT LAB MED, EINSTEIN COL MED, BRONX, NY, 81- *Concurrent Pos:* Consult chemist, Area Reference Lab. *Honors & Awards:* Van Slyke Award, Am Asn Clin Chemists, 69, Ames Award, 75. *Mem:* Am Chem Soc; Am Asn Clin Chem. *Res:* Pyrazine chemistry; automated biochemical analyses. *Mailing Add:* 129 Patton Blvd New Hyde Park NY 11040

KLEIN, CHRISTOPHER FRANCIS, b Los Angeles, Calif, Sept 11, 43; m 73; c 2. LASERS, ELECTRO-OPTICS. *Educ:* Calif State Univ, Long Beach, BS, 67, MS, 72. *Prof Exp:* Mem res & develop staff electro-optic design, Autonetics Div, NAm Rockwell, 67-72; mem res & develop staff laser design, Hughes Aircraft Co, 72-75; RES LASER SPECTROSCOPY, LASER SYSTMS DESIGN & ANAL, AEROSPACE CORP, 75- *Concurrent Pos:* Instr physics, El Camino Col, 76-77. *Res:* Laser spectroscopy; laser design; laser damage to optical materials. *Mailing Add:* Aerospace Corp D8-1205 2350 E El Segundo Blvd El Segundo CA 90245

KLEIN, CLAUDE A, b Strasbourg, France, Nov 4, 25; nat US; m 50; c 1. PHYSICS. *Educ:* Univ Paris, EE, 51, PhD(physics), 55. *Prof Exp:* Asst to mgr, Mil Dept, French AEC, 55-57; PRIN SCIENTIST, RES DIV, RAYTHEON CO, 57- *Concurrent Pos:* Vis lectr, Univ Lyons, 53-54, Univ Paris, 54-56 & Univ Lowell, 62-63. *Mem:* Fel Am Phys Soc; Inst Elec & Electronics Engrs. *Res:* Solid state physics; lasers and infrared; systems engineering. *Mailing Add:* Raytheon Co Res Div 28 Seyon St Waltham MA 02154

KLEIN, CORNELIS, b Haarlem, Holland, Sept 4, 37; US citizen; m 60; c 2. MINERALOGY, PETROLOGY. *Educ:* McGill Univ, BSc, 58, MSc, 60; Harvard Univ, PhD(geol), 65. *Prof Exp:* Res assoc geol, Harvard Univ, 63-65, lectr, 65-69, assoc prof mineral, 69-72; PROF MINERAL, IND UNIV, BLOOMINGTON, 72- *Concurrent Pos:* Allston Burr sr tutor, 66-70; assoc ed, Am Mineralogist, 77-82; Guggenheim fel, 78. *Mem:* Fel Mineral Soc Am; fel Geol Soc Am; Mineral Asn Can; Microbeam Anal Soc; fel AAAS. *Res:* Precambrian iron formation; chemical, optical and x-ray properties of amphiboles; minerals in meteorites; mineralogy and petrology of lunar rocks; electron probe analysis of minerals. *Mailing Add:* Dept Geol Ind Univ Bloomington IN 47401

KLEIN, DAVID HENRY, b Milwaukee, Wis, May 28, 33; m 54; c 2. ANALYTICAL METHODS DEVELOPMENTS, ENVIRONMENTAL CHEMISTRY. *Educ:* Albion Col, BA, 54; Case Western Reserve Univ, PhD, 59. *Prof Exp:* Instr chem, Calif Inst Technol, 59-60; asst prof, Los Angeles State Col, 60-64; from assoc prof to prof chem, Hope Col, 64-81, chmn dept, 69-73; PROJ SCIENTIST, PARKE DAVIS CO, 81- *Concurrent Pos:* NSF fel, Scripps Inst Onceanog, 68-69; vis scientist, Oak Ridge Nat Lab, 73-74. *Mem:* AAAS. *Res:* Kinetics of nucleation; precipitation and co-precipitation; mercury and other heavy metals in the environment; geochemistry and marine chemistry; environmental effects of coal combustion. *Mailing Add:* Parke Davis Co 182 Howard Ave Holland MI 49423

KLEIN, DAVID JOSEPH, b Los Angeles, Calif, Aug 3, 22; m 45; c 2. RADIOLOGICAL PHYSICS. *Educ:* Calif Inst Technol, BS, 43, PhD(physics), 51. *Prof Exp:* Asst prof radiol, Med Sch, Univ Southern Calif, 74-; consult, Appl Info Methods, Inc, 71- *Concurrent Pos:* Asst, Calif Inst Technol, 46-51; res engr, NAm Aviation, Inc, 51-52, sr engr, 53-58, sr physicist, 59-63, mem tech staff, Autonetics Div, NAm Rockwell Corp, 63-71; consult, Advan Info Methods, Inc, 71-72; ASST RADIATION PHYSICIST, LOS ANGELES COUNTY/USC MED CTR, 72- Concurrent. *Mem:* Am Asn Physicists Med; Am Phys Soc. *Res:* Solid state physics; reactor fuels; x-ray diffraction; electron diffraction and microscopy; radiation effects; semiconductors; dosimetry; diagnostic radiological physics; tomography; image quality; resolution; modulation transfer function; diagnostic quality assurance. *Mailing Add:* 2339 Kenilworth Ave Los Angeles CA 90039

KLEIN, DAVID ROBERT, b Fitchburg, Mass, May 18, 27; m 55; c 3. MAMMALIAN ECOLOGY. *Educ:* Univ Conn, BS, 51; Univ Alaska, MS, 53; Univ BC, PhD(zool), 63. *Prof Exp:* Biologist, US Fish & Wildlife Serv, 55-59; biologist, Alaska Dept Fish & Game, 59-61, res dir, 61-62; DIR, ALASKA COOP WILDLIFE RES UNIT & PROF WILDLIFE ECOL, UNIV ALASKA, 62- *Concurrent Pos:* NSF inst grant, 63-64; Bur Sport Fisheries & Wildlife grant, 64-65; Bur Land Mgr grant, 65-67; vis res biologist, Kalo Game Biol Sta, Denmark, 67; vis prof, Univ Oslo, 71-72. *Mem:* AAAS; Wildlife Soc; Arctic Inst NAm. *Res:* Effects of vegetational quality on the growth and development of individuals and populations; man's impact on the environment. *Mailing Add:* Alaska Coop Wildlife Res Unit Univ of Alaska Fairbanks AK 99701

KLEIN, DAVID XAVIER, b Milwaukee, Wis, Oct 18, 08; m 34; c 3. ORGANIC CHEMISTRY. *Educ:* Univ Chicago, BS, 30. *Prof Exp:* Res chemist, Manhattan proj, E I du Pont de Nemours & Co, 30-46; res dir, Aspinook Corp, 46-48; mgr res, Heyden Div, Heyden-Newport Chem Corp, 48-59, vpres Heyden Div, Tenneco Chem, Inc, 60-67, pres, 67-70, coord foreign investments, 70-73; CONSULT, 74- *Mem:* Am Chem Soc; Asn Res Dirs (secy-treas, 53-54); Chem Mkt Res Asn. *Res:* Organic intermediates; anthraquinone wool, acetate and vat dyes; organic silicones; cellulose application; commercial development. *Mailing Add:* 98 Yantacaw Brook Rd Upper Montclair NJ 07043

KLEIN, DEANA TARSON, b Chicago, Ill, Jan 7, 25; m 47. MYCOLOGY. *Educ:* Univ Chicago, BS, 47, MS, 48, PhD(bot), 52. *Prof Exp:* Res asst, Food Res Inst, Univ Chicago, 52-53; res asst chem embryol, Columbia Univ, 54-55, USPHS res fel, Dept Zool, 55-57; USPHS res fel microbiol & immunol, Albert Einstein Col Med, 57-58, instr, 58-62, asst prof, 62-66; asst prof biol sci, Hunter Col, 66-67; assoc prof biol, 67-71, PROF BIOL, ST MICHAEL'S COL, VT, 71- *Mem:* Mycol Soc Am; Bot Soc Am. *Res:* Physiology microorganisms and stress in angiosperm. *Mailing Add:* Dept of Biol St Michael's Col Winooski VT 05404

KLEIN, DOLPH, b New York, NY, May 2, 28; m 56; c 4. CLINICAL MICROBIOLOGY. *Educ:* City Col New York, BS, 50; Rutgers Univ, PhD(microbiol), 61; Am Bd Med Microbiol, dipl, 77. *Prof Exp:* Med technologist, Manhattan Gen Hosp, 50-51; lab asst microbiol, New York City Dept Health, 51-53; bacteriologist, Beth Israel Hosp, NY, 53-54; chief med technologist, Lakeside Hosp, Copiague, 54-57; res asst biophys, Sloan-Kettering Inst Cancer Res, 57-58; res asst agr microbiol, Rutgers Univ, 58-61; res microbiologist, Monsanto Co, Mo, 61-62, sr res microbiologist, Monsanto Res Corp, Mass, 62-63; res assoc biophys chem, Purdue Univ, 63-67; asst prof biochem, Univ Minn, Minneapolis, 67-71, asst prof microbiol & asst dir, Diag Microbiol Lab, Med Ctr, 72-74; ASSOC PROF MICROBIOL, MED CTR, DUKE UNIV, 74-, DIR, CLIN MICROBIOL LAB, DUKE HOSP, 74- *Mem:* Am Soc Microbiol. *Res:* Anticancer agents; bacterial dissimilation of streptomycin; evaluation of antimicrobial agents and their modes of action; physicochemical basis of biological stability in structural proteins. *Mailing Add:* Dept of Microbiol & Immunol Duke Univ Med Ctr Durham NC 27710

KLEIN, DONALD ALBERT, b Bridgeport, Conn, Sept 11, 35; m 56; c 4. MICROBIOLOGY. *Educ:* Univ Vt, BS, 57, MS, 61; Pa State Univ, PhD(microbiol), 66. *Prof Exp:* Asst qual control, Nat Dairy Prod Corp, Vt, 57-58; instr food microbiol, Univ Vt, 58-61; res asst microbiol, Pa State Univ, 62-66; asst prof, Ore State Univ, 67-70; from asst prof to assoc prof, 70-78, PROF MICROBIOL, COLO STATE UNIV, 78- *Concurrent Pos:* Vis prof, Univ Kiel, 75 & Univ Copenhagen, 78. *Mem:* Am Soc Microbiol; Am Soc Agron. *Res:* Mined land reclamation microbiology; rhizosphere microbiology; microbial transformation of hydrocarbons and pesticides; soil ecology. *Mailing Add:* Dept of Microbiol Colo State Univ Ft Collins CO 80523

KLEIN, DONALD FRANKLIN, b New York, NY, Sept 4, 28; c 4. PSYCHIATRY, PSYCHOPHARMACOLOGY. *Educ:* Colby Col, BA, 47; State Univ NY Downstate Med Ctr, MD, 52; Am Bd Psychiat & Neurol, dipl psychiat, 59. *Prof Exp:* Intern, USPHS Hosp, Staten Island, NY, 52-53; resident, Creedmoor State Hosp, 53-54 & 56-58; sr asst surg & staff psychiatrist, USPHS Hosp, Lexington, Ky, 54-56; res assoc psychiat, Creedmoor Inst Psychobiol Studies, 57-59; res assoc, Hillside Hosp, 59-64, dir res, 65-70, med dir for eval, 70-72, dir dept psychiat, res & evaluation, Long Island Jewish-Hillside Med Ctr, 72-76; DIR RES, NY STATE PSYCHIAT INST, 76-; PROF PSYCHIAT, COL PHYSICIANS & SURGEONS, COLUMBIA UNIV, 78- *Concurrent Pos:* Pvt pract, 56-; candidate, New York Psychoanal Inst, 57-61; USPHS ment health career investr, 61-64, sr staff psychiatrist, 65; NIMH grants, 61-; attend psychiatrist, Queens Hosp Ctr, 66-; adj prof psychol, Queens Col, NY, 69-; mem Hofheimer Prize Bd, Am Psychiat Asn, 69-75 & task force methadone & narcotic antagonist eval, 71-73; mem clin pharmacol study sect, NIMH, 71-75 & Neuropharmacol Adv Comt, Food & Drug Admin, 71; prof psychiat, Col Med, State Univ NY Stony Brook, 72-76. *Honors & Awards:* A E Bennett Neuropsychiat Res Award, 64; Res Award, Nat Asn Pvt Psychiat Hosps, 65 & 71. *Mem:* Fel Am Col Neuropsychopharmacol (pres, 81); fel Am Psychiat Asn; Am Psychopath Asn (treas, 72, pres, 78); Int Neuropsychol Soc; fel Royal Col Psychiat. *Res:* Diagnosis and drug treatment of psychiatric disorders; psychiatric case studies, treatment, drugs and outcome; age of onset of drug abuse in psychiatric inpatients; phobic anxiety syndrome complicated by drug dependence and addiction. *Mailing Add:* Dept of Psychiatry Columbia Univ New York NY 10027

KLEIN, DONALD LEE, b Brooklyn, NY, Dec 19, 30; m 52; c 6. INORGANIC CHEMISTRY. *Educ:* Polytech Inst Brooklyn, BSCh, 52; Univ Conn, MS, 56, PhD(chem), 59. *Prof Exp:* Engr, Sylvania Elec Prod, Inc, 52-54; asst, Univ Conn, 54-55, asst instr, 55-58; mem tech staff, Bell Tel Labs, Inc, 58-67; SR CHEMIST, DATA SYSTS DIV, IBM CORP, 67- *Mem:* Am Chem Soc; Electrochem Soc. *Res:* Electrochemistry; photochemistry; semiconductor materials and processing. *Mailing Add:* Gen Technol Div E Fishkill Fac IBM Corp Hopewell Junction NY 12533

KLEIN, DOUGLAS J, b Portland, Ore, Nov 8, 42; m 66. MOLECULAR PHYSICS, QUANTUM CHEMISTRY. *Educ:* Ore State Univ, BSc, 64; Univ Tex, Austin, MA, 67, PhD(chem), 69. *Prof Exp:* Instr chem, Univ Tex, Austin, 69; Air Force Off Sci Res-Nat Res Coun fel, Princeton Univ, 69-70, univ fel, 70-71; asst prof physics, Univ Tex, Austin, 71-78; asst prof, 79-80, ASSOC PROF PHYSICS & CHEM, TEX A&M UNIV, GALVESTON, 81- *Concurrent Pos:* Vis asst prof, Rice Univ, Houston, 79. *Mem:* Am Chem Soc; Am Phys Soc. *Res:* Theoretical models for molecules and solids, with special emphasis on correlation effects and group-theoretic methods. *Mailing Add:* Dept Marine Sci Tex A&M Univ Galveston TX 77553

KLEIN, EDMUND, b Vienna, Austria, Oct 22, 21; Can citizen; m 52; c 5. MEDICINE, DERMATOLOGY. *Educ:* Univ Toronto, BA, 47, MD, 51. *Prof Exp:* Nat Res Coun fel, Univ Labs, Harvard Med Sch, 51-52, Children's Cancer Res Found fel, Children's Med Ctr, 52-53, res assoc, 53-55, assoc clin path, 54-56; asst resident, Mass Gen Hosp, 58-59, res assoc, 59-60; asst prof med, Sch Med, Tufts Univ, 59-60, asst prof dermat, 60-61; assoc prof exp path, Grad Sch, 62-70, RES PROF MED DERMAT, SCH MED, STATE UNIV NY BUFFALO, 70-; CHIEF DERMAT, ROSWELL PARK MEM INST, 61- *Concurrent Pos:* Clin & res fel dermat, Mass Gen Hosp, 56-58, teaching fel, 58-59; consult, Children's Cancer Res Found, Children's Med Ctr & Acute Leukemia Task Froce, Nat Cancer Inst; mem adv comt biol effects of optical masers, US Army Med Res & Develop Command, Off Surgeon Gen, DC. *Honors & Awards:* Lasker Immunol Award, 72; Founders' Award Immunol, 75. *Mem:* Am Asn Cancer Res; Am Soc Exp Pathologists; Soc Invest Dermat; Am Acad Dermat; Am Soc Clin Pharmacol & Therapeut. *Res:* Biological effects of lasers; lipid transport; hemorrhagic diathesis; cutaneous neoplasms. *Mailing Add:* Dept of Dermat Roswell Park Mem Inst Buffalo NY 14203

KLEIN, EDWARD LAWRENCE, b Roscoe, Pa, Feb 17, 36; m 63; c 4. WOOD ENERGY, FOREST PRODUCTS. *Educ:* Pa State Univ, BS, 58, MS, 61; Baylor Univ, MBA, 63; La State Univ, PhD(forestry mkt), 68. *Prof Exp:* Asst dist forester, Md Dept of Forestry, 58-60; instr in charge mkt res, La State Univ, 65-68; mkt analyst, US Forest Serv, Princeton, WVa, 68-69; supvr econ sect, Tenn Valley Auth, 69-73; mfg mgr, Indust Wood & Pallet Co, 73-75; staff asst to dir, Div Forestry, Tenn Valley Auth, Norris, 75-77, proj leader wood energy, 77-79; DIR MKT, ENERCO ASSOCS, LANGHORNE, PA, 79- *Mem:* Soc Am Foresters; Forest Prod Res Soc. *Res:* Economics of new plant sites and construction; production of saw mills and pallet plants; utilization of biomass as an energy source. *Mailing Add:* 205 W Park Ave Langhorne PA 19047

KLEIN, ELENA BUIMOVICI, b Bucharest, Romania, Nov 12, 30; m 62; c 1. MICROBIOLOGY, INFECTIOUS DISEASES. *Educ:* Univ Bucharest, MD, 53. *Prof Exp:* Sr res scientist microbiol, Cantacuzino Inst, Bucharest, 53-72; res scientist virol, Bellevue Hosp, NY Univ, 72-73; ASST PROF PEDIAT, ROOSEVELT HOSP, COLUMBIA UNIV, 73-; DIR, VIRUS LAB, ST LUKE'S-ROOSEVELT HOSP CTR, 80- *Mem:* Romanian Soc Infectious Path; Am Soc Microbiol; fel Soc Infectious Dis. *Res:* Epidemiology of diptheria; genetics of enteroviruses; epidemiology of poliomyelities; congenital rubella; cell mediated immunity in viral infections; viral vaccines. *Mailing Add:* 27 Nob Ct New Rochelle NY 10804

KLEIN, ELIAS, b Leipzig, Ger, Oct 26, 24; m 48; c 3. PHYSICAL CHEMISTRY. *Educ:* Tulane Univ, MS, 52, PhD(phys chem), 54. *Prof Exp:* Res chemist, Southern Regional Res Lab, USDA, 54-55, invest head, 55-58; res chemist phys chem, Courtaulds, Inc, Ala, 58-60, sect head, 60-62, mgr res dept, 62-64; dir res & develop, 64-67; dir phys chem, 67, DIR LAKE PONTCHARTRAIN LAB, GULF SOUTHERN RES INST, 67- *Concurrent Pos:* Consult, Kalvar Corp, 52-55; adj prof, Loyola Univ, La, 69- *Mem:* Am Chem Soc; Sci Res Soc Am; Am Soc Artificial Internal Organs. *Res:* Kinetics; classical thermodynamics; cellulose and fiber chemistry; membrane transport; polymer properties; hemodialysis; reverse osmosis. *Mailing Add:* Lake Pontchartrain Lab Gulf Southern Res Inst PO Box 26500 New Orleans LA 70126

KLEIN, FRANCIS MICHAEL, b Wilkes Barre, Pa, Nov 1, 41; m 64; c 5. ORGANIC CHEMISTRY. *Educ:* King's Col, Pa, BS, 63; Univ Notre Dame, PhD(org chem), 67. *Prof Exp:* NIH fel, Iowa State Univ, 67-68; asst prof, 68-73, asst dean, 78-79, ASSOC PROF CHEM, CREIGHTON UNIV, 73- *Mem:* AAAS; Am Chem Soc (chmn sect, 72). *Res:* Organic photochemistry; reaction mechanisms, especially stereochemical factors; molecular orbital calculations of reaction energetics; electrophilic addition reactions. *Mailing Add:* Dept of Chem Creighton Univ Omaha NE 68178

KLEIN, GEORGE DEVRIES, b s'Gravenhage, Neth, Jan 21, 33; US citizen; div; c 3. SEDIMENTOLOGY, OCEANOGRAPHY. *Educ:* Wesleyan Univ, BA, 54; Univ Kans, MA, 57; Yale Univ, PhD(geol), 60. *Prof Exp:* Part-time geologist, State Geol Surv, Kans, 55-56; asst instr, Univ Kans, 56-57; lab instr, Yale Univ, 57-58 & 59-60; res geologist, Sinclair Res, Inc, 60-61; asst prof geol, Univ Pittsburgh, 61-63; asst prof, Univ Pa, 63-66, assoc prof, 66-69; assoc prof, 70-72, PROF GEOL, UNIV ILL, URBANA, 72- *Concurrent Pos:* Vis fel, Oxford Univ, 69; vis assoc prof geol & geophys, Univ Calif, Berkeley; vis prof oceanog, Ore State Univ, 74; vis exchange prof geophys sci, Univ Chicago, 79-80. *Honors & Awards:* Outstanding Paper Award, 1970 J Sedimentary Petrol, Soc Econ Paleontologists & Mineralogists, 72. *Mem:* AAAS; Geol Soc Am; Am Asn Petrol Geol; Soc Econ Paleontologists & Mineralogists; Int Asn Sedimentol. *Res:* Recent sediments; sedimentary and sandstone petrology; origin of primary structures; directional properties of sediments; marine geology; turbidites; sedimentation on tidal flats; tidalites; marginal basins; deep-ocean sediment transport; petroleum sandstone reservoir prediction and diagenesis. *Mailing Add:* 245 Natural Hist Bldg Univ Ill 1301 W Green St Urbana IL 61801

KLEIN, GERALD I(RWIN), b Brooklyn, NY, Sept 22, 28; m 48; c 4. ELECTRICAL ENGINEERING. *Educ:* Cooper Union, BEE, 48; Polytech Inst Brooklyn, MEE, 53. *Prof Exp:* Asst head, Radar & Microwave Electronics Sect, Naval Mat Lab, NY, 48-55; chief, Oscillators & Amplifiers Sect, Evans Signal Lab, NJ, 55-58; mgr, Microwave Tubes Sect, Electronic Tube Div, Westinghouse Elec Corp, 58-65, mgr microwave tech lab, Aerospace Div, Md, 65-68; vpres eng & mfg, Solitron Microwave, 68-70; ADV ENGR, WESTINGHOUSE ELEC CORP, 70- *Mem:* Sr mem Inst Elec & Electronics Engrs. *Res:* Microwave electronics; electromagnetic theory; microwave plasmas; electron tubes. *Mailing Add:* Westinghouse Elec Corp Systs Devleop Div PO Box 746-Ms339 Baltimore MD 21208

KLEIN, GERALD WAYNE, b Seattle, Wash, Mar 28, 39; m 58; c 3. POLYMER CHEMISTRY. *Educ:* Seattle Pac Col, BS, 60; Yale Univ, PhD(org chem), 65. *Prof Exp:* NSF fel, Gothenburg Univ, 64-65; asst prof chem, Univ Wyo, 65-69; NIH spec res fel & vis prof, Columbia Univ, 69-70; sr res chemist, 70-77, RES ASSOC, EASTMAN KODAK CO, 77- *Mem:* Am Chem Soc. *Res:* Novel synthetic polymers as vehicles, mordants and chemically active components of photographic systems; photographic science; polymeric films. *Mailing Add:* Res Labs Eastman Kodak Co Rochester NY 14650

KLEIN, HANNAH RAY, analytical chemistry, see previous edition

KLEIN, HAROLD GEORGE, b Jersey City, NJ, Mar 14, 29; m 65. VERTEBRATE ZOOLOGY. *Educ:* Cornell Univ, BS, 53, MS, 54, PhD(vert zool), 58. *Prof Exp:* Instr biol, Swarthmore Col, 57-58; asst prof zool, Pa State Univ, 59-62; asst prof, 62-65, ASSOC PROF BIOL, STATE UNIV NY COL PLATTSBURGH, 65- *Mem:* Ecol Soc Am; Am Soc Mammal; Animal Behav Soc. *Res:* Ecological research on vertebrate animals, particularly mammals. *Mailing Add:* Dept of Biol Sci State Univ of NY Col Plattsburgh NY 12901

KLEIN, HAROLD PAUL, b New York, NY, Apr 1, 21; m 42; c 2. MICROBIAL PHYSIOLOGY, EXOBIOLOGY. *Educ:* Brooklyn Col, BA, 42; Univ Calif, Berkeley, PhD(bact, biochem), 50. *Prof Exp:* Chemist, US Civil Serv, 42-43; instr bact, Armstrong Jr Col, 46-47; asst, Univ Calif, 47-50; res fel, Am Cancer Soc, Mass Gen Hosp, 50-51; from instr to asst prof microbiol, Univ Wash, Seattle, 51-55; from asst prof to prof biol, Brandeis Univ, 55-63, chmn dept, 56-63; chief exobiol div, 63-64, DIR LIFE SCI, AMES RES CTR, NASA, 64- *Concurrent Pos:* Am Cancer Soc fel, 50; vis prof, Univ Calif, 60-61; NSF sr fel, 63; mem, Joint US-USSR Space Med & Biol Working Group, 71-; leader biol team, Viking Mission to Mars, 75-77. *Mem:* AAAS; Am Soc Microbiol; Am Chem Soc; Am Soc Biol Chem; Int Acad Astronaut. *Res:* Microbial metabolism; formation of adaptive enzymes; lipid synthesis. *Mailing Add:* Life Sci Directorate Ames Res Ctr NASA Moffett Field CA 94035

KLEIN, HARVEY GERALD, b New York, NY, Oct 22, 30; m 57. PHARMACEUTICS, INSTRUMENTATION. *Educ:* City Col New York, BS, 53; NY Univ, MS, 57; Purdue Univ, PhD(chem), 61. *Prof Exp:* Chemist plastic additives res, Cent Res Div, Am Cyanamid Co, Stamford, Conn, 61-63, sr mkt analyst, Com Develop Div, Wayne, NJ, 63-66, tech rep & liaison, Washington, DC, 66-67; drug & health care financial analyst, R W Pressprich & Co, 67-69, Wertheim & Co, 69-70 & Andresen & Co, 71-72; pres, Klein Assocs, 73-80, VPRES, KLEIN BIOMED CONSULTS, 81- *Mem:* Am Chem Soc; Am Inst Ultrasound Med; Am Inst Chemists; Inst Elec & Electronics Engrs; Sigma Xi. *Res:* Medical diagnostic instrumentation and pharmaceutical development. *Mailing Add:* 215 W 90th St New York NY 10024

KLEIN, HOWARD JOSEPH, b Kokomo, Ind, July 5, 41; m 64; c 5. METALLURGICAL ENGINEERING. *Educ:* Purdue Univ, BS, 63; Univ Ala, MS, 65; Univ Tenn, PhD(metall eng), 69. *Prof Exp:* Engr, 69-71, sr engr process metall, 72-73, group leader process metall & ceramics, 73-75, sect mgr, 75-77, dir res & develop, stellite div, 78-80, OPERS MGR, HIGH TECHNOL DIV, CABOT CORP, 80- *Concurrent Pos:* Mem, Comt Electroslag Remelting & Plasma Melting Technol, Nat Mat Adv Bd, 74-75 & Comt Joint Coop Electro Metall, US State Dept, 76-; mem comt review US-USSR Agreement Coop Fields Sci & Technol, Nat Acad Sci, 77. *Honors & Awards:* Von Karman Award, Theodore Von Karman Mem Found, 74; IR 100, Indust Res, 75 & 77. *Mem:* Am Soc Metals; Am Inst Mining, Metall & Petrol Engrs. *Res:* Process metallurgy in the specialty metals industry, specifically primary and secondary melting processes, process modeling, computer process control; also strengthening and oxidation mechanisms for high temperature and corrosion resistant materials. *Mailing Add:* High Technol Mat Div 1020 W Park Ave Kokomo IN 46901

KLEIN, IMRICH, b Kosice, Czech, Sept 14, 28; US citizen; m 50; c 2. PLASTICS & CHEMICAL ENGINEERING. *Educ:* Israel Inst Technol, BS, 56; Case Inst Technol, MS, 58, PhD(chem eng), 59. *Prof Exp:* Res asst, Israel Inst Technol, 55-56; chem engr, Israel Govt, 56-57; res engr, E I du Pont de Nemours & Co, 59-61 & Esso Res & Eng Co, 61-63; sr res engr, Eng Res Cent, Western Elec Co, 63-68; PRES, SCI PROCESS & RES, INC, 68- *Mem:* Am Chem Soc; Am Inst Chem Engrs; Soc Plastics Engrs; Am Inst Chemists. *Res:* Plastics extrusion and processing; development of computerized physical models; computer technology and programming; numerical analysis; polymerization kinetics; design and analysis of experiments; multicomponent phase equilibria; semicrystalline polyolefins; separation processes; chemical process development. *Mailing Add:* 70 S Adlaide Ave Highland Park NJ 08904

KLEIN, JAMES H(ENRY), b Boston, Mass, Oct 12, 20; m 55; c 4. CHEMICAL ENGINEERING. *Educ:* Mass Inst Technol, BS & MS, 43, ScD(chem eng), 50. *Prof Exp:* Maintenance engr, Union Oil Co, 43-46; engr, Quinton Engrs Ltd, 46-47; res assoc, Mass Inst Technol, 47-50, engr & bus mgr, Lexington Proj, 48, instr, 48-49; proj engr, Am Res & Develop Co, 50-51; tech dir, Inst Inventive Res, Div Southwest Res Inst, 51-53; tech consult, State of Mass, 53-56; mem tech staff, Thompson Ramo-Wooldridge, 56-57;

dir eng, Stanley Aviation Corp, 58; CONSULT ENGR, 58-; PRES, KLEIN AEROSPACE, INC, 66- *Concurrent Pos:* Consult, Baird-Atomic, 50-56 & Southwest Res Inst, 53-56; dir res, Cook Batteries, 59-63; vpres res, Frost Eng Develop Corp, 61-64; vpres, Aerospace Eng Sales Co, 61-70. *Mem:* Am Chem Soc; Electrochem Soc; Am Inst Chem Engrs; Am Inst Physics; Air Pollution Control Asn. *Res:* Heat and mass transfer; photosynthesis; energy storage and conversion; nuclear engineering; medical instrumentation; air pollution; bio-engineering; development and commercialization of new ideas and inventions. *Mailing Add:* PO Box 906 Breckenridge CO 80424

KLEIN, JAN, b Opava, Czech, Jan 18, 36; m 69; c 3. BIOLOGY, IMMUNOGENETICS. *Educ:* Charles Univ, Prague, MS, 58; Czech Acad Sci, PhD(genetics), 64. *Prof Exp:* Res assoc genetics, Inst Exp Biol & Genetics, Prague, 64-65; res assoc, Sch Med, Stanford Univ, 68-69; from asst prof to assoc prof, Univ Mich, Ann Arbor, 69-74; from assoc prof to prof microbiol, Univ Tex Health Sci Ctr, Dallas, 74-78; DIR DEPT IMMUNOGENETICS, MAX PLANCK INST BIOL, 78- *Concurrent Pos:* Levere K Purcell & Truman St John Mem fels genetics, Sch Med, Stanford Univ, 65-66; NIH grant; Nat Inst Dent Res grant, 69; managing ed, Immunogenetics; mem immunobiol study sect, NIH. *Honors & Awards:* Elisabeth Goldschmidt Mem lectr; Rabbi Schacknai Mem Prize, Transplantation Soc. *Mem:* Am Asn Immunol; Transplantation Soc. *Res:* Transplantation genetics; cellular immunology. *Mailing Add:* Dept of Immunogenetics Corrensstrasse 42 7400 Tübingen 1 Germany, Federal Republic of

KLEIN, JERRY ALAN, b Neenah, Wis, Apr 19, 45; m 66; c 2. CHEMICAL ENGINEERING. *Educ:* Univ Wis, BS, 67; Princeton Univ, PhD(chem eng), 72. *Prof Exp:* Develop engr, 72-78, GROUP LEADER ENVIRON CONTROL TECHNOL, CHEM TECHNOL DIV, OAK RIDGE NAT LAB, 78- *Res:* Environmental control technology for coal conversion processes. *Mailing Add:* Chem Technol Div PO Box X Oak Ridge TN 37830

KLEIN, JOHN PETER, b Milwaukee, Wis, Dec 30, 50. RELIABILITY, COMPETING RISKS. *Educ:* Univ Wis, Milwaukee, BA, MS, 75; Univ Mo, PhD(statist), 80. *Prof Exp:* Asst math, Univ Wis, Milwaukee, 74-75, statist, Univ Mo, 75-80; ASST PROF STATIST, OHIO STATE UNIV, 80- *Concurrent Pos:* Researcher, Oak Ridge Nat Labs, 76-77; consult, Ohio State Comprehensive Cancer Ctr, 81- *Mem:* Biomet Soc; Am Statist Asn. *Res:* Competing risk theory. *Mailing Add:* #4 583 Harley Dr Columbus OH 43202

KLEIN, JOHN SHARPLESS, b Ossining, NY, Sept 9, 22; m 63; c 2. APPLIED MATHEMATICS. *Educ:* Haverford Col, BS, 43; Mass Inst Technol, SM, 49; Univ Mich, PhD, 59. *Prof Exp:* Instr math, Williams Col, 49-51, Oberlin Col, 54-55 & Case Inst Technol, 55-56; asst prof, Univ RI, 56-58 & Wilson Col, 59; assoc prof, Lafayette Col, 59-60, Wilson Col, 60-63 & Monmouth Col, NJ, 63-64; head dept, 64-74, PROF MATH, HOBART & WILLIAM SMITH COLS, 64- *Mem:* Soc Indust & Appl Math; Math Asn Am. *Res:* Integral transforms. *Mailing Add:* Dept of Math Hobart & William Smith Cols Geneva NY 14456

KLEIN, LARRY L, b Chicago, Ill, Jan 24, 53. ORGANIC CONDUCTORS, CARBOHYDRATE CHEMISTRY. *Educ:* Ill Inst Technol, BS, 75; Mich State Univ, PhD(chem), 80. *Prof Exp:* NIH fel chem, Harvard Univ, 80-82; ASST PROF CHEM, TEX A&M UNIV, 82- *Mem:* Am Chem Soc. *Res:* Organic synthesis of natural products. *Mailing Add:* Dept Chem Box 64 Harvard Univ Cambridge MA 02138

KLEIN, LEROY, b Newark, NJ, Oct 1, 26; m 58; c 3. BIOCHEMISTRY, MEDICAL RESEARCH. *Educ:* Syracuse Univ, BA, 50; Boston Univ, MA, 52, PhD(biochem), 58; Case Western Reserve Univ, MD, 65. *Prof Exp:* From instr to assoc prof biochem in orthop surg, 63-77, from sr instr to asst prof biochem, 65-71, PROF BIOCHEM IN ORTHOP & MACROMOLECULAR SCI, CASE WESTERN RESERVE UNIV, 77-, ASSOC PROF BIOCHEM, 71- *Concurrent Pos:* Res fel biochem, Case Western Reserve Univ, 58-60, res fel orthop, 60-63, instr orthop surg, 63-65; Kappa Delta res award, 63, res grants, 63- *Mem:* Am Fedn Clin Res; Am Soc Biol Chem; Orthop Res Soc; Geront Soc; Am Soc Bone & Mineral Res. *Res:* Connective tissue metabolism and diseases; collagen and mineral turnover in experimental and metabolic bone diseases, aging, wound healing. *Mailing Add:* Dept Macromolecular Sci Case Western Reserve Univ Cleveland OH 44106

KLEIN, LEWIS S, b Youngstown, Ohio, Sept 2, 32; m 60. THEORETICAL PHYSICS. *Educ:* Union Col, NY, BS, 54; Yale Univ, MS, 55, PhD(physics), 58. *Prof Exp:* Fulbright fel & res physicist, Nat Ctr Sci Res, France, 58-59; instr physics, Northwestern Univ, 59-60; sr res staff, Nat Bur Stand, 60-65; assoc prof, 65-70, PROF PHYSICS, HOWARD UNIV, 70- *Mem:* Am Phys Soc. *Res:* Field theory; statistical mechanics; plasma physics. *Mailing Add:* Dept of Physics Howard Univ Washington DC 20001

KLEIN, MARTIN, b New York, NY, June 25, 24; m 80; c 3. HISTORY OF PHYSICS. *Educ:* Columbia Univ, AB, 42, AM, 44; Mass Inst Technol, PhD(physics), 48. *Prof Exp:* Asst physics, Columbia Univ, 42-44, physicist, Underwater Sound Reference Lab, 44-45; mem, Opers Res Group, Washington, DC, 45-46; res assoc physics, Mass Inst Technol, 46-49; from instr to prof, Case Inst Technol, 49-67; EUGENE HIGGINS PROF HIST PHYSICS, YALE UNIV, 73- *Concurrent Pos:* Nat Res fel, Dublin Inst Advan Studies, 52-53; Guggenheim fel, Inst Lorentz, Leiden, 58-59; mem, Inst Advan Study, 72; Van der Waals prof, Univ Amsterdam, 74; vis prof, Rockefeller Univ, 75. *Mem:* Nat Acad Sci; fel AAAS; fel Am Phys Soc; Hist Sci Soc; Acad Int Hist Sci. *Res:* History of modern physics; statistical mechanics. *Mailing Add:* Dept Hist Sci Yale Univ Box 2036 New Haven CT 06520

KLEIN, MARYROSE SILVIA, b Attleboro, Mass, Aug 12, 47; m 70; c 1. DEVELOPMENTAL BIOLOGY. *Educ:* Boston Univ, AB, 68; NY Univ, MS, 72, PhD(cell biol), 78. *Prof Exp:* ASSOC, YALE UNIV, 78- *Concurrent Pos:* Instr, Yale Univ, 80 & 82. *Mem:* Soc Protozoologists; Am Soc Cell Biol; Soc Develop Biol. *Res:* Developmental biology and genetics; mammalian reproductive biology. *Mailing Add:* Dept Biol Box 6666 Yale Univ New Haven CT 06511

KLEIN, MAX, b New Bedford, Mass, Feb 5, 25; wid; c 3. CHEMICAL PHYSICS, THERMODYNAMICS. *Educ:* Univ Mass, BS, 48; Univ Md, PhD(physics), 62. *Prof Exp:* Electronics engr comput memory, Nat Bur Standards, 50-55, physicist thermodynamics, 55-63; physicist chem physics, Weizmann Inst Sci, 63-65; physicist thermodynamics, Nat Bur Standards, 65-67; sect chief thermodynamics, 67-77, SUPVRY PHYSICIST THERMODYNAMICS, NAT BUR STANDARDS, 77- *Concurrent Pos:* Mem fac grad sch, NIH, 66-76; mem adv comt grad sch, Dept Agr, 67-72. *Honors & Awards:* Dept Silver Medal, US Dept Com. *Mem:* Am Phys Soc; Am Inst Chem Engrs; AAAS; Sigma Xi. *Mailing Add:* 618 Hyde Rd Silver Spring MD 20902

KLEIN, MELVIN PHILLIP, b Denver, Colo, July 27, 21; m 60; c 2. BIOPHYSICS, BIOPHYSICAL SPECTROSCOPY. *Educ:* Univ Calif, Berkeley, AB, 52, PhD(biophys), 59. *Prof Exp:* Physicist, Radiation Lab, 52-59, biophysicist, Lawrence Radiation Lab, 59-69, BIOPHYSICIST & ASSOC DIR, CHEM BIODYN LAB, LAWRENCE BERKELEY LAB, UNIV CALIF, 69- *Concurrent Pos:* Vis mem tech staff, Bell Tel Labs, Murray Hill, NJ, 60-61; mem biophys & biophys chem study sect, Div Res Grants, NIH, 69-74; mem adv comt, Stable Isotopes Resource, Los Alamos Sci Labs, 75; mem exec comt, Stanford Magnetic Resonsance Lab, Stanford Univ, 76; sabbatical vis, Biophys Group, Ecole Polytech, Palaiseau & Synchrotron Radiation Lab, Univ Paris, 76-77; John Simon Guggenheim Mem Found, 76; chmn, Gordon Res Conf Magnetic Resonance, 77. *Mem:* Biophys Soc; Am Phys Soc. *Res:* Nitrogen fixation; photosynthesis; magnetic resonance spectroscopy; x-ray spectroscopy with synchrotron radiation; membranes. *Mailing Add:* Chem Biodyn Lab Univ Calif Berkeley CA 94720

KLEIN, MICHAEL, b Chicago, Ill, Mar 5, 46; m 80. MEDICINAL CHEMISTRY, MASS SPECTROMETRY. *Educ:* Univ Ill, BS, 67, PhD(med chem), 71. *Prof Exp:* Appointee chem, Chem Div, Argonne Nat Lab, Ill, 72-74; sr res chemist mass spectrometry, liquid chromatography & forensic drug chem, Testing & Res Lab, 74-78, SR RES CHEMIST, REGULATORY CONTROL DIV, DRUG ENFORCEMENT ADMIN, US DEPT JUSTICE, 78- *Concurrent Pos:* Presidential internship, Argonne Nat Lab, Ill, 72-73. *Honors & Awards:* Spec Achievement Award, Drug Enforcement Admin, US Dept Justice, 78. *Mem:* Am Chem Soc; Am Pharmaceut Asn. *Res:* Identification and quantitation of trace impurities in illicit drugs for forensic purposes; techniques applied include organic synthesis, mass spectrometry, high and resolution, gas and liquid chromatography, nuclear magnetic resonance, infrared; drug control decisions based on actual and potential abuse. *Mailing Add:* US Dept Justice Regulatory Control Div Washington DC 20537

KLEIN, MICHAEL, b New York, NY, June 30, 17; m 50; c 3. ANATOMY. *Educ:* City Col New York, BS, 38; Univ Calif, Los Angeles, MA, 46, PhD(endocrinol), 48. *Prof Exp:* Asst zool, Univ Calif, Los Angeles, 45-47; from asst prof to assoc prof cancer res, Univ Fla, 51-56; assoc dir cancer res, Michael Reese Hosp, Chicago, Ill, 56-57; from asst prof to assoc prof anat, Col Med, Univ Tenn, 57-63; head bioassay sect, Carcinogenesis Studies Br, 63-66, prog dir carcinogenesis, 66-67, RES PLANNING OFFICER, OFF DIR, NAT CANCER INST, 67- *Concurrent Pos:* Nat Cancer Inst fel, Univ Calif, Los Angeles, 49-51. *Mem:* Am Asn Cancer Res; Am Soc Exp Path. *Res:* Pathogenesis and etiology of cancer; infant carcinogenesis; carcinogenesis bioassay; experimental pathology. *Mailing Add:* Nat Cancer Inst Bldg 31A-10A52 Bethesda MD 20014

KLEIN, MICHAEL GARDNER, b Rockford, Ill, Jan 14, 41; m 64; c 2. ENTOMOLOGY. *Educ:* Univ Wis-Madison, BS, 63, MS, 65, PhD(entom), 72. *Prof Exp:* RES ENTOMOLOGIST, HORT INSECTS RES LAB, SCI & EDUC AGR RES SERV, USDA, 69- *Mem:* Entom Soc Am; Soc Invert Path; Sigma Xi; Int Orgn Biol Control Noxious Animals & Plants. *Res:* Studies on the use of attractants, juvenile hormone-like compounds and biological control agents against horticultural insects. *Mailing Add:* USDA Japanese Beetle Res Lab Ohio Agr Res & Develop Ctr Wooster OH 44691

KLEIN, MICHAEL JOHN, b Ames, Iowa, Jan 19, 40; m 62; c 3. RADIO ASTRONOMY. *Educ:* Iowa State Univ, BS, 62; Univ Mich, MS, 66, PhD(astron), 68. *Prof Exp:* Asst res engr, Radio Astron Lab, Univ Mich, 63-64; Nat Res Coun-NASA resident res assoc, 68-69, sr scientist radio astron, Space Sci Div, 69-73, MEM TECH STAFF, SPACE SCI DIV, JET PROPULSION LAB, CALIF INST TECHNOL, 73- *Mem:* Am Inst Elec & Electronics Eng; Am Astron Soc; Int Astron Union; Int Union Radio Sci. *Res:* Measuring and interpretating radio frequency emission of galactic and extragalactic radio sources and the planets and satellites of the solar system. *Mailing Add:* Jet Propulsion Lab Calif Inst of Technol 4800 Oak Grove Dr Pasadena CA 91103

KLEIN, MICHAEL LAWRENCE, b London, Eng, Mar 13, 40; m 62; c 2. THEORETICAL CHEMISTRY. *Educ:* Bristol Univ, BSc, 61, PhD(theoret chem), 64. *Prof Exp:* Ciba Found fel physics, Univ Genoa, 64-65; Imp Chem Industs fel theoret chem, Bristol Univ, 65-67; res assoc physics, Rutgers Univ, 67-68; SR RES OFF CHEM, NAT RES COUN CAN, 68- *Mem:* Am Phys Soc; Royal Soc Chem; Can Inst Physics; Chem Inst Can. *Res:* Physical chemistry; solid state physics. *Mailing Add:* Nat Res Coun Can Chem Div 100 Sussex Dr Ottawa ON K1A 0R6 Can

KLEIN, MICHAEL W, b Teglas, Hungary, Mar 29, 31; US citizen; m 55; c 2. SOLID STATE PHYSICS, STATISTICAL MECHANICS. *Educ:* Univ Colo, BS, 56; Cornell Univ, PhD(physics), 62. *Prof Exp:* Asst physics, Cornell Univ, 56-61; res physicist, Lincoln Labs, Mass Inst Technol, 61-62 & Sperry Rand Res Ctr, Mass, 62-68; assoc prof physics, Wesleyan Univ, 68-71; assoc prof physics, Bar-Ilan Univ, Israel, 71-77; vis prof, Physics Dept, Univ Ill, 77-79; PROF PHYSICS, WORCESTER POLYTECH INST, 79- *Concurrent Pos:* Vis assoc prof, Brandeis Univ, 67-68. *Mem:* Am Phys Soc. *Res:* Theory of magnetism; solid state physics; statistical mechanics; plasma physics; glassy and amorphous systems. *Mailing Add:* Dept Physics Worcester Polytech Inst Worcester MA 01609

KLEIN, MILES VINCENT, b Cleveland, Ohio, Mar 9, 33; m 56; c 2. PHYSICS. *Educ:* Northwestern Univ, BS, 54; Cornell Univ, PhD(physics), 61. *Prof Exp:* NSF fel physics, Stuttgart Tech Univ, 61-62; from asst prof to assoc prof, 62-69, PROF PHYSICS, UNIV ILL, URBANA, 69- *Mem:* Fel Am Phys Soc; Optical Soc Am. *Res:* Raman scattering in solids; low temperature thermal conductivity studies in solids; lattice dynamics; optical properties of solids. *Mailing Add:* Dept of Physics Univ of Ill Urbana IL 61801

KLEIN, MILTON M, b New York, NY, Apr 19, 17; m 51; c 1. FLUID DYNAMICS. *Educ:* NY Univ, MS, 50, PhD(physics), 56. *Prof Exp:* Physicist aerodyn, Nat Adv Comt Aeronaut, 42-47, aeronaut res scientist, 48-50; instr physics, NY Univ, 50-55; physicist, Gen Elec Co, 55-61; physicist nuclear debris studies, Geophys Corp Am, 61-63, re-entry physics, Lincoln Lab, 63-64 & plasma physics & hydrodyn, GCA Corp, 64-67; RES PHYSICIST, AIR FORCE CAMBRIDGE RES LABS, BEDFORD, 67- *Concurrent Pos:* Lectr, Grad Sch, Univ Pa, 57-58. *Mem:* Am Phys Soc. *Res:* Fluid dynamics; diffusion; turbulence; heat transfer; interaction of buoyant turbulent jets with air; dissipation of fog by heat; cloud physics; meteorology. *Mailing Add:* 54 Burlington St Lexington MA 02173

KLEIN, MORTON, b New York, NY, Aug 9, 25; m 49; c 2. OPERATIONS RESEARCH. *Educ:* Duke Univ, BS, 46; Columbia Univ, MS, 52, EngScD, 57. *Prof Exp:* Ord engr, Picatinny Arsenal, US Army, 50-54; asst indust eng, 54-56, from instr to assoc prof opers res, 56-68, chmn div math methods & opers res, 68-77, PROF OPERS RES, COLUMBIA UNIV, 68-, CHMN DEPT INDUST ENG & OPER RES, 81- *Mem:* Opers Res Soc Am; Inst Mgt Sci; Am Inst Indust Eng. *Res:* Network flow theory; medical applications; optimal schedules for medical examinations. *Mailing Add:* 301A SW Mudd Bldg Columbia Univ New York NY 10027

KLEIN, MORTON, b Philadelphia, Pa, Nov 30, 14; m 36; c 2. VIROLOGY. *Educ:* Univ Pa, BS, 38, MS, 40, PhD(immunol), 42. *Prof Exp:* Asst instr bact, Univ Pa, 40-42; res assoc, Dept Med, Univ Chicago, 42-43; res assoc, Virus Infections & Chemother, Sch Med, Univ Pa, 43-48; asst prof bact, Jefferson Med Col, 48-50; assoc prof, 50-57, PROF MICROBIOL, SCH MED, TEMPLE UNIV, 57- *Mem:* Fel AAAS; Am Soc Microbiol; fel Am Acad Microbiol. *Res:* Inactivation of viruses; immunology of viral infections; role of macrophages in resistance to infection. *Mailing Add:* Dept of Microbiol Temple Univ Sch of Med Philadelphia PA 19140

KLEIN, MORTON JOSEPH, b Chicago, Ill, Feb 26, 28; m 53; c 3. INORGANIC CHEMISTRY. *Educ:* Univ Ill, BS, 48; Ill Inst Technol, PhD(chem), 53. *Prof Exp:* Assoc chemist catalysis, 53-54, res chemist org chem, 54-56, asst supvr propellant res, 56-59, supvr, 59-62, asst dir chem res, 62-65, dir appl chem, 65-69, dir chem res, 69-75, dir chem & chem eng res, 75-77, V PRES RES OPERS, IIT RES INST, 77- *Mem:* Am Chem Soc; Am Inst Aeronaut & Astronaut; Am Inst Chem; Int Ozone Inst (pres, 75-). *Res:* Synthesis and evaluation of new high energy materials; research management. *Mailing Add:* IIT Res Inst 10 W 35th St Chicago IL 60616

KLEIN, NATHAN, b New York, NY, July 29, 31; m 52; c 5. PHYSICAL CHEMISTRY. *Educ:* City Col New York, BS, 51; Columbia Univ, MA, 52; Univ Del, PhD(chem), 67. *Prof Exp:* Res asst biochem, Sloan-Kettering Inst Cancer Res, 52; chemist, Edgewood Arsenal, 55-66, group leader radiation chem, US Army Nuclear Defense Lab, 66-74, GROUP LEADER, US ARMY BALLISTIC RES LABS, 74- *Mem:* Am Chem Soc; Sigma Xi; fel Am Inst Chem. *Res:* Physical chemistry of aqueous solutions; reactions rates of high energy compounds; chemical kinetics of propellants and explosives; high temperature, high pressure reaction studies. *Mailing Add:* US Army Ballistic Res Labs Aberdeen Proving Ground MD 21005

KLEIN, NELSON HAROLD, b New York, NY, Mar 6, 42; m 66; c 2. PHYSICS. *Educ:* Drexel Univ, BS, 64, MS, 68, PhD(physics), 72. *Prof Exp:* Assoc prof physics, 72-78, CHMN DEPT SCI, BUCKS COUNTY COMMUN COL, 78-, PROF PHYSICS, 80- *Mem:* Am Asn Physics Teachers. *Mailing Add:* Dept of Sci Bucks County Commun Col New Town PA 18940

KLEIN, PAUL ALVIN, b Weehawken, NJ, Feb 1, 41; m 63; c 2. VIROLOGY, IMMUNOLOGY. *Educ:* Rutgers Univ, New Brunswick, BA, 63; Univ Fla, PhD(med sci), 67. *Prof Exp:* ASSOC PROF PATH, COL MED, UNIV FLA, 69- *Mem:* AAAS; Am Asn Immunologists; Reticuloendothelial Soc. *Res:* Viral immunology; membrane antigens; immunogenicity; tumor immunology. *Mailing Add:* Dept of Path Univ of Fla Col of Med Gainesville FL 32601

KLEIN, PETER DOUGLAS, b Elmhurst, Ill, Nov 30, 27; m 50, 68; c 3. ANALYTICAL CHEMISTRY, BIOCHEMISTRY. *Educ:* Antioch Col, BS, 48; Wayne State Univ, MS, 50, PhD(physiol chem), 54. *Prof Exp:* From asst biochemist to sr biochemist, Div Biol Med Res, Argonne Nat Lab, 69-72; prof med, Univ Chicago, 72-80; mem staff, Div Biol & Med Res, Argonne Nat Lab, 76-80; PROF PEDIAT, BAYLOR COL MED, 80-; DIR, STABLE ISOTOPE LAB, CHILDREN'S NUTRIT RES CTR, 80- *Mem:* Am Soc Mass Spectrometry; Am Asn Study Liver Dis; Am Soc Biol Chemists; Am Gastroenterol Asn; Am Soc Clin Nutrit. *Res:* Application of stable isotope tracer methodology and mass spectrometry to clinical research in nutrition and gastroenterology; development of non-invasive diagnostic and functional assessments in premature and neonatal infants. *Mailing Add:* Children's Nutrit Res Ctr 6608 Fannin Rm 519 Houston TX 77030

KLEIN, PHILIPP HILLEL, b New York, NY, Sept 14, 26; m 53; c 3. PHYSICAL INORGANIC CHEMISTRY. *Educ:* Syracuse Univ, BS, 48, MS, 51, PhD(phys chem), 53. *Prof Exp:* Asst chem, Syracuse Univ, 48-49, res asst, 51-52; res assoc, Knolls Atomic Power Lab, Gen Elec Co, 52-56, phys chemist, Electronics Lab, 56-61; mem sci staff, Sperry Rand Res Ctr, 61-66; head dielec mat sect, Electronics Res Ctr, NASA, Mass, 66-70; head crystals & pure mat sect, 70-73, HEAD DIELEC MAT SECT, US NAVAL RES LAB, 73- *Mem:* Fel Am Inst Chem; Sigma Xi; Inst Elec & Electronics Engrs; Am Ceramic Soc; Am Phys Soc. *Res:* Effects of nuclear radiation on gases and dielectric solids; thermoelectricity; compound semiconductors; thermal properties of solids; electronically and optically active solids; crystal growth. *Mailing Add:* Code 6822 US Naval Res Lab Washington DC 20375

KLEIN, RALPH, b Pittsburgh, Pa, Jan 24, 18; wid; c 2. PHYSICAL CHEMISTRY. *Educ:* Carnegie Inst Technol, BS, 38; Univ Minn, MS, 40; Univ Pittsburgh, PhD(chem), 50. *Prof Exp:* Phys chemist, US Bur Mines, 38-39, Chem Warfare Serv, 40-41, US Bur Mines, 46-56, Olin Mathieson Chem Corp, 56-60 & Melpar, Inc, 60-61; chief surface chem sect, 61-74, SR SCIENTIST, NAT BUR STANDS, WASHINGTON, DC, 74- *Mem:* Am Chem Soc; Am Phys Soc. *Res:* Low temperature chemistry; surface phenomena. *Mailing Add:* 7105 Plantation Lane Rockville MD 20852

KLEIN, RICHARD JOSEPH, b Lugoj, Romania, June 11, 26; US citizen; m 57; c 1. MICROBIOLOGY, EXPERIMENTAL MEDICINE. *Educ:* Inst Med, Bucharest, Romania, MD, 53, DSc(virol), 67. *Prof Exp:* From instr to asst prof microbiol, Inst Med, Bucharest, 49-54; sr res scientist, Cantacuzino Inst, Bucharest, 51-72; ASSOC PROF MICROBIOL, SCH MED, MED CTR, NY UNIV, 72-, ASSOC PROF MICROBIOL, SCH DENT, 77- *Mem:* Am Soc Microbiol; Brit Soc Gen Microbiol; NY Acad Sci. *Res:* Virology; experimental chemotherapy; antiviral drugs; epidemiology; genetics of enteroviruses; herpes simplex virus infections. *Mailing Add:* Med Ctr 550 First Ave New York NY 10016

KLEIN, RICHARD LESTER, b Hempstead, NY, Nov 6, 29; m 53; c 2. PHARMACOLOGY, CELL PHYSIOLOGY. *Educ:* Hofstra Univ, BA, 51, MA, 52; Vanderbilt Univ, PhD(biol, chem), 57. *Prof Exp:* Instr pharmacol, Vanderbilt Univ, 58-59; from asst prof to assoc prof, 59-66, prof pharmacol, 66-81, PROF PHARMACOL & TOXICOL, MED CTR, UNIV MISS, 81- *Concurrent Pos:* Nat Heart Inst fel pharmacol, Vanderbilt Univ, 57-59; NIH career prog award, 62-72; vis prof, Biophys Lab, Wenner-Gren Inst, 63-64; vis prof, Karolinska Inst, 69-70. *Mem:* Am Soc Pharmacol & Exp Therapeut; Electron Micros Soc Am; Soc Neurosci. *Res:* Sympathetic nerve and catecholamine storage visicles, including permeability, enzyme activity, composition, histochemistry and ultrastructure; human serum dopamine beta-hydroxylase and sympathetic homeostasis. *Mailing Add:* Dept of Pharmacol Univ of Miss Med Ctr Jackson MS 39216

KLEIN, RICHARD M, b Philadelphia, Pa, Nov 10, 37. INORGANIC CHEMISTRY, ORGANIC CHEMISTRY. *Educ:* Williams Col, BA, 59; Univ Ill, MS, 62, PhD(polymer chem), 63. *Prof Exp:* Mem staff sales develop spec prod, Rohm and Haas Co, 63-65, mgr sales develop, Pa, 65-66, mgr int opers sales develop, 66-68; asst managing dir, Triton Chem SAfrica, 68-69; asst to pres int opers, Tanatex Chem Corp, NJ, 69-70; pres, Ionac Chem Co, 70-78; GROUP VPRES CHEM, SYBRON CORP, 78- *Concurrent Pos:* Pres, Gamlen Chem Co NAm, 75-78. *Mem:* Am Chem Soc. *Res:* Chemical management and development. *Mailing Add:* Sybron Corp Birmingham Rd Birmingham NJ 08011

KLEIN, RICHARD M, b Chicago, Ill, Mar 17, 23; m 47. PLANT PHYSIOLOGY. *Educ:* Univ Chicago, BS, 47, MS, 48, PhD(bot), 51. *Prof Exp:* Am Cancer Soc fel bot, Univ Chicago, 51-53; res assoc, NY Bot Garden, 53-55, assoc cur, 55-57, Alfred H Caspary cur plant physiol, 57-67; PROF BOT, UNIV VT, 67- *Mem:* Am Soc Plant Physiol; Bot Soc Am; Am Soc Photobiol. *Res:* Growth and development of plants; photobiology. *Mailing Add:* Dept of Bot Univ of Vt Burlington VT 05401

KLEIN, RICHARD MORRIS, b Brooklyn, NY, Apr 26, 42; m 64; c 2. MATERIALS SCIENCE, GLASS SCIENCE. *Educ:* State Univ NY Col Ceramics, Alfred, BS, 63, PhD(ceramic sci), 67. *Prof Exp:* MEM TECH STAFF, GTE LABS, INC, 66-, PRIN INVESTR, 75-, ACTG RES MGR, 81- *Mem:* Am Ceramic Soc; Nat Inst Ceramic Engrs; Soc Glass Technol; Sigma Xi. *Res:* Preparation of telecommunication-grade optical fibers and characterization of their optical and mechanical properties; optical and electrical properties of oxide and non-oxide glasses. *Mailing Add:* GTE Labs Inc 40 Sylvan Rd Waltham MA 02254

KLEIN, ROBERT HERBERT, b New York, NY, Dec 5, 32; m 61; c 3. PHYSICS. *Educ:* Columbia Univ, AB, 53; Carnegie Inst Technol, PhD(physics), 63. *Prof Exp:* Asst physics, Carnegie Inst Technol, 53-55; assoc scientist, Avco Res & Adv Develop Corp, 56-57; solid state physicist, Electronic Res Directorate, Air Force Cambridge Res Ctr, Mass, 57-59; asst theoret physics, Carnegie Inst Technol, 59-63; res scientist, Courant Inst, NY Univ, 63-65; res assoc physics, Case Inst Technol, 65-67; ASSOC PROF PHYSICS, CLEVELAND STATE UNIV, 67-, DIR FIRST COL, 75- *Mem:* Am Phys Soc. *Res:* Theoretical physics. *Mailing Add:* Dept of Physics Cleveland State Univ Cleveland OH 44115

KLEIN, ROBERT MELVIN, b New York, NY, Dec 17, 49; m 75; c 1. ANATOMY, CELL BIOLOGY. *Educ:* City Univ New York, BA, 70; NY Univ, MS, 73, PhD(anat), 74. *Prof Exp:* Fel, Marquette Univ, 74-75; asst prof, 75-81, ASSOC PROF ANAT, MED CTR, UNIV KANS, 81- *Concurrent Pos:* Assoc scientist, Mid-Am Cancer Ctr, 75-; NIH Travel Award, Tel Aviv, Israel, 77; prin investr, NIH grant, 78-82; prin investr, Am Heart Asn grant, 81-82. *Mem:* Am Asn Anatomists; Cell Kinetics Soc; Soc Develop Biol; NY Acad Sci; Am Soc Cell Biol. *Res:* Influence of autonomic nervous system on growth and differentiation of neonatal digestive system; pulmonary hypertension. *Mailing Add:* Dept Anat Univ Kans Med Ctr 39th & Rainbow Kansas City KS 66103

KLEIN, S WAYNE, b Canonsburg, Pa, Jan 20, 28; m 55; c 3. MEDICINE. *Educ:* Univ Pittsburgh, BA, 49, MS, 52; Johns Hopkins Univ, MD, 56. *Prof Exp:* Asst biophys, Univ Pittsburgh, 49-52; NSF fel biophys, Johns Hopkins Univ, 57-58, asst pediat, 58-59, from instr to asst prof, 59-63; pediatrician & dir pediat virus labs, Baltimore City Hosps, 59-63, asst chief pediatrician, 63-68; ASSOC PROF PEDIAT, STATE UNIV NY STONY BROOK, 69-; DIR NEONATOL, NASSAU COUNTY MED CTR, 68- *Res:* Virology; pediatrics; viral infections of prenatal and neonatal life. *Mailing Add:* Nassau County Med Ctr 2201 Hempstead Turnpike East Meadow NY 11554

KLEIN, SHERWIN JARED, b Toledo, Ohio, Jan 13, 19; m 43; c 2. PSYCHOPHYSIOLOGY. *Educ:* Western Reserve Univ, AB, 41; Univ Pa, MA, 47, PhD, 51. *Prof Exp:* Asst psychol, Western Reserve Univ, 40-41, instr, 46-51; sepc proj scientist, Air Crew Equip Lab, Naval Air Eng Ctr, 51-65; coordr, 65-74, PROF PSYCHOL, WRIGHT STATE UNIV, 65- *Concurrent Pos:* Assoc & lectr, Grad Sch Educ, Univ Pa, 59-65. *Mem:* Fel AAAS; Am Psychol Asn; Psychonomic Soc; Soc Psychophysiol Res. *Res:* Neurophysiology; biophysics; electrophysiological correlates of behavior, especially quantitative measures of stress; relationships of electrophysiological patterns to performance in mental and motor work. *Mailing Add:* Dept of Psychol Wright State Univ Dayton OH 45431

KLEIN, SIGRID MARTA, b Koenigsberg, Ger, May 1, 32. MICROBIOLOGY, BIOCHEMISTRY. *Educ:* Univ Kiel, Staatsexamen, 57; Brigham Young Univ, MS, 61, PhD(microbiol), 64. *Prof Exp:* Res asst biochem, Sloan-Kettering Lab, 58-59, res assoc microbiol, Brigham Young Univ, 64-67; fel, Charles F Kettering Labs, 67-70; RES ASSOC BIOCHEM, BRIGHAM YOUNG UNIV, 70- *Mem:* Am Soc Microbiol. *Res:* Organization of photosynthetic membranes; intermediary metabolism in blue-green algae. *Mailing Add:* 972 W 200 N Provo UT 84601

KLEIN, STANLEY, engineering & solid mechanics, see previous edition

KLEIN, V(ERNON) A(LFRED), b Marion, Tex, Sept 10, 18; m 50; c 2. CHEMICAL ENGINEERING. *Educ:* Univ Tex, BSChE, 40, MSChE, 42. *Prof Exp:* Instr chem eng, Univ Tex, 41-42; asst supt org chem prod, Dow Chem Co, 42-44, res & develop engr & group leader org res, 44-51, tech specialist, 51-56, sr tech specialist, 56-60, consult, 60-63, systs specialist, 63-68, SR PROCESS SPECIALIST, DOW CHEM CO, 68- *Mem:* Am Chem Soc; Am Inst Chem Engrs; Sigma Xi. *Res:* High pressure vapor-liquid equilibrium; physical chemistry. *Mailing Add:* 63 Plantation Ct Lake Jackson TX 77566

KLEIN, VLADISLAV, b Brezolupy, Czech, Feb 7, 29; m 56; c 1. AERONAUTICS, FLIGHT DYNAMICS. *Educ:* Mil Acad Czech, dipl ing, 49, CSc, 62; Cranfield Inst Technol, PhD(flight dynamics), 74. *Prof Exp:* Res scientist flight dynamics, Aeronaut Res & Test Inst, Prague-Letnany, Czech, 54-70; sr res officer, Cranfield Inst Technol, 70-75; res scientist, 75-78, RES PROF FLIGHT DYNAMICS, GEORGE WASHINGTON UNIV, 78- *Mem:* Soc Natural Philosophy; Am Inst Aeroanut & Astronaut. *Res:* Flight dynamics; flight test data analysis; system identification; control theory. *Mailing Add:* George Washington Univ Mail Stop 161 Hampton VA 23665

KLEIN, WILLIAM, b Philadelphia, Pa, Apr 1, 43; m 67; c 2. STATISTICAL MECHANICS. *Educ:* Temple Univ, BS, 65, PhD(physics), 72. *Prof Exp:* Res scientist physics, Univ Cologne, 74-76; asst prof, 76-81, ASSOC PROF PHYSICS, BOSTON UNIV, 81- *Res:* Mathematics and physics of phase transitions. *Mailing Add:* Dept of Physics Boston Univ Boston MA 02215

KLEIN, WILLIAM ARTHUR, b St Paul, Minn, Aug 30, 29; m 52; c 4. ORGANIC CHEMISTRY. *Educ:* Col St Thomas, BS, 51; Univ Md, PhD(org chem), 56. *Prof Exp:* Sr chemist, Minn Mining & Mfg Co, 56-61, res supvr, 61-64, res mgr, 64-67, tech mgr, 67-69, TECH DIR DECORATIVE PROD DIV, 3M CO, ST PAUL, 69- *Mem:* Am Chem Soc. *Res:* Phenolic resins; addition polymers; exocyclic dienes; coated abrasives; decorative films. *Mailing Add:* 427 W County Rd C St Paul MN 55113

KLEIN, WILLIAM H, b New York, NY, Apr 16, 19; m 42; c 2. METEOROLOGY. *Educ:* City Col New York, BS, 38, MS, 40; Mass Inst Technol, SM, 44; NY Univ, PhD, 64. *Prof Exp:* Res asst, Mass Inst Technol, 43-45; supvr meteorologist extended forecast div, US Weather Bur, 46-64, dir tech develop lab, 64-74, DIR, SYSTS DEVELOP OFF, NAT WEATHER SERV, NAT OCEANIC & ATMOSPHERIC ADMIN, DEPT COM, 74- *Honors & Awards:* Dept Com Meritorious Award, 64; Meritorious Serv Gold Medal, US Dept Com, 74; Outstanding Contrib Advan Appl Meteorol, Am Meteorol Soc, 75. *Mem:* AAAS; fel Am Meteorol Soc; Am Geophys Union; Royal Meteorol Soc. *Res:* Statistical forecasting; synoptic climatology; extended forecasting; objective methods. *Mailing Add:* Nat Weather Serv 8060 13th St Silver Spring MD 20910

KLEIN, WILLIAM MCKINLEY, JR, plant taxonomy, see previous edition

KLEIN, WILLIAM RICHARD, b Grayling, Mich, July 8, 37; m 56; c 4. ACOUSTICS. *Educ:* Cent Mich Univ, AB, 59; Mich State Univ, MS, 62, PhD(physics), 64; Pepperdine Univ, MBA, 80. *Prof Exp:* Asst prof, Southern Ill Univ, 66-69; from assoc prof to prof physics, Murray State Univ, 69-76; MGR RES & ENG, TIDELAND SIGNAL CORP, 76- *Mem:* Am Asn Physics Teachers; Acoust Soc Am. *Res:* Interaction of light with ultrasound; acoustic birefringence; marine navigational aids; non-linear acoustics. *Mailing Add:* Tideland Signal Corp PO Box 52430 Houston TX 77052

KLEINBERG, ISRAEL, b Toronto, Ont, May 1, 30; m 55; c 4. ORAL BIOLOGY. *Educ:* Univ Toronto, DDS, 52; Univ Durham, PhD(physiol & biochem), 58; Royal Co Dentists Can, FRCD(C), 69. *Prof Exp:* Demonstr, Univ Durham, 55-58; from asst prof to prof biochem, Univ Man, 58-73; PROF & CHMN, DEPT ORAL BIOL & PATH, STATE UNIV NY STONY BROOK, 73- *Concurrent Pos:* Mem assoc comt dent res, Nat Res Coun Can, 59-60, exec mem, 60-65; consult, Nat Inst Dent Res, NIH, 74-81. *Mem:* Int Asn Dent Res. *Res:* Metabolism of the dental bacterial plaque; plaque formation; saliva composition and its oral microbial effects; microchemical and oral diagnostic techniques; biomedical instrumentation development; gingival crevice fluid and its relation to oral and systemic disease. *Mailing Add:* Dept of Oral Biol & Path State Univ NY Stony Brook NY 11794

KLEINBERG, JACOB, b Passaic, NJ, Feb 14, 14; m 42; c 2. INORGANIC CHEMISTRY. *Educ:* Randolph-Macon Col, BS, 34; Univ Ill, MS, 37, PhD(chem), 39. *Prof Exp:* Asst chem, Univ Ill, 37-39; asst prof, James Millikin Univ, 40-43; assoc prof, Col Pharm, Univ Ill, 43-46; from asst prof to assoc prof, 46-51, chmn dept, 63-70, PROF CHEM, UNIV KANS, 51- *Mem:* Am Chem Soc. *Res:* Reactions in non-aqueous solvents; unfamiliar oxidation states of the elements. *Mailing Add:* Dept of Chem Univ of Kans Lawrence KS 66045

KLEINBERG, WILLIAM, b New York, NY, Jan 24, 11; m 41; c 2. PHYSIOLOGY. *Educ:* NY Univ, BS, 32, MS, 35; Princeton Univ, PhD(physiol, endocrinol), 43. *Prof Exp:* Asst biol, NY Univ, 32-33, teaching fel, 33-36, asst, 36-41; instr biol, Princeton Univ, 41-44; instr pharmacol, Col Physicians & Surgeons, Columbia Univ, 44-45; asst prof & Upjohn fel, Princeton Univ, 45-46; dir, Princeton Labs, Inc, 47-74, CONSULT, PRINCETON LAB PROD CO, 74-77. *Concurrent Pos:* Res assoc, Princeton Univ, 46-50, vis biologist, 50-65, sr vis biologist, 65-76. *Mem:* Endocrine Soc; NY Acad Sci; Reticuloendothelial Soc. *Res:* Blood; protein hormones; enzymes; immunological diagnostics; development of diagnostic tests. *Mailing Add:* 50 Woodland Dr Princeton NJ 08540

KLEINEBERG, GERD A, analytical chemistry, see previous edition

KLEINER, ALEXANDER F, JR, b New York, NY, June 18, 42; m 65; c 2. MATHEMATICS. *Educ:* Univ St Thomas, Tex, BA, 64; Tex A&M Univ, MS, 66, PhD(math), 69. *Prof Exp:* Instr math, Tex A&M Univ, 66-69; asst prof, 69-74, ASSOC PROF MATH, DRAKE UNIV, 74- *Mem:* Math Asn Am; Am Math Soc. *Res:* Summability theory, particularly the set of series summed by a regular matrix method; topological and related properties of ordered fields; convolution and Fourier series. *Mailing Add:* Dept of Math Drake Univ Des Moines IA 50311

KLEINER, BEAT, b Bern, Switz, Nov 27, 43; m 70; c 2. APPLIED STATISTICS. *Educ:* Swiss Fed Inst Technol, dipl, 68, Dr Sc Math (statist), 71. *Prof Exp:* Fel statist, Swiss Nat Sci Found, 71-72; MEM TECH STAFF STATIST, BELL LABS, 72- *Concurrent Pos:* Vis lectr, Yale Univ, 76, Swiss Fed Inst Technol, Zurich, 77-78 & Stanford Univ, 79. *Mem:* Am Statist Asn. *Res:* Time series analysis; data analysis; graphical techniques in statistics. *Mailing Add:* Bell Labs Murray Hill NJ 07974

KLEINER, WALTER BERNHARD, b Plainfield, NJ, Mar 1, 18; m 44; c 4. ELECTROCHEMISTRY. *Educ:* Rutgers Univ, BS, 39; Ohio State Univ, PhD(electrochem), 46. *Prof Exp:* Anat & control chemist, Calco Chem Div, Am Cyanamid Co, NJ, 39-40; asst chem, Ohio State Univ, 40-43; res engr, Battelle Mem Inst, 44; res & develop electrochemist, Manhattan Proj, Dayton, 45; res electrochemist, Am Smelting & Refining Co, 47-52; from asst prof to assoc prof, 68-74, PROF CHEM, ESSEX COUNTY COL, 74-; RES DIR, KLEINER ELECTROCHEM CO, 52- *Concurrent Pos:* Instr chem, Rutgers Univ, 51-52; res dir, Spiral Glass Pipe Co, 53-55; res electrochemists, Hanson-Van Winkle-Munning Co, 58-61, res dir, Electrochem Mach Div, 61-63; mem, Am Electroplaters Soc Res Comt, Nat Bur Standards; res dir, Ionic Mach Co, 63-65; asst prof chem, Upsala Col, 65-66; lectr chem, Newark Col Eng, 66-67; res dir, View-Formall Co, BC, 67. *Mem:* AAAS; Am Chem Soc; Electrochem Soc; Am Electroplaters Soc; Am Soc Metals. *Res:* Electrochemical machining; electroplating-electrodeposition. *Mailing Add:* 1845 First St Dunellen NJ 08812

KLEINERMAN, JEROME, b Pittsburgh, Pa, July 7, 24; m 44; c 3. PATHOLOGY, PHYSIOLOGY. *Educ:* Univ Pittsburgh, BS, 43, MD, 46; Am Bd Path, dipl, 52. *Prof Exp:* Demonstr path, Sch Med, Case Western Reserve Univ, 51-52, from instr to assoc prof, 52-72; assoc dir, St Luke's Hosp, 57-64, head, Dept Path Res & Clin Path, 65-70, assoc dir med res, 70-80, dir, Div Path Res, 76-80; prof path, Sch Med, Case Western Reserve Univ, 72-80, dir dept, 76-80; PROF & CHMN, DEPT PATHOL, MT SINAI MED SCH, 80- *Concurrent Pos:* Res fel physiol, Grad Sch Med, Univ Pa, 50-51; Am Heart Asn res fel, Cleveland Metrop Gen Hosp, 52-54, asst pathologist, 52-62, vis assoc pathologist, 62-; lectr, Sch Med, Univ Pittsburgh, 63-; attend pulmonary dis, Vet Admin Hosp, 65-; consult pathologist, Saranac Lab, Trudeau Found; mem path B study sect NIH, 65- *Mem:* Am Soc Exp Pathologists; fel Am Soc Clin Pathologists; Am Asn Pathologists & Bacteriologists; Am Heart Asn; Col Am Pathologists. *Res:* Experimental pathology; pulmonary emphysema and physiology; cerrbral blood flow; experimental renal disease; electron microscopy. *Mailing Add:* Mt Sinai Sch Med 1 Gustave L Levy Place New York NY 10029

KLEINFELD, ERWIN, b Vienna, Austria, Apr 19, 27; nat US; m 68. ALGEBRA. *Educ:* City Col New York, BS, 48; Univ Pa, MA, 49; Univ Wis, PhD(math), 51. *Prof Exp:* Instr math, Univ Chicago, 51-53; from asst prof to prof, Ohio State Univ, 53-62; prof, Syracuse Univ, 62-68; PROF MATH, UNIV IOWA, 68- *Concurrent Pos:* Vis lectr, Yale Univ, 56-57; partic conf algebra, Bowdoin Col, 57; res assoc, Cornell Univ, 58; vis lectr, Univ Calif, Los Angeles, 59, Stanford Univ, 60, Inst Defense Anal, 61-62 & Agency Int Develop Educ, India, 64-65; consult ed, Charles E Merrill Publ Co, 63-; vis prof, Emory Univ, 76-77. *Mem:* Am Math Soc. *Res:* Algebra and the foundations of projective geometry. *Mailing Add:* Dept of Math Univ of Iowa Iowa City IA 52242

KLEINFELD, MARGARET HUMM, b St Louis, Mo, Apr 7, 38; m 59, 68; c 2. MATHEMATICS. *Educ:* Univ Rochester, BA, 60; Syracuse Univ, MS, 63, PhD(math), 65. *Prof Exp:* Asst prof math, Syracuse Univ, 65-68; asst prof, 68-75, ASSOC PROF MATH, UNIV IOWA, 76- *Mem:* Am Math Soc; Asn Women in Math. *Res:* Non associative ring theory; algebra. *Mailing Add:* Dept of Math Univ of Iowa Iowa City IA 52240

KLEINFELD, RUTH GRAFMAN, b New York, NY, Feb 9, 28; m 48, 73. CELL BIOLOGY, REPRODUCTIVE BIOLOGY. *Educ:* Brooklyn Col, BS, 49; Univ Wis, MA, 51; Univ Chicago, PhD(cell biol), 53. *Prof Exp:* Res assoc prev med, Yale Univ, 56-57; res assoc path, Ohio State Univ, 57-62; assoc prof pharmacol, State Univ NY Syracuse, 62-70; assoc prof anat, 70-72, PROF ANAT & REPROD BIOL, UNIV HAWAII, MANOA, 72-, CHMN, 80- *Concurrent Pos:* USPHS fel physiol, Ohio State Univ, 53-55, Mary S Muellhaupt scholar, 55-56; USPHS res career develop award pharmacol, State Univ NY Syracuse, 62-70; mem NIH Reproductive Biol Study Sect. *Mem:* Histochem Soc; Am Soc Cell Biol; Am Asn Anat; Soc Develop Biol. *Res:* Cellular aspects of reproductive biology; cell replication and cytodifferentiation; decidualization and implantation in early pregnancy; carcinogenesis; cytochemistry and cell-fine structure. *Mailing Add:* Dept of Anat & Reprod Biol Univ of Hawaii at Manoa Honolulu HI 96822

KLEINHENZ, MARGIE JOYCE, human anatomy, see previous edition

KLEINHENZ, WILLIAM A, b Baltimore, Md, Oct 18, 21; m 49; c 4. MECHANICAL ENGINEERING, METALLURGY. *Educ:* Duke Univ, BS, 43; Univ Minn, MS, 52; Pa State Univ, PhD, 66. *Prof Exp:* Assoc prof, 46-80, PROF MECH ENG, UNIV MINN, MINNEAPOLIS, 80-, ASSOC HEAD DEPT, 46- *Concurrent Pos:* Proj engr, G H Tennant Co, 49-52; instr, St Paul Area Tech Sch, 62-68. *Mem:* Am Soc Mech Engrs; Am Soc Eng Educ. *Res:* Elasticity properties of metals at elevated temperatures; dynamics, controls and experimental stress analysis; fluidics research. *Mailing Add:* Inst of Technol Univ of Minn Minneapolis MN 55455

KLEINHOFS, ANDRIS, b Dobele, Latvia, Dec 25, 37; US citizen; m 65; c 2. GENETICS, AGRONOMY. *Educ:* Univ Nebr, Lincoln, BS, 58, MS, 64, PhD(genetics), 67. *Prof Exp:* Instr genetics, Univ Nebr, Lincoln, 65-67; from asst prof to assoc prof, 67-77, PROF GENETICS, WASH STATE UNIV, 77- *Mem:* AAAS; Genetics Soc Am. *Res:* Genetics and biochemistry of nitrate reduction in plants; chloroplast development; uptake and fate of exogenous DNA by plants; mechanisms of chemical mutagenesis. *Mailing Add:* Prog in Genetics Wash State Univ Pullman WA 99163

KLEINHOLZ, LEWIS HERMANN, b New York, NY, May 18, 10. PHYSIOLOGY. *Educ:* Colby Col, BS, 30; Harvard Univ, MA, 35, PhD(biol), 37; US Army Sch Aviation Med, dipl, 42. *Hon Degrees:* DSc, Colby Col, 63. *Prof Exp:* Instr biol, Colby Col, 30-33; asst, Harvard Univ, 35-37, Sheldon traveling fel, Plymouth & Naples Biol Stas, 37-38, instr biol, 40-41; proj engr, Aero-Med Lab, Wright Field, 45-46; from asst prof to assoc prof, 46-50, PROF BIOL, REED COL, 50- *Concurrent Pos:* Res investr, Marine Biol Lab, Woods Hole, 33-67, dir invert zool, 50-54, trustee, 50-; asst, Radcliffe Col, 36-37; instr, Cambridge Jr Col, 38-42; Jones Scholar, Long Island Biol Sta, 40; Guggenheim fel, Harvard Univ, 45-46; Fulbright fel, 51-52; NSF fac fel, 58; consult, NIH, 60-65; vis res prof, Med-Kem Inst, Univ Lund, 61-62; mem US Nat Comt, Int Union Biol Sci Comt Int Biol Stas, 62-; mem, Sci Adv Bd, Wesleyan Univ, 64-67; Porter scholar, Bermuda Biol Sta; adv comt & pub adv bd, Naples Zool Sta; consult, US Off Educ, 75- *Mem:* Am Soc Zool; Soc Gen Physiol; NY Acad Sci. *Res:* Biochemistry; physiology of endocrine systems of vertebrates and invertebrates; physiology of nervous system and chromatophores; physiology and specificity of neurosecretory hormones. *Mailing Add:* Dept of Biol Reed Col Portland OR 97202

KLEINKOPF, GALE EUGENE, b Twin Falls, Idaho, Oct 2, 40; m; c 1. PLANT PHYSIOLOGY. *Educ:* Univ Idaho, BS, 63; Univ Calif, Davis, PhD(plant physiol), 70. *Prof Exp:* Chemist, Aerojet Gen Corp, 63-64; res assoc agron, Univ Calif, Davis, 64-70, fel plant sci, 70-72; asst prof plant ecol, Univ Calif, Los Angeles, 72-75; ASSOC PROF CROP PHYSIOL, UNIV IDAHO, 75- *Mem:* AAAS; Crop Sci Soc Am; Am Soc Plant Physiol. *Res:* Carbon and nitrogen cycling in some crop species as affected by environmental stress. *Mailing Add:* Res & Exten Ctr Univ of Idaho Kimberly ID 83341

KLEINKOPF, MERLIN DEAN, b Macomb, Ill, Feb 1, 26; m 49; c 3. GEOPHYSICS. *Educ:* Monmouth Col, Ill, BS, 49; Univ Mo-Rolla, BS, 51; Columbia Univ, PhD(geol), 55. *Prof Exp:* Seismic comput geologist, Atlantic Refining Co, 51-52; geologist-geophysicist, Standard Oil Co Calif, 55-57, geologist, 57-58, lead geophysicist gravity & magnetics, 58-62 & 64-65, dist explor geologist, 62-64, prof specialist gravity & magnetics, 65-66; res geophysicist, Br Regional Geophys, US Geol Surv, Colo, 66-70, dep asst to chief geologist, 70-72, RES GEOPHYSICIST, US GEOL SURV, 72- *Concurrent Pos:* Leader, US Deleg Geophysicists to USSR, 71. *Mem:* Geol Soc Am; Am Inst Mining, Metall & Petrol Engrs; Soc Explor Geophysicists; Am Asn Petrol Geologists; Soc Econ Geologists. *Res:* Gravity and magnetic model studies using electronic computer; regional geophysical studies of Belt Basin, Northwestern Montana; geophysical studies of porphyry copper, Sonora, Mexico; geophysical studies of Arabian Shield, Saudi Arabia. *Mailing Add:* US Geol Surv MS 964 Box 25046 Fed Ctr Denver CO 80225

KLEINMAN, ARTHUR MICHAEL, b New York, NY, Mar 11, 41; m 65; c 2. PSYCHIATRY, MEDICAL ANTHROPOLOGY. *Educ:* Stanford Univ, AB, 62, MD, 67; Harvard Univ, MA, 74. *Prof Exp:* Lectr anthrop, Harvard Univ, 74-76; clin instr psychiat, Mass Gen Hosp & Harvard Med Sch, 75-76; assoc prof & adj assoc prof, 76-79, PROF PSYCHIAT & ADJ PROF ANTHROP, UNIV WASH, 79- *Concurrent Pos:* Intern med, New Haven Hosp, Yale Univ, 67-68; resident psychiat, Mass Gen Hosp, 72-75; Dupont Warren fel, Harvard Med Sch, 74-75 & Milton Fund fel, 75-76; Found Fund Res Psychiat fel, 74-76; prin investr, NIMH res grant, Univ Wash, 78-79; ed-in-chief, Cult, Med & Psychiat, 76- *Honors & Awards:* Wellcome Medal Med Anthrop, Royal Anthrop Inst, 80. *Mem:* AAAS; fel Am Anthrop Asn; Soc Med Anthrop; Am Psychosom Soc. *Res:* Psychological anthropology depression and cross cultural studies of somatization, therapeutic relationships and indigenous healing; applied anthropology; anthropology of medical beliefs and practices. *Mailing Add:* Dept of Psychiat & Behav Sci Univ of Wash Seattle WA 98195

KLEINMAN, CHEMIA JACOB, b Sandomierz, Poland, Feb 1, 32; US citizen; m 55; c 2. PHYSICS. *Educ:* Yeshiva Univ, BA, 53; NY Univ, MS, 56, PhD(physics), 65. *Prof Exp:* Physicist, Mat Lab, Brooklyn Naval Shipyard, 56-57; engr microwave res, Ford Instrument Co, 57-60; lectr physics, City Col New York, 60-64; PROF PHYSICS, LONG ISLAND UNIV, 64-, CHMN DEPT, 80- *Concurrent Pos:* Instr, Yeshiva Univ, 54-55, 58-60; consult, Budd-Lewyt Corp, 56-57; res fel, NY Univ, 65; NASA fel, Goddard Space Flight Ctr, 66; NSF fel, Univ Colo, Boulder, 67; assoc res scientist, NY Univ, 69, consult, 71. *Mem:* Am Phys Soc. *Res:* Atomic and electromagnetic scattering and bound state problems. *Mailing Add:* Dept of Physics Long Island Univ Brooklyn NY 11201

KLEINMAN, LEONARD, b New York, NY, July 25, 33; m 57; c 2. SOLID STATE PHYSICS. *Educ:* Univ Calif, Los Angeles, BA, 55, MA, 56; Univ Calif, Berkeley, PhD(physics), 60. *Prof Exp:* Res assoc physics, Univ Chicago, 60-61; asst prof, Univ Pa, 61-64; assoc prof, Univ Southern Calif, 64-67; PROF PHYSICS, UNIV TEX, AUSTIN, 67- *Mem:* Fel Am Phys Sov. *Res:* Energy band theory; theory of electronhypherphonon interactions; theory of tunneling in superconductors and semiconductors; covalent bonding and theory of cohesive energies; electron gas theory; theory of metal surfaces. *Mailing Add:* Dept of Physics Univ of Tex Austin TX 78712

KLEINMAN, LEONARD I, b Brooklyn, NY, June 29, 35; m 61; c 3. PHYSIOLOGY, NEONATOLOGY. *Educ:* Columbia Col, AB, 56; State Univ NY, MD, 60. *Prof Exp:* From intern to resident pediat, Mass Gen Hosp, 60-62; from asst prof to assoc prof, 66-75, PROF PHYSIOL & PEDIAT, COL MED, UNIV CINCINNATI, 75- *Concurrent Pos:* Res fel physiol, Harvard Univ, 62-65; Fulbright res scholar, Univ Milan, 65-66. *Mem:* Am Physiol Soc; Soc Pediat Res; Am Pediat Soc; Soc Exp Biol Med; AAAS. *Res:* Respiratory, renal and neonatal physiology. *Mailing Add:* Dept of Pediat Univ of Cincinnati Col of Med Cincinnati OH 45267

KLEINMAN, MICHAEL THOMAS, b Brooklyn, NY, Mar 8, 42; m 65; c 2. ENVIRONMENTAL & OCCUPATIONAL HEALTH, ANALYTICAL CHEMISTRY. *Educ:* City Univ NY, BS, 65; Polytechnic Inst Brooklyn, MS, 71; NY Univ, PhD(environ health), 77. *Prof Exp:* Radiochemist, US Atomic Energy Comn, 63-65, physical scientist, 65-72; asst res scientist, NY Univ Med Ctr, 72-77; DIR AEROSOL LAB, RANCHO LOS AMIGOS HOSP, 77- *Concurrent Pos:* Consult, Con Ed NY, 74-76, Equitable Environ Asn, 75-77, Intersoc Comt,75-77 & Nat Resources Defense Coun, 76-77; consult, 74-; guest lectr, Univ Calif, Irvine, 79- *Mem:* Air Pollution Control Asn; AAAS; Am Geophys Union. *Res:* Health effects of pollutant aerosols and gases in humans and animals; chemical alterations of airborne pollutants; development of methods for the generation and characterizations of air pollutants; industrial hygiene. *Mailing Add:* Rancho Los Amigos Hosp 7601 E Imperial Hwy Downey CA 90242

KLEINMAN, RALPH ELLIS, b New York, NY, July 27, 29; m 55; c 2. APPLIED MATHEMATICS. *Educ:* NY Univ, BA, 50; Univ Mich, MA, 51; Delft Univ Technol, PhD(appl math), 61. *Prof Exp:* Res asst math, Univ Mich, Ann Arbor, 51-53, res assoc, 55-58, from assoc res mathematician to res mathematician, 59-68; assoc prof, 68-72, PROF MATH, UNIV DEL, 72- *Concurrent Pos:* Danish Nat Found Tech Sci grant, Lab Electromagnetic Theory, Tech Univ Denmark, 65-66; vis prof math, Univ Strathclyde, 72; Nat Res Coun sr resident res assoc, Air Force Cambridge Res Labs, 74-75. *Mem:* Am Math Soc; Edinburgh Math Soc; Gesellschaft Angewandte Math & Mech; Soc Indust & Appl Math; Inst Elec & Electronic Engrs. *Res:* Classical electromagnetic theory; propagation and scattering of electromagnetic and acoustic waves; boundary value problems; integral equations; partial differential equations; special functions. *Mailing Add:* Dept of Math Univ of Del Newark DE 19711

KLEINMAN, RAPHAEL, b Budapest, Hungary, Nov 12, 43; Israeli citizen; m 69; c 2. HUMAN IMMUNOLOGY. *Educ:* Hebrew Univ, Jerusalem, BSc, 68, MSc, 70; Tel-Aviv Univ, PhD(immunol), 75. *Prof Exp:* Res asst immunol, Hebrew Univ, Jerusalem, 68-70; res assoc, Tel-Aviv Univ, 70-75; instr, Univ Ill Med Ctr, 75-78; ASST PROF IMMUNOL, DEPT MICROBIOL, UNIV GA, 78-, MEM FAC GERONT, 79- *Mem:* Am Soc Microbiol; AAAS. *Res:* Generation and regulation of various forms of immune response in humans and mice; specific and nonspecific cytotoxic responses against autologous and heterologous lumphyocytes and tumor cells; bacteria-immune system interactions immunology of aging. *Mailing Add:* Dept of Microbiol Univ of Ga Athens GA 30602

KLEINMAN, ROBERTA WILMA, b New York, NY, Oct 10, 42. ORGANIC CHEMISTRY, CONSERVATION CHEMISTRY. *Educ:* Barnard Col, Columbia Univ, AB, 64; Rutgers Univ, NB, PhD(org chem), 69. *Prof Exp:* NIH fel chem, Rutgers Univ, NB, 69-70, instr, 70-71, fel, 71-72; asst prof chem, Univ Mich-Dearborn, 72-79; Lectr, Univ Mich-Ann Arbor, 79-82; CONSERV CHEMIST, PANHANDLE-PLAINS HIST MUS, TEX, 82- *Concurrent Pos:* Consult, Henry Ford Mus, Dearborn, 79-80. *Mem:* Am Chem Soc; AAAS. *Res:* Carbene additions to steroid analogues; micelle formation and catalysis; synthetic polynucleotides as catalysts of enzymatic ractions; nucleic acid interactions; identification of natural dyes on textiles; stability studies of natural dyes. *Mailing Add:* Conserv Dept Panhandle-Plains Hist Mus Canyon TX 79016

KLEINMANN, DOUGLAS ERWIN, b Chicago, Ill, July 11, 42; m 70; c 2. ASTRONOMY, PHYSICS. *Educ:* Rice Univ, BA, 64, PhD(space sci), 69; Mass Inst Technol, SM, 80. *Prof Exp:* Fel astron, Rice Univ, 68-70; astronomer, Smithsonian Astrophys Observ, Smithsonian Inst, 70-79; PROG MGR, HONEYWELL ELECTRO-OPTICS, 80- *Concurrent Pos:* Lectr, Harvard Col Observ, Harvard Univ, 71-79; res affil, Mass Inst Technol, 73-79; mem infrared instrument definition team, Space Telescope, NASA, 73-77. *Mem:* Am Astron Sooc; Int Astrophys Union; Am Optical Soc. *Res:* Infrared devices, infrared astronomy; instrumentation using infrared devices. *Mailing Add:* 15 Hastings Rd Lexington MA 02173

KLEINROCK, LEONARD, b New York, NY, June 13, 34; m 54; c 2. COMPUTER SCIENCE. *Educ:* City Col New York, BEE, 57; Mass Inst Technol, SMEE, 59, PhD(elec eng), 63. *Prof Exp:* Asst engr, Photobell Co, NY, 51-57; res asst, Servomechanism Lab, Mass Inst Technol, 57-58, res asst, Electronics Res Lab, 58-61, staff mem, Lincoln Lab, 63; from asst prof to assoc prof, 63-70, PROF COMPUT SCI, UNIV CALIF, LOS ANGELES, 70- *Concurrent Pos:* Consult, Babcock Electronics Corp, Calif & Beckman Instruments Inc, 64, Jet Propulsion Lab, Calif Inst Technol, 64-, TRW Systs Group, 65-, Solid State Radiation, Inc, 65-, Cubic Corp, 66, Magnavox Res Labs, 67, Assoc Comput Mach, 67-, Technol Serv Corp, 68-, US Army Comput Syst Command, 71- & Off Emergency Preparedness, Exec Off President, 68-; prin investr, Advan Res Projs Agency, Dept Defense Contract, 69-; pres, Linkabit Corp, 68-69; pres, Technol Transfer Inst, 76-; mem adv coun sci & eng, City Col New York. *Mem:* Nat Acad Eng; Opers Res Soc Am; fel Inst Elec & Electronics Engrs. *Res:* Communication theory; digital computer applications; operations research; queueing theory; computer systems modeling and analysis. *Mailing Add:* Comput Sci Dept 3732 Boelter Hall Univ of Calif Los Angeles CA 90024

KLEINSCHMIDT, ALBERT WILLOUGHBY, b Clinton, Iowa, Mar 20, 13; m 43; c 3. ORGANIC CHEMISTRY. *Educ:* Iowa State Univ, BS, 35; Purdue Univ, PhD(org chem), 41. *Prof Exp:* Res chemist, Cent Soya Co, Inc, 40-44, Beatrice Foods Inc, Ill, 44-47 & Am Maize Prod Co, Inc, 47-58; res chemist, J R Short Milling Co, 58-63, lab mgr, 63-67, tech dir, 67-69, vpres, 69-79; RETIRED. *Mem:* Am Chem Soc; Am Oil Chem Soc; Am Asn Cereal Chem; Inst Food Technol; Am Soc Brewing Chem. *Res:* Oil; fats; carbohydrates. *Mailing Add:* 452 King St Oviedo FL 32765

KLEINSCHMIDT, R STEVENS, b Boston, Mass, Oct 8, 25; wid; c 4. CIVIL ENGINEERING, WATER POWER ENGINEERING. *Educ:* Harvard Univ, AB, 49, SM, 51, ScD(civil eng), 58. *Hon Degrees:* Dr Community Develop, Unity Col, Maine, 76. *Prof Exp:* Res engr, Harvard Univ, 50-58; asst engr water supply & sewage disposal, Camp Dresser & McKee, Mass, 58-59; asst prof hydraul & sanit eng, Northeastern Univ, 59-62; hydraul engr, Great Northern Paper Co, Maine, 62-66; independent consult engr, 66-70; partner, 70-80, CHMN BD & SR VPRES, KLEINSCHMIDT & DUTTING CONSULT ENGRS, 80- *Honors & Awards:* Herschel Prize, 51. *Mem:* Am Soc Civil Engrs; Am Consult Engrs Coun; Sigma Xi. *Res:* Hydraulics as applied to sanitary engineering. *Mailing Add:* Kleinschmidt & Dutting Consult Engrs 73 Main St Pittsfield ME 04967

KLEINSCHMIDT, ROGER FREDERICK, b New York, NY, May 12, 19; m 45; c 3. ORGANIC CHEMISTRY, PETROLEUM TECHNOLOGY. *Educ:* Lehigh Univ, BS, 40; Columbia Univ, PhD(org chem), 44. *Prof Exp:* Asst chem, Columbia Univ, 41-44; res chemist, Interchem Corp, NY, 44 & Gen Aniline & Film Corp, 46-52; group leader org chem, Phillips Petrol Co, 52-57, sr group supvr, 57-59, sect mgr org chem synthesis, 59-65, mgr hydrocarbon chem br, 65-68, vpres res & develop, Phillips Sci Corp, 68-71, licensing rep, Phillips Petrol Co, 71-74, PLANNING CONSULT NATURAL RESOURCES, PHILLIPS PETROL CO, 74-, PROG MGR TERTIARY RECOVERY PETROL, ENERGY RES & DEVELOP ADMIN-PHILLIPS PETROL CO PROJ, 75-, MEM STAFF CORP PLANNING NORWEG INDUST DEVELOP, 81- *Concurrent Pos:* Instr, Exten, Okla State Univ, 53- *Mem:* Soc Petrol Engrs. *Res:* Synthetic organic chemicals; acetylene chemistry; polymerization; pressure reactions; petrochemicals from olefins and diolefins; naphthenes; non-aromatic cyclics; organometallic catalysts and intermediates; industrial organic chemistry; enhanced recovery of oil; micellar/polymer recovery methods; exploration and production planning, economics and budgets. *Mailing Add:* Phillips Petrol Co Bartlesville OK 74004

KLEINSCHMIDT, WALTER JOHN, b Wabash Co, Ill, Apr 11, 18; m 42; c 1. BIOCHEMISTRY. *Educ:* Ind Univ, BS, 40; Univ Minn, MS, 49, PhD(biochem), 50. *Prof Exp:* Sr res biochemist, Biol Pharmacol Res Div, 50-66, RES SCIENTIST, BIOL RES DIV, LILLY RES LABS, 66- *Mem:* AAAS; Am Chem Soc; Am Soc Biol Chem. *Res:* Antiviral agents; interferon; viruses; virus inhibition; aging; nucleic acids. *Mailing Add:* Lilly Res Labs Indianapolis IN 46285

KLEINSCHUSTER, JACOB JOHN, b Northampton, Pa, July 5, 43; m 70; c 3. ORGANIC POLYMER CHEMISTRY. *Educ:* Va Mil Inst, BS, 64; Pa State Univ, MS, 66, PhD(chem), 72. *Prof Exp:* Res chemist, 72-74, sr res chemist, 74-75, supvr org polymer chem, 75-78, sr supvr, 79-82, TECH SUPT, E I DU PONT DE NEMOURS & CO, INC, 82- *Mem:* Am Chem Soc. *Res:* High performance organic industrial fibers. *Mailing Add:* 1010 Corntassel Trail Martainsville VA 24112

KLEINSCHUSTER, STEPHEN J, III, b Bath, Pa, June 3, 39; m 66; c 2. DEVELOPMENTAL BIOLOGY, IMMUNOTHERAPY. *Educ:* Colo State Univ, BS, 63, MS, 66; Ore State Univ, PhD(zool), 70. *Prof Exp:* Fel develop biol, Univ Chicago, 71; asst prof biol, Metrop State Col, Denver, 71-73; affil prof bot & plant path, Colo State Univ, 73, assoc prof anat, 75-77, chmn exec comt anat, 76-77; actg head, 80-81, DIR ANIMAL TUMOR PROG, ANIMAL, DAIRY & VET SCI, UTAH STATE UNIV, 77-, PROF & HEAD, ANIMAL, DAIRY & VET SCI DEPT, 81- *Concurrent Pos:* Consult, NASA, 71-77; prin investr, NIH, Cancer Immunoprophylaxis Contracts, 77-81 & Immunotherapy Procurement Contracts, 75-81; Impact Rev Group, Dept Agr, State Utah, 77; surg oncol res group, LDS Hosp, Salt Lake City, Utah, 79-; organizer & dir, Vet Sci Tissue Culture Facil, Utah State Univ, 79- *Mem:* AAAS; Am Asn Anatomists; Am Asn Vet Anatomists; NY Acad Sci; Am Soc Animal Sci. *Res:* Cancer biology; immunotherapy and immunoprophylaxis; molecular biology of development and morphogenesis. *Mailing Add:* Animal Dairy Vet Sci Dept Utah State Univ UMC 48 Logan UT 84322

KLEINSMITH, LEWIS JOEL, b Detroit, Mich, Apr 13, 42; m 64; c 2. CELL BIOLOGY, BIOCHEMISTRY. *Educ:* Univ Mich, BS, 64; Rockefeller Univ, PhD(life sci), 68. *Prof Exp:* From asst prof to assoc prof zool, Univ Mich, Ann Arbor, 68-74; vis prof biochem, Univ Fla, Gainesville, 74-75; PROF BIOL SCI, UNIV MICH, ANN ARBOR, 75- *Concurrent Pos:* Lectr vis biologists prog, Am Inst Biol Sci, 69-71; Guggenheim fel, 74-75. *Honors & Awards:* Henry Russel Award, 71; Distinguished Serv Award, Univ Mich, 71. *Mem:* Am Inst Biol Sci; Sigma Xi; Am Soc Cell Biol; NY Acad Sci; Am Soc Biol Chemists. *Res:* Biochemistry of cell nucleus; role of nuclear proteins in regulating gene function; nucleoprotein chemistry and function; biochemical regulatory mechanisms; regulation of normal and malignant cell growth. *Mailing Add:* Div Biol Sci Krause Nat Sci Bldg Univ of Mich Ann Arbor MI 48109

KLEINSPEHN, GEORGE GEHRET, b Middlebury, Vt, Mar 27, 24; m 47; c 2. ORGANIC CHEMISTRY. *Educ:* Colgate Univ, AB, 44; Johns Hopkins Univ, AM, 47, PhD(chem), 51. *Prof Exp:* Jr chemist, Clinton Eng Works-Tenn Eastman Corp, 44-46; jr instr, Johns Hopkins Univ, 46-49, res assoc & univ fel, 51-56; sr res assoc & treas, Monadnock Res Inst, 56-59; res assoc, Johns Hopkins Univ, 60; chemist, US Army Ballistic Res Labs, 60-63, chief org chem sect, Chem Br, 63-67; PROF CHEM, HOOD COL, 67-, DEPT CHAIR, 79- *Concurrent Pos:* USPHS fel, NIH, 51-52; consult, US Army Ballistic Res Labs, 68. *Mem:* AAAS; Am Chem Soc; NY Acad Sci; Sigma Xi. *Res:* Nitrogenous heterocyclic compounds, especially pyrroles and porphyrins; organic substances of high nitrogen content. *Mailing Add:* Dept of Chem Hood Col Frederick MD 21701

KLEINSTEUBER, TILMANN CHRISTOPH WERNER, b Berlin, Ger, July 16, 34. PHYSICS, PHYSICAL CHEMISTRY. *Educ:* Univ Hamburg, BSc, 56; Univ Munich, PhD(phys chem), 61. *Prof Exp:* Res assoc phys chem, Univ Munich, 61-63; res assoc, Amherst Col, 63-64, asst prof chem, 64-65; asst prof, 65-68, ASSOC PROF PHYSICS, KING'S COL, PA, 68-, CHMN DEPT, 65- *Mem:* Am Asn Physics Teachers; Am Chem Soc. *Res:* Calorimetry at high and low temperatures; thermodynamics of metals and alloys; surface chemistry; gas chromatography. *Mailing Add:* Dept of Physics King's Col Wilkes-Barre PA 18711

KLEINT, R(ODERIC) E(MIL), b Arling, Idaho, Sept 8, 26; m 49; c 4. ENGINEERING. *Educ:* Univ Southern Calif, BS, 47; Ore State Col, MS, 49. *Prof Exp:* Design engr nuclear reactor group, Hanford works, Gen Elec Co, 47-48; asst, Ore State Col, 48-49; res engr, AEC, 49-51; res metallurgist, Naval Ord Test Sta, 51-53; res engr & supvr metals sect, NAm Aviation Corp, 53-57, vpres & gen mgr, Ultrasonic Test & Res Lab, 57-60; supvr mat & processes, Rocketdyne Div, NAm Aviation, Inc, 60-76, MEM TECH STAFF, ROCKETDYNE DIV, ROCKWELL INT CORP, 76- *Concurrent Pos:* Instr, Iowa State Col, 49-51. *Mem:* Am Soc Metals; Am Soc Nondestructive Testing. *Res:* Metallurgy; nondestructive testing. *Mailing Add:* 21500 California St #111 Woodland Hills CA 91367

KLEINZELLER, ARNOST, b Ostrava, Czech, Dec 6, 14; m 43; c 2. CELL PHYSIOLOGY. *Educ:* Univ Brno, Czech, MD, 38; Univ Sheffield, PhD(biochem), 42. *Hon Degrees:* DSc, Czech Acad Sci, 59; MA, Univ Pa, 73. *Prof Exp:* Med Res Coun grant biochem, Cambridge Univ, 43-44; head lab cell metab, Czech Inst Health, 46-48; assoc prof fermentation chem & head dept, Prague Tech Univ, 48-52; assoc prof biochem, Charles Univ, Prague, 52-55; head lab cell metab, Czech Acad Sci, 56-66; vis prof physiol, Univ Rochester, 66-67; PROF PHYSIOL, SCH MED, UNIV PA, 67- *Concurrent Pos:* Rockefeller fel, Cambridge Univ, 41-42; mem, Acad Leopoldina, 66-; mem & secy, US Nat Comt Physiol Sci, 76-; Fogarty Sr Int Fel, 80. *Mem:* Biophys Soc; Am Physiol Soc; Am Soc Cell Biol; Soc Gen Physiol; Brit Biochem Soc. *Res:* Intermediate metabolism; transport of electrolytes and sugars across cell membranes. *Mailing Add:* Dept of Physiol Univ of Pa Sch of Med Philadelphia PA 19104

KLEIS, JOHN DIEFFENBACH, b Hamburg, NY, Feb 1, 12; m 51; c 3. PHYSICS, METALLURGY. *Educ:* Univ Buffalo, BA, 32, MA, 33; Yale Univ, PhD(physics), 36; Harvard Bus Sch, AMP, 57. *Prof Exp:* Physicist elec contacts, Fansteel, Inc, 36-57, vpres res refractory metals, 57-63, vpres & gen mgr elec & electronic prod, 63-69; vpres res elec contacts, 69-70, pres, Cooper Div, 70-78, VPRES & TECHNOL DIR PRECIOUS METALS GROUP, STERNDENT CORP, 78- *Mem:* Soc Automotive Engrs; fel Am Soc Testing & Mat; Inst Elec & Electronic Engrs. *Res:* Solid state, areas relating to bonding procedures and bonding, interconnect materials; precious metals, metallurgy of Al and AliSi materials. *Mailing Add:* 161 Clapboard Ridge Rd Greenwich CT 06830

KLEIS, ROBERT W(ILLIAM), b Martin, Mich, Nov 30, 25; m 49; c 2. AGRICULTURAL ENGINEERING. *Educ:* Mich State Univ, BS, 49, MS, 51, PhD(agr eng), 57. *Prof Exp:* Instr agr eng, Mich State Univ, 49-51; instr, Univ Ill, 51-53, asst prof, 53-56; prof & head dept, Univ Mass, Amherst, 57-66; prof & chmn dept, 66-67, ASSOC DIR AGR EXP STA, UNIV NEBR, LINCOLN, 67-, DEAN INT PROGS, 76- *Concurrent Pos:* Dir, Midamerica Int Agr Consortium, Inc, 76-; consult, Indust, 50- & Int Agr Develop, 75-; dir, Int Collab Res Support Prog, 78- *Mem:* Fel Am Soc Agr Engrs; Am Soc Eng Educ; Nat Asn Univ Dirs Int Progs; Agr Exp Sta Dir Asn. *Res:* Materials handling systems for agriculture; product processing; food and feed preservation; farm operations mechanization. *Mailing Add:* Int Progs Off 210 Ag Hall Univ of Nebr Lincoln NE 68483

KLEIS, WILLIAM DELONG, b Akron, Ohio, Feb 26, 24; m 64; c 4. ATMOSPHERIC PHYSICS. *Educ:* Univ Colo, AB, 49; Univ Chicago, MS, 52. *Prof Exp:* With US Air Force, 52-68, chief forecaster, Weather Detachment, Eng, 52-56, climat officer, March AFB, Calif, 56-61, chief forecaster, Turkey, 61-62, chief sci serv br, Andrews AFB, Md, 64-68; PROG DEVELOP SCIENTIST, OFF PROGS, ENVIRON RES LABS, NAT OCEANIC & ATMOSPHERIC ADMIN, 69- *Mem:* Am Meteorol Soc; Am Geophys Union; for mem Royal Meteorol Soc. *Res:* Aeronomy; upper atmospheric physics and chemistry; solar-terrestrial physics; meteorology; remote sensing of the atmosphere. *Mailing Add:* Off Progs-Rx3 Environ Res Labs Nat Oceanic & Atmospheric Admin Boulder CO 80302

KLEIST, JOHN RAYMOND, geology, see previous edition

KLEITMAN, DANIEL J, b New York, NY, Oct 4, 34; m 64; c 2. MATHEMATICS. *Educ:* Cornell Univ, AB, 54; Harvard Univ, AM, 55, PhD, 58. *Prof Exp:* NSF fel physics, Copenhagen Univ, 58-59 & Harvard Univ, 59-60; asst prof, Brandeis Univ, 60-66; assoc prof, 66-69, PROF MATH, MASS INST TECHNOL, 69-, HEAD DEPT, 79- *Concurrent Pos:* Consult, Nuclear Regulatory Comn, Gen Acct Off, 73-81; managing ed, SIAM J Algebraic & Discrete Methods, 75; ed, J Networks. *Mem:* Am Math Soc; Oper Res Soc Am; Soc Indust & Appl Math; Am Acad Arts & Sci; NY Acad Sci. *Res:* Combinatorial mathematics; graph theory; numeration and optimization; applications to operations research. *Mailing Add:* Dept of Math Mass Inst of Technol Cambridge MA 02139

KLEITMAN, DAVID, b New York, NY, June 28, 31; m 52; c 3. SOLID STATE PHYSICS. *Educ:* Cornell Univ, BA, 52; Purdue Univ, MS, 53, PhD(physics), 58. *Prof Exp:* Group head labs & head display res, David Sarnoff Res Ctr, RCA, 57-67; vpres & dir res & develop, Signetics Corp, 67-78, vpres res, 78-80; PRES, PROTRACOA, 80-; DIR TECHNOL, BRANSON/IPC, 81- *Mem:* Inst Elec & Electronics Engrs; AAAS. *Res:* Semiconductors; radiation damage; luminescence; optical amplification; color television system and display system management; integrated circuits, their materials, processing devices, circuits design and applications in computers, communications and consumer and industrial systems; semiconductor devices for integrated circuits, microwave, power, computer, instrumentation, optical and novel applications and systems; computer software; plasma processing. *Mailing Add:* 12387 Stonebrook Dr Los Altos Hills CA 94022

KLEITSCH, WILLIAM PHILIP, b Cincinnati, Ohio, July 12, 12. SURGERY. *Educ:* Univ Ill, BS, 34, MD & MS, 37; Am Bd Surg, dipl. *Prof Exp:* Instr surg, Col Med, Univ Ill, 38-42; from asst prof to assoc prof, Col Med, Univ Nebr, Omaha, 55-66; assoc prof, Sch Med, Creighton Univ, 55-66; CHIEF SURG, VET ADMIN HOSP, PHOENIX, 66- *Concurrent Pos:* Lectr, Col Dent, Univ Nebr, Omaha, 47-50; chief surg serv, Vet Admin Hosp, Nebr, 46-66; mem staff, Good Samaritan Hosp; consult, Phoenix Indian Med Ctr. *Mem:* AAAS; Am Thoracic Soc; AMA; Asn Mil Surg US; Nat Tuberc & Respiratory Dis Asn. *Mailing Add:* 2201 E Solano Dr Phoenix AZ 85016

KLEKOWSKI, EDWARD JOSEPH, JR, b Brooklyn, NY, Oct 24, 40. BOTANY, GENETICS. *Educ:* NC State Univ, BS, 62, MS, 64; Univ Calif, Berkeley, PhD(bot), 68. *Prof Exp:* Asst prof, 68-73, ASSOC PROF BOT, UNIV MASS, AMHERST, 73- *Mem:* Bot Soc Am. *Res:* Pteridology; genetic and evolutionary studies of homosporous ferns. *Mailing Add:* Dept of Bot Univ of Mass Amherst MA 01003

KLEM, EDWARD BENSON, molecular biology, cell biology, see previous edition

KLEMA, ERNEST DONALD, b Wilson, Kans, Oct 4, 20; m 53; c 2. NUCLEAR PHYSICS. *Educ:* Univ Kans, AB, 41, AM, 42; Rice Inst, PhD(physics), 51. *Prof Exp:* Jr scientist, Los Alamos Sci Lab, 43-46; sr physicist nuclear physics, Oak Ridge Nat Lab, 50-56; assoc prof nuclear eng, Univ Mich, 56-58; prof nuclear & sci eng, Northwestern Univ, 58-68, chmn dept eng sci, 60-67; dean col eng, 68-73, PROF ENG SCI, TUFTS UNIV, 68-, ADJ PROF INT POLITICS, FLETCHER SCH LAW & DIPLOMACY, 73- *Mem:* Fel Am Phys Soc; fel Am Nuclear Soc; sr mem Inst Elec & Electronics Engrs. *Res:* Angular correlations of gamma rays; fission cross sections; empirical nuclear models; semiconductor detectors; science and technology policy. *Mailing Add:* 53 Adams St Medford MA 02155

KLEMANN, LAWRENCE PAUL, b Cincinnati, Ohio, Aug 13, 43; m 63; c 2. ORGANOMETALLIC CHEMISTRY. *Educ:* Univ Mass, BS, 65, PhD(chem), 69. *Prof Exp:* Staff chemist, 69-80, RES ASSOC, EXXON RES & ENG CO, 80- *Mem:* Am Chem Soc; Electrochem Soc. *Res:* Investigations of the solution properties of polyamine chelated lithium compounds; investigation of alkali metal organic electrolytes; synthesis of five membered metallocycles using butadienyl-dilithium reagents; homogeneous and heterogeneous catalysis involving carbon monoxide and hydrogen. *Mailing Add:* Exxon Res & Eng Co Box 45 Linden NJ 07036

KLEMAS, VYTAUTAS, b Klaipeda, Lithuania, Nov 29, 34; US citizen; m 60; c 3. OPTICAL PHYSICS, MARINE STUDIES. *Educ:* Mass Inst Technol, BS, 57, MS, 59; Univ Brunswick, PhD(optical physics), 65. *Prof Exp:* Mgr optical physics & space explor, Space Div, Gen Elec Co, 59-71; assoc prof, 71-80, PROF MARINE STUDIES, UNIV DEL, 80-, DIR REMOTE SENSING CTR, 75- *Concurrent Pos:* Fel, Gen Elec Co, 63; consult, Environ Protection Agency, NASA, NSF & AID, Peru, 74- & United Nations Develop Prog, India, 77-; mem comn natural resources, Nat Acad Sci, 75-78; mem, Ocean Policy Comt, Nat Acad Sci; mem adv comts, NASA, 75-; prog mgr, Scientists & Engrs Econ Develop, NSF, 77-78; mem, Man & the Biosphere, UNESCO, 77- *Honors & Awards:* Achievement Medal, Korean Advan Inst Sci & Merit Award, India Remote Sensing Agency, 78. *Mem:* Inst Elec & Electronics Engrs; Asn Am Geographers; Am Geophys Union; Am Soc Photogram. *Res:* Management of coastal and fishery resources; remote sensing of environment, especially physical and biological coastal processes; third world resources development; oil pollution monitor. *Mailing Add:* Col of Marine Studies Univ of Del Newark DE 19711

KLEMCHUK, PETER PAUL, b Oakville, Conn, Oct 31, 28; m 49; c 5. ORGANIC CHEMISTRY. *Educ:* Mass Inst Technol, BS, 50; Rutgers Univ, MS, 56, PhD(org chem), 57. *Prof Exp:* Chemist, Merck & Co, Inc, 50-56; chemist, Esso Res & Eng Co, 57-59; chemist, Stauffer Chem Co, 59-60; TECH MGR, CIBA-GEIGY CORP, 60- *Mem:* AAAS; Am Chem Soc; Soc Plastics Engrs. *Res:* Polymer stabilization; polymer additives. *Mailing Add:* Plastics & Additives Div Saw Mill & River Rd Ardsley NY 10502

KLEMENS, PAUL GUSTAV, b Vienna, Austria, May 24, 25; m 50; c 2. PHYSICS. *Educ:* Univ Sydney, BSc, 46, MSc, 48; Oxford Univ, DPhil(theoret physics), 50. *Prof Exp:* Prin res officer, Nat Standards Lab, Sydney, Australia, 50-59; physicist, Westinghouse Res Labs, 59-64, mgr transport properties, Solids Dept, 64-67; chmn dept, 67-74, PROF PHYSICS, UNIV CONN, 67- *Mem:* Fel Am Phys Soc; fel Brit Inst Physics & Phys Soc. *Res:* Theoretical solid state and low temperature physics, particularly thermal conductivity of solids and other non-equilibrium and transport properties. *Mailing Add:* Dept of Physics Univ of Conn Storrs CT 06268

KLEMENT, ALFRED WILLIAM, JR, b Bryan, Tex, Nov 8, 23; m 45; c 2. HEALTH PHYSICS, ENVIRONMENTAL SCIENCES. *Educ:* US Mil Acad, BS, 45; Univ Calif, Berkeley, MBioradiol, 52; Am Bd Health Physics, dipl. *Prof Exp:* Radiation effects specialist, Radiation Effects Weapons Br, Div Biol & Med, AEC, 57-59, sci analyst, 59-62, nuclear fallout specialist, Fallout Studies Br, 62-65, actg chief, 64-65, asst chief, 65-66, sci liaison dir canal studies group, Atlantic-Pac Interoceanic Canal Study Comn, Nev Opers Off, 66-70; AEC rep, Spec Studies Group, Radiation Progs, Environ Protection Agency, 70-72; CONSULT, 72- *Mem:* AAAS; fel Am Pub Health Asn; Health Physics Soc; fel Royal Soc Health. *Res:* Radiological physics; biophysics; nuclear weapons effects; radioactive fallout. *Mailing Add:* 10105 Summit Ave Kensington MD 20795

KLEMENT, VACLAV, b Pilsen, Czech, May 7, 35; m 67; c 2. RADIATION ONCOLOGY, MICROBIOLOGY. *Educ:* Charles Univ, Prague, MD, 59; Czech Acad Sci, Prague, PhD(biol), 64. *Prof Exp:* Vis scientist viral oncol, Nat Inst Allergy & Infectious Dis, NIH, 67-68; res fel pediat, 68-69; from asst prof to assoc prof pediat, 69-79, ASSOC PROF RADIATION ONCOL & MICROBIOL, SCH MED, UNIV SOUTHERN CALIF, 79- *Concurrent Pos:* Res fel, Czech Acad Sci, 64-67; sr res training grant, WHO, 67-68; dir virol prog, USPHS Contract, Nat Cancer Inst, 75-78; clin assoc radiation oncol, Los Angeles County, Comprehensive Cancer Ctr, Univ Southern Calif, 78-79. *Mem:* Am Asn Cancer Res; Int Asn Comp Res Leukemia & Related Dis; Am Col Radiol. *Res:* Viral carcinogensis and tumor biology; mechanisms of interactions of oncogenic viruses with the host cells; latency of oncogenic viruses. *Mailing Add:* Sch of Med 2025 Zonal Ave Los Angeles CA 90033

KLEMENT, WILLIAM, JR, b Chicago, Ill, Sept 30, 37. MATERIALS SCIENCE. *Educ:* Calif Inst Technol, BS, 58, PhD(eng sci), 62. *Prof Exp:* Asst res geophysicist, Inst Geophys & Planetary Physics, Univ Calif, Los Angeles, 62-64; Miller res fel physics, Univ Calif, Berkeley, 64-66; asst prof eng, 66-67, ASSOC PROF ENG, UNIV CALIF, LOS ANGELES, 67- *Concurrent Pos:* NATO fel, Royal Inst Technol, Sweden, 63; Guggenheim Mem Found fel, Australian Nat Univ, 68-69; Ford Found Prog, Univ Chile, 73; vis scientist, Nat Physical Res Lab, Pretoria, SAfrica, 74-76 & Inorganic Chem Lab, Oxford Univ, 79. *Res:* Phase transformations; archaeological, ethrographic and historical materials. *Mailing Add:* 163 Hawthorne Elmhurst IL 60126

KLEMER, ANDREW ROBERT, b St Clair, Pa, June 4, 42; m 63; c 4. PHYSIOLOGICAL ECOLOGY, LIMNOLOGY. *Educ:* La Salle Col, BA, 64; Univ Minn, PhD(ecol), 73. *Prof Exp:* Consult limnol, Dept Sci & Indust Res, NZ, 73-74; vis scientist algal physiol, Cawthron Inst, 74-75; ASST PROF BIOL & ENVIRON SCI, STATE UNIV NY, PURCHASE, 76- *Concurrent Pos:* Nat Res Adv Coun NZ, res fel, 73-75; State Univ NY Res Found fac res fel, 77 & 79. *Mem:* Phycol Soc Am; Am Soc Limnol & Oceanog; Int Asn Theoret & Appl Limnol; AAAS. *Res:* Factors that limit the distribution and affect the community structure of phytoplankton; physiological mechanisms involved in responses to those factors. *Mailing Add:* Div of Natural Sci State Univ NY Purchase NY 10577

KLEMM, DONALD J, b Detroit, Mich, Jan 13, 38. FRESHWATER BIOLOGY, ECOLOGY. *Educ:* Valley City State Col, BS, 63; Eastern Mich Univ, MS & SpecS, 70; Univ Mich, Ann Arbor, PhD(fisheries), 74. *Prof Exp:* Res assoc malacol, Mollusk Div, Mus Zool, Univ Mich, Ann Arbor, 72-74; RES AQUATIC BIOLOGIST, ENVIRON MONITORING & SUPPORT LAB, US ENVIRON PROTECTION AGENCY, 74- *Mem:* Am Soc Limnol & Oceanog; Int Asn Theoret & Appl Limnol; Int Asn Great Lakes Res; NAm Benthol Soc; Brit Freshwater Biol Asn. *Res:* Stream, lake and marsh ecology; ecology of polluted waters; invertebrate and fish zoology; macroinvertebrate and fish methodology, parasitology, physiology and toxicology; systematics and ecology of freshwater fish macroparasites, insects, mollusks, annelids, and especially Hirudinea of the world. *Mailing Add:* Environ Monitoring & Support Lab US Environ Protection Agency Cincinnati OH 45268

KLEMM, JAMES L, b South Bend, Ind, Oct 30, 39; m 81; c 2. APPLIED MATHEMATICS, COMPUTER SCIENCE. *Educ:* Univ Chicago, BS, 61; Purdue Univ, MS, 63; Mich State Univ, PhD(eng mech), 70. *Prof Exp:* Asst math, Purdue Univ, 61-65; asst prof, Ind Univ Pa, 65-67; asst, Dept Metall, Mech & Mat Sci, Mich State Univ, 67-69, res assoc, 70; asst prof eng sci, Univ Cincinnati, 70-77; sr publ, 77-80, SR SYSTS ANALYST, NCR CORP, 80- *Concurrent Pos:* Partic, NSF Inst Appl Math & Mech, Mich State Univ, 67. *Res:* St Venant boundary value problems in two and three dimensional theories of classical elasticity; computer applications in manufacturing. *Mailing Add:* SE/CIMEG NCR Corp Dayton OH 45479

KLEMM, LEROY HENRY, b Maple Park, Ill, July 31, 19; m 45; c 3. ORGANIC CHEMISTRY. *Educ:* Univ Ill, BS, 41; Univ Mich, MS, 43, PhD(org chem), 45. *Prof Exp:* Res chemist, Am Oil Co, Tex, 44-45; fel, Univ Res Found, Ohio State Univ, 46; instr chem, Harvard Univ, 46-47; from instr to asst prof, Ind Univ, 47-52; from asst prof to assoc prof, 52-63, PROF CHEM, UNIV ORE, 63- *Concurrent Pos:* Fel, Guggenheim Mem Found, Med Res Coun Labs, London & Swiss Fed Inst Tech, Zurich, 58-59; vis prof, Univ Cincinnati, 65-66; Fulbright-Hays res fel & NATO res grant, Aarhus Univ, Denmark & Univ Groningen, Netherlands, 72-73; vis prof, La Trobe Univ & sr assoc, Univ Melbourne, Australia, 79-80. *Mem:* AAAS; Am Chem Soc. *Res:* Synthesis of carbocyclic and heterocyclic compounds; organic reactions occurring on surfaces; stereochemistry; chromatography; heterogeneous catalysis; electrochemistry. *Mailing Add:* Dept of Chem Univ of Ore Eugene OR 97403

KLEMM, REBECCA JANE, b Bloomington, Ind, Feb 21, 50. STATISTICS, OPERATIONS RESEARCH. *Educ:* Miami Univ, BS, 71, Iowa State Univ, MS, 73, PhD(statist), 76. *Prof Exp:* asst prof statist, Temple Univ, 76-80; MEM FAC STATIST, SCH BUS ADMIN, GEORGETOWN UNIV, 80- *Concurrent Pos:* US Dept Energy fac fel, Sch Bus, Am Assembly Col, 78-79. *Mem:* Am Statist Asn; Opers Res Soc Am; Inst Mgt Sci. *Res:* Statistical education; constrained least squares, econometric model building. *Mailing Add:* Sch Bus Admin Nevils Bldg Georgetown Univ Washington DC 20057

KLEMM, RICHARD ANDREW, b Bloomington, Ind, Mar 13, 48; m 80; c 1. THEORETICAL SOLID STATE PHYSICS. *Educ:* Stanford Univ, BS, 69; Harvard Univ, MA, 72, PhD(physics), 74. *Prof Exp:* Fel, Stanford Univ, 74-76; asst prof physics, Ames Lab, Iowa State Univ, 76-81; assoc prof, 81; STAFF PHYSICIST, EXXON RES & ENG CO, 82- *Concurrent Pos:* Vis scientist, Univ, BC, 78 & 79, Univ Hamburg, 80. *Mem:* Am Phys Soc. *Res:* Theory of condensed matter involving superconductivity; p-wave superconductivity; lower dimensional conductors; charge-density waves and spin-glasses. *Mailing Add:* Exxon Res & Eng Co PO Box 45 Linden NJ 07036

KLEMM, ROBERT DAVID, b Youngstown, Ohio, Sept 13, 29; div; c 1. VERTEBRATE MORPHOLOGY. *Educ:* Capital Univ, BS, 57; Ohio Univ, MS, 59; Southern Ill Univ, PhD(vert zool), 64. *Prof Exp:* Asst prof biol, Capital Univ, 64-67; asst prof anat, Col Vet Med, Kans State Univ, 67-70; asst prof, Mich State Univ, 70-72, invests leader, Avian Anat Invests, USDA, 70-72; assoc prof, 72-79, PROF ANAT, DEPT ANAT & PHYSIOL, COL VET MED, KANS STATE UNIV, 79- *Concurrent Pos:* Guest prof, Zentrum für Anat u Cytobiol Der Justus-Liebig Univ Giessen WGer, 79-80. *Mem:* Am Asn Anatomists; Electron Micros Soc Am; Am Asn Vet Anatomists; Am Soc Zoologists. *Res:* Gross, light and electron microscopy studies of vertebrate structure with special reference to avian morphology; avian anatomy, especially functional anatomy and evolutionary problems involved in Aves. *Mailing Add:* Dept of Anat & Physiol Col Vet Med Kans State Univ Manhattan KS 66506

KLEMM, WALDEMAR ARTHUR, JR, b Elgin, Ill, July 10, 34; m 59; c 3. SILICATE CHEMISTRY. *Educ:* Univ Calif, Riverside, BA, 56; Ore State Univ, MS, 67. *Prof Exp:* Res chemist propellant chem, Lockheed Propulsion Co, 59-66; group leader cement chem, Tech Ctr, Am Cement Corp, 66-70; assoc specialist geochem, Inst Geophys & Planetary Physics, Univ Calif, 70-72; sr res scientist, Gen Portland Inc, 72-75; SR SCIENTIST CEMENT CHEM, MARTIN MARIETTA LABS, 75- *Concurrent Pos:* Chmn cementing subcomt, Indust Liaison Comt, Geothermal Resources Prog, Univ Calif, 71-72; vchmn solid-liquid interactions cement hydration, Gordon Res Conf, 75-76; mem comt chem additions & admixtures for concrete, Transp Res Bd, 76-79. *Mem:* Am Ceramic Soc. *Res:* High-temperature silicate chemistry; cement clinkering reactions; admixture interactions; expansive cements; cement hydration. *Mailing Add:* Martin Marietta Labs 1450 S Rolling Rd Baltimore MD 21227

KLEMM, WILLIAM ARTHUR, b Chicago, Ill, Dec 11, 19. CHEMICAL ENGINEERING. *Educ:* Univ Ill, BS, 40; Mass Inst Technol, ScD, 46. *Prof Exp:* Asst, Mass Inst Technol, 40-42, res worker, Nat Defense Res Comt contract, 42-46; asst prof chem eng, Okla Agr & Mech Col, 46-48, assoc prof, 48-50; res engr, Metals Div Res, Kaiser Aluminum & Chem Corp, Calif, 50-53, res group leader, 53-69; assoc prof chem eng, Ind Inst Technol, 69-75; assoc prof, 75-81, PROF CHEM ENG, SDAK SCH MINES & TECHNOL, 81- *Concurrent Pos:* Asst lectr, Birmingham, 59-60. *Mem:* Am Chem Soc; Am Inst Chem Engrs; Am Ceramic Soc; Am Soc Eng Educ. *Res:* Flame thrower jets; high rate combustion and temperature measurement; fluidized retorting of oil shale and of wood; ignition temperatures; heat transfer; trajectories of thickened fuel jets; design and operation of aluminum reduction cells; refractory hard metals; biomass processing and utilization. *Mailing Add:* Dept of Chem Eng SDak Sch Mines & Technol Rapid City SD 57701

KLEMM, WILLIAM ROBERT, b South Bend, Ind, July 24, 34; m 57; c 2. NEUROSCIENCES. *Educ:* Auburn Univ, DVM, 58; Univ Notre Dame, PhD(biol), 63. *Prof Exp:* NIH fel, 60-63; assoc prof physiol & pharmacol, Iowa State Univ, 63-66; assoc prof, 66-70, PROF, TEX A&M UNIV, 70- *Mem:* Am Physiol Soc; Soc Neurosci. *Res:* Animal hypnosis; theta rhythm; brain stem functions; animal electroencephalography; psychopharmacology. *Mailing Add:* Dept Vet Anat Tex A&M Univ College Station TX 77843

KLEMME, HUGH DOUGLAS, b Belmond, Iowa, Jan 24, 21; m 43; c 3. PETROLEUM GEOLOGY. *Educ:* Coe Col, AB, 42; Princeton Univ, MA, 48, PhD(geol), 49. *Prof Exp:* Regional geologist, Standard Oil Co, 49-51; staff geologist, Am Overseas Petrol, Ltd, 51-58, mgr explor, 58-63, asst chief geologist, 63-69; vpres explor, Lewis G Weeks Assocs, Ltd, Westport, 69-76; sr vpres, Weeks Petrol Corp, Westport, 76-79; pres, Geo Basins Ltd, 80-81. *Mem:* Geol Soc Am; Am Asn Petrol Geologists; AAAS; Am Geophys Union; Am Petrol Inst. *Res:* Regional petroleum geology; regional tectonics; basin studies; petroleum formation, migration and accumulation. *Mailing Add:* 112 Rowayton Woods Dr Norwalk CT 05854

KLEMMEDSON, JAMES OTTO, b Ft Collins, Colo, Aug 20, 27; m 52; c 4. SOIL SCIENCE, FOREST & RANGE ECOLOGY. *Educ:* Univ Calif, Berkeley, BS, 50, PhD(soil sci), 59; Colo State Univ, MS, 53. *Prof Exp:* Soil conservationist, Soil Conserv Serv, USDA, 50-51; instr forestry, Colo State Univ, 51-52, res asst range mgt, 52-53; instr, Mont State Univ, 53-55; res asst forestry, Univ Calif, Berkeley, 55-56, soils & plant nutrit, 56-59; range scientist, Int Forest & Range Exp Sta, USDA, 59-66; prof forestry, 66-80, PROF RANGE MGT, UNIV ARIZ, 66-, RES SCIENTIST, AGR EXP STA, 80- *Mem:* Soc Am Foresters; Soc Range Mgt; Ecol Soc Am; Soil Sci Soc Am; Am Soc Agron. *Res:* Nutrient balance in forest, range and shrub ecosystems; ecology of forest and range ecosystems; influence of cultural practices on nutrient balance. *Mailing Add:* Sch of Renewable Natural Resources Univ of Ariz Tucson AZ 85721

KLEMMER, HOWARD WESLEY, b Sask, Can, 22; nat US; m 60; c 1. MICROBIOLOGY. *Educ:* Univ Sask, BS, 49, MS, 50; Univ Wis, PhD(bact), 54. *Prof Exp:* Microbiologist, Pineapple Inst Hawaii, 54-63; microbiologist, Pac Biomed Res Ctr, Univ Hawaii, 63-75, proj dir, Community Studies Pesticides, 65-75; RETIRED. *Mem:* AAAS; Am Soc Microbiol; Am Phytopath Soc; Am Chem Soc; fel Am Inst Chem. *Res:* Sanitary and industrial microbiology; environmental pollution. *Mailing Add:* 4915 Kalanianaole Honolulu HI 96821

KLEMOLA, ARNOLD R, b Pomfret, Conn, Feb 20, 31. ASTRONOMY. *Educ:* Ind Univ, AB, 53; Univ Calif, Berkeley, PhD(astron), 62. *Prof Exp:* Res asst astron, Yale Univ, 61-63, res staff astronomer, 63-67; asst res astronomer, 67-77, ASSOC RES ASTRONOMER, LICK OBSERV, UNIV CALIF, SANTA CURZ, 77- *Mem:* Am Astron Soc; Int Astron Union. *Res:* Photographic astrometry. *Mailing Add:* Lick Observ Univ of Calif Santa Cruz CA 95064

KLEMOLA, TAPIO, b Pori, Finland, July 20, 34; m 55; c 2. MATHEMATICS. *Educ:* Univ Helsinki, MS, 56, PhD(math), 59. *Prof Exp:* Asst math, Univ Helsinki, 56-58; Aaltonen Saatio & Govt Finland grant, Paris, 59; actg asst prof, Univ Oulu, 59-60; asst prof, Univ Windsor, 60-62; NSF grant, Inst Adv Study, 62-63; lectr & res assoc, Johns Hopkins Univ, 63-64; vis prof, 64-65, ASSOC PROF MATH, UNIV MONTREAL, 65- *Concurrent Pos:* Swiss Govt grant, Swiss Fed Inst Technol, 71-72. *Mem:* Am Math Soc; Can Math Cong. *Res:* Complex manifolds and spaces; differential operators on manifolds. *Mailing Add:* Dept of Math Univ of Mont CP 6128 Montreal PQ H3C 3J7 Can

KLEMPERER, MARTIN R, b New York, NY, June 26, 31; m 59; c 3. HEMATOLOGY, ONCOLOGY. *Educ:* Dartmouth Col, AB, 53; NY Univ, MD, 57. *Prof Exp:* Instr pediat, Harvard Med Sch, 65-67, assoc, 67-69, asst prof, 69-70, tutor med sci, 67-70; assoc prof pediat, 70-74 & med, 71-74, PROF PEDIAT & MED, SCH MED, UNIV ROCHESTER, 74- *Concurrent Pos:* Res fel pediat, Harvard Med Sch, 63-65; fel hemat & med, Children's Hosp Med Ctr, Boston, Mass, 63-65, asst med, 65-66, res assoc immunol & hemat, 66-68, assoc med, immunol & hemat, 68-70; sr assoc pediatrician, Strong Mem Hosp, Med Ctr, Univ Rochester, 70- *Mem:* Soc Pediat Res; Am Fedn Clin Res; Int Soc Exp Hematol; Am Soc Hemat; NY Acad Sci. *Res:* Hereditary and acquired defects of the serum complement system; role of the complement system in inflammation; therapy of childhood malignancies. *Mailing Add:* Dept of Pediat Univ of Rochester Med Ctr Rochester NY 14642

KLEMPERER, WALTER GEORGE, b Saranac Lake, NY, Apr 2, 47. INORGANIC CHEMISTRY. *Educ:* Harvard Univ, BA, 68; Mass Inst Technol, PhD(chem), 73. *Prof Exp:* Asst prof, 73-78, ASSOC PROF CHEM, COLUMBIA UNIV, 78- *Concurrent Pos:* Alfred P Sloan Found fel, 76; Camille & Henry Dreyfus Found grant, 78. *Mem:* Am Chem Soc; The Chem Soc. *Mailing Add:* Dept of Chem Columbia Univ New York NY 10027

KLEMPERER, WILLIAM, b New York, NY, Oct 6, 27; m 49; c 3. PHYSICAL CHEMISTRY. *Educ:* Harvard Univ, AB, 50; Univ Calif, PhD, 54. *Prof Exp:* Instr chem, Univ Calif, 54; from instr to assoc prof, 54-65, PROF CHEM, HARVARD UNIV, 65- *Honors & Awards:* John Price Wetherill Medal, Franklin Inst, 78; The Irving Langmuir Award in Chem Physics, Am Soc Phys, 80. *Mem:* Nat Acad Sci; Am Chem Soc; Am Acad Arts & Sci; Am Phys Soc. *Res:* Molecular structure; molecular spectroscopy. *Mailing Add:* Dept Chem Harvard Univ Cambridge MA 02138

KLEMPNER, DANIEL, b Brooklyn, NY, June 4, 43. PHYSICAL CHEMISTRY, POLYMER SCIENCE. *Educ:* Rensselaer Polytech Inst, BS, 64; Williams Col, MS, 68; State Univ NY Albany, PhD(phys chem), 70. *Prof Exp:* Engr, Sprague Elec Co, Mass, 64-68; vis scientist, Univ Mass, Amherst, 70-72; MEM FAC, POLYMER INST, UNIV DETROIT, 72- *Mem:* AAAS; Am Chem Soc; Am Inst Chem Engrs; Am Phys Soc; Am Inst Chem. *Res:* Electrical properties of materials; inter-penetrating polymer networks; high pressure effects on polymers; x-ray diffraction studies of polymers; morphological and viscoelastic studies on polymers; theories of fusion and blending of polymers, flammability. *Mailing Add:* Polymer Inst Univ Detroit 4001 W McNichols Rd Detroit MI 48221

KLEMS, GEORGE J, b Brno, Czech, May 4, 36; US citizen; m 68; c 2. METALLURGY. *Educ:* Harvard Univ, AB, 58; Ill Inst Technol, MS, 61; Case Western Reserve Univ, PhD(metall & mat sci), 71. *Prof Exp:* Res asst solid state physics & mat sci, Ill Inst Technol, 58-61 & x-ray crystallog, 61-64; res metallurgist, Res Ctr, Repub Steel Corp, 64-73; mkt develop Metallurgist, Molycorp, Inc, 73-76; PROD METALLURGIST HIGH STRENGTH STEELS, STEEL GROUP, FLAT ROLLED DIV, REPUB STEEL CORP, 76- *Mem:* Am Soc Metals; Am Inst Mech Engrs; Soc Automotive Engrs; Sigma Xi. *Res:* Phase transformations; alloy development. *Mailing Add:* Repub Steel Corp 1418 Repub Bldg PO Box 6778 Cleveland OH 44101

KLEMS, JOSEPH HENRY, b Cincinnati, Ohio, July 14, 42; m 67. ENERGY CONSERVATION. *Educ:* Univ Chicago, SB, 64, SM, 65, PhD(physics), 70. *Prof Exp:* Res assoc physics, Lab Nuclear Studies, Cornell Univ, 70-73; asst res physicist, Univ Calif, Davis, 73-78; STAFF SCIENTIST, LAWRENCE BERKELEY LAB, 78- *Mem:* Am Phys Soc; AAAS; Sigma Xi; Int Solar Energy Soc. *Res:* Experimental high energy physics; energy-efficient windows and lighting systems; solar energy; wind energy; distributed energy technologies. *Mailing Add:* Energy & Environ Div Lawrence Berkeley Lab Berkeley CA 94720

KLENDER, GERALD, plastics chemistry, see previous edition

KLENKE, EDWARD FREDERICK, JR, b New York, NY, May 22, 16; m 38; c 2. CHEMICAL ENGINEERING. *Educ:* Newark Col Eng, BS, 40. *Prof Exp:* Sr supvr, Kankakee Ord Works, 41-44; chem engr, Manhattan Proj, Univ Chicago, Hanford, Wash, 44-45; res chem & engr, pigments dept, 45-64, sr res engr, 64-69, res supvr, 69-74, coordr new facil, 74-77, SAFETY, HEALTH & ENVIRON COORDR, E I DU PONT DE NEMOURS & CO, INC, 77- *Concurrent Pos:* Eng consult, 46-51. *Mem:* Am Inst Chem Engrs. *Res:* Colored pigments research; process design and development. *Mailing Add:* 15 Wedgewood Dr Liberty Corner NJ 07938

KLENKNECHT, KENNETH S(AMUEL), b Washington, DC, July 24, 19; m 47; c 3. AEROSPACE & AERONAUTICAL ENGINEERING. *Educ:* Purdue Univ, BS, 42. *Prof Exp:* Proj engr, NASA Lewis Res Ctr, 42-51, head opers eng sect & aeronaut res scientist, NASA Flight Res Ctr, Calif, 51-59, mem, Space Task Group, Langley Field, Va, 59-61, tech asst to dir, NASA Johnson Space Ctr, 61-62, mgr, Proj Mercury, 62-63, dep mgr, Gemini Prog, 63-67, mgr, Command & Serv Modules, Apollo Spacecraft Prog, 67-70, mgr, Skylab Prog, 70-74, dir flight opers, 74-76, asst mgr, Orbiter Proj, 76-77, dep assoc adminr space transp systs, Europ Opers, NASA HQ, Washington, DC, 77-79, asst mgr, Orbiter Proj & vehicle mgr, Orbiter 102, NASA Johnson Space Ctr, 79-81; SR SPACE TRANSP SYST TECH ADV, MARTIN MORIELLO AEROSPACE, DENVER, COLO, 81- *Honors & Awards:* NASA Group Achievement Award, 62; NASA Exceptional Serv Medal, 69; NASA Distinguished Serv Medal, 69 & 73; NASA Medal for Outstanding Leadership, 63 & 81; John J Montgomery Award, Nat Soc Aerospace Prof, 63; W RAndolph Lovelace, II Award, Am Astronaut Soc, Inc, 75. *Mem:* Fel Am Astronaut Soc; corresp mem Int Acad Astronaut; assoc fel Am Inst Aeronaut & Astronaut. *Res:* Space science. *Mailing Add:* 825 Front Range Rd Littleton CO 80120

KLENS, PAUL FRANK, b Scranton, Pa, July 21, 18; m 47; c 4. MICROBIOLOGY. *Educ:* Syracuse Univ, AB, 40, MS, 42, PhD(microbiol), 51. *Prof Exp:* Asst bot, Syracuse Univ, 40-42, instr bact & mycol, 45-51; chemist & mat engr, Carrier Corp, NY, 42-45; chief germicides unit, QM Res & Develop, US Dept Army, 51-53; chief microbiol lab, Nuodex Prods Co, NJ, 54-58; assoc prof, 58-61, dean arts & sci, 66-74, PROF BIOL, LOCK HAVEN STATE COL, 61- *Mem:* Am Soc Microbiol; Soc Indust Microbiol. *Res:* Physiology of fungi; microbiological deterioration; industrial microbiology; water pollution studies. *Mailing Add:* Dept of Biol Lock Haven State Col Lock Haven PA 17745

KLEPCZYNSKI, WILLIAM J(OHN), b Philadelphia, Pa, Apr 16, 39; m 61. ASTRONOMY. *Educ:* Univ Pa, AB, 61; Georgetown Col, MA, 64; Yale Univ, PhD(astron), 69. *Prof Exp:* Astronomer, Nautical Almanac Off, 61-71, ASTRONOMER, TIME SERV DIV, US NAVAL OBSERV, 71- *Mem:* AAAS; Am Astron Soc; Am Inst Navig; Int Astron Union. *Res:* Planetary motion; masses of the planets; motion of minor planets; observations of minor planets; eclipsing variable stars. *Mailing Add:* 6614 Weatherford Ct McLean VA 22101

KLEPFER, HAROLD H(OLMES), b Cedar Falls, Iowa, May 28, 31; m 52; c 5. METALLURGY. *Educ:* Carleton Col, AB, 53; Iowa State Univ, PhD(metall), 57. *Prof Exp:* Asst metall, Inst Atomic Res, Iowa State Univ, 53-57; res metallurgist, Vallecitos Atomic Lab, Gen Elec Co, 57-61, mgr metall res, 61-66, mgr fuels & mat develop, 66-69, mgr nuclear fuels mfg, 69-71, mgr develop mgt, Nuclear Fuels Prod Dept, 71-76, mgr technol & develop, Boiling Water Reactor Syst Div, 76-77, gen mgr, Nuclear Technol Dept, 77-79, MGR NUCLEAR FUEL & SERV ENG DEPT, NUCLEAR ENG DIV, GEN ELEC CO, 79- *Mem:* Am Nuclear Soc. *Res:* Physical metallurgy and mechanical metallurgy, especially nuclear reactor fuel and structural alloys. *Mailing Add:* Nuclear Eng Div 175 Curtner Ave San Jose CA 95125

KLEPINGER, LINDA LEHMAN, b Hammond, Ind, Mar 27, 41. BIOLOGICAL ANTHROPOLOGY. *Educ:* Ind Univ, AB, 63; Univ Kans, MPhil, 71, PhD(anthrop), 72. *Prof Exp:* Asst prof, 72-79, ASSOC PROF ANTHROP, UNIV ILL, URBANA, 79- *Mem:* Am Anthrop Asn; Am Asn Phys Anthropologists; AAAS; Soc Am Archaeol; Paleopath Asn. *Res:* Biological relationships of prehistoric populations; dental pathology in prehistoric South America; paleopathology of New and Old World populations; paleodemography of New World populations; chemical analyses of archaeological bone. *Mailing Add:* Dept Anthrop Univ Ill 607 S Matthews Urbana IL 61801

KLEPPA, OLE JAKOB, b Oslo, Norway, Feb 4, 20; m 48; c 2. PHYSICAL CHEMISTRY. *Educ:* Norwegian Tech Univ, ChE, 46, Dr techn(chem), 56. *Prof Exp:* Instr, Inst Study Metals, Univ Chicago, 49-50; res supvr, Dept Chem & Metall, Norwegian Defense Res Estab, 50-51; asst prof chem, Inst Study Metals, 52-57, assoc prof, Inst Study Metals & Dept Chem, 58-62, chmn calorimetry conf, 66-67, assoc dir, James Franck Inst, 68-71, dir, 71-77, PROF, DEPT CHEM & GEOPHYS SCI, UNIV CHICAGO, 62- *Concurrent Pos:* Consult, Argonne Nat Lab. *Mem:* Am Chem Soc; Am Inst Mining, Metall & Petrol Eng; Am Ceramic Soc; Norweg Chem Soc. *Res:* Thermodynamics; thermochemistry; electrochemistry; chemical and physical metallurgy; solid state chemistry; fused salts. *Mailing Add:* James Franck Inst Univ of Chicago 5640 Ellis Ave Chicago IL 60637

KLEPPER, DAVID LLOYD, b New York, NY, Jan 25, 32. ARCHITECTURAL ACOUSTICS, ELECTROACOUSTICS. *Educ:* Mass Inst Technol, BS, 53, MS, 57. *Prof Exp:* Sr consult acoust, Bolt Beranek & Newman, Inc, 57-71; PRES ACOUST, KLEPPER MARSHALL KING ASSOC LTD, 71- *Mem:* Fel Acoust Soc Am; fel Audio Eng Soc; US Inst Theatre Technol; Inst Noise Control Eng. *Mailing Add:* Klepper Marshall King Assoc Ltd 96 Haarlem Ave White Plains NY 10603

KLEPPER, ELIZABETH LEE (BETTY), b Memphis, Tenn, Mar 8, 36. PLANT PHYSIOLOGY. *Educ:* Vanderbilt Univ, BA, 58; Duke Univ, AM, 63, PhD(bot), 66. *Prof Exp:* Teacher high sch, Tenn, 60-61; teaching asst bot, Duke Univ, 63-64; res scientist, Div Irrig Res, Commonwealth Sci & Indust Res Orgn Griffith, Australia, 66-68; asst prof bot, Auburn Univ, 68-72; res scientist, Battelle Northwest Labs, 72-74; sr res scientist, Ecosysts Dept, 74-76; MEM STAFF, SCI & EDUC ADMIN-AGR RES, USDA, 76- *Mem:* AAAS; Am Inst Biol Sci; Bot Soc Am; Am Soc Plant Physiol; Am Soc Agron. *Res:* Plant water and ion relationships. *Mailing Add:* Sci & Educ Admin-Agr Res USDA PO Box 370 Pendleton OR 97810

KLEPPER, JOHN RICHARD, b Dayton, Ohio, Sept 20, 47; m 69. ULTRASONIC IMAGING, DIGITAL IMAGE PROCESSING. *Educ:* Ohio State Univ, BS, 69; Washington Univ, MA, 75, PhD(physics), 80. *Prof Exp:* Res asst, Biomed Comput Lab, Washington Univ, 77-80; res bioengr, 80-81, DIR, DEPT PHYS SCI, INST APPL PHYSIOL & MED, 81- *Concurrent Pos:* Affil asst prof elec eng, Univ Wash, 82- *Mem:* Inst Elec & Electronics Engrs; Eng in Med & Biol Soc. *Res:* Development of computer aided ultrasonic imaging systems for use in medical diagnosis; ultrasonic tissue characterization, through application of computed tomographic techniques; blood flow analysis, through Doppler shift measurements. *Mailing Add:* Inst Appl Physiol & Med 701 16th Ave Seattle WA 98122

KLEPPNER, ADAM, b New York, NY, June 5, 31; m 58. MATHEMATICAL ANALYSIS. *Educ:* Yale Univ, BS, 53; Univ Mich, MA, 54; Harvard Univ, PhD(math), 60. *Prof Exp:* From asst prof to assoc prof, 61-68, PROF MATH, UNIV MD, COLLEGE PARK, 68- *Concurrent Pos:* Vis prof, Univ Colo, 70-71 & Univ Calif, Berkeley, 75. *Mem:* Am Math Soc. *Res:* Group representations; functional analysis. *Mailing Add:* Dept of Math Univ of Md College Park MD 20742

KLEPPNER, DANIEL, b New York, NY, Dec 16, 32; m 58; c 3. PHYSICS. *Educ:* Williams Col, BA, 53; Cambridge Univ, BA, 55; Harvard Univ, PhD(physics), 59. *Prof Exp:* Res fel physics, Harvard Univ, 59-60, from instr to asst prof, 60-66; assoc prof, 66-73, PROF PHYSICS, MASS INST TECHNOL, 73- *Concurrent Pos:* Alfred P Sloan Found fel, 62-66. *Mem:* Fel Am Phys Soc; fel AAAS. *Res:* Atomic resonance physics; atomic structure; high precision measurements. *Mailing Add:* Dept of Physics Mass Inst Technol Cambridge MA 02179

KLEPSER, HARRY JOHN, b Buffalo, NY, Mar 10, 08; m 36; c 3. STRATIGRAPHY, GEOLOGY. *Educ:* Syracuse Univ, AB, 32, MA, 33; Ohio State Univ, PhD(geol), 37. *Prof Exp:* Asst geol, Ohio State Univ, 34; assoc prof geol & geog, Capital Univ, 36-43 & SDak State Col, 43-44; geologist, US Geol Surv, Ky, 44-45; from asst prof to prof, 46-78, head dept, 61-72, EMER PROF GEOL, UNIV TENN, KNOXVILLE, 78- *Mem:* AAAS; Geol Soc Am; Am Asn Petrol Geol. *Res:* Fluorspar deposits; lower Mississippian rocks of the highland rim in southern Kentucky and Tennessee; Chattanooga shale of Tennessee. *Mailing Add:* Dept of Geol Univ of Tenn Knoxville TN 37916

KLERER, JULIUS, b New York, NY, July 19, 28; m 61. PHYSICAL CHEMISTRY, SOLID STATE CHEMISTRY. *Educ:* NY Univ, BA, 49, MS, 55, PhD(phys chem), 58. *Prof Exp:* Instr phys chem, Brooklyn Col, 57-58; group leader, Radio Corp Am, 58-60; supvry mem tech staff, Bell Tel Labs, 60-67; assoc prof, 67-80, PROF CHEM ENG, COOPER UNION, 80- *Mem:* Electrochem Soc; Royal Soc Chem; NY Acad Sci. *Res:* Solid state chemistry concerned with thin films of oxides and metals, their preparation and properties both on semiconductors and semiconducting oxides. *Mailing Add:* Sch of Eng & Sci Cooper Union Cooper Sq New York NY 10009

KLERER, MELVIN, b New York, NY, Feb 17, 26; m 51; c 2. COMPUTER SCIENCE. *Educ:* NY Univ, BA, 48, MS, 50, PhD(theoret physics), 54. *Prof Exp:* Tutor physics, City Col New York, 52-53, instr, 54-57; sr res assoc, dir comput & data processing facil & head comput sci prog, Hudson Labs, Columbia Univ, 57-67; prof indust eng, NY Univ, 67-73; vis scientist, Weizman Inst Sci, 73-74; PROF COMPUT SCI, POLYTECH INST NEW YORK, 74- *Mem:* Am Fedn Info Processing Socs; AAAS; Asn Comput Mach; Inst Elec & Electronics Engrs; Pattern Recognition Soc. *Res:* Computer science programming language and compiler design; artificial intelligence and pattern recognition. *Mailing Add:* Div Comput Sci Polytech Inst 333 Jay St Brooklyn NY 11201

KLERLEIN, JOSEPH BALLARD, b Baltimore, Md, Dec 16, 48; m 70; c 3. FINITE MATHEMATICS. *Educ:* Furman Univ, BS, 70; Vanderbilt Univ, PhD(math), 75. *Prof Exp:* Instr, 74-75, ASST PROF MATH, WESTERN CAROLINA UNIV, 75- *Mem:* Am Math Soc; Math Asn Am. *Res:* Graph theory especially the study of traversability in cayley color graphs; line graphs for directed graphs. *Mailing Add:* Dept of Math Western Carolina Univ Cullowhee NC 28723

KLERMAN, GERALD L, b New York, NY, Dec 20, 28. PSYCHIATRY. *Educ:* Cornell Univ, AB, 50; NY Univ, MD, 54. *Prof Exp:* Asst prof psychiat, Med Sch, Yale Univ, 65-70; prof psychiat, Harvard Med Sch, 70-77; ADMINR, ALCOHOL, DRUG ABUSE & MENTAL HEALTH ADMIN, 77- *Concurrent Pos:* Dir, Conn Mental Health Ctr, 67-69; supt, Erich Lindemann Mental Health Ctr, Boston, 70-76; dir, Cobb Psychiat Res Lab, Mass Gen Hosp, 76-77; consult, Am Med Asn, 67-77, Nat Inst Mental Health, 61-77, Med Letter, 68-77. *Honors & Awards:* Hofheimer Prize, Am Psychiat Asn, 69. *Mem:* AAAS; Am Med Asn; Am Psychiat Asn; Am Psychopath Asn; Inst Med. *Mailing Add:* 5600 Fishers Lane Rockville MD 20857

KLERMAN, LORRAINE VOGEL, b New York, NY, July 10, 29; m 54; c 4. PUBLIC HEALTH. *Educ:* Cornell Univ, BA, 50; Harvard Univ, MPH, 53, DrPH, 62. *Prof Exp:* Mem staff vol health agencies, NJ, 52-56; fac assoc res, Florence Heller Grad Sch Advan Studies Social Welfare, 62-65; asst prof pub health, Dept Epidemiol & Pub Health, Sch Med, Yale Univ, 65-70, res assoc, 70-71, consult, 71-73; lectr, 71-73, ASSOC PROF PUB HEALTH, FLORENCE HELLER GRAD SCH ADVAN STUDIES SOCIAL WELFARE, BRANDEIS UNIV, 73- *Mem:* Fel Am Pub Health Asn; fel Soc Pub Health Educators; Nat Alliance Concerned with Sch-Age Parents. *Res:* Maternal and child health; handicapped children; child welfare; adolescent parenting. *Mailing Add:* Florence Heller Grad Sch Brandeis Univ Waltham MA 02254

KLESSIG, DANIEL FREDERICK, b Fond du Lac, Wis, Feb 24, 49. MOLECULAR BIOLOGY, BIOCHEMISTRY. *Educ:* Univ Wis-Madison, BS, 71; Univ Edinburgh, BSc, 73; Harvard Univ, PhD(molecular biol, biochem), 78. *Prof Exp:* Fel, Cold Spring Harbor Lab, 78, jr staff scientist tumor virol, 79-80; MEM FAC, DEPT CELL & MOLEC BIOL, UNIV UTAH, 80- *Res:* Control of gene expression in eukaryotes using abortive infections of simian cells by human adenovirus as a model system. *Mailing Add:* Dept Cell & Molec Biol Univ Utah Salt Lake City UT 84132

KLESTADT, BERNARD, b Buren, Ger, Jan 31, 25; nat US; m 56; c 1. ELECTRICAL ENGINEERING. *Educ:* Columbia Univ, BS, 49, MS, 50; Univ Southern Calif, PhD(elec eng), 58. *Prof Exp:* Elec engr, Aircraft Radiation Lab, Wright Air Develop Ctr, 49; asst proj engr, Sperry Gyroscope Co, 50; mem tech staff, Systs Develop Labs, Hughes Aircraft Co, 50-58, sr staff engr, 58-62, sr scientist, 62-63, asst mgr flight control systs dept, 63-66, mgr missile control systs dept, 66-69, sr scientist, Space & Commun Group, 69-76, sr scientist, Missiles Systs Group, 76-81, MGR, CONTROL SYSTS DEPT, HUGHES AIRCRAFT CO, 81- *Concurrent Pos:* Lectr, Univ Southern Calif, 56-58. *Mem:* Sigma Xi; Inst Elec & Electronics Engrs; NY Acad Sci. *Res:* Servomechanisms; circuit theory; guidance and control systems; automatic computation; space flight development. *Mailing Add:* Missile Systs Group Fallbrook & Roscoe Blvds Canoga Park CA 91304

KLETSKY, EARL J(USTIN), b Springfield, Mass, July 22, 30; m 58; c 1. ELECTRICAL ENGINEERING. *Educ:* Mass Inst Technol, BS, 51, MS, 53; Syracuse Univ, PhD(elec eng), 61. *Prof Exp:* Torchiana fel & res engr elec eng, Univ Delft, 55-56; elec engr, Gen Electronics Labs, 56-57; from instr to asst prof, 57-67, asst dir, Lab Sensory Commun, 64-74, ASSOC PROF ELEC ENG, SYRACUSE UNIV, 67-, COORDR, BIOENG PROG, 73- *Concurrent Pos:* Admin dir, Inst Sensory Res, Syracuse Univ, 74-80. *Mem:* Inst Elec & Electronics Engrs; Acoust Soc Am. *Res:* Biosimulation; analog and digital simulation of sensory systems; modeling of sensory information processing. *Mailing Add:* Col Eng Syracuse Univ 203 Link Hall Syracuse NY 13210

KLETT, JAMES ELMER, b Cincinnati, Ohio, May 20, 47. ORNAMENTAL HORTICULTURE, NURSERY PRODUCTION. *Educ:* Ohio State Univ, BS, 69; Univ Ill, MS, 71, PhD(hort), 74. *Prof Exp:* Res asst ornamental hort, Univ Ill, 69-72, teaching asst, 72-74; asst prof, ornamental hort, SDak State Univ 74-77, assoc prof, 77-79; ASSOC PROF ORNAMENTAL HORT, COLO STATE UNIV, 79- *Concurrent Pos:* Water Qual Inst grant, SDak State Univ, 76, new chem prod grants. *Mem:* Am Soc Hort Sci; Am Hort Soc; Int Plant Propagators Soc; Am Asn Bot Gardens & Arboretums; Sigma Xi. *Res:* Herbaceous and woody ornamental plant evaluation research; woody ornamental nutrition and cold hardiness research; media and photoperiod studies with floriculture crops. *Mailing Add:* Dept Hort Colo State Univ Ft Collins CO 80523

KLETZIEN, ROLF FREDERICK, b Beloit, Wis, Dec 15, 46; m 69; c 2. BIOCHEMISTRY. *Educ:* Univ Wis, BS, 70, PhD(oncol), 74. *Prof Exp:* Fel biochem, Princeton Univ, 74-75; Harvard Univ, 75-77; ASSOC PROF BIOCHEM, WVA UNIV, 77- *Mem:* Am Soc Cellular Biol. *Res:* Regulation of cellular function and metabolism. *Mailing Add:* Dept Biochem Sch Med WVa Univ Morgantown WV 26506

KLEVANS, EDWARD HARRIS, b Roaring Spring, Pa, Oct 13, 35; m 59; c 2. PLASMA PHYSICS, RESEARCH ADMINISTRATION. *Educ:* Pa State Univ, BS, 57; Univ Mich, MS, 58, PhD(nuclear eng), 62. *Prof Exp:* Sr scientist, Jet Propulsion Lab, Calif Inst Technol, 62-66; from asst prof to assoc prof, 66-76, PROF NUCLEAR ENG, PA STATE UNIV, 76-, ASSOC DEAN RES, 80- *Mem:* Am Phys Soc; Am Nuclear Soc. *Res:* Plasma physics; thermonuclear engineering. *Mailing Add:* 103 W Marylyn Ave State College PA 16801

KLEVAY, LESLIE MICHAEL, b Chicago, Ill. NUTRITION, INTERNAL MEDICINE. *Educ:* Univ Wis, Madison, BS, 56, MD, 60; Harvard Univ, MS, 62, DSc(hyg, nutrit), 65. *Prof Exp:* Teaching asst chem, Univ Wis, Madison, 55-57; intern med, St Louis City Hosp, Mo, 60-61; from instr to asst prof internal med, Col Med, Univ Cincinnati, 65-72, from asst prof to assoc prof environ health, 65-72; RES MED OFFICER, HUMAN NUTRIT LAB, SCI & EDUC ADMIN-AGR RES, USDA, 72- *Concurrent Pos:* Asst, Wash Univ, 60-61; consult, Off Int Res, NIH, 67, Ky Dept Health, 68-69, Div Chronic Dis Progs, Health Serv & Ment Health Admin, 69- & Nat Ctr Health Statist, 70; assoc prof internal med, Univ NDak, 72; Joseph Goldberger vis prof clin nutrit. *Mem:* Am Fedn Clin Res; Soc Exp Biol & Med; Am Inst Nutrit; Am Soc Clin Nutrit. *Res:* Experimental atherosclerosis; interrelationships of nutrients; mammalian metabolism of insecticides; metabolism of metallic trace elements; nutritional aspects of the human environment; nutritional problems of underdeveloped countries; epidemiology of ischemic heart disease. *Mailing Add:* Sci & Educ Admin-Agr Res USDA PO Box 7166 Grand Forks ND 58201

KLEVECZ, ROBERT RAYMOND, b Stratford, Conn, Feb 8, 39; m 61; c 2. CELL BIOLOGY, MOLECULAR BIOLOGY. *Educ:* Ga Inst Technol, BS, 62; Univ Tex, PhD(cell biol), 66. *Prof Exp:* SR RES SCIENTIST, CITY OF HOPE MED CTR, 67- *Concurrent Pos:* Fel, Yale Univ, 66, Nat Cancer Inst res fel enzyme chem, 66-67. *Mem:* AAAS; Am Soc Cell Biol. *Res:* Cellular regulatory mechanisms; cellular clocks and oscillators; control of growth and division in mammalian cells in culture; periodic gene function and the temporal organization of RNA and enzyme synthesis. *Mailing Add:* Dept of Biol City of Hope Med Ctr Duarte CA 91010

KLEVEN, STANLEY H, b Dawson, Minn, June 24, 40; m 60; c 3. VETERINARY MICROBIOLOGY, AVIAN MEDICINE. *Educ:* Univ Minn, St Paul, BS, 63, DVM, 65, PhD(microbiol), 70. *Prof Exp:* Pvt pract, 65-66; instr vet microbiol, Univ Minn, 66-67, res fel, 67-70; asst prof med microbiol, 70-73, assoc prof, 73-78, PROF AVIAN MED & MED MICROBIOL, POULTRY DIS RES CTR, UNIV GA, 78-, HEAD DEPT AVIAN MED, 73- *Mem:* AAAS; Am Vet Med Asn; Am Asn Avian Path; World Vet Poultry Asn. *Res:* Respiratory infections of poultry; avian tumor viruses; avian mycoplasmosis. *Mailing Add:* Poultry Dis Res Ctr Univ Ga 953 College Station Rd Athens GA 30605

KLEYN, DICK HENRY, b Heemstede, Netherlands, Oct 29, 29; US citizen; m 62; c 1. DAIRY SCIENCE, BIOCHEMISTRY. *Educ:* Ohio State Univ, BS, 53; Cornell Univ, MS, 56, PhD(dairy sci), 60. *Prof Exp:* Asst prof dairy sci, Univ Fla, 59-60; food technologist, Gen Foods Corp, 60-62; exten specialist dairy tech, Ohio State Univ, 62-63; assoc res specialist dairy sci, 63-80, PROF FOOD SCI, RUTGERS UNIV, NEW BRUNSWICK, 80- *Mem:* Am Dairy Sci Asn; Inst Food Technol. *Res:* Chemistry of milk; freezing point studies; factors affecting chemical composition; analytical methods for estimating phosphatase activity in milk; yogurt-digestibility and manufacture. *Mailing Add:* Dept of Food Sci Rutgers Univ New Brunswick NJ 08903

KLIBANOV, ALEXANDER M, b Moscow, USSR, July 15, 49; US citizen; m 72; c 1. APPLIED ENZYMOLOGY, BIOTECHNOLOGY. *Educ:* Moscow Univ, MS, 71, PhD(chem enzym), 74. *Prof Exp:* Res chemist, Moscow Univ, 74-77; res assoc, Univ Calif, San Diego, 78-79; ASST PROF APPL BIOCHEM & HENRY L DOHERTY PROF, MASS INST TECHNOL, 79- *Mem:* Am Chem Soc; Am Soc Microbiol. *Res:* Mechanisms of enzyme inactivation; stabilization of enzymes; immobilized enzymes and cells; enzymes as catalysts in organic syntheses; enzymes for energy conversion and storage; enzymes for waste water treatment. *Mailing Add:* Rm 16-209 Mass Inst Technol Cambridge MA 02139

KLICK, CLIFFORD C, b Strausstown, Pa, Aug 31, 18; m 47; c 6. SOLID STATE PHYSICS. *Educ:* Muhlenberg Col, AB, 39; Harvard Univ, MA, 47; Carnegie Inst Technol, ScD(physics), 49. *Prof Exp:* Asst elec eng, Mass Inst Technol, 41-42; assoc physicist, Radiation Lab, Johns Hopkins Univ, 42-45; physicist, Naval Res Lab, 49-52, head luminescent mat sect, 53-67, supt mat sci div, 67-77; mem staff, Off Naval Res, London, 77-79; RETIRED. *Concurrent Pos:* Consult, US Army, 45. *Mem:* Fel Am Phys Soc; Sigma Xi. *Res:* Color centers and luminescent centers in solids. *Mailing Add:* 5355 Nevada Ave NW Washington DC 20015

KLICKA, JOHN KENNETH, b Chicago, Ill, Dec 9, 33; m 54; c 7. COMPARATIVE ENDOCRINOLOGY, CHEMICAL CARCINOGENESIS. *Educ:* Northern Ill Univ, BS, 57, MS, 58; Univ Ill, Urbana, PhD(physiol, endocrinol), 62. *Prof Exp:* From instr to prof physiol & biochem, Wis State Univ, Oshkosh, 62-79; RES ASSOC, VET ADMIN HOSP, UNIV MINN, 79- *Concurrent Pos:* NIH training prog fel, Med Sch, Univ Minn, 65-67; career develop award environ toxicol, Nat Inst Environ Health Sci, NIH, 81-84. *Mem:* AAAS; Am Soc Zool; Am Physiol Soc; NY Acad Sci; Sigma Xi. *Res:* Mechanism by which estrogens act to induce renal tumors in Syrian golden hamsters. *Mailing Add:* 15017 Stevens Ave S Burnsville MN 55337

KLIEFORTH, HAROLD ERNEST, b San Francisco, Calif, July 6, 27; m 54; c 2. METEOROLOGY. *Educ:* Univ Calif, Los Angeles, BA, 49, MA, 51. *Prof Exp:* Res meteorologist, Univ Calif, Los Angeles, 51-56; field dir flight group meteorol, Air Force Cambridge Res Labs, Edwards Air Force Base, Calif, 58-61, chief, Exp Meteorol Br, 61-65; RES PROF ATMOSPHERIC SCI, DESERT RES INST, UNIV NEV, RENO, 65- *Honors & Awards:* Paul Tuntland Mem Res Award, Soaring Soc Am, 54. *Mem:* AAAS; Am Meteorol Soc; Royal Meteorol Soc. *Res:* Mountain meteorology; air flow over mountains; mountain lee waves; meso-scale meteorology; synoptic meteorology and climatology; severe storms; snow water resources; macrophysics of clouds. *Mailing Add:* Desert Res Inst Univ of Nev Syst PO Box 60220 Reno NV 89506

KLIEGER, PAUL, b Milwaukee, Wis, Oct 26, 16; m 42; c 1. CIVIL ENGINEERING. *Educ:* Univ Wis, BS, 39. *Prof Exp:* Mat inspector & state engr, Wis, 39; engr farm planning, Soil Conserv Serv, 39-41; sr res engr, 41-60, mgr field res sect, 60-63 & concrete res sect, 63-71, DIR CONCRETE MAT RES DEPT, PORTLAND CEMENT ASN, 71- *Concurrent Pos:* Mem, Hwy Res Bd & US Comt on Large Dams. *Honors & Awards:* Award of Merit, Am Soc Testing & Mat, 75, Frank Richart Award, 77. *Mem:* Am Soc Testing & Mat; Am Concrete Inst. *Res:* Cement and concrete. *Mailing Add:* 2050 Valencia Dr Northbrook IL 60062

KLIEJUNAS, JOHN THOMAS, b Sheboygan, Wis, May 4, 43; m 68; c 1. PLANT PATHOLOGY. *Educ:* Univ Wis-Stevens Point, BS, 65; Univ Minn, MF, 67; Univ Wis-Madison, PhD(plant path), 71. *Prof Exp:* Fel plant path, Univ Wis-Madison, 71-72; jr plant pathologist, Univ Hawaii, Hilo, 72-75, asst plant pathologist, 75-79; PLANT PATHOLOGIST PAC SOUTHWEST REGION, US FOREST SERV, 79- *Mem:* Am Phytopath Soc; Mycol Soc Am; Soc Am Foresters. *Res:* Epidemiology and control of forest nursery disease and other diseases of Californian and Hawaiian forest trees. *Mailing Add:* Forest Pest Mgt 630 Sansome St San Francisco CA 94111

KLIEM, PETER O, b Berlin, Ger, May 13, 38; US citizen; m 62; c 1. ANALYTICAL CHEMISTRY, PHOTOGRAPHIC CHEMISTRY. *Educ:* Bates Col, BS, 60; Northeastern Univ, MS, 65. *Prof Exp:* Asst scientist to sr scientist, 60-66, dept mgr to sr develop mgr, 66-75, div vpres negative res & develop, 75-77, asst corp vpres res, 77-80, VPRES RES, POLAROID CORP, 80- *Mem:* Am Chem Soc; Soc Photog Sci & Eng; Indust Res Inst. *Res:* Photographic research and development. *Mailing Add:* Polaroid Corp 1265 Main St Waltham MA 02154

KLIER, KAMIL, b Prague, Czech, Mar 21, 32; m 61; c 2. PHYSICAL CHEMISTRY. *Educ:* Charles Univ, Prague, dipl chem, 54; Czech Acad Sci, CSc(phys chem), 61. *Prof Exp:* Res fel surface phys chem, Inst Phys Chem, Czech Acad Sci, 54-57, asst, 57-61, res scientist, 61-67; vis prof physics & chem of solids & surfaces, 67-68, res assoc prof, 68-73, PROF CHEM, LEHIGH UNIV, 73-, DIR, CATALYSIS LAB, 75-, ASSOC DIR, CTR SURFACE RES, 78- *Concurrent Pos:* Int Atomic Energy Agency fel radiation chem surfaces, Wantage Res Labs, Eng, 59-60; consult catalysis, spectros & separation processes. *Mem:* Am Chem Soc; Sigma Xi. *Res:* Physics and chemistry of solids; surface chemistry; chemisorption; catalysis. *Mailing Add:* Dept of Chem Lehigh Univ Bethlehem PA 18015

KLIEWER, JOHN WALLACE, b Lanigan, Sask, Jan 20, 24; US citizen; m 54; c 4. MEDICAL ENTOMOLOGY. *Educ:* Bethel Col, Kans, BA, 50; Univ Utah, MS, 52; Univ Kans, PhD(entom), 62. *Prof Exp:* Asst prof biol sci, Bethel Col, Kans, 53-56; sr vector control specialist & proj leader, Calif State Dept Pub Health, 60-67; proj officer, Aedes Aegypti Eradication Prog, USPHS, 67-69, sr res entomologist, Malaria Prog, Ctr Dis Control, 69-72; PROJ OFFICER, PESTICIDE PROG, ENVIRON PROTECTION AGENCY, 72- *Concurrent Pos:* Consult, WHO, 66-; adj prof prev med, Med Univ SC. *Mem:* AAAS; Entom Soc Am; Am Mosquito Control Asn; NY Acad Sci. *Res:* Ecology and behavior of insects, mites and ticks. *Mailing Add:* Epidemiol Studies Prog Med Univ SC Charleston SC 29403

KLIEWER, KENNETH L, b Mountain Lake, Minn, Dec 31, 35; m 59; c 3. THEORETICAL SOLID STATE PHYSICS. *Educ:* Univ Minn, BS, 57, MS, 59; Univ Ill, PhD(physics), 64. *Prof Exp:* From asst prof to assoc prof, Iowa State Univ, 63-69, prof physics, 69-81; ASSOC DIR PHYS RES, ARGONNE NAT LAB, 81- *Concurrent Pos:* Guest prof, Univ Hamburg, Ger, 72-73; Free Univ, Berlin, 74 & Fritz-Haber Inst, Berlin, 75; sr physicist, Ames Lab, US Dept Energy, 69-81, asst prof dir solid state physics, 74-78, assoc dir sci & technol, 78-81, mem staff, Mat Sci Div, Off Energy Res, 79-80; vis scientist, Rockwell Int Sci Ctr, 76. *Mem:* Am Phys Soc; AAAS; Am Asn Univ Professors. *Res:* Optical properties of solids, particularly metals; lattice dynamics; surface physics; photoemission. *Mailing Add:* Argonne Nat Lab 9700 S Capitol Ave Argonne IL 60439

KLIEWER, WALTER MARK, b Escondido, Calif, Dec 10, 33; m 62; c 1. BIOCHEMISTRY, PLANT PHYSIOLOGY. *Educ:* Calif State Polytech Col, BS, 55; Cornell Univ, MS, 58, PhD(agron), 61. *Prof Exp:* Scientist, Soil Conserv Serv, USDA, 55; fel, Ore State Univ, 61-63; asst biochemist, 63-68, assoc biochemist, 68-74, BIOCHEMIST, UNIV CALIF, DAVIS, 74- *Mem:* Am Soc Plant Physiol; Am Soc Enol; Am Soc Hort Sci. *Res:* Effect of environment on fruit quality and growth and development of grapevines; organic acid, amino acid and carbohydrate metabolism of grapevines; translocation; photosynthesis; plant growth regulators; fruit coloration; mineral nutrition. *Mailing Add:* Dept of Vicicult & Enol Univ of Calif Davis CA 95616

KLIGER, DAVID SAUL, b Newark, NJ, Nov 3, 43; m 79. PHYSICAL CHEMISTRY. *Educ:* Rutgers Univ, BS, 65; Cornell Univ, PhD(phys chem), 70. *Prof Exp:* NIH res fel phys chem, Harvard Univ, 70-71; ASSOC PROF PHYS CHEM, UNIV CALIF, SANTA CRUZ, 71- *Concurrent Pos:* Petro Res Fund-Am Chem Soc res grant, Univ Calif, Santa Cruz, 71-74; NIH res grant, 73; NSF res grant, 76- *Mem:* NY Acad Sci; Am Soc Photobiol. *Res:* Molecular spectroscopy of electronically excited states; spectroscopic studies of visual pigments. *Mailing Add:* Div of Natural Sci II Univ of Calif Santa Cruz CA 95064

KLIGERMAN, MORTON M, b Philadelphia, Pa, Dec 26, 17; m 56; c 3. RADIOTHERAPY. *Educ:* Temple Univ, BS, 38, MD, 41, MSc, 48; Am Bd Radiol, dipl, 46. *Hon Degrees:* MA, Yale Univ, 58. *Prof Exp:* Instr radiol, Temple Univ, 47-48; from instr to assoc prof, Col Physicians & Surgeons, Columbia Univ, 48-58; prof & chmn dept, Sch Med, Yale Univ, 58-72, Robert E Hunter prof radiol, 58-72; PROF RADIOL & DIR CANCER RES CTR, SCH MED, UNIV N MEX, 72-, ASST DIR RADIOTHER, LOS ALAMOS SCI LAB, 72- *Concurrent Pos:* Asst & asst attend radiologist, Presby Hosp, 48-56, attend radiologist, 56-58; radiologist-in-chief, Yale-New Haven Hosp, 58-72. *Mem:* Am Asn Cancer Res; Am Cancer Soc; Am Col Radiol; Am Soc Therapeut Radiol (pres, 68-69); Asn Univ Radiol (pres, 67-68). *Res:* Applied radiation techniques; clinical cancer research in combined chemotherapy and radiotherapy and in preoperative irradiation; animal experimental radiotherapy; heavy particle irradiation; radiation sensitization in cell systems. *Mailing Add:* Dept Radiol Univ NMex 620 Camino de Salud NE Albuquerque NM 87131

KLIGMAN, ALBERT MONTGOMERY, b Philadelphia, Pa, Mar 17, 16; m 42; c 3. DERMATOLOGY. *Educ:* Pa State Univ, BS, 39; Univ Pa, PhD(bot), 42, MD, 47; Am Bd Dermat & Syphilol, dipl, 51. *Prof Exp:* Dir res, J B Swayne Co, Pa, 39-44; intern, N Div, Albert Einstein Med Ctr, 47-48; resident dermat, Univ Hosp, 48-51, prof, Div Grad Med, Hosp Univ Pa, 58-72, from instr to assoc prof, 48-57, PROF DERMAT, SCH MED, UNIV PA, 57- *Mem:* AAAS; Soc Invest Dermat; Soc Exp Biol & Med; AMA; Am Acad Dermat. *Res:* Medical mycology; dermatologic allergy. *Mailing Add:* Duhiring Lab Rm 244 Univ Pa 36th & Hamilton Walk Philadelphia PA 19104

KLIGMAN, RONALD LEE, b Philadelphia, Pa, Aug 20, 40; m 68; c 2. STATISTICAL MECHANICS, ACOUSTICS. *Educ:* Temple Univ, BA, 62; Am Univ, MS, 67, PhD(physics), 68. *Prof Exp:* Asst prof physics, Sweetbriar Col, 68-69; physicist acoustics, Naval Ship Res & Develop Ctr, 69-71; asst prof physics, Robert Col, 71-72; RES PHYSICIST STATIST MECH & ACOUSTICS, NAVAL SURFACE WEAPONS CTR, 72- *Mem:* Am Phys Soc. *Res:* Statistical mechanics applied to phase transitions in solids; transport theory in ionized media; wave propagation and scattering, acoustic and electromagnetic. *Mailing Add:* 1394 Canterbury Way Rockville MD 20854

KLIJANOWICZ, JAMES EDWARD, b Baltimore, Md, Sept 24, 44; m 75; c 1. ORGANIC CHEMISTRY. *Educ:* Loyola Col, Md, BS, 66; Carnegie-Mellon Univ, MS, 69, PhD(org chem), 71. *Prof Exp:* Sr res chemist, 70-78, res lab head, Chemiphotog Systs Lab, 78-81, RES LAB HEAD, PHOTOG MECHANISMS LAB, EASTMAN KODAK CO, 81- *Mem:* AAAS; Am Chem Soc. *Res:* Mechanisms of photographic chemical reactions. *Mailing Add:* Eastman Kodak Co Kodak Park Bldg 82A Rochester NY 14650

KLIMAN, ALLAN, b Boston, Mass, Dec 20, 33; m 56; c 2. INTERNAL MEDICINE. *Educ:* Harvard Univ, AB, 54, MD, 58. *Prof Exp:* Res assoc org chem, Harvard Univ, 53-54, res assoc endocrinol, 55; intern, Beth Israel Hosp, 58-59; chief, Clin Ctr Blood Bank, NIH, 59-61; instr, 61-71, ASST CLIN PROF MED, HARVARD MED SCH, 71-; CHIEF HEMAT-ONCOL DEPT, MASS REHAB HOSP, 74- *Concurrent Pos:* Mem, Red Cross Blood Prog, 64-74; clin assoc med, Mass Gen Hosp. *Mem:* Am Fedn Clin Res; Am Soc Hemat. *Res:* Hematology; blood transfusion; serum hepatitis; automation of laboratory procedures; plasmapheresis; cancer chemotherapy; clinical pharmacology. *Mailing Add:* 125 Nashua St Boston MA 02114

KLIMAN, GERALD BURT, b Boston, Mass, July 28, 31; m 60; c 1. ELECTRICAL ENGINEERING. *Educ:* Mass Inst Technol, SB, 55, SM, 59, ScD(elec eng), 65. *Prof Exp:* Teaching asst elec eng, Mass Inst Technol, 57-61, instr, 61-65; asst prof, Rensselaer Polytech Inst, 65-71; electromagnetic engr advan propulsion equip prog, Transp Technol Ctr, 71-75, prin engr, Fast Breeder Reactor Dept, 75-77, ELEC ENGR, CORP RES & DEVELOP, GEN ELEC CO, 77- *Mem:* Inst Elec & Electronics Engrs; Am Phys Soc. *Res:* Magnetohydrodynamics; Alfven waves in wave guides with non uniform magnetic fields; flow in pipes; electromagnetic pumps; electrical machines and materials. *Mailing Add:* Corp Res & Develop Gen Elec Co Schenectady NY 12301

KLIMAN, HARVEY LOUIS, b Boston, Mass, May 28, 42; m 66. PHYSICAL CHEMISTRY, POLYMER PHYSICS. *Educ:* Boston Univ, AB, 63; Princeton Univ, MA, 66, PhD(phys chem), 70. *Prof Exp:* SR RES CHEMIST POLYMER CHEM & PHYSICS, TEXTILE FIBERS DEPT, TEXTILE RES LAB, E I DU PONT DE NEMOURS & CO, INC, 69- *Mem:* AAAS; Am Chem Soc. *Res:* High pressure physical chemistry of solutions; hydrophobic interactions in biochemical macromolecules; physical chemistry and physics of fiber forming polymers; textile yarn process engineering; computer modelling. *Mailing Add:* E I du Pont de Nemours & Co Inc RD 2 Box 48H Chadds Ford PA 19317

KLIMCZAK, WALTER JOHN, b New Haven, Conn, Nov 17, 16; m 54; c 5. MATHEMATICS. *Educ:* Yale Univ, PhD(math), 48. *Prof Exp:* Instr, Yale Univ, 43-47; instr & asst prof math, Univ Rochester, 47-51; from asst prof to prof, 51-74, SEABURY PROF MATH & NATURAL PHILOS, TRINITY COL, CONN, 74- *Mem:* Am Math Soc; Math Asn Am. *Res:* Differential operators of infinite order. *Mailing Add:* Dept of Math Trinity Col Hartford CT 06106

KLIMISCH, RICHARD L, b Yankton, SDak, Jan 1, 38; m 62; c 2. CATALYSIS, ENVIRONMENTAL HEALTH. *Educ:* Loras Col, BS, 60; Purdue Univ, PhD(org chem), 64. *Prof Exp:* Res chemist, Explosives Dept, Exp Sta, E I du Pont de Nemours & Co, Inc, 64-67; sr res chemist, 67-71, supvry res chemist, Fuels & Lubrication Dept, 71-73, asst dept head, Phys Chem Dept, 73-75, DEPT HEAD, ENVIRON SCI DEPT, GEN MOTORS RES LABS, 75- *Mem:* Am Chem Soc; Sigma Xi. *Res:* Catalysis; air pollution; surface chemistry; atmospheric chemistry. *Mailing Add:* Environ Sci Dept GM Res Labs 12 Mile & Mound Rds Warren MI 48090

KLIMKO, EUGENE M, b Youngstown, Ohio, Mar 13, 39. MATHEMATICS. *Educ:* Ohio State Univ, BS, 61, MS, 64, PhD(math), 67. *Prof Exp:* Sr res eng, NAm Aviation, Inc, 62-65; asst prof math, 67-75; MEM FAC, DEPT PROBABILITY & STATIST, STATE UNIV NY BINGHAMTON, 75- *Mem:* Am Math Soc; Inst Math Statist. *Res:* Application of ratio ergodic theorems to Glivenko-Cantelli theorem and to convergence of information ratios. *Mailing Add:* Dept of Math Sci State Univ NY Binghamton NY 13901

KLIMPEL, RICHARD ROBERT, b Billings, Mont, Sept 23, 39; m 58; c 2. MINERAL PROCESSING, ENGINEERING MATHEMATICS. *Educ:* NDak State Univ, BS, 61, MS, 62; Pa State Univ, PhD(mat sci), 64. *Prof Exp:* Teaching asst math, NDak State Univ, 61-62; res assoc fuel sci, Pa State Univ, 62-64; res mgr math, 64-77; SCIENTIST ENG, DOW CHEM CO, 77- *Concurrent Pos:* Lectr math, Saginaw Valley State Col, 65-75; adj prof mineral eng, Pa State Univ, 78- *Mem:* Sigma Xi; Am Inst Mining Engrs; Am Inst Chem Engrs; Am Chem Soc. *Res:* Mining chemicals; math modeling of engineering processes; operations research; engineering research in grinding, flotation, solids separation and other related particulate handling processes. *Mailing Add:* 1776 Bldg Dow Chem Co Midland MI 48640

KLIMSTRA, PAUL D, b Erie, Ill, Aug 25, 33; m 57; c 2. MEDICINAL CHEMISTRY. *Educ:* Augustana Col, BA, 55; Univ Iowa, MS, 57, PhD, 59. *Prof Exp:* Res chemist, 59-70, from asst dir to dir chem res, 70-73, dir preclin res & develop, 73-74, VPRES NORTH AM PRECLIN RES & DEVELOP, G D SEARLE & CO, 74- *Concurrent Pos:* Mem, Intra-Sci Res Found & Indust Res Inst. *Mem:* Sigma Xi; Am Pharmaceut Asn; NY Acad Sci; Am Soc Pharmacol & Exp Therapeut; Pharmaceut Mfrs Asn. *Res:* Steroids; heterocyclics. *Mailing Add:* G D Searle & Co 4901 Searle Pkwy Skokie IL 60077

KLIMSTRA, WILLARD DAVID, b Erie, Ill, Dec 25, 19; m 42; c 3. WILDLIFE MANAGEMENT, VERTEBRATE ECOLOGY. *Educ:* Blackburn Col, BA, 39; Maryville Col, BA, 41; Iowa State Univ, MS, 48, PhD(econ zool), 49. *Prof Exp:* Student work mgr, Blackburn Col, 38-39; asst instr bot, Univ NC, 41-42, lectr, Sch Pub Health, 42; foreman consol, Nat Munitions Corp, 42-45; asst coop wildlife res unit, Iowa State Univ, 46-47, res assoc, 47-49; from asst prof to assoc prof, 49-59, actg dir, Coal Utilization & Res Ctr, 76-77, PROF ZOOL, SOUTHERN ILL UNIV, CARBONDALE, 59-, DIR COOP WILDLIFE RES LAB, 51-, DIR GRAD STUDIES IN ZOOL, 73- *Concurrent Pos:* Wildlife consult, Ill Natural Hist Surv, 52 & Nat Pest Control Asn. *Honors & Awards:* Kaplan ResAward, Sigma Xi. *Mem:* Fel AAAS; Am Soc Zool; Wildlife Soc (pres, 73-74); hon mem Nat Pest Control Asn; NY Acad Sci. *Res:* Life history, ecology and management of vertebrates; ecology of disturbed lands by mineral extraction. *Mailing Add:* Coop Wildlife Res Lab Southern Ill Univ Carbondale IL 62901

KLINCK, HAROLD RUTHERFORD, b Gormley, Ont, Sept 24, 22; m 51; c 5. AGRONOMY, PLANT BREEDING. *Educ:* Ont Agr Col, BSA, 50; McGill Univ, MSc, 52, PhD, 55. *Prof Exp:* Lectr, 54-56, from asst prof to assoc prof, 56-71, PROF AGRON, MACDONALD COL, MCGILL UNIV, 71- *Mem:* Am Soc Agron; Can Soc Agron (secy-treas, 55-58, pres elect, 65-66, pres, 66-67); fel Agr Inst Can. *Res:* Oat and barley breeding. *Mailing Add:* Dept Plant Sci Macdonald Col McGill Univ 21111 Lakeshore Rd Ste Anne de Bellevue PQ H9X 1C0 Can

KLINCK, ROSS EDWARD, b Kitchener, Ont, Dec 1, 38; m 63; c 1. PHYSICAL CHEMISTRY. *Educ:* Univ Western Ont, BSc, 60, PhD(chem), 65. *Prof Exp:* Res assoc physics, Duke Univ, 64-66; asst prof chem, Univ Conn, 66-71; assoc prof chem, Urbana Col, 71-76, coordr sci, 74-76; ASSOC PROF CHEM, ADIRONDACK COMMUNITY COL, 76-, CHMN SCI DIV, 78-, PROF CHEM, 79- *Mem:* Am Chem Soc; Am Phys Soc; Chem Inst Can. *Res:* High resolution nuclear magnetic resonance spectroscopy related to conformational studies and barriers to rotation; electron paramagnetic resonance of organic single crystals. *Mailing Add:* Adirondack Community Col Glens Falls NY 12801

KLINE, BERRY JAMES, b Mont Alto, Pa, Jan 9, 41; m 63; c 2. PHARMACEUTICAL CHEMISTRY. *Educ:* Philadelphia Col Pharm, BS, 62; Temple Univ, MS, 65; Univ Wis, PhD(pharm), 68. *Prof Exp:* Sr analyst, Vick Divisions Res Div, Richardson-Merrell, Inc, 68-69; Sr scientist, Ciba Pharmaceut Co, 69-72, sr staff scientist, CIBA-Geigy Pharmaceut, 72-76; ASSOC PROF & DIR, ANAL SERV, SCH PHARM, MED COL VA, 76- *Mem:* Am Pharmaceut Asn; Acad Pharmaceut Sci; Am Chem Soc; fel Am Found Pharmaceut Educ. *Res:* Homogeneous solution kinetics; complexation interactions; pharmaceutical analysis, especially gas and high performance liquid chromatography. *Mailing Add:* Med Col of Va Box 581 MCV Sta Richmond VA 23298

KLINE, BRUCE CLAYTON, b Grand Rapids, Mich, June 22, 37; m 63; c 1. MOLECULAR BIOLOGY, MICROBIOLOGY. *Educ:* Aquinas Col, BS, 59; Mich State Univ, MS, 66, PhD(microbiol), 68. *Prof Exp:* Microbiologist, Mich Dept Health, 60-63; instr microbial genetics, Mich State Univ, 68; asst prof biochem, Univ Tenn, Knoxville, 71-75; CONSULT, DEPT CELL BIOL, MAYO CLIN, ROCHESTER, MINN, 75-, PROF, 76-; ASSOC PROF MICROBIOL, UNIV MINN, 80- *Concurrent Pos:* NIH fel, Univ Calif, San Diego, 68-70. *Mem:* Am Soc Microbiol; fel Am Acad Microbiol. *Res:* Mechanism and control of DNA duplication in procaryotic organisms. *Mailing Add:* Dept Cell Biol Guggenheim Bldg Mayo Clin Rochester MN 55901

KLINE, CHARLES HOWARD, b Pittsfield, Mass, Oct 22, 18; m; c 4. PHYSICAL CHEMISTRY. *Educ:* Princeton Univ, AB, 40, PhD(phys chem), 44. *Prof Exp:* Supvr, Chem & Metall Prog, Chem Div, Gen Elec Co, 46-49, mgr prod planning, 49-52; mgr chem develop div, Climax Molybdenum Co, 52-56; sci dir, Shulton, Inc, 56-59; PRES, CHARLES H KLINE & CO, Inc, 59- *Concurrent Pos:* Dir, Rosario Resources Corp, 68-80. *Mem:* Am Inst Mining, Metall & Petrol Engrs; Am Chem Soc; Soc Chem Indust; Com Develop Asn; Chem Mkt Res Asn. *Res:* Applications and marketing of chemicals and minerals. *Mailing Add:* Charles H Kline & Co 330 Passaic Ave Fairfield NJ 07006

KLINE, DANIEL LOUIS, b Philadelphia, Pa, Dec 25, 17; m 45; c 3. PHYSIOLOGY. *Educ:* Purdue Univ, BS, 42; Columbia Univ, PhD(physiol), 46. *Prof Exp:* Instr physiol, Col Physicians & Surgeons, Columbia Univ, 45; instr, Long Island Col Med, 46-47; Nat Res Coun fel physiol chem, Sch Med, Yale Univ, 47-49, asst prof, 49-52, from asst prof to assoc prof physiol, 52-66; PROF PHYSIOL & CHMN DEPT, COL MED, UNIV CINCINNATI, 66- *Concurrent Pos:* Guggenheim fel, 58-59. *Honors & Awards:* Harold Lamport Award, NY Acad Sci, 79. *Mem:* AAAS; Sigma Xi; Soc Exp Biol & Med; Int Soc Thrombosis & Haemostasis; Am Physiol Soc. *Res:* Purification of plasminogen and plasmin; mechanism of activation. *Mailing Add:* Dept of Physiol Univ of Cincinnati Col of Med Cincinnati OH 45267

KLINE, DAVID G, b Philadelphia, Pa, Oct 13, 34; m 58; c 3. NEUROSURGERY. *Educ:* Univ Pa, AB, 56, MD, 60. *Prof Exp:* From intern to resident surg, Univ Mich, Ann Arbor, 60-62; res investr neurosurg, Walter Reed Gen Hosp & Inst Res, 62-64; teaching assoc, Univ Mich & res investr, Kresge Neurosurg Labs, 64-67; instr surg & neurosurg, 67-68, asst prof neurosurg, 68-70, assoc prof surg & neurosurg, 70-71, assoc prof neurosurg, 71-73, prof surg & neurosurg, 73-76, chmn div, 71-76, PROF NEUROSURG & CHMN DEPT, SCH MED, LA STATE UNIV, NEW ORLEANS, 76- *Concurrent Pos:* Vis investr, Delta Regional Primate Ctr, 67-; vis surgeon, Charity Hosp, New Orleans, 67-; mem staff, Southern Baptist Hosp, Hotel Dieu, Touro Infirmary & Ochsner Clin & Found, 67-; consult, Keesler AFB, 69-, USPHS Hosp, 71- & Vet Admin Hosp, 74; secy, Am Bd Neurol Surg. *Honors & Awards:* Frederick A Coller Award, Am Col Surgeons, 67. *Mem:* Cong Neurol Surg; Asn Acad Surg; Am Asn Neurol Surg; Soc Univ Surgeons; Res Soc Neurosurgeons. *Res:* Peripheral nerve injuries and their repair; computer utilization for neurosurgical research; hepatic encephalopathy. *Mailing Add:* Dept of Surg Div of Neurosurg La State Univ Med Ctr New Orleans LA 70112

KLINE, DONALD EDGAR, b DuBois, Pa, Aug 28, 28; m 49; c 3. PHYSICS. *Educ:* Pa State Univ, BS, 51, MS, 53, PhD(physics), 55. *Prof Exp:* Instr eng mech, Pa State Univ, 54-55, asst prof physics, 55-56, vis physicist, Nuclear Reactor Facility, 56-57; staff res physicist, HRB-Singer, Inc, 57-61; from assoc prof to prof nuclear eng, 61-68, PROF MAT SCI, PA STATE UNIV, 68- *Concurrent Pos:* Consult, Jet Propulsion Lab, Calif Inst Technol, NASA, HRB-Singer, Inc, Avco Corp, Pfaudler & Hershey Med Ctr. *Mem:* Am Phys Soc; Am Nuclear Soc; Am Soc Eng Educ. *Res:* Radiation effects; dosimetry; polymer physics; polymer concrete, wood, biomaterials. *Mailing Add:* 107 Walker Bldg Pa State Univ University Park PA 16802

KLINE, EDWARD SAMUEL, b Philadelphia, Pa, June 26, 24; m 50; c 2. BIOCHEMISTRY. *Educ:* Univ Pa, AB, 48; George Washington Univ, MS, 55, PhD(biochem), 61. *Prof Exp:* Clin bacteriologist, Grad Hosp, Univ Pa, 50-51; chemist, Publicker Indust, Inc, 51-52; bacteriologist, Ft Detrick, 52-54; bacteriologist, Walter Reed Army Inst Res, 54-57; biochemist, Armed Forces Inst Path, 57-61; fel, Dept Chem, Ind Univ, 61-63; asst prof, 63-68, ASSOC PROF BIOCHEM, MED COL VA, VA COMMONWEALTH UNIV, 68- *Mem:* AAAS; Sigma Xi. *Res:* Metabolic control mechanisms; metabolic effects of alcohol. *Mailing Add:* Dept of Biochem Med Col of Va Richmond VA 23298

KLINE, EDWIN A, b Salina, Kans, Apr 29, 18; m 43; c 3. ANIMAL SCIENCE. *Educ:* Kans State Univ, BS, 42 & 43; Washington State Univ, MS, 48; Iowa State Univ, PhD(swine, nutrit), 53. *Prof Exp:* Instr meats, Kans State Univ, 42-43; 4-H Club agent, Sedgwick County, Kans, 43-44; cattle buyer & meat sales, Cudahy Packing Co, 44-45; instr animal sci, Washington State Univ, 45-48; PROF ANIMAL SCIENCE & FOOD TECHNOL, IOWA STATE UNIV, 48- *Mem:* Am Soc Animal Sci; Am Meat Sci Asn. *Res:* Effect of breeding, feeding and management on carcass composition of meat animals; teaching and research in the production of quality meat. *Mailing Add:* Dept Animal Sci Iowa State Univ Ames IA 50010

KLINE, FRANK MENEFEE, b Cumberland, Md, May 14, 28; m 53; c 2. PSYCHIATRY. *Educ:* Univ Md, BS, 50, MD, 52. *Prof Exp:* Intern med, Cincinnati Gen Hosp, 52-53; psychiat resident, Brentwood Vet Admin Hosp, Los Angeles, 55-58; consult, E Los Angeles Probation Off, 60-63; psychiat consult, Univ High Sch & Francis Blend Sch Blind, Los Angeles, 66-67; regional chief, West Cent Ment Health Serv, Los Angeles County, 67-68; assoc dir, Psychiat Outpatient Dept, Los Angeles County-Univ Southern Calif Med Ctr, 68-74; assoc prof psychiat, Sch Med, Univ Southern Calif, 74-78; CHIEF PSYCHIAT, LONG BEACH VET MED CTR, 77-; PROF PSYCHIAT & VCHMN DEPT, UNIV CALIF, IRVINE, 78- *Concurrent Pos:* Pvt pract, 58-; instr, Exten Div, Southern Calif Psychoanal Inst, 64-67, instr, Inst, 67-, mem exec coun, 70-71; pres bd trustees, Community Clin, Westwood Hosp, 66-67; fac mem, Los Angeles Ctr Group Psychother, 67-69. *Mem:* Fel Am Psychiat Asn. *Res:* Evaluation of psychotropic drugs; training of psychiatric residents and evaluation of the best methods for accomplishing this; group psychotherapy, particularly as a device for maintaining competence in practicing psychotherapists; historical evolution of psychoanalytic and psychodynamic theory. *Mailing Add:* Long Beach Vet Med Ctr 5910 E Seventh St Long Beach CA 90822

KLINE, GORDON MABEY, b Trenton, NJ, Feb 9, 03; m 26; c 1. PLASTICS CHEMISTRY, POLYMER CHEMISTRY. *Educ:* Colgate Univ, AB, 25; George Washington Univ, MS, 26; Univ Md, PhD(chem), 34. *Prof Exp:* Res chemist, State Dept Health, NY, 26-28 & Picatinny Arsenal, Dept of War, 28-29; chief plastics sect, Nat Bur Standards, 29-52, chief, Div Polymers, 52-63; consult, 64-69; SCI EDITOR, 69- *Concurrent Pos:* Tech ed, Mod Plastics, 36-; ed dir & consult, Mod Plastics Encycl, 36-60; chmn, Fed Specifications Plastics Tech Comt, 41-54; tech investr, US Army, Europe, 45; chmn tech comt plastics & US deleg, Int Orgn Standardization, var US & foreign countries, 51-78; hon secy, Plastics & High Polymers Sect, Int Union Pure & Appl Chem, 51-59, from vpres to pres, 59-67. *Honors & Awards:* Am Inst Chem Honor Award, 52; Gold Medal, Dept Com, 53; Am Soc Testing & Mat Award, 54; Rosa Award, Nat Bur Standards, 65; Plastics Hall of Fame, 73. *Mem:* Am Chem Soc; Am Soc Testing & Mat; Soc Plastics Eng; Soc Plastics Indust; fel Am Inst Chem. *Res:* Adhesives; polymers. *Mailing Add:* One North Golfview Apt 602 Lake Worth FL 33460

KLINE, IRA, b Plainfield, NJ, July 7, 24; m 45; c 2. CANCER. *Educ:* Am Univ, BS, 48; George Washington Univ, MS, 50, PhD, 57. *Prof Exp:* Biologist, Nat Cancer Inst, 48-57; head dept cancer chemother & res & develop, Microbiol Assocs, Inc, 57-65, asst dir, 65-75; expert consult, Nat Cancer Inst, 75-78, HEALTH SCI ADMINR, DIV RES GRANTS, NIH, 78- *Concurrent Pos:* Consult biologist, Microbiol Assocs, Inc, 55-57. *Mem:* Soc Exp Biol & Med; Am Asn Cancer Res; NY Acad Sci; Am Soc Pharmacol & Exp Therapeut. *Res:* Scientific responsibility of review of grants related to cancer experimental therapeutics. *Mailing Add:* Exp Therapeut Study Sect Div Res Grants NIH Bethesda MD 20205

KLINE, IRWIN KAVEN, b Canton, Ohio, Mar 18, 31; m 56; c 4. MEDICINE, PATHOLOGY. *Educ:* Columbia Univ, AB, 53; Western Reserve Univ, MD, 57; Am Bd Path, dipl, 62. *Prof Exp:* Intern, Mt Sinai Hosp, Cleveland, 57-58; resident path, Michael Reese Hosp, Chicago, 58-63, USPHS trainee, 60-63; instr, Univ Ill Col Med, 63-64; asst prof, Sch Med & assoc pathologist, Hosp, Boston Univ, 64-66; clin assoc path, Harvard Med Sch, 66-68; asst pathologist, Mass Gen Hosp, 68-69; clin assoc prof path, Sch Med, Temple Univ, 69-74, clin prof, 74-79; DIR PATH, LANKENAU HOSP, 69-; PROF PATH, JEFFERSON MED COL, THOMAS JEFFERSON UNIV, PA, 79- *Concurrent Pos:* Pathologist & chief anat path, Cambridge City Hosp, 66-68. *Mem:* Int Soc Lymphology; Col Am Pathologists; Am Soc Clin Path; Am Asn Path; fel Am Col Cardiologists. *Res:* Cardiac disease, principally infections and immunologic myocarditis and the effect of the obstructed cardiac lymphatics. *Mailing Add:* Dept of Path Lankenau Hosp City Line & Lancaster Ave Philadelphia PA 19151

KLINE, JACOB, b Boston, Mass, Aug 3, 17; m 57; c 3. BIOMEDICAL ENGINEERING. *Educ:* Mass Inst Technol, BSc, 42, MSc, 51; Iowa State Univ, PhD, 62. *Prof Exp:* Electronics engr, Int Tel & Tel Co, 42-46 & Continental TV & Electronic Co, 46-48; asst elec eng, Mass Inst Technol, 48-51, res engr, 51-52; from asst prof to assoc prof, Univ RI, 52-66; coordr biomed eng prog, 62-66, dir, Med Instrumentation Lab, 70-78, PROF BIOMED ENG & DIR DEPT, UNIV MIAMI, 66- *Concurrent Pos:* Consult, 48-; NASA-Am Soc Eng Educ fel, Stanford Univ & NASA Ames Res Ctr, 65, 66. *Mem:* Asn Advan Med Instrumentation; Inst Elec & Electronics Engrs; Am Soc Artificial Organs; NY Acad Sci; Sigma Xi. *Res:* Biomedical engineering and electronic instrumentation as applied to medical electronics; artificial hearts; patient safety problems. *Mailing Add:* Dept Biomed Eng Univ Miami Coral Gables FL 33124

KLINE, JAMES MARTIN, b Dayton, Ohio, Mar 4, 26; m 56; c 2. SOLID STATE PHYSICS. *Educ:* Univ Cincinnati, BSME, 49, MS, 51; Univ Ky, PhD(physics), 64. *Prof Exp:* Instr gunfire control, US Naval Officers Candidate Sch, 53; asst prof physics & astron, Univ Miss, 55-58; instr physics, Univ Ky, 60-61; assoc prof physics & astron, Murray State Univ, 64-66, prof, 66-79, chmn dept, 70-75 ; SUPVR DESIGN, TIDELAND SIGNAL CORP, 80- *Concurrent Pos:* Danforth assoc, 70-79. *Mem:* Am Asn Physics Teachers. *Res:* Astronomy in ancient America; optical and electrical properties of semiconductors. *Mailing Add:* Tideland Signal Corp 4310 Directors Row Houston TX 77092

KLINE, JENNIE KATHERINE, b Boston, Mass, Jan 15, 50. EPIDEMIOLOGY. *Educ:* Univ Chicago, BA, 72; Columbia Univ, MS, 74, PhD(epidemiol), 77. *Prof Exp:* SR RES SCIENTIST, NY STATE PSYCHIAT INST, 75- *Concurrent Pos:* Res assoc, Sch Pub Health, Columbia Univ, 77-; res assoc epidemiol, Gertrude H Sergievsky Ctr, Columbia Univ, 78- *Mem:* Soc Epidemiol Res; Int Epidemiol Asn. *Res:* Epidemiology of fetal defects and spontaneous abortions; mental retardation; cerebral palsy; epilepsy. *Mailing Add:* Gertrude H Sergievsky Ctr 630 W 168th St New York NY 10032

KLINE, JERRY ROBERT, b Minneapolis, Minn, May 20, 32; m 54; c 4. SOIL CHEMISTRY, ANALYTICAL CHEMISTRY. *Educ:* Univ Minn, BS, 57, MS, 60; Univ Minn, PhD(soil sci), 64. *Prof Exp:* Res assoc neutron activation appl to soils, Argonne Nat Lab, 64-65; assoc scientist, PR Nuclear Ctr, 65-66, dir terrestrial ecol proj, 66-68; ecologist, Radiol & Environ Res Div, Argonne Nat Lab, 68-74; sr land use analyst, US Nuclear Regulatory Comn, 74-76, sect leader, 76-80; ADMIN JUDGE, ATOMIC SAFETY & LICENSING BD, US NAT RES COUN, 80- *Concurrent Pos:* Adj prof, Univ Ill, Chicago Circle, 72-76. *Mem:* Soil Sci Soc Am; AAAS; Ecol Soc Am; Sigma Xi. *Res:* Terrestrial ecology; trace elements in environmental systems; water relationships in soil-plant systems. *Mailing Add:* 13624 Middlevale Lane Silver Spring MD 20906

KLINE, JOHN V(IRGIL), b Washington, DC, May 30, 20; m 41; c 2. SPECTROSCOPY. *Educ:* Oberlin Col, AB, 41; Purdue Univ, MS, 49, PhD(physics), 52. *Prof Exp:* Chemist, Beacon Res Lab, Tex Co, 41-46; asst, Purdue Univ, 46-50; asst prof physics, Univ Redlands, 51-52 & Colo Agr & Mech Col, 52-56; assoc prof, 56-66, PROF PHYSICS, COLO SCH MINES, 66- *Concurrent Pos:* Vis staff mem, Los Alamos Sci Lab. *Mem:* AAAS; Optical Soc Am; Inst Elec & Electronics Engrs; Am Asn Physics Teachers; Asn Comput Mach. *Res:* Determination of wavelengths and line structures in near infrared, minicomputers and interfacing to real-time instruments; computer analysis of instrument aberrations. *Mailing Add:* Dept of Physics Colo Sch of Mines Golden CO 80401

KLINE, KENNETH A(LAN), b Chicago, Ill, July 11, 39; m 60; c 4. ENGINEERING MECHANICS, MECHANICAL ENGINEERING. *Educ:* Univ Minn, BS, 61, PhD(eng mech), 65. *Prof Exp:* Sr res engr, Esso Prod Res Co, Standard Oil Co, NJ, 65-66; assoc prof, 66-73, PROF MECH ENG, WAYNE STATE UNIV, 73- *Concurrent Pos:* Prin investr, NSF res grants, 67-68, 69-71, 72-75, 76-78 & 80-82; sr US scientist award, Alexander von Humboldt-Stiftung, 72-73; coprin investr, Dept Energy res grant, 77-79. *Mem:* Soc Rheology; Soc Automotive Engrs; Am Soc Mech Engrs. *Res:* Computer-aided structural analysis; boundary integral method of structural analysis; optimal design; rheology of fluid suspensions. *Mailing Add:* Dept of Mech Eng Wayne State Univ Detroit MI 48202

KLINE, LARRY KEITH, b Buffalo, NY, Oct 20, 39; m 61; c 3. MOLECULAR BIOLOGY. *Educ:* Valparaiso Univ, BS, 61; Pa State Univ, MS, 65; State Univ NY Buffalo, PhD(biochem), 70. *Prof Exp:* Asst cancer res scientist, Roswell Park Mem Inst, 65-67; NIH fel, Yale Univ, 69-71; asst prof, 71-74, ASSOC PROF BIOL SCI, STATE UNIV NY COL BROCKPORT, 74- *Mem:* AAAS; Sigma Xi. *Res:* Nucleic acid biosynthesis and function in mammalian cells. *Mailing Add:* Dept Biol Sci State Univ NY Col Brockport NY 14420

KLINE, LEO V(IRGIL), b West Salem, Ohio, Feb 22, 29; m 50; c 2. ENGINEERING. *Educ:* Univ Akron, BME, 50; Ohio State Univ, MSc, 51, PhD(mech eng), 54. *Prof Exp:* Res assoc eng, Ohio State Res Found, 53-54; res engr, Redstone Arsenal, US Army, 54-56; from asst prof to assoc prof eng sci, Purdue Univ, 56-61; mgr explor eng, 61-65, mgr advan technol, 65-67, tech asst to vpres & group exec, 67-68, systs mgr, Publ Systs, 68-70, mgr Prod Components & Technol Systs Develop Div, 70-74, dir tech staff, Gen Prod Div, 74-77, mgr disk prod technol, Gen Prod Div Lab, 77-78, div dir oper, 78-80, DIR PROD & PROCESS ENG, CORP HQ, IBM CORP, 80- *Concurrent Pos:* Consult, Midwest Appl Sci Corp, 56, Gen Motors Corp, 57, IBM Corp, 59 & Gen Tech Corp, 59. *Mem:* Soc Eng Sci; fel Am Soc Mech Engrs; Am Soc Eng Educ. *Res:* Engineering sciences; continuum mechanics; stress analysis; systems analysis. *Mailing Add:* IBM Corp Old Orchard Rd 9 Val Armonk NY 10504

KLINE, MORRIS, b New York, NY, May 1, 08; m 39; c 3. APPLIED MATHEMATICS. *Educ:* NY Univ, BSc, 30, MSc, 32, PhD(math), 36. *Prof Exp:* Instr math, Wash Sq Col, NY Univ, 30-36; asst, Inst Adv Study, 36-38; instr math, NY Univ, 38-42; physicist & radio engr, Signal Corps Eng Labs, NJ, 42-45; from asst prof to prof, 45-76, dir, Div Electromagnetic Res, Courant Inst Math Sci, 46-66, chmn math dept, 59-70, EMER PROF MATH, WASH SQ COL, NY UNIV, 76- *Concurrent Pos:* Lectr, New Sch Soc Res, 39-40 & Hunter Col, 40-41; consult, Reeves Instrument Corp, NY, 45-56; vis prof, Stanford Univ, 58, 61 & 66; Fulbright lectr, Ger, 58-59; Guggenheim fel, 58-59; vis distinguished prof, Brooklyn Col, City Univ New York, 74-76; assoc ed, Arch Hist Exact Sci, 70- *Mem:* Am Math Soc; Math Asn Am; Inst Elec & Electronics Eng. *Res:* Topology; electromagnetic theory; ultrahigh frequency radio theory; pedagogy; history of mathematics. *Mailing Add:* 1024 E 26th St Brooklyn NY 11210

KLINE, NATHAN SCHELLENBERG, b Philadelphia, Pa, Mar 22, 16; div; c 1. PSYCHIATRY, PSYCHOPHARMACOLOGY. *Educ:* Swarthmore Col, BA, 38; NY Univ, MD, 43; Clark Univ, MA, 51. *Prof Exp:* Intern & resident, St Elizabeth's Hosp, Washington, DC, 43-44; mem staff, Vet Admin Hosp, Lyons, NJ, 46-50; dir res, Worcester State Hosp, Mass, 50-52; dir res, Rockland State Hosp, 52-75; DIR, ROCKLAND RES INST, 75- *Concurrent Pos:* Consult physician, Lenox Hill Hosp; assoc, Columbia Greystone Proj, 47-50 & NY State Brain Res Proj, 48-50; permanent vis prof psychiat, Univ Calif, San Mateo, 72-; clin prof psychiat, Col Physicians & Surgeons, Columbia Univ, 73-80; clin prof psychiat, New York Univ, 79- *Honors & Awards:* Adolf Meyer Award, Asn Improv Ment Health, 56; Albert Lasker Award, Am Pub Health Asn, 57 & Albert Lasker Clin Res Award, 64; Henry Wisner Miller Award, Manhattan Soc Ment Health; Comdr, Order Toussaint-Louverture & Grand Officer, Legion of Honor & Merit, Repub of Haiti, 59; Knight, Serenissimi Mil Order St Mary Glorious, 61; Knight Grand Comdr, Liberian Humane Order African Redemption, Repub of Liberia, 63. *Mem:* Fel AAAS; fel Am Psychiat Asn; Am Psychol Asn; Asn Res Nerv & Ment Dis; fel Am Col Physicians. *Res:* Psychopharmacol development and implementation of interdisciplinary models techniques for describing, predicting and controlling abnormal behavior, thought processes and effect. *Mailing Add:* Rockland Res Inst Orangeburg NY 10962

KLINE, ORAL LEE, b Reynolds, Ind, Sept 12, 05; m 29; c 3. BIOCHEMISTRY. *Educ:* Univ Wis, BS, 29, MS, 31, PhD(biochem, nutrit), 34. *Prof Exp:* Asst agr chem, Col Agr, Univ Wis, 29-36; biochemist, Food & Drug Admin, 36-47, dir nutrit res, 47-58, food div, 58-59, nutrit div, 59-62, asst comnr sci resources, 62-66; exec officer, 71-76, DIR OFF NUTRIT SCI SERV, AM INST NUTRIT, 66- *Concurrent Pos:* Vis prof, Mich State Univ, 63-66; mem, Nutrit Found Sci Adv & US Nat comts, Int Union Nutrit Sci, 64-69; mem chem codex comt, Nat Acad Sci, 65. *Honors & Awards:* Distinguished Serv Award, Dept Health, Educ & Welfare, 56; C A Elvehjem Award, Am Inst Nutrit, 71; exec officer, Nat Nutrition Consortium, 76-79. *Mem:* AAAS; Am Chem Soc; Soc Exp Biol & Med; Asn Off Anal Chem; Am Inst Nutrit (treas, 53, pres, 65). *Res:* Development of biochemical and biological methods for nutritionally important substances; human and animal nutritional requirements. *Mailing Add:* 9416 Holland Ct Bethesda MD 20814

KLINE, RALPH WILLARD, b Omaha, Nebr, Sept 23, 17; m 46; c 2. FOOD SCIENCE. *Educ:* Univ Omaha, AB, 39; Iowa State Univ, PhD(poultry prod technol), 45. *Prof Exp:* mem staff, Food Res Div, Armour & Co, 42-80; CONSULT, 80- *Mem:* Am Chem Soc; Poultry Sci Asn; Inst Food Technologists. *Res:* Technology of egg and poultry products. *Mailing Add:* 4940 E Laurel Lane Scottsdale AZ 85254

KLINE, RAYMOND MILTON, b St Louis, Mo, Feb 25, 29; m 51; c 4. ELECTRICAL ENGINEERING. *Educ:* Univ Mo-Rolla, BS, 51; Iowa State Univ, MS, 54; Purdue Univ, PhD(elec eng), 62. *Prof Exp:* Systs engr, Sperry Gyroscope Co, NY, 54-57; sr systs engr, Aircraft Div, McDonnell Aircraft Co, Mo, 57-59; instr elec eng, Purdue Univ, 59-62; from asst prof to assoc prof, 62-77, PROF ELEC ENG, WASH UNIV, 77- *Mem:* Inst Elec & Electronics Engrs; Am Soc Eng Educ; Asn Comput Mach. *Res:* Design and application of information processing systems including digital computers, switching theory, especially areas in the field of artificial intelligence, pattern recognition and learning machines; image processing. *Mailing Add:* Dept of Elec Eng Wash Univ St Louis MO 63130

KLINE, RICHARD HENRY, b Bernville, Pa, Sept 7, 23; m 49; c 3. ORGANIC CHEMISTRY. *Educ:* Franklin & Marshall Col, BS, 43; Univ Pittsburgh, PhD(org chem), 52. *Prof Exp:* Res chemist, Pittsburgh Coke & Chem Co, 52-54; sr res chemist, 54-73, RES SCIENTIST, GOODYEAR TIRE & RUBBER CO, 73- *Mem:* Am Chem Soc. *Res:* Organic synthesis; age resistors for rubbers and plastics; aging of polymers. *Mailing Add:* Res Div Goodyear Tire & Rubber Co Akron OH 44316

KLINE, RICHARD WILLIAM, b Philadelphia, Pa, Dec 33, 42. POLYMER RHEOLOGY, ENERGY ENGINEERING. *Educ:* Mass Inst Technol, SB, 64, SM, 65, PhD(chem eng), 70. *Prof Exp:* res engr, Milliken, Inc, 70-75; group leader, Lockwood Greene Engrs, 75-76; SR DEVELOP ENGR, CRYOVAC DIV, W R GRACE & CO, 76- *Concurrent Pos:* Consult, Am Hoechst, 78-79, Batchelder-Blasius, Inc, 77-81, City Landrum, 80. *Mem:* Am Inst Chem Engrs; Soc Plastics Engrs; Sigma Xi. *Res:* Simulation and modelling of plasticating extrusion, including extruder screws and dies; development of rheological theory. *Mailing Add:* 701 Ridgedale Dr Spartanburg SC 29301

KLINE, ROBERT JOSEPH, b Minocqua, Wis, Nov 6, 21; m 55; c 5. INORGANIC CHEMISTRY. *Educ:* Univ Wis, BS, 47, PhD(chem), 53. *Prof Exp:* From asst prof to assoc prof, 53-63, PROF INORG CHEM, OHIO UNIV, 63- *Mem:* Am Chem Soc. *Res:* Colloidal electrolytes; coordination compounds; actinide elements. *Mailing Add:* Dept of Chem Ohio Univ Athens OH 45701

KLINE, RONALD ALAN, b Wilkes-Barre, Pa, June 28, 52; m 81. ENGINEERING. *Educ:* Johns Hopkins Univ, BES, 74, MSE, 75, PhD(mech & mat sci), 78. *Prof Exp:* Res asst, Johns Hopkins Univ, 72-78; sr res scientist, Gen Dynamics Corp, 78-79; SR RES ENGR, GEN MOTORS RES LABS, 79- *Mem:* Adhesion Soc Am; Am Soc Nondestructive Testing. *Res:* Mechanical behavior of fiber reinforced composite materials and adhesively bonded composite joints. *Mailing Add:* Eng Mech Dept Gen Motors Res Labs Warren MI 48090

KLINE, STEPHEN JAY, b Los Angeles, Calif, Feb 25, 22; m 46; c 3. MECHANICAL ENGINEERING. *Educ:* Stanford Univ, BS, 43, MS, 49; Mass Inst Technol, ScD, 52. *Prof Exp:* Res analyst turbomach, Aerophys Lab, NAm Aviation, Inc, 46-48; asst mech eng, Stanford Univ, 48-50; from instr to asst prof, Mass Inst Technol, 50-52; from asst prof to assoc prof, Stanford 52-57, prof mech eng, 57-61, dir thermosci div, 61-73. *Concurrent Pos:* Consult, Gen Elec Co, 57- & Gen Motors Co, 57- *Honors*

& Awards: Melville Medal, Am Soc Mech Engrs, 59, Golden Eagle Award, 64, Bucraino Medal, 65, Fluids Eng Award, 75; George Stephenson Medal, Brit Inst Mech Engrs, 66. *Mem:* Nat Acad Eng; Am Soc Mech Engrs. *Res:* Internal flow; thermodynamics. *Mailing Add:* Dept of Mech Eng Rm 501-G Stanford Univ Stanford CA 94305

KLINE, TONI BETH, b Los Angeles, Calif, Aug 23, 50; m 76. INSECT ENDOCRINOLOGY, ORGANIC CHEMISTRY. *Educ:* Univ Calif, Berkeley, AB, 73; Univ Calif, San Francisco, MS, 76; Univ Ala, Birmingham, PhD(chem), 80. *Prof Exp:* Teaching asst org chem, Dept Pharmaceut Chem, Univ Calif, 74-76; teaching asst org chem, Dept Chem, Univ Ala, 76-78, teaching asst biochem, 78; res assoc, Dept Chem, Ore State Univ, 79-80; res assoc, Dept Chem, State Univ NY, 80-82; ASSOC PROF, DEPT PHARMACOL, MT SINAI MED SCH, 82- *Concurrent Pos:* Res asst, Univ Ala, 76-79. *Mem:* AAAS; Am Chem Soc. *Res:* Use of organic chemistry in investigating chamsims of drug actions and natural product synthesis; biogenesis, pharmacognosy and ecology; structure activity relationships of all biologically active compounds. *Mailing Add:* Dept Pharmacol Mt Sinai Sch Med Gustave Levy Pl New York NY 10029

KLINE, VIRGINIA MARCH, b Cleveland, Ohio, Jan 26, 26. PLANT ECOLOGY. *Educ:* Univ Wis, BS, 47, MS, 75, PhD(bot), 76. *Prof Exp:* STAFF ECOLOGIST, UNIV WIS ARBORETUM & LECTR BOT, UNIV WIS, 76- *Mem:* Am Inst Biol Sci; Ecol Soc Am; Sigma Xi. *Res:* Community ecology; prairie, temperate forest, wetland; relationship of climate and geology to vegetation; succession; management of natural vegetation. *Mailing Add:* 322 Birge Hall Bot Univ of Wis Madison WI 53706

KLINEDINST, KEITH ALLEN, b York, Pa, Nov 8, 44; m 74; c 2. PHYSICAL CHEMISTRY, MATERIALS SCIENCE. *Educ:* Franklin & Marshall Col, BA, 66; Stanford Univ, MS, 70, PhD(chem), 72. *Prof Exp:* Res assoc, Advan Fuel Cell Res Lab, Pratt & Whitney Aircraft, United Technol Corp, 72-76; MEM TECH STAFF LITHIUM BATTERY RES, GTE LABS INC, GEN TEL & ELECTRONICS CORP, 76- *Mem:* Sigma Xi; Am Chem Soc; Electrochem Soc. *Res:* Fuel cell electrochemistry; lithium batteries; heterogeneous catalysis; porous electrode research and development. *Mailing Add:* GTE Labs Inc 40 Sylvan Rd Waltham MA 02254

KLINEDINST, PAUL EDWARD, JR, b York, Pa, Dec 29, 33; m 67; c 2. ORGANIC CHEMISTRY. *Educ:* Lehigh Univ, BS, 55; Univ Calif, Los Angeles, PhD(chem), 59. *Prof Exp:* Fel chem, NSF, Harvard Univ, 59-60; from asst prof to assoc prof, 60-69, PROF CHEM, CALIF STATE UNIV, NORTHRIDGE, 69- *Mem:* Am Chem Soc; Sigma Xi. *Res:* Organic reaction mechanisms; salt effects and ion pairs in solvolysis and related reactions. *Mailing Add:* Dept of Chem Calif State Univ Northridge CA 91330

KLINEFELTER, HARRY FITCH, b Baltimore, Md, Mar 20, 12; m 44, 67; c 3. CLINICAL MEDICINE. *Educ:* Univ Va, BA, 33; Johns Hopkins Univ, MD, 37. *Prof Exp:* Asst med, Harvard Univ, 41-42; from instr to asst prof, 43-65, ASSOC PROF MED, SCH MED, JOHNS HOPKINS UNIV, 65- *Mem:* Am Rheumatism Asn; fel Am Col Physicians; AMA; Am Soc Internal Med; World Med Asn. *Res:* Rheumatology; endocrinology; alcoholism; clinical research in rheumatology. *Mailing Add:* 550 N Broadway Baltimore MD 21205

KLINENBERG, JAMES ROBERT, b Chicago, Ill, June 17, 34; m 59; c 4. INTERNAL MEDICINE, RHEUMATOLOGY. *Educ:* Johns Hopkins Univ, AB & AM, 55; George Washington Univ, MD, 59. *Prof Exp:* From asst prof to assoc prof, 66-73, PROF MED, UNIV CALIF, LOS ANGELES, 73-, VCHMN DEPT, 72-, ASST DEAN, SCH MED, 80-; DIR DEPT MED, CEDARS-SINAI MED CTR, 72- *Concurrent Pos:* Consult, Wadsworth Vet Admin Hosp & Sepulveda Vet Admin Hosp; consult, Calif Regional Med Progs, Inland Area VI; chmn, Calif State Arthritis Coun; fel, Arthritis Found, 66-70, clin scholar; attend physician, Cedars-Sinai Med Ctr, 72-; mem, US Pharmacopeia Adv Panel Number 1 Allergy, Immunol & Connective Tissue Dis, 75-; mem bd trustees, Arthritis Found, 78-; chmn, Nat Arthritis Adv Bd, 81- *Mem:* Fel Am Col Physicians; Am Rheumatism Asn; Am Fedn Clin Res; Asn Prog Dirs in Internal Med; Am Fedn Clin Res. *Res:* Clinical investigation in purine metabolism and gout. *Mailing Add:* Cedars-Sinai Med Ctr 8700 Beverly Blvd Los Angeles CA 90048

KLING, GERALD FAIRCHILD, b Lewisburg, Pa, Dec 12, 41; m 64; c 1. SOIL SCIENCE. *Educ:* Purdue Univ, BS, 68; Cornell Univ, MS, 73, PhD(soil sci), 74. *Prof Exp:* ASST PROF SOIL SCI, ORE STATE UNIV, 74- *Mem:* Am Soc Agron; Soil Sci Soc Am; Int Soc Soil Sci; Sigma Xi. *Res:* Quantification of the dynamic soil system so that predictions can be made regarding the probable effects of various land use changes on the system. *Mailing Add:* Dept of Soil Sci Ore State Univ Corvallis OR 97331

KLING, HARRY P(EARCE), b New York, NY, Dec 23, 17; m 45; c 2. PHYSICAL METALLURGY. *Educ:* Calif Inst Technol, BS, 45; Mass Inst Technol, SM, 46, ScD, 49. *Prof Exp:* Asst metall, Mass Inst Technol, 47-49; sr engr & sect head cent eng labs, Atomic Energy Div, Sylvania Elec Prod, Inc, 49-59; mgr nuclear components & dir res & develop, Nuclear Div, Martin Co, 59-63; V PRES & TECH DIR, HITTMAN ASSOC INC, 63- *Concurrent Pos:* Instr, Polytech Inst Brooklyn, 50-59 & Cath Univ, 65- *Mem:* Am Soc Metals. *Res:* High temperature oxidation of gas turbine alloys; mechanism of creep; metals fabrication; niobium oxidation; fuel element fabrication processes; nuclear fuels; control rods; reactor components; direct energy conversion systems; radio-isotope power systems; compact nuclear reactors. *Mailing Add:* 11401 Manor Rd Baltimore MD 21234

KLING, OZRO RAY, b Peru, Ind, May 3, 42; m 66; c 2. REPRODUCTIVE ENDOCRINOLOGY. *Educ:* Butler Univ, BS, 65; Ind Univ, Bloomington, PhD(zool), 69. *Prof Exp:* Res assoc, Div Steroid Res, Sch Med, Ohio State Univ, 69-70, asst prof gynec-obstet, physiol & biophys, 70-75, ASSOC PROF GYNEC & OBSTET & ASSOC PROF PHYSIOL & BIOPHYS, SCH MED, UNIV OKLA, 75- *Concurrent Pos:* Ford Found res fel, Human Reproductive Endocrinol Res Unit, Karolinska Inst, Stockholm, 74-75. *Mem:* Endocrine Soc; Am Soc Primatologists; Soc Study Reproduction; Int Primatological Soc; Soc Exp Biol & Med. *Res:* Human and subhuman primate reproductive endocrine physiology; endocrine of the primate ovary; endocrine regulation of pregnancy and fetal development. *Mailing Add:* Dept Gynec & Obstet Univ Okla Health Sci Ctr Oklahoma City OK 73190

KLINGBEIL, WERNER WALTER, b Onoway, Alta, June 19, 32; m 66; c 2. APPLIED MECHANICS, APPLIED MATHEMATICS. *Educ:* Univ Alta, BSc, 54; Col Aeronaut, Eng, dipl, 56; Brown Univ, SM, 64, PhD(appl math), 66. *Prof Exp:* Stress engr, Avro Aircraft Ltd, Can, 56-59; res engr, Allied Res Assocs, Inc, 59-61; res scientist, 66-71, sr res scientist, 71-82, RES ASSOC, RES CTR, UNIROYAL, INC, 82- *Mem:* Sigma Xi. *Res:* Stress analysis and design of engineering structures; deformation and flow behavior of polymeric materials; finite elasticity; viscoelasticity; composite materials; tire mechanics. *Mailing Add:* Corp Tire Res & Develop World Hq Uniroyal Inc Middlebury CT 06749

KLINGBERG, WILLIAM GENE, b Wichita, Kans, Sept 17, 16; m 41; c 4. PEDIATRICS, HEMATOLOGY. *Educ:* Univ Wichita, AB, 38; Washington Univ, MD, 43. *Prof Exp:* From instr to assoc prof pediat, Sch Med, Washington Univ, 48-60; PROF PEDIAT & CHMN DEPT, SCH MED, WVA UNIV, 60- *Concurrent Pos:* Consult, US Army, Ft Leonard Wood, Mo, 47-60 & Div Crippled Children's Serv, State of Mo, 47-60; vis prof, Sch Med, Univ Ankara, 57-58; consult, US Air Force Hosp, Scott AFB, 58-60. *Mem:* Am Pediat Soc; Am Acad Pediat; Am Fedn Clin Res. *Res:* Hematology research and cancer chemotherapy in children. *Mailing Add:* Dept of Pediat WVa Univ Sch of Med Morgantown WV 26506

KLINGE, ALBERT FREDERICK, b Dudleytown, Ind, May 8, 23; m 53; c 2. AGRICULTURAL ENGINEERING. *Educ:* Purdue Univ, BS, 52, MS, 55; Univ Calif, Los Angeles, PhD(eng hydraul), 66. *Prof Exp:* Asst eng, Purdue Univ, 52-55; assoc, Univ Calif, Los Angeles, 55-62, lectr, 62-63; assoc prof, 65-68, PROF AGR ENG, UNIV MAINE, ORONO, 68- *Mem:* Am Soc Agr Engrs; Am Soc Eng Educ. *Res:* Hydraulics, water and soil resource management; waste management. *Mailing Add:* Dept of Agr Eng Univ of Maine Orono ME 04473

KLINGEBIEL, ALBERT ARNOLD, b Hinton, Iowa, Oct 1, 10; m 37; c 4. SOIL SCIENCE. *Educ:* Iowa State Univ, BS, 36, MS, 37. *Prof Exp:* Res asst range reseeding, Intermt Forest & Range Exp Sta, US Forest Serv, 37-38; soil scientist, Soil Conserv Serv, USDA, 38-42, dir training, 42-46, state soil scientist, 46-52, Ill state dir soil & water mgt res, Agr Res Serv, 52-54, from asst dir to dir soil surv interpretations, Soil Conserv Serv, 54-73; SOILS CONSULT, 73- *Concurrent Pos:* Soils consult, Int Bank Reconstruct & Develop, Mex, 73-75, Econ Res Serv, USDA, DC, 75-76, Nat Res Coun, DC, 75, Remote Sensing Inst & SDak State Univ, 77-81. *Honors & Awards:* Superior Serv Award, USDA, 50. *Mem:* Fel Am Soc Agron; Fel Soil Sci Soc Am; Am Soc Planning Off; Int Soc Soil Sci; Soil Conserv Soc Am. *Res:* Soil classification and interpretation; soil and water management; land use planning. *Mailing Add:* 2413 Countryside Dr Silver Spring MD 20904

KLINGELE, HAROLD OTTO, b Niagara Falls, NY, Aug 4, 37. ANALYTICAL CHEMISTRY, ORGANIC CHEMISTRY. *Educ:* Mass Inst Technol, BSc, 59; Yale Univ, MS, 61; Cornell Univ, PhD(org chem), 65. *Prof Exp:* Instr pharmacol, Univ Louisville, 65-66, asst prof, 66-71; PRES, HOK ASSOCS, 71- *Concurrent Pos:* Sr res assoc, Dept Chem, State Univ New York Buffalo, 73-75; mgr, treas & chem consult, Peninsula Chem Anal Ltd, 76-78; chem consult & chem analysis, HOK Assoc, 71-82; vis indust chemist, Chem Dept, Canisius Col, Buffalo, NY, 80; pres, Soap Factory Stores, Inc, 80. *Mem:* Am Chem Soc; Royal Soc Chem. *Res:* Forensics; analytical method development; industrial problems involving chemistry; drug analysis; organophosphorous heterocycles; carcinogens; toxicology; environmental chemistry; organic synthesis. *Mailing Add:* 1169 Oak Pl Niagara Falls NY 14304

KLINGEMAN, PETER C, b Evanston, Ill, May 31, 34; m 57; c 2. HYDRAULIC ENGINEERING, HYDROLOGY. *Educ:* Northwestern Univ, BS, 57, MS, 59; Univ Calif, Berkeley, PhD(civil eng), 65. *Prof Exp:* Asst prof civil eng, NDak State Univ, 59; res engr, Univ Calif, Berkeley, 62-64; Ford Found Prog vis prof hydraul eng, Catholic Univ Chile, 64-66; from asst prof to assoc prof, 66-75, PROF CIVIL ENG, ORE STATE UNIV, 75-; DIR, ORE WATER RESOURCES RES INST, 75- *Mem:* Am Soc Civil Eng; Am Geophys Union; Int Asn Hydraul Res. *Res:* Development of river basins and estuaries, including basin hydrology, sediment transport and related aspects of water resources development. *Mailing Add:* Dept Civil Eng Ore State Univ Corvallis OR 97331

KLINGEN, THEODORE JAMES, b St Louis, Mo, Oct 7, 31; m 58; c 2. PHYSICAL INORGANIC CHEMISTRY. *Educ:* St Louis Univ, BS, 53, MS, 55; Fla State Univ, PhD(chem), 62. *Prof Exp:* Nuclear res officer, Res Div, Spec Weapons Ctr, US Air Force, NMex, 55-57; analyst chem, McDonnell Aircraft Corp, 57-58; fel, Fla State Univ, 58-60, asst, 60-62; res scientist, Res Div, McDonnell Aircraft Corp, 62-64; from asst prof to assoc prof, 64-70, dir, Ctr Radiation Res, 72-74, PROF CHEM, UNIV MISS, 70- *Concurrent Pos:* Grants, US Dept of Energy & NSF. *Mem:* Am Chem Soc; Am Phys Soc; Am Nuclear Soc. *Res:* Radiation chemistry of plastic crystals; radiation induced polymerization of organo-substituted carboranes; radiation chemistry of semiconductor materials; effects of lattice defects on thermodynamic properties. *Mailing Add:* Dept of Chem Univ of Miss University MS 38677

KLINGENBERG, JOSEPH JOHN, b Bellevue, Ky, Nov 16, 19; wid; c 5. ANALYTICAL CHEMISTRY. *Educ:* Xavier Univ, Ohio, BS, 41; Univ Cincinnati, MS, 47, PhD(chem), 49. *Prof Exp:* From instr to assoc prof, 49-60, PROF CHEM, XAVIER UNIV, OHIO, 60- *Concurrent Pos:* Vis lectr, Univ Cincinnati, 66, 69 & 75; sci adv, Food & Drug Admin, 67-72; vis lectr, Univ Ky, 76 & 77; vis scientist, Va Polytech Inst & State Univ, 81-82. *Mem:* Am Chem Soc. *Res:* Chemistry of zirconium; mandelic acid derivatives. *Mailing Add:* Dept of Chem Xavier Univ Cincinnati OH 45207

KLINGENER, DAVID JOHN, b Meadville, Pa, Sept 4, 37; m 60; c 1. ZOOLOGY. *Educ:* Swarthmore Col, BA, 59; Univ Mich, MA, 61, PhD(zool), 64. *Prof Exp:* Instr zool & cur mammals, Mus Zool, Univ Mich, 63-64; asst prof, 64-70, ASSOC PROF ZOOL, UNIV MASS, AMHERST, 70- *Mem:* Am Soc Mammal; Soc Study Evolution; Am Soc Zool; Soc Vert Paleont. *Res:* Comparative anatomy and paleontology of bats and rodents. *Mailing Add:* Dept of Zool Univ of Mass Amherst MA 01002

KLINGENSMITH, GEORGE BRUCE, b Pittsburgh, Pa, Dec 6, 34; m 60; c 1. PHYSICAL CHEMISTRY, ORGANIC CHEMISTRY. *Educ:* Univ Pittsburgh, BSc, 57, PhD(phys-org chem), 63. *Prof Exp:* Fel phys & org chem, Pa State Univ, 63-64; res supvr, Shell Chem Co Woodbury, 66-74, STAFF RES CHEMIST, SHELL DEVELOPMENT CO, 74- *Mem:* Am Chem Soc. *Res:* Reactions and physical properties of aromatic systems; solvent effects; crystallization and crystal structure of polymers; nuclear magnetic resonance spectroscopy. *Mailing Add:* 1828 Milford Houston TX 77006

KLINGENSMITH, MERLE JOSEPH, b Grenora, NDak, Mar 27, 32; m 59; c 2. PLANT PHYSIOLOGY. *Educ:* Wheaton Col, Ill, BS, 54; Univ Mich, MS, 56, PhD(bot), 59. *Prof Exp:* Lab asst bact, Fla State Univ, 54-55; asst bot, Univ Mich, 55-56; vis asst prof bot & bact, Ohio Wesleyan Univ, 59-60; asst prof bot, Colgate Univ, 60-65; from asst prof to assoc prof, 65-76, PROF BIOL, ROCHESTER INST TECHNOL, 76- *Mem:* Fel AAAS; Bot Soc Am; Am Soc Plant Physiol; Am Sci Affiliation. *Res:* Plant nutrition; exogenous growth regulators; radiation effects on plant growth. *Mailing Add:* Dept of Biol Rochester Inst of Technol Rochester NY 14623

KLINGENSMITH, RAYMOND W, b Pittsburgh, Pa, Mar 21, 31; m 53; c 2. NUCLEAR PHYSICS. *Educ:* Hanover Col, AB, 53; Miami Univ, MA, 55; Ohio State Univ, PhD(elastic scattering), 63. *Prof Exp:* Physicist, Westinghouse Elec Corp, 56-57; prin physicist, Battelle Mem Inst, 57-63, proj leader nuclear physics, 63-68, prog mgr strategic technol, 68-74, supvr, Hot Lab, 74-77, mgr, Hot Lab & assoc sect mgr nuclear mat technol, Battelle-Columbus, 77-81, PROJ MGR, OFF NUCLEAR WEAPONS TECHNICIAN/SPECIALIST INTEGRATION, BATTELLE PROJ MGR DIV, 81- *Res:* Low energy scattering as related to nuclear structure physics; nuclear weapons effects; strategic technology; nuclear materials technology; hot cell technology and operations; research management. *Mailing Add:* Battelle Proj Mgt Div 505 King Ave Columbus OH 43201

KLINGER, ALLEN, b New York, NY, Apr 2, 37; div; c 2. COMPUTER SCIENCE, ENGINEERING. *Educ:* Cooper Union, BEE, 57; Calif Inst Technol, MS, 58; Univ Calif, Berkeley, PhD(elec eng), 66. *Prof Exp:* Mem tech staff electronics, Hughes Aircraft Co, 57; electronics engr elec systs, ITT Labs, 58-59; electronics systs engr comput systs, Syst Develop Corp, 59-63; sr res engr electronics systs, Jet Propulsion Lab, 64-65, consult, 78; researcher math, Rand Corp, 65-67; PROF COMPUT SCI, UNIV CALIF, LOS ANGELES, 67- *Concurrent Pos:* Consult, Syst Develop Corp, 67-68 & 78-, res dept, Gateways Hosp, 71-72, Rand Corp, 67-69 & 72-73, Int Bank Reconstruction & Develop, 74 & Calif Inst Technol, 78-; sr radar systs specialist, Litton Industs, 68-69; prin investr, NSF, 68-71 & Air Force Off Sci Res, 70-77; chmn, Conf Data Strut Pattern Recognition & Comput Graphics, 74-75; distinguished lectr, Int Elec & Electronic Engrs, 76-77; pres, Data Structure & Display Co, 76-; consult radiol dept, Long Beach Mem Hosp, 77-78 & US Army Eng Topogr Labs, 78-79 & 80- *Mem:* Inst Elec & Electronics Engrs. *Res:* Structural pattern recognition; image data bases; search and statistical analysis. *Mailing Add:* 3531 C Boelter Hall Univ of Calif Los Angeles CA 90024

KLINGER, HAROLD P, b Brooklyn, NY, July 20, 29; m 59. GENETICS. *Educ:* Harvard Univ, BA, 52; Univ Basel, MD, 59, PhD, 63. *Prof Exp:* Res asst neurosurg, New York Med Col, 45-52; demonstr anat, Univ Basel, 55-57, from second asst to first asst, 59-61, dir cytogenetics res unit, 61-63; from asst prof to assoc prof anat & genetics, 63-72, PROF GENETICS, ALBERT EINSTEIN COL MED, 72- *Concurrent Pos:* Ed, Cytogenetics & Cell Genetics, 60-; NIH career develop award, 65-74; mem adv comt, Pop Coun, Rockefeller Univ, 71- *Mem:* Genetics Soc Am; Am Soc Human Genetics; Am Asn Phys Anthrop; NY Acad Sci; Swiss Anat Soc. *Res:* Cytogenetics; role of chromosomal aberrations in human development; somatic cell genetics; gene regulation and interaction in normal and malignant cells. *Mailing Add:* Dept of Genetics Albert Einstein Col of Med Bronx NY 10461

KLINGER, LAWRENCE EDWARD, b Chicago, Ill, Nov 18, 29; m 53; c 4. BACTERIOLOGY. *Educ:* Loyola Univ, Ill, BS, 51; Ill Inst Technol, MS, 53. *Prof Exp:* Res chemist, Swift & Co, 52-54, asst to dir labs, 54-55, div head, Res Labs, 55-59, asst to vpres res, 59-61, div head, Res Labs, 61-62, gen mgr new prod develop dept, 62-68, dir planning & acquisitions, Swift Chem Co, 68-69, plant mgr, 69-70, sr admin asst, 70-71, dir pub responsibility, 71-77, DIR QUAL ASSURANCE, SWIFT & CO, 78- *Concurrent Pos:* Dir, Food Update, 75-79; steering comt, Nutrit Planning Conf, Food & Drug Admin, 75-76. *Mem:* Inst Food Technol (treas, 57 & 58); Am Soc Qual Control; Soc Nutrit Educ; Coun Agr Sci & Technol; Asn Food & Drug Off. *Res:* New products development; nutrition education; food safety. *Mailing Add:* Swift & Co 1919 Swift Dr Oak Brook IL 60521

KLINGER, WILLIAM RUSSELL, b Columbia City, Ind, Feb 9, 39; m 60; c 1. MATHEMATICS. *Educ:* Taylor Univ, BS in Ed, 61; Ohio State Univ, MSc, 67, PhD(math, educ), 73. *Prof Exp:* Teacher math, Marion Community Schs, Ind, 61-68; instr, Ohio State Univ, 68-73; asst prof, 73-74, ASSOC PROF MATH, MARION COL, 74-, HEAD DEPT, 73- *Concurrent Pos:* Mem assoc fac, Ind Univ, Kokomo, 73- *Mem:* Math Asn Am. *Res:* Necessary and sufficient conditions for continuity in metric spaces and topological spaces. *Mailing Add:* Dept of Math Marion Col Marion IN 46952

KLINGHAMMER, ERICH, b Kassel, Ger, Feb 28, 30; m 58; c 1. ETHOLOGY, PSYCHOLOGY. *Educ:* Univ Chicago, AB, 58, PhD(psychol), 62. *Prof Exp:* From instr to asst prof psychol, Univ Chicago, 63-68; ASSOC PROF PSYCHOL, PURDUE UNIV, LAFAYETTE, 68- *Concurrent Pos:* Pres, NAm Wildlife Park Found, 72-; sci ed, Grzimek's Animal Life Encycl. *Mem:* AAAS; Am Ornith Union; Animal Behav Soc. *Res:* Ethology; imprinting; effects of early experience on adult behavior; behavior mechanisms in canids development and motivation. *Mailing Add:* Dept of Psychol Sci Purdue Univ Lafayette IN 47907

KLINGHOFFER, JUNE F, b Philadelphia, Pa, Feb 12, 21; m 47; c 1. INTERNAL MEDICINE. *Educ:* Univ Pa, BA, 41; Woman's Med Col Pa, MD, 45; Am Bd Internal Med, cert, 51; Spec Bd Rheumatology, cert, 76. *Prof Exp:* Intern, Albert Einstein Med Ctr, 45, resident internal med, 45-47; fel path, 47-48, clin asst med, 48-50, dir student health serv, 48-51, from instr to assoc prof, 50-69, PROF MED, MED COL PA, 69- *Concurrent Pos:* Consult physician, Vet Admin Hosp, Philadelphia, 70-; consult, The Inglis House. *Honors & Awards:* Lindback Award for Distinguished Teaching, 65; Commonwealth Citation, Commonwealth Bd of Med Col Pa, 73; Golden Apple Award, 74; Outstanding Educator Am Award, 75. *Mem:* Am Med Women's Asn; Asn Women Sci; Am Asn Univ Prof; AMA; Am Rheumatism Asn. *Mailing Add:* Med Col of Pa 3300 Henry Ave Philadelphia PA 19129

KLINGLER, EUGENE H(ERMAN), b Ft Wayne, Ind, Sept 3, 32; m 54; c 6. ELECTRICAL ENGINEERING. *Educ:* Ind Inst Technol, BSEE, 53; NMex State Univ, MSEE, 57; Carnegie Inst Technol, PhD(elec eng), 61. *Prof Exp:* Servomech engr, Bell Aircraft Corp, 53-55; instr, NMex State Univ, 57; proj engr, Carnegie Inst Technol, 57-61; staff engr, Space Tech Labs, 61-62; chief electronics engr, Fairchild Camera & Instrument Corp, 62; sr mem tech staff, Northrop Space Labs, 62-63; mgr eng res lab, NAm Aviation Inc, Okla, 63-65; chmn dept elec eng, Ind Inst Technol, 65-69; prof & chmn dept, Univ Detroit, 69-70; PRES & CHMN BD, EUGENE KLINGLER INC, 70- *Concurrent Pos:* Instr, Ind Inst Technol, 58. *Mem:* Inst Elec & Electronics Engrs. *Res:* Synthesis of artificial dielectric materials by means of control of electric and magnetic losses as a function of frequency. *Mailing Add:* 5045 Charing Cross Rd Bloomfield MI 48013

KLINGLESMITH, DANIEL ALEXANDER, III, astrophysics, computer science, see previous edition

KLINGMAN, DARWIN DEE, b Dickinson, NDak, Feb 5, 44; m 64. OPERATIONS RESEARCH, MATHEMATICAL STATISTICS. *Educ:* Wash State Univ, BA, 66, MA, 67; Univ Tex, Austin, PhD, 69. *Prof Exp:* Teaching asst, Wash State Univ, 66-67; teaching assoc, 68-69, from asst prof to assoc prof oper res & computer sci, 69-76, PROF OPER RES & COMPUTER SCI, UNIV TEX, AUSTIN, 76- *Concurrent Pos:* Consult, Tex Water Develop Bd, 71-72, Farah Mfg Co, 72-, Mathematica, Inc, 72-73 & Univac, 73-76. *Mem:* Oper Res Soc Am; Math Prog Soc; Asn Comput Mach. *Res:* Mathematical programming and computational algorithms and comparisons. *Mailing Add:* Dept of Statist Univ of Tex Austin TX 78712

KLINGMAN, DAYTON L, b Neosho Falls, Kans, Feb 10, 13; m 41; c 4. AGRONOMY. *Educ:* Univ Nebr, BSc, 38, PhD(agron), 54; Purdue Univ, MSc, 42. *Prof Exp:* Asst agronomist & asst prof agron, Univ Wyo, 42-48; agronomist, Crops Res Div, 48-52, sr agronomist & coordr weed invests, 53-56, leader weed invests-grazing lands, 57-72, chief, Turfgrass Lab, 72-74, chief, Field Crops Lab, 74-76, CHIEF, WEED SCI LAB, USDA, 76- *Mem:* AAAS; Am Soc Agron; Weed Sci Soc Am; Soc Range Mgt. *Res:* Technique study of use of cages in pasture research; small grain improvement; weed control in pastures and field crops. *Mailing Add:* Beltsville Agr Res Ctr-West USDA Beltsville MD 20705

KLINGMAN, GERDA ISOLDE, b Berlin, Ger, May 6, 24; US citizen; m 53; c 1. PHARMACOLOGY. *Educ:* Fordham Univ, BS, 52; Med Col Va, PhD(pharmacol), 56. *Prof Exp:* Res assoc, Dept Pharmacol & Physiol, Med Sch, Duke Univ, 55-57; instr, Dept Pharmacol & Exp Therapeut, Sch Med, Johns Hopkins Univ, 57-61; from instr to assoc prof, 61-73, PROF BIOCHEM PHARMACOL, STATE UNIV NY BUFFALO, 73- *Concurrent Pos:* Career develop award, NIH, 62-67. *Mem:* Am Soc Pharmacol & Exp Therapeut. *Res:* Neuropharmacology; neurochemistry, adrenergic nervous system and catecholamine metabolism; acute and chronic tolerance; drug dependence; nerve growth factor and nerve growth factor antiserum. *Mailing Add:* Dept of Biochem Pharmacol State Univ of NY Buffalo NY 14260

KLINGMAN, JACK DENNIS, b Johnson City, NY, Apr 21, 27; m 53; c 1. BIOCHEMISTRY. *Educ:* Syracuse Univ, BA, 51; Med Col Va, MS, 53; Duke Univ, PhD(biochem), 58. *Prof Exp:* Res assoc pharmacol, Med Col Va, 53; asst biochem, Duke Univ, 54-55; res assoc neurochem, Johns Hopkins Univ, 58-61; from instr to assoc prof, 61-73, PROF BIOCHEM, STATE UNIV NY BUFFALO, 73- *Concurrent Pos:* Mem fac, Dept Biochem, Sch Med, Monash Univ, Australia, 71-72; Hayes-Fulbright fel, 71-72. *Mem:* AAAS; Am Chem Soc; Neurochem Soc; Am Soc Biol Chem. *Res:* N15-ethanolamine metabolism; purification and mechanism of renal glutaminase; C14-glucose metabolism in surviving superior cervical ganglion; biochemical events in excitation; phospholipid and amino acid metabolism. *Mailing Add:* Dept of Biochem State Univ of NY Buffalo NY 14214

KLINGSBERG, CYRUS, b Philadelphia, Pa, Nov 12, 24; m 50. SOLID STATE CHEMISTRY, CERAMICS. *Educ:* Univ Pa, BA, 48; Bryn Mawr Col, MA, 49; Pa State Univ, PhD(geo chem), 58. *Prof Exp:* Res mgr, G F Pettinos Inc, 50-51; petrologist, Simonds Abrasive Co, 51-54; asst geochem, Pa State Univ, 54-57; res chemist, Corning Glass Works, NY, 57-59; ceramist, Off Naval Res, 59-63, liaison scientist ceramics, London, 63-64, ceramist, 64-66; exec secy, Comt Radioactive Waste Mgt, Nat Acad Sci-Nat Res Coun, 66-75; sr res assoc, Arhco, 76-77; proj engr, 77-80, SR STAFF SCIENTIST, US DEPT ENERGY, 80- *Mem:* Fel Am Ceramic Soc; Mineral Soc Am; Sigma Xi; Geol Soc Am. *Res:* Solid state chemistry of ceramics, minerals and ionic solids; synthesis and characterization of crystalline phases; management of radioactive wastes. *Mailing Add:* 118 Monroe St Rockville MD 20850

KLINGSBERG, ERWIN, b Philadelphia, Pa, Mar 13, 21; m 45; c 3. ORGANIC CHEMISTRY. *Educ:* Univ Pa, BS, 41; Univ Rochester, PhD(chem), 44. *Prof Exp:* Res chemist, Schering Corp, 44-46; res chemist, Am Cyanamid Co, 46-65, prin res scientist, 65-81. *Concurrent Pos:* Assoc prof, City Col New York, 63-64; Brit Govt traveling fel, 72; vis prof, Univ Caen, France, 73 & Univ Sci Tech Lang, Montpellier, France, 73-74. *Mem:* Fel AAAS; Am Chem Soc. *Res:* Dyestuffs; anthraquinone derivatives; heteroaromatic compounds of nitrogen and sulfur. *Mailing Add:* 1597 Deer Path Mountainside NJ 07092

KLINK, JOEL RICHARD, b Nevada, Ohio, June 28, 35; m 59; c 2. ORGANIC CHEMISTRY. *Educ:* Ohio State Univ, BS, 57, PhD(chem), 64. *Prof Exp:* Instr chem, Ohio Northern Univ, 61-63; from asst to assoc prof, 63-71, PROF CHEM, UNIV WIS-EAU CLAIRE, 71-, CHMN DEPT, 78- *Mem:* Am Chem Soc; Nat Sci Teachers Asn. *Res:* Mechanisms of aromatic rearrangement reactions; synthesis and properties of heterocyclic compounds. *Mailing Add:* Dept of Chem Univ of Wis Eau Claire WI 54701

KLINK, WILLIAM H, b Chicago, Ill, Sept 29, 37; m 59. THEORETICAL PHYSICS. *Educ:* Univ Mich, BA, 59; Johns Hopkins Univ, PhD(physics), 64. *Prof Exp:* From asst prof to assoc prof, 65-77, PROF PHYSICS & ASTRON, UNIV IOWA, 77- *Concurrent Pos:* Fulbright grant, Univ Heidelberg, 64-65. *Res:* Elementary particle physics, primarily using group theory. *Mailing Add:* Dept of Physics & Astron Univ of Iowa Iowa City IA 52240

KLINKE, DAVID J, b Detroit, Mich, Feb 27, 32; m 64; c 3. ORGANIC CHEMISTRY. *Educ:* Mich State Univ, BS, 54, PhD(org chem), 63. *Prof Exp:* Teacher jr high sch, Mich, 54-55 & high sch, 55-59; res chemist petrol additives, Jackson Lab, 63-66, prod supvr miscellaneous org intermediates, Chambers Works, 66-68, supvr mgt training & personnel develop, 68-71, prod supvr dyes, 71-74, SR SUPVR MAT DISTRIB, E I DU PONT DE NEMOURS & CO, INC, 74- *Mem:* Am Chem Soc. *Res:* Thiophene chemistry; organo-metallics. *Mailing Add:* RR 3 Box 228 Woodstown NJ 08098

KLINKHAMMER, MICHAEL DENNIS, b Cogswell, NDak, Jan 2, 44. PHYSICAL CHEMISTRY. *Educ:* NDak State Univ, BS, 66, PhD(phys chem), 72. *Prof Exp:* Fel adsorption activated carbon, Empire State Paper Res Inst, State Univ NY, 72-73; CHEMIST, DT NAVAL SHIP RES & DEVELOP CTR, 74- *Mem:* Am Chem Soc; Am Soc Testing & Mat. *Res:* Evaluation of synthetic crudes, fuels and lubes derived from coal, shale and tar sands; predictive test development for characterizing candidate Navy liquid lubricants. *Mailing Add:* DT Naval Ship Res & Develop Ctr Code 2832 Annapolis MD 21402

KLINMAN, JUDITH POLLOCK, b Philadelphia, Pa, Apr 17, 41; m 63; c 2. BIOCHEMISTRY, PHYSICAL ORGANIC CHEMISTRY. *Educ:* Univ Pa, AB, 62, PhD(org chem), 66. *Prof Exp:* Fel phys org chem, Isotopes Dept, Weizmann Inst, 66-67; assoc, Inst Cancer Res, 68-70, res assoc biochem, 70-72, asst mem, 72-77, assoc mem, 77-78; ASSOC PROF CHEM, UNIV CALIF, BERKELEY, 78- *Concurrent Pos:* Asst prof med biophys, Univ Pa, 74-78. *Mem:* Am Chem Soc; Am Soc Biol Chemists. *Res:* Mechanism and regulation of enzyme action. *Mailing Add:* Dept of Chem Univ of Calif Berkeley CA 94708

KLINMAN, NORMAN RALPH, b Philadelphia, Pa, Mar 23, 37; m 78; c 2. IMMUNOLOGY. *Educ:* Haverford Col, AB, 58; Jefferson Med Col, MD, 62; Univ Pa, PhD(microbiol), 65. *Prof Exp:* Fel immunol, Univ Pa, 62-66, Weizmann Inst, 66-67 & Nat Inst Med Res, London, 67-68; from asst prof to assoc prof microbiol, Sch Med, Univ Pa, 68-75, prof path, 75-78; MEM STAFF, SCRIPPS CLIN & RES FOUND, 78- *Concurrent Pos:* NIH res fel, 62-63; Helen Hay Whitney Found res fel, 63-66; Am Cancer Soc res scholar, 66-68; adj prof, Univ Calif, San Diego, 79- *Mem:* Am Asn Immunol; Am Asn Exp Pathologists. *Res:* Structure, activity and synthesis of antibody. *Mailing Add:* Dept Immunopath Scripps Clin & Res Found La Jolla CA 92037

KLINT, ROBERT V(ICTOR), mechanical engineering, see previous edition

KLINTWORTH, GORDON K, b Ft Victoria, Rhodesia, Aug 4, 32; US citizen; m 57; c 3. PATHOLOGY, ANATOMY. *Educ:* Univ Witwatersrand, BSc, 54, MB, BCh, 57, BSc(Hons), 61, PhD(anat), 65. *Prof Exp:* Intern med & surg, Johannesburg Hosp, 58-59, sr house physician, psychiat, 59-60, registr, Neurol & Neurosurg, 60-61; assoc, 64-66, from asst prof to assoc prof, 66-73, PROF PATH, MED CTR, DUKE UNIV, 73-, PROF OPTHAL, 68- *Concurrent Pos:* Louis B Mayer scholar, 72. *Mem:* AAAS; Am Asn Pathologists; Sigma Xi; Int Soc Neuropath; Tissue Cult Asn. *Res:* Diseases of the eye and nervous system; infectious diseases; secondary effects of increased intracranial pressure; human genetics and diseases of the cornea. *Mailing Add:* Dept Path Duke Univ Med Ctr Durham NC 27710

KLINZING, GEORGE ENGELBERT, b Natrona Heights, Pa, Mar 22, 38; m 69; c 2. CHEMICAL ENGINEERING. *Educ:* Univ Pittsburgh, BS, 59; Carnegie Inst Technol, MS, 61, PhD(chem eng), 63. *Prof Exp:* From asst prof to assoc prof, 63-81, PROF CHEM ENG, UNIV PITTSBURGH, 81- *Concurrent Pos:* Consult, Univ Develop Proj, Ecuador, 63-66; hon prof, Cent Univ Ecuador, 66. *Mem:* Am Inst Chem Engrs; Am Soc Eng Educ. *Res:* Solid/gas flow systems; electrostatics; mass transfer in partially miscible systems; molecular hydrogen permeation; photo conversion. *Mailing Add:* Benedum Eng Hall Univ of Pittsburgh Pittsburgh PA 15261

KLIONSKY, BERNARD LEON, b Binghamton, NY, Oct 8, 25; m 50; c 4. MEDICINE, PATHOLOGY. *Educ:* Harvard Univ, AB, 47; Hahnemann Med Col, MD, 52; Am Bd Path, dipl, 57. *Prof Exp:* Nat Cancer Inst trainee path, Med Ctr, Univ Kans, 53-55, Am Cancer Soc clin fel, 55-57, fel path, 56-57, from instr to assoc prof, 56-61; assoc prof, 61-70, PROF PATH, SCH MED, UNIV PITTSBURGH, 71- *Res:* Intrauterine fetal growth retardation; yellow hyaline membranes. *Mailing Add:* Magee Womens Hosp Univ of Pittsburgh Sch of Med Pittsburgh PA 15213

KLIORE, ARVYDAS J(OSEPH), b Kaunas, Lithuania, Aug 5, 35; US citizen; m 60. PLANETARY SCIENCE, ATMOSPHERIC PHYSICS. *Educ:* Univ Ill, BS, 56; Univ Mich, MS, 57; Mich State Univ, PhD(elec eng), 62. *Prof Exp:* Engr, Armour Res Found, Ill Inst Technol, 57-59; instr elec eng, Mich State Univ, 61-62; sr res engr, 62-64, res specialist, 64-66, RES SCIENTIST ANAL, JET PROPULSION LAB, CALIF INST TECHNOL, 66- *Concurrent Pos:* Lectr, Univ Calif, Los Angeles, 63-64; vchmn, Comt Space Res, 75-78. *Honors & Awards:* Medal Exceptional Sci Achievement, NASA, 73. *Mem:* AAAS; Am Astron Soc; Am Geophys Union. *Res:* Space astronomy; radio propagation experiments to measure planetary atmospheres; spacecraft radio propagation experiments to study the atmospheres and ionospheres of planets and their satellites. *Mailing Add:* Jet Propulsion Lab 4800 Oak Grove Dr Pasadena CA 91103

KLIOZE, OSCAR, b Baltimore, Md, Jan 2, 19; m 43; c 3. PHARMACEUTICAL CHEMISTRY. *Educ:* George Washington Univ, BS, 40; Va Polytech Inst, BS, 44; Univ Md, PhD(pharmaceut chem), 49. *Prof Exp:* Jr chemist, Baltimore Paint & Color Works, Inc, 40-41 & Bur Plant Indust, USDA, 41-42 & 46; jr biochemist, Manhattan Proj, US Army Engrs, 44-46; res assoc biochem, Northwestern Univ, 49-50; res chemist pharmaceut chem, Chas Pfizer & Co, Inc, 50-54, res supvr, 54-58; dir prod develop, 58-60 & prod develop & qual control, 60-64, dir, 65-81, VPRES PHARM RES & ANAL SERV, A H ROBINS CO, INC, 81- *Concurrent Pos:* Lectr, Med Col Va, 66-75. *Mem:* Am Chem Soc; Am Pharmaceut Asn; Am Inst Chem; Parenteral Drug Asn. *Res:* Relationship of chemical structure to biological activity; pharmaceutical research and development; physiological effects of radiant energy; plant biochemistry; protein synthesis. *Mailing Add:* Res Labs A H Robins Co Inc 1211 Sherwood Ave Richmond VA 23220

KLIP, DOROTHEA A, b The Hague, Netherlands, Sept 27, 21; m 55; c 4. ANALYSIS & FUNCTIONAL ANALYSIS, APPLIED MATHEMATICS. *Educ:* State Univ Utrecht, Dra(theoret physics), 62. *Prof Exp:* Asst prof, physiol, 63-73, ASSOC PROF PHYSIOL & BIOPHYS, UNIV ALA, BIRMINGHAM, 73-, ASST PROF INFO SCI, 71- *Concurrent Pos:* Reviewer, NSF. *Mem:* AAAS; Asn Comput Mach; Sigma Xi; Soc Indust & Appl Math. *Res:* Design and implementation of algorithms for the solution of nonlinear (polynomial) equations; symbolic algebraic manipulation by computer. *Mailing Add:* Dept of Physiol & Biophys Univ of Ala Birmingham AL 35294

KLIP, WILLEM, b Rotterdam, Neth, Nov 26, 17; US citizen; m 55; c 4. BIOPHYSICS. *Educ:* Univ Utrecht, MD, 46, PhD(bact), 51, PhD(theoret physics), 55, DSc(physics), 62. *Prof Exp:* Staff mem of Dr H C Burger, Dept Med Physics, Univ Utrecht, 53-58; PROF MED PHYSICS, DEPT PHYSIOL MED & PHYSICS, UNIV ALA, BIRMINGHAM, 58- *Res:* Medical and theoretical physics. *Mailing Add:* Dept of Physiol Med & Physics Univ of Ala Univ Sta Birmingham AL 35294

KLIPHARDT, RAYMOND A(DOLPH), b Chicago, Ill, Mar 18, 17; m 45; c 5. ENGINEERING SCIENCES. *Educ:* Ill Inst Technol, BS, 38, MS, 48. *Prof Exp:* Instr graphics & math, NPark Col, 38-43; asst math, Ill Inst Technol, 43-44; asst civil eng, 45-46, from asst prof to assoc prof eng graphics, 46-58, from assoc prof to prof eng sci, 58-70, PROF ENG SCI & APPL MATH, NORTHWESTERN UNIV, 70-, CHMN DEPT, 78- *Concurrent Pos:* Campus coordr, Khartoum Proj, USAID; consult, Appl Math Div, Argonne Nat Lab. *Mem:* AAAS; Am Soc Eng Educ; Asn Comput Mach. *Res:* Abstract geometry; computer automation. *Mailing Add:* Dept of Eng Sci & Appl Math Northwestern Univ Evanston IL 60201

KLIPPENSTEIN, GERALD LEE, protein chemistry, deceased

KLIPPLE, EDMUND CHESTER, b Cuero, Tex, July 5, 06; m 28; c 3. MATHEMATICAL ANALYSIS. *Educ:* Univ Tex, BA, 26, PhD(pure math), 32. *Prof Exp:* Instr math, Univ Tex, 26-27; instr, San Antonio Jr Col, 27-29; instr, Univ Tex, 29-35; from instr to prof, 35-71, EMER PROF MATH, TEX A&M UNIV, 71- *Mem:* AAAS; Am Math Soc; Math Asn Am. *Res:* Point set theory; real variables; Laplace transformations; spaces in which there exist contiguous points. *Mailing Add:* Dept of Math Tex A&M Univ College Station TX 77843

KLIPSTEIN, DAVID HAMPTON, b New York, NY, July 25, 30; m 55, 72; c 8. ENGINEERING MANAGEMENT, ALTERNATIVE ENERGY UTILIZATION. *Educ:* Princeton Univ, BSE, 52; Mass Inst Technol, SM, 56, ScD, 63. *Prof Exp:* Res engr, Am Cyanamid Corp, 51-54; dir, Bound Brook Sta, Sch Chem Eng Practice, Mass Inst Technol, 58-60; mkt rep, Union Carbide Chem Corp, 62-69, mkt develop mgr, Develop Div, 69-70, prod mgr acrylate monomers & polymers, 70-71, mkt mgr, Trade Chem Intermediates, 71-72; bus develop mgr, Res Cottrell Inc, 72-73, vpres planning & develop oper, Air Pollution Control Group, 73-74, vpres particulate opers, 74-76, DIR ADVAN TECHNOL CORP DEVELOP, RES COTTRELL INC, 76-, DIR, BIPHASE ENERGY SYSTS, 80- *Concurrent Pos:* Mem, Environ AdV Comt, Fed Energy Admin, 74-76. *Mem:* Am Chem Soc; Am Inst Chem Eng; Geothermal Resources Coun. *Res:* Commercial development; optimization of combustion processes, precombustion fuel cleaning, high efficiency energy conversion systems, load leveling controls. *Mailing Add:* Res Cottrell Inc Box 1500 Somerville NJ 08876

KLIPSTEIN, FREDERICK AUGUST, b Greenwich, Conn, June 5, 28; m 65; c 3. MEDICINE. *Educ:* Williams Col, BA, 50; Columbia Univ, MD, 54; Am Bd Internal Med, dipl, 63; Am Bd Clin Nutrit, dipl, 67. *Prof Exp:* From intern to asst resident, Med Serv, Presby Hosp, NY, 54-56; NIH trainee, Col Physicians & Surgeons, Columbia Univ, 58-59; Postgrad Med Sch, London, Eng, 59-60; chief med resident, Francis Delafield Hosp, New York, 60-61; instr med, Col Physicians & Surgeons, Columbia Univ, 61-63, assoc, 63-65, asst prof, 65-68; assoc prof, 68-72, PROF MED, SCH MED & DENT, UNIV ROCHESTER, 72- *Concurrent Pos:* Asst physician, Presby Hosp, NY, 60-68; Am Cancer Soc advan clin fel, 61-63; clin asst vis physician, First Med Div, Bellevue Hosp, 63-68; consult, Greenwich Hosp, Conn, 63-68 & Harlem

Hosp, 66-68; vis physician, Francis Delafield Hosp, 66-68; physician, Strong Mem Hosp, Med Ctr, Univ Rochester; dir trop malabsorption unit, Univ Rochester-Univ PR, San Juan, 70-73; assoc prof, Sch Med, Univ PR, San Juan, 70-73. *Mem:* Am Fedn Clin Res; Am Gastroenterol Asn; Am Soc Hemat; Am Soc Clin Nutrit; Am Soc Trop Med. *Res:* Diarrheal disorders; tropical malabsorption. *Mailing Add:* Dept of Med Univ of Rochester Med Ctr Rochester NY 14642

KLIR, GEORGE JIRI, b Prague, Czech, Apr 22, 32; m 62; c 2. SYSTEMS & COMPUTER SCIENCE. *Educ:* Tech Univ, Prague, MS, 57; Czech Acad Sci, PhD(comput sci), 64. *Prof Exp:* Res asst, Res Inst Telecommun, Prague, 51-52; lectr, Charles Univ, 62-64; lectr elec eng, Univ Baghdad, 64-66; lectr comput sci, Univ Calif, Los Angeles, 66-68; assoc prof elec eng, Fairleigh Dickinson Univ, 68-69; assoc prof, 69-72, PROF COMPUT SCI, SCH ADVAN TECHNOL, STATE UNIV NY, BINGHAMTON, 72-, CHMN DEPT SYSTS SCI, 76- *Concurrent Pos:* Ed, Czech Acad Sci, Prague, 62-63; IBM Systs Res Inst fel, 69; Ed-in-chief, Int J Gen Systs, Am Soc Cybernet, 74; Neth Inst Advan Studies fel, 75-76; Japan Soc Promotion Sci fel, 80. *Honors & Awards:* Advancing Gen Systs Res Award, Neth Soc Systs Res, 76; Outstanding Contribution to Systs Res & Cybernet Award, Austrian Soc Cybernet Studies. *Mem:* Sr mem Inst Elec & Electronics Engrs (pres); Philos Sci Asn; Soc Gen Systs Res (pres, 81); Soc Indust & Applied Math; Int Fed Systs Res (pres, 80-). *Res:* Switching and automata theory; logical design of digital computers; digital codes; cybernetic methodology; general systems theory and methodology; logical design of computers; computer architecture; discrete mathematics. *Mailing Add:* Dept of Systs Sci State Univ NY Binghamton NY 13901

KLISIEWICZ, JOHN MICHAEL, b Stanley, Wis, Jan 3, 29; m 59; c 3. PLANT PATHOLOGY. *Educ:* Wis State Col, River Falls, BS, 51; Univ Wis, PhD(plant path), 60. *Prof Exp:* RES PLANT PATHOLOGIST, USDA, 61- *Mem:* Am Phytopath Soc. *Res:* Diseases of oilseed crops; root rotting and vascular invading fungi; biological control of weeds. *Mailing Add:* Dept of Plant Path Col of Agr Univ of Calif Davis CA 95616

KLITGAARD, HOWARD MAYNARD, b Harlan, Iowa, Oct 16, 24; m 45; c 5. PHYSIOLOGY. *Educ:* Univ Iowa, BA, 49, MS, 50, PhD(physiol), 53. *Prof Exp:* Instr physiol, Univ Iowa, 51-53; from instr to prof, 53-78, asst chmn dept, 61-66, vchmn dept, 67-78, ADJ PROF, MED COL WIS, 78-; CHMN BASIC MED SCI, MARQUETTE UNIV SCH DENT, 78- *Concurrent Pos:* Consult, Vet Admin Hosp, Wood, Wis, 57- *Mem:* AAAS; Endocrine Soc; Am Physiol Soc; Soc Exp Biol & Med; Int Asn Dent Res. *Res:* Physiology and biochemistry of the thyroid hormone, endocrines and metabolism; radioisotope methodology. *Mailing Add:* Dept Basic Sci Marquette Univ Sch of Dent Milwaukee WI 53233

KLIVINGTON, KENNETH ALBERT, b Cleveland, Ohio, Sept 23, 40; m 68; c 1. ACADEMIC ADMINISTRATION, NEUROSCIENCE, COGNITIVE SCIENCE. *Educ:* Mass Inst Technol, SB, 62; Columbia Univ, MS, 64; Yale Univ, PhD(neurosci), 67. *Prof Exp:* Res engr electronics, Electronics Res Lab, Columbia Univ, 62-64; asst res neuroscientist, Univ Calif, San Diego, 67-68; dir res urban design, Fisher-Jackson Assocs, 68-69; prog officer sci, Alfred P Slaoan Found, 69-81; VPRES RES & DEV, ELECTRO-BIOL INC, 81- *Concurrent Pos:* Vis scientist, Univ Calif, San Diego, 73; consult, Nat Res Coun, 75-; vis comt, Dept Physchiat, Mass Inst Technol, 81- *Mem:* AAAS; Soc Neurosci; Bioelec Repair & Growth Soc; Cognitive Sci Soc. *Res:* Electromagnetic properties of biological tissues; neural correlates of behavior; neural information processing. *Mailing Add:* Electro-Biol Inc 300 Fairfield Rd Fairfield NJ 07006

KLIWER, JAMES KARL, b Abilene, Kans, Dec 17, 28; m 63. PHYSICS. *Educ:* Univ Colo, BS, 57, MS, 59, PhD, 63. *Prof Exp:* Asst, Nuclear Physics Lab, Univ Colo, 57-63; res assoc, 63-65, from asst prof to assoc prof, 65-75, PROF PHYSICS, UNIV NEV, RENO, 75- *Res:* Atomic and nuclear spectroscopy. *Mailing Add:* Dept of Physics Univ of Nev Reno NV 89557

KLOBUCHAR, RICHARD LOUIS, b Chicago, Ill, Oct 15, 48; m 71. NAVAL ANALYSIS. *Educ:* Univ Ill, BS, 70; Carnegie-Mellon Univ, MS, 72, PhD(chem), 75. *Prof Exp:* Res assoc nuclear chem, Brookhaven Nat Lab, 75-77; mem prof staff, Ctr Naval Analyses, 77-81; DIR ADV TECHNOL, INC, 81- *Mem:* Am Chem Soc; Am Nuclear Soc; Am Phys Soc. *Res:* Scientific analysis of naval weapons systems; analytical support of fleet activities; applications of positronium chemistry; high energy nuclear reactions. *Mailing Add:* 758 Suffolk Ln Virginia Beach VA 23452

KLOCK, BENNY LEROY, b Washington, DC, Oct 29, 34; m 57; c 3. ASTRONOMY. *Educ:* Cornell Univ, BA, 56, MS, 60; Georgetown Univ, PhD(astron), 64. *Prof Exp:* Tech asst dir six-inch transit circle div, 60-69, dir, Northern Transit Circle Div, 69-76, CHIEF INSTRUMENTATION BR, US NAVAL OBSERV, 76- *Honors & Awards:* NSF int grant, 74. *Mem:* AAAS; Am Astron Soc; Int Astron Union. *Res:* Design and development of transit circle instrumentation; microcomputer systems; determination of star positions; automation of telescopes; electro-optics system design. *Mailing Add:* US Naval Observ Washington DC 20390

KLOCK, GLEN ORVAL, b Portland, Ore, Aug 26, 37; m 58; c 4. FOREST SOILS. *Educ:* Ore State Univ, BS, 59, PhD(soil physics), 68; Iowa State Univ, MS, 63. *Prof Exp:* Res assoc soil physics, Ore State Univ, 64-67; prin res soil scientist, Pac Northwest Forest & Range Exp Sta, USDA Forest Serv, 68-82; PRIN SCIENTIST, G O KLOCK & ASSOC, 82- *Honors & Awards:* Unit Super Serv Award Sci & Educ, USDA, 74. *Mem:* Am Soc Agron; Soil Sci Soc Am; Soil Conserv Soc Am; Int Soil Sci Soc; Am Forestry Assoc. *Res:* Water resource and plant nutrient management for maintaining and enhancing the productivity of forest ecosystems in the western United States. *Mailing Add:* G O Klock & Assoc 2113 Sunrise Circle Wenatchee WA 98801

KLOCK, HAROLD F(RANCIS), b Miami Beach, Fla, Mar 21, 29; m 55; c 3. ELECTRICAL ENGINEERING. *Educ:* Northwestern Univ, BS, 52, MS, 54, PhD(elec eng), 56. *Prof Exp:* Lectr elec eng, Northwestern Univ, 56; asst prof, Case Western Reserve Univ, 56-62; prof lectr, 62-64; systs engr, Bailey Meter Co, Ohio, 64-66; PROF ELEC ENG, OHIO UNIV, 66- *Concurrent Pos:* Consult, Reliance Elec & Mfg Co, Nat Cash Register Co & Curtiss-Wright Corp. *Mem:* Inst Elec & Electronics Engrs; Asn Comput Mach; Soc Indust & Appl Math. *Res:* Feedback control systems; switching theory. *Mailing Add:* Dept of Eng Ohio Univ Athens OH 45701

KLOCK, JOHN W, b Orange, NJ, Nov 12, 28; m 53; c 2. SANITARY ENGINEERING. *Educ:* Southern Calif Univ, BE, 51; Univ Calif, Berkeley, MS, 56, PhD(sanit eng), 60. *Prof Exp:* PROF ENG, ARIZ STATE UNIV, 60- *Concurrent Pos:* Consult, Ariz Health Planning Authority, USPHS, 51-55, Commun Disease Ctr, 60- & Off Surgeon Gen, 61- *Mem:* Am Water Works Asn; Water Pollution Control Asn. *Res:* Communicable disease control; water pollution; waste water reclamation. *Mailing Add:* Col of Eng Ariz State Univ Tempe AZ 85281

KLOCKE, ROBERT ALBERT, b Buffalo, NY, Oct 4, 36; c 3. PULMONARY DISEASES, PULMONARY PHYSIOLOGY. *Educ:* Manhattan Col, BS, 58; State Univ NY Buffalo, MD, 62. *Prof Exp:* Res asst prof med, 70-71, from asst prof to assoc prof med, 71-78, from asst prof to assoc prof physiol, 76-81, PROF MED, STATE UNIV NY BUFFALO, 78-, CHIEF PULMONARY DIV, DEPT MED, 77-, PROF PHYSIOL, 81- *Concurrent Pos:* Chief pulmonary lab, Walter Reed Gen Hosp, Washington, DC, 63-66; mem attend staff, E J Meyer Mem Hosp, Buffalo, 70- *Mem:* Am Physiol Soc; Am Thoracic Soc; Am Fedn Clin Res. *Res:* Pulmonary gas exchange, particularly the rates of chemical reactions of carbon dioxide and oxygen in blood. *Mailing Add:* E J Meyer Mem Hosp 462 Grider St Buffalo NY 14215

KLOEPFER, HENRY WARNER, b Roseville, Ohio, Feb 25, 13; m 36; c 4. HUMAN GENETICS. *Educ:* Ohio Univ, BS, 34, MA, 38; Muskingum Col, BA, 35; Ohio State Univ, PhD(human genetics), 42. *Prof Exp:* Instr, Ohio Pub Sch, 35-36; asst zool, Ohio State Univ, 39-42; prof biol & head dept, Dakota Wesleyan Univ, 42-46; prof biol & chmn div, dean of men & acad dean, 46-47; prof biol & acad dean, Col of Ozarks, 47-52; assoc prof anat, 52-77, EMER ASSOC PROF ANAT, SCH MED, TULANE UNIV, 77- *Concurrent Pos:* Danforth vis lectr, Asn Am Cols, 62-66. *Mem:* Am Soc Human Genetics (treas, 58-60); Genetics Soc Am; World Fedn Neurol (secy, 61-65); Int Dermatoglyphics Asn (pres, 74-). *Res:* Genetics of rare genes; detection of genetic carrier. *Mailing Add:* 3033 La Ave Pkwy New Orleans LA 70125

KLOET, WILLEM MARINUS, b Neth. NUCLEAR PHYSICS. *Educ:* Univ Utrecht, PhD(theoret physics), 73. *Prof Exp:* Res assoc theoret physics, Inst Fisica Teorica, Sao Paulo, 68-70, Univ Md, 73-75 & Los Alamos Sci Lab, 75-77; ASST PROF THEORET PHYSICS, RUTGERS UNIV, 77- *Mem:* Am Phys Soc; AAAS. *Res:* Theoretical nuclear physics. *Mailing Add:* Dept of Physics & Astron Rutgers Univ New Brunswick NJ 08903

KLOETZEL, JOHN ARTHUR, b Cambridge, Mass, Mar 21, 41; m 62; c 4. CELL BIOLOGY, PROTOZOOLOGY. *Educ:* Univ Southern Calif, BA, 62; Johns Hopkins Univ, PhD(biol), 67. *Prof Exp:* NIH fel biol, Univ Colo, 67-70; asst prof, 70-75, ASSOC PROF BIOL, UNIV MD BALTIMORE COUNTY, 75- *Concurrent Pos:* Fel, Alexander von Humboldt Found, WGer, 78. *Mem:* Soc Protozool; Am Soc Cell Biol. *Res:* Fine-structural aspects of cellular function, development and differentiation. *Mailing Add:* Dept of Biol Sci Univ of Md Baltimore County Catonsville MD 21228

KLOETZEL, MILTON CARL, b Detroit, Mich, Aug 28, 13; m 38; c 4. ORGANIC CHEMISTRY. *Educ:* Univ Mich, BS, 34, PhD(org chem), 37. *Prof Exp:* Du Pont fel chem, Univ Mich, 37-38; instr, Harvard Univ, 38-41; from asst prof to assoc prof, DePauw Univ, 41-45; from asst prof to prof, 45-58, dean grad sch, 58-68, vpres res & grad affairs, 67-70, acad vpres, 70-75, EMER ACAD VPRES, UNIV SOUTHERN CALIF, 75- *Mem:* Am Chem Soc. *Res:* Chemistry of polycyclic and heterocyclic compounds; Diels-Alder reaction; chemistry of nitroparaffins. *Mailing Add:* Apt 1106A 425 Ena Rd Honolulu HI 96815

KLOKHOLM, ERIK, b Nykobing, Denmark, Mar 13, 22; US citizen; m 43. SOLID STATE PHYSICS. *Educ:* Mass Inst Technol, BS, 51; Temple Univ, PhD(physics), 60. *Prof Exp:* From res asst to head struct & metals br, Labs Res & Develop, Franklin Inst, 51-59; res physicist, Moorehead Patterson Res Ctr, Am Mach & Foundry Co, 59-61; assoc prof physics, State Univ NY Col Ceramics, Alfred Univ, 61-62; res staff mem, Thomas J Watson Res Ctr, 62-73, RES PROJ MGR, MFR RES LABS, DATA SYSTS DIV, IBM CORP, 73- *Mem:* NY Acad Sci. *Res:* Structure and properties of solids, particularly thin metallic films; crystallographic aspects of solid state physics. *Mailing Add:* 64 Willard Terr Stamford CT 06903

KLOMP, EDWARD, b Detroit, Mich, Oct 18, 30; m 59; c 3. MECHANICAL ENGINEERING, FLUID MECHANICS. *Educ:* Wayne State Univ, BS, 52, MS, 53. *Prof Exp:* Res engr, 53-59, assoc sr res engr, 59-65, sr res engr, 65-77, staff res engr, 77-80, SR STAFF RES ENGR, RES LABS, GEN MOTORS CORP, WARREN, 80- *Concurrent Pos:* Instr, Wayne State Univ, 55-65. *Mem:* Am Soc Mech Engrs; Soc Automotive Engrs; Sigma Xi. *Res:* Fluid mechanics relating to turbomachinery and internal combustion engines. *Mailing Add:* 36237 Acton Dr Mt Clemens MI 48043

KLOMPARENS, WILLIAM, b Holland, Mich, Jan 2, 22; m 49; c 3. PLANT PATHOLOGY. *Educ:* Mich State Univ, BS, 49, MS, 50, PhD, 53. *Prof Exp:* Asst dir agr prod div, 65-68, DIR AGR RES & DEVELOP, UPJOHN CO, 68- *Mem:* Am Phytopath Soc. *Res:* Agricultural pesticides, especially systemics; turf diseases; shade and forest diseases. *Mailing Add:* 124 S Prairie Ave Kalamazoo MI 49001

KLONTZ, EVERETT EARL, b Akron, Ohio, Sept 28, 21; m 42; c 3. PHYSICS. *Educ:* Kent State Univ, BS, 42; Univ Ill, MS, 43; Purdue Univ, PhD(physics), 52. *Prof Exp:* Asst physics, Univ Ill, 42-44; instr, Bowling Green State Univ, 44; asst, 46-52, res assoc & asst prof, 52-62, ASSOC PROF PHYSICS, PURDUE UNIV, WEST LAFAYETTE, 62- *Mem:* Am Phys Soc; Am Asn Physics Teachers. *Res:* Effects of high energy particle irradiations on physical properties of crystals. *Mailing Add:* Dept of Physics Purdue Univ West Lafayette IN 47901

KLOPATEK, JEFFREY MATTHEW, b Milwaukee, Wis, Dec 5, 44; m 67; c 1. ECOLOGY, BOTANY. *Educ:* Univ Wis-Milwaukee, BS, 71, MS, 74; Univ Okla, PhD(bot), 78. *Prof Exp:* Res assoc ecol, Okla Biol Surv, 73-76; res ecologist, Environ Sci Div, Oak Ridge Nat Lab, 76-81; PROF & RES ECOLOGIST, DEPT BOT & MICROBIOL, ARIZ STATE UNIV, 81- *Concurrent Pos:* Consult, Elec Power Res Inst; lectr, Univ Tenn, 80-81; chmn, Municipal Planning Comn, Farragut, Tenn, 80-81. *Mem:* Ecol Soc Am; Int Asn Ecol; Am Inst Biol Sci; Int Asn Aquatic Vascular Plant Biologists; Interdisciplinary Group Ecol Develop & Energy. *Res:* Regional ecology; energy analysis; urban ecology; wetland ecology; plant ecology and the integration of natural and cultural systems. *Mailing Add:* Dept Bot Ariz State Univ Tempe AZ 85287

KLOPFENSTEIN, CHARLES E, b Los Angeles, Calif, July 6, 40; m 63. PHYSICAL ORGANIC CHEMISTRY, CHEMICAL INSTRUMENTATION. *Educ:* Univ Ore, BA, 62, PhD(chem), 66. *Prof Exp:* Asst prof chem, 66-80, DIR LABS, UNIV ORE, 66-, ASSOC PROF, 80- *Concurrent Pos:* NATO res fel, Lab Org Chem, Swiss Fed Inst Technol, 66-67. *Mem:* Am Chem Soc. *Res:* Synthesis of aromatic heterocyclic compounds; calculation of physical properties of aromatic compounds; computer analysis of physical data. *Mailing Add:* Dept of Chem Univ of Ore Eugene OR 97403

KLOPFENSTEIN, KENNETH F, b Mt Pleasant, Iowa, Mar 13, 40; m 61; c 3. MATHEMATICS. *Educ:* Iowa Wesleyan Col, BA, 61; Colo State Univ, MS, 63; Purdue Univ, PhD(math), 67. *Prof Exp:* Instr math, Wabash Col, 66-67; asst prof, 67-73, ASSOC PROF MATH, COLO STATE UNIV, 73- *Mem:* Math Asn Am; Am Math Soc. *Res:* Hilbert space; operator theory; mathematics education. *Mailing Add:* Dept of Math Colo State Univ Ft Collins CO 80521

KLOPFENSTEIN, RALPH WALTER, b Aberdeen, SDak, June 3, 23; m 48, 54; c 3. APPLIED MATHEMATICS. *Educ:* Univ Wash, Seattle, BS, 44; Iowa State Col, MS, 51, PhD(math), 54. *Prof Exp:* Instr math, SDak Sch Mines & Technol, 46-48; elec engr antennas, Victor Div, Radio Corp Am, 48-50; instr math, Iowa State Col, 50-53; res engr antennas & microwaves, Radio Corp Am Labs, 53-57, head math serv, 57-62; dir comput ctr, Iowa State Univ, 62-63; RES ENGR NUMERICAL ANAL & DIGITAL COMPUT, RCA LABS, 63- *Mem:* Am Math Soc; Soc Indust & Appl Math; Am Math Asn; As Comput Mach; Inst Elec & Electronics Eng. *Res:* Electromagnetic theory, antennas and cavities; electrical networks; numerical analysis; digital and scientific computation. *Mailing Add:* PO Box 537 Princeton NJ 08540

KLOPFENSTEIN, WILLIAM ELMER, b Paris, Ohio, Dec 23, 35; m 60; c 3. BIOCHEMISTRY. *Educ:* Pa State Univ, BS, 58, MS, 61, PhD(biochem), 64. *Prof Exp:* Asst technologist food res, Gen Foods Corp, 58; instr biochem, Pa State Univ, 60-64; asst prof, 64-72, ASSOC PROF BIOCHEM & ASSOC BIOCHEMIST, AGR EXP STA, KANS STATE UNIV, 72-, CHMN GRAD BIOCHEM GROUP, 77- *Mem:* Am Chem Soc; Sigma Xi; Am Soc Biol Chemists; Am Oil Chem Soc. *Res:* Structure and function of lipids; physical properties of lipids; binding of lipids to proteins. *Mailing Add:* Dept of Biochem Kans State Univ Manhattan KS 66502

KLOPFER, PETER HUBERT, b Berlin, Ger, Aug 9, 30; m 55; c 3. ZOOLOGY. *Educ:* Univ Calif, Los Angeles, AB, 52; Yale Univ, PhD(zool), 57. *Prof Exp:* Head sci dept, Windsor Mountain Sch, Mass, 52-53 & 55-56; USPHS fel, Cambridge Univ, 57-58; from asst prof to assoc prof zool, 58-68, PROF ZOOL & DIR FIELD STA ANIMAL BEHAV, DUKE UNIV, 68- *Concurrent Pos:* Nat Inst Ment Health career develop award, 65; Alexander von Humboldt Prize, 79-80. *Honors & Awards:* Nat Inst Ment Health Res Scientist Award, 70. *Mem:* Fel AAAS; Ecol Soc Am; Brit Ornith Union; fel Animal Behav Soc; Int Soc Res Aggression. *Res:* Behavior and ecology, especially analysis of the development of species-specific behavior in birds and mammals; maternal-filial relations and aggression. *Mailing Add:* Dept of Zool Duke Univ Durham NC 27706

KLOPMAN, GILLES, b Brussels, Belg, Feb 24, 33; m 57. CHEMISTRY. *Educ:* Free Univ Brussels, Lic es Sci, 56, Dr es Sci, 60. *Prof Exp:* Res assoc org chem, Cyanamid Europ Res Inst, 60-67; assoc prof chem, 67-69, PROF CHEM, CASE WESTERN RESERVE UNIV, 69-, CHMN, CHEM DEPT, 81- *Concurrent Pos:* Welch fel, Univ Tex, 65-66. *Mem:* Am Chem Soc; The Chem Soc; Swiss Chem Soc; Belg Chem Soc; Am Asn Univ Professors. *Res:* Applied theoretical organic chemistry; chemical reactivity; nucleophilic reactivity; quantum mechanical calculation of large organic molecules; quantitative structure activity relationship of carcinogenic molecules. *Mailing Add:* Dept of Chem Case Western Reserve Univ Cleveland OH 44106

KLOPOTEK, DAVID L, b Green Bay, Wis, Jan 11, 42; m 63; c 2. ORGANIC CHEMISTRY. *Educ:* St Norbert Col, BA, 64; Utah State Univ, PhD(chem), 68. *Prof Exp:* Res assoc chem, E I du Pont de Nemours & Co, Inc, 67-68; asst prof, 68-71, ASSOC PROF CHEM, ST NORBERT COL, 71- *Concurrent Pos:* NSF grant, 71-73; Res Corp grant, 72-74. *Mem:* Am Chem Soc. *Res:* Chemistry of compounds containing nitrogen-fluorine bonds; reactivity of fluoronitrene with nucleophiles. *Mailing Add:* Dept of Chem St Norbert Col DePere WI 54115

KLOPP, CALVIN TREXLER, b Atlantic City, NJ, Dec 7, 12; m; c 3. SURGERY. *Educ:* Swarthmore Col, BA, 34; Harvard Univ, MD, 38. *Prof Exp:* Intern surg, Boston City Hosp, Mass, 39-40; rotating intern med, Reading Hosp, Pa, 40-41; resident, Mem Hosp, New York, 41-44; from asst clin prof to assoc prof, 46-60, Warwick prof surg, Sch Med, 60-76, med dir, Univ Clin, 68-76, EMER PROF SURG, SCH MED, GEORGE WASHINGTON UNIV, 76- *Concurrent Pos:* Consult, various hosps, 46- *Mem:* Am Radium Soc; Am Asn Cancer Res; Am Col Surgeons; James Ewing Soc; Am Thyroid Asn. *Res:* Cancer. *Mailing Add:* 4119 61st Ave Terrace W Bradenton FL 33507

KLOPPING, HEIN LOUIS, b Utrecht, Holland, Feb 7, 21; nat US; m 50; c 2. ORGANIC CHEMISTRY, BIOCHEMISTRY. *Educ:* State Univ Utrecht, BS, 41 & 43, MS, 46, PhD(chem), 51. *Prof Exp:* Lab asst, Med Chem Lab, State Univ Utrecht, 44-45, asst & instr org chem, 46-47; chem engr, Standard Oil Co, 47; res chemist & group leader, Inst Org Chem, State Univ Utrecht, 47-51; res chemist, 51-55, res scientist, 55-62, RES ASSOC, E I DU PONT DE NEMOURS & CO, INC, 62- *Mem:* Am Chem Soc; Sigma Xi. *Res:* Organic synthesis; agricultural chemicals; drugs; cancer research; protein chemistry; cell metabolism; structure versus odor; electrophysiology. *Mailing Add:* Exp Sta Bldg 324 E I du Pont de Nemours & Co Wilmington DE 19898

KLOS, EDWARD JOHN, b Hamilton, Ont, June 27, 25; m 49; c 2. PLANT PATHOLOGY. *Educ:* Ont Agr Col, BSAg, 50; Cornell Univ, PhD(plant path), 54. *Prof Exp:* Asst plant path, Cornell Univ, 50-54; from asst prof to assoc prof, 54-67, PROF PLANT PATH, MICH STATE UNIV, 67-, CHMN DEPT, 80- *Mem:* Am Phytopath Soc. *Res:* Effect of Erwinia herbicola on fire blight of pome fruits; population studies of Erwinia amylovora; resistance or tolerance of Venturia inaequalis to fungicides; control of tree fruit diseases by chemicals and other means. *Mailing Add:* Dept of Bot & Plant Path Mich State Univ East Lansing MI 48824

KLOS, WILLIAM ANTON, b Houston, Tex, Aug 14, 36; m 63; c 1. ELECTRICAL ENGINEERING. *Educ:* Univ Houston, BS, 63 & 64, PhD(elec eng), 69. *Prof Exp:* Res asst elec eng, Univ Houston, 66-69; prin engr, Lockheed Electronics Co, Tex, 69-70; assoc prof, 70-80, PROF ELEC ENG, UNIV SOUTHWESTERN LA, 80-, HEAD DEPT, 70- *Mem:* Inst Elec & Electronics Engrs; Acoust Soc Am; Am Soc Eng Educ; Am Geophys Union; Nat Soc Prof Engrs. *Res:* Electromagnetic wave propagation; radar cross-section and radar systems. *Mailing Add:* Dept of Elec Eng Box 873 Univ of Southwestern La Lafayette LA 70504

KLOSE, JULES ZEISER, b St Louis, Mo, Aug 7, 27; m 58; c 4. ATOMIC PHYSICS, VACUUM ULTRAVIOLET RADIOMETRY. *Educ:* Wash Univ, St Louis, AB, 49; Univ Rochester, MS, 53; Cath Univ Am, PhD(physics), 58. *Prof Exp:* Physics aid, US Naval Gun Factory, 48; instr, Dunford Sch, Mo, 49; asst physics, Univ Rochester, 49-53; from asst prof to assoc prof, US Naval Acad, 53-61; PHYSICIST, NAT BUR STANDARDS, 61- *Concurrent Pos:* Res assoc & lectr, Univ Mich, 60-61. *Mem:* Am Phys Soc; Am Asn Physics Teachers; Sigma Xi. *Res:* Vacuum ultraviolet radiometry; measurement of atomic lifetimes and transition probabilities; ultrasonics; thermal relaxation in gases; cosmic rays. *Mailing Add:* Nat Bur Standards Washington DC 20234

KLOSE, THOMAS RICHARD, b Adelaide, Australia, Apr 20, 46; m 74; c 2. ORGANIC CHEMISTRY. *Educ:* Univ Adelaide, BSc, 67, Hons, 68, PhD(org chem), 72. *Prof Exp:* Fel org chem, Res Inst Med & Chem, 72-74 & Mass Inst Technol, 74-75; RES CHEMIST ORG CHEM, EASTMAN KODAK CO RES LABS, 75- *Mem:* Am Chem Soc. *Res:* Synthesis of novel dyes and pigments for use in non-silver imaging systems. *Mailing Add:* Eastman Kodak Co Res Labs 1669 Lake Ave Rochester NY 14650

KLOSEK, RICHARD C, b Olyphant, Pa, Feb 18, 33; m 56; c 3. MICROBIOLOGY. *Educ:* Univ Scranton, BS, 54; St John's Univ, MS, 56, PhD(microbiol), 60. *Prof Exp:* From asst prof to assoc prof, 60-74, PROF MICROBIOL, FAIRLEIGH DICKINSON UNIV, 74- *Concurrent Pos:* Res grants, Fairleigh Dickinson Univ, 61-62 & 71; res grant, Jomol Pharmaceut Corp, 63-64, consult, 65; mem, Smithsonian Inst, 74. *Mem:* Fel AAAS; Am Acad Microbiol; Soc Protozool; Sigma Xi. *Res:* Protozoan nutrition and cellular chemistry, especially pathways associated with carbohydrate, protein and lipid metabolism; isolation and functional aspects of chemotherapeutic agents utilized in bacterial, fungal and viral diseases. *Mailing Add:* Dept of Biol Sci Fairleigh Dickinson Univ Rutherford NJ 07070

KLOSNER, JEROME M, b New York, NY, Mar 23, 28; m 65; c 3. APPLIED MECHANICS, STRUCTURAL DYNAMICS. *Educ:* City Col New York, BCE, 48; Columbia Univ, MS, 50; Polytech Inst Brooklyn, PhD(appl mech), 59. *Prof Exp:* Sr stress analyst, Repub Aviation Corp, 52-56; sr scientist appl mech, Res & Advan Develop Div, Avco Corp, 56; res assoc, 56-59, res asst prof, 59-62, assoc prof, 62-67, PROF APPL MECH, POLYTECH INST NEW YORK, 67- *Concurrent Pos:* Consult, Res & Advan Develop Div, Avco Corp, Gen Appl Sci Labs, Fed Trade Comn, Res Ctr, Ingersoll-Rand Corp & Technautics Corp; consult, Weidlinger Assocs, Consult Engrs, 76-; mem comt on recommendations US Army basic sci res, Nat Res Coun, 76-79. *Mem:* Am Soc Mech Engrs; assoc fel Am Inst Aeronaut & Astronaut; Soc Rheol; fel Am Soc Civil Engrs. *Res:* Structural Dynamics; hydroelasticity; acoustic radiation. *Mailing Add:* Dept of Mech & Aerospace Eng 333 Jay St Brooklyn NY 11201

KLOSTERMAN, EARLE WAYNE, b Plankinton, SDak, Oct 3, 19; m 45; c 3. ANIMAL HUSBANDRY. *Educ:* SDak State Col, BS, 42; Cornell Univ, MS, 43; PhD(animal husb), 46. *Prof Exp:* Asst animal husb, Cornell Univ, 42-46; asst prof, SDak State Col, 46-47; assoc prof, NDak Col, 47-52; assoc prof, Ohio Agr Exp Sta, 52-68, PROF ANIMAL SCI & ASSOC CHMN DEPT, OHIO AGR RES & DEVELOP CTR, 68- *Mem:* AAAS; Am Soc Animal Sci. *Res:* Nutrient requirements of sheep; function of trace minerals in sheep and swine nutrition; methianine content and utilization of various feed stuffs by chicks and rats; protein requirements and value of urea for fattening lamb; nutrient requirements of beef cattle, beef cattle breeding and management. *Mailing Add:* Ohio Agr Res & Develop Ctr Wooster OH 44691

KLOSTERMAN, ELLIOT LEE, b Mt Vernon, Wash, Oct 13, 48; m 71; c 3. ENERGY TECHNOLOGY, LASER TECHNOLOGY. *Educ:* Univ Wash, BS, 70, MS, 71. *Prof Exp:* RES SCIENTIST, MAT SCI NORTHWEST, INC, 71- *Res:* Energy conversion; laser physics; high temperature and unsteady gas dynamics; non equilibrium gas chemistry. *Mailing Add:* Math Sci Northwest Inc 2755 Northup Way Bellevue WA 98004

KLOSTERMAN, HAROLD JOSEPH, b Mooreton, NDak, Jan 11, 24; m 46; c 7. BIOCHEMISTRY. *Educ:* NDak State Univ, BS, 46, MS, 49; Univ Minn, PhD(biochem), 55. *Prof Exp:* From asst to assoc chemist, 46-57, prof agr biochem & chmn dept, 57-68, PROF BIOCHEM & CHMN DEPT, NDAK STATE UNIV, 68- *Mem:* Am Chem Soc. *Res:* Isolation and characterization of natural products. *Mailing Add:* Dept of Biochem NDak State Univ Fargo ND 58102

KLOSTERMEYER, EDWARD CHARLES, b Omaha, Nebr, Feb 25, 19; m 41; c 2. ENTOMOLOGY. *Educ:* Univ Nebr, BSc, 40, MSc, 42; State Col Wash, PhD, 52. *Prof Exp:* Asst entom, Univ Nebr, 40-42; asst, Univ Calif, 46-47; asst entomologist, Irrig Exp Sta, 47-58, assoc entomologist, 58-62, entomologist, 62-81, prof, 75-81, EMER PROF ENTOM, WASH STATE UNIV, 81- *Mem:* Entom Soc Am. *Res:* Field crop insect control; insect pollination; bee behavior. *Mailing Add:* Dept of Entom Wash State Univ Pullman WA 99164

KLOSTERMEYER, LYLE EDWARD, b Oakland, Calif, Dec 4, 44. ENTOMOLOGY. *Educ:* Wash State Univ, BS, 68; NDak State Univ, MS, 74; Univ Nebr, PhD(entom), 78. *Prof Exp:* Res asst dept entom, NDak State Univ, 70-73 & Univ Nebr, 73-78; asst prof entom, Dept Agr Biol, 78-80, ASST PROF ENTOM, DEPT ENTOM & PLANT PATH, UNIV TENN, 80- *Mem:* Entom Soc Am; Sigma Xi. *Res:* Biology and control of forage and pasture insects. *Mailing Add:* Dept Entom & Plant Path PO Box 1071 Univ Tenn Knoxville TN 37901

KLOTZ, ARTHUR PAUL, b Milwaukee, Wis, Sept 28, 13; m 41; c 4. CLINICAL MEDICINE. *Educ:* Univ Chicago, SB & MD, 38. *Prof Exp:* Asst in med, Univ Chicago, 49-51, instr, 51-54; from asst prof to prof med, Med Ctr, Univ Kans, 54-75, dir, Div Gastroenterol, 54-75; DIR GASTROINTESTINAL LAB, BOSWELL MEM HOSP, SUN CITY, 75- *Concurrent Pos:* Consult, Menorah Hosp, Vet Hosp, Kansas City, Mo & Wadsworth, Kans; mem, Gastroenterol Res Group; res collabr, Brookhaven Nat Lab, NY; pvt pract clin gastroenterol, 75-; ed, Boswell Hosp Proc, 80- *Mem:* Am Soc Gastrointestinal Endoscopy; Soc Nuclear Med; Am Gastroenterol Asn; Am Pancreatic Asn; Am Col Physicians. *Res:* Gastric secretions; pancreatic function; liver disease; ulcerative colitis; small bowel absorption in humans by perfusion technique. *Mailing Add:* 9802 112th Ave Sun City AZ 85351

KLOTZ, EUGENE ARTHUR, b Fredericksburg, Iowa, June 25, 35; m 57; c 2. MATHEMATICS. *Educ:* Antioch Col, BS, 58; Yale Univ, PhD(math), 65. *Prof Exp:* Actg instr math, Yale Univ, 62-63; instr, 63-69, assoc prof, 69-77, PROF MATH, SWARTHMORE COL, 77- *Concurrent Pos:* NSF sci fac fel, 74; prin investr, prog math educ using info technol, NSF-Nat Inst Educ, 81-82. *Mem:* Am Math Soc; Math Asn Am; Asn Comput Mach; Asn Develop Comput Based Instrnl Systs. *Res:* Real-time microcomputer color graphics units for mathematics instruction, using video arcade technology; social science mathematics. *Mailing Add:* Dept of Math Swarthmore Col Swarthmore PA 19081

KLOTZ, FREDERICK SUCCOP, theoretical physics, see previous edition

KLOTZ, IRVING MYRON, b Chicago, Ill, Jan 22, 16; m 47, 66. PHYSICAL BIOCHEMISTRY. *Educ:* Univ Chicago, SB, 37, PhD(chem), 40. *Prof Exp:* Asst chem, Univ Chicago, 37-39; Abbott res assoc, 40, Nat Defense Res Comt assoc, 41-42, from instr to prof, 42-63, MORRISON PROF CHEM, NORTHWESTERN UNIV, EVANSTON, 63- *Concurrent Pos:* Lalor fel, 47-48; chmn biophys & biophys chem, Study Sect, NIH, 63-66; mem corp & trustee, Marine Biol Lab, Woods Hole; Reilly lectr, Univ Notre Dame; Mack lectr, Ohio State Univ; Barton lectr, Univ Okla; Gooch-Stephens lectr, Baylor Univ; Welch lectr, Univ Tex, 73; Winzler lectr, Fla State Univ, 77; Steiner lectr, Oberlin, 81. *Honors & Awards:* Lilly Award, 49; Midwest Award, Am Chem Soc, 70. *Mem:* Nat Acad Sci; fel Am Acad Arts & Sci; Am Chem Soc; Am Soc Biol Chem; fel Royal Soc Med. *Res:* Structure and function of proteins and polymers; spectroscopy; biochemical energetics; thermodynamics. *Mailing Add:* Dept of Chem Northwestern Univ Evanston IL 60201

KLOTZ, JAMES ALLEN, b Milwaukee, Wis, Oct 18, 22; m 26; c 3. PETROLEUM ENGINEERING, APPLIED MATHEMATICS. *Educ:* Northwestern Univ, BS, 44; Univ Mich, MS, 47. *Prof Exp:* Engr, Manhattan Proj, US Naval Res Lab, 44-46; res engr, Oil Field Res Div, Calif Res Corp, 47-58; petrol engr, Arabian Am Oil Co, 58-60; res technologist, Pure Oil Co, 60-62; sr res technologist, 62-65; eng assoc, 66-70, supvr, Arctic Ocean & reservoir eng res, 70-81, SUPVR WELLBORE MECH RES, UNION OIL CO CALIF, 81- *Concurrent Pos:* Mem tech adv comt, Sucker Rod Pumping Res, Inc, 61-64; mem drilling domain comt, Div Prod, Am Petrol Inst, 61-64, mem adv comt fundamental res origin & recovery of petrol, 65, mem tech adv comt, Ocean Margin Drilling Proj, 79-81, mem prod res adv comt, 81- *Mem:* AAAS; Soc Petrol Engrs; Am Inst Chem Engrs. *Res:* Oil well drilling; reservoir engineering; thermal secondary recovery; application of computer methods to oil fild engineering; application of operations research methods to oil field engineering; offshore and arctic engineering for oil production. *Mailing Add:* Union Res Ctr Union Oil Co of Calif PO Box 76 Brea CA 92621

KLOTZ, JEROME HAMILTON, b Loma Linda, Calif, June 21, 34; m 56; c 2. BIOSTATISTICS. *Educ:* Univ Calif, Berkeley, AB, 56, PhD(statist), 60. *Prof Exp:* Lectr math & statist, McGill Univ, 60-61; asst prof statist, Univ Calif, Berkeley, 61-62; asst prof, Harvard Univ, 62-65; assoc prof, 65-69, PROF STATIST, UNIV WIS-MADISON, 69- *Concurrent Pos:* Consult

statistician clin oncol, Univ Wis, 72-; prof statist, Cent Oncol Group, 72- & Wis Clin Cancer Ctr, 73-; prof, Ohio State Univ, 81-82. *Mem:* Fel Inst Math Statist; Am Statist Asn; Biometrics Soc. *Res:* Nonparametric methods; computer techniques; components of variance; biostatistical methods. *Mailing Add:* Dept of Statist Univ of Wis Madison WI 53706

KLOTZ, JOHN WILLIAM, b Pittsburgh, Pa, Jan 10, 18; m 42; c 7. GENETICS, PHILOSOPHY OF SCIENCE. *Educ:* Univ Pittsburgh, MS, 40, PhD(genetics), 47; Concordia Sem, BD, 41. *Prof Exp:* Lab asst, Univ Pittsburgh, 40; instr, Concordia Collegiate Inst, 41-43; prof sci, Bethany Lutheran Col, 43-45; from assoc prof to prof biol, physiol & nature study, Concordia Teachers Col, 45-59; prof natural sci, Concordia Sr Col, 59-74; PROF PRACTICAL THEOL, CONCORDIA SEM, 74-, DIR GRAD STUDIES, 77- *Concurrent Pos:* Registr, Bethany Lutheran Col, 44-45. *Mem:* AAAS; Am Genetic Asn; Nat Sci Teachers Asn; Nat Asn Biol Teachers. *Res:* Genetics of Habrobracon and Mormoniella; ecology; physiology; lethals, semi-lethals and an inversion in Habrobracon juglandis. *Mailing Add:* 5 Seminary Terr St Louis MO 63105

KLOTZ, LOUIS HERMAN, b Elizabeth, NJ, May 21, 28; m 66; c 2. CIVIL ENGINEERING. *Educ:* Pa State Univ, BSCE, 51; NY Univ, MCE, 56; Rutgers Univ, New Brunswick, PhD(civil eng), 67. *Prof Exp:* Struct engr, firms, NY & NJ metrop area, 51-56; civil engr, Ebasco Int Corp, New York, 56-58, construct proj engr defense electronic prod, Missile & Surface Radar Div, Radio Corp Am , NJ, 58-59; res assoc civil eng, Univ Ill, Urbana, 59-61; consult engr, Ohio & NJ, 61-65; asst prof, 65-69, acting chmn dept, 69-71, chmn dept, 71-73, ASSOC PROF CIVIL ENG, UNIV NH, 69-; PRES, DURHAM INST, 80- *Concurrent Pos:* Ed, Energy Sources, Promises & Probs, 80. *Mem:* AAAS; Am Soc Civil Engrs; Am Soc Eng Educ; Int Asn Bridge & Struct Engrs; NY Acad Sci. *Res:* applications of linear graph system; mathematical models and computer applications in structures, foundations and soil mechanics; small hydro-power technical and economic analyses and design. *Mailing Add:* Dept of Civil Eng Kingsbury Hall Univ of NH Durham NH 03824

KLOTZ, LYNN CHARLES, b Trenton, NJ, Nov 25, 40; c 1. PHYSICAL BIOCHEMISTRY. *Educ:* Princeton Univ, AB, 65; Univ Calif, San Diego, PhD(chem), 71. *Prof Exp:* Res asst molecular biol, Princeton Univ, 61-62, res assoc, 65-66; asst prof biochem, Harvard Univ, 71-74, assoc prof, 74-80; WITH BIOTECHANICA INT, 80- *Mem:* AAAS; Fedn Am Scientists; Sigma Xi. *Res:* Physical studies of DNA and chromosomes; evolution of DNA and chromosomes. *Mailing Add:* Biotechanica Int 85 Bolton St Cambridge MA 02140

KLOTZ, RICHARD LAWRENCE, b Philadelphia, Pa, Jan 4, 50; m 75; c 2. BIOLOGY. *Educ:* Denison Univ, BS, 72; Univ Conn, MS, 75, PhD(bot), 79. *Prof Exp:* ASST PROF BIOL, STATE UNIV NY CORTLAND, 79- *Mem:* Phycol Soc Am; Am Soc Limnol & Oceanog; AAAS; Sigma Xi. *Res:* Effects of pollutants on algae, including heavy metal, sewage, and agricultural pollution and acid precipitation; response of streams to agriculture. *Mailing Add:* Dept Biol Sci State Univ NY Box 2000 Cortland NY 13045

KLOTZBACH, ROBERT J(AMES), b New York, NY, Aug 27, 22; m 46; c 1. CHEMICAL ENGINEERING. *Educ:* Fordham Univ, BS, 43. *Prof Exp:* Develop engr, Oak Ridge Nat Lab, 46-48, design engr, 48-53, design problem leader, 53, chmn long range planning group, Chem Technol Div, 53-55; proj engr, Union Carbide Nuclear Div, 55-57, mgr eng dept, 57-65, mgr, Union Carbide Mining & Metals Div, 65-69, asst dir eng, 69, dir eng, 69-72, DIR TECHNOL, UNION CARBIDE METALS DIV, UNION CARBIDE CORP, 72- *Mem:* Am Chem Soc; Am Nuclear Soc; Am Inst Chem Engrs. *Res:* Solvent extraction; power reactor fuel reprocessing; mining and milling; ion exchange. *Mailing Add:* 5140 Dana Dr Lewiston NY 14092

KLOUDA, MARY ANN ABERLE, b Peoria, Ill, Jan 8, 37; m 62; c 4. PHYSIOLOGY. *Educ:* Col Notre Dame, Calif, BA, 58; Loyola Univ, Ill, PhD(physiol), 64. *Prof Exp:* Res assoc physiol, Loyola Univ, Ill, 64-65; from instr to asst prof, Univ Mass, Amherst, 65-71; lectr, 74-79, asst prof, 79-82, ASSOC PROF BIOL, COL OF OUR LADY OF THE ELMS, 82- *Mem:* Assoc Am Physiol Soc; Sigma Xi. *Res:* Cardiac response to sympathetic stimulation; effects of cardiac sympathectomy. *Mailing Add:* 2 Greenwood Ln South Hadley MA 01075

KLOVAN, JOHN EDWARD, geology, see previous edition

KLOWDEN, MARC JEFFREY, b Chicago, Ill, June 6, 48; m 70. MEDICAL ENTOMOLOGY. *Educ:* Univ Ill, Chicago Circle, BS, 70, MS, 73, PhD(biol), 76. *Prof Exp:* Res asst biol, Univ Ill, Chicago Circle, 70-73, teaching asst biol, 73-76; RES ASSOC, DEPT ENTOMOL, UNIV GA, 76- *Mem:* AAAS; Entom Soc Am; Sigma Xi; Am Soc Trop Med & Hyg; Am Mosquito Control Asn. *Res:* Physiology of mosquito host-seeking. *Res:* Insect transmission of human enteropathogens; insect tissue culture. *Mailing Add:* Dept of Entomol Univ of Ga Athens GA 30602

KLUBA, RICHARD MICHAEL, b Altoona, Pa, July 16, 47; m 81. FOOD SCIENCE, ANALYTICAL CHEMISTRY. *Educ:* Pa State Univ, BS, 69, MS, 73; Cornell Univ, PhD(food sci), 77. *Prof Exp:* Res assoc, 77-80, DIR RES, TAYLOR WINE CO INC, 80- *Mem:* Inst Food Technol; Am Soc Enologists; Sigma Xi. *Res:* Wine chemistry; analytical instrumentation. *Mailing Add:* Taylor Wine Co Inc Hammondsport NY 14840

KLUBEK, BRIAN PAUL, b Buffalo, NY, Apr 21, 48; m 72; c 3. SOIL MICROBIOLOGY, MICROBIAL ECOLOGY. *Educ:* Colo State Univ, BS, 71; Ore State Univ, MS, 74; Utah State Univ, PhD(microbiol ecol), 77. *Prof Exp:* Res assoc microbiol, NC State Univ, 77-78; ASST PROF SOIL MICROBIOL, SOUTHERN ILL UNIV, CARBONDALE, 78- *Concurrent Pos:* Comt mem, Pesticide Waste Mgt Task Force, Ill Environ Protection Agency, 81-; prin investr, Ill Inst Environ Qual, 81- *Mem:* Am Soc Microbiol; Am Soc Agron; Soil Sci Soc Am; Sigma Xi. *Res:* Symbiotic nitrogen fixation; biological sulfur oxidation in strip mine soils; disposal of waste pesticide solutions. *Mailing Add:* Dept Plant & Soil Sci Southern Ill Univ Carbondale IL 62901

KLUBES, PHILIP, b Brooklyn, NY, June 23, 35; m 64; c 2. PHARMACOLOGY. *Educ:* Queens Col, NY, BS, 56; Univ Minn, MS, 59, PhD(biochem), 62. *Prof Exp:* Res fel bact, Harvard Med Sch, 62-63; res assoc microbiol, Sch Med, Univ Southern Calif, 63-64, instr, 64-65; asst res prof, 65-70, asst prof, 70-73, assoc prof, 73-79, PROF PHARMACOL, MED CTR, GEORGE WASHINGTON UNIV, 79- *Concurrent Pos:* Res fel, USPHS, 62-63 & Bank Am/Giannini Med Found, 63-64. *Mem:* Am Chem Soc; Am Asn Cancer Res; Am Soc Pharmacol & Exp Therapeut; AAAS. *Res:* Studies on the mechanism of action and physiological disposition of anticancer agents. *Mailing Add:* Dept of Pharmacol Med Ctr George Washington Univ Washington DC 20037

KLUCAS, ROBERT VERNON, b Montevideo, Minn, Oct 19, 40; m 66; c 2. MICROBIAL BIOCHEMISTRY, PLANT BIOCHEMISTRY. *Educ:* SDak State Col, BS, 62; Univ Wis, MS, 64, PhD(biochem), 67. *Prof Exp:* Res asst biochem, Univ Wis, 62-67; res assoc plant physiol, Ore State Univ, 67-69; asst prof biochem, 69-75, assoc prof, 75-81, PROF BIOCHEM, UNIV NEBR, LINCOLN, 81- *Concurrent Pos:* NIH fel, Ore State Univ, 67-68. *Mem:* Am Soc Plant Physiol; Am Soc Microbiol. *Res:* Biological nitrogen fixation. *Mailing Add:* Lab Agr Biochem Univ Nebr Lincoln NE 68583

KLUENDER, HAROLD CLINTON, b Baraboo, Wis, Jan 28, 44; m 69; c 2. ORGANIC CHEMISTRY, MEDICINAL CHEMISTRY. *Educ:* Univ Wis-Stevens Point, BS, 66; Univ Wis-Madison, MS, 68; Wesleyan Univ, PhD(org chem), 71. *Prof Exp:* Res assoc org chem, Pharmaceut Dept, Univ Wis, 72-73; RES SCIENTIST & SUPVR MED CHEM, NATURAL PROD LAB, MILES LABS, INC, 73- *Concurrent Pos:* NIH fel org chem, Harvard Univ, 70-72. *Mem:* Am Chem Soc; AAAS. *Res:* Prostanoids, chemistry and biological activity. *Mailing Add:* Miles Labs Inc PO Box 40 Elkhart IN 46515

KLUEPFEL, DIETER, b Zurich, Switz, Oct 7, 30; Can citizen; m 59; c 2. MICROBIOLOGY, BIOCHEMISTRY. *Educ:* Swiss Fed Inst Technol, Dipl sc nat, 54, Dr sc nat, 56. *Prof Exp:* Res asst microbiol, Swiss Fed Inst Technol, 54-56, res assoc biochem, 56-57; Nat Res Coun Can fel, 57-58; res scientist microbiol, Lepetit SPA, Milan, Italy, 59-61, head lab biochem, 61-65; sr res scientist microbiol, Ayerst Labs, 65-70, res assoc, 70-75; RES PROF, INST A FRAPPIER, UNIV QUE, MONTREAL, 75- *Concurrent Pos:* Lectr, Univ Montreal, 70-78; adj prof, Univ Concordia, Montreal, 78- *Res:* Microbial metabolism; biosynthesis of natural products; biodegradation and bioconversion; isolation of secondary metabolites and antibiotics. *Mailing Add:* Inst Armand-Frappier Univ Que Montreal Ville de Laval PQ H7N 4Z3 Can

KLUETZ, MICHAEL DAVID, b Wausau, Wis, June 20, 48. BIOPHYSICAL CHEMISTRY. *Educ:* Univ Wis-Madison, BS, 71; Univ Ill, Urbana, PhD(phys chem), 75. *Prof Exp:* ASST PROF CHEM, UNIV IDAHO, 75-, ASST PROF BIOCHEM, 80- *Mem:* Am Chem Soc; Biophys Soc. *Res:* Biophysical, particularly magnetic resonance, studies of enzyme systems which are responsible for the degradation of several physiologically important polyamines and histamine in both plant and animal systems. *Mailing Add:* Dept of Chem Univ of Idaho Moscow ID 83843

KLUG, DENNIS DWAYNE, b Milwaukee, Wis, Aug 22, 42; m 62; c 1. PHYSICAL CHEMISTRY. *Educ:* Univ Wis-Milwaukee, BS, 64; Univ Wis-Madison, PhD(phys chem), 68. *Prof Exp:* Fel, 68-70, RES CHEMIST, NAT RES COUN CAN, 70- *Mem:* Sigma Xi. *Res:* Experimental and theoretical studies of lattice vibrations in crystalline and disordered solids; far-infrared and high pressure techniques and instrumentation. *Mailing Add:* Div of Chem Nat Res Coun of Can Ottawa ON K1A 0R9 Can

KLUG, MICHAEL J, b Milwaukee, Wis, Mar 7, 41; m 69. MICROBIOLOGY, ECOLOGY. *Educ:* SDak State Univ, BS, 63; Univ Iowa, MS, 66, PhD(microbiol), 69. *Prof Exp:* NIH res fel microbiol, Univ Ill, Urbana, 69-70; mem staff, 70-80, ASSOC PROF, W K KELLOGG BIOL STA, MICH STATE UNIV, 80- *Mem:* AAAS; Am Chem Soc; Am Soc Microbiol; Am Inst Biol Sci. *Res:* Ecology and metabolism of heterotrophic bacteria in natural waters and insects. *Mailing Add:* W K Kellogg Biol Sta Mich State Univ Hickory Corners MI 49060

KLUG, WILLIAM STEPHEN, b Parkersburg, WVa, Sept 2, 41; m 62; c 3. BIOLOGY. *Educ:* Wabash Col, BA, 63; Northwestern Univ, PhD(develop genetics), 68. *Prof Exp:* Instr biol, Wabash Col, 63-65, asst prof, 68-73; assoc prof biol & chmn dept, 73-78, PROF BIOL, TRENTON STATE COL, 79- *Mem:* Genetics Soc Am; Am Soc Zool; Soc Cell Biol; Soc Develop Biol; Sigma Xi. *Res:* Developmental genetics in the ovarian system of Drosophila melanogaster. *Mailing Add:* Dept of Biol Trenton State Col Trenton NJ 08625

KLUGE, ARNOLD GIRARD, b Glendale, Calif, July 27, 35; m 59; c 2. VERTEBRATE ZOOLOGY. *Educ:* Univ Southern Calif, BA, 57, MS, 60, PhD(biol), 64. *Prof Exp:* Lectr embryol, Univ Southern Calif, 64; asst prof comp anat, San Fernando Valley State Col, 64-65; asst prof comp anat & embryol, 65-66, assoc prof zool, 74-76, ASSOC CUR, MUS ZOOL, UNIV MICH, ANN ARBOR, 66-, PROF ZOOL, 76- *Concurrent Pos:* Res asst, Los Angeles Ment Health Asn grant, 58; NSF grants, 59 & 69-71, USPHS grant, 60-61; Fulbright scholar, Australia, 61-62; Am Philos Soc grant, 69; Guggenheim fel, 71-72; NSF fel, 60, Sigma Xi & Sci Res Soc Am fel, 63. *Mem:* AAAS; Am Soc Ichthyol & Herpet; Soc Study Evolution; Soc Syst Zool. *Res:* Evolution; numerical taxonomy; herpetology. *Mailing Add:* Dept of Zool Univ of Mich Ann Arbor MI 48104

KLUGE, JOHN PAUL, b St Louis, Mo, July 7, 37; m 58; c 4. VETERINARY PATHOLOGY, COMPARATIVE PATHOLOGY. *Educ:* Univ Mo, BS & DVM, 62; Iowa State Univ, MS, 65; George Washington Univ, PhD(comp path), 68; Am Col Vet Path, dipl, 70. *Prof Exp:* Res vet, Nat Animal Dis Lab, 62-68; from assoc prof to prof path, 68-75, PROF VET PATH & CHMN DEPT, IOWA STATE UNIV, 75- *Concurrent Pos:* Consult, Agr Res Serv & Animal & Plant Health Inspection Serv, USDA. *Mem:* AAAS; Am Vet Med Asn; Wildlife Dis Asn; Conf Res Workers Animal Dis; Am Col Vet Path. *Res:* Comparative pathology of infectious diseases and neoplasms. *Mailing Add:* Dept of Vet Path Iowa State Univ Ames IA 50011

KLUGER, MATTHEW JAY, b Brooklyn, NY, Dec 14, 46; m 67; c 2. PHYSIOLOGY. *Educ:* Cornell Univ, BS, 67; Univ Ill, MS, 69, PhD(zool), 70. *Prof Exp:* NIH fel, Yale Univ & J B Pierce Found Lab, 70-72; asst prof, 72-76, assoc prof, 76-81, PROF PHYSIOL, MED SCH, UNIV MICH, ANN ARBOR, 81- *Mem:* Am Physiol Soc; Am Soc Zoologists; Soc Exp Biol Med. *Res:* Temperature regulation and bioenergetics; evolution and adaptive value of fever; host responses to infection. *Mailing Add:* 7620 Med Sci II Univ of Mich Med Sch Ann Arbor MI 48109

KLUGER, RONALD H, b Newark, NJ, Dec 22, 43; m 69; c 2. ORGANIC CHEMISTRY, BIOCHEMISTRY. *Educ:* Columbia Univ, AB, 65; Harvard Univ, AM, 66, PhD(chem), 69. *Prof Exp:* NIH fel biochem, Brandeis Univ, 69-70; asst prof chem, Univ Chicago, 70-74; asst prof, 74-76, assoc prof, 76-81, PROF CHEM, UNIV TORONTO, 81- *Concurrent Pos:* Sloan Found fel, 73. *Mem:* Chem Inst Can; Am Chem Soc. *Res:* Mechanisms of biochemical catalysis and related organic reaction mechanisms; thiamin, biotin and enzymes; enzyme inhibitors based on mechanistic analysis; functional group interactions and reactive intermediates. *Mailing Add:* Dept of Chem Univ of Toronto Toronto ON M5S 1A1 Can

KLUGHERZ, PETER D(AVID), b Brooklyn, NY, Feb 25, 42; m 62; c 4. CHEMICAL ENGINEERING. *Educ:* Cornell Univ, BChE, 63, PhD(chem eng), 69. *Prof Exp:* SR CHEMIST, RES LABS, ROHM AND HAAS CO, PHILADELPHIA, 68- *Mem:* Am Chem Soc; Am Inst Chem Engrs; Catalysis Soc. *Res:* Heterogeneous catalytic oxidation; monomer process research. *Mailing Add:* 760 Killdeer Lane Huntingdon Valley PA 19006

KLUIBER, RUDOLPH W, b Chicago, Ill, Feb 20, 30; m 55. INORGANIC CHEMISTRY. *Educ:* Univ Ill, BS, 50; Columbia Univ, AM, 52; Univ Wis, PhD(chem), 54. *Prof Exp:* Chemist, Plastics Div, Union Carbide Corp, 54-64; res assoc, Princeton Univ, 64-66; from asst prof to assoc prof, 66-71, PROF CHEM, RUTGERS UNIV, NEWARK, 71- *Mem:* Am Chem Soc. *Res:* Metal chelate compounds. *Mailing Add:* Dept of Chem Rutgers Univ Newark NJ 07102

KLUKSDAHL, HARRIS EUDELL, b Bismarck, NDak, Mar 4, 33; m 57; c 3. EXTRACTIVE MATALLURGY, CATALYSIS. *Educ:* Western Wash State Col, BA, 54; Univ Wash, PhD(inorg chem), 58. *Prof Exp:* Res chemist, E I du Pont de Nemours & Co, 58-60; SR RES ASSOC, CHEVRON RES CO, 60- *Mem:* AAAS. *Res:* Heterogeneous hydroprocessing catalysts for petroleum refining. *Mailing Add:* Chevron Res Co 576 Standard Ave Richmond CA 94802

KLUMPAR, DAVID MICHAEL, b Jacksonville, Fla, Apr 14, 43; m 64; c 2. SPACE PHYSICS. *Educ:* Univ Iowa, BA, 65, MS, 68; Univ NH, PhD(physics), 73. *Prof Exp:* Res assoc physics, Univ NH, 72-74; res assoc space physics, Inst Phys Sci, 74-77, RES SCIENTIST, CTR SPACE SCI, UNIV TEX, DALLAS, 78- *Mem:* Am Geophys Union; assoc mem Sigma Xi; Am Phys Soc. *Res:* Investigations of the low energy charged particle environment in the earth's near magnetosphere and interactions between the magnetosphere and ionosphere, especially at high latitudes in the auroral region. *Mailing Add:* Ctr for Space Studies Univ of Tex PO Box 688 Richardson TX 75080

KLUMPP, THEODORE GEORGE, b New York, NY, May 15, 03; m 34; c 6. INTERNAL MEDICINE. *Educ:* Princeton Univ, BS, 24; Harvard Univ, MD, 28. *Hon Degrees:* DSc, Philadelphia Col Pharm, 43, New Eng Col Pharm, 61 & Albany Med Col, 64; LLD, Univ Chattanooga, 60. *Prof Exp:* Intern, Peter Bent Brigham Hosp, 29-30; asst resident physician, Lakeside Hosp, Cleveland, 30-32; instr & asst clin prof internal med, Med Sch, Yale Univ, 32-36; chief drug div, Food & Drug Admin, Fed Security Agency, Washington, DC, 36-41; dir drugs, food & phys ther & secy coun pharm & chem, Am Med Asn, Ill, 41-42; mem bd gov, Sterling-Winthrop Res Inst, 46-60, pres, Winthrop Labs Div, Sterling Drug, Inc, 42-70, chmn, 70-73, mem bd dirs & vpres, Sterling Drug, Inc, 60-73. *Concurrent Pos:* Assoc physician, New Haven Hosp, 32-36, chief hemat clin & dir med lab, 33-36; adj clin prof, Med Sch, George Washington Univ, 40-41; attend physician, Gallinger Munic Hosp, 41; mem pharmaceut mfrs indust adv comt & penicillin producers indust adv comt, War Prod Bd, 42-47; chmn bd gov, Nat Vitamin Found, 47-56; dir, Sterwin Chem, Inc, 49-70; chmn task force on handicapped, Off Defense Mobilization, Washington, DC, 51-52; pres, Nat Pharmaceut Coun, Inc, 53-55; chmn med serv task force, Hoover Comn on Orgn Exec Br Govt, 53-55; mem study comt fed aid to pub health, Comn Inter-Govt Rels, Washington, DC, 54; mem, Nat Adv Coun Voc Rehab, 55-59; consult surgeon, Chesapeake & Ohio RR, 56-; mem bd vis, Sch Pub Health, Harvard Univ, 58-64 & Med & Dent Schs, 64-70; mem med adv comt, Off Voc Rehab, 60-62; mem health resources adv comt, Off Emergency Planning, Exec Off of President, 62-69; mem, NY State Voc Rehab Coun, 67-73; secy, Nat Fund Med Educ, 68-69, pres, 69-71, chmn, 71-75, vpres, 75-80; mem bd trustees, Brooklyn Col Pharm, Long Island Univ, 68-77, chmn, 74-77; mem comt on aging, Coun Med Serv, AMA; mem, Gov Coun Rehab, NY & Found Trop Med; mem bd trustees, Affil Cols & Univs, Inc, 72-; med consult, President's Coun Phys Fitness & Sports, 73-; assoc ed, Med Times, 73-; mem bd trustees, Human Resources Sch, NY, 74- & Arnold & Marie Schwartz Col Pharm & Health Sci, Long Island Univ, 77-; chmn bd dirs, Nat Asn Human Develop, 74-80. *Mem:* AAAS; fel Am Soc Clin Invest; fel Am Col Physicians; fel AMA. *Res:* Therapeutics; materia medica; medical pharmacology; hematology; physiological chemistry. *Mailing Add:* 90 Park Ave New York NY 10016

KLUN, JEROME ANTHONY, b Ely, Minn, May 4, 39; m 66; c 3. ENTOMOLOGY. *Educ:* Univ Minn, Duluth, BS, 61; Iowa State Univ, PhD(entom), 65. *Prof Exp:* Res asst, Iowa State Univ, 61-65; RES SCI & EDUC ADMIN-AGR RES, USDA, 65- *Concurrent Pos:* Assoc prof entom, Iowa State Univ, 69-77. *Mem:* AAAS; Am Chem Soc; Entom Soc Am. *Res:* Chemical factors associated with host plant resistance to insects; insect sex pheromones. *Mailing Add:* USDA Agr Res BARC Beltsville MD 20705

KLUNDT, IRWIN LEE, b Pasco, Wash, Aug 7, 36; m 59; c 3. ORGANIC CHEMISTRY. *Educ:* State Col Wash, BS, 58; Mont State Univ, MS, 59; Wayne State Univ, PhD(org chem), 63. *Prof Exp:* Chemist, Detroit Inst Cancer Res, 63; sr res scientist, Pac Northwest Labs, Battelle Mem Inst, 65-66; proj leader, Aldrich Chem Co, 66, group leader, 66-71, biochem tech mgr, 71-73, tech serv mgr, 73-74, VPRES, ALDRICH CHEM CO, INC, 74-, DIR, 78-, VPRES, SIGMA-ALDRICH CORP, 75-, DIR, SIGMA CHEM CO, 78- *Mem:* Am Chem Soc; NY Acad Sci. *Res:* Aliphatic and alicyclic chemistry; small ring compounds; carbohydrates. *Mailing Add:* 2320 Kevenauer Dr Brookfield WI 53005

KLUS, JOHN P, b Goodman, Wis, June 13, 35; m 61; c 4. STRUCTURAL & CIVIL ENGINEERING. *Educ:* Mich Technol Univ, BS, 57, MS, 61; Univ Wis, PhD(civil eng), 65. *Prof Exp:* Appraiser, Am Appraisal Co, 57-58; res engr designer, Eng & Res Develop Labs, Va, 58-59; instr, Mich Technol Univ, 60-61; instr drawing, Univ Wis, 61-62; struct designer, Warzyn Eng Co, 62; from instr to assoc prof, 62-70, chmn dept, 67-70, PROF STRUCT & CHMN, DEPT ENG & APPL SCI, UNIV WIS-EXTENSION, 70- *Concurrent Pos:* Fulbright scholar, Finland, 66-67; chmn, Working Group Continuing Educ Engrs, UNESCO, 73-; gen chmn, 1st World Conf Continuing Eng Educ, 79. *Mem:* AAAS; Am Soc Civil Engrs; Am Soc Eng Educ; Nat Soc Prof Engrs; Am Public Works Asn. *Res:* Structural design; continuing education research, esthetics water towers, renewable resources. *Mailing Add:* Dept of Eng & Appl Sci Univ of Wis-Exten 432 N Lake St Madison WI 53706

KLUSMAN, RONALD WILLIAM, b Batesville, Ind, June 16, 41; m 64; c 2. GEOCHEMISTRY. *Educ:* Ind Univ, Bloomington, BS, 64, MS, 67, PhD(geochem), 69. *Prof Exp:* Instrumental analyst geochem, Ind Geol Surv, 64-67; asst prof, Purdue Univ, 69-72; assoc prof, 72-77, PROF GEOCHEM, COLO SCH MINES, 77-, PROF CHEM, 80- *Mem:* Geol Soc Am; Soc Environ Geochem & Health. *Res:* Trace elements in geological and environmental systems; instrumental analysis; computer applications in geology. *Mailing Add:* Dept of Chem & Geochem Colo Sch of Mines Golden CO 80401

KLUSS, BYRON CURTIS, b Luzerne, Iowa, May 25, 28. CELL BIOLOGY. *Educ:* Univ Iowa, BA, 49, MS, 55, PhD(zool), 57. *Prof Exp:* Asst zool, Univ Iowa, 53-57; instr, Albion Col, 57-59; from asst prof to assoc prof biol, 59-66, dir spec progs, 70-75, prof biol, 66-80, PROF ZOOL, CALIF STATE UNIV, LONG BEACH, 80- *Concurrent Pos:* Lalor Found fel, 58; Fulbright fel, Assiut, 65-66. *Mem:* Am Soc Zool; Am Soc Cell Biol; Electron Micros Soc Am. *Res:* Cytology; bioluminescence; electron microscopy. *Mailing Add:* Dept of Biol Calif State Univ Long Beach CA 90840

KLUTCHKO, SYLVESTER, b Wilkes-Barre, Pa, Sept 2, 33; m 62; c 3. SYNTHETIC ORGANIC CHEMISTRY. *Educ:* Pa State Univ, BS, 55. *Prof Exp:* From asst scientist to scientist org chem, 55-75, SR SCIENTIST ORG CHEM, WARNER-LAMBERT CO, INC, ANN ARBOR, 75- *Mem:* Am Chem Soc. *Res:* Heterocyclic synthesis of certain chromones which have been studied as antiallergy agents, especially their chemistry and preparation by novel synthetic precedure. *Mailing Add:* 5143 Pratt Rd Scio Twp Ann Arbor MI 48103

KLUTE, ARNOLD, b Galein, Mich, Sept 24, 21; m 48; c 4. AGRONOMY. *Educ:* Mich State Col, BS, 47, MS, 48; Cornell Univ, PhD(soil physics), 51. *Prof Exp:* Res engr, Schlumberger Well Surv Corp, 51-53; from asst prof to prof agron, Univ Ill, 53-70; PROF SOILS, COLO STATE UNIV, 70-; RES LEADER IRRIG & SOIL-PLANT-WATER RELS, AGR RES SERV, USDA, FT COLLINS, 78- *Concurrent Pos:* With US Salinity Lab, Riverside, Calif, 60; soil scientist, Sci & Educ Admin-Agr Res, USDA, 70-78. *Honors & Awards:* Soil Sci Award, Am Soc Agron, 65. *Mem:* Am Soc Agron; Soil Sci Soc Am; Am Geophys Union. *Res:* Investigations of the transport of water, gases, heat, and solutes in soils. *Mailing Add:* 1112 Parkwood Dr Ft Collins CO 80525

KLUVER, J(OHAN) W(ILHELM), b Monaco, Nov 13, 27; m 64; c 2. COMMUNICATIONS. *Educ:* Royal Inst Technol, Sweden, Engr, 51; Univ Calif, MS, 55, PhD, 57. *Prof Exp:* Engr TV develop, Thomson-Houston Co, France, 53-54; asst prof elec eng, Univ Calif, 57-58; mem tech staff, Bell Tel Labs, 58-68; PRES, EXPS IN ART & TECHNOL, INC, 68- *Mem:* Assoc Am Phys Soc; Assoc Inst Elec & Electronics Engrs; Optic Soc Am; Soc Info Display. *Res:* Microwave electronics; electron dynamics; electron devices; microwave tubes; gas lasers; optics. *Mailing Add:* Exps in Art & Technol Inc 49 E 68th St New York NY 10021

KLYCE, STEPHEN DOWNING, b Arlington, Mass, Oct 30, 42; m 64; c 3. PHYSIOLOGY. *Educ:* Univ Mass, BS, 64; Yale Univ, PhD(physiol), 71. *Prof Exp:* Res assoc ocular physiol, Yale Univ, 71-72; res assoc, 72-75, sr res assoc ocular physiol, Stanford Univ, 75-79; PROF OPHTHAMOL, MED SCH, LA STATE UNIV, 79- *Concurrent Pos:* Co-prin investr res grant, Nat Eye Inst, NIH, 72-79; consult, Vet Admin Hosp, Palo Alto, Calif, 76-79. *Mem:* Asn Res Vision & Ophthal; Biophys Soc; Am Physiol Soc; Int Soc Eye Res. *Res:* Physiology and biophysics of membrane transport and permeability in epithelial tissues. *Mailing Add:* Eye Ctr La State Univ 136 S Roman St New Orleans LA 70112

KMAK, WALTER S(TEVEN), b Garfield, NJ, June 5, 28; m 59; c 4. CHEMICAL ENGINEERING. *Educ:* Pa State Univ, BS, 49; Univ Ill, MS, 50, PhD, 56. *Prof Exp:* Res chem engr, Esso Res & Eng Co, 55-64, sr engr, 64-74, eng assoc, 74-79, SR ENG ASSOC, EXXON RES & ENG CO, 79- *Mem:* Am Chem Soc; Am Inst Chem Engrs. *Res:* Chemical reaction kinetics; catalytic reforming; engineering computer applications. *Mailing Add:* Exxon Res & Eng Co PO Box 101 Florham Park NJ 07932

KMETEC, EMIL PHILIP, b Carlinville, Ill, Sept 29, 27; m 55; c 5. BIOLOGICAL CHEMISTRY. *Educ:* Univ Chicago, MS, 53; Univ Wis, PhD(plant physiol), 57. *Prof Exp:* Asst bot, Univ Chicago, 50-52; asst plant physiol, Iowa State Univ, 52-53; asst, Univ Wis, 53-57, res assoc, 57; res assoc

biochem, Sch Med, La State Univ, 57-60; sr instr biochem & pediat, Sch Med, Western Reserve Univ, 60-61, asst prof, 61-64; from assoc prof to prof biol, 64-75, PROF BIOL CHEM, SCH MED & COL SCI & ENG, WRIGHT STATE UNIV, 75-, ASST VPRES ACAD AFFAIRS, 79- *Mem:* AAAS; Am Chem Soc; NY Acad Sci; Sigma Xi. *Res:* RNA metabolism and protein synthesis; synthesis and control of kidney membranes; purine metabolism. *Mailing Add:* Dept of Biol Chem Wright State Univ Dayton OH 45431

KMETKO, EDWARD ANDREW, physics, see previous edition

KMETZ, JOHN MICHAEL, b Johnstown, Pa, Jan 14, 43; m 66; c 3. HISTOLOGY, CYTOCHEMISTRY. *Educ:* Pa State Univ, BS, 64, PhD(physiol), 68. *Prof Exp:* Asst prof biol, Pa State Univ, 68-73; res dir, Sci Unlimited Res Found, 73-78; ASST PROF BIOL SCI, KEAN COL NJ, 78- *Mem:* NY Acad Sci; Am Inst Biol Sci. *Res:* Quantitative histochemistry and cytophotometry. *Mailing Add:* Dept of Biol Morris Ave Union NJ 07083

KMIECIK, JAMES EDWARD, b New Waverly, Tex, Feb 11, 36; m 59; c 1. ORGANIC CHEMISTRY. *Educ:* St Edwards Univ, BS, 56; Univ Tex, MA, 60, PhD(chem), 61. *Prof Exp:* Res chemist, Cities Serv Res & Develop Co, 61-64; sr res chemist, Columbia Carbon Co, 64-66; sr res chemist, 66-68, proj chemist, 68-70, mgr amine prod develop, Mkt Dept, 70-77, MGR NEW PROD DEVELOP, COM DEVELOP DIV, JEFFERSON CHEM CO, 77- *Mem:* Soc Aerospace Mat & Process Engrs; Am Chem Soc. *Res:* Synthesis of organic nitrogen heterocyclic compounds; reactions of carbon monoxide with organic compounds; reactions of aliphatic and aromatic nitro compounds. *Mailing Add:* Mkt Dept Com Develop Div Jefferson Chem Co PO Box 430 Bellaire TX 77401

KNAAK, JAMES BRUCE, b Milwaukee, Wis, Aug 20, 32; m 58; c 3. BIOCHEMISTRY, TOXICOLOGY. *Educ:* Univ Wis, BS, 54, MS, 57, PhD(biochem, dairy husb), 62. *Prof Exp:* Res asst dairy husb, biochem & entom, Univ Wis, 56-61; Union Carbide Indust fel biochem, Mellon Inst, 61-66, sr fel, 67; sr res chemist, Niagara Chem Div, FMC Corp, 67-71; group leader agr chem, CIBA-Geigy Corp, 71-73; STAFF TOXICOLOGIST, CALIF DEPT FOOD & AGR, 73- *Mem:* AAAS; Am Chem Soc; Soc Toxicol; NY Acad Sci; fel Am Inst Chem. *Res:* Toxicology and metabolism of organophosphate and carbamate insecticides; urea and s-triazine herbicides; metabolism of industrial chemicals; biochemical pharmacology; dermal dose response and dermal absorption studies; environmental monitoring; behavioral and biochemical pharmacology. *Mailing Add:* Calif Dept of Food & Agr 1220 N St Sacramento CA 95814

KNABE, GEORGE W, JR, b Grand Rapids, Mich, June 29, 24; m 54; c 4. PATHOLOGY. *Educ:* Univ Md, MD, 49. *Prof Exp:* Fel path, Cleveland Clin Found, 50-51; resident path, Henry Ford Hosp, Detroit, 53-54; chief lab serv, Vet Admin Ctr, Dayton, Ohio, 55-57; med ed adv, Int Coop Admin, 57-59; asst prof path & chief clin lab, Sch Med, Puerto Rico, 59-60; prof path & chmn dept, Sch Med, Univ SDak, 60-72, dean sch med, 67-72; assoc dean clin affairs, 72-75, PROF PATH, SCH MED, UNIV MINN, DULUTH, 72- *Concurrent Pos:* Mem staff, Va Munic Hosp, Virginia, Minn, 77- *Mem:* AMA; Am Soc Clin Pathologists; Col Am Pathologists; Int Acad Pathologists. *Res:* Infectious disease. *Mailing Add:* Va Munic Hosp 901 Ninth St N Virginia MN 55792

KNABESCHUH, LOUIS HENRY, b Louisville, Ky, Jan 31, 26; m 50; c 7. RUBBER CHEMISTRY. *Educ:* Univ Louisville, BS, 51, MS, 52, PhD(chem), 54. *Prof Exp:* Chemist, E I du Pont de Nemours & Co, Inc, Ky, 54-55, CHEMIST, E I DU PONT DE NEMOURS & CO, INC, 55- *Mem:* Am Chem Soc. *Res:* Hydrocarbon rubbers, primarily ethylenepropylene copolymers. *Mailing Add:* E I du Pont de Nemours & Co Inc PO Box 3269 Beaumont TX 77704

KNACKE, ROGER FRITZ, b Sttutgart, Ger, June 22, 41; US citizen. ASTROPHYSICS, ASTRONOMY. *Educ:* Univ Calif, Berkeley, BA, 63, PhD(physics), 69. *Prof Exp:* Fel astron, Lick Observ, Univ Calif, 70-71; asst prof astron, 71-74, assoc prof, 74-79, PROF ASTRON, DEPT EARTH SCI, STATE UNIV NY STONY BROOK, 79- *Concurrent Pos:* Vis scientist, Max Plank Inst Nuclear Physics, Heidelberg, Ger, 78- *Mem:* Am Astron Soc. *Res:* Composition of interstellar grains; molecular abundances in stellar atmospheres; infrared astronomy; planetary atmospheres. *Mailing Add:* Dept of Earth & Space Sci State Univ NY Stony Brook NY 11790

KNAEBEL, KENT SCHOFIELD, b Cincinnati, Ohio, Aug 20, 51; m 73; c 2. CHEMICAL ENGINEERING. *Educ:* Univ Ky, BSChE, 73; Univ Del, MChE, 78, PhD(chem eng), 80. *Prof Exp:* Chem engr, Tenn Eastman Co; instr chem eng, Univ Del, 79-80; ASST PROF CHEM ENG, OHIO STATE UNIV, 80- *Concurrent Pos:* Vis scientist, Brookhaven Nat Lab, 81. *Mem:* AAAS; Am Chem Soc; Am Inst Chem Engrs; Am Soc Eng Educ. *Res:* Separation process: cyclic sorption, including both gas and liquid phase versions; computer applications: real-time, data-acquisitoin, interactive computer-graphic design techniques, simulation and process design. *Mailing Add:* Dept Chem Eng Ohio State Univ 140 W 19th Ave Columbus OH 43210

KNAFF, DAVID BARRY, b New York, NY, June 5, 41; m 62; c 1. PHOTOBIOLOGY. *Educ:* Mass Inst Technol, BS, 62; Yale Univ, MS, 63, PhD(chem), 66. *Prof Exp:* Biochemist, Dept Cell Physiol, Univ Calif, Berkeley, 66-76; assoc prof chem, 76-80, PROF CHEM, TEX TECH UNIV, 80- *Mem:* Biophys Soc; Am Soc Photobiol; Am Soc Plant Physiol; AAAS; Am Soc Biol Chemists. *Res:* Electron transport in plants and photosynthetic bacteria with emphasis on the roles of cytochromes and iron-sulfur proteins. *Mailing Add:* Dept of Chem Tex Tech Univ PO Box 4260 Lubbock TX 79409

KNAGGS, EDWARD ANDREW, b Oak Park, Ill, July 28, 22; m 47; c 2. ORGANIC CHEMISTRY. *Educ:* YMCA Col, BS, 45; Ill Inst Technol, MS, 53. *Prof Exp:* Pilot plant technician, Glue Div, Swift & Co, 42; asst chemist, Inst Gas Technol, 42-45; res chemist, Ninol Labs, Inc, 45-49; chief chemist & plant engr, 49-58; assoc tech dir, 58-62, asst to gen mgr, 65-69, DIR RES

& DEVELOP, STEPAN CHEM CO, 62-, TECH DIR INDUST CHEM DIV, 69- *Mem:* AAAS; Am Chem Soc; Am Oil Chemists' Soc; Water Pollution Control Fedn; Am Water Works Asn. *Res:* Organic synthesis; organic sulfur compounds; desulfurization of gas and petroleum; SO3 sulfation and sulfonation; surface-active agents. *Mailing Add:* 715 Colwyn Terr Deerfield IL 60015

KNAKE, ELLERY LOUIS, b Gibson City, Ill, Aug 26, 27; m 51; c 2. WEED SCIENCE, AGRONOMY. *Educ:* Univ Ill, BS, 49, MS, 50, PhD(agron), 60. *Prof Exp:* Teacher, High Sch, Ill, 50-56; instr plant sci, Voc Agr Serv, 56-60, from asst prof to assoc prof agron, 60-69, PROF AGRON, UNIV ILL, URBANA, 69- *Concurrent Pos:* ed, Weeds Today Mag, 78-82; mem comt on integrated pest mgt, Off Technol Assessment, 79. *Honors & Awards:* Crops & Soils Mag Award, Am Soc Agron, 67; Outstanding Exten Worker, Weed Sci Soc Am, 72; Outstanding Contrib Agr, Ciba-Geigy, 72; Educr Award, Midwest Agr Chem Asn, 75; Funk Award, Col Agr, Univ Ill, 78; Exten Award, Am Soc Agron, 78. *Mem:* Fel Weed Sci Soc Am (pres, 74); fel Am Soc Agron. *Res:* Competitive effects of giant foxtail; cultivation versus chemical weed control; herbicide incorporation; improving effectiveness of pre-emergence herbicides; site of herbicide uptake. *Mailing Add:* N323 Turner Hall Univ Ill 1102 S Goodwin Ave Urbana IL 61801

KNAP, JAMES E(LI), b Denver, Colo, Oct 5, 26; m 49; c 6. CHEMICAL ENGINEERING. *Educ:* Univ Colo, BS, 49; Univ Ill, MS, 51, PhD(chem eng), 53. *Prof Exp:* Asst chem eng, Ill, 49-50; chem engr, Process Develop Lab, Carbide & Carbon Chem Co, 52-55; group leader, Res & Develop Dept, Union Carbide Chem Div, 55-68, asst mgr, Invest Recovery Dept, 68-74, GEN MGR, INVEST RECOVERY DEPT, UNION CARBIDE CORP, 74- *Honors & Awards:* Bronze Medal & Chromium Plating Award, Am Electroplaters Soc, 67; Distinguished Serv Award, Am Inst Chem Engrs, 73. *Mem:* Am Chem Soc; Am Inst Chem Engrs; Am Electroplaters Soc; Nat Soc Prof Engrs. *Res:* High pressure reactions; reaction kinetics; reactions of carbon monoxide; organometallic reactions; vapor plating; unit operations. *Mailing Add:* 110 Elizabeth St Charleston WV 25311

KNAPHUS, GEORGE, b McCallsburg, Iowa, Aug 31, 24; m 47; c 4. PLANT PATHOLOGY. *Educ:* Univ Northern Iowa, BA, 49; Iowa State Univ, MS, 51, PhD(plant path), 64. *Prof Exp:* Prin & teacher, High Sch, Iowa, 58-62; from instr to assoc prof bot, 62-72, PROF BOT, IOWA STATE UNIV, 72-, PROF SEC EDUC, 80- *Mem:* Am Phytopath Soc; Bot Soc Am; Am Inst Biol Sci. *Res:* Fungistasis of soil fungi. *Mailing Add:* Dept of Bot & Plant Path Iowa State Univ Ames IA 50011

KNAPP, ALPHIA EUGENE, engineering mechanics, see previous edition

KNAPP, ANTHONY WILLIAM, b Morristown, NJ, Dec 2, 41; m 63; c 2. ANALYSIS, LIE GROUPS. *Educ:* Dartmouth Col, BA, 62; Princeton Univ, MA, 64, PhD(math), 65. *Prof Exp:* C L E Moore instr math, Mass Inst Technol, 65-67; from asst prof to assoc prof, 67-75, PROF MATH, CORNELL UNIV, 75- *Concurrent Pos:* Mem, Inst Advan Study, NJ, 68-69 & 75-76; invited address, Int Congress Math, 74; res assoc, Princeton Univ, 71; prof d'exchange, Univ de Paris-Sud, Orsay, 72-; vis assoc prof, Rice Univ, 73; vis scholar, Univ Chicago, 81. *Mem:* Am Math Soc. *Res:* Bounded functions on groups; boundary values of harmonic functions; representations of semi-simple Lie groups. *Mailing Add:* Dept of Math Cornell Univ Ithaca NY 14853

KNAPP, CHARLES FRANCIS, b Evansville, Ind, Mar 28, 40; m 68; c 2. BIOENGINEERING, AEROSPACE ENGINEERING. *Educ:* St Procopius Col, BA, 62; Univ Notre Dame, BS, 63, MS, 65, PhD(aerospace eng), 68. *Prof Exp:* Asst prof, 68-80, ASSOC PROF MECH ENG, UNIV KY, 80- *Concurrent Pos:* Prin investr, NASA grant; co-investr, USAF & US Pub Health Serv grants. *Mem:* Am Inst Aeronaut & Astronaut. *Res:* Response of mammalian organisms to centrifugally simulated gravities and related stress environments; cardiovascular changes during whole body vibration; computer modeling of the cardiovascular system; childbirth simulation; blood rheology. *Mailing Add:* Wenner-Gren Aeronaut Res Lab Univ of Ky Lexington KY 40506

KNAPP, CHARLES H, b New York, NY, June 8, 31; m 55; c 4. ELECTRICAL ENGINEERING. *Educ:* Univ Conn, BSEE, 53, PhD(elec eng), 62; Yale Univ, ME, 56. *Prof Exp:* Eng trainee, RCA Victor Div, Radio Corp Am, 53; assoc engr, Res Div, Int Bus Mach Corp, 56-57; from instr to assoc prof, 57-74, PROF ELEC ENG, UNIV CONN, 74- *Concurrent Pos:* Consult, Elec Boat Div, Gen Dynamics Corp, 61-78, Unimatir Inc, 80. *Mem:* Inst Elec & Electronics Engrs. *Res:* Automatic control; estimation and identification; communications and signal processing. *Mailing Add:* Dept of Elec Eng Box U-157 Univ of Conn Storrs CT 06268

KNAPP, DANIEL ROGER, b Evansville, Ind, July 29, 43. PHARMACOLOGY. *Educ:* Univ Evansville, BA, 65; Ind Univ, Bloomington, PhD(org chem), 69. *Prof Exp:* NIH fel, Univ Calif, Berkeley, 69-70; asst prof exp med, Col Med, Univ Cincinnati, 71-72; asst prof, 72-78, ASSOC PROF PHARMACOL, MED UNIV SC, 78- *Mem:* Am Chem Soc; Am Soc Mass Spectrometry; Am Soc Pharmacol & Exp Therapeut. *Res:* Organoanalytical chemistry; mass spectrometry; stable isotopes; drug metabolism. *Mailing Add:* Med Univ of SC 171 Ashley Ave Charleston SC 29403

KNAPP, DAVID EDWIN, b El Paso, Tex, July 9, 32; m 54; c 4. NUCLEAR PHYSICS. *Educ:* Calif Inst Technol, BS, 53; Univ Rochester, MA, 59, PhD(physics), 61. *Prof Exp:* Res scientist, Long Beach Div, Douglas Aircraft Co, Inc, 54-55, consult, 55-57, res scientist, 57-58, res scientist, Missile & Space Systs Div, 61-62, chief nuclear res br, 62-64, asst chief scientist nuclear dept, 64-69, chief scientist, Donald W Douglas Labs, Richland, Wash, 69-74, chief scientist, 74-76, PRIN STAFF ENGR, McDONNELL DOUGLAS ASTRONAUTICS CO, 76- *Mem:* AAAS; Am Phys Soc; Am Inst Aeronaut & Astronaut. *Res:* Elementary particle physics; energy conversion; nuclear power sources and propulsion. *Mailing Add:* McDonnell Douglas Astron Co 5301 Bolsa Ave Huntington Beach CA 92647

KNAPP, EDWARD ALAN, b Salem, Ore, Mar 7, 32; m 54; c 4. PHYSICS. *Educ:* Pomona Col, BA, 54; Univ Calif, PhD(physics), 58. *Prof Exp:* Group leader, 59-68, asst div leader, 68-72, assoc div lab, 72-76, alt div leader, 76-77, DIV LEADER, ACCELERATOR TECHNOL DIV, LOS ALAMOS SCI LAB, UNIV CALIF, 78- *Concurrent Pos:* Consult, Sci Applications, Inc & EMI Ther Systs, Inc, 71- *Mem:* AAAS; Am Phys Soc. *Res:* Medical application of accelerators and accelerator produced particles to cancer therapy; application of particle accelerators; high energy nuclear physics; photomeson processes and pi meson interactions; high energy linear accelerators, microwave cavities and related electromagnetic phenomena; applied physics. *Mailing Add:* Los Alamos Sci Lab PO Box 1663 Los Alamos NM 87544

KNAPP, FRANCIS MARION, b Caldwell, Idaho, Oct 17, 24; c 2. CARDIOVASCULAR PHYSIOLOGY, NEUROPHYSIOLOGY. *Educ:* Col Idaho, AB, 49; Univ Southern Calif, MS, 55, PhD(physiol), 60. *Prof Exp:* Asst physiol, Sch Med, Univ Southern Calif, 54-59; res assoc, Thudichum Lab, State Res Hosp, Galesburg, Ill, 61-64; from asst prof to assoc prof physiol & biol, Duquesne Univ, 64-70; chmn, Dept Biol, Stetson Univ, 70-77; ASSOC DIR ACAD AFFAIRS, PA STATE UNIV, NEW KENSINGTON, 78- *Concurrent Pos:* NIH fel, Karolinska Inst, Sweden, 60-61. *Mem:* AAAS; Am Physiol Soc; Am Inst Biol Sci; Microcirc Soc; Am Soc Zool. *Res:* Cerebro-vascular and peripheral blood flow problems; neurophysiology and central nervous system; behavioral studies and drug action. *Mailing Add:* Pa State Univ 3550 Seventh Street Rd New Kensington PA 15068

KNAPP, FRED WILLIAM, b Princeton, Ill, Oct 14, 28; m 58; c 2. ENTOMOLOGY. *Educ:* Univ Ill, BS, 56; Kans State Univ, MS, 58, PhD(entom), 61. *Prof Exp:* Asst entom, Kans State Univ, 56-58, asst instr, 58-60, instr, 60-61; from asst prof to assoc prof, 61-71, PROF ENTOM, UNIV KY, 71- *Concurrent Pos:* Consult, Louisville-Jefferson County Pub Health, 61-65; entom adv, Agr Ctr Northeast, Thailand, 68-70; consult pesticide indust, 71- *Mem:* Entom Soc Am; Am Mosquito Control Asn; Thailand Agr Soc. *Res:* Medical and veterinary entomology; insecticides; application methods and residues; pest management; integrated control of insects affecting man and animals. *Mailing Add:* Dept Entomol Univ Ky Lexington KY 40506

KNAPP, FREDERICK WHITON, b Danbury, Conn, Mar 19, 15; m 48. FOOD CHEMISTRY. *Educ:* Univ Calif, Davis, BS, 35, MS, 56, PhD(agr chem), 60. *Prof Exp:* Asst biochemist, Univ Fla, 60-67, assoc prof food sci & assoc biochemist, Inst Food & Agr Sci, 67-77; RETIRED. *Mem:* Inst Food Technologists. *Res:* Use and control of enzymes in food processing; protein recovery from animal by-products. *Mailing Add:* 4410 Eastshore Dr North Bend OR 97459

KNAPP, GAYLE, b Norwich, NY, July 31, 49. MOLECULAR BIOLOGY. *Educ:* Barnard Col, AB, 71; Univ Ill, PhD(biochem), 77. *Prof Exp:* Fel molecular biol, Dept Chem, Univ Calif, San Diego, 77-81; ASST PROF MICRO-MOLECULAR BIOL, DEPT MICROBIOL, UNIV ALA, BIRMINGHAM, 81- *Mem:* Am Chem Soc; Sigma Xi. *Res:* Biosynthesis of eukaryotic (yeast) tRNA's, in particular those which arise through splicing of intron-containing RNA precursors; nucleic acid structure and how altering structure affects the biological activity of the nucleic acid. *Mailing Add:* Dept Microbiol Box 11 SDB Univ Ala Birmingham AL 35294

KNAPP, GILLIAN REVILL, b; m 68. RADIO ASTRONOMY. *Educ:* Univ Edinburgh, BSc, 66; Univ Md, PhD(astron), 72. *Prof Exp:* Asst astron, Univ Md, 66-72, teaching assoc, 72-74; res fel astron, 74-80, VIS ASSOC RADIO ASTRON, CALIF INST TECHNOL, 80- *Mem:* Royal Astron Soc; Am Astron Soc. *Res:* Interstellar microwave spectroscopy. *Mailing Add:* Owens Valley Radio Observ Calif Inst of Technol Pasadena CA 91125

KNAPP, GORDON GRAYSON, b Miami, Ariz, Nov 26, 30; m 55; c 4. ORGANIC CHEMISTRY. *Educ:* Ore State Col, BS, 52; Univ Wis, MS, 53, PhD(chem), 57. *Prof Exp:* Res chemist, 56-63, res supvr, 66-69, RES ASSOC, ETHYL CORP, 63- *Mem:* Am Chem Soc. *Res:* Petrochemical research, especially lubricant additives; hydrometallurgy; industrial organic chemicals. *Mailing Add:* Ethyl Corp 1600 W Eight Mile Rd Ferndale MI 48220

KNAPP, HAROLD ANTHONY, JR, b Berlin, NH, Mar 20, 24; m; c 3. TECHNICAL ADMINISTRATION. *Educ:* Mass Inst Technol, BSc, 48, PhD(math), 53. *Prof Exp:* Opers analyst, Opers Eval Group, Off Chief Naval Opers, 50-55; opers analyst, Off Gen Mgr, Hqs, US AEC, 55-60, opers analyst, Fallout Studies Br, Div Biol & Med, 60-63, mem staff, systs eval div, Inst Defense Anal, 63-81; DEP DIR, JOINT PROG OFF, OFF SECY DEFENSE, 81- *Concurrent Pos:* Mem adv comt civil defense, Nat Acad Sci, 61-71; mem strategic command & control task force, Defense Sci Bd, 73-74. *Mem:* Sigma Xi. *Res:* Mathematical and theoretical physics; theory of relativity; strategic command and control; weapons systems evaluation; origin, distribution, biological and environmental effects of radioactive fallout; military applications of space. *Mailing Add:* 21900 Davis Mill Rd Germantown MD 20874

KNAPP, JOHN SAMUEL, b Wilkinsburg, Pa, Feb 20, 23; m 51; c 3. CHEMISTRY. *Educ:* Univ Pittsburgh, BS, 43. *Prof Exp:* Chemist, 43-45 & 46-67, TECH DIR, FED LABS, INC, 67- *Res:* General analytical chemistry; development of pyrotechnic items; electroplating. *Mailing Add:* 623 Orchard Hill Dr Fox Chapel PA 15238

KNAPP, JOHN WILLIAMS, b Huntington, WVa, Dec 9, 32; m 57; c 3. CIVIL & SANITARY ENGINEERING. *Educ:* Va Mil Inst, BS, 54; Johns Hopkins Univ, MSE, 62, PhD(sanit eng, water resources), 65. *Prof Exp:* Admin asst, Chesapeake & Potomac Tel Co, 54; off engr, Concrete Pipe & Prod Co, 58-59; instr civil eng, Va Mil Inst, 59-61; res asst sanit eng, Johns Hopkins Univ, 61-64; from asst prof to assoc prof, 64-68, head dept, 66-71, PROF CIVIL ENG, VA MIL INST, 68- *Mem:* Am Soc Civil Engrs; Am Water Works Asn; Water Pollution Control Fedn; Nat Soc Prof Engrs. *Res:* Urban hydrology; economics and systems analysis; water supply and treatment; waste treatment and disposal; radioactive waste disposal. *Mailing Add:* Dept of Civil Eng Va Mil Inst Lexington VA 24450

KNAPP, JOSEPH LEONCE, JR, b New Boston, Tex, Nov 6, 37; m 57; c 2. AGRICULTURAL CHEMISTRY. *Educ:* Miss State Univ, BS, 60, PhD(entom), 65; Kans State Univ, MS, 62. *Prof Exp:* Scientist host plant resistance entom, USDA, 62-65; supvr field entom, Int Minerals & Chem Co, 65; entomologist, Upjohn Co, 69-70, plant scientist, 70-77; mem staff, 77-80, ASSOC PROF ENTOMOL & NEMATOL, UNIV FLA, 80- *Mem:* Entom Soc Am. *Res:* Field research and development of insecticides, fungicides, herbicides and plant growth regulators for use on a wide range of agronomic crops. *Mailing Add:* Univ of Fla AREC PO Box 1088 Lake Alfred FL 33850

KNAPP, KARL, b La Jolla, Calif, May 28, 37; m 71. MECHANICAL ENGINEERING, PHYSICS. *Educ:* Calif Inst Technol, BS, 59, MS, 60, PhD(mech eng), 65. *Prof Exp:* Asst prof mech eng, Calif Stte Col, Long Beach, 64-68; vpres eng, Cheeseboro Prod Corp, 68-70; pres, Kardel Prod Corp, Los Angeles, 70-75; PROD AREA MGR RES & SPEC PROJS, ASTRO RES CORP, 75- *Concurrent Pos:* Sr engr, Electro-Optical Systs, 65-68. *Mem:* Am Inst Aeronaut & Astronaut. *Res:* Heat transfer to supercritical fluids; food refrigeration; dry ice refrigeration systems; space structures; deployable structures. *Mailing Add:* Astro Res Corp 6390 Cindy Lane Carpinteria CA 93013

KNAPP, KENNETH T, b Jacksonville, Fla, June 9, 30; m 54; c 3. ENVIRONMENTAL CHEMISTRY. *Educ:* Univ Fla, BS, 54, PhD(chem), 60. *Prof Exp:* Chemist, Res Div, Procter & Gamble Co, 60-63, chemist, Foods Div, 63-65; chemist, Int Latex & Chem Corp, 65-67; chemist, Southern Res Inst, 67-70; head anal sect, Vick Chem Co, Mt Vernon, NY, 70-71; chief non-metal sect, Div Atmos Surveillance, 71-73, chief, Particulate Emissions Res Sect, 73-80, CHIEF, STATIONARY SOURCES EMISSIONS RES BR, ENVIRON SCI RES LAB, ENVIRON PROTECTION AGENCY, RESEARCH TRIANGLE PARK, 80- *Mem:* Am Chem Soc; Am Oil Chem Soc. *Res:* Instrumental analysis, especially gas chromatography, x-ray analysis; infrared spectroscopy, ultraviolet and visible spectroscopy, isolation and identification of naturally occurring compounds; measurement and characterization of air pollutants from source emissions. *Mailing Add:* 317 Glasgow Rd Cary NC 27511

KNAPP, LESLIE W, b Port Byron, NY, Nov 17, 29; m 57; c 2. ICHTHYOLOGY. *Educ:* Cornell Univ, BS, 52, PhD(vert zool), 64; Univ Mo, MA, 58. *Prof Exp:* Supvr vert, 63-68, dep dir, 68-72, SUPVR VERT, OCEANOG SORTING CTR, SMITHSONIAN INST, 72-, DIR, 81. *Mem:* Am Soc Ichthyol & Herpet; Soc Syst Zool; Am Fisheries Soc. *Res:* Systematic ichthyology, particularly the families Percidae and Platycephalidae. *Mailing Add:* Oceanog Sorting Ctr Smithsonian Inst Washington DC 20560

KNAPP, MALCOLM HAMMOND, b Orange, NJ, Sept 20, 39; m 70; c 2. INDUSTRIAL ORGANIC CHEMISTRY. *Educ:* Rutgers Univ, BS, 61. *Prof Exp:* Chemist electrochem, Nuodex Div, Heyden Newport Corp, 64-66, sr chemist organometallics synthesis, Nuodex Div, Tenneco Chem, Inc, 67-70, lab mgr lubricants, Res & Develop Dept, 71-80, MGR, LUBRICANTS RES & DEVELOP, TENNECO CHEM, INC, 80- *Mem:* Soc Automotive Engrs; Am Soc Testing & Mat; Am Soc Lubrication Engrs. *Res:* Development of synthetic lubricants, novel base fluids, additives; test development. *Mailing Add:* 316 Raymond Ct Bridgewater NJ 08807

KNAPP, MALCOLM ROBERT, b Indianapolis, Ind, Sept 12, 43; m 65; c 2. CHEMICAL ENGINEERING. *Educ:* Johns Hopkins Univ, BES, 65, MSE, 68; Carnegie-Mellon Univ, PhD(chem eng), 73. *Prof Exp:* Staff scientist ceramics, Res & Develop Ctr, 72-76, RES ENGR INSULATION, WIRE & CABLE DEPT, GEN ELEC CO, 76- *Concurrent Pos:* Key reader, Metall Trans, 76- *Mem:* Am Inst Chem Engrs. *Res:* Experimental high temperature heterogeneous catalysis and kinetics, associated heat and mass transfer and thermodynamics; mass spectroscopy. *Mailing Add:* Gen Elec Co 1285 Boston Ave 25DE-15 Bridgeport CT 06602

KNAPP, RICHARD ALLEN, solid state physics, optics, see previous edition

KNAPP, ROBERT HAZARD, JR, b Boston, Mass, May 18, 44. THEORETICAL PHYSICS, TECHNOLOGY STUDIES. *Educ:* Harvard Col, BA, 65; Oxford Univ, PhD(theoret physics), 68. *Prof Exp:* Res physicist, Carnegie-Mellon Univ, 68-70; lectr, Calif State Polytech Col, 70-72; MEM FAC PHYSICS, EVERGREEN STATE COL, 72- & ASST ACAD DEAN, 76- *Mem:* Am Phys Soc; Fedn Am Scientists; Soc Values Higher Educ; AAAS. *Res:* Scale effects in technological systems and organization; design of college-level interdisciplinary studies. *Mailing Add:* Evergreen State Col Olympia WA 98505

KNAPP, ROBERT LESTER, b Keokuk, Iowa, Nov 17, 21; m 42; c 4. ORGANIC CHEMISTRY. *Educ:* Brown Univ, ScB, 43. *Prof Exp:* Jr res chemist, Naugatuck Chem Div, US Rubber Co, 46-48, sr res chemist plastics, 48-52, sr group leader, 52-57, sect mgr Kralastic res & develop, 57-60, prod supt, Synthetic Rubber Plant, 60-63, sales mgr Kralastic, 64-66; dir mkt, Uniroyal, Inc, 66-69, group mgr plastics res & develop, Uniroyal Chem Div, 69-76, dir bus develop & planning, 77-81, dir, Int Bus Develop, 81; CONSULT, 81- *Mem:* Am Chem Soc; Soc Plastics Eng. *Res:* High polymers, both synthesis and physical behavior, particularly polyesters and gum plastics. *Mailing Add:* 189 Alder Lane North Falmouth MA 02556

KNAPP, ROGER DALE, b Natchez, Miss, Sept 6, 43. NUCLEAR MAGNETIC RESONANCE SPECTROSCOPY. *Educ:* Miss State Univ, BS, 64; Univ Houston, PhD(chem), 74. *Prof Exp:* ASST PROF, BAYLOR COL MED, 81- *Mem:* Inst Elec & Electronics Engrs. *Res:* Biopolymer structure by carbon 13 nuclear magnetic resonance; computer, instrument interface. *Mailing Add:* 4508 Birch St Belcaire TX 77401

KNAPP, STEPHEN LAURENCE, b Washington, DC, Nov 22, 42. ASTRONOMY, INSTRUMENTATION. *Educ:* Trinity Col, Conn, BS, 65; Univ Md, PhD(astron), 74. *Prof Exp:* Assoc engr astron, Owens Valley Radio Observ, 74-75, fel astron, 75-77, MEM TECH STAFF, JET PROPULSION LAB, CALIF INST TECHNOL, 77- *Mem:* Am Astron Soc. *Res:* Charge coupled device imagers; astronomical stellar . instrument development; measurements of stellar diameters. *Mailing Add:* 1776 Oakdale St Pasadena CA 91106

KNAPP, STUART EDWARD, veterinary parasitology, see previous edition

KNAPP, THEODORE MARTIN, b Berkeley, Calif, Sept 2, 47; div; c 2. EMERGENCY MEDICINE. *Educ:* Univ Calif, Berkeley, BA; Univ Tenn, Knoxville, PhD(physiol psychol), 73. *Prof Exp:* Vis lectr & res assoc psychol, Univ Houston, 73-74; res assoc psycho-physiol, Baylor Col Med, 74-75; fel, Tex Res Inst Ment Sci, 75; assoc neuropsychologist, Midwest Res Inst, 75-81; ASST PROF ALLIED HEALTH, UNIV KANS, 81- *Concurrent Pos:* Consult ed, Physiol & Behav & Psychophysiology, 75- *Mem:* Soc Neurosci; Am Soc Allied Health Prof. *Res:* Learning styles, biofeedback, physiological reeducation, issues in emergency medical training. *Mailing Add:* Dept Allied Health Sci Univ Kans Kansas City KS 66103

KNAPP, WAYNE ROBERT, b Alamosa, Colo, May 13, 47; m 76. CROP SCIENCE, AGRONOMY. *Educ:* Colo State Univ, BS, 69; Purdue Univ, MS, 72, PhD(crop sci), 74. *Prof Exp:* Asst prof, 74-80, ASSOC PROF CROP SCI & EXTEN GRAIN CROPS, DEPT AGRON, CORNELL UNIV, 80- *Mem:* Am Soc Agron; Crop Sci Soc Am. *Res:* Production and management of field crops, particularly corn, wheat, oats, barley, sorghum, soybeans and buckwheat. *Mailing Add:* 145 Emerson Cornell Univ Ithaca NY 14853

KNAPP, WILLIAM ARNOLD, JR, b Atlanta, Ga, Oct 4, 25; m 50; c 3. VETERINARY PHARMACOLOGY, TOXICOLOGY. *Educ:* Univ Ga, DVM, 51, MS, 64. *Prof Exp:* Asst prof vet med & surg, Univ Ga, 51-52; pvt practice, 52-54; asst prof physiol & pharmacol, Sch Vet Med, Univ Ga, 54-62; dir res, Morris Res Labs, Inc, 62-65; assoc dir & res coordr, Toxicol Div, Hazleton Labs, Inc, 65-68, pres, Hazleton Res Animals, Inc, 68-71; dir animal sci-prod div, Flow Labs Inc, Rockville, Md, 71-78, pres, Flow Res Animals Inc, 71-77; VPRES, FLOW LABS INC, McLEAN, VA, 76- *Mem:* Am Soc Vet Physiol & Pharmacol; Vet Med Asn; Am Asn Lab Animal Sci; Indust Vet Asn (pres, 69-70); Am Col Vet Toxicologists. *Res:* veterinary pharmacology; drug evaluations; toxicology; nutrition; research administration and general management. *Mailing Add:* Flow Labs Inc Westgate Res Park McLean VA 22102

KNAPP, WILLIAM G(ERARD), b Dayton, Ohio, Aug 9, 20; m 44; c 4. CHEMICAL ENGINEERING. *Educ:* Univ Dayton, BChE, 42; Ohio State Univ, MSc, 47, PhD(chem eng), 49. *Prof Exp:* Res chem engr, 49-56, res pilot plant group leader, 57-71, SR RES GROUP LEADER, ORG CHEM DIV, MONSANTO CHEM CO, 71- *Mem:* Am Chem Soc; Am Inst Chem Engrs. *Res:* Distillation; fluid mechanics. *Mailing Add:* 1216 Selma Ave Webster Groves MO 63119

KNAPP, WILLIAM JOHN, b Toronto, Ont, Sept 11, 16; m 43; c 2. CERAMIC ENGINEERING, MATERIALS SCIENCE. *Educ:* Alfred Univ, BS, 39; Mass Inst Technol, ScD(ceramics), 42. *Prof Exp:* Res chemist, NAm Cement Corp, NY, 42-43; sr res ceramist, Pa Salt Mfg Co, 46-47; asst prof ceramics, Mo Sch Mines, 47-49; from asst prof to assoc prof, 49-57, vchmn, Dept Eng, 61-66, asst dean sch eng & appl sci, 69-75, PROF ENG & APPL SCI, UNIV CALIF, LOS ANGELES, 57- *Concurrent Pos:* Fulbright Award, Norway, 55-56; Univ Calif, Los Angeles eng educ proj, Gadjah Mada, Jogjakarta, 60-61. *Mem:* Fel Am Ceramic Soc (vpres, 74-75); Nat Inst Ceramic Engrs. *Res:* Thermodynamics of ceramic mixtures; prestressed ceramics and structural applications. *Mailing Add:* Dept Mat Univ Calif Los Angeles CA 90024

KNAPPE, LAVERNE F, b Ellsworth, Wis, Jan 8, 22; m 44; c 3. MECHANICAL ENGINEERING, APPLIED MECHANICS. *Educ:* Univ Minn, BME, 44, MSME, 47, PhD(mech eng), 53. *Prof Exp:* Mech engr, Barber Colman Co, 47-50; instr mech eng, Univ Minn, 50-53; res engr, Am Mach & Foundry Co, 53-55; consult, Booz, Allen & Hamilton, Inc, 55-57; mgr mech anal lab, Int Bus Mach Corp, 57-70, SR ENGR, IBM CORP, 70- *Concurrent Pos:* Consult, Gen Mills, Inc, 51-53. *Mem:* Am Soc Mech Engrs; Soc Exp Stress Anal; NY Acad Sci. *Res:* Research and development of computer-aided mechanical design systems, including engineer-computer communication, analytical design procedures, system modeling and design optimization. *Mailing Add:* Advan Technol Dept IBM Corp Rochester MN 56472

KNAPPENBERGER, HERBERT ALLAN, b Reading, Pa, May 24, 32; m 57; c 3. INDUSTRIAL ENGINEERING, APPLIED STATISTICS. *Educ:* Pa State Univ, BS, 57, MS, 60; NC State Univ, PhD(exp statist), 66. *Prof Exp:* Apprentice draftsman, Textile Mach Works, Pa, 50-54; instr indust eng, Pa State Univ, 58-60; from instr to asst prof, NC State Univ, 60-68; from assoc prof to prof, Univ Mo-Columbia, 68-77; MEM STAFF, DEPT INDUST ENG, WAYNE STATE UNIV, 77-, CHMN OPERS RES, 81- *Concurrent Pos:* Mem health serv res training comt, Nat Ctr Health Serv Res & Develop. *Mem:* Am Inst Indust Engrs; Am Statist Asn; Opers Res Soc Am; Am Soc Eng Educ. *Res:* Health care systems design; patient scheduling systems design; automated radiology systems design; resource allocation on large systems. *Mailing Add:* Dept of Indust Eng Wayne State Univ Detroit MI 48202

KNAPPENBERGER, PAUL HENRY, JR, b Reading, Pa, Sept 5, 42; m 63; c 2. SCIENCE ADMINISTRATION, ASTRONOMY. *Educ:* Franklin & Marshall Col, AB, 64; Univ Va, MA, 66, PhD(astron), 68. *Prof Exp:* Chmn dept astron, Fernbank Sci Ctr, Atlanta, 68-72; DIR, SCI MUS VA, 73- *Concurrent Pos:* Instr astron, Emory Univ & adj prof, Ga State Univ, 70-72; asst prof, Va Commonwealth Univ, 73-; adj assoc prof, Univ Richmond, 74-;

bd mem, Asn Sci & Technol Ctrs. *Mem:* Am Astron Soc; AAAS. *Res:* Astronomical interferometry; astronomical applications of image converters and intensifiers; development of educational activities in astronomy; design and evaluation of interactive exhibits in science. *Mailing Add:* Sci Mus of Va Richmond VA 23220

KNATTERUD, GENELL LAVONNE, b Minot, NDak. BIOSTATISTICS. *Educ:* Macalester Col, BA, 52; Univ Minn, MS, 59, PhD(biostatist), 63. *Prof Exp:* Asst biochemist, Pillsbury Mills Res Labs, 52-53; teaching asst anat, Univ Minn, 54-56, statistician, Biostatist Div, 56-57, sr statistician, 58-60, instr, Sch Pub Health, 60-62; anal statistician, Off Biomet, Consult Sect, NIMH, 63-64; asst prof epidemiol & biostatist, Pakistan Med Res Ctr, Univ Md, 66-67, from asst prof to assoc prof, Inst Int Med, 67-72, assoc prof, 72-73, PROF EPIDEMIOL & PREV MED, UNIV MD, BALTIMORE, 73- *Concurrent Pos:* Mem nat cancer adv comt, Nat Bladder-Prostate Cancer Projs, 72-74; vpres, Md Med Res Inst, 74-; mem lipid metab adv comt, Nat Heart & Lung Inst, 75- *Mem:* AAAS; Am Diabetes Asn; Am Pub Health Asn; Am Statist Asn; Biomet Soc. *Res:* Design, methods and applications of clinical trials; epidemiology of cardiovascular disease and diabetes. *Mailing Add:* Dept of Social & Prev Med Univ of Md Baltimore MD 21210

KNAUER, BRUCE RICHARD, b New York, NY, Nov 24, 42. ORGANIC CHEMISTRY. *Educ:* Cooper Union, BChE, 63; Cornell Univ, MS, 65, PhD(chem), 69. *Prof Exp:* US Air Force Off Aerospace Res fel, Univ Ga, 68-70; asst prof, 70-78, ASSOC PROF ORG CHEM, STATE UNIV NY COL ONEONTA, 78- *Mem:* Am Chem Soc. *Res:* Electron spin resonance; polycyclic aromatic hydrocarbons; reaction mechanisms. *Mailing Add:* Dept of Chem State Univ NY Col Oneonta NY 13820

KNAUFF, RAYMOND EUGENE, b Venus, Pa, July 22, 25; m 49; c 1. BIOCHEMISTRY. *Educ:* Capital Univ, BS, 47; Univ Mich, MS, 49, PhD(biol chem), 52. *Prof Exp:* Chem technician, Barneby-Cheney Eng Co, 44; org chemist, Dow Chem Co, 45, anal chemist, 46, biochemist toxicol, 47; biochemist, Univ Mich Hosp, 47-49, asst biol chem, Med Sch, 49-50; endocrinologist, Upjohn Co, 51-55; head bioanal dept, G D Searle Co, 56-57; asst prof biochem, Univ Mich, 57-61; assoc prof biochem, Sch Med, Temple Univ, 61-74; prof physiol chem, 74-80, PROF BIOCHEM & CHMN DEPT, PHILADELPHIA COL OSTEOP MED, 80- *Concurrent Pos:* Dir res, Cystic Fibrosis Res Inst, 61-67. *Mem:* AAAS; Am Chem Soc; Am Inst Chemists; NY Acad Sci. *Res:* Biological chemistry; endocrine biochemistry; bioanalytical chemistry; protein and amino acid chemistry and metabolism; cystic fibrosis. *Mailing Add:* 37 Meade Rd Ambler PA 19002

KNAUFT, DAVID A, b Evergreen Park, Ill, May 10, 51; m 78. PLANT BREEDING, FARMING SYSTEMS. *Educ:* Univ Wis-Madison, BS, 73; Cornell Univ, PhD(plant breeding), 77. *Prof Exp:* Vis instr genetics, Agron & Soils Dept, Clemson Univ, 77-78; ASST PROF PLANT BREEDING & GENETICS, AGRON DEPT, UNIV FLA, 78- *Mem:* Am Soc Agron; Am Peanut Res & Educ Soc; Am Genetic Asn; Crop Sci Soc Am. *Res:* Genetic factors important in the improvement of cultivated peanuts, including genetic stability, response to stress environments, disease resistance and intercropping. *Mailing Add:* Agron Dept Univ Fla 2183 McCarty Hall Gainesville FL 32611

KNAUS, EDWARD ELMER, b Leroy, Sask, Jan 7, 43; m 74. MEDICINAL CHEMISTRY. *Educ:* Univ Sask, BSP, 65, MSc, 67, PhD(pharmaceut chem), 70. *Prof Exp:* Med Res Coun Can fel chem, Tex A&M Univ, 70-71 & Univ BC, 71-72; asst prof, 72-80, PROF MED CHEM, UNIV ALTA, 80- *Mem:* Am Chem Soc; Can Pharmaceut Asn; Chem Inst Can. *Res:* Synthesis of new nitrogen heterocycles and diagnostic agents; structure-activity studies; drug design. *Mailing Add:* Fac of Pharm & Pharmaceut Sci Univ of Alta Edmonton AB T6G 2N8 Can

KNAUS, JOSEPH A(NTHONY), b Wayland, NY, July 16, 18; m 44; c 5. CHEMICAL ENGINEERING. *Educ:* Univ Notre Dame, BS, 40; Mass Inst Technol, MS, 42. *Prof Exp:* Res engr petrol & chem res, M W Kellogg Co, 42-48, res supvr, 48-53, sect head, 53-55, assoc dir, 55-65; mgr fluid catalysts, Socony Mobil Oil Co, 65-67; PRIN ENGR, BECHTEL CORP, 67- *Mem:* Am Chem Soc. *Res:* Petroleum, chemicals, petrochemicals and coal processing. *Mailing Add:* 2093 Plantation Houston TX 77024

KNAUS, RONALD MALLEN, b San Jose, Calif, June 9, 37; m 60; c 2. RADIOECOLOGY, RADIOBIOLOGY. *Educ:* San Jose State Univ, AB, 60, MA, 62; Ore State Univ, PhD(radiation biol), 71. *Prof Exp:* Teacher, Fremont Union High Sch Dist, 60-65 & Fresno City Col, 65-68; researcher biochem, Ore State Univ, 68-71; teacher biol, Univ Tex, Arlington, 71-74; TEACHER-RESEARCHER RADIOECOL, LA STATE UNIV, 74- *Concurrent Pos:* Consult, Comprehensive Planning Inst, Dallas, 76- & City & Parish, East Baton Rouge, 77-; prin investr, Lake Restoration Proj, City Baton Rouge, 77- *Mem:* AAAS; Sigma Xi; Ecol Soc Am; Health Physics Soc. *Res:* Investigation into the behavior of stable metal tracers in the lotic environment; sorption of stable tracers to exposed roots in stream waters. *Mailing Add:* Nuclear Sci Ctr La State Univ Baton Rouge LA 70803

KNAUSENBERGER, WULF H, b Vienna, Austria, May 3, 43; US citizen; m 67; c 4. ELECTRONICS ENGINEERING. *Educ:* Pa State Univ, BS, 65, PhD(solid state sci), 69. *Prof Exp:* Res assoc, Pa State Univ, 69-70; mem tech staff, 70-78, TECH SUPVR, BELL LABS, 78- *Mem:* Inst Elec & Electronics Engrs; Int Electronics Packaging Soc. *Res:* Analysis of electronic system design, electronic packaging and interconnection system design. *Mailing Add:* Bell Labs Whippany NY 07981

KNAUSS, JAMES FREDERICK, plant pathology, see previous edition

KNAUSS, JOHN ATKINSON, b Detroit, Mich, Sept 1, 25; m 54; c 2. OCEANOGRAPHY. *Educ:* Mass Inst Technol, BS, 46; Univ Mich, MA, 49; Univ Calif, Los Angeles, PhD(oceanog), 59. *Prof Exp:* Oceanographer, Navy Electronics Lab, 47-48; oceanogr, Off Naval Res, 49-51; res staff, Scripps Inst Oceanog, 51-53; oceanogr, Off Naval Res, 53-54; oceanogr, Scripps Inst Oceanog, 55-62; DEAN, GRAD SCH OCEANOG, UNIV RI, 62-, PROVOST MARINE AFFAIRS, 69- *Concurrent Pos:* Mem, President's Comn Marine Sci, Eng & Resources, 67-68; chmn, Ocean Sci Comt, Nat Acad Sci, 71-73, Ocean Policy Comt, Nat Acad Sci, 72-, Univ Nat Oceanog Lab Syst, 74-75; mem, Nat Adv Comt Oceans & Atmosphere, 77-, chmn, 81- *Honors & Awards:* Sea Grant Asn Award, 74. *Mem:* Am Geophys Union; AAAS; Am Meterol Soc. *Res:* Ocean circulation; law of the sea; marine affairs. *Mailing Add:* Grad Sch of Oceanog Univ of RI Kingston RI 07881

KNAVEL, DEAN EDGAR, b Windber, Pa, Sept 5, 24; m 47; c 3. HORTICULTURE. *Educ:* Pa State Univ, BS, 54; Univ Del, MS, 56; Mich State Univ, PhD(hort), 59. *Prof Exp:* From asst prof to assoc prof hort, 59-78, PROF HORT, UNIV KY, 78- *Mem:* Am Soc Hort Sci. *Res:* Breeding, nutrition and minimum tillage of vegetable crops. *Mailing Add:* Dept of Hort Univ of Ky Lexington KY 40506

KNAZEK, RICHARD ALLAN, b Cleveland, Ohio, Mar 23, 42; m 67; c 2. MEDICINE, ENGINEERING. *Educ:* Case Inst Technol, BS, 62; Lehigh Univ, MS, 64; Ohio State Univ, MD, 69; Am Bd Internal Med, dipl, 74. *Prof Exp:* Engr cryogenic res, Air Prod & Chem, 62-63; engr plastics develop, E I du Pont de Nemours & Co, Inc, 63-65; intern med, Duke Hosp, 69-70, resident, 70-71; INVESTR MED, NIH, 71- *Concurrent Pos:* Vis fac, W A Jones Cell Sci Ctr, 73-76; vis lectr, Univ Toronto & Mass Gen Hosp, 74; contract officer, Breast Cancer Task Force, Nat Cancer Inst, 74-80; PhD thesis adv, Univ Del, 76-77. *Mem:* Endocrine Soc; Am Asn Cancer Res; Soc Exp Biol Med. *Res:* Developer of artificial capillary cell culture technique to grow solid organs in vitro; study of the control of prolactin receptors in liver and mammary cancer. *Mailing Add:* Nat Cancer Inst NIH 9000 Rockville Pike Bethesda MD 20014

KNEALE, SAMUEL GEORGE, b Tulsa, Okla, Dec 13, 21; m 45; c 2. MATHEMATICS. *Educ:* Univ Kans, AB, 47, MA, 48; Harvard Univ, PhD(math), 53. *Prof Exp:* Consult math, Philco Corp, Pa, 51-56, Gen Elec Co, 56-59 & Avco Corp, Ohio, 59-61; PRIN SCIENTIST MATH, OPERS RES INC, 61- *Mem:* Am Math Soc; Soc Indust & Appl Math; Math Asn Am; Opers Res Soc Am. *Res:* Applied mathematics, including probability theory and statistics, game theory, systems analysis, and other aspects of operations research. *Mailing Add:* Opers Res Inc 1400 Spring St Silver Spring MD 20910

KNEBEL, HARLEY JOHN, b Iowa City, Iowa, Nov 10, 41; m 69; c 2. GEOLOGICAL OCEANOGRAPHY, MARINE GEOLOGY. *Educ:* Univ Iowa, BA, 65; Univ Wash, MS, 67, PhD(oceanog), 72. *Prof Exp:* Res asst oceanog, Univ Wash, 65-67; oceanogr, Nat Oceanic & Atmospheric Admin, Atlantic Oceanog & Meteorol Labs, 67-69; res assoc, Univ Wash, 69-73; OCEANOGR, OFF MARINE GEOL, US GEOL SURV, 73- *Concurrent Pos:* Texaco fel oceanog, Univ Wash, 71-72. *Mem:* AAAS; Am Geophys Union; fel Geol Soc Am; Sigma Xi. *Res:* Sedimentology; estuarine, nearshore, and continental shelf sedimentary processes and stratigraphy; statistics applied to geological oceanography; mass movements of sediments on continental slopes; clay mineralogy; submarine canyon development. *Mailing Add:* Off of Marine Geol US Geol Surv Woods Hole MA 02543

KNECHEL, WILLIAM FRANKLIN, b Catasaqua, Pa, June 11, 24. ORGANIC CHEMISTRY. *Educ:* Muhlenberg Col, BS, 49. *Prof Exp:* Chemist, 49-50, from res chemist to sr res chemist, 52-68, RES ASSOC, RES LAB, EASTMAN KODAK CO, 68- *Mem:* Am Chem Soc; Soc Photog Sci & Eng. *Res:* Searching for new and improving existing color formers for color photographic systems. *Mailing Add:* Res Labs Eastman Kodak Co 343 State St Rochester NY 14650

KNECHT, ALBERT T, petroleum microbiology, biochemistry, see previous edition

KNECHT, CHARLES DANIEL, b Halethorpe, Md, Mar 22, 32; m 54; c 2. VETERINARY SURGERY, NEUROLOGY. *Educ:* Univ Pa, VMD, 56; Univ Md, College Park, BS, 60; Univ Ill, Urbana, MS, 66; Am Col Vet Surgeons, dipl, 69; Am Col Vet Internal Med, dipl & cert neurol, 74. *Prof Exp:* Assoc vet, Broad St Vet Hosp, Richmond, Va, 56; assoc vet, Wertz Mem Animal Hosp, Pittsburgh, 58-59; assoc vet, Towson Vet Hosp, Md, 59-64; from instr to asst prof vet med & surg, Col Vet Med, Univ Ill, Urbana, 64-68, assoc prof vet surg, 68-70; prof med & surg, Col Vet Med, Univ Ga, 70-72; prof & chief of surg, Sch Vet Sci & Med, Purdue Univ, West Lafayette, 72-79; PROF & HEAD, DEPT SMALL ANIMAL SURG & MED, SCH VET MED, AUBURN UNIV, 79- *Concurrent Pos:* Abstractor, Chirurgia Veterinaria, WGer, 66-68; mem grad fac, Univ Ill, Urbana, 68-70, Univ Ga, 71-72 & Purdue Univ, 72-; abstractor, J World & Europ Vet Surgeons, 68-72; chmn exam comt, Am Col Vet Internal Med, 74-77. *Mem:* Am Vet Med Asn; Am Col Vet Surg; Am Asn Vet Neurol (pres, 74-75); Am Asn Vet Clinicians; Asn Am Vet Med Cols. *Res:* Orthopedic surgery; neurosurgery; bioengineering. *Mailing Add:* Dept Small Animal Surg & Med Sch Vet Med Auburn Univ Auburn AL 36849

KNECHT, DAVID JORDAN, b Elgin, Ill, June 2, 30; m 57; c 1. MAGNETOSPHERIC PHYSICS. *Educ:* Univ Ill, BS, 51, MS, 52; Univ Wis, PhD(physics), 58. *Prof Exp:* Proj assoc nuclear physics, Univ Wis, 58-59; proj officer physics div, Air Force Spec Weapons Ctr, 59-61, res physicist spec proj div, 61-63; sci dir space physics br, Air Force Weapons Lab, 63-64; RES PHYSICIST, SPACE PHYSICS LAB, AIR FORCE CAMBRIDGE RES LABS, 64- *Mem:* Am Geophys Union; Am Phys Soc. *Res:* Study and prediction of magnetospheric storms through measurements of geomagnetic pulsations by a nationwide network of magnetic ground stations and measurement of particles and fields within the magnetosphere. *Mailing Add:* 56 South Rd Bedford MA 01730

KNECHT, LAURANCE A, b Elgin, Ill, Mar 16, 32; m 66; c 1. ANALYTICAL CHEMISTRY, PHYSICAL CHEMISTRY. *Educ:* Univ Ill, BS, 53; Univ Minn, PhD(anal chem), 59. *Prof Exp:* Instr chem, Iowa State Univ, 60-63; asst prof, Univ Cincinnati, 63-68; assoc prof, 68-77, PROF CHEM, MARIETTA COL, 78- *Mem:* AAAS; Am Chem Soc. *Res:* Electroanalytical techniques. *Mailing Add:* Dept of Chem Marietta Col Marietta OH 45750

KNECHT, WALTER LUDWIG, b Ludwigsburg, Ger, Feb 2, 09; US citizen; m 35; c 3. PHYSICS, CHEMISTRY. *Educ:* Univ Munich, MS, 32; Univ Berlin, PhD(quantum electronics), 34. *Prof Exp:* Res physicist, Fernseh A G, Berlin, 34-37; dir res high vacuum sci & microwav electronics, Flugfunk Forschungs Inst, Munich, 38-45; dir div head electronic mat, Dept Econ, Munich, 45-47; sect chief electron tube & molecular electronics, Air Force Aeronaut Systs Div, Ohio, 47-60; sr scientist, Air Force Avionics Lab, Dayton, 61-79; SUPVR PHYSICIST & TECH AREA MGR, AIR FORCE MAT LAB, DAYTON, 79- *Concurrent Pos:* Mem, Armed Serv Electron Device Comt, Defense Dept, 49-60; consult, indust, univs & govt agencies, 50-; mem adv group dir defense res, 54-62; chmn, Nat Conf Aerospace Electronics, 63. *Honors & Awards:* Lilienthal Award, 38; Air Force Res & Pub Awards, 55-67. *Mem:* Inst Elec & Electronics Eng. *Res:* Laser components designed for satellite space laser communication systems; integrated optical circuits for compact electrooptical systems and progressive fiber optics; material purification; processing and development for military systems, including missles and high energy lasers. *Mailing Add:* 1616 Mercer Ct Yellow Springs OH 45387

KNECHTLI, RONALD (C), b Geneva, Switz, Aug 14, 27; nat US; m 53; c 3. PHYSICS. *Educ:* Swiss Fed Inst Technol, Dipl, 50, PhD(elec eng), 55. *Prof Exp:* Res engr, Brown Boveri & Co, Switz, 50-51; asst, Mass Inst Technol, 51-52; res engr, Brown Boveri & Co, 52-53; res engr, Res Labs, Radio Corp Am, 53-58; SR SCIENTIST, RES LABS, HUGHES AIRCRAFT CO, 58- *Mem:* Am Inst Aeronaut & Astronaut; Am Phys Soc; Sigma Xi; Inst Elec & Electronics Eng. *Res:* Photovoltaic and electrochemical devices. *Mailing Add:* 22929 Ardwick St Woodland Hills CA 91364

KNEE, DAVID ISAAC, b New York, NY, July 13, 34; m 59; c 2. MATHEMATICS. *Educ:* City Col New York, BS, 56; Mass Inst Technol, PhD(math), 62. *Prof Exp:* Mathematician, Arde Assocs, NJ, 56; instr math, Columbia Univ, 62-65; asst prof, 65-69, ASSOC PROF MATH, HOFSTRA UNIV, 69- *Mem:* Math Asn Am. *Res:* Algebra; group theory; representation theory; mathematical linguistics. *Mailing Add:* Dept of Math Hofstra Univ Hempstead NY 11550

KNEE, TERENCE EDWARD CREASEY, b Brussels, Belg, Apr 20, 32; m 56; c 2. PHYSICAL ORGANIC CHEMISTRY. *Educ:* Trinity Col, Dublin, BASc, 53; Mass Inst Technol, PhD(chem), 56. *Prof Exp:* Instr chem, Franklin Tech Inst, 55-56; res chemist, DuPont Co Can, 57-60, res supvr, E I du Pont de Nemours & Co, Inc, 60-70, sr supvr, 70-72, tech supt, 72-76, tech supt, Chattanooga Res & Develop Sect, 76-80. *Mem:* Am Chem Soc. *Res:* Synthetic textile fibers; polymer chemistry; reaction mechanisms. *Mailing Add:* 228 Masters Rd Hixson TN 37343

KNEEBONE, LEON RUSSELL, b Bangor, Pa, May 28, 20; m 45; c 3. MYCOLOGY. *Educ:* Pa State Univ, BS, 42, PhD(bot), 50. *Prof Exp:* Asst bot, 47-50, asst prof, 50-53, assoc prof bot & plant path, 53-60, PROF BOT & PLANT PATH, PA STATE UNIV, 60- *Concurrent Pos:* Consult mushroom indust, 53-; past pres & mem, Int Comn Mushroom Sci. *Mem:* AAAS; Bot Soc Am; Mycol Soc Am; Am Phytopath Soc; Am Inst Biol Sci. *Res:* Mushroom culture, especially spawn and strain development, diseases. *Mailing Add:* 117 Buckhout Lab Pa State Univ University Park PA 16802

KNEEBONE, WILLIAM ROBERT, b Eveleth, Minn, July 11, 22; m 48; c 3. AGRONOMY, PLANT BREEDING. *Educ:* Univ Minn, BS, 47, MS, 50, PhD(plant genetics), 51. *Prof Exp:* Asst grass breeding, Univ Minn, 47-50; res agronomist, Okla Agr Exp Sta & Crop Res Div Agr Res Serv, USDA, 51-63; PROF AGRON, UNIV ARIZ, 63- *Concurrent Pos:* Consult revegetation & golf course maintainence. *Mem:* Fel AAAS; Am Soc Agron; Coun Agr Sci & Technol; Soc Econ Bot. *Res:* Breeding; genetics; seed production; factors involved in stand establishment, vigor and spread of forage and turf grasses; water use by grasses. *Mailing Add:* Dept of Plant Sci Univ of Ariz Tucson AZ 85721

KNEECE, ROLAND ROYCE, JR, b Tifton, Ga, Oct 15, 39; m 63. MATHEMATICS, OPERATIONS RESEARCH. *Educ:* Ga Inst Technol, BS, 61, MS, 62; Univ Md, PhD(math), 70. *Prof Exp:* Mem staff opers res, Inst Defense Anal, Arlington, 67-74; MEM STAFF, MANPOWER, RESERVE AFFAIRS & LOGISTICS, OFF SECY DEFENSE, 74- *Concurrent Pos:* Prof lectr, Am Univ, 69- *Mem:* Am Math Soc; Asn Comput Mach. *Res:* Operator theory; functional analysis; strictly singular operators; computer technology. *Mailing Add:* Off Asst Secy Defense Manpower & Reserve Affairs Pentagon Washington DC 20301

KNEEN, ERIC, b Battleford, Sask, Mar 23, 09; nat US; m 35; c 2. AGRICULTURAL BIOCHEMISTRY, ENZYMOLOGY. *Educ:* Univ Alta, BSc, 31; Univ Minn, MS, 33, PhD(agr biochem), 42. *Prof Exp:* Instr agr biochem, Univ Minn, 34-36; from asst agr chemist to assoc agr chemist, Exp Sta, Univ Nebr, 36-45, asst plant pathologist, 36-43; prof milling indust, Kans State Col, 46; dir res, Kurth Malting Corp, 46-73, vpres, 53-73; RETIRED. *Concurrent Pos:* Enzyme consult, 43-46; sci ed, Am Soc Brewing Chemists J, 74- *Honors & Awards:* Cincinnati Achievement Award, Master Brewers Asn Am, 54. *Mem:* Fel AAAS; Am Chem Soc; Am Soc Brewing Chem (pres, 58-59); Am Asn Cereal Chem; Master Brewers Asn Am. *Res:* Biochemistry of malting and brewing; enzymes and enzyme inhibitors. *Mailing Add:* 1105 Highland Dr Box 642 Elm Grove WI 53122

KNEIP, G(EORGE) D(EWEY), JR, b Cleveland, Ohio, Jan 18, 25; m 49; c 2. METALLURGY. *Educ:* Case Inst Technol, BS, 45, MS, 48; Mass Inst Technol, ScD, 52. *Prof Exp:* Proj engr, S K Wellman Co, 50-53; head metallurgist, Carbide & Carbon Chem Co, 53-62; tech dir, Supercon Div, Nat Res Corp, Mass, 62-66; SR SCIENTIST, INSTRUMENT DIV, VARIAN ASSOCS, 66- *Mem:* Am Phys Soc; Am Soc Metals; Sigma Xi. *Res:* Physics of metals. *Mailing Add:* 24 Palm Court Menlo Park CA 94025

KNEIP, THEODORE JOSEPH, b St Paul, Minn, Dec 20, 26; m 51; c 6. ANALYTICAL CHEMISTRY, ENVIRONMENTAL CHEMISTRY. *Educ:* Univ Minn, BCh, 50; Univ Ill, MS, 52, PhD, 54. *Prof Exp:* Chemist, Mallinckrodt Chem Works, 54-59, head, Anal Res Lab, 59-61, asst mgr urianium div, Anal Lab, 61-63, mgr, Lab Supply Res, 63-67; asst dir & actg dir, Lab Environ Studies, 68-70, DEP DIR, LAB ENVIRON STUDIES, INST ENVIRON MED, MED CTR, NY UNIV, 70-, RES PROF, 75- *Concurrent Pos:* Chmn & mem subcomt 6-metals I, Intersoc Comt Methods Air Sampling & Anal; consult, US NIH, Nat Oceanic & Atmospheric Admin, NY City Dept of Health & Var Industs; sr res scientist & head environ qual lab, NY Univ Med Ctr, 67- *Mem:* AAAS; Inst Standards Orgn (secy, 75-); Am Chem Soc; Am Pub Health Asn; Am Soc Testing & Mat. *Res:* Analysis, wet and instrumental; sampling and evaluation of natural and polluted environmental systems, air, water, biota; toxicological studies in aquatic and mammalian species. *Mailing Add:* Inst of Environ Med 550 First Ave New York NY 10016

KNEISSL, GERHART JOSEF, b Zieditz on Eger, Czech, Oct 16, 35; m 63; c 2. MECHANICAL ENGINEERING. *Educ:* Graz Tech Univ, Dipl ing, 63; Okla State Univ, PhD(mech eng), 67. *Prof Exp:* Instrumentation engr, Nat Bur Stand, 65-67; proj engr, Dunn Anal Instruments Div, Block Eng Inc, 67-70; prod line mgr, 70-76, MKT MGR, DIGILAB, INC, 76- *Mem:* Am Soc Testing & Mat; Electrochem Soc. *Res:* Instrumentation for air pollution process control; Fourier transform data systems for nuclear magnetic resonance; spectroscopy; nuclear magnetic resonance accessories. *Mailing Add:* Digilab Inc 237 Putnam Ave Cambridge MA 02139

KNELL, MARTIN, b Harvard, Ill, Feb 9, 20; m 49; c 2. ORGANIC CHEMISTRY. *Educ:* Univ Ill, BS, 43; Northwestern Univ, PhD(chem), 50. *Prof Exp:* Res chemist, Sinclair Refining Co, 49-51; fel, Mellon Inst, 51-52; res chemist, Geigy Chem Corp, 52-70, RES MGR PLASTICS & ADDITIVES DIV, CIBA-GEIGY CORP, 70- *Mem:* Am Chem Soc. *Res:* Organic synthesis; metal complexing agents; antioxidants; fluorochemicals; germicides; plastic additives. *Mailing Add:* Ciba-Geigy Corp Ardsley NY 10502

KNELLER, WILLIAM ARTHUR, b Cleveland, Ohio, Apr 7, 29; m 51; c 4. ENGINEERING GEOLOGY, ECONOMIC GEOLOGY. *Educ:* Miami Univ, AB, 51, MS, 55; Univ Mich, PhD(econ geol), 64. *Prof Exp:* Asst prof geol, Eastern Mich Univ, 56-59; PROF GEOL & CHMN DEPT, UNIV TOLEDO, 61-, DIR, EITEL INST FOR SILICATE RES, 76- *Mem:* Fel Geol Soc Am; Soc Econ Geologists; Soc Econ Paleontologists & Mineralogists. *Res:* Coal characterization for industrial use, coal petrology and petrography; industrial mineralogy; economic geology of industrial rocks and minerals; characterization of waste materials for industrial use; geochemistry of chert; concrete petrology. *Mailing Add:* 1761 Cherrylawn Dr Toledo OH 43614

KNEPPER, WILLIAM A(LBERT), b Wilkinsburg, Pa, Jan 10, 25; m 50; c 4. CHEMICAL ENGINEERING. *Educ:* Carnegie Inst Technol, BS, 49. *Prof Exp:* Insulation engr, Gen Elec Co, 49; proj engr, Chem Eng Div, Res Lab, Carnegie-Ill Steel Co, 49-52; supvr technologist, Raw Mat Div, US Steel Res Lab, 52-55, asst div chief, 55-59, res engr, Raw Mat, 59-60, div chief, Ore Reduction, 60-65, CHIEF STAFF ENGR, BLAST FURNACES & AGGLOMERATION, US STEEL ENG, 65- *Mem:* Am Inst Chem Engrs; Am Inst Mining, Metall & Petrol Engrs; Brit Iron & Steel Inst. *Res:* Blast furnace and agglomeration. *Mailing Add:* US Steel Corp 600 Grant St Pittsburgh PA 15230

KNEPTON, JAMES CANNIE, JR, b Jacksonville, Fla, Jan 4, 26; m 47; c 4. PHYSIOLOGY. *Educ:* Univ Fla, BS, 49, MS, 51. *Prof Exp:* From instr to asst prof biol, Wesleyan Col, 50-55; asst prof, Memphis State Univ, 55-61; instr, Pensacola Jr Col, 61-63; res biologist, US Naval Aerospace Med Inst, 63-70, sci staff asst, Naval Aerospace Med Res Lab, 70-72, RES PHYSIOLOGIST, NAVAL AEROSPACE MED RES LAB, 72- *Mem:* Bioelectromagnetics Soc. *Res:* Electromagnetic radiation effects on nonhuman primates conditioned behavior. *Mailing Add:* Code L33JK Bldg 1953 Naval Aerospace Med Res Lab Pensacola FL 32508

KNEVEL, ADELBERT MICHAEL, b St Joseph, Minn, Oct 20, 22; m 50; c 5. MEDICINAL CHEMISTRY. *Educ:* NDak State Univ, BS, 52, MS, 53; Purdue Univ, PhD(med chem), 57. *Prof Exp:* Instr pharmaceut chem, NDak State Univ, 53-54; from instr to assoc prof med chem, 54-65, asst dean, Sch Pharm & Pharm Sci, 68-75, PROF MED CHEM, SCH PHARM & PHARM SCI, PURDUE UNIV, WEST LAFAYETTE, 65-, ASSOC DEAN, 75- *Mem:* AAAS; Am Chem Soc; Am Pharmaceut Asn; fel Acad Pharmaceut Sci. *Res:* Methods development for drugs; drug metabolites in biological systems; studies of mechanism of drug action. *Mailing Add:* Sch of Pharm & Pharm Sci Purdue Univ West Lafayette IN 47907

KNIAZUK, MICHAEL, b Wilkes-Barre, Pa, June 12, 14; m 36. ELECTRONICS. *Educ:* NY Univ, BEE, 41. *Prof Exp:* Lab asst, 32-33, technician, 33-37, res assoc, 37-43, asst dir, Res Labs, 46-60, MGR BIOELECTRONICS LAB, MERCK INST THERAPEUT RES, 60- *Mem:* AAAS; Am Phys Soc; Inst Elec & Electronics Engrs. *Res:* Design and development of electronic instruments for biological research. *Mailing Add:* Biophysics Dept Res Div Merck & Co PO Box 2000 Rahway NJ 07065

KNIAZZEH, ALFREDO G(IOVANNI) F(RANCESCO), b New York, NY, July 31, 38; m 68; c 2. MECHANICAL ENGINEERING, PHYSICAL CHEMISTRY. *Educ:* Mass Inst Technol, BS, 59, MS, 61, PhD(mech eng), 66. *Prof Exp:* Physicist, Electronics Res Ctr, NASA, 66-70; from scientist to sr scientist, 70-78, ASST LAB MGR, POLAROID CORP, 78- *Mem:* Am Phys Soc; Am Vacuum Soc. *Res:* Thin films; physical electronics; mechanics of materials; photochemistry; chemical kinetics; thermodynamics; radiation transport; fluid mechanics; direct energy conversion; electrochemistry; optics. *Mailing Add:* 76 Prince St West Newton MA 02165

KNICKLE, HAROLD NORMAN, b Boston, Mass, Jan 6, 36; m 63; c 2. CHEMICAL ENGINEERING. *Educ:* Univ Mass, BSME, 62; Rensselaer Polytech Inst, MS, 65, PhD(nuclear eng), 69. *Prof Exp:* Engr nuclear eng, Knolls Atomic Power Lab, Gen Elec Co, 62-66; ASSOC PROF CHEM ENG, UNIV RI, 69- *Concurrent Pos:* Res prof, Pittsburgh Energy Technol Ctr, 77-80. *Mem:* Am Chem Soc; Am Inst Chem Engrs; Am Soc Eng Educ; Sigma Xi. *Res:* Mass transfer including azeotropic and extractive distillation, gas absorption, and leaching; heat transfer including single and two phase flow and insulation properties; design including mass transfer and heat transfer equipment; multiphase flow. *Mailing Add:* Dept of Chem Eng Univ of RI Kingston RI 02881

KNIEBES, DUANE VAN, b Marquette, Mich, May 17, 26; m 50; c 3. ANALYTICAL CHEMISTRY, RESEARCH ADMINISTRATION. *Educ:* Mich State Univ, BS, 48; Ill Inst Technol, MS, 54. *Prof Exp:* Asst chemist, 49-51, supvr, Instrumental Anal Lab, 51-54, head, Anal Div, 54-57, asst res dir, 57-62, assoc dir, 62-69, dir opers, 69-75, ASST VPRES EDUC SERV, INST GAS TECHNOL, 75- *Mem:* Am Chem Soc; Air Pollution Control Asn; Am Soc Testing & Mat; Am Gas Asn. *Res:* Odorization of natural and liquid propage gases; analysis of gaseous fuels; management of research and research facilities; design and operation of engineering education and technician training programs in natural gas technology. *Mailing Add:* 9S 135 Nantucket Dr Westmont IL 60559

KNIEVEL, DANIEL PAUL, b West Point, Nebr, Jan 29, 43; m 65; c 2. CROP PHYSIOLOGY. *Educ:* Univ Nebr, Lincoln, BS, 65; Univ Wis-Madison, MS, 67, PhD(agron, biochem), 68. *Prof Exp:* Crop physiologist plant sci, Univ Wyo, 68-72; asst prof, 72-75, ASSOC PROF CROP PHYSIOL, PA STATE UNIV, UNIVERSITY PARK, 75- *Concurrent Pos:* NSF grant, 69-72; crop sci adv, Pa State Univ-US AID, Grad Sch Develop Proj Argentina, 72-74; vis scientist, Sea Educ Admin, USDA, 80-81; assoc ed, Agron J, 78-83. *Mem:* Am Soc Agron; Crop Sci Soc Am; Am Soc Plant Physiol; Coun Agr Sci & Technol. *Res:* physiology of forage and grain yield; physiology of crop response to environmental stress; computer simulation of crop growth and development. *Mailing Add:* Dept of Agron Pa State Univ University Park PA 16802

KNIFFEN, DONALD AVERY, b Kalamazoo, Mich, Apr 27, 33; m 52; c 3. ASTROPHYSICS. *Educ:* La State Univ, BS, 59; Wash Univ, St Louis, MA, 60; Cath Univ Am, PhD, 67. *Prof Exp:* PHYSICIST, GODDARD SPACE FLIGHT CTR, NASA, 60- *Concurrent Pos:* Lectr, Univ Md, 78-; proj scientist, Gamma Ray Observ, 79- *Mem:* AAAS; Am Astron Soc; Am Phys Soc; Am Geophy Union. *Res:* Galactic and solar cosmic rays, including both charged particles and gamma rays; trapped radiation. *Mailing Add:* Code 662 Goddard Space Flight Ctr Greenbelt MD 20771

KNIGGE, KARL MAX, b Brooklyn, NY, July 17, 26; m 48; c 3. NEUROENDOCRINOLOGY. *Educ:* Rutgers Univ, BS, 50; Univ Mich, PhD(anat), 53. *Prof Exp:* Instr anat, Univ Pittsburgh, 53-55; asst prof, Univ Calif, Los Angeles, 55-59; from assoc prof to prof, Univ Cincinnati, 59-65; prof anat & chmn dept, Sch Med & Dent, 65-79, PROF & DIR, NEUROENDOCRINE UNIT, UNIV ROCHESTER, 80- *Mem:* Endocrine Soc; Am Physiol Soc; Soc Exp Biol & Med; Am Asn Anatomists; NY Acad Sci. *Res:* Neuroendocrinology. *Mailing Add:* Neuronendocrine Unit Box 609 Univ Rochester Sch of Med & Dent Rochester NY 14642

KNIGHT, ALAN CAMPBELL, b Hartford, Conn, Nov 2, 22; m 48; c 2. POLYMER SCIENCE. *Educ:* Ore State Col, BS, 48; Univ Calif, Berkeley, PhD(chem), 50. *Prof Exp:* Chemist, E I du Pont de Nemours & Co, Inc, Wilmington, 50-55, asst tech supt mfg, 55-56, tech supt, 56-58, sr supvr res & develop, 58-67, res assoc, 67-73, RES ASSOC, POLYMER PROD DEPT, WASHINGTON LAB, E I DU PONT DE NEMOURS & CO, INC, 73- *Mem:* Am Chem Soc. *Res:* Reaction kinetics and mechanisms; polymer synthesis; degradation mechanisms; stabilization; relation of structure to properties; manufacture of heavy organic chemicals; applied mathematics; computer applications; applied physical theory. *Mailing Add:* Du Pont Washington Works PO Box 1217 Parkersburg WV 26101

KNIGHT, ALLEN WARNER, b Grand Rapids, Mich, Feb 7, 32; m 55; c 4. AQUATIC ECOLOGY, WATER POLLUTION. *Educ:* Western Mich Univ, BS, 59; Mich State Univ, MS, 61; Univ Utah, PhD(zool), 65. *Prof Exp:* Asst prof entom & zool, Mich State Univ, 65-68; from asst prof to assoc prof, 68-76, PROF HYDROBIOL, UNIV CALIF, DAVIS, 76- *Concurrent Pos:* Consult, Stanford Res Inst, 70-75, Calif State Water Resources Control Bd, 76-81 & Wickland Oil Co, 81-; mem, Inst Ecol, Univ Calif. *Mem:* AAAS; Ecol Soc Am; Am Soc Limnol & Oceanog; Inst Soc Limnol; Entom Soc Am. *Res:* Pollution ecology; effect of environmental factors and pollutants on aquatic life; aquaculture, culture of freshwater prawn; clam (Corbicula); growth metabolism studies of aquatic life; hydrobiology. *Mailing Add:* Dept of Water Sci & Eng Univ of Calif Davis CA 95616

KNIGHT, ANNE BRADLEY, b Durham, NC, July 7, 42. BIOCHEMISTRY, PHYSIOLOGY. *Educ:* Univ NC, Chapel Hill, BA, 64, PhD(biochem), 72. *Prof Exp:* Res technician membrane transport, Med Sch, Univ NC, 64-67, res asst, 71-72; res assoc erythrocyte metab, Dept Physiol, Duke Univ, 72-75; instr anat & physiol, NC Cent Univ, 75; ASST PROF ANAT & PHYSIOL, WINTHROP COL, 75- *Concurrent Pos:* NIH res fel, Duke Univ, 72-74. *Mem:* Sigma Xi; Biophys Soc; AAAS. *Res:* Erythrocytes; comparative metabolism and transport; cellular volume regulation; interaction of active and passive transport with metabolism. *Mailing Add:* Dept of Biol Winthrop Col Rock Hill SC 29733

KNIGHT, ARTHUR ROBERT, b St John's, Nfld, Feb 24, 38; m 59; c 6. PHOTOCHEMISTRY. *Educ:* Mem Univ Nfld, BSc, 58, MSc, 60; Univ Alta, PhD(chem), 62. *Prof Exp:* Fel chem, Univ Alta, 62-64; from asst prof to assoc prof chem, 64-76, head dept, 76-81, PROF CHEM, UNIV SASK, 76-, DEAN, COL ART & SCI, 81- . *Mem:* Fel Can Inst Chem. *Res:* Reactions of radicals produced in photolytic decompositions; primary process studies in photolyses; photochemistry and photophysics of sulfur containing compounds. *Mailing Add:* Col Arts & Sci Univ of Sask Saskatoon SK S7N 0W0 Can

KNIGHT, BRUCE L, b Kansas City, Mo, Jan 4, 42; m 64; c 1. CHEMICAL & PETROLEUM ENGINEERING. *Educ:* Univ Kans, BS, 64; Univ Colo, MS, 65, PhD(chem eng), 69. *Prof Exp:* Res engr, Denver Res Ctr, 69-75, sr petrol engr, 75-77, environ coordr, 77-81, SR RES ENGR, MARATHON OIL CO, 81- *Mem:* Am Inst Chem Engrs; Soc Petrol Engrs; Am Petrol Inst. *Res:* Cryogenic heat transfer through porous media; tertiary oil recovery processes. *Mailing Add:* Marathon Oil Co PO Box 269 Littleton CO 80160

KNIGHT, BRUCE WINTON, (JR), b Milwaukee, Wis, Dec 4, 30; m 73; c 2. BIOPHYSICS, APPLIED MATHEMATICS. *Educ:* Dartmouth Col, BS, 52. *Prof Exp:* Staff mem, Los Alamos Sci Lab, 55-61; MEM FAC, ROCKFELLER UNIV, 61- *Res:* Neurophysiology of vision; applied theoretical physics. *Mailing Add:* Rockefeller Univ 230 York Ave New York NY 10021

KNIGHT, CHARLES ALFRED, b Chicago, Ill, Mar 28, 36; m 62. CLOUD PHYSICS. *Educ:* Univ Chicago, MS, 57, PhD(geol), 59. *Prof Exp:* Res scientist arctic ice, Univ Wash, 59-61; prog scientist cloud physics, Lab Atmospheric Sci, 62-74, head, Microphys Sect, Nat Hail Res Exp, 74-80, HEAD, CONNECTIVE STORMS DIV, NAT CTR ATMOSPHERIC RES, 80- *Concurrent Pos:* Mem fac, Colo State Univ, 69-, Univ Colo, 73- & Univ Wyo, 77- *Honors & Awards:* Publications Prize, Nat Ctr Atmospheric Res, 70. *Mem:* Am Meteorol Soc; Glaciol Soc. *Res:* Structure of hail; hail formation in relation to severe storm structure; hail suppression; ice crystal nucleation and growth. *Mailing Add:* Nat Ctr Atmospheric Res Boulder CO 80307

KNIGHT, CLAUDE ARTHUR, b Petoskey, Mich, Oct 17, 14; m 43; c 3. MOLECULAR BIOLOGY. *Educ:* Alma Col, Mich, BS, 36; Pa State Col, PhD(biochem), 40. *Prof Exp:* Asst biochem, Pa State Col, 38-40; fel, Rockefeller Inst, 40-42, asst, 42-45, assoc, 45-48; assoc prof, 48-55, prof virol, 55-64, prof molecular biol, 64-78, chmn, 76-78, EMER PROF MOLECULAR BIOL, UNIV CALIF, BERKELEY, 78- *Mem:* Am Soc Biol Chem. *Res:* Chemistry of viruses and cell components. *Mailing Add:* Dept of Molecular Biol Univ of Calif Berkeley CA 94720

KNIGHT, CLIFFORD BURNHAM, b Rockville, Conn, Jan 6, 26; m 56; c 1. INSECT ECOLOGY. *Educ:* Univ Conn, BA, 50, MA, 52; Duke Univ, PhD(invert ecol), 57. *Prof Exp:* Instr biol, 56-57, from asst prof to assoc prof zool, 57-64, dir grad studies biol, 73-81, PROF ZOOL, EAST CAROLINA UNIV, 64- *Mem:* Ecol Soc Am; Nat Audubon Soc; Am Inst Biol Sci. *Res:* Ecology of Collembola in forest communities of North Carolina; benthic invertebrate estuarine ecology. *Mailing Add:* Dept of Biol ECarolina Univ Greenville NC 27834

KNIGHT, DAVID BATES, b Louisville, Ky, Sept 23, 39; m 65; c 2. ORGANIC CHEMISTRY. *Educ:* Univ Louisville, BS, 61; Duke Univ, MA, 63, PhD(org chem), 66. *Prof Exp:* Vis assoc chem, Ohio State Univ, 66-67 & 77-78; asst prof, 67-73, ASSOC PROF CHEM, UNIV NC, GREENSBORO, 78- *Mem:* AAAS; Am Chem Soc. *Res:* Protium-deuterium exchange in hydrocarbons; chemistry of fulvenes. *Mailing Add:* Dept of Chem Univ of NC Greensboro NC 27414

KNIGHT, DENNIS HAL, b Clear Lake, SDak, Dec 24, 37; m 67; c 2. PLANT ECOLOGY. *Educ:* Augustana Col, SDak, BA, 59; Univ Wis-Madison, MS, 61, PhD(bot), 64. *Prof Exp:* Instr bot, with Peace Corps, Loja, Ecuador, 64-66; from asst prof to assoc prof, 66-79, PROF BOT, UNIV WYO, 79- *Mem:* AAAS; Ecol Soc Am; Am Inst Biol Sci; Soc Range Mgt. *Res:* Ecology of Great Plains and Rocky Mountain vegetation; tropical plant ecology; impact of vegetation structure on ecosystem function. *Mailing Add:* Dept of Bot Univ of Wyo Laramie WY 82071

KNIGHT, DOUGLAS WAYNE, b Batavia, NY, Oct 7, 38; m 61; c 3. COMPUTER SCIENCE. *Educ:* Ariz State Univ, BS, 61, MS, 69, PhD(elec eng), 75. *Prof Exp:* Geophysicist seismol, Shell Oil Co, 61-67; fac assoc programming, Ariz State Univ, 71-73; contractor, Govt Electronics Div, Motorola, 73-74; programming supvr, Trans Test Ctr, Dynalectron Corp, 74-79; prog mgr, Kentron Int, 79; DEPT CHMN COMPUT SCI TECHNOL FAC, UNIV SOUTHERN COLO, 80- *Concurrent Pos:* Referee, Fed Info Processing Standard, 73; owner, Computerland, Colorado Springs, 78- *Mem:* Data Processing Mgt Asn; Asn Comput Mach. *Res:* Microprocessing applications and software in testing environments; real-time dynamic structures testing; role playing simulations. *Mailing Add:* Univ Southern Colo 2200 N Bonforte Pueblo CO 81001

KNIGHT, FRANK B, b Chicago, Ill, Oct 11, 33; m 70; c 3. MATHEMATICS, MATHEMATICAL STATISTICS. *Educ:* Cornell Univ, BA, 55; Princeton Univ, PhD(math), 59. *Prof Exp:* Res asst math, Univ Minn, 59-60, from instr to asst prof, 60-63; from asst prof to assoc prof, 63-69, PROF MATH, UNIV ILL, URBANA, 69- *Res:* Prbability theory; differential equations; continuous time stochastic processes. *Mailing Add:* Dept of Math Univ of Ill Urbana IL 61801

KNIGHT, FRED BARROWS, b Waterville, Maine, Dec 12, 25; m 45; c 3. FOREST ENTOMOLOGY. *Educ:* Univ Maine, BSF, 49; Duke Univ, MF, 50, DF(forest entom), 56. *Prof Exp:* Entomologist, Bur Entom & Plant Quarantine, NC, 50-51 & Colo, 51-54; entomologist, Forest Insect & Dis Lab, US Forest Serv, Colo, 54-60; from assoc prof to prof forestry, Univ Mich, 60-72, chmn dept, 66-70; PROF FOREST RESOURCES & DIR SCH, UNIV MAINE, ORONO, 72-, ASSOC DIR, MAINE AGR EXP STA, 76- *Concurrent Pos:* Vis prof, Sch Forestry, Univ Canterbury, 70; from vpres to pres, Forestry Res Orgn, Asn State Col & Univ, 76-80. *Mem:* AAAS; Soc Am Foresters; Entom Soc Am; Soil Conserv Soc Am; Wildlife Soc. *Res:* Forest insect population, biological control; silviculture; forest ecology. *Mailing Add:* Sch of Forest Resources Univ of Maine Orono ME 04469

KNIGHT, FRED G, b Fargo, NDak, May 23, 20; div; c 2. EARTH SCIENCES. *Educ:* Colo Sch Mines, Geol Engr, 42. *Prof Exp:* Computer-party chief, Seismograph Serv Corp, 42-46; geophysicist, 47-53, dist geologist, Gulf & West Coasts, 53-61, adv sr staff geologist, 61-65, div explor mgr, 65-67, coord mgr explor, US & Can, 67-72, ASSOC RES DIR EXPLOR, MARATHON OIL CO, 72- *Mem:* Am Asn Petrol Geologists; Soc Explor Geophysicists. *Mailing Add:* Marathon Oil Co PO Box 269 Littleton CO 80120

KNIGHT, GORDON RAYMOND, b Oakland, Calif, Oct 6, 40; m 62; c 2. ELECTROOPTICS, ELECTRICAL ENGINEERING. *Educ:* Mass Inst Technol, SB, 62; Stanford Univ, MS, 64, PhD(elec eng), 67. *Prof Exp:* Engr commun theory, Lockheed Missiles &Space Co, 62-63; eng specialist, Sylvania Electronic Defense Labs, 63-69; mem res staff coherent optics, Ampex Corp, 69-70; mgr, Optical Storage Area, Palo Alto Res Ctr, Xerox Corp, 70-80; DIR ENG, OPTIMEN, UNIT SHUGART ASSOCS, 80- *Mem:* Optical Soc Am; Inst Elec & Electronics Engrs. *Res:* Holography; optical storage systems. *Mailing Add:* Optimen Unit Shugart Assocs 150 Charcot Ave San Jose CA 94131

KNIGHT, HOMER TALCOTT, b Rochelle, Ill, June 2, 23; m 48; c 2. ANALYTICAL CHEMISTRY. *Educ:* Northern Ill State Teachers Col, BS, 47; Colo State Col, MA, 48; Univ Ill, MS, 50; Univ Wis, PhD(chem), 52. *Prof Exp:* Chemist, Fansteel Metall Corp, Ill, 52-57, asst dir res, 57-63, tech dir, 63-65; tech asst to gen mgr, Gen Instruments Corp, SC, 65; mgr, Newport Facil, Elpac, Inc, 65-68; asst prof, 69-74, ASSOC PROF ANAL CHEM, UNIV WIS-PARKSIDE, 74- *Mem:* Am Chem Soc; Soc Appl Spectros. *Mailing Add:* Univ Wis-Parkside PO Box 2000 Kenosha WI 53141

KNIGHT, JAMES ALBERT, JR, b La Grange, Ga, Oct 16, 20; m 48; c 3. ORGANIC CHEMISTRY. *Educ:* Wofford Col, BS, 42; Ga Inst Technol, MS, 44; Pa State Univ, PhD(chem), 50. *Prof Exp:* From asst prof to assoc prof, Inst, 50-58, res assoc prof, Eng Exp Sta, 58-62, RES PROF CHEM, ENG EXP STA, GA INST TECHNOL, 62- *Mem:* AAAS; Forest Prod Res Soc; Am Chem Soc. *Res:* Pyrolytic and carbon technologies utilizing agricultural and forestry materials; radiation chemistry of organic systems; synthetic organic chemistry; gas and liquid chromatography. *Mailing Add:* Eng Exp Sta-Area 2 Ga Inst Technol Altanta GA 30332

KNIGHT, JAMES ALLEN, b St George, SC, Oct 20, 18; m 63. PSYCHIATRY. *Educ:* Wofford Col, AB, 41; Duke Univ, BD, 44; Vanderbilt Univ, MD, 52; Tulane Univ, MPH, 62. *Prof Exp:* Intern, Grady Mem Hosp, Atlanta, Ga, 52-53; asst resident pediat & obstet, Duke Univ Hosp, 53-54; instr psychiat, Sch Med, Tulane Univ, 55-58; asst prof, Col Med, Baylor Univ, 58-61, asst dean, 60-61; assoc prof, Sch Med, Tulane Univ, 61-63; prof psychiat, Union Theol Sem, NY, 63-64; prof psychiat & assoc dean, Sch Med, Tulane Univ, 64-74; dean, Col Med, Tex A&M Univ, 74-77; PROF PSYCHIAT, LA STATE UNIV SCH OF MED, NEW ORLEANS, 78- *Concurrent Pos:* Resident, Tulane Serv, Charity Hosp, New Orleans, 55-58, chief resident, 57-58. *Mem:* Am Psychiat Asn; Acad Psychoanal; Group Advan Psychiat. *Res:* Interrelationships of religion and psychiatry; suicide; motivation; psychosomatic medicine; ethics and human values; medical student maturation. *Mailing Add:* La State Univ Sch of Med 1542 Tulane Ave New Orleans LA 70112

KNIGHT, JAMES MILTON, b Jacksonville, Fla, Feb 20, 33; m 67; c 2. THEORETICAL PHYSICS. *Educ:* Spring Hill Col, BS, 54; Univ Md, PhD(physics), 60. *Prof Exp:* Res assoc & instr physics, Univ Md, 60-61; res assoc, Duke Univ, 63-65; assoc prof physics, 65-77, PROF PHYSICS & ASTRON, UNIV SC, 77- *Mem:* Am Phys Soc. *Res:* Elementary particle, field and scattering theory. *Mailing Add:* Dept of Physics Univ of SC Columbia SC 29208

KNIGHT, JAMES WILLIAM, b Alexandria, La, Nov 27, 48; m 70. REPRODUCTIVE PHYSIOLOGY. *Educ:* Univ Southwestern La, BS, 70; Univ Fla, MS, 72, PhD(reprod physiol), 75. *Prof Exp:* Fel reprod physiol, Univ Mo, 75-76; ASST PROF REPROD PHYSIOL, VA POLYTECH INST & STATE UNIV, 76- *Mem:* Am Soc Animal Sci; Soc Study Reprod; Endocrine Soc. *Res:* Conceptus-maternal interrelationships; uterine protein secretions; placental function; endocrinology of gestation. *Mailing Add:* Dept of Animal Physiol Va Polytech Inst & State Univ Blacksburg VA 24061

KNIGHT, JERE DONALD, b Deer River, Minn, July 2, 16; m 81. PHYSICAL CHEMISTRY. *Educ:* St John's Univ, Minn, BS, 38; Univ Minn, PhD(phys chem), 48. *Prof Exp:* Instr, St John's Prep Sch, Minn, 38-40; asst chem, Univ Minn, 41-42; asst, Nat Defense Res Comt Chicago, 42-43; jr chemist, Metall Lab, 43; assoc chemist, Clinton Labs, Tenn, 43-45; instr chem, Univ Ill, 48, res assoc physics, 48-49; MEM STAFF, LOS ALAMOS NAT LAB, 49- *Concurrent Pos:* Vis researcher, Brookhaven Nat Lab, 54-55. *Honors & Awards:* Clark Medal, Am Chem Soc, 80. *Mem:* AAAS; Am Chem Soc; fel Am Phys Soc. *Res:* Radiochemistry; nuclear structure and reactions; chemical and nuclear studies with mesons. *Mailing Add:* MS 514 Los Alamos Nat Lab Los Alamos NM 87545

KNIGHT, JOHN C (IAN), b Musselburgh, Scotland, June 16, 26; US citizen; m 63; c 1. UNDERWATER ACOUSTICS, OPERATIONS RESEARCH. *Educ:* Univ Edinburgh, BSc, 50, PhD(physics), 53. *Prof Exp:* Asst physics, Univ Edinburgh, 52-54; sr sci officer, Admiralty, Eng, 54-58, prin sci officer, Home Fleet, 58-59; mem staff opers res, Saclant Anti-Submarine Warfare Res Ctr, Italy, 59-63; prin sci officer, Ministry of Defence, Eng, 63-65; sr staff mem, Opers Res Inc, Md, 65-68; sr staff & dep dir, John D Kettelle Corp, Va, 68-70; head, Systs Anal Group, Acoust Div, Naval Res Lab, 70-80; prin scientist, EG & G Wash Anal Serv Ctr, 80; MEM PRIN STAFF, SUMMIT RES CORP, 80- *Concurrent Pos:* Consult comt undersea warfare, Nat Acad Sci, 67-70; staff scientist, Commander Oceanog Syst Atlantic, 74-77. *Mem:* Acoust Soc Am; Opers Res Soc Am; Sigma Xi. *Res:* Beta and gamma ray spectroscopy; military operations research; analysis of naval system performance. *Mailing Add:* 3403 Fessenden St NW Washington DC 20008

KNIGHT, KATHERINE LATHROP, b Jackson, Mich, May 13, 41. BIOCHEMISTRY, IMMUNOLOGY. *Educ:* Elmira Col, BA, 62; Ind Univ, PhD(chem), 66. *Prof Exp:* Res assoc, 66-68, from asst prof to assoc prof, 68-75, PROF MICROBIOL, UNIV ILL MED CTR, CHICAGO, 75- *Concurrent Pos:* NIH res career develop award, 70-75. *Mem:* AAAS; Am Chem Soc; Am Asn Immunologists. *Res:* Immunochemistry; immunogenetics; protein chemistry. *Mailing Add:* Dept of Microbiol Univ of Ill Med Ctr Chicago IL 60680

KNIGHT, KENNETH LEE, b Saunemin, Ill, Mar 16, 15; m 44; c 5. ENTOMOLOGY. *Educ:* Ill State Univ, BEd, 37; Univ Ill, MS, 39, PhD(entom), 41. *Prof Exp:* Med entomologist, Med Serv Corps, US Dept Navy, 41-62; prof med entom, Iowa State Univ, 62-66; prof syst entom, Univ Ga, 66-68; head, Dept Entom, NC State Univ, 68-80; RETIRED. *Mem:* Entom Soc Am, 74-75, secy-treas, 81-83); Soc Syst Zool; Am Mosquito Control Asn (pres, 73-74); Sigma Xi. *Res:* Medical entomology; taxonomy, morphology and biology of mosquitoes. *Mailing Add:* Dept of Entom NC State Univ Raleigh NC 27650

KNIGHT, LARRY V, b Pocatello, Idaho, Mar 13, 35; m 58; c 6. PHYSICS. *Educ:* Brigham Young Univ, BS, 58, MS, 59; Stanford Univ, PhD(physics), 65. *Prof Exp:* Res assoc physics, Stanford Univ, 65-69; asst prof physics, 69-77, ASSOC PROF PHYSICS & ASTRON, BRIGHAM YOUNG UNIV, 77- *Concurrent Pos:* Mem tech staff, Hewlett-Packard Co, 64-69; vpres, Holograf Corp, 70-72; consult, Lawrence Livermore Lab, 75- *Mem:* Am Phys Soc. *Res:* Low temperature physics; fundamental constants; magnetic resonance; electron spectroscopy; quantum electronics; holography; laser fusion; plasma physics. *Mailing Add:* Dept of Physics Brigham Young Univ Provo UT 84601

KNIGHT, LEE H, JR, b Westville, Fla, July 8, 28; m 60; c 1. MECHANICAL ENGINEERING. *Educ:* Univ SC, BS, 57; Ga Inst Technol, MS, 62. *Prof Exp:* Res asst, Ga Inst Technol, 57-69, asst res engr, 60-62; sr engr, Lockheed Ga Co, 62-64; br head mech eng, Ga Inst Technol, 64-67; ASST DIR SERV, SKIDAWAY INST OCEANOG, 67- *Res:* Heat and mass transfer; underwater propulsion systems; electromechanical equipment for oceanographic research. *Mailing Add:* Skidaway Inst of Oceanog PO Box 13687 Savannah GA 31406

KNIGHT, LON BISHOP, JR, b Milledgeville, Ga, Apr 24, 44; m 66; c 2. PHYSICAL CHEMISTRY. *Educ:* Mercer Univ, BS, 66; Univ Fla, PhD(chem), 70. *Prof Exp:* Res assoc phys chem, Univ Fla, 70-71; asst prof, 71-75, ASSOC PROF CHEM, FURMAN UNIV, 75- *Mem:* Am Chem Soc. *Res:* Study of reactions of metal atoms in the gas phase at low temperatures; metallic transport mechanisms; ESR matrix isolation of high temperature species. *Mailing Add:* Dept of Chem Furman Univ Greenville SC 29613

KNIGHT, LUTHER AUGUSTUS, JR, b Clarendon, Ark, Dec 19, 30; m 55; c 2. AQUATIC BIOLOGY. *Educ:* Ark State Col, BS, 57; Univ Miss, MS, 61, PhD(biol), 69. *Prof Exp:* Teacher, high sch, Ark, 56-57 & Mo, 57-64; asst prof & asst res prof, 68-72, assoc prof, 72-81, PROF BIOL & CUR ZOOL MUS, UNIV MISS, 81- *Mem:* Am Soc Limnol & Oceanog; Am Micros Soc; Sigma Xi. *Res:* Taxonomy, ecology and distribution of Rotifera; water quality as related to freshwater plankton and biological productivity in reservoirs; trace elements in aquatic organisms. *Mailing Add:* Dept of Biol Univ of Miss University MS 38677

KNIGHT, LYMAN COLEMAN, b Wooster, Ohio, Nov 2, 15; m 37; c 3. MATHEMATICS. *Educ:* Col Wooster, BS, 37; Kent State Univ, MA, 41; Univ Pittsburgh, DEd(math educ), 58. *Prof Exp:* Teacher pub schs, Ohio, 37-40; instr math & band, Northeastern Okla Jr Col, 40-42; from asst prof to assoc prof, 42-59, PROF MATH, MUSKINGUM COL, 59-, PROF COMPUT SCI, 81- *Concurrent Pos:* Consult, Nat Defense Educ Act. *Mem:* AAAS; Am Math Soc; Math Asn Am; Am Statist Asn. *Res:* Mathematical education; training of elementary and secondary teachers; undergraduate curriculum in mathematics in liberal arts colleges. *Mailing Add:* Dept of Math Muskingum Col New Concord OH 43762

KNIGHT, RALPH AMBER, b Salt Lake City, Utah, Aug 12, 20; m 42; c 2. BACTERIOLOGY. *Educ:* Univ Utah, BS, 48, MS, 49, PhD, 58. *Prof Exp:* Bacteriologist, State Dept Health, Utah, 49-51; bacteriologist, Vet Admin Hosp, 51-58, res bacteriologist, 58-62; asst prof med & assoc microbiol, 62-69, ASSOC PROF CLIN PATH & MED, MED COL PA, 69-, ASST PROF MICROBIOL, 81- *Res:* Bacteriology of pulmonary disease; aspects of tuberculosis and nontubercular chest disease. *Mailing Add:* Dept of Path Med Col of Pa Philadelphia PA 19129

KNIGHT, ROBERT ARTHUR, parasitology, see previous edition

KNIGHT, ROBERT HALLOWELL, molecular biology, cell biology, see previous edition

KNIGHT, SAMUEL BRADLEY, b Bowman, SC, Dec 25, 13; m 37; c 2. CHEMISTRY. *Educ:* Clemson Agr Col, BS, 34; Univ NC, MS, 37, PhD, 38. *Prof Exp:* Asst chem, Univ NC, 34-38; from asst prof to assoc prof, Davidson Col, 38-41; from asst prof to assoc prof, 41-45, prof, 50-80, EMER PROF CHEM, UNIV NC, CHAPEL HILL, 80- *Mem:* Am Chem Soc. *Res:* Electrochemistry, absorption spectra; flame photometry; analysis of small quantities of metals. *Mailing Add:* Dept of Chem Univ of NC Chapel Hill NC 27514

KNIGHT, STEPHEN, b San Mateo, Calif, Feb 24, 38; m 59; c 3. EXPERIMENTAL PHYSICS. *Educ:* Beloit Col, BS, 59; Yale Univ, MS, 60, PhD(physics), 64. *Prof Exp:* Mem tech staff, 64-68; supvr explor device tech group, 68-71; supvr optical mat properties group, 71-72; supvr displays group, 72-73; supvr opto-isolators group, 73-78, supvr govt systs support, 78-80; supvr technol options, 80-81, HEAD ELECTRONICS TECHNOL PLANNING, BELL TEL LABS, 81- *Concurrent Pos:* Assoc ed, Inst Elec & Electronic Engr Trans Electron Devices, ed, 78- *Mem:* Am Phys Soc; sr mem

Inst Elec & Electronics Engrs; Electron Devices Soc. *Res:* Low temperature physics, turbulent superfluid helium; semiconductor physics, bulk negative resistance; light emitting diodes; magnetic bubble materials; integrated circuit planning; high performance technology evaluation. *Mailing Add:* Rm 2D329 Bell Tel Labs Murray Hill NJ 07974

KNIGHT, VERNON, b Osceola, Mo, Sept 6, 17; m 46; c 4. MEDICINE. *Educ:* William Jewell Col, AB, 39; Harvard Univ, MD, 43; Am Bd Internal Med, dipl. *Prof Exp:* Asst prof med, Med Col, Cornell Univ, 53-54; assoc prof, Sch Med, Vanderbilt Univ, 54-59; clin dir, Nat Inst Allergy & Infectious Dis, Md, 59-66; PROF MED & CHMN DEPT MICROBIOL & IMMUNOL, BAYLOR COL MED, 66- *Concurrent Pos:* Mem, Nat Adv Allergy & Infectious Dis Coun; prof consult, US Army Med Res Inst of Infectious Dis, Ft Detrick. *Mem:* Soc Exp Biol & Med; Am Soc Clin Invest; Am Clin & Climat Asn; Am Col Physicians. *Res:* Infectious disease. *Mailing Add:* 11735 Green Bay Dr Houston TX 77024

KNIGHT, WALTER DAVID, JR, b New York, NY, Oct 14, 19; m 45, 72; c 3. SOLID STATE PHYSICS, ATOMIC AND MOLECULAR PHYSICS. *Educ:* Middlebury Col, AB, 41; Duke Univ, MA, 43, PhD(physics), 50. *Prof Exp:* Instr physics, Duke Univ, 43-44; instr, Trinity Col, 46-50; from asst prof to assoc prof, 50-61, asst dean col lett & sci, 59-61, assoc dean, 61-63, dean, 67-72, PROF PHYSICS, UNIV CALIF, BERKELEY, 61- *Concurrent Pos:* Alfred P Sloan fel, 56-59; Guggenheim fel, 61; Miller fel, 79. *Mem:* Fel AAAS; fel Am Phys Soc. *Res:* Study of metal microclusters by molecular beam methods. *Mailing Add:* Dept of Physics Univ of Calif Berkeley CA 94720

KNIGHT, WALTER REA, b Cortland, Ohio, Apr 25, 32; m 54; c 4. PSYCHOBIOLOGY. *Educ:* Baldwin-Wallace Col, AB, 54; Pa State Univ, MS, 56, PhD(psychol), 61. *Prof Exp:* Instr psychol, 56-57, asst prof, 57-58, 60-65, assoc prof, 65-68, PROF PSYCHOL & BIOL, HIRAM COL, 68-, CHMN DEPT PSYCHOL, 66- *Concurrent Pos:* NIMH spec res training fel, Univ Fla, 64-66. *Mem:* AAAS; Am Psychol Asn; Animal Behav Soc. *Res:* Neural, hormonal and early experience factors in animal social behavior and social stress. *Mailing Add:* Dept of Biol Hiram Col Hiram OH 44234

KNIGHT, WILLIAM ALLEN, JR, b St Louis, Mo, Oct 5, 14; m 41; c 3. GASTROENTEROLOGY. *Educ:* Drury Col, AB, 36; St Louis Univ, MD, 40; Am Bd Int Med cert, 51. *Prof Exp:* Asst int med, 47-48, instr, 48-49, sr instr, 49-51, asst prof med, 51-55, dir int med, Housestaff & Residency Training Prog, 50-59, DIR, DIV GASTROENTEROL, SCH MED, ST LOUIS UNIV, 54-, ASSOC PROF MED, 55- *Concurrent Pos:* Area consult int med, US Vet Admin, 56-60; dir int med, St Louis City Hosp, St Louis Univ Med Serv, 48-55 & Firmin Desloge Hosp, 55-58; dir, Dept Internal Med, St Mary's Health Ctr, 65-80, emer dir, Cancer Res & Treatment Ctr, 81- *Mem:* Am Col Gastroenterol; Am Soc Gastrointestinal Endoscopy; Am Gastroenterol Asn; Am Asn Study Liver Dis; fel Am Col Phys. *Res:* Qualitative and quantitative analysis of pancreatic secretions, proteins and electrolytes in the normal and diseased pancreas to aid in the diagnosis of pancreatic disease. *Mailing Add:* St Mary's Health Ctr 6420 Clayton Rd St Louis MO 63117

KNIGHT, WILLIAM ERIC, b Lacon, Ala, July 24, 20; m 44. PLANT BREEDING. *Educ:* Ala Polytech Inst, BS, 42, MS, 48; Pa State Univ, PhD(agron), 51. *Prof Exp:* Teacher, Vet Voc Agr, State Dept Educ, Fla, 46-47; asst soils res, Ala Polytech Inst, 47-48; res agronomist plant breeding & genetics, 51-81, ADJ PROF AGRON, EXP STA, SCI & EDUC ADMIN, USDA, MISS STATE UNIV, 81- *Concurrent Pos:* Mem, South Pasture & Forage Crop Improvement Conf. *Mem:* Am Soc Agron; Crop Sci Soc Am; Am Genetic Asn; Am Forage & Grassland Coun. *Res:* Genetic and plant breeding in annual Trifolium species; plant improvement by breeding. *Mailing Add:* Box 272 Miss Mississippi State MS 39762

KNIGHTEN, JAMES LEO, b Lafayette, La, Apr 1, 43; m 70; c 2. ELECTROMAGNETICS, ELECTROMAGNETIC PULSE ENGINEERING. *Educ:* La State Univ, BS, 65, MS, 68; Iowa State Univ, PhD(elec eng), 76. *Prof Exp:* Asst prof electromagnetics, Iowa State Univ, Ames, 76-77; staff engr, 77-80, MGR ELECTROMAGNETICS, IRT CORP, 80- *Mem:* Inst Elec & Electronics Engrs. *Res:* Nuclear electromagnetic pulse effects on systems; numerical methods; nuclear electromagnetic pulse hardening of ground launched Cruise missile; assessment of electromagnetic pulse coupling to ground based command, control and communications facilities, tactical systems, aircraft and missiles. *Mailing Add:* IRT Corp PO Box 80817 San Diego CA 92138

KNIGHTEN, ROBERT LEE, b Marshfield, Ore, May 7, 40; m 63; c 2. ALGEBRA. *Educ:* Mass Inst of Technol, BS, 62, PhD(math), 66. *Prof Exp:* Mathematician, Navy Electronics Lab, Calif, 57-64; instr math, Mass Inst Technol, 64-66 & Univ Chicago, 66-68; asst prof, Univ Ill, Chicago Circle, 68-71; asst prof, 71-76, ASSOC PROF MATH, UNIV PR, 76- *Mem:* AAAS; Am Math Soc; Math Asn Am; Soc Indust & Appl Math. *Res:* Applications of category theory to commutative algebra; algebraic geometry and homotopy theory. *Mailing Add:* Dept Math Univ PR Box BF Rio Piedras PR 00931

KNIGHTS, JOHN CHRISTOPHER, b Felixstowe, Eng, July 2, 47. PHYSICS. *Educ:* Univ Sussex, BSc, 68; Univ Cambridge, MA & PhD(physics), 72. *Prof Exp:* Imp Chem Industs fel, Univ Cambridge, 72-73; RES SCIENTIST PHYSICS, PALO ALTO RES CTR, XEROX CORP, 73- *Concurrent Pos:* Res fel, Sidney Sussex Col, Cambridge, Eng, 72-73. *Res:* Transport properties of amorphous and crystalline semiconductors. *Mailing Add:* Xerox Palo Alto Res Ctr 3333 Coyote Hill Rd Palo Alto CA 94304

KNIKER, WILLIAM THEODORE, b Sequin, Tex, Aug 30, 29; m 65; c 4. ALLERGY, IMMUNOLOGY. *Educ:* Univ Tex, BA, 50, MD, 53; Am Bd Pediat, dipl; 59; Conjoint Bd Allergy & Immunol, dipl, 74. *Prof Exp:* Intern, Henry Ford Hosp, Detroit, 53-54; resident pediat, Univ Tex Med Br, 56-58; chief resident, Med Ctr, Univ Ark, 58-59, from instr to asst prof pediat, 59-62,

from asst prof to assoc prof pediat & path, 65-69; assoc prof pediat & microbiol, 69-71, PROF PEDIAT & MICROBIOL, UNIV TEX MED SCH, SAN ANTONIO, 71- *Concurrent Pos:* Res fel infectious dis, Am Thoracic Soc, 59-62; res fel, Div Exp Path, Scripps Clin & Res Found, Calif, 62-65; asst dir clin res unit, Univ Ark Med Ctr, 65-69, dir sect immunol-allergy, 69-; NIH res career develop award, 68-69. *Mem:* Am Asn Path; Am Asn Immunologists; Soc Pediat Res; Am Soc Nephrology; Am Acad Allergy. *Res:* Immunopathology, mechanisms of hypersensitivity and immunological diseases; immunochemistry of mycobacterial antigens; primate immunology; pediatrics. *Mailing Add:* Dept of Pediat Univ of Tex Health Sci Ctr San Antonio TX 78284

KNILL, LAMAR M, b Denver, Colo, Aug 4, 24; m 51; c 3. RADIOBIOLOGY. *Educ:* Colo State Univ, BS, 51, MS, 56, PhD(physiol), 65. *Prof Exp:* Res physiologist, Biochem Res Div, US Vet Admin Hosp, Albuquerque, NMex, 56-58; tech rep, Braun Chem Co, Calif, 58-60; from asst prof to assoc prof, 60-69, PROF PHYSIOL, CALIF STATE POLYTECH UNIV, POMONA, 69-, DIR, EQUINE RES CTR, 80- *Concurrent Pos:* Consult, Ministry Educ & Relig, Athens, Greece, 72. *Mem:* Am Chem Soc; Sigma Xi; Am Nuclear Soc; NY Acad Sci. *Res:* Immunochemistry; radiation biology; physiology. *Mailing Add:* Dept of Biol Sci Calif State Polytech Univ Pomona CA 91766

KNILL, RONALD JOHN, b Chicago, Ill, Feb 20, 35; m 58; c 3. TOPOLOGY. *Educ:* Marquette Univ, BS, 56; Univ Notre Dame, MS, 60, PhD(math), 62. *Prof Exp:* NSF fel, Univ Calif, Berkeley, 62-63; from asst prof to assoc prof, 63-74, PROF MATH, TULANE UNIV, 74- *Mem:* Am Math Soc; Math Asn Am; Math Soc France. *Res:* Fixed point theory; dynamical systems. *Mailing Add:* Dept of Math Tulane Univ New Orleans LA 70118

KNIPE, DAVID MAHAN, b Lancaster, Ohio, Aug 6, 50; m 73; c 2. VIROLOGY, CELL BIOLOGY. *Educ:* Case Western Reserve Univ, BA, 72; Mass Inst Technol, PhD(cell biol), 72. *Prof Exp:* fel, 76-79, ASST PROF VIROL, DEPT MICROBIOL, UNIV CHICAGO, 79- *Mem:* Am Soc Microbiol; Am Soc Virol; AAAS. *Res:* How herpes simplex virus replicates in and interacts with its host cell; molecular biological and genetic approaches to study how viral and cellular proteins are transported into the cell nucleus. *Mailing Add:* Dept Microbiol & Molecular Genetics Harvard Med Sch 25 Shattuck St Boston MA 02115

KNIPE, RICHARD HUBERT, b Salmon, Idaho, Sept 12, 27; m 57; c 3. CHEMICAL PHYSICS. *Educ:* Calif Inst Technol, BS, 50; Duke Univ, PhD(physics), 54. *Prof Exp:* Physicist, 54-57, aeronaut power plant res engr, 57-62, phys chemist, 62, RES PHYSICIST, NAVAL WEAPONS CTR, 62- *Mem:* Am Phys Soc; Am Chem Soc. *Res:* Quantum theory of molecules; gas phase chemical kinetics and mechanism. *Mailing Add:* Code 3852 Naval Weapons Ctr China Lake CA 93555

KNIPFEL, JERRY EARL, b Calgary, Alta, June 30, 41; m 66; c 2. NUTRITION, BIOCHEMISTRY. *Educ:* Univ Sask, BSA, 65, MSc, 67; McGill Univ, PhD(nutrit), 73. *Prof Exp:* Chemist, Health Protection Br, Nutrit Res Div, Health & Welfare Can, 67-69, res scientist, 69-73; RES SCIENTIST, FORAGE PROD & UTILIZATION SECT, RES STA, AGR CAN, 73- *Concurrent Pos:* Asst ed, Can J Animal Sci, 77-80, Comt Animal Sci, 80-83; lectr, Dept Biol, Univ Regina, 78; consult, Topline Feeds, Inc, Swift Current, 74; mem, Exp Comt Animal Nutrit, 81-84, Forage Crops, 79-82, prog review comt, Agr Can Western Region, 80; sci authority, Res Br, Agr Can, Contract Res Progs, 79-; asst prof biol, Univ Regina, 81. *Mem:* Can Soc Animal Sci; Nutrit Soc Can; Can Asn Lab Animal Sci. *Res:* Nutrition in relation to fetal development and post partum performance; nitrogen metabolism in ruminants; evaluation of nutritional quality and nutrient availability; improvement in nutritional value of roughage. *Mailing Add:* Forage Prod & Utilization Sect Res Sta Agr Can Swift Current SK S9H 3X2 Can

KNIPLING, EDWARD FRED, b Port Lavaca, Tex, Mar 20, 09; m 34; c 5. ENTOMOLOGY. *Educ:* Tex A&M Univ, BS, 30; Iowa State Univ, MS, 32, PhD(entom), 47. *Hon Degrees:* DSc, Catawba Col, 62; NDak State Univ, 70, Clemson Univ, 70, Fla State Univ, 75. *Prof Exp:* Field asst, Bur Entom & Plant Quarantine, USDA, 30, from jr entomologist to assoc entomologist, 31-42, sr entomologist, Off Sci Res & Develop contract, 42-46, prin entomologist, 46-53, dir, Entom Res Div, Agr Res Serv, 53-71, sci adv, 71-73, CONSULT, USDA, 73- *Honors & Awards:* Medal, Typhus Comn; US Army Medal for Merit; King's Medal for Cause of Freedom; Distinguished Serv Award, USDA; Hoblitzelle Nat Award, 60; Rockefeller Pub Serv Award, 64; Nat Medal Sci, 66; President's Award Distinguished Fed Civilian Serv, 71. *Mem:* Nat Acad Sci; AAAS; Entom Soc Am; Am Soc Trop Med & Hyg; Am Mosquito Control Asn. *Res:* Biology, ecology, population dynamics and control of insects. *Mailing Add:* 2623 Military Rd Arlington VA 22207

KNIPMEYER, HUBERT ELMER, b Sharon, Conn, Nov 7, 29; m 52; c 4. ORGANIC CHEMISTRY, RESEARCH ADMINISTRATION. *Educ:* Mass Inst Technol, SB, 51; Univ Ill, PhD(chem), 57. *Prof Exp:* Res chemist, Cent Res Dept, 56-60, tech investr, Film Dept, 60-61, res chemist, 61-62, staff scientist, 62-63, tech rep, 64-65, group mgr, 65-69, res mgr, Ohio, 69-71, prod mgr, 71-74, tech mgr, Film Dept, 74-75, mgr mkt develop & customer serv, 76, lab supt, 77, RES MGR, PLASTIC PROD & RESINS DEPT & PROG MGR CORP AUTOMOTIVE DEVELOP, CORP PLANS DEPT, E I DU PONT DE NEMOURS & CO, INC, 78- *Mem:* Am Chem Soc. *Res:* Physical organic chemistry; organic synthesis; heterocyclic organic chemistry; polyimide, polyester and polyolefin chemistry. *Mailing Add:* Plastic Prod & Resins Dept E I du Pont de Nemours & Co Wilmington DE 19898

KNIPP, ERNEST A, (JR), b Houston, Tex, Oct 10, 29; m 79. CHEMICAL ENGINEERING. *Educ:* Rice Univ, BS, 50, MS, 52; Yale Univ, PhD(chem eng), 58. *Prof Exp:* Fel chem, Univ NC, 57-59; asst prof chem eng, Mich Col Mining & Technol, 59; fel chem, Rice Univ, 60; res chem engr, Humble Oil & Ref Co, 61-63, sr res chem engr, 63-65, Esso Res & Eng Co, 65-68, res specialist, 68-71; INDEPENDENT CONSULT, 71- *Mem:* Am Chem Soc; Am Inst Chem Engrs; Asn Comput Mach; Royal Soc Chem. *Res:* Computer applications. *Mailing Add:* PO Box 3041 Houston TX 77001

KNIPPLE, WARREN RUSSELL, b Johnstown, Pa, May 28, 34; m 59; c 2. INDUSTRIAL CHEMISTRY, PETROLEUM CHEMISTRY. *Educ:* Univ Pittsburgh, BS, 59; Case Western Reserve Univ, MS, 61, PhD(chem), 68. *Prof Exp:* Sr chemist, Res Dept, Standard Oil Co (Ohio), 59-68; sr res chemist, 68-69, prod mgr chem, 69-70, chem opers mgr, 70-72, GEN MGR, CLEVELAND REFRACTORY METALS DIV, CHASE BRASS & COPPER CO, INC, 72- *Mem:* Am Chem Soc; AAAS; Am Mgt Asn. *Res:* Organic synthesis; organometallic research; heterogeneous catalysis; peroxide chemistry; aromatic substitution; rhenium chemistry; ion exchange and solvent extraction technology. *Mailing Add:* Cleveland Refractory Metals Div 29855 Aurora Rd Solon OH 44139

KNISELEY, RICHARD NEWMAN, b Wichita, Kans, Jan 23, 30; m 51; c 2. SPECTROCHEMISTRY, ANALYTICAL INSTRUMENTATION. *Educ:* Univ Kansas City, BA, 51; Iowa State Univ, MS, 54, PhD, 71. *Prof Exp:* Res assoc spectros, Inst Atomic Res, 55-59, from assoc chemist to chemist, 59-74, sr chemist, Ames Lab, Dept Energy, 74, ASST DIR ENVIRON PROGS, IOWA STATE UNIV, 79- *Mem:* Optical Soc Am; Soc Appl Spectros; Microbeam Anal Soc; Sigma Xi. *Res:* High temperature, stable molecules; electron microprobe analysis; instrument design and development; inductively coupled plasma excitation sources; determination of trace metals in environmental and biomedical samples; microbiological air quality; photoacoustic spectroscopy. *Mailing Add:* Ames Lab Dept of Energy Iowa State Univ Ames IA 50011

KNISELY, WILLIAM HAGERMAN, b Houghton, Mich, Feb 3, 22; m 47; c 5. ANATOMY. *Educ:* Univ Chicago, PhB, 47, BS, 50; Med Col SC, MS, 52, PhD, 54. *Prof Exp:* Asst anat, Med Col SC, 49-50 & 51-54; from instr to asst prof med & from instr to assoc prof anat, Duke Univ, 54-59; prof anat & chmn dept, Univ Ky, 59-63; dir inst biol & med, Mich State Univ, 63-70; vchancellor health affairs, Univ Tex Syst, 70-73, prof anat & cell biol, 70-75, asst to chancellor health affairs, 73-75; vpres acad affairs, 75, PRES, MED UNIV SC, 75-, PROF ANAT, 75- *Concurrent Pos:* Univ res fel med, Duke Univ, 54-57, Am Heart Asn fel, 55-57, USPHS sr res fel, 57-59; mem, Nat Adv Coun Educ for Health Prof, 68-71, chmn policy plan comn, 69-71, vchmn, Study Comn on Dietetics, 69-71; comnr, Navajo Health Authority, 72-76; mem adv comt, Regional Health Serv Res Inst, Univ Tex Health Sci Ctr San Antonio, 73-75 & Univ Tex Austin Ctr Social Work, 74-75; mem bd dirs, Holy Cross Hosp, 73-75; consult, Regions IX & X, Dept Health, Educ & Welfare, 73-79 & Dept Med & Surg, Vet Admin, 74-; assoc mem, Inst Soc, Ethics & Life Sci, 74-75; gen adj prof, Union Grad Sch, Yellow Springs, Ohio, 74- *Mem:* AAAS; Geront Soc; Am Heart Asn; Am Asn Anatomists; Microcirc Soc. *Res:* Anatomy, physiology, pharmacology and pathology of small blood vessels, especially the lung. *Mailing Add:* Med Univ SC Charleston SC 29401

KNISKERN, VERNE BURTON, b Negaunee, Mich, Oct 16, 21; m 42; c 3. PARASITOLOGY. *Educ:* Univ Mich, BS, 47, MS, 48, PhD(zool), 50. *Prof Exp:* From assoc prof to PROF ZOOL, EASTERN ILL UNIV, 50- *Mem:* Am Micros Soc; Am Soc Parasitol; Wildlife Dis Asn. *Res:* Parasitology; protozoology; genetics; histology; malacology; medical biology. *Mailing Add:* Dept of Zool Eastern Ill Univ Charleston IL 61920

KNITTEL, MARTIN DEAN, b Torrington, Wyo, Dec 19, 32; m 56; c 3. MICROBIOLOGY. *Educ:* Willamette Univ, BS, 55; Ore State Univ, MS, 62, PhD(microbiol), 65. *Prof Exp:* Bacteriologist, Ore Agr Div, 55-56; med technologist, Doctors' Clin, 58-59; aquatic biologist, Ore Fish Comn, 62-63; sr res microbiologist, Norwich Pharmacal Co, 65-66; microbiologist, Pac Northwest Water Lab, Fed Water Pollution Control Admin, 66-69; sr engr, Jet Propulsion Lab, 69-71; res microbiologist, Pac Northwest Water Lab, 71-74, RES MICROBIOLOGIST, WESTERN FISH TOXICOL STA, ENVIRON PROTECTION AGENCY, 74- *Mem:* AAAS; Am Soc Microbiol. *Res:* Physiology of the bacterium Sphaerotilus natans as is related to its growth in polluted streams; microbiology of waste treatment; detection of pathogenic organisms in waste water; biochemistry of waste water treatment; effect of stress on disease in fish. *Mailing Add:* Rt 3 Box 404 Corvallis OR 97330

KNIZE, RANDALL JAMES, b Tacoma, Wash, Feb 4, 53; m 79. ATOMIC COLLISIONS, SURFACE PHYSICS. *Educ:* Univ Chicago, BA & MS, 75; Harvard Univ, MA, 76, PhD(physics), 81. *Prof Exp:* Res asst, Harvard Univ, 76-81; RES PHYSICIST, PRINCETON UNIV, 80- *Mem:* Am Phys Soc; Am Vacuum Soc. *Res:* Fundamental atomic physics; impurity control and hydrogen recycling in controlled thermonuclear devices. *Mailing Add:* Plasma Physics Lab Princeton Univ PO Box 451 Princeton NJ 08544

KNOBELOCH, F X CALVIN, b Tell City, Ind, Aug 5, 25; m 53; c 3. SPEECH PATHOLOGY, AUDIOLOGY. *Educ:* Ind Univ, BSEd, 49; Univ Fla, PhD(speech path, audiol), 59. *Prof Exp:* Assoc prof speech & dir speech & hearing clin, Univ Miss, 59-60; asst chief speech path & audiol, Vet Admin Regional Off, Louisville, Ky, 60-62, chief speech path & audiol, Winston-Salem, NC, 62-66 & Durham, NC, 66-69; assoc dir, 69-80, DIR INTERDISCIPLINARY TRAINING & COMMUN DISORDERS SPECIALIST, DIV DISORDERS OF DEVELOP & LEARNING, BIOL SCI RES CTR, UNIV NC, CHAPEL HILL, 80- *Concurrent Pos:* Clin assoc prof, Inst Speech & Hearing Sci & Dept Pediat, Univ NC, Chapel Hill, 77-; assoc prof, Shaw Univ, 72-79; adj assoc prof, Speech, Lang & Auditory Path Prog, East Carolina Univ, 72-80. *Mem:* Fel Am Speech, Language & Hearing Asn. *Res:* Hearing and language development in high risk and normal infants. *Mailing Add:* Div Disorders of Develop & Learning Univ NC Biol Sci Res Ctr Chapel Hill NC 27514

KNOBIL, ERNST, b Berlin, Ger, Sept 20, 26; nat US. ENDOCRINOLOGY, PHYSIOLOGY. *Educ:* Cornell Univ, BS, 48, PhD(zool), 51. *Hon Degrees:* Dr, Univ de Bordeaux, France, 81. *Prof Exp:* Milton res fel, Biol Res Lab, Sch Dent Med, Harvard Univ, 51-53, instr physiol, Med Sch, 53-55, assoc, 55-57, asst prof, 57-61; Richard Beatty Mellon prof physiol & chmn dept, Sch Med, Univ Pittsburgh, 61-81, dir, Ctr Res Primate Reprod, 67-81; H WAYNE HIGHTOWER PROF PHYSIOL & DEAN, MED SCH, UNIV TEX HEALTH SCI CTR, HOUSTON, 81- *Concurrent Pos:* Markle scholar acad med, 56-61; mem human growth & develop study sect, NIH, 64-66, chmn reproductive biol study sect, 66-68, mem primate res ctr adv comt, 69-73, mem, Corpus Luteum Panel, Contraceptive Develop Br, 69-71; tenth Bowditch lectr, Am Physiol Soc, 65; mem adv coun, Inst Lab Animal Resources, Nat Acad Sci, 66-69; mem physiol test comt, Nat Bd Med Examr, 70-74; mem liaison comt med educ, AMA-Am Asn Med Cols, 72-74; Gregory Pincus Mem lectr, Laurentian Hormone Conf, 73; consult, Sch Med, Univ Mich, 73, Med Sch, Harvard Univ, 73-74, Pop Off, Ford Found, 74-75, Uniformed Serv Univ Health Sci, 75; Am Fertil Soc Upjohn lectr, 74; Kathleen M Osborn Mem lectr, Sch Med, Univ Kans, 74; Hopkins-Md lectr reproductive endocrinol, 74; mem comt priorities & planning, Fedn Am Socs Exp Biol, 74; mem pop res comt, Ctr Pop Res, Nat Inst Child Health & Human Develop, 74-77; Karl Paschkis lectr, Philadelphia Endocrine Soc, 75; consult, Human Reproduction Unit, WHO, 76-; mem bd adv gynec, Alza Corp, 76-78; first transatlantic lectr, Soc Endocrinol Gt Brit, 79; Lawson Wilkins Pediat Endocrine Soc lectr, 80; mem med adv bd, Nat Pituitary Agency, 80; ed-in-chief, Sect Endocrinol & Metab, Am J Physiol, 79-82; ed, Annual Rev Physiol, 74-77. *Honors & Awards:* Ciba Award, Endocrine Soc, 61; Bard lectr, Sch Med, Johns Hopkins Univ, 81; Herbert M Evans Mem lectr, Univ Calif, 81. *Mem:* Int Soc Neuroendocrinol; Am Physiol Soc (pres, 78-79); Int Soc Endocrinol; Endocrine Soc (pres, 76-77); Int Soc Res Biol Reprod. *Res:* Physiology of the pituitary gland; reproductive physiology. *Mailing Add:* Univ Tex Med Sch PO Box 20708 Houston TX 77025

KNOBL, GEORGE MARTIN, JR, organic chemistry, see previous edition

KNOBLER, CHARLES MARTIN, b Newark, NJ, June 1, 34; m 57; c 2. PHYSICAL CHEMISTRY. *Educ:* NY Univ, BA, 55; Pa State Univ, PhD(molecular physics), 61. *Prof Exp:* Res assoc phys chem, Ohio State Univ, 61-62; fel chem eng, Calif Inst Technol, 62-64; from asst prof to assoc prof, 64-77, PROF CHEM, UNIV CALIF, LOS ANGELES, 77- *Mem:* Am Chem Soc; Am Phys Soc. *Res:* Thermodynamics of liquids and liquid mixtures; equation of state. *Mailing Add:* Dept of Chem Univ of Calif Los Angeles CA 90024

KNOBLER, ROBERT LEONARD, b New York, NY, Nov 10, 48; m 79. NEUROIMMUNOLOGY, NEUROVIROLOGY. *Educ:* City Col New York, BS, 69; State Univ NY Brooklyn, MD & PhD(anat), 75. *Prof Exp:* Intern med & psychiat, Kings County Hosp Ctr, State Univ NY, 75-76, resident neurol, 76-79; FEL IMMUNOPATH, SCRIPPS CLIN & RES FOUND, 79-, CLIN COORDR, MULTIPLE SCLEROSIS CLIN, GEN CLIN RES CTR, 81- *Mem:* Am Acad Neurol; Am Asn Anatomists; Am EEG Soc; Sigma Xi; Soc Neurosci. *Res:* Viral and immune mechanisms of central nervous system diseases; ultrastructure of neurocellular relationships; clinical neurophysiology. *Mailing Add:* Scripps Clin & Res Found 10666 N Torrey Pines Rd La Jolla CA 92037

KNOBLOCH, EDGAR, b Praha, Czechoslovakia, Mar 30, 53; UK citizen; m 77. ASTROPHYSICS, PHYSICS. *Educ:* Cambridge Univ, BA, 74; Harvard Univ, AM, 75, PhD(astron), 78. *Prof Exp:* Res asst astron, Harvard Univ, 76-78; ASST PROF PHYSICS, UNIV CALIF, BERKELEY, 78- *Concurrent Pos:* Jr fel, Harvard Soc Fels, 78-80; Alfred P Sloan res fel, 80-82. *Mem:* Jr mem Am Astron Soc; Am Phys Soc; Sigma Xi. *Res:* Astrophysical fluid dynamics; magnetohydrodynamics (dynamo theory); stochastic processes; stellar dynamics. *Mailing Add:* Dept Physics Univ Calif Berkeley CA 94720

KNOBLOCH, FRED WILLIAM, b Englewood, NJ, Nov 1, 28; m 55; c 4. FUTURIST-TECHNOLOGY FORECASTING, POLYMER CHEMISTRY. *Educ:* Rutgers Univ, BS, 51; Rensselaer Polytech Inst, MS, 54, PhD, 59. *Prof Exp:* Res chemist, Wright Air Develop Ctr, 52-55; res chemist, E I du Pont de Nemours & Co, Inc, 59-62, sr res chemist, 62-64, res assoc, 64-65, res supvr, Pioneering Res Div, 65-69, RES DEVELOP SUPVR, TEXTILE RES LAB, E I DU PONT DE NEMOURS & CO, INC, 69- *Mem:* Am Chem Soc. *Res:* Synthetic rubber; textile fibers; high temperature plastics; organo-inorganic polymers. *Mailing Add:* Textile Res Lab E I du Pont de Nemours & Co Inc Wilmington DE 19898

KNOBLOCH, HILDA, b New York, NY, Dec 14, 15; m 42. PEDIATRICS. *Educ:* Barnard Col, Columbia Univ, BA, 36; NY Univ, MD, 40; Johns Hopkins Univ, MPH, 51, DrPH, 55; Am Bd Pediat, dipl, 47; Am Bd Prev Med, dipl, 54. *Prof Exp:* Asst clin child develop, Sch Med, Yale Univ, 45-46; clin asst child guid clin, Mt Sinai Hosp, NY, 47-49; pediat consult, Maternity & Newborn Div, New York City Health Dept, 49-50; res assoc, Maternal & Child Health Div, Sch Hyg & Pub Health, Johns Hopkins Univ, 51-55, asst prof, 55; assoc prof pediat, Col Med, Ohio State Univ, 55-62, asst prof psychiat, 58-66; prof pediat, Univ Ill Col Med, 66-67; prof, Mt Sinai Sch Med, 67-70; prof pediat, Alabany Med Col, 70-82. *Concurrent Pos:* Pvt pract, NY, 47-49; asst clin vis pediatrician, Bellevue Hosp, NY, 47-49; dir clin child develop, Children's Hosp, 56-64, dir div child develop, 64-66; med specialist, NY State Off Mental Retardation & Develop Disabilities, 70-81. *Mem:* Fel Soc Res Child Develop; fel Am Acad Pediat; Am Pediat Soc; Am Acad Cerebral Palsy; fel Am Orthopsychiat Asn. *Res:* Developmental assessment and infant neurology, especially etiologic factors in neuropsychiatric disabilities of childhood. *Mailing Add:* 230 E Oglethorpe Ave Savannah GA 31401

KNOBLOCH, IRVING WILLIAM, b Buffalo, NY, Mar 1, 07; m 34; c 3. BOTANY. *Educ:* Univ Buffalo, BA, 30, MA, 32; Iowa State Col, PhD(bot), 42. *Prof Exp:* Asst biologist, Univ Buffalo, 28-30; dir bot gardens, City of Buffalo, 31-33; wildlife technician, US Fish & Wildlife Serv, 33-37; instr bot, Iowa State Col, 42-43; asst prof bot, Univ Buffalo, 43-45; from asst prof to prof natural sci, 45-59, prof bot, 59-76, EMER PROF BOT, MICH STATE UNIV, 76- *Mem:* Bot Soc Am; Am Fern Soc(vpres, 65-66, pres, 66-69); Am Inst Biol Sci; Am Asn Univ Professors. *Res:* Structure of economic plants; cytology of plants; morphology; agrostology; hybrids and evolution; pteridophytes. *Mailing Add:* Dept of Bot & Plant Path Mich State Univ East Lansing MI 48823

KNOBLOCH, JAMES OTIS, b Thibodaux, La, Jan 9, 20; m 50; c 3. ORGANIC CHEMISTRY. *Educ:* La State Univ, BS, 41; Univ Notre Dame, MS, 47, PhD(chem), 49. *Prof Exp:* Inspector, Radford Ord Works, 41-42; shift supvr acid plant, Pa Ord Works, US Rubber Co, 42-43; chem engr, Magnesium Plant, Mathieson Alkali Works, 43-44; chemist, Synthetic Rubber Plant, Firestone Tire & Rubber Co, 44-45; chemist, Whiting Res Labs, Standard Oil Co (Ind), 49-59, sr res scientist, 59-70, SR RES CHEMIST, STANDARD OIL CO (IND), AMOCO RES CTR, AMOCO CHEM CORP, 70- *Mem:* Am Chem Soc; Am Inst Chem. *Res:* Structure of petroleum sulfonic acids; reactions of ozonides; synthesis of trifluoromethyl olefins; reduction of acetylenic glycols; oxidation studies; aromatic acid halogenations; polyanhydrides; fire retardants. *Mailing Add:* 7S 242 Green Acres Dr Naperville IL 60540

KNOBLOCK, EDWARD C, b Cortez, Colo, Apr 5, 20; m 43; c 4. BIOCHEMISTRY. *Educ:* Western State Col Colo, AB, 42; Univ Md, MS, 59. *Prof Exp:* Instr chem, Med Dept, US Army Enlisted Schs, 45-47, chief lab sect, 47-50, chief chem, 406th Med Gen Lab, Japan, 50-53, asst chief biophys, Walter Reed Army Inst Res, 54-57, chief biochem, 57-61, dir, Div Biochem, 61-70; asst prof, 70-81, ASSOC PROF PATH, MED SCH, UNIV MD, BALTIMORE, 81-, DIR CLIN CHEM, UNIV HOSP, 70- *Concurrent Pos:* Mem biochem study sect, NIH, 63-70; mem comt space med, NASA, 65-70. *Mem:* Sr mem Am Asn Clin Chemists; sr mem Am Chem Soc. *Res:* Clinical biochemistry, with emphasis on interactions between micronutrients, enzymes and hormones; improved use of analytical chemistry to clinical problems. *Mailing Add:* Dept of Clin Path Univ of Md Hosp Baltimore MD 21201

KNOCHE, HERMAN WILLIAM, b Stafford, Kans, Nov 15, 34; m 55; c 2. AGRICULTURAL BIOCHEMISTRY. *Educ:* Kans State Univ, BS, 59, PhD(biochem), 63. *Prof Exp:* From instr to assoc prof biochem & nutrit, 62-73, PROF, DEPT AGR BIOCHEM, UNIV NEBR, 73-, HEAD DEPT, 74- *Concurrent Pos:* Consult, Physicians Path Lab, Univ Nebr, 66-70; hon res assoc & NIH fel, Harvard Univ, 71-72; grants, NSF, Nebr Wheat Comn & AEC, 71-72, NSF, 80-83; consult, Norden Labs, Inc, 73- & Vet Hosp, Lincoln, Nebr, 75- *Mem:* AAAS; Am Chem Soc; Am Soc Biol Chemists. *Res:* Biochemistry and structure of lipids; lipid metabolism in plants and plant parasites; radioactive tracer methodology. *Mailing Add:* Dept Agr Biochem Univ of Nebr Lincoln NE 68583

KNOCK, FRANCES ENGELMANN, b Chicago, Ill, July 8, 21; m 43. SURGERY, ORGANIC CHEMISTRY. *Educ:* Univ Chicago, BS, 40, PhD(org chem), 43, MD, 54; Am Bd Surg, dipl, 60. *Prof Exp:* Asst, Univ Chicago, 40-42; assoc org chemist, Armour Res Found, 43-46, org chemist, 46-50, chem consult, 50-51; chem consult, Merck Sharp & Dohme, 54-56; DIR, KNOCK RES FOUND, 55-; CLIN ASST PROF SURG, UNIV ILL COL MED, 61- *Concurrent Pos:* Dir, Nat Registry Rare Chemists, 45-50; resident, Presby Hosp, 55-59, adj surg, 59-61, asst attend surgeon, 61-69; staff physician, Surg Serv, Vet Anmin Hosp, Hines, 62-74; consult, E R Squibb & Sons, 64-66; attend surg staff, Augustana Hosp, 68-; lectr pharmacol, Loyola Univ, Hines, 72- *Mem:* Fel AAAS; fel Am Geriat Soc; Am Chem Soc; AMA; fel Am Inst Chemists. *Res:* Surgical-chemical therapy of cancer; preferential effect on cancer by drugs inhibiting DNA polymerases; chromosomal nonhistone proteins in gene control; surgery for coronary artery disease-radical cardioomentopexy; chemical kinetics; synthesis of monomers, catalysts and promoters; Grignard reagents. *Mailing Add:* 416 Country Lane Glenview IL 60025

KNOCKEMUS, WARD WILBUR, b Des Plaines, Ill, Jan 29, 34; m 64; c 3. INORGANIC CHEMISTRY. *Educ:* Knox Col, BA, 55; Pa State Univ, MS, 58; Univ Nebr, PhD, 69. *Prof Exp:* From asst prof to assoc prof chem, Morningside Col, 61-70; asst prof chem, Behrend Campus, Pa State Univ, 70-74; PROF CHEM & CHMN DEPT, HUNTINGDON COL, 74- *Concurrent Pos:* Consult, Great Lakes Res Inst, Pa, 70- *Mem:* Am Chem Soc; Space Studies Inst. *Res:* Chemistry of metal-organic chelates; hydrolysis of oxymolybdenum chelates; adduct type compounds of octamolybdic acid. *Mailing Add:* Dept of Chem Huntingdon Col Montgomery AL 36106

KNODEL, ELINOR LIVINGSTON, b New York, NY. BIOCHEMISTRY, NEUROSCIENCES. *Educ:* Columbia Univ, AB, 69; Yale Univ, MS, 72; Univ Conn, PhD(biochem), 76. *Prof Exp:* Res fel, Univ Conn, 74-76; res fel neuroendocrinol, Rockefeller Univ, 76-77; res fel neurochem, Mayo Clin, 78-80; PROCESS CHEMIST, CLIN SYSTS DIV, E I DU PONT DE NEMOURS & CO, 80- *Mem:* AAAS; Asn Women Sci; Asn Clin Chem; Soc Neurosci. *Res:* Biochemistry of neural transmission in the brain and its regulation by hormones and drugs; automated clinical chemistry tests. *Mailing Add:* Clin Systs Div E I Du Pont de Nemours & Co Wilmington DE 19898

KNODEL, RAYMOND WILLARD, b Butte, NDak, June 10, 32; m 59; c 3. MATHEMATICS EDUCATION. *Educ:* Minot State Col, BS, 55; Univ Northern Colo, MA, 60, DEduc(math educ), 70. *Prof Exp:* Instr sci, Ashley High Sch, NDak, 55-56; instr math, Mandan Sr High Sch, 56-59 & Anaconda Sr High Sch, Mont, 60-61; PROF MATH, BEMIDJI STATE COL, 61- *Res:* Team teaching mathematics and arithmetic methods to prospective elementary school teachers. *Mailing Add:* Dept of Math Bemidji State Col Bemidji MN 56601

KNODT, CLOY BERNARD, b Hastings, Minn, Feb 20, 17; m 40; c 3. DAIRY SCIENCE. *Educ:* Univ Minn, BS, 40, PhD(dairy husb), 44; Univ Conn, MS, 42. *Prof Exp:* Lab technician, Univ Minn, 37-40, asst physiol, 41-44; from instr to asst prof, Cornell Univ, 44-45; from assoc prof to prof dairy prod, Pa State Col, 46-54; cattle specialist, Gen Mills, Inc, 54-56; dir res, Burrus Mills, Inc, 57; res farm, Cargill, Inc, 57-61; head dept nutrit res, Squibb Inst Med Res, 61-62; DIR RES & DEVELOP, A O SMITH HARVESTORE PROD, INC, 62- *Mem:* AAAS; Am Chem Soc; Am Soc Animal Sci; Soc Exp Biol & Med; Am Dairy Sci Asn. *Res:* Nutrition, housing and management of farm livestock; agricultural sciences. *Mailing Add:* 26573 W Taylor St Barrington IL 60010

KNOEBEL, LEON KENNETH, b Shamokin, Pa, Dec 7, 27. PHYSIOLOGY. *Educ:* Pa State Univ, BS, 50, MS, 52; Univ Rochester, PhD(physiol), 55. *Prof Exp:* Instr physiol, Univ Rochester, 55; from asst prof to assoc prof, 55-70, PROF PHYSIOL, SCH MED, IND UNIV, INDIANAPOLIS, 70- *Mem:* AAAS; Am Physiol Soc. *Res:* Gastrointestinal digestion and absorption of lipid. *Mailing Add:* Dept of Physiol Ind Univ Sch of Med Indianapolis IN 46207

KNOEBEL, SUZANNE BUCKNER, b Ft Wayne, Ind, Dec 13, 26. INTERNAL MEDICINE, CARDIOLOGY. *Educ:* Goucher Col, AB, 48; Ind Univ, Indianapolis, MD, 60. *Prof Exp:* From asst prof to prof, 66-77, HERMAN C & ELLNORA D KRANNERT PROF MED, SCH MED, IND UNIV, INDIANAPOLIS, 77- *Mem:* Fel Am Col Cardiol; Asn Univ Cardiologists; Am Fedn Clin Res; Am Heart Asn. *Res:* Myocardial blood flow; arrhythmias in coronary artery disease; computer analysis of cardiovascular data. *Mailing Add:* Ind Univ Med Ctr 1100 W Michigan Indianapolis IN 46223

KNOECHEL, EDWIN LEWIS, b Milwaukee, Wis, June 15, 31; m 53; c 2. PHARMACY. *Educ:* Univ Wis, BS, 53, MS, 55, PhD(pharm), 58. *Prof Exp:* Res assoc prod res & develop, 58-65, HEAD MAT INSPECTION, CONTROL DIV, UPJOHN CO, 65- *Mem:* Am Pharmaceut Asn. *Res:* Control activities associated with Food and Drug Administration, especially good manufacturing practices, self inspection, raw material evaluation, contract processor inspections, determination of mesh analysis, bulk volume, dissolution rates, surface area and particle size distributions, solids technology and in-process testing. *Mailing Add:* Control Div 7000 Portage St Kalamazoo MI 49001

KNOEDLER, ELMER L, b Gloucester, NJ, Feb 12, 12; m 41. CHEMICAL ENGINEERING. *Educ:* Cornell Univ, ME, 34; Columbia Univ, MS, 36, PhD(chem eng), 52. *Prof Exp:* Mem tech staff, Atlantic Refining Co, Pa, 34-35; asst supt, Davis Emergency Equip Co, NJ, 36-37; develop engr & supt iron powder prod, Metals Disintegrating Co, 39-41; sr proj engr, Sheppad T Powell, 41-58, SR PROJ ENGR & PARTNER, SHEPPARD T POWELL ASSOCS, 58- *Mem:* Am Chem Soc; Am Soc Mech Eng; Inst Elec & Electronics Engrs; Am Inst Chemists; Am Inst Chem Eng. *Res:* Industrial water; boiler feedwater; corrosion; industrial waste waters. *Mailing Add:* Sheppard T Powell Assocs 31 Light St Baltimore MD 21202

KNOEPFLER, NESTOR B(EYER), b New Orleans, La, Oct 1, 18; m 43; c 3. CHEMICAL ENGINEERING, CHEMISTRY. *Educ:* Tulane Univ, BE, 40. *Prof Exp:* Lab asst, Southern Cotton Oil Co, 40-41; asst mgr, Southern Photocraft, 45-50 fel, Nat Cottonseed Prod Asn, Southern Regional Res Lab, USDA, 50-52, asst chem engr, 52-55, assoc chem engr, 55-56, tech asst to dir, 56-58, asst to dir, 58-60, res chem engr, 60-66, head, Cotton Prod Invests Eng & Develop Lab, 66-73, res leader, textile chem eng, eng & develop, 73-79, CONSULT CHEM ENGR, USDA, 79- *Honors & Awards:* USDA Superior Serv Awards, 55 & 65; Cotton Batting Indust Award, 65 & 78. *Mem:* Am Oil Chem Soc; Sigma Xi; Am Asn Textile Chem & Colorists. *Res:* Processing of Southern grown agricultural products, especially oilseeds, fruits, vegetables, pine gum; mechanical processing and chemical finishing of cotton. *Mailing Add:* Eng & Develop Lab PO Box 19687 New Orleans LA 70179

KNOERR, KENNETH RICHARD, b Milwaukee, Wis, Sept 2, 27; m 52; c 3. FORESTRY. *Educ:* Univ Idaho, BS, 52; Yale Univ, MF, 55, PhD, 61. *Prof Exp:* Res forester meteorol & asst proj leader snow physics studies, Pac Southwest Forest & Range Exp Sta, US Forest Serv, 56-61, proj leader forest microclimate studies, Cent States Forest Exp Sta, 61; asst prof forest climat, 61-67, assoc prof forest meteorol, 67-72, assoc prof biometeorol, 67-81, prof forest meteorol, 72-81, assoc prof bot, 76-81, PROF FORESTRY & ENVIRON STUDIES, SCH FORESTRY, DUKE UNIV, 81- *Concurrent Pos:* Mem, Nat Acad Sci Adv Comt Climat, US Weather Bur, 65- *Mem:* AAAS; Soc Am Foresters; Am Meteorol Soc; Am Geophys Union; Int Asn Sci Hydrol. *Res:* Micrometeorology and microclimatology of forests related to surface energy balance; evapotranspiration and watershed management. *Mailing Add:* Dept of Bot Duke Univ Durham NC 27706

KNOKE, JAMES DEAN, b Des Moines, Iowa, Mar 22, 41; m 69; c 2. BIOSTATISTICS. *Educ:* Univ Iowa, BA, 63; Stanford Univ, MS, 65; Univ Calif, Los Angeles, PhD(biostatist), 70. *Prof Exp:* Opers res analyst, Autonetics Div, NAm Rockwell Corp, 65-68; asst prof biomet, Case Western Reserve Univ, 71-78; ASSOC PROF BIOSTATIST, UNIV NC, 78- *Mem:* Am Statist Asn; Biometric Soc. *Res:* Statistical methodology and biomedical applications. *Mailing Add:* Dept of Biostatist Univ NC Chapel Hill NC 27514

KNOKE, JOHN KEITH, b Detroit, Mich, Mar 31, 30; m 56; c 2. ENTOMOLOGY. *Educ:* Univ Wis, BS, 52, MS, 59, PhD(entom), 62. *Prof Exp:* Entomologist, Cacao Entom, Inter-Am Inst Agr Sci, 60-63; proj assoc, Univ Wis-Madison, 63, asst prof, 63-67; RES ENTOMOLOGIST, AGR RES SERV, USDA, OHIO AGR RES & DEVELOP CTR, 67- *Concurrent Pos:* Collab, Univ Wis-Madison, 60-63; adj assoc prof entom, Ohio Agr Res & Develop Ctr & Ohio State Univ, 67- *Mem:* Entom Soc Am; Latin Am Phytotech Asn; Am Phytopath Soc. *Res:* Control of insects attacking vegetables, especially through the use of systemic insecticides; study of all phases of entomology relative to production of Theobroma cacao L; epidemiology of virus diseases of corn. *Mailing Add:* Dept of Entom Ohio Agr Res & Develop Ctr Wooster OH 44691

KNOLL, ANDREW HERBERT, b West Reading, Pa, Apr 23, 51; m 74. PALEONTOLOGY, GEOLOGY. *Educ:* Lehigh Univ, BA, 73; Harvard Univ, AM, 74, PhD(geol), 77. *Prof Exp:* ASST PROF GEOL, OBERLIN COL, 77- *Concurrent Pos:* Assoc ed, Palebiol, 80-83; mem, Comt Planetary Biol & Chem Evolution, US Space Sci Bd, 80-83. *Mem:* Geol Soc Am; Bot Soc Am; Soc Econ Paleontologists & Mineralogists; Sigma Xi; Paleont Soc. *Res:* Precambrian biological evolution; evolution of land plants; Precambrian sedimentary geology. *Mailing Add:* Dept Geol Oberlin Col Oberlin OH 44074

KNOLL, GLENN F, b St Joseph, Mich, Aug 3, 35; m 57; c 3. NUCLEAR ENGINEERING. *Educ:* Case Western Reserve Univ, BS, 57; Stanford Univ, MS, 59; Univ Mich, PhD(nuclear eng), 63. *Prof Exp:* From asst prof to assoc prof, 62-77, PROF NUCLEAR ENG, UNIV MICH, ANN ARBOR, 77-, CHMN DEPT, 81- *Concurrent Pos:* Fulbright travel grant & vis scientist, Nuclear Res Ctr, Karlsruhe, Ger, 65-66; consult, Univ Hosp, Ann Arbor, Mich & Bendix Corp, Mich. *Mem:* AAAS; Am Nuclear Soc; Am Phys Soc; Inst Elec & Electronics Engrs; Am Asn Physicists Med. *Res:* Neutron spectroscopy; radiation detection and measurements; radioisotope imaging; medical instrumentation; neutron cross sections. *Mailing Add:* 3891 Waldenwood Ann Arbor MI 48105

KNOLL, HENRY ALBERT, b Englewood, NJ, Dec 10, 22; m 47; c 2. VISION. *Educ:* Univ Rochester, BS, 44; Ohio State Univ, MS, 48, PhD(physiol optics), 50. *Prof Exp:* Asst physiol optics, Ohio State Univ, 46-49; asst prof optics, Los Angeles Col Optom, 50-52, assoc prof geomet optics, 52-53, dean 53-55; from asst res biophysicist to assoc res biophysicist, Med Ctr, Univ Calif, Los Angeles, 55-58; res engr, 58-59, dept head, Lens Prod Develop & Instrument Res, 60-62 & Biophys Res & Develop, 62-66, SR SCIENTIST, BIOPHYS RES & DEVELOP, BAUSCH & LOMB INC, 66- *Mem:* AAAS; Optical Soc Am; Am Acad Optom. *Res:* Pupillary size changes associated with accommodation and convergence; refractive state of the eye in the absence of optical stimuli to accommodation; point source thresholds of the human eye; optics of ophthalmic lenses; infrared communication systems; contact lens research and development. *Mailing Add:* Bausch & Lomb Inc Rochester NY 14602

KNOLL, JACK, b Ashland, Wis, Feb 17, 24; m 48; c 1. ANIMAL PHYSIOLOGY. *Educ:* Mich State Univ, BS, 50, MS, 59, PhD(physiol), 62. *Prof Exp:* Asst physiol, Mich State Univ, 57-61; from asst prof to assoc prof, 62-76, prof, 76-81, EMER PROF BIOL, UNIV NEV, RENO, 81- *Mem:* AAAS; Nat Audubon Soc. *Res:* Ion transport across natural biological membranes; fish physiology. *Mailing Add:* Dept of Biol Univ of Nev Reno NV 89557

KNOLL, KENNETH MARK, b Pittsburgh, Pa, Apr 10, 41; m 63; c 2. GLACIAL GEOLOGY, PETROLEUM GEOLOGY. *Educ:* Antioch Col, BA, 64; Univ Wash, MS, 67; Univ Kans, PhD(glacial geol), 73. *Prof Exp:* Instr geol, Univ Wash, 68; asst prof, Winona State Col, 69-71; geologist, Shell Oil Co, 73-78; geologist, Rocky Mountain Div, Koch Explor Co, 78-80; GEOL MGR, FRONTIER GROUP, SOHIO PETROL CO, 80- *Mem:* Geol Soc Am; Sigma Xi; Am Asn Petrol Geologists. *Res:* Petroleum exploration geology of Rocky Mountains using seismic, magnetics and geophysical well logging techniques. *Mailing Add:* Frontier Group 100 Pine St Denver CO 80202

KNOLLENBERG, ROBERT GEORGE, b Mattoon, Ill, Aug 28, 39; m 66; c 3. INSTRUMENTATION. *Educ:* Eastern Ill Univ, BS, 61; Univ Wis-Madison, MS, 64, PhD(cloud physics), 67. *Prof Exp:* Res asst, Univ Wis-Madison, 64-66; scientist, NCAR Res Aviation, Colo, 67-69; asst prof geophys sci, Univ Chicago, 69-72; vis prof atmospheric sci, Colo State Univ, 73-75; PRES, PARTICLE MEASURING SYSTS, INC, 72-, CHIEF RES EXEC, 76- *Mem:* Am Meteorol Soc; Am Chem Soc; Am Inst Physics; Inst Elec & Electronics Engrs; Optical Soc Am. *Res:* Particle physics research and instrumentation development applied to the development of particle size spectrometers. *Mailing Add:* Particle Measuring Systs Inc 1855 S 57th Ct Boulder CO 80301

KNOLLMAN, GILBERT CARL, b Cleveland, Ohio, Mar 14, 28; m 59; c 2. MATERIAL SCIENCE, ULTRASONICS. *Educ:* Ga Inst Technol, BS, 49, MS, 50, PhD(physics), 61. *Prof Exp:* Instr physics, Ga Inst Technol, 49-50, res physicist, Eng Exp Sta, 50-62, asst prof math, Inst, 52-60; res scientist, Res Labs, Lockheed Missiles & Space Co, 62-63, head, Hydrospace Physics Lab, 62-70, staff scientist, 63-64, sr staff scientist, 64-66, SR MEM, LOCKHEED PALO ALTO RES LABS, 66-, DIR, ADV ACOUSTICS LAB, 71- *Concurrent Pos:* NSF grant, 60-61; consult, Ga Tech Res Inst, 62-65 & Lockheed Calif Co, 64-67; fel, Stanford Univ, 65-66; consult, Saratoga Systs, 70-76; mem Lockheed Res Comt, 70-71, chmn, 72-73; staff, Lockheed Eng Sci, 72-74; consult, Naval Weapons Lab, 73-; staff, Lockheed Mat Sci, 74- *Mem:* Fel AAAS; fel Am Phys Soc; Am Asn Physics Teachers; Sigma Xi; fel Am Inst Physics. *Res:* Quantum field theory; quantum and statistical mechanics; many-body theory; superconductivity and superfluidity; liquid state physics; theoretical acoustics and hydrodynamics; orbital and wave mechanics; electromagnetic theory; viscoelasticity; ultrasonics; underwater acoustics and electronics; material sciences; nondestructive test and evaluation; ocean science. *Mailing Add:* Dept 52/35 Bldg 204 Lockheed Palo Alto Res Labs Palo Alto CA 94304

KNOLLMUELLER, KARL OTTO, b Regensburg, Ger, July 12, 31; US citizen; m 68. INDUSTRIAL ORGANIC CHEMISTRY. *Educ:* Univ Munich, MS, 58, PhD(chem), 60. PXChemist, Diversey Corp, Ill, 60; from res chemist to sr res chemist, 60-74, res assoc, 74-78, SR RES ASSOC, OLIN CORP, NEW HAVEN, 78- *Mem:* Am Chem Soc; AAAS. *Res:* Inorganic and organic phosphorus compounds; sequestration agents; metal treatment chemicals; high temperature stable polymers; functional fluids; organosilicon chemicals. *Mailing Add:* 28 Apple Tree Lane Hamden CT 06518

KNOP, CHARLES M(ILTON), b Chicago, Ill, Feb 18, 31. ELECTROMAGNETIC ENGINEERING, ELECTRICAL ENGINEERING. *Educ:* Ill Inst Technol, BSEE, 54, MSEE, 60, PhD(elec eng), 63. *Prof Exp:* Mem tech staff antenna res, Hughes Aircraft Co, 54-55; res asst, Princeton Univ, 55-56; asst engr, Armour Res Found, Ill, 56-58, assoc engr, 58-60; sr engr, Res Lab, Systs Div, Bendix Corp, 60-61; asst dir res & develop, Hallicrafters Co, 61-64; mem sr staff, Nat Eng Sci Co, Calif, 64-65; assoc dir antenna design, Andrew Corp, 65-67, res consult, 67-68; independent consult electrodyn, 68-70; MGR RES & DEVELOP, ANDREW CORP, 70- *Concurrent Pos:* Lectr, Dept Elec Eng, Ill Inst Technol, 66-72. *Mem:* Inst Elec & Electronics Engrs; Am Phys Soc. *Res:* Electromagnetic wave radiation, propagation, scattering and diffraction as related to antennas and communication systems; waveguiding systems. *Mailing Add:* Andrew Corp 10500 W 153rd St Orland Park IL 60462

KNOP, CHARLES PHILIP, b Detroit, Mich, May 23, 27; m 52; c 9. INORGANIC CHEMISTRY. *Educ:* Aquinas Col, BS, 52; Mich State Univ, PhD(chem), 58. *Prof Exp:* Chemist, Haviland Prod Co, 52-53; asst, Mich State Univ, 53-58; res asst prof, 65-70, chmn dept, 69, assoc prof, 70-76, PROF CHEM, GRAND VALLEY STATE COL, 76-, CHMN DEPT, 74- *Mem:* Am Chem Soc. *Res:* Pollution abatement; plating wastes recovery. *Mailing Add:* Dept of Chem Grand Valley State Col Allendale MI 49401

KNOP, HARRY WILLIAM, JR, b Chicago, Ill, June 20, 20; m 50. PHYSICS. *Educ:* Ripon Col, BA, 42; Univ Wis, PhD(physics), 48. *Prof Exp:* Res physicist, Photoprods Dept, 49-56, res supvr, 56-60, sales tech supvr, 60-65, field sales mgr, 65-66, mgr, Rochester Res & Develop, 66-69, res mgr, Exp Sta Lab, 69-73, dir Du Pont Photo Prods, Japan, 73-75, LAB DIR, DU PONT PHOTO PRODS, EXP STA LAB, E I DU PONT DE NEMOURS & CO, 76- *Mem:* Am Phys Soc; Soc Motion Picture & TV Eng; Soc Photo Scientists & Engrs. *Res:* Physics of photography, solid state physics. *Mailing Add:* 313 Brockton Rd Sharpley Wilmington DE 19803

KNOP, OSVALD, b Kurim, Czech, July 11, 22; nat Can; m 51. INORGANIC CHEMISTRY, SOLID STATE CHEMISTRY. *Educ:* Masaryk Univ, Czech, BS, 46; Laval Univ, DSc(phys chem), 57. *Prof Exp:* Asst, Calif Inst Technol, 49; lectr indust chem, Dept Chem Eng, NS Tech Col, 50-53, from asst prof to assoc prof chem, 53-64; assoc prof, 64-69, PROF CHEM, DALHOUSIE UNIV, 69-, HARRY SHIRREFF PROF CHEM RES, 81- *Mem:* Fel Chem Inst Can; Royal Soc Chem. *Res:* Structural inorganic and solid state chemistry; computer-simulation methods; application of combinatorial analysis and graph theory to chemistry and physics. *Mailing Add:* Dept of Chem Dalhousie Univ Halifax NS B3H 4J3 Can

KNOP, ROBERT EDWARD, b Detroit, Mich, Dec 10, 39; div; c 2. PHYSICS. *Educ:* Univ Calif, Berkeley, AB, 62; Univ Md, College Park, PhD(physics), 69. *Prof Exp:* Res assoc physics, Rutgers Univ, New Brunswick, 68-70; staff physicist, Fla State Univ, 70-75; ASSOC PROF COMPUT SCI, MANKATO STATE UNIV, 81- *Mem:* AAAS; Asn Comput Mach. *Res:* Techniques of machine computation, particularly with applications to experimental particle physics; experimental particle physics; Monte Carlo algorithms. *Mailing Add:* Comput Sci Mankato State Univ Mankato MN 56001

KNOPF, DANIEL PETER, b Louisville, Ky, July 28, 16; m 44; c 4. CHEMISTRY. *Educ:* Univ Louisville, AB, 38, MS, 40, JD, 68. *Prof Exp:* Night supt, 42-45, plant mgr, 45-52, mgr labs, 52-66, DIR LABS, BROWN-FORMAN DISTILLERS CORP, 66- *Mem:* AAAS; Am Chem Soc; Am Soc Testing & Mat; Am Bar Asn; Am Pub Health Asn. *Mailing Add:* Distillery & Flavor Consult 118 Beechwood Rd Louisville KY 40207

KNOPF, FRITZ L, b Aurora, Ohio, June 6, 45; c 2. WILDLIFE ECOLOGY, ORNITHOLOGY. *Educ:* Hiram Col, Ohio, BA, 67; Utah State Univ, MS, 73, PhD(wildlife ecol), 76. *Prof Exp:* Instr, Utah State Univ, 75-76; asst prof wildlife ecol, Okla State Univ, 76-79; RES WILDLIFE BIOLOGIST, US FISH & WILDLIFE SERV, 80- *Mem:* Wildlife Soc; Cooper Ornith Union; Am Ornithologists Union. *Res:* Habitat preference and utilization by wild birds and mammals and management of that habitat; avian behavioral ecology. *Mailing Add:* Denver Wildlife Res Ctr 1300 Blue Spruce Fort Collins CO 80524

KNOPF, RALPH FRED, b Muskegon, Mich, Mar 26, 26; m 54; c 3. INTERNAL MEDICINE. *Educ:* Univ Mich, BS, 51, MD, 54; Am Bd Internal Med, dipl, 63. *Prof Exp:* Intern med, Virginia Mason Hosp, Seattle, Wash, 54-55, resident internal med, 55-56; resident internal med, 56-58, resident ophthal, 58-59, fel internal med, 59-62, from instr to assoc prof, 62-73, PROF INTERNAL MED, MED CTR, UNIV MICH, ANN ARBOR, 73- *Mem:* Am Fedn Clin Res; Am Diabetes Asn; Endocrine Soc. *Res:* Diabetes mellitus; inter-relationship between carbohydrate, protein and lipid metabolism and insulin glucagon and growth hormone secretion. *Mailing Add:* Dept of Internal Med Univ of Mich Med Ctr Ann Arbor MI 48104

KNOPF, ROBERT JOHN, b West New York, NJ, Apr 18, 32; div; c 3. ORGANIC CHEMISTRY, POLYMER CHEMISTRY. *Educ:* Gettysburg Col, BA, 54; Princeton Univ, MA, 56, PhD(org chem), 57. *Prof Exp:* Chemist, 57-66, group leader res & develop, 66-70, res scientist, 70-75, prod develop mgr, 74-76, SR DEVELOP SCIENTIST, ETHYLENE OXIDE/GLYCOL DIV, UNION CARBIDE CORP, SOUTH CHARLESTON, 75- *Mem:* Am Chem Soc. *Res:* Flame retardants for plastics; chemistry of isocyanates; polyurethane foams, coatings and elastic fibers; aldol condensation chemistry; condensation polymerizations in solution; polyethers; hydrogel polymers; photocure coatings intermediates; surfactant intermediates; ethlyene oxide derivatives. *Mailing Add:* 900 Sunset Dr St Albans WV 25177

KNOPKA, W N, b Buffalo, NY, Dec 1, 38; m 65; c 3. FIBER TECHNOLOGY, WIRE TECHNOLOGY. *Educ:* Canisius Col, BS, 61; Seton Hall Univ, MS, 63, PhD(org chem), 65. *Prof Exp:* Sr res chemist, Cent Res & Develop, FMC Corp, NJ, 65-69, group leader, Fiber Div, Pa, 69-73, prod mgr, 73-76, agr chem, 76-77; dir, Fabric Develop, 77-79, DIR ELASTOMER & CHEM RES, GOODYEAR TIRE & RUBBER CO, 79- *Res:* Specialty organic chemical intermediates; fiber processing; wire process technology; condensation and addition polymers; synthetic rubbers; rubber chemicals. *Mailing Add:* Goodyear Tire & Rubber Co 142 Goodyear Blvd Akron OH 44316

KNOPOFF, LEON, b Los Angeles, Calif, July 1, 25; m 61; c 3. GEOPHYSICS, PHYSICS. *Educ:* Calif Inst Technol, BS, 44, MS, 46, PhD(physics), 49. *Prof Exp:* From asst prof to assoc prof physics, Miami Univ, 48-50; from res assoc to assoc res geophysicist, Inst Geophysics, 50-56, assoc prof geophys, 56-57, PROF GEOPHYS, 57- & PHYSICS, 59-, UNIV CALIF, LOS ANGELES, RES MUSICOLOGIST, 61- *Concurrent Pos:* Mem earth sci panel, NSF, 59-62; sr fel NSF, Cambridge Univ, 60-61; secy gen, Int Upper Mantle Comt & chmn US comt, 63-71; vis prof, Univ

Karlsruhe, 66 & Technische Hochschule, Karlsruhe, Ger, 66; chmn comt math geophys, Int Union of Geophys & Geophysicists, 71-; assoc dir, Inst Geophys & Planetary Physics, Univ Calif, Los Angeles, 72-; vis prof, Harvard Univ, 72 & Univ Chile, Santiago, 73; mem US nat comt, Int Union Geophys & Geophysicists, 73-77; Harold Jeffreys lectr, Royal Astron Soc, 76; Guggenheim fel, 76-77. *Honors & Awards:* Emil Wiechert Medal, Ger Geophys Soc, 78. *Mem:* Nat Acad Sci; Am Acad Arts & Sci; Am Phys Soc; Seismol Soc Am; Am Geophys Union. *Res:* Elastic wave propagation; theoretical and observational seismology; acoustics of solids; physics and chemistry of deep interior of earth; physics of high pressures; systematic musicology. *Mailing Add:* Inst Geophys & Planetary Physics Univ of Calif Los Angeles CA 90024

KNOPP, JAMES A, b Grand Rapids, Mich, Oct 26, 40; m 62; c 2. BIOPHYSICAL CHEMISTRY. EDCarleton Col, BA, 62; Univ Ill, PhD(biophys chem), 67. *Prof Exp:* Investr biol div, Oak Ridge Nat Lab, 67-69, biophysicist, 67-69; asst prof, 69-74, ASSOC PROF BIOCHEM, NC STATE UNIV, 74- *Mem:* Am Chem Soc; Am Soc Biol Chemists. *Res:* Physical chemistry of proteins; fluorescence techniques in biochemistry. *Mailing Add:* Dept of Biochem PO Box 5050 NC State Univ Raleigh NC 27650

KNOPP, MARVIN ISADORE, b Chicago, Ill, Jan 4, 33; m 57; c 3. NUMBER THEORY, MATHEMATICAL ANALYSIS. *Educ:* Univ Ill, BS, 54, AM, 55, PhD(math), 58. *Prof Exp:* Asst math, Univ Ill, 54-58; res mathematician, Space Tech Labs, 58-59; fel math, NSF Inst Advan Study, 59-60; from asst prof to prof math, Univ Wis, Madison, 60-70; prof math, Univ Ill, Chicago Circle, 70-76; PROF MATH, TEMPLE UNIV, 76- *Concurrent Pos:* Res grants, NSF, 60-; mathematician, Nat Bur Standards, 63-64; vis prof, Math Inst, Univ Basel, Switz, 68-69, Ohio State Univ, 79; visitor, Inst Advan Study, 75-78. *Mem:* Am Math Soc. *Res:* Construction of automorphic forms; uniformization and Riemann surfaces; Eichler cohomology of automorphic forms; period functions of generalized automorphic integrals. *Mailing Add:* Dept of Math Temple Univ Philadelphia PA 19122

KNOPP, PAUL JOSEPH, b San Antonio, Tex, Jan 3, 34; m 63; c 3. MATHEMATICS. *Educ:* Spring Hill Col, BS, 57; Harvard Univ, AM, 58; Univ Texas, PhD(math), 62. *Prof Exp:* Lectr & instr math, Spring Hill Col, 59-60; asst prof, Univ Mo, 62-64; asst prof math, Univ Houston, 64-68, assoc prof, 68-80. *Concurrent Pos:* Assoc dir comt undergrad prog in math, Math Asn Am, 71-72, dir, 72-73. *Mem:* Math Asn Am; Am Math Soc. *Res:* Matrix theory. *Mailing Add:* 9726 Braesmont Houston TX 77096

KNOPP, WALTER, b Ostrava, Czech, Oct 22, 22; US citizen; m 51; c 2. PSYCHIATRY. *Educ:* Univ Heidelberg, MD, 50; Am Bd Psychiat & Neurol, dipl, 61. *Prof Exp:* Intern med, Univ Heidelberg Hosp, 50, resident pediat, 51; toxicologist, European Lab, US Army Med Ctr, Ger, 52-54; intern, Glens Falls Hosp, NY, 54-55; psychiat resident, Springfield State Hosp, Sykesville, Md, 55-58, chief serv, Men's Group, 58-60; from instr to assoc prof, 60-70, PROF PSYCHIAT, COL MED, OHIO STATE UNIV, 70- *Concurrent Pos:* Attend staff physician, Ohio State Univ Hosps, 60-, coordr preclin educ, 66- & premed educ, 73-, asst prof, Sch Soc Work, 64-67, adv, Grad Sch, 65-, asst prof phys med, Univ, 66-67; consult, Vet Admin Hosp, Chillicothe, Ohio, 61-, Vet Admin Ment Hyg Clin, Columbus, 65-76 & Athens Ment Health Ctr; dipl mem psychiat Pan-Am Med Asn, 65-75. *Mem:* Fel Am Psychiat Asn; Soc Neurosci; NY Acad Sci; Int Col Neuropsychopharmacol. *Res:* Bridging the gaps between neuro-sciences, human behavior and patient oriented therapeutic research and between behavioral sciences, biological sciences and educational technology and research. *Mailing Add:* Dept of Psychiat Ohio State Univ Col of Med Columbus OH 43210

KNOPPERS, ANTONIE THEODOOR, b Kapelle, Neth, Feb 27, 15; nat US; m 39; c 4. PHARMACOLOGY. *Educ:* Univ Amsterdam, MD, 39; Univ Leyden, PharD, 41. *Hon Degrees:* DSc, Worcester Polytech Inst, 65. *Prof Exp:* First asst, Pharmacol Inst, Univ Amsterdam, 40-43; dir pharmacol, Amsterdamsche Chininefabriek, 43-49; mem managing bd combination Amsterdamsche, Bandoengsche en Nederlandsche Kininefabrieken, 50-52; mgr med serv, Merck-NAm, Inc, 52-53, dir med serv, Merck Sharp & Dohme Int Div, 53-55, dir sci activities, 55, vpres & gen mgr, 55-57, pres, 57-67, from sr vpres to pres, Merck & Co, 67-74, vchmn, 74-75. *Concurrent Pos:* Mem, Malaria Comn Netherlands, 51-53; mem, Coun Foreign Rels; trustee, US Coun, Int Chamber of Com; mem bd dirs, Neth-Am Found; dir, Scott Paper Co, Hewlett-Packard Co, Mathematica, Inc & John Wiley & Sons, Inc; Eisenhower exchange fels, Drew Univ & Salk Inst. *Mem:* fel NY Acad Sci. *Res:* Physiology and pharmacology of the regulation of the body temperature; chemotherapy of malaria, especially chemoresistance; cardiovascular pharmacology. *Mailing Add:* 38 Lenox Rd Summit NJ 07901

KNORR, DIETRICH W, b Waidhofen, Austria, July 3, 44; m 68; c 2. FOOD SCIENCE & TECHNOLOGY. *Educ:* Univ Agr, Austria, dipling, 71, Dr, 74. *Prof Exp:* Asst prof, dept food technol, Univ Agr, Vienna, 74-78; ASSOC PROF FOOD PROCESSING, UNIV DEL, 78- *Concurrent Pos:* Vis prof food sci, Western Regional Res Ctr-USDA, 76-77 & Cornell Univ, 78. *Mem:* Int Biomet Soc; Inst Food Technologist; Am Asn Cereal Chemists; Am Oil Chem Soc; Asn Austrian Food & Biotechnologists. *Res:* Food processing; food protein technology; protein functionality; food wastes and nutrient recycling; food quality; appropriate intermediate food technology. *Mailing Add:* Dept Food Sci & Human Nutrit Univ Del Newark DE 19711

KNORR, GEORGE E, b Munich, Ger, Jan 29, 29; m 60; c 3. PLASMA PHYSICS. *Educ:* Munich Tech Univ, Vordiplom, 51, dipl, 54; Univ Munich, PhD(physics), 63. *Prof Exp:* Physicist, Philips Corp, C H F Mueller AG, 55-58; res asst, Max Planck Inst Physics, 58-65; res fel plasma physics, Princeton Univ, 63-64; res assoc, Inst Plasma Physics, Garching, Ger, 65-66; asst prof & res assoc physics, Univ Calif, Los Angeles, 66-67; assoc prof physics & astron, 67-74, PROF PHYSICS, UNIV IOWA, 74- *Mem:* Am Phys Soc. *Res:* Radiation from plasmas; confinement and instabilities of plasmas; wave propagation, non-linear effects, numerical methods and computer simulation of plasmas. *Mailing Add:* Dept of Physics & Astron Univ of Iowa Iowa City IA 52240

KNORR, PHILIP NOEL, b Mitchell, Nebr, Apr 9, 16; m 64. FOREST ECONOMICS, RESOURCE MANAGEMENT. *Educ:* Univ Calif, BS, 38; Duke Univ, MF, 40; Univ Minn, PhD(forest econ), 63. *Prof Exp:* Timber supvr & mapper, US Forest Serv, 38-39, jr forester, Southern Forest Exp Sta, New Orleans, 41; asst res forester, Weyerhaeuser Co, 46-48; asst prof forest mgt, Ore State Univ, 48-51; from asst to instr forest mgt, Univ Minn, 54-59; assoc prof forestry, 59-66, PROF FORESTRY, UNIV ARIZ, 66-, RES SCIENTIST, AGR RES STA, 76- *Honors & Awards:* Ford-Bartlett Award, Am Soc Photogram, 66. *Mem:* Fel AAAS; Soc Am Foresters; Am Econ Asn; Am Agr Econ Asn; Am Soc Photogram. *Res:* Decision making in forest management; remote sensing, including photo-interpretation; decision making in renewable resources policy. *Mailing Add:* Dept of Forestry Mgt Col of Agr Univ of Ariz Tucson AZ 85721

KNORR, THOMAS GEORGE, b Buffalo, NY, Apr 14, 32; m 56; c 5. SOLID STATE PHYSICS. *Educ:* Canisius Col, BS, 53; Case Inst Technol, MS, 55, PhD(physics), 58; Univ Detroit, MA, 78. *Prof Exp:* Asst, Case Inst Technol, 53-58; from instr to asst prof physics, Univ Dayton, 58-60; sr physicist, Battelle Mem Inst, 60-65; assoc prof, 65-77, PROF PHYSICS, WHEELING COL, 77- *Mem:* Am Phys Soc; Am Inst Physics; Am Asn Physics Teachers. *Res:* Thin films; defect properties and structure; radiation damage; linguistics; surface structures. *Mailing Add:* Dept of Physics Wheeling Col Wheeling WV 26003

KNOSPE, WILLIAM H, b Oak Park, Ill, May 26, 29; m 54; c 3. HEMATOLOGY. *Educ:* Univ Ill, Urbana, AB, 51, BS, 52; Univ Ill Med Ctr, MD, 54; Univ Rochester, MS, 62. *Prof Exp:* Chief med serv, US Army Hosp, Berlin, Ger, 58-61; attend physician, Walter Reed Gen Hosp, Washington, DC, 63-64, asst chief hemat serv, 64-66; assoc dir hemat sect & chief radio hemat lab, Presby-St Luke's Hosp, 67-73, DIR CLIN HEMAT SECT, RUSH-PRESBY-ST LUKE'S MED CTR, 74-; ASSOC PROF MED, UNIV ILL COL MED, 69-; PROF MED, RUSH MED COL, 74- *Concurrent Pos:* Attend staff, Presby-St Luke's Hosp, 68-, attend physician, 71-; assoc prof med, Col Med, Univ Ill, 69-72 & Rush Med Col, 71-74; prin investr, Southeastern Cancer Study Group, 69-80 & Polycythemia Vera Study Group, 78-; vis prof med, Dept Hematol, Univ Basel, Switz, 80-81. *Mem:* Fel Am Col Physicians; Am Soc Hemat; Am Fedn Clin Res; Radiation Res Soc; Sigma Xi. *Res:* Radiation effects upon bone marrow; role of sinusoidal microcirculation in aplastic anemias; regulation of hematopoietic stem cells; clinical investigation of leukemia and lymphomas. *Mailing Add:* Rush-Presby-St Luke's Med Ctr 1753 W Congress Pkwy Chicago IL 60612

KNOTEK, MICHAEL LOUIS, b Norfolk, Nebr, Nov 23, 43; m 69; c 3. SOLID STATE PHYSICS, SURFACE PHYSICS. *Educ:* Iowa State Univ, BS, 66; Univ Calif, Riverside, MS, 69, PhD(physics), 72. *Prof Exp:* Physicist amorphous semiconductors, Naval Weapons Ctr, 70-72; MEM TECH STAFF SUPERIONIC CONDUCTORS & SURFACE PHYSICS, SANDIA LAB, 73-, SUPVR, SURFACE PHYSICS DIV, 79- *Concurrent Pos:* Consult, Bourns Inc, 70. *Mem:* Am Vacuum Soc. *Res:* Transport properties of amorphous and disordered semiconductors; transport properties of superionic conductors, especially related to surface and interface properties; surface studies of photocatalytic properties of rutile and related materials; surface science; electron and photon stimulated desorption. *Mailing Add:* Sandia Lab Albuquerque NM 87117

KNOTH, WALTER HENRY, JR, b New York, NY, Feb 18, 30; m 53; c 2. HETEROPOLYANIONS, BORON HYDRIDES. *Educ:* Syracuse Univ, BS, 50; Pa State Univ, PhD(chem), 54. *Prof Exp:* RES CHEMIST, E I DU PONT DE NEMOURS & CO, INC, 53- *Mem:* Am Chem Soc; Sigma Xi. *Res:* Organo-silicon and organoboron chemistry; boron hydrides; nitrogen complexes; transition metal chemistry. *Mailing Add:* Central Res Dept E I du Pont de Nemours & Co Inc Wilmington DE 19898

KNOTT, DONALD MACMILLAN, b Boston, Mass, Oct 20, 19; m 43; c 4. INDUSTRIAL ORGANIC CHEMISTRY. *Educ:* Mass Inst Technol, SB, 41, PhD(org Chem), 47. *Prof Exp:* With Gen Elec Co, 47-54; with Chas Pfizer & Co, 54-63, chem consult, 63-68; PRES, CHEMCONSUL INC, 68- *Mem:* Am Chem Soc; Com Develop Asn; Tech Asn Pulp & Paper Indust. *Res:* Commercial chemical development; pulp and paper technology; wood science and technology. *Mailing Add:* 73 Cutler Rd Greenwich CT 06830

KNOTT, DOUGLAS RONALD, b New Westminster BC, Nov 10, 27; m 50; c 4. PLANT GENETICS. *Educ:* Univ BC, BSA, 48; Univ Wis, MS, 49, PhD, 52. *Prof Exp:* From asst prof to assoc prof, 52-65; prof & head dept, 65-75, PROF CROP SCI, UNIV SASK, 75- *Mem:* Am Soc Agron; Genetics Soc Am; Genetics Soc Can; Agr Inst Can; Can Soc Agron. *Res:* Genetics and cytogenetics of rust resistance in wheat. *Mailing Add:* Dept of Crop Sci Univ of Saskatchewan Saskatoon SK S7N 0W0 Can

KNOTT, FRED NELSON, b Oxford, NC, July 18, 33; m 55; c 4. ANIMAL NUTRITION. *Educ:* NC State Col, BS, 55; NC State Univ, MS, 62; Va Polytech Inst, PhD(animal nutrit), 68. *Prof Exp:* Res asst, 55-56, agr exten agent, 56-57, assoc prof, 72-79, exten dairy specialist, 57-65, EXTEN DAIRY SPECIALIST DAIRY HUSB, NC STATE UNIV, 67-, PROF, 79- *Concurrent Pos:* Mem exten serv team to Virgin Islands, 78. *Mem:* Am Dairy Sci Asn; Sigma Xi. *Res:* Utilization of urea by dairy cattle as a supplement to protein nutrition. *Mailing Add:* Dept of Animal Sci NC State Univ PO Box 5127 Raleigh NC 27650

KNOTT, JOHN RUSSELL, b Chicago, Ill, Nov 6, 11; m 35; c 3. NEUROPHYSIOLOGY. *Educ:* Univ Iowa, BA, 35, MA, 36, PhD, 38. *Prof Exp:* Res assoc psychol, 38-41, asst prof, 41-48, from assoc prof to prof psychiat, 48-74, EMER PROF PSYCHIAT, UNIV IOWA, 74-; PROF NEUROL, TUFTS UNIV, 77- *Concurrent Pos:* Vpres, Inst Fedn Socs Electroencephalog & Clin Neurophysiol, 57-61; head div electroencephalog & neurophysiol, Univ Psychopath Hosp, 58-74; mem neurol A study sect, NIH, 67-71, mem neurol prog proj rev comt B, 72-76; vis prof psychiat, La State Univ, 69-71; prof neurol, Sch Med, Boston Univ, 75-77; consult electroencephalography, 80- *Mem:* Am Electroencephalog Soc (pres, 57). *Res:* Neurophysiological bases of behavior. *Mailing Add:* 5 Miles Dr Quincy MA 01269

KNOTT, ROBERT F(RANKLIN), b Toronto, Ont, May 26, 23; m 52; c 1. CHEMICAL ENGINEERING, ORGANIC CHEMISTRY. *Educ:* Univ Toronto, BASc, 50, MASc, 51, PhD(chem eng), 53. *Prof Exp:* Res chemist, Can Indust Ltd, 53-55, group leader, 55-57, supt res, Explosives Div, 57-64, res mgr, Explosives & Ammuniton Div, 64-67, corp planning mgr, 67-71; head, NAm Dept, ICI London, Eng, 71-74; gen mgr, Can Safety Fuse Co, Brownsburg, Que, 74-77; pres, CXA Ltd, Brownsburg, Que, 77-80; EXPLOSIVES COORDR & CHMN, ICI EXPLOSIVES INT, LONDON, ENG, 80- *Mem:* Fel Chem Inst Can. *Res:* Shock wave studies; detonation phenomenon; effects of explosives on materials; blasting effects on rock; forming of metals under high loading rates. *Mailing Add:* I C House Millbank London SW1 England

KNOTTS, GLENN RICHARD, b East Chicago, Ind, May 16, 34. PHARMACOLOGY, PUBLIC HEALTH. *Educ:* Purdue Univ, BS, 56, MS, 60, PhD(clin pharm, pub health), 68; Ind Univ, MS, 64. *Hon Degrees:* Dr Med Sci, Union Col, 75; ScD, Ricker Col, 75. *Prof Exp:* Instr chem, San Antonio Col, 58-60; admin asst, AMA, 60-61, res assoc, 61-62, from asst dir to dir off adv eval, Div Sci Activ, 62-69; exec dir, Am Health Asn, 69-72; prof & coordr grad studies & res, Dept Allied Health Sci, Kent State Univ, 72-75; PROF MED JOUR, ED-IN-CHIEF, HEAD DEPT INFO & PUBL, UNIV TEX SYST CANCER CTR, M D ANDERSON HOSP & TUMOR INST, 75-, DIR EDUC RESOURCES, 79- *Concurrent Pos:* Vis lectr health & safety educ, Ind Univ, 62-64; vis prof health educ, Madison Col, 64, Utah State Univ, 65 & Union Col, 65-69; lectr pharmacol & toxicol, Purdue Univ, 68-69; vis prof allied health sci, Kent State Univ, 69-72 & adj prof, 75-; vis prof, Sch Med, Pahlavi Univ, Iran, 70; consult ed, Clin Pediat, 71-; contrib ed, Ann Allergy, 72-; prof biomed commun, Sch Allied Health Sci, Tex Health Sci Ctr, Houston, 76- & prof behav sci, Sch Pub Health, 77-; exec editor, Cancer Bull, 76- *Mem:* Sr mem Am Chem Soc; fel Am Sch Health Asn; fel Am Pub Health Asn; Am Pharmaceut Asn; fel Am Inst Chemists. *Res:* Pharmacal sciences; health education; author or coauthor of over 30 publications. *Mailing Add:* Univ of Tex Syst Cancer Ctr Tex Med Ctr Houston TX 77030

KNOWLER, LLOYD A, b Hedrick, Iowa, Jan 30, 08; m 35; c 2. ACTUARIAL SCIENCE, STATISTICS. *Educ:* Univ Iowa, BA, 32, MS, 34, PhD(math, actuarial sci, statist), 37. *Prof Exp:* Asst math & astron, Univ Iowa, 32-34; actuary, State Old Age Assistance Comn, Iowa, 34-35; asst math & astron, Univ Iowa, 35-37; instr, Hunter Col, 37-39; from asst prof to prof math, 39-65, chmn dept math & astron, 46-59, prof prev med & environ health, 46-80, prof math sci, 65-80, EMER PROF STATIST & PREV MED & ENVIRON HEALTH, UNIV IOWA, 80- *Concurrent Pos:* Bur Census math statist adv to India, Int Coop Admin, US Dept State, 60-61; consult actuary & statist qual control, indust & govt; mem qual control staff, Univ Calif, Los Angeles, Univ Colo, Univ Ill, Univ Mich, Northwestern Univ, Purdue Univ & Univ Wis; mem bd trustees, Teachers Ins & Annuity Asn, 58-62, mem bd dir & treas, Exec Comt, Blue Shield of Iowa, mem, Joint Mgt Comt & Joint Finance Comt, Blue Cross/Blue Shield of Iowa; deleg, Int Cong Voluntary Health Serv, London. *Honors & Awards:* Shewhart Medal, 62 & Oakley Award, 68, Am Soc Qual Control. *Mem:* Am Math Soc; Am Soc Eng Educ; fel Am Soc Qual Control; fel Am Soc of Pension Actuaries; Sigma Xi. *Res:* Actuarial science; biostatistics; medical statistics; operations research; statistical quality control. *Mailing Add:* Div of Math Sci Univ of Iowa Iowa City IA 52240

KNOWLES, BARBARA B, b New York, NY, Feb 27, 37; m 59; c 2. GENETICS, CELL BIOLOGY. *Educ:* Middlebury Col, AB, 58, Ariz State Univ, MS, 63, PhD(zool), 65. *Prof Exp:* Res asst drosophila genetics, Ariz State Univ, 62-65; res fel genetics, Univ Calif, Berkeley, 65-66; res asst, 67-71, res assoc, 72-76, ASSOC PROF, WISTAR INST ANAT & BIOL, 77- *Concurrent Pos:* Career develop award, Nat Inst Allergy & Infectious Dis, 75; mem, Univ Pa Immunol Grad Group, 77- *Mem:* Am Soc Human Genetics; Genetics Soc Am. *Res:* Immunogenetics; genetic control of human cell surface molecules; murine immune response genes to tumor specific antigens; cell surface molecules of preimplantation stage mouse embryos. *Mailing Add:* Wistar Inst of Anat & Biol 36th St at Spruce Philadelphia PA 19104

KNOWLES, CECIL MARTIN, b Newton, Miss, Jan 6, 18; m 48; c 2. ORGANIC CHEMISTRY. *Educ:* Miss Col, BA, 39; Univ Tex, MA, 41, PhD(org chem), 43. *Prof Exp:* Instr chem, Univ Tex, 39-42; chemist, GAF Corp, NY, 43-51, mgr tech serv & com develop, 51-67; vpres & dir res, Trylon Chem, Inc, 68-72; VPRES & TECH DIR, CHEM SPECIALTIES GROUPS, EMERY INDUST, INC, 72- *Res:* Surface active agents; organic chemical specialties. *Mailing Add:* Chem Specialties Group PO Box 628 Mauldin SC 29662

KNOWLES, CHARLES ERNEST, b Ogden, Utah, Mar 7, 37; m 60; c 4. PHYSICAL OCEANOGRAPHY. *Educ:* Univ Utah, BS, 60; Tex A&M Univ, MS, 67, PhD(phys oceanog), 70. *Prof Exp:* Res scientist phys oceanog, Tex A&M Univ, 69-70; asst prof phys oceanog, 70-76, assoc prof geosci, 76-81, ASSOC PROF MARINE SCI & ENG, NC STATE UNIV, 81- *Concurrent Pos:* Consult, Res Triangle Inst, 70- *Mem:* Am Geophys Union. *Res:* Isunami-island interaction including numerical modeling of Tsunami wave modification and recovery of incident tsunami in deep water from records taken at island shoreline; coastal dynamics studies near Pamlico Sound, North Carolina. *Mailing Add:* Dept of Geosci NC State Univ Raleigh NC 27607

KNOWLES, CHARLES OTIS, b Tallassee, Ala, Feb 1, 38; m 59; c 3. ENTOMOLOGY. *Educ:* Auburn Univ, BS, 60, MS, 62; Univ Wis, PhD(entom), 65. *Prof Exp:* From asst prof to prof, 65-74, PROF ENTOM, UNIV MO-COLUMBIA, 74- *Mem:* Entom Soc Am; Am Chem Soc; Soc Toxicol; Soc Environ Toxicol & Chem; Int Soc Study Xenobiotics. *Res:* Toxicology of insecticides; comparative insect biochemistry; mode of action and metabolism of acaricides; environmental impact of pesticides. *Mailing Add:* Univ of Missouri-Columbia Columbia MO 65201

KNOWLES, DAVID M, b Saginaw, Mich, July 22, 27; m 45; c 2. GEOLOGY. *Educ:* Mich Technol Univ, BS, 54, MS, 55; Columbia Univ, PhD(geol), 67. *Prof Exp:* Chief geologist, Can Javelin Ltd, 54-69; ASSOC PROF GEOL, LAKE SUPERIOR STATE COL, 69- *Mem:* Geol Soc Am; Geol Asn Can; Can Inst Mining & Metall. *Res:* Structural geology of Labrador Trough formations near Wabush Lake; superposed folds, Hudsonian events and Grenville Province events. *Mailing Add:* Earth Sci Dept Lake Superior State Col Sault Ste Marie MI 49783

KNOWLES, HAROLD LORAINE, b Chicago, Ill, Aug 21, 05; m 31; c 1. PHYSICS. *Educ:* Phillips Univ, BA, 26; Univ Kans, PhD(physics), 31. *Prof Exp:* Asst instr physics, Univ Kans, 27-31; from instr to prof physics, 31-54, prof phys sci, Univ Fla, 54-72, head dept, 54-67, EMER PROF PHYS SCI, UNIV FLA, 72- *Concurrent Pos:* Supvr sig corps contract proj, War Res Lab, Fla Eng & Indust Exp Sta, 44-45. *Mem:* Am Phys Soc; Am Asn Physics Teachers. *Res:* Dielectric constant measurements; direction finder for atmospherics; physical sciences in general education. *Mailing Add:* 1424 NW 12th Rd Gainesville FL 32605

KNOWLES, HARROLD B, b Berkeley, Calif, July 28, 25; m 49; c 2. PHYSICS. *Educ:* Univ Calif, Berkeley, AB, 47, MA, 51, PhD(physics), 57. *Prof Exp:* Res asst oceanog, Univ Wash, 48-50; res asst physics, Univ Calif, Berkeley, 51-57; sr exp physicist, Lawrence Radiation Lab, Univ Calif, Livermore, 57-61; res assoc, Yale Univ, 61-64; assoc prof, 64-77, PROF PHYSICS, WASH STATE UNIV, 77- *Concurrent Pos:* Vis staff mem, Los Alamos Sci Lab, 73-74; vis staff consult, Los Alamos Sci Lab, 74- *Mem:* Am Phys Soc; Am Asn Physicists in Med. *Res:* Nuclear physics; accelerator design; protection against radiation hazards; radiological physics; charged particle optics, track detectors. *Mailing Add:* Dept of Phys 644 Phys Sci Wash State Univ Pullman WA 99164

KNOWLES, HARVEY C, JR, b Glen Cove, NY, Aug 12, 15; m 42; c 2. INTERNAL MEDICINE. *Educ:* Yale Univ, BS, 37; Columbia Univ, MD, 42; Am Bd Internal Med, dipl. *Prof Exp:* Dir metab lab, 52-69, PROF MED, COL MED, UNIV CINCINNATI, 69- *Concurrent Pos:* USPHS fel, 50-52; Markle scholar, 52- *Mem:* AAAS; fel Am Col Physicians; Am Diabetes Asn; Am Fedn Clin Res. *Res:* Metabolic disorders. *Mailing Add:* 234 Goodman St Cincinnati OH 45229

KNOWLES, HUGH SHALER, b Hynes, Iowa, Sept 23, 04; m 28; c 3. ELECTRONIC ENGINEERING. *Educ:* Columbia Univ, AB, 28. *Prof Exp:* Engr, Hammarlund Mfg Co, New York, 27-28; gen mgr parts div, Silver Marshall, Inc, Chicago, 28-30; chief engr, Jensen Mfg Co, Chicago, 31-50, vpres, 40-50; CONSULT ENGR, 36- *Concurrent Pos:* Lectr grad physics, Univ Chicago, 35-36; pres & dir res, Indust Res Prod, Inc, Elk Grove Village, 46-, Knowles Electronics, Inc, Franklin Park, 54-; pres, Knotts Edward Corp, Franklin Park, 65-, Synchro-Start Prod, Inc, 68- & Financial Corp, Ill, 69-; chmn bd, Knowles Electronics, Ltd, Burgess Hill, Eng, 61-; mem US deleg, Electrotech Comn TC29, 53 & 54, head deleg, 55 & 57; head deleg, US Int Orgn Standardization TC 43, 55; mem, Acoust Standards Bd, 58-60. *Mem:* Nat Acad Eng; fel Inst Elec & Electronics Engrs (pres, 45-47); Radio Mfr Asn; Am Inst Physics; Audio Eng Soc (pres, 65-66). *Res:* Loudspeakers and room acoustics; telephone receivers; microphones. *Mailing Add:* Knowles Electronics Inc 3100 N Mannheim Rd Franklin Park IL 60131

KNOWLES, JAMES KENYON, b Cleveland, Ohio, Apr 14, 31; m 52; c 3. APPLIED MATHEMATICS. *Educ:* Mass Inst Technol, SB, 52, PhD(math), 57. *Prof Exp:* Instr math, Mass Inst Technol, 57-58; from asst prof to assoc prof, 58-65, PROF APPL MECH, CALIF INST TECHNOL, 65- *Mem:* Am Soc Mech Engrs; Am Math Soc; Soc Indust & Appl Math. *Res:* Mathematical theory of elasticity. *Mailing Add:* Thomas Lab Calif Inst of Technol Pasadena CA 91107

KNOWLES, JOHN APPLETON, III, b Portchester, NY, Nov 20, 35; m 59; c 2. DRUG METABOLISM. *Educ:* Middlebury Col, AB, 58; Ariz State Univ, PhD(anal chem), 66. *Prof Exp:* Res chemist, Orchem Dept, Chambers Works, E I du Pont de Nemours & Co, 66-68; res scientist, 68-78, MGR DRUG KINETICS SECT, WYETH LABS, AM HOME PROD CORP, 78- *Mem:* AAAS; Am Chem Soc. *Res:* Analysis of drugs and their metabolites. *Mailing Add:* Wyeth Labs PO Box 8299 Philadelphia PA 19101

KNOWLES, JOHN WARWICK, b Toronto, Ont, Dec 9, 20; m 43; c 5. NUCLEAR PHYSICS. *Educ:* Univ Toronto, BA, 43; McGill Univ, PhD(physics), 47. *Prof Exp:* Res physicist nuclear physics, Nat Res Coun, 43-45; asst res officer gen physics, 47-54, assoc res officer, 54-58, SR RES OFFICER NUCLEAR PHYSICS, ATOMIC ENERGY CAN LTD, 58- *Mem:* Fel Am Phys Soc; Can Asn Physicists. *Res:* Low energy nuclear physics, crystal diffraction of neutron capture x-rays; precision measurements of reference x-rays; photo fission and related photo nuclear reactions. *Mailing Add:* Chalk River Nuclear Lab Atomic Energy of Can Ltd Chalk River ON K0J 1J0 Can

KNOWLES, M B, b Newton, Miss, Jan 4, 21; m 42; c 3. ORGANIC CHEMISTRY. *Educ:* Miss Col, BA, 42; Univ Tex, PhD(org chem), 49. *Prof Exp:* Chemist, E I du Pont de Nemours & Co, 42-44; sr res chemist, Tenn Eastman Co, 49-60, sr chemist & head dept, 60-63, supt, Res Pilot Plants, 63-67, sr res assoc, 67, asst div supt, 67-73, div supt, 73-81; PLANT MGR, HOLSTON DEFENSE CORP, 81- *Mem:* Am Chem Soc; Am Inst Chemists; Soc Plastics Engrs; AAAS. *Res:* Organic synthesis; process development and design. *Mailing Add:* Tenn Eastman Co Kingsport TN 37662

KNOWLES, PAULDEN FORD, b Unity, Sask, Can, Apr 18, 16; nat US; m 43; c 1. AGRONOMY. *Educ:* Univ Sask, BSA, 38, MSc, 40; Univ Calif, PhD(genetics), 43. *Prof Exp:* Assoc prof plant sci, Univ Alta, 46-47; from asst prof to assoc prof agron, 47-59, chmn dept agron & range sci, 70-75, PROF AGRON & AGRONOMIST, AGR EXP STA, UNIV CALIF, DAVIS, 59- *Mem:* Bot Soc Am; Soc Econ Bot; Am Soc Agron. *Res:* Oil crops including flax, safflower, sunflower, soybeans and rapeseed. *Mailing Add:* Dept of Agron & Range Sci Univ of Calif Davis CA 95616

KNOWLES, RICHARD N, b Wilmington, Del, Aug 8, 35; m 57; c 3. ORGANIC CHEMISTRY. *Educ:* Oberlin Col, BA, 57; Univ Rochester, PhD(chem), 60. *Prof Exp:* Res chemist, 60-73, res supvr, 73, develop supvr, Indust Chem Dept, 73-75, tech supt, 75, prod supt, 76-77, mfg mgr, 78-80, ASST PLANT MGR, E I DU PONT DE NEMOURS & CO, INC, 80- *Mem:* Am Chem Soc; Am Ornith Union. *Res:* Herbicides, fungicides, insecticides, pharmaceutical agents, azo catalysts and flame retardants; colloidal silica; production of organic and inorganic chemicals in volumes ranging from lab scale to bulk commodities. *Mailing Add:* 18 Main St Henry Clay Wilmington DE 19807

KNOWLES, ROGER, b Halifax, Eng, July 7, 29; m 63; c 2. MICROBIOLOGY. *Educ:* Univ Birmingham, BSc, 53; Univ London, PhD, 57. *Prof Exp:* From asst prof to prof, 57-71, PROF MICROBIOL, MACDONALD COL, MCGILL UNIV, 71- *Mem:* Soil Sci Soc Am; Am Soc Microbiol; Can Soc Microbiol. *Res:* Soil and aquatic microbiology; forest soils; nitrogen fixation; denitrification; nutrification. *Mailing Add:* Dept of Microbiol Macdonald Col McGill Univ Quebec PQ H9X 1C0 Can

KNOWLES, STEPHEN H, b New York, NY, Feb 28, 40; m 65; c 2. RADIO ASTRONOMY. *Educ:* Amherst Col, BA, 61; Yale Univ, PhD(astron), 68. *Prof Exp:* Astronomer, US Naval Observ, 61, ASTRONOMER, US NAVAL RES LAB, 61- *Mem:* AAAS; Int Union Radio Sci; Am Astron Soc; Int Astron Union. *Res:* Radar astronomy; celestial mechanics; radio spectroscopy; very long baseline interferometry. *Mailing Add:* US Naval Res Lab Code 4132 Washington DC 20375

KNOWLTON, CARROLL BABBIDGE, JR, b Nashua, NH, Oct 11, 26; m 50; c 2. ENTOMOLOGY. *Educ:* Amherst Col, BA, 50; Cornell Univ, MS, 58, PhD(entom), 61. *Prof Exp:* From asst prof to assoc prof zool, 61-70, prof, 70-81, PROF BIOL, ORANGE COUNTY COMMUNITY COL, 81-, CHMN, DEPT BIOL & HEALTH SCI, 70- *Mem:* AAAS; Am Inst Biol Sci; Entom Soc Am; Lepidop Soc; Soc Syst Zool. *Res:* Mechanisms of survival in the Arthropoda, especially the Insecta. *Mailing Add:* Dept of Biol & Health Sci Orange County Community Col Middletown NY 10940

KNOWLTON, DAVID ALMY, b Washington, DC, June 20, 38; div; c 2. REFRACTORIES RESEARCH, PRODUCT DEVELOPMENT. *Educ:* Capital Univ, BS, 61; Ohio State Univ, MSc, 67, PhD(biochem), 69. *Prof Exp:* Instr, Ohio State Univ, 70-71, asst prof, 71-73; researcher, Battelle Mem Inst, 73-76; res chemist, 77-81, DIR NEW PROD DEVELOP, GUNNING REFRACTORIES INC, 82- *Concurrent Pos:* Consult, Cent Labs, State Ohio & Consolidated Biomed Labs, 71-73. *Mem:* Sigma Xi; Am Chem Soc; Am Ceramic Soc. *Res:* Development of carbon-bonded refractory, especially products for use in the manufacture of iron and steel. *Mailing Add:* PO Box 223 Wheelersburg OH 45694

KNOWLTON, FLOYD M(ARION), b Milan, Ind, Jan 18, 18; m 41; c 3. CHEMICAL ENGINEERING. *Educ:* Purdue Univ, 39. *Prof Exp:* From process operator to res chemist, Joseph E Seagram & Sons, Inc, 39-42; supvr chem control div, Pa Ord Works, 42-43; develop engr, Naugatuck Chem Div, US Rubber Co, 43-45; develop engr, Bristol Labs Div, Briston-Myers Co, 45-50, dept head, Chem Develop Pilot Plant, 50-58, mgr chem develop, 58-67, dir develop, 67-75, dir develop spec projs, Indust Div, 75-81; RETIRED. *Mem:* Am Chem Soc; Am Inst Chem Engrs. *Res:* Industrial fermentations; recovery processes; organic syntheses. *Mailing Add:* 40 Churchill Ct Fayetteville NY 13066

KNOWLTON, FREDERICK FRANK, b Springville, NY, Nov 24, 34; m 61; c 4. WILDLIFE RESEARCH. *Educ:* Cornell Univ, BS, 57; Mont Stat Col, MS, 59; Purdue Univ, PhD(ecol, physiol), 64. *Prof Exp:* Proj biologist, Mont Fish & Game Dept, 59; lectr biol, Univ Mo, Kansas City, 64; WILDLIFE BIOLOGIST, US FISH & WILDLIFE SERV, 64- *Concurrent Pos:* Vis assoc prof, Cornell Univ, 71; assoc prof wildlife sci, Utah State Univ, 72- *Mem:* Wildlife Soc ; Am Soc Mammal; Wildlife Dis Asn; Nat Audubon Soc. *Res:* Dynamics and mechanisms of natural vertebrate populations; especially mammalian physiology and phenomenoon of predation; ungulates; the larger carnivores. *Mailing Add:* Predator Ecol & Behav Proj Utah State Univ UMC J2 Logan UT 84322

KNOWLTON, GEORGE FRANKLIN, b Farmington, Utah, July 28, 01; m 25; c 2. ENTOMOLOGY. *Educ:* Utah State Univ, BS, 23, MA, 25; Ohio State Univ, PhD(entom), 32. *Prof Exp:* Asst entomologist, Exp Sta, 25-30, assoc entomologist, 30-40, res assoc prof entom, 40-45, exten entomologist, 43-67 & 69-70, prof zool & entom, 45-67, EMER PROF ZOOL & ENTOM, UTAH STATE UNIV, 67- *Concurrent Pos:* Leader, Grasshopper & Mormon Cricket Control, Utah State Univ, 37-54; entomologist chg insect & rodent control unit, 9th Serv Command, US Army Engrs, 44-45. *Mem:* Fel AAAS; fel Entom Soc Am (vpres, Am Asn Econ Entom, 41-42); Soc Syst Zool; fel Herpetologists League. *Res:* Desert arthropod ecology; aphids; bird and lizard food habits; western insects. *Mailing Add:* Dept Biol 53 Utah State Univ Logan UT 84322

KNOWLTON, GREGORY DEAN, b Santa Barbara, Calif, Jan 6, 46; div; c 1. ANALYTICAL CHEMISTRY. *Educ:* San Jose State Univ, BS, 74, MS, 76; Ariz State Univ, PhD(chem), 82. *Prof Exp:* Res geochemist, Lawrence Livermore Nat Lab, 75 & 76; res assoc, Ariz State Univ, 76-79; anal lab mgr, Commerce Metal Refiners, 79-80; ANAL CHEMIST & PRIN INVESTR, TALLEY INDUST ARIZ, 80- *Concurrent Pos:* Instr chem, Phoenix Col, 78-80. *Mem:* Am Chem Soc; AAAS; Sigma Xi. *Res:* Analytical chemistry, methods, development and diagnostics; solid propellant gas generators, research, formulation and development. *Mailing Add:* Talley Indust Ariz PO Box 849 Mesa AZ 85201

KNOWLTON, KENNETH C(HARLES), b Springville, NY, June 6, 31; m 54; c 5. COMPUTER SCIENCE, COMMUNICATIONS. *Educ:* Cornell Univ, BEng, 53, MS, 55; Mass Inst Technol, PhD(commun sci), 62. *Prof Exp:* Res assoc electron micros, Cornell Univ, 56-57; res asst mach trans natural lang, Mass Inst Technol, 57-62; MEM TECH STAFF, SPEECH & COMMUN RES DEPT, BELL TEL LABS, 62- *Concurrent Pos:* Mem, Nat Comt Elec Eng Films, 67-71; vis prof Univ Calif, Santa Cruz, 71-72. *Mem:* AAAS; Asn Comput Mach. *Res:* Development of programming languages such as a computer language for producing animated movies and a low-level list processing language. *Mailing Add:* Bell Tel Labs Mountain Ave Murray Hill NJ 07974

KNOWLTON, NANCY, b Evanston, Ill, May 30, 49. BEHAVIORAL ECOLOGY, MARINE ECOLOGY. *Educ:* Harvard Univ, AB, 71; Univ Calif, Berkeley, PhD(zool), 78. *Prof Exp:* NATO fel, Univ Liverpool & Cambridge Univ, Eng, 78-79; ASST PROF BIOL, YALE UNIV, 79- *Mem:* Sigma Xi; Soc Study Evolution; Ecol Soc Am; Animal Behav Soc; Am Soc Zoologists. *Res:* Sexual selection; evolution of aggression; coral reef ecology; crustaceans; anemone commensals. *Mailing Add:* Dept Biol Yale Univ PO Box 6666 New Haven CT 06511

KNOWLTON, ROBERT CHARLES, b Gardner, Mass, Aug 3, 29; m 52; c 1. CHEMICAL ENGINEERING. *Educ:* Northeastern Univ, BS, 52; Newark Col Eng, MS, 58. *Prof Exp:* Appl Engr, Worthington Corp, 52-55; serv engr, Eng Dept, 55-58, res engr, Textile Fibers Dept, 58-65, sr res engr, 65-75, DEVELOP ASSOC, TEXTILE FIBERS DEPT, E I DU PONT DE NEMOURS & CO, INC, 75- *Mem:* Am Inst Chem Engrs; Textured Yarn Asn Am. *Res:* Synthetic fibers; spinning, drawing, and processing of polyester fibers; texturing of continuous filament yarns. *Mailing Add:* Textile Res Lab Chestnut Run Wilmington DE 19898

KNOWLTON, ROBERT EARLE, b Summit, NJ, Oct 14, 39; m 63; c 2. INVERTEBRATE ZOOLOGY, MARINE BIOLOGY. *Educ:* Bowdoin Col, AB, 60; Univ NC, Chapel Hill, PhD(zool), 70. *Prof Exp:* Asst zool, Univ NC, Chapel Hill, 60-64; res asst fisheries, Inst Marine Sci, 64-65; from instr to asst prof biol, Bowdoin Col, 65-72; asst prof, 72-75, ASSOC PROF BIOL, GEORGE WASHINGTON UNIV, 75-, ASST DEAN, 80- *Concurrent Pos:* Teaching fel zool, Univ NC, Chapel Hill, 62-63; vis lectr biol, Univ Southern Maine, 72-80. *Mem:* AAAS; Am Inst Biol Sci; Am Soc Zool. *Res:* Autecology of decapod larvae; plankton ecology; sound production of Crustacea. *Mailing Add:* Dept of Biol Sci George Washington Univ Washington DC 20052

KNOX, ANDREW GIBSON, b Philadelphia, Pa, Apr 26, 23; m 47; c 3. PHYSICAL CHEMISTRY. *Educ:* Williams Col, AB, 47; Univ Pa, MS, 48, PhD(chem), 50. *Prof Exp:* Res chemist polymer chem, Nylon Res Div, 50-54, res supvr, 54-59, tech supvr, 59-62, res supvr, 62-72, SPECIALIST, TEXTILE RES LAB, E I DU PONT DE NEMOURS & CO, 72- *Mem:* Am Chem Soc; Sigma Xi. *Res:* Polymer chemistry; melt spinning; textile chemistry. *Mailing Add:* Textile Res Lab E I du Pont de Nemours & Co Inc Wilmington DE 19898

KNOX, BRUCE E(LWIN), b Binghamton, NY, Aug 4, 31; m 53; c 3. MATERIALS SCIENCE. *Educ:* Rensselaer Polytech Inst, BS, 53; Syracuse Univ, MS, 58; Pa State Univ, PhD(fuel technol), 63. *Prof Exp:* Res asst, Syracuse Univ, 56-57; res asst shock tube chem, Pa State Univ, 57-59 & 60-62, instr geochem, 63, asst prof solid state technol, 63-67, solid state sci, 67-68 & mat sci, 68-69, ASSOC PROF MAT SCI, PA STATE UNIV, 69-, ASST DIR, MAT RES LAB, 75- *Mem:* AAAS; fel Am Inst Chemists; Am Chem Soc; Am Soc Eng Educ; Mat Res Soc. *Res:* Mass spectrometry; vapor species of solid materials; laser-solid interaction; thin films; characterization of materials; chemical kinetics; trace elements in disease; materials science and engineering education; auger electron spectrometry; ion scattering spectrometry. *Mailing Add:* Mat Res Lab Pa State Univ University Park PA 16802

KNOX, BURNAL RAY, b Pineville, Mo, Mar 29, 31; m 55; c 3. FLUVIAL GEOMORPHOLOGY, SPELEOLOGY. *Educ:* Univ Ark, BS, 53, MS, 57; Univ Iowa, PhD(geol), 66. *Prof Exp:* Explor geologist, Gulf Oil Corp, 56-58; teacher high sch, Kans, 59-62; from asst prof to assoc prof, 65-76, PROF GEOL SCI, SOUTHEAST MO UNIV, 76- *Mem:* Geol Soc Am; Nat Asn Geol Teachers; Am Sci Affil; Nat Speleol Soc. *Res:* Geomorphic evolution of Ozarks and Mississippi-Ohio rivers confluence area; Karst geomorphology and speleology of southeast Missouri; correlation of landforms with quaternary events, particularly climatic changes as controls of landscape evolution. *Mailing Add:* Dept of Earth Sci Southeast Mo State Univ Cape Girardeau MO 63701

KNOX, CHARLES EMERY, plastics chemistry, see previous edition

KNOX, CHARLES KENNETH, b Minneapolis, Minn, Nov 19, 38. NEUROPHYSIOLOGY, ENGINEERING. *Educ:* Univ Minn, Minneapolis, BS, 61, MS, 62, PhD(physiol), 69. *Prof Exp:* Asst prof, 69-76, ASSOC PROF PHYSIOL, UNIV MINN, MINNEAPOLIS, 76- *Concurrent Pos:* NIH res fel, Nobel Inst Neurophysiol, Stockholm, 69-70; NIH res grant, 73-76 & 76-79. *Mem:* Am Physiol Soc; Soc Neurosci; NY Acad Sci. *Res:* Neural control of respiration. *Mailing Add:* Lab of Neurophysiol Dept Physiol 424 Millard Hall Univ of Minn Minneapolis MN 55455

KNOX, DAVID LALONDE, b Chicago, Ill, Sept 3, 30; m 58; c 3. OPHTHALMOLOGY. *Educ:* Baylor Univ, MD, 55. *Prof Exp:* ASSOC PROF OPHTHAL, SCH MED, JOHNS HOPKINS UNIV, 62-, ASST DEAN ADMIS, 76- *Res:* Neuro-medical ophthalmology. *Mailing Add:* Dept of Ophthal Johns Hopkins Univ Sch of Med Baltimore MD 21205

KNOX, ELLIS GILBERT, b Sterling, Ill, Mar 25, 28; m 48; c 2. NEW CROP INTRODUCTION. *Educ:* Univ Ill, BS, 49, MS, 50; Cornell Univ, phD(soils), 54. *Prof Exp:* From asst prof to prof soils, Ore State Univ, 54-73; pedologist, Aero Serv Corp, Bogota, Colombia, 73-75; EXEC OFFICER SOIL & LAND USE TECHNOL, INC, 75- *Concurrent Pos:* Soil scientist, Soil Conserv Serv, USDA, 62-63; consult, Interam Inst Agr Sci, Turrialba, Costa Rica, 66; tech officer, Food & Agr Org UN, Turrialba, Costa Rica, 69-70. *Mem:* AAAS; Soil Sci Soc Am; Sigma Xi; Soil Conserv Soc Am; Am Soc Agron. *Res:* Soil classification and mapping; soil survey interpretations; land resource and land use evaluation; analysis of crop production-marketing-consumption systems; biomass crops; development of crop systems; land resource inventory and management. *Mailing Add:* 11021 Wood Elves Way Columbia MD 21044

KNOX, FRANCIS STRATTON, III, b Wilmington, Del, Jan 28, 41; m 65; c 1. PHYSIOLOGY, BIOMEDICAL ENGINEERING. *Educ:* Brown Univ, BA, 63; Iowa State Univ, MS, 66; Univ Ill, PhD(physiol & biomed eng), 71. *Prof Exp:* Grad teaching asst zool, Iowa State Univ, 63-66; USPHS trainee biomed eng, Med Ctr, Univ Ill, 66-70; chief bioinstrumentation br, US Army Aeromed Res Lab, 70-73; asst prof, Med Ctr, La State Univ, Shreveport, 73-76, mem Grad Fac, 74-80, assoc prof physiol & biophys, 76-80; RES PHYSIOLOGIST & GROUP LEADER CREW BIOTECHNOL GROUP, BIOMED APPLN RES DIV, AEROMED RES LAB, US ARMY, 80- *Concurrent Pos:* Consult physiol & bioeng, US Army Aeromed Res Lab, Ft Rucker, Ala, 73-; affil asst prof bioeng, La Tech Univ, 75- *Mem:* Sigma Xi; Asn Res Vision & Ophthal; Am Burn Asn; Inst Elec & Electronics Engrs; Soc Neurosci. *Res:* Quantitative physiology; systems analysis of physiological systems; use of biomedical instrumentation and computers to study physiological systems and to create economical, comprehensive diagnostic and patient monitoring systems. *Mailing Add:* US Army Aeromedical Res Lab Biomed Appln Div PO Box 577 Ft Rucker AL 36362

KNOX, GAYLORD SHEARER, b Bangkok, Thailand, Oct 18, 23; US citizen; m 46; c 3. MEDICINE, RADIOLOGY. *Educ:* Tulane Univ, MD, 51; Am Bd Radiol, cert, 58. *Prof Exp:* Intern gen med, Charity Hosp, New Orleans, 51-52; pvt pract, La, 52-53; physician, US Army, Ft Bliss, Tex, 53-55, resident radiol, Walter Reed Army Hosp, 55-58, chief radiol serv, Hosp, Bad Canstatt, Ger, 58-61; assoc prof radiol, Univ Okla, 61-65; chief, Dept Radiol, Baltimore City Hosps, 65-79; RADIOLOGIST, GREATER LAUREL BELTSVILLE HOSP, 79- *Concurrent Pos:* Consult, Vet Admin Hosp, Oklahoma City, 61-65 & Perry Point, Md, 65-; asst prof, Sch Med, Johns Hopkins Univ, 65-; assoc prof, Sch Med, Univ Md, Baltimore City, 65-; active consult, Sinai Hosp Baltimore, 66-; pres, Chesapeake Physicians, 73-78, Chesapeake Casualty Ins Co, Denver, 74-78. *Mem:* Radiol Soc NAm; fel Am Col Radiol; AMA; Soc Nuclear Med; Am Inst Ultrasound Med. *Res:* Clinical radiology, particularly skeletal and visceral changes in the aging process and vascular changes in aging. *Mailing Add:* Dept of Radiol Greater Laurel Beltsville Hosp Laurel MD 20707

KNOX, JACK ROWLES, b Hot Springs, Ark, Feb 8, 29; m 53; c 2. POLYMER SCIENCE. *Educ:* La State Univ, BS, 50, MS, 52; Univ Del, PhD(phys chem), 63. *Prof Exp:* Res chemist, E I du Pont de Nemours & Co, 52-60; res chemist, Avisun Corp, 60-61, group leader polymer struct, 61-63; mgr polymer physics, Continental Can Co, 63-65; sect leader polymer properties, Avisun Corp, 65-70; SR RES ASSOC, AMOCO CHEMICALS CORP, 70- *Mem:* Soc Rheology (pres, 76-77); Am Chem Soc; Am Phys Soc. *Res:* Thermal analysis; polymer rheology, structure and analysis; mechanical properties. *Mailing Add:* Amoco Chemicals Corp PO Box 400 Naperville IL 60566

KNOX, JAMES CLARENCE, b Platteville, Wis, Nov 29, 41; m 64; c 2. GEOMORPHOLOGY, PHYSICAL GEOGRAPHY. *Educ:* Univ Wis-Platteville, BS, 63; Univ Iowa, PhD(geog), 70. *Prof Exp:* From asst prof to assoc prof, 68-76, PROF GEOG, UNIV WIS-MADISON, 77-, DIR CTR GEOL ANAL, INST ENVIRON STUDIES, 73- *Concurrent Pos:* Assoc ed, Geog Annals, 78-81, Ann Am Quaternary Asn, 78- *Mem:* Asn Am Geogr; Am Quaternary Asn; AAAS; Geol Soc Am; Soil Conserv Soc Am. *Res:* Fluvial geomorphology; paleoclimatology and paleohydrology of the Quaternary; effects of present-day climate variation and land use on stream flow characteristics and sedimentation problems. *Mailing Add:* Dept of Geog 324 Sci Hall Univ of Wis Madison WI 53706

KNOX, JAMES L(ESTER), b Youngstown, Ohio, July 30, 19; m 46; c 5. ELECTRICAL ENGINEERING. *Educ:* Univ Tenn, BS, 42; Univ Mich, MSE, 54; Ohio State Univ, PhD(elec eng), 62. *Prof Exp:* Instr elec eng, Univ Tenn, 42-43; engr, Gen Elec Co, 43-46; Am Baptist For Mission Soc missionary assigned as instr physics, Univ Shanghai, 47-48; asst prof eng, Cent Philippine Univ, 48-50, tech dir eng, Radio Sta DYSR, 50-51, assoc prof, Cent Philippine Univ, 51-59, prof & dean, 62-65; instr elec eng, Ohio State Univ, 60-61, res assoc, Res Found, 61-62; assoc prof, 65-69, PROF ELEC ENG, MONT STATE UNIV, 69- *Concurrent Pos:* Prof elec eng, Univ Petrol & Minerals, Dhahran, Saudi Arabia, 73-75 & 76-78. *Mem:* Inst Elec & Electronics Engrs; Instrument Soc; Am Soc Eng Educ. *Res:* Electromagnetics; electric power; instrumentation; community acoustics; remote sensing. *Mailing Add:* Dept Elec Eng Mont State Univ Bozeman MT 59715

KNOX, JAMES RUSSELL, JR, b Bonne Terre, Mo, May 28, 41; m 65; c 2. PHYSICAL BIOCHEMISTRY, X-RAY CRYSTALLOGRAPHY. *Educ:* Univ Mo-Rolla, BS, 63; Boston Univ, PhD(phys chem), 67. *Prof Exp:* Fel crystallog, Oxford Univ, 66-69; res assoc biophysics, Dept Molecular Biochem, Yale Univ, 69-70; assoc prof, 70-80, PROF BIOPHYS, BIOL SCI GROUP, UNIV CONN, 80- *Concurrent Pos:* NIH grant, 72-; NSF grant, 76-; vis prof, Harvard Biol Labs, 77; grant, Merck Sharpe & Dohme Co, 78- *Mem:* AAAS; Am Chem Soc; Am Crystallog Asn; Sigma Xi; Biophys Soc. *Res:* Enzyme structure and function by means of x-ray analysis; penicillin-binding proteins; biodegradable polymer design; Beta-lactamases and transpeptidases. *Mailing Add:* Biol Sci Group Univ of Conn Storrs CT 06268

KNOX, JOHN MACMURRAY, b Sheboygan, Wis, Nov 21, 46; m 69; c 2. PHYSICS. *Educ:* Gustavus Adolphus Col, BA, 68; Univ Wyo, MS, 77, PhD(physics), 81. *Prof Exp:* RES FEL & ASST PROF PHYSICS, INST PAPER CHEM, 81- *Mem:* Am Phys Soc. *Res:* Optical and electrical properties of pulp slurries and of paper; gas phase electron capture; negative ion and optically modified mass spectra. *Mailing Add:* Inst Paper Chem PO Box 1039 Appleton WI 54912

KNOX, JOSEPH BLATT, b Pittsburgh, Pa, Jan 11, 24; m 48; c 2. METEOROLOGY, APPLIED PHYSICS. *Educ:* Univ Calif, Los Angeles, BA, 49, MA, 50, PhD(physics, meteorol), 55. *Prof Exp:* Instr & asst prof meteorol, Univ Calif, Los Angeles, 55-58, physicist, Plowshare Div, 58-63, group leader theoret physics, 63-70, group leader fluid mech, Earth Sci Div, 70-72, group leader atmospheric sci, Physics Dept, 72-74, DIV LEADER ATMOSPHERIC SCI, PHYSICS DEPT, LAWRENCE LIVERMORE LAB, UNIV CALIF, 74- *Concurrent Pos:* Consult, Rand Corp, Calif, 56-58; exten lectr, Univ Calif, 57-58; consult Calif State Dept Water Resources & environ sci, Bechtel Corp, 67-74; vis lectr, Univ Calif, Davis, 72; meteorol adv comt, Environ Protection Agency, 74-75. *Mem:* Am Meteorol Soc; Am Nuclear Soc; Am Geophys Union; NY Acad Sci; Air Pollution Control Asn. *Res:* Fallout physics; dynamic and synoptic meteorology; applied physics problems associated with effects of underground nuclear explosions; spatial and temporal distribution of air pollutants of conventional or nuclear origin. *Mailing Add:* Lawrence Livermore Lab Univ of Calif PO Box 808 Livermore CA 94550

KNOX, KENNETH L, b Winnipeg, Man, Sept 18, 20; US citizen; m 42; c 3. CHEMICAL ENGINEERING. *Educ:* Univ Saskatchewan, BE, 42, MSc, 46; Columbia Univ, PhD(chem eng), 49. *Prof Exp:* Res engr, Yerkes Res & Develop Lab, 48-52, develop supvr, Cellophane Plants, NY, Iowa & Kans, 52-60, tech supt Cellophane Lab, Kans, 60-63, RES ASSOC, CIRCLEVILLE RES & DEVELOP LAB, E I DU PONT DE NEMOURS & CO INC, NY, 63- *Mem:* Am Chem Soc; Am Inst Chem Engrs. *Res:* Industrial research on polyester film. *Mailing Add:* 327 Meadow Lane Circleville OH 43113

KNOX, KERRO, b Philadelphia, Pa, June 17, 24; m 49; c 4. INORGANIC CHEMISTRY. *Educ:* Yale Univ, BS, 45, PhD(phys chem), 50; Cambridge Univ, PhD(phys chem), 52. *Prof Exp:* From instr to assoc prof chem, Univ NC, 51-56; mem tech staff, Bell Tel Labs, 56-63; assoc prof chem, Case Western Reserve Univ, 63-69; PROF CHEM, CLEVELAND STATE UNIV, 69- *Mem:* Am Crystallog Asn. *Res:* X-ray crystallography. *Mailing Add:* Dept of Chem Cleveland State Univ Cleveland OH 44115

KNOX, KIRVIN L, b Sayre, Okla, Aug 9, 36; m 58; c 3. NUTRITION. *Educ:* Fresno State Col, BS, 58; Colo State Univ, MS, 60; Univ Calif, PhD(physiol, nutrit), 64. *Prof Exp:* Lab supt, Escalon Packers Inc, 60; asst prof animal sci, Colo State Univ, 64-65, from asst prof to assoc prof animal sci & physiol, 65-72, dir metab lab, 65-72; PROF NUTRIT SCI & HEAD DEPT, UNIV CONN, 72- *Concurrent Pos:* Co-investr, NIH res grant, 65-68 & prin investr, 66-69; Am Cancer Soc res grant, 66-68; sabbatical leave, Univ Calif, Berkeley, 78-79. *Mem:* Am Dairy Sci Asn; Am Soc Animal Sci; Am Inst Nutrit; NY Acad Sci; AAAS. *Res:* Comparative nutrition as related to energy and vitamin metabolism; behavioral response to nutrition. *Mailing Add:* Dept of Nutrit Sci Univ of Conn Storrs CT 06268

KNOX, LARRY WILLIAM, b Mishawaka, Ind, Nov 10, 42; m 64; c 1. PALEONTOLOGY. *Educ:* Ind Univ, AB, 65, AM, 71, PhD(geol), 74. *Prof Exp:* ASST PROF GEOL, TENN TECHNOL UNIV, 74- *Mem:* Geol Soc Am; Paleont Soc; Paleont Asn; Soc Econ Paleontologists & Mineralogists. *Res:* Paleontology and biostratigraphy of paleozoic microfossils. *Mailing Add:* Box 5125 Tenn Technol Univ Cookeville TN 38501

KNOX, ROBERT ARTHUR, b Washington, DC, Jan 15, 43; m 66; c 2. PHYSICAL OCEANOGRAPHY. *Educ:* Amherst Col, AB, 64; Mass Inst Technol-Woods Hole Oceanog Inst, PhD(oceanog), 71. *Prof Exp:* Res assoc, Mass Inst Technol, 71-73; RES ASST OCEANOGR, SCRIPPS INST OCEANOG, 73-, ACAD ADMINR, 80- *Mem:* Sigma Xi; Am Meteorol Soc; Am Geophys Union. *Res:* Equatorial ocean dynamics and circulation; structure and dynamics of oceanic mixed layer; acoustic sensing of ocean circulation. *Mailing Add:* Scripps Inst Oceanog A-030 Univ of Calif at San Diego La Jolla CA 92093

KNOX, ROBERT SEIPLE, b Franklin, NJ, July 13, 31; m 54; c 3. CONDENSED MATTER, BIOPHYSICS. *Educ:* Lehigh Univ, BS, 53; Univ Rochester, PhD(physics, optics), 58. *Prof Exp:* Res assoc physics, Univ Ill, 58-59, res asst prof, physics, 59-60; from asst prof to assoc prof, 60-68, Chmn Dept, 69-74, PROF PHYSICS, UNIV ROCHESTER, 68- *Concurrent Pos:* Consult, Solid State Sci Div, Argonne Nat Lab, 59-69, Naval Res Lab, 60-70 & Xerox Corp, 63-; NSF sr fel, Univ Leiden, 67-68; fel, Soc Prom Sci, Kyoto, Japan, 79. *Mem:* Fel Am Phys Soc; Am Soc Photobiol; Am Asn Physics Teachers. *Res:* Optical and electrical properties of ionic and molecular crystals; theory of photosynthesis biosecond spectroscopy. *Mailing Add:* Dept of Physics & Astron Univ of Rochester Rochester NY 14627

KNOX, WALTER EUGENE, b Norcatur, Kans, July 21, 18; m 48; c 3. MEDICINE. *Educ:* Univ Nebr, AB, 39; Harvard Univ, MD, 43. *Prof Exp:* Intern, Presby Hosp, New York, 43; resident med, Med Sch, NY Univ, 44-46; mem sci staff, Enzyme Lab, Columbia Univ, 46-47, assoc med, Col Physicians & Surgeons, 47-48; res assoc, Rheumatic Fever Res Inst & instr med, Med Sch, Northwestern Univ, 48-49; USPHS spec res fel, Cambridge Univ & Nat Inst Med Res, 49-51; assoc prof biochem, Sch Med, Tufts Univ, 52-53; from asst prof to assoc prof, 53-69, PROF BIOL CHEM, HARVARD MED SCH, 69-; MEM STAFF, CANCER RES INST, NEW ENG DEACONESS HOSP, MASS, 53- *Concurrent Pos:* Asst physician, Presby Hosp, New York, 47-48; jr asst physician, Sch Med, Tufts Univ & Boston Dispensary, 53-59, asst physician, 59-, sr clin instr, 63-70; sect ed, Biol Abstracts, 56-; vis prof & chmn, Med Sch, Am Univ Beirut, 61-62; mem metab study sect, USPHS, 62-65, chmn, 64-65; ed, Enzyme, 68- & Biochimica et Biophysica Acta, 78- *Mem:* Am Soc Biol Chem; Am Chem Soc; Am Soc Human Genetics; hon mem, Japanese Biochem Soc; Am Asn Cancer Res. *Res:* Enzymes of intermediary metabolism; mechanism of biological action of compounds; regulation of metabolism. *Mailing Add:* Cancer Res Inst New Eng Deaconess Hosp Boston MA 02215

KNOX, WALTER ROBERT, b Childress, Tex, July 18, 26; m 48; c 3. ORGANIC CHEMISTRY, PETROCHEMISTRY. *Educ:* Baylor Univ, BS, 47; Univ Iowa, MS, 49, PhD(org chem), 50. *Prof Exp:* Control chemist, Fibreboard Prod, Inc, 47; res chemist, Gen Aniline & Film Corp, 50-52; chemist, Hydrocarbons & Polymers Div, Monsanto Co, 52-54, sr res chemist, 54-56, group leader, 56-62, mgr res, 62-70, dir res, Petrochem Div, Monsanto Polymers & Petrochem Co, 70-80, TECHNOL DIR SPEC ASST, MONSANTO INT CO, 80- *Mem:* Am Chem Soc; Catalysis Soc. *Res:* Catalysts and catalytic interconversions, especially with hydrocarbons; monomer synthesis; surfactant synthesis; general organic synthesis. *Mailing Add:* Monsanto Chem Int Co 800 N Lindbergh Blvd St Louis MO 63166

KNOX, WILLIAM JORDAN, b Pomona, Calif, Mar 21, 21; m 48; c 4. NUCLEAR PHYSICS. *Educ:* Univ Calif, BS, 42, PhD(physics), 51. *Prof Exp:* Asst chem, Metall Lab, Univ Chicago, 42-43; from jr chemist to chemist, Clinton Labs, Oak Ridge, 43-46; jr technologist, Hanford Eng Works, 44-45; chemist, Radiation Lab, Univ Calif, 46, physicist, 47-51; asst prof physics, Yale Univ, 51-53; physicist, AEC, Washington, DC, 53-55 & consult, 55-56; asst prof physics, Yale Univ, 55-59; assoc prof physics, Univ Calif, Davis, 60-66, chmn dept, 63-66; actg dir Crocker Nuclear Lab, 66-67 & 78-79; chmn dept, 71-75, PROF PHYSICS, UNIV CALIF, DAVIS, 66- *Concurrent Pos:* Vis sci, Europ Ctr Nuclear Res, 73-74; sr Fulbright Hayes Prog res fel France, Comt Int Exchange Persons, 73-74; vis scientist, Lawrence Berkeley Lab, 81-82. *Mem:* Am Phys Soc; Am Asn Physics Teachers. *Res:* Nuclear reactions; nuclear structure; plutonium and fission product chemistry; particle production. *Mailing Add:* Dept of Physics Univ of Calif Davis CA 95616

KNUCKLES, JOSEPH LEWIS, b Lumberton, NC, Mar 17, 24. PARASITOLOGY. *Educ:* NC Cent Univ, BS, 48, MS, 50; Univ Conn, PhD(parasitol), 59. *Prof Exp:* Instr biol, Bishop Col, 50-52, chmn dept sci, 51-52; instr biol & math, 56-59, coordr biol, 59-67, asst to acad dean, 71, dir summer sch, 71, actg head, Div Sci & Math, 73-75, actg head, Div Arts Scis, 75-76, chmn, Dept Biol & Phys Sci, 67-78, coodr, Area Biol, 78-80 PROF BIOL, FAYETTEVILLE STATE UNIV, 59- *Concurrent Pos:* Sigma Xi grant, 58; consult, NC Teachers Asn, 59; NC Acad Sci grant, 60; NSF stipend, 64; dir coop prog, Fayetteville State Univ, 70; dir consortium prom acad excellence & dir sci improv & exp biol prog; Title III grants, 72-76. *Mem:* AAAS; Am Entom Soc; Am Soc Parasitol; Am Asn Univ Professors; Am Pub Health Asn. *Res:* Transmission of disease agents by flies; general parasitology. *Mailing Add:* Area Biol Fayetteville State Univ Fayetteville NC 28301

KNUDSEN, DENNIS RALPH, b Warren, Minn, July 22, 43; m 65; c 2. PHYSICAL CHEMISTRY. *Educ:* NDak State Univ, BS, 65, PhD(phys chem), 70. *Prof Exp:* RES CHEMIST, US NAVAL SURFACE WEAPONS CTR, 70- *Mem:* Am Chem Soc; Am Conf Govt Indust Hygienists. *Res:* Thermodynamics of solutions; determination of chemical compounds in air; chemical instrument development; combustion. *Mailing Add:* US Naval Surface Weapons Ctr Code G-51 Dahlgren VA 22448

KNUDSEN, ERIC INGVALD, b Palo Alto, Calif, Oct 7, 49; m 75. NEUROSCIENCE, BIOLOGY. *Educ:* Univ Calif, Santa Barbara, BA, 71, MA, 73; Univ Calif, San Diego, PhD(neurosci), 76. *Prof Exp:* res fel neurosci, Calif Inst Technol, 76-80; MEM FAC, DEPT NEUROSCI, STANFORD SCH MED, 80- *Mem:* Acoust Soc Am; AAAS; Soc Neurosci. *Res:* Neurophysiology, anatomy and ethology related to the evolution of the auditory system, specifically encoding of space by the auditory system. *Mailing Add:* Dept Neurobiol Stanford Sch Med Stanford CA 94305

KNUDSEN, GEORGE ANDREW, JR, b New London, Conn, Feb 10, 37; m 69; c 3. PHYSICAL ORGANIC CHEMISTRY. *Educ:* Univ Md, College Park, BS, 63; Mass Inst Technol, PhD(org chem), 67; sr res chemist, Enjay Chem Lab, Esso Res & Eng Co, Linden, 67-74, STAFF CHEMIST, EXXON CHEM CO, 74- *Mem:* Am Chem Soc. *Res:* Peroxygen compounds; sulfonation chemistry; polyelectrolytes; process chemistry; olefin hydration; oxidation electrochemistry. *Mailing Add:* 1932 Mary Ellen Lane Scotch Plains NJ 07076

KNUDSEN, HAROLD KNUD, b San Francisco, Calif, Aug 6, 36; m 58; c 2. ELECTRICAL ENGINEERING. *Educ:* Univ Calif, Berkeley, BS, 58, MS, 60, PhD(elec eng), 62. *Prof Exp:* Staff mem data systs anal, Lincoln Lab, Mass Inst Technol, 62-66; assoc prof, 66-74, PROF ELEC ENG, UNIV NMEX, 74- *Mem:* Inst Elec & Electronics Engrs. *Res:* Data systems analysis; system theory, especially the application of theories of optimization. *Mailing Add:* Dept of Elec Eng Univ of NMex Albuquerque NM 87131

KNUDSEN, J(AMES) G(EORGE), b Youngstown, Alta, Mar 27, 20; nat US; m 47; c 2. CHEMICAL ENGINEERING. *Educ:* Univ Alta, BS, 43, MS, 44; Univ Mich, PhD(chem eng), 50. *Prof Exp:* Asst prof chem eng, 49-53, assoc prof, 53-57, asst dean, 59-71, assoc dean, 71-81, PROF ENG, ENG EXP STA, ORE STATE UNIV, 57- *Concurrent Pos:* Nat Sci sr fel, Cambridge Univ, 61-62; eng consult. *Honors & Awards:* Founders Award, Am Inst Chem Engrs, 77. *Mem:* Am Inst Chem Engrs (pres, 81); Am Chem Soc; Nat Soc Prof Engrs. *Res:* Fluid mechanics; heat transfer; mass transfer; relationship between these processes; applied mathematics. *Mailing Add:* Eng Exp Station Ore State Univ Corvallis OR 97331

KNUDSEN, JAMES FREDERICK, b Boston, Mass, Sept 3, 46; m 74. MEDICAL PHYSIOLOGY. *Educ:* Univ Maine, Orono, BS, 68; Univ NH, MS, 70; Med Col Ga, PhD(endocrinol), 74. *Prof Exp:* NIH FEL PHYSIOL, SCH MED, UNIV MD, BALTIMORE, 74- *Mem:* Sigma Xi; Soc Study Reproduction; Am Asn Anatomists; Am Fertil Soc; Am Soc Zoologists. *Res:* Regulation of female reproduction by the central nervous system, as well as the various interdependent factors involved in this process. *Mailing Add:* Dept of Physiol Univ of Md Sch of Med Baltimore MD 21201

KNUDSEN, JENS WERNER, JR, b Brooklyn, NY, Nov 13, 28; m 54; c 1. ZOOLOGY. *Educ:* Pac Lutheran Col, BA, 52; Univ Southern Calif, MS, 54, PhD(zool), 57. *Prof Exp:* Cur entom, Allan Hancock Found, 52-53; asst zool, Univ Southern Calif, 57; instr, 57-58, from asst prof to assoc prof, 58-70, PROF BIOL, PAC LUTHERAN UNIV, 70-, REGENCY PROF, 77- *Concurrent Pos:* Researcher, US Fish & Wildlife Serv, 57-58. *Mem:* AAAS; Am Soc Ichthyol & Herpet. *Res:* Carcinology on crab life cycles, growth and reproduction; amphibian and coleopteran life histories. *Mailing Add:* Dept of Biol Pac Lutheran Univ Tacoma WA 98447

KNUDSEN, JOHN R, b Brooklyn, NY, July 12, 16; m 42; c 2. APPLIED MATHEMATICS. *Educ:* NY Univ, BS, 37, PhD(math), 51. *Prof Exp:* Instr math, NY Univ, 39-51, from asst prof to assoc prof, 51-72, asst dean & budget officer, 66-72; MEM TECH STAFF, EDUC CTR, BELL TEL LABS, 72- *Concurrent Pos:* Consult, Bell Tel Labs, NJ, 57-72. *Mem:* Am Math Soc; Math Asn Am. *Res:* Self-study instructional techniques. *Mailing Add:* 13 Huntley Rd Holmdel NJ 07733

KNUDSEN, THOMAS PAUL, mass spectrometry, physical organic chemistry, see previous edition

KNUDSEN, WILLIAM CLAIRE, b Provo, Utah, Dec 12, 25; m 48; c 4. PHYSICS. *Educ:* Brigham Young Univ, BS, 50; Univ Wis, MS, 52, PhD(physics), 54. *Prof Exp:* Res physicist geophys, Calif Res Corp Div, Standard Oil Co, Calif, 54-62; res physicist geophys, Lockheed Aircraft Corp, 62-67, STAFF SCIENTIST, LOCKHEED RES LAB, 67- *Mem:* Am Phys Soc; Am Geophys Union. *Res:* Low temperature physics; exploration geophysics; ground water hydrology; planetary atmospheres; planetary ionospheres. *Mailing Add:* Lockheed Res Lab 52-12 Bldg 205 3251 Hanover St Palo Alto CA 94304

KNUDSON, ALFRED GEORGE, JR, b Los Angeles, Calif, Aug 9, 22; m 76; c 3. MEDICINE, GENETICS. *Educ:* Calif Inst Technol, BS, 44, PhD(biochem, genetics), 56; Columbia Univ, MD, 47. *Prof Exp:* Chmn dept pediat, City of Hope Med Ctr, Calif, 56-62, chmn dept biol, 62-66; prof pediat & assoc dean, Health Sci Ctr, State Univ NY Stony Brook, 66-69; prof biol & pediat & assoc dir educ, Univ Tex M D Anderson Hosp & Tumor Inst, Houston, 69-70; prof med genetics & dean, Univ Tex Grad Sch Biomed Sci, 70-76; DIR, INST CANCER RES, FOX CHASE CANCER CTR, 76- *Mem:* AAAS; Am Asn Cancer Res; Am Pediat Soc; Am Soc Human Genetics; Asn Am Physicians. *Res:* Cancer; medical genetics. *Mailing Add:* 7701 Burholme Ave Inst Cancer Res Fox Chase Philadelphia PA 19111

KNUDSON, ALVIN RICHARD, b Minneapolis, Minn, Aug 17, 34; m 60; c 3. ATOMIC PHYSICS. *Educ:* Catholic Univ, AB, 54; Johns Hopkins Univ, PhD(physics), 60. *Prof Exp:* Res asst nuclear physics, Johns Hopkins Univ, 57-58 & 59-60; res physicist, US Naval Res Lab, 60-67, head charged particle reactions sect, 67-70, HEAD MAT ANAL SECT, NAVAL RES LAB, 70- *Mem:* Am Phys Soc. *Res:* Use of high energy ion beams for materials analysis; study of ion-atom collisions at MV energies through high and low resolution measurements of the emitted x-rays. *Mailing Add:* US Naval Res Lab Code 6673 Washington DC 20375

KNUDSON, DOUGLAS MARVIN, b Anoka, Minn, June 11, 36; m 57; c 2. FOREST RECREATION. *Educ:* Colo State Univ, BS, 59, MS, 60; Purdue Univ, PhD(forest econ), 65. *Prof Exp:* Forester, Purdue Univ-Agr Univ Brazil, 60-62, asst prof forestry, 65-67; asst prof, 67-69, ASSOC PROF FORESTRY, PURDUE UNIV, WEST LAFAYETTE, 69- *Concurrent Pos:* Wilderness planner, Nat Park Serv, 70; res assoc, US Forest Serv, 79; consult corp engrs, US Forest Serv, 80-81. *Honors & Awards:* Hon Prof, Fed Univ Vicosa, 68. *Mem:* Soc Am Foresters; Nat Recreation & Park Asn; Commonwealth Forestry Asn; Asn Interpretive Naturalists; Int Asn Torch Clubs (pres, 78-79). *Res:* outdoor recreation economics and planning. *Mailing Add:* Dept of Forestry & Natural Resources Purdue Univ West Lafayette IN 47907

KNUDSON, RONALD JOEL, b Chicago, Ill, Feb 22, 32; m 71. PULMONARY PHYSIOLOGY. *Educ:* Yale Univ, BS, 53; Northwestern Univ, MD, 57. *Prof Exp:* Intern, Chicago Wesley Mem Hosp, 57-58; fel surg, Ochsner Found Hosp, New Orleans, 59-63; fel thoracic surg, Overholt Thoracic Clin, Boston, 63-64; res fel pulmonary physiol, Boston Univ Med Ctr, 64-66 & Sch Pub Health, Harvard Univ, 66-68; asst prof physiol & med, Sch Med, Yale Univ, 68-70; assoc prof internal med, 70-75, PROF INTERNAL MED, COL MED, UNIV ARIZ, 75-, ASSOC DIR DIV RESPIRATORY SCI, 74- *Concurrent Pos:* Dir respiratory serv, Ariz Med Ctr, Tucson, 74- *Mem:* Am Physiol Soc; Am Thoracic Soc; AAAS; Am Col Chest Physicians. *Res:* Respiratory mechanics; airway dynamics; respiratory structure and function relationships. *Mailing Add:* Div of Respiratory Sci Univ of Ariz Col of Med Tucson AZ 85724

KNUDSON, VERNIE ANTON, b Olsburg, Kans, Sept 18, 32; m 54; c 3. LIMNOLOGY. *Educ:* Bethany Col, BS, 54; Ft Hays Kans State Col, MS, 59; Okla State Univ, PhD(zool), 70. *Prof Exp:* Instr biol, Bethany Col, 59-60; instr, Dodge City Col, 60-63; partic, Acad Yr Inst, Univ Ore, 64-65; asst prof fisheries & wildlife, Mich State Univ, 66-69; asst prof biol sci, 71-77, asst prof, 77-80, ASSOC PROF NATURAL RESOURCES TECHNOL, LAKE SUPERIOR STATE COL, 80- *Mem:* Am Inst Biol Sci; Am Chem Soc. *Res:* Water quality; eutrophication; nutrient removal by algae. *Mailing Add:* Dept of Biol Sci Lake Superior State Col Sault Ste Marie MI 49783

KNUDTSON, JOHN THOMAS, b Charleston, SC, July 3, 45. PHYSICAL CHEMISTRY. *Educ:* Colo Col, BS, 67; Columbia Univ, MS, 69, PhD(chem), 72. *Prof Exp:* Res assoc chem, Univ Utah, 72-74 & Univ Wis, 74-75; ASST PROF CHEM, NORTHERN ILL UNIV, 75- *Mem:* Am Phys Soc. *Res:* Laser spectroscopy and chemical dynamics. *Mailing Add:* 524 S Sixth St De Kalb IL 60115

KNULL, HARVEY ROBERT, b Thorsby, Alta, Sept 15, 41; m 65; c 2. BIOCHEMISTRY. *Educ:* Univ Alta, BSc, 63; Univ Nebr, MS, 65; Pa State Univ, PhD(biochem), 70. *Prof Exp:* Fel neurochem, Dept Biochem, Mich State Univ, 70-73; asst prof oral biol, Univ Man, 73-78, assoc prof, 78-80; ASSOC PROF BIOCHEM, UNIV NDAK, 80- *Mem:* Int Soc Neurochem; Am Soc Neurochem; Soc Complex Carbohydrates; Can Biochem Soc; Can Fedn Biol Sci. *Res:* Neurochemistry; axonal transport; brain energy metabolism; compartmentation of glycolytic enzymes; proteoglycans; carbohydrate metabolism. *Mailing Add:* Dept Biochem Univ NDak Grand Forks ND 58202

KNUTH, DONALD ERVIN, b Milwaukee, Wis, Jan 10, 38; m 61; c 2. COMPUTER SCIENCE, MATHEMATICS. *Educ:* Case Inst Technol, BS & MS, 60; Calif Inst Technol, PhD(math), 63. *Prof Exp:* From asst prof to prof math, Calif Inst Technol, 63-68; prof, 68-77, FLETCHER JONES PROF COMPUT SCI & PROF ELEC ENG, STANFORD UNIV, 77- *Concurrent Pos:* Consult, Burroughs Corp, 60-68; staff mathematician, Commun Res Div, Inst Defense Anal, 68-69; Guggenheim Found fel, 72. *Honors & Awards:* G M Hopper Award, 71; A M Turing Award, Asn for Comput Mach, 74; J B Priestley Award, 81; W McDowell Award, Inst Elec & Electron Engrs, 80. *Mem:* Nat Acad Sci; Nat Acad Eng; Soc Indust & Appl Math; Asn Comput Mach; Math Asn Am. *Res:* Analysis of algorithms; combinatorial theory; programming languages; history of computer science; typography. *Mailing Add:* Comput Sci Dept Stanford Univ Stanford CA 94305

KNUTH, ELDON L(UVERNE), b Luana, Iowa, May 10, 25; m 73; c 4. MOLECULAR DYNAMICS, COMBUSTION. *Educ:* Purdue Univ, BS, 49, MS, 50; Calif Inst Technol, PhD(aeronaut eng), 53. *Prof Exp:* Group leader aerothermodyn, Aerophys Develop Corp, 53-56; assoc res engr, 56-58, assoc prof, 59-65, gen chmn, Heat Transfer & Fluid Mech Inst, 59, head, Chem, Nuclear & Thermal Div, 63-65, chmn, Dept Energy & Kinetics, 69-75, PROF ENG, UNIV CALIF, LOS ANGELES, 65-, HEAD MOLECULAR-BEAM LAB, 61- *Concurrent Pos:* Consult, Marquardt Aircraft Corp, 58-60, Jet Propulsion Lab & TRW Inc, 79-; Alexander von Humboldt Found fel, 75. *Honors & Awards:* Award, Am Inst Aeronaut & Astronaut, 50. *Mem:* Am Phys Soc; Am Inst Aeronaut & Astronaut; Am Inst Chem Engrs; Am Vacuum Soc; Combustion Inst. *Res:* Combustion; thermodynamics and statistical mechanics; transport phenomena and properties; free-molecule flows and molecular beams. *Mailing Add:* Dept Chem Nuclear & Thermal Eng 5531 Boelter Hall Univ Calif Los Angeles CA 90024

KNUTSON, CARROLL FIELD, b Santa Monica, Calif, Mar 14, 24; m 48; c 4. GEOSCIENCES SCIENCE. *Educ:* Stanford Univ, BS, 50, MS, 51; Univ Calif, Los Angeles, PhD(geol), 59. *Prof Exp:* Reservoir engr, Continental Oil Co, 51-54, from prod engr to sr prod engr, 54-58, sr res engr, 58-61, res group leader, 61-66, res assoc, 66-67; chief geologist, Cer Geonuclear Corp, 67-74; consult geologist, C F Knutson & Assocs, 74-76; VPRES, C K GEOENERGY, 76- *Concurrent Pos:* Environ dir, Western Oil Shale Corp, 75-76. *Mem:* Geol Soc Am; Am Asn Petrol Geol; Soc Petrol Engrs; Am Geophys Union; Soc Independent Prof Earth Scientists. *Res:* Formation evaluation; rock mechanics; subsurface nuclear engineering geology; hydrology, environmental geology; development of energy with minimum adverse environmental impact. *Mailing Add:* 3376 S Eastern Ave Suite 145 CK Geoenergy Corpe Las Vegas NV 89109

KNUTSON, CHARLES DWAINE, b Milbank, SDak, Sept 23, 34; m 55; c 4. COMPUTER SCIENCES. *Educ:* SDak Sch Mines & Technol, BS, 56; Brown Univ, PhD(physics), 62. *Prof Exp:* Asst instr math, SDak Sch Mines & Technol, 54-55, asst instr math & physics, 55-56; math asst, Sperry Rand Univac, 55; lab asst, Knolls Res Lab, Gen Elec Co, 56; res asst, Brown Univ, 56-61; sr res physicist, Cent Res Labs, 61-68, SUPVR COMPUT-ASSISTED RES & DEVELOP, CENT RES LABS, MINN MINING & MFG CO, 68- *Mem:* Int Transactional Anal Asn. *Res:* Energy systems, psychology, systems modeling and microcomputers; computer science; education technology; glass structure; nuclear magnetic resonance; solid state physics computer applications. *Mailing Add:* Cent Res Lab 208-1 3M Co 3M Ctr St Paul MN 55144

KNUTSON, CLARENCE ARTHUR, JR, b Minot, NDak, June 18, 37; m 59; c 2. ORGANIC CHEMISTRY. *Educ:* Concordia Col, Moorhead, Minn, BA, 59; NDak State Univ, MS, 61. *Prof Exp:* RES CHEMIST, NORTHERN REGIONAL RES CTR, AGR RES SERV, USDA, 61- *Mem:* Am Chem Soc; Am Asn Cereal Chemists. *Res:* Carbohydrate chemistry; composition structure and properties of cereal polysaccharides; quantitative analytical methods. *Mailing Add:* 5927 Tampico Dr Peoria IL 61614

KNUTSON, DONALD IVAR, mathematics, see previous edition

KNUTSON, HERBERT CLAUS, b Crawfordsville, Iowa, Sept 6, 15; m 39; c 1. ENTOMOLOGY. *Educ:* Iowa Wesleyan Col, AB, 36; Southern Methodist Univ, MS, 37; Univ Minn, PhD(entom), 41. *Prof Exp:* Asst entom, Univ Minn, 37-39; instr biol, Southern Methodist Univ, 39-40; asst entom, Univ Minn, 40-41; from instr to prof zool, Univ RI, 41-53, head dept, 48-53; head dept & chief entomologist, Exp Sta, 53-76, PROF ENTOM, KANS STATE UNIV, 53-, ENTOMOLOGIST, EXP STA, 76- *Concurrent Pos:* Adminr, State RI Div Entom & Plant Indust, 46-48; state entomologist, Kans, 53-63; exam, Educ Testing Serv; spec consult, USPHS; secy-treas, Cent Plant Protection Bd, 54-57; mem, Nat Plant Bd, 57-59; Entom Soc Am del, 12th Int Cong Entom, Canberra, Australia, 72; coun mem, Asn D'Acridologie, Paris, 72. *Honors & Awards:* Alumni Merit Award, Iowa Wesleyan Col, 61. *Mem:* Entom Soc Am; Pan Am Acridological Soc. *Res:* Insects affecting man and animals; agricultural insects; habits and economic importance of acrididae. *Mailing Add:* Dept of Entom Kans State Univ Manhattan KS 66506

KNUTSON, KENNETH WAYNE, b Williams, Minn, Feb 11, 32; m 57; c 2. PLANT PATHOLOGY. *Educ:* Univ Minn, BS, 54, MS, 56, PhD(plant path), 60. *Prof Exp:* Asst plant pathologist, Univ Idaho, 60-64; EXTEN ASSOC PROF, COLO STATE UNIV, 64- *Mem:* Potato Asn Am. *Res:* Potato diseases and other cultural problems; soil-borne fungi; viruses. *Mailing Add:* Shepardson Bldg Colo State Univ Ft Collins CO 80523

KNUTSON, LLOYD VERNON, b Ottawa, Ill, July 4, 34; m 57; c 2. ENTOMOLOGY. *Educ:* Macalester Col, BA, 57; Cornell Univ, MS, 59, PhD(limnol), 63. *Prof Exp:* Res assoc entom, Cornell Univ, 63-68; res entomologist, Syst Entom Lab, 68-73, CHMN, INSECT IDENTIFICATION & BENEFICIAL INSECT INTROD INST, AGR RES CTR, AGR RES SERV, USDA, BELTSVILLE, 73- *Concurrent Pos:* Sci cooperator, Royal Inst Natural Sci, Belgium, 65-; resident ecologist, Smithsonian Inst, 71-72. *Mem:* Entom Soc A; Am Soc Parasitologists; Entom Soc Washington; Soc Syst Zool (treas, 71-74); Ecol Soc Am. *Res:* Taxonomy and biology of Diptera, especially malacophagous and entomophagous groups, Asiloidea, Syrphoidea, Empididae; phylogeny of Sciomyzoidea; biological control of pest molluscs; taxonomic services. *Mailing Add:* Beltsville Agr Res Ctr-West Agr Res Serv USDA Beltsville MD 20705

KNUTSON, ROGER M, b Montevideo, Minn, Jan 3, 33; m 57; c 5. BOTANY, PLANT LIFE HISTORIES. *Educ:* St Olaf Col, BA, 57; Mich State Univ, MS, 61, PhD(plant path), 65. *Prof Exp:* From asst prof to assoc prof, 64-74, PROF BIOL, LUTHER COL, IOWA, 74- *Concurrent Pos:* NSF sci fac fel, Univ Ga, 71-72. *Mem:* AAAS; Am Inst Biol Sci. *Res:* plant thermoregulation. *Mailing Add:* Dept of Biol Luther Col Decorah IA 52101

KNUTTGEN, HOWARD G, b Yonkers, NY, May 5, 31; m 61; c 2. APPLIED PHYSIOLOGY. *Educ:* Springfield Col, BS, 52; Pa State Univ, MS, 53; Ohio State Univ, PhD(phys educ), 59. *Prof Exp:* Instr phys educ, Ohio State Univ, 54-59; asst prof anat & physiol, 61-65, assoc prof physiol, 65-71, assoc dean, 75-80, PROF PHYSIOL, COL ALLIED HEALTH PROFESSIONS, BOSTON UNIV, 71-, CHMN, DEPT HEALTH SCI, 80- *Concurrent Pos:* Ed-in-chief, Med & Sci in Sports, 74- *Mem:* AAAS; Am Col Sports Med; Am Physiol Soc. *Res:* Human performance; exercise physiology; muscle metabolism. *Mailing Add:* Boston Univ University Rd Boston MA 02215

KNYCH, EDWARD THOMAS, b Chicago, Ill, Oct 8, 42; m 65; c 3. PHARMACOLOGY. *Educ:* Loyola Univ, Chicago, BS, 64; Creighton Univ, MS, 66; WVa Univ, PhD(pharmacol), 70. *Prof Exp:* Fel pharmacol, Univ Wis, 70-72; ASST PROF PHARMACOL, UNIV MINN, 72- *Mem:* AAAS; Sigma Xi. *Res:* Mechanism of polypeptide hormone action and effect of drugs of abuse on hormone release. *Mailing Add:* Dept of Pharmacol Univ of Minn Duluth MN 55812

KNYSTAUTAS, EMILE J, Can citizen. ATOMIC PHYSICS. *Educ:* Univ Montreal, BSc, 65; Univ Conn, MS, 67, PhD(physics), 69. *Prof Exp:* Asst prof, 71-76, ASSOC PROF PHYSICS, LAVAL UNIV, 76- *Concurrent Pos:* Foreign guest worker, Nat Bur Standards, Washington, DC, 78-79. *Mem:* Can Asn Physicists. *Res:* Atomic spectroscopy; stopping powers; accelerator technology. *Mailing Add:* Dept Phys Laval Univ Quebec PQ G1K 7P4 Can

KO, CHE MING, b Szechuan, China, Jan 7, 43; US citizen; m 74; c 2. HEAVY-ION PHYSICS, MEDIUM-ENERGY PHYSICS. *Educ:* Tunghai Univ, Taiwan, BSc, 65; McMaster Univ, Can, MSc, 68; State Univ NY, Stony Brook, PhD(physics), 73. *Prof Exp:* Res assoc, McMaster Univ, 73-74; vis scientist nuclear physics, Max Planck Inst, 74-77; res assoc, Mich State Univ, 77-78; staff physicist, Lawrence Berkeley Lab, 78-80; ASST PROF, TEX A&M UNIV, 80- *Mem:* Am Phys Soc. *Res:* Theoretical nuclear physics, especially the studies of dissipative processes and particle productions in heavy-ion reactions. *Mailing Add:* Physic Dept Tex A&M Univ College Station TX 77843

KO, EDMOND INQ-MING, b Hong Kong, July 8, 52. CHEMICAL CATALYSIS. *Educ:* Univ Wis, Madison, BS, 74; Stanford Univ, MS, 75, PhD(chem eng), 80. *Prof Exp:* ASST PROF CHEM ENG, CARNEGIE-MELLON UNIV, 80- *Mem:* AAAS; Am Inst Chem Engrs; Am Chem Soc. *Res:* Synthesis and characterization of heterogeneous catalysts; adsorption and reaction of gases on solid surfaces. *Mailing Add:* Dept Chem Eng Carnegie-Mellon Univ Pittsburgh PA 15213

KO, H(SIEN) C(HING), b Formosa, Apr 28, 28; m 55; c 3. ELECTRICAL ENGINEERING, RADIO ASTRONOMY. *Educ:* Nat Taiwan Univ, BS, 51; Ohio State Univ, MSc, 53, PhD(elec eng), 55. *Prof Exp:* Asst, Radio Wave Res Labs, Formosa, 51-52; res asst, Radio Observ, Ohio State Univ, 52-55, from instr to assoc prof elec eng, 55-63, asst dir, Radio Observ, 57-66, PROF ELEC ENG & ASTRON, OHIO STATE UNIV, 63-, CHMN, DEPT ELEC ENG, 77- *Mem:* Int Union Radio Sci; fel Inst Elec & Electronics Engrs; Am Astron Soc; fel Royal Astron Soc. *Res:* Space physics; electromagnetic theory and antennas; electronics and communications. *Mailing Add:* Dept of Elec Eng Ohio State Univ 2015 Neil Ave Columbus OH 43210

KO, HON-CHUNG, b Canton, China, June 27, 37; m 68; c 1. PHYSICAL CHEMISTRY. *Educ:* Chung Chi Col, BS, 59; Univ Va, MS, 62; Carnegie Inst Technol, PhD(phys chem), 64. *Prof Exp:* Res chemist, Rocket Power Res Lab, Maremont Corp, 63-67 & Space Sci Inc, 67-68; res assoc chem, Univ Chicago, 69-70, Univ Pittsburgh, 70-72 & Univ Lethbridge, 72-74; RES CHEMIST, ALBANY RES CTR, BUR MINES, 74- *Mem:* Sigma Xi; Am Chem Soc. *Res:* Thermochemistry; thermodynamics; calorimetry; molten salts; solvent effects; high temperature chemistry; low-temperature heat capacities. *Mailing Add:* Albany Res Ctr Bur Mines Albany OR 97321

KO, HON-YIM, b Hong Kong, China, Jan 18, 40; m 64; c 2. SOIL & ROCK MECHANICS. *Educ:* Univ Hong Kong, BSc, 62; Calif Inst Technol, MS, 63, PhD(civil eng), 66. *Prof Exp:* Res fel eng, Calif Inst Technol, 66-67; asst prof, 67-70, assoc prof, 70-75, PROF CIVIL ENG, UNIV COLO, BOULDER, 75- *Concurrent Pos:* Consult, Jet Propulsion Lab, Calif Inst Technol, 67-69, prin investr, NSF, Air Force Off Sci Res, US Bur Reclamation & US Bur Mines res grants, 67-; consult, Martin Marietta Corp, 70- & Sandia Corp, 79-81. *Honors & Awards:* DOW Outstanding Young Faculty, Am Soc Eng Educ, 75; Huber Res Prize, Am Soc Civil Engrs, 79. *Mem:* Am Soc Civil Engrs; Am Soc Eng Educ; Soc Exp Stress Anal. *Res:* Fundamental mechanical properties of soil, rock and other geological materials, and the analysis of engineering problems in geotechnics; centrifugal modeling of geotechnical structures; geotechnical engineering. *Mailing Add:* Dept of Civil Eng Univ of Colo Boulder CO 80309

KO, HOWARD WHA KEE, b Vancouver, BC, Can, Jan 1, 27; m 56; c 3. BIOPHYSICS. *Educ:* Univ BC, BA, 50, MA, 52; Purdue Univ, PhD(biophys), 57. *Prof Exp:* RES ASSOC BIOPHYS, UPJOHN CO, 57- *Mem:* Biophys Soc; NY Acad Sci. *Res:* Characterization of macromolecules and correlation of their biological activity with their physical chemical parameters; molecular biology; chemical assays and their automation; creation of radioimmunoassays; pharmacokinetics; drug metabolism. *Mailing Add:* Res Div Upjohn Co Kalamazoo MI 49001

KO, PAK LIM, b Hong Kong, Mar 4, 37; Can citizen; m 64; c 2. TRIBOLOGY. *Educ:* Univ Strathclyde, BSc, 63; Univ BC, MASc, 65; PhD(tribology), 70. *Prof Exp:* Fel mech eng, Univ BC, 69-70; RES ENGR, CHALK RIVER NUCLEAR LABS, ATOMIC ENERGY CAN LTD, 70- *Mem:* Inst Mech Engrs, Eng; Can Soc Mech Eng. *Res:* Autonomous quasiharmonic and forced vibration of frictional systems; friction and galling mechanisms of sliding solids in high temperature water environment; flow-induced vibration and tube fretting-wear in steam generator and heat exchanger units. *Mailing Add:* Eng Res Br Atomic Energy of Can Ltd Chalk River ON K0J 1J0 Can

KO, WEN HSIUNG, b Fukien, China, Apr 12, 23; US citizen; m 57; c 4. BIONICS. *Educ:* Nat Amoy Univ, BS, 46; Case Inst Technol, MS, 56, PhD(elec eng), 59. *Prof Exp:* Engr, Taiwan Telecommun Admin, 46-54; from asst prof to assoc prof elec eng, 59-67, assoc prof surg, Sch Med, 64-70, actg dir, Eng Design Ctr, 70-71, PROF ELEC & BIOMED ENG, CASE WESTERN RESERVE UNIV, 67-, DIR, ELECTRONICS DESIGN CTR, 71- *Concurrent Pos:* Mem biomed eng training comt, NIH, 66-70, mem oviduct panel, Contraceptive Develop Br, Ctr Pop Res, 71; NIH fel, Sch Med, Stanford Univ, 67-68; mem, NASA Life Sci Prog Space Sci Bd, Nat Acad Sci, 69-70. *Honors & Awards:* Cecon Award, Electronics Rep Asn, 70. *Mem:* Fel Inst Elec & Electronics Engrs; Int Inst Med Electronics & Biol Eng; Int Soc Biotelemetry; Biomed Eng Soc. *Res:* Microelectronic instrumentation and technology; medical instrumentation; implant electronic transducers, telemetry and stimulators. *Mailing Add:* Electronics Design Ctr Case Western Reserve Univ Cleveland OH 44106

KO, WEN-HSIUNG, b Chao Chow, Taiwan, May 14, 39; m 68; c 2. PLANT PATHOLOGY, SOIL MICROBIOLOGY. *Educ:* Nat Taiwan Univ, BS, 62; Mich State Univ, PhD(plant path), 66. *Prof Exp:* From res assoc to assoc prof, 66-76, PROF PLANT PATH, UNIV HAWAII, HILO, 76- *Mem:* Am Phytopath Soc. *Res:* Ecology of soil-borne diseases; general soil microbiology; fungal physiology. *Mailing Add:* Agr Exp Sta 461 Lanikauia St Hilo HI 96720

KO, WINSTON TAI-KAN, b Shanghai, China, Apr 5, 43; m 70; c 2. HIGH ENERGY PHYSICS. *Educ:* Carnegie Inst Technol, BS, 65; Univ Pa, MS, 66, PhD(physics), 71. *Prof Exp:* Asst res physicist, 70-72, asst prof, 72-76, ASSOC PROF PHYSICS, UNIV CALIF, DAVIS, 76- *Mem:* Am Phys Soc. *Res:* Experimental high energy physics; elementary particle physics; hadronic interactions; inclusive reactions; computer analysis of experimental data; photon-photon interactions; particle spectroscopy. *Mailing Add:* Dept of Physics Univ of Calif Davis CA 95616

KOBALLA, THOMAS RAYMOND, JR, b Manchester, NH, June 28, 54. ATTITUDE CHANGE. *Educ:* East Carolina Univ, BS, 76, MA, 78; Pa State Univ, PhD, 81. *Prof Exp:* ASST PROF, PIKEVILLE COL, 81- *Res:* Systematic design of attitude change paradigms in changing attitudes toward science. *Mailing Add:* 203 Spilman Apts Poplar St Pikeville KY 41501

KOBAYASHI, ALBERT S(ATOSHI), b Chicago, Ill, Dec 9, 24; m; c 3. MECHANICAL ENGINEERING. *Educ:* Tokyo Univ, BS, 47; Univ Wash, MS, 52; Ill Inst Technol, PhD(mech eng), 58. *Prof Exp:* Tool engr, Konishiroku Photo Indust, Japan, 47-50 design engr, Ill Tool Works, 53-55; res engr exp stress anal, Armour Res Found, Ill Inst Technol, 55-58; from asst prof to assoc prof, 58-65, PROF MECH ENG, UNIV WASH, 65- *Concurrent Pos:* Mem staff, Boeing Co, Wash, 58-75; assoc ed, J Appl Mech, 77-, Trans Japan Soc Composite Mats, 74- *Honors & Awards:* B J Lazan Award, Soc Exp Stress Anal, 81. *Mem:* Fel Soc Exp Stress Anal; fel Am Soc Mech Engrs; Soc Eng Sci. *Res:* Fracture mechanics; experimental stress analysis; theories of elasticity; plasticity; theory of structures and dynamic response of structures; author of over 180 publications. *Mailing Add:* Dept of Mech Eng Univ of Wash Seattle WA 98195

KOBAYASHI, F(RANCIS) M(ASAO), b Seattle, Wash, Nov 19, 25; m 63; c 3. ENGINEERING MECHANICS. *Educ:* Univ Notre Dame, BS, 47, MS, 48, ScD(eng mech), 53. *Prof Exp:* Asst prof eng mech, 48-58, assoc prof eng sci, 58-59, 60-64, asst vpres res & sponsored progs, 68-71, PROF ENG SCI, UNIV NOTRE DAME, 64-, ASST VPRES ADVAN STUDIES, RES & SPONSORED PROGS, 71- *Concurrent Pos:* Asst dir eng sci prog, NSF, 59-60. *Res:* Fluid mechanics; wave resistance; systems engineering; operations research. *Mailing Add:* Univ of Notre Dame Notre Dame IN 46556

KOBAYASHI, GEORGE S, b San Francisco, Calif, Nov 25, 27; m 56; c 4. MYCOLOGY, BIOCHEMISTRY. *Educ:* Univ Calif, Berkeley, BS, 52; Tulane Univ, PhD(microbiol), 63. *Prof Exp:* Chemist enol, Roma Wine Co, Calif, 52; sr lab technician mycol, Sch Pub Health, Univ Calif, Berkeley, 52-59; from instr to assoc prof, 64-77, PROF MYCOL, SCH MED, WASHINGTON UNIV, 77- *Concurrent Pos:* Assoc dir, Microbiol Labs, Barnes Hosp, St Louis, 65-; assoc ed, Cutaneous Path, 74-; consult, Bur of Biologics, Food & Drug Admin, 74-76; mem NIH study sect, Nat Inst Allergy & Infectious Dis. *Mem:* AAAS; Int Soc Human & Animal Mycol; NY Acad Sci; Med Mycol Soc Am; Infectious Dis Soc. *Res:* Immunology and biochemistry of medically important fungi. *Mailing Add:* Dept of Med Washington Univ Sch of Med St Louis MO 63110

KOBAYASHI, RIKI, b Webster, Tex, May 13, 24; m; c 2. CHEMICAL ENGINEERING, CHEMICAL PHYSICS. *Educ:* Rice Inst, BS, 44; Univ Mich, MSE, 47, PhD(chem eng), 51. *Prof Exp:* From asst prof to assoc prof, 51-65, prof, 65-67, LOUIS CALDER PROF CHEM ENG, RICE UNIV, 67- *Concurrent Pos:* Res engr, Continental Oil Co, Okla. *Honors & Awards:* Meritorious Award, Cryog Eng Conf Comt, 65. *Mem:* Fel Am Inst Chem Engrs; fel Am Inst Chemists; Am Inst Physics, Am Inst Mining & Metal Engrs; Am Chem Soc. *Res:* Thermodynamic and transport properties of fluids and solids, particularly at advanced pressures, cryogenic temperatures. *Mailing Add:* Rice Univ PO Box 1892 Houston TX 77001

KOBAYASHI, SHIRO, b Gotsu, Japan, Feb 21, 24; m 61. MECHANICAL ENGINEERING. *Educ:* Univ Tokyo, BS, 46; Univ Calif, Berkeley, MS, 57, PhD(mech eng), 60. *Prof Exp:* Asst prof indust eng, 61-65, assoc prof mech eng, 65-68, PROF MECH ENG, UNIV CALIF, BERKELEY, 68- *Concurrent Pos:* Battelle vis prof, Ohio State Univ, 67-68; E A Taylor vis prof, Univ Birmingham, 70. *Honors & Awards:* Blackall Mach Tool & Gage Award, 63. *Mem:* Am Soc Mech Engrs; Japan Soc Tech Plasticity. *Res:* Materials processing, machining and forming. *Mailing Add:* Dept of Mech Eng Univ of Calif Berkeley CA 94720

KOBAYASHI, SHOSHICHI, b Kofu, Japan, Jan 4, 32; m 57; c 2. MATHEMATICS. *Educ:* Univ Tokyo, BS, 53; Univ Wash, PhD(math), 56. *Prof Exp:* Mem staff, Inst Advan Study, 56-58; res assoc math, Mass Inst Technol, 58-60; asst prof, Univ BC, 60-62; from asst prof to assoc prof, 62-66, chmn dept, 78-81, PROF MATH, UNIV CALIF, BERKELEY, 66- *Concurrent Pos:* A P Sloan fel, 64-66; lectr, Univ Tokyo, 65; vis prof, Univ Mainz, 66, Univ Bonn, 69 & 78 & Mass Inst Technol, 70; assoc ed, Duke J Math, 70-80; ed, J Differential Geometry, 73-; Guggenheim fel, 77-78; vis prof, Univ Tokyo, 81. *Mem:* Am Math Soc; Math Soc Can; Math Soc Japan; Math Soc France; Swiss Math Soc. *Res:* Differential geometry and functions of several complex variables. *Mailing Add:* Dept of Math Univ of Calif Berkeley CA 94720

KOBAYASHI, YUTAKA, b San Francisco, Calif, Mar 11, 24; m 54. BIOCHEMISTRY. *Educ:* Iowa State Col, BS, 46, MS, 50; Univ Iowa, PhD(biochem), 53. *Prof Exp:* Res assoc, Rheumatic Fever Res Inst, Chicago, Ill, 53-57; sr scientist, Worcester Found for Exp Biol, Inc, 57-74; MGR, LSC APPLN LAB, NEW ENG NUCLEAR CORP, 74- *Mem:* Am Chem Soc; Am Soc Pharmacol & Exp Therapeut; Am Soc Biol Chemists. *Res:* Intermediary metabolism of amino acids and biogenic amines; amine oxidases. *Mailing Add:* 549 Albany St Boston MA 02118

KOBE, DONALD HOLM, b Seattle, Wash, Jan 13, 34. QUANTUM PHYSICS. *Educ:* Univ Tex, Austin, BS, 56; Univ Minn, Minneapolis, MS, 59, PhD(physics), 61. *Prof Exp:* Vis asst prof physics, Ohio State Univ, 61-63; Fulbright lectr, Nat Taiwan Univ & Taiwan Norm Univ, 63-64; vis scientist, Quantum Chem Inst, Univ Uppsala, 64-66; vis asst prof physics, H C Oersted Inst, Copenhagen Univ, 66-67 & Northeastern Univ, 67-68; assoc prof, 68-75, PROF PHYSICS, N TEX STATE UNIV, 75- *Mem:* AAAS; Am Phys Soc; Am Sci Affil; Am Asn Physics Teachers. *Res:* Quantum theory of many-particle systems; applications to superfluid helium; quantum theory of radiation; interaction of electromagnetic radiation and matter. *Mailing Add:* Dept of Physics NTex State Univ Denton TX 76203

KOBER, ALFRED ERNEST, b Somerville, NJ, Dec 25, 40; m 68; c 1. FUEL CHEMISTRY, ORGANIC CHEMISTRY. *Educ:* Univ Fla, BS, 63, PhD(org chem), 67. *Prof Exp:* Res chemist fuel additives, Esso Res & Eng Co, 67-71; teacher chem, Seabreeze Sr High Sch, 71-73; res mgr fuel additives, Apollo Chem Corp, 73-80, ASSOC DIR RES, APOLLO TECHNOLOGIES, 80- *Concurrent Pos:* Consult, Apollo Chem Corp, 71-73. *Mem:* Am Chem Soc; Combustion Inst; Air Pollution Control Asn. *Res:* Coal technology; deposit formation in coal-fired boilers, coal handling aids (freeze conditoners, dust control, etc); flue gas conditioning agents. *Mailing Add:* Apollo Technologies Inc One Apollo Dr Whippany NJ 07981

KOBER, C(ARL) L(EOPOLD), b Vienna, Austria, Nov 22, 13; nat US; m 42; c 2. MECHANICAL ENGINEERING. *Educ:* Vienna Univ, PhD, 35; Vienna Tech Univ, Dr phil habil, 38. *Prof Exp:* From tech asst to vpres prod, Elin, Inc, Austria, 36-40; chief radar dept, GEMA GmbH, Ger, 40-45; mgr, Proschwitz Indust, Austria, 46-48; mgr, Secowerk, 48-49; consult, Wright Air Develop Ctr, Wright-Patterson Air Force Base, Ohio, 49-55; tech dir, Tech Div, Gen Mills, Inc, Minn, 55-58; vpres ord opers, Crosley Div, Avco Corp, 58-61; dir manned space opers, Denver Div, Martin Marietta Corp, 61-73; PRES, DENVER MINERAL EXPLOR CORP, 73- *Concurrent Pos:* Prof, Colo State Univ, 63-79. *Mem:* Inst Elec & Electronics Engrs. *Res:* Ordnance; missile detection; plasma physics; data processing; remote sensing geology. *Mailing Add:* 605 Front Range Rd Littleton CO 80120

KOBER, EHRENFRIED H, b Chemnitz, Ger, Mar 16, 21; nat US; m 51; c 3. ORGANIC CHEMISTRY. *Educ:* Univ Halle, MS, 48; Univ Berlin, PhD, 50. *Prof Exp:* Res chemist, Asid-Serum-Inst, Ger, 48-50; res assoc & instr org chem, Univ Berlin, 50-51; res assoc, Olin Mathieson Chem Corp, NY, 52-57; res specialist, 57-58, mgr, 58-61, assoc dir res, 61-64, tech dir, 64-69; DIR DEVELOP, WASAGCHEMIE GMBH, 69- *Res:* Organic chemistry; pharmaceuticals; lubricants; fluoro compounds; pesticides; biocides; hydraulic fluids; polymers; heterocycles. *Mailing Add:* Beethovenstrasse 9 8261 Aschauam Inn West Germany

KOBERNICK, SIDNEY D, b Montreal, Que, May 7, 19; nat US; m 41; c 3. PATHOLOGY. *Educ:* McGill Univ, BSc, 41, MD, CM, 43, MSc, 49, PhD(exp path), 51; Am Bd Path, cert path anat, 53, cert clin path, 59. *Prof Exp:* Asst prof path, McGill Univ, 51-52; CLIN PROF PATH, WAYNE STATE UNIV, 53-; DIR LABS, SINAI HOSP, DETROIT, 52- *Concurrent Pos:* adj prof med technol, Wayne State Univ. *Mem:* Soc Exp Biol & Med; Am Asn Path & Bact; fel Am Soc Clin Path; fel Col Am Pathologists; Electron Micros Soc Am. *Res:* Experimental atherosclerosis; tissue hypersensitivity; morphological pathology. *Mailing Add:* Sinai Hosp Dept of Lab Med 6767 W Outer Dr Detroit MI 48235

KOBERSTEIN, JEFFREY THOMAS, b Milwaukee, Wis, Sept 27, 52; m 75; c 2. POLYMER CHEMISTRY, CHEMICAL ENGINEERING. *Educ:* Univ Wis, BS, 74; Univ Mass, PhD(chem eng), 79. *Prof Exp:* Fel, Ctr Res Macromolecules, 79-80; ASST PROF CHEM ENG, PRINCETON UNIV, 80- *Concurrent Pos:* Vis asst prof, Univ Wis, 81. *Mem:* Am Chem Soc; Am Phys Soc; Am Inst Chem Engrs. *Res:* Polymer morphology; structure property relationships in block copolymers; polymer-polymer interfaces; microphase separation; small angle x-ray, neutron and light scattering; polymer blends; compatibility. *Mailing Add:* Dept Chem Eng Princeton Univ Princeton NJ 08544

KOBILINSKY, LAWRENCE, b New York, NY, Nov 7, 46; m 71; c 1. IMMUNOLOGY, BIOCHEMISTRY. *Educ:* City Univ New York, BS, 69, MA, 71, PhD(biol), 77. *Prof Exp:* Res asst biophys, Columbia Presbyterian Med Ctr, 69-70; lectr biol, City Univ New York, 70-71; Brooklyn Col, 72-74; Hunter Col, 74-75 & John Jay Col Criminal Justice, 75-77; res fel immunol, Sloan Kettering Inst Cancer Res, 77-80. *Concurrent Pos:* Adj asst prof, John Jay Col Criminal Justice, City Univ New York, 77- *Mem:* Sigma Xi; AAAS; NY Acad Sci; Am Chem Soc. *Res:* Relationship between feline leukemia virus induced lymphosarcoma and complement activation in vivo and in vitro. *Mailing Add:* 285 Lockwood Ave Northfield IL 60093

KOBLE, ROBERT A(DAMS), b Shamokin, Pa, Sept 24, 22; m 47; c 3. CHEMICAL ENGINEERING. *Educ:* Bucknell Univ, BS, 44; Univ WVa, MS, 52, PhD(chem eng), 53. *Prof Exp:* Chem engr, Celanese Corp Am, 44 & 46-49; process design engr, 52-58, process eval engr, 58-61, tech asst to dir opers res, 61-64, process consult field serv comput, 65-67, dir systs modeling, Eng Sci Comput Dept, 67-70, consult systs modeling, Process Anal, 70-75, thermodyn consult, 75-78, SR RES ENGR RES & DEVELOP, PHILLIPS PETROL CO, 78- *Concurrent Pos:* Spec lectr, Okla State Univ. *Mem:* Am Inst Chem Engrs. *Res:* Process simulation and optimization computer systems; fluidization of solids; adsorption and kinetics; thermodynamics of nonideal solutions; high pressure technology; hydrometallurgy; coal gasification; coal liquifaction; alternate energy resources. *Mailing Add:* 1803 Skyline Dr Bartlesville OK 74003

KOBLICK, DANIEL CECIL, b San Francisco, Calif, May 13, 22; m 60; c 2. PHYSIOLOGY. *Educ:* Univ Calif, AB, 44; Univ Ore, PhD(biol), 57. *Prof Exp:* Instr biol, Univ Ore, 57-58; asst prof zool, Univ Mo, 58-59; USPHS fel, Univ Calif, Berkeley, 59-60; asst res physiologist, 60-63; ASSOC PROF PHYSIOL, ILL INST TECHNOL, 63- *Mem:* Fel AAAS; Am Physiol Soc; Biophys Soc; Soc Gen Physiol. *Res:* Ion transport; bioelectricity; invertebrate physiology. *Mailing Add:* Dept of Biol Ill Inst of Technol Chicago IL 60616

KOBLUK, DAVID RONALD, b Feb 4, 49; Can citizen. PALEOECOLOGY, MARINE GEOLOGY. *Educ:* McGill Univ, BSc, 71, MSc, 73; McMaster Univ, PhD(geol), 76. *Prof Exp:* ASST PROF PALEONT, UNIV TORONTO, 77- *Concurrent Pos:* Fel, Mem Univ Nfld, 76-77; Nat Res Coun Can oper grant, 77-78; Earthwatch res grants, 77, 78 & 79; Connaught grant, Univ Toronto, 78. *Mem:* Am Asn Petrol Geologists; Can Soc Petrol Geologists; Soc Econ Paleontologists & Mineralogists; Paleont Asn; fel Explorers Club. *Res:* Ecology of modern and ancient coral reefs; processes of marine biological erosion; cavity-dwelling marine organisms; invertebrate evolution and community ecology. *Mailing Add:* Earth & Planetary Sci Div Erindale Col Univ Toronto Mississauga ON L5L 1C6 Can

KOBRIN, ROBERT JAY, b New York, NY, Nov 4, 37; m 69; c 3. CHEMICAL INSTRUMENTATION. *Educ:* City Col New York, BS, 60; Univ Del, PhD(phys chem), 69. *Prof Exp:* Jr chemist anal chem, Sonneborn Chem & Refining Co, 60-61; sr chem, 61-73, RES ASSOC AUTOMATION SYST, MOBIL RES & DEVELOP CORP, 74- *Mem:* Asn Comput Mach; Sigma Xi; Am Chem Soc. *Res:* Laboratory automation; information systems and computer networks; analytical instrumentation. *Mailing Add:* Paulsboro Lab Mobil Res & Develop Corp Paulsboro NJ 08066

KOBRINE, ARTHUR, b Chicago, Ill, Oct 9, 43; m 69; c 2. NEUROSURGERY. *Educ:* Northwestern Univ, BS, 64, MD, 68; George Washington Univ, PhD(physiol), 79. *Prof Exp:* Resident neurosurg, Walter Reed Hosp, 70-73; asst chief, 73-75; asst prof, 75-77, assoc prof, 77-79, PROF NEUROSURG, GEORGE WASHINGTON UNIV, 79- *Mem:* Soc Neurol Surgeons; Am Phys Soc; Am Bd Neurol Surg. *Mailing Add:* 2150 Pennsylvania Ave NW Washington DC 20037

KOBSA, HENRY, b Vienna, Austria, May 4, 29; nat US; m 80; c 2. PHYSICAL CHEMISTRY. *Educ:* Univ Vienna, PhD(chem), 56. *Prof Exp:* Res chemist, Dacron Res Lab, 56-58, res chemist, Pioneering Res Lab, Del, 58-61, sr res chemist, 61, res assoc, 61-62, res supvr, 62-64, res supvr, Benger Res Lab, Va, 64-65, tech supvr, Lycra Tech Sect, Va, 65-66, sr supvr, 66-68, sr supvr, May Plant Tech Sect, 68-69, res mgr, Dacron Res Lab, 69-73, tech supt, Indust Tech Sect, Kinston plant, NC, 73-77, RES FEL, PIONEERING RES LAB, E I DU PONT DE NEMOURS & CO, DEL, 77- *Mem:* Am Chem Soc. *Res:* Photochemistry of polymers and dyes; energy transfer phenomena; polymer physics; polymerization kinetics; diffusion. *Mailing Add:* 111 Greenspring Rd Greenville DE 19807

KOBURGER, JOHN ALFRED, b Queens, NY, Apr 20, 31; m 52; c 4. FOOD MICROBIOLOGY. *Educ:* Kans State Univ, BS, 59, MS, 60; NC State Col, PhD(food microbiol), 62. *Prof Exp:* Res asst, Res Labs, Nat Dairy Prod Corp, 56-57; from asst prof to assoc prof food microbiol, WVa Univ, 62-69; PROF FOOD MICROBIOL, DEPT FOOD SCI, UNIV FLA, 69- *Mem:* Am Chem Soc; Am Dairy Sci Asn; Am Soc Microbiol; Inst Food Technol. *Res:* Physiology of microorganisms important to the food industry. *Mailing Add:* Dept of Food Sci Univ of Fla Gainesville FL 32611

KOBYLNYK, RONALD WILLIAM, b Calgary, Alta, Aug 19, 42. LASER ENTOMOLOGY. *Educ:* Univ Calgary, BSc, 63; Univ Guelph, Ont, MSc, 65, PhD(entom), 72. *Prof Exp:* eval officer insecticides, Agr Can, 70-80; MEM STAFF, PESTICIDE CONTROL BR, MINISTRY ENVIRON, VICTORIA, 80- *Mem:* Entom Soc Can. *Res:* Effects of laser radiation on insects. *Mailing Add:* Pesticide Control Br Ministry Environ 810 Blanshard St Victoria BC V8V 1X5 Can

KOCAN, RICHARD M, microbiology, public health, see previous edition

KOCATAS, BABUR M(EHMET), b Istanbul, Turkey, Apr 7, 27; m 55. CHEMICAL ENGINEERING. *Educ:* Robert Col, Istanbul, BS, 47; Univ Tex, MS, 53, PhD(chem eng), 62. *Prof Exp:* Design engr, Union Carbide Chem Co, 56-57; lectr math, Univ Tex, 57-62; sr res engr, 62-76, SR RES GROUP LEADER, MONSANTO CO, 76- *Mem:* Am Chem Soc; Am Inst Chem Engrs. *Res:* Process design and development; micro pilot planting; distillation; fuel cells; mathematical modeling; systems engineering; air pollution control. *Mailing Add:* Monsanto Co 800 N Lindbergh Blvd St Louis MO 63166

KOCH, ALAN R, b St Louis, Mo, Oct 6, 30; m 56; c 3. PHYSIOLOGY. *Educ:* Univ Mich, BS, 51; Columbia Univ, PhD(pharmacol), 55. *Prof Exp:* Asst pharmacol, Columbia Univ, 53-55; res instr, Col Med, Univ Utah, 55-57; from res instr to res asst prof of physiol, Univ Wash, 59-65; ASSOC PROF ZOOPHYSIOL, MED SCH, WASH STATE UNIV, 66- *Concurrent Pos:* USPHS fel, 55-58. *Mem:* Biophys Soc; Am Physiol Soc. *Res:* Renal physiology; ion transport in brain; active ion transport. *Mailing Add:* Dept of Physiol Wash State Univ Sch of Med Pullman WA 99164

KOCH, ARTHUR LOUIS, b St Paul, Minn, Oct 25, 25; m 47; c 2. THEORETICAL BIOLOGY, BACTERIAL PHYSIOLOGY. *Educ:* Calif Inst Technol, BS, 48; Univ Chicago, PhD(biochem), 51. *Prof Exp:* Res assoc & instr, Univ Chicago, 51-52 & 53-56; from asst prof to assoc prof biochem, Col Med, Univ Fla, 56-63, prof biochem & microbiol, 63-67; PROF MICROBIOL, IND UNIV, BLOOMINGTON, 67- *Concurrent Pos:* Assoc scientist, Argonne Nat Lab, 52-56; Guggenheim fel, 60-61 & 81-82. *Mem:* Am Soc Microbiol; Am Chem Soc; Am Soc Biol Chemists; Biophys Soc; Genetics Soc Am. *Res:* Enzyme and haploid evolution; active transport systems; microbial growth physiology; microbial response to toxic and antibiotic substances. *Mailing Add:* Dept of Microbiol Ind Univ Bloomington IN 47401

KOCH, CARL FRED, b Washington, DC, July 13, 32; m 78; c 1. PALEONECOLOGY, BIOSTRATIGRAPHY. *Educ:* Univ Md, BS, 57, MS, 61; George Washington Univ, PhD(geol), 77. *Prof Exp:* Engr, Appl Physics Lab, Johns Hopkins Univ, 58-61; Rixan Electronics Inc, 62-67 & Seismic Data Anal Ctr, 68-77; ASST PROF GEOL, OLD DOMINION UNIV, 78- *Concurrent Pos:* Geologist, US Geol Surv, 77-; res assoc, Smithsonian Inst, 81- *Mem:* Geol Soc Am; Paleont Soc; Int Paleont Inst. *Res:* Geologic data for restricted time intervals of large geographic extent; biosphere history; arrantitative paleonecology and biostratigraphy using upper cretaceous molluscs. *Mailing Add:* Dept Geophys Sci Old Dominion Univ Norfolk VA 23508

KOCH, CARL MARK, environmental engineering, water resources, see previous edition

KOCH, CHARLES FREDERICK, b Tarrytown, NY, Mar 23, 32. MATHEMATICS. *Educ:* Union Col, BS, 53; Univ Ill, MS, 57, PhD(math), 61. *Prof Exp:* Instr math, Univ Minn, 61-64; asst prof math, Kans State Univ, 64-66; ASST PROF MATH, SOUTHERN ILL UNIV, CARBONDALE, 66- *Mem:* Am Math Soc; Math Asn Am. *Res:* Summability of sequences and series. *Mailing Add:* Dept of Math Southern Ill Univ Carbondale IL 62901

KOCH, CHRISTIAN BURDICK, b Elko, Nev, Feb 26, 22; m 47; c 3. WOOD SCIENCE, FORESTRY. *Educ:* Univ Idaho, BS, 47, MS, 49; Univ Mich, Ann Arbor, PhD(wood technol), 64. *Prof Exp:* Res officer, Forest Prod Lab, Commonwealth Sci & Indust Res Orgn, Melbourne, Australia, 47-49; asst prof wood sci, Utah State Univ, 50-51; from asst prof to assoc prof, 51-64, PROF WOOD SCI, WVA UNIV, 64-; WOOD SCIENTIST, 74- *Concurrent Pos:* Lectr, Univ Mich, 61-62. *Mem:* Soc Am Foresters; Forest Prod Res Soc; Soc Wood Sci & Technol. *Res:* Physical properties of wood; hardwood utilization; behavior of wood subjected to high compressive stresses. *Mailing Add:* Div of Forestry WVa Univ Morgantown WV 26506

KOCH, DAVID GILBERT, b Milwaukee, Wis, Aug 6, 45; m 74; c 2. INFRARED ASTRONOMY, ASTROPHYSICS. *Educ:* Univ Wis-Madison, BS, 67; Cornell Univ, MS, 71, PhD(physics), 72. *Prof Exp:* Sr scientist x-ray astron, Am Sci & Eng, 72-76; staff scientist, 76-77; ASTROPHYSICIST INFRARED ASTRON, ASTROPHYS OBSERV, SMITHSONIAN INST, 77- *Concurrent Pos:* Assoc, Harvard Col Observ, 77- *Honors & Awards:* Group Achievement Award, NASA, 78. *Mem:* AAAS; Am Astron Soc. *Res:* Infrared, x-ray and gamma-ray astrophysics with particular emphasis on spaceborne instrumentation and computer aided data reduction. *Mailing Add:* Smithsonian Astrophys Observ 60 Garden St Cambridge MA 02138

KOCH, DAVID WILLIAM, b Frankfort, Kans, Nov 22, 42; m 66. AGRONOMY. *Educ:* Kans State Univ, BS, 64, MS, 66; Colo State Univ, PhD(agron), 71. *Prof Exp:* Asst prof, 71-77, ASSOC PROF CROP PHYSIOL, UNIV NH, 77- *Mem:* Am Soc Agron. *Res:* Minimum tillage establishment of forage crops; forage crop managemnt; methods of forage conservation. *Mailing Add:* Dept of Plant Sci Univ of NH Durham NH 03824

KOCH, DONALD LEROY, b Dubuque, Iowa, June 3, 37; m 62; c 3. STRATIGRAPHY, GROUNDWATER GEOLOGY. *Educ:* State Univ Iowa, BS, 59, MS, 67. *Prof Exp:* Res geologist, 59-71, chief subsurface geol, 71-75, asst state geologist, 75-80, STATE GEOLOGIST & DIR, IOWA GEOL SURV, 80- *Mem:* Nat Water Well Asn. *Res:* Carbonate petrology and carbonate hydrology, defining the relationship of primary and secondary porosity to parameters of water availability and water quality. *Mailing Add:* 1431 Prairie du Chien Rd Iowa City IA 52240

KOCH, ELIZABETH ANNE, b Toronto, Ohio, Oct 8, 36; m 73. BIOCHEMICAL GENETICS, ELECTRON MICROSCOPY. *Educ:* Mt Union Col, BS, 58; Northwestern Univ, PhD(genetics), 64. *Prof Exp:* Teacher gen sci & eng, Ely Jr High Sch, Elyria, Ohio, 58-59; instr gen biol & genetics,

Hope Col, 63-64; res assoc electron microscopy & genetics, Northwestern Univ, 64-69; asst prof, 69-74, ASSOC PROF BIOCHEM & GENETICS, CHICAGO MED SCH, 74- *Concurrent Pos:* Fel, Cancer Inst, NIH, 64-66; lectr, Eve Div, Northwestern Univ, 65-72. *Mem:* Am Soc Cell Biol; Genetics Soc Am; AAAS; Sigma Xi; Am Asn Univ Prof. *Res:* Ultrastructural localization of proteins using immune chemical methods; oogenesis. *Mailing Add:* Dept of Biochem 2020 W Ogden Ave Chicago IL 60612

KOCH, FREDERICK BAYARD, b St Paul, Minn, Aug 15, 35; m 63; c 3. PHYSICAL METALLURGY. *Educ:* Carleton Col, BA, 57; Univ Minn, Minneapolis, MS, 62; Northwestern Univ, PhD(mat sci), 67. *Prof Exp:* Mem staff, Sci Lab, Ford Motor Co, 60-62; MEM TECH STAFF, BELL TEL LABS, 67- *Mem:* Am Inst Metall Engrs; Electrochem Soc. *Res:* Discrete wiring methods for circuit board development. *Mailing Add:* 184 Kent Pl Blvd Summit NJ 07901

KOCH, GARY MARLIN, b Pottsville, Pa, Nov 7, 41. ORNAMENTAL HORTICULTURE. *Educ:* Pa State Univ, BS, 63, MS, 65, PhD(hort), 70. *Prof Exp:* Asst prof ornamental hort, 70, assoc prof plant sci, 70-77, PROF PLANT SCI, CALIF STATE UNIV, FRESNO, 77- *Mem:* Am Soc Hort Sci. *Res:* Plant materials and usage; commercial floriculture; floral design; turfgrass production. *Mailing Add:* Dept of Plant Sci Calif State Univ Fresno CA 93710

KOCH, GEORGE SCHNEIDER, JR, b Washington, DC, Oct 30, 26; m 73; c 3. ECONOMIC GEOLOGY, STATISTICS. *Educ:* Harvard Univ, SB, 48, PhD(econ geol), 55; Johns Hopkins Univ, MA, 49. *Prof Exp:* Geologist, US Geol Surv, 48-52; chief geologist, Minera Frisco, SA, Mex, 52-56; asst prof geol, Ore State Univ, 56-62; res geologist, US Bur Mines, 62-71; PROF GEOL, UNIV GA, 71- *Concurrent Pos:* Consult, firms in mineral indust & US govt. *Mem:* Soc Econ Geol; Am Inst Mining, Metall & Petrol Eng; Int Asn Math Geol. *Res:* Statistical analysis of geological data; exploration for and evaluation of mineral deposits; precious and nonferrous metal and uranium deposits. *Mailing Add:* Dept of Geol Univ of Ga Athens GA 30602

KOCH, HEINZ FRANK, b Berlin, Ger, June 21, 32; US citizen; m 58; c 2. PHYSICAL ORGANIC CHEMISTRY, FLUORINE CHEMISTRY. *Educ:* Haverford Col, BS, 54, MS, 56; Cornell Univ, PhD(org chem), 60. *Prof Exp:* Res chemist, Univ Calif, Berkeley, 60-62; res chemist, Plastics Dept, E I du Pont de Nemours & Co, 62-65; from asst prof to assoc prof, 65-70, Chmn, Dept Chem, 67-79, Chmn, Div Fluorine Chem, 77, PROF ORG CHEM, ITHACA COL, 70- *Concurrent Pos:* NSF faculty fel, Univ Calif, Berkeley, 71-72, vis prof, 72-73; vis prof, Univ Grenoble, France, 79 & Univ Auckland, NZ, 79-80. *Mem:* Am Chem Soc (secy-treas, Div Fluorine Chem, 74-75); The Chem Soc; NY Acad Sci; Sigma Xi. *Res:* Physical organic studies of reaction mechanisms, particularly fluorohalocarbon chemistry; studies of 1, 2 elimination reactions, carbanions and isotope effects. *Mailing Add:* Dept of Chem Ithaca Col Ithaca NY 14850

KOCH, HENRY GEORGE, b Mt Holly, NJ, May 22, 48; m 68; c 2. MEDICAL ENTOMOLOGY. *Educ:* Okla State Univ, BS, 71, MS, 74; NC State Univ, PhD(entom), 77. *Prof Exp:* RES ENTOMOLOGIST, LONE STAR TICK RES LAB, SCI & EDUC ADMIN-AGR RES, USDA, 77- *Concurrent Pos:* Adj assoc prof entom, Okla State Univ, 78- *Mem:* Entom Soc Am. *Res:* Acarology, tick ecology and biology; host suitability; acarid susceptibility. *Mailing Add:* Lone Star Tick Lab USDA Agr PO Box 588 Poteau OK 74953

KOCH, HERMAN WILLIAM, b New York, NY, Sept 28, 20; m 45; c 5. PHYSICS. *Educ:* Queens Col, NY, BS, 41; Univ Ill, MS & PhD(physics), 44. *Prof Exp:* Res physicist, Univ Ill, 44-45 & Clinton Labs, Oak Ridge, 45-46; asst prof res nuclear physics, Univ Ill, 46-49; physicist, High Energy Radiation Sect, Nat Bur Stand, 49-62, chief, Radiation Physics Div, 62-66; DIR, AM INST PHYSICS, 66- *Concurrent Pos:* Mem, Numerical Data Adv Bd; chmn, US Nat Comt, Comt Data Sci & Technol; vchmn, Copyright Clearance Ctr; pres, Nat Fedn Abstracting & Indexing Serv. *Mem:* Acoust Soc Am; Soc Rheology; Am Astron Soc; Am Crystallog Asn; Am Asn Physicists Med. *Res:* Nuclear physics research on 20 million electron volt, 50 million electron volt and 180 million electron volt synchrotron; development of high-energy x-ray spectrometer; Bremsstrahlung production; radiation physics research from 50 kiloelectron volts to 180 million electron volts; studies of science information flow. *Mailing Add:* Am Inst of Physics 335 E 45th St New York NY 10017

KOCH, HOWARD A(LEXANDER), b Evanston, Ill, June 15, 22; m 43; c 2. CHEMICAL ENGINEERING. *Educ:* Northwestern Univ, BS, 43, MS, 46, PhD(chem eng), 49. *Prof Exp:* Asst chem engr, Northwestern Univ, 46, res supvr, 46-49; proj leader, Reservoir Mechs, Atlantic Refining Co, 49-59, sr reservoir engr, 59-61, div reservoir engr, 61-63, mgr, Block 31 Unit Opers, 63-67, dist mgr, Rocky Mt-Mid Continent Dist, 67-69, res eng mgr, Atlantic Richfield Co, 69-73, VPRES ENG, ARCO OIL & GAS CO, 73- *Mem:* Am Inst Chem Engrs; Am Inst Mining, Metall & Petrol Engrs. *Res:* Unit operations; gas absorption; reservoir mechanics; fluid flow and mass transfer. *Mailing Add:* Atlantic Richfield Co PO Box 2819 Dallas TX 75221

KOCH, J FREDERICK, b Berlin, Ger, June 1, 37; US citizen; m 61; c 2. SOLID STATE PHYSICS. *Educ:* NY Univ, BA, 58; Univ Calif, Berkeley, PhD(physics), 62. *Prof Exp:* Actg asst prof physics, Univ Calif, Berkeley, 62-63; from asst prof to prof physics, Univ Md, College Park, 63-73; PROF PHYSICS, TECH UNIV MUNCHEN, 73- *Mem:* Am Phys Soc; Deutsche Phys Gesellschaft. *Mailing Add:* Dept of Physics E16 Tech Univ of Munchen 8046 Garching Germany Federal Republic of

KOCH, KAY FRANCES, b Tremont, Ill, June 18, 36; m 71. ORGANIC CHEMISTRY. *Educ:* Univ Ill, BS, 58; Univ Calif, Berkeley, PhD(org chem), 62. PXInstr chem, Wellesley Col, 61-63, asst prof, 63-66; SR ORG CHEMIST, RES LABS, ELI LILLY CO, 66- *Concurrent Pos:* Nat Inst Gen Med Sci spec fel, 64-65. *Mem:* Am Chem Soc; NY Acad Sci; Am Soc Microbiol. *Res:* Photochemistry of highly conjugated cyclic organic and other organic compounds; biosynthesis of quinones in insects and study of defensive secretions of insects; fermentation products chemistry; antibiotics, especially amino glycosides. *Mailing Add:* The Lilly Res Labs Eli Lilly & Co Indianapolis IN 46206

KOCH, MELVIN VERNON, b Chicago, Ill, June 12, 40. PHARMACEUTICAL CHEMISTRY. *Educ:* St Olaf Col, BA, 62; Univ Iowa, MS, 64, PhD(med chem), 67. *Prof Exp:* Res chemist, 67-69, proj leader fine organics, 69-71, group leader, 71-74, GROUP LEADER PHARMACEUT CHEM, DOW CHEM USA, 74- *Mem:* Am Chem Soc; Sigma Xi. *Mailing Add:* Dow Chem Co 574 Bldg Midland MI 48640

KOCH, PETER, b Missoula, Mont, Oct 15, 20; m 50. WOOD SCIENCE & TECHNOLOGY. *Educ:* Mont State Univ, BS, 42; Univ Wash, PhD(wood sci), 54. *Hon Degrees:* DSc, Univ Maine, Orono, 80. *Prof Exp:* Asst to pres, Stetson-Ross Mach Co, Wash, 46-52; consult engr, 52-55; assoc prof wood sci, Mich State Univ, 55-57; vpres & dir, Champlin Co, NH, 57-62; res & writing, 62-63; CHIEF WOOD SCIENTIST & PROJ LEADER, SOUTHERN FOREST EXP STA, FOREST SERV, USDA, PINEVILLE, 63- *Concurrent Pos:* Adj prof wood & paper sci, NC State Univ, 73-; mem comt renewable resources for indust mat, Nat Res Coun, 75. *Honors & Awards:* Superior Serv Honor Award, USDA, 68 & Unit Superior Serv Award, 73; Forest Prod Res Soc & Hitchcock's Woodworking Digest Award, 68; John Scott Award, City of Philadelphia Bd Dirs of City Trusts, 74. *Mem:* Am Soc Mech Engrs; Nat Soc Prof Engrs; Wood Wood Sci & Technol; Forest Prod Res Soc (pres, 72-73); fel Int Acad Wood Sci. *Res:* Wood machining processes; improved utilization of southern woods, especially southern pines. *Mailing Add:* 376 Windermere Blvd Alexandria LA 71301

KOCH, RICHARD, b NDak, Nov 24, 21; m 44; c 5. PEDIATRICS. *Educ:* Univ Rochester, MD, 51; Univ Calif, AB, 58. *Prof Exp:* From instr to prof pediat, Sch Med, Univ Southern Calif, 55-75, head div child develop, 65-75; dep dir, Calif State Dept Health Chg ment health, develop, disabilities & drug abuse, 75-76; PROF CLIN PEDIAT, SCH MED, UNIV SOUTHERN CALIF, 76-; DIR PKU NAT COLLAB STUDY, 76-; ACTG HEAD, CHILDREN'S HOSP LOS ANGELES, 80- *Concurrent Pos:* Dir, Child Develop Clin, Los Angeles Children's Hosp, 55-75; dir, Regional Ctr for Developmentally Disabled. *Mem:* Acad Pediat; Am Asn Ment Deficiency. *Res:* Mental retardation in children; metabolic diseases. *Mailing Add:* 4650 Sunset Blvd Los Angeles CA 90027

KOCH, RICHARD CARL, b Pittsburgh, Pa, Aug 10, 30; m 47; c 4. MEDICINAL CHEMISTRY. *Educ:* Cornell Univ, BA, 52; Yale Univ, PhD(org chem), 57. *Prof Exp:* Res chemist, Res & Eng Div, Monsanto Chem Co, 57-59; chemist, 59-66, proj leader, 66-68, sect mgr, 68-72, asst dir, 72-76, DIR, CENT RES DIV, PFIZER, INC, 76- *Mem:* Am Chem Soc; Sigma Xi. *Res:* Discovery and development of animal health drugs. *Mailing Add:* Cent Res Div Pfizer Inc Groton CT 06340

KOCH, RICHARD MONCRIEF, b Hutchinson, Kans, Jan 29, 39. GEOMETRY. *Educ:* Harvard Univ, AB, 61; Princeton Univ, PhD(math), 64. *Prof Exp:* Instr math, Univ Pa, 64-66; asst prof, 66-70, ASSOC PROF MATH, UNIV ORE, 70- *Mem:* Am Math Soc; Math Asn Am. *Res:* Differential geometry, particularly pseudogroups. *Mailing Add:* Dept of Math Univ of Ore Eugene OR 97403

KOCH, ROBERT B, b St Paul, Minn, May 14, 23; m 45; c 5. BIOCHEMISTRY. *Educ:* Univ Minn, BS, 48, PhD(biochem), 52. *Prof Exp:* Chief chem & microbiol br, Qm Food & Container Inst, US Army, 57-61; res sect head, Honeywell Inc, 61-65, staff scientist, 65-73; PROF BIOCHEM, MISS STATE UNIV, 73- *Mem:* Am Soc Biol Chem; Am Chem Soc; NY Acad Sci. *Res:* Enzyme purification and kinetics; enzymology of subcellular particles and organelles; biochemical mechanism of olfaction; properties of adenoxine triphosphatase system; soybean lipoxygenase isozymes. *Mailing Add:* Dept of Biochem Miss State Univ Mississippi State MS 39762

KOCH, ROBERT CHARLES, b Redick, Ill, June 5, 22; div; c 2. RUBBER CHEMISTRY, POLYMER CHEMISTRY. *Educ:* Univ Ill, BS, 43. *Prof Exp:* Jr chem engr, 43-44, 46-48, chem engr, 48-50, advan tire engr, 52-57, supvr off-hwy & tractor compounds, 57-63, supvr passenger tire compounds, 63-67, supvr truck tire compounds, 67-70, mgr heavy duty compounds, 70-75, MGR TIRE & RUBBER TECHNOL, CENT RES, FIRESTONE TIRE & RUBBER CO, 75- *Mem:* Am Chem Soc. *Res:* Rubber compounding for tire and industrial use. *Mailing Add:* Cent Res 1200 Firestone Pkwy Akron OH 44317

KOCH, ROBERT HARRY, b York, Pa, Dec 19, 29; m 59; c 4. ASTRONOMY. *Educ:* Univ Pa, AB, 51, MA, 55 & PhD(astron), 59. *Prof Exp:* Instr astron, Amherst & Mt Holyoke Cols, 59-60, from asst prof to assoc prof, Joint Dept Astron, Amherst, Mt Holyoke & Smith Cols & Univ Mass, 60-66; assoc prof astron, Univ NMex,66-67; assoc prof, 67-69, actg chmn dept, 68-73, PROF ASTRON, UNIV PA, 69- *Mem:* AAAS; Am Astron Soc; Int Astron Union. *Res:* Photoelectric photometry, polarimetry, visible band and ultraviolet spectroscopy and evolution of eclipsing variable stars. *Mailing Add:* 210 Roberts Rd Ardmore PA 19003

KOCH, ROBERT JACOB, b Chicago, Ill, Apr 17, 26; m 57; c 2. MATHEMATICS. *Educ:* Tulane Univ, La, PhD(math), 53. *Prof Exp:* From asst prof to assoc prof, 53-62, PROF MATH,LA STATE UNIV, BATON ROUGE, 62- *Mem:* Am Math Soc. *Res:* Topological semigroups. *Mailing Add:* Dept of Math La State Univ Baton Rouge LA 70803

KOCH, ROBERT MILTON, b Sioux City, Iowa, May 15, 24; m 46; c 3. ANIMAL BREEDING. *Educ:* Mont State Col, BS, 48; Iowa State Col, MS, 50, PhD(animal breeding, genetics), 53. *Prof Exp:* From asst prof to assoc prof animal husb, 50-59, chmn dept, 59-66, PROF ANIMAL SCI, UNIV NEBR, 59- *Concurrent Pos:* Supt, Ft Robinson Beef Cattle Res Sta, 54-57. *Honors & Awards:* Animal Breeding & Genetics Award, Am Soc Animal Sci, 76. *Mem:* Am Soc Animal Sci. *Res:* Beef cattle breeding; population genetics. *Mailing Add:* US Meat Animal Res Ctr Clay Center NE 68933

KOCH, RONALD JOSEPH, b Cincinnati, Ohio, June 30, 39; m 61; c 4. PHYSICS, MATERIALS SCIENCE. *Educ:* Xavier Univ, Ohio, BS, 61; Johns Hopkins Univ, PhD(physics), 69. *Prof Exp:* From res spectrochemist to sr res spectrochemist, 69-75, sr res chemist, 75-78, SR RES PHYSICIST, ARMCO INC, 78- *Mem:* Am Iron & Steel Inst; Am Soc for Testing & Mat. *Res:* X-rayphysics and diffraction; auger spectroscopy; surface analysis. *Mailing Add:* Armco Inc 703 Curtis St Middletown OH 45043

KOCH, RONALD N, b Pittsburgh, Pa, Aug 19, 41; m 63; c 3. FLOW MEASUREMENT. *Educ:* Carnegie-Mellon Univ, BSME, 63. *Prof Exp:* Develop engr, 63-76, MGR ENG, ROCKWELL INT, 76- *Mem:* Am Water Works Asn; Am Soc Sanit Engrs; Asn Mech Engrs; Int Water Supply Asn; Nat Micrographics Asn. *Res:* New product development activities for equipment in the field of flow measurement. *Mailing Add:* 400 N Lexington Ave Pittsburgh PA 15208

KOCH, RUDY G, b Richland Center, Wis, Sept 26, 39; m 61; c 3. SCIENCE EDUCATION, PLANT TAXONOMY. *Educ:* Concordia Teacher's Col, Nebr, BSEd, 61; Univ Mo-Kansas City, MA, 63; Ore State Univ, MS, 65; Okla State Univ, EdD, 68, Univ Nebr, PhD(bot), 75. *Prof Exp:* Asst prof biol, St John's Col, Kans, 63-67; asst cur plant taxon, Nebr State Mus, Lincoln, 67-68; Asst prof, 68-77, ASSOC PROF BIOL, UNIV WIS-SUPERIOR, 68-, CHMN DEPT, 77- *Mem:* Am Soc Plant Taxon; Am Bryol & Lichenological Soc; Nat Asn Biol Teachers; Int Asn Plant Taxon. *Res:* Curriculum development in biology; systematic studes of Bidens in North Cental United States; flora of Northwestern Wisconsin. *Mailing Add:* Dept of Biol Univ Wis Superior WI 54880

KOCH, RUSSELL WILLIAM, b St Louis, Mo, May 21, 41; m 63; c 3. ORGANIC CHEMISTRY, POLYMER SCIENCE. *Educ:* DMillikin Univ, BS, 63; Univ Akron, MS, 68; Va Polytech Inst & State Univ, PhD(org chem), 73. *Prof Exp:* CHEMIST ORG CHEM, FIRESTONE TIRE & RUBBER CO, 63-, ASSOC SCIENTIST, 78- *Concurrent Pos:* Res asstship, NSF, 68-72. *Mem:* Am Chem Soc; Adhesion Soc. *Res:* Adhesives; polyurethane chemistry; polymer synthesis; organic synthesis and exploratory research. *Mailing Add:* Firestone Cent Res S Main & Wilbeth Rd Akron OH 44317

KOCH, STANLEY D, b Cleveland, Ohio, Feb 10, 24; m 58; c 3. ORGANIC CHEMISTRY, POLYMER CHEMISTRY. *Educ:* Univ Ill, BA, 47; Cornell Univ, PhD(org chem), 50. *Prof Exp:* Fel, Univ Chicago, 50-51; res chemist, Jackson Lab, E I du Pont de Nemours & Co, 51-54 & Glendale Plaskon Lab, Barrett Div, Allied Chem Corp, 54-57; sr res chemist, Boston Lab, Monsanto Res Corp, 57-59, group leader, 59-64, res mgr, 64, Dayton Lab, 65-69; dept head, Horizons Res, Inc, 69-73; sec head, photo cure, Dwight P Joyce Res Ctr, Glidden-Durkee Div, SCM Corp, 74-77; develop assoc, Washington Res Ctr, W R Grace & Co, 77-78; MGR POLYMERIC COATINGS RES, ENTHONE, INC, 79- *Mem:* Am Chem Soc. *Res:* Coatings; radiation curing; herbicides. *Mailing Add:* PO Box 1900 Enthone Inc New Haven CT 06508

KOCH, STEPHEN ANDREW, b Jamaica, NY, Nov 19, 48; m 75. INORGANIC CHEMISTRY. *Educ:* Fordham Univ, BS, 70; Mass Inst Technol, PhD(chem), 75. *Prof Exp:* Assoc inorg chem, Tex A&M Univ, 75-77 & Cornell Univ, 78; ASST PROF CHEM, STATE UNIV NY, 78- *Mem:* Am Chem Soc. *Res:* Structural, electronic and reactivity properties of transition metal compound; bioinorganic chemistry; catalysis. *Mailing Add:* Dept of Chem State Univ of NY Stony Brook NY 11794

KOCH, STEPHEN DOUGLAS, b New York, NY, Dec 16, 40; m 68; c 2. PLANT TAXONOMY. *Educ:* Swarthmore Col, BA, 62; Univ Mich, MS, 64, PhD(plant taxon), 69. *Prof Exp:* Instr bot, Duke Univ, 67-68; asst prof, NC State Univ, 68-73; PROF-INVESTR BOT, POSTGRAD COL, CHAPINGO, MEX, 73- *Mem:* AAAS; Am Soc Plant Taxonomists; Int Asn Plant Taxonomists; Mex Bot Soc. *Res:* Grass systematics. *Mailing Add:* Centro Botanica Colegio de Postgraduados 56230 Chapingo Edo Mexico

KOCH, TAD H, b Mt Vernon, Ohio, Jan 1, 43. ORGANIC CHEMISTRY. *Educ:* Ohio State Univ, BS, 64, Iowa State Univ, PhD(org photochem), 68. *Prof Exp:* Asst prof, 68-74, ASSOC PROF ORG CHEM, UNIV COLO, BOULDER, 74- *Concurrent Pos:* Grants, Petrol Res Fund, 68-72 & 77-79, Res Corp, 69-70, Gen Med Sci Inst, 74-76. *Mem:* Am Chem Soc; Royal Chem Soc. *Res:* Mechanistic and synthetic photochemistry; free radical chemistry. *Mailing Add:* Dept of Chem Univ of Colo Boulder CO 80309

KOCH, THEODORE AUGUR, b Schenectady, NY, Oct 21, 25; m 52; c 5. PHYSICAL CHEMISTRY, CATALYSIS. *Educ:* St Michael's Col, BS, 46, MS, 47; Univ Pa, PhD(chem), 52. *Prof Exp:* Instr chem, Univ Vt, 46 & Drexel Inst, 47-51; CHEMIST, PETROCHEMICALS DEPT, E I DU PONT DE NEMOURS & CO, INC, 52- *Mailing Add:* 1500 Ridge Rd Holly Oak Wilmington DE 19809

KOCH, THOMAS RICHARD, b Strasburg, Pa, Oct 9, 44; m 68; c 3. CLINICAL CHEMISTRY, ANALYTICAL CHEMISTRY. *Educ:* Lebanon Valley Col, BS, 66; Univ Md, PhD(anal chem), 70; Am Bd Clin Chem, dipl, 76. *Prof Exp:* Trainee clin chem, State Univ NY, Buffalo, 70-72; clin chemist, St Joseph Hosp, 72-75; ASST PROF PATH & ASSOC DIR CLIN CHEM, SCH MED, UNIV MD, 75- *Concurrent Pos:* Consult, Vet Admin Hosp, 76-80 & Food & Drug Admin, USPHS, 77- *Mem:* Am Asn Clin Chem. *Res:* Trace elements in human disease; bilirubin measurement. *Mailing Add:* Dept of Path 22 S Green St Baltimore MD 21201

KOCH, WALTER THEODORE, b Orwigsburg, Pa, Jan 4, 23; m 46; c 3. ORGANIC CHEMISTRY. *Educ:* Albright Col, BS, 44; Rutgers Univ, MS, 50, PhD(org chem), 51. *Prof Exp:* Asst gen chem, Rutgers Univ, 47-50; res chemist, Merck & Co, Inc, 51-53 & Am Viscose Corp, 53-63; res chemist, 63-66, SECT LEADER, FMC CORP, 66- *Mem:* Am Chem Soc. *Res:* High polymers; cellophane, coatings; thermoplastic films. *Mailing Add:* 4 E Langhorne Ave Havertown PA 19083

KOCH, WILLIAM AUGUST, b Chicago, Ill, Mar 28, 17; m 40; c 3. FACILITES ENGINEERING, RESOURCE MANAGEMENT. *Prof Exp:* Mech eng, Univ Fla, 37-40; prob dir, Rocket Res Div, Aberdeen Proving Ground, 43-46, aero res engr supersonics, Wind Tunnels Br, Ballistic Res Lab, 46-58, aero res instrumentation engr, 58-61, asst plant engr, 61-69; housing mgt engr, 69-77, FACILITIES MGT ENGR, US ARMY TEST & EVAL COMMAND, 77-, CERT PLANT ENGR, 78- *Mem:* AAAS; Am Inst Aeronaut & Astronaut; Am Inst Plant Engrs. *Res:* Solid rocket weaponry design and development; supersonic wind tunnels design, instrumentation, operations. *Mailing Add:* 320 Law St Aberdeen MD 21001

KOCH, WILLIAM EDWARD, b York, Pa, Nov 22, 33; m 61; c 2. ANATOMY. *Educ:* Univ Pa, AB, 56, AM, 59; Stanford Univ, PhD(biol), 62. *Prof Exp:* From instr to asst prof anat, Sch Med, Yale Univ, 62-68; assoc prof, 68-75, PROF ANAT, SCH MED, UNIV NC, CHAPEL HILL, 68-, ADJ PROF ZOOL, 77- *Mem:* AAAS; Am Soc Zoologists; Am Asn Anatomists; Soc Develop Biol. *Res:* Study of embryonic tissue interacting and differentiating in vitro. *Mailing Add:* Dept of Anat Univ of NC Sch of Med Chapel Hill NC 27514

KOCH, WILLIAM GEORGE, b Forsyth, Mont, May 16, 24; m 51; c 1. PHYSICAL CHEMISTRY. *Educ:* Univ Notre Dame, BS, 47; Mont State Univ, MA, 53. *Prof Exp:* Asst chemist, Great Western Sugar Co, Colo, 54-55; asst prof, 55-58, assoc prof, 59, chmn dept, 74-77, PROF CHEM, UNIV NORTHERN COLO, 59- *Mem:* AAAS; Am Chem Soc. *Res:* Carbon isotope effects in decarboxylation reactions; effect of deuterium on carbon isotope effects; kinetics in the reaction between organolithium compounds and ether. *Mailing Add:* Dept of Chem Div of Sci Univ of Northern Colo Greeley CO 80631

KOCH, WILLIAM JULIAN, b Durham, NC, May 17, 24; m 47; c 4. MYCOLOGY. *Educ:* Univ NC, MA, 50, PhD(bot, plant physiol, zool), 55. *Prof Exp:* From asst to assoc prof, 47-74, PROF BOT, UNIV NC, CHAPEL HILL, 74- *Concurrent Pos:* Vis investr, Mich Biol Sta, 56, Highlands Biol Sta, 57, 58 & Int Bot Cong, Can, 59. *Mem:* AAAS; Bot Soc Am; Mycol Soc Am; Am Soc Plant Taxon; Electron Micros Soc Am. *Res:* Culture, comparative morphology, sexuality and mobility of fungus of reproductive cells; fungi parasitic on algae. *Mailing Add:* Dept of Bot Univ of NC Chapel Hill NC 27514

KOCHAKIAN, CHARLES DANIEL, b Haverhill, Mass, Nov 18, 08; m 40; c 1. ENDOCRINOLOGY, BIOCHEMISTRY. *Educ:* Boston Univ, AB, 30, AM, 31; Univ Rochester, PhD(physiol chem), 36. *Prof Exp:* Instr physiol, Sch Med & Dent, Univ Rochester, 36-40, assoc, 40-44, from asst prof to assoc prof endocrinol, 44-51; prof res biochem, Sch Med, Univ Okla, 51-57; prof physiol & biophys, 57-61, prof biochem & prof & dir exp endocrinol, 61-79, prof physiol & biophys, 65-79, EMER PROF BIOCHEM, MED & DENT SCHS, UNIV ALA, BIRMINGHAM, 79- *Concurrent Pos:* Assoc, Jackson Mem Lab, 46-49; mem panel hormones, Comt Growth, Nat Res Coun, 49-51, mem panel appraisers handbk biol data, 49-; vis Claude Bernard prof, Inst Exp Med Surg, Univ Montreal, 50; assoc dir, Okla Med Res Found, 51-53, head dept biochem & endocrinol, 51-57, coordr res, 53-55; consult, Dent Sch Comt, Okla Dent Asn, 54-57; consult, Univ Tex M D Anderson Hosp & Tumor Inst Houston, 56; actg coordr res, Univ Ala, Birmingham, 60-61; consult, Div Int Med Educ, Asn Am Med Cols, 64-70; mem panel drugs for metab disturbances, Drug Efficacy Study, Nat Acad Sci-Nat Res Coun, 67-69; mem metab & endocrine eval comt, Vet Admin Hosp, 69-71; mem nomenclature comt, Int Union Physiol Sci, 69- *Honors & Awards:* Claude Bernard Medal, Univ Montreal, 50; Medal, Osaka Endocrine Soc, 62. *Mem:* AAAS; Am Chem Soc; Am Physiol Soc; Am Soc Biol Chemists; Endocrine Soc. *Res:* Steroid biochemistry; protein; carbohydrate and fat metabolism; enzymes; hormones. *Mailing Add:* Lab of Exp Endocrinol Univ of Ala Med Ctr Birmingham AL 35294

KOCHAN, IVAN, b Ukraine, Aug 20, 23; nat US; m 49; c 3. IMMUNOLOGY. *Educ:* Univ Man, BSc, 53; MSc, 55; Stanford Univ, PhD(med microbiol), 58; Am Bd Med Microbiol, dipl. *Prof Exp:* Res assoc, Stanford Univ, 58-59; assoc prof microbiol, Baylor Univ, 59-61, prof & chmn dept, 61-67; PROF MICROBIOL, MIAMI UNIV, 67-; PROF MICROBIOL, SCH MED, WRIGHT STATE UNIV, 74- *Mem:* AAAS; Am Asn Immunologists; Reticuloendothelial Soc; Am Soc Microbiol; Am Thoracic Soc. *Res:* Study of transferrin-iron-mycobactin interplay in host-parasite relationship; nutritional immunity; role of fatty acids in cellular immunity and immunological diseases. *Mailing Add:* Dept of Microbiol Miami Univ Oxford OH 45056

KOCHAN, ROBERT GEORGE, b Prince Albert, Sask, Oct 25, 49; m 72; c 4. EXERCISE PHYSIOLOGY, BIOCHEMISTRY. *Educ:* Univ Sask, BA, 71; Univ Toledo, PhD(exercise physiol), 78. *Prof Exp:* Teaching asst, Univ Sask, 71-73 & Univ Toledo, 73-77; fel biochem, Med Col Ohio, 77-79, res assoc, 79-80; ASST PROF EXERCISE PHYSIOL, UNIV WIS-MADISON, 80- *Concurrent Pos:* Res fel, Juvenile Diabetes Found, 77-79. *Mem:* Am Col Sports Med. *Res:* Exercise metabolism; glycogen synthesis; insulin action mechanism; diabetes control. *Mailing Add:* Biodynamics Lab Univ Wis-Madison Madison WI 53706

KOCHAN, WALTER J, b Plainfield, NJ, July 15, 22; m 48; c 1. PLANT PHYSIOLOGY. *Educ:* Utah State Univ, BS, 50, MS, 52; Rutgers Univ, PhD(plant physiol), 55. *Prof Exp:* Asst horticulturist, Univ Idaho, 55-57; asst plant biochemist, Div Indust Res, Wash State Univ, 57; from asst horticulturist to assoc horticulturist, 57-70, RES PROF HORT, EXP STA, UNIV IDAHO, 70- *Mem:* Am Soc Plant Physiologists. *Res:* Mineral nutrition of plants; post-harvest physiology of tree fruits. *Mailing Add:* Br Exp Sta Univ of Idaho Parma ID 83660

KOCHEN, JOSEPH ABRAHAM, b Antwerp, Belg, July 12, 31; m 55; c 4. PEDIATRICS, HEMATOLOGY. *Educ:* McGill Univ, BSc, 52, PhD(biochem), 56; Univ Rochester, MD, 60. *Prof Exp:* Asst res prof pediat, Albert Einstein Col Med, 60-67, asst prof, 67-71, assoc prof, 71-77, prof, 77-78; PROF PEDIAT, MED COL, CORNELL UNIV, 78- *Concurrent Pos:* Attend physician & head pediat hemat serv, Montefiore Hosp & Med Ctr 68-78, North Shore Univ Hosp, 78- *Mem:* Am Acad Pediat; Soc Pediat Res; Am Soc Clin Oncol; Am Soc Hemat; Biochem Soc. *Res:* Blood diseases of childhood; red blood cell physiology; oncology. *Mailing Add:* 5 Walworth Ave Scarsdale NY 10583

KOCHEN, MANFRED, b Vienna, Austria, July 4, 28; nat US; m 54; c 2. INFORMATION SCIENCE. *Educ:* Mass Inst Technol, BS, 50; Columbia Univ, MA, 51, PhD(appl math), 55. *Prof Exp:* Asst, Spectros Lab, Mass Inst Technol, 49-50; mathematician aeroelasticity res, Biot & Arnold Co, 50-52; lectr math, Columbia Univ, 52-53; mem staff, Electronic Comput Proj, Inst Advan Study, 53-55; Ford fel math models in behav sci, Harvard Univ, 55-56; staff mathematician, Thomas J Watson Res Ctr, Int Bus Mach Corp, 56-58, mem res tech staff, 58-60, mgr info retrieval proj, 60-63, exchange vis expert at Euratom, Italy, 63-64; assoc prof math biol, 65-69, PROF INFO SCI & URBAN/REGIONAL PLANNING & RES MATHEMATICIAN, MENT HEALTH RES INST, 69- *Concurrent Pos:* Consult, Paul Rosenberg Assocs, 53-55, RCA Res Lab, 65, United Aircraft Corp, 66-69, Rand Corp, 68- & Sci Ctr Berlin, 78-; assoc ed, Behav Sci, 68-70, J Asn Comput Mach, 72- & managing ed, Human Systs Mgt, 79-; hon res assoc, Harvard Univ, 73-74; pres, Wise Fund, 75-; vis prof, Rockefeller Univ, 80-81. *Mem:* Am Math Soc; Am Soc Info Sci; Fedn Am Scientists; Am Phys Soc; fel AAAS. *Res:* Information systems and organization of knowledge; models for information-seeking behavior, problem representation solving, cognitive learning processes; decentralization theory; science of science; social planning; artificial intelligence; decision support systems. *Mailing Add:* 2026 Devonshire Ann Arbor MI 48104

KOCHEN, SIMON BERNARD, b Antwerp, Belg, Aug 14, 34; nat US. MATHEMATICS. *Educ:* McGill Univ, BSc, 54, MSc, 55; Princeton Univ, MA, 56, PhD(math), 58. *Prof Exp:* Demonstr physics, McGill Univ, 52-53; asst lectr math, Princeton Univ, 57-58; Nat Res Coun Can res assoc & asst prof, Univ Montreal, 58-59; from asst prof to prof, Cornell Univ, 59-67; PROF MATH, PRINCETON UNIV, 67- *Concurrent Pos:* Guggenheim fel, 62-63; mem, Inst Advan Study, 66-67. *Honors & Awards:* Cole Prize, Am Math Soc, 67. *Mem:* Am Math Soc; Asn Symbolic Logic. *Res:* Mathematical logic. *Mailing Add:* Dept of Math Princeton Univ Princeton NJ 08540

KOCHER, CARL A, b Seattle, Wash, Feb 14, 42; m 68; c 3. EXPERIMENTAL ATOMIC PHYSICS. *Educ:* Univ Calif, Berkeley, AB, 63, PhD(physics), 67. *Prof Exp:* Fel, Oxford Univ, 67-68; vis scientist, Mass Inst Technol, 68-69; lectr, Columbia Univ, 69-73; asst prof, 73-78, ASSOC PROF PHYSICS, ORE STATE UNIV, 78- *Concurrent Pos:* Fel, NSF, 67-69; prin investr, US Dept Energy, 78- *Mem:* Sigma Xi; Am Phys Soc; Am Asn Physics Teachers; Fedn Am Scientists. *Res:* Atomic collisions; radiative and autoionization processes; high Rydberg states; computer instrumentation. *Mailing Add:* Dept Physics Ore State Univ Corvallis OR 97331

KOCHER, CHARLES WILLIAM, b Johnson City, NY, May 16, 32; m 54; c 3. NUCLEAR PHYSICS. *Educ:* Harpur Col, BA, 54; NC State Col, MS, 56; Ind Univ, PhD(nuclear physics), 61. *Prof Exp:* Res assoc physics, Solid State Physics Group, Brookhaven Nat Lab, 60-62; sr staff scientist, Phys Res Lab, Budd Co, 62-65; scientist, 65-67, SR RES PHYSICIST, ANAL LAB, DOW CHEM USA, 67- *Mem:* AAAS; Am Chem Soc; Am Phys Soc. *Res:* Nuclear research reactors and decay schemes; Mossbauer effect; solid state physics, corrosion testing; metalorganic chemistry. *Mailing Add:* 5316 Dale St Midland MI 48640

KOCHER, DAVID CHARLES, b Washington, DC, Nov 9, 41; m 77. PHYSICS, ENVIRONMENTAL SCIENCES. *Educ:* Univ Md, BS, 63; Univ Wis-Madison, MS, 65, PhD(physics), 70. *Prof Exp:* Res assoc physics, Univ Birmingham, 70-71; res assoc, 71-76, RES ASSOC PHYSICS & ENVIRON SCI, OAK RIDGE NAT LAB, 76- *Mem:* Am Phys Soc; Am Nuclear Soc; Health Physics Soc. *Res:* Development of models and data bases for the assessment of health and safety impacts on man from energy production technologies. *Mailing Add:* Health & Safety Res Div PO Box X Oak Ridge TN 37830

KOCHER, FRANK T, b Marietta, Pa, Sept 14, 19; m 46; c 2. MATHEMATICS. *Educ:* Bloomsburg State Col, BS, 40; Pa State Univ, MA, 49. *Prof Exp:* High sch teacher, Pa, 40-44; teacher, Admiral Farragut Acad, Fla, 45-46; instr math, DuBois Campus, 46-50, from instr to asst prof, 50-66, assoc prof math, Pa State Univ, University Park, 66-81, supervr math, Exten, 50-81; vis lectr math, Baylor Univ, Tex, 80- *Concurrent Pos:* Assoc ed, Am Math Monthly, 81-82. *Mem:* Math Asn Am; Nat Coun Teachers of Math. *Res:* Education; theorems on polynomial sets of Type One. *Mailing Add:* Dept Math Baylor Univ Waco PA 76798

KOCHER, HARIBHAJAN S(INGH), b Lyall Pur, WPakistan, Sept 29, 34; m; c 2. FLUID MECHANICS. *Educ:* Okla State Univ, BS, 57; Purdue Univ, MS, 59; Mich State Univ, PhD(fluid mech), 63. *Prof Exp:* Lectr mech eng, Indian Inst Technol, New Delhi, 62-63; develop engr, Civilian Atomic Power Dept, Can Gen Elec Co, 63-64; sr res physicist, Delco Prod Div, Gen Motors Corp, NY, 64-66; SCIENTIST, XEROX CORP, 66- *Concurrent Pos:* Adj asst prof, Univ Rochester, 76- *Mem:* Am Soc Mech Engrs; Inst Elec & Electronics Engrs. *Res:* Thermal properties of metals; heat transfer in nuclear reactors and electrical motors; boundary layer studies; fluid flow instability. *Mailing Add:* 800 Phillips Rd Webster Res Ctr Xerox Corp Webster NY 14580

KOCHERT, GARY DEAN, b Louisville, Ky, Oct 12, 39; m 63; c 2. BOTANY. *Educ:* Ind Univ, AB, 63, PhD(microbiol), 67. *Prof Exp:* From asst prof to assoc prof, 67-78, PROF BOT, UNIV GA, 78-, CHMN DEPT, 81- *Mem:* Phycol Soc Am. *Res:* Algology; cell differentiation; experimental control of sexuality in algae. *Mailing Add:* Dept of Bot Univ of GA Athens GA 30601

KOCHHAR, DEVENDRA M, b Sailkot, India, Mar 10, 38; m 62; c 2. ANATOMY, EMBRYOLOGY. *Educ:* Punjab Univ, India, BSc, 58, MSc, 59; Univ Fla, PhD(anat), 64. *Prof Exp:* Instr anat, Univ Fla, 64-65; vis scientist, Karolinska & Wenner-Grens Insts, Stockholm, Sweden, 65-66; vis scientist, Strangeways Res Lab, Cambridge, 66-67; guest investr, Rockefeller Univ, 67-68; from asst prof to assoc prof anat, Univ Iowa, 68-71; from assoc prof to prof, Univ Va, 71-76; PROF ANAT, JEFFERSON MED COL, 76- *Concurrent Pos:* Consult pharmaceut indust, Environ Protection Agency & Food & Drug Admin. *Mem:* Am Soc Cell Biol; Am Asn Anatomists; Teratology Soc (pres, 82-83); Europ Teratology Soc. *Res:* Experimental teratology; cell and organ culture; whole embryo culture; development of skeletal system; cleft palate; audio tutorial systems in medical education; amino acid analogues in abnormal development; congenital abnormalities of limb. *Mailing Add:* Dept Anat Jefferson Col Med 1020 Locust St Philadelphia PA 19107

KOCHHAR, MAN MOHAN, b Lahore, Pakistan, Sept 14, 32; US citizen; m 54; c 3. MEDICINAL CHEMISTRY, BIOCHEMICAL TOXICOLOGY. *Educ:* Punjab Univ, India, BS, 53; Univ Tex, Austin, MS, 61, PhD(med chem), 64. *Prof Exp:* Chief chemist, Dr Nayer Chem Works, India, 54-55; med rep, Geigy Pharmaceut, India, 55-58; asst med chem, Univ Tex, Austin, 59-63, spec instr, Col Pharm, 63-64; from asst prof to assoc prof pharm & pharmaceut chem, 64-75, prof toxicol, 75-81, PROF PHARMACOL & TOXICOL, AUBURN UNIV, 81- *Concurrent Pos:* Lederle fac awards, 64 & 65; grant-in-aid, Auburn Univ, 65-68; Nat Inst Drug Abuse award, 73; Dept Ment Health award, State of Ala, 74; dir, Drug Screening Training Prog, Auburn Univ & Drug Anal Lab, 73- *Mem:* Am Acad Clin Toxicol; Am Chem Soc; Am Asn Clin Chem; Am Pub Health Asn; Can Acad Clin Anal Toxicol. *Res:* Structure-activity relationships among psychotropic and antineoplastic agents; biochemical approach to toxicology including analytical toxicology. *Mailing Add:* Sch of Pharm Auburn Univ Auburn AL 36830

KOCHHAR, RAJINDAR KUMAR, b Nurmahal, India, Aug 1, 22; US citizen; m 54; c 2. POLYMER CHEMISTRY. *Educ:* Panjab Univ, India, BS, 45; Univ Delhi, MS, 48; Univ Tex, Austin, PhD(phys org chem), 65; Univ Mo-Kansas City, MBA, 69. *Prof Exp:* Mgr, Rita Ice Creams, India, 51-55; asst med res, Lady Hardinge Med Col, Delhi, 55-58; factory mgr, I B Misra & Co, 58-59; res chemist, 64-68, sr res chemist, Gulf Res & Develop Co, 68-77, mgr polymerization res, 77-81, DIR PROCESS CHEM, PLASTICS DIV, GULF OIL CHEM CO, 81- *Mem:* Am Chem Soc. *Res:* Color and chemical constitution; dyes for nylon; research on medicinal plants; fixed oils; polymer synthesis and characterization; polyolefin development. *Mailing Add:* 610 Brenwick Katy TX 77450

KOCHI, JAY KAZUO, b Los Angeles, Calif, May 17, 28; m 59; c 1. ORGANOMETALLIC CHEMISTRY, PHYSICAL ORGANIC CHEMISTRY. *Educ:* Univ Calif, Los Angeles, BS, 49; Iowa State Univ, PhD(chem), 52. *Prof Exp:* Instr org chem, Harvard Univ, 52-55; NIH fel, Cambridge Univ, 55-56; vis asst prof, Iowa State Univ, 56; chemist, Shell Develop Co, 57-62; from assoc prof to prof chem, Case Western Reserve Univ, 62-69; EARL BLOUGH PROF CHEM, IND UNIV, BLOOMINGTON, 69- *Honors & Awards:* James Flack Norris Award, Am chem Soc, 81. *Mem:* Am Chem Soc; Royal Soc Chem. *Res:* Mechanisms of organic reactions catalyzed by metal complexes; application of metal complexes to organic synthesis; electron-transfer and charge-transfer processes in organic chemistry; photochemistry of organometallic compounds; application of electron spin resonance spectroscopy to organic and organometallic free radicals and to the mechanism of homolytic reactions. *Mailing Add:* Dept of Chem Ind Univ Bloomington IN 47401

KOCHMAN, STANLEY OSCAR, b New York, NY, July 18, 46; m 69; c 3. MATHEMATICS. *Educ:* Kenyon Col, AB, 66; Univ Chicago, MS, 67, PhD(math), 70. *Prof Exp:* Gibbs instr math, Yale Univ, 70-72; asst prof, Purdue Univ, West Lafayette, 72-77; asst prof, 77-80, ASSOC PROF MATH, UNIV WESTERN ONT, 80- *Concurrent Pos:* Lectr, Mass Inst Technol, 73-74. *Mem:* Am Math Soc; Can Math Soc; Math Asn Am. *Res:* Algebraic topology, especially homology operations and Cobordism theory. *Mailing Add:* Dept of Math Univ of Western Ont London ON N6A 5B7 Can

KOCHWA, SHAUL, b Vienna, Austria, Apr 30, 15; nat US; m 40; c 1. BIOCHEMISTRY, IMMUNOCHEMISTRY. *Educ:* Hebrew Univ Jerusalem, MSc, 40, PhD(immunol), 49; Harvard Univ, MPH, 53. *Prof Exp:* Chief chemist, Gordon Co, Israel, 43-45; med lab dir, Bikur Cholim Hosp, Jerusalem, 45-47; assoc dir immunochem, Rogoff Med Res Inst, Beilinson Hosp, 55-58; sr res assoc, Mt Sinai Hosp, 59-66; assoc prof med, 66-72, PROF PATH, MT SINAI SCH MED, 72-, PROF MED, 79- *Mem:* Am Asn Immunologists; Am Chem Soc; Harvey Soc; Am Soc Hemat; NY Acad Sci. *Res:* Physicochemistry and purification of proteins, toxins, antibodies and enzymes; protein-protein interaction and complex formation. *Mailing Add:* Mt Sinai Sch of Med Dept of Path Fifth Ave & 100th St New York NY 10029

KOCH-WESER, DIETER, b Kassel, Ger, July 13, 16; nat US; m 50; c 2. EXPERIMENTAL PATHOLOGY, PREVENTIVE MEDICINE. *Educ:* Univ Sao Paulo, MD, 43; Northwestern Univ, MS, 50, PhD, 56. *Prof Exp:* Asst med, Hosps & Clin, Sao Paulo, Brazil, 44-47; asst path, Hektoen Inst Med Res, Cook County Hosp, Chicago, 49-51; from instr to asst prof med, Grad Sch Med, Univ Chicago, 51-56; assoc prof, Sch Med, Western Reserve Univ, 57-62; chief, Latin-Am Off, NIH, Brazil, 62-64; assoc prof, Sch Pub Health, 64-71, PROF PREV & SOCIAL MED, MED SCH, HARVARD UNIV, 71-, ASSOC DEAN INT PROGS, 67- *Honors & Awards:* Couto Prize, Acad Med, Brazil, 45. *Mem:* Am Soc Clin Invest; Am Thoracic Soc; AMA; Am Col Chest Physicians. *Res:* Isotope and biochemical studies in tuberculosis, hypersensitivity and liver diseases. *Mailing Add:* Dept of Prev & Social Med Harvard Med Sch Boston MA 02115

KOCH-WESER, JAN, b Berlin, Ger, Oct 30, 30; US citizen. INTERNAL MEDICINE, CLINICAL PHARMACOLOGY. *Educ:* Univ Chicago, AB, 50; Harvard Med Sch, MD, 54. *Prof Exp:* Intern med, Mass Gen Hosp, 54-55, asst resident, 55-56, resident, 59; from instr to assoc prof pharmacol, Harvard Med Sch, 62-75; assoc dir res ctr & chief med res, 75-76, DIR RES CTR & V PRES RES, MERRELL INT, 76- *Concurrent Pos:* Assoc physician & chief hypertension & clin pharmacol unit, Mass Gen Hospp 66-75; mem med adv bd, Coun High Blood Pressure Res, Am Heart Asn; mem sci adv bd, Pan Am Health Orgn; mem pharmacol-toxicol rev comt & prog comt, Nat Inst Gen Med Sci; mem bd trustees, US Pharmacopeial Coun; USPHS res fel pharmacol, Harvard Med Sch, 60-61, Burroughs Wellcome scholar clin pharmacol, 66-71; USPHS spec res fel, 62 & grant, 64-75. *Mem:* Am Col Cardiol; Am Fedn Clin Res; Am Soc Clin Pharmacol & Therapeut; Am Soc Pharmacol & Exp Therapeut; Cardiac Muscle Soc. *Res:* Cardiovascular physiology and pharmacology; clinical pharmacology and human therapeutics; adverse drug reactions; drug metabolism and pharmacokinetics; antiarrhythmic, antihypertensive and anticoagulant drugs. *Mailing Add:* Merrell Int Res Ctr 16 rue d'Ankara 67000 Strasbourg France

KOCIBA, RICHARD JOSEPH, b Harbor Beach, Mich, Apr 8, 39; m 66; c 2. VETERINARY PATHOLOGY, TOXICOLOGY. *Educ:* Mich State Univ, BS, 64, DVM, 66, MS, 69, PhD(path), 70. *Prof Exp:* Practr, Milford Vet Clin, 66-67; instr anat, Mich State Univ, 67-68, NIH fel path, 68-70; res pathologist, 70-80, SR ASSOC SCIENTIST, TOXICOL RES LAB, DOW CHEM CO, 80- *Concurrent Pos:* Adj asst prof path, Mich State Univ, 81- *Mem:* Am Vet Med Asn; Am Col Vet Pathologists; Soc Toxicol; Soc Pharmacol & Environ Pathologists. *Res:* Design, conduction, evaluation and interpretation of research in the area of acute and chronic toxicity, with special emphasis on carcinogenesis and pathology. *Mailing Add:* Toxicol Res Lab 1803 Bldg Dow Chem Co Midland MI 48640

KOCK, WINSTON E(DWARD), b Cincinnati, Ohio, Dec 5, 09; m 39; c 3. ENGINEERING PHYSICS. *Educ:* Univ Cincinnati, EE, 32, MS, 33; Univ Berlin, PhD(physics), 34. *Hon Degrees:* DSc, Univ Cincinnati, 52. *Prof Exp:* Teaching fel, Univ Cincinnati, 34-35 & Inst Advan Study, 35-36; fel, Indian Inst Sci, 36; res engr, Baldwin Piano Co, Ohio, 36-38, dir electronic res, 38-42; res engr microwaves, Bell Tel Labs, Inc, 42-51, dir acoust res, 51-55, dir audio & video systs res, 55-56; chief scientist, Systs Div, Bendix Corp, 56-57, dir & gen mgr res labs, 58-62, vpres res, 62-64; dir, NASA Electronics Res Ctr, Mass, 64-66; vpres & chief scientist, Bendix Corp, 66-72; DIR, HERMAN SCHNEIDER LAB, UNIV CINCINNATI, 72- *Concurrent Pos:* Mem Hartwell comt, US Defense Dept, 50, Teota comt, US Dept Army, 52 & Lamplight comt, Off Naval Res, 53; mem Nobska comt, Nat Acad Sci, 56, space study comt, 65, comt undersea warfare, 68-; mem bd gov, Am Inst Physics, 56-62; mem comt, Air Res & Develop Command-Nat Acad Sci, 57; consult, Secy Defense, 58-, mem adv panel electronics, 59-; mem Atlantis comt, 60, mem study comt, Inst Defense Anal, 63; mem bd dirs, Atomic Indust Forum, 66, chmn space nuclear comt; NSF appointee, US-Japan Holography Comn, 67; mem res & develop task group, Defense Sci Bd, 67; mem bd dirs, Roanwell Corp, 68-; mem bd trustees, Argonne Univs Asn, 68-, mem bd dirs & reactor res comt; chmn bd trustees, Western Col for Women, 68-70. *Honors & Awards:* Naval Ord Award, 46, Distinguished Pub Serv Medal, US Navy, 64; Weakley Award, Nat Security Indust Asn, 75. *Mem:* Fel Am Phys Soc; fel Acoust Soc Am; fel Inst Elec & Electronics Engrs; hon fel Indian Acad Sci; Sigma Xi. *Res:* Acoustics; microwaves; antennas; glow discharge oscillators; electronic organ; wave-guide lens antenna; artificial microwave dielectrics; acoustic lens; coaxial transistor; underwater sound; automatic speech recognition; narrow band television; microwave-acoustic analogs. *Mailing Add:* 822-B Rhodes Hall Univ of Cincinnati Cincinnati OH 45221

KOCKS, U(LRICH) FRED, b Dusseldorf, Ger, Nov 25, 29; nat US; m 54; c 4. MATERIALS SCIENCE. *Educ:* Univ Gottingen, dipl physics, 54; Harvard Univ, PhD(appl physics), 59. *Hon Degrees:* DrTech, Tampere Univ Tech, 82. *Prof Exp:* Lectr & res fel, Harvard Univ, 59-61, asst prof, 61-65; SR SCIENTIST, ARGONNE NAT LAB, 65- *Concurrent Pos:* Vis prof, Munich Tech Univ, 64, Aachen Tech Univ, 71-72 & McMaster Univ, 78; Humboldt award, Fed Repub Ger, 79. *Mem:* Am Inst Mining, Metall & Petrol Engrs. *Res:* Mechanics and thermodynamics of solids; defects in crystals; strengthening mechanisms; kinetics of plasticity and creep. *Mailing Add:* Mat Sci Div Argonne Nat Lab Argonne IL 60439

KOCON, RICHARD WILLIAM, b Fall River, Mass, Apr 18, 42; m 68; c 2. CLINICAL CHEMISTRY, MEDICAL LABORATORY SCIENCE. *Educ:* Southeastern Mass Univ, BS, 70; Providence Col, PhD(chem), 73. *Prof Exp:* Org Chem, Rhode Island Hosp, 74-77; LAB DIR, DAMON MED LAB, INC, 79- *Mem:* Am Asn Clin Chem. *Res:* Clinical chemistry, specifically clinical application of radioimmunoassay procedures and enzyme-linked immunosorbent blocking assay techniques. *Mailing Add:* 438 Oakland Pkwy Franklin MA 02038

KOCSIS, JAMES JOSEPH, b Barberton, Ohio, Aug 13, 20; m 52; c 4. PHARMACOLOGY. *Educ:* Ohio State Univ, BA, 43; Univ Chicago, MS, 52, PhD(pharmacol), 56. *Prof Exp:* From instr to assoc prof, 56-74, PROF PHARMACOL, JEFFERSON MED COL, 74- *Mem:* Am Chem Soc; Am Soc Pharmacol & Exp Therapeut. *Res:* Bioassay; drug metabolism. *Mailing Add:* Dept of Pharmacol Jefferson Med Col Philadelphia PA 19107

KOCUREK, MICHAEL JOSEPH, b New York, NY, Jan 6, 43; m 67; c 2. PAPER SCIENCE, ENGINEERING. *Educ:* State Univ NY, BS, 64, MS, 67; Syracuse Univ, PhD(paper sci & eng), 71. *Prof Exp:* assoc prof paper sci, 70-80, PROF PAPER SCI & ENG, UNIV WIS-STEVENS POINT, 80-, CHMN DEPT, 70- *Concurrent Pos:* Mem acad adv coun, Tech Asn Pulp & Paper Indust, 71-, mem prof develop oper coun, 76-, chmn continuing educ div, 76-78, mem US-Can joint textbook comt, 78-, instr intro to pulp & paper tech, 75- *Mem:* Tech Asn Pulp & Paper Indust. *Res:* Wood and pulping chemistry; paper and fiber physics. *Mailing Add:* Dept Paper Sci & Eng Univ of Wis Stevens Point WI 54481

KOCURKO, MICHAEL JOHN, b Orange, Calif, Jan 28, 45; div. GEOLOGY, SEDIMENTOLOGY. *Educ:* Midwestern Univ, BS, 66; Univ Wis-Milwaukee, MS, 68; Tex Tech Univ, PhD(geol), 72. *Prof Exp:* Explor geologist, Union Oil Co Calif, 68-69 & 72-75; asst prof geol, Tulane Univ, 75-79; ASSOC PROF GEOL, MIDWESTERN STATE UNIV, WICHITA FALLS, TEX, 79- *Mem:* Soc Econ Paleontologists & Mineralogists. *Res:* Application of modern carbonate depositional environments and post-depositional history to the paragenesis of carbonate rocks. *Mailing Add:* Dept Geol Midwestern State Univ Wichita Falls TX 76308

KODA, ROBERT T, b Watsonville, Calif, June 18, 33; m 59; c 2. PHARMACEUTICAL CHEMISTRY. *Educ:* Univ Southern Calif, PharmD, 61, PhD(pharmaceut chem), 68. *Prof Exp:* Asst prof, 68-74, fel, 69, ASSOC PROF PHARMACEUT CHEM & ASSOC DEAN, UNIV SOUTHERN CALIF, 75- *Concurrent Pos:* Fel acad admin internship prog, Am Coun Educ, 71. *Mem:* Am Pharmaceut Asn. *Res:* Synthesis of compounds of potential biological activity; determination of pharmacokinetic parameters of drugs of current clinical interest. *Mailing Add:* Sch of Pharm Univ of Southern Calif Los Angeles CA 90033

KODAMA, ARTHUR MASAYOSHI, b Honolulu, Hawaii, Dec 17, 31; m 59; c 1. PHYSIOLOGY. *Educ:* Washington Univ, BA, 54; Univ Calif, Berkeley, PhD(physiol), 63, MPH, 78. *Prof Exp:* Res physiologist, Univ Calif, Berkeley, 63-77; asst prof physiol, 78-80, MEM FAC, DEPT PUB HEALTH SCI, SCH PUB HEALTH, UNIV HAWAII, 80- *Mem:* AAAS; Am Physiol Soc. *Res:* Environmental physiology and space biology; occupational health and industrial hygiene. *Mailing Add:* Sch Pub Health Univ Hawaii 1960 East-West Rd Honolulu HI 96822

KODAMA, GOJI, b Sakai City, Japan, Dec 2, 27; m 57; c 2. INORGANIC CHEMISTRY. *Educ:* Tokyo Inst Technol, BE, 51; Univ Mich, Ann Arbor, MS, 52, PhD(chem), 58. *Prof Exp:* From res assoc to instr chem, Univ Mich, 58-60; res fel, Harvard Univ, 60-61; from asst prof to prof, Tokyo Sci Univ, 61-69; assoc res prof, 69-80, RES PROF CHEM, UNIV UTAH, 80- *Mem:* Am Chem Soc. *Res:* Reactions of boron hydrides with various bases; transition metal-boron hydride complexes. *Mailing Add:* Dept of Chem Univ of Utah Salt Lake City UT 84112

KODAMA, HIDEOMI, b Tokyo, Japan, Oct 9, 31; m 59; c 3. MINERALOGY. *Educ:* Tokyo Univ Educ, BSc, 56, MSc, 58, DSc(mineral), 61. *Prof Exp:* Japanese Soc Promoting Sci fel & lectr, Int Christian Univ, Tokyo, 61-62; Nat Res Coun Can fel, 62-64; res scientist, Soil Res Inst, Can Dept Agr, 64-77, RES SCIENTIST, CHEM & BIOL RES INST, AGR CAN, 78- *Concurrent Pos:* Vis scientist, Nat Ctr Sci Res, Orleans, France, 69-70. *Mem:* Mineral Soc Am; Clay Minerals Soc; Can Soc Soil Sci; Int Asn Study Clay; Mineral Soc Japan. *Res:* Structure and genesis of interstratified clay minerals; fine structure analysis of layer silicates; crystal chemistry of silicate minerals; interactions between clay minerals and soil organic matter. *Mailing Add:* Mineral Lab Soil Sect Cent Exp Farm Ottawa ON K1A 0C6 Can

KODAMA, JIRO KENNETH, b Reedley, Calif, Mar 4, 24; m 51; c 5. PHARMACOLOGY, TOXICOLOGY. *Educ:* Univ Calif, AB, 51, MS, 55, PhD(pharmacol), 57. *Prof Exp:* Instr pharmacol, Med Sch & toxicol, Sch Pub Health, Univ Calif, 57-59; from asst dept chief toxicol & pharmacol to sr pharmacologist, Hazleton Labs, Inc, 59-63; pharmacologist, Shell Develop Co, 63-66, supvr pharmacol dept, 66-68, vis Shell scientist, Tunstall Lab, Shell Res Ltd, Eng, 69-70, staff toxicologist, Agr Div, Shell Chem Co, 70-77; staff toxicologist, 77-80, TECH LIAISON REP, STANDARD OIL CO, CALIF, 81- *Mem:* AAAS; Am Soc Pharmacol & Exp Therapeut; Soc Toxicol. *Res:* Drug research and development; pharmacotoxic characterization of chemical warfare agents; mechanisms of toxic actions of organophosphorus chemicals and cytotoxic alkylating agents; toxicology and safety evaluation of industrial and agricultural chemicals; preclinical evaluation of pharmaceuticals; forensic toxicology; technical management. *Mailing Add:* Standard Oil Co of Calif PO Box 1272 Richmond CA 94802

KODAMA, ROBERT MAKOTO, b Kauai, Hawaii, May 30, 32; m 64; c 2. CELL PHYSIOLOGY. *Educ:* Univ Hawaii, BA, 55; Univ Ill, PhD(physiol), 67. *Prof Exp:* Phys sci aide, US Fish & Wildlife Serv, 55-56; med technologist, Mt Sinai Hosp, Chicago, Ill, 59; asst cell physiol, Med Ctr, Univ Ill, 60-62, physiol, 66-67; from asst prof to assoc prof, 67-76, PROF BIOL, DRAKE UNIV, 76- *Res:* Biological transport; endocrinology; electron microscopy. *Mailing Add:* Dept of Biol Drake Univ Des Moines IA 50311

KODITSCHEK, LEAH K, b Lithuania, May 20, 17; US citizen; m 48; c 2. MICROBIAL ECOLOGY. *Educ:* Hunter Col, AB, 39; Oberlin Col, MA, 40; Rutgers Univ, PhD(bact), 66. *Prof Exp:* Lab asst, Wasserman Lab, New York Dept Health, 41-42; lab asst biochem, Internal Med Lab, NY State Psychiat Inst, 42; jr prof asst climatic res, US Signal Corps Res Labs, 42-43; vitamin analyst, Burroughs Wellcome & Co, 43-44 & 45-46; microbiologist, Res Labs, Merck & Co, Inc, 46-51; asst prof sci, Paterson State Col, 59-60; assoc prof, 61-72, PROF BIOL, MONTCLAIR STATE COL, 72- *Mem:* AAAS; Environ Mutagen Soc; Am Soc Microbiol. *Res:* Microbial nutrition; monitoring marine and fresh water and sediment for bacteria resistant to antibiotic and heavy metals, in relation to R plasmid transfer in aquatic ecosystems and its value as pollution indicator. *Mailing Add:* 409 Highland Ave Upper Montclair NJ 07043

KODRES, UNO ROBERT, b Tartu, Estonia, May 21, 31; nat US; m 59; c 2. MATHEMATICS. *Educ:* Wartburg Col, BA, 54; Iowa State Univ, MS, 56, PhD(math), 58. *Prof Exp:* Staff mathematician, Prod Develop Lab, Int Bus Mach Corp, 58-63; ASSOC PROF MATH, NAVAL POSTGRAD SCH, 63-, ACTG CHMN COMPUT SCI GROUP, 75- *Concurrent Pos:* Consult, IBM Corp, 67-69 & Collins Radio Co, 67-69. *Mem:* Math Asn Am; Asn Comput Mach; Soc Indust & Appl Math; Sigma Xi. Graph theory; applied military applications of microcomputers. *Mailing Add:* Dept of Comput Sci Naval Postgrad Sch Monterey CA 93940

KODRICH, WILLIAM RALPH, b Cooperstown, NY, Aug 26, 33; m 60. ECOLOGY. *Educ:* Hartwick Col, BA, 55; Univ Pittsburgh, PhD(biol), 67. *Prof Exp:* Assoc prof, 67-74, PROF BIOL, CLARION STATE COL, 74- *Mem:* Ecol Soc Am; Am Soc Mammalogists. *Res:* Physiological rates of small mammals living freely in their natural environments; relative thyroid release rates of 131-I of mammals living at different altitudes; bioenergetics of mammals in natural environments. *Mailing Add:* Dept of Biol Clarion State Col Clarion PA 16214

KOE, B KENNETH, b Astoria, Ore, Apr 15, 25; m 55; c 2. NEUROCHEMISTRY. *Educ:* Reed Col, BA, 45; Univ Wash, MS, 48; Calif Inst Technol, PhD(chem), 52. *Prof Exp:* Res fel chem, Calif Inst Technol, 52-54; assoc chemist, Southwest Res Inst, 54-55; res chemist, 55-74, sr res investr, 74-79, RES ADV, PFIZER INC, 79- *Mem:* Am Soc Pharmacol & Exp Therapeut; Soc Neurosci; Am Col Neuropsychopharmacol. *Res:* Alcohol metabolism; biochemical psychotherapeutic drugs; psycho pharmacology; neurtransmitters. *Mailing Add:* Dept of Pharmacol Pfizer Inc Groton CT 06340

KOEFERL, MICHAEL TALLYN, toxicology, pharmacology, see previous edition

KOEGLE, JOHN S(TUART), b Rochester, Pa, Jan 8, 26; m 50; c 5. CHEMICAL ENGINEERING. *Educ:* Purdue Univ, BChE, 48; Kans State Col, MS, 49; Ohio State Univ, PhD(chem eng). 51. *Prof Exp:* Res chem engr, Monsanto Co, 51-56, res design engr, 56-61, res group leader, 61-63, pilot plant dir marine colloids, 63-68, dir eng marine colloids, 68-70, dir develop marine colloids, Maine, 70-71; dir eng, Technol, Res & Develop, Inc, 71-74; sr process eng, Pedco, 74-77; dir process eng, Velsicol, 77-80; SR PROCESS ENG & PROJ MGR, PEDCO, 80- *Mem:* Am Chem Soc; Am Inst Chem Engrs. *Res:* Plant design, process and product developmet; evaluation, design, construction and maitenance of all research equipment. *Mailing Add:* PEDCO 11499 Chester Rd Cincinnati OH 45246

KOEHL, GEORGE MARTIN, b College Point, NY, July 24, 09; m 35; c 2. OPTICS. *Educ:* Univ NC, AB, 31; George Washington Univ, AM, 33. *Prof Exp:* Pub sch teacher, NY, 34-37; assoc, 37-46, assoc prof, 46-52, asst dean jr col, 47-53, dean, 53-63, assoc dean col arts & sci, 63-72, PROF PHYSICS, GEORGE WASHINGTON UNIV, 52- *Concurrent Pos:* Pub sch teacher, Washington, DC, 37-42 & 45-46; physicist, Carnegie Inst, 43-45. *Honors & Awards:* Naval Ord Develop Award. *Mem:* Am Phys Soc; Am Asn Physics Teachers. *Res:* Interior ballistics measurements; diffraction of ultrasonic sound waves. *Mailing Add:* 515 Mansfield Rd Silver Spring MD 20910

KOEHL, WILLIAM JOHN, JR, b Newport, Ky, July 27, 35; m 60. FUEL SCIENCE, AIR POLLUTION. *Educ:* Xavier Univ, Ohio, BS, 55, MS, 57; Univ Ill, PhD(org chem), 60. *Prof Exp:* Sr res chemist, Cent Res Div Lab, Socony Mobil Oil Co Inc, NJ, 60-68; sr res chemist, 68-76, SUPV CHEMIST, PROD RES & TECHNOL SERV DIV, MOBIL RES & DEVELOP CORP, 76- *Mem:* Am Chem Soc. *Res:* Electrochemical synthesis of organic compounds; automotive fuels and exhaust emissions. *Mailing Add:* Res Dept Mobil Res & Develop Corp Paulsboro NJ 08066

KOEHLER, ANDREAS MARTIN, b Weimar, Ger, Jan 21, 30; US citizen; m 52; c 3. MEDICAL PHYSICS, ACCELERATOR PHYSICS. *Educ:* Harvard Univ, BS, 50. *Prof Exp:* Proj engr mech design, Hesse-Eastern Corp, 51-53; tech assoc, accelerator physics, 53-61, asst dir, 61-77, DIR ACCELERATOR MED PHYSICS, CYCLOTRON LAB, HARVARD UNIV, 77- *Res:* Radiation therapy using beams of charged particles; radiation physics and dosimetry of protons; radiography using protons and alpha particles; proton activation analysis; accelerator design for medical applications. *Mailing Add:* Harvard Cyclotron Lab 44 Oxford St Cambridge MA 02138

KOEHLER, CARLTON SMITH, b Holyoke, Mass, July 20, 32; m 54; c 3. ECONOMIC ENTOMOLOGY. *Educ:* Univ Mass, BS, 54; Cornell Univ, MS, 56, PhD(econ entom), 58. *Prof Exp:* Res assoc econ entom, Cornell Univ, 58-59, asst prof entom & plant path, 59-62; lectr, Univ Calif, Berkeley, 62-69, from asst entomologist to entomologist, 62-75, prof entom, 69-75; prof entom & head dept, Ore State Univ, 75-76; EXTEN ENTOMOLOGIST, UNIV CALIF, BERKELEY, 76- *Concurrent Pos:* Spec field staff mem, Rockefeller Found, 68-69; consult, Int Rice Res Inst, 70-71 & Rockefeller Found, 70-; Ford Found travel fel, 71. *Mem:* Entom Soc Am. *Res:* Biology; ecology; control of insects and mites of importance in urban environments. *Mailing Add:* 28 Giannini Hall Univ of Calif Berkeley CA 94720

KOEHLER, DALE ROLAND, b Milwaukee, Wis, Oct 13, 32; m 55; c 4. RADIATION EFFECTS ON QUARTZ. *Educ:* Auburn Univ, BS, 54, MS, 55; Univ Ala, PhD(physics), 64. *Prof Exp:* Physicist, Signal Eng Labs, NJ, 55 & Army Ballistic Missile Agency, Ala, 57-58; physicist, Phys Sci Lab, Army Missile Command, 58-64, chief radiation physics br, 64-67; mgr advan res lab, Bulova Watch Co, 67-77; PHYSICIST, SANDIA LABS, 77- *Res:* Ionizing radiation effects on quartz crystal resonators, primarily on frequency and acoustic loss changes; development of quartz purification and radiation hardness assurance technologies; quartz transducer development. *Mailing Add:* Sandia Labs Org 2531 Albuquerque NM 87115

KOEHLER, DON EDWARD, b Urbana, Ill, May 10, 42. PLANT PHYSIOLOGY. *Educ:* Univ Ill, BS, 64; Purdue Univ, MS, 67; Mich State Univ, PhD(biochem), 72. *Prof Exp:* Fel develop biol, Univ Chicago, 72-74; fel plant physiol, Univ Calif, Riverside, 74-77; ASST PROF PLANT SCI, TEX A&M UNIV, 77- *Mem:* Am Soc Plant Physiologists; AAAS; Am Inst Biol Sci. *Res:* Hormonal control of enzyme induction and developmental processes in plants. *Mailing Add:* Dept of Plant Sci Tex A&M Univ College Station TX 77843

KOEHLER, DONALD OTTO, b Evansville, Ind, Feb 12, 37; m 63; c 1. PURE MATHEMATICS. *Educ:* Hanover Col, AB, 58; Ind Univ, Bloomington, MA, 60, PhD(math), 68. *Prof Exp:* Instr math, Hanover Col, 63-65; asst prof, DePauw Univ, 67-68; asst prof, 68-73, assoc prof math, 73-80, PROF MATH & STATIST, MIAMI UNIV, 80- *Mem:* Math Asn Am; Sigma Xi; Am Math Soc. *Res:* Functional analysis; semi-inner-product spaces; isometries on normed linear spaces; norms arising from multilinear functionals; numerical range of element in lmc algebra and operator on locally convex topological vector space. *Mailing Add:* Dept of Math Miami Univ Oxford OH 45056

KOEHLER, FRED EUGENE, b Naylor, Mo, Jan 25, 23; m 47; c 4. SOIL FERTILITY. *Educ:* Univ Mo, BS, 43, MS, 50, PhD(soils), 51. *Prof Exp:* Soil scientist, USDA & asst agronomist, Univ Nebr, 51-57; assoc soil scientist, 58-66, SOIL SCIENTIST & PROF SOILS, WASH STATE UNIV, 66- *Mem:* Am Soc Agron; Soil Sci Soc Am. *Res:* Soil fertility and soil chemistry. *Mailing Add:* Dept of Agron & Soils Wash State Univ Pullman WA 99164

KOEHLER, HELMUT A, b Berlin, Ger, Mar 10, 33; US citizen; m 69. NUCLEAR PHYSICS, SOLID STATE PHYSICS. *Educ:* Gen Motors Inst, BSE, 61; Univ Mich, MSE, 64, PhD(nuclear sci), 68. *Prof Exp:* PHYSICIST, LAWRENCE LIVERMORE LAB, UNIV CALIF, 68- *Concurrent Pos:* Tech consult serv, 68- *Mem:* Am Phys Soc. *Res:* Lasers and new laser systems and their appropriate application; neutron imaging and measurement systems. *Mailing Add:* Lawrence Livermore Lab Univ of Calif Box 808 Livermore CA 94550

KOEHLER, HENRY MAX, b Offenbach, Ger, Oct 13, 31; nat US; m 57. SCIENTIFIC INFORMATION, TRANSLATION. *Educ:* Roosevelt Univ, BS, 52, MS, 57, MBA, 62. *Prof Exp:* Sr water chemist, Water Bur, Chicago, 53-54; asst biochem, Med Sch, Northwestern Univ, 54-55; asst chem, Roosevelt Univ, 55-56, sr chemist, Div Chem, 56-64; ed supvr, Oral Res Abstr, Am Dent Asn, 64-72, ed updates, 70-79, ed, Oral Res Abstr, 74-79; CONSULT ED, 80- *Concurrent Pos:* Mem, State of Ill Weather Modification Bd, 74-77. *Mem:* Fel AAAS; fel Am Inst Chemists; Am Chem Soc; Am Med Writers' Asn; Am Translr Asn. *Res:* Abstract preparation; editing; translation. *Mailing Add:* 211 E Chicago Ave Chicago IL 60611

KOEHLER, JAMES K, b Darmstadt, Ger, June 7, 33; US citizen; m 57; c 5. CELL BIOLOGY. *Educ:* Univ Ill, BS, 55; Univ Calif, Berkeley, MS, 58, PhD(biophys), 61. *Prof Exp:* Asst prof physics, NMex Highlands Univ, 62-63; from asst prof to assoc prof, 63-75, PROF BIOL STRUCT, UNIV WASH, 75- *Concurrent Pos:* NIH fel, Swiss Fed Inst Technol, 61-62; vis lectr, Dept Anat, Univ Malaya, 71-72. *Mem:* Electron Micros Soc Am; Am Asn Anat; Am Soc Cell Biologists; Am Soc Study Reproduction. *Res:* Fine structure of cells and tissues; cryobiology. *Mailing Add:* Dept of Biol Struct Univ of Wash Seattle WA 98195

KOEHLER, JAMES STARK, b Oshkosh, Wis, Nov 10, 14; m 40; c 2. PHYSICS. *Educ:* Wis State Teachers Col, BEd, 35; Univ Mich, PhD, 40. *Prof Exp:* Rackham fel, Univ Mich, 40-41; Westinghouse res fel, 41-42; instr physics, Carnegie Inst Technol, 42-46, assoc prof, 46-50; assoc prof, 50-53, PROF PHYSICS, UNIV ILL, URBANA, 53- *Concurrent Pos:* Guggenheim fel, 57; mem solid state adv comt, Oak Ridge Nat Lab. *Mem:* Fel Am Phys Soc. *Res:* Effects of internal rotation on molecular spectra; plastic deformation of solids; radiation damage; point defects produced by quenching, irradiation and ion bombardment. *Mailing Add:* Dept of Physics Univ of Ill Urbana IL 61801

KOEHLER, LAWRENCE D, b Grand Rapids, Mich, Feb 19, 32; m 60; c 3. DEVELOPMENTAL BIOLOGY, PHYSIOLOGY. *Educ:* Otterbein Col, BS, 54; Mich State Univ, PhD(zool), 60. *Prof Exp:* From asst prof to assoc prof, 60-68, PROF BIOL, CENT MICH UNIV, 68-, CHMN DEPT, 75- *Concurrent Pos:* NIH spec res fel, Inst Molecular Evolution, Univ Miami, 68-69. *Mem:* Am Soc Zoologists; Am Soc Cell Biologists; Am Soc Study Reproduction; Int Soc Develop Biol; Electron Micros Soc Am. *Res:* gametogenesis and fertilization, including ultrastructural changes in gametes and early zygotes. *Mailing Add:* Dept Biol Cent Mich Univ Mt Pleasant MI 48859

KOEHLER, MARK E, b Dayton, Ohio, July 6, 49; m 70; c 1. INSTRUMENTATION. *Educ:* Univ Dayton, BS, 71; Wright State Univ, MS, 73; Case Western Reserve Univ, PhD(chem), 78. *Prof Exp:* Chemist, 78-80, SECT LEADER, GLIDDEN COATINGS & RESINS, DIV SCM CORP, 80- *Mem:* Am Chem Soc. *Res:* Development and computer interfacing of laboratory instrumentation; areas of computer applications in chemistry; scientific computing and analog and digital electronics. *Mailing Add:* 16775 Elderdale Dr Middleburg Heights OH 44130

KOEHLER, P RUBEN, b Berlin, Ger, Apr 29, 31; US citizen; m; c 2. RADIOLOGY. *Educ:* Univ Bern, MD, 56. *Prof Exp:* Assoc radiol, Albert Einstein Med Ctr, Philadelphia, Pa, 61-62; instr, Sch Med, Temple Univ, 62-64; from asst prof to prof, Sch Med, Washington Univ, 64-70; PROF RADIOL, COL MED, UNIV UTAH, 70-, CHIEF, DIV DIAG RADIOL, 80- *Mem:* Am Col Radiol; Am Roentgen Ray Soc; Radiol Soc NAm; Asn Univ Radiologists; Int Soc Lymphology. *Res:* Lymphology; visceral arteriography. *Mailing Add:* Dept of Radiol Univ of Utah Col of Med Salt Lake City UT 84112

KOEHLER, PHILIP EDWARD, b Kansas City, Mo, Mar 30, 43; m 66; c 2. FOOD SCIENCE. *Educ:* Emporia Kans State Col, BS, 65; Okla State Univ, PhD(biochem), 69. *Prof Exp:* From asst prof to assoc prof, 69-76, mem staff, 76-80, PROF FOOD SCI, UNIV GA, 80- *Mem:* Am Chem Soc; Inst Food Technologists; Sigma Xi. *Res:* Food safety and toxicology; food colorants. *Mailing Add:* Dept of Food Sci Univ of Ga Athens GA 30602

KOEHLER, PHILIP GENE, b Doylestown, Pa, July 21, 47; m 74. ENTOMOLOGY. *Educ:* Catawba Col, AB, 69; Cornell Univ, PhD(entom), 72. *Prof Exp:* Asst prof, 75-80, ASSOC PROF EXTEN ENTOM, UNIV FLA, 80- *Concurrent Pos:* Coordr grant, Develop 4-H Integrated Pest Mgt Curric, 78-79. *Mem:* Am Mosquito Control Asn; Entom Soc Am; Am Registry Prof Entomologists; Sigma Xi. *Res:* Livestock, poultry and dairy pest management; household and structural pest management; pasture pest management. *Mailing Add:* 214 Newell Hall Univ of Fla Gainesville FL 32611

KOEHLER, RICHARD FREDERICK, JR, b New York, NY, Mar 27, 45; m 69; c 2. PHYSICS, ELECTRICAL ENGINEERING. *Educ:* Mass Inst Technol, BS, 67; Stanford Univ, MS, 68, PhD(elec eng), 72. *Prof Exp:* Assoc scientist, 72-75, scientist, 75-78, sr scientist, 78-80, AREA MGR, XEROX CORP, 80- *Mem:* Soc Photog Scientists & Engrs. *Res:* Physics and materials of the xerographic system. *Mailing Add:* 800 Lauren Ct Webster NY 14580

KOEHLER, THOMAS RICHARD, b Toledo, Ohio, Aug 8, 32; m 61. PHYSICS. *Educ:* Seattle Univ, BS, 54; Calif Inst Technol, PhD(physics), 60. *Prof Exp:* Physicist, Aeronutronic Div, Ford Motor Co, 59-60; STAFF PHYSICIST, SAN JOSE RES LAB, IBM CORP, 60- *Mem:* Am Phys Soc. *Res:* Theoretical solid state and low temperature physics. *Mailing Add:* IBM Res K32 281 5600 Cottle Rd San Jose CA 95193

KOEHLER, TRUMAN L, JR, b Allentown, Pa, Apr 9, 31; m 54; c 3. STATISTICS. *Educ:* Muhlenberg Col, BS, 52; Rutgers Univ, MS, 57. *Prof Exp:* Engr qual control, Sylvania Elec Prod Inc, 52-57; statistician, Am Cyanamid Co, 57, head qual control sect, Org Chem Div, 57-62, mgr systs anal, 62-66, mfg mgr, Org Pigments Dept, 66-68, dir mkt, Pigments Div, 68-70, mgr titanium dioxide dept, 70-77, dir planning, 77-79, gen mgr, Spec Prods Dept, 79-80; EXEC VPRES & CHIEF OPER OFFICER, SODYECO DIV, MARTIN MARIETTA CHEM, 81- *Concurrent Pos:* Lectr, Rutgers Univ, 57-; partic, NSF TV Prog, Pursuit of Perfection, 65- *Honors & Awards:* Award, Rochester Inst Technol, 64. *Mem:* Fel Am Soc Qual Control; Am Statist Asn; Am Inst Chem Engrs. *Res:* Design and analysis of experimental programs; numerical analysis and computing. *Mailing Add:* 5222 Winding Brook Rd Charlotte NC 28211

KOEHLER, WALLACE CONRAD, b Chicago, Ill, Aug 25, 20; m 43; c 2. PHYSICS. *Educ:* Univ Chicago, BS, 43, MS, 48; Univ Tenn, PhD(physics), 53. *Hon Degrees:* Dr, Univ Grenoble, France, 79. *Prof Exp:* Jr physicist x-ray diffraction, Argonne Nat Lab, 45-48; asst prof physics, Va Polytech Inst, 48-49; physicist, 49-64, group leader neutron diffraction, 64-79, sect head crystal physics, 72-79, DIR, NAT CTR SMALL ANGLE SCATTERING RES, OAK RIDGE NAT LAB, 78- *Concurrent Pos:* Fulbright & Guggenheim fels, Univ Grenoble, 58-59; Carbide Corp fel, 79. *Mem:* Fel Am Phys Soc; Am Crystallog Asn. *Res:* Solid state physics; magnetism; crystallography; neutron scattering. *Mailing Add:* Oak Ridge Nat Lab Oak Ridge TN 37830

KOEHLER, WILBERT FREDERICK, b Braddock, Pa, Feb 20, 13; m 36; c 2. OPTICAL PHYSICS. *Educ:* Allegheny Col, BS, 33; Cornell Univ, MA, 34; Johns Hopkins Univ, PhD(physics), 49. *Prof Exp:* Pub sch instr, Pa, 34-36; instr, Punahou Acad, Hawaii, 36-43; instr physics, Johns Hopkins Univ, 46-48; assoc prof, Naval Postgrad Sch, 48-51; sect head phys optics, Naval Ord Test Sta, 51-54, res scientist, 54-58, head physics div, 58-61; asst dean, 61-62, dean progs, 62-76, EMER DEAN & DISTINGUISHED EMER PROF PHYSICS, NAVAL POSTGRAD SCH, 76- *Mem:* Am Phys Soc; fel Optical Soc Am; Am Asn Physics Teachers; Am Soc Eng Educ. *Res:* Multiple-beam interferometry; optical constants; surface smoothness; specific heats of gases; solid state physics. *Mailing Add:* 52 Alta Mesa Circle Monterey CA 93940

KOEHLER, WILLIAM HENRY, b Houston, Tex, Feb 17, 39. INORGANIC CHEMISTRY. *Educ:* Southern Methodist Univ, BS, 60, MS, 62; Univ Tex, Austin, PhD(chem), 69. *Prof Exp:* Instr chem, Southern Methodist Univ, 61-63; res scientist, Tracor, Inc, Tex, 68-69; asst prof, 69-74, ASSOC PROF CHEM, TEX CHRISTIAN UNIV, 74-, ACTG DEAN GRAD SCH, 78-, VCHANCELLOR ACAD AFFAIRS, 80- *Concurrent Pos:* Vpres, Tex Christian Univ Res Found. *Mem:* Nat Coun Univ Res Adminr; Am Chem Soc. *Res:* Raman spectroscopy; reflection and transmission spectroscopy; characterization of metal-ammonia solutions; synthesis and reaction mechanisms in nonaqueous solvents. *Mailing Add:* Grad Sch Tex Christian Univ Ft Worth TX 76109

KOEHN, PAUL V, b Bristol, Conn, Jan 10, 31; m 63; c 3. BIOCHEMISTRY. *Educ:* Bates Col, BS, 52; Cent Mo State Col, MSEd, 58; Univ Conn, PhD(biochem), 64. *Prof Exp:* Jr chemist, Am Cyanamid Co, 52-55; instr gen chem, Cent Mo State Col, 56-58; instr biochem, Univ Conn, 63-64; assoc prof biochem, 67-70, head dept, 69-70, fac res grant, 71, PROF BIOCHEM, STATE UNIV NY COL ONEONTA, 69-, CHMN DEPT, 70- *Concurrent Pos:* NY State Res Found grant, 68-70; fac grants, State Univ NY, 74 & 77. *Mem:* Am Chem Soc; Sigma Xi. *Res:* Synthesis of phosphopeptides and structural studies of proteins. *Mailing Add:* Dept of Chem State Univ of NY Oneonta NY 13820

KOEHN, RICHARD KARL, b Niles, Mich, Aug 25, 40; m 65; c 1. POPULATION GENETICS. *Educ:* Western Mich Univ, BA, 63; Ariz State Univ, PhD(genetics), 67. *Prof Exp:* Trainee immunol, Univ Kans, 67, asst prof zool, 67-70; vis scientist genetics, Aarhus Univ, 70-71 & 76-77; assoc prof ecol & evolution & provost biol sci, 71-80, PROF ECOL & EVOLUTION & DEAN BIOL SCI, STATE UNIV NY STONY BROOK, 80- *Concurrent Pos:* NSF & NIH grants; NATO sr sci fel, 70; assoc ed, J Soc Study Evolution, 75-77; George C Marshall fel, Denmark, 76-77; ed, Marine Biol Letters, 78- *Mem:* AAAS; Am Soc Naturalists; Genetics Soc Am; Soc Study Evolution. *Res:* Evolutionary genetics of natural populations, particularly marine invertebrates; protein function, structure and adaptation. *Mailing Add:* Dept Ecol & Evolution State Univ NY Stony Brook NY 11790

KOELLA, WERNER PAUL, b Zurich, Switz, Apr 13, 17; nat US; m 55; c 3. NEUROPHYSIOLOGY. *Educ:* Univ Zurich, MD, 42. *Prof Exp:* Resident neurosurg, Univ Zurich, 43-45, resident physiol, 45-48, head asst dept, 48-51; res assoc neurophysiol, Univ Minn, 51-52, assoc prof, 52-55; mem staff, Worcester Found Exp Biol, 57-68; chmn dept pharmacol & med, Robapharm Ag, 68-70; sr mem staff, Lab Neurophysiol, Ciba-Geigy Ltd, 70-82; RETIRED. *Concurrent Pos:* Prof affil, Clark Univ, 57-, Boston Univ, 59 & Univ Berne, 70. *Mem:* AAAS; Am Physiol Soc; Am Soc Pharmacol & Exp Therapeut; fel Am Col Neuropsychopharmacol; NY Acad Sci. *Res:* Cerebellum; vestibular apparatus; subcortical-cortical relationships; sleep; organization of autonomic functions; neuropharmacology. *Mailing Add:* Buchenstrasse 1 4104 Oberwil Switzerland

KOELLE, GEORGE BRAMPTON, b Philadelphia, Pa, Oct 8, 18; m 54; c 3. PHARMACOLOGY. *Educ:* Philadelphia Col Pharm & Sci, BSc, 39; Univ Pa, PhD(pharmacol), 46; Johns Hopkins Univ, MD, 50. *Hon Degrees:* DSc, Philadelphia Col Pharm & Sci, 65; Dr Med, Univ Zurich, 72. *Prof Exp:* Bioassayist, LaWall & Harrisson, Pa, 39-42; asst prof pharmacol, Columbia Univ, 50-52; prof, Grad Div Med, 52-65, dean, 57-59, prof pharmacol & chmn dept, 59-81, DISTINGUISHED PROF, SCH MED, UNIV PA, 81- *Concurrent Pos:* Consult, pharmaceut indust, 51-, Philadelphia Gen Hosp, 53-71, Valley Forge Army Hosp, 54-70, Army Chem Corps, 56-61, Philadelphia Naval Hosp, 57-; Hachmeister lectr, Med Sch, Georgetown Univ, 52; Merck lectr, Med Sch, McGill Univ, 55; vis lectr, Philadelphia Col Pharm & Sci, 55-57, trustee, 62-; consult, Study Sect Pharmacol & Exp Therapeut, NIH, 58-62, chmn, 65-68, bd sci counr, Nat Heart Inst, 60-64, chmn eval clin ther adv comt, Nat Inst Neurol Dis & Stroke, 68-70, mem, Nat Adv Neurol Dis & Stroke Coun, 70-74; ed, Pharmacol Rev, 59-62; spec lectr, Univ London, 62; vis lectr, Biophys Inst, Univ Brazil, 62; Guggenheim fel & vis prof, Inst Physiol, Univ Lausanne, 63-64; secy-gen, Int Union Pharmacol, 66-69, vpres, 69-72; prof & actg chmn dept pharmacol, Med Sch, Pahlavi Univ, Iran, 69-70; P K Smith lectr, George Washington Univ, 71; vis prof, Polish Acad Sci, 79. *Honors & Awards:* Abel Prize & Borden Award, 50. *Mem:* Nat Acad Sci; fel AAAS (vpres, 71); Am Soc Pharmacol & Exp Therapeut (pres, 65-66); Brit Pharmacol Soc; Soc Neurosci. *Res:* Neuropharmacology; histochemistry; electron microscopy; anticholinesterase agents; neurohumoral transmitters. *Mailing Add:* Dept of Pharmacol Univ of Pa Sch of Med G3 Philadelphia PA 19104

KOELLER, RALPH CARL, b Chicago, Ill, Aug 9, 33; m 75; c 2. MECHANICAL ENGINEERING, CONTINUUM MECHANICS. *Educ:* Ill Inst Technol, BS, 57, MS, 59, PhD(mech), 63. *Prof Exp:* Res & teaching asst mech eng, Ill Inst Technol, 59-62; instr, Univ Colo, 62-63; asst prof, 63-79, PROF MECH ENG, UNIV COLO, 79- *Concurrent Pos:* Univ Colo Fac fel, Univ Calif, Berkeley, 65-66; consult, Colo Instruments Inc, 69, Dow Chem Co, 70-71, Dieterich Standards Corp, 73 & Hewlett-Packard Co, 74; resident fac fel, Am Soc Eng Educrs, 74-75; vis asst prof, Cornell Univ, 76-77; consult, Ponderosa Assoc, 78- *Mem:* Am Soc Mech Engrs. *Res:* Thermomechanical field theory; plate and shell theory; tire mechanics. *Mailing Add:* Dept of Mech Eng 1100 14th St Denver CO 80202

KOELLER, RAYMOND C(HARLES), b Chicago, Ill, May 14, 25; m 49; c 2. CHEMICAL ENGINEERING. *Educ:* Univ Ill, BS, 49, MS, 50, PhD(chem eng), 52. *Prof Exp:* Res engr, Pan Am Petrol Corp, 52-57, tech group leader, 57-60, res group supvr, 60-62; planning supvr, 62-67, dir planning develop & procedures, 67-71, mgr investment res, 71-77, DIR INVESTOR RELS, STAND OIL CO, INC, 77- *Mem:* Financial Analysts Fedn; Am Inst Mining, Metall & Petrol Engrs. *Res:* Diffusion in compressed liquids; hydrocarbon fluid phase behavior; fluid flow in porous media; primary and secondary oil recovery methods, economics and finance of corporate long range planning. *Mailing Add:* Stand Oil Co of Ind 200 E Randolph Chicago IL 60601

KOELLING, DALE DEAN, b Great Bend, Kans, May 8, 41; m 68; c 2. SOLID STATE SCIENCE. *Educ:* Kans State Univ, BS, 63; Mass Inst Technol, PhD(physics), 68. *Prof Exp:* Res assoc, Northwestern Univ, 68-72; PHYSICIST SOLID STATE SCI, ARGONNE NAT LAB, 72- *Mem:* Am Phys Soc. *Res:* Electronic structure and resulting properties primarily in metallic or semiconducting actinide, rare-earth, or transition element materials. *Mailing Add:* Solid State Sci Div Argonne Nat Lab Argonne IL 60439

KOELLING, MELVIN R, b Sullivan, Mo, July 18, 37; m 59. FORESTRY. *Educ:* Univ Mo, BS, 59, MS, 61, PhD(bot), 64. *Prof Exp:* Assoc plant physiol, Northeast Forest Exp Sta, USDA, 64-67; from asst prof to assoc prof, 67-77, PROF FORESTRY & EXTEN SPECIALIST, MICH STATE UNIV, 77- *Mem:* AAAS; Am Inst Biol Sci; Ecol Soc Am; Soc Am Foresters. *Res:* Botany; improvement of sugar maple with respect to sap production; maple sap physiology. *Mailing Add:* Dept of Forestry Mich State Univ East Lansing MI 48824

KOELSCH, THEODORE ALLEN, b Fairfield, Ill, Apr 12, 51. EXPERIMENTAL ROCK DEFORMATION. *Educ:* Occidental Col, BA, 73; Univ Ill Champaign-Urbana, MS, 76, PhD(geol), 79. *Prof Exp:* Res geologist, 79-80, SR RES GEOLOGIST, EXXON PROD RES CO, 80- *Mem:* Am Geophys Union; Am Asn Petrol Geologists; Soc Explor Geophysicists. *Res:* Experimental rock deformation; analytical structural geology; engineering geology. *Mailing Add:* Exxon Prod Res Co PO Box 2189 Houston TX 77001

KOELSCHE, CHARLES L, b Seattle, Wash, Sept 23, 06; m 44. INORGANIC CHEMISTRY, ANALYTICAL CHEMISTRY. *Educ:* Univ Southern Calif, AB, 28, MS, 30; Ind Univ, EdD(gen educ), 53. *Prof Exp:* Pub sch teacher sci & math, 29-42; Fed Security Agency inspector, US Food & Drug Admin, 42-44; assoc prof chem & chmn dept, Univ Alaska, 44-47; assoc prof, Ariz State Univ, 47-52; assoc prof phys sci, Wis State Col, Eau Claire, 52-57; prof sci educ & chem, Univ Toledo, 57-58; specialist for sci, US Off Educ, 58-59; spec asst to dir off sci personnel, Nat Acad Sci-Nat Res Coun, 59-60; prof sci educ, Univ Ga, 60-74; consult sci educ, 74-78; chmn dept sci, Athens Acad, 78-81; RETIRED. *Concurrent Pos:* NSF Summer & In-serv Insts Sci Teachers, Univ Ga, 61-73. *Res:* Chemistry; physics; physical science; science education. *Mailing Add:* 1397 Coyote Rd Prescott AZ 86301

KOELSCHE, GILES ALEXANDER, b Ashland, Ore, Sept 3, 08; m 30; c 2. INTERNAL MEDICINE. *Educ:* Pac Union Col, BS, 30; Col Med Evangelists, MD, 31; Univ Minn, MS & PhD(med), 35. *Prof Exp:* Fel, Mayo Found, Univ Minn, 31-35; asst, 35-37, from instr to assoc prof, 37-74, consult, Div Med, Mayo Clin, 37-74, EMER ASSOC PROF CLIN MED, MAYO GRAD SCH MED, UNIV MINN, 74- *Mem:* Emer fel Am Acad Allergy; emer fel Am Col Allergists (pres, 60-61). *Res:* Newer therapy for asthma, hay fever and perennial allergic rhinitis; management of chronic urticaria; problems of immunologic tolerance and organ transplantation; auto-immune diseases; immunology in relation to cancer. *Mailing Add:* 13825 Crown Point Sun City AZ 85351

KOELTZOW, DONALD EARL, b Clovis, NMex, May 9, 44; m 65; c 3. BIOCHEMISTRY, ORGANIC CHEMISTRY. *Educ:* NMex Inst Mining & Technol, BS, 66; Univ Ill, MS, 68, PhD(biochem), 70. *Prof Exp:* Fel med microbiol, Stanford Univ, 70-71; assoc res scientist pharmacol, Univ Iowa, 77-78; asst prof, 71-77, ASSOC PROF CHEM, LUTHER COL, 77-, CHMN DEPT, 78- *Concurrent Pos:* US Army med res grant, 73-75. *Mem:* Am Chem Soc; Am Soc Microbiol; AAAS; Midwest Asn Chem Teachers Lib Arts Cols. *Res:* Structure and function of membrane components, particularly carbohydrates and lipids. *Mailing Add:* Dept of Chem Luther Col Decorah IA 52101

KOELZER, VICTOR A, b Seneca, Mo, May 3, 14; m 50; c 1. HYDRAULIC ENGINEERING. *Educ:* Univ Kans, BS, 37; Univ Iowa, MS, 39. *Prof Exp:* Jr engr, US Geol Surv, Iowa, 38-40; jr asst engr, Corps Engrs, Ky, 40-42; from sr engr to head engr, Bur Reclamation, Washington, DC, 46-48 & 54-56 & Colo, 48-54; from hydraul engr to vpres, Harza Eng Co, Ill, 56-69; chief eng & environ sci, Nat Water Comn, 69-76; PRES, ENG FARMS INC, 76- *Concurrent Pos:* Mem comt water, Nat Acad Sci, 65-67; teacher, Colo State Univ, Ft Collins, 72-; consult, 72- *Honors & Awards:* Julian Hinds Award, Am Soc Civil Engrs, 75. *Mem:* Am Soc Civil Engrs; Am Geophys Union; Sigma Xi; Am Water Resources Asn. *Res:* Hydrology; sedimentation; hydropower; water resources; development and operating of irrigation land. *Mailing Add:* 1604 Miramont Ft Collins CO 85024

KOEN, BILLY VAUGHN, b Graham, Tex, May 2, 38; m 67; c 2. NUCLEAR ENGINEERING. *Educ:* Univ Tex, Austin, BA, 60, BS, 61; Mass Inst Technol, SM, 62, ScD(nuclear eng), 68; Saclay Nuclear Res Ctr, France, dipl eng, 63. *Prof Exp:* Asst prof, 68-71, assoc prof nuclear eng, 71-80, ASSOC PROF MECH ENG, UNIV TEX, AUSTIN, 80- *Concurrent Pos:* Foreign collabr, French Atomic Energy Comn, 71-72. *Mem:* Am Nuclear Soc; Am Soc Eng Educ; NY Acad Sci. *Res:* Nuclear reactor kinetics; engineering education. *Mailing Add:* Dept of Mech Eng N 217 Univ of Tex Austin TX 78712

KOENG, FRED R, b Wilmington, Del, Aug 6, 41; m 63; c 1. ORGANIC CHEMISTRY. *Educ:* Franklin & Marshall Col, AB, 63; Northwestern Univ, PhD(org chem), 70. *Prof Exp:* Chemist, Rohm and Haas Co, 65-67; sr res chemist, 70-80, RES ASSOC, EASTMAN KODAK CO, 80- *Mem:* AAAS; Soc Photog Scientists & Engrs. *Res:* Photographic systems research. *Mailing Add:* Eastman Kodak Co 343 State St Rochester NY 14650

KOENIG, ALBERT A, b Baltimore, Md, Feb 2, 45; m 68; c 3. LOW TEMPERATURE PHYSICS, LASERS. *Educ:* Loyola Col, Md, BS, 66; Duke Univ, PhD(physics), 74. *Prof Exp:* Res assoc physics, Haverford Col, 74-75; energy engr, Space Systs Div, 75-80, PROJ ENGR, ADV ENERGY PROGS DIV, GEN ELEC CO, 80- *Res:* High temperature solar energy systems design and thermal modelling; experimental and theoretical interests in critical phenomena utilizing laser spectroscopy. *Mailing Add:* Gen Elec Corp Adv Energy Progs Div 501 Allendale Rd King of Prussia PA 19406

KOENIG, CHARLES JACOB, b St Marys, Ohio, June 3, 11; m 52; c 5. CERAMIC ENGINEERING. *Educ:* Ohio State Univ, BCerE, 32, MS, 33, PhD(ceramic eng), 35, CE, 48. *Prof Exp:* Res engr, Eng Exp Sta, 35-41, prof, 56-73, EMER PROF CERAMIC ENG, OHIO STATE UNIV, 73-; SR RES ENGR, EDWARD ORTON JR CERAMIC FOUNDATION, 73- *Concurrent Pos:* Dir res, Am Nepheline Corp, 45-66 vpres res & dir, 60-64, pres, 64-66; dir, Indust Minerals Can, Ltd, 47-65, vpres res, 60-66; trustee, Whiteware Div, Am Ceramic Soc, 63-66; consult, Anchor Hocking Corp, 73-76 & Gorham Div, Textron, Inc, 76- *Mem:* Fel Am Ceramic Soc; Am Soc Testing & Mat; Nat Inst Ceramic Engrs. *Res:* Electrical porcelain; dinnerware; tile; glass; porcelain enamel; sanitary porcelain; refractories; multiple fluxes for promoting glassy phases in whiteware bodies; effect of furnace atmosphere in firing ceramics; pyrometric cones. *Mailing Add:* 1521 Guilford Rd Columbus OH 43221

KOENIG, CHARLES LOUIS, b Yonkers, NY, Oct 11, 11; m; c 4. PHYSICAL CHEMISTRY. *Educ:* NY Univ, BS, 32, PhD(chem), 36. *Prof Exp:* Sr chemist, Solvay Process Co, NY, 36-45; res chemist, Lithaloys Corp, 45-46; chief res br, AEC, 46-47; chmn dept chem & chem eng res, Armour Res Found, 47-49; asst dir res, Stanford Res Inst, 50-51; vpres, Southwest Res Inst, 51-56; OWNER, LOUIS KOENIG RES, 56- *Concurrent Pos:* Asst ed, Chem Abstr, 49-; adv, Saline Water Conservion Prog, Secy Interior, 52-56; adv advan waste treatment prog, USPHS, 60-63. *Mem:* AAAS; Sigma Xi; Am Chem Soc; Am Water Works Asn; Am Inst Chem Engrs. *Res:* Phase relations of aqueous systems; water resources; waste disposal; cost engineering; market research; economics. *Mailing Add:* Louis Koenig Res Rte 10 Box 108 San Antonio TX 78258

KOENIG, DANIEL RENE, b Rouen, France, Oct 6, 36; US citizen; m 58; c 2. NUCLEAR ENGINEERING. *Educ:* Univ Calif, Berkeley, BS, 59, MS, 65, PhD(eng sci), 66. *Prof Exp:* Physicist, Defense Atomic Support Agency, 65-67; PHYSICIST, LOS ALAMOS SCI LAB, UNIV CALIF, 69- *Concurrent Pos:* Vis physicist, Ctr Nuclear Studies, France, 67-68; Saclay, 79-80. *Honors & Awards:* Teller Award, Am Nuclear Soc, 66. *Mem:* Am Nuclear Soc. *Res:* Surface physics phenomena such as thermionic emission and surface ionization; detection and theoretical transport of neutron, gamma and x-ray radiations; application of heat pipes to solar energy; design of fast-spectrum nuclear reactors for space applications; design of small solar thermodynamic engines. *Mailing Add:* 129 Huddleson St Santa Fe NM 87501

KOENIG, EDWARD, b New York, NY, Nov 10, 28; m 53; c 3. NEUROBIOLOGY, NEUROCHEMISTRY. *Educ:* Franklin & Marshall Col, BA, 56; Univ Pa, PhD(physiol), 61. *Prof Exp:* From asst prof to assoc prof, 63-75, PROF PHYSIOL, STATE UNIV NY BUFFALO, 75- *Concurrent Pos:* Res career prog award, Nat Inst Neurol Dis & Stroke, 68-73. *Mem:* AAAS; Am Physiol Soc; Am Soc Neurochem; Int Soc Neurochem; Soc Neurosci. *Res:* Control and regulation of protein synthesis in the neuron and its major subdivisions as they relate to the altered functional and growth rate; microchemistry; microanalysis. *Mailing Add:* Dept of Physiol State Univ of NY Buffalo NY 14214

KOENIG, ELDO C(LYDE), b Marissa, Ill, Oct 17, 19; m 50; c 4. ELECTRICAL ENGINEERING. *Educ:* Wash Univ, St Louis, BS, 43; Ill Inst Technol, MS, 49; Univ Wis, PhD(elec eng), 56. *Prof Exp:* Test engr, Allis Chalmers Mfg Co, 44-46, engr, 46-52, supvr comput lab, 54-57, engr in chg eng anal, 57-62; assoc prof numerical anal, 62-64, ASSOC PROF COMPUT SCI, ASSOC PROF INSTR RES LAB EDUC & ASSOC DIR SYNNOETICS LAB, SCH EDUC, UNIV WIS-MADISON, 64- *Honors & Awards:* Noble Prize, 51. *Mem:* AAAS; Am Math Soc; Soc Indust & Appl Math; Asn Comput Mach; assoc mem Inst Elec & Electronics Engrs. *Res:* Engineering and mathematical analysis and research for computers; systems and design; intelligent properties of systems. *Mailing Add:* Synnoetics Lab Sch Educ Univ of Wis Madison WI 53706

KOENIG, HAROLD, b New York, NY, Mar 16, 21; m 45; c 2. NEUROLOGY. *Educ:* Rutgers Univ, BS, 42; Chicago Med Sch, MD, 47; Northwestern Univ, MS, 45; Univ Pa, PhD(anat), 48. *Prof Exp:* Res assoc anat, Med Sch, Univ Wash, 47; from instr to asst prof, Univ Pa, 47-49; from asst prof to assoc prof, Chicago Med Sch, 49-54; from asst prof to assoc prof neurol, 57-63, PROF NEUROL, NORTHWESTERN UNIV, CHICAGO, 63-; CHIEF NEUROL, VET ADMIN LAKESIDE MED CTR, 57- *Concurrent Pos:* Resident physician, Univ Chicago Clin, 55; mem, Vet Admin Prog Comt Psychiat, Neurol & Psychol, 61-63; sr physician, Vet Admin, 71-75. *Mem:* Am Soc Cell Biol; Histochem Soc; Sigma Xi; NY Acad Sci; Am Acad Neurol. *Res:* Metabolic bases of neurological disease; nucleic acid and protein metabolism in nervous system; effects of nucleic acid antimetabolites; experimental neuropathology; lysosomes and other storage particles; neurochemistry; neurohistochemistry; electron microscopy. *Mailing Add:* Neurol Serv Vet Admin 333 E Huron St Chicago IL 60611

KOENIG, HARVEY STEVEN, textile chemistry, polymer chemistry, see previous edition

KOENIG, HERMAN E, b Marissa, Ill, Dec 12, 24; m 49; c 3. ELECTRICAL ENGINEERING. *Educ:* Univ Ill, BS, 47, MS, 49, PhD(elec eng), 53. *Prof Exp:* Asst prof elec eng, Univ Ill, 53-54 & 55-56 & Mass Inst Technol, 54-55; assoc prof, 56-59, chmn dept elec eng & systs sci, 69-75, PROF ELEC ENG, MICH STATE UNIV, 59-, DIR SYSTS SCI PROG, 67-, DIR CTR ENVIRON QUAL, 75-, OFF VPRES RES & GRAD STUDIES, 80- *Concurrent Pos:* Consult, Reliance Elec & Eng Co, Ohio, 51-54 & Lear Siegler, Inc, Mich, 63-65. *Mem:* Am Soc Eng Educ; Soc Eng Sci; Inst Elec & Electronics Engrs. *Res:* Theory of electrical networks and other physical systems; transportation; business and other socio-economic systems; operations research; industrialized ecosystem design and management; energy and energy resources. *Mailing Add:* Dir Ctr for Environ Qual Mich State Univ East Lansing MI 48824

KOENIG, INGE RABES, b Heuchelheim, Ger, Dec 1, 21; US citizen; wid; c 1. PHYSICAL CHEMISTRY. *Educ:* Univ Marburg, PhD(phys chem), 45. *Prof Exp:* Docent chem, Agr Col Friedberg, Ger, 45-47; res assoc, Inst Metal Res, Univ Marburg, 47-49; docent chem, Voc Educ Inst, Univ Frankfurt, 49-55; from asst prof to assoc prof, 61-70, PROF PHYS CHEM, SAN JOSE STATE UNIV, 70- *Concurrent Pos:* Fulbright res fel, Stanford Univ, 54. *Res:* Chemical thermodynamics. *Mailing Add:* Dept of Chem San Jose State Univ San Jose CA 95192

KOENIG, JACK L, b Cody, Nebr, Feb 12, 33; m 53; c 4. POLYMER CHEMISTRY, PHYSICAL CHEMISTRY. *Educ:* Yankton Col, BA, 56; Univ Nebr, MS, 58, PhD(chem), 60. *Prof Exp:* Mem staff, Plastics Dept, E I du Pont de Nemours & Co, 59-63; from asst prof to assoc prof chem, 63-70, PROF MACROMOLECULAR SCI, CASE WESTERN RESERVE UNIV, 70- *Concurrent Pos:* Consult, Diamond Alkali Co & Sohio Res, Ohio & anal res div, Esso Res & Eng Co, NJ, 59-63; NSF & NASA res grants, 65-78; consult instrument prod div, E I du Pont de Nemours & Co, Del, 63- *Honors & Awards:* Res Award, Sigma Xi, 70. *Mem:* Am Chem Soc; Am Phys Soc; Soc Appl Spectros. *Res:* Spectroscopy of polymeric materials. *Mailing Add:* Dept of Macro Sci University Circle Case Western Reserve Univ Cleveland OH 44106

KOENIG, JAMES J(ACOB), b Le Mars, Iowa, Sept 4, 18; m 51; c 4. CHEMICAL ENGINEERING. *Educ:* Iowa State Col, BS, 39. *Prof Exp:* Foreman, Procter & Gamble Mfg Co, Kans, 40-41; gen foreman & tech supvr, Tenn, 41-44; asst dir prod div, NY Opers Off, USAEC, 46-47, asst area mgr, Mo, 47-52, chief, Fla Field Off, 52-56; res engr, Aluminum Co Am, 56-67, sr res engr, 67-77; MEM STAFF, JAMES J KOENIG CONSULT, INC, 81- *Mem:* Am Inst Chem Engrs; Sigma Xi; Tech Asn Pulp & Paper Indust; Fedn Socs Coatings Technol. *Res:* Explosives loading; uranium extraction and metallurgy; alumina chemicals. *Mailing Add:* 129 Country Club Acres Belleville IL 62223

KOENIG, JANE QUINN, b Seattle, Wash, Sept 16, 35; c 2. RESPIRATORY PHYSIOLOGY. *Educ:* Univ Wash, BS, 59, MS, 61, PhD(physiol psychol), 63. *Prof Exp:* Fel neurophysiol, Med Sch, Stanford Univ, 63-65; asst prof, Med Sch, 66-70, vis scientist, 70-71, actg asst prof physiol, Dept Zool, 72-73, ASST PROF, DEPT ENVIRON HEALTH, SCH PUB HEALTH & COMMUNITY MED, UNIV WASH, 74- *Mem:* AAAS; Fedn Am Scientists; Union Concerned Scientists. *Res:* Effects of acute exposures to air pollutants upon respiratory physiology in human volunteers. *Mailing Add:* Dept Environ Health SC-34 Univ Wash Seattle WA 98195

KOENIG, JOHN HENRY, b St Marys, Ohio, Apr 9, 09; m 42; c 2. CERAMIC ENGINEERING. *Educ:* Ohio State Univ, BChE, 31, MSc, 36, PhD(ceramic eng), 38. *Prof Exp:* Res chemist, Gen Elec Co, Mass, 31-35; res engr, Hall China Co, Ohio, 38-42; dir sch ceramics, NJ Ceramic Res Sta, 45-70, adj prof ceramics, 70, EMER PROF, RUTGERS UNIV, 70- *Concurrent Pos:* Pres, VI Int Glass Cong, 62-65. *Honors & Awards:* Jeppson Award, Am Ceramic Soc, 63; Award Merit, Am Soc Testing & Mat, 69. *Mem:* Hon mem Am Ceramic Soc; fel Am Soc Testing & Mat; Ceramic Educ Coun (pres, 55-56). *Mailing Add:* 1967 H-Rd Delta CO 81416

KOENIG, JOHN WALDO, b Newark, NJ, July 19, 20; m 50; c 1. PALEONTOLOGY. *Educ:* Columbia Univ, BS, 47; Univ Kans, MS, 51. *Prof Exp:* Sci illusr, Kans State Geol Surv, 47-51; geol engr, Phillips Petrol Co, 51-54; geologist, Mo Geol Surv & Water Resources, 54-65, Continental Oil Co, 65-66 & Mo Geol Surv, 66-67; TECH ED, UNIV MO-ROLLA, 67- *Concurrent Pos:* Lectr art, Univ Mo-Rolla, 74-80. *Mem:* Am Artists Prof League; Asn Earth Sci Ed. *Res:* Invertebrate paleontology; Bryozoa and Crinoidea; Mississippian stratigraphy. *Mailing Add:* Grad Sch Res Off Univ Mo Rolla MO 65401

KOENIG, KARL E, b Washington, DC, Dec 27, 47. AMINO ACID SYNTHESIS. *Educ:* Univ Tex, Austin, BS, 70; Univ Southern Calif, PhD(chem), 74. *Prof Exp:* Fel chem, Univ Calif, Los Angeles, 74-76; sr res chemist, asymmetric catalysis, Corp Res Labs, 76-79, res specialist, Corp Res & Develop Biomed Prog, 79-81, RES SPECIALIST, NUTRIT CHEM DIV, MONSANTO, 81- *Mem:* Am Chem Soc. *Res:* Homogeneous catalysis; drugs based on low molecular weight polyelectrolytes; asymmetric synthesis; nutritional chemicals; selective complexation of transition metals; organosilicon chemistry. *Mailing Add:* Monsanto Corp 800 N Lindbergh T-3F St Louis MO 63167

KOENIG, KARL JOSEPH, b Milwaukee, Wis, Jan 9, 20; m 59; c 1. GEOLOGY. *Educ:* Univ Ill, BS, 41, MS, 46, PhD, 49. *Prof Exp:* Stratigrapher, Shell Oil Co, Tex, 49-55; ASSOC PROF GEOL, TEX A&M UNIV, 55- *Mem:* Soc Econ Paleont & Mineral; Geol Soc Am; Am Asn Petrol Geol. *Res:* Miocene stratigraphy and paleontology; sedimentation and clay mineralogy. *Mailing Add:* Dept of Geol Tex A&M Univ College Station TX 77843

KOENIG, LLOYD RANDALL, b St Louis, Mo, July 17, 29; m 55; c 2. METEOROLOGY. *Educ:* Washington Univ, BSChE, 50; Univ Chicago, MS, 59, PhD(meteorol), 62. *Prof Exp:* Instr chem eng, US Naval Postgrad Sch, 50-53; res asst meteorol, Univ Chicago, 57-59, res assoc, 60-62; chief atmospheric sci br, Missile & Space Systs Div, Douglas Aircraft Co, 62-66; PHYS SCIENTIST, RAND CORP, SANTA MONICA, 66- *Mem:* Am Geophys Union; Am Meteorol Soc; Sigma Xi. *Res:* Cloud physics, including natural and artificial precipitation mechanisms, scavenging, effects of atmospheric processes on the atmosphere. *Mailing Add:* 258 Notteargentor Rd Pacific Palisades CA 90272

KOENIG, MILTON G, b Moberly, Mo, Aug 23, 27; m 56; c 3. THERMODYNAMICS. *Educ:* Wayne State Univ, BSME, 56, MSME, 57. *Prof Exp:* From instr to asst prof, 56-65, ASSOC PROF MECH ENG, WAYNE STATE UNIV, 65- *Mem:* Soc Automotive Eng. *Res:* Thermodynamics and its applications; automotive design; vehicle dynamics and handling. *Mailing Add:* Dept Mech Eng Wayne State Univ Detroit MI 48202

KOENIG, NATHAN HART, b NH, Apr 18, 15; m 40; c 3. TEXTILE CHEMISTRY. *Educ:* Univ Chicago, BS, 37; Calif Inst Technol, PhD(chem), 50. *Prof Exp:* Chem lab instr, Cent YMCA Col, Chicago, 37-41; asst chem, US Regional Res Lab, USDA, Ill & Calif, 41-42; explosives inspector, Green River Ord Plant, 42-43; sr res chemist, Shell Develop Co, 50-54; chemist, US Regional Res Labs, Pa, 54-57, chemist fiber sci, Western Regional Res Ctr, 57-81; RETIRED. *Mem:* AAAS; Am Asn Textile Chemists & Colorists; Am Chem Soc. *Res:* Proton-olefin complexes; isolation of trace amounts of insecticides; sulfur derivatives of fats; wool chemistry. *Mailing Add:* 824 Ramona Ave Albany CA 94706

KOENIG, PAUL EDWARD, b Gallup, NMex, May 30, 29; m 50; c 8. ORGANIC CHEMISTRY. *Educ:* Univ Ariz, BS, 50, MS, 52; Univ Iowa, PhD(chem), 55. *Prof Exp:* Chemist, Ethyl Corp, 55-58; from asst prof to assoc prof chem, 58-70, vchancellor acad affairs, 70-81, PROF CHEM, LA STATE UNIV, BATON ROUGE, 70- *Concurrent Pos:* Asst head dept chem, La State Univ, Baton Rouge, 63-67, assoc dean grad sch, 67-70. *Mem:* Am Chem Soc. *Res:* Organic reaction mechanisms; physical organic chemistry; organic synthesis; reactions of metal nitrides with organic compounds; structure of tertiary amides. *Mailing Add:* Dept of Chem La State Univ Baton Rouge LA 70803

KOENIG, SEYMOUR HILLEL, b Manchester, NH, July 16, 27; m 47; c 2. BIOPHYSICS. *Educ:* Columbia Univ, BS, 49, MA, 50, PhD, 52. *Prof Exp:* Asst physics, Columbia Univ, 49-51; mem staff, Watson Res Lab, 52-64, from asst dir to dir, 64-70, dir gen sci, Res Ctr, 70-71, STAFF MEM PHYS SCI DEPT, WATSON RES CTR, IBM CORP, 71- *Concurrent Pos:* From adj asst prof to adj prof, Dept Elec Eng, Columbia Univ, 57-68, lectr, Dept Art Hist & Archeol, 70-76, adj prof, 76- consult, Physics Div, Los Alamos Sci Lab, 59-; mem gov coun, Am Phys Soc, 70-74. *Mem:* Fel Am Phys Soc; Biophys Soc; Sigma Xi; Am Soc Biol Chemists; NY Acad Sci. *Res:* Low temperature electrical transport in semiconductors and semi-metals; inelastic neutron scattering by solids; biophysics of proteins; nuclear magnetic relaxation in protein solutions; protein-water interactions; laser light scattering from macromolecule and virus solutions. *Mailing Add:* IBM T J Watson Res Ctr PO BOX 218 Yorktown Heights NY 10598

KOENIG, THOMAS W, b Kansas City, Mo, Feb 11, 38; m 61; c 2. ORGANIC CHEMISTRY. *Educ:* Southern Methodist Univ, BS, 59; Univ Ill, MS, 61, PhD(chem), 63. *Prof Exp:* From asst prof to assoc prof, 63-74, PROF CHEM, UNIV ORE, 74- *Mem:* Am Chem Soc. *Res:* Mechanisms of organic reactions. *Mailing Add:* Dept of Chem Univ of Ore Eugene OR 97403

KOENIG, VIRGIL LEROY, b Kansas City, Mo, Oct 10, 13; m 49; c 4. BIOCHEMISTRY. *Educ:* Univ Mo-Kansas City, AB, 36; Okla State Univ, MS, 38; Univ Colo, PhD(biochem), 40. *Prof Exp:* Chief chemist, State Bd Agr, Okla, 37-38; asst, Univ Colo, 39-40; Copavin fel, Univ Minn, 40-41; res biochemist, Armour Labs, 41-48; staff mem, Los Alamos Sci Lab, Univ Calif, 48-54; from asst prof to assoc prof biochem, Med Sch, Northwestern Univ, 54-60; prin scientist, Gen Mills, Inc, 60-63; chmn dept, 63-71, PROF BIOCHEM, UNIV TEX MED BR, GALVESTON, 63- *Concurrent Pos:* Prin scientist, US Vet Admin Res Hosp, 54-56. *Mem:* AAAS; Am Soc Biol Chemists; Am Chem Soc; Radiation Res Soc; Soc Exp Biol & Med. *Res:* Antioxidants in foods; ovarianthyroid relationship; stilbestrol; effects of radiation on proteins and nucleic acids; physico-chemical properties of nucleic acids from bacteria; critical ultracentrifugal studies on proteins and nucleic acids; infrared spectroscopy of organic compounds; proteins of crystalline lens; urinary and pituitary gonadotrophins; wheat flour proteins; physical characterization of immunoglobulins. *Mailing Add:* Dept of Biochem Univ of Tex Med Br Galveston TX 77550

KOENIGSBERG, ERNEST, b New York, NY, Apr 15, 23; m 55; c 2. OPERATIONS RESEARCH, MANAGEMENT SCIENCE. *Educ:* NY Univ, BA, 48; Iowa State Univ, PhD(theoret physics), 53. *Prof Exp:* Sr physicist, Midwest Res Inst, 53-55; group leader, EMI Eng Develop, 55-57; sect head opers res, Midwest Res Inst, 57-58; mgr mgt serv, Touche, Ross, Bailey & Smart, 58-61; mgr tech serv, CEIR Inc, 61-64; prof indust, Univ Pa, 64-65; vpres, Matson Res Corp, 65-69; sr vpres & tech dir, Manalytics Inc, 69-72; SR LECTR, SCHS BUS ADMIN, UNIV CALIF, BERKELEY, 72- *Concurrent Pos:* Vis lectr, Stanford Univ, 60; vis lectr, Univ Calif, Berkeley, 61-63, grad sch bus admin, 63-64, lectr, 66-72; mem comt future port develop, Maritime Transp Res Bd, Nat Acad Eng, 74-75. *Mem:* Fel Royal Statist Soc; Opers Res Soc; Inst Mgt Sci (vpres, 61-65). *Res:* Application of operations research to business, commercial and non-military government problems; queue theory; inventory theory; linear programming; transportation, distribution and energy development. *Mailing Add:* Schs of Bus Admin Univ of Calif Berkeley CA 94720

KOEPF, ERNEST HENRY, b Bruceville, Tex, Jan 23, 12; m 38; c 2. CHEMICAL ENGINEERING. *Educ:* Univ Tex, BS, 34, MS, 36, PhD(chem eng), 39. *Prof Exp:* Chem engr, Atlantic Refining Co, 39-52; vpres & gen mgr, Texas City Chem, Inc, 52-54; admin coordr, Crude Oil Producing Dept, Atlantic Refining Co, 54-55; mgr res & tech servs, 55-65, gen mgr Francorelab, 65-68, vpres res & tech servs, 68-78, V PRES RES & DEVELOP, CORE LABS, INC, 78- *Concurrent Pos:* Engr, AAAS, Interstate Oil Compact Comn Res Comt & Am Petrol Inst; pres, Ocean Pollution Control, Inc, 71-72, Ecol Audits, Inc, 72-78, P-V-T, Inc, 75-78 & Syndrill Carbide Diamond Co, 80- *Mem:* Am Chem Soc; Am Inst Mining, Metall & Petrol Engrs. *Res:* High pressure phase behavior of hydrocarbons; petroleum reservoir operation; physical properties of oil reservoir rock and their contained fluids; distribution and flow of hydrocarbons in porous media; environmental protection. *Mailing Add:* 3607 Greenbrier Dallas TX 75225

KOEPF, GEORGE F, b Buffalo, NY, Nov 30, 11; m 39; c 2. ENDOCRINOLOGY. *Educ:* Univ Buffalo, MD, 37. *Prof Exp:* Intern & resident, Buffalo Gen Hosp, 37-39; asst med, Johns Hopkins Univ, 39-41; asst clin prof med, Sch Med, Univ Buffalo, 41-78; PRES, TREAS & FOUNDER, MED FOUND BUFFALO, 56- *Concurrent Pos:* NIH grant, 50-55; physician, Buffalo Gen Hosp, 73-76, consult med, 76- *Mem:* Am Physiol Soc; Endocrine Soc; Am Diabetes Asn; Soc Nuclear Med. *Res:* Molecular endocrinology; mode of action of hormones. *Mailing Add:* Med Found of Buffalo 73 High St Buffalo NY 14203

KOEPKE, BARRY GEORGE, b Detroit, Mich, Oct 27, 37. MATERIALS SCIENCE. *Educ:* Univ Ill, BS, 60, MS, 62; Iowa State Univ, PhD(metall), 68. *Prof Exp:* Res engr metall, Rocketdyne Div, NAm Aviation, 62-64; prin res scientist mat sci, 68-73, sr prin res scientist, 73-78, staff scientist, 78-79, group leader mat & process res, 79-80, PROG MGR, HONEYWELL SYSTS & RES CTR, 81- *Concurrent Pos:* Adj prof mat sci, Univ Minn, 76-; dir Ceramics Prog Div Mat Res, NSF, 80-81. *Mem:* Am Ceramic Soc; Am Soc Metals; Sigma Xi. *Res:* Studies of the mechanical properties and fracture behavior of ceramic materials, the nature and extent of surface damage introduced into dielectrics by machining and polishing; low cost composite silicon photovoltaic solar cells; production of ceramics with tailored microstructures. *Mailing Add:* Honeywell Inc 10701 Lyndale Ave S Bloomington MN 55420

KOEPKE, GEORGE HENRY, b Toledo, Ohio, Jan 1, 16; m 40; c 2. MEDICINE. *Educ:* Univ Toledo, BS, 45; Univ Cincinnati, MD, 49; Am Bd Phys Med & Rehab, dipl, 55. *Prof Exp:* Intern, Toledo Hosp, 49-50; resident, Univ Mich Hosp, 50-52, instr phys med & rehab, Med Sch, Univ, 52-53; pvt pract, 53-54; from asst prof to prof phys med & rehab, Med Ctr, Univ Mich, Ann Arbor, 54-76; RETIRED. *Concurrent Pos:* Consult, Vet Admin Hosp, Ann Arbor, 55-75, Lapeer State Home & Training Sch, 64- & Mary Free Bed Hosp, Grand Rapids, 71-76; mem staff, Saginaw Community Hosp, St Mary's Hosp, Saginaw Gen Hosp & St Luke's Hosp; chmn, Am Bd Phys Med & Rehab, 76; Am Bd Phys Med & Rehab; emer mem prof adv coun, United Cerebral Palsy Asn. *Mem:* Fel Am Acad Phys Med & Rehab; Am Asn Electromyog & Electrodiag; Am Acad Orthop Surg; Am Cong Rehab Med; AMA. *Res:* Physical medicine and rehabilitation; electromyography and prosthetics. *Mailing Add:* 830 S Jefferson Saginaw MI 48601

KOEPKE, JOHN ARTHUR, b Milwaukee, Wis, Mar 25, 29; m 55; c 4. CLINICAL PATHOLOGY, HEMATOLOGY. *Educ:* Valparaiso Univ, BA, 51; Univ Wis, MD, 56; Marquette Univ, MS, 64. *Prof Exp:* Instr path, Marquette Univ, 58-60; from asst prof to assoc prof, Univ Ky, 61-70; assoc clin prof med technol, Col Med, Univ Iowa, 70-71, prof path & vchmn dept, 72-79; PROF PATH & MED DIR, TRANSFUSION SERV & HEMAT LABS, COL MED, DUKE UNIV, 80- *Concurrent Pos:* From asst pathologist to assoc pathologist, Univ Ky Hosp, 61-71; attend pathologist, Vet Admin Hosp & consult, USPHS, 63-71; vis scientist, Karolinska Inst, Sweden, 67-68; dir lab, Lexington Clin, 71-72; attend pathologist, Univ Iowa Hosp & Clins, 72-; chief lab serv, Vet Admin Hosp, Iowa City, 72-78; vis colleague, Royal Postgrad Med Sch, London, Eng. *Mem:* Col Am Pathologists; Am Soc Hemat; Am Soc Clin Path; Am Asn Blood Banks. *Res:* Blood coagulation; flow cytometry; immunohematology; quality assurance systems. *Mailing Add:* Med Ctr Duke Univ PO Box 3712 Durham NC 27710

KOEPNICK, RICHARD BORLAND, b Dayton, Ohio, Feb 5, 44. SEDIMENTARY PETROLOGY. *Educ:* Univ Colo, BA, 67; Univ Kans, MS, 69, PhD(geol), 76. *Prof Exp:* asst prof, Dept Geol, Williams Col, 75-77; RES GEOLOGIST, MOBIL FIELD RES LAB, 77- *Mem:* Soc Econ Paleontologists & Mineralogists; Am Asn Petrol Geologists; Paleont Soc. *Res:* Upper Cambrian paleoenvironments, western United States; diagenesis of carbonate rocks and sandstones. *Mailing Add:* Mobil Field Res Lab Box 900 Dallas TX 75221

KOEPP, LEILA H, b Haifa, Israel, July 7, 45; US citizen; m 69; c 2. SCIENCE EDUCATION. *Educ:* Messiah Col, BA, 68; NTex State Univ, MS, 70; Col Med & Dent NJ, PhD(microbiol), 81. *Prof Exp:* Instr microbiol, Montclair State Col, 74-76, instr biol, anat & physiol, Fairleigh Dickson Univ, Madison, 76-77; asst med microbiol & researcher microbiol, Col Med & Dent NJ, 78-81; ASST PROF BIOL, ANAT & PHYSIOL, BLOOMFIELD COL, NJ, 81- *Concurrent Pos:* Bacteriologist clin microbiol, Overlook Hosp, Summit, NJ, 75-81. *Mem:* Am Soc Microbiol. *Res:* Molecular basis for the biological activity of the slime glycolipoprotein of Pseudomonas aeruginosa. *Mailing Add:* Dept Math & Natural Sci Bloomfield Col Bloomfield NJ 09003

KOEPP, STEPHEN JOHN, b Los Angeles, Calif, Apr 24, 46; m 69; c 2. ZOOLOGY, CYTOPATHOLOGY. *Educ:* Messiah Col, BA, 68; NTex State Univ, MS, 70, PhD(biol), 73. *Prof Exp:* Asst prof, 73-78, ASSOC PROF BIOL, MONTCLAIR STATE COL, 78- *Mem:* Electron Micros Soc Am; AAAS; Am Soc Parasitologists. *Res:* Histopathologic and cytopathologic response of aquatic fauna following toxic exposure to heavy metals. *Mailing Add:* Dept of Biol Montclair State Col Upper Montclair NJ 07043

KOEPPE, DAVID EDWARD, b Sheboygan, Wis, 1939. PLANT BIOCHEMISTRY, PLANT PHYSIOLOGY. *Educ:* Wis State Univ-Oshkosh, BS, 62; Univ Okla, MNS, 65, PhD(bot, plant physiol), 68. *Prof Exp:* Teacher high schs, Wis, 62-64, 65-66; res assoc, 68-69, from asst prof to assoc prof, 69-77, PROF PLANT PHYSIOL, UNIV ILL, URBANA, 77- *Mem:* Am Soc Plant Physiol; Scand Soc Plant Physiol; Crop Sci Soc Am; Am Soc Agron. *Res:* Plant active processes affected by environment variables; plant mitochondria; plant-plant interactions mediated by chemicals; plant physiological responses to toxic materials. *Mailing Add:* N-217 Turner Hall Dept of Agron Univ of Ill Urbana IL 61801

KOEPPE, JOHN K, b Beaver Dam, Wis, July 20, 44. INSECT PHYSIOLOGY, ENDOCRINOLOGY. *Educ:* Hope Col, BA, 67; Tulane Univ, PhD(biol), 71. *Prof Exp:* Fel insect physiol, Northwestern Univ, 71-73; res fel biochem, Roche Inst Molecular Biol, 73-75; ASST PROF ZOOL, UNIV NC, CHAPEL HILL, 75- *Mem:* Am Soc Zoologists; Entom Soc Am. *Res:* Molecular analysis of the mode of action of the juvenile hormone during insect vitellogenesis. *Mailing Add:* Dept of Zool Univ of NC Chapel Hill NC 27514

KOEPPE, OWEN JOHN, b Cedar Grove, Wis, May 29, 26; m 50; c 3. BIOCHEMISTRY. *Educ:* Hope Col, AB, 49; Univ Ill, MS, 51, PhD(biochem), 53. *Prof Exp:* Asst chem, Univ Ill, 49-51, asst biochem, 51-52; USPHS res fel, Univ Minn, 53-55; from asst prof to assoc prof, 55-61, chmn dept, 68-73, PROF BIOCHEM, SCH MED, UNIV MO-COLUMBIA, 61-, PROVOST ACAD AFFAIRS, 73- *Mem:* Am Chem Soc; Am Soc Biol Chemists. *Res:* Mechanism of enzyme action; peptide bond synthesis. *Mailing Add:* Dept of Biochem Univ of Mo Sch of Med Columbia MO 65201

KOEPPE, ROGER ERDMAN, b Amoy, China, May 2, 22; m 47; c 5. BIOCHEMISTRY. *Educ:* Hope Col, AB, 44; Univ Ill, MS, 47, PhD(biochem), 50. *Prof Exp:* Asst, Univ Ill, 46-48 & 50-51; res assoc, Univ Tenn, 51-52; from instr to assoc prof chem, 52-59; assoc prof, 59-60, PROF BIOCHEM, OKLA STATE UNIV, 60-, HEAD DEPT, 63- *Concurrent Pos:* NIH sr fel, Univ Pa, 66-67; Sigma Xi lectr, 74. *Mem:* AAAS; Am Chem Soc; Am Soc Biol Chemists; Brit Biochem Soc. *Res:* Metabolism, including enzymology, of acetate, mannose, pyruvate and glutamate in mammalian brain and liver; neurochemistry. *Mailing Add:* Dept of Biochem Okla State Univ Stillwater OK 74074

KOEPPEN, ROBERT CARL, b Oshkosh, Wis, Jan 1, 31; m 54; c 2. BOTANY, RESEARCH ADMINISTRATION. *Educ:* Wis State Col, Oshkosh, BS, 54; Univ Wis, MS, 57, PhD(bot, forest prod), 62. *Prof Exp:* Teacher high schs, Wis; plant taxonomist, 62-75, proj leader, Ctr Wood Anat Res, taxonomist, 75-80, RES STAFF FOREST PROD TECHNOLOGIST, US FOREST PROD LAB, 80- *Concurrent Pos:* Lectr, Univ Wis, 61- *Mem:* Am Soc Plant Taxon; Int Asn Wood Anat; Forest Prod Res Soc. *Res:* Taxonomic wood anatomy and wood identification, especially of the Leguminosae. *Mailing Add:* FPER Rm 3836-S Forest Serv USDA PO Box 2417 Washington DC 20013

KOEPPL, GERALD WALTER, b Chicago, Ill, Dec 4, 42. CHEMICAL PHYSICS. *Educ:* Ill Inst Technol, BSc, 65, PhD(chem), 69. *Prof Exp:* NIH res fel chem, Harvard Univ, 69-70, res fel, 70; from instr to asst prof, 70-74, ASSOC PROF CHEM, QUEENS COL, NY, 74- *Concurrent Pos:* Proj dir res grant, Res Found City Univ New York, 71-76; Sloan Found fel, 75-79. *Mem:* Am Chem Soc; NY Acad Sci; Am Phys Soc; Fedn Am Scientists. *Res:* Classical mechanical trajectory studies of the statistical theories of chemical reaction dynamics; trajectory studies of organic reaction mechanisms; model dynamical studies of reaction at active enzyme sites. *Mailing Add:* Dept of Chem Queens Col Flushing NY 11367

KOEPSEL, WELLINGTON WESLEY, b McQueeney, Tex, Dec 5, 21; m 50; c 3. ELECTRICAL ENGINEERING. *Educ:* Univ Tex, BS, 44, MS, 51; Okla State Univ, PhD(elec eng), 60. *Prof Exp:* Res scientist elec eng, Univ Tex, 48-51; res engr aerophys lab, NAm Aviation, Inc, 51; asst prof, Southern Methodist Univ, 51-56 & Okla State Univ, 56-58; assoc prof, Southern Methodist Univ, 58-59, Univ NMex, 60-63 & Duke Univ, 63-64; head dept, 64-76, PROF ELEC ENG, KANS STATE UNIV, 64- *Mem:* Inst Elec & Electronics Engrs; Nat Soc Prof Engrs. *Res:* Feedback control systems; microcomputer and digital control systems. *Mailing Add:* 2815 Illinois Lane Manhattan KS 66502

KOEPSELL, PAUL L(OEL), b Canova, SDak, June 17, 30; m 52; c 3. CIVIL ENGINEERING. *Educ:* SDak State Univ, BS, 52; Univ Wash, Seattle, MS, 54; Okla State Univ, PhD, 65. *Prof Exp:* Stress analyst, Aircraft Structures, Boeing Airplane Co, 52-57; asst prof civil eng, 58, assoc prof, 59-65, dir res & data processing, 65-76, PROF CIVIL ENG, SDAK STATE UNIV, 67-, DIR COMPUT CTR, 76-, HEAD, DEPT COMPUT SCI, 81- *Mem:* Am Soc Civil Engrs; Am Concrete Inst; Nat Soc Prof Engrs; Asn Comput Mach. *Res:* Structural components; approximate analysis of structures; application of matrix methods to structural analysis. *Mailing Add:* Comput Ctr Box 2201 SDak State Univ Brookings SD 57007

KOERBER, GEORGE G(REGORY), b Akron, Ohio, Aug 30, 24; m 51; c 3. ELECTRICAL ENGINEERING. *Educ:* Hiram Col, BA, 48; Purdue Univ, MS, 50, PhD(phys chem), 52. *Prof Exp:* Mem tech staff component develop, Bell Tel Labs, Inc, 52-56; assoc prof mech, Rensselaer Polytech Inst, 56-58; assoc prof eng mech, Mich Col Mining & Technol, 58-59; assoc prof theoret & appl mech, 60-61, assoc prof elec eng, 61-65, PROF ELEC ENG, IOWA STATE UNIV, 65- *Res:* Applied mathematics; properties of solids. *Mailing Add:* Dept of Elec Eng Iowa State Univ Ames IA 50010

KOERBER, THOMAS WILLIAM, b Milwaukee, Wis, Jan 12, 33; m 57; c 4. ENTOMOLOGY. *Educ:* Univ Wis, 56, MS, 57; Univ Calif, Berkeley, PhD(entom), 67. *Prof Exp:* Lab asst, Lake States Forest Exp Sta, 53-54, entomologist, Pac Southwest Forest & Range Exp Sta, 57-64, RES ENTOMOLOGIST, PAC SOUTHWEST FOREST & RANGE EXP STA, US FOREST SERV, 64- *Concurrent Pos:* Secy-treas, Western Forest Insect Work Conf, 71-72; chmn insect comt, Calif Forest Pest Control Action Coun, 78-79. *Mem:* Entom Soc Am; Entom Soc Can; Lepidop Soc. *Res:* Insects destroying the seeds of forest trees; insects defoliating forest trees; testing of insecticides and pheromones to control forest insects; impact of insects on forest productivity. *Mailing Add:* Pac SW Forest & Range Exp Sta US Forest Serv Box 245 Berkeley CA 94701

KOERBER, WALTER LUDWIG, b Berlin, Ger, Aug 3, 12; US citizen; m 37; c 1. BIOCHEMISTRY, MICROBIOLOGY. *Educ:* Univ Frankfurt, PhD(org chem, bact), 36. *Prof Exp:* Fel, Sch Hyg & Trop Med, Univ London, 36-37; asst head dept bact, E R Squibb & Sons, 39-42 & Mfg Pilot Plant, 42-44, head microbiol develop, Squibb Inst Med Res, 44-51, tech adv, Squibb-Rome, 52-53, tech dir, Squibb-Sao Paulo, 54-55, dir int res & develop inst, 56-57, dir & regional coordr, 57-58, dir int res, Squibb Inst Med Res, 58-63, coordr, 63-70, dir, 65-69, dir sci affairs, Squibb Europe Ltd, 70-77; CONSULT, REVLON HEALTH CARE GROUP, 78- *Concurrent Pos:* Consult to Badger Ltd, London, Govt Pakistan, 64. *Mem:* Am Chem Soc; Am Asn Immunol; Am Soc Microbiol. *Res:* Fermentations; biologicals; natural products; development of pharmaceuticals. *Mailing Add:* Dr Lechner-Weg 17 A-5310 Mondsee Austria

KOERING, MARILYN JEAN, b Brainerd, Minn, Jan 7, 38. ANATOMY, REPRODUCTIVE PHYSIOLOGY. *Educ:* Col St Scholastica, BA, 60; Univ Wis-Madison, MS, 63, PhD(anat), 67. *Prof Exp:* Res asst chem, Col St Scholastica, 60-61; instr anat, Univ Wis, 63-64; res trainee reproductive physiol, Ore Primate Res Ctr, 66-67; NIH fel, Primate Res Ctr, Univ Wis-Madison, 67-68, proj assoc, 68-69; asst prof, 69-73, assoc prof, 73-79, PROF ANAT, MED CTR, GEORGE WASH UNIV, 79- *Concurrent Pos:* Guest worker, Pregnancy Res Br, Nat Inst Child Health & Human Develop, 77- *Mem:* AAAS; Am Asn Anatomists; Electron Micros Soc Am; Soc Study Reproduction. *Res:* Cyclic changes in ovarian morphology as observed in light and electron microscopy; correlation of reproductive morphology with physiology. *Mailing Add:* Dept Anat George Washington Univ Med Ctr Washington DC 20037

KOERKER, FREDERICK WILLIAM, b Milwaukee, Wis, June 9, 13; m 37; c 3. INORGANIC CHEMISTRY. *Educ:* Univ Wis, BS, 34, MS, 36. *Prof Exp:* Asst chem, Univ Wis, 34-36; analyst, Main Lab, 36-37, chemist, Chlorine Dept, 37-41, asst supt, 41-53, tech expert electrochem planning, 53-62, tech expert, Chem Dept, 62-68, mgr qual standards, 68-78, CONSULT, DOW CHEM CO, 78- *Mem:* Am Chem Soc; Electrochem Soc. *Res:* Electrolytic production of chlorine, caustic and allied products; specifications and methods of analysis for general chemicals. *Mailing Add:* 4103 Dyckman Rd Midland MI 48640

KOERKER, ROBERT LELAND, b Saginaw, Mich, Jan 10, 43. PHARMACOLOGY. *Educ:* Kalamazoo Col, BA, 65; Emory Univ, PhD(pharmacol), 70. *Prof Exp:* Asst biologist microbiol, Biochem Res Lab, Dow Chem Co, 63-64, asst chemist, Dept Chem Res Lab, 65; NIH res fel pharmacol, Univ Colo Med Ctr, 70-73; USPHS res fel, Emory Univ, 73-74; asst prof pharmacol, La State Univ Med Ctr, 74-80; ASSOC PROF

PHARMACOL, MED SCH, WRIGHT STATE UNIV, 80- *Mem:* Tissue Cult Asn; Sigma Xi; AAAS; Int Asn Dent Res; Am Soc Pharmacol & Exp Therapeut. *Res:* Toxicity of aldehydes, alcohols, organo-mercurials and other agents in cultured mouse neuroblastoma cells; characterization of uptake and storage mechanisms in cultured mouse neuroblastoma cells. *Mailing Add:* Dept Pharmacol Colonial Glenn Hgwy Dayton OH 45431

KOERNER, DIONA HEATHER, biochemistry, endocrinology, see previous edition

KOERNER, E(RNEST) L(EE), JR, b Cleveland, Ohio, Mar 17, 31; m 53; c 6. CHEMICAL ENGINEERING. *Educ:* Univ Dayton, BChE, 53; Iowa State Col, MS, 55, PhD(chem eng), 56. *Prof Exp:* Asst chem eng, Ames Lab, AEC, Iowa State Col, 53-56; res engr & sect leader extractive processes, Union Carbide Metals Co, 57-59; res specialist, Monsanto Co, 59-67; sr res specialist, Kerr-McGee Corp, 67, sr res group leader, 67-70; PRES, TECHNOL RES & DEVELOP INC, 70- *Mem:* Am Inst Chem Engrs; Am Inst Mining, Metall & Petrol Engrs; Am Inst Plant Engrs; Nat Soc Prof Engrs. *Res:* Extractive metallurgical processes; liquid-liquid extraction; high temperature extractive metallurgical processes; phosphoric acid; reactive metals; biological and enzyme treatment of waste waters. *Mailing Add:* Technol Res & Develop Inc 4619 N Santa Fe Oklahoma City OK 73118

KOERNER, HAROLD ELTON, b Freeport, Ill, Mar 2, 05; m 30; c 3. VERTEBRATE PALEONTOLOGY. *Educ:* Univ Colo, BA, 29, MA, 30; Yale Univ, PhD(geol), 39. *Prof Exp:* Asst geol, Univ Colo, 29-30; from instr to assoc prof, Lafayette Col, 30-47; from assoc prof to prof, 47-71, asst head dept, 49-70, assoc chmn dept, 70-71, EMER PROF GEOL SCI, UNIV COLO, BOULDER, 71- *Mem:* AAAS; Soc Vert Paleont; Paleont Soc; Geol Soc Am. *Res:* Vertebrate paleontology; stratigraphy; sedimentation. *Mailing Add:* Dept of Geol Sci Univ of Colo Boulder CO 80304

KOERNER, HEINZ, b Komotau, May 9, 42; German citizen. AQUATIC BIOLOGY, ECOLOGY. *Educ:* Free Univ Berlin, PhD(biol), 70. *Prof Exp:* Res scientist bot & pharmacol, Schering A G, Berlin, 70-71; ASST CUR AQUATIC BIOL, ACAD NAT SCI, 71- *Mem:* Int Phycol Soc; Phycol Soc Am; Sigma Xi. *Res:* Diatom morphology and taxonomy; diatom ecology; aquatic ecology (with emphasis on biological water quality assessment by diatom community analysis). *Mailing Add:* Div of Limnol & Ecol 19th St & The Pkwy Philadelphia PA 19103

KOERNER, JAMES FREDERICK, b Charles City, Iowa, June 30, 29; m 58; c 2. BIOCHEMISTRY. *Educ:* Iowa State Col, BS, 50, PhD(biochem), 56. *Prof Exp:* Res assoc biochem, Iowa State Col, 50-52, asst, 52-56; USPHS fel, Mass Inst Technol, 56-58, res assoc, 58-61; from asst prof to assoc prof, 61-72, PROF BIOCHEM, MED UNIV MINN, MINNEAPOLIS, 72- *Mem:* AAAS; Am Soc Biol Chemists. *Res:* Neurochemistry; acidic amino acids as excitatory neurotransmitters. *Mailing Add:* Dept Biochem Univ Minn Med Sch 435 Delaware St S E Minneapolis MN 55455

KOERNER, ROBERT M, b Philadelphia, Pa, Dec 2, 33; m 59; c 3. SOIL MECHANICS. *Educ:* Drexel Inst Technol, BSCE, 56, MSCE, 63; Duke Univ, PhD(soil mech), 68. *Prof Exp:* Engr & supt, Conduit & Found Corp, 56-60; engr analyst, Dames & Moore, 60-62; engr & supt, J J Skelly, Inc, 62-63; instr, Pa Mil Col, 64-65; NSF teaching intern, Duke Univ, 65-67, instr, part-time, 67-68; from asst prof to assoc prof, 68-76, PROF CIVIL ENG, DREXEL UNIV, 76- *Mem:* Am Soc Civil Engrs; Am Soc Eng Educ. *Res:* Foundation engineering; particle mechanics; powder metallurgy. *Mailing Add:* Dept of Civil Eng Drexel Univ Philadelphia PA 19104

KOERNER, WILLIAM ELMER, b Neenah, Wis, Nov 3, 23; m 47; c 2. PHYSICAL CHEMISTRY, ANALYTICAL CHEMISTRY. *Educ:* Univ Wis, BS, 46, PhD(phys chem), 49. *Prof Exp:* Res phys chemist, 49-54, group leader phys chem, 54-64, mgr, Phys Sci Ctr, 64-80, DIR PHYS SCI, MONSANTO CO, 80- *Mem:* AAAS; Soc Appl Spectros; Am Chem Soc; Sigma Xi. *Res:* Chemical reaction kinetics; thermochemistry; physical analytical chemistry. *Mailing Add:* 5642 Murdoch Ave St Louis MO 63109

KOERTING, LOLA ELISABETH, b Munich, Ger, Jan 31, 24; US citizen; m 53; c 2. GENETICS, CYTOLOGY. *Educ:* Munich Tech Univ, BS, 47, MS, 49, PhD(biol, agr), 53. *Prof Exp:* Res asst plant genetics, Munich Tech Univ, 48-53; chief histol & ultrasonics, New Eng Inst Med Res, 54-55; res assoc forest genetics, Sch Forestry, Yale Univ, 55-58; res fel cytogenetics, New Eng Inst Med Res, 65-73; CONSULT GENETICIST, KITCHAWAN RES LAB, BROOKLYN BOT GARDEN, NY, 75- *Mem:* AAAS; Environ Mutagen Soc; Bot Soc Am; Sigma Xi; Tissue Cult Asn. *Res:* Cytogenetics; induced chromosome abnormalities and mutations; tissue culture. *Mailing Add:* PO Box 551 Ridgefield CT 06877

KOESTER, CHARLES JOHN, b Niagara Falls, NY, Jan 26, 29; m 53; c 4. OPTICS. *Educ:* Carnegie Inst Technol, BS, 50; Univ Rochester, PhD(physics, optics), 55. *Prof Exp:* Asst, Univ Rochester, 50-55; physicist, Am Optical Co, 55-58; res assoc, Nat Bur Standards, 58-59; physicist, Am Optical Corp, 59-65, appl res mgr, Framingham Res Lab, 65-75, dir res, Sci Instrument Div, 75-77; ASST PROF BIOPHYS OPHTHAL, COLUMBIA UNIV COL PHYSICIANS & SURGEONS, 78- *Concurrent Pos:* Lectr ophthal, Columbia Univ, 70-; indust rep, Food & Drug Admin Ophthalmic Device Classification Panel, 74-78. *Mem:* Optical Soc Am; Asn Res Vision & Ophthal. *Res:* Ophthalmic instruments, microscopes, and optical instruments in medicine; polarized light, interference and polarizing microscopes, image enhancement in fiber optics, laser photocoagulation and laser eye protection. *Mailing Add:* Edward S Harkness Eye Inst 635 W 165th St New York NY 10032

KOESTER, LOUIS JULIUS, JR, b Galveston, Tex, Jan 25, 25; m 46; c 2. EXPERIMENTAL HIGH ENERGY PHYSICS, NUCLEAR PHYSICS. *Educ:* Univ Wis, BS, 47, PhD(physics), 51. *Prof Exp:* Res assoc, 51-55, from asst prof to assoc prof, 55-63, PROF PHYSICS, UNIV ILL, URBANA, 63- *Concurrent Pos:* Mem, Phys Sci Study Comt, 56-60; vis scientist, Europ Orgn

Nuclear Res, 58-59; consult, Electronics Div, Argonne Nat Lab, 60-73. *Mem:* Fel Am Phys Soc. *Res:* Structure of light nuclei; particle detectors; photodisintegration; high energy physics. *Mailing Add:* Dept of Physics Univ of Ill Urbana IL 61801

KOESTERER, MARTIN GEORGE, b Rochester, NY, July 2, 33; m 58; c 4. MICROBIOLOGY. *Educ:* Univ Rochester, AB, 55; Syracuse Univ, MS, 57. *Prof Exp:* Res supvr sterilization, Wilmot Castle Co, 59-64; sr microbiologist & prog mgr sterilization & planetary quarantine, Valley Forge Space Technol Ctr, Gen Elec Co, 65-75; mgr microbiol res, Ethicon Inc, 75-77; CONSULT INDUST, 77-; MEM STAFF MICROBIOL & STERILIZATION TECHNOL, WYETH LABS, INC, 78- *Concurrent Pos:* Spec lectr, Grad Sch Environ Sci, Drexel Univ, 69-70; guest lectr, Contamination Control Sem, Rochester Inst Technol, 71-75; consult microbial contamination control & sterilization, 69- *Honors & Awards:* NASA Tech Brief, 72. *Mem:* Am Soc Microbiol; Inst Environ Sci; Soc Indust Microbiol; Am Soc Testing & Mat. *Res:* Resistance of bacterial spores to dry heat, moist heat, irradiation, various chemical agents; bioburden and microbial contamination control as it pertains to good manufacturing practices on pharmaceutical, biomedical devices and products; biological indicator development; sterilization development and validation. *Mailing Add:* Wyeth Labs, Inc PO Box 565 West Chester PA 19380

KOESTLER, ROBERT CHARLES, b Elizabeth, NJ, Oct 31, 32; m 58; c 3. PESTICIDE CHEMISTRY. *Educ:* Cornell Univ, BA, 54; Univ NC, Chapel Hill, PhD(org chem), 61. *Prof Exp:* Res chemist, Am Viscose Div, FMC Corp, 61-65; sr res chemist, 65-77, PROJ LEADER, PENNWALT CORP, 77- *Concurrent Pos:* Mem, Gov Bd, Int Symposium Controlled Release Bioactive Mat. *Mem:* Am Chem Soc. *Res:* Organometallics; films and coatings; organic synthesis; microencapsulation and controlled release technology. *Mailing Add:* Pennwalt Corp 900 First Ave King of Prussia PA 19406

KOESTNER, ADALBERT, b Hatzfeld, Rumania, Sept 10, 20; US citizen; m 51; c 2. VETERINARY PATHOLOGY. *Educ:* Univ Munich, DMV, 51; Ohio State Univ, MSc, 57, PhD, 59. *Prof Exp:* Res assoc bact, Vet Col, Univ Munich, 51-52; from instr to assoc prof, 55-64, chmn, Dept Vet Pathobiol, 72-81, PROF VET PATH, OHIO STATE UNIV, 64-; CHMN PATH, MICH STATE UNIV, 81- *Mem:* AAAS; Am Asn Pathologists; Soc Neurosci; Am Vet Med Asn; Am Asn Cancer Res. *Res:* Comparative neuropathology; comparative and experimental oncology. *Mailing Add:* Dept of Vet Pathobiol Ohio State Univ Columbus OH 43210

KOETHE, SUSAN M, b San Diego, Calif, Sept 4, 45; m 68; c 1. IMMUNOLOGY. *Educ:* San Diego State Col, BS, 67; Harvard Univ, PhD(immunol), 74. *Prof Exp:* NIH fel, 74-76, asst prof, 76-81, ASSOC PROF PATH, MED COL WIS, 81- *Concurrent Pos:* Chmn, Milwaukee Immunol Group, 78-82. *Mem:* Am Asn Immunologists. *Res:* Immunoregulation in myasthenia gravis and multiple sclerosis. *Mailing Add:* 8700 W Wisconsin Ave Milwaukee WI 54226

KOETKE, DONALD D, b Chicago, Ill, Dec 12, 37; m 59; c 3. HIGH ENERGY PHYSICS, LOW ENERGY NUCLEAR PHYSICS. *Educ:* Concordia Col, Ill, BS, 59; Northwestern Univ, Ill, MS, 63, PhD(physics), 68. *Prof Exp:* Assoc prof physics, Concordia Col, Ill, 67-77; PROF PHYSICS, VALPARAISO UNIV, 77- *Concurrent Pos:* Vis scientist, Argonne Nat Lab, 69 & 71-82. *Mem:* Am Phys Soc; Am Asn Physics Teachers; Sigma Xi. *Res:* Experiments in neutrino physics; low energy nuclear cross-section measurements relative to solar neutrino production. *Mailing Add:* Dept of Physics Valparaiso Univ Valparaiso IN 46383

KOETZLE, THOMAS F, b Brooklyn, NY, Oct 15, 43; m 67; c 2. PHYSICAL CHEMISTRY, CHEMICAL CRYSTALLOGRAPHY. *Educ:* Harvard Univ, BA, 64, MA, 65, PhD(chem), 70. *Prof Exp:* Res assoc chem, 70-73, assoc chemist, 73-75, CHEMIST, BROOKHAVEN NAT LAB, 75- *Concurrent Pos:* AEC fel, 70-71; NIH fel, 71-73; prin investr, Protein Data Bank, 75- *Mem:* AAAS; NY Acad Sci; Am Chem Soc; Am Crystallog Asn. *Res:* Applications of neutron and x-ray diffraction to the analysis of chemical bonding and structures. *Mailing Add:* Dept of Chem Brookhaven Nat Lab Upton NY 11973

KOEVENIG, JAMES L, b Postville, Iowa, Mar 18, 31; m 54; c 2. BOTANY, BIOLOGY. *Educ:* Univ Iowa, BA, 55, PhD(sci educ), 61; State Col Iowa, MA, 57. *Prof Exp:* Elem sch teacher, 55-56; res assoc, Univ Iowa, 61; asst prof zool, San Diego State Col, 61-62; res consult, Biol Sci Curric Study, Univ Colo, 62-64; from assoc prof to prof bot & biol, Univ Kans, 64-72; PROF BIOL, UNIV CENT FLA, 72- *Concurrent Pos:* Vis lectr, Univ Colo, 63-64; mem eval panel, Comn Undergrad Educ in Biol, 65; NSF sci fac fel, Princeton Univ, 67-68. *Mem:* AAAS; Bot Soc Am; Mycol Soc Am; Nat Asn Biol Teachers; Am Inst Biol Sci. *Res:* Morphology of slime molds; physiology of spore and seed germination; plant development; science education-evaluation. *Mailing Add:* Dept of Biol Sci Univ Cent Fla Box 25000 Orlando FL 32816

KOFF, RAYMOND STEVEN, b Brooklyn, NY, June 11, 39; m 60; c 2. INTERNAL MEDICINE, GASTROENTEROLOGY. *Educ:* Adelphi Col, BA, 58; Albert Einstein Col Med, MD, 62; Am Bd Internal Med, dipl. *Prof Exp:* Intern med, Barnes Hosp, Washington Univ, 62-63; asst resident, 63-64; teaching fel, Tufts Univ & Lemuel Shattuck Hosp, 64-65, res fel, 65-66; clin & res fel, Mass Gen Hosp, Harvard Med Sch, 66-68, res fel, 68-69; asst prof, 69-74, assoc prof, 74-78, PROF, SCH MED, BOSTON UNIV & VET ADMIN MED CTR, 79- *Concurrent Pos:* NIH trainee gastroenterol, Mass Gen Hosp, 66-69; clin investr, Vet Admin, 69-72, chief hepatology sect, 73- *Mem:* Soc Epidemiol Res; Am Asn for Study Dis of Liver; fel Am Col Physicians; Am Gastroenterol Asn; Int Asn Study Liver. *Res:* Viral hepatitis; drug hepatotoxicity; chronic hepatitis. *Mailing Add:* Vet Admin Med Ctr 150 S Huntington Ave Boston MA 02130

KOFFLER, DAVID, b New York, NY, Mar 28, 34; c 3. IMMUNOPATHOLOGY. *Educ:* State Univ NY, MD, 58. *Prof Exp:* Res fel, Mt Sinai Hosp, 59-60; NIH trainee, 60-63; instr path, Col Physicians & Surgeons, Columbia Univ, 63-66; from asst prof to assoc prof path, Mt Sinai Sch Med, 66-69, asst dean acad affairs, 66-72, prof, 69-76; PROF PATH & DIR LAB MED, HAHNEMANN MED COL & HOSP, 76- *Concurrent Pos:* NIH spec res fel, 63-66; asst attend pathologist, Mt Sinai Hosp, 63-71, attend pathologist, 71-; guest investr, Rockefeller Univ, 66-78, adj prof, 78- *Mem:* Am Soc Clin Invest; Am Asn Path & Bact; Am Soc Exp Path; Am Asn Nephrology; Am Rheumatism Asn. *Mailing Add:* Dept of Path 230 N Broad St Philadelphia PA 19102

KOFFLER, HENRY, b Vienna, Austria, Sept 17, 22; nat US; m 46. MICROBIOLOGY. *Educ:* Univ Ariz, BS, 43; Univ Wis: Wis, MS, 44, PhD(bact), 47. *Prof Exp:* From asst prof to assoc prof bact, Purdue Univ, West Lafayette, 47-52, coordr res, 49-59, prof biol, 52-74, asst to dean grad sch, 57-59, asst dean, 59-60, head dept biol sci, 59-75, F L Hovde Distinguished prof, 74-75; PROF BIOCHEM & MICROBIOL & VPRES ACAD AFFAIRS, UNIV MINN, MINNEAPOLIS, 75- *Concurrent Pos:* Guggenheim fel, Sch Med, Case Western Reserve Univ, 53-54; mem, Comn Undergrad Educ in Biol Sci, 66-69, vchmn, 66-67, chmn, 67-69; mem, Purdue Res Found, 67-; consult-examr, NCent Asn Cols, 67-; mem, 2nd-7th Int Cong Biochem, Paris, Brussels, Vienna, Moscow & Tokyo; mem, 6th-8th & 10th Int Cong Microbiol, Rome, Stockholm, Montreal & Mexico City; mem, 9th & 11th Int Bot Cong, Montreal & Seattle; mem, 1st-3rd Int Biophys Cong, Stockholm, Vienna & Boston; mem, 5th Int Cong Electron Micros, Philadelphia, 16th Int Zool Cong, Washington, DC, 4th Int Cong Chemother, Washington, DC, 24th Int Cong Physiol Sci, 1st Int Cong Bact, Jerusalem & 1st Int Cong Int Asn Microbiol Soc, Tokyo. *Honors & Awards:* Eli Lilly & Co Award, 57. *Mem:* Am Soc Biol Chemists; Biophys Soc; Am Soc Microbiol; fel Am Acad Microbiol; Am Soc Cell Biologists. *Res:* Biosynthesis of carbohydrates; chemistry, biosynthesis and mechanism of action of antibiological peptides; structure and biosynthesis of flagellin and bacterial flagella; self-assembly of macromolecular structures; molecular bases for biological stability. *Mailing Add:* Off of VPres Acad Affairs Univ of Minn Minneapolis MN 55455

KOFFYBERG, FRANCOIS PIERRE, b Eindhoven, Neth, Nov 17, 34; m 59; c 3. SOLID STATE SCIENCE. *Educ:* Free Univ, Amsterdam, Drs, 59. *Prof Exp:* Nat Res Coun Can fel, 59-62; res chemist, Corning Glass Works, NY, 62-65; assoc prof chem, 65-67, actg head physics, 67-68, assoc prof, 68-74, PROF PHYSICS, BROCK UNIV, 74- *Mem:* AAAS; Am Asn Physics Teachers; Can Asn Physicists. *Res:* Point defects and dislocations in crystals; semiconductivity of oxides and glasses; solar cells. *Mailing Add:* Dept of Physics Brock Univ St Catharines ON L2S 3A1 Can

KOFLER, RICHARD ROBERT, b Milwaukee, Wis, July 4, 35; m 59; c 3. PHYSICS. *Educ:* Marquette Univ, BS, 58; Univ Wis, MS, 60, PhD(elem particle physics), 64. *Prof Exp:* Res assoc physics, Univ Wis, 64-65; asst prof, 65-69, ASSOC PROF PHYSICS, UNIV MASS, AMHERST, 69- *Mem:* Am Inst Physics. *Res:* High energy elementary particle physics. *Mailing Add:* Dept of Physics Univ of Mass Amherst MA 01002

KOFOID, MELVIN J(ULIUS), b Portland, Ore, July 16, 10; m 41; c 2. ELECTRICAL ENGINEERING. *Educ:* Ore State Col, BS, 33, MS, 35, PhD(elec eng), 42. *Prof Exp:* Elec & hydraul engr, Bingham Pump Co, Ore, 35-37; res engr lamp div, Westinghouse Elec Co, NJ, 37, res lab, Pa, 38-46; assoc prof elec eng, Ore State Col, 46-50; res specialist, 50-58, STAFF MEM, SCI RES LABS, BOEING AIRPLANE CO, 58- *Mem:* Fel Inst Elec & Electronics Engrs; Am Phys Soc. *Res:* Plasma physics; gaseous electrical conductors; dielectrics; high voltage insulation. *Mailing Add:* 18625 Beverly Rd Seattle WA 98166

KOFORD, JAMES SHINGLE, b Cheyenne, Wyo, July 26, 38. ELECTRICAL ENGINEERING. *Educ:* Stanford Univ, BS, 59, MS, 60, PhD(elec eng), 64. *Prof Exp:* Res asst mem tech staff, Stanford Electronics Lab, 60-64; proj engr, IBM Components Div, 64-66; mem tech staff, Fairchild Semiconductor Corp, 66-69, sr mem tech staff, 69-73; vpres develop, Packet Commun, Inc, 73-75; mgr, Network Develop Lab, Boeing Comput Servs, 75-81; DIR, COMPUT AIDED DESIGN, LSI LOGIC INC, 81- *Mem:* AAAS; Inst Elec & Electronics Engrs; Asn Comput Mach. *Res:* Adaptive pattern-recognition systems; speech recognition; threshold elements, adaptation algorithms; computer-aided design for microelectronic circuits, logic simulation, graphic data processing. *Mailing Add:* 1480 Chukar Ct Sunnyvale CA 94087

KOFRANEK, ANTON MILES, b Chicago, Ill, Feb 5, 21; m 42; c 2. FLORICULTURE. *Educ:* Univ Minn, BS, 47; Cornell Univ, MS, 49, PhD, 50. *Prof Exp:* Asst, Cornell Univ, 47-50; from asst prof to prof floricult, Univ Calif, Los Angeles, 50-67; PROF ENVIRON HORT, UNIV CALIF, DAVIS, 67- *Concurrent Pos:* Vis prof, Hebrew Univ, Israel, 72-73. *Honors & Awards:* Am Carnation Soc Res Award, 74. *Mem:* Fel Am Soc Hort Sci; Am Orchid Soc. *Res:* Photoperiod and temperature in floricultural plants; post harvest physiology; floriculture crop production. *Mailing Add:* Dept of Environ Hort Univ of Calif Davis CA 95616

KOFRON, JAMES THOMAS, JR, b Petersburg, Va, Mar 11, 28; m 60; c 4. PHOTOGRAPHIC CHEMISTRY. *Educ:* Univ Notre Dame, BS, 52; Mass Inst Technol, PhD(org chem), 56. *Prof Exp:* Res assoc chem, 56-75, SR RES ASSOC, RES LABS, EASTMAN KODAK CO, 75- *Mem:* AAAS; Am Chem Soc; Soc Photog Scientists & Engrs. *Res:* Reaction mechanisms in chemistry of photographic processes. *Mailing Add:* Res Labs Eastman Kodak Co Rochester NY 14650

KOFRON, WILLIAM G, b Petersburg, Va, Aug 9, 34. ORGANIC CHEMISTRY. *Educ:* Univ Notre Dame, BS, 56; Univ Rochester, PhD(chem), 61. *Prof Exp:* Res assoc chem, Duke Univ, 60-62; fel, Columbia Univ, 62-63; sr chemist, Med Chem Dept, Geigy Res Labs, NY, 63-65; asst prof, 65-70, assoc prof, 70-76, PROF CHEM, UNIV AKRON, 76- *Mem:* Am Chem Soc; Brit Soc Chem Indust. *Res:* Chemistry of carbanions; heterocyclic chemistry. *Mailing Add:* Dept of Chem Univ of Akron Akron OH 44325

KOFSKY, IRVING LOUIS, b New York, NY, Mar 29, 25; m 69; c 3. PHYSICS. *Educ:* Syracuse Univ, BA, 45, PhD(physics), 52. *Prof Exp:* Instr physics, Syracuse Univ, 47-51; asst prof, Smith Col, 52-56; physicist, Tech Opers, Inc, 57-68; PRES & TECH DIR, PHOTOMETRICS INC, 68- *Mem:* Am Phys Soc; Am Astron Soc; Am Asn Physics Teachers. *Res:* Extensive showers in cosmic radiation; weapons effects; gaseous electronics; atmospheric optics; photometry, image analysis and scanning theory. *Mailing Add:* PhotoMetrics Inc 4 Arrow Dr Woburn MA 01803

KOFT, BERNARD WALDEMAR, b Hammonton, NJ, Nov 21, 21; m 44; c 5. BACTERIOLOGY. *Educ:* Rutgers Univ, BS, 43; Univ Pa, MS, 47, PhD(bact), 50. *Prof Exp:* From instr to asst prof bact, Jefferson Med Col, 50-57; from asst prof to assoc prof, 57-67, PROF MICROBIOL, RUTGERS UNIV, 67- *Mem:* Am Soc Microbiol; Am Inst Biol Sci; fel NY Acad Sci. *Res:* Bacterial nutrition; metabolism; vitamin synthesis; cellulose degradation. *Mailing Add:* Dept of Microbiol Rutgers Univ New Brunswick NJ 08903

KOGA, ROKUTARO, b Nagoya, Japan, Aug 18, 42; US citizen. ASTROPHYSICS. *Educ:* Univ Calif, Berkeley, BA, 66; Univ Calif, Riverside, PhD(physics), 74. *Prof Exp:* Physicist, Berkeley Sci Labs, 66-69; fel, Univ Calif, Riverside, 74; res assoc astrophys, Case Western Reserve Univ, 74-76, sr res assoc astrophys, 77-78, asst prof physics, 79-80; RES PHYSICIST SPACE & ASTROPHYS, AEROSPACE CORP, 81- *Mem:* Am Phys Soc; Sigma Xi; NY Acad Sci; Am Geophys Union. *Res:* Measurements of heavy ions in space using satellite based sensors; search for solar neutrons using a unique balloon borne detector. *Mailing Add:* Space Sci Lab Aerospace Corp Los Angeles CA 90009

KOGA, TOYOKI, b Japan, Apr 1, 12; div; c 2. THEORETICAL PHYSICS. *Educ:* Univ Tokyo, MS, 37, DSc, 48. *Prof Exp:* Asst prof aeronaut, Nagoya Univ, 40-48, prof mech eng & appl physics, 48-59; res scientist, Eng Ctr, Univ Southern Calif, 59-63; prof mech eng, Univ NC, 63-64; mem prof staff, TRW Systs, Inc, 67-69; RES & WRITING, 69- *Concurrent Pos:* Fulbright sr res fel, Calif Inst Technol, 55-56; vis prof, Univ Calif, 56-59 & Grad Ctr, Polytech Inst Brooklyn, 64-67. *Mem:* Am Phys Soc. *Res:* Gas dynamics; kinetic theory of gases; thermodynamics; kinetic theory of quantum mechanical systems; revision of quantum mechanics; theory of elementary particles. *Mailing Add:* 3061 Ewing Ave Altadena CA 91001

KOGAN, MARCOS, b Rio de Janeiro, Brazil, June 9, 33; m 53; c 2. ENTOMOLOGY, ECOLOGY. *Educ:* Univ Rural do Rio de Janeiro, BS, 61; Univ Calif, Riverside, PhD(entom), 69. *Prof Exp:* Entomologist res, S Cent Inst Agr Res, Rio de Janeiro, 61-63; biologist res, Inst Oswaldo Cruz, Rio de Janeiro, 63-66; res fel entom, Univ Calif, Riverside, 66-69, res assoc, 69; assoc entomologist res, Ill Natural Hist Surv, Urbana, 69-76; assoc prof agr entom, 73-77, PROF ENTOM & AGR ENTOM, UNIV ILL, URBANA, 77-; ENTOMOLOGIST, ILL NATURAL HIST SURV, URBANA, 76- *Concurrent Pos:* Consult soybean entom Brazil, 74-78, Korea, 78-79; mem sci deleg to Repub China, 81. *Mem:* Entom Soc Am; AAAS; Brazilian Entom Soc. *Res:* Management of soybean insect pests; soybean resistance to insects; insect plant interactions; nutrition of phytophagous insects; bionomics of Strepsiptera; international cooperation in soybean entomology and crop protection. *Mailing Add:* 172 Natural Resources Bldg Univ of Ill Urbana IL 61801

KOGAN, YURY, cancer, environmental medicine, see previous edition

KOGEL, MARCUS DAVID, b Austria, Sept 28, 03; nat US; m 30; c 2. PUBLIC HEALTH, ACADEMIC ADMINISTRATION. *Educ:* NY Med Col, MD, 27; Am Bd Prev Med, dipl. *Hon Degrees:* DHL, Yeshiva Univ, 52 & NY Med Col, 53. *Prof Exp:* From intern to chief resident physician, Metrop Hosp, NY, 27-29; from dep med supt to med supt, Cumberland Hosp, 30-35; med supt, Queens Gen Hosp, 35-41; gen med supt & dir bur med & hosp servs, Dept Hosps, New York, 46-49, comnr hosps, 49-54; dean col, 53-67, prof prev & environ med & chmn dept, 54-59, dean Sue Golding Grad Div, 56-67, Atran prof social med, 60-67, EMER DEAN, ALBERT EINSTEIN COL MED, 67- *Concurrent Pos:* Chief med officer civil defense, New York, 49-53; vpres med affairs & sci, Yeshiva Univ, 67-69. *Mem:* Fel Am Pub Health Asn; Asn Teachers Prev Med; Asn Am Med Cols; fel Am Col Prev Med; fel NY Acad Med. *Res:* Preventive and environmental medicine. *Mailing Add:* Lincoln B 1038 C V Boca Raton FL 33434

KOGELNIK, H W, b Graz, Austria, June 2, 32; m 64; c 3. PHYSICS, ELECTRONICS. *Educ:* Vienna Tech Univ, Dipl Ing, 55, Dr Tech, 58; Oxford Univ, DPhil(electromagnetic theory), 60. *Prof Exp:* Asst prof electronics, Inst High frequency Electronics, Vienna, Austria, 55-58; Brit Coun scholar, Oxford Univ, 58-60; mem staff electronics res, 61-67, head coherent optics, Res Dept, 67-76, DIR, ELECTRONICS RES LAB, BELL LABS, 76- *Mem:* AAAS; Am Phys Soc; fel Inst Elec & Electronics Engrs; fel Optical Soc Am. *Res:* Lasers; integrated optics; optical communication. *Mailing Add:* Bell Labs Holmdel NJ 07733

KOGER, LAVON M, b Cove, Ore, Sept 25, 15; m 42; c 3. VETERINARY MEDICINE. *Educ:* State Col Wash, BSc, 41, DVM, 42. *Prof Exp:* Pvt pract, 42-64; ASSOC PROF VET MED, WASH STATE UNIV, 64- *Mem:* Am Vet Med Asn; Am Animal Health Asn; Asn Bovine Practitioners. *Res:* Use of electrocautery in the control of bovine cancer-eye; veterinary use of isonicotinic acid hydrozide; animal identification; artificial pigmentation and depigmentation of animal skin; pregnancy diagnosis in the ewe; history of the livestock industry of the Nez Perce; calcium chloride chemosurgery. *Mailing Add:* Dept of Vet Med Wash State Univ Pullman WA 99163

KOGER, MARVIN, b Colgate, Okla; m 38; c 4. ANIMAL BREEDING, GENETICS. *Educ:* NMex Col, BS, 39; Kans State Univ, MS, 41; Univ Mo, PhD(physiol), 43. *Prof Exp:* From instr to assoc prof animal husb, NMex Col, 43-51; prof animal husb & animal geneticist, 51-80, PROF ANIMAL SCI, AGR EXP STA, UNIV FLA, 80- *Mem:* Am Soc Animal Sci; Am Dairy Sci Asn. *Res:* Nutritional deficiencies of sorghums; effects of hyperthyroidism; genetics of cattle and sheep; physiology of reproduction. *Mailing Add:* Dept of Animal Sci Univ of Fla Gainesville FL 32611

KOGON, IRVING CHARLES, b Brooklyn, NY, Aug 8, 23; m 48; c 2. ORGANIC CHEMISTRY. Educ: Brooklyn Col, BA, 48, MA, 51; Polytech Inst Brooklyn, PhD(chem), 54. Prof Exp: Asst org chem, Brooklyn Col, 49-51; res assoc, Univ Wis, 53-54; RES ASSOC, POLYMER PROD DEPT, EXP STA, E I DU PONT DE NEMOURS & CO, INC, 54- Mem: AAAS; Am Chem Soc; fel Am Inst Chemists. Res: Synthesis of antispasmodics, antihistamines and local anesthetics; heterocyclic vinyl monomers; mechanism of organic reactions; chemistry of isocyanates and polyurethanes; structure of antibiotics and synthetic rubbers; polymer chemistry. Mailing Add: 1420 Drake Rd Green Acres Wilmington DE 19803

KOGOS, L(AURENCE), b Boston, Mass, July 24, 29; m 51; c 2. CHEMICAL ENGINEERING. Educ: Northeastern Univ, BS, 51. Prof Exp: Chem engr, Sawyer-Tower, Inc, 51-52, chief res engr, 52-53, dir tech sales, 55, tech dir, 56-58, gen mgr, 58-59; exec vpres, Farrington Texol Corp, 59-63; gen mgr, Dynamic Coaters, Inc, 63-70; dir opers, Plymouth Rubber Co, Inc, 70-72; pres, Polymeric Fabricants Div, Whittaker Corp, 72-73; pres, Plastics Div, W R Grace & Co, 73-79; VPRES & GEN MGR, ROPER PLASTICS, INC, NEW YORK, 80- Mem: Am Chem Soc; Am Soc Plastics Engrs; Am Inst Chem Engrs. Res: Application of protective and decorative coatings to fabrics. Mailing Add: 6 Calumet Rd Westport CT 06880

KOGUT, JOHN BENJAMIN, b Brooklyn, NY, Mar 6, 45. THEORETICAL PHYSICS. Educ: Princeton Univ, BA, 67; Stanford Univ, MS, 68, PhD(physics), 71. Prof Exp: Assoc physics, Inst Advan Study, 71-73 & Tel Aviv Univ, 73; res assoc, Cornell Univ, 73-74, from asst prof to assoc prof, 74-78; PROF PHYSICS, UNIV ILL, 78- Concurrent Pos: Sloan Found fel & NSF grant, Cornell Univ, 76-78; NSF grant, Univ Ill, 78- Mem: Am Phys Soc. Res: Theory of elementary particles; field theory and statistical mechanics. Mailing Add: Loomis Lab Univ of Ill Urbana IL 61801

KOGUT, LEONARD S, inorganic chemistry, see previous edition

KOGUT, MAURICE D, b Brooklyn, NY, July 7, 30; m 59; c 3. PEDIATRICS, ENDOCRINOLOGY. Educ: NY Univ, BA, 51, MD, 55. Prof Exp: Intern pediat, Bellevue Hosp, New York, 55-56, resident, 56-57; chief resident, Children's Hosp, Los Angeles, 59-60, USPHS fel endocrinol, 60-62; from instr to assoc prof, 62-73, prof pediat, 73-80, assoc head dept, 75-80, CLIN PROF MED, SCH MED, UNIV SOUTHERN CALIF, 80-; HEAD DIV ENDOCRINOL & METAB & PROG DIR, CLIN RES CTR, CHILDREN'S HOSP, 71- Mem: Endocrine Soc; Am Diabetes Asn; Am Acad Pediat; Soc Pediat Res; Am Pediat Soc. Res: Carbohydrate metabolism in idiopathic hypoglycemia; growth hormone and insulin metabolism in hypopituitarism; the role of circulating insulin and glucagon in children with genetic predisposition to diabetes mellitus; uric acid metabolism. Mailing Add: Children's Hosp 4650 Sunset Blvd Los Angeles CA 90027

KOH, EUSEBIO LEGARDA, applied mathematics, see previous edition

KOH, KWANG KUK, b Seoul, Korea, Sept 7, 34; m 63; c 3. CHEMICAL ENGINEERING. Educ: Seoul Nat Univ, BS, 58; Univ Iowa, MS, PhD(chem eng), 68. Prof Exp: Res engr, Ham Tai Coal Mining Co, 60-63; dir, Korea Chem Eng Res Lab, 63-64; sr res engr, Exxon Res & Eng Co, 68-75; ADMINR, ANG COAL GASIFICATION CO, 75- Concurrent Pos: Instr, Seoul Nat Univ, 63-64. Mem: Am Inst Chem Engrs; Am Chem Soc. Res: Utilization of coal; gasification and liquifaction of coal. Mailing Add: ANG Coal Gasification Co One Woodward Ave Detroit MI 48226

KOH, KWANGIL, b Seoul, Korea, July 8, 31; m 58; c 3. MATHEMATICS. Educ: Auburn Univ, BS, 59, MS, 60; Univ NC, PhD(math), 64. Prof Exp: From instr to assoc prof, 64-68, PROF MATH, NC STATE UNIV, 68- Mem: Am Math Soc; Math Asn Am. Res: Algebra; theory of rings. Mailing Add: Dept of Math NC State Univ Raleigh NC 27607

KOH, P(UN) K(IEN), b China, Jan 31, 14; nat US; m 67; c 2. PHYSICAL METALLURGY. Educ: Mass Inst Technol, DSc, 39. Prof Exp: Head, Metall Sect, Stand Oil Co, Ind, 45-47; assoc dir res & staff scientist, Allegheny Ludlum Steel Corp, 48-60; res engr, Bethlehem Steel Corp, 60-66; prof of mat sci, 66-76, EMER PROF MECH ENG, TEX TECH UNIV, 76- Concurrent Pos: Lectr, Ill Inst Technol, 46-47, Univ Pittsburgh, 53-58 & Stevens Inst Technol, 65-66; hon assoc dir, Metal Indust Res Inst, Kaosiung, Taiwan; tech adv, Indust Technol Res Inst, Taiwan, Repub China. Mem: Fel Am Inst Chemists. Res: X-ray diffraction; electron microprobe; metal physics; polymers; environmental engineering. Mailing Add: Dept of Mech Eng Tex Tech Univ Lubbock TX 79409

KOH, ROBERT CY, b Shanghai, China, May 23, 38; m 61; c 1. FLUID MECHANICS, APPLIED MATHEMATICS. Educ: Calif Inst Technol, BS, 60, MS, 61, PhD(appl mech, math), 64. Prof Exp: Res fel eng, Calif Inst Technol, 64-65; mem tech staff, Hughes Res Co, 65-66; SR SCIENTIST, TETRA TECH INC, 66- Mem: Int Asn Hydraul Res. Res: Fluid mechanics; applied mathematics. Mailing Add: 212 S Marengo Ave Pasadena CA 91101

KOH, SEVERINO LEGARDA, b Manila, Philippines, Jan 8, 27; m 52; c 5. THEORETICAL & APPLIED MECHANICS, THERMAL SCIENCES. Educ: NY Univ, BS, 50; Nat Univ, Manila, BS, 52; Pa State Univ, MS, 57; Purdue Univ, PhD(eng sci), 62. Prof Exp: Meteorologist-in-chg marine unit, Weather Bur, Manila, 48-54; res asst hydrodyn lab, Johns Hopkins Univ, 54-55; instr mech, Pa State Univ, 55-57; instr eng sci, Purdue Univ, 57-59; res assoc viscoelasticity, Gen Tech Corp, 59-61; mech engr, Major Appliance Lab, Gen Elec Co, 61-62; from asst prof to prof aeronaut & eng sci, Purdue Univ, 62-73, prof mech eng, 73-80, asst head, Div Interdisciplinary Eng Studies, 77-80, head, Dept Eng, 80-81; PROF & CHMN MECH & AEROSPACE ENG, WVA UNIV, 81- Concurrent Pos: Mem, President's Fact-Finding Comt, Philippines, 53-54; res assoc, B G Bantegui & Assocs, Manila, 53-54; scientist-consult, Gen Tech Corp, 62-; Standard Oil Co (Ind) Found teaching award, 67; vis prof & res assoc, Clausthal Tech Univ, 68-69; vis prof, Univ Karlsruhe, 69; Humboldt vis prof, Univ Bonn, 74-75; Balik

scientist, Philippines, 76; consult, 3IE, Inc, 77- & Batelle Northwest, 78; dir, The Eng Sci Perspective, 70-73 & 78-80, ed-in-chief, 76- Mem: Soc Eng Sci (secy, 63-68); Am Acad Mech; Am Soc Eng Educ; Am Soc Mech Engrs; Soc Rheology. Res: Elasticity; viscoelasticity; fluid dynamics; rheology of nonlinear materials; composite materials; testing of materials; sandwich structures; micromechanics; solar energy systems; geotechnical engineering problems; heat and mass transfer. Mailing Add: Mech & Aerospace Eng WVa Univ Morgantown WV 26506

KOH, YOUNG O, statistics, computer science, see previous edition

KOHAN, MELVIN IRA, b Boston, Mass, Mar 11, 21; m 43; c 4. ORGANIC POLYMER CHEMISTRY. Educ: Harvard Univ, AB, 42; Univ Ill, PhD(chem), 50. Prof Exp: Chemist, Dept Electrochem, 42-44 & 46-47, chemist, Dept Plastics, 50-62, sr res chemist, 62-74, res assoc, Dept Plastics, 74-80, RES ASSOC, POLYMER PRODUCTS DEPT, EXP STA, E I DU PONT DE NEMOURS & CO, INC, 80- Mem: Am Chem Soc; Soc Plastic Engrs; Sigma Xi. Res: Polymer chemistry; plastics engineering; nylon plastics technology. Mailing Add: Polymer Prods Dept E I du Pont de Nemours Co Inc Wilmington DE 19898

KOHANE, THEODORE, b New York, NY, Apr 20, 23; m 55; c 2. PHYSICS. Educ: City Col New York, BS, 44; Rutgers Univ, PhD(physics), 53. Prof Exp: Physicist, Nat Adv Comt Aeronaut, 44-46; asst physics & instr, NY Univ, 46-48; asst & fel, Rutgers Univ, 48-53; MEM RES STAFF, RAYTHEON RES DIV, WALTHAM, 53- Mem: Am Phys Soc; Optical Soc Am. Res: Nuclear magnetic resonance; magnetic and electrical properties of ferrites; microwaves; optical properties of solids. Mailing Add: 43 Hobart Rd Sudbury MA 01776

KOHEL, RUSSELL JAMES, b Omaha, Nebr, Nov 30, 34; m 57; c 3. PLANT GENETICS. Educ: Iowa State Univ, BS, 56; Purdue Univ, MS, 58, PhD(plant breeding), 59. Prof Exp: RES GENETICIST COTTON, USDA, SCI & EDUC & AGR RES SERV, 59- Mem: Am Soc Plant Physiologists; fel Am Soc Agron; Am Genetic Asn; Genetics Soc Am. Res: Qualitative and quantitative genetics of the cotton plant. Mailing Add: Dept of Soil & Crop Sci Tex A&M Univ College Station TX 77843

KOHIN, BARBARA CASTLE, b Providence, RI, Dec 11, 32; m 59; c 3. MOLECULAR PHYSICS. Educ: Col William & Mary, BS, 53; Univ Md, MS, 56, PhD(physics), 60. Prof Exp: Res assoc molecular physics, Cath Univ Am, 59-61; physicist theoret physics, Inst Battelle, Geneva, Switz, 61-62; instr physics, Mass State Col Worcester, 64-67; asst prof physics, Clark Univ, 67-68 & 71-78; ASSOC DIR, OFF SPEC STUDIES, COL OF THE HOLY CROSS, 78- Concurrent Pos: Res assoc, Mass Inst Technol, 73-74. Res: Quantum chemistry; solid state physics; elementary and atomic physics. Mailing Add: 11 Berwick St Worcester MA 01602

KOHIN, ROGER PATRICK, b Chicago, Ill, Mar 2, 31; m 59; c 3. PHYSICS. Educ: Univ Notre Dame, BSEE, 53; Univ Md, PhD(physics), 60. Prof Exp: Scientist physics, Battelle Mem Inst, Geneva, Switz, 61-62; asst prof, 62-67, chmn dept, 74-76, ASSOC PROF PHYSICS, CLARK UNIV, 67- Concurrent Pos: Vis scientist, Inst J Stefan, Ljubljana, Yugoslavia, 68-69; Indo-Am fel, Indian Inst Tech-Kanpur, 76-77. Mem: Am Phys Soc; Optical Soc Am. Res: Electron-spin resonance spectroscopy; radiation damage of solids; experimental ferroelectric materials; organic semiconductors; organic and inorganic free radicals. Mailing Add: Dept of Physics Clark Univ Worcester MA 01610

KOHL, A(RTHUR) L(IONEL), b Ont, Can, Aug 21, 19; nat US; m 43; c 3. CHEMICAL ENGINEERING. Educ: Univ Southern Calif, BE, 43, MS, 47. Prof Exp: Res engr, Turco Prod, Inc, 42-44 & 46-47; chief chem eng res, Fluor Corp Ltd, 47-60; group leader process develop, Atomics Int, 60-68, proj engr & proj mgr advan develop, 68-78, PROG MGR COAL GASIFICATION, ENERGY SYSTS GROUP, ROCKWELL INT, 78- Honors & Awards: Outstanding Achievement Award, Am Inst Chem Engrs, 66. Mem: Am Inst Chem Engrs. Res: Protective treatments for magnesium alloys; gas purification; process equipment; saline water conversion; chemical process development; nuclear reactor fuels and materials; nuclear reactor component development; coal conversion. Mailing Add: Energy Systs Group Rockwell Int PO Box 309 Canoga Park CA 91304

KOHL, DANIEL HOWARD, b Cleveland, Ohio, July 30, 28; m 50; c 4. PLANT PHYSIOLOGY. Educ: Univ Calif, Berkeley, BS, 60; Washington Univ, PhD(molecular biol), 65. Prof Exp: Asst prof bot, 65-70, assoc prof, 70-79, sr fel, Ctr Biol Natural Systs, 71-81, PROF BIOL, WASHINGTON UNIV, 79- Mem: Am Soc Plant Physiol; Soil Sci Soc Am. Res: N isotope distribution in various components of N cycle. Mailing Add: Dept of Biol Box 1137 Washington Univ St Louis MO 63130

KOHL, DAVID MARTIN, developmental biology, biochemistry, see previous edition

KOHL, FRED JOHN, b Cleveland, Ohio, Jan 1, 42. PHYSICAL CHEMISTRY. Educ: Case Inst Technol, BS, 63; Case Western Reserve Univ, PhD(chem), 68. Prof Exp: RES CHEMIST, LEWIS RES CTR, NASA, 68- Mem: Am Chem Soc; Am Soc Mass Spectrometry; Combustion Inst. Res: Hot corrosion of superalloys; oxidation of metals; high temperature vaporization and thermodynamics; mass spectrometry; oxidation/vaporization processes; high temperature chemistry; vaporization of refractories; materials science experiments in space; combustion process related to corrosion. Mailing Add: NASA Lewis Res Ctr 21000 Brookpark Rd Cleveland OH 44135

KOHL, HARRY CHARLES, JR, b St Louis, Mo, Aug 6, 19; m 41; c 1. FLORICULTURE, PLANT PHYSIOLOGY. Educ: Univ Ill, BS, 40, MS, 48; Cornell Univ, PhD(hort), 50. Prof Exp: Assoc exten specialist floricult, Rutgers Univ, 50-53; asst prof, Univ Calif, Los Angeles & asst plant physiologist, 57-62; prof floricult & plant physiologist, 62-77, prof & chairperson, Plant Phys Grad Group, 77-80, EMER PROF ENVIRON HORT, UNIV CALIF, DAVIS, 80- *Mem:* Am Soc Plant Physiol; Am Soc Hort Sci; Bot Soc Am; Int Soc Soil Sci. *Res:* Control of plant growth and differentiation; preharvest and post-harvest physiology of flowers; mineral translocation; root aeration; salinity tolerance. *Mailing Add:* Dept of Environ Hort Univ of Calif Davis CA 95616

KOHL, JEROME, b Montreal, Que, Mar 13, 18; nat US; m 45; c 2. CHEMICAL ENGINEERING. *Educ:* Calif Inst Technol, BS, 40; NC State Univ, MS, 75. *Prof Exp:* Chem & proj engr, Avon Refinery, Tidewater Assoc Oil Co, Calif, 43-46, asst supt, 46-48; chem engr, Tracerlab, Inc, 48-51, sect leader, Mobile Radiochem Lab, 51-53, chief engr, 53-58, mgr eng & develop, 58-60; coordr spec prod, Gen Atomic Div, Gen Dynamics Corp, 60-64; mkt mgr, Oak Ridge Tech Enterprises, 65-69; NUCLEAR ENG EXTEN SPECIALIST, NC STATE UNIV, 69- *Concurrent Pos:* Instr & lectr, Univ Calif, Berkeley & San Diego, 47-64; lectr, Univ Delft, 56. *Mem:* Am Nuclear Soc; Am Inst Chem Engrs. *Res:* Radiation monitoring instrumentation; industrial applications of radioisotopes; measurement of nuclear radiations; energy conservation; co-generation; management of hazardous waste. *Mailing Add:* Dept of Nuclear Eng NC State Univ Box 5636 Raleigh NC 27650

KOHL, JOHN C(LAYTON), b New York, NY, June 22, 08; m 35; c 2. CIVIL ENGINEERING. *Educ:* Univ Mich, BSE, 29. *Hon Degrees:* MA, Univ Pa, 73. *Prof Exp:* From draftsman to inspector construct, Cincinnati Union Terminal Co, 29-30; instr civil eng, Carnegie Inst Technol, 31-37; asst dir cent develop lab, Pittsburgh Plate Glass Co, 37-38; res & develop engr, Pittsburgh Corning Corp, 38-44 & 46; from asst prof to prof civil eng, Univ Mich, 46-66, dir transp inst, 55-66; exec secy div eng, Nat Acad Sci-Nat Res Coun, 66-68; sr assoc, Wilbur Smith & Assocs, 68-70; comnr, NJ Dept Transp, 70-74; prof, 74-76, EMER PROF CIVIL & URBAN ENG, UNIV PA, 76- *Concurrent Pos:* Consult, Am Buslines, Inc, 48, Haugh & Keenan Transfer & Storage Co, 49 & Fruehauf Trailer Co, 50; asst adminr, US Housing & Home Finance Agency, DC, 61-66; chmn, Tristate Regional Planning Comn, 70-71; vchmn, Gov Comn Transit Financing, 71-73; mem transp res bd, Nat Acad Sci-Nat Res Coun; mem, Transp Res Forum; vis sr fel, Dept Civil Eng, Princeton Univ, 76-81. *Mem:* Am Soc Civil Engrs; Am Soc Traffic & Transp; hon mem Inst Transp; hon mem Am Pub Works Asn. *Res:* Transportation engineering and economics; urban transportation planning; rail network analysis. *Mailing Add:* 700 Maple Leaf Lane Moorestown NJ 08057

KOHL, JOHN LESLIE, b Zanesville, Ohio, Apr 27, 41; m 65; c 2. EXPERIMENTAL ATOMIC PHYSICS, SOLAR PHYSICS. *Educ:* Muskingum Col, BS, 63; Univ Toledo, MS, 66, PhD(physics), 69. *Prof Exp:* Res fel physics, 69-72, res assoc physics, Harvard Col Observ, 72-76, ASTROPHYSICIST & LECTR, SMITHSONIAN ASTROPHYS OBSERV, HARVARD UNIV, 76- *Concurrent Pos:* Nat Sci Found fel. *Mem:* Am Phys Soc; Am Astron Soc; Int Astron Union; Am Geophys Union. *Res:* Experimental studies of atomic and molecular processes needed to understand astrophysical and laboratory plasmas; experimental studies of solar wind generation using space instrumentation. *Mailing Add:* Ctr for Astrophysics 60 Garden St Cambridge MA 02138

KOHL, RICHARD NIEMES, b Cincinnati, Ohio, Nov 12, 15. PSYCHIATRY. *Educ:* Univ Cincinnati, BA, 38, MD, 42. *Prof Exp:* Res psychiatrist, Payne Whitney Clin, New York Hosp, 44-49; from asst prof to assoc prof psychiat, Med Col, Cornell Univ, 49-71; clin dir, 62-64, med dir, 65-80, ATTEND PSYCHIATRIST & DEPT MED DIR, PAYNE WHITNEY CLIN, NEW YORK HOSP, 80-; PROF PSYCHIAT, MED COL, CORNELL UNIV, 71- *Concurrent Pos:* From asst attend psychiatrist to assoc attend psychiatrist, New York Hosp, 49-59, attend psychiatrist, 59-; expert examr, Munic Civil Serv Comn, New York, 50-; attend psychiatrist, Vet Admin Hosp, Montrose, NY, consult, 62-70. *Honors & Awards:* Physician's Recognition Award in Continuing Med Educ, AMA, 70. *Mem:* Am Acad Arts & Sci; Asn Am Med Cols; Am Acad Psychiat & Law; Am Psychiat Asn. *Res:* Administrative and hospital psychiatry; psychiatric illnesses of medical students and physicians; family and forensic psychiatry; resident training. *Mailing Add:* Payne Whitney Clin New York Hosp 525 E 68th St New York NY 10021

KOHL, ROBERT A, b Harvey, Ill, Jan 22, 36; m 57; c 4. SOIL PHYSICS, IRRIGATION. *Educ:* Purdue Univ, BS, 58; Utah State Univ, MS, 60, PhD(soils, irrig), 63. *Prof Exp:* Agr missionary, Lutheran Mission, Nigeria, 63-66; res soil scientist, Snake River Conserv Res Ctr, Agr Res Serv, USDA, Idaho, 67-74; ASSOC PROF PLANT SCI, S DAK STATE UNIV, 75- *Mem:* Soil Sci Soc Am; Am Soc Agron. *Res:* Water management; sprinkler irrigation. *Mailing Add:* Dept of Plant Sci SDak State Univ Brookings SD 57007

KOHL, SCHUYLER G, b Philadelphia, Pa, Feb 22, 13; m 43; c 1. MEDICINE. *Educ:* Univ Md, BS, 36, MD, 40; Columbia Univ, MS, 52, DrPH, 54; Am Bd Obstet & Gynec, dipl, 51. *Prof Exp:* Asst obstet, Univ Md, 42-49, instr, 49-50; res assoc obstet & gynec, 50-51, from asst prof to assoc prof, 51-62, from asst dean to assoc dean, 58-71, PROF OBSTET & GYNEC, STATE UNIV NY DOWNSTATE MED CTR, 62- *Concurrent Pos:* Consult, Nat Inst Neurol Dis & Stroke, mem hosp facil res study sect, 58-60, mem human ecol study sect, 60-65; lectr, Columbia Univ, 59-; consult, Pan Am Health Orgn, 60- *Mem:* Asn Planned Parenthood Physicians; Soc Gynec Invest; Am Pub Health Asn; AMA; Asn Am Med Cols. *Res:* Application of statistical methods to clinical practice. *Mailing Add:* Dept of Obstet & Gynec State Univ NY Downstate Med Ctr Brooklyn NY 11203

KOHL, WALTER H(EINRICH), b Kitzingen, Bavaria, Ger, Jan 22, 05; nat US; m 32; c 1. ELECTRONICS. *Educ:* Dresden Tech Univ, Dipl Ing, 28, Dr Ing, 30. *Prof Exp:* Demonstr physics, Dresden Tech Univ, 28-30; develop engr, Rogers Electronic Tubes, Toronto, 31-40, proj engr, 41-43, chief engr, vpres & dir, 44-45; sect head vacuum tube lab, Collins Radio Co, Iowa, 46-48, consult to dir res, 49-52; res assoc electronics res lab, Stanford Univ, 52-58; sr eng specialist, Mt View Components Lab, Sylvania Elec Prod, Inc, 58-61; consult mat & technol for electron devices, 62-66; sr scientist microwave lab, Electronics Res Ctr, NASA, 66-68, chief univ affairs off, 68-70; consult mat & technol for electron devices, 70-78; RETIRED. *Concurrent Pos:* Lectr, Univ Toronto, 35-40; consult, Stanford Res Inst, 56-58 & Off Asst Secy Defense, 57. *Mem:* AAAS; fel Inst Elec & Electronics Engrs; fel Am Ceramic Soc; Sigma Xi; Am Soc Metals. *Res:* Materials and techniques for electron devices. *Mailing Add:* 36 Woodleigh Rd Watertown MA 02172

KOHLAND, WILLIAM FRANCIS, b Chester, Pa, May 13, 25; m 56; c 1. PETROLOGY, ATMOSPERIC SCIENCE. *Educ:* Bucknell Univ, AB, 51; Univ Tenn, Knoxville, MS, 52, PhD(earth sci), 69. *Prof Exp:* Asst prof geol & earth sci, Edinboro State Col, 59-67; PROF GEOL & EARTH SCI, MID TENN STATE UNIV, 67- *Concurrent Pos:* Consult, field geologist. *Mem:* Geol Soc Am; Nat Asn Geol Teachers; Am Soc Agron; Soil Sci Soc Am; Int Soil Sci Soc. *Res:* Relationships of soil formation to underlying rock; metasomatic changes in rocks; mineral identification. *Mailing Add:* Dept of Geol & Earth Sci Mid Tenn State Univ Box 416 Murfreesboro TN 37132

KOHLBRENNER, PHILIP JOHN, b South Bend, Ind, Nov 17, 31; m 57; c 6. ORGANIC CHEMISTRY. *Educ:* Purdue Univ, BS, 53; State Univ NY Col Forestry, Syracuse Univ, PhD(org chem), 58. *Prof Exp:* Res chemist synthetic org chem, Cowles Chem Co, 57-58; res chemist, 58-64, group leader synthetic org chem, 64-76, dept head basic pharmaceut, Lederle Labs Div, 76-80, ASSOC DIR REGULATORY AFFAIRS, MED RES DIV, AM CYANAMID CO, 80- *Mem:* Am Chem Soc; Am Pharmaceut Asn; Acad Pharmaceut Sci. *Res:* Synthetic organic chemistry. *Mailing Add:* 9 Borger Pl Pearl River NY 10965

KOHLER, BRYAN EARL, b Heber City, Utah, June 9, 40; m 60; c 3. PHYSICAL CHEMISTRY. *Educ:* Univ Utah, BA, 62; Univ Chicago, PhD(chem), 67. *Prof Exp:* Fermi Inst res fel chem, Univ Chicago, 67; NSF fel, Calif Inst Technol, 67-68; from asst prof to assoc prof, Harvard Univ, 69-75; assoc prof, 75-77, PROF CHEM, WESLEYAN UNIV, 77-, CHMN CHEM, 80- *Concurrent Pos:* Grants, Am Chem Soc, Harvard Univ, 69-70, Advan Res Proj Agency, 69-, NIH, 69- & NSF, 72-; Sloan Found fel, 74-76; fel, Alexander von Humboldt, 79; vis fel, Joint Inst Lab Astrophysics, 78; fel, Alfred P Sloan Found, 74. *Mem:* Am Phys Soc; NIH; Am Phys Soc; NY Acad Sci; Biophys Soc . *Res:* Investigation of the electronic structure of molecules and molecular crystals using the techniques of magnetic resonance and optical spectroscopy; electronic properties of biomolecules; dynamics of excitation. *Mailing Add:* Dept of Chem Wesleyan Univ Middletown CT 06457

KOHLER, CARL, b Hamilton, Ont, June 24, 30; m 50; c 4. MARINE BIOLOGY, ICHTHYOPLANKTON. *Educ:* McMaster Univ, BA, 53; McGill Univ, MSc, 56, PhD(zool), 60. *Prof Exp:* Asst conservationist, Royal Bot Gardens, Ont, 51; from asst technician to technician, 53-56, from asst scientist to sr scientist, 56-67, head groundfish prog, 67-73, HEAD FISHERY BIOL SECT, BIOL STA, FISHERIES RES BD CAN, 73- *Concurrent Pos:* Demonstr, McGill Univ, 55-56 & 58-59. *Mem:* Am Fisheries Soc. *Res:* Fishery biology and biostatistics; fishery management. *Mailing Add:* Biol Sta Fisheries Res Bd Can St Andrews NB E0G 2X0 Can

KOHLER, CONSTANCE ANNE, b Flushing, NY, Jan 9, 43. PHARMACOLOGY, BIOCHEMISTRY. *Educ:* St John's Univ, NY, BS, 65; Med Ctr, Univ Calif, San Francisco, PhD(pharmacol), 73. *Prof Exp:* Fel pharmacol, Roche Inst Molecular Biol, NJ, 72-74; res pharmacologist, 74-80, SR RES SCIENTIST, LEDERLE LABS, DIV AM CYANAMID, NY, 80- *Mem:* AAAS; Am Heart Asn; Am Chem Soc; NY Acad Sci; Sigma Xi. *Res:* Atherosclerosis and thrombosis; platelet biochemistry; arachidonic acid metabolism; cell culture; growth factors. *Mailing Add:* Med Res Div Am Cyanamid Co Pearl River NY 10965

KOHLER, DONALD ALVIN, b Rainier, Ore, Oct 29, 28; m 59; c 2. NUCLEAR PHYSICS, PLASMA PHYSICS. *Educ:* Univ Ore, BS, 51, MS, 52; Calif Inst Technol, PhD(physics), 59. *Prof Exp:* Res assoc nuclear physics, Stanford Univ, 59-62, res assoc, 62-63, lectr, 62-65; res scientist, 65-73, staff scientist, 73-79, SR STAFF SCIENTIST, LOCKHEED PALO ALTO RES LAB, 79- *Mem:* AAAS; Am Phys Soc. *Res:* Optical spectroscopy; pressure effects of foreign gases upon absorption lines; experimental low-energy nuclear physics, particularly of the light nuclei; cosmology and astrophysics; x-ray physics and instrumentation; laser-plasma interaction; laser fusion power experimental studies; elementary particle physics; weak interactions. *Mailing Add:* Lockheed Palo Alto Res Lab Bldg 203 Palo Alto CA 94304

KOHLER, ELAINE ELOISE HUMPHREYS, b Paris, France, Feb 5, 39; US citizen; m. PEDIATRIC ENDOCRINOLOGY. *Educ:* Radcliffe Col, BA, 60; Boston Univ, MD, 64. *Prof Exp:* Intern pediat, Milwaukee Children's Hosp, 64-65, resident, 65-66, chief resident, 66-67; instr, 68-71, asst prof pediat, 71-80, CHIEF METAB SECT, MED COL WIS, 78-, ASSOC PROF PEDIAT, 80- *Concurrent Pos:* Dir, Milwaukee Poison Ctr, 71-77; lectr, Marquette Univ, 71-72. *Mem:* Am Acad Pediat; Am Diabetes Asn; Ambulatory Pediat Asn; Wilkins Pediat Endocrine Soc. *Res:* Juvenile diabetes mellitus; glycohydrolase metabolism; growth problems in infancy; chondrodystrophies. *Mailing Add:* Milwaukee Children's Hosp 1700 W Wisconsin Ave Milwaukee WI 53233

KOHLER, ERWIN MILLER, b Cincinnati, Ohio, June 24, 30; m 54; c 2. VETERINARY MICROBIOLOGY. *Educ:* Ohio State Univ, DVM, 55, MS, 63, PhD(microbiol, immunol), 65. *Prof Exp:* Vet, Winchester Animal Hosp, Va, 55-62; from asst prof to assoc prof, 65-73, PROF INFECTIOUS DISEASES DOMESTIC ANIMALS, VET SCI DEPT, OHIO AGR RES & DEVELOP CTR, 73-, CHMN DEPT, 76- *Mem:* Am Vet Med Asn; Am Soc Microbiol; Conf Res Workers Animal Diseases; Am Asn Swine Practitioners. *Res:* Studies of colibacillosis of gnotobiotic and conventional swine; studies of the oral immunization of sows as an aid in the prevention of neonatal enteric colibacillosis of pigs. *Mailing Add:* Dept of Vet Sci Ohio Agr Res & Develop Ctr Wooster OH 44691

KOHLER, GEORGE OSCAR, b Milwaukee, Wis, Apr 9, 13; m 40; c 3. BIOCHEMISTRY, BIOCHEMICAL ENGINEERING. *Educ:* Univ Wis, BS, 34, MS, 36, PhD(biochem), 38. *Prof Exp:* Asst, Univ Wis, 34-39, Cerophyl Labs grant, 38-39; assoc dir res, Cerophyl Labs, Inc, 39-50, vpres & dir res, 50-54, dir res, Alfalfa Dehydration & Milling Co, 54-55; pres, Cerophyl Labs, Inc, 55-56; res leader, Western Regional Res Ctr, Sci & Educ Admin-Agr Res, USDA, 56-81; OWNER, G O KOHLER & ASSOC, 81- *Mem:* Am Inst Nutrit; Am Chem Soc; Inst Food Technologists; Am Asn Cereal Chemists; Poultry Sci Asn. *Res:* Chicken and guinea pig nutrition; hormone assay and synthesis; vitamin assay; isolation of compounds from natural materials; process development; amino acid analysis; protein isolates from leaves and oilseeds. *Mailing Add:* 2259 Tamalpais Ave El Cerrito CA 94530

KOHLER, HEINZ, b Duisburg, Ger, Sept 11, 39; m 65; c 2. PROTEIN CHEMISTRY, IMMUNOLOGY. *Educ:* Univ Munich, MD, 65. *Prof Exp:* Res fel, Max Planck Inst Biochem, 65-67; res assoc, Div Biol Sci, Ind Univ, 67-70; asst prof, Dept Path, 70-74, ASSOC PROF, DEPTS PATH & BIOCHEM, UNIV CHICAGO, 74- *Concurrent Pos:* Res career develop award, USPHS, 73. *Mem:* Fedn Am Soc Exp Biol. *Res:* Relationship of function and structure of proteins; regulation of immune response. *Mailing Add:* La Rabida Univ of Chicago Inst E 65th St at Lake Mich Chicago IL 60649

KOHLER, PETER FRANCIS, b Milwaukee, Wis, Apr 14, 35; m 62; c 3. IMMUNOLOGY. *Educ:* Princeton Univ, AB, 57; Columbia Univ, MD, 61. *Prof Exp:* From asst prof to assoc prof, 67-76, PROF MED, UNIV COLO MED CTR, 76-, HEAD DIV CLIN IMMUNOL, 75- *Mem:* Am Soc Clin Invest; Am Asn Immunologists; Am Acad Allergy. *Res:* Immunopathogenic mechanisms in disease; complement; immunology of hepatitis B virus infection. *Mailing Add:* Univ of Colo Med Ctr Denver CO 80231

KOHLER, R RAMON, b Midway, Utah, July 24, 31; m 56; c 7. SPEECH PATHOLOGY, AUDIOLOGY. *Educ:* Brigham Young Univ, BS, 58, MS, 61; Univ Utah, PhD(speech path), 67. *Prof Exp:* Speech pathologist mobile unit, Mont Soc Crippled Children, 59; teacher elem, Idaho Falls Pub Schs, 60-62; speech pathologist, Daggett, Hinckley & Newberry Pub Schs, 62-65 & Salt Lake City Pub Schs, 66-68; asst prof, 68-71, PROF SPEECH PATH & HEAD DEPT, UNIV WYO, 71- *Concurrent Pos:* Consult & team mem, Wyo Cleft Palate Eval Team, 68- *Mem:* Am Cleft Palate Asn; Am Speech & Hearing Asn. *Res:* Velopharyngeal closure in cleft palate children and its effect upon speech. *Mailing Add:* Dept of Speech Path & Audiol Box 3311 Univ Sta Laramie WY 82071

KOHLER, ROBERT HENRY, b Philadelphia, Pa, Apr 25, 33. PHYSICS. *Educ:* Mass Inst Technol, BS, 55, PhD(physics), 60. *Prof Exp:* Res assoc exp physics, Columbia Univ, 60-63; asst prof physics, NY Univ, 63-65; vis asst prof, Rutgers Univ, 65-66; PROF PHYSICS, STATE UNIV NY COL BUFFALO, 66- *Mem:* Am Phys Soc; Am Asn Physics Teachers. *Res:* Lasers and quantum electronics; optical pumping. *Mailing Add:* Dept of Physics State Univ of NY Col Buffalo NY 14222

KOHLER, SIGURD H, b Uppsala, Sweden, Dec 1, 28; wid. NUCLEAR PHYSICS. *Educ:* Univ Uppsala, Fil Kand, 51, Fil Mag, 52, Fil Lic, 56, Fil Dr(theoret physics), 59. *Prof Exp:* Asst, Inst Meteorol, Univ Uppsala, 50-53 & Inst Theoret Physics, 53-57; fel theoret physics, Cern, Geneva, Switz, 57-59; res assoc, Cornell Univ, 59-60; asst res physicist, Univ Calif, Los Angeles, 60-61; spec res, AEC Sweden, Uppsala, 61-63; asst res physicist, Univ Calif, San Diego, 63-65; vis assoc prof physics, Rice Univ, 65-68; PROF PHYSICS, UNIV ARIZ, 68- *Mem:* Am Phys Soc. *Res:* Many body problems. *Mailing Add:* Dept of Physics Univ of Ariz Tucson AZ 85721

KOHLHAW, GUNTER B, b Elbing, Ger, May 5, 31; m 59. BIOCHEMISTRY. *Educ:* Univ Freiburg, MS, 59, PhD(biochem), 62. *Prof Exp:* Res asst gen biochem, Univ Freiburg, 62-64; NATO fel intracellular regulation, 64-66, from asst prof to assoc prof, 66-73, PROF BIOCHEM, PURDUE UNIV, WEST LAFAYETTE, 73- *Mem:* Am Chem Soc; Am Soc Biol Chemists; Am Soc Microbiol; Ger Soc Biol Chem. *Res:* Enzymology; metabolic regulation. *Mailing Add:* Dept of Biochem Purdue Univ West Lafayette IN 47906

KOHLHEPP, SUE JOANNE, b Kittanning, Pa, July 15, 39. ANALYTICAL BIOCHEMISTRY. *Educ:* WVa Wesleyan Col, BS, 61; Pa State Univ, MS, 63, PhD(biophys), 69. *Prof Exp:* Teacher physics & phys sci, Marple-Newtown Sch Dist, Pa, 63-66; res assoc clin chem, St Anthony Hosp, Louisville, Ky, 69-74; res assoc biochem, Ore State Univ, 75-77; RES ASSOC, GILBERT RES LAB, PROVIDENCE MED CTR, PORTLAND, 77- *Concurrent Pos:* Assoc prof biochem, Catherine Spalding Col, 71. *Mem:* AAAS; Biophys Soc; Am Soc Microbiol; NY Acad Sci; fel Am Inst Chemists. *Res:* Identification and quantitation of metabolic products of the anti-tumor agent 1-2-chloroethyl-3-cyclohexyl-1-nitrosourea in rats, monkeys and humans as a means of deducing the mechanisms of action of the drug and decreasing its toxicity; infectious diseases such as molecular mechanism of aminoglycoside renal toxicity and subcellular distribution of gentamicin in renal cortical tissue; mechanism of action of toxins from Clostridium difficila. *Mailing Add:* Providence Med Ctr NE 49th & Glesan Sts Portland OR 97213

KOHLI, DILIP, b Kanpur, India, July 22, 47; m 77. MECHANICAL ENGINEERING. *Educ:* Indian Inst Technol, Kanpur, BS, 69, MS, 71; Okla State Univ, PhD(mech eng), 73. *Prof Exp:* Res asst mech eng, Okla State Univ, 71-73, assoc, 74; assoc & instr, Rensselaer Polytech Inst, 74-75; asst prof, 76-79, ASSOC PROF MECH ENG, UNIV WIS-MILWAUKEE, 79- *Concurrent Pos:* Consult, Procter & Gamble, 76-, Burroughs Corp, 77- & Control Data Corp, 78-; vis scientist, Univ Fla, Gainesville, 78- *Mem:* Am Soc Mech Engrs; Am Soc Eng Educ. *Res:* Kinematics and dynamics of machinery, vibrations, rotor dynamics and machine elements; robotics and manipulators. *Mailing Add:* Mech Eng Dept Univ Wis PO Box 413 Milwaukee WI 53201

KOHLI, JAI DEV, b Jullundur City, India, Dec 27, 18; m 46; c 3. MEDICAL PHARMACOLOGY. *Educ:* Glancy Med Sch, Amritsar, India, Dipl, 42; Univ Chicago, MS, 51; Univ Man, PhD(pharmacol), 65. *Prof Exp:* Res fel pharmacol, Indian Coun Med Res, 42-50; jr sci officer, Coun Sci & Indust Res, India, 51-59, sr sci officer, 59-61; asst prof, Univ Man, 61-65; res scientist pharmacol, Food & Drug Directorate, Can, 65-70; asst dir, Indust Toxicol Res Ctr, 70-75; assoc prof, 75-78, RES PROF PHARMACOL, UNIV CHICAGO, 79- *Concurrent Pos:* Fulbright fel, 50; Wellcome res fel, 61. *Mem:* Sigma Xi; Am Soc Pharmacol & Exp Therapeut; Pharmacol Soc Can; Indian Pharmacol Soc. *Res:* Receptor pharmacology; medicinal plants; cardiovascular pharmacology; dopamine and analogs. *Mailing Add:* Dept of Pharmacol 947 E 58th St Chicago IL 60637

KOHLMAN, DAVID L(ESLIE), b Houston, Tex, Oct 13, 37; m 59; c 2. AEROSPACE ENGINEERING. *Educ:* Univ Kans, BS, 59, MS, 60; Mass Inst Technol, PhD(aeronaut, astronaut), 63. *Prof Exp:* Res engr, Boeing Co, 63-64; from asst prof to assoc prof, 64-70, chmn dept, 67-72, prof aerospace eng, 70-81, DIR, FLIGHT RES LAB, UNIV KANS, 81- *Concurrent Pos:* Consult, Centron Corp, 66-, Beech Aircraft Corp, 69-70, Bell Helicopter Co, 70, Cessna Aircraft Co, 74, NASA, 75-77, Gates Learjet, 78-, Piaggio, 78- & Singer-Link, 81-; pres, Kohlman Aviation Corp, 77-; mem, Flight Mech Panel, NAtlantic Treat Org-Adv Group Aeronaut Res & Develop, 81- *Mem:* Assoc fel Am Inst Aeronaut & Astronaut; Am Soc Eng Educ. *Res:* Aerodynamic design of aircraft; aircraft stability and control; flight simulation; aircraft ice protection systems; flight testing. *Mailing Add:* Box 100C RR 4 Lawrence KS 66044

KOHLMAYR, GERHARD FRANZ, b Klagenfurt, Austria, Nov 30, 30; m 63. MATHEMATICAL PHYSICS. *Educ:* Graz Tech Univ, BS, 51, PhD(theoret physics), 59. *Prof Exp:* Sci asst, Darmstadt Tech Univ, 59-60; fel, Von Humboldt Found, 60-61; staff scientist, 61-71, sr appl mathematician, Pratt & Whitney Aircraft, 71-74, FOUNDER, MATHMODEL CONSULT BUR, 74- *Concurrent Pos:* Adj asst prof, Rensselaer Polytech Inst, 61-66. *Mem:* Am Math Soc; Soc Indust & Appl Math. *Res:* Acoustical duct lining theory; inconsistency of Zermelo-Fraenkel set theory; neutron transport theory; mathematical foundation of electrodynamic theory; elementary particle theory; functional analysis; nonlinear differential equations; transient heat transfer; numerical operational calculus; generalized functions. *Mailing Add:* 80 Founders Rd Glastonbury CT 06033

KOHLMEIER, RONALD HAROLD, b Craig, Nebr, Oct 16, 36; m 63; c 3. VETERINARY PHYSIOLOGY, NUTRITIONAL PHYSIOLOGY. *Educ:* Univ Nebr, BS, 59; Iowa State Univ, PhD(ruminant nutrit), 66, DVM, 68. *Prof Exp:* Farmer, 59; eng change notice coordr, RCA Missile Div, 60; asst nutritionist, Iowa State Univ, 60-66, res assoc nutrit & physiol, 66-68, asst prof, 68-70, assoc prof nutrit & physiol & res ruminant nutritionist & vet, 70-73; res ruminant nutritionist & vet, Agr Res Serv, USDA & Assoc Prof Animal Sci, Univ Nebr, 73-75; mgr tech serv processing group, 75-80, MGR FEED SCI SERVS, THE ANDERSONS, 80- *Concurrent Pos:* Nutrit consult for Dr Richard Hubbard, Gowrie Vet Serv, 68-73. *Mem:* Am Soc Animal Sci; Am Asn Bovine Practioners; Am Vet Med Asn; Am Asn Swine Practitioners. *Res:* Animal nutrition and usage of feed additives; animal nutrition and disease interrelationships. *Mailing Add:* The Andersons PO Box 119 Maumee OH 43537

KOHLMEYER, JAN JUSTUS, b Berlin, Ger, Mar 15, 28; wid. MYCOLOGY. *Educ:* Univ Berlin, Dr rer nat(bot), 55. *Prof Exp:* Res asst mycol, Bundesanstalt f Materialprüfung, Berlin-Dahlem, Ger, 56-59 & Bot Mus, 60-64; asst prof, Inst Fisheries Res, 64-69, assoc prof, Inst Marine Sci, 69-74, PROF, INST MARINE SCI, UNIV NC, 74- *Concurrent Pos:* Res assoc, Univ Wash, 59-60 & Duke Univ, 63-64. *Mem:* Mycol Soc Am; Brit Mycol Soc; Am Inst Biol Sci; Ger Soc Mycol; Sigma Xi. *Res:* Marine mycology; taxonomy of fungi; animal-fungus relationships; phytopathology. *Mailing Add:* Inst of Marine Sci Univ of NC Morehead City NC 28557

KOHLS, CARL WILLIAM, b Rochester, NY, Mar 14, 31. MATHEMATICS. *Educ:* Univ Rochester, AB, 53; Purdue Univ, MS, 55, PhD(math), 57. *Prof Exp:* Asst math, Purdue Univ, 57; instr, Columbia Univ, 57-58; asst prof, Univ Ill, 58-61; from asst prof to assoc prof, 61-70, PROF MATH, SYRACUSE UNIV, 70- *Concurrent Pos:* Res assoc & vis asst prof, Univ Rochester, 60-61. *Mem:* Am Math Soc; Math Asn Am. *Res:* Theory of dynamical systems. *Mailing Add:* 200 Carnegie Bldg Syracuse Univ Syracuse NY 13210

KOHLS, DONALD W, b Minneapolis, Minn, Oct 21, 34; m 62; c 2. EXPLORATION GEOLOGY. *Educ:* Carleton Col, BA, 56; Univ Minn, MS, 58, PhD(geol), 61. *Prof Exp:* Res scientist, NJ Zinc Co, 64-74, gen mgr & asst to pres, NJ Zinc Explor Co, 74-76; VPRES EXPLOR, GOLD FIELDS MINING CORP, 76- *Mem:* Am Asn Petrol Geologists; Am Inst Mining, Metall & Petrol Engrs; Geol Soc Am; Soc Econ Paleont & Mineral; Soc Econ Geologists. *Res:* Economic geology; petrology; mineralogy; geochemistry; field mapping. *Mailing Add:* Gold Fields Mining Corp 200 Union Blvd Suite 500 Lakewood CO 80228

KOHLS, ROBERT E, b Portage, Wis, Mar 15, 31; m 54; c 4. VETERINARY PARASITOLOGY, ENTOMOLOGY. *Educ:* Univ Wis, BS, 53, MS, 55, PhD, 58. *Prof Exp:* Proj asst dept vet sci, Univ Wis, 58; dir res, Specifide, Inc, Ind, 58-59; vet parasitologist, Upjohn Co, 59-68; chief parasitol, 68-73, chief avian prod develop, 73-75, chief feed additives, 75-77, Norwich Pharmacal Co; CHIEF PARASITOL, W AGRO CHEM INC, 77- *Concurrent Pos:* Assoc ed, Vet Parasitol, 76-80. *Mem:* Am Soc Parasitol. *Res:* Insect taxonomy; Diptera and Coleoptera. *Mailing Add:* RD-4 Guilford Rd Norwich NY 13815

KOHLSTAEDT, KENNETH GEORGE, b Indianapolis, Ind, May 10, 08; m 35; c 2. MEDICINE. *Educ:* Ind Univ, BS, 30, MD, 32. *Hon Degrees:* DSc, Ind Univ, 77. *Prof Exp:* Intern, Indianapolis Gen Hosp, 32-33, resident med, 33-34, resident neuropsychiat, 34-36; assoc, 37-47, from asst prof to prof med,

Sch Med, Ind Univ, Indianapolis, 47-78, spec asst to dean, 74-77; RETIRED. *Concurrent Pos:* Asst supt, Indianapolis Gen Hosp, 36-44, med dir, 45; dir, Lilly Lab Clin Res, 45-60, dir clin res div, Eli Lilly & Co, 54-60, exec dir med res, 60-64, vpres med res, 64-73; chmn med adv comt, Coun High Blood Pressure Res, Am Heart Asn; mem drug res bd, Nat Acad Sci. *Honors & Awards:* Henery Elliot Award, Am Soc Clin Pharmacol & Therapeut, 78. *Mem:* Am Soc Clin Pharmacol & Therapeut (vpres, 74-75); master Am Col Physicians; Soc Exp Biol & Med; Am Physiol Soc; fel AMA. *Res:* Research administration; clinical pharmacology; cardiovascular research. *Mailing Add:* 1430 Paseo De Marcia Palm Springs CA 92262

KOHMAN, TRUMAN PAUL, b Champaign, Ill, Mar 8, 16; m 45; c 3. NUCLEAR CHEMISTRY. *Educ:* Harvard Univ, AB, 38; Univ Wis, PhD(inorg & anal chem), 43. *Prof Exp:* Asst chem, Univ Wis, 38-42; res assoc metall lab, Univ Chicago, 42-44 & 45-46; chemist, Hanford Eng Works, Wash, 44-45; res assoc, Argonne Nat Lab, 46; fel chem, Inst Nuclear Studies, Univ Chicago, 46-48; from asst prof to assoc prof, 48-57, PROF CHEM, CARNEGIE-MELLON UNIV, 57- *Concurrent Pos:* NSF fel, Max-Planck Inst Chem, 57-58; vis prof, Indian Inst Technol, Kanpur, 62-63. *Honors & Awards:* Am Chem Soc Award, 62. *Mem:* Fel AAAS; Am Chem Soc; fel Am Phys Soc; Geochem Soc; Am Astron Soc. *Res:* Artificial and natural radioactivity; techniques of radioactivity measurement; yields of nuclear reactions; geochronometry; meteorites; cosmochemistry. *Mailing Add:* Dept of Chem Carnegie-Mellon Univ Pittsburgh PA 15213

KOHN, ALAN JACOBS, b New Haven, Conn, July 15, 31; m 59; c 4. ZOOLOGY. *Educ:* Princeton Univ, AB, 53; Yale Univ, PhD(zool), 57. *Prof Exp:* Res assoc zool, Marine Lab, Univ Hawaii, 54-56; Anderson fel, Bingham Oceanog Lab, Yale Univ, 58; asst prof zool, Fla State Univ, 58-61; from asst prof to assoc prof, 61-67, PROF ZOOL, UNIV WASH, 67- *Concurrent Pos:* Biologist, Yale Exped to Seychelles Islands, 57-58; partic, Int Indian Ocean Exped, 63; sr vis res assoc, Smithsonian Inst, 67; vis prof, Univ Hawaii, 68; Guggenheim Found fel, 74; adj cur malacol, Thomas Burke Mem Wash State Mus, 71-; adj prof, Inst Environ Studies, 78- *Mem:* Fel AAAS; Ecol Soc Am; Am Soc Zool (treas, 71-73); Am Soc Naturalists; Soc Syst Zool. *Res:* Ecology and systematics of marine mollusks; coral reefs. *Mailing Add:* Dept of Zool Univ of Wash Seattle WA 98195

KOHN, ERWIN, b Vienna, Austria, Aug 23, 23; nat US; m 49; c 6. PHYSICAL CHEMISTRY, POLYMER CHEMISTRY. *Educ:* Univ Ill, BS, 48; Univ Notre Dame, MS, 50; Univ Tex, PhD(chem), 56. *Prof Exp:* From res chemist to sr res chemist, Monsanto Co, Tex, 55-62, res specialist, 62-66; assoc prof chem, Southwestern Okla State Univ, 66-68; assoc prof polymer chem, NDak State Univ, 68-72, dir NSF prog, 71-72; SR PROJ SCIENTIST, DEVELOP DIV, MASON & HANGER CO, 72- *Mem:* fel, Am Inst Chemists; Am Chem Soc; Am Phys Soc; Electron Micros Soc Am; Soc Plastics Engrs. *Res:* Physical and physical-organic chemistry; analytical chemistry; liquid and gel permeation chromatography; x-ray analysis; explosives analysis; kinetics and mechanisms; Ziegler-Natta polymerization; structure of polyolefins; polymer characterization; organometallic chemistry; kinetic isotope effects; surface analysis. *Mailing Add:* 3613 Nebraska Amarillo TX 79109

KOHN, GUSTAVE K, b Syracuse, NY, Feb 12, 10; m 50; c 3. CHEMISTRY. *Educ:* NY Univ, BS, 30. *Prof Exp:* Control chemist, Ortho Div, Chevron Chem Co, Standard Oil Co, Calif, 46-51, res chemist, 51-54, group leader org synthesis, 54-56, chief res chemist, 56-62, mgr cent res labs, 62-70, sr res scientist, 70-75; pesticide prod adv to govt India, UN Indust Develop Orgn, New Delhi, 75-76; res dir, 76-78, SR SCIENTIST, ZOECON CORP, PALO ALTO, 79- *Mem:* AAAS; Am Chem Soc; Entom Soc Am; Am Inst Biol Sci. *Res:* Synthesis of biologically active and agriculturally useful compounds; organophosphate insecticides; halo-organic fungicides and plant growth regulators. *Mailing Add:* 975 Calif St Palo Alto CA 94304

KOHN, HAROLD WILLIAM, b Newark, NJ, Nov 9, 20; m 57; c 4. ENVIRONMENTAL SCIENCE. *Educ:* Univ Mich, Ann Arbor, BS, 43; Syracuse Univ, PhD(chem), 53. *Prof Exp:* Asst chem, Syracuse Univ, 48-53; res engr, Battelle Mem Inst, 52-53; chemist, Oak Ridge Nat Labs, 47-48 & 54-73; STAFF SCIENTIST ENVIRON, OHIO ENVIRON PROTECTION AGENCY, 73- *Concurrent Pos:* Vis lectr, Univ Calif, Berkeley, 63-64; vis prof, Dickinson Col, 71-72. *Mem:* Am Chem Soc; Health Physics Soc; Am Nuclear Soc. *Res:* Effects of ionizing radiations on heterogeneous catalysts; radiation chemistry of surfaces; molten salt chemistry; power plant siting and productivity; environmental impacts. *Mailing Add:* 147 Chatham Rd Columbus OH 43214

KOHN, HERBERT MYRON, b Chicago, Ill, Feb 24, 35; m 57; c 2. NEUROPSYCHOLOGY, ELECTROENCEPHALOGRAPHY. *Educ:* Univ Ill, BA, 58; Roosevelt Univ, MA, 60; Ill Inst Technol, PhD(psychol), 65. *Prof Exp:* Med res assoc, Ill State Psychiat Inst, 60-67; dir, Darrow Mem Lab, Inst Juv Res, 68-70; res scientist, Ill State Pediat Inst, 71-72; asst prof, 72-75, ASSOC PROF PSYCHIAT, RUTGERS MED SCH, COL MED & DENT NJ, 75-, CHIEF NEURODIAG LAB, 72- *Concurrent Pos:* Lectr, Roosevelt Univ, 65-72; asst prof, Ill Inst Technol, 67-72 & Abraham Lincoln Sch Med, Univ Ill, 68-72; lectr, Northeastern Ill State Univ, 70-72 & Univ Ill, Chicago Circle, 72; assoc psychobiol, Grad Fac, Rutgers Univ, 72-78; adj assoc prof, Grad Sch of Appl & Prof Psychol, Rutgers Univ, 76- *Mem:* Am Psychol Asn; Psychonomic Soc; Int Neuropsychol Soc. *Res:* Neural bases of human behavior; primate behavior; vision and effects of early brain damage. *Mailing Add:* Rutgers Med Sch Dept Psychiat Col of Med & Dent of NJ Piscataway NJ 08854

KOHN, JACK ARNOLD, b Trenton, NJ, July 17, 25; m 51; c 2. CRYSTALLOGRAPHY. *Educ:* Univ Mich, BS, 47, MS, 48, PhD(mineral), 50. *Prof Exp:* Asst mineral, Univ Mich, 48-50, res assoc, 50-51; mineralogist, Electrotech Lab, US Bur Mines, 51-55; physicist & dep dir solid state sci div, 55-69, dep dir inst explor res, 69-71, dep dir technol, 71-73, DIR ELECTRONIC MAT RES, ELECTRONICS TECHNOL & DEVICES LAB, US ARMY ELECTRONICS RES & DEVELOP COMMAND, FT MONMOUTH, 74- *Concurrent Pos:* Consult mineralogist, US Bur Mines, 50-51. *Honors & Awards:* Prize, Army Sci Conf, 59, 62 & 70; Army Tech Achievement Award, 63; Meritorious Civilian Serv Award, 64. *Mem:* Mat Res Soc; Fel AAAS; fel Mineral Soc Am; Am Crystallog Asn. *Res:* Crystallography of electronic and magnetic materials; twinning; polymorphism; polytypism; general x-ray crystallography. *Mailing Add:* 47 Birchwood Ct Tinton Falls NJ 07724

KOHN, JAMES P(AUL), b Dubuque, Iowa, Oct 31, 24; m 58; c 3. CHEMICAL ENGINEERING. *Educ:* Univ Notre Dame, BS, 51; Univ Mich, MSE, 52; Univ Kans, PhD, 56. *Prof Exp:* Chem engr, Reilly Tar & Chem Corp, 46-51; from asst prof to assoc prof, 55-64, PROF CHEM ENG, UNIV NOTRE DAME, 64- *Concurrent Pos:* Consult, Eng Enterprises; dir, Solar Lab for Thermal Appln, 74- *Mem:* AAAS; Am Chem Soc; Am Inst Chem Engrs. *Res:* Heterogeneous phase equilibrium; applied thermodynamics; unsteady state diffusion; physical properties; molecular transport. *Mailing Add:* Dept of Chem Eng Univ of Notre Dame Notre Dame IN 46556

KOHN, JOSEPH JOHN, b Prague, Czech, May 18, 32; nat US; m 66; c 3. MATHEMATICS. *Educ:* Mass Inst Technol, BS, 53; Princeton Univ, MA, 54, PhD(math), 56. *Prof Exp:* Instr math, Princeton Univ, 56-57; mem, Inst Advan Study, 57-58; from asst prof to prof math, Brandeis Univ, 58-68; PROF MATH, PRINCETON UNIV, 68-, CHMN DEPT, 74- *Concurrent Pos:* Ed, Transactions of Am Math Soc, Advances Math & Annals Math. *Honors & Awards:* Steele Prize, Am Math Soc, 79. *Mem:* Am Acad Arts & Sci; Am Math Soc. *Res:* Several complex variables; partial differential equations. *Mailing Add:* Dept of Math Princeton Univ Princeton NJ 08540

KOHN, KURT WILLIAM, b Austria, Sept 14, 30; nat US; m 56; c 2. CHEMICAL PHARMACOLOGY. *Educ:* Harvard Univ, AB, 52, PhD(biochem), 66; Columbia Univ, MD, 56. *Prof Exp:* Clin assoc, Nat Cancer Inst, 57-59, SR INVESTR, NAT CANCER INST, 59-, CHIEF LAB MOLECULAR PHARMACOL, 68- *Mem:* Am Chem Soc; Am Asn Cancer Res; Am Asn Biol Chemists. *Res:* Effects of chemotherapeutic agents on structure and function of desoxyribonucleic acid. *Mailing Add:* 11519 Gainsborough Rd Potomac MD 20854

KOHN, LEONARD DAVID, b New York, NY, Aug 1, 35; m 62; c 2. BIOCHEMICAL PHARMACOLOGY. *Educ:* Columbia Univ, BA, 57, MD, 61. *Prof Exp:* Intern med, Columbia Presby Med Ctr, 61-62, asst resident, 62-63, sr resident, 63-64; res assoc, Lab Biochem & Metab, 64-66, med res officer, Lab Biochem Pharmacol, 66-74, CHIEF SECT BIOCHEM OF CELL REGULATION, LAB BIOCHEM PHARMACOL, NAT INST ARTHRITIS, METAB & DIGESTIVE DIS, 74- *Concurrent Pos:* Vis prof, Dept Med, Univ Liege, Belg, 70-71. *Mem:* Am Soc Biol Chemists. *Res:* Mechanism by which hormones interact with membrane components to elicit functional responses; enzymatic conversion of precursors of collagen to collagen; enzymes concerned with solute transport across membranes. *Mailing Add:* Bldg 4 Rm B1-31 Nat Insts of Health Bethesda MD 20014

KOHN, MICHAEL, b Budapest, Hungary, June 18, 34; US citizen; m 55; c 1. BIOMEDICAL ENGINEERING, NEUROPHYSIOLOGY. *Educ:* City Univ New York, BEE, 60, MEE, 68; NY Univ, PhD(elec eng), 74. *Prof Exp:* Res engr, 57-68, DIR, BIOENG DEPT, ROCKLAND RES INST, 68- *Concurrent Pos:* Consult, Mnemotron Corp, 61-62. *Res:* Development of biomedical instrumentation; analysis of electrophysiological data. *Mailing Add:* Rockland Res Inst Orangeburg NY 10962

KOHN, MICHAEL CHARLES, b Brooklyn, NY, July 29, 41; m 71. BIOCHEMISTRY, THEORETICAL CHEMISTRY. *Educ:* Mass Inst Technol, BS, 64; Univ SC, PhD(chem), 70. *Prof Exp:* Technician chem, Gen Latex & Chem Co, 62; consult, BB Chem Co, 62-63; fel, Univ Tex, Austin, 69-71; chemist, Naval Undersea Res & Develop Ctr, 71-73; SR RES INVESTR & ADJ ASSOC PROF, UNIV PA, 74- *Concurrent Pos:* Nat Res Coun grant, Naval Undersea Res & Develop Ctr, 71-73. *Mem:* Am Chem Soc; Sigma Xi; Soc Comput Simulation; NY Acad Sci. *Res:* Valence force field calculations of strain energy; molecular orbital theory; statistical mechanics of polymer solutions; biomedical computer models; sensitivity analysis; graph-theoretical analysis of metabolic networks. *Mailing Add:* Dept of Comput & Info Sci Moore Sch D2 Univ of Pa Philadelphia PA 19104

KOHN, ROBERT ROTHENBERG, b Cleveland, Ohio, June 14, 25; m 52; c 4. EXPERIMENTAL PATHOLOGY. *Educ:* Univ Wis, BS, 49; Univ Mich, AM, 51, PhD(zool), 53; Western Reserve Univ, MD, 57. *Prof Exp:* USPHS fel path, 57-60, from asst prof to assoc prof, 60-70, PROF PATH, CASE WESTERN RESERVE UNIV, 70- *Mem:* AAAS; Am Soc Path; Geront Soc. *Res:* Chemical and physical changes associated with diabetes and aging processes. *Mailing Add:* Inst of Path Case Western Reserve Univ Cleveland OH 44106

KOHN, WALTER, b Vienna, Austria, Mar 9, 23; nat US; m 47; c 2. PHYSICS. *Educ:* Univ Toronto, BA, 45, MA, 46; Harvard Univ, PhD(physics), 48. *Hon Degrees:* LLD, Univ Toronto, 67, DSc, Univ Paris, 80, Branders Univ, 81; DPhil, Hebrew Univ, Jerusalem, 81. *Prof Exp:* Indust physicist, Sutton Horsley Co, Can, 41-43; geophysicist, Koulomzine, Que, 44 & 46; instr physics, Harvard Univ, 48-50; from asst prof to prof, Carnegie Inst Technol, 50-60; chmn dept, Univ Calif, San Diego, 61-63, prof physics, 60-79; DIR INST THEORET PHYSICS, SANTA BARBARA, 79- *Concurrent Pos:* Nat Res Coun fel, 51; NSF fel, 58 & sr fel, Univ Paris, 67; Guggenheim fel, 63; vis prof, Superior Normal School, Paris, 63-64 & Hebrew Univ, Jerusalem, 70; Battelle distinguished vis prof, Univ Wash, 74; mem solid state sci panel, Nat Acad Sci; ed, J Non-Metals & J Physics & Chem of Solids. *Honors & Awards:* Oliver E Buckley Prize, 61; Davisson Germer Prize, 77. *Mem:* Nat Acad Sci; fel Am Acad Arts & Sci; fel Am Phys Soc. *Res:* Theory of solids; surface physics; collision theory. *Mailing Add:* Dept of Physics Univ of Calif at San Diego La Jolla CA 92093

KOHNKE, ELTON EVERETT, b Clear Lake, SDak, Mar 28, 24; m 48; c 3. PHYSICS. *Educ:* SDak State Col, BS, 48; Northwestern Univ, MS, 50, PhD(physics), 55. *Prof Exp:* Lectr, Univ Minn, Duluth, 52-53; from asst prof to assoc prof, 55-64, actg head dept, 68-70, PROF PHYSICS, OKLA STATE UNIV, 64- *Mem:* Am Ceramic Soc; Am Phys Soc; Am Asn Physics Teachers. *Res:* Semiconductors; surfaces; ceramics. *Mailing Add:* Dept of Physics Okla State Univ Stillwater OK 74074

KOHNKE, HELMUT, b Rostov, Russia, Aug 6, 01; nat US; m 36; c 2. AGRONOMY. *Educ:* Univ Berlin, BSc, 25, DrAgr, 26; Univ Alta, MSc, 32; Ohio State Univ, PhD(soils), 34. *Prof Exp:* Exten agronomist, Ger, 26-27; instr Ger, Univ Alta, 29-30; soil surveyor, Soil Conserv Serv, USDA, 34-35, chg soil dept, Northern Appalachian Watershed Exp Sta, 35-39, Ind Agr Hydrol Studies, 39-43; soil scientist, 43-70, EMER PROF AGRON, PURDUE UNIV, WEST LAFAYETTE, 70- *Concurrent Pos:* Exec dir comt sci & soc, Ind Acad Sci, 70-72; soil conserv consult UN, Food & Agr Orgn, Bulgaria, 72; consult soil scientist, Corn Prod Syst, Inc, Ill, 75. *Mem:* Fel AAAS; fel Am Soc Agron; Soil Sci Soc Am. *Res:* Soil fertility; physics; conservation; hydrology; run-off chemistry. *Mailing Add:* 208 Forest Hill Dr West Lafayette IN 47906

KOHOUT, FRANCIS ANTHONY, b St Paul, Minn, Apr 24, 24; m 49. HYDROLOGY, GEOLOGICAL OCEANOGRAPHY. *Educ:* Univ Minn, AB, 49; Univ Miami, MS, 67. *Prof Exp:* Res hydrologist, US Geol Surv, 49-79; CONSULT, HYDROGEOLOGIC, 79- *Concurrent Pos:* Liaison officer, US Geol Surv to US Off Saline Water, 67-70; consult, UN Develop Prog, 77. *Honors & Awards:* Robert E Horton Award, Am Geophys Union, 60. *Mem:* Geol Soc Am; Am Geophys Union; Am Water Resources Asn; Nat Water Well Asn; Int Asn Hydrogeologists. *Res:* Interrelations of coastal hydrology and oceanography; intrusion of sea water into coastal fresh-water aquifers; occurrence of relict fresh ground water beneath the Outer Continental Shelf. *Mailing Add:* 64 Muskegat Rd East Falmouth MA 02536

KOHOUT, FREDERICK CHARLES, III, b Flint, Mich, June 19, 40; m 61; c 3. PHYSICAL ANALYTICAL CHEMISTRY, LUBRICATION SCIENCE. *Educ:* Mich State Univ, BS, 62; Pa State Univ, PhD(phys chem), 66. *Prof Exp:* Mem staff, Cent Res Div, 66-73, mem staff, Prod Res Div, 73-81, MGR MAT SCI & ENVIRON SERV, PROCESS RES DIV, MOBIL RES & DEVELOP, PAULSBORO LAB, 81- *Mem:* Am Chem Soc; Am Soc Lubrication Engrs. *Res:* Development of marine diesel lubricants, gear lubricants and greases; analytical chemistry of petroleum; environmental science. *Mailing Add:* Prod Res Lab Mobil Res & Develop Corp Paulsboro NJ 08066

KOHR, CHARLES BYRON, b York, Pa, July 27, 39; m 61; c 3. PHYSICS. *Educ:* Franklin & Marshall Col, AB, 61; Univ Md, PhD(physics), 67. *Prof Exp:* From asst prof to assoc prof, 64-70, PROF PHYSICS, MILLERSVILLE STATE COL, 70-, CHMN DEPT, 72- *Concurrent Pos:* NSF acad year exten grant, 67-69; vis prof, Univ Utah, 72. *Mem:* Am Phys Soc; Am Asn Physics Teachers. *Res:* Theory of nuclear structure, especially giant dipole resonance in heavy nuclei; oxygen-16. *Mailing Add:* Dept of Physics Millersville State Col Millersville PA 17551

KOHRMAN, ARTHUR FISHER, b Cleveland, Ohio, Dec 19, 34; m 55; c 4. PEDIATRICS. *Educ:* Univ Chicago, AB & BS, 55; Western Reserve Univ, MD, 59. *Prof Exp:* NIH trainee & spec fel pediat, Stanford Univ, 65-68; from asst prof to assoc prof, 68-77, prof med educ res & develop, 77-80, ASSOC DEAN EDUC PROG, COL HUMAN MED, MICH STATE UNIV, 77-, PROF DEPT PEDIAT & HUMAN DEVELOP, 80- *Concurrent Pos:* Consult to Surgeon Gen, US Air Force Europe, 63-65. *Mem:* Lawson Wilkins Prod Endocrinol Soc; AAAS; Am Acad Pediat; Am Fedn Clin Res; Soc Pediat Res. *Res:* Developmental endocrinology and biochemistry; effects of environmental agents on human development; medical education research and development. *Mailing Add:* Off of the Dean Mich State Univ East Lansing MI 48824

KOHUT, ROBERT IRWIN, otolaryngology, see previous edition

KOHUT, ROBERT JOHN, b Cannonsburg, Pa, Nov 19, 43. POLLUTANT EFFECTS ON VEGETATION, VEGETATION STRESS CONSULTING. *Educ:* Pa State Univ, BS, 65, MS, 72, PhD(plant path), 75. *Prof Exp:* Res fel, Dept Plant Path, Univ Minn, 75-77; plant pathologist, Environ Res & Technol, 77-80; RES ASSOC, BOYCE THOMPSON INST, CORNELL UNIV, 80- *Concurrent Pos:* Affil fac, Dept Plant Path, Colo State Univ, 78-80; comt mem, Colo Gov Air Pollution Tech Working Comt, 79-80, Toxic Substances Subcomt, Environ Protection Agency Sci Adv Bd, 80- *Mem:* Am Phytopath Soc; Air Pollution Control Asn. *Res:* Field and laboratory research evaluating the effects of air pollutants on growth and yield of agricultural crops and on native plants and plant communities. *Mailing Add:* Boyce Thompson Inst Cornell Univ Ithaca NY 14853

KOIDE, FRANK T, b Honolulu, Hawaii, Dec 25, 35. BIOMEDICAL & ELECTRONIC ENGINEERING. *Educ:* Univ Ill, BSEE, 58; Clarkson Col Technol, MS, 61; Univ Iowa, PhD(physiol), 66. *Prof Exp:* Engr res div, Collins Radio Co, 59-61; asst prof elec eng, physiol & biomed eng, Iowa State Univ, 66-68; prin res scientist, Life Sci Div, Technol Inc, Tex, 68-69; assoc prof elec eng, assoc prof physiol, 72-74, PROF ELEC ENG & PHYSIOL, UNIV HAWAII, 74- *Concurrent Pos:* Instr, Cedar Rapids Adult Educ, 60-61; consult, Collins Radio Co, 61-63; NASA-Am Soc Eng Educ fac fel, 67; consult, Shared Clin Eng Servs Hawaii & Acupuncture Asn Hawaii, 74-; external examr, Chinese Univ Hong Kong, 77- *Mem:* Sigma Xi; Asn Advan Med Instrumentation; Inst Elec & Electronic Engrs; AAAS. *Res:* Application of engineering techniques in solution of biomedical problems; membrane physiology; electrophysiology; nerve; bioinstrumentation; nutrition. *Mailing Add:* Dept of Elec Eng Univ Hawaii 2540 Dole St Honolulu HI 96822

KOIDE, SAMUEL SABURO, b Honolulu, Hawaii, Oct 6, 23; m 60; c 3. BIOCHEMISTRY, INTERNAL MEDICINE. *Educ:* Univ Hawaii, BS, 45; Northwestern Univ, MD, 53, MS, 54, PhD, 60. *Prof Exp:* Assoc, Sloan-Kettering Inst, 61-65, asst prof biochem, 64-65; asst dir biomed div, 65-70, ASSOC DIR & SR SCIENTIST, CTR FOR BIOMED RES, POP COUN, ROCKEFELLER UNIV, 70- *Concurrent Pos:* Asst prof, Cornell Univ, 61-69; Nat Inst Arthritis & Metab Dis career develop award, 63-65. *Honors & Awards:* Joseph A Capps Prize Med Res, 58. *Mem:* Biochem Soc; Endocrine Soc; Am Col Physicians; Am Soc Biol Chemists; Soc Exp Biol & Med. *Res:* Mechanism of hormone action; metabolism of steroids; nucleic acid metabolism. *Mailing Add:* Biomed Div Pop Coun Rockefeller Univ New York NY 10021

KOIKE, HIDEO, b Hilo, Hawaii, Mar 10, 21; m 48; c 3. PHYTOPATHOLOGY. *Educ:* Univ Hawaii, BA, 44; Kans State Univ, MS, 51, PhD(bact), 56. *Prof Exp:* Asst, Kans State Univ, 49-51; asst pathologist, Exp Sta, Hawaiian Sugar Planters Asn, 52-54; asst, Kans State Univ, 54-56; assoc pathologist, Exp Sta, Hawaiian Sugar Planters Asn, 57-66; res microbiologist sugarcane & sweet sorghum invest, Tobacco & Sugar Crops Res Br, Crops Res Div, Agr Res Serv, Univ PR, Gurabo, 66-69; RES PLANT PATHOLOGIST, US SUGARCANE FIELD LAB, USDA, 69- *Mem:* Fel AAAS; Am Phytopath Soc; Int Soc Plant Path; Sigma Xi. *Res:* Sugarcane pathology. *Mailing Add:* US Sugarcane Field Lab USDA Box 470 Houma LA 70361

KOIKE, THOMAS ISAO, b Watsonville, Calif, July 27, 27; m 55; c 2. PHYSIOLOGY. *Educ:* Univ Calif, Berkeley, AB, 51, PhD(physiol), 58. *Prof Exp:* Jr res physiologist, Univ Calif, Berkeley, 58-61; USPHS fel animal physiol, Univ Calif, Davis, 61-63, asst specialist physiol, 63-64, asst res physiologist, 64-65; from asst prof to assoc prof, 65-78, PROF PHYSIOL, MED CTR, UNIV ARK, LITTLE ROCK, 78- *Concurrent Pos:* Co-prin investr grants, Nat Inst Arthritis & Metab Dis, 63-65; NIH grant, 66-72. *Mem:* AAAS; Am Physiol Soc; Soc Exp Biol & Med; NY Acad Sci; Am Asn Univ Professors. *Res:* Regulation of body fluids. *Mailing Add:* Dept of Physiol Univ of Ark Med Ctr Little Rock AR 72201

KOIRTYOHANN, SAMUEL ROY, b Washington, Mo, Sept 11, 30; m 52; c 3. ANALYTICAL CHEMISTRY. *Educ:* Univ Mo, BS, 53, MS, 58, PhD(agr chem), 66. *Prof Exp:* Chemist, Oak Ridge Nat Lab, 59-63; from instr to asst prof, 63-70, assoc prof agr chem, 70-80, PROF CHEM, UNIV MO-COLUMBIA, 80- *Mem:* Am Chem Soc; Soc Appl Spectros. *Res:* Determination of trace elements in biological and agricultural materials using spectrographic and other instrumental methods. *Mailing Add:* Environ Trace Substances Ctr Rte 3 Columbia MO 65201

KOISTINEN, DONALD PETER, b Lake Norden, SDak, Nov 19, 27; m 59; c 3. METAL PHYSICS. *Educ:* Univ Mich, BS, 52; Wayne State Univ, MS, 58. *Prof Exp:* Res physicist, 52-58, sr res physicist, 58-69, SUPVRY RES PHYSICIST METAL PHYSICS, RES LABS, GEN MOTORS CORP, 69- *Mem:* Am Phys Soc. *Res:* Mechanics of large-scale plasticity in metals; strain hardening; precipitation; crystalline deformation mechanisms and transformations; fatigue in metals; surface hardening techniques. *Mailing Add:* Res Lab Gen Motors Corp Physics Dept G M Tech Ctr Warren MI 48090

KOIVO, ANTTI J, b Vaasa, Finland, Apr 9, 32; m 69; c 2. ELECTRICAL ENGINEERING, BIOENGINEERING. *Educ:* Inst Technol, Finland, dipl eng, 56; Cornell Univ, PhD(elec eng), 63. *Prof Exp:* Design engr, Oy Stroemberg Ab, Finland, 57-59; from asst prof to assoc prof, 64-78, PROF ELEC ENG, PURDUE UNIV, WEST LAFAYETTE, 78- *Mem:* sr mem Inst Elec & Electronics Engrs; Sigma Xi. *Res:* Robitic manipulation control; application of system theory and pattern recognition to biomedical problems; blood pressure control with microcomputers. *Mailing Add:* Dept of Elec Eng Purdue Univ West Lafayette IN 47907

KOIZUMI, CARL JAN, b Reno, Nev, Jan 7, 43; m 68; c 1. NUCLEAR GEOPHYSICS, SOLID STATE PHYSICS. *Educ:* Univ Nev, Reno, BS, 65, MS, 71, PhD(physics), 77; Ariz State Univ, MS, 67. *Prof Exp:* Res geophysicist, Bendix Field Eng Corp, 77-81; RES PHYSICIST, AUSTIN RES CTR, GEARHART INDUST, 82- *Mem:* Am Soc Testing & Mat. *Res:* Calibration of devices used for uranium detection; gamma-ray logging theory; fission neutron logging theory; Mossbauer spectroscopic studies of hydrides of intermetallic compounds. *Mailing Add:* Austin Res Ctr Gearhart Indust Suite 103 2525 Wallingwood Austin TX 78746

KOIZUMI, KIYOMI, b Kobe, Japan, Sept 4, 24; m 54; c 1. PHYSIOLOGY, BIOCHEMISTRY. *Educ:* Tokyo Women's Med Col, MD, 47; Wayne State Univ, MS, 51; Kobe Med Col, PhD(physiol), 57. *Prof Exp:* Fel physiol, State Univ NY Downstate Med Ctr, 51-52, from instr to asst prof, 52-60; vis lectr, Kobe Med Col, 60-61; assoc prof, 63-70, PROF PHYSIOL, STATE UNIV NY DOWNSTATE MED CTR, 70- *Concurrent Pos:* Hon res fel, Aberdeen Univ, 62; NIH res grants, 55-; NSF grants, 74-78. *Mem:* Soc Neurosci; Int Brain Res Orgn; Am Physiol Soc; Harvey Soc; NY Acad Sci. *Res:* Neurophysiology. *Mailing Add:* Dept of Physiol State Univ NY Downstate Med Ctr Brooklyn NY 11203

KOJIMA, HARUO, b Japan, May 18, 45; m 70; c 2. LOW TEMPERATURE PHYSICS. *Educ:* Univ Calif, Los Angeles, BS, 68, MS, 70, PhD(physics), 72. *Prof Exp:* Adj asst prof, Univ Calif, Los Angeles, 72-73; res assoc, Univ Calif, San Diego, 73-75; asst prof, 75-80, ASSOC PROF PHYSICS, RUTGERS UNIV, 80- *Mem:* Am Phys Soc. *Res:* Experimental investigation of superfluid phases of helium at ultra low temperatures. *Mailing Add:* Dept of Physics Rutgers Univ New Brunswick NJ 08903

KOJOIAN, GABRIEL, b Providence, RI, Dec 11, 27; m 53; c 2. ASTRONOMY, RADIO ASTRONOMY. *Educ:* Brown Univ, BSc, 52; Univ Calif, Berkeley, DPhil(physics), 66. *Prof Exp:* Head theoret div physics, Div Lab Electronics, Tracerlab, 66-67; Nat Acad Sci res fel, NASA-Ames Res

Ctr, 67-69; lectr, Dept Physics, Univ Mass, Amherst, 69-71; staff scientist astron, Northeast Radio Observ, Mass Inst Technol, 72-73; assoc prof, Pahlavi Univ, Shiraz, Iran, 75-76; vis assoc prof, 76-80, ADJ ASSOC PROF PHYSICS & ASTRON, UNIV WIS-EAU CLAIRE, 80- Concurrent Pos: Invited guest, Am Acad Sci, Soviet Socialist Repub, 76; exchange scientist, Nat Acad Sci & Soviet Acad Sci, 78. Mem: Am Astron Soc; AAAS. Res: Radio-continuum measurements of galactic and extragalactic objects. Mailing Add: Dept of Physics Univ of Wis Eau Claire WI 54701

KOK, BESSEL, plant physiology, deceased

KOK, LOKE-TUCK, b Ipoh, Malaysia, Nov 10, 39; m 66. ENTOMOLOGY. Educ: Univ Malaya, BAgrSc Hons, 63, MAgrSc, 65; Univ Wis-Madison, PhD(entom), 71. Prof Exp: Tutor, Univ Malaya, 63-65, from asst lectr to lectr, 65-71; asst prof, 72-78, ASSOC PROF ENTOM, VA POLYTECH INST & STATE UNIV, 78- Concurrent Pos: Res scholar, Int Rice Res Inst, Philippines, 64; from res asst to res assoc, Univ Wis-Madison, 68-71. Mem: Entom Soc Can; Entom Soc Am; Weed Sci Soc Am; Int Orgn Biol Control. Res: Biological control of insect and weed pests of forage and field crops in Virginia, with special emphasis on the control of Carduus thistles using introduced beneficial insects. Mailing Add: Dept of Entom Va Polytech Inst & State Univ Blacksburg VA 24061

KOKALIS, SOTER GEORGE, b East Chicago, Ind, Jan 29, 36. INORGANIC CHEMISTRY. Educ: Purdue Univ, BSc, 58; Univ Ill, MSc, 60, PhD(inorg chem), 62. Prof Exp: Asst inorg chem, Univ Ill, 59-62; asst prof, Washington Univ, 62-64 & Univ Ill, Chicago Circle, 64-67; assoc prof, Chicago State Col, 67-69; ASSOC PROF INORG CHEM, WILLIAM RAINEY HARPER COL, 69- Mem: AAAS; Am Chem Soc; Royal Soc Chem. Res: Synthesis and chemical properties of inorganic ring structures; analysis of electron delocalization in heterocyclic compounds; phosphonitrilic compounds and their applications. Mailing Add: Dept of Chem William Rainey Harper Col Palatine IL 60067

KOKAME, GLENN MEGUMI, b Waimea, Hawaii, July 7, 26; m 53; c 2. SURGERY, THORACIC SURGERY. Educ: Univ Hawaii, BA, 50; Tulane Univ, BS, 52, MD, 55; Am Bd Surg, dipl, 62; Am Bd Thoracic Surg, dipl, 63. Prof Exp: From asst prof surg, Sch Med, Tulane Univ, 55-67; asst prof, 67-71, ASSOC PROF SURG, SCH MED, UNIV HAWAII, 71- Concurrent Pos: Am Cancer Soc adv clin fel, 64-66. Mem: Fel Am Col Surgeons; AMA; Am Asn Cancer Res; Am Soc Clin Oncol. Res: Regional chemotherapy of cancer; hyperbaric oxygenation in medicine; immunology of cancer; vascular surgery; heterotransplantation of human cancer and tissue culture; transplantation of organs. Mailing Add: Dept of Surg Univ of Hawaii Sch of Med Honolulu HI 96822

KOKATNUR, MOHAN GUNDO, b Belgaum, India, Mar 19, 30; m 63; c 2. CLINICAL BIOCHEMISTRY, NUTRITION. Educ: Univ Poona, BS, 51; Univ Nagpur, BS, 53; Univ Ill, Urbana, PhD(food sci, biochem, nutrit), 59. Prof Exp: Res assoc food sci & lipids, Univ Ill, Urbana, 59-61; Coun Sci & Indust Res Pool fel biochem & nutrit, Cent Food Res Inst, Mysore, India, 61-63; res assoc nutrit biochem, Univ Ill, Urbana, 63-66; asst prof, 66-72, ASSOC PROF PATH, LA STATE UNIV MED CTR, NEW ORLEANS, 72-; ASSOC DIR, CLIN CHEM LAB, CHARITY HOSP, NEW ORLEANS, 78- Concurrent Pos: La Heart Asn sr res grant-in-aid, 67-69; mem coun arteriosclerosis, Am Heart Asn, 68. Mem: Am Soc Clin Nutrit; Am Inst Nutrit; fel Am Heart Asn; Am Asn Clin Chemists; Soc Exp Biol Med. Res: Lipid chemistry, biochemistry and metabolism; importance of lipids and nutrition in atherosclerosis; lipids and atherosclerosis; clinical chemistry methodology; vitamin E deficiency and fat oxidation. Mailing Add: Dept of Path La State Univ Med Ctr New Orleans LA 70112

KOKEN, JAMES E, b New York, NY, May 8, 12; m 47; c 2. CHEMISTRY. Educ: Columbia Univ, AB, 33; NY Univ, AM, 40; Pa State Univ, EdD, 59. Prof Exp: High sch instr, NJ, 42-47; from assoc prof to prof chem & chmn dept sci, 47-76, EMER PROF CHEM, MILLERSVILLE STATE COL, 76- Mem: Am Chem Soc. Res: General chemistry. Mailing Add: 1125 Richmond Rd Lancaster PA 17603

KOKENGE, BERNARD RUSSELL, b Dayton, Ohio, Dec 7, 39; m 59; c 2. INORGANIC CHEMISTRY. Educ: Univ Dayton, BS, 61; Ohio Univ, PhD(inorg chem), 66. Prof Exp: Lab technician, Wright-Patterson AFB, summers 60 & 61; sr res chemist, 65-66, group leader inorg chem & isotopic fuels, 66-72, plutonium processing mgr, Mound Lab, 72-77, MGR NUCLEAR TECHNOL, MONSANTO RES CORP, MIAMISBURG, 77- Mem: Am Chem Soc. Res: Synthesis of various compounds of plutonium for use as isotopic fuels; high temperature vapor pressure of various plutonium-oxide compounds; management of plutonium fuel fabrication and nuclear waste treatment facilities. Mailing Add: 252 Orchard Hill Dr Dayton OH 45449

KOKERNOT, ROBERT HUTSON, b Alpine, Tex, Aug 14, 21; m 46; c 4. EPIDEMIOLOGY, VIROLOGY. Educ: Agr & Mech Col Tex, DVM, 46; Baylor Univ, MD, 50; Johns Hopkins Univ, MPH, 52, DrPH, 61; Am Bd Med Microbiol, cert, 61; Am Bd Prev Med, dipl. Prof Exp: Epidemiologist, Calif State Health Dept, 52-53; mem staff, Rockefeller Found, 53-63; prof epidemiol & asst dir ctr zoonoses res, Univ Ill, 63-68; prof epidemiol & chmn dept pathobiol & comp med, Univ Tex, Houston, 68-73; CHMN DEPT PREV MED & COMMUNITY HEALTH, TEX TECH UNIV, 73- Mem: Am Col Prev Med; Am Soc Trop Med & Hyg; Am Pub Health Asn; Am Asn Immunologists; NY Acad Sci. Res: Arthropod-borne virus diseases. Mailing Add: 17 Brentwood Club Lubbock TX 79416

KOKESH, FRITZ CARL, b Minneapolis, Minn, Jan 12, 43; m 69; c 2. ORGANIC GEOCHEMISTRY. Educ: Lewis Univ, BSc, 65; Ohio State Univ, PhD(org chem), 69. Prof Exp: NIH fel, Harvard Univ, 69-71; asst prof biochem, Univ Guelph, 72-77; RES CHEMIST, PHILLIPS PETROL CO, 77- Mem: Am Chem Soc. Res: Origin and mechanism of petroleum formation; organic geochemical methods for petroleum exploration. Mailing Add: Res Ctr Phillips Petrol Co Bartlesville OK 74004

KOKJER, KENNETH JORDAN, b Beatrice, Nebr, Feb 27, 41. ELECTRICAL ENGINEERING, COMPUTER SCIENCE. Educ: Nebr Wesleyan Univ, BS, 63; Univ Ill, Urbana-Champaign, MS, 67, PhD(biophys), 70. Prof Exp: Asst prof, 70-76, ASSOC PROF ELEC ENG, UNIV ALASKA, FAIRBANKS, 76- Concurrent Pos: Vis scientist, Tohoku Univ, Sendai, Japan, 81. Mem: Inst Elec & Electronics Engrs; Comput Soc; Soc Comput Simulation. Res: Applications of computers to real time support of biological research laboratories; personal data communications via satellites. Mailing Add: Dept of Elec Eng Univ of Alaska Fairbanks AK 99701

KOKKINAKIS, DEMETRIUS MICHAEL, b Heraklion, Crete, March 5, 50. ENZYMOLOGY, METABOLISM. Educ: Nat Univ Athens, BS, 73; Pa State Univ, MS, 75; WVa Univ, PhD(biochem), 77. Prof Exp: Grad asst biochem, WVa Univ Plant Sci, 75-77, res assoc, 77-78; fel med biochem, Sch Med, Tex Tech Univ, 78-80; fel, 80-81, ASSOC PATH, MED SCH, NORTHWESTERN UNIV, 81- Concurrent Pos: Res award, R Welch Found, 79. Mem: Am Chem Soc. Res: Metabolism of pancreatic carcinogens (nitrosamines) by various organs: evaluate the significance of each metabolic pathway in the activation of the parent compound to its carcinogen form; interaction of nitrosamines and their metabolites with cellular macromolecules. Mailing Add: Dept Path Northwestern Univ Med Sch 303 E Chicago Ave Chicago IL 60611

KOKNAT, FRIEDRICH WILHELM, b Muenster, Ger, Feb 19, 38; m 64; c 2. INORGANIC CHEMISTRY, X-RAY CRYSTALLOGRAPHY. Educ: Univ Giessen, BS, 59, MS, 63, PhD(chem), 65. Prof Exp: Instr chem, Univ Giessen, 64-66; fel, Iowa State Univ, 66-69; instr, Boone Jr Col, 68-69; asst prof, 69-74, assoc prof, 74-80, PROF CHEM, YOUNGSTOWN STATE UNIV, 80- Mem: Am Chem Soc; Am Crystallog Asn; Ger Chem Soc; Sigma Xi. Res: Structural inorganic chemistry; transition metal cluster compounds; phase relationships and stabilization of low oxidation states by formation of complexes and double salts. Mailing Add: Dept of Chem Youngstown State Univ Youngstown OH 44555

KOKORIS, LOUIS A, b Chicago, Ill, June 27, 24; wid; c 3. ALGEBRA. Educ: Univ Chicago, SB, 47, SM, 48, PhD(math), 52. Prof Exp: From instr to asst prof math, Univ Wash, 52-55; asst prof, Wash Univ, 55-58; assoc prof, 58-63, PROF MATH, ILL INST TECHNOL, 63- Concurrent Pos: Vis lectr, Yale Univ, 56-57. Mem: Am Math Soc; Math Asn Am; Sigma Xi; Am Asn Univ Professors. Res: Non-associative algebras. Mailing Add: Dept of Math Ill Inst Technol Chicago IL 60616

KOKOROPOULOS, PANOS, b Thessaloniki, Greece, Aug 10, 27; US citizen; m 60; c 3. ENVIRONMENTAL ENGINEERING, PHYSICAL CHEMISTRY. Educ: Univ Thessaloniki, Greece, BS, 55; Univ Dayton, MS, 64; Univ Akron, PhD(civil eng), 72. Prof Exp: Assoc res chemist solid state chem & tech info, Univ Dayton, 63-65; dir tech info, Ctr Info Syst, Univ Akron, 65-69, asst prof chem technol, 69-71; assoc prof environ eng, 73-80, PROF CIVIL ENG, SOUTHERN ILL UNIV, EDWARDSVILLE, 80- Concurrent Pos: Consult, Granite City Works, Am Steel Foundries, 77; tech reviewer, US Dept Energy, 80 & 81. Mem: Am Chem Soc; Am Soc Civil Engrs; Am Soc Testing & Mat; Solar Energy Soc; Am Soc Eng Educ. Res: Methane production by anaerobic digestion of livestock wastes; solar energy utilization; retrofitting of existing homes; centralized solar systems for multi-housing developments. Mailing Add: 414 W Union #6 Edwardsville IL 62025

KOKOSKI, CHARLES JOSEPH, b Chicopee Falls, Mass, June 2, 27; m 52; c 3. PHARMACY. Educ: Univ Md, BS, 51, MS, 53, PhD(pharm), 56. Prof Exp: From asst prof to assoc prof pharm, George Washington Univ, 56-64; biochemist, Food & Drug Admin, Dept Health, Educ & Welfare, Washington, DC, 64-77; CHIEF, DIV TOXICOL, FOOD ADDITIVES EVAL BR, FOOD & DRUG ADMIN, 77- Mem: AAAS; Am Pharmaceut Asn; Soc Toxicol; Soc Cosmetic Chemists. Res: Toxicology; pharmaceutical and cosmetic product development. Mailing Add: 4504 Maple Ave Halethorpe MD 21227

KOKOSKI, ROBERT JOHN, pharmacy, pharmacognosy, see previous edition

KOKOSZKA, GERALD FRANCIS, b Meriden, Conn, Sept 26, 38; m 61; c 3. PHYSICAL INORGANIC CHEMISTRY. Educ: Univ Conn, BA, 60; Univ Md, MS, 64, PhD(phys PhD(chem physics), 66. Prof Exp: Res scientist, Inorg Chem Sect, Nat Bur Standards, 61-68; from asst prof to assoc prof, 68-73, PROF CHEM, STATE UNIV NY COL PLATTSBURGH, 73- Concurrent Pos: State Univ NY Res Found grants, 68 & 70; Res Corp grant, 69; Petrol Res Found grants, 70, 71-73 & 74-82. Mem: Am Chem Soc; Am Phys Soc; The Chem Soc. Res: Electron spin resonance of metal complexes, free radicals, minerals, low-dimensional systems and biochemical systems. Mailing Add: Dept of Chem State Univ NY Col Arts & Sci Plattsburgh NY 12901

KOKOTAILO, GEORGE T, b Willingdon, Alta, June 21, 19; US citizen; m 53; c 2. SOLID STATE PHYSICS. Educ: Univ Alta, BSc, 41, MSc, 48; Temple Univ, PhD(physics), 55. Prof Exp: Physicist, Ont Res Found, 41-42 & Defense Indust Ltd, 42-44; physicist, Nat Res Coun Can, 44-45, sr res physicist, Socony Mobil Oil Co, 48-60, RES ASSOC, MOBIL RES & DEVELOP CORP, 60- Concurrent Pos: Adj prof, Drexel Inst Technol, 58- Mem: Am Phys Soc; Am Chem Soc; Electron Micros Soc Am; Am Crystallog Asn. Res: Radiowave propagation; cloud chamber physics; rubber physics; x-ray spectroscopy; x-ray absorption fine structure; crystal structure; anomolous transmission of x-rays and electrons; chemistry and structure of zeolites. Mailing Add: 98 N American Woodbury NJ 08096

KOKTA, MILAN RASTISLAV, b Brno, Czech, Mar 22, 41; m 70. SOLID STATE CHEMISTRY. Educ: Inst Chem Technol, Pardubice, MS, 68; Newark Col Eng, DESc, 72. Prof Exp: Staff chemist inorg chem res, Lachema, Czech, 65-68; mem tech staff, Bell Labs, 72-73; staff chemist res, Allied Chem

Corp, 73-77; STAFF SCIENTIST, UNION CARBIDE CORP, 77- *Mem:* Am Chem Soc; Sigma Xi; Am Asn Crystal Growth. *Res:* Liquid phase epitaxy; crystal chemistry of oxide and chalcogenide compounds; relation between structure and physical properties; magnetism; phase relations in oxide systems with respect to crystal growth; crystal growth of electrooptical materials. *Mailing Add:* Union Carbide Corp 8888 Balboa Ave San Diego CA 92123

KOLAIAN, JACK H, b Troy, NY, July 22, 29; m 60; c 3. COLLOID CHEMISTRY, SURFACE CHEMISTRY. *Educ:* Cornell Univ, BS, 56; Purdue Univ, MS, 58, PhD(clay chem), 60. *Prof Exp:* Asst, Purdue Univ, 56-60; res assoc, Cornell Univ, 60; sr chemist, Bellaire Lab, 60-64, group leader chem res, 64-68, res chemist, 68-73, GROUP LEADER CATALYSTS-REFINING, BEACON RES LAB, CHEM PROD DEVELOP, TEXACO, INC, 74- *Mem:* Am Chem Soc. *Res:* Oil production; catalysts; petroleum refining. *Mailing Add:* Texaco Inc PO Box 509 Beacon NY 12508

KOLAKOWSKI, DONALD LOUIS, b Chicago, Ill, Jan 7, 44. PSYCHOMETRICS, HUMAN QUANTITATIVE GENETICS. *Educ:* Knox Col, BA, 66; Univ Chicago, MA, 67, PhD(measurement & statist), 70. *Prof Exp:* Asst prof biobehav sci, 70-74, ASST PROF BEHAV SCI, UNIV CONN HEALTH CTR, 74- *Concurrent Pos:* Prin investr, NIH & NIMH grants, Univ Conn, 73-82. *Honors & Awards:* Res Career Develop Award, Nat Inst Dental Res, 75-80. *Mem:* Am Soc Human Genetics; Behav Genetics Asn; Psychometric Soc; Soc for Study Social Biol; Am Educ Res Asn. *Res:* Inheritance of mental traits, cranio-facial structures, disease susceptibility, and their measurement in diverse human populations; human behavioral genetics; dental anthropology. *Mailing Add:* Dept Behav Sci-Community Health Univ of Conn Health Ctr Farmington CT 06032

KOLAR, JOHN JOSEPH, b Raynesford, Mont, June 14, 22; m 55; c 2. PLANT BREEDING. *Educ:* Mont State Col, BS, 50, MS, 52; Iowa State Col, PhD(plant breeding), 55. *Prof Exp:* Asst agronomist, 56-69, assoc prof agron & assoc agronomist, 69-77, RES PROF AGRON, UNIV IDAHO, 77- *Mem:* Crop Sci Soc Am; Am Soc Agron; Sigma Xi; Western Soc Crop Sci; Coun Agr Sci & Technol. *Res:* Bean breeding and production. *Mailing Add:* Univ of Idaho Res & Exten Ctr Kimberly ID 83341

KOLAR, JOSEPH ROBERT, JR, b Chicago, Ill, Sept 26, 38; m 72; c 1. VETERINARY VIROLOGY. *Educ:* Southern Ill Univ, Carbondale, BA, 65, MA, 68, PhD(microbiol), 72. *Prof Exp:* Res assoc dent med, Dent Res Ctr, Univ NC, 72-73; prod mgr virus, Armour-Baldwin Labs, 73-74; res scientist vet virol, 74-77, RES DIR, FROMM LABS, INC, SALSBURY LABS, 77- *Mem:* Am Tissue Cult Asn. *Res:* Applied research in development of veterinary viral vaccines. *Mailing Add:* 141 W Lilac Lane Grafton WI 53024

KOLAR, MICHAEL JOSEPH, b Cleveland, Ohio, Apr 8, 39; m 61; c 5. ENGINEERING, MECHANICAL ENGINEERING. *Educ:* John Carroll Univ, BS, 61, MS, 63; Case Western Reserve Univ, PhD(eng), 68. *Prof Exp:* Res engr thermal sci, Am Gas Asn, 61-62; nuclear engr, Lewis Res Ctr, NASA, 62-69; asst prof math, Cleveland State Univ, 69-73; mgr eng anal, Gilbert/Commonwealth, 73-78; PROG MGR, ELEC POWER RES INST, 78- *Mem:* Am Nuclear Soc; Am Soc Eng Educ; Am Soc Mech Engrs; Soc Exp Stress Anal. *Res:* Steam turbines; power plant reliability. *Mailing Add:* Elec Power Res Inst 3412 Hillview Ave Palo Alto CA 94303

KOLAR, OSCAR CLINTON, b Los Angeles, Calif, Sept 26, 28; Div; c 3. NUCLEAR CRITICALITY SAFETY, PHYSICS. *Educ:* Univ Calif, Los Angeles, BA, 49; Univ Calif, PhD(physics), 55. *Prof Exp:* SR PHYSICIST, LAWRENCE LIVERMORE LAB, UNIV CALIF, 55- *Concurrent Pos:* Regist prof nuclear engr, Calif, 76. *Mem:* Am Phys Soc; Sigma Xi; Am Nuclear Soc; Am Asn Physics Teachers; AAAS. *Res:* Nuclear physics, especially nuclear reactions; reactor physics, including criticality hazards evaluation; geophysics; seismology. *Mailing Add:* Lawrence Livermore Nat Lab L-303 Univ of Calif PO Box 808 Livermore CA 94550

KOLASA, KATHRYN MARIANNE, b Detroit, Mich, July 26, 49. NUTRITION, ANTHROPOLOGY. *Educ:* Mich State Univ, BS, 70; Univ Tenn, Knoxville, PhD(food sci), 74. *Prof Exp:* Test kitchen home economist, Kellogg Co, 71; asst prof, 74-80, ASSOC PROF COMMUNITY NUTRIT, MICH STATE UNIV, 80- *Concurrent Pos:* Res assoc, Home Learning Ctr Res Proj, Off Educ, 74-75. *Mem:* Am Inst Nutrit; Soc Nutrit Educ; Inst Food Technologists; Comt Nutrit Anthrop. *Res:* Interactions of nutrition and culture upon the health of the individual and family in the US and the developing world. *Mailing Add:* Food Sci & Human Nutrit & Mich State Univ East Lansing MI 48824

KOLAT, ROBERT S, b Bay City, Mich, May 8, 31; m 54; c 4. ANALYTICAL CHEMISTRY. *Educ:* Mich State Univ, BS, 58; Iowa State Univ, PhD(phys chem), 61. *Prof Exp:* Res chemist, Am Cyanamid Co, 61-65; res chemist, 65-73, RES MGR, DOW CHEM CO, MIDLAND, 73- *Mem:* AAAS; Am Chem Soc. *Res:* Chelation; bomb calorimetry; aerosol research. *Mailing Add:* 3370 Parkway Dr Bay City MI 48706

KOLATA, DENNIS ROBERT, b Rockford, Ill, June 9, 42; m 63; c 2. STRATIGRAPHY, INVERTEBRATE PALEONTOLOGY. *Educ:* Northern Ill Univ, BS, 68, MS, 70; Univ Ill, PhD(geol), 73. *Prof Exp:* Geologist explor & develop, Texaco Inc, 73-74; assoc geologist, 74-80, GEOLOGIST, ILL STATE GEOL SURV, 80- *Mem:* Paleontol Soc; Paleont Asn. *Res:* Stratigraphy and paleontology of Paleozoic rocks in the Eastern Interior of North America. *Mailing Add:* Ill State Geol Surv Natural Resources Bldg Champaign IL 61820

KOLB, ALAN CHARLES, b Hoboken, NJ, Dec 14, 28. PHYSICS. *Educ:* Ga Inst Technol, BS, 49; Univ Mich, MS, 50, PhD(theoret physics), 55. *Prof Exp:* Supt plasma physics div, Naval Res Lab, 55-70, pres & chief exec officer, 70-78, CHMN & CHIEF EXEC OFFICER, MAXWELL LABS INC, 78- *Concurrent Pos:* Adj prof, Univ Md, College Park, 68-70; vis prof, Cath Univ Am, 65-68. *Mem:* Am Phys Soc; NY Acad Sci. *Res:* Plasma physics and controlled thermonuclear research; theoretical and experimental spectroscopy; hydrodynamics and very high Mach number shock waves; electron beam research; high voltage engineering; laser development. *Mailing Add:* 9244 Balboa Ave San Diego CA 92123

KOLB, BRYAN EDWARD, b Calgary, Alta, Nov 10, 47. NEUROPSYCHOLOGY, PHYSIOLOGICAL PSYCHOLOGY. *Educ:* Univ Calgary, BSc, 68, MSc, 70; Pa State Univ, PhD(psychol), 73. *Prof Exp:* Fel psychol, Univ Western Ont, 73-75; med res coun fel, Montreal Neurol Inst, 75-76; asst prof, 76-78, ASSOC PROF PSYCHOL, UNIV LETHBRIDGE, 78- *Mem:* Soc Neurosci; Am Psychol Asn; Can Psychol Asn; Int Neuropsychol Soc; Animal Behav Soc. *Res:* Frontal lobe function in mammals; recovery of function following brain damage; cortical control of praxic movements. *Mailing Add:* Dept of Psychol Univ of Lethbridge Lethbridge AB T1K 3M4 Can

KOLB, CHARLES EUGENE, JR, b Cumberland, Md, May 21, 45; m 65; c 2. CHEMICAL KINETICS, ATMOSPHERIC CHEMISTRY. *Educ:* Mass Inst Technol, SB, 67; Princeton Univ, MA, 68, PhD(phys chem), 71. *Prof Exp:* Sr res scientist, 71-75, dir, Ctr Chem & Environ Physics, 77-80, tech dir, Appl Sci Div, 80-81, PRIN RES SCIENTIST, AERODYNE RES INC, 75-, VPRES & DIR, APPL SCI DIV, 81- *Concurrent Pos:* Hon res fel atmospheric chem, Ctr Earth & Planetary Physics, Harvard Univ, 76-; res affil, Spectros Lab, Mass Inst Technol, 81- *Mem:* Combustion Inst; Am Chem Soc; Am Phys Soc; Optical Soc Am. *Res:* Experimental and theoretical studies of inelastic energy exchange in hyperthermal molecular collisions; chemistry and physics of trace atmospheric species; chemical kinetics and spectroscopy of combustion and gas lasers. *Mailing Add:* Aerodyne Res Inc Crosby Dr Bedford Res Park Bedford MA 01730

KOLB, CHARLES RUDOLPH, b Vicksburg, Miss, Apr 14, 20; m 51; c 1. GEOLOGY. *Educ:* La State Univ, BS, 48, MS, 50, PhD, 60. *Prof Exp:* Instr, La State Univ, 47-48; eng geologist, Snare Eng Corp, Chile, 50-51; geologist & chief geol, Waterways Exp Sta, 51-61; chief scientist, Arctic Test Ctr, Alaska, 62-64; chief geologist, Waterways Exp Sta, 65-74; RETIRED. *Concurrent Pos:* Consult geologist. *Honors & Awards:* Outstanding Performance Award, Corps Engrs, US Army, 58, 70 & Arctic Test Ctr, 64. *Mem:* Fel AAAS; fel Geol Soc Am; Am Asn Petrol Geologists; Am Inst Prof Geologists. *Res:* Alluvial geology and its significance in engineering problems in the lower Mississippi Alluvial Valley; uses of aerial photo interpretation in selecting sites for airfields, locks and other engineering structures; quantitative geomorphology; military terrain analysis; arctic research and development. *Mailing Add:* 3314 Highland Dr Vicksburg MS 39180

KOLB, DORIS KASEY , b Louisville, Ky, Aug 4, 27; m 48; c 3. ORGANIC CHEMISTRY. *Educ:* Univ Louisville, BS, 48; Ohio State Univ, MSc, 50, PhD(chem), 53. *Prof Exp:* Chemist info res, Standard Oil Co, (Ind), 53-57; assoc prof chem & head dept, Corning Community Col, 61-62, chemist, 59-62; PROF CHEM, ILL CENT COL, 67- *Mem:* Am Chem Soc. *Res:* Sugars; fatty acid solubility; petroleum chemistry; plastics. *Mailing Add:* Dept of Chem Ill Cent Col East Peoria IL 61635

KOLB, EDWARD JOHN, research administration, ionospheric physics, see previous edition

KOLB, EDWARD WILLIAM, b New Orleans, La, Oct 2, 51; m 72; c 2. COSMOLOGY, SUPERNOVAE. *Educ:* Univ New Orleans, BS, 73; Univ Tex, PhD(physics), 78. *Prof Exp:* Fel astrophysics, Calif Inst Technol, 78-80; J Robert Opphenheimer res fel, 80-81, MEM STAFF ASTROPHYSICS, LOS ALAMOS NAT LAB, 80- *Mem:* Am Phys Soc. *Res:* Application of particle physics to the study of the early universe; cosmology; neutrine processes in supernovae; weak interactions. *Mailing Add:* Theoret Div MSB288 Los Alamos Nat Lab Los Alamos NM 87545

KOLB, FELIX OSCAR, b Vienna, Austria, Nov 12, 12; nat US. MEDICINE. *Educ:* Univ Calif, AB, 41, MD, 43; Am Bd Internal Med, cert endocrinol & metab. *Prof Exp:* Asst med, Univ Calif, 46-49; asst, Mass Gen Hosp, 50-51; asst, 51-53, from clin instr to asst clin prof, 52-59, assoc clin prof & assoc res physician, 59-68, res physician, Metab Unit, 53-59 & 68-81, CLIN PROF MED, SCH MED, UNIV CALIF, SAN FRANCISCO, 68- *Mem:* Endocrine Soc; AMA; Am Diabetes Asn; fel Am Col Physicians; Am Fedn Clin Res. *Res:* Metabolic bone disease; renal tubular disorders and renal stones, including cystinuria; adrenal adrenogenic disorder, including etiology of hirsutism. *Mailing Add:* 3580 California St San Francisco CA 94118

KOLB, FREDERICK J(OHN), JR, b Rochester, NY, May 7, 17; m 42; c 4. RECORDING MEDIA. *Educ:* Mass Inst Technol, SB, 38, SM, 39, ScD(chem eng), 47. *Prof Exp:* Chem engr, 42-73, PROJ COORDR, EASTMAN KODAK CO, 73- *Concurrent Pos:* Instr, Univ Rochester, 45. *Mem:* AAAS; Am Chem Soc; Soc Motion Picture & TV Engrs; Am Inst Chem Engrs; Inst Elec & Electronics Engrs. *Res:* Physical and chemical properties of photographic and magnetic media; theory and practice of magnetic and photographic recording systems, especially from the viewpoint of information theory; production of cellulose ester and polyester films; cine film manufacture and applications; effects of radiation on motion-picture films; development manufacture and applications of magnetic recording media; storage and retrieval of audio and visual information; international standardization. *Mailing Add:* 211 Oakridge Dr Rochester NY 14617

KOLB, HARRY JOHN, b Buffalo, NY, June 5, 18; m; c 2. CHEMISTRY. *Educ:* Hamilton Col, BS, 40; Haverford Col, MS, 41; Northwestern Univ, PhD(chem), 43. *Prof Exp:* Proj engr, Naval Res Lab, Washington, DC, 43-44; res chemist, E I du Pont de Nemours & Co, Inc, NY, 45-50, res supvr, Del, 50-66, TECH SERV MGR, E I DUPONT DE NEMOURS & CO, INC, 66- *Concurrent Pos:* Mem body armour comt, Nat Res Coun. *Mem:* Sigma Xi. *Res:* Thermodynamics of dehydration of alcohols; crystallography; corrosion chemistry; polymer chemistry; textile research. *Mailing Add:* Taylor La CDRCRFT Wilmington DE 19898

KOLB, HELGA ELLEN THOR, neuroanatomy, see previous edition

KOLB, KENNETH EMIL, b Louisville, Ky, Jan 21, 28; m 48; c 3. ORGANIC CHEMISTRY. *Educ:* Univ Louisville, BS, 48; Ohio State Univ, PhD(chem), 53. *Prof Exp:* Chemist, Nat Distillers, 48, Standard Oil Co, Ind, 53-58 & Corning Glass Works, 58-65; CHEMIST, BRADLEY UNIV, 65- *Mem:* Am Chem Soc; Soc Plastics Eng; The Chem Soc. *Res:* Electro-organic chemistry; electrophilic bromination and aklylation; iodine organic complexes; furan chemistry. *Mailing Add:* Dept of Chem Bradley Univ Peoria IL 61625

KOLB, LAWRENCE COLEMAN, b Baltimore, Md, June 16, 11; m 37; c 3. PSYCHIATRY. *Educ:* Trinity Col, Dublin, BA, 32; Johns Hopkins Univ, MD, 34; Am Bd Psychiat & Neurol, dipl, 42. *Prof Exp:* Intern med, Strong Mem Hosp, NY, 34-35, intern surg, 35-36; asst dispensary neurologist, Sch Med, Johns Hopkins Univ, 36-38, instr neurol, 39-41; resident psychiatrist, Milwaukee Sanitarium, 41-42; dir res, Div Ment Hyg, USPHS, 46-49; consult, Mayo Clin, 49-54; comnr, NY State Dept Ment Hyg, 75-77; prof, 54-75, EMER PROF PSYCHIAT, COL PHYSICIANS & SURGEONS, COLUMBIA UNIV, 76- DISTINGUISHED PHYSICIAN, US VET ADMIN, 78- & PROF PSYCHIAT, ALBANY MED COL, 78- *Concurrent Pos:* Fel, Sch Med, Johns Hopkins Univ, 36-38; Markle Found fel, Nat Hosp, London, 38; consult, US Navy, Washington, DC, 46-49, USPHS, 54-62 & NIMH; res assoc, Wash Sch Psychiat, 47-49; assoc prof, Univ Minn, 49-53; chmn dept psychiat & dir psychiat serv, Presby Hosp, New York, 54-74, pres med bd, 62-64, trustee, 71-73; dir, NY State Psychiat Inst, New York, 54-74; dir & mem bd dirs, Res Fedn Ment Hyg Inc, 54-75, pres & chmn bd, 60-75; mem comt, Navy Med Res, Nat Res Coun, 56-59; dir, Am Bd Psychiat & Neurol, 60-68, pres, 68; assoc comnr res, NY State Dept Ment Hyg, 68-69; ed, Yearbk Psychiat & Appl Ment Health, 71-; pres adv bd, PR Inst Psychiat, 72. *Honors & Awards:* Henry Wisner Miller Mem Award, First Oscar K Diamond Award, 71; Joan Plehn Award Humane Serv, Ment Health Asn New York & Bronx Counties, 72; mem, Johns Hopkins Soc Scholars, 72. *Mem:* Am Acad Arts & Sci; Am Neurol Asn; hon fel Royal Col Psychiat; Am Psychiat Asn (pres, 68); Asn Res Nerv & Ment Dis (pres, 59). *Res:* Psychiatry and psychoanalysis; neurology. *Mailing Add:* Vet Admin Med Ctr 113 Holland Ave Albany NY 12208

KOLB, LEONARD H, b Chicago, Ill, Feb 2, 13; m; c 4. SURGERY, ONCOLOGY. *Educ:* Univ Ill, BS, 35, MD, 38. *Prof Exp:* Intern, Mt Sinai Hosp, Chicago, 37-39, resident surg, 39-40, ASSOC PROF SURG, RUSH MED SCH & MT SINAI HOSP, 48- *Concurrent Pos:* Sr attend surgeon, Mt Sinai Hosp, 46- *Mem:* Fel Am Col Surgeons; AMA; Am Asn Cancer Res; Am Asn Cancer Educ; Soc Clin Oncol. *Res:* Cancer. *Mailing Add:* 30 N Michigan Ave Chicago IL 60602

KOLBECK, ANDREW GERARD, polymer physics, glass technology, see previous edition

KOLBECK, RALPH CARL, b Wausau, Wis, Sept 2, 44; m 66; c 2. PHYSIOLOGY, BIOCHEMISTRY. *Educ:* Univ Minn, BA, 66, PhD(physiol, biochem), 70. *Prof Exp:* Res fel cardiac physiol, Stone Res Lab, Univ Minn, Minneapolis, 70-73; instr med, 73-77, asst prof med & asst dir hemodynamic res, 77-80, ASSOC PROF MED & DIR MYOCARDIAL RES, MED COL GA, 80-, LECTR PHYSIOL, 77- *Concurrent Pos:* Ga Heart Asn grant, 74-76; Gen Res Support grant, 74-76; NIH grant, 75-78; Am Heart Asn grant, 76-78; Ga Heart Asn Investr, 78- *Mem:* Am Fed Clin Res; Soc Exp Biol Med; assoc Am Physiol Soc; Am Heart Asn; Sigma Xi. *Res:* Sugar transport modified by insulin and muscular activity; calcium uptake by rabbit myocardium; subcellular calcium localization in canine myocardium; smooth muscle contractility. *Mailing Add:* Dept of Med Med Col of Ga Augusta GA 30901

KOLBEZEN, MARTIN (JOSEPH), b Pueblo, Colo, Apr 16, 14; m 53. PESTICIDE CHEMISTRY. *Educ:* Colo State Univ, BS, 39; Univ Utah, MS, 41, PhD(org chem), 50. *Prof Exp:* Nat Defense Res Coun fel, Iowa State Univ, 41-42; asst, Univ Utah, 39-41, 47-48; anal chemist, US Bur Mines, Utah, 42-44; asst insect toxicologist, 50-56, asst chemist, Plant Path, 56-58, assoc chemist, 58-64, chemist & lectr, 64-81, EMER CHEMIST & LECTR, PLANT PATH, CITRUS EXP STA, UNIV CALIF, RIVERSIDE, 81- *Mem:* Am Chem Soc. *Res:* Chemistry and mode of action of pesticides; residue analysis and development of methods of analysis; climatic and biological breakdown of pesticides; soil fumigation measurements and techniques. *Mailing Add:* Dept of Plant Path Univ of Calif Riverside CA 92502

KOLBYE, ALBERT CHRISTIAN, JR, b Philadelphia, Pa, Feb 15, 35. PUBLIC HEALTH. *Educ:* Harvard Col, AB, 57; Temple Univ, MD, 61; Johns Hopkins Univ, MPH, 65; Univ Md, JD, 66. *Prof Exp:* Intern med, Univ Hosps, Madison, Wis, 62; resident physician, Div Chronic Dis, USPHS, 62-65, chief field staff, Heart Dis Control Prog, 65-67, assoc dir sci, Nat Ctr Smoking & Health, 67-68, staff dir & exec secy, Comn Pesticides & Environ Health, Dept Health, Educ & Welfare, 69, dir off standards & compliance, Consumer Protection & Environ Health Serv, USPHS, 69-70, dep dir, Bur Foods, 70-72, ASSOC DIR SCI, BUR FOODS, FOOD & DRUG ADMIN, 72-, ASST SURGEON GEN, USPHS, 71- *Honors & Awards:* Meritorious Serv Medal, Food & Drug Admin, USPHS, 71 & 75. *Mem:* Fel Am Pub Health Asn; fel Am Col Prev Med; fel Am Col Legal Med; fel Am Acad Clin Toxicol; Am Acad Forensic Med. *Res:* Epidemiology of heavy metal toxicity, halogenated hydrocarbons; environmental contaminants; epidemiology of cancer and carcinogenesis; medicolegal aspects of clinical and epidemiological research; medicolegal aspects of malpractice. *Mailing Add:* 4802 Ft Sumner Dr Bethesda MD 20016

KOLCHIN, ELLIS ROBERT, b New York, NY, Apr 18, 16; m 40; c 2. MATHEMATICS. *Educ:* Columbia Univ, AB, 37, PhD(math), 41. *Prof Exp:* Instr math, Hofstra Col & lectr Barnard Col, 40-41; Nat Res fel, Inst Advan Study, 41-42; from instr to assoc prof, 46-58, prof, 58-76, ADRAIN PROF MATH, COLUMBIA UNIV, 76- *Concurrent Pos:* Guggenheim fel, 54-55 & 61-62; NSF sr fel, 60-61. *Mem:* AAAS; Am Acad Arts & Sci; Am Math Soc. *Res:* Differential algebra and algebraic groups. *Mailing Add:* Dept of Math Columbia Univ New York NY 10027

KOLDER, HANSJOERG E, b Vienna, Austria, Nov 29, 26; m 55; c 3. OPHTHALMOLOGY, PHYSIOLOGY. *Educ:* Univ Vienna, MD, 50. *Prof Exp:* Asst physiol, Univ Vienna, 51-59, docent, 59; vis asst prof, Emory Univ, 59-63, assoc prof, 63-68; assoc prof, 68-73, PROF OPHTHAL, UNIV IOWA, 73- *Concurrent Pos:* Europ Coun res fel aviation med, Karolinska Inst, Sweden, 58 & 61. *Mem:* AAAS; Am Acad Ophthal & Otolaryngol; Am Physiol Soc; Biophys Soc. *Res:* Aviation and sensory physiology; ophthalmic electrodiagnosis; cataract management. *Mailing Add:* Dept of Ophthal Univ of Iowa Hosps Iowa City IA 52240

KOLDEWYN, WILLIAM A, b Odgen, Utah, Apr 23, 42; m 67; c 2. PHYSICS. *Educ:* Weber State Col, BS, 67; Wesleyan Univ, PhD(physics), 76. *Prof Exp:* Electro-mech engr, Xytex Corp, 74-75; sr mem tech staff, Ball Aerospace Syst Div, Ball Corp, 75-78; staff physicist, Off Prod Div, IBM, 78-80; PRIN MEM TECH STAFF, BALL AEROSPACE SYST DIV, BALL CORP, 80- *Mem:* Am Phys Soc. *Res:* Remote sensing from spacecraft; high precision control systems; high accuracy measurements of physcial constants. *Mailing Add:* 933 Columbia Place Boulder CO 80303

KOLDOVSKY, OTAKAR, b Olomouc, Czech, Mar 31, 30; m 71. DEVELOPMENTAL PHYSIOLOGY, GASTROENTEROLOGY. *Educ:* Charles Univ, Prague, MD, 55; Czech Acad Sci, Prague, PhD(develop physiol), 62. *Hon Degrees:* MA, Univ Pa, 74. *Prof Exp:* Scientist nutrit biochem & develop physiol, Inst Physiol, Czech Acad Sci, 56-68; res assoc, Dept Pediat, Stanford Univ, 68-69; from asst prof to prof pediat, Univ Pa, 69-79; PROF PEDIAT & PHYSIOL, UNIV ARIZ, 80- *Concurrent Pos:* Vis scientist, Dept Pediat, Stanford Univ, 65 & Dept Biochem, Univ Lund, Sweden, 67-68. *Honors & Awards:* Spec Award, Czech Acad Sci, 67. *Mem:* Am Inst Nutrit; Am Physiol Soc; Am Pediat Soc; Am Gastroenterol Soc; Perinatal Res Soc. *Res:* Role of hormonal and dietary factors in expression of normal developmental patterns of gastrointestinal functions. *Mailing Add:* Dept Pediat Univ Ariz 1501 N Campbell St Tuscon AZ 85724

KOLEK, ROBERT LOUIS, b Pittsburgh, Pa, Feb 5, 36; m 68; c 2. PLASTICS TECHNOLOGY, MATERIALS SCIENCE. *Educ:* Univ Pittsburgh, BS, 58, MS, 61. *Prof Exp:* Chemist fiber glass, PPG Industs, 61-68; FEL SCIENTIST PLASTICS, WESTINGHOUSE ELEC CO, 68- *Mem:* Soc Plastics Engrs; Am Chem Soc; Am Asn Testile Technol. *Res:* Reinforced plastics; composite material; textile technology. *Mailing Add:* Res & Develop Ctr 1310 Beulah Rd Pittsburgh PA 15235

KOLENBRANDER, HAROLD MARK, b Sibley, Iowa, Oct 7, 38; m 58; c 3. METABOLISM, ENZYMOLOGY. *Educ:* Cent Col, Iowa, BA, 60; Univ Iowa, PhD(biochem), 64. *Prof Exp:* From asst prof to prof chem, Cent Col, Iowa, 64-71; asst to pres, Grand Valley State Col, 71-72, dean, Col Planning, 72-75; vpres acad affairs, 75-80, PROF CHEM, PROVOST & DEAN, CENT COL, IOWA, 75- *Concurrent Pos:* USPHS grant amino acid metab, 65-68, spec fel, 69-70; vis scientist, Case Western Reserve Univ, 70. *Mem:* The Chem Soc; Biochem Soc; Sigma Xi. *Res:* Histidine metabolism and the associated enzymes. *Mailing Add:* Cent Col Pella IA 50219

KOLER, ROBERT DONALD, b Casper, Wyo, Feb 14, 24; m 45; c 2. MEDICAL GENETICS, HEMATOLOGY. *Educ:* Univ Ore, MD, 47; Am Bd Internal Med, dipl, 55. *Prof Exp:* Intern, Med Sch, Univ Ore, 47-48, resident hemat, 48-49; instr basic sci, Med Dept Res & Grad Sch, US Army, 49-50, chief gen med, 181st Gen Hosp, 50-51; resident med, 51-53, clin assoc med & hemat, 53-56, from asst prof to assoc prof, 56-64, head div hemat & exp med, 64-67, PROF MED & HEMAT, MED SCH, UNIV ORE, 64-, HEAD DIV MED GENETICS, 67- *Concurrent Pos:* USPHS res fel & hon res asst, Univ Col, Univ London, 60-61. *Mem:* Am Soc Hemat; Am Fedn Clin Res; fel Am Col Physicians; Am Soc Human Genetics; Int Soc Hemat. *Res:* Medical and human genetics; characterization of hemoglobin and red cell enzymes. *Mailing Add:* Dept Med Genetics L-103 Sch Med Ore Health Sci Univ Portland OR 97201

KOLESAR, PETER JOHN, b New York, NY, Nov 25, 36; c 2. OPERATIONS RESEARCH, STATISTICAL ANALYSIS. *Educ:* Queens Col, NY, BA, 59; Columbia Univ, BSIE, 59, MS, 61, PhD(opers res), 64. *Prof Exp:* Systs analyst appl statist, Procter & Gamble Co, 59-61; lectr opers res, Imp Col, Univ London, 64-65; asst prof, Columbia Univ, 65-70; assoc prof, Univ Montreal, 70-71; sr analyst, Rand Corp, 71-72; assoc prof comput sci, City Col New York, 72-75; assoc prof, 75-77, PROF MGT SCI, COLUMBIA UNIV, 77- *Concurrent Pos:* Consult, Rand Corp, 72-, NY State, 73-, Mt Sinai Hosp, 74-, NY City 80- & Citibank, 81- *Honors & Awards:* Lanchester Prize, Opers Res Soc Am, 75; NATO Syst Sci Prize, 76. *Mem:* Opers Res Soc Am; Inst Mgt Sci; fel AAAS; Am Statist Assoc. *Res:* Application of operations research to urban problems and transportation; applied optimization; probability and statistics particularly in litigation, clinical trial and public systems analysis. *Mailing Add:* Uris Hall Columbia Univ New York NY 10027

KOLESAR, PETER THOMAS, b Bridgeport, Conn, Oct 14, 42; m 65; c 2. GEOCHEMISTRY, PETROLOGY. *Educ:* Rensselaer Polytech Inst, BS, 66, MS, 68; Univ Calif, Riverside, PhD(geol), 73. *Prof Exp:* Fel isotope geochem, Inst Geophys & Planetary Physics, Univ Calif, Riverside, 73-74; asst prof, 74-80, ASSOC PROF GEOL, UTAH STATE UNIV, 80- *Concurrent Pos:* Co-prin investr, Utah State UniV Fac res grant, 77- & Off Water Res & Technol, US Dept Interior, 78- *Mem:* Sigma Xi; Soc Econ Paleontologists & Mineralogists; Geochem Soc. *Res:* Deciphering carbonate rocks; their original depositional environments, the changes which they have undergone (diagenesis) and the chemistry of fluids responsible for those changes; investigation of geothermal resources. *Mailing Add:* Dept of Geol (07) Utah State Univ Logan UT 84322

KOLESARI, GARY LEE, b Milwaukee, Wis, Aug 5, 48; m 73. TERATOLOGY. *Educ:* Univ Wis-Milwaukee, BS, 71; Med Col Wis, MS, 73, PhD(anat), 76, MD, 77. *Prof Exp:* asst prof anat & teratology, 78-81, ASST ADJ PROF DEPT ANAT, MED COL WIS, 81- *Mem:* Teratology Soc; AMA. *Res:* Teratology, environmental and abuse drug related. *Mailing Add:* Dept of Anat PO Box 26509 Milwaukee WI 53226

KOLESKE, JOSEPH VICTOR, b Stratford, Wis, Jan 23, 30; m 51; c 2. POLYMER CHEMISTRY. *Educ:* Univ Wis, BS, 58; Inst of Paper Chem, MS, 60, PhD, 63. *Prof Exp:* sr res scientist, 63-77, RES ASSOC, POLYMER SCI, CHEMICALS & PLASTICS, UNION CARBIDE CORP, 77- *Mem:* Am Chem Soc. *Res:* Polymer physical chemistry; high solids; polyurethane; powder; water borne coatings. *Mailing Add:* Union Carbide Corp Tech Ctr PO Box 8361 South Charleston WV 25303

KOLETSKY, SIMON, pathology, deceased

KOLF, RICHARD C, fluid mechanics, see previous edition

KOLFF, WILLEM JOHAN, b Leiden, Holland, Feb 14, 11; nat US; m 37; c 5. EXPERIMENTAL MEDICINE, CLINICAL MEDICINE. *Educ:* State Univ Leiden, MD, 38; State Univ Groningen, PhD, 46. *Hon Degrees:* DSc, Allegheny Col, 60, Tulane Univ, 75; MD, Univ Turin, 69, Univ Rostock, 75, Univ Bologna, Italy, 77 , hon mem Austrian Soc Nephrology, 78 & DSc, Univ L'Aquila, Italy, 81. *Prof Exp:* Asst path anat, State Univ Leiden, 34-36; asst med, State Univ Groningen, 38-41; head dept, Munic Hosp, Kampen, 41-50; prof clin invest, Educ Found, Cleveland Clin Found, 50-67, mem staff res div, 50-63, mem surg div & head dept artificial organs, 58-67; PROF SURG, RES PROF ENG, DIR INST BIOMED ENG & HEAD DIV ARTIFICIAL ORGANS, COL MED, UNIV UTAH, 67- *Concurrent Pos:* Pvt docent, Med Sch, State Univ Leiden, 49-51. *Honors & Awards:* Landsteiner Silver Medal, Neth Red Cross, 42; Frances Amory Award, Am Acad Arts & Sci, 48; Addingham Gold Medal, Univ Leeds, 62; K Award, Nat Kidney Dis Found, 63; Oliver Sharpey Prize, Royal Col Physicians, 63; Cameron Prize, Univ Edinburgh, 64; Gairdner Prize, Gairdner Found, Can, 66; 1st Gold Medal, Neth Surg Soc, 70; Ubbo Emmius Medal, State Univ Groningen, 70; Comdr, Order of Orange, Nassau, Neth, 70; Leo Harvey Prize, 72; Austrian Gewerbeverein's Wilhelm-Exner Award, 80. *Mem:* AAAS; fel Am Col Physicians; Am Heart Asn; hon fel AMA; Am Physiol Soc. *Res:* Kidney transplantation; application of heart-lung machines; development of artificial heart inside the chest; avoidance of thrombosis on plastics; development of blood oxygenators; new types of artificial kidneys and dialysis techniques; development of techniques for organ preservation for transplantation and visual prosthesis. *Mailing Add:* Div of Artificial Organs Univ of Utah Col of Med Salt Lake City UT 84112

KOLHOFF, M(ARVIN) J(OSEPH), b Goodland, Ind, Oct 22, 15; m 37; c 2. ENGINEERING. *Educ:* Purdue Univ, BSEE, 39. *Prof Exp:* Mem staff, Gen Elec Co, NY, 39-42, requisition engr control eng div, Locomotive & Car Equip Dept, Pa, 42-46, admin asst, 46-51, proj engr, 51, asst mgr lab, 51-53, mgr, 53-56, chmn opers res & synthesis study, 56-59, prog planning engr gen eng lab, NY, 59-60, consult eng applns, 60-63, mgr design eval, Gen Purpose Control Dept, 63-66, adminr modern eng course, NY, 66-71, staff assoc tech res, Corp Tech Staff, Gen Elec Co, Conn, 71-79; SR PARTNER, KOLHOFF ASSOCIATES, FLA, 80- *Mem:* Inst Elec & Electronics Engrs; Nat Soc Prof Engrs. *Res:* Technical resources and technological implications of legislative and regulatory issues related to environment, safety and other protection of consumers and public; engineering administration. *Mailing Add:* Kolhoff Assocs 342 N 14th St Quincy FL 32351

KOLI, ANDREW KAITAN, b Bombay, India, Aug 1, 25; US citizen; m 58; c 2. ORGANIC CHEMISTRY. *Educ:* Univ Bombay, BSc, 55; Howard Univ, MS, 64, PhD(chem), 68. *Prof Exp:* Develop chemist res, Dow Chem Co, 55-61; res asst, Howard Univ, 61-66, res assoc, 66-67, instr, Dept Pharm, 67-68; PROF CHEM, SC STATE COL, 68- *Mem:* Am Chem Soc; Sigma Xi; Indian Chem Soc; Am Soc Microbiol. *Res:* Organic synthesis and environmental pollution. *Mailing Add:* SC State Col Box 1633 Orangeburg SC 29117

KOLIN, ALEXANDER, b Odessa, Russia, Mar 12, 10; nat US; m 51. BIOPHYSICS. *Educ:* Prague Ger Univ, PhD(physics), 34. *Prof Exp:* Res fel biophys, Reese Hosp, Chicago, 35-37; physicist, Mt Sinai Hosp, NY, 38-41; res assoc civil eng, Columbia Univ, 41-46, instr physics, 44-45; asst prof, NY Univ, 45-46; asst prof, Univ Chicago, 46, actg chmn col physics, 47-50, chmn, 50-53, assoc prof, 53-55; assoc res biophysicist, 56-61, prof, 61-76, EMER PROF BIOPHYS, SCH MED, UNIV CALIF, LOS ANGELES, 77- *Concurrent Pos:* Res fel, Med Sch, NY Univ, 41-42; instr, City Col NY, 41-44. *Honors & Awards:* John Scott Medal, 65; Albert F Sperry Medal, 67; Humboldt Award, 77; Founder's Award, Electrophoresis Soc, 80. *Mem:* AAAS; Biophys Soc; Am Phys Soc; Sigma Xi; Am Physiol Soc. *Res:* Photoelectric effects; Geiger counters; gas discharges; biophysics of circulation of blood; electromagnetic measurement of fluid flow and turbulence; isoelectric focusing; electromagnetophoresis; electrophoresis; cell electrophoresis; studies of vasomotion and blood flow. *Mailing Add:* Molecular Biol Inst Univ of Calif Los Angeles CA 90024

KOLINER, RALPH, b New York, NY, Mar 20, 17; m 42; c 1. CIVIL ENGINEERING. *Educ:* Cooper Union, BChE, 39; Univ Pa, MS, 48, PhD(civil eng), 56. *Prof Exp:* Naval architect, Philadelphia Naval Shipyard, 40-46; instr mech eng, Drexel Inst, 46; instr & asst prof civil eng, Univ Pa, 46-57; assoc prof, 57-67, PROF CIVIL ENG, VILLANOVA UNIV, 67- *Concurrent Pos:* Consult, 46-; lectr & coordr, Rutgers Univ, 53-67. *Honors & Awards:* Farrell Award, Villanova Univ, 81. *Mem:* Am Soc Eng Educ; Am Soc Civil Engrs; Am Concrete Inst; Eng Honor Soc. *Res:* Reinforced concrete; fluid and applied mechanics; engineering materials. *Mailing Add:* Dept of Civil Eng Villanova Univ Villanova PA 19085

KOLIPINSKI, MILTON CHARLES, marine ecology, see previous edition

KOLIWAD, KRISHNA M, b Byadgi, India, Feb 27, 38; m 67; c 2. MICROELECTRONICS, SEMICONDUCTORS. *Educ:* Karnatak Univ, India, BSc, 58, MSc, 60; Rensselaer Polytech Inst, MS, 64; Cornell Univ, PhD(mat sci), 67. *Prof Exp:* Res assoc mat sci, Cornell Univ, 67; res assoc solid state physics, Univ Md, College Park, 67-68; res assoc mat sci, Cornell Univ, 68-70; mem tech staff semiconductor, Tex Instruments, Inc, 70-75; MEM TECH STAFF, JET PROPULSION LAB, CALIF INST TECHNOL, 75- *Res:* Development of low cost silicon crystal growth technology for terrestrial solar energy application; photovoltaic devices. *Mailing Add:* 429 Paulette Place La Canada CA 91011

KOLKER, HAROLD JERROLD, b St Louis, Mo, Oct 4, 37. THEORETICAL CHEMISTRY. *Educ:* Wash Univ, AB, 59; Columbia Univ, PhD(phys chem), 62. *Prof Exp:* NSF fel theoret chem, Columbia Univ, 62-63; from res scientist to sr res scientist, United Aircraft Res Labs, 63-67, sr theoret physicist, 67-80. *Mem:* Am Phys Soc. *Res:* Quantum mechanics; electric and magnetic interactions in molecules; chemical kinetics; theory of atomic and molecular collisions; theory of carbon formation in flames. *Mailing Add:* 28 Huntington St Apt C-3 Hartford CT 06105

KOLLAR, EDWARD JAMES, b Forest City, Pa, Mar 3, 34; m 63; c 5. ORAL BIOLOGY, EMBRYOLOGY. *Educ:* Univ Scranton, BS, 55; Syracuse Univ, MS, 59, PhD(zool), 63. *Prof Exp:* Instr zool, Univ Chicago, 63-66, asst prof biol, 66-67, asst prof anat, 67-71; assoc prof, 71-75, PROF ORAL BIOL, SCH DENT MED, UNIV CONN, FARMINGTON, 76- *Concurrent Pos:* Vis fac, W Alton Jones Cell Sci Ctr, Lake Placid, NY, 71-75; mem educ comt, Tissue Cult Asn, 74-78; bd dir, cranio-facial group, Int Asn Dent Res, 78-81; nat bd exam comt, Am Dent Asn, 78-; ed, Arch Oral Biol; vpres & prog dir, Craniofacial Group, Asn Dent Res, 81-82. *Honors & Awards:* Quantrell Teaching Award, Univ Chicago, 68, Ryerson Fac Fel, 69; Fogerty Int Fel, 78, Nat Acad Sci Exchange Fel, 78; Isaac Schour Mem Award, Int Asn Dent Res, 81. *Mem:* Int Asn Develop Biol; Soc Develop Biol; Am Asn Anatomists; Tissue Cult Asn; Int Soc Differentiation. *Res:* Development of skin, teeth and cranial neural crest; the role of collagen during morphogenesis; teratology. *Mailing Add:* Dept Oral Biol Sch Dent Med Univ Conn Health Ctr Farmington CT 06032

KOLLAR, WILLIAM L, b Akron, Ohio, Jan 31, 26; m 48; c 3. POLYMER CHEMISTRY. *Educ:* Univ Akron, BS, 49, MS, 55. *Prof Exp:* Jr chemist, 51-57, from res chemist to sr res chemist,57-70, group leader, mat chem & polymer characterization, Res & Develop, 70-80, SECT HEAD, ANAL SERV & MICROS, GEN TIRE & RUBBER CO, 80- *Mem:* Am Chem Soc. *Res:* Polymer characterization. *Mailing Add:* Res & Develop Ctr 2990 Gilchrist Rd Akron OH 44305

KOLLEN, WENDELL JAMES, b Adrian, Mich, Feb 22, 35; m 55; c 4. SURFACE PHYSICS. *Educ:* Hope Col, AB, 64; Clarkson Col Technol, MS, 67, PhD(physics), 69. *Prof Exp:* Res physicist, 69-74, SR PHYSICIST, TECH CTR, OWENS-ILL, INC, 74- *Mem:* Am Phys Soc; Am Vacuum Soc. *Res:* Vacuum ultramicrogravimetry; gas-solid interactions; chemical physics; high temperature corrosion; catalysis; gas and vapor transport in polymers. *Mailing Add:* Tech Ctr Owens-Ill Inc One Sea Gate Toledo OH 43666

KOLLER, CHARLES RICHARD, b North Manchester, Ind, Nov 16, 20; m 44; c 5. TEXTILE FIBERS, NONWOVEN FABRICS. *Educ:* Manchester Col, AB, 43; Purdue Univ, MS, 48, PhD(chem), 50. *Prof Exp:* Asst, Purdue Univ, 46-49; res chemist, 50-60, sr res chemist, 60-62, res supvr, 62-67, RES ASSOC, E I DU PONT DE NEMOURS & CO, 67- *Mem:* Am Chem Soc; Sigma Xi; fel Am Inst Chem; Fiber Soc. *Res:* Textile and inorganic fibers; nonwoven fabrics; condensation and vinyl polymerization; nitroparaffins; polymer and textile chemistry; fiber and textile engineering; fiber reinforced composites; engineered fabrics design and evaluation; biopolymers. *Mailing Add:* Pioneering Res Lab Du Pont Exp Sta Wilmington DE 19898

KOLLER, EARL LEONARD, b Brooklyn, NY, Dec 8, 31; m 56; c 2. PHYSICS. *Educ:* Columbia Univ, AB, 52, MA, 58, PhD(physics), 59. *Prof Exp:* Asst physics, Columbia Univ, 52-59; from instr to assoc prof physics, 59-69, PROF PHYSICS, STEVENS INST TECHNOL, 69- *Honors & Awards:* Ottens Res Award, 63. *Mem:* Am Phys Soc; Sigma Xi; Am Asn Univ Prof. *Res:* High energy nuclear physics, especially particle physics; investigation of strange particle and pi meson properties; K meson decays; pi-p, K-p, p-p and p-d interactions using the Fermilab 30 inch bubble chamber hybrid system; neutron interactions using bubble chamber techniques. *Mailing Add:* Dept of Physics Stevens Inst of Technol Hoboken NJ 07030

KOLLER, GLENN R, b Buffalo, NY, Nov 25, 51. GEOSTATISTICS. *Educ:* State Univ NY, Buffalo, BA, 73; Syracuse Univ, MS, 76, PhD(geol), 78. *Prof Exp:* Geologist, Savannah River Lab, Dept Energy, 78-80; MATH GEOLOGIST, AMOCO PROD RES, 80- *Res:* Mathematical and statistical manipulation of geologic data in the area of petroleum exploration. *Mailing Add:* 7409 S 77 East Ave Tulsa OK 74133

KOLLER, JAMES EDWARD, b Edgemont, SDak, July 30, 22; m 44; c 5. PHOTOGRAPHIC CHEMISTRY. *Educ:* Creighton Univ, BS, 47, MS, 49; Univ Nebr, PhD(chem), 53. *Prof Exp:* Instr chem, Creighton Univ, 47-51; res chemist, 53-73, supt, Film Emulsion Div, 73-75, asst mgr film mfg, 75-79, mgr paper mfg, 79-80, MGR FILM MFG, EASTMAN KODAK CO, 80- *Mem:* Soc Photog Scientists & Engrs. *Res:* Formulation of photographic emulsions. *Mailing Add:* Kodak Park Div Eastman Kodak Co Rochester NY 14650

KOLLER, NOEMIE, b Vienna, Austria, Aug 21, 33; US citizen; m 56; c 2. NUCLEAR PHYSICS, SOLID STATE PHYSICS. *Educ:* Columbia Univ, BA, 53, MA, 55, PhD(physics), 58. *Prof Exp:* Fel physics, Columbia Univ, 58-60; from asst prof to assoc prof, 60-70, PROF PHYSICS, RUTGERS UNIV, NEW BRUNSWICK, 70- *Mem:* Fel Am Phys Soc. *Res:* Spectroscopy of low lying nuclear levels; study of hyperfine interactions at nuclei in ionized atoms or in solids. *Mailing Add:* Dept of Physics Rutgers Univ New Brunswick NJ 08903

KOLLER, ROBERT DENE, b Sidney, Nebr, Mar 7, 45; m 66; c 1. PHYSICAL CHEMISTRY, STATISTICS. *Educ:* Univ Nebr, BS, 67, PhD(theoret chem), 72. *Prof Exp:* Anal chemist, Com Solvents Corp, 67 & 68; fel theoret chem, Mellon Inst, Carnegie Mellon Univ, 72-73; SR SCIENTIST CHEM, ROHM & HAAS CO, 73- *Mem:* Am Chem Soc. *Res:* The application of computer and statistical techniques for analysis of chemical problems arising in industrial research. *Mailing Add:* PO Box 245 Harleysville PA 19438

KOLLIG, HEINZ PHILIPP, b Bonn, Ger, May 19, 28; US citizen; m 51; c 2. ANALYTICAL CHEMISTRY, CLINICAL CHEMISTRY. *Educ:* Univ Bonn, Ger, BS, 50; Fla Inst Technol, BS, 69. *Prof Exp:* Chemist clin chem, Univ Bonn, Ger, 51-57; chemist power plant chem, City Bonn, Ger, 57-59; res chemist, Univ Ala, 59-60; anal chemist microanal, Southern Res Inst, 60-68; anal chemist environ health, TWA Kennedy Space Ctr, Fla, 68-71; RES CHEMIST WATER, US ENVIRON PROTECTION AGENCY, 71- *Mem:* Am Chem Soc; Am Phys Soc. *Res:* Ecology. *Mailing Add:* 250 Dogwood Hill NW Watkinsville GA 30677

KOLLMAN, GERALD EUGENE, plant physiology, see previous edition

KOLLMAN, PETER ANDREW, b Iowa City, Iowa, July 24, 44; m 70; c 1. THEORETICAL CHEMISTRY, BIOPHYSICAL CHEMISTRY. *Educ:* Grinnell Col, BA, 66; Princeton Univ, PhD(chem), 70. *Prof Exp:* NATO fel theoret chem, Cambridge Univ, 70-71; asst prof, 71-76, assoc prof, 76-80, PROF CHEM & PHARMACEUT CHEM, SCH PHARM, UNIV CALIF, SAN FRANCISCO, 80- *Concurrent Pos:* Career develop award, Nat Inst Gen Med Sci, 74. *Mem:* Am Chem Soc; Am Phys Soc; Sigma Xi. *Res:* Application of quantum mechanics and molecular mechanics to intermolecular interactions and to structure activity relationships in biological systems. *Mailing Add:* Dept of Pharmaceut Chem Univ of Calif San Francisco CA 94143

KOLLMANN, GEORGE, radiobiology, biochemistry, see previous edition

KOLLMORGEN, G MARK, b Bancroft, Nebr, June 23, 32; m 54; c 4. CELL BIOLOGY, IMMUNOLOGY. *Educ:* Univ Iowa, BA, 57, MA, 60, PhD(radiation biol), 63. *Prof Exp:* Instr biol sci, Univ Iowa, 58-60, instr radiation biol, 61-63; resident res assoc, Argonne Nat Lab, 63-65, asst biologist, 65-66; asst mem, Okla Med Res Found, 66-69; from asst prof to assoc prof, 66-74, PROF RADIOL, SCH MED, UNIV OKLA, 74-; assoc mem, 69-76, MEM OKLA MED RES FOUND, 76- *Mem:* Am Asn Cancer Res; Am Soc Cell Biol; Soc Exp Biol & Med; Tissue Cult Asn; Sigma Xi. *Res:* Effects of dietary fat on tumor incidence and immune responses; serum factors which inhibit immune responses; influence of prostaglandins on tumor growth and transplantability; effects of products derived from cyclooxygenase and lipoxygenase pathways on function of natural killer cells. *Mailing Add:* Okla Med Res Found 825 NE 13th St Oklahoma City OK 73104

KOLLROS, JERRY JOHN, b Vienna, Austria, Dec 29, 17; nat US; m 42; c 2. EMBRYOLOGY, CELL BIOLOGY. *Educ:* Univ Chicago, SB, 38, PhD(zool), 42. *Prof Exp:* Asst zool, Univ Chicago, 40-42, neurosurg, 43-45, toxicity lab, 45, instr zool, Col, 45-46; assoc, 46-47, from asst prof to assoc prof, 47-57, actg chmn, 54-55, chmn dept, 55-77, PROF ZOOL, UNIV IOWA, 57- *Concurrent Pos:* Consult, Am Col Dictionary & Random House Dictionary of the English Language; consult div inst progs, NSF, 64-66; mem cell biol study sect, NIH, 60-64, biol sci training rev comt, NIMH, 66-70; Comn Undergrad Educ Biol Sci, 67-71, chmn, 69-71. *Mem:* AAAS; Am Soc Cell Biol; Soc Develop Biol; Am Asn Anat; Am Soc Zool (treas, 59-62). *Res:* Control of skin gland development and segregation of skin regions; development of behavior in Amphibia; experimental embryology of amphibian central nervous system; amphibian metamorphosis; regeneration of Amphibia. *Mailing Add:* Dept of Zool Univ of Iowa Iowa City IA 52242

KOLM, HENRY HERBERT, b Vienna, Austria, Sept 10, 24; nat US; m 53; c 4. MAGNETISM. *Educ:* Mass Inst Technol, SB, 50, PhD(physics), 54. *Prof Exp:* Asst low temperature physics, 50-54, mem res staff, Lincoln Lab, 54-60, SR SCIENTIST & LECTR DEPT AERONAUT & ASTRONAUT, MASS INST TECHNOL NAT MAGNET LAB, 60- *Mem:* Am Phys Soc; Am Inst Aeronaut & Astronaut; Inst Elec & Electronic Engrs. *Res:* Hydrodynamics of liquid helium; semiconductor surface physics; cyclotron resonance in solids; design of pulsed and continous high-field solenoid magnets; superconductivity; magnetic separation; magnetic levitation and propulsion of high speed vehicles; applications of magnetism; piezoelectricity. *Mailing Add:* Weir Meadow Wayland MA 01778

KOLMAN, BERNARD, b Havana, Cuba, July 4, 32; US citizen; m 57; c 2. MATHEMATICS. *Educ:* Brooklyn Col, BS, 54; Brown Univ, ScM, 56; Univ Pa, PhD(math), 65. *Prof Exp:* Prin mathematician, Univac Div, Sperry Rand Corp, 57-64; asst prof, 64-68, assoc prof, 68-76, PROF MATH, DREXEL UNIV, 76- *Mem:* Am Math Soc; Math Asn Am; Soc Indust & Appl Math; Asn Comput Mach. *Res:* Lie algebras; operations research. *Mailing Add:* Dept of Math Drexel Univ 32nd & Chestnut St Philadelphia PA 19104

KOLMAN, WILFRED AARON, clinical pharmacology, biometrics, see previous edition

KOLMEN, SAMUEL NORMAN, b Brownsville, Tex, Mar 20, 30; m 54; c 2. PHYSIOLOGY. *Educ:* Univ Tex, BA, 54, PhD(physiol), 57. *Prof Exp:* From asst prof to prof physiol, Univ Tex Med Br Galveston, 58-75, head div physiol, Shriners Burns Inst, 68-70, res coordr, 70-75; PROF PHYSIOL & CHMN DEPT, SCH MED, WRIGHT STATE UNIV, 75-, PROG DIR, 81- *Concurrent Pos:* Kempner fel med, London Hosp Med Col, Univ London, 57-58; mem coun thrombosis, Am Heart Asn. *Mem:* AAAS; Soc Exp Biol & Med; Am Physiol Soc; Brit Biochem Soc; Microcirc Soc. *Res:* Adsorptive phenomena related to biological processes; fibrinogen metabolism, storage and distribution; lymphatic circulation; microcirculation; burn physiopathology. *Mailing Add:* Dept of Physiol Wright State Univ Sch of Med Dayton OH 45431

KOLNER, S(AMUEL) J(AMES), b Brooklyn, NY, July 26, 22; m 46; c 2. CHEMICAL ENGINEERING. *Educ:* Univ Fla, BS, 44. *Prof Exp:* Proj engr separation studies, Res & Develop Dept, 46-48, pilot plant supvr, 49-57, sect mgr polyolefin develop, 58-60, br mgr petrochem develop, 60-66, managing dir, Polyolefins NV, Antwerp, 66-68, dir polymer opers, Europe-Africa, 68-75; mgr polyolefin mfg, Phillips Petrol Co, 75-79; ADAMS TERMINAL PLANT MGR, 79- *Mem:* Am Inst Chem Engrs. *Res:* Evaluation and development of separation techniques and devices; development of processes for manufacture of petrochemicals and plastics. *Mailing Add:* 2303 College Green Houston TX 77058

KOLOBIELSKI, MARJAN, b Warsaw, Poland, Aug 17, 15; nat US; m 48; c 1. PETROLEUM CHEMISTRY, FUEL SCIENCE. *Educ:* Univ Lodz, MPhil, 48; Univ Paris, PhD(phys sci), 54. *Prof Exp:* Mem res staff, French Nat Ctr Sci Res, Ecole Normale Superieure, Paris, 49-55; fel org chem, Northwestern Univ, 55-56; res fel, Mellon Inst, 56-63; res chemist, Borden Chem Co, 63-64; res chemist, Coating & Chem Lab, Aberdeen Proving Ground, 64-74, RES CHEMIST, US ARMY MOBILITY EQUIP RES & DEVELOP CTR, 74- *Mem:* Am Chem Soc; Combustion Inst; Chem Soc Fr; Am Inst Chemists; Am Soc Testing & Mat. *Res:* Development of new products, fuels and lubricants. *Mailing Add:* 6710 Sherwood Rd Baltimore MD 21239

KOLODNER, IGNACE IZAAK, b Warsaw, Poland, Apr 12, 20; nat US; m 48, 68; c 3. MATHEMATICS. *Educ:* Univ Grenoble, Dipl, 40, NY Univ, PhD(math), 50. *Prof Exp:* Asst, Col Eng, NY Univ, 47-48, asst, Inst Math Sci, 48-51, res assoc, 51-53, sr scientist, 53-56; prof math, Univ NMex, 56-64; head dept, 64-71, PROF MATH, CARNEGIE-MELLON UNIV, 64- *Concurrent Pos:* Instr, Wash Sq Col, NY Univ, 48-51; lectr, Stevens Inst Tech, 50-53; consult, Underwater Mine Comt, Nat Res Coun, 55, Courant Inst Math Sci, 56-60, 69; Sandia Corp, 56-68 & Lawrence Radiation Lab, 60-67; vis mem, Math Res Ctr, Univ Wis-Madison, 62; sch math study group, Stanford Univ, 65; Fulbright lectr Universidad de la Republica, Montevideo, Uruguay, 67; Sussman vis prof, Israel Inst Technol, Haifa, 72-73; adj prof, Univ Pittsburgh, 76-77 & 78-79. *Mem:* Am Phys Soc; Am Math Soc; Math Asn Am; Soc Indust & Appl Math; Soc Natural Philos. *Res:* Differential equations; integral equations; mathematical physics. *Mailing Add:* Dept of Math Carnegie-Mellon Univ Pittsburgh PA 15213

KOLODNER, RICHARD DAVID, b Morristown, NJ, Apr 3, 51. MOLECULAR BIOLOGY. *Educ:* Univ Calif, Irvine, BS, 71, PhD(biol), 75. *Prof Exp:* res fel molecular biol, 75-78, ASST PROF BIOL CHEM, SCH MED & SIDNEY FARBER CANCER INST, HARVARD UNIV, 79- *Concurrent Pos:* Fel, Cystic Fibrosis Found, 75-76 & NIH, 76-78; jr fac res award, Am Cancer Soc, 81- *Res:* Mechanism of genetic recombination in procaryotes and eucaryotes; the biogenesis of mitochondria and chloroplasts; DNA structure. *Mailing Add:* 328 Commercial Ave # 34 Boston MA 02116

KOLODNY, GERALD MORDECAI, b Brookline, Mass, Apr 22, 37; m 64; c 3. RADIOLOGY. *Educ:* Harvard Univ, AB, 58; Northwestern Univ, Chicago, MD, 62; Am Bd Radiol, dipl, 67; Am Bd Nuclear Med, dipl, 74. *Prof Exp:* Intern med, Stanford Univ Med Ctr, 62-63; resident radiol, Mass Gen Hosp, 63-66; Picker Found fel biol, Mass Inst Technol, 66-69; asst radiol, Mass Gen Hosp, 69-71; from instr to asst prof, 69-75, ASSOC PROF RADIOL, HARVARD MED SCH, 75-; asst radiologist, Mass Gen Hosp, 71-75, assoc radiologist & dir, Radiol Res Lab, 75-79; DIR, DIV NUCLEAR MED, BETH ISRAEL HOSP, 79- *Concurrent Pos:* Picker Found grant, 69-71; res assoc biochem, Huntington Labs, Harvard Univ, 69-70, assoc chmn curric, Div Med Sci, 74- *Mem:* Am Soc Cell Biol; Tissue Cult Asn; Inst Elec & Electronics Engrs; Soc Nuclear Med; Radiol Soc NAm. *Res:* Gene regulation; RNA biochemistry; cell to cell communication; contact inhibition; electronics and computers in medicine; nuclear medicine; cellular radiation biology. *Mailing Add:* Div Nuclear Med Beth Israel Hosp Boston MA 02215

KOLODNY, NANCY HARRISON, b Brooklyn, NY, Mar 30, 44; m 64; c 3. PHYSICAL CHEMISTRY. *Educ:* Wellesley Col, BA, 64; Mass Inst Technol, PhD(phys chem), 69. *Prof Exp:* Dean class of 76, 72-74, dir, Sci Ctr, 74-77, ASST PROF CHEM, WELLESLEY COL, 69- *Concurrent Pos:* Radcliffe Inst scholar, 70-72; res fel med, Mass Gen Hosp, Boston, 71-72. *Mem:* Am Chem Soc. *Res:* Electron spin resonance spectroscopy of charge transfer complexes in solution; nuclear magnetic resonance spectroscopy of protein-nucleic acid interactions. *Mailing Add:* Dept of Chem Wellesley Col Wellesley MA 02181

KOLODZIEJ, BRUNO J, b Chicago, Ill, Aug 27, 34; m 58; c 3. MICROBIOLOGY, MICROBIAL PHYSIOLOGY. *Educ:* Northern Ill Univ, BSEd, 58; Northwestern Univ, MS, 60, PhD(biol), 63. *Prof Exp:* NIH fel microbial physiol, Univ Chicago, 63-65; res assoc, Albert Einstein Med Ctr, Pa, 65-66; asst prof, 66-71, ASSOC PROF MICROBIOL, OHIO STATE UNIV, 71- *Mem:* AAAS; Am Soc Microbiol; Sigma Xi. *Res:* Elucidation and characterization of bacterial cell surface components with emphasis on membrane binding-transport proteins associated with sugar and amino acid transport and structure and function of exocellular capsule material. *Mailing Add:* Dept of Microbiol Ohio State Univ Columbus OH 43210

KOLOGISKI, RUSSELL LEE, b Anderson, Ind, Aug 19, 46. PLANT ECOLOGY. *Educ:* Univ NC, Charlotte, BS, 71; NC State Univ, PhD(bot), 77. *Prof Exp:* Botanist, Ctr Natural Areas, Smithsonian Inst, 72-73; plant ecologist, Northern Prairie Wildlife Res Ctr, 76-80; ENDANGERED SPECIES BOTANIST, US FISH & WILDLIFE SERV, ALBUQUERQUE, NM, 80- *Mem:* Am Inst Biol Sci; Am Soc Plant Taxonomists; Ecol Soc Am. *Res:* Community plant ecology: pocosin vegetation, grasslands of the Northern Great Plains; rare and endangered plants of the Southwestern United States. *Mailing Add:* US Fish & Wildlife Serv PO Box 1306 Albuquerque NM 87103

KOLOR, MICHAEL GARRETT, b Brooklyn, NY, May 1, 34; m 57; c 4. FOOD CHEMISTRY, MASS SPECTROMETRY. *Educ:* Queen's Univ New York, BS, 56. *Prof Exp:* Res chemist, Res Ctr, Nat Dairy Corp, 56-59; assoc res chemist, 59-62, res chemist, 62-65, sr res chemist, 65-70, proj res leader, 70-72, res specialist, 72-78, SR RES SPECIALIST, TECH CTR, GEN FOODS CORP, 78- *Mem:* Am Soc Mass Spectrometry. *Res:* Mass spectrometry; gas chromatography; food and flavor chemistry; natural products chemistry; identification of volatile flavor components in foodstuffs. *Mailing Add:* Gen Foods Tech Ctr 555 S Broadway Tarrytown NY 10591

KOLP, BERNARD J, b Caroll, Iowa, Oct 20, 28; m 52; c 3. AGRONOMY, PLANT BREEDING. *Educ:* Iowa State Univ, BS, 54; Kans State Univ, MS, 55, PhD, 58. *Prof Exp:* Asst prof agron, 57-70, PROF PLANT BREEDING, UNIV WYO, 70- *Res:* Drought resistance and emergence of wheat; nitrate content in oats; winter hardiness in wheat. *Mailing Add:* Plant Sci Div Univ of Wyo Univ Sta Box 3354 Laramie WY 82070

KOLPAK, MIROSLAV MICHAL, b Czechoslovakia, Jan 30, 41; US citizen; m 67; c 2. OFFSHORE ENGINEERING. *Educ:* Cooper Union, BCE, 63; Mass Inst Technol, MS, 65, PhD(hydronamics), 70. *Prof Exp:* RES ASSOC OFFSHORE ENG, RES CTR, AMOCO PROD CO, 70- *Mem:* Soc Petrol Engrs. *Res:* Development of computer models for simulating hurricane generated winds, waves and currents, floating vessel moorings and responses in rough seas. *Mailing Add:* 8720 S 71 E Ave Tulsa OK 74133

KOLSKI, THADDEUS L(EONARD), b Chicago, Ill, Nov 29, 28; m 55; c 2. INORGANIC CHEMISTRY. *Educ:* Ill Inst Technol, BS, 50; St Louis Univ, MS, 54, PhD(inorg chem), 57. *Prof Exp:* RES CHEMIST, E I DU PONT DE NEMOURS, 56- *Concurrent Pos:* Ed, High-Solids Coatings, 79-81. *Res:* Oxidation of niobium and niobium alloys; anodic characteristics of tantalum and niobium; electrolytic capacitators; surface and boron chemistry; white and colored pigments. *Mailing Add:* 1116 Graylyn Rd Chatham Wilmington DE 19803

KOLSKY, HARWOOD GEORGE, b Portland, Ore, Jan 18, 21; m 42; c 4. PHYSICS, COMPUTER SCIENCE. *Educ:* Univ Kans, BS, 43, MS, 47; Harvard Univ, PhD(physics), 50. *Prof Exp:* Asst instr physics, Univ Kans, 46-47; mem staff, Weapons Div & Theoret Div, Los Alamos Sci Lab, 50-52, assoc group leader, Hydrodyn Group, Theoret Div, 52-57; sr planning rep prod planning, 57-59, proj coordr stretch comput, 59, asst mgr, 438 L Proj, Omaha, 59-60, mgr systs sci res lab, San Jose, 61-62, spec proj, Adv Systs Develop Lab, 62-64, univ prog, Palo Alto, 64-66, mgr atmospheric physics dept, 66-69, IBM FEL, IBM SCI CTR, IBM CORP, 69- *Mem:* Am Phys Soc; Asn Comput Mach; Inst Elec & Electronics Eng. *Res:* Digital computer application and design; compressible fluid hydrodynamics; nuclear moments by molecular beam technique; numerical meteorology. *Mailing Add:* 18950 Lynbrook Court Saratoga CA 95070

KOLSKY, HERBERT, b London, Eng, Sept 22, 16; m 45; c 3. PHYSICS, MECHANICS. *Educ:* Imp Col, Univ London, BSc, 37; Univ London, PhD(phys chem), 40, DSc(physics), 57. *Prof Exp:* Head dept physics, Akers Res Labs, Imp Chem Industs Ltd, 46-56; Fulbright vis prof eng, Brown Univ, 56-58; sr prin sci officer, Ministry Supply, UK, 58-60; PROF APPL PHYSICS, BROWN UNIV, 60- *Concurrent Pos:* Vis prof, Imperial Col, 68, METU, Ankara, 68, Oxford Univ, 74, Berkeley, 78 & ETH, Zurich, 78-79 & 80. *Mem:* Soc Eng Sci; Acoust Soc Am; fel Brit Inst Physics; Brit Soc Rheol (pres, 59-60); Am Soc Rheol. *Res:* Stress waves in solids; viscoelasticity; rate of strain effects in metals; dynamic fracture phenomena; experimental techniques; stress birefringence. *Mailing Add:* Div of Appl Math Brown Univ Providence RI 02912

KOLSRUD, GRETCHEN SCHABTACH, b Schenectady, NY, Jan 9, 39. GENETICS, HUMAN FACTORS ENGINEERING. *Educ:* McGill Univ, BSc, 60; Johns Hopkins Univ, MA, 63, PhD(psychol), 66. *Prof Exp:* Prin res scientist physiol psychol, Systs & Res Ctr, Honeywell Inc, 66-67; sr syst scientist human factors eng, Serendipity Inc, 67-71; staff scientist, BioTechnol Inc, 71-73; prog mgr, NASA, 73-74; prog mgr Transp Prog, 74-76, asst to dir, New & Emerging Technol, 76-78, actg group mgr, Health Group, 78, group mgr, genetics & pop, 78-81, MGR, HUMAN RESOURCES GROUP, OFF TECHNOL ASSESSMENT, US CONG, 81- *Concurrent Pos:* Consult, Flight Mgt Systs, 67 & Nat Hwy Traffic Safety Admin, 71. *Mem:* AAAS; Human Factors Soc (secy & treas, 74-75); NY Acad Sci; Sigma Xi. *Res:* Science policy; emerging technologies in biological sciences and in medicine; relationships between society and technology. *Mailing Add:* Off Technol Assessment US Cong Washington DC 20510

KOLSTAD, GEORGE ANDREW, b Elmira, NY, Dec 10, 19; m 44; c 3. NUCLEAR PHYSICS, EARTH SCIENCES. *Educ:* Bates Col, BS, 43; Yale Univ, PhD(physics), 48. *Prof Exp:* Asst physics, Wesleyan Univ, 43-44; res assoc radar, Harvard Univ, 44-45; spec asst physics, Yale Univ, 45-46, asst, 46-47, instr, 48-50; with physics & math prog, Div Res, US Atomic Energy Comn, 50-52, head, 52-73; sr physicist & head geosci prog, Div Phys Res, US Energy Res & Develop Admin, 73-77, SR PHYSICIST & HEAD GEOSCI PROG, OFF ENERGY RES, DIV ENG, MATH & GEOSCI, US DEPT OF ENERGY, 77- *Concurrent Pos:* Guest staff mem, Inst Theoret Physics, Copenhagen, 56-57; trustee, Bates Col, 58-64 & Laytonsville Elem Sch, 66-71; mem bd dirs, Sandy Springs Friends Sch, 71-77; mem, European-Am Nuclear Data Comt, 60-73; US del, Int Nuclear Data Comt, Int Atomic Energy Agency, 63-73, chmn, 70-72; mem, Fed Coun Sci & Technol, Ad Hoc Comt Int Geodyn Proj, 73-78; liaison mem, Geophys Res Bd, Nat Acad Sci, 73-, Geol Bd, 80- *Honors & Awards:* Spec Serv Award, US Atomic Energy Comn, 60. *Mem:* Fel Am Phys Soc; Am Geophys Union; Soc Explor Geophysicists. *Res:* Mass spectroscopy; radar countermeasures; a linear accelerator for the production of high intensity gamma rays and neutrons; earth sciences and solar-terrestrial physics. *Mailing Add:* 7920 Brink Rd Oak Hill Laytonsville MD 20760

KOLTHOFF, IZAAK MAURITS, b Almelo, Holland, Feb 11, 94; nat US. ANALYTICAL CHEMISTRY. *Educ:* State Univ Utrecht, PhD(chem), 18. *Hon Degrees:* DSc, Univ Chicago, 54; Dr, State Univ Groningen, 64; PhD, Brandeis Univ & The Hebrew Univ of Jerusalem, 74. *Prof Exp:* Conservator, Pharmaceut Inst, State Univ Utrecht, 17-27, privat docent appl electrochem, 24-27; prof & head div, 27-62, EMER PROF ANAL CHEM, UNIV MINN, MINNEAPOLIS, 62- *Concurrent Pos:* Hon prof, Lima & La Plata; consult, Phillips Petrol Co; chmn comt anal chem & mem comt Fulbright scholars, Nat Res Coun; vpres, Int Union Pure & Appl Chem. *Honors & Awards:* Comdr, Order of Orange-Nassau, 47; Nichols Medal, Am Chem Soc, 49, Fisher Award, 50 & Minn Award, 60; Charles Medal, Charles Univ, Prague; Willard Gibbs Medal, 64; Polarographic Medal, Brit Polarographic Soc, 64; first recipient, Kolthoff Gold Medal, Acad Pharmaceut Sci, 67; Olin-Palladium Medal Award, Electrochem Soc, 81. *Mem:* Nat Acad Sci; AAAS; Am Chem Soc; Electrochem Soc; Am Acad Arts & Sci. *Res:* Macromolecular compounds; physical chemistry; acid-base indicators; theory of acids and bases; volumetric analysis; potentiometric, conductometric and amperometric titrations; polarography; properties of crystalline precipitates; kinetics and mechanism of emulsion polymerization; nonaqueous chemistry; proteins. *Mailing Add:* Campus Club Univ of Minn Minneapolis MN 55455

KOLTUN, DANIEL S, b Brooklyn, NY, Dec 7, 33; m 56; c 2. THEORETICAL PHYSICS, NUCLEAR PHYSICS. *Educ:* Harvard Col, AB, 55; Princeton Univ, PhD(physics), 61. *Prof Exp:* Res assoc physics, Princeton Univ, 60-61; NSF vis fel nuclear physics, Weizmann Inst, 61-62 & Inst Theoret Phys, Copenhagen, 62; res assoc physics, 62-63, from asst prof to assoc prof, 63-74, PROF PHYSICS, UNIV ROCHESTER, 74- *Concurrent Pos:* Res assoc ctr theoret physics, Mass Inst Technol, 69-70; Alfred P Sloan res fel, 69-71; vis prof, Tel Aviv Univ, 76-77 & J S Guggenheim fel, 76-77. *Mem:* Am Phys Soc. *Res:* Theoretical nuclear spectroscopy; many-body theory; interaction of nuclei with mesons. *Mailing Add:* Dept of Physics & Astron Univ of Rochester Rochester NY 14627

KOLTUN, STANLEY PHELPS, b Bogalusa, La, Mar 5, 25; m 55; c 3. CHEMICAL ENGINEERING. *Educ:* La State Univ, BSChE, 48. *Prof Exp:* Chem engr, Proc Design Unit, 56-59, cost engr, Cost & Design Unit, 59-63, proj leader, Food Prod Invests, 63-70, res chem engr oilseed prod ees, 70-76, ACTING RES LEADER OILSEED PROD RES, SOUTHERN REGIONAL RES CTR, USDA, 76- *Honors & Awards:* Superior Serv Award, US Dept Agr, 76. *Mem:* Am Inst Chem Engrs; Nat Soc Prof Engrs; Am Oil Chemists' Soc; Asn Off Anal Chemists; Sigma Xi. *Res:* Detoxification and inactivation of aflatoxin contaminated oilseeds; oilseed solvent extraction; food dehy- dration; utilization of oilseed proteins as human food; oilseed meals; cottonseed; peanuts; sweetpotatoes; human nutrition; food safety. *Mailing Add:* Southern Regional Res Ctr PO Box 19687 New Orleans LA 70179

KOLTUN, WALTER LANG, b New York, NY, Apr 23, 28; m 62; c 2. BIOPHYSICAL CHEMISTRY. *Educ:* Mass Inst Technol, BS, 48, PhD(biochem), 52. *Prof Exp:* Asst biol, Mass Inst Technol, 51-52, res assoc, 52-53; asst prof biochem, Sch Med, Univ Va, 55-56; res assoc, Med Col, Cornell Univ, 56-59; consult biophysics, Univ Calif, Berkeley, 59-61; staff mem, Sci Resources Planning Off, NSF, 61-64, prog dir molecular biol, 64-65; spec asst, Off Vpres & Secy & Inst Secy for Found, Mass Inst Technol, 65-68; dir prog advan study, Bolt, Beranek & Newman, 68-70; ASST DIR RESOURCES, HARVARD-MASS INST TECHNOL HEALTH PROG, 70- *Mem:* AAAS; Fedn Am Sci; Am Soc Biol Chem. *Res:* Structure, function and interaction of macromolecules, particularly proteins. *Mailing Add:* Rm 26-142 Mass Inst Technol Cambridge MA 02139

KOLYER, JOHN M, b East Williston, NY, June 30, 33; m 60; c 4. ORGANIC CHEMISTRY, POLYMER CHEMISTRY. *Educ:* Hofstra Col, BA, 55; Univ Pa, PhD(org chem), 60. *Prof Exp:* Technician pesticides, Olin Mathieson Chem Corp, NY, 55-56; res chemist, FMC Corp, NJ, 60-62; res chemist, Thompson Chem Co, Mass, 62-63; sr res chemist, Plastics Div, Allied Chem Corp, 64-65, group leader, 65-67, tech supvr, Morristown, 67-71; MEM TECH STAFF, AUTONETICS DIV, ROCKWELL INT CORP, 73- *Concurrent Pos:* Mem, Lepidoptera Found, 65-73. *Mem:* Am Chem Soc; Lepidop Soc. *Res:* Preparation processes for plastics additives and monomers; polymerization processes and fabrication methods; polymer modifications; lepidopterological research. *Mailing Add:* Autonetics Div Rockwell Int Corp 3370 Miraloma Ave Anaheim CA 92803

KOMAI, LEO G, b Los Angeles, Calif, Dec 29, 25; m 52; c 4. LASERS. *Educ:* Univ Calif, Los Angeles, BA, 49, MA, 52, PhD(physics), 59. *Prof Exp:* Physicist, Hughes Aircraft Co, Calif, 57-61; sr physicist, Electro-Optical Systs, Inc, 61-62; asst mgr laser develop dept, 62-72, mgr laser develop dept, 72-77, chief scientist, Laser & Electro-Optical Syst Lab, Laser Syst Div, 77-80, CHIEF SCIENTIST, LASER ENG LAB, ELECTRO-OPTICAL ENG DIV, HUGHES AIRCRAFT CO, CULVER CITY, 80- *Res:* Laser range finder-designator development. *Mailing Add:* Hughes Aircraft Co 2000 E El Segundo Blvd El Segundo CA 90245

KOMANDURI, RANGACHARY, b India; US citizen; m 78. MATERIALS ENGINEERING. *Educ:* Osmania Univ, India, BE, 64, ME, 66; Monash Univ, Australia, PhD(mech eng), 72. *Prof Exp:* Res scholar mech eng, Monash Univ, Australia, 68-71; res engr & asst prof, Carnegie Mellon Univ, 72-77; SCI STAFF MAT & MFG ENG, CORP RES & DEVELOP, GEN ELEC CO, 77- *Concurrent Pos:* Consult, Samanta Metal Forming Corp, 74-76, Babcox & Wilcox, 76, Mat Characterization Ltd, Pittsburgh, 76 & Shepped Envelope Co, Mass, 77; adj prof mech eng, Rensselaer Polytech Inst, 78. *Honors & Awards:* F W Taylor Award, Int Inst Prod Eng Res, 77; Blackall Mach Tool & Gauge Award, Am Soc Mech Eng, 81. *Mem:* Am Soc Mech Engrs; assoc mem Inst Engrs India; corresp mem Int Inst Prod Eng Res. *Res:* Manufacturing research in grindings and machining; friction and wear; vibrations in machining; high speed machining; machining of difficult to machine superalloys. *Mailing Add:* Bldg K-1 Rm 4A37 Gen Elec Co Schenectady NY 12309

KOMAR, ARTHUR BARAWAY, b Brooklyn, NY, Mar 26, 31; m 52; c 2. THEORETICAL PHYSICS. *Educ:* Princeton Univ, AB, 52, PhD(physics), 56. *Prof Exp:* Fel, Scandinavian-Am Found, Inst Theoret Physics, Denmark, 56-57; asst prof physics, Syracuse Univ, 58-60, assoc prof, 60-63; dean, Belfer Grad Sch Sci, 69-78; assoc prof physics, Yeshiva Univ, 63-66, prof, 66-80. *Mem:* Am Phys Soc. *Res:* General relativity and quantum field theory. *Mailing Add:* 562 W 26th St New York NY 10471

KOMAR, PAUL D, b Grand Rapids, Mich, Dec 2, 39; m 62; c 1. OCEANOGRAPHY, MARINE GEOLOGY. *Educ:* Univ Mich, BA, 61, MS, 62 & 65; Univ Calif, San Diego, PhD(oceanog), 69. *Prof Exp:* Nato fel, Scripps Inst Oceanog, 69-70; asst prof, 70, assoc prof, 70-78, PROF OCEANOG, ORE STATE UNIV, 78- *Concurrent Pos:* Nato fel, Univ St Andrews, 69-71. *Mem:* Soc Econ Paleont & Mineral; Am Geophys Union; Geol Soc Am. *Res:* Transport of sand on beaches; mechanics of turbidity current flow. *Mailing Add:* Dept of Oceanography Ore State Univ Corvallis OR 97331

KOMARKOVA, VERA, b Pisek, Czech, Dec, 25, 42. PLANT ECOLOGY. *Educ:* Charles Univ, Czech, MSc, 64; Univ Colo, PhD(biol), 76. *Prof Exp:* RES ASSOC, INST ARTIC & ALPINE RES, UNIV COLO, BOULDER, 76-, ASST PROF, DEPT ENVIRON POP & ORGANISMIC BIOL, 79- *Concurrent Pos:* Prin investr, 79- *Mem:* AAAS; Am Inst Biol Sci; Ecol Soc Am; Int Soc Vegetation Sci. *Res:* Phytosociology; photogeography; vegetation mapping; methods of vegetation analysis; environment-vegetation relationship; community development; vegetation and environmental data management; effects of perturbation. *Mailing Add:* Inst Artic & Alpine Res Univ Colo Box 450 Boulder CO 80309

KOMARMY, JULIUS MICHAEL, b Franklin, NJ, Oct 19, 26; m 52; c 4. PHYSICAL CHEMISTRY, ORGANIC CHEMISTRY. *Educ:* Southwestern Mo State Col, BS, 49; Univ Ark, MS, 52, PhD, 58. *Prof Exp:* Asst chem, Univ Ark, 49-52, instr, 52-54, 56-67; instr, Flint Jr Col, 57-61; supvr chem, Res Dept, 61-65, supvr chem res, 65-66, RES SCIENTIST, AC SPARK PLUG DIV, GEN MOTORS CORP, 66- *Mem:* AAAS; Am Chem Soc; Soc Automotive Eng; Am Soc Testing & Mat. *Res:* Automotive applications of plastics and elastomers; fuels and lubricants and filtration processes; catalyst development for automotive exhaust environmental controls; materials development for fabrication of large liquid crystal displays. *Mailing Add:* 1636 Miller Rd Flint MI 48503

KOMINEK, LEO ALOYSIUS, b Chicago, Ill, Apr 11, 37; m 59; c 4. MICROBIOLOGY, BIOCHEMISTRY. *Educ:* St Joseph's Col, Ind, BS, 59; Univ Ill, PhD(microbiol), 64. *Prof Exp:* Res assoc, 64-72, sr scientist microbiol, 72-78, res mgr, 78-79, SR SCIENTIST, UPJOHN CO, 79- *Mem:* Am Soc Microbiol; Am Chem Soc; Sigma Xi; AAAS; NY Acad Sci. *Res:* Biochemical aspects of bacterial sporulation; microbial metabolism; antibiotic biosynthesis; steroid bioconversion. *Mailing Add:* Fermentation Res & Develop Upjohn Co 7000 Portage Rd Kalamazoo MI 49002

KOMINZ, DAVID RICHARD, b Rochester, NY, Apr 2, 24; div; c 3. PROTEIN CHEMISTRY. *Educ:* Univ Rochester, MD, 47; Harvard Univ, BA, 50. *Prof Exp:* Intern, Gorgas Hosp, CZ, 47-48; res fel phys chem lab, Harvard Univ, 50-51; from sr asst surgeon to med dir, Nat Inst Arthritis & Metab Dis, 51-65, chief, NIH Pac Off, Tokyo, 66-68, med dir, Nat Inst Arthritis, Metab & Digestive Dis, 68-76, chief sect bioenergetics, Lab Biophys Chem, 70-76; assoc dir, Nat Bladder Cancer Proj, 76-78; RES PROF PHYSIOL, UNIV MASS MED SCH, 78- *Mem:* AAAS; Am Chem Soc; Am Soc Biol Chem; Biophys Soc. *Res:* Amino acid analysis; comparative biochemistry of muscle proteins; protein modifications; biophysical studies of interactions of muscle proteins and muscle model systems. *Mailing Add:* Dept of Physiol 55 N Lake Ave Worcester MA 01605

KOMISARUK, BARRY RICHARD, b New York, NY, Apr 4, 41; m 61; c 2. PSYCHOBIOLOGY, NEUROPHYSIOLOGY. *Educ:* City Univ New York, BS, 61; Rutgers Univ, PhD(neuroendocrinol), 65. *Prof Exp:* NIMH fel neuroendocrinol, Univ Calif, Los Angeles, 65-66; asst prof zool, 66-68, assoc prof, 68-72, PROF ZOOL, RUTGERS UNIV, NEWARK, 72- *Concurrent Pos:* NIMH res grant, Rutgers Univ, Newark, 66-79, NIMH Res Scientist Develop Award, 69-79; NSF res grant, Rutgers Univ, Newark, 79- *Mem:* AAAS; Soc Neurosci; Endocrine Soc; Am Physiol Soc; Int Soc Psychoneuroendocrinol. *Res:* Neurophysiological bases of species characteristic, hormonally influenced behavior, analgesic mechanisms. *Mailing Add:* Inst of Animal Behav Rutgers Univ Newark NJ 07102

KOMKOV, VADIM, b Moscow, Russia, Aug 18, 19; US citizen; m 46; c 5. ENGINEERING MECHANICS, APPLIED MATHEMATICS. *Educ:* Polish Univ, Dipl Ing, 48; Univ Utah, PhD, 64. *Prof Exp:* Design engr mech eng, Dawson & Mason Co, 48-50, Wellmann, Smith & Owen Corp, 51-53 & Anglo-Am Corp, 53-57; asst prof, Univ Utah, 57-64; vis res prof, Math Res Ctr, Univ Wis, 64-65; assoc prof math, Fla State Univ, 65-69; prof math, Tex Tech Univ, 69-78; ed, Math Rev, 78-80; CHMN, DEPT MATH, WVA UNIV, 80- *Concurrent Pos:* Consult, US Army, 73-78. *Mem:* Am Inst Aeronaut & Astronaut; Am Math Soc. *Res:* Mathematical theory of elasticity; continuum mechanics; differential equations; non-standard analysis; control theory. *Mailing Add:* WVa Univ Morgantown WV 26506

KOMM, HORACE, b Russia, Dec 30, 16; nat US; m 47; c 3. MATHEMATICS. *Educ:* Univ Buffalo, BA, 37; Univ Mich, MA, 38, PhD(math), 42. *Prof Exp:* Structures engr, Curtiss-Wright Corp, 42-44, asst to chief mathematician, Res Lab, 44-46; instr math, Univ Rochester, 46-48, asst prof, 48-52; assoc prof, Univ of the South, 52-53; asst prof, Rensselaer Polytech Inst, 53-62; chmn dept, 71-77, PROF MATH, HOWARD UNIV, 71- *Mem:* Am Math Soc; Math Asn Am. *Res:* Dimension of partially ordered sets; general and algebraic topology. *Mailing Add:* Dept of Math Howard Univ Washington DC 20001

KOMMEDAHL, THOR, b Minneapolis, Minn, Apr 1, 20; m 51; c 3. PLANT PATHOLOGY. *Educ:* Univ Minn, BS, 45, MS, 47, PhD(plant path), 51. *Prof Exp:* With bur plant indust, USDA, 43-46; instr, Agr Exp Sta, Univ Minn, 46-51; asst prof, Agr Exp Sta, Ohio State Univ, 51-53; asst prof plant path, 53-57, assoc prof plant path, 57-63, PROF PLANT PATH, UNIV MINN, ST PAUL, 63- *Concurrent Pos:* Assoc ed, Am Phytopath Soc, 50-52, ed-in-chief, 64-66, coordr publ, 78-82; consult, botanist & taxonomist, Div Plant Indust, State Dept Agr, Dairy & Food, Minn, 54-60; Guggenheim fel, Waite Agr Res Inst, Australia, 61-62; Fulbright fel, Univ Iceland, 68; consult, McGraw-Hill Co. *Honors & Awards:* Award of Excellence, Weed Sci Soc Am, 64. *Mem:* Fel AAAS; Am Inst Biol Sci; Am Phytopath Soc (vpres, 69, pres, 71); Mycol Soc Am; Int Soc Plant Path. *Res:* Flax and corn diseases; weed ecology; root diseases and ecology of root-infecting fungi; biological control root diseases. *Mailing Add:* Dept of Plant Pathol 304 Stakman Hall Univ of Minn St Paul MN 55108

KOMORNICKI, ANDREW, b Louth, Eng, Oct 23, 48; US citizen. THEORETICAL CHEMISTRY. *Educ:* Univ Wis-Milwaukee, BS, 70; State Univ NY Buffalo, PhD(theoret chem), 74. *Prof Exp:* Res assoc, Univ Tex, Austin, 73-74 & Univ Rochester, NY, 74-76; Nat Res Coun assoc, Ames Res Ctr, NASA, Moffett Field, Calif, 76-78; RES SCIENTIST & PRES, POLYATOMICS RES INST, 78- *Concurrent Pos:* Samuel B Silbert fel, 72-73; Nat Res Coun fel, 76; mem, Bd Dir, Molecular Res Inst, Atherton, Calif, 79. *Mem:* Am Chem Soc; Am Phys Soc. *Res:* Theoretical chemistry; molecular quantum mechanics; molecular spectroscopy, infrared and raman vibrational intensities; dynamics of chemical reactions; author or coauthor of over 40 publications. *Mailing Add:* Polyatomics Res Inst Suite 420 1101 San Antonio Rd Mountain View CA 94043

KOMOROSKI, RICHARD ANDREW, b St Louis, Mo, Feb 4, 47. PHYSICAL CHEMISTRY, ANALYTICAL CHEMISTRY. *Educ:* St Louis Univ, BS, 69; Ind Univ, PhD(phys chem), 73. *Prof Exp:* Fel chem, Fla State Univ, 73-76; SR RES CHEMIST, DIAMOND SHAMROCK CORP, 76- *Mem:* Am Chem Soc; The Chem Soc; Soc Appl Spectros. *Res:* Nuclear magnetic resonance spectroscopy; structure of synthetic and biological macromolecules. *Mailing Add:* T R Evans Res Ctr PO Box 348 Painesville OH 44077

KOMOTO, ROBERT GORDON, b Ontario, Ore, Oct 23, 48. INDUSTRIAL ORGANIC CHEMISTRY, INORGANIC CHEMISTRY. *Educ:* Ore State Univ, BS, 70; Stanford Univ, PhD(inorg chem), 74. *Prof Exp:* CHEMIST, CHEVRON RES CO, STANDARD OIL CO CALIF, 74- *Mem:* Am Chem Soc. *Res:* Organometallic chemistry; homogeneous catalysis; synthetic polymer chemistry; pesticides. *Mailing Add:* Chevron Res Co 576 Standard Ave Richmond CA 94802

KOMYATHY, JOSEPH CHARLES, b Kulpmont, Pa, Oct 23, 22; m 52; c 7. INORGANIC CHEMISTRY, ANALYTICAL CHEMISTRY. *Educ:* City Col NY, BS, 47; Purdue Univ, MS, 49; Okla State Univ, PhD(chem), 53. *Prof Exp:* ANAL CHEMIST, TEXACO RES CTR, 52- *Mem:* Sigma Xi. *Res:* Analysis of petroleum products; development of analytical methods for petroleum products. *Mailing Add:* Texaco Res Ctr Beacon NY 12508

KONAR, AHMET FERIT, b Adapazari, Turkey, Aug 15, 30; m 59; c 3. ELECTRICAL ENGINEERING, CONTROL SYSTEMS. *Educ:* State Acad Istanbul, dipl, 52; Univ Mich, MS, 57 & 61; Univ Minn, PhD(control sci), 69. *Prof Exp:* Control engr, Seyhan Hydroelec Proj, 53-55; develop engr, Kuhlman Elec Co, Mich, 57-60, res mgr, 60-61; sr res scientist, MPG Res Lab, Honeywell, Inc, Minn, 62-64; asst prof elec eng & chmn dept, Mid East Tech Univ, Ankara, 64-65; prin scientist res dept, Systs & Res Div, Honeywell, Inc, Minn, Ankara, 69-70; sr prin scientist info sci, 70-73, proj staff scientist control sci, 73-77, SECT CHIEF SYSTS & CONTROL SCI, SYSTS & RES CTR, HONEYWELL, INC, 77- *Honors & Awards:* H W Sweatt Award, Digital Control, Honeywell, Inc, 73. *Mem:* Inst Elec & Electronics Engrs; Illum Eng Soc; Instrument Soc Am; Simulation Coun. *Res:* Computer controlled systems; optimal control and estimation; digital filtering; multisensor navigation. *Mailing Add:* Systs & Res Ctr Res Dept 2600 Ridgeway Pkwy Minneapolis MN 55413

KONDE, ANTHONY JOSEPH, b Passaic, NJ, Jan 15, 12; m 40; c 1. PHYSICAL CHEMISTRY. *Educ:* Trenton State Col, BS, 34; Columbia Univ, MA, 37; Fordham Univ, PhD, 63. *Prof Exp:* Sci teacher & chmn high schs, NJ, 35-42; from instr to prof chem, univ col, St John's Univ, NY, 42-62, chmn dept, 46-62; prof chem, Pace Univ, 62-70, Harold Blancke prof, 70-80, chmn dept, 64-80. *Concurrent Pos:* Instr chem, St Francis Col, NY & Panzer Col, 58-61. *Mem:* Fel Am Inst Chem; Am Chem Soc; NY Acad Sci; AAAS. *Res:* Chemical instrumentation; chemistry education. *Mailing Add:* 29 Great Hill Terrace Short Hills NJ 07078

KONDIS, THOMAS JOHN, b Munhall, Pa, Sept 14, 33; m 57; c 2. INDUSTRIAL CHEMISTRY. *Educ:* Duquesne Univ, BS, 55. *Prof Exp:* Res asst emission spectros, Mellon Inst Indust Res, 57-58; chief chemist, Res & Qual Control, Duquesne Brewing Co, 58-60; scientist anal chem, 60-62, scientist org finishes, 62-68, sr scientist powder & pigments, 68-76, STAFF SCIENTIST POWDER & FORGINGS, ALUMINUM CO AM, 76- *Honors & Awards:* IR 100 Award, Indust Res Mag, 75. *Mem:* Am Chem Soc; Tech Asn Pulp & Paper Indust; Sigma Xi. *Res:* Organo-aluminum compounds; physics and chemistry of aluminum powder; aluminum as an energy source in propellants, explosives and blasting agents; aluminum surface chemistry and lubrication. *Mailing Add:* Alcoa Labs Alcoa Center PA 15069

KONDO, EDWARD SHINICHI, b Victoria, BC, Sept 5, 39; m 70; c 1. FOREST PATHOLOGY. *Educ:* Univ Toronto, BScF, 64, MScF, 66, PhD(plant path), 70. *Prof Exp:* Res officer, 69-71, RES SCIENTIST FOREST PATH, CAN FORESTRY SERV, DEPT ENVIRON, 71- *Concurrent Pos:* Adj prof, Forestry Fac, Univ Toronto, 72-74. *Res:* Vascular wilt tree diseases; Dutch elm disease; urban forestry; tree and fungus physiology, mycology, chemotherapy of tree diseases. *Mailing Add:* Can Forestry Serv Box 490 Dept of Environ Sault Ste Marie ON P6A 5M7 Can

KONDO, NORMAN SHIGERU, b Honolulu, Hawaii, Oct 30, 41; m 71; c 1. ORGANIC CHEMISTRY. *Educ:* Univ Hawaii, BA, 63; Univ Calif, Riverside, PhD(chem), 67. *Prof Exp:* Res assoc biophys, Argonne Nat Lab, 71-73; asst prof chem, Fed City Col, 73-77; ASSOC PROF CHEM, UNIV DC, 77- *Concurrent Pos:* NIH fel, Johns Hopkins Univ, 67-69 & fel, 69-71; NIH grant, Fed City Col, Univ DC, 75- *Mem:* Am Chem Soc; Biophys Soc. *Res:* Synthesis and conformational studies on nucleic acid constituents. *Mailing Add:* Dept of Chem Univ of the DC Washington DC 20005

KONDO, YOJI, b Hitachi, Japan, May 26, 33; US citizen; m 65; c 3. ASTRONOMY, ASTROPHYSICS. *Educ:* Tokyo Univ Foreign Studies, BA, 58; Univ Pa, MS, 63, PhD(astron), 65. *Prof Exp:* Nat Acad Sci res assoc astron & space sci, Goddard Space Flight Ctr, 65-68, astronr, 68-69, chief astrophys sect, Johnson Space Ctr, 69-77, ASTROPHYSICIST, GODDARD

SPACE FLIGHT CTR, NASA, 78- *Concurrent Pos:* Mem adj grad fac, Univ Houston, 68-74, adj prof, 74-77; adj assoc prof, Univ Okla, 71-72, adj prof, 72-; ed, Earth & Extraterrestrial Sci, 74-79 & Comments Astrophysics, 79-; adj prof, Univ Pa, 78-; consult, NASA Hq, 81-82. *Mem:* AAAS; Am Astron Soc; Int Astron Union. *Res:* Astronomical observations from space; interacting close binary stars; interstellar medium; active galactic nuclei. *Mailing Add:* Lab Astron & Solar Physics Code 683 Goddard Space Flight Ctr Greenbelt MD 20771

KONDO, YOSHIO, b Kaeleku, Hawaii, Oct 26, 10; m 32; c 1. ZOOLOGY. *Educ:* Univ Hawaii, BA, 40, MA, 47; Harvard Univ, PhD, 55. *Prof Exp:* Asst malacol, 35-42, asst malacologist, 43-50, terrestrial malacologist, 50-55, chmn dept zool, 69-74, malacologist, 56-80, EMER MALACOLOGIST, BERNICE P BISHOP MUS, 80- *Concurrent Pos:* Pac Sci Bd Achatina Res, 49-52; Guggenheim fel, 53-55; spec consult, US Army, US Navy & Bd Agr & Forestry, Hawaii, 57-; mem expeds, Mangarevan, 34, Micronesian, 35-36, Henry G Lapham Exped, Fiji, 38, Hawaii-Philippines Sulu, 57, Solomon Islands & Juan Fernandez, 66, New Hebrides, Tonga & Samoa, 67, Loyalty & Fiji Islands, 68 & Marquesas, 69. *Mem:* Soc Syst Zool; Soc Study Evolution; Am Malacol Union; Sigma Xi. *Res:* Anatomy of Tornatellinidae-Achatinellidae; anatomy of Partulidae; anatomy of Amastridae. *Mailing Add:* Bishop Mus PO Box 19000 A Honolulu HI 96819

KONDRA, PETER ALEXANDER, b Mikado, Sask, July 30, 11; m 39; c 3. POULTRY GENETICS. *Educ:* Univ Man, BSA, 34, MSc, 43; Univ Minn, PhD(poultry genetics), 53. *Prof Exp:* Poultry inspector, Man Dept Agr, 36-40; asst poultry, Univ Man, 40-43, mgr hatchery, 44-45; asst poultry specialist, Man Dept Agr, 45-46; from asst prof to assoc prof poultry sci, Univ Man, 46-64, prof poultry sci, 64-78. *Concurrent Pos:* Mem poultry breeding comt, Can Dept Agr, 53-; exchange scientist, Acad Sci, USSR, 64, adv, Thailand 68-69, Brazil, 74 & Costa Rica, 78. *Mem:* Poultry Sci Asn; World Poultry Sci Asn; Genetics Soc Can; Agr Inst Can. *Res:* Poultry breeding biology; incubation; housing. *Mailing Add:* 60 Purdue Ft Garry Winnipeg MB R3T 3C7 Can

KONECCI, EUGENE B, b Chicago, Ill, Jan 7, 25; m; c 2. MEDICAL PHYSIOLOGY. *Educ:* Roosevelt Univ, BS, 48; Univ Bern, PhD(med physiol), 50. *Prof Exp:* Res scientist, US Air Force Sch Aviation Med, 50-56; chief physiol & toxicol & develop eng inspector, I G Norton AFB, Calif, 56-57; chief life sci, Douglas Aircraft Co, 57-62; dir human factor systs, Off Advan Res & Tech Hqs, NASA, Washington, DC, 62-64, sr prof staff mem manned space flight, spacecraft & missions, Nat Aeronaut & Space Coun, Exec Off Pres, 64-66; PROF MGT, AEROSPACE ENG & CLIN MED & ALICE G K KLEBERG PROF INTERDISCIPLINARY RES, UNIV TEX, AUSTIN, 66- *Concurrent Pos:* Mem staff, US Air Force Command & Staff Sch, Maxwell AFB, Ala, 52; chmn bioastronaut comt, Int Astronaut Fedn, 62-65; academician, Int Acad Astronaut, Paris, 65-; mem bd dirs, Appl Devices Corp, New York, 67-71, SysteMed, Inc, Newport Beach, Calif, 68-71 & Applied Solar Energy Corp, 79-; founder & pres, Inteck Assocs, 68-71; co-founder, Amerigenics Inc, 75- & Pangea Inc, 77- *Honors & Awards:* John Jeffries Award, 64. *Mem:* Am Astronaut Soc (pres, 68-69); assoc fel Am Inst Aeronaut & Astronaut; Am Soc Cybernet; Radiation Res Soc; Aerospace Indust Life Sci Asn. *Res:* Research and development management. *Mailing Add:* Grad Sch of Bus Univ of Tex BEB-203F Austin TX 78712

KONECKY, MILTON STUART, b Omaha, Nebr, July 29, 22; m 48; c 2. ORGANIC CHEMISTRY. *Educ:* Creighton Univ, BS, 44, MS, 48; Univ Ill, PhD(chem), 58. *Prof Exp:* Chemist, Omaha Grain Exchange Labs, Nebr, 47-50; chemist pesticide chem res br, Entom Res Div, USDA, Md, 50-54; sr chemist, 57-60, res assoc, 61-63, sect head, 63-69, SR STAFF ADV, EXXON RES & ENG CO, 69- *Mem:* AAAS; Sigma Xi; Am Chem Soc; NY Acad Sci. *Res:* Agricultural chemicals; petrochemicals; olefin and diolefin utilization; biodegradation methods for and synthesis of detergents; industrial, trade sales and specialty resins for surface coatings; heterogeneous catalysis. *Mailing Add:* Exxon Res & Eng Co PO Box 121 Linden NJ 07036

KONECNY, JAN, b Prague, Czech, Apr 20, 28; nat US; m 55; c 2. PHYSICAL BIOCHEMISTRY. *Educ:* Cornell Univ, BA, 50; Univ Calif, PhD(chem), 54. *Prof Exp:* Asst chem, Univ Calif, 50-53; instr, Reed Col, 53-54; instr, Wash State Univ, 54-56; chemist, US Naval Ord Lab, 56-57 & Shell Develop Co, 58-63; chemist, 63-66, SR SCIENTIST, CIBA-GEIGY LTD, SWITZ, 66- *Concurrent Pos:* Ford Found fel, Reed Col, 53-54. *Mem:* Swiss Soc Microbiol. *Res:* Chemical kinetics; immobilization of enzymes; isolation characterization of enzymes and their applications. *Mailing Add:* Ciba-Geigy Ltd Werk Klybeck Basel Switzerland

KONEN, HARRY P, b Dayton, Ky, Sept 18, 40; m 71. NUMERICAL ANALYSIS. *Educ:* St Thomas Univ, BA, 62; Tex A&M Univ, MS, 65, PhD(math), 67. *Prof Exp:* Instr math, San Jacinto Col, 66-69; asst prof, 69-74, ASSOC PROF MATH, SAM HOUSTON STATE UNIV, 74- *Mem:* Soc Indust & Appl Math; Math Asn Am; Asn Comput Mach; Sigma Xi. *Res:* Fifth-order Runge-Kutta methods for the numerical solution of differential equations. *Mailing Add:* Dept of Math Sam Houston State Univ Huntsville TX 77341

KONETZKA, WALTER ANTHONY, b Pa, Sept 8, 23; m 49; c 4. MICROBIAL PHYSIOLOGY. *Educ:* Univ Md, BS, 50, MS, 52, PhD(bact), 54. *Prof Exp:* Asst, Univ Md, 50-51; fel, Walter Reed Army Med Ctr, 52-54; microbiologist, Merck & Co, 54-55; from asst prof to prof bact, Ind Univ, Bloomington, 55-66; prof biol sci, Univ Md, Baltimore County, 66-68; PROF MICROBIOL, IND UNIV, BLOOMINGTON, 68- *Mem:* AAAS; Am Soc Microbiol; Brit Soc Gen Microbiol. *Res:* Microbial metabolism of environmentally important molecules; mutagenesis in bacteria resulting from metabolic conversions; magnetotaxis in bacterial cells. *Mailing Add:* Dept of Biol Jordan Hall Ind Univ Bloomington IN 47401

KONG, JIN AU, b Kiangsu, China, Dec 27, 42; US citizen; m 70; c 2. ELECTRICAL ENGINEERING. *Educ:* Nat Taiwan Univ, BS, 62; Chiao Tung Univ, MS, 65; Syracuse Univ, PhD(elec eng), 68. *Prof Exp:* Res engr elec eng, Syracuse Univ, 68-69; asst prof, 69-73, assoc prof, 73-80, PROF ELEC ENG, MASS INST TECHNOL, 80- *Concurrent Pos:* Vinton Hayes fel eng, Mass Inst Technol, 69-71; consult remote sensing technol, Off Tech Coop, UN, 77-79, Raytheon Co, Lincoln Lab & Hughes Aircraft Co, 80. *Mem:* Inst Elec & Electronics Engrs; Am Phys Soc; Optical Soc Am; Am Geophys Union; Am Soc Eng Educ. *Res:* Electromagnetic Wave Theory. *Mailing Add:* 36-383 Mass Inst of Technol Cambridge MA 02139

KONG, YI-CHI MEI, b Boston, Mass, Feb 2, 34; c 2. IMMUNOLOGY, MICROBIOLOGY. *Educ:* Wellesley Col, BA, 55; Univ Mich, MS, 57, PhD(microbiol), 61. *Prof Exp:* Res assoc, Univ Mich, 60-61; asst res bacteriologist, Naval Biol Lab, Univ Calif, Berkeley, 61-66; from asst prof to assoc prof, 66-77, PROF IMMUNOL & MICROBIOL, SCH MED, WAYNE STATE UNIV, 77- *Concurrent Pos:* Mem immunol sci study sect, NIH, 74-77 & bacteriol mycol study sect, 81-84. *Mem:* AAAS; Transplantation Am Soc Microbiol; Am Asn Immunologists. *Res:* Mechanisms of immunologic tolerance; transplantation antigens and immunity; immunogenetic and cellular control of autoimmunity; effect of adjuvants. *Mailing Add:* Dept of Immunol & Microbiol Wayne State Univ Sch of Med Detroit MI 48201

KONHAUSER, JOSEPH DANIEL EDWARD, b Ford City, Pa, Oct 5, 24; m 48; c 1. MATHEMATICS. *Educ:* Pa State Univ, BS, 48, MA, 51, PhD(math), 63. *Prof Exp:* Instr math, Pa State Univ, 50-55; sr engr, HRB-Singer, Inc, 55-61, staff mathematician, 61-65; assoc prof math, Univ Minn, Minneapolis, 65-68, assoc dir col geom proj, Minnemath Ctr, 66-68; assoc prof, 68-70, chmn dept, 69-81, PROF MATH, MACALESTER COL, 70- *Mem:* Am Math Soc; Math Asn Am; The Math Asn. *Res:* Applied mathematics; geometry; biorthogonal polynomial sets. *Mailing Add:* Dept of Math Macalester Col St Paul MN 55105

KONHEIM, ALAN G, b Brooklyn, NY, Oct 17, 34; m 57; c 2. MATHEMATICS. *Educ:* Polytech Inst Brooklyn, BEE, 55, MS, 57; Cornell Univ, PhD(math), 60. *Prof Exp:* Res staff mem math, Thomas J Watson Res Lab, 60-69, res staff mem, IBM Res Lab, Switz, 69-74, mem staff, 74-77, RES STAFF MEM, THOMAS J WATSON RES LAB, IBM CORP, 77- *Mem:* Am Math Soc; Math Asn Am; Soc Indust & Appl Math. *Res:* Probability theory; harmonic analysis. *Mailing Add:* Thomas J Watson Res Lab IBM Corp PO Box 218 Yorktown Heights NY 10598

KONICEK, DONALD E, b Buhl, Idaho, Mar 26, 29; c 2. PLANT PATHOLOGY. *Educ:* Univ Idaho, BS, 53, MS, 57; Ore State Univ, PhD(plant path, nematol), 61. *Prof Exp:* Asst plant path, Ore State Univ, 60-61; NEMATOLOGIST PLANT PATH, CALIF STATE DEPT AGR, 61- *Mem:* Am Phytopath Soc; Soc Nematol. *Res:* Regulatory plant pathology; nematology. *Mailing Add:* 3712 Thornwood Dr Sacramento CA 95821

KONIG, RONALD H, b Albany, NY, Aug 12, 32. STRUCTURAL GEOLOGY, ECONOMIC GEOLOGY. *Educ:* St Lawrence Univ, BS, 54; Cornell Univ, MS, 56, PhD(geol), 59. *Prof Exp:* From asst prof to assoc prof, 59-71, chmn dept geol, 71-80, PROF, UNIV ARK, FAYETTEVILLE, 71- *Mem:* Geol Soc Am; Soc Econ Geol. *Res:* Areal geologic mapping; geologic investigation of mineral deposits. *Mailing Add:* Dept of Geol Univ of Ark Fayetteville AR 72701

KONIGSBACHER, KURT S, b Switz, , 23; nat US; m 45; c 2. ORGANIC CHEMISTRY, BIOCHEMISTRY. *Educ:* Dartmouth Col, BA, 44; Swiss Fed Inst Technol, DrSc Tech, 49. *Prof Exp:* Group leader org chem, Foster D Snell, Inc, 49-50; group leader, Evans Res & Develop Corp, 50-57, assoc develop mgr, 57-60, develop mgr, 60-63, vpres, 63-68, sr vpres, 68-69; vpres, Foster D Snell, Inc, Booz, Allen & Hamilton, Inc, 69-74; vpres opers, William T Thompson Co, 74-75; VPRES, HERBERT V SHUSTER, INC, 75- *Concurrent Pos:* Guest lectr, NY Univ, 55. *Mem:* Am Chem Soc; Am Inst Chem; Inst Food Technol; NY Acad Sci; Am Soc Testing & Mat. *Res:* Biochemistry of foods and food products; product development; pharmaceuticals; market research; enzymes; dehydrated and intermediate moisture compressed foods; canless sterilization of foods; performance testing; cosmetics; health and beauty aids. *Mailing Add:* 128 Dogwood Lane Stamford CT 06903

KONIGSBERG, ALVIN STUART, b New York, NY, Apr 28, 43; m 66; c 2. ATMOSPHERIC SCIENCE, BIOMETEOROLOGY. *Educ:* City Col NY, BS, 63; Syracuse Univ, MS, 65, PhD(physics), 69. *Prof Exp:* Res assoc physics, Atmospheric Sci Res Ctr, State Univ NY, Albany, 65; teaching asst, Syracuse Univ, 63-68; from asst prof to assoc prof, 68-77, chmn dept physics, 77-79, DIR INNOVATIVE STUDIES, STATE UNIV NY COL NEW PALTZ, 79- *Concurrent Pos:* Aeronaut & Space res fel, NASA & Am Asn Eng Educ, 73 & 74. *Mem:* AAAS; Am Asn Physics Teachers. *Res:* Oxidant pollution; condensation nuclei studies; light scattering instrumentation; alternate energy systems. *Mailing Add:* Dept Geol Sci State Univ of NY Col New Paltz NY 12561

KONIGSBERG, IRWIN R, b Brooklyn, NY, May 6, 23; m 54; c 2. DEVELOPMENTAL BIOLOGY. *Educ:* Brooklyn Col, BA, 48; Johns Hopkins Univ, PhD(biol), 52. *Prof Exp:* Jr instr biol, Johns Hopkins Univ, 49-51; asst prof, Lab Chem Embryol, Sch Med, Univ Colo, 52-58; biologist, Geront Br, NIH, Baltimore City Hosps, 58-61; staff mem, Dept Embryol, Carnegie Inst Washington, 61-66; prof, 66-77, COMMONWEALTH PROF BIOL, UNIV VA, 77-; RES ASSOC, DEPT EMBRYOL, CARNEGIE INST WASHINGTON, 66- *Concurrent Pos:* Assoc prof, Johns Hopkins Univ, 64-66; instr, Embryol Training Prog, Marine Biol Lab, 66-68; mem molecular biol study sect, Div Res Grants, NIH, 66-70. *Mem:* AAAS; Am Asn Anatomists; Am Soc Zoologists; Am Soc Cell Biol; Soc Develop Biol. *Res:* Regulation of proliferation and differentiation of embryonic muscle cells in culture; regeneration of adult muscle fibers; properties of myoblasts from regenerating normal and dystrophic muscle. *Mailing Add:* 1714 Kenwood Lane Charlottesville VA 22901

KONIGSBERG, MOSES, b Montreal, Que, Can, Sept 21, 12; nat US; m 39; c 2. ORGANIC CHEMISTRY. *Educ:* Ohio State Univ, AB, 35, PhD(org chem), 39. *Prof Exp:* Atlas Powder Co fel, Ohio State Univ, 39-40; res chemist, Nat Starch Prod, Inc, NY, 40-46; res chemist & vpres, Polymer Industs, Inc, 46-54, vpres res & develop, 54-58, commercial develop, 58-61; VPRES & TECH DIR, HUDSON INDUSTS CORP, 61- *Mem:* AAAS; Am Chem Soc; NY Acad Sci. *Res:* Natural and synthetic polymers; industrial adhesives. *Mailing Add:* Hudson Industries Corp 19 Hutton Ave West Orange NJ 07052

KONIGSBERG, WILLIAM HENRY, b New York, NY, Apr 5, 30; m 56; c 1. BIOCHEMISTRY. *Educ:* Rensselaer Polytech Inst, BSc, 52; Columbia Univ, PhD(chem), 56. *Prof Exp:* Asst prof biochem, Rockefeller Inst, 58-64; assoc prof biochem, 64-74, assoc prof molecular biophys & biochem & human genetics, 74-77, PROF MOLECULAR BIOPHYS & BIOCHEM & HUMAN GENETICS, YALE UNIV, 77- *Res:* Protein chemistry; structure of hemoglobin; structure and function of proteins, peptides and natural products; antibodies; virus proteins. *Mailing Add:* Dept of Biochem Yale Univ Sch of Med New Haven CT 06510

KONIJN, HENDRIK SALOMON, b Amsterdam, Netherlands, Mar 17, 18; nat US. STATISTICS, ECONOMICS. *Educ:* Columbia Univ, MA, 42; Univ Calif, PhD(statist), 54. *Prof Exp:* Jr staff mem, Nat Bur Econ Res, NY, 41-42; statistician, Combined Shipping Adj Bd, DC, 42-45; res analyst, Off Strategic Servs, 45 & Off Far Eastern Affairs, US Dept State, 45-47, statist consult econ res, Univ Calif, 53-54; lectr agr econ, Univ Calif Berkeley, 54-56; sr lectr econ statist, Sydney, 56-61; vis assoc prof, Cowles Found, Yale Univ, 61-62; vis prof statist, Univ Minn, 62-63; prof, City Col NY, 63-65; PROF STATIST, TEL-AVIV UNIV, 65- *Mem:* Fel AAAS; fel Am Statist Asn; Economet Soc; Inst Math Statist; Royal Statist Soc. *Res:* Statistical methodology; econometric studies. *Mailing Add:* Dept of Statist Tel-Aviv Univ 69978 Tel Aviv Israel

KONIKOFF, JOHN JACOB, b Philadelphia, Pa, May 1, 21; m 44; c 2. BIOMEDICAL ENGINEERING, CLINICAL PHARMACOLOGY. *Educ:* Drexel Univ, BSME, 55; Union Grad Sch, PhD(biomed eng sci), 72. *Prof Exp:* Proj engr, US Naval Air Mat Ctr, 42-46, specialist chem & pyrotechnics, US Naval Air Develop Ctr, 47-49; sr mech engr, Philco Corp, 49-50; chief develop engr, Thermal Res & Eng Corp, 50-56; mgr phys biol opers, Space Sci Lab, Gen Elec Co, 56-64, consult scientist, Res & Eng Dept, 65-70; res instr, Jefferson Med Col, 68-71, res asst prof physiol & orthop surg, 71-75, RES ASSOC PROF, DEPT ORTHOP SURG, JEFFERSON MED COL, THOMAS JEFFERSON UNIV, 76-, CONSULT ORTHOP SURGEON, 71-; SR CLIN RES SCIENTIST, HOFFMANN-LA ROCHE INC, 73- *Concurrent Pos:* Deleg, Int Astronaut Fedn Cong, Athens, Greece, 65 & New York, 68, Int Fedn Med & Biol Eng, Stockholm, 67; consult prof, La State Univ, 69-70; consult scientist, Gen Elec Co, 70-73; consult coop wildlife res unit, Pa State Univ, 71-73; consult scientist, 78- *Honors & Awards:* Aerospace Appln Award, Am Inst Aeronaut & Astronaut, 70; Breakthrough 60 Award, Gen Elec Co, 60. *Mem:* AAAS; Am Soc Clin Pharm & Therapeut; Soc Biomed Eng; Sigma Xi; NY Acad Sci. *Res:* Role bioelectric potentials play in mediating homeostasis, particularly studies related to wound repair enhancement and tissue regeneration; development of artificial tendons; biomedical instrumentation; investigation of safety and efficacy of new and investigational drugs in man. *Mailing Add:* 32 Fenton Dr Short Hills NJ 07078

KONIKOW, LEONARD FRANKLIN, b Far Rockaway, NY, Jan 26, 46; m 66; c 2. HYDROLOGY, GEOLOGY. *Educ:* Hofstra Univ, BA, 66; Pa State Univ, MS, 69, PhD(geol), 73. *Prof Exp:* Geologist, Geraghty & Miller Inc, 66; instr geol, Hofstra Univ, 66; HYDROLOGIST, US GEOL SURV, 72- *Concurrent Pos:* Assoc ed, Water Resource Res. *Mem:* Geol Soc Am; Am Geophys Union. *Res:* Transport and dispersion of solutes in flowing ground water. *Mailing Add:* US Geol Surv 431 National Ctr Reston VA 22092

KONINGSTEIN, JOHANNES A, b Velsen, Netherlands, Nov 30, 33; Can citizen; m 59; c 2. CHEMISTRY, CHEMICAL PHYSICS. *Educ:* Univ Amsterdam, Drs & Dr(chem), 65. *Prof Exp:* Fel, Nat Res Coun Can, 59-62; mem res staff, Bell Tel Labs, 62-65; from asst prof to assoc prof, 65-72, PROF CHEM, CARLETON UNIV, 72- *Concurrent Pos:* Vis prof, Nat Res Coun Can, 69- *Mem:* Am Phys Soc; Chem Inst Can. *Res:* Molecular and atomic research; electronic Raman spectroscopy. *Mailing Add:* Dept of Chem Carleton Univ Ottawa ON K1S 5B6 Can

KONISHI, FRANK, b Ft Lupton, Colo, Dec 2, 28; m 50; c 3. NUTRITION. *Educ:* Colo State Univ, BS, 50, MS, 52; Cornell Univ, PhD(animal nutrit), 58. *Prof Exp:* Asst, Colo State Univ, 50-52 & Cornell Univ, 52-54, 57-58; radiobiologist, US Naval Radiol Defense Lab, 58-61; assoc prof nutrit, 61-65, chmn dept, 65-77, PROF NUTRIT, SOUTHERN ILL UNIV, CARBONDALE, 66-, PROF, SCH MED, 74- *Mem:* Am Inst Nutrit; Am Dietetic Asn; Soc Exp Biol & Med; Am Pub Health Asn; NY Acad Sci. *Res:* Nutritional dietary surveys; obesity; energy metabolism. *Mailing Add:* Div of Human Develop Southern Ill Univ Carbondale IL 62901

KONISHI, MASAKAZU, b Kyoto, Japan, Feb 17, 33. BIOLOGY. *Educ:* Hokkaido Univ, BS, 56, MS, 58; Univ Calif, Berkeley, PhD(zool), 63. *Prof Exp:* Alexander von Humboldt Found fel, 63-64; Int Brain Res Orgn-UNESCO fel, 64-65; asst prof zool, Univ Wis, 65-66; from asst prof to assoc prof biol, Princeton Univ, 70-75; prof biol, 75-79, BING PROF BEHAV BIOL, CALIF INST TECHNOL, 79- *Honors & Awards:* Newcomb Cleveland Prize, AAAS, 78. *Mem:* AAAS; Am Soc Zoologists; Am Soc Naturalists; Acoust Soc Am; Soc Neurosci. *Res:* Behavior and neurobiology. *Mailing Add:* Calif Inst of Technol Div of Biol 216-76 Pasadena CA 91125

KONISKY, JORDAN, b Providence, RI, Apr 8, 41; m 67; c 2. MICROBIAL PHYSIOLOGY. *Educ:* Providence Col, BA, 63; Univ Wis, Madison, PhD(genetics), 68. *Prof Exp:* Res assoc genetics, Univ Wis, Madison, 68; NIH fel molecular biophys & biochem, Yale Univ, 68-70; asst prof, 70-75, assoc

prof, 75-81, PROF MICROBIOL, UNIV ILL, URBANA, 81- *Honors & Awards:* Career Develop Award, NIH, 75. *Mem:* Am Soc Microbiol; AAAS. *Res:* Effects of colicins on bacteria; regulation of gene expression in bacteria; functions of bacterial membrane. *Mailing Add:* Dept of Microbiol Univ of Ill Urbana IL 61801

KONIZER, GEORGE BURR, b Wilmington, Del, Dec 24, 42; m 66; c 2. PHYSICAL ORGANIC CHEMISTRY. *Educ:* Univ Del, BA, 64, MBA, 76; Univ SC, PhD(chem), 69. *Prof Exp:* Res chemist, Dacron Res Lab, 69-71 & Textile Res Lab, 71-75, sr res chemist, Textile Res Lab, 75-78, supvr res & develop orlon, 78-81, SUPVR RES & DEVELOP NYLON, E I DU PONT DE NEMOURS & CO, INC, 81- *Concurrent Pos:* Fel, State Univ NY Col Forestry, Syracuse Univ, 68-69. *Mem:* Am Chem Soc; Sigma Xi. *Res:* Fiber research. *Mailing Add:* 2008 N Brailsford Rd Camden SC 29020

KONKEL, DAVID ANTHONY, b Washington, DC, Feb 20, 48; m 70. RECOMBINANT DNA, MOLECULAR GENETICS. *Educ:* Boston Col, BS, 70; Mass Inst Technol, PhD(biochem), 77. *Prof Exp:* Asst biochem, Dept Biol, Mass Inst Technol, 70-77; staff fel, Lab Molecular Genetics, Nat Inst Child & Human Develop, 77-80; ASST PROF CELL BIOL, DEPT HUMAN GENETICS & CELL BIOL, UNIV TEX MED BR GALVESTON, 80- *Concurrent Pos:* Prin investr grants, NSF, 80-83 & NIH, 82-84. *Mem:* AAAS; Sigma Xi. *Res:* Recombinant DNA technology to study the structure and regulation of genes encoding human hexosaminidase isotymes A and B and those encoding chicken myoglobin. *Mailing Add:* Dept Human Genetics & Cell Biol Div Cell Biol Univ Tex Med Br Galveston TX 77550

KONKEL, PHILIP M, b Brush, Colo, May 5, 12; m 36. PETROLEUM GEOLOGY. *Educ:* Univ Wyo, BA, 34, MA, 35. *Prof Exp:* Geologist, Ohio, 40-55, asst chief geologist, 55-61, geologist, Tulsa Div, 61-65, explor mgr, 65-74, EXPLOR CONSULT, 74- *Mem:* Am Asn Petrol Geologists; Soc Explor Geophys. *Res:* Petroleum exploration. *Mailing Add:* 3153 E 38th St Tulsa OK 74105

KONKLE, GEORGE MELVIN, b Sebewaing, Mich, Sept 4, 19; m 42; c 5. CHEMISTRY. *Educ:* Mich State Univ, BS, 41. *Prof Exp:* Chemist, Frederick Stearns & Co, 41-42; mgr, Silastic Sect, Prod Eng Labs, 46-65, gen mat develop, 65-68, tech dir, Chem Prod Div, 68-69, mgr fluids, Tech Serv & Develop, 69-71, mgr tech support, 71-75, mgr corp res, 75-80, MGR ANAL DEPT, DOW CORNING CORP, 80- *Mem:* Am Chem Soc; AAAS. *Res:* Silicones; elastomers. *Mailing Add:* Dow Corning Corp Midland MI 48640

KONNEKER, WILFRED R, b Akron, Ohio, Feb 20, 22; m 46; c 1. MEDICAL PHYSICS, NUCLEAR PHYSICS. *Educ:* Ohio Univ, BS, 43, MS, 46; Univ Wash, PhD(physics), 50. *Prof Exp:* Sr res chemist, Monsanto Co, 46; instr physics, Ohio Univ, 46-47 & Univ Wash, 47-50; vpres nuclear res & develop div, Nuclear Corp Am, 50-55, vpres, NJ, 55-58; pres, Nuclear Consult Corp, 58-66; vpres & gen mgr, Nuclear Div, 66-69, Diag Div, 69-70, vpres & gen mgr, New Ventures Div, 70-74, CONSULT, MALLINCKRODT CHEM WORKS, INC, 74- *Concurrent Pos:* Mem, Mo State AEC, 60-75; spec adv, US AEC, 69 & 70. *Mem:* Am Phys Soc; Am Nuclear Soc; Health Physics Soc; Am Asn Physicists in Med; Soc Nuclear Med. *Res:* Application of radiant energy to the medical field; nuclear instrumentation. *Mailing Add:* RR 2 Kiefer Creek Rd Manchester MO 63011

KONNER, MELVIN JOEL, biological anthropology, behavioral biology, see previous edition

KONNERTH, KARL LOUIS, b Mt Pleasant, Pa, Aug 15, 32. MEDICAL ELECTRONICS, BIO-MEDICAL ENGINEERING. *Educ:* Carnegie Inst Technol, BS, 54, MS, 55, PhD(elec eng), 61. *Prof Exp:* Asst prof elec eng, Carnegie Inst Technol, 61-64; staff res engr, Thomas J Watson Res Ctr, 64-74, mgr, I/O Systs, IBM Res Div, 74-77, MGR ADVAN TECHNOL, IBM BIOMED SYSTS, IBM CORP, 77- *Honors & Awards:* Outstanding Innovation Award, IBM Corp, 76. *Mem:* Sr mem Inst Elec & Electronic Engrs; Asn Advan Med Instrumentation. *Res:* Investigation of new types of bio-medical instrumentation. *Mailing Add:* IBM Biomed Systs 110 S Bedford Rd Mt Kisco NY 10549

KONNERUP, NELS MILLARD, veterinary public health, see previous edition

KONO, TETSURO, b Tokyo, Japan, May 17, 25; m 61; c 3. PHYSIOLOGY, BIOCHEMISTRY. *Educ:* Univ Tokyo, BA, 47, PhD(anal chem), 58. *Prof Exp:* Instr agr chem, Univ Tokyo, 47-58 & 60-63; from asst prof to assoc prof, 63-74, PROF PHYSIOL, SCH MED, VANDERBILT UNIV, 74- *Mem:* Japanese Biochem Soc; Am Soc Biochem. *Res:* Mechanism of insulin action. *Mailing Add:* Dept of Physiol Vanderbilt Univ Sch of Med Nashville TN 37232

KONONENKO, OLEG K, b Kharkov, Ukraine, Sept 5, 18; m 39; c 2. ORGANIC CHEMISTRY, PHARMACEUTICAL CHEMISTRY. *Educ:* State Univ Kharkov, Chemist, 39; Ukrainian Tech Univ, Ger, PhD, 49. *Prof Exp:* Res chemist & lectr, Ukrainian Pharmaceut Inst, 39-41; supt, Lab Pharmaceut Prod, 41-43; res chemist, Inst Chem Tech, Ukrainian Acad Sci, 43-44; lab asst, Berg & Huetten, AG, 44-45; teacher pub sch, Allendorf, 45-47; assoc prof org & pharmaceut chem, Ukrainian Tech Univ, Germany, 47-51; chem operator, S B Penick & Co, 51-52; res chemist, Allied Chem & Dye Corp, 52-54; chief chemist, Herstein Labs, Inc, 54-61, pres, 61-77; SPEC LECTR, NJ INST TECHNOL, 77- *Res:* Synthetic organic chemistry; intermediates; pharmaceuticals; fine organics; high polymers; polyurethanes; sucrochemistry; analytical and physical chemistry; custom synthesis and development of rare organics, inorganics and biochemicals. *Mailing Add:* 1019 Birch St Boonton NJ 07005

KONOPKA, ALLAN EUGENE, b Chicago, Ill, Feb 26, 50; m 73; c 2. MICROBIOLOGY. *Educ:* Univ Ill, Urbana, BS, 71; Univ Wash, MS, 73, PhD(microbiol), 75. *Prof Exp:* Res assoc microbiol, Univ Wis-Madison, 75-77; ASST PROF BIOL, PURDUE UNIV, 77- *Mem:* Am Soc Microbiol; Am Soc Limnol & Oceanog; Phycol Soc Am. *Res:* Microbial ecology; physiological ecology of planktonic blue-green algae; buoyancy regulation by procaryotic microorganisms. *Mailing Add:* Dept of Biol Sci Purdue Univ West Lafayette IN 47907

KONOPKA, EDWARD ALEXANDER, b Newark, NJ, Oct 13, 19; m 45; c 3. BACTERIOLOGY. *Educ:* Univ Ky, BS, 42. *Prof Exp:* Microbiologist growth factors, Merck & Co, NJ, 45-47; dir diag lab, Montclair Biochem Lab, 47-48; sr bacteriologist microbial chemother, 48-63, assoc dir chemother, 63-67, head bacterio-mycol, 67-75, mgr microbiol, 75-78, DIR MICROBIOL RES, CIBA PHARMACEUT CO, 78- *Mem:* Soc Indust Microbiol; fel Am Acad Microbiol; Am Soc Microbiol; Sigma Xi; NY Acad Sci. *Res:* General chemotherapy; tuberculosis; leprosy; medical mycology; experimental antimicrobial chemotherapy and general bacteriology; parasitology. *Mailing Add:* Ciba-Geigy Corp 556 Morris Ave Summit NJ 07901

KONOPKA, RONALD J, b Cleveland, Ohio, Oct 19, 47. NEUROBIOLOGY. *Educ:* Univ Dayton, BS, 67; Calif Inst Technol, PhD(biochem), 72. *Prof Exp:* Fel biol, Stanford Univ, 72-74; ASST PROF BIOL, CALIF INST TECHNOL, 74- *Concurrent Pos:* NSF fel, 72-73; mem sci adv bd, Found Res Hereditary Dis, 72-; Helen Hay Whitney fel, 73-74. *Mem:* AAAS; Genetics Soc Am. *Res:* Circadian rhythm; behavior genetics of Drosophila. *Mailing Add:* Beckman Behav Biol Lab Calif Inst of Technol Pasadena CA 91125

KONORT, MARK D, b Sliven, Bulgaria, Nov 20, 18; nat US; m 52; c 2. ORGANIC CHEMISTRY. *Educ:* Univ Toulouse, DiplIngChim, 40; Rutgers Univ, MS, 50, PhD(org chem), 52. *Prof Exp:* Chemist, Matam Corp, 42-44; develop chemist, R J Prentiss & Co, 47; asst, Rutgers Univ, 48-52; sr res chemist, 52-56, prin res chemist, 56-59, res assoc, 59-63, sr res assoc, 63-72, res scientist, 72-81, SR RES SCIENTIST, LEVER BROS CO, 81- *Mem:* Am Chem Soc; Sigma Xi. *Res:* Lubricating and cutting oils; insecticides; substituted phenanthrenes and hydrophenanthrenes; detergents; edible products; organic synthesis. *Mailing Add:* Lever Bros Co 45 River Rd Edgewater NJ 07020

KONOWALOW, DANIEL DIMITRI, b Cleveland, Ohio, Apr 28, 29; m 78. THEORETICAL CHEMISTRY. *Educ:* Ohio State Univ, BS, 53; Univ Wis, PhD(chem), 61. *Prof Exp:* Chemist, Plastics Dept, E I du Pont de Nemours & Co, Del, 60-62; asst dir Theoret Chem Inst, Univ Wis, 62-65; asst prof, 65-69, assoc prof, 69-80, PROF CHEM, STATE UNIV NY BINGHAMTON, 80- *Mem:* Am Chem Soc; AAAS; Am Phys Soc. *Res:* Calculation and correlation of physical properties of atoms and molecules by quantum-mechanical methods; intramolecular and intermolecular interactions; theoretical spectroscopy. *Mailing Add:* Dept of Chem State Univ of NY Binghamton NY 13901

KONRAD, DUSAN, b Brno, Czech, Jan 7, 35; US citizen; m 72; c 2. ELECTROCHEMISTRY. *Educ:* Masaryk Univ, Czech, MS, 57; Czech Acad Sci, PhD(chem), 62. *Prof Exp:* Instr inorg chem, Masaryk Univ, Czech, 57-62; res scientist phys chem, J Heyrovsky Inst Polarography, Czech Acad Sci, 63-66; res chemist, Govt Assay Off, Czech, 67-68; sr res fel, Rudjer Boskovic Inst, Yugoslavia, 68-69; res fel chem, Calif Inst Technol, 70-71; sr scientist electrochem, Technol Ctr, ESB Inc, Yardley, Pa, 71-78; MEM TECH STAFF, TEX INSTRUMENTS, INC, DALLAS, 78- *Mem:* Electrochem Soc. *Res:* Electrochemical instrumentation; automatized data taking and processing; electrode impedance in Laplace plane analysis; electrochemistry of lead-acid cell; non-stoichiometric oxide electrodes; porous electrodes; computer software systems. *Mailing Add:* Tex Instruments Inc MS 145 PO Box 225936 Dallas TX 75265

KONRAD, GERHARD T(HIES), b Konigsberg, Ger, Feb 23, 35; US citizen; m 64; c 2. ELECTRICAL ENGINEERING. *Educ:* Univ Mich, BSE, 57, MSE, 60, PhD(elec eng), 69. *Prof Exp:* Asst res engr, Univ Mich, 60-61, assoc res engr, 61-69; staff mem, Lincoln Lab, Mass Inst Technol, 69-72; staff mem, 72-77, HEAD KLYSTRON DEPT, STANFORD LINEAR ACCELERATOR CTR, 77- *Concurrent Pos:* Consult, Litton Indust, 79- & Valvo, Ger, 78- *Mem:* Inst Elec & Electronics Engrs; Am Phys Soc; Nat Soc Prof Engrs; Sigma Xi. *Res:* Electron devices; microwave circuits; electron optics; high-voltage techniques; vacuum techniques; plasma physics; electromagnetic theory. *Mailing Add:* Stanford Linear Accelerator Ctr PO Box 4349 MS 30 Stanford CA 94305

KONRAD, JOHN GREY, soil chemistry, water chemistry, see previous edition

KONRAD, MICHAEL WARREN, molecular biology, see previous edition

KONRADI, ANDREI, space physics, see previous edition

KONSLER, THOMAS RHINEHART, b Henderson, Ky, Apr 17, 25; m 54; c 8. HORTICULTURE. *Educ:* Univ Ky, BS, 55; NC State Univ, MS, 57, PhD(exp statist), 61. *Prof Exp:* From asst prof to assoc prof, 60-78, PROF HORT SCI, MOUNTAIN HORT CROPS RES STA, NC STATE UNIV, 78- *Mem:* Am Soc Hort Sci; Biomet Soc. *Res:* Cultural practices and plant breeding with vegetable crops. *Mailing Add:* Mountain Hort Crops Res Sta RR 2 Fletcher NC 28732

KONSTAM, AARON HARRY, b Bronx, NY, Aug 11, 36; m 61. COMPUTER SCIENCES, PROGRAMMING LANGUAGES. *Educ:* Polytech Inst Brooklyn, BS, 57; Pa State Univ, PhD(phys org chem), 61. *Prof Exp:* Instr chem, Brooklyn Col, 61-62; fel & res assoc phys org chem, Israel Inst Technol, 62-64; sr res chemist, Monsanto Res Corp, 65-69; dir comput ctr & assoc prof math, Lindenwood Cols, 69-72; ASSOC PROF COMPUT SCI, TRINITY UNIV, 72- *Concurrent Pos:* Treas, 77-80, vpres, Vanguard Systs Corp, 80- *Mem:* AAAS; Asn Comput Mach. *Res:* Artificial intelligence, computer assisted instruction and programming languages. *Mailing Add:* Box 273 Trinity Univ San Antonio TX 78284

KONTOS, HERMES A, b Lefka, Cyprus, Dec 13, 33; US citizen; m 60; c 2. MEDICINE, PHYSIOLOGY. *Educ:* Nat Univ Athens, MD, 58; Med Col Va, PhD(physiol), 67; Am Col Physicians, dipl, 69. *Prof Exp:* From instr to assoc prof, 64-72, PROF MED, MED COL VA, 72-, CHMN DIV CARDIO PULMONARY MED, 81- *Concurrent Pos:* USPHS res career develop award, 67-72; Markle scholar acad med, 69-74. *Mem:* Am Fedn Clin Res; Am Heart Asn; Am Physiol Soc; Am Soc Clin Invest. *Res:* Circulatory physiology and pathophysiology. *Mailing Add:* Dept of Med Med Col of Va Richmond VA 23298

KONTRAS, STELLA B, b Newport News, Va, June 28, 28; m 47; c 3. PEDIATRICS, GENETICS. *Educ:* Ohio State Univ, BA, 48, MA, 49, MD, 53. *Prof Exp:* Intern med, 54, instr pediat, 54-60, asst prof pediat & anat, 60-66, assoc prof pediat, 66-69, PROF PEDIAT, COL MED, OHIO STATE UNIV, 69- *Concurrent Pos:* Resident pediat, Ohio State Univ, 55 & 56, resident path, 57-58; consult, Ohio Dept Health, 62-70; NIH spec fel cancer, Ohio State Univ, 63-64; dir, Med Genetics Ctr, Children's Hosp, Columbus, 65-71, vchmn, Dept Pediat, 80. *Mem:* Soc Pediat Res; Am Soc Hemat; Am Soc Human Genetics. *Res:* Hematology. *Mailing Add:* Dept of Pediat Ohio State Univ Col of Med Columbus OH 43210

KONYA, CALVIN JOSEPH, b Cleveland, Ohio, June 23, 43. MINING ENGINEERING, BLASTING. *Educ:* Mo Sch Mines, BS, 66; Univ Mo-Rolla, MS, 68 & 70, PhD(mining eng), 72. *Prof Exp:* From asst prof to assoc prof mining eng, WVa Univ, 71-78; assoc prof, 78-81, PROF MINING ENG & CHMN DEPT, OHIO STATE UNIV, 81- *Concurrent Pos:* Mgr tech servs, Precision Blasting Servs, 73-78; exchange scientist, Nat Acad Sci, 75. *Mem:* Soc Explosives Engrs (pres, 75-77); Am Inst Mining, Metall & Petrol Engrs. *Res:* Rock mechanics; explosives engineering. *Mailing Add:* Mining Eng Prog Ohio State Univ Columbus OH 43210

KONZ, STEPHAN A, b Milwaukee, Wis, Nov 25, 33; m 58; c 5. INDUSTRIAL ENGINEERING. *Educ:* Univ Mich, BS, 56, MBA, 56; Univ Iowa, MS, 60; Univ Ill, PhD(indust eng), 64. *Prof Exp:* Indust engr, Westinghouse Elec Corp, 56-57 & Collins Radio Co, 58-60; instr mech & indust eng, Univ Ill, 60-64; from asst prof to assoc prof, 64-69, PROF INDUST ENG, KANS STATE UNIV, 69- *Mem:* Am Inst Indust Engrs; Human Factors Soc; Am Soc Qual Control; Am Indust Hyg Asn; Am Soc Heat, Refrig & Air-Conditioning Engrs. *Res:* Human factors, especially design of industrial jobs; heat stress; inspection. *Mailing Add:* Dept of Indust Eng Kans State Univ Manhattan KS 66506

KONZAK, CALVIN FRANCIS, b Devils Lake, NDak, Oct 17, 24; div; c 2. GENETICS, PLANT BREEDING. *Educ:* NDak Agr Col, BS, 48; Cornell Univ, PhD, 52. *Prof Exp:* Assoc geneticist, Dept Biol, Brookhaven Nat Lab, 51-57; assoc prof & assoc agronomist, 57-62, PROF AGRON & AGRONOMIST, WASH STATE UNIV, 62-, PROF GENETICS, 66- *Concurrent Pos:* Spec adv plant breeding & genetics sect, Joint Food & Agr Orgn-Int Atomic Energy Agency Div Food & Agr, Vienna, 65-67; Food & Agr consult, Crop Res & Introd Ctr, Izmir, Turkey, 71; sci adv, Plant Breeding & Genetics Sect, Joint Food & Agr Orgn-Int Atomic Energy Agency Div Atomic Food & Agr, 73-74. *Mem:* AAAS; Genetics Soc Am; fel Am Soc Agron; Crop Sci Soc Am; Radiation Res Soc. *Res:* Breeding semidwarf oats for improved yield and tolerance to barley yellow dwarf virus; genetics of reduced height and other traits in wheat; induction of useful mutations in wheat and oats; development and application of electronic data capture and management systems for plant breeding; agronomic crop research. *Mailing Add:* Dept of Agron & Soils Wash State Univ Pullman WA 99163

KONZELMAN, LEROY MICHAEL, b Jersey City, NJ, May 27, 36; m 60; c 3. ORGANIC CHEMISTRY. *Educ:* St Peter's Col, NJ, BSc, 58; Seton Hall Univ, MSc, 64, PhD(org chem), 66. *Prof Exp:* Chemist, Schering Corp, NJ, 60-65; res chemist, 66-72, group leader dyes & intermediates dept, 72-74, CHIEF CHEMIST DYES & INTERMEDIATES MFG DEPT, AM CYANAMID CO, BOUND BROOK, 74- *Mem:* Am Chem Soc; NY Acad Sci; Sigma Xi. *Res:* Process and product development of organic dyes, their intermediates, and a variety of associated industrial intermediates. *Mailing Add:* 61 Elm St Flourham Park NJ 07932

KONZO, SEICHI, b Tacoma, Wash, Aug 2, 05; m 32; c 2. MECHANICAL ENGINEERING. *Educ:* Univ Wash, BS, 27; Univ Ill, MS, 29. *Prof Exp:* Asst mech eng, 27-32, res assoc, 32-34, res asst prof, 34-36, res assoc prof, 36-40, res prof, 40-47, prof, 47-71, assoc head dept, 63-70, EMER PROF MECH ENG, UNIV ILL, URBANA, 71- *Concurrent Pos:* Consult, Ill State Geol Surv; coordr eng teachers prog, Ford Found; eng consult, 71- *Honors & Awards:* F Paul Anderson Medal, Am Soc Heat, Refrig & Air-Conditioning. *Mem:* Am Soc Eng Educ; Am Soc Heat, Refrig & Air-Conditioning Engrs; Am Soc Mech Engrs. *Res:* Heating and heat transfer; air conditioning; fluid flow; combustion. *Mailing Add:* Small Homes Coun-Bldg Res Coun Univ of Ill Urbana IL 61820

KOO, BENJAMIN, b Shanghai, China, Apr 4, 20; US citizen. STRUCTURAL ENGINEERING, APPLIED MECHANICS. *Educ:* St John's Univ, BS, 41; Cornell Univ, MS, 42, PhD(struct eng), 46. *Prof Exp:* Struct engr, 42-55; engr concrete & found sect, M H Treadwell Co, 55-61; proj engr, Am Car & Foundry Div, ACF Industs, 61-65; PROF CIVIL ENG, UNIV TOLEDO, 65- *Mem:* Am Soc Civil Engrs; Am Soc Eng Educ; Am Concrete Inst; Sigma Xi. *Res:* Structural reliability in reinforced concrete members and frames; traile train freight car patent; cushioned underframe system patent. *Mailing Add:* Dept of Civil Eng Univ of Toledo Toledo OH 43606

KOO, DELIA WEI, b Hankow, China, May 14, 21; US citizen; m 43; c 3. MATHEMATICS, STATISTICS. *Educ:* St John's Univ, China, BA, 41; Radcliffe Col, AM, 42, PhD(eng philol), 47; Mich State Univ, MA, 54. *Prof Exp:* Instr math, Mich State Univ, 55-56; lectr, Douglass Col, Rutgers Univ, 56-57; instr, Mich State Univ, 57-58; from asst prof to assoc prof, 65-77, PROF MATH, EASTERN MICH UNIV, 77- *Mem:* Math Asn Am; Inst Math Statist; Economet Soc. *Mailing Add:* Dept of Math Eastern Mich Univ Ypsilanti MI 48197

KOO, FRANCIS KEH SHING, b Kiating, China, Oct 21, 14; US citizen; m 48. GENETICS, RADIOBIOLOGY. *Educ:* Nantung Univ & Nat Szechwan Univ, BS, 38; Univ Minn, PhD(plant genetics), 50. *Prof Exp:* Asst agronomist, Szechwan Agr Exp Sta, instr, Tsingmukwan High Sch & head, Farm Mgt & Rural Indust Div, Farmer's Bank China, 38-44; res asst, Univ Minn, 50-51, res fel, 51-53, joint proj leader, Oats & Rye Improv Projs, 53-61; PROF BIOL, UNIV PR, MAYAGUEZ, 61-; HEAD & SR SCIENTIST, TROP AGRO-SCI DIV, PR NUCLEAR CTR, 68- *Concurrent Pos:* Assoc scientist, Trop Agro-Sci Div, PR Nuclear Ctr, 61-67, chief scientist, 68. *Mem:* AAAS; Genetics Soc Am; Radiation Res Soc. *Res:* Genetics, cytogenetics and breeding of crop plants; genetic recombination mechanism; seed radiobiology; effect of multiple ionization in genetic systems; environmental mutagenesis. *Mailing Add:* Ctr for Energy & Environ Res Col Sta Mayaguez PR 00708

KOO, GLORIA CHAN, b Chunking, China, Nov 22, 44; US citizen. IMMUNOLOGY, ELECTRON MICROSCOPY. *Educ:* Goshen Col, BA, 65; Temple Univ, PhD(immunol), 70. *Prof Exp:* Med technologist, RI Hosp, 66-67; fel immunogenetics, 70-72, res assoc, 72-74, ASSOC IMMUNOGENETICS, MEM SLOAN-KETTERING INST, 74- *Concurrent Pos:* Asst prof, Med Col, Cornell Univ, 75- *Honors & Awards:* Fac Res Award, Am Cancer Soc, 78. *Res:* Immunobiology, immunogenetics, and reproductive biology. *Mailing Add:* Mem Sloan-Kettering Cancer Ctr 1075 York Ave New York NY 10021

KOO, PETER H, b Shanghai, China; US citizen; m 67; c 2. CANCER IMMUNOLOGY & BIOLOGY. *Educ:* Univ Wash, BA, 64; Univ Md, PhD(biochem), 70. *Prof Exp:* Fel immunol, Johns Hopkins Univ, 71-74; staff fel, NIH, 74-75; asst prof oncol, Johns Hopkins Univ, 75-77; ASST PROF IMMUNOL & MICROBIOL, COL MED, NORTHEASTERN OHIO UNIV, 77- *Concurrent Pos:* Asst prof, Dept Chem, Kent State Univ, 78-, asst prof, Dept Biol, 80-; prin investr, Nat Cancer Inst, NIH, 78-, Am Cancer Soc, 78-79 & Pediat of Akron, Inc, 78-79. *Mem:* Sigma Xi; NY Acad Sci; AAAS. *Res:* Structure and function of Alpha-2 macroglobulins; characterization of nonspecific tumor cytotoxic soluble factors in serum; characterization of immunological parameters in spontaneous regression of cancer. *Mailing Add:* Col Med Northeastern Ohio Univ State Rte 44 Rootstown OH 44272

KOO, ROBERT CHUNG JEN, b Shanghai, China, Mar 20, 21; nat US; m 49; c 3. POMOLOGY. *Educ:* Cornell Univ, BS, 44; Univ Fla, MS, 50, PhD(fruit crops), 53. *Prof Exp:* Interim asst biochemist, Citrus Exp Sta, 53-57, from asst horticulturist to assoc horticulturist, 57-68, PROF & HORTICULTURIST, AGR RES & EDUC CTR, UNIV FLA, 69- *Honors & Awards:* Presidential Gold Medal Award, Fla State Horticult Soc, 65; Res Award, Fla Fruit & Vegetable Asn, 75. *Mem:* Am Soc Hort Sci; Am Agron Soc. *Res:* Plant nutrition of citrus; irrigation and water management. *Mailing Add:* Agr Res & Educ Ctr Univ of Fla Lake Alfred FL 33850

KOO, TED SWEI-YEN, b China, Feb 4, 10; nat US; m 37; c 4. FISH BIOLOGY. *Educ:* Amoy Univ, BS, 34; Lingnan Univ, MS, 37; Univ Wash, PhD(fisheries), 55. *Prof Exp:* Asst prof biol, Amoy Univ, 37-39, assoc prof, Fukien Med Col, 39-41; from assoc prof to prof, Amoy Univ, 41-47; sci asst fisheries, Univ Wash, 48-54, sr fishery biologist, 54-56, from res asst prof to res assoc prof, 56-64; prof fishery biol, Univ Md, 64-79; RETIRED. *Mem:* Am Fisheries Soc; Am Inst Fishery Res Biol. *Res:* Age, growth and life history of estuarine and anadromous fishes. *Mailing Add:* 802 Gest Dr Mountain View CA 94040

KOOB, ROBERT DUANE, b Graettinger, Iowa, Oct 14, 41; m 60; c 5. PHYSICAL CHEMISTRY. *Educ:* Univ Northern Iowa, BA, 62; Univ Kans, PhD(chem), 67. *Prof Exp:* Instr high sch, Iowa, 63-64; res assoc chem, Univ Kans, 67; from asst prof to assoc prof, 67-72, chmn dept, 73-77, PROF CHEM, N DAK STATE UNIV, 72- DIR, WATER RESOURCES RES INST, 74- *Mem:* Am Chem Soc; Sigma Xi. *Res:* Radiation chemistry; photochemistry; mass spectrometry. *Mailing Add:* Dept of Chem NDak State Univ Fargo ND 58102

KOOB, ROBERT PHILIP, b Philadelphia, Pa, Jan 3, 22; m 54; c 3. ORGANIC CHEMISTRY. *Educ:* Villanova Col, BS, 43; Univ Pa, MS, 47, PhD(chem), 49. *Prof Exp:* Asst instr, Univ Pa, 43-44, 46-49; asst prof chem, Villanova Col, 49-55; from asst prof to assoc prof, 55-59, PROF CHEM, ST JOSEPH'S COL, PA, 59- *Concurrent Pos:* Res chemist, E I du Pont de Nemours & Co, 47; asst prof, Rosemont Col, 51-52. *Mem:* Am Chem Soc. *Res:* Phase and reaction rate studies; effects of solvent on reaction; extensions of the Fries Rearrangement. *Mailing Add:* Dept of Chem St Joseph's Col City Line Ave at 54th St Philadelphia PA 19131

KOOBS, DICK HERMAN, b Hinsdale, Ill, July 22, 28; m 55. PATHOLOGY, BIOLOGICAL CHEMISTRY. *Educ:* Andrews Univ, BA, 50; Loma Linda Univ, MD, 55; Univ Calif, Los Angeles, PhD(biol chem), 65; Am Bd Path, dipl, 66. *Prof Exp:* Intern, Robert B Green Mem Hosp, San Antonio, Tex, 55-56; resident physician path, White Mem Hosp, Los Angeles, 56-59; asst prof, 65-78, ASSOC PROF PATH, SCH MED, LOMA LINDA UNIV, 78- *Mem:* Int Acad Path. *Res:* Experimental and molecular pathology, particularly heart disease. *Mailing Add:* Dept of Path Loma Linda Univ Sch of Med Loma Linda CA 92354

KOOH, SANG WHAY, b Seoul, Korea, Oct 5, 30; m 56; c 3. PEDIATRICS. *Educ:* Yan-Sei Univ, MD, 55; Univ Toronto, PhD(physiol), 67; Am Acad Pediat, dipl, 61; FRCP, 68. *Prof Exp:* Fel pediat, Michael Reese Hosp & Med Ctr, 60-62; sr res fel, Res Inst, Hosp Sick Children, Toronto, 62-67; ASSOC PROF, DEPT PHYSIOL & DEPT PEDIAT, UNIV TORONTO, 68- *Concurrent Pos:* Sr staff physician, Hosp Sick Children, 68- *Mem:* Soc Pediat Res; Can Soc Clin Investigation. *Res:* Metabolism bone diseases in children; metabolism of vitamin D in human and in experimental animals; regulation of bone mineralization. *Mailing Add:* 555 Univ Ave Toronto ON M5G 1X8 Can

KOOI, CLARENCE F, energy conversion, see previous edition

KOOI, KENNETH ASHLEY, b Muskegon, Mich, Oct 31, 22; m 49; c 4. ELECTROENCEPHALOGRAPHY. *Educ:* Univ Mich, MD, 46, MS, 52. *Prof Exp:* From clin instr to asst clin prof psychiat, Col Med, Univ Utah, 54-59; from asst prof to assoc prof psychiat, 59-67, PROF ELECTROENCEPHALOGRAPHY, MED SCH, UNIV MICH, ANN ARBOR, 67-, CHIEF EEG LAB, MED CTR, 64- *Concurrent Pos:* Dir, EEG Lab, Vet Admin Hosp, Salt Lake City, Utah & attend neurol, Salt Lake City County Hosp, 54-59; consult, Wayne County Gen Hosp, Eloise, 60- *Mem:* Am EEG Soc (secy, 61-64, pres, 66-67); Am Acad Neurol; Am Epilepsy Soc; Am EEG Soc. *Res:* Cerebral evoked potentials; normative studies of spontaneous cerebral activity; epilepsy and other disorders of the brain. *Mailing Add:* EEG Lab Univ of Mich Med Ctr Ann Arbor MI 48104

KOOIJ, THEO, b Dordrecht, Netherlands, Nov 29, 33; m 56; c 3. ACOUSTIC SIGNAL PROCESSING, ELECTRONICS ENGINEERING. *Educ:* Delft Univ Technol, BSc, 58, MSc, 61; Cath Univ Am, PhD(elec eng), 77. *Prof Exp:* Jr res scientist, Saclant ASW Res Ctr, La Spezia, Italy, 61-65, sr res scientist & teamleader underwater acoustics, 65-68; sci adv sonar interpretation, US Naval Ship Res & Develop Ctr, Washington, DC, 68-74, head target physics br, Ocean Sci Dept, Naval Underwater Systs Ctr, New London, Conn, 74-76; tech dir, Acoust Res Ctr, 76-78, PROG MGR, TACTICAL TECHNOL OFF, DEFENSE ADVAN RES PROJS AGENCY, 78- *Concurrent Pos:* Lectr, Am Univ, 68-69. *Mem:* Acoust Soc Am; Netherlands Royal Inst Eng; Am Soc Cybernet; Inst Elec & Electronics Engrs. *Res:* Theoretical, model and computer simulated, and full scale experimental research in detection and classification of underwater targets; design and development of digital sonar signal processing systems. *Mailing Add:* Tactical Tech Off Defense Adv Res Proj 1400 Wilson Blvd Arlington VA 22209

KOONCE, ANDREA LAVENDER, b Denver, Colo, Dec 31, 51. FOREST PATHOLOGY, TROPICAL FORESTRY. *Educ:* Ariz State Univ, BS, 73; Ore State Univ, MS, 80, PhD(forest sci), 81. *Prof Exp:* Researcher, US Forest Serv, 78; teacher pathol & ecol, Ore State Univ, 75-78, res asst, 75-81; PROF ECOL, BOT, PATHOL & HEAD GENETIC RES, ESCUELA NACIONAL DE CIENCIAS FORESTALES, 81- *Concurrent Pos:* Consult, Lew Roth Forest, 80-81. *Mem:* Soc Am Foresters; Soc Trop Foresters. *Res:* Tree improvement of tropical pines, hardwoods and legumes; tree disease-fire interactions; tree physiology. *Mailing Add:* c/o Lewis F Roth Dept Bot Ore State Univ Corvallis OR 97331

KOONCE, KENNETH LOWELL, b Lake Charles, La, Sept 6, 39; m 62; c 3. EXPERIMENTAL STATISTICS. *Educ:* Univ Southwestern La, BS, 61; La State Univ, MS, 63; NC State Univ, PhD(animal genetics), 68. *Prof Exp:* Instr animal sci, NC State Univ, 67; from asst prof to assoc prof, 67-76, PROF EXP STATIST, LA STATE UNIV, BATON ROUGE, 76- *Mem:* Biomet Soc; Am Soc Animal Sci; Am Soc Info Sci; Am Statist Asn. *Mailing Add:* Dept of Exp Statist La State Univ Baton Rouge LA 70803

KOONIN, STEVEN ELLIOT, b Brooklyn, NY, Dec 12, 51; m 75. THEORETICAL NUCLEAR PHYSICS. *Educ:* Calif Inst Tech, BS, 72; Mass Inst Technol, PhD(physics), 75. *Prof Exp:* Asst prof theoret physics, 75-78, assoc prof physics, 78-81, PROF THEORET PHYSICS, CALIF INST TECHNOL, 81- *Concurrent Pos:* Consult, Lawrence Berkeley Lab, Lawrence Livermore Lab, Los Alamos Sci Lab & Oak Ridge Nat Lab, 77-; res fel, Niels Bohr Inst, 76-77; Alfred P Sloan Found res fel, 77-79. *Mem:* Am Phys Soc; AAAS. *Res:* Nuclear reaction models; heavy ion physics. *Mailing Add:* Dept of Physics Calif Inst of Technol 106-38 Pasadena CA 91125

KOONS, CHARLES BRUCE, b Oklahoma City, Okla, Nov 14, 29; m 56; c 3. ORGANIC CHEMISTRY. *Educ:* Southern Ill Univ, BS, 51; Univ Minn, PhD(org chem), 58. *Prof Exp:* Res chemist, Jersey Prod Res Co, Div Standard Oil Co, NJ, 58-64; sr res chemist, 64-75, RES ASSOC, EXXON PROD RES CO, 75- *Mem:* Am Chem Soc; Am Soc Testing & Mat. *Res:* Kinetics of aromatic substitution reactions; organic geochemistry, involving studies of the origin, migration and accumulation of petroleum; environmental chemistry, involving the fate of petroleum in the marine environment. *Mailing Add:* Exxon Production Res Co PO Box 2189 Houston TX 77001

KOONS, DAVID SWARNER, b Fresno, Calif, June 17, 30; div; c 2. CHEMICAL ENGINEERING, PETROLEUM ENGINEERING. *Educ:* Calif Inst Technol, BS, 52, MS, 55; Univ Colo, PhD(chem eng), 60. *Prof Exp:* Process engr, Texaco Inc, 52-54; res asst, Exp Sta, Univ Colo, 60; sr res technologist, Mobil Oil Co Inc, 60-77; STAFF ENGR, MOBIL CORP, 77- *Mem:* Am Chem Soc; Am Inst Chem Engrs; Am Inst Mining, Metall & Petrol Engrs. *Res:* Simultaneous fluid flow; heat transfer and reaction kinetics of processes for recovering oil from underground reservoirs; pneumatic conveying of solids and petroleum refining. *Mailing Add:* Mobil Corp PO Box 5444 Denver CO 80219

KOONS, DONALDSON, b Seoul, Korea, Aug 23, 17; US citizen; m 44; c 4. GEOMORPHOLOGY. *Educ:* Columbia Univ, AB, 39, AM, 41, PhD(geol), 45. *Hon Degrees:* DSc, Col of Wooster, 74; Unity Col, 76. *Prof Exp:* Instr geol & geog, Carleton Col, 42-43; lectr geol, Columbia Univ, 46; asst prof, WVa Univ, 46-47; asst prof, 47-50, prof, 50-75, DANA PROF GEOL, COLBY COL, 75-, HEAD DEPT, 47- *Concurrent Pos:* Comnr, Maine Dept of

Conserv, 73-75. *Mem:* Fel AAAS; fel Geol Soc Am; fel Am Geog Soc. *Res:* Areal geology; dynamic geomorphology; geology of Colorado Plateau; Pleistocene Glaciation of Maine. *Mailing Add:* Dept of Geol Colby Col Waterville ME 04901

KOONS, LAWRENCE FRANKLIN, physical chemistry, see previous edition

KOONTZ, FRANK P, b Baltimore, Md, Nov 13, 32; m 60; c 3. MICROBIOLOGY. *Educ:* Univ Md, BS, 58, MS, 60, PhD(biochem, microbiol), 62. *Prof Exp:* NIH fel, Oxford Univ, 62-64; asst prof prev med, 64-70, asst dir, State Hygienic Lab, 67-77, ASSOC PROF PREV MED & ENVIRON HEALTH, UNIV IOWA, 70-, PRIN BACTERIOLOGIST, 73- *Concurrent Pos:* Prin microbiologist, State Hygienic Lab, 64-67; consult, Univ Hosp, Iowa, 64- *Mem:* Am Soc Microbiol; fel Am Pub Health Asn. *Res:* Influence of cervico-vaginal flora on post-partum infection rates; microbiologic problems in obstetrics; taxonomy of non-fermenting gram-negative rods; pre-surgical decontamination in oral surgery; scope and control of venereal disease problems. *Mailing Add:* State Hygienic Lab Univ of Iowa Iowa City IA 52240

KOONTZ, HAROLD VIVIEN, b Pendleton, Ore, Sept 9, 28; m 65; c 2. PLANT PHYSIOLOGY, HORTICULTURE. *Educ:* Ore State Univ, BS, 52; Wash State Univ, PhD(plant physiol), 57. *Prof Exp:* Lectr & jr agronomist, plant physiol, Univ Calif, Davis, 57-60; biol scientist, Hanford Atomic Prod Oper, Gen Elec Co, 60-61; asst prof, 61-66, ASSOC PROF PLANT PHYSIOL, UNIV CONN, 66- *Concurrent Pos:* Mem staff, Int Atomic Energy Agency, Taiwan, 68-69. *Mem:* Int Soc Soiless Cult; Am Soc Plant Physiol; Scandinavian Soc Plant Physiol; Biol Photog Asn. *Res:* Absorption; translocation and redistribution of materials in plants; scientific photography; hydroponics. *Mailing Add:* Biol Sci Group Bot Sect Univ Conn Storrs CT 06268

KOONTZ, WARREN WOODSON, JR, b Lynchburg, Va, June 10, 32; m 57; c 2. UROLOGY. *Educ:* Va Mil Inst, BA, 53; Univ Va, MD, 57. *Prof Exp:* From intern to resident surg, New York Hosp, 57-62, resident urol, 62-66; from instr to asst prof, Med Col Va, 66-69; asst prof, Harvard Univ, 69-70; PROF UROL & CHMN DEPT, MED COL VA, 70- *Concurrent Pos:* Asst urologist, Mass Gen Hosp, 69-70; consult, McGuire Vet Admin Hosp, 70- & Portsmouth Naval Hosp, 71- *Mem:* Am Col Surgeons; Am Urol Asn; Soc Pediat Urol; Soc Univ Urol. *Res:* Pediatric urology; urinary tract cancer. *Mailing Add:* Dept of Urol Med Col of Va Richmond VA 23298

KOOP, CHARLES EVERETT, b Brooklyn, NY, Oct 14, 16; m 38; c 4. SURGERY. *Educ:* Dartmouth Col, AB, 37; Cornell Univ, MD, 41; Univ Pa, ScD(med), 47. *Hon Degrees:* LLD, Eastern Baptist Col, 60; MD, Univ Liverpool, 68; LHD, Wheaton Col, 73. *Prof Exp:* From asst instr to instr surg, 42-47, assoc, 47-48, from asst prof to assoc prof, 48-59, PROF PEDIAT SURG, UNIV PA, 59-, PROF PEDIAT, 76- *Concurrent Pos:* Surgeon-in-chief, Children's Hosp; consult, US Naval Hosp, 64-; ed, J Pediat Surg; dep asst secy health, USPHS, 80, surg gen, 81. *Mem:* Soc Univ Surgeons; Am Surg Asn; fel Am Col Surgeons; Brit Asn Paediat Surg; Am Pediat Surg Asn. *Res:* Pediatric surgical techniques; neo-natalogy; childhood tumors. *Mailing Add:* Children's Hosp One Children's Ctr Philadelphia PA 19104

KOOP, JOHN C, b Myitkyina, Burma, Mar 6, 19; US citizen; m 43; c 8. STATISTICS. *Educ:* Univ Rangoon, BSc, 42; NC State Univ, PhD(statist), 58. *Prof Exp:* Chief labor statist, Directorate Labour, Govt Burma, 48-58; mem, Int Labour Off, Switzerland, 59-60; vis asst prof exp statist, NC State Univ, 60-61, vis assoc prof, 61-65, assoc prof, 65-66; sr adv sampling in agr & head res training, Dominion Bur Statist, Can, 66-70; SR GROUP SCIENTIST, STATIST SCI ADMIN, RES TRIANGLE INST, 70- *Mem:* Fel Am Statist Asn; Royal Statist Soc; Burma Res Soc; Int Asn Survey Statisticians; Int Statist Inst. *Res:* Sampling theory for finite universes derived on basis of axioms; theory of ratio estimation; theory of functional relationships for a finite universe; unified theory of estimation for sample surveys taking into account response and measurement errors; statistical inference; demographic study of minority community in Burma. *Mailing Add:* 3201 Clark Ave Raleigh NC 27607

KOOPMAN, DAVID WARREN, b Caro, Mich, Mar 14, 35; m 60; c 2. PLASMA PHYSICS. *Educ:* Amherst Col, BA, 57; Univ Mich, MS, 59, PhD(physics), 64. *Prof Exp:* Res asst prof, 64-68, res assoc prof, 68-73, PROF, INST PHYS SCI & TECHNOL, UNIV MD, COLLEGE PARK, 73- *Concurrent Pos:* Consult, Naval Res Lab, Washington, DC, 74- *Mem:* Inst Elec & Electronics Engrs; Nuclear & Plasma Sci Soc; Am Phys Soc. *Res:* Experimental shock wave, plasma spectroscopy, and atomic collision studies; laser-plasma and ionization phenomena; laser applications; controlled fusion research. *Mailing Add:* Inst for Phys Sci & Technol Univ of Md College Park MD 20742

KOOPMAN, FRANCIS CHRISTIAN, b Rapid City, SDak, July 5, 21; m 54; c 3. HYDROLOGY. *Educ:* SDak Sch Mines & Technol, BS, 49. *Prof Exp:* Hydraul engr, Water Resources Div, US Geol Surv, 50-58; engr-in-charge hydrol, Daniel, Mann, Johnson & Mendenhall, Thailand, 58-60; hydraul engr, US Geol Surv, 60-63; supvry hydrologist & chief invests, Water Resources Div, 63-75, chief, Instrument Sect, Gulf Coast Hydrosci Ctr, 75-80; RETIRED. *Honors & Awards:* US Geol Surv Award, 66. *Res:* Geophysical and geochemical parameters under high pressure environment; research and development of instruments in hydrologic work. *Mailing Add:* 108 Romaneda Bay St Louis MS 39520

KOOPMAN, KARL FRIEDRICH, b Honolulu, Hawaii, Apr 1, 20. MAMMALOGY. *Educ:* Columbia Univ, BA, 43, MA, 45, PhD(zool), 50. *Prof Exp:* Instr biol, Middletown Collegiate Ctr, 49-50 & Queens Col, NY, 52-58; asst cur, Acad Natural Sci, Philadelphia, 58-59 & Chicago Natural Hist Mus, 59-61; asst cur, 61-66, assoc cur, 66-78, CUR, AM MUS NATURAL

HIST, 78- *Honors & Awards:* Newberry Prize, 49; Gerrit S Miller Jr Award, 77. *Mem:* Am Soc Mammal; Soc Syst Zool; Soc Study Evolution. *Res:* Systematic mammalogy; taxonomy and zoogeography of bats; paleontology and zoogeography of West Indian mammals. *Mailing Add:* Dept of Mammal 79th St & Central Park W New York NY 10024

KOOPMAN, KENNETH H(ENRY), b Westport, Conn, Sept 8, 16; m 39; c 2. METALLURGICAL ENGINEERING. *Educ:* Rensselaer Polytech Inst, BME, 38, MME, 58. *Prof Exp:* Metall asst, Bethlehem Steel Co, 38-40; res metallurgist, Union Carbide Corp, 40-47, develop & proj engr, Linde Develop Lab, 47-55; mgr welding metall & develop lab, Knolls Atomic Power Lab, Gen Elec Co, 55-58; from asst dir to dir, 58-76, EXEC DIR, WELDING RES COUN, 76- *Honors & Awards:* Davis Silver Medal, Am Welding Soc, 58. *Mem:* Am Welding Soc; Am Soc Metals; Soc Naval Archit & Marine Engrs; Am Soc Mech Engrs. *Res:* Metallurgical, welding, structural and pressure vessel research. *Mailing Add:* Welding Res Coun 345 E 47th St New York NY 10017

KOOPMAN, RICHARD J(OHN) W(ALTER), b St Louis, Mo, June 24, 05; m 34; c 1. ELECTRICAL ENGINEERING. *Educ:* Univ Mo, BS, 28, PhD, 42; Yale Univ, MS, 33. *Prof Exp:* Test engr, Gen Elec Co, 28-30; instr elec eng, Yale Univ, 30-32 & Mich Col Mining & Technol, 35-37; from asst prof to assoc prof, Univ Kans, 37-43; head electro-mech sect, Cornell Aeronaut Lab, 43-46; assoc prof, 46-49, chmn dept, 49-65, prof, 49-72, Samuel C Sachs Prof, 72-73, EMER SAMUEL C SACHS PROF ELEC ENG, WASHINGTON UNIV, 73- *Concurrent Pos:* Consult chmn, Nat Comt Aerospace Instrumentation, 59-60; consult var utility co, testing labs & ins co, 78- *Mem:* Am Soc Eng Educ; fel Inst Elec & Electronics Engrs. *Res:* Electrical machinery; servo motors; response of instruments and systems; causes and effects of electrical failure; direct simulation of electrical machinery; investigations of electrical damage in transformers, distribution systems, etc. *Mailing Add:* 2201 St Clair Brentwood MO 63144

KOOPMAN, RICHARD NELSON, b Buffalo, NY, Nov 26, 45; m 70; c 2. MECHANICAL ENGINEERING. *Educ:* Wash Univ, BS, 68; Univ Minn, MS, 69, PhD(mech eng), 75. *Prof Exp:* Mech engr, Phys Sci Lab, US Army Missle Command, Redstone Arsenal, Ala, 70-71; heat transfer anal, Govt & Aero Prods Div Honeywell Inc, Minneapolis, 73-75; mech engr, Reactor Anal & Safety Div & Components Technol Div, Agronne Nat Lab, 75-80; MEM TECH STAFF, BELL LABS, 80- *Mem:* Am Soc Mech Engrs. *Res:* Heat transfer of electronic components and packages. *Mailing Add:* Bell Labs 600 Mountain Ave Murray Hill NJ 07974

KOOPMANS, LAMBERT HERMAN, b Chicago, Ill, July 23, 30; m 55; c 4. MATHEMATICAL STATISTICS. *Educ:* San Diego State Col, AB, 52; Univ Calif, PhD, 58. *Prof Exp:* Asst statist, Univ Calif, 52-56, assoc biostatist, 57-58; mem staff, Sandia Corp, 58-64; assoc prof math & statist, 64-68, chmn dept, 69-74, PROF MATH & STATIST, UNIV NMEX, 68- *Concurrent Pos:* Consult, Sandia Corp, 64-72; Westinghouse Corp, 65-67; civil eng fac & dept path, Univ NMex, 76-77, diabetes proj, 78-82 & Vet Admin Hosp, Albuquerque, 78-79; sabbatical leave fac math, Univ Calif, Santa Cruz, 71-72; vis prof statist, Princeton Univ, 75. *Mem:* Fel Am Statist Asn; Biomet Soc; fel Inst Math Statist; Bernouli Soc. *Res:* Data analysis; time series analysis. *Mailing Add:* Dept of Math Univ of NMex Albuquerque NM 87131

KOOPOWITZ, HAROLD, b East London, SAfrica, Sept 10, 40; m 69; c 1. NEUROPHYSIOLOGY, INVERTEBRATE ZOOLOGY. *Educ:* Rhodes Univ, SAfrica, BSc, 62, MSc, 64; Univ Calif, Los Angeles, PhD(zool), 68. *Prof Exp:* Asst prof, 68-75, ASSOC PROF BIOL, UNIV CALIF, IRVINE, 75- *Mem:* Brit Soc Exp Biol; Am Soc Zool; Soc Gen Physiol; Soc Neurosci. *Res:* Organization of flatworm nervous systems; electrophysiology of vision in insect eyes. *Mailing Add:* Dept of Develop & Cell Biol Univ of Calif Irvine CA 92717

KOOSER, ROBERT GALEN, b Mankato, Minn, July 23, 41; m 66. PHYSICAL CHEMISTRY. *Educ:* St Olaf Col, BA, 63; Cornell Univ, PhD(chem), 68. *Prof Exp:* Asst prof, 68-72, ASSOC PROF CHEM, KNOX COL, ILL, 72- *Mem:* Am Chem Soc; Am Phys Soc. *Res:* Electron spin resonance, primarily spin relaxation processes of organic and inorganic singlet systems in solution. *Mailing Add:* Dept of Chem Knox Col Galesburg IL 61401

KOOSIS, PAUL, b Los Angeles, Calif, Apr 20, 29. MATHEMATICAL ANALYSIS. *Educ:* Univ Calif, Berkeley, BA, 50, PhD(math), 54. *Prof Exp:* Instr math, Univ Mich, 54-55; asst instr math sci, NY Univ, 55-57, 59-60; Fulbright fel to France, 57-58; NSF fels, 58-59, 60-61; from asst prof to assoc prof, Fordham Univ, 62-63; from asst prof to assoc prof, 63-70, PROF MATH, UNIV CALIF, LOS ANGELES, 70- *Mem:* Am Math Soc; Math Soc France. *Res:* Classical harmonic analysis; complex variable theory; theory of approximation. *Mailing Add:* Dept of Math 6364 Math Sci Bldg Univ of Calif Los Angeles CA 90024

KOOSTRA, WALTER L, b Berea, Ky, May 15, 34; m 54; c 4. MICROBIOLOGY. *Educ:* Univ SDak, BA, 62, MA, 63, PhD(microbiol), 68. *Prof Exp:* Asst prof, 68-77, ASSOC PROF MICROBIOL, UNIV MONT, 77- *Mem:* AAAS; Am Soc Microbiol; Sigma Xi. *Res:* Physiology of mycoplasmas and bacterial L-phase organisms; bacterial lipids; cell wall and membrane structure and physiology. *Mailing Add:* Dept of Microbiol Univ of Mont Missoula MT 59812

KOOTSEY, JOSEPH MAILEN, b Houston, Tex, Sept 3, 39; m 61; c 2. PHYSIOLOGY. *Educ:* Pac Union Col, BA, 60; Brown Univ, ScM, 64, PhD(physics), 66. *Prof Exp:* Asst prof physiol & biophys, Loma Linda Univ, 67-69; prof biophys, Andrews Univ, 76-79; asst prof physiol & pharmacol, 71-76, COORDR EDUC RES & DEVELOP, DEPT PHYSIOL, DUKE UNIV, 79- *Concurrent Pos:* Bank Am-Giannini Found grant, Loma Linda Univ, 65-67; NIH spec fel, Duke Univ, 69-71. *Mem:* AAAS; Am Physiol Soc; Biophys Soc; Am Phys Soc; Am Heart Asn. *Res:* Cardiac electrophysiology; computer simulation in physiology; medical education. *Mailing Add:* Dept of Physiol Box 3709 Duke Univ Med Ctr Durham NC 27710

KOOYMAN, GERALD LEE, b Salt Lake City, Utah, June 16, 34; m 62; c 2. COMPARATIVE PHYSIOLOGY. *Educ:* Univ Calif, Los Angeles, AB, 57; Univ Ariz, PhD(zool), 66. *Prof Exp:* Res asst antarctic seal studies, Univ Ariz, 63-66; NSF fel, Anat & Physiol of Marine Mammals, London Hosp Med Col, Eng, 66-67; res physiologist, 67-68, from asst res physiologist to assoc res physiologist, 68-78, RES PHYSIOLOGIST, SCRIPPS INST OCEANOG, UNIV CALIF, SAN DIEGO, 78- *Concurrent Pos:* NSF grant, 68- *Mem:* AAAS; Am Soc Zool; sci fel Zool Soc London; Am Physiol Soc. *Res:* Behavior and physiology of diving in aquatic birds and mammals, especially pressure effects; comparative respiratory physiology and anatomy of vertebrates. *Mailing Add:* PRL A-004 Scripps Inst Oceanog La Jolla CA 92093

KOOZEKANAI, SAID H, b Mash-had, Iran, Mar 15, 33; m 65. ELECTRICAL ENGINEERING, BIOMEDICAL ENGINEERING. *Educ:* Univ Tehran, Electro-Mech Eng, 56; Brown Univ, PhD(elec eng), 61; Univ Dayton, MS, 69. *Prof Exp:* Sr res scientist, Raytheon Res Div, Mass, 61-65; from asst prof to assoc prof, 66-76, PROF ELEC ENG, OHIO STATE UNIV, 76- *Mem:* Am Inst Physics; Am Phys Soc; Inst Elec & Electronics Engrs. *Res:* Quantum electronics; lasers; antennas and propagation. *Mailing Add:* Dept of Elec Eng Ohio State Univ Columbus OH 43210

KOPAL, ZDENEK, b Litomysl, Czech, Apr 4, 14, nat US; m 38; c 3. ASTRONOMY. *Educ:* Charles Univ, Prague, DSc(astron), 37. *Hon Degrees:* MSc, Univ Manchester, 55; DSc, Univ Patras, 71, Univ Krakow, Poland, 74. *Prof Exp:* Res assoc astron, Harvard Univ, 40-42; mem staff, Mass Inst Technol, 42-45, res assoc appl math, 45-47, assoc prof, 48-51, mem court gov, 64-67, prof astron & head dept, 51-81, EMER PROF, VICTORIA UNIV MANCHESTER, 81- *Concurrent Pos:* Mem, Solar Eclipse Exped, Japan, 36; pres comn 42, Int Astron Union, 48-55; res assoc, Harvard Col Observ, 46-51, lectr, 49-51; mem, Nat Adv Comt Aeronaut, 49-52; vpres, Int Found Pic-du-Midi, 62, pres, 78; ed-in-chief, Astrophys & Space Sci, 68-; ed, Moon J, 70- & Icarus. *Honors & Awards:* von Neumann Medal, Univ Brussels, 66; Gold Medal, Czech Acad Sci, 69, Copernicus Medal, Univ Krakow, 74. *Mem:* Am Astron Soc; fel Royal Astron Soc; Int Acad Astronaut; Explorers Club. *Res:* Theory of close binary systems; mathematical astronomy; numerical analysis. *Mailing Add:* Dept of Astron Victoria Univ of Manchester Manchester England United Kingdom

KOPCHICK, JOHN JOSEPH, b Punxsutawney, Pa, Nov 2, 50; m 76. VIROLOGY. *Educ:* Ind Univ Pa, BS, 72, MS, 75; Grad Sch Biomed Sci, Univ Tex, 80. *Prof Exp:* AM CANCER SOC FEL, ROCHE INST MOLECULAR BIOL, 80- *Mem:* Sigma Xi; Am Soc Microbiol. *Res:* Determining the biological activity of cloned retavira DNA molecules; biological activity is assoyed by introduction of DNA molecules into eucaryotic cells via microinjection. *Mailing Add:* Roche Inst Molecular Biol Nutley NJ 07110

KOPCHIK, RICHARD MICHAEL, b Punxsutawney, Pa, Apr 29, 41; m 64; c 2. POLYMERIC CHEMICAL REAGENTS. *Educ:* Carnegie-Mellon Univ, BS, 63; Univ Rochester, PhD(org chem), 68. *Prof Exp:* Res chemist polymers, 69-80, SR RES ASSOC, ROHM & HAAS CO, 80- *Mem:* Am Chem Soc; Sigma Xi; Soc Plastics Eng. *Res:* Organic chemistry; free radical reactions; chemical modification of polymers; organo-phosphorous chemistry; continuous preparation and processing of polymers; polymer chemistry; polymeric sorbents; engineering plastics. *Mailing Add:* Rohm & Haas Co 727 Norristown Rd Spring House PA 19477

KOPECKY, KARL RUDOLPH, b Hradec Kralove, Czech, Oct 5, 32; US citizen; m 63; c 2. ORGANIC CHEMISTRY. *Educ:* Iowa State Col, BS, 54; Univ Calif, Los Angeles, PhD, 59. *Prof Exp:* Instr chem, Univ Calif, Los Angeles, 59; NIH fel, Calif Inst Technol, 59-61; from asst prof to assoc prof, 61-77, PROF CHEM, UNIV ALTA, 77- *Mem:* Am Chem Soc; Chem Inst Can. *Res:* Thermal reactions of styrene; radicals from chiral sources; peroxide reactions; chemiluminescent compounds; reactions of stable radicals. *Mailing Add:* Dept of Chem Univ of Alta Edmonton AB T6G 2G2 Can

KOPELMAN, JAY B, b New York, NY, Feb 24, 39. INTERNATIONAL ENERGY SCIENCES. *Educ:* Rensselaer Polytech Inst, BS, 60; Northwestern Univ, PhD(physics), 65. *Prof Exp:* Res assoc physics, Univ Colo, Boulder, 64-66, asst prof, 66-74, asst dean grad sch, 68-74; mgr energy modeling prog, Stanford Res Inst, 74-78; MGR SPEC STUDIES, ELEC POWER RES INST, 78- *Mem:* AAAS; Am Phys Soc. *Res:* Energy technology; energy economics; modelling. *Mailing Add:* Elec Power Res Inst 3412 Hillview Ave Palo Alto CA 94303

KOPELMAN, RAOUL, b Vienna, Austria, Oct 21, 33; US citizen; m 55; c 3. PHYSICAL CHEMISTRY. *Educ:* Israel Inst Technol, BS, 55, dipl eng, 56, MSc, 57; Columbia Univ, PhD(chem), 60. *Prof Exp:* Res assoc chem, Harvard Univ, 60-62; lectr, Israel Inst Technol, 62-64; res fel, Calif Inst Technol, 64-65, sr res fel, 65-66; from asst prof to assoc prof, 66-71, PROF CHEM, UNIV MICH, ANN ARBOR, 71- *Mem:* Am Phys Soc. *Res:* Excitons and phonons in molecular cyrstals and aggregates; group and quantum theory of nonrigid molecules and molecular solids; low temperature, tunable-laser, time resolved, micro-spectroscopy; the physics of photosynthesis; solar-energy spectral concentrators. *Mailing Add:* Dept of Chem Univ of Mich Ann Arbor MI 48109

KOPF, ALFRED WALTER, b Buffalo, NY, June 21, 26; m 49; c 4. MEDICINE, ONCOLOGY. *Educ:* Cornell Univ, BA, 48, MD, 51; NY Univ, MS, 55; Am Bd Dermat, dipl, 57. *Prof Exp:* Intern, Cleveland City Hosp, Ohio, 51-52; clin resident dermat & syphil, Skin & Cancer Unit, Univ Hosp, 53-54, organizer oncol sect, 54, asst dermat & syphil, Post-Grad Med Sch & Univ Hosp, 54-55, instr, Post-Grad Med Sch, 57-59, asst clin prof, 59-61, from asst prof to assoc prof, 61-66, PROF DERMAT, SCH MED & POST-GRAD MED SCH, NY UNIV, 66-, ASSOC DIR DERMAT SERV, MED CTR, 68- *Concurrent Pos:* Pvt pract dermat, New York, 55-; from asst attend to assoc attend dermat, Univ Hosp, NY Univ Med Ctr, 58-63, assoc attend med staff, 63-64, attend, 64-; from co-ed to sr ed, Yearbook Dermat, 63-70; mem bd dirs, Inst Dermat Commun & Educ, 63-70; vis physician, Bellevue Med Ctr, 64; mem dermat training grants comt, Nat Inst Arthritis & Metab Dis, 67-71; trustee, Dermat Found, 68-72; mem, Am Bd Dermat, 72, 78. *Mem:* AAAS; Soc Invest Dermat (pres, 80); Am Acad Dermat (pres, 80); Am Dermat Asn (treas); AMA. *Res:* Cutaneous oncology, especially neoplasms of the melanocyte including clinical and basic studies on pigmented nevi and malignant melanoma. *Mailing Add:* Dept of Dermat NY Univ Sch of Med New York NY 10016

KOPF, PETER W, b Philadelphia, Pa, Apr 23, 44; m 70. PHYSICAL CHEMISTRY, POLYMER CHEMISTRY. *Educ:* Rutgers Col, AB, 66; Univ Rochester, PhD(phys chem), 70. *Prof Exp:* CHEMIST, RES & DEVELOP DEPT, UNION CARBIDE CORP, BOUND BROOK, 70- *Mem:* Am Chem Soc; Sigma Xi. *Res:* Nuclear magnetic resonance spectroscopy; electron paramagnetic resonance spectroscopy; polymer microstructural analysis; stable and transient free radicals; engineering thermoplastics; computer assisted calculations and simulations; polymer synthesis; thermoset reaction mechanisms; surface chemistry; dynamic mechanical analysis. *Mailing Add:* Box 120 RD 1 Belle Mead NJ 08502

KOPF, RUDOLPH WILLIAM, b Munich, Ger, Sept 10, 22; US citizen; m 49; c 2. STRATIGRAPHY, STRUCTURAL GEOLOGY. *Educ:* Univ Buffalo, BA, 50, MA, 52. *Prof Exp:* Instr geol, Univ Buffalo, 50-51; oceanogr, US Navy Hydrographic Off, 52; geologist, US Geol Surv, 52-56; geol engr, USAEC, 56-61; GEOLOGIST, US GEOL SURV, 61- *Concurrent Pos:* West Coast rep, Geol Names Comt, US Geol Surv, 61- *Honors & Awards:* Award of Merit, Dept Interior Safety Coun, 69. *Mem:* Paleont Soc; Geol Soc Am. *Res:* Mechanics of thrust faulting; origin of thrust breccia, clastic pipes and dikes, diatremes and mud volcanoes; uranium-vanadium deposits, stratigraphy, and structure of parts of Colorado plateaus, basin and range province; auriferous placers in California; diamonds in California. *Mailing Add:* US Geol Surv Tech Reports Unit 345 Middlefield Rd Menlo Park CA 94025

KOPFLER, FREDERICK CHARLES, b New Orleans, La, Aug 14, 38; m 61; c 4. ENVIRONMENTAL CHEMISTRY. *Educ:* Southeastern La Col, BS, 60; La State Univ, MS, 62, PhD(food sci), 64. *Prof Exp:* Res chemist milk proteins, Agr Res Serv, USDA, 64-66, supvry chemist, 66-71; supvry chemist water supply progs div, 71-79, CHIEF, CHEM & STATIST SUPPORT BR, HEALTH EFFECTS RES LAB, ENVIRON PROTECTION AGENCY, 79- *Concurrent Pos:* Adj asst prof, Univ Ala, 68-73. *Mem:* Sigma Xi; AAAS; Am Water Works Asn; Am Chem Soc. *Res:* Isolation of toxic organic chemicals from water using reverse osmosis; identification of toxic organics with computerized gc-mass spectrometry; high performance liquid chromatography. *Mailing Add:* 1835 Loisdale Ct Cincinnati OH 45230

KOPIN, IRWIN J, b New York, NY, Mar 27, 29; m 52; c 3. INTERNAL MEDICINE, PHARMACOLOGY. *Educ:* McGill Univ, BSc, 51, MD, 55. *Prof Exp:* Intern med, Boston City Hosp, 55-56, resident, 56-57; res assoc, NIH, 57-60; resident med, Columbia-Presby Med Ctr, 60-61; actg chief, Sect Med, Lab Clin Sci, 61-63, actg chief, Lab Clin Sci, 68-69, CHIEF, SECT MED, LAB CLIN SCI, NIMH, 63-, CHIEF, LAB CLIN SCI, 69- *Mem:* AAAS; Asn Am Physicians; Am Soc Biol Chemists; Am Soc Clin Invest; Am Soc Pharmacol & Exp Therapeut. *Res:* Biochemical pharmacology. *Mailing Add:* Lab of Clin Sci Nat Inst of Ment Health Bethesda MD 20014

KOPITO, LOUIS ELIEZER, b Haifa, Israel, Sept 20, 21; US citizen; m 47; c 2. NUTRITION. *Educ:* Tri-State Col, BS, 43; Columbia Univ, MS, 49. *Prof Exp:* Engr Cities Serv Oil Co, NY, 47-50; chief engr, Capitol Steel Corp, NY, 50-53; consult engr, 53-56; sr scientist, Baird-Atomic, Inc, 56-63; res assoc pediat, Harvard Med Sch, 68-69, prin assoc, 69-75; res assoc path, 63-71, RES ASSOC CLIN NUTRIT, CHILDREN'S HOSP MED CTR, 71-; SR RES SCIENTIST, MASS INST TECHNOL, 75- *Concurrent Pos:* Consult, Baird-Atomic, Inc, 63-66, Orion Res Inc, 63- & Jarell-Ash Div, Fisher Sci Co, 65-68; contributor, panel on zinc, Nat Acad Sci, 73. *Mem:* Soc Appl Spectros; Optical Soc Am; Am Chem Soc; NY Acad Sci; Am Inst Chem. *Res:* Spectrochemical analysis of human tissues; study of mineral metabolism in toxicology; environmental health; cystic fibrosis and other inborn errors of metabolism; pathology. *Mailing Add:* 204 Clinton Rd Brookline MA 02146

KOPKO, RONALD JOSEPH, chemical engineering, lubrication engineering, see previous edition

KOPLIN, JAMES RAY, b Monte Vista, Colo, June 9, 34; m 56; c 3. POPULATION ECOLOGY. *Educ:* Univ Mont, BS, 59, MS, 62; Colo State Univ, PhD(zool), 67. *Prof Exp:* Asst prof biol, State Univ NY Albany, 65-67; from asst prof to assoc prof wildlife, 67-76, dir grad studies, Sch Natural Resources, 70-74, chmn dept wildlife mgt, 74-77, PROF WILDLIFE, HUMBOLDT STATE UNIV, 76- *Mem:* Ecol Soc Am; Am Ornith Union; Cooper Ornith Soc; Wilson Ornith Soc. *Res:* Predator-prey dynamics; impact of predators on their prey; energetics of predators; inter and intra-specific interactions of birds and mammals. *Mailing Add:* Dept of Wildlife Mgt Humboldt State Univ Arcata CA 95521

KOPLOVE, H MICHAEL, b Philadelphia, Pa, Oct 13, 48. FERMENTATION TECHNOLOGY. *Educ:* Univ Pa, BS, 70; Mass Inst Technol, PhD(biochem eng), 77. *Prof Exp:* Res assoc, Squibb Corp, 70-72; sr engr, Union Carbide Corp, 77-79; sr res engr, Lederle Lab Med Res Div, Am Cyanamid, 79-80; SECT LEADER, SCHERING-PLOUGH CORP, 80- *Honors & Awards:* W H Peterson Award, Am Chem Soc, 74. *Mem:* Am Chem Soc; Am Inst Chem Engrs. *Res:* Fermentation process technology, with emphasis on antibiotic production processes; unsteady state continuous cultures for enzyme production. *Mailing Add:* Schering-Plough Corp Union NJ 07083

KOPLOW, JANE, b Ulm, Ger, Mar 15, 48; US citizen. MICROBIOLOGY, MOLECULAR BIOLOGY. *Educ:* Univ Wis, BA, 70; Univ Pa, MS, 73, PhD(molecular biol), 77. *Prof Exp:* fel virol, Sch Med, Washington Univ, 78-79, fel immunol & membranes, 79-81. *Res:* Synthesis of microbial membranes; defense mechanisms of pathogens. *Mailing Add:* 7146 Tulane St St Louis MO 63130

KOPLYAY, JANOS BERNATH, b Budapest, Hungary, June 24, 24; US citizen; m 58; c 4. APPLIED MATHEMATICS, COMPUTER SCIENCE. *Educ:* Royal Hungarian Air Force Acad, BS, 43; Royal Hungarian Polytech Inst, MS, 49; Northwestern Univ, MA, 64, PhD(math, psychol), 66. *Prof Exp:* Elec engr, Hungarian Utilities, Budapest, 48-49; chief engr electronic mech, Ygnis AG, Switz, 49-51; asst chief engr mech eng, Sociedade Paulista de Inst Gerais, Brazil, 51-55; engr design, Rochester & Goodell Engrs Inc, 56-63; asst prof math & psychol, Northwestern Univ, 65-68; SR RES SCIENTIST MATH & COMPUT SCI, AIR FORCE HUMAN RES LAB, US AIR FORCE SYSTS COMMAND, 68- *Concurrent Pos:* Consult, US Armed Serv & Friendly Allied Nations, 74-; charter mem, US Air Force Tech Adv Bd, 75-; prof math, San Antonio Col, 75- *Mem:* Math Asn Am; Mil Testing Asn; Am Statist Asn; Asn Comput Mach. *Res:* Mathematics; aerospace medicine; computer science. *Mailing Add:* AFHRL/MOM Brooks AFB San Antonio TX 78235

KOPP, EUGENE H(OWARD), b New York, NY, Oct 1, 29; m 50; c 3. ELECTRICAL ENGINEERING. *Educ:* City Col New York, BEE, 50, MEE, 53; Univ Calif, Los Angeles, PhD(eng), 65. *Prof Exp:* Proj engr, Polarad Electronics Corp, 50-53 & Kaye-Halbert Corp, 53-54; proj engr, Precision Radiation Instruments, Inc, 54-56, chief engr, 56-58; from asst prof to prof eng, Calif State Col, Los Angeles, 58-73, dean sch eng, 67-73; vpres acad affairs, West Coast Univ, 73-79; SR SCIENTIST, HUGHES AIRCRAFT CO, 80- *Concurrent Pos:* Res fel, Univ Leeds, 66-67; adj fac, Univ Calif, Los Angeles, 79- *Honors & Awards:* Excellence in Eng Educ Award, Western Elec Co, Inc, 67. *Mem:* Sr mem Inst Elec & Electronics Engrs. *Res:* Microwave components and antennas; educational administration. *Mailing Add:* PO Box 1351 South Pasadena CA 91030

KOPP, HARRIET GREEN, b New York, NY, June 18, 17; m 48, 72. AUDIOLOGY, CLINICAL PSYCHOLOGY. *Educ:* Brooklyn Col, BA, 37, MA, 39; Columbia Univ, dipl, 40, PhD(speech path, psychol), 62. *Prof Exp:* Instr speech path, Brooklyn Col, 37-39; res asst speech sci & path, Columbia Univ, 39-40; instr deaf educ, Ind Univ, 40-41; res asst speech sci & path, Columbia Univ, 41-43; res assoc speech sci, Bell Labs, 43-46; asst prof speech path, audiol & deaf, East Mich Univ, 46-48; dir speech & audiol, Pub Schs, Mich, 48-55; dir speech & audiol clin, Rehab Inst, Detroit, 55-59; prin deaf educ, Detroit Day Sch Deaf, 59-70; PROF SPEECH PATH & AUDIOL, SAN DIEGO STATE UNIV, 70-, ACTG DEAN, COL HUMAN SERV, 80- *Concurrent Pos:* Mem fac, Wayne State Univ, 59-70; consult, US Dept Health, Educ & Welfare, 63-; mem, Nat Adv Comt Educ Deaf, 66-69, chmn, 70-72. *Mem:* Fel Am Speech & Hearing Asn; AAAS; Conf Execs Am Schs for Deaf; Alexander Graham Bell Asn for Deaf; NY Acad Sci. *Res:* Physiologic phonetics; cognitive processing; analysis and synthesis of speech; speech pathology. *Mailing Add:* Dept of Commun Dis San Diego State Univ San Diego CA 92182

KOPP, JAY PATRICK, b Buffalo Center, Iowa, 38. PHYSICS. *Educ:* Loras Col, BS, 59; Univ Wis, MS, 61; Northwestern Univ, PhD(physics), 68. *Prof Exp:* Instr physics, Loras Col, 61-64; res assoc, Solid State Physics Lab, Swiss Fed Inst Technol, 67-69; ASST PROF PHYSICS, LORAS COL, 69- *Mem:* Am Phys Soc; Am Asn Physics Teachers; Swiss Phys Soc. *Res:* Experimental solid state physics using nuclear magnetic resonance and magnetization measurements to study magnetic properties of rare earth systems, principally indirect exchange mechanisms. *Mailing Add:* Dept of Physics Loras Col Dubuque IA 52001

KOPP, JOHN F, b Cincinnati, Ohio, Sept 9, 26; m 52; c 1. ANALYTICAL CHEMISTRY. *Educ:* Xavier Univ, Ohio, BS, 49, MS, 55. *Prof Exp:* Phys sci aid, Sanit Eng Ctr, US Pub Health Serv, 49-51, jr chemist, 51-54, res chemist, Health Field Hqs, 54-62, spectrochemist, Water Quality Sect, 62-67, Fed Water Pollution Control Admin, US Dept Interior, 67-70, spectrochemist, Anal Qual Control Lab, 70-74, BR CHIEF PHYSICS & CHEM, ENVIRON MONITORING & SUPPORT LAB, ENVIRON PROTECTION AGENCY, 74- *Mem:* Am Chem Soc; Soc Appl Spectros; Am Soc Test & Mat. *Res:* Emission spectroscopy; analysis for trace quantities of toxic elements; determination of zinc and copper in toxicology; trace elements in water; method development and applied research; water and waste samples. *Mailing Add:* Environ Monitoring & Supp Lab 26 St Clair St Cincinnati OH 45268

KOPP, MANFRED KURT, b Koenigsberg, Ger, Mar 8, 32; US citizen; m 58; c 1. INSTRUMENTATION. *Educ:* Univ Buenos Aires, Argentina, BSEE, 62; Univ Tenn, BSEE, 70, MSEE, 75. *Prof Exp:* Develop engr nuclear instrumentation, Comision Nac de Energia Atomica, Buenos Aires, Arg, 56-67; RES ENGR INSTRUMENTATION, OAK RIDGE NAT LAB, 67- *Mem:* Inst Elec & Electronics Engrs; Sigma Xi. *Res:* Low noise electronics; position sensitive proportional counters; radiation detectors, and basic measurement science. *Mailing Add:* Bldg 3500 PO Box X Oak Ridge TN 37830

KOPP, OTTO CHARLES, b Brooklyn, NY, July 22, 29; m 54; c 4. GEOLOGY. *Educ:* Univ Notre Dame, BS, 51; Columbia Univ, MA, 55, PhD(geol), 58. *Prof Exp:* Res asst, Columbia Univ, 55-58; from asst prof to assoc prof, 58-68, PROF GEOL, UNIV TENN, KNOXVILLE, 68- *Concurrent Pos:* Consult, Oak Ridge Nat Lab, 59-77, res partic, 77- *Honors & Awards:* Centennial of Sci Award, Univ Notre Dame, 65; Distinguished Prof Award, Am Fedn of Mineral Soc, 76. *Mem:* Fel Geol Soc Am; fel Mineral Soc Am; Sigma Xi; Nat Asn Geol Teachers; Am Inst Mining, Metall & Petrol Engrs. *Res:* Mineralogy; crystallography; petrology; petrography; hydrothermal synthesis of silicates and sulfides; coal geology; differential thermal analysis. *Mailing Add:* Dept of Geol Sci Univ of Tenn Knoxville TN 37996

KOPP, RICHARD E, b Brooklyn, NY, July 12, 31; m 53; c 4. SYSTEMS ANALYSIS, CONTROL THEORY. *Educ:* Polytech Inst Brooklyn, BEE, 53, MEE, 57, DEE(control theory), 61. *Prof Exp:* Res engr comput, Grumman Aircraft Eng Corp, 53-57, group leader comput res, 57-63, sect head, 63-74, DIR SYST SCI RES, GRUMMAN AEROSPACE CORP, 74-

Concurrent Pos: Adj prof, Polytech Inst Brooklyn, 61- *Mem:* Inst Elec & Electronics Engrs; Am Inst Aeronaut & Astronaut. *Res:* Electronics; control theory; astrodynamics; computing; marine sciences; mathematics; data processing; image processing; filtering; simulation. *Mailing Add:* Grumman Aerospace Corp Bethpage NY 11714

KOPP, ROGER ALAN, b Detroit, Mich, Feb 17, 40; m 62; c 3. SOLAR PHYSICS, LASER FUSION. *Educ:* Univ Mich, BS, 61; Harvard Univ, MA, 63, PhD(astron), 68. *Prof Exp:* Staff scientist, High Altitude Observ, Nat Ctr Atmospheric Res, 66-76; STAFF MEM, LOS ALAMOS NAT LAB, 76- *Concurrent Pos:* Vis scientist, Max Planck Inst Physics & Astrophys, 71-72, 79-80. *Mem:* Am Astron Soc; Am Geophys Union; Int Astron Union. *Res:* Heating of the solar corona; origin and dynamics of the solar wind; structure of the chromosphere-corona transition region; laser fusion target design and experiments; laser-plasma interactions. *Mailing Add:* Los Alamos Nat Lab Los Alamos NM 87545

KOPPEL, GARY ALLEN, b Cleveland, Ohio, Aug 8, 43; m 66; c 2. ORGANIC CHEMISTRY. *Educ:* Case Western Reserve Univ, 65; Univ Pittsburgh, PhD(org chem), 69. *Prof Exp:* NIH fel org chem, Columbia Univ, 69-70; res scientist org chem, 70-80, RES ASSOC, ELI LILLY & CO, 80- *Concurrent Pos:* Lectr chem, Butler Univ, 71- *Mem:* Sigma Xi; AAAS. *Res:* Synthesis of natural products; development of new cephalosporins; new synthetic methods in the synthesis of penicillins and cephalosporins. *Mailing Add:* 7823 Sunset Ln Indianapolis IN 46260

KOPPEL, LOWELL B, b Chicago, Ill, Sept 13, 35; m 57; c 2. CHEMICAL ENGINEERING. *Educ:* Northwestern Univ, BS, 57, PhD(chem eng), 60; Univ Mich, MSE, 58. *Prof Exp:* Instr chem eng, Calif Inst Technol, 60-61; from asst prof to assoc prof, 61-67, PROF CHEM ENG, PURDUE UNIV, 67- *Concurrent Pos:* Consult, Argonne Nat Lab, 62- *Mem:* Am Chem Soc; Am Inst Chem Engrs. *Res:* Process control; transport phenomena; applied mathematics; process simulation and optimization. *Mailing Add:* 2234 Carberry Dr West Lafayette IN 47907

KOPPELMAN, ELAINE, b Brooklyn, NY, Mar 28, 37; m 70. MATHEMATICS. *Educ:* Brooklyn Col, BA, 57; Yale Univ, MA, 59; Johns Hopkins Univ, PhD(hist sci), 69. *Prof Exp:* From instr to asst prof, 61-74, ASSOC PROF MATH, GOUCHER COL, 74- *Mem:* Math Asn Am; Hist Sci Soc. *Res:* History of modern mathematics, particularly the development of algebra during the nineteenth and twentieth centuries. *Mailing Add:* Dept of Math Goucher Col Towson MD 21204

KOPPELMAN, LEE EDWARD, b New York City, NY, May 19, 27; m 48; c 4. ENVIRONMENTAL SCIENCE. *Educ:* City Col, New York, BEE, 50; Pratt Inst Grad Sch Architecture, IASP, 64; NY Univ Grad Sch, DPA, 70. *Hon Degrees:* LD, Long Island Univ, 78. *Prof Exp:* PROF, PLANNING & RESOURCE MGT, STATE UNIV NY, STONY BROOK, 67- *Concurrent Pos:* Dir planning, Suffolk County Planning Comn, 60-; exec dir regional planning, Long Island Regional Planning Bd, 65-; appointee, Coastal Zone Mgt Adv Coun, Nat Oceanic & Atmospheric Admin, 73-75, Nat Shoreline Erosion Adv Panel, US Army, 74-81; adj prof, Grad Sch Environ Sci & Forestry, Syracuse Univ, 75-; consult, US Dept Housing & Urban Develop, 75-78, UN Off Ocean Econ & Technol, 81. *Mem:* Am Planning Asn; Sigma Xi. *Res:* Integraton of coastal zone sciences and the regional planning process, including pollution studies of surface waters and the institutional management mechanisms required for coastal development. *Mailing Add:* Long Island Regional Planning Bd Vet Hwy Happauge NY 11788

KOPPELMAN, RAY, b Chicago, Ill, Aug 25, 22; m 46; c 2. BIOCHEMISTRY, BIOLOGY. *Educ:* Univ Chicago, BS, 44, PhD(biochem), 52. *Prof Exp:* Asst biochem, Univ Chicago, 47-52; from instr to asst prof, 52-63, assoc prof biochem & head col biol sect, 63-67, assoc dean, Col Biol Div, 65-67; head, Nat Sci Found Liaison Staff, New Delhi, 67-69; V PRES RES & GRAD STUDIES, W VA UNIV, 70- *Concurrent Pos:* N Cent Asn consult-exam, grad record exam. *Mem:* AAAS; Am Soc Biol Chem; Am Inst Biol Sci. *Res:* Metabolism of virus-infected bacterial and animal cell systems. *Mailing Add:* Stewart Hall WVa Univ Morgantown WV 26506

KOPPENAAL, THEODORE J, b Milwaukee, Wis, Dec 19, 31; m 54; c 3. METALLURGY. *Educ:* Univ Wis, BS, 54; Univ Ill, MS, 58; Northwestern Univ, PhD(metall), 61. *Prof Exp:* Asst metallurgist, Argonne Nat Lab, Ill, 62-66, assoc metallurgist, 66-67; supvr phys metall, aeronutronic div, Ford Aerospace & Commun Corp, 67-79; dir eng, heavy metals div, Aerojet Ordnance Co, 79-81; PRES, KOPPENAAL & ASSOC, 81- *Mem:* Fel Am Soc Metals. *Res:* Technical consultant; technical marketing for diversified programs related to materials science and engineering. *Mailing Add:* Koppenaal & Assoc 14701 Sweeten St Irvine CA 92714

KOPPENHEFFER, THOMAS LYNN, b Harrisburg, Pa, May 23, 42; m 67. BIOCHEMISTRY, IMMUNOLOGY. *Educ:* Bloomsburg State Col, BS, 64; Williams Col, MA, 66; Boston Univ, PhD(biol), 70. *Prof Exp:* Asst prof biol, Boston Univ, 70-71; assoc surg, Harvard Med Sch, 72-73; ASST PROF BIOL, WILLIAMS COL, 73- *Concurrent Pos:* Res fel surg, Harvard Med Sch, 71-72. *Mem:* AAAS. *Res:* Tumor immunology; biology of endogenous RNA viruses. *Mailing Add:* Dept of Biol Williams Col Williamstown MA 01267

KOPPERL, SHELDON JEROME, b Cleveland, Ohio, Sept 11, 43; m 67; c 2. HISTORY OF SCIENCE, NUTRITION. *Educ:* Case Inst Technol, BS, 65; Univ Wis, Madison, PhD(chem, hist sci), 70. *Prof Exp:* Asst prof hist sci, 70-72, asst prof health sci, 72-75, assoc prof, 75-81, PROF, SCH HEALTH SCI, GRAND VALLEY STATE COL, 81- *Mem:* Am Chem Soc; Hist Sci Soc; Soc Hist Technol. *Res:* Historical studies in inorganic, physical and organo-metallic chemistry, chiefly since 1800; studies in the history of medicine, especially early 20th century. *Mailing Add:* Sch of Health Sci Grand Valley State Col Allendale MI 49401

KOPPERMAN, RALPH DAVID, b New York, NY, Feb 17, 42; div; c 2. MATHEMATICAL LOGIC. *Educ:* Columbia Col, AB, 62; Mass Inst Technol, PhD(math), 65. *Prof Exp:* Lectr math, Boston Univ, 63-65; asst prof, Univ RI, 65-67; asst prof, 67-71, ASSOC PROF, CITY COL NEW YORK, 71- *Mem:* Am Math Soc; Asn Symbolic Logic. *Res:* Model theory; topological rings and modules; distance spaces, continuity spaces and uniform spaces. *Mailing Add:* Dept of Math City Col of NY New York NY 10031

KOPPLE, KENNETH D(AVID), b Philadelphia, Pa, Oct 21, 30; m 60. ORGANIC CHEMISTRY. *Educ:* Mass Inst Technol, SB, 51, PhD(chem), 54. *Prof Exp:* Instr org chem, Univ Chicago, 54-56, asst prof, 56-62; res chemist, Gen Elec Co Res Lab, 62-65; assoc prof, 65-71, PROF CHEM, ILL INST TECHNOL, 71- *Concurrent Pos:* J S Guggenheim Found fel, Lab Chem Biodynamics, Univ Calif, Berkeley, 64-65; NIH res career develop award, 70-75; for res guest, SNAM Progetti Laboratori Ricerche di Base, Rome, Italy, 74. *Mem:* Am Chem Soc; fel AAAS; Am Soc Biol Chemists; Royal Soc Chem. *Res:* Peptide chemistry, synthesis and spectroscopic determination of comformation; nuclear magnetic resonance; electron transfer reactions. *Mailing Add:* Dept of Chem Ill Inst of Technol Chicago IL 60616

KOPPLIN, J(ULIUS) O(TTO), b Appleton, Wis, Feb 6, 25; m 50; c 4. ELECTRICAL ENGINEERING, MATERIALS SCIENCE. *Educ:* Univ Wis, BS, 49; Purdue Univ, MS, 54, PhD(elec eng), 59. *Prof Exp:* Corrosion engr, Northern Ind Pub Serv Co, 49-53; instr elec eng, Purdue Univ, 54-58; asst prof, Univ Ill, 58-61; vis asst prof, Mass Inst Technol, 61; assoc prof, Univ Ill, 62-68; prof elec eng & head dept, Univ Tex, El Paso, 68-75; PROF ELEC ENG & CHMN DEPT, IOWA STATE UNIV, 75- *Mem:* Inst Elec & Electronics Engrs; Am Soc Eng Educ. *Res:* Superconductivity; electric and magnetic properties of materials; liquid and solid surface phenomena. *Mailing Add:* Dept of Elec Eng Iowa State Univ Ames IA 50011

KOPRIWA, BEATRIX MARKUS, b Donau, Austria, July 18, 26; m 57. HISTOLOGY. *Educ:* Univ Vienna, cert teaching, 50, PhD(mineral), 55. *Prof Exp:* Res asst, 58-63, lectr, 63-66, asst prof, 66-69, ASSOC PROF HISTOL, DEPT ANAT, McGILL UNIV, 69- *Res:* Development and improvement of a variety of radioautographic methods on the light and electron microscopic level; procedures are developed which provide high resolution and high sensitivity for quantitative electron microscopic radioautography. *Mailing Add:* Dept of Anat McGill Univ Montreal PQ H3A 2B2 Can

KOPROWSKA, IRENA, b Warsaw, Poland, May 12, 17; nat US; m 38; c 2. PATHOLOGY, CYTOLOGY. *Educ:* Warsaw Med Sch, MD, 39. *Prof Exp:* Intern med, Villejuif Lunatic Asylum, France, 40; asst pathologist, Rio de Janeiro City Hosps, 42-44; res asst & asst pathologist, Med Col, Cornell Univ & New York Hosp, 45-46; res asst appl immunol, Pub Health Res Inst, City of New York, 46-47; asst pathologist, New York Infirmary, 47-49; res fel & assoc anat, Med Col, Cornell Univ, 49-54; asst prof path, State Univ NY Downstate Med Ctr, 54-57; from assoc prof to prof, Hahnemann Med Col, 57-70; PROF PATH & DIR CYTOL SERV, HEALTH SCI CTR, TEMPLE UNIV, 70- *Concurrent Pos:* Res fel, Med Col, Cornell Univ, 49-54; USPHS res grants, 54-; Runyon Mem Fund grant, 55-56; Am Cancer Soc grant, 58-61; lectr, France, Poland, India & Iran, 52-; consult, WHO, 62- *Mem:* AAAS; Am Soc Cytol; Am Asn Cancer Res; Am Soc Exp Path; Am Soc Clin Pathologists. *Res:* Studies of progressive morphologic cellular changes, especially neoplastic progression in human beings, mice and in tissue culture systems. *Mailing Add:* Path/Cytol Div 3401 N Broad St Philadelphia PA 19140

KOPROWSKI, HILARY, b Warsaw, Poland, Dec 5, 16; nat US; m 38; c 2. BIOLOGY. *Educ:* Univ Warsaw, MD, 39. *Hon Degrees:* Var from Univ Helsinki, Finland, Ludwig Maximillian Univ, Munich, WGer & Widener Col, Chester, Pa. *Prof Exp:* Mem staff, Yellow Fever Res Serv, Rockefeller Found & Ministry Educ, Brazil, 40-44; mem staff res div, Am Cyanamid Co, 44-46, asst dir viral & rickettsial res, Lederle Labs, NY, 46-57; PROF MICROBIOL, FAC ARTS & SCI & WISTAR PROF RES MED, UNIV PA, 57-, DIR, WISTAR INST ANAT & BIOL, 57- *Concurrent Pos:* Consult, Nat Cancer Inst, NIH & USPHS, 62-70; mem expert comt on rabies, WHO, Switz, 50; assoc ed, Virology, 55-60, J Bact, 56-60 & Cancer Res, 57-61; mem study sect, NIH, 56; dir, Am Asn Cancer Res, 63-66; Fulbright scholar, Max Planck Inst Physiol of Behav, Ger, 71; Alexander Von Humbolt Sr Scientist Award, Max Planck Inst, W Ger. *Honors & Awards:* Comdr, Order of Merit; Chevalier, Order of the Royal Lion, Belg; Alvarenga Prize; Polish Millennium Award, Alfred Jurzykowski Found, 66. *Mem:* Nat Acad Sci; NY Acad Med; NY Acad Sci (pres, 59); AAAS. *Res:* Cell biology, virology, and immunology; cancer; vaccine against poliomyelitis, hog cholera and rabies. *Mailing Add:* Wistar Inst 36th & Spruce Sts Philadelphia PA 19104

KORACH, MALCOLM, b New York, NY, Apr 25, 22; m 46; c 3. ORGANIC CHEMISTRY. *Educ:* Yale Univ, BS, 42, PhD(chem), 48. *Prof Exp:* Asst, Manhattan Proj, Columbia Univ, 43 & Oak Ridge Inst Nuclear Studies, 44-46; res chemist, org group leader & asst dir res, 49-70, dir res, 70-74, MGR RES, CHEM DIV, PPG INDUSTS, 74- *Mem:* Am Chem Soc. *Res:* Heavy organic chemicals; chlorinated organics; hydrogen peroxide and its utilization. *Mailing Add:* Chem Div PPG Industs One Gateway Ctr Pittsburgh PA 15222

KORAN, ZOLTAN, b Hungary, May 27, 34; Can citizen; m 68; c 4. FOREST PRODUCTS, PULP TECHNOLOGY. *Educ:* Univ BC, BSc, 59, MF, 61; Syracuse Univ, PhD(forestry), 64. *Prof Exp:* Asst prof forestry, Univ N H, 63-64; res scientist pulp & paper, Pulp & Paper Res Inst Can, 65-68; asst prof forestry, Univ Toronto, 68-73; res scientist, Que Indust Res Ctr, 73-76; PROF ENG, UNIV QUE, 76- *Mem:* Forest Prod Res Soc; Int Asn Wood Anat; Can Pulp & Paper Asn; Micros Soc Can. *Res:* Cytology, anatomy and ultrastructure of wood, bark, fiber and paper; thermomechanical pulping; pulp and paper properties; forest products and utilization; composite boards; wood finishing and impregnation; x-ray, light and electron microscopic studies; material science engineering. *Mailing Add:* Dept Eng Univ Que CP 500 Trois-Rivieres PQ G9A 5H7 Can

KORANT, BRUCE DAVID, b Brooklyn, NY, Aug 9, 43; m 69; c 1. VIROLOGY. *Educ:* Brooklyn Col, BS, 65; Pa State Univ, MS, 67, PhD(microbiol), 69. *Prof Exp:* BIOCHEMIST VIROL, CENT RES DEPT, EXP STA, E I DU PONT DE NEMOURS & CO, INC, 69- *Mem:* Am Soc Microbiol; Am Soc Cell Biol. *Res:* Animal virology; bacteriophages; virus structure and replication; effects of viruses on cells; protein chemistry; proteolytic enzymes. *Mailing Add:* Cent Res Dept Exp Sta E I du Pont de Nemours & Co Inc Wilmington DE 19898

KORANYI, ADAM, b Szeged, Hungary, July 13, 32; US citizen. MATHEMATICS. *Educ:* Univ Szeged, dipl, 54; Univ Chicago, PhD(math), 59. *Prof Exp:* Instr math, Harvard Univ, 59-60; asst prof, Univ Calif, Berkeley, 60-64; vis asst prof, Princeton Univ, 64-65; assoc prof math, Belfer Grad Sch, Yeshiva Univ, 65-68; prof, 68-79; PROF MATH, WASHINGTON UNIV, 79- *Mem:* Am Math Soc. *Res:* Symmetric spaces; Lie groups; theory of functions of several complex variables. *Mailing Add:* Math Dept Washington Univ St Louis MO 63130

KORCAK, RONALD FRANK, b New York, NY, Mar 29, 47; m 71; c 1. SOIL SCIENCE, AGRONOMY. *Educ:* Cornell Univ, BS, 68; Univ Md, MS, 73, PhD(soil chem, fertil), 77. *Prof Exp:* SOIL SCIENTIST FRUIT NUTRIT, FRUIT LAB, USDA, 77- *Mem:* Am Soc Agron; Soil Sci Soc Am; Am Soc Hort Sci; Coun Agr Sci & Technol. *Res:* Nutritional disorders of apples; calcium nutrition of fruit; blueberry adaptation to mineral soils; the effect of soil root environment on fruit nutrition; utilization of waste products in orchards. *Mailing Add:* Fruit Lab Beltsville Agr Res Ctr USDA Beltsville MD 10705

KORCEK, STEFAN, b Trnava, Czech, May 28, 34; m 65; c 2. PHYSICAL ORGANIC CHEMISTRY, LUBRICANTS CHEMISTRY. *Educ:* Slovak Tech Univ, Bratislava, MS, 57, PhD(chem, chem eng & fuel technol), 67. *Prof Exp:* Assoc prof chem kinetics & reactors design, Dept Chem & Technol Petrol, Slovak Tech Univ, 57-68; fel phys org chem, Div Chem, Nat Res Coun, Ottawa, Can, 68-70; sr res scientist, 71-76, prin res scientist assoc, 76-81, STAFF SCIENTIST LUBRICANT CHEM & PHYS ORG CHEM, RES FUELS & LUBRICANTS DEPT, FORD MOTOR CO, DEARBORN, MICH, 81- *Concurrent Pos:* Vis res off, Div Chem, Nat Res Coun, Ottawa, Can, 70-71. *Honors & Awards:* F R McFarland Award, Soc Automotive Engrs, 81. *Mem:* Am Chem Soc; Soc Automotive Engrs. *Res:* Kinetics and mechanisms of autoxidation and inhibited oxidation of organic substrates in liquid phase at elevated temperatures; mechanism of action of antioxidants; automotive lubricants, their chemistry and degradation in service; reactions of lubricant antioxidant additives in engines; author or coauthor of over 40 publications. *Mailing Add:* 4778 Crestview Ct Birmingham MI 48010

KORCHAK, ERNEST I(AN), b Opava, Czech, Feb 15, 34; Australian citizen; m 59; c 3. CHEMICAL ENGINEERING. *Educ:* Univ Melbourne, BChE, 57; Mass Inst Technol, SM, 61, ScD(chem eng), 64. *Prof Exp:* Res engr chem eng, Imp Chem Industs, Australia & NZ, 58-59; chem engr, Halcon Int, Inc, 64-67; sales exec, Sci Design Co, Inc, 67-71; vpres & gen mgr, Halcon Catalyst Industs, 71-75, pres, Halcon Res & Develop Corp, 75-80, PRES, SCI DESIGN CO, 81- *Mem:* Am Chem Soc; Am Inst Chem Engrs. *Res:* Gas flow and turbulence, application to packed beds; process research and development of organic chemical processes, special emphasis on kinetics and separations. *Mailing Add:* Sci Design Co 2 Park Ave New York NY 10016

KORCHIN, LEO, b Brooklyn, NY, July 1, 14; wid; c 2. ORAL SURGERY. *Educ:* Cornell Univ, BS, 36; NY Univ, DDS, 41; Georgetown Univ, MS, 54; Am Bd Oral & Maxillofacial Surg, dipl. *Prof Exp:* Chief oral surg sect, Army Hosp, US Army, Ft Jay, NY, 48-52, instr oral surg & asst prof mil sci & tactics, Sch Dent, Georgetown Univ, 52-54, chief oral surg sect, Rodriguez Army Hosp, PR, 54-57, chief oral surg br, Dent Detachment, Ft Devens, Mass, 57-62, chief dent clin & oral surg sect, 97th Gen Hosp, Frankfurt, Ger, 62-65, chief dent serv & oral surg & dir dent intern training prog, Martin Army Hosp, Ft Benning, Ga, 65-67; assoc prof oral surg, 67-72, dir dept surg sci, 72-75, PROF ORAL & MAXILLOFACIAL SURG, SCH DENT, UNIV PR, SAN JUAN, 72-, DIR DEPT SURG SCI, 78-, ASST DEAN FOR CLIN INSTR, 81- *Concurrent Pos:* Fel oral path, Armed Forces Inst Path, 75-76. *Honors & Awards:* Novice Award, Int Asn Dent Res, 54. *Mem:* Am Soc Oral & Maxillofacial Surgeons; Am Acad Oral Path; Am Dent Asn; Am Asn Dent Schs; Int Asn Oral Surgeons. *Res:* Effects of starch sponge implanted in bone. *Mailing Add:* Asst Dean Clin Instr Univ of PR Sch of Dent San Juan PR 00936

KORCHYNSKY, M(ICHAEL), b Kiev, Ukraine, Apr 11, 18; nat US; m 51; c 3. PHYSICAL METALLURGY, MATERIALS SCIENCE. *Educ:* Tech Univ Lviv, Dipl Ing, 42. *Prof Exp:* Asst metall, Tech Univ Lviv, 42-44; chief engr, US Army, Ger, 45-50; res metallurgist phys metall, Metals Res Labs, Union Carbide Metals Co, 51-60, tech supvr, Tech Dept, 60-61; res supvr alloy & high strength steels, Jones & Laughlin Steel Corp, 61-65, asst dir res new prod develop, Graham Res Lab, 65-70, dir prod res, 70-73; DIR ALLOY DEVELOP, METALS DIV, UNION CARBIDE CORP, 73- *Concurrent Pos:* Sr develop fel, Union Carbide Corp, 79. *Honors & Awards:* Am Iron & Steel Inst Medal, 65; Howe Mem lectr, Asn Inst Mining, Metall & Petrol Eng, 83. *Mem:* Fel Am Soc Metals; Am Inst Mining, Metall & Petrol Engrs; Brit Metals Soc; Am Iron & Steel Inst; Japan Iron & Steel Inst. *Res:* Physical metallurgy of steels; materials for high-temperature service; nuclear fuels; alloy design and development; technology and application of high-strength, low-alloy steels; management of industrial research and product development; technological marketing. *Mailing Add:* Union Carbide Corp Metals Div Robinson Plaza II Rte 60 Pittsburgh PA 15205

KORDA, EDWARD J(OHN), b Duluth, Minn, Nov 17, 18; m 45; c 3. METALLURGICAL ENGINEERING, MATERIALS SCIENCE. *Educ:* Univ Minn, BMetE, 47; Stevens Inst Technol, MS, 51. *Prof Exp:* Lab asst chem, Duluth Jr Col, 38-39; lab asst metallog, Univ Minn, 39-41; scientist metall res, 47-48; mem res staff metall, Manhattan Proj, 44-46; proj engr metall eng, Curtiss Wright Corp, NJ, 48-49 & 50-56; prof metall eng, Drexel

Inst, 56-65; dir ed & res, Del Sci Labs, Inc, 65; electron microscopist, Corning Glass Works, 65-66, sr res scientist, 66-75, res supvr, 75-79; vis prof, Atlanta Univ, 79-81; RES SUPVR, CORNING GLASS WORKS, 81- *Concurrent Pos:* Laboratorian, Am Steel & Wire Co, Minn, 39-41; res engr metall, Stevens Inst Technol, 49-50, instr, 49-51. *Mem:* Am Soc Testing & Mat; Am Soc Metals; Electron Micros Soc Am; Am Ceramic Soc; Sigma Xi. *Res:* Electron microscopy and optics; metallography; physical metallurgy; solid state physics, x-ray analysis; ceramography; optical microscopy; image analysis; electron diffraction. *Mailing Add:* RD 3 Box 386 Hornby Rd Corning NY 14830

KORDA, PETER E, b Budapest, Hungary, Dec 5, 31; US citizen; m 54; c 4. ENGINEERING MECHANICS, STRUCTURAL ENGINEERING. *Educ:* Budapest Tech Univ, Dipl Eng, 54; Ohio State Univ, PhD(eng mech), 64. *Prof Exp:* Struct designer, Indust Bldg Design Off, Hungary, 54-56, Livesley & Henderson, Eng, 56-57 & Dominion Bridge Co, Ltd, Can, 57-60; asst proj design, 60-61, res assoc & instr eng mech, 61-63, from asst prof to prof, 64-71, PROF, SCH ARCHIT, OHIO STATE UNIV, 71- *Concurrent Pos:* Consult engr, Miller & Korda, 64-67, pres, Korda Eng Co Consult Engrs, 67- *Mem:* Am Soc Civil Engrs; Concrete Inst Am; Int Asn Shell Struct; Nat Soc Prof Engrs; Am Soc Eng Educ. *Res:* Shallow shell theory with computer applications; dynamic stability and structural damping. *Mailing Add:* 5544 Dublin Rd Dublin OH 43017

KORDAN, HERBERT ALLEN, b St Louis, Mo, Apr 10, 26; m 49; c 3. DEVELOPMENTAL PHYSIOLOGY, PLANT MORPHOGENETICS. *Educ:* Univ Calif, Los Angeles, BA, 55, MS, 58, PhD(plant sci), 61. *Prof Exp:* Fel tumorigenesis, Cedars of Lebanon Hosp, Los Angeles, 61-62; res staff mem plant physiol & consult, Stanford Res Inst, 63; asst res plant physiologist, Univ Calif, Los Angeles, 63-65; asst prof biol, Mt St Mary's Col, Calif, 64-66; assoc prof, Gustavus Adolphus Col, 66-67; UNIV LECTR BOT, UNIV BIRMINGHAM, 68- *Concurrent Pos:* US Pub Health Serv fel, Univ Leeds, 67-68. *Mem:* Soc Exp Biol; fel Bot Soc Edinburgh; fel Royal Micros Soc; Sigma Xi. *Res:* Comparative cytology; morphology and physiology of growing and non-growing plant cells. *Mailing Add:* Dept Plant Biol Univ of Birmingham PO Box 363 Birmingham England United Kingdom

KORDESCH, KARL VICTOR, b Vienna, Austria, Mar 18, 22; nat US; m 46; c 4. ELECTROCHEMISTRY. *Educ:* Univ Vienna, PhD(chem), 48. *Prof Exp:* Asst & lectr chem, Chem Inst, Univ Vienna, 46-48, asst prof, 48-53; chem engr, Signal Corps Eng Labs, NJ, 53-55; res chemist & group leader, Develop Dept, 55-70, sr res assoc, Parma Res Lab, Union Carbide Corp, 70-74, corp res fel, Battery Prod Div, 74-77; PROF, TECH UNIV GRAZ, AUSTRIA, 77-; DIR, INST INORG CHEM TECHNOL, 77-; CONSULT ELECTROCHEM, 77- *Honors & Awards:* Nat Energy Award, Austria, 81. *Mem:* Am Chem Soc; Electrochem Soc; Austrian Chem Soc; Int Electrochem Soc (secy, 81). *Res:* Electrochemical systems; batteries, especially with alkaline electrolytes; hydrogen-oxygen fuel cells; carbon electrodes; test and control instruments; electronic circuitry. *Mailing Add:* Carnerigesse 18 Graz A-8010 Austria

KORDOVA, NONNA, b Krasnodar, USSR; Can citizen; m 45. RICKETTSIAL DISEASES. *Educ:* Charles Univ, Prague, MD, 45; Czech Acad Sci, PhD(med virol), 60. *Prof Exp:* Res assoc pediat, Children's Hosp, Komensky Univ, 45-54, asst prof, 54-56; res assoc rickettsioses, Inst Virol, Czech Acad Sci, 56-60, sr scientist, 60-66, chief lab, 66-68; res assoc, Univ Kans, 68-69; assoc prof, 70-74, PROF, MED COL, UNIV MAN, 74- *Honors & Awards:* Recognition Dipl, Czech Acad Sci, 65. *Mem:* Can Soc Microbiol; Am Soc Microbiol; Can Pub Health Asn. *Res:* Pathogenesis of chlamydial diseases; parasite-host interactions at the cellular and subcellular level. *Mailing Add:* Dept of Med Microbiol Univ of Man Med Col Winnipeg MB R3T 2N2 Can

KORDYBAN, EUGENE S, b Ukraine, May 20, 28; m 53; c 6. FLUID MECHANICS. *Educ:* Univ Detroit, BME, 54; State Univ NY Buffalo, MS, 60, PhD(mech eng), 69. *Prof Exp:* Engr, Linde Div, Union Carbide Corp, 54-64, sr engr, 64-69; asst prof, 69-72, assoc prof civil eng, 72-81, PROF MECH ENG, UNIV DETROIT, 81- *Concurrent Pos:* NSF res grant, 70-72. *Mem:* Am Soc Mech Engrs. *Res:* Polyphase flow, especially slug flow, basic fluid mechanics, flow visualization techniques and flow measurement. *Mailing Add:* Dept of Civil Eng Univ of Detroit Detroit MI 48221

KORECKY, BORIVOJ, b Prague, Czech, Sept 9, 29; m; c 2. MEDICAL PHYSIOLOGY. *Educ:* Charles Univ, Prague, MD, 55; Czech Acad Sci, PhD, 61. *Prof Exp:* From asst prof to assoc prof path physiol, Charles Univ, Prague, 55-66; assoc prof, 66-71, PROF PHYSIOL, UNIV OTTAWA, 71- *Concurrent Pos:* Med Res Coun Can res fel, 63-64. *Mem:* Can Physiol Soc; Am Physiol Soc. *Res:* Cardiovascular and respiratory physiology. *Mailing Add:* Dept of Physiol Fac of Med Univ of Ottawa Ottawa ON K1N 9A9 Can

KOREIN, JULIUS, b New York, NY, Sept 27, 28; m 57; c 3. NEUROLOGY. *Educ:* NY Univ, BA, 49, MD, 53. *Prof Exp:* Intern, Maimonides Hosp, Brooklyn, 53-54; asst resident neurol, Mt Sinai Hosp, 54-55; asst & chief resident, NY Univ-Bellevue Hosp Ctr, 55-57; from asst prof to assoc prof, 61-72, assoc dir anal & comput methodology, Dept Radiol, 68-72, PROF NEUROL, MED CTR, NY UNIV, 72- *Concurrent Pos:* Fel, Mt Sinai Hosp, 53-54, asst attend, 59-70, spec trainee, 60-61; spec trainee, NY Univ-Bellevue Hosp Ctr, 59-60; vis asst, Bellevue Hosp, 59-68, vis assoc, 68-72, attend, 72-, dir EEG, 61-70, chief, 70-; attend physician, Vet Admin Hosp, Manhattan, 61-73, consult, 73-; asst attend, NY Univ Hosp, 61-72, attend, 71-; consult, Health Ins Plan of Greater New York, 63-65, Gen Elec Corp, 66-67, Children's Bur, Dept Health, Educ & Welfare, 66-71, Int Info Processing, 67-70, Task Force, Nat Prog Dermat, 69-72 & Nat Inst Neurol Dis & Stroke, 71-74; proj dir, Health Res Coun Grants, City of New York, 63-65 & Nat Cancer Inst, 66-70; prin investr, USV Pharmaceut Corp, 63-72, Warner-Lambert Inst, 66-67, Nat Ctr Health Serv Res & Develop, 66-70 & Hoffmann-La Roche Labs, 69-70; co-investr, Nat Inst Neurol Dis & Stroke, 65-67, proj dir & vchmn study cerebral death, 71-72; co-investr sensory feedback ther, Inst Crippled & Disabled Res & Rehab Ctr, 72-; assoc ed, Am Soc Cybernet Forum, 74-80; mem adv bd, Int J Neurosci; adv, President's Comn Study Ethical Problems Med, Biomed & Behav Res, Washington DC, 80-81. *Mem:* AAAS; AMA; Am Neurol Asn; Am Acad Neurol; Asn Res Nerv & Ment Dis. *Res:* Computer applications in capture, storage, retrieval and analysis of narrative medical data for the purpose of patient care and clinical research; sensory feedback therapy in neuromuscular disorders; electroencephalography and behavior, including computer analysis of the electroencephalogram, effects of drugs on the electroencephalogram and behavior, diagnosis of brain death and operant conditioning of normal and abnormal electroencephalograph activity and their behavioral correlates; pathophysiology and treatment of segmental torsion dystonia; models of neurophysiological structures. *Mailing Add:* Dept of Neurol NY Univ Med Ctr New York NY 10016

KORENBROT, JUAN IGAL, b Mexico City, Mex, Nov 29, 47; m 72; c 1. BIOPHYSICS. *Educ:* Johns Hopkins Univ, MA, 71, PhD(biophys), 72. *Prof Exp:* Res assoc biophys, Johns Hopkins Univ, 71-72; res assoc physiol, Univ Calif, Los Angeles, 72-73, lectr, 73-74; asst prof, 74-80, ASSOC PROF PHYSIOL, UNIV CALIF, SAN FRANCISCO, 80- *Concurrent Pos:* Vis scientist biochem, Nat Polytech Inst, 73. *Mem:* Soc Neurosci. *Res:* Molecular mechanisms of ion transport; reconstitution of biological ion translocator in model membranes; mechanisms of function of Rhodopsins. *Mailing Add:* Dept of Physiol Univ of Calif Sch of Med San Francisco CA 94122

KORENJAK, ALLEN J, electrical engineering, computer science, see previous edition

KORENMAN, STANLEY G, b New York, NY, Jan 21, 33; m 56; c 3. ENDOCRINOLOGY, BIOCHEMISTRY. *Educ:* Princeton Univ, AB, 54; Columbia Univ, MD, 58. *Prof Exp:* Intern, Second Div, Bellevue Hosp & Mem Hosp, New York, 58-59, asst resident med, 50-61; clin assoc, Endocrinol Br, Nat Cancer Inst, 61-63, med officer & sr investr, 63-66; from asst prof to assoc prof med, Sch Med, Univ Calif, 66-70; prof med & biochem & chief endocrinol div, Sch Med, Univ Iowa, 70-74; PROF MED & CHMN DEPT, UNIV CALIF, LOS ANGELES, 74-, ASSOC DEAN RES EDUC, SAN FERNANDO VALLEY PROG, 81- *Concurrent Pos:* Collab investr, Lab Chem Biol, Inst Arthritis & Metab Dis, 64-65; clin instr, Med Ctr, George Washington Univ, 65-66; coordr regional med prog, Dept Med, Harbor Gen Hosp, 68-70, dir clin res ctr, 69-70; mem, Reproductive Biol Study Sect, 70-73; mem, Breast Cancer Task Force, 72; chmn dept med, San Fernando Valley Prog; chief med, Vet Admin Med Ctr, Sepulveda. *Mem:* Am Soc Clin Invest; fel Am Col Physicians; Am Fedn Clin Res; Endocrine Soc; Asn Am Physicians. *Res:* Molecular mechanisms of hormone action both on normal targets and on responsive neoplasms. *Mailing Add:* Vet Admin Med Ctr Sepulveda CA 91343

KORENMAN, VICTOR, b Brooklyn, NY, Feb 5, 37; m 68. THEORETICAL SOLID STATE PHYSICS. *Educ:* Princeton Univ, AB, 58; Harvard Univ, MA, 59, PhD(physics), 66. *Prof Exp:* Res assoc, 65-67, asst prof, 67-73, assoc prof, 73-79, PROF PHYSICS, UNIV MD, 79- *Concurrent Pos:* Fel, Alfred P Sloan Found, 71. *Mem:* AAAS; Am Phys Soc; Fedn Am Scientists. *Res:* Theory of itinerant ferromagnetism. *Mailing Add:* Dept of Physics Univ of Md College Park MD 20742

KORENSTEIN, RALPH, b Havannah, Cuba, Dec 6, 51; US citizen; m 76. INORGANIC CHEMISTRY, SOLID STATE CHEMISTRY. *Educ:* Polytech Inst Brooklyn, BS, 73; Brown Univ, PhD(chem), 77. *Prof Exp:* MEM TECH STAFF CHEM, TEX INSTRUMENTS INC, 76- *Mem:* Am Chem Soc. *Res:* Crystal growth of oxides by liquid phase epitaxy; synthesis of new inorganic compounds; thin film technology. *Mailing Add:* Tex Instruments Inc PO Box 225936 MS 145 Dallas TX 75265

KORETZ, JANE FAITH, b New York, NY, Aug 12, 47. IMAGE ANALYSIS, TENSOR ANALYSIS. *Educ:* Swarthmore Col, BA, 69; Univ Chicago, PhD(biophysics), 74. *Prof Exp:* Adj asst prof human physiol, Kean Col, NJ, 77; ASST PROF, DEPT BIOL, RENSSELAER POLYTECH INST, 77- *Concurrent Pos:* Vis scientist, Cell Biophysics Unit, Med Res Coun, London, 74-76; res affil, Dept Physiol, NJ Med Sch, 76-77. *Mem:* Biophys Soc; Inst Elec & Electronics Engrs; Soc Comput Simulation; NY Acad Sci; Asn Women in Sci. *Res:* Structural analysis of native and reconstituted skeletal muscle, thick filaments and nyosin rod aggregates; computer-based modelling of human and Rhesus monkey visual accommodation; etiology of presbyopia. *Mailing Add:* Dept Biol Rensselaer Polytech Inst Troy NY 12181

KOREVAAR, JACOB, b Netherlands, Jan 25, 23; nat US, m; c 8. MATHEMATICS. *Educ:* Univ Leiden, PhD(math), 49. *Hon Degrees:* Dr, Univ Gothenburg, 78. *Prof Exp:* Asst math, Delft Univ Technol, 44-46, prof, 51-53; res assoc, Math Ctr, Univ Amsterdam, 47-49; from asst prof to prof, Univ Wis, 53-64; chmn dept, Univ Calif, San Diego, 71-73, prof math, 64-74; PROF, MATH INST, UNIV AMSTERDAM, 74-, DIR, 80- *Concurrent Pos:* Mem Nat Sci Found fel comt, 64-66; vis prof math, Univ Amsterdam, 74-76. *Honors & Awards:* Reynolds Teaching Award, 58. *Mem:* AAAS; Am Math Soc; London Math Soc; Math Asn Am; Soc Indust & Appl Math. *Res:* Approximation; complex analysis; distributions; Fourier analysis; Tauberian theorems. *Mailing Add:* Math Inst Roetersstraat 15 Amsterdam Neth

KORF, RICHARD PAUL, b Bronxville, NY, May 28, 25; m 59; c 4. MYCOLOGY, TAXONOMY. *Educ:* Cornell Univ, BSc, 46, PhD(mycol), 50. *Prof Exp:* Asst plant path, 47-50, from asst prof to assoc prof, 51-60, PROF MYCOL, CORNELL UNIV, 60-, PROF BOT, 82- *Concurrent Pos:* Lectr, Glasgow Univ, 50-51; Fulbright res prof & NSF sr fel, Yokohama Nat Univ, Japan, 57-58; chmn, Nomenclature Secretariat, Int Mycol Asn, 72-77; co-ed, Mycotaxon J, 74-; adj prof, Copenhagen Univ, 78. *Mem:* Mycol Soc Am (secy-treas, 65-68, vpres, 68-69, pres, 70-71); Brit Mycol Soc; Mycol Soc Fr; Mycol Soc Japan; Int Asn Plant Taxon. *Res:* Taxonomic mycology; taxonomy of discomycetes; life histories and genetics of ascomycetes; botanical nomenclature; fungi of Asia, Neotropics and Macaronesia. *Mailing Add:* Plant Path Herbarium Cornell Univ Ithaca NY 14853

KORFHAGE, ROBERT R, b Syracuse, NY, Dec 2, 30; m 55; c 4. MATHEMATICS, COMPUTER SCIENCE. *Educ:* Univ Mich, BSE, 52, MS, 55, PhD(math), 62. *Prof Exp:* Engr comput res lab, United Aircraft Corp, 52-54; asst prof math, NC State Col, 60-62; from asst prof to assoc prof math & comput sci, Purdue Univ, 62-70; dir, Comput Sci/Opers Res Ctr, 70-72, PROF COMPUT SCI, SOUTHERN METHODIST UNIV, 70-, ACTG CHMN, COMPUT SCI & ENG, 81- *Concurrent Pos:* Consult, Proj Comput in Eng Educ, Univ Mich, 62, Eli Lilly & Co, 64-66, Indianapolis Hosp Develop Asn, 65-66, Los Alamos Sci Lab, 65-76, Alpha Systs, Inc, 70-, Xerox Corp, 77- & On-Line Data, Inc, 78- *Mem:* Am Math Soc; Asn Comput Mach. *Res:* Finite mathematical structures; logic and algorithms; non-numeric uses of computers; information retrieval; library information systems. *Mailing Add:* Dept of Comput Sci Southern Methodist Univ Dallas TX 75275

KORFMACHER, WALTER AVERILL, b St Louis, Mo, Nov 6, 51; m 74; c 1. MASS SPECTROMETRY, ENVIRONMENTAL ANALYSIS. *Educ:* St Louis Univ, BSCh, 73; Univ Ill, Urbana, MS, 75, PhD(anal chem), 78. *Prof Exp:* Teaching asst, Chem Div, Univ Ill, Urbana, 73-75, res asst, 75; res assst, Chem Div, Colo State Univ, Ft Collins, 76-78; CHEMIST, NAT CTR TOXICOL RES, FOOD & DRUG ADMIN, 78- *Mem:* Sigma Xi; Am Chem Soc; AAAS; Am Soc Mass Spectrometry. *Res:* Environmental analytical methods, particularly in trace organic quantitative methods; development of capillary gas chromatography combined with atmospheric pressure ionization mass spectrometry. *Mailing Add:* Chem Div Nat Ctr Toxicol Res Jefferson AR 72079

KORGEN, BENJAMIN JEFFRY, b Duluth, Minn, Jan 6, 31; m 59; c 3. PHYSICAL OCEANOGRAPHY. *Educ:* Univ Minn, BS, 56; Univ Mich, MA, 58; Ore State Univ, PhD(phys oceanog), 69. *Prof Exp:* Asst prof phys oceanog, Univ N C Chapel Hill, 69-74; writing & consult, 74-78; OCEANOGR, US NAVAL OCEANOG OFF & RES ASSOC, TULANE UNIV, 78- *Mem:* AAAS; Am Geophys Union; Am Soc Limnol & Oceanog; Geol Soc Am. *Res:* Circulation of continental shelf waters; near-bottom processes; underwater acoustics; terrestrial heat flow; marine geophysics; geothermal energy. *Mailing Add:* 219 Loop Dr Slidell LA 70458

KORGEN, REINHARD LUNDE, mathematics, deceased

KORGES, EMERSON, b Victoria, Tex, Aug 6, 11; m 42; c 1. ELECTRICAL ENGINEERING, PHYSICS. *Educ:* Tex Col Arts & Indust, BS, 31, MS, 42; Colo State Univ, MEE, 57. *Prof Exp:* Instr eng, 42-47, from asst prof to assoc prof, 47-57, PROF ELEC ENG, TEX A&I UNIV, 57- *Concurrent Pos:* Consult, Tex A&I Univ, 57- *Mem:* Am Soc Eng Educ; Inst Elec & Electronics Engrs. *Res:* Corrosion and performance of copper-to-aluminum and aluminum-to-aluminum non tension electrical connectors. *Mailing Add:* Dept of Elec Eng PO Box 2275 Kingsville TX 78363

KORIN, AMOS, b Rehovoth, Israel, Sept 11, 44; m 67; c 3. MEMBRANE SCIENCE, SEPARATION TECHNOLOGY. *Educ:* Technion Israel Inst Technol, BSc, 67; Weizmann Inst Sci, MSc, 72, PhD(polymer chem), 78. *Prof Exp:* Sr proj mgr, Israel Atomic Energy Comn, 67-73; proj engr, Weizmann Inst Sci, 73-78; dept head water distillation, Mehorot Water Co, 78-79; DIR MEMBRANE DEVELOP, GELMAN SCI, INC, 79- *Concurrent Pos:* Lectr chem & physics, Col Eng, Tel Aviv, 73-77; consult, Amplast Co, Israel, 78-79. *Mem:* Israel Inst Chem Eng; Am Chem Soc; Filtration Soc. *Res:* Novel polymer systems; polymeric ultra filtration and microporous membranes; separation systems and their application in industrial and medical fields. *Mailing Add:* 1854 Glenwood Ann Arbor MI 48104

KORIN, BASIL PETER, b Oxford, Conn, Sept 15, 32; m 59; c 1. MATHEMATICAL STATISTICS. *Educ:* Univ Conn, BA, 57; Stanford Univ, MS, 60; George Washington Univ, PhD(statist), 67. *Prof Exp:* Mathematician, Lockheed Missiles & Space Co, 57-60; math statistician, US Bur Census, 60-61; from instr to assoc prof math & statist, 61-74, PROF MATH & STATIST, AMERICAN UNIV, 74- *Mem:* Inst Math Statist; Am Statist Asn. *Res:* Statistics; multivariate analysis. *Mailing Add:* Dept Statistics & Comp Sci Am Univ Washington DC 20016

KORINEK, GEORGE JIRI, b Jicin, Czech, July 8, 27; m 58. PHYSICAL CHEMISTRY. *Educ:* Univ BC, MSc, 54, PhD(metall), 56. *Prof Exp:* Fel, Nat Res Coun Can, 56-57; proj leader, Metals Res Lab, Union Carbide Metals Co, 57-61; group leader, Rare Metals Div, Ciba Ltd, Switz, 61-65, mgr, Rare Metals Dept, Ciba Corp, 65-70; managing dir, 70-74, PRES, H C STARCK, INC, 74- *Mem:* Electrochem Soc; Am Soc Metals; Am Inst Mining, Metall & Petrol Eng. *Res:* Physical chemistry of extractive metallurgy; catalysis; hydrometallurgy; refractory metals; Ta capacitors. *Mailing Add:* H C Starck Inc 280 Park Ave New York NY 10017

KORITALA, SANBASIVAROA, b India, Apr 10, 32; nat US; m 61; c 2. LIPID CHEMISTRY. *Educ:* Andhra Univ, India, BS, 52; Nagpur Univ, BS, 54; Ohio State Univ, MS, 57, PhD(physiol chem), 60. *Prof Exp:* Res assoc & instr physiol chem, Ohio State Univ, 61-63; RES CHEMIST, NORTHERN REGIONAL RES CTR, AGR RES SERV, USDA, 63- *Concurrent Pos:* Abstr ed, Am Oil Chemists Soc, 75- *Mem:* Am Chem Soc; Am Oil Chemists Soc. *Res:* Selective hydrogenation of vegetable oils to improve their flavor stability and to modify their functional properties for application in margarines, cooking and other food uses; preparations of selective and active catalysts for hydrogenation of animal and vegetable oils. *Mailing Add:* Northern Regional Res Ctr Agr Res Serv USDA Peoria IL 61604

KORITNIK, DONALD RAYMOND, b Rock Springs, Wyo, Feb 28, 46; m 80. REPRODUCTIVE ENDOCRINOLOGY, ATHEROSCLEROSIS. *Educ:* Univ Wyo, BS, 68, MS, 73, PhD(animal sci), 77. *Prof Exp:* Fel, Reprod Endocrinol Prog, Univ Calif, San Francisco, 77-80; ASST PROF COMP MED, BOWMAN GRAY SCH MED, WAKE FOREST UNIV, 80- *Mem:* Endocrine Soc; Soc Study Reprod. *Res:* Regulation of metabolism by reproductive hormones especially changes in lipid and carbohydrate metabolism; alterations in hormone concentrations and binding of hormones to carrier serum proteins during pregnancy and around the time of puberty; factors in atherosclerosis. *Mailing Add:* Dept Comp Med Bowman Gray Sch Med 300 S Hawthorne Rd Winston-Salem NC 27103

KORITZ, GARY DUANE, b DeKalb, Ill, May 18, 44; m 68; c 2. VETERINARY MEDICINE, PHARMACOLOGY. *Educ:* Univ Ill, Urbana, BS, 66, DVM, 68, PhD(vet pharmacol), 75. *Prof Exp:* Clinician pvt pract, Dundee Animal Hosp, 68-70; asst prof, 75-79, ASSOC PROF PHARMACOL, COL VET MED, UNIV ILL, URBANA, 79- *Concurrent Pos:* NIH fel, Univ Ill, Urbana, 73-74. *Mem:* Am Vet Med Asn; Am Col Vet Toxicol; Am Col Vet Pharmacol & Therapeut; Am Soc Vet Physiologists & Pharmacologists. *Res:* Comparative pharmacology including therapeutics, pharmacokinetics and drug disposition. *Mailing Add:* Col Vet Med Univ Ill Urbana IL 61801

KORITZ, SEYMOUR BENJAMIN, b Boston, Mass, Nov 25, 21; m 51; c 4. BIOCHEMISTRY. *Educ:* Univ Mass, BS, 44; Univ Wis, PhD(biochem), 51. *Prof Exp:* Res assoc, Ohio State Univ, 52-53; staff biochemist, Worcester Found Exp Biol, 53-59; from asst prof to prof biochem, Sch Med, Univ Pittsburgh, 59-68; PROF BIOCHEM, MT SINAI SCH MED, 68- *Concurrent Pos:* Am Cancer Soc fel, Brussels, 51-52. *Mem:* Am Chem Soc; Am Soc Cell Biol; Am Soc Biol Chemists. *Res:* Mode of action of steroid and adrenocorticotropic hormones. *Mailing Add:* Dept Biochem Mt Sinai Sch Med Fifth Ave at 100th St New York NY 10029

KORK, JOHN O, b Mt Vernon, NY, Nov 7, 38; m 62; c 2. MATHEMATICS, STATISTICS. *Educ:* Colo State Univ, MS, 63; Univ Tenn, PhD(math), 69. *Prof Exp:* ASST PROF MATH, COLO SCH MINES, 69- *Concurrent Pos:* Mathematician, US Geol Surv, 74- *Mem:* Am Math Soc; Am Statist Asn; Sigma Xi. *Res:* Information and sufficiency in sequential tests; geo-statistics and applications of statistics in mining; analysis of data. *Mailing Add:* 300 Plateau Pkwy Golden CO 80401

KORK, JYRI, aeronautical engineering, see previous edition

KORMAN, N(ATHANIEL) I(RVING), b Providence, RI, Feb 23, 16; m 41; c 2. ELECTRONICS, COMPUTER SCIENCE. *Educ:* Worcester Polytech Inst, BS, 37; Mass Inst Technol, MS, 38; Univ Pa, PhD(elec eng), 58. *Prof Exp:* Student engr, RCA Corp, 38-40, develop engr, 40-44, eng group leader, 44-48, eng group supvr, 48-50, adminr radar systs activities, 50-52, mgr develop eng group, 52-54, mgr systs eng group, 54, asst chief engr, 54-56, chief systs, 57-58, dir advan mil systs, 58-63, dir tech progs, 63-65, chief engr graphic systs div, 65-66, dir med electronics plans & progs, 66-69; PRES, VENTURES RES & DEVELOP GROUP, 69- *Mem:* Assoc fel Am Inst Aeronaut & Astronaut; sr mem Am Astronaut Soc; Asn Comput Mach; fel Inst Elec & Electronics Engrs. *Res:* Advanced development of frequency modulation transmitters; microwave and waveguide components for radar and television; development of microwave studio-to-transmitter link; fire control radar; frequency modulation techniques; waveguide techniques; systems engineering. *Mailing Add:* 371 Riverside Dr Princeton NJ 08540

KORMENDY, JOHN, b Graz, Austria, June 13, 48; Can citizen. ASTRONOMY. *Educ:* Univ Toronto, BSc, 70; Calif Inst Technol, PhD(astron), 76. *Prof Exp:* Parisot fel astron, Univ Calif, Berkeley, 76-78; sr vis fel, Inst Astron, Cambridge, 78 & 80; STAFF MEM, DOMINION ASTROPHYS OBSERV, 80- *Concurrent Pos:* Fel astron, Kitt Peak Nat Observ, 78-79; sr fel, Inst Astron, Univ Cambridge, Eng, 78-80. *Mem:* Am Astron Soc; Int Astron Union; Astron Soc Pac. *Res:* Extragalactic observational astronomy, with particular emphasis on the structure of normal and peculiar galaxies; theoretical dynamics of the structure of galaxies; astronomical image processing. *Mailing Add:* Dominion Astrophys Observ 5071 W Saanich Rd Victoria BC V8X 4M6 Can

KORN, ALFRED, b Long Island City, NY, July 19, 30. STRUCTURAL & CIVIL ENGINEERING. *Educ:* Purdue Univ, BS, 52; Univ Ill, Urbana, MS, 61; Washington Univ, DSc(appl mech, struct), 67. *Prof Exp:* Designer, Bell Aircraft Corp, NY, 52-53; engr, Sverdrup & Parcel Eng Co, Mo, 55-59 & 61-63; lectr, Washington Univ, 63-66; asst prof civil eng, Univ Ky, 67-69; assoc prof, 69-75, PROF CIVIL ENG, SOUTHERN ILL UNIV, EDWARDSVILLE, 75- *Mem:* Am Concrete Inst; Am Soc Civil Engrs; Int Asn Bridge & Struct Eng. *Res:* Structural mechanics; elastic and inelastic frame stability; plastic design; numerical and computer analysis of structures. *Mailing Add:* Dept Eng Sch Sci & Eng Southern Ill Univ Edwardsville IL 62026

KORN, DAVID, b Providence, RI, Mar 5, 33; m 55; c 3. PATHOLOGY, MOLECULAR BIOLOGY. *Educ:* Harvard Univ, BA, 54, MD, 59. *Prof Exp:* Res assoc biochem, Nat Inst Arthritis & Metab Dis, 61-63, staff mem, 63-68, staff pathologist, NIH, 64-68; PROF PATH & CHMN DEPT, SCH MED, STANFORD UNIV, 68- *Mem:* AAAS; Am Soc Biol Chemists; Am Soc Exp Path; Am Soc Cell Biol; Int Acad Path. *Res:* Biochemistry; nucleic acid biochemistry; regulation of gene expression. *Mailing Add:* Dept of Path Stanford Univ Sch of Med Stanford CA 94305

KORN, EDWARD DAVID, b Philadelphia, Pa, Aug 3, 28; m 50; c 2. BIOCHEMISTRY, CELL BIOLOGY. *Educ:* Univ Pa, AB, 49, PhD(biochem), 54. *Prof Exp:* Asst instr physiol chem, Univ Pa, 49-51; biochemist, Nat Heart Inst, 54-69, HEAD SECT CELLULAR BIOCHEM & ULTRASTRUCT, NAT HEART & LUNG INST, 69-, CHIEF, LAB CELL BIOL, 74- *Mem:* Am Soc Biol Chem. *Res:* Mechanisms of fat transport; biochemistry of lipoproteins; structure and metabolism of polyunsaturated fatty acids; biochemical cytology; membrane biology; pinocytosis and phagocytosis; cell motility; cytoplasmic actin and myosin. *Mailing Add:* Lab of Cell Biol Nat Heart & Lung Inst Bethesda MD 20205

KORN, GRANINO A(RTHUR), b Berlin, Ger, May 7, 22; nat US; m 48; c 2. COMPUTER SCIENCE, ELECTRICAL ENGINEERING. *Educ:* Brown Univ, BA, 42, PhD(physics), 48; Columbia Univ, MA, 42. *Prof Exp:* Proj engr, Sperry Gyroscope Co, 47-48; head anal group, Airplane Div, Curtiss-Wright Corp, 48-49; staff engr, Lockheed Aircraft Co, 49-52; INDUST CONSULT, 52-; PROF ELEC ENG, UNIV ARIZ, 57- *Concurrent Pos:* Consult, Nat Acad Sci, Chile, 61; mem, NIH-Nat Adv Res Coun, 78-79. *Honors & Awards:* Sr Sci Award, Soc Comput Simulation, 68; Humboldt Prize, Humboldt Found, WGer, 76. *Mem:* Int Asn Analog Comput; fel Inst Elec & Electronics Engrs; Soc Comput Simulation. *Res:* Dare computer systems for simulation; microdare laboratory-automation software; mini-microcomputer system design. *Mailing Add:* 6801 Opatas St Tucson AZ 85715

KORN, ROY JOSEPH, b Chicago, Ill, July 25, 20; m 55; c 4. MEDICAL ADMINISTRATION. *Educ:* Northwestern Univ, BS, 42, MD, 46. *Prof Exp:* Intern med, Wesley Mem Hosp, Chicago, Ill, 45-46; resident internal med, Vet Admin Hosp, Hines, Ill, 49-52; staff physician, Vet Admin Hosp, Omaha, Nebr, 52-53; from asst chief to chief med serv, West Side Vet Admin Hosp, Chicago, Ill, 53-62; adv & prof med, Chiengmai Med Sch, Thailand, 62-64; chief of staff, Vet Admin Hosp, Indianapolis, 65-72; PROF MED, ABRAHAM LINCOLN SCH MED, UNIV ILL, 72-; CHIEF OF STAFF, VET ADMIN WEST SIDE HOSP, CHICAGO, 72- *Concurrent Pos:* Instr, Univ Nebr, 52-53; from asst prof to assoc prof, Col Med, Univ Ill, 55-64; prof, Chicago Med Sch, 64-65; clin prof med, Sch Med, Ind Univ-Purdue Univ, Indianapolis, 65-72. *Mem:* Fel Am Col Physicians. *Res:* Liver disease. *Mailing Add:* Vet Admin West Side Hosp 820 S Damen Ave Chicago IL 60612

KORNACKER, KARL, b Chicago, Ill, Oct 14, 37; m 60, 79; c 2. SUPERSTRONG INTERACTIONS, GENETIC ENGINEERING. *Educ:* Mass Inst Technol, BS, 58, PhD(neurophysiol), 62. *Prof Exp:* Res assoc biol, Mass Inst Technol, 62-68; asst prof biophys, 68-69, ASSOC PROF, OHIO STATE UNIV, 69- *Mem:* AAAS; Am Soc Info Sci. *Res:* Unified gauge field theory; control of gene expression; pattern recognition. *Mailing Add:* Ohio State Univ Columbus OH 43210

KORNBERG, ARTHUR, b Brooklyn, NY, Mar 3, 18; m 43; c 3. BIOCHEMISTRY. *Educ:* City Col New York, BS, 37; Univ Rochester, MD, 41. *Prof Exp:* Intern, Strong Mem Hosp, Rochester, 41-42; asst surgeon to med dir, NIH, 42-53, chief enzyme & metab sect, 47-53; prof microbiol & head dept, Sch Med, Wash Univ, 53-59; head dept, 59-69, PROF BIOCHEM, STANFORD UNIV SCH MED, 59- *Honors & Awards:* Nobel Prize in med & physiol, 59; Paul-Lewis Award, Am Chem Soc, 51; Nat Medal Sci, Royal Soc, 79. *Mem:* Nat Acad Sci; Am Chem Soc; Am Soc Biol Chem (pres, 65-66). *Res:* Enzymatic studies of DNA replication, membrane biochemistry. *Mailing Add:* Dept of Biochem Stanford Univ Sch of Med Stanford CA 94305

KORNBERG, HARRY ALEXANDER, b Chicago, Ill, Aug 18, 14; m 37; c 3. RADIATION BIOLOGY. *Educ:* Univ Ill, BS, 38; State Col Wash, MS, 40; Univ Tex, PhD(biochem), 42. *Prof Exp:* Instr, Univ Tex, 40-41, res assoc, 42; Abbott-Glidden-Lilly fel, Northwestern Univ, 42-43; asst prof, Ore State Col, 46-47; head biol div, Gen Elec Co, 47-50, mgr biol oper, 50-65, mgr biol dept, Battelle-Northwest, 65-68, assoc mgr environ & life sci div, 68-69, consult to dir, 69-71, sr staff scientist, 71-73; mem planning staff, 74-77, PROJ MGR, ENVIRON ASSESSMENT DEPT, BONNEVILLE POWER ADMIN, ELEC POWER RES INST, 79- *Concurrent Pos:* Mem path effects of radiation comt & chmn subcomt inhalation hazards, Nat Acad Sci; del, Harwell Confs Passage of Fission Prods through Biol Chains, 55-58; spec adv, German Elec Utility Indust & Swedish State Power Bd, 77- *Mem:* Bioelectromagnetics Soc. *Res:* Biological effects of radiation; metabolism and hazards of radioactive materials; biological effects of electric fields; radiation biology. *Mailing Add:* Elec Power Res Inst PO Box 10412 Palo Alto CA 94303

KORNBERG, ROGER DAVID, b St Louis, Mo, Apr 24, 47. BIOCHEMISTRY. *Educ:* Harvard Univ, BA, 67; Stanford Univ, PhD(chem), 71. *Prof Exp:* Fel, Nat Cystic Fibrosis Res Found, 72; mem sci staff cell biol, Med Res Coun Lab Molecular Biol, Cambridge, Eng, 74-75; asst prof biol chem, Harvard Med Sch, 76-78; PROF STRUCT BIOL, SCH MED, STANFORD UNIV, 78- *Res:* 3-D organization of cells, especially structure of chromosomes. *Mailing Add:* Dept of Struct Biol Stanford Univ Sch of Med Stanford CA 94305

KORNBERG, THOMAS B, b Washington, DC, Nov 10, 48. CELL BIOLOGY, DEVELOPMENTAL BIOLOGY. *Educ:* Columbia Col, New York, BA, 70; Columbia Univ, PhD(biochem), 73. *Prof Exp:* Res assoc biochem, Princeton Univ, 73-75; res assoc develop biol, Med Res Coun Lab Molecular Biol, Cambridge Univ, UK, 75-76; mem staff, Molecular Biol Inst, Univ Calif, Los Angeles, 76-77; ASST PROF BIOCHEM & BIOPHYS, UNIV CALIF, SAN FRANCISCO, 78- *Res:* Genetic and biochemical description of the cellular events which govern determination in higher organisms. *Mailing Add:* Dept Biochem & Biophys Univ Calif San Francisco CA 94143

KORNBLITH, CAROL LEE, b Chicago, Ill, Sept 6, 45. PHYSIOLOGICAL PSYCHOLOGY, NEUROBIOLOGY. *Educ:* Univ Mich, AB, 66, AM, 68; Calif Inst Technol, PhD(biol), 72. *Prof Exp:* Fel psychol, Princeton Univ, 72-74; asst prof, Univ NC, 74-80, interdisciplinary fel neurosci, 80-81; ASSOC PROF PSYCHOL, ILL STATE UNIV, 81- *Mem:* Soc Neurosci; Sigma Xi; AAAS. *Res:* Development and function of sexually dimorphic brain regions in the rat as revealed by deoxyglucose autoradiography and the development of feeding behavior and its relation to reinforcement. *Mailing Add:* Dept Psychol Ill State Univ Normal IL 61761

KORNBLITH, LESTER, JR, b Chicago, Ill, Apr 27, 17; m 40; c 3. NUCLEAR ENGINEERING. *Educ:* Mass Inst Technol, SB, 38. *Prof Exp:* Chief engr, Enrico Fermi Inst Nuclear Studies, Univ Chicago, 47-55; mgr reactor tech oper, Vallecitos Atomic Lab, Gen Elec Co, 56-63; asst dir reactors, Div Compliance, US Atomic Energy Comn, 63-67, asst dir tech progs, 67-72, mem atomic safety & licensing bd panel, US Nuclear Regulatory Comn, 72-79; VPRES & PRIN ENGR, NAT NUCLEAR CORP, 79- *Concurrent Pos:* consult engr, 79- *Mem:* Fel Am Nuclear Soc; Inst Elec & Electronics Engrs; AAAS. *Res:* Design, construction and operation of nuclear reactors and accelerators. *Mailing Add:* Nat Nuclear Corp 6708 Tulip Hill Terr Bethesda MD 20816

KORNBLUM, NATHAN, b New York, NY, Mar 22, 14; m 47; c 4. ORGANIC CHEMISTRY. *Educ:* NY Univ, BS, 35, MS, 37; Univ Ill, PhD(org chem), 40. *Prof Exp:* Hall res instr, Oberlin Col, 40-42; Nat Res Coun fel chem, Harvard Univ, 42-43; from asst prof to assoc prof, 43-53, PROF CHEM, PURDUE UNIV, 53- *Concurrent Pos:* Fulbright sr scholar, Univ Col, London, 52-53; Guggenheim mem fel, Swiss Fed Inst Technol, 53, NSF fel, 64-65; vis prof org chem, Swiss Fed Inst Technol, 73-74; vis prof, Nat Ctr Sci Res, France, 75, Univ Marseilles, 78 & Univ Kyoto, Japan, 79. *Mem:* Am Chem Soc. *Res:* Reaction mechanisms and their application to synthetic organic chemistry. *Mailing Add:* Dept of Chem Purdue Univ West Lafayette IN 47907

KORNBLUM, RONALD NORMAN, b Chicago, Ill, Dec 5, 33. PATHOLOGY. *Educ:* Univ Calif, Los Angeles, BA, 55, MD, 59. *Prof Exp:* Resident gen path, Santa Clara County Hosp, 62-66; resident neuropath, Md Dept Ment Hyg, 66-67; fel forensic path, Md Postmortem Exam, 67-68; asst med examr, state med exam off, Md, 68-73; MED EXAMR, VENTURA COUNTY, CALIF, 73- *Concurrent Pos:* Lectr pub health admin, Johns Hopkins Univ, 69- *Mem:* Am Acad Forensic Sci; Am Soc Clin Pathologists; Col Am Pathologists. *Res:* Forensic pathology; investigation into causes of sudden death in infancy syndrome; investigation of craniocerebral injuries and shock in relation to cerebral anoria. *Mailing Add:* 3291 Loma Vista Rd Ventura CA 93003

KORNBLUM, SAUL S, b Far Rockaway, NY, Feb 24, 34; m 58; c 2. PHYSICAL PHARMACY, PHYSICAL CHEMISTRY. *Educ:* Brooklyn Col Pharm, BS, 55; Columbia Univ, MS, 57; Rutgers Univ, PhD(pharm, phys chem), 63. *Prof Exp:* Instr chem, Newark Col Eng, 59-61; asst prof phys pharm, Brooklyn Col Pharm, L I Univ, 62-66; sr scientist, Sandoz Pharmaceut, 66-67, mgr, 67-73, ASSOC SECT HEAD PROD DEVELOP & CLIN PROD, SANDOZ, INC, 73- *Concurrent Pos:* CIBA res grant, 61-62. *Honors & Awards:* Lunsford Richardson Award, 63. *Mem:* Am Pharmaceut Asn; Acad Pharmaceut Sci; NY Acad Sci; Parenteral Drug Asn. *Res:* Solid state kinetics; dissolution of poorly water-soluble drugs; sustained-release dosage forms; pharmaceutical dosage form design and evaluation; preformulation stability evaluation for new drugs. *Mailing Add:* 144 Short Hills Ave Springfield NJ 07081

KORNEFF, THEODORE, electronics, see previous edition

KORNEGAY, ERVIN THADDEUS, b Faison, NC, Mar 16, 31; m 56; c 3. ANIMAL SCIENCE. *Educ:* NC State Univ, BS, 53, MS, 60; Mich State Univ, PhD(animal nutrit), 63. *Prof Exp:* Asst agr agent, NC State Univ, 56-59, asst 59-60; asst, Mich State Univ, 60-63; asst res prof, Animal Nutrit, Rutgers Univ, 63-67; assoc prof, 67-73, PROF ANIMAL SCI, VA POLYTECH INST & STATE UNIV, 73- *Mem:* Am Soc Animal Sci; NY Acad Sci; Am Inst Nutrit. *Res:* Unrease immunization; evaluation of feedstuffs for swine; nitrogen metabolism; sow management and nutrition; artificial rearing of baby pigs; trace mineral availability and interactions. *Mailing Add:* Dept of Animal Sci Va Polytech Inst & State Univ Blacksburg VA 24061

KORNEL, LUDWIG, b Jaslo, Poland, Feb 27, 23; m 52; c 2. ENDOCRINOLOGY, BIOCHEMISTRY. *Educ:* Wroclaw Univ, MD, 50; Univ Birmingham, PhD(endocrinol, steroid biochem), 58. *Prof Exp:* Intern med, surg, gynec & pediat, Wroclaw Univ Hosp, 49-50; from intern to resident med, Hadassah Univ Hosp, Jerusalem, 50-54; asst physician & instr, Hadassah Med Sch, Hebrew Univ, Israel, 54-55; lectr med, Univ Birmingham, 56-57; asst physician med & pub health, Hadassah Univ Hosp & Pub Health Ctr, Jerusalem, 57-58; from asst prof to prof med, Med Ctr, Univ Ala, 61-67, assoc prof biochem, 65-67, dir steroid sect & consult endocrinol, 63-67; DIR STEROID UNIT, RUSH-PRESBY-ST LUKE'S MED CTR, 67-, SR ATTEND PHYSICIAN & SR SCIENTIST, 71-; PROF MED & BIOCHEM, RUSH MED COL, 70- *Concurrent Pos:* Res fel hemat, Hosp Broussai, Univ Paris, 51-52; Brit Coun res scholar med & steroid chem, Univ Birmingham, 55-57; res fel endocrinol & metab, Med Ctr, Univ Ala, Birmingham, 58-59; USPHS trainee, Inst Steroid Biochem, Univ Utah, 59-61; mem ed abstracting staff, Exerpta Medica, 56-57; prin investr steroid metab hypertension, NIH Res Grant Proj, 60-; hon vis prof, Polish Acad Sci, Warsaw, 65; prof med, Col Med, Univ Ill, 67-71; attend physician, Presby-St Luke's Hosp, Chicago, 67-71, assoc biochemist, 67-70, sr biochemist on sci staff, 70-71; vis prof, Kanazawa Univ, Japan, 73; nat corresp, Fedn Am Socs Exp Biol, 75- *Mem:* AAAS; Am Fedn Clin Res; Endocrine Soc; fel Am Soc Clin Pharmacol & Therapeut; Am Physiol Soc. *Res:* Metabolism and mechanism of action of steroidal hormones, especially relation of corticosteroids to mechanism of arterial hypertension. *Mailing Add:* Rush-Presby-St Luke's Med Ctr 1753 W Congress Pkwy Chicago IL 60612

KORNET, MILTON JOSEPH, b East Chicago, Ind, Dec 31, 35; m 62; c 3. PHARMACEUTICAL CHEMISTRY, ORGANIC CHEMISTRY. *Educ:* Purdue Univ, BS, 57; Univ Ill, PhD(pharmaceut chem), 63. *Prof Exp:* Chemist, Abbott Labs, 57-59; res assoc org synthesis, Northwestern Univ, 62-63; asst prof, 63-67, ASSOC PROF PHARMACEUT CHEM, UNIV KY, 67- *Mem:* Am Chem Soc; Acad Pharmaceut Sci. *Res:* Synthesis of local anesthetics; heterocyclic organic chemistry; medicinal chemistry. *Mailing Add:* Col of Pharm Univ of Ky Lexington KY 40506

KORNETSKY, AARON, b Chelsea, Mass, June 1, 30; m 53; c 2. FOOD SCIENCE. *Educ:* Univ Mass, BS, 52; Univ Md, MS, 54, PhD(food technol), 56. *Prof Exp:* Asst hort, Univ Md, 52-56; asst technologist res & develop, Birds Eye Div, Gen Foods Corp, 56-58; food technologist & prod mgr, Giant

Food, Inc, Washington, DC, 58-64; food technologist & prod mgr, 64-75, MGR NEW PROD DEVELOP & QUAL CONTROL, STOP & SHOP INC, 75- Mem: Inst Food Technologists. Mailing Add: 57 Lantern Lane Sharon MA 02067

KORNETSKY, CONAN, b Portland, Maine, Feb 9, 26; m 49; c 2. PSYCHOLOGY, PSYCHOPHARMACOLOGY. Educ: Univ Maine, BA, 48; Univ Ky, MS, 51, PhD(psychol), 52. Prof Exp: Res scientist, NIMH, 52-59; assoc prof, 59-62, PROF PSYCHIAT & PHARMACOL, SCH MED, BOSTON UNIV, 62- Concurrent Pos: NIH sr res fel, Boston Univ, 59-62, NIH res scientist award, 62-70, NIMH res scientist award, 70-; mem psychopharmacol study sect, NIH, 62-67, mem clin psychopharmacol res rev comt, NIMH, 67-71; mem comt tobacco habituation, Am Cancer Soc, 66-70; mem panel behav modification drugs for hyperkinetic children, Dept Health, Educ & Welfare, 71; mem merit rev bd neurobiol, Vet Admin, 72-76; mem psychopharmacol agents adv comt, Food & Drug Admin, 73-77. Mem: Am Soc Pharmacol & Exp Therapeut; Am Psychol Asn; Am Col Neuropsychopharmacol; Int Col Neuropsychopharmacol; Psychonomic Soc. Res: Animal models of behavioral deficits seen in schizophrenic patients; behavioral and neuropsychological studies of the action of antipsychotic and analgesic drugs. Mailing Add: Dept of Psychiat Boston Univ Sch of Med Boston MA 02118

KORNFEIL, FRED, b Vienna, Austria, Feb 14, 24; nat US; m 53. PHYSICAL CHEMISTRY, ELECTROCHEMISTRY. Educ: Univ Vienna, MS, 50, PhD(chem), 53. Prof Exp: Chemist, Power Sources Div, 53-59, phys scientist, Explor Res Div E, 59-71, phys scientist, Power Sources Area, Electronics Technol & Devices Lab, US Army Electronics Command, Ft Monmouth, 71-78; RETIRED. Mem: Am Chem Soc; Electrochem Soc. Res: Fuel cells; battery test techniques; kinetics of electrode processes. Mailing Add: Seven Lakes Box 672 West End NC 27376

KORNFELD, EDMUND CARL, b Philadelphia, Pa, Feb 24, 19; m 45. MEDICINAL CHEMISTRY. Educ: Temple Univ, AB, 40, AM, 42; Harvard Univ, MA, 44, PhD(org chem), 46. Prof Exp: Res chemist, Off Sci Res & Develop Contract, Harvard Univ, 45; res chemist, 46-65, RES ADV, ELI LILLY & CO, 65- Mem: Am Chem Soc. Res: Rubber chemistry; organic structural determination; synthetic organic medicinals; organic chemicals development; medicinal chemistry of indol derivatives and ergot alkaloids. Mailing Add: Eli Lilly & Co Indianapolis IN 46285

KORNFELD, JOSEPH M, b New York, NY, Mar 21, 26; m 51; c 2. MICROBIOLOGY. Educ: Brooklyn Col, BS, 56; Univ Wis, MS, 58, PhD(bact), 61. Prof Exp: Instr bact, Univ Wis, 61-63; asst prof, Univ Conn, 63-69; RES MICROBIOLOGIST, CONN STATE DEPT HEALTH, 70- Mem: Am Soc Microbiol; Brit Soc Gen Microbiol; Brit Biochem Soc. Res: Fungal physiology; morphogenesis. Mailing Add: Conn State Dept of Health 10 Clinton St Hartford CT 06103

KORNFELD, LOTTIE, b Vienna, Austria, Feb 8, 25; US citizen. IMMUNOBIOLOGY. Educ: Col Wooster, BA, 45; Ohio State Univ, MS, 47; Univ Chicago, PhD(microbiol), 60. Prof Exp: Asst bact, Ohio State Univ, 45-47; bacteriologist, Viral & Rickettsial Res Div, Lederle Labs, Am Cyanamid Co, 47-54; res asst bact, Univ Mich, 54-55; res asst bact, Dept Med, Univ Chicago, 55-60, res assoc, Dept of Med & Argonne Cancer Res Hosp, 60-61; res fel, Dept Exp Path, Scripps Clin & Res Found, Calif, 61-63; res microbiologist, US Naval Radiol Defense Lab, 63-69 & Letterman Army Inst Res, 69-72; microbiologist, Div Biomed & Environ Res, US Atomic Energy Comn, 72-74; HEALTH SCIENTIST ADMINR, NIH, 74- Concurrent Pos: Lectr, Dept Microbiol, San Francisco State Col, 69-71. Mem: AAAS; Am Soc Microbiol; Radiation Res Soc; Reticuloendothelial Soc; Am Asn Immunologists. Res: Immunology; host resistance; effects of irradiation on host-parasite relationship; science administration. Mailing Add: Div Res Grants NIH Bethesda MD 20205

KORNFELD, MARIO O, b Zagreb, Yugoslavia, July 9, 27; m 56; c 1. NEUROPATHOLOGY. Educ: Univ Zagreb, MD, 53, ScD, 64. Prof Exp: Staff pathologist, Inst Path, Gen Hosp, Zagreb, 59-64; instr neuropath, Col Physicians & Surgeons, Columbia Univ, 67-68; asst prof, 68-70, assoc prof path & neuropath, 70-80, PROF PATH, SCH MED, UNIV NMEX, 80- Concurrent Pos: Trainee & fel, Col Physicians & Surgeons, Columbia Univ, 64-67; staff pathologist, Bernalillo County Med Ctr, Albuquerque, 70; attend neuropathologist, Vet Admin Hosp, 70- Honors & Awards: Matthew T Moore Award, Am Asn Neuropath. Mem: Assoc Am Asn Neuropathologists; Am Asn Pathologists; Asn Res Neuropath Ment Dis. Res: Histopathology of inner ear and temporal bone; ultrastructural aspects of neurolipidoses, peripheral nervous system diseases and astroglia in metabolic encephalopathies; morphometry of secretion in pituitary adenomonas. Mailing Add: Dept of Path Univ of NMex Sch of Med Albuquerque NM 87116

KORNFELD, STUART ARTHUR, b St Louis, Mo, Oct 4, 36; m 59; c 3. HEMATOLOGY. Educ: Dartmouth Col, AB, 58; Washington Univ, MD, 62. Prof Exp: from asst prof to assoc prof, 66-72, PROF MED & BIOCHEM, SCH MED, WASHINGTON UNIV, 66- Concurrent Pos: Mem cell biol study sect, NIH, 74-77; assoc ed, J Clin Invest, 77-81, ed, 81-82. Mem: Am Soc Hemat; Am Soc Biol Chemists; Am Soc Clin Invest. Res: Studies of the structure, biosynthesis and function of glycoproteins, especially those which are found on the surface of normal and malignant cells; targeting of newly synthesized acid hydroloses to lysosomes. Mailing Add: Sch of Med Washington Univ St Louis MO 63110

KORNFIELD, IRVING LESLIE, b Jacksonville, NC, July 16, 45; m 68; c 2. EVOLUTIONARY BIOLOGY. Educ: Syracuse Univ, AB, 68; State Univ NY, Stony Brook, NY, 72, PhD(ecol), 74. Prof Exp: Fel, Smithsonian Inst, 74-75; res collabr, Dept Genetics, Hebrew Univ, 75-76; ASST PROF ZOOL, UNIV MAINE, 77- Concurrent Pos: Assoc, Danforth Found, 80- Mem: Am Soc Ichthyologists & Herpetologists; Genetics Soc Am; Soc Study Evolution. Res: Evolutionary genetics of fishes; biochemical systematics. Mailing Add: Dept of Zool Univ of Maine Orono ME 04469

KORNFIELD, JACK I, b New York, NY. SATELLITE METEOROLOGY. Educ: City Col New York, BS, 61; Northeastern Univ, MS, 63; Univ Wis, PhD(meteorol), 73. Prof Exp: Sr analyst, Space Res Corp, 73-74; sr mathematician, GTE, 74-76; sr scientist, Agr Res Inst Israel, 76-77; sr colorimetrist, SCI, Inc, Tex, 77-78; sr scientist, Systs & Appl Sci Corp, 78-79; mem advan prog staff, OAO Corp, 79-80; ASSOC PROG DIR METEOROL, NSF, 81- Mem: Am Meteorol Soc; Am Geophys Union; Sigma Xi; AAAS. Res: Remote sensing to extract parameters of the earth's land, ocean and atmosphere systems; climate and hydrological modeling; colorimetry applied to the display and analysis of information; balistic analysis. Mailing Add: 1121 University Blvd West Silver Spring MD 20902

KORNFILT, JAK, b Istanbul, Turkey, Apr 6, 51; m 76. THERMAL-HYDRAULICS, COMPUTER MODELING. Educ: Bogazici Univ, Istanbul, BSc, 74, MS, 76; Univ Mich, Ann Arbor, PhD(nuclear eng), 81. Prof Exp: SR ENGR THERMAL-HYDRAULIC DEVELOP, WESTINGHOUSE ELEC CORP, 81- Mem: Am Nuclear Soc; AAAS; Sigma Xi. Res: Nuclear power plant modeling; heat transfer and fluid flow models; computer code development; numerical analysis. Mailing Add: 2051 Hampstead Dr Pittsburgh PA 15235

KORNGUTH, STEVEN E, biochemistry, see previous edition

KORNHAUSER, ALAIN LUCIEN, b Beaurepaire, France, June 12, 44; US citizen; m 65. ASTRODYNAMICS, TRANSPORTATION. Educ: Pa State Univ, BS, 65, MS, 67; Princeton Univ, MA, 69, PhD(aerospace sci), 71. Prof Exp: Res asst cavitation, Ord Res Lab, 67; asst prof astrodyn, Univ Minn, Minneapolis, 71-77; assoc prof, 77-78, PROF, DEPT CIVIL ENG, PRINCETON UNIV, 78-, DIR, TRANSPORTATION PROG, 76- Concurrent Pos: Consult, Princeton Univ 71- & Optimal Data Co, 71- Honors & Awards: R T Knapp & Melville Medal, Am Soc Mech Eng, 70. Mem: Am Soc Mech Eng; Am Inst Aeronaut & Astronaut; Am Astronaut Soc. Res: Optimal space flight; cavitation; urban transportation; computer graphics; freight railroad operations and planning analysis. Mailing Add: Dept of Civil Eng Princeton Univ Princeton NJ 08540

KORNHAUSER, EDWARD T(HEODORE), b Louisville, Ky, June 30, 25; m 45, 78; c 3. ELECTRICAL ENGINEERING. Educ: Cornell Univ, BEE, 45; Harvard Univ, MS, 47, PhD(appl physics), 49. Prof Exp: Instr appl physics, Harvard Univ, 49-51; asst prof physics, 51-56, assoc prof physics, PROF ENG, BROWN UNIV, 63- Concurrent Pos: NATO fel & vis lectr, Bristol Univ, 59-60; visitor dept eng sci, Oxford Univ, 67; acad visitor, Imperial Col, London, 74; vis prof, Univ Calif, San Diego, 81-82. Mem: Sr mem Inst Elec & Electronics Engrs. Res: Electromagnetic theory; acoustics; applied mathematics; solid state physics. Mailing Add: Div of Eng Brown Univ Providence RI 02912

KORNICKER, LOUIS SAMPSON, b Brooklyn, NY, May 23, 19; m 51; c 3. GEOLOGY. Educ: Univ Ala, BS, 41 & 42; Columbia Univ, MA, 54, PhD, 58. Prof Exp: Prod supvr trinitrotoluene, Tech Invest Group, Hercules Powder Co, 42-44; sr process engr & pilot plant supt, Cities Serv Ref Co, 44-47; treas & plant supt, Uncle Sam Chem Co, Inc, 47-54; asst, Columbia Univ, 54-57; asst dir, Inst Marine Sci, Univ Tex, 57-60; geologist, Off Naval Res, Chicago, 60-61; from assoc prof to prof oceanog, Tex A&M Univ, 61-64; assoc cur, 64-67, CUR DIV CRUSTACEA, US NATURAL HIST MUS, SMITHSONIAN INST, 67- Concurrent Pos: Adj prof biol, George Washington Univ, 70- Mem: Soc Syst Zool; Crustacean Soc. Res: Marine geology; micropaleontology; paleoecology; ecology; ostracodes; coral reefs; ostracoda systematics and ecology. Mailing Add: 10400 Lake Ridge Dr Oakton VA 22124

KORNREICH, HELEN KASS, b Newark, NJ, Sept 4, 31; m 65. PEDIATRICS, RHEUMATOLOGY. Educ: Rutgers Univ, BS, 52; Hahnemann Med Col, MD, 56. Prof Exp: From instr to asst prof, 63-70, ASSOC PROF PEDIAT, SCH MED, UNIV SOUTHERN CALIF, 70- Concurrent Pos: Arthritis & Rheumatism Found fel pediat rheumatology, Childrens Hosp, Los Angeles, Calif, 63-65. Mem: Am Rheumatism Asn; Am Acad Pediat. Res: Connective tissue diseases of childhood; medical education. Mailing Add: Childrens Hosp 4650 Sunset Blvd Los Angeles CA 90027

KORNREICH, PHILIPP G, b Vienna, Austria, Nov 4, 31; US citizen; m 60; c 3. SOLID STATE PHYSICS, MICROWAVE ACOUSTICS. Educ: Carnegie Inst Tech, BS, 62; Univ Pa, PhD(elec eng), 67. Prof Exp: Sr res engr thin film technol res, Sperry Rand Univac, 60-66; res assoc solid state physics res, Univ Pa, 66-67; from asst prof to assoc prof, 67-78, PROF ELEC ENG, SYRACUSE UNIV, 78- Concurrent Pos: Consult, Gen Elec Co; consult & co-founder, DEFT Labs. Mem: Am Phys Soc; Inst Elec & Electronics Engrs; Sigma Xi; AAAS; Soc Photo-Optical Instrumentation Engrs. Res: Phonon microwave oscillator; variable delay magnetic strip line; directional dependence of photoconductivity; direct electronic fourier transforms of images; systems with delay and memory; vibrational modes of superlattices. Mailing Add: Dept of Elec & Comput Eng Syracuse Univ Syracuse NY 13210

KORNS, MICHAEL EDWARD, medicine, pathology, see previous edition

KORNSTEIN, EDWARD, b New York, NY, Sept 7, 29; m 58. ELECTROOPTICS, ENGINEERING MANAGEMENT. Educ: NY Univ, BS, 51; Drexel Inst Technol, MS, 54. Prof Exp: Physicist optics, Radio Corp Am, 51-57 & Phys Res Lab, Boston Univ, 58; consult optics, 59-60; physicist, Radio Corp Am, 60-70; vpres, Optel Corp, 70-72; PRES, KORTRON CONSULTS, 72-; VPRES, OBJECT RECOGNITION SYSTS, INC, 77- Mem: Soc Motion Picture & TV Engrs; Optical Soc Am; Inst Elec & Electronics Engrs; Soc Info Display. Res: Infrared optical and detection systems; aerial reconnaissance and data processing systems; physical optics; laser devices and systems; electro-optical displays; electronic digital timepieces; pattern recognition. Mailing Add: 10 Channing Way RD 1 Cranbury NJ 08512

KOROBKIN, IRVING, b New York, NY, Oct 18, 25; m 47; c 4. PHYSICS, SYSTEMS ANALYSIS. *Educ:* City Col New York, BME, 45; Columbia Univ, BS, 48; Univ Md, PhD(physics), 60. *Prof Exp:* Instr physics, CitY Col New York, 47-48; instr mech eng, Syracuse Univ, 48-51; res scientist & adminr fluid dynamics, US Naval Ord Lab, 51-61; sr systs analyst, IBM CORP, 61-68; OPERS RES ANALYST MIL OPERS RES, NAVAL SURFACE WEAPON CTR, 68- *Concurrent Pos:* Consult, Missile & Space Vehicle Dept, Gen Elec Co, 56-59; assoc prof lectr, George Washington Univ, 57-66. *Honors & Awards:* Meritorious Civil Serv Award, Naval Ord Lab, 57. *Mem:* Sigma Xi; assoc fel Am Inst Aeronaut & Astronaut; AAAS. *Res:* High speed fluid dynamics; reentry physics; nuclear weapons effects; military systems analyst with emphasis on strategic warfare. *Mailing Add:* Naval Surface Weapon Ctr Dept Navy Silver Spring MD 20910

KOROL, BERNARD, psychopharmacology, see previous edition

KOROS, AURELIA M CARISSIMO, b Boston, Mass, Aug 28, 34; m 57; c 5. IMMUNOLOGY, CELL BIOLOGY. *Educ:* Radcliffe Col, AB, 56; Univ Pittsburgh, MS, 60, PhD(microbiol), 65. *Prof Exp:* Res asst cell physiol, Sch Med, Harvard Univ, 56-58; Am Cancer Soc Inst res grant immunol, Sch Med, Univ Pittsburgh, 65-66, from instr to asst prof microbiol, 66-73, res asst prof obstet & gynec, 73-75, res asst prof path, 75-76; res assoc, Allegheny Gen Hosp, Pittsburgh, 77-78, asst biologist, Cancer Res Unit, 78-80; MEM STAFF, ALLEGHENY COUNTY HEALTH DEPT, 80-, GRAD SCH PUB HEALTH, UNIV PITTSBURGH, 81- *Concurrent Pos:* NIH grants, 66-74, NCI grants, 80-83; Health Res & Serv Found grants, 69 & 70. *Mem:* AAAS; Am Soc Microbiol; Am Asn Immunologists; NY Acad Sci. *Res:* Elucidation of the mechanism by which antigen and antibody regulate the proliferation of antibody-producing cells; immunological relations in maternal-fetal interactions; immunoregulation in tumor models. *Mailing Add:* 154 Maple Heights Rd Pittsburgh PA 15232

KOROS, PETER J, b Berlin, Ger, July 14, 32; US citizen; m 57; c 5. METALLURGY, MATERIALS SCIENCE. *Educ:* Drexel Univ, BS, 54; Mass Inst Technol, SM, 55. *Hon Degrees:* ScD, Mass Inst Technol, 58. *Prof Exp:* Res engr & sr res engr, 58-63, res supvr steelmaking, 63-65, chief process metallurgist, Qual Control Div, 65-75, dir process metall res, 75-78, dir res spec projs, 78-80, MGR PROCESS DEVELOP & QUAL CONTROL, JONES & LAUGHLIN STEEL CORP, 80- *Honors & Awards:* Toy Award, 62 & McKune & Herty Mem Awards, 63, Am Inst Mining, Metall & Petrol Engrs; Jalmet Award, Jones & Laughlin Steel Corp, 63; Gold Medal, Am Iron & Steel Inst, 77; Design & Appln Award, Int Magnesium Asn, 78. *Mem:* Am Iron & Steel Inst; Am Inst Mining, Metall & Petrol Engrs; Am Soc Metals. *Res:* Process and quality control in steel production; physical chemistry of iron and steelmaking; applied research in steelmaking, coal and cokemaking development. *Mailing Add:* Jones & Laughlin Steel Corp Gateway 2 #9E Pittsburgh PA 15263

KOROS, WILLIAM JOHN, b Omaha, Nebr, Aug 31, 47; m 70. POLYMER SCIENCE & ENGINEERING. *Educ:* Univ Tex, Austin, BS, 69, MS, 75, PhD(chem eng), 77. *Prof Exp:* Engr polymer processing, E I Du Pont de Nemours & Co, 69-73; asst prof, 77-80, ASSOC PROF CHEM ENG, NC STATE UNIV, 80- *Concurrent Pos:* Prin investr dual mode sorption & transport in glassy polymers, NSF grant, 77-79, 80-82; Army Res Off grant, 80-83; res award, Sigma Xi, 80. *Mem:* Am Inst Chem Eng; Sigma Xi. *Res:* Sorption and transport of low molecular weight compounds such as gases, solvents, monomers and additives in the polymeric solid state. *Mailing Add:* Dept of Chem Eng NC State Univ Raleigh NC 27650

KOROSTOFF, EDWARD, b Philadelphia, Pa, Feb 25, 21; m 51; c 3. DENTAL MATERIALS. *Educ:* Univ Pa, BS, 41, MS, 50, PhD(metall eng), 61. *Prof Exp:* Lectr dent mat sci, Univ Pa, 63-65, from asst prof to assoc prof biomat, Sch Dent Med, Sch Med & Col Eng & Appl Sci, 65-75, PROF RESTORATIVE DENT, SCH DENT MED, UNIV PA, 75- *Concurrent Pos:* USPHS career develop award, Univ Pa, 66; chmn med-dent mat comt, Metall Soc, 69-71. *Mem:* Soc Biomat; Orthop Res Soc; Int Asn Dent Res; AAAS. *Res:* Stress generated electrical potentials in bone and dentin; viscoelastic properties of bone and dentin; electric stimulation of bone remodeling. *Mailing Add:* Sch of Dent Med Univ of Pa Philadelphia PA 19174

KOROTEV, RANDALL LEE, b Green Bay, Wis, May 15, 49; m 74. GEOCHEMISTRY, ANALYTICAL CHEMISTRY. *Educ:* Univ Wis-Madison, BS, 71, PhD(chem), 76. *Prof Exp:* Proj assoc soil sci, Univ Wis-Madison, 76-79; SR RES SCIENTIST GEOCHEM, WASHINGTON UNIV, 79- *Mem:* Geochem Soc; Am Ornithologists Union. *Res:* Factors affecting the distribution of elements in geologic and environmental systems; chemical analysis by neutron activation and atomic absorption spectrophotometry. *Mailing Add:* Dept Earth & Planetary Sci PO Box 1169 Washington Univ St Louis MO 63130

KORPEL, ADRIANUS, b Rotterdam, Neth, Feb 18, 32; m 56; c 1. OPTICS, ACOUSTICS. *Educ:* Delft Technol Univ, MSEE, 56, PhD, 69. *Prof Exp:* Res engr commun, Postmaster Gen Dept, Melbourne, Australia, 56-60; div chief laser appln, Zenith Radio Corp, 60-73, dir res eng physics, 73-77; PROF ELEC ENG, UNIV IOWA, 77- *Mem:* Am Phys Soc; fel Inst Elec & Electronics Engrs; Optical Soc Am. *Res:* Information and communication theory; microwaves; laser optics; acoustic holography and microscopy; acoustooptics; nonlinear waves. *Mailing Add:* Div of Info Eng Univ of Iowa Iowa City IA 52242

KORPELA, SEPPO ANTERO, b Finland, Apr 8, 43; US citizen; m 65; c 2. MECHANICAL ENGINEERING. *Educ:* Brigham Young Univ, BES, 67; Univ Mich, MSc, 69, PhD(mech eng), 72. *Prof Exp:* Asst prof, 72-77, ASSOC PROF MECH ENG, OHIO STATE UNIV, 77- *Mem:* Sigma Xi. *Res:* Heat transfer. *Mailing Add:* Dept of Mech Eng 206 W 18th Ave Columbus OH 43210

KORPMAN, RALPH ANDREW, b New York, NY, Aug 9, 52. HEMATALOGY, MEDICAL INFORMATION SCIENCE. *Educ:* Loma Linda Univ, BA, 71, MD, 74. *Prof Exp:* Intern, Med Ctr, 74-75, resident path, 75-78, fel hemat, 78-79, ASST PROF HEMAT & PATH & DIR LABS, LOMA LINDA UNIV, 79- *Concurrent Pos:* Dir, Med Data Corp, 76-81; consult, Technician Instruments Corp, 78-81; mem comput adv comt, Am Soc Clin Path, 78-; sci adv, HBO & Co, 81- *Honors & Awards:* Sheard-Sanford Award, Am Soc Clin Pathologists, 76. *Mem:* Fel Col Am Pathologists; fel Am Soc Clin Path; NY Acad Sci. *Res:* Characterization of cellular membranes, especially red blood cells, laboratory quality control, applications of computers to medical care and instrument design and evaluation. *Mailing Add:* PO Box 548 Loma Linda CA 92354

KORR, IRVIN MORRIS, b Philadelphia, Pa, Aug 24, 09; m 39; c 1. PHYSIOLOGY, NEUROSCIENCES. *Educ:* Univ Pa, BA, 30, MA, 31; Princeton Univ, PhD(cellular physiol), 35. *Prof Exp:* Asst instr physiol, Princeton Univ, 32-33; instr, Col Med, NY Univ, 36-43; sr physiologist, Signal Lab, US War Dept, Ft Monmouth, NJ, 43-44; physiol investr wound ballistics, Princeton Univ, 45; from prof & chmn div physiol sci to distinguished prof & dir prog neurobiol, 45-75, EMER PROF PHYSIOL, KIRKSVILLE COL OSTEOP MED, 75-; PROF MED EDUC, TEX COL OSTEOP MED, 78- *Concurrent Pos:* Procter fel, Princeton Univ, 35-36; Am Philos Soc; Am Acad Arts & Sci, Plotz Found, Warner Inst Therapeut Res, Am Osteop Asn, NIH & Off Naval Res res grants; investr, Aviation Res Labs, Columbia Univ, 42-43; prof biomech, Col Osteop Med, Mich State Univ, 75-78. *Mem:* AAAS; Am Physiol Soc; Soc Exp Biol & Med; Soc Neurosci; Am Soc Neurochem. *Res:* Bioluminescence; oxidation-reduction potentials; cellular metabolism; renal physiology; aviation and climatic physiology; human spinal reflexes; referred pain mechanisms; interchange between somatic and autonomic nervous systems; trophic functions of nerves. *Mailing Add:* Tex Col Osteop Med Camp Bowie at Montgomery Fort Worth TX 76107

KORRINGA, JAN, b Heemstede, Netherlands, Mar 31, 15; m 43; c 3. THEORETICAL PHYSICS, GEOPHYSICS. *Educ:* Delft Univ Technol, DSc, 42. *Prof Exp:* From asst to instr physics, Delft Univ Technol, 41-46; from lectr to sr lectr, Univ Leiden, 46-53; from assoc prof to prof physics, Ohio State Univ, 53-80; SR RES ASSOC, CHEVRON OIL FIELD RES CO, 80- *Concurrent Pos:* Guggenheim fel, 63; vis prof, Univ Besancon, 63 & Univ Paris, 68; consult, Chevron Oil Field Res Co, 55- & Union Carbide Nuclear Co, 57-80. *Mem:* Fel Am Phys Soc; Netherlands Phys Soc. *Res:* Statistical physics; metals physics; theory of solids; theory of heterogeneous materials. *Mailing Add:* Chevron Oil Field Res Co PO Box 446 La Habra CA 90631

KORSCH, DIETRICH G, b Waren-Mueritz, Ger, Nov 30, 37; US citizen; m 66; c 2. MIRROR OPTICS. *Educ:* Univ Tuebingen, Ger, BS, 63, MS, 65, Dr rer Nat, 69. *Prof Exp:* Asst to pres, Univ Tuebingen, 66-68, res asst appl optics, 68-70; staff engr optics, Bendix Aerospace Systs, 70-73; eng consult, Sperry Rand Support Serv, 73-76; vpres sci, TAI Corp, 77-81; PRES, KORSCH OPTICS, INC, 81- *Mem:* Optical Soc Am; Soc Optical Eng; Astron Soc Pac; Ger Astron Soc. *Res:* Design and development of advanced telescope systems; development of new design and optimization techniques for all-reflective imaging systems; studies in geometric optics pertaining to the design and analysis of mirror systems from near-normal to grazing incidence. *Mailing Add:* 10111 Bluff Dr Huntsville AL 35803

KORSH, JAMES F, b Philadelphia, Pa, June 16, 38; m 62; c 3. COMPUTER SCIENCE, OPERATIONS RESEARCH. *Educ:* Univ Pa, BS, 60, PhD(comput sci), 66; Univ Ill, MS, 62. *Prof Exp:* Asst prof comput sci, Univ Pa, 66-71; sr res fel, Calif Inst Technol, 71-72; assoc prof, 72-76, PROF COMPUT SCI, TEMPLE UNIV, 77- *Mem:* Asn Comput Mach; Inst Elec & Electronic Engrs. *Res:* Quantitative methods in computer systems; analysis of algorithms. *Mailing Add:* Dept of Comput & Info Sci Temple Univ Philadelphia PA 19122

KORSON, ROY, b Philadelphia, Pa, Oct 24, 22; m 46. PATHOLOGY. *Educ:* Univ Pa, AB, 43; Jefferson Med Col, MD, 47; Am Bd Path, dipl, 56. *Prof Exp:* Asst, 50-51, asst prof, 51-52 & 54-57, assoc prof, 57-67, PROF PATH, COL MED, UNIV VT, 67-, ACTG CHMN DEPT, 74- *Concurrent Pos:* Nat Cancer Inst res fel, Columbia Univ, 48-49 & Col Med, Univ Vt, 49-50; USPHS sr res fel, 58-63; resident, Mary Fletcher Hosp, Burlington, Vt, 51-52. *Mem:* AAAS; Am Asn Pathologists; Col Am Pathologists; Int Acad Path; Sigma Xi. *Res:* Cytochemistry; histopathology; electron microscopy. *Mailing Add:* Med Alumni Bldg Univ of Vt Col of Med Burlington VT 05401

KORSRUD, GARY OLAF, b Peterborough, Ont, Mar 23, 42; m 65; c 3. ANALYTICAL CHEMISTRY, TOXICOLOGY. *Educ:* Univ Sask, BSA, 64, MSc, 66; Univ Calif, Davis, PhD(nutrit), 70. *Prof Exp:* Res asst, Univ Sask, 64-66; teaching asst animal sci, Univ Calif, Davis, 66-67, res asst, 67-70; res scientist, Health & Welfare Can, 70-77; RES SCIENTIST, AGR CAN, 77- *Mem:* Agr Inst Can; Can Soc Animal Sci; Can Soc Nutrit Sci; Soc Toxicol Can; Am Col Vet Toxicologists. *Res:* nutritional and biochemical aspects of veterinary toxicology; human carbohydrate nutrition research and advising; lipid nutrition; detection and assessment of chemically induced liver damage; food chemistry and residue analysis research. *Mailing Add:* Animal Path Lab Agr Can 116 Vet Rd Saskatoon SK S7N 2R3 Can

KORST, DONALD RICHARDSON, b Janesville, Wis, July 17, 24; m 48; c 3. INTERNAL MEDICINE. *Educ:* Univ Wis, MD, 48. *Prof Exp:* Intern, Grad Hosp, Univ Pa; resident internal med, Univ Hosp, Univ Wis-Madison; chief radioisotope serv & hematologist, Ann Arbor Vet Admin Hosp, 55-65; assoc prof med, Sch Med, Univ Wis-Madison, 65-70, asst dean educ, 71, dir independent study prog, 72, coordr educ, Dept Med, 74, prof & asst dean educ admin, 70-79, head sect gen internal med, 77-79; dir educ internal med, Madison Gen Hosp, 65-79; PROF MED, SCH MED, BOSTON UNIV, 79-, CHIEF, SECT GEN INTERNAL MED, 79- *Concurrent Pos:* Fel hemat, Med Sch, Univ Wis; asst prof internal med, Sch Med, Univ Mich, 55-65; consult, St Joseph Mercy Hosp, Ann Arbor, Mich, 58-65. *Mem:* AAAS; Am Soc Nuclear Med; Am Soc Hemat; AMA; Am Fedn Clin Res. *Res:* General medicine and health care; medical education. *Mailing Add:* 720 Harrison Ave Dobil Boston MA 02118

KORST, HELMUT HANS, b Vienna, Austria, Jan 4, 16; US citizen; m 42; c 4. MECHANICAL ENGINEERING, GAS DYNAMICS. *Educ:* Vienna Tech Univ, dipl ing, 41, Dr tech Sc, 47. *Prof Exp:* Res engr, Maschinenfabrik Augsburg-Nurnberg AG, Ger, 41-45; asst prof mech eng, Vienna Tech Univ, 45-48; vis lectr gas dynamics, 48-49, assoc prof mech eng, 49-51, head dept mech & indust eng, 62-74, PROF MECH ENG, UNIV ILL, URBANA, 51-, PROF INDUST ENG, 80- *Concurrent Pos:* Vis prof, Kans State Univ, 50, Va Polytech Inst, 54 & Vienna Tech Univ, 57; design specialist, Gen Dynamics Convair, Ft Worth, 55; sr fel, NSF, 57; consult, Gen Elec Co, 59; propulsion specialist, Rocketdyne Div, NAm Aviation, 60 & 65-68; owner, H H Korst engrs consult, Urbana, Ill, 56-; consult, Adv Group Aeronaut Res & Develop, NATO, 64 & US Army Missile Command, 71- *Mem:* Fel Am Soc Mech Engrs; fel Am Inst Aeronaut & Astronaut; Am Soc Eng Educ; Sigma Xi. *Res:* Internal and external aerodynamics; jet and rocket propulsion; heat transfer. *Mailing Add:* 3 Eton Ct Champaign IL 61820

KORST, JAMES JOSEPH, b Joliet, Ill, Nov 24, 31; m 60; c 3. ORGANIC CHEMISTRY. *Educ:* Univ Ill, BS, 53; Dartmouth Col, MA, 55; Univ Wis, PhD(org chem), 59. *Prof Exp:* Chemist, Chas Pfizer & Co, Inc, 59-70, supvr, 70-71, mgr qual control, 71-73, OPERS MGR, QUALITY CONTROL, PFIZER INC, 73- *Mem:* Am Chem Soc. *Res:* Structures of steroid intermediates; tetracycline chemistry; quality control aspects of organic chemicals and pharmaceuticals; quality control management. *Mailing Add:* Qual Control Dept Pfizer Inc Groton CT 06340

KORST, WILLIAM LAWRENCE, b Joliet, Ill, Mar 23, 22; m 54; c 4. INORGANIC CHEMISTRY, PHYSICAL CHEMISTRY. *Educ:* Univ Chicago, PhB, 46, SB, 47, SM, 49; Univ Southern Calif, PhD, 56. *Prof Exp:* Asst res chemist, Univ Calif, 56-57; asst prof chem, Polytech Inst Brooklyn, 57-58; sr res chemist, Atomics Int Div, NAm Aviation, Inc, 58-59, res specialist, 59-67; instr chem, Los Angeles City Col, 69-70; from instr to asst prof, 75-80, assoc prof, 75-80, PROF CHEM, WEST LOS ANGELES COL, 80- *Concurrent Pos:* Vis prof, Tech Univ Vienna, 78. *Mem:* Am Chem Soc. *Res:* X-ray diffraction and crystal structures; solid-state chemistry; heavy metal hydrides; high-vacuum and high-temperature techniques; atmospheric chemistry. *Mailing Add:* 7106 Quartz Ave Canoga Park CA 91306

KORT, MARGARET ALEXANDER, b Jerusalem, Jordan, Jan 16, 28; US citizen. HISTOLOGY, CELL BIOLOGY. *Educ:* Georgetown Col, BS, 58; Univ Louisville, MS, 60; Univ Northern Colo, EdD, 68. *Prof Exp:* Instr biol, Coe Col, 61-63; PROF BIOL, SOUTHWEST BAPTIST COL, 67- *Mem:* AAAS; Nat Sci Teachers Asn. *Res:* Acid phosphatase patterns in the involuting rat uterus. *Mailing Add:* Dept of Biol Southwest Baptist Col Bolivar MO 65613

KORTANEK, KENNETH O, b Chicago, Ill, Nov 13, 36; c 1. OPERATIONS RESEARCH, SYSTEMS ANALYSIS. *Educ:* Northwestern Univ, BSBA, 58, MA, 59, PhD(eng sci), 64. *Prof Exp:* Asst prof appl math & indust adminr, Univ Chicago, 65-66; assoc prof opers res, Cornell Univ, 66-69; PROF MATH SCIENCES, CARNEGIE-MELLON UNIV, 69- *Concurrent Pos:* Vis prof, Col Eng, Va Polytech Inst & State Univ, 79 & Univ NC, 81; pres, Kwel Corp, 81; mem, Int Symp Semi-Infinite Prog & Applns, 81. *Mem:* Opers Res Soc Am; Inst Mgt Sci; Am Math Soc; Economet Soc; Soc Indust & Appl Math. *Res:* Linear programming; duality theory in mathematical programming; multiple person game theory; equilibrium theory in economic systems; theory and applications of semi-infinite programming and design of telecommunications networks. *Mailing Add:* Dept of Math Carnegie-Mellon Univ Pittsburgh PA 15213

KORTE, WILLIAM DAVID, b Chicago, Ill, Oct 11, 37; m 64; c 3. ORGANIC CHEMISTRY. *Educ:* Northwestern Univ, BA, 60; Univ Mich, MS, 62; Univ Calif, Davis, PhD(chem), 66. *Prof Exp:* From asst prof to assoc prof, 66-75, chmn dept, 77-80, PROF CHEM, CALIF STATE UNIV, CHICO, 75- *Concurrent Pos:* Am Chem Soc-Petrol Res Fund res grants, 70-72. *Mem:* AAAS; Am Chem Soc. *Res:* Stereochemistry; organometallic reaction mechanisms; organic analysis. *Mailing Add:* Dept Chem Calif State Univ Chico CA 95929

KORTELING, RALPH GARRET, b Madanapalle, SIndia, Jan 2, 37; US citizen; m 61; c 2. NUCLEAR CHEMISTRY. *Educ:* Hope Col, AB, 58; Univ Calif, Berkeley, PhD(chem), 63. *Prof Exp:* Fel chem, Carnegie Inst Technol, 62-63, asst prof, 63-65; assoc prof, 65-70, ASSOC PROF CHEM, SIMON FRASER UNIV, 70- *Mem:* Am Phys Soc. *Res:* High energy nuclear reactions. *Mailing Add:* Dept of Chem Simon Fraser Univ Burnaby BC V5A 1S6 Can

KORTH, GARY E, b Tremonton, Utah, Feb 27, 38; m 61; c 5. METALLURGY, MATERIALS SCIENCE. *Educ:* Univ Utah, BS, 63, PhD(metall), 68. *Prof Exp:* Test lab engr, Gen Dynamics-Convair, 64-68; MAT RES SCIENTIST, EG&G IDAHO, INC, 68- *Mem:* Am Soc Testing & Mat; Am Soc Mech Engrs. *Res:* Elevated temperature fatigue and creep fatigue; mechanical properties; neutron irradiation effects of metals; transmission electron microscopy. *Mailing Add:* EG&G Idaho Inc PO Box 1625 ARAI Idaho Falls ID 83415

KORTIER, WILLIAM E, b Fostoria, Ohio, Nov 10, 34; m 56; c 3. PHYSICS, NUCLEAR ENGINEERING. *Educ:* Capital Univ, BS, 56; Ohio Univ, MS, 58. *Prof Exp:* Prog coordr, NASA, 58-61; asst prof mgr, Nuclear Div, Martin Co, 61-63; assoc div chief nuclear auxiliary power, Battelle Mem Inst, Ohio, 63-68, chief mat systs, Eng Div, 68-69; sr proj engr, 69-72, PROJ MGR, NUCLEAR ENERGY SYSTS, WESTINGHOUSE ELEC CORP, 72- *Mem:* Am Nuclear Soc. *Res:* Pressurized water reactor; nuclear steam supply systems; reactor operations. *Mailing Add:* Nuclear Energy Systs Div Westinghouse Elec PO Box 355 Pittsburgh PA 15230

KORTRIGHT, JAMES MCDOUGALL, b Huntington, NY, Apr 3, 27; m 52; c 2. MEDICAL PHYSICS, RADIOLOGICAL PHYSICS. *Educ:* Cornell Univ, AB, 49; Purdue Univ, MS, 53, PhD(physics), 63. *Prof Exp:* From instr to asst prof, Temple Univ, 62-66; assoc prof physics, Rose-Hulman Inst Technol, 66-72; physicist, Radiol Sci Dept, Calif Col Med, Univ Calif, Irvine, 72-73; physicist, St Francis Hosp, Lynwood, Cal, 73-74; MED PHYSICIST, RADIATION CALIBRATION CO, 74- *Mem:* Am Asn Physicists Med. *Res:* X-ray diffraction; radiation damage; semiconductor properties; gamma ray scattering; radiological and health physics. *Mailing Add:* PO Box 6432 Orange CA 92667

KORTSCHAK, HUGO PETER, b Chicago, Ill, Sept 4, 11; m 37; c 4. PLANT CHEMISTRY. *Educ:* Yale Univ, BS, 33; Univ Zurich, PhD(phys chem), 36. *Prof Exp:* Res assoc, Hawaiian Sugar Planters Asn, 37-40, assoc technologist, 41-47, assoc biochemist, 47-60, sr biochemist, physiol & biochem dept, 60-76; RES AFFIL, LYON ARBORETUM, 76- *Concurrent Pos:* Chmn bioconversion sect, Comt Alt Energy Sources Hawaii, 74-76. *Honors & Awards:* Charles F Kettering Award, Am Soc Plant Physiologists, 80; The Rank Prize, Nutrit & Agron, Rank Found, London, Eng, 81. *Mem:* AAAS; Am Chem Soc. *Res:* Photosynthesis; translocation; air pollution; carbon cycle in C-4 plants. *Mailing Add:* 2428 Ferdinand Ave Honolulu HI 96822

KORVER, GAILERD LEE, b Orange City, Iowa, Apr 16, 42; m 68; c 2. POLYMER CHEMISTRY. *Educ:* Hope Col, BA, 64; Wash State Univ, PhD(chem), 69. *Prof Exp:* Sr res chemist, Polyester Res & Develop Div, Goodyear Tire & Rubber Co, 68-79; SPECIALIST ENGR MAT TECHNOL, COM AIRPLANE CO, BOEING CO, 77- *Mem:* Am Chem Soc; Sigma Xi. *Res:* Secondary deuterium isotope effects in allylic rearrangements; improving the stability of polyethylene terephthalate towards chemical degradation; flammability testing in the development of aircraft interior materials. *Mailing Add:* 16501 SE 30th St Bellevue WA 98008

KORY, MITCHELL, b Brooklyn, NY, Jan 6, 14; m 43; c 2. BIOLOGICAL SCIENCE, MEDICINE. *Educ:* Univ Calif, Los Angeles, AB, 42, PhD(physiol bact), 53. *Prof Exp:* Instr bact, Univ Kans, 46-51; sr res biochemist res labs, 53-63, mgr pub info, 63-66, MGR MED EDUC SERV, ELI LILLY & CO, 66- *Mem:* Am Soc Biol Chemists; Brit Biochem Soc. *Res:* Infectious diseases including effects on host physiology and biochemistry; role and nature of host defenses; microbiology; antibiotic pharmacokinetics; antibiotic mechanisms of action and resistance including genetic aspects; therapeutic and ecological considerations of antibiotic development. *Mailing Add:* Med Educ Serv Eli Lilly & Co 307 E McCarty St Indianapolis IN 46285

KORY, ROSS CONKLIN, b Petersburg, Va, Sept 17, 18; m 47; c 3. MEDICINE, PHYSIOLOGY. *Educ:* Columbia Univ, AB, 38, MD, 42. *Prof Exp:* Asst path, Emory Univ, 47-48; instr med, Sch Med, Vanderbilt Univ, 49-53; from asst prof to assoc prof, Med Col Wis, 54-60, prof clin res, 60-72; assoc chief of staff & chief pulmonary function lab, Wood Vet Admin Hosp, Milwaukee, 54-72; asst dean, 72-75, PROF MED, COL MED, UNIV S FLA, 72-; MED DIR RESPIRATORY SERV, TAMPA GEN HOSP, 75- *Concurrent Pos:* Vis lectr, Univ Valle, Colombia, 63; attend staff, St Joseph's & Univ Community Hosps, Tampa, Fla, 72-; chief of staff, Tampa Vet Admin Hosp, 72-75. *Mem:* Am Physiol Soc; fel Am Col Physicians; fel Am Col Chest Physicians; Thoracic Soc; Am Fedn Clin Res. *Res:* Pulmonary physiology; obstructive pulmonary disease; sputum viscosity; electron microscopy of lung and sputum; non-obstructive pulmonary over-inflation; phonopneumography. *Mailing Add:* 108 Martinique Ave Tampa FL 33606

KORYTNYK, WALTER, b Caslav, Czech, Apr 21, 29; nat US; m 57; c 3. MEDICINAL CHEMISTRY, BIOCHEMISTRY. *Educ:* Univ Adelaide, BSc, 53 & 54, PhD(org chem), 57, DSc, 74. *Prof Exp:* Fel, Univ Adelaide, 57; fel, Am Cyanamid Co, Purdue Univ, 58-59; chemist, Fruit & Vegetable Chem Lab, USDA, Calif, 59-60; sr cancer res scientist, Roswell Park Mem Inst, 60-67; res assoc biochem, Univ Calif, Berkeley, 67-68; assoc cancer res scientist, 68-76, PRIN CANCER RES SCIENTIST, ROSWELL PARK MEM INST, 76-; RES PROF CHEM & DIR GRAD STUDIES, MED CHEM PROG, STATE UNIV NY BUFFALO, 81- *Concurrent Pos:* Prin investr, USPHS grant, 66-83; sci exchange vis, Poland, 70; res prof biol, Niagara Univ, 76- *Mem:* Am Chem Soc; The Chem Soc; NY Acad Sci; Am Asn Cancer Res; Am Soc Biol Chemists. *Res:* Plasma membrane modifiers and inhibitors; carbohydrate chemistry and biochemistry; application of NMR spectroscopy to chemistry and pharmacology; vitamin B6 and anticancer agents. *Mailing Add:* Dept of Exp Therapeut 666 Elm St Roswell Park Mem Inst Buffalo NY 14263

KOS, CLAIR MICHAEL, b Washington, Iowa, Aug 6, 11; m 36; c 3. OTOLOGY. *Educ:* Univ Nebr, BSc & MD, 37; Harvard Univ, dipl, 39. *Prof Exp:* Intern, Bishop Clarkson Mem Hosp, Omaha, Nebr, 37-38; resident, Mass Eye & Ear Infirmary, 39-41; assoc surg, Div Otolaryngol, Duke Univ, 46-47; from asst prof to prof otolaryngol, Col Med, Univ Iowa, 47-60; dir, Iowa Found Otol, 60-80; pres, Otol Med serv, PC, 71-80; RETIRED. *Concurrent Pos:* Consult, Surgeon Gen, US Air Force Hosp, Washington, DC, 41-70; emer consult, 70-; US Air Force mem, Nat Res Coun; mem bioacoust, Nat Acad Sci-Nat Res Coun; dir, Am Bd Otolaryngol; exec secy-treas, Am Acad Ophthal & Otolaryngol, 69-78; exec vpres, Am Acad Otolaryngol, 78 & 79. *Honors & Awards:* Gold Medal, Am Cong Rehab Med, 51; Award, Am Acad Ophthal & Otolaryngol, 54. *Mem:* Am Laryngol, Rhinol & Otol Soc; Am Geriat Soc; Am Otol Soc (past pres); AMA; Am Col Surgeons. *Res:* Physiology of hearing. *Mailing Add:* Otol Med Serv PC 2440 Towncrest Dr Iowa City IA 52240

KOS, EDWARD STANLEY, b Chicago, Ill, Aug 10, 28; m 52; c 2. MICROBIOLOGY. *Educ:* Loyola Univ, Ill, BS, 50; Marquette Univ, MS, 52; Univ Ill, PhD(microbiol), 58. *Prof Exp:* Actg instr life sci, Univ Calif, Riverside, 57-58; instr microbiol, Col Med, Univ Ill, 58-60; prof biol & chmn dept, Parsons Col, 60-61; assoc prof, 61-69, PROF BIOL, ROCKHURST COL, 69- *Mem:* Am Soc Microbiol. *Res:* Nutrition and metabolism of bacteria; Melanin pigmentation in Azotobacter chrococcum. *Mailing Add:* Dept of Biol Rockhurst Col Kansas City MO 64110

KOS, JOSEPH FRANK, b Montreal, Que. SOLID STATE PHYSICS. *Educ:* Univ Waterloo, BSc, 62; Univ Ottawa, PhD(physics), 67. *Prof Exp:* Asst prof physics & astron, Regina Campus, Univ Sask, 67-71, assoc prof, 71-74; assoc prof, 74-81, PROF PHYSICS & ASTRON, UNIV REGINA, 81- *Mem:* Can Asn Physicists; Electrochem Soc Am; Solar Energy Soc Can Inc. *Res:* Measurements of electron transport properties of metals; design and construction of gravitational antenna; photoelectrochemical conversion of solar energy to electricity or to production of hydrogen gas. *Mailing Add:* Dept Physics & Astron Univ Regina Regina SK S4S 0A2 Can

KOSAK, ALVIN IRA, b New York, NY, Feb 29, 24; m 58; c 3. ORGANIC CHEMISTRY. *Educ:* City Col New York, BS, 43; Ohio State Univ, PhD(org chem), 48. *Prof Exp:* Res chemist, Socony-Vacuum Oil Co, 43-45; asst chem, Ohio State Univ, 45-46, asst instr, 48; Jewett fel, Harvard Univ, 48-49; asst prof, Univ Cincinnati, 49-52; asst prof indust med, 52-56, assoc prof chem, 56-62, chmn dept, 62-65, head, All-Univ Dept, 65-77, actg dean fac arts & sci, 77-78, PROF CHEM, NY UNIV, 62- *Concurrent Pos:* USPHS spec fel, Univ Zurich, 62. *Mem:* Fel AAAS; Am Chem Soc; fel NY Acad Sci. *Res:* Thiophene chemistry; natural products; polynuclear hydrocarbons. *Mailing Add:* Dept of Chem RM 509 NY Univ 4 Washington Pl New York NY 10003

KOSAK, JOHN R, b Wilmington, Del, May 18, 30; m 57; c 3. INDUSTRIAL ORGANIC CHEMISTRY. *Educ:* Univ Del, BS, 51, MS, 52; Mich State Univ, PhD(org chem), 57. *Prof Exp:* Instr org & gen chem, Ferris State Col, 55-56; sr chemist, 57-80, RES ASSOC, E I DU PONT DE NEMOURS & CO, INC, 80- *Mem:* Am Chem Soc; Catalysis Soc. *Res:* Catalysis; catalytic hydrogenation. *Mailing Add:* E I du Pont de Nemours & Co Inc 1007 Market St Wilmington DE 19898

KOSANKE, ROBERT MAX, b Park Ridge, Ill, Sept 4, 17; m 41; c 2. PALEOBOTANY. *Educ:* Coe Col, BA, 40; Univ Cincinnati, MS, 42; Univ Ill, PhD(paleobot), 52. *Prof Exp:* Lab instr geol, Coe Col, 39-40; asst bot, Univ Cincinnati, 40-43; asst, Ill Geol Surv, 43, from asst geologist to geologist, 43-63; GEOLOGIST, US GEOL SURV, 63- *Concurrent Pos:* Assoc prof bot, Univ Ill, 59-63. *Mem:* AAAS; fel Geol Soc Am; Bot Soc Am; Soc Econ Geol; Paleont Soc. *Res:* Spore studies of coal beds of Pennsylvania age; Pennsylvanian stratigraphy and paleobotany. *Mailing Add:* US Geol Surv MS 919 Box 25046 Denver Fed Ctr Denver CO 80225

KOSANOVICH, ROBERT JOSEPH, b Monroe, Mich, Sept 27, 38; m 60; c 3. MATHEMATICS. *Educ:* Eastern Mich Univ, BS, 60, MA, 62; Univ Detroit, MA, 63; Mich State Univ, PhD, 72. *Prof Exp:* PROF MATH, FERRIS STATE COL, 65-, HEAD DEPT, 75- *Mailing Add:* Dept Math Ferris State Col Big Rapids MI 49307

KOSASKY, HAROLD JACK, b Winnipeg, Man, Oct 19, 27; m 55; c 3. OBSTETRICS, GYNECOLOGY. *Educ:* Univ Man, BA, 48, MD, 53; FRCS, 60; mem, Royal Col Obstetricians & Gynecologists, 60; Am Bd Obstet & Gynec, dipl, 64. *Prof Exp:* Rotating intern, Deer Lodge Vet & Grace Hosps, Winnipeg, Can, 52-53; resident gen surg, Colonel Belcher Hosp, Calgary, 53-54; resident psychiat, Warren State Hosp, Warren, Pa, 55-56; asst resident obstet & gynec, Chicago Lying-In Hosp, Univ Chicago, 56-58, sr res, 58-59; from asst prof to assoc prof, Sch Med, Univ Louisville, 61-65; INSTR OBSTET & GYNEC, HARVARD MED SCH, 66- *Concurrent Pos:* Exchange fel, Univ Durham, 59-60; dir dept obstet & gynec, Cambridge Hosp, 68-70, jr assoc surgeon, Peter Bent Brigham Hosp, 66-80, obstetrician & gynecologist, Boston Hosp Women, 66-80; consult, Jordan Hosp, 69-; active staff, Brigham & Women's Hosp, 80- *Mem:* Fel Am Col Obstetricians & Gynecologists; fel Am Col Surgeons; Asn Profs Gynec & Obstet. *Res:* Endocrinology; gynecologic surgery; infertility; clinical and gynecology. *Mailing Add:* Dept of Obstet & Gynec Harvard Med Sch Boston MA 02115

KOSBAB, FREDERIC PAUL GUSTAV, b Berlin, Ger, Mar 29, 22; US citizen; m 51. PSYCHIATRY, INTERNAL MEDICINE. *Educ:* Univ Berlin, MD, 45; Am Bd Psychiat & Neurol, dipl, 63. *Prof Exp:* Intern, Army Hosps & Refugee Infirmary, Friedland, WGer, 45-46; resident internal med, Dist Hosp, Hannoversch Muenden, WGer, 46-48 & Evangel Hosp, Goettingen-Weende, WGer, 48-51; pvt pract internal med, 51-55; rotating intern, Swed Covenant Hosp, Chicago, Ill, 56-57; staff physician I, Psychiat Serv, Manteno State Hosp, Ill, 57-58; resident psychiat, Col Med, Univ Nebr, 58-59; staff physician II, Psychiat Serv, Northern State Hosp, Sedro-Woolley, Wash, 59-60; resident psychiat, Sch Med, Univ Wash, 60-61 & Northern State Hosp, Sedro-Woolley, Wash, 61-62; clin instr psychiat, Med Sch, Univ Ore, 62-64; from asst prof to prof psychiat, Med Col Va, Va Commonwealth Univ, 64-73, dir residency training in psychiat, 66-69, from actg chmn dept to assoc chmn dept, 69-73; med dir, E Plains Ment Health Ctr, 74-77; chief psychiat servs, Hampton, Va Med Ctr, 77-82; PROF PSYCHIAT & CHMN DEPT, SCH MED, ORAL ROBERTS UNIV, TULSA, 82- *Concurrent Pos:* Consult, WGer Vet Admin, Landau, 52-56 & Residency Training Prog, East State Hosp, Williamsburg, Va, 68-73; sr staff psychiatrist & unit med dir, Ore State Hosp, Salem, 62-63; pvt pract psychiat, 63-; mem, Med Col Va Hosps, 64-73; attend & consult, McGuire Vet Admin Hosp, Richmond, Va, 64-73; chmn, Comt Postgrad Training in Psychiat, 67-70; mem dean's comt, Richmond Vet Admin Hosp, 69-70; prof dir NIMH grant, 69-73; prof, Dept Psychiat & Behavioral Sci, Eastern Va Med Sch, 77-82. *Mem:* Fel Am Psychiat Asn; fel Royal Soc Med; hon fel, Arbeitsgemeinschaft F Katathymes Bilderleben, WGer. *Res:* Contribution to the problem of superfetation and superfecundation in twins; camptocormia in the female; introduction of a buddy system for hospitalized geriatric patients; symbol formation; affective imagery and its didactic uses in psychiatry; teaching and learning in medical school. *Mailing Add:* Oral Roberts Univ Sch Med 7777 S Lewis Ave Tulsa OK 74171

KOSCHMANN, ARNOLD H(ERMAN), b Freeport, Ill, Nov 30, 26; m 51; c 4. ELECTRICAL ENGINEERING. *Educ:* Valparaiso Univ, AB, 48; Purdue Univ, BSEE, 50, MS, 51, PhD, 54. *Prof Exp:* Asst math, Purdue Univ, 51-52; asst prof elec eng, Univ Minn, 54-57; assoc prof elec eng, Univ NMex, 57-63, chmn dept, 62-71, assoc dean, Col Eng, 74-76, prof, 63-80. *Concurrent Pos:* Consult, Minneapolis, Honeywell Co, 54-57, Kirtland AFB, 59- & Dikewood Corp; sr staff engr, Hughes Aircraft Co, 78-79. *Mem:* Inst Elec & Electronics Engrs. *Res:* Statistical problems in communication and control systems; time varying systems; adaptive control systems. *Mailing Add:* 1212 Espanola NE Albuquerque NM 87108

KOSCHMIEDER, ERNST LOTHAR, b Danzig, Ger, May 1, 29; m 62; c 2. METEOROLOGY, FLUID DYNAMICS. *Educ:* Univ Bonn, dipl physics, 58, Dr rer nat(physics), 63. *Prof Exp:* Res fel atmospheric sci, Harvard Univ, 63-65; res assoc, Univ Chicago, 65-67; vis asst prof, Univ Okla, 67-68; asst prof, 68-69, ASSOC PROF ATMOSPHERIC SCI, UNIV TEX, AUSTIN, 69- *Concurrent Pos:* Consult, Apollo XIV & XVII Convection Exp, Lockheed Space & Missiles Co, 71-74; mem, Ctr Statist Mech, Univ Tex, Austin, 72-; sr vis fel, Nat Ctr Atmospheric Res, Colo, 73-74; lectr, 17th Int Solvay Cong Physics, Brussels, 78; vis sci, Centre d'Etudes Nucleaires, Saclay, France, 81. *Mem:* Am Phys Soc. *Res:* Application of fluid dynamics to problems of atmospheric motions, particularly the use of model experiments. *Mailing Add:* E Cockrell Jr Hall 9.126 Univ of Tex Austin TX 78712

KOSCO, JOHN C(ARROLL), b Du Bois, Pa, Sept 20, 32; m 56; c 6. METALLURGY. *Educ:* Univ Notre Dame, BS, 54; Princeton Univ, MSE, 56; Pa State Univ, PhD(metall), 58. *Prof Exp:* Res metallurgist, Stackpole Carbon Co, 58-66, chief engr metals, 66-67, dir metall res, 67-71; DIR POWDER METALL RES, KEYSTONE CARBON CO, 71- *Mem:* Am Soc Metals; Am Inst Mining, Metall & Petrol Engrs; Am Chem Soc. *Res:* Powder metallurgy of ferrous and non-ferrous materials, high temperature materials and electrical contacts; electrical ceramics and thermoelectric materials; coatings and metal joining. *Mailing Add:* Keystone Carbon Co Powder Metall Res Dept St Marys PA 15857

KOSEL, GEORGE EUGENE, b Rochester, NY, July 22, 23; m 50; c 3. ELECTROPHOTOGRAPHY. *Educ:* Cornell Univ, AB, 44; Univ Rochester, MS, 51. *Prof Exp:* Res assoc biochem, Atomic Energy Comn, Univ Rochester, 47-50; chief biochemist dental res, Passaic Gen Hosp, NJ, 50-54; mgr res graphic arts, 54-67, mgr res, Electrostatic Div, 67-70, asst dir res, 70-75, DIR BASIC CHEM RES, PHILIP A HUNT CHEM CORP, 75- *Mem:* AAAS; Am Chem Soc; Am Crystallog Asn; Soc Photog Sci & Eng. *Res:* Fluoride metabolism; solid state and physical chemistry; powders and liquid developers for electrophotography. *Mailing Add:* 181 North Ave Park Ridge NJ 07656

KOSEL, PETER BOHDAN, b Northeim, Ger, Aug 20, 46; Australian citizen; m 73; c 2. MICROELECTRONIC DEVICES. *Educ:* Univ Sydney, Australia, BSc, 68; Univ New South Wales, Australia, PhD(elec eng), 76. *Prof Exp:* Prof officer elec eng, Univ NSW, 73-80; ASSOC PROF ELEC ENG, UNIV CINCINNATI, 80- *Mem:* Inst Elec & Electron Engrs. *Res:* High speed charge-coupled devices in gallium arsenite and fabrication technology of compound semiconductor devices; computer aided design and simulation of signal processing devices and circuits; submicron-line lithography and very-large-scale integration pattern generation. *Mailing Add:* Elec Eng Dept ML #30 Univ Cincinnati Cincinnati OH 45221

KOSERSKY, DONALD SAADIA, b Waterbury, Conn, Oct 16, 32; m 60. PHARMACOLOGY. *Educ:* Univ Conn, BA, 57, MS, 68; Univ of the Pac, PhD, 71. *Prof Exp:* Res assoc, Sch Med, Univ NC, Chapel Hill, 71-73; asst prof, Northeastern Univ, 73-77, assoc prof pharmacol, 77-81; ASSOC PROF PHARMACOL & COORDR GRAD PROG, MASS COL PHARM & ALLIED HEALTH SCI, 81- *Mem:* AAAS; Am Soc Pharmacol & Exp Therapeut; Neurosci Soc. *Res:* Autonomic and central nervous system pharmacology; pharmacology of addiction and drugs of abuse; classical pharmacology. *Mailing Add:* Mass Col Pharm & Allied Health Sci 179 Longwood Ave Boston MA 02115

KOSH, JOSEPH WILLIAM, b Hempstead, Tex, Sept 30, 40. NEUROPHARMACOLOGY. *Educ:* Univ Tex, BSPharm, 64, MSPharm, 67; Univ Colo, PhD(pharmacol), 71. *Prof Exp:* Asst prof pharmacol, Univ SC, 71-75, assoc prof, 75-80. *Mem:* AAAS; Sigma Xi. *Res:* Cardiovascular and neuropharmacology; pharmacology of gamma-aminobutyric acid intermediates and relation to convulsive threshold. *Mailing Add:* 3514 Bronte Rd Columbia SC 29210

KOSHEL, RICHARD DONALD, b Argo, Ill, Feb 1, 36; m 62; c 2. NUCLEAR PHYSICS. *Educ:* Univ Ill, BS, 58, MS, 59; Univ Kans, PhD(theoret nuclear physics), 63. *Prof Exp:* From asst prof to assoc prof, 63-73, PROF PHYSICS, OHIO UNIV, 73-, ASSOC DEAN, COL ARTS & SCI, 80- *Concurrent Pos:* Vis prof, Fla State Univ, 69-70 & Univ Md, 78-79. *Mem:* Am Phys Soc; Am Asn Physics Teachers. *Res:* Theoretical nuclear physics and numerical analysis; nuclear structure using many body techniques and nuclear reactions. *Mailing Add:* Dept Physics Ohio Univ Athens OH 45701

KOSHER, ROBERT ANDREW, b Key West, Fla, Mar 1, 45; m 68; c 3. DEVELOPMENTAL BIOLOGY. *Educ:* Wilkes Col, BA, 67; Temple Univ, PhD(biol), 72. *Prof Exp:* NIH fel anat, Sch Med, Univ Pa, 72-74; asst prof, 74-80, ASSOC PROF ANAT, UNIV CONN HEALTH CTR, 80- *Mem:* Soc Develop Biol; Am Soc Zoologists; Am Asn Anatomists. *Res:* The role of extracellular matrix components in tissue interactions and other developmental processes; the control of somite chondrogenesis by extracellular matrix components produced by the embryonic notochord and spinal cord. *Mailing Add:* Dept of Anat Univ of Conn Health Ctr Farmington CT 06032

KOSHI, JAMES H, b Agate, Colo, June 13, 19; m 77. DAIRY SCIENCE, ANIMAL SCIENCE. *Educ:* Colo Agr & Mech Col, BS, 48; Univ Minn, PhD(dairy sci), 55. *Prof Exp:* Dairy specialist & prof, Univ Hawaii, 55-74; gen mgr agr, Micronesian Develop Co, Tinian, 75-77; consult dairy prod, Hawaiian Agron Co Int, Iran, 77-78; GEN MGR, 50TH STATE DAIRY FARMERS COOP, 79- *Concurrent Pos:* Consult & prof, Kasetsart Univ Thailand, 62-65. *Mem:* Am Dairy Sci Asn; Sigma Xi. *Res:* All areas of dairy cattle management and milk production. *Mailing Add:* 2333 Kapiolani Blvd Apt 2011 Honolulu HI 96826

KOSHLAND, DANIEL EDWARD, JR, b New York, NY, Mar 30, 20; m 45; c 5. BIOCHEMISTRY. *Educ:* Univ Calif, BS, 41; Univ Chicago, PhD(chem), 49. *Prof Exp:* Anal chemist, Shell Chem Co, 41-42; asst, Manhattan Dist, Univ Chicago, 42-43, res assoc, Oak Ridge, 43-44, group leader, 44-46; fel, Harvard Univ, 49-51; assoc biochemist, Brookhaven Nat Lab, 51-54, biochemist, 54-56, sr biochemist, 56-65; PROF BIOCHEM, UNIV CALIF, BERKELEY, 65- *Concurrent Pos:* Affiliate, Rockefeller Inst, 58-65; mem panel, USPHS, 59-64; vis fel, All Souls Col, Oxford, 72; fel, Guggenheim Found, 72. *Honors & Awards:* Harvey Soc lectr; Walker-Ames lectr, Univ Wash; Rennebohm lectr, Univ Wis; Carter Wallace lectr, Princeton Univ; Christian Herter lectr, NY Univ; O M Shaffer lectr, Wash Univ; Marion lectr, Nat Res Coun Can, 73; Nieuwland lectr, Univ Notre Dame, 74; John Edsall Lectr, Harvard Univ, 78; T Duckett Jones Award, Helen Hay Whitney Found, 77; Distinguished Lectr Award, Soc Gen Physiol, 78. *Mem:* Nat Acad Sci; AAAS; Am Chem Soc; Am Soc Biol Chem (pres, 73-74); coun mem, Am Acad Arts & Sci. *Res:* Mechanism of enzyme action; regulation and control of enzyme activity; biochemistry of sensory systems; chemotaxis as a model sensory system. *Mailing Add:* Dept of Biochem 401 Biochem Bldg Univ of Calif Berkeley CA 94720

KOSHLAND, MARIAN ELLIOTT, b New Haven, Conn, Oct 25, 21; m 45; c 5. IMMUNOLOGY. *Educ:* Vassar Univ, BA, 42; Univ Chicago, MS, 43, PhD(bact), 49. *Prof Exp:* Asst, Cholera Proj, Off Sci Res & Develop, Chicago, 43 & 44-45; asst, Comn Air Borne Dis, Colo, 43-44; jr chemist, Atomic Bomb Proj, Manhattan Dist, Tenn, 45-46; from assoc bacteriologist to bacteriologist, Brookhaven Nat Lab, 53-65; from assoc res immunologist to res immunologist, 65-70, PROF BACT & IMMUNOL, UNIV CALIF, BERKELEY, 70- *Concurrent Pos:* Fel bact & immunol, Harvard Univ, 49-51; mem, Nat Sci Bd, NSF, 76-82. *Mem:* Nat Acad Sci; Am Asn Immunologists (pres, 82-83); Am Soc Biol Chemists; Sigma Xi; Am Acad Microbiologists. *Res:* Mechanism of antibody biosynthesis; roles of J chain and IgM in the differentiation of antibody-forming cells; genetic control of J and heavy chain synthesis. *Mailing Add:* Dept of Bact & Immunol Univ of Calif Berkeley CA 94720

KOSHUBA, WALTER J(OSEPH), b St Paul, Minn, Aug 22, 17; m 45; c 2. METALLURGY, CERAMICS. *Educ:* Univ Minn, BMetE, 40. *Prof Exp:* Asst res engr, Allis-Chalmers Mfg Co, 41-43, asst supt res eng, 43-45, supt, 45-46; consult, Bergen Precision Castings, 46; exp engr & gen supt, Solar Aircraft Co, 46-47; sr metallurgist, Nuclear Engine Propulsion Aircraft Div, Fairchild Engine & Airplane Corp, 47, prin metallurgist, 47-49, head mat sect, 49-51; supvr metall & ceramic eng, Aircraft Nuclear Propulsion Dept, Gen Elec Co, 51-56, mgr tech prod, 56-61; mgr, Nuclear Div, Beryllium Corp, 61-64, mgr, Alloy Div, 65-70; mgr mfg technol, Kawecki Beryllium Industs, 70-72; mgr facil & equip eng, Nuclear Div, United Nuclear Corp, 72-74, VPRES ENG, URANIUM RECOVERY CORP, UNITED NUCLEAR CORP, 74-, VPRES SPECIAL PROJS, URANIUM RECOVERY CORP & PRODECO & BIOSERVS, INC, SUBSIDIARIES, 79- *Mem:* Am Soc Metals; Am Ceramic Soc; Am Inst Mining, Metall & Petrol Engrs; Nat Inst Ceramic Engrs; fel Am Inst Chemists. *Res:* Heat treatment of heavy forgings; metallurgy of heat resistant alloys; high temperature materials; materials for nuclear reactors; molding materials for precision casting; beryllium and beryllium alloy technology; equipment engineering; facilities design and construction of chemical plants. *Mailing Add:* Uranium Recovery Corp Box 765 Mulberry FL 33860

KOSHY, K THOMAS, b Kerala, India, Sept 22, 24; m 50; c 2. PHARMACY, PHARMACEUTICAL CHEMISTRY. *Educ:* Kerala Univ, India, BSc, 43; Benares Hindu Univ, BPharm, 48; Univ Iowa, MS, 58, PhD(pharm, pharmaceut chem), 60. *Prof Exp:* Mfg chemist, Sterling Pharmaceut, India, 48-49; jr sci asst, Inspectorate of Gen Stores Lab, 49-51; med serv rep, Parke Davis & Co, Ltd, 51-56; asst col pharm, Univ Iowa, 60-61; sr res pharmacist, Miles Labs, Inc, 61-66; SR RES SCIENTIST, UPJOHN CO, 66- *Mem:* Am Pharmaceut Asn; Am Chem Soc. *Res:* Analytical methods development for drugs and pharmaceuticals; kinetic studies and stability testing of pharmaceuticals; residue analysis in plants and animals; metabolism in plants and animals; photolysis of pesticides and herbicides. *Mailing Add:* Upjohn Co Kalamazoo MI 49001

KOSIBA, WALTER LOUIS, b Braddock, Pa, Feb 13, 21. PHYSICAL CHEMISTRY. *Educ:* Canisius Col, BS, 43; Ohio State Univ, MSc, 49, PhD(chem), 51. *Prof Exp:* Res assoc, S A M Labs, Columbia Univ, 44-45; chemist, Phys Chem, Uranium, Tenn Eastman Corp, 45-46; res chemist, Phys Chem Solids, Vitro Corp Am, 51-53; assoc physicist, Brookhaven Nat Lab, 53-58; mem res staff, Gen Atomic Div, Gen Dynamics Corp, 58-61; consult, European Atomic Energy Community, Belgium, 61-63; sr scientist, Nuclear Dept, Douglas Aircraft Co, Inc, 64-66 & Aerospace Corp, 66; asst to dir, NAm Rockwell Sci Ctr, 66-70; SPECIALIST, LA JOLLA RADIOCARBON & TRITIUM LAB, UNIV CALIF, SAN DIEGO, 71- *Concurrent Pos:* Consult, Int Atomic Energy Agency, Austria, 61. *Mem:* AAAS; Am Chem Soc. *Res:* Materials sciences; radiation effects; solid state chemistry; radiocarbon dating. *Mailing Add:* 3920 Ingraham St Apt 118 San Diego CA 92109

KOSIER, FRANK J, b Lansing, Mich, July 2, 34; m 52; c 2. MATHEMATICS. *Educ:* Mich State Univ, BS, 56, MS, 57, PhD(math), 60. *Prof Exp:* Instr math, Univ Calif, Berkeley, 60-61 & Univ Wis, 61-63; asst prof, Syracuse Univ, 63-64 & Univ Wis-Madison, 64-66; assoc prof, 66-69, PROF MATH, UNIV IOWA, 69- *Mem:* Am Math Soc; Math Asn Am. *Res:* Non-associative rings. *Mailing Add:* Dept of Math Univ of Iowa Iowa City IA 52240

KOSIEWICZ, STANLEY TIMOTHY, b Chicago, Ill, July 21, 44; c 1. ANALYTICAL CHEMISTRY. *Educ:* Univ Ill, BS, 67; Univ Wis, MS, 69, PhD(anal chem), 73. *Prof Exp:* Process engr chem eng, Olin Corp, 68-69; STAFF MEM ANAL CHEM, LOS ALAMOS NAT LAB, UNIV CALIF, 73- *Mem:* AAAS. *Res:* Transuranium radioactive waste degradation; thermogravimetry; trace element geochemistry and archaeology; automation of analytical instrumentation; electron spectroscopy chem analysis; auger electron spectroscopy. *Mailing Add:* Los Alamos Nat Lab MS 740 Los Alamos NM 87545

KOSIKOWSKI, FRANK VINCENT, b Torrington, Conn, Jan 10, 16; m 44; c 1. FOOD SCIENCE. *Educ:* Univ Conn, BS, 39; Cornell Univ, MS, 41, PhD(dairy chem), 44. *Prof Exp:* Instr, 42-44, res assoc, 44-45, from asst prof to assoc prof, 45-52, PROF FOOD SCI, CORNELL UNIV, 52- *Concurrent Pos:* Consult, Food & Agr Orgn, UN, 52-; Fulbright res scholar, France, 55; State Dept exchange scholar, Ireland, 59; mem expert adv comt food hyg, WHO, 70. *Honors & Awards:* Borden Award, Am Dairy Sci Asn, 55, Pfizer Award, 60; Pfizer Award, Am Dairy Sci Asn, 60. *Mem:* AAAS; Am Chem Soc; Am Dairy Sci Asn; Inst Food Technol. *Res:* Chemistry and bacteriology of milk and cheese products, especially flavor reactions, analytical methods and enzyme activity; foods from fermentations; international food development. *Mailing Add:* Dept Food Sci Stocking Hall Cornell Univ Ithaca NY 14853

KOSINSKI, ANTONI A, b Warsaw, Poland, May 25, 30; div; c 1. MATHEMATICS. *Educ:* Univ Warsaw, PhD, 56. *Prof Exp:* Asst prof inst math, Polish Acad Sci, 56-59 & Univ Calif, Berkeley, 59-62; mem Inst Adv Study, 62-64; assoc prof math, Univ Calif, Berkely, 64-66; PROF MATH, RUTGERS UNIV, 66- *Mem:* Am Math Soc. *Res:* Topology and differential topology. *Mailing Add:* Dept of Math Rutgers Univ New Brunswick NJ 08903

KOSINSKI, ROBERT JOSEPH, b Montclair, NJ, Jan 8, 49. POPULATION ECOLOGY, LIMNOLOGY. *Educ:* Seton Hall Univ, BS, 72; Rutgers Univ, PhD(ecol), 77. *Prof Exp:* ASST PROF BIOL, TEX A&M UNIV, 77- *Mem:* AAAS; Ecol Soc Am; Am Soc Limnol & Oceanog; Am Soc Naturalists. *Res:* stream ecology; primary productivity in streams; effects of pesticides in streams; computer modeling of antigenic variation of trypanosome infections; use of computers as teaching tools. *Mailing Add:* Dept of Biol Col of Sci Tex A&M UniV College Station TX 77843

KOSIUR, DAVID RICHARD, b Buffalo, NY, Dec 9, 50. GEOCHEMISTRY. *Educ:* State Univ NY Buffalo, BA, 72, MS, 75; Univ Calif, Los Angeles, PhD(geochem), 78. *Prof Exp:* RES GEOCHEMIST, CHEVRON OIL FIELD RES CO, 78- *Mem:* Mineral Soc Am; Int Zeolite Asn; Clay Minerals Soc. *Res:* Quantitative x-ray diffractometry of mineralogical phases; formation and diagenesis of clays and zeolites; crystal growth. *Mailing Add:* PO Box 446 La Habra CA 90631

KOSKI, RAYMOND ALLEN, b Corvallis, Ore, Aug 21, 51; m 79. GENE EXPRESSION IN YEAST. *Educ:* Stanford Univ, BS, 73; Yale Univ, MPhil, 75, PhD(biol), 78. *Prof Exp:* Fel molecular biol, Inst Molecular Biol II, Univ Zurich, 78; fel, Dept Microbiol, Univ Geneva, 78-79; fel, Dept Genetics, Univ Wash, 79-81; RES SCIENTIST, APPL MOLECULAR GENETICS INC, 81- *Res:* Structure and function of yeast promoters; expression of heterologous genes in yeast. *Mailing Add:* Appl Molecular Genetics Inc 1892 Oak Terr Lane Newbury Park CA 91320

KOSKI, WALTER S, b Philadelphia, Pa, Dec 1, 13; m 40; c 4. PHYSICAL CHEMISTRY. *Educ:* Johns Hopkins Univ, PhD(phys chem), 42. *Prof Exp:* Res chemist, Hercules Powder Co, 42-43; group leader, Los Alamos Sci Lab, 44-47; assoc prof phys chem, 47-55, chmn dept, 55-74, PROF CHEM, JOHNS HOPKINS UNIV, 55- *Concurrent Pos:* Physicist, Brookhaven Nat Lab, NY, 47-48; consult chem corps, US Army, 49- *Mem:* Am Chem Soc; fel Am Phys Soc. *Res:* Radioactive and stable isotopes as tracers; chemistry of boron hydrides; electron and nuclear magnetic resonance; mass spectroscopy; nuclear chemistry; ion-molecule reactions; reactive scattering of ions: mechanism of drug action. *Mailing Add:* Dept Chem Johns Hopkins Univ Baltimore MD 21218

KOSKO, ERYK, b Odessa, Russia, Aug 30, 04; Can citizen; m 44; c 2. AEROSPACE ENGINEERING. *Educ:* Danzig Tech Univ, Dipl Eng, 32; Polish Univ Abroad, London, Dr Tech Sci, 68. *Prof Exp:* Design engr, Nat Aircraft Works, Poland, 33-34; engr aircraft airworthiness, Aeronaut Res Inst, 35-39; chief stress engr, Nat Air Navig Co, Brazil, 41; asst prof aircraft struct, Polytech Sch, Montreal, 43-45; chief stress engr, Fairchild Aircraft Ltd Can, 46; asst chief stress engr, A V Roe Can Ltd, 47-59; sr res officer, Nat Aeronaut Estab, Nat Res Coun Can, 59-70; eng consult, 70-80; RETIRED. *Concurrent Pos:* Spec lectr & sci consult, Inst Aerophys, Univ Toronto, 55-57; session lectr dept mech eng, Univ Ottawa, 68-70; fac eng, Carleton Univ, 70-71. *Mem:* Assoc fel Can Aeronaut & Space Inst. *Res:* Structural theory; static and dynamic analysis of complex structures, especially matrix methods as applied to aeronautical and other structures. *Mailing Add:* 2106 Woodcrest Rd Ottawa ON K1H 6H8 Can

KOSKY, PHILIP GEORGE, b London, Eng, Mar 25, 39; m 64; c 2. CHEMICAL ENGINEERING, COAL SCIENCE. *Educ:* Univ London, BSc, 61; Univ Calif, Berkeley, MS, 63, PhD(chem eng), 66. *Prof Exp:* Res asst chem eng, Univ Calif, Berkeley, 61-66; sr sci officer, Atomic Energy Res Estab, Harwell, Eng, 66-68; staff scientist, Res & Develop Ctr, Gen Elec Co, 68-75; assoc prof mech eng & mech, Lehigh Univ, 75-77; staff scientist, 77-80, MGR, FUEL SCI UNIT, GEN ELEC RES & DEVELOP CTR, 80- *Concurrent Pos:* Adj assoc prof, Union Col NY, 70-75. *Mem:* AAAS. *Res:* Thermodynamics; energy research; fuel science with specialty in coal; heat transfer and nuclear engineering. *Mailing Add:* Gen Elec Res & Develop Ctr Schenectady NY 12301

KOSLOW, JULIAN ANTHONY, b Los Angeles, Calif, May 14, 47; m 79; c 1. FISHERIES OCEANOGRAPHY. *Educ:* Harvard Univ, BA, 69; Univ Wash, BA, 73; Univ Calif, San Diego, PhD(biol oceanog), 80. *Prof Exp:* Field & lab worker, Fisheries Res Inst, Univ Wash, 72 & 74; field & lab worker, Nat Marine Fisheries Serv, 73; res asst biol oceanog, Scripps Inst Oceanog, Univ Calif, San Diego, 74-79; ASST PROF FISHERIES OCEANOG, OCEANOG DEPT, DALHOUSIE UNIV, 80- *Concurrent Pos:* Lectr, Scripps Inst Oceanog, Univ Calif, San Diego,, 78. *Honors & Awards:* E W Fager Award, Scripps Inst Oceanog, 80; Chapman-Schaefer Award, Marine Technol Soc, 75. *Res:* Structure of marine zooplankton communities, influence of fish populations, climatic change, physical oceanography and plankton behavior; the regulation between stock and recruitment in fish populations, interactions with biological and climatic change and larval ecology; effect of fisheries management on fishing communities. *Mailing Add:* Oceanog Dept Dalhousie Univ Halifax NS B3H 4J1 Can

KOSLOW, STEPHEN HUGH, b New York, NY, Oct 14, 40; m 62; c 2. PHARMACOLOGY, PSYCHOPHARMACOLOGY. *Educ:* Columbia Univ, BS, 62; Univ Chicago, PhD, 67. *Prof Exp:* Fel pharmacol, Karolinska Inst, Stockholm, Sweden, 68-69; NIMH staff fel, Lab Preclin Pharmacol, St Elizabeth's Hosp, Washington, DC, 70-73, chief unit neurobiol & appl mass spectrometry, Lab Preclin Pharmacol, 73-75, chief, Biol Res Sect, Clin Res Br, 75-81, CHIEF NEUROSCI RES BR, DIV EXTRAMURAL RES, NIMH, 81- *Concurrent Pos:* Dir, Clin Res Br Collab Prog Psychol Depression, NIMH, 75-, Presidential Comn Mental Health, Special Asst Res Panel, 78. *Mem:* Am Soc Pharmacol & Exp Therapeut; Soc Neurosci; Am Col Neuropsychopharmacol; Soc Biol Psychiat; Am Soc Neurochem. *Res:* Neuropharmacology and psychopharmacology; depression and schizophrenia; neurotransmitters; metabolites and central nervous system function; neuroendocrinology. *Mailing Add:* NIMH Parklawn Bldg Rm 10-C-23 5600 Fishers Lane Rockville MD 20857

KOSMAHL, HENRY G, b Wartha, Ger, Dec 14, 19; US citizen; m 43; c 3. ELECTRON PHYSICS. *Educ:* Dresden Tech Univ, MS, 43; Darmstadt Tech Univ, DS(electron physics), 49. *Prof Exp:* Asst prof physics, Darmstadt Tech Univ, 49-51; res physicist, AEG-Telefunken Res Ctr, Ger, 52-56; head power amplifier, Electron Lab, US Army, 56-62; HEAD POWER AMPLIFIER, LEWIS RES CTR, NASA, 62- *Concurrent Pos:* Consult, Aeronautical Systs & Space Div, US Air Force, Dayton, 62- *Honors & Awards:* Sci Achievement Medal, NASA, 74. *Mem:* Fel Inst Elec & Electronic Engrs. *Res:* Interaction of charged particles with waves and matter. *Mailing Add:* NASA Lewis Res Ctr 21000 Brookpark Rd Cleveland OH 44135

KOSMAN, DANIEL JACOB, b Chicago, Ill, Nov 29, 41; m 64; c 2. BIOCHEMISTRY. *Educ:* Oberlin Col, BA, 63; Univ Chicago, PhD(phys org chem), 68. *Prof Exp:* Res assoc biophys, Univ Hawaii, 68-69; Cornell Univ res assoc molecular biol, Dept Chem, Cambridge Univ & Med Res Coun Lab of Molecular Biol, Cambridge, Eng, 69-70; from asst prof to assoc prof, 70-81, PROF BIOCHEM, STATE UNIV NY BUFFALO, 81- *Mem:* AAAS; Am Chem Soc. *Res:* Mechanism of enzyme action; enzyme modification; bioinorganic chemistry; protein biosynthesis. *Mailing Add:* Dept of Biochem Farber Hall State Univ of NY Buffalo NY 14214

KOSMAN, MARY ELLEN, b Denver, Colo, Mar 27, 26; m 53; c 1. PHARMACOLOGY. *Educ:* Univ Denver, BA, 50, MA, 51; Northwestern Univ, PhD(physiol psychol), 53. *Prof Exp:* Res assoc neuropharmacol, Col Med, Univ Ill, Chicago, 53-55 & 62-65, SR SCIENTIST, DIV DRUGS, AMA, 69- *Concurrent Pos:* Fel pharmacol, Univ Ill, Chicago, 66-69. *Mem:* Am Soc Clin Pharmacol Therapeut; AAAS. *Res:* Psychopharmacology; literature in the area of clinical pharmacology. *Mailing Add:* Dept of Drugs AMA 535 N Dearborn St Chicago IL 60610

KOSMAN, WARREN MELVIN, b Chicago, Ill, Mar 23, 46; m 70; c 1. CHEMICAL PHYSICS. *Educ:* Valparaiso Univ, BS, 67; Univ Chicago, MS, 69, PhD(chem physics), 74. *Prof Exp:* Instr chem, Valparaiso Univ, 69-70, instr math, 70-71; asst prof chem, Ohio State Univ, 74-77; ASST PROF CHEM, VALPARAISO UNIV, 77- *Mem:* Am Chem Soc. *Res:* Molecular spectroscopy and ab initio molecular orbital calculations of atoms and small molecules. *Mailing Add:* Dept of Chem Valparaiso Univ Valparaiso IN 46383

KOSMOLAK, FREDERICK GRAHAM, b Minnedosa, Man, Mar 8, 47; m 67; c 2. CEREAL CHEMISTRY. *Educ:* Univ Man, BSc, 69, PhD(biochem), 73. *Prof Exp:* RES SCIENTIST CEREAL CHEM, RES BR, AGR CAN, 74- *Mem:* Am Asn Cereal Chemists; Sigma Xi. *Res:* Biochemical methods for assisting plant breeders. *Mailing Add:* 699 Patricia Winnipeg MB R3T 3A8 Can

KOSONOCKY, WALTER F, solid state electronics, see previous edition

KOSOWER, EDWARD MALCOLM, b Brooklyn, NY, Feb 2, 29; m 61; c 2. ORGANIC CHEMISTRY. *Educ:* Mass Inst Technol, SB, 48; Univ Calif, Los Angeles, PhD(chem), 52. *Prof Exp:* NIH res fel org chem, Univ Calif, 52-53 & Harvard Univ, 53-54; asst prof chem, Lehigh Univ, 54-56; from instr to asst prof, Univ Wis, 56-61; from assoc prof to prof, 61-72, ADJ PROF CHEM, STATE UNIV NY STONY BROOK, 72- *Concurrent Pos:* Alfred P Sloan fel, 60-64; NSF fel, Weizmann Inst Sci, Israel, 68-69; prof, Tel-Aviv Univ, 72-; John Simon Guggenheim fel, 77-78; vis prof, Kyoto, Japan, 78. *Mem:* Am Chem Soc; Royal Soc Chem; Am Soc Biol Chem; Soc Neurosci. *Res:* Charge-transfer spectra; pyridinium ion chemistry; solvent effects on spectra; stable free radicals; molecular medicine; neurophysiology; glutathione in chemistry, biochemistry, biology and medicine; fluorescence mechanisms; membrane mobility agents; mechanism of cell fusion; bimanes (diazabicyclo(3.3.0) octadienediones). *Mailing Add:* Dept Chem State Univ NY Stony Brook NY 11790

KOSOWSKY, DAVID I, b New York, NY, Feb 27, 30; m 54; c 3. HEALTH SCIENCES, ELECTRONICS. *Educ:* City Col New York. BEE, 51; Mass Inst Technol, SM, 52, ScD(network theory), 55. *Prof Exp:* Res asst & staff mem, Res Lab Electronics, Mass Inst Technol, 51-55; dir crystal div, Hermes Electronics Co, 55-60; vpres, Itek Electro-Prod Co, 60-61; PRES, DAMON CORP, 61- *Concurrent Pos:* bd gov, New Eng Aquarium, 68-; vpres, Univ Hosp Boston, 70-; vchmn, Childrens Hosp Med Ctr, 76- *Mem:* Inst Elec & Electronics Engrs; Sigma Xi; AAAS; NY Acad Sci. *Res:* Network theory; statistical theory of communication; crystal filters; voltage controlled crystal oscillators; spectrum analyzers; health service delivery systems; medical and electronic instrumentation. *Mailing Add:* 100 Dudley Rd Newton MA 02159

KOSS, DONALD A, b Dodge County, Minn, Oct 23, 38; m 64; c 2. METALLURGICAL ENGINEERING, MATERIALS SCIENCE. *Educ:* Univ Minn, Minneapolis, BS, 60; Yale Univ, MS, 62, PhD(mat sci), 64. *Prof Exp:* Fel metall, Oxford Univ, 64-65; res assoc metall, Advan Mat Res & Develop Lab, Pratt & Whitney Aircraft Div, United Aircraft Corp, 65-70; PROF METALL ENG, MICH TECHNOL UNIV, 70- *Concurrent Pos:* NSF fac prof develop award & vis staff scientist, Los Alamos Sci Lab, 78-79. *Mem:* Am Inst Mining, Metall & Petrol Engrs; Am Soc Metals. *Res:* Mechanical properties of metals and alloys; fracture; strengthening mechanisms in alloys and composites. *Mailing Add:* Dept of Metall Eng Mich Technol Univ Houghton MI 49931

KOSS, LEOPOLD GEORGE, b Danzig, Poland, Oct 2, 20; nat US;; m; c 3. PATHOLOGY, CYTOLOGY. *Educ:* Univ Bern, MD, 46. *Prof Exp:* Asst path, St Gallen, Switz, 47 & Long Island Col Med, 49; instr, Col Med, State Univ NY Downstate Med Ctr, 50-52; from assoc dir to dir cytol, Mem Hosp Cancer & Allied Dis, 52-60, from asst attend pathologist to assoc attend pathologist, 53-60, chief cytol serv & attend pathologist, 60-70; prof path, Jefferson Med Col, 70-73; PROF PATH & CHMN DEPT, ALBERT EINSTEIN COL MED & CHMN DEPT PATH, MONTEFIORE HOSP & MED CTR, 73- *Concurrent Pos:* From asst to assoc, Sloan-Kettering Inst, 53-60, head secy cytopath, 60-70; from asst prof to assoc prof, Sloan-Kettering Div, Med Col, Cornell Univ, 54-70; vis pathologist, James Ewing Hosp, 60-68; consult, NY State Dept Health, 62-; pathologist-in-chief, Sinai Hosp Baltimore, Inc, 70-73. *Honors & Awards:* Wien Award, 61; Goldblatt Award, 62; Alfred P Sloan Award Cancer Res, 64; Papanicolaou Award, Am Soc Cytol, 66. *Mem:* Fel Am Soc Clin Pathologists; Am Asn Pathologists & Bacteriologists; Am Soc Cytol (pres, 62); James Ewing Soc; Int Acad Path. *Res:* Cytology and pathology of cancer. *Mailing Add:* Montefiore Hosp & Med Ctr 111 E 210th St Bronx NY 10467

KOSS, MICHAEL CAMPBELL, b Ann Arbor, Mich, Sept 24, 40. PHARMACOLOGY. *Educ:* NY Univ, BA, 66; Columbia Univ, PhD(pharmacol), 71. *Prof Exp:* From asst to assoc prof, 71-81, PROF PHARMACOL, COL MED, UNIV OKLA, 81- *Mem:* Asn Res Vision & Ophthal; Soc Neurosci; Am Soc Pharmacol & Exp Therapeut. *Res:* Neuropharmacology; neurophysiology; brain stem regulatory mechanisms; autonomic nervous system. *Mailing Add:* Dept of Pharmacol Univ of Okla Col of Med Oklahoma City OK 73104

KOSSACK, CARL FREDERICK, b Chicago, Ill, May 30, 15; m 40; c 6. APPLIED STATISTICS. *Educ:* Univ Calif, Los Angeles, BA, 35, MS, 36; Univ Mich, PhD(math), 39. *Prof Exp:* From instr to asst prof math, Univ Ore, 39-46; mathematician, US Dept Navy, 46-47; from assoc prof to prof math, Purdue Univ, 47-59, dir statist lab, 48-56, head dept, 56-59; mgr statist & opers res, Int Bus Mach Corp, 59-62; dir lab comput sci, Grad Res Ctr Southwest, 62-65; head, Dept Statist & Comput Sci, 65-81, EMER PROF STATIST, UNIV GA, 81- *Concurrent Pos:* Data processing expert, Food & Agr Orgn, UN, India, 69-70; consult, Dir Gen Econ Agr, Mex, 75-79. *Mem:* AAAS; Am Math Soc; Biomet Soc; fel Am Statist Asn; Inst Math Statist. *Res:* Operations research; foundation of theory of probability; classification techniques in statistics; information systems and planning, personnel systems. *Mailing Add:* Dept of Statist & Comput Sci Univ of Ga Athens GA 30602

KOSSIAKOFF, ALEXANDER, b St Petersburg, Russia, June 26, 14; US citizen; m 39; c 2. PHYSICAL CHEMISTRY. *Educ:* Calif Inst Technol, BS, 36; Johns Hopkins Univ, PhD(chem), 38. *Prof Exp:* Fel, Calif Inst Technol, 38-39; instr chem, Cath Univ, 39-42; tech aide, Nat Defense Res Comt, 42-43; dep dir res, Allegheny Ballistics Lab, George Washington Univ, 44-46; physicist, Appl Physics Lab, 46-48, asst dir, 48-61, assoc dir, 61-66, dep dir, 66-69, dir, 69-80, EMER DIR & CHIEF SCIENTIST, APPL PHYSICS LAB, JOHNS HOPKINS UNIV, 80- *Concurrent Pos:* Consult tech adv panel aeronaut, Defense Dept, 54-58; mem panel launching & handling comt guided missiles, Res & Develop Bd, 48-52; Carmrand comt, Nat Planning Asn, 62- *Honors & Awards:* Cert Merit, President, 48; Distinguished Pub Serv Award, US Navy, 68. *Mem:* Am Inst Chemists. *Res:* Prediction and determination of molecular structure; relation between molecular structure and physical and chemical properties; mechanism of chemical reactions; mechanism of neural processes; administration of research; computer languages. *Mailing Add:* Appl Physics Lab Johns Hopkins Rd Laurel MD 20707

KOSSLER, WILLIAM JOHN, b Charleston, SC, Mar 26, 37; m 61; c 3. PHYSICS. *Educ:* Mass Inst Technol, BS, 59; Princeton Univ, PhD(physics), 64. *Prof Exp:* Staff mem nuclear physics, Mass Inst Technol, 64-66, asst prof physics, 66-69; from asst prof to assoc prof physics, 69-78, PROF PHYSICS, COL WILLIAM & MARY, 78- *Res:* Experimental nuclear and solid state physics. *Mailing Add:* Dept of Physics Col of William & Mary Williamsburg VA 23185

KOSSMANN, CHARLES EDWARD, b Brooklyn, NY, Apr 20, 09; m 46; c 2. MEDICINE. *Educ:* NY Univ, BS, 28, MD, 31, MedScD, 38. *Prof Exp:* House physician, Bellevue Hosp, 31-33; asst med, Heart Sta, Univ Hosp, Univ Mich, 34; asst, Sch Med, NY Univ, 34-38, from instr to prof, 38-67, head cardiovasc sect, 64-67; chmn div circulatory dis, 67-74, PROF MED, 67-76, PROF EMER, COL MED, UNIV TENN, MEMPHIS, 76- *Concurrent Pos:* Chief peripheral vascular dis clin, NY Univ Hosp, 36-41, from assoc attend physician to attend physician, 49-67; asst clin vis physician, Bellevue Hosp, 34-40, from asst vis physician to vis physician, 40-67, consult physician, 68-, chief adult cardiac clin, 40-56; adj physician, Lenox Hill Hosp, 37-46, assoc physician, 46-49, attend physician, 49-64, consult physician, 64- *Mem:* Fel AAAS; Asn Am Physicians; Asn Univ Cardiol; master Am Col Physicians; fel AMA. *Res:* Cardiovascular diseases; physiology of circulation; aviation medicine. *Mailing Add:* Div of Circulatory Dis Univ of Tenn Col of Med Memphis TN 38163

KOSSOY, AARON DAVID, b New York, NY, Aug 19, 36; m 70. ANALYTICAL & ORGANIC CHEMISTRY. *Educ:* City Col New York, BS, 58; Polytech Inst Brooklyn, PhD(org chem), 66. *Prof Exp:* Anal chemist, Trubek Labs, Inc, 58-61; fel chem, Univ Calif, Berkeley, 66-69; sr anal chemist, 69-80, RES SCIENTIST, ELI LILLY RES LABS, 80- *Mem:* Am Chem Soc. *Res:* Peptide synthesis and characterization; spectroscopic characterization of organic compounds; organic synthesis and structure determination. *Mailing Add:* 7627 Almaden Ct Indianapolis IN 46278

KOSSUTH, SUSAN, b Boston, Mass, Apr 28, 46. PLANT PHYSIOLOGY, GENETICS. *Educ:* Colo State Univ, BS, 68, MS, 71; Yale Univ, MS, 72, MPhil, 73, PhD(tree physiol-genetics), 74. *Prof Exp:* Consult, Fla Citrus Comn, 74-76; asst prof tree physiol, Univ Ark, 76-77; asst res scientist, Univ Fla, 77-78; PROJ LEADER, US FOREST SERV, 79- *Concurrent Pos:* Adj asst prof, Univ Fla, 74-76; prin investr, Weyerhaeuser Corp, Eli-Lilly Co, Ark Kraft Co, Southern Regional Educ Bd, 76; co-prin investr, Fla Citrus Comn, 77-79. *Mem:* Am Soc Plant Physiol; Sigma Xi; Soc Am Foresters; Am Forestry Asn; Plant Growth Regulator Soc Am. *Res:* Reproductive physiology and breeding and improvement of Southern pines; vegetative propagation of pines; flowering in pines; early genetic testing of pines; effects of ultraviolet light on plants. *Mailing Add:* SE Forest Exp Sta PO Box 70 Olustee FL 32072

KOSTANT, BERTRAM, b New York, NY, May 24, 28; m 49; c 1. MATHEMATICS. *Educ:* Purdue Univ, BS, 50; Univ Chicago, MS, 51, PhD(math), 54. *Prof Exp:* NSF fel, Inst Advan Study, 53-54, mem, 54-56; from asst prof to prof math, Univ Calif, Berkeley, 56-63; PROF MATH, MASS INST TECHNOL, 63- *Concurrent Pos:* Higgins lectr, Princeton Univ, 55-56; mem, Miller Inst Bassic Res, 58-59; Guggenheim fel, Paris, France, 59-60; prof, Oxford Univ. *Mem:* Nat Acad Sci; Am Acad Arts & Sci; Am Math Soc. *Res:* Operator theory; Lie groups; representation theory; differential geometry. *Mailing Add:* Dept of Math Mass Inst of Technol Cambridge MA 02139

KOSTELNICEK, RICHARD J, b Chicago, Ill, May 16, 42; m 67. ELECTRICAL ENGINEERING. *Educ:* Univ Ill, Urbana, BS, 64, MS, 65, PhD(elec eng), 69. *Prof Exp:* SR RES ASSOC, ESSO PROD RES CO, 69- *Mem:* AAAS; Soc Explor Geophys; Inst Elec & Electronics Engrs. *Res:* Antennas; plasma physics; wave propagation in inhomogeneous media; geoscience. *Mailing Add:* Esso Prod Res Co PO Box 2189 Houston TX 77001

KOSTELNIK, ROBERT J, b Homestead, Pa, Nov 9, 46; m 69. CHEMISTRY. *Educ:* Univ Pittsburgh, BS, 68; Carnegie-Mellon Univ, MS & Phd(chem), 71. *Prof Exp:* Fel chem, Mellon Inst, 72; sr res assoc polymer sci, Midland Macromolecular Inst, 73-77; mem staff, Gen Elec Co, 77-79; MEM STAFF, ARCO CHEM CO, 79- *Mem:* Am Chem Soc; Sigma Xi. *Res:* Spectroscopic studies of interactions of drugs with enzymes and nucleic acids; mechanism of drug action; polymer-polymer interactions; nuclear magnetic resonance spectroscopy; thermoplastics; polymer synthesis. *Mailing Add:* 3801 W Chester Pike Arco Chem Co Newtown Square PA 19073

KOSTENBADER, KENNETH DAVID, JR, b Allentown, Pa, May 6, 41; m 77. VIROLOGY. *Educ:* Albright Col, BS, 64. *Prof Exp:* Microbiologist I salmonella, Pa Dept Health, Philadelphia, 65-66; res asst, 66-67, RES SPECIALIST VIROL, FOOD RES INST, UNIV WIS-MADISON, 67- *Concurrent Pos:* Consult, WHO Collab Ctr on Food Virol, Food Res Inst, Univ Wis-Madison, 75- *Mem:* AAAS; Am Soc Microbiol. *Res:* Occurrence, transmission and detection of animal and human viruses in food, water and wastewater. *Mailing Add:* Dept of Food Microbiol & Toxicol 1925 Willow Dr Madison WI 53706

KOSTENBAUDER, HARRY BARR, b Danville, Pa, Apr 9, 29. PHARMACY. *Educ:* Phila Col Pharm, BSc, 51; Temple Univ, MSc, 53; Univ Wis, PhD(pharm), 56. *Prof Exp:* Asst pharm, Temple Univ, 51-53 & Univ Wis, 55; from asst prof to prof, Temple Univ, 56-68; PROF PHARM & ASSOC DEAN RES, COL PHARM, UNIV KY, 68- *Mem:* Am Pharmaceut Asn; NY Acad Sci; fel Acad Pharmaceut Sci (pres, 71-72). *Res:* Drug binding by macromolecules; drug stability; pharmacokinetics. *Mailing Add:* Col of Pharm Univ of Ky Lexington KY 40506

KOSTER, DAVID F, b Houston, Tex, Nov 3, 36; m 59; c 5. PHYSICAL CHEMISTRY, SPECTROSCOPY. *Educ:* St Thomas Univ, BA, 59; Tex A&M Univ, MS, 63, PhD(chem), 65. *Prof Exp:* Chemist, Diamond Alkali Co, 59-60; res fel, Mellon Inst, 64-67; asst prof, 67-71, assoc prof 71-81, PROF CHEM, SOUTHERN ILL UNIV, CARBONDALE, 81- *Mem:* Am Chem Soc; Sigma Xi. *Res:* Infrared laser induced reactions; nuclear magnetic resonance; Raman and infrared spectroscopy; structure and conformation studies of polyatomic molecules; IR laser induced reactions. *Mailing Add:* Dept of Chem Southern Ill Univ Carbondale IL 62901

KOSTER, GEORGE FRED, b New York, NY, Apr 9, 27; m 51; c 3. PHYSICS. *Educ:* Mass Inst Technol, SB, 48, PhD(physics), 51. *Prof Exp:* Res assoc, 51-52, Lincoln Lab, 52-55, from asst prof to assoc prof, 56-64, PROF PHYSICS, MASS INST TECHNOL, 64- *Concurrent Pos:* Guggenheim fel, 55-56. *Mem:* Am Phys Soc. *Res:* Theoretical physics including theory of solids and molecular theory. *Mailing Add:* Dept of Physics Mass Inst of Technol Cambridge MA 02139

KOSTER, ROBERT ALLEN, b Grand Rapids, Mich, July 12, 41; m 63; c 2. ORGANIC CHEMISTRY. *Educ:* Hope Col, AB, 63; Univ Mich, Ann Arbor, MS, 65, PhD(chem), 68. *Prof Exp:* Res chemist, 68-70, proj leader, Org Chem Prod Res, 70-80, RES LEADER, STYRENE PLASTICS, DOW CHEM USA, 80- *Res:* Carbonium ion chemistry; reaction mechanisms via kinetic studies; process development on fine organic chemicals; chemistry of 2.2.1 bicyclic systems; polymer process development. *Mailing Add:* 400 Hollybrook Dr Midland MI 48640

KOSTER, W(ILLIAM) P(FEIFFER), b Fords, NJ, Apr 18, 29; m 54; c 4. METALLURGICAL ENGINEERING. *Educ:* Rutgers Univ, BS, 50; Univ Cincinnati, MS, 51, PhD(metall eng), 53. *Prof Exp:* Staff mem, 53-57, vpres, 57-78, DIR METALL ENG, METCUT RES ASSOC INC, 57-, PRES, 78- *Honors & Awards:* Gold Medal, Soc Mfg Engrs. *Mem:* Fel Am Soc Metals; Am Inst Mining, Metall & Petrol Eng. *Res:* Mechanical engineering. *Mailing Add:* Metcut Res Assocs 3980 Rosslyn Dr Cincinnati OH 45209

KOSTER, WILLIAM HENRY, b Teaneck, NJ, Apr 20, 44; m 68; c 1. SYNTHETIC ORGANIC CHEMISTRY. *Educ:* Colby Col, BA, 66; Tufts Univ, PhD(chem), 72. *Prof Exp:* Fel beta-lactam antibiotics, 72, GROUP LEADER BETA-LACTAM ANTIBIOTICS, SQUIBB INST MED RES, 72- *Mem:* Am Chem Soc. *Res:* Synthesis and modification of beta-lactam antibiotics; chemistry of cephalosporins and penicillins. *Mailing Add:* E R Squibb & Sons Inc PO Box 4000 Princeton NJ 08540

KOSTER VAN GROOS, AUGUST FERDINAND, b Leeuwarden, Netherlands, Jan 9, 38; m 71. GEOCHEMISTRY. *Educ:* Univ Leiden, BSc, 58, MS, 62, PhD(exp petrol), 66. *Prof Exp:* Res assoc, Goddard Space Flight Ctr, NASA, 66-68; asst prof petrol, State Univ Utrecht, 68-70; asst prof, 70-75, ASSOC PROF GEOL SCI, UNIV ILL, CHICAGO CIRCLE, 75- *Mem:* AAAS; Am Geophys Union. *Res:* Genesis of carbonatite, experimental work in synthetic systems containing carbon dioxide and water at elevated pressure and temperature; salt-silicate-water systems; studies of liquid immiscibility occurring in rocks; partitioning of minor elements in multi- phase systems. *Mailing Add:* Dept of Geol Sci Univ of Ill at Chicago Circle Chicago IL 60680

KOSTINER, EDWARD S, b New York, NY, Feb 25, 40; m 60; c 2. SOLID STATE CHEMISTRY. *Educ:* Tufts Univ, BS, 60; Polytech Inst Brooklyn, PhD(inorg chem), 66. *Prof Exp:* Asst prof chem, Cornell Univ, 66-72; assoc prof chem, 72-77, PROF CHEM, UNIV CONN, 77- *Mem:* Am Chem Soc; NY Acad Sci; Am Asn Crystal Growth; Mineral Soc Am; Am Crystallog Asn. *Res:* Crystal growth; crystal and structural chemistry of apatites and other halophosphates and orthophosphates; Mossbauer effect spectroscopy. *Mailing Add:* Inst of Mat Sci Univ of Conn Storrs CT 06268

KOSTISHACK, DANIEL F(RANK), b Pittsburgh, Pa, Mar 25, 40; m 66; c 2. ELECTRICAL ENGINEERING, SOLID STATE PHYSICS. *Educ:* Carnegie Inst Technol, BS, 63, MS, 65; Carnegie-Mellon Univ, PhD(elec eng), 68. *Prof Exp:* mem res staff, 67-81, GROUP LEADER, LINCOLN LAB, MASS INST TECHNOL, 81- *Res:* Solid-state and high frequency devices and circuits; solid-state imaging devices and electro-optical systems. *Mailing Add:* Lincoln Lab Box 73 Mass Inst of Technol Lexington MA 02173

KOSTIUK, THEODOR, b Plauen, Ger, Aug 12, 44; m 70. SPACE PHYSICS. *Educ:* City Col New York, BS, 66; Syracuse Univ, PhD(physics), 73. *Prof Exp:* Nat Acad Sci resident res assoc, 73-74, SPACE SCIENTIST INFRARED ASTROPHYS, GODDARD SPACE FLIGHT CTR, NASA, 74- *Mem:* Am Phys Soc; Optical Soc Am; Soc Photo-Optical Instrument Engrs; Fedn Am Scientists; Am Inst Physics. *Res:* Study the atmospheres of planets, stars and the earth's stratosphere using infrared heterodyne spectroscopy; ultra-high resolution infrared spectroscopy; discovery of the first natural laser (carbon dioxide on Mars). *Mailing Add:* Code 693 NASA Goddard Space Flight Ctr Greenbelt MD 20771

KOSTIW, LUBA LISZCZYNSKA, microbiology, biochemistry, see previous edition

KOSTKOWSKI, HENRY JOHN, physics, see previous edition

KOSTOFF, MORRIS R, b Jamestown, NDak, Dec 2, 33; m 55; c 5. NUCLEAR PHYSICS, ACOUSTICS. *Educ:* Pac Lutheran Univ, BS, 62; Univ Tex, Austin, PhD(physics), 67. *Prof Exp:* Res asst nuclear physics, Ctr Nuclear Studies, Univ Tex, Austin, 63-66; engr-scientist, Sci & Systs Div, Tracor, Inc, 66-70, sr scientist, 70-79, PRIN SCIENTIST, ANAL & APPL RES DIV, APPL SCI GROUP, TRACOR INC, 79- *Concurrent Pos:* Asst prof physics, Southwestern Univ, Tex, 71-74. *Mem:* Am Phys Soc. *Res:* Spin polarization measurements for elastic and inelastic proton scattering; systems analysis and simulation of signal processors for sonar systems; propagation of acoustic waves in water medium. *Mailing Add:* 8904 Laurel Grove Dr Austin TX 78758

KOSTREVA, DAVID ROBERT, b Milwaukee, Wis, Aug 14, 45; m 75; c 3. ANESTHESIOLOGY. *Educ:* Univ Wis, Milwaukee, Ba, 72; Med Col Wis, MS, 74, PhD(physiol), 76. *Prof Exp:* Fel, Am Heart Asn, 76-77 & Nat Heart, Lung and Blood Inst, NIH, 77-78; asst prof physiol & anesthesia, 78-81, ASSOC PROF ANESTHESIOL, MED COL WIS, 81- *Concurrent Pos:* Chmn, Ad Hoc Study Sect, NIMH, 81. *Mem:* Am Physiol Soc; Am Neurosci; Sigma Xi; Soc Exp Biol & Med. *Res:* Neural control of circulation and respiration in dogs, cats, and monkeys using afferent and efferent recording techniques and brain mapping studies of visceral reflexes using the carbon-fourteen-deoxyglucose technique. *Mailing Add:* Res Serv 151 Vet Admin Ctr Wood WI 53193

KOSTROUN, VACLAV O, b Brasov, Rumania, Dec 30, 38; US citizen; m 63; c 2. NUCLEAR PHYSICS, ATOMIC PHYSICS. *Educ:* Univ Wash, BSc, 61, MSc, 63; Univ Ore, PhD(physics), 68. *Prof Exp:* Res assoc & lectr, 68-70, asst prof, 70-77, ASSOC PROF APPL & ENG PHYSICS, CORNELL UNIV, 77- *Mem:* AAAS; Am Phys Soc. *Res:* Experimental low energy nuclear physics, structure and radioactivity; experimental and theoretical atomic physics; radiative and non-radiative processes in atoms; interaction between atomic and nuclear systems. *Mailing Add:* Sch of Appl & Eng Physics Cornell Univ Ithaca NY 14853

KOSTRZEWA, RICHARD MICHAEL, b Trenton, NJ, July 22, 43; m 65; c 8. PHARMACOLOGY, NEUROSCIENCE. *Educ:* Philadelphia Col Pharm & Sci, BS, 65, MS, 67; Univ Pa, PhD(pharmacol), 71. *Prof Exp:* Res pharmacologist, Vet Admin Hosp, New Orleans, 71-75; asst prof physiol, La

State Univ Med Ctr, New Orleans, 75-78; ASSOC PROF PHARMACOL, E TENN STATE UNIV, 78- *Concurrent Pos:* Asst prof pharmacol, Tulane Univ Med Ctr, New Orleans, 74-75; prin investr, NIH grant, 75-81, March Dimes grant, 77-79 & Am Parkinson's Dis Asn grant, 77-78. *Mem:* Am Soc Pharmacol & Exp Therapeut; Neurosci Soc; AAAS; Histochem Soc. *Res:* Development of monoaminergic neurons; association of neuronal development with regenerative sprouting; Parkinson's disease; neurotoxins. *Mailing Add:* Col of Med E Tenn State Univ Johnson City TN 37601

KOSTYO, JACK LAWRENCE, b Elyria, Ohio, Oct 1, 31; m 53; c 2. PHYSIOLOGY, ENDOCRINOLOGY. *Educ:* Oberlin Col, AB, 53; Cornell Univ, PhD(zool), 57. *Hon Degrees:* MD, Univ Goteborg, 78. *Prof Exp:* From asst prof to prof physiol, Duke Univ, 59-68; prof physiol & chmn dept, Emory Univ, 68-79; PROF PHYSIOL & CHMN DEPT, MED SCH, UNIV MICH, 79- *Concurrent Pos:* Nat Res Coun fel, Harvard Med Sch, 57-59; Lederle med fac award, 61-64; mem endocrinol study sect, NIH, 67-71; chmn educ comt, Am Physiol Soc, 70-76; vis foreign scientist, Swed Med Res Coun, 72; mem physiol test comt, Nat Bd Med Examr, 74-77; mem Com Med Physiol; Int Union Physiol Sci; pres Asn Chmn Dept Physiol, 79-80; Ed-in-Chief, Endocrinol. *Honors & Awards:* Ernst Oppenheimer Mem Award, Endocrine Soc, 69; Oppenheimer Award, Endocrine Soc, 69. *Mem:* Am Physiol Soc; Endocrine Soc; Soc Exp Biol & Med. *Res:* Mechanism of action of pituitary growth hormone; relationship between structure and functions of growth hormone; nature of growth hormone in blood. *Mailing Add:* Dept Physiol Univ Mich Med Sch 1335 E Catherine Ann Arbor MI 48109

KOSTYRKO, GEORGE JURIJ, b Ukraine, May 9, 37; US citizen. CIVIL ENGINEERING. *Educ:* City Col New York, BChE, 57; Univ Mich, Ann Arbor, MSE, 58; Sacramento State Col, MS, 63; Univ Calif, Davis, PhD(civil eng), 69. *Prof Exp:* Develop engr, Air Prod Inc, Pa, 57; Aerojet-Gen Corp, Calif, 58-61, sr res engr, 61-68; ASSOC PROF CIVIL ENG, SACRAMENTO STATE COL, 68-, HEAD PROG APPL MECH, 71- *Concurrent Pos:* NSF grant, Sacramento State Col, 71-72. *Mem:* Sigma Xi. *Res:* Detection of static and dynamic stresses in solids and structures by means of acoustic wave propagation, holography and photoelasticity. *Mailing Add:* 1721 Cathay Way Sacramento CA 95825

KOSUGE, TSUNE, b Merino, Colo, Nov 28, 25; m 52; c 2. PLANT BIOCHEMISTRY, PLANT PATHOLOGY. *Educ:* Univ Colo, BA, 52; Wash State Univ, MS, 55; Univ Calif, Berkeley, PhD(comp biochem), 59. *Prof Exp:* Res asst plant path, Wash State Univ, 52-55; res asst plant biochem, Univ Calif, Berkeley, 55-58; jr res biochemist, 59-61, asst res plant pathologist, 61-62, asst plant pathologist, 62-66, assoc prof plant path, 66-71, PROF PLANT PATH, UNIV CALIF, DAVIS, 71-, CHMN DEPT, 74- *Mem:* Am Soc Plant Physiol; Am Phytopath Soc. *Res:* Biosynthesis of aromatic compounds in higher plants; metabolism of indoleacetic acid by plant pathogens; biochemistry of plant disease. *Mailing Add:* Dept of Plant Path Univ of Calif Davis CA 95616

KOSZALKA, THOMAS R, b Rochester, NY, Jan 25, 27; m 54; c 3. BIOCHEMISTRY. *Educ:* Univ Rochester, BA, 50, PhD, 59. *Prof Exp:* From instr to asst prof biochem, Sch Med & Dent, Univ Rochester, 59-65; assoc prof radiol, 65-70, assoc prof biochem, 67-75, PROF RADIOL, JEFFERSON MED COL, 70-, PROF BIOCHEM, 75- *Concurrent Pos:* Assoc dir, Eleanor Roosevelt Res Labs & dir, Harry Bock Labs, 65- *Res:* Developmental biochemistry; creatine metabolism. *Mailing Add:* Stein Res Ctr Jefferson Med Col Philadelphia PA 19107

KOSZTARAB, MICHAEL, b Bucharest, Romania, July 7, 27; US citizen; m 53; c 1. ENTOMOLOGY. *Educ:* Hungarian Univ Agr Sci, HortE, 51; Ohio State Univ, PhD(entom), 62. *Prof Exp:* Exten asst, Hungarian State Bur Plant Protection, 47-50; asst prof hort entom, Hungarian Univ Agr Sci, 51-56; consult entomologist, Insect Control & Res Inc, Md, 57-58, asst dir res, 59-60; assoc prof, 62-68, PROF ENTOM, VA POLYTECH INST & STATE UNIV, 68- *Concurrent Pos:* NSF res grant, 63-75. *Mem:* Entom Soc Am; Soc Syst Zool; Sigma Xi; hon mem Hungarian Entom Soc. *Res:* Systematics and biological control of scale insects (Homoptera and Coccoidea) in North America and Europe. *Mailing Add:* Dept of Entom VA Polytech Inst & State Univ Blacksburg VA 24061

KOT, PETER ALOYSIUS, b Stanley, Wis, Jan 13, 32; m 58; c 6. CARDIOVASCULAR PHYSIOLOGY. *Educ:* Marquette Univ, MS, 56, MD, 57. *Prof Exp:* Intern med, Med Ctr, 57-58, resident, 58-60, instr physiol, 60-64, instr med, 63-64, from asst prof to assoc prof physiol, 64-76, ASST PROF MED, MED SCH, GEORGETOWN UNIV, 64-, PROF PHYSIOL, 76- *Concurrent Pos:* Fel coun circulation, Am Heart Asn, 63, investr, 64-69; lectr physiol, US Naval Dent Sch, Bethesda, Md, 66-71; lectr, US Army Inst Dent Res, 68-71. *Mem:* AAAS; Am Fedn Clin Res; Am Physiol Soc; Soc Exp Biol & Med; NY Acad Sci. *Res:* Cardiovascular physiology, especially hemodynamic effects of the prostaglandins and their precursors. *Mailing Add:* Georgetown Univ Med Sch 3900 Reservoir Rd NW Washington DC 20007

KOT, RICHARD ANTHONY, b Syracuse, NY, May 22, 41; m 61; c 3. METALLURGY, MATERIALS SCIENCE. *Educ:* LeMoyne Col, BS, 64; Syracuse Univ, MS, 67, PhD(solid state sci), 69. *Prof Exp:* Res metallurgist, 69-74, supvr, 74-75, sect chief, 75-78, res adv, 78-80, sr res adv, 80-81, ASST DIV HEAD METALLURGICAL, REPUBLIC STEEL RES CTR, 81- *Mem:* Am Soc Metals; Am Inst Mining, Metall & Petrol Engrs; Sigma Xi; NY Acad Sci. *Res:* Physical metallurgy; plastic deformation; recrystallization. *Mailing Add:* Republic Steel Res Ctr 6801 Brecksville Rd Independence OH 44131

KOTANSKY, D(ONALD) R(ICHARD), b Hinsdale, Ill, July 28, 39; m 62; c 3. FLUID MECHANICS, AERODYNAMICS. *Educ:* Gen Motors Inst, BME, 62; Mass Inst Technol, SM, 62, MechE, 64, ScD(fluid mech), 66. *Prof Exp:* Asst prof mech eng, Purdue Univ, 65-68; sr & proj propulsion engr, Ft Worth Div, Gen Dynamics Corp, 68-70; sr group engr propulsion 70-73, sr scientist, McDonnel Douglas Res Lab, 73-77, sect chief, 77-80, BR CHIEF TECHNOL, AERODYN, MCDONNELL AIRCRAFT CO, MCDONNELL DOUGLAS CORP, 80- *Concurrent Pos:* Vis Caterpillar prof, Bradley Univ, 66-67; consult, Allison Div, Gen Motors Corp, Ind, 67-68. *Mem:* Assoc fel Am Inst Aeronaut & Astronaut; Am Soc Mech Engrs; Sigma Xi. *Res:* Theoretical and experimental investigations of external and internal aerodynamics, including laminar and turbulent flows, boundary layers, rotational and secondary flows, jet and multiple jet dominated flows, unsteadiness, acoustics and shock boundary layer interaction. *Mailing Add:* 15400 Clover Ridge Dr Chesterfield MO 63017

KOTCH, ALEX, b Edwardsville, Pa, Aug 18, 26; m 52; c 4. SCIENCE & ACADEMIC ADMINISTRATION. *Educ:* Pa State Col, BS, 46, MS, 47; Univ Ill, PhD(org chem), 50. *Prof Exp:* Asst org chem, Pa State Col, 46-47 & Univ Ill, 47-49; Fulbright fel, Delft Tech Univ, 50-51; Little fel, Mass Inst Tech, 51-52; res chemist, Cent Res Dept, Exp Sta, E I du Pont de Nemours & Co, 52-54, Org Chem Dept, Jackson Lab, 54-59; assoc prog dir chem, Nat Sci Found, 59-63, prog dir org chem, 63-65; chief biosci div, Off Saline Water, US Dept Interior, 65-66; staff assoc, Sci Develop Eval Group, Div Instnl Progs, Nat Sci Found, 66-67; prof chem & assoc chmn dept, Univ Wis-Madison, 67-77; asst dir info, educ & int progs, 77-78, spec asst to dir, 78-79, br chief, Acad & Univ Progs, 78-81, PRIN MGR, UNIV RES & STORAGE PROGS, SOLAR ENERGY RES INST, 81- *Concurrent Pos:* Consult-exam, N Cent Asn Cols & Schs, 69- *Mem:* AAAS; Am Chem Soc; Am Asn Univ Prof; Int Solar Energy Soc. *Res:* Synthetic organic chemistry; polymers; heterocyclics; fluorescent whitening agents; dyes; science research and academic administration. *Mailing Add:* 1905 Zang St Golden CO 80401

KOTCHER, EMIL, b Passaic, NJ, July 19, 13; m 40; c 3. MEDICAL MICROBIOLOGY. *Educ:* Wesleyan Univ, AB, 37, MA, 38; Johns Hopkins Univ, ScD(parasitol) 41, Am Bd Med Microbiol, Dipl. *Prof Exp:* Under biol aide, Tenn Valley Auth, 39-40, jr biol aide, 40; asst biologist, State Bd Health, Miss, 41-43, med entomologist & epidemiologist, 46-47; assoc prof microbiol, 47-63, res prof med parasitol & dept head, 63-68, dept head, 68-77, PROF MICROBIOL & IMMUNOL, SCH MED, LA STATE UNIV, SHREVEPORT, 68- *Concurrent Pos:* Pub health lab consult, Spec Tech & Econ Mission, Mutual Security Agency, Assoc States Indo-China, Saigon, 53-55; dir div pub health labs, State Dept Health, Ky, 58-60. *Mem:* AAAS; Am Soc Parasitol; Am Soc Microbiol; Am Soc Trop Med & Hyg; Sigma Xi. *Res:* Filaroid nematodes; household anophelism; immunity of murine typhus; epidemiology of murine typhus, brucellosis and malaria; microbiology of vaginitis and trichomonal vaginitis histoplasmosis; tinea capitis. *Mailing Add:* Dept of Microbiol & Immunol La State Univ Sch of Med Shreveport LA 71130

KOTCHOUBEY, ANDREW, b Florence, Italy, Mar 31, 38; US citizen; m 68; c 4. COMPUTER SCIENCE, APPLIED MATHEMATICS. *Educ:* Stevens Inst Technol, ME, 59; Columbia Univ, MA, 61, PhD(appl math), 66. *Prof Exp:* Supvr comput installation, Watson Sci Comput Lab, IBM Corp, 60-62, res asst appl math, Watson Lab, 62-66, sr staff mem appl math & comput, 66-69; dir info systs, Interway Corp, 69-71; pres, subsidiary I/W Data Systs, Inc, 71-73; V PRES, AUTOMATECH GRAPHICS CORP, 73- *Concurrent Pos:* Assoc grad facil math, Columbia Univ, 67-68, adj asst prof, 68-69. *Mem:* AAAS; Asn Comput Mach; Sigma Xi; Soc Indust & Appl Math. *Res:* Calculations in atomic and molecular physics; mathematical physics; numerical analysis. *Mailing Add:* 50 E 96th St New York NY 10028

KOTHANDARAMAN, GOPALAN, b Shiyali, India, Dec 21, 46. CHEMISTRY, PHYSICAL CHEMISTRY. *Educ:* Univ Madras, BS, 66; Indian Inst Technol, Madras, MS, 68; Univ Calif, Davis, PhD(chem), 73. *Prof Exp:* Res asst prof chem, Univ Pittsburgh, 73-77; PRIN SCIENTIST, PHYS SCI INC, 77- *Mem:* Am Phys Soc; Int Soc Magnetic Resonance; Sigma Xi. *Res:* Optical detection of magnetic resonance; spectroscopy of molecular excited states; coal gasification; infrared and visible laser applications; chemical kinetics. *Mailing Add:* Phy Sci Inc 30 Commerce Way Woburn MA 01801

KOTHE, KENNETH RALPH, geophysics, see previous edition

KOTHMANN, MERWYN MORTIMER, b Castell, Tex, Jan 30, 40; m 62; c 3. RANGE SCIENCE, RANGE MANAGEMENT. *Educ:* Tex A&M Univ, BS, 61, PhD(range sci), 68; Utah State Univ, MS, 63. *Prof Exp:* Res asst range nutrit, Utah State Univ, 63-64; res asst range nutrit, 64-67, asst prof range mgt, Tex Agr Exp Sta, 67-70, ASSOC PROF RANGE SCI, TEX A&M UNIV, 70- *Mem:* Soc Range Mgt; Am Soc Animal Sci. *Res:* Reactions of natural vegetation and livestock to various grazing management systems; nutrition of range livestock and botanical and chemical characteristics of diets of grazing animals. *Mailing Add:* Dept of Range Sci Tex A&M Univ College Station TX 77843

KOTHNY, EVALDO LUIS, b Buenos Aires, Argentina, Oct 6, 25; US citizen; m 60; c 2. AIR POLLUTION, GEOCHEMISTRY. *Educ:* Univ Buenos Aires, MS, 55, PhD(chem), 64. *Prof Exp:* Plant chemist, Coplan Br, US Rubber Co, Argentina, 55-56; res chemist, Compania Quimica, Buenos Aires, 56-57; asst anal instrumentation, Univ Buenos Aires, 57-60 & 61-63; asst specialist qual control, Monsanto, Argentina, 60-61; sr specialist, Gen Elec, Argentina, 61-64; RES CHEMIST, AIR & INDUST HYG LAB, STATE DEPT HEALTH, CALIF, 64- *Mem:* Am Chem Soc; Asn Off Anal Chem; Asn Explor Geochem; fel Am Inst Chem. *Res:* Industrial inorganic preparative chemistry; trace inorganic analysis; geochemistry; environmental chemistry; geochemistry of noble metals; nitrogen oxides analysis; geochemical cycle of mercury; platinum and palladium in the environment; exploration of noble metals; biogeochemistry of palladium. *Mailing Add:* 20 Rheem Blvd Orinda CA 94563

KOTHS, JAY SANFORD, b Taylor, Mich, July 22, 26; m 47; c 3. FLORICULTURE. *Educ:* Mich State Univ, BS, 48; Purdue Univ, MS, 50; Univ Mass, PhD, 67. *Prof Exp:* Instr floricult, Purdue Univ, 48-50; greenhouse mgr, Kemble-Smith Co, Iowa, 50-53; asst greenhouse mgr, A

Washburn & Sons, Ill, 53-54; gen mgr, A Weiler Greenhouse, Wis, 54-55; PROF FLORICULTURE, UNIV CONN, 55- *Mem:* Am Soc Agron; Am Soc Hort Sci; Soil Sci Soc Am; Int Soc Hort Sci; Am Hort Soc. *Res:* Automation of greenhouse microclimate; greenhouse crop fertility control; biological control of soilborne diseases; pollution effects on soil nitrification. *Mailing Add:* Dept of Plant Sci Col Agr Box U-67 Univ of Conn Storrs CT 06268

KOTICK, MICHAEL PAUL, b Buffalo, NY, Dec 28, 40; m 65; c 2. ORGANIC CHEMISTRY, MEDICINAL CHEMISTRY. *Educ:* State Univ NY Buffalo, BS, 62, PhD(med chem), 68; Ind Univ, MS, BA, 81. *Prof Exp:* Res asst med chem, Sch Pharm, State Univ NY Buffalo, 63-68; fel org chem, Walker Labs, Sloan-Kettering Inst Cancer Res, 68-69; res scientist, Molecular Biol Dept, 69-75, sr res scientist, Chem Dept, 75-81, PRIN RES SCIENTIST, BIOTECHNOL GROUP, MILES LABS, 81- *Mem:* AAAS; Am Chem Soc. *Res:* Chemistry of oligonucleotides, nucleosides, carbohydrates, narcotic drugs; medicinal chemistry; recombinant DNA technology. *Mailing Add:* Chem Dept Miles Labs 1127 Myrtle St Elkhart IN 46514

KOTILA, PAUL MYRON, b Hancock, Mich, Oct 14, 50. AQUATIC ECOLOGY, ENTOMOLOGY. *Educ:* Mich Technol Univ, BS, 72, MS, 74; Univ Wis-Madison, PhD(entom), 78. *Prof Exp:* ASST PROF BIOL, ALLEGHENY COL, 78- *Mem:* AAAS; Am Fisheries Soc; Entom Soc Am; N'Am Benthological Soc; Sigma Xi. *Res:* Effects of impoundments, toxicants and other disturbances on stream insects; ecology of aquatic invertebrates. *Mailing Add:* Biol Dept Allegheny Col Meadville PA 16335

KOTIN, LEON, b Brooklyn, NY, Jan 6, 24; m 48; c 2. MATHEMATICS. *Educ:* NY Univ, BS, 48, MS, 50, PhD(math), 58. *Prof Exp:* Chem lab technician, Off Sci Res & Develop, Columbia Univ, 42-43; asst math, Washington Univ, 50-51; MATHEMATICIAN, US ARMY COMMUN-ELECTRONICS COMMAND, FT MONMOUTH, 51- *Concurrent Pos:* Lectr, Fairleigh Dickinson Univ, 57-59 & Monmouth Col, NJ, 55-56 & 61-76. *Mem:* Am Math Soc; Math Asn Am; Soc Indust & Appl Math. *Res:* Ordinary differential equations. *Mailing Add:* US Commun Res & Develop Command Ft Monmouth NJ 07703

KOTIN, LEONARD, b New York, NY, June 3, 32. PHYSICAL CHEMISTRY. *Educ:* Queens Col, BS, 54; Harvard Univ, AM, 55, PhD(chem physics), 60. *Prof Exp:* Res assoc chem, Inst Study Metals, Chicago, 59-61; asst prof, Wash Univ, 61-65; ASST PROF CHEM, UNIV ILL, CHICAGO CIRCLE, 65- *Concurrent Pos:* Res assoc, Nat Acad Sci-Nat Res Coun, 59-61. *Mem:* AAAS; Am Chem Soc; NY Acad Sci. *Res:* Equilibrium and transport properties of synthetic and biological macromolecules; polyelectrolytes; thermodynamics and statistical mechanics of condensed phases. *Mailing Add:* Dept of Chem Univ of Ill at Chicago Circle Chicago IL 60680

KOTIN, PAUL, b Chicago, Ill, Aug 13, 16; m 70; c 2. PATHOLOGY. *Educ:* Univ Ill, BS, 37, MD, 40; Am Bd Path, dipl, 53. *Prof Exp:* From instr to prof path, Univ Southern Calif, 51-60, Paul Peirce prof, 60-62; chief carcinogenesis studies br, Nat Cancer Inst, 62-63, sci dir etiology, 64-66; dir div environ health sci, Nat Inst Environ Health Sci, 66-69, dir, Inst, 69-71; prof path, vpres health sci & dean sch med, Temple Univ, 71-74; sr vpres health, safety & environ, Johns-Manville Corp, 74-81. *Concurrent Pos:* Res fel path, Sch Med, Univ Southern Calif, 49-50, NSF sr fel, 59-60; med microbiologist, Los Angeles County Gen Hosp, 50-51; attend staff pathologist, 51-62. *Honors & Awards:* Knudsen Award, Am Occup Med Asn, 81; Gehrmann Lectr, Am Acad Occup Med, Nashville, 81. *Mem:* Am Asn Cancer Res; Am Asn Pathologists & Bacteriologists; fel Col Am Pathologists. *Res:* Mechanisms of carcinogenesis; experimental cancer production; environmental factors in cancer; air pollution; teratogenesis. *Mailing Add:* 4505 S Yosemite #339 Denver CO 80237

KOTLARSKI, IGNACY ICCHAK, b Warsaw, Poland, July 29, 23; US citizen. MATHEMATICS. *Educ:* Univ Warsaw, MA, 52; Wroclaw Univ, PhD(math), 61; Warsaw Tech Univ, Docent, 67. *Prof Exp:* Lectr math & statist, Planning & Statist Acad, Warsaw, 50-53; asst sampling inspection, Math Inst, Polish Acad Sci, 53-54; lectr math, Warsaw Tech Univ, 54-68; vis prof, Rome Univ, 68-69 & Univ Md, College Park, 69; PROF MATH & STATIST, OKLA STATE UNIV, 69- *Concurrent Pos:* Mem staff sampling inspection, Polish Stand Comt, 50-53; lectr math, Army Tech Acad, Warsaw, 53-59. *Mem:* Inst Math Statist; Am Math Soc; Math Asn Am; Soc Indust & Appl Math. *Res:* Characterization problems in probability; mathematical modeling. *Mailing Add:* Dept Math & Statist Okla State Univ Stillwater OK 74074

KOTLIAR, ABRAHAM MORRIS, b Brooklyn, NY, Oct 8, 26; m 55; c 4. PHYSICAL CHEMISTRY, POLYMER PHYSICS. *Educ:* Adelphi Col, BA, 49; Polytech Inst Brooklyn, PhD(chem), 55. *Prof Exp:* Res assoc & fel chem, Duke Univ, 55-56; chemist radiation effects, US Naval Res Lab, 56-60; chemist polymer physics, Esso Res & Eng Co, 60-64; group leader, 64-66, SR SCIENTIST, ALLIED CHEM CORP, 66- *Mem:* Am Chem Soc; Am Phys Soc; Soc Rheology; Sigma Xi. *Res:* Solution properties; molecular weight distributions; random processes; rheology and mechanical properties of plastics. *Mailing Add:* Allied Chem Corp PO Box 1021R Morristown NJ 07960

KOTNIK, LOUIS JOHN, b Cleveland, Ohio, Oct 2, 25; m 74; c 6. ORGANIC CHEMISTRY, CHEMICAL ENGINEERING. *Educ:* Case Inst Technol, BS, 45, BS, 49, PhD(chem eng), 60. *Prof Exp:* Instr chem, John Carroll Univ, 48-49; nat pres, Young Christian Students, 49-50; res chemist, Strong Cobb & Co, 50-53; proj chemist, Weyerhaeuser Timber Co, 53-56; res asst chem, Case Inst Technol, 56-58 & Ursuline Col, Ohio, 57-58; res technologist corrosion, Appl Res Div, US Steel Corp, 59-62; res engr, Lewis Labs, NASA, 62-64; from assoc prof to prof chem, 64-74, head dept phys sci, 66-74, dean bus & sci, 74-76, MEM ADV COMT, ETHNIC HERITAGE CTR, CUYAHOGA COMMUNITY COL, 71-, PROF CHEM, 76- *Concurrent Pos:* Chmn comt teaching chem in urban two-year cols, Two-Year Col Chem Conf, 70; mem bd trustees & exec comt, Newman Found, 70-73.

Mem: Am Chem Soc; fel Am Inst Chemists. *Res:* Corrosion; liquid metal corrosion; biochemistry; teaching methods; preparation of teaching materials. *Mailing Add:* Cuyahoga Community Col 2900 Community Col Cleveland OH 44115

KOTOK, ALAN, b Philadelphia, Pa, Nov 9, 41. COMPUTER SCIENCE. *Educ:* Mass Inst Technol, BS, 62, MS, 66. *Prof Exp:* SR CONSULT ENGR COMPUT ARCHIT & TELECOMMUN, DIGITAL EQUIP CORP, 62- *Concurrent Pos:* Lectr, Mass Inst Technol, 72-; vis lectr, Univ Calif, Berkeley, 75-76. *Res:* Computer architecture; computer structures; telephone switching systems. *Mailing Add:* MR1-2/E47 200 Forest St Marlborough MA 01752

KOTOVYCH, GEORGE, b Jan 3, 41; Can citizen; m 75; c 3. BIOPHYSICAL CHEMISTRY. *Educ:* Univ Man, BSc, 63, MSc, 64, PhD(phys chem), 68. *Prof Exp:* Nat Res Coun Can fel bio-phys chem, Lawrence Radiation Lab, Univ Calif, Berkeley, 68-69; asst prof, 70-76, ASSOC PROF CHEM, UNIV ALTA, 76- *Mem:* Chem Inst Can; Am Chem Soc; Can Biochem Soc. *Res:* Application of nuclear magnetic resonance techniques to the study of biological systems; chemistry and structure-activity relationships of the prostaglandins and prostacyclins; chemistry of vitamin D; chemistry of vitamin D. *Mailing Add:* Dept of Chem Univ of Alta Edmonton AB T6G 2G2 Can

KOTT, EDWARD, b Toronto, Ont, Mar 25, 39. ZOOLOGY. *Educ:* Univ Toronto, BA, 60, PhD(ecol), 65. *Prof Exp:* Lectr zool, Lakehead Col, 63-65; assoc scientist fisheries res, Bedford Inst Oceanog, 65-69; ASST PROF BIOL, WATERLOO LUTHERAN UNIV, 69- *Mem:* Am Soc Mammalogists; Soc Syst Zool. *Res:* Mammalian and fish population ecology. *Mailing Add:* Dept Biol Waterloo Lutheran Univ Waterloo ON N2L 3G1 Can

KOTTAS, HARRY, b Milligan, Nebr, Oct 24, 10; m 38; c 2. MECHANICAL ENGINEERING. *Educ:* Univ Nebr, BSc, 32, MSc, 33. *Prof Exp:* Mech engr food processing, Roberts Dairy Co, Nebr, 33-36 & Swift & Co, 36-37; chief mech eng div, Nat Adv Comt Aeronaut, Ohio, 37-52; chief tech panels, Redstone Arsenal, Ala, 52-56; asst dir eng, AK Div, Avco Mfg Corp, Ind, 56-59; chief spec prod eng, Curtiss-Wright Corp, 59-60; chief engr, Tuthill Spring Co, Ill, 60-62; mgr eng, Int Staple & Mach Co, Pa, 62-64; mfg mgr, Am Device Mfg Co, 64-69; prof design & drafting technol, Lake Land Col, 69-76; PRES, K-SERV, 76- *Mem:* AAAS. *Res:* Product-market characteristics; mobile vehicles materials handling; industrial noise phenomena; tillage components; fluid and solid metal flow phenomena; automated packaging; engineering and industrial human factors; manufacturing optimization. *Mailing Add:* 403 S Randall St Steeleville IL 62288

KOTTER, F(RED) RALPH, b Salt Lake City, Utah, Dec 8, 15; m 49; c 5. ELECTRICAL MEASUREMENTS, HIGH VOLTAGE PHENOMENA. *Educ:* Univ Utah, BS, 37; George Washington Univ, AM, 40; Mass Inst Technol, ScD, 55. *Prof Exp:* Physicist, Nat Bur Standards, 37-47; from instr to asst prof elec eng, Mass Inst Technol, 47-54; physicist, Nat Bur Standards, 55-81; CONSULT, 81- *Mem:* Fel Am Phys Soc; Inst Elec & Electronics Engrs. *Res:* Precise electrical measurements; high voltage measurements. *Mailing Add:* Nat Bur of Standards Washington DC 20234

KOTTKE, BRUCE ALLEN, b Blue Earth, Minn, Jan 22, 29; m 79; c 2. EXPERIMENTAL PATHOLOGY, INTERNAL MEDICINE. *Educ:* Hamline Univ, BS, 51; Univ Minn, Minneapolis, MD, 54, PhD, 62. *Prof Exp:* Consult, Mayo Found & Clin, 62-71; from asst prof to assoc prof med, 62-76, PROF MED, MAYO GRAD SCH MED, UNIV MINN, 76- *Concurrent Pos:* Fel int med, Mayo Found, 57-61; mem coun arteriosclerosis, Am Heart Asn, mem coun atherosclerosis, mem coun thrombosis, fel coun circulation. *Mem:* Am Heart Asn; Am Fedn Clin Res. *Res:* Atherosclerosis; cholesterol metabolism; bile acid metabolism. *Mailing Add:* Mayo Clin Rochester MN 55901

KOTTKE, FREDERIC JAMES, b Hayfield, Minn, May 26, 17; m 39; c 4. PHYSICAL MEDICINE. *Educ:* Univ Minn, BS & MS, 41, PhD(physiol), 44, MD, 45; Am Bd Phys Med & Rehab, dipl, 49. *Prof Exp:* Asst physiol, 39-40, instr, 41-44, from asst prof to assoc prof, 47-52, dir div, 49-52, assoc prof, 52-53, PROF PHYS MED & REHAB, UNIV MINN, MINNEAPOLIS, 53-, HEAD DEPT, 52- *Concurrent Pos:* Baruch fel phys med, Univ Minn, Minneapolis, 46-47; mem, Am Bd Phys Med & Rehab, 55-, chmn, 64-70; consult, Minneapolis Vet Admin Hosp, 56; mem, Minn Gov Adv Comt Voc Rehab, 56-60; mem exec comt, prog chmn & vpres, Int Cong Phys Med, 60; mem med adv comt, Off Voc Rehab, 60-67; mem med res study sect, Voc Rehab Admin, 61-63; secy & mem bd dirs & mem expert med comt, Am Rehab Found, 64; mem, Minn State Bd Health, 64-67, Med Adv Comt, Social & Rehab Serv, 68-69 & Coun Cerebrovasc Dis & Coun Clin Cardiol, Am Heart Asn. *Honors & Awards:* Distinguished Serv Key, Am Cong Phys Med & Rehab, 61; Sidney Licht Lectr Rehab Med, Univ Pa, 79; Frank H Krusen Award, Am Acad Phys Med & Rehab, 79. *Mem:* Fel AMA; fel Am Cong Phys Med & Rehab (vpres, 54-58, pres elect, 59-60, pres, 60); Am Acad Phys Med & Rehab (mem bd dir, 73-76, pres-elect, 77, pres, 78); Int Soc Rehab Disabled; Nat Rehab Asn. *Res:* Circulation; neuromuscular diseases; poliomyelitis; rehabilitation; work of the heart. *Mailing Add:* Univ Hosp Univ of Minn Box 297 Minneapolis MN 55455

KOTTLE, SHERMAN, physical chemistry, see previous edition

KOTTLOWSKI, FRANK EDWARD, b Indianapolis, Ind, Apr 11, 21; m 45; c 3. ECONOMIC GEOLOGY, COAL GEOLOGY. *Educ:* Ind Univ, AB, 47, AM, 49, PhD(econ geol), 51. *Prof Exp:* Asst geologist econ geol, State Geol Surv, Ind, 46-51; econ geologist, 51-66, asst dir & sr geologist, 66-73, DIR, N MEX BUR MINES & MINERAL RESOURCES, 73- *Concurrent Pos:* Asst, Ind Univ, 47-48, instr, 50; fac assoc, NMex Inst Mining & Technol, 54-73; adj prof, 74-; ed, Am Asn Petrol Geologists, 71-75; chmn, Nat Acad Sci Codes Comt, 80-81. *Mem:* Fel AAAS; Soc Econ Geol; fel Geol Soc Am; Soc Econ Paleont & Mineral; Am Asn Petrol Geologists. *Res:* Coal geology; Pennsylvanian and Permian stratigraphy; Cenozoic sediments and volcanic rocks; industrial minerals and rocks; areal mapping in Indiana, New Mexico and Montana; measuring stratigraphic sections. *Mailing Add:* 703 Sunset Dr Socorro NM 87801

KOTTMAN, CLIFFORD ALFONS, b San Diego, Calif, Aug 3, 42; m 66; c 3. MATHEMATICS. *Educ:* Loyola Univ, Los Angeles, BS, 64; Univ Iowa, MS, 66, PhD(math), 69. *Prof Exp:* Asst prof math, La State Univ, 69-70; asst prof, 70-75, assoc prof math, ORE STATE UNIV, 75-77; MATHEMATICIAN DEFENSE MAPPING AGENCY, 77- *Concurrent Pos:* Consult in nondestructive testing. *Mem:* AAAS; Am Math Soc; Math Asn Am; Am Soc Photogram. *Res:* Functional analysis; Banach spaces; photogrammetry. *Mailing Add:* Defense Mapping Agency 6500 Brookes Lane Washington DC 20315

KOTTMAN, ROY MILTON, b Thornton, Iowa, Dec 22, 16; m 41; c 4. ANIMAL BREEDING. *Educ:* Iowa State Univ, BS, 41, PhD(animal breeding), 52; Univ Wis, MS, 48. *Hon Degrees:* LLD, Col Wooster, 72. *Prof Exp:* Asst, Univ Wis, 47-48; asst prof animal husb, Iowa State Univ, 46-47, 49-52, assoc prof, 52-54, prof & assoc dean agr, 54-58; dean col agr, Forestry & Home Econ & dir, Agr Exp Sta, Univ WVa, 58-60; DEAN COL AGR & HOME ECON & DIR OHIO AGR RES & DEVELOP CTR, OHIO STATE UNIV, 60-, DIR COOP EXTEN SERV, 64- *Concurrent Pos:* Asst to dean, Iowa State Univ, 50-51, asst dean, 51-54. *Mem:* Sigma Xi; fel Am Soc Animal Sci. *Res:* Population genetics; genetic improvement of swine, beef cattle and sheep. *Mailing Add:* Off of the Dean Col of Agr & Home Econ Ohio State Univ Columbus OH 43210

KOTTMEIER, PETER KLAUS, b Munich, Ger, Feb 1, 28; m 56; c 4. SURGERY. *Educ:* Univ Munich, MD, 51, Ohio State Univ, MMSc, 60. *Prof Exp:* Asst instr surg, State Univ NY Downstate Med Ctr, 57-60; instr, Ohio State Univ, 60-61; from asst prof to assoc prof, 67-70, PROF SURG, STATE UNIV NY DOWNSTATE MED CTR, 70-, DIR PEDIAT SURG SERV, UNIV HOSP, 67-, DIR PEDIAT SURG SERV, KINGS COUNTY HOSP, BROOKLYN, 62- *Mem:* Fel Am Acad Pediat; fel Am Col Surgeons; fel Am Pediat Surg Asn. *Res:* Pediatric surgery. *Mailing Add:* Dept of Surg State Univ NY Downstate Med Ctr Brooklyn NY 11203

KOTULA, ANTHONY W, b Holyoke, Mass, June 12, 29; m 57; c 2. FOOD SCIENCE. *Educ:* Univ Mass, BS, 51, MS, 54; Univ Md, PhD(food sci), 64. *Prof Exp:* Proj leader, 54-67, invests leader, 67-71, SUPVRY RES FOOD TECHNOLOGIST, CHIEF MEAT SCI RES LAB, ANIMAL SCI INST, AGR RES SERV, USDA, 71- *Concurrent Pos:* Res award, Poultry Sci Res Asn, 67. *Mem:* Poultry Sci Asn; Inst Food Technologists; World Poultry Sci Asn; Am Meat Sci Asn; Am Soc Animal Sci. *Res:* Maintaining and improving quality of animal products. *Mailing Add:* Meat Sci Res Lab Agr Res Serv USDA Beltsville MD 20705

KOTVAL, PESHO SOHRAB, b Nagpur, India, Aug 31, 42; US citizen; m 65; c 2. MEDICAL ENGINEERING, MANAGEMENT SCIENCE. *Educ:* Univ Nagpur, BSc, 60; Univ Sheffield, MMet, 62, PhD(phys metall), 65; Pace Univ, MBA, 77. *Prof Exp:* Scientist, res assoc & mgr superally metall, Stellite Div, Union Carbide Corp, 66-70; vis scientist metall, Res Inst Advan Studies, 70-71; sr group leader metals & ceramics, Corp Res Lab, Union Carbide Corp, 71-78, res mgr mat sic, Med Prod Div, 78-80. *Concurrent Pos:* Fel, Sheffield Univ, 65-66; adj prof physics, Ind Univ, 67-68; adj prof mgt econ, Pace Univ, 77-80. *Honors & Awards:* Coatings Award, Am Soc Metals, 73. *Mem:* Fel Am Soc Metals; Brit Inst Metallurgists. *Res:* Superalloys for high temperature gas turbines and corrosion resistance; powder metdllurgy; crystal growth; process development; low cost solar cells; medical instruments. *Mailing Add:* 8 Verne Pl Hartsdale NY 10530

KOTYK, MICHAEL M, b Ford City, Pa, Mar 10, 29; m 52; c 5. METALLURGY, CERAMICS. *Educ:* Pa State Univ, BS, 54, MS, 56; NC State Univ, PhD(metall, ceramics), 68. *Prof Exp:* Instr metall, Pa State Univ, 54-56; sr technologist, US Steel Corp, 56-63; assoc dir metall & ceramics div, US Army Res Off, 63-68; sect supvr, Appl Res Lab, 68-73, div chief sheet prod res, 73-82, DIV CHIEF BASIC RES DIV, US STEEL CORP, 82- *Mem:* Am Soc Metals; Am Inst Mining, Metall & Petrol Engrs; fel Am Chem Soc; Iron & Steel Inst Japan. *Res:* Formability of sheet steels; gases in metals; physical and mechanical properties of ferrous alloys; phase equilibria studies. *Mailing Add:* US Steel Res Monroeville PA 15146

KOTZ, ARTHUR RUDOLPH, b Eau Claire, Wis, Feb 21, 33; m 55; c 3. SOLID STATE ELECTRONICS. *Educ:* Univ Minn, BA, 55; Univ Wis, MS, 62, PhD(solid state physics), 66. *Prof Exp:* Jr physicist, 55-57, sr physicist, 57-58, supvr phys res, 58-60, proj leader, 60-61, res specialist, 66-68, sr res specialist, 68-70, mgr electronic imaging group, 70-73, CORP SCIENTIST, 3M CO, 73- *Mem:* Am Phys Soc; Soc Photog Sci & Eng. *Res:* Electrical transport properties of organic semiconductors; electron beam recording; gas discharge devices; photoeffects in solids, including photoconductivity, photovoltaic effect and photoemission; electrophotography; electronic imaging; electrography; reprography; electronic printing. *Mailing Add:* Electronic Info Technol Sector Lab 201-3Se 3M Co 3M Cent St Paul MN 55144

KOTZ, JOHN CARL, b Massillon, Ohio, June 27, 37; m 61; c 2. INORGANIC CHEMISTRY, ORGANOMETALLIC CHEMISTRY. *Educ:* Wash & Lee Univ, BS, 59; Cornell Univ, PhD(inorg chem), 64. *Prof Exp:* NIH fel chem, Manchester Col Sci & Technol, Eng, 63-64 & Ind Univ, 64-65; asst prof, Kans State Univ, 65-70; PROF CHEM, STATE UNIV NY COL ONEONTA, 70- *Concurrent Pos:* Fulbright lectr & res scholar, Portugal, 79. *Mem:* Am Chem Soc; Royal Soc Chem. *Res:* Synthetic organometallic chemistry; electrochemistry of organometallic compounds. *Mailing Add:* Dept Chem State Univ NY Col Oneonta NY 13820

KOTZ, SAMUEL, b Harbin, China, Aug 28, 30; m 63; c 3. MATHEMATICAL STATISTICS, APPLIED PROBABILITY. *Educ:* Hebrew Univ, Israel, MSc, 56; Cornell Univ, PhD(math statist), 60. *Prof Exp:* Instr math, Bar-ilan Univ, Israel, 56-58, lectr, 60-62; res assoc, Inst Statist, Univ NC, 62-63; sr res fel indust eng, Univ Toronto, 63-64, assoc prof, 64-67; prof math, Temple Univ, 67-79; PROF STATIST, UNIV MD, 79- *Concurrent Pos:* Assoc ed, J Am Statist Asn; Distinguished vis prof, Bucknell

Univ, 77; co-ed Encycl Statist Sci. *Mem:* Am Math Soc; fel Am Statist Asn; fel Inst Math Statist; London Math Soc; Int Statist Inst. *Res:* Information theory; statistical distribution theory; scientific terminology; probabilistic models with special applications to business and engineering. *Mailing Add:* Dept Mgt & Statist Univ MD College Park MD 20742

KOTZEBUE, KENNETH LEE, b San Antonio, Tex, Dec 4, 33; m 54; c 3. ELECTRICAL ENGINEERING. *Educ:* Univ Tex, BS, 54; Univ Calif, Los Angeles, MS, 56; Stanford Univ, PhD(elec eng), 59. *Prof Exp:* Sr engr, Tex Instruments, Inc, 58-59; mem tech staff elec eng, Watkins-Johnson Co, 59-63; dept head solid state devices res & develop, 63-64; assoc prof, 64-68, PROF ELEC ENG, UNIV CALIF, SANTA BARBARA, 68- *Mem:* Inst Elec & Electronics Engrs. *Res:* Microwave solid-state device electronics. *Mailing Add:* Dept of Elec Eng Univ of Calif Santa Barbara CA 93106

KOTZIG, ANTON, b Kocovce, Czech, Oct 22, 19; Can citizen; m 44; c 1. MATHEMATICS. *Educ:* Univ Bratislava, Czech, RNDr, 47; Charles Univ, Prague, Czech, Dr Sc, 61. *Prof Exp:* Head dept statistics, Cent Bur Social Ins, Bratislava, 42-50; from assoc prof to prof math, Univ Econ, Bratislava, 51-59; dir, Math Inst, Slovak Acad Sci, Bratislava, 59-63; prof & dean, Univ Bratislava, 64-69; vis prof, Univ Calgary, 69-70; CHIEF RES MATH, CTR MATH RES, UNIV MONTREAL, 70- *Honors & Awards:* State Prize, Czech Republic, 69. *Mem:* Am Math Soc; Opers Res Soc Am; Can Math Cong. *Res:* Discrete mathematics; combinatorics; operations research; optimization; econometrics. *Mailing Add:* Ctr of Math Res PO Box 6128 Univ of Montreal Montreal PQ H3C 3J7 Can

KOUBA, DELORE LOREN, b Lincoln, Nebr, Apr 18, 19; m 41. CHEMICAL ENGINEERING, ORGANIC CHEMISTRY. *Educ:* Univ Nebr, BSc, 41. *Prof Exp:* Anal chemist, Smokeless Powder Plant, Hercules, Inc, NJ, 41-42, lab supvr, 42, chief chemist, 42-43, anal chemist, Res & Develop Res Ctr, Del, 43-46, explosives chemist, 46-50, res chemist, 50-78, SR RES CHEMIST, RES & DEVELOP RES CTR, HERCULES, INC, DEL, 79- *Mem:* Am Chem Soc. *Res:* Smokeless powder testing; high explosives; semi-plant nitration; oxidation of aromatic compounds and hazardous chemicals evaluation; synthetic lubricants. *Mailing Add:* 1808 Windermere Ave Wilmington DE 19804

KOUBA, RUDOLPH FRANK, biochemistry, physical organic chemistry, see previous edition

KOUBEK, EDWARD, b Bayshore, NY, July 25, 37; m 63; c 2. INORGANIC CHEMISTRY. *Educ:* State Univ NY Albany, BS, 59; Brown Univ, PhD(chem), 64. *Prof Exp:* Fel, Bell Tel Labs, NJ, 63-64; from asst prof to assoc prof, 67-75, PROF CHEM, US NAVAL ACAD, 75- *Mem:* Am Chem Soc. *Res:* Kinetics and mechanisms of inorganic reactions. *Mailing Add:* Dept of Chem US Naval Acad Annapolis MD 21402

KOUCKY, FRANK LOUIS, JR, b Chicago, Ill, June 24, 27; m 49; c 4. MINERALOGY, GEOCHEMISTRY. *Educ:* Univ Chicago, MS, 53, PhD(geol), 56. *Prof Exp:* Instr phys sci, Navy Pier, Univ Ill, 51-55; from instr to asst prof, Mont Sch Mines, 55-57; asst prof & dir field camp, Univ Ill, 57-71; from asst prof to assoc prof, Univ Cincinnati, 60-71; PROF GEOL, COL WOOSTER, 71- *Concurrent Pos:* Assoc, Danforth Found. *Mem:* Am Mineral Soc; Geol Soc Am; Am Asn Petrol Geol; Geochem Soc; Clay Mineral Soc. *Res:* X-ray crystallography; sulfide and sulfosalt minerals; geology of Wyoming and Montana; Precambrian geology; ancient technology related to mining and smelting; archaeological geology of Cyprus, Israel and Jordan. *Mailing Add:* Dept of Geol Col of Wooster Wooster OH 44691

KOUL, HIRA LAL, b Srinagar, Kashmir, May 27, 43. MATHEMATICAL STATISTICS. *Educ:* Univ Jammu & Kashmir, India, BA, 62, Univ Poona, MA, 64; Univ Calif, Berkeley, PhD(math statist), 67. *Prof Exp:* Asst, Univ Calif, Berkeley, 65-67; asst prof statist, 68-72, assoc prof, 72-77, PROF STATIST & PROBABILITY, MICH STATE UNIV, 77- *Mem:* Inst Math Statist. *Res:* Nonparametric statistics; weak convergence of probability measures and its application to statistics; inference in reliability theory. *Mailing Add:* Dept of Statist & Probability Mich State Univ East Lansing MI 48823

KOUL, MAHARJ KISHEN, b Srinagar, India, Sept 10, 41. MATERIALS SCIENCE, METALLURGY. *Educ:* Univ Jammu & Kashmir, BSc, 59; Banaras Hindu Univ, BSc, 63; Mass Inst Technol, PhD(mat sci), 68. *Prof Exp:* Metall asst, Union Carbide India Pvt Ltd, 63-65; res asst mat sci, Mass Inst Technol, 65-68, fel, 68-69; res scientist, Res & Develop, Mining & Metals Div, Union Carbide Corp, 69-70; proj engr, New Prod Develop, 70-76; mgr, Steel Res & Develop, Foote Mineral Co, 76-79; exec vpres, Div Indian Metals & Ferro Alloys Ltd, Newmont Mining Co, 79-80; SR RES SCIENTIST, JOHNSON & JOHNSON, 80- *Mem:* Am Inst Mining, Metall & Petrol Engrs; Am Soc Metals. *Res:* Electron microscopic investigation of phase transformation and deformation behavior in Beta-isomorphous titanium alloys; strengthening mechanisms and their application to the development of high strength-low alloy steels; dissolution kinetics of solids in liquid metals; thermodynamics and its application to metallurgical phenomenon; boron steel developments; deoxidation, desulfurization and sulfide modification in steel; dental alloy development. *Mailing Add:* Johnson & Johnson 20 Lake Dr CN 7060 East Windsor NJ 08520

KOUL, OMANAND, b Kashmir, India, Feb 17, 47; m 71; c 3. NEUROCHEMISTRY, GLYCOLIPIDS. *Educ:* Banaras Hindu Univ, India, MSc, 68, PhD(zool), 74. *Prof Exp:* Lectr physiol & biochem, Banaras Hindu Univ, India, 70-74; asst prof genetics & biol, Govind Ballabh Pant Univ Agr & Technol, India, 75-76; RES ASSOC BIOCHEM, EUNICE KENNEDY SHRIVER CTR MENTAL RETARDATION, 76- *Concurrent Pos:* Res fel, Dept Neurol, Mass Gen Hosp, 76- *Mem:* Am Soc Neurochem; Soc Gerantol. *Res:* Brain function in health and disease; enzymology of lipids; metabolism of glycolipids in animals and cell cultures; myelin biosynthesis during development. *Mailing Add:* Dept Biochem Eunice Kennedy Shriver Ctr 200 Trapelo Rd Waltham MA 02254

KOULOURIDES, THEODORE I, b Preveza, Greece, Sept 11, 25; US citizen; m 56; c 3. DENTISTRY, ORAL BIOLOGY. *Educ:* Nat Univ Athens, Dent Surgeon, 50; Univ Rochester, MS, 58; Univ Ala, DMD, 60. *Prof Exp:* From asst prof to assoc prof, 60-69, PROF DENT, MED CTR, UNIV ALA, BIRMINGHAM, 69-; SR SCIENTIST, INST DENT RES, 71- *Concurrent Pos:* Fel pedodontics, Guggenheim Dent Clin, New York, 55; fel, Eastman Dent Dispensary, Rochester, NY, 55-56; USPHS res career develop award, 63-68. *Mem:* Am Dent Asn; Am Col Dent; Sigma Xi; Int Dent Fedn; Int Asn Dent Res. *Res:* Biological mineralization, especially factors involved in dental caries and calculus formation. *Mailing Add:* Inst of Dent Res Univ Sta Birmingham AL 35294

KOUNOSU, SHIGERU, b Tokyo, Japan, Aug 23, 28; m 61; c 2. HIGH ENERGY PHYSICS, THEORETICAL PHYSICS. *Educ:* Fukushima Univ, Japan, BEd, 51; Univ Pa, MS, 63, PhD(physics), 65. *Prof Exp:* Res assoc physics, Princeton Univ, 65-67; asst prof, 67-70, ASSOC PROF PHYSICS, UNIV LETHBRIDGE, 70- *Mem:* Am Phys Soc. *Res:* Elementary particle physics. *Mailing Add:* Dept of Physics Univ of Lethbridge Lethbridge AB T1K 3H4 Can

KOUNTZ, SAMUEL L, surgery, deceased

KOURANY, MIGUEL, b Panama City, Panama, Sept 16, 24; m 53; c 4. MICROBIOLOGY, PUBLIC HEALTH. *Educ:* Iowa State Col, BS, 50; Loyola Univ, Chicago, MS, 53; Univ Mich, Ann Arbor, MPH, 54, PhD(epidemiol sci), 63. *Prof Exp:* Dir, Pub Health Lab, 54-63, CHIEF BACT DEPT, GORGAS MEM LAB, 63- *Concurrent Pos:* Consult,Pan Am Health Orgn Lab Serv in various countries, 71-; supv ad honoratium, Pub Health Lab Serv, Ministry Health, 63-; mem, Epert Adv Panel Health Lab Serv, WHO, 67-; mem, Pan Am Health Org Sci Adv Comt to Zoonosis Ctr, Argentina, 74- *Mem:* Am Soc Trop Med & Hyg; AAAS; Panamanian Soc Microbiol & Parasitol (pres, 68, 69 & 78). *Res:* Intracellular infections; etiological agents of diarrheal disease; ecology of vibrio parahaemolyticus; zoonosis in Panama. *Mailing Add:* Lab Conmemorativo Gorgas Apartado 6991 Panama 5 Panama

KOURI, DONALD JACK, b Hobart, Okla, July 25, 38; m 65; c 2. THEORETICAL CHEMISTRY. *Educ:* Okla Baptist Univ, BA, 60; Univ Wis, MS, 62, PhD(phys chem), 65. *Prof Exp:* Instr chem & physics, Okla Baptist Univ, 62-63; res assoc physics & mem joint inst lab astrophys, Univ Colo, 65-66; asst prof chem, Midwestern Univ, 66-67; from asst prof to assoc prof, 67-73, PROF CHEM & PHYSICS, UNIV HOUSTON, 73- *Concurrent Pos:* Fel, A P Sloan Found, 72-; Weizmann Inst fel, 73; J S Guggenheim fel, 78-79; fel Inst Advan Studies, Hebrew Univ, Jerusalem, 78-79. *Honors & Awards:* US Sr Scientist Award, Alexander von Humboldt Found, 73. *Mem:* Fel Am Phys Soc; Am Chem Soc; Am Asn Physics Teachers. *Res:* Theoretical research on quantum mechanical scattering phenomena; reactive and nonreaction molecular collisions; approximations for inelastic and reactive collisions. *Mailing Add:* Dept of Chem Univ of Houston Houston TX 77004

KOUSHANPOUR, ESMAIL, b Teheran, Iran, June 9, 34; US citizen; m78; c 4. PHYSIOLOGY, BIOPHYSICS. *Educ:* Columbia Univ, AB, 58; Mich State Univ, MS, 61, PhD(physiol), 63. *Prof Exp:* Asst prof, 63-68, ASSOC PROF PHYSIOL, MED SCH, NORTHWESTERN UNIV, ILL, 68- *Concurrent Pos:* Nat Heart Inst fel, 65- *Mem:* AAAS; Am Physiol Soc; NY Acad Sci; Am Heart Asn. *Res:* Mathematical and experimental analyses of the cardiovascular and renal regulators; mechanism of the baroceptor process in the carotid sinus; role of carotid sinus in renal hypertension. *Mailing Add:* Dept Physiol Northwestern Univ Med Sch Chicago IL 60611

KOUSKOLEKAS, COSTAS ALEXANDER, b Thessaloniki, Greece, May 10, 27; m 58; c 2. ENTOMOLOGY. *Educ:* Univ Thessaloniki, Dipl agr, 51; Univ Mo-Columbia, MS, 58; Univ Ill, Urbana, PhD(entom), 64. *Prof Exp:* Teacher agron, Am Farm Sch, Thessaloniki, 54-56; res assoc agr entom, Natural Hist Surv & Agr Exp Sta, Univ Ill, Urbana, 62-63; consult, Doxiadis Assocs Int, Athens, Greece, 64-65; sr res officer entom, Benaki Phytopath Inst, Athens, 65-67; ASSOC PROF ENTOM, AUBURN UNIV, 67- *Mem:* Entom Soc Am; Int Orgn Biol Control. *Res:* Biology and control of insects of ornamentals and vegetables; integrated pest management. *Mailing Add:* Dept of Zool-Entom Auburn Univ Auburn AL 36830

KOUSKY, VERNON E, b Detroit, Mich, Nov 2, 43; m 73; c 3. DYNAMIC METEOROLOGY. *Educ:* Pa State Univ, BS, 65, MS, 67; Univ Wash, PhD(atmospheric sci), 70. *Prof Exp:* Asst prof meteorol, Univ Utah, 70-75; prof collabr, Inst Astron & Geophys, Univ Sao Paulo, 75-77; ASSOC RESEARCHER & RESEARCHER, INST SPACE RES, BRAZIL, 77- *Mem:* Am Meteorol Soc; Meteorol Soc Japan. *Res:* Synoptic meteorology; diagnostic study of wave motions in the tropical stratosphere; severe local storms; jetstream formation; tropopause deformation; atmospheric teleconnections; tropical meteorology; climate anomalies. *Mailing Add:* Dept Meteorol CP515/Inst de Pesquisasa Espaciais 12200 Sao Jose dos Campos Brazil

KOUTS, HERBERT JOHN CECIL, b Bisbee, Ariz, Dec 18, 19; m 42; c 2. PHYSICS. *Educ:* La State Univ, BS, 41, MS, 46; Princeton Univ, PhD(physics), 52. *Prof Exp:* Assoc physicist, Brookhaven Nat Lab, 50-51, asst group leader, 51-52, group leader reactor physics, 52-58, sr scientist & assoc div head, 58-73; dir, Div Reactor Safety Res, AEC, 73-75; dir, Off Nuclear Regulatory Res, US Nuclear Regulatory Comn, 75-76; CHMN DEPT NUCLEAR ENERGY, BROOKHAVEN NAT LAB, 77- *Concurrent Pos:* Mem adv comt reactor safeguards, AEC, 62-66, chmn, 65; mem, Europ-Am Comt Reactor Physics, Europ Nuclear Energy Agency, 62-68; mem, Mayor's Tech Adv Comt on Radiation, New York, 69-73; chmn, Nuclear Adv Comt, Hall of Sci, New York, 69-73; prin adv reactor safety, NY State Atomic & Space Develop Authority, 69-73. *Honors & Awards:* E O Lawrence Award, AEC, 63 & Distinguished Serv Award, 75; Distinguished Serv Award, US Nuclear Regulatory Comn, 76. *Mem:* Nat Acad Eng; fel Am Nuclear Soc. *Res:* Elementary particle physics; shielding and physics of nuclear reactors. *Mailing Add:* 249 S Country Rd Brookhaven NY 11719

KOUTSKY, JAMES A, b Cleveland, Ohio, Dec 1, 39. CHEMICAL ENGINEERING, POLYMER SCIENCE. *Educ:* Case Inst Technol, BS, 61, MS, 63, PhD(polymer sci), 66. *Prof Exp:* From asst prof to assoc prof, 66-77, PROF CHEM ENG, UNIV WIS-MADISON, 77- *Concurrent Pos:* Du Pont Young Fac res grant, 68-69. *Mem:* Am Phys Soc; Am Inst Chem Engrs; Am Chem Soc; Soc Plastics Engrs. *Res:* Solid state characterization of macromolecules by electron and optical microscopy, electron and x-ray diffraction and differential thermal analysis. *Mailing Add:* Dept of Chem Eng Univ of Wis Madison WI 53706

KOUVEL, JAMES SPYROS, b Jersey City, NJ, May 23, 26; m 53; c 2. SOLID STATE PHYSICS. *Educ:* Yale Univ, BEng, 46, PhD(phys & elec eng), 51. *Prof Exp:* Res engr, Microwave Devices, Fed Telecommun Labs, NJ, 47-48; res fel physics, Univ Leeds, 51-53; res fel solid state physics, Harvard Univ, 53-55; physicist, Res & Develop Ctr, Gen Elec Co, 55-69; PROF PHYSICS, UNIV ILL, CHICAGO CIRCLE, 69- *Concurrent Pos:* Guggenheim fel, 67-68; consult, Argonne Nat Lab, 69-, mem rev comts, Solid State Sci & Mat Sci Div, 70-72, vis scientist, 73-74; mem, Mat Res Adv Comt, NSF, 80- *Mem:* Fel Am Phys Soc. *Res:* Properties of magnetic materials; critical phenomena; phase transitions; ferroelectricity. *Mailing Add:* Dept Physics Univ Ill Chicago IL 60680

KOUZEL, BERNARD, b New York, NY, Aug 21, 20; m 48; c 3. CHEMICAL ENGINEERING. *Educ:* City Col New York, BChE, 41; Univ Southern Calif, MSChE, 63. *Prof Exp:* Chem engr, Air Prod, Inc, Pa, 48-54; tech ed, Rocketdyne Div NAm Aviation, Inc, Calif, 54-55; develop engr, Res Dept, 55-63, sr develop engr, 63-69, ENG ASSOC, SCI & TECHNOL DIV, UNION OIL CO OF CALIF, 69- *Concurrent Pos:* Mem tech data subcomt, Refining Div, Am Petrol Inst. *Mem:* Am Inst Chem Engrs. *Res:* Methods for prediction and correlation of physical properties; development of computer calculation procedures for process design; Stretford technology for treatment of sulfur-plant tail gas; hydrogen sulfide abatement procedures for geothermal energy systems. *Mailing Add:* Res Dept Union Oil Co of Calif PO Box 76 Brea CA 92621

KOUZES, RICHARD THOMAS, b Arlington, Va, July 8, 47; m 70. NUCLEAR PHYSICS. *Educ:* Mich State Univ, BS, 69; Princeton Univ, MA, 72, PhD(physics), 74. *Prof Exp:* Sr systs analyst, Univ Comput Co, 70-71; res assoc nuclear physics, Cyclotron Facil, Ind Univ, Bloomington, 75-76; RES STAFF & LECTR, PRINCETON UNIV, 76- *Mem:* Am Phys Soc; Sigma Xi. *Res:* Investigation of multiple nucleon transfer reactions for the measurement of masses far from stability. *Mailing Add:* 111 Mountain Ave Princeton NJ 08540

KOVAC, JEFFREY DEAN, b Cleveland, Ohio, May 29, 48; m 73; c 1. PHYSICAL CHEMISTRY. *Educ:* Reed Col, BA, 70; Yale Univ, MPhil, 72, PhD(chem), 74. *Prof Exp:* Res assoc chem, Mass Inst Technol, 74-76; ASST PROF CHEM, UNIV TENN, 76- *Mem:* AAAS; Am Phys Soc; Am Chem Soc. *Res:* Statistical mechanics of polymers and simple fluids; equilibrium and non equilibrium thermodynamics; rubber elasticity; structure of coal. *Mailing Add:* Dept of Chem Univ of Tenn Knoxville TN 37996

KOVACH, EUGENE GEORGE, b Irvington, NJ, May 18, 22; m 50; c 5. ORGANIC CHEMISTRY, SCIENCE ADMINISTRATION. *Educ:* Wayne State Univ, BS, 43, MS, 44; Harvard Univ, MA, 48, PhD, 49. *Prof Exp:* Res tutor, Harvard, 46-49; instr, Univ Fla, 49-50, asst prof, 51-54; asst prof, Colgate Univ, 50-51; sci adv, US Naval Forces, Germany, 54-57; chem prog, Nat Sci Found, 57-59; asst sci adv, Int Sci & Tech Affairs, US Dept State, 59-65, actg dir, Off Gen Sci Affairs, 65-70; dep asst secy gen for sci affairs, NATO, 70-76; with Div of Policy Res, NSF, 76-78; mem staff, Off Technol Policy, 78-80, DIR, OFF ADVAN TECHNOL, US DEPT OF STATE, 80- *Mem:* AAAS; Am Chem Soc; Ger Chem Soc; Sigma Xi. *Res:* Structure of natural products; chelate compounds; theoretical organic chemistry; science education and administration; international relations. *Mailing Add:* Off Advan Technol US Dept of State Washington DC 20520

KOVACH, JACK, b Rices Landing, Pa, Mar 23, 40; m 65; c 2. GEOLOGY. *Educ:* Waynesburg Col, BSc, 62; Ohio State Univ, MSc, 67, PhD(geol), 74. *Prof Exp:* Asst prof, 68-77, ASSOC PROF GEOL, MUSKINGUM COL, 77- *Concurrent Pos:* Res assoc, Nat Res Coun, Nat Acad Sci, 79-80; assoc, US Geol Surv, Denver. *Mem:* Geol Soc Am; AAAS; Soc Econ Paleontologists & Mineralogists. *Res:* Strontium isotope geochemistry and rubidium-strontium geochronology; biogeochemistry of nonmarine mollusk shells; composition of atmospheric precipitation; Silurian stratigraphy and paleontology; biogeochemistry and isotopic composition of conodonts. *Mailing Add:* Dept of Geol Muskingum Col New Concord OH 43762

KOVACH, LADIS DANIEL, b Budapest, Hungary, Nov 21, 14; nat US; m 45; c 3. MATHEMATICS. *Educ:* Case Inst Technol, BS, 36, MS, 48; Western Reserve Univ, MA, 40; Purdue Univ, PhD(math), 51. *Prof Exp:* Elec draftsman, Picker X-ray Corp, 37-40; chief elec draftsman, Am Shipbldg Co, 41-44; sr elec designer, Ohio Crankshaft Co, 44-48; instr math, Purdue Univ, 48-51; design specialist, Douglas Aircraft Co, 51-61; prof math & head dept math & physics, Pepperdine Col, 58-68, PROF MATH, NAVAL POST-GRAD SCH, 68- *Concurrent Pos:* Instr, Case Inst Technol, 46-48; vis lectr, Pepperdine Col, 57-58. *Mem:* Math Asn Am; Soc Computer Simulation; Sigma Xi. *Res:* Analog computing; nonlinear differential equations; algebra; teacher education. *Mailing Add:* 69 Paseo Hermoso Salinas CA 93908

KOVACH, STEPHEN MICHAEL, b Whiting, Ind, Mar 23, 25; m 49; c 4. PETROLEUM CHEMISTRY. *Educ:* Univ Ill, BS, 50. *Prof Exp:* Res chemist, Sinclair Res, Inc, 51-64; GROUP LEADER CATALYSIS, ASHLAND OIL & REF CO, 64- *Mem:* Fel Am Inst Chem; Am Chem Soc; Catalysis Soc. *Res:* Use and application of catalysts and catalysis to petroleum processing, petrochemical production and chemicals. *Mailing Add:* Res & Develop Ashland & Refining Co Ashland KY 41101

KOVACHEVICH, RUDY, biochemistry, pathology, see previous edition

KOVACHICH, GYULA BERTALAN, b Budapest, Hungary, Mar 27, 36; m 64; c 2. NEUROCHEMISTRY. Educ: Haverford Col, BA, 62; Univ Pa, PhD(pharmacol), 75. Prof Exp: Res asst neurochem, Ciba-Geigy Corp, 64-69; instr pharmacol, 75-77, res assoc, 77-80, ASST PROF, DEPT PHARMACOL, SCH MED, UNIV PA, 80- Concurrent Pos: Primary investr neurochem, Inst Environ Med, Univ Pa Med Ctr, 75- Res: Oxygen toxicity of the central nervous system; regulation of pyrovate dehydrogenase complex. Mailing Add: Inst for Environ Med Univ of Pa Med Ctr Philadelphia PA 19174

KOVACIC, JERALD J, b Sheboygan, Wis, Mar 12, 41. ALGEBRA. Educ: Stanford Univ, BS, 62; Columbia Univ, MA, 63, PhD(math), 68. Prof Exp: Instr, Princeton Univ, 68-70; asst prof, Fordham Univ, 70-74; asst prof, 74-80, ASSOC PROF MATH, BROOKLYN COL, 80- Concurrent Pos: Prin investr, NSF, 71- Mem: Am Math Soc; Math Asn Am. Res: Galois theory in differential algebra. Mailing Add: Dept of Math Brooklyn Col Brooklyn NY 11210

KOVACIC, JOSEPH EDWARD, b Youngstown, Ohio, Apr 4, 30; div; c 5. ORGANIC CHEMISTRY. Educ: Univ Ohio, BS, 52, MS, 53. Prof Exp: Chemist nylon res labs, E I du Pont de Nemours & Co, 55-56; teaching asst chem, Fla State Univ, 56-57; res chemist, Resinous Prod Lab, Dow Chem Co, 57-60, org chemist, Chem-Physics Res Lab, 60-63; actg head anal sect, Silicone Div, Stauffer Chem Co, 63-65; sr develop engr, Adv Tech Div, 65-68; group supvr, Mat & Process Eng, Anal Serv Lab, 68-69, PRIN CHEM ENGR & GROUP SUPVR, CHEM & ANAL SERV LAB, UNIVAC, SPERRY RAND CORP, 69- Mem: fel Am Inst Chem. Res: Infrared spectroscopy; infrared spectra of chelates; polymer chemistry; scanning electron microscopy; gas chromatography. Mailing Add: Sperry-Univac Mat Eng MS U0S23 St Paul MN 55165

KOVACIC, PETER, b Wylandville, Pa, Aug 1, 21; m 46; c 6. ORGANIC CHEMISTRY. Educ: Hanover Col, AB, 43, DSc, 64; Univ Ill, PhD(chem), 46. Prof Exp: Asst org chem, Mass Inst Technol, 46-47; instr, Columbia Univ, 47-48; res chemist, E I du Pont de Nemours & Co, 48-55; from asst prof to prof chem, Case Inst Technol, 55-68; PROF CHEM, UNIV WIS, MILWAUKEE, 68- Mem: Am Chem Soc. Res: N-Halamines; adamantanes; azahomoadamantanes; homoadamantanes; azoalkanes; bicyclo-3.3.1-nonanes; rearrangements; nitrenium ions; aromatic substitution; metal halides; polymerization of aromatic nuclei; environmental chemistry. Mailing Add: Dept Chem Univ Wis Milwaukee WI 53201

KOVACS (NAGY), HANNA, b Szeged, Hungary, Oct 31, 19; US citizen; m 50; c 2. ORGANIC CHEMISTRY. Educ: Univ Szeged, PhD(org chem), 45. Prof Exp: Res assoc org chem, Univ Szeged, 44-46, physiol, 46-50; res assoc org chem, Univ Budapest, 50-56; res assoc bact, Univ Basel, 57 & Detroit Inst Cancer Res, 58-59; res assoc peptide chem, St John's Univ, NY, 59-63; res chemist, Naval Appl Sci Lab, Brooklyn, 63-70; CLIN CHEMIST, MT SINAI HOSP, NEW YORK, 70- Mem: Nat Acad Clin Biochem; Am Chem Soc; NY Acad Sci; Sigma Xi; Am Asn Clin Chem. Res: Author or coauthor of twenty-eight publications in the field of peptide, heterocyclic, polymer, medicinal and clinical chemistry. Mailing Add: 117 Onslow Pl Kew Gardens NY 11415

KOVACS, ARTHUR Z, b Aug 20, 35; US citizen; m; c 2. SYSTEMS ENGINEERING. Educ: Wabash Col, AB, 57; Duke Univ, PhD(high energy physics, math), 63. Prof Exp: Teaching asst physics, Duke Univ, 57-58, res asst, 58-59, instr, 59-60, res asst, 60-61; res assoc, Northwestern Univ, Evanston, 61-62; res assoc, Purdue Univ, 62-64, asst prof, 64-68; assoc prof indust & syts eng, Univ Dayton, 68-78; prof physics & head dept, Bethany Col, WVa, 78-81; PROF PHYSICS & HEAD DEPT, ROCHESTER INST TECHNOL, ROCHESTER, NY, 81- Concurrent Pos: Consult, Aguacult Prog, Bodega Marine Lab, Univ Calif, Davis, 74-75 & Cause Proj NSF, Bethany Col, WVa, 81-84. Mem: Sr mem Am Inst Indust Engrs; AAAS; Am Phys Soc; Inst Mgt Sci; Am Soc Eng Educ. Mailing Add: Physics Dept Rochester Inst Technol One Lomb Mem Dr Rochester NY 14623

KOVACS, BELA A, b Nagykoros, Hungary, Aug 28, 21; Can citizen; m 52. PHARMACOLOGY, ALLERGY. Educ: Med Univ Szeged, MD, 46; Univ London, DrPhil(pharmacol), 61. Prof Exp: From asst prof to assoc prof pharmacol, Med Univ Szeged, 49-56; asst prof, 61-64, assoc prof pharmacol & exp med, 64-69, ASSOC PROF EXP MED, McGILL UNIV, 69-; SCI ADV, DEPT NAT HEALTH & WELFARE, FOOD & DRUG DIRECTORATE, 69- Concurrent Pos: Res fel org chem, Univ Basel, 56-57; res fel pharmacol, Nat Inst Med Res, London, 57-61; lectr, Sch Pharm, Univ London, 59-61. Mem: Am Soc Pharmacol & Exp Therapeut; Pharmacol Soc Can; Brit Pharmacol Soc; Am Col Clin Pharmacol & Therapeut; Can Soc Immunol. Res: Histamine and antihistaminics; inflammation; gastric secretion; pulmonary edema. Mailing Add: Dept of Health & Welfare Bur of Drugs Ottawa ON K1S 3M6 Can

KOVACS, CHARLES JEFFREY, radiation biology, cell biology, see previous edition

KOVACS, EVE MARIA, b Budapest, Hungary, Apr 13, 25; m 52. MEDICINE. Educ: Univ Szeged, MD, 52. Prof Exp: Lectr pharmacol, Univ Szeged, 52-54, lectr internal med, 54-55, asst prof, 55-56; pharmacologist, Geigy AG, Switz, 57-58; lectr, 61-64, ASST PROF PHARMACOL, McGILL UNIV, 64-; SCI ADV, DEPT NAT HEALTH & WELFARE, FOOD DIRECTORATE, 70- Concurrent Pos: Cancer res fel, Dept Pharmacol, Univ London, 58-61. Mem: Pharmacol Soc Can; Am Soc Pharmacol & Exp Therapeut; Int Soc Biochem Pharmacol; Can Med Asn. Res: Cancer immunology; allergy; histamine; histamine metabolites; gastric secretion. Mailing Add: Bur Chem Safety Food Directorate Dept of Nat Health & Welfare Ottawa PQ H3G 1Y6 Can

KOVACS, EVE VERONIKA, b Melbourne, Australia, Nov 12, 54. COMPUTER SCIENCE. Educ: Univ Melbourne, BSc, 76, PhD(physics), 80, dipl comput sci, 80. Prof Exp: Vis Scientist, Stanford Linear Accelerator Ctr, 80-81; RES ASSOC, ROCKEFELLER UNIV, 81- Mem: Am Phys Soc. Res: Monte Carlo simulations of lattice guage theories with particular emphasis on finite size effects and the interquark potential. Mailing Add: Dept Physics Rockefeller Univ Box 272 New York NY 10021

KOVACS, JOSEPH, b Nagykoros, Hungary, Mar 21, 15; US citizen; m 50; c 2. BIO-ORGANIC CHEMISTRY. Educ: Univ Szeged, PhD(org chem), 42. Prof Exp: Asst prof org chem, Univ Szeged, 42-50, privatdocent, 50; assoc prof, Eotvos Lorand Univ, Budapest, 50-56; res assoc, Inst Org Chem, Univ Basel, 56-57 & Wayne State Univ, 57-58; assoc prof, 58-59, PROF ORG CHEM, ST JOHN'S UNIV, NY, 59- Concurrent Pos: NIH grants, 59- Mem: Am Chem Soc; The Chem Soc; Swiss Chem Soc. Res: One hundred eleven publications in the field of amino acids, peptides and proteins; stereochemistry and alloids. Mailing Add: 117 Onslow Pl Kew Gardens NY 11415

KOVACS, JULIUS STEPHEN, b Trenton, NJ, Aug 20, 28; m 56; c 2. THEORETICAL PHYSICS. Educ: Lehigh Univ, BS, 50; Ind Univ, MS, 52, PhD, 55. Prof Exp: Asst prof physics, Univ Toledo, 54-55; res assoc, Ind Univ, 55-56; from asst prof to assoc prof, 56-68, PROF PHYSICS, MICH STATE UNIV, 68-, ASSOC CHMN DEPT, 77- Res: Meson physics; elementary particles. Mailing Add: Dept of Physics & Astron Mich State Univ East Lansing MI 48823

KOVACS, KALMAN T, b Szeged, Hungary, July 11, 26; Can citizen; m 62. ENDOCRINOLOGY, ELECTRON MICROSCOPY. Educ: Univ Szeged, Hungary, MD, 50; Univ Liverpool, PhD(path), 66; FCAP & FRCP(C), 73; FRCPath, 80. Prof Exp: Demonstr & lectr, Dept Path, Univ Szeged, 50-54, sr lectr, Dept Med, 54-68; vis scientist exp med, Univ Montreal, 68-71; asst prof, 71-80, PROF PATH, UNIV TORONTO, 80-; PATHOLOGIST, ST MICHAEL'S HOSP, TORONTO, 80- Concurrent Pos: Res fel path, Docent Univ Szeged, 60 & Crosby res fel, Univ Liverpool, 64-65. Honors & Awards: Hungarian Acad Sci Award, 68. Mem: Int Acad Path; Am Path Soc; Can Micros Soc. Res: Morphologic study of endocrine glands, especially human pituitaries and pituitary adenomas; correlation of structural features with secretory activity. Mailing Add: Dept Path St Michael's Hosp 30 Bond St Toronto ON M5B 1W8 Can

KOVACS, SANDOR J, JR, b Budapest, Hungary, Aug 17, 47; US citizen. CARDIOLOGY. Educ: Cornell Univ, BS, 69; Calif Inst Technol, MS, 72, PhD(theoret physics), 76; Univ Miami, MD, 79. Prof Exp: Res asst theoret physics, Calif Inst Technol, 71-77; RES FEL CARDIOL, DIV CARDIOL, DEPT MED, WASHINGTON UNIV, 82- Concurrent Pos: Med consult & lectr, Nat Asn Underwater Instrs, 74- Mem: Sigma Xi; Int Soc Gen Relativity & Gravitation. Res: Noninvasive cardiological diagnostic methods including cardiac electrophysiology and arrythmia detection and analysis. Mailing Add: 234 Crandon Dr Clayton MO 63105

KOVAL, CARL ANTHONY, b York, Pa, June 28, 52; m 74. CHEMISTRY. Educ: Juniata Col, BS, 74; Calif Inst Technol, PhD(chem), 79. Prof Exp: Fel, Purdue Univ, 78-80; ASST PROF CHEM, UNIV COLO, 80- Mem: Am Chem Soc; Sigma Xi. Res: Catalysis of multi-electron processes by polynuclear transition metal complexes; steric inhibition of exothermic redox reactions. Mailing Add: Dept Chem Campus Box 215 Univ Colo Boulder CO 80309

KOVAL, CHARLES FRANCIS, b Ashland, Wis, May 10, 38; m 57; c 3. ENTOMOLOGY, AGRICULTURAL RESEARCH ADMINISTRATION. Educ: Northland Col, BA, 60; Univ Wis, MS, 63, PhD(entom), 66. Prof Exp: Res asst, 60-65, from instr to assoc prof, 65-73, PROF ENTOM, UNIV WIS-MADISON, 73-, DIR, UNIV WIS EXP FARMS, 80- Concurrent Pos: Farm entomologist, Univ Wis-Madison, 65-80. Mem: Entom Soc Am. Res: Insect management on fruit, turf and ornamentals with emphasis on minimizing pesticide usage; biological research on cranberry insects; urban forestry. Mailing Add: Univ Exp Farms Univ of Wis Madison WI 53706

KOVAL, DANIEL, b Fitchburg, Mass, Nov 28, 22; m 45; c 2. MATHEMATICS. Educ: Worcester Polytech Inst, BS, 44; Boston Univ, AM, 52, PhD(math), 65. Prof Exp: Physicist radiation lab, Mass Inst Technol, 44-46; asst prof appl math & physics, Atlantic Union Col, 46-60; assoc prof math, Columbia Union Col, 60-71; chmn dept, 71-77, PROF MATH, PAC UNION COL, 71- Mem: Math Asn Am. Res: Partial differential equations. Mailing Add: Dept Math Pac Union Col Angwin CA 94508

KOVAL, E(DWARD) J(OHN), chemical engineering, see previous edition

KOVAL, LESLIE R(OBERT), b Rochester, NY, Jan 12, 33; m 56; c 3. ENGINEERING MECHANICS, STRUCTURAL ACOUSTICS. Educ: Univ Rochester, BS, 55; Cornell Univ, MS, 57, PhD(mech), 61. Prof Exp: McMullen fel, Cornell Univ, 55-56, instr eng mech, 58-61; mem tech staff, Ramo-Wooldridge Corp, 57-58; mem tech staff, TRW Systs Group, 61-66, staff engr, TRW Systs, Inc, Calif, 66-69; US Agency Int Develop vis prof, Fed Univ Rio de Janeiro, 69-70; assoc prof mech & aerospace eng, 71-76, PROF MECH ENG, UNIV MO-ROLLA, 76- Concurrent Pos: Consult, Fed Systs Div, Int Bus Mach, Inc, 59 & Lockheed-Calif Co, 78-; lectr, Univ Southern Calif, 62-69; mem tech staff, Litton Ship Systs, Calif, 71. Mem: Am Soc Mech Engrs; Acoust Soc Am; Am Acad Mech; Am Inst Aeronaut & Astronaut. Res: Vibrations and dynamic response of shell structures; liquid sloshing in rigid and flexible tanks; wobble damping of spinning spacecraft; liquid behavior in low-gravity environments; acoustics; structure-borne noise propagation. Mailing Add: Dept of Mech Eng Univ of Mo Rolla MO 65401

KOVAL, THOMAS MICHAEL, b Brownsville, Pa, Nov 20, 50. CELL BIOLOGY, RADIATION BIOLOGY. *Educ:* Pa State Univ, BS, 72; Ohio State Univ, MS, 74, PhD(zool), 76. *Prof Exp:* Nat Res Serv award fel physiol & biophys, Univ Ill, 76-77; res assoc cancer res, Allegheny Gen Hosp, 77-79; ASST PROF RADIATION THER & NUCLEAR MED, HAHNEMANN MED COL, 79- *Concurrent Pos:* Partic, NATO Advan Study Inst, Italy, 78. *Mem:* Radiation Res Soc; Am Soc Cell Biol; Tissue Cult Asn; Sigma Xi; Am Soc Photobiol. *Res:* Cell and molecular biology; oncogenesis, aging, DNA repair mechanisms; cell differentiation; radiation biology; mechanisms of radioresistance of cultured lepidopteran insect cells. *Mailing Add:* 230 N Broad St Dept Radiation Ther Hahnemann Med Col Philadelphia PA 19102

KOVALAK, WILLIAM PAUL, b Detroit, Mich, Apr 12, 46; m 70; c 3. AQUATIC BIOLOGY. *Educ:* Eastern Mich Univ, BS, 67; Univ Mich, MS, 69, PhD(fisheries), 75. *Prof Exp:* Asst prof biol, Allegheny Col, 75-78; ASST PROF AQUATIC BIOL, UNIV MICH, DEARBORN, 78- *Concurrent Pos:* Biol systs scientist, Detroit Edison, 79- *Mem:* NAm Benthological Soc. *Res:* Behavioral ecology of stream insects; ecology of Great Lakes fishes. *Mailing Add:* Dept Nat Sci Univ Mich Dearborn MI 48128

KOVAR, FREDERICK RICHARD, b Cleveland, Ohio, Sept 20, 33; m 62; c 4. NUCLEAR PHYSICS, PLASMA PHYSICS. *Educ:* John Carroll Univ, BS, 55; Wash Univ, St Louis, MA, 57, PhD(physics), 63. *Prof Exp:* Instr physics, St Bonaventure Univ, 59-61; SR PHYSICIST & PROJ MGR, LAWRENCE LIVERMORE LAB, UNIV CALIF, 63- *Concurrent Pos:* Consult, Bradford Components Co, NY, 60. *Mem:* Am Phys Soc. *Res:* Hydrodynamics, strategic analysis, and nuclear energy. *Mailing Add:* Lawrence Livermore Lab Univ of Calif PO 808 Livermore CA 94550

KOVAR, JAN BERNARD, carbohydrate chemistry, physical organic chemistry, see previous edition

KOVAR, JOHN ALVIS, b Ennis, Tex, Nov 30, 32; c 2. SOIL MORPHOLOGY. *Educ:* Tex Tech Univ, BS, 56; Tex A&M Univ, MS, 63; Iowa State Univ, PhD(agron), 67. *Prof Exp:* Soil scientist, Soil Conserv Serv, USDA, 53-56 & 59-60; res asst soil anal, Tex A&M Univ, 60-62; res assoc soil surv, Iowa State Univ, 62-67; AREA DIR, TENN VALLEY AUTHORITY, 67- *Concurrent Pos:* Fel Welder Wildlife Found. *Mem:* Soil Sci Soc Am; Am Soc Agron; Coun Agr Sci & Technol; Sigma Xi; Int Soc Soil Sci. *Res:* Soil morphology and genesis; soil fertility. *Mailing Add:* Tenn Valley Authority Okla State Univ Dept Agron Stillwater OK 04078

KOVATCH, GEORGE, b Scranton, Pa, Feb 20, 34; m 68; c 2. ELECTRONICS & SYSTEMS ENGINEERING. *Educ:* Princeton Univ, BSE, 55; Cornell Univ, MS, 60, PhD, 62. *Prof Exp:* Engr electronics, Gen Elec Co, 55-56, 57-60; instr control eng, Cornell Univ, 60-62; sr eng specialist control & guid systs, Martin Co, 62-64; lab chief control & info systs, NASA, 64-67, dept dir, Off Control Theory & Appln, 67-70; proj mgr, 70-76, CHIEF, TRANSP INDUST ANAL BR, TRANSP SYSTS CTR, US DEPT TRANSP, 76- *Concurrent Pos:* Mem vis sci staff, Res Inst Adv Studies, Md, 62-64; vis lectr, Brown Univ, 68-70; mem, Transp Res Forum. *Mem:* Inst Elec & Electronics Engrs. *Res:* Analysis and synthesis of automatic control and guidance systems utilizing modern control theory and techniques; analysis of intermodal transportation systems including new urban systems. *Mailing Add:* Transp Systs Ctr Kendall Sq Cambridge MA 02142

KOVATS, ZOLTAN, b Oroshaza, Hungary; US citizen; c 2. UNSTEADY AERODYNAMICS, ENGINEERING VIBRATIONS. *Educ:* Tech Univ Budapest, MS, 56. *Prof Exp:* Jr engr mech eng, Rust Eng Co, 57-58; design engr optical & syst design, Am Optical Co, Div J W Fecker, 58-61; sr res engr fluid mech res, Cent Res Div, Rockwell Mgr Co, 61-67; sr res scientist dynamics vibration res, 67-78, FEL ENGR AERODYNAMIC RES, RES & DEVELOP CTR, WESTINGHOUSE ELEC CORP, 78- *Mem:* Am Soc Mech Engrs; Am Inst Aeronaut & Astronaut; Am Acad Mech. *Mailing Add:* 1314 Denniston Ave Pittsburgh PA 15217

KOVESI-DOMOKOS, SUSAN, b Budapest, Hungary, Aug 16, 39; US citizen; m 67. ELEMENTARY PARTICLE PHYSICS. *Educ:* Eotvos Lorand Univ, dipl physics, 63. *Prof Exp:* Res asst theoret physics, Eotvos Lorand Univ, 62-63; res assoc, Cent Res Inst Physics, Budapest, 63-68; assoc res scientist, 69-74, asst prof theoret physics, 74-80, ASSOC PROF PHYSICS, JOHNS HOPKINS UNIV, 80- *Concurrent Pos:* Vis sci consult, Rutherford Lab, Eng, 73; vis scientist, Europ Orgn Nuclear Res, Switz, 75-76; vis sci staff mem, Deutsches Electronen-Synchrotron, Hamburg, Ger, 76. *Mem:* Ital Phys Soc; Europ Phys Soc. *Res:* Strong interactions of elementary particles at high energy; critical phenomena. *Mailing Add:* Dept of Physics Johns Hopkins Univ Baltimore MD 21218

KOVITZ, ARTHUR A(BRAHAM), b Detroit, Mich, Aug 6, 28; m 57; c 2. FLUID DYNAMICS. *Educ:* Univ Mich, BSE, 50, MS, 51; Princeton Univ, PhD(aeronaut eng), 57. *Prof Exp:* Rocket res engr, Bell Aircraft Corp, NY, 51-52; res assoc, Princeton Univ, 57, asst dir proj Squid, 57-58; from asst prof to assoc prof, 58-69, actg chmn dept mech eng & astronaut sci, 71-73, PROF MECH ENG, NORTHWESTERN UNIV, EVANSTON, 69- *Concurrent Pos:* Consult, Aeronaut Res Assocs, Princeton, 57-58, Bendix Aviation Corp, 60, Am Mach & Foundry, 62 & Argonne Nat Labs, 79-80. *Mem:* Am Phys Soc; Combustion Inst. *Res:* Interfacial fluid mechanics; aerothermochemistry; classical fluid mechanics. *Mailing Add:* Dept Mech & Nuclear Eng Technol Inst Northwestern Univ Evanston IL 60201

KOVNER, JACOB L, b Brockton, Mass, Sept 12, 12; m 49. FOREST BIOMETRY. *Educ:* Yale Univ, BS, 34; State Univ NY, MF, PhD, 55. *Prof Exp:* Statistician, Ben Burk, Inc, 35-42; res forester, US Forest Serv, USDA, 51-55, math statistician, 55-80; RETIRED. *Mem:* Soc Am Foresters; Am Statist Asn; Am Geophys Union; Biomet Soc; Inst Math Statist. *Res:* Biometry; sampling methods, especially line transect for wildlife; nearest neighbor distance sampling. *Mailing Add:* 2120 W Prospect St Ft Collins CO 80526

KOWAL, CHARLES THOMAS, b Buffalo, NY, Nov 8, 40; m 68; c 1. ASTRONOMY. *Educ:* Univ Southern Calif, BS, 63. *Prof Exp:* Res asst astron, Calif Inst Technol, 63-65 & Univ Hawaii, 65-66; res asst, 66-75, assoc scientist, 76-77, scientist astron, 78-81, MEM PROF STAFF, CALIF INST TECHNOL, 81- *Honors & Awards:* James Craig Watson Medal, Nat Acad Sci, 79. *Mem:* Am Astron Soc; Int Astron Union. *Res:* Supernovae; planetary satellites; asteroids; comets. *Mailing Add:* Dept of Astrophys Calif Inst of Technol Pasadena CA 91125

KOWAL, GEORGE M, b July 6, 38; US citizen; m 63; c 4. NUCLEAR ENGINEERING, MECHANICAL ENGINEERING. *Educ:* Univ Detroit, BS, 61; Pa State Univ, MS, 64. *Prof Exp:* Nuclear eng radiation protection, Elec Boat Div, Gen Dynamics Corp, 64-67; nuclear proj engr gen anal, 67-73; DEPT MGR APPL ENG ANAL, GILBERT ASSOCS INC, 73- *Concurrent Pos:* Mem indust prof adv coun, PaState Univ, 73-77; instr, Reading Area Community Col, 76-; adj assoc prof, Drexel Univ, 76- *Mem:* Am Nuclear Soc. *Res:* Analysts associated with nuclear power generation, especially nuclear safety, shielding, heaalth physics, fuel management, licensing, regulation and emergency core cooling systems. *Mailing Add:* Gilbert Assocs Inc PO Box 1498 Reading PA 19603

KOWAL, JEROME, b New York, NY, Mar 16, 31; m 58; c 2. INTERNAL MEDICINE, BIOCHEMISTRY. *Educ:* Tufts Univ, BS, 52; Johns Hopkins Univ, MD, 56. *Prof Exp:* Steroid trainee, Worcester Found Exp Biol, 62-63; from asst prof to assoc prof med, Mt Sinai Sch Med, 65-70; assoc prof, 70-74, PROF MED, SCH MED, CASE WESTERN RESERVE UNIV, 74-, ASSOC DEAN VET AFFAIRS, 77-; CHIEF STAFF, CLEVELAND VET ADMIN MED CTR, 77- *Concurrent Pos:* Fel endocrinol, Mt Sinai Sch Med, 60-61; fel molecular biol, Albert Einstein Col Med, 63-65; chief med serv, Cleveland Vet Admin Hosp, 73-77. *Mem:* AAAS; Endocrine Soc; Am Soc Clin Invest; Am Soc Biol Chemists; fel NY Acad Sci. *Res:* Mechanisms of hormone and enzyme action; biochemical regulation of adrenal cells. *Mailing Add:* Chief of Staff 10701 East Blvd Cleveland OH 44106

KOWAL, NORMAN EDWARD, b Paterson, NJ, Sept 3, 37; m 62; c 3. WASTEWATER TREATMENT, COMPUTER SIMULATION. *Educ:* New York Univ, BA, 58; Duke Univ, MA, 60, PhD(plant ecol), 66; WVa Univ, MD, 77. *Prof Exp:* Instr bot, Univ Philippines, 63-65; asst & assoc prof biol, Clark Col, 65-67; fel systs ecol, Oak Ridge Nat Lab, 67-68; fel entom, Univ Ga, 68-69; asst prof biol, WVa Univ, 69-73; RES MED OFFICER, HEALTH EFFECTS RES LAB, US ENVIRON PROTECTION AGENCY, 77- *Mem:* AAAS; Am Soc Microbiol; Soc Environ Geochem & Health; Water Pollution Control Fedn. *Res:* Health effects of nonconventional municipal wastewater treatment, including land treatment, wastewater aquaculture, and land application of sludge; human exposure to and health effects of cadmium; computer simulation of pharmacodynamics; environmental exposure assessment. *Mailing Add:* Health Effects Res Lab US Environ Protection Agency Cincinnati OH 45268

KOWAL, ROBERT RAYMOND, b Paterson, NJ, Apr 23, 39. SYSTEMATIC BOTANY, BIOMETRY. *Educ:* Cornell Univ, BA, 60, PhD(plant taxon & ecol), 68. *Prof Exp:* Fel biomath, Dept Exp Statist, NC State Univ, 67-69; vis asst prof biol, Kans State Univ, 69-71; asst prof, 71-76, ASSOC PROF BOT, UNIV WIS-MADISON, 76- *Mem:* AAAS; Bot Soc Am; Soc Study Evolution; Am Soc Plant Taxon; Am Inst Biol Sci. *Res:* Systematics of Senecio aureus and allied species; multivariate analysis, especially canonical analysis, as a tool in plant systematics; estimation of genetic variability in natural populations. *Mailing Add:* Dept of Bot Univ of Wis Madison WI 53706

KOWALAK, ALBERT DOUGLAS, b Portsmouth, Va, Aug 14, 36; div; c 2. PHYSICAL INORGANIC CHEMISTRY. *Educ:* Col William & Mary, BS, 58; Va Polytech Inst, MS, 63, PhD(chem), 65. *Prof Exp:* Teacher chem high sch, Va, 58-59; rubber chemist, O'Sullivan Rubber Corp, 60; teacher math high sch, Va, 60-61; res asst, Air Force Off Sci Res, 63; instr inorg chem, Rose Polytech Inst, 65-67; asst prof, 67-71, ASSOC PROF CHEM, LOWELL TECHNOL INST, 71-, CHMN DEPT, 77- *Honors & Awards:* Fulbright lectr, Univ Repub, Montevideo, Uruguay. *Mem:* Am Chem Soc. *Res:* Kinetics of the arsenic-chromium reaction in various buffer solutions. *Mailing Add:* Dept of Chem Univ of Lowell Lowell MA 01854

KOWALCZYK, LEON S(TANISLAW), b Motycz, Poland, May 3, 08; m 33. CHEMICAL ENGINEERING. *Educ:* Warsaw Sch Eng, dipl, 31, DSc(eng), 36. *Prof Exp:* Dep to chief, Res Sta, Polish State Spirit Monopoly, 35-39; asst prof chem eng & dep to head dept, Polish Univ Col Eng, 47-50; from assoc prof to prof, 50-73, chmn dept, 59-73, EMER PROF CHEM ENG, UNIV DETROIT, 73- *Concurrent Pos:* Dir, Pub Health Serv (IR), 56- *Mem:* Am Inst Chem Engrs; Inst Chem Engrs, UK. *Res:* Reaction kinetics; chemical reactor design. *Mailing Add:* 287 Third St Bonita Springs FL 33923

KOWALENKO, CHARLES GRANT, b Saskatoon, Sask, May 14, 46; m 71; c 2. SOIL SCIENCE. *Educ:* Univ Sask, BSA, 68, MSc, 70; Univ BC, PhD(soil sci), 74. *Prof Exp:* Res scientist, Soil Res Inst, 74-78, RES SCIENTIST, AGR CAN RES STA, 78- *Concurrent Pos:* Assoc ed, Can J Soil Sci. *Mem:* Can Soc Soil Sci; Int Soc Soil Sci; Agron Soc Am; Soil Sci Soc Am; Agr Inst Can-BC Inst Agrologists. *Res:* Studies on the nutrient requirements of a wide range of crops including forages, vegetables, and fruit; primary specializationin nitrogen and sulfur but also concerned with entire range of nutrients, both macro and micro. *Mailing Add:* Agr Can Res Sta Box 1000 Agassiz BC V0M 1A0 Can

KOWALEWSKI, EDWARD JOSEPH, b Mt Carmel, Pa, Apr 21, 20; m 42; c 3. FAMILY MEDICINE. *Educ:* Gettysburg Col, BS, 42; George Washington Univ, MD, 45. *Prof Exp:* Pvt pract, 33-71; PROF FAMILY MED & CHMN DEPT, SCH MED, UNIV MD, BALTIMORE, 72- *Honors & Awards:* Clarence E Shaffner Award, 71. *Mem:* Am Acad Family Physicians (pres, 69-70); Soc Teachers Family Med. *Res:* Teaching of family medicine; core content of family medicine. *Mailing Add:* Dept of Family Med Univ of Md Sch of Med Baltimore MD 21201

KOWALIK, JANUSZ SZCZESNY, b Krzemieniec, Poland, Feb 28, 34; m 59; c 1. COMPUTATIONAL MATHEMATICS. *Educ:* Gdansk Tech Univ, MSc, 57; Polish Acad Sci, Dr Techn Sc, 61. *Prof Exp:* Head comput ctr, Cent Shipbuilding Design Off, Poland, 61-64; res fel, Royal Norweg Coun Sci & Indust Res, 64-66; res fel comput sci, Inst Advan Studies, Australian Nat Univ, 66-67; sr specialist & mgr math anal, Boeing Comput Serv, Inc, 67-73; mem fac, Dept Comput Sci, Sir George Williams Univ, 73-74; DIR SYSTS & COMPUT & PROF COMPUT SCI, WASH STATE UNIV, 74- *Mem:* Opers Res Soc Am; Asn Comput Mach. *Res:* Parallel processing, high speed computing, management, and organization for computing on campus. *Mailing Add:* Systs & Comput Wash State Univ Pullman WA 99164

KOWALIK, VIRGIL C, b Sinton, Tex, Feb 8, 32; m 59. MATHEMATICS. *Educ:* St Mary's Univ, Tex, BS, 53; Univ Tex, MA, 59, PhD(math), 66. *Prof Exp:* Instr math & physics, St Edward's Univ, 61-63; from asst prof to assoc prof, 65-69, chmn dept, 66-80, PROF MATH, TEX A&I UNIV, 69- *Mem:* Am Math Soc; Am Soc Eng Educ; Math Asn Am. *Res:* Uniqueness and existence theorems for differential equations in complex space, application of functional analysis techniques to these theorems; real variables; functional analysis; generalized derivatives. *Mailing Add:* Dept of Math Tex A&I Univ Kingsville TX 78363

KOWALSKI, BRUCE RICHARD, b Chicago, Ill, Mar 7, 42; m 74; c 2. ANALYTICAL CHEMISTRY. *Educ:* Millikin Univ, BA, 65; Univ Wash, PhD, 69. *Prof Exp:* Chemist, Shell Develop Co, Emerville, Calif, 69-71 & Houston, Tex, 71-72; asst prof, Colo State Univ, 72-73; asst prof, 74-75, assoc prof, 75-77, PROF, UNIV WASH, 78- *Concurrent Pos:* Chemist, Lawrence Livermore Lab, Univ Calif, 71-72 & consult, 72-; pres, Infometrix, 77-; mem, Dir Res Appln, NSF; Alexander von Humboldt Award, 80. *Honors & Awards:* Res Award, Eli Lilly Res Lab, 76. *Mem:* Pattern Recognition Soc: Am Chem Soc; AAAS; NY Acad Sci; Chemometrics Soc (pres). *Res:* Chemometrics-the development of novel mathematical approaches for improving the measurement process; application of pattern recognition and other multivariant analysis methods to chemical data. *Mailing Add:* Lab for Chemometrics Univ Wash Seattle WA 98195

KOWALSKI, CHARLES JOSEPH, b Chicago, Ill, May 8, 38; m 62; c 3. STATISTICS, BIOMETRICS. *Educ:* Roosevelt Univ, BS, 62; Mich State Univ, MS, 65; Univ Mich, Ann Arbor, PhD(biostatist), 68. *Prof Exp:* Asst prof dent, Sch Dent, 68-74, ASSOC PROF DENT, SCH DENT, UNIV MICH, ANN ARBOR, 74-; ASST DIR STATIST RES LAB, 71-; DIR BIOMET LAB, DENT RES INST, 68- *Concurrent Pos:* Consult, Statist Res Lab, 68-71; Nat Football League, 69 & Parke, Davis & Co, 70. *Mem:* Am Statist Asn; Biomet Soc; Inst Math Statist; Int Asn Dent Res; Am Asn Phys Anthrop. *Res:* Multivariate statistical analysis, especially as applied to biomedical research; problems in growth and development; sequential and time series analysis. *Mailing Add:* Sch of Dent Univ of Mich Ann Arbor MI 48109

KOWALSKI, DAVID FRANCIS, b Chester, Pa, Feb 20, 47; m 81; c 1. BIOCHEMISTRY. *Educ:* LaSalle Col, BA, 68; Purdue Univ, PhD(chem), 74. *Prof Exp:* Chemist, USDA Eastern Regional Lab, 68; asst, Purdue Univ, 69-73; RES SCIENTIST BIOCHEM, ROSWELL PARK MEM INST, 74- *Res:* Structure, reactivity and functions of supercoiled DNA; occurrence, properties and functions of DNA topoisomerses. *Mailing Add:* Roswell Park Mem Inst 666 Elm St Buffalo NY 14263

KOWALSKI, DONALD T, b Dearborn, Mich, Mar 23, 38; c 3. MYCOLOGY. *Educ:* Univ Mich, BS, 60, MS, 61, PhD(bot), 64. *Prof Exp:* From asst prof to assoc prof, 64-73, PROF BIOL, CALIF STATE UNIV, CHICO, 73- *Concurrent Pos:* NSF res grants, 65-75. *Mem:* Mycol Soc Am; Am Bryol & Lichenological Soc; Brit Mycol Soc. *Res:* Developmental and cytological studies in the Ascomycetes and taxonomy of Myxo mycetes; biosystematics of Myxomycetes; lichen distribution. *Mailing Add:* Dept of Biol Calif State Univ Chico CA 95929

KOWALSKI, JOHN BERNARD, microbial genetics, see previous edition

KOWALSKI, KENNETH L, b Chicago, Ill, July 24, 32; m 60; c 2. THEORETICAL NUCLEAR PHYSICS. *Educ:* Ill Inst Technol, BS, 54; Brown Univ, PhD(physics), 63. *Prof Exp:* Aeronaut res scientist, Nat Adv Comt Aeronaut, 54-56; res assoc physics, Brown Univ, 62; res assoc, 62-63, from asst prof to assoc prof, 63-73, chmn dept, 71-76, PROF PHYSICS, CASE WESTERN RESERVE UNIV, 73- *Concurrent Pos:* Vis prof, Inst Theoret Physics, Univ Louvain, 68-69; exec officer dept physics, Case Western Reserve Univ, 70-71. *Mem:* Am Phys Soc. *Res:* Scattering theory; nuclear physics; particle physics. *Mailing Add:* Dept of Physics Case Western Reserve Univ Cleveland OH 44106

KOWALSKI, LUDWIK, b Warsaw, Poland, Oct 24, 31; m 67. NUCLEAR PHYSICS, NUCLEAR CHEMISTRY. *Educ:* Warsaw Tech Univ, ME, 55; Univ Paris, MS, 62, PhD(nuclear physics), 63. *Prof Exp:* Res assoc nuclear chem, Columbia Univ, 64-69; assoc prof, 69-78, PROF PHYSICS, MONTCLAIR STATE COL, 78- *Res:* Experimental nuclear physics; high energy fission; nuclear reactions at low energies; heavy ion nuclear reactions; application of semiconductor detectors and mica track detectors for nuclear research. *Mailing Add:* Dept of Physics & Earth Sci Montclair State Col Upper Montclair NJ 07043

KOWALSKI, STANLEY BENEDICT, b Wishart, Sask, Feb 23, 35; m 61; c 2. NUCLEAR PHYSICS. *Educ:* Univ Sask, BEng, 57, MSc, 58; Mass Inst Technol, PhD(physics), 63. *Prof Exp:* Res physicist, 63-64, asst prof physics, 64-77, SR RES SCIENTIST, MASS INST TECHNOL, 64- *Mem:* Am Phys Soc. *Res:* Photonuclear reactions; accelerator physics. *Mailing Add:* Dept of Physics Mass Inst Technol Cambridge MA 02139

KOWALSKI, STEPHEN WESLEY, b Bayonne, NJ, June 24, 31; m 55, 71; c 5. INORGANIC CHEMISTRY, SCIENCE EDUCATION. *Educ:* Fairleigh Dickinson Univ, BS, 53; NY Univ, MA, 54, PhD(sci educ), 64. *Prof Exp:* Instr, Upsala Col, 53-54 & NY Univ, 54-55; teacher high sch, NJ, 55-56; chmn, Physics-Geosci Dept, 68-72, PROF SCI, MONTCLAIR STATE COL, 56- *Concurrent Pos:* Res chemist & consult, Shulton, Inc, 53-56; guest lectr, Upsala Col, 54-65 & Fairleigh Dickinson Univ, 55-64, res chemist, Hoffmann-La Roche, 56-67, consult, sr assoc, Danforth Found, 62-; coordr-supvr, Summer Sci Insts, AID, India, 66 & 67; coordr & supvr sci & math, MA in Teaching Prog, 68-69; consult, NSF & Memory Flavors, Inc. *Mem:* AAAS; Am Chem Soc; Nat Sci Teachers Asn. *Res:* Consumer testing; polyethylene permeability; synthetic flavor derivatives; chromatography; consumer science. *Mailing Add:* Dept of Physics-Geosci Montclair State Col Upper Montclair NJ 07043

KOWALSKI, TADEUSZ, b Kutno, Poland, Nov 2, 22; Can citizen; m 51; c 2. ENGINEERING, HYDRODYNAMICS. *Educ:* Glasgow Univ, BSc, 44; Stevens Inst Technol, MS, 63; Univ Waterloo, PhD(mech eng), 69. *Prof Exp:* Res asst ship hydrodyn, Brit Ship Res Asn, 47-49; lectr mech eng, McGill Univ, 49-51; res engr ship res, Davidson Lab, Stevens Inst Technol, 60-63; asst prof mech eng, US Naval Acad, 63-66; lectr mech eng, Univ Waterloo, 66-69; PROF OCEAN ENG, UNIV RI, 69- *Mem:* Fel Royal Inst of Naval Architects; Soc Naval Archit & Marine Eng. *Res:* Ship hydrodynamics ship model research on novel propulsion, drag reducing and motion reducing systems; pressure and velocity measurements in liquids; application of drag reducing agents to waterborne craft; environmental measurements in the coastal zone. *Mailing Add:* Dept of Ocean Eng Univ of RI Kingston RI 02881

KOWALSKY, ARTHUR, b Utica, NY, Nov 16, 23. BIOPHYSICAL CHEMISTRY. *Educ:* Clarkson Col Technol, BS, 47; Univ Chicago, MS, 50, PhD(chem), 54. *Prof Exp:* Res assoc, Brookhaven Nat Lab, 54-56 & Univ Minn, 58-62; res assoc, Johnson Found, Univ Pa, 62-63, asst prof, 63-69; assoc scientist, Papanicolaou Cancer Res Inst, 69-71; assoc prof biophys, Albert Einstein Col Med, 71-78; PROG DIR BIOPHYSICS, NSF, 78- *Concurrent Pos:* Res fel physiol chem, Univ Minn, 56-58. *Mem:* Am Chem Soc; Am Soc Biol Chemists; Biophys Soc; AAAS. *Res:* Protein structure; nuclear magnetic resonance; mechanism of ion and electron transfer. *Mailing Add:* Nat Sci Found 1800 G St NW Washington DC 20550

KOWANKO, NICHOLAS, b Charkov, Ukraine, June 7, 34; div; c 2. ORGANIC CHEMISTRY. *Educ:* Univ Adelaide, BSc, 56, PhD(org chem), 61. *Prof Exp:* Teacher high sch, Australia, 57; Fulbright travel grant to US, 60; res assoc chem, Univ Calif, Berkeley, 61; fel, Univ Minn, 61-62, asst prof, 62-64; sr chemist cent res labs, Minn Mining & Mfg Co, 64-68; chmn dept chem, 69-73, assoc prof, 68-77, PROF CHEM, MOORHEAD STATE UNIV, 77- *Concurrent Pos:* Instr chem exten div, Univ Minn, 62-68. *Mem:* Am Chem Soc; Royal Soc Chem; Royal Australian Chem Inst. *Res:* Catalysis and desulfurization of organic compounds by metals; structure and synthesis of natural products, biosynthesis of natural products; direct fluorination studies. *Mailing Add:* Dept of Chem Moorhead State Univ Moorhead MN 56560

KOWARSKI, A AVINOAM, b Tel-Aviv, Israel, Dec 30, 27; m 50; c 2. PEDIATRICS, ENDOCRINOLOGY. *Educ:* Hebrew Univ, MD, 55. *Prof Exp:* Asst physician, Hadassah Univ Hosp, Israel, 55-62, chief physician, 65-67; from instr to asst prof, 67-72, ASSOC PROF PEDIAT, SCH MED, JOHNS HOPKINS UNIV, 72-; PROF & DIR PEDIAT ENDOCRINOL, SCH MED, UNIV MD, 81- *Concurrent Pos:* Fel pediat endocrinol, Sch Med, Johns Hopkins Univ, 62-65. *Mem:* Endocrine Soc; Am Pediat Soc; Soc Pediat Res; Am Fedn Clin Res. *Res:* Human metabolism of hormones in healthy and diseased children and adults; growth hormone; diabetes; hypoglycemia; hypertension. *Mailing Add:* Pediat Endocrinol HHT 10-047 Sch Med Univ Md Baltimore MD 21201

KOWARSKI, CHANA ROSE, b Kaunas, Lithuania, June 1, 29; US citizen; m 50; c 2. PHARMACEUTICS. *Educ:* Sch Pharm, Switz, BS, 53; Sch Pharm, Israel, PhD(pharm chem), 62. *Prof Exp:* Chief pharmacist, RAFA Labs, Israel, 53-59; teaching fel, Sch Pharm, Israel, 57-62; fel phys chem, Hebrew Univ, Jerusalem, 66-67; fel, 63-65, vis prof, 67-69, assoc prof, 69-75, PROF PHARM, TEMPLE UNIV, 75- *Honors & Awards:* Lederle Res Award, 76. *Mem:* Am Pharmaceut Asn; Am Pharmaceut Soc; Sigma Xi; Am Asn Cols Pharm. *Res:* Absorption and bioavailability of drugs using the nonthrombogenic continuous withdrawal method; exemplary subjects include sulfamthiazole, sulfaethylthiadiazole, aspirin; radioimmunoassay of drugs, steroids. *Mailing Add:* 2405 Sugar Cone Rd Baltimore MD 21209

KOWEL, STEPHEN THOMAS, b Philadelphia, Pa, Nov 20, 42; m 70; c 3. ELECTRICAL ENGINEERING, APPLIED PHYSICS. *Educ:* Univ Pa, BSEE, 64, PhD(elec eng), 68; Polytech Inst Brooklyn, MSEE, 66. *Prof Exp:* Assoc elec eng, Moore Sch, Univ Pa, 68-69; from asst prof to assoc prof, 69-79, PROF ELEC ENG, SYRACUSE UNIV, 79- *Concurrent Pos:* Princ investr, Syracuse Univ; grants & res contracts, NSF, US Army Night Vision & Electrooptics Lab, US Air Force Rome Air Develop Ctr, 71-; consult, Electronics Lab, Gen Elec Co, 76-; vpres, Deft Labs, Inc, 76- *Mem:* Sr mem Inst Elec & Electronics Engrs; Sigma Xi; AAAS; Soc Photo-Optical Instrumentation Engrs. *Res:* Acoustooptics and electrooptics; optical imaging with surface acoustic waves; electron devices; optical and electronic applications of polymers. *Mailing Add:* Dept of Elec & Comput Eng Syracuse Univ Syracuse NY 13210

KOWERT, BRUCE ARTHUR, b Fredericksburg, Tex, Feb 11, 42. PHYSICAL CHEMISTRY. *Educ:* Univ Tex, Austin, BS, 64, PhD(chem), 71. *Prof Exp:* Res assoc phys chem, Phys Chem Inst, Univ Basel, 71-73 & Univ Calif, Los Angeles, 73-75; asst prof phys chem, Mich State Univ, 75-77; mem fac chem, 77-80, ASSOC PROF CHEM, ST LOUIS UNIV, 80- *Mem:* Am Chem Soc. *Res:* Spin relaxation, molecular motion in liquids, electron transfer reactions, and the electronic structure of organic ion radicals employing electron spin resonance. *Mailing Add:* Dept of Chem 221 N Grand Blvd St Louis MO 63103

KOWKABANY, GEORGE NORMAN, b Jacksonville, Fla, Sept 16, 23. ORGANIC CHEMISTRY. *Educ:* Univ Fla, BS, 47; Yale Univ, MS, 49, PhD(chem), 51. *Prof Exp:* Fel carbohydrate res, Ohio State Univ, 50-52; chemist, Nat Bur Standards, 52-53; from instr to asst prof, 53-60, ASSOC PROF ORG CHEM, CATH UNIV AM, 60- *Concurrent Pos:* NIH spec fel, Univ Ferrara, 63-64; vis assoc prof, Med Sch, Univ Miami, 70-71; res chemist, USDA, Beltsville, Md, 80-81. *Mem:* Fel AAAS; fel Am Inst Chemists; Am Chem Soc. *Res:* Paper chromatography; separation of amino acids and carbohydrates; structures of polysaccharides; enzymology. *Mailing Add:* Dept of Chem Cath Univ of Am Washington DC 20017

KOWLES, RICHARD VINCENT, b Ivanhoe, Minn, May 9, 32; m 56; c 5. GENETICS. *Educ:* Winona State Col, BS, 54, MS, 63; St Mary's Col Minn, MS, 67; Univ Minn, St Paul, PhD(genetics), 72. *Prof Exp:* Teacher high schs, Minn, 54-68; instr biol, Univ Wis-River Falls, 71-72, asst prof, 72-74; assoc prof, 74-77, PROF BIOL, ST MARY'S COL, MINN, 77- *Mem:* Genetics Soc Am; Am Genetic Asn; Soc Study Evolution; Radiation Res Asn. *Res:* Chromosome aberrations; supernumerary chromosomes in maise; cytogenetics of endosperm in maize. *Mailing Add:* Dept of Biol St Mary's Col Winona MN 55987

KOWN, BONG TAICK, nuclear engineering, see previous edition

KOYAL, SANKAR NATH, b Calcutta, India; m 65; c 1. PHYSIOLOGY, NUTRITION. *Educ:* Univ Col Sci, Calcutta, dipl diet, 55, MS, 59, PhD(physiol), 64. *Prof Exp:* Asst res officer, Dept Physiol, Univ Col Sci, Calcutta, 62-63; sr lectr physiol, Inst Technol & Appl Nutrit, Calcutta, 64-65; fel, Inst Phys Med & Rehab, NY Univ Med Ctr, 65-66; res scientist physiol, Univ Nijmegen, Holland, 66-67; instr anesthesiol, State Univ NY Downstate Med Ctr, 67-68; sr sci officer grade I, Defense Inst Physiol & Allied Sci, India, 68-69; respiratory & exercise physiologist, Div Respiratory Physiol & Med, Harbor Gen Hosp-Sch Med, Univ Calif, Los Angeles, 71-76; asst prof, Dept Physiol & Med, Sch Med, Univ Southern Calif, 77-90; ASST PROF & DIR, EXERCISE PHYSIOL LAB, WHITE MEM MED CTR, LOMA LINDA UNIV, 80- *Mem:* Am Col Sports Med; Am Physiol Soc; Brit Asn Sports Med; Physiol Soc India; Am Thoracic Soc. *Res:* Respiratory, cardiovascular and metabolic control mechanisms during exercise in health and disease; health consequences of chronic inhalation of smoke in human subjects; chemosensitivity with progestrone level in normal women. *Mailing Add:* Dept Cardiol Loma Linda 1720 Brooklyn Ave 1231 Los Angeles CA 90033

KOYAMA, RICHARD YUTAKA, solid state electronics, solid state physics, see previous edition

KOYAMA, TETSUO, b Tokyo, Japan, Oct 9, 35. SYSTEMATIC BOTANY, ECONOMIC BOTANY. *Educ:* Tokyo Univ, BSc, 56, MA, 58, PhD(bot), 61. *Prof Exp:* Vis assoc prof bot, Ryukyus Univ, 58-59; asst prof, Tokyo Univ, 61-63; res assoc taxon, 63-64, assoc cur, 64-67, cur taxon, 67-78, SR CUR, NY BOT GARDEN, 78- *Concurrent Pos:* Lectr, Fac Arts & Sci, Nippon Univ, 61; assoc prof, Tamagawa Univ, 61-62, vis prof, Sch Agr, 74-; Nat Res Coun Can res fel, 61-63; adj prof, City Univ New York, 71-; corresp mem, Am Mus Natural Hist, 74-; vis prof, Bot Inst, Aarhus Univ, Denmark, 77-78. *Mem:* Am Soc Plant Taxon; Asn Trop Biol (secy-treas, 65-67); Bot Soc Japan; Int Asn Plant Taxonomists; Japanese Soc Trop Agr. *Res:* Phylogenetic studies and taxonomic monograph of the monocotyledonous family Cyperaceae employing anatomical, palynological and cytological approaches; taxonomic monograph of the Liliaceous genera Smilax and Heterosmilax; inventory studies of economic plants, with special emphasis on the tropics; Asia botany. *Mailing Add:* NY Bot Garden Bronx Park Bronx NY 10458

KOZAK, ANTAL, b Tiszapuspoki, Hungary, May 22, 36; Can citizen; m 63; c 2. FOREST BIOMETRICS. *Educ:* Univ BC, BSF, 59, MF, 61, PhD(biomet), 63. *Prof Exp:* Res asst data processing, Univ BC, 62-63; res off statist, Can Dept Forestry, 63-65; from asst prof to assoc prof, 65-72, PROF FAC FORESTRY, UNIV BC, 72- *Concurrent Pos:* Vis lectr, Univ BC, 63-65. *Mem:* Am Statist Asn; Biomet Soc; Can Inst Forestry. *Res:* Application of statistics for forestry problems. *Mailing Add:* Fac of Forestry Univ of BC Vancouver BC V6T 1E1 Can

KOZAK, EDWARD JOSEPH, b Chicago, Ill, Aug 21, 19; m 60; c 3. PROSTHODONTICS. *Educ:* Univ Ill, BS, 55, DDS, 57. *Prof Exp:* Instr prosthdontics, Col Dent, Univ Ill, 57-59; asst prof, Dent Sch, Northwestern Univ, 59-61; from asst prof to assoc prof, 61-69, PROF PROSTHODONTICS, COL DENT, UNIV ILL MED CTR, 69- *Concurrent Pos:* Pvt pract, 57-; lectr postgrad prosthodontics, 61- *Mem:* Am Dent Asn; Am Prosthodont Soc. *Res:* Removable partial dentures. *Mailing Add:* 5202 S Lotus Ave Chicago IL 60638

KOZAK, GARY S, b Pittsburgh, Pa, June 13, 38; m 57; c 3. ANALYTICAL CHEMISTRY, PHYSICAL CHEMISTRY. *Educ:* Ind Univ, BS, 60; Univ Ariz, PhD(chem), 63. *Prof Exp:* Sr assoc chemist, 63-64, staff chemist, 64-66, proj chemist, 66-68, proj mgr & develop chemist, 68-69, mgr PhD recruitment progs, 69-71, mgr educ & sci rels, IBM World Trade Corp, 71-74, dir sci & contrib progs, IBM Europe, Paris, 74-78, dir spec univ prog, 78-81, PROG DIR TECH PERSONNEL RESOURCES, IBM CORP, 81- *Mem:* AAAS; Am Chem Soc; Am Inst Chem. *Res:* Kinetic studies with electrogenerated halogens; fluorescence; photosensitive polymers; epoxy resins and laminates. *Mailing Add:* Dept 785 IBM Corp 44 S Broadway White Plains NY 10601

KOZAK, JOHN JOSEPH, b Cleveland, Ohio, Sept 14, 40; m 69; c 3. CHEMICAL PHYSICS, BIOPHYSICAL CHEMISTRY. *Educ:* Case Inst Technol, BS, 61; Princeton Univ, PhD(chem), 65. *Prof Exp:* NIH fel chem, Free Univ Brussels, 65-67; res assoc, Univ Chicago, 67-68; asst prof, 68-72, assoc prof, 72-75, PROF CHEM, UNIV NOTRE DAME, 76- *Concurrent Pos:* Chmn, Prog Unified Sci, Univ Notre Dame, 70-; vis prof, Free Univ Brussels, 75, Ecole Polytechnique Federale de Lausanne, 78. *Mem:* Am Chem Soc. *Res:* Interacting radiation and matter; investigations of liquid dissolved state; theory of phase transitions; studies on nature of irreversibility. *Mailing Add:* Dept Chem Univ Notre Dame Notre Dame IN 46556

KOZAK, SAMUEL J, b Peabody, Mass, Apr 13, 31; m 59; c 2. GEOLOGY. *Educ:* Bates Col, BS, 54; Brown Univ, MS, 58; Univ Iowa, PhD(geol), 61. *Prof Exp:* Asst prof, 61-70, PROF GEOL, WASHINGTON & LEE UNIV, 70- *Mem:* Geol Soc Am; Nat Asn Geol Teachers. *Res:* Structural geology; igneous and metamorphic petrology; geology of the Central Appalachians. *Mailing Add:* Dept of Geol Washington & Lee Univ Lexington VA 24450

KOZAK, WLODZIMIERZ MACIEJ, b Warsaw, Poland, May 7, 27; m 74; c 1. VISUAL PHYSIOLOGY, PSYCHOPHYSICS. *Educ:* Univ Lodz, MS, 51; Univ Sydney, PhD(visual electrophysiol), 64; Polish Acad Sci, DSc(visual electrophysiol), 66. *Prof Exp:* Asst prof neurophysiol, Nencki Inst Exp Biol, Univ Lodz, 46-56, assoc prof & sr scientist, Nencki Inst Exp Biol, Polish Acad Sci, Warsaw, 56-64, head, Lab Electrophysiol, 64-67 & Lab Afferent Systs, 67-68; vis assoc res prof visual physiol, State Univ NY Buffalo, 68-70; assoc prof, 70-73, PROF PHYSIOL & BIOENG, CARNEGIE-MELLON UNIV, 74- *Concurrent Pos:* Recipient habilitation grant, Div Natural Sci, Polish Acad Sci, 65-66; Brit Coun visitor, Gt Brit, 65, Polish Acad Sci & USSR Acad Sci visitor, USSR, 65, Karolinska Inst visitor, Sweden, 66, visitor, Sch Med, Johns Hopkins Univ, Chile, 70 & NSF visitor, Japan, 78; Wellcome Trust fel, Inst Ophthal, Univ London, 68; United Health Found Western NY grant & Res Found grant, State Univ NY Albany, 69-70; Scaife Fund grant & Ford Found grant, Carnegie-Mellon Univ, 71-72, Health Res & Serv Found grant, 73-75, NSF grant, 76-77 & Juv Diabetes Found grant, 78-; lectr, Univ Lodz, 52-55 & Warsaw Tech Univ, 65; sr scientist dept med, Shadyside Hosp, Pittsburgh, 75-; vis fel, Australian Nat Univ, Canberra, 79. *Honors & Awards:* Sci Award, Div Natural Sci, Polish Acad Sci, 55. *Mem:* AAAS; NY Acad Sci; Int Brain Res Orgn; Polish Inst Arts & Sci Am; Asn Res Vision & Ophthal. *Res:* Electrophysiology and conditioning of salivary secretion; plasticity and memory traces of spinal cord reflexes; eye optics; electrophysiology of retina and visual pathway; oscillatory components of electroretinograms and evoked potentials; electroretinograms in diabetic retinopathy; coding of brightness and color information in eye and brain; subjective color sensations; computer Fourier analysis; neurophysiology. *Mailing Add:* Biomed Eng Prog Wean Hall 1325 Carnegie-Mellon Univ Pittsburgh PA 15213

KOZAM, GEORGE, b Union City, NJ, Mar 28, 24; m 53. ANATOMY, PATHOLOGY. *Educ:* NY Univ, BA, 45, MS, 46, PhD(human anat), 50, DDS, 53. *Prof Exp:* Asst biol, NY Univ, 46-47, instr anat, Dent Col, 47-50, instr bact, 53-54; from asst prof to assoc prof, 58-71, PROF ANAT, COL MED & DENT NJ, 71- *Concurrent Pos:* Vis asst prof path, Dent Col, Fairleigh Dickinson Univ, 64-65. *Mem:* Am Dent Asn; fel Am Acad Oral Path; NY Acad Sci; Int Asn Dent Res. *Res:* Capillary fragility; circulation in dental pulp; respiration of rat and rabbit dental pulp; effects of local anesthetics on the respiration of dental pulp; research on trigeminal nerve; effect of eugenol on nerve transmission and oral mucous membranes. *Mailing Add:* Dept of Anat Col of Med & Dent of NJ Newark NJ 07103

KOZARICH, JOHN WARREN, b Jersey City, NJ, June 20, 49; m 72. BIOLOGICAL CHEMISTRY, BIOCHEMISTRY. *Educ:* Boston Col, BS, 71; Mass Inst Technol, PhD(biol chem), 75. *Prof Exp:* NIH fel biochem, Harvard Univ, 74-77; ASST PROF PHARMACOL, YALE UNIV, 77- *Mem:* Am Chem Soc; assoc mem Sigma Xi. *Res:* Design of enzyme inhibitors; mechanisms of enzyme action; chemistry and biochemistry of modified nucleosides. *Mailing Add:* Dept of Pharmacol Sch of Med Yale Univ 333 Cedar St New Haven CT 06510

KOZAWA, AKIYA, b Japan, Jan 2, 28; m 53; c 2. ELECTROCHEMISTRY. *Educ:* Nagoya Univ, DrEng(electrochem), 59. *Prof Exp:* Instr appl chem, Nagoya Univ, 52-59, asst prof, 59-62; asst prof electrochem, Western Reserve Univ, 63-64; sr res assoc, 64-74, CORP RES FEL, PARMA TECH CTR, UNION CARBIDE CORP, 74- *Concurrent Pos:* Res assoc, Duke Univ, 56-57 & Western Reserve Univ, 57-59. *Mem:* Electrochem Soc. *Res:* Batteries, fuel cells. *Mailing Add:* Parma Tech Ctr Union Carbide Corp Cleveland OH 44130

KOZEK, WIESLAW JOSEPH, b Poniatowka, Poland, Feb 6, 39; US citizen; m 71; c 3. IMMUNOLOGY, ULTRASTRUCTURE. *Educ:* Canisius Col, BS, 61; Tulane Univ, MS, 67, PhD(parasitol), 69. *Prof Exp:* Fel, Dept Microbiol, Univ Chicago, 69-71, Dept Immunol & Med Microbiol, Univ Fla, Gainesville, 71-72; asst res parasitologist, Calif Primate Res Ctr, Univ Calif, Davis, 73-77; SCIENTIST, INT COLLABR INFECTIOUS DIS RES PROG, TULANE UNIV, CALI, COLOMBIA, 77- *Concurrent Pos:* Adj assoc prof, Dept Trop Med, Tulane Sch Pub Health & Trop Med, 80-; prin investr human filariasis, Int Collabr Infectious Dis Res Prog, Cali, Colombia, 80- *Mem:* Am Soc Trop Med & Hyg; Royal Soc Trop Med & Hyg; Am Soc Parasitologists; Sigma Xi; AAAS. *Res:* Medical helminthology; immunology, morphology, ultrastructure, animal models, and host-parasite relationship of filariae; epidemiology of human filariases in Colombia; culture of helminth cells; characterization of intracellular microorganisms of filarids; host-parasite relationships of trichinella spiralis. *Mailing Add:* CIDEIM Apartado Aereo 5390 Cali Colombia

KOZEL, PHILIP C, horticulture, plant physiology, see previous edition

KOZEL, THOMAS RANDALL, b Ft Dodge, Iowa, Jan 31, 46. MEDICAL MYCOLOGY, MEDICAL BACTERIOLOGY. *Educ:* Univ Iowa, BA, 67, MS, 69, PhD(microbiol), 71. *Prof Exp:* Instr microbiol, Univ Iowa, 69-70; asst prof, 71-75, dir med admis, 72-76, ASSOC PROF MICROBIOL, UNIV NEV, RENO, 75-, CHMN DEPT, 76- *Concurrent Pos:* vis assoc prof, Rockefeller Univ, 80-81. *Mem:* Am Soc Microbiol; Harvey Soc. *Res:* Cellular and molecular mechanisms of infection and resistance in systemic mycoses. *Mailing Add:* Sch of Med Sci Univ of Nev Reno NV 89507

KOZELKA, ROBERT M, b Minneapolis, Minn, July 20, 26; m 50; c 4. STATISTICS. *Educ:* Univ Minn, BA, 47, MA, 48; Harvard Univ, PhD(math), 53. *Prof Exp:* From instr to asst prof math, Tufts Univ, 49-53; asst prof, Univ Nebr, 53-57; from asst prof to assoc prof, 57-66, PROF MATH, WILLIAMS COL, 66- *Concurrent Pos:* Vis assoc prof math, Univ NC, Chapel Hill, 63-64;

vis prof anthrop & sociol, Univ Tex, Austin, 70-71. *Mem:* Inst Math Statist; Am Statist Asn; Math Asn Am. *Res:* Applications of mathematics and statistics to behavioral science. *Mailing Add:* Williams Col Williamstown MA 01267

KOZENY, O(RAL) A(NTHONY), chemical engineering, deceased

KOZIAR, JOSEPH CLEVELAND, b Baltimore, Md, Jan 6, 46; m 68; c 1. POLYMER CHEMISTRY, ORGANIC CHEMISTRY. *Educ:* Johns Hopkins Univ, BA, 68, PhD(org chem), 75. *Prof Exp:* Res chemist process develop, Diamond Shamrock Corp, 69-71; RES CHEMIST PLASTICS & COATINGS, ROHM AND HAAS CO, 75- *Mem:* Am Chem Soc; AAAS. *Res:* Polymer synthesis and characterization; monomer synthesis; organic photochemistry. *Mailing Add:* Rohm and Haas Res Labs PO Box 219 Bristol PA 19007

KOZICKI, WILLIAM, b Kenora, Ont, June 11, 31; m 63; c 1. THERMODYNAMICS. *Educ:* Univ Toronto, BASc, 53, MASc, 57; Calif Inst Technol, PhD(thermodyn), 62. *Prof Exp:* Process engr, Textile Fibres Div, Du Pont of Can, 53-55; res fel thermodyn, Calif Inst Technol, 61-62; from asst prof to assoc prof, 62-71, PROF CHEM ENG, UNIV OTTAWA, 71-, ASSOC DEAN ENG, 76- *Res:* Transport phenomena: rheology and flow of complex systems with particular emphasis on characterization of polymer adsorption and its role in improved oil recovery, turbulent drag reduction and as filtration aid. *Mailing Add:* 21 River Rd Nepean ON K1K 3V2 Can

KOZICKY, EDWARD LOUIS, b Elberon, NJ, Feb 11, 18; m 41; c 3. WILDLIFE MANAGEMENT. *Educ:* Univ Maine, BS, 41; Pa State Col, MS, 42, PhD(zool), 48. *Prof Exp:* Chief res, State Div Fish & Game, NJ, 48; leader, Co-op Wildlife Res Unit, Iowa State Col, 48-56; DIR CONSERV CTR, WINCHESTER-WESTERN DIV, OLIN CORP, 56- *Concurrent Pos:* Dir, Wildlife Legis Fund. *Mem:* Wildlife Soc (pres, 69-70); Am Forestry Asn. *Res:* Life history, ecology and management of game birds and mammals; the development, evaluation and improvement of game animal census techniques; development and promotion of shooting preserves. *Mailing Add:* Conserv Dept Olin Corp East Alton IL 62024

KOZIK, EUGENE, b Duquesne, Pa, Sept 22, 24; m 56; c 2. COMPUTER SCIENCE, OPERATIONS RESEARCH. *Educ:* Univ Pittsburgh, BS, 49, ML, 50, PhD, 60. *Prof Exp:* Engr, Gulf Oil Corp, 48-50; tech adminstr res & develop, Wright Air Develop Ctr, 53-57; mgt sci consult, Univ Pittsburgh, 59-60; mgr planning & controls, Gen Dynamics Corp, 60-61; prog mgr mgt sci, Opers Res, Inc, 61-62; dir adv studies, Burroughs Corp, 62-66; mgr info sci, Gen Elec Co, 66-70; PRES, KOZIK & ASSOCS, 70- *Concurrent Pos:* Lectr, Duquesne Univ, 60, Univ Rochester, 61 & Pa State Univ, 64-; mem, Int Comt Sci Mgt, Hist Eval Res Orgn, McLean, Va, 62-, comput comt, Am Inst Planners, 67- & urban info & measurement comt, Nat Acad Sci, 68- *Res:* Management and information science; intergrated management system; data management; computer technology. *Mailing Add:* 38 Rabbit Run Rd Malvern PA 19355

KOZIKOWSKI, ALAN PAUL, b Menominee, Mich, Oct 27, 48; m 75. ORGANIC CHEMISTRY. *Educ:* Univ Mich, BS, 70; Univ Calif, Berkeley, PhD(org chem), 74. *Prof Exp:* NIH fel org chem, Harvard Univ, 74-76; asst prof, 76-80, ALFRED P SLOAN FEL ORG CHEM, UNIV PITTSBURGH, 76-, ASSOC PROF & CAMILLE & HENRY DREYFUS TEACHER SCHOLAR, 80- *Mem:* Am Chem Soc; The Chem Soc; Sigma Xi. *Res:* Synthetic organic chemistry; synthesis of alkaloids and carbohydrates; organometallics. *Mailing Add:* Dept of Chem Univ of Pittsburgh Pittsburgh PA 15260

KOZIKOWSKI, BARBARA ANN, b Chicago, Ill, Jan 20, 54. PHYSICAL CHEMISTRY. *Educ:* Loyola Univ, BS, 75; Univ Ill, Chicago Circle, MS, 77, PhD(phys chem), 81. *Prof Exp:* STAFF SCIENTIST, PROCTER & GAMBLE CO, 81- *Mem:* Am Chem Soc; Soc Appl Spectroscopy. *Res:* Electronic structure of heavy transition metal complexes by means of cryogenic absorption; magnetic circular dichroism; emission and two-proton excitation techniques. *Mailing Add:* Procter & Gamble Co Miami Valley Cincinnati OH 45247

KOZINSKI, ANDRZEJ, b Poland, Oct 1, 25; m 49; c 1. MEDICINE. *Educ:* Univ Warsaw, MD, 50, PhD(biochem), 56. *Prof Exp:* Res assoc, State Inst Health, Poland, 50-55; asst prof, Inst Biochem, Polish Acad Sci, 55-57; res assoc, Virus Lab, Univ Calif, 57-58; asst prof, Inst Microbiol, Rutgers Univ, 58-59; assoc prof biochem, 62-68, PROF HUMAN GENETICS, UNIV PA, 68- *Concurrent Pos:* NIH fel biochem, Johns Hopkins Univ, 59-62. *Res:* Biochemistry of DNA replication; structure of phage chromosome. *Mailing Add:* Dept Human Genetics Univ Pa Philadelphia PA 19104

KOZLIK, R(OLAND) A(RTHUR), metallurgy, metallurgical engineering, see previous edition

KOZLOFF, EUGENE NICHOLAS, b Teheran, Iran, Sept 26, 20; nat US; m 44; c 1. ZOOLOGY. *Educ:* Univ Calif, AB, 42, MA, 46, PhD(zool, protozool), 50. *Prof Exp:* Asst zool, Univ Calif, 44, lectr micros technol, 45; from instr to prof biol, Lewis & Clark Col, 45-66, chmn dept, 60-66; PROF ZOOL, UNIV WASH, 66- *Concurrent Pos:* Guggenheim fel, 53-54; vis prof, Inst Marine Biol, Univ Ore, 57-60 & 64; vis prof, Friday Harbor Labs, Univ Wash, 61 & 62, resident assoc dir, 66-73; vis prof, Pac Marine Sta, 63; dir, NSF Inst Col Teachers, Univ Ore, 64. *Mem:* Soc Protozool; Am Micros Soc. *Res:* Cytology, morphology and taxonomy of protozoa; commensal ostracods; acoel and rhabdocoel Turbellaria; orthonectid Mesozoa; development of kinorhynchs. *Mailing Add:* Dept of Zool Univ of Wash Seattle WA 98195

KOZLOFF, LLOYD M, b Chicago, Ill, Oct 15, 23; m 47; c 4. VIROLOGY, MOLECULAR BIOLOGY. *Educ:* Univ Chicago, BS, 43, PhD(biochem), 48. *Prof Exp:* Res assoc biochem, Univ Chicago, 49-52, from asst prof to prof, 52-64; prof microbiol, Univ Colo Med Ctr, Denver, 64-80, chmn dept, 66-76,

assoc dean fac affairs, 76-79; PROF MICROBIOL & DEAN, GRAD DIV, UNIV CALIF, SAN FRANCISCO, 81- *Concurrent Pos:* Mem virol & rickettsiology study sect, NIH, 63-68; ed, J Virol, 66-74; vchmn, Virol Sect, Am Soc Microbiol, 74-75, chmn, 75-76; Found Microbiol lectr, 75-76. *Mem:* Hon fel AAAS; Am Soc Microbiol; Am Soc Biol Chemists; Am Chem Soc. *Res:* Virus structure, function and assembly; reactions during viral invasion. *Mailing Add:* Grad Div S-140 Univ Calif San Francisco CA 94143

KOZLOSKI, RICHARD PETER, b Derby, Conn, June 25, 46. WATER POLLUTION ANALYSIS. *Educ:* Univ Conn, BA, 68; Va Polytech Inst & State Univ, PhD(chem), 77. *Prof Exp:* ASST AGR SCIENTIST, CONN AGR EXP STA, 79- *Mem:* Am Chem Soc. *Res:* Development of purge and trap techniques for water pollution analysis and aflatoxin analysis; aflatoxin analysis. *Mailing Add:* Conn Agr Exp Sta PO Box 1106 New Haven CT 06504

KOZLOWSKI, ADRIENNE WICKENDEN, b Hackensack, NJ, Apr 26, 41; m 68, 77. INORGANIC CHEMISTRY. *Educ:* MacMurray Col, AB, 62; Univ Conn, MS, 64, PhD(chem), 68. *Prof Exp:* Res asst phys chem, Univ Conn, 68, fel biol sci, 69-70; asst prof, 70-77, ASSOC PROF CHEM, CENT CONN STATE COL, 77- *Concurrent Pos:* Lectr, Univ Copenhagen, 69. *Res:* Coordination compounds; infrared, electronic spectra and magnetic properties of complexes; ligand reactions; role of transition metal ions in biological systems. *Mailing Add:* Dept Chem Cent Conn State Col New Britain CT 06050

KOZLOWSKI, BETTY ANN, b Dothan, Ala, Dec 14, 43; m 78. NUTRITION. *Educ:* Ala Col, BS, 65; Univ Tenn, Knoxville, PhD(nutrit), 70. *Prof Exp:* Res asst nutrit, Univ Tenn, Knoxville, 69-70; asst prof, Auburn Univ, 70-74; asst prof, 74-77, CHIEF NUTRIT, NISONGER CTR MENTAL RETARDATION & DEVELOP DISABILITIES, OHIO STATE UNIV, 74-, ASSOC PROF NUTRIT, DEPT HUMAN NUTRIT & FOOD MGT, 77- *Mem:* Sigma Xi. *Res:* Utilization of inorganic sulfate and its relationship to the metabolism of the sulfur-containng amino acids; nutritional needs, and ways of meeting them in persons with developmental disabilities. *Mailing Add:* Nisonger Ctr 1580 Cannon Dr Ohio State Univ Columbus OH 43210

KOZLOWSKI, DON ROBERT, b St Louis, Mo, Dec 5, 37; m 60; c 3. AVIONICS. *Educ:* Univ St Louis, BS, 59; Washington Univ, St Louis, MS, 67. *Prof Exp:* Sr engr, McDonnell Aircraft Co, McDonnell Douglas Corp, 59-62; mgr prog develop, Electronic Specialty Co, 62-64; vpres, Aerospace Systs Corp, 64-65; sect mgr advan reconnaissance systs, 65-72, sr prog engr, 72-80, CHIEF PROG ENGR ADVAN ENG, MCDONNELL AIRCRAFT CO, MCDONNELL DOUGLAS CORP, 80- *Concurrent Pos:* Dir & consult, US Air Force/Air Force Systs Command Offensive Air Support Mission Anal, 74-76. *Honors & Awards:* Meritorious Civilian Serv Medal, US Air Force/Air Force Systs Command, 78. *Mem:* Inst Elec & Electronics Engrs; Am Soc Photogram; Am Inst Aeronaut & Astronaut; Am Defense Preparedness Asn. *Res:* Avionics, displays and data processing systems for reconnaissance and intelligence; communications and electronic warfare; aircraft systems design. *Mailing Add:* 1810 Millshire Riverview MO 63136

KOZLOWSKI, GERALD P, b Grand Rapids, Mich, Dec 24, 42. NEUROENDOCRINOLOGY. *Educ:* Aquinas Col, BS, 64; Mich State Univ, MS, 67; Univ Ill, Urbana-Champaign, PhD(anat), 71. *Prof Exp:* Technician histopath, Mich State Univ, 64-65, asst instr anat, 65-66; res assoc, Univ Mo-Columbia, 67-68; instr, Univ Ill, Urbana-Champaign, 68-70; teaching fel, Sch Med & Dent, Univ Rochester, 71-73; asst prof anat, Col Vet Med & Biomed Sci, Colo State Univ, 73-76, assoc prof, 76-78; ASSOC PROF NEUROBIOL & ANAT, UNIV TEX HEALTH SCI CTR, HOUSTON, 78- *Concurrent Pos:* NIH grant, 74-78; ed, Histochem. *Mem:* Am Asn Anatomists; Int Soc Neuroendocrinologists; Biol Stain Comn. *Res:* Light and electron microscopic immunocytochemistry for visualization of releasing-hormones and neuropeptides of the hypothalamus; vasopressin, oxytocin and neurophysin; scanning and high-voltage electron microscopy of the median eminence. *Mailing Add:* Dept of Neurobiol & Anat PO Box 20708 Houston TX 77025

KOZLOWSKI, ROBERT H, b Duquesne, Pa, May 17, 28; m 51; c 2. ORGANIC CHEMISTRY. *Educ:* St Mary's Col Calif, BS, 50; Northwestern Univ, PhD(chem), 55. *Prof Exp:* Res chemist, 55-60, sr res chemist, 60-64, supvry res chemist, 64-66, sr res assoc, Petrol Process Res & Develop, Chevron Res Co Div, 66-76, litigation support coordr, Secy's Dept, 76-77, LITIGATION SUPPORT CONSULT, SECY'S DEPT, STANDARD OIL CO CALIF, 78- *Mem:* Am Chem Soc; Am Soc Enol. *Res:* Petroleum processing; hydrocarbon reactions and mechanisms. *Mailing Add:* 420 Michigan Ave Berkeley CA 94707

KOZLOWSKI, THEODORE R, b Niagara Falls, NY, Dec 21, 37; m 61; c 5. PHYSICAL INORGANIC CHEMISTRY. *Educ:* Niagara Univ, BS, 59; Rensselaer Polytech Inst, PhD(phys inorg chem), 63. *Prof Exp:* Sr chemist, 63-64, res chemist, 66-70, mgr indust prod develop, 70-73, mgr prod div, 73-77, MGR INDUST PROD DEVELOP TECH STAFF DIV, CORNING GLASS WORKS, 77- *Mem:* AAAS; fel Am Inst Chemists; Am Chem Soc; Sigma Xi. *Res:* Physical chemistry and vibrational spectra of molten salts; decomposition kinetics of inorganic materials; glass-molten salt interactions; high strength glasses and glass ceramics by ion exchange from molten salts; high strength materials. *Mailing Add:* Corning Glass Works Sullivan Park Corning NY 14830

KOZLOWSKI, THEODORE THOMAS, b Buffalo, NY, May 22, 17; m 54. PLANT PHYSIOLOGY, FOREST BIOLOGY. *Educ:* Syracuse Univ, BS, 39; Duke Univ, MA, 41, PhD(plant physiol), 47. *Hon Degrees:* DSc, Univ Louvain, Belgium, 78. *Prof Exp:* Asst, Duke Univ, 46; from asst prof to prof bot & head dept, Univ Mass, 47-58; prof, 58-61 & 65-72, chmn dept, 61-64, A J RIKER PROF FORESTRY, UNIV WIS, MADISON, 72-; DIR BIOTRON, 77- *Concurrent Pos:* Vis prof, Univ Pa, 54; vis scientist, Soc Am Foresters, 63, 66, 68, 69 & 70; Fulbright sr res scholar & exchange lectr,

Oxford Univ, 64-65; vis biologist, Am Inst Biol Sci, 69-71; Int Shade Tree Conf res fel, 69, 70 & 71-; George Lamb lectr, Univ Nebr, 74; ed, Physiol-Ecol Book Series, Acad Press; res collabr, US Forest Serv; consult, UN Food & Agr Orgn, Nat Park Serv, Oak Ridge Nat Lab, Stanford Res Inst, NSF, Acad Press & several com orgns; George S Long lectr, Univ Washington, 78. *Honors & Awards:* Auth Award, Int Shade Tree Conf, 71; Barrington Moore Res Award Biol Sci, Soc Am Foresters, 74; Arboricult Res Award, Int Soc Arboricult, 76. *Mem:* Soc Am Foresters; Am Soc Plant Physiol; Bot Soc Am; Ecol Soc Am; Am Inst Biol Sci. *Res:* Physiology of woody plants; plant water relations; physiological ecology. *Mailing Add:* Dept of Forestry Russell Labs Univ of Wis Madison WI 53706

KOZMA, ADAM, b Cleveland, Ohio, Feb 2, 28; wid; c 2. OPTICAL PHYSICS, ELECTROOPTICS. *Educ:* Univ Mich, BSE, 52, MSE, 64; Wayne State Univ, MSEM, 61; Univ London, PhD(elec eng), 68 & dipl, Imp Col, 69. *Prof Exp:* Design engr, US Broach Co, Mich, 51-56, sales engr, 56-58; asst mech & electrooptical design, Inst Sci & Technol, Univ Mich, Ann Arbor, 58-61, res assoc, 61-63, assoc res engr, 63-65, res head optics group, Radar & Optics Lab, 65-69; gen mgr, Electrooptics Ctr, Radiation Div, Harris, Inc, 69-73; sr res engr & mgr, Electromagnetics & Electronics Dept, 73-75, mgr tech staff, 75-76, VPRES & DIR, RADAR & OPTICS DIV, ENVIRON RES INST MICH, 76- *Concurrent Pos:* Consult, Conductron Corp, 65-66, IBM Systs Develop Div, 66-67, UK Atomic Weapons Estab, 67-68 & Radiation Inc, Fla, 68-69; on leave, Imp Col, Univ London, 66-68, acad visitor & lectr, 67-68; consult phys sci directorate, USAMRDEL, MICOM, Redstone, Ala, 74-78. *Mem:* Fel Optical Soc Am; Inst Elec & Electronics Engrs; Am Defense Preparedness Asn; Sigma Xi. *Res:* Coherent optics with application to signal processing and optical correlation; holography; application of lasers and holography to storage and retrieval; speckle effects in coherent systems; synthetic aperture radar systems and applications. *Mailing Add:* PO Box 8618 Ann Arbor MI 48107

KOZUB, RAYMOND LEE, b Ladysmith, Wis, June 16, 40; m 65; c 2. NUCLEAR PHYSICS. *Educ:* Wis State Univ-River Falls, BS, 62; Mich State Univ, MS, 64, PhD(physics), 67. *Prof Exp:* Asst prof physics, Tex A&M Univ, 67-71, res scientist, Cyclotron Inst, 71-72; res assoc chem, Columbia Univ, 72-74; asst prof physics, Queen's Univ, Kingston, Ont, 74-77; assoc prof, 77-80, PROF PHYSICS, TENN TECHNOL UNIV, 80- *Mem:* Am Phys Soc; AAAS; Sigma Xi. *Res:* Nuclear structure studies; transfer reactions; stripping reactions to unbound final states; isobaric analog states; nuclear lifetime measurements; heavy ion reactions. *Mailing Add:* Dept of Physics Tenn Technol Univ Cookeville TN 38501

KRA, IRWIN, b Poland, Jan 5, 37; US citizen; m 61; c 3. MATHEMATICS. *Educ:* Polytech Inst Brooklyn, BS, 60; Columbia Univ, MA, 64, PhD(math), 66. *Prof Exp:* C L E Moore instr math, Mass Inst Technol, 66-68; from asst prof to assoc prof, 68-71, chmn dept, 75-81, PROF MATH, STATE UNIV NY STONY BROOK, 72- *Concurrent Pos:* Guggenheim Found fel, 70-71; actg chmn dept math, State Univ NY Stony Brook, 70-71, actg provost, Div Math Sci, 71-72. *Mem:* Am Math Soc. *Res:* One complex variable, particularly moduli of Riemann surfaces and Kleinian groups. *Mailing Add:* Dept of Math State Univ of NY at Stony Brook Stony Brook NY 11794

KRAAKEVIK, JAMES HENRY, b Chicago, Ill, Feb 18, 28; m 50; c 5. ATMOSPHERIC PHYSICS. *Educ:* Wheaton Col, Ill, BS, 48; Univ Md, PhD(physics), 57. *Prof Exp:* Physicist, US Naval Res Lab, 48-54, res sect head, 54-58; from asst prof to assoc prof, 58-70, PROF PHYSICS, WHEATON COL, ILL, 70-, CHMN DEPT, 61- *Concurrent Pos:* Teacher, Titcombe Col, Nigeria, 64-66, prin, 66-67; consult, US Naval Res Lab, 58-, Ill State Water Surv, 61-64 & Coronet Instr Films, 62-65; educ secy, Sudan Interior Mission, 69-70, educ consult, 70-; educ consult, Ministry Educ, Sudan, 73- *Mem:* Am Geophys Union; Am Asn Physics Teachers; AAAS; Am Meteorol Soc. *Res:* Electrical properties of atmosphere and relationship with meteorology; electrical characteristics of upper atmosphere and relationship with radiation; conduction of electricity through gases; characteristics of sub-micron particles in the atmosphere. *Mailing Add:* Dept of Physics Wheaton Col Wheaton IL 60187

KRAAY, GERRIT JACOB, b Amsterdam, Netherlands, Oct 14, 35; m 63; c 4. GENETICS. *Educ:* State Agr Univ Wageningen, BSc, 60, MSc, 63, PhD, 67. *Prof Exp:* Res scientist, Found for Blood Group Res, Wageningen, Netherlands, 63; res scientist, Dept Animal Sci, State Agr Univ Wageningen, 64-67; asst prof vet bact, Univ Guelph, 67-69, asst prof biomed sci, 69-72; HEAD BLOOD TYPING SECT, ANIMAL DIS RES INST EAST, CAN DEPT AGR, 72- *Mem:* Royal Dutch Soc Agr Sci; Int Soc Animal Bloodgroup Res; Genetics Soc Can. *Res:* Population genetics of blood groups and serum-protein polymorphisms in animals; immuno-reproduction. *Mailing Add:* Animal Dis Res Inst East 801 Fallowfield Rd Ottawa ON K2H 8P9 Can

KRABACHER, BERNARD, b Cincinnati, Ohio, Dec 25, 25. PHYSICAL ORGANIC CHEMISTRY. *Educ:* Univ Cincinnati, Chem Eng, 49, PhD(phys org chem), 61. *Prof Exp:* Chemist, Emery Industs, Inc, 49-57, group leader ozone res, 61-63; assoc prof, 63-66, PROF CHEM, WVA STATE COL, 66-, CHMN DEPT, 76- *Mem:* Am Chem Soc; fel Am Inst Chemists. *Res:* Reactions of organic compounds with cobalt carbonyls and ozone; preparation of unusual compounds; reaction mechanisms. *Mailing Add:* Dept of Chem WVa State Col Institute WV 25112

KRABBE, GREGERS LOUIS, b Roskilde, Denmark, Jan 5, 20; nat US; m 55; c 2. MATHEMATICAL ANALYSIS. *Educ:* Univ Calif, AB, 49, MS, 51, PhD, 54. *Prof Exp:* Assoc prof math, Purdue Univ, 54-60 & Yale Univ, 60-61; NATO fel, Univ Rennes, 61-62; assoc prof, 62-68, PROF MATH, PURDUE UNIV, 68- *Mem:* Am Math Soc. *Res:* Algebraic operational calculus, as applied to lumped systems; theory of linear operators; spectral theory; functional and harmonic analysis; electrical engineering, linear networks, signal and system analysis. *Mailing Add:* Div of Math Sci Purdue Univ Lafayette IN 47907

KRABBENHOFT, HERMAN OTTO, b Detroit, Mich, July 15, 45; m 76; c 1. ORGANIC CHEMISTRY. *Educ:* Wayne State Univ, BS, 69; Univ Mich, MS, 71, PhD(chem), 74. *Prof Exp:* STAFF CHEMIST ORG CHEM, GEN ELEC CORP RES & DEVELOP CTR, 76- *Concurrent Pos:* NIH grant chem, Univ Calif, Berkeley, 75-76. *Mem:* Am Chem Soc. *Res:* Structure and mechanism in organic chemistry; organic synthesis. *Mailing Add:* 6 Arcadian Dr Scotia NY 12302

KRABBENHOFT, KENNETH LOUIS, b Page, NDak, Feb 24, 31; m 55; c 3. MICROBIOLOGY. *Educ:* Univ Valparaiso, BA, 53; NDak State Univ, MS, 56; Ore State Univ, PhD(microbiol), 65. *Prof Exp:* Instr biol, Mankato State Col, 58-62; asst prof, NMex State Univ, 65-67; assoc prof, 67-70, PROF BIOL, MANKATO STATE UNIV, 70- *Concurrent Pos:* NASA res grant, 65-67; NSF res grant, 69-71. *Mem:* AAAS; Am Soc Microbiol; Inst Food Technologists. *Res:* Mechanisms of radiation resistance in microorganisms. *Mailing Add:* Dept of Biol Mankato State Univ Mankato MN 56001

KRABEC, CHARLES FRANK, JR, b St Louis, Mo, Oct 18, 49. ELECTROOPTICS. *Educ:* Wash Univ, BS, 71; Univ Mo, MS, 76. *Prof Exp:* PHYSICIST ELECTROOPTICS, US AIR FORCE AVIONICS LAB, 77- *Mem:* Am Phys Soc. *Res:* Transverse electric pulsed chemical lasers; atmospheric propagation of laser radiation. *Mailing Add:* Air Force Avionics Lab AFAL/DHO-1 Wright-Patterson AFB OH 45433

KRABILL, DAVID MILTON, b Sterling, Ohio, July 8, 14; m 40; c 4. MATHEMATICS. *Educ:* Col Wooster, BA, 36; Ohio State Univ, PhD(math), 41. *Prof Exp:* Asst instr math, Ohio State Univ, 36-40; instr, Potomac State Col, 40-42; assoc prof, 46-50, PROF MATH, BOWLING GREEN STATE UNIV, 50- *Mem:* Am Math Soc; Soc Indust & Appl Math; Math Asn Am; Nat Coun Teachers Math. *Res:* Numerical analysis, especially linear systems, differential equations, roots of polynomials. *Mailing Add:* 510 Brownwood Court Bowling Green OH 43402

KRACHER, ALFRED, b Vienna, Austria, Sept 21, 45; m 74; c 2. METEORITICS, COSMOCHEMISTRY. *Educ:* Univ Vienna, PhD(chem), 74. *Prof Exp:* Res asst chem, Univ Vienna, 72-74, res asst petrol, 74-76; staff scientist mineral & petrol, Mus Natural Hist, Vienna, 76-81; RESEARCHER EARTH SCI, INST METEORITICS, UNIV NMEX, 81- *Concurrent Pos:* Researcher chem, Inst Geophysics, Univ Calif, Los Angeles, 77-78. *Mem:* Meteoritical Soc; AAAS. *Res:* Petrology and composition of meteorites; computer application to petrologic problems. *Mailing Add:* Inst Meteoritics Univ NMex Albuquerque NM 87131

KRACKOV, MARK HARRY, b Brooklyn, NY, June 2, 32; m 54; c 2. ORGANIC CHEMISTRY. *Educ:* Univ Calif, Berkeley, BS, 55; Ore State Univ, PhD(org chem), 62. *Prof Exp:* Instr chem, Ore State Univ, 61-62; USPHS fel org chem, Sch Med, Yale Univ, 62-65; RES CHEMIST, JACKSON LAB, ORG CHEMS DEPT, E I DU PONT DE NEMOURS & CO, 65- *Mem:* Am Chem Soc; AAAS; Sigma Xi; Catalysis Soc. *Res:* Synthesis and physical properties of heterocyclic nitrogen, sulfur and selenium compounds; chemical synthesis of polynucleotides; labelling compounds via neutron activation; photopolymerization; reverse osmosis membranes; organic chemical process development; catalysis. *Mailing Add:* Chem & Pigments Dept Jackson Lab E I du Pont de Nemours & Co Wilmington DE 19898

KRAEGER, SPRING JULIET, medical microbiology, see previous edition

KRAELING, ROBERT RUSSELL, b Pittsburgh, Pa, Aug 22, 42; m 62; c 5. ANIMAL SCIENCE. *Educ:* Univ Md, BS, 64, MS, 67; Iowa State Univ, PhD(animal sci physiol reprod), 70. *Prof Exp:* Res asst, Swine Res Br, Animal Husb Res Div, Agr Res Serv, USDA, 64-66, agr res technician, 66-67, agr res scientist, 67; res assoc, Iowa State Univ, 67-70; res animal physiologist, Animal Physiol & Genetics Inst, Reproduction Lab, Md, 70-74, Animal Prod Lab, Russell Agr Res Ctr, Athens, 74-77, SUPVR RES PHYISOLOGIST, ANIMAL PHYSIOL RES UNIT, RUSSELL RES CTR, AGR RES SERV, USDA, 77- *Concurrent Pos:* Adj asst prof, Dept Animal & Dairy Sci, Univ Ga, 74-, mem grad fac, 79- *Mem:* Am Soc Animal Sci; Soc Study Reproduction; Sigma Xi. *Res:* Determining the physiological and endocrinolgoical factors which control puberty, ovulation, corpus luteum function and the post-partum interval in swine and cattle and the effects of environment and management systems. *Mailing Add:* Richard B Russell Agr Res Ctr USDA PO Box 5677 Athens GA 30613

KRAEMER, DUANE CARL, b Willow, Wis, Oct 27, 33; m 60; c 2. REPRODUCTIVE PHYSIOLOGY, MEDICINE. *Educ:* Univ Wis, BS, 55; Tex A&M Univ, MS, 60, BS, PhD(physiol of reprod) & DVM, 66. *Prof Exp:* Asst scientist, Southwest Found Res & Educ, 66-75; assoc prof, 75-77, PROF VET PHYSIOL & PHARMACOL, COL VET MED, TEX A&M UNIV, 77- *Mem:* Soc Study Reprod; Sigma Xi; Am Vet Med Asn; Am Soc Animal Sci; Am Asn Lab Animal Sci. *Res:* Reproductive gamete physiology; contraceptive development and testing. *Mailing Add:* Dept of Vet Physiol & Pharmacol Tex A&M Univ Col of Vet Med College Station TX 77843

KRAEMER, HELENA CHMURA, b Derby, Conn, July 10, 37; m 62; c 2. BIOSTATISTICS. *Educ:* Smith Col, BA, 58; Stanford Univ, PhD(statist), 63. *Prof Exp:* Actg asst prof, 64-69, res assoc, 69-72, asst prof, 72-75, ASSOC PROF BIOSTATIST, DEPT PSYCHIAT & BEHAV SCI, SCH MED, STANFORD UNIV, 75- *Concurrent Pos:* Lectr, Div Biostatist, Dept Community & Prev Med, Stanford Univ, 71- *Mem:* Am Statist Asn; Inst Math Sci; Psychomet Soc. *Res:* Development of statistical methods for use in clinical and behavioral research, with particular emphasis on correlational methods. *Mailing Add:* Dept of Psychiat & Behav Sci Stanford Univ Sch of Med Stanford CA 94305

KRAEMER, HERBERT F(ARADAY), chemical engineering, deceased

KRAEMER, J HUGO, b Albany, NY, Apr 7, 09; m 35. FORESTRY. *Educ:* Univ Idaho, BS, 34; Harvard Univ, MF, 35; Yale Univ, PhD(growth-strength rels red pine), 43. *Prof Exp:* Land survr, NY State Conserv Dept, 29; survr, Off Div Eng, NY Cent RR, Albany, 29-31; trail construct survr, US Forest Serv, Idaho, 31; road & trail locator, US Off Indian Affairs, Wash, 33; asst technician, US Forest Serv, NH, 34, jr forester, Northeastern Forest Exp Sta, 35-37; instr forestry, Mich State Col, 37-41; instr eng sci & mgt war training prog, Yale Univ, 42-43; sr econ analyst & chief forest resources unit, Bd Econ Warfare & For Econ Admin, 43-45; sr econ analyst & attache for forestry & lumber indust, For Serv Auxiliary, US Dept State, Norway, Sweden, Denmark, Finland & Ger, 45-46; sr commodity specialist, Lumber-Paper Div, US Tariff Comn, 47; assoc res prof forestry & dir wood res lab, Purdue Univ, 47-51; commodity-indust analyst & chief wood conserv sect, Nat Prod Authority, 51-52; chief, Div Forestry & adv forestry to Govt Repub Korea, UN Korean Reconstruct Agency, 53-54; guest prof forestry, Seoul Nat Univ, 54; consult forester, J Hugo Kraemer Assocs, 55-59. *Concurrent Pos:* Owner-mgr, High Valley Forest, 57-; vis prof forest mgt & econ, Univ Philippines, 62-64. *Mem:* Soc Am Foresters; Philippine Soc Advan Res; Sigma Xi. *Res:* Forest management; silviculture; forestry economics; wood technology; foreign forest resources and forestry. *Mailing Add:* J Hugo Kraemer Assocs Patent Rd RD 1 Box 233 Peru NY 12972

KRAEMER, JOHN FRANCIS, b St Louis, Mo, June 20, 41. ORGANIC CHEMISTRY, POLYMER CHEMISTRY. *Educ:* St Louis Univ, BS, 63; Loyola Univ, MS, 65, PhD(org chem), 68. *Prof Exp:* ORG CHEMIST, INT MINERALS & CHEM CORP, 68- *Mem:* Am Chem Soc. *Res:* Organic synthesis; synthesis of biologically active compounds; interactions of biologically active molecules with metal ions. *Mailing Add:* Int Minerals & Chem Corp 1331 S First St Terre Haute IN 47808

KRAEMER, LOUISE MARGARET, b New York, NY, Dec 26, 10. PHYSICAL CHEMISTRY, BIOCHEMISTRY. *Educ:* Univ Pa, AB, 43; Univ Chicago, PhD(chem), 49. *Prof Exp:* Asst engr, Brown Instrument Co, 43-45; asst chem, Univ Chicago, 45-49; res assoc med, Univ Minn, 49-51; assoc chemist, Argonne Nat Lab, 51-53; asst prof natural sci, Univ Chicago, 53-59, assoc prof phys sci, 59-64; prof chem, New Col, 64-65; prof, 66-76, EMER PROF PHYS SCI, UNIV COLO, BOULDER, 76- *Mem:* AAAS; Am Chem Soc. *Res:* Enzymes in wheat germ; porphyrin chemistry; color centers in alkali halides. *Mailing Add:* 2568 Sixth St Boulder CO 80302

KRAEMER, LOUISE RUSSERT, b Milwaukee, Wis, Dec 17, 23; m 50; c 4. MALACOLOGY. *Educ:* Marquette Univ, BS, 45; Univ Mich, Ann Arbor, MS, 47, PhD(malacol), 66. *Prof Exp:* Asst zool & fisheries, Univ Mich, Ann Arbor, 46-48; asst prof zool, 48-50, instr, 56-58 & 59-66, from asst prof to assoc prof, 66-77, PROF ZOOL, UNIV ARK, FAYETTEVILLE, 77- *Mem:* AAAS; Am Malacol Union (pres, 81-82); Am Soc Zoologists; Sigma Xi; Animal Behav Soc. *Res:* Functional morphology; behavior of freshwater mollusks; nervous systems and reproductive systems of Lampsilis and Corbicula; macrobenthic communities in lotic systems. *Mailing Add:* Dept of Zool Univ of Ark Fayetteville AR 72701

KRAEMER, PAUL MICHAEL, b Philadelphia, Pa, Mar 19, 30. CELL BIOLOGY. *Educ:* Univ Colo, BA, 57; Tulane Univ, MPH, 59, DrPH, 61; Univ Pa, PhD(microbiol), 64. *Prof Exp:* Group leader exp pathol, 79-81, STAFF MEM CELLULAR BIOL, LOS ALAMOS NAT LAB, 64- *Concurrent Pos:* Fel, Wistar Inst, 61-64; ed, J Cellular Physiol; cellular physiol study sect, NIH, 77-81. *Mem:* Am Soc Biol Chemists; Am Soc Cell Biol; Am Soc Exp Path. *Res:* Mammalian cell surface complex carbohydrates; heteroploidy in mammalian cells; tumor biology. *Mailing Add:* Exp Pathol Group MS 888 Los Alamos Nat Lab Los Alamos NM 87545

KRAEMER, RICHARD JOHN, b Nov 13, 34; m; c 3. PHARMACOLOGY, TOXICOLOGY. *Educ:* Univ Wis, BS, 62; Univ Colo, MS, 65, PhD(pharmacol), 68. *Prof Exp:* Proj asst, Dept Anesthesiol, Sch Med, Univ Wis, 58-62; res asst, Dept Med, Vet Admin Hosp, Denver, Colo, 62-63; fel pharmacol & exp therapeut, Sch Med, Johns Hopkins Univ, 68-70; asst prof, Dept Anesthesiol, Sch Med, Univ Wis, 70-73, asst prof, Dept Pharmacol, 70-75, asst prof, Dept Prev Med & asst dir, Ctr Environ Toxicol, 74; assoc prof & asst dean, Sch Pharm, Univ Colo, Boulder, 75-80. *Mem:* NY Acad Sci; AAAS; Sigma Xi; Fedn Am Socs Exp Biol. *Mailing Add:* 1077 Albion Rd Boulder CO 80303

KRAEMER, ROBERT WALTER, b Philadelphia, Pa, Jan 27, 35; m 60; c 3. EXPERIMENTAL HIGH ENERGY PHYSICS. *Educ:* La Salle Col, BA, 57; Johns Hopkins Univ, PhD(physics), 62. *Prof Exp:* Instr physics, Johns Hopkins Univ, 61-62, res assoc, 62-64; res assoc, 64-65, from asst prof to assoc prof, 65-74, PROF PHYSICS, CARNEGIE-MELLON UNIV, 74- *Mem:* Am Phys Soc. *Res:* High energy experimental nuclear physics; bubble chamber physics. *Mailing Add:* Dept of Physics Carnegie-Mellon Univ Pittsburgh PA 15213

KRAEUTER, JOHN NORMAN, b Glen Gardner, NJ, Mar 26, 42; m 70. BIOLOGICAL OCEANOGRAPHY, MARINE ECOLOGY. *Educ:* Fla State Univ, BA, 64; Col William & Mary, MA, 66; Univ Del, PhD(biol sci), 71. *Prof Exp:* Res fel biol sci, Marine Inst, Univ Ga, 71-73; res assoc, Skidaway Inst Oceanog, Ga, 73-74; asst marine scientist & asst prof, 74-80, ASSOC MARINE SCIENTIST, VA INST MARINE SCI & ASSOC PROF, UNIV VA & COL WILLIAM & MARY, 81- *Concurrent Pos:* bus mgr, J Estuaries, Estuarine Res Fedn, 78- *Mem:* Atlantic Estuarine Res Soc (pres, 77-79); Estuarine Res Fedn (treas, 82); Malacol Soc London; AAAS; Am Malacol Union. *Res:* Systematics and ecology of scaphopod mollusks; zoogeography of the western Atlantic marine invertebrates; benthic infaunal ecology. *Mailing Add:* Va Inst Marine Sci Wachapreague VA 23480

KRAFFT, JOSEPH MARTIN, b Alexandria, Va, Jan 13, 23. PHYSICS. *Educ:* Cath Univ Am, Washington, DC, BME, 43, PhD, 51. *Prof Exp:* Various positions teaching, eng, patent search & writing, DC, 41-49; physicist res & develop terminal ballistics, dynamic plastic flow & fracture fatigue mech, 48-

70, head, Mech Mat Br, 70-81, CONSULT, STRUCTURAL INTEGRITY BR, NAVAL RES LAB, WASHINGTON, DC, 81- *Concurrent Pos:* Tech ed, Trans, Am Soc Mech Engrs, J Eng Mat & Technol, 78-81. *Mem:* Fel Am Soc Metals; fel Am Soc Testing & Mat; Am Soc Mech Engrs. *Mailing Add:* Code 58301 Naval Res Lab Washington DC 20375

KRAFT, ALAN M, b Passaic, NJ, May 24, 25; m 51; c 2. PSYCHIATRY. *Educ:* Chicago Med Sch, MD, 51. *Prof Exp:* Staff psychiatrist, Vet Admin Hosp, Denver, Colo, 55-57; chief psychiatrist, Ment Health Ctr Am, 58-61; dir, Ft Logan Ment Health Ctr, 61-67; PROF PSYCHIAT & CHMN DEPT, ALBANY MED COL, 67- *Concurrent Pos:* Fel psychiat, Menninger Sch Psychiat, 52-55; consult, Vet Admin Hosp, Albany, NY, 71-; dir, Capital Dist Psychiat Ctr, Albany, 67-79. *Mem:* Am Psychiat Asn. *Res:* Treatment of chronic schizophrenia; program evaluation. *Mailing Add:* Dept of Psychiat Albany Med Col Albany NY 12208

KRAFT, ALLEN ABRAHAM, b New York, NY, 1923; m 47; c 2. FOOD TECHNOLOGY. *Educ:* Cornell Univ, BS, 47, MS, 49; Iowa State Col, PhD(food technol), 53. *Prof Exp:* Asst food technol & bact, Iowa State Col, 49-53; asst poultry prod technologist, Animal & Poultry Husb Res Br, Agr Res Serv, USDA, 53-59; from asst prof to assoc prof, 59-72, PROF FOOD TECHNOL, IOWA STATE UNIV, 72-, PROF MICROBIOL, 81- *Mem:* Fel AAAS; Poultry Sci Asn; Inst Food Technologists; Am Soc Microbiol; World Poultry Sci Asn. *Res:* Microbiology and technology of meat and poultry products. *Mailing Add:* Food Res Lab Dept Food Technol Iowa State Univ Ames IA 50010

KRAFT, CHRISTOPHER COLUMBUS, JR, b Phoebus, Va, Feb 28, 24; m 50; c 2. AEROSPACE ENGINEERING. *Educ:* Va Polytech Inst, BS, 44. *Hon Degrees:* DEng, Ind Inst Technol, 66 & St Louis Univ, 67. *Prof Exp:* Aeronaut res engr, Langley Aeronaut Lab, Nat Adv Comt Aeronaut, Va, 45-48, space task group, 58-59, supvry aeronaut res engr, 59-61, asst chief flight opers div, 61-62, chief div, 62-63, dir flight opers, 63-69, dep dir ctr, 69-72, DIR CTR, MANNED SPACECRAFT CTR, NASA, 72- *Honors & Awards:* Outstanding Leadership Medal, NASA, 63, Distinguished Serv Medal, 69; Arthur S Flemming Award, 63; Spirit of St Louis Award, Am Soc Mech Engrs, 66; Louis W Hill Award, Am Inst Aeronaut & Astronaut, 70; Space Flight Award, Am Astronaut Soc, 70. *Mem:* Nat Acad Eng; fel Am Inst Aeronaut & Astronaut; fel Am Astronaut Soc. *Res:* Aerospace engineering. *Mailing Add:* Johnson Space Ctr NASA Houston TX 77058

KRAFT, DAVID WERNER, b Worms, Ger, Apr 21, 33; nat US; m 58; c 3. PHYSICS. *Educ:* City Col New York, BS, 54; Pa State Univ, PhD(physics), 59. *Prof Exp:* Res physicist, Pa State Univ, 59-60; sr physicist, Philips Labs Div, NAm Philips Co, Inc, 60-64 & Electronics Systs Div, Loral Corp, 64; sr res physicist, Cent Res Div, Am Cyanamid Co, 65; res scientist, Hudson Labs, Columbia, 65-68; from assoc prof to prof physics, Cooper Union, 68-76; vis prof opers res, Grad Sch Bus Admin, NY Univ, 76-77; dir Manpower Placement Div & Sr Staff Adv Planning, Am Inst Physics, 77-79; DEP EXEC SECY, AM PHYS SOC, 79- *Concurrent Pos:* Consult electronic systs div, Loral Corp, 65; vis scientist & consult, Gen Tel & Electronics Labs, 69-70; vis scientist, NY Univ, 72-74 & Philips Labs Div, NAm Philips Co, 75; consult, NY Tel Co, 76-77 & Am Inst Physics, 77; adj prof opers res, Grad Sch Bus Admin, NY Univ, 69- *Mem:* Am Phys Soc; Am Asn Physics Teachers; NY Acad Sci; AAAS. *Res:* Ultrasonic absorption; scattering of elastic waves; magnetic, optical and elastic properties of solids; atmospheric physics; operations and economic analysis; scientific manpower utilization; science administration. *Mailing Add:* Am Inst Physics 335 E 45th St New York NY 10017

KRAFT, DONALD J, b Strasburg, NDak, Nov 9, 36; m 60; c 4. PLANT PHYSIOLOGY. *Educ:* NDak State Univ, BS, 59, PhD(plant physiol), 68. *Prof Exp:* Teacher high sch, NDak, 61-62; chmn dept sci, 62-63; asst prof biol, St Mary's Col Minn, 68-69; asst prof, 69-72, assoc prof, 72-79, PROF, BEMIDJI STATE UNIV, 79- *Concurrent Pos:* Prin investr grants, NIH, 68-69 & Minn State Col Bd, 69-70 & 73-74. *Mem:* AAAS; Am Soc Plant Physiologists; Sigma Xi. *Res:* Biochemistry of seed germination as a means to eliminate noxious weeds through natural components of seeds rather than through use of sprays. *Mailing Add:* Dept of Biol Bemidji State Univ Bemidji MN 56601

KRAFT, EDWARD MICHAEL, b Cincinnati, Ohio, Nov 13, 44; m 71; c 1. AERODYNAMICS, WIND TUNNEL TECHNOLOGY. *Educ:* Univ Cincinnati, BS, 68; Univ Tenn, MS, 72, PhD(aerodyn eng), 75. *Prof Exp:* Res asst, Space Inst, Univ Tenn, 68-69; proj engr, Sverdrup/Aro, Inc, 69-72, res engr, 72-78, engr supv, 78-80; ASST MGR, CALSPAN FIELD SERV, INC, 81- *Concurrent Pos:* Asst prof, Space Inst, Univ Tenn, 77- *Mem:* Am Inst Aeronaut & Astronaut. *Res:* Wind tunnel wall interference, including subsonic, transonic and vertical/short take off and landing theories and development of the adaptive wall concept. *Mailing Add:* PWT/4T MS 600 Calspan Field Serv, Inc Arnold Afs TN 37389

KRAFT, ELISE, organic chemistry, deceased

KRAFT, GERALD F, b Salinas, Calif, Feb 22, 28; m 48, 79; c 4. ENTOMOLOGY. *Educ:* San Jose State Col, BA, 54; Wash State Univ, MS, 56; Ore State Univ, PhD(entom), 62. *Prof Exp:* Asst prof zool, 61-66, chmn dept biol, 71-74, ASSOC PROF BIOL, WESTERN WASH UNIV, 66-, CHMN DEPT BIOL, 77- *Concurrent Pos:* City of Bellingham grant, 62-64; dir inst freshwater studies, Western Wash State Col, 64-68; US Dept Interior grant, 66-; res assoc, Univ Calif, Berkeley, 68-69. *Mem:* Entom Soc Am. *Res:* General entomology; aquatic insects. *Mailing Add:* Dept of Biol Western Wash Univ Bellingham WA 98225

KRAFT, IRVIN ALAN, b Huntington, WVa, Nov 20, 21; m 51; c 4. PSYCHIATRY. *Educ:* NY Univ, MD, 49. *Prof Exp:* Asst prof psychiat, 57-61, asst prof pediat, 58-61, assoc prof psychiat & pediat, 61-77, CLIN PROF PSYCHIAT, BAYLOR COL MED, 77-; CLIN PROF MENT HEALTH,

UNIV TEX SCH PUB HEALTH HOUSTON, 75- *Concurrent Pos:* Med dir, Tex Inst Family Psychiat, 64-79. *Mem:* Fel Am Psychiat Asn; fel Am Acad Psychoanal; fel Am Acad Child Psychiat; life fel Am Orthopsychiat Asn. *Res:* Child psychiatry; psychoanalysis. *Mailing Add:* 2423 Gramercy Houston TX 77030

KRAFT, JOHN CHRISTIAN, b Schwenksville, Pa, Nov 15, 29; m 55; c 2. GEOLOGY, STRATIGRAPHY. *Educ:* Pa State Univ, BS, 51; Univ Minn, MS, 52, PhD(micropaleont), 55. *Prof Exp:* Geologist, Shell Can Ltd, 55-61, div stratigrapher, 61-64; from asst prof to assoc prof, 64-71, PROF GEOL, UNIV DEL, 71-, CHMN DEPT, 69- *Mem:* fel AAAS; Am Asn Petrol Geologists; fel Geol Soc Am; Soc Econ Paleont & Mineral; Am Inst Prof Geologists. *Res:* Geology of coasts; Holocene sedimentary environments; Ordovician and Holocene Ostracoda; archaeological geology. *Mailing Add:* Dept of Geol Univ of Del Newark DE 19711

KRAFT, JOHN M, b Gary, Ind, July 14, 38; m 64; c 2. PLANT PATHOLOGY. *Educ:* Ariz State Univ, BSc, 60; Univ Minn, St Paul, MS, 62; Univ Calif, Riverside, PhD(plant path), 66. *Prof Exp:* Res asst plant path, Univ Minn, St Paul, 60-62 & Univ Calif, Riverside, 62-66; RES PLANT PATHOLOGIST, CROP RES DIV, AGR RES SERV, USDA, 66- *Concurrent Pos:* Mem grad fac, Dept Plant Path, Wash State Univ. *Mem:* Am Phytopath Soc. *Res:* Soil-borne diseases of peas and their etiology, biology of the fungi and nematodes, their control and the nature and inheritance of resistance when found; control of soil-borne diseases of peas; breeding for root disease resistance in peas. *Mailing Add:* Irrigated Agr Res & Exten Ctr Prosser WA 99350

KRAFT, KENNETH J, b Dows, Iowa, Mar 3, 30; m 68; c 1. INVERTEBRATE ECOLOGY. *Educ:* Bemidji State Col, BS, 52; Univ NDak, MS, 53; Univ Minn, PhD(entom), 58. *Prof Exp:* Instr biol, Univ Minn, 56-58; asst prof, Moorhead State Col, 58-59 & Bemidji State Col, 59-61; asst prof, 61-64, ASSOC PROF BIOL, MICH TECHNOL UNIV, 64- *Mem:* Entom Soc Am. *Res:* Ecology of aquatic insects. *Mailing Add:* Dept Biol Sci Mich Technol Univ Houghton MI 49931

KRAFT, LELAND M, JR, b Gloversville, NY, Feb 27, 42; m 67; c 2. CIVIL ENGINEERING, SOIL MECHANICS. *Educ:* Ohio State Univ, BCE & MS, 65, PhD(civil eng), 68. *Prof Exp:* Res asst soil mech, Ohio State Univ, 63-66, res assoc, 66-68, res assoc civil eng, 68-69; asst prof soil mech, Dept Civil Eng, Auburn Univ, 69-72; proj eng, 72-74, MGR, SPEC PROJS GROUP, MCCELLAND ENG, INC, HOUSTON, 74- *Concurrent Pos:* Soil engr, Columbus Testing Lab, Ohio, 68-69; mem, Transp Res Bd, Nat Acad Sci-Nat Res Coun. *Mem:* Am Soc Civil Engrs; Int Soc Soil Mech & Found Eng; Coastal Soc; Marine Technol Soc. *Res:* Application of statistical and probability concepts to soil mechanics and foundation engineering; analysis and design of earth structures, product control and acceptance specification of earthwork; marine geotechnical engineering. *Mailing Add:* 2020 Briargreen Dr Houston TX 77077

KRAFT, LISBETH MARTHA, b Vienna, Austria, May 16, 20; nat US. PATHOLOGY, RADIOBIOLOGY. *Educ:* Cornell Univ, BS, 42, DVM, 45. *Prof Exp:* Asst parasitol, Cornell Univ, 45-46 & nutrit, Harvard Univ, 46; bacteriologist, NY State Dept Health, 47-49; asst, Yale Univ, 49-51, from instr to asst prof, 51-55; asst prof, NY Univ, 55-57; res assoc path & vet, Sch Med, Yale Univ, 57-61; asst dir, New York City Bur Labs & assoc mem, Pub Health Res Inst, 61-65; staff scientist, Bioquest Div, Becton Dickinson Co, 65-66; res vet, Oak Ridge Assoc Univs, 66-68; owner, L M Kraft Assocs, 68-74; specialist, Space Sci Lab, Univ Calif, Berkeley, 74-75; assoc scientist dept physics, Univ San Francisco, 75-77; RES SCIENTIST, AMES RES CTR, NASA, 77- *Concurrent Pos:* Consult, Sloan-Kettering Inst Cancer Res, NY, 59-61. *Honors & Awards:* Griffin Award, Am Asn Lab Animal Sci, 72; Charles River Prize, Am Vet Med Asn, 81. *Mem:* AAAS; Am Soc Microbiol; Am Vet Med Asn; Am Asn Lab Animal Sci; Am Col Lab Animal Med. *Res:* Central nervous system effects of cosmic ray (homogeneous differential equation) particles as applicable to manned spaceflight safety standards; investigations on health status of animals in spaceflight research; laboratory animal medicine and science. *Mailing Add:* PO Box 28 Moffett Field CA 94035

KRAFT, PATRICIA LYNN, b Somerville, NJ. TOXICOLOGY. *Educ:* Rutgers Col Agr & Environ Sci, BS, 72; Mass Inst Technol, PhD(toxicol), 79. *Prof Exp:* SR TOXICOLOGIST, BEST FOODS RES & ENG CTR, CPC NORTH AM, 80- *Mem:* Am Inst Nutrit; Am Col Toxicol; Inst Food Technologists. *Res:* Effect of diet on mainetnance of health and progression of disease; effect of dietary fat on adipose tissue compositon; immune function and drug metabolism. *Mailing Add:* 1120 Commerce Ave Union NJ 07083

KRAFT, R(ALPH) WAYNE, b Collingswood, NJ, Jan 14, 25; m 48; c 4. SYSTEMS THEORY, PHYSICAL METALLURGY. *Educ:* Lehigh Univ, BS, 48; Univ Mich, MS, 56, PhD(metall eng), 58. *Prof Exp:* Metallurgist, Am Brake Shoe Co, 48-54; instr metall, Univ Mich, 54-58; group leader mat res, United Aircraft Corp, 58-62; from assoc prof to prof metall eng, 62-67, N J Zinc Prof, 67-78, PROF METALL ENG, LEHIGH UNIV, 78- *Mem:* Fel AAAS; fel Am Soc Metals; Soc Gen Systs Res. *Res:* General systems theory and the philosophy of science and religion; analysis of cosmic processes using thermodynamic and information theory concepts; evolutionary ideas of thinkers such as Teihard de Chardin. *Mailing Add:* Dept of Metall Lehigh Univ Bethlehem PA 18015

KRAFT, ROBERT PAUL, b Seattle, Wash, June 16, 27; m 49; c 2. ASTRONOMY. *Educ:* Univ Wash, BS, 47, MS, 49; Univ Calif, PhD(astron), 55. *Prof Exp:* Instr math & astron, Whittier Col, 49-51; NSF fel, Mt Wilson & Palomar Observs, 55-56; asst prof astron, Ind Univ, 56-58 & Univ Chicago, 58-59; mem staff, Mt Wilson & Palomar Observs, 60-67; actg dir, 68-70, 71-73 & 80-81, PROF ASTRON & ASTRONR, LICK OBSERV, UNIV CALIF, SANTA CRUZ, 67-, DIR, LICK OBSERV, 81- *Concurrent Pos:* Warner Prize lectr, Am Astron Soc, 62; chmn bd studies astron & astrophys, Univ Calif, Santa Cruz, 68-70 & 78-80; vis fel, Univ Colo, 70. *Mem:* Nat Acad Sci; Am Astron Soc (pres, 74-76); Am Acad Arts & Sci; Int Astron Union. *Res:* Stellar spectroscopy; galactic structure. *Mailing Add:* Lick Observ Univ of Calif Santa Cruz CA 95064

KRAFT, SUMNER CHARLES, b Lynn, Mass, Aug 21, 28; m 63; c 3. INTERNAL MEDICINE, GASTROENTEROLOGY. *Educ:* Tufts Col, BS, 48; Boston Univ, AM, 49; Univ Chicago, MD, 55; Am Bd Internal Med, dipl, 62, Am Bd Gastroenterol, dipl, 65. *Prof Exp:* From instr to assoc prof, 59-73, PROF MED & COMT IMMUNOL, SCH MED, UNIV CHICAGO, 74- *Concurrent Pos:* USPHS spec res fel, 61-66, USPHS res career develop award, 67-71; res fel, Div Allergy, Immunol & Rheumatol, Scripps Clin & Res Found, La Jolla, Calif, 64-66; vis affil prof med, Uniformed Serv, Univ Health Sci, Bethesda, 79- *Honors & Awards:* William Beaumont Award, 77. *Mem:* AAAS; Am Col Physicians; Am Fedn Clin Res; Am Gastroenterol Asn; Am Soc Gastrointestinal Endoscopy. *Res:* Gastrointestinal immunology. *Mailing Add:* Dept Med Univ of Chicago Hosps 950 E 59th St Box 400 Chicago IL 60637

KRAFT, WILLIAM GERALD, b Evansville, Ind, July 15, 44; m 77. MICROBIOLOGY. *Educ:* Purdue Univ, BS, 66; Univ Wash, MS, 72; Ind Univ, PhD(microbiol), 77. *Prof Exp:* res eng chem, Dow Chem Co, 66-68; SR RES MICROBIOLOGIST, NORWICH-EATON PHARMACEUT, 77- *Mem:* Am Soc Microbiol. *Res:* Develop sporulation media for bacillus spores; thermal resistance of aerobic bacilli spores and define sterilization cycles for pharmaceutical products; microbial ecology of natural and synthetic substances. *Mailing Add:* 23 Brown Ave Norwich NY 13815

KRAG, WILLIAM ERIC, b Brooklyn, NY, Aug 7, 28; m 51; c 4. PHYSICS. *Educ:* Mass Inst Techno), SB, 50, PhD(physics), 59. *Prof Exp:* Asst, Mass Inst Technol, 50-52, PHYSICIST, LINCOLN LAB, MASS INST TECHNOL, 52- *Mem:* Am Phys Soc; Inst Elec & Electronic Engrs; Sigma Xi; AAAS. *Res:* Solid state physics; semiconductors; imaging devices. *Mailing Add:* Mass Inst Technol PO Box 73 Lexington MA 02173

KRAHENBUHL, JAMES LEE, b Appleton, Wis, Oct 7, 42; m 65; c 1. INFECTIOUS DISEASES, TUMOR IMMUNOLOGY. *Educ:* Univ Wis-Madison, BS, 64, MS, 67, PhD(med microbiol), 70. *Prof Exp:* Fel, Palo Alto Med Res Found, 70-71, sr res assoc immunol & infectious dis, 72-79; CHIEF, LEPROSY RES UNIT, USPHS HOSP, SAN FRANCISCO, 79- *Concurrent Pos:* Fel med, Med Ctr, Stanford Univ, 70-71, res assoc, 72-78; Pub Health Serv Res Career Develop Award, Nat Inst Allergy & Infectious Dis, 74-79. *Mem:* AAAS; Am Asn Immunologists; Soc Exp Biol & Med; Am Soc Microbiol; Int Leprosy Asn. *Res:* Mechanisms of host resistance to intracellular pathogens and tumors. *Mailing Add:* Leprosy Res Unit USPHS Hosp 15th Ave & Lake St San Francisco CA 94118

KRAHL, NAT W(ETZEL), b Houston, Tex, Sept 30, 21; m 49; c 5. STRUCTURAL ENGINEERING. *Educ:* Rice Inst, BA, 42, BS, 43; Univ Ill, MS, 50, PhD(civil eng), 63. *Prof Exp:* Asst civil eng, Rice Inst, 43-44; struct engr, Walter P Moore, Consult Engr, 46-49, chief design engr, 50-57; asst prof civil eng, 57-64, assoc prof struct eng, 64-68, chmn, Dept Civil Eng, 72-77, PROF CIVIL ENG & ARCHIT, RICE UNIV, 68- *Concurrent Pos:* Consult engr, 57-; partner, Krahl & Gaddy Engrs, 69-76; prin, Nat Krahl & Assocs, Consult Engrs, 76- *Honors & Awards:* State-of-the-Art Award, Am Soc Civil Engrs, 74. *Mem:* Am Soc Civil Engrs; Am Concrete Inst; Int Asn Bridge & Struct Engrs; Int Asn Shell Struct; Am Consult Engrs Coun. *Res:* Structural design of buildings; concrete behavior under triaxial stress; stability of tensile cracks in concrete beams; analysis of space frames; polymer concrete; behavior, analysis, and design of structural systems. *Mailing Add:* Dept of Civil Eng Rice Univ PO Box 1892 Houston TX 77001

KRAHLER, STANLEY EARL, b Canton, Ohio, May 11, 18; m 44; c 2. ORGANIC CHEMISTRY. *Educ:* Knox Col, AB, 39; Univ Va, PhD(org chem), 42. *Prof Exp:* Asst chem, Univ Va, 39-40; res chemist, Jackson Lab, 42-55, chemist, Chambers Works, plant technol sect, 55-60, res chemist, Jackson Lab, 60-62, sr res chemist, 62-67, res assoc, 67-71, res assoc, Chambers Works, 71-75, RES ASSOC, JACKSON LAB, E I DU PONT DE NEMOURS & CO, 75- *Mem:* Am Chem Soc. *Res:* Organic and quinoline chemistry; fluorohydrocarbons; dyestuffs; lepidine derivatives; aromatic isocyanates; surfactants; textile finishes; fluorinated textile auxiliaries. *Mailing Add:* Jackson Lab E I du Pont de Nemours & Co Wilmington DE 19898

KRAHLING, JEFFREY BUREN, b Grass Valley, Calif, Feb 7, 49; m 72. BIOCHEMISTRY, PLANT PHYSIOLOGY. *Educ:* Univ Calif, Santa Cruz, AB, 71; Univ Calif, Riverside, PhD(plant physiol), 77. *Prof Exp:* RES ASSOC, DEPT BIOCHEM, MICH STATE UNIV, 76- *Mem:* Am Soc Plant Physiologists. *Res:* Peroxisomes; fatty acid oxidation. *Mailing Add:* 637 Cornell East Lansing MI 48823

KRAHMER, ROBERT LEE, b Forest Grove, Ore, Dec 28, 32; m 57; c 2. FOREST PRODUCTS. *Educ:* Ore State Univ, BS, 58, MS, 60; State Univ NY Col Forestry, Syracuse Univ, wood prod eng), 62. *Prof Exp:* Instr forest prod, 59-60, asst prof, forest res labs, 62-67, assoc prof, 67-77, PROF FOREST PROD, ORE STATE UNIV, 77- *Mem:* Forest Prod Res Soc; Soc Wood Sci & Technol; Int Asn Wood Anat. *Res:* Light and electron microscope studies of fine structure of wood; variability of anatomical properties of wood. *Mailing Add:* Forest Prod Dept Ore State Univ Corvallis OR 97331

KRAHN, ROBERT CARL, b Minneapolis, Minn, Dec 1, 41; m 78; c 2. ORGANIC CHEMISTRY. *Educ:* Univ Minn, BChE, 63; Univ Wash, PhD(org chem), 68. *Prof Exp:* Res chemist, Org Chem Dept, 68-73, process chemist, 73-78, SR CHEMIST, CHEM, DYES & PIGMENTS DEPT, JACKSON LAB, E I DU PONT DE NEMOURS & CO, INC, 78- *Mem:* Am Chem Soc; Sigma Xi; AAAS. *Res:* Emulsion polymerization; monomer synthesis; flurochemicals; surfactant chemistry; ethoxylation; textile finishing. *Mailing Add:* 17 Polaris Dr N Star Newark DE 19711

KRAHNKE, HAROLD C, b Beloit, Wis, Oct 12, 07; m 31; c 2. PHYSIOLOGICAL CHEMISTRY, PHARMACY. *Educ:* Univ Wis, BS, 40, MS, 41. *Prof Exp:* Pharmacist, Retail Pharm, 26-36; res asst physiol chem, Univ Wis, 40-41; res chemist, Lakeside Labs, Inc, 41-47, chief control chemist, 47-52, chief pharmaceut div, 52-62; dir pharmaceut dept, Lakeside Labs Div, Colgate-Palmolive Co, 62-73. *Mem:* Am Chem Soc; Am Pharmaceut Asn; Acad Pharmaceut Sci. *Res:* Pharmaceutical research and product development; formulation and manufacturing procedures; synthesis of organic medicinal compounds; quality control of pharmaceuticals. *Mailing Add:* 6770 N Yates Rd Milwaukee WI 53217

KRAHULA, JOSEPH L(OUIS), b Czech, July 22, 23; nat US; m 59; c 2. MECHANICS. *Educ:* Rensselaer Polytech Inst, BME, 46, MS, 50; Univ Ill, PhD(mech), 52. *Prof Exp:* Instr mech, Rensselaer Polytech Inst, 46-50; asst, Univ Ill, 50-52; from asst prof to assoc prof, 52-67, PROF MECH, HARTFORD GRAD CTR, RENSSELAER POLYTECH INST, 67- *Mem:* Assoc fel Am Inst Aeronaut & Astronaut; Int Asn Bridge & Struct Engrs. *Res:* Vibrations and elasticity. *Mailing Add:* Hartford Grad Ctr 275 Windsor St Hartford CT 06120

KRAICER, JACOB, b Toronto, Ont, Oct 28, 31; m 57; c 2. ENDOCRINOLOGY, NEUROENDOCRINOLOGY. *Educ:* Univ Toronto, BA, 54, MD, 58, PhD(physiol), 62. *Prof Exp:* Rotating intern med, Toronto Gen Hosp, 58-59; res assoc physiol, Banting & Best Dept Med Res, Univ Toronto, 61-62; from asst prof to assoc prof, 64-72, PROF PHYSIOL, QUEEN'S UNIV, ONT, 72- *Concurrent Pos:* Med Res Coun Can fel, Endocrinol Lab, Fac Med, Laval Univ, 62-63 & Animal Morphol Lab, Free Univ Brussels, 63-64; Med Res Coun Can scholar, 64-66; ed, Can J Physiol & Pharmacol, 81- *Mem:* Int Soc Neuroendocrinol; Am Physiol Soc; Endocrine Soc; Can Physiol Soc; Can Soc Endocrinol & Mutabolism. *Res:* Mechanism and related peptides and of regulation of corticotrophin and growth hormone secretion in the adenohypophysis. *Mailing Add:* Dept Physiol Botterell Hall Queen's Univ Kingston ON K7L 3N6 Can

KRAICER, PERETZ FREEMAN, b Toronto, Ont, Aug 15, 32; m 58, 81; c 4. REPRODUCTIVE PHYSIOLOGY, ENDOCRINOLOGY. *Educ:* Univ Toronto, BA, 55; Weizmann Inst Sci, Israel, PhD(reproductive physiol), 60. *Prof Exp:* Res asst exp biol, Weizmann Inst Sci, 60-62, res assoc, 62-65, sr scientist, 65-69; sr lectr zool, 65-68, assoc prof, 69-76, dir, Soferman Inst Fertil, 69-82, PROF ENDOCRINOL, TEL AVIV UNIV, 77-, PROF ZOOL, 77- *Concurrent Pos:* Vis scientist, Biomed Div, Pop Coun, NY, 75-76; vis prof obstet & gynec, Univ Med & Dent, NJ. *Mem:* Israel Soc Study Fertil (secy, 75-); Int Soc Res Reproduction; Brit Soc Study Fertil; Israel Endocrine Soc; Israel Soc Physiol & Pharmacol. *Res:* Comparative biology of reproduction, ovulation, fertilization, endocrinology of carbohydrate metabolism, ovum implantation and decidual cell growth and differentiation. *Mailing Add:* Dept of Zool George S Wise Ctr for Life Sci Tel Aviv Univ Ramat Aviv Israel

KRAICHNAN, ROBERT HARRY, b Philadelphia, Pa, Jan 15, 28; m 54; c 1. STATISTICAL MECHANICS. *Educ:* Mass Inst Technol, BS, 47, PhD, 49. *Prof Exp:* Mem, Inst Advan Study, 49-50; mem tech staff, Bell Tel Labs, Inc, 50-52; res assoc, Electronics Res Lab, Columbia Univ, 52-56; inst math sci, NY Univ, 56-59, sr res scientist, 59-62; INDEPENDENT CONSULT, 62- *Concurrent Pos:* Consult, Naval Res Lab, 57-59 & NASA, 61-; assoc physics, Woods Hole Oceanog Inst, 60-; res affiliate, Mass Inst Technol, 63- *Mem:* Fel Am Phys Soc; Acoust Soc Am; Italian Phys Soc. *Res:* Quantum and classical statistical mechanics; random processes; turbulence, quantum field and relativity theory; acoustics. *Mailing Add:* Dublin NH 03444

KRAIHANZEL, CHARLES S, b New Bedford, Mass, Sept 6, 35; m 57; c 5. INORGANIC CHEMISTRY. *Educ:* Brown Univ, ScB, 57; Univ Wis, MS, 59, PhD(chem), 62. *Prof Exp:* From asst prof to assoc prof, 62-70, PROF INORG CHEM, LEHIGH UNIV, 70- *Mem:* AAAS; Am Chem Soc. *Res:* Syntheses, reactions, nature of bonding and physical properties, such as infrared, electronic, and nuclear magnetic resonance spectroscopies, of inorganic and organometallic compounds, especially of transition metals. *Mailing Add:* Dept of Chem Seeley G Mudd Bldg 6 Bethlehem PA 18015

KRAIMAN, EUGENE ALFRED, b Philadelphia, Pa, Apr 11, 29; m 56. POLYMER CHEMISTRY. *Educ:* Univ Pa, BS, 50; Univ Ill, MS, 51, PhD(chem), 53. *Prof Exp:* Res chemist, Union Carbide Plastics Co, 53-56 & Hooker Chem Co, 56-58; supvr, Plastics Div, Nopco Chem Co, 58-61; res sect head, Sun Chem Corp, 61-68; PRES, POLYMER SYSTS CORP, 68- *Mem:* Am Chem Soc. *Res:* Polyurethanes; organic chemicals; elastomers; coatings; adhesives; ultraviolet radiation cured systems. *Mailing Add:* 50 Greendale Rd Cedar Grove NJ 07009

KRAINES, DAVID PAUL, b Chicago, Ill, Mar 7, 41; m 64; c 2. TOPOLOGY. *Educ:* Oberlin Col, AB, 61; Univ Calif, Berkeley, MA, 63, PhD(math), 65. *Prof Exp:* Instr math, Mass Inst Technol, 65-67; asst prof, Haverford Col, 67-70, actg chmn, 68-69; guest prof, Aarhus Univ, 70-71; asst prof, 71-73, ASSOC PROF MATH, DUKE UNIV, 73- *Mem:* Am Math Soc. *Res:* Algebraic topology. *Mailing Add:* Dept of Math Duke Univ Durham NC 27706

KRAINTZ, LEON, b Johnstown, Pa, Oct 3, 24; m 49; c 3. PHYSIOLOGY, ENDOCRINOLOGY. *Educ:* Harvard Univ, AB, 50; Rice Inst, MA, 52, PhD(biol), 54. *Prof Exp:* Res scientist exp med, Univ Tex M D Anderson Hosp & Tumor Inst, 51-52, from instr to assoc prof physiol, Dent Br, 54-62; prof biol, Rice Univ, 62-64; assoc prof oral biol, 64-66, PROF ORAL BIOL & HON PROF PHYSIOL, UNIV BC, 66-, HEAD DEPT ORAL BIOL, 69- *Concurrent Pos:* USPHS spec fel physiol, Howard Florey Inst Exp Physiol, Univ Melbourne, 68-69; asst, Rice Inst, 51-52; vis instr, Col Med, Baylor Univ, 56-63; vis lectr, Univ St Thomas, Tex, 57-63. *Mem:* Fel AAAS; Endocrine Soc; Soc Nuclear Med; Am Physiol Soc; Can Physiol Soc. *Res:* Radioisotopic techniques in biology and medicine; protein hormones; mineral metabolism; salivation. *Mailing Add:* Dept of Oral Biol Fac of Dent Univ of BC Vancouver BC V6T 1W5 Can

KRAITCHMAN, JEROME, b New York, NY, Mar 5, 26; m 57; c 3. INSTRUMENTATION, MATERIALS SCIENCE ENGINEERING. *Educ:* Syracuse Univ, AB, 48; Columbia Univ, AM, 50, PhD(chem physics), 54. *Prof Exp:* Asst, Columbia Univ, 49-53; res physicist, Res Labs, Westinghouse Elec Corp, 53-66; res physicist, Glass Res Ctr, PPG Industs, Inc, 66-75; supvr, Cent Res Facil, 76-80, ASST DIR, MAT RES LAB, CARNEGIE-MELLON UNIV, 80- *Mem:* Am Phys Soc. *Res:* Materials science; microwave spectroscopy; molecular structure; dielectrics; semiconductors; physics and chemistry of surfaces; thin films; adhesion. *Mailing Add:* 2409 Collins Rd Pittsburgh PA 15235

KRAJEWSKI, JOHN J, b Chicago, Ill, Mar 27, 31; m 59; c 2. SYNTHETIC ORGANIC CHEMISTRY, POLYMER CHEMISTRY. *Educ:* Loyola Univ Ill, BS, 53, MS, 54; Carnegie Inst Technol, PhD(org chem), 58. *Prof Exp:* Res chemist, Swift & Co, 58-60, div head, 60-62; res chemist, Int Minerals & Chem Corp, 62-67, synthetic org specialist, 67-70; res chemist, 70-73, tech mgr, 73-79, MGR POLYMER DEVELOP, DE SOTO, INC, 79- *Mem:* Am Chem Soc. *Res:* Organic synthesis; polymers; natural products; plant growth regulants; fungicides; photopolymerization; organic photoconductors. *Mailing Add:* 932 Valley Stream Dr Wheeling IL 60090

KRAJINA, VLADIMIR JOSEPH, b Slavice, Czech, Jan 30, 05; Can citizen; m 30; c 2. PLANT ECOLOGY, PLANT TAXONOMY. *Educ:* Charles Univ, Prague, ScD(bot), 27. *Hon Degrees:* LLD, Notre Dame Univ, 73. *Prof Exp:* Asst, Bot Inst, Charles Univ, 25-33, docent habil plant taxon & ecol, 34-45, prof bot & head, Div Plant Sociol & Ecol, Bot Inst, 45-48; spec lectr, 49-51, from asst prof to prof, 54-73, HON PROF BOT, UNIV BC, 73- *Concurrent Pos:* Res fel, Yale Univ & Univ Honolulu, 29-30 & Charles Univ & Masaryk Nat Res Coun, 37; vis prof, Univ Hawaii, 61-62; hon assoc, Bernice P Bishop Mus, 63-; mem & chmn, BC Ecol Reserves Comt, 68-; chmn ecol subcomt, Standards Comt Pac Bot, 71-; mem adv comt, Ecol Reserves Act, 72-, asn comt ecol reserves, Nat Res Coun Can, 75-; assoc ed, Syesis, 73- *Honors & Awards:* George Lawson Medal, Can Bot Asn, 72. *Mem:* AAAS; Bot Soc Am; Ecol Soc Am; Am Soc Plant Taxon; Soc Am Foresters. *Res:* Forest autecology and synecology; grassland; reforestation; ecological classification; plant taxonomy of Central Europe, Pacific North America, Western Canadian Arctic, and Hawaiian Islands; taxonomy of vascular plants, bryophytes and lichens; experimental forest tree nutrition; conservation of nature, including ecological reserves in Canada, especially British Columbia. *Mailing Add:* Dept of Bot Univ of BC Vancouver BC V6T 2B1 Can

KRAKAUER, HENRY, b Jaworzno, Poland, May 31, 39; US citizen; m 74. IMMUNOLOGY, BIOCHEMISTRY. *Educ:* Yeshiva Univ, BA & BHL, 60; NY Univ, MD, 64; Yale Univ, PhD(phys chem), 68. *Prof Exp:* asst prof chem, Wash State Univ, 68-74, assoc prof biochem, 74-79; CHIEF, GENETICS & TRANSPLANTATION BIOL BR, NAT INST ALLERGY & INFECTIOUS DIS, NIH, 79- *Mem:* Am Chem Soc; Am Soc Biol Chemists; Biophys Soc; Am Asn Immunol. *Res:* Immunogenetics; immunobiology; immunochemistry; thermodynamics of macromolecular complexes. *Mailing Add:* Genetics & Transplantation Biol Br Nat Inst Allergy & Infectious Dis Bethesda MD 20205

KRAKAUER, TERESA, b China; US citizen. BIOCHEMISTRY, CELL BIOLOGY. *Educ:* Wash State Univ, BSc(chem) & BSc(biochem), 71; Iowa State Univ, PhD(biochem), 75. *Prof Exp:* Res assoc biochem, Wash State Univ, 75-78; NIH staff fel biochem, Nat Inst Arthritis, Metab & Digestive Dis, 78-80, NIH STAFF FEL, NAT INST DENT RES, 80- *Mem:* Am Chem Soc; Sigma Xi; Biophys Soc. *Res:* Molecular biology; cell surface proteins; molecular basis of immunogenicity; developmental biology; gene transfer. *Mailing Add:* NIH Bldg 30 Rm 329 Bethesda MD 20014

KRAKE, GUSS LAWRENCE, b Minneapolis, Minn, June 20, 35; m 63; c 2. ELECTRICAL ENGINEERING, MATHEMATICS. *Educ:* Univ Minn, BS, 59, MSEE, 61. *Prof Exp:* Res engr, Univac Div, Sperry Rand Corp, 61-63, proj engr, 63-65; electronic engr, NStar Res & Develop Inst, 65-67, sr engr, 67-71; SR RES ENGR, CARGILL INC, 71- *Concurrent Pos:* Instr exten div, Univ Minn, 62-70. *Mem:* Inst Elec & Electronics Engrs. *Res:* Special purpose computer development; industrial instrumentation research and development; electro-optical development including laser applications; automation and computer systems utilization; sonic and ultrasonic device and system development; computer memory development. *Mailing Add:* 6939 Harriet Ave S Richfield MN 55423

KRAKOFF, IRWIN HAROLD, b Columbus, Ohio, July 20, 23; m 46; c 3. MEDICINE. *Educ:* Ohio State Univ, BA, 43, MD, 47; Am Bd Internal Med, dipl. *Prof Exp:* Res fel, Sloan-Kettering Inst Cancer Res, 53-54, from asst to assoc, 54-61, assoc mem, 61-69, chief div chemother res, 70-72, chief med oncol serv, 70-74, head lab clin chemother & pharmacol, 73-76, mem, 69-76, assoc chmn dept med, attend physician & chief clin chemother serv, 74-76; DIR VT REGIONAL CANCER CTR, 76-; PROF MED, UNIV VT, PROF PHARMACOL, 77- *Concurrent Pos:* Spec fel, Mem Hosp Cancer & Allied Dis, 53-55, clin asst, 55-58, from asst attend physician to assoc attend physician, 58-69, attend physician physician, 69-76, chief, Med Oncol Serv, 69-74; Sloan award cancer res, 65-; res assoc, Med Col, Cornell Univ, 55-58, from asst prof to assoc prof med, 58-75, prof, 75-76. *Mem:* Harvey Soc; Am Asn Cancer Res; Am Col Physicians; Am Fedn Clin Res; Am Soc Pharmacol & Exp Therapeut. *Res:* Cancer chemotherapy. *Mailing Add:* Vt Regional Cancer Ctr Univ of Vt Burlington VT 05401

KRAKOW, BURTON, b Brooklyn, NY, Feg 12, 28. PHYSICAL CHEMISTRY, SPECTROSCOPY. *Educ:* City Col New York, BS, 49; Brooklyn Col, MA, 58; Mass Inst Technol, PhD(phys chem), 62. *Prof Exp:* Jr engr extractive metall, Metall Lab, Sylvania Elec Prod, 54-57; sr phys chemist molecular spectros, Control Instrument Div, Warner & Swasey Co, 62-69; sr prin develop engr, Honeywell Inc, 69-73; res engr, ARO Inc, 73-78; PROJ MGR ADV TECHNOL, NY STATE ENERGY RES & DEVELOP AUTHORITY, 78- *Mem:* Am Chem Soc; Am Phys Soc; Coblentz Soc. *Res:* Infrared spectroscopy; radiant heat transfer; spectroscopic pyrometry; infrared instrumentation; solar energy conversion. *Mailing Add:* NY State Energy Res & Agency Bldg 2 Empire State Plaza Albany NY 12223

454 / KRAKOW

KRAKOW, JOSEPH S, b New York, NY, Dec 23, 29; m 55; c 2. BIOCHEMISTRY, MOLECULAR BIOLOGY. Educ: Univ Mich, BS, 55; Yale Univ, PhD(pharmacol), 61. Prof Exp: USPHS fel biochem, NY Univ, 61-63; assoc res biochemist, Space Sci Lab, Univ Calif, Berkeley, 63-71, lectr, Dept Med Physics, 64-71; PROF BIOL SCI, HUNTER COL, 71- Concurrent Pos: Biochem Study Sect, NIH, 75-, chmn, 78. Mem: Am Chem Soc; Am Soc Biol Chem. Res: Nucleic acids; enzymology. Mailing Add: Dept of Biol Sci Hunter Col New York NY 10021

KRAKOWER, GERALD W, b Brooklyn, NY, Nov 14, 29; m 59; c 6. ORGANIC CHEMISTRY. Educ: Yeshiva Univ, BA, 51; Columbia Univ, MA, 53; Wayne State Univ, PhD(org chem), 58. Prof Exp: Fel, USPHS, Weizmann Inst Sci, Israel, 58-59; sr res chemist, Squibb Inst Med Res, Olin Mathieson Chem Corp, NJ, 59-68; ASSOC PROF CHEM, BAR-ILAN UNIV, ISRAEL, 68- Mem: The Chem Soc. Res: Structure and stereochemistry of natural products; steroid chemistry; conformational analysis. Mailing Add: Dept of Chem Bar-Ilan Univ Ramat-Gan Israel

KRAKOWSKI, FRED, b Zuoz, Switz, July 31, 27; m 58; c 1. MATHEMATICS. Educ: Swiss Fed Inst Technol, DSc(math), 57. Prof Exp: From instr to asst prof math, Univ Calif, Davis, 57-67; assoc prof, Sacramento State Col, 67-70, PROF MATH, CALIF STATE UNIV, SACRAMENTO, 70- Mem: Am Math Soc. Res: Algebra. Mailing Add: Genferstl 30 8002 Zurich Switzerland

KRAKOWSKI, MARTIN, b Lodz, Poland, Aug 18, 25; nat US; m 53. MATHEMATICS. Educ: Univ Ill, BS, 49, MS, 50; Carnegie Inst Technol, PhD(math), 53. Prof Exp: Physicist, Anderson Phys Lab, Ill, 47-51; proj mathematician, Carnegie Inst Technol, 51-53; res physicist, Calif Res Corp Div, Standard Oil Co Calif, 53-57; sr engr, Radio Corp Am, NJ, 57-58; res mathematician, Hughes Aircraft Co, Calif, 58-60; chief, Bus Anal Sect, Martin-Marietta, Colo, 60-61; consult indust & govt, 61-67; prof opers res, Sch Bus Admin, Tulane Univ, 67-69; CONSULT OPERS RES, ECON & SOC SCI, 69- Concurrent Pos: Vis prof opers res, Drexel Univ, 79-80. Mem: Fr Asn Econ & Tech Cybernet; Opers Res Soc Am. Res: Operations research; statistics and probability; management sciences; applied mathematics; economics; demography. Mailing Add: Suite 237 5301 Westbard Circle Bethesda MD 20016

KRAL, ROBERT, b Highland Park, Ill, Feb 28, 26; m 57; c 1. PLANT TAXONOMY. Educ: NC State Col, BS, 52; Fla State Univ, PhD(bot), 59. Prof Exp: Asst bot, Fla State Univ, 55-58; instr, Northeast La State Col, 58-59; asst prof, Va Polytech Inst, 59-65; from asst prof to assoc prof biol, 65-73, PROF BIOL, VANDERBILT UNIV, 73- Res: Vascular plant taxonomy; floristics of southeastern coastal plain; studies in Annonaceae, Cyperaceae and Xyridaceae. Mailing Add: Dept of Gen Biol Vanderbilt Univ Nashville TN 37240

KRALL, ALBERT RAYMOND, b Eaton, Ohio, July 23, 22; m 45, 67; c 8. BIOCHEMISTRY. Educ: Univ Wis, BS, 50, MS, 52, PhD(biochem), 53. Prof Exp: Asst biochem, Univ Wis, 50-53; assoc biochemist, Biol Div, Oak Ridge Nat Lab, 53-55; assoc plant physiol, Univ Minn, 55-56; sr biochemist, Res Inst Advan Studies, Md, 56-60; from asst prof to assoc prof psychiat & biochem, Sch Med, Univ Miami, 60-65; assoc prof, Sch Med, Univ NC, 65-69; PROF BIOCHEM, MED UNIV SC, 69- Concurrent Pos: NIH career develop award, 61-65 & 66-69; vis prof, Dept Zool, Univ Col, Dublin, 79-; Fogarty sr int fel, USPHS, 79-80. Mem: AAAS; Am Soc Cell Biol; Am Chem Soc; Sigma Xi; Am Soc Biol Chemists. Res: Biochemistry and toxicology of lead; biochemistry of calcium and magnesium; calcium transport in mitochondria and its regulation; carbon monoxide metabolism. Mailing Add: Dept of Biochem Med Univ of SC Charleston SC 29425

KRALL, ALLAN M, b Bellefonte, Pa, Feb 25, 36; m 58; c 4. MATHEMATICS. Educ: Pa State Univ, BS, 58; Univ Va, MA, 60, PhD(math), 63. Prof Exp: From asst prof to assoc prof, 63-71, PROF MATH, PA STATE UNIV, 71- Concurrent Pos: Grants, NASA, 65-69 & US Air Force, 77-79. Mem: Math Asn Am; Am Math Soc. Res: Differential operators. Mailing Add: Dept of Math Pa State Univ University Park PA 16802

KRALL, HARRY LEVERN, b York, Pa, June 13, 07; m 34, 63; c 2. MATHEMATICS. Educ: Gettysburg Col, BS, 27, MS, 28; Brown Univ, PhD(math), 32. Prof Exp: Instr math, Gettysburg Col, 27-28 & Brown Univ, 28-32; from instr to assoc prof, Pa State Col, 33-48; prof, 48-76, EMER PROF MATH, PA STATE UNIV, UNIVERSITY PARK, 76- Mem: Am Math Soc; Math Asn Am. Res: Analysis; differential equations; special functions. Mailing Add: 346 E Irvin Ave State College PA 16801

KRALL, JOHN MORTON, b Bellefonte, Pa, July 28, 38; m 67; c 2. BIOSTATISTICS. Educ: Pa State Univ, BA, 60; Univ Iowa, MS, 62, PhD(statist), 69. Prof Exp: Mathematician, Comput Br, NIH, 62-65; asst prof biomet, Univ Tex MD Anderson Hosp & Tumor Inst Houston, 69-70; asst prof pub health & prev med, 70-73, assoc prof biostatist, 73-79, PROF BIOSTATIST, WVA UNIV, 79- Mem: Biomet Soc; Am Statist Asn; Soc Clin Trials. Res: Development of methodology for medical statistical applications; study of factors affecting survival. Mailing Add: Dept Commun Med WVa Univ Med Ctr Morgantown WV 26506

KRALL, NICHOLAS ANTHONY, b Kansas City, Kans, Feb 16, 32; m 54; c 6. PHYSICS. Educ: Univ Notre Dame, BSc, 54; Cornell Univ, PhD(theoret physics), 59. Prof Exp: Mem res staff solid state physics, RCA Labs, NJ, 54; mem res staff theoret physics, John Jay Hopkins Lab Pure & Appl Sci, Gen Atomic Div, Gen Dynamics Corp, 59-67; asst mgr theory, Gen Atomic Controlled Fusion Res Prog, 67; prof physics, Univ Md, College Park, 67-73; vis res prof physics, Univ Calif, San Diego, 73-74; dir lab appl plasma studies, Sci Applns Inc, 74-78, vpres, 77-78; VPRES, JAYCOR, SAN DIEGO, 78- Concurrent Pos: Dir joint prog plasma physics, Naval Res Lab, Univ Md, 71-73; Guggenheim Found fel, 73-74. Mem: Fel Am Phys Soc; Sigma Xi;

AAAS. Res: Controlled thermonuclear fusion; plasma physics; high energy nuclear physics; electron scattering; application of dispersion relation technique to atomic physics; magnetohydrodynamics; plasma stability theory. Mailing Add: Jaycor San Diego CA 92138

KRAM, DAVID, b Mar 13, 49; US citizen. CYTOGENTICS, MUTAGENESIS. Educ: Univ Conn, BA, 71, PhD(develop biol), 76. Prof Exp: STAFF FEL GERONT, NAT INST AGING, BALTIMORE CITY HOSP, 76-79; BIOLOGIST, OFF TOXIC SUBSTANCES, US ENVIRON PROTECTION AGENCY, 79-; ADJ ASSOC PROF RADIOL, SCH MED, GEORGE WASHINGTON UNIV, 79- Mem: Soc Cell Biol; Environ Mutagenesis Soc; Genetic Toxicol Soc; Geront Soc; Teratol Soc. Res: Alterations in DNA repair and cellular replication as a function of aging; analysis of sister chromatid exchanges as a screen for environmental mutagens; transplacental mutagenesis; use of invitro cell lines for promutagen metabolism. Mailing Add: Sch Med George Washington Univ 2300 Eye St NW Ross Hall Rm 13 Washington DC 20037

KRAMBECK, FREDERICK JOHN, chemical engineering, see previous edition

KRAMER, AARON R, b New York, NY, Apr 26, 32; m 60; c 3. MECHANICAL ENGINEERING, INSTRUMENTATION. Educ: State Univ NY Maritime Col, BME, 54; City Col New York, MME, 63. Prof Exp: Appl engr instr, Bailey Meter Co, 56-63; assoc prof eng, 63-71, PROF ENG, STATE UNIV NY, MARITIME COL, 71- Concurrent Pos: Consult, Simulation Autodyn Inc, 67- & Stone & Webster Eng Corp, 73-; Inst Environ Sci res grant, 68-69; Maritime Admin, US Dept Commerce res grant, 69-73. Mem: Instrument Soc Am; Am Soc Mech Engrs; Am Soc Eng Educ. Res: Automatic control design and analysis; simulation of mechanical, chemical processes and energy management techniques with analogue, digital and hybrid computers; instrumentation and data collection systems and analysis. Mailing Add: 15 Sutton Rd Monsey NY 10952

KRAMER, A)FRED WILLIAM, JR, b Astoria, NY, Jan 19, 30; m 59; c 2. MORPHOLOGICAL BIOLOGY. Educ: Fordham Univ, BS, 56, MS, 59. Prof Exp: Jr pharmacologist cardiovasc physiol, Res Labs, Burroughs Wellcome & Co, 56-59; RES BIOLOGIST EXP PATH, LEDERLE LABS, AM CYANAMID CO, 59- Concurrent Pos: Instr, Bronx Community Col, 61-72, asst prof, 72- Res: Cardiovascular pharmacology of anti-arhythmia compounds; normal and pathological morphology and technical data of laboratory animals; development of practical techniques for use in experimental pathology. Mailing Add: 206 Lake Rd Valley Cottage NY 10989

KRAMER, AMIHUD, b Drohobyck, Austria-Hungary, May 7, 13; nat US; m 39; c 2. FOOD SCIENCE. Educ: Univ Md, BS, 38, MS, 39, PhD(hort), 42. Prof Exp: Farm mgr, Herzliah, Palestine, 33-34; coop agt, Soil Conserv Serv, USDA, 39-41; food res chemist, Nat Canners Asn, Washington, DC, 41-44; res assoc, 44-47, assoc prof hort, 48-49, prof, 49-80, EMER PROF, FOOD SCI PROG, UNIV MD, COLLEGE PARK, 80- Concurrent Pos: Asst, Univ Md, 38-41; lectr, City Col New York, 58-59; Consult food processing specialist, US Opers Mission, Israel, 54, 60 & 69, Ecuador, 62 & 63, Thailand, 65 & 67, Malaya, 67, PR, 65, 66, 67 & 71, Ghana, 68, Brazil, 70 & 77, Venezuela, 70, 74, 78 & 81, Korea, 72, India, 73, Egypt, 78, Jamaica, 80, Mexico, 80 & 81 & Paraguay, 81; dir, Govt-Indust Oyster Res Proj, 59-62; sci adv, Refrig Res Found, 60-80, dir, 80-; Sigma Xi res award, 79. Honors & Awards: Woodbury Award, 50 & 52; Nicholas Appert Award, Inst Food Technologists, 76. Mem: Fel AAAS; fel Am Soc Hort Sci; fel Am Soc Qual Control; fel Am Inst Chemists; assoc Am Statist Asn. Res: Nutritive value of foods; quality control in food production and processing; quality measurements; product development; food preservation. Mailing Add: Col Agr F-1122 Univ Md College Park MD 20742

KRAMER, BERNARD, b New York, NY, Nov 12, 22; m 46; c 2. SOLID STATE PHYSICS. Educ: City Col New York, BS, 42; NY Univ, PhD(physics), 52. Prof Exp: Physicist, Fed Tel & Radio Corp, 42-47; instr, Brooklyn Col, 47-49; res asst, NY Univ, 49-52, res assoc, 52-65, res scientist, 65-69; lectr 53-55, from asst prof to assoc prof, 55-66, chmn dept physics & astron, 60-71, PROF PHYSICS, HUNTER COL, CITY UNIV NEW YORK, 66- Concurrent Pos: Vis prof, Munich Technol Univ, 59-60; vis fel, Princeton Univ, 73-74; sci collab, Brookhaven Nat Lab, 80-81; vis scholar, Univ Del, 81. Mem: Am Phys Soc. Res: Luminescence; photoconductivity; photovoltaic effects. Mailing Add: Dept Physics & Astron Hunter Col 695 Park Ave New York NY 10021

KRAMER, BRIAN DALE, b Pottsville, Pa, Nov 17, 42; m 67. PHYSICAL ORGANIC CHEMISTRY. Educ: Pa State Univ, BS, 64; Harvard Univ, PhD(chem), 68. Prof Exp: Res chemist, New Enterprises Res Div, 68, sr res chemist, Cent Res Div, 68-73, res supvr, 73-76, res scientist, Chem Sci Div, 76-79, RES SCIENTIST, MAT SCI DIV, HERCULES INC, 79-, PROJ LEADER PAPER CHEM, 80- Mem: AAAS; Am Chem Soc; Tech Asn Pulp Paper Indust. Res: Kinetics and mechanisms of 1, 2 cycloaddition reactions; photochemical generation of reactive intermediates; Ziegler polymerization of alpha-olefins; physical and chemical characterzation of organic polymers; radiation chemistry; chemical additives for paper. Mailing Add: Res Ctr Hercules Inc Wilmington DE 19899

KRAMER, BRUCE MICHAEL, b New York City, NY, July 23, 49. MECHANICAL ENGINEERING. Educ: Mass Inst Technol, SB & SM, 72, PhD(mech eng), 79. Prof Exp: ASST PROF MECH ENG, MASS INST TECHNOL, 79- Concurrent Pos: Chmn, Zoom Telephonics, Inc, Boston, 76-; consult, 79- Mem: Am Soc Mech Engrs; Am Soc Metals; Sigma Xi. Res: Basic physics and chemistry of the wear process, particularly in severe wear, such as that encountered in the metal-cutting process. Mailing Add: Rm 35-234 Mass Inst Technol 77 Mass Ave Cambridge MA 02139

KRAMER, CHARLES EDWIN, b Lancaster, Pa, Apr 1, 47; m 69; c 2. POLYMER SYNTHESIS. *Educ:* Franklin & Marshall Col, BS, 69; Northeastern Univ, MS, 71, PhD(chem), 75. *Prof Exp:* Res chemist, Celanese Corp, 74-77; sr res assoc, 77-81, ASST DIR RES, ALBANY INT CORP, 81- *Mem:* Am Chem Soc; Sigma Xi. *Res:* Polymer chemistry; monomer and polymer synthesis; polymer flammability; membrane science; polymer blends; polymer structure-property relationships. *Mailing Add:* 1000 Providence Hwy Dedham MA 02026

KRAMER, CHARLES LAWRENCE, b Leavenworth, Kans, Apr 4, 28; m 51; c 2. MYCOLOGY. *Educ:* Univ Kans, BA, 50, MS, 53, PhD(bot), 57. *Prof Exp:* Asst prof biol, Western Ill Univ, 57-58; from asst prof to assoc prof, 58-73, PROF BOT, KANS STATE UNIV, 73- *Concurrent Pos:* Grants, USPHS, 58- & NSF, 67- *Mem:* Am Mycol Soc; Int Asn Plant Taxon; Brit Mycol Soc. *Res:* Kansas fungi, especially parasitic forms; taxonomy of Taphinales; aeromycology. *Mailing Add:* Div of Biol Kans State Univ Manhattan KS 66506

KRAMER, CLYDE YOUNG, b Lebanon, Pa, Feb 2, 25; m 44; c 1. STATISTICS. *Educ:* Va Polytech Inst, BS, 51, MS, 53, PhD(bot), 57. *Prof Exp:* PROF STATIST, VA POLYTECH INST & STATE UNIV, 51- *Concurrent Pos:* Consult, Dept Health, Educ & Welfare, 58-; mem, Study Sect, NIH, 58- *Honors & Awards:* Presidential Citation Merit. *Mem:* Fel Am Statist Asn; Inst Math Statist; Biomet Soc. *Res:* Design and analysis of variance, range tests; multivariate analysis. *Mailing Add:* Box 255 Christianburg VA 24073

KRAMER, DAVID, b New York, NY, Apr 17, 34; m 55; c 2. METALLURGY. *Educ:* Mass Inst Technol, BS, 55; Columbia Univ, MS, 57. *Prof Exp:* Sr engr, Atomics Int Div, NAm Aviation, Inc, 57-62, mem tech staff, Sci Ctr, 62-66, proj engr, 66-70, mgr phys metall, 70-75, MGR, MAT DEVELOP ENERGY SYSTS GROUP, ROCKWELL INT CORP, 75- *Concurrent Pos:* sr ed, Effects Radiation Mat, Am Soc Testing & Mat, 81. *Mem:* Am Inst Mining, Metall & Petrol Engrs; Am Soc Testing & Mat; Am Soc Metals; Metal Properties Coun. *Res:* Radiation effects on metals, materials for coal conversion systems; materials for high energy batteries. *Mailing Add:* 8900 DeSoto Ave Canoga Park CA 91304

KRAMER, DAVID BUCKLEY, b Turtle Creek, Pa, Oct 21, 27; m 76; c 2. MECHANICAL ENGINEERING, COMPUTER SCIENCE. *Educ:* Univ Pittsburgh, BS, 50; Carnegie-Mellon Univ, MS, 53; Univ Md, PhD(mech eng), 75. *Prof Exp:* Res engr analog comput, Westinghouse Elec Corp, 50-52; res engr process control, E I du Pont de Nemours & Co, Inc, 53-61; RES ENGR OPERS RES, ORI, INC, 61- *Mem:* Am Soc Mech Engrs; Opers Res Soc Am. *Res:* Acoustical holography; nonlinear programming; nuclear weapons effects; inventories; scheduling. *Mailing Add:* ORI Inc 1400 Spring St Silver Spring MD 20910

KRAMER, EARL SIDNEY, b Chippewa Falls, Wis, Nov 13, 40. MATHEMATICS. *Educ:* Wis State Univ, Eau Claire, BS, 62; Univ Mich, MS, 64 & 66, PhD(math), 69. *Prof Exp:* Temp lectr, Univ Birmingham, 69-70; asst prof, 70-74, ASSOC PROF MATH, UNIV NEBR, LINCOLN, 74- *Mem:* Am Math Soc. *Res:* Existence of various combinatorial structures. *Mailing Add:* Dept of Math Univ of Nebr Lincoln NE 68508

KRAMER, EDWARD J(OHN), b Wilmington, Del, Aug 5, 39; m 63; c 3. MATERIALS SCIENCE. *Educ:* Cornell Univ, BChE, 62; Carnegie-Mellon Univ, PhD(metal & mat sci), 67. *Prof Exp:* NATO fel metall, Oxford Univ, 66-67; asst prof mat sci & eng, 67-72, ASSOC PROF MAT SCI & ENG, CORNELL UNIV, 72- *Concurrent Pos:* Vis scientist, Argonne Nat Lab, 74-75. *Mem:* Am Phys Soc; Am Inst Mining, Metall & Petrol Engrs; Am Soc Metals. *Res:* Flux motion and pinning in type II superconductors; deformation and fracture of polymeric materials. *Mailing Add:* Dept of Mat Sci & Eng Cornell Univ Ithaca NY 14850

KRAMER, ELIZABETH, b Milwaukee, Wis, June 7, 18. DIETETICS, BIOCHEMISTRY. *Educ:* Alverno Col, BSE, 43; De Paul Univ, MS, 48; St Louis Univ, PhD(chem), 54. *Prof Exp:* Instr biol & math, high sch, Ill, 43-47; instr biol, Alverno Col, 47-49, assoc prof chem & chmn dept, 54-69, prof chem, 69-79; DIETITIAN, VET ADMIN MED CTR, MILWAUKEE, WIS, 81- *Concurrent Pos:* Fel biochem, Univ Iowa, 69-70. *Mem:* Am Dietetic Asn; Sigma Xi. *Res:* Studies of drug binding, especially aspirin, salicylates and D-tubocurarine to purified proteins of human blood as well as to serum and plasma using fluorometric and gel filtration techniques. *Mailing Add:* Dept of Chem Alverno Col Milwaukee WI 53215

KRAMER, ELMER E, b New Orleans, La, Sept 22, 14; m 47; c 2. MEDICINE. *Educ:* Tulane Univ, BS, 35, MD, 38; Am Bd Obstet & Gynec, dipl. *Prof Exp:* Intern, Hotel Dieu Hosp, New Orleans, La, 38-39, resident, 39-40; asst obstet & gynec, Med Col, Cornell Univ, 46-49, from instr to prof clin obste & gynec, 49-70, prof clin path, 69-79, prof obstet & gynec, 70-79; ASSOC DIR, NEW YORK HOSP, 79- *Concurrent Pos:* Intern, NY Lying-In-Hosp, 46, from asst resident to resident, 46-50, asst pathologist, 50-56, pathologist, 56-; asst attend obstetrician & gynecologist, NY Hosp, 50-53, attend pathologist, 69-; consult, Payne Whitney Psychiat Clin, 52-56, from assoc attend obstetrician & gynecologist to attend obstetrician & gynecologist, 53-57; consult, Lenox Hill Hosp, 74-79; Am Bd Qual Assurance & Utilization Rev Physicians, 78-; Am Col Utilization Rev Physicians, 78- *Mem:* AMA; fel Am Col Surgeons; Am Col Obstetricians & Gynecologists. *Res:* Obstetrical and gynecological pathology. *Mailing Add:* New York Hosp 525 E 68th St New York NY 10021

KRAMER, FRANCIS R, b Chicago, Ill, Aug 19, 30; m 54; c 4. CHEMICAL ENGINEERING. *Educ:* Calif Inst Technol, BS, 52; Purdue Univ, PhD(chem eng), 59. *Prof Exp:* Jr engr, Bechtel Corp, 52; proj engr, Edgewood Arsenal, 54-55; res develop engr, Textile Fibers Dept, 59-61, sr res develop engr, 61-62, supvr develop, 62-64, sr supvr, 64-65, sr supvr develop, 65-68, tech supt, Kinston Plant, 68-70, process supt, Spruance Fibers Plant, 70-71, supt nomex prod, 71-73, venture mgr sontara, 73-76, tech mgr qiana, 76-77, tech mgr

nylon & dacron indust, 78-80, TECH MGR DACRON STAPLE, FIBERFILL, FIBER SURFACE RES, E I DU PONT DE NEMOURS & CO, INC, 81- *Mem:* Am Inst Chem Engrs. *Res:* Synthetic fiber technology; heat transfer. *Mailing Add:* E I du Pont de Nemours & Co Inc Nemours Bldg #4525 Wilmington DE 19898

KRAMER, FRANKLIN, b Brooklyn, NY, Mar 6, 23; m 51; c 2. CHEMICAL ENGINEERING. *Educ:* City Col New York, BS, 44; Polytech Inst Brooklyn, MS, 47. *Prof Exp:* Res chem engr, Cent Res Labs, Gen Foods Corp, 44-53, res supvr, Atlantic Gelatin Div, 53-56, tech supt, 56-59; mgr res & develop, Walter Baker Chocolate Co, 59-62 & Cracker Jack Co Div, Borden Co, Ill, 62-65; mgr equip & process develop, Kitchens of Sarah Lee Div, Consol Foods Corp, Ill, 65-68; mem staff, La Touraine Coffee, 68-73, vpres mfg & eng, La Touraine-Bickford's Foods, Inc, 71-73; vpres mfg, Seapak Div, W R Grace & Co, 73-75; MGR SYSTS COMMERCIALIZATION, CENT RES DIV, GEN FOODS CORP, 75- *Mem:* Sr mem Am Chem Soc; sr mem Am Inst Chem Engrs; Inst Food Technol. *Res:* Development of food processes from lab bench scale through commercialization; technical administration and management. *Mailing Add:* 132 Holbrook Rd Briarcliff Manor NY 10510

KRAMER, FRED RUSSELL, b New York, NY, July 7, 42; m 65; c 2. MOLECULAR BIOLOGY, BIOCHEMISTRY. *Educ:* Univ Mich, BS, 64; Rockefeller Univ, PhD(molecular biol), 69. *Prof Exp:* Am Cancer Soc fel, Inst Cancer Res, 69-71, res assoc molecular biol, 71-72, instr, 72-73, asst prof, human genetics & develop, 73-80, SR RES ASSOC, INST CANCER RES, COL PHYSICIANS & SURGEONS, COLUMBIA UNIV, 73- *Res:* Evolution and synthesis of nucleic acids in vitro; computer applications in molecular biology. *Mailing Add:* Inst Cancer Res Columbia Univ 701 West 168 St New York NY 10032

KRAMER, GEORGE MORTIMER, b Brooklyn, NY, May 15, 29; m 51; c 2. PHYSICAL ORGANIC CHEMISTRY. *Educ:* Queen's Col NY, BS, 51; Univ Pa, MS, 55, PhD(phys chem), 57. *Prof Exp:* Chemist, Frankford Arsenal, Pa, 51-52; chemist, Process Res Div, Esso Res & Eng Co, 57-64, Baytown Res & Develop Div, Tex, 65-66, res assoc, Cent Basic Res Lab, 66-69, res assoc, 69-78, SR RES ASSOC, CORP RES LAB, EXXON RES & ENG CO, NJ, 78- *Mem:* Am Chem Soc. *Res:* Pressure-volume-temperature behavior of gases; equation of state; surface chemistry; thermochemical data; acid catalyzed alkylation and isomerization; catalysis; hydride transfer reactions; free radical reactions; carbonium ion rearrangement mechanisms and acid characterization; uranium chemistry. *Mailing Add:* Corp Res Lab Exxon Res & Eng Co Linden NJ 07036

KRAMER, GERALD M, b Gloucester, Mass, June 11, 22; m 45; c 2. PERIODONTOLOGY, DENTISTRY. *Educ:* Tufts Univ, DMD, 44; Reisman Clin, cert, 52; Am Bd Periodont, dipl. *Prof Exp:* Instr periodont, Sch Dent Med, Univ Pa, 55-60; from asst prof to assoc prof, 63-68, PROF PERIODONT & CHMN DEPT, SCH GRAD DENT, BOSTON UNIV, 68- *Concurrent Pos:* Head periodont sect, Beth Israel Hosp, Boston & Boston Univ Hosp, 68- *Mem:* AAAS; Am Dent Asn; fel Am Col Dent; Am Acad Periodont; hon mem Periodont Soc SAfrica. *Res:* Clinical periodontics and oral medicine. *Mailing Add:* 90 Humphrey St Swampscott MA 01907

KRAMER, HENRY HERMAN, b New York, NY, Aug 19, 30; m 59; c 3. NUCLEAR MEDICINE, DIAGNOSTIC MEDICINE. *Educ:* Columbia Univ, BA, 52, MA, 53; Univ Ind, PhD(phys chem), 60. *Prof Exp:* Res chemist nuclear methods anal, Union Carbide Corp, Nuclear Res Ctr, 60-65, group leader, Nucleonics Res & Develop, 66-73, sr group leader, Tarrytown Tech Ctr, 73-76, mgr, Sterling Forest Res Ctr, 76-78; V PRES RES & DEVELOP, MEDI PHYSICS INC, 78- *Mem:* AAAS; Am Chem Soc; Am Nuclear Soc; Soc Nuclear Med; Am Col Nuclear Physicians. *Res:* Radiochemicals; radiodiagnostics; nuclear methods of analysis; clinical microbiology; educational aids; biomedical significance of trace elements; nucleonics in industry and ore body exploration; diagnostic medicine. *Mailing Add:* 3911 Campolindo Dr Moraga CA 94556

KRAMER, IRVIN RAYMOND, b Baltimore, Md, Sept 18, 12; m 35. METALLURGY. *Educ:* Johns Hopkins Univ, BS, 35, MS, 47, DE, 51. *Prof Exp:* Chemist, Am Radiator & Standard Sanit Mfg Corp, Md, 35-38; metallurgist & chief spec alloys sect, Naval Res Lab, 38-46, metallurgist, phys scientist & head mech & mat br, Off Naval Res, 46-51; asst to pres, Horizons Titanium Corp, NY, 51-53; vpres, Mercast Corp, NY, 53-55; chief mat res, Martin Co, 55-68 & Metals Sci Res Dept, Martin Marietta Corp, 68-71, mgr independent progs, 71-74; tech adv, Reisman Dent Lab, Naval Ship Res & Develop Ctr, 75-81; RES PROF, UNIV MD, 81- *Concurrent Pos:* Mem, heat resistant mat comt, Nat Adv Comt Aeronaut, metall panel, Res & Develop Bd, Dept Nat Defense & comt ship steel, Nat Res Coun, 44. *Honors & Awards:* Burgess Mem Award, Severn Tech Soc, 78. *Mem:* Fel Am Soc Metals; Am Inst Mining, Metall & Petrol Engrs; Sigma Xi; Severn Tech Soc. *Res:* Hardenability of steels; effects of alloying elements on mechanical and physical properties of metals; iron-manganese-nickel alloys; age-hardening steels; dynamic behavior of metals and phenomena of plastic deformation; surface effect as related to flow and fracture of metals. *Mailing Add:* Naval Ship Res & Develop Ctr Annapolis MD 21402

KRAMER, J DAVID R, JR, b Bayonne, NJ, Oct 29, 35; m 66. ELECTRICAL ENGINEERING. *Educ:* Univ Pa, BSEE, 57; Mass Inst Technol, MS, 58, ScD(elec eng), 64. *Prof Exp:* Mem tech staff, 64-69, group leader, 69-79, ASSOC DEPT HEAD, MITRE CORP, 79- *Concurrent Pos:* Lectr, Northeastern Univ, 65-68. *Mem:* Inst Elec & Electronics Engrs. *Res:* Systems optimization; signal design and processing; operations research. *Mailing Add:* 26 Fairbanks Rd Lexington MA 02173

KRAMER, JAMES PHILLIP, systematic entomology, see previous edition

KRAMER, JAMES RICHARD, b Marine City, Mich, Oct 27, 31; m 55; c 4. GEOCHEMISTRY, AQUATIC CHEMISTRY. *Educ:* Mass Inst Technol, BS, 53; Univ Mich, MS, 54, PhD(geol), 58. *Prof Exp:* Asst, Res Lab, Carter Oil Co, 54; instr geol, Univ Mich, 57-58; fel, Nat Res Coun Can, Western Ont Univ, 58-59, lectr, 59-61, asst prof, 61-63; res assoc, Univ Mich, 63-64; from asst prof to assoc prof, Syracuse Univ, 64-68; assoc prof, 68-71, PROF GEOL, McMASTER UNIV, 71- *Mem:* Am Geol Soc; Mineral Soc Am; Geochem Soc; Am Asn Petrol Geologists; Am Chem Soc. *Res:* Physical chemistry of carbonate minerals; limnological investigation of the Great Lakes; sedimentation and facies analysis of the Proterozoic sediments of Canada; aquatic chemistry of shield lakes. *Mailing Add:* Dept of Geol McMaster Univ Hamilton ON L8S 4M1 Can

KRAMER, JERRY MARTIN, b Bronx, NY, Dec 16, 42; m 70; c 2. CHEMICAL PHYSICS. *Educ:* Univ Calif, Berkeley, BS, 65; Univ Chicago, PhD(chem), 71. *Prof Exp:* Res assoc chem, Case Western Reserve Univ, 71-72; MEM TECH STAFF, GEN TEL & ELECTRONICS LABS, 72- *Mem:* Am Phys Soc; Am Chem Soc. *Res:* Laser chemistry; arc and discharge physics; low energy ion-electron excitation of inorganic phosphors; photodissociation of gaseous ions; chemical kinetics. *Mailing Add:* Gen Tel & Electronics Labs 40 Sylvan Rd Waltham MA 02154

KRAMER, JOHN D(UDLEY), chemical engineering, deceased

KRAMER, JOHN J(ACOB), b Pittsburgh, Pa, July 9, 31; m 56; c 3. PHYSICAL METALLURGY, MATERIAL SCIENCE. *Educ:* Carnegie Inst Technol, BS, 53, MS & PhD(metall), 56. *Prof Exp:* Sr engr, magnetic mat develop sect, Westinghouse Elec Corp, 56-60, res metallurgist, res lab, 60-63, supv metallurgist, 63-64, sect mgr, 64-65, adv metallurgist, 65; assoc prof elec eng, 65-69, PROF ELEC ENG, UNIV DEL, 69- *Concurrent Pos:* Phys metallurgist, ballistics res lab, Aberdeen Proving Grounds, Md, 57. *Mem:* Am Soc Metals; Am Inst Mining, Metall & Petrol Engrs. *Res:* Application of thermodynamics; surfaces; grain and crystal growth; solid state reactions; magnetic and electrical properties of solids. *Mailing Add:* 410 Arbour Dr Newark DE 19713

KRAMER, JOHN KARL GERHARD, b Bololo, Congo, Oct 6, 39; Can citizen; m 68. BIOCHEMISTRY, ORGANIC CHEMISTRY. *Educ:* Univ Man, BSc, 63, MSc, 65; Univ Minn, Minneapolis, PhD(biochem), 68. *Prof Exp:* Hormel fel, Hormel Inst, Univ Minn, Austin, 68-70; Nat Res Coun Can fel, Univ Ottawa, 70-71; RES SCIENTIST, ANIMAL RES CTR, RES BR, AGR CAN, OTTAWA, 71- *Res:* Pesticide metabolism in animals; lipid biochemistry and nutrition. *Mailing Add:* Animal Res Ctr Res Br Agr Can Ottawa ON K1A 0C6E Can

KRAMER, JOHN PAUL, b Elgin, Ill, Mar 13, 28; div; c 2. INSECT PATHOLOGY. *Educ:* Beloit Col, BS, 50; Univ Mo, MS, 52; Univ Ill, PhD(entom), 58. *Prof Exp:* Asst res prof entom, NC State Col, 58-59; asst entomologist econ entom, Ill Natural Hist Surv, 59, assoc entomologist, 59-65; assoc prof, 65-75, PROF INSECT PATH, CORNELL UNIV, 75- *Concurrent Pos:* Lectr, 8th Int Cong Microbiol, Montreal, 62, dept biol sci, Northwestern Univ, 64, 2nd Int Conf Protozool, London, 65 & Dept Biol, Ithaca Col, 81; consult, Environ Biol Unit, WHO, Geneva, 62-; mem trop med & parasitol study sect, NIH, 66-69; NSF vis insect pathologist, Japan, 67; mem, Eval Panel Life Sci, Nat Res Coun, 69-; NIH-Off Naval Res res grant microbiol, 71-; vis biologist, Arctic Health Res Ctr, Inst Arctic Biol, Alaska, 72 & WHO res agreement, 78- *Mem:* Soc Invert Path; Int Orgn Biol Control. *Res:* Infectious diseases of insects, especially those caused by microsporidians and entomophthorans; ecology of microsporidians; epidemiology of diseases of insects. *Mailing Add:* Dept of Entom Cornell Univ Ithaca NY 14850

KRAMER, JOHN WILLIAM, b Dearborn, Mich, Aug 17, 35; m 59; c 2. CLINICAL PATHOLOGY. *Educ:* Mich State Univ, BSc, 58, DVM, 60, MSc, 68; Univ Calif, Davis, PhD(comp path), 72; Am Col Vet Pathologists, dipl & cert vet clin path. *Prof Exp:* Vet, NZ Dept Agr, 60-64; adv clin path, Mich State Univ, Nsukka, Nigeria, 64-66, asst instr, Univ, 66-68; trainee, Col Vet Med, Univ Calif, Davis, 68-72; assoc prof, 72-77, PROF VET CLIN SURG & MED, COL VET MED, WASH STATE UNIV, 77- *Mem:* Am Vet Med Asn; Am Soc Vet Clin Pathologists; Am Col Vet Pathologists. *Res:* Pathophysiology of carbohydrate metabolism; an inherited muscular disorder of Laborador retrievers; Chediak-Higashi syndrome of cats; lactate acidosis of dogs. *Mailing Add:* Dept of Vet Clin Surg & Med Col of Vet Med Wash State Univ Pullman WA 99163

KRAMER, JULIAN, b New York, NY, Jan 30, 25; m 48; c 2. BIOLOGY. *Educ:* City Col New York, BS, 47; George Washington Univ, MS, 54. *Prof Exp:* Bacteriologist, Div Antibiotics, 51-65, microbiologist, Div Antibiotics & Insulin Cert, 65-70, DEP DIR, DIV DRUG BIOL, FOOD & DRUG ADMIN, DEPT HEALTH, EDUC & WELFARE, DC, 70- *Res:* Antibiotics; bioassay; cytology and cytogenetics; biometrics; insulin. *Mailing Add:* 3506 Napier St Silver Spring MD 20906

KRAMER, KARL JOSEPH, b Evansville, Ind, Aug 20, 42; m 66; c 2. ENTOMOLOGY, BIOCHEMISTRY. *Educ:* Purdue Univ, BS, 64; Univ Ariz, PhD(chem), 71. *Prof Exp:* Res assoc biochem, Univ Chicago, 71-74; RES CHEMIST BIOCHEM, USDA, 74- *Concurrent Pos:* NIH fel, 71; asst prof biochem, Kans State Univ, 74-78, assoc prof, 78- *Mem:* Am Soc Biol Chemists; Am Chem Soc; Entom Soc Am; Am Inst Biol Sci; AAAS. *Res:* Insect biochemistry; endocrinology; physiology. *Mailing Add:* US Grain Mkt Res Lab 1515 College Ave Manhattan KS 66502

KRAMER, MAX, b New York, NY, Mar 23, 09; m 37; c 1. MATHEMATICS. *Educ:* City Col New York, BA, 30; Columbia Univ, MA, 31, PhD(math), 50. *Prof Exp:* Instr math, Univ Ill, 45-49, ; asst prof, NMex State Univ, 49-52, assoc prof, 52-57; from asst prof to assoc prof, San Jose State Col, 57-63, prof, 63-76, EMER PROF MATH, SAN JOSE STATE UNIV, 76- *Mem:* Math Asn Am. *Res:* Applied mathematics, particularly in the field of meteorology; mathematics education. *Mailing Add:* 4175 Page Mill Rd Los Altos Hills CA 94022

KRAMER, MILTON, b Chicago, Ill, Nov 11, 29; c 4. PSYCHIATRY. *Educ:* Univ Ill, BS, 50, BS, 52, MD, 54; Am Bd Psychiat & Neurol, dipl & cert psychiat, 61. *Prof Exp:* Assoc dir res, Dept Psychiat, 72-80, PROF PSYCHIAT, SCH MED, UNIV CINCINNATI, 72-, DIR, DREAM & SLEEP LAB & SLEEP DISORDERS CTR, 80- *Concurrent Pos:* Pvt practr psychiat, Cincinnati, 60-; clinician psychiat, Outpatient Dept, Cincinnati Gen Hosp, 61- & attend staff psychiatrist, 65-; consult, Coun Drugs, AMA, 62-; dir psychiat res, Vet Admin Hosp, Cincinnati, 63- & asst chief, Dept Psychiat, 64-80; Upjohn Co grant, 70-72; mem, Therapeut Care Comt, Group Advan Psychiat, 70-; res investr, Wm S Merrell Co, 70-72 & Upjohn, 70-; proj dir sonic boom res data anal, Fed Aviation Admin, 70-72; prin investr, US Vet Admin, 75-; mem, Ohio Ment Health & Ment Retardation Adv Bd, 71-75; mem staffs, Christian R Holmes Hosp, Jewish Hosp & Good Samaritan Hosp. *Mem:* Fel Am Psychiat Asn; AMA; Asn Psychophysiol Study Sleep (mem exec comt, 71); sci assoc Am Acad Psychoanal; Am Col Psychiat. *Res:* Psychology and psychophysiology of dreaming; drugs and sleep. *Mailing Add:* Dept Psychiat 59 Sch Med Univ Cincinnati Cincinnati OH 45220

KRAMER, MORTON, b Baltimore, Md, Mar 21, 14; m 39; c 4. BIOSTATISTICS, EPIDEMIOLOGY. *Educ:* Johns Hopkins Univ, AB, 34, ScD, 39. *Prof Exp:* Asst biostatist, Sch Hyg & Pub Health, Johns Hopkins Univ, 37-38; instr prev med, Col Med, NY Univ, 38; statistician, State Dept Health, NY, 39-40; asst prof biostatist, Sch Trop Med, Univ PR & statistician, Insular Dept Health, San Juan, 40-42; econ analyst, US Dept Treas, DC, 42-43; assoc biostatist, Sch Med, Western Reserve Univ, 43-46; chief info & res, Off Int Health Rels, USPHS, DC, 46-49, chief biomet br, NIMH, 49-75, dir div biometry & epidemiol, 75-76; PROF DEPT MENT HYG, SCH HYG & PUB HEALTH, JOHNS HOPKINS UNIV, 76- *Concurrent Pos:* Consult ment health unit, WHO, 59-; mem expert panel health statist, WHO, 61-; vis scientist, Dept Pub Health Admin, London Sch Hyg & Trop Med & Soc Med Res Unit Med Res Coun, Eng, 68-69. *Honors & Awards:* Superior Serv Award, Dept Health, Educ & Welfare, 62, Distinguished Serv Award, 74; Rema Lapousse Award, Am Pub Health Asn, 73. *Mem:* Hon fel Am Psychiat Asn; fel Am Pub Health Asn; fel Am Statist Asn; fel Am Orthopsychiat Asn; Am Epidemiol Soc. *Res:* Epidemiology of mental disorders; application of biostatistical and epidemiologic methods to planning mental health and related human services and evaluating their effectiveness; classification of mental disorders. *Mailing Add:* Dept of Ment Hyg Johns Hopkins Univ Baltimore MD 21205

KRAMER, NICHOLAS WILLIAM, b Burkettsville, Ohio, May 4, 21; m 43; c 6. AGRONOMY, GENETICS. *Educ:* Ohio State Univ, BSc, 43, PhD(agron), 49. *Prof Exp:* Asst agron, Ohio State Univ, 42-44 & 46-47, asst instr, 48-49, asst prof, univ & asst agronomist, Ohio Agr Exp Sta, 50; asst agronomist, Sorghum Invests, Tex Agr Exp Sta, 50-51, assoc agronomist, 51-58, agronomist, 58-60; agronomist, Paymaster Seeds Div, 60-61, res dir, 62-67, sorghum res dir, Acco Seed Div, Anderson, Clayton & Co, 67-80, SORGHUM RES DIR, CARGILL SEEDS, 80- *Concurrent Pos:* Asst, Ohio Dept Agr, 42-44; prof agron, Tex Tech Univ, 59-60; mem, Nat Coun Com Plant Breeders. *Mem:* Fel AAAS; fel Am Soc Agron; AAAS; Am Soc Agron; Crop Sci Soc Am. *Res:* Field crops; sorghum breeding and genetics; corn breeding; industrial utilization of sorghum; crop management under dry conditions. *Mailing Add:* Cargill Res PO Box 1630 Plainview TX 79072

KRAMER, NOAH HERBERT, b New York, NY, Apr 10, 24; m 54; c 3. ELECTRICAL ENGINEERING. *Educ:* Mich State Univ, BS, 47, MS, 49, PhD(elec eng), 51. *Prof Exp:* Asst, Mich State Univ, 47-49, instr, 49-51; engr, Int Bus Mach Corp, 51-57 & Stelma, Inc, 57-70; mgr transmission planning, Int Tel & Tel Corp, 73-78; pres, N H Kramer & Assocs, 78-79; mem staff, Am Satellite Corp, 79-80; TECH MGR, LITTON DATA COMMAND SYSTS, 80- *Mem:* Inst Elec & Electronics Engrs. *Res:* Communication systems and equipment; digital data transmission; digital techniques; solid state electronics; computer peripherals. *Mailing Add:* 43 Old Logging Rd Stamford CT 06903

KRAMER, NORMAN CLIFFORD, b New York, NY, Aug 16, 28; m 54; c 5. INTERNAL MEDICINE, IMMUNOLOGY. *Educ:* The Citadel, BS, 48; George Washington Univ, MS, 50, MD, 54; Am Bd Internal Med, dipl, 63. *Prof Exp:* Consult biochem, Vet Admin Hosp, Martinsburg, WVa, 50-53; from instr to assoc prof, 60-74, PROF INT MED, GEORGE WASHINGTON UNIV, 74- *Concurrent Pos:* USPHS res fel, 59-60, USPHS res career develop award, 61-66; dir, Washington Regional Histocompatability Typing Lab; dir, Hemopheresis Serv, George Washington Univ Med Ctr. *Mem:* Fel Am Col Physicians; Am Fedn Clin Res; Am Asn Clin Histocompitibility Test; Am Soc Artificial Internal Organs; Int Soc Nephrology. *Res:* Pathophysiology and immunology of diseases of the kidney. *Mailing Add:* Div Renal Dis George Washington Univ Med Ctr Washington DC 20037

KRAMER, PAUL ALAN, b Hartford, Conn, July 22, 42; m 64; c 2. PHYSICAL PHARMACY, BIOPHARMACEUTICS. *Educ:* Rensselaer Polytech Inst, BChE, 64; Univ Wis, MS, 66, PhD(pharm), 68. *Prof Exp:* Res biochemist, Walter Reed Army Inst Res, 68-71; asst prof phys pharm, Purdue Univ, 71-76; ASSOC PROF PHARM & LAB MED, UNIV CONN, 76- *Res:* Pharmacokinetics of drugs in the elderly; drug acetylation in man; effect of drugs on neonatal behavioral development. *Mailing Add:* Dept of Pharm Univ of Conn Health Ctr Farmington CT 06032

KRAMER, PAUL JACKSON, b Brookville, Ind, May 8, 04; m 31; c 2. PLANT PHYSIOLOGY. *Educ:* Miami Univ, AB, 26; Ohio State Univ, MS, 29, PhD(plant physiol), 31. *Hon Degrees:* LittD, Miami Univ, 66; DSc, Univ NC, 66 & Ohio State Univ, 72; Dr, Univ Paris, 75. *Prof Exp:* Asst bot, Ohio State Univ, 28-31; from instr to prof, 31-54, Duke prof, 54-74, EMER PROF BOT, DUKE UNIV, 74- *Concurrent Pos:* Mem agr bd, Nat Res Coun, 58-60, mem comt wartime modification biol teaching; prog dir regulatory biol, NSF, 60-61, consult, 60-65, mem divisional comt, Div Biol & Med, 62-65, chmn, 64-65; chmn phytron bd, Duke Univ & NC State Univ, 62-78; mem comt int biol proj, Nat Acad Sci-Nat Res Coun, 63-64; mem comt agr sci, USDA,

65-68; vis comt, Harvard Univ, 65-71; mem nat comt, Int Bot Cong, 65-71; bd trustees, Biol Abstr, 66-71, pres, 71; chmn comt to rev US Int Biol Prog, Nat Acad Sci-Nat Res Coun, 73-75; consult, Sarah P Duke Gardens, 74-78; vis prof, Univ Tex, 76; Walker-Ames vis prof, Univ Wash, 77. *Honors & Awards:* Cert of Merit, Bot Soc Am, 56; Soc Am Foresters Award, 61; Am Inst Biol Sci Distinguished Serv Award, 77. *Mem:* Nat Acad Sci; Am Acad Arts & Sci; AAAS; Am Philos Soc; Bot Soc Am (vpres, 59, pres, 64). *Res:* Plant and soil water relations and absorption of water by plants; physiology of woody plants; effects of environmental factors on plants. *Mailing Add:* Dept of Bot Duke Univ Durham NC 27706

KRAMER, PAUL ROBERT, b Montclair, NJ, Nov 17, 35; m 64; c 2. PHYSICS. *Educ:* Cornell Univ, BA, 57; Rutgers Univ, MS, 59, PhD(physics), 66. *Prof Exp:* Instrumentation specialist physics, State Univ NY Stony Brook, 64-66, asst prof, 66-70; assoc prof, 70-75, chmn dept, 77-81, PROF PHYSICS, AGR & TECH COL, STATE UNIV NY, FARMINGDALE, 75-, DEAN ACAD SERV, 81- *Concurrent Pos:* Dir, Comput Assisted Instr, State Univ NY Stony Brook, 67-68, proj coordr, Instr Resources Ctr, 68-70. *Mem:* Am Phys Soc; Am Asn Physics Teachers; Inst Elec & Electronics Engrs. *Res:* Instructional technology using computers and other media; improvement of instruction in physics and other fields. *Mailing Add:* Dean Acad Serv State Univ of NY Agr & Tech Col Farmingdale NY 11735

KRAMER, RAYMOND ARTHUR, b Buffalo, NY, Dec 7, 29; m 55. ANALYTICAL CHEMISTRY. *Educ:* Canisius Col, BS, 54; Rensselaer Polytech Inst, PhD(anal chem), 59. *Prof Exp:* Technician, Aluminum Co Am, NY, 48-54; asst, Rensselaer Polytech Inst, 54-58; phys chemist, Alcoa Res Labs, 58-67, ANAL CHEMIST, ALCOA TECH CTR, ALUMINUM CO AM, 67- *Mem:* Am Chem Soc; Soc Appl Spectros. *Res:* Neutron activation analysis; x-ray diffraction and fluorescence; characterization of ultra-pure aluminum and gallium; emission spectroscopy; aluminum in fusion reactors. *Mailing Add:* Alcoa Tech Ctr Alcoa Center PA 15069

KRAMER, RAYMOND EDWARD, b Warren, Ohio, Feb 2, 19; m 47; c 3. ELECTRICAL ENGINEERING, PHYSICS. *Educ:* Heidelberg Col, BSc, 43; Case Inst Technol, MSc, 50. *Prof Exp:* Asst prof, 50-54, chmn dept, 54-78, assoc prof, 54-78, PROF ELEC ENG, YOUNGSTOWN STATE UNIV, 78- *Concurrent Pos:* Consult elec engr, US Steel Corp, 51 & ARC Res Inc, 51-53; consult develop engr, Westinghouse Elec Corp, 54 & 55 & Ohio Bell Tel, 61. *Mem:* Inst Elec & Electronics Engrs; AAAS. *Res:* Spark machining; ferromagnetic domains and computer cores; particle physics; electrical, kinetic and quantum properties of fundamental particles; gravity waves. *Mailing Add:* Dept of Elec Eng 410 Wick Ave Youngstown OH 44503

KRAMER, RICHARD JOHN, b Fairmont, Minn, May 27, 38; m 68; c 3. PLANT ECOLOGY, ENVIRONMENTAL MANAGEMENT. *Educ:* St John's Univ Minn, BA, 60, Ariz State Univ, MS, 62; Rutgers Univ, New Brunswick, PhD(bot), 68. *Prof Exp:* Instr biol, Mary Baldwin Col, 67-68, asst prof, 68-72; consult ecologist, Howard, Needles, Tammen & Dergendoff, Dept Environ Qual & Conserv, 72-81; CONSULT ECOLOGIST, ENVIRON RESOURCES MGT, INC, 81- *Concurrent Pos:* Mem gen fac, Grad Sch, USDA, 73-78. *Mem:* Nat Asn Environ Prof; Ecol Soc Am; Am Inst Biol Sci; Am Forestry Asn; Torrey Bot Club. *Res:* Plant synecology; autecology of the saguaro cactus in south central Arizona; synecology and mapping of plant associations; large scale phenological studies and mapping in eastern deciduous forest biome. *Mailing Add:* Environ Resources Mgt Inc PO Box 357 Wes Chester PA 19380

KRAMER, RICHARD MELVYN, b Brooklyn, NY, Dec 20, 35; m 57; c 3. HERBICIDES, PLANT GROWTH REGULATORS. *Educ:* Polytech Inst Brooklyn, BChE, 57, MChE, 60, PhD(chem eng), 63; St Louis Univ, MBA, 71. *Prof Exp:* Res assoc electrodialysis, bioferm div, Int Minerals & Chem Co, 62-63, develop engr, 63-65, sr process engr, 65-66; sr res engr, 66-73, sr res group leader, 73-79, RES MGR, MONSANTO CO, LATIN AM, 79- *Mem:* Am Chem Soc. *Res:* Herbicide and plant growth regulator research and development; pesticide residue chemistry; pesticide formulation and environmental science. *Mailing Add:* 800 N Lindbergh Blvd Monsanto Res Ctr St Louis MO 63166

KRAMER, ROBERT, b Boston, Mass, Apr 25, 27; m 50; c 4. ELECTRICAL & SYSTEMS ENGINEERING. *Educ:* Mass Inst Technol, SB, 49, SM, 52, ScD(elec eng), 59. *Prof Exp:* Proj engr, Servomech Lab, Mass Inst Technol, 49-62, lectr elec eng, Univ, 59-62, staff engr, Lincoln Lab, 62-69; sr consult, Harrington, Davenport & Curtis, Inc, 69-71; STAFF ENGR, LINCOLN LAB, MASS INST TECHNOL, 71- *Mem:* Inst Elec & Electronics Engrs; Optical Soc Am. *Res:* Optical and data systems. *Mailing Add:* Lincoln Labs L382 PO Box 73 Lexington MA 02173

KRAMER, SHELDON J, b Chicago, Ill, Aug 17, 38; m 62; c 3. CHEMICAL ENGINEERING. *Educ:* Univ Ill, Urbana, BSChE, 60; Princeton Univ, MAChE, 62, PhD(chem eng), 66. *Prof Exp:* Chem engr, Gul Res & Develop Co, 65-68; sr proj chem engr, Res & Develop Dept, 68-77, RES ENGR, AMOCO RES CTR, 77- *Mem:* Am Inst Chem Eng; Am Chem Soc. *Res:* Petroleum refining. *Mailing Add:* Amoco Oil Co H-1 PO Box 400 Naperville IL 60566

KRAMER, SHERMAN FRANCIS, b Elcho, Wis, Nov 15, 28; m 59; c 4. PHARMACY, PHARMACOLOGY. *Educ:* Univ Wis, BS, 50, PhD(pharm), 60. *Prof Exp:* Res assoc, 60-66, SECT HEAD, UPJOHN CO, 66- *Mem:* Am Pharmaceut Asn; Acad Pharmaceut Sci. *Res:* Pharmaceutical product research and development. *Mailing Add:* 11090 Higley Circle W Schoolcraft MI 49087

KRAMER, SOL, b Philadelphia, Pa, Aug 22, 19; m 60; c 2. BIOLOGY, ETHOLOGY. *Educ:* Brooklyn Col, BA, 39; Mass State Col, MS, 42; Univ Ill, PhD(entom & zool), 48. *Prof Exp:* Lab instr zool, Mass State Col, 41-42; asst entom, Univ Ill, 46-47, fel, 47-48; Nat Res Coun fel insect physiol, Univ Cambridge, 48-49; asst prof zool, Univ Wis, 49-53; res assoc histol, NY Univ,

54-55; Guggenheim fel ethology, Max Planck Inst Physiol of Behav, 55-56 & USPHS res fel, 56-57; NSF sr fel muscle physiol, Woods Hole Marine Biol Lab, Mass, 58; assoc prof biol, State Univ NY Stony Brook, 59-63, prof, 63-65; prof biol sci in psychiat, Div Biol Sci & Col Med, 65-73, chief, Div Behav Sci, 66-69, res prof ethol & dir, Comp Behav Lab, 74-76, dir, Ethol Lab, 76-79, PROF RES ETHOL, COL VET MED, UNIV FLA, GAINESVILLE, 76- *Concurrent Pos:* Lectr col vis biol prog, Am Inst Biol Sci, 62-72; consult interdisciplinary commun prog, NY Acad Sci, 63-71. *Mem:* Am Soc Zoologists; Animal Behav Soc; Asn Behav Sci & Med Educ. *Res:* Comparative animal behavior; human development; biological basis of personality; muscle physiology; comparative morphology; physiology. *Mailing Add:* Dept of Metab Univ of Fla Col of Vet Med Gainesville FL 32610

KRAMER, STANLEY PHILLIP, b Baltimore, Md, Oct 7, 23; m 62; c 2. MEDICINAL CHEMISTRY, PHARMACOLOGY. *Educ:* Univ Md, BS, 49, PhD(med chem), 55. *Prof Exp:* Res assoc cancer chemother, Sinai Hosp Baltimore, Inc, 55-68; sci instrument specialist, 68-71, sr sci instrument specialist, Florence Agreement Prog, 71-76, PROG MGR, FLORENCE AGREEMENT STAFF, US DEPT COM, 76- *Concurrent Pos:* Res assoc, Sch Med, Johns Hopkins Univ, 55-60, asst surg, 60-68. *Mem:* AAAS; Am Chem Soc; Am Asn Cancer Res; Electron Micros Soc Am; Nat Soc Med Res. *Res:* Cancer chemotherapy; toxicology; enzymology; biochemistry; alkylating agents; esterase; lipase; amidase; trypsin; clinical chemistry. *Mailing Add:* Spec Import Prog US Dept Com Washington DC 20230

KRAMER, STANLEY ZACHARY, b Philadelphia, Pa, Sept 10, 21; m 41; c 1. NEUROPHARMACOLOGY. *Educ:* Univ Pa, AB, 52, PhD(physiol), 58. *Prof Exp:* Asst instr physiol, Univ Pa, 53-58; instr, Vassar Col, 58-60; instr, NY Med Col, 60-64, asst prof physiol, 64-67; assoc prof, 67-76, PROF BIOL, SETON HALL UNIV, 76- *Res:* Effects of drugs on brain electrical activity and behavior; neurophysiology. *Mailing Add:* Dept of Biol Seton Hall Univ South Orange NJ 07079

KRAMER, STEPHEN LEONARD, b Philadelphia, Pa, July 22, 43; m; c 2. EXPERIMENTAL HIGH ENERGY PHYSICS, MEDICAL PHYSICS. *Educ:* Drexel Inst Technol, BS, 66; Purdue Univ, MS, 67, PhD(physics), 71. *Prof Exp:* Res asst high energy physics, 71-74, asst physicist, 74-81, PHYSICIST, ARGONNE NAT LAB, 81- *Mem:* Am Phys Soc; Sigma Xi; Am Asn Physicists Med; AAAS. *Res:* Meson and baryon spectroscopy; production dynamics; radiographic imaging; applications of particle accelerators to medical research; high energy accelerator system design and application; nuclear instrumentation; accelerator physics. *Mailing Add:* Argonne Nat Lab Argonne IL 60439

KRAMER, THEODORE TIVADAR, b Novi-Sad, Yugoslavia, Jan 4, 28; US citizen; m 57; c 3. VETERINARY MICROBIOLOGY, IMMUNOLOGY. *Educ:* Nat Vet Sch, Alfort, France, DVM, 52; Univ Strasbourg, dipl, 53; Colo State Univ, MSc, 63, PhD(microbiol), 65; Am Col Vet Microbiol, dipl, 70. *Prof Exp:* Res off microbiol, Can Dept Agr, 57-60; jr pathologist, Colo State Univ, 60-65; asst prof microbiol, Univ Col, Nairobi, Kenya, 65-67; assoc prof vet microbiol, Western Vet Col Med, Univ Sask, 67-70; prof microbiol & head dept, Sch Vet Med, Auburn Univ, 71-80; PROF VET MICROBIOL & PREV MED & CHMN DEPT, COL VET MED, IOWA STATE UNIV, 80- *Mem:* Am Soc Microbiol; Can Vet Med Asn; Can Soc Immunol. *Res:* Experimental colibacillosis in piglets; immunoglobulins of bovine colostrum; vaccine against bovine vibriosis; maternal immunity and the newborn; cell-mediated immunity to infectious diseases of animals. *Mailing Add:* Dept Vet Microbiol & Prev Med Col Vet Med Iowa State Univ Ames IA 50011

KRAMER, VERNON A, b Marcellus, Wash, Mar 11, 24; m 50; c 2. MATHEMATICS. *Educ:* Univ Wash, BS, 47, MS, 49; Univ Calif, PhD(math), 54. *Prof Exp:* Instr math, Univ Ariz, 50-52; asst prof, 54-61, ASSOC PROF MATH, UNIV CALIF, RIVERSIDE, 61- *Mem:* Am Math Soc; Math Asn Am. *Res:* Perturbation theory; differential operators. *Mailing Add:* Dept of Math Univ of Calif Riverside CA 92502

KRAMER, WILLIAM GEOFFREY, b Pittsburgh, Pa, Sept 16, 48; m 73. PHARMACY, PHARMACOKINETICS. *Educ:* Univ Pittsburgh, BS, 71; Ohio State Univ, PhD(pharm), 76. *Prof Exp:* ASST PROF PHARMACEUT, COL PHARM, UNIV HOUSTON, 76- *Concurrent Pos:* Res assoc, Inst Cardiovasc Studies, Col Pharm, Univ Houston, 77- *Mem:* Am Pharmaceut Asn; Acad Pharmaceut Sci; AAAS; Sigma Xi; Am Soc Clin Pharmacol & Therapeut. *Res:* Pediatric pharmacokinetics; effects of disease and other abnormal conditions on drug pharmacokinetics; application of computers in pharmacokinetic data analysis and dosage regimen design. *Mailing Add:* Dept of Pharmaceut Univ Houston 1441 Moursund St Houston TX 77030

KRAMER, WILLIAM J, b Coldwater, Ohio, Oct 13, 19. ORGANIC CHEMISTRY, ANALYTICAL CHEMISTRY. *Educ:* Univ Fribourg, Lic es Sci, 52, ScD(chem), 53. *Prof Exp:* From instr to assoc prof, 53-68, PROF CHEM, ST JOSEPH'S COL IND, 68-, CHMN DEPT, 77- *Mem:* Am Chem Soc. *Res:* Reactivity of methyl groups in substituted benzene rings; history and philosophy of science. *Mailing Add:* Dept of Chem St Joseph's Col Rensselaer IN 47978

KRAMER, WILLIAM S, b Butte, Nebr, Jan 10, 22; m 44; c 4. DENTISTRY. *Educ:* Univ Nebr, BSc, 46, DDS, 48, MSc, 54; Am Bd Pedodont, dipl. *Prof Exp:* Instr operative dent, 48-52, prof operative dent, 54-58, chem dept, pedodont, 58-80, PROF PEDODONT, UNIV NEBR, LINCOLN, 80- *Concurrent Pos:* Dir, Dent Asst Utilization Prog; past examr, Am Bd Pedodont, exec secy, 74- *Mem:* Am Acad Pedodont (pres, 78-); Int Asn Dent Res. *Res:* Clinical studies on local anesthetic solutions; morphology of the primary dentition; physical properties of gold foil; ultrasonic sterilization; pedodontic failures. *Mailing Add:* Dept Pedodont Col Dent Univ Nebr Lincoln NE 68503

KRAMERICH, GEORGE L, b Aliquippa, Pa, Nov 26, 29; m 54; c 3. CONTROL & ELECTRICAL ENGINEERING. *Educ:* Fla State Univ, BS, 63, MS, 64; Case Western Reserve Univ, PhD(control eng), 70. *Prof Exp:* Teaching asst eng sci, Fla State Univ, 63-64; teaching asst elec eng, Case Western Reserve Univ, 64-69; from asst prof to assoc prof, 69-77, PROF ELEC ENG, CLEVELAND STATE UNIV, 77- *Concurrent Pos:* Consult, Gen Elec Lighting Res Lab, 70-, Chemstress Consults, 77-, Gould Instrument Div, 77- & Ohio Legis Serv Comn, 78-79. *Mem:* Sr mem Instrument Soc Am; Inst Elec & Electronics Engrs; Am Soc Eng Educ. *Res:* Economic and management decision making applied to the evaluation of advanced process control technology; computer simulation. *Mailing Add:* Cleveland State Univ Dept of Elec Eng 1983 E 24th St Cleveland OH 44115

KRAMISH, ARNOLD, b Denver, Colo, June 6, 23; m 52; c 2. NUCLEAR PHYSICS, INTERNATIONAL RELATIONS. *Educ:* Univ Denver, BS, 45; Harvard Univ, MA, 47. *Prof Exp:* Mass spectroscopist, Oak Ridge Nat Lab, 44-45; physicist, Los Alamos Sci Labs, 45-46; staff physicist, AEC, 47-51 & physics dept, Rand Corp, Calif, 51-69; adj prof int studies, Univ Miami, 69-73; US sci liaison attache, UNESCO, 70-73; counr sci & technol, US Mission, Orgn Econ Coop & Develop, 74-76; sr scientist, Res & Develop Assocs, Arlington, 76-80; TECHNOL CONSULT, 81- *Concurrent Pos:* Consult, Int Bank Reconstruct & Develop, 58; fel, Coun For Rels, 58-59; consult, NSF, 59-62; prof in residence, Univ Calif, Los Angeles, 65-66; Guggenheim fel, 66-67; mem, Adv Coun, Inst Future, 74- *Mem:* Inst Strategic Studies; fel Int Inst Strategic Studies. *Res:* Fission physics; applied nuclear energy; political and economic implications of nuclear energy; research and development policy and planning; science policy; international energy policy. *Mailing Add:* 2065 Wethersfield Ct Reston VA 22091

KRAML, MICHAEL JOSEPH ANTHONY, b Montreal, Que, Mar 31, 31; m 60; c 3. BIOCHEMISTRY, ORGANIC CHEMISTRY. *Educ:* Loyola Col, Can, BSc, 53; Univ Montreal, MSc, 54, PhD(biochem), 56. *Prof Exp:* Fel, Univ Montreal, 56-57; BIOCHEMIST, AYERST RES LABS, 57- *Mem:* Can Fedn Biol Soc; Can Biochem Soc; Can Soc Clin Chem; Am Heart Asn; Am Pharmaceut Asn. *Res:* Metabolism of drugs and natural products; enzymatic and chemical analytical methods; cholesterol biosynthesis; drugs as enzyme inhibitors. *Mailing Add:* Ayerst Labs PO Box 6115 Montreal PQ H3C 3J1 Can

KRAMM, KENNETH ROGER, b San Francisco, Calif, Apr 15, 45; m 69; c 2. BEHAVIOR-ETHOLOGY, SCIENCE ADMINISTRATION. *Educ:* Calif State Col, Long Beach, BA, 67; Univ Calif, Irvine, MS, 69, PhD(biol), 71. *Prof Exp:* Assoc prof, 74-78, PROF BIOL, MICH TECHNOL UNIV, 78-; CONSULT, PETRO TECH INST, HOUSTON, 81- *Concurrent Pos:* Consult, Chronobiol Labs, Med Sch, Univ Minn, 73-; prin investr res grants, US Forest Serv, 75-76 & 76-78 & Mich Dept Natural Resources, 78-79, NSF, 80-81. *Mem:* Sigma Xi; Int Soc Chronobiol; Nat Sci Teachers Asn. *Res:* Chronobiology; behavior modeling; training for petroleum. *Mailing Add:* 802 Patchester Houston TX 77079

KRAMP, ROBERT CHARLES, b Alexandria, Va, Aug 2, 42; m 65; c 2. RADIATION BIOLOGY, ENDOCRINOLOGY. *Educ:* Univ Md, BS, 64; Univ Okla, MS, 69; Univ Tenn, PhD(radiation biol), 73. *Prof Exp:* Fel endocrinol, Inst Clin Biochem, 73-75; res instr, Vanderbilt Univ, 75-78; ASST PROF BIOL, VA POLYTECH INST & STATE UNIV, 78- *Mem:* Am Diabetes Asn; Europ Asn Study Diabetes. *Res:* Diabetes; transplantation of pancreatic islet tissue in mice; experimental and genetic diabetes in rodents. *Mailing Add:* Dept of Biol Va Polytech Inst & State Univ Blacksburg VA 24061

KRAMPITZ, LESTER ORVILLE, b Maple Lake, Minn, July 9, 09; m 32; c 1. BACTERIOLOGY, MICROBIOLOGY. *Educ:* Macalester Col, BA, 31; Iowa State Col, PhD(bact), 42. *Hon Degrees:* DSc, Macalester Col, 58. *Prof Exp:* Asst, Rockefeller Inst, 42-43; asst prof bact, Indust Sci Res Inst, Iowa State Col, 43-46; assoc prof biochem, 46-48, prof microbiol & dir dept, 48-79, EMER PROF, SCH MED, CASE WESTERN RESERVE UNIV, 79- *Concurrent Pos:* Fulbright res scholar, Univ Munich, 55-56; mem biochem study sect, NIH, 54-58, mem bact study sect, 59-64, mem res career award comt, Nat Inst Gen Med Sci, 64-68, mem microbiol training comt, 70-74. *Mem:* Nat Acad Sci; Am Soc Microbiol; Am Soc Photobiol; Am Acad Microbiol; NY Acad Sci. *Res:* Metabolism of bacteria using isotopes; antivitamin studies; hydrogen function of biophotolysis of water; mode of action of thiamin diphosphate. *Mailing Add:* Dept of Microbiol Case Western Reserve Univ Sch Med Cleveland OH 44106

KRANBUEHL, DAVID EDWIN, b Madison, Wis, Apr 16, 43; m 66; c 2. PHYSICAL CHEMISTRY, POLYMER PHYSICS. *Educ:* DePauw Univ, BA, 65; Univ Wis, PhD(chem), 69. *Prof Exp:* Res chemist polymers, Nat Bur Standards, 69-70; ASSOC PROF CHEM, COL WILLIAM & MARY, 70- *Concurrent Pos:* Nat Acad Sci fel, 69-70; consult, Nat Bur Standards, 70- *Mem:* Am Chem Soc. *Res:* Physical properties of polymers; dielectric phenomena; molecular dynamics in the liquid and glassy state. *Mailing Add:* Dept of Chem Col of William & Mary Williamsburg VA 23185

KRANC, GEORGE M(AXIMILIAN), b Lodz, Poland, Feb 1, 20; nat US. ELECTRICAL ENGINEERING. *Educ:* St Andrews Univ, BSc, 44; Columbia Univ, MS, 53, DEng Sc(elec eng), 56. *Prof Exp:* Radio engr, Jewel Radio Co, 49-51; asst elec eng, Columbia Univ, 51-53, from instr to assoc prof, 53-62; vis prof, Polytech Inst Brooklyn, 62-63; assoc prof, 63-71, PROF SCH ENG, CITY COL NEW YORK, 71- *Concurrent Pos:* Consult, Gen Appl Sci Labs, 57 & Norden Labs, 58-59; sci ed, Scripta Technica Inc, 63-71. *Mem:* Inst Elec & Electronics Engrs. *Res:* Control systems theory, particularly sampled data systems and optimal controls. *Mailing Add:* Dept of Elec Eng Sch of Eng City Col of New York New York NY 10031

KRANC, STANLEY CHARLES, b Peoria, Ill, Sept 29, 42. MECHANICAL ENGINEERING, CHEMICAL PHYSICS. *Educ:* Northwestern Univ, BS, 64, PhD(mech eng), 69. *Prof Exp:* Asst prof eng sci, Fla State Univ, 67-71; from asst prof to assoc prof, 71-78, PROF ENG, UNIV SOUTH FLA, 71- *Mem:* Am Inst Aeronaut & Astronaut; Newcomen Soc; Am Soc Mech Engrs. *Res:* Gas dynamics; plasma physics; combustion; two phase flow. *Mailing Add:* Dept Civil Eng & Mech Col Eng Univ SFla Tampa FL 33620

KRANE, KENNETH SAUL, b Philadelphia, Pa, May 15, 44; m 66; c 1. EXPERIMENTAL NUCLEAR PHYSICS. *Educ:* Univ Ariz, BS, 65; Purdue Univ, MS, 67, PhD(physics), 70. *Prof Exp:* Res assoc physics, Los Alamos Sci Lab, 70-72 & nuclear chem, Lawrence Berkeley Lab, 72-74; asst prof, 74-78, ASSOC PROF PHYSICS, ORE STATE UNIV, 78- *Mem:* Am Phys Soc; Am Asn Physics Teachers. *Res:* Angular distributions and correlations of gamma rays; nuclear spectroscopy; nuclear physics at ultralow temperatures; beta decay; x-rays in muonic atoms; intermediate energy nuclear physics. *Mailing Add:* Dept of Physics Ore State Univ Corvallis OR 97331

KRANE, STANLEY GARSON, b New York, NY, Feb 16, 37. CELL BIOLOGY, MOLECULAR BIOLOGY. *Educ:* City Col New York, BS, 57; Mich State Univ, MS, 58; Calif Inst Technol, PhD(biochem), 66. *Prof Exp:* Res fel biochem, Brandeis Univ, 66-67; asst prof biol, Univ Mass, Boston, 68-75; asst prof, 75-80, ASSOC PROF BIOL, FITCHBURG STATE COL, 80- *Mem:* AAAS; Am Inst Biol Sci. *Res:* Mutagenesis of microorganisms. *Mailing Add:* Dept of Biol Fitchburg State Col Fitchburg MA 01420

KRANE, STEPHEN MARTIN, b New York, NY, July 15, 27; m 52; c 4. MEDICINE, BIOCHEMISTRY. *Educ:* Columbia Col, AB, 46; Columbia Univ, MD, 51; Am Bd Internal Med, dipl, 58. *Hon Degrees:* AM, Harvard Univ, 68. *Prof Exp:* Asst, Harvard Med Sch, 55-59, instr, 59-60, assoc, 60-63, from asst prof to assoc prof, 63-72, PROF MED, HARVARD MED SCH, 72-; PHYSICIAN, MASS GEN HOSP, 69- *Concurrent Pos:* Fel med, Harvard Med Sch, 53-55; fel, Sch Med, Wash Univ, 56; Guggenheim fel, Oxford Univ, 73-74; assoc physician, Mass Gen Hosp, 66-69. *Mem:* Am Soc Clin Invest; Endocrine Soc; Asn Am Physicians; Am Rheumatism Asn; Am Fedn Clin Res. *Res:* Connective tissue biology and metabolism; internal medicine and rheumatology; transport mechanisms. *Mailing Add:* Mass Gen Hosp Boston MA 02114

KRANICH, WILMER LEROY, b Philadelphia, Pa, Nov 20, 19; m 50; c 3. CHEMICAL ENGINEERING, SYNTHETIC FUELS. *Educ:* Univ Pa, BS, 40; Cornell Univ, PhD(chem eng), 44. *Prof Exp:* Instr chem eng, Cornell Univ, 41-44; asst prof, Princeton Univ, 46-48; assoc prof, 48-49, head dept, 58-75, PROF CHEM ENG, WORCESTER POLYTECH INST, 49-, DEAN GRAD STUDIES, 75- *Concurrent Pos:* Consult, Arthur D Little, Inc, 49-74 & Norton Co, 64-68. *Mem:* Am Chem Soc; Am Soc Eng Educ; Am Inst Chem Engrs; Sigma Xi. *Res:* Process development; chemical kinetics. *Mailing Add:* Dept of Chem Eng Worcester Polytech Inst Worcester MA 01609

KRANNICH, LARRY KENT, b Pekin, Ill, Sept 5, 42. INORGANIC CHEMISTRY. *Educ:* Ill State Univ, BS, 63, MS, 65; Univ Fla, PhD(inorg chem), 68. *Prof Exp:* Asst chem, Ill State Univ, 63-65; asst, Univ Fla, 65-68, res asst, 68; asst prof, Univ Miss, 68-69; asst prof, 69-72, actg chmn dept, 74-75, assoc prof, 72-76, PROF & CHMN DEPT CHEM, UNIV ALA, BIRMINGHAM, 76- *Concurrent Pos:* Vis prof, Tech Univ Vienna, 69. *Mem:* Am Chem Soc. *Res:* Chemistry of the arsenic-nitrogen bond; chemistry of chloramine and its reaction with group V bases. *Mailing Add:* Dept of Chem Univ of Ala Birmingham AL 35294

KRANTZ, ALLEN, b New York, NY, Jan 25, 40. ORGANIC CHEMISTRY. *Educ:* City Col New York, BS, 61; Yale Univ, MS, 62, PhD(chem), 67. *Prof Exp:* Fel, Univ Reading, 67-68; asst prof, 68-74, ASSOC PROF ORG CHEM, STATE UNIV NY STONY BROOK, 74- *Concurrent Pos:* Petrol Res Fund grant, 68-71; Res Corp grant, 68-; State Univ NY Res Found fac fel & grant in aid, 69-70; NATO sr fel, 75; NSF grants, 74, 76 & 77; NIH grant, 77-81. *Mem:* Am Chem Soc; The Chem Soc. *Res:* Drug design; photochemistry of matrix isolated species; mechanism of reactions of heterocycles; bio-organic chemistry. *Mailing Add:* Syntex Can Inc 2100 Syntex Ct Mississauga ON L5M 2B3 Can

KRANTZ, DAVID S, b New York, NY, Feb 9, 49; m 82. MEDICAL PSYCHOLOGY, BEHAVIORAL MEDICINE. *Educ:* City Col New York, BS, 71; Univ Tex, Austin, PhD(psychol), 75. *Prof Exp:* Asst prof psychol, Univ Southern Calif, 75-78; asst prof, 78-82, ASSOC PROF MED PSYCHOL, UNIFORMED SERV UNIV HEALTH SCI, 82- *Mem:* Am Psychol Asn; Am Psychosomatic Soc; Soc Psychophysiol Res; Acad Behav Med Res. *Res:* Behavioral and psychophysiological factors in cardiovascular disorders; psychological stress and techniques of stress-reduction, particularly in health care settings. *Mailing Add:* Dept Med Psychol Uniformed Serv Univ Health Sci 4301 Jones Bridge Rd Bethesda MD 20814

KRANTZ, GERALD WILLIAM, b Pittsburgh, Pa, Mar 12, 28; m 55; c 3. ENTOMOLOGY. *Educ:* Univ Pittsburgh, BSc, 51; Cornell Univ, PhD, 55. *Prof Exp:* From asst prof to assoc prof, 55-65, PROF ENTOM, ORE STATE UNIV, 65- *Concurrent Pos:* Microzoologist, Am Quintana Roo Exped, 65, zoologist & dep leader, Exped II, 68; lectr, Acarology Lab, Ohio State Univ, 67, 71 & 73. *Honors & Awards:* Acarology Award, Ohio State Univ, 71. *Mem:* Entom Soc Am (mem, Gov Bd, 71-76, chmn, 75-76). *Res:* Systematics and behavior of Acari diversi. *Mailing Add:* Dept of Entom Ore State Univ Corvallis OR 97331

KRANTZ, KARL WALTER, b Waterbury, Conn, May 9, 18; m 42; c 2. ORGANIC CHEMISTRY, POLYMER CHEMISTRY. *Educ:* Univ Conn, BS, 39, MS, 40; Stanford Univ, PhD(chem), 51. *Prof Exp:* Asst chem, Stanford Univ, 40-41; instr, Univ Conn, 42-43; res chemist, E I du Pont de Nemours & Co, 45-50; res chemist, 50-60, SPECIALIST SILICONE RES TECHNOL, SILICONE PROD DEPT, GEN ELEC CO, 60- *Mem:* Am Chem Soc; fel Am Inst Chemists. *Res:* Aliphatic diamines; local anesthetics; fluorocarbons; catalytic oxidation of hydrocarbons; silicones. *Mailing Add:* 1219 Hedgewood Lane Schenectady NY 12309

KRANTZ, KERMIT EDWARD, b Oak Park, Ill, June 4, 23; m 46. MEDICINE. *Educ:* Northwestern Univ, BS, 45, BM & MS, 47, MD, 48; Am Bd Obstet & Gynec, dipl. *Hon Degrees:* LittD, William Woods Col, 71. *Prof Exp:* Asst zool, Northwestern Univ, 43, resident anat, Med Sch, 44-47; intern obstet & gynec, New York Lying-In-Hosp, Cornell Univ, 47-48; asst resident, New York Hosp, 48-50; from instr to asst prof, Univ Vt, 51-55; asst prof, Sch Med, Univ Ark, 55-59; dean clin affairs, Med Ctr Col Health Sci & Hosp, 72-74, PROF OBSTET & GYNEC & CHMN DEPT, SCH MED, UNIV KANS, 59-, PROF ANAT, 63-, ASSOC TO EXEC V CHANCELLOR FACIL DEVELOP, MED CTR, 74- *Concurrent Pos:* NY Acad Med Bowen-Brooks fel, New York Hosp, 48-50; res fel, Col Med, Univ Vt, 50-51; Markle scholar, Sch Med, Univ Kans, 57-62; asst, Med Sch, Northwestern Univ, 46-47, cur mus, 44-47; consult, Div Maternal & Child Health & Welfare, Vt State Dept Health, 52-55 & Surgeon Gen, US Air Force, 64-; pres, Int Family Planning Res Asn, Inc, 75-76. *Mem:* AAAS; Am Asn Anatomists; found fel Am Col Obstetricians & Gynecologists; Am Med Writers Asn; Am Col Surgeons. *Res:* Human placenta; anatomy and physiology; female anatomy, urethra, bladder, vagina, uterus, tubes and ovaries; renal function in pregnancy. *Mailing Add:* Univ of Kans Med Ctr Kansas City KS 66103

KRANTZ, REINHOLD JOHN, b Bradford, Pa, Aug 12, 15; m 37; c 4. ORGANIC CHEMISTRY. *Educ:* Greenville Col, AB, 36; Univ Ill, MS, 37; Mich State Col, PhD(org chem), 47. *Prof Exp:* Control chemist, Kendall Refrig Co, 37-38; instr chem & math, Moberly Jr Col, 38-41 & chem, Mich State Col, 41-47; from asst prof to assoc prof, 47-60, prof, 60-81, EMER PROF CHEM, UNIV REDLANDS, 81- *Concurrent Pos:* Lectr, Pakistan Univ, 58-59; chemist, Off Naval Res, 51-; dir div sci & math, Univ Redlands, 61-73; mem bd, Redlands-Highland-Yucaipa Resource Conserv Dist, 69- *Mem:* AAAS; Am Chem Soc. *Res:* Fragmentation of tertiary alcohols; organosilicon compounds; reaction of alkenes, 1-alkenes and formaldehyde. *Mailing Add:* Dept of Chem Div of Natural Sci Univ of Redlands Redlands CA 92373

KRANTZ, SANFORD B, b Chicago, Ill, Feb 6, 34; m 58; c 4. INTERNAL MEDICINE, HEMATOLOGY. *Educ:* Univ Chicago, AB & BS, 55, MD, 59. *Prof Exp:* Intern med, Univ Chicago Hosps, 60-61, asst resident, 61-62, res assoc, 63-64; asst prof med, Univ Chicago Hosps & Argonne Cancer Res Hosp, 65-68; asst chief hemat serv, Clin Ctr, NIH, 68-70; assoc prof, 70-75, PROF MED & DIR HEMAT, SCH MED, VANDERBILT UNIV, 75-; CHIEF HEMAT UNIT, VET ADMIN HOSP, NASHVILLE, 70- *Concurrent Pos:* USPHS fel, Univ Chicago Hosps, 62-64; NATO fel biochem, Univ Glasgow, 64-65; Leukemia Soc scholar, 65-68. *Honors & Awards:* Joseph A Capps Prize, Inst Med Chicago, 64. *Mem:* AAAS; Am Soc Clin Invest; Am Fedn Clin Res; Am Soc Hemat. *Res:* Erythropoietin; erythropoietic diseases; polycythemia and red cell aplasia; friend virus polycythemia in mice. *Mailing Add:* 838 Rodney Dr Nashville TN 37203

KRANTZ, STEVEN GEORGE, b San Francisco, Calif, Feb 3, 51; m 74. SEVERAL COMPLEX VARIABLES. *Educ:* Univ Calif, Santa Cruz, BA, 71; Princeton Univ, PhD(math), 74. *Prof Exp:* asst prof math, Univ Calif, Los Angeles, 74-81; ASSOC PROF MATH, PA STATE UNIV, UNIVERSITY PARK, 81- *Concurrent Pos:* NSF res fel, 75- *Mem:* Am Math Soc. *Res:* Function theory on pseudoconvex domains in complex n-space; harmonic analysis of Euclidean spaces, real function theory, differentiability of functions, and interpolation theory. *Mailing Add:* Dept Math Pa State Univ University Park PA 16802

KRANTZ, WILLIAM BERNARD, b Freeport, Ill, Jan 27, 39; m 68; c 1. COAL GASIFICATION, HYDRODYNAMIC STABILITY THEORY. *Educ:* St Joseph's Col, Ind, BA, 61; Univ Ill, Urbana, BS, 62; Univ Calif, Berkeley, PhD(chem eng), 68. *Prof Exp:* Asst prof, 68-77, assoc prof, 77-79, PROF CHEM ENG, UNIV COLO, BOULDER, 79- *Concurrent Pos:* Consult, Dow Chem Co, Mich, 69-71; Fulbright-Hays lectr, Istanbul Tech Univ, 74-75; NSF, NATO sr fel, Univ Essex, Eng, 75; consult, Laramie Energy Technol Ctr, Dept Energy, 76-; dir, Thermodyn & Mass Transfer Prog, NSF, 77-78; mem area adv comt, US Coun Int Exchange Scholar, Int Commun Agency, 77-80; consult, US Dept Commerce, 79-80; Fulbright-Hays sr res fel, Aachen Tech Univ, WGer, 81-82. *Honors & Awards:* Ralph R Teetor Award, Soc Automotive Engrs, 72; Spec Achievement & Outstanding Performance Awards, NSF, 78; George Westinghouse Award, Am Soc Eng Educ, 80. *Mem:* AAAS; Am Inst Chem Engrs; Am Soc Eng Educ; Am Chem Soc; Sigma Xi. *Res:* Underground coal gasification; development of membrane separations technologies; modeling of periglacial geophysical processes; transport processes in dynamic interfaces; particle dynamics in unsteady flows; research administration and planning; science education. *Mailing Add:* Dept of Chem Eng Univ of Colo Boulder CO 80309

KRANZ, EUGENE FRANCIS, b Toledo, Ohio, Aug 17, 33; m; c 6. AERONAUTICAL ENGINEERING. *Educ:* St Louis Univ, BS. *Prof Exp:* Flight test engr, McDonnell Aircraft Co, 54-55; supvr carrier flight test maintenance & checkout, Holloman AFB, NMex, 58-60; FLIGHT DIR GEMINI, APOLLO & SKYLAB MISSIONS, MANNED SPACECRAFT CTR, NASA, 64-, CHIEF FLIGHT CONTROL DIV, 69-, FLIGHT OPERS DIR SHUTTLE PROG, 80- *Concurrent Pos:* Flight controller, Mercury Missions. *Honors & Awards:* Lawrence Sperry Award, Am Inst Aeronaut & Astronaut, 67. *Mailing Add:* Manned Spacecraft Ctr NASA Houston TX 77058

KRANZER, HERBERT C, b New York, NY, Apr 10, 32; m 58; c 3. APPLIED MATHEMATICS. *Educ:* NY Univ, BA, 52, PhD(math), 57. *Prof Exp:* Asst math, NY Univ, 52-57, assoc res scientist, 57-58, instr, 58-59; assoc prof, 59-63, PROF MATH, ADELPHI UNIV, 63- *Concurrent Pos:* Consult, Los Alamos Sci Lab, 56-68; NSF sr fel, 66; vis prof, Imp Col London, 66-67; vis scholar, Columbia Univ, 76-77. *Honors & Awards:* Putnam Awards, 51 & 52. *Mem:* Am Math Soc; Soc Indust & Appl Math; Math Asn Am; AAAS. *Res:* Magnetohydrodynamics; numerical analysis; Weiner-Hopf problems; conservation laws. *Mailing Add:* Dept of Math Adelphi Univ Garden City NY 11530

KRANZLER, ALBERT WILLIAM, b Bismarck, NDak, July 11, 16; m 39; c 2. MATHEMATICS. *Educ:* Univ NDak, BS, 37; Univ Minn, MS, 50. *Prof Exp:* Prin pub sch, NDak, 37-41; teacher, SDak, 41-42; instr training div, Sioux Falls Army Air Force Sch, 42-43; prin pub sch, Colo, 43-45; assoc prof math, 45-61, actg head dept, 61-68, PROF MATH, SDAK STATE UNIV, 61- *Mem:* Math Asn Am; Am Math Soc. *Res:* Reorganization of high school mathematics curriculum. *Mailing Add:* Dept of Math SDak State Univ Brookings SD 57007

KRAPCHO, ANDREW PAUL, b Alden, Pa, Mar 6, 32; m 58; c 3. ORGANIC CHEMISTRY. *Educ:* Pa State Univ, BS, 53; Harvard Univ, MA, 57, PhD(chem), 58. *Prof Exp:* Instr chem, Smith Col, 57-59; res fel, Pa State Univ, 59-60; from asst prof to assoc prof, 60-67, PROF CHEM, UNIV VT, 67- *Concurrent Pos:* Fulbright scholar, France, 68-69. *Mem:* Am Chem Soc. *Res:* Chemistry of thiones and photochemistry of cyclic ketones; physical-organic chemistry; metal-amine reductions; solvolytic studies of spirane systems; sesquiterpene syntheses; bivalent carbon species. *Mailing Add:* Dept of Chem Univ of Vt Burlington VT 05405

KRAPF, GEORGE, b Millvale, Pa, July 20, 22; m 46. ANALYTICAL CHEMISTRY. *Educ:* Univ Pittsburgh, BS, 44. *Prof Exp:* Instr chem, sec schs, WPa, 44-50; res chemist, 50-70, SR RES CHEMIST, US STEEL RES LABS, 70- *Mem:* Am Chem Soc. *Res:* Polarography, thermal analysis and second phase analysis in steels. *Mailing Add:* Thompson Manor 307 Russell St Pittsburgh PA 15209

KRAPU, GARY LEE, b Oakes, ND, Mar 12, 44; m 67. WILDLIFE RESEARCH, ANIMAL ECOLOGY. *Educ:* NDak State Univ, BS, 66; Iowa State Univ, MS, 68, PhD(animal ecol), 72. *Prof Exp:* RES SCIENTIST, NORTHERN PRAIRIE WILDLIFE RES CTR, US FISH & WILDLIFE SERV, 71- *Mem:* Wildlife Soc; Ecol Soc Am; Am Ornithologist's Union; Wilson Soc. *Res:* Ecological aspects of waterfowl reproduction; sandhill crane biology; feeding ecology and nutrition; reproductive physiology; lipid storage; bioenergetics; marsh ecology. *Mailing Add:* Northern Prairie Wildlife Res Ctr PO Box 1747 Jamestown ND 58401

KRASAVAGE, WALTER JOSEPH, b Luzerne, Pa, Mar 12, 33; m 55; c 4. INDUSTRIAL TOXICOLOGY. *Educ:* King's Col, BS, 55; Univ Rochester, MS, 63. *Prof Exp:* Technician parasitol, Merck Inst Therapeut Res, 55-56; sr res assoc, Atomic Energy Proj, Dept Radiation Biol & Biophys, Sch Med & Dent, Univ Rochester, 58-65; SR TOXICOLOGIST INDUST TOXICOL, HEALTH SAFETY & HUMAN FACTORS LAB, EASTMAN KODAK CO, 65- *Concurrent Pos:* Instr biol, Rochester Inst Technol, 63-65. *Mem:* Soc Toxicol; Teratol Soc; Environ Mutagen Soc. *Res:* Subchronic and chronic toxicology of industrial chemicals, especially reproduction and embryo-fetotoxicity. *Mailing Add:* Toxicol Sect Eastman Kodak Co Rochester NY 14650

KRASHES, DAVID, b Brooklyn, NY, Jan 31, 25; m 56; c 1. METALLURGY. *Educ:* Rensselaer Polytech Inst, BS, 49, MS, 52, PhD(metall), 58. *Prof Exp:* Res assoc metall, Rensselaer Polytech Inst, 53-54; mem staff, Nuclear Metals, Inc, 55-57; assoc prof, Worcester Polytech Inst, 57-65; PRES, MASS MAT RES, INC, 65-, PRES, LEHIGHTESING LABS, 72-, PRES, CONN METALL INC, 81- *Concurrent Pos:* Consult, Wyman-Gordon Co, 59- & Reed Rolled Thread Die Co, 60-; dir, Richard D Brew Co. *Mem:* Fel Am Soc Metals (treas, 71-73, vpres, 80-81, pres, 81-82); Am Inst Mining, Metall & Petrol Engrs; Am Soc Testing & Mat; Am Foundry Soc. *Res:* Failure analysis of metals and mechanical products; solving industrial manufacturing problems relating to materials; fabrication; microscopy; economic studies. *Mailing Add:* Mass Mat Res Inc 241 W Boylston St West Boylston MA 01583

KRASHIN, BERNARD R(OBERT), b Buffalo, NY, Nov 9, 18; m 46; c 2. METALS. *Educ:* Western Reserve Univ, BS, 41. *Prof Exp:* Chemist, Cosma Labs Co, 41-43, dir metals labs, 43-45, chief chemist & asst tech dir, 45-50; vpres, Colton Chem Co Div, Air Reduction Co, Inc, 50-56, pres, 56-62; pres, Macco Chem Co Div, Glidden Co, 62-64, vpres & gen mgr, 64-67, vpres opers, Glidden-Durkee Div, 67-70, VPRES & GEN MGR, MACCO ADHESIVES GROUP, SCM CORP, 71- *Mem:* Am Chem Soc; Am Ord Asn; Am Inst Chem. *Res:* Fungicides; vinyl resins; emulsions, wax and synthetic resin; process for fusion of bronze to steel; fungicide for ropes, nets and twine; radiological physics; synthetic resins; analytic chemistry. *Mailing Add:* Macco Adhesives SCM Corp Glidden Coatings & Resins Div Wickliffe OH 44092

KRASKIN, KENNETH STANFORD, b Kearny, NJ, Dec 28, 29; m 54; c 2. MICROBIOLOGY. *Educ:* Rutgers Univ, BS, 51, MS, 55, PhD(bact), 57. *Prof Exp:* Lab instr bact, Rutgers Univ, 54-57; microbiologist, Rohm & Haas Co, 57-70; head microbiol, Personal Prod Co, 71-77, DIR APPL RES, PERSONAL PROD CO, JOHNSON & JOHNSON, 77- *Mem:* Am Soc Microbiol; Sigma Xi; Soc Indust Microbiol. *Res:* Antibiotics; enzyme fermentations; sterility; disinfectants; biodegradation; vaginal microbiology and physiology. *Mailing Add:* 14 N Garden Terr Milltown NJ 08850

KRASNA, ALVIN ISAAC, b New York, NY, June 23, 29; m 55; c 3. BIOCHEMISTRY. *Educ:* Yeshiva Col, BA, 50; Columbia Univ, PhD(biochem), 55. *Prof Exp:* Res worker, 54-56, from instr to assoc prof, 56-70, PROF BIOCHEM, COLUMBIA UNIV, 70- *Concurrent Pos:* Guggenheim Mem Found fel, 62-63. *Mem:* AAAS; Am Chem Soc; Harvey Soc; Am Soc Biol Chemists. *Res:* Mechanism of enzyme action; intermediary metabolism; bioconversion of solar energy; nucleic acids. *Mailing Add:* Col of Physicians & Surgeons Columbia Univ New York NY 10032

KRASNER, JOSEPH, b Buffalo, NY, Jan 10, 26; m 53; c 2. BIOCHEMISTRY. *Educ:* Univ Buffalo, BS, 48, EdM, 50, MA, 63, PhD(biochem), 65. *Prof Exp:* High sch teacher, 50-51; asst cancer res scientist, Roswell Park Mem Inst, 51-61; res assoc, Children's Hosp, Buffalo, NY, 65-66; assoc res prof pediat, 66 79, ASSOC RES PROF OBSTET & GYNEC, STATE UNIV NY-BUFFALO, 79-; CANCER RES SCIENTIST

II, ROSWELL PARK MEM INST, BUFFALO, 79- *Concurrent Pos:* Dir core labs, Children's Hosp, NY, 66-72. *Mem:* AAAS; Am Chem Soc; NY Acad Sci; Am Asn Clin Chemists; Am Soc Pharmacol & Exp Therapeut. *Res:* Biochemical changes during mammalian development and the effect of endogenous and exogenous compounds on development; drug-protein interactions during development and in pathological situations; physical biochemical techniques as used to study the antibody confirming site. *Mailing Add:* 60 Snughaven Tonawanda NY 14150

KRASNER, ROBERT IRVING, b Providence, RI, Dec 3, 29; m 64; c 2. BACTERIOLOGY. *Educ:* Providence Col, BS, 51; Boston Univ, AM, 52, PhD(biol), 56. *Prof Exp:* From instr to assoc prof, 58-65, PROF BIOL, PROVIDENCE COL, 65- *Concurrent Pos:* Mem, La State Univ Sch Med Interam Training Prog Trop Med in Cent Am, 62, adv coun clin labs, RI Dept Health, 62- & US Army Biol Labs, Ft Detrick, Md, 65-66; vis prof, Sch Med, Georgetown Univ, 69-71. *Mem:* AAAS; Am Soc Microbiol. *Res:* Medical bacteriology; host-parasite relationships. *Mailing Add:* Dept of Biol Providence Col Providence RI 02918

KRASNER, SOL H, b St Louis, Mo, June 14, 23; m 58; c 4. PHYSICS. *Educ:* Univ Calif, Los Angeles, AB, 57, MA, 48; Univ Chicago, PhD(physics), 55. *Prof Exp:* Jr physicist, Argonne Nat Lab, 49-53; nuclear physicist, Off Naval Res, 55-63; prof lectr, 63-71, ASSOC PROF PHYSICS, UNIV CHICAGO, 70-, DEAN STUDENTS, DIV PHYS SCI, 63- *Concurrent Pos:* Asst to the chmn & dept counselor, Univ Chicago, 76- *Mem:* Am Phys Soc; Am Asn Physics Teachers. *Res:* Nuclear reactor physics; scientific administration. *Mailing Add:* Dept of Phys Phys Sci Div Univ of Chicago Chicago IL 60637

KRASNEY, JOHN ANDREW, b Long Beach, Calif, Nov 29, 40; m 64; c 5. CARDIOVASCULAR PHYSIOLOGY. *Educ:* Elmhurst Col, BS, 62; Univ Wis-Madison, PhD(physiol), 66. *Prof Exp:* From instr to assoc prof physiol, Albany Med Col, 67-74; ASSOC PROF PHYSIOL, STATE UNIV NY BUFFALO, 74- *Concurrent Pos:* Nat Heart Inst fel physiol, Univ Wis-Madison, 66-67. *Mem:* Am Physiol Soc; Can Physiol Soc; Am Heart Asn. *Res:* Neural control of the cardiovascular system, specifically mechanisms controlling regional blood flow during environmental stress, such as exercise or arterial hypoxia; pulmonary and coronary circulation; physiology of the renal prostaglandins; regulation of respiration in exercise. *Mailing Add:* Dept of Physiol Sherman Hall State Univ of NY Schs Med & Dent Buffalo NY 14214

KRASNO, LOUIS RICHARD, b Chicago, Ill, Sept 2, 14; m 40; c 1. MEDICINE. *Educ:* Northwestern Univ, BS, 36, MS, 37, PhD(physiol), 39, MD, 44. *Prof Exp:* Asst physiol, Northwestern Univ, 36-39; instr, Chicago City Jr Col, 39-40; instr, Med Sch, Northwestern Univ, 40-47; asst prof clin sci, Univ Ill, 47-57; ASST PROF MED, STANFORD UNIV, 57-; DIR CLIN RES, UNITED AIR LINES, 57- *Concurrent Pos:* Practicing physician, Ill, 47-57. *Mem:* Soc Exp Biol & Med; fel Int Col Angiol; fel AMA; fel Aerospace Med Asn; fel Am Col Cardiol. *Res:* Aviation medicine; physiology; cardiovascular medicine. *Mailing Add:* United Air Lines Int Airport San Francisco CA 94128

KRASNOFF, EUGENE L, b Brooklyn, NY, Mar 19, 30; m 62; c 2. FLUID DYNAMICS. *Educ:* Rensselaer Polytech Inst, BAeroE, 52; Case Inst Technol, MSAeroE, 54; Rutgers Univ, PhD(mech eng), 70. *Prof Exp:* Res asst, mech eng dept, Case Inst Technol, 52-54; res engr, United Aircraft Res Labs, 54-56; staff res engr, Allied Res Assoc, Inc, 56-58; eng specialist, New Devices Lab, TRW, Inc, 58-59; sr eng specialist, 59-60, head fluid mech group, 60-63; mem tech staff, 63-69, asst chief fluid mech, 69-75, chief spec prod, 75-81, CHIEF CONCEPT DEVELOP SECT, INGERSOLL-RAND RES, INC, 81- *Concurrent Pos:* Res assoc, Rutgers Univ, 67-69. *Mem:* Am Inst Aeronaut & Astronaut; Am Phys Soc; Am Acad Mech; AAAS. *Res:* Theoretical and experimental studies in fluid dynamics and mechanics, including gas dynamics, hydraulics, turbulence, unsteady flows, stresswaves in gasses, liquids and solids; concepting and development of new mechanical devices. *Mailing Add:* 210 Hamilton Ave Princeton NJ 08540

KRASNOW, FRANCES, b New York, NY, Oct 16, 94; m 30; c 1. BIOCHEMISTRY. *Educ:* Columbia Univ, BS & AM, 17, PhD(bact, chem, biochem), 22. *Hon Degrees:* LHD, Jewish Theol Sem of America, 74. *Prof Exp:* Asst biochem, Col Physicians & Surgeons, Columbia Univ, 19-22; instr, 22-32, Rhein-Levy Res Fund fel, 20-28; asst dir & head fundamental sci, Sch Dent Hyg, Guggenheim Dent Clin, 32-44, dir res, 44-52; RES CONSULT, 52- *Concurrent Pos:* Consult biochemist, Dept Dermat, Skin & Cancer Unit, NY Postgrad Med Sch & Hosp, Columbia Univ, 23-44; fel, Lehn-Fink Res Fund, NJ, 25-26; consult biochemist, NY State Labor Dept, 29; spec consult, NY Bur Dent Info, 40; res dir, Universal Coatings, Inc, 52-72; specialist clin chem, Am Bd Clin Chem, 53- *Mem:* AAAS; Am Chem Soc; fel Am Inst Chemists; Int Asn Dent Res (ed, vpres, pres, 34-60); assoc fel NY Acad Med; fel NY Acad Sci. *Res:* Skin disease; syphilis; cholesterol; phospholipids; biochemistry of saliva; caries; place of nutrition in dentistry; correlation between metabolic inorganic-organic levels in blood, saliva, urine and tooth conditions. *Mailing Add:* 405 E 72nd St New York NY 10021

KRASNOW, MARVIN ELLMAN, b Chicago, Ill, Apr 27, 24; m 49; c 5. PHYSICAL CHEMISTRY. *Educ:* Ohio State Univ, PhD(chem), 52. *Prof Exp:* Res assoc electron scattering, Ohio State Univ, 52-53; res chemist polyethylene, Visking Corp, 53-56; mgr chem, Physics & Petrol Lab, Inland Testing Labs, 56-59; dir govt res & develop, Hallicrafters Co, 59-64; COORDR INDUST RELS, COL ENG, UNIV ILL, URBANA, 64- *Mem:* Inst Elec & Electronics Engrs; Optical Soc Am; Am Inst Physics; Am Soc Eng Educ. *Res:* Electron scattering by gases; investigation of structure of polyethylene; interaction of electromagnetic radiation with matter; evaluation of fuels and lubricants; quantum phenomena. *Mailing Add:* 803 Brighton Dr Urbana IL 61801

KRASNOW, RICHARD ALLEN CHRISTIAN, b Washington, DC, Mar 21, 45. CELL BIOLOGY, THEORETICAL BIOLOGY. *Educ:* Mass Inst Technol, SB, 67, PhD(physics), 73. *Prof Exp:* Res fel biophys, Harvard Med Sch, 73-75; res fel, Biol Labs, Harvard Univ, 75-81. *Concurrent Pos:* NIH fel, Biol Labs, Harvard Univ, 75-76; sci fel, Comt Agr, US House Rep, mem subcomt, Dept Phys Sci, Res & Foreign Agr, 81-82; cong sci & eng fel, AAAS, 81-82. *Mem:* AAAS. *Res:* Circadian rhythms; cell growth; bioluminescience; computers in biology. *Mailing Add:* 16 Divinity Ave Harvard Univ Biol Labs Cambridge MA 02138

KRASNY, HARVEY CHARLES, b Highpoint, NC, July 27, 45; m 79; c 1. DRUG METABOLISM, PHARMACOKINETICS. *Educ:* Lynchburg Col, BS, 67; Univ NC, MS, 69, PhD(biochem), 76. *Prof Exp:* RES SCIENTIST, WELLCOME RES LABS, BURROUGHS WELLCOME CO, 69- *Mem:* Am Soc Clin Pharmacol & Therapeut; Am Soc Pharmacol & Exp Therapeut; Soc Toxicol; Sigma Xi; NY Acad Sci. *Res:* Drug metabolism and the pharmacokinetic disposition of nucleic acid antagonist in animals and in man. *Mailing Add:* Dept Exp Therapeut Burroughs Wellcome Co Research Triangle Park NC 27709

KRASS, ALLAN S(HALE), b Milwaukee, Wis, May 16, 35. THEORETICAL PHYSICS, SCIENCE POLICY. *Educ:* Cornell Univ, BS, 58; Stanford Univ, PhD(theoret physics), 63. *Prof Exp:* Res assoc physics, Univ Iowa, 62-64; lectr, Univ Calif, Santa Barbara, 64-65; asst prof, 65-72; lectr, Princeton Univ, 72-73; vis lectr, Open Univ Gr Brit, 73-74; assoc prof, 74-79, PROF PHYSICS & SCI POLICY, HAMPSHIRE COL, 81- *Concurrent Pos:* Consult, Off Technol Assessment, US Cong, 76-; NSF fac fel, 76-77; vis researcher, Stockholm Instrnl Peace Res Inst, 80-81. *Res:* Elementary particle physics; theoretical high energy physics; science policy, especially energy, arms control and environmental. *Mailing Add:* Sch of Natural Sci Hampshire Col Amherst MA 01002

KRASS, DENNIS KEITH, b Cincinnati, Ohio, Dec 24, 47; m 71; c 1. SYNTHETIC ORGANIC CHEMISTRY, AGRICULTURAL CHEMISTRY. *Educ:* Univ Cincinnati, BS, 69; Univ Ala, PhD(org chem), 75. *Prof Exp:* SR RES CHEMIST, PPG INDUSTS, INC, BARBERTON, OHIO, 75- *Mem:* Am Chem Soc; Int Soc Heterocyclic Chemists; AAAS. *Res:* Synthesis of novel heterocyclic organic compounds for potential application of herbicidal agents. *Mailing Add:* PPG Indust PO Box 31 Barberton OH 44203

KRASSNER, STUART M, b New York, NY, Aug 21, 35. PARASITOLOGY. *Educ:* Brooklyn Col, BS, 57; Johns Hopkins Univ, ScD(parasitol), 61. *Prof Exp:* NIH fel, int coop med res & training prog, Johns Hopkins Univ-Sch Trop Med, Univ Calcutta, 61-62; guest investr & NIH res trainee, Rockefeller Univ, 62-65; instr invert zool, Hunter Col, 64-65; asst prof organismic biol, 65-69, assoc prof develop & cell biol, 69-73, assoc dean grad div, 74-76, assoc dean biol sci, 77-80, JOINT PROF DEVELOP & CELL BIOL & MED MICROBIOL, UNIV CALIF, IRVINE, 73- *Concurrent Pos:* Vchmn dept develop & cell biol, Univ Calif, Irvine, 69-73. *Mem:* AAAS; Am Soc Parasitol; Soc Protozool; Am Soc Trop Med Hyg. *Res:* Immune responses in hemoflagellate infections. *Mailing Add:* Dept of Develop & Cell Biol Univ of Calif Irvine CA 92717

KRASTINS, GUNAR, nuclear engineering, see previous edition

KRATOCHVIL, BYRON, b Osmond, Nebr, Sept 15, 32; m 60; c 4. ANALYTICAL CHEMISTRY. *Educ:* Iowa State Univ, BS, 57, MS, 59, PhD(anal chem), 61. *Prof Exp:* Instr chem, Univ Wis, Madison, 61-62, asst prof, 62-67; assoc prof, 67-71, PROF CHEM, UNIV ALTA, 71- *Concurrent Pos:* Guest worker, Nat Bur Standards, Washington, DC, 80-81. *Mem:* AAAS; Am Chem Soc; Chem Inst Can. *Res:* Electron transfer reactions; metal complex studies; nonaqueous solvents; solvent-solute interactions; analysis using nonaqueous solvents; clinical analysis; sampling for chemical analysis. *Mailing Add:* Dept of Chem Univ of Alta Edmonton AB T6G 2G2 Can

KRATOCHVIL, CLYDE HARDING, physiology, biochemistry, see previous edition

KRATOCHVIL, JIRI, b Prague, Czech, June 11, 44; m 72; c 1. ELECTROCHEMISTRY, BIOMEDICAL SCIENCES. *Educ:* Southampton Univ, PhD(electrochem), 72. *Prof Exp:* Fel electrochem, Univ Okla, 72-73; lectr physiol, St Thomas' Hosp Med Sch, London, 73-75; res fel, Webb-Waring Lung Inst, Denver, 75-76; sr chemist electrochem, Beckman Instruments Inc, 77-79; MGR RES & DEVELOP, CRITIKON INC, SALT LAKE CITY, UTAH, 79- *Mem:* Fel The Chem Soc; Am Chem Soc. *Res:* Ion-selective electrodes; electrochemistry of membranes; polarography; biomedical transducers; semiconductor technology; semiconductor packaging. *Mailing Add:* 9144 S Winter Wren Dr Sandy UT 84092

KRATOHVIL, JOSIP, b Morovic, Yugoslavia, Feb 26, 28; m 52; c 2. COLLOID CHEMISTRY, POLYMER PHYSICAL CHEMISTRY. *Educ:* Univ Zagreb, BS, 52, PhD(chem), 54. *Prof Exp:* Asst chem, Med Sch, Univ Zagreb, 52-59; res fel, Nat Res Coun Can, 59-60; res assoc, 60-64, from asst prof to assoc prof, 64-67, PROF CHEM, CLARKSON COL TECHNOL, 67-, DIR, INST COLLOID & SURFACE SCI, 81- *Mem:* AAAS; Am Chem Soc; Fine Particle Soc; NY Acad Sci; Sigma Xi. *Res:* Coagulation and stability of colloids; light scattering; physical biochemistry; polymer chemistry; micellar systems; bile salts; polyelectrolytes and macromolecules in solutions. *Mailing Add:* Dept of Chem Clarkson Col Technol Potsdam NY 13676

KRATTIGER, JOHN TRUBERT, b Denison, Tex, Aug 30, 16; wid; c 1. MATHEMATICS. *Educ:* Austin Col, BA, 38; Southern Methodist Univ, MA, 39; Univ Okla, EdD, 58. *Prof Exp:* Asst math, Southern Methodist Univ, 39-40; teacher pub sch, Tex, 40-41; instr, Col Ozarks, 41-44; instr, Univ Okla, 46-48; assoc prof, 48-65, PROF MATH, SOUTHEASTERN OKLA STATE UNIV, 65-, VPRES STUDENT SERV, 75- *Mem:* Math Asn Am; Personnel & Guid Asn. *Res:* Educational guidance. *Mailing Add:* Box 4116 Southeastern Okla State Univ Durant OK 74701

KRATZ, HOWARD RUSSEL, b Mattoon, Wis, Nov 2, 16; m 42; c 2. EXPERIMENTAL PHYSICS. *Educ:* Ripon Col, AB, 38; Univ Wis, PhD(physics), 42. *Prof Exp:* Asst physics, Univ Wis, 38-40; asst spectros, Princeton Univ, 40-42; res assoc, Metall Lab, Univ Chicago, 42-44, Los Alamos Sci Lab, 44-46, Northwestern Univ, 46, Res Lab, Gen Elec Co, 46-59, Gulf Gen Atomic Inc, 59-70 & Gulf Radiation Technol, Calif, 70-72; sr res scientist, Systs, Sci & Software, 72-79; RETIRED. *Mem:* Am Phys Soc. *Res:* Ultraviolet and infrared spectroscopy; thermal conduction and transfer; plasma physics; explosion phenomena; accelerator development; nuclear weapons effects; instrumentation. *Mailing Add:* 2620 Kanuga Pines Rd Hendersonville NC 28739

KRATZEL, ROBERT JEFFREY, b New York, NY, Feb 5, 49; m 75. IMMUNOHEMATOLOGY, MICROBIOLOGY. *Educ:* Hofstra Univ, BA, 71; State Univ NY, Buffalo, MA, 73, PhD(microbiol), 77. *Prof Exp:* Trainee lab med, Erie County Lab, E J Meyer Mem Hosp, Buffalo, 77; dir tech serv, 78-81, DIR BUFFALO REGION, AM RED CROSS BLOOD SERV, 81- *Concurrent Pos:* Clin instr, Dept Microbiol, State Univ NY, Buffalo, 77-; clin asst prof, Dept Microbiol, State Univ NY Buffalo, 81-; mem bd dir, Blood Bank Asn NY State Inc. *Mem:* Am Asn Blood Banks; Am Soc Microbiol. *Res:* The chemical characterization and localization of blood group antigens on blood and tissue cells. *Mailing Add:* Buffalo Regional 786 Delaware Ave Buffalo NY 14209

KRATZER, D DAL, b Amazonia, Mo, Dec 16, 37; m 63; c 2. ANIMAL BREEDING, STATISTICS. *Educ:* Univ Mo, BS, 59; Iowa State Univ, MS, 64, PhD(animal breeding), 65. *Prof Exp:* Asst animal breeding, Iowa State Univ, 59-62, res assoc animal breeding & comput sci, 62-65, asst prof animal sci & comput sci, 65-68; from asst prof to prof animal sci & statist, Univ Ky, 68-77; BIOSTATISTICIAN, THE UPJOHN CO, 78- *Mem:* Am Soc Animal Sci; Biomet Soc. *Res:* Behavior of domestic animals. *Mailing Add:* The Upjohn Co Kalamazoo MI 49001

KRATZER, FRANK HOWARD, b Baldwinsville, NY, Jan 24, 18; m 46; c 3. NUTRITION. *Educ:* Cornell Univ, BS, 40; Univ Calif, PhD(animal nutrit), 44. *Prof Exp:* Asst poultry husb, Univ Calif, 40-43, res assoc, 43-44; assoc prof, Colo Agr & Mech Col, 44-45; asst prof, Col Agr & Environ Sci, 45-49, assoc prof, 49-55, prof poultry husb, 55-76, chmn dept, 76-81, PROF AVIAN SCI, COL AGR & ENVIRON SCI, UNIV CALIF, DAVIS, 76- *Concurrent Pos:* NSF fel, 59-60; guest prof, Justus Liebig Univ, Giessen, Ger, 68-69. *Honors & Awards:* Nat Turkey Fedn Res Award, 49; Am Feed Mfrs Res Award, 60; CPC Res Award, 73. *Mem:* Am Chem Soc; Soc Exp Biol & Med; Am Inst Nutrit; Poultry Sci Asn; Biochem Soc. *Res:* Nutrition of poultry amino acid requirements of chickens and turkeys; vitamin needs and function; minerals and mineral availability; growth inhibitors. *Mailing Add:* Dept Avian Sci Univ Calif Davis CA 95616

KRATZER, REINHOLD, b Kaaden, CSR, Nov 14, 28. POLYMER CHEMISTRY. *Educ:* Univ Munich, Dr rer nat(inorg chem), 60. *Prof Exp:* Res asst inorg chem, Univ Southern Calif, 60-62; res chemist, Naval Ord Lab, Corona, Calif, 62-64; sr scientist, MHD Res Inc, Hercules Powder Co, 64-66; spec mem adv tech staff, Marquardt Corp, 66, mgr chem res, 66-70; MGR CHEM DEPT, ULTRASYSTS INC, 70- *Mem:* Am Chem Soc; Royal Soc Chem; Ger Chem Soc; AAAS; NY Acad Sci. *Res:* Hydrides of low atomic weight elements and their Lewis base adducts; organometallic chemistry of these elements; phosphonitriles; arc and glow discharge processes; degradation and flammability of polymers; mechanism of acid formation in coal mines; corrosion and oxidation inhibition in lubricating fluids; fluids-seals interactions. *Mailing Add:* 1425 Seacrest Dr Corona Del Mar CA 92625

KRATZKE, ALBERT WILLIAM, applied mathematics, see previous edition

KRAUHS, JANE MORRISON, b Norfolk, Va, Oct 14, 47; m 73. NEUROCYTOLOGY, SENSORY PHYSIOLOGY. *Educ:* Duke Univ, BS, 69; Ind Univ, MA, 71, PhD(zool), 75. *Prof Exp:* Res assoc, Med Sci Prog, Ind Univ, 73-75; res assoc, Dept Physiol & Biophysics, 75-76, fel, 76-79, RES ASST PROF, DEPT PHYSIOL, UNIV TEX MED BR, GALVESTON, 79- *Concurrent Pos:* Prin investr, Am Heart Asn, 79-82 & NIH, 81-; mem, Basic Sci Coun, Am Heart Asn. *Mem:* Am Asn Anatomists; Am Soc Cell Biol; Biophys Soc; Soc Neurosci. *Res:* Ultrastructure and function of sensory receptors, particularly aortic baroreceptors and airway stretch receptors. *Mailing Add:* Dept Physiol & Biophys Univ Tex Med Br Galveston TX 77550

KRAUS, ALFRED ANDREW, JR, b Richmond, Calif, May 24, 25; m 49; c 4. PHYSICS. *Educ:* Mass Inst Technol, BS, 49; Calif Inst Technol, PhD(physics), 53. *Prof Exp:* Asst, Calif Inst Technol, 50-52; res assoc nuclear physics, Rice Univ, 53-55; from res assoc to instr physics, Univ Pac, 55-61, chmn dept, 56-61; from assoc prof to prof, NMex Highlands Univ, 61-64, chmn dept physics & math, 63-64; phys sci proj dir, Killgore Res Ctr, West Tex State Univ, 64-65 & 67-68, dir, 65-67, prof physics, 64-68; OWNER, CANYON RES CO, 68- *Concurrent Pos:* Radiol physicist, San Joaquin Gen Hosp, 57-60. *Mem:* Am Phys Soc. *Res:* Nuclear physics; computers; relativistic astrophysics. *Mailing Add:* Canyon Res Co 133 Virginia St NE Albuquerque NM 87108

KRAUS, ALFRED PAUL, b Vienna, Austria, June 24, 16; nat US; m 44; c 2. MEDICINE. *Educ:* Univ Chicago, MD, 41. *Prof Exp:* Intern, Michael Reese Hosp, Ill, 41-42, asst resident & resident internal med, 42-44, resident dept hemat res, 48; chief hemat sect, Vet Admin Hosp, Ala, 49; asst chief, Kennedy Vet Admin Hosp, Tenn, 50-52; from asst prof to prof, 53-81, chief sect hemat, 64-81, dir, Ctr Res & Serv Sickle Cell Dis, 74-79, EMER PROF MED, COL MED, UNIV TENN, MEMPHIS, 81- *Concurrent Pos:* Consult hematologist, Baptist Mem Hosp, 53-, Le Bonheur Children's Hosp, Methodist Hosp & St Joseph's Hosp; vis asst prof, Univ Indonesia, 55-56; investr natural hist sickle cell dis, 79- *Mem:* AAAS; Am Soc Hemat; fel AMA; fel Am Col Physicians; Am Fedn Clin Res. *Res:* Hematology; sickle cell disease; abnormal hemoglobins; hemorrhagic diseases; red cell enzymes. *Mailing Add:* Univ of Tenn Col of Med Memphis TN 38163

KRAUS, ARTHUR SAMUEL, b New York, NY, Aug 2, 25; m 46; c 3. EPIDEMIOLOGY. *Educ:* City Col New York, BS, 49; Columbia Univ, MS, 53; Univ Pittsburgh, ScD(biostatist), 58. *Prof Exp:* Biostatistician, NY State Dept Health, 50-57; chief, Div Statist, Res & Rec, Md State Dept Health, 58-62; asst dir, Off Res, New York City Dept Health, 62-65; head dept biostatist, Montefiore Hosp & Med Ctr, Bronx, NY, 65-66; PROF BIOSTATIST, DEPT COMMUNITY HEALTH & EPIDEMIOL, QUEEN'S UNIV ONT, 66- *Concurrent Pos:* Consult biostatist, Ont Dept Health, 66- *Mem:* Fel Am Pub Health Asn; Am Heart Asn; Can Pub Health Asn; Soc Epidemiol Res. *Res:* Epidemiologic and health care studies, particularly regarding the elderly and conditions which are disabling to them, such as stroke, dementia, incontinence, deafness and depression. *Mailing Add:* Dept Commun Hlth & Epidemiol Queen's Univ Kingston ON K7L 3N6 Can

KRAUS, ERIC BRADSHAW, b Liberec, Czech, Mar 22, 12; m 42; c 3. METEOROLOGY. *Educ:* Charles Univ, Prague, PhD(geophysics), 46. *Prof Exp:* Sr res officer, Div Radiophysics, Commonwealth Sci & Indust Res Orgn, Australia, 46-49; authority meteorologist, Snowy Mt, Hydro-Elec Authority, 52-61; sr scientist, Woods Hole Oceanog Inst, 61-66; prof meteorol & phys oceanog, 66-77, chmn div atmospheric sci, 69-77, dir, Coop Inst Marine & Atmospheric Studies, 77-81, EMER PROF, UNIV MIAMI, 81-; SR RES ASSOC, COOP INST RES ENVIRON SCI, 81- *Concurrent Pos:* Lectr, Univ Sydney, 47-51; mem, Australian Nat Comt Geophys & Geod, 49-55; convener sub-comt oceanog, 52-55; chief, UN tech assistance mission, Nairobi, Kenya, 55-56; mem panel water resources develop, World Meteorol Orgn, 55-56; adj prof, Yale Univ, 61-63; dir, NATO Atmospheric Studies Inst, Urbino Italy 75, trustee, Univ Corp Atmospheric Res, 74-80, dir NATO Atmospheric Res Inst, Bonas, France, 81, vis prof, Paris, France, 81. *Mem:* Am Meteorol Soc; Am Geophys Union; Royal Meteorol Soc. *Res:* physical oceanography; dynamic climatology and climatic change; air-sea interaction. *Mailing Add:* Coop Inst Res Environ Sci Univ Colo Boulder CO 80303

KRAUS, FRANK JOSEPH, b Austria, Dec 14, 11; nat US; m 43; c 2. CHEMISTRY. *Educ:* Graz Univ, Austria, PhD(chem), 33. *Prof Exp:* Chief chemist & prod mgr, Joseph E Seagram & Sons, Inc, 39-44; vpres & gen mgr, Barton Distilling Co, 44-69; PROD ADV, JAMES B BEAM DISTILLING CO, 69- *Mem:* AAAS; Am Chem Soc. *Mailing Add:* James B Beam Distilling Co 500 N Mich Ave Chicago IL 60611

KRAUS, GEORGE ANDREW, b Buffalo, NY, June 28, 50. ORGANIC CHEMISTRY. *Educ:* Univ Rochester, BS, 72; Columbia Univ, PhD(chem), 76. *Prof Exp:* asst prof, 76-81, PROF, DEPT CHEM, IOWA STATE UNIV, 81- *Concurrent Pos:* DuPont young fac grant, 76-78; 3M Young Fac grant, 81-82. *Mem:* AAAS; Am Chem Soc; fel The Chem Soc. *Res:* Active in the development of new synthetic methods and the application of these methods to the total synthesis of natural products; interests include kinetic anions, electrochemistry and thermal chemistry. *Mailing Add:* Dept of Chem Iowa State Univ Ames IA 50011

KRAUS, GERARD, b Prague, Czech, Feb 25, 20; nat US; m 46; c 2. PHYSICAL CHEMISTRY. *Educ:* Southern Methodist Univ, BS, 43; Univ Cincinnati, MS, 45, DSc(chem physics), 47. *Prof Exp:* Instr chem physics, Univ Cincinnati, 47-49, asst prof appl sci, 49-52; sect head, 53-59, br mgr, 59-67, SR SCIENTIST, SYNTHETIC RUBBER BR, PHILLIPS PETROL CO, 67- *Mem:* Am Chem Soc. *Res:* Polymer and surface chemistry; rheology. *Mailing Add:* Phillips Petrol Co 106 RB-6 Res & Develop Div Bartlesville OK 74004

KRAUS, HARRY, b Czech, July 23, 32; US citizen; m 55, 78; c 2. APPLIED MECHANICS, MECHANICAL ENGINEERING. *Educ:* NY Univ, BME, 53; Univ Pittsburgh, MS, 58, PhD(mech eng), 61. *Prof Exp:* Jr design engr, Bettis Atomic Power Lab, Westinghouse Elec Corp, 53-54, assoc design engr, 56-58, engr appl mech, 58-61, sr engr, 61-62; staff scientist, Pratt & Whitney Aircraft Div, United Aircraft Corp, 62-66; assoc prof eng, State Univ NY, Stony Brook, 66-68; assoc dean, 69-70, dean, 70-72, PROF MECH, HARTFORD GRAD CTR, 68- *Concurrent Pos:* Lectr, Univ Pittsburgh, 61-62; adj asst prof, Rensselaer Polytech Inst, 62-; consult, Exxon Res & Eng Co, 66- *Mem:* Am Soc Mech Engrs; Orthopaedic Res Soc. *Res:* Structural analysis of industrial equipment; mechanics of solids, particularly in theories of shells, elasticity, thermal stresses and vibrations; orthopaedic biomechanics; sports medicine. *Mailing Add:* Hartford Grad Ctr 275 Windsor St Hartford CT 06120

KRAUS, JAMES ELLSWORTH, b Rocky Ford, Colo, Nov 19, 09; m 35; c 1. HORTICULTURE. *Educ:* Colo State Col, BS, 32; Univ Wis, MS, 34; Cornell Univ, PhD(veg crops), 40. *Prof Exp:* Asst hort, Univ Wis, 33-34; asst veg crops, Cornell Univ, 39-40; asst physiologist, Bur Plant Indust, USDA, 36-41; assoc horticulturist, Aberdeen br exp sta, Idaho, 41-44; plant breeder, Calif Packing Corp, Ill, 44-45; assoc horticulturist, Univ Idaho, 45-47, horticulturist, Agr Exp Sta, 48-49, assoc dir, 49-55, dir, Agr Exp Sta & Agr Exten Serv & dean, Col Agr, 55-72, prof hort & head dept, 48-49, prof plant sci, 49-72, EMER DEAN COL AGR & EMER PROF PLANT SCI, UNIV IDAHO, 72- *Mem:* Am Soc Hort Sci. *Res:* Culture and physiology of potatoes; genetics and breeding hybrid onions; culture and physiology of freezing and canning crops; vegetable seed production. *Mailing Add:* 718 E First St Moscow ID 83843

KRAUS, JESS F, b Los Angeles, Calif, Apr 4, 36; m 57; c 5. EPIDEMIOLOGY, ENVIRONMENTAL HEALTH. *Educ:* Sacramento State Col, BA, 59, MS, 63; Univ Calif, Berkeley, MPH, 64; Univ Minn, Minneapolis, PhD(environ epidemiol), 67. *Prof Exp:* Instr epidemiol & environ health, Univ Minn, 67-68; adj asst prof, Univ Cincinnati, 68-69; asst prof, 69-74, assoc prof, 74-80, PROF COMMUNITY HEALTH, SCH MED, UNIV CALIF, DAVIS, 80- *Concurrent Pos:* Chief environ epidemiol, USPHS, 68-69, epidemiologist, Bur Environ Mgt, 69-71; fel coun epidemiol, Am Heart Asn. *Mem:* Am Pub Health Asn; Soc Epidemiol Res; Asn Teachers Prev Med. *Res:* Design and execution of community and epidemiologic research involving the interrelationship of man with his physical environment. *Mailing Add:* Dept of Community Health Univ of Calif Sch of Med Davis CA 95616

KRAUS, JOHN DANIEL, b Ann Arbor, Mich, June 28, 10; m 41; c 2. ELECTRICAL ENGINEERING, ASTRONOMY. *Educ:* Univ Mich, BS, 30, MS, 31, PhD(physics), 33. *Prof Exp:* Asst physics, Univ Mich, 31-32, res assoc, Dept Eng Res, 34-35, res physicist, Dept Physics, 36-37; res physicist, Physicist Res Co, 37-38; independent res & consult, Ann Arbor, 38-40; physicist, Naval Ord Lab, 40-43; res assoc, Radio Res Lab, Harvard Univ, 43-46; from assoc prof to prof elec eng, 46-71, TAINE G McDOUGAL PROF ELEC ENG & ASTRON, OHIO STATE UNIV, 71-, DIR, RADIO OBSERV, 52- *Honors & Awards:* Sullivant Medal, 70. *Mem:* Nat Acad Eng; Am Phys Soc; Am Astron Soc; Inst Elec & Electronics Engrs. *Res:* Electromagnetic theory; antennas; radio astronomy. *Mailing Add:* Radio Observ Ohio State Univ Columbus OH 43210

KRAUS, JOHN FRANKLYN, b Brooklyn, NY, Nov 12, 29; m 57; c 5. FOREST GENETICS. *Educ:* Univ Mich, BSF, 53, MF, 56; Univ Minn, PhD(forestry), 66. *Prof Exp:* Res forester, Southeastern Forest Exp Sta, 56-64, plant geneticist, 64-72, PLANT GENETICIST, GA FORESTRY CTR, US FOREST SERV, 72- *Mem:* AAAS; Soc Am Foresters. *Res:* Breeding improved strains of southern pines. *Mailing Add:* So Forest Fire Lab Ga Forest Ctr Riggins Mill Rd Po Box 5106 Macon GA 31208

KRAUS, JON ERIC, b Cambridge, Mass, May 16, 51; m 77. FUNCTIONAL ANALYSIS, OPERATOR ALGEBRAS. *Educ:* Univ Calif, Santa Barbara, BA, 72; Univ Calif, Berkeley, MA, 75, PhD(math), 77. *Prof Exp:* Hill res instr math, 77-79, ASST PROF MATH, STATE UNIV NY BUFFALO, 79- *Mem:* Am Math Soc; Math Asn Am. *Res:* Operator algebras including von Neumann and C-algebras; noncommutative dynamical systems. *Mailing Add:* Dept of Math State Univ of NY Buffalo NY 14214

KRAUS, KENNETH WAYNE, b Waterloo, Iowa, Oct 20, 35; m 56; c 4. ORGANIC CHEMISTRY. *Educ:* Loras Col, BS, 57; Univ Calif, Berkeley, PhD(chem), 60. *Prof Exp:* From asst prof to assoc prof, 60-72, chmn dept, 65-69 & 70-71, PROF CHEM, LORAS COL, 72, ASST TO VPRES ACAD AFFAIRS, 73- *Concurrent Pos:* NSF grant, 64-66; lectr, Dept Chem, Calif State Col Long Beach, 69-70. *Mem:* Am Chem Soc. *Res:* Mechanism and use of the reaction of organocadmium reagents with acid chlorides, dipole moments, syntheses and structure proof. *Mailing Add:* Dept of Chem Loras Col Dubuque IA 52001

KRAUS, LORRAINE MARQUARDT, b Suffern, NY, Sept 6, 22; m 44; c 2. BIOCHEMISTRY. *Educ:* Mt Mary Col, BS, 43; Univ Tenn, MS, 52, PhD, 56. *Prof Exp:* Res technician, Dept Endocrinol & Metab Dis, Michael Reese Hosp, 43-44, 48; instr chem, Univ Indonesia, 55-56; res assoc, 57-60, from asst prof to assoc prof, 60-72, PROF BIOCHEM, CTR HEALTH SCI, UNIV TENN, MEMPHIS, 72- *Concurrent Pos:* Mem, Blood Dis & Resources Adv Comt, Blood Div, Nat Heart, Lung & Blood Inst, 79-83. *Mem:* Int Soc Hemat; Am Chem Soc; Am Soc Hemat; Am Soc Human Genetics; Am Soc Biol Chemists. *Res:* Biosynthesis of abnormal human hemoglobins; erythropoietin; tissue culture of hemic cells; immunochemistry; chemistry of sickle cell disease. *Mailing Add:* Dept of Biochem Univ of Tenn Ctr for Health Sci Memphis TN 38163

KRAUS, OLEN, b Berwick, Pa, Apr 7, 24; m 46; c 2. PHYSICS. *Educ:* Pa State Univ, BS, 50; Mich State Univ, MS, 52, PhD(physics), 65. *Prof Exp:* Physicist, Nat Bur Standards, 55-62; chmn dept physics, Univ SDak, 62-67; chmn dept, 67-77, PROF PHYSICS 67- & ASSOC DEAN, COL OF ARTS & SCI, UNIV NDAK, 77- *Mem:* Am Phys Soc; Am Asn Physics Teachers. *Res:* Nuclear magnetic resonance; quantum mechanics; mathematical physics; electron resonance. *Mailing Add:* Dept of Physics Univ of NDak Grand Forks ND 58201

KRAUS, SAMUEL, b Irvington, NJ, Mar 15, 25; m 54; c 3. AEROTHERMODYNAMICS, FLUID MECHANICS. *Educ:* Rensselaer Polytech Inst, BAeroEng, 44, MAeroEng, 49. *Prof Exp:* Jr engr, preliminary aeronaut design, propeller div, Curtiss-Wright Corp, 46-47; aeronaut res engr, Ames Res Ctr, NASA, 49-62; res specialist, space div, 62-67, lead engr, S-II aerothermodynamics, 67-69; lead engr, 69-80, MEM TECH STAFF, SHUTTLE AERODYN LOADS, SPACE TRANSP & SYSTS GROUP, ROCKWELL INT CORP, 69-, TECH COORDR, AIRLOADS EVAL & AERO SCI, 80- *Mem:* Assoc fel Am Inst Aeronaut & Astronaut; Sigma Xi. *Res:* Experimental and theoretical research in aerothermodynamics; planning, development and utilization of corporate experimental facilities; preflight prediction and postflight verification of aerospace vehicle environment; ignition overpressure; wake recirculation; venting of aerospace vehicles. *Mailing Add:* 6108 Monero Dr Rancho Palos Verdes CA 90274

KRAUS, SHIRLEY RUTH, b New York, NY, Dec 24, 19; m 46; c 2. PHYSIOLOGY, PHARMACOLOGY. *Educ:* Hunter Col, BA, 40; Cornell Univ, MA, 42; Univ Ill, PhD(physiol), 46. *Prof Exp:* Asst dept exp biol, Am Mus Natural Hist, NY, 40-41; hematologist, Jewish Mem Hosp, 41; asst biol & chem, Adelphi Col, 42-43, instr, Sch Nursing, 43; asst dept zool & physiol, Univ Ill, 43-46; high sch teacher, 46-47; physiologist, Gastroenterol Res Lab, Mt Sinai Hosp, 47-48; biochemist, Cancer Res Found, Harlem Hosp, 48-50; lectr physiol, Col Dent, NY Univ, 50-51; pharmacologist, Cancer Res & Metab Unit, Mt Alto Hosp, Washington, DC, 51-53; instr pharmacol, Sch Med, Howard Univ, 55-56; assoc prof, 57-65, prof pharmacol, Brooklyn Col Pharm, 65-75, PROF PHARMACOL & PHYSIOL, ARNOLD & MARIE SCHWARTZ COL PHARM & HEALTH SCI, LONG ISLAND UNIV, 75-, DIR, DIV PHARMACOTHERAPEUT & HEALTH SCI, 79- *Concurrent Pos:* instr, Eve Sch, Brooklyn Col, 47-48; assoc prof, State Univ NY Downstate Med Ctr, 69-70; vis fel clin pharmacol, Cornell Univ Med Col, 77-78; mem, Instnl Rev Bd, Clin Drug Investr Inc, 81. *Mem:* Soc Exp Biol & Med; Endocrine Soc; Am Physiol Soc; Am Soc Pharmacol & Exp Therapeut; fel Am Soc Clin Pharmacol & Therapeut. *Res:* Alloxan diabetes-anaphylaxis and granuloma pouch formation; pituitary-adrenal stress response in alloxan diabetes; anti-estrogenic action of B glycyrrhetinic acid; hyperthermia on blood platelets in male rats; corticosterone and adrenocorticotropic hormone in alloxan diabetic rats. *Mailing Add:* Arnold & Marie Schwartz Col Pharm Long Island Univ 75 DeKalb Ave Brooklyn NY 11201

KRAUS, WILLIAM LUDWIG, b Augsburg, Ger, Aug 12, 22; nat US; m 56; c 4. CARDIOLOGY. *Educ:* Harvard Med Sch, MD, 52. *Prof Exp:* Intern med, Roosevelt Hosp, New York, 52-53, asst resident, 53-55; mem med staff, Baylor Univ Hosp, 59-60; DIR CARDIAC LAB, ST PAUL HOSP, 60- *Concurrent Pos:* Life Inst Med Res Fund fel, Harvard Med Sch, 57-59; asst, Peter Bent Brigham Hosp, Boston, 57-59; mem med staff, Gaston Hosp, 59-60 & Parkland Mem Hosp, 59-; clin prof med, Univ Tex Health Sci Ctr, 59- *Mem:* Fel Am Col Cardiol; fel Am Col Physicians; Am Fedn Clin Res. *Res:* Cardiovascular physiology. *Mailing Add:* Cardiac Lab St Paul Hosp Dallas TX 75235

KRAUSCHE, DOLORES SMOLENY, b Cleveland, Ohio, Jan 27, 42. PHYSICS, ELECTRICAL ENGINEERING. *Educ:* Univ Fla, BS, 65, MS, 67, BSEE, 67, PhD(physics, astron), 75. *Prof Exp:* Res asst radioastron, 65-75, fel physics, 76-77, RES PHYSICIST, UNIV FLA, 78- *Concurrent Pos:* Interim engr, Electronic Commun Inc, 67; prin staff mem, Oper Res Inc, 78- *Mem:* Am Astron Soc; assoc mem Sigma Xi; assoc mem Inst Atmospheric Optics & Remote Sensing. *Res:* Electromagnetic phenomena relating to engineering problems and astronomical research. *Mailing Add:* PO Box 271 Gainesville FL 32602

KRAUSE, DALE CURTISS, b Wichita, Kans, Dec 27, 29; c 2. OCEANOGRAPHY, MARINE GEOLOGY. *Educ:* Calif Inst Technol, BS, 52; Univ Calif, Los Angeles, MS, 57; Univ Calif, San Diego, PhD, 61. *Prof Exp:* Mining geologist, Cerro de Pasco Corp, Peru, 52-54; res asst marine geol, Univ Calif, 56-61; asst res prof, 62-66, assoc prof, 66-72, prof, 72-73, ADJ PROF OCEANOG, GRAD SCH OCEANOG, UNIV RI, 73-; DIR, DIV MARINE SCI, UNESCO, 73- *Concurrent Pos:* Consult, various industs; NSF fel, NZ Oceanog Inst, 61-62; exchange fel, Nat Acad Sci-USSR Acad Sci, Moscow, 67-68; fel, Cambridge Univ, United Kingdom, 68-69; res oceanographer, Nat Oceanic & Atmospheric Admin, Miami, 72-73. *Mem:* Geol Soc Am; AAAS; Am Geophys Union. *Res:* Origin and evolution of the sea floor, ocean basins and continents. *Mailing Add:* Div Marine Sci UNESCO Paris 75700 France

KRAUSE, DANIEL, JR, b Sudbury, Mass, Feb 21, 45; m 75. CHEMICAL OCEANOGRAPHY. *Educ:* Univ Mass, BS, 66, PhD(physics), 72. *Prof Exp:* RES ASSOC OCEANOG, AMHERST COL, 72- *Mem:* Sigma Xi; Am Phys Soc; Am Geophys Union. *Res:* Mass spectrometric and gasometric studies of gases dissolved in water. *Mailing Add:* 734 Bay Rd S Amherst MA 01002

KRAUSE, DAVID WILFRED, b Medicine Hat, Alta, Feb 15, 50; m 78. ANATOMY. *Educ:* Univ Alta, BSc, 71, MSc, 76; Univ Mich, PhD(geol), 82. *Prof Exp:* ASST PROF ANAT, STATE UNIV NY, STONY BROOK, 82- *Honors & Awards:* Anna M Jackson Award, Am Soc Mammalogists, 81. *Mem:* Am Soc Mammalogists; Geol Asn Can; Sigma Xi; Soc Syst Zool; Soc Vert Paleont. *Res:* Evolution of late Mesozoic and early Cenozoic vertebrates, particularly mammals, and the form and function of the mammalian dentition and postcranial skelton. *Mailing Add:* Dept Anat Sci Health Sci Ctr State Univ Stony Brook NY 11794

KRAUSE, ELIOT, b New York, NY, June 7, 38; m 59; c 3. POPULATION GENETICS. *Educ:* Cornell Univ, BS, 60; Purdue Univ, MS, 63, PhD(genetics), 68. *Prof Exp:* Res asst pop genetics, Purdue Univ, 60-65; instr, 65-68, ASST PROF BIOL, SETON HALL UNIV, 68- MEM: AAAS; Genetics Soc Am; Biomet Soc; Am Genetic Asn. *Res:* Cytogenetic research with various mutagens using human lymphocytes as detected by sister chromatic exchange; selection of quantitative traits in Tribolium castaneum using genotype-environment, nutrition, interactions; investigation of disease resistance to mouse malaria using various genetic strains of mice. *Mailing Add:* Dept of Biol Seton Hall Univ South Orange NJ 07079

KRAUSE, ERNST HENRY, b Milwaukee, Wis, May 2, 13; m 39, 74; c 4. PHYSICS. *Educ:* Univ Wis, BS, 34, MS, 35, PhD(physics), 38. *Prof Exp:* Physicist, Naval Res Lab, 38-51, assoc dir res, 51-54; dir res labs, Missile Systs Div, Lockheed Aircraft Corp, 54-55; pres & chmn bd dirs, Systs res Corp, 55-56; vpres & mem bd dirs, Aeronutronic Systs, Inc, 56-59, dir tech staff, Aeronutronic Div, Ford Motor Co, 59-62; vpres & gen mgr, San Bernardino Opers, 62-68, sr vpres develop, Aerospace Corp, 68-78; MGT & TECH CONSULT, 78- *Concurrent Pos:* Mem sci adv bd, Univ Redlands, 64- & Orange State Col, 64-; mem bd dirs & pres, World Affairs Coun-Inland Empire, Calif. *Mem:* fel Am Phys Soc. *Res:* Theoretical and experimental physics; electronics; atomic and nuclear physics; upper atmosphere; missile and space systems; radio-astronomy; radar; guidance and navigation systems. *Mailing Add:* 1919 Glenwood Lane Newport Beach CA 92660

KRAUSE, EUGENE FRANKLIN, b Kenosha, Wis, Apr 7, 37; m 59; c 2. MATHEMATICS. *Educ:* Univ Wis, BS, 59, MA, 60, PhD(math), 63. *Prof Exp:* From instr to assoc prof, 63-76, PROF MATH, UNIV MICH, ANN ARBOR, 76- *Mem:* Nat Coun Teachers Math; Math Asn Am. *Res:* Mathematics education. *Mailing Add:* Dept of Math Univ of Mich Ann Arbor MI 48104

KRAUSE, GARY F, b Waverly, Kans, Jan 29, 34; m 56; c 3. STATISTICS. *Educ:* Kans State Univ, BS, 58, MS, 59; Va Polytech Inst, PhD(statist), 63. *Prof Exp:* Asst prof statist, Kans State Univ, 63-65; assoc prof statist, Univ Mo-Columbia, 66-70, prof, 70-80. *Mem:* Am Statist Asn; Biomet Soc; Wildlife Soc. *Res:* Design and analysis of experiments and statistical models in biology. *Mailing Add:* 607 Westridge Columbia MO 65201

KRAUSE, HELMUT, b Eichenstein, Ger, July 25, 28; Can citizen; m 56; c 3. FOREST SOILS. *Educ:* Univ Freiburg, Diplom Forstwirt, 54; Univ Wis, PhD(soil sci), 60. *Prof Exp:* Instr soil sci, Univ Wis, 59-61; res scientist, Can Dept Forestry & Rural Develop, 61-66; asst prof, 66-70, assoc prof, 70-76, PROF FOREST SOILS, UNIV NB, 76- *Concurrent Pos:* Vis assoc prof, Dept Soil Sci, Univ Fla, 73-74. *Mem:* AAAS; Soil Sci Soc Am; Can Soc Soil Sci; Can Inst Forestry. *Res:* Mineral requirements of forest tree seedlings, plantations and stands; chemistry of plant nutrients in forest soils; nutrient cycling in forest ecosystems. *Mailing Add:* Dept of Forest Resources Univ of NB Fredericton NB E3B 5A3 Can

KRAUSE, HELMUT G L, b Koenigsberg, Ger, Nov 10, 11, US citizen; m 55; c 1. LOW DENSITY AERODYNAMICS, THERMODYNAMICS. *Educ:* Albertus Univ, Ger, PhD(astron), 38. *Prof Exp:* Sci res asst, Koenigsberg Univ Observ, 37-44; res scientist, Inst Ballistics, Ger Air Force Acad, 44-45 & Carl Zeiss Optical Factory, 45-47; sci res asst, Inst Theoret Physics, Univ Jena, 47 & Hamburg Univ Observ, 47-48; tech physicist, Glycerine & Aliphatic Acid Factory, 49-50; dep chief, Astronaut Res Inst, Univ Stuttgart, 51-54; sr res scientist, Res Inst Physics Jet Propulsion, 54-57; spec asst space sci, Army Ballistic Missile Agency, Ala, 57-60; sci adv studies off, Marshall Space Flight Ctr, NASA, 60-65, sci adv to dir aero-astrodyn lab, 65-74; mgr bur anal res, 75-78; AEROSPACE SCIENTIST, MARSHALL SPACE FLIGHT CTR, NASA, 78- *Honors & Awards:* Ernst Heinckel Space Flight Award, 51. *Mem:* Assoc fel Am Inst Aeronaut & Astronaut; sr mem Am Astronaut Soc; Am Astron Soc; fel Brit Interplanetary Soc; Ger Soc Rocket & Space Flight. *Res:* Rocket ballistics, space mechanics and astronautical sciences; first-order perturbation theory used for Explorer I and Vanguard I; author or coauthor of 50 scientific publications. *Mailing Add:* 2718 Briarwood Dr Huntsville AL 35801

KRAUSE, HERBERT FRANCIS, b Woodbury, NJ, Mar 10, 42; m 70; c 2. ATOMIC PHYSICS, CHEMICAL PHYSICS. *Educ:* Drexel Univ, BS, 65; Univ Pittsburgh, PhD(physics), 71. *Prof Exp:* RES ASSOC ATOMIC & MOLECULAR PHYSICS, OAK RIDGE NAT LAB, 71- *Mem:* Am Phys Soc; Am Asn Physics Teachers; AAAS. *Res:* Atomic and molecular beam research; thermal-high energies; molecular dynamics studies involving inner and outer shell excited species. *Mailing Add:* Oak Ridge Nat Lab PO Box X Oak Ridge TN 37830

KRAUSE, HORATIO HENRY, b St Paul, Minn, Oct 11, 18; m 50; c 2. INORGANIC CHEMISTRY. *Educ:* St Mary's Col Minn, BS, 39; Univ Minn, PhD(chem), 55. *Prof Exp:* Teacher pvt sch, 39-43; instr chem & physics, De LaSalle Mil Acad, 43-48; asst, Univ Minn, 49-54; prin chemist, 55-57, proj leader chem, 57-62, sr chemist, 62-70, prin res scientist, 70-80, SR RES SCIENTIST, BATTELLE MEM INST, 80- *Mem:* AAAS; Am Soc Mech Engrs; Am Soc Mech Eng; Nat Asn Corrosion Engrs. *Res:* High temperature chemistry, deposits and corrosion in boilers and incinerators; molten salts; solid propellants; air pollution; sulfur oxides. *Mailing Add:* Battelle Mem Inst 505 King Ave Columbus OH 43201

KRAUSE, IRVIN, b New York, NY, July 18, 32; m 53; c 3. MECHANICAL ENGINEERING. *Educ:* City Col New York, BME, 54; Columbia Univ, MS, 55; NY Univ, EngScD(mech eng), 60. *Prof Exp:* Lectr graphics, City Col New York, 54-59; asst mech eng, NY Univ, 59-60; res scientist, Res Div, American-Standard Corp, 60-63; assoc prof mech eng & dir mat labs, Fairleign Dickinson Univ, 63-66; chief res & develop, Diehl Div, Singer Co, 66-70, mgr eng, Indust Prod Div, 70-76; dir eng, Acushnet Co, 76-78; MGR MFG TECHNOL, ARTHUR D LITTLE, INC, 78- *Concurrent Pos:* Consult, Army Res Off NC, 64- *Mem:* AAAS; Am Soc Mech Engrs; Sigma Xi; Soc Mfg Engrs. *Res:* Visco-elastic behavior of polymeric materials; fracture in brittle materials; kinematics and mechanism synthesis; tunnel diode accelerometers; laser system metrology; electric motors and controls; automated production systems; computerization and automation as applied to the design and manufacturing activities in industry. *Mailing Add:* Arthur D Little Inc Acorn Park Cambridge MA 02742

KRAUSE, JOSEF GERALD, b Kearny, NJ, Mar 21, 42; m 63; c 2. ORGANIC CHEMISTRY. *Educ:* Hobart Col, BS, 63; Northeastern Univ, PhD(org chem), 67. *Prof Exp:* NSF res fel org chem, Univ Mass, 67-68; PROF CHEM, NIAGARA UNIV, 68- *Concurrent Pos:* Sigma Xi res grant-in- aid, Niagara Univ, 68-69. *Mem:* Am Chem Soc. *Res:* Organic nitrogen compounds; organic synthesis; reaction mechanisms; bicyclic ring systems. *Mailing Add:* Dept of Chem Niagara University NY 14109

KRAUSE, LEONARD ANTHONY, b Hartford, Conn, May 13, 25; m 55, 68; c 4. BIOCHEMISTRY. *Educ:* Univ Conn, BA, 50, MS, 51; Univ Cincinnati, ScD(indust health, med), 62; Am Bd Indust Hyg, dipl. *Prof Exp:* Instr physiol & zool, Univ Conn, 49-51; biochemist-indust hygienist, Bur Labs, Conn, 51-55, sr indust hygienist, 56-59; chief indust hyg-air pollution, Resources Res, DC, 61-62; dir environ hyg, Nat Insts Health, 62-63; mgr environ hyg serv, 63-75, DIR ENVIRON MENTAL HYG & TOXICOL, OLIN CORP, 75- *Mem:* AAAS; Am Indust Hyg Asn; Air Pollution Control Asn; Am Pub Health Asn. *Res:* Physiology of invertebrates; aspects of metal fume fever; use of vaporphase chromatography; insecticides and effects on human metabolism. *Mailing Add:* 19 Wellsweep Rd Branford CT 06405

KRAUSE, LLOYD O(SCAR), b Hamburg, Wis, Oct 23, 18; m 42; c 2. ELECTRICAL ENGINEERING. *Educ:* Rose Polytech Inst, BS, 40; Syracuse Univ, MEE, 64, PhD(elec eng), 66. *Prof Exp:* Test engr, Gen Elec Co, 40-41, prog engr, 41-43, develop engr, 43-47, proj engr, 47-52, asst sect engr, 52-53, mgr elec eng, 53-63, consult engr, Electronics Lab, 63-67; tech adv, Autonetics Div, NAm Rockwell Corp, 67-76; SYSTS ANALYST, SPACE DIV, ROCKWELL INT CORP, 76- *Honors & Awards:* Coffin Award, Gen Elec Co, 53. *Mem:* Sigma Xi; Electronic Industs Asn; Inst Elec & Electronics Engrs. *Res:* Radio frequency and microwave radiators; antennas; transmission lines and networks; solid state microwave; paramagnetic amplifiers; phase shifters; switches; ferrites; ferroelectrics; ground screens; electronic systems; computer reliability; correlation loops; low angle radiation. *Mailing Add:* 4015 Topside Lane Corona Del Mar CA 92625

KRAUSE, LUCJAN, b Poznan, Poland, Jan 8, 28; nat Can; m 50; c 6. PHYSICS, ATOMIC & MOLECULAR COLLISIONS. *Educ:* Univ London, BSc, 51, DSc(physics), 68; Univ Toronto, MA, 53, PhD(physics), 55. *Prof Exp:* Assoc prof physics, Memorial Univ, 55-58 & Assumption Univ, 58-63; PROF PHYSICS & HEAD DEPT, UNIV WINDSOR, 63- *Concurrent Pos:* Hon res fel, Univ Col, Univ London, 70-71; adj prof eng sci, Wayne State Univ, Detroit, 72-; fel Churchill Col, Cambridge. *Mem:* Am Phys Soc; Can Asn Physicists; fel Brit Inst Physics. *Res:* Inelastic collisions of excited atoms and molecules, sensitized fluorescence and quenching, lifetimes of excited atomic and molecular states. *Mailing Add:* Dept of Physics Univ of Windsor Windsor ON N9B 3P4 Can

KRAUSE, MANFRED OTTO, b Stuttgart, Ger, Mar 11, 31; m 63. ATOMIC PHYSICS, CHEMICAL PHYSICS. *Educ:* Univ Stuttgart, Diplom Phys, 57; Max Planck Inst, Dr rer nat, 60. *Prof Exp:* Sr scientist mass spectrometry, Wm H Johnston Lab, Inc, Md, 60-63; SR SCIENTIST ELECTRON SPECTROMETRY, OAK RIDGE NAT LAB, 63- *Concurrent Pos:* Exchange prof, Lab Curie, Paris France, 75; Humboldt awardee, Stiftung, Ger, 75-76. *Mem:* AAAS; Sigma Xi; fel Am Phys Soc. *Res:* Transuranic chemistry; electron spectrometry; x-ray analysis; photoionization; atomic and molecular physics. *Mailing Add:* Oak Ridge Nat Lab Box X TRL Oak Ridge TN 37830

KRAUSE, MARGARIDA OLIVEIRA, b Lisbon, Portugal, Jan 13, 31; Can citizen; m 56; c 3. CELL BIOLOGY, GENETICS. *Educ:* Univ Lisbon, BSc, 53; Univ Wis, MSc, 57, PhD(cell biol), 60. *Prof Exp:* Res assoc cell biol, Univ Wis, 60-61 & Univ Toronto, 63-66; res assoc, 66-70, assoc prof, 70-76, PROF CELL BIOL, UNIV NB, 76- *Concurrent Pos:* Res grants, Banting Res Found, 65 & 67, Med Res Coun Can, 65-66, Nat Res Coun Can, 67-78, Nat Cancer Inst Can, 76-79 & Natural Sci & Eng Res Coun Can, 78-82; mem, Can Nat Comt Int Union Biol Soc, 80-83; mem int sci & technol affairs, 81-84. *Mem:* Biol Coun Can; Am Soc Cell Biol; Can Soc Cell Biol. *Res:* Role of chromosomal proteins and small nuclear RNA in gene expression; chromatin template activity and structure-cellcycle control and cancer transformation; hormone induction. *Mailing Add:* Dept of Biol Univ of NB Fredericton NB E3B 5A3 Can

KRAUSE, PAUL CARL, JR, b Reynolds, Nebr, Jan 27, 32; m 53; c 4. ELECTRICAL ENGINEERING. *Educ:* Univ Nebr, BS, 56 & 57, MS, 58; Univ Kans, PhD(elec eng), 61. *Prof Exp:* Instr elec eng, Univ Kans, 58-61; res elec engr, Allis-Chalmers Mfg Co, 61-62; asst prof elec eng, Univ Wis-Milwaukee, 62-65; assoc prof, Univ Wis-Madison, 65-70; PROF ELEC ENG, PURDUE UNIV, 70- *Concurrent Pos:* Consult, Allis-Chalmers Mfg Co, 63-66. *Mem:* Sr mem Inst Elec & Electronics Engrs; Am Soc Eng Educ. *Res:* Electric machines, power systems and control systems; hybrid computer applications in analysis of systems. *Mailing Add:* Dept of Elec Eng Purdue Univ West Lafayette IN 47907

KRAUSE, PAUL FREDERICK, b Racine, Wis, July 30, 45; m 70; c 1. PHYSICAL CHEMISTRY. *Educ:* Dubuque Univ, BS, 67; Univ Iowa, PhD(chem), 72. *Prof Exp:* Res asst chem, Univ Iowa, 68-72; res assoc, Univ Pittsburgh, 72-73; res assoc, 73-74, instr, 74, teaching fel & vis asst prof chem, Miami Univ, 74-77; ASST PROF CHEM, UNIV CENT ARK, 77- *Mem:* Sigma Xi. *Res:* Molecular spectroscopy and its use for structural considerations, particularly in the solid state. *Mailing Add:* Dept of Chem Univ of Cent Ark Conway AR 72032

KRAUSE, RALPH A(LVIN), b San Francisco, Calif, Nov 11, 09; m 34, 76; c 4. ENGINEERING. *Educ:* Univ Calif, BA, 32. *Prof Exp:* Biophys res, Inst Exp Biol, Univ Calif, 30-33; radio engr, Remler Co, 32-37; electronic res engr, Instrumentation Res & Develop Dept, Calif Res Corp, 37-41; electronics res, Off US Secy Navy, 41-45; sci br, Off Naval Res, 45-46; asst dir, Lab Nuclear Sci & Eng, Mass Inst Technol, 46-47; asst to pres, Raytheon Mfg Co, Mass, 47-48; dir res, Stanford Res Inst, 48-54, assoc dir, 54-64; dir dept appl sci, UNESCO, 64-68; int consult, Res Anal Corp, 68-69; RETIRED. *Concurrent Pos:* Sr eng consult, Brookhaven Nat Lab & Res & Develop Bd. *Mem:* AAAS; Am Soc Naval Engrs; Sigma Xi; Am Nuclear Soc; Solar Energy Soc; Inst Elec & Electronics Engrs. *Res:* Laboratory organization and research administration; electronic engineering; electrical masking of nerves; electro-encephalographic equipment design; radio speech input design; acoustic engineering; magnetostrictive pressure gauges; nuclear research administration; health physics and nuclear instrumentation; radar; loran; radio and radar counter measures. *Mailing Add:* 550 Battery St Apt 2109 San Francisco CA 94111

KRAUSE, RALPH M, b New York, NY, Nov 23, 31; m 60; c 2. MATHEMATICS. *Educ:* Harvard Univ, BA, 53, MA, 54, PhD(math), 59. *Prof Exp:* Asst prof math, Univ Ill, 58-60 & Ill Inst Technol, 60-62; PROG DIR, NAT SCI FOUND, 62- *Mem:* Am Math Soc; Math Asn Am. *Res:* Topology. *Mailing Add:* Nat Sci Found 1800 G St NW Washington DC 20550

KRAUSE, REGINALD FREDERICK, b Moyers, WVa, July 4, 12; m 43. BIOCHEMISTRY. *Educ:* WVa Univ, AB, 35, BS, 36, MS, 39; Univ Rochester, PhD(biochem), 42; Univ Vt, MD, 51. *Prof Exp:* Asst pharmacol, Univ Rochester, 39-42; instr, Univ Vt, 42, res assoc biochem, Col Med, 45-51; prof biochem & chmn dept, 51-77, EMER PROF BIOCHEM, MED CTR, W VA UNIV, 77- *Mem:* Am Chem Soc. *Res:* Lipid biochemistry; aviation physiology; microchemical determinations of vitamins; biochemistry of vitamin A and carotene; biochemical study of lipids of bone marrow in normal and anemic animals; lipid metabolism in atherosclerosis. *Mailing Add:* 901 Hawthorne Ave Morgantown WV 26505

KRAUSE, RICHARD MICHAEL, b Marietta, Ohio, Jan 4, 25. MICROBIOLOGY, IMMUNOLOGY. *Educ:* Marietta Col, AB, 47; Western Reserve Univ, MD, 52. *Hon Degrees:* DSc, Marietta Col, 78, Sch Med & Dent, Univ Rochester, 79, Med Col Ohio, 81. *Prof Exp:* Intern med, Barnes Hosp, 52-53, asst resident, 53-54; asst, Rockefeller Inst, 54-57, from asst prof to assoc prof, 57-62; from assoc prof to prof, Sch Med, Wash Univ, 62-66; from assoc to prof microbiol & immunol & sr physician, Univ Hosp, Rockefeller Univ, 66-75; DIR, NAT INST ALLERGY & INFECTIOUS DIS, 75-, ASST SURGEON GEN, 77- *Concurrent Pos:* Mem coun rheumatic fever & congenital heart dis & mem coun epidemiol, Am Heart Asn, mem res comt, 63-66; mem comn streptococcal and staphylococcal dis, Armed Forces Epidemiol Bd, 63-72; chmn allergy & immunol A study sect, NIH, 66-70; consult & mem, Coccal Expert Comt, WHO, 67- & mem steering comt, Biomed Sci Working Group, 78; mem bd dirs, Asthma & Allergy Found Am, 76-; mem bd dirs, NY Heart Asn, 67-73; mem infectious dis adv comt, Nat Inst Allergy & Infectious Dis, 70-74; mem bd dirs, Royal Soc Med Found, Inc, 71-77, treas, 73-75. *Honors & Awards:* Repub Egypt Order of Gumhuria

Award, 80. *Mem:* Nat Acad Sci; Inst Med-Nat Acad Sci; Am Soc Clin Invest; Harvey Soc; Asn Am Physicians. *Res:* Pathogenesis and epidemiology of streptococcal diseases; immunochem, studies on streptococcal antigens; immunogenetics; antibody structure and mechanisms that generate antibody diversity. *Mailing Add:* NIH Bldg 31 Rm 7A03 Nat Inst Allergy Bethesda MD 20205

KRAUSE, RONALD ALFRED, b Boston, Mass, Oct 30, 31; m 52, 77; c 2. INORGANIC CHEMISTRY. *Educ:* Ohio State Univ, BSc, 56, PhD(chem), 59. *Prof Exp:* Res scientist, Am Cyanamid Co, Conn, 59-62; asst prof, 62-67, assoc prof, 67-77, PROF CHEM, UNIV CONN, 78- *Concurrent Pos:* Consult, Arco, 78-81; guest prof, Univ Copenhagen, Denmark, 68-69 & 76. *Mem:* Am Chem Soc; Nat Speleol Soc. *Res:* Synthesis, reactions, structure and spectra of coordination compounds. *Mailing Add:* Dept Chem Univ Conn Storrs CT 06268

KRAUSE, SONJA, b St Gall, Switz, Aug 10, 33; nat US; m 70. PHYSICAL CHEMISTRY. *Educ:* Rensselaer Polytech Inst, 54; Univ Calif, PhD(phys chem), 57. *Prof Exp:* Res chemist, Rohm & Haas Co, Pa, 57-64; US Peace Corps vol, Lagos Univ, Nigeria, 64-65 & Gondar Health Col, Ethiopia, 65-66; asst prof chem, Univ Southern Calif, 66-67; asst prof, 67-72, assoc prof, 72-78, PROF CHEM, RENSSELAER POLYTECH INST, 78- *Concurrent Pos:* Mem coun, Gordon Res Conf, 81- *Mem:* AAAS; Am Chem Soc; fel Am Phys Soc; Biophys Soc; NY Acad Sci. *Res:* Dilute solution properties of polymers; block copolymers; polymer compatibility; transient electric birefringence; muscle proteins. *Mailing Add:* Dept of Chem Rensselaer Polytech Inst Troy NY 12181

KRAUSE, THOMAS OTTO, b Grand Rapids, Mich, May 5, 44. THEORETICAL PHYSICS, NUCLEAR PHYSICS. *Educ:* Mass Inst Technol, BS, 66; Ohio State Univ, PhD(physics), 73. *Prof Exp:* Vis asst prof, Dept Physics, Ohio State Univ, 73-76; ASST PROF, DEPT PHYSICS, TOWSON STATE UNIV, 76- *Mem:* Am Phys Soc; Sigma Xi. *Res:* Scattering theory, especially nuclear, with nonlocal potentials; gravitation; theoretical astrophysics. *Mailing Add:* Dept of Physics Towson State Univ Towson MD 21204

KRAUSE, WILLIAM JOHN, b Glasgow, Mont, Mar 24, 42; m 67; c 2. ANATOMY, HISTOLOGY. *Educ:* Augustana Col, BA, 64; Univ Iowa, MS, 66; Univ Mo-Columbia, PhD(anat), 69. *Prof Exp:* Lectr anat, Monash Univ, 69-71; asst prof, 71-76, ASSOC PROF ANAT, UNIV MO-COLUMBIA, 76- *Mem:* Am Asn Anatomists; Anat Soc Gt Brit & Ireland. *Res:* Postnatal development of respiratory, urinary and digestive systems. *Mailing Add:* Dept of Anat Univ of Mo Columbia MO 65201

KRAUS-FRIEDMANN, NAOMI, b Budapest, Hungary, July 4, 33; div; c 1. PHYSIOLOGY. *Educ:* Hebrew Univ, Jerusalem, MSc, 60, PhD(biochem), 65. *Prof Exp:* Res assoc, Columbia Univ, 65-66; res assoc physiol, Vanderbilt Univ, Nashville, 66-68; instr biochem, Sch Med, Univ Pa, 68-74; asst prof, 74-78, ASSOC PROF PHYSIOL, SCH MED, UNIV TEX, HOUSTON, 78- *Concurrent Pos:* Vis prof, Eidenossische Tech, Zurich, 80-82. *Mem:* Am Physiol Soc; Am Soc Biol Chemists. *Res:* Hormonal regulation of gluconeogenesis; role of calcium and other ions in regulation of metabolic processes. *Mailing Add:* Sch Med Univ Tex PO Box 20708 Houston TX 77025

KRAUSHAAR, JACK JOURDAN, b Newark, NJ, Sept 6, 23; m 51; c 3. NUCLEAR PHYSICS. *Educ:* Lafayette Col, BS, 44; Syracuse Univ, MS, 48, PhD, 52. *Prof Exp:* Asst physics, Syracuse Univ, 46-50; res assoc nuclear spectros, Brookhaven Nat Lab, 51-53; instr physics, Stanford Univ, 53-56; from asst prof to assoc prof, 56-63, PROF PHYSICS, UNIV COLO, BOULDER, 63- *Concurrent Pos:* Fulbright award, Free Univ, Amsterdam, 67-68; fac fel, Tri-Univ Meson Facil, Univ BC, Vancouver, 78-79. *Mem:* AAAS; fel Am Phys Soc; Fedn Am Sci. *Res:* Nuclear reactions and spectroscopy; pi meson interactions and scattering; energy and environmental problems in the United States. *Mailing Add:* Dept of Physics & Astrophys Univ of Colo Boulder CO 80302

KRAUSHAAR, WILLIAM LESTER, b Newark, NJ, Apr 1, 20; m 43; c 3. PHYSICS. *Educ:* Lafayette Col, BS, 42; Cornell Univ, PhD(physics), 49. *Prof Exp:* Physicist, Nat Bur Stand, 42-45; res assoc, Mass Inst Technol, 49-51, from asst prof to prof physics, 51-65; PROF PHYSICS, UNIV WIS-MADISON, 65- *Mem:* Nat Acad Sci; Fel Am Acad Arts & Sci; fel Am Phys Soc. *Res:* High energy astrophysics; space science; cosmic rays. *Mailing Add:* Chamberlin Hall Dept Physics Univ of Wis Madison WI 53706

KRAUSKOPF, JOHN, b New York, NY, Mar 30, 28; m 52; c 3. PSYCHOPHYSIOLOGY. *Educ:* Cornell Univ, AB, 49; Univ Tex, PhD, 53. *Prof Exp:* Asst psychol, Cornell Univ, 49-50; asst, Univ Tex, 50-52, res assoc, 52-53; USPHS fel, Brown Univ, 56-57, asst prof, 57-59; asst prof, Rutgers Univ, 59-62; res assoc, Univ Md, 62-64; res scientist, Inst Behav Res, 64-66; MEM TECH STAFF, BELL LABS, 66- *Concurrent Pos:* Vis asst prof, Bryn Mawr Col, 59-60; mem vision comt, Armed Forces-Nat Res Coun, 60- *Res:* Vision; visual perception. *Mailing Add:* 85 Oak Ridge Ave Summit NJ 03104

KRAUSKOPF, KONRAD BATES, b Madison, Wis, Nov 30, 10; m 36; c 4. GEOCHEMISTRY. *Educ:* Univ Wis, AB, 31; Univ Calif, PhD(chem), 34; Stanford Univ, PhD(geol), 39. *Hon Degrees:* DSc, Univ Wis-Milwaukee, 71. *Prof Exp:* Instr chem, Univ Calif, 34-35; actg instr phys sci, Dept Geol, 35-39, from asst prof to assoc prof geol, 39-50, prof, 50-76, EMER PROF GEOCHEM, STANFORD UNIV, 76- *Concurrent Pos:* Fulbright & Guggenheim fels, Norway, 52-53; NSF fac fel, Ger, 60-61; chmn bd, Radioactive Waste Mgt, Nat Acad Sci, 81- *Honors & Awards:* Day Medal, Geol Soc Am, 61. *Mem:* Nat Acad Sci; Geol Soc Am (pres, 67); Am Geol Inst (pres, 64); Geochem Soc (pres, 70); Soc Econ Geologists. *Res:* Petrology of igneous and metamorphic rocks; physical chemistry of ore solutions; trace elements in sea water and in sedimentary rocks. *Mailing Add:* Dept of Geol Stanford Univ Stanford CA 94305

KRAUSMAN, PAUL RICHARD, b Washington, DC, Nov 17, 46; m 66; c 2. WILDLIFE ECOLOGY. *Educ:* Ohio State Univ, BS, 68; NMex State Univ, MS, 71; Univ Idaho, PhD(wildlife sci), 76. *Prof Exp:* Res asst environ alteration, Aeromed Res Lab, NMex, 68-71; res asst, Environ Res Lab & Radiation Lab, Brooks AFB, Tex, 71-72; asst prof wildlife ecol, Auburn Univ, 76-78; ASST PROF WILDLIFE ECOL & ASST RES ASSOC, UNIV ARIZ, 78- *Concurrent Pos:* Welder wildlife fel ecol, 72-76. *Mem:* Wildlife Soc; Am Soc Mammalogists; Soc Range Mgt. *Res:* Ungulate ecology. *Mailing Add:* Sch Renewable Natural Resources Univ of Ariz Tucson AZ 85720

KRAUSS, ALAN ROBERT, b Chicago, Ill, Oct 3, 43; m 65; c 1. PHYSICS. *Educ:* Univ Chicago, BS, 65; Purdue Univ, MS, 69, PhD(physics), 72. *Prof Exp:* Res assoc surface physics, James Franck Inst, Univ Chicago, 71-74; asst physicist, 74-80, PHYSICIST SURFACE PHYSICS, ARGONNE NAT LAB, 80- *Mem:* Am Phys Soc; Am Vacuum Soc. *Res:* Surface physics and chemistry; sputtering; secondary ion emission and ion-bombardment phenomena; applications to thermonuclear fusion devices. *Mailing Add:* Chem Div 9700 S Cass Ave Argonne IL 60439

KRAUSS, BEATRICE HILMER, b Honolulu, Hawaii, Aug 4, 03. PLANT PHYSIOLOGY, ETHNOBOTANY. *Educ:* Univ Hawaii, BS, 26, MS, 30. *Prof Exp:* From asst plant physiologist to plant physiologist, Pineapple Res Inst Hawaii, 26-68; lectr ethnobot & res affil pineapple physiol, 68-73, RES AFFIL HAWAIIAN ETHNOBOT, LYON ARBORETUM, UNIV HAWAII, MANOA, 74- *Mem:* Fel AAAS. *Res:* Morphology and anatomy of pineapple plant; pineapple nutrition, especially micronutrients; Hawaiian ethnobotany. *Mailing Add:* Harold L Lyon Arboretum 3860 Manoa Rd Honolulu HI 96822

KRAUSS, GEORGE, b Philadelphia, Pa, May 14, 33; m 60; c 4. PHYSICAL METALLURGY, METALLURGICAL ENGINEERING. *Educ:* Lehigh Univ, BS, 55; Mass Inst Technol, MS, 58, ScD, 61. *Prof Exp:* Mem staff div sponsored res, Mass Inst Technol, 61-62; NSF fel, Max-Planck Inst Iron Res, 62-63; from asst prof to prof metall, Lehigh Univ, 63-75, dir electron micros lab, 69-75; AMAX FOUND PROF PHYS METALL, COLO SCH MINES, 75- *Concurrent Pos:* Ed, J Heat Treating, Prof Engr Pa & Co, 78- *Mem:* Am Inst Mining, Metall & Petrol Engrs; fel Am Soc Metals; Electron Micros Soc Am. *Res:* Mechanical and fracture behavior of steels; microstructural characterization by light and electron microscopy; failure analysis; author of over 90 publications. *Mailing Add:* Dept Metall Eng Colo Sch Mines Golden CO 80401

KRAUSS, ROBERT WALLFAR, b Cleveland, Ohio Dec 27, 21; m 47; c 2. PLANT PHYSIOLOGY. *Educ:* Oberlin Col, BA, 47; Univ Hawaii, MS, 49; Univ Md, College Park, PhD(bot), 51. *Prof Exp:* Asst bot, Univ Hawaii, 47-49; asst bot, Univ Md, College Park, 49-51; res assoc plant physiol, 51-55, from asst prof to prof, 55-73, head dept bot, 64-73; dean col sci, Ore State Univ, 73-80; EXEC DIR, FEDN AM SOC EXP BIOL, 79- *Concurrent Pos:* Res fel, Carnegie Inst, 51-55; biologist, Coastal Studies Inst, La State Univ, 58-59; mem, Nat Res Coun, 59-60; sr res affil, Chesapeake Biol Lab, 68-73; chmn ed bd, Space Biol & Med, 69-73; mem bd dirs, Ed Projs Inc, 69-; consult, US Air Force Sch Aviation Med, NASA & NSF; mem corp, Marine Biol Lab, Woods Hole, Mass. *Honors & Awards:* Darbaker Award, Bot Soc Am, 56; Presidents Leadership Award, Am Inst Biol Sci, 74. *Mem:* Phycol Soc Am (pres, 64); Bot Soc Am; Am Soc Plant Physiol; Am Inst Biol Sci (secy-treas, 63-69, vpres, 72, pres, 73). *Res:* Algal physiology and biochemistry. *Mailing Add:* Fedn Am Soc Exp Biol 9650 Rockville Pike Bethesda MD 20814

KRAUSZ, ALEXANDER STEPHEN, b Budapest, Hungary, Sept 16, 24; Can citizen; m 49. MATERIALS SCIENCE, MECHANICAL ENGINEERING. *Educ:* Budapest Tech Univ, BSc, 51; Queen's Univ, Ont, MSc, 59; Univ Toronto, PhD(metall), 65. *Prof Exp:* Mgr mfg, Gamma Instrument Co, Hungary, 49-52; res off plastic deformation, Nat Res Coun Can, 59-70; assoc prof, 70-72, PROF MECH ENG & CHMN DEPT, UNIV OTTAWA, 72- *Mem:* Am Soc Metals; Eng Inst Can. *Res:* Fracture mechanics; deformation kinetics, thermally activated plastic flow and fracture and deformation processes in manufacturing. *Mailing Add:* 10d-300 Queen Elizabeth Driveway Ottawa ON K1S 3M6 Can

KRAUSZ, FRANK GORDON, physics, see previous edition

KRAUT, EDGAR A, b Cleveland, Ohio, May 4, 34; m 62. PHYSICS. *Educ:* Univ Calif, Los Angeles, AB, 56, MA, 57, PhD(physics), 62. *Prof Exp:* Res geophysicist, Univ Calif, Los Angeles, 57-63, asst prof physics & geophysics, 63-67; mem tech staff, 67-69, GROUP LEADER SOLID STATE PHYSICS, SCI CTR, NORTH AM ROCKWELL CORP, 69- *Concurrent Pos:* NSF travel grant to Int Acoustics Conf, 62. *Mem:* AAAS; Am Phys Soc. *Res:* Theoretical and mathematical physics; wave propagation; physics of semiconductor surfaces and interfaces; heterojunctions; energy bands. *Mailing Add:* NAm Rockwell Corp Sci Ctr PO Box 1085 Thousand Oaks CA 91360

KRAUT, JOSEPH, b New York, NY, Dec 5, 26; m 53; c 3. PHYSICAL BIOCHEMISTRY. *Educ:* Bucknell Univ, BS, 50; Calif Inst Technol, PhD(phys chem), 54. *Prof Exp:* From instr to asst prof biochem, Univ Wash, 53-62; assoc prof, 62-66, PROF CHEM, UNIV CALIF, SAN DIEGO, 66- *Honors & Awards:* Keilin Medal, Brit Biochem Soc, 80. *Mem:* AAAS; Am Chem Soc; Am Crystallog Asn; Am Soc Biol Chem. *Res:* Structure, function and evolution of biological macromolecules; x-ray diffraction crystallography. *Mailing Add:* Dept of Chem Univ of Calif San Diego La Jolla CA 92093

KRAUTER, ALLAN IRVING, b Newark, NJ, Oct 15, 41; m 68; c 3. MECHANICAL ENGINEERING. *Educ:* Stevens Inst Technol, ME, 63; Stanford Univ, MS, 64, PhD(mech eng), 68. *Prof Exp:* Asst prof mech eng, Cornell Univ, 68-74; sr consult engr & mgr, Technol Dept, Shaker Res Corp, 75-81; PROG MGR, MECH SYSTS, CARRIER CORP, 81- *Mem:* Am Soc Mech Engrs; Soc Automotive Engrs. *Res:* Vibrations and dynamics of mechanical systems; simulation of mechanical and economic system behavior. *Mailing Add:* Res Div Carrier Corp Carrier Parkway Syracuse NY 13221

KRAUTHAMER, GEORGE MICHAEL, b Ger, Sept 14, 26; nat US; m 53; c 6. NEUROSCIENCE. *Educ:* City Col New York, BS, 51, MA, 52; NY Univ, PhD(psychol), 59. *Prof Exp:* Asst psychophysiol, Sch Med, NY Univ, 57-59, instr psychol, 59-60; res assoc, Univ Paris, 63-66; asst prof, Col Physicians & Surgeons, Columbia Univ, 67-69; assoc prof, 69-79, PROF ANAT, RUTGERS MED SCH, 79- *Concurrent Pos:* USPHS res fel, Ctr Study Physiol of Cent Nerv Syst, Univ Paris, 60-63; res assoc, Hillside Hosp, Glen Oak, NY, 59-60; lectr psychol, City Col New York, 59-60; asst to exec secy, Int Brain Res Orgn-UNESCO, 65-68. *Mem:* AAAS; Am Physiol Soc; Soc Neurosci; Am EEG Soc; NY Acad Sci. *Res:* Electrophysiology and neuroanatomy of brain; behavior correlates of brain function; effects of brain injury; perception and intersensory relationships; electroencephalography; drug effects. *Mailing Add:* Dept of Anat Bldg 4102 Rutgers Med Sch New Brunswick NJ 08903

KRAVITZ, EDWARD, b Philadelphia, Pa, Sept 1, 20. SCIENCE EDITING. *Educ:* Philadelphia Col Pharm & Sci, BSc, 48, & MSc, 49, DSc, 52. *Prof Exp:* Supvry res scientist, US Navy Dept, 52-56; chemist, Eastern Regional Res Lab, USDA, 56-58; asst chief pub health lab, City Philadelphia, 58; asst dir clin lab, hosp & assoc clin path, Med Col Pa, 58-59; dir, Newark Med Labs, Del, 59-64; managing ed, Cancer Res, 64-69; microbiologist & tech ed-writer, US FDA, 69-75; INFO SCIENTIST, 75- *Concurrent Pos:* Asst to lab dir, Eastern Pa Psychiat Inst, 58-59; dir labs, Bissell Hosp, Wilmington, Del, 61. *Honors & Awards:* Commendation Award, US Navy Dept, 53. *Res:* Biochemistry; clinical chemistry; enzymology; microbiological physiology; physico-chemical phenomena of microorganisms; disinfection; public health; bacteriology; immunology; parasitology; intermediary metabolism; nutrition; cytochemistry; hematology; clinical pathology; analytical chemistry; behavioral science; information science; technical administration. *Mailing Add:* PO Box 38 Wynnewood PA 19096

KRAVITZ, EDWARD ARTHUR, b New York, NY, Dec 19, 32; m 58; c 2. BIOCHEMISTRY, NEUROCHEMISTRY. *Educ:* City Col New York, BS, 54; Univ Mich, PhD(biochem), 59. *Prof Exp:* Nat Heart Inst fel biochem, 59-60; Nat Inst Neurol Dis & Blindness res fel neurophysiol & neuropharmacol, 60-61, instr neurophysiol & neuropharmacol, 61-63, assoc, 63-66, from asst prof to assoc prof, 66-69, PROF NEUROBIOL, HARVARD MED SCH, 69- *Concurrent Pos:* USPHS spec fel, 61-64, career develop award, 66-71. *Mem:* Soc Neurosci; Am Acad Arts & Sci; Am Soc Biol Chemists. *Res:* Biochemical studies on single physiologically identified nerve cells; metabolism of gamma-aminobutyric acid and other neurotransmitters in the lobster nervous system; amines and neurohormones in lobsters. *Mailing Add:* Dept of Neurobiol Harvard Med Sch Boston MA 02115

KRAVITZ, HENRY, b Poland, Oct 18, 18; Can citizen; m 42; c 1. PSYCHIATRY, PSYCHOANALYSIS. *Educ:* McGill Univ, BA, 45, MD, CM, 49, dipl psychiat, 54; Royal Col Physicians & Surgeons Can, cert psychiat, 54; FRCP(C). *Prof Exp:* Assoc prof, 67-72, PROF PSYCHIAT, McGILL UNIV, 72-; CHMN PSYCHIAT, JEWISH GEN HOSP & DIR, INST COMMUNITY & FAMILY PSYCHIAT, 67- *Concurrent Pos:* Training analyst, Can Psychoanal Inst, 62-, assoc dir, 68-, dir, 80-; chmn bd examiners, Royal Col Physicians & Surgeons, 78- *Mem:* Fel AAAS; fel Am Col Psychiat; fel Am Psychiat Asn; Can Psychoanal Soc (pres, 68-71). *Res:* Theoretical and practical considerations for unwed mothers; use of methadone and other substitute therapies in drug addiction; psychiatric education. *Mailing Add:* Dept of Psychiat Jewish Gen Hosp Montreal PQ H3T 1E2 Can

KRAVITZ, LAWRENCE C, b New York, NY, July 27, 32; m 58; c 3. PHYSICS, ELECTRONICS. *Educ:* Kans Univ, BS, 54; Air Force Inst Technol, MS, 55; Harvard Univ, PhD(physics), 63. *Prof Exp:* Physicist solid state, Corp Res & Develop Ctr, Gen Elec Co, 63-71, mgr display prog, 72-73; dir electronics, 73-78, dir, Air Force Off Sci Res, 78-81; DIR RES, BENDIX ADVAN TECHNOL CTR, 81- *Mem:* Inst Elec & Electronics Engrs. *Res:* Solid state science. *Mailing Add:* Bendix Advan Technol Ctr 9140 Old Annapolis Rd Columbia MD 21045

KRAWETZ, ARTHUR ALTSHULER, b Chicago, Ill, Oct 30, 32. ANALYTICAL CHEMISTRY, PHYSICAL CHEMISTRY. *Educ:* Northwestern Univ, BS, 52; Univ Chicago, SM, 53, PhD(chem), 55; Am Inst Chemists, cert. *Prof Exp:* Vpres, 54-74, PRES, PHOENIX CHEM LAB, INC, CHICAGO, 74- *Mem:* Am Chem Soc; Am Soc Testing & Mat; Am Inst Chem; Royal Soc Chem. *Res:* Fuel and lubricant technology; spontaneous ignition; flammability; air and water pollution; forensic chemistry; differential thermal analysis; solution chemistry; thermodynamics; molecular spectroscopy; industrial hygiene; safety; hydraulic fluids; protective coatings; rubber and plastic. *Mailing Add:* 1010 Isabella St Evanston IL 60201

KRAWIEC, STEVEN STACK, b Corvallis, Ore, Nov 4, 41; m 65; c 2. MOLECULAR BIOLOGY. *Educ:* Brown Univ, AB, 63; Yale Univ, PhD(microbiol), 68. *Prof Exp:* Trainee, Univ Wis-Madison, 68-69, Nat Inst Gen Med Sci fel, 69-70; asst prof, 70-76, chmn, 76-78, ASSOC PROF BIOL, LEHIGH UNIV, 76- *Concurrent Pos:* Fogarty int fel, Autonomous Univ Madrid, 78-79. *Mem:* Am Soc Microbiol; AAAS; Sigma Xi. *Res:* Characterization of nucleic acid organization; acquisitive evolution. *Mailing Add:* Dept of Biol Wms Bldg 31 Lehigh Univ Bethlehem PA 18015

KRAY, LOUIS ROBERT, b San Bernardino, Calif, Oct 20, 38; m 58; c 5. PETROLEUM CHEMISTRY. *Educ:* Univ Calif, Riverside, BA, 61, PhD(org chem), 65. *Prof Exp:* Researcher, 65-67; RES CHEMIST ORG CHEM, CHEVRON RES CO, STAND OIL CO CALIF, RICHMOND, 67- *Mem:* Am Chem Soc. *Res:* Fuel additive synthesis and development. *Mailing Add:* 1348 Yukon Way Apt 26 Novato CA 94947

KRAYBILL, EDWARD K(READY), b Lancaster, Pa, June 3, 17; m 39; c 1. ELECTRICAL ENGINEERING. *Educ:* Pa State Col, BS, 39, EE, 51; Univ Mich, MSE, 48, PhD, 66. *Prof Exp:* From instr to assoc prof elec eng, Duke Univ, 39-71, asst to dean, Col Eng, 53-62, asst dean, 62-66, assoc dean, 66-71;

DIR & PROF ENG, WORTHINGTON SCRANTON CAMPUS, PA STATE UNIV, 71- *Mem:* Am Soc Eng Educ; Illum Eng Soc; Inst Elec & Electronics Engrs; Nat Soc Prof Engrs; Am Asn Higher Educ. *Res:* Higher education. *Mailing Add:* Worthington Scranton Campus Pa State Univ University Park PA 16802

KRAYBILL, HENRY LAWRENCE, b Washington, DC, Apr 13, 18; m 44; c 2. EXPERIMENTAL HIGH ENERGY PHYSICS. *Educ:* Univ Chicago, SB, 38, PhD(physics), 49. *Prof Exp:* From instr to asst prof, 48-57, ASSOC PROF PHYSICS, YALE UNIV, 57- *Mem:* Am Phys Soc; Am Asn Physics Teachers. *Res:* High energy particles; bubble chamber analysis of hadron interactions. *Mailing Add:* Sloan Physics Lab Yale Univ New Haven CT 06520

KRAYBILL, HERMAN FINK, b Marietta, Pa, June 27, 14; c 3. BIOCHEMISTRY, TOXICOLOGY. *Educ:* Franklin & Marshall Col, BS, 36; Univ Md, MS, 38, PhD(biochem), 41. *Prof Exp:* Instr chem, Univ Md, 36-39; res chemist, Swift & Co, 41-43; res biochemist, Moorman Mfg Co, Ill, 46 & Nat Dairy Res Labs, Md, 46-48; res assoc, Nat Res Coun, DC, 48-49; res biochemist, Bur Animal Indust, USDA, 49-53; supvry biochemist & chief chem div, Army Med Nutrit Lab, 53-59; sr scientist, Curtiss Wright Corp, NJ, 59-60; sr biochemist & scientist adminstr, Div Radiation Health, Nat Cancer Inst, 60-63; chief pesticides prog, USPHS, 63-66; asst dir biol sci res, Bur Sci & asst dir sci coord, Bur Foods, Food & Drug Admin, 66-72; SCI COORDR ENVIRON CANCER, NAT CANCER INST, 72- *Concurrent Pos:* Lectr biochem, Univ Colo & Univ Denver, 55-59. *Mem:* AAAS; Am Chem Soc; Am Inst Nutrit; Soc Toxicol; NY Acad Sci. *Res:* Food research; fat enzymes; animal and human nutrition; dairy products; meats and fishery products; allergy; cancer; toxicology of irradiated foods; pesticides. *Mailing Add:* Nat Cancer Inst 7910 Woodmont Ave Bethesda MD 20205

KRAYBILL, RICHARD R(EIST), b Dover, NH, July 31, 20; m 45; c 4. CHEMICAL ENGINEERING, POLYMER PROCESSING. *Educ:* Purdue Univ, BChE, 42; Univ Mich, MS, 43, PhD(chem eng), 53. *Prof Exp:* Asst res engr, Calif Res Corp, 44-46; from asst prof to assoc prof chem eng, Univ Rochester, 50-67; TECH ASSOC DEVELOP, MFG EXP DIV, EASTMAN KODAK CO, ROCHESTER, 67- *Concurrent Pos:* Sr lectr, Univ Rochester, 78-79. *Mem:* AAAS; Am Chem Soc; Am Soc Eng Educ; fel Am Inst Chem Engrs; Soc Plastics Engrs. *Res:* Fluid flow; heat transfer; extrusion. *Mailing Add:* 1289 Calkins Rd Pittsford NY 14534

KRAYCHY, STEPHEN, b Redwater, Alta, Feb 18, 28; nat US; m54; c 3. ORGANIC CHEMISTRY, NUCLEAR MEDICINE. *Educ:* Univ Alta, BSc, 50; Univ Wis, PhD(org chem), 55. *Prof Exp:* Asst mem, Sloan-Kettering Inst Cancer Res, 54-56; sr investrchem res, G D Searle & Co, 56-71, asst dir biochem res, 71-73, asst dir drug metab-radiochem, 73-75, mgr radiopharmaceut, Searle Labs, 75-78, SR RES SCIENTIST, G D SEARLE & CO, 78- *Mem:* Am Chem Soc. *Res:* Synthesis of steroids; steroid metabolism; misrobiological transformations of steroids; drug metabolism; radiochemicals; research and development of radiopharmaceuticals; anti-infective agents. *Mailing Add:* G D Searle & Co PO Box 5110 Chicago IL 60680

KRAYER, OTTO, b Kondringen, Ger, Oct 22, 99; nat US; m 39. PHARMACOLOGY. *Educ:* Univ Freiburg, MD, 26. *Hon Degrees:* MA, Harvard Univ, 42; MD, Univ Freiburg, 57; MD, Univ Gottingen, 62 & Tech Univ Munich, 73. *Prof Exp:* Asst pharmacol, Univ Freiburg, 26-27; asst pharmacol, Univ Berlin, 27-29, lectr pharmacol & toxicol, 29-32, actg head dept pharmacol, 30-32, prof extraordinarius pharmacol & toxicol, 32-34; Rockefeller fel, Univ Col, Univ London, 34; vis prof pharmacol & head dept, Am Univ Beirut, 34-37; assoc prof pharmacol, 37-39, assoc prof comp pharmacol, 39-51, prof pharmacol, 51-54, Wilder prof, 54-63, G A Pfeiffer prof, 64-66, head dept, 39-66, EMER PROF PHARMACOL, HARVARD MED SCH, 66- *Concurrent Pos:* Ed, Ergebnisse der Physiologie, 33-35 & 49-80; lectr, Harvard Med Sch, 36 & Mayo Found, 47 & 52; ed, Pharmacol Rev, Am Soc Pharmacol & Exp Therapeut, 48-53, ed-in-chief, 54-59; mem pharmacol study sect, USPHS, 50-54; univ lectr, Aberdeen Univ, 55; Litchfield lectr, Oxford Univ, 55; spec lectr, Univ Col, Univ London, 55; Fahr lectr, Univ Minn, 56; univ lectr, Univ Helsinki, 61; vis centennial prof, Howard Univ, 66; vis prof pharmacol, Ariz Med Col, 72-82. *Honors & Awards:* Torald Sollmann Award, Am Soc Pharmacol & Exp Therapeut, 61; Schmiedeberg Award, Ger Pharmacol Soc, 64; Res Achievement Award, Am Heart Asn, 69. *Mem:* Nat Acad Sci; Am Acad Arts & Sci; Am Soc Pharmacol & Exp Therapeut (pres, 57); Ger Acad Natural Scientists Leopoldina; corresp mem Swiss Acad Med Sci. *Res:* Pharmacology of the circulation and autonomic nervous system. *Mailing Add:* 3940 E Timrod St Apt 202 Tucson AZ 85711

KRAYNAK, MATTHEW EDWARD, b Scranton, Pa, Dec 19, 27; m 68. NUTRITION. *Educ:* Scranton Univ, BS, 50; Univ Tenn, MS, 52, PhD(biochem), 56. *Prof Exp:* Instr chem, Univ Tenn, 53-55; asst prof biochem & vis chmn dept, Indonesia, 56-60; asst prof, Univ Tenn, 61-62; from asst prof to assoc prof, 62-69, PROF CHEM & NUTRIT, UNIV OKLA, 69- *Concurrent Pos:* Mem Okla Nutrit Task Force. *Mem:* AAAS; Am Chem Soc; Am Dietetic Asn. *Res:* Nutritional availability of plant galactosides; biochemistry of galactosemia and lactose intolerance. *Mailing Add:* Burton Hall Univ of Okla 610 Elm St Norman OK 73019

KRBECHEK, LEROY O, b Thief River Falls, Minn, May 21, 34; m 60; c 3. ORGANIC CHEMISTRY. *Educ:* Univ NDak, BS, 57; Univ Mich, MS & PhD, 61. *Prof Exp:* Chemist, Aerospace Corp, 61-64 & Int Minerals & Chem Corp, 64-69; sr res chemist, James Ford Bell Res Ctr, Gen Mills, Inc, 69-72, sr res chemist, Gen Mills Chem Inc, 72-80, SR RES CHEMIST, HENKEL INC, 80- *Mem:* Am Chem Soc. *Res:* Organic azides and synthesis. *Mailing Add:* Henkel Inc 2010 E Hennepin Ave Minneapolis MN 55413

KRC, JOHN, JR, b Chicago, Ill, May 17, 20; m 49; c 5. CHEMICAL MICROSCOPY, CRYSTALLOGRAPHY. *Educ:* Univ Chicago, BS, 43. *Prof Exp:* Chemist, E J Brach & Sons, 47, Swift & Co, 48 & Armour Res Found, Ill Inst Technol, 49-61; sr res pharmacist, 61-80, RES ASSOC, WARNER-LAMBERT/PARKE-DAVIS PHARMACEUT RES DIV, 80- *Concurrent Pos:* Adj prof, Sch Pharm, Univ Mich, Ann Arbor, 70- *Mem:* Am Crystallog Asn. *Res:* Chemical, x-ray and optical crystallography; chemical microscopy; phase diagrams; thermal stability; crystallization kinetics; solvation; polymorphism; recrystallization; nucleation and crystal growth; physical properties of nonhomogeneous solids. *Mailing Add:* 26669 Huntington Rd Huntington Woods MI 48070

KREAM, BARBARA ELIZABETH, b New York, NY, Mar 11, 48. BIOCHEMISTRY, ENDOCRINOLOGY. *Educ:* Mt Holyoke Col, BA, 69; Yale Univ, PhD(molecular biophys, biochem), 74. *Prof Exp:* NIH fel, Dept Biochem, Univ Wis, 74-77; res assoc, 77-78, instr med & endocrinol, 78-79, ASST PROF, DEPT MED, DIV ENDOCRINOL & METAB, UNIV CONN HEALTH CTR, 79- *Concurrent Pos:* Res grants, Am Diabetes Asn, 78-79, Juvenile Diabetes Found, 79-81, Proctor & Gamble Co, 81 & NIH, 81- *Mem:* Sigma Xi; Endocrine Soc; AAAS; Am Soc Bone & Mineral Res. *Res:* Bone and calcium metabolism; vitamin D receptors; mechanism of action of hormones; effect of insulin on collagen synthesis in normal and diabetic bone; hormonal regulation of bone collager synthesis. *Mailing Add:* Dept of Med Univ of Conn Health Ctr Farmington CT 06032

KREAM, JACOB, b New York, NY, Apr 16, 19; m 42; c 4. BIOCHEMISTRY, CLINICAL CHEMISTRY. *Educ:* City Col New York, BS, 42; Columbia Univ, PhD(biochem), 52; Nat Registry Clin Chem, dipl. *Prof Exp:* Asst, Rockefeller Inst Med Res, 43; chemist, Kellex Corp, 43-44 & Pyridium Corp, 44-46; asst biochem, Columbia Univ, 46-49; biochemist, Inst Cancer Res, 50-52 & US Vet Admin Hosp, NY, 52-53; res assoc biochem, Columbia Univ, 53-54; chief, Dept Clin Chem, Hosp for Joint Dis, 54-65; DIR CORE LAB, CLIN RES CTR, SR INVESTR, STEROID INST, MONTEFIORE HOSP & MED CTR, 65-; ASSOC PROF LAB MED, ALBERT EINSTEIN COL MED, 78- *Concurrent Pos:* Mem bd exam, Bur Labs, NY Dept Health; lectr, Hunter Col, 51-65; lectr-consult, US Naval Hosp, St Albans, NY, 58-62; consult clin radioimmunoassay, Union Carbide Corp, 75- *Mem:* AAAS; Am Chem Soc; Am Asn Clin Chem; fel Am Inst Chem; Sigma Xi. *Res:* Enzymology; purine and pyrimidine metabolism; purine analogs and cancer; nucleic acid chemistry; polypeptide metabolism; clinical chemistry; automated clinical methods; steroid analysis; radioimmunoassay; competitive protein binding analysis; episodic secretion of pituitary hormones; radioisotopes. *Mailing Add:* Montefiore Hosp & Med Ctr Clin Res Ctr 111 E 210 St New York NY 10467

KREAR, HARRY ROBERT, b Pittsburgh, Pa, Apr 13, 22. ETHOLOGY, ECOLOGY. *Educ:* Pa State Univ, BSF, 49; Univ Wyo, MS, 53; Univ Colo, PhD(ecol, ethology), 65. *Prof Exp:* Biologist wildlife res, Mont Fish & Game Dept, 53-54; explor & res, Arctic Wildlife Range Exped, 56; instr biol, Univ Colo, 60-61; asst prof, Mankato State Col, 65-66; chmn div sci & math, US Int Univ, Colo Alpine Campus, 67-73; ASSOC PROF BIOL SCI, MICH TECHNOL UNIV, 73- *Concurrent Pos:* Vis lectr zool, NSF Insts, Univ Colo, 59-64. *Mem:* Animal Behav Soc; Ecol Soc Am; Am Soc Mammalogists. *Res:* Ecology of selected vertebrates of Ungava; reproduction of cow fur seal; Arctic wildlife range; ecology of muskrats; behavior and ecology of sea otters; ecology and ethology of pikas. *Mailing Add:* Dept of Biol Sci Mich Technol Univ Houghton MI 49931

KREASKY, JOSEPH BERNARD, entomology, see previous edition

KREBILL, RICHARD G, b Upland, Calif, Mar 9, 36; m 58; c 3. FOREST PATHOLOGY. *Educ:* Univ Calif, Berkeley, BS, 58; Univ Wis, PhD(plant path), 62. *Prof Exp:* Plant pathologist, 62-76, ASST DIR, ROCKY MOUNTAIN FOREST & RANGE EXP STA, US FOREST SERV, 79- *Mem:* Am Phytopath Soc; Soc Am Foresters. *Res:* Tree diseases; rust fungi; shrub diseases; research administration. *Mailing Add:* Rocky Mountain Forest & Exp Sta Ariz State Univ Tempe AZ 85287

KREBS, CHARLES THEODORE, b Glens Falls, NY, Feb 7, 46; m 76. MARINE BIOLOGY. *Educ:* Boston Univ, AB, 68, PhD(biol), 76. *Prof Exp:* Instr, 74-76, ASST PROF BIOL, ST MARY'S COL MD, 76- *Mem:* AAAS; Am Inst Biol Sci; Estuarine & Brackish Water Sci Asn; Sigma Xi. *Res:* Ecology and behavior of marine invertebrates with emphasis on the effects of pollutants; the effects of petroleum and chlorinated hydrocarbons on marine and estuarine organisms. *Mailing Add:* Div of Natural Sci & Math St Mary's Col of Md St Mary's City MD 20686

KREBS, EDWIN GERHARD, b Lansing, Iowa, June 6, 18; m 45; c 3. BIOCHEMISTRY. *Educ:* Univ Ill, AB, 40; Washington Univ, MD, 43. *Prof Exp:* Intern & asst resident, Barnes Hosp, St Louis, 44-45; NIH res fel, Washington Univ, 46-48, from asst prof to prof biochem, 48-68; prof biochem & chmn dept, Sch Med, Univ Calif, Davis, 68-77; investr, 77-80, SR INVESTR, HOWARD HUGHES MED INST, 80-; PROF & CHMN DEPT PHARMACOL, SCH MED, UNIV WASH, SEATTLE, 77- *Concurrent Pos:* Guggenheim fel, 59, 66. *Mem:* Nat Acad Sci; Am Acad Arts & Sci; Am Soc Biol Chemists; Am Chem Soc. *Res:* Enzyme chemistry; regulation of metabolism; mechanism of action of hormones; protein phosphorylation. *Mailing Add:* SJ-30 Howard Hughes Med Inst Seattle WA 98195

KREBS, JAMES JOHN, b St Louis, Mo, Feb 28, 32. EXPERIMENTAL SOLID STATE PHYSICS. *Educ:* St Louis Univ, BS, 54, PhD(physics), 59. *Prof Exp:* PHYSICIST MAGNETIC RESONANCE, US NAVAL RES LAB, 58- *Concurrent Pos:* Nat Res Coun res assoc, 58-59; vis fel, Princeton Univ, 75-76. *Mem:* Am Phys Soc. *Res:* Investigation of electron-nuclear interactions by means of magnetic double resonance; resonance and optical absorption in exchange coupled systems; deep impurity resonance in III-V semiconductors; properties of ultra-thin magnetic single crystals. *Mailing Add:* Code 6891 Naval Res Lab Washington DC 20375

KREBS, JOHN S, b New Orleans, La, Dec 3, 24; m 56; c 2. BIOPHYSICS, RADIATION BIOLOGY. *Educ:* La State Univ, BS, 48; Univ Calif, PhD(biophys), 58. *Prof Exp:* Asst pharmacol, Med Sch, La State Univ, 48-49; biologist, US Naval Radiol Defense Lab, 54-69; SR BIOPHYSICIST, STANFORD RES INST, 69- *Mem:* Am Physiol Soc; Radiation Res Soc. *Res:* Metabolism of sulfobromophthalein by the liver; permanent damage in mammals caused by ionizing radiation; kinetics of accumulation of ionizing radiation damage by repeated radiation exposure; kinetics of cell proliferation. *Mailing Add:* Life Sci Div Stanford Res Inst Menlo Park CA 94025

KREBS, JULIA ELIZABETH, b Baton Rouge, La, Mar 29, 43. ECOLOGY, BIOLOGY. *Educ:* Oberlin Col, AB, 65; Boston Col, MEd, 69; Univ Ga, MSc, 72, PhD(zool & ecol), 77. *Prof Exp:* ASST PROF BIOL, FRANCIS MARION COL, 77- *Mem:* Ecol Soc Am. *Res:* Nutrient cycling; effect of man on natural systems; bird populations. *Mailing Add:* Dept of Biol Francis Marion Col Florence SC 29501

KREBS, ROBERT DIXON, b Gowanda, NY, Mar 12, 31; m 54; c 3. SOIL MECHANICS, FOUNDATION ENGINEERING. *Educ:* Rutgers Univ, BS, 52, PhD(soil sci), 56; Purdue Univ, MSE, 59. *Prof Exp:* From asst to assoc prof agron, Va Polytech Inst, 55-57; instr eng geol, Purdue Univ, 58-59; ASSOC PROF CIVIL ENG, VA POLYTECH INST & STATE UNIV, 59-, ASST HEAD DEPT, 70- *Concurrent Pos:* Assoc, Hwy Res Bd, Nat Acad Sci-Nat Res Coun. *Mem:* Fel AAAS; Am Soc Civil Engrs; Am Soc Eng Educ. *Res:* Soil mechanics, physics, mineralogy and chemistry; soils and geologic engineering; soil genesis and classification; soil stabilization; soil behavior. *Mailing Add:* Dept of Civil Eng Va Polytech Inst & State Univ Blacksburg VA 24061

KREBS, ROBERT EDWARD, b Shippensburg, Pa, Aug 4, 22; c 3. SCIENCE EDUCATION, BIOLOGY. *Educ:* Shippensburg State Col, BS, 48; Western Md Col, MEd, 52; Univ Fla, EdD(admin sci), 58. *Prof Exp:* Asst prof biol & chem, Univ Fla, 52-61; lectr space sci, NASA, Washington, DC, 61-62; sci specialist, US Off Educ, 63-66; dir res, Pace Univ, NY, 66-68; dir res & develop, Cent Wash Univ, 68-72; assoc vpres, Govs State Univ, Ill, 72-78; ASSOC DEAN, RES ADMIN, MED CTR, UNIV ILL, 78- *Concurrent Pos:* Sci ed adv, Univ Fla State Mus, 54-56; fel, NSF Chem Inst, 61; inst consult, NSF, 64-66; admin coordr, USAID, India, 65-66; proj dir, State Wash grants, 67-78. *Mem:* Soc Res Adminrs; Nat Coun Univ Res Adminrs. *Res:* Research administration and research grant-contract management. *Mailing Add:* Univ of Ill Med Ctr Grad Col PO Box 6998 Chicago IL 60680

KREBS, WILLIAM H, b Detroit, Mich; c 2. INDUSTRIAL HYGIENE. *Educ:* Univ Mich, Ann Arbor, BS, 60, MPH, 63, MS, 65, PhD, 70; Bd Cert Safety Prof, cert; Am Bd Indust Hyg, cert. *Prof Exp:* Res asst indust health, Sch Pub Health, Univ Mich, Ann Arbor, 62; indust hygienist, Lumbermens Mutual Casualty Co, Ill, 63-64; indust hygienist, Indust Hyg Dept, 70-77, mgr, 77-81, DIR, TOXIC MAT CONTROL ACTIVITY, GEN MOTORS CORP, 81- *Mem:* AAAS; NY Acad Sci; Am Indust Hyg Asn; Am Acad Indust Hyg; Soc Occup & Environ Health. *Res:* Formation of ferruginous bodies. *Mailing Add:* Toxic Mat Control Activity 3044 W Grand Blvd Detroit MI 48202

KREBS, WILLIAM NELSON, b Santa Monica, Calif, Sept 4, 48. MICROPALEONTOLOGY. *Educ:* Univ Calif, Los Angeles, BS, 70; Univ Calif, Davis, PhD(geol), 77. *Prof Exp:* MICROPALEONTOLOGIST, AMOCO PROD CO, 78- *Mem:* Paleont Soc; Soc Econ Paleontologists & Mineralogists; Sigma Xi. *Res:* Ecology, paleoecology, preservation and biostratigraphy of marine and lacustrine diatoms. *Mailing Add:* Amoco Prod Co 1321 E 10th Ave 9 Denver CO 80218

KREDICH, NICHOLAS M, b Chicago, Ill, Sept 23, 35; m 57; c 3. INTERNAL MEDICINE, BIOCHEMISTRY. *Educ:* Duke Univ, BA, 57; Univ Mich, MA, 60, MD, 62. *Prof Exp:* Intern internal med, Duke Hosp, Durham, NC, 62-63, asst resident, 63-64; res assoc molecular biol, Nat Inst Arthritis & Metab Dis, 64-66, staff assoc, 66-68; asst prof, 68-73, assoc prof, 73-80, PROF INTERNAL MED, MED CTR, DUKE UNIV, 80- *Concurrent Pos:* Nat Inst Arthritis & Metab Dis res grant, 68-81; investr, Howard Hughes Med Inst, 73- *Res:* Regulation of metabolic pathways, including feedback inhibition and repression and induction of enzymes; bacterial and human genetics; sulfur metabolism in bacteria; adenosine deaminase deficiency; immunodeficiency disease; genetics; molecular biology. *Mailing Add:* Dept of Med & Biochem Duke Med Ctr Box 3100 Durham NC 27710

KREEGER, RUSSELL LOWELL, b Amherst, Ohio, Jan 24, 46; m 73; c 2. ORGANIC CHEMISTRY, POLYMER CHEMISTRY. *Educ:* Kent State Univ, BS, 68; Ohio State Univ, Columbus, PhD(org chem), 76. *Prof Exp:* RES SCIENTIST, CHEM & PLASTICS DIV, UNION CARBIDE CORP, 76- *Mem:* Am Chem Soc; Sigma Xi. *Res:* Research and development; organic chemicals process research; Friedel-Crafts catalysts; organic synthesis; polymer chemistry, particularly water-soluble polymers. *Mailing Add:* 462 New Ctr Rd Somerville NJ 08876

KREER, JOHN B(ELSHAW), b Brooklyn, NY, Sept 25, 27; m 57; c 2. ELECTRICAL ENGINEERING. *Educ:* Iowa State Col, BS, 51; Univ Ill, MS, 54, PhD(elec eng), 56. *Prof Exp:* From instr to asst prof elec eng, Univ Ill, 55-59; from assoc prof to prof, Univ WVa, 59-64; assoc prof, 64-68, PROF ELEC ENG, MICH STATE UNIV, 68-, CHMN DEPT ELEC ENG & SYSTS SCI, 77- *Concurrent Pos:* Mem, Transp Res Bd. *Mem:* Inst Elec & Electronics Engrs; Inst Transp Engrs; Am Soc Eng Educ; Nat Soc Prof Engrs. *Res:* Computer traffic control. *Mailing Add:* Dept of Elec Eng & Systs Sci Mich State Univ East Lansing MI 48824

KREEVOY, MAURICE M, b Boston, Mass, Aug 28, 28; m 53; c 2. PHYSICAL CHEMISTRY, CHEMICAL KINETICS. *Educ:* Univ Calif, Los Angeles, BS, 50; Mass Inst Technol, PhD, 54. *Prof Exp:* Res assoc chem, Pa State Univ, 53-55; NSF fel, Univ Utah, 55-56; from asst prof to assoc prof, 56-64, PROF CHEM, UNIV MINN, MINNEAPOLIS, 64- *Concurrent Pos:*

Consult, Gen Mills, Inc, 59-; Sloan Found fel, 60-64; NSF sr fel, Oxford Univ, 62-63; partic, US Acad Sci exchange prog with Coun of Acad Socialist Fed Repub of Yugoslavia, 69-70; consult, Ventron Corp, 75- *Mem:* Am Chem Soc; The Chem Soc; Croatian Chem Soc; Sigma Xi. *Res:* Physical and theoretical organic chemistry; chemical kinetics in solution; isotope effects; structure and dynamics of transition states. *Mailing Add:* Dept of Chem Univ of Minn Minneapolis MN 55455

KREFT, ANTHONY FRANK, III, b Detroit, Mich, May 28, 48; m 79. ORGANIC CHEMISTRY, MEDICINAL CHEMISTRY. *Educ:* Univ Mich, BS, 70; Columbia Univ, MPh, 73, PhD(org chem), 76. *Prof Exp:* SR RES SCIENTIST ORG CHEM, WYETH RES LABS, 78- *Concurrent Pos:* Fel, Stanford Univ, 76-78. *Mem:* NY Acad Sci. *Res:* Design and synthesis of drugs of medicinal interest. *Mailing Add:* Wyeth Labs PO Box 8299 Philadelphia PA 19101

KREGLEWSKI, ALEXANDER, b Warsaw, Poland, June 3, 27; m 54; c 1. THERMODYNAMICS, PETROLEUM CHEMISTRY. *Educ:* Univ Warsaw, MSc, 51; Polish Acad Sci, DrSc(phys chem), 56, Docent Dr, 62. *Prof Exp:* Res chemist, Inst Phys Chem, Polish Acad Sci, 51-58, head lab phase equilibrium, 61-66; fel phys chem, Carnegie Inst Technol, 58-60; assoc prof, Tex A&M Univ, 66-67; vis assoc prof chem eng, Ohio State Univ, 68-69; assoc prof chem, Tex A&M Univ, 69-71; SR RES CHEMIST, THERMODYNAMICS RES CTR, TEX A&M UNIV, 71- *Mem:* Am Chem Soc. *Res:* Experimental and theoretical research on equilibrium properties of fluids and fluid mixtures; industrial research on separation and purification of mixtures. *Mailing Add:* Thermodynamics Res Ctr Tex A&M Univ College Station TX 77843

KREH, DONALD WILLARD, b Frederick, Md, Mar 17, 37; m 66; c 4. ORGANIC CHEMISTRY. *Educ:* Univ Richmond, BS, 59, MS, 61; Va Polytech Inst, PhD(org chem), 66. *Prof Exp:* Chemist, Great Lakes Res Corp, 66-67; chemist, 67-68, SR CHEMIST, TENN EASTMAN CO, 69- *Mem:* Am Chem Soc. *Res:* Reactions and synthesis of small ring sulfides, sulfoxides and sulfones; synthesis of photographic chemicals, antioxidants, stabilizers, and industrial chemical intermediates. *Mailing Add:* Tenn Eastman Co Kingsport TN 37660

KREH, E(DWARD) J(OSEPH), JR, b Pittsburgh, Pa, Feb 26, 15; m 38; c 3. ENGINEERING. *Educ:* Carnegie Inst Technol, BS, 37. *Prof Exp:* Design engr, Westinghouse Elec Corp, 37-42; plant engr, Camillus Cutlery Co, 46-51; mgr equip develop, 51-56, mem div mgr staff, Stress Corrosion & Hydraul Fields, Bettis Plant, 56-58, div apparatus engr, 58-59, mgr, Nuclear Core Dept, 59-61, mgr, Core Mat Dept, 61-65, mgr cent labs, 65-67, mgr opers, Bettis Plant, 67-72, mgr, Prod Assurance, Westinghouse Pressurized Water Reactors Div, 72-79, CONSULT ENGR, WESTINGHOUSE ELEC CORP, 79- *Mem:* Am Soc Mech Engrs; Nat Asn Corrosion Engrs; Am Inst Mgt. *Res:* Thermal, mechanical and electrical design; corrosion studies; development of fabrication processes for nuclear reactors; development and management of quality assurance systems to assure reactor safety and reliability. *Mailing Add:* Westinghouse Elec Corp PO Box 355 Pittsburgh PA 15230

KREHBIEL, EUGENE B, b Moundridge, Kans, July 29, 30; m 57; c 3. EMBRYOLOGY, ENDOCRINOLOGY. *Educ:* Bethel Col, Kans, BS, 57; Kans State Univ, MS, 61, PhD(zool), 63. *Prof Exp:* Instr zool, Kans State Univ, 62-63; asst prof, 63-72, PROF ZOOL, EASTERN ILL UNIV, 72- *Mem:* AAAS; Am Soc Zoologists. *Res:* Developmental biology; reproductive system of bovine embryos. *Mailing Add:* Dept of Zool Eastern Ill Univ Charleston IL 61920

KREIBICH, GERT, b Komotau, Czech, Nov 14, 39; Ger citizen; m 66; c 1. CELL BIOLOGY. *Educ:* Univ Heidelberg, dipl chem, 65, Dr rer nat, 68. *Prof Exp:* Fel chem carcinogenesis, Ger Cancer Res Ctr, Heidelberg, 65-70; res assoc cell biol, Rockefeller Univ, 70-72; aast prof, 72-75, ASSOC PROF CELL BIOL, MED CTR, NY UNIV, 75- *Concurrent Pos:* Res fel, Ger Res Soc, 70-72; NIH res career develop award, 77-82; mem cell biol study sect, NIH, 78-82. *Mem:* Ger Soc Biol Chem; NY Acad Sci; Am Soc Cell Biol; Am Soc Biol Chemists. *Res:* Structure and function of subcellular membranes in eukaryotic cells; function of membrane bound polysomes in membrane biogenesis. *Mailing Add:* Dept of Cell Biol Sch of Med NY Univ 550 First Ave New York NY 10016

KREIBICH, ROLAND, b Glasert, Bohemia, July 30, 22; m 58. ORGANIC CHEMISTRY. *Educ:* Univ Graz, Magister Pharmaciae, 49, PhD(chem), 51. *Prof Exp:* Res chemist, Can Westinghouse, 52-54 & Durez Plastics, Inc, 54-56; proj engr, Gen Elec, 57-58; MGR, POLYMER RES DEPT, WEYERHAEUSER CO, 58- *Mem:* Am Chem Soc. *Res:* Polymers; resins. *Mailing Add:* Weyerhaeuser Co Tacoma WA 98477

KREIDER, DONALD LESTER, b Lancaster, Pa, Dec 5, 31; m 52; c 3. MATHEMATICAL LOGIC. *Educ:* Lebanon Valley Col, BS, 53; Mass Inst Technol, PhD(math), 59. *Prof Exp:* Instr, Lebanon Valley Col, 52-53; asst, Mass Inst Technol, 53-55, instr math, 55-60; from asst prof to assoc prof, 60-68, PROF MATH, DARTMOUTH COL, 68- *Mem:* Am Math Soc; Asn Symbolic Logic; Math Asn Am. *Res:* Recursive functions; automata theory. *Mailing Add:* Dept of Math Dartmouth Col Hanover NH 03755

KREIDER, EUNICE S, b Ohio, June 5, 41; m 63. INTERNATIONAL PRODUCT DEVELOPMENT. *Educ:* Goshen Col, BA, 63; Purdue Univ, PhD(chem), 67; Northwestern Univ, MM, 77. *Prof Exp:* From res investr to sr res investr, G D Searle & Co, 67-74, group leader, 74-76, dir, Prog Planning & Qual Assurance, 76-78, assoc dir, 78-80, dir proj mgt, Preclin Res & Develop, 80-81; DIR, INT PROD DEVELOP, ORTHO PHARMACEUT CORP, 81- *Mem:* Sigma Xi; Am Chem Soc; NY Acad Sci. *Res:* Heterocyclic medicinal chemicals; drug safety testing and GLP'S; project management. *Mailing Add:* Ortho Pharmaceutical Corp Raritan NJ 08869

KREIDER, HENRY ROYER, b Baltimore, Md, Dec 31, 11; m 36; c 2. PHYSICAL CHEMISTRY, ORGANIC CHEMISTRY. *Educ:* Univ Toledo, BA, 33; Ohio State Univ, MS, 35, PhD(chem), 36. *Prof Exp:* Chemist, Am Med Asn, Chicago, 36-42 & Mead Johnson & Co, Ind, 42-45; exec asst to vpres, William S Merrell Co, 45-50, assoc dir res, 50-56; dir res, Chesebrough-Ponds, Inc, 56-59; exec vpres, Viobin Corp, 59-60; dir res, Sherman Labs, 60-68; dir prod develop, Cooper Labs, Inc, 68-71; CONSULT DRUG COSMETIC INDUSTS, 71- *Mem:* AAAS; Am Chem Soc; Soc Cosmetic Chem; Am Pharmaceut Asn; Asn Res Dirs. *Res:* Development of foods, drugs & cosmetics; vitamins; proteins; fats; micronutrients. *Mailing Add:* 1937 Ill Ave NE St Petersburg FL 33703

KREIDER, JACK LEON, b Afton, Okla, Mar 12, 41; m 67; c 3. ANIMAL SCIENCE, REPRODUCTIVE PHYSIOLOGY. *Educ:* Okla State Univ, BS, 68; Univ Ky, MS, 70, PhD(animal sci), 71. *Prof Exp:* Asst prof animal sci, Univ Mo-Columbia, 72; from asst prof to assoc prof animal sci, La State Univ, Baton Rouge, 73-79; ASSOC PROF ANIMAL SCI, TEX A&M UNIV, 79- *Mem:* Am Soc Animal Sci. *Res:* Reproductive physiology and endocrinology of the mare as related to improving efficiency of production of horses, particularly the perparturient period; reproductive physiology of the stallion, particularly semen physiology. *Mailing Add:* Dept Animal Sci Tex A&M Univ College Station TX 77843

KREIDER, JOHN WESLEY, b Philadelphia, Pa, Mar 24, 37; m 63; c 2. CANCER RESEARCH, TUMOR IMMUNOLOGY. *Educ:* La Salle Col, AB, 59; Univ Pa, MD, 63. *Prof Exp:* Mem fac path, Med Sch, Univ Pa, 67-68; MEM FAC PATH, HERSHEY MED CTR, 68- *Concurrent Pos:* Career develop award, USPHS, 69; mem, Path B Study Sect, NIH, 79- *Mem:* Am Asn Pathologists; Am Asn Cancer Res; Am Asn Immunologists. *Res:* Frost regulation of tumor growth; neoplastic cell differentiation. *Mailing Add:* Dept Path Hershey Med Ctr Hershey PA 17033

KREIDER, KENNETH GRUBER, b Lancaster, Pa, May 21, 37; m 61; c 3. METALLURGY, MATERIALS SCIENCE. *Educ:* Mass Inst Technol, SB, 59, SM, 61, ScD, 63. *Prof Exp:* Res supvr, United Aircraft Res Labs, 65 Labs, 65-73; DIV CHIEF, NAT BUR STANDARDS, 73- *Mem:* Combustion Inst; Am Soc Testing & Mat; Am Inst Mining, Metall & Petrol Engrs; Am Soc Mech Engrs; Am Soc Metals. *Res:* Industrial energy conservation; instrumentation for harsh environments; thermal properties of materials; metal matrix composites; infrared thermography. *Mailing Add:* Nat Bur Standards Bldg 221 Rm B252 Washington DC 20234

KREIDER, LEONARD CALE, b Sterling, Ohio, Feb 16, 10; m 33; c 3. CHEMISTRY. *Educ:* Goshen Col, AB, 31; Ohio State Univ, MSc, 33, PhD(org chem), 36. *Prof Exp:* Preparations asst, Ohio State Univ, 31-32, asst chem, 32-36; res chemist, Rockefeller Inst, 36-37; from asst prof to prof chem, Bethel Col Kans, 37-49, chmn, Div Natural Sci, 46-49; chemist tech serv, Res Ctr, B F Goodrich Co, 49-50, pioneering res, 50-56 & org res, 56-59, sr res chemist polymerization res, 59-75; RETIRED. *Mem:* Am Chem Soc; Sigma Xi. *Res:* Development of catalyst for manufacture of cis-1, 4-polyisoprene and for Hydrin rubbers; oligosaccharides; alkaline degradation of carbohydrates; galacturonic acid chemistry; pigment reinforcement in rubber; sodium catalyzed rubbers; polyester urethane rubbers; rubber hysteresis; aluminum alkyls; metalloorganic catalyzed polymerizations. *Mailing Add:* 408 Highland Ave Wadsworth OH 44281

KREIDER, MARLIN BOOKS, b Campbelltown, Pa, Nov 7, 22. ENVIRONMENTAL PHYSIOLOGY. *Educ:* Houghton Col, AB, 47; Univ Md, MS, 50, PhD(zool, physiol), 53. *Prof Exp:* Res physiologist environ physiol, US Army Res Inst Environ Med, 53-70; PROF BIOL PHYSIOL, WORCESTER STATE COL, 70- *Concurrent Pos:* Asst prof, Eastern Nazarene Col, 55-70. *Mem:* Fel Am Col Sports Med; Int Soc Biometeorol; Am Sci Affil. *Res:* Responses of man and animal to extremes of heat and cold; nature and rate of acclimatization and cross acclimatization; effect of environmental poisons on response to these extremes. *Mailing Add:* Dept of Biol Worcester State Col Worcester MA 01602

KREIDL, NORBERT J(OACHIM), b Atzgersdorf, Austria, July 3, 04; US citizen; m 34; c 3. PHYSICS, GLASS SCIENCE. *Educ:* Univ Vienna, PhD(physics), 28. *Hon Degrees:* PhD, Alfred Univ, 71, & Univ Vienna, 78. *Prof Exp:* Fel glass sci, Kaiser Wilhelm Inst, 29; mgr res, Schreiber & Nephews, Rapotin, Czech, 29-39; asst prof glass sci, Pa State Col, 39-43; head glass div, Bausch & Lomb, Inc, 43-55, dir mat res & develop, 55-64; prof ceramics, Rutgers Univ, 64-66; prof ceramic eng, 66-75, EMER PROF CERAMIC ENG, UNIV MO-ROLLA, 76- *Concurrent Pos:* Consult numerous industs, 39-43 & 64-; chmn infrared transmitters comt, mat adv bd, Nat Acad Sci-Nat Res Coun, 68 & mem submergencies comt, 69; pres, Int Comn Glass, 69-72; mem, Glass Comn, Univ Space Res Assoc, 73-; Sci Coun, 80-; adj prof chem eng, Univ N Mex, 78-; adj prof physics, Col Santa Fe, 80- *Honors & Awards:* Toledo Award, Am Ceramic Soc, 67, Jepson Award, 69. *Mem:* Fel Am Ceramic Soc; Brit Soc Glass Technol; hon mem Ger Glass Technol Asn. *Res:* Glass structure and properties; radiation effects. *Mailing Add:* 1433 Canyon Rd Santa Fe NM 87501

KREIDL, TOBIAS JOACHIM, b Rochester, NY, May 6, 54. DIGITAL IMAGE PROCESSING. *Educ:* Univ Vienna, Austria, PhD(astron), 79. *Prof Exp:* Res assoc, Ruhr Univ, Bochum, WGer, 79-80; ASTRONOMER, LOWELL OBSERV, 80- *Concurrent Pos:* Lectr comput sci, Northern Ariz Univ, 81. *Mem:* Am Astron Soc. *Res:* Digital image processing and image processing systems; photometry of peculiar A-type stars; computer analysis of astronomical data of various nature. *Mailing Add:* Lowell Observ PO Box 1269 Flagstaff AZ 86002

KREIDLER, ERIC RUSSELL, b Lock Haven, Pa, July 21, 39; m 68; c 2. PHASE EQUILIBRIA, LUMINESCENCE. *Educ:* Pa State Univ, BS, 61, MS, 63, PhD(ceramic sci), 67. *Prof Exp:* Res chemist, Gen Elec Co, 66-80; ASSOC PROF CERAMIC ENG, OHIO STATE UNIV, 80- *Concurrent Pos:* Consult, Gen Elec Co, 80-; contributing ed, Communications of the Am

Ceramic Soc, 81-; assoc ed, Phase Diagrams for Ceramists, 81- *Mem:* Fel Am Ceramic Soc; Electrochem Soc; AAAS. *Res:* Determination of phase diagrams; crystal chemistry and luminescence of inorganic materials; phosphors and luminescence; oxide thermionic cathodes; depreciation in fluorescent lamps; dielectric and metallic thin films; glass-metal composites. *Mailing Add:* Ohio State Univ 394 Watts Hall 2041 Col Rd Columbus OH 43210

KREIER, JULIUS PETER, b Philadelphia, Pa, Nov 30, 26; m 55; c 2. PROTOZOOLOGY, IMMUNOLOGY. *Educ:* Univ Pa, VMD, 53; Univ Ill, MS, 59, PhD, 62. *Prof Exp:* Vet, Agr Res Serv, USDA, 53-56; instr vet physiol, Univ Ill, 56-59, instr vet path & hyg, 59-61, USPHS fel, 61-62; from asst prof to assoc prof, 62-72, PROF MICROBIOL, OHIO STATE UNIV, 72- *Concurrent Pos:* Vis prof, State Univ de Sao Paulo, Botucatu, Brazil, 81. *Mem:* Am Soc Trop Med Hygiene; Soc Protozoologists; Am Soc Parasitol; Am Asn Immunol; Am Soc Microbiol. *Res:* Immunity to plasmodia; isolation of plasmedical antigens; nature of Anaplasma, Eperythrozoon, Hemobartonella; host responses to blood inhabiting protozoa, Plasmodia babesia and Trypanosomes. *Mailing Add:* Dept Microbiol Ohio State Univ Columbus OH 43210

KREIFELDT, JOHN GENE, b Manistee, Mich, Oct 7, 34; m 64; c 2. ENGINEERING DESIGN, BIOMEDICAL ENGINEERING. *Educ:* Univ Calif, Los Angeles, BS, 61; Mass Inst Tech, MS, 64; Case Western Reserve Univ, PhD(biomed eng), 69. *Prof Exp:* assoc prof, 69-80, PROF BIOMED & HUMAN FACTORS ENG, TUFTS UNIV, 80- *Concurrent Pos:* Vpres, Appl Ergonomics Corp; consult, New Eng Med Ctr, Boston, Mass, 70-, Gillette Co, 71-, E I du Pont de Nemours, Inc, 72-, Dacom, 75, Johnson & Johnson, 76- & Bard-Parker, 79; USPHS grants, Tufts Univ & New Eng Med Ctr, 71-81; Nat Res Coun associateship, NASA-Ames Res Ctr, 73; Dept Health, Educ & Welfare grant; NASA grants. *Mem:* Human Factors Soc; Inst Elec & Electronics Eng; Am Soc Eng Educ. *Res:* Electromyographic processing and control; man-machine system design; air traffic control studies; computers in automation of radiotherapy treatment multidimensional scaling in design; mathematical models of human operators; consumer product design. *Mailing Add:* Dept of Eng Design Tufts Univ Medford MA 02155

KREIGHBAUM, WILLIAM EUGENE, b Elkhart, Ind, June 17, 34; m 61; c 2. MEDICINAL CHEMISTRY. *Educ:* Wabash Col, AB, 56; Ind Univ, PhD(org chem), 60. *Prof Exp:* Bristol Labs res fel org chem, Ind Univ, 60-61; sr res scientist, 61-67, group leader, 68-69, sr investr, 70-73, PRIN INVESTR, MEAD JOHNSON RES CTR, MEAD JOHNSON & CO, 74- *Mem:* Am Chem Soc; Int Soc Heterocyclic Chem. *Res:* Synthesis and pharmacological activity of organic sulfur compounds; heterocyclic compounds containing sulfur or nitrogen; chemistry of the sympathetic nervous system. *Mailing Add:* Dept Chem Res Mead Johnson Pharmaceut Div Evansville IN 47721

KREILICK, ROBERT W, b Kalamazoo, Mich, Jan 3, 38; m 59; c 2. PHYSICAL CHEMISTRY. *Educ:* Wash Univ, AB, 59, PhD(magnetic resonance), 64. *Prof Exp:* From asst prof to assoc prof, 64-71, PROF CHEM, UNIV ROCHESTER, 71- *Concurrent Pos:* Alfred P Sloan fel, 69-71. *Mem:* Am Chem Soc. *Res:* Nuclear magnetic resonance and electron spin resonance; biophysical chemistry; study of biologically important metal complexes. *Mailing Add:* Dept of Chem Univ of Rochester Rochester NY 14627

KREILING, DARYL, b Minatare, Nebr, May 18, 36; m 56; c 3. MATHEMATICS. *Educ:* Chadron State Col, BS, 61; Bowling Green State Univ, MA, 63; Univ Wyo, PhD(math), 69. *Prof Exp:* Instr math, Univ Wyo, 66-69; from asst prof to assoc prof math, Western Ill Univ, 73-80, asst dean, 74-80; PROF MATH, UNIV TENN, 80- *Mem:* Am Math Soc; Math Asn Am. *Res:* Associative and non-associative rings; radicals of rings and ring-like structures. *Mailing Add:* Martin Sch Arts & Sci Univ Tenn Martin TN 38238

KREILING, WILLIAM H(ERMAN), b Brooklyn, NY, Dec 20, 23; m 51; c 2. CHEMICAL ENGINEERING. *Educ:* Polytech Inst Brooklyn, BChE, 49. *Prof Exp:* Chem res engr pilot plant design, M W Kellogg Co Div, Pullman, Inc, 42-49; dept chemist paper coatings, Lowe Paper Co, 49-53, res chemist, 53-55, gen foreman coatings dept, 55-57, tech supt finishing mill, 57-58, qual control supvr, 58-59; chem engr coating develop, Keuffel & Esser Co, 59-64, mgr process eng, 64-68; sect leader, paper & coatings group, Corp Res Ctr, Int Paper Co, 68-70, sr res assoc paper develop, Corp Res & Develop Div, 70-78; sr develop engr, Specialty Papers & Packaging Div, 78-80, SR DEVELOP ENGR, LAMINATING & COATINGS DIV, LUDLOW CORP, 80- *Mem:* Tech Asn Pulp & Paper Indust; fel Am Inst Chem; NY Acad Sci. *Res:* Protective, decorative, printing and photographic coatings and specialty papers. *Mailing Add:* 154 Wolf Swamp Rd Longmeadow MA 01106

KREIMER, HERBERT FREDERICK, JR, b Cincinnati, Ohio, Feb 19, 36; m 61; c 2. MATHEMATICS. *Educ:* Yale Univ, BS, 58, PhD(math), 62. *Prof Exp:* From asst prof to assoc prof, 62-77, PROF MATH, FLA STATE UNIV, 77- *Concurrent Pos:* Univ Res Coun grant, 64 & 67; vis assoc prof, Northwestern Univ, 65-66; NSF grant, 65-66 & 68-71. *Mem:* Am Math Soc; Math Asn Am. *Res:* Ring theory and homological algebra. *Mailing Add:* Dept of Math Fla State Univ Tallahassee FL 32306

KREINER, HOWARD WILLIAM, b Philadelphia, Pa, Apr 20, 24; m 57; c 2. OPERATIONS RESEARCH. *Educ:* Univ Pa, BS, 44; Mass Inst Technol, MS, 54. *Prof Exp:* From opers analyst to sr scientist, Opers Eval Group, US Dept Navy, 47-66; staff scientist, Spec Warfare Lab, Airtronics, Inc, 66-68; systs analyst, Commun Satellite Corp, 68-71; consult, Cybernetics Res Inst, 71-72; systs analyst, Dept Defense, Off Dir, Defense Res & Eng, 72-77; systs analyst, Syst Planning Corp, 77-79; SYSTS ANALYST & STUDY DIR, CTR NAVAL ANALYSES, 79- *Mem:* Opers Res Soc Am; Sigma Xi. *Res:* Development of improved methods of testing and measuring systems reliability. *Mailing Add:* Ctr Naval Analysis 2000 N Beauregard St Alexandria VA 22311

KREIPKE, MERRILL VINCENT, b Evansville, Ind, Feb 14, 16; m 37; c 2. GEOTECHNICAL ENGINEERING, CIVIL ENGINEERING. *Educ:* Purdue Univ, BS, 36. *Prof Exp:* Resident engr & city engr, Evansville, Ind, 36-39; inspector, US Army Engrs Dist, Ky, 39-41, jr engr, 41-42, asst engr, 42-44, engr, 46-51, civil engr, 51-56 & Off Chief Engrs, US Dept Army, 56-61, engr, Off Chief Res & Develop, 61-69, chief geophys sci br, US Army Res Off, 69-74, chief mil res & develop team, Chief Engrs, Dept Army, 74-75; CONSULT, 75- *Concurrent Pos:* Permanent secy, quadripartite standing working group ground mobility, Armies of US, UK, Can & Australia, 59-66; proj officer for US, NATO long-term sci study land-based mobility, 66-; US nat leader, NATO long-term sci study mobility interface, 69-; exec mem & US leader, subgroup T-ground mobility, Tech Coop Prog, US, UK, Can & Australia, 69-; US nat leader, NATO long-term sci study on Arctic opers, 71- *Honors & Awards:* Meritorious Civilian Serv Medal, Dept Army, 66. *Mem:* Am Soc Civil Engrs; Soc Am Mil Engrs; Nat Soc Prof Engrs; Int Soc Soil Mech & Found Eng; Int Soc Terrain-Vehicle Systs. *Res:* Soil mechanics; terrain-vehicle interaction; quantitative terrain evaluation; design and construction of earth and rockfill dams; rapid earthwork; soil stabilization; soil surfacings. *Mailing Add:* 3060 Hazelton St Falls Church VA 22044

KREIS, RONALD W, b Passaic, NJ, Oct 20, 42; m 69; c 1. PHYSICAL CHEMISTRY. *Educ:* Ursinus Col, BS, 64; Univ Del, PhD(chem), 69. *Prof Exp:* Res scientist chem, Uniroyal Inc, 69-77; MGR TECH SERV, ALCOLAC CHEM CORP, 77- *Mem:* Am Chem Soc; Sigma Xi; Tech Asn Pulp & Paper Indust. *Res:* Latex and colloid chemistry; adhesion of rubber; paper chemicals. *Mailing Add:* Alcolac Chem Corp 3440 Fairfield Rd Baltimore MD 21226

KREIS, WILLI, b Ebnat, Switz, Nov 3, 24; m 62; c 4. CLINICAL PHARMACOLOGY, CHEMOTHERAPY. *Educ:* Univ Zurich, MD, 54; Univ Basel, PhD(org chem), 57. *Prof Exp:* Res mem biochem pharmacol, Sandoz, Ltd, Basel, Switz, 58-61; res assoc, Sloan-Kettering Inst Cancer Res, 61-64, assoc, 64-69; asst prof, 67-72, chmn biochem unit, 74-75, ASSOC PROF BIOCHEM, SLOAN-KETTERING DIV, GRAD SCH MED SCI, CORNELL UNIV, 72-, ASSOC MEM, SLOAN-KETTERING INST CANCER RES, 69- *Concurrent Pos:* Damon Runyon grant, 73; Nat Cancer Inst grant, 75; asst attend clin pharmacologist, Dept Med, Mem Hosp, 75-; Am Cancer Soc grants, 76, 78, 79, 80 & 81; assoc prof pharmacol & therapeut, Sloan-Kettering Div Grad Sch Med Sci, Cornell Univ, 80- *Mem:* Swiss Med Soc; Swiss Chem Soc; Am Asn Cancer Res; NY Acad Sci; Am Soc Biol Chemists. *Res:* Biochemical pharmacology of anticancer drugs; experimental and clinical pharmacology of cancer; biochemistry of nucleic acids. *Mailing Add:* Sloan-Kettering Inst Cancer Res 145 Boston Post Rd Rye NY 10580

KREISER, THOMAS HARRY, b Ono, Pa, Aug 12, 35; m 79; c 3. BIOCHEMISTRY. *Educ:* Lebanon Valley Col, BS, 58; Univ Nebr, MS, 60, PhD(chem), 65. *Prof Exp:* Res biochemist, 62-69, SR RES BIOCHEMIST, MILES LABS, INC, 69- *Mem:* Am Chem Soc; Sigma Xi. *Res:* Isolation and purification of enzymes and m-RNA; enzymatic synthesis of biologically active DNA. *Mailing Add:* Miles Labs Inc Elkhart IN 46515

KREISHMAN, GEORGE PAUL, b Nurnberg, Ger, Jan 28, 46; US citizen; m 72; c 2. BIOPHYSICAL CHEMISTRY. *Educ:* Univ Wis-Milwaukee, BS, 67; Calif Inst Technol, PhD(chem), 72. *Prof Exp:* Fel chem, Int Chem Nuclear Corp, 71-72; fel biophys, Univ Pittsburgh, 72-74; vis teaching asst chem, Mich Technol Univ, 74-75; asst prof, 75-81, ASSOC PROF CHEM, UNIV CINCINNATI, 81- *Mem:* Am Chem Soc; Biophys Soc. *Res:* Application of nuclear magnetic resonance spectroscopy and electrochemical techniques to the study of biologically important systems. *Mailing Add:* Dept of Chem Univ of Cincinnati Cincinnati OH 45221

KREISLE, LEONARDT F(ERDINAND), b Austin, Tex, Oct 22, 22. MECHANICAL ENGINEERING. *Educ:* Univ Tex, BS, 44, MS, 51; Cornell Univ, PhD(mach design, eng mech & servomech), 55. *Prof Exp:* Instr, Univ Tex, 42-43, instr eng drawing, 43-44; mech engr struct design, Robert E McKee, Gen Contractor, 44-45; instr mech eng, 45-49, asst prof, 49-53 & 55-56, assoc prof, 56-67, PROF MECH ENG, UNIV TEX, AUSTIN, 67-, COUNR, COL ENG, 66- *Concurrent Pos:* Res engr, Univ Tex, Austin, 51 & 52-53; vis instr, Cornell Univ, 53-55. *Mem:* AAAS; Am Soc Mech Engrs; Am Soc Eng Educ; Nat Soc Prof Engrs. *Res:* Transient analyses of linear and nonlinear dynamic systems; design of machine elements for dynamic and fatigue conditions; measurement engineering. *Mailing Add:* Dept of Mech Eng Univ of Tex Austin TX 78712

KREISLER, MICHAEL NORMAN, b Bronx, NY, Oct 30, 40; m 63; c 3. HIGH ENERGY PHYSICS. *Educ:* Princeton Univ, AB, 62; Stanford Univ, MS, 63, PhD(physics), 66. *Prof Exp:* From instr to asst prof physics, Joseph Henry Labs, Princeton Univ, 66-72; assoc prof, 72-76, grad dean res, 75-77, PROF PHYSICS, UNIV MASS, AMHERST, 76- *Concurrent Pos:* Sci Assoc, Europ Orgn Nuclear Res, Geneva, 78-79. *Mem:* Am Phys Soc; Sigma Xi. *Res:* Investigation of the strong interactions of neutrons, especially cross sections; study of the decays of multi-pionic resonances such as the eta meson; search for rare phenomena in weak interactions, kaon decays, beta decay of Lambda hyperon; search for tachyons; polarization in inclusive reactions; charm searches; macron accelerators. *Mailing Add:* Dept of Physics Univ of Mass GRC Tower C Amherst MA 01003

KREISMAN, NORMAN RICHARD, b Chicago, Ill, June 26, 43. NEUROPHYSIOLOGY. *Educ:* Ariz State Univ, BA, 65; Univ Mich, MS, 68; Med Col Pa, PhD(physiol), 71. *Prof Exp:* Instr, 71-73, asst prof, 73-79, ASSOC PROF PHYSIOL, SCH MED, TULANE UNIV, 79- *Mem:* Am Epilepsy Soc; Soc Neurosci; Am Heart Asn. *Res:* Electrophysiological and metabolic relationships in brain in physiological and pathophysiological states; epilepsy; anticonvulsant drug mechanisms. *Mailing Add:* Dept Physiol Sch Med Tulane Univ New Orleans LA 70112

KREITER, VICTOR PETER, JR, immunochemistry, deceased

KREITH, FRANK, b Vienna, Austria, Dec 15, 22; nat US; m 51; c 3. SOLAR ENGINEERING, THERMODYNAMICS. *Educ:* Univ Calif, BS, 45; Univ Calif, Los Angeles, MS, 49; Univ Paris, Dr Univ Paris(sci), 65. *Prof Exp:* Res engr, Jet Propulsion Lab, Calif Inst Technol, 45-49; asst prof mech eng, Univ Calif, 51-53; assoc prof, Lehigh Univ, 53-59; prof mech eng, 59-68, fac res assoc, Inst Behav Sci, 71-77, prof, 68-81, EMER PROF CHEM ENG, UNIV COLO, BOULDER, 81-; CHIEF, THERMAL CONVERSION, SOLAR ENERGY RES INST, 77- *Concurrent Pos:* Consult, Proj Squid, 50, Air Prod, Inc, 55-57, Metals Disintegrating Co, 57-69, Beech Aircraft Co, 59 & Nat Ctr Atmos Res, 67-69; mem staff, Nat Bur Standards, 61-63; Fulbright grants & vis lectr, France, Israel & Spain, 64-65; mem, Nat Adv Group Aeronaut Res & Develop-NATO, 64-65; fac res asst, Inst Arctic & Alpine Res, 65-71; NATO sr fel, 75; pres, Environ Consult Serv, 75-77. *Mem:* Fel Am Soc Mech Engrs; Am Inst Chem Engrs; Inst Soc Solar Energy. *Res:* Heat transfer; boundary layer theory; solar engineering; solar energy thermal conversion. *Mailing Add:* 1485 Sierra Dr Boulder CO 80302

KREITH, KURT, b Vienna, Austria, May 3, 32; US citizen; m 57. MATHEMATICS. *Educ:* Univ Calif, Berkeley, AB, 53, MA, 57, PhD(math), 60. *Prof Exp:* Asst prof math, Univ Calif, Davis, 60-63; phys sci officer, US Arms Control & Disarmament Agency, 63-65; assoc prof, 65-69, PROF MATH, UNIV CALIF, DAVIS, 69- *Mem:* Am Math Soc; Math Asn Am. *Res:* Differential equations and differential operators in Hilbert space. *Mailing Add:* Dept of Math Univ of Calif Davis CA 95616

KREITZBERG, CARL WILLIAM, b Missoula, Mont, Mar 25, 37; m 58; c 4. METEOROLOGY. *Educ:* Univ Wash, BS, 59, PhD(meteorol), 63. *Prof Exp:* Res physicist, Meteorol Lab, Air Force Cambridge Res Labs, 63-67; asst prof meteorol, Pa State Univ, 67-71; assoc prof, 71-76, PROF PHYSICS & ATMOSPHERIC SCI, DREXEL UNIV, 77- *Mem:* AAAS; Am Meteorol Soc; Sigma Xi. *Res:* Atmospheric structure, dynamics and prediction on the mesoscale, especially scale interactions due to clouds and boundary layer processes as determined from numerical simulation and field experiments. *Mailing Add:* Dept of Physics & Atmospher Sci Drexel Univ Philadelphia PA 19104

KREITZMAN, STEPHEN NEIL, b New York, NY, Sept 6, 39; m 62. BIOCHEMISTRY, NUTRITION. *Educ:* Hofstra Univ, BA, 61; Mass Inst Technol, PhD(nutrit biochem & metab), 69. *Prof Exp:* Assoc prof nutrit biochem, 69-77, ASSOC PROF ORAL BIOL, SCH DENT, EMORY UNIV, 69- *Mem:* Int Asn Dent Res. *Res:* Role of enzymes in the demineralization of the calcified tissues of bones and teeth; dental caries; relationship between nutrition and learning in school children. *Mailing Add:* Emory Univ Sch of Dent 1462 Clifton Rd NE Atlanta GA 30322

KREIZINGER, JEAN DOLLOFF, b Presque Isle, Maine, Oct 17, 31; div; c 3. GENETICS. *Educ:* Univ Maine, BS, 53; Cornell Univ, MS, 56, PhD(genetics), 58; Univ Conn, MBA, 81. *Prof Exp:* Asst prof biol, Danbury State Col, 65-67; NIH res fel human genetics, Univ Tex M D Anderson Hosp & Tumor Inst, 67-69, res assoc biol, Univ Tex, Houston, 69-71; assoc prof, 71-79, PROF BIOL, WESTERN CONN STATE COL, 79- *Concurrent Pos:* Vis prof, Cornell Univ, 81. *Mem:* Genetics Soc Am; Crop Sci Soc Am; Agron Soc Am. *Res:* Chemical mutagenesis; plant and human cytogenetics. *Mailing Add:* Dept of Biol Western Conn State Col Danbury CT 06810

KREJSA, RICHARD JOSEPH, b Cleveland, Ohio, Apr 4, 33; m 62; c 6. VERTEBRATE ZOOLOGY, RESOURCE MANAGEMENT. *Educ:* Mich State Univ, BS, 54; Univ Calif, Los Angeles, MA, 58; Univ BC, PhD(zool), 65. *Prof Exp:* Asst cur fishes, Scripps Inst Oceanog, Univ Calif, 58-59; instr gen zool & biol, Western Wash State Col, 64-65; vis asst prof zool, Univ Hawaii, 65-66; Nat Inst Dent Res trainee comp calcification, Col Physicians & Surgeons, Columbia Univ, 66-68; from asst prof to assoc prof, 68-78, PROF BIOL SCI, CALIF POLYTECH STATE UNIV, 78- *Concurrent Pos:* NSF stipend, Summer Inst Animal Behav, Utah State Univ, 65; co-chmn & bd dirs, San Luis Obispo Environ Ctr. *Honors & Awards:* Frederick H Stoye Award, Am Soc Ichthyologists & Herpetologists, 63. *Mem:* Am Soc Zoologists; Am Soc Ichthyologists & Herpetologists. *Res:* Experimental and comparative embryology of fish skin and scales; systematics and behavior of fresh water sculpins; comparative morphology of vertebrate skin. *Mailing Add:* Biol Sci Dept Calif Polytech State Univ San Luis Obispo CA 93407

KREKELER, CARL HERMAN, b Levenworth, Kans, Jan 12, 20; m 44; c 2. ZOOLOGY, ENTOMOLOGY. *Educ:* Concordia Sem, BA, 41; Univ Chicago, PhD(zool), 55. *Prof Exp:* Instr biol, Bethany Col, 42-44; PROF BIOL, VALPARAISO UNIV, 47- *Mem:* Ecol Soc Am; Soc Study Evolution; Soc Syst Zoologists; Nat Speleol Soc. Res; Speciation pattern in cave beetles; systematic entomology. *Mailing Add:* Dept of Biol Valparaiso Univ Valparaiso IN 46383

KREKORIAN, CHARLES O'NEIL, b Los Angeles, Calif, Apr 17, 41; m 67; c 2. ANIMAL BEHAVIOR. *Educ:* Calif State Col, Los Angeles, BA, 63, MA, 66; Univ Toronto, PhD(zool), 70. *Prof Exp:* Res assoc behav res, Am Inst Res, 64-66; from asst prof to assoc prof, 70-79, PROF ZOOL, SAN DIEGO STATE UNIV, 79- *Mem:* AAAS; Animal Behav Soc. *Res:* Ethology of fish and reptiles with emphasis on their agonistic and gamopractic behavior. *Mailing Add:* Dept of Zool 5402 College Ave San Diego State Univ San Diego CA 92182

KRELL, ROBERT DONALD, b Toledo, Ohio, Dec 2, 43; m 66; c 2. IMMUNOPHARMACOLOGY. *Educ:* Univ Toledo, BS, 66; Ohio State Univ, PhD(pharmacol), 72. *Prof Exp:* Fel, Sch Hyg & Pub Health, Johns Hopkins Univ, 72-73; sr scientist pharmacol, SmithKline Corp, 73-81; MGR, PULMONARY PHARMACOL SECT, STUART PHARMACEUT, 81- *Mem:* Soc Neurosci; AAAS; Am Acad Allergy; Am Soc Pharmacol & Exp Therapeut; Am Thoracic Soc. *Res:* Biochemical, pharmacological, physiological and immunological investigation into the mechanisms of asthma, immediate-type hypersensitivity reactions and chronic obstructive pulmonary diseases. *Mailing Add:* Stuart Pharmaceut Wilmington DE 19897

KREMBS, G(EORGE) M(ICHAEL), b Merrill, Wis, Sept 2, 34; m 57; c 5. ELECTRICAL ENGINEERING. *Educ:* Notre Dame Univ, BS, 56; Stanford Univ, PhD, 59. *Prof Exp:* Elec engr, Ampex Corp, 57-58; group supvr solid state mat, Philco Res Labs, 59-61, sect mgr solid state mat, Ford-Philco Appl Res Labs, 61-64; staff engr, Systs Develop Div, 64-65, mgr adv graphic technol, 65-68, mgr adv display systs, 68-70, mgr, Eng Dept Adv Systs Develop, 70-77, mgr display prod technol, 77-78, mgr adv display prod, 78-79, MGR ADV DISPLAY TECHNOL, IBM CORP, 79- *Concurrent Pos:* Guest lectr, IBM Systs Res Inst, New York, 80- *Mem:* Inst Elec & Electronics Engrs; Asn Comput Mach; Electrochem Soc; Soc Info Displays. *Res:* Computer displays; electronic scanning; graphic image processing; electro-optical systems; television engineering; broadband communications; electron tube devices; solid state device and materials technology; transistor circuit design. *Mailing Add:* IBM Corp PO Box 120 Kingston NY 12401

KREMENAK, CHARLES ROBERT, b Newell, Iowa, Apr 17, 31; m 54; c 4. MAXILLOFACIAL GROWTH & DEVELOPMENT. *Educ:* Univ Iowa, DDS, 55, MS, 61. *Prof Exp:* Instr pedodontics, 59-61, asst prof orthodont, 61-69, asst prof otolaryngol & maxillofacial surg, 66-69, assoc prof, 69-72, PROF ORTHODONT, OTOLARYNGOL & MAXILLOFACIAL SURG, UNIV IOWA, 72-, HEAD DIV, 69- *Concurrent Pos:* Prog writer & consult, Encycl Britannica Films, Inc, 61-62; Nat Inst Dent Res fel, Univ Iowa, 63-64, Nat Inst Dent Res investr cleft palate prog proj, 65-71, co-prin investr, 71- *Mem:* Int Asn Dent Res; AAAS; Am Cleft Palate Asn. *Res:* Maxillofacial growth, especially elucidation of maxillofacial growth control systems; cleft palate habilitation with emphasis on prevention of postsurgical growth aberration; role of the median nasal apparatus in midfacial growth and development. *Mailing Add:* Maxillofacial Growth Div Univ of Iowa Dent Res Lab Iowa City IA 52242

KREMENTZ, EDWARD THOMAS, b Newark, NJ, Apr 30, 17; m 46; c 5. SURGERY. *Educ:* Wesleyan Univ, AB, 39; Univ Rochester, MD, 43; Am Bd Surg, dipl, 52. *Prof Exp:* Asst surg, Yale Univ, 43, 44-48, asst resident surg path, 45-46, instr surg, 48-50, Childs fel med res, 48-49; from instr to assoc prof surg, 50-61, PROF SURG, TULANE UNIV, 61-, CANCER TEACHING COORDR, 53-, AM CANCER SOC PROF CLIN ONCOL, 77- *Concurrent Pos:* Fel, New Haven Hosp, 43, 44-45, asst resident, 46-48, assoc resident, 48-49, chief resident, 49-50; sr vis surgeon, Charity Hosp, La, 50-; surgeon, Touro Infirmary, 57-63, sr assoc, 63-; dir Cancer Res Clin, Tulane Univ, 62-75; consult surg, various hosps, 50- *Mem:* Am Cancer Soc; Soc Univ Surgeons; Soc Exp Biol & Med; Am Col Surgeons; Am Asn Cancer Res. *Res:* Cancer chemotherapy; experimental surgery; immunotherapy; author or coauthor of 221 publications. *Mailing Add:* 1430 Tulane Ave New Orleans LA 70112

KREMER, JAMES NEVIN, b Montclair, NJ, July 19, 45; m 69; c 2. BIOLOGICAL OCEANOGRAPHY, ECOLOGY. *Educ:* Princeton Univ, BA, 67; Univ RI, PhD(oceanog), 75. *Prof Exp:* Res asst marine ecol, Grad Sch Oceanog, Univ RI, 70-75; ASST PROF BIOL SCI, UNIV SOUTHERN CALIF, 76- *Concurrent Pos:* NATO fel, 75-76. *Mem:* Am Soc Limnol & Oceanog; Estuarine Res Fedn; Am Geophys Union; Sigma Xi. *Res:* Marine plankton ecology; systems ecology and computer simulation, especially physical processes and nutrient dynamics in plantonic systems. *Mailing Add:* Dept of Biol Sci Univ of Southern Calif Los Angeles CA 90007

KREMER, LEWIS A(LBERT), b Stanton, Nebr, Aug 13, 24; m 46; c 4. CHEMICAL ENGINEERING. *Educ:* Univ Nebr, BS, 48; Iowa State Univ, MS, 49. *Prof Exp:* Res investr indust & biochem dept, 49-56, res supvr, 56-68, tech supt, Cleveland Plant, 68-73, tech supt, East Chicago Plant, 73-80, STAFF ASSOC TRAINING, CHEM DEVELOP & PROD DEPT, E I DU PONT DE NEMOURS & CO, INC, 80- *Mem:* Am Inst Chem Engrs; Sigma Xi. *Res:* Process for organic and inorganic chemicals. *Mailing Add:* Chem & Pigments Dept E I du Pont de Nemours & Co Inc Wilmington DE 19898

KREMERS, HOWARD EARL, b Urbana, Ill, Sept 21, 17; m 40; c 3. INDUSTRIAL CHEMISTRY. *Educ:* Western Reserve Univ, AB, 39; Syracuse Univ, MS, 41; Univ Ill, PhD(chem), 44. *Prof Exp:* Chemist, Lindsay Light & Chem Co, 44-46, dir res, 46-51, dir res, Lindsay Chem Co, 51-56, secy, 56-58, vpres mkt develop, Lindsay Chem Div, Am Potash & Chem Corp, 59-60, dist mgr, 60-63, mgr mkt develop & tech serv, 63-69; mgr mkt res & develop, 69-70, mgr mkt serv, 70-71, DIR MKT SERV, KERR-MCGEE CHEM CORP, 72- *Mem:* Am Chem Soc. *Res:* Rare earths; thorium. *Mailing Add:* Kerr-McGee Chem Corp Kerr-McGee Ctr Oklahoma City OK 73125

KREMKAU, FREDERICK WILLIAM, b Mechanicsburg, Pa, Apr 30, 40; m 67; c 1. BIOACOUSTICS. *Educ:* Cornell Univ, BEE, 63; Univ Rochester, MS, 69, PhD(elec eng), 72. *Prof Exp:* Teaching asst elec eng, Univ Rochester, 67-69, res asst, 69-72; instr med, 72-74, RES ASST PROF MED, BOWMAN GRAY SCH MED, 74- *Concurrent Pos:* Consult, NSF, 74-75. *Mem:* Sigma Xi; Inst Elec & Electronic Engrs; AAAS; NY Acad Sci; Am Inst Ultrasound Med. *Res:* Biological effects of ultrasound; acoustic properties of biological material. *Mailing Add:* Dept of Med Bowman Gray Sch of Med Winston-Salem NC 27103

KREMP, GERHARD OTTO WILHELM, b Berlin, Ger, Nov 14, 13; nat US; m 40; c 3. GEOLOGY. *Educ:* Reichs Univ, Posen, Ger, Dr rer nat, 45. *Prof Exp:* Sci asst geol, Univ Gottingen, 45-47; geologist, Geol Surv, Nordhein-Westfalen, Ger, 48-54; sr res assoc geol, Pa State Univ, 55-59; geologist, US Geol Surv, 59-60; prof geosci, 60-79, EMER PROF, UNIV ARIZ, 80- *Concurrent Pos:* Palynological consult, Kremp Palynologic Data Retrieval Res Proj, Atlantic Richfield, Am Oil Co, Chevron, Exxon, Gulf, Mobil, Texaco, Union Oil Co & Geol Surv Can & Phillips Petrol Co, 68- *Honors & Awards:* Prof Gunnar Erdtman Int Medal for Palynol, Palynological Soc India, 70. *Mem:* Am Paleont Soc; Am Fern Soc; Ger Paleont Soc; Palynological Soc India; Am Asn Stratig Palynologists. *Res:* Palynology; paleobotany; coal geology; paleontology. *Mailing Add:* Dept of Geosciences Univ of Ariz Tucson AZ 85721

KREMPL, ERHARD, b Regensburg, Ger, Mar 5, 34; m 61; c 2. MECHANICS. *Educ:* Munich Tech Univ, Dipl Ing, 56, Dr Ing(mech of mat), 62. *Prof Exp:* Res proj engr, Munich Tech Univ, 56-64; mech of mat engr, Gen Elec Co, NY, 64-68; assoc prof mech, 68-75, PROF MECH & DIR, MECH MAT LAB, RENSSELAER POLYTECH INST, 75- *Concurrent Pos:* Consult, govt & indust. *Mem:* Fel Am Soc Mech Engrs; Am Soc Exp Stress Anal; Am Soc Testing & Mat; Soc Eng Sci; Am Acad Mech. *Res:* Mechanics of deformation and fracture behavior of metals and composites; creep, fatigue, fracture; applications to power plant such as steam and gas turbines and nuclear reactors; constitutive equation theory to describe time-dependent material behavior; inelastic analysis. *Mailing Add:* Dept Mech & Aeronaut Rensselaer Polytech Inst Troy NY 12181

KREMSER, THURMAN RODNEY, b Temple, Pa, Aug 29, 32; m 58; c 4. PHYSICS. *Educ:* Lehigh Univ, BS, 54, MS, 56; Temple Univ, PhD(physics), 68. *Prof Exp:* PROF PHYSICS & CHMN DEPT, ALBRIGHT COL, 56- *Mem:* Am Asn Physics Teachers. *Mailing Add:* Dept of Physics Albright Col PO Box 516 Reading PA 19603

KREMZNER, LEON T, b Poland, Sept 16, 24; US citizen; m 56; c 3. BIOCHEMISTRY. *Educ:* Seton Hall Univ, BS, 49; Rutgers Univ, MS, 52, PhD(biochem), 55. *Prof Exp:* Res chemist biochem, Gen Foods Corp, 49-51; asst, Bur Biol Res, Rutgers Univ, 52-55; proj leader, Res Ctr, Gen Foods Corp, 55-58; res assoc neurochem, Col Physicians & Surgeons, Columbia Univ, 59-63; neurochemist, Bur Res, NJ Neuropsychiat Inst, 63-67; asst prof, 67-73, ASSOC PROF NEUROCHEM, COL PHYSICIANS & SURGEONS, COLUMBIA UNIV, 73- *Mem:* NY Acad Sci; Am Soc Biol Chemists. *Res:* Enzyme chemistry; intermediate metabolism; cholinergic system; histamine and polyamine metabolism; neurochemistry. *Mailing Add:* Col of Physicians & Surgeons Columbia Univ New York NY 10032

KRENDEL, EZRA SIMON, b New York, NY, Mar 5, 25; m 50; c 3. OPERATIONS RESEARCH, HUMAN FACTORS ENGINEERING. *Educ:* Brooklyn Col, BA, 45; Mass Inst Technol, ScM, 47; Harvard Univ, AM, 49. *Hon Degrees:* MA, Univ Pa, 71. *Prof Exp:* From res engr to mgr engr, Psychol Lab, Labs Res & Develop, Franklin Inst, 49-63; tech dir opers res, Res Labs, 63-66; dir, Mgt Sci Ctr, 67-69; chmn bd adv, Ctr, 69-70; PROF OPERS RES, WHARTON SCH, UNIV PA, 66- *Concurrent Pos:* Consult to indust, res, non-profit, local & fed govt orgn, 67-; NATO vis guest lectr in univs & res insts, Greece, Turkey, Eng, Italy, France & Ger, 68-71. *Honors & Awards:* Louis E Levy Gold Medal, Franklin Inst, 60. *Mem:* Fel AAAS; fel Inst Elec & Electronics Engrs; fel Am Psychol Asn; fel Human Factors Soc; Opers Res Soc Am. *Res:* Human control dynamics, tracking, decision making and power output; command control and man-machine systems design; application of control engineering methods to political, social and cultural institutions. *Mailing Add:* Wharton Sch Univ of Pa Philadelphia PA 19174

KRENER, ARTHUR JAMES, b Brooklyn, NY, Oct 8, 42. APPLIED MATHEMATICS, SYSTEMS THEORY. *Educ:* Col of the Holy Cross, BS, 64; Univ Calif, Berkeley, MA, 67, PhD(math), 71. *Prof Exp:* Asst prof, 71-76, assoc prof, 76-80, PROF MATH, UNIV CALIF, DAVIS, 80- *Concurrent Pos:* Res fel eng & appl physics, Harvard Univ, 74-75; Fullbright Hays fel, Univ Rome, 79; vis sr res fel, Imperial Col, London, 80-81. *Mem:* Soc Indust & Appl Math; Am Math Soc; Inst Elec & Electronics Engrs. *Res:* Nonlinear systems theory; stochastic processes. *Mailing Add:* Dept of Math Univ of Calif Davis CA 95616

KRENITSKY, THOMAS ANTHONY, b Throop, Pa, Sept 13, 38. BIOCHEMISTRY. *Educ:* Scranton Univ, BS, 59; Cornell Univ, PhD(biochem), 63. *Prof Exp:* Fel biochem, Sloan-Kettering Inst Cancer Res, 63-64; res assoc, Yale Univ, 64-66; sr res biochemist, 66-68, HEAD ENZYMOLOGY, WELLCOME RES LABS, 68- *Concurrent Pos:* Adj assoc prof, Dept Biochem & Nutrit, Univ NC, Chapel Hill, 76- *Mem:* Am Chem Soc; Am Soc Biol Chemists. *Res:* Specificities, mechanisms and phylogenetic relationships of the enzymes involved in purine and pyrimidine metabolism; purine and pyrimidine hydroxylating enzymes, ribosyltransferases, phosphoribosyltransferases, nucleoside and nucleotide kinases, and nucleotide interconverting enzymes. *Mailing Add:* Wellcome Res Labs 3030 Cornwallis Rd Research Triangle Park NC 27709

KRENOS, JOHN ROBERT, b New Britain, Conn, Sept 4, 45. CHEMICAL PHYSICS. *Educ:* Univ Conn, BA, 67; Yale Univ, MS, 68, PhD(chem), 72. *Prof Exp:* Fel chem, Harvard Univ, 72-73; asst prof, 73-78, ASSOC PROF CHEM, DOUGLASS COL, RUTGERS UNIV, 78- *Mem:* Am Phys Soc; Am Chem Soc; AAAS. *Res:* Energy transfer in hyperthermal collisions and collisions involving electronically excited reactants; molecular beam chemiluminescence; model calculations of chemical reactions. *Mailing Add:* Dept of Chem Douglass Col Rutgers Univ New Brunswick NJ 08903

KRENZ, JERROLD H(ENRY), b Buffalo, NY, Apr 24, 34. ELECTRICAL ENGINEERING. *Educ:* Univ Buffalo, BS, 56; Stanford Univ, MS, 58, PhD(elec eng), 64. *Prof Exp:* Engr antennas, Lockheed Missile Systs, Lockheed Aircraft Corp, 56-57; engr microwave tubes, Gen Elec Microwave Lab, 58-61; asst prof elec eng, 63-77, dir eng honors prog, 69-73, assoc prof, 77-81, PROF ELEC ENG, UNIV COLO, BOULDER, 81- *Concurrent Pos:* Consult, Gen Elec Co, 62. *Mem:* Inst Elec & Electronics Engrs; Int Solar Energy Soc; AAAS. *Res:* Energy systems and policy; modeling; economic studies. *Mailing Add:* Dept of Elec Eng Univ of Colo Boulder CO 80309

KRENZELOK, EDWARD PAUL, b Ladysmith, Wis, Mar 11, 47. TOXICOLOGY, PHARMACY. *Educ:* Univ Wis, BS, 71; Univ Minn, PhD(pharm), 74. *Prof Exp:* asst prof, 74-81, ASSOC PROF PHARM, UNIV MINN, 81- *Concurrent Pos:* Dir toxicol, Hennepin Poison Ctr, Hennepin County Med Ctr, Minneapolis, 76- & mem fac toxicol, Dept Emergency Med, 78-; Minneapolis Community Health Serv grant poison prev prog children in day care ctrs, 77-; consult, Emergency Med Serv Div, Minn Dept Health, Minneapolis, 78 & Emergency Med Serv Div, Metrop Coun, St Paul, 78-;

chmn, Dept Prof Educ, Nat Poison Ctr Network, Pittsburgh, 78- *Mem:* Am Asn Poison Ctr; Am Soc Hosp Pharm; Am Acad Clin Toxicol; Nat Poison Ctr Network. *Res:* Poison education and prevention for preschoolers; study toxicity of acetaminophen, corrosives and caustics; drugs of abuse; nonprescription. *Mailing Add:* Hennepin Poison Ctr 701 Park Ave Minneapolis MN 55415

KREPINSKY, JIRI J, b Prague, Czech, July 15, 34; m 68; c 2. ORGANIC CHEMISTRY, BIOCHEMICAL GENETICS. *Educ:* Charles Univ, Prague, MSc, 57, Dr rer nat, 66; Czech Acad Sci, PhD(chem), 61. *Prof Exp:* Res asst org chem, Inst Org Chem & Biochem, Czech Acad Sci, 57-61, res assoc natural prod, 61-66 & 67-68; vis scientist, Inst Org Chem, Univ Milan, 66-67; fel synthesis natural prod, Univ NB, 68-70, lectr, 70-72; dir, Chem Res Lab of Simes, Milan, 72-75; sr res scientist, Dept Med Genetics, 76-80, ASSOC PROF, DEPT MED BIOPHYS & MED GENETICS, UNIV TORONTO, 80-; SR STAFF SCIENTIST, LUDWIG INST CANCER RES, TORONTO BR, 81- *Concurrent Pos:* Mem bot exped, Soviet Cent Asia, 61; consult, Ont Cancer Inst, 78- *Mem:* Am Chem Soc; The Chem Soc. *Res:* Determination of molecular mechanisms of mutagenesis and carcinogenesis by alkylating agents; determination of structures of biologically important compounds and their total synthesis such as oligosccharides of glycoproteins, and studies of their biological functions; roles of glycoproteins and proteoglycans, and their higher-order structures in malignancy; in particular colon cancer. *Mailing Add:* Dept of Med Genetics Med Sci Bldg Univ of Toronto Toronto ON M5S 1A1 Can

KREPS, DAVID PAUL, b Pottstown, Pa, Jan 13, 43; m 65; c 2. MICROBIOLOGY, IMMUNOLOGY. *Educ:* Manchester Col, 64; Ohio State Univ, MS, 68; Chicago Med Sch, PhD(microbiol), 76. *Prof Exp:* Teaching asst microbiol, Ohio State Univ, 65-67; ASSOC PROF BIOL, MANCHESTER COL, 67- *Concurrent Pos:* Res asst microbiol, Chicago Med Sch, 74-75; Res Corp res grant, 78-79; dir, NSF Int Soc Educ Planners grant, Manchester Col, 78-81. *Mem:* Sigma Xi; Am Soc Microbiol. *Res:* Immunological responses to salmonella typhimurium vaccines and cell fractions in inbred and outbred mice. *Mailing Add:* Dept of Biol Manchester Col North Manchester IN 46962

KRESCH, ALAN J, b New York, NY, June 25, 31. PHYSICAL CHEMISTRY, DATA PROCESSING. *Educ:* Cornell Univ, AB, 52; Rutgers Univ, PhD(solution kinetics), 61. *Prof Exp:* Sr res chemist, Nat Cash Register Co, Ohio, 60-73, STAFF RES ASSOC, APPLETON PAPERS INC, 73- *Mem:* AAAS; Am Chem Soc. *Res:* Solution kinetics of inorganic polymers; reversible photochemical reactions in solution; color technology; laboratory computer. *Mailing Add:* Appleton Papers Inc PO Box 359 Appleton WI 54912

KRESGE, ALEXANDER JERRY, b Wilkes-Barre, Pa, July 17, 26; m 50, 63; c 3. PHYSICAL ORGANIC CHEMISTRY. *Educ:* Cornell Univ, BA, 49; Univ Ill, PhD(chem), 53. *Prof Exp:* Asst, Univ Ill, 49-51; Fulbright scholar, Univ Col, Univ London, 53-54; res assoc, Purdue Univ, 54-55 & Mass Inst Technol, 55-57; assoc chemist, Brookhaven Nat Lab, 57-60; from asst prof to prof chem, Ill Inst Technol, 60-74; chmn chem group, 74-78, PROF CHEM, SCARBOROUGH COL, UNIV TORONTO, 74- *Concurrent Pos:* Guggenheim fel, 64; NSF sr fel, 64-65; vis lectr, Bedford Col, London, 64-65; vis prof, Oxford Univ, 65; guest of Inst, Mass Inst Technol, 65; vis prof, Univ Toronto, 70-71, Univ Mich, 79, Univ Lausanne, 81 & Tech Univ Denmark, 82; vis scientist, Fritz Haber Inst, 81. *Mem:* Am Chem Soc; The Chem Soc. *Res:* Reaction mechanisms; isotope effects; acid-base catalysis; kinetics. *Mailing Add:* Dept of Chem Scarborough Col Univ of Toronto West Hill ON M1C 1A4 Can

KRESGE, EDWARD NATHAN, b Noxen, Pa, Aug 14, 35; m 63. POLYMER CHEMISTRY. *Educ:* Univ Tampa, BS, 57; Univ Fla, PhD(chem), 61. *Prof Exp:* Res chemist, 61-63, proj leader elastomers, 63-75; HEAD ELASTOMERS EXPLOR RES, ELASTOMERS TECHNOL DIV, EXXON CHEM CO, 75-, CHIEF POLYMER SCIENTIST, 78- *Mem:* AAAS; Am Chem Soc. *Res:* Elastomer, morphology, polymer rheology and physics. *Mailing Add:* Exxon Chem Co Elastomers Tech Div Linden NJ 07036

KRESHECK, GORDON C, b North Tonawanda, NY, Sept 3, 33; m 61; c 3. PHYSICAL BIOCHEMISTRY. *Educ:* Ohio State Univ, BS, 55, MS, 59, PhD(dairy technol), 61. *Prof Exp:* Res asst biochem, Nobel Med Inst, Stockholm, Sweden, 62-63; vis scientist, Procter & Gamble Co, 63; NIH res fel chem, Cornell Univ, 63-65; asst prof, 65-68, assoc prof, 68-78, PROF CHEM, NORTHERN ILL UNIV, 78-, DIR, CTR BIOCHEM & BIOPHYS STUDIES, 75- *Concurrent Pos:* Assoc ed, Bull Thermodynamics & Thermochem, 71-76. *Mem:* AAAS; Am Chem Soc; Biophys Soc; Am Soc Biol Chemists. *Res:* Protein chemistry; solution calorimetry; surfactants. *Mailing Add:* Dept of Chem Northern Ill Univ De Kalb IL 60115

KRESHOVER, SEYMOUR J, b New York, NY, June 22, 12; m 46; c 4. DENTAL PATHOLOGY. *Educ:* NY Univ, BA, 34, MD, 49; Univ Pa, DDS, 38; Yale Univ, PhD(clin med, path), 42; Am Bd Oral Med, dipl. *Hon Degrees:* DSc, State Univ NY Buffalo, 61, Univ Pa, 67 & Boston Univ, 69; DOdont, Gothenburg Univ, 73; DSc, Univ Mich, 75. *Prof Exp:* Asst instr, Sch Med, Univ Ill, 38-39; clin asst dent surg, Yale Univ, 42-43; teaching fel histoanat, NY Univ, 46-47, instr, 47; prof oral path & dir dent res, Grad & Postgrad Study, Med Col Va, 49-56; assoc dir, Nat Inst Dent Res, 46-66, dir, 66-75; vis prof oral biol, State Univ NY, Buffalo, 75-80. *Concurrent Pos:* Assoc trustee, Bd Med Educ & Res, Univ Pa, 56-66; chmn comn dent res, Int Dent Fedn, 61-67. *Honors & Awards:* USPHS Meritorious Serv Medal, 65; Pierre Fouchard Medal, 72; Callahan Medal, 72; USPHS Distinguished Service Medal, 75. *Mem:* Am Dent Asn; Am Pub Health Asn; Am Acad Oral Path; Int Asn Dental Res (pres, 62). *Res:* Dental histology and embryology; dental pathology; prenatal factors in congenital defects. *Mailing Add:* 838 John Anderson Dr Ormond Beach FL 32074

KRESPAN, CARL GEORGE, b Erie, Pa, Aug 10, 26; m 49; c 3. ORGANIC CHEMISTRY. *Educ:* Univ Rochester, BS, 48; Univ Minn, PhD(org chem), 52. *Prof Exp:* Res chemist, 52-60, res supvr org chem, 60-70, RES SCIENTIST, CENT RES DEPT, E I DU PONT DE NEMOURS & CO, 70- *Mem:* Am Chem Soc. *Res:* Organic fluorine chemistry; free radical, sulphur, cyanocarbon and macroheterocycle chemistry. *Mailing Add:* E I du Pont de Nemours & Co Ctr Res Develop Dept Exp Sta Wilmington DE 19898

KRESS, BERNARD HIRAM, b New York, NY, Apr 18, 17; m; c 3. ORGANIC CHEMISTRY. *Educ:* City Col New York, BS, 38; Columbia Univ, MA, 40, PhD(org chem), 47. *Prof Exp:* Asst biochem, Col Physicians & Surgeons, Columbia Univ, 38-40; jr biochemist neuropsychiat res unit, US Vet Admin, Long Island, 41-42; res chemist, Fed Telecommun Labs, NJ, 42-46 & Celanese Corp Am, 47-48; sr res chemist & group leader, Plaskon Div, Libbey-Owens-Ford Glass Co, 49-53; dir org res, Quaker Chem Prod Co, 53-64; mgr polymer res & develop, 64-70, SR SCIENTIST, QUAKER CHEM CORP, 70- *Mem:* Am Chem Soc; Am Asn Textile Chem & Colorists; Am Tech Asn Pulp & Paper Indust; Am Soc Lubrication Eng; fel Am Inst Chem. *Res:* High polymers; textile, metal and paper chemicals. *Mailing Add:* 4018 Kottler Dr Lafayette Hill PA 19444

KRESS, DONNIE DUANE, b American Falls, Idaho, Mar 17, 42; m 70; c 2. GENETICS, ANIMAL BREEDING. *Educ:* Univ Idaho, BS, 64; Univ Wis, MS, 66, PhD(genetics & animal sci), 69. *Prof Exp:* NIH fel quant genetics, Univ Minn, 69-70; asst & assoc prof, 70-80, PROF GENETICS & ANIMAL BREEDING, MONT STATE UNIV, 80- *Mem:* Am Soc Animal Sci; Sigma Xi. *Res:* Quantitative genetics and animal breeding; selection, genetic by environment interaction; maternal ability and beef sire evaluation. *Mailing Add:* Dept of Animal & Range Sci Mont State Univ Bozeman MT 59717

KRESS, LANCE WHITAKER, b Camp Lejeune, NC, Sept 2, 45; m 69; c 3. PHYTOPATHOLOGY. *Educ:* Pa State Univ, BS, 68, MS, 72; Va Polytech Inst & State Univ, PhD(plant path), 78. *Prof Exp:* Jr res aide, Pa State Univ, 72-73; res assoc, Va Polytech Inst & State Univ, 75-80; ASST ECOLOGIST, ARGONNE NAT LAB, 80- *Mem:* Am Phytopath Soc; Air Pollution Control Asn; Sigma Xi. *Res:* Evaluating the impacts of low concentrations of air pollutants and pollutant combinations on the growth and marketable yield of important agricultural field crops and forest tree species. *Mailing Add:* RER 203 Argonne Nat Lab 9700 S Cass Ave Argonne IL 60439

KRESS, LAWRENCE FRANCIS, b Milwaukee, Wis, Oct 5, 36; m 59; c 4. BIOCHEMISTRY. *Educ:* Marquette Univ, BS, 59, MS, 61, PhD(physiol), 64. *Prof Exp:* NSF fel biochem, Med Sch, Dartmouth Univ, 64-66; Am Heart Asn adv res fel, 66-68, sr res scientist, 68-78, res scientist IV, 78-80, RES CANCER SCIENTIST V, ROSWELL PARK MEM INST, 80- *Mem:* Am Soc Biol Chemists; Int Soc Toxinol. *Res:* Enzymology; proteolytic enzymes and their inhibitors; interactions between snake venom proteinases and plasma proteinase inhibitors. *Mailing Add:* Roswell Park Mem Inst 666 Elm St Buffalo NY 14263

KRESS, THOMAS JOSEPH, b Indianapolis, Ind, Oct 31, 40; m 65; c 4. ORGANIC CHEMISTRY. *Educ:* Xavier Univ Ohio, BS, 62, MS, 64; Ohio Univ, PhD(org chem), 67. *Prof Exp:* Res assoc, Ohio Univ, 67-68; sr org chemist, 68-74, res scientist, 74-80, RES ASSOC, ELI LILLY & CO, 80- *Mem:* Int Soc Heterocycle Chem; Am Chem Soc; Royal Soc Chem. *Res:* The synthesis and reactions of nitrogen heterocycles. *Mailing Add:* Res Chem Bldg 45 Eli Lilly & Co Indianapolis IN 46204

KRESS, THOMAS SYLVESTER, b Kingsport, Tenn, Dec 5, 33; m 56; c 3. NUCLEAR ENGINEERING, AEROSOL SCIENCE. *Educ:* Univ Tenn, BS, 56, MS, 65, PhD(eng sci), 71. *Prof Exp:* Engr aircraft nuclear propulsion, Pratt & Whitney Aircraft, 56-59; engr reactor safety, 59-76, prog mgr & group leader advan reactor syst, Nuclear Div, 76-80, MGR, NUCLEAR RES COUN, UNION CARBIDE CORP, 80- *Mem:* AAAS; Am Soc Mech Engrs; Am Nuclear Soc; Nat Soc Prof Engrs. *Res:* Thermal sciences, heat ransfer, fluid transfer, fluid mechanics and thermodynamics; nuclear safety; aerosol science. *Mailing Add:* Oak Ridge Nat Lab PO Box Y Bldg 9108 Oak Ridge TN 37830

KRESSE, JEROME THOMAS, b Buffalo, NY, Dec 29, 31; m 62; c 5. ORGANIC CHEMISTRY. *Educ:* Mich State Univ, BS, 58; Univ Fla, PhD(org chem), 65. *Prof Exp:* Asst prof chem, Muskingum Col, 65-66; asst prof, 66-69, assoc prof chem & chmn dept chem & physics, 69-74, chmn, Div Math & Natural Sci, 74-78, PROF CHEM, D'YOUVILLE COL, 74- *Mem:* AAAS; Am Asn Univ Prof; Am Chem Soc. *Res:* Studies of factors influencing the stereochemistry of the Wittig reaction; synthesis of amino acid antagonists. *Mailing Add:* Dept of Chem & Physics D'Youville Col 320 Porter Ave Buffalo NY 14201

KRESSEL, HENRY, b Vienna, Austria, Jan 24, 34; US citizen; m 56; c 2. SOLID STATE PHYSICS. *Educ:* Yeshiva Col, BA, 55; Harvard Univ, MS, 56; Univ Pa, MBA, 59, PhD(metall), 65. *Prof Exp:* Engr, Semiconductor Div, Radio Corp Am, 59-61, group head microwave develop, 61-63, group device physics, Tech Progs Lab, 65-66, mem tech staff, RCA Labs, 67-69, group head, 69-77, lab dir, 77-79, STAFF VPRES, RCA LABS, 79- *Honors & Awards:* Achievement Award, RCA Corp, 62, 68 & 69; David Sarnoff Medal, 73. *Mem:* Fel Am Phys Soc; fel Inst Elec & Electronics Engrs. *Res:* New semiconductor devices, particularly in area of microwaves and optical devices; lasers; properties of defects in semiconductors. *Mailing Add:* RCA Labs Princeton NJ 08540

KRESTA, JIRI ERIK, b Kosice, Czech, Apr 19, 34. POLYMER CHEMISTRY, CHEMICAL ENGINEERING. *Educ:* Inst Chem Technol, Prague, MChE, 57; Tech Univ Prague, MS, 64; Czech Acad Sci, PhD(polymer sci), 67. *Prof Exp:* Res assoc, Res Inst Synthetic Rubber, Gottwaldov, Czech, 57-62; res scientist, Res Inst Macromolecular Chem, Brno, 62-69; res assoc, Dept Chem, Wayne State Univ, 69-71; RES PROF POLYMER SCI, DEPT CHEM & CHEM ENG, POLYMER INST, UNIV DETROIT, 71- *Mem:* Am Chem Soc; Soc Plastics Engrs; Czech Chem Soc. *Res:* Reaction kinetics and catalysis of polyreactions; characterization, flammability degradation and stabilization of polymers, morphological and viscoelastic studies of polymers; research in polyurethanes; cellular materials, polyolefins; elastomers; thermostable polymers; plastics failure. *Mailing Add:* Polymer Inst Univ Detroit 4001 W McNichols Detroit MI 48221

KRESTENSEN, ELROY R, b New York, NY, Sept 6, 21; m 48; c 1. ENTOMOLOGY. *Educ:* Univ Fla, BSA, 49, MS, 51; Univ Md, PhD(entom), 62. *Prof Exp:* Asst entom, Univ Fla, 49-51; interim instr, 51-52; entomologist, Fla Bd Health, 52-54; from instr to asst prof, 55-67, ASSOC PROF ENTOM, SHARPSBURG RES CTR, UNIV MD, 67- *Mem:* Entom Soc Am. *Res:* Insect pests and control methods for fruit. *Mailing Add:* Univ Md Sharpsburg Res Ctr Keedysville MD 21756

KRETCHMAN, DALE WARREN, b Berrien Springs, Mich, Sept 7, 31; m 52; c 4. HORTICULTURE. *Educ:* Mich State Univ, BS, 53, MS, 54, PhD(hort), 58. *Prof Exp:* Asst horticulturist, Citrus Exp Sta, Univ Fla, 58-63; assoc prof, 63-67, PROF HORT, OHIO AGR RES & DEVELOP CTR, OHIO STATE UNIV, 67- *Mem:* Am Soc Hort Sci. *Res:* Culture and physiology of vegetable crops. *Mailing Add:* Dept of Hort Ohio Agr Res & Develop Ctr Wooster OH 44691

KRETCHMAR, ARTHUR LOCKWOOD, b London, Eng, July 20, 21; nat US; m 43; c 4. BIOCHEMISTRY. *Educ:* Harvard Univ, BS, 43; Wayne State Univ, MD, 47; Univ Mich, MS, 50, PhD, 58. *Prof Exp:* Intern surg, Univ Hosp, Univ Mich, 47-48; res assoc, Univ, 50-52; chief scientist, Med Div, Oak Ridge Inst Nuclear Studies, 54-66; prof, Col Med, 64-66, assoc prof res, 66-69, prof res mem res ctr, 69-76, PROF, DEPT FAMILY PRACT, UNIV TENN, 76- *Mem:* AAAS; Int Epidemiol Asn; Am Soc Exp Path. *Mailing Add:* Dept of Family Pract 1924 Alcoa Hwy Knoxville TN 37920

KRETCHMER, NORMAN, b New York, NY, Jan 20, 23; m 42; c 3. NUTRITIONAL SCIENCE, PEDIATRICS & OBSTETRICS. *Educ:* Cornell Univ, BS, 44; Univ Minn, MS, 45, PhD(physiol chem), 47; State Univ NY, MD, 52; Am Bd Pediat, dipl. *Prof Exp:* Asst physiol chem, Univ Minn, 44-45, jr scientist, 45-47; asst prof biochem & path, Col Med, Univ Vt, 47-48; res assoc path, Long Island Col Med, State Univ NY, 48-52; Commonwealth fel med & intern, Montefiore Hosp, 52-53; asst prof biochem & pediat, Med Col, Cornell Univ, 53-56; from asst prof to assoc prof pediat, 56-59; from prof to Harold K Faber prof, Sch Med, Stanford Univ, 59-74, exec head dept, 56-59; dir, Nat Inst Child Health & Human Develop, 74-81; PROF NUTRIT, UNIV CALIF, BERKELEY, 81-; PROF OBSTET & PEDIAT, UNIV CALIF, SAN FRANCISCO, 81- *Concurrent Pos:* Asst resident, NY Hosp, 53-54, asst pediatrician outpatients, 54-55, pediatrician, 54-55, asst attend pediatrician, 55-59; Commonwealth Fund traveling fel, Univ Paris & St Mary's Hosp, London, 57 & Atomic Energy Lab, Saclay, Paris, 65-66; pediatrician-in-chief, Stanford Hosp, 59-69; spec consult, WHO, 67-69; mem bd sci coun, Nat Inst Child Health & Human Develop, 69-71; chmn prog human biol, Stanford Univ, 69-72; vir prof, Univ Lagos, 70; pres, Int Orgn Study Human Develop, 70-; Guggenheim fel, 73-74; consult lectr, Nat Naval Med Ctr, 74- *Honors & Awards:* Johnson Award, Am Acad Pediat, 58, Borden Award, 69. *Mem:* Inst Med-Nat Acad Sci; AAAS; Am Pediat Soc; Am Soc Biol Chemists; Am Soc Clin Nutrit. *Res:* Perinatology; human development; developmental biology; maternal and child health; biochemical development of the intestine; lactose intolerance; pyrimidine biosynthesis; enzymatic adaptations to nutrients; diabetes mellitus. *Mailing Add:* Dept Nutrit Sci 309 Morgan Hall Univ Calif Berkeley CA 94720

KRETCHMER, RICHARD ALLAN, b Tracy, Minn, Dec 12, 40; m 67. SYNTHETIC ORGANIC CHEMISTRY. *Educ:* Univ Minn, BChem, 62; Univ Wis, PhD(org chem), 66; Chicago-Kent Col Law, JD, 75. *Prof Exp:* USPHS fel chem, Columbia Univ, 66-68; from asst prof to assoc prof chem, Ill Inst Technol, 68-76; PATENT ATTORNEY, PATENTS & LICENSING DEPT, STANDARD OIL CO, IND, 76- *Concurrent Pos:* Law firm assoc, 75- *Mem:* Am Chem Soc. *Res:* Organic chemistry; structure and synthesis; chemistry of natural products; the organic chemistry of mercury. *Mailing Add:* 270 Walker Ave Clarendon Hills IL 60514

KRETSCHMER, ALBERT EMIL, JR, b New York, NY, Nov 15, 25; m 49; c 3. TROPICAL AGROSTOLOGY. *Educ:* Univ Fla, BA, Al; Rutgers Univ, PhD(soil chem), 52. *Prof Exp:* Soil chemist, Everglades Exp Sta, 52-55, AGRONOMIST, AGR RES CTR, UNIV FLA, 55- *Concurrent Pos:* Consult soil chemist, Univ Fla-AID Prog, Costa Rica, 58-60, chief, 69-70; pvt consult tropical pastures, overseas. *Mem:* Am Soc Agron; Sigma Xi; Am Grasslands Coun. *Res:* Evaluation of tropical pasture legumes and grasses; micro and macro nutrient requirements of forages; management of grass-legume mixtures. *Mailing Add:* Agr Res Ctr PO Box 248 Univ of Fla Ft Pierce FL 33454

KRETSINGER, ROBERT, b Denver, Colo, Mar 20, 37. MOLECULAR BIOLOGY. *Educ:* Univ Colo, AB, 58; Mass Inst Technol, PhD(biophys), 64. *Prof Exp:* Helen Hay Whitney Found fel, Med Res Coun Lab Molecular Biol, Cambridge Univ, Eng, 64-65; fel, Int Molecular Biol, Geneva, Switz, 66-67; assoc prof, 67-75, PROF BIOL, UNIV VA, 75-, CHMN DEPT, 79- *Mem:* Am Crystallog Asn. *Res:* Protein structure determination by x-ray crystallography; function and evolution of calcium modulated proteins. *Mailing Add:* Dept Biol Univ Va Charlottesville VA 22901

KRETZ, RALPH, Can citizen. PETROLOGY, GEOCHEMISTRY. *Educ:* Univ Chicago, PhD(geol), 58. *Prof Exp:* Geologist, Geol Surv Can, 58-61; sr lectr geol, Univ Queensland, 61-65; assoc prof, 67-71, PROF GEOL, UNIV OTTAWA, 71- *Mem:* Geochem Soc; Mineral Asn Can. *Res:* Chemical composition and texture of metamorphic rocks. *Mailing Add:* Dept Geol Univ Ottawa Ottawa ON K1N 6N5 Can

KRETZMER, ERNEST R(UDOLF), b Ger, Dec 24, 24; nat US; m 54. ELECTRONICS. *Educ:* Worcester Polytech Inst, BS, 45; Mass Inst Technol, SM, 46, ScD(elec eng), 49. Mass Inst Technol, 45-49, res assoc, 49; mem tech Mass Inst Technol, 45-49, res assoc, 49; mem tech staff, 49-, dept head, 65-70, DIR, BELL TEL LABS, INC, 70- *Mem:* Fel Inst Elec & Electronics Engrs. *Res:* Pulse modulation; phase measurement; redundancy in television; coded facsimile; transistor applications; electronic telephone system development; data communication. *Mailing Add:* 13 Blue Hills Dr Holmdel NJ 07733

KREUTEL, RANDALL WILLIAM, JR, b Norwood, Mass, May 3, 34. ELECTRICAL ENGINEERING, ELECTROPHYSICS. *Educ:* Northeastern Univ, BS, 61, MS, 64; George Washington Univ, DSc(electrophys), 78. *Prof Exp:* Res eng antennas, Sylvania Electron Syst, 57-66; mem tech staff, 66-68, mgr, Antennas Dept, 68-77, sr staff scientist res & develop, 77-79, dir optical commun, 79-81, DIR, DIV DEVELOP ENG, COMSAT LABS, COMMUNICATIONS SATELLITE CORP, 81- *Mem:* Inst Elec & Electronics Engrs; Int Sci Radio Union; Am Inst Aeronaut & Astronaut. *Res:* Antennas, microwave circuits, fiber optics and communications. *Mailing Add:* COMSAT Labs 22300 Comsat Dr Clarksburg MD 20734

KREUTNER, WILLIAM, b Brooklyn, NY, Feb 20, 41; m 63; c 2. PHARMACOLOGY, BIOCHEMISTRY. *Educ:* Brooklyn Col, BS, 62; Univ Minn, PhD(pharmacol), 67. *Prof Exp:* PRIN SCIENTIST, SCHERING CORP, 67- *Concurrent Pos:* Adj asst prof biochem, Fairleigh Dickinson Univ, 72. *Mem:* Am Asn Clin Immunol & Allergy; Am Diabetes Asn; NY Acad Sci; Am Soc Pharmacol Exp Ther. *Res:* Interrelationships between lipid, protein, and carbohydrate metabolism as it relates to diabetes mellitus allergy, inflammation; prostaglandins; leukotrienes; cyclic nucleotides. *Mailing Add:* Schering Corp 60 Orange St Bloomfield NJ 07003

KREUTZER, RICHARD D, b Evergreen Park, Ill, June 23, 36. CYTOGENETICS, BIOCHEMISTRY OF LEISHMANIA. *Educ:* Univ Ill, BS, 63, MS, 65, PhD(zool), 68. *Prof Exp:* Instr zool, Univ Ill, Urbana, 67-69; asst prof, 69-74, assoc prof, 74-79, PROF BIOL, YOUNGSTOWN STATE UNIV, 79- *Concurrent Pos:* Chief vector, Biol Sect, Gorgas Mem Lab, 77-79. *Mem:* Am Soc Zoologists; Am Mosquito Control Asn; Genetics Soc Am; Entom Soc Am; Am Soc Trop Med Hyg. *Res:* Genetics; invertebrates; parasitology; entomology; cytogenetics and evolution of anophelines; isozyme studies on insects and protozoan parasites. *Mailing Add:* Dept of Biol Youngstown State Univ Youngstown OH 44555

KREUTZER, WILLIAM ALEXANDER, b Gunnison, Colo, Apr 13, 08; m 39; c 3. PLANT PATHOLOGY. *Educ:* Colo Agr Col, BS, 30, MS, 32; Iowa State Col, PhD(plant path), 39. *Prof Exp:* From instr to asst prof bot, Colo Agr Col, 31-34; asst bot & plant path, Iowa State Col, 34-36; from asst prof to prof, Colo State Col, 36-46; plant pathologist, Agr Lab, Shell Develop Co, 46-62; prof, 62-74, EMER PROF BOT & PLANT PATH, COLO STATE UNIV, 74- *Mem:* Fel AAAS; Am Phytopath Soc; Mycol Soc; NY Acad Sci. *Res:* Soil fungicides and soil microecology. *Mailing Add:* 868 Gregory Rd Ft Collins CO 80524

KREUZ, JOHN ANTHONY, b Buffalo, NY, Sept 18, 33; m 57; c 6. ORGANIC POLYMER CHEMISTRY. *Educ:* St Bonaventure Univ, BS, 55; Univ Notre Dame, PhD(org chem), 60. *Prof Exp:* Res chemist, 59-64, staff scientist, 65-77, RES ASSOC, E I DU PONT DE NEMOURS & CO, INC, 77- *Mem:* Am Chem Soc. *Res:* Alkaline decomposition of aliphatic disulfides; addition and condensation polymerizations; polyimides and other high temperature polymers; organic semiconductors; polymer surface chemistry, polyimide and other adhesives. *Mailing Add:* Circleville Res Lab PPD E I du Pont de Nemours & Co Inc Circleville OH 43113

KREUZER, JAMES LEON, b Syracuse, NY, Feb 28, 30; m 51; c 2. ORGANIC CHEMISTRY. *Educ:* Hartwick Col, BS, 51; Rensselaer Polytech Inst, PhD(chem), 59. *Prof Exp:* Res chemist, K-B Prod Corp, NY, 51-52; from asst prof to assoc prof chem, 58-68, PROF CHEM, SIENA COL, 68- *Concurrent Pos:* Vis prof, Rensselaer Polytech Inst, 60-63; NY State Health Dept spec grant, NY State Health Dept Labs, 61; spec instr, Hudson Valley Community Col, 64-69, prof, 70- *Mem:* Am Chem Soc. *Res:* Synthetic organic chemistry; hydrazines; explosives; reduction of alkoxy benzenes. *Mailing Add:* Dept of Chem Siena Col Loudonville NY 12211

KREUZER, LLOYD BARTON, b Los Angeles, Calif, Aug 26, 40. MICROCOMPUTERS, MICROCOMPUTER OPERATING SYSTEMS. *Educ:* Swarthmore Col, BA, 62; Princeton Univ, PhD(physics), 66. *Prof Exp:* Mem tech staff physics, Bell Tel Labs, NJ, 66-73; vpres, Diax Corp, Calif, 73-74; mem tech staff, Hewlett-Packard Lab, 74-78; vpres eng, 78-81, VPRES ADV DEVELOP, DYNABYTE INC, 81- *Mem:* Am Phys Soc; Inst Elec & Electronics Engrs. *Res:* Nonlinear optics; optical parametric effects; experimental gravitation; air pollution detection by IR laser; optoacoustic spectroscopy; microcomputers and microcomputer software. *Mailing Add:* 2156 Sand Hill Rd Menlo Park CA 94025

KREVANS, JULIUS RICHARD, b New York, NY, May 1, 24; m 50; c 4. MEDICINE. *Educ:* NY Univ, BS, 44, MD, 46. *Prof Exp:* Intern, Queens Gen Hosp, 46-47; resident path, Flushing Hosp, 47; fel hemat, Johns Hopkins Univ Hosp, 50-51; asst resident, 51-52, resident, 52-53, dir blood bank, 53-63, from assoc prof to prof med, Sch Med, 60-71, dean acad affairs, 69-71; PROF MED & DEAN SCH MED, UNIV CALIF, SAN FRANCISCO, 71- *Concurrent Pos:* Vis hematologist, Baltimore City Hosps, 53-63, physician-in-chief, 63-; asst prof, Johns Hopkins Univ, 55-60. *Mem:* Am Soc Hemat; assoc Am Col Physicians; Am Fedn Clin Res; Int Soc Hemat. *Res:* Hematology. *Mailing Add:* Sch of Med Univ of Calif San Francisco CA 94143

KREWER, SEMYON E, b Moscow, Russia, Mar 10, 15; nat US; m 39; c 1. PHYSICS. *Educ:* Tech Hochsch Berlin, dipl, 37. *Prof Exp:* Asst to Prof Fermi & Szilard, Columbia Univ, 38-40; dir res, Photovolt Corp, 40-65, vpres, 59-65; OWNER, KREWER RES LABS, 65- *Concurrent Pos:* Consult energy, US Senator Moynihan, NY, 77- *Mem:* Optical Soc Am; Arthritis Found; Am Congress Rehab Med; NY Acad Sci. *Res:* Design of scientific instruments for industry and medical research; pH meters and electrodes; supersensitive photometers; densitometers; colorimeters; fluorescence meters; rheumatoid hand gymnasium; design of simple test for tightness of intrinsic hand muscles. *Mailing Add:* Krewer Res Labs PO Box 111 Point Lookout NY 11569

KREY, LEWIS CHARLES, b New York, NY, Oct 1, 44; m 67. NEUROENDOCRINOLOGY. *Educ:* Brown Univ, AB, 66; Duke Univ, PhD(physiol), 71. *Prof Exp:* Res assoc & fel physiol, Univ Pittsburgh Sch Med, 71-73, asst prof, 73-75; asst prof physiol psychol, 75-81, ASSOC PROF NEUROENDOCRINOL, ROCKEFELLER UNIV, 81- *Concurrent Pos:* Irma T Hirschl Found fel, 80- *Mem:* Endocrine Soc; Sigma Xi. *Res:* Role of hypothalamic and hypophyseal steroid receptors in the neuroendocrine regulation of anterior pituitary gland function; in particular, the control of gonadotropin release in several mammalian species. *Mailing Add:* Rockefeller Univ 1230 York Ave New York NY 10021

KREY, PHILIP W, b Brooklyn, NY, June 18, 27; m 52; c 5. RADIOCHEMISTRY, ENVIRONMENTAL SCIENCE. *Educ:* St Francis Col, BS, 48; Duquesne Univ, MS, 50. *Prof Exp:* Chemist, Nuclear Defense Lab, 50-55, chief radio chem div, 55-57; mgr radiochem div, Isotopes, Inc, 57-64; dir radioactivity in surface air prog, 65-67, dir stratospheric radioactivity prog, Health & Safety Lab, 67-75, environ scientist, US Energy Res & Develop Admin & US Dept Energy, 75-80, DIR, ANAL CHEM DIV, ENVIRON MEASUREMENTS LAB, US DEPT ENERGY, 80- *Concurrent Pos:* Mem task group on C-14 waste disposal, Nat Coun Radiation Protection & Measurements, 75- *Mem:* AAAS; NY Acad Sci. *Res:* Behavior and transport of artificial and natural radioactivity; trace metal and gaseous pollutants in the environment, including soil, troposphere and stratosphere from both local and global sources of contamination. *Mailing Add:* Environ Measurements Lab US Dept of Energy New York NY 10014

KREY, PHOEBE REGINA, b Ambridge, Pa; m 60; c 3. RHEUMATOLOGY. *Educ:* Northeastern Univ, BS, 55; Boston Univ, MD, 60. *Prof Exp:* Intern, Newton-Wellesley Hosp, 60-61; clin fel rheumatology, Boston City Hosp & res fel, Univ Hosp, 63-69; instr med, Boston Univ Med Sch, 69-74, asst prof, 74-75; asst prof med & dir rheumatology, 75-77, ASSOC PROF MED, COL MED & DENT, NJ, 77- *Mem:* Am Rheumatism Asn; Reticuloendothelial Soc; Electron Micros Soc Am. *Res:* Rheumatoid arthritis, fine structure and culture of the synovial membrane; gout, systemic lupus erythematons; immune experimental arthritis in animals. *Mailing Add:* Rheumatology Div NJ Col of Med 100 Bergen St Newark NJ 07103

KREYSA, FRANK JOSEPH, b Stankov, Czech, Apr 21, 19; nat US; m 50; c 4. ORGANIC CHEMISTRY, RESOURCE MANAGEMENT. *Educ:* Macalester Col, BA, 40; Columbia Univ, MA, 43, PhD(org chem), 48. *Prof Exp:* Anal chemist, Rockefeller Inst, 40-41; asst chem, Col Pharm, Columbia Univ, 43-44; from instr to assoc prof chem, St John's Univ NY, 46-55; from sr res chemist to asst to vpres Europ develop, W R Grace & Co, NY & Md, 55-61; from sr prof assoc to vpres, Smithsonian Inst Sci Info Exchange, DC, 61-73; CHIEF, SCI SERV DIV, BUR ALCOHOL, TOBACCO & FIREARMS, TREAS DEPT, WASHINGTON, DC, 73- *Concurrent Pos:* Tech consult, Chemo Puro Mfg Co, NY & NJ, 51-55; chmn bd trustees, Am Soc Safety Res, 66-70; comnr, Sci Manpower Comn, 69-73. *Mem:* AAAS; Am Inst Chem; Am Chem Soc; Am Acad Forensic Sci; Am Soc Crime Lab Dirs. *Res:* Research and development management; forensic science; instrumentation; analytical chemistry. *Mailing Add:* 10805 Pebble Brook Lane Potomac MD 20854

KREZANOSKI, JOSEPH Z, b Mundare, Alta, Apr 14, 27; nat US; m 49, 54; c 3. PHARMACEUTICAL CHEMISTRY. *Educ:* Univ Calif, BS, 51, MS, 53, PhD(pharmaceut chem), 56. *Prof Exp:* Asst pharm, Univ Calif, 51-56; asst prof, Med Col Va, 56-59; dir pharmaceut res & develop, Barnes-Hind Labs, Inc, 59-67; vpres & tech adv, Flow Pharmaceut, Inc, 67-77; DIR RES & DEVELOP, COOPER LABS, INC, 77- *Honors & Awards:* Borden Award, 51; Brunswick Award, 51. *Mem:* AAAS; Am Pharmaceut Asn; Am Chem Soc; assoc Am Acad Dermat; Am Mgt Asn. *Res:* Physical pharmacy; mechanism of drug action at the cellular level; pharmaceutical formulation. *Mailing Add:* Cooper Labs Inc 455 E Middlefield Rd Mountain View CA 94043

KREZEL, JOHN ROBERT, b Portsmouth, Va, May 25, 45; m 68; c 2. ENGINEERING MECHANICS, COMPUTER SCIENCE. *Educ:* Va Polytech Inst, BS, 68; Old Dominion Univ, MS, 74. *Prof Exp:* PHYSICIST, DAVID TAYLOR NAVAL SHIP RES & DEVELOP CTR, 64- *Concurrent Pos:* Instr comput sci, Old Dominion Univ, 75. *Res:* Dynamic response of submarines and other structures to underwater explosion attack. *Mailing Add:* David W Taylor Naval Ship Underwater Explosions Res Div Portsmouth VA 23709

KRIBEL, ROBERT EDWARD, b Pittsburgh, Pa, Sept 17, 37; m 59; c 4. PLASMA PHYSICS, MAGNETOHYDRODYNAMICS. *Educ:* Univ Notre Dame, BS, 59; Univ Calif, San Diego, MS, 66, PhD(physics), 68. *Prof Exp:* Res asst plasma physics, Gulf Gen Atomic Inc, Gulf Oil Corp, 63-65 & Univ Calif, San Diego, 65-68; staff assoc, Gulf Gen Atomic Inc, Gulf Oil Corp, 68-69; asst prof physics, Drake Univ, 70-73; assoc prof & head dept physics, James Madison Univ, 74-78; PROF & HEAD DEPT PHYSICS, AUBURN UNIV, 78- *Concurrent Pos:* Lectr, Univ San Diego, 67-68; consult, Cornell Univ, 70-71. *Mem:* Am Phys Soc. *Res:* Plasma production; confinement and stability. *Mailing Add:* Dept of Physics Auburn Univ Auburn AL 36830

KRICHER, JOHN C, b Philadelphia, Pa, Feb 7, 44; m 68. ECOLOGY. *Educ:* Temple Univ, BA, 66; Rutgers Univ, NB, PhD(zool), 70. *Prof Exp:* From asst prof to assoc prof, 70-80, PROF BIOL, WHEATON COL, MASS, 80- *Concurrent Pos:* Cottrell sci grants, Res Corp, 74 & 75. *Mem:* AAAS; Ecol Soc Am; Am Ornith Union; Cooper Ornith Soc. *Res:* Bird species diversity in relation to secondary succession; species diversity of intertidal communities; tropical bird species diversity; ecology of migrant birds in the tropics; range expansions of North American birds. *Mailing Add:* Biol Dept Wheaton Col Norton MA 02766

KRICHEVSKY, MICAH I, b Chicago, Ill, May 4, 31; m 52; c 2. MICROBIOLOGY, BIOCHEMISTRY. *Educ:* Univ Conn, BA, 52; Univ Ill, MS, 55, PhD(dairy sci), 58. *Prof Exp:* Asst dairy sci, Univ Ill, 53-57, 58; biochemist, Nat Inst Allergy & Infectious Dis, 58-59; biochemist, Nat Heart Inst, 59-61; biochemist, 61-68, chief environ mechanisms sect, 68-74, CHIEF MICROBIAL SYSTEMATICS SECT, NAT INST DENT RES, 74- *Mem:* Am Soc Microbiol. *Res:* Biochemical differentiation in slime molds; metabolic pathways in bacteria; automation and computer technology in biomedical research. *Mailing Add:* Nat Inst of Dent Res Bethesda MD 20014

KRICK, H(AROLD) D(AVID), SR, chemical engineering, deceased

KRICK, IRVING PARKHURST, b San Francisco, Calif, Dec 20, 06. METEOROLOGY, PHYSICS. *Educ:* Univ Calif, Berkeley, BA, 28; Calif Inst Technol, MS, 33, PhD(meteorol), 34. *Prof Exp:* Weather forecasting, Western Air Express, 32-33; staff mem meteorol, Calif Inst Technol, 33-35, from asst prof to prof, 35-48, head dept, 42-48; PRES WEATHER FORECASTING & MODIFICATION, IRVING P KRICK ASSOC INC, 50- *Concurrent Pos:* Consult meteorol dept, Am Air Lines Inc, 35-36; major chief long range res & forecasting sect, US Army Air Force, 42-44; dep dir weather serv, Europ Theatre Oper, 44; chief, Weather Info Sect, 45, mem sci adv group, 45-46; consult, US Adv Comt Weather, 56-57; consult & official weather engr, VIII Olympic Winter Games, 58-60; consult, White House, 65- *Honors & Awards:* Croix de Guerre Avec Etoile Vermeil, France, 44; Legion Merit, US, 46. *Mem:* Am Water Works Asn; Am Geophys Union; assoc fel Am Inst Aeronaut & Astronaut; fel Royal Soc Arts; Royal Meteorol Soc. *Res:* Extensive original work in weather forecasting and weather modification. *Mailing Add:* Irving P Krick Assoc Inc 748 Vella Rd Palm Springs CA 92262

KRICK, MERLYN STEWART, b Shillington, Pa, Jan 13, 38; m 68. NUCLEAR SCIENCE. *Educ:* Albright Col, BS, 59; Univ Pa, PhD(physics), 66. *Prof Exp:* Res assoc physics, Univ Rochester, 66-68; res appointee, Los Alamos Sci Lab, 68-70; from asst prof to assoc prof nuclear eng, Kans State Univ, 70-75; MEM STAFF NUCLEAR SAFEGUARDS, LOS ALAMOS NAT LAB, UNIV CALIF, 75- *Mem:* Am Phys Soc; Am Nuclear Soc; Inst Elec & Electronics Engrs. *Res:* Nuclear safeguards; nuclear instrumentation; delayed neutron physics. *Mailing Add:* Group Q-1 Los Alamos Nat Lab PO Box 1663 Los Alamos CA 87545

KRIDEL, DONALD JOSEPH, b Rochester, NY, Apr 2, 16; m 45; c 6. CHEMICAL ENGINEERING. *Educ:* Univ Rochester, BS, 37; Mass Inst Technol, ScD, 40. *Prof Exp:* Staff engr, 40-64, asst supt, 64-66, SUPT, EASTMAN KODAK CO, 66- *Mem:* Am Chem Soc; Am Inst Chem Engrs. *Res:* Photographic chemicals. *Mailing Add:* Apt 825 Sam Houston Dr Victoria TX 77901

KRIDER, EDMUND PHILIP, b Chicago, Ill, Mar 22, 40. ATMOSPHERIC ELECTRICITY, ATMOSPHERIC PHYSICS. *Educ:* Carleton Col, BA, 62; Univ Ariz, MS, 64, PhD(physics), 69. *Prof Exp:* Grad teaching asst physics, Univ Ariz, 62-64, grad res asst, 67-69, res assoc, 69; Nat Acad Sci resident res assoc, Manned Spacecraft Ctr, NASA, 69-71; asst res prof, Inst Atmospheric Physics, 71-75, asst prof, 73-75, assoc prof, 75-80, PROF, DEPT ATMOSPHERIC SCI & INST ATMOSPHERIC PHYSICS, UNIV ARIZ, 80- *Concurrent Pos:* Prin investr numerous res grants & contracts, 71-; adv, NASA, 76; mem, Lightning & Sferics Subcomn, Int Comn Atmospheric Elec, 76-; assoc ed, J Geophys Res, 77-80. *Mem:* Sigma Xi; Am Meteorol Soc; Am Geophys Union; Am Asn Physics Teachers. *Res:* Lightning and atmospheric electricity; cosmic ray physics. *Mailing Add:* Inst of Atmospheric Physics Univ of Ariz Tucson AZ 85721

KRIDER, JAKE LUTHER, b Lewistown, Ill, Dec 12, 13; m 36. ANIMAL NUTRITION. *Educ:* Univ Ill, BS, 39, MS, 41; Cornell Univ, PhD(animal husb), 42. *Prof Exp:* Asst animal husb, Univ Ill, 39-40 & Cornell Univ, 40-42; assoc, Univ Ill, 42-43, asst prof swine husb, 43-46, assoc prof, 46-47, prof animal sci, 47-50, dir feed res & nutrit, 50-51; vpres & dir feed sales, McMillen Feed Div, Cent Soya Co, Inc, 51-56, vpres & dir pub rels, 56-59, vpres personnel develop & pub rels, 59-63; prof, 63-79, EMER PROF ANIMAL SCI, PURDUE UNIV, 79- *Mem:* Hon fel Am Soc Animal Sci (vpres, 67-68, pres, 68-69); Poultry Sci Asn. *Res:* Nutritive requirements of the baby pig; value of pastures; causes of reproductive failures in sows; vitamin B-12 in baby pig nutrition; dose range antibiotic protocols; choline requirement and choline-methiorine responses of young pigs. *Mailing Add:* 1305 Ravinia Rd West Lafayette IN 47906

KRIEBEL, HOWARD BURTT, b Philadelphia, Pa, July 31, 21; m 49; c 2. FOREST GENETICS, MOLECULAR BIOLOGY CELL CULTURE. *Educ:* Haverford Col, BA, 46; Yale Univ, MF, 48, PhD, 56. *Prof Exp:* Instr forestry, Univ NH, 49-52; from instr to assoc prof forestry, Ohio Agr Res & Develop Ctr, 53-62, from asst prof to prof bot & plant path, Ohio State Univ, 55-69, PROF FORESTRY, OHIO AGR RES & DEVELOP CTR, 62-, PROF GENETICS, OHIO STATE UNIV, 69- *Concurrent Pos:* Vis scientist, Royal Col Forestry, Stockholm, 63; actg chmn, Dept Forestry, Ohio Agr Res & Develop Ctr, 66-69; Fulbright lectr, Univ Zagreb, 71-72. *Mem:* Fel AAAS; Soc Am Foresters; Am Soc Plant Physiologists; hon mem Asn Genetic Socs Yugoslavia. *Res:* Heritability studies; incompatibility systems; molecular biology of embryogenesis; developmental regulation of gene expression; hybrid and ecotype testing. *Mailing Add:* Dept of Forestry Ohio Agr Res & Develop Ctr Wooster OH 44691

KRIEBEL, MAHLON E, b Garfield, Wash, Nov 18, 36; m 56; c 3. PHYSIOLOGY, COMPARATIVE PHYSIOLOGY. *Educ:* Wash State Univ, BS, 58; Univ Wash, MS, 64, PhD(zool), 67. *Prof Exp:* Fel, Albert Einstein Col Med, 67-69; ASSOC PROF PHYSIOL, STATE UNIV NY UPSTATE MED CTR, 69- *Concurrent Pos:* Mem, Marine Biol Lab, Woods Hole. *Mem:* Am Soc Cell Biologists. *Res:* Physiology of tunicate heart; neurophysiology of fish oculomotor neurons; degranulation of mast cells; squid chromatophore nerve-muscle studies; transmitter release at the n-m junction. *Mailing Add:* Dept of Physiol State Univ of NY Upstate Med Ctr Syracuse NY 13210

KRIEBEL, RICHARD MARVIN, b WReading, Pa, Apr 12, 47; m 66; c 4. NEUROANATOMY. *Educ:* Albright Col, BA, 69; Temple Univ, PhD(anat), 74. *Prof Exp:* Instr & asst prof anat, Med Col Va, Va Commonwealth Univ, 73-75; asst prof anat, 75-80, ASSOC PROF ANAT & NEUROBIOL, COL MED, UNIV VT, 80- *Res:* Neuroendocrine control of osmoregulation in fishes and synaptology of thalamic nuclei in mammals with specific interest in lateral geniculate. *Mailing Add:* Dept Anat Col Med Given Bldg Univ Vt Burlington VT 05401

KRIEBLE, JAMES G(ERHARD), b NJ, Oct 23, 20; m 43; c 3. CHEMICAL ENGINEERING. *Educ:* Princeton Univ, BS, 42, PhD(chem eng), 49. *Prof Exp:* Res assoc chem process eng, Res Lab, Gen Elec Co, NY, 49-57, process engr, Refractory Metals Lab, 57-61, mgr powder prod eng, 61-68, MGR ENG, REFRACTORY METAL POWDER & GAS OPER, GEN ELEC CO, 68- *Concurrent Pos:* Fel, Textile Res Inst, 49. *Mem:* Am Chem Soc; Am Inst Chem Engrs; NY Acad Sci. *Res:* Development and economic evaluation of processes for refractory metals and gases used in lamps. *Mailing Add:* 3646 Tolland Cleveland OH 44122

KRIEG, ARTHUR F, b East Orange, NJ, Oct 23, 30; m 56; c 3. PATHOLOGY. *Educ:* Yale Univ, AB, 52; Tufts Univ, MD, 56. *Prof Exp:* Rotating intern, Western Reserve Univ, 56-57, resident path, 57-60, resident, New Eng Deaconess Hosp, 63-64; asst prof, State Univ NY Upstate Med Ctr, 64-68; assoc prof, 68-71, PROF PATH & DIR CLIN LABS, HERSHEY MED CTR, PA STATE UNIV, 71- *Mem:* Fel Acad Clin Lab Physicians & Scientists; fel Am Soc Clin Pathologists; fel Col Am Pathologists. *Res:* Clinical pathology; clinical laboratory computerization. *Mailing Add:* Milton S Hershey Med Ctr Pa State Univ Hershey PA 17033

KRIEG, DANIEL R, b Taylor, Tex, May 19, 43; m 65; c 2 PLANT PHYSIOLOGY, BIOCHEMISTRY. *Educ:* Tex A&M Univ, BS, 65, PhD(plant physiol), 70. *Prof Exp:* From asst prof to assoc prof, 70-77, PROF PLANT PHYSIOL, TEX TECH UNIV, 77- *Mem:* Am Soc Plant Physiologists; Crop Sci Soc Am; Am Soc Agron. *Res:* Sorghum and cotton, physiological responses to environmental stress; environmental effects on biochemical changes in germinating cotton seeds; drought tolerance and photosynthetic activity of sorghum; environmental effects on seed development of grain sorghum. *Mailing Add:* Plant Physiol Lab Plant & Soil Sci Dept Tex Tech Univ Lubbock TX 79409

KRIEG, DAVID CHARLES, b Bradford, Pa, June 10, 36; m 58; c 3. ANIMAL BEHAVIOR, VERTEBRATE ZOOLOGY. *Educ:* Mansfield State Col, BS, 58; St Bonaventure Univ, MS, 61, PhD(biol), 64. *Prof Exp:* Instr biol high sch, NY, 59-62; asst prof zool, State Univ NY Col Cortland, 62-64; grad asst, St Bonaventure univ, 64-67; ASSOC PROF BIOL, STATE UNIV NY COL NEW PALTZ, 67- *Concurrent Pos:* Frank M Chapman grants, Am Mus Natural Hist, 66, 71, 72 & 73. *Honors & Awards:* Marcia Brady Tucker Award, Am Ornith Union, 66. *Mem:* AAAS; Am Ornith Union; Am Soc Zoologists; Animal Behav Soc; Am Soc Ichthyologists & Herpetologists. *Res:* Comparative behavior of genus Sialia; hybridization of bluebirds in great plains. *Mailing Add:* Dept of Biol State Univ of NY Col New Paltz NY 12561

KRIEG, DAVID RONALD, b Lorain, Ohio, Apr 4, 28; m 65. GENETICS. *Educ:* Ohio State Univ, BS, 50; Univ Rochester, PhD(biophys), 57. *Prof Exp:* Res assoc biophys, Univ Rochester, 52-53, asst biol, 55-56; biologist, Biol Div, Oak Ridge Nat Lab, 57-64; assoc prof, 65-80, EMER PROF BACT, UNIV CALIF, LOS ANGELES, 80- *Concurrent Pos:* Nat Insts Health fel, Stanford Univ, 63-64. *Mem:* AAAS. *Mailing Add:* Dept of Bact 5304 Life Sci Bldg Univ of Calif Los Angeles CA 90024

KRIEG, NOEL ROGER, b Waterbury, Conn, Jan 11, 34. MICROBIOLOGY. *Educ:* Univ Conn, BA, 55, MS, 57; Univ Md, PhD(microbiol), 60. *Prof Exp:* Asst bact, Univ Conn, 55-57 & microbiol, Univ Md, 57-60; from asst prof to assoc prof, 60-70, PROF BACT, VA POLYTECH INST & STATE UNIV, 70- *Honors & Awards:* Carski Distinguished Teaching Award, Am Soc Microbiol, 78. *Mem:* Am Soc Microbiol. *Res:* Nutrition, taxonomy and motility of Spirillum. *Mailing Add:* Dept of Biol Va Polytech Inst & State Univ Blacksburg VA 24061

KRIEG, RICHARD EDWARD, JR, b New York, NY, Oct 16, 42; m 66; c 3. BACTERIOLOGY. *Educ:* Rutgers Univ, New Brunswick, BS, 64; Iowa State Univ, MS, 66, PhD(bact), 68. *Prof Exp:* Res microbiologist, US Air Force Sch Aerospace Med, 68-70; biomed analyst biomed, Aerospace Med Div, 70-73; res microbiologist, Armed Forces Inst Path, 73-74; INSTR BACT, UNIV MD, 73-, TECH ADV, 77-; CHIEF BACT, ARMED FORCES INST PATH, 74- *Mem:* Am Soc Microbiol; AAAS; Sigma Xi; fel Am Acad Microbiol. *Res:* Pathogenicity of mycobacterial skin infections; epidemiology and etiology of Legionnaires' disease; numerical taxonomy; deoxyribonucleic acid base ration analysis. *Mailing Add:* Armed Forces Inst of Path 6825 16th NW Washington DC 20306

KRIEG, WENDELL JORDAN, b Lincoln, Nebr, Apr 13, 06; m 48; c 2. NEUROANATOMY. *Educ:* Univ Nebr, BSc, 28; NY Univ, MS, 31, PhD(anat), 35. *Prof Exp:* Instr anat, Univ Nebr, 28-29; instr, Col Dent, NY Univ, 29-32, from instr to asst prof, Col Med, 32-44; assoc prof neurol, Inst Neurol, 44-46, prof neurol & dir inst, Med Sch, 46-48, prof anat, 48-73, EMER PROF ANAT, MED SCH, NORTHWESTERN UNIV, CHICAGO, 73- *Concurrent Pos:* Mem corp, Marine Biol Lab, Woods Hole. *Mem:* Am Neurol Asn; Am Asn Anatomists. *Res:* Originator of electroneuroprosthesis; structure and connections of cerebral cortex and diencephalon of rat, monkey and man; illustration of nervous system; design of stereotaxic machines. *Mailing Add:* 1236 Hinman Evanston IL 60202

KRIEGE, OWEN HOBBS, b Toledo, Ohio, Nov 6, 29; m 52; c 3. APPLIED CHEMISTRY. *Educ:* Ohio State Univ, BSc, 51, MSc, 52, PhD(anal chem), 54. *Prof Exp:* Staff mem, Los Alamos Sci Lab, 54-60; sr chemist, Res & Develop Ctr, Westinghouse Elec Corp, 60-66; group leader anal chem, Adv Mat Res & Develop Lab, 66-67, group leader anal & struct chem, 67-68, res supvr, 68-70, tech supvr appl chem, 71-76, ASST MGR, MAT ENG & RES LAB, PRATT & WHITNEY AIRCRAFT, 76- *Mem:* Am Chem Soc. *Res:* Analytical chemistry of refractory materials; phase separations in superalloys; trace analysis in complex alloys; atomic absorption; polymer chemistry; electroplating. *Mailing Add:* Pratt & Whitney Aircraft Mat Eng & Res Lab Aircraft Rd Middletown CT 06457

KRIEGEL, MONROE W(ERNER), b Giddings, Tex, July 30, 12; m 42; c 1. CHEMICAL ENGINEERING. *Educ:* Univ Tex, BS, 34, MS, 36, PhD(chem eng), 39. *Prof Exp:* Instr chem, Univ Tex, 34-36, res assoc, bur indust chem, 37-39; assoc prof chem eng, Tex Col Arts & Indust, 39-40; sr geochemist, Carter Oil Co, 40-45, res engr & group supvr, 45-49, head prod & pipe line res, 49-58; dir tech placement & col rels, Jersey Prod Res Co, 58-64; prof chem eng, eng exten, 64-78, asst dir exten, 64-66, dir, 66-78, EMER PROF CHEM ENG, OKLA STATE UNIV, 78-; CONSULT CONTINUING ENG EDUC, 78- *Concurrent Pos:* Field test engr, oil & gas div, Tex RR Comn, 39. *Honors & Awards:* Distinguished Serv Award, Am Soc Eng Educ, 77, Pioneer Award, 78. *Mem:* Soc Petrol Engrs; Am Inst Chem Engrs; Am Soc Eng Educ. *Res:* Microgas analysis; geochemistry; corrosion in hydrogen sulphide; geochemical method of prospecting for petroleum; personnel selection; research management; hiring, training and placement of technical personnel; continuing engineering education; industry-university relations. *Mailing Add:* 2123 Countryside Dr Stillwater OK 74074

KRIEGER, ALLEN STEPHEN, b New York, NY, Feb 23, 41; m 66; c 2. SOLAR PHYSICS. *Educ:* Mass Inst Technol, BS, 62, PhD(physics), 67. *Prof Exp:* Res assoc cosmic ray physics, Ctr Space Res, Mass Inst Technol, 67-68; sr scientist, 68-71, staff scientist, 72-73, sr staff scientist, 74-77, dir solar res, 78-79, VPRES SPACE SYSTS, AM SCI & ENG INC, 80- *Mem:* Am Phys Soc; Am Astron Soc. *Res:* Solar physics; x-ray astronomy. *Mailing Add:* Am Sci & Eng Inc 955 Massachusetts Ave Cambridge MA 02139

KRIEGER, BARBARA BROCKETT, b Madison, Wis, Jan 27, 47. CHEMICAL ENGINEERING, CHEMICAL PHYSICS. *Educ:* Univ Wis-Madison, BS, 68; Wayne State Univ, MS, 72, PhD(chem eng), 75. *Prof Exp:* Res engr, Inst Francais du Petrole, 68-69; res technician auto emission control, Gen Motor Res Labs, 70-71; res asst, Wayne State Univ, 71-75; asst prof, 75-80, ASSOC PROF CHEM ENG, UNIV WASH, 80- *Concurrent Pos:* Consult, Rocket Res Corp, 77-, Hanford Energy Develop Lab, 78- & Nat Acad Adv Bd, Environ Protection Agency, 76- *Mem:* Am Inst Chem Engrs; Am Chem Soc; AAAS; Sigma Xi. *Res:* Chemical kinetics, chemical physics and transport related to chemical reaction engineering as applied to high temperature-high energy phenomena such as combustion, pyrolysis, laser and plasma processing, air pollution and atmospheric chemistry. *Mailing Add:* Benson Hall BF-10 Univ Wash Seattle WA 98195

KRIEGER, CARL HENRY, b Milwaukee, Wis, Aug 14, 11; m 40; c 3. BIOCHEMISTRY, RESEARCH ADMINISTRATION. *Educ:* Univ Wis, BS, 33, MS, 38, PhD(biochem), 40. *Prof Exp:* Res assoc, Alumni Res Found, Univ Wis, 34-40, lab mgr, 40-50, dir gen labs, 50-55; dir basic res, Campbell Soup Co, 55-57, dir basic res & prod develop, 57-60, pres, Campbell Soup Co Res Inst, 60-76, vpres prod res, 61-76, pres, Campbell Inst Food Res, 66-76; DIR TECHNOL RESOURCES, INC, 75- *Concurrent Pos:* Mem indust adv comt canned meat, Res & Develop Assoc Mil Food/Packaging Syst, 59-62, dir, 73-74; mem sci res comt, Nat Canners Asn, 60-74; mem comt res life sci, Nat Acad Sci-Nat Res Coun, 66-69, mem comt fruit & vegetable prod, Adv Bd Mil Personnel Supplies, 68-71, mem, Food Nutrit Bd, 69-72, mem, Bd Agr & Renewable Resources, 73-76; mem tech adv comt, Inst Human Nutrit, Columbia Univ, 66-72; mem sci & tech adv comt, AID, 67-72; mem, Monell Chem Senses Ctr, Nat Adv Coun, 68-; chmn food & nutrit liaison comt, Nutrit Found Inc, 70-72; mem sci adv bd, Nat Ctr Toxicol Res, 72-76; trustee, Campbell Soup Co Res Inst, 60-76. *Mem:* Fel AAAS; Am Chem Soc; Am Inst Nutrit; Animal Nutrit Res Coun; fel Inst Food Technol. *Res:* Fats; dairy products; fermentation; proteins; carbohydrates; flavors; microbiology and nutrition as applied to foods; development of new food products in heat processed, frozen and dehydrated food areas. *Mailing Add:* 722 Sussex Rd Wynnewood PA 19096

KRIEGER, DOROTHY T, b New York, NY, Feb 17, 27; m 53; c 2. PHYSIOLOGY. *Educ:* Columbia Univ, AB, 45, MD, 49. *Prof Exp:* Loewenberg fel hemat, Mt Sinai Hosp, 52; USPHS fel neuroendocrinol, Mt Sinai Hosp & Presby Hosp, 54-55; asst attend physician, Presby Hosp, 55-56; res assoc endocrinol & chief endocrine clin, Mt Sinai Hosp, 56-69, from asst prof to assoc prof, Mt Sinai Sch Med, 66-72, PROF MED & DIR DIV ENDOCRINOL, MT SINAI SCH MED, 72- *Concurrent Pos:* Mem endocrinol study sect, Nat Inst Arthritis, Metab & Digestive Dis, 71-75; attend physician, Mt Sinai Hosp, 72-; chairperson, Endocrinol Study Sect, Nat Inst Arthritis, Metab & Digestive Dis, 80-82. *Mem:* Am Physiol Soc; Asn Am Physicians; Endocrine Soc (vpres, 74-75); Am Fedn Clin Res; Am Soc Clin Invest. *Res:* Neuroendocrinology; hypothalamic regulation of pituitary-adrenal function; neural regulation of growth hormone; neural regulation of adrenal circadian periodicity; endocrinology; brain peptides. *Mailing Add:* 1148 Fifth Ave New York NY 10028

KRIEGER, EDUARDO MOACYR, b Cerro Largo, Brazil, June 27, 28; m 56; c 2. MEDICAL PHYSIOLOGY. *Educ:* Fac Med Porto Alegre, MD, 53. *Prof Exp:* Asst prof physiol, Fac Med Porto Alegre, 54-57; asst prof, 57-62, prof livre-docente, 62-67, assoc prof, 67-73, PROF PHYSIOL, FAC MED RIBEIRAO PRETO, UNIV SAO PAULO, 73-, CHMN DEPT, 74- *Concurrent Pos:* Staff mem & vpres, Comt Postgrad Prog Med Sch, Fac Med Ribeirao Preto, Univ Sao Paulo, 71-76, coordr, Prog Postgrad Studies Physiol, Dept Physiol, 72-76. *Mem:* Brazilian Soc Advan Sci; Brazilian Soc Physiol; Brazilian Soc Cardiol; Brazilian Nat Acad Sci. *Res:* Cardiovascular physiology; experimental hypertension; resetting of the baroreceptor during hypotension and hypertension; activity of the renin-angiotensin system in different physiological conditions. *Mailing Add:* Dept of Physiol Sch of Med 14.100 Ribeirao Preto Sao Paulo Brazil

KRIEGER, HENRY ALAN, b Denver, Colo, May 7, 36; m 57; c 2. MATHEMATICS. *Educ:* Rensselaer Polytech Inst, BAE, 57; Brown Univ, PhD(appl math), 64. *Prof Exp:* Bateman res fel math, Calif Inst Technol, 64-65, asst prof, 65-68; asst prof, 68-71, ASSOC PROF MATH, HARVEY MUDD COL, 71- *Concurrent Pos:* Vis assoc prof statist, Israel Inst Technol, 74-75. *Mem:* Am Math Soc; Math Asn Am. *Res:* Mathematical analysis, particularly abstract harmonic analysis and probability theory; measure theory. *Mailing Add:* Dept of Math Harvey Mudd Col Claremont CA 91711

KRIEGER, HOWARD PAUL, b Brooklyn, NY, July 2, 18; m 53; c 2. NEUROLOGY. *Educ:* Harvard Univ, SB, 41; Long Island Col Med, MD, 44; Am Bd Psychiat & Neurol, dipl. *Prof Exp:* Intern, Long Island Col Med Hosp, 44-45, resident, Long Island Col Med, 46-47; resident, 49-51, fel Columbia Univ, 51; asst attend neurologist, 52-59, assoc attend neurologist, 59-62; chief div neurol, Beth Israel Med Ctr, 60-77; ATTEND NEUROLOGIST, MT SINAI HOSP, 62-, PROF NEUROL, MT SINAI SCH MED, 75-; ATTEND NEUROLOGIST, BETH ISRAEL MED CTR, 60- *Concurrent Pos:* Fel, NY Univ-Bellevue Med Ctr, 47-48; USPHS fel, 48-49, spec fel, 51; Nat Found Infantile Paralysis fel, 52, 54; consult neurologist, US Marine Hosp, 57-75; clin prof neurol, Mt Sinai Med Sch, 66-75. *Mem:* Am Psychol Asn; Am Neurol Asn; Am Acad Neurol; Am Fedn Clin Res; NY Acad Sci. *Res:* Neurophysiology; neuroendocrinology. *Mailing Add:* Dept of Neurol Mt Sinai Med Sch New York NY 10029

KRIEGER, IRVIN MITCHELL, b Cleveland, Ohio, May 14, 23; m 65; c 1. PHYSICAL CHEMISTRY. *Educ:* Case Inst Technol, BS, 44, MS, 48; Cornell Univ, PhD(phys chem), 51. *Prof Exp:* Asst, Cornell Univ, 47-48; instr chem, 49-51, from asst prof to assoc prof phys chem, 51-68, PROF PHYS CHEM & MACROMOLECULAR SCI, CASE WESTERN RESERVE UNIV, 68- *Concurrent Pos:* Sci res coun fel, Univ Bristol, 77-78. *Mem:* Am Chem Soc; Soc Rheol (pres, 77-79); Am Inst Chem Eng. *Res:* Rheology and statistical mechanics of colloids and polymers. *Mailing Add:* 15691 Fenemore Rd East Cleveland OH 44112

KRIEGER, JEANNE KANN, b Hartford, Conn, Apr 16, 44; m 66; c 2. PHYSICAL ORGANIC CHEMISTRY. *Educ:* Bryn Mawr Col, BA, 66; Mass Inst Technol, PhD(org chem), 71. *Prof Exp:* Res assoc chem, Mass Inst Technol, 71-72, instr, 72-75, lectr, 75-78; proj leader, 78-80, ASST TO DIR MGR, NEW ENGLAND NUCLEAR, 81- *Mem:* Am Chem Soc; AAAS. *Res:* Nuclear magnetic resonance exchange calculations; mechanistic organometallic chemistry. *Mailing Add:* 44 Webester Rd Lexington MA 02173

KRIEGER, JOSEPH BERNARD, b Brooklyn, NY, July 10, 37; m 64. THEORETICAL SOLID STATE PHYSICS, ATOMIC PHYSICS. *Educ:* Columbia Univ, AB, 59, PhD(physics), 65. *Prof Exp:* From asst prof to assoc prof physics, Polytech Inst Brooklyn, 65-72; assoc prof, 72-74, PROF PHYSICS, BROOKLYN COL, 74- *Concurrent Pos:* Vis assoc prof, Brooklyn Col, 71-72; chmn dept, Brooklyn Col, 76-80; acad assoc, Calif Inst Technol, 79. *Mem:* Fel Am Phys Soc. *Res:* Transport theory in solids; surface physics; calculation of atomic expectation values; exact quantization conditions and Wentzel-Kramer-Brillouin energy eigenvalues; electron states. *Mailing Add:* Dept Physics Brooklyn Col Brooklyn NY 11210

KRIEGER, ROGER B, b Milwaukee, Wis, May 4, 41; m 68, 79. MECHANICAL ENGINEERING. *Educ:* Univ Wis, Madison, BS, 64, PhD(mech eng), 68. *Prof Exp:* Res engr, French Inst Petrol, 68-69; SR STAFF RES ENGR, ENGINE RES DEPT, GEN MOTORS RES LABS, 69- *Mem:* Soc Automotive Engrs; Am Soc Mech Engrs; Combustion Inst. *Res:* Combustion; pollutant formation and destruction during combustion; combustion modelling and internal combustion engine simulation. *Mailing Add:* Engine Res Dept Gen Motors Res Labs Warren MI 48090

KRIEGER, STEPHAN JACQUES, b San Francisco, Calif, Aug 2, 37; m 58; c 4. THEORETICAL PHYSICS. *Educ:* Univ Calif, Berkeley, BS, 59, PhD(physics), 63. *Prof Exp:* Res physicist, Carnegie Inst Technol, 63-66; assoc prof physics, Univ Ill, Chicago Circle, 71-78, prof, 78-80; STAFF SCIENTIST, LAWRENCE LIVERMORE NAT LAB, 80- *Mem:* Am Phys Soc. *Res:* Nuclear structure; many body problem. *Mailing Add:* L-71 Lawrence Livermore Nat Lab PO Box 808 Livermore CA 94550

KRIEGER, THEODORE JOSEPH, b New York, NY, July 27, 18; wid; c 2. THEORETICAL PHYSICS. *Educ:* City Col New York, BS, 39; Columbia Univ, MA, 40; Purdue Univ, PhD(physics), 52. *Prof Exp:* Physicist, Battelle Mem Inst, 52-55; physicist, Knolls Atomic Power Lab, Gen Elec Co, 55-59; PHYSICIST, BROOKHAVEN NAT LAB, 61- *Mem:* Am Phys Soc. *Res:* Nuclear reaction theory; statistical theory of nuclear cross sections; statistical phenomena:; reactor physics. *Mailing Add:* Dept Nuclear Energy T 130 Brookhaven Nat Lab Upton NY 11973

KRIEGH, JAMES DOUGLAS, b Dodge City, Kans, Dec 29, 28. CIVIL ENGINEERING. *Educ:* Univ Colo, BS, 55, MS, 58. *Prof Exp:* Asst, Cryogenics Lab, Nat Bur Standards, Colo, 53-54; asst, Eng Exp Sta, Univ Colo, 54-55, instr civil eng, 55-58; from asst prof to assoc prof, 58-69, PROF CIVIL ENG, UNIV ARIZ, 69-, PROF ENG MECH, 81- *Concurrent Pos:* NSF fac fel, Univ Colo, 63-64; comt chmn, Hwy Res Bd, Nat Acad Sci-Nat Res Coun, 64-70. *Mem:* Am Soc Civil Engrs; Am Concrete Inst. *Res:* Epoxy resins for concrete construction and structural adhesives. *Mailing Add:* Dept of Civil Eng Univ of Ariz Tucson AZ 85721

KRIEGMAN, GEORGE, b Chicago, Ill, Sept 14, 17; m 41; c 4. PSYCHIATRY, PSYCHOANALYSIS. *Educ:* Univ Ill, BA, 39, MS, 42, MD, 43. *Prof Exp:* From intern to resident med, St Elizabeth Hosp, DC, 43-45; consult psychistrist, Child Care Bur, Va Dept Pub Welfare, 47-52; asst prof ment hyg, Sch Nursing, Med Col Va, 50-58, assoc med, 56-58, asst clin prof psychiat, 59-64, assoc clin prof, 64-68, CLIN PROF PSYCHIAT, MED COL VA, VA COMMONWEALTH UNIV, 68-, CHMN, CLIN FAC COMT, DEPT PSYCHIAT, 81- *Concurrent Pos:* Consult psychiatrist, Family &

Children's Serv Soc Richmond, Va, 47-73; pvt pract psychoanal & psychiat, 47-; lectr psychiat, Richmond Prof Inst, Sch Social Work, Col William & Mary, 51-58; consult psychiatrist, Vet Admin Hosp, 52-57 & Richmond Children's Aid Soc, 58-60; instr, Wash Psychoanal Inst, 58-61; lectr psychiat, Sch Med, Univ Va, 58-62; mem adv bd, Southern Regional Educ Bd Continuing Educ Ment Health, 67-69; mem, Va Ment Health & Ment Retardation Prof Adv Bd, 71- *Mem:* Life fel Am Psychiat Asn; Am Psychoanal Asn; fel Am Acad Psychoanal. *Res:* The PaTE Report, a psychometric procedure for evaluation of emotional problems; continuing education program for mental health workers. *Mailing Add:* Kriegman Clin Ltd 106 Thompson St Richmond VA 23221

KRIEGSMAN, HELEN, b Pittsburg, Kans, Feb 27, 24. MATHEMATICS. *Educ:* Kans State Teachers Col Pittsburg, BS, 44, MS, 47; Ohio State Univ, PhD(math educ), 64. *Prof Exp:* Teacher, High Sch, Kans, 44-47; from instr to assoc prof, 47-67, PROF MATH & CHMN DEPT, PITTSBURG STATE UNIV, 67- *Mem:* Math Asn Am; Am Math Soc; Nat Coun Teachers Math. *Res:* Curriculum and methods of teaching mathematics on the secondary school and college levels. *Mailing Add:* Dept of Math Pittsburg State Univ Pittsburg KS 66762

KRIEGSMANN, GREGORY A, b Chicago, Ill, Sept 20, 46; m 69; c 2. APPLIED MATHEMATICS. *Educ:* Marquette Univ, BS, 69; Univ Calif, Los Angeles, MS, 70, PhD(appl math), 74. *Prof Exp:* Instr math, Courant Inst, NY Univ, 74-76; mem tech staff, Hughes Aircraft Co, 76-77; asst prof math, Univ Nebr, 77-79, assoc prof, 79-80; ASSOC PROF APPL MATH, NORTHWESTERN UNIV, 80- *Mem:* Soc Indust Appl Math; Am Math Soc. *Res:* Numerical and asymstotic analysis of wave propagation; bifurcation problems in the physical sciences. *Mailing Add:* Dept Eng Sci & Appl Math Northwestern Univ Evanston IL 60201

KRIENKE, ORA KARL, JR, b Seattle, Wash, Jan 31, 31; m 60; c 2. ASTRONOMY. *Educ:* Seattle Pac Col, BA, 53, MA, 55; Univ Wash, MS, 59 & 69, PhD(astron), 73. *Prof Exp:* Instr math, 53-59, asst prof physics & math, 59-63, assoc prof physics, math & philos, 63-71, PROF PHYSICS, MATH & PHILOS, SEATTLE PAC UNIV, 71-, DIR, SCH NAT & MATH SCI, 80- *Concurrent Pos:* Vis lectr, Univ Wash, 64 & 68. *Mem:* AAAS; Am Asn Physics Teachers; Am Astron Soc. *Res:* Structure of galaxies, especially irregular type II galaxies. *Mailing Add:* 917 NW 103rd Seattle WA 98177

KRIENS, RICHARD DUANE, b Belmond, Iowa, Oct 16, 32; m 67; c 3. ORGANIC CHEMISTRY. *Educ:* Iowa State Teachers Col, BA, 56; Iowa State Univ, PhD(org chem), 63. *Prof Exp:* Teacher, High Sch, Iowa, 57-58; asst prof chem, Iowa Wesleyan Col, 63-65; assoc prof, 65-73, PROF CHEM, ASHLAND COL, 73- *Mem:* Am Inst Chem; Royal Soc Chem; Am Chem Soc. *Res:* Free radical organic chemistry; reaction mechanisms in organic chemistry. *Mailing Add:* Dept of Chem Ashland Col Ashland OH 44805

KRIER, CAROL ALNOTH, b Bismarck, NDak, July 22, 28; m 57; c 2. MATERIAL SCIENCE ENGINEERING, MANUFACTURING TECHNOLOGY. *Educ:* St Martin's Col, BS, 50; Univ Pittsburgh, PhD(chem), 55. *Prof Exp:* Lab asst fuel oils, State Labs Dept, NDak, 45-46; asst instr chem, Pvt Sch, Wash, 48-50; asst, Univ Pittsburgh, 50-51, asst phys chem, 51-55; prin chemist, proj leader & sr scientist, Battelle Mem Inst, 55-62; metals res specialist, Boeing Co, 62-67, supvr mat stress & environ simulation, 67-70, mgr advan develop & spec studies, 70-71, ENG MGR, BOEING AEROSPACE CO, 71- *Concurrent Pos:* Consult, Defense Metals Info Ctr, 59-62; mat adv bd mem, Nat Acad Sci, 61-69. *Honors & Awards:* NASA-Apollo Achievement Award, 70; Apollo/Saturn V Roll of Honor, 71; Apollo 11 Manned Flight Awareness Award, 71. *Mem:* Am Chem Soc; Am Soc Metals. *Res:* Thermodynamics; calorimetry; cryogenics; theory of metals and alloys; extractive metallurgy; refractory, structural and electronic materials; high temperature coatings for metals; oxidation of metals and alloys; alkali metals; platinum-group metals; high temperature corrosion; physical metallurgy; vapor deposition; manufacturing processes. *Mailing Add:* Boeing Aerospace Co PO Box 3999 Seattle WA 98124

KRIESEL, DOUGLAS CLARE, b Owatonna, Minn, July 22, 37; m 59; c 3. MEDICINAL CHEMISTRY. *Educ:* Univ Minn, BS, 60, PhD(med chem), 65. *Prof Exp:* Prof med chem, Sch Pharm, Southwestern State Col, Okla, 65-72; RES SCIENTIST PHARMACEUT PRODS DIV, ABBOTT LABS, 76- *Concurrent Pos:* Res grants, Mead Johnson Labs, 66-67 & Okla Heart Asn, 67-68. *Mem:* Am Chem Soc; Am Pharmaceut Asn; Acad Pharmaceut Sci. *Res:* Synthesis formulation and development of pharmaceutical dosage forms of analgesics, antineoplastics, antivirals, and cardiovascular agents. *Mailing Add:* Abbott Labs North Chicago IL 60064

KRIGBAUM, WILLIAM RICHARD, b Ill, Sept 29, 22; m 46; c 3. PHYSICAL CHEMISTRY. *Educ:* Millikin Univ, BS, 44; Univ Ill, MS, 48, PhD(chem), 49. *Hon Degrees:* DSc, Millikin Univ, 66. *Prof Exp:* Nat Res Coun fel, Cornell Univ, 49-50, res assoc & instr, 50-52; from instr to prof, 52-69, JAMES B DUKE PROF CHEM, DUKE UNIV, 69-, CHMN DEPT, 76- *Concurrent Pos:* Sloan res fel, 56-60; NSF sr fel, 59-60; mem adv panel chem, NSF. *Mem:* Am Chem Soc; Am Phys Soc; Am Crystallog Asn. *Res:* Wide and low angle x-ray diffraction; physical chemical studies of polymers in solution and in bulk state; physical chemistry of macromolecules. *Mailing Add:* 2504 Wilson St Durham NC 27705

KRIGMAN, MARTIN ROSS, b New York, NY, Sept 4, 33; m 58; c 3. NEUROPATHOLOGY, NEUROBIOLOGY. *Educ:* Columbia Col, BA, 54; Cornell Univ, MD, 58; Am Bd Path, dipl anat path, 63, dipl neuropath, 64. *Prof Exp:* From instr to asst prof path, Sch Med, Yale Univ, 61-66; asst prof path, 66-69, course dir neurobiol, 69-72, assoc prof, 69-81, PROF PATH, SCH MED, UNIV NC, CHAPEL HILL, 81- *Concurrent Pos:* Spec fel neuropath, 61-64; consult, Dept Path, Moses Cone Hosp, Greensboro, NC. *Mem:* NY Acad Sci; Am Asn Neuropath; Am Asn Pathologists & Bacteriologists; Int Acad Path; Am Soc Exp Pathologists. *Res:* Experimental neuropathology and neurobiology. *Mailing Add:* Dept of Path Univ of NC Sch of Med Chapel Hill NC 27514

KRIGSVOLD, DALE THOMAS, b Grant Co, Minn, June 21, 37; m 82. PLANT PATHOLOGY, PLANT ECOLOGY. *Educ:* Old Dominion Univ, BS, 73; Va Polytech Inst & State Univ, PhD(plant path), 79. *Prof Exp:* PLANT PATHOLOGIST, TROP RES DIV, UNITED FRUIT CO, 79- *Mem:* Am Phytopath Soc. *Res:* Etiology and control of post-harvest diseases on commercially produced tropical fruits and vegetables, primarily bananas; ecology of soil-borne plant pathogens, primarily fungal spore germination as affected by soil fungistasis and the host plant. *Mailing Add:* Trop Res United Fruit Co La Lima Honduras Central America

KRIKORIAN, ABRAHAM D, b Worcester, Mass, May 5, 37. PLANT PHYSIOLOGY. *Educ:* Mass Col Pharm, BS, 59; Cornell Univ, PhD(plant physiol), 65. *Prof Exp:* From teaching asst to teaching assoc plant physiol, Cornell Univ, 60-64, from instr to asst prof, 63-66; asst prof biol sci, 66-71, ASSOC PROF BIOL SCI, STATE UNIV NY STONY BROOK, 71- *Mem:* AAAS; Am Soc Pharmacog; Int Soc Plant Morphol; Int Asn Plant Tissue Cult; Soc Develop Biol. *Res:* Physiological and morphological aspects of growth and development in flowering plants; morphogenesis and biochemical differentiation; nitrogen metabolism; production of secondary products and retention of biochemical potentialities by cells and tissues grown in culture. *Mailing Add:* Dept Biochem State Univ NY Stony Brook NY 11794

KRIKORIAN, ESTHER, b Chelsea, Mass. SOLID STATE PHYSICS, MATERIALS SCIENCE. *Educ:* Columbia Univ, BS, 50, PhD(phys chem), 57. *Prof Exp:* Lab asst phys chem, Columbia Univ, 49-50; fel, Brookhaven Nat Lab, 56-58; instr, Hunter Col, 60-61; staff scientist physics, 61-66, SR STAFF SCIENTIST PHYSICS, POMONA DIV, GEN DYNAMICS CORP, 66- *Mem:* Am Phys Soc; Am Vacuum Soc. *Res:* Crystal physics; infrared anisotropy in single crystals; a-decay in polonium-210; nucleation and growth of thin films of semiconductors, metals and dielectrics; epitaxial growth; organic semiconductors; semiconductor devices including electronic and electrooptical; integrated optics. *Mailing Add:* Pomona Div PO Box 2507 Pomona CA 91766

KRIKORIAN, JOHN SARKIS, JR, b Providence, RI, Sept 18, 41. ELECTRICAL ENGINEERING, APPLIED MATHEMATICS. *Educ:* Univ RI, BS, 63; Syracuse Univ, MS, 67, PhD(elec eng), 68. *Prof Exp:* Res specialist elec eng, Elec Boat Div, Gen Dynamics Corp, Groton, Conn, 68-73; ASST PROF, UNIV RI, 73- *Concurrent Pos:* Lectr elec eng, Univ Conn, 69. *Mem:* Inst Elec & Electronics Engrs; Sigma Xi. *Res:* Functional analysis approach to the stability of nonlinear systems; phase-lock loop operation in presence of noise; measurement and study of burst noise in semiconductors; development of small low-head hydro facilities. *Mailing Add:* 5 Thayer Pl Warwick RI 02888

KRIKORIAN, OSCAR HAROLD, b Fresno, Calif, Nov 22, 30; m 53; c 2. HIGH TEMPERATURE CHEMISTRY. *Educ:* Fresno State Col, BS, 52; Univ Calif, PhD(chem), 55. *Prof Exp:* RES CHEMIST, LAWRENCE LIVERMORE NAT LAB, 55- *Mem:* Fel Am Inst Chemists; Am Chem Soc. *Res:* High temperature chemistry; preparation and determination of physical properties of materials for use at temperatures of 1000-3000 degrees centigrade; thermodynamic properties of gaseous species that exist at high temperatures. *Mailing Add:* Lawrence Livermore Nat Lab PO Box 808 L-369 Livermore CA 94550

KRIKORIAN, SAMUEL EDWARD, JR, b Providence, RI, May 11, 30; m 58; c 4. MOLECULAR SPECTROSCOPY. *Educ:* Brown Univ, ScB, 51; Mass Inst Technol, PhD(org chem), 67. *Prof Exp:* Develop chemist, Procter & Gamble Co, 57-60, flavor chemist, 60-63; assoc prof chem, US Naval Acad, 67-69; ASSOC PROF MED CHEM, SCH PHARM, UNIV MD, BALTIMORE, 69- *Concurrent Pos:* Sci adv, Baltimore Dist Lab, Food & Drug Admin, 71-81; sr res fel, Chem Systs Lab, US Army ARRADCOM, 81- *Mem:* Am Chem Soc; Soc Appl Spectros; Coblentz Soc; Sigma Xi. *Res:* Analysis of drugs; near-infrared spectroscopy. *Mailing Add:* Dept of Med Chem Univ of Md Sch of Pharm Baltimore MD 21201

KRIKOS, GEORGE ALEXANDER, b Old Phaleron, Greece, Sept 17, 22; US citizen; m 49; c 3. PATHOLOGY. *Educ:* Univ Pa, DDS, 49; Univ Rochester, PhD(path), 59. *Prof Exp:* NIH res fel path, Univ Rochester, 54-58; from asst prof to prof, Sch Dent Med, Univ Pa, 58-68; prof path, 68-74, PROF ORAL BIOL & CHMN DEPT PATHOBIOL, SCH DENT, UNIV COLO, DENVER, 68- *Concurrent Pos:* Assoc prof oral path, Grad Sch Arts & Sci, Div Grad Educ, Sch Med, Univ Pa, 62-68, chmn dept path, 64-68. *Mem:* AAAS; Am Soc Exp Path; Am Acad Oral Path; Am Dent Asn; Int Asn Dent Res. *Res:* Connective tissue research. *Mailing Add:* Univ of Colo Sch of Dent C-285 Denver CO 80262

KRILL, ARTHUR MELVIN, b Burlington, Colo, Oct 17, 21; m 44; c 3. MECHANICAL ENGINEERING. *Educ:* Univ Colo, BS, 43, MS, 51. *Prof Exp:* Prod engr, Pratt-Whitney Aircraft Div, United Aircraft Corp, 42, exp test engr, 43-47; from instr to assoc prof mech engr, Col Eng, Univ Denver, 47-62, coord coop plan, 48-56, head admin eng, 51-52, proj supvr, 51-56; dir opers anal unit, Denver Res Inst, 55-62, head mech div, 56-62; pres, Falcon Res & Develop, 62-70; pres, Ken R White Co, 63-76 ; chmn, 76-78, PRES, ARTHUR M KRIL CONSULTS, 79- *Concurrent Pos:* Consult, Bond Eng Co, 50-52; pres, Falcon Res & Develop Co, 62-70; mem, Colo State Air Pollution Variance Bd. *Mem:* AAAS; Am Soc Mech Engrs; Am Soc Eng Educ; Nat Soc Prof Engrs; Am Inst Consult Engrs. *Res:* Theoretical and applied mechanics; operations research; behavioral sciences; magnetohydrodynamics. *Mailing Add:* 450 Westwood Dr Denver CO 80206

KRILL, FRANCIS M(ARION), b St Louis, Mo, Oct 2, 21; div; c 5. PHYSICAL METALLURGY. *Educ:* Univ Mo, BS, 43. *Prof Exp:* Res metallurgist, Aluminum Co Am, Ohio, 43-46; metallurgist, Manhattan Proj, Los Alamos Sci Lab, 46-47; HEAD METALLOG SECT, ALLOY RES, CTR TECHNOL, KAISER ALUMINUM & CHEM CORP, 48- *Mem:* Am Soc Metals. *Res:* Metallography of aluminum alloys. *Mailing Add:* Kaiser Aluminum & Chem Corp PO Box 877 Pleasanton CA 94566

KRIM, MATHILDE, b Como, Italy, July 9, 26; US citizen; m 58; c 1. CYTOGENETICS, VIROLOGY. *Educ:* Geneva Univ, BS, 48, PhD(cytogenetics), 53. *Prof Exp:* Jr scientist & res assoc cancer res, Weizmann Inst, 53-59; res assoc virol, Div Virus Res, Med Col, Cornell Univ, 59-62; assoc, 62-75, ASSOC & MEM, SLOAN-KETTERING INST CANCER RES, 75- *Concurrent Pos:* Mem, President's Comt Ment Retardation, 66-69, jury, Lasker Awards, 68-, adv comt health protection & dis prev, Secy, Dept Health, Educ & Welfare, 69-70, Nat Endowment for Humanities, 69-73, Comt of 100 for Nat Health Ins, 69- & panel of consult conquest of cancer, Comt Labor & Pub Welfare, US Senate, 71; consult spec virus cancer prog & mem adv comt, Nat Colorectal Cancer Prog, Nat Cancer Inst, 71; trustee, Rockefeller Found, 71-; co-chmn, Nat Comt to Save our Schs of Health, 71-; mem bd trustees, Nat Biomed Res Found; mem bd dirs, Inst Soc, Ethics & Life Sci; pres, Comn Study Ethnical Probs in Med, Biomed & Behav Res, 80- *Mem:* AAAS; Am Cancer Soc; Am Asn Ment Deficiency. *Res:* Structure of chromosomes; prenatal determination of sex; aberrations in human sexual development; cell biology and mechanisms of oncogenic transformation; interferon research. *Mailing Add:* 33 E 69th St New York NY 10021

KRIMEN, LEWIS IRVIN, organic chemistry, see previous edition

KRIMIGIS, STAMATIOS MIKE, b Chios, Greece, Sept 10, 38; US citizen; m 68; c 2. SPACE PHYSICS. *Educ:* Univ Minn, BPhys, 61; Univ Iowa, MS, 63, PhD(physics), 65. *Prof Exp:* Res assoc space physics, Univ Iowa, 65-66, asst prof physics, 66-68; from sr staff scientist to supvr space physics, 68-74, head space physics & instrumentation group, 74-79, CHIEF SCIENTIST, SPACE DEPT, APPL PHYSICS LAB, JOHNS HOPKINS UNIV, 79- *Concurrent Pos:* Co-investr, Mariner IV & Injun IV, 63, Orbiting Geophys Observ-4, Explorer 33 & 35 & Injun V, 65, Mariner V Venus, 66, prin investr, Interplanetary Monitoring Platform on 7 & 8, 67; mem var NASA adv comts on space invests; prin investr, Low Energy Charged Particle Exp, 72 & Active Magnetospheric Particle Tracer Explorers, 77; co-prin investr, Galileo Mission, Energetic Particle Detector Exp, 77 & co-investr, Int Solar-Polar Mission, LAN Exp, 77. *Mem:* AAAS; fel Am Geophys Union; Am Phys Soc. *Res:* Space plasma physics; solar and heliospheric physics; geomagnetically trapped radiation; planetary magnetospheres; cosmic rays; particle instrumentation. *Mailing Add:* Appl Physics Lab Johns Hopkins Univ Laurel MD 20810

KRIMM, SAMUEL, b Morristown, NJ, Oct 19, 25; m 49; c 2. PHYSICS, BIOPHYSICS. *Educ:* Polytech Inst Brooklyn, BS, 47; Princeton Univ, MA, 49, PhD(phys chem), 50. *Prof Exp:* Fel, 50-52, from instr to assoc prof physics, 52-63, assoc dean res, Col Lit Sci & Arts, 72-75, PROF PHYSICS, UNIV MICH, ANN ARBOR, 63-, CHMN BIOPHYSICS RES DIV, 76- *Concurrent Pos:* Consult, B F Goodrich Co & Allied Chem Corp; NSF sr fel, 62-63; chmn, Gordon Res Conf, 68; mem, Mat Res Adv Comt, NSF, 81- *Honors & Awards:* Am Phys Soc High Polymer Physics Prize, 77. *Mem:* AAAS; Am Chem Soc; Biophys Soc; fel Am Phys Soc; Am Crystallog Asn. *Res:* Infrared spectroscopy; x-ray diffraction; high polymers; protein structure; membrane structure. *Mailing Add:* Dept of Physcis Univ of Mich Ann Arbor MI 48109

KRIMMEL, PETER, b Erie, Pa, June 23, 17. MEDICINAL CHEMISTRY. *Educ:* Pa State Col, BS, 39, PhD(chem), 45; Northwestern Univ, MS, 41. *Prof Exp:* Instr chem, Pa State Col, 44-45; res chemist, 46-78, CONSULT, G D SEARLE & CO, 79- *Mem:* AAAS; Am Chem Soc. *Res:* Organic chemistry applied to pharmaceuticals; chemistry of kojic acid derivatives; spasmolytics; diuretics; cardioactive drugs; anti-atherosclerotic drugs; anti-virals and antibiotics; adamantane derivatives. *Mailing Add:* G D Searle & Co Dept Med Chem PO Box 5110 Chicago IL 60680

KRIMMER, EDWARD CHARLES, b Youngstown, Ohio, Dec 31, 33; m 58; c 3. PHARMACOLOGY, PSYCHOPHARMACOLOGY. *Educ:* Univ Pittsburgh, BS, 68, PhD(pharmacol), 74. *Prof Exp:* Fel pharmacol, Univ Pittsburgh, 74-76, asst prof, 76-81, ASSOC PROF PHARMACOL, UNIV PITTSBURGH, 81- *Concurrent Pos:* Consult, ICI US, 74-75; fel, Nat Inst Drug Abuse grant, 74-76; co-investr, NIMH grant, 76-; investr, Nat Inst Drug Abuse grant, 79- *Mem:* AAAS; Behav Pharmacol Soc; Sigma Xi; Soc Stimulus Properties Drugs (secy-treas, 78-80); Soc Neurosci. *Res:* Investigate the stimulus properties of various sedatives, axiolytics, narcotics and cannabinoids and the pharmacological antagonism or enhancement of these perceived effects. *Mailing Add:* Dept of Pharmacol Univ Pittsburgh Sch Pharm Pittsburgh PA 15261

KRINER, WILLIAM ARTHUR, b Pottsville, Pa, Feb 8, 31; m 57; c 2. INORGANIC CHEMISTRY. *Educ:* West Chester State Col, BS, 53; Univ Pa, PhD(inorg chem), 59. *Prof Exp:* Res chemist, Rohm and Haas Co, Pa, 59-61; lectr chem, Univ Pa, 62-65; asst prof, 65-70, ASSOC PROF CHEM, ST JOSEPHS UNIV, PA, 70- *Mem:* Am Chem Soc. *Res:* Small ring heterocyclics of Group IV preparation and reactivity; organometallic polymers; synthesis of novel organosilicon compounds; silicon hydride chemistry; boron cyanides and siloxy aluminum compounds. *Mailing Add:* Dept of Chem St Josephs Univ Philadelphia PA 19131

KRING, JAMES BURTON, b Monett, Mo, May 25, 21; m 47; c 5. ENTOMOLOGY. *Educ:* Rockhurst Col, BS, 47; Kans State Col, MS, 48, PhD(entom), 52. *Prof Exp:* Asst Instr Kans State Col, 50; asst biol, Rockhurst Col, 50; from asst entomologist to entomologist, Conn Agr Exp Sta, 51-77; PROF & HEAD DEPT ENTOMOL, UNIV MASS, 77- *Concurrent Pos:* Mem grad fac, Univ Conn, 59- ENTOMOLOGIST, CONN AGR EXP STA, UNIV CONN, 61-, MEM GRAD FAC, UNIV, 59- *Mem:* Entom Soc Am (pres, 79); AAAS; Royal Entom Soc London. *Res:* Ecology and systematics of Aphidae; control of economic pests and tobacco; behavior of vectors of plant diseases. *Mailing Add:* Dept of Entomol Univ of Mass Amherst MA 01003

KRINITZSKY, E(LLIS) L(OUIS), b Norfolk, Va, July 1, 24; m 52. ENGINEERING GEOLOGY. *Educ:* Va Polytech Inst, BS, 45; Univ NC, MS, 47; La State Univ, PhD(geol), 50. *Prof Exp:* Asst prof geol, Southwestern La Inst, 46-47; geologist, Army Corps Engrs, 48-53; sr geologist, Creole Petrol Corp, 53-61; vis prof, Univ Houston, 62-63; CHIEF GEOL RES, WATERWAYS EXP STA, ARMY CORPS ENGRS, 63- *Mem:* Fel Geol Soc Am; Am Asn Petrol Geol; Am Inst Prof Geol; Am Soc Civil Engrs; Int Soc Soil Mech & Found Engrs. *Res:* Engineering geology; river engineering; earthquake hazards, x-radiography. *Mailing Add:* Dept of the Army Corps of Engrs PO Box 631 Vicksburg MS 39180

KRINSKY, HERMAN Y, b Hudson, NY, Aug 6, 24; m 48; c 2. CHEMICAL ENGINEERING, THERMODYNAMICS. *Educ:* Univ Del, BChE, 48; Columbia Univ, MS, 51. *Prof Exp:* From instr to assoc prof, 51-66, chmn dept, 64-74, PROF CHEM ENG, PRATT INST, 66- *Mem:* Am Chem Soc; Am Inst Chem Eng. *Res:* Thermodynamics of irreversible processes, particularly as applied to transport. *Mailing Add:* Dept of Chem Eng Pratt Inst Brooklyn NY 11205

KRINSKY, NORMAN IRVING, b Iron River, Mich, June 29, 28; m 60; c 2. BIOCHEMISTRY. *Educ:* Univ Southern Calif, BA, 48, MS, 50, PhD(biochem), 53. *Prof Exp:* USPHS fel, Harvard Univ, 53-55, Nat Coun to Combat Blindness fel, 55-56, instr biol, 56-59, lectr, 59-60, from asst prof pharmacol to prof biochem, 60-70, PROF BIOCHEM & PHARMACOL, SCH MED, TUFTS UNIV, 70- *Concurrent Pos:* Vis prof, Sch Med, Boston Univ, 81-82; res assoc, Boston Vet Admin Med Ctr, 81-82. *Mem:* Am Chem Soc; Biophys Soc; NY Acad Sci; Am Soc Photobiol (secy-treas, 75-81, pres, 82-83); Am Soc Biol Chemists. *Res:* Function of carotenoids; photosensitization; mechanisms of membrane damage. *Mailing Add:* Dept of Biochem & Pharmacol Tufts Univ Sch of Med Boston MA 02111

KRINSKY, SAMUEL, b Brooklyn, NY, Jan 14, 45; m 72. STATISTICAL MECHANICS, ACCELERATOR PHYSICS. *Educ:* Mass Inst Technol, BS, 66; Yale Univ, PhD(physics), 71. *Prof Exp:* Res assoc physics, Inst Theoret Physics, State Univ NY Stony Brook, 71-73; asst physicist, 73-75, assoc physicist, 75-78, PHYSICIST, BROOKHAVEN NAT LAB, 78- *Res:* Particle beam dynamics in storage rings, undulators and wigglers as sources of synchrotron radiation; free electron lasers. *Mailing Add:* Brookhaven Nat Lab Upton NY 11973

KRINSKY, WILLIAM LEWIS, b Brooklyn, NY, Jan 10, 47; m 70; c 1. MEDICAL ENTOMOLOGY, PARASITOLOGY. *Educ:* Yale Univ, AB, 67, MD, 74; Cornell Univ, PhD(entom), 74. *Prof Exp:* Res assoc med entom, Rocky Mountain Lab, Nat Inst Allergy & Infectious Dis, 74-77; ASST PROF EPIDEMIOL, SECT MED ENTOM, DEPT EPIDEMIOL & PUB HEALTH, SCH MED, YALE UNIV, 77- *Concurrent Pos:* Fac affil entomol, Peabody Mus Natural Hist, Yale Univ, 80- *Mem:* Entom Soc Am; Am Soc Parasitologists; Am Soc Trop Med & Hyg; Royal Soc Trop Med & Hyg. *Res:* Medical entomology, acarology and parasitology; arthropod-borne parasites; protozoans; vector-parasite interactions and mechanisms of transmission. *Mailing Add:* Sect Med Entom Sch Med Yale Univ PO Box 3333 New Haven CT 06510

KRINSLEY, DAVID, b Chicago, Ill, Jan 9, 27; m 58; c 3. SEDIMENTOLOGY. *Educ:* Univ Chicago, PhB, 48, SB & SM, 50, PhD(geol), 56. *Prof Exp:* Asst geol, Univ Ill, 54-55, instr, 55-56; micropaleontologist & geochemist oceanog & geochem, Lamont Geol Observ, Columbia Univ, 56-57; from instr to prof geol, Queens Col, NY, 57-76, chmn dept geol & geog, 62-65, assoc dean fac, 66-70, actg dean fac, 70; chmn dept, 76-82, PROF GEOL, ARIZ STATE UNIV, 76- *Concurrent Pos:* Grants, Am Philos Soc, 59, Petrol Res Fund, Am Chem Soc, 60 & NASA, 76-; overseas fel, Churchill Col, Cambridge Univ, 70-71. *Mem:* Fel AAAS; Geochem Soc; Soc Econ Paleont & Mineral; Geol Soc Am. *Res:* Surface textures of sand grains via electron microscopy. *Mailing Add:* 312 E Geneva Dr Tempe AZ 85282

KRIPALANI, KISHIN J, b Karachi, W Pakistan, Oct 3, 37; m 66; c 2. DRUG METABOLISM, BIOPHARMACEUTICS. *Educ:* Univ Bombay, BSc Hons, 57, BSc, 59; Univ Calif, PhD(pharmaceut chem), 66. *Prof Exp:* Staff scientist, Worcester Found Exp Biol, Shrewsbury, Mass, 67-68, NIH fel steroid biochem, 68-69; RES GROUP LEADER DRUG METAB, SQUIBB INST MED RES, E R SQUIBB & SONS, INC, 69- *Mem:* Am Chem Soc; NY Acad Sci. *Res:* Drug metabolism; drug-protein interactions; biotransformations, and biopharmaceutics of drugs in animal species and humans, mechanism of drug-induced drug-enzyme interactions. *Mailing Add:* Dept of Drug Metab Squibb Inst for Med Res New Brunswick NJ 08903

KRIPKE, BENJAMIN JOSHUA, anesthesiology, see previous edition

KRIPKE, BERNARD ROBERT, b Washington, DC, Aug 25, 39; m 79; c 1. VISION, LEARNING DISABILITIES. *Educ:* Harvard Col, AB, 59; Harvard Univ, AM, 60, PhD(math), 64. *Prof Exp:* Staff mem math, Mass Inst Technol, 62-63; asst prof, Univ Tex, Austin, 63-64 & Univ Calif, Berkeley, 64-69; vis lectr vision, Hadassah Hosp, Hebrew Univ, 69-70; vis fel biophysics, Ohio State Univ, 70-72; res instr, 72-76, ASST PROF PHYSIOL, SCH MED, UNIV UTAH, 76- *Concurrent Pos:* Consult, Utah State Budget Off, 80-81 & Utah State Div Data Processing, 81-82. *Mem:* AAAS; Soc Neurosci. *Res:* Effects of visual deprivation on cat striate cortex; hereditary learning disability; analytic functions of several complex variables; approximation in banach spaces. *Mailing Add:* Dept Physiol Univ Utah 410 Chipeta Way Salt Lake City UT 84108

KRIPKE, DANIEL FREDERICK, b Washington, DC, Oct 12, 41; c 2. SLEEP DISORDERS, BIOLOGICAL RHYTHMS. *Educ:* Harvard Col, BA, 61; Col Physicians & Surgeons, Columbia Univ, MD, 65. *Prof Exp:* Intern, Bronx Municipal Hosp Ctr, 65-66; resident psychiat, Albert Einstein Col Med, 68-72; asst prof, 71-78, assoc prof, 78-82, PROF, DEPT PSYCHIAT, UNIV CALIF, SAN DIEGO, 82- *Concurrent Pos:* Attending physician, Dept

Psychiat, Univ Hosp, Univ Calif, San Diego, 71-; staff psychiatrist, San Diego Vet Admin Med Ctr & dir, Sleep Disorders Clinic, 72-, clin investr biol rhythms, 72-76, dir psychiat, Emergency Evaluation & Crisis Serv, 76-77; ed, J Sleep Res, 79-80; consult, US Surgeon Gen Proj Sleep, 80. *Mem:* AAAS; Asn Psychophysiol Study Sleep; Int Soc Chronobiol; Soc Psychophysiol Res; Am Psychiat Soc. *Mailing Add:* Dept Psychiat 116A Vet Admin Med Ctr 3350 La Jolla Village Dr San Diego CA 92161

KRIPKE, MARGARET LOUISE (COOK), b Concord, Calif, July 21, 43. CANCER, IMMUNOBIOLOGY. *Educ:* Univ Calif, Berkeley, AB, 65, MA, 67, PhD(immunol), 70. *Prof Exp:* Teaching asst immunol, Univ Calif, Berkeley, 65-66; res assoc, Ohio State Univ, Columbus, 70-72; res assoc, Sch Med, Univ Louisville, 72; asst prof path, Col Med, Univ Utah, 72-75; sr prin scientist cancer, 75-79, DIR, CANCER BIOL PROG, FREDERICK CANCER RES CTR, 79- *Concurrent Pos:* Chancellors distinguished lectr, Univ Calif, Berkeley, 80. *Honors & Awards:* Edna Roe Mem lectr, Int Cong Photo Biol, 80. *Mem:* Am Asn Cancer Res; Am Soc Photobiol; Transplantation Soc; AAAS; Soc Investigative Dermat. *Res:* Mechanisms of immunologic responses to tumors; relationship between the immune system and carcinogenesis; nature and significance of tumor antigens using the system of experimental ultraviolet carcinogenesis; effects of ultraviolet radiation on immunologic processes. *Mailing Add:* Frederick Cancer Res Ctr PO Box B Frederick MD 21701

KRIPPAEHNE, WILLIAM W, b Douglas, Alaska, Nov 3, 17; m 49; c 7. SURGERY. *Educ:* Univ Wash, BS, 43; Univ Ore, MD, 46; Am Bd Surg, dipl, 56. *Prof Exp:* From instr to assoc prof, 53-65, actg chmn, 64-65, PROF SURG & CHMN DEPT, MED SCH, UNIV ORE, 65- *Concurrent Pos:* Consult, Vet Admin Hosp, Portland, Ore, 59- *Mem:* Soc Surg Oncol; Am Col Surgeons. *Res:* Cancer; healing of vascular prostheses; tissue transplantation. *Mailing Add:* Dept of Surg Univ of Ore Med Sch Portland OR 97201

KRISCH, ALAN DAVID, b Philadelphia, Pa, Apr 19, 39; m 61; c 1. HIGH ENERGY PHYSICS. *Educ:* Univ Pa, BA, 60; Cornell Univ, PhD(physics), 64. *Prof Exp:* Instr physics, Cornell Univ, 64; from asst prof to assoc prof, 64-68, PROF PHYSICS, UNIV MICH, ANN ARBOR, 68- *Concurrent Pos:* Guggenheim fel, 71; trustee, Argonne Univ Assoc, 72-73 & 80-, chmn, Argonne ZGS Users Group, 74-76 & 78-79; vis prof, Niels Bohr Inst, Copenhagen, 75-76. *Mem:* AAAS; fel Am Phys Soc. *Res:* Experiments on high energy elastic and inelastic scattering of strongly interacting particles; experiments on spin dependence of strong interactions; phenomenology of strong interactions. *Mailing Add:* Randall Lab of Physics Univ of Mich Ann Arbor MI 48104

KRISCH, JEAN PECK, b Washington, DC, May 23, 39; m 61; c 1. HIGH ENERGY THEORETICAL PHYSICS, ASTROPHYSICS. *Educ:* Univ Md, BS, 60; Cornell Univ, MS, 62, PhD(physics), 65. *Prof Exp:* Teaching asst physics, Cornell Univ, 60-65; res assoc, 65-75, LECTR PHYSICS, UNIV MICH, 76- *Mem:* Am Asn Physics Teachers. *Res:* High energy particle physics; general relativity. *Mailing Add:* Dept of Physics Univ of Mich Ann Arbor MI 48104

KRISCH, ROBERT EARLE, b Philadelphia, Pa, Jan 29, 37; m 70. BIOPHYSICS. *Educ:* Univ Pa, BA, 56, MS, 62, PhD(physics), 64; Temple Univ, MS, 60. *Prof Exp:* Instr physics, Univ Pa, 64-65; asst biophysicist, Argonne Nat Lab, 65-72, biophysicist, Div Biol & Med Res, 72-77; SPEC FEL, DEPT RADIATION THERAPY, HARVARD MED SCH, 77- *Mem:* Radiation Res Soc; Biophys Soc. *Res:* Radiation biology. *Mailing Add:* Dept of Radiation Therapy 50 Binney St Boston MA 02115

KRISE, GEORGE MARTIN, b San Antonio, Tex, May 12, 19; m 43; c 2. PHYSIOLOGY. *Educ:* Univ Tex, BS, 46, MA, 48, PhD(zool), 52. *Prof Exp:* From instr to asst prof biol, St Edward's Univ, 49-51; res scientist physiol, Univ Tex, 52-58, ; admin officer, Dept Biol, 69-74, PROF PHYSIOL, TEX A&M UNIV, 58- *Res:* Microbial physiology; effects of ionizing radiations on various species. *Mailing Add:* Dept of Biol Tex A&M Univ College Station TX 77843

KRISHAN, AWTAR, b Sprinagar, India, Oct 11, 37; US citizen; m 55; c 3. CANCER RESEARCH & CHEMOTHERAPY. *Educ:* Panja Univ, India, PhD(zool), 63; Univ Western Ont, PhD(anat), 64. *Prof Exp:* Res prof cytogenetics, Univ Minn, St Paul, 65-66; cytologist, Children's Cancer Res Inst, Boston, 66-71, chief cancer res, Div Exp Path & Lab Cytokinetics, 72-77; assoc prof, 77-79, PROF ONCOL, MED SCH, UNIV MIAMI, 79- *Concurrent Pos:* Chief, Div Cytokinetics, Comp Cancer Ctr, State Fla, 77- *Honors & Awards:* Collip Medal, Univ Western Ont, 65. *Mem:* Am Asn Cancer Res; Cell Kinetics Soc Am; Electron Micros Soc (pres, 75-76). *Res:* Tumor cell kinetics; effect of cancer chemotheraphy on tumor growth; use of laser flow cytometry for monitoring drug uptake. *Mailing Add:* Med Sch Univ Miami R-71 PO Box 016960 Miami FL 33101

KRISHEN, ANOOP, b Ludhiana, India, Aug 7, 27; m 57; c 2. ANALYTICAL CHEMISTRY. *Educ:* Univ Panjab, India, BSc, 48, MSc, 49; Univ Pittsburgh, PhD, 57. *Prof Exp:* Lectr chem, Govt Col, Ludhiana, India, 49-50; res asst anal chem, Nat Phys Lab, India, 50-52; sr res chemist, B F Goodrich Co Res Ctr, 57-62; chief chemist, Synthetics & Chem Ltd, India, 62-63; SR RES CHEMIST, RES DIV, GOODYEAR TIRE & RUBBER CO, 63- *Mem:* Am Chem Soc. *Res:* Pyrolysis-gas chromatography; high speed liquid chromatography; instrumental analysis; gas chromatography. *Mailing Add:* Goodyear Tire & Rubber Co Res Div 142 Goodyear Blvd Akron OH 44316

KRISHEN, KUMAR, b Srinagar, India, June 22, 39; US citizen; m 61; c 3. ELECTRONICS, REMOTE SENSING. *Educ:* Univ Jammu & Kashmir, BA, 59; Univ Calcutta, BTech, 62, MTech, 63; Kans State Univ, MS, 66, PhD(electronics), 68. *Prof Exp:* Res fel, Univ Calcutta, 64-65; res asst & instr elec eng, Kans State Univ, 65-68, asst prof, 68-69; staff scientist & engr earth observ, Lockheed Electronics Co, 69-76; proj mgr earth resources microwave prog, 76-78, mgr advan microwave prog, 68-81, COORDR ADV PROG, EXP SYST DIV, JOHNSON SPACE CTR, NASA, 81- *Concurrent Pos:* Consult applns investr, NASA, 69-76, proj leader, Skylab Microwave Sensors Eval Team, 73-75, mem, NASA active microwave workshops, 74-77, mem agr panel earth resources, 76-77, chmn water resources panel, Microwave Remote Sensing Symp, 77; reviewer, Radio Sci, 75-; memm, Synthetic Aperture Radar Team, NASA, 76-80; lectr, Univ Houston, 77- *Honors & Awards:* Gold Medal, Calcutta Univ, 62, Silver Medal, 63; Highest Merit Award, J&K Univ; Commendation Except Performance, NASA, 71 & 74. *Mem:* Sr mem Inst Elec & Electronics Engrs; Am Soc Eng Educ; Am Inst Aeronaut & Astronaut; Radio Physics & Electronics Asn; Sigma Xi. *Res:* Applications of microwaves to the field of remote sensing of earth resources and ocean/weather phenomena and human health; developing specifications for space borne microwave systems for earth resources, ocean and weather sensing microwave sensors. *Mailing Add:* NASA Johnson Space Ctr Code ED6 Houston TX 77058

KRISHER, LAWRENCE CHARLES, b Rochester, NY, Aug 21, 33. CHEMICAL PHYSICS. *Educ:* Syracuse Univ, AB, 55; Harvard Univ, AM, 57, PhD(chem), 59. *Prof Exp:* NSF fel physics, Columbia Univ, 59-61, asst prof, 61-63; from asst prof to assoc prof, 63-75, PROF PHYSICS, INST PHYS SCI & TECHNOL, UNIV MD, COLLEGE PARK, 75- *Res:* Microwave spectroscopy; molecular dynamics; molecular structure; radioastronomy. *Mailing Add:* Inst Phys Sci & Technol Univ of Md College Park MD 20742

KRISHNA, C R, b Bangalore, India, May 31, 39; m 74; c 3. ENGINEERING, COMBUSTION. *Educ:* Indian Inst Sci, ME, 61; State Univ NY, Stony Brook, PhD(eng), 74. *Prof Exp:* Engr, Hindustan Aeronaut Ltd, India, 61-69; res assoc, 74-76, ASSOC ENGR, BROOKHAVEN NAT LAB, 76- *Mem:* Combustion Inst. *Res:* Fluidized beds; coal-slurries. *Mailing Add:* Dept of Eng Brookhaven Nat Lab Upton NY 11973

KRISHNA, KUMAR, b Dehradun, India, June 21, 30; US citizen; m 60. ZOOLOGY, ENTOMOLOGY. *Educ:* Agra Univ, BS, 50; Univ Lucknow, MS, 52; Univ Chicago, PhD(zool), 61. *Prof Exp:* Res asst, Forest Res Inst, India, 52-54; teaching asst biol, Univ Ill at Chicago Circle, 58-60; res assoc, Univ Chicago, 60-62; from instr to assoc prof, 62-74, PROF BIOL, CITY COL NEW YORK, 74- *Concurrent Pos:* Res assoc, Am Mus Natural Hist, 62-; NSF res grant, 62- *Mem:* Am Soc Zoologists; Soc Syst Zoologists; Int Union Study Soc Insects. *Res:* Taxonomy, ecology, zoogeography and evolution of termites; general evolutionary theory. *Mailing Add:* Dept Biol City Col of New York 139th St at Convent Ave New York NY 10031

KRISHNAIAH, PARUCHURI RAMA, b India, July 15, 32; nat US; m 60. STATISTICS. *Educ:* Univ Madras, BSc, 54; Univ Minn, MA, 57, PhD(statist), 63. *Prof Exp:* Sr statistician, Appl Math Dept, Remington Rand Univac, 60-63; res math statistician, Aerospace Res Labs, Wright Patterson AFB, 63-75, math statistician, Air Force Flight Dynamics Lab, 75-76; PROF DEPT MATH & STATIST, UNIV PITTSBURGH, 76- *Concurrent Pos:* Chmn Int Symp Multivariate Anal, Dayton, Ohio, 65, 68, 72 & 75; vis scientist, Indian Statist Inst, Calcutta, 66; ed, J Multivariate Anal; chmn, Symp Appln Statistics, 76; chmn, Fifth Int Symp Multivariate Anal, 78; gen ed, Statistics & Develop in Statist. *Mem:* Fel AAAS; Am Statist Asn; Inst Math Statist. *Res:* Theoretical research in multivariate analysis; application of statistics in physical, engineering and behavioral sciences. *Mailing Add:* Dept of Math & Statist Univ of Pittsburgh Pittsburgh PA 15260

KRISHNAMOORTHY, GOVINDARAJALU, b Tanjore, India, Jan 1, 31; m 56; c 1. STRUCTURAL MECHANICS, CIVIL ENGINEERING. *Educ:* Col Eng, Guindy, India, BSCE, 52; Ill Inst Technol, MSCE, 60, PhD(struct), 65. *Prof Exp:* Jr engr, Madras Hwy Dept, India, 52-57; from instr to asst prof civil eng, Ill Inst Technol, 61-68; from asst prof to assoc prof, 68-74, PROF CIVIL ENG, SCH ENG, SAN DIEGO STATE UNIV, 74- *Concurrent Pos:* Consult, IIT Res Inst, 67-, Rohr Corp, 69-70 & SAI, La Jolla. *Mem:* Am Soc Civil Engrs; Am Soc Eng Educ. *Res:* Buckling of shells; computer applications in structures; analysis and design of ocean structures; reinforced concrete masonry structures; dynamic and thermal response of mountings on main cooling pipe of nuclear reactors; computer graphics; computer aided design. *Mailing Add:* Dept of Civil Eng Col of Eng San Diego State Univ San Diego CA 92115

KRISHNAMURTHY, RAMANATHAPUR GUNDACHAR, b Mysore, India, May 8, 31; m 60; c 3. FOOD CHEMISTRY, BIOCHEMISTRY. *Educ:* Univ Mysore, BS, 51; Rutgers Univ, MS, 64, PhD(food sci), 65. *Prof Exp:* Lab asst metall, Indian Inst Sci, India, 51-54; sci asst food technol, Cent Food Technol Res Inst, Mysore, 54-61; res asst food sci, Rutgers Univ, 61-63, res fel, 63-65, asst res prof, 65-66; res chemist, Best Foods Div, Corn Prod Co, 66-67; group leader, 67-77, SR GROUP LEADER EDIBLE OIL PROD, RES & DEVELOP DIV, KRAFT, INC, 77- *Honors & Awards:* Award of Merit, Am Oil Chemists Soc, 74. *Mem:* Am Chem Soc; Am Oil Chemists Soc; Inst Food Technol. *Res:* Autoxidation and thermal oxidation of fats and oils; investigation of flavors and flavor percursors in foods; chemistry and technology of oils and fats and products derived from them. *Mailing Add:* 3059 Crestwood Lane Glenview IL 60025

KRISHNAMURTHY, SUBRAMANIAN, b Trichinopoly, Madras, India, Dec 27, 40; US citizen; m 67; c 1. POLYMER SCIENCE, CHEMICAL ENGINEERING. *Educ:* Univ Bombay, BS, 63; Johns Hopkins Univ, MS, 67; Univ Akron, PhD(polymer sci), 71. *Prof Exp:* Chem engr, Firestone Plastics Co, 66-67; res assoc membranes, Univ Akron, 71-73; develop chemist, AMF Ben Hogan Co, Subsid Am Machine & Foundry, Inc, 73-75, mgr prod develop plastics & elastomers, 75-80; mem tech staff, Tex Instruments, 80-81; SR PROCESS ENGR, D M INTERNATIONAL INC, 81- *Mem:* Am Chem Soc; Am Inst Chem Engrs; Soc Plastics Engrs. *Res:* Materials selection, evaluation and processing; mold and tool design and engineering toward high precision, close tolerance parts and products. *Mailing Add:* D M International Inc 2912 W Pafford St Houston TX 77036

KRISHNAMURTHY, SUNDARAM, b Coimbatore, Madras, India, Nov 26, 44; m 75. ORGANIC CHEMISTRY. *Educ:* Univ Madras, BSc, 64, MSc, 66; Purdue Univ, PhD(chem), 71. *Prof Exp:* Sr res assoc chem, Purdue Univ, West Lafayette, 71-80; MEM RES STAFF, RES LAB, EASTMAN KODAK CO, 80- *Mem:* Am Chem Soc. *Res:* Synthesis and application of trialkylborohydrides in stereospecific and reguospecific organic synthesis; selective reductions; organometallics in organic synthesis. *Mailing Add:* Eastman Kodak Co Res Lab Bldg 82 Kodak Park Rochester NY 14650

KRISHNAMURTI, CUDDALORE RAJAGOPAL, b Cuddalore, India, Apr 16, 29; m 53; c 2. ANIMAL PHYSIOLOGY, ANIMAL BIOCHEMISTRY. *Educ:* Univ Madras, BVSc, 51, MVSc, 61; Univ Alta, PhD(animal nutrit), 66. *Prof Exp:* Asst lectr physiol, parasitol & bact, Madras Vet Col, 55-59; bacteriologist, Inst Vet Prev Med, Ranipet, 62; res assoc animal nutrit, Univ Alta, 66-67; assoc prof, 67-75, PROF & ACTING HEAD, DEPT ANIMAL SCI, UNIV BC, 75- *Mem:* Agr Inst Can; Nutrit Soc Can; Can Soc Animal Sci. *Res:* Biochemical investigations on rumen microorganisms; fetal physiology; digestion, absorption and metabolism of nutrients by the ruminant animal, especially metabolic disorders. *Mailing Add:* Dept of Animal Sci Univ of BC Vancouver BC V6T 1E1 Can

KRISHNAMURTI, PULLABHOTLA V, b Gudivada, India, Mar 1, 23; m 49; c 5. VETERINARY MICROBIOLOGY. *Educ:* Univ Madras, BVSc, 49, DVP, 58; Univ Wis-Madison, MS, 61; Tex A&M Univ, PhD(vet microbiol), 67. *Prof Exp:* State vet, Andhra Vet Serv, India, 48-54; instr vet sci & exten vet, Exten Training Ctr, 55-56; asst lectr, Andhra Vet Col, 57-58; res asst, Univ Wis-Madison, 59-63; researcher poultry dis, Hy-line Poultry Farms, Iowa, 64-65; res asst vet microbiol, Tex A&M Univ, 65-66; from asst prof to assoc prof, sch vet med, Tuskegee Inst, 66-69; assoc prof microbiol, 69-74, PROF BIOL, SAVANNAH STATE COL, 74- *Mem:* Am Vet Med Asn; Am Soc Parasitol; Poultry Sci Asn; Am Asn Avian Path. *Res:* Parasites and parasitism; plasmodium in Wisconsin chickens; cultivation of Histomonas meleagridis free of bacteria and its demonstration in tissues and cell cultures using fluorescent labeled antibody techniques; therapeutic agents in canine distemper. *Mailing Add:* Dept of Biol Savannah State Col Savannah GA 31404

KRISHNAMURTI, RUBY EBISUZAKI, b Haney, BC, Oct 23, 34; m 60. PHYSICS, FLUID MECHANICS. *Educ:* Univ Western Ont, BSc, 57; Univ Chicago, MS, 60; Univ Calif, Los Angeles, PhD(physics), 67. *Prof Exp:* Res assoc fluid mech, Stanford Univ, 67; assoc prof oceanog, 71-75, SR RES ASSOC, GEOPHYS FLUID DYNAMICS INST, FLA STATE UNIV, 67-, PROF OCEANOG, 75- *Concurrent Pos:* Asst prof oceanog, Fla State Univ, 68-71. *Mem:* Am Phys Soc; Am Meteorol Soc; Am Geophys Union. *Res:* Geophysical fluid dynamics, particularly theoretical and experimental studies of convection and ocean circulation modelling. *Mailing Add:* Dept of Oceanog Fla State Univ Tallahassee FL 32306

KRISHNAMURTI, TIRUVALAM N, b Madras, India, Jan 10, 32; nat US. METEOROLOGY, ATMOSPHERIC SCIENCE. *Educ:* Univ Delhi, BS, 51; Andhra Univ, India, MS, 53; Univ Chicago, PhD(meteorol), 59. *Prof Exp:* Prof meteorol, Univ Calif, Los Angeles, 60-67; assoc prof, 67-70, PROF METEOROL, FLA STATE UNIV, 70- *Concurrent Pos:* Mem, Global Atmospheric Res Prog working group on struct of the trop atmosphere, 69-71; mem, Adv Panel to Nat Oceanic & Atmospheric Admin on Nuclear Metal Conf, 71-73; consult synoptic subprog, GATE, Nat Acad Sci, 73-74; external examr, Univ Nairobi, Kenya, 73-76 & McGill Univ PhD students, 74-77; consult, MONEX Comt, World Meteorol Orgn, 75-76; vis lectr, Ctr Theoret Physics, Trieste, Italy, 75; mem, US Global Atmospheric Res Prog, 75-; assoc ed, J Atmospheric Sci, 75-; chmn, US MONEX Panel, Nat Acad Sci, 76-; mem, Working Group on Numerical Experimentation Global Atmospheric Res Prog, Joint Organizing Comt; mem, Comt Atmospheric Sci, Nat Acad Sci, 79- *Honors & Awards:* Half-Century Award, Am Meteorol Soc, 74 & 76. *Mem:* Fel Am Meteorol Soc; Am Geophys Union; fel Royal Meteorol Soc; Meteorol Soc Japan. *Res:* Dynamic and synoptic meteorology, including diagnostic and prognostic studies of tropical and mid-latitude systems using real input data together with analyses of tropical weather systems using satellite and aircraft information in sparse conventional data areas. *Mailing Add:* Dept of Meteorol Fla State Univ Tallahassee FL 32306

KRISHNAN, KAMALA SIVASUBRAMANIAM, b Tiruchirappalli, India, Nov 12, 37; US citizen; m 58; c 3. OPTICAL PHYSICS, SOLID STATE SCIENCE. *Educ:* Univ Madras, MA, 57; Indian Inst Sci, Bangalore, DIISc, 60; Univ Fla, PhD(physics), 66. *Prof Exp:* Res scientist solid state physics, Res Div, Am Standard Inc, 65-68; sr res physicist, Stanford Res Inst, 68-77; MGR ELECTRO-OPTICS, SYSTS CONTROL TECHNOL, INC, 77- *Concurrent Pos:* Vis prof mat sci, San Jose State Univ, 74- *Mem:* Am Phys Soc; Optical Soc Am; Sigma Xi. *Res:* Optical and infrared systems; laser physics and applications; nonlinear optics; applied statistics; remote sensing; oceanography. *Mailing Add:* Systs Control Inc 1801 Page Mill Rd Palo Alto CA 94304

KRISHNAN, VENKATANAMA, b Madras, India, Oct 20, 29. ELECTRICAL & SYSTEMS ENGINEERING. *Educ:* Univ Madras, BSc, 48; Banares Hindu Univ, BSc, 53; Princeton Univ, MSE, 59; Univ Pa, PhD(elec eng), 63. *Prof Exp:* Instr chem, Loyola Col, Madras Univ, 48-49; sr res asst elec eng, Indian Inst Sci Bangalore, 53-56; instr, Princeton Univ, 57-58; asst prof, Villanova Univ, 58-61; assoc, Moore Sch Elec Eng, Pa, 61-64; asst prof, Polytech Inst Brooklyn, 64-66, assoc prof, 66-76; MEM FAC, DEPT ELEC ENG, SAN FRANCISCO STATE UNIV, 76- *Mem:* Inst Elec & Electronics Engrs. *Res:* Inertial navigation systems; control theory; electronic circuits and solid state physics. *Mailing Add:* Dept of Elec Eng 1600 Holloway San Francisco CA 94132

KRISHNAN, VIAKALATHUR SANKRITHI, b Madras, India, Oct 11, 19; m 54; c 2. MATHEMATICS. *Educ:* Univ Madras, dipl, 39, MSc, 43, BT, 46; Presidency Col Madras, BA, 40, MA, 41; Univ Paris, DSc, 51. *Prof Exp:* Asst prof math, Govt Madras, 46-49; reader, Univ Madras, 52-57, prof, 57-69; PROF MATH, TEMPLE UNIV, 69- *Concurrent Pos:* Mem, Nat Sch Math Textbks Comt, India, 60-61; univ fel, Univ Chicago, 62; vis prof, State Univ NY Buffalo, 64-66 & Univ Ottawa, 66-67. *Mem:* Am Math Soc; Math Asn Am; Math Soc Can; Math Soc France; Indian Math Soc. *Res:* Algebra, including ordered structures; topology; category theory. *Mailing Add:* Dept of Math Temple Univ N Broad St Philadelphia PA 19122

KRISHNAPPAN, BOMMANNA GOUNDER, b Madras, India, Jan 15, 43; Can citizen; m 72; c 2. HYDRAULICS, FLUID MECHANICS. *Educ:* Madras Univ, BE, 66; Univ Calgary, MSc, 68; Queen's Univ, Ont, PhD(civil eng), 72. *Prof Exp:* Res scientist, Can Ctr Inland Waters, 72-77; flow syst engr, Ont Hydro, 77-78; RES SCIENTIST HYDRAUL, NAT WATER RES INST, CAN CTR INLAND WATERS, ONT, 78- *Concurrent Pos:* Asst, Nat Res Coun Can, 66-72. *Res:* Sediment transport in open channel flows; dispersion of mass in open channels; mathematical models for river morphology; thermal models. *Mailing Add:* Environ Hydraul Sect CCIW 867 Lakeshore Rd Burlington ON L7R 4R6 Can

KRISHNAPRASAD, PERINKULAM S, b Bombay, India, May 15, 49. SYSTEM THEORY. *Educ:* Indian Inst Technol, BTech, 72; Syracuse Univ, MS, 73; Harvard Univ, PhD(eng), 77. *Prof Exp:* Asst prof systs eng, Case Inst Technol, 77-80; ASST PROF ELEC ENG, UNIV MD, 80- *Mem:* Inst Elec & Electronics Engrs; Am Math Soc. *Res:* System theory and applications to modeling; geometric methods applied to problems in systems; control theory and nonlinear mechanics. *Mailing Add:* Dept Elec Eng Univ Md College Park MD 20742

KRISHTALKA, LEONARD, b Montreal, Can, Jan 30, 46. MAMMALIAN PALEONTOLOGY. *Educ:* Univ Alta, BSc, 69, MSc, 71; Tex Tech Univ, Lubbock, PhD(biol & vert paleont), 75. *Prof Exp:* Fel, 75-76, res fel, 76-77, asst cur, 77-80, ASSOC CUR, CARNEGIE MUS NATURAL HIST, 80- *Concurrent Pos:* Adj lectr, Univ Pittsburgh, 76-77, adj asst prof, 77-80, adj assoc prof, 80- *Mem:* Soc Vert Paleont; AAAS. *Res:* Origin, evolution, relationships, paleocology and systematics of early Tertiary and Mesozoic mammals, especially primates, insectivores and multituberculates; African Neogene hominids and microfaunal paleontology. *Mailing Add:* Sect Vert Fossils Carnegie Mus Carnegie Mus Natural Hist Pittsburgh PA 15213

KRISS, JOSEPH P, b Philadelphia, Pa, May 15, 19; m 48; c 3. INTERNAL MEDICINE. *Educ:* Pa State Col, BS, 39; Yale Univ, MD, 43. *Prof Exp:* Asst med, Sch Med, Yale Univ, 43-44, instr, 44-45; res fel metab, Sch Med, Univ Wash, 46-48; asst med, 48-50, clin instr, 50-52, asst clin prof, 52-56, assoc clin prof, 56-57, assoc prof, 57-62, PROF MED & RADIOL, SCH MED, STANFORD UNIV, 62- *Concurrent Pos:* Intern, New Haven Hosp, Conn, 43-44, asst resident, 44, assoc resident, 44-45, resident, 45; consult, Vet Admin Hosp, San Francisco, 49-59 & Palo Alto, 59-; USPHS spec fel biochem, Stanford Univ, 66-67. *Mem:* Endocrine Soc; Am Soc Nuclear Med; Am Fedn Clin Res; Am Thyroid Asn; Asn Am Physicians. *Res:* Nuclear medicine; endocrinology; thyroid disorders; nuclear cardiology. *Mailing Add:* Div of Nuclear Med Stanford Med Ctr Palo Alto CA 94305

KRISS, MICHAEL ALLEN, b San Diego, Calif, Dec 14, 40; m 63; c 3. PHYSICS, COMPUTER SCIENCES. *Educ:* Univ Calif, Los Angeles, AB, 62, MS, 64, PhD(physics), 69. *Prof Exp:* res assoc, Color Photog Div, 69-79, RES ASSOC PHYSICS DIV, RES LABS, EASTMAN KODAK, 79-; LECTR, UNIV COL, UNIV ROCHESTER, 76- *Mem:* Soc Photograph Scientist & Engrs; Sigma Xi. *Res:* Photographic sciences; photographic research with emphasis on the mechanisms of color reproduction and image structure photographic film systems; development of methods to measure and evaluate the color reproduction and image structure of photographic and non-photographic systems; image processing by use of computers. *Mailing Add:* Physics Div Res Labs Eastman Kodak Co 1669 Lake Ave Rochester NY 14650

KRIST, F KEVIN, b New York, NY, Nov 10, 38; m 70; c 2. INORGANIC CHEMISTRY, PHYSICAL CHEMISTRY. *Educ:* Fordham Univ, BS, 60; Yale Univ, MS, 61, PhD(phys chem, inorg chem), 66. *Prof Exp:* Sr engr, Fairchild Camera & Instrument Corp, 66-68; sr scientist laser develop, Control Data Corp, TRG Div, 68-71; sci instr chem & physics, St Mary's High Sch, 71-78; asst prof chem, Elmira Col, 78-80. *Concurrent Pos:* Adj asst prof chem, Queen's Col, 77-78. *Mem:* Am Chem Soc. *Res:* Kinetics of inorganic excited states and its relation to solar energy conversion. *Mailing Add:* 5 Lisa Ct Glen Westover Newark DE 19711

KRISTA, LAVERNE MATHEW, b Webster, SDak, Dec 24, 31; m 64; c 3. VETERINARY ANATOMY. *Educ:* SDak State Univ, BS, 58, MS, 60; Univ Minn, PhD(poultry sci), 66, DVM, 69. *Prof Exp:* Res asst, SDak State Univ, 58-60; res asst poultry nutrit & phys, Univ Minn, 60-69; asst prof, 69-73, assoc prof, 73-81, PROF VET ANAT & HISTOL, AUBURN UNIV, 81- *Mem:* Sigma Xi; Am Asn Vet Anat; World Poultry Sci; Am Vet Med Asn. *Res:* Nutrition; atherosclerosis; cardiovascular physiology. *Mailing Add:* Dept of Vet Anat & Histol Auburn Univ Sch of Vet Auburn AL 36830

KRISTAL, MARK BENNETT, b New York, NY, Apr 19, 44; m 67; c 1. BIOPSYCHOLOGY. *Educ:* Rutgers Univ, BA, 65; Kans State Univ, MS, 70, PhD(psychol), 71. *Prof Exp:* Trainee behav genetics & neuroendocrinol, Jackson Lab, 71-73; asst prof, 73-78, ASSOC PROF PSYCHOL, STATE UNIV NY BUFFALO, 78- *Concurrent Pos:* Dir, Biopsychol Prog, Psychol Dept, State Univ NY, Buffalo, 78- *Mem:* AAAS; Behav Genetics Asn; Soc Neurosci; Animal Behav Soc. *Res:* Neural, endocrine, and genetic bases of maternal, ingestive and sexual behaviors; functions of the hypothalamus; limbic-hypothalamic function interactions. *Mailing Add:* State Univ NY Dept of Psychol 4320 Ridge Lea Rd Buffalo NY 14226

KRISTIAN, JEROME, b Milwaukee, Wis, June 5, 34; m 55; c 1. PHYSICS, ASTRONOMY. *Educ:* Univ Chicago, MS, 56, PhD(physics), 62. *Prof Exp:* Mem staff, Argonne Nat Lab, 57-59; vis lectr physics & math, Univ Tex, 62-64; asst prof astron, Univ Wis, 64-67; MEM STAFF, MT WILSON & LAS CAMPANAS OBSERV, CARNEGIE INST WASHINGTON, 67- *Mem:* Am Phys Soc; Am Astron Soc; Int Astron Union. *Mailing Add:* 813 Santa Barbara St Pasadena CA 91101

KRISTIANSEN, MAGNE, b Elverum, Norway, Apr 14, 32; nat US; m 57; c 2. PULSED POWER TECHNOLOGY, PLASMA PHYSICS. *Educ:* Univ Tex, BS, 61, PhD(elec eng), 67. *Prof Exp:* Res engr, Univ Tex, 63-66; from asst prof to prof elec eng, 66-77, P W HORN PROF ELEC ENG, TEX TECH UNIV, 77- *Concurrent Pos:* NSF grants, 67- & US Atomic Energy Comn grant, 67-72; US Army & Air Force grants, 69- & 80-; consult to various industs; vis staff mem, Los Alamos Sci Lab; contractor, Sandia Labs & US Navy, 77-79; US Air Force sci adv bd, 81-; assoc ed, Trans Plasma Sci, Inst Elec & Electronics Engrs, 79- *Mem:* AAAS; Am Nuclear Soc; fel Inst Elec & Electronics Engrs; Am Phys Soc; Am Soc Eng Educ. *Res:* Plasma dynamics, pulsed power technology and physical electronics; high power switching and radio frequency wave propagation and technology. *Mailing Add:* Dept of Elec Eng Tex Tech Univ Lubbock TX 79409

KRISTIANSON, BRYANT NEIL, b Ogden, Iowa, Nov 19, 38; m 64; c 2. NUCLEAR ENGINEERING. *Educ:* Iowa State Univ, BS, 60, MS, 61, PhD(nuclear eng), 64. *Prof Exp:* Asst nuclear engr, Argonne Nat Lab, 63-69; asst prof physics, Wheaton Col, Ill, 69-74; ENGR, 74- *Mem:* Am Soc Mech Eng; Am Asn Physics Teachers. *Res:* Computer program development and use as applied to problems of physics and engineering design. *Mailing Add:* PO Box 17 Naperville IL 60566

KRISTMANSON, DANIEL D, b Vancouver, BC, Oct 10, 29; m 56; c 2. CHEMICAL ENGINEERING. *Educ:* Univ BC, BASc, 53; Univ London, PhD(chem eng), 60. *Prof Exp:* Develop engr, Consolidated Mining & Smelting Co Can, Ltd, 53-56, fertilizer mfg, 60-62; from asst prof to assoc prof, 62-68, PROF CHEM ENG, UNIV NB, 68- *Mem:* Chem Inst Can; Air Pollution Control Asn. *Res:* Mixing in reactors and natural streams; atomization of liquids. *Mailing Add:* Dept of Chem Eng Univ of NB Fredericton NB E3B 5A3 Can

KRISTOFFERSEN, THORVALD, b Denmark, May 6, 19; nat US; m 48; c 1. FOOD SCIENCE. *Educ:* Royal Vet & Agr Col, Denmark, BS, 44; Iowa State Univ, MS, 48, PhD(dairy bact), 54. *Prof Exp:* Asst milk & milk prod, Govt Res Inst Denmark, 44-46; lab asst cheese, Iowa State Univ, 46-54; res assoc sanitizers, 55-56, from asst prof to assoc prof dairy technol, 56-63, PROF DAIRY TECHNOL, OHIO STATE UNIV, 63-, CHMN DEPT, 72- *Honors & Awards:* Pfizer-Paul Lewis Award Cheese Res, 65. *Mem:* Fel AAAS; Am Soc Microbiol; Am Dairy Sci Asn; Inst Food Technol. *Res:* Mechanism of flavor development in cheese; enzyme system of milk, its function and purpose; butter and its physical structure; dairy sanitizers; analysis and evaluation of dairy products. *Mailing Add:* Dept of Food Sci & Nutrit Ohio State Univ Columbus OH 43210

KRITCHEVSKY, DAVID, b Kharkov, Russia, Jan 25, 20; nat US; m 47; c 3. LIPID METABOLISM, NUTRITION. *Educ:* Univ Chicago, BS, 39, MS, 42; Northwestern Univ, PhD(chem), 48. *Prof Exp:* Jr chemist, Ninol Labs, 41-42, chemist, 42-46; asst & quiz instr, 46-48; Am Cancer Soc fel, Swiss Fed Inst Technol, 48-50; mem staff, Radiation Lab, Univ Calif, 50-52; res chemist, Lederle Labs Div, Am Cyanamid Co, 52-57; asst prof, Sch Med, 57-65, prof, Sch Vet Med, 65-67, Wistar prof biochem, 67-72, PROF BIOCHEM IN SURG, SCH VET MED, UNIV PA, 72-, CHMN GRAD GROUP MOLECULAR BIOL, 71- MEM, WISTAR INST, 57-, ASSOC DIR, 75- *Honors & Awards:* Borden Award, Am Inst Nutrit, 74; Philadelphia Sect Award, Am Chem Soc, 77; Award, Am Col Nutrit, 78. *Mem:* AAAS; Soc Exp Biol & Med; Am Soc Biol Chem; Am Chem Soc. *Res:* Synthesis and metabolism of compounds labeled with isotopic carbon and hydrogen; experimental atherosclerosis; organic synthesis; steroids; biology of deuterium oxide; lipid metabolism. *Mailing Add:* Wistar Inst 36th & Spruce Sts Philadelphia PA 19104

KRITIKOS, HARALAMBOS N, b Tripolis, Greece, Mar 8, 33; US citizen; m 64. ELECTRICAL ENGINEERING. *Educ:* Worcester Polytech Inst, BS, 54, MS, 56; Univ Pa, PhD(elec eng), 61. *Prof Exp:* Res asst elec eng, Worcester Polytech Inst, 54-56; from asst instr to assoc prof, 56-76, PROF ELEC ENG, MOORE SCH ELEC ENG, UNIV PA, 76- *Concurrent Pos:* Res fel, Calif Inst Technol, 66; exec ed, Inst Elec & Electronics Engrs Trans of Geosci Electronics, 76-80. *Mem:* Inst Elec & Electronics Engrs. *Res:* Diffraction theory; antennas; propagation; microwave hazards; remote sensing; electromagnetic field theory. *Mailing Add:* Moore Sch of Elec Eng Univ of Pa 200 S 33rd St Philadelphia PA 19104

KRITZ, ARNOLD H, b Providence, RI, Jan 6, 35; m 57; c 3. PLASMA PHYSICS. *Educ:* Brown Univ, ScB, 56; Yale Univ, MS, 57, PhD(physics), 61. *Prof Exp:* Res asst, Yale Univ, 57-61; sr physicist, Space Sci Lab, Gen Dynamics/Astronaut, 61-63, staff scientist, 63-65; sr staff physicist, Aeronaut Res Assocs Princeton, Inc, 65-69; from asst prof to prof, 69-76, chmn dept physics & astron, 71-77, PROF PHYSICS, HUNTER COL, 76- *Concurrent Pos:* Lectr, New Haven Col, 59-60 & Southern Conn State Col, 60-61; asst prof, San Diego State Col, 63-64; consult, Oak Ridge Nat Lab, 74-; sci adj, Ctr Plasma Physics Res, Ecole Polytech Lausanne, 75-76; vis res fel, Princeton Univ, 77- *Mem:* AAAS; Am Phys Soc; Am Asn Physics Teachers. *Res:* Nonequilibrium statistical mechanics; kinetic description of plasma; microwave interactions with inhomogeneous plasma; radio frequency heating of toroidal plasmas. *Mailing Add:* 69 Lillie St Princeton Junction NJ 08550

KRITZ, J(ACOB), b Brooklyn, NY, Dec 12, 18; m 49; c 2. ELECTRONICS, ELECTROACOUSTICS. *Educ:* City Col New York, BEE, 39; Polytech Inst Brooklyn, MEE, 49. *Prof Exp:* Engr signal corps, US War Dept, 40-44; MacKay Radio & Tel, 45-48; sr res engr, Radio Receptor Co, 48-49; W L Maxson Corp, 49-56; head res labs, Arma Div, Am Bosch Arma Corp, 56-61; pres, Janus Prod Inc, 61-66; eng mgr sonar systs, Marquardt Corp, 66-67; chief electroacoustic technol, Kollsman Instrument Corp, 67-69; ENG DEPT HEAD, SYSTS MGR DIV, SPERRY CORP, 69-, RES DEPT HEAD, SPERRY MARINE SYSTS, 72. *Concurrent Pos:* Adj prof grad sch, Polytech Inst Brooklyn, 57-60. *Honors & Awards:* Dr Samuel N Burka Award, Am Inst Navig, 69. *Mem:* Sr mem Inst Elec & Electronics Engrs; Acoust Soc Am. *Res:* Navigation aids, especially poppler sonar, radio-radar, inertial, ultrasonic instrumentation including flowmeters and densitometers. *Mailing Add:* Sperry Marine Systs MS 35114 Marcus Ave Great Neck NY 11020

KRITZMAN, JULIUS, b Lawrence, Mass, Sept 15, 24; m 50; c 2. MEDICINE, HEMATOLOGY. *Educ:* Harvard Univ, AB, 47; Boston Univ, MD, 51; Am Bd Internal Med, dipl, 58, dipl hemat, 74, dipl med oncol, 75. *Prof Exp:* Res fel hemat, New Eng Ctr Hosp, 53-54; clin instr med, Sch Med, 54-58, sr instr, 59-62, asst clin prof, 62-67, asst prof, 67-75, ASSOC CLIN PROF MED, SCH MED, TUFTS UNIV, 75-; STAFF INTERNAL MED, NEW ENG MED CTR HOSPS, 67- *Concurrent Pos:* Physician, Med Clin, Boston Dispensary, 58-; res assoc, Arthur G Rotch Lab, 60-; attend physician, Boston Vet Admin Hosp, 60-; asst vis physician, Beth Israel Hosp, 61-67, assoc in med, 67-; instr, Harvard Med Sch, 61-70. *Mem:* Am Soc Hemat; Am Col Physicians. *Res:* Synthesis and function of antibodies, especially the use of in vitro systems for study of antibody synthesis; medical oncology. *Mailing Add:* 171 Harrison Ave Boston MA 02111

KRIVAK, THOMAS GERALD, b Johnstown, Pa, Oct 21, 40; m 63; c 3. INORGANIC CHEMISTRY. *Educ:* Univ Pittsburgh, BS, 62, MEd, 64; Univ Notre Dame, PhD(inorg chem), 69. *Prof Exp:* Res asst chem, Radiation Labs, Mellon Inst, 62-64; SR RES CHEMIST, INDUST CHEM DIV, PPG INDUSTS, 69- *Mem:* Am Chem Soc; Sigma Xi. *Res:* Silica pigments for paint, paper, plastics and rubber applications. *Mailing Add:* 2222 H Vue Dr Akron OH 44312

KRIVANEK, NEIL DOUGLAS, b Milwaukee, Wis, June 11, 44; m 69. TOXICOLOGY. *Educ:* Univ Wis, BS, 66; Wayne State Univ, MS, 68, PhD(physiol), 72. *Prof Exp:* Instr toxicol, Dept Occup & Environ Health, Col Med, Wayne State Univ, 72-74; res toxicologist, 74, CONSULT, HASKELL LAB TOXICOL & INDUST MED, E I DU PONT DE NEMOURS & CO, INC, 75- *Mem:* Am Chem Soc; Am Indust Hyg Asn; Am Bd Indust Hyg Asn; Sigma Xi. *Res:* Biochemical mechanisms of industrial toxicology; methods development for measuring toxic effects. *Mailing Add:* Haskell Lab E I du Pont de Nemours & Co Inc Newark DE 19711

KRIVANEK, ONDREJ LADISLAV, b Prague, Czech, Aug 1, 50; Brit citizen. ELECTRON MICROSCOPY, ELECTRON SPECTROSCOPY. *Educ:* Univ Leeds, BSc, 71; Univ Cambridge, PhD(physics), 76. *Prof Exp:* Res fel physics, Cavendish Lab, Cambridge, 75-76; res consult electron micros, Bell Lab, 76-77; asst res engr mat sci, Univ Calif, Berkeley, 77-80; ASST PROF SOLID STATE SCI, ARIZ STATE UNIV, 81- *Mem:* Am Phys Soc; Electron Micros Soc Am; Brit Inst Physics. *Res:* High resolution and analytical electron microscopy; atomic structure of crystalline defects and interfaces; electron optics; the structure of disordered materials; nitrogen ceramics; electron energy loss spectroscopy. *Mailing Add:* Ctr Solid State Sci Ariz State Univ Tempe AZ 85287

KRIVIS, ALAN FREDERICK, b New York, NY, Sept 27, 31; m 56; c 3. ANALYTICAL CHEMISTRY. *Educ:* Columbia Univ, AB, 52, MA, 54; Univ Mich, MS, 56, PhD(electrochem), 58. *Prof Exp:* Bio-analyst, Sloan-Kettering Inst, 52-53; mem pigment synthesis staff, Res Div, Interchem Corp, 53; res assoc phys & anal chem, Upjohn Co, 57-61; group supvr, Chem Div Res, Olin Mathieson Chem Corp, 61-66; ASSOC PROF CHEM, UNIV AKRON, 66- *Mem:* AAAS; fel Am Inst Chem; Electrochem Soc; Am Chem Soc; Am Microchem Soc. *Res:* Analytical chemistry including chromatography and electro-chemistry of inorganic and organic systems; biologically active materials; water and air analyses. *Mailing Add:* Dept of Chem Univ of Akron Akron OH 44325

KRIVIT, WILLIAM, b Jersey City, NJ, Nov 28, 25; m 51; c 4. PEDIATRICS, HEMATOLOGY. *Educ:* Duke Univ, 42-44; Tulane Univ, MD, 48; Am Bd Pediat, dipl, 53, dipl pediat hemat, 75. *Prof Exp:* Intern, Charity Hosp, New Orleans, 48-49; resident pediat, Col Med, Univ Utah, 49-50, chief resident, 50-51; PROF PEDIAT, MED SCH, UNIV MINN, MINNEAPOLIS, 51-, HEAD DEPT, 79- *Mem:* Soc Pediat Res; Am Soc Hemat; Soc Exp Biol & Med; NY Acad Sci. *Mailing Add:* Dept of Pediat Univ of Minn Med Sch Minneapolis MN 55455

KRIVOY, WILLIAM AARON, b Newark, NJ, Jan 2, 28. PHARMACOLOGY. *Educ:* Georgetown Univ, BS, 48; George Washington Univ, MS, 49, PhD(pharmacol), 53. *Prof Exp:* Pharmacologist, Chem Corps Med Labs, Army Chem Ctr, Md, 50-54; USPHS res fel pharmacol, Sch Med, Univ Pa, 54-55 & Sch Med, Univ Edinburgh, 55-57; instr, Sch Med, Tulane Univ, 57-59; from asst prof to assoc prof, Col Med, Baylor Univ, 59-63; PHARMACOLOGIST, ADDICTION RES CTR, NAT INST DRUG ABUSE, 68- *Mem:* Am Soc Pharmacol & Exp Therapeut; NY Acad Sci; Am Col Neuropsychopharmacol; Am Soc Clin Pharmacol & Therapeut; Biophys Soc. *Res:* Neuropharmacology and neurophysiology; autonomic agents and psychochemicals; neuroendocrinology; neurosciences; physiology; psychopharmacology. *Mailing Add:* Addiction Res Ctr PO Box 12390 Nat Inst Drug Abuse Lexington KY 40583

KRIZ, GEORGE JAMES, b Brainard, Nebr, Sept 20, 36; m 60; c 3. AGRICULTURAL ENGINEERING, SOIL SCIENCE. *Educ:* Iowa State Univ, BSAE, 60, MSAE, 62; Univ Calif, Davis, PhD(eng), 65. *Prof Exp:* Teaching asst agr eng, Iowa State Univ, 60-62; asst engr, Univ Calif, Davis, 64-65, lectr groundwater hydrol, 65; from asst prof to assoc prof biol & agr eng, NC State Univ, 65-73, assoc head dept, 69-73; PROF & DIR RES, NC AGR EXP STA, 73- *Concurrent Pos:* Consult, Int Basic Econ Corp & Indian Inst Technol, 67. *Mem:* Am Soc Agr Engrs. *Res:* Animal waste management; saturated flow in porous media, especially soil water relationships. *Mailing Add:* 302 Oak Ridge Rd Cary NC 27511

KRIZ, GEORGE STANLEY, JR, b Santa Cruz, Calif, Oct 20, 39; m 66; c 3. PHYSICAL ORGANIC CHEMISTRY. *Educ:* Univ Calif, Berkeley, BS, 61; Ind Univ, PhD(org chem), 66. *Prof Exp:* Foreign asst chem, Univ Montpellier, 65-66; vis res assoc, Ohio State Univ, 66-67; asst prof, 67-72, exec asst to dean arts & sci, 75-77, assoc prof, 77-79, PROF CHEM, WESTERN WASH UNIV, 79- *Mem:* AAAS; Am Chem Soc; Soc Automotive Engrs; The Chem Soc. *Res:* Deuterium kinetic isotope effects; mechanisms of organic reactions; thermochemistry of organic processes; nuclear magnetic resonance spectroscopy; linear free energy relationships; plant phenolic substances; automotive chemistry. *Mailing Add:* Dept of Chem Western Wash Univ Bellingham WA 98225

KRIZAN, JOHN ERNEST, b Lansford, Pa, Dec 12, 34; m 58; c 2. THEORETICAL PHYSICS. *Educ:* Lehigh Univ, BS, 56, MS, 59, PhD(pysics), 62. *Prof Exp:* From asst prof to assoc prof, 62-71, PROF PHYSICS, UNIV VT, 71- *Concurrent Pos:* Vis assoc prof, Univ Rochester, 69-70. *Mem:* AAAS; NY Acad Sci; Am Phys Soc. *Res:* Statistical mechanics; relativistic statistical mechanics; physics of plasmas; quantum and classical electrodynamics. *Mailing Add:* Dept of Physics Univ of Vt Burlington VT 05401

KRIZEK, DONALD THOMAS, b Cleveland, Ohio, June 25, 35; m 62; c 3. ENVIRONMENTAL PHYSIOLOGY. *Educ:* Western Reserve Univ, BA, 57; Univ Chicago, MS, 58, PhD(bot), 64. *Prof Exp:* Res & develop officer, Arctic, Desert, Tropic Info Ctr, Res Studies Inst, Air Univ, 58-62; instr bot & biol, Univ Chicago, 64-66; res plant physiologist, Phyto-Eng Lab, 66-72, RES PLANT PHYSIOLOGIST, PLANT STRESS LAB, BELTSVILLE AGR RES CTR, AGR RES SERV, USDA, 72- *Concurrent Pos:* Instr, Montgomery Ctr, Univ Ala, 59-61; USDA rep, White House Task Force Inadvertent Modification Stratosphere, 75-78; consult, NASA, 79- *Mem:* Am Soc Plant Physiol; Am Soc Hort Sci; Brit Soc Exp Biol; Japanese Soc Plant Physiol; Scand Soc Plant Physiol. *Res:* Plant growth and development; senescence of vascular plants; photoperiodism and photomorphogenesis; plant growth regulators; plant stress; controlled environments; environmental physiology; carbon dioxide enrichment; plant growth chambers; ultra-violet radiation effects; water stress. *Mailing Add:* Plant Stress Lab USDA Agr Res Ctr Beltsville MD 20705

KRIZEK, RAYMOND JOHN, b Baltimore, Md, June 5, 32; m 64; c 2. GEOTECHNICAL ENGINEERING. *Educ:* Johns Hopkins Univ, BE, 54; Univ Md, MS, 61; Northwestern Univ, PhD(soil mech), 63. *Prof Exp:* Instr civil eng, Univ Md, 57-61; lectr soil mech, Cath Univ, 61; from asst prof to assoc prof, 63-70, PROF CIVIL ENG, NORTHWESTERN UNIV, 70-, CHMN DEPT, 80- *Concurrent Pos:* Consult, 63- *Honors & Awards:* C A Hogentogler Award, Am Soc Testing & Mat, 70; Walter L Huber Res Prize, Am Soc Civil Engrs, 71. *Mem:* Am Soc Civil Engrs. *Res:* Soil-structure interaction of buried conduits; use of dredgings for landfill; relationship between soil fabric and its engineering properties; constitutive relations for soils; flow through porous media; disposal of solid waste materials; soil stabilization by chemical grouting. *Mailing Add:* Dept of Civil Eng Northwestern Univ Evanston IL 60201

KRIZEK, THOMAS JOSEPH, b Milwaukee, Wis, Dec 1, 32; m 59; c 3. PLASTIC SURGERY, RECONSTRUCTIVE SURGERY. *Educ:* Marquette Univ, BS, 54, MD, 57. *Hon Degrees:* MA, Yale Univ, 74. *Prof Exp:* Asst prof plastic surg, Johns Hopkins Univ & Univ Md, 66-68; assoc prof, Sch Med, Yale Univ, 68-73, prof plastic surg, 73-78, assoc dean grad & continuing educ, 75-77; prof surg, Col Physicians & Surgeons, Columbia Univ & Chief, Div Plastic & Reconstructive Surg, Columbia-Presby Med Ctr, 78-81; PROF SURG, UNIV SOUTHERN CALIF & CHIEF, DIV PLASTIC SURG, LOS ANGELES COUNTY, UNIV SOUTHERN CALIF, MED CTR, 81- *Mem:* Am Asn Plastic Surgeons; Asn Hand Surg (pres, 80-81); Am Asn Surg of Trauma; Am Burn Asn; Am Col Surgeons. *Res:* Surgical infection, particularly as related to burns and other trauma; surgery and epidemiology of head and neck cancer; aging. *Mailing Add:* Univ Southern Calif Med Ctr 1200 N State St Los Angeles CA 90033

KRNJEVIC, KRESIMIR, b Zagreb, Yugoslavia, Sept 7, 27; m 54; c 2. NEUROPHYSIOLOGY. *Educ:* Univ Edinburgh, MB, ChB, 49, BSc, 51, PhD(physiol), 53. *Prof Exp:* Beit Mem res fel, Univ Edinburgh, 51-54; res assoc & actg asst prof, Univ Wash, 54-56; from prin sci officer to sr prin sci officer, ARC Inst Animal Physiol, Eng, 59-65; HEAD DEPT ANESTHESIA RES, McGILL UNIV, 65-, DRAKE PROF & CHMN DEPT PHYSIOL, 78- *Concurrent Pos:* Prof physiol, McGill Univ, 64-65. *Mem:* Am Physiol Soc; Can Physiol Soc; Int Soc Neurochem; Soc Neurosci; Royal Soc Can. *Res:* Central synaptic mechanisms. *Mailing Add:* Dept of Anesthesia Res McGill Univ McIntyre Bldg Montreal PQ H3G 1Y6 Can

KROC, ROBERT LOUIS, b Chicago, Ill, June 19, 07; m 34; c 2. PHYSIOLOGY. *Educ:* Oberlin Col, BA, 29, MA, 31; Univ Wis, PhD(zool, physiol), 33. *Hon Degrees:* DSc, Oberlin Col, 79. *Prof Exp:* Asst, Univ Wis, 30-33; from instr to asst prof zool, Ind Univ, 33-44; biologist, Res Div, Maltine Co, 44-47; dir physiol res, Chilcott Labs Div, 47-51, Warner-Chilcott Labs Div, Warner-Hudnut, Inc, 51-58 & Warner-Lambert Res Inst, 58-69; PRES, THE KROC FOUND, 69- *Mem:* Endocrine Soc; Am Physiol Soc; Am Thyroid Asn; NY Acad Sci. *Res:* Endocrinology, especially thyroid and reproductive physiology. *Mailing Add:* The Kroc Found PO Box 547 Santa Ynez CA 93460

KROCHMAL, ARNOLD, b New York, NY, Jan 30, 19; m 56, 70; c 3. ECONOMIC BOTANY. *Educ:* NC State Col, BS, 42; Cornell Univ, MS, 51, PhD(econ bot), 52. *Prof Exp:* Instr hort, NMex Col Agr & Mech Arts, 47-49 Fulbright prof hort, Am Farm Sch, Greece, 52-53; instr agr, State Univ NY Agr & Tech Inst Delhi, 53-54; chmn, Sci Div, Morris Brown Col, 54-55; assoc prof hort, Ariz State Univ, 55-57; chief res adv, Univ Wyo Team, Afghanistan, 57-59; assoc prof agr, Western Carolina Col, 59-60; chmn dept hort, Pan Am Sch Agr, Honduras, 60-61; res botanist & asst in charge crops res div, VI, 61-66, proj leader & res botanist, Northeastern Forest Exp Sta, Berea, Ky, 66-71, prin econ botanist, Southeastern Forest Exp Sta, 71-82, PRIN ECON BOTANIST, INST TROP FORESTRY, PUERTO RICO, USDA, 82- *Concurrent Pos:* Consult trop fruit prod, Surinam Govt, 64; consult, Thai Tapioca Asn, Thailand, 64 & Agr Develop Corp, Jamaican Govt, 65; adj prof bot, NC State Univ, 71-77; adj prof biol, Univ NC, Asheville, 75-; collabr, Nat Acad Sci, 75; working party leader, Int Union Forestry Res Orgns structure of trop rain forests, 77-; adj prof forestry, NC State Univ, 78- *Mem:* Caribbean Food Crops Soc (secy, treas, 63-64). *Res:* Production and associated problems of fruit, vegetable and industrial crops in tropics; culture of wild plants for drug sources; wildlife feed and nitrogen fixation; endangered, rare and threatened plants; natural areas. *Mailing Add:* Southeastern Forest Exp Sta 113 Veterans Dr Asheville NC 28805

KROCHMAL, JEROME J(ACOB), b New York, NY, Dec 17, 30; m 52; c 3. ORGANIZATION DEVELOPMENT, ORGANIZATIONAL EFFECTIVENESS. *Educ:* Ga Inst Technol, BCerE, 52. *Prof Exp:* Staff mem ceramics, Battelle Mem Inst, 52; staff mem ceramics & graphites, US Air Force Propulsion Lab, 54-57; staff mem, US Air Force Lab, 57-60, sr proj officer, 60-69, sr plans analyst, 71-75, SR MGT ANALYST, AERONAUT LABS, US AIR FORCE, 75- *Concurrent Pos:* Staff consult, Mat Adv Bd, Nat Acad Sci-Nat Res Coun, 60-61; Stanford-Sloan fel, 69-70. *Mem:* Orgn Develop Network; Orgn Develop Inst. *Res:* Research and development organization effectiveness; transitioning of new technology to systems concepts and hardware; goal oriented research and development; synergistic problem solving in advanced technology. *Mailing Add:* 5331 Birchbend Ct Dayton OH 45415

KROCHTA, WILLIAM G, b Piney Fork, Ohio, Sept 24, 30; m 54; c 3. ANALYTICAL CHEMISTRY. *Educ:* Mt Union Col, BS, 52; Purdue Univ, MS, 54, PhD(chem), 57. *Prof Exp:* Sr res chemist, Columbia-Southern Chem Corp, 56-59, supvr, 59-62; SR SUPVR, CHEM DIV, PPG INDUSTS, BARBERTON, 62- *Mem:* Am Chem Soc; Am Indust Hyg Asn. *Res:* Absorption spectroscopy; gas chromatography. *Mailing Add:* 237 Tanglewood Trail Wadsworth OH 44281

KROEGER, DONALD CHARLES, b Boise, Idaho, Sept 18, 25; m 48; c 2. PHARMACOLOGY. *Educ:* Ore State Col, BS, 47; Purdue Univ, MS, 49, PhD(pharmacol), 51. *Prof Exp:* From asst prof to assoc prof pharmacol, Univ Houston, 51-56; from asst prof to assoc prof, 56-64, PROF PHARMACOL, UNIV TEX DENT BR, HOUSTON, 64-, CHMN DEPT, 68- *Mem:* AAAS; Am Pharmaceut Asn; Soc Exp Biol & Med; Am Soc Pharmacol & Exp Therapeut; Int Asn Dent Res. *Res:* Neuropharmacology; electrophysiological stimulation and recording of autonomic neural centers in the brain and relationship of chemical changes in tissues to brain stimulation. *Mailing Add:* Dept of Pharmacol Dent Br Univ of Tex Med Ctr PO Box 20068 Houston TX 77025

KROEGER, PETER G, b Swinoujscie, Poland, Apr 26, 30; US citizen; m 58; c 2. FLUID DYNAMICS, HEAT TRANSFER. *Educ:* Inst Technol, Aachen, WGer, ME, 56; Case Western Reserve Univ, PhD(mech eng), 72. *Prof Exp:* Res engr, Gen Elec Co, 62-67 & 72-74, Kennecott Copper Co, 67-72; RES ENGR, BROOKHAVEN NAT LAB, 74- *Mem:* Am Soc Mech Engrs. *Res:* Analysis of thermal and fluid dynamics systems and processes; nuclear reactor thermohydraulics; phase change processes such as freezing and melting; dynamics of propulsion plants. *Mailing Add:* Bldg 703 Brookhaven Nat Lab Upton NY 11973

KROEKER, RICHARD MARK, b Bakersfield, Calif, Sept 7, 52; m 78. ELECTRON TUNNELING. *Educ:* Washington Univ, St Louis, BA, 74; Univ Calif, Santa Barbara, PhD(physics), 79. *Prof Exp:* Fel, Physics Dept, Univ Calif, Santa Barbara, 79-80; fel, 80-81, STAFF ENGR, GEN PROD DIV, IBM CORP, SAN JOSE, 81- *Mem:* Am Phys Soc. *Res:* Physical chemistry of surfaces, including monolayer spectroscopy, radiation chemistry of thin films and mechanisms of heterogeneous catalysis. *Mailing Add:* G11/025 IBM Corp 5600 Cottle Rd San Jose CA 95193

KROEKER, WARREN DEAN, biochemistry, see previous edition

KROEMER, HERBERT, b Weimar, Ger, Aug 25, 28; m 50; c 5. SEMICONDUCTORS. *Educ:* Univ Gottingen, dipl, 51, Dr rer nat, 52. *Prof Exp:* Res scientist, Ger Post Off Lab, 52-54 & labs, Radio Corp Am, 54-57; res group leader, Ger Philips Lab, 57-59; sr scientist, Varian Assocs, 59-66; head New Phenomena Sect, Semiconductor Res & Develop Lab, Fairchild, 66-68; prof elec eng, Univ Colo, Boulder, 68-76; PROF ELEC ENG, UNIV CALIF, SANTA BARBARA, 76- *Honors & Awards:* J Ebers Award, Inst Elec & Electronics Engrs, 73. *Mem:* Fel Am Phys Soc; fel Inst Elec & Electronics Engrs; Electrochem Soc. *Res:* Semiconductor physics and exploratory research on new device principles; physics and technology of semiconductor materials and devices; heterojunctions; molecular beam epitaxy. *Mailing Add:* Dept Elec & Comput Eng Univ of Calif Santa Barbara CA 93106

KROENBERG, BERNDT, b Riga, Latvia, Oct 31, 36; m 59; c 1. FOOD SCIENCE, NUTRITION. *Educ:* Inst Divi Thomae, MS, 61, PhD(biochem), 63. *Prof Exp:* Instr Ger, Our Lady Cincinnati Col, 61-63; instr, Xavier Univ, Ohio, 62-63; group leader leaf chem, Brown & Williamson Tobacco Corp, 63-66; mgr emulsion develop, Celanese Coatings Co, 66-69; dir prod develop res, 69-76, DIR LICENSING, ROSS LABS DIV, ABBOTT LABS, COLUMBUS, 76- *Mem:* AAAS; Am Chem Soc; Licencing Exec Soc. *Res:* Isolation and identification of natural products of animal and plant origin; amino acids, alkaloids, sterols; medicinal use of natural products; infant and geriatric foods; pediatric and obstetrics and gynecology drugs; diagnostic kits; enteral feeding pumps. *Mailing Add:* 501 Greenglade Ave Worthington OH 43085

KROENERT, JOHN THEODORE, b Arkansas City, Kans, Nov 28, 21; m 47; c 2. ELECTRICAL ENGINEERING, COMMUNICATIONS. *Educ:* Purdue Univ, BSEE, 43. *Prof Exp:* Res engr sonar, US Navy Underwater Sound Lab, 43-51; br head servodyn group, 51-55; sr engr sonar develop, Ultrasonic Corp, 55-56; engr supvr airborne sonar, Light Mil Electronic Equip, Gen Elec Co, 56-58; sr engr, 58-61, prin engr, Submarine Signal Div, 61-64, CONSULT ENGR, RAYTHEON CORP, 64- *Mem:* Sr mem Inst Elec & Electronics Engrs; Acoust Soc Am. *Res:* Sonar signal processing; detection, classification, location, and underwater telephony. *Mailing Add:* Raytheon Co PO Box 360 Portsmouth RI 02871

KROENING, JOHN LEO, b Princeton, Minn, Aug 18, 34; m 56; c 4. PHYSICS. *Educ:* Univ Minn, Minneapolis, BS, 56, MS, 59, PhD(physics), 62. *Prof Exp:* Res assoc physics, Univ Minn, Minneapolis, 62-65; asst prof, Duluth, 65-68, ASSOC PROF PHYSICS, UNIV MINN, DULUTH, 68- *Mem:* Am Geophys Union. *Res:* Atmospheric physics and electricity; small ion content; atmospheric ozone distribution; chemiluminescent detection; atmospheric aerosol-effect on ozone and small ion content; stratosphere-troposphere transport. *Mailing Add:* Sch of Physics & Astron Univ of Minn Duluth MN 55812

KROENKE, LOREN WILLIAM, b Milwaukee, Wis, July 2, 38. MARINE GEOLOGY. *Educ:* Univ Wis-Madison, BS, 60; Univ Hawaii, MS, 68, PhD(geol), 72. *Prof Exp:* Proj asst marine geol & geophys, Geophys & Polar Res Ctr, Univ Wis, 61-63; asst geophys, 63-66, jr geophysicist, 67-72, asst geophysicist, 72-75, ASSOC GEOPHYSICIST MARINE GEOL & GEOPHYS, HAWAII INST GEOPHYS, UNIV HAWAII, 75- *Concurrent Pos:* Tech adv, Comt Coord, Joint Prospecting Mineral Resources SPac Offshore Areas, Econ Comn Asia & Far East, UN, 72-73; sci adv, US-Japan Coop Prog Marine Sea-Bottom Surv Panel, 73-74; marine geologist & regional adv, UN Develop Prog, 74-76; mem, Adv Panel Ocean Margin, Joint Oceanog Inst Deep Earth Sampling-Int Prog Ocean Drilling, 74- *Mem:* Am Geophys Union; Seismol Soc Am; Geol Soc Am; AAAS; Sigma Xi. *Res:* Marine geology and geodynamics of the Pacific Ocean Basin with particular reference to the formation and deformation of oceanic crust and continental margins in the southwest Pacific. *Mailing Add:* Hawaii Inst of Geophys Univ Hawaii 2525 Correa Rd Honolulu HI 96822

KROENKE, WILLIAM JOSEPH, b Cleveland, Ohio, Aug 16, 34; m 61; c 2. CHEMISTRY. *Educ:* Case Inst Technol, BS, 56, PhD(inorg chem), 63. *Prof Exp:* Chemist, Nat Carbon Res Lab, Union Carbide Corp, 56-61; res chemist, Res Ctr, 63-65, sr res chemist, 65-70, res assoc, 70-74, sr res assoc, 74-80, RES & DEVELOP FEL, B F GOODRICH CO, 80- *Mem:* Am Chem Soc. *Res:* Inorganic and organometallic chemistry; goechemistry; smoke retarders; synthesis; coordination numbers; molecular and crystal structure; property-structure relationships; solid state chemistry; phase relationships; fire retardants; catalysis; polymers; high-temperature chemistry. *Mailing Add:* 8485 Sunnydale Dr Brecksville OH 44141

KROES, ROGER L, b Racine, Wis, Dec 3, 35; m 64; c 2. SOLID STATE PHYSICS. *Educ:* Marquette Univ, BS, 57; Univ Mo-Columbia, PhD(physics), 68. *Prof Exp:* PHYSICIST, MARSHALL SPACE FLIGHT CTR, NASA, 68- *Mem:* Am Phys Soc. *Res:* Color centers in alkaline earth oxides; optical properties of solids; crystal characterization. *Mailing Add:* Space Sci Lab NASA Marshall Space Flight Ctr Huntsville AL 35812

KROGDAHL, WASLEY SVEN, b Springfield, Ill, Jan 17, 19; m 42; c 3. COSMOLOGY. *Educ:* Univ Chicago, BS, 39, PhD(astron), 42. *Prof Exp:* Jr physicist, Naval Ord Lab, 42-43; instr physics, Army Specialized Training Prog, Ripon Col, 43-44; assoc prof math & astron, Univ SC, 44-45; instr, Yerkes Observ, 45-46; asst prof astron & astrophys, Dearborn Observ, Northwestern Univ, Ill, 46-58; assoc prof math & astron, 58-64, PROF MATH & ASTRON, UNIV KY, 64- *Mem:* Am Astron Soc; Royal Astron Soc. *Res:* Theoretical astrophysics; relativistic cosmology. *Mailing Add:* Dept of Physics & Astron Univ of Ky Lexington KY 40506

KROGER, F(ERDINAND) A(NNE), b Amsterdam, Netherlands, Sept 11, 15; m 57; c 2. PHYSICAL CHEMISTRY, THERMODYNAMICS. *Educ:* Univ Amsterdam, BSc, 34, Drs, 37, PhD(phys chem), 40. *Prof Exp:* Res worker, Philips Res Labs, Netherlands, 38-40, res group leader, 40-58; sci adv, Mullard Res Labs, Eng, 58-64; PROF MAT SCI & CHEM, UNIV SOUTHERN CALIF, 64-, DAVID PACKARD PROF ELEC ENG, 72- *Concurrent Pos:* Corresp, Royal Dutch Acad Sci, 78. *Mem:* Electrochem Soc; Am Ceramics Soc. *Res:* Solid state luminescence; compound semiconductors; imperfection chemistry. *Mailing Add:* Dept of Mat Sci Univ Southern Calif Univ Park Los Angeles CA 90007

KROGER, HANNS H, b Hamburg, Ger, Sept 25, 26; m 59; c 2. INORGANIC CHEMISTRY, ELECTROCHEMISTRY. *Educ:* Univ Hamburg, Cand, 53, Dipl, 56, Dr rer nat (chem, mineral), 58. *Prof Exp:* Sci asst chem, Univ Hamburg, 56-59; chemist, Accumulatorenfabrik AG, Ger, 59-61; electrochemist, NY, 62-65, ELECTROCHEMIST, BATTERY BUS SECT, GEN ELEC CO, FLA, 65- *Mem:* Electrochem Soc. *Res:* Battery technology; analytical chemistry. *Mailing Add:* Gen Elec Co PO Box 114 Gainesville FL 32602

KROGER, HARRY, b Brooklyn, NY, Aug 13, 36; m 58; c 3. SOLID STATE ELECTRONICS, EXPERIMENTAL SOLID STATE PHYSICS. *Educ:* Univ Rochester, BS, 57; Cornell Univ, PhD(physics), 62. *Prof Exp:* Mem res staff, 62-68, group leader microwave semiconductors, 68-69, mgr semiconductor device dept, 69-75, MGR ADVAN DEVICE DEPT, SPERRY RES CTR, 75- *Mem:* Inst Elec & Electronic Eng; Am Phys Soc. *Res:* Soft x-ray spectroscopy; semiconductor memories; conduction through thin insulators; microwave semiconductor devices; Josephson devices. *Mailing Add:* Advan Device Dept Sperry Res Ctr Sudbury MA 01776

KROGER, LARRY A, b Hastings, Nebr, Dec 6, 43; m 68; c 2. NUCLEAR PHYSICS, MEDICAL PHYSICS. *Educ:* Hastings Col, BA, 66; Univ Wyo, PhD(physics), 72. *Prof Exp:* Res assoc physics & NSF-Nat Res Coun fel, Nat Reactor Testing Sta, 71-73; res assoc, Univ Pa, 73-75; sr physicist, Emergency Care Res Inst, 75-78; HEALTH PHYSICIST, MED SYST DIV, GEN ELEC CO, 78- *Concurrent Pos:* Lectr energy. *Mem:* Am Inst Physics; AAAS; Am Asn Physicist Med; Sigma Xi; Am Phys Soc. *Res:* Medical applications of x and gamma rays and performance of radiology systems; study of radioactivity and nuclear decay schemes; radiation safety. *Mailing Add:* Gen Elec Med Systs Div PO Box 414 Milwaukee WI 53201

KROGER, MANFRED, b Bad Oeynhausen, WGer, May 19, 33; Can citizen; m 62; c 3. FOOD SCIENCE. *Educ:* Univ Man, BSA, 61; Pa State Univ, MS, 63, PhD(food chem), 66. *Prof Exp:* Asst dairy sci, 61-63, instr, 63-66, asst prof food sci, 66-72, assoc prof, 72-78, PROF FOOD SCI, PA STATE UNIV, UNIVERSITY PARK, 78- *Concurrent Pos:* Tech ed, Dairy & other journals; consult, food indust. *Mem:* AAAS; Am Chem Soc; Am Dairy Sci; Inst Food Technologists; World Future Soc. *Res:* Food flavor chemistry; pesticide residue analysis; analysis and chemistry of food contaminants; environmental quality; food safety; food laws and regulations; instrumental analysis of fat and protein in foods; milk processing; dairy products manufacture; yogurt quality. *Mailing Add:* 104 Borland Lab Pa State Univ University Park PA 16802

KROGER, MARLIN G(LENN), b Hampton, Nebr, Jan 22, 26; m 49; c 1. ELECTRONIC ENGINEERING, OPERATIONS ANALYSIS. *Educ:* Univ Nebr, BS, 49. *Prof Exp:* Res engr, RCA Labs, 49-52; sr proj engr, Motorola Inc, 52-56, chief engr, 56-60, assoc dir res & develop, 60-63; asst to pres, Autonetics Div, NAm Aviation Inc, 63-66, vpres info systs, 66-76; PRES, M G KROGER ASSOC, 76- *Concurrent Pos:* Consult, Off Secy Defense & Inst Defense Anal, 60- *Honors & Awards:* RCA Award, 51. *Mem:* Inst Elec & Electronics Engrs. *Res:* Information systems research; space electronics. *Mailing Add:* M G Kroger Assoc 1117 Via Gioleta Palos Verdes Estates CA 90274

KROGH, LESTER CHRISTENSEN, b Ruskin, Nebr, Aug 22, 25; m 46; c 2. ORGANIC CHEMISTRY. *Educ:* Univ Nebr, BS, 45, MS, 48; Univ Minn, PhD(chem), 52. *Prof Exp:* Asst, Univ Nebr, 46-48; asst, Univ Minn, 48-51; sr chemist, 52-55, mgr res group, 55-59, mgr res & develop group, Abrasives Lab, 59-60, asst tech dir, 60-62, tech dir, 62-64, dir, Chem Res Lab, Cent Res Labs, 64-65, corp tech planning & coordr, 65-69, gen mgr, New Bus Ventures Div, 69-70, exec dir, Cent Res Labs, 70-73, vpres, Com Chem Div, 73-81, RES & DEVELOP VPRES, INDUST & CONSUMER SECTOR, MINN MINING & MFR CO, 81- *Mem:* Am Chem Soc. *Res:* Preparation and reaction of polymers; fluorocarbons and the Michael reactions; coated abrasives; analysis of research projects; technology transfer. *Mailing Add:* 1390 W Skillman Ave St Paul MN 55113

KROGH, THOMAS EDVARD, b Peterborough, Ont, Jan 12, 36; m 61; c 4. GEOCHEMISTRY. *Educ:* Queen's Univ, Ont, BSc, 59, MSc, 61; Mass Inst Technol, PhD(isotope geol), 64. *Prof Exp:* Fel, Carnegie Inst Dept Terrestrial Magnetism, 64-66, mem sci staff, Carnegie Inst Geophys Lab, 66-75; DIR GEOCHRONOLOGY LAB, MINERAL & GEOL DEPT, ROYAL ONT MUS, 75- *Mem:* Can Mineral Asn. *Res:* Isotope geology; use of isotopic variation in nature as natural tracers in geological processes; geochronology and genesis of rock systems; uranium-lead dating of zircon and low level lead isotopic analyses. *Mailing Add:* Dept of Geol 100 Queen's Park Toronto ON M5S 2C5 Can

KROGMANN, DAVID WILLIAM, b Washington, DC, Oct 21, 32; m 58; c 3. BIOLOGY. *Educ:* Cath Univ Am, AB, 53; Johns Hopkins Univ, PhD(biochem), 57. *Prof Exp:* Fel biochem, Johns Hopkins Univ, 57-58; res assoc, Univ Chicago, 58-60; from asst prof to prof, Wayne State Univ, 60-67; PROF BIOCHEM, PURDUE UNIV, WEST LAFAYETTE, 67- *Res:* Biological chemistry; biochemistry of electron transport and phosphate metabolism in photosynthesis. *Mailing Add:* Dept of Biochem Purdue Univ West Lafayette IN 47907

KROGSTAD, BLANCHARD ORLANDO, b Winger, Minn, Oct 6, 21; m 46; c 3. INSECT ECOLOGY, INVERTEBRATE ECOLOGY. *Educ:* Bemidji State Col, BA, 46; Univ Minn, MA, 48, PhD, 51. *Prof Exp:* Asst prof biol, St Olaf Col, 51-54; from asst prof to assoc prof, 54-63, PROF BIOL, UNIV MINN, DULUTH, 63-, HEAD DEPT, 78- *Concurrent Pos:* Mem staff, Rockefeller Found, Chapingo, Mex, 63-64; researcher, Mexican Inst Coffee, Xalapa, 70-71. *Mem:* Ecol Soc Am; Entom Soc Am; Sigma Xi; Am Inst Biol Sci. *Res:* Ecology of insects and other invertebrates. *Mailing Add:* 5705 Juniata St Duluth MN 55804

KROGSTAD, DONALD JOHN, b New York, NY, Feb 18, 43; m 65; c 2. MEDICINE, BIOLOGY. *Educ:* Bowdoin Col, AB, 65; Harvard Med Sch, MD, 69. *Prof Exp:* Intern, mass Gen Hosp, Boston, 69-70, asst resident, 70-71, sr resident, 75-76, clin & res fel med, 76-78; epidemic intel serv officer, Parasitic Dis Div & Parasitic Dis Drug Serv, Ctr Dis Control, Ga, 71-73; lectr physiol & med, Med Asst Training Sch, Lilongue, Malawi, 73-75; ASST PROF MED & PATH, SCH MED, WASHINGTON UNIV, 78- *Concurrent Pos:* Physician, Lilongue Gen Hosp, 73-75; dir, Microbiol Lab, Barnes Hosp, St Louis, 78-; consult, Jewish Hosp, St Louis, 78- *Mem:* Am Soc Microbiol; Am Soc Trop Med & Hyg; Am Col Physicians; Am Asn Pathologists; Am Col Epidemiology. *Res:* Mechanisms of drug resistance; pathogenicity; epidemiology of nosocomial infection. *Mailing Add:* Microbiol Lab Barnes Hosp St Louis MO 63110

KROH, GLENN CLINTON, b Philadelphia, Pa, Dec 20, 41; m 67; c 1. PLANT ECOLOGY. *Educ:* Pa State Univ, BS, 66, MS, 70; Mich State Univ, PhD(plant ecol), 75. *Prof Exp:* ASST PROF BIOL, TEX CHRISTIAN UNIV, 75- *Mem:* Ecol Soc Am; Am Inst Biol Sci; AAAS. *Res:* The effects of intra and interspecific competition on the strategies of annual herbs with regard to how they partition available resources into roots, shoots and reproductive tissue. *Mailing Add:* Dept of Biol Tex Christian Univ Ft Worth TX 76129

KROHMER, JACK STEWART, b Cleveland, Ohio, Nov 7, 21; m 46; c 3. DIAGNOSTIC & THERAPEUTIC RADIOLOGICAL PHYSICS. *Educ:* Western Reserve Univ, BS, 43, MA, 47; Univ Tex, PhD(biophysics), 61. *Prof Exp:* Sec assoc radiol physics, Atomic Energy Med Res Proj, Western Reserve Univ, 47-57; prof, Univ Tex, Southwestern Med Sch, 57-63; res prof, Roswell Park Mem Inst, 63-66; assoc, Geisinger Med Ctr, 66-72 & Radiol Assocs Erie, 72-79; PROF RADIOL & RADIATION ONCOLOGY, WAYNE STATE UNIV, SCH MED, 79- *Concurrent Pos:* Chief physicist, Univ Hosp Cleveland, 47-57 & Parkland Mem Hosp, Dallas, Tex, 57-63; Physicist, Radiation Ctr, Fort Worth, Tex, 58-63; prof biophysics, State Univ NY, Buffalo, 63-66 & physics, Bucknell Univ, Lewisburg, Pa, 66-72; pres, Erie Clinic Inc, Pa, 73-76; dir, Div Radiol Physics, Wayne State Univ, 79-; assoc mem staff, Mt Carmel Mercy Hosp & Detroit Receiving Hosp, 80-, Harper-Grace Hosp, 82- *Mem:* Am Asn Physicists Med (pres, 74-75); Am Bd Radiol; Radiol Soc NAm (vpres, 79); Am Roetgen Ray Soc; Health Physics Soc. *Res:* Biological effects of radiation; radiation imaging; uses of radioactive materials; radiation therapy and radiation protection. *Mailing Add:* Dept Radiol Detroit Receiving Hosp Univ Health Ctr 4201 St Antoine Detroit MI 48201

KROHN, ALBERTINE, b Toledo, Ohio, Nov 28, 24. CHEMISTRY. *Educ:* Univ Toledo, BS, 46, MS, 49; Univ Mich, MS, 51, PhD(phys chem), 56. *Prof Exp:* Asst, State Geol Surv, Ill, 46; instr math & chem, 47-51, from asst prof to assoc prof chem, 51-63, PROF CHEM, UNIV TOLEDO, 63- *Mem:* Am Chem Soc; Sigma Xi. *Res:* Electrodeposition of copper-lead alloys; codeposition of molybdenum with iron, cobalt, nickel, copper and zinc; internal reflection spectroscopic studies of electrodeposited alloys; chemical education, examinations and tests in science; computers in chemical education. *Mailing Add:* Dept of Chem Univ of Toledo Toledo OH 43606

KROHN, BURTON JAY, b St Louis, Mo, Feb 25, 41; m 67; c 2. MOLECULAR PHYSICS. *Educ:* Vanderbilt Univ, BA, 64; Ohio State Univ, MS, 66, PhD(physics), 71. *Prof Exp:* Fel chem physics, Battelle Mem Inst, 71-72; res assoc infrared spectros, Fla State Univ, 73-74; STAFF MEMBER MOLECULAR PHYSICS, THEORET DIV, LOS ALAMOS NATLAB,74- *Mem:* Am Phys Soc. *Res:* Quantum-mechanical theory; modeling and computations of energies and properties of vibrating, rotating polyatomic molecules; analysis of positions of absorption lines and band- and line-intensities in high-resolution infrared spectra. *Mailing Add:* Theoret Div Los Alamos Nat Lab Los Alamos NM 87545

KROHN, KENNETH ALBERT, b Stevens Point, Wis, June 19, 45; m 68; c 1. NUCLEAR CHEMISTRY. *Educ:* Andrews Univ, BA, 66; Univ Calif, Davis, PhD(chem), 71. *Prof Exp:* Instr radiation sci, Washington Univ, 71-73; asst prof radiol, Sch Med, Univ Calif, Davis, 73-78, assoc prof, 78-81, assoc dir, Crocker Nuclear Lab, 78-80; ASSOC PROF RADIOL & RADIATION ONCOL, SCH MED, UNIV WASH, SEATTLE, 81- *Concurrent Pos:* Mem comt radiopharmaceut & radioassay, Am Col Nuclear Physicians, 75-78. *Mem:* Am Chem Soc; Soc Nuclear Med; Radiation Res Soc; AAAS; Sigma Xi. *Res:* Application of isotopes to biological problems; development of new cyclotron produced radiopharmaceuticals for diagnostic procedures for cancer and heart disease; halogen and technetium chemistry and chemical effects of nuclear transformations. *Mailing Add:* Dept Radiol-Nuclear Med RC-70 Univ Wash Hosp Seattle WA 98195

KROHN, NORMAN F, electrical engineering, see previous edition

KROHN, VICTOR EUGENE, JR, b Milwaukee, Wis, Oct 26, 24. PHYSICS. *Educ:* Washington & Jefferson Col, BA, 47; Case Inst Technol, MS, 51, PhD(physics), 52. *Prof Exp:* Asst physics, Case Inst Technol, 49-52; assoc physicist, Argonne Nat Lab, 52-58; res specialist, Atomics Int, 58-60; mem tech staff, Thompson Ramo-Wooldridge, Inc, 60-62; PHYSICIST, ARGONNE NAT LAB, 62- *Mem:* Am Phys Soc. *Res:* Nuclear physics; secondary ion emission; neutron decay; reactor physics; electron-neutron interaction; electric propulsion; electrohydrodynamic; ion microscopy; ultracold neutrons. *Mailing Add:* Argonne Nat Lab Argonne IL 60439

KROL, ARTHUR J, b Chicago, Ill, Dec 3, 25. DENTISTRY. *Educ:* Loyola Univ, Ill, DDS, 47, BS, 48. *Prof Exp:* Instr full dentures, Sch Dent, Northwestern Univ, 53-54; prof prosthodont & chmn dept, Sch Dent, Loyola Univ, Ill, 54-64; prof prosthodont, Sch Dent, Univ of the Pac, 64-76; CHIEF DENT SERV, VET ADMIN MED CTR, 74-; PROF PROSTHODONT, SCH DENT, UNIV CALIF, SAN FRANCISCO, 74- *Concurrent Pos:* Consult, Vet Admin Hosps, Hines & West Side, Chicago, Ill, 57-61, Dwight, Ill, 61-64 & Palo Alto, Calif, 64-; consult, Vet Admin Hosp, Livermore, Calif, 67- & Letterman Army Hosp, San Francisco, 69- *Mem:* Am Dent Asn; Am Prosthodont Soc; Int Asn Dent Res; Int Col Appl Nutrit; Am Col Dent. *Res:* Prosthodontics; factors involved in denture retention, especially the application of the principles of hydraulics in establishing peripheral seal; new removable partial denture designs for esthetics and plaque reduction. *Mailing Add:* Vet Admin Med Ctr San Francisco CA 94121

KROL, GEORGE J, b Wilno, Poland, June 6, 36; US citizen; m 62; c 3. PHYSICAL CHEMISTRY, ANALYTICAL CHEMISTRY. *Educ:* Univ Rochester, BS, 58; Rutgers Univ, PhD(phys anal chem), 68. *Prof Exp:* Res technician, Med Sch, Univ Rochester, 58-59; chemist, Hoffmann-La Roche Inc, 60-62; res asst phys chem, Rutgers Univ, 63-67; sr res chemist, 67-75, sect head, Ayerst Labs, Inc, 75-78; SUPVR, MILES PHARMACEUT INC, 78. *Mem:* Am Chem Soc. *Res:* Biochemistry; radiochemistry and kinetics; analytical method development, especially chromatography; bioavailability assay. *Mailing Add:* Prod Develop Lab Miles Pharmaceut Inc West Haven CT 06516

KROL, JOSEPH, b Warsaw, Poland, Jan 14, 11; US citizen; m 52. MECHANICAL & INDUSTRIAL ENGINEERING. *Educ:* Warsaw Tech Univ, MS, 37; Univ London, PhD(mech eng), 47. *Prof Exp:* Chief tech off, Boryszew Co, Ltd, Poland, 37-39; asst works engr, George Clark Co, Ltd, Eng, 40-41; tech off ammunition prod, Brit Ministry Supply, 41-45; res scientist, Univ London, 46-47; consult engr, Howard Smith Paper Mills Co, Ltd, Can, 48-51; assoc prof mech eng, Univ Man, 51-56; prof indust eng, 56-80, prof systs eng, 69-80, EMER PROF INDUST & SYSTS ENG, GA INST TECHNOL, 80- *Honors & Awards:* Stephenson Prize, Brit Inst Mech Eng, 51. *Mem:* AAAS; Am Soc Mech Eng; Sigma Xi; fel Inst Mech Eng; Inst Mgt Sci. *Res:* Economic analysis and computer simulation of complex systems. *Mailing Add:* Apt 1416 710 Peachtree St Northeast Atlanta GA 30308

KROLIK, JULIAN H, b Detroit, Mich, Apr 4, 50. THEORETICAL ASTROPHYSICS. *Educ:* Mass Inst Technol, BS, 71; Univ Calif, Berkeley, PhD(physics), 77. *Prof Exp:* Mem staff, Inst Advan Study, Mass Inst Technol, 77-79, scientist, Ctr Theoret Physics & Space Res, 79-81; RES ASSOC, SMITHSONIAN CTR ASTROPHYS, HARVARD UNIV, 81- *Concurrent Pos:* Lectr, Dept Astron, Harvard Univ, 81- *Mem:* Am Astron Soc. *Mailing Add:* Smithsonian Ctr Astrophys 60 Garden St Cambridge MA 02138

KROLL, ARTHUR STANLEY, b Dunkirk, NY, Apr 26, 42; c 2. PHYSICS. *Educ:* State Univ NY, Brockport, BS, 68. *Prof Exp:* Q C optical engr, Kodak Apparatus Div, 68-69, RES PHYSICIST, RES LABS, EASTMAN KODAK CO, 69- *Res:* Electrophotography; basic studies in image quality and development mechanisms. *Mailing Add:* Eastman Kodak Co Kodak Park Rochester NY 14650

KROLL, BERNARD HILTON, b Brooklyn, NY, Sept 8, 22; m 47; c 3. STATISTICS, SYSTEMS SCIENCE. *Educ:* Brooklyn Col, BA, 47. *Prof Exp:* Air transp economist, Civil Aeronaut Bd, 48-51; anal statistician, Nat Inst Ment Health, 51-58; supvry statistician, Nat Inst Neurol Dis & Blindness, 58-67, supvry systs analyst, Nat Inst Neurol & Commun Disorders & Stroke, 67-77, assoc chief off biomet & epidemiol, 77-81; CONSULT SYSTS, 80- *Mem:* Fel AAAS; Asn Systs Mgt; fel Am Pub Health Asn; fel Royal Soc Health. *Res:* Design of management and administrative systems involving the use of computers; management of epidemiologic and statistical research in medical and related fields; epidemiology, manpower and information systems. *Mailing Add:* 3507 Farthing Dr Wheaton MD 20906

KROLL, CHARLES L(OUIS), b Boston, Mass, Sept 15, 23; m 46, 56; c 6. CHEMICAL ENGINEERING. *Educ:* Yale Univ, BE, 44; Mass Inst Technol, SM, 49, ScD(chem eng), 51. *Prof Exp:* Field engr, E I du Pont de Nemours & Co, 46-47; res assoc chem eng, Mass Inst Technol, 48-50; res chemist, Celanese Corp Am, 51-52; head, eng sect microbiol pilot plant, Squibb Inst Med Res, Div Olin Mathieson Chem Corp, 52-55, tech data mgr, 55-64, assoc dir drug regulatory affairs, 64-72, DIR REGULATORY OPERS, SQUIBB CORP, NEW BRUNSWICK, 72- *Mem:* Am Chem Soc; Am Inst Chem Engrs. *Res:* Heat transfer to air at high temperatures and low Reynolds numbers; theoretical supersonic performance of a ducted rocket; industrial fermentations. *Mailing Add:* 4 Corn Lane Shrewsbury NJ 07704

KROLL, EMANUEL, b New York, NY, Feb 26, 19; m 43; c 2. BIOCHEMISTRY. *Educ:* City Col New York, BS, 42; Canisius Col, MS, 46. *Prof Exp:* Chemist, Chem Construct Co, 42-43 & Fedders Mfg Co, 43-44; res chemist, Manhattan Proj, Linde Air Prod Co, 44-46; vpres res, Chem Res Assocs, 46-51; dir res, Heparin, Inc, 51-52; tech dir pharmaceut divs, Int Latex Corp, 52-69; dir res & develop, Standard Chem Prod, Inc, Henkel Co, 69-74; MGR RES SERVS, INT PLAYTEX, INC, 74- *Mem:* AAAS; Am Chem Soc; Soc Cosmetic Chem; Am Pharmaceut Asn. *Res:* Drug and cosmetic product development; protein, amino acid and enzyme research; organic synthesis; antiseptics; iodine compounds; ion exchange; chemical specialty product development; quality control; regulatory agency liaison administration. *Mailing Add:* 121 Robertson Dr Wyckoff NJ 07481

KROLL, JOHN ERNEST, b Los Angeles, Calif, Aug 15, 40; m 73. FLUID DYNAMICS, PHYSICAL OCEANOGRAPHY. *Educ:* Univ Calif, Los Angeles, BS, 63, MS, 66; Yale Univ, PhD(eng & appl sci), 73. *Prof Exp:* Res fel phys oceanog, Nova Oceanog Lab, 72-75; instr, Mass Inst Technol, 75-76; asst prof, 76-80, ASSOC PROF APPL MATH, OLD DOMINION UNIV, 81- *Mem:* Soc Indust & Appl Math; Am Geophys Union. *Res:* Theoretical investigation of the generation and propagation of inertial oscillations. *Mailing Add:* Dept of Math Old Dominion Univ Norfolk VA 23508

KROLL, NORMAN MYLES, b Tulsa, Okla, Apr 6, 22; m 45; c 4. MATHEMATICAL PHYSICS. *Educ:* Columbia Univ, AB, 42, AM, 43, PhD(physics), 48. *Prof Exp:* Asst physics, Columbia Univ, 42-44, mem sci staff, radiation lab, 43-62, from asst prof to prof physics, 49-62; chmn dept, 63-65, PROF PHYSICS, UNIV CALIF, SAN DIEGO, 62- *Concurrent Pos:* Nat Res Coun fel, Inst Advan Study, 48-49; Guggenheim fel, Rome, 55-56; mem staff, Jason Div, Inst Defense Anal, 60-; NSF sr fel, Europ Orgn Nuclear Res, 65-66. *Mem:* Nat Acad Sci; fel Am Phys Soc. *Res:* Nonlinear optics; microwave and nuclear physics; magnetron design; quantized field theories; elementary particle theory. *Mailing Add:* Dept of Physics Univ of Calif La Jolla CA 92093

KROLL, ROBERT J, b Cincinnati, Ohio, May 1, 28; m 54; c 5. AEROSPACE & STRUCTURAL ENGINEERING. *Educ:* Univ Cincinnati, BS, 49, MS, 56; Mich State Univ, PhD(appl mech), 62. *Prof Exp:* Engr reinforced concrete, Pollak Steel Co, 49-51; sr engr stress & design, Gen Elec Co, 52-57; from asst prof aeronaut eng to prof aerospace eng, 57-68, acting head dept, 70-71, 78-79, BRADLEY JONES PROF AEROSPACE ENG, UNIV CINCINNATI, 75- *Concurrent Pos:* Consult, Gen Elec Corp, 57-, Univ Dayton Res Div, 62-63, Aeronca Mfg Corp, 64-, Rockwell Standard Corp, 64-, Cincinnati Shaper Co, 65- & Cincinnati Industs, 67-; NASA-Am Soc Eng Educ sci fac fel, 64. *Mem:* Assoc fel Am Inst Aeronaut & Astronaut; Soc Exp Stress Anal; Am Soc Eng Educ; Sigma Xi. *Res:* Thermal stresses and stability; energy methods applied to lightweight structures; structural testing using strain gages and photostress; experimental wave propagation. *Mailing Add:* 2579 Beechmar Dr Cincinnati OH 45230

KROM, MELVEN R, b Hospers, Iowa, Oct 4, 31; m 53. MATHEMATICS. *Educ:* Univ Iowa, BA, 54, MS, 57; Univ Mich, PhD(math), 63. *Prof Exp:* Asst prof, 63-69, assoc prof, 69-76, PROF MATH, UNIV CALIF, DAVIS, 76- *Mem:* Asn Symbolic Logic; Math Asn Am; Am Math Soc. *Res:* Mathematical logic. *Mailing Add:* Dept of Math Univ of Calif Davis CA 95616

KROM, MICHAEL DAVID, b London, Eng, Mar 2, 50; m 77; c 1. GEOCHEMISTRY, MARINE SEDIMENTOLOGY. *Educ:* Queen's Col, Cambridge, 71; Edinburgh Univ, PhD(geochem), 76. *Prof Exp:* Higher sci officer anal chem, Water Res Ctr, Medmenham Bucks, 76-77; FEL GEOCHEM, DEPT GEOL & GEOPHYS, YALE UNIV, 77- *Concurrent Pos:* Vis assoc prof, Dept Earth & Environ Sci, Wesleyan Univ, Middletown, Conn, 80-81. *Mem:* Geochem Soc; Am Soc Limnol & Oceanog; Geol Soc Am. *Res:* Understanding the natural geochemical processes as they affect the marine environment and most particularly, the sediments quantifying how man has modified those processes. *Mailing Add:* Dept Geol & Geophysics Yale Univ New Haven CT 06520

KROMAN, RONALD AVRON, b Minneapolis, Minn, Mar 30, 27; m 62; c 3. GENETICS. *Educ:* Univ Minn, PhD(zool), 57. *Prof Exp:* From asst prof to assoc prof, 59-69, PROF BIOL, CALIF STATE UNIV, LONG BEACH, 69- *Concurrent Pos:* Consult revision jr high & high sch math curricula, Sch Math Study Group & Calif State Dept Educ. *Res:* Soc Study Evolution; Am Genetic Asn; Genetics Soc Am; Am Inst Biol Sci; Sigma Xi. Res: Drosophila genetics; tumors; melanin metabolism; eye pigmentation; symbiotic associations in the Acarina. *Mailing Add:* Dept of Biol Calif State Univ Long Beach CA 90840

KROMANN, PAUL ROGER, b Racine, Wis, Nov, 15, 29; m 60. PHYSICAL CHEMISTRY. *Educ:* Hope Col, AB, 52; Univ Calif, PhD, 57. *Prof Exp:* Chemist org synthesis, Hope Col, 52; asst chem, Univ Calif, 52-55; chemist, Plastics Fundamental Res Lab, Dow Chem USA, Mich, 57-71; ASST PROF CHEM, FT VALLEY STATE COL, 71- *Mem:* Am Chem Soc. *Res:* Radiation chemistry; photochemistry; fluorescence lifetimes. *Mailing Add:* 348 Clairmont Warner Robins GA 31093

KROMANN, RODNEY P, b Stockton, Calif, Sept 3, 31; m 79; c 4. ANIMAL NUTRITION. *Educ:* Calif State Polytech Col, BS, 58; Univ Calif, Davis, MS, 60, PhD(nutrit), 66. *Prof Exp:* Asst prof nutrit, NMex State Univ, 63-68; nutritionist, Shell Develop Co, 68-70; asst prof nutrit, Wash State Univ, 71-73, assoc prof, 73-78; PRES, NUTRIT INT, 78- *Concurrent Pos:* Nutrit consult, 67-68. *Mem:* AAAS; Am Soc Animal Sci; Am Inst Nutrit; Am Inst Chem. *Res:* Animal bioenergetics and nutrient and energy metabolism; mathematical modeling of protein and fat synthesis and of heat loss for the determination of maintenance by a radiometer. *Mailing Add:* Nutrit Int Box 143-G Rte 1 Palouse WA 99161

KROMBEIN, KARL VON VORSE, b Buffalo, NY, May 26, 12; m 42; c 3. ENTOMOLOGY. *Educ:* Cornell Univ, BS, 34, AM, 35, PhD(entom), 60; Univ Peradeniya, Sri Lanka, PhD(zool), 80. *Prof Exp:* Asst, NY State Exp Sta, 36-38; entomologist, Niagara Sprayer & Chem Co, NY, 39-40; assoc entomologist, Bur Entom & Plant Quarantine, USDA, 41-42, entomologist & invests leader, 46-65; chmn dept entom, 65-71, sr entomologist, 71-80, SR SCIENTIST, SMITHSONIAN INST, 80- *Concurrent Pos:* Civilian consult, Surgeon Gen, US Air Force, 72-79, emer consult, 79- *Mem:* Fel AAAS; Am Entom Soc; hon mem Egyptian Entom Soc; Entom Soc Am. *Res:* Systematics, bionomics, ecology and behavior of Hymenoptera Aculeata. *Mailing Add:* Dept of Entom NHB Stop 105 Smithsonian Inst Washington DC 20560

KROMER, LAWRENCE FREDERICK, b Sandusky, Ohio, Sept 1, 50. NEUROBIOLOGY, NEURAL REGENERATION. *Educ:* Univ Chicago, BA, 72, PhD(anat), 77. *Prof Exp:* Fel, Dept Histol, Univ Lung, Sweden, 77-79; asst res neuroscientist, Univ Calif, San Diego, 79-81; ASST PROF, DEPT ANAT & NEUROBIOL, UNIV VT, 81- *Concurrent Pos:* Prin investr, pvt found res grants, NIH, 79-; fel, A P Sloan Found, 80- *Mem:* Soc Neurosci; Int Soc Develop Neurosci; Am Asn Anatomists; AAAS. *Res:* Development and regeneration in the mammalian central nervous system by utilizing and intracephalic implantation technique which allows the transplantation of embryonic and neonatal neural tissue into the brain of neonatal and adult rodents. *Mailing Add:* Dept Anat & Neurobiol Given Med Bldg Univ Vt Burlington VT 05405

KROMER, RALPH EUGENE, b Boise, Idaho, Oct 23, 33; m 56; c 3. SYSTEMS ANALYSIS. *Educ:* Univ Colo, BS, 56; Southern Methodist Univ, MS, 66; Stanford Univ, PhD(statist), 70. *Prof Exp:* Systs engr, Gen Elec Co, 59-63; systs engr, Tex Instruments, Inc, 63-73, mgr comput systs, 73-77, DIR COMPUT SCI LAB, CENT RES LAB, TEX INSTRUMENTS, INC, 77- *Mem:* Am Statist Asn; Inst Math Statist. *Res:* Computer systems research; speech processing and word recognition. *Mailing Add:* Cent Res Labs PO Box 5936 MS 132 Dallas TX 75222

KROMHOUT, ROBERT ANDREW, b Elgin, Ill, Oct 23, 23; m 50; c 3. CHEMICAL PHYSICS. *Educ:* Univ Ill, PhD(physics), 52. *Prof Exp:* From instr to asst prof physics, Univ Ill, 52-56; from asst prof to assoc prof, 56-65, head dept, 60-62, PROF PHYSICS, FLA STATE UNIV, 65- *Mem:* Fel AAAS; Am Phys Soc; Am Asn Physics Teachers. *Res:* Phase transitions; statistical mechanics; adsorption theory. *Mailing Add:* Dept of Physics Fla State Univ Tallahassee FL 32306

KROMMINGA, ALBION JEROME, b Mille Lacs Co, Minn, June 20, 33; div; c 2. THEORETICAL PHYSICS. *Educ:* St Cloud State Col, BS, 55; Univ Minn, PhD(physics), 61. *Prof Exp:* Asst prof physics, Iowa State Univ, 61-63 & Idaho State Univ, 63-65; assoc prof, 65-69, PROF PHYSICS, CALVIN COL, 69- *Mem:* Am Phys Soc; Sigma Xi; Am Sci Affil. *Res:* Theory of decay of isobaric analogue states; deuteron stripping and other direct nuclear reactions; nuclear structure, simple shell model calculations; many body problem, liquid helium 4. *Mailing Add:* Dept of Physics Calvin Col Grand Rapids MI 49506

KRON, GERALD EDWARD, b Milwaukee, Wis, Apr 6, 13; m 46; c 5. ASTRONOMY. *Educ:* Univ Wis, BS, 33, MS, 34; Univ Calif, PhD(astrophys), 38. *Prof Exp:* Jr astronr, Lick Observ, Univ Calif, 38-42, asst astronr, 42-47, assoc astronr, 47-52, astronr, 52-65; dir, US Naval Observ, Flagstaff Sta, 65-73; sr res fel, Australian Nat Univ, 74-76; RETIRED. *Concurrent Pos:* Res assoc, Mass Inst Technol, 40-41 & Calif Inst Technol, 42-45; physicist, US Naval Ord Test Sta, Calif, 45; astron res, Pinecrest Observ, Flagstaff, Ariz, 76- *Mem:* AAAS; Am Astron Soc; Int Astron Union; Royal Astron Soc. *Res:* Electronic camera research and development; investigation of integrated properties of globular clusters; distribution of interstellar reddening. *Mailing Add:* Pinecrest Observ 416 N Bertrand St Flagstaff AZ 86001

KRONAUER, RICHARD ERNEST, b Paterson, NJ, Aug 5, 25; m 48; c 3. MECHANICAL ENGINEERING, BIOMEDICAL PHYSICS. *Educ:* Stevens Inst Technol, MechEng, 47; Harvard Univ, SM, 48, PhD, 51. *Prof Exp:* From instr to assoc prof, 51-64, PROF MECH ENG, HARVARD UNIV, 64- *Concurrent Pos:* Consult, Pratt & Whitney Aircraft Div, United Aircraft Corp, 51-58, Flow Corp, 53-59, Baldwin-Lima-Hamilton Corp, 56-61 & Arthur D Little Co, 61-; NSF fel, 64 & 71; NIH int fel, 78. *Mem:* Am Soc Mech Engrs; Am Inst Aeronaut & Astronaut. *Res:* Fluid dynamics and turbulence; nonlinear oscillations; respiratory control and infant death; visual system information processing; human circadian oscillators. *Mailing Add:* 324 Pierce Hall Harvard Univ Cambridge MA 02138

KRONBERGER, KARLHEINZ, b Vienna, Austria, Jan 24, 40. POLYMER CHEMISTRY, ORGANIC CHEMISTRY. *Educ:* Vienna Tech Univ, Dipl Ing, 64; Univ Nebr, PhD(org chem), 67. *Prof Exp:* Res assoc, Mass Inst Technol, 67-68; sr res chemist, 68-78, RES SECT MGR, RES DIV, ROHM AND HAAS CO, 78- *Mem:* Am Chem Soc; Austrian Chem Soc. *Res:* Coatings and polymer research. *Mailing Add:* Res Div Rohm and Haas Co Spring House PA 19477

KRONE, LAWRENCE JAMES, b Chicago, Ill, Sept 8, 40; m 68; c 2. VECTOR CONTROL, SOLID WASTE MANAGEMENT. *Educ:* North Park Col, BS, 63; Yale Univ, MPH, 67; Univ Ill, PhD(entom), 71. *Prof Exp:* Asst prof environ health, Dept Health, Ore State Univ, 72-75; proj dir, 75-77, EXEC DIR ENVIRON HEALTH, NAT ENVIRON HEALTH ASN, 77- *Concurrent Pos:* Pub health sanitarian, Benton County Health Dept, Ore, 73-74 & Nat Park Serv, 75; honorarium fac, Univ Denver & Univ Colo, 81; consult, Prof Exam Serv, 78- *Res:* Environmental health science, educational and professional roles in environmental health; entomology. *Mailing Add:* Nat Environ Health Asn 1200 Lincoln St Suite 704 Denver CO 80203

KRONE, LESTER H(ERMAN), JR, b St Louis, Mo, Oct 8, 31; m 53; c 3. MANAGEMENT SCIENCE. *Educ:* Wash Univ, BS, 52, DSc(chem eng), 55; Univ Ill, MS, 53. *Prof Exp:* Group leader process develop dept, Uranium Div, Mallinckrodt Chem Works, 55-56; appl sci rep, Int Bus Mach Corp, 56-57, mgr appl sci, Mo, 57-58; mgr oper anal, Monsanto Co, 58-68; independent consult, 68-73; MGR PROD PLANNING & MKT, McDONNELL-DOUGLAS AUTOMATION CO, 73- *Concurrent Pos:* Lectr, Wash Univ; assoc prof, Southern Ill Univ. *Mem:* Asn Comput Mach; Am Inst Chem Engrs; Opers Res Soc Am; Inst Mgt Sci. *Res:* Applied mathematics; computer techniques; operations research; mathematical programming, statistics and simulation. *Mailing Add:* 749 Chatelet Woods St Louis MO 63135

KRONE, RALPH WERNER, b Berlin, Ger, May 18, 19; US citizen; m 52; c 3. NUCLEAR PHYSICS. *Educ:* Antioch Col, BS, 42; Univ Ill, MS, 43; Johns Hopkins Univ, PhD, 49. *Prof Exp:* From asst prof to assoc prof, 48-61, actg chmn dept, 65-66, prof physics, 61-81, PROF PHYSICS & ASTRON, UNIV KANS, 81- *Mem:* Fel Am Phys Soc. *Res:* Nuclear structure; spectroscopy of light and medium light nuclei. *Mailing Add:* Dept of Physics Univ of Kans Lawrence KS 66044

KRONE, RAY B, b Long Beach, Calif, June 7, 22; m 46; c 2. HYDRAULIC & SANITARY ENGINEERING. *Educ:* Univ Calif, BS, 50, MS, 58, PhD(sanit eng), 62. *Prof Exp:* From asst to assoc res engr, Univ Calif, Berkeley, 50-64, lectr, 62-64; assoc prof civil eng, 64-70, chmn dept, 68-72, PROF CIVIL ENG, UNIV CALIF, DAVIS, 70-, ASSOC DEAN RES, COL ENG, 72- *Concurrent Pos:* Consult, US Army Corps Engrs, 60- *Mem:* AAAS; Am Geophys Union; Water Pollution Control Fedn; Am Soc Civil Engrs. *Res:* Soil science; particle transport; properties of water; soil water relations. *Mailing Add:* Dept of Civil Eng Univ of Calif Davis CA 95616

KRONENBERG, KLAUS JOHANNES, b Solingen, Ger, Mar 28, 21; US citizen; m 48; c 3. PHYSICS. *Educ:* Univ Gottingen, dipl, 48; Clausthal Tech Univ, Dr rer nat, 53. *Prof Exp:* Asst, Physics Inst, Univ Gottingen, 45-48, Ger Mining Acad, 48-52 & Deutsche Edelstahlwerke, 53; scientist, Ind Steel Prod Co, 53-63; staff scientist, Gen Dynamics/Pomona, 63-72; assoc prof, Calif State Polytech Univ/Pomona, 73-81; RES DIR & VPRES, TRIG INT, 81- *Concurrent Pos:* Guest lectr, Harvey Mudd Col; spec award, Alexander von Humboldt Found, Bonn, Ger. *Mem:* Am Inst Physics; Inst Elec & Electronics Engrs. *Res:* Electron microscopy; magnetism; thin films; metallurgy; meteorology; geophysics; astrophysics; fluid physics. *Mailing Add:* Dept of Physics Calif State Polytech Univ Pomona CA 91768

KRONENBERG, MARVIN L, b Chicago, Ill, July 3, 29; m 58; c 3. PHYSICAL CHEMISTRY, ELECTROCHEMISTRY. *Educ:* Univ Chicago, MS, 51; Western Reserve Univ, PhD(electochem), 59. *Prof Exp:* Res electrochemist, Nat Bur Standards, 51-53; Harshaw Chem Co, 56-57 & Union Carbide Corp, 59-65; proj leader electrochem, Sohio Res, 65-66; sr res assoc, Union Carbide Parma Tech Ctr, 66-77; electrochemist, Battery Bus Dept, Gen Elec, 77-80; STAFF CHEMIST, ARGONNE NAT LAB, 80- *Concurrent Pos:* Part-time instr, Cuyahoga Community Col, 66-77. *Honors & Awards:* Heise Award, Electrochem soc. *Mem:* Electrochem Soc; Am Chem Soc. *Res:* Electrochemical energy conversion devices; electrochemical catalysis and kinetics; corrosion and abrasion resistant coatings; electropolishing; electroanalytical methods; aluminum electrowinning; nonaqueous batteries; ambient temperature secondary batteries. *Mailing Add:* Argonne Nat Lab 9700 S Cass Ave Argonne IL 60439

KRONENBERG, RICHARD SAMUEL, b Chicago, Ill, Aug 7, 38; m 63; c 3. MEDICINE, PHYSIOLOGY. *Educ:* Northwestern Univ, BA, 60, MD, 63. *Prof Exp:* USPHS res fel, Cardiovasc Res Inst, Med Ctr, Univ Calif, San Francisco, 68-70; asst prof med, 70-74, assoc prof med, 74-78, PROF MED & HEAD, PULMONARY DIV, UNIV MINN HOSP, 70-, LECTR PHYSIOL, 70- *Concurrent Pos:* Consult, Vet Admin Hosp, Minneapolis, 71- *Mem:* AAAS; Am Physiol Soc; fel Am Col Physicians; Am Fedn Clin Res; Am Thoracic Soc. *Res:* Respiratory physiology; pulmonary disease. *Mailing Add:* Univ of Minn Hosp Minneapolis MN 55455

KRONENBERG, STANLEY, b Krosno, Poland, May 3, 27; US citizen; m 53; c 2. PHYSICS. *Educ:* Univ Vienna, PhD(physics, math, chem), 52. *Prof Exp:* Physicist, 53-81; CHIEF, HIGH ENERGY PROCESSING BR, ELECTRONIC TECH & DEVICES LAB, US ARMY ELECTRONICS RES & DEVELOP COMMAND, 70- *Concurrent Pos:* Army liaison rep, Nat Res Coun-Nat Acad Sci, 61-; consult, Fed Emergency Mgt Agency & Dept Energy. *Honors & Awards:* Meritorious Civil Serv Award, 61. *Mem:* Am Phys Soc; Am Nuclear Soc. *Res:* Nuclear radiation applications in solid state physics; dosimetry. *Mailing Add:* US Army Electronics Res & Develop Command ET&DL DELET-ER Ft Monmouth NJ 07703

KRONENTHAL, RICHARD LEONARD, b New York, NY, Oct 6, 28; m 49; c 2. POLYMER CHEMISTRY, SURGICAL DEVICES. *Educ:* Brooklyn Col, BS, 51; Polytech Inst Brooklyn, PhD(chem), 55. *Prof Exp:* Sr proj chemist org chem, Colgate Palmolive Co, 54-57; mgr dept org & polymer chem, 57-68, assoc dir res, 68-72, DIR RES, ETHICON, INC, JOHNSON & JOHNSON, 72- *Concurrent Pos:* Instr, Polytech Inst Brooklyn, 58-64. *Mem:* AAAS; Am Chem Soc; Am Soc Artificial Internal Organs; Am Inst Chem; Royal Soc Chem. *Res:* Chemistry of proteins; surgical devices; biomaterials; biodegradable polymers. *Mailing Add:* 33 Garwood Rd Fair Lawn NJ 07410

KRONENWETT, FREDERICK RUDOLPH, b Newark, NJ, July 29, 23; m 50; c 5. BACTERIOLOGY. *Educ:* Upsala Col, BSc, 48; Rutgers Univ, MS, 50, PhD(dairy bact), 54. *Prof Exp:* Dir qual control, Hohneker Dairy Co, 54-57; fel, Rutgers Univ, 58; from instr to assoc prof biol sci, 58-69, PROF BIOL SCI, FAIRLEIGH DICKINSON UNIV, 69-; DIR, AM BIOL CONTROL LABS, 57- *Concurrent Pos:* Lectr, Upsala Col, 58-59; chmn adv panel biol indicators, US Pharmacopeia; consult, Bergen Pines Hosp, 59; dir bioanal lab, NJ Bd Med Examr, 59; expert adv, Int Atomic Energy Agency, Vienna, 72. *Mem:* Am Soc Microbiol; Am Pub Health Asn; Inst Food Technologists; NY Acad Sci. *Res:* Identification of thermophilic bacteria; thermal death time studies on Brucella abortus; food poisoning; general microbiology; sterilization and disinfection; irradiation microbiology and dosimetry. *Mailing Add:* Dept of Biol Fairleigh Dickinson Univ Rutherford NJ 07070

KRONER, KLAUS E(RLENDUR), b Gottingen, Ger, July 19, 26; nat US; m 59; c 2. INDUSTRIAL ENGINEERING, ENGINEERING GRAPHICS. *Educ:* Col Wooster, BA, 49; NY Univ, BEE, 57; Am Int Col, MBA, 62. *Prof Exp:* Instr eng drawing, NY Univ, 50 & 51-55; instr eng graphics, Univ Maine, 55-57; from asst prof to assoc prof basic eng, 57-69, ASSOC PROF INDUST ENG & OPERS RES, UNIV MASS, AMHERST, 69-, ASST HEAD, 81- *Concurrent Pos:* Res scientist, indust develop div, Ga Inst Technol, 71. *Mem:* Am Soc Eng Educ. *Res:* Computer graphics; engineering economy; plant location and layout; industrial development. *Mailing Add:* Dept of Indust Eng & Opers Res Univ of Mass Sch of Eng Amherst MA 01003

KRONFELD, DAVID SCHULTZ, b Auckland, NZ, Nov 5, 28; m 57; c 2. NUTRITION, VETERINARY PHYSIOLOGY. *Educ:* Univ Queensland, BVSc, 52, BSc, 54, MVSc, 57, DSc(biochem), 72; Univ Calif, Davis, PhD(physiol), 59; Am Col Vet Internal Med, dipl, 73. *Hon Degrees:* MA, Univ Pa, 71. *Prof Exp:* Demonstr physiol, Univ Queensland, 53-54, lectr vet physiol, 54-57; lectr vet med, Univ Calif, Davis, 58-59, asst prof physiol, 59-60; from asst prof to assoc prof pharmacol, 60-67, PROF NUTRIT, SCH VET MED, UNIV PA, 67-, CHIEF SECT NUTRIT, 81- *Mem:* Am Dairy Sci Asn; Am Physiol Soc; Am Vet Med Asn; Am Inst Nutrit. *Res:* Nutrition and high performance of exercise, growth, pregnancy and lactation; metabolic disorders, ketosis, hypercholesterolemia, hypoglycemia, hypocalcemia, hypomagnesemia; tracer methodology, kinetic analysis, regulatory models; preventive medicine, health economics. *Mailing Add:* Sch of Vet Med Univ of Pa Kennett Square PA 19348

KRONGELB, SOL, b Jersey City, NJ, Aug 15, 32; m 53; c 3. PHYSICS. *Educ:* NY Univ, BS, 53; Mass Inst Technol, MS, 55, PhD, 58. *Prof Exp:* Asst physics, Res Lab Electronics, Mass Inst Technol, 54-58; assoc, 58-60, MEM RES STAFF, IBM CORP, 60- *Mem:* Am Vacuum Soc; Inst Elec & Electronics Engr. *Res:* Microwave spectroscopy; paramagnetic resonance; parametric devices; semiconductor technology; thin film adhesion; deposition and properties of magnetic and glass thin films; device fabrication technology. *Mailing Add:* Thomas J Watson Res Ctr PO Box 218 Yorktown Heights NY 10598

KRONISH, DONALD PAUL, b New York, NY, July 15, 26; m 54; c 1. MICROBIOLOGY, MICROBIAL BIOCHEMISTRY. *Educ:* Hunter Col, BS, 49; NY Univ, MS, 56. *Prof Exp:* Res asst dept chem eng, Columbia Univ, 51-52; microbiologist, Schwartz Labs, NY, 52-53, Gold Leaf Pharmacal Co, 53-54 & Nepera Chem Co, 54-56; assoc scientist microbiol, Warner Chilcott Labs, 56-61, scientist, 61-66, sr scientist, Dept Diag Res, 66-74, SR RES ASSOC, DEPT DIAG RES, WARNER-LAMBERT RES INST, 74- *Mem:* Am Soc Microbiol; NY Acad Sci; Am Acad Microbiol. *Res:* Antibiotic resistance, microbial transformations; biochemistry of the bacterial cell wall; fermentation and antibiotic isolation; diagnostic product research. *Mailing Add:* Dept of Microbiol & Immunol Gen Diag Div Warner-Lambert Co Morris Plains NJ 07950

KRONK, HUDSON V, b Port Jervis, NY, Oct 6, 38; m 59; c 3. MATHEMATICS. *Educ:* Rensselaer Polytech Inst, BS, 59; Mich State Univ, MS, 60, PhD(math), 64. *Prof Exp:* Lectr math, Kalamazoo Col, 63; asst prof, 64-68, ASSOC PROF MATH, STATE UNIV NY BINGHAMTON, 68- *Mem:* Am Math Soc; Math Asn Am. *Res:* Graph theory. *Mailing Add:* Dept of Math State Univ NY at Binghamton Binghamton NY 13901

KRONMAL, RICHARD AARON, b Los Angeles, Calif, May 3, 39; m 60; c 3. BIOSTATISTICS. *Educ:* Univ Calif, Los Angeles, AB, 61, PhD(biostatist), 64. *Prof Exp:* From instr to assoc prof, 64-75, PROF BIOSTATIST, SCH PUB HEALTH, UNIV WASH, 75-, CHMN BIOMATH GROUP, 73- *Concurrent Pos:* Career develop award, 68-73; mem, Renal Cardiovasc Ad Comt, Food & Drug Admin. *Mem:* Fel Am Statist Asn; Soc Study Human Biol; AAAS; Biomet Soc. *Res:* Mathematical statistics; statistical computing; public health and epidemiology. *Mailing Add:* Dept of Biostatist Sch of Pub Health Univ of Wash Seattle WA 98195

KRONMAN, JOSEPH HENRY, b New York, NY, Apr 4, 31; m 61; c 3. ANATOMY, DENTISTRY. *Educ:* NY Univ, BS, 52, DDS, 55; Columbia Univ, cert orthodont, 59; Med Col Va, PhD(anat), 62. *Prof Exp:* Instr anat, Med Col Va, 61-62; assoc prof orthodont, 62-68, asst to dean, Grad Sch Arts & Sci, 64-69, dir postdoctoral studies, Sch Dent Med, 64-70, dir growth & develop div, 68-69, PROF ORTHODONT, SCH DENT MED, TUFTS UNIV, 68- *Mem:* Am Asn Orthodont; Am Asn Anatomists; Int Asn Dent Res; Int Soc Craniofacial Biol. *Res:* Growth and development; caries; histochemistry; endocrinology; physiology of salivary glands. *Mailing Add:* 136 Harrison Ave Boston MA 02111

KRONMAN, MARTIN JESSE, b New York, NY, Sept 30, 27; m 65; c 3. PHYSICAL CHEMISTRY. *Educ:* Rutgers Univ, BS, 50; Temple Univ, PhD, 55. *Prof Exp:* Nat Heart Inst fel, Purdue Univ, 55-56; phys chemist, Eastern Regional Res Lab, USDA, 56-61; head biochem lab, US Army Natick Labs, 61-68; PROF BIOCHEM, STATE UNIV NY UPSTATE MED CTR, 68- *Honors & Awards:* Chem of Milk Award, Am Chem Soc, 68. *Mem:* AAAS; Am Chem Soc; Am Soc Biol Chemists. *Res:* Physico-chemical properties of proteins and nucleic acids; theory and technique of light scattering; optical rotation dispersion, absorption and emission spectra as applied to biological macromolecules; protein denaturation in enzyme action. *Mailing Add:* 113 Cumberland Ave Syracuse NY 13210

KRONSTAD, WARREN ERVIND, b Bellingham, Wash, Mar 3, 32; m 52; c 4. GENETICS, AGRONOMY. *Educ:* Wash State Univ, BS, 57, MS, 59; Ore State Univ, PhD(crop sci, genetics), 63. *Prof Exp:* Sr exp aide genetics, Wash State Univ, 59; from instr to assoc prof genetics & agron, 59-72, PROF PLANT BREEDING & AGRON CROP SCI, ORE STATE UNIV, 72- *Concurrent Pos:* Consult, US AID, Turkey, 67-, Washington, DC, 69, Ecuador, Korea, & People's Repub China; Alexander von Humboldt award, 81. *Mem:* Am Soc Agron; Crop Sci Soc Am. *Res:* Cereal improvement; environment-genotype interaction; use of biometrical models to partition genetic variation; disease resistance; influence of chelating agents on genetic recombination; aluminum tolerance in plants. *Mailing Add:* Dept of Crop Sci Ore State Univ Corvallis OR 97331

KRONSTEIN, KARL MARTIN, b Heidelberg, Ger, Feb 9, 28; US citizen; m 60; c 3. ALGEBRA. *Educ:* Georgetown Univ, BS, 51; Harvard Univ, AM, 52, PhD(math), 64. *Prof Exp:* Instr math, Reed Col, 57-58; from instr to asst prof, 58-69, ASSOC PROF MATH, UNIV NOTRE DAME, 69- *Concurrent Pos:* NATO res fel, Univ Frankfurt, 64-65. *Mem:* Am Math Soc; Math Asn Am. *Res:* Finite group theory, particularly Schur index. *Mailing Add:* Dept of Math Univ of Notre Dame Notre Dame IN 46556

KRONSTEIN, MAX, b Basel, Switz, Oct 7, 95; nat US; m 48; c 2. POLYMER CHEMISTRY. *Educ:* Univ Leipzig, PhD(chem), 22. *Prof Exp:* Chemist in charge prod varnishes & insulating mat, Elec Varnish Div, Brown Boveri Co, Ger, 22-38; develop chemist, William Zinsser & Co, NY, 39-43; chief chemist, Res Div, Titeflex, Inc, NJ, 43-46; from res assoc to sr res scientist & proj dir, Res Div, Sch Eng & Sci, NY Univ, 46-73; RES ASSOC CHEM, MANHATTAN COL, 73- *Mem:* Am Chem Soc; fel Am Inst Chem; Fedn Socs Paint Technol; Sigma Xi. *Res:* Formation of three-dimensional units in polymerization of organic material and metal-organics; formation of metal-organic complexes and basic principles of film-formation; mechanism of underwater coatings; surface reactions on galvanized steel. *Mailing Add:* Dept of Chem Manhattan Col Riverdale NY 10471

KROODSMA, DONALD EUGENE, b Zeeland, Mich, July 7, 46; m 68; c 3. ANIMAL COMMUNICAION, BEHAVIORAL ECOLOGY. *Educ:* Hope Col, BA, 68; Ore State Univ, PhD(zool), 72. *Prof Exp:* Fel, animal behav, Rockefeller Univ, 72-74, asst prof, 74-80; ASSOC PROF ZOOL, UNIV MASS, AMHERST, 80- *Concurrent Pos:* Mem adv panel, psychobiol, NSF, 80 & prin investr, grants, 76- *Mem:* Am Soc Naturalists; Am Ornithologists Union; Animal Behav Soc; Cooper Ornith Soc; Ecol Soc Am. *Res:* Diversity of vocal behaviors among birds; development, evolution, and functions of these diverse vocal communication systems. *Mailing Add:* Dept Zool Univ Mass Amherst MA 01003

KROODSMA, ROGER LEE, b Zeeland, Mich, Jan 23, 44. WILDLIFE ECOLOGY, ORNITHOLOGY. *Educ:* Hope Col, BA, 66; ND State Univ, MS, 68, PhD(zool), 70. *Prof Exp:* Asst prof biol, Union Univ, Jackson, Tenn, 70-73; res assoc ecol, Univ Ga, Athens, 73-74; mgr environ impacts prog, 77-79, MEM RES STAFF, ENVIRON SCI DIV, OAK RIDGE NAT LAB, 74- *Mem:* Wildlife Soc; Ecol Soc Am; Am Ornithologists Union. *Res:* Community ecology of birds in man-affected habitats, such as transmission line rights-of-way and pine plantations; edge effect. *Mailing Add:* Environ Sci Div Oak Ridge Nat Lab Oak Ridge TN 37830

KROOK, LENNART PER, b Ekshärad, Sweden, Aug 28, 24; m 58; c 2. VETERINARY PATHOLOGY. *Educ:* Royal Vet Col Sweden, DVM, 53, PhD(vet path), 57. *Prof Exp:* From asst prof to assoc prof vet path, Royal Vet Col Sweden, 51-57; assoc prof, Res Inst Nat Defense, Sundbyberg, 58; assoc prof, Sch Vet Med, Kans State Univ, 58-59; assoc prof, 59-65, PROF VET PATH, NY STATE COL VET MED, CORNELL UNIV, 65-, ASSOC DEAN POSTDOCTORAL EDUC, 81- *Mem:* Am Inst Nutrit; Int Acad Path. *Res:* Nutritional pathology. *Mailing Add:* Dept of Path Cornell Univ Ithaca NY 14853

KROON, JAMES LEE, b Grand Rapids, Mich, Apr 24, 26; m 52; c 3. SCIENCE EDUCATION. *Educ:* Calvin Col, AB, 48; Purdue Univ, MS, 51, PhD(chem), 54. *Prof Exp:* Asst, Purdue Univ, 48-51; chemist, Dow Chem Co, 53-58, proj leader, 58-69; assoc prof, 69-79, PROF CHEM, BETHEL COL, 79- *Mem:* Am Chem Soc; Sigma Xi; Am Sci Affiliation. *Res:* Polarography; electrochemistry; aerosols. *Mailing Add:* Dept of Natural Sci Bethel Col Mishawaka IN 46545

KROON, PAULUS ARIE, b Rotterdam, Neth, June 1, 45; NZ citizen; m 68; c 2. PHYSICAL BIOCHEMISTRY. *Educ:* Univ Auckland, BS, 67, MS, 68; Calif Inst Technol, PhD(chem), 75. *Prof Exp:* Res assoc, Life Sci Dept, Univ Pittsburgh, 75-77; SR RES BIOCHEMIST, MERCK SHARP & DOHME RES LABS, 77- *Concurrent Pos:* Res scientist, Biosci Div, Jet Propulsion Lab, 70-73. *Mem:* NY Acad Sci; AAAS. *Res:* Nuclear magnetic resonance spectroscopy; fluorescence spectroscopy; model and biological membranes; structure, function and metabolism of plasma lipoproteins. *Mailing Add:* Merck Sharp & Dohme Res Labs Box 2000 Rahway NJ 07065

KROON, R(EINOUT) P(IETER), b Hoorn, Holland, Aug 4, 07; nat US; m; c 3. MECHANICAL ENGINEERING. *Educ:* Polytech Acad, Zurich, MS, 30. *Prof Exp:* Develop engr, Westinghouse Elec Corp, 31-37, mgr, Exp Div & Steam Div, 37-45, eng mgr, Aviation Gas Turbine Div, 45-54; dir res, 54-57, chief engr adv, Design & Develop Dept, 57-58, adv systs planning, 58-60; prof, 60-75, EMER PROF MECH ENG, UNIV PA, 75- *Honors & Awards:* Spirit of St Louis Award, 50; Longstreth Medal, 63. *Mem:* Hon mem Am Soc Mech Engrs; assoc fel Am Inst Aeronaut & Astronaut. *Res:* Mechanics; turbomachinery; biomechanics. *Mailing Add:* Apt 93 Kendal Kennett Square PA 19348

KROONTJE, WYBE, b Rotterdam, Netherlands, Aug 2, 22; nat US; m 48; c 1. AGRONOMY. *Educ:* Cornell Univ, BS, 51; Univ Nebr, MS, 53, PhD(soils), 56. *Prof Exp:* Asst, Univ Nebr, 51-56; assoc prof, 56-74, PROF AGRON, VA POLYTECH INST & STATE UNIV, 74- *Concurrent Pos:* Prof & chmn dept soil sci, Ataturk Univ, Turkey, 63-65. *Mem:* Am Soc Agron; Soil Sci Soc Am; Int Soil Sci Soc; Turkish Soil Sci Soc. *Res:* Soil fertility and management of tobacco, soybeans and field crops; transformation and uptake of nitrogen; development of agronomic and higher education. *Mailing Add:* Dept of Agron Va Polytech Inst & State Univ Blacksburg VA 24061

KROOPNICK, PETER MICHAEL, b Detroit, Mich, Jan 31, 42; m 68. OCEANOGRAPHY, GEOCHEMISTRY. *Educ:* Wayne State Univ, BS, 63; Univ Calif, Berkeley, MS, 65; Univ Calif, San Diego, PhD(earth sci), 71. *Prof Exp:* ASSOC PROF CHEM OCEANOG, UNIV HAWAII, MANOA, 71-; RESEARCHER, HAWAII INST GEOPHYS, 71- *Mem:* AAAS; Am Geophys Union. *Res:* Chemical oceanography; stable isotopes, application to oceanographic transport phenomenon; carbon, oxygen-nutrient cycles; air-sea interactions; paleotemperature. *Mailing Add:* Dept of Oceanog Univ of Hawaii Honolulu HI 96822

KROOTH, ROBERT S, genetics, deceased

KROP, STEPHEN, b New York, NY, Sept 24, 11; m 34; c 4. PHARMACOLOGY, TOXICOLOGY. *Educ:* George Washington Univ, BS, 39; Georgetown Univ, MS, 40; Cornell Univ, PhD(pharmacol), 42. *Prof Exp:* Asst pharmacol, Med Col, Cornell Univ, 39-42, instr, 42-44; from instr to asst prof, Sch Med, Yale Univ, 44-46; chief pharmacol sect, Med Div, Army Chem Ctr, Md, 46-48, dep chief physiol div, Chem Corps Med Labs, 52-57; assoc mem, Squibb Inst Med Res, 48-49; dir pharmacol div, Warner Inst Therapeut Res, Div Warner-Hudnut, Inc, 49-51; res assoc & asst dir chem-biol coord ctr, Nat Res Coun, 51-52; chief pharmacol dept, Ethicon Res Found Div, Johnson & Johnson Co, NJ, 57-63; chief drug pharmacol br, US Food & Drug Admin, 63-79; CONSULT, 79- *Concurrent Pos:* Prof lectr, Med Sch, Georgetown Univ, 51-58, 63-; spec lectr, Med Sch, Univ Md, 52-57. *Mem:* Soc Toxicol; Am Soc Pharmacol & Exp Therapeut; Soc Exp Biol & Med; Am Physiol Soc; Harvey Soc. *Res:* Pharmacology of central nervous system; circulation; nerve-muscle; smooth muscle; local anesthetics; methods; respiration; toxicology. *Mailing Add:* 7908 Birnam Wood Dr McLean VA 22102

KROPF, ALLEN, b Queens, NY, Oct 3, 29; m 50; c 3. BIOPHYSICAL CHEMISTRY. *Educ:* Queens Col, NY, BS, 51; Univ Utah, PhD(chem), 54. *Hon Degrees:* MA, Amherst Col, 69. *Prof Exp:* Chemist, Appl Physics Lab, Johns Hopkins Univ, 54-56; Am Cancer Soc res fel chem vision, Harvard Univ, 56-58; from instr to assoc prof chem, 58-68, PROF CHEM, AMHERST COL, 68- *Concurrent Pos:* NSF sci fac fel, Univ Calif, Berkeley, 62-63; NIH spec res fel, Weizmann Inst Sci, 68-69; vis prof biophys, Kyoto Univ, 75-76; vis prof phys chem, Hebrew Univ, 76. *Mem:* Biophys Soc. *Res:* Photochemistry of visual pigments; preparation and properties of visual figments. *Mailing Add:* Dept of Chem Amherst Col Amherst MA 01002

KROPF, DONALD HARRIS, b Watertown, Wis, Mar 8, 31; m 62; c 3. MEAT SCIENCE, ANIMAL HUSBANDRY. *Educ:* Univ Wis, BS, 52, PhD(animal husb), 57; Univ Fla, MS, 53. *Prof Exp:* Res asst meat sci, Univ Fla, 52-53 & Univ Wis, 53-56; asst prof animal husb, Clemson Univ, 58-62; assoc prof, 62-72, PROF ANIMAL SCI & MEAT RES SCI, KANS STATE UNIV, 72- *Mem:* AAAS; Am Soc Animal Sci; Am Meat Sci Asn; Inst Food Technologists. *Res:* Meat color; effect of freezing system and rate packaging; display temperature and lighting on color; muscle histochemistry; carcass and live animal evaluation; processing and quality control. *Mailing Add:* Dept of Animal Sci & Indust Weber Hall Kans State Univ Manhattan KS 66506

KROPFLI, ROBERT ANTHONY, b Cleveland, Ohio, Aug 29, 40. RADAR METEOROLOGY, ATMOSPHERIC SCIENCE. *Educ:* Case Inst Technol, BS, 61; Cornell Univ, MS, 66. *Prof Exp:* Assoc physicist radar meteorol, Johns Hopkins Appl Physics Lab, 61-63, sr physicist, 66-74; PHYSICIST RADAR METEOROL, WAVE PROPAGATION LAB, NAT OCEANIC & ATMOSPHERIC ADMIN, 74- *Mem:* Am Meteorol Soc. *Res:* Application of radar and other remote sensors to improve understanding of atmospheric processes. *Mailing Add:* Wave Propagation Lab 325 Broadway Boulder CO 80302

KROPP, HELMUT, b Darmstadt, Ger, Feb 29, 36; US citizen; m 58; c 2. MEDICAL RESEARCH. *Educ:* Upsala Col, BSc, 70. *Prof Exp:* Apprentice chem, E Merck GMBH, Ger, 52-53, lab technician, 55-60, res biologist, 60-71, sr res biologist, 71-76, RES FEL, MERCK INST, MERCK & CO INC, 76- *Mem:* Am Soc Microbiol. *Res:* Biological and biochemical design and evaluation of new chemotherapeutic agents; mechanistic studies of drug action in the pharmacological and enzymological disciplines. *Mailing Add:* Merck Inst Merck & Co Inc Rahway NJ 07065

KROPP, JAMES EDWARD, b Chicago, Ill, July 25, 39; m 61; c 3. ORGANIC CHEMISTRY. *Educ:* Wabash Col, BA, 61; Univ Colo, PhD(org chem), 65. *Prof Exp:* Res chemist, Film Dept, E I du Pont de Nemours, Inc, 65-67; SR CHEMIST, MINN MINING & MFG CO, 67- *Mem:* Am Chem Soc. *Res:* Organic synthesis, mechanisms, stereochemistry; polymer synthesis, mechanisms, morphology, solvent effects. *Mailing Add:* Bldg 207-1W 3M Ctr St Paul MN 55144

KROPP, JOHN LEO, b Salem, Ore, June 26, 34; m 59; c 4. PHYSICAL CHEMISTRY, SPECTROSCOPY. *Educ:* Univ Santa Clara, BS, 56; Univ Notre Dame, PhD(phys chem), 61. *Prof Exp:* Res assoc radiation lab, Univ Notre Dame, 61-62; mem tech staff, 62-80, SR PROJ ENGR, TRW SYSTS GROUP, 80- *Mem:* AAAS; Am Chem Soc; Am Phys Soc. *Res:* Photochemistry of large organic molecules, especially fluorescence and phosphorescence of aromatic hydrocarbons; solar energy conversion; development of instrument systems especially space-oriented instruments. *Mailing Add:* 315 Via San Sebastian Redondo Beach CA 90277

KROPP, PAUL JOSEPH, b Springfield, Ohio, June 29, 35; m 63; c 2. ORGANIC CHEMISTRY. *Educ:* Univ Notre Dame, BS, 57; Univ Wis, PhD(org chem), 62. *Prof Exp:* Res chemist, Procter & Gamble Co, 61-70; PROF CHEM, UNIV NC, CHAPEL HILL, 70- *Concurrent Pos:* Alfred P Sloan Found res fel, 72; vis prof, Univ Calif, Los Angeles, 77-78. *Mem:* Am Chem Soc; Royal Soc Chem. *Res:* Photochemistry; stereochemistry; organic synthesis. *Mailing Add:* Dept Chem Univ NC Chapel Hill NC 27514

KROPP, WILLIAM A, b Hazelton, Pa, Nov 23, 28; m 52; c 1. PHYSICS. *Educ:* Muhlenberg Col, BS, 52. *Prof Exp:* Physicist, Argonne Nat Lab, 52-53; physicist, Savannah River Lab, 53-55, supvr instrumentation, 55-64, supvr, Exp Sta, 64-68, mgr electronics, 68-70, mgr appl physics, 70-74, mgr div progs, Du Pont Eng Res Div, 74-75, mgr eng test ctr, 75-77, DIR ENG TECHNOL LAB, E I DU PONT DE NEMOURS & CO, INC, 77- *Concurrent Pos:* Mem int comt nondestructive testing, AEC, 62-64; consult, Int Comn Reactor Safety, 63-64. *Res:* Measurement of physical properties of textile fibers; development of analog and digital information systems; nuclear reactor instruments and nondestructive testing. *Mailing Add:* 158 Oldbury Rd Westgate Farms Wilmington DE 19808

KROPP, WILLIAM RUDOLPH, JR, b Chicago, Ill, Nov 10, 36; m 63; c 2. COSMIC RAY PHYSICS, ELEMENTARY PARTICLE PHYSICS. *Educ:* DePaul Univ, BS, 58; Case Inst Technol, PhD(physics), 64. *Prof Exp:* Res assoc, Case Inst Technol, 64-66; asst res physicist, 66-67, asst prof physics, 67-73, assoc res physicist 73-80, RES PHYSICIST, UNIV CALIF, IRVINE, 80- *Mem:* Am Phys Soc; Am Asn Physics Teachers. *Res:* Low background detection systems; neutrino interactions; cosmic rays. *Mailing Add:* Dept of Physics Univ of Calif Irvine CA 92717

KROPSCHOT, RICHARD HENRY, cryogenics, solid state physics, see previous edition

KROSCHEWSKY, JULIUS RICHARD, b Taylor, Tex, Dec 14, 24; m 46; c 3. BOTANY, PHYTOCHEMISTRY. *Educ:* Univ Tex, BA, 47, MA, 49, PhD(bot), 67. *Prof Exp:* Instr biol, Lee Col, Tex, 49-52, Odessa Col, 54-59 & high sch, Calif, 60-61; assoc prof, St Edward's Univ, 61-67; PROF BIOL, BLOOMSBURG STATE COL, 67- *Mem:* AAAS; Phytochem Soc NAm. *Res:* Determination of structures and taxonomic significances of flavonoid compounds of plants. *Mailing Add:* Dept of Biol Bloomsburg State Col Bloomsburg PA 17815

KROSS, ROBERT DAVID, b Brooklyn, NY, Apr 25, 31; m 52; c 2. POLYMER CHEMISTRY, ANALYTICAL CHEMISTRY. *Educ:* Brooklyn Col, BS, 52; Iowa State Col, PhD(phys chem), 56. *Prof Exp:* Anal group leader, Rayonier, Inc, 57-59; chief chemist, Food & Drug Res Labs, 59-66; res dir, Foster D Snell, 66-69; dir, Kross Ref Lab, 69-80; vpres & dir res, Hydro Optics, Inc, 73-80; PRES, KROSS-LINK LABS, 81-; VPRES, MKT-TECH INDUST LTD, 81- *Res:* Consulting and analysis in nutrition, pharmaceuticals, cosmetics, plastics and polymers; life sciences; biochemistry; infrared spectroscopy; physical analytical chemistry; federal regulations pertaining to chemically-oriented products; environmental sciences. *Mailing Add:* Kross-Link Labs PO Box 374 Bellmore NY 11710

KROTKOV, ROBERT VLADIMIR, b Toronto, Ont, July 17, 29; m 58; c 4. ATOMIC PHYSICS. *Educ:* Queen's Univ, Ont, BA, 51, MA, 52; Princeton Univ, PhD, 58. *Prof Exp:* Instr physics, Palmer Lab, Princeton Univ, 56-58, res asst, 58-60; from instr to asst prof, Yale Univ, 60-66; assoc prof, 66-73, PROF PHYSICS, UNIV MASS, AMHERST, 73- *Mem:* Am Phys Soc. *Res:* Relativity and gravitation. *Mailing Add:* Dept of Physics Univ of Mass Amherst MA 01002

KROUSE, HOWARD ROY, b Norfolk Co, Ont, Jan 8, 35; m 58; c 2. PHYSICS, CHEMISTRY. *Educ:* McMaster Univ, BSc, 56, PhD(physics), 60. *Prof Exp:* From asst prof to prof physics, Univ Alta, 60-71, asst chmn dept, 70-71; PROF PHYSICS & CHMN DEPT, UNIV CALGARY, 71- *Concurrent Pos:* NATO fel & res assoc, Univ Calif, San Diego, 66-67; exchange scientist, USSR, 69; vis scientist, Japan, 71; res grants, Nat Res Coun Can, Defence Res Bd Can & Geol Surv Can. *Mem:* AAAS; Am Geophys Union; Am Phys Soc; Geochem Soc; Can Asn Physicists. *Res:* Isotope fractionation studies in physical, geological, chemical, biological and environmental processes; mass spectrometry. *Mailing Add:* Dept of Physics Univ of Calgary Calgary AB T2N 1N4 Can

KROUSKOP, THOMAS ALAN, b Washington, DC, July 11, 45; m 68; c 3. BIOENGINEERING, BIOMATERIALS. *Educ:* Carnegie Inst Technol, BS, 67; Carnegie-Mellon Univ, MS, 69, PhD(civil eng, biotechnol), 71. *Prof Exp:* Design engr, Gen Analytics Inc, 68; asst prof, 71-74, assoc prof, 74-78, ASST PROF BIOENG, TEX A&M UNIV, 78- *Concurrent Pos:* Consult, Sampson Corp, 70-71; consult, Tex Heart Inst, 75- *Mem:* Am Soc Testing & Mat; Rehab Eng Soc NAm; Am Cong Rehab Med. *Res:* Design of prosthetic appliances; materials for use as medical implants; effects of mechanical stress on soft tissue metabolism; development of assistive devices for the physically handicapped. *Mailing Add:* Inst for Rehab & Res 1333 Moursund Ave Houston TX 77025

KROW, GRANT REESE, b Reading, Pa, June 30, 41; m 70; c 2. ORGANIC CHEMISTRY. *Educ:* Albright Col, BS, 63; Princeton Univ, MFA, 64, PhD(chem), 67. *Prof Exp:* Res assoc chem, Ohio State Univ, 67-69; asst prof, 69-74, assoc prof, 74-80, PROF CHEM, TEMPLE UNIV, 80- *Mem:* Am Chem Soc. *Res:* stereochemistry; chemistry of heterocycles; synthesis of anticancer natural products. *Mailing Add:* Dept Chem Temple Univ Philadelphia PA 19122

KRUBINER, ALAN MARTIN, b New York, NY Apr 6, 41; m 62; c 2. ORGANIC CHEMISTRY. *Educ:* Queens Col, BS, 61; Univ Calif, Berkeley, PhD(org chem), 65; Seton Hall Univ, JD, 74. *Prof Exp:* Sr chemist, Hoffman-La Roche, Inc, 64-70, patent chemist, 70-74; patent atty, 74-77, supvry patent atty, 77-79, asst patent coun, 79-81, DIR PATENT LAW & LICENSING, SYNTEX CORP, 81- *Mem:* Am Chem Soc. *Res:* Proprietary information, primarily in health care area. *Mailing Add:* Syntex Corp Patent Dept 3401 Hillview Ave Palo Alto CA 94304

KRUCKEBERG, ARTHUR RICE, b Los Angeles, Calif, Mar 21, 20; m 42, 53; c 5. BOTANY. *Educ:* Occidental Col, AB, 41; Univ Calif, Berkeley, PhD(bot), 51. *Prof Exp:* Asst biol, Occidental Col, 39-41; field asst, Carnegie Inst, 41; asst biol, Stanford Univ, 41-42; asst bot, Univ Calif, Berkeley, 46-51; from instr to assoc prof, 51-63, PROF BOT, UNIV WASH, 64-, CHMN DEPT, 71- *Concurrent Pos:* Instr, Occidental Col, 46. *Mem:* Am Soc Plant Taxon. *Res:* Experimental plant taxonomy; edaphic ecology of serpentine soils. *Mailing Add:* Dept of Bot Univ of Wash Seattle WA 98195

KRUCZYNKSI, WILLIAM LEONARD, b Buffalo, NY, July 18, 43; m 66; c 2. RESOURCE MANAGEMENT. *Educ:* Caniscus Col, BS, 65; Univ NC, Chapel Hill, PhD(marine biol), 71. *Prof Exp:* Asst prof biol, Hartwick Col, 70-74; asst prof res, Fla A&M Univ, 74-79; LIFE SCIENTIST, US ENVIRON PROTECTION AGENCY, 79- *Concurrent Pos:* Consult, Environ Anal, Inc, 72-75, Conservation Consult, Inc, 77 & Tex A&M Univ & Tex Instruments, Inc, 78-79; vis prof, Col Ctr Finger Lakes, 73; res assoc, Fla State Univ, 74-77; vpres, Environ Systs Serv, Inc, 74-76. *Mem:* Am Soc Zoologists; AAAS; Ecol Soc Am; Estuarine Res Fedn. *Res:* Ecology of a crab symbiotic with mollusk hosts; systematics of marine isopod crustaceans; ecology of seline marshes. *Mailing Add:* 640 Applewood Lane Marietta GA 30064

KRUEGEL, ALICE VIRGINIA, b Louisville, Ky, May 29, 39; m 65; c 2. ORGANIC CHEMISTRY, FORENSIC SCIENCE. *Educ:* Spalding Col, Louisville, BA, 61; Univ Ky, PhD(org chem), 72. *Prof Exp:* Res chemist, Drug Enforcement Admin, Spec Testing & Res Lab, 70-78, SUPVRY CHEMIST FORENSIC DRUG CHEM, DRUG ENFORCEMENT ADMIN, WESTERN REGIONAL LAB, 78- *Mem:* Am Chem Soc; Am Acad Forensic Sci. *Res:* Forensic drug analysis; identification of impurities in illictly manufactured drugs. *Mailing Add:* Drug Enforcement Admin Western Regional Lab Box 36075 San Francisco CA 94102

KRUEGER, ALBERT PAUL, b Butte, Mont, Mar 17, 02; m 22; c 2. MEDICAL ECOLOGY. *Educ:* Stanford Univ, AB, 25, MD, 29; Am Bd Microbiol, dipl. *Prof Exp:* Asst bact & exp path, Stanford Univ, 27-28, actg instr, 28-29, instr & asst prof, 29; assoc gen physiol, Rockefeller Inst, 29-31; from assoc prof to prof bact, 31-57, lectr med, 32-57, chmn dept bact, 46-52, EMER PROF BACT, UNIV CALIF, BERKELEY, 57-; CHMN BD MED CONSULT, NAVAL BIOL LAB, 62- *Concurrent Pos:* Asst vis physician, Univ Hosp, Univ Calif, Berkeley, 31-56, consult, Student Health Serv, 32-57; grant, Comt Sci Res, AMA, 38; prin investr, Off Naval Res, Task V, Calif, 46-50; sci dir, US Naval Biol Lab, 50-54, chmn bd adv, 54-56. *Honors &. Honors & Awards:* William F Peterson Award, Int Soc Biometeorol, 66. *Mem:* Am Soc Microbiol; fel Am Pub Health Asn; fel Am Acad Microbiol; Int Soc Biometeorol; fel Royal Soc Health. *Res:* Biometeorology; experimental pathology and aerobiology; biological effects of gaseous ions. *Mailing Add:* Earl Warren Hall Univ Calif Sch Pub Health Berkeley CA 94720

KRUEGER, CHARLES ROBERT, b Milwaukee, Wis, June 21, 38; m 65; c 2. FORAGE CROP MANAGEMENT, FORAGE CROP UTILIZATION. *Educ:* Univ Wis-Madison, BS, 60, MS, 63, PhD(agron), 67. *Prof Exp:* Asst prof extension, Dept Agron, Univ Wis-Madison, 67-70; assoc prof res & teaching, Dept Plant Sci, SDak State Univ, 70-73, prof & head admin, res & teaching, 73-78; ASST DIR ADMIN, OHIO AGR RES & DEVELOP CTR, OHIO STATE UNIV, WOOSTER, 78- *Mem:* Am Soc Agron; Crop Sci Soc Am; Coun Agr Sci & Technol; Am Dairy Sci Soc; Am Soc Animal Sci. *Res:* Interdisciplinary research on forage crop production, management and utilization; determination of forage nutritive value by in vitro and in vivo methods; pasture and forage systems for beef cattle; establishment and use of warm-season perennial grasses; interseeding of native rangeland to improve productivity. *Mailing Add:* Ohio Agr Res & Develop Ctr Ohio State Univ Wooster OH 44691

KRUEGER, DAVID ALLEN, b Sidney, Mont, Aug 21, 39; m 61; c 4. THEORETICAL PHYSICS. *Educ:* Mont State Univ, BS, 61; Univ Wash, PhD(physics), 67. *Prof Exp:* Wis Alumni Res Found res assoc physics, Univ Wis, Madison, 67-69; asst prof, 69-72, assoc prof, 72-80, PROF PHYSICS, COLO STATE UNIV, 80- *Concurrent Pos:* Vis prof, Watson Res Lab, Int Bus Mach Corp, Yorktown Heights, NY, 75; mem tech staff, Sandia Lab, Albuquerque, 78-79; vis prof, Dept Energy, Energy Technol Ctr, Bartlesville, Okla, 80. *Mem:* AAAS; Am Phys Soc. *Res:* Theoretical many-body problem; dynamics of second order phase transitions; system size effects on phase transitions; fluids (stability of flow in porous media); thermal physics. *Mailing Add:* Dept of Physics Colo State Univ Ft Collins CO 80523

KRUEGER, EUGENE REX, b Grand Island, Nebr, Mar 30, 35; m 57; c 3. MATHEMATICS, COMPUTER SCIENCES. *Educ:* Rensselaer Polytech Inst, BS, 57, MS, 60, PhD(appl math), 62. *Prof Exp:* Physicist, Res Ctr, Int Bus Mach Corp, 57-58; vis fel, Math Res Ctr, Univ Wis, 62-63; asst prof math, Univ Colo, Boulder, 63-68, from asst prof to prof math & comput sci, 68-74, dir, Comput Ctr, 67-74; PROF COMPUT SCI, ORE STATE UNIV, 74-; VCHANCELLOR EDUC SYST, ORE STATE SYST HIGHER EDUC, 74- *Mem:* Soc Indust & Appl Math; Math Asn Am; Asn Comput Mach. *Res:* Fluid mechanics with emphasis on hydrodynamic stability; mathematical methods of physics; numerical analysis; interactive computer graphics. *Mailing Add:* Ore State Syst Higher Educ PO Box 3175 Eugene OR 97403

KRUEGER, GEORGE CORWIN, b Seattle, Wash, Nov 29, 22. OPTICS. *Educ:* Reed Col, AB, 45; Brown Univ, PhD(physics), 51. *Prof Exp:* From instr to assoc prof, 50-62, PROF PHYSICS, UNIV MAINE, ORONO, 62- *Concurrent Pos:* Air Force Weapons Lab, NMex, 65-66. *Mem:* Am Phys Soc; Optical Soc Am. *Res:* Atmospheric turbulence and heat transfer; physical optics; electromagnetic theory. *Mailing Add:* Dept of Physics Univ of Maine Orono ME 04473

KRUEGER, JACK N, b St Paul, Minn, Aug 29, 22; m 58; c 2. ELECTRICAL & AGRICULTURAL ENGINEERING. *Educ:* Univ Minn, BEE, 44, MS, 49. *Prof Exp:* Instr elec eng, Univ Minn, 44-49; res prof agr eng, Univ Ky, 49-51; consult engr, 51-55; assoc prof elec eng, Va Polytech Inst, 55-56; head, Electromech Develop Dept, Pillsbury Mills, Inc, 56-58; assoc prof elec eng, SDak State Univ, 58-59; assoc prof, 59-69, PROF ELEC ENG, UNIV N DAK, 69- *Mem:* Inst Elec & Electronics Engrs. *Res:* Electrical power and machinery; electrical instrumentation; biomedical and industrial electronics; environmental conditioning of production, processing and storage areas for agricultural products; forensic engineering; solar and wind energy systems. *Mailing Add:* Dept of Elec Eng Univ of NDak Grand Forks ND 58202

KRUEGER, JAMES ELWOOD, b Marinette, Wis, Apr 2, 26; m 53; c 3. ORGANIC CHEMISTRY. *Educ:* Univ Wis, BS, 49; Mass Inst Technol, PhD(org chem), 54. *Prof Exp:* Res fel chem, Harvard Med Sch, 53-55; chemist, Dow Chem Co, 55-61; CHEMIST, LEDERLE LABS DIV, AM CYANAMID CO, 61- *Mem:* AAAS; Am Chem Soc; Sigma Xi; Acad Pharmaceut Sci. *Res:* Pharmaceutical science. *Mailing Add:* 6 Lucille Blvd New City NY 10956

KRUEGER, JAMES HARRY, b Milwaukee, Wis, May 18, 36; m 59; c 3. INORGANIC CHEMISTRY. *Educ:* Univ Wis-Madison, BS, 58; Univ Calif, Berkeley, PhD(chem), 61. *Prof Exp:* From asst prof to assoc prof, 61-76, PROF CHEM, ORE STATE UNIV, 76- *Mem:* Am Chem Soc. *Res:* Kinetics and mechanisms of inorganic reactions; synthesis and characterization of transition metal complexes containing thiolate amino acid ligands. *Mailing Add:* Dept of Chem Ore State Univ Corvallis OR 97331

KRUEGER, KEATHA KATHRINE, b Faulk Co, SDak, Nov 15, 21. BIOCHEMISTRY. *Educ:* Univ SDak, BA, 43; Univ Wis, MS, 45, PhD(biochem), 48. *Prof Exp:* Assoc biochem, Med Sch, Univ SDak, 48-49, asst prof, 49-56; from asst ed to assoc ed, Chem Abstracts Serv, 56-61, head dept biochem, 61-63; sci commun officer, Nat Inst Arthritis & Metab Dis, 63-74, diabetes prog dir, 74-77, DIABETES SPECIALIST, NAT INST ARTHRITIS, DIABETES, DIGESTIVE & KIDNEY DIS, 77- *Concurrent Pos:* Exec secy, Nat Comn Diabetes, 75-76. *Mem:* AAAS; Am Chem Soc; Am Diabetes Asn; Am Med Writers Asn; NY Acad Sci. *Res:* Diabetes program administration; metabolic diseases. *Mailing Add:* Westwood Bldg Rm 626 NIADDKD Bethesda MD 20014

KRUEGER, KENNETH KAY, b Wharton, Tex, Feb 17, 49; m 70; c 2. PHYSIOLOGICAL GENETICS. *Educ:* Tex A&M Univ, BS, 71, MS, 72, PhD(poultry sci), 76. *Prof Exp:* Asst prof poultry sci, NC State Univ, 76-78; gen mgr, Tarheel Turkey Hatchery, 78; DIR RES, HYBRID TURKEYS LTD, 78- *Mem:* Worlds Poultry Sci; Poultry Sci Asn. *Res:* Reproductive physiology of the male and female turkey as influenced by management, environment, nutrition and genetic selection. *Mailing Add:* RR 1 New Hamburg ON N0B 2G0 Can

KRUEGER, PAUL A, b Madison, SDak, Feb 4, 06; m 32; c 5. ORGANIC CHEMISTRY. *Educ:* Sioux Falls Col, AB, 27; Northwestern Univ, MS, 29; Pa State Col, PhD(org chem), 32. *Prof Exp:* Jr patent exam, US Patent Off, 27-28; res chemist, Mallinckrodt Chem Works, 32-42, asst tech dir, 42-46 & prod develop, 46-53, mgr, Develop Dept, 54-60, dir mkt res indust chem, 56-60 & corporate develop, 60-63, asst to pres, 64-71, asst secy, 66-71; DIR CORP DEVELOP, NEWHARD, COOK & CO, INC, 73- *Concurrent Pos:* Stock broker, Stix Friedman & Co, Inc, 72. *Mem:* Am Chem Soc; Com Develop Asn; Chem Mkt Res Asn. *Mailing Add:* 5052 Westminster Pl St Louis MO 63108

KRUEGER, PAUL CARLTON, b Louisville, Ky, June 1, 36; m 65. INORGANIC CHEMISTRY, PHYSICAL CHEMISTRY. *Educ:* Marquette Univ, BS, 58; Case Inst Technol, PhD(chem), 63. *Prof Exp:* Res chemist, Air Reduction Co, Inc, 63-65, SR RES CHEMIST, CENT RES LABS, AIRCO, INC, 65- *Mem:* Am Chem Soc. *Res:* Chelate, silicon and slag chemistry; coordination compounds; inorganic and high temperature polymers; ferroalloy production; cutting of metals; corrosion of stainless steel alloys; development of stainless steel alloys. *Mailing Add:* Cent Res Labs Airco Inc 100 Mountain Ave Murray Hill NJ 07974

KRUEGER, PETER GEORGE, b Lodz, Poland, May 20, 40; US citizen; div; c 3. PHYSICS, BIOPHYSICS. *Educ:* Loma Linda Univ, La Sierra Campus, BA, 62; Univ Calif, Riverside, MA, 66, PhD(physics), 70. *Prof Exp:* Physicist, Naval Weapons Ctr, 62-77 & Naval Air Systs Command, Washington, DC, 77-78; physicist, Naval Weapons Ctr, 78-18; STAFF SCIENTIST, NAVAL AIR SYSTS COMMAND, WASHINGTON, DC, 81- *Mem:* Am Phys Soc. *Res:* Optical properties of multilayer dielectric mirrors; the theory of ring laser gyro and their performance sensitivities to mirror characteristics and bias mechanizations. *Mailing Add:* 110 Patrick St SE Voemma VA 22180

KRUEGER, PETER J, b Altona, Man, Nov 11, 34; m 59; c 3. PHYSICAL CHEMISTRY, SPECTROSCOPY. *Educ:* Univ Man, BSc, 55, MSc, 56; Oxford Univ, DPhil(infrared spectros), 58. *Prof Exp:* Fel, Org Spectrochem Sect, Div Pure Chem, Nat Res Coun Can, Ont, 58-59; asst prof chem, Univ

Alta, 59-64, assoc prof, 64-66; head dept chem, 66-70, vdean fac arts & sci, 70-72, mem bd govs, 70-73, PROF CHEM, UNIV CALGARY, 66-, ACAD V PRES, 76- *Concurrent Pos:* Vis scientist, Nat Res Coun Can, Ottawa, 66-67. *Honors & Awards:* Coblentz Award Spectros, Coblentz Soc, 67; Gerhard Herzberg Award, Spetros Soc Can, 73. *Mem:* Am Chem Soc; Chem Inst Can; Spectros Soc Can; Royal Soc Chem; Coblentz Soc. *Res:* Organic spectrochemistry; infrared and Raman spectra of organic compounds; normal coordinate analysis of vibrational spectra; molecular structure determination. *Mailing Add:* Dept of Chem Univ of Calgary Calgary AB T2N 1N4 Can

KRUEGER, ROBERT A, b Oak Park, Ill, Dec 29, 35; m 59; c 3. ORGANIC CHEMISTRY. *Educ:* Knox Col, AB, 57; Kans State Univ, PhD(org chem), 65. *Prof Exp:* Chemist, Visking Div, Union Carbide Corp, 57-58 & 60; res chemist, 65-69, sect leader, 69-72, tech adminr, 72-73, facility mgr, 73-75, vpres res & develop eng, 77-78, vpres additives & specialty polymers & develop function, 77-79, sr vpres elastomers, latex & specialty chem, 79-80, sr vpres & gen mgr, Polyvinyl Chloride Div, 80-81, SR VPRES STAFF SUPPORT SERV, B F GOODRICH CHEM CO, 81- *Mem:* Am Chem Soc; Indust Res Inst. *Res:* Synthesis and reactions of carbenes; olefin synthesis; antioxidants; polyvinyl chloride stabilization; organometallic chemistry. *Mailing Add:* 3359 Purdue St Cuyahoga Falls OH 44221

KRUEGER, ROBERT CARL, b Philadelphia, Pa, Oct 11, 20; m 47; c 2. BIOCHEMISTRY. *Educ:* Univ Pa, BS, 42; Columbia Univ, PhD(biochem), 48. *Prof Exp:* Res assoc immunochem, Col Physicians & Surgeons, Columbia Univ, 47-50; asst prof, 50-56, ASSOC PROF BIOL CHEM, COL MED, UNIV CINCINNATI, 56- *Concurrent Pos:* Res assoc, Brookhaven Nat Lab, 59-60; vis scientist, Univ Brussels, 66-67; NIH spec fel, 66-67. *Mem:* Am Soc Biol Chemists. *Res:* RNA synthesis; deoxribonucleoprotein structure and function. *Mailing Add:* Dept of Biol Chem Univ of Cincinnati Col of Med Cincinnati OH 45219

KRUEGER, ROBERT GEORGE, b Duluth, Minn, Apr 22, 38; m 60; c 2. IMMUNOLOGY, VIROLOGY. *Educ:* Col St Thomas, BS, 60; Univ Detroit, MS, 62; Univ Chicago, PhD(microbiol), 66. *Prof Exp:* Asst prof immunol, New York Med Col, 66-67; asst prof microbiol, Univ Wash, 67-71; assoc prof, Mayo Grad Sch Med, Univ Minn & Mayo Med Sch, 71-75; dir, Lab Molecular Oncol, Christ Hosp Inst Med Res, Cincinnati, 75-81, dir, Div Tumor Biol, 78-81; prof exp med & assoc prof microbiol, Col Med, Univ Cincinnati, 75-81; REGIONAL MED ASSOC, SMITH KLINE & FRENCH LABS, 81- *Concurrent Pos:* USPHS grants, 67-81; Am Cancer Soc grant, 69-71; consult microbiol & immunol, Mayo Clin, 71-75. *Mem:* AAAS; Am Asn Immunologists; Soc Exp Biol & Med; Am Soc Microbiol; Am Diabetes Asn. *Res:* Genetic regulation of immunoglobulin synthesis; mechanisms of neoplastic transformation by oncogenic viruses; protein synthesis in differentiated mammalian cells; structure of oncogenic viruses. *Mailing Add:* Christ Hosp Inst Med Res 2141 Auburn Ave Cincinnati OH 45219

KRUEGER, ROBERT HAROLD, b Sioux City, Iowa, Jan 25, 26; m 56; c 3. PHYSICAL CHEMISTRY. *Educ:* Morningside Col, BS, 50; Northwestern Univ, MS, 55; Loyola Univ, PhD(chem), 67. *Prof Exp:* Chemist, Cent Com Co, 51-54 & Diversey Corp, Ill, 54-56; res chemist, 56-62, sr res chemist, 62-70, group leader, 70-78, MGR PHYS CHEM, ROY C INGERSOLL RES CTR, BORG-WARNER CORP, 78- *Mem:* Am Chem Soc; Am Soc Testing & Mat; Nat Asn Corrosion Engrs. *Res:* Development of materials for bearings and seals; cement additives; new fluids for refrigeration; corrosion, friction and wear of materials; development of corrosion and scale inhibitors; plasma treatment of metals; protective coatings; sensors. *Mailing Add:* 1125 Skylark Dr Palatine IL 60067

KRUEGER, ROBERT JOHN, b Milwaukee, Wis, Apr 15, 48. PHARMACOGNOSY, PHARMACEUTICAL CHEMISTRY. *Educ:* Univ Conn, BS, 71; Univ Iowa, PhD(pharm), 75. *Prof Exp:* Asst prof, 75-80, ASSOC PROF PHARMACOG, FERRIS STATE COL, 80- *Concurrent Pos:* NDEA fel, 71-74; Eli Lilly & Co fel, 74-75. *Mem:* AAAS; Am Soc Pharmacog; Am Chem Soc; Phytochem Soc NAm; Am Asn Col Pharm. *Res:* Plant tissue culture; microbial transformations; isolation and identification of natural products; application of high pressure liquid chromatography to natural product isolation. *Mailing Add:* Sch of Pharm Ferris State Col Big Rapids MI 49307

KRUEGER, ROBERT WILLIAM, b Philadelphia, Pa, Nov 16, 16; m 41; c 2. PHYSICS. *Educ:* Univ Calif, Los Angeles, AB, 37, MA, 38, PhD(physics), 42. *Prof Exp:* Res physicist, Douglas Aircraft Co, 42-46; asst chief, Missiles Div, Rand Corp, 47-53; pres, Planning Res Corp, 54-73; PRES, PROF SERV INT, 73- *Concurrent Pos:* Pres-founder, Nat Coun Prof Serv Firms, 71-74, dir, 71- *Mem:* Am Phys Soc; Opers Res Soc Am. *Res:* Operations research; systems engineering; aerodynamics; propulsion; quantum mechanics; spectroscopy. *Mailing Add:* 1016 Moraga Dr Los Angeles CA 90049

KRUEGER, ROLAND FREDERICK, b Fond du Lac, Wis, Oct 18, 18; m 43; c 3. WELLBORE MECHANICS, OIL RECOVERY. *Educ:* Ripon Col, BA, 39; Univ Ill, MA, 41. *Prof Exp:* Lab instr, Univ Ill, 39-41; physicist, Tenn Eastman Corp, 41-42, Holston Ord Works, 42, Calif, 43, tech supvr, Oak Ridge, 43-44, asst dept supt, 44-46; physicist & res engr, Douglas Aircraft Co, Calif, 46-48; physicist & res engr, 48-51, sect leader, Prod Res Dept, 51-55, sr sect leader, 55-62, supvr, 62-81, MGR, UNION OIL CO, 81- *Concurrent Pos:* Sr tech ed, J Petrol Technol, 79- *Mem:* Am Inst Mining, Metall & Petrol Eng; Am Petrol Inst; AAAS. *Res:* Isotope separation; mass spectroscopy; combustion; spectrophotometry; thermodynamics; flow of fluids in porous media; production mechanics; formation damage in oil and gas wells; oil recovery processes. *Mailing Add:* 561 Peralta Hills Dr Anaheim CA 92807

KRUEGER, RUSSELL FRANCIS, b Milwaukee, Wis, Sept 1, 26; m 56; c 3. MICROBIOLOGY. *Educ:* Marquette Univ, BS, 50; Bowling Green State Univ, MA, 51; Mich State Univ, PhD, 58. *Prof Exp:* Res asst parasitol & pharmacol, Abbott Labs, 51-55; res asst microbiol & pub health, Mich State Univ, 55-58; dir biol res, Grove Labs, Mo, 58-64; dept head infectious dis res,

64-74, assoc dir biol sci, 74-77, ASSOC DIR SCI ADMIN, MERRELL-NAT LABS, MERRELL DOW PHARMACEUTICALS INC, 77- *Mem:* AAAS; Am Soc Parasitol; Am Soc Microbiol; Am Soc Trop Med & Hyg. *Res:* Chemotherapy of infectious diseases; host resistance; interferon inducers. *Mailing Add:* Merrell Dow Pharmaceuticals Inc 2110 E Galbraith Rd Cincinnati OH 45215

KRUEGER, WALTER L(AWRENCE), b Menomonie, Wis, Jan 18, 27; m 50; c 3. PLASTICS ENGINEERING. *Educ:* NDak State Univ, BS, 49, MS, 50. *Prof Exp:* Chemist, Tape Lab, 51-61, res specialist, 61-66, res specialist, Eng Res, 66-77, sr res specialist, 75-81, sr res specialist, 3M Cent Res Pilot Develop Lab, 78-81, STAFF SCIENTIST, 3M CENT RES PROCESS TECHNOL LAB, 81- *Mem:* Soc Plastics Eng. *Res:* Computer modeling of plastics extruders; computer designing of plastics film and sheet dies; research and development of film extrusion lines and screw plasticizing injection molding equipment; diffusion. *Mailing Add:* 3M Co 3M Ctr Bldg 208-1 St Paul MN 55144

KRUEGER, WILLIAM ARTHUR, b Milford, Iowa, Mar 24, 41. AGRONOMY. *Educ:* Univ Minn, BS, 63; Univ Ill, PhD(agron), 68. *Prof Exp:* Asst prof agron, 68-74, ASSOC PROF PLANT & SOIL SCI, UNIV TENN, KNOXVILLE, 74- *Mem:* Plant Growth Regulator Soc; Weed Sci Soc Am. *Res:* The effects that herbicides exert on the physiology of plants, particularly mode of action and basis of selectivity. *Mailing Add:* Dept of Plant & Soil Sci Univ of Tenn Knoxville TN 37916

KRUEGER, WILLIAM CLEMENT, b Medford, Ore, Aug 19, 42; m 65; c 2. RANGE SCIENCE. *Educ:* St Mary's Col, Calif, BS, 64; Humboldt State Col, MS, 67; Utah State Univ, PhD(range sci), 70. *Prof Exp:* Res technician range sci, Intermountain Forest & Range Exp Sta, 67-70; asst prof, Humboldt State Col, 70-71; asst prof, 71-75, leader rangeland resources prog, 75-80, HEAD, DEPT RANGELAND RESOURCES, ORE STATE UNIV, 81- *Concurrent Pos:* Head, Dept Range Sci, Colo State Univ, 80-81. *Mem:* Soc Range Mgt. *Res:* Range livestock nutrition concentrating on forage palatability; interaction of livestock grazing, wildlife and timber production through integration of management systems. *Mailing Add:* Rangeland Resources Dept Ore State Univ Corvallis OR 97331

KRUEGER, WILLIAM E, b St Louis, Mo, June 26, 40. ORGANIC CHEMISTRY. *Educ:* Univ Notre Dame, BS, 62; Univ NH, PhD(org chem), 67. *Prof Exp:* Res fel org chem, Univ Ill, Chicago Circle, 66; asst prof, 66-72, ASSOC PROF CHEM, STATE UNIV NY COL PLATTSBURGH, 72- *Mem:* Am Chem Soc. *Res:* Partially reduced pyridines; nitrenes; phosphorus additions. *Mailing Add:* Dept of Chem State Univ NY Col at Plattsburgh Plattsburgh NY 12901

KRUEGER, WILLIE FREDERICK, b Riesel, Tex, Oct 12, 21; m 46; c 2. POULTRY HUSBANDRY, GENETICS. *Educ:* Tex A&M Univ, BS, 43, MS, 49; Univ Mo, PhD(genetics, animal breeding), 52. *Prof Exp:* Teacher & prin pub sch, Tex, 41-42; flock supvr, Tex Poultry Improv Asn, 42-43; instr poultry husb, Miss State Univ, 46-47; asst, Agr & Mech Col Tex, 47-49; asst, Univ Mo, 49-50, from instr to asst prof, 50-53; from asst prof to assoc prof, 53-59, PROF POULTRY SCI, TEX A&M UNIV, 59-, HEAD DEPT, 72- *Mem:* Poultry Sci Asn; Am Genetic Asn. *Res:* Application of the principles of population genetics to poultry; embryology; embryology and incubation of chicken and turkey eggs; environmental factors influencing chickens and turkeys. *Mailing Add:* Dept of Poultry Sci Tex A&M Univ College Station TX 77843

KRUER, WILLIAM LEO, b Louisville, Ky, Apr 20, 42; m 65; c 3. PLASMA PHYSICS. *Educ:* Univ Louisville, BS, 64, MS, 65; Princeton Univ, MA, 67, PhD(astron), 69. *Prof Exp:* Res assoc, Plasma Physics Lab, Princeton Univ, 69-70, mem res staff, 70-72; GROUP LEADER LASER PLASMA THEORY & SIMULATION, LAWRENCE LIVERMORE LAB, 72- *Concurrent Pos:* Lectr, Univ Calif, Davis/Livermore, 76-; affil mem Ctr Plasma Physics & Fusion Eng, Univ Calif, Los Angeles, 76-; fel Am Phys Soc. *Mem:* Am Phys Soc. *Res:* Plasma theory; computer simulation of plasmas; nonlinear plasma waves; plasma heating; laser fusion. *Mailing Add:* Lawrence Livermore Lab L-477 Livermore CA 94550

KRUG, EDWARD CHARLES, b New Brunswick, NJ, Aug 24, 47. ENVIRONMENTAL GEOCHEMISTRY. *Educ:* Rutgers Univ, BSc, 75, MSc, 78, PhD(environ geochem), 81. *Prof Exp:* ASS'T SOIL SCIENTIST, CONN AGR EXP STA, 80- *Mem:* Soil Sci Soc Am; Water Pollution Control Fedn. *Res:* Reactions, weathering, and biogeochemical cycling of elements and materials in soil, water, and lake sediment. *Mailing Add:* Conn Agr Exp Sta PO Box 1106 New Haven CT 06504

KRUG, JOHN CHRISTIAN, b Toronto, Can, July 11, 38; m 74; c 2. MYCOLOGY. *Educ:* Univ Toronto, BSc, 63, MA, 64, PhD(mycol), 70. *Prof Exp:* Fel mycol, Inst of Bot, Swiss Fed Inst Technol, 70-72; fel, Univ Waterloo, 73; res assoc & fel, Univ Toronto, 73-74; res assoc & asst cur crytogamic bot, Royal Ont Mus, 74-75; res assoc mycol, 75-77, LECTR, UNIV TORONTO, 77-, ASST CUR, 81- *Concurrent Pos:* Collabr, Excerpta Botanica Sectio A: Taxonomica et Chorologica, 75-; res fel, Royal Ontario Mus, 78- *Mem:* Can Bot Asn; Brit Mycol Soc; Mycol Soc Am; Am Bryolog & Lichenolog Soc; Brit Lichen Soc. *Res:* Systematic and phytogeographical studies of Coprophilous Ascomycetes; Ascomycetes of over-wintering twigs; phytogeographical studies of fleshy fungi in Southern Ontario. *Mailing Add:* Dept of Bot Univ of Toronto Toronto ON M5S 1A1 Can

KRUGER, CHARLES HERMAN, JR, b Oklahoma City, Okla, Oct 4, 34; m 77; c 4. MECHANICAL ENGINEERING. *Educ:* Mass Inst Technol, SB, 56, PhD(mech eng), 60; Univ London, dipl, Imp Col, 57. *Prof Exp:* From instr to asst prof mech eng, Mass Inst Technol, 59-60; res scientist, Res Labs, Lockheed Missiles & Space Co, Calif, 60-62; from asst prof to assoc prof, 62-70, PROF MECH ENG, STANFORD UNIV, 70- *Concurrent Pos:* Sr fel, Nat Sci Found, 68-69; mem hearing bd, Bay Area Air Pollution Control Dist,

70-; chmn, Steering Comt, Eng Aspects of Magnetohydrodyn, 78-81; vis prof, Princeton, 78-79; vis scientist, Norwegian Inst Technol, 79; mem, Environ Studies Bd, Nat Acad Sci, 80- *Honors & Awards:* Fluid & Plasmadynamics Award & Medal, Am Inst Aeronaut & Astronaut, 79. *Mem:* Am Phys Soc; Am Soc Mech Engrs; Air Pollution Control Asn; Am Inst Aeronaut & Astronaut; Combustion Inst. *Res:* Physical gas dynamics; partially ionized plasmas; magnetohydrodynamics; combustion; air pollution. *Mailing Add:* Dept Mech Eng Stanford Univ Stanford CA 94305

KRUGER, FRED ALBERT, b New Brunswick, NJ, June 8, 21; m 45; c 3. BIOCHEMISTRY, ENDOCRINOLOGY. *Educ:* Rutgers Univ, BS, 42; Ohio State Univ, MD, 51. *Prof Exp:* Asst prof physiol chem, 56-58, ASSOC PROF MED, COL MED, OHIO STATE UNIV, 58-, PROF PHYSIOL CHEM, 64- *Mem:* Am Chem Soc; Biophys Soc. *Res:* Metabolism; mechanism of action of hormones and drugs; lipid metabolism; lipoproteins; diabetes. *Mailing Add:* Dept of Physiol Chem Ohio State Univ Col of Med Columbus OH 43210

KRUGER, FRED W, b Chicago, Ill, Dec 17, 21; m 47; c 3. MECHANICAL ENGINEERING. *Educ:* Univ Purdue, BS, 43, BS, 47; Univ Notre Dame, MS, 54. *Prof Exp:* Instr mech eng, 47-55, chmn dept, 55-65, dean col eng, 65-72, VPRES, VALPARAISO UNIV, 74- *Concurrent Pos:* Consult, McDonnell Aircraft Co, Caterpillar Tractor Co, Argonne Nat Lab, Northern Ill Gas Co & Ind State Bd Registr Prof Eng; mem city coun, City of Valparaiso, 72- & City Planning Comn, 76- *Mem:* Am Soc Mech Engrs; Am Soc Eng Educ. *Res:* Heat power systems. *Mailing Add:* Off of the VPres Valparaiso Univ Valparaiso IN 46383

KRUGER, FREDRICK CHRISTIAN, b St Paul, Minn, Apr 1, 12; m 36; c 2. ECONOMIC GEOLOGY. *Educ:* Univ Minn, BS, 35, MS, 36; Harvard Univ, PhD, 41. *Prof Exp:* Asst, Univ Minn, 35-36; instr geol, Dartmouth Col, 36-38; asst, Harvard Univ, 38-41; from asst geologist to asst chief geologist, Cerro de Pasco Copper Corp, 41-49; lectr geol, Northwestern Univ, 49; from assoc prof to prof, Univ Tenn, 49-52; asst chief geologist, Reynolds Metals Co, 52-57; chief geologist to vpres mining & explor div, Int Minerals & Chem Corp, 57-66; head dept, 66-74, prof mineral eng, 66-78, Donald Steel chair econ geologist, 71-78, assoc dean, 72-78, EMER PROF, STANFORD UNIV, 77-; CONSULT, 80- *Concurrent Pos:* Asst, Radcliffe Col, 38-41; Krumb lectr, Am Inst Mining, Metall & Petrol Eng, 68. *Honors & Awards:* Hardinge Award, Am Inst Mining, Metall & Petrol Eng, 72. *Mem:* Fel Am Geol Soc; Soc Econ Geol; Am Inst Mining, Metall & Petrol Eng; Can Inst Mining & Metall; Peruvian Geol Soc. *Res:* Mining geology; administration. *Mailing Add:* 145 Wildwood Way Woodside CA 94062

KRUGER, JAMES EDWARD, b Winnipeg, Man, Oct 14, 38; m 60; c 1. ENZYMOLOGY, CEREAL CHEMISTRY. *Educ:* Univ Man, BSc, 60, MSc, 63; Univ Sask, PhD(phys org), 65. *Prof Exp:* RES SCIENTIST CHEM CEREAL, GRAIN RES LAB, 66- *Mem:* Am Asn Cereal Chemists; Chem Inst Can; Am Asn Plant Physiologists. *Res:* Wheat systems such as amylase, proteases, polyphenol, and oxidoases; high performance liquid chromatography of sugars and proteins; automation of analytical techniques in cereal chemistry; pre-harvest sprouting problems. *Mailing Add:* 1425-303 Main St Winnipeg MB R3C 3G9 Can

KRUGER, JEROME, b Atlanta, Ga, Feb 7, 27; m 55; c 2. PHYSICAL CHEMISTRY, CORROSION. *Educ:* Ga Inst Technol, BS, 48, MS, 50; Univ Va, PhD(chem), 53. *Prof Exp:* Phys chemist, Naval Res Lab, 52-55; phys chemist, 55-66, LEADER CORROSION & ELECTRODEPOSITION GROUP, NAT BUR STANDARDS, 66- *Concurrent Pos:* Lectr, Univ Md, 59-69, prof, 69- *Honors & Awards:* Silver Medal, US Dept Com, 62, Gold Medal, 72; Blum Award, Electrochem Soc; Willis R Whitney Award, Nat Asn Corrosion Eng, 76. *Mem:* AAAS; Am Soc Testing Mat; Electrochem Soc; Sigma Xi; Nat Asn Corrosion Eng. *Res:* Corrosion; metallic oxidation; ellipsometry; electrochemistry. *Mailing Add:* Corrosion & Electrodepos Group Nat Bur of Standards Washington DC 20234

KRUGER, LAWRENCE, b New Brunswick, NJ, Aug 15, 29; m 61; c 2. NEUROANATOMY, NEUROPHYSIOLOGY. *Educ:* Wagner Col, BS, 49; Yale Univ, PhD(physiol), 54. *Prof Exp:* Asst physiol, Yale Univ, 50-53, asst neurophysiol, Inst Living, Conn, 53-54; USPHS fel physiol, Johns Hopkins Univ, 55-58; Nat Res Coun fel, Col France, 58; Nat Res Coun fel anat, Oxford Univ, 58-59; USPHS sr res fel anat, 59-60, from asst prof to assoc prof, 60-66, PROF ANAT, UNIV CALIF, LOS ANGELES, 66- *Concurrent Pos:* Lederle med fac award, 61-64; mem, Int Brain Res Orgn, UNESCO; Wellcome vis prof, 81. *Mem:* AAAS; Am Asn Anatomists; Am Physiol Soc; Soc Neurosci. *Res:* Cutaneous receptors and their central nervous system representation; organization of the visual system in vertebrates with particular reference to the midbrain; thalamo-cortical relations; electron microscopy of neural degeneration. *Mailing Add:* Dept Anat 73-235 Health Sci Ctr Univ of Calif Los Angeles CA 90024

KRUGER, OWEN L, b Oak Park, Ill, Dec 1, 32; m 54; c 4. CERAMICS, METALLURGY. *Prof Exp:* Metall engr, Ill Inst Technol, 54; metallurgist, Continental Foundry & Mach Co, 54-55; assoc metallurgist, Argonne Nat Lab, 57-69; assoc chief, Plutonium Technol & Mat, Thermodyn Div, Columbus Div, Battelle Mem Inst, 69-77; SR ENGR & COST ANALYIST, EXXON NUCLEAR CO, INC, 77- *Mem:* Fel Am Ceramic Soc; Am Nuclear Soc. *Res:* Light water reactor fuel fabrication; plutonium ceramics and metallurgy; fast reactor fuel development. *Mailing Add:* Exxon Nuclear Co Inc 2101 Horn Rapids Rd Richland WA 99352

KRUGER, PAUL, b Jersey City, NJ, June 7, 25; div; c 3. NUCLEAR CIVIL ENGINEERING. *Educ:* Mass Inst Technol, BS, 50; Univ Chicago, MS, 52, PhD(nuclear chem), 54. *Prof Exp:* Asst instr nuclear & phys chem, Univ Chicago, 50-53; res physicist, Res Labs Div, Gen Motors Corp, 53-54; vpres & head, Dept Phys Sci, Nuclear Sci & Eng Corp, Pa, 54-60; mgr nuclear proj, Hazelton-Nuclear Sci Corp, 60-62; PROF NUCLEAR CIVIL ENG, STANFORD UNIV, 62- *Mem:* Fel Am Nuclear Soc; Am Soc Civil Engrs. *Res:* Nuclear methods in civil engineering and environmental sciences; environmental radioactivity; nuclear explosion engineering; geothermal engineering. *Mailing Add:* Dept of Civil Eng Stanford Univ Stanford CA 94305

KRUGER, RICHARD PAUL, b Chicago, Ill, July 27, 44; m 69; c 2. ELECTRICAL ENGINEERING. *Educ:* Purdue Univ, BS, 67; Univ Mo, MS, 68, PhD(elec eng), 71; Univ NMex, MBA, 79. *Prof Exp:* Asst prof elec eng & radiol, Univ Southern CAlif, Calif, 71-75; STAFF MEM ELEC ENG, LOS ALAMOS NAT LAB, UNIV CALIF, 75- *Concurrent Pos:* Consult, Rockwell Corp, 73, Aerospace Corp, 75 & Univ Southern Calif, 76-77. *Mem:* Sr mem Inst Elec & Electronics Engrs; Sigma Xi. *Res:* Computer image processing applied to biomedical and industrial images; industrial automation; pattern recognition; computed tomography. *Mailing Add:* Los Alamos Nat Lab Los Alamos NM 87545

KRUGER, ROBERT A(LAN), b Oklahoma City, Okla, Dec 4, 35; m 58; c 4. MECHANICAL ENGINEERING, APPLIED PHYSICS. *Educ:* Mass Inst Technol, SB, 57, PhD(mech eng), 61. *Prof Exp:* NSF fel, Cambridge Univ, 57-58; sr engr, Convair Div, Gen Dynamics Corp, 61-62, staff mem, Gen Atomic Div, 62-67; head radiation-hydrodyn dept, Systs, Sci & Software, 67-68, mgr theoret sci div, 68-71, vpres & dir opers, 71, pres, 71-75; consult, 76; PRES, HORIZONS TECHNOL, INC, 76- *Mem:* Am Soc Mech Engrs; Am Inst Aeronaut & Astronaut; Sigma Xi. *Res:* High energy fluid dynamics; interaction of plasmas and solids; gas dynamics; ablation; boiling heat transfer; computers; microprocessors. *Mailing Add:* 2640 Saint Tropez Pl La Jolla CA 92037

KRUGH, THOMAS RICHARD, b Pittsburgh, Pa, May 3, 43; m 70; c 1. BIOPHYSICAL CHEMISTRY. *Educ:* Univ Pittsburgh, BS, 65; Pa State Univ, PhD(phys chem), 69. *Prof Exp:* NIH fel, Stanford Univ, 69-70; from asst prof to assoc prof, 70-78, PROF CHEM, UNIV ROCHESTER, 78- *Mem:* AAAS; Biophys Soc; Am Chem Soc. *Res:* Biophysical chemistry; drug-nucleic acid complexes; carcinogen-nucleic acid complexes; structures of nucleic acids; nuclear magnetic resonance. *Mailing Add:* Dept of Chem Univ of Rochester Rochester NY 14627

KRUGLAK, HAYM, b Ukraine, Mar 24, 09; m 41; c 2. PHYSICS. *Educ:* Univ Wis, BA, 34, MA, 36; Univ Minn, PhD, 51. *Prof Exp:* Instr pub sch, Wis, 36-38 & Milwaukee Voc Jr Col, 38-42, supvr radio training, 42-44; vis asst prof physics, Princeton Univ, 44-46; instr, Univ Minn, 46-51, asst prof physics, astron & gen studies, 51-54; assoc prof, 54-57, prof, 57-77, EMER PROF PHYSICS, WESTERN MICH UNIV, 78- *Mem:* Am Asn Physics Teachers; Am Asn Univ Prof; fel AAAS; Am Asn Physics Teachers. *Res:* Performance tests in laboratory instruction; design of laboratory and demonstration apparatus; physics, mathematics and astronomy education. *Mailing Add:* Dept of Physics Western Mich Univ Kalamazoo MI 49008

KRUGMAN, SAUL, b New York, NY, Apr 7, 11; m 40; c 2. MEDICINE. *Educ:* Med Col Va, MD, 39. *Prof Exp:* NIH res fel, 48-50; assoc prof, 54-60, chmn dept, 60-74, PROF PEDIAT, SCH MED, NY UNIV, 60- *Concurrent Pos:* Consult, Staten Island Develop Ctr, 56-; mem comn viral infections, US Armed Forces Epidemiol Bd, 59-73; dir pediat serv, Bellevue & Univ Hosps, 60-74; mem nat adv coun, Nat Inst Allergy & Infectious Dis, 65-69, chmn infectious dis adv comt, mem comt viral hepatitis, Nat Res Coun; mem, WHO Expert Panel Virus Dis. *Mem:* Nat Acad Sci; Am Pediat Soc; Soc Pediat Res; Am Epidemiol Soc; Am Acad Pediat. *Res:* Infectious diseases of children with special emphasis on viral infections. *Mailing Add:* Dept of Pediat NY Univ Sch of Med New York NY 10016

KRUGMAN, STANLEY LIEBERT, b St Louis, Mo, June 8, 32; m 58; c 2. FOREST GENETICS, FOREST PHYSIOLOGY. *Educ:* Univ Mo, BS, 54; Univ Calif, MS, 56, PhD(plant physiol), 61. *Prof Exp:* Res asst forestry, Univ Calif, 58-60, res specialist, 60-62; plant physiologist forest genetics, Pac Southwest Forest Range & Exp Sta, 62-66, proj leader genetics res proj, Inst Forest Genetics, 66-71, chief br genetic & related res, 71-74, prin res forest geneticist, 74-81, DIR, TIMBER MGT RES, US FOREST SERV, 81- *Concurrent Pos:* Res assoc, Agr Exp Sta, Univ Calif, 62-71; Nat Genetics Resources Bd, USDA, 78- *Mem:* Soc Am Foresters; Soc Plant Physiol; AAAS. *Res:* Pigments, hormones and reproductive physiology as related to trees; forest and tree improvement. *Mailing Add:* 6515 Dryden Dr McLean VA 22101

KRUH, DANIEL, b Brooklyn, NY, May 22, 34; m 61; c 2. TECHNICAL MANAGEMENT, PRODUCT DEVELOPMENT. *Educ:* WVa Wesleyan Col, BS, 55; Rensselaer Polytech Inst, PhD(org chem), 63. *Prof Exp:* Res chemist, Hercules Powder Co, 63-66; specialist, Insulating Mat Dept, Gen Elec Co, 66-70, mgr wire enamel develop, 70-72; res assoc, 72-75, sr res scientist, 75-76, SUPVR POLYMER TECH SERV, JOHNSON & JOHNSON DENTAL PRODS CO, 76- *Mem:* Am Chem Soc; Soc Plastics Eng; Royal Soc Chem; Am Inst chem. *Res:* Antiradiation drugs; phthalocyanine pigments; polyamide-imides; chemical and light cured polyesters; high performance polymers in coatings and composites; dental materials; reinforcing fillers; analytical methods development; materials characterization. *Mailing Add:* 8 Braddock St East Brunswick NJ 08816

KRUH, ROBERT FRANK, b St Louis, Mo, June 15, 25; m 48; c 2. PHYSICAL CHEMISTRY. *Educ:* Wash Univ, AB, 48, PhD(chem), 51. *Prof Exp:* Asst prof chem, DePauw Univ, 51-52; from asst prof to prof chem & dean col arts & sci, Univ Ark, 52-67; PROF CHEM & DEAN GRAD SCH, KANS STATE UNIV, 67- *Concurrent Pos:* Vis prof, Wash Univ, 60-61; mem coun res policy and grad educ, Nat Asn State Univs & Land Grant Cols, 68-72; mem policy comt, Coun Grad Schs, US, 69-73, chmn, Bd Dirs, 78-79; mem bd trustees, Argonne Univ Asn, 70-77; pres, Kans State Univ Res Found, 70-; mem, Grad Record Exam Bd, 77-, chmn, 80-81. *Mem:* Sigma Xi; AAAS; Am Chem Soc; fel Am Inst Chemists; Am Phys Soc. *Res:* Crystallography; x-ray diffraction; structure of liquids. *Mailing Add:* Grad Sch Kans State Univ Manhattan KS 66506

KRUIDENIER, FRANCIS JEREMIAH, b Cedar Rapids, Iowa, June 28, 13; m 43; c 6. HELMINTHOLOGY. *Educ:* Univ Mich, BS, 36, MS, 38, PhD(zool), 51. *Prof Exp:* Asst zool, Univ Mich, 43-44, fel, 44-48; from instr to assoc prof, 48-60, PROF ZOOL, UNIV ILL, URBANA, 61- *Concurrent*

Pos: Secy, World Fedn Parasitologists, 60-71. *Mem:* AAAS; Am Soc Parasitologists (secy, 60-62, secy-treas, 63-65, vpres, 66); Am Micros Soc; Electron Micros Soc Am; Am Soc Zoologists. *Res:* Electron microscopy; histochemistry and immunology. *Mailing Add:* Dept of Genetics & Develop Univ of Ill Urbana IL 61801

KRUKOWSKI, MARILYN, b New York, NY, May 3, 32; m 55; c 1. PHYSIOLOGY, DEVELOPMENTAL BIOLOGY. *Educ:* Brooklyn Col, BA, 54; NY Univ, MS, 62, PhD(biol), 65. *Prof Exp:* Res asst endocrinol exp cardiovasc dis, NY Med Col, Flower & Fifth Ave Hosps, 56-62, res assoc, 62-66, asst prof pharmacol & coinvestr endocrinol and exp cardiovasc dis, 66-69, instr pharmacol, 64-66; from res asst prof to asst prof, 69-75, ASSOC PROF BIOL, WASH UNIV, 75- *Mem:* AAAS. *Res:* Calcium metabolism and bone development; osteogenesis in birds and mammals as influenced by parathyroid hormone, calcitonin and steroids. *Mailing Add:* Dept of Biol Wash Univ St Louis MO 63130

KRULL, IRA STANLEY, b New York, NY, Oct 21, 40; m 73. ANALYTICAL CHEMISTRY. *Educ:* City Col New York, BS, 62; NY Univ, MS, 66, PhD(chem), 68. *Prof Exp:* Weizmann fel chem, Weizmann Inst Sci, 70-73; asst scientist, Boyce Thompson Inst, 73-76; sr scientist chem, Thermo Electron Corp, 77-79; SR SCIENTIST, NORTHEASTERN UNIV, 79- *Concurrent Pos:* Union Carbide fel, 68-70. *Mem:* Am Chem Soc; The Chem Soc; Am Asn Cancer Res; NY Acad Sci; Asn Off Anal Chemists. *Res:* Synthetic organic chemistry; mechanisms of chemical carcinogenesis; trace organic analytical chemistry; mechanisms of organic reactions. *Mailing Add:* Northeastern Univ 360 Huntington Ave Boston MA 02115

KRULL, JOHN NORMAN, b Albany, NY, July 31, 39; m 63; c 2. ECOLOGY, WILDLIFE BIOLOGY. *Educ:* State Univ NY Col Forestry, Syracuse Univ, BS, 61, MS, 63, PhD(wetland ecol), 67. *Prof Exp:* Asst prof Southern Ill Univ, 67-71; assoc prof, 71-75, PROF WILDLIFE BIOL & CONSERV, CENT MICH UNIV, 75- *Mem:* Soc Am Foresters; Conserv Educ Asn; Soil & Water Conserv Soc; Wildlife Soc. *Res:* Wetland ecology, especially green-tree reservoir ecology, waterfowl use and production from various wetland habitats, and aquatic plant-invertebrate associations; wildlife management investigations; conservation. *Mailing Add:* Dept of Biol Cent Mich Univ Mt Pleasant MI 48859

KRULWICH, TERRY ANN, b New York, NY, Apr 7, 43; m 73; c 2. BIOCHEMISTRY, MICROBIAL PHYSIOLOGY. *Educ:* Goucher Col, BA, 64; Univ Wis-Madison, MS, 66, PhD(bact), 68. *Prof Exp:* NIH trainee bact, Univ Wis, 68; NSF fel molecular biol, Albert Einstein Col Med, 68-70; asst prof, 70-74, assoc prof, 74-81, PROF BIOCHEM & DEAN GRAD SCH, MT SINAI SCH MED, 81- *Mem:* AAAS; Am Soc Microbiol; Am Chem Soc; Am Soc Biol Chemists; NY Acad Sci. *Res:* Microbial bioenergetics; alkalophilic and acidophilic bacteria. *Mailing Add:* Dept of Biochem Mt Sinai Sch of Med New York NY 10029

KRUM, ALVIN A, b Fresno, Calif, May 14, 28; m 54; c 2. PHYSIOLOGY. *Educ:* Univ Calif, AB, 50, PhD(physiol), 57. *Prof Exp:* Res physiologist, Univ Calif, 57-61; from asst prof to assoc prof, 61-73, PROF PHYSIOL, MED CTR, UNIV ARK, LITTLE ROCK, 73- *Concurrent Pos:* Fel, Steroid Training Prog, Univ Utah, 58-59; Lederle Med Fac Award, 64-67. *Mem:* AAAS; Am Physiol Soc; Endocrine Soc; Soc Exp Biol & Med. *Res:* Endocrinology; steroid biosynthesis; metabolism. *Mailing Add:* Dept of Physiol Univ of Ark Med Ctr Little Rock AR 72201

KRUM, JACK KERN, b Kansas City, Mo, Mar 17, 22; m 46; c 4. FOOD TECHNOLOGY. *Educ:* Hope Col, AB, 44; Mich State Univ, MS, 48; Univ Mass, PhD(food tech), 49. *Prof Exp:* Assoc prof food technol, Univ Tenn, 49-50; food technologist in charge prod control labs, Oscar Mayer & Co, 50-52; res chemist, Nat Biscuit Co, 52-56; asst tech dir, Sterwin Chem Inc, 56-61, tech dir, 61-69; asst res dir, R T French Co, 69-70, dir res & develop, 71-72, vpres & dir res & develop, 72-73; tech dir, ITT Paniplus Co, 73-79; PRES, TECH INC, 80- *Concurrent Pos:* Mem food additive comt, Flavoring Extract Mfrs Asn US, 61-72, chmn, 67-71; mem indust comt, Food Protection Comn, Nat Acad Sci, 64-66, White House Conf Food Nutrit & Health, 69 & tech comt, Grocery Mfrs Am, 70-73. *Mem:* Am Asn Cereal Chem; Soc Indust Microbiol; Inst Food Technol. *Res:* Food additives; new product development; fermentation; nutrition; food processing; dry mixes; food additives; dehydration; food flavors; stabilizers, emulsifiers and enrichment research administration. *Mailing Add:* Tech Inc 9718 Overbrook Rd Leawood KS 66206

KRUMBEIN, AARON DAVIS, b New York, NY, Apr 6, 21; m 50; c 3. REACTOR PHYSICS, PLASMA PHYSICS. *Educ:* Brooklyn Col, AB, 41; NY Univ, PhD(physics), 51. *Prof Exp:* Lab asst physics, Bartol Res Found, 41-42; asst, NY Univ, 42-46, asst, Cosmic Ray Proj, 46-47, consult physicist, Upper Atmosphere Res, Res Div, 47-49; sr scientist, Solid State Physics, US Naval Ord Lab, 55; asst prof physics, Univ Md, 50-56; adv scientist, Develop Div, United Nuclear Corp, 56-71; SR SCIENTIST-A, SOREQ NUCLEAR RES CTR, YAVNE, ISRAEL, 71- *Concurrent Pos:* Vis asst prof, Yeshiva Univ, 61-70; vis sr res assoc, Plasma Physics Group, Univ Md, 78-79. *Mem:* Israel Phys Soc (treas, 75-78); Am Nuclear Soc; Israel Nuclear Soc; Am Phys Soc. *Res:* Gaseous electronics; nuclear detectors; nuclear reactor and reactor shielding physics; intermetallic semiconductors; Geiger-Müller counters; radiation transport; space physics; laser produced plasma; thermonuclear reactors. *Mailing Add:* 9 Lutzki St Rehovot Israel

KRUMBEIN, SIMEON JOSEPH, b Brooklyn, NY, Jan 12, 31; m 57; c 3. ELECTROCHEMISTRY, SURFACE PHYSICS. *Educ:* Brooklyn Col, BS, 56; NY Univ, PhD(phys chem), 61. *Prof Exp:* Chemist, TRG, Inc, 56-57; phys chemist, Fuel Cell Lab, Gen Elec Co, 61-64; sr scientist, Res Div, Burndy corp, 64-69; asst prof, Stern Col, Yeshiva Univ, 69-75, assoc prof chem, 75-79; SR ENG SCIENTIST, RES DIV, AMP, INC, 77- *Concurrent Pos:* Consult, US Army Electronic Components Lab, 70; coadj asst prof chem, Univ Coll, Rutgers Univ, 72-74; consult, Res Div, AMP, Inc, 73-76. *Mem:* Am Chem Soc; Electrochem Soc; fel Am Inst Chem; Am Soc Testing & Mat. *Res:* Experimental methods in fuel cell research; electrical contact phenomena; metallic corrosion; experimental electrode kinetics; contact materials; environmental testing; electric contact phenomena. *Mailing Add:* AMP Inc Box 3608 Harrisburg PA 17105

KRUMDIECK, CARLOS L, b Lima, Peru, Nov 11, 32; m; c 2. BIOCHEMISTRY, NUTRITION. *Educ:* San Marcos Univ, Lima, BMed & MD, 58; Tulane Univ La, PhD(biochem), 64. *Prof Exp:* Resident med, Hosp 2nd of May, Lima, Peru, 58-59; biochemist, Hektoen Inst Med Res, Chicago, Ill, 59-60; Rockefeller Found fel biochem, Tulane Univ La, 60-62 & 64, USPHS fel, 62-63; prof biochem, Univ Cayetano Heredia, Peru, 65-70; assoc prof biochem & pediat, Med Sch, Univ Ala, 70-76, assoc dir nutrit prog, 73-76; assoc prof, 76-81, PROF BIOCHEM, UNIV ALA, BIRMINGHAM, 81-, assoc prof pediat, 76- *Mem:* Am Soc Biol Chemists; Sigma Xi. *Res:* Biochemistry of folic acid polyglutamates; biochemical assessment of nutrient status; pathogenesis of atherosclerosis. *Mailing Add:* Dept of Biol Univ of Ala Med Ctr Birmingham AL 35294

KRUMHANSL, JAMES ARTHUR, b Cleveland, Ohio, Aug 2, 19; m 44; c 3. SOLID STATE PHYSICS, APPLIED MATHMATICS. *Educ:* Univ Dayton, BS, 39; Case Inst Technol, MS, 40; Cornell Univ, PhD(physics), 43. *Hon Degrees:* DSc, Case Western Reserve, 80. *Prof Exp:* Instr physics, Cornell Univ, 43-44; physicist, Stromberg-Carlson Co, 44-46; from asst prof to assoc prof physics & appl math, Brown Univ, 46-48; from asst prof to assoc prof physics, Cornell Univ, 48-55; from asst dir res to assoc dir res, Nat Carbon Co, 55-58; dir lab atomic & solid state physics, 60-64, PROF PHYSICS, CORNELL UNIV, 59- *Concurrent Pos:* Consult to var industs, 46-; mem adv comts, AEC, Dept Defense & Nat Acad Sci, 56-; ed, J Appl Physics, 57-60; Guggenheim fel, 59-60; assoc ed, Solid State Commun, 63- & Rev Mod Physics, 68-73; NSF sr fel, Oxford Univ, 66-67; mem gov bd, Am Inst Physics, 73-; ed, Phys Rev Lett, 74-; asst dir, math phys sci & eng, NSF, 77-79; adj prof physics, Univ Pa, 82-; fel, Los Alamos Nat Lab. *Mem:* Fel Am Phys Soc; Am Asn Univ Prof; AAAS; Am Asn Physics Teachers; Sigma Xi. *Res:* Materials science; applied mathematics; carbon science and technology; research administration. *Mailing Add:* 1577 Taughannock Blvd Trumansburg NY 14886

KRUMINS, SOLVEIG AUD, b Oslo, Norway. CELL BIOLOGY, RECEPTOLOGY. *Educ:* City Col NY, BS, 69; NY Univ, MS, 72, PhD(biol), 78. *Prof Exp:* Fel assoc biol sci, Univ Md, 78-80; FOGARTY VIS FEL BIOPHYSICS & ENDOCRINOL, ENDOCRINOL & REPROD RES BR, NAT INST CHILD HEALTH & HUMAN DEVELOP, 81- *Res:* Cell surfaces; receptor-ligand interactions; lipoproteins, neurotransmitters; endocrinology; cell biology; biochemistry. *Mailing Add:* Biophysics & Endocrinol Sect Nat Inst Child Health Develop Bethesda MD 20205

KRUMM, CHARLES FERDINAND, b Macomb, Ill, Aug 3, 41; m 67. ELECTRICAL ENGINEERING. *Educ:* Univ Mich, BSE, 63, MSE, 65, PhD(elec eng), 70. *Prof Exp:* Res asst, Electron Physics Lab, Univ Mich, 65-69; sr res scientist, Res Div, Raytheon Co, 69-76; DEPT MGR, HUGHES RES LABS, 76- *Mem:* Inst Elec & Electronics Engrs. *Res:* Survenite design; fabrication and testing of Gallium Arsenic & Silicon integrated circuits including ion implantation; electron beam and optical lithography; high resolution dry processing and molecular beam epitaxy. *Mailing Add:* Hughes Res Labs 3011 Malibu Canyon Rd Malibu CA 90265

KRUMMEL, WILLIAM MARION, b New York, NY, Aug 15, 28; m 62; c 3. BIOMEDICAL ENGINEERING, ELECTRICAL ENGINEERING. *Educ:* City Col New York, BEE, 49; Columbia Univ, MS, 63; NY Univ, PhD(biomed eng), 67. *Prof Exp:* Engr, Control Div, Gen Elec Co, 49-54; systs engr, 56-62; asst prof elec eng, Univ Conn, 67-69 & NY Univ, 69-71, adj assoc prof, 71-73; assoc prof math, Bronx Community Col, City Univ New York, 71-73; assoc dean, Westchester Community Col, 73-80; PRES, NORWALK STATE TECH COL, 80- *Mem:* AAAS; Inst Elec & Electronics Engrs; NY Acad Sci; Sigma Xi. *Res:* Application of mathematical and engineering techniques to experimental and theoretical biomedical problems; application of electrical engineering techniques to industrial process control. *Mailing Add:* Norwalk State Tech Col Norwalk CT 06854

KRUMMENACHER, DANIEL, b Geneva, Switz, Mar 14, 25; m 51. GEOLOGY, CHEMISTRY. *Educ:* Univ Geneva, dipl chem eng, 52, PhD(geol), 59. *Prof Exp:* Res scientist, Univ Geneva, 59-62, assoc prof geochem, 62-68; from asst prof to assoc prof, 68-74, PROF GEOL, SAN DIEGO STATE UNIV, 74- *Concurrent Pos:* Researcher mass spectros, Univ Calif, Berkeley, 60-61, res assoc, 67-68. *Mem:* Geol Soc Am. *Res:* Isotope geology; geochronometry. *Mailing Add:* Dept of Geol San Diego State Univ San Diego CA 92115

KRUMREI, W(ILLIAM) C(LARENCE), b Cleveland, Ohio, Mar 31, 24; m 52; c 2. PROCESS DEVELOPMENT, PRODUCT DEVELOPMENT. *Educ:* Case Inst Technol, BS, 50; Mass Inst Technol, MS, 51. *Prof Exp:* Develop engr, Process Develop Dept, 51-54, tech brand mgr, Soap Prod Res Dept, 54-55, sect head, 55-58, assoc dir, Foods Div, Prod Develop Dept, 58-62, assoc dir, Household Soap Prod Develop Div, 62-63, dir prod develop, Household Soap Div, 63-70, dir tech govt rels, 70-72, SR DIR, CORP RES & DEVELOP DEPT, PROCTER & GAMBLE CO, 72- *Concurrent Pos:* Mem adv comt, NIH, 77-78. *Mem:* AAAS; Am Mgt Asn; Sigma Xi; NY Acad Sci; Am Indust Health Counc. *Res:* Oil, food and detergent chemistry and processing. *Mailing Add:* Procter & Gamble Co Ivorydale Tech Ctr Cincinnati OH 45217

KRUPA, PAUL L, b New York, NY, Jan 2, 29; m 61; c 2. PARASITOLOGY, ELECTRON MICROSCOPY. *Educ:* St Francis Col, NY, BS, 53; NY Univ, MS, 56, PhD(parasitol), 62. *Prof Exp:* From instr to assoc prof, 59-76, PROF BIOL, CITY COL NEW YORK, 76- *Concurrent Pos:* USPHS biomed sci support grant, 70-71; City Univ New York fac res grant, 71-72. *Mem:* AAAS; Am Soc Parasitol; Am Soc Trop Med & Hyg; Electron Micros Soc Am; Am Soc Cell Biol. *Res:* Electron microscopy and cytochemistry of platyhelminth parasites. *Mailing Add:* Dept of Biol City Col New York Convent Ave at 139th St New York NY 10031

KRUPA, SAGAR, b Madras, India, Oct 11, 40; US citizen; m 67. PHYTOPATHOLOGY, AIR POLLUTION. *Educ:* Andhra Univ, BSc, 59; Univ Wis, MS, 68; Univ Uppsala, PhD(plant physiol), 71. *Prof Exp:* Swed Nat Sci Res Coun res fel physiol bot, Inst Physiol Bot, Univ Uppsala, 72; res fel soil sci, Dept Microbiol, 72-73 & plant path, 73-74, asst prof, 74-80, ENVIRON PATHOLOGIST, 74-, ASSOC PROF PLANT PATH & PLANT PHYSIOL, DEPT PLANT PATH, UNIV MINN, ST PAUL, 80- *Concurrent Pos:* Docent, Inst Physiol Bot, Univ Uppsala, 73- *Mem:* Am Phytopath Soc; Air Pollution Control Asn. *Res:* Atmospheric chemistry and effects of air pollution on vegetation. *Mailing Add:* Dept of Plant Path Univ of Minn St Paul MN 55108

KRUPKA, LAWRENCE RONALD, b New York, NY, Mar 7, 33; m 58. PLANT PATHOLOGY. *Educ:* Cornell Univ, BS, 54; Univ Del, MS, 56; La State Univ, PhD, 59. *Prof Exp:* Asst plant path, Univ Del, 54-56 & La State Univ, 56-58; asst pathologist, Univ Nebr, 59-60; biologist, Rohm and Haas Chem Co, Pa, 61-63; asst prof biol, Philadelphia Col Pharm, 63-65; from asst prof to assoc prof, 65-68, PROF NATURAL SCI, MICH STATE UNIV, 68-, CHMN DEPT GREAT ISSUES & INTERDEPT COURSES, 73- *Concurrent Pos:* USPHS fel, 59-60; co-dir, sci, technol & human values, NSF. *Mem:* Mycol Soc Am; Am Phytopath Soc; Soc Indust Microbiol. *Res:* Host-parasite relationships of plant pathogens, especially rusts; respiration studies; enzyme and organic acid metabolism; drug toxicity; effects of science and technology upon society. *Mailing Add:* Dept of Natural Sci Mich State Univ East Lansing MI 48823

KRUPKA, MILTON CLIFFORD, b New York, NY, Jan 1, 24; m 54; c 3. HIGH TEMPERATURE PHYSICAL CHEMISTRY, MATERIALS SCIENCE. *Educ:* Brooklyn Col, BA, 44; Univ NMex, MS, 58, PhD(phys chem), 62. *Prof Exp:* Jr chemist, SAM Labs, Columbia Univ, 44-45; asst chemist, 45-46, lab supvr explosives, 46-50, proj engr weapons develop, 50-59, mat scientist high temp chem, 59-71, staff mem & asst mgr high temp chem, 71-75, MEM STAFF, TECHNOLOGY & ENVIRON ASSESSMENT, NEW ENERGY TECHNOLOGY & CONVERSION SYSTS, LOS ALAMOS NAT LAB, UNIV CALIF, 76- *Mem:* Fel Am Inst Chemists; Am Chem Soc; Sigma Xi; Sci Res Soc. *Res:* Elucidation of high temperature thermodynamics and properties of various refractory materials; ultrahigh pressure and temperature research; preparation of new materials and new superconductors; corrosion research in natural silicate melts; technology assessment. *Mailing Add:* Los Alamos Nat Lab PO Box 1663 Los Alamos NM 87545

KRUPKA, RICHARD MORLEY, biochemistry, see previous edition

KRUPKE, WILLIAM F, b Springfield, Mass, Jan 30, 37; m 61. SOLID STATE PHYSICS. *Educ:* Rensselaer Polytech Inst, BS, 58; Univ Calif, Los Angeles, MA, 60, PhD(spectros), 66. *Prof Exp:* Mem tech staff laser res, Minneapolis Regulator Co, 61-62; mem tech staff solid state res, Aerospace Corp, 62-66; staff physicist, Hughes Aircraft Co, Culver City, 66-74; MEM STAFF, LAWRENCE LIVERMORE NAT LAB, 74- *Mem:* Am Phys Soc. *Res:* Spectroscopic research on solid and gaseous systems as related to the dynamics of lasers; electronic structure of rare earth elements in solids; transition intensities and energy transfer processes. *Mailing Add:* Lawrence Livermore Nat Lab L-470 PO Box 5508 Livermore CA 94550

KRUPP, EDWIN CHARLES, b Chicago, Ill, Nov 18, 44; m 68; c 1. ASTRONOMY. *Educ:* Pomona Col, BA, 66; Univ Calif, Los Angeles, MA, 68, PhD(astron), 72. *Prof Exp:* Cur, 72-74, actg dir, 74-76, DIR ASTRON, GRIFFITH OBSERV, CITY LOS ANGELES, 76- *Concurrent Pos:* Inst, El Camino Col, 69-74 & Univ Southern Calif, 74-75; consult, Los Angeles County Supt Sch, Community Col Consortium, 74-; lectr & course coord, Univ Calif Exten, 75- *Mem:* Am Astron Soc; Sigma Xi; fel Explorer's Club. *Res:* Archaeoastronomy. *Mailing Add:* Griffith Observ 2800 E Observatory Rd Los Angeles CA 90027

KRUPP, IRIS M, b New Orleans, La, May 1, 28. PARASITOLOGY, DERMATOLOGY. *Educ:* La State Univ, BS; Tulane Univ, MS, 55, PhD(parasitol), 58, MD, 71. *Prof Exp:* Res asst, Sch Med, Tulane Univ, 49-53; instr vet parasitol, Mich State Col, 53-54; asst, 54-58, from instr to asst prof trop med & pub health, 59-66, assoc prof trop med & pub health, 66-81, CLIN ASSOC PROF MED, MED SCH, TULANE UNIV, 81- *Concurrent Pos:* Observer res technol, London Sch Hyg & Trop Med, 59-60; consult, USPHS grant, 60-65; intern, USPHS Hosp, 71-72; res fel, Vet Admin Hosp, New Orleans, 72-73; mem adv bd parasitic dis & consult to surgeon gen, Dept Army, 73-75; resident dermat, Charity Hosp, New Orleans, 73-76. *Mem:* Am Soc Parasitol; Am Soc Trop Med & Hyg; Am Acad Dermat; Am Asn Immunologists. *Res:* Immunology of parasitic infections. *Mailing Add:* Dept of Trop Med & Pub Health Tulane Univ of La Med Sch New Orleans LA 70112

KRUPP, MARCUS ABRAHAM, b El Paso, Tex, Feb 12, 13. MEDICINE, METABOLISM. *Educ:* Stanford Univ, AB, 34, MD, 39; Am Bd Int Med, dipl, 47. *Prof Exp:* Dir clin path, Vet Admin Hosp, San Francisco, 46-50; dir, Palo Alto Med Clin Lab, 50-50, DIR, PALO ALTO MED RES FOUND, 50- *Concurrent Pos:* Asst clin prof, Sch Med, Stanford Univ, 46-56, assoc clin prof, 56-65, clin prof, 65- *Mem:* Am Col Physicians; Am Fedn Clin Res; AAAS. *Res:* Renal physiology; water and electrolyte metabolism. *Mailing Add:* Palo Alto Med Res Found Palo Alto CA 94301

KRUPP, PATRICIA POWERS, b New York, NY. GROSS ANATOMY, EXPERIMENTAL MORPHOLOGY. *Educ:* Beaver Col, BA, 64; Hahnemann Med Col, PhD(anat), 70. *Prof Exp:* Asst instr nursing anat & physiol, Pa State Univ, Ogontz Campus, 63-66; sr instr gross anat, Hahnemann Med Col, 70-71, asst prof, 71-72; asst prof, 72-78, ASSOC PROF ANAT, COL MED, UNIV VT, 78- *Mem:* Am Asn Anatomists; AAAS; NY Acad Sci; Am Fedn Clin Res; Am Women Sci. *Res:* Experimental modification of thyroid gland structure and function; effects of diet, drugs, spontaneous hypertension and chronic stimulation. *Mailing Add:* Dept of Anat Col of Med Univ of Vt Burlington VT 05401

KRUSBERG, LORIN RONALD, PLANT PATHOLOGY. *Educ:* Univ Del, BS, 54; NC State Col, MS, 56, PhD(plant path), 59. *Prof Exp:* From asst prof to assoc prof, 60-70, PROF PLANT PATH, UNIV MD, COLLEGE PARK, 70- *Concurrent Pos:* Fel, NSF, Rothamsted Exp Sta, Eng, 59-60. *Mem:* Am Phytopath Soc; Soc Nematol. *Res:* Biology and control of nematodes parasitic on corn, soybeans and vegetables. *Mailing Add:* Dept Bot Univ Md College Park MD 20742

KRUSCHWITZ, WALTER HILLIS, b Edgerton, Ohio, July 20, 20; m 47; c 2. PHYSICS. *Educ:* Taylor Univ, AB, 42; Vanderbilt Univ, MA, 48; Univ Mich, PhD(higher ed), 61. *Prof Exp:* Assoc prof physics, Cumberland Univ, 48-50; asst prof physics & math, Union Univ, Tenn, 51-60, prof & head physics dept, 61-63; prof physics, Mobile Col, 63-67; assoc prof physics & educ, 67-69, assoc prof phys sci & physics, 69-72, ASSOC PROF PHYSICS, UNIV SFLA, 73- *Mem:* Am Asn Physics Teachers. *Res:* Measurement of the velocity of a gas immediately before combustion; undergraduate college physics research and its sponsorship; science education. *Mailing Add:* Dept of Physics Univ of SFla Tampa FL 33620

KRUSE, ARTHUR HERMAN, b Easton, Kans, Feb 5, 28; m 54; c 2. MATHEMATICS. *Educ:* Univ Kans, BA, 49, MA, 51; Univ Chicago, PhD(math), 56. *Prof Exp:* Res assoc math, Univ Kans, 54-60, from instr to asst prof, 54-60; RES PROF MATH SCI, NMEX STATE UNIV, 60- *Mem:* Am Math Soc; Math Asn Am. *Res:* Topology; axiomatic set theory; analysis. *Mailing Add:* Res Ctr NMex State Univ University Park NM 88003

KRUSE, CARL WILLIAM, b Aline, Okla, June 2, 27; m 49; c 4. COAL DESULFURIZATION, COAL ANALYSES. *Educ:* Bethany-Nazarene Col, AB, 50; Univ Kans, MS, 52; Univ Ill, PhD(chem), 58. *Prof Exp:* Res chemist, Phillips Petrol Co, 52-54 & Ill State Geol Surv, 54-56; group leader org chem, Phillips Petrol Co, 57-64, sect mgr, 64-68; assoc prof, Mid-Am Nazarene Col, 68-74, prof chem, 74-78, chmn div environ serv, 68-78; chemist, 78-80, HEAD MINERALS ENG SECT, ILL STATE GEOL SURV, 80- *Concurrent Pos:* Consult, Midwest Res Inst, 68-74 & Oak Ridge Nat Labs, Energy Res & Develop Admin, 75. *Mem:* Am Chem Soc; Am Inst Chem Engrs; AAAS. *Res:* Aromatic and aliphatic halides; alkylation of aromatics; acetylenic and olefinic compounds; organoaluminum compounds; energy problems; low temperature carbonization of coal; beneficiation of coal and coal char. *Mailing Add:* Ill State Geol Surv 615 E Peabody Dr Champaign IL 61820

KRUSE, CONRAD EDWARD, b Philadelphia, Pa, Sept 14, 23; m 49; c 2. BACTERIOLOGY. *Educ:* Philadelphia Col Pharm, BSc, 49, DSc(bact), 53; Univ Wis, MSc, 51. *Prof Exp:* Instr bact, Philadelphia Col Pharm, 51-56; res assoc, can div, Crown Cork & Seal Co, Pa, 56-57 & Col Dept, Lea & Febiger, 57-60; asst prof biol sci, Drexel Inst, 60-67; ASSOC PROF BIOL, URSINUS COL, 67- *Concurrent Pos:* Dept supvr bact, Children's Hosp, Philadelphia, 53-56; instr, Misericordia Hosp, Philadelphia, 55-56. *Mem:* AAAS; Am Soc Microbiol; Am Pharmaceut Asn; Inst Food Technologists. *Res:* Industrial and medical microbiology; biochemistry; food technology; development of pharmaceutical and food products; development of biochemical fuel cell. *Mailing Add:* Dept of Biol Ursinus Col Collegeville PA 19426

KRUSE, CORNELIUS WOLFRAM, b College Station, Tex, Feb 19, 13; m 39; c 4. PUBLIC HEALTH, SANITARY ENGINEERING. *Educ:* Mo Sch Mines, BSCE, 34, CE, 39; Harvard Univ, MSSE, 40; Univ Pittsburgh, DrPH, 61; Am Acad Environ Engrs, dipl. *Prof Exp:* Inspector flood control works, US Army Engrs, Memphis Dist, 34-35; eng aide health & safety dept, Tenn Valley Authority, 35-38, resident sanit engr, 38-44, staff sanit engr, 44-45; from instr to assoc prof sanit eng, 45-50, PROF ENVIRON HEALTH, SCH HYG & PUB HEALTH, JOHNS HOPKINS UNIV, 60- *Concurrent Pos:* Consult, USPHS, 47, Tenn Valley Authority, 48-61, WHO, Liberia, 50, Southeast Asia, 53 & West Pac, 59; mem comt sanit eng & environ, Med Sci Div, Nat Res Coun, 51-53; vis prof & head pub health eng, Inst Hyg, Manila, 53-55; mem, Md State Bd Health & Ment Hyg, 60-; mem comn environ hyg, Armed Forces Epidemiol Bd, 63- *Mem:* Am Indust Hyg Asn; Am Pub Health Asn; Am Soc Civil Eng; Am Water Works Asn; Am Soc Trop Med & Hyg. *Res:* Ecological techniques for mosquito control, aircraft dispersion of larvicides, adulticides and herbicides; fundamental properties and behavior of infectious agents in the external environment, including bacteria, viruses, protozoa and helminths. *Mailing Add:* Sch of Hyg & Pub Health Johns Hopkins Univ Baltimore MD 21205

KRUSE, FERDINAND HOBERT, b Council Bluffs, Iowa, July 9, 25; m 47; c 3. PHYSICAL CHEMISTRY. *Educ:* Iowa State Col, BSc, 45; Univ NMex, MSc, 51; Univ Calif, Los Angeles, PhD(phys chem), 56. *Prof Exp:* Chemist, Gen Elec Co, Mass, 45-46; instr inorg chem, Iowa State Col, 46-48; res chemist phys chem, Esso Res & Eng Co, 56-57; mem staff, Los Alamos Sci Lab, 57-67; SR CHEMIST CORP TECH, TECH CTR, OWENS-ILL, INC, 68- *Concurrent Pos:* Fulbright lectr, Univ Alexandria, 65-66. *Mem:* Am Crystallog Asn. *Res:* X-ray crystallography; single crystal structure analysis; optical properties of crystalline compounds; inorganic chemistry of actinide elements; chemistry of tellurium and selenium; digital computer programming and applications; analytical chemistry; x-ray fluorescence spectroscopy. *Mailing Add:* 4716 Crestridge Rd S Toledo OH 43623

KRUSE, JURGEN M, b Berlin, Ger, Apr 27, 27; nat US; m 51; c 3. CHEMISTRY. *Educ:* Harvard Univ, AB, 49; Purdue Univ, MS, 50, PhD(chem), 52. *Prof Exp:* Res chemist & group leader, E I du Pont de Nemours & Co, Inc, 52-64, res assoc, 63-67; mgr anal lab, Itek Corp, 67-75; specialist, US Postal Serv, 75-76; dir advan develop, Coulter Systs Corp, 76-80. *Mem:* Am Chem Soc. *Res:* Analytical chemistry; catalysis. *Mailing Add:* Bldg 1 Apt 9 45 Jefferson Rd Branford CT 06405

KRUSE, KIPP COLBY, b Norfolk, Nebr, Nov 21, 49; m 75; c 2. BEHAVIORAL ECOLOGY. *Educ:* Wayne State Col, BSE, 71; Univ SDak, MA, 73; Univ Nebr, PhD(Ecol), 78. *Prof Exp:* Instr biol, Univ Nebr, 78-79; ASST PROF ZOOL, EASTERN ILL UNIV, 79- *Mem:* Sigma Xi; Soc Study Amphibians & Reptiles. *Res:* Aspects of sexual selection in the anura as well as testing certain components of optimal foraging theory. *Mailing Add:* Dept Zool Eastern Ill Univ Charleston IL 61920

KRUSE, LAWRENCE IVAN, b Springfield, Vt, Dec 21, 58; m 80. PHARMACEUTICAL CHEMISTRY. *Educ:* Mass Inst Technol, BS, 76, PhD(chem), 79. *Prof Exp:* ASSOC SR INVESTR MED CHEM, SMITH KLINE & FRENCH LABS, 79- *Mem:* Am Chem Soc. *Res:* Design and synthesis of selective enzyme inhibitors; synthesis of unnatural amino acids and antitumor-antimetabolic agents of potential therapeutic ability; stereoelectronic effects in organic chemistry; indole and other heterocyclic chemistry. *Mailing Add:* Smith Kline & French Labs 1500 Spring Garden St Philadelphia PA 19101

KRUSE, OLAN ERNEST, b Coupland, Tex, Sept 6, 21; m 42; c 2. PHYSICS. *Educ:* Tex Col Arts & Indust, BS, 42; Univ Tex, MA, 49, PhD, 51. *Prof Exp:* Jr radio engr, Signal Corps Labs, Camp Evans, NJ, 42-43; from asst prof to prof physics & chmn dept, Stephen F Austin State Col, 51-56; PROF PHYSICS & CHMN DEPT, TEX A&I UNIV, 56- *Mem:* Am Asn Physics Teachers; Nat Sci Teachers Asn. *Res:* Electronic circuitry; mechanics; electricity and magnetism; multiple scattering of charged particles by thin soils. *Mailing Add:* Dept of Physics Tex A&I Univ Kingsville TX 78363

KRUSE, PAUL WALTERS, JR, b Hibbing, Minn, Nov 24, 27; m 54; c 9. SOLID STATE PHYSICS, ELECTROOPTICS. *Educ:* Univ Notre Dame, BS, 51, MS, 52, PhD(physics), 54. *Prof Exp:* Physicist, Farnsworth Electronics Co, 54-56; sr res scientist, Res Ctr, Minn-Honeywell Regulator Co, 56-59, prin res scientist, 59-60, staff scientist, 60-69, sr staff scientist, 70-77, prin staff scientist, 78-80, PRIN RES FEL, CORP TECHNOL CTR, HONEYWELL, INC, 80. *Concurrent Pos:* Mem, US Army Sci Adv Panel, 65-77, ground warfare panel, President's Sci Adv Comt, 70-72, comt mat for electromagnetic radiation detection devices, Nat Acad Sci, 71-73 & Army Countermine Adv Comt, 71-74; mem planning comt, Third Int Photoconductivity Conf, 69-71; chmn, US Army ERADCOM Technol Panel, 75-76; mem, US Army Near-Millimeter Wave Technol Base Develop Study, 76-77; consult, Army Sci Bd, 78-; Mem comt phys sci, adv bd military personnel supplies, Nat Res Coun, Nat Acad Sci, 69-71, NATO rev panel Pres's Sci Adv Comt & Vietnam Panel, 71-72 & US/USSR Tech Balance Assessment Study, US Naval Res Adv Comt, 79-80. *Honors & Awards:* Recipient, H W Sweatt Award, Honeywell, Inc, 66; Alan Gordon Mem Award, Int Soc Optical Eng, 81. *Mem:* Fel Am Phys Soc; assoc fel Am Inst Aeronaut & Astronaut; Optical Soc Am; sr mem Inst Elec & Electronics Engrs. *Res:* Electrooptical physics; nonlinear optics; infrared detectors; crystal growth; solid state devices; lasers. *Mailing Add:* Honeywell Corp Technol Ctr 10701 Lyndale Ave S Bloomington MN 55420

KRUSE, ROBERT LEROY, b Jacksonville, Fla, Jan 7, 41. COMBINATIONS, FINITE MATHEMATICS. *Educ:* Pomona Col, BA, 60; Calif Inst Technol, MS, 62, PhD(math), 64. *Prof Exp:* Staff mem, Sandia Lab, 64-70; assoc prof math, Emory Univ, 73-76; chmn dept, 76-79, PROF MATH, ST MARY'S UNIV, HALIFAX, 79- *Concurrent Pos:* Fulbright-Hays grant & vis reader, Univ Canterbury, NZ, 70-72. *Mem:* Am Math Soc; Can Math Soc; Australian Math Soc; Asn Comput Mach; Can Info Processing Soc. *Res:* Data structures; program transformations; applications of computers in abstract algebra; finte rings. *Mailing Add:* Dept Math St Mary's Univ Halifax NS B3H 3C3 Can

KRUSE, ROBERT LOUIS, b Fairmont, Minn, Aug 23, 38; m 64; c 2. CHEMICAL ENGINEERING, POLYMER CHEMISTRY. *Educ:* Univ Minn, Minneapolis, BS, 60; Univ Ill, Urbana, MS, 62; Columbia Univ, EngSciD(chem eng), 67. *Prof Exp:* Chem engr, Esso Res & Eng Co, NJ, 61-64; chem engr, 67-70, res group leader, 70-78, SCI FEL, MONSANTO CO, 78- *Concurrent Pos:* Lectr polymer processing, Univ Mass, 67-68; lectr math, Western New Eng Col, 68-; lectr polymer characterization, St Joseph Col, Conn, 70-71. *Mem:* Am Chem Soc; Soc Rheol. *Res:* Polymerization kinetics; rheology and surface properties of polymers; molecular characterization; continuum properties. *Mailing Add:* 444 Michael Sears Rd Belchertown MA 01007

KRUSE, ULRICH ERNST, b Berlin, Ger, May 22, 29; nat US. PHYSICS. *Educ:* Harvard Univ, PhD(physics), 54. *Prof Exp:* From instr to asst prof physics, Univ Chicago, 54-59; from asst prof to assoc prof, 59-69, PROF PHYSICS, UNIV ILL, URBANA, 69- *Mem:* Fel Am Phys Soc. *Res:* Experimental nuclear physics. *Mailing Add:* Dept of Physics Univ of Ill Urbana IL 61803

KRUSE, WALTER, b Heide, Ger, Oct 6, 28; m 60; c 2. INORGANIC CHEMISTRY, PHYSICAL CHEMISTRY. *Educ:* Univ Cologne, PhD, 58. *Prof Exp:* Fel, Univ Chicago, 58-60; asst kinetics, Max Planck Inst Phys Chem, 60-64; res chemist, Hercules Res Ctr, Del, 64-71; res chemist, Atlas Chem Industs, Inc, 71-74; res chemist, ICI United States, Inc, 74-79, SR RES CHEMIST, ICI AMERICAS, INC, 79- *Mem:* Am Chem Soc. *Res:* Preparative inorganic chemistry; complex chemistry; oxidation of olefins; hydrogenation of carbohydrates; homogeneous catalysis. *Mailing Add:* ICI Americas Inc Wilmington DE 19897

KRUSEN, EDWARD MONTGOMERY, b Philadelphia, Pa, Feb 7, 20; m 48; c 2. MEDICINE. *Educ:* Univ Pa, BA, 41, MD, 44; Univ Minn, MS, 50. *Prof Exp:* Med dir phys ther sch, 51-71, prof phys ther, Univ, 58-71, CHIEF DEPT PHYS MED & REHAB, BAYLOR UNIV MED CTR, 50- *Concurrent Pos:* From asst prof to assoc prof phys med & rehab, Univ Tex Health Sci Ctr, 51-61, chmn dept, 51-55, clin prof phys med & rehab, 61-; area consult, Vet Admin, 54-; chmn med adv bd, United Cerebral Palsy, Tex, 55-73; consult, Elizabeth Kenney Found, 55-57 & Am Rehab Found, 57-; chmn, Coun Med Dirs Phys Ther Schs, 60; mem, Am Bd Phys Med & Rehab, 65-77, Gov Coun Develop Disabilities, 71 & Residency Review Comt, 76- *Honors & Awards:* Tex Award Planning Voc Rehab, 68. *Mem:* AMA; Am Rheumatism Asn; Am Cong Rehab Med; Am Acad Phys Med & Rehab. *Res:* Cervical syndrome; backache; hemiplegia; hemiplegia; rehabilitation of the elderly; electromyography. *Mailing Add:* Dept of Phys Med & Rehab Baylor Univ Med Ctr Dallas TX 75246

KRUSHENSKY, RICHARD D, b Ferndale, Mich, June 3, 32; m 60; c 1. GEOLOGY, VOLCANOLOGY. *Educ:* Wayne State Univ, BS, 55, MS, 57; Ohio State Univ, PhD(geol), 60. *Prof Exp:* Geologist, Orinoco Mining Co Div, US Steel Corp, 60-62; geologist, Br Spec Projs, 62-63, Br Mil Geol, 63-64 & Br Int Geol, 64-70, GEOLOGIST BR EASTERN ENVIRON GEOL, DEP CHIEF, OFF ENVIRON GEOL, US GEOL SURV, 70- *Mem:* Geol Soc Am. *Res:* Mineral exploration and training of local personnel in Turkey; study of Irazu Volcano, Costa Rica and other active and inactive volcanoes in Central America; volcanic petrology and petrography; volcanology; mineral exploration; regional geology of volcanogenic and intrusive rocks in Southwestern Puerto Rico. *Mailing Add:* Off of Environ Geol Nat Ctr Reston VA 22092

KRUSIC, PAUL JOSEPH, b Trieste, Italy, Nov 28, 34; m 56; c 3. ELECTRON SPIN RESONANCE, FREE RADICAL CHEMISTRY. *Educ:* Wesleyan Univ, BA, 59; Univ Calif, Berkeley, PhD(chem), 66. *Prof Exp:* Chemist, Cent Res Lab, Gen Elec Co, NY, 59-61; RES CHEMIST, CENT RES DEPT, E I DU PONT DE NEMOURS & CO, INC, 66- *Concurrent Pos:* Vis scholar, Centre d'Etudes Nucleaires de Grenoble, France, 81-82. *Mem:* Am Chem Soc. *Res:* Microwave spectroscopy; electron spin resonance spectroscopy; free radical chemistry; organometallic reaction mechanisms; homogeneous catalysis; organometallic photochemistry; autoxidation of hydrocarbons. *Mailing Add:* Cent Res Dept E I du Pont de Nemours & Co Inc Wilmington DE 19898

KRUSKAL, JOSEPH BERNARD, b New York, NY, Jan 29, 28; m 53; c 2. MATHEMATICS. *Educ:* Univ Chicago, PhB & BS, 48, MS, 49; Princeton Univ, PhD, 54. *Prof Exp:* Instr math, Princeton Univ, 55; res instr, Univ Wis, 56-58; asst prof, Univ Mich, 58-59; MEM TECH STAFF, BELL LABS, 59- *Concurrent Pos:* Vis prof, Yale Univ, 66-67, Columbia Univ, 76, Rutgers Univ, 77; assoc ed jour, Soc Indust & Appl Math, 67-70. *Mem:* Am Math Soc; Soc Indust & Appl Math; fel AAAS; fel Am Statist Asn; Psychometric Soc (pres, 74-75). *Res:* Statistics, psychometrics and statistical linguistics. *Mailing Add:* Dept of Math Bell Labs Murray Hill NJ 07974

KRUSKAL, MARTIN DAVID, b New York, NY, Sept 28, 25; m 50; c 3. MATHEMATICAL PHYSICS, APPLIED MATHEMATICS. *Educ:* Univ Chicago, BS, 45; NY Univ, MS, 48, PhD(math), 52. *Prof Exp:* Asst & instr math, NY Univ, 46-51; RES SCIENTIST, PLASMA PHYSICS LAB, PRINCETON UNIV, 51-, SR RES ASSOC, 59-, PROF ASTROPHYS SCI, 61-, PROF MATH, 81- *Concurrent Pos:* Consult, Los Alamos Sci Lab, 53-59, radiation lab, Univ Calif, 54-57, Oak Ridge Nat Lab, 55-58, 63-, Radio Corp Am, 60-62 & IBM Corp, 63-; assoc head theoret div, Plasma Physics Lab, Princeton Univ, 56-64, lectr astron, univ, 59-61; NSF sr fel, 59-60. *Mem:* Am Math Soc; Math Asn Am; Am Phys Soc. *Res:* Plasma physics; general mathematics; asymptotic phenomena; logic; magnetohydrodynamics; controlled fusion; relativity; minimal surfaces. *Mailing Add:* Dept of Astrophys Princeton Univ Princeton NJ 08540

KRUSKAL, WILLIAM HENRY, b New York, NY, Oct 10, 19; m 42; c 3. STATISTICS. *Educ:* Harvard Univ, SB, 40, MS, 41; Columbia Univ, PhD(math statist), 55. *Prof Exp:* Mathematician, US Naval Proving Ground, 41-46; vpres, Kruskal & Kruskal, Inc, 46-48; lectr math, Columbia Univ, 49-50; from instr to prof, 50-73, chmn dept, 66-73, dean, Div Social Sci, 74-79, ERNEST DEWITT BURTON DISTINGUISHED SERV PROF STATIST & COL, UNIV CHICAGO, 73-, DEAN, DIV SOCIAL SCI, 80- *Concurrent Pos:* Vis asst prof, Univ Calif, Berkeley, 55-56; ed, Annals Math Statist, Inst Math Statist, 58-61; chmn math sci panel & mem cent planning comt, Behav & Soc Sci Surv Comt, 66-70; mem adv comt, Encycl Britannica, 66-76, adv comt probs census enumeration, Nat Res Coun, 69-71 & President's Comn Fed Statist, 70-71; fel, Ctr Advan Study in Behav Sci, 70-71; NSF sr fel, 70-71; trustee, Nat Opinion Res Ctr, 70-; dir, Social Sci Res Coun, 75-78; chmn comt Nat Statist, Nat Acad Sci-Nat Res Coun, 71-78; mem adv coun, NSF, 77-; mem adv comt, Fed Statist Syst Reorgn, 78-80; John Simon Guggenheim Mem Found fel, 79-80. *Honors & Awards:* Ronald A Fisher Mem lectr, Comt Pres Statist Socs, 78. *Mem:* Fel AAAS; fel Inst Math Statist (pres, 70-71); fel Am Statist Asn (vpres, 72-74, pres, 82); Int Statist Inst; Am Math Soc. *Res:* Theoretical statistics, especially nonparametric analysis and analysis of variance; public policy aspects of statistics. *Mailing Add:* Dept Statist Univ Chicago Chicago IL 60637

KRUTAK, JAMES JOHN, SR, b Atlanta, Ga, Apr 5, 42; m 60, 80; c 5. ORGANIC CHEMISTRY, PHYSICAL CHEMISTRY. *Educ:* La State Univ, BS, 64; Univ NC, PhD(org chem), 67. *Prof Exp:* Sr res chemist, 69-75, RES ASSOC, TENN EASTMAN CO, EASTMAN KODAK CO, 75- *Concurrent Pos:* Coordr, Photog Chem Res Lab, Eastman Kodak, 73- *Mem:* Am Chem Soc. *Res:* Synthesis of natural products; development of novel indole synthesis; study of mechanisms of indole forming reactions using stable and radioactive isotope tracer methodology; cycloaddition reactions; chemical uses of lasers; photographic dye and developer synthesis and related technology. *Mailing Add:* Res Dept Tenn Eastman Co PO Box 511 Kingsport TN 37660

KRUTAK, PAUL RUSSELL, b Pueblo, Colo, Oct 6, 34; m 55; c 5. GEOLOGY, MICROPALEONTOLOGY. *Educ:* La State Univ, BS, 56, MS, 60, PhD(geol), 63. *Prof Exp:* Jr geologist, Pan Am Petrol Corp, Wyo, 56-57; asst geol, La State Univ, 58-63; asst prof, Ball State Univ, 63-65 & Eastern NMex Univ, 65-70; PROF, UNIV NEBR, LINCOLN, 70- *Concurrent Pos:* Geol Soc Am grant, 65-66; Sigma Xi grant, 67; Fulbright res award, 80-81. *Mem:* Am Asn Petrol Geol; Soc Econ Paleont & Mineral; Geol Soc Am; Paleont Soc; Paleont Res Inst. *Res:* Ostracode; sedimentary petrology; reconnaissance areal geology; organism-substrate interactions in modern environments as well as fossil. *Mailing Add:* Dept Geol Univ Nebr 418 Morrill Hall Lincoln NE 68588

KRUTCHEN, CHARLES M(ARION), b Gadsden, Ala, Sept 7, 34; m 59; c 4. CHEMICAL ENGINEERING. *Educ:* Vanderbilt Univ, BE, 56; Cornell Univ, PhD(chem eng), 64. *Prof Exp:* Chem engr, Res Ctr, Hercules Powder Co, 56-58, res engr, Fiber Dept, 62-64; sr res engr, Res Div, W R Grace & Co, 64-66; staff chem engr, Gen Elec Res & Develop Ctr, 66-76; eng assoc, Res & Develop Lab, Edison, NJ, 76-77, RES SUPVR, PLASTICS DIV, MOBIL CHEM, CANANDAIGUA, NY, 77- *Mem:* Am Inst Chem Engrs; Am Chem Soc; AAAS; Soc Plastics Engrs. *Res:* Chemical process studies; polymer fiber, film and foam technology; polymer processing; morphology-physical property relationships in polymers. *Mailing Add:* Plastics Div 100 North St Canandaigua NY 14424

KRUTCHKOFF, DAVID JAMES, b Eureka, Calif, June 7, 38; m 66; c 3. ORAL PATHOLOGY, DENTISTRY. *Educ:* Univ Calif, Berkeley, AB, 60; Wash Univ, DDS, 64; Univ Mich, MS, 70. *Prof Exp:* Res path, Wash Univ, 67-68; Nat Inst Dent Res fel & instr oral path, Univ Mich, 68-70; asst prof oral path, Univ Louisville, 70-73; ASSOC PROF ORAL DIAGNOSIS, UNIV CONN, 73- *Mem:* Int Asn Dent Res; Am Acad Oral Path. *Res:* Dental caries; clinical studies; dental enamel; infrared internal reflection spectroscopy. *Mailing Add:* Dept of Anat Path Univ of Conn Health Ctr Farmington CT 06032

KRUTCHKOFF, RICHARD GERALD, b Brooklyn, NY, Dec 23, 33; m 60; c 2. APPLIED STATISTICS. *Educ:* Columbia Univ, AB, 56, MA, 58, PhD(math statist), 64. *Prof Exp:* Instr physics, Wilkes Col, 58-60; lectr, Queens Col, NY, 60-64; from asst prof to assoc prof, 64-68, PROF STATIST, VA POLYTECH INST & STATE UNIV, 68- *Concurrent Pos:* Ed, J Statist Comput & Simulation, 73- *Mem:* AAAS; fel Am Statist Asn; Inst Math Statist; Biomet Soc; Water Pollution Control Fedn. *Res:* Statistical inference; empirical Bayes decision theory; water pollution statistics. *Mailing Add:* Dept of Statist Va Polytech Inst & State Univ Blacksburg VA 24061

KRUTTER, HARRY, b Boston, Mass, Mar 17, 11; m 35; c 1. PHYSICS. *Educ:* Mass Inst Technol, 32, SM, 33, PhD(physics), 35. *Prof Exp:* Teaching fel physics, Mass Inst Technol, 33-35; instr, Purdue Univ, 35-36; asst prof petrol eng, Pa State Col, 36-42; res assoc & staff mem, Mass Inst Technol, 42-45; chief scientist, Field Sta, Naval Res Lab, 46-49, tech dir, Aero Electronics & Elec Lab, 49-56, chief scientist, 56-67, tech dir, 67-73, CONSULT, NAVAL AIR DEVELOP CTR, 73- *Concurrent Pos:* Lectr, Wharton Sch, Univ Pa, 73-79. *Honors & Awards:* Distinguished Civilian Serv Award, US Navy, 56 & US Dept Defense, 57. *Mem:* Am Phys Soc; fel Inst Elec & Electronics Eng; assoc fel Am Inst Aeronaut & Astronaut. *Res:* X-ray crystal structure; theory of metals; flow of gases through porous media; antennas; radar; electronics. *Mailing Add:* Naval Air Develop Ctr Warminster PA 18974

KRUTZSCH, PHILIP HENRY, b St Louis, Mo, July 12, 19; m 40; c 2. ANATOMY, ZOOLOGY. *Educ:* San Diego State Col, BA, 43; Univ Calif, MA, 48; Univ Kans, PhD(zool), 53. *Prof Exp:* Asst, Univ Calif, 47-48; asst instr, Univ Kans, 48-52, asst, 49; instr anat, Sch Med, Univ Pittsburgh, 53-54; asst prof, Univ Tex Health Sci Ctr, Dallas, 55-56; assoc prof, Sch Med, Univ Pittsburgh, 57-64; head dept, 64-73, PROF ANAT, COL MED, UNIV ARIZ, 64- *Mem:* Am Soc Mammal; Am Asn Anatomists; Am Soc Zoologists. *Res:* Physiology of reproduction; hematology of hypothermia and studies of brown adipose tissue. *Mailing Add:* Dept of Anat Univ of Ariz Col of Med Tucson AZ 85721

KRUUS, JAAN, b Kuimetsa, Estonia, July 23, 36; Can citizen; m 62; c 4. ELECTRICAL ENGINEERING, INSTRUMENTATION. *Educ:* Univ Toronto, BASc, 59; Univ Ill, MS, 61, PhD(elec eng), 63. *Prof Exp:* Engr, Spruce Falls Power & Paper Co, Ont, 59-60; asst prof elec eng, Queen's Univ, Ont, 63-65; assoc prof, Univ Ottawa, 65-69; head, Instrumentation Sect, Hydrol Sci Div, Inland Waters Br, 69-74, coordr remote sensing, Off Sci Adv, 74-78, planning analyst, Atmospheric Environ Serv, 78-80, DIR, DATA ACQUISITION SERV BR, ENVIRON CAN, 80- *Concurrent Pos:* McLaughlin Sci Fund res grant & Nat Res Coun Can grant, 65-66. *Mem:* Inst Elec & Electronics Engrs. *Mailing Add:* Environ Can 4905 Dufferinst Downsview ON M3H 5T4 Can

KRUUS, PEETER, b Tallinn, Estonia, July 8, 39; Can citizen; m 63; c 4. PHYSICAL CHEMISTRY. *Educ:* Univ Toronto, BSc, 61, PhD(phys chem), 65; Tech Univ Denmark, Lic Techn, 63. *Prof Exp:* From asst prof to assoc prof, 65-77, PROF CHEM, CARLETON UNIV, 77- *Concurrent Pos:* Sci adv, Sci Coun Can, 69-70; res scientist, Cominco Ltd, 79-80. *Mem:* Chem Inst Can. *Res:* Structure and dynamics in liquids and solutions; cavitation-induced chemical reactions. *Mailing Add:* Dept Chem Carleton Univ Ottawa ON K1S 5B6 Can

KRUUV, JACK, b Tartu, Estonia, June 1, 38; Can citizen; m 60; c 3. BIOPHYSICS, RADIOBIOLOGY. *Educ:* Univ Waterloo, BASc, 62, MSc, 63; Univ Western Ont, PhD(biophys), 66. *Prof Exp:* Ont Cancer Found fel & lectr, Victoria Hosp, 66; fel, Argonne Nat Lab, 66-67; from asst prof to assoc prof physics, 67-77, PROF PHYSICS & BIOL, UNIV WATERLOO, 77- *Concurrent Pos:* Vis prof biophysics, Pa State Univ, 74-75. *Mem:* Radiation Res Soc; Cryobiol Soc. *Res:* Cancer research; radiation biophysics; research with synchronized tissue culture cells; effects of low oxygen atmospheres on cells; radiotherapy of cancer cells; repair of radiation and freeze-thaw damage; cryobiology; multi-cellular tissue culture systems; hypothermia; hyperthermia; cryobiology. *Mailing Add:* Dept of Physics Univ of Waterloo Waterloo ON N2L 3G1 Can

KRYDER, MARK HOWARD, b Portland, Ore, Oct 7, 43; m 65; c 2. MAGNETIC BUBBLES DEVICES, MAGNETIC RECORDING. *Educ:* Stanford Univ, BS, 65; Calif Inst Technol, MS, 66, PhD(elec eng, physics), 70. *Prof Exp:* NSF res fel, Calif Inst Technol, 69-71; scientist solid state physics, Univ Regensburg, 71-73; res staff mem, IBM Res Ctr, 73-75, mgr explor bubble devices, 75-78; assoc prof, 78-80, PROF ELEC ENG, CARNEGIE-MELLON UNIV, 80- *Concurrent Pos:* Consult, IBM, Gen Elec, Nat Semiconductor Corp & Motorola. *Mem:* Am Phys Soc; Inst Elec & Electronics Eng. *Res:* Applied magnetics; magnetic bubble devices and magnetic recording devices including materials, fabrication, device design and use in systems. *Mailing Add:* Dept of Elec Eng Carnegie-Mellon Univ Pittsburgh PA 15213

KRYGER, ROY GEORGE, b Brooklyn, NJ, June 7, 36; m 58; c 2. PHYSICAL ORGANIC CHEMISTRY. *Educ:* Atlantic Union Col, AB, 57; Stevens Inst Technol, MS, 66; Boston Univ, PhD(org chem), 73. *Prof Exp:* Chemist qual control, Lederle Lab Div, Am Cyanamid Co, 57-58; chemist food analyst, US Army Med Res & Nutrit Lab, 59-60; anal methods develop & antibiotic res & develop chemist, Lederle Lab Div, Am Cyanamid Co, 60-66; PROF CHEM, ATLANTIC UNION COL, 81-, CHMN DEPT, 66- *Mem:* Am Chem Soc; AAAS; Nat Sci Teachers Asn. *Res:* Relative and absolute reactivities of free radicals and relation of structure of free radicals to their reactivity. *Mailing Add:* George Hill Rd South Lancaster MA 01561

KRYNICKI, VICTOR EDWARD, b Jersey City, NJ, Feb 16, 49; m 70; c 2. NEUROPHYSIOLOGY. *Educ:* Yale Univ, BA, 69; State Univ NY Albany, MA, 72; Columbia Univ, PhD(psychol), 76. *Prof Exp:* Res scientist, Inst Res in Ment Retardation, 72-73; res psychologist, Queens Children's Psychiat Ctr, 76-78; assoc prof psychiat, New York Med Col, 78-79; PROG EVAL SPECIALIST, QUEENS CHILDREN'S PSYCHIAT CTR, 79- *Mem:* Am Psychol Asn; Int Neuropsychol Soc. *Res:* Psychophysiology of sleep; ultradian rhythms during sleep; neuropsychological research on the functions of the cerebral hemispheres in normal subjects and psychiatric patients. *Mailing Add:* Queens Children's Psychiat Ctr 74-03 Commonwealth Blvd Bellerose NY 11426

KRYNITSKY, JOHN ALEXANDER, b Far Rockaway Beach, NY, June 15, 18; m 49; c 1. PETROLEUM FUELS, CHEMISTRY. *Educ:* Univ Md, BS, 39; Univ NC, PhD(org chem), 43. *Prof Exp:* Asst chem, Univ NC, 39-43; chemist, Naval Res Lab, DC, 43-44 & 45-64; staff asst, Off Def Defense Res & Eng, 64-67; dir tech opers, 67-81, CONSULT, FUELS & PETROL PROD, DEFENSE FUEL SUPPLY CTR, 81- *Mem:* Am Chem Soc; Am Soc Testing & Mat. *Res:* Fuels; lubricants; petroleum products; organic materials; synthetic organic chemistry; detection and identification of organic substances; preparations and properties of some highly chlorinated hydrocarbons; hydrazine; aircraft and rocket fuels. *Mailing Add:* 4904 Cumberland Ave Cameron Sta Chevy Chase MD 20815

KRYSAN, JAMES LOUIS, b Calmar, Iowa, Mar 12, 34; m 60; c 3. INSECT PHYSIOLOGY. *Educ:* Iowa State Teachers Col, BA, 61; Univ Ill, MS, 64, PhD(entom), 65. *Prof Exp:* Asst prof biol, St Mary's Col, Minn, 65-68; ENTOMOLOGIST, NORTHERN GRAIN INSECTS RES LAB, SCI & EDUC ADMIN-AGR RES, USDA, 68- *Mem:* Entom Soc Am; AAAS; Am Soc Nat; Coleopterists Soc. *Res:* Physiology and biochemistry of the insect egg; biosystematics of Diabrotica. *Mailing Add:* Northern Grain Insects Res Lab Brookings SD 57006

KRYSIAK, HENRY R, b Wilmington, Del, Aug 8, 21; m 56; c 3. ORGANIC CHEMISTRY. *Educ:* Univ Del, BS, 50; Purdue Univ, MS, 52, PhD(chem), 54. *Prof Exp:* Res chemist, Rayon Res Div, 54-55, SR RES CHEMIST, NYLON TECH DIV, TEXTILE FIBERS DEPT, E I DU PONT DE NEMOURS & CO, 55- *Res:* Steric and electrical effects of trimethylsilyl group in aromatic systems; Teflon yarn development; adhesives for polyamide and polyester tire cords; coated fabrics; dyeing assistants and fire retardants development; textile printing; flame retardants for polyamide fibers; antistatic fabrics. *Mailing Add:* Textile Fibers Dept E I du Pont de Nemours & Co Wilmington DE 19898

KRYTER, KARL DAVID, b Indianapolis, Ind, Oct 13, 14; m 46; c 3. PSYCHOPHYSIOLOGY, PSYCHOACOUSTICS. *Educ:* Butler Univ, AB, 39; Univ Rochester, PhD(psychol), 43. *Prof Exp:* Fel psycho-acoust, Harvard Univ, 42-46; asst prof psychol, Univ Wash, St Louis, 46-48; dir human factors oper res lab, US Air Force, 48-52 & oper appln lab, Cambridge Res, 52-57; head psychoacoust dept, Bolt Beranek & Newman, Inc, 57-65; STAFF SCIENTIST, SRI INT, 65- *Concurrent Pos:* Pres, Acousis Co; mem comt hearing, bioacoust & biomech, Nat Acad Sci-Nat Res Coun, 57-, chmn exec coun, 61-64; mem adv panel psychol & soc sci, Off Asst Secy Defense, 58-63; chmn subcomt psychoacoust instruments, Int Orgn Standardization & Int Electrotechnol Comn, 62-; adv, President's Comt Sci & Technol. *Mem:* Fel AAAS; Soc Eng Psychol (pres, 66); Am Psychol Asn; Acoust Soc Am (pres elect, 71); Human Factors Soc. *Res:* Audition; psychoacoustics; speech communication; electrophysiology. *Mailing Add:* SRI Int 333 Ravenswood Ave Menlo Park CA 94025

KRYWOLAP, GEORGE NICHOLAS, b Ukraine, Jan 4, 36; US citizen; m 57; c 1. MICROBIAL ECOLOGY. *Educ:* Drexel Univ, BS, 60; Pa State Univ, MS, 62, PhD(microbiol), 64. *Prof Exp:* Asst prof microbiol, Schs Pharm & Dent, 64-70, assoc prof, 70-77, PROF MICROBIOL, UNIV MD, 77- *Mem:* AAAS; Am Soc Microbiol; Int Asn Dent Res; Brit Soc Gen Microbiol. *Res:* Antibiotics; production of antibiotics by mycorrhizal fungi; microbial ecology of the oral cavity; microbiology of the periodontum. *Mailing Add:* Dept Microbiol Sch Dent Univ Md 666 W Baltimore St Baltimore MD 21201

KRZANOWSKI, JOSEPH JOHN, JR, b Hartford, Conn, Feb 4, 40; m 63; c 2. PHARMACOLOGY, PHYSIOLOGY. *Educ:* Univ Conn, BS, 62; Univ Tenn, MS, 65, PhD(pharmacol, physiol), 68. *Prof Exp:* Fel pharmacol, Med Sch, Washington Univ, 68-71; asst prof, 71-75, ASSOC PROF PHARMACOL, COL MED, UNIV SOUTH FLA, 75-, VCHMN DEPT, 81- *Concurrent Pos:* NIH pulmonary young investr award, 74-76. *Mem:* Am Soc Pharmacol & Exp Therapeut. *Res:* Autonomic pharmacology; smooth muscle pharmacology; histochemistry; pulmonary and cardiac cyclic nucleotides; prostaglandins; pulmonary and immunopharmacol. *Mailing Add:* Dept Pharmacol & Therapeut Col Med Univ SFla Tampa FL 33612

KRZEMINSKI, LEO FRANCIS, b Greenport, NY, July 3, 25; m 53; c 3. METABOLISM, ANALYTICAL BIOCHEMISTRY. *Educ:* Hofstra Col, BA, 50; Purdue Univ, MS, 55, PhD(biochem), 59. *Prof Exp:* Asst biochem, Fla State Univ, 50-51; jr anal chemist, Off State Chemist, Purdue Univ, 51-59; assoc chemist, Am Meat Inst Found, Ill, 59-64; res assoc, 64-75, RES HEAD BIOCHEM, UPJOHN CO, 75- *Mem:* Am Chem Soc. *Res:* Antioxidants and autoxidation of fat; biosynthesis of carotenes in Neurospora crassa; pesticide and drug residues in animal tissue; residue method development and metabolism in chemical agents. *Mailing Add:* Biochem & Residue Anal Upjohn Co Henrietta St Kalamazoo MI 49001

KRZEMINSKI, STEPHEN F, b Philadelphia, Pa, Dec 26, 43; m 66; c 3. PHYSICAL CHEMISTRY, ANALYTICAL CHEMISTRY. *Educ:* La Salle Col, BA, 65; Univ Pittsburgh, PhD(phys chem), 69. *Prof Exp:* Sr res chemist, Bristol Res Labs, 69-75, proj leader, Res Div, 75-77, mgr, Govt Regulatory Rels, 77-80, CORP MGR, GOVT RELS & PROD STANDARDS, AGR CHEM-NORTH AM, ROHM AND HAAS CO, 80- *Mem:* Am Chem Soc. *Res:* Transition metal chemistry; coordination compounds; Mossbauer spectroscopy; pesticide residues; metabolism and environmental fate of pesticides; drug delivery systems; pharmacokinetics. *Mailing Add:* Rohm and Haas Co Independence Mall West Philadelphia PA 19105

KSHIRSAGAR, ANANT MADHAV, b Satara, India, Aug 16, 31; m 57. STATISTICS, OPERATIONS RESEARCH. *Educ:* Univ Bombay, MSc, 51; Univ Manchester, PhD(statist), 61, DSc, 76. *Prof Exp:* Lectr statist, Univ Bombay, 51-63; sr sci officer, Defence Sci Lab, India, 63-68; asso prof statist, Southern Methodist Univ, 68-71; prof statist, Tex A&M Univ, 71-77; PROF BIOSTAT, UNIV MICH, 77- *Mem:* Fel Am Statist Asn; fel Inst Math Statist. *Res:* Design of experiments; multivariant and discriminant analysis; renewal theory, especially Markovian renewal theory. *Mailing Add:* Dept of Biostatist Univ of Mich Ann Arbor MI 48109

KSIENSKI, A(HARON), b Warsaw, Poland, June 23, 24; nat US; m 54; c 2. ELECTRICAL ENGINEERING. *Educ:* Univ Southern Calif, MS, 52, PhD(elec eng), 58. *Prof Exp:* Consult engr, W L Schott Co, Calif, 52-53; staff engr, Wiancko Eng Co, 53-57; staff engr, Antenna Res Dept, Hughes Aircraft Co, 58-60, sr staff engr, 60, head res staff, 60-67; PROF ELEC ENG & TECH DIR COMMUN SYSTS, ELECTROSCI LAB, OHIO STATE UNIV, 67- *Concurrent Pos:* Lectr, Univ Southern Calif, 54-57; assoc ed, Antennas, Inst Elec & Electronics Engrs, 70-72. *Honors & Awards:* Lord Brabazon, Inst Radio & Electronic Engrs, London, 67 & 76. *Mem:* Fel Inst Elec & Electronics Engrs; Int Union Radio Sci. *Res:* Antennas and antenna systems; information theory; data processing; radar detection and identification; target identification; signal processing arrays communication. *Mailing Add:* Dept of Elec Eng Ohio State Univ 2015 Neil Ave Columbus OH 43210

KSIR, CHARLES JOSEPH, b Albuquerque, NMex, May 19, 45; m 67; c 1. PSYCHOPHARMACOLOGY. *Educ:* Univ Tex, Austin, BA, 67; Ind Univ, Bloomington, PhD(psychol), 71. *Prof Exp:* Fel Neurobiol, Worcester Found Exp Biol, 71-72; asst prof, 72-76, assoc prof, 76-80, PROF PSYCHOL, UNIV WYO, 80- *Mem:* Behav Pharmacol Soc; Psychonomic Soc; AAAS; Sigma Xi; Soc Neurosci. *Res:* Behavioral pharmacology; operant conditioning. *Mailing Add:* Dept of Psychol Box 3415 Univ of Wyo Laramie WY 82071

KSYCKI, MARY JOECILE, b Du Bois, Ill, May 26, 13. RADIATION CHEMISTRY. *Educ:* St Louis Univ, BSc, 36, MS, 40, PhD(chem), 42. *Prof Exp:* Instr chem, Le Clerc Col, 42-43, prof & head dept, 43-49; prof, Webster Col, 49-50; head dept sci pvt sch, Ill, 50-54; prof & head dept, Notre Dame Col, Mo, 54-77; PROF CHEM & CHMN SCI, ST MARY'S COL, MICH, 77- *Concurrent Pos:* Assoc radiation proj, Univ Notre Dame, 58; fel, Univ Okla, 61 & 63, Univ Ill, 62 & Kans State Univ, 64; NIH res award, 61-64; NSF res grant, 63-65; Japan Soc Promotion Sci res grant, Kyoto Univ, 71. *Honors & Awards:* Chemist of the Year Award, St Louis Univ Chemists Asn, 64. *Mem:* Am Chem Soc; Nat Sci Teachers Asn. *Res:* Electrodeposition of molybdenum; alloxan diabetes; electrodeposition potentials of copper, nickel and cobalt; radiation chemistry; effects of drugs on iodine metabolism; protective power of nucleotides against gamma ray inactivation of ribonuclease. *Mailing Add:* Dept Chem St Mary's Col Orchard Lake MI 48033

KU, ALBERT B, b Changsha, China, June 15, 33; m 65; c 2. ENGINEERING MECHANICS, APPLIED MATHEMATICS. *Educ:* Univ Taiwan, BSCE, 56; Va Polytech Inst, MSCE, 61; Ohio State Univ, PhD(soil mech), 65. *Prof Exp:* Jr engr, Mil Construct Comt, 58-59; engr, Kai-Nan Eng Corp, 59-60; asst prof, 64-68, assoc prof eng mech, 68-76, PROF ENG MECH, UNIV DETROIT, 76- *Concurrent Pos:* Consult, Chrysler Corp, 66- & Burrough's Corp, 70- *Mem:* Am Soc Mech Engrs; Am Acad Mech. *Res:* Rheological properties of bituminous concrete; linear viscoelasticity; nonlinear mechanics; static and dynamic stability; finite element analysis. *Mailing Add:* Dept of Eng Mech Col of Eng Univ of Detroit Detroit MI 48221

KU, AUDREY YEH, b Taiwan. ORGANIC CHEMISTRY, POLYMER CHEMISTRY. *Educ:* Providence Col, Taiwan, BS, 71; Eastern Ill Univ, MS, 73; State Univ NY, Buffalo, PhD(chem), 77. *Prof Exp:* Teaching & res asst chem, Eastern Ill Univ, 72-73 & State Univ NY, Buffalo, 73-77; fel chem, Ohio State Univ, 77-78; res chemist, Union Carbide Corp, 78-80; SR RES CHEMIST, MONSANTO CO, 80- *Mem:* Am Chem Soc; Sigma Xi. *Mailing Add:* 800 N Linderbergh Blvd T 4 F St Louis MO 63166

KU, CHIA-SOON, b Nanking, China, Apr 15, 46; m 76. CHEMICAL ENGINEERING, APPLIED CHEMISTRY. *Educ:* Nat Taiwan Univ, BS, 68; Worcester Polytech Inst, MS, 71; Pa State Univ, PhD(chem eng), 77. *Prof Exp:* Asst prof chem eng, Lafayette Col, 77-78; sr chem engr, Appl Sci Div, Versar Inc, 78-79; SR RES ENGR, NAT BUR STANDARDS, 79- *Mem:* Am Inst Chem Engrs; Am Chem Soc; Am Soc Automotive Engrs; Am Soc Lubrication Engrs. *Res:* Tribiology; oxidation bench test development for lubricating oils; oil degradation mechanisms; additive response studies for lubricants; oxidation stability of oil versus oil compositon; friction and wear mechanism and bench test developments. *Mailing Add:* 19819 Wheelwright Dr Gaithersburg MD 20879

KU, EDMOND CHIU-CHOON, b Canton, China, Aug 11, 32; US citizen; m 59; c 2. BIOCHEMISTRY. *Educ:* Taiwan Prov Col, BS, 56; Va Polytech Inst, PhD(biochem), 62. *Prof Exp:* Res scientist biochem, Parke, Davis & Co, 63-67; NIH spec res fel, Cornell Univ, 67-69; SR STAFF SCIENTIST BIOCHEM, CIBA-GEIGY CORP, 70- *Mem:* Am Chem Soc. *Res:* Enzyme kinetics and its application to the study of drug action at molecular level; regulatory mechanism involved in the biosynthesis and degradation of prostaglandins at subcellular level. *Mailing Add:* Biochem Subdiv Ciba-Geigy Corp Ardsley NY 10502

KU, HAN SAN, b Hsin-Chu, Taiwan, Nov 20, 35; m 65; c 2. PLANT PHYSIOLOGY, BIOCHEMISTRY. *Educ:* Nat Taiwan Univ, BS, 58; Osaka Univ, MS, 63; Univ Calif, Davis, PhD(plant physiol), 68. *Prof Exp:* Lectr agr, Taipei Agr Prof Sch, 57-58; asst plant physiol, Nat Taiwan Univ, 60-61; res asst, Univ Calif, Davis, 64-68, NIH fel ethylene biosynthesis, 68; NSF fel ethylene physiol, Purdue Univ, 68-70; res biologist, Allied Chem Res Lab, 70-71, biologist & res leader plant sci, 72-73; plant biochemist, Mich State Univ, 73-74; SR RES ASSOC BIOCHEM, T R EVANS RES CTR, 74- *Honors & Awards:* Japanese Food Sci Soc Award, 66; Campbell Award, Am Inst Biol Sci, 69. *Mem:* AAAS; Am Soc Plant Physiologists; Am Soc Agron; Am Soc Hort; Soil Sci Soc Am. *Res:* Ethylene biogenesis and action in plant tissue; plant growth regulator; photorespiration; nitrogen fixation; crop production pesticide. *Mailing Add:* T R Evans Res Ctr PO Box 348 Painesville OH 44077

KU, HARRY HSIEN HSIANG, b Peking, China, Mar 3, 18; US citizen; m 42; c 1. MATHEMATICAL STATISTICS, ENGINEERING. *Educ:* Purdue Univ, BS, 40, MSE, 41; George Washington Univ, MS, 60, PhD, 68. *Prof Exp:* Civil engr, M W Kellogg Co, 42-43; tech counselor, Embassy Repub China, 43-58; math statistician, 59-79, CHIEF STATIST ENG DIV, CTR APPL MATH, NAT ENG LAB, NAT BUR STANDARDS, 78- *Mem:* AAAS; fel Am Statist Asn; Inst Math Statist; Int Statist Inst. *Res:* Statistical analysis of measurement data in engineering and physical sciences; propagation of error, precision and accuracy; application of information theory in analysis of multi-dimensional contingency tables and Markov chains. *Mailing Add:* Statist Eng Div A334 Admin Bldg Washington DC 20234

KU, HSU-TUNG, b Formosa, Oct 24, 33; m 64. TOPOLOGY. *Educ:* Taiwan Prov Norm Univ, BSc, 61; Tulane Univ, MSc, 64, PhD(math), 67. *Prof Exp:* Mem math, Inst Adv Study, 67-68; asst prof, 68-73, assoc prof, 73-79, PROF MATH, UNIV MASS, AMHERST, 79- *Concurrent Pos:* Vis mem math, Inst Adv Study, 77. *Mem:* Am Math Soc. *Res:* Transformation groups; algebraic topology. *Mailing Add:* Dept Math Univ Mass Amherst MA 01003

KU, MEI-CHIN HSIAO, b Formosa, Nov 1, 37; m 64. TOPOLOGY. *Educ:* Taiwan Norm Univ, BSc, 61; Syracuse Univ, MS, 64; Tulane Univ, La, PhD(math), 67. *Prof Exp:* Mathematician, Inst Advan Study, 67-68; asst prof, 70-76, ASSOC PROF MATH, UNIV MASS, AMHERST, 76- *Concurrent Pos:* Vis mem, Inst Advan Study, 77. *Mem:* Math Asn Am. *Res:* Transformation groups. *Mailing Add:* Dept Math & Statist Univ Mass Amherst MA 01002

KU, PEH SUN, b Shangtung, China, Aug 23, 22; US citizen; m 57; c 2. ENVIRONMENTAL PHYSICS. *Educ:* Nat Cent Univ, BS, 47; Univ Rochester, MS, 55; Yale Univ, DEng(chem eng), 60. *Prof Exp:* Chem engr, Chinese Petrol Corp, Taiwan, 47-54; res asst, Carnegie Inst Technol, 54-55; res engr, Boeing Co, 60-65; theoret physicist, Reentry Systs Div, Gen Elec Co, 65-69, staff scientist, 69-70; chem engr air pollution control, 70-73, SR ENGR, NUCLEAR & EMISSION CONTROL ENG, CONSOL EDISON CO, NEW YORK, 73- *Mem:* AAAS; Am Chem Soc; Am Phys Soc; Am Inst Aeronaut & Astronaut; Am Geophys Union. *Res:* Acoustics; high temperature thermodynamics and transport properties of matter; physical properties of matter under high pressures; chemical kinetics; control and dispersion of air pollutants in the atmosphere and their removal from industrial processes; novel methods of energy conversion. *Mailing Add:* 244 Old State Rd Berwyn PA 19312

KU, ROBERT TIEN-HUNG, b Shanghai, China, Jan 19, 47; US citizen; m 71; c 2. PLASMA PHYSICS, LASER SPECTROSCOPY. *Educ:* Univ Ill, Urbana, BS, 67, MS, 68, PhD(elec eng), 73. *Prof Exp:* Res asst, Gaseous Electronics Lab, Univ Ill, 67-73; mem tech staff, Optics Div, Lincoln Lab, Mass Inst Technol, 73-81; MEM TECH STAFF, LASER DEVELOP DEPT, BELL LABS, 81- *Mem:* Am Phys Soc; Inst Elec & Electronics Engrs; Optical Soc Am; NSF fel; Sigma Xi. *Res:* Laser and optical components for fiber communication systems; laser spectroscopy studies of pollutant gases; laser diagnostics of plasma and chemically excited media. *Mailing Add:* Bell Labs 2525 N 12 St Reading PA 19604

KU, TEH-LUNG, b Shanghai, China, Aug 30, 37; m 70; c 2. GEOCHEMISTRY, GEOCHRONOLOGY. *Educ:* Nat Taiwan Univ, BS, 59; Columbia Univ, PhD(geochem), 66. *Prof Exp:* Trainee geochem, Lamont Geol Observ, Columbia Univ, 66-67; asst scientist, Woods Hole Oceanog Inst, 67-69; assoc prof, 69-75, PROF GEOCHEM, UNIV SOUTHERN CALIF, 75- *Mem:* AAAS; Am Geophys Union; Int Asn Quaternary Res; Geol Soc China. *Res:* Isotope geochemistry; chemical oceanography; geochronology; pleistocene geology; climatology; hydrogeochemistry. *Mailing Add:* Dept of Geol Sci Univ of Southern Calif Los Angeles CA 90007

KU, THOMAS HSIU-HENG, nuclear chemistry, radiochemistry, see previous edition

KU, TIMOTHY TAO, b Chaochow, China, Mar 26, 26; m 50; c 2. FORESTRY. *Educ:* Nanking Univ, BS, 48; Mich State Univ, MF, 50, PhD(forest ecol, silvicult), 54. *Prof Exp:* Forester, T S Coile, Inc, Forest Land Consults, 56-58; from asst prof to assoc prof, 59-63, PROF FORESTRY, UNIV ARK, MONTICELLO, 63- *Mem:* Soc Am Foresters; Soil Sci Soc Am. *Res:* Silviculture; forest soils and ecology; biomass production and nutrient cycling in forest stands, site evaluation and classification, and applied silviculture. *Mailing Add:* Dept of Forest Resources Univ of Ark Monticello AR 71655

KU, VICTOR CHIA-TAI, b Nanking, China, July 15, 42; US citizen; m 72; c 2. ELECTRICAL ENGINEERING, COMPUTER SCIENCE. *Educ:* Cheng Kung Univ, Taiwan, BS, 66; Rutgers Univ, MS, 69; Univ Pittsburgh, PhD(elec eng), 73. *Prof Exp:* Sr engr, Stromberg Carlson Corp, Gen Dynamic Corp, 73-74; mem tech staff, RCA Labs, 75-76; mem tech staff elec eng, Bell Labs, 76-79; eng mgr, Wang Labs, Inc, 79, GEN MGR, WANG COMPUT LTD, TAIWAN, 80- *Mem:* Inst Elec & Electronics Engrs; Sigma Xi; Chinese Inst Engrs. *Res:* Design automation especially logic and fault simulation, testing, placement and routing; interactive graphic computer systems; computer manufacturing, research and development; ideographic computer design. *Mailing Add:* Wang Comput Taiwan Ltd NO2 Sci Rd 1 Ind Park HSINCHU Taiwan 07733 Republic China

KU, VICTORIA FENG, b Peking, China, Mar 14, 30; US citizen; m 50; c 2. ORGANIC CHEMISTRY. *Educ:* Barat Col, BS, 50; Univ Ark, MS, 64, PhD(chem), 76 . *Prof Exp:* Chemist, Mich State Health Dept Lab, 52-56 & Hercules Powder Co, 57-59; asst prof, 69-75, ASSOC PROF CHEM, UNIV ARK, MONTICELLO, 76- *Mem:* Am Chem Soc. *Mailing Add:* Univ Ark PO Box 3067 Monticello AR 71655

KU, Y(U) H(SIU), b Wusih, China, Dec 24, 02; m 29; c 7. ELECTRICAL ENGINEERING, SYSTEMS ENGINEERING. *Educ:* Mass Inst Technol, SB, 25, SM, 26, ScD, 28. *Hon Degrees:* MA & LLD, Univ Pa, 72. *Prof Exp:* Prof elec eng & head dept, Chekiang Univ, 29-30; dean eng, Cent Univ, China, 31-32; pres, 44-45, prof elec eng, 47-49; dean eng, Tsing Hua China, 32-37; vminister, Ministry Ed, 38-44; educ comnr, Shanghai Munic Govt, 45-47; vis prof elec eng, Mass Inst Technol, 50-52; vis prof, 52-54, prof, 54-71, EMER PROF ELEC & SYSTS ENG, UNIV PA, 72- *Concurrent Pos:* Dir, Aeronaut Res Lab, China, 34-37 & Electronics Res Lab, 35-37; head, Chinese Educ Mission to India, 43; chief Chinese deleg, Int Tech Cong, Paris, 46; mem gen assembly, Int Union Theoret & Appl Mech, 46-84; consult, Gen Elec Co, NY, 51-55, Univac, 52-53, Radio Corp Am, 59-60; hon prof, Shanghai Jiao-Tong Univ, 79- *Honors & Awards:* Lamme Medal, Inst Elec & Electronics Engrs, 72. *Mem:* Am Soc Eng Educ; fel Inst Elec & Electronics Engrs; Brit Inst Elec Engrs; Chinese Inst Eng (vpres, 45-46); Chinese Inst Elec Engr (pres, 40-41). *Res:* Analysis and control of linear and nonlinear systems; electric energy conversion; transient circuit analysis. *Mailing Add:* Dept Systs Eng Univ Pa Philadelphia PA 19104

KUAN, TEH S, b Maymyo, Burma; US citizen. NATURAL GAS TECHNOLOGY. *Educ:* Univ BC, BSc, 65; Univ Southern Calif, PhD(chem), 69. *Prof Exp:* Fel chem physics, Univ Southern Calif, 69; res assoc spectros, Univ Calif, Los Angeles, 69-71; sr chemist photo chem, Eastman Kodak Co, 71-80; sr scientist hydrogen tech, Arco Solar Co, 80-82; SR SCIENTIST PETROL CHEM, ATLANTIC RICHFIELD CO, 82- *Mem:* Int Asn Hydrogen Energy; Electrochem Soc; Am Chem Soc. *Res:* Petroleum chemistry; hydrogen energy; metal hydrides; spectroscopy; analytical chemistry; electrochemistry; thin film sputtering technology; far-infrared technology; intermolecular potentials; low temperature solid states; photographic science; coating technology, ceramics-injection molding. *Mailing Add:* Atlantic Richfield Co 20717 Prairie St Chatsworth CA 91311

KUAN, TIONG H, b Manila, Philippines, June 24, 45; Chinese citizen. POLYMER SCIENCE. *Educ:* De La Salle Col, Philippines, BS, 67; Univ Akron, MS, 70, PhD(polymer sci), 73. *Prof Exp:* RES SCIENTIST RUBBER RES & ENG, RES CTR, GEN TIRE & RUBBER CO, 72- *Mem:* Am Chem Soc; Soc Rheology. *Res:* dynamic, mechanical and failure properties of rubbers and blends in general; polymer structure - property relationships. *Mailing Add:* Gen Tire & Rubber Co Res Ctr 2990 Gilchrist Rd Akron OH 44305

KUBAS, GREGORY JOSEPH, b Cleveland, Ohio, Mar 12, 45; m 73. TRANSITION-METAL & SMALL MOLECULE CHEMISTRY. *Educ:* Case Inst Technol, BS, 66; Northwestern Univ, PhD(inorg chem), 70. *Prof Exp:* Fel chem, Princeton Univ, 71-72; MEM STAFF CHEM, LOS ALAMOS NAT LAB, UNIV CALIF, 72- *Mem:* Am Chem Soc. *Res:* Coordination chemistry of sulfur dioxide, structure and reactivity of transition metal SO2 complexes; synthesis, characterization and structure of organometallic iron-sulfur clusters and small molecule complexes of molybdenum and tungsten. *Mailing Add:* Los Alamos Nat Lab PO Box 1663 Los Alamos NM 87545

KUBE, WAYNE R(OBERT), b Mancelona, Mich, May 3, 22; m 48; c 3. CHEMICAL ENGINEERING. *Educ:* Mich Tech Univ, BS, 44, MS, 46. *Prof Exp:* Engr prod, Linde Air Prods Co, 44-45; asst chem eng, Mich Tech Univ, 45-46, instr, 46-48; chem engr res, Bur Mines, US Dept Interior, 48-52; from asst prof to prof chem eng, Univ NDak, 52-80; RETIRED. *Mem:* Am Chem Soc; Am Soc Eng Educ; fel Am Inst Chem Engrs. *Res:* Solid fuels; carbonization, gasification, drying and other thermal treatment. *Mailing Add:* Dept of Chem Eng Univ of NDak Grand Forks ND 55202

KUBENA, LEON FRANKLIN, b Caldwell, Tex, July 6, 40; m 68; c 2. NUTRITION, TOXICOLOGY. *Educ:* Tex A&M Univ, BS, 65, PhD(poultry sci), 70. *Prof Exp:* Res nutritionist, SCent Poultry Res Lab, Animal Sci Div, 70-75, RES CHEMIST BIOCHEM & NUTRIT, VET TOXICOL & ENTOM LAB, AGR RES SERV, USDA, COLLEGE STATION, TEX, 76- *Concurrent Pos:* Mem fac, Tex A&M Univ, 80- *Mem:* Poultry Sci Asn; Asn Off Anal Chemists; AAAS; World Poultry Sci Asn. *Res:* Interrelationships of environment and nutrition; toxicology of environmental toxicants in poultry with special emphasis on interaction of these toxicants. *Mailing Add:* PO Drawer GE Energy Res Lab Univ Tex College Station TX 77841

KUBERSKY, EDWARD SIDNEY, b Brooklyn, NY, Feb 25, 47; m 69; c 2. LIMNOLOGY, ECOLOGY. *Educ:* City Univ NY, Brooklyn, BS, 67; Ind Univ, MA, 68, PhD(zool), 73. *Prof Exp:* Instr, 72-73, asst prof, 73-81, ASSOC PROF BIOL, UPSALA COL, 81-, CHMN DEPT, 79- *Concurrent Pos:* Proj dir, NSF grant, 72-74 & 76-77; Danforth assoc, 80- *Mem:* Int Asn Theoret & Appl Limnol; Freshwater Biol Asn; Am Soc Limnol & Oceanog. *Res:* Ecology and taxonomy of cladocera; paleolimnology. *Mailing Add:* Dept of Biol Upsala Col East Orange NJ 07019

KUBES, GEORGE JIRI, b Prague, Czech, Feb 14, 34; Can citizen; m 59; c 2. PULP CHEMISTRY. *Educ:* Tech Univ, Prague, MSc, 58; Tech Univ, Bratislava, PhD(pulp chem). *Prof Exp:* Supvr res group, NBohemian Pulp & Paper Mill, Czech, 58-62, mgr res pulping, papermaking & pollution, 62-67; head pulping group, Pulp & Paper Res Inst Czech, 68; sr res chemist, CIP Res Ltd, Can, 69-72; res scientist pulping, 72-77, HEAD CHEM PULPING & BLEACHING SECT, PULP & PAPER RES INST CAN, 77- *Concurrent Pos:* Indust consult, Chem Eng Designing Inst, Czech, 58-68; lectr, Chem Eng Fac, Tech Univ, 62-67. *Mem:* Can Pulp & Paper Asn; Tech Asn Pulp & Paper Indust; Chem Inst Can. *Res:* Pulping with an effort to develop a sulphur-free pulping and chlorine-free bleaching process; consultant services to pulp and paper manufacturing industry all over the world; improvements in existing processes, pulping of tropical wood species and annual plants. *Mailing Add:* Chem Pulping & Bleaching Sect 570 St Johns Blvd Pointe Claire PQ H9R 3J9 Can

KUBICA, GEORGE P, b Little Falls, NY, June 18, 29; m 53; c 2. MEDICAL BACTERIOLOGY. *Educ:* Cornell Univ, BA, 51; Univ Mich, MA, 52; Univ Wis, PhD(med bact), 55. *Prof Exp:* Actg chief, Tuberc Unit, Commun Dis Ctr, USPHS, 55-62, chief, 62-69; mem & head mycobact sect, Trudeau Inst, Inc, 69-74; MICROBIOLOGIST CONSULT, CTR DIS CONTROL, 74- *Concurrent Pos:* Instr, Sch Med, Emory Univ, 59-69. *Mem:* Sigma Xi; Am Thoracic Soc; Am Soc Microbiol; Int Union Against Tuberculosis; fel Am Acad Microbiol. *Res:* Tuberculosis. *Mailing Add:* Ctr Dis Control Atlanta GA 30333

KUBICEK, WILLIAM GEORGE, b Medford, Minn, Jan 6, 13; m 35; c 1. PHYSIOLOGY. *Educ:* Univ Minn, BS, 42, PhD(physiol), 46. *Prof Exp:* Technician, Inst Exp Med, Mayo Clin, 36-39; technician, Inst Exp Med, Mayo Clin, 36-39; technician, Dept Physiol, 39-42, asst, 42-43, from instr physiol to prof physiol & clin res, 43-77, PROF PHYS MED & REHAB, UNIV MINN, MINNEAPOLIS, 77- *Concurrent Pos:* Mem, Int Physiol Cong, Oxford, 47. *Mem:* Am Physiol Soc; Soc Exp Biol & Med; Inst Elec & Electronics Engrs. *Res:* Biophysics; circulatory system; high altitude; emergency water supply; hypertension; bulbar poliomyelitis; muscle physiology; methods and results of stimulation of certain autonomic nerves in relation to arterial blood pressure in the dog; impedance cardiography. *Mailing Add:* Dept of Phys Med & Rehab Univ of Minn Minneapolis MN 55455

KUBIK, ROBERT N, b Honolulu, Hawaii, Nov 17, 31; m 55; c 4. COMPUTER SCIENCE, CONTROL SYSTEMS. *Educ:* Univ Calif, Berkeley, AB, 54. *Prof Exp:* Programmer, Atomic Energy Div, Babcock & Wilcox Co, 57-61, sr programmer, 61-62, prog supvr, 62-63, chief comput serv, 63-66; acct rep, IBM Corp, 67; prin engr, Nuclear Power Generating Dept, Babcock & Wilcox Co, 68-69, chief instrument develop, Res & Develop Div, 69-71, mgr process control, Lynchburg Res Ctr, 71-72, mgr indust systs, Babcock & Wilcox Co, 72-76, MGR ADVAN CONTROL & EXP PHYSICS LAB, LYNCHBURG RES CTR, BABCOCK & WILCOX CO, 76- *Mem:* Inst Elec & Electronics Engrs; Am Soc Nondestructive Testing; Am Nuclear Soc. *Res:* methodology; nondestructive examination. *Mailing Add:* Lynchburg Res Ctr PO Box 1260 Lynchburg VA 24505

KUBIN, ROSA, b Poelten, Austria, Dec 15, 06; nat US; m 31. BIOCHEMISTRY, VETERINARY PATHOLOGY. *Educ:* St Poeltner Obergym, Austria, BS, 25; Univ Vienna, MS, 29, PhD(org chem), 31. *Prof Exp:* Asst, Austrian Chem Works, 31-35 & Syngala, Inc, Austria, 35-38; AMA fel, Med Sch, Univ Ore, 38, Lilly fel, 39-40, asst, 40-41; asst prof biochem & clin path, Med Sch, Middlesex Univ, 41-47; asst prof chem, Univ Mass, 47-49; assoc prof biochem, New Eng Col Pharm, 50-51; CONSULT VET PATHOLOGIST, 51- *Concurrent Pos:* Lectr, Wellesley Col, 55-57 & Concord Acad, 57-61; teacher advan chem & molecular biol, Waltham High Sch, 61-73. *Mem:* Fel AAAS; Am Chem Soc; NY Acad Sci. *Res:* Medical biochemistry; bleaching of textiles; hormone extraction; laboratory methods applied in veterinary clinical pathology; diseases in veterinary medicine. *Mailing Add:* 19 Appleton St Waltham MA 02154

KUBINSKI, HENRY A, b Warsaw, Poland, Jan 15, 33; m 59; c 3. ONCOLOGY, MOLECULAR BIOLOGY. *Educ:* Univ Warsaw, MD, 55. *Prof Exp:* Res assoc microbiol, Sch Med, Univ Warsaw, 54-55, instr, 56-60; instr, Found Res Poliomyelitis & Multiple Sclerosis, Hamburg, Ger, 61-64; res assoc, 64, from asst prof to assoc prof, 65-74, PROF SURG, UNIV WISMADISON, 75- *Mem:* Am Asn Cancer Res; Am Soc Biol Chemists; Biophys Soc; NY Acad Sci; Am Soc Neurochem. *Res:* Neurochemistry and oncology of the central nervous system; cellular regulatory mechanisms; chemical carcinogenesis. *Mailing Add:* 4605 Med Sci Ctr 1300 Univ Ave Madison WI 53706

KUBINSKY, EUGENE JOSEPH, wood science & technology, see previous edition

KUBIS, JOSEPH JOHN, b New York, NY, Apr 15, 38; m 68. THEORETICAL PHYSICS. *Educ:* Mass Inst Technol, SB, 59; Princeton Univ, AM, 61, PhD(physics), 64. *Hon Degrees:* MA, Cambridge Univ, 67. *Prof Exp:* Asst prof physics, Tex A&M Univ, 64-67; sr res physicist, Cavendish Lab & fel, Clare Hall, Cambridge Univ, 67-69; asst prof physics, Mich State Univ, 69-71; MEM TECH STAFF, THEORY & COMPUT DIV, KMS FUSION, INC, 71- *Concurrent Pos:* Consult, Brookhaven Nat Lab, 67 & Los Alamos Sci Lab, 68 & 71. *Mem:* Am Phys Soc; Europ Phys Soc; Ital Phys Soc. *Res:* Lasers; plasma physics; elementary particles; scattering theory; dispersion relations; applied mathematics; numerical analysis; statistics; computing. *Mailing Add:* KMS Fusion Inc PO Box 1567 Ann Arbor MI 48106

KUBISEN, STEVEN JOSEPH, JR, b Iowa City, Iowa, June 21, 52; m 77. PHYSICAL ORGANIC CHEMISTRY, ORGANIC CHEMISTRY. *Educ:* Cornell Univ, AB, 74; Harvard Univ, MA, 75, PhD(org chem), 78. *Prof Exp:* RES CHEMIST, UNION CARBIDE CORP, 78- *Mem:* Am Chem soc; Sigma Xi. *Res:* Phosphate ester hydrolysis; process chemistry; epoxidation chemistry; natural oils chemistry. *Mailing Add:* One River Rd Bound Brook NJ 08805

KUBITSCHEK, HERBERT ERNEST, b Oak Park, Ill, June 9, 20; m 43; c 4. BIOPHYSICS. *Educ:* Univ Chicago, SB, 42; Univ Ill, MS, 47, PhD(physics), 49. *Prof Exp:* USPHS fel biophys, Inst Radiobiol & Biophys, Univ Chicago, 49-51; assoc physicist, 51-69, SR BIOPHYSICIST, ARGONNE NAT LAB, 70- *Concurrent Pos:* Minna-James-Heineman fel, Univ Groningen, 74; adj prof, Northern Ill Univ, 71- *Res:* Variation and growth of microorganisms. *Mailing Add:* Argonne Nat Lab 9700 S Cass Ave Argonne IL 60439

KUBLER, DONALD GENE, b Easton, Md, Apr 4, 23; m 52; c 4. ORGANIC CHEMISTRY. *Educ:* Univ SC, BS, 47; Univ Md, PhD(chem), 52. *Prof Exp:* Instr chem, Univ SC, 47-48; chemist, Develop Dept, Union Carbon Chem Co, WVa, 52-58; asst prof chem, Univ SC, 58-59 & Hampden-Sydney Col, 59-61; assoc prof, 61-65, chmn dept, 67-72, PROF CHEM, FURMAN UNIV, 65- *Concurrent Pos:* NSF fac fel sci, Clemson Univ, 75. *Mem:* Am Chem Soc; Sigma Xi. *Res:* Structure and mechanism for acetal and carbohydrate hydrolysis. *Mailing Add:* Dept of Chem Furman Univ Greenville SC 29613

KUBLER, HANS JAKOB, b Ger, Sept 11, 22; m 60. FOREST PRODUCTS. *Educ:* Univ Hamburg, dipl wood tech, 50, Dr rer nat(wood sci), 57. *Prof Exp:* Res asst wood tech, Nat Res Ctr Wood Prod, Ger, 50-54, proj leader wood sci, 59-66; ASSOC PROF WOOD SCI, UNIV WIS-MADISON, 67- *Concurrent Pos:* Proj leader, Ger Res Asn, 57-58; Fulbright fel, US Forest Prod Lab, Madison, Wis, 58-59; exchange scientist, Acad Wood Tech, Leningrad, USSR, 62; int ed, Forest Prod Res Soc, 67-74. *Mem:* Forest Prod Res Soc; Soc Wood Sci & Technol. *Res:* Wood at low temperatures; growth stresses in trees; drying of wood; cracks in stems of trees; self heating of wood and other organic materials; wood as building material. *Mailing Add:* Russell Lab 1630 Linden Dr Madison WI 53706

KUBO, RALPH TERUO, b Hilo, Hawaii, Mar 28, 42; m 67; c 2. IMMUNOLOGY. *Educ:* Univ Calif, Los Angeles, BA, 65; Univ Hawaii, MS, 67, PhD(microbiol), 70. *Prof Exp:* Asst prof microbiol, Univ Hawaii, Honolulu, 70-71; sr fel, 71-73; MEM IMMUNOL, NAT JEWISH HOSP & RES CTR, 73-; ASSOC PROF, DEPT MICROBIOL, IMMUNOL & MED, MED SCH, UNIV COLO, 80- *Concurrent Pos:* Assoc ed, J Immunol & Develop Comp Immunol, 78- *Mem:* Am Soc Microbiol; Sigma Xi; Am Asn Immunologists; NY Acad Sci; Brit Soc Immunol. *Res:* Regulation of expression of immunoglobulins during B-cell differentiation; characterization of the structure and function of T-cell antigen recognition molecules. *Mailing Add:* Dept of Med 3800 Colfax Ave Denver CO 80206

KUBOSE, DON AKERU, b Japan, Dec 28, 36; US citizen; m 62; c 3. PHYSICAL CHEMISTRY, EXPLOSIVES. *Educ:* Univ Ill, BS, 58; Univ Notre Dame, PhD(phys chem), 62. *Prof Exp:* Res chemist, Naval Radiol Defense Lab, 62-69; RES CHEMIST RES & DEVELOP, NAVAL SURFACE WEAPONS CTR, 69- *Mem:* AAAS. *Res:* Explosives chemistry; analytical procedures for microgram quantities of explosives; photochemistry of explosives; mass spectrometry of explosives; detonation chemistry. *Mailing Add:* 3700 Roseneath St Olney MD 20832

KUBOTA, MITSURU, b Eleele, Hawaii, Sept 25, 32; m 56; c 2. INORGANIC CHEMISTRY. *Educ:* Univ Hawaii, BA, 54; Univ Ill, MS, 58, PhD, 60. *Prof Exp:* From instr to assoc prof, 59-71, PROF CHEM, HARVEY MUDD COL, 71- *Concurrent Pos:* NSF fel, Univ NC, Chapel Hill, 66-67; Fulbright-Hays advan res fel, Univ Sussex, Eng, 73-74; NIH spec fel, Calif Inst Technol, 74-75. *Mem:* AAAS; Am Chem Soc; The Chem Soc. *Res:* Organometallic chemistry; homogeneous catalysis; inorganic synthesis. *Mailing Add:* Dept of Chem Harvey Mudd Col Claremont CA 91711

KUBOTA, TOSHI, b Westmoreland, Calif, Feb 25, 26; m 52; c 3. AERONAUTICS. *Educ:* Univ Tokyo, BEng, 47; Calif Inst Technol, MS, 52, PhD(aeronaut), 57. *Prof Exp:* From asst prof, 57-59, res fel, 57-59, from asst prof to assoc prof, 59-71, PROF AERONAUT, CALIF INST TECHNOL, 71- *Concurrent Pos:* Consult, AER, Inc, 57-59, Calif Div, Lockheed Aircraft Corp, 59-61, NESCO, 61-62, NAm Aviation, 62-, TRW Systs Group, 68- & Aerospace, 69- *Mem:* Am Inst Aeronaut & Astronaut; Phys Soc Japan. *Res:* Hypersonic aerodynamics and heat transfer. *Mailing Add:* Firestone Flight Sci Lab Calif Inst of Technol Pasadena CA 91109

KUBU, EDWARD THOMAS, b New York, NY, Nov 19, 26; m 51. PHYSICAL CHEMISTRY, POLYMER PHYSICS. *Educ:* NY Univ, BA, 49; Princeton Univ, MA, 51, PhD(chem), 52. *Prof Exp:* Sect leader, Textile Physics Sect, Res Ctr, B F Goodrich Co, 52-59; supvr characterization res, Cent Res Lab, 59-61, asst dir lab res, 61-62, dir fibers div, 62-63, dir res & develop, 63-68, asst to pres, 68-70, dir fibers div, 70-73, dir tech opers, 73-77, MGR GOVT & INDUST LIAISON, ALLIED CORP, 77- *Concurrent Pos:* Bd trustees exec comt, Textile Res Inst, 71-; mem adv bd, Textile Res Inst Regulatory Tech Info Ctr. *Mem:* Am Chem Soc; Am Phys Soc; Fiber Soc; Sigma Xi. *Res:* Physical, chemical and mechanical properties of high polymers; manufacture and use of synthetic fibers; impact of government regulations on synthetic fiber, plastics and chemical manufacture and use. *Mailing Add:* Fibers & Plastics Co Allied Corp Box 31 Petersburg VA 23804

KUBY, STEPHEN A, b Jersey City, NJ, Aug 5, 25; m 63. BIOCHEMISTRY. *Educ:* NY Univ, AB, 48; Univ Wis, MS, 51, PhD(biochem), 53. *Prof Exp:* USPHS fel, Johnson Found Med Physics, Univ Pa, 53-54; res assoc, Inst Enzyme Res, Univ Wis, 54-55; USPHS fel, Med Nobel Inst, Stockholm, Sweden, 55-56; asst prof biochem, 56-63, assoc prof biochem & assoc res prof med, 63-69, PROF BIOCHEM & RES PROF MED, LAB STUDY HEREDITARY & METAB DIS, COL MED, UNIV UTAH, 69- *Concurrent Pos:* Mem physiol chem study sect, NIH, 68-72. *Mem:* AAAS; NY Acad Sci; Am Chem Soc; Am Soc Biol Chemists. *Res:* Chemistry of isolated enzymes and their catalyzed reactions; applications of enzyme chemistry to study of inherited and metabolic disorders. *Mailing Add:* Lab Study Hereditary & Metab Dis Univ of Utah Col of Med Salt Lake City UT 84132

KUC, JOSEPH, b New York, NY, Nov 24, 29; m 54; c 3. PLANT BIOCHEMISTRY, PLANT PATHOLOGY. *Educ:* Purdue Univ, BS, 51, MS, 53, PhD(biochem), 55. *Prof Exp:* Asst biochem, Purdue Univ, 51-54, from asst prof to prof, 55-74; PROF PLANT PATH, UNIV KY, 74- *Concurrent Pos:* Fulbright fel, 60 & 66; fel, Brazilian Coffee Inst, 69 & 71; Alexander von Humboldt Found res prize. *Honors & Awards:* Campbell Award, Am Phytopath Soc. *Mem:* Am Chem Soc; fel Am Phytopath Soc; Am Soc Plant Physiol; Phytochem Soc; fel Am Inst Chemists. *Res:* Biochemistry of disease resistance in plants; synthesis of natural products; plant immunization. *Mailing Add:* Dept of Plant Path Univ of Ky Lexington KY 40506

KUCERA, CLARE H, b Laurel, Mont, Sept 20, 25; m 50; c 5. ORGANIC CHEMISTRY. *Educ:* Mont State Col, BS, 51; Purdue Univ, MS, 54, PhD(chem), 56. *Prof Exp:* Chemist, 56-57, from res chemist to sr res chemist, 57-66, lab group leader, 66-67, sect supvr res & eng, 67-71, res mgr, 72-76, SR RES SPECIALIST, DOWELL DIV, DOW CHEM CO, 76- *Mem:* Am Chem Soc. *Res:* Organic synthesis; stereochemistry of the 2-ethyl-cyclohexanols; organic acid corrosion inhibitors, especially acetylenic compounds; synthesis of acetylenic compounds; development of oilwell fracturing fluids; rheology of fracturing fluids; synthesis of orthophosphate esters; development of oilwell cements; synthesis of cement additives; synthesis and development of drilling fluids. *Mailing Add:* Dowell Div Dow Chem Co 1150 N Utica Tulsa OK 74110

KUCERA, LOUIS S, b New Prague, Minn, June 23, 35; m 59; c 4. VIROLOGY, ONCOLOGY. *Educ:* St John's Univ, Minn, BA, 57; Creighton Univ, MS, 59; Univ Mo, PhD(microbiol), 64. *Prof Exp:* Res bacteriologist, Radioisotope Serv, Vet Admin Hosp, Omaha, Nebr, 60; res asst virol, Sect Microbiol, Mayo Clin, 64-65, res assoc, 65-66, res assoc, Virol Lab, St Jude Res Hosp, Memphis, Tenn, 66-68, staff mem, 68-70; from asst prof to assoc prof, 70-80, PROF MICROBIOL, BOWMAN GRAY SCH MED, WAKE FOREST UNIV, 80- *Concurrent Pos:* Reviewer, Human Cell Biol Prog, NSF. *Mem:* AAAS; Am Soc Microbiol; fel Am Acad Microbiol; Sigma Xi; Am Soc Virol. *Res:* Biochemistry of virus-DNA synthesis; role of herpes-type viruses in tumorigenesis; consequences of herpes simplex virus-host cell interaction at supraoptimal temperatures; mechanism of stimulation of host cell DNA synthesis by herpes simplex virus; tumor promoter-herpesvirous interactions. *Mailing Add:* Dept of Microbiol Bowman Gray Sch of Med Winston-Salem NC 27103

KUCERA, THOMAS J, b Oak Park, Ill, Feb 22, 25; m 64; c 3. ORGANIC CHEMISTRY. *Educ:* Loyola Univ, Ill, BS, 45; Ill Inst Technol, MS, 52; Purdue Univ, PhD, 53. *Prof Exp:* Res chemist, Miner Labs, Mid-West Div, Arthur D Little, Inc, 45-50; Fulbright scholar, Univ Auckland, 53-54; res fel, Purdue Univ, 54-55; asst to pres, Mid-West Labs, 55-56; mgr chem res, Charles Bruning Co, Inc, 56-61; consult, 61-64; vpres res & eng, Apeco Corp, 64-81; CONSULT, 82- *Mem:* AAAS; Am Chem Soc; The Chem Soc; Soc Photog Sci & Eng. *Res:* Photoreproduction; organic photoreactions; inorganic photoconductors; electrostatics; organic mechanisms. *Mailing Add:* 3126 Thayer St Evanston IL 60007

KUCESKI, VINCENT PAUL, b Superior, Wis, Apr 1, 20; m 44; c 2. ORGANIC CHEMISTRY. *Educ:* Univ Wis, BS, 42, MS, 48, PhD(chem), 50. *Prof Exp:* Res chemist, Southern Cotton Oil Co, 50-52; sr chemist, 52-59, dir res, 59-71, vpres res, 71-74, V PRES RES & DEVELOP, C P HALL CO ILL, 74- *Mem:* Am Chem Soc; Am Inst Chemists; Am Oil Chemists Soc. *Res:* Oxidations of organic compounds; oils and fats; analytical organic chemistry. *Mailing Add:* C P Hall Co of Ill 7300 S Central Ave Chicago IL 60638

KUCHAR, NORMAN RUSSELL, b Cleveland, Ohio, June 22, 39; m 67; c 2. COMPUTER-AIDED ENGINEERING, PROCESS ANALYSIS. *Educ:* Case Inst Technol, BS, 61, MS, 65; Case Western Reserve Univ, PhD(eng), 67. *Prof Exp:* Fluid dynamicist fluid physics, Space Sci Lab, 67-69, group leader biofluid mech, Environ Sci Lab, 69-72, mech engr, 72-80, MGR-PROCESS TECHNOL, CORP RES & DEVELOP, GEN ELEC CO, 80- *Mem:* Am Soc Mech Engrs; Am Inst Aeronaut & Astronaut. *Res:* Fluid dynamics; heat transfer; mathematical simulation of industrial processes; process control; computer-aided design; computer-aided manufacturing. *Mailing Add:* Corp Res & Develop PO Box 43 Schenectady NY 12301

KUCHAREK, THOMAS ALBERT, b Cleveland, Ohio, Nov 16, 39; m 63; c 2. PLANT PATHOLOGY. *Educ:* Kent State Univ, BS, 62; Univ Minn, MS, 65, PhD(plant path), 69. *Prof Exp:* Asst plant path, Univ Minn, 62-65; instr, Okla State Univ, 65-68 & Univ Minn, 69; asst prof & asst exten plant pathologist, 70-74, assoc prof, 75-80, PROF PLANT PATH & EXTEN PLANT PATHOLOGIST, UNIV FLA, 80- *Mem:* Am Phytopath Soc. *Res:* Diagnosis and control of diseases on field crops and vegetables. *Mailing Add:* Dept of Plant Path Univ of Fla Gainesville FL 32601

KUCHEL, OTTO GEORGE, b Spis Stara Ves, Czech, June 22, 24; Can citizen; m 53; c 3. NEPHROLOGY. *Educ:* Charles Univ, Prague, MD, 50, PhD(endocrinol), 56, ScD(nephrology), 65. *Prof Exp:* Instr int med, Safarik Univ, Kosice, 56; asst prof, III Dept Med, Charles Univ, Prague, 57-65; instr, Vanderbilt Univ, 66; prof, III Dept Med, Charles Univ, Prague, 67-68; PROF NEPHROLOGY, CLIN RES INST, UNIV MONTREAL, 68-, DIR LAB SYMPATHETIC NERV SYSTEM, INST, 75- *Concurrent Pos:* Mem serv nephrology, Hotel-Dieu Hosp & Univ Montreal, 68; mem hypertension task force, NIH, 75-79; mem, Coun High Blood Pressure Res, Cleveland. *Honors & Awards:* Res Award, Asn French Speaking Physicians Can, 72. *Mem:* Endocrine Soc; Royal Soc Med. *Res:* Clinical nephrology and endocrinology related to research of mechanisms of hypertension, particularly the role of the sympathetic nervous system, adrenals and the kidney. *Mailing Add:* Clin Res Inst of Montreal 110 Pine Ave W Montreal PQ H2W 1R7 Can

KUCHERLAPATI, RAJU SURYANARAYANA, b Kakinada, India, Jan 18, 43. HUMAN GENETICS. *Educ:* Andhra Univ, India, BSc, 60, MSc, 62; Univ Ill, Urbana, PhD(genetics), 72. *Prof Exp:* Res fel human genetics, Yale Univ, 72-75; ASST PROF HUMAN GENETICS, PRINCETON UNIV, 75- *Concurrent Pos:* Damon Runyon Cancer Fund res fel, Yale Univ, 73-74, NIH fel, 74-75. *Mem:* AAAS; Genetics Soc Am. *Res:* Human gene mapping; study of regulation of gene action in human cells; genetics of malignancy. *Mailing Add:* Dept of Biochem Sci Princeton Univ Princeton NJ 08544

KUCHINSKAS, EDWARD JOSEPH, b Maspeth, NY, Feb 11, 27; m 52; c 1. BIOCHEMISTRY. *Educ:* Queen's Col, NY, BS, 49; Cornell Univ, PhD, 54. *Prof Exp:* Instr biochem, Med Col, Cornell Univ, 54-56; from asst prof to assoc prof, 56-67, from asst dean to assoc dean sch grad studies, 67-73, PROF BIOCHEM, STATE UNIV NY DOWNSTATE MED CTR, 67- *Mem:* AAAS; Am Chem Soc; Soc Exp Biol Med; Harvey Soc; Am Soc Biol Chemists. *Res:* Metabolic effects of cysteine analogues, especially vitamin requirements and enzyme activation; catalase; semisynthetic penicillins; S-methyl group oxidations; peroxidative mechanisms; metabolism of penicillamine. *Mailing Add:* Dept of Biochem Box 8 State Univ NY Downstate Med Ctr Brooklyn NY 11203

KUCHLER, ROBERT JOSEPH, b Pittsburgh, Pa, Mar 28, 28; m 58; c 3. MICROBIOLOGY. *Educ:* Univ Pittsburgh, BS, 50, MS, 52; Univ Mich, PhD, 58. *Prof Exp:* Asst bact, WVa Univ, 52-54 & Univ Mich, 54-58; bacteriologist & head dept, William Singer Res Lab, Allegheny Gen Hosp, 58-62; from asst prof to prof bact, 62-75, PROF MICROBIOLOGY, RUTGERS UNIV, 75-, CHMN DEPT, 77-, DIR COORD GRAD PROG MICROBIOL, 78- *Mem:* Am Soc Microbiol; Tissue Cult Asn; Am Soc Cell Biol. *Res:* Development of metazoan cell populations in tissue culture with emphasis on their permeability to small molecular species and on the organization of macromolecules within these cells; viral nucleic acids. *Mailing Add:* Dept of Microbiol Rutgers Univ New Brunswick NJ 08903

KUCHNIR, FRANCA TABLIABUE, b Russe, Bulgaria, July 18, 35; US citizen; m 60; c 2. MEDICAL PHYSICS, RADIOLOGICAL SCIENCE. *Educ:* Univ San Paulo, BS, 58; Univ Ill, MS, 62, PhD(physics), 65. *Prof Exp:* Res asst physics, Univ Ill, 60-65; fel, Argonne Nat Lab, 66-68; asst prof, Univ Ill, 69-70; asst physicist, Argonne Nat Lab, 70-71; trainee, 71-73, asst prof, 73-74, ASSOC PROF MED PHYSICS, UNIV CHICAGO, 74-, DIR, SECT MED PHYSICS, 81- *Concurrent Pos:* Prog dir, Nat Res Serv Awards, Nat Cancer Inst, 79- *Mem:* Am Phys Soc; Am Asn Physicists Med; Radiation Res Soc. *Res:* Experimental nuclear physics; radiation physics and dosimetry specifically related to neutrons as applied to radiobiology, radiation therapy and diagnosis. *Mailing Add:* Dept of Radiol Univ of Chicago 950 E 59th St Chicago IL 60637

KUCHNIR, MOYSES, b Sao Paulo, Brazil, May 18, 36; US citizen; m 60; c 2. LOW TEMPERATURE PHYSICS, CRYOGENICS. *Educ:* Univ Sao Paulo, BS, 57; Univ Ill, Urbana, MS, 62, PhD(physics), 66. *Prof Exp:* Mem staff solid state physics, Argonne Nat Lab, 66-68, asst physicist, 68-73; proj assoc cryogenics, Univ Wis-Madison, 73; prof physics, Univ Estadual Campinas, Brazil, 74; physicist, 74-80, APPL SCIENTIST, FERMI NAT ACCELERATOR LAB, 80- *Mem:* AAAS; Am Phys Soc. *Res:* Motion of ions and sound propagation in quantum fluids; dilution refrigerators; cryogenic equipment and techniques; superconducting magnets for accelerators; properties of materials at low and ultra low temperatures. *Mailing Add:* 934 Parkside Elmhurst IL 60126

KUCK, DAVID JEROME, b Muskegon, Mich, Oct 3, 37. COMPUTER SCIENCE. *Educ:* Univ Mich, Ann Arbor, BS, 59; Northwestern Univ, MS, 60, PhD(eng), 63. *Prof Exp:* Ford fel & asst prof elec eng, Mass Inst Technol, 63-65; from asst to assoc prof, 65-72, PROF COMPUT SCI, UNIV ILL, URBANA-CHAMPAIGN, 72- *Concurrent Pos:* Nat Sci Found res grant, 70-; consult, Burroughs Corp, 72- & Los Alamos Nat Lab, 78-; assoc ed, Inst Elec & Electronics Engrs Trans Comput, 73-75, Asn Comput Mach Database Systs, 77-, Int J Comput & Info Sci, 77-, J Asn Comput Mach, 80- & J Digital Systs, 80-; pres, Kuck & Assoc, Inc. *Res:* Computer system and software organization; design of high performance processors, parallel memories, memory hierarchies, and related software; algorithm development for special purpose and high performance machines; information retrieval and database systems. *Mailing Add:* 222 Digital Comput Lab Univ Ill 1304 W Springfield Urbana IL 61801

KUCK, JAMES CHESTER, b New Orleans, La, Dec 24, 12; m 69. AGRICULTURAL BIOCHEMISTRY, ORGANIC CHEMISTRY. *Educ:* La State Univ, Baton Rouge, BS, 38. *Prof Exp:* Prof, New Orleans Pub Sch Syst, 38-41; prof math & sci, Rugby Mil Acad, New Orleans, 41-42; asst chemist, La State Bd Health, 42; sr res chemist, Celotex Corp, Marrero, La, 42-49; RES CHEMIST, SOUTHERN REGIONAL RES CTR, SCI & EDUC ADMIN, AGR RES, USDA, NEW ORLEANS, 53- *Mem:* Am Oil Chemists Soc; Sigma Xi. *Res:* Chemical and physical properties of oil-bearing seed, especially cottonseed, peanuts, soybean, sunflower, rape and properties relating to improvements in present industrial processing and development of higher quality and utility of these products. *Mailing Add:* 1373 Madrid St New Orleans LA 70122

KUCK, JOHN FREDERICK READ, JR, b Savannah, Ga, Jan 27, 18; m 49; c 5. BIOCHEMISTRY. *Educ:* Va Polytech Inst, BS, 39, MS, 40; Univ NC, PhD(biochem), 51. *Prof Exp:* Chemist, Nat Adv Comn Aeronaut, 40-46; prof chem, St Procopius Col, 50-51; res assoc surg, Col Med, Wayne State Univ, 51-56; res assoc, Kresge Eye Inst, 57-63; asst prof, 63-69, assoc prof, 69-78, PROF OPHTHAL, SCH MED, EMORY UNIV, 78-, ASST PROF BIOCHEM, 63- *Mem:* AAAS; Am Chem Soc; Asn Res Vision & Ophthal. *Res:* Lens metabolism; diabetic and radiation cataracts. *Mailing Add:* Eye Res Lab Emory Univ Atlanta GA 30322

KUCK, JULIUS ANSON, b Willimantic, Conn, Jan 6, 07; m 55; c 2. ORGANIC CHEMISTRY. *Educ:* Hamilton Col, AB, 28; Cornell Univ, PhD(org chem), 32. *Prof Exp:* Asst chem, Cornell Univ, 28-32; fel, City Col New York, 34-35, tutor, 35-36, from instr to assoc prof, 37-64; vis prof & actg chmn dept, Inter-Am Univ, PR, 65-66; from asst prof to assoc prof chem, Stamford Br, Univ Conn, 66-77; RES ASSOC DEPT CHEM, BANNOW SCI CTR, FAIRFIELD UNIV, 77- *Concurrent Pos:* Consult, Am Cyanamid Co, 43-64. *Mem:* Am Chem Soc; AAAS; Am Microchem Soc. *Res:* Synthetic organic chemistry; aliphatic boric acids; cardiac lactones; microanalysis; analytical methods and development. *Mailing Add:* Dept of Chem N Benson Rd Fairfield CT 06430

KUCZENSKI, RONALD THOMAS, b Detroit, Mich, July 27, 44. PSYCHOPHARMACOLOGY. *Educ:* Univ Notre Dame, BS, 66; Mich State Univ, PhD(biochem), 70. *Prof Exp:* Res psychobiologist psychiat, Univ Calif, San Diego, 70-73, asst prof, 73-74; ASST PROF PHARMACOL, VANDERBILT UNIV, 74-, ASST PROF BIOCHEM, 80- *Res:* Regulation of biochemical events of central nervous system synaptic transmission and relationship to effects of pharmacological manipulations on behavioral parameters. *Mailing Add:* 117 Alton Rd Nashville TN 37205

KUCZKOWSKI, JOSEPH EDWARD, b Buffalo, NY, Nov 18, 39; m 65; c 4. ALGEBRA. *Educ:* Canisius Col, BS, 61; Purdue Univ, MS, 63, PhD(math), 68. *Prof Exp:* From instr to asst prof math, Purdue Univ, 66-71; assoc prof, 71-75, PROF MATH, IND UNIV-PURDUE UNIV, INDIANAPOLIS, 75- *Mem:* Am Math Soc; Math Asn Am; Nat Coun Teachers Math. *Res:* Subsemigroups of groups with emphasis on subsemigroups of nilpotent groups; semigroups satisfying certain non-tautological laws. *Mailing Add:* Dept of Math Sci Ind Univ-Purdue Univ Indianapolis IN 46205

KUCZKOWSKI, ROBERT LOUIS, b Buffalo, NY, Aug 2, 38; m 62; c 3. PHYSICAL INORGANIC CHEMISTRY. *Educ:* Canisius Col, BS, 60; Harvard Univ, MA, 62, PhD(chem), 64. *Prof Exp:* Nat Acad Sci res fel chem, Nat Bur Standards, 64-66; from asst prof to assoc prof, 66-74, PROF CHEM, UNIV MICH, ANN ARBOR, 74- *Mem:* Am Chem Soc. *Res:* Microwave spectroscopy of inorganic compounds. *Mailing Add:* Dept of Chem 3020 Chem Bldg Univ of Mich Ann Arbor MI 48109

KUCZYNSKI, EUGENE RAYMOND, b Chicago, Ill, Jan 1, 25; m 46; c 5. ENVIRONMENTAL SCIENCES, MATERIAL SCIENCE ENGINEERING. *Educ:* Univ Chicago, PhB, 47, BS, 48; Drexel Univ, MS, 71. *Prof Exp:* Engr electrochem, Burgess Battery Co, 48-51; prin scientist, Leeds & Northrup Co, 51-73; mgr res & eng, Dohrmann Div, Envirotech Corp, 73-80; dir res & develop, Bacharach Co, 80-81; proj mgr, Versatec, 81-82; CONSULT, 82- *Concurrent Pos:* Prin investr, Army Chem Ctr, Edgewood, 62-63; regist prof engr, Pa Environ, 73- & Calif Control Syst, 76- *Mem:* Am Chem Soc; Instrument Soc Am; Air Pollution Control Asn; Water Pollution Control Fedn; Electrochem Soc. *Res:* Development and manufacturing introduction of small systems conbining mechanical design, electronics, materials and manufacturability in aesthelically pleasing housing; process monitoring instrumentation and computer peripheral devices. *Mailing Add:* 10178 Myer Pl Cupertino CA 95014

KUCZYNSKI, GEORGE CZESLAW, b Krakow, Poland, Apr 20, 14; nat US; m; c 3. MATERIALS SCIENCE. *Educ:* Cracow Tech Univ, MA, 36; Univ South Wales, BSc, 42; Mass Inst Technol, ScD(metall), 46. *Prof Exp:* Teacher, pub sch, Poland, 36-39; teacher, Army Personnel Training Sch, Scotland, 42-43; asst, State Col Wash, 43-44; consult engr, Baldwin Locomotive Co, Pa, 45-46; sr engr, Sylvania Elec Prods, Inc, NY, 46-49; consult engr, Colombia, SAm, 49-50; aeronaut scientist, Nat Adv Comt Aeronaut, Ohio, 50-51; assoc prof, 51-55, prof metall, 55-80, PROF, DEPT METALL ENG & MAT SCI, UNIV NOTRE DAME, 80- *Concurrent Pos:* Lectr, Polytech Inst Brooklyn, 47-49. *Mem:* Am Phys Soc; fel Am Ceramic Soc. *Res:* Physics of solids; order-disorder transformations; diffusion in solids; sintering and powder technology; ceramics; semi-conductors; color centers. *Mailing Add:* Box E Notre Dame IN 46556

KUDENOV, JERRY DAVID, b Lynwood, Calif, Dec 19, 46; m 69; c 1. INVERTEBRATE ZOOLOGY, POLLUTION BIOLOGY. *Educ:* Univ Calif, San Diego, BA, 68; Univ of the Pac, MSc, 70; Univ Ariz, PhD(zool), 74. *Prof Exp:* RES SCIENTIST ZOOL & POLLUTION BIOL, MARINE POLLUTION STUDIES GROUP, FISHERIES & WILDLIFE DIV, AUSTRALIA, 74- *Mem:* Am Soc Zoologists; Sigma Xi; AAAS; Australian Marine Sci Asn; NZ Marine Sci Asn. *Res:* Feeding biology and population dynamics of spionid polychaetes in stressed or polluted habitats; taxonomy, systematics and zoogeography of polychaetous annelids. *Mailing Add:* Marine Studies Group 605 Flinders St Exten Melbourne Victoria 3000 Australia

KUDER, JAMES EDGAR, b Madang, New Guinea, Dec 28, 39; US citizen; m 62; c 2. ORGANIC CHEMISTRY. *Educ:* Capital Univ, BS, 62; Ohio Univ, PhD(org chem), 68. *Prof Exp:* Chemist water anal, US Geol Surv, Ohio, 62-63; res fel, Rensselaer Polytech Inst, 68-69; scientist, Res Labs, Xerox Corp, 69-77; RES ASSOC, CELANESE RES CO, 77- *Mem:* Am Chem Soc; The Chem Soc; Electrochem Soc. *Res:* Electronic structure and properties of organic dyes; photochemical rearrangements; quantum chemistry; reactions and spectroscopic studies of heterocyclic compounds; organic electrochemistry. *Mailing Add:* Celanese Res Co 86 Morris Ave Summit NJ 07901

KUDER, ROBERT CLARENCE, b North Baltimore, Ohio, Dec 31, 18; m 42; c 7. PLASTICS CHEMISTRY. *Educ:* Ohio State Univ, AB, 39; Northwestern Univ, PhD(org chem), 42. *Prof Exp:* Jr chemist, Ethyl Gasoline Corp, 39; res chemist, Stand Oil Co, Ind, 42-46; asst prof chem, Univ Dayton, 46-48; sr res chemist, Barrett Div, Allied Chem Corp, 48-52, asst supvr res, 52-57, supvr polymer res, 57; tech dir, Bemis Bros Bag Co, 57-58; dir res & develop, Mol-Rez Div, Am Petrochem Corp, 58-63; res assoc, Gen Mills, Inc, 63-68; tech dir resins, 68-77, TECH DIR, MINNEAPOLIS COATINGS & CHEM DIV, WHITTAKER CORP, 77- *Mem:* Am Chem Soc. *Res:* Polyesters; polyurethanes. *Mailing Add:* Minneapolis Coatings & Chem Div 3134 California St N E Minneapolis MN 55418

KUDLICH, ROBERT A, b Pottsville, Pa, Jan 16, 26; m 51; c 1. ELECTRICAL ENGINEERING, COMPUTER SCIENCE. *Educ:* Lafayette Col, BSEE, 50; Harvard Univ, MS, 51; Univ Ill, PhD(elec eng), 54. *Prof Exp:* Mem tech staff comput systs & logical design, Bell Tel Lab, Inc, 54-59; dir comput res & develop, AC Spark Plug Div, Gen Motors Corp, 59-63; prog dir, AC Electronics Div, Wis, 63-69; mgr, Air Traffic Control Systs, 69-74; prod assurance mgr, 74-80, MGR, RADAR SYSTS LAB, EQUIP DIV, RAYTHEON CO, WAYLAND, 80- *Concurrent Pos:* Consult, Defense Sci Bd Task Force Electronic Test Equip, 75-77. *Mem:* Inst Elec & Electronics Engrs; Am Fedn Info Processing Soc (vpres, 72-73); Sigma Xi. *Res:* Systems engineering; radar systems development. *Mailing Add:* 158 Kings Grant Rd Weston MA 02193

KUDMAN, IRWIN, b Brooklyn, NY, Feb 20, 36; m 59; c 2. METALLURGY, PHYSICS. *Educ:* NY Univ, BMetEng, 58, MS, 60. *Prof Exp:* Assoc engr, Radio Corp Am, 60-62, mem tech staff mats, Res Lab, RCA Corp, 62-72; vpres, Princeton Infrared Equip, Inc, 72-76; PRES, INFRARED ASSOCS, INC, 76- *Honors & Awards:* RCA Labs Achievement Award, 67. *Res:* Optical, electrical and thermal properties of semiconductor materials and alloy systems. *Mailing Add:* 14A Jules Lane New Brunswick NJ 08901

KUDO, AKIRA, b Japan, Apr 6, 39; m 74; c 2. ENVIRONMENTAL SCIENCES, WATER CHEMISTRY. *Educ:* Kyoto Univ, Japan, BSc, 63, MSc, 65; Univ Tex, Austin, PhD(environ health eng), 69. *Prof Exp:* RES OFFICER BIOL, NAT RES COUN CAN, 71- *Concurrent Pos:* Vis prof, Univ Ottawa, Can, 75-; vis scientist, Japan, 76 & France, 81; assoc ed, J Environ Conserv Eng, 80- *Mem:* Int Asn Water Pollution Res; Am Soc Civil Eng; Am Water Pollution Control Fedn. *Res:* Distribution, transport, transformation, and transfer of heavy metal pollutants, including radioactive materials, in the aquatic systems such as rivers, lakes, and estuaries. *Mailing Add:* Div Biol 100 Sussex Dr Ottawa ON K1A 0R6 Can

KUDO, ALBERT MASAKIYO, b New Westminster, BC, May 30, 37; m 62; c 2. PETROLOGY, VOLCANOLOGY. *Educ:* Univ Toronto, BS, 60; McMaster Univ, MS, 62; Univ Calif, San Diego, PhD(earth sci), 67. *Prof Exp:* Lab instr geol, McMaster Univ, 60-62; res asst geochem, Univ Calif, San Diego, 62-66; asst prof, 66-71, ASSOC PROF GEOL, UNIV NMEX, 71- *Mem:* Am Geophys Union; Geochem Soc; Geol Soc Am. *Res:* Igneous petrology of basalts and andesites of Rio Grande Rift; igneous petrology of some absaroka intrusive rocks. *Mailing Add:* Dept of Geol Univ of NMex Albuquerque NM 87131

KUDRYK, VAL, b Chipman, Alta, Mar 2, 24; US citizen; m 51; c 3. METALLURGY, CHEMICAL ENGINEERING. *Educ:* Univ Alta, BASc, 46; Univ BC, MASc, 48; Columbia Univ, PhD(metall eng), 53. *Prof Exp:* Proj engr process develop, Chem Construct Corp, 50-56; asst vpres, Nichols Eng & Res Corp, 56-58; vpres technol res & develop, Accurate Specialties Co, 58-61; self-employed consult, 61-65; asst mgr process design, Lummus Eng, 65-68, MGR RES & DEVELOP, ASARCO, INC, 68- *Mem:* Am Inst Mining, Metall & Petrol Engrs; Indust Res Inst. *Res:* Research and development of new and improved methods for extracting non-ferrous metals from ores. *Mailing Add:* Cent Res Labs 901 Oak Tree Rd South Plainfield NJ 07080

KUDZIN, STANLEY FRANCIS, b Jersey City, NJ, Mar 1, 26; m 50; c 3. ORGANIC CHEMISTRY. *Educ:* Fordham Univ, BS, 47, MS, 49, PhD(chem), 51. *Prof Exp:* Res & tech serv chemist, E I du Pont de Nemours & Co, 51-56; tech supvr, Ciba Co, Inc, 56-60; assoc prof org chem, Clemson Col, 60-61; ed, Acad Press, Inc, 61-62; assoc prof, 62-70, PROF CHEM, STATE UNIV NY COL NEW PALTZ, 70- *Concurrent Pos:* Consult, Acad Press, Inc. *Mem:* AAAS; Am Chem Soc. *Res:* Chemical education and literature. *Mailing Add:* Dept of Chem State Univ NY Col at New Paltz New Paltz NY 12561

KUEBLER, JOHN RALPH, JR, b Indianapolis, Ind, Oct 22, 24; m 57; c 2. INDUSTRIAL CHEMISTRY. *Educ:* Univ Wis, BS, 48; Univ Ill, MS, 49, PhD, 51. *Prof Exp:* Inorg res chemist, Mallinckrodt Chem Works, 51-70, QUAL CONTROL MGR, CALSICAT DIV, MALLINCKRODT, INC, 70- *Mem:* Am Chem Soc; Am Soc Qual Control. *Res:* Inorganic stereochemistry; inorganic analytical methods development. *Mailing Add:* Calsicat Div Mallinckrodt Inc 1707 Gaskell St Erie PA 16503

KUEBLER, ROY RAYMOND, JR, b Shamokin, Pa, Oct 10, 11. MATHEMATICAL STATISTICS. *Educ:* Dickinson Col, AB, 33; Univ Pa, AM, 47; Univ NC, PhD(statist), 58. *Prof Exp:* Libr asst, Dickinson Col, 33-35, asst treas & supt grounds & bldgs, 35-41, from instr to assoc prof math, 41-42 & 46-55; mathematician, Off Chief of Ord, Dept Army, 55-56; assoc prof, 58-62, prof, 62-76, EMER PROF BIOSTATIST, UNIV NC, CHAPEL HILL, 76- *Mem:* Am Math Soc; Biomet Soc; Math Asn Am; fel Am Statist Asn; Inst Math Statist. *Res:* Statistical design of experiments; problem and statistical exposition. *Mailing Add:* 96 Willow Terr Chapel Hill NC 27514

KUEBLER, WILLIAM FRANK, JR, b Kansas City, Mo, Feb 21, 16; m 45; c 2. CHEMISTRY. *Educ:* Univ Kans, BA, 38. *Prof Exp:* Pharmaceut chemist, Peerless Serum Co, Kans, 38-40; pharmaceut tablet maker, Geo A Breon & Co, Mo, 40-41; chief control chemist, Thompson-Hayward Chem Co, 41-42, res chemist, 46-51; res chemist, Jensen-Salsbery Labs Div, Richardson-Merrell, Inc, 51-54, group leader, 54-57, dir pharmaceut res & develop, 57-59, res adminr, 59-61, asst to res dir proj planning & anal, 61-65; asst to tech dir, Marion Labs, Inc, 65-70 & Knoll Pharmaceut Co; exec admin asst to vpres-sci dir, Knoll Pharmaceut Co, 70-71; dir regulatory affairs, 71-72; exec vpres, Bavley-Kuebler Assocs, 72-74; tech dir, Bio-Eval, Inc, 74-79; CONSULT, 79- *Mem:* Am Chem Soc; Biomet Soc; Am Statist Asn; fel Am Inst Chem. *Res:* Clinical investigations; protocols; biostatistics; data interpretation. *Mailing Add:* 534 Fairmount Ave Chatham NJ 07928

KUECKER, JOHN FRANK, b Webster, SDak, Mar 21, 32; m 58; c 4. PHYSICAL CHEMISTRY. *Educ:* Northern State Col, BS, 54; SDak Sch Mines & Technol, BS, 58; Univ Nebr, MS, 63, PhD(chem), 65. *Prof Exp:* Teacher high sch, SDak, 54-55 & 56-57; asst prof chem, Doane Col, 63-65; from asst prof to assoc prof, 65-71, head dept, 69-72, PROF CHEM, KEARNEY STATE COL, 71- *Mem:* AAAS; Am Chem Soc; Nat Sci Teachers Asn. *Res:* Viscosity of aqueous salt solutions; ultracentrifugation of inorganic polymer solutions. *Mailing Add:* Dept of Chem Kearney State Col Kearney NE 68847

KUEHL, FREDERICK ALBERT, JR, b Malden, Mass, Nov 9, 16; m 41; c 6. ORGANIC CHEMISTRY. *Educ:* Wesleyan Univ, AB, 39; Harvard Univ, PhD, 42. *Prof Exp:* res assoc, 43-64, asst dir bio-org chem, 64-66, dir, Bio-org Res Lab, Inst, 66-69, sr investr, 69-72, sr scientist, 72-81, DISTINGUISHED SR SCIENTIST, MERICK INST THERAPEUT RES, MERCK & CO, 81-; res assoc, 43-64, asst dir bio-org chem, 64-66, dir bio-org res lab, Inst, 66-69, sr investr, 69-72, SR SCIENTIST, MERCK INST THERAPEUT RES, MERCK & CO, INC, 72- *Mem:* Am Chem Soc. *Res:* Isolation and structure determination of biologically active natural products; antibiotics; vitamins; hormones; enzymes; roles of phostaglandins and cyclic nucleotides in cell function. *Mailing Add:* Merck Inst for Therapeut Res Rahway NJ 07065

KUEHL, HANS H(ENRY), b Detroit, Mich, Mar 16, 33; m 65; c 2. ELECTRICAL ENGINEERING. *Educ:* Princeton Univ, BSEE, 55; Calif Inst Technol, MS, 56, PhD(elec eng), 59. *Prof Exp:* Mem tech staff, Hughes Aircraft Co, 58-59; res scientist plasmas, Eng Ctr, 59-60, from asst prof to assoc prof, 60-72, PROF ELEC ENG, UNIV SOUTHERN CALIF, 72- *Concurrent Pos:* Res fel, Calif Inst Technol, 59-60. *Mem:* Am Phys Soc; fel Inst Elec & Electronics Engrs; Int Sci Radio Union. *Res:* Plasma physics; electromagnetic theory; antennas. *Mailing Add:* Dept of Elec Eng Univ of Southern Calif Los Angeles CA 90007

KUEHL, LEROY ROBERT, b Ketchikan, Alaska, Aug 15, 31; m 59; c 3. BIOCHEMISTRY. *Educ:* Iowa State Univ, BS, 53; Ore State Univ, MS, 55; Univ Calif, Berkeley, PhD(comp biochem), 61. *Prof Exp:* NIH fel, Max Planck Inst Biol, Tübingen, Ger, 62-65; from instr to assoc prof, 65-80, PROF BIOCHEM, UNIV UTAH, 80- *Mem:* Fedn Am Soc Exp Biol. *Res:* Biochemistry of the cell nucleus; chromosomal proteins. *Mailing Add:* Dept Biochem Sch Med Univ Utah Salt Lake City UT 84112

KUEHLER, CHRISTOPHER WULFE, chemical engineering, see previous edition

KUEHN, CHRISTA GISELA, b Hof, Ger, Mar 17, 47; US citizen. INDUSTRIAL CHEMISTRY. *Educ:* Ohio Univ, BS, 69; Stanford Univ, PhD(inorg chem), 75. *Prof Exp:* Res assoc phys chem, Max Planck Inst Phys Chem, Gottingen, Ger, 69-70; asst chem, Stanford Univ, 70-74; res chemist, FMC Corp, 74-78; RES CHEMIST, OCCIDENTAL RES CORP, 78- *Concurrent Pos:* Fulbright fel, Univ Gottingen & Max Planck Inst Phys Chem, 69-70. *Mem:* Am Chem Soc. *Res:* Sodium carbonate manufacture; interaction of simple sulfur ligands with transition metals; phosphorus manufacture. *Mailing Add:* Occidental Res Corp PO Box 19601 Irvine CA 92713

KUEHN, GLENN DEAN, b Terry, Mont, Apr 13, 42; m 65. BIOCHEMISTRY. *Educ:* Concordia Col, BA, 64; Wash State Univ, PhD(chem), 68. *Prof Exp:* NIH fel, Univ Calif, Los Angeles, 68-70; asst prof, 70-74, assoc prof, 74-80, PROF CHEM, NMEX STATE UNIV, 80- *Concurrent Pos:* Am Cancer Soc res support award, 71-76; NSF res support award, 73-75; NIH res support award, 74-77, 77-80 & 80-85. *Mem:* AAAS; Am Chem Soc; Fedn Am Soc Exp Biol; Am Soc Microbiol. *Res:* Biochemistry of cell differentiation and development in the slime mold Physarum polycephalum; biosynthesis and regulatory functions of polyamines; carbon dioxide fixation in autotrophs; regulatory enzymology. *Mailing Add:* Dept of Chem Box 3C NMex State Univ Las Cruces NM 88003

KUEHN, HAROLD HERMAN, b Orange, NJ, June 17, 27; m 55; c 2. MICROBIOLOGY, MYCOLOGY. *Educ:* Mont State Univ, AB, 50; Univ Ill, MS, 52, PhD(bot), 54. *Prof Exp:* Asst prof biol, NMex Highlands Univ, 54-55; sr res mycologist, Grain Processing Corp, Iowa, 58-61; res mycologist, Campbell Soup Co, NJ, 61; res microbiologist, Rohm and Haas Co, Pa, 61-70; PROF BIOL, MERCER COUNTY COMMUNITY COL, 70- *Mem:* Bot Soc Am; Mycol Soc Am. *Res:* Industrial mycology; Gymnoascaceae; soil fungi; water molds; mucorales; fungal enzymes. *Mailing Add:* Biol Dept PO Box B Mercer County Community Col Trenton NJ 08690

KUEHN, JEROME H, b Minneapolis, Minn, July 20, 20; m 45; c 3. FISH BIOLOGY, FISHERIES ADMINISTRATION. *Educ:* Univ Minn, BS, 42, MS, 49. *Prof Exp:* Aquatic biologist aide, 46, aquatic biologist, 47-52, asst wildlife projs coordr, 52-56, supvr, Survs & Inventories Unit, 56-66, natural resource planning dir, 66-79, CHIEF FISHERIES, STATE NATURAL RESOURCES DEPT, MINN, 79- *Mem:* Am Fisheries Soc. *Res:* Techniques of fisheries survey procedures; development of fisheries management investigations; fish toxicants; natural resource planning; environmental impact review; water resources planning. *Mailing Add:* 120 Park Ave Mahtomedi MN 55115

KUEHN, LORNE ALLAN, b Sault Saint Marie, Ont, Jan 28, 43; m; c 2. BIOPHYSICS. *Educ:* Univ Alta, BSc, 63; York Univ, PhD(physics), 68. *Prof Exp:* Defence serv sci officer physics, Defence Res Estab Toronto, 66-71; DIR, BIOSCI DIV, DEFENCE & CIVIL INST ENVIRON MED, 71- *Concurrent Pos:* Mem proj rev group develop pneumatic decompression comput, Dept Indust, Trade & Com, 71-75; tech secy, Adv Panel Arctic Med & Climatic Physiol, Defence Res Bd, 71-75; Can observer, Human Biol Working Party, Sci Comt for Anarctic Res, 75-; chmn, NAm Affairs Comt, Under Sea Med Soc, 80-81. *Mem:* Arctic Inst NAm; Canadian Physiol Soc; Can Asn Physicists; assoc fel Aerospace Med Asn; Undersea Med Soc. *Res:* Development of decompression theories and operational computers;

development of measuring techniques in environmental stress, particularly in extreme heat and extreme cold; diagnosis and treatment of accidental and occupational hypothermia. *Mailing Add:* Defence & Civil Inst of Environ Med Box 2000 Downsview ON M3M 3B9 Can

KUEHNE, DONALD LEROY, b Oak Park, Ill, Jan 24, 52. CHEMICAL ENGINEERING. *Educ:* Cornell Univ, BS, 73; Calif Inst Technol, MS, 75, PhD(chem eng), 79. *Prof Exp:* RES ENGR, CHEVRON OIL FIELD RES CO, STANDARD OIL CO, 78- *Mem:* Am Inst Chem Engrs; Soc Petrol Engrs. *Res:* Enhanced oil recovery by chemical flooding; properties and field applications of mobility control polymers; automated chemical analysis. *Mailing Add:* 2309 N Maplewood St Orange CA 92665

KUEHNE, MARTIN ERIC, b Floral Park, NY, May 29, 31; m 53; c 1. ORGANIC CHEMISTRY. *Educ:* Columbia Univ, AB, 52, PhD(chem), 56; Harvard Univ, MA, 53. *Prof Exp:* Sr chemist, Chem Res Dept, Ciba Pharmaceut Prod, Inc, 55-61; from asst prof to assoc prof & Sloan fel, 61-68, chmn dept, 76-78, PROF CHEM, UNIV VT, 68- *Mem:* Am Chem Soc. *Res:* Synthetic and degrative problems in natural products; general organic chemistry; medicinal chemistry. *Mailing Add:* Dept of Chem Univ of Vt Burlington VT 05401

KUEHNE, ROBERT ANDREW, b Austin, Tex, June 22, 27; m 55; c 4. ZOOLOGY. *Educ:* Southern Methodist Univ, BS, 49, MS, 50; Univ Mich, PhD(zool), 58. *Prof Exp:* Aquatic biologist, State Game & Fish Comn, Tex, 50-53; instr zool, Univ Mich, 57-58; from instr to asst prof, 58-66, ASSOC PROF ZOOL, UNIV KY, 66- *Concurrent Pos:* Sci fac fel, Freshwater Biol Asn, Eng, 65-66; vis prof, Hebrew Univ Jerusalem, 71. *Mem:* AAAS; Am Fisheries Soc; Am Soc Ichthyologists & Herpetologists; Ecol Soc Am. *Res:* Ecology, behavior and taxonomy of freshwater fishes; stream ecology. *Mailing Add:* Dept of Biol Sci Univ of Ky Lexington KY 40506

KUEHNER, CALVIN CHARLES, b Put-in-Bay, Ohio, Dec 12, 22; m 47; c 3. MEDICAL MICROBIOLOGY, PUBLIC HEALTH. *Educ:* Ohio State Univ, BS, 49, MS, 50, PhD(mycol), 53. *Prof Exp:* Zymologist, Fermentation Div, Northern Regional Res Lab, Peoria, Ill, 51-54; asst prof microbiol, Univ Detroit, 54-58; assoc prof biol, Univ Windsor, 58-67; prof & chmn dept, St Dominic Col, 67-69; prof microbiol, Moraine Valley Community Col, 69-75; CHMN MICROBIOL & PUB HEALTH & DIR, BASIC SCI DIV, NAT COL CHIROPRACTIC, 75- *Concurrent Pos:* Consult microbiol, Palos Med Labs, Palos Heights, Ill, 74-76; assoc ed, J Manipulative & Physiol Therapeut, 78- *Mem:* Am Inst Biol Sci; Am Soc Microbiol; Am Pub Health Asn. *Res:* Teaching of general and medical micrbiology; relation of disease incidence to natural cycles. *Mailing Add:* Nat Col of Chiropractic 200 E Roosevelt Rd Lombard IL 60148

KUEHNER, JOHN ALAN, b Lennoxville, Que, Oct 8, 31; m 55; c 3. NUCLEAR PHYSICS. *Educ:* Bishop's Univ, BSc, 51; Queen's Univ, Ont, MA, 54; Univ Liverpool, PhD(physics), 56. *Prof Exp:* Res officer, Chalk River Nuclear Labs, 56-66; PROF PHYSICS, MCMASTER UNIV, 66- *Mem:* Am Phys Soc; Can Asn Physicists. *Res:* Nuclear structure studies using reactions induced with accelerated ion beams. *Mailing Add:* Dept of Physics McMaster Univ Hamilton ON L8S 4K1 Can

KUEHNER, RICHARD LOUIS, b Plumville, Pa, Nov 21, 17; m 42; c 1. BACTERIOLOGY. *Educ:* Allegheny Col, AB, 40; Yale Univ, PhD(bact), 43. *Prof Exp:* Sr res engr, York Corp, 43-57; group leader, 57-62, mgr environ sci, 62-73, STAFF SCIENTIST, ROY C INGERSOLL RES CTR DIV, BORG-WARNER CORP, 73- *Mem:* AAAS; Am Soc Microbiol; Am Soc Heat, Refrig & Air-Conditioning Eng; Am Chem Soc; Am Pub Health Asn. *Res:* Bacterial taxonomy; air sanitation; air quality control; taxonomic studies of the enterococci; food preservation; environmental biology; air pollution. *Mailing Add:* Ingersoll Res Ctr Borg-Warner Cp Wolf & Algonquin Rd Des Plaines IL 60018

KUEHNERT, CHARLES CARROLL, b Springdale, Ark, Nov 21, 30; m 68. PLANT MORPHOGENESIS. *Educ:* Mankato State Col, BA, 53; Purdue Univ, MS, 55, PhD(bot), 59. *Prof Exp:* Asst bot, Purdue Univ, 53-58, res asst, 59; Nat Res Coun Can fel & res assoc biol, Univ Sask, 60-62; res assoc, Brookhaven Nat Lab, 62-64; from asst prof to assoc prof bot, 64-71, ASSOC PROF BOT, SYRACUSE UNIV, 71- *Concurrent Pos:* Res collabr, Brookhaven Nat Lab, 64-67; vis prof, 65-66; asst botanist, 70-71; adv except undergrad, NSF undergrad res partic prog, Syracuse Univ, 66-67 & adv except sec sch students, NSF Pre-Col Studies Ctr, 68 & 71; sci consult, L W Singer Publ Co, 67; organizing co-chmn, Int Conf Dynamics Meristem Cell Pop, Univ Rochester, 71. *Mem:* AAAS; Am Fern Soc; Bot Soc Am. *Res:* Dynamics of meristem cell populations; cell biology; cell population kinetics; developmental and experimental morphology. *Mailing Add:* 504-506 Biol Res Labs Syracuse Univ 130 College Pl Syracuse NY 13210

KUEKER, DAVID WILLIAM, b Denver, Colo, Dec 14, 43; m 64. LOGIC. *Educ:* Univ Calif, Los Angeles, BA, 64, MA, 66, PhD(math), 67. *Prof Exp:* Actg asst prof math, Univ Calif, Los Angeles, 67-68; Hildebrandt res instr, Univ Mich, Ann Arbor, 68-70, asst prof, 70-73; asst prof, 73-76, ASSOC PROF MATH, UNIV MD, COLLEGE PARK, 76- *Mem:* Am Math Soc; Asn Symbolic Logic. *Res:* Mathematical logic, especially model theory for both finitary and infinitary languages. *Mailing Add:* Dept Math Univ Md College Park MD 20742

KUELLMER, FREDERICK JOHN, b Chicago, Ill, Mar 28, 24; m 48; c 4. PETROLOGY. *Educ:* Univ Chicago, SB, 48, SM, 49, PhD(geol), 52. *Prof Exp:* Geologist, NMex Bur Mines & Mineral Resources, 52-64; prof geol & head dept, Univ Ill, Chicago Circle, 64-66; sr geologist, 66-74, vpres acad affairs, 66-76, actg chmn, Geosci Dept, 80-81, PROF GEOL, NMEX INST MINING & TECHNOL, 66- *Concurrent Pos:* NSF res fel, NMex Inst Mining & Technol, 59-60; prof geol, 59-64. *Mem:* Fel Geol Soc Am; fel Mineral Soc Am; Geochem Soc; Am Geophys Union. *Res:* Structure and petrogenesis of tertiary igneous rocks; coal petrology; alkali feldspars in tertiary porphyries; reaction kinetics of deformed quartz; system of barite, fluorite and calcite. *Mailing Add:* Box 1043 Socorro NM 87801

KUEMMEL, DONALD FRANCIS, b Milwaukee, Wis, Dec 27, 27; m 49; c 3. ANALYTICAL CHEMISTRY. *Educ:* Marquette Univ, BS, 50, MS, 52; Purdue Univ, PhD(anal chem), 56. *Prof Exp:* Chemist, Allis-Chalmers Mfg Co, Wis, 51-53; RES CHEMIST, PROCTER & GAMBLE CO, 55- *Mem:* Am Chem Soc. *Res:* Chromatography; separations. *Mailing Add:* Procter & Gamble Co Miami Valley Labs PO Box 175 Cincinnati OH 45247

KUEMPEL, JOHN RICKEY, analytical chemistry, inorganic chemistry, see previous edition

KUENHOLD, KENNETH ALAN, b Cleveland, Ohio. ATOMIC PHYSICS, ENGINEERING PHYSICS. *Educ:* Cornell Univ, BEP, 64; Ohio State Univ, PhD(physics), 73. *Prof Exp:* Asst prof, 73-76, ASSOC PROF PHYSICS, UNIV TULSA, 76-, CHMN ENG PHYSICS, 80- *Concurrent Pos:* Adj res partic, Oak Ridge Assoc Univs, 73- *Mem:* Am Phys Soc; Am Asn Physics Teachers. *Res:* X-ray production from ion induced reactions; quantitative analysis with x-ray fluorescence. *Mailing Add:* Dept of Physics Univ of Tulsa Tulsa OK 74104

KUENZEL, WAYNE JOHN, b Philadelphia, Pa, Jan 22, 42. POULTRY PHYSIOLOGY, ORNITHOLOGY. *Educ:* Bucknell Univ, BS, 64, MS, 66; Univ Ga, PhD(zool), 69. *Prof Exp:* NIH fel neurophysiol, Cornell Univ, 71-73, res assoc, 73-74; asst prof poultry sci, 74-78, ASSOC PROF PHYSIOL, UNIV MD, COLLEGE PARK, 78- *Concurrent Pos:* Sabbatical leave, Scotland, 81. *Mem:* AAAS; World's Poultry Sci Asn; Poultry Sci Asn; Am Ornithologists Union; Am Soc Zoologists. *Res:* Avian physiology; regulation of food and water intake; neuroanatomy; neurobiology; energy metabolism. *Mailing Add:* Dept Poultry Sci Univ Md College Park MD 20742

KUENZI, NORBERT JAMES, b Beaver Dam, Wis, Aug 5, 35; m 60; c 5. MATHEMATICS. *Educ:* Wis State Univ-Eau Claire, BS, 59; Univ Ill, Urbana, MA, 63; Univ Iowa, PhD(statist), 69. *Prof Exp:* Teacher high sch, Wis, 59-62; asst prof, 64-66 & 69-70, assoc prof, 70-80, PROF MATH, UNIV WIS-OSHKOSH, 80-, CHAIRPERSON DEPT, 76- *Mem:* Inst Math Statist; Am Statist Asn; Math Asn Am. *Res:* Probability theory; mathematical statistics. *Mailing Add:* Dept of Math Univ of Wis-Oshkosh Oshkosh WI 54901

KUENZI, W DAVID, b Seattle, Wash, May 28, 37; m 62; c 3. GEOLOGY. *Educ:* Wash State Univ, BS, 59; Univ Mont, MS, 61, PhD(geol), 66. *Prof Exp:* From instr to assoc prof geol, Western Mich Univ, 64-74, prof, 74-80. *Mem:* Geol Soc Am; Am Asn Petrol Geologists; Soc Econ Paleontologists & Mineralogists; Paleont Soc; Soc Vert Paleont. *Res:* Tertiary stratigraphy, sedimentation and geologic history in the intermontane basins of the Northern Rocky Mountains; Triassic paleontology; Holocene sedimentation of Southwestern Guatemala. *Mailing Add:* 813 Berkshire Dr Kalamazoo MI 49007

KUENZLER, EDWARD JULIAN, b West Palm Beach, Fla, Nov 11, 29; m 65; c 2. ECOLOGY. *Educ:* Univ Fla, BS, 51; Univ Ga, MS, 53, PhD(ecol), 59. *Prof Exp:* From res asst to res assoc marine biol, Woods Hole Oceanog Inst, 59-64, assoc scientist, 64-65; assoc prof environ sci & eng, 65-70, PROF ENVIRON SCI & ENG, UNIV NC, CHAPEL HILL, 70- *Concurrent Pos:* Prog dir biol oceanog, NSF, Washington, DC, 71-72; prog area dir, Environ Chem & Biol, 80- *Mem:* Estuarine Res Fedn; Ecol Soc Am; Am Soc Limnol & Oceanog; Phycol Soc; Elisha Mitchell Sci Soc (pres, 79-). *Res:* Ornithology; spider populations; energy and nutrient flow through marine animal populations; nutrition of marine phytoplankton; ecology of estuaries; aquatic and wetland ecology. *Mailing Add:* Dept of Environ Sci & Eng Univ of NC Chapel Hill NC 27514

KUEPER, THEODORE VINCENT, b Dubuque, Iowa, Aug 13, 41; m 63; c 3. EXPERIMENTAL STATISTICS. *Educ:* Iowa State Univ, BS, 63. *Prof Exp:* Scientist biochem, 63, statistician exp statist, 63-67, head statist, 67-70, res mgr sci serv, 70-74, res mgr new prod develop, 74-78, dir formulated food res, 78-81, DIR FOOD RES, RES & DEVELOP CTR, SWIFT & CO, 81- *Mem:* Inst Food Technologists. *Res:* New food products, both consumer and industrial; statistical analysis, experimental design and computer applications in regard to food research and development. *Mailing Add:* 1919 Swift Dr Oak Brook IL 60521

KUESEL, DONALD CHARLES, b Milwaukee, Wis, Mar 6, 25; m 48; c 2. FOOD SCIENCE. *Educ:* Univ Wis, BSc, 52, MSc, 53, PhD(dairy & food indust), 55. *Prof Exp:* Asst dairy & food indust, Univ Wis, 52-53 53-55; mgr prod develop, Campbell Soup Co, 55-64; dir res & develop, 64-69, dir qual assurance & res, 69-75, VPRES QUAL ASSURANCE & RES, LARSEN CO, 75- *Mem:* Inst Food Technologists. *Res:* Quality assurance; product development; agricultural research departments. *Mailing Add:* Larsen Co PO Box 1127 Green Bay WI 54305

KUESEL, THOMAS ROBERT, b Richmond Hill, NY, July 30, 26; m 59; c 2. CIVIL ENGINEERING. *Educ:* Yale Univ, BEng, 46, MEng, 47. *Prof Exp:* Mem staff, 47-63, proj mgr, San Francisco, 67-68, PARTNER, SR VPRES & DIR, PARSONS, BRINCKERHOFF, QUADE & DOUGLAS, NEW YORK, 68- *Concurrent Pos:* Asst mgr eng, Parsons Brinckerhoff-Tudor-Bechtel, San Francisco, 63-67; vchmn, OECD Tunneling Conf, Washington, DC, 70; mem, US Nat Comt Tunneling Technol, 72-74. *Mem:* Nat Acad Eng; fel Am Soc Civil Eng; fel Am Consult Engrs Coun; Int Asn Bridge, Struct Eng. *Res:* designer over 100 bridges, 60 tunnels & numerous other structures in 36 states and 20 foreign countries. *Mailing Add:* Parsons Brinckerhoff One Penn Plaza 250 W 34th St New York NY 10119

KUETHER, CARL ALBERT, b Ripon, Wis, Oct 15, 15; m 39; c 2. BIOCHEMISTRY. *Educ:* Miami Univ, AB, 36; Wayne State Univ, MS, 40; George Washington Univ, PhD(biochem), 43. *Prof Exp:* Asst chem, Miami Univ, 33-36 & Oberlin Col, 36-38; from asst to instr biochem, George Washington Univ, 40-43; from instr to sr instr, Western Reserve Univ, 43-46; asst prof, Univ Wash, 46-51; biochemist, Res Labs, Eli Lilly & Co, 51-60;

assoc prof chem, Youngstown Univ, 60-62; assoc prog dir metab biol, NSF, 62-65; PROG ADMINR, NAT INST GEN MED SCI, 65- *Mem:* AAAS; Am Chem Soc. *Res:* Biosciences research administration. *Mailing Add:* Pharmacol Sci Prog Nat Inst Gen Med Sci Bethesda MD 20205

KUETTNER, KLAUS E, b Bunzlau, Ger, June 25, 33; m 75. BIOCHEMISTRY. *Educ:* Univ Freiburg, MS, 58; Univ Berne, PhD(pharmaceut chem), 61. *Prof Exp:* Res assoc biochem, Ciba Pharmaceut Co, Switz, 61-62; fel, Div Biol & Med Res, Argonne Nat Lab, 62-64; from instr to asst prof biol chem, Univ Ill Col Med, 64-70; assoc prof, 72-77, PROF BIOCHEM, RUSH MED COL, 77-, CHMN DEPT, 79, ASSOC BIOCHEMIST, RUSH PRESBY-ST LUKE'S MED CTR, 66-, PROF & SR SCIENTIST, ORTHOP SURG, 79- *Concurrent Pos:* Res assoc biochem, Presby-St Luke's Hosp, 64-66. *Mem:* Soc Complex Carbohydrates; Orthop Res Soc; Int Asn Dent Res; Am Soc Biol Chemists; Am Soc Cell Biol. *Res:* Biochemistry of connective tissue; biochemical changes during cartilage calcification, vascular and tumor invasion; bone formation and development. *Mailing Add:* 426-B W Webster Chicago IL 60614

KUFF, EDWARD LOUIS, b Baltimore, Md, June 1, 24; m 47; c 1. MOLECULAR BIOLOGY. *Educ:* Johns Hopkins Univ, AB, 43, MD, 47; Washington Univ, PhD(cytol), 52. *Prof Exp:* Intern med, Barnes Hosp, Washington Univ, 47-48, instr anat, Sch Med, 48-52; med officer, 52-65, head tumor-host rels sect, Lab Biochem, 65-68, actg chief lab biochem, 69-73, HEAD BIOSYNTHESIS SECT, NAT CANCER INST, 68- *Concurrent Pos:* Vis scientist, Virol Sect, Weizmann Inst Sci, Rehovot, Israel, 74-75. *Mem:* Am Soc Biol Chemists; Am Asn Cancer Res. *Res:* Biochemical basis of cell structure; protein and nucleic acid biosynthesis; molecular biology of oncogenic viruses. *Mailing Add:* 6020 Dellwood Pl Bethesda MD 20034

KUFFNER, ROY JOSEPH, b New York, NY, Mar 15, 22; m 47, 78; c 4. PHYSICAL CHEMISTRY. *Educ:* Col of Ozarks, BS, 44; Vanderbilt Univ, PhD(phys chem), 54. *Prof Exp:* Asst prof chem, Emory Univ, 53-54; asst prof phys chem, Fisk Univ, 54-56; from assoc prof to prof, Lowell Tech Inst, 56-67; prof chem, Chicago State Univ, 67-70; chmn, Div Natural Sci & Math, 70-77, prof chem & chmn, Div Nat Sci, 70-79, COORDR PHYSICAL SCI, ALVERNO COL, 80- *Mem:* Am Asn Univ Prof; AAAS; Am Chem Soc; Sigma Xi. *Res:* Surface chemistry; surface tension of aqueous solutions; kinetics and statistical mechanics of surface formation; surface chemical thermodynamics. *Mailing Add:* Phys Sci Div Alverno Col 3401 S 39th St Milwaukee WI 53215

KUGEL, HENRY W, b 40; US citizen. NUCLEAR FUSION RESEARCH. *Educ:* Canisius Col, BS, 62; Univ Notre Dame, PhD(physics), 67. *Prof Exp:* Res assoc nuclear physics, Univ Notre Dame, 67; res assoc, Univ Wis, 68-70; res fel nuclear & atomic physics, Rutgers Univ & Bell Lab, 70-72; asst prof atomic physics, Rutgers Univ, 72-78; RES PHYSICIST, PRINCETON PLASMA PHYSICS LAB, 78- *Mem:* Am Phys Soc; AAAS; Sigma Xi. *Res:* Neutral beam operations for the pox tokamak; optimizing neutral beam heating performance and the developmentof neutral beam diagnositcs. *Mailing Add:* Princeton Plasma Physics Lab PO Box 451 Princeton NJ 08544

KUGEL, ROBERT BENJAMIN, b Chicago, Ill, May 2, 23; m 50; c 4. PEDIATRICS, ACADEMIC ADMINISTRATION. *Educ:* Univ Mich, AB, 45, MD, 46. *Prof Exp:* Intern, Univ Hosp, Univ Mich, 47, resident pediat, 48-50; Commonwealth Fund fel, Child Study Ctr, Yale Univ, 50-52; instr, Univ, 52-53; res assoc, Sch Hyg & Pub Health & asst prof pediat, Johns Hopkins Univ, 55-56; assassoc prof, Col Med, Univ Iowa & dir child develop clin, Univ Hosp, 56-63; from prof med sci to prof child health, Brown Univ, 63-66; found prof pediat, 66-69, chmn dept pediat, 66-69; prof pediat & dean Col Med, Univ Nebr, Omaha, 69-74; prof pediat & vpres health sci, Univ NMex Health Sci ctr, 74-76; exec vchancellor, Univ Kans Med Ctr, 76-77; vpres community health plan, Georgetown Univ, Washington, DC, 77-80; MED DIR, FLOWER HOSP, NEW YORK, NY, 81- *Concurrent Pos:* Dir sch health, Baltimore Health Dept, Md, 55-56; mem, President's Comn on Ment Retardation, 66-70; consult, State Hosp & Sch, Woodward, Iowa; Ment Retardation Br, Div Hosp & Med Facilities, USPHS, Health Res Facilities Br, NIH & US Children's Bur; chief admin officer, Bernalillo County Med Ctr, Albuquerque, NMex, 74-76. *Honors & Awards:* Mildred Thomson Award, 73. *Mem:* Soc Res Child Develop; fel Am Asn Ment Deficiency; fel Am Acad Pediat; Am Pediat Soc; Am Acad Polit & Social Sci. *Res:* Child development; medical ecology; mental retardation. *Mailing Add:* 1249 Fifth Ave Dept Deiatrics Flower Hosp New Rochelle NY 10029

KUGELMAN, IRWIN JAY, b Brooklyn, NY, Feb 15, 37; m 58; c 4. ENVIRONMENTAL ENGINEERING. *Educ:* Cooper Union, BCE, 58; Mass Inst Technol, SM, 60, ScD(civil eng), 63. *Prof Exp:* Asst prof civil eng, NY Univ, 62-65; res scientist process res, Am-Standard Corp, 65-70; res sanit engr, Phys & Chem Res Sect, Advan Waste Treatment Prog, 70-74, chief pilot & field eval, Munic Environ Res Lab, US Environ Protection Agency, 74-81; DIR, CTR MARINE & ENVIRON SYST, LEHIGH UNIVERSITY, 81- *Concurrent Pos:* US Pub Health Serv res grant, 64-65; consult, Nat Acad Sci Patomic Estuary Study, 76-79, Sci Adv Comt, Univ Ill, 80 & Notre Dame, 80- *Mem:* Am Soc Civil Engrs; Am Water Works Asn; Water Pollution Control Fedn. *Res:* Treatment of water and wastes. *Mailing Add:* Ctr Marine Environ Syts Lehigh Univ Bethleham PA 18105

KUGLER, LAWRENCE DEAN, b Orange, Calif, Feb 18, 41; m 62; c 2. GENERAL MATHEMATICS. *Educ:* Calif Inst Technol, BS, 62; Univ Calif, Los Angeles, MA, 65, PhD(math), 66. *Prof Exp:* PROF MATH, UNIV MICH-FLINT, 66- *Concurrent Pos:* NSF grants, 67-71. *Mem:* Am Math Soc; Math Asn Am. *Res:* Application of nonstandard analysis to the theory of almost periodic functions; division algebra. *Mailing Add:* Dept of Math Univ of Mich Flint MI 48503

KUH, ERNEST SHIU-JEN, b Peking, China, Oct 2, 28; nat US; m 57; c 2. ELECTRICAL ENGINEERING. *Educ:* Univ Mich, BS, 49; Mass Inst Technol, SM, 50; Stanford Univ, PhD, 52. *Prof Exp:* Mem tech staff, Bell Tel Labs, NJ, 52-56; assoc prof, 56-62, Miller res prof, 65-66, chmn, Dept Elec Eng & Comput Sci, 68-72, dean Col Eng, 73-80, PROF ELEC ENG, UNIV CALIF, BERKELEY, 62- *Concurrent Pos:* Consult, Res Lab, Int Bus Mach Corp, 57-62; NSF sr fel, 62-63; mem adv panel elec sci, NSF, 76-77, vis comt, Gen Motors Inst, Sci Adv Bd, Mills Col & Peer Rev Panel, Nat Bur Standards; Alexander von Humboldt award, 77; mem adv panel eng, NSF, 79- *Honors & Awards:* Guillemin-Cauer Award, Inst Elec & Electronics Engrs, 73; Lamme Award, Am Soc Eng Educ, 81; Educ Medal, Inst Elec & Electronics Engrs, 81. *Mem:* Nat Acad Eng; fel Inst Elec & Electronics Engrs; Acad Sinica; fel AAAS. *Res:* Network and system theory. *Mailing Add:* Dept Elec Eng & Comput Sci Univ Calif Berkeley CA 94720

KUHAR, MICHAEL JOSEPH, b Scranton, Pa, Mar 10, 44; m 69; c 2. NEUROPHARMACOLOGY, NEUROBIOLOGY. *Educ:* Univ Scranton, BS, 65; Johns Hopkins Univ, PhD(biophys, pharmacol), 70. *Prof Exp:* Fel psychiat, Sch Med, Yale Univ, 70-72; asst prof, 72-76, assoc prof, 76-81, PROF NEUROSCI, PHARMACOL & PSYCHIAT, SCH MED, JOHNS HOPKINS UNIV, 81- *Mem:* AAAS; Soc Neurosci; Am Soc Neurochem; Am Soc Pharmacol & Exp Therapeut; Am Col Neuropsychopharmacol. *Res:* Interaction of drugs with central nervous system neurotransmitters. *Mailing Add:* Dept of Pharmacol Johns Hopkins Univ Sch of Med Baltimore MD 21205

KUHI, LEONARD VELLO, b Hamilton, Ont, Oct 22, 36; nat US; m 60; c 2. ASTROPHYSICS. *Educ:* Univ Toronto, BASc, 58; Univ Calif, Berkeley, PhD(astron), 63. *Prof Exp:* Carnegie fel astron, Mt Wilson & Palomar Observs, 63-65; from asst prof to assoc prof, 65-74, chmn dept, 75-76, PROF ASTRON, UNIV CALIF, BERKELEY, 74-, DEAN PHYS SCI, 76- *Concurrent Pos:* Foreign prof, Col de France, Paris, 72-73; vis prof, Joint Inst Lab Astrophys, Boulder, 69, Inst d'Astrophysique, Paris, 72-73 & Univ Heidelberg, Landessternwarte, 78; Alexander von Humbolt US sr scientist fel, 80-81. *Mem:* Fel AAAS; Astron Soc Pac (pres, 78-80); Int Astron Union; Am Astron Soc; Royal Astron Soc Can. *Res:* Pre-main sequence stellar evolution; extended stellar atmospheres and mass flow problems. *Mailing Add:* Dept of Astron Univ of Calif Berkeley CA 94720

KUHL, DAVID EDMUND, b St Louis, Mo, Oct 27, 29; m 54; c 1. NUCLEAR MEDICINE, RADIOLOGY. *Educ:* Temple Univ, AB, 51; Univ Pa, MD, 55. *Prof Exp:* Chief, Nuclear Med Div, Dept Radiol, Hosp Univ Pa, 63-76, vchmn, 75-76; CHIEF, DIV NUCLEAR MED, DEPT RADIOL SCI, SCH MED, UNIV CALIF, LOS ANGELES, 76-, ASSOC DIR & CHIEF, LAB BIOMED & ENVIRON SCI, LAB NUCLEAR MED, 76-, VCHMN, DEPT RADIOL, 77- *Concurrent Pos:* Mem, Adv Comt, med uses isotopes, US Atomic Energy Comn, Nat Res Coun, 67-79, Comt Radiol, Nat Acad Sci, 67-71 & Radiation Study Sect, NIH, 68-73; chmn, Diagnostic Radiol Comt, Nat Cancer Inst, NIH, 73-77. *Honors & Awards:* Jung Prize, Ernst Jung Found, Ger, 81. *Mem:* Soc Nuclear Med; fel Am Col Radiol; Am Col Radiol; Asn Univ Radiol; Int Soc Cerebral Blood Flow & Metabol. *Res:* Radionuclide imaging. *Mailing Add:* Lab Nuclear Med Univ Calif Sch Med Los Angeles CA 90024

KUHL, FRANK PETER, JR, b New York, NY, Oct 28, 35; m 64; c 5. ELECTRICAL ENGINEERING. *Educ:* Columbia Univ, BSEE, 57, MSEE, 58; Yale Univ, MEng, 61, DEng, 63. *Prof Exp:* Engr, Sperry Gyroscope Co, NY, 62-63; sr engr, Missile Systs Div, Digital Systs Dept, Raytheon Co, 63-65; asst prof elec eng, Union Col, NY, 65-67 & US Naval Acad, 68-73; eng specialist, Singer-Kearfott, 74-76; sr engr, Avionics Div, ITT, 76-78; PROJ LEADER, US ARMY ARMAMENT RES & DEVELOP COMMAND, 78- *Mem:* Sr mem Inst Elec & Electronics Engrs. *Res:* Pattern recognition by use of computers, specifically in the areas of handprinted letters and numbers; polarized radar backscatter of solid objects in free space; video images of airplanes. *Mailing Add:* 64 E Shawnee Trail Wharton NJ 07885

KÜHL, GÜNTER HINRICH, b Geesthacht, Ger, Jan 2, 28; m 57; c 3. INORGANIC CHEMISTRY. *Educ:* Brunswick Tech Univ, dipl, 55, Dr rer nat(chem), 57. *Prof Exp:* Res chemist, Kali-Chemie AG, Ger, 60-61; sr res chemist, Cent Res Div, Socony Mobil Oil Co, 62-69; sr res chemist, 69-75, ASSOC CHEMIST, PROCESS RES & TECH SERV DIV, MOBIL RES & DEVELOP CORP, 75- *Concurrent Pos:* USPHS fel, Ind Univ, 57-59. *Mem:* Soc Ger Chem; Am Chem Soc; Int Zeolite Asn. *Res:* Preparation and properties of organo-metallic acetylene compounds and catalysts for the mineral oil industry; preparation and investigation of hydrogenphosphato-carbonato-apatites; preparation and chemistry of zeolites; phosphato complexes; zeolite crystallization and chemistry; catalyst research and development for application in petroleum industry. *Mailing Add:* Process Res & Tech Serv Div Mobil Res & Develop Corp Paulsboro NJ 08066

KUHLERS, DARYL LYNN, b Mason City, Iowa, Nov 2, 45; m 76; c 1. ANIMAL BREEDING. *Educ:* Iowa State Univ, BS, 67; Univ Wis, MS, 70, PhD(animal sci & genetics), 73. *Prof Exp:* Asst prof animal sci, Iowa State Univ, 74-78; ASSOC PROF ANIMAL & DAIRY SCI, AUBURN UNIV, 78- *Concurrent Pos:* Res assoc, Univ Wis, 73-74; consult, US Feed Grains Coun, 77. *Mem:* Am Soc Animal Sci. *Res:* Swine breeding; genetics; selection and swine production. *Mailing Add:* Animal & Dairy Sci Bldg Auburn Univ Auburn AL 36830

KUHLMAN, ELMER GEORGE, b Beaver Dam, Wis, Dec 15, 34; m 61; c 3. PLANT PATHOLOGY. *Educ:* Univ Wis, BS, 56; Ore State Univ, PhD(plant path), 61. *Prof Exp:* Plant pathologist, Southeastern Forest & Range Exp Sta, 61-68, prin plant pathologist, 68-71, supvry plant pathologist, 71-73, PRIN PLANT PATHOLOGIST, FORESTRY SCI LAB, SOUTHEASTERN FOREST & RANGE EXP STA, US FOREST SERV, 73- *Concurrent Pos:* Adj prof plant path, NC State Univ, 75-; assoc ed, Plant Disease, 78-81. *Mem:* Mycol Soc Am; Am Phytopath Soc. *Res:* Ecological studies of soil organisms; epidemiology of pitch canker disease; effect of environment and mycoparasites on sporulation by Cronartium fusiforms; hyperparasites and hypovirulence; taxionomy of Gibberella Fujikuroi and Mostierella. *Mailing Add:* Southeastern Forest & Range Exp Sta PO Box 12254 Research Triangle Park NC 27709

KUHLMAN, JOHN MICHAEL, b Akron, Ohio, June 1, 48; m 78; c 2. MECHANICAL ENGINEERING. *Educ:* Case Western Reserve Univ, BS, 70, MS, 73, PhD(eng), 75. *Prof Exp:* asst prof, 74-80, assoc prof mech eng, Dept Mech Eng & Mech, Old Dominion Univ, 80-81. *Concurrent Pos:* NSF grant, 78-80, prin investr, Langley Res Ctr, NASA grant, 80-81. *Mem:* Am Soc Mech Engrs; Am Soc Eng Educ; Am Inst Aeronaut & Astronaut. *Res:* Experimental and theoretical fluid mechanics and aerodynamics. *Mailing Add:* Dept of Mech Eng & Mech Old Dominion Univ Norfolk VA 23508

KUHLMANN, GEORGE EDWARD, b Bronxville, NY, Apr 7, 42. ORGANIC CHEMISTRY, PHYSICAL CHEMISTRY. *Educ:* City Col New York, BS, 64; Syracuse Univ, MS, 65, PhD(org chem), 68. *Prof Exp:* Proj chemist, 68-71, res chemist, 71-78, STAFF RES CHEMIST, AMOCO CHEM CORP, 78- *Mem:* AAAS; Am Chem Soc; The Chem Soc. *Res:* Sulfur chemistry; aromatic acids; hydrocarbon oxidation. *Mailing Add:* Amoco Chem Corp PO Box 400 Naperville IL 60540

KUHLMANN, KARL FREDERICK, b Ogden, Utah, Feb 3, 37; m 62; c 2. BIOPHYSICAL CHEMISTRY, ANALYTICAL DATA SYSTMES. *Educ:* Johns Hopkins Univ, BA, 59; Univ Utah, PhD(chem), 63. *Prof Exp:* Res fel chem, Harvard Univ, 62-64 & Int Bus Mach fel, Comput Ctr, 63-64; Alumni Res Found fel, Univ Wis, 64-65; asst prof, Dartmouth Col, 65-71; assoc prof, Stanford Univ, 71-73; phys chemist, Life Sci Div, Stanford Res Inst, 73-81; SR DEVELOP ENGR, NELSON ANAL INC, 81- *Mem:* Am Phys Soc. *Res:* Magnetic resonance; structure and relaxation in liquids; drug design; binding of drugs to macromolecules. *Mailing Add:* 20370 Town Ctr Lane Nelson Anal Inc Cupertino CA 95014

KUHLTHAU, A(LDEN) R(OBERT), b New Brunswick, NJ, Apr 29, 21; m 43; c 3. TRANSPORTATION, SYSTEMS ENGINEERING. *Educ:* Wake Forest Col, BS, 42; Univ Va, MS, 44, PhD(physics), 48. *Prof Exp:* Asst physics, Wake Forest Col, 41-42 & Off Sci Res & Develop & Naval Bur Ord contracts, 42-48; asst prof, Univ NH, 48-51; asst dir, Ord Res Lab, 51-54, dir, Res Lab Eng Sci, Univ, 54-67, assoc dean sch eng & appl sci, 59-67, assoc provost for res, 67-71, pres, Univ Space Res Asn, 69-75, prof aerospace eng, 59-77, PROF TRANSP, DEPT CIVIL ENG, UNIV VA, 77- *Mem:* Am Inst Aeronaut & Astronaut; Transp Res Bd. *Res:* Rarefied gas dynamics; human factors in transportation; air transportation systems. *Mailing Add:* Dept of Civil Eng Thornton Hall Univ of Va Charlottesville VA 22901

KUHN, ALBIN OWINGS, b Woodbine, Md, Jan 31, 16; m 38; c 5. AGRONOMY. *Educ:* Univ Md, BS, 38, MS, 39, PhD(agron), 48. *Prof Exp:* From instr to prof & head dept agron, 39-55, asst to pres, 55-58, exec vpres, 58-65, vpres, Baltimore Campuses, 65-67, chancellor, 67-71, chancellor, Univ Md, Baltimore, 71-80, EXEC VPRES SYSTS, UNIV MD, ADELPHI, 80- *Mem:* Fel Am Soc Agron. *Res:* Pasture management; plant breeding; weed control. *Mailing Add:* Elkins Bldg Univ Md Syst Adelphi MD 20783

KUHN, CEDRIC W, b Milroy, Ind, Dec 23, 30; m 56; c 2. PLANT PATHOLOGY. *Educ:* Purdue Univ, BS, 56, MS, 58, PhD(plant path), 60. *Prof Exp:* Grad asst, Purdue Univ, 56-60; from asst plant pathologist to assoc plant pathologist, 60-68, head dept plant path, 66-68, assoc prof, 68-70, PROF PLANT PATH, UNIV GA, 70- *Mem:* Am Phytopath Soc. *Res:* Plant virus research. *Mailing Add:* Dept Plant Path Univ of Ga Athens GA 30602

KUHN, CHARLES, III, b Cambridge, Mass, May 18, 33; m 59; c 3. PATHOLOGY. *Educ:* Harvard Univ, AB, 55; Washington Univ, MD, 59. *Prof Exp:* Intern path, Barnes Hosp, St Louis, Mo, 59-60, asst resident, 60-61, resident, 61-62; Am Cancer Soc fel, 62-63, from instr to assoc prof, 65-76, PROF PATH, SCH MED, WASHINGTON UNIV, 76- *Concurrent Pos:* Vis prof biochem, Univ Manchester, UK, 80-81. *Mem:* Am Soc Cell Biologists; Am Thoracic Soc; Int Acad Path. *Res:* Pulmonary ultrastructure; pulmonary connective tissue; experimental emphysema. *Mailing Add:* Dept of Path Washington Univ Sch of Med St Louis MO 63110

KUHN, DAISY ANGELIKA, b Heidelberg, Ger, Aug 3, 30. MICROBIOLOGY. *Educ:* Univ Pa, AB, 52; Univ Calif, PhD(microbiol), 60. *Prof Exp:* Asst bact, Univ Calif, 57-59; from instr to assoc prof microbiol, 59-71, PROF BIOL, CALIF STATE UNIV, NORTHRIDGE, 71- *Mem:* AAAS; Am Soc Microbiol; Brit Soc Gen Microbiol; Can Soc Microbiologists. *Res:* Systematics of bacteria; microbial ecology. *Mailing Add:* Dept of Biol Calif State Univ Northridge CA 91330

KUHN, DAVID TRUMAN, b Tucson, Ariz, Apr 4, 40; m 68; c 2. GENETICS. *Educ:* Colo State Col, BA, 63; Univ Utah, MS, 65; Ariz State Univ, PhD(zool), 68. *Prof Exp:* Asst prof biol, Creighton Univ, 68-70; asst prof, 70-72, assoc prof, 72-79, PROF BIOL, UNIV CENT FLA, 79- *Concurrent Pos:* Sabbatical, Univ Geneva, Switz, 78. *Mem:* AAAS; Genetics Soc Am; Soc Study Evolution; Sigma Xi; Am Soc Zool. *Res:* Developmental and population genetics of Drosophila. *Mailing Add:* Dept of Biol Sci Univ Cent Fla Orlando FL 32816

KUHN, HANS HEINRICH, b Uzwil, Switz, Jan 12, 24; m 54; c 2. ORGANIC CHEMISTRY. *Educ:* Swiss Fed Inst Technol, ChemEng, 49, Dr Sci Tech(org chem), 54. *Prof Exp:* Res chemist, Dewey & Almy Div, W R Grace & Co, 57-60; group leader textile chem, 60-61, sect leader, 61-65, MGR POLYMER RES, MILLIKIN RES CO, 65- *Concurrent Pos:* Asst to Prof H Hopff, Swiss Fed Inst Technol, 53-57; hon consult for Switz, SC & NC. *Mem:* Am Chem Soc; Am Asn Textile Chemists & Colorists; Swiss Chem Soc; Swiss Chem Asn. *Res:* Chemistry of epoxy steroids, aliphatic and aromatic epoxides; polymer chemistry, specifically oriented toward textile applications. *Mailing Add:* 176 W Park Dr Spartanburg SC 29301

KUHN, HAROLD WILLIAM, b Santa Monica, Calif, July 29, 25; m 49; c 3. MATHEMATICS. *Educ:* Calif Inst Technol, BS, 47; Princeton Univ, MA, 48, PhD(math), 50. *Prof Exp:* Fine instr math, Princeton Univ, 49-50; Fulbright res scholar, dept sci, Univ Paris, 50-51; lectr, Princeton Univ, 51-52; from asst prof to assoc prof, Bryn Mawr Col, 52-59; assoc prof, 59-63, PROF MATH & ECON, PRINCETON UNIV, 63- *Concurrent Pos:* Exec secy, div math, Nat Acad Sci-Nat Res Coun, 57-58 & 59-61; NSF fel & vis mem, London Sch Econ, 58-59 & 71-72; sr consult, Mathematica, Inc, 61-; mem adv comt, Army Res Off, 62-65 & div math, Nat Res Coun, 63-65 & 69-71; NSF fel, Univ Rome, 65-66. *Mem:* Am Math Soc; Soc Indust & Appl Math (pres, 53-54); fel Economet Soc; Math Asn Am. *Res:* Mathematical economics; mathematical programming; combinatorial problems. *Mailing Add:* Dept of Math Fine Hall Box 37 Princeton Univ Princeton NJ 08540

KUHN, HOWARD A, b Pittsburgh, Pa, Dec 6, 40; m 62; c 4. MECHANICAL ENGINEERING, METALLURGICAL ENGINEERING. *Educ:* Carnegie-Mellon Univ, BS, 62, MS, 63, PhD(mech eng), 66. *Prof Exp:* Instr mech eng, Carnegie-Mellon Univ, 65-66; asst prof, Drexel Univ, 66-67, from asst prof to assoc prof metall eng, 67-74; assoc prof, 75-77, PROF METALL ENG & MECH ENG, UNIV PITTSBURGH, 77- *Concurrent Pos:* Consult, Appl Res Lab, US Steel Corp, 63-65, RCA Defense Electronic Prod, 66 & Metals Lab, TRW, Inc, 67. *Mem:* Am Soc Metals; Am Soc Mech Engrs; Am Powder Metall Inst. *Res:* Fracture in metalworking processes; metal flow analysis; process design. *Mailing Add:* 5408 Peach Dr Gibsonia PA 15044

KUHN, JOHN KENNETH, b Longview, Ill, July 23, 32; m 60; c 2. ANALYTICAL CHEMISTRY. *Educ:* Univ Ill, BS, 65. *Prof Exp:* Chemist, Ill State Geol Surv, 57-59; mgr mat anal chem, 59-79, ASSOC DIR, INST MINING & MINERALS RES, UNIV KY, 79- *Mem:* AAAS; Am Soc Testing Mat; Am Chem Soc. *Res:* Coal and energy research; environmental chemistry; x-ray fluorescence analysis; analytical methods and procedures; mineral analysis and geochemical evaluation. *Mailing Add:* Inst Mining & Minerals Res PO Box 13015 Lexington KY 40512

KUHN, LESLIE A, b South Falls, NY, May 10, 24; m 50; c 2. CARDIOLOGY. *Educ:* State Univ NY Downstate Med Ctr, MD, 48. *Prof Exp:* Assoc prof med, 66-75, assoc attend cardiologist, Hosp, 66-75, CLIN PROF MED, MT SINAI SCH MED, 75-, ATTEND CARDIOLOGIST, MT SINAI HOSP, NEW YORK, 75-, DIR, CORONARY CARE UNIT, 70-, CONSULT, CORONARY CARE UNIT, 81- *Concurrent Pos:* Prin investr, Nat Heart Inst res grant, 60; fel coun clin cardiol, Am Heart Asn, 65-; consult cardiologist, US Vet Admin Hosp, Bronx, 69- *Mem:* Fel Am Col Cardiol; fel Am Col Physicians; Am Fedn Clin Res; Am Soc Artificial Internal Organs; Am Col Chest Physicians. *Res:* Hemodynamic and cardiac metabolic effects of pharmacological agents and methods of mechanical circulatory support in experimental and clinical acute myocardial infarction with shock. *Mailing Add:* Div of Cardiol Mt Sinai Sch of Med New York NY 10029

KUHN, MARTIN CLIFFORD, b Tucson, Ariz, Apr 4, 40; m 63; c 3. METALLURGY. *Educ:* Colo Sch Mines, Met Eng, 63, MS, 67, PhD(metall), 68. *Prof Exp:* Sr res engr, Anaconda Co, 68-72, supvr mineral processing, 72-74, mgr process technol, 74-75; proj mgr, Hazen Res, 75-76; mgr, Tech Develop Ctr, Mineral Sci Div, UOP Inc, 76-79; VPRES & GEN MGR, MINERALS SEPARATION CORP, 79- *Concurrent Pos:* Vpres new ventures, Mountain States Mineral Enterprises Inc. *Mem:* Am Inst Mining Metall & Petrol Engrs; Soc Mining Engrs; Mining & Metallurgical Soc Am; Am Mining Congress. *Res:* Mineral processing; froth flotation; hydrometallurgy; extractive metallurgy; heavy media and ultrasonics. *Mailing Add:* Minerals Separation Corp Interstate 10 & Vail Rd Vail AZ 85641

KUHN, MATTHEW, b Sacalaz, Rumania, Mar 19, 36; Can citizen. ELECTRICAL ENGINEERING, SOLID STATE PHYSICS. *Educ:* Queen's Univ, Ont, BSc, 62; Univ Waterloo, MASc, 63, PhD(elec eng), 67. *Prof Exp:* Advan Res Proj Agency fel, Div Eng, Brown Univ, 67-68; mem staff device res & develop, Bell Tel Labs Inc, 68-70, supvr electroluminescent device develop, 70-73, mgr, Elec Mat & Process Dept, 73-76, mgr, Advan Technol Lab, 76-79, DIR, TECH DEPT, BELL NORTHERN RES LTD, 79- *Mem:* Inst Elec & Electronics Engrs; Am Inst Physics; Electrochem Soc. *Res:* Solid state device physics; electroluminescence; semiconductor-insulator interface physics; solid state display development; silicon integrated circuit research. *Mailing Add:* Bell Northern Res Ltd PO Box 3511 Sta C Manotick ON K1Y 4H7 Can

KUHN, PETER MOUAT, b Janesville, Wis, Feb 2, 20; m 41. METEOROLOGY, ATMOSPHERIC CHEMISTRY & PHYSICS. *Educ:* Univ Wis, BS, 51, MS, 52, PhD(meteorol), 62. *Prof Exp:* Res meteorologist, US Weather Bur, Washington, DC, 52-54; res assoc meteorol, Univ Wis, 54-56; res meteorologist, US Weather Bur, Univ Wis, 56-67; PROJ LEADER, RADIATION GROUP, ATMOSPHERIC PHYS & CHEM LAB, NAT OCEANIC & ATMOSPHERIC ADMIN RES LABS, 67-, CHIEF THERMAL MODIFICATION BR, 70-; SR RES SCI, NORTHROP SERVS, INC, AMES RES CTR, NASA, CALIF, 80- *Concurrent Pos:* Staff meteorologist, WKOW-TV, 54-56. *Mem:* AAAS; fel Explorers Club; fel Optical Soc Am; Sigma Xi; Am Meteorol Soc. *Res:* Experimental meteorology, especially infrared radiation measurements surface through 30 kilometers. *Mailing Add:* Atmospheric Physics & Chem Lab Nat Oceanic & Atmospheric Admin Boulder CO 80302

KUHN, RAYMOND EUGENE, b Biloxi, Miss, Sept 6, 42; m 64. IMMUNOBIOLOGY, PARASITOLOGY. *Educ:* Carson-Newman Col, BS, 65; Univ Tenn, PhD(zool), 68. *Prof Exp:* Assoc prof, 68-80, PROF BIOL, WAKE FOREST UNIV, 80- *Mem:* Am Soc Parasitologists; Am Asn Immunol; Am Soc Trop Med & Hyg. *Res:* Immunology of parasitic diseases. *Mailing Add:* Dept of Biol Wake Forest Univ Winston-Salem NC 27109

KUHN, THOMAS S, b Cincinnati, Ohio, July 18, 22; div; c 3. HISTORY OF PHYSICS, CONCEPTUAL CHANGE. *Educ:* Harvard Univ, SB, 43, AM, 46, PhD(physics), 49. *Prof Exp:* Asst prof, Gen Educ & Hist Sci, Harvard Univ, 51-57; prof, Univ Calif, Berkeley, 58-64; prof hist sci, Princeton Univ, 64-79; PROF PHILOS & HIST SCI, MASS INST TECHNOL, 79- *Concurrent Pos:* Lectr, Lowell Inst, 51; proj dir, Sources Hist Quantum Physics, 61-64; mem bd dir, Social Sci Res Coun, 64-66, Inst Advan Study, Princeton, 72-79 & Assembly Behav & Social Sci, Nat Acad Sci, Nat Res

Coun, 80- *Honors & Awards:* Howard T Behrman Award, Princeton Univ, 77. *Mem:* Nat Acad Sci; Am Philos Soc; Am Acad Arts & Sci; Hist Sci Soc; Am Philos Asn. *Res:* Reconstruction of out-of-date scientific ideas; description and abstract analysis of the way language and ideas change in scientific development. *Mailing Add:* Dept Linguistics & Philos Mass Inst Technol 20D-213 Cambridge MA 02139

KUHN, TRUMAN HOWARD, b Glendora, Calif, Oct 31, 08; m 32; c 2. GEOLOGY. *Educ:* Calif Inst Technol, BS, 30; Univ Ariz, PhD(geol), 40. *Prof Exp:* Engr geologist, Los Angeles County Flood Control Dist, Calif, 31-37; geologist, Ariz Molybdenum Corp, 38-39 & Magma Copper Co, 40-42; from asst prof to prof geol, 42-74, dean grad sch, 53-56, dean fac, 56-68, vpres admin affairs, 68-74, interim chief exec officer, summer 70; vpres acad affairs, 71-72, actg dir, Potential Gas Agency, Mineral Resources Inst, 74-76, EMER VPRES, COLO SCH MINES, 74- *Concurrent Pos:* Consult geologist, 42-; geologist, US Geol Surv, 51-53 & CSM Res Inst, 53-70; consult, Istanbul Tech Univ, Turkey, 63-66 & Univ Zambia, Lusaka, 66-67; mem, US Consortium Comt, Univ Petroleum & Minerals, Dhahran, Saudi Arabia, 70-73, chmn, 73-75; AID consult, Lemigas Acad, Cepu, Indonesia, 74. *Honors & Awards:* Bliss Medal, Soc Am Mil Engrs, 68; Mineral Indust Educ Award, Am Inst Mining, Metall & Petrol Engrs, 74. *Mem:* Fel Geol Soc Am; Soc Econ Geologists; Am Soc Eng Educ; Am Inst Mining, Metall & Petrol Engrs; Sigma Xi. *Res:* Mineral deposits; mining geology; mineralography; engineering geology. *Mailing Add:* 14 Carriage Hill Circle Casselberry FL 32707

KUHN, WILLIAM E(RIK), b Toronto, Ont, Feb 27, 22; nat US; m 54; c 2. MATERIALS SCIENCE, POWDER METALLURGY. *Educ:* Univ Toronto, BASc, 44. *Prof Exp:* Res fel eng & metall, Ont Res Found, Can, 44-48; metall, Univ Notre Dame, 48-49; sr res engr, Metall Dept, Titanium Alloy Mfg Co, 49-52; sr engr, Carborundum Co, 52-58, supvr & mgr metall dept, 58-63; head metall dept, Spindletop Res, Inc, Ky, 63-68, mgr mat & processing div, 68-70; RES ASSOC PROF MAT SCI, UNIV CINCINNATI, 70- *Concurrent Pos:* Pres, Dymatron Inc, 72-; dir, Hemotec Inc, 75-; prin investr, NSF grant, 72-77 & NIH grant, 75-77. *Honors & Awards:* Leonard Medal, Can Inst Mining & Metall, 51. *Mem:* Electrochem Soc; Am Soc Metals; Brit Inst Metals; Soc Biomat. *Res:* Materials technology including ferrous and nonferrous metals; arc and plasma technology re arc melting, furnacing and synthesis of compounds; powder metallurgy; fibers and ultrafine particles; ceramics; bio-materials; biomaterials and powder metallurgy; mechanical alloying; comminution. *Mailing Add:* 2085 Fallon Rd Lexington KY 40504

KUHN, WILLIAM FREDERICK, b Kittanning, Pa, Apr 1, 30; m 53; c 4. ANALYTICAL CHEMISTRY, SPECTROCHEMISTRY. *Educ:* St Vincent Col, BS, 57; Univ Richmond, MS, 62. *Prof Exp:* Chemist, 57-59, res chemist, 59-62, group leader tech info, 62-64, sr scientist mass spectros, 64-69, facil leader instrument sect, 69-72, proj leader smoke condensate, 72-74, mgr biochem res, 74-81, MGR ANALYTICAL RES, PHILIP MORRIS, USA, 81- *Honors & Awards:* William J Poehlman Award, Soc Appl Spectros, 75. *Mem:* Soc Appl Spectros; Am Soc Testing & Mat; Am Chem Soc; Am Soc Mass Spectrometry. *Res:* Spectroscopic methods; chromatographic techniques; computer applications; technical information; environmental pollution; tobacco and smoke composition; ionization phenomena; entomology. *Mailing Add:* Philip Morris USA PO Box 26583 Richmond VA 23261

KUHN, WILLIAM LLOYD, b Grafton, WVa, Dec 23, 25; m 51; c 2. PHARMACOLOGY. *Educ:* WVa Wesleyan Col, BS, 49; Univ Cincinnati, PhD(pharmacol), 57. *Prof Exp:* Jr biochemist, William S Merrell Co, 51-54; asst pharmacol, Univ Cincinnati, 54-55; pharmacologist, 56-57, dept head pharmacol, 57-62, assoc dir biol sci, 62-64, dir biol sci, 64-69, dir res planning & coord, 69-73, VPRES RES PLANNING & COORD, MERRELL-NAT LABS, 73- *Res:* Pharmacology and physiology of neuromuscular junction; central nervous system; heart and circulation; chemical structure; pharmacological activity relationships. *Mailing Add:* 318 Whitthorne Dr Cincinnati OH 45215

KUHN, WILLIAM R, b Columbus, Ohio, May 7, 38; m 57; c 3. PLANETARY ATMOSPHERES, CLIMATOLOGY. *Educ:* Capital Univ, BS, 61; Univ Colo, PhD(astro-geophys), 66. *Prof Exp:* Fel astro-geophys, Univ Colo, 66-67; asst prof, 67-71, assoc prof atmosphere & ocean sci, 72-77, PROF ATMOSPHERIC OCEANIC SCI, UNIV MICH, ANN ARBOR, 77-, DEPT CHMN, 80- *Mem:* Am Geophys Union; Am Astron Soc. *Res:* Radiation and photochemical studies applicable to planetary atmospheres and the prebiotic earth atmosphere; climatology; photochemistry of outer planets. *Mailing Add:* Dept of Atmos & Oceanic Sci Univ of Mich Ann Arbor MI 48104

KUHNEN, SYBIL MARIE, b Haledon, NJ, Sept 12, 17. BOTANY. *Educ:* Montclair State Col, BA, 41; Columbia Univ, MA, 46; NY Univ, PhD(sci educ), 60. *Prof Exp:* Pub sch teacher, NJ, 41-43; asst bot, Columbia Univ, 43-46; from instr to assoc prof bact & bot, 46-66, chmn dept, 69-76, PROF BIOL, MONTCLAIR STATE COL, 66- *Concurrent Pos:* Consult, 55- *Mem:* AAAS; Bot Soc Am; Nat Sci Teachers Asn. *Res:* Plant ecology. *Mailing Add:* Dept of Biol Montclair State Col Upper Montclair NJ 07043

KUHNLEY, LYLE CARLTON, b Buffalo, Minn, Dec 23, 25; m 53; c 4. MICROBIOLOGY. *Educ:* Univ Minn, BA, 49; Univ Tex, MA, 55, PhD(bact), 61. *Prof Exp:* Bacteriologist, Ariz State Dept Health, 49-50, 53-55; assoc prof, 59-81, EMER PROF BIOL, TEX TECH UNIV, 81- *Mem:* AAAS; Am Soc Microbiol. *Res:* Inducible enzyme formation; rumen microbiology; ecology of coliphage; geomicrobiological prospecting; resistance mechanisms. *Mailing Add:* PO Box 496 Monroe OR 97456

KUHNS, ELLEN SWOMLEY, b Chester, Pa, Feb 6, 19; m 74; c 1. PHYSICS, RESEARCH ADMINISTRATION. *Educ:* Coe Col, BA, 41; Johns Hopkins Univ, PhD(physics), 46. *Prof Exp:* Instr astron, Teachers Col, Johns Hopkins Univ, 41-45; instr physics, Conn Col, 45-46; asst prof, NJ Col for Women, Rutgers Univ, 46-51; physicist, 51-66, head, Optical Physics Div, 66-68, res mgr, 68-70, planning officer, 70-74, tech prog mgt off, Naval Electronics Lab Ctr, 74-77; DEP INDEPENDENT RES & INDEPENDENT EXP DEVELOP DIR, NAVAL OCEAN SYSTS CTR, 77- *Mem:* Fel Am Phys Soc. *Res:* Ultrasonics; underwater acoustics. *Mailing Add:* 875 Albion St San Diego CA 92106

KUHNS, WILLIAM JOSEPH, b Allentown, Pa, Sept 2, 18; m 41; c 7. IMMUNOHEMATOLOGY. *Educ:* Muhlenberg Col, BS, 40; Lehigh Univ, MS, 42; Johns Hopkins Univ, MD, 48. *Prof Exp:* Chemist, Lederle Labs Div, Am Cyanamid Corp, 42-44; serologist, Blood Bank Hosp, Johns Hopkins Univ, 44-46; fel, Baltimore Rh Typing Lab, 46-48; intern med, Salt Lake County Gen Hosp, 49-50; intern microbiol, Col Med, NY Univ, 50-51; vis investr & asst physician, Hosp, Rockefeller Inst, 51-54; assoc prof path, Sch Med, Univ Pittsburgh, 54-59; assoc prof path, Sch Med, NY Univ, 60-77; PROF PATH, UNIV NC & DIR TRANSFUSION SERV, NC MEM HOSP, 77- *Concurrent Pos:* Dir, Cent Blood Bank, Pittsburgh, 54-59; mem attend staff & dir transfusion serv, Bellevue & Univ Hosp, 60-77; Lister Inst, Univ London, 74-75. *Mem:* Harvey Soc; Am Soc Clin Invest; Soc Exp Biol & Med; Tissue Culture Asn; Am Asn Immunologists. *Res:* Blood banking; blood groups and their precursors on cultured cells; glycosyltransferase enzymes; blood groups on cells on culture; blood groups in infrahuman species; effects of transfusion; blood groups and antibodies in transplantation. *Mailing Add:* Dept of Path Univ NC Sch Med Chapel Hill NC 27514

KUHR, RONALD JOHN, b Appleton, Wis, Dec 29, 39; m 61; c 3. AGRICULTURAL CHEMISTRY, INSECT TOXICOLOGY. *Educ:* Univ Wis, BS, 63; Univ Calif, Berkeley, PhD(agr chem), 66. *Prof Exp:* NIH fel, Pest Infestation Lab, Slough, Eng, 66-68; from asst prof to assoc prof insect toxicol, NY State Agr Exp Sta, 73-77; prof entom, assoc dir res & assoc dir, Agr Exp Sta, Cornell Univ, 77-80; PROF & HEAD, DEPT ENTOM, NC STATE UNIV, 80- *Mem:* AAAS; Am Chem Soc; Entom Soc Am; Soc Toxicol. *Res:* Metabolism of carbamate insecticide chemicals in plants and insects; environmental degradation of pesticides. *Mailing Add:* NC State Univ Entom Dept Raleigh NC 27650

KUIDA, HIROSHI, b Ogden, Utah, Oct 23, 25; m 51; c 4. INTERNAL MEDICINE, PHYSIOLOGY. *Educ:* Univ Utah, BS, 49, MD, 51. *Prof Exp:* Intern med, Salt Lake County Gen Hosp & Univ Utah, 51-52, asst resident, 52-53; fel cardiol, Harvard Med Sch & Peter Bent Brigham Hosp, 53-54, res fel, 54-56; res fel physiol, Univ Minn, 56-57; chief resident med, 57-58, instr, 58-61, asst res prof, 61-64, assoc prof, 64-69, assoc prof physiol, 65-69, PROF MED & PHYSIOL, COL MED, UNIV UTAH, 69-, CHIEF DIV CARDIOL, 80- *Concurrent Pos:* USPHS fel, 53-55, res career develop award, Am Heart Asn res fel, 55-57. *Mem:* Am Physiol Soc; Am Fedn Clin Res. *Res:* Pulmonary vascular hemodynamics; hemodynamics of endotoxin shock; pathophysiology of pulmonary hypertensive heart disease in cattle. *Mailing Add:* Dept of Med Univ of Utah Col of Med Salt Lake City UT 84112

KUIJT, JOB, b Velsen, Holland, May 25, 30; nat Can; m 59. PLANT ANATOMY, PLANT MORPHOLOGY. *Educ:* Univ BC, BA, 54; Univ Calif, MA, 55, PhD(anat), 58. *Prof Exp:* From instr to asst prof biol & bot, Univ BC, 59-68; assoc prof, 68-70, PROF BIOL, UNIV LETHBRIDGE, 70- *Mem:* Bot Soc Am. *Res:* Structure and taxonomy of parasitic angiosperms; systematics; floristics of Southern Alberta. *Mailing Add:* Dept of Biol Univ of Lethbridge Lethbridge AB T1K 3M4 Can

KUIKEN, KENNETH (ALFRED), b Chicago, Ill, Oct 14, 18; m 44; c 2. BIOCHEMISTRY. *Educ:* Geneva Col, BS, 39; Univ Pittsburgh, PhD(biochem), 43. *Prof Exp:* Assoc nutritionist & assoc prof biochem & nutrit, Exp Sta, Agr & Mech Col Tex, 43-50; mem staff, Cellulose & Specialties Tech Div, 50-74, SR RES CHEMIST, BUCKEYE CELLULOSE CORP, 74- *Mem:* AAAS; Tech Asn Pulp & Paper Indust; Am Chem Soc; Soc Exp Biol & Med; fel Am Oil Chemists' Soc. *Res:* Microbiological methods of amino acid analysis; cottonseed processing; nutritional requirements of laboratory and farm animals; manufacture and application of wood and cotton cellulose; analytical methods for cellulose. *Mailing Add:* Buckeye Cellulose Corp 2899 Jackson Ave Memphis TN 38108

KUIPER, EDWARD, hydraulic engineering, see previous edition

KUIPER, LOGAN KEITH, b Oskaloosa, Iowa, Sept 12, 40; m 72; c 1. GROUNDWATER HYDROLOGY, GEOPHYSICS. *Educ:* Univ Iowa, BA, 62, MS, 65, PhD(physics), 69; Calif Inst Technol, MS, 63. *Prof Exp:* Asst prof physics, SDak Sch Mines, 70; res geologist, Iowa Geol Surv, 72-80; HYDROLOGIST, US GEOL SURV, 79- *Mem:* Am Geophys Union; Int Asn Hydrol Sci; Nat Waterwell Asn; Soc Indust & Appl Math; Soc Exp Geophysicists. *Res:* Groundwater hydrology and particularly the mathematical modelling; geophysics, mostly resistivity and seismic. *Mailing Add:* US Geol Surv 711 East 8th 3rd Foor Austin TX 78701

KUIPER, THOMAS BERNARDUS HENRICUS, b Amersfoort, Neth, July 14, 45; Can citizen; m 70. RADIOASTRONOMY. *Educ:* Loyola Col, Montreal, BSc, 66; Univ Md, PhD(astron), 73. *Prof Exp:* Sr scientist, 75-77, MEM TECH STAFF ASTRON, JET PROPULSION LAB, CALIF INST TECHNOL, 77- *Concurrent Pos:* Resident res assoc, US Nat Res Coun & Jet Propulsion Lab, 73-75. *Mem:* Am Astron Soc; Can Astron Soc; Int Astron Union; AAAS; Int Union Radio Sci. *Res:* Spectroscopy observations with emphasis on instrumentation and techniques; very large baseline interferometer; solar physics; radio search for extraterrestrial intelligence and evolution of civilization in space. *Mailing Add:* JPL T-1166 Calif Inst of Technol Pasadena CA 91109

KUIPER-GOODMAN, TINE, b Leeuwarden, Netherlands, Sept 11, 37; m 61; c 1. ELECTRON MICROSCOPY, TOXICOLOGY. *Educ:* McMaster Univ, BSc, 61, MSc, 63; Nat Res Coun Can & Ontario fels & PhD(histol, embryol), Univ Ottawa, 67. *Prof Exp:* RES SCIENTIST CELL TOXICOL & TOXICOLOGIST, HEALTH PROTECTION BR, BUR CHEM SAFETY,

NAT HEALTH & WELFARE DEPT, CAN, 66- *Mem:* Electron Micros Soc Am; Can Soc Cell Biol; Micros Soc Can; Can Asn Pathologists; Am Soc Toxicol. *Res:* Effect of exogenous substances that may be present in food on cell organelles of animal tissues; risk assessment of mycotoxins and natural toxicants present in food; development of quantitative morphological methods. *Mailing Add:* Nat Health & Welfare Bur of Chem Safety Tunney's Pasture ON K1A 0L2 Can

KUIPERS, BENJAMIN JACK, b Grand Rapids, Mich, April 7, 49; m 75; c 2. INTELLIGENT SYSTEMS. *Educ:* Swarthmore Col, BA, 70; Mass Inst Technol, PhD(math), 77. *Prof Exp:* Systs Programmer, Psychol Dept, Harvard Univ, 70-72; res assoc, Div Study Res Educ, Mass Inst Technol, 77-78; ASST PROF COMPUT SCI, DEPT MATH, TUFTS UNIV, 78- *Concurrent Pos:* Vis scientist, Lab Comput Sci, Mass Inst Technol, 80- *Mem:* NY Acad Sci; Sigma Xi; Asn Comput Mach; Cognitive Sci Soc; Am Asn Artificial Intelligence. *Res:* Human commonsense knowledge, and use artificial intelligence techniques to build computer models of knowledge of space and causality, concentrating on their role in the problem-solving strategies of expert physicians. *Mailing Add:* Dept Math Tufts Univ Medford MA 02155

KUIPERS, JACK, b Grand Rapids, Mich, Mar 27, 21; m 48; c 5. MATHEMATICS. *Educ:* Calvin Col, AB, 43; Univ Mich, BSEE, 43, MSE, 59, Info & ContE, 66. *Prof Exp:* Asst to dir res, Elec Sorting Mach Co, 46-50; proj engr, Lear, Inc, 50-53; chief engr, R C Allen Bus Mach, Inc, 53-54; sr proj engr, Lear, Inc, 54-59; sr physicist, Cleveland Pneumatic Industs, 59-62; lectr aerospace eng, Inst Sci & Technol, Univ Mich, 62-65, assoc res engr, Univ, 65-67; ASSOC PROF MATH, CALVIN COL, 67- *Concurrent Pos:* Consult, Precision Prod Dept, Nortronics Div, Northrop Corp, 67-, Precision Prod Dept & Avionics Div, Lear Jet Industs, 67-, Polhemus Navigation Sci, Inc & Advan Technol Systs, Univ Austin Co, Cleveland, Ohio, 75- *Mem:* Inst Elec & Electronics Engrs; Math Asn Am. *Res:* Automatic control; analog-digital computer simulation; special purpose computer design; navigation and guidance control and instrumentation; coordinate converters for gyroscope inertial reference systems; mathematical models and optimization. *Mailing Add:* Dept of Math Calvin Col Grand Rapids MI 49506

KUIST, CHARLES HOWARD, b West Chester, Pa, Apr 24, 31; m 55; c 5. PHYSICAL CHEMISTRY, POLYMER CHEMISTRY. *Educ:* Lafayette Col, AB, 53. *Prof Exp:* Chemist, Extrax Co, 53-55; asst instr chem, Newark Col Eng, 55-59; chemist, Nat Starch & Chem Corp, 59-61, proj supvr, 61-65, sect leader, 65-69, mgr cent res, 69-74; VPRES RES & DEVELOP, CHOMERICS, INC, 74- *Concurrent Pos:* Spec lectr, Eve Div, Newark Col Eng, 58-60. *Mem:* AAAS; Am Chem Soc; Am Phys Soc; Am Soc Testing & Mat. *Res:* Photochemistry and radiation chemistry of polymers; accelerated weathering of plastics; physical interactions of latex particles; behavior of polymers at interfaces; electroanalytical instrumentation. *Mailing Add:* Chomerics Inc 77 Dragon Ct Woburn MA 01801

KUITERT, LOUIS CORNELIUS, b Spring Lake, Mich, Aug 20, 12; m 46; c 3. ENTOMOLOGY. *Educ:* Kalamazoo Col, BA, 39; Univ Kans, MA, 40, PhD(entom), 47. *Prof Exp:* Asst entomologist, State Entom Comn, Kans, 40-41; high sch instr, 41-42; asst instr biol, Univ Kans, 46-47; asst prof entom, Kans State Col, 47-48; from asst entomologist to assoc entomologist, 48-55, head dept, 61-66, ENTOMOLOGIST, AGR EXP STA, UNIV FLA, 55-, PROF ENTOM, UNIV, 66- *Mem:* Entom Soc Am. *Res:* Control of insect and arachnid pests of woody ornamentals, pastures, tobacco; taxonomy of western hemisphere water scorpions; biology and control of tobacco insects. *Mailing Add:* 2842 SW First Ave Gainesville FL 32607

KUIVILA, HENRY GABRIEL, b Fairport Harbor, Ohio, Sept 17, 17; m 43; c 3. ORGANIC CHEMISTRY. *Educ:* Ohio State Univ, BSc, 42, MA, 44; Harvard Univ, PhD(chem), 48. *Prof Exp:* Jr chemist, Manhattan Proj, Monsanto Chem Co, Ohio, 44-46; from asst prof to prof chem, Univ NH, 48-64; chmn dept, 64-69, PROF CHEM, STATE UNIV NY ALBANY, 64- *Concurrent Pos:* NSF sr fel & Guggenheim fel, 59; vis prof, Japan Soc Promotion of Sci, 73. *Mem:* Fel AAAS; Am Chem Soc. *Res:* Organic reaction mechanisms; organometallic chemistry; photochemistry. *Mailing Add:* Dept of Chem State Univ NY Albany NY 12203

KUJAWA, FRANK B, geochemistry, see previous edition

KUKACHKA, BOHUMIL FRANCIS, b Montgomery, Minn, Dec 1, 15; m 38; c 1. PLANT ANATOMY. *Educ:* Univ Minn, BS, 37, PhD(wood technol), 42. *Prof Exp:* Asst forestry, Univ Minn, 37-42; from instr to asst prof, La State Univ, 42-45; wood technologist, Forest Prod Lab, 45-74, WOOD TECHNOLOGIST, PIONEER RES UNIT, FOREST PROD RES LAB, US FOREST SERV, 74- *Concurrent Pos:* Lectr, Univ Wis-Madison. *Mem:* Int Asn Wood Anat. *Res:* Wood structure and identification; systematic anatomy of the woods of the Sapotaceae; properties of tropical timbers. *Mailing Add:* Forest Prod Lab US Forest Serv Madison WI 53705

KUKAL, GERALD COURTNEY, b St Louis, Mo, Oct 1, 43; m 63; c 4. LOG ANALYSIS, PETROLEUM GEOLOGY. *Educ:* Southwest Mo Univ, BS, 67; Purdue Univ, MS, 73. *Prof Exp:* Teacher geol, Riverview Gardens Sch Dist, 67-70; teaching asst & instr geol, Purdue Univ, 70-73; field engr, Dresser Atlas, 73-77; SR GEOLOGIST & FORMATION EVALUATION SPECIALIST, CER CORP, 77- *Mem:* Soc Prof Well Log Analysts; Am Asn Petrol Geologists; Development of log interpretation systems for low-permeability gas reservoirs: these systems are improved mathematical models or procedures to quantity porosity, permeability, saturation, lithology and for geologic interpretations such as formation water geochemistry and basin hydrodynamics. *Mailing Add:* 5010 Reno Ct Las Vegas NV 89119

KUKIN, IRA, b New York, NY, Apr 4, 24; m 54; c 3. ENVIRONMENTAL CHEMISTRY. *Educ:* City Col New York, BS; Harvard Univ, MA, 50, PhD(inorg chem), 51. *Prof Exp:* Instr chem, Sampson Col, 46-48; group leader, Gulf Res & Develop Co, 51-57; res dir & scientist, res Sonneborn Chem & Ref Corp, DiV Witco Corp, 57-63; PRES & FOUNDER, APOLLO CHEM CORP, 63- *Concurrent Pos:* Subsidiary, Economics Lab, Inc, St Paul, 80. *Mem:* Am Chem Soc; Nat Asn Corrosion Engrs. *Res:* Energy conservation; pollution control; consultant with government agencies on air pollution. *Mailing Add:* Apollo Technol Inc 1 Apollo Dr Whippany NJ 07981

KUKKONEN, CARL ALLAN, b Duluth, Minn, Jan 25, 45; m 68; c 2. THEORETICAL PHYSICS, TECHNOLOGICAL ASSESSMENT. *Educ:* Univ Calif, Davis, BS, 68; Cornell Univ, MS, 71, PhD(physics), 75. *Prof Exp:* Res assoc physics, Purdue Univ, 75-77; RES STAFF, FORD MOTOR CO, 77- *Mem:* Am Phys Soc. *Res:* Theory of electrons in metals; direct injection diesel engines; design and development of small high speed direct injection diesel engines for passenger cars; technological assessment of hydrogen as an alternative automotive fuel. *Mailing Add:* Res Staff Ford Motor Co Dearborn MI 48121

KUKLA, MICHAEL JOSEPH, b Frankfort, Ger, Sept 23, 47; US citizen; m 69; c 3. PHARMACEUTICAL CHEMISTRY. *Educ:* Kalamazoo Col, BA, 69; Ohio State Univ, PhD(org chem), 74. *Prof Exp:* Res investr chem, G D Searle & Co, 74-78; SR SCIENTIST, MCNEIL PHARMACEUT, 78- *Mem:* Am Chem Soc. *Res:* Synthesis of heterocyclic ring systems which may alter functions in the central nervous system. *Mailing Add:* McNeil Pharmaceut Spring House PA 19477

KUKOLICH, STEPHEN GEORGE, b Appleton, Wis, Feb 3, 40. PHYSICAL CHEMISTRY, STRUCTURAL CHEMISTRY. *Educ:* Mass Inst Technol, BS, 62, DSc(physics), 66. *Prof Exp:* Instr physics, Mass Inst Technol, 66-68; asst prof chem, Univ Ill, 68-69 & Mass Inst Technol, 69-74; assoc prof, 74-79, PROF CHEM, UNIV ARIZ, 79- *Concurrent Pos:* NSF res grant, 70-74, 74-77 & 77-79, Am Chem Soc, 77-79, 79-81. *Mem:* Am Phys Soc; Sigma Xi; Am Chem Soc. *Res:* High resolution microwave spectroscopy; molecular Zeeman effect; molecular beam maser spectroscopy; electric and magnetic interactions in molecules; electron paramagnetic resonance spectroscopy of biological molecules; molecular relaxation studies. *Mailing Add:* Dept of Chem Univ of Ariz Tucson AZ 85721

KUKSIS, ARNIS, b Valka, Latvia, Dec 3, 27; nat Can; m 53; c 4. BIOCHEMISTRY. *Educ:* Iowa State Col, BS, 51, MS, 53; Queen's Univ, Ont, PhD(biochem), 56. *Prof Exp:* Res fel org chem, Royal Mil Col, Ont, 56-58. *Prof Exp:* Res assoc biochem, Queen's Univ, Ont, 58-59, asst prof, 60-65; asst prof, Banting & Best Dept Med Res, 65-68, assoc prof, 68-74, PROF, DEPT BIOCHEM & BANTING & BEST DEPT MED RES, C H BEST INST, UNIV TORONTO, 74- *Concurrent Pos:* Med Res Coun Can med res assoc, 60-; fel coun arteriosclerosis, Am Heart Asn. *Mem:* Am Oil Chem Soc; Can Biochem Soc; Brit Am Soc Biol Chemists; Am Inst Nutrit. *Res:* Composition of food fats; mechanics of lipid digestion and absorption; metabolism of triglycerides and phospholipids, sterols and bile acids; chromatographic separations of lipids. *Mailing Add:* Banting & Best Dept of Med Res C H Best Inst Univ of Toronto Toronto ON M5G 1L6 Can

KULA, ERIC BERTIL, b New York, NY, July 4, 29; m 51; c 2. PHYSICAL METALLURGY. *Educ:* Mass Inst Technol, BS, 48, MS, 52, ScD(metall), 54. *Prof Exp:* Metallurgist, Domnarvet's Steelworks, Sweden, 48-49; asst, Royal Inst Technol, Sweden, 49-50; asst, Mass Inst Technol, 50-54; SUPVRY METALLURGIST, US ARMY MAT & MECH RES CTR, WATERTOWN, 56-, DIV CHIEF, 79- *Mem:* Am Soc Metals; Am Inst Mining, Metall & Petrol Engrs. *Res:* Mechanical behavior of metals; high strength steels; failure analysis. *Mailing Add:* 23 Mason St Lexington MA 02173

KULACKI, FRANCIS ALFRED, b Baltimore, Md, May 21, 42. MECHANICAL ENGINEERING, HEAT TRANSFER. *Educ:* Ill Inst Technol, BSME, 63, MSGE, 66; Univ Minn, PhD(mech eng), 71. *Prof Exp:* ASSOC PROF MECH ENG, OHIO STATE UNIV, 71- *Concurrent Pos:* Consult, Battelle Mem Inst, 73-76, Anchor Hocking Corp, 73-, Argonne Nat Lab, 74- & CVI Corp, Div Penwalt, 78- *Mem:* Sigma Xi; Am Soc Mech Engrs; Am Soc Eng Educ. *Res:* Fluid mechanics and transport phenomena; currently active in fields of natural convection, hydrodynamic stability, electrofluidmechanics, catalytic combustion and two-phase flow. *Mailing Add:* Dept of Mech Eng 206 W 18th Ave Columbus OH 43210

KULAK, GEOFFREY LUTHER, b Edmonton, Alta, Nov 26, 36; m 58; c 2. CIVIL ENGINEERING. *Educ:* Univ Alta, BSc, 58; Univ Ill, Urbana, MS, 61; Lehigh Univ, PhD(civil eng), 67. *Prof Exp:* Design engr, Bridge Br, Prov of Alta Dept Hwy, 58-60; instr civil eng, Univ Alta, 61-62; asst prof, NS Tech Col, 62-64; res asst, Lehigh Univ, 64-67; assoc prof, NS Tech Col, 67-70; PROF CIVIL ENG, UNIV ALTA, 70- *Concurrent Pos:* Mem, Res Coun Struct Conn, 67- *Mem:* Am Soc Civil Engrs; Can Standards Asn. *Res:* Strength and behavior of steel structures; strength of high-strength bolts and welds; behavior of welded and bolted connections; fatigue strength of steel structures. *Mailing Add:* Dept of Civil Eng Univ of Alta Edmonton AB T6G 2G7 Can

KULCINSKI, GERALD LA VERN, b LaCrosse, Wis, Oct 27, 39; m 61; c 3. NUCLEAR ENGINEERING. *Educ:* Univ Wis, BS, 61, MS, 62, PhD(nuclear eng), 65. *Prof Exp:* Asst scientist nuclear rockets, Los Alamos Sci Lab, 63; sr res scientist & group leader radiation damage reactor mats, Battelle Northwest Lab, 65-72; adj prof nuclear eng, Ctr Grad Study, Richland, 68-71; PROF NUCLEAR ENG, UNIV WIS, 72- *Concurrent Pos:* Consult var industs, 73-; mem adv comt, Elec Power Res Inst, 75-77 & Dept Chem Eng, Princeton Univ, 76-; mem fusion assessment resource comt, Nat Acad Sci, 76-77. *Honors & Awards:* Curtis McGraw Res Award, Am Soc Eng Educ, 78. *Mem:* Am Soc Testing & Mat; fel Am Nuclear Soc; Am Phys Soc. *Res:* Fission reactors; fusion reactor design; materials; radiation damage; environmental effects; nuclear power. *Mailing Add:* 6013 Greentree Rd Madison WI 53711

KULCZYCKI, LUCAS LUKE, b Jurjampol, Poland, Aug 19, 11; US citizen; m; c 2. PEDIATRICS. *Educ:* Univ Lwow, BSc, 34, DVM, 36; Univ Edinburgh, MB BCh, 44, MD, 46; Univ London, dipl pub health, 48; Royal Col Physicians & Surgeons Can, cert pediat, 58. *Prof Exp:* Resident physician med & surg, Raigmore Hosp, Dept Health, Scotland, 46-47; asst physician, London Exec Coun, Eng, 47-50; med dir pub health, Local Health Unit, Dept Health, Winnipeg, Can, 51-53; residential training pediat, Children's Hosp Med Ctr, Boston, Mass, 53-55, asst physician, 55-62; DIR CYSTIC FIBROSIS CARE, TEACHING & RES CTR, CHILDREN'S HOSP DC, 62-; PROF PEDIAT, GEORGETOWN UNIV, 72- *Concurrent Pos:* Res fel, Children's Hosp Med Ctr, Boston, 55-61; instr, Harvard Med Sch, 56-62; clin dir, Wrentham State Sch, 57-58; consult pediatrician, Dept Health Maine & Maine Med Ctr, Portland, 58-68; clin assoc prof pediat, Georgetown Univ, 62-67, assoc prof, 67-72; consult pediatrician & co-worker, Children's Hosp, Boston, Mass, 62-68; guest worker, NIH, 62-68; consult pediatrician, Children's Convalescent Hosp, Washington, DC, 63-70. *Mem:* Fel Am Acad Pediat; fel Am Col Chest Physicians; AMA; fel NY Acad Sci; hon mem Polish Pediat Soc; fel Royal Soc Health. *Res:* Cystic fibrosis in caucasians and negroes; cyctic fibrosis, tuberculosis and allergy; upper respiratory tract in cystic fibrosis; hearing and cystic fibrosis; bronchoscopy and bronchial lavage in cystic fibrosis; impact of cystic fibrosis on the patient and his parents; patient home care. *Mailing Add:* Cystic Fibrosis Ctr Georgetown Univ Med Ctr Washington DC 20007

KULEVSKY, NORMAN, b New York, NY, July 28, 35; m 61; c 3. PHYSICAL CHEMISTRY. *Educ:* Brooklyn Col, BS, 56; Univ Mich, MS, 58, PhD, 63. *Prof Exp:* From asst prof to assoc prof, 62-74, PROF CHEM, UNIV NDAK, 74- *Mem:* Am Chem Soc. *Res:* Molecular and charge transfer complexes; hydrogen bonding studies. *Mailing Add:* Dept of Chem Univ of NDak Grand Forks ND 58201

KULFINSKI, FRANK BENJAMIN, b New Brunswick, NJ, May 30, 30; m 56; c 3. ECOLOGY, CELL BIOLOGY. *Educ:* Rutgers Univ, BS, 52; Univ Mass, MS, 54; Iowa State Col, PhD(ecol), 57. *Prof Exp:* Instr bot, Iowa State Col, 56-57; asst prof biol sci, Western Ill Univ, 57-60; assoc prof biol, Ill Wesleyan Univ, 60-69; assoc prof, 69-77, PROF BIOL SCI, SOUTHERN ILL UNIV, EDWARDSVILLE, 77- *Concurrent Pos:* Vis assoc prof zool, Southern Ill Univ, Carbondale, 68; instr, Civil Serv Comn Workshop Environ Impact Statements, 73-77; consult biol portions environ impact statements, eng firms, 71-81. *Res:* Cytology; phycology; pathology; ecology. *Mailing Add:* Dept of Biol Sci Southern Ill Univ Edwardsville IL 62025

KULGEIN, NORMAN GERALD, b Bridgeport, Conn, Mar 6, 34; m 60; c 2. ENGINEERING, APPLIED PHYSICS. *Educ:* Mass Inst Technol, BS, 55, MS, 56; Harvard Univ, PhD(eng, appl physics), 60. *Prof Exp:* Res scientist, Aerospace Sci Lab, 60-67, STAFF SCIENTIST & MGR AEROPHYS GROUP, LOCKHEED PALO ALTO RES LAB, 67- *Concurrent Pos:* Lectr, Univ Santa Clara, 63-; Stanford Univ, 69-70. *Mem:* Am Inst Aeronaut & Astronaut; Combustion Inst. *Res:* High temperature viscous flows; radiation gas dynamics; hydrodynamics; reentry vehicle hardening technology; infrared systems analysis. *Mailing Add:* 711 Gailen Ave Palo Alto CA 94303

KULHAWY, FRED HOWARD, b Topeka, Kans, Sept 8, 43; m 66. GEOTECHNICAL ENGINEERING. *Educ:* Newark Col Eng, BSCE, 64, MSCE, 66; Univ Calif, Berkeley, PhD(civil eng), 69. *Prof Exp:* Asst inst civil eng, Newark Col Eng, 64-66; soils engr, Storch Engrs, 66; res asst & jr res specialist, Univ Calif, Berkeley, 66-69; assoc, Raamot Assoc PC, 69-71; from asst prof to assoc prof, Syracuse Univ, 69-76; assoc prof, 76-81, PROF CIVIL ENG, CORNELL UNIV, 81- *Concurrent Pos:* Numerous consults to govt agencies, indust firms, eng & archit consults & attys, 69- *Honors & Awards:* Edmund Friedman Young Eng Award, Am Soc Civil Eng, 74. *Mem:* Am Soc Civil Eng; fel Geol Soc Am; Int Soc Rock Mech; Int Soc Soil Mech & Found Eng; Int Asn Eng Geol. *Res:* Numerical methods applications in geotechnical engineering; soil and rock stress-strain-strength behavior; model and full-scale behavior of geotechnical structures. *Mailing Add:* Sch Civil & Environ Eng Cornell Univ Ithaca NY 14853

KULIER, CHARLES PETER, b Chicago, Ill, Aug 11, 35; m 59; c 2. SYNTHETIC ORGANIC CHEMISTRY, STRUCTURAL CHEMISTRY. *Educ:* Ill Wesleyan Univ, BS, 57; Univ Kans, PhD(org chem), 62. *Prof Exp:* Asst chem, Ill Wesleyan Univ, 56-57 & Univ Kans, 57-61; res assoc & fel org chem, Johns Hopkins Univ, 62-63; from assoc res chemist to res chemist, 63-70, sr res chemist, 70-72, sr scientist, 72-75, RES ASSOC, PARKE, DAVIS & CO, 76- *Mem:* Am Chem Soc. *Res:* Organic synthesis in the area of steroids, terpenes and heterocyclic compounds; use of newer reaction methods for preparation of organic compounds of potential medicinal use; process research. *Mailing Add:* 1181 Oak Hampton Rd Holland MI 49423

KULIK, MARTIN MICHAEL, b Brooklyn, NY, Apr 20, 32; m 62; c 3. PLANT PATHOLOGY. *Educ:* Cornell Univ, BS, 54; La State Univ, MS, 56, PhD(plant path), 59. *Prof Exp:* Plant pathologist, Seed Br, 61-63, res plant pathologist, Field Crops & Animal Prod Res Br, 63-72, Seed Res Lab, Agr Mkt Res Inst, 72-79, RES PLANT PATHOLOGIST, PLANT GENETICS & GERMPLASM INST, USDA, 79- *Mem:* AAAS; Am Soc Agron; Am Phytopath Soc; Mycol Soc Am; Can Phytopath Soc. *Res:* Seedborne fungi and diseases of seeds. *Mailing Add:* 5100 Moorland Lane Bethesda MD 20814

KULIN, GERSHON, b Webster, Mass, Aug 21, 26; m 56. FLUID MECHANICS, HYDRAULICS. *Educ:* Worcester Polytech Inst, BS, 48; Carnegie Inst Technol, MS, 50; Mass Inst Technol, ScD, 55. *Prof Exp:* Res hydraul engr fluid mech, Nat Bur Standards, 55-60; res scientist, Hydronautics Inc, 60-62; res hydraul engr, 62-65, chief hydraul sect, 65-75, RES HYDRAUL ENGR, NAT BUR STANDARDS, 75- *Concurrent Pos:* Assoc prof, lectr, George Washington Univ, 62-64. *Mem:* Am Soc Civil Eng; Am Geophys Union; Water Pollution Control Fedn. *Res:* Water waves; viscous flow problems. *Mailing Add:* 8484 16th Silver Spring MD 20910

KULINSKI, EDMUND S(YLVESTER), mechanical engineering, applied mechanics, see previous edition

KULJIAN, ERNEST SAM, b Fresno, Calif, Feb 13, 21; m 44; c 3. ANALYTICAL CHEMISTRY. *Educ:* Univ Southern Calif, AB, 43, MS, 48; Univ of the Pac, PhD(chem), 64. *Prof Exp:* Asst chem, Univ Southern Calif, 43-44; anal chemist, Am Cyanamid Co, 44-45; instr chem, Univ Dayton, 47; res & develop chemist, Cutter Labs, 47; instr chem, George Pepperdine Col, 49-51; MEM STAFF DEPT CHEM, LOS ANGELES PIERCE COL, 51- *Concurrent Pos:* Fulbright exchange teacher, Suderland Tech Col, Eng, 59-60; NSF fel, 62-63; expert in chem, higher col teacher training, UNESCO, Libya, 66-68. *Honors & Awards:* Mfg Chemists Asn Award, 76. *Mem:* Am Chem Soc. *Res:* Pi olefin complexes of platinum and palladium; water chemistry. *Mailing Add:* 8020 Whiteoak Ave Northridge CA 91325

KULKA, JOHANNES PETER, b Vienna, Austria, Feb 7, 21; nat US. PATHOLOGY, PSYCHIATRY. *Educ:* Cornell Univ, AB, 41; Johns Hopkins Univ, MD, 44; Am Bd Path, dipl. *Prof Exp:* Intern path, Strong Mem Hosp, NY, 44-45; asst res, Mass Gen Hosp, Boston, 45-47; instr anat, Harvard Med Sch, 47-49, instr path, 49-52, assoc, 52-58, clin assoc, 58-61, from asst clin prof to assoc clin prof, 61-70; resident psychiat, McLean Hosp, 70-73; child psychiat trainee, South Shore Ment Health Ctr, Quincy, Mass, 73-74; GEN PHYSICIAN HEALTH SERV & CLIN INSTR MED, TUFTS UNIV, 75- *Concurrent Pos:* Pathologist, Lovett Mem, 47-52; assoc path, Peter Bent Brigham Hosp, 55-58, asst med, 58-61, assoc staff, 61-70; pathologist, Robert B Brigham Hosp, Boston, 55-58, clin & res assoc, 58-61, pathologist, 61-70; clin fel psychiat, Harvard Med Sch, 70-73 & McLean Hosp, 73-74; mem courtesy staff, Lawrence Mem Hosp, Medford, Mass, 75- *Mem:* Am Asn Path & Bact; Am Soc Exp Path; Soc Exp Biol & Med. *Res:* Pathology of rheumatic diseases, cold injury and microcirculatory disorder; psychosomatic disorders. *Mailing Add:* 33 Farrar Rd Lincoln MA 01773

KULKARNI, ANANT SADASHIV, b Kolhapur, India, July 31, 34; m 60; c 2. CLINICAL PHARMACOLOGY, IMMUNOLOGY. *Educ:* Podar Med Col, GFAM (MD), 58; Univ Minn, PhD(pharmacol), 66. *Prof Exp:* Intern med, Sisters Hosp, Buffalo, NY, 59-60; surg resident, St Anthony's Hosp St Louis, 60-61; res asst pharmacol, Univ Wis, 61-62; res asst pharmacol, Univ Minn, 62-65; sr scientist, Mead Johnson Res Ctr, 65-67; res pharmacologist, Dow Human Health Res Lab, 67-71, clin monitor, Med Dept, Dow Chem Co, 71-73; sect head neuropsychiat & assoc dir clin res, Abbott Lab, 73-75; assoc dir, 75-77, DIR CLIN RES, GEN MED & NEUROPSYCHIAT, G D SEARLE & CO, 78- *Concurrent Pos:* Vis lectr, Med Ctr, Ind Univ, Indianapolis, 68-71, clin asst prof, 71-73. *Mem:* Acad Psychosom Med; Am Soc Pharmacol & Exp Therapeut; Soc Neurosci; Am Psychol Asn; Am Pharmaceut Asn. *Res:* CNS pharmacology; clinical psychopharmacology; animal behavior; rheumatology; drug behavior interactions. *Mailing Add:* G D Searle & Co Med Res Box 5110 Chicago IL 60680

KULKARNI, ASHOK VASANT, b Karwar, India, May 20, 47; m 74. COMPUTER SCIENCES, PATTERN RECOGNITION. *Educ:* Indian Inst Technol, BTech, 68; Univ Calif, Berkeley, MS, 69; Univ Md, PhD(comput sci), 76. *Prof Exp:* Syst analyst comput sci, Control Data Corp, 69-72; ASST ENG MGR PATTERN RECOGNITION, COULTER BIOMED RES CORP, COULTER ELECTRON INC, 75- *Mem:* Sigma Xi; Inst Elec & Electronic Engrs. *Res:* Automated cytology; image processing; interactive graphics and computer systems software and hardware design. *Mailing Add:* 1068 Belmont St No 2 Watertown MA 02172

KULKARNI, BIDY, b Maharashtra, India, Apr 18, 30; m 57; c 2. REPRODUCTIVE ENDOCRINOLOGY, MATERNAL & CHILD HEALTH. *Prof Exp:* Jr sci asst biochem & steroid chem, Nat Chem Lab, Poona, India, 52-56, sr sci asst steroid chem, 56-61; fel steroid biochem, Clark Univ, 61-64; fel org chem, Nat Res Coun Can, 64-66; sr sci officer biochem, Nat Chem Lab, Poona, 66-67; staff scientist, Dept Endocrinol, Div Clin Sci, Southwest Found Res & Educ, 67-70; asst prof obstet & gynec, Pritzker Sch Med, Univ Chicago, 70-73; assoc prof obstet & gynec & dir reproductive endocrinol, Stritch Sch Med, Loyola Univ Chicago, 73-79; DIR, REPRODUCTIVE ENDOCRINOL LABS, DEPT OBSTET & GYNEC, COOK COUNTY HOSP, CHICAGO, 79-, SR SCI OFFICER, 80- *Concurrent Pos:* Dir labs, Sect Gynecic Endocrinol, Michael Reese Hosp & Med Ctr, 70-73; dir perinatal ctr labs, Forster G McGaw Hosp, Maywood, 73-77; consult, Gottlieb Mem Hosp, 79-; assoc prof, Chicago Med Sch, 80- *Mem:* AAAS; Endocrine Soc; Soc Study Reproduction; Am Chem Soc; NY Acad Sci. *Res:* Natural and contraceptive steroid metabolism in the man and nonhuman primates; methods in hormone assay involving competitive protein binding and radioimmunoassays; clinical endocrinology and population control research; steroid biochemistry. *Mailing Add:* Cook County Hosp 1825 W Harrison Chicago IL 60612

KULKARNI, PADMAKAR VENKATRAO, b Inamhongal, India, Nov 1, 42; m 68; c 2. NUCLEAR CHEMISTRY, RADIOPHARMACEUTICALS. *Educ:* Janata Col, BS, 63; Rensselaer Polytech Inst, MS, 72, PhD(chem), 73. *Prof Exp:* Sci officer trainee radiochem, Bhabha Atomic Res Ctr, Bombay, 63-64, sci officer, 64-68; radiopharmaceut specialist, Cambridge Nuclear Radiopharm Corp, Mass, 72-73; isotope chemist, Abbott Diag Div, Abbot, Ill, 73-76; ASST PROF, UNIV TEX SOUTHWESTERN MED SCH, 76- *Concurrent Pos:* Radiopharmaceut scientist, Parkland Mem Hosp, Dallas, Tex, 76- *Mem:* Am Chem Soc; Soc Nuclear Med; AAAS. *Res:* Development of radioisotope labeled compounds as radiopharmaceuticals for diagnostic purposes; development of radioimmunoassay systesm; diagnostic nuclear cardiology; radioisotope tracer techniques in health sciences. *Mailing Add:* Dept of Radiol 5323 Harry Hines Blvd Dallas TX 75235

KULKARNY, VIJAY ANAND, b Karwar, India, May 3, 47. FLUID DYNAMICS, APPLIED PHYSICS. *Educ:* Indian Inst Technol, Bombay, BTech, 69; Calif Inst Technol, MS, 70, PhD(aeronaut), 75. *Prof Exp:* From res fel to sr res fel aeronaut, Calif Inst Technol, 75-78; MEM TECH STAFF, ENG SCI LAB, TRW DEFENSE & SPACE SYSTS GROUP, 78- *Concurrent Pos:* Instr aeronaut, Calif Inst Technol, 76-77; consult, TRW Defense & Space Systs Group, 78. *Mem:* Am Phys Soc; Sigma Xi. *Res:* Gas dynamics; acoustics; shock waves and associated linear and nonlinear wave phenomena in multidimensions and inhomogeneous media; dynamics of vortex interactions and vorticity dominated flows; flow and acoustics of high energy pulsed gas lasers. *Mailing Add:* TRW Defense & Space Systs Group One Space Park Redondo Beach CA 90278

KULKE, BERNHARD, b Freiburg, Ger, Nov 29, 32; US citizen; m 62; c 2. ELECTRON BEAMS, PULSED POWER. *Educ:* Univ Colo, BS, 55; Stanford Univ, MS, 60, PhD(microwave electronics), 65. *Prof Exp:* Mem tech staff, Bell Tel Labs Inc, 55-58; asst prof elec eng, Syracuse Univ, 65-67; physicist, Electronics Res Ctr, NASA, 67-70; chief radar beacon sect, Dept Transp, Cambridge Univ, 70-74; GROUP LEADER ACCELERATOR TECHNOL, LAWRENCE LIVERMORE LAB, 74- *Mem:* Inst Elec & Electronics Engrs; Am Phys Soc. *Res:* Design and construction of state-of-the-art, high current, induction linear accelerator of an X-band, cyclotron resonance oscillator; experimental, 100 kilowatt, traveling wave klystron; electron beam diagnostics, antenna design, radar systems analysis and solid state device characterization. *Mailing Add:* Lawrence Livermore Lab Code 153 PO Box 808 Livermore CA 94550

KULKOSKY, PAUL JOSEPH, b Newark, NJ, Mar 3, 49; m 78. PHYSIOLOGICAL PSYCHOLOGY. *Educ:* Columbia Col, BA, 71, MA, 72; Univ Wash, PhD(psychol), 75. *Prof Exp:* Staff fel, Nat Inst Alcohol Abuse & Alcoholism, 76-80; instr, Cornell Univ Med Col, 80-82; ASST PROF PSYCHOL, UNIV SOUTHERN COLO, 82- *Concurrent Pos:* Affiliate prof psychol, Am Univ, 77-80. *Mem:* Psychonomic Soc; AAAS. *Res:* Regulatory behaviors in mammals, including the learned and physiological controls of ingestive behaviors. *Mailing Add:* Dept Psychol Univ Southern Colo Pueblo CO 81001

KULL, FREDERICK CHARLES, SR, b Newark, NJ, Apr 10, 19; m 43; c 5. BACTERIOLOGY. *Educ:* Villanova Univ, BS, 41; Ind Univ, MA, 49; Univ Mich, PhD(bact), 52; Am Bd Med Microbiol, dipl. *Prof Exp:* Chemist, Sherwin-Williams Co, NJ, 41-43; asst bact, Ind Univ, 47-49; from asst to instr, Univ Mich, 49-51; sr bacteriologist, Ciba-Geigy Pharmaceut Co, 52-58; dir virol, 58-59, dir bact, 59-61, dir sci info ctr, 61-68; adminr, 68-77, DIR ADMIN, RES, DEVELOP & MED, BURROUGHS WELLCOME CO, 77- *Concurrent Pos:* Instr, Rutgers Univ, 55-58; adj prof, Sch Pharm, Univ NC, 72- *Mem:* Am Acad Microbiol; Am Soc Microbiol. *Res:* Medical information; documentation; biological sciences; virology; enzymology. *Mailing Add:* Wellcome Res Labs Burroughs Wellcome Co Research Triangle Park NC 27709

KULL, FREDRICK J, b Marion, Ohio, Mar 9, 35; m 66; c 2. BIOCHEMISTRY. *Educ:* Kent State Univ, BS, 60; Ohio State Univ, MSc, 62; Brandeis Univ, PhD(biochem), 67. *Prof Exp:* Assoc biochemist, Biol Div, Oak Ridge Nat Lab, 62-63; investr, 67-69; asst prof, 69-75, ASSOC PROF BIOL, STATE UNIV NY BINGHAMTON, 75- *Mem:* AAAS; Am Chem Soc; Sigma Xi; NY Acad Sci; Am Soc Biol Chemists. *Res:* Mechanism of yeast phosphoglucose isomerase; effects of hydrocortisone on enzyme induction and RNA synthesis; heterologous aminoacylation between Neurospora crassa and Escherichia coli; mammalian peptidyl-digonucleotidyl complexes; mammalian aminoacylation reactions; mammalian alkaline ribonuclease and ribonuclease inhibitor. *Mailing Add:* Dept of Biol Sci State Univ of NY Binghamton NY 13901

KULL, LORENZ ANTHONY, b Chicago, Ill, Dec 25, 37; div; c 2. NUCLEAR PHYSICS. *Educ:* Ill Inst Technol, BSc, 63; Mich State Univ, PhD(physics), 67. *Prof Exp:* Physicist, Gulf Gen Atomic, Inc, 67-69; physicist, 69-75, vpres & mgr appl sci & technol group, 75-79, EXEC VPRES, SCI APPLICATIONS, INC, 79- *Mem:* Am Phys Soc; Am Nuclear Soc; Inst Nuclear Mat Mgt. *Res:* Development of nuclear materials assay instrumentation; experimental studies of direct particle transfer reactions with light nuclei; experimental studies of photoneutron cross-sections, threshold photoneutrons and photo fission; modeling and analysis of nuclear fuel cycle systems. *Mailing Add:* Sci Applns Inc PO Box 2351 La Jolla CA 92037

KULLA, JEAN B, b Washington, DC, Sept 9, 49. PETROPHYSICS, ORGANIC GEOCHEMISTRY. *Educ:* Univ Md, BS, 72; Univ Champaign, Ill, MS, 75, PhD(geol), 79. *Prof Exp:* Res geologist, 78-79, sr res geologist, 80-81, RES SPECIALIST, EXXON PROD RES CO, 82- *Mem:* Am Asn Petrol Geologists; Sigma Xi; Grad Women Sci; Geochem Soc. *Res:* Physics and chemistry of shales and how these properties change with increases in temperature and pressure as the shale undergoes burial. *Mailing Add:* Box 2189 Houston TX 77001

KULLBACK, JOSEPH HENRY, b Washington, DC, July 16, 33; m 60; c 3. MATHEMATICAL STATISTICS. *Educ:* George Washington Univ, BA, 55; Stanford Univ, MS, 57, PhD(math statist), 60. *Prof Exp:* Mathematician, Stanford Res Inst, 60-67; math statistician, US Naval Res Lab, 67-81; TECH DIR, CTEC INC, 81- *Concurrent Pos:* Prof lectr, George Washington Univ, 77- *Mem:* Inst Math Statist; Am Statist Asn; Opers Res Soc Am; Soc Indust & Appl Math. *Res:* Operation research; simulation techniques. *Mailing Add:* CTEC Inc 6862 Elm St McLean VA 22101

KULLBACK, SOLOMON, b Brooklyn, NY, Apr 3, 07; m 30; c 2. MATHEMATICAL STATISTICS, APPLIED STATISTICS. *Educ:* City Col New York, BS, 27; Columbia Univ, MA, 29; George Washington Univ, PhD(math), 34. *Prof Exp:* Prof, 38-75, EMER PROF STATIST, GEORGE WASHINGTON UNIV, 75- *Mem:* Inst Math Statist; Am Statist Asn; Royal Statist Soc. *Res:* Information theory; analysis of count or categorical data. *Mailing Add:* Dept of Statist George Washington Univ Washington DC 20052

KULLBERG, RUSSELL GORDON, b Flint, Mich, Aug 4, 22; m 45; c 2. BOTANY. *Educ:* Univ Mich, BS, 49, MS, 50; Mich State Univ, PhD(bot), 66. *Prof Exp:* Assoc prof, 65-77, PROF BIOL, SOUTHEAST MO STATE UNIV, 77- *Mem:* AAAS; Phycol Soc Am; Ecol Soc Am; Am Soc Limnol & Oceanog; Am Micros Soc. *Res:* Phycology; ecology of hot spring algae. *Mailing Add:* Dept of Biol Southeast Mo State Univ Cape Girardeau MO 63701

KULLER, ROBERT G, b Baltimore, Md, Nov 29, 26; m 59; c 5. MATHEMATICS. *Educ:* Swarthmore Col, AB, 48; Univ Mich, MS, 49, PhD(math), 55. *Prof Exp:* Instr math, Dartmouth Col, 53-55; from instr to asst prof, Wayne State Univ, 55-59; asst prof, Dartmouth Col, 61-62 & Univ Colo, 62-65; assoc prof, Wayne State Univ, 65-68; ASSOC PROF MATH, NORTHERN ILL UNIV, 68- *Concurrent Pos:* Vis lectr, Nat Taiwan Univ, 60-61. *Mem:* Am Math Soc; Math Asn Am; Soc Indust & Appl Math. *Res:* Functional analysis; computers in undergraduate mathematics curriculum. *Mailing Add:* Dept of Math Northern Ill Univ De Kalb IL 60115

KULLERUD, GUNNAR, b Odda, Norway, Nov 12, 21; m 47; c 5. GEOCHEMISTRY. *Educ:* Tech Univ Norway, MSc, 46, PhD, 48; Univ Oslo, DSc, 54. *Prof Exp:* Instr, Univ Chicago, 48-49; res assoc, 49-52; res assoc, Univ Oslo, 52-54; sr staff mem, Geophys Lab, Carnegie Inst, 54-71; head dept, 70-76, PROF GEOSCI, PURDUE UNIV, WEST LAFAYETTE, 70- *Concurrent Pos:* Adj prof, Lehigh Univ, 62-71; vis prof, Univ Heidelberg, 64-70; hon collabr, Div Meteorites, Smithsonian Inst, 64-71; mem comt on chem of solar syst, Space Sci Bd, 64-72; consult prof, Tex Tech Univ, 68-71; co-ed Mineralium Deposita & Chem Geol. *Honors & Awards:* A H Dumont Award, Belg Geol Soc, 65. *Mem:* Geochem Soc; Soc Econ Geologists; fel Am Mineral Soc; fel Geol Soc Am; Norweg Acad Sci. *Res:* Sulfide phase equilibria; geochemistry of ore deposits, meteorites; mineralogy-geochemistry of coal. *Mailing Add:* Dept of Geosci Purdue Univ West Lafayette IN 47907

KULLMAN, DAVID ELMER, b Kenosha, Wis, May 27, 40; m 65; c 2. MATHEMATICS EDUCATION. *Educ:* Northwestern Univ, BA, 62; Cornell Univ, MA, 63; Univ Kans, PhD(math), 69. *Prof Exp:* High sch teacher, Ill, 63-65; from asst prof to assoc prof, 69-81, PROF MATH, MIAMI UNIV, 81- *Mem:* Nat Coun Teachers Math; Sch Sci & Math Asn; Math Asn Am. *Res:* Geometry point-set topology; history of mathematics; problem solving and applications in school mathematics. *Mailing Add:* Dept of Math & Statist Miami Univ Oxford OH 45056

KULLNIG, RUDOLPH K, b Kirchberg, Lower Austria, Oct 2, 18; US citizen; m 54. PHYSICAL ORGANIC CHEMISTRY. *Educ:* Univ Ottawa, Can, PhD(chem), 58. *Prof Exp:* Chemist, Bell-Craig Ltd, Ont, 52-55; asst res chemist, 58-64, res chemist & group leader, 64-68, SECT HEAD, STERLING WINTHROP RES INST, 68- *Mem:* Am Chem Soc. *Res:* Nuclear magnetic resonance spectroscopy; indoles and other heterocyclic compounds. *Mailing Add:* Sterling Winthrop Res Inst Rensselaer NY 12144

KULM, LAVERNE DUANE, b Mobridge, SDak, Feb 17, 36; m 62. GEOLOGICAL OCEANOGRAPHY. *Educ:* Monmouth Col, BA, 59; Ore State Univ, PhD(oceanog), 65. *Prof Exp:* From asst prof to assoc prof, 64-74, PROF OCEANOG, ORE STATE UNIV, 74- *Concurrent Pos:* Fel, Marathon Oil Co, 71. *Mem:* AAAS; Soc Econ Paleontologists & Mineralogists; fel Geol Soc Am; Am Geophys Union. *Res:* Continental margin structure, tectonics, sedimentation; deep-sea sedimentation. *Mailing Add:* Sch of Oceanog Ore State Univ Corvallis OR 97331

KULMAN, HERBERT MARVIN, b Sayre, Pa, June 12, 29; m 59; c 2. ENTOMOLOGY. *Educ:* Pa State Univ, BS, 52; Duke Univ, MF, 55; Univ Minn, PhD, 60. *Prof Exp:* Entomologist, Southeastern Forest Exp Sta, USDA, 56-57; asst prof entom, WVa Univ, 59-62; from asst to assoc prof forest entom, Va Polytech Inst, 62-69; assoc prof, 69-72, PROF ENTOM, FISHERIES & WILDLIFE, UNIV MINN, ST PAUL, 72- *Mem:* Entom Soc Am. *Res:* Forest entomology, especially biological control and damage evaluation. *Mailing Add:* Dept Entom Fisheries & Wildlife Univ of Minn St Paul MN 55108

KULP, BERNARD ANDREW, b Columbus, Ohio, Aug 3, 23; m 52; c 9. PHYSICS. *Educ:* Univ Minn, BEE, 46; Ohio State Univ, MS, 47, PhD(physics), 55. *Prof Exp:* Asst, Ohio State Univ, 46-47; res metallurgist, Carnegie-Ill Steel Corp, 47-48; res engr, Battelle Mem Inst, 48-55; physicist, Linde Co, 55-58; physicist, Aerospace Res Lab, Wright-Patterson AFB, 58-69; chief scientist, Air Force Armament Lab, Eglin AFB, 69-75; CHIEF SCIENTIST & DIR LABS, AIR FORCE SYSTS COMMAND, 75- *Mem:* Fel AAAS; Am Phys Soc; Am Defense Preparedness Asn. *Res:* Solid state physics; radiation damage; electrooptics; ordnance engineering. *Mailing Add:* Air Force Systs Command/DLZ Andrews AFB MD 20334

KULP, JOHN LAURENCE, b Trenton, NJ, Feb 11, 21; m 44; c 3. GEOCHEMISTRY. *Educ:* Wheaton Col, BS, 42; Ohio State Univ, MS, 43; Princeton Univ, MA, 44, PhD(chem), 45. *Hon Degrees:* Wooster Col, ScD, 69. *Prof Exp:* Chemist, Nat Aniline Div, Allied Chem & Dye Corp, NY, 42; phys chemist, Manhattan Proj, 44-45; Kemp fel, Columbia Univ, 45-46; univ fel, 46-47; from lectr to prof geochem, 47-65; adj prof, 65-68; pres, Teledyne Isotopes, 65-75; VPRES RES & DEVELOP, WEYERHAEUSER CO, 76- *Concurrent Pos:* Dir, Lamont Geochem Lab, 54-56; NSF fel, 58-59. *Honors & Awards:* Newcomb Cleveland Award, AAAS, 51. *Mem:* Am Chem Soc; fel Geol Soc Am; fel Geochem Soc; fel Mineral Soc; Am Phys Soc. *Res:* Plutonium hazard from nuclear weapons devices; carbon dioxide cycle in the air and ocean; clay mineral deposits in North America; origin of uranium deposits in the Colorado plateau; geologic mapping of the moon from its gamma ray spectra; detection of underground nuclear explosions. *Mailing Add:* Weyerhaeuser Technol Ctr Tacoma WA 98477

KULP, STUART S, b Pennsburg, Pa, July 19, 25; m 50; c 3. ORGANIC CHEMISTRY. *Educ:* Gettysburg Col, BA, 50; Lehigh Univ, MS, 53, PhD(chem), 57. *Prof Exp:* Instr gen & anal chem, Lehigh Univ, 55-57; PROF CHEM & HEAD DEPT, MORAVIAN COL, 57- *Mem:* Am Chem Soc; Sigma Xi; Am Inst Chemists. *Res:* Synthesis and study of tautomerism of 2-cyanocycloalkanones, especially five and six numbered rings. *Mailing Add:* 328 Hillcrest Ave Bethlehem PA 18017

KULSRUD, HELENE E, b New York, NY, July 6, 33; m 55; c 3. APPLIED MATHEMATICS, SYSTEM ANALYSIS. *Educ:* Smith Col, BA, 53; Univ Chicago, MS, 55. *Prof Exp:* Programmer, Int Bus Mach Inc, NY, 54-55; res asst astron, Princeton Univ, 56; head programmer, Educ Testing Serv, 56-57; mem tech staff, RCA Labs, RCA Corp, 57-66; res assoc, Yale Univ, 66-67; sr staff mem, Aeronaut Res Assocs Princeton, Inc, 67-68; RES STAFF MEM, INST DEFENSE ANAL, 68- *Mem:* Asn Comput Mach. *Res:* Design of computer languages, particularly debugging languages and tools. *Mailing Add:* 201 Wendover Dr Princeton NJ 08540

KULSRUD, RUSSELL MARION, b Lindsborg, Kans, Apr 10, 28; m 55; c 3. PLASMA PHYSICS. *Educ:* Univ Md, BA, 49; Univ Chicago, MS, 52, PhD(physics), 54. *Prof Exp:* Mem staff physics, Proj Matterhorn, Princeton Univ, 54-59, sr res assoc, 59-64, head theoret sect, Plasma Physics Lab, 64-66; prof appl sci & astron, Yale Univ, 66-67; PROF LECTR ASTROPHYS SCI, PRINCETON UNIV, 67- *Concurrent Pos:* Consult, Oak Ridge Nat Lab, 55, RCA Corp, 60 & Gen Atomic Div, Gen Dynamics Corp, 60. *Mem:* Fel Am Phys Soc; Int Astron Union; Am Astron Soc. *Res:* Plasma physics with application to controlled fusion reactor research; astrophysics. *Mailing Add:* Plasma Physics Lab Princeton Univ Princeton NJ 08541

KULWICH, ROMAN, b New York, NY, Oct 18, 25; m 48; c 3. BIOCHEMISTRY. *Educ:* Univ Fla, BS, 49, PhD(animal nutrit), 51. *Prof Exp:* Animal nutritionist & animal husbandman, Animal Husb Res Div, Agr Res Serv, USDA, 51-57, biochemist & supvry chemist, Mkt Qual Res Div, Agr Mkt Serv, Plant Indust Sta, Beltsville, 57-62; grants assoc, Div Res Grants, NIH, 62-63; scientist adminr, Nat Inst Child Health & Human Develop, 63-64, endocrinol prog dir extramural prog, Nat Inst Arthritis & Metab Diseases, 64-69; health scientist adminr, Nat Ctr Health Serv Res & Develop, 69-71; asst for rev & eval, 71-73, asst dir extramural progs, Nat Inst Allergy & Infectious Dis, 73-78; CONSULT, 78- *Mem:* AAAS; Am Inst Nutrit. *Res:* Nutritional and biochemical research on trace mineral and sulfur metabolism in laboratory and farm animals involving the use of radioactive tracers; body composition research involving 4-pi low level gamma ray measurements; biomedical science administration. *Mailing Add:* Rte 1 Box 3286 Belleview FL 32620

KULWICKI, BERNARD MICHAEL, b Detroit, Mich, July 3, 35. CHEMICAL ENGINEERING, MATERIALS SCIENCE. *Educ:* Univ Detroit, BChE, 58; Univ Mich, MSE, 60, PhD(chem eng), 63. *Prof Exp:* Res fel, Inst Solid State Physics, Czech Acad Sci, 63-64; proj engr semiconductor mat res, 64-69, sect leader, 69-70, br mgr active mat develop, Mat & Elec Prod Group, Mat & Controls Div, 71-79, SR MEM TECH STAFF, ADVAN DEVELOP, TEX INSTRUMENTS INC, 80- . *Mem:* AAAS; Am Ceramic Soc; Electrochem Soc; Am Chem Soc. *Res:* Phase equilibria; thermodynamic and electrical properties of semiconducting materials; ferroelectric materials; thermistors; ceramic varistors. *Mailing Add:* Tex Instruments Inc 34 Forest St M/S 10-13 Attleboro MA 02703

KUMAGAI, LINDY FUMIO, b Rock Springs, Wyo, Aug 5, 27; m 52; c 3. MEDICINE. *Educ:* Univ Utah, BA, 49, MS, 50, MD, 54. *Prof Exp:* Asst anat, Sch Med, Univ Utah, 49-54; med intern, Mass Mem Hosp, 54-55; USPHS res fel, Thorndyke Mem Lab, Boston City Hosp, Harvard Med Sch, 55-57; asst resident med, Univ Hosp, Utah, 57-58, from instr to assoc prof, Col Med, 58-69, asst dean, 68-69; assoc prof, 69-71, PROF INTERNAL MED, SCH MED, UNIV CALIF, DAVIS, 71-, HEAD ENDOCRINE SECT, 69- *Concurrent Pos:* Clin investr, Vet Admin Hosp, Salt Lake City, Utah, 58-61; chief radioisotope serv, 61-69; assoc ed, Endocrinology, 73-77; mem, Endocrine Study Sect, Dept Health & Human Sci, NIH, 80-; mem, Calif Bd Med Quality Assurance, 80- *Mem:* Endocrine Soc. *Res:* Metabolism of adrenocortical and thyroidal hormones. *Mailing Add:* Dept of Internal Med Univ of Calif Sch of Med Davis CA 95616

KUMAI, MOTOI, b Nagano, Japan, Mar 22, 20; m 48; c 2. CLOUD PHYSICS, ELECTRON MICROSCOPY. *Educ:* Sci Univ Tokyo, BS, 41; Hokkaido Univ, PhD(physics), 57. *Prof Exp:* Res assoc physics, Hokkaido Univ, 42-55, lectr, 55-58; res assoc cloud physics, Univ Chicago, 58-61; RES PHYSICIST ATMOSPHERIC SCI, US ARMY COLD REGIONS RES & ENG LAB, 61- *Mem:* Am Meteorol Soc; Int Glaciol Soc; Sigma Xi; Phys Soc Japan; Meteorol Soc Japan. *Res:* Physics of atmosphere, research on snow crystal nuclei, and ice fog nuclei; electron diffraction of ice and aerosols and attenuation of infrared radiation; scanning electron microscopy. *Mailing Add:* US Army Cold Regions Res & Eng Lab 72 Lyme Rd Hanover NH 03755

KUMAMOTO, JUNJI, b Sacramento, Calif, May 9, 24; m 50; c 4. PHYSICAL ORGANIC CHEMISTRY. *Educ:* Univ Calif, Los Angeles, BS, 50; Univ Chicago, PhD(phys org chem), 53. *Prof Exp:* NSF grant, Harvard Univ, 53-55; chemist, Shell Develop Co, 55-60 & res lab, IBM Corp, 60-66; LECTR & CHEMIST, UNIV CALIF, RIVERSIDE, 66- *Mem:* Am Chem Soc; NY Acad Sci. *Res:* Reaction mechanisms of phosphate ester hydrolysis; free radical-metal ion reactions; relationship between structure and spectra. *Mailing Add:* Dept of Plant Sci Univ of Calif Riverside CA 92502

KUMAR, AJIT, b Binar, India, Mar 2, 40; m 71; c 1. CELL BIOLOGY, MOLECULAR GENETICS. *Educ:* Binar Univ, India, BSc, 58, MSc, 60; Univ Chicago, PhD(biol), 68. *Prof Exp:* Fel biochem, Albert Einstein Col Med, 68-71; res assoc, Harvard Med Sch, 71-75, asst prof microbiol & molecular genetics, 77; tutor biochem & molecular biol, Harvard Univ, 77-79; ASSOC PROF BIOCHEM, SCH MED, GEORGE WASHINGTON UNIV, 79- *Concurrent Pos:* Vis fel microbiol, Uppsala Univ, Sweden, 71; vis scientist biochem, Cambridge Univ, 77; assoc prof genetics, George Washington Univ, 80-; guest res scientist, Lab Biochem, Nat Cancer Inst, NIH, 80- *Mem:* Am Soc Cell Biol; Am Soc Biol Chemists. *Res:* RNA protein complexes and their role in eukaryotic gene expression. *Mailing Add:* Dept Biochem Sch Med & Health Sci George Washington Univ 2300 Eye St NW Washington DC 20037

KUMAR, ALOK, b Meerut, India, Sept 22, 51; m 80. COMPUTER AIDED DESIGN. *Educ:* Indian Inst Technol, Kanpur, India, BTech, 72, MTech, 76; Univ Houston, PhD(mech eng), 80. *Prof Exp:* Asst prof mech eng, Univ Wis-Platteville, 79-81; ASST PROF MECH ENG, UNIV DEL, NEWARK, 81- *Concurrent Pos:* Res & teaching asst, Indian Inst Technol, Kanpur, India, 73-76; res & teaching fel, Univ Houston, 76-79. *Mem:* Am Soc Mech Engrs; Soc Mfg Engrs; Am Soc Eng Educ. *Res:* Computer-aided design; kinematics; robotics and mechanical manipulator characterization; design and control; mathematical modeling of manufacturing processes; biomechanics. *Mailing Add:* 26-12 Winterhaven Dr Newark DE 19702

KUMAR, CIDAMBI KRISHNA, b Madras, India, Sept 24, 37; m 68; c 2. ASTROPHYSICS, ATOMIC PHYSICS. *Educ:* Andhra Univ, India, BSc, 57; Univ Wis, MS, 65; Univ Mich, PhD(astron), 69. *Prof Exp:* Jr sci officer nuclear physics, AEC, India, 58-63; Carnegie fel atomic physics & astrophys, Carnegie Inst Washington Dept Terrestrial Magnetism, 70-72; asst prof, 72-77, ASSOC PROF PHYSICS & ASTRON, HOWARD UNIV, 77- *Concurrent Pos:* Res assoc, Carnegie Inst Washington Dept Terrestrial Magnetism, 73- *Mem:* Am Astron Soc. *Res:* Spectrophotometry of galaxies and comets; beam-foil spectroscopy; radio astronomy. *Mailing Add:* Dept of Physics & Astron Howard Univ Washington DC 20059

KUMAR, GANESH N, b Madras, India, Oct 4, 48; m 75. POLYMER SCIENCE, CHEMICAL ENGINEERING. *Educ:* Univ Madras, BTech, 70; Clarkson Col Technol, MS, 72; Case Western Reserve Univ, PhD(polymer sci), 75. *Prof Exp:* Assoc scientist, Xerox Corp, 74-78; sr res scientist, 78-80, mgr polymer res, 80-81, DIR POLYMER SCI, JOHNSON & JOHNSON DENT PROD CO, 81- *Mem:* Am Chem Soc; Am Phys Soc; Int Asn Dent Res; NAm Thermal Analysis Soc. *Res:* Polymer structure property relationships; polymer mechanical and rheological properties; polymer blends and composites. *Mailing Add:* Johnson & Johnson Dent Prods Co 20 Lake Dr CN 7060 East Windsor NJ 08520

KUMAR, KAPLESH, b Lucknow, India, Nov 9, 47; m 74; c 2. MATERIALS SCIENCE. *Educ:* Indian Inst Technol, Kanput, BTech, 69, Stevens Inst Technol, MS, 71; Mass Inst Technol, ScD, 75. *Prof Exp:* Staff scientist, 75-80, CHIEF, MAT DEVELOP SECT, CHARLES STARK DRAPER LAB, INC, 80- *Res:* Samarium-cobalt permanent magnets; metal matrix composites; ion implantation; chemical vapor deposition; dimensional stability; flex lead corrosion; printed circuit board adhesion degradation. *Mailing Add:* 25 Redwing Rd Wellesley MA 02181

KUMAR, LALIT, b Lahore, India, Feb 16, 39; m 64; c 3. ALTERNATE ENERGY. *Educ:* Indian Inst Technol, BTech, 61; Univ Hawaii, MS, 69; Univ Ill, PhD(agr eng), 72. *Prof Exp:* Planning engr, Hindustan Tractors Ltd, 62-66; lectr, Univ Dares Salaam, Tanzania, 73-75; head, Agr Eng Dept, Univ Zambia, 75-78; DIR ENG, NAT STOVE WORKS INC, 79- *Mem:* Am Soc Mech Engrs; Am Soc Agr Engrs. *Res:* Behavior of soil and fruits under static and dynamic loading; energy absorption by the fruit; mathematical modelling. *Mailing Add:* 54 W Main St Cobleskill NY 12043

KUMAR, MAHESH C, b Montgomery, WPakistan, Sept 21, 35; wid; c 2. VETERINARY MICROBIOLOGY, PUBLIC HEALTH. *Educ:* Univ Bihar, BVSc & AH, 58; Univ Minn, Minneapolis, MS, 64, PhD(vet microbiol), 67. *Prof Exp:* Vet asst surg, Animal Husb Dept, Univ Bihar, 58-61; res fel, 67, res assoc vet microbiol, Univ Minn, St Paul, 67-76; DIR VET SERVS, MILE HIGH TURKEY HATCHERY, LONGMONT, COLO, 76- *Mem:* Am Vet Med Asn; Am Asn Avian Path; Poultry Sci Asn; Am Soc Microbiol; Conf Res Workers Animal Diseases. *Res:* Poultry diseases; mycoplasma and salmonella infections in turkeys; elimination of salmonella from turkeys and their environment; prevention and treatment of diseases in turkeys. *Mailing Add:* Mile High Turkey Hatchery 711 S Bowen St Longmont CO 80501

KUMAR, PRADEEP, b Allahabad, India, Jan 1, 49; m 74. NONLINEAR PHENOMENA. *Educ:* Univ Lucknow, India, BSc, 66; Indian Inst Technol, Kanpur, MSc, 68; Univ Calif, San Diego, PhD(physics), 73. *Prof Exp:* Res assoc physics, Univ Wis-Milwaukee, 73-75; res assoc, Univ Southern Calif, 75-77, asst prof, 77-78; ASST PROF PHYSICS, UNIV FLA, 79- *Concurrent Pos:* Nordita prof, Helsinki Univ Technol, Finland, 78-79. *Mem:* Am Phys Soc; NY Acad Sci; AAAS. *Res:* Theoretical ultra low temperature physics; nonlinear phenomena; solitons; magnetism. *Mailing Add:* Phys Dept Univ Fla Gainesville FL 32601

KUMAR, ROMESH, b Rajpura, India, Oct 18, 44; m 76; c 2. CHEMICAL ENGINEERING. *Educ:* Panjab Univ, BSc, 65; Univ Calif, Berkeley, MS, 68, PhD(chem eng), 72. *Prof Exp:* Appointee, 72-74, asst chem engr, 74-76, CHEM ENGR & GROUP LEADER ENVIRON CHEM, ARGONNE NAT LAB, 76- *Mem:* Am Inst Chem Engrs. *Res:* Food processing; fast breeder reactor safety analysis; transformation and transport of environmental pollutants. *Mailing Add:* Chem Eng Div Argonne Nat Lab Argonne IL 60439

KUMAR, SHIV SHARAN, b Bannu, India, Mar 15, 39; m 64; c 3. ASTRONOMY. *Educ:* Univ Mich, PhD(astron), 62. *Prof Exp:* Asst astron, Univ Observ, Univ Mich, 57-60; astrophysicist, Smithsonian Astrophys Observ, 60-61; res assoc, Goddard Inst Space Studies, 62-63; staff mem, Phys Res Lab, India, 63-65; asst prof, 65-68, ASSOC PROF ASTRON, UNIV VA, 68- *Mem:* Fel AAAS; Int Astron Union; Am Astron Soc; fel Royal Astron Soc. *Res:* Stellar atmospheres; stellar structure and evolution; origin of the solar system; celestial mechanics. *Mailing Add:* Leander McCormick Observ Box 3818 Univ Sta Charlottesville VA 22903

KUMAR, SHRAWAN, b Allahabad, India, July 1, 39. BIOMECHANICS, ERGONOMICS. *Educ:* Univ Allahabad, BSc, 59, MSc, 62; Univ Surrey, PhD(physiol), 71. *Prof Exp:* Lectr zool, Univ Allahabad, 62-66; pool officer orthop, All-India Inst Med Sci, 73-74; res assoc rehab med, Univ Toronto, 74-77; asst prof, 77-79, assoc prof, 79-81, PROF PHYS THER, UNIV ALTA, 82-, ASSOC PROF BIOMED ENG, 80- *Concurrent Pos:* Fel eng, Univ

Dublin, 71-73; asst prof biomed eng, Univ Alta, 77-80. *Mem:* Am Soc Biomech; Can Med & Biol Eng Soc; Human Factors Soc; Human Factors Soc Can. *Res:* Work physiology; occupational biomechanics; tissue biomechanics. *Mailing Add:* Dept of Phys Ther Univ of Alta Edmonton AB T6G 2G4 Can

KUMAR, SOMA, b Lucknow, India, May 16, 24; m 55; c 3. BIOCHEMISTRY. *Educ:* Univ Lucknow, BSc, 44, MSc, 45; Univ Md, PhD, 53. *Prof Exp:* Res assoc, Univ Md, 53-54; lectr biochem, Univ Lucknow, 54-56; asst prof, All-India Inst Med Sci, New Delhi, 56-58; from asst prof to assoc prof, 58-72, PROF CHEM, GEORGETOWN UNIV, 72- *Mem:* AAAS; Am Chem Soc; Am Soc Biol Chemists. *Res:* Biosynthesis of fatty acids. *Mailing Add:* Dept of Chem Georgetown Univ Washington DC 20057

KUMAR, SUDHIR, b Saharanpur, India, Oct 31, 33. ENGINEERING MECHANICS. *Educ:* Agra Univ, BSc, 50, MSc, 52; Indian Inst Sci, Bangalore, AIISc, 55; Pa State Univ, PhD(eng mech), 58. *Prof Exp:* Demonstr physics, Bareilly Col, Agra Univ, 50-51; res asst eng mech, Pa State Univ, 55-57, res assoc, 57-58, asst prof, 58-59; asst solid mech br, Eng Sci Div, Off Ord Res, US Army, 58-59, chief, 59-62, assoc dir, Eng Sci Div, US Army Res Off-Durham, 62-71; PROF MECH & MECH & AEROSPACE ENG, ILL INST TECHNOL, 71- *Concurrent Pos:* Vis lectr, Duke Univ, 58-62, vis assoc prof, 62-71 & NC State Univ, 68-71. *Honors & Awards:* Res & Develop Achievement Award, US Army, 66. *Mem:* Am Inst Aeronaut & Astronaut; Indian Soc Theoret & Appl Mech; Am Soc Metals; Am Helicopter Soc; Am Acad Mech. *Res:* High speed ground transportation; rocket boosting; helicopters; materials. *Mailing Add:* Dept of Mech & Mech & Aerospace Eng Ill Inst of Technol Chicago IL 60616

KUMAR, SUDHIR, b Anjhi, India, Sept 16, 42; m 68; c 2. BIOCHEMISTRY, NEUROCHEMISTRY. *Educ:* Univ Rajasthan, India, BS, 59, MS, 61; Univ Lucknow, India, PhD(biochem), 66. *Prof Exp:* Res assoc pharmacol, Baylor Col Med, 67-68; sr res scientist, NY State Res Inst Neurochem, 68-69; chief biochemist pediat, Methodist Hosp, Brooklyn, 69-73; res biochemist hematol, Vet Admin Hosp, Brooklyn, 73-75; asst prof, 76-79, ASSOC PROF BIOCHEM & NEUROL SCI, MED SCH, RUSH UNIV, 79-; DIR PERINATAL RES & LAB, CHRIST HOSP, OAK LAWN, ILL, 75-, DIR PEDIAT RES, 79- *Concurrent Pos:* Int Brain Res Org res fel award, UNESCO & Govt France, 71; Dreyfus Med Found fel, 71 & 73; consult scientist med res, Vet Admin Hosp, Hines, Ill, 76-79. *Mem:* Fel NY Acad Sci; Am Soc Biol Chemists; Am Inst Nutrit; Am Soc Neurochem; Soc Exp Biol & Med. *Res:* Study of vitamin B12 metabolism; effect of malnutrition on brain development and its correlation to mental retardation; changes in levels of nucleic acids and enzymes of purine catabolism; changes in amino acid levels; developing brain and metabolic disorders in newborn; perinatal medicine and development of screening tests for metabolic disorders in newborn. *Mailing Add:* 18901 Springfield Flossmoor IL 60422

KUMAR, SURIENDER, b Panjab, India, Dec 5, 38; m 65; c 4. ORGANIC CHEMISTRY, BIOCHEMISTRY. *Educ:* Univ Delhi, BSc, 58, MSc, 60; Boston Univ, PhD(org chem), 67. *Prof Exp:* Lectr chem, Deshbandhu Col, Delhi, 60-62; fel, Cornell Univ, 66-68; fel, Univ Wis-Madison, 68; res chemist, Vet Admin Hosp, 68-70; asst prof biochem, 71-75, assoc prof, 75-81, PROF BIOCHEM, COL MED & DENT NJ, 81- *Mem:* AAAS; Am Chem Soc; fel Am Inst Chemists; NY Acad Sci; Am Soc Biol Chemists. *Res:* Mechanism of action of enzymes controlling fatty acid synthesis; enzyme kinetics; subunit interaction and cooperative phenomenon; interaction of model compounds with enzymatic active sites; structure-biological activity relationships. *Mailing Add:* Dept of Biochem Col of Med & Dent of NJ Newark NJ 07103

KUMAR, VIJAY, b Punjab, India, Apr 15, 45; m 73. LABORATORY MEDICINE, IMMUNOLOGY. *Educ:* Panjab Univ, BS, 66, MS, 68; State Univ NY Buffalo, PhD(biochem), 73; Am Bd Med Microbiol, dipl; Am Bd Med Lab Immunol, dipl. *Prof Exp:* Teaching asst biochem, State Univ NY Buffalo, 69-73; fel, E J Meyer Mem Hosp, 73-74, fel immunol, Erie County Lab, E J Meyer Mem Hosp, 74-76; ASST DIR, IF TESTING SERV, BUFFALO, 76-; ASST PROF, DEPT MICROBIOL, STATE UNIV NY, BUFFALO, 80- *Concurrent Pos:* From clin instr to clin asst prof, Dept Microbiol, State Univ NY Buffalo, 74-76. *Mem:* Am Soc Microbiol. *Res:* Isolation of proteins, enzymes, autoimmunity, and immunochemistry. *Mailing Add:* 219 Sherman Hall State Univ of NY Buffalo NY 14214

KUMAR, VINAY, b Montgomery, India, Dec 24, 44; m 72; c 2. CANCER, IMMUNOLOGY. *Educ:* Poona Univ, BSc, 62; Punjab Univ, MBBS, 67; All India Inst Med Sci, MD(path), 72. *Prof Exp:* Tutor path, All India Inst Med Sci, 69-72; from inst to asst prof, 72-78, ASSOC PROF PATH & MICROBIOL, SCH MED, BOSTON UNIV, 78- *Concurrent Pos:* Med Found Inc fel, Boston, 74-76; prin investr, Nat Cancer Inst, 77- *Honors & Awards:* Cancer Res Scholar Award, Am Cancer Soc, 78. *Mem:* Am Asn Immunol; Sci Res Soc NAm. *Res:* Tumor immunology; virus induced cancer; bonemarrow transplantation. *Mailing Add:* Dept Pathol Southwestern Med Sch Dallas TX 75235

KUMARAN, A KRISHNA, b Govada, India, July 17, 32; US citizen; m 56; c 1. DEVELOPMENTAL BIOLOGY. *Educ:* Univ Madras, BSc, 50, MSc, 55, PhD(zool), 59. *Prof Exp:* Demonstr zool, Sri Venkateswara Univ, India, 55-57, lectr, 57-62; NIH trainee, Western Reserve Univ, 62-65; reader, Osmania Univ, India, 65-68; sr res assoc biol, Case Western Reserve Univ, 68-69; assoc prof, 69-73, PROF BIOL, MARQUETTE UNIV, 73-, NSF RES GRANTS, 70- *Concurrent Pos:* NIH res grant, 75- *Mem:* AAAS; Entom Soc Am; Am Soc Cell Biol; Am Soc Zoologists; Int Soc Develop Biol. *Res:* Insect development; role of hormones in control of insect development; nucleic acid metabolism in insect development; role of hormones in control of insect development; nucleic acid synthesis and its relation with differentiation in insects. *Mailing Add:* Dept of Biol Marquette Univ Milwaukee WI 53233

KUMAROO, KUZIYILETHU KRISHNAN, b Kerala, India, Apr 6, 31; m 67; c 2. BIOCHEMISTRY. *Educ:* Kerala Univ, India, BSc, 55; Univ NC, PhD(biochem), 69. *Prof Exp:* Chemist, Capsulation Serv, India, 55-56; clin chemist, Grant Med Col, Bombay, 56-57; petrol chemist, Kuwait Oil Co, Arabia, 57-63; res asst biochem, Univ NC, Chapel Hill, 63-68; NIH trainee, Univ Mich Med Ctr, 68-71; asst prof biochem, Univ NC, Chapel Hill, 71-79; RES BIOCHEMIST, DEPT HYPERBARIC MED, NAVAL MED RES INST, BETHESDA, MD, 79- *Mem:* Sigma Xi; AAAS; Coun Except Children; Nat Asn Retarded Citizens; Am Chem Soc. *Res:* Biochemistry of circulating blood factors and cells that regulate pulmonary, cardiovascular and central nervous system functions in normal and pathological conditions; cerebral ischemia and thrombosis; biochemistry of decompression sickness; regulatory role of proteases; basic chromosomal proteins in differentiating cells. *Mailing Add:* Dept Hyperbaric Med Naval Med Res Inst Bethesda MD 20814

KUMBAR, MAHADEVAPPA M, b Tallur, India, Nov 15, 39; m; c 1. PHYSICAL CHEMISTRY, BIOPHYSICS. *Educ:* Karnatak Univ, India, BSc, 61, MSc, 63; Adelphi Univ, PhD(phys chem), 69. *Prof Exp:* Lectr, Parle Col, India, 63-65; res assoc biophys, Adelphi Univ, 69-71. *Concurrent Pos:* adj asst prof biophys, Adelphi Univ, 71-79, adj assoc prof, 79- *Mem:* Am Chem Soc. *Res:* Statistical mechanics of macromolecules; dynamic and mechanical properties, conformational changes and conformational studies. *Mailing Add:* Dept of Chem Adelphi Univ Garden City NY 11530

KUMINS, CHARLES ARTHUR, b New York, NY, Jan 13, 15; m 40; c 3. SURFACE CHEMISTRY. *Educ:* City Col New York, BS, 36; Polytech Inst Brooklyn, MS, 41. *Prof Exp:* Jr chemist, Titanium Div, Nat Lead Co, NJ, 37-41; res chemist & group leader, Wyandotte Chem Co, Mich, 41-42; sr res chemist, Res Labs, Interchem Corp, 42-50, head dept inorg & phys chem, 50-54, dir dept, 54-59, dir textile chem, 59-63, asst dir, 63-67; dir res lab, Charles Bruning Co, 67-71; dir res & develop, Graphics Develop Lab, Addressograph-Multigraph Co, 71-73; dir res & develop, Tremco Corp, 73-80; vpres sci & technol, Sherwin Williams Co, 80-81; CONSULT, 82- *Concurrent Pos:* Secy & trustee, Paint Res Inst, 75- *Honors & Awards:* Roon Awards, Fed Socs Coatings Technol, 65 & 76; Matticello lectr, 79; Sci Achievement Award, Fed Soc Coatings Technol. *Mem:* AAAS; Am Chem Soc; fel Am Inst Chemists. *Res:* Rheology and particle size; colloids and surface chemistry; high temperature reactions; inorganic pigments; metallo-organics; iron compounds; alumina silicates; physical chemistry of polymers; transport phenomena in polymers; photochemistry; imaging systems; electrophotography; sealants and adhesives. *Mailing Add:* Epping Rd Cleveland OH 44104

KUMKUMIAN, CHARLES SIMON, b Meriden, Conn, June 17, 20; m 61; c 4. MEDICINAL CHEMISTRY. *Educ:* Temple Univ, BS, 44, MS, 51; Univ Md, PhD(med chem), 62. *Prof Exp:* Instr, Temple Univ, 47-51; instr chem, Univ Md, 57-60; asst ed, Chem Abstr Serv, 62-63; chemist, Bur Med, 64-68, supvry chemist, Bur Drugs, 68-72, ASST ASSOC DIR NEW DRUG EVAL, BUR DRUGS, US FOOD & DRUG ADMIN, 72- *Mem:* Am Chem Soc; Am Pharmaceut Asn. *Res:* Synthesis and biological activity of steroids; structure activity relationships; analytical chemistry. *Mailing Add:* 5919 Holland Rd Rockville MD 20851

KUMLER, MARION LAWRENCE, b Salem, Ore, Nov 18, 14; m 45; c 1. PLANT ECOLOGY, ENVIRONMENTAL STUDIES. *Educ:* Asbury Col, AB, 36; Boston Univ, MTh, 39; Ore State Univ, BS, 41, MS, 59, PhD(bot), 63. *Prof Exp:* Instr gen bot & plant physiol, Ore State Univ, 60-63; asst prof gen bot, plant ecol & physiol, Univ Wyo Team, Kabul Univ, Afghanistan, 63-65; assoc prof, 65-77, PROF BOT, SOUTHERN ILL UNIV, EDWARDSVILLE, 77- *Concurrent Pos:* Team leader APP team, Univ Tenn Overseas Prog, Tamil Nadu, India, 70-72; co-proj dir, Mo Bot Garden, St Louis, 73-74. *Mem:* Ecol Soc Am; AAAS; Am Soc Agron. *Res:* Plant succession in areas of hostile environment and physiological adaptations shown in adaptation of plants to these environments; plant distribution on hills surrounding Kabul, Afghanistan; nodulation studies with soybeans. *Mailing Add:* Dept of Biol Sci Southern Ill Univ Edwardsville IL 62025

KUMLER, PHILIP L, b Columbus, Ohio, May 23, 41; m 63; c 1. ORGANIC CHEMISTRY, POLYMER CHEMISTRY. *Educ:* Miami Univ, BA, 62; Univ Rochester, PhD(chem), 67. *Prof Exp:* Jr chemist indust res, Procter & Gamble Co, 62, summer staff, Indust Soap & Chem Prod, 63 & 64; fac asst chem, Wabash Col, 64; NATO fel, Univ Copenhagen, 67-68; fel & res assoc, Univ Chicago, 68-69, NIH fel, 69-70, fel & res assoc, 70; from asst prof to assoc prof chem, Saginaw Valley State Col, 70-76; assoc prof, 76-80, PROF CHEM, STATE UNIV NY, FREDONIA, 80- *Concurrent Pos:* Vis res assoc macromolecular sci, Case Western Reserve Univ, 81. *Mem:* AAAS; Am Chem Soc; Sigma Xi; NY Acad Sci. *Res:* Organic photochemistry of amine oxides and other organic species; organoselenium photochemistry; electron spin resonance studies of polymer transitions; polymer chemistry and physics. *Mailing Add:* Dept of Chem State Univ of NY Fredonia NY 14063

KUMLI, KARL F, b Denver, Colo, Oct 9, 27; m 53; c 2. ORGANIC CHEMISTRY. *Educ:* Kans State Teachers Col, AB, 55; Univ Kans, PhD(chem), 59. *Prof Exp:* Res chemist, Celanese Chem Corp, 59-61; res scientist, Weyerhaeuser Co, 61-64; from asst prof to assoc prof, 64-71, PROF CHEM, CALIF STATE UNIV, CHICO, 71-, CHMN DEPT, 75- *Mem:* Am Chem Soc. *Res:* Stereochemistry and mechanisms of reactions of the phosphorus atom; synthesis and characterization of polyoxymethylene, phenol-formaldehyde, epoxy. *Mailing Add:* 1340 Manchester Rd Chico CA 95926

KUMMEL, BERNHARD, b Racine, Wis, Aug 13, 19; m 46. PALEONTOLOGY. *Educ:* Univ Wis, BA, 41, MA, 42; Columbia Univ, PhD(geol), 49. *Prof Exp:* Topographer, US Coast & Geod Surv, Va, 43; geologist, Peruvian Govt, 43-46; Nat Res Coun fel, 46-47; geologist, Bur Econ Geol, Univ Tex, 47-48; from asst prof to assoc prof geol, Univ Ill, 48-52; assoc prof geol, Harvard Univ, 52-62, prof, 62-80. *Mem:* AAAS; Paleont Soc; Geol

Soc Am; Am Asn Petrol Geologists; Soc Econ Paleontologists & Mineralogists. *Res:* Triassic paleontology and stratigraphy; regional stratigraphy of Peru; Permian-Triassic boundary problems of world. *Mailing Add:* 29 Fresh Pond Place Cambridge MA 02138

KUMMER, HANS JACOB, applied mathematics, see previous edition

KUMMER, JOSEPH T, b Baltimore, Md, Oct 21, 19; m 47; c 4. SOLID STATE CHEMISTRY. *Educ:* Johns Hopkins Univ, BE, 41, PhD(chem eng), 45. *Prof Exp:* Fel catalysis, Mellon Inst, 45-51; assoc scientist, Dow Chem Co, 51-60; SR STAFF SCIENTIST, SCI LAB, FORD MOTOR CO, 60- *Honors & Awards:* Mobay Award, Am Chem Soc, 81. *Mem:* Am Chem Soc. *Res:* Catalysis; electrochemistry; plant process design; heat engines. *Mailing Add:* Ford Motor Co Res Lab PO Box 2053 Dearborn MI 48121

KUMMER, KEITH F, b Wauwatosa, Wis, May 28, 23; m 48; c 4. MECHANICAL ENGINEERING. *Educ:* Univ Wis, BS, 52. *Prof Exp:* Indust engr, Harnischfeger Corp, 52-53; design engr, Line Mat Co, 53-54; teacher, Milwaukee Sch Eng, 54-65; assoc prof mech eng, 65-73; INSTR, MACH TOOL OPER PROG, WAUKESHA COUNTY TECH INST, 75- *Res:* Mechanics. *Mailing Add:* 1236 S 113th St West Allis WI 53214

KUMMER, MARTIN, b Glarus, Switz, June 11, 36; m 67. MATHEMATICAL PHYSICS, APPLIED MATHEMATICS. *Educ:* Swiss Fed Inst Technol, predipl math, 57, dipl math phyiscs, 59, PhD(math Physics), 62. *Prof Exp:* Asst theoret physics, Swiss Fed Inst Technol, 60-64; NSF res assoc, Univ Mich, 64-66; from asst prof to assoc prof, 66-75, PROF MATH, UNIV TOLEDO, 75- *Concurrent Pos:* Sabbatical leave, Courant Inst, NY Univ, 78; res grant, Swiss Fed Inst Technol, 81. *Mem:* Am Phys Soc; Math Asn Am; Int Asn Math Physicists; Am Math Soc. *Res:* Statistical mechanics; application of group theory to physical problems; differential equations, in particular their application to mechanics; hamiltonian and celestial mechanics. *Mailing Add:* Dept of Math Univ of Toledo Toledo OH 43606

KUMMER, W(OLFGANG) H(ELMUT), b Stuttgart, Ger, Oct 10, 25; nat US; m 56; c 4. ELECTRICAL ENGINEERING. *Educ:* Univ Calif, BS, 46, MS, 47, PhD(elec eng), 54. *Prof Exp:* Asst elec eng, Univ Calif, 46-50, lectr, 50-53; mem tech staff, Bell Tel Labs, 53-59; head res sect, Antenna Dept, 59-66, sr scientist, Antenna Dept, 66-76, CHIEF SCIENTIST, RADAR MICROWAVE LAB, HUGHES AIRCRAFT CO, CULVER CITY, 76- *Concurrent Pos:* Mem comns B & F, Int Sci Radio Union. *Mem:* Fel Inst Elec & Electronics Engrs (pres, Antennas & Propagation Soc, 74). *Res:* Electromagnetic theory; signal processing and electronically scanned antennas and tropospheric propagation beyond the horizon; microwave field; slot radiators in wave-guides. *Mailing Add:* Hughes Aircraft Co Radar Systs Group PO Box 92426 Los Angeles CA 90009

KUMMEROW, FRED AUGUST, b Berlin, Ger, Oct 4, 14; nat US; m 42; c 3. FOOD SCIENCE. *Educ:* Univ Wis, BS, 39, MS, 41, PhD(biochem), 43. *Prof Exp:* Assoc nutritionist, Clemson Col, 43-45; assoc prof chem, Kans State Col, 45-50; assoc prof food chem, 50-59, PROF FOOD CHEM, UNIV ILL, URBANA, 59- *Concurrent Pos:* Mem, Assocs Food & Container Inst, Chicago; mem comn arteriosclerosis, Am Heart Asn. *Mem:* AAAS; Am Chem Soc; Am Oil Chem Soc; Am Dairy Sci Asn; Poultry Sci Asn. *Res:* Nutrition; biochemistry; fat and oil chemistry. *Mailing Add:* Dept Food Sci Univ Ill Urbana IL 61801

KUMMLER, RALPH H, b Jersey City, NJ, Nov 1, 40; m 62; c 3. CHEMICAL ENGINEERING, ENVIRONMENTAL ENGINEERING. *Educ:* Rensselaer Polytech Inst, BS, 62; Johns Hopkins Univ, PhD(chem eng), 66. *Prof Exp:* Res chemist, Gen Elec Space Sci Lab, 65-70; assoc prof, 70-74, CHMN & PROF CHEM ENG, WAYNE STATE UNIV, 74- *Concurrent Pos:* Consult, Gen Elec Space Sci Lab, 70-74, Phys Dynamics Inc, 70-78, Urban Sci Appl, 77- & KMS Fusion, 77; mem sci adv bd, Environ Protection Agency, 76-78. *Mem:* Am Inst Chem Engrs; Am Chem Soc; Air Pollution Control Asn; Am Inst Chem. *Res:* Chemical kinetics; environmental chemistry and transport including computer simulation of natural and polluted air and aquatic environments; chemiluminescence and hydrocarbon reactivity; synthetic fuels, oil shale processing in situ. *Mailing Add:* Dept Chem Eng Wayne State Univ Detroit MI 48202

KUMOSINSKI, THOMAS FRANCIS, b Philadelphia, Pa, Apr 19, 41. PHYSICAL CHEMISTRY. *Educ:* Drexel Univ, BSc, 64, PhD(phys chem), 73. *Prof Exp:* PHYS CHEMIST BIOCHEM, EASTERN REGIONAL LAB, US DEPT AGR, 61- *Mem:* Am Chem Soc. *Res:* Physical chemistry of biological macromolecules; theoretical and experimental quantum chemistry; small angle x-ray and light scattering; general spectroscopy of small molecular weight biological systems, porphyrins, flavins, etc. *Mailing Add:* US Dept of Agr 600 E Mermaid Ln Philadelphia PA 19118

KUMPEL, PAUL GREMMINGER, JR, b Riverside, NJ, Sept 5, 35; m 60; c 2. TOPOLOGY. *Educ:* Trenton State Col, BS, 56; Brown Univ, PhD(math), 64. *Prof Exp:* Instr math, Lafayette Col, 56-59; asst, Brown Univ, 59-63, instr, 63-64; asst prof math, 64-72, dir teacher prep, Div Math Sci, 71-74, ASSOC PROF MATH, STATE UNIV NY STONY BROOK, 72- *Concurrent Pos:* Sci Res Coun sr vis fel, Univ Hull, 71; dir undergrad prog math, 76-82; vis scholar, Wesleyan Univ, 78. *Mem:* Math Asn Am. *Res:* Topology of H-spaces. *Mailing Add:* Dept of Math State Univ of NY Stony Brook NY 11794

KUN, ERNEST, b Sopron, Hungary, Oct 22, 19; nat US. BIOCHEMISTRY, PHARMACOLOGY. *Educ:* Eotvos Lorand Univ, Budapest, MD, 43. *Prof Exp:* Asst physiol, Eotvos Lorand Univ, 39-43, asst prof pharmacol, 44-46; asst, Univ Chicago, 46-47, res assoc, 47-49; asst prof med & pharmacol & lectr biochem, Tulane Univ, 49-53; fel, Inst Enzyme Res, Univ Wis, 53-56; lectr pharmacol, 56-60, assoc prof, 60-65, PROF EXP PHARMACOL, BIOCHEM & BIOPHYS & EXP THERAPEUT, MED CTR, UNIV CALIF, SAN FRANCISCO, 65- *Concurrent Pos:* Estab investr, Am Heart Asn,

56-61. *Mem:* AAAS; Am Chem Soc; Am Soc Pharmacol & Exp Therapeut; Soc Exp Biol & Med; Am Soc Biol Chemists. *Res:* Enzymology of dehydrogenases; enzymes of sulfur metabolism; metabolic regulation studies by F-containing substrate homologs; bioenergetics; molecular mechanisms of growth regulation in eukaryotic cells at the chromatin level (poly adenosine diphosphate R). *Mailing Add:* Surge 103 Dept of Pharmacol Univ of Calif Med Ctr San Francisco CA 94143

KUN, KENNETH ALLAN, b Brooklyn, NY, July 14, 30; m 55; c 2. POLYMER CHEMISTRY. *Educ:* Brooklyn Col, BS, 52; Polytech Inst Brooklyn, MS, 55; Yale Univ, MS, 59, PhD(chem), 61. *Prof Exp:* Chemist, US Elec Mfg Co, 52-53, Warner-Chilcott Res Labs, 53-55 & Am Cyanamid Co, 55-57; asst redox polymers, Yale Univ, 57-60; sr res chemist, 60-66, Far East regional mgr indust chem, Foreign Opers Div, Tokyo, 66-72, sales/mkt coordr, Latin Am Opers, Int Div, 72-76, mem staff corp hq, Rohm & Haas Co, 76-78; dir mkt, Specialty Chem Div, Church & Dwight Co Inc, 78-79; dir specialty chem res, Calgon Corp, Div Merck & Co Inc, 79-81; CHIEF TECH OFFICER & VPRES, POLYCHROME CORP, DIV DAINIPPON INK & CHEM, 81- *Mem:* AAAS; Am Chem Soc. *Res:* Synthesis of monomers and polymers; application of polymers for surface coatings, fibers, redox polymers and ion-exchange resins; structures of porous solids; pharmaceuticals; batteries and dry cells. *Mailing Add:* Polychrome Corp PO Box 817 Yonkers NJ 10702

KUNA, ROBERT ALAN, b Newark, NJ, Oct 4, 44; m 67; c 2. ANIMAL PHYSIOLOGY. *Educ:* Parsons Col, BS, 67; New York Univ, MS, 70; PhD(biol), 73. *Prof Exp:* Sr toxicologist, Lakeside Labs, 73-75; TOXICOLOGIST, EXXON CORP, 75- *Mem:* Soc Toxicol; Europ Soc Toxicol; Am Indust Hyg Asn; Environ Mutagen Soc. *Res:* Initiation, identification, toxicological evaluation and consultation on the health hazards associated with industrial chemicals and petroleum products on a worldwide basis. *Mailing Add:* PO Box 235 East Millstone NJ 08873

KUNA, SAMUEL, b Velke Levare, Czech, May 7, 12; nat US; m 36; c 2. PHARMACOLOGY. *Educ:* NY Univ, BA, 43, PhD(biol), 56; Temple Univ, MA, 49. *Prof Exp:* Mem, Merck Inst Therapeut Res, 34-43, res asst to dir, 43-50, res assoc & head pharmacol res unit, 50-57; head pharmacol dept, Bristol-Myers Prod Div, Bristol-Myers Co, 57-62, asst dir res & develop, 63-67; dir pharmacol & toxicol, Calgon Consumer Prod Co Div, Merck & Co, 67-74, dir biol res, 74-80; PROF & DIR TOXICOL PROG, GRAD SCH, RUTGERS UNIV, 80- *Concurrent Pos:* Head biol control dept, Merck Inst Therapeut Res, 47-50, 53-56; instr, Temple Univ, 47-50. *Mem:* AAAS; Am Soc Pharmacol & Exp Therapeut; Am Pharmaceut Asn; Soc Toxicol; NY Acad Sci. *Res:* Action of chemical agents on interchange of tissue fluids; analgesics; physiology of the stomach; psychopharmacology; product development. *Mailing Add:* Rutgers Univ Grad Sch Nelson Blvd Bush Campus New Brunswick NJ 08903

KUNASZ, IHOR ANDREW, b Montlucon, France, Sept 24, 39; US citizen; m 65; c 2. ECONOMIC GEOLOGY. *Educ:* Case Western Reserve Univ, BA, 63; Pa State Univ, MS, 68, PhD(geol), 70. *Prof Exp:* Staff geologist, 70-72, CHIEF GEOLOGIST, FOOTE MINERAL CO, 72- *Concurrent Pos:* Chmn, Chem & Metall Minerals Tech Comt, Soc Mining Eng, Am Inst Mining Eng, 76-77. *Mem:* Soc Mining Eng, Am Inst Mining Eng; Geol Soc Am; Geochem Soc; Shevchenko Sci Soc. *Res:* Economic and exploration geology associated with industrial minerals, especially saline deposits and lithium deposits of the world. *Mailing Add:* Foote Mineral Co Rt 100 Exton PA 19341

KUNCE, HENRY WARREN, b St Louis, Mo, Apr 18, 25; m 48; c 5. COMPUTER SIMULATION, MATHEMATICAL COMMUNICATION. *Educ:* Wash Univ, BA, 46; McCormick Theol Sem, Chicago, BD & MDiv, 49; Univ Miami, MSIE, 71, PhD(statist), 76, (physiol), 79. *Prof Exp:* Clergyman, Ohio & Mo, 49-61; planner-analyst parish develop, Bd Missions, United Presby Church, Mo & Fla, 61-70; systs analyst, Clin Campesina, Homestead, Fla, 70-71; res scientist sociocybernetics, Univ Miami, 71-72; CHIEF MGR SYST ENG, MGT INFO SYST & OPERS RES, METROP DADE COUNTY GOVT, FLA, 72-; ADJ MATH FAC, UNIV MIAMI, CORAL GABLES, FLA, 80- *Mem:* Opers Res Soc Am; Am Inst Indust Engrs; Inst Mgt Sci; Soc Comput Simulation; AAAS. *Res:* Sociocybernetics, the application of cybernetics to the dynamics of human interaction and social structures, using systems analysis and computer simulation of stochastic and deterministic mathematical models, a discrete finite state automata, and a continuous model analyzed by phase space analysis; applicaitons made in management; counseling education; personnel problems. *Mailing Add:* 5025 SW 74th Terr Miami FL 33143

KUNDEL, HAROLD LOUIS, b New York, NY, Aug 15, 33. RADIOLOGY. *Educ:* Columbia Univ, AB, 55, MD, 59; Temple Univ, MA, 63. *Prof Exp:* Intern med, Mary Imogene Bassett Hosp, Cooperstown, NY, 59-60; resident radiol, Temple Univ Hosp, 60-63; resident radiobiol, Sch Aerospace Med, 63-64; James Picker Found advan acad fel physiol, Sch Med, Temple Univ, 64-66, attend radiologist, Univ Hosp, 66-80, prof radiol, 68-80; WILSON PROF RES RADIOL, UNIV PA, 80- *Concurrent Pos:* attend radiologist, Hosp Univ Pa, 80- *Honors & Awards:* Mem Award, Asn Univ Radiologists, 63 *Mem:* AAAS; Am Col Radiol; Asn Univ Radiologists. *Res:* Image information processing and analysis; visual perception; diagnostic decision making. *Mailing Add:* Dept of Radiol Hosp Univ Pa Philadelphia PA 19104

KUNDERT, ESAYAS G, b Rüti, Switz, May 7, 18; US citizen; m 54; c 3. ALGEBRA. *Educ:* Swiss Fed Inst Technol, dipl, 45, Dr Math, 50. *Prof Exp:* Asst prof math, Univ Tenn, 50-51; from asst prof to prof, La State Univ, 51-62; PROF MATH, UNIV MASS, AMHERST, 62- *Concurrent Pos:* US Army grant, 52-53. *Res:* Algebraic geometry and algebraic topology. *Mailing Add:* Dept of Math Univ of Mass Amherst MA 01002

KUNDIG, FREDERICKA DODYK, b Nashville, Tenn, Apr 22, 24; m 64; c 1. CELL PHYSIOLOGY, VERTEBRATE PHYSIOLOGY. *Educ:* Univ Rochester, PhD(pharmacol), 61. *Prof Exp:* Res assoc biochem, Rackham Arthritis Res Unit, Univ Mich, Ann Arbor, 61-65 & Johns Hopkins Univ, 65-67; from asst prof to assoc prof, 67-73, PROF VERT ANAT & PHYSIOL & CELL BIOL, TOWSON STATE UNIV, 73- *Res:* Cell surface phenomena; hormones and enzyme activity. *Mailing Add:* Dept of Biol Sci Towson State Univ Baltimore MD 21204

KUNDSIN, RUTH BLUMFELD, b New York, NY, July 30, 16; m; c 2. MEDICAL MICROBIOLOGY. *Educ:* Hunter Col, BA, 36; Boston Univ, MA, 49; Harvard Univ, ScD(microbiol), 58. *Hon Degrees:* ScD, Lowell Tech Inst, 75. *Prof Exp:* Res bacteriologist, Sch Pub Health, Harvard Univ, 36-37 & Sch Med, Univ Pa, 37-38; res bacteriologist, Peter Bent Brigham Hosp, 51-58, asst surg, 58-64, mem assoc staff, 64-70, hosp epidemiologist, 70-81, res assoc, Harvard Med Sch, 61-76, ASSOC PROF MICROBIOL & MOLECULAR GENETICS, HARVARD MED SCH, 76-; PRES, KUNDSIN LAB INC, 81- *Mem:* AAAS; Am Soc Microbiol; World Med Asn; NY Acad Sci; Am Venereal Disease Asn. *Res:* Dynamics of disinfection as applied to environmental bacteriology; sanitary bacteriology; maintenance of standards for a hygienic environment; epidemiology of staphylococcal disease; skin disinfection; mycoplasmas and reproductive failure in humans. *Mailing Add:* 721 Huntington Ave Boston MA 02115

KUNDT, JOHN FRED, b Denver, Colo, Dec 21, 26; m 48; c 2. DENDROLOGY, FORESTRY EDUCATION. *Educ:* WVa Univ, BS, 52; NC State Univ, PhD(forestry), 72. *Prof Exp:* Mgt chief, Forest Mgt Serv, Div Forestry, Va, 52-57; forest supvr prod, Union Camp Paper Corp, 57-64; fel dendrol, NC State Univ, 64-69; asst prof bot, genetics & plant taxon, State Univ NY, 69-73; ASSOC PROF & EXTEN FORESTRY SPECIALIST, UNIV MD, 74- *Mem:* Soc Am Foresters. *Res:* Effects of adding composted sewage sludge to newly planted Pinus Taeda and Pinus Virginiana; developing pine hybrids between Pinus Taeda and Pinus Rigida by selecting superior parental phenotypes, and producing experimental seed orchard; developing a Pinus Virginiana seed orchard to produce seed for Christmas tree production. *Mailing Add:* Dept Hort Univ Md College Park MD 20742

KUNDU, MUKUL RANJAN, b Calcutta, India, Feb 10, 30; m 58; c 3. RADIOPHYSICS, ELECTRONICS. *Educ:* Univ Calcutta, BSc, 49, MSc, 51; Univ Paris, DSc(radio astron), 57. *Prof Exp:* Asst, Coun Sci & Indust Res, Univ Calcutta, 52-54; French Govt scholar radio astron, Ecole Normale Superieure & Maudon Observ, 54-56; asst, Nat Ctr Sci Res, Ministry Educ, France & Meudon Observ, 56-58; sr res fel, Nat Phys Lab, India, 58-59; res assoc solar radio astron, Observ, Univ Mich, 59-62; assoc prof astron, Cornell Univ, 62-65 & Tata Inst Fundamental Res, Bombay, 65-68; actg dir astron, 78-79, PROF PHYSICS & ASTRON, UNIV MD, COLLEGE PARK, 68-, DIR ASTRON, 80- *Concurrent Pos:* Sr res assoc, Nat Acad Sci-Nat Res Coun, 74-75. *Honors & Awards:* Sr US Scientist Award, Alexander von Humboldt Found, 78. *Mem:* Int Astron Union; sr mem Inst Elec & Electronics Engrs; Am Astron Soc; assoc Brit Inst Radio Eng; fel Royal Astron Soc. *Res:* Solar and galactic radio astronomy. *Mailing Add:* Astron Prog Univ of Md College Park MD 20742

KUNDU, SUKHAMAY, computer science, combinatorial mathematics, see previous edition

KUNELIUS, HEIKKI TAPANI, b Konginkangas, Finland, Mar 21, 40; Canadian citizen; m 71; c 2. PLANT SCIENCE. *Educ:* Univ Helsinki, BSA & MSc, 66; Univ Man, PhD(plant sci), 70. *Prof Exp:* Res asst plant path, Agr Res Ctr, 66; RES SCIENTIST PLANT SCI, AGR CAN, RES BR, 70- *Concurrent Pos:* Fel plant sci, Univ Man, 70; mem expert comt, Forage Breeding, Can, 79-; study leave, New Zealand-Australia, 79-80. *Mem:* Can Soc Agron; Am Soc Agron; Agr Inst Can; Finnish Asn Agr Grad; Swed Seed Asn. *Res:* Physiology and management of forage grasses and legumes; conservation and utilization of forage crops; minimum tillage for pasture renovation. *Mailing Add:* Agr Can Res Sta PO Box 1210 Charlottetown PE C1A 7M8 Can

KUNESH, JERRY PAUL, b Kewaunee, Wis, Jan 19, 38; m 61; c 3. CLINICAL PHARMACOLOGY, MEDICINE. *Educ:* Iowa State Univ, DVM, 61, MS, 66, PhD(physiol), 69. *Prof Exp:* Instr vet med & surg, 61-62, NIH fel physiol, 64-65, asst prof physiol & pharmacol, 65-70, assoc prof pharmacol & med, 70-75, PROF VET MED & SURG, IOWA STATE UNIV, 75- *Mem:* Am Asn Swine Practitioners; Am Asn Bovine Practitioners; Am Vet Med Asn. *Res:* Porcine hemorrhagic syndromes and clinical evaluation of antimicrobial agents as well as their mechanisms of action. *Mailing Add:* Dept of Vet Clin Sci Iowa State Univ Ames IA 50010

KUNG, CHING, b Kwang Tung, China, Apr 28, 39; US citizen; m 65; c 3. GENETICS, NEUROBIOLOGY. *Educ:* Chung Chi Col, Chinese Univ Hong Kong, dipl, 63; Univ Pa, PhD(biol), 68. *Prof Exp:* Fel genetics, Ind Univ, Bloomington, 68-70; fel electrophysiol, Univ Calif, Los Angeles, 70-71; from asst prof to assoc prof molecular biol, Univ Calif, Santa Barbara, 71-74; assoc prof, 74-77, PROF MOLECULAR BIOL & GENETICS, UNIV WIS-MADISON, 77- *Mem:* AAAS; Genetic Soc Am; Am Soc Cell Biol. *Res:* Genetic dissection of the excitable membrane in paramecium; electrophysiological, biochemical and ultrastructural studies of normal and mutant with altered membrane functions and behavior. *Mailing Add:* Lab of Molecular Biol Univ of Wis Madison WI 53706

KUNG, ERNEST CHEN-TSUN, b Ping-tung, Taiwan, China, Jan 1, 31; m 59; c 3. METEOROLOGY. *Educ:* Nat Univ Taiwan, BS, 53; Univ Ariz, MS, 59; Univ Wis, PhD(meteorol), 63. *Prof Exp:* Specialist agron, Taiwan Prov Govt, 54-58; proj assoc meteorol, Univ Wis, 63; res meteorologist, Geophys Fluid Dynamics Lab, Environ Sci Serv Admin, 63-67; assoc prof, 67-70, PROF ATMOSPHERIC SCI, UNIV MO-COLUMBIA, 70- *Concurrent Pos:* NSF grants, 67-69, 70-75, 76-78, 78-81 & 81-84; pres grad fac senate, Univ Mo-Columbia, 77-78. *Mem:* Am Meteorol Soc; foreign mem Royal Meteorol Soc; Meteorol Soc Japan. *Res:* Atmospheric general circulation; dynamic meteorology; dynamic climatology; long-range forecasting. *Mailing Add:* Dept of Atmospheric Sci Univ of Mo Columbia MO 65211

KUNG, HAROLD HING CHUEN, b Hong Kong, Oct 12, 49; m 71. PHYSICAL CHEMISTRY. *Educ:* Univ Wis-Madison, BS, 71; Northwestern Univ, MS, 72, PhD(chem), 74. *Prof Exp:* Res chemist, E I du Pont de Nemours & Co, Inc, 74-76; asst prof, 76-81, ASSOC PROF CHEM ENG, NORTHWESTERN UNIV, 81- *Mem:* Am Chem Soc; Am Inst Chem Engrs. *Res:* Surface chemistry and physics; catalysis; electrocatalysis; solid state photochemistry. *Mailing Add:* Dept of Chem Eng Northwestern Univ Evanston IL 60201

KUNG, HSIANG-TSUNG, b Shanghai, China, Nov 9, 45; m 70; c 2. COMPUTER SCIENCE, MATHEMATICS. *Educ:* Nat Tsing Hua Univ, BS, 68; Univ NMex, MA, 70; Carnegie-Mellon Univ, PhD(math), 74. *Prof Exp:* Res assoc, 73-74, asst prof, 74-78, assoc prof, 78-82, PROF COMPUT SCI, CARNEGIE-MELLON UNIV, 82- *Concurrent Pos:* Archit consult, ESL, Inc, 82. *Mem:* Asn Comput Mach; Inst Elec & Electronics Engrs. *Res:* Computer algorithms; computational complexity; parallel computation; multiprocessors; very large scale integration; database systems; numerical analysis. *Mailing Add:* Dept of Comput Sci Carnegie-Mellon Univ Pittsburgh PA 15213

KUNG, SHAIN-DOW, b Lini, China, Mar 14, 35; US citizen; m 64; c 3. MOLECULAR BIOLOGY. *Educ:* Chung Hsing Univ, Taiwan, BSc, 58; Univ Guelph, MSc, 65; Univ Toronto, PhD(bot), 68. *Prof Exp:* Instr bot, Chung Hsing Univ, Taiwan, 58-62; res assoc biochem, Univ Toronto, 68-71 & biol, Univ Calif, Los Angeles, 71-74; asst prof, 74-77, assoc prof, 77-82, PROF BIOL, UNIV MD, BALTIMORE COUNTY, 82- *Mem:* AAAS; Am Soc Plant Physiologists. *Res:* Biochemistry and genetics of chloroplast protein; properties, function and evolution of chloroplast DNA; biology of protoplast. *Mailing Add:* Dept of Biol Sci Univ of Md Baltimore County Catonsville MD 21228

KUNIANSKY, SIDNEY, b Atlanta, Ga, Aug 31, 16; m 41; c 3. CHEMICAL ENGINEERING. *Educ:* Ga Inst Technol, BS, 37; Univ Cincinnati, PhD(chem eng), 41. *Prof Exp:* Chem engr, E I du Pont de Nemours & Co, Inc, Ind, 41-42, Ala, 42-43, Del, 43, Tenn, 44, Wash, 44-45, NJ, 45-49; intel analyst, US Air Force, 49-56; consult, US govt, 56-73 & Washington, DC, 80-81. *Concurrent Pos:* Consult, Va State Water Control Bd, Alexandria. *Mem:* Am Inst Chem Engrs. *Res:* Flow of fluids through v-notch weirs; foreign chemical engineering developments. *Mailing Add:* 3724 Hummer Rd Annandale VA 22003

KUNIN, ARTHUR SAUL, b Brooklyn, NY, Aug 11, 25; m 59; c 4. MEDICINE, PHYSIOLOGICAL CHEMISTRY. *Educ:* Columbia Univ, BA, 48; Univ Vt, MD, 52. *Prof Exp:* Intern med, Peter Bent Brigham Hosp, Boston, Mass, 52-54, jr asst resident, 53-54; NIH fel, Med Sch, Boston Univ, 54-56; sr asst resident, Peter Bent Brigham Hosp, 56-57; from instr to asst prof, 57-68, ASSOC PROF, COL MED, UNIV VT, 68- *Concurrent Pos:* Lederle Med fac award, Col Med, Univ Vt, 65-68; NIH spec fel, Mass Gen Hosp & Harvard Med Sch, 62-64; Am Col Physicians Willard Thompson traveling scholar, Univ Col Hosp Med Sch, London, 64; vis prof, Inst Chem Med, Univ Bern, 70-71; fel Dept Physiol, Harvard Med Sch, 78-79. *Mem:* Am Col Physicians; Am Fedn Clin Res. *Res:* Renal physiology; mitochondrial metabolism; nutrition in renal disease; nephrology; diseases of metabolism; metabolic bone diseases and the intermediary metabolism of epiphyseal cartilage. *Mailing Add:* Col Med Unit Vt Burlington VT 05401

KUNIN, CALVIN MURRY, b Burlington, Vt, May 3, 29; m 52; c 3. INTERNAL MEDICINE, PREVENTIVE MEDICINE. *Educ:* Columbia Univ, AB, 49; Cornell Univ, MD, 53. *Prof Exp:* Intern med, New York Hosp, 53-54; sr asst surg, USPHS, 54-56; asst resident, Peter Bent Brigham Hosp, Boston, 56-57; res fel, Harvard Med Sch, 57-59; from asst prof to assoc prof med & prev med, Sch Med, Univ Va, 59-70; prof med & assoc chmn dept, Univ Wis-Madison, 70-79; chief med, Vet Admin Hosp, 70-70; PROF MED & CHMN DEPT MED, COL MED, OHIO STATE UNIV, 79- *Mem:* Am Fedn Clin Res; Am Asn Immunologists; Am Assoc Physicians; Am Soc Clin Invest; Soc Exp Biol & Med. *Res:* Epidemiology; antibiotic therapy virology. *Mailing Add:* 410 W 10th Ave Dept Med Ohio State Univ Columbus OH 43210

KUNIN, ROBERT, b West New York, NJ, July 16, 18; m 42; c 2. PHYSICAL CHEMISTRY. *Educ:* Rutgers Univ, BS, 39, PhD(colloidal chem), 42. *Prof Exp:* Assoc chemist, Tenn Valley Authority, 42-44; sr chemist, Manhattan Proj, Columbia Univ, 44-45; Gulf fel, Mellon Inst, 45-46; lab head chg res & develop ion exchange resins, 46-59, res assoc, 59-70, sr staff assoc, Rohm & Haas Co, 70-76; CONSULT, 76- *Concurrent Pos:* Lectr, Univ Pa & Am Univ. *Honors & Awards:* Franklin Inst Gold Medal, 66. *Mem:* AAAS; Am Chem Soc; Am Inst Chem Engrs; Electrochem Soc; Israel Chem Soc. *Res:* Desalination; adsorption; liquid extraction; theory and application of ion exchange; inorganic chemistry of phosphates, uranium fluorides; analytical chemistry of inorganic constituents; ion exchange in silicates; electrochemistry of membrane processes; catalysis; water treatment and purification. *Mailing Add:* 1318 Moon Dr Yardley PA 19067

KUNISHI, HARRY MIKIO, b Honolulu, Hawaii, Aug 30, 32; m 59. SOIL CHEMISTRY. *Educ:* Univ Hawaii, BS, 55, MS, 56; Univ Wash, BS, 58; Univ Wis, PhD(soils), 63. *Prof Exp:* SOIL SCIENTIST, AGR RES SERV, USDA, 62- *Mem:* Int Soc Soil Sci; Am Soc Agron; Clay Minerals Soc; Am Chem Soc; Int Asn Study Clays. *Res:* Chemistry and mineralogy of potassium in soils; adsorption and movement of radionuclides in soils; phosphate reactions in field and streams; rates of phosphate supplied to plants by acid soils of southeastern United States; phosphorus and nobelium-tillage; model of phosphorus transport. *Mailing Add:* Rm 201 Bldg 007 Bay Area Res Ctr-W Beltsville MD 20705

KUNISI, VENKATASUBBAN S, b Kottayam, India; m 74; c 1. ORGANIC CHEMISTRY. *Educ:* Univ Madras, India, BSc, MSc; Unliv Kans, PhD(chem), 75. *Prof Exp:* Fel, Emory Univ, 74-76; lectr, Tex A&M Univ, 76-79; assoc prof, Univ Fla, 79-80; ASST PROF CHEM, UNIV NFLA, 81- *Mem:* Am Chem Soc. *Res:* Bio-organic mechanisms; chemical and enzyme catalysis; organic reaction mechanisms; solution kinetics; istope effectss. *Mailing Add:* Dept Natural Sci Univ NFla Jacksonville FL 32216

KUNKA, ROBERT LEONARD, b Chicago, Ill, Aug 30, 47; m 78; c 1. PHARMACOKINETICS, BIOPHARMACEUTICS. *Educ:* Univ Ill, BS, 70; Univ NC, Chapel Hill, PhD(pharmaceut), 77. *Prof Exp:* ASST PROF PHARMACEUT, UNIV PITTSBURGH, 78- *Mem:* Am Pharmaceut Asn; Acad Pharmaceut Sci; Am Asn Col Pharm. *Res:* Protein binding of drugs; effect of disease states on pharmacokinetics and biopharmaceutics; computer modeling of drugs; bioavailability testing; secretion of drugs in body fluids. *Mailing Add:* 712 Salk Hall Univ Pittsburgh Pittsburgh PA 15261

KUNKEE, RALPH EDWARD, b San Fernando, Calif, July 30, 27. BIOCHEMISTRY, ENOLOGY. *Educ:* Univ Calif, AB, 50, PhD(biochem), 55. *Prof Exp:* Asst biochemist, Univ Calif, 50-53; res biochemist, E I du Pont de Nemours & Co, 55-60; asst res biochemist, 60-63, PROF ENOL, UNIV CALIF, DAVIS, 63- *Mem:* AAAS; Am Soc Microbiol; Am Soc Enol (secy-treas, 81-83). *Res:* Intermediary metabolism and control; fermentation; microbiology. *Mailing Add:* Dept of Viticult & Enol Univ of Calif Davis CA 95616

KUNKEL, HARRIOTT ORREN, b Olney, Tex, July 3, 22; m 60; c 2. BIOCHEMISTRY, NUTRITION. *Educ:* Tex A&M Univ, BS, 43, MS, 48; Cornell Univ, PhD(biochem), 50. *Prof Exp:* Instr biochem, Univ Wis, 50-51; from asst prof to assoc prof animal sci & biochem, 51-57, assoc dir exp sta, 62-68, dean col agr & actg dir, Tex Agr Exp Sta, 68-72, PROF ANIMAL SCI, BIOCHEM & BIOPHYS, TEX A&M UNIV, 57-, DEAN AGR, 72- *Mem:* Am Chem Soc; Am Soc Animal Sci; Am Soc Biol Chemists; Am Inst Nutrit; Soc Exp Biol & Med. *Res:* Ruminant metabolism; science administration. *Mailing Add:* Off of Dean of Agr Tex A&M Univ College Station TX 77843

KUNKEL, HENRY GEORGE, b New York, NY, Sept 9, 16; m 49; c 3. MEDICINE. *Educ:* Princeton Univ, AB, 38; Johns Hopkins Univ, MD, 42. *Hon Degrees:* MD, Univ Uppsala, 65. *Prof Exp:* Intern, Bellevue Hosp, New York, 42-43; asst res physician, Rockefeller Hosp, 45-47; assoc liver dis res, 47-49, assoc mem, 49-52, MEM & PROF IMMUNOL, ROCKEFELLER UNIV & SR PHYSICIAN, HOSP, 52- *Honors & Awards:* Gairdner Award, 62; Allergy Found Award, 65; Dameshek Award, 72; City of Hope Res Award, 74; T Duckett Jones Award, 74; Am Col Physicians Award, 75; Passano Award, 75; Lasker Award, 75. *Mem:* Nat Acad Sci; Nat Inst Med; Am Soc Biol Chemists; Soc Clin Invest (pres, 63); Am Asn Immunologists (pres, 74). *Res:* Immunology; disease; biochemistry. *Mailing Add:* Dept of Immunol Rockefeller Univ New York NY 10021

KUNKEL, JOSEPH GEORGE, b Oceanside, NY, Aug 17, 42; m 64; c 2. DEVELOPMENTAL BIOLOGY, INSECT PHYSIOLOGY. *Educ:* Columbia Col, AB, 64; Case Western Reserve Univ, PhD(biol), 68. *Prof Exp:* Trainee biomet, Case Western Reserve Univ, 68; NIH trainee develop biol, Yale Univ, 68-70; asst prof, 70-76, ASSOC PROF ZOOL, UNIV MASS, 76- *Concurrent Pos:* Instr biol, Yale Univ, 69-70; prin investr, NIH-Biomed Res Support grant & vis scholar, Dept Biochem, Univ Calif, Berkeley, 77-78. *Mem:* AAAS; Am Soc Zoologists. *Res:* Insect physiology and development; chemistry and function of vitellogenin; evolution; biometry. *Mailing Add:* Dept of Zool Univ of Mass Amherst MA 01003

KUNKEL, REINOLD WALTER, b New Salem, NDak, May 25, 20; m 48; c 4. DAIRY SCIENCE. *Educ:* NDak State Univ, BS, 41; Univ Minn, MS, 43, PhD(dairy sci, agr biochem), 48. *Prof Exp:* From asst to instr, Univ Minn, 41-46, res assoc, 46-47; assoc scientist, Kraft Foods Co, 48-57; res mgr, Sealtest Foods, Nat Dairy Prod Corp, 59-62; lab mgr, Res & Develop Div, 62-75, DIR REGULATORY SCI, RES & DEVELOP DIV, KRAFT, INC, 75- *Mem:* Am Dairy Sci Asn; Inst Food Technologists. *Res:* Dairy products; confections; fruit and vegetable products. *Mailing Add:* Res & Develop Div Kraft Inc 801 Waukegan Rd Glenview IL 60025

KUNKEL, WILLIAM ECKART, b Berlin, Ger, Mar 25, 36; nat US; m 69; c 2. ASTRONOMY. *Educ:* Univ Calif, Berkeley, BA, 59; Univ Tex, Austin, PhD(astron), 67. *Prof Exp:* Jr astronr, Interam Observ Cerro Tololo, 67-70, assoc astronr, 70-77; mem staff, Brazilian Nat Observ, 77-79; ASTRONOMER, MAX PLANCK INST ASTRON, GER, 80- *Mem:* Am Astron Soc; Int Astron Union. *Res:* Solar neighborhood flare stars; dwarf galaxies, photometry. *Mailing Add:* Max Planck Inst Astron 6900 Konigstuhl I Heidelberg Germany

KUNKEL, WULF BERNARD, b Eichenau, Ger, Feb 6, 23; nat US; m 47; c 2. PLASMA PHYSICS. *Educ:* Univ Calif, BA, 48, PhD(physics), 51. *Prof Exp:* Asst res engr aerodyn, 51-54, lectr, 53-67, assoc res eng, 54-55, physicist, Lawrence Berkeley Lab, 56-70, PROF PHYSICS, UNIV CALIF, BERKELEY, 67-, GROUP LEADER MAGNETIC FUSION ENERGY RES PROJ, LAWRENCE BERKELEY LAB, 70- *Concurrent Pos:* Guggenheim fel, 55-56 & 72-73; consult, Aerospace Corp, 61-71; ed, Plasma Physics, 70-80; Alexander von Humboldt award, 80. *Mem:* Fel Am Phys Soc. *Res:* Physics of ionized gases; magnetohydrodynamics; controlled-fusion research. *Mailing Add:* Lawrence Berkeley Lab Univ of Calif Berkeley CA 94720

KUNKLE, DONALD EDWARD, b New Kensington, Pa, Mar 9, 28; m 50; c 3. PHYSICS, MATHEMATICS. *Educ:* Lafayette Col, BS, 50. *Prof Exp:* Res physicist spectros, 50-55, group leader nondestructive testing, 55-62, process control, Alcoa Res Lab, 62-70; staff physicist process technol, 70-80, MGR PROD ANALYSIS & TEST SYSTS, QUALITY CONTROL, KAISER ALUMINUM & CHEM CORP, 80- *Mem:* Am Soc Non-destructive Testing; Anal Chem Appl Spectros; Am Soc Testing & Mat. *Res:* Applied emission spectroscopy; eddy current testing; new principles of radiation thickness gauging for non-ferrous rolling mills; closed loop process control systems; quality control in metals industry. *Mailing Add:* 311 Dover Dr Walnut Creek CA 94598

KUNKLE, GEORGE ROBERT, b Elyria, Ohio, Mar 27, 34; m 58; c 4. ENVIRONMENTAL GEOLOGY, HYDROLOGY. *Educ:* Iowa State Univ, BS, 56; Univ Mich, MS, 58, PhD(geol), 61. *Prof Exp:* Geologist, Res Coun Alta, Can, 60-62 & US Geol Surv, 62-66; asst prof geol, Univ Toledo, 66-71; pres & environ consult, Earthview, Inc, 71-77; sr scientist, Jones & Henry Eng, LTD, 77-80; ASSOC & MGR, NEYER, TISCO & HINDO, LTD, 80- *Mem:* Nat Water Well Asn; Am Soc Testing & Mat; Am Inst Prof Geologists. *Res:* Groundwater resources and environmental geology; influence of land use and natural processes on the quality and quantity of ground and surface waters. *Mailing Add:* 6277 Sundance Trail Brighton MI 48116

KUNKLE, HERMAN MELVIN, JR, b Richmond, Va, Dec 19, 46; m 70; c 1. CELL BIOLOGY, DEVELOPMENTAL BIOLOGY. *Educ:* Carson-Newman Col, BS, 72; Univ Tenn, PhD(anat), 76. *Prof Exp:* Fel cell biol, Dept Pharmacol, Baylor Col Med, 76-78; ASST PROF ANAT, UNIV ALA, BIRMINGHAM, 78- *Concurrent Pos:* Am Cancer Soc grant, 76. *Mem:* Soc Study Reprod; AAAS. *Res:* Developmental cell biology and chromatin structure. *Mailing Add:* Dept of Anat Univ of Ala Birmingham AL 35294

KUNO, MOTOY, b Mukden, Manchuria, Aug 20, 28; m 56; c 3. PHYSIOLOGY. *Educ:* Kyoto Univ, MD, 54, PhD(physiol), 60. *Prof Exp:* Rockefeller Found fel, Univ Utah, 57-58, NIH fel, 58-59, res assoc physiol, 61-64; asst prof pharmacol, Yamaguchi Med Col, 60-61; vis assoc prof physiol, Nat Polytech Inst Mex, 64-65; res assoc, Yale Univ, 65-67; assoc prof, Univ Utah, 67-71; PROF PHYSIOL, UNIV NC, CHAPEL HILL, 71- *Res:* Neuropharmacology; neurophysiology. *Mailing Add:* Dept of Physiol Univ of NC Sch of Med Chapel Hill NC 27514

KUNOS, GEORGE, b Budapest, Hungary, May 14, 42; m 67; c 2. PHARMACOLOGY. *Educ:* Budapest Med Univ, MD, 66; McGill Univ, PhD(pharmacol), 73. *Prof Exp:* Lectr physiol, Dept of Med, Budapest Med Univ, 66-67, asst prof, 67-71; fel & lectr, 71-74, asst prof, Dept Pharmacol & Therapeut, 74-79, ASSOC PROF PHARMACOL, MCGILL UNIV, 79- *Concurrent Pos:* Scholar, Med Res Coun Que, 75-81. *Mem:* Am Soc Pharmacol & Exp Therapeut; Can Soc Clin Invest; Can Pharmacol Soc; Soc Exp Biol & Med. *Res:* The physiology and pharmacology of the autonomic nervous system; adrenergic receptor mechanisms; hormonal control of adrenergic receptors; opioid-adrenergic interactions in hypertension. *Mailing Add:* Dept Pharmacol McGill Univ 3655 Drummond Street Montreal PQ H3G 1Y6 Can

KUNSELMAN, A(RTHUR), RAYMOND, b Witchita Falls, Tex, Feb 22, 42; m 63; c 2. NUCLEAR PHYSICS, PARTICLE PHYSICS. *Educ:* Univ Calif, Berkeley, BA, 64, MA, 65, PhD(physics), 69. *Prof Exp:* Physicist, Lawrence Berkeley Lab, 69; FAC MEM PHYSICS, UNIV WYO, 69- *Concurrent Pos:* Consult, Rutherford Lab, Eng, 75. *Mem:* Am Asn Physics Teachers; Sigma Xi. *Res:* Muonic and hadronic atoms. *Mailing Add:* Dept of Physics Univ Wyo Laramie WY 82071

KUNTZ, GARLAND PARKE PAUL, b Fort Worth, Tex. CORROSION. *Educ:* Fla State Univ, BS, 66; Case Western Reserve Univ, MS, 69, PhD(chem), 72; Univ Alta, MSc, 82. *Prof Exp:* Fel, Dept Chem, Case Western Reserve Univ, 72-73; res assoc, Univ Alta, 73-75; ASSOC PROF PHYSICS & CHEM, CONCORDIA COL, EDMONTON, 75- *Mem:* Nat Asn Corrosion Engrs. *Res:* Corrosion of steels in an aqueous hydrogen sulfide environment. *Mailing Add:* Dept Sci Concordia Col Edmonton AB T5B 4E4 Can

KUNTZ, IRVING, b New York, NY, Feb 16, 25; m 77; c 2. POLYMER CHEMISTRY, ORGANIC CHEMISTRY. *Educ:* City Col New York, BS, 48; Polytech Inst Brooklyn, MS, 50, PhD(chem), 55. *Prof Exp:* Res chemist, Sprague Elec Co, Mass, 50-53; from sr chemist to sect head, Esso Res & Eng Co, 55-63, res assoc, 63-68, SR RES ASSOC, EXXON CHEM CO, 68- *Res:* Organic reaction mechanisms; polymer chemistry; ionic polymerizations; kinetics. *Mailing Add:* Exxon Chem Co PO Box 45 Linden NJ 07036

KUNTZ, IRWIN DOUGLAS, JR, b Nashville, Tenn, Aug 31, 39; m 61; c 3. PHYSICAL CHEMISTRY. *Educ:* Princeton Univ, AB, 61; Univ Calif, Berkeley, PhD(chem), 65. *Prof Exp:* Asst prof chem, Princeton Univ, 65-71; assoc prof, 71-76, PROF CHEM, UNIV CALIF, SAN FRANCISCO, 77- *Mem:* AAAS. *Res:* Physical chemistry of liquid state; hydration of macromolecules; spectroscopic studies of biological materials and fast reactions in biological systems. *Mailing Add:* Dept of Pharmaceut Chem Univ of Calif San Francisco CA 94143

KUNTZ, MEL ANTON, b Minneapolis, Minn, July 4, 39; m 67. GEOLOGY, PETROLOGY. *Educ:* Carleton Col, BA, 61; Northwestern Univ, MS, 64; Stanford Univ, PhD(geol), 68. *Prof Exp:* Asst prof geol, Amherst Col, 68-74; GEOLOGIST, US GEOL SURV, 74- *Mem:* Mineral Soc Am; Geol Soc Am. *Res:* Petrogenesis of epizonal and catazonal plutons; application of experimental studies to natural igneous and metamorphic rocks; geology of Colorado; petrogenesis of basalts; basalts of Snake River Plain, Idaho; geology of intermountain western United States. *Mailing Add:* US Geol Surv Mail Stop 913 Box 25046 Denver Fed Ctr Denver CO 80225

KUNTZ, RICHARD A, b Lakewood, NJ, Sept 7, 39; m 60; c 2. MATHEMATICS. *Educ:* Monmouth Col, BS, 64; Univ Md, MA, 67, PhD(math), 69. *Prof Exp:* Teaching asst math, Univ Md, 64-68; asst prof, 68-72, assoc prof, 72-76, chmn dept, 74-76, PROF MATH, MONMOUTH COL, NJ, 76-, DEAN GRAD SCH, 76- *Mem:* Am Math Soc; Math Asn Am. *Res:* Abstract algebra; ideal theory in commutative rings. *Mailing Add:* Dept of Math Monmouth Col West Long Branch NJ 07764

KUNTZ, ROBERT ELROY, b Lawton, Okla, Feb 23, 16; m 38; c 2. PARASITOLOGY, HELMINTHOLOGY. *Educ:* Univ Okla, BA, 39, MS, 40; Univ Mich, PhD(zool), 47; Am Bd Med Microbiol, dipl. *Prof Exp:* Asst zool, Univ Okla, 38-40; teaching fel, Univ Mich, 40-43; mem staff, Naval Med Sch, Bethesda, Md, 43, head epidemiol teams, SPac, 43-45, res parasitologist,

Naval Med Res Inst, 45-48, head parasitol dept, Naval Med Res Unit 3, Cairo, 48-53, instr, Naval Med Sch, 53-57, head parasitol dept, Naval Med Res Unit 2, Taipei, 57-62, res parasitologist & head tech serv dept, Naval Med Res Inst, 62-64; HEAD PARASITOL DEPT, SOUTHWEST FOUND RES & EDUC, 64- Concurrent Pos: Exam parasitol, Fac Med, Ain Shams Univ, Cairo, 50-52; res prof Univ Md & adj prof, microbiol, Univ Tex Med Sch, San Antonio; consult, Parasitic Div, WHO. Mem: Am Soc Trop Med & Hyg; Am Soc Parasitologists; Am Micros Soc; Int Primatol Soc; SW Asn Parasitol. Res: Biology of schistosomes and other helminths; survey-type investigations on parasites of man and lower vertebrates; epidemiology of helminth diseases and zoogeography of parasites of vertebrates, especially the parasites of primates. Mailing Add: Parasitol Dept Southwest Found Res & Educ San Antonio TX 78284

KUNTZ, ROBERT ROY, b Barry, Ill, Apr 10, 37; m 59; c 1. PHYSICAL CHEMISTRY. Educ: Culver-Stockton Col, BA, 59; Carnegie Inst Technol, MS, 62, PhD(chem), 63. Prof Exp: From asst prof to assoc prof, 62-71, chmn dept, 78-79, assoc chair, 79-81, PROF CHEM, UNIV MO-COLUMBIA, 71- Concurrent Pos: Assoc prog dir, NSF, 73-74. Mem: Am Soc Photobiol; Sigma Xi; Am Chem Soc; Am Phys Soc; Radiation Res Soc. Res: Photolysis and radiolysis of organic compounds, free radical kinetics, radiation protection; flash photolysis; photobiology. Mailing Add: Dept of Chem Univ of Mo Columbia MO 65201

KUNTZMAN, RONALD GROVER, b New York, NY, Sept 17, 33. BIOCHEMISTRY, PHARMACOLOGY. Educ: Brooklyn Col, BS, 55; George Washington Univ, MS, PhD(biochem), 62. Prof Exp: Chemist, USPHS, 55-62; sr biochemist, Wellcome Res Labs, Burroughs & Co, 62-70, dep head biochem pharmacol dept, 67-70; assoc dir dept biochem & drug metab, 70-72, assoc dir biol res, 72-73, ASST VPRES & DIR EXP THERAPEUT, HOFFMANN-LA ROCHE INC, 73- Honors & Awards: John Jacob Abel Award, Am Soc Pharmacol & Exp Therapeut, 69. Mem: Am Soc Pharmacol & Exp Therapeut (secy-treas, 81-83); Am Soc Biol Chemists. Res: Biochemical effects and metabolism of drugs and steroid hormones, induced enzyme syntheses; syntheses metabolism and storage of biogenic amines; preclinical development of new drugs; pharmacokinetics and efficacy studies on new therapeutics. Mailing Add: Hoffmann-La Roche Inc Nutley NJ 07110

KUNZ, ALBERT BARRY, b Philadelphia, Pa, Oct 2, 40; m 64; c 1. CHEMICAL PHYSICS, SOLID STATE SCIENCE. Educ: Muhlenberg Col, BS, 62; Lehigh Univ, MS, 64, PhD(physics), 66. Prof Exp: Res assoc physics, Lehigh Univ, 66-69; res asst prof, 69-71, from asst prof to assoc prof, 71-76, PROF PHYSICS, UNIV ILL, URBANA, 76- Concurrent Pos: Consult, US Air Force Aerospace Res Lab, 71 & E I du Pont de Nemours & Co, Inc, 73-79; adj prof physics, Mich Technol Univ, 81- Mem: Am Phys Soc; Sigma Xi. Res: Solid state, atomic and molecular theory; band theory of solids, solid state spectroscopy; spectra of ions, atoms and molecules; theory of ground state properties of polyatomic systems; theory of catalysis is being developed. Mailing Add: Dept of Physics Univ of Ill Urbana IL 61801

KUNZ, ALBERT L, b Bloomington, Ind, Oct 3, 33; m 57; c 5. PHYSIOLOGY. Educ: Ind Univ, AB, 56, MD, 59; Ohio State Univ, MS, 65. Prof Exp: Instr, 62-63, asst prof, 65-69, assoc prof, 69-76, PROF PHYSIOL, OHIO STATE UNIV, 76- Concurrent Pos: Nat Heart Inst fel, 63-65; Alexander Von Humboldt fel, 74-75. Res: Respiratory control; anomalous viscosity of blood. Mailing Add: Dept of Physiol Ohio State Univ Columbus OH 43210

KUNZ, BERNARD ALEXANDER, b Montreal, Que, Mar 5, 52. DNA REPAIR, MUTAGENESIS. Educ: McGill Univ, Que, BSc, 74; Brock Univ, Ont, MSc, 76; York Univ, PhD(molecular genetics), 81. Prof Exp: VIS FEL, NAT INST ENVIRON HEALTH SCIENCES, 81- Mem: Genetics Soc Can; Environ Mutagen Soc; AAAS; NY Acad Sci. Res: Effects of thymidylate starvation on inter- and intra-chromosomal recombination in yeast; mutagen specificity in E coli; kinetics of induced recombination and mutation. Mailing Add: Nat Inst Environ Health Sci PO Box 12233 Research Triangle Park NC 27709

KUNZ, HANS JOSEPH, physics, physical chemistry, see previous edition

KUNZ, HAROLD RUSSELL, b Troy, NY, Oct 3, 31; m 56; c 2. THERMODYNAMICS, HEAT TRANSFER. Educ: Rensselaer Polytech Inst, BME, 53, MS, 58, PhD(heat transfer), 66. Prof Exp: Jr engr heat transfer & fluid mech res, Pratt & Whitney Aircraft Div, 53-54, anal engr, 54-57, sr anal engr, 57-60, asst proj engr heat transfer res, 60-63, proj engr heat transfer & fuel cell res, 63-68, sr proj engr, 68-74, sr proj engr, Power Systs Div, 75, SR PROJ ENGR FUEL CELL RES, POWER SYSTS DIV, UNITED TECHNOLOGIES CORP, 75- Concurrent Pos: Adj asst prof, Hartford Grad Ctr, 66-70, adj assoc prof, 70- Mem: Electrochem Soc; Am Soc Mech Engrs. Res: Thermodynamics; single-phase and two-phase fluid mechanics and heat transfer; electrochemistry; electrocatalysis. Mailing Add: United Technologies Corp PO Box 109 South Windsor CT 06074

KUNZ, KAISER SCHOEN, b New Middletown, Ind, Oct 16, 15; m 44; c 3. PHYSICS. Educ: Univ Ind, AB, 36; Univ Cincinnati, AM, 37, PhD(theoret physics), 39. Prof Exp: Instr math, Univ Cincinnati, 39-42; instr electronics, Cruft Lab, Harvard Univ, 42-45, res assoc, 45-46, res fel, 46-47, lectr appl math, comput lab, 47-49; assoc prof elec eng, Case Inst Technol, 49-51; from res physicist to head interpretation res dept, Schlumberger Well Surv Corp, 51-60; res prof physics & elec eng, 60-76, RES PROF PHYSICS, N MEX STATE UNIV, 76- Mem: Fel AAAS; Am Phys Soc; Inst Elec & Electronics Engrs, Am Asn Physics Teachers. Res: Propagation of electromagnetic waves in dynamic media; quantum electronics and lasers; electrodynamics; field theory; numerical analysis. Mailing Add: Dept of Physics NMex State Univ Las Cruces NM 88003

KUNZ, NANCE KAY DICCIANI, b Philadelphia, Pa, Oct 18, 47; m 70. KINETICS & CATALYSIS, TRANSPORT PROCESSES. Educ: Villanova Univ, BS, 69; Univ Va, MS, 70; Univ Pa, PhD(chem eng), 77. Prof Exp: Supt water treatment, City Philadelphia, 72-74; res engr, 77-78, res mgr, 78-81, DIR RES, AIR PRODS & CHEMS, INC, 81- Mem: Am Inst Chem Engrs; Soc Women Engrs. Res: Mass transfer; three phase fluid dynamics; heterogeneous kinetics and catalysis; separations science. Mailing Add: Air Prods & Chems Inc Box 538 Allentown PA 18105

KUNZ, SIDNEY EDMUND, b Fredericksburg, Tex, Dec 24, 35; m 60; c 3. ENTOMOLOGY, ECOLOGY. Educ: Tex A&M Univ, BS, 58, MS, 62; Okla State Univ, PhD(entom), 67. Prof Exp: Surv entomologist, Okla State Univ, 61-64, exten entomologist, 64-67; res entomologist, Kerrville, 67-69, res entomologist, College Sta, 69-77, RES LEADER, RES ENTOMOLOGIST, SCI & EDUC AGR RES SERV, USDA, 77- Concurrent Pos: Entom consult, Food & Agr Orgn UN Develop Prog, Mauritius, 73-74 & USAID, Tanzania, Samalia, 82. Mem: Entom Soc Am; Am Registry Prof Entomologists; Sigma Xi. Res: Biology, ecology and area integrated pest management control of biting flies of cattle, horn flies and stable flies. Mailing Add: Sci & Educ Agr Res Serv USDA PO Box 232 Kerrville TX 78028

KUNZ, WALTER ERNEST, b Chattanooga, Tenn, Apr 17, 18; m 43; c 5. RADIATION PHYSICS. Educ: Davidson Col, BS, 40; Univ Tenn, PhD(physics), 54. Prof Exp: Physicist, Oak Ridge Nat Lab, 52-54, US Naval Res Lab, 54-58 & AEC, 58-62; STAFF MEM, LOS ALAMOS SCI LAB, 62- Mem: Am Phys Soc. Res: Nuclear reaction at low energy; gamma ray measurements; extreme ultraviolet; solar x-rays; research and development on safeguards for fissionable materials. Mailing Add: Group Q-2 MS 562 Los Alamos Sci Lab Los Alamos NM 87545

KUNZE, ADOLF WILHELM GERHARD, b Philadelphia, Pa, Aug 23, 36; m 67; c 2. GEOPHYSICS. Educ: Pa State Univ, BS, 63, PhD(geophys), 73. Prof Exp: Nat Res Coun res assoc lunar geophys, Johnson Space Ctr, NASA, Houston, 73-74; asst prof, 74-79, ASSOC PROF GEOL, UNIV AKRON, 79- Mem: Am Geophys Union; Soc Explor Geophysicists; Sigma Xi. Res: Tectonophysics: isostatic adjustment processes and rheologic behavior of geologic models; planetology, particularly interpretation of planetary gravity anomalies and satellite imagery. Mailing Add: Dept of Geol Univ of Akron Akron OH 44325

KUNZE, DIANA LEE, b Winthrop, Mass, Dec 19, 39. MEDICAL PHYSIOLOGY. Educ: Stetson Univ, BS, 61; Emory Univ, MS, 66; Univ Utah, PhD(physiol), 70. Prof Exp: Researcher neurophysiol, Nat Ctr Sci Res, France, 71-72; res assoc cardiovasc physiol, Univ Utah, 72-73; asst prof cardiovasc physiol, 73-78, ASSOC PROF PHYSIOL & BIOPHYSICS, UNIV TEX MED BR GALVESTON, 78- Res: Studies of control mechanisms of cardiac rhythm by neural input and by local factors. Mailing Add: Dept of Physiol & Biophys Univ of Tex Med Br Galveston TX 77550

KUNZE, GEORGE WILLIAM, b Warda, Tex, Sept 16, 22; m 48; c 2. SOIL MINERALOGY. Educ: Tex A&M Univ, BS, 48, MS, 50; Pa State Univ, PhD(soil mineral), 52. Prof Exp: From asst prof to assoc prof, 52-60, assoc dean, 67-68, PROF SOIL & CROPS SCI, TEX A&M UNIV, 60-, DEAN GRAD COL, 68- Concurrent Pos: Consult ed, Soil Sci, 58-; grad prog consult, Bangladesh Agr Univ, 70 & Grad Sch Agr Sci, Castelar, Arg, 72; mem, Fed Adv Comt for Affirmative Action in Employment Pract in Inst of Higher Educ, Adv to Secy of Labor & Secy of HEW, 74-76; vpres, Conf Southern Grad Schs, 79-80, pres, 80-81. Mem: Fel AAAS; fel Am Soc Agron; Soil Sci Soc Am; Clay Minerals Soc; fel Mineral Soc Am. Res: Soil chemistry. Mailing Add: Grad Col Tex A&M Univ College Station TX 77843

KUNZE, JAY FREDERICK, b Pittsburgh, Pa, Feb 24, 33; m 56; c 3. PHYSICS. Educ: Carnegie Inst Technol, BS, 54, MS, 55, PhD(nuclear physics), 59. Prof Exp: Proj physicist & asst, Carnegie Inst Technol, 54-58; physicist, Idaho Test Sta, Gen Elec Co, 58-65, mgr nuclear technol, 65-69; mgr oper & anal, Aerojet Nuclear Corp, 69-70, mgr reactor technol, LPT, 70-74; mgr geothermal & adv technol, EG&G Idaho, Inc, 74-78; VPRES & GEN MGR, ENERGY SERV INC, 78- Concurrent Pos: Site leader, Air Force res solar eclipse expeds, 54-55; affil prof, Univ Idaho, 59-; assoc prof, Univ Utah, 69- Mem: Am Nuclear Soc; Nat Soc Prof Engrs. Res: Geothermal energy; experimental reactor physics and reactor analysis; experimental high energy physics; astronomy. Mailing Add: Rt 4 Box 224 Idaho Falls ID 83402

KUNZE, OTTO ROBERT, b Warda, Tex, May 27, 25; m 51; c 4. ENGINEERING, AGRICULTURE. Educ: Tex A&M Univ, BS, 50; Iowa State Univ, MS, 51; Mich State Univ, PhD(agr eng), 64. Prof Exp: Agr & indust engr, Cent Power & Light Co, 51-56; assoc prof, 57-61, 64-69, PROF ELEC POWER & PROCESSING, TEX A&M UNIV, 69- Concurrent Pos: Consult, post-harvest rice processing, India, 75; mem, Tex Air Control Bd, 78- Mem: Fel Am Soc Agr Engrs; Am Asn Cereal Chemists; AAAS; Nat Soc Prof Engrs. Res: Electric power and processing in agriculture; physical properties of agricultural products; hygroscopicity of rice and its effects on the grain; moisture absorption in low-moisture rough rice and rapid moisture removal in grains. Mailing Add: Dept of Agr Eng Tex A&M Univ College Station TX 77843

KUNZE, RAY A, b Des Moines, Iowa, Mar 7, 28; m 51; c 5. MATHEMATICS. Educ: Univ Chicago, BS, 50, MS, 51, PhD(math), 57. Prof Exp: Asst prof math, Brandeis Univ, 60-62; from assoc prof to prof, Wash Univ, 63-69; chmn dept, 69-74, PROF MATH, UNIV CALIF, IRVINE, 69- Concurrent Pos: Consult, Inst Defense Anal, 54-, Prentice Hall & McGraw Hill, 61- Mem: Am Math Soc. Res: Harmonic analysis; representations of Lie Groups. Mailing Add: Dept of Math Univ of Calif Irvine CA 92664

KUNZE, RAYMOND J, b La Grange, Tex, Oct 25, 28; m 51; c 2. SOIL PHYSICS. Educ: Tex A&M Univ, BS, 51, MS, 56; Iowa State Univ, PhD(soil physics), 60. Prof Exp: Asst, Tex A&M Univ, 54-56; from asst to res assoc, Iowa State Univ, 56-60, NSF res fel & asst prof soil physics, 60-62; soil scientist, 62-65, RES SOIL SCIENTIST, SCI & EDUC ADMIN-AGR RES, USDA, 65-; PROF SOIL SCI, MICH STATE UNIV, 70-, ASSOC CHMN, 80- Concurrent Pos: Assoc prof soils, Mich State Univ, 65-70; vis prof, Purdue Univ, 74. Mem: Am Soc Agron; Soil Sci Soc Am. Res: Measurement of unsaturated flow of moisture in soils; predictions, by computer techniques and analysis, of water movement and distribution in the profile based on measured characteristics of the soil; expertise in operating double-gamma beam for simultaneous, nondestructive, two-component soil and water analysis. Mailing Add: Dept of Soil Sci Mich State Univ East Lansing MI 48824

KUNZLE, HANS PETER, b Kreuzlingen, Switz, Sept 1, 40; m 68; c 3. MATHEMATICAL PHYSICS. Educ: Swiss Fed Inst Technol, dipl, 64; Univ London, PhD(relativity), 67. Prof Exp: Res asst, Kings Col, Univ London, 67-68; lectr & asst res mathematician, Univ Calif, Berkeley, 68-70; asst prof, 70-73, assoc prof, 73-80, PROF MATH, UNIV ALTA, 80- Mem: Am Math Soc; Am Phys Soc; Can Math Soc. Res: Mathematical problems in general relativity; applications of differential geometry to physics, especially relativistic mechanics and field theories. Mailing Add: Dept Math Univ Alta Edmonton AB T6G 2G1 Can

KUNZLER, JOHN EUGENE, b Willard, Utah, Apr 25, 23; m 50; c 4. PHYSICAL CHEMISTRY. Educ: Univ Utah, BS, 45; Univ Calif, PhD(phys chem), 50. Prof Exp: Asst, Purdue Univ, 45-46; from asst to res assoc, Univ Calif, 46-52; mem tech staff, 52-61, head metal physics res dept, 61-69, DIR ELECTRONIC MAT & DEVICE LAB, BELL TEL LABS, INC, 69- Honors & Awards: John Price Wetherill Award, Franklin Inst, 64. Mem: AAAS; Am Chem Soc; fel Am Phys Soc. Res: Electrical, thermal and magnetic properties of solids at low temperatures; Fermi surface; galvanomagnetic and magnetothermal effects; high purity metals; high-field superconductivity; superconducting magnets; low temperature heat capacity and related thermal effects. Mailing Add: Rm 2D-333 Tel Labs PO Box 261 Murray Hill NJ 07974

KUO, ALBERT YI-SHUONG, b Tayuan, Taiwan, Nov 4, 39; m 65; c 1. PHYSICAL OCEANOGRAPHY, HYDRODYNAMICS. Educ: Nat Taiwan Univ, BS, 62; Univ Iowa, MS, 65; Johns Hopkins Univ, PhD(fluid mech), 70. Prof Exp: Jr instr fluid mech, Johns Hopkins Univ, 67-69, res assoc, 70; assoc marine scientist, 70-78, SR MARINE SCIENTIST & HEAD HYDRAULICS SECT, VA INST MARINE SCI, 78- Concurrent Pos: Asst prof, Univ Va & Col William & Mary, 70-73, assoc prof, 73-80, prof 81- Mem: Am Phys Soc; Am Soc Civil Engrs. Res: Turbulence, diffusion, dispersion; estuarine mathematical model; estuarine hydrodynamics; sediment transport; coastal circulation. Mailing Add: Dept of Phys Oceanog & Hydraulics Va Inst Marine Sci Gloucester Point VA 23062

KUO, BENJAMIN CHUNG-I, b China, Oct 5, 30; m 54; c 1. ELECTRICAL ENGINEERING. Educ: Univ NH, BS, 54; Univ Ill, MS, 56, PhD(elec eng), 58. Prof Exp: Plant engr, Laible Mfg Co, 53-54; asst, 54-57, from asst prof to assoc prof, 58-66, PROF ELEC ENG, UNIV ILL, URBANA, 66- Mem: Inst Elec & Electronics Engrs. Res: Feedback control systems; sampled-data systems. Mailing Add: 3206 Valleybrook Dr Champaign IL 61820

KUO, CHAN-HWA, b Shanghai, China, Oct 7, 31; US citizen; m 57; c 3. ORGANIC CHEMISTRY. Educ: Hartwick Col, BS, 57; Rensselaer Polytech Inst, MS, 58; Polytech Inst Brooklyn, PhD(org chem), 75. Prof Exp: Res chemist, 58-74, SR RES CHEMIST, MERCK & CO, INC, 74- Mem: Sigma Xi. Res: Synthesis of griseofulvin, fluoro- and polychlorogriseofulvin, estrone, prostaglandin E1; synthesis and conformational analysis of pantetheine analogs; synthesis and relative configurational studies of the chiral lactone derived from thermozymocidin (myriocin). Mailing Add: 105 E Nassau Ave S Plainfield NJ 07080

KUO, CHAO-YING, immunochemistry, see previous edition

KUO, CHENG-YIH, b Tainan, Taiwan, Apr 2, 42. POLYMER SCIENCE. Educ: Nat Taiwan Univ, BS, 66; Univ Akron, MS, 69, PhD(polymer sci), 73. Prof Exp: Fel, Inst Polymer Sci, Univ Akron, 73-75; sr chemist, 75-80, ASSOC SCIENTIST COATINGS RES, GLIDDEN-DURKEE DIV, SCM CORP, 80- Mem: Am Chem Soc. Res: Morphology and physical properties of block copolymers; solution properties of polymers and characterization of organic coatings. Mailing Add: Dwight P Joyce Res Ctr PO Box 8827 Strongsville OH 44136

KUO, CHIANG-HAI, b Tainan, Taiwan, Feb 10, 36; m 59; c 2. CHEMICAL & PETROLEUM ENGINEERING. Educ: Nat Taiwan Univ, BS, 57; Univ Houston, MS, 61, PhD(chem eng), 64. Prof Exp: Teaching asst, Nat Taiwan Univ, 57-59; engr, Shell Develop Co, 62-64, res engr, 64-70; assoc prof, 70-77, PROF CHEM ENG, MISS STATE UNIV, 77- Honors & Awards: Award, Am Inst Chem Engrs, 64; Bronze Medal Award, US Environ Protection Agency, 75. Mem: Am Inst Chem Engrs; Am Inst Mining, Metall & Petrol Engrs. Res: Mass transfer and chemical reactions; applied mathematics; flow through porous media; heat transfer; petroleum recovery processes; air and water pollution control. Mailing Add: Dept of Chem Eng Miss State Univ Mississippi State MS 39762

KUO, CHING-MING, b Taipei, Taiwan, Sept 23, 35; m 62; c 3. REPRODUCTIVE PHYSIOLOGY, ICHTHYOLOGY. Educ: Nat Taiwan Univ, BSc, 58; Scripps Inst Oceanog, Univ Calif, San Diego, PhD(marine biol), 74. Prof Exp: Lab instr zool, Nat Taiwan Univ, 60-64; res asst ichthyol, Scripps Inst Oceanog, 64-70; res assoc physiol, Oceanic Inst, 70-72, head aquaculture, 72-74, sr research physiol, 75-80; SR SCIENTIST PHYSIOL, INT CTR LIVING AQUATIC RESOURCES MGT, 80- Mem: Am Soc Zoologists; Sigma Xi. Res: Process and mechanism involved in gonadal maturation and ovulation; control of ovarian development and induced ovulation of marine teleosts; artificial propagation and genetic improvement of cultured fish. Mailing Add: Int Ctr Living Aquatic Resources Mgt MCC PO Box 1501 Makati Metro Manila 96795 Philippines

KUO, CHO-CHOU, b Taiwan, Sept 12, 34; m 64; c 1. MEDICAL MICROBIOLOGY. Educ: Nat Taiwan Univ, MD, 60; Univ Wash, PhD(prev med), 70. Prof Exp: Fel, 67-71, asst prof, 71-76, assoc prof, 76-80, PROF PATHOBIOL, UNIV WASH, 80- Mem: Am Pub Health Asn; Am Col Prev Med; Am Soc Microbiol; Am Asn Immunologists. Res: Microbiology and immunology of the Chlamydia Trachomatis organisms which cause eye and genital infection, development of diagnostic methods and prevention of the disease. Mailing Add: Dept of Pathobiol SC-38 Univ of Wash Seattle WA 98195

KUO, ERIC YUNG-HUEI, b Chiayi, Taiwan, Aug 8, 34; US citizen; m 68; c 2. ONCOLOGY, VETERINARY MEDICINE. Educ: Nat Taiwan Univ, BS, 60; Univ Ill, Urbana, MS, 66, PhD(vet med sci), 70. Prof Exp: Asst vet parasitol, Dept Vet Med, Nat Taiwan Univ, 61-63; res asst vet physiol, Col Vet Med, Univ Ill, Urbana, 63-69; res assoc endocrinol, Dept Physiol, Sch Med, Boston Univ, 69-71; sr investr vet endocrinol, 71-74, prin investr oncol, Mason Res Inst, 75-76; vet med officer, USDA, 76-80. Concurrent Pos: Vet, Southeast Vet Hosp, Taiwan, 61-63; lectr, Grad Div, Anna Maria Col, Mass, 76- Mem: AAAS; Endocrine Soc; Am Vet Med Asn. China. Res: The roles of infection, infection hormonal imbalance, radiation and immunosuppression in mammary oncogenesis; the responses of hosts and tumors to surgery, radiation and chemotherapy. Mailing Add: 2455 Sedgefield Dr Chapel Hill NC 27514

KUO, FRANKLIN F(A-KUN), b China, Apr 22, 34; m 58; c 2. ELECTRICAL ENGINEERING. Educ: Univ Ill, BS, 55, MS, 56, PhD(elec eng), 58. Prof Exp: Asst prof elec eng, Polytech Inst Brooklyn, 58-60; mem tech staff, Bell Tel Labs, Inc, 60-66; PROF ELEC ENG, UNIV HAWAII, 66- Concurrent Pos: Mem Cosine comt, Nat Acad Eng, 65-; liaison scientist, US Off Naval Res, London, 71-72; consult ed, Prentice-Hall, Inc; dir info systs, Off Secy Defense, 76-77. Mem: Fel Inst Elec & Electronics Engrs; Asn Comput Mach. Res: Digital computers; information transmission; computer networks; data communications. Mailing Add: Dept of Elec Eng Univ of Hawaii Honolulu HI 96822

KUO, HARNG-SHEN, b Hangchow, China, June 9, 35; m 67; c 1. CHEMISTRY, BIOCHEMISTRY. Educ: Cheng Kung Univ Taiwan, BS, 59; La State Univ, New Orleans, MS, 66; Pa State Univ, PhD(chem), 70. Prof Exp: Analyst cement, Taiwan Chi Hsin Co, 61; engr, Taiwan Fertilizer Co, 61-64; chemist & fel, Lawrence Berkeley Lab, 70-71; anal res chemist, 71-72, radiation safety officer, 72-75, SR ANAL RES CHEMIST, CUTTER LABS, 75- Mem: Am Chem Soc. Mailing Add: Cutter Labs Fourth & Parker Sts Berkeley CA 94710

KUO, HSIAO-LAN, b Mancheng, China, Jan 7, 15; m 49; c 3. DYNAMIC METEOROLOGY, FLUID DYNAMICS. Educ: Tsing Hua Univ, BS, 37; Univ Chicago, PhD(meteorol), 48. Prof Exp: From res assoc meteorol to res meteorologist, Mass Inst Technol, 49-57; vis assoc prof meteorol, Univ Chicago, 57-58; supvr res meteorol & hurricane res proj, Mass Inst Technol, 58-62; PROF METEOROL, UNIV CHICAGO, 62- Res: Dynamics of planetary atmospheres and atmospheric vortices; general circulation; atmospheric radiation; high atmosphere. Mailing Add: Dept of Geophys Sci Univ of Chicago Chicago IL 60637

KUO, J(AMES) CHENG-WU, b Amoy City, China, Feb 7, 38; m 62; c 1. CHEMICAL ENGINEERING. Educ: Univ Taiwan, BS, 57; Univ Wash, Seattle, MS, 62; Univ Minn, PhD(chem eng), 65. Prof Exp: Res chem engr, Cent Res Div Lab, Mobile Oil Corp, 66-67; sr res engr, Process Res & Tech Serv Div, Mobil Oil Res & Develop Co, 67-80; WITH SCHERING CORP, 80- Mem: Am Inst Chem Eng. Res: Chemical kinetics; chemical reactor theory; applied mathematics; automotive emission control research. Mailing Add: Schering Corp 60 Orange St Bloomfield NJ 07003

KUO, JOHN TSUNG-FEN, b Hangchow, China, Apr 1, 22; m 57; c 3. GEOPHYSICS. Educ: Univ Redlands, BS, 52; Calif Inst Technol, MS, 54; Stanford Univ, PhD(geophys), 58. Hon Degrees: ScD, Univ Redlands, 78. Prof Exp: From instr to asst prof geol & geophys, San Jose State Col, 56-60; res scientist, Lamont Geol Observ, 60-64, assoc prof, 64-69, PROF MINING & GEOPHYSICS, COLUMBIA UNIV, 69- Concurrent Pos: Res assoc, Stanford Univ, 58-60; NSF sr fel, Cambridge Univ, 70-71; consult. Mem: Seismol Soc Am; Am Geophys Union; Soc Explor Geophys; fel Geol Soc Am; fel Royal Astron Soc. Res: Acoustic, elastical EM wave scattering and deffractions; geophysical exploration; solid earth and ocean dynamics. Mailing Add: Henry Krumb Sch of Mines Columbia Univ New York NY 10027

KUO, JYH-FA, b Taiwan, China, May 19, 33; m 65; c 2. BIOCHEMISTRY, PHARMACOLOGY. Educ: Nat Taiwan Univ, BS, 57; SDak State Univ, MS, 61; Univ Ill, Urbana, PhD(biochem), 64. Hon Degrees: Dr, Linkoping Univ, Sweden, 80. Prof Exp: Res biochemist, Lederle Labs, Am Cyanamid Co, 64-68; from asst prof to assoc prof pharmacol, Sch Med, Yale Univ, 68-72; assoc prof, 72-76, PROF PHARMACOL, SCH MED, EMORY UNIV, 76- Concurrent Pos: NIH res career develop award, 71-75; vis professorship, Swedish Med Res Coun, Linkoping Univ, Sweden, 79. Mem: AAAS; Am Soc Biol Chemists; Am Soc Pharmacol & Exp Therapeut; Am Chem Soc. Res: Action of hormones; role of cyclic adenocine monophosphate, cyclic guanosine monophosphate, cyclic cytidine monophosphate, calcium and protein kinases in cellular function and metabolism. Mailing Add: Dept of Pharmacol Emory Univ Sch of Med Atlanta GA 30322

KUO, MINGSHANG, b Kaohsiung, Taiwan, Oct, 11, 49; m 74; c 2. SPECTROSCOPY, CHROMATOGRAPHY. Educ: Nat Tsing-Hua Univ, Taiwan, BS, 71; Mich State Univ, PhD(chem), 79. Prof Exp: SCIENTIST ANAL CHEM, UPJOHN CO, 79- Mem: Am Chem Soc. Res: Development of analytical methods for pharmaceuticals and chemicals; identification of chemical structures of impurities and by-products of chemical processes. Mailing Add: Upjohn Co 7700 Portage Rd Kalamazoo MI 49001

KUO, PAO-KUANG, b Hopei, China, Feb 23, 35; m 61; c 2. THEORETICAL PHYSICS. *Educ:* Nat Taiwan Univ, BSc, 57; Univ Minn, PhD(physics), 64. *Prof Exp:* Instr physics, Cornell Univ, 64-66; from res assoc to instr, Mass Inst Technol, 66-68; vis lectr, Johns Hopkins Univ, 68-69; asst prof, 69-71, ASSOC PROF PHYSICS, WAYNE STATE UNIV, 71- *Mem:* Am Phys Soc. *Res:* Quantum electrodynamics; theory of elementary particles and coherence phenomena. *Mailing Add:* Dept of Physics Wayne State Univ Detroit MI 48202

KUO, PETER TE, b Fukien, China, Mar 21, 16; m 49; c 2. INTERNAL MEDICINE. *Educ:* St John's Univ, China, MD, 39; Univ Pa, MSc, 49, DSc(med), 50. *Prof Exp:* From asst to asst prof med, Med Sch, St John's Univ, China, 40-46; from instr to prof, Sch Med, Univ Pa, 50-73, sr staff mem, Robinette Found Cardiovasc Res, Hosp Univ Pa, 52-73; PROF MED & DIR CARDIOVASC DIV, RUTGERS MED SCH, COL MED & DENT NJ, 73- *Concurrent Pos:* Consult cardiol & probs lipid metab; estab investr, Am Heart Asn, 55-60; USPHS career develop award, 61-66. *Honors & Awards:* Sci Award, Am Chinese Asn. *Mem:* Fel Gerontol Soc; fel Am Col Physicians; fel Am Col Cardiol; Am Soc Clin Nutrit; Am Nutrit Inst. *Res:* Blood and tissue lipids and their relationship to the problem of arteriosclerosis; circulatory hemodynamics. *Mailing Add:* Dept of Med Div Cardiovasc Dis Rutgers Med Sch Piscataway NJ 08854

KUO, SHAN SUN, b Nanking, China, Nov 22, 22; m 58; c 1. APPLIED MATHEMATICS, COMPUTER SCIENCE. *Educ:* Nat Chung Cheng Univ, China, BEng, 44; Ohio State Univ, MSc, 48; Harvard Univ, MEng, 54; Yale Univ, DEng, 58. *Prof Exp:* Instr, Nat Chung Cheng Univ, China, 44-46; lectr, Formosa Inst Technol, 46-47; struct engr, Ohio State Univ, 48-52; engr, Carew Steel Prod Corp, 52-53; engr, Fay Spofford & Thorndike, 54-55; from asst prof to assoc prof civil eng, Tufts Univ, 58-64, dir comput ctr, 61-64; prof math, 64-77, PROF COMPUT SCI, UNIV NH, 77-, DIR COMPUT CTR, 64- *Mem:* Am Math Soc; Asn Comput Mach; Am Soc Civil Engrs; Am Soc Mech Engrs; Am Soc Eng Educ. *Res:* Numerical analysis; computer applications. *Mailing Add:* Dept of Math Univ of NH Durham NH 03824

KUO, SHIOU, b Ping-Tung, Taiwan, Oct 8, 43; m 69; c 3. SOIL CHEMISTRY, PHYSICAL CHEMISTRY. *Educ:* Chung-Hsing Univ, Taiwan, BS, 66; Utah State Univ, MS, 70; Univ Maine, PhD(soil chem), 73. *Prof Exp:* Res assoc soils, Iowa State Univ, 74-75; res assoc agron, Univ Calif, Davis, 75-78; ASST SOIL SCIENTIST, WESTERN WASH RES & EXTEN CTR, WASH STATE UNIV, 78- *Mem:* Am Soc Agron; Soil Sci Soc Am; Chinese Agr Asn; Sigma Xi. *Res:* Nitrogen transformations in soils and their relation to the nitrogen uptake by plant; cations and anions reactions with soil colloidal particals and the plant growth. *Mailing Add:* Western Wash Res & Exten Ctr Wash State Univ Puyallup WA 98371

KUO, THOMAS TZU SZU, b Peiping, China, July 31, 32; m 62; c 2. THEORETICAL PHYSICS. *Educ:* Naval Col Eng, Taiwan, BS, 54; Tsing Hua Univ, Taiwan, MS, 59; Univ Pittsburgh, PhD(physics), 64. *Prof Exp:* From instr to asst prof physics, Princeton Univ, 64-68; vis scientist, Argonne Nat Lab, 68 & 69; assoc prof, 68-72, PROF PHYSICS, STATE UNIV NY STONY BROOK, 72- *Concurrent Pos:* Nordita guest prof physics, Univ Oslo, 74-75 & 78; vis prof, Julich Nuclear Res Ctr, WGer, 79; hon prof, Inst High Energy Physics, China, Jilin Univ & Fudan Univ, 81. *Honors & Awards:* Humboldt Award Sr Am Scientists, 77. *Mem:* Fel Am Phys Soc. *Res:* Theoretical nuclear physics; nuclear structure and the free nucleon nucleon interaction; nuclear shell model; many body problems. *Mailing Add:* Dept of Physics State Univ NY Stony Brook NY 11790

KUO, TZEE-KE, b Peking, China, Apr 13, 37; m 61. HIGH ENERGY PHYSICS. *Educ:* Nat Taiwan Univ, BS, 57; Univ Chicago, MS, 60; Cornell Univ, PhD(physics), 63. *Prof Exp:* Res assoc physics, Brookhaven Nat Lab, 63-65; asst prof, 65-68, assoc prof, 68-77, PROF PHYSICS, PURDUE UNIV, WEST LAFAYETTE, 77- *Mem:* Am Phys Soc. *Res:* Elementary particle physics. *Mailing Add:* Dept of Physics Purdue Univ West Lafayette IN 47907

KUO, YEN-LONG, b Taipei, Taiwan, Nov 18, 36; m 66; c 1. ELECTRICAL ENGINEERING. *Educ:* Taipei Inst Technol, Taiwan, Dipl elec eng, 57; Okla State Univ, MS, 61; Univ Calif, Berkeley, PhD(elec eng), 66. *Prof Exp:* Actg asst prof elec eng, Univ Calif, Berkeley, 66; asst prof, Purdue Univ, 66-70; MEM TECH STAFF ELEC ENG, BELL TEL LABS INC, 70- *Mem:* Inst Elec & Electronics Engrs. *Res:* Computer-aided circuit analysis and synthesis; nonlinear distortion analysis; system theory. *Mailing Add:* Bell Tel Labs Inc 1600 Osgood St North Andover MA 01845

KUPCHIK, EUGENE JOHN, b Wallington, NJ, Aug 26, 29; m 65. ORGANOMETALLIC CHEMISTRY. *Educ:* Rutgers Univ, BS, 51, PhD(org chem), 59. *Prof Exp:* Res chemist, Union Carbide Plastics Co, 54-55; instr org chem, Rutgers Univ, 58-60; from asst prof to assoc prof, 60-68, PROF ORG CHEM, ST JOHN'S UNIV, NY, 68- *Mem:* Am Chem Soc. *Res:* Reaction mechanisms; organometallic chemistry; organotin compounds; biological properties of organometallic compounds; forensic chemistry. *Mailing Add:* Dept of Chem St John's Univ Jamaica NY 11439

KUPCHIK, HERBERT Z, b Brooklyn, NY, Dec 6, 40; m 64; c 2. CANCER. *Educ:* Bethany Col, BS, 62; Wayne State Univ, MS, 65, PhD(biochem), 67. *Prof Exp:* Asst chem, Wayne State Univ, 62-63, res asst biochem, 64-67; assoc med, 69-71, assoc biol chem, 71-72, prin res assoc biochem, Harvard Med Sch, 72-78; asst prof, 76-82, ASSOC PROF MICROBIOL, SCH MED, BOSTON UNIV, 82- *Concurrent Pos:* Instr biochem & org chem, Marygrove Col, 64-65; NIH fel enzym, Cancer Res Inst, New Eng Deaconess Hosp, Boston, 67-69; res fel enzym, Harvard Med Sch, 68-69; clin assoc, Thorndike Mem Lab, 69-73; res assoc, Mallory Gastroenterol Lab, Boston City Hosp, 69-74, sr res assoc, 74-80; res assoc, Sch Med, Boston Univ, 71-76, mem staff, Hubert H Humphrey Cancer Res Ctr, 80-; mem spec sci staff, Boston City Hosp & Mallory Inst Path, 78- *Mem:* Am Asn Pathologists; Am Asn Clin Chem; Am Asn Cancer Res; Am Fedn Clin Res; NY Acad Sci. *Res:* Metabolic disorders of tyrosine metabolism; treatment of connective tissue disease; enzymology of cancer; glutamine metabolism; immunology of hepatitis; diagnosis and treatment of cancer; tumor immunology; tumor biology. *Mailing Add:* Mallory Inst of Path Boston City Hosp Boston MA 02118

KUPEL, RICHARD E, b Peoria, Ill, Nov 8, 20; m 46; c 1. ORGANIC CHEMISTRY, INORGANIC CHEMISTRY. *Educ:* Monmouth Col, Ill, BS, 48. *Prof Exp:* Chemist, Gen Elec Co, Wash, 48-50, supvr mass spectrometry lab, 50-52, chemist, Ohio, 52-54, unit leader instrumental anal lab, 54-61; asst chief lab phys & chem anal br, Nat Inst Occup Safety & Health, USPHS, 61-73, hazard eval coordr, 73-80; CONSULT, SKC INC, 80- *Concurrent Pos:* Chmn subcomt seven, Intersoc Comt Manual Methods Ambient Air Sampling & Anal. *Mem:* Am Chem Soc; Am Conf Govt Indust Hyg; Am Indust Hyg Asn; Soc Appl Spectros (pres elect, 65). *Res:* Quantitative analytical methods for analysis of trace elements in biological tissues and environmental samples using emission spectrographic, mass spectrometric, x-ray diffraction, gas chromatographic and spectrophotometric procedures and instrumentation; charcoal tube for sampling organic vapors; K-2 spot test of asbestos. *Mailing Add:* SKC Inc 3935 Freeman Ave Hamilton OH 45015

KUPER, ALAN B(IRK), b Chicago, Ill, Nov 8, 24; m 49; c 3. SOLID STATE ELECTRONICS, APPLIED PHYSICS. *Educ:* Univ Chicago, BS, 49; Univ Ill, MS, 52, PhD(physics), 55. *Prof Exp:* Res assoc metall chem, Princeton Univ, 55-57; mem tech staff, Bell Tel Labs, NJ, 57-64; assoc prof elec eng, Case Western Reserve Univ, 64-80. *Concurrent Pos:* Summer fel, NASA Lewis Res Ctr, 77 & 78. *Mem:* Electrochem Soc; Int Solar Energy Soc. *Res:* Experimental solid-state physics; semiconductor materials and devices; surface phenomena; energy systems; solar energy; solar photovoltaics. *Mailing Add:* 2265 Delaware Dr Cleveland OH 44106

KUPER, J B HORNER, b New York, NY, Nov 5, 09; m 37; c 1. PHYSICS, ELECTRONICS. *Educ:* Williams Col, AB, 30; Princeton Univ, PhD(physics), 38. *Prof Exp:* From physicist to asst physicist, Wash Biophys Inst, 37-40; assoc physicist, NIH, 40-41; from mem staff to assoc group leader, Radiation Lab, Mass Inst Technol, 41-46; from sr engr to head dept, Fed Telecommun Labs, NY, 46; head electronics Div, 47-48, chmn instrumentation & health physics dept, 48-70, chmn environ sci study group, 70-72, asst to dir, 72-74, CONSULT, BROOKHAVEN NAT LAB, 75- *Concurrent Pos:* Ed, Rev Sci Instruments, Am Inst Physics, 54-79. *Mem:* Fel Am Phys Soc; Health Physics Soc; fel Inst Elec & Electronics Engrs. *Res:* General instrumentation; spectrophotometers; Geiger counters and other equipment for radioactive research; microwave plumbing; general electronics; health physics; electronic instrumentation and editorial work. *Mailing Add:* Brookhaven Nat Lab Upton NY 11973

KUPERMAN, ALBERT SANFORD, b New York, NY, Aug 1, 31; m 56; c 2. PHARMACOLOGY. *Educ:* NY Univ, AB, 52; Cornell Univ, PhD(pharmacol), 57. *Prof Exp:* Res fel pharmacol, Med Col, Cornell Univ, 57-58, instr, 58-59; asst prof, Col Med, NY Univ, 59-61; asst prof, Med Col, Cornell Univ, 61-65; assoc prof, Hunter Col, 65-68, prof biol sci, 68; Rockefeller Found vis prof & actg chmn dept pharmacol, Fac Med Sci, Mahidol Univ, Thailand, 68-75; ASSOC DEAN EDUC AFFAIRS, ALBERT EINSTEIN COL MED, 75- *Concurrent Pos:* USPHS fel, 57-59. *Mem:* Am Soc Pharmacol & Exp Therapeut; fel Am Col Clin Pharmacol. *Res:* General pharmacology; physiology and pharmacology of excitable cells. *Mailing Add:* Off of Educ Albert Einstein Col of Med Bronx NY 10461

KUPFER, CARL, b New York, NY, Feb 9, 28. OPHTHALMOLOGY. *Educ:* Yale Univ, AB, 48; Johns Hopkins Univ, MD, 52. *Prof Exp:* Intern & asst resident, Wilmer Eye Inst, Johns Hopkins Hosp, 52-53, lab asst biostatist, Med Sch, Johns Hopkins Univ, 53-54 & 57-58; from instr to asst prof ophthal, Harvard Med Sch, 60-66; prof & chmn dept, Sch Med & res affil, Primate Ctr, Univ Wash, 66-70; DIR, NAT EYE INST, 70- *Concurrent Pos:* Res fel ophthal, Wilmer Eye Inst, 57-58; res fel, Harvard Med Sch, 58-60; prog dir ophthal training grant, Mass Eye & Ear Infirmary, 62-66; mem vision res training comt, NIH, 63-64, mem neurol prog proj B, 67-69; mem adv comt basic & clinical res, Nat Soc Prev Blindness, 69-; clin assoc prof, Howard Univ, 70-; mem sci adv panel, Res to Prevent Blindness, Inc, 71-75; mem sci adv comt, Fight for Sight, 71-; chmn proj & priorities comt, Int Agency Prevention Blindness, 75-; mem bd dirs, Am Found Overseas Blind, Inc, 75- *Honors & Awards:* Spec Citation, Secy Health, Educ & Welfare, 72; Dept Health, Educ & Welfare Super Serv Award, 73. *Mem:* Am Physiol Soc; Asn Res Vision & Ophthal; Am Acad Ophthal & Otolaryngol; Am Ophthal Soc. *Res:* Intraocular pressure and neurophysiology; glaucoma; neuro-ophthalmology. *Mailing Add:* Bldg 31 Nat Eye Inst Bethesda MD 20205

KUPFER, DAVID, b Warsaw, Poland, Nov 27, 28; US citizen; m 61; c 3. BIOCHEMICAL PHARMACOLOGY, DRUG METABOLISM. *Educ:* Univ Calif, Los Angeles, BA, 52, PhD(biochem), 58. *Prof Exp:* Scientist, Worcester Found Exp Biol, 58-60; intermediate scientist & fel, Weizmann Inst Sci, 61-62; res scientist, Lederle Labs, Am Cyanamid Co, 62-71; SR SCIENTIST, WORCESTER FOUND EXP BIOL, 71- *Mem:* Am Chem Soc; Am Soc Biol Chemists; Soc Pharmacol & Exp Therapeut. *Res:* Drug-drug interactions; prostaglandin metabolism; hepatic monoxygenases; hormonal activity of environmental pollutants. *Mailing Add:* Worcester Found Exp Biol Shrewsbury MA 01545

KUPFER, DONALD HARRY, b Los Angeles, Calif, Oct 4, 18; m 52; c 2. STRUCTURAL GEOLOGY. *Educ:* Calif Inst Technol, BS, 40; Univ Calif, Los Angeles, AM, 42; Yale Univ, MS, 51, PhD(geol), 51. *Prof Exp:* Geologist, Gladding McBean & Co, 41-42 & US Geol Surv, 42-55; from asst prof to assoc prof, 55-66, prof, 66-80, EMER PROF GEOL, LA STATE UNIV, BATON ROUGE, 81- *Concurrent Pos:* Indust mineral consult, 58-; NSF sr fel, NZ, 62-63; Cent Treaty Orgn minerals mapping consult, Turkey, 66 & Pakistan, 67; fel, Salt Domes, Spain & Ger, 69, Can, Mexico, Israel, 79. *Honors & Awards:* A I Levorsen Award, 75. *Mem:* AAAS; Am Asn Petrol Geologists; Am Geophys Union. *Res:* Earthquakes; faults; salt domes; nonmetal mining; computer tectonics; areal geology; Gulf Coast geology; geopressures; energy resources. *Mailing Add:* 5984 Hibiscus Dr Baton Rouge LA 70808

KUPFER, SHERMAN, b Jersey City, NJ, Apr 28, 26; m 51; c 3. INTERNAL MEDICINE, PHYSIOLOGY. *Educ:* Cornell Univ, MD, 48. *Prof Exp:* Res fel physiol, Sch Med, Western Reserve Univ, 49-50; res fel, Med Col, Cornell Univ, 50-51, from instr to asst prof physiol, 55-66; assoc prof med, 66-72, from assoc dean to sr assoc dean, 68-80, PROF MED MT SINAI SCH MED, 72-, DEP DEAN, 80-, ASSOC PROF PHYSIOL, 68- *Concurrent Pos:* Asst to dir med res, Mt Sinai Hosp, 56-58, res assoc, 58-60, asst attend physician, 60-65, dir clin res ctr, 63-, assoc attend physician, 65-72, attend physician, 72- *Mem:* Am Physiol Soc. *Res:* Renal and cardiovascular physiology. *Mailing Add:* Mt Sinai Sch of Med One E 100th St New York NY 10029

KUPFERBERG, HARVEY J, b New York, NY, Jan 4, 33; m 62; c 2. PHARMACOLOGY. *Educ:* Univ Calif, Los Angeles, BS, 55; Univ Southern Calif, PharmD, 59; Univ Calif, San Francisco, PhD(pharmacol), 62. *Prof Exp:* USPHS fel pharmacol, Univ Calif, San Francisco, 60-62 & 62-63; staff fel, Nat Heart Inst, 63-65; from instr to asst prof, Univ Minn, Minneapolis, 65-71; PHARMACOLOGIST, EPILEPSY BR, NEUROL DIS PROG, NAT INST NEUROL & COMM DIS & STROKE, 71- *Concurrent Pos:* USPHS res grant, 66-69. *Mem:* AAAS; Am Pharmaceut Asn; Acad Pharmaceut Sci; Am Soc Pharmacol & Exp Therapeut; Soc Toxicol. *Res:* Pharmacodynamics; metabolism of drugs; mechanism of action of anticonvulsant drugs. *Mailing Add:* Epilepsy Br Neurol Dis Prog Nat Inst Neurol & Comm Dis & Stroke Bethesda MD 20014

KUPFERBERG, KENNETH MAURICE, b Flushing, NY, Nov 6, 19; m 46; c 3. PHYSICS, ELECTRONICS. *Educ:* Queen's Col, NY, BS, 41; NY Univ, MS, 43, PhD(physics), 47. *Prof Exp:* Asst physics, NY Univ, 41-43, instr, 43-44; res physicist, radiation lab, Columbia Univ, 44; res physicist, Manhattan Proj, Los Alamos Sci Lab, 44-46; dir res, 46-68, chief engr, 68-80, DIR ENG, KEPCO, INC, 80- *Mem:* Am Phys Soc; Am Asn Physics Teachers; Inst Elec & Electronics Engrs. *Res:* Cosmic rays; mesotron investigations; nuclear and neutron physics; nuclear fission; development of instruments for teaching electronics; design and development of regulated power units. *Mailing Add:* Kepco Inc 131-38 Sanford Ave Flushing NY 11352

KUPFERBERG, LENN C, b Flushing, NY, July 27, 51; m 76; c 1. MAGNETIC METALS. *Educ:* Trinity Col, Conn, BS, 73; Univ Rochester, NY, MA, 75, PhD(physics), 79. *Prof Exp:* Assoc fel physics, Mass Inst Technol, 78-80; ASST PROF PHYSICS, WORCESTER POLYTECH INST, 80- *Concurrent Pos:* Vis scientist physics, Mass Inst Technol, 80- *Mem:* Am Phys Soc; AAAS; Am Asn Physics Teachers; Sigma Xi. *Res:* Phase transitions and critical phenomina; magnetism and magnetic material; experimental physics; picosecond lasers and spectroscopy. *Mailing Add:* Dept Physics Worcester Polytech Inst Worcester MA 01609

KUPFERMAN, ALLAN, b New York, NY, Aug 5, 35; m 59; c 2. PHARMACOLOGY, OPHTHALMOLOGY. *Educ:* Univ Bridgeport, BA, 59; Clark Univ, AM, 61; Univ Vt, PhD(pharmacol), 66. *Prof Exp:* Asst prof pharmacol, 69-78, ASSOC PROF PHARMACOL & OPHTHAL, SCH MED, BOSTON UNIV, 78- *Res:* Pharmacokinetics of topically applied steroids in the eye. *Mailing Add:* Dept of Pharmacol Boston Univ Sch of Med Boston MA 02118

KUPFERMAN, STUART L, b New York, NY, June 30, 37; m 66. PHYSICAL OCEANOGRAPHY, WASTE DISPOSAL. *Educ:* Polytech Inst Brooklyn, BS, 59; Harvard Univ, AM, 64, PhD(physics), 67. *Prof Exp:* Res assoc phys oceanog, Univ RI, 68-70; ASST prof phys oceanog, Univ Del, 70-78; VIS INVESTR, WOODS HOLE OCEANOG INST, 78- *Concurrent Pos:* Grants, Univ Del Res Found, 71-72 & NSF, 71-78. *Mem:* AAAS; Am Geophys Union; Am Soc Limnol & Oceanog; Am Phys Soc; Am Meteorol Soc. *Res:* Use of radioactive and chemical tracers to study movement and mixing of water masses. *Mailing Add:* Sandia Nat Lab PO Box 5800 Albuquerque NM 87185

KUPFERMANN, IRVING, b New York, NY, Jan 26, 38; m 65; c 2. NEUROPSYCHOLOGY. *Educ:* Univ Fla, BS, 59; Univ Chicago, PhD(biopsychol), 64. *Prof Exp:* Res fel, Harvard Med Sch, 65-66; from instr to assoc prof, NY Univ Med Sch, 66-73; ASSOC RES SCIENTIST, NY STATE PSYCHIAT INST, 73-; ASSOC PROF MED PSYCHOL, COL PHYSICIANS & SURGEONS, COLUMBIA UNIV, 74- *Concurrent Pos:* NIMH res scientist develop award, 69; mem, NIMH Neuropsychol Study Sect, 75- *Honors & Awards:* Richard Temple Award, Univ Chicago, 65. *Mem:* Am Soc Zoologists; Soc Neurosci. *Res:* Invertebrate behavior and learning; neural mechanisms of learning and motivation; mechanisms of habituation and dishabituation in the marine mollusk, Aplysia; feeding behavior in Aplysia. *Mailing Add:* Col of Physicians & Surgeons Columbia Univ New York NY 10032

KUPIECKI, FLOYD PETER, b Bronson, Mich, May 1, 26; m 50; c 2. BIOCHEMISTRY. *Educ:* Western Mich Univ, BS, 50; Univ Notre Dame, PhD(chem), 53. *Prof Exp:* Res chemist, Mich Chem Corp, 53-55; res assoc org chem & biochem, Univ Pa, 55-56; from res assoc to instr biochem, Univ Mich, 56-59; Fulbright fel, Biochem Inst, Helsinki, Finland, 59-60; RES SCIENTIST, UPJOHN CO, 60- *Mem:* Am Soc Biol Chemists; Am Chem Soc. *Res:* Diabetes research; lipid metabolism and adipose tissue enzymes; metabolism in islets of diabetic animals. *Mailing Add:* Dept of Diabetes & Atherosclerosis Res Upjohn Co Kalamazoo MI 49001

KUPKE, DONALD WALTER, b Omaha, Nebr, Mar 16, 22; m 49; c 5. BIOCHEMISTRY. *Educ:* Valparaiso Univ, AB, 47; Stanford Univ, MS, 49, PhD(chem), 52. *Prof Exp:* Nat Res Coun fel med sci, Carlsberg Lab, Denmark, 52-53 & Uppsala Univ, Sweden, 53-54; USPHS fel, Carlsberg Lab & Stanford Univ, 55; mem staff, Carnegie Inst, Stanford Univ, 55-56; from asst prof to assoc prof, 57-66, chmn dept, 64-66, PROF BIOCHEM, SCH MED, UNIV VA, 66- *Mem:* AAAS; Am Soc Biol Chemists; Am Chem Soc; Biophys Soc; Am Soc Plant Physiol. *Res:* Protein and virus biophysical chemistry; chloroplast proteins; magnetic balancing methods; density, viscosity and osmotic pressure. *Mailing Add:* Dept of Biochem Univ of Va Sch of Med Charlottesville VA 22908

KUPP, ROBERT W(ILLIAM), b Detroit, Mich, July 28, 23; m 46; c 2. NUCLEAR ENGINEERING. *Educ:* Wayne State Univ, BS, 47. *Prof Exp:* Opers supvr gaseous diffusion, Carbide & Carbon Chem Corp, Div Union Carbide Corp, 45-47; process engr, Eng Div, Vitro Corp Am, 47-52, proj engr chem plants, 52-53, nuclear process engr, Atomic Power Develop Assocs, 53-54, chief nuclear engr, Eng Div, 54-60; sr assoc, 60-69, VPRES FINANCING SERV DIV, S M STOLLER CORP, 69- *Concurrent Pos:* Lectr, City Col New York; adj assoc prof, NY Univ, 62- *Mem:* Am Nuclear Soc; Am Inst Chem Eng. *Res:* Engineering consulting on nuclear power projects. *Mailing Add:* S M Stoller Corp 227 Beechwood Rd Ridgewood NJ 07450

KUPPENHEIMER, JOHN D, JR, b Orange, NJ, Sept 15, 41; m 64. OPTICS. *Educ:* Lafayette Col, BS, 63; Boston Univ, MA, 65; Worcester Polytech Inst, PhD(physics), 69. *Prof Exp:* Fel physics, Worcester Polytech Inst, 69-70, asst prof, 70-71; scientist, Diffraction Ltd, Inc, 71-72; asst mgr, Diffraction Ltd Div, Sanders Assocs, 72-73; dir Optical Metrology Lab, 73-79, SR PRIN PHYSICIST, SANDER ASSOCS, 79-; ADJ PROF PHYSICS, UNIV LOWELL, 75- *Mem:* Optical Soc Am; Sigma Xi. *Res:* Quantum optics; photon count statistics; lasers; optical constants of semiconductors; atmospheric optics; optical guidance; optical counter measures; development of IR lasers. *Mailing Add:* 100 Brookfield Rd Tewksbury MA 01876

KUPPERIAN, JAMES EDWARD, JR, b Milwaukee, Wis, Apr 7, 25; m 62; c 2. SPACE SCIENCE, ASTRONOMY. *Educ:* Webb Inst Naval Archit, NY, BS, 46; Univ Del, MS, 48; Univ NC, PhD, 52. *Prof Exp:* Physicist, Naval Res Lab, 54-58; br head astrophys, 58-70, dept proj mgr, orbiting astron observ, 70-75, proj mgr, orbiting satellites, 75-79, ASSOC DIR PROJS SPACE SCI, GODDARD SPACE FLIGHT CTR, NASA, 79- *Concurrent Pos:* Proj mgr & proj scientist Explorer XI, Goddard Space Flight Ctr, NASA, 59-62; mem astron subcomt, NASA, 60-64, proj scientist orbiting astron observ, Goddard Space Flight Ctr, 60- *Honors & Awards:* Except Sci Achievement Award, NASA, 69. *Mem:* Am Astron Soc; Int Astron Union. *Res:* Ultraviolet astronomy; upper atmospheric physics; optics. *Mailing Add:* 2702 Lyn Pl Bowie MD 20715

KUPPERMAN, HERBERT SPENCER, b Newark, NJ, Apr 12, 15; m 42; c 2. ENDOCRINOLOGY. *Educ:* Univ Wis, BA, 36, MA, 37, PhD(endocrinol), 40, MD, 45. *Prof Exp:* Nat Res Coun fel exp med, Sch Med, Univ Ga, 42-46, sr res fel endocrinol, 46-47, res assoc, 47; res assoc therapeut, 47-53, ASSOC PROF MED, COL MED, NY UNIV, 53-; DIR, ROCHE CLIN LABS, 75- *Mem:* Endocrine Soc; fel AMA; fel Am Col Physicians; fel Am Col Obstet & Gynec; fel Acad Psychosom Med. *Res:* Physiology of reproduction; antihormones; pharmacology; endocrines and cardiovascular drugs; clinical and assay endocrinology. *Mailing Add:* Roche Clin Labs Raritan NJ 08869

KUPPERMAN, MORTON, b New York, NY, Mar 19, 18; m 46. MATHEMATICAL STATISTICS. *Educ:* City Col New York, BS, 38; George Washington Univ, MA, 50, PhD(math statist), 57. *Prof Exp:* Statistician, Gen Staff, US War Dept, 40-41 & Europ Cent Inland Transp Orgn, France, 46; statistician, Med Statist Div, Off Army Surgeon Gen, 47-55; mathematician, Nat Security Agency, 55-73; sr lectr math statist, Univ Leicester, Eng, 73-78; RETIRED. *Concurrent Pos:* Prof lectr, George Washington Univ, 57-73. *Mem:* Inst Math Statist; Royal Statist Soc; Math Asn Am; Am Statist Asn. *Res:* Distribution theory; application of information theory to multivariate analysis and statistical inference; counterexamples in probability and statistics. *Mailing Add:* 2 Stoughton Ave Leicester LE2 2DR England

KUPPERMAN, ROBERT HARRIS, b New York, NY, May 12, 35; m 67; c 1. APPLIED MATHEMATICS, OPERATIONS RESEARCH. *Educ:* NY Univ, BA, 56, PhD(appl math), 62. *Prof Exp:* Instr math, NY Univ, Pratt Inst & Hunter Col, 56-60; sr engr, Jet Propulsion Lab, Calif Inst Technol, 60-62; exec adv opers res, Douglas Aircraft Co, Inc, 62-64; mem sr staff, Inst Defense Anal, 64-67; asst dir natural resource anal ctr, Exec Off of President, 67-70, dep asst dir, President's Off Emergency Preparedness, 70-71, asst dir, 71-73; chief scientist, US Arms Control & Disarmament Agency, 73-79; EXEC DIR, CTR STRATEGIC & INT STUDIES, GEORGETOWN CTR, 79- *Concurrent Pos:* Prin engr, Repub Aviation Corp, 59-60; consult, US Civil Serv Comn, 65 & US Army Security Agency, Army Intel & Army Electronic Warfare Bd, 66; lectr, Univ Md, 65, vis prof govt & polit, 74-76; expert consult, Exec Off President, 67-68; dep exec dir, President's Property Rev Bd, 70-73. *Honors & Awards:* Outstanding Serv Awards, Exec Off President, 68-71, Order of Paul Revere Patriot, 70; Presidential Citations, 71-73, Distinguished Serv Award, Exec Off President, 73. *Mem:* NY Acad Sci; fel Opers Res Soc; Soc Indust & Appl Math; Int Inst Strategic Studies; Mil Opers Res Soc. *Res:* Strategic analysis and arms race stability; conversational computer systems and crisis management; conventional arms transfers; terrorism. *Mailing Add:* 2832 Ellicott St NW Washington DC 20008

KUPPERMANN, ARON, b Sao Paulo, Brazil, May 6, 26; nat US; m 51; c 4. CHEMICAL PHYSICS. *Educ:* Univ Sao Paulo, Brazil, ChemE, 48, CE, 53; Univ Notre Dame, PhD(phys chem), 56. *Prof Exp:* Asst prof phys chem, Cath Univ Sao Paulo, 49-50 & chem, Inst Aeronaut Technol, 50-51; head anodizing sect, Ajax Indust & Trade Co, 52; res assoc phys chem, Radiation Proj, Univ Notre Dame, 53-55; from instr to assoc prof, Univ Ill, 55-63; pROF CHEM PHYSICS, CALIF INST TECHNOL, 63- *Concurrent Pos:* Resident res assoc, Argonne Nat Lab, 57; res assoc, Inst Atomic Energy, Sao Paulo, 59-60; Reilly lectr, Univ Notre Dame, 65; NSF fel, 68-69; Guggenheim fel, 76-77; consult, Jet Propulsion Lab, 65-69 & TRW Systs Group, 70-77; chmn joint chem study group, Nat Acad Sci-Nat Res Coun, Brazil, 73-76. *Honors & Awards:* Venable lectr, Univ NC, 67; Werner lectr, Univ Kans, 68. *Mem:* Fel Am Inst Chem; fel Am Phys Soc; Am Chem Soc; AAAS. *Res:* Experimental and theoretical chemical dynamics; collisions in crossed molecular beams; laser spectroscopy and photochemistry; radiation chemistry; low energy electron impact phenomena, experiment and theory; variable angle photoelectron spectroscopy. *Mailing Add:* Dept of Chem Calif Inst of Technol Pasadena CA 91125

KUPPERS, JAMES RICHARD, b Newland, Ind, Aug 4, 20; m; c 4. PHYSICAL CHEMISTRY. *Educ:* Univ Fla, BS, 43, PhD(chem), 57; La State Univ, MS, 47. *Prof Exp:* Food technologist, United Fruit Co, 47-49, assoc biochemist, 49-54; res chemist textile fibers dept, E I du Pont de Nemours & Co, 57-60; assoc prof chem, Pfeiffer Col, 60-64; assoc prof, 65-68, PROF CHEM, UNIV NC, CHARLOTTE, 68- *Mem:* AAAS; Am Chem Soc; NY Acad Sci. *Res:* Surface chemistry; membrane phenomena; solution thermodynamics. *Mailing Add:* Dept of Chem Univ of NC Charlotte NC 28223

KUPSCH, WALTER OSCAR, b Amsterdam, Neth, Mar 2, 19; nat Can; m 45; c 3. GEOLOGY. *Educ:* Univ Amsterdam, BSc, 43; Univ Mich, MS, 48, PhD(geol), 50. *Prof Exp:* Dir, Inst North Studies, 65-72, dir, Churchill River Study, 73-76, PROF GEOL, UNIV SASK, 50- *Concurrent Pos:* Prin geologist, Geol Surv, Sask, 50-56, consult, 56-; ed, Musk-Ox; mem, Sci Coun Can, 76-82; mem, NWT Sci Adv Bd, 76-, petrol adv, 80- *Mem:* Fel Arctic Inst NAm; fel Geol Asn Can; fel Geol Soc Am; Am Asn Petrol Geol; fel Royal Soc Can. *Res:* Stratigraphy; geomorphology; glacial geology. *Mailing Add:* Dept of Geol Sci Univ of Sask Saskatoon SK S7N 0W0 Can

KUPSTAS, EDWARD EUGENE, b Eynon, Pa, Aug 1, 21; m 57; c 5. ORGANIC CHEMISTRY. *Educ:* Fordham Col, BS, 51, MS, 53, PhD(chem), 58. *Prof Exp:* RES CHEMIST, TEXTILE FIBERS DEPT, E I DU PONT DE NEMOURS & CO, INC, 55- *Mem:* Am Chem Soc. *Res:* Structure and synthesis of ichtiamin; dyes; polymers; polyesters. *Mailing Add:* 1614 Hardee Rd Kingston NC 28501

KURAJIAN, GEORGE MASROB, b Highland Park, Mich, Oct 28, 26; m 55; c 3. ENGINEERING MECHANICS, MECHANICAL ENGINEERING. *Educ:* Univ Detroit, BME, 48, ME, 63; Univ Mich, MSE, 53. *Prof Exp:* From instr to asst prof eng mech, Univ Detroit, 48-64; from asst prof to assoc prof, 64-72, PROF MECH ENG & ENG MECH, UNIV MICH-DEARBORN, 72-, CHMN DEPT MECH ENG, 75- *Concurrent Pos:* Consult, indust & govt agencies, 54- *Mem:* Am Soc Eng Educ; Am Soc Mech Engrs; Soc Exp Stress Anal; Indust Math Soc; Int Asn Vehicle Design. *Res:* Design and stress analysis of structural shells; space frames; amphibious vehicles; chemical machinery; automotive components; automotive dynamometers and test cells; physical testing laboratory projects; mechanical design; finite element; solid mechanics; theories of failure; fatigue. *Mailing Add:* Dept of Mech Eng Sch of Eng Univ of Mich Dearborn MI 48128

KURAMITSU, HOWARD KIKUO, b Los Angeles, Calif, Oct 18, 36; m 70; c 2. BIOCHEMISTRY. *Educ:* Univ Calif, Los Angeles, BS, 57, PhD(biol chem), 62. *Prof Exp:* Jr res biochemist, Sch Med, Univ Calif, Los Angeles, 61-62; res fel bact, Harvard Med Sch, 62-63; res assoc microbiol, Sch Med, Univ Southern Calif, 63-67; asst prof, 67-70, assoc prof, 70-79, PROF MICROBIOL, MED SCH, NORTHWESTERN UNIV, CHICAGO, 79- *Mem:* AAAS; Am Soc Biol Chemists; Am Soc Microbiol; Int Asn Dent Res. *Res:* Regulation of carbohydrate metabolism in oral microorganisms. *Mailing Add:* Dept Microbiol-Immunol Northwestern Univ Med Sch Chicago IL 60611

KURATA, F(RED), b Rialto, Calif, June 4, 14; m 46; c 4. CHEMICAL ENGINEERING. *Educ:* Calif Inst Technol, BS, 34; Univ Mich, MSE, 39, PhD(chem eng), 41. *Prof Exp:* Chemist, Fruit Industs, Inc, 34-36; res assoc chem eng, Eng Res Inst, Univ Mich, 41-43; plant engr, Protected Steel Prod Co, 43-44; chem engr, Res & Develop, Atlas Powder Co, 44-47; from asst prof to prof, 47-60, distinguished prof & mem Ctr Res Eng Sci, 60-77, EMER PROF CHEM & PETROL ENG, UNIV KANS, 77- *Concurrent Pos:* Consult; Ford Found adv, Fac Sanit Eng, Indust Eng & Petrol Eng, Nat Univ Eng, Peru, 65-67. *Mem:* AAAS; Am Soc Eng Educ; Am Chem Soc; Nat Soc Prof Eng; Am Inst Mining, Metall & Petrol Engrs. *Res:* Reaction kinetics; cryogenics; thermodynamics; low temperature properties of fluids. *Mailing Add:* Dept of Chem Eng Univ of Kans Lawrence KS 66044

KURATH, DIETER, b Evanston, Ill, Oct 17, 21; m 45; c 4. THEORETICAL NUCLEAR PHYSICS. *Educ:* Brown Univ, AB, 42; Univ Chicago, PhD(physics), 51. *Prof Exp:* Asst, Univ Chicago, 47-51; assoc physicist, 51-60, SR PHYSICIST, ARGONNE NAT LAB, 60- *Concurrent Pos:* Guggenheim fel, 57-58; vis prof, Univ Wash, 61-62 & State Univ NY Stony Brook, 69-70; sr vis fel, Nuclear Physics Lab, Oxford Univ, 73-74. *Mem:* Am Phys Soc. *Res:* Shell model of nuclear structure. *Mailing Add:* Argonne Nat Lab Argonne IL 60439

KURATH, PAUL, b St Gallen, Switz, June 18, 24; nat US; div; c 5. ORGANIC CHEMISTRY. *Educ:* Swiss Fed Inst Technol, dipl, 48, DSc, 51. *Prof Exp:* Res assoc & fel pharmaceut chem, Univ Kans, 51-53 & org chem, Univ Rochester, 54-58; RES CHEMIST, RES DIV, ABBOTT LABS, 58- *Mem:* Am Chem Soc; The Chem Soc; Swiss Chem Soc. *Res:* Organic synthesis; natural products; steroids; antibiotics; peptides. *Mailing Add:* Res Div D-482 Abbott Labs North Chicago IL 60064

KURATH, SHELDON FRANK, b Moscow, Idaho, Mar 29, 28; m 54; c 3. POLYMER CHEMISTRY, RHEOLOGY. *Educ:* Univ Wis, BS, 50, MS, 51, PhD(chem), 54. *Prof Exp:* Res aide, Inst Paper Chem, Lawrence Univ, 53-65; assoc prof phys chem, 65-69, PROF CHEM, UNIV WIS-OSHKOSH, 69- *Mem:* Am Chem Soc; Soc Rheol; Am Inst Chem Eng; Tech Asn Pulp & Paper Indust. *Res:* Non-Newtonian flow of polymers and pigment suspensions; polymer viscoelasticity; colloid chemistry; solar energy. *Mailing Add:* Dept of Chem Univ of Wis Oshkosh WI 54901

KURATLE, HENRY, III, b Wilmington, Del, Sept 26, 41; m 63; c 2. BIOLOGY, AGRICULTURE. *Educ:* Univ Del, BS, 63, MS, 65, PhD(biol), 68. *Prof Exp:* RES BIOLOGIST, PLANT RES LAB, E I DU PONT DE NEMOURS & CO, INC, 68- *Res:* Metabolism of herbicides by plants; absorption and translocation of herbicides in plants; biological evaluation of chemicals on plants. *Mailing Add:* DuPont Plant Res Lab 900 Wilson Rd Wilmington DE 19803

KURCHACOVA, ELVA S, b Oriente, Cuba, Aug 5, 21; m 44; c 2. ORGANIC CHEMISTRY. *Educ:* Univ Havana, DSc(physics, chem), 45. *Prof Exp:* Dir res, Linner Labs, Cuba, 45-61; assoc res chemist, 61-78, SR ASSOC RES SCIENTIST, MILES LABS, INC, 78- *Concurrent Pos:* Pres & dir, Yelene Prod, 51-61. *Mem:* AAAS; Am Chem Soc; NY Acad Sci. *Res:* Pharmaceuticals; organic synthesis; development of medicinal drugs. *Mailing Add:* 321 O'Neff St Elkhart IN 46514

KURCZEWSKI, FRANK E, b Erie, Pa, May 24, 36; m 59; c 4. ENTOMOLOGY. *Educ:* Allegheny Col, BS, 58; Cornell Univ, MS, 62, PhD(insect taxon), 64. *Prof Exp:* Res assoc entom, Univ Kans, 64-66, vis asst prof, 66; from asst prof to prof entom, 66-77, PROF ENVIRON & FOREST BIOL, STATE UNIV NY COL ENVIRON SCI & FORESTRY, 77- *Concurrent Pos:* NSF fel, 64-65; NIH fel, 65-66. *Res:* Comparative behavior and systematics of digger wasps; insect behavior. *Mailing Add:* Dept of Entom State Univ NY Col Environ Sci Syracuse NY 13210

KURCZYNSKI, THADDEUS WALTER, b Hamtramck, Mich, Oct 31, 40; m 63, 79; c 2. HUMAN GENETICS, NEUROLOGY. *Educ:* Univ Mich, BS, 62, MS, 63; Case Western Reserve Univ, PhD(human genetics), 69. *Prof Exp:* From intern to resident neurol, Univ Mich Hosps, 70-73; resident pediat, Children's Hosp Mich, 73-74; fel pediat neurol, Albert Einstein Col Med, 74-76; asst prof, Dept Pediat, Div Pediat Neurol, Dept Med, Div Neurol & Human Genetics & Genetics Ctr, Case Western Reserve Univ, 76-81; ASSOC PROF, DEPT PEDIAT & NEUROSCI & DIR, GENETICS CTR NORTHWEST OHIO, MED COL OHIO, 81- *Mem:* Am Soc Human Genetics; Am Acad Neurol; Child Neurol Soc. *Res:* Medical genetics; pediatric neurology. *Mailing Add:* Dept Pediat Med Col Ohio C S 10008 Toledo OH 43699

KUREY, THOMAS JOHN, b Boston, Mass, Feb 21, 37. NUCLEAR PHYSICS, REACTOR PHYSICS. *Educ:* Boston Col, BS, 58; Pa State Univ, MS, 61, PhD(physics), 63. *Prof Exp:* Physicist, Knolls Atomic Power Lab, Gen Elec Co, 64-80. *Mem:* Am Phys Soc; Am Nuclear Soc. *Res:* Beta and gamma spectroscopy; applications of solid state nuclear detectors; electron spin resonance study of decay of unstable free radicals in gamma irradiated solids; reactor physics analytical methods; critical experiments. *Mailing Add:* 28 Val de Penas Lane Clifton Park NY 12065

KURFESS, JAMES DANIEL, b Perrysburg, Ohio, Nov 8, 40; m 66; c 2. ASTROPHYSICS. *Educ:* Case Inst Technol, BS, 62, MS, 63, PhD(physics), 67. *Prof Exp:* Res assoc space sci, Rice Univ, 67-69; ASTROPHYSICIST, E O HULBURT CTR SPACE RES, US NAVAL RES LAB, 69- *Concurrent Pos:* Mem data base group study uses sci balloons, Nat Acad Sci, 75; mem, Sci Adv Panel Long Duration Balloon Develop Prog; prin investr, Oriented Scintillation Spectros Exp, Gamma Ray Observ, NASA. *Mem:* Am Phys Soc; Am Astron Soc. *Res:* Hard x-ray and gamma-ray observations of solar and extra-solar sources using balloons and satellite instrumentation; development of long duration balloon-borne capabilities. *Mailing Add:* Code 7128 US Naval Res Lab Washington DC 20375

KURFMAN, VIRGIL BENSON, b Perry, Ill, Sept 7, 30; m 50; c 2. PHYSICAL CHEMISTRY. *Educ:* Univ Ill, BS, 51; Northwestern Univ, PhD(chem), 55. *Prof Exp:* Asst chem, Northwestern Univ, 51-53; from res chemist to res specialist, 54-80, RES ASSOC, DOW CHEM CO, 81- *Mem:* Am Chem Soc. *Res:* Physical chemistry of metallic interfaces; nucleation; catalysis; thin film composites. *Mailing Add:* Dow Chem Co Bldg 1776 E 7 A Midland MI 48640

KURIAKOSE, AREEKATTUTHAZHAYIL, b Palai, India, Aug 20, 33; Canadian citizen; m 60; c 3. PHYSICAL CHEMISTRY, CERAMICS. *Educ:* Univ Madras, India, BSc, 53, MA, 55, PhD(chem), 61. *Prof Exp:* Lectr chem, St Thomas Col, Palai, India, 55-56; res engr, Norton Res Corp Can Ltd, 66-69, sr res engr, 69-75, supvr mat res abrasives, 75-81; RES SCIENTIST, DEPT ENERGY, MINES & RESOURCES, GOVT CAN, 81- *Mem:* Chem Inst Can; Can Soc Chem Engrs; Can Asn Phys. *Res:* High temperature chemistry; abrasive materials; ceramics microstructure and properties; solid electrolytes and energy storage and generating systems. *Mailing Add:* Canadian Dept Energy Mines & Resources 405 Rochester St Niagara Falls ON K1A 0G1 Can

KURIGER, WILLIAM LOUIS, b Waterloo, Iowa, Aug 7, 33; m 56; c 7. ELECTRICAL ENGINEERING. *Educ:* Univ Iowa, BSEE, 58; Iowa State Univ, ME, 63, PhD(elec eng), 66. *Prof Exp:* Engr, Collins Radio Co, 58-64; asst prof, 66-70, assoc prof, 70-80, PROF ELEC ENG, UNIV OKLA, 80- *Mem:* Inst Elec & Electronics Engrs; Optical Soc Am. *Res:* Laser applications; electronics. *Mailing Add:* Sch of Elec Eng Univ of Okla Norman OK 73019

KURIHARA, NORMAN HIROMU, b Oxnard, Calif, Mar 23, 38; m 65. ORGANIC CHEMISTRY. *Educ:* Univ Calif, Santa Barbara, BA, 61; Univ Calif, Davis, PhD(org chem), 65. *Prof Exp:* Res fel, Univ Calif, 65-66; RES SPECIALIST, AGR ORG DEPT, DOW CHEM CO, 66- *Mem:* Am Chem Soc. *Res:* Agricultural and pesticide chemistry. *Mailing Add:* Dow Chem Co 2800 Mitchell Dr Walnut Creek CA 94598

KURIHARA, YOSHIO, b Korea, Oct 24, 30; m 60; c 2. METEOROLOGY. *Educ:* Univ Tokyo, BA, 53, PhD(geophys), 62. *Prof Exp:* Tech officer, Japan Meteorol Agency, 53-59; res officer, Meteorol Res Inst, 59-63; res meteorologist, Geophys Fluid Dynamics Lab, US Weather Bur, 63-65; res officer, Meteorol Res Inst, 65-67; res meteorologist, Environ Sci Serv Admin, 67-70, RES METEOROLOGIST, GEOPHYS FLUID DYNAMICS LAB, NAT OCEANIC & ATMOSPHERIC ADMIN, 70- *Honors & Awards:* Meteorol Soc Japan Award, 75. *Mem:* fel Am Meteorol Soc; Am Geophys Union; Meteorol Soc Japan. *Res:* Numerical analysis of meteorological data; construction of statistical-dynamical model of the atmosphere; simulation of the hurricane. *Mailing Add:* Geophys Fluid Dynamics Lab Princeton Univ PO Box 308 Princeton NJ 08540

KURIS, ARMAND MICHAEL, b New York, NY, May 16, 42. PARASITOLOGY, MARINE ECOLOGY. *Educ:* Tulane Univ, BS, 63; Univ Calif, Berkeley, MA, 66, PhD(zool), 71. *Prof Exp:* Asst prof zool, Univ Fla, 73-74; asst prof zool & marine sci, Univ NC, Chapel Hill, 74-75; ASST PROF BIOL SCI, UNIV CALIF, SANTA BARBARA, 75- *Concurrent Pos:* NIH fel, G W Hooper Found, Univ Calif, San Francisco, 71-72; NIH fel, Dept Zool, Univ Mich, Ann Arbor, 72-73; actg asst prof, Bodega Marine Lab, Univ Calif, Bodega Bay, 73, 74 & 75; prin investr, Marine Sci Inst, Univ Calif, Santa Barbara, 78- *Mem:* Am Soc Ichthyol & Herpetol; AAAS; Ecol Soc Am; Soc Protozool; Am Soc Parasitol. *Res:* Parasite ecology; biological control; crustacean biology; molting physiology; crustacean viruses; competition; parasitic castration; shrimp taxonomy; limb regeneration; population biology. *Mailing Add:* Dept of Biol Sci Univ of Calif Santa Barbara CA 93106

KURITZKES, ALEXANDER MARK, b Leipzig, Ger, May 3, 24; nat US; m 55; c 2. ORGANIC CHEMISTRY. *Educ:* Univ Calif, BA, 48; Univ Basel, PhD(chem), 59. *Prof Exp:* Res chemist, R J Strasenburgh Co, NY, 49-52; RES CHEMIST, MATTIN LABS, MEARL CORP, 59- *Mem:* AAAS; Am Chem Soc; Sigma Xi. *Res:* Isolation and determination of structures of natural products; organic analytical chemistry; spectroscopy. *Mailing Add:* Henry L Mattin Labs Mearl Corp Ossining NY 10562

KURIYAMA, MASAO, b Tokyo, Japan, Oct 29, 31; m 58; c 1. SOLID STATE PHYSICS, CRYSTALLOGRAPHY. *Educ:* Tokyo Metrop Univ, BS, 53; Univ Tokyo, MS, 55, DSc(physics), 58. *Prof Exp:* Res assoc, Tokyo Metrop Univ, 58-59; res assoc x-ray physics, Inst Solid State Physics, 59-62; sr scientist, Westinghouse Elec Corp, 62-66; assoc prof physics, Univ Tokyo, 66-67; PHYSICIST, NAT MEASUREMENT LAB, NAT BUR STANDARDS, 67- *Mem:* Am Crystallog Asn; Am Phys Soc; NY Acad Sci; Phys Soc Japan. *Res:* Magnetism; x-ray dynamical diffraction; crystal perfection; crystal growth; x-ray inelastic scattering; synchrotron radiation topography, x-ray nondestructive evaluation. *Mailing Add:* Nat Bur of Standards Bldg 223 Rm B266 Washington DC 20234

KURKJIAN, CHARLES R(OBERT), b Wanamassa, NJ, Dec 7, 29; m 55; c 3. CERAMICS. *Educ:* Rutgers Univ, BS, 52; Mass Inst Technol, ScD(ceramics), 55. *Prof Exp:* Res assoc glass, Mass Inst Technol, 55-57; fel, Univ Sheffield, England, 57-59; MEM TECH STAFF INORG CHEM, BELL TEL LABS, 59- *Mem:* Fel Am Ceramic Soc; fel Brit Soc Glass Technol. *Res:* Glass; ceramics; general high temperature inorganic chemistry. *Mailing Add:* Bell Tel Labs Murray Hill NJ 07974

KURKOV, VICTOR PETER, b Zrenjanin, Yugoslavia, Mar 29, 36; US citizen; m 57; c 2. ORGANIC CHEMISTRY. *Educ:* NY Univ, BChE, 63; Columbia Univ, MA, 65, PhD(org chem), 67. *Prof Exp:* Res asst biochem, Col Med, NY Univ, 58-63; res chemist, 67-74, SR RES CHEMIST, CHEM RES DEPT, CHEVRON RES CO, 74- *Mem:* Am Chem Soc. *Res:* Free radical reactions; oxidation; homogeneous catalysis; new petrochemical processes; polymer chemistry. *Mailing Add:* Chevron Res Co Chem Res Dept 576 Standard Ave Richmond CA 94802

KURLAND, ALBERT A, b Wilkesbarre, Pa, June 29, 14; m 41; c 2. PSYCHIATRY. *Educ:* Univ Md, BS, 36, MD, 40. *Prof Exp:* Staff psychiatrist, Spring Grove State Hosp, State of Md, 49-53, dir med res, 53-60, dir res, Dept Ment Hyg, 60-69, dir, Md Psychiat Res Ctr, 69-77; RES PROF PSYCHIAT, SCH MED, UNIV MD, 79- *Mem:* AMA; Am Psychiat Asn. *Res:* Chlorpromazine in the treatment of schizophrenia; clinical reaction and tolerance to lysergic acid diethylamine tartrate in chronic schizophrenia; the drug placebo and its psychodynamic and conditional reflex action; comparative effectiveness of eight phenothiazines; author of over 185 publications in clinical Psychopharmacology. *Mailing Add:* Dept Psychiat Sch Med Univ Md Baltimore MD 21201

KURLAND, JEFFREY ARNOLD, b New York, NY, Nov 19, 43; m 67. PRIMATOLOGY. *Educ:* Cornell Univ, BA, 67; Harvard Univ, PhD(anthrop), 76. *Prof Exp:* Res assoc primatol, Primate Res Inst, Kyoto Univ, 72-73; instr anthrop, Harvard Univ, 74-75; ASST PROF ANTHROP, PA STATE UNIV, UNIVERSITY PARK, 75- *Mem:* AAAS; Animal Behav Soc; Int Primatol Soc; Soc Study Evolution. *Res:* Primate sociobiology and behavioral ecology; crab-eating, rhesus, Japanese and barbary macaques. *Mailing Add:* Dept of Anthrop Pa State Univ University Park PA 16802

KURLAND, JONATHAN JOSHUA, b Boston, Mass, Jan 11, 39; m 64; c 2. PHYSICAL ORGANIC CHEMISTRY. *Educ:* Univ Pa, BA, 60; Harvard Univ, MA, 64, PhD(chem), 68. *Prof Exp:* Res assoc chem, Columbia Univ, 67-68; chemist, 68-75, PROJ SCIENTIST, UNION CARBIDE CORP, 75- *Mem:* Am Chem Soc. *Res:* Oxidation and free-radical chemistry; kinetics and mechanism of autoxidations. *Mailing Add:* 1617 Kirklee Rd Charleston WV 25314

KURLAND, LEONARD T, b Baltimore, Md, Dec 24, 21; m 42; c 5. MEDICINE, EPIDEMIOLOGY. *Educ:* Johns Hopkins Univ, BA, 42, DrPH, 51; Univ Md, MD, 45; Harvard Univ, MPH, 48. *Prof Exp:* Intern, Univ Hosp, Univ Md, 45; asst resident, Glenn Dale Sanatorium, 46; asst dir, Div Tuberc Control & Sanatoria, State of Mass, 46-47; epidemiologist, NIMH, 48-50; res assoc epidemiol, Johns Hopkins Univ, 50-52; res asst & fel, Mayo Clin, 52-55; chief epidemiol br, Nat Inst Neurol Dis & Blindness, 55-64; PROF EPIDEMIOL, MAYO GRAD SCH MED, UNIV MINN & CHMN DEPT MED STATIST & EPIDEMIOL, MAYO CLIN, 64- *Concurrent Pos:* Res assoc, Mayo Clin, 53-55; chmn comt nomenclature, biomet & genetics, World Fedn Neurol, 54-64; fel, Armed Forces Inst Path, 55-56; vis lectr, Med Col SC, 56; prof lectr, Georgetown Univ, 57-60; clin prof neurol, Howard Univ, 60-64. *Mem:* Am Soc Human Genetics; fel AMA; fel Am Pub Health Asn; Am Neurol Asn; Am Epidemiol Soc (pres, 74). *Res:* Human ecology; medical record systems; geographic pathology; human genetics as applied to neurology; epidemiology of chronic disease. *Mailing Add:* 200 1st St SW Rochester MN 55901

KURLAND, ROBERT JOHN, b Denver, Colo, Apr 2, 30; m 64; c 4. NUCLEAR MAGNETIC RESONANCE, BIOPHYSICAL CHEMISTRY. *Educ:* Calif Inst Technol, BS, 51; Harvard Univ, MA, 53, PhD(chem physics), 55. *Prof Exp:* Nat Bur Stand-Nat Res Coun res assoc, 56-58; from instr to assoc prof chem, Carnegie-Mellon Univ, 58-68; ASSOC PROF CHEM, STATE UNIV NY BUFFALO, 68- *Mem:* Am Chem Soc; Am Phys Soc; Biophys Soc. *Res:* Nuclear magnetic resonance of paramagnetic molecules, biologically relevant systems and heavy nuclear species. *Mailing Add:* Dept Chem Acheson Hall State Univ NY Buffalo NY 14214

KURMES, ERNEST A, b Brooklyn, NY, Jan 19, 31; m 56; c 2. FORESTRY. *Educ:* Lehigh Univ, BA, 53; Yale Univ, MS, 57, MF, 58, PhD(forest ecol), 61. *Prof Exp:* Asst prof forestry, Southern Ill Univ, Carbondale, 61-67; assoc prof, 67-80, PROF FORESTRY, NORTHERN ARIZ UNIV, 80- *Mem:* AAAS; Soc Am Foresters; Ecol Soc Am. *Res:* Forest ecology; regeneration of forest tree species. *Mailing Add:* Sch Forestry Fac Box 4098 Northern Ariz Univ Flagstaff AZ 86011

KURMIS, VILIS, forestry, see previous edition

KURNICK, ALLEN ABRAHAM, b Kaunas, Lithuania, Mar 15, 21; nat US; m 42; c 2. CHEMISTRY, NUTRITION. *Educ:* Calif State Polytech Col, BS, 53; Agr & Mech Col, Tex, MS, 55, PhD(biochem, nutrit), 57. *Prof Exp:* Asst biochem & nutrit, Agr & Mech Col, Tex, 53-57; asst prof poultry sci, Univ Ariz, 57-59, prof & head dept, 59-62; assoc mgr tech & res serv, 62-66, dir tech serv, 66-73, dir dept agr & animal health, 73-75, gen mgr, 75-79, VPRES-DIR RES & DEVELOP, ROCHE CHEM DIV, HOFFMANN-LA ROCHE INC, 80- *Mem:* AAAS; Am Chem Soc; Poultry Sci Asn; Am Inst Nutrit. *Res:* Unidentified factors required for reproduction; enzyme systems in the developing chick embryo; metabolism and nutrition of mineral elements; vitamins in animal nutrition; biochemistry. *Mailing Add:* 33 Beachmont Terr North Caldwell NJ 07006

KURNICK, JOHN EDMUND, b New York, NY, Feb 9, 42; m 69; c 2. HEMATOLOGY, ONCOLOGY. *Educ:* Harvard Univ, BA, 62; Univ Chicago, MD, 66. *Prof Exp:* Intern, Univ Wash Hosps, 66-67; resident med, Stanford Univ Hosps, 67-68; fel hemat, 68-70, asst prof med, Univ Colo Med Ctr & chief, Hemat Serv, Denver Vet Admin Hosp, 73-78; ASSOC CLIN PROF MED (HEMAT/ONCOL), UNIV CALIF, IRVINE, 79- *Mem:* Am Col Physicians; Am Fedn Clin Res; Am Soc Clin Oncol; Am Soc Hemat; Int Soc Exp Hemat. *Res:* Hematopoietic cellular differentiation and control of granulopoiesis; erythropoiesis in anemias of chronic diseases and uremia; chemotherapy of malignant disorders. *Mailing Add:* 1760 Termino Ave Long Beach CA 90804

KURNICK, NATHANIEL BERTRAND, b Brooklyn, NY, Nov 8, 17; m 40; c 3. BIOCHEMISTRY, MEDICINE. *Educ:* Harvard Univ, BA, 36, MD, 40; Am Bd Internal Med, dipl, 51, cert oncol, 73, cert hemat, 74. *Prof Exp:* Workman fel med & biochem, Mass Gen Hosp, Harvard Univ, 40-41; intern, Mt Sinai Hosp, NY, 41-42, resident med, 46-47; Nat Res Coun & Am Cancer Soc res fel biochem & cytochem, Rockefeller Inst, 47-48 & Karolinska Nobel Inst, Stockholm, 48-49; asst prof med & dir lab cell res, Med Sch, Tulane Univ, 49-54; assoc clin prof med, Univ Calif, Los Angeles, 54-65, assoc internist, 59-65; assoc prof med in residence & assoc internist, 65-68, chmn div med, 66-71, CLIN PROF MED, UNIV CALIF, IRVINE, 68- *Concurrent Pos:* Vis physician, Charity Hosp, New Orleans, La, 49-54 & Touro Infirmary, 52-54; consult, Charity Hosp, Pineville, La, 54-59, consult, 59-; vis physician, Harbor Gen Hosp, Torrance Calif, 54-59, consult, 59-66; vis physician, Los Angeles County Hosp, 65-68; chmn dept med, Long Beach Community Hosp, 66-67; staff mem var hosps; dir oncol-hemat lab, Long Beach Community Hosp, 81- *Mem:* Histochem Soc; Am Soc Hemat; Soc Exp Biol & Med; Int Soc Hemat; Int Soc Exp Hemat. *Res:* Nucleic acids; chemistry and metabolism; nucleolytic enzymes; cytochemistry; hematology; oncology; radiation biology. *Mailing Add:* 1760 Termino Ave # 100 Long Beach CA 90804

KURNOW, ERNEST, b New York, NY, Oct 21, 12; m 38; c 3. STATISTICS. *Educ:* City Col New York, BS, 32, MS, 33; NY Univ, PhD(econ), 51. *Prof Exp:* From instr to prof econ, Schs Bus, 48-62, chmn quant anal area, 62-76, PROF STATIST, SCHS BUS, NY UNIV, 62-, CHMN DOCTORAL PROG, GRAD SCH BUS ADMIN, 76- *Concurrent Pos:* Lincoln Found grant, 58-61; study dir, Tri-State Transp Comt, 64-66, Finance Mass Transit, 71-72 & Gov Spec Comn, 71-72; Fulbright grant, Athens, Greece, 66-67; consult, Tri-State Regional Planning Comn, 73-75 & New York City Temp Comn City Finances, 75-76. *Mem:* Fel Am Statist Asn; Int Statist Inst; Inst Mgt Sci; Am Econ Asn; Am Inst Decision Sci. *Res:* Applications of statistics in fields of transportation and state and local government; design of sampling studies. *Mailing Add:* NY Univ 100 Trinity Pl New York NY 10006

KUROBANE, ITSUO, b Tochigi, Japan, Dec 23, 44; m 73; c 1. PHARMACOLOGY, BIOLOGICAL CHEMISTRY. *Educ:* Univ Tokyo, MS, 72, PhD(radiation genetics), 75. *Prof Exp:* assoc researcher biol, Dalhousie Univ, 75-79; res assoc, Univ Wis-Madison, 79-80; RES ASSOC, MED SCH, NORTHWESTERN UNIV, 80- *Concurrent Pos:* Guest scientist, Atlantic Regional Lab, Nat Res Coun Can, 75-79. *Mem:* AAAS; Radiation Res Soc; Am Chem Soc; Am Soc Microbiol. *Res:* Biosynthesis and biological activity of secondary metabolites; nuclear magnetic resonance spectroscopy in biological fields; radiation and isotope effects in biological systems; drug-receptor interactions. *Mailing Add:* Dept Pharmacol Med Sch Northwestern Univ Chicago IL 60611

KURODA, PAUL KAZUO, b Fukuoka, Japan, Apr 1, 17; nat US; m 53; c 3. CHEMISTRY. *Educ:* Univ Tokyo, BS, 39, ScD(inorg chem), 44. *Prof Exp:* Asst prof chem, Univ Tokyo, 44-49; fel, Univ Minn, 49-52; from asst prof to prof, 52-81, DISTINGUISHED PROF CHEM, UNIV ARK, FAYETTEVILLE, 81- *Concurrent Pos:* Assoc chemist, Argonne Nat Lab, 57-58. *Honors & Awards:* Nuclear Appln Award, Am Chem Soc, 78. *Mem:*

AAAS; Am Phys Soc; Geochem Soc; Am Chem Soc; Am Geophys Union. *Res:* Natural radioactivity; nuclear and radiochemistry; cosmochemistry; geochemistry; spontaneous fission; low-level counting; radioactive fallout. *Mailing Add:* Rm 8 Chem Bldg Dept Chem Univ Ark Fayetteville AR 72701

KUROHARA, SAMUEL S, b Hilo, Hawaii, Apr 21, 31; m 56; c 3. RADIOBIOLOGY, RADIOTHERAPY. *Educ:* Wash Univ, BA, 53, MD, 57; Univ Rochester, PhD(radiobiol), 64. *Prof Exp:* Intern gen med, Jewish Hosp, St Louis, 57-58; res radiol, Strong Mem Hosp, 58-61, asst radiotherapist, 61-64; radiotherapist, US Naval Hosp, San Diego, 64-66; assoc dir radiother & assoc chief cancer res, Roswell Park Mem Inst, NY, 66-68; asst dir radiother, Med Ctr, 68-74, prof radiol, 68-74, CLIN PROF RADIOL, SCH MED, UNIV SOUTHERN CALIF, 75-; ASSOC RADIOTHERAPIST, WHITTIER ONCOL MED CLIN, 75- *Concurrent Pos:* Instr radiol, Sch Med, Univ Rochester, 61-64; clin consult, Roswell Park Mem Inst, NY, 68-; specialist physician, Los Angeles County Univ Southern Calif Med Ctr, 68-; consult, Tech Serv Corp, 60-71, Good Samaritan Hosp, Los Angeles, 69-72, Whittier Oncol Med Clin, 71- & Alpha Omega Serv, 73- *Mem:* Radiol Soc NAm; AMA; Am Soc Therapeut Radiol; Radiation Res Soc. *Res:* Computer applications in the study of medical and biological data; computer application to automated system in radiotherapy; effects of ionizing radiation on normal tissues; mechanisms of tumor control with radiation. *Mailing Add:* Dept of Radiation Ther OPD 1P-17 LAC-USC Med Ctr Los Angeles CA 90033

KUROSAKA, MITSURU, b Snenyang, China, Mar 26, 35; US citizen; m 63; c 3. MECHANICAL ENGINEERING, APPLIED MATHEMATICS. *Educ:* Univ Tokyo, BS, 59, MS, 61; Calif Inst Technol, PhD(mech eng), 68. *Prof Exp:* Design engr, Hitachi Ltd, 61-63; grad res & teaching asst, Calif Inst Technol, 63-67; eng specialist, AiResearch Mfg Co, 67-69; fluid mech engr, Gen Elec Res & Develop Ctr, 69-77; assoc prof, 77-79, PROF MECH & AEROSPACE ENG, UNIV TENN SPACE INST, 79- *Concurrent Pos:* Consult, Gen Elec Co, ARO, Inc & AiResearch Mfg Co. *Mem:* Assoc fel Am Inst Aeronaut & Astronaut; Am Soc Mech Engrs; Sigma Xi. *Res:* Aerothermodynamics of gas turbines; aeroacoustics; unsteady flow, aeroelasticity; nonlinear waves; two-phase flow. *Mailing Add:* Dept Mech & Aerospace Eng Univ Tenn Space Inst Tullohoma TN 37388

KUROSE, GEORGE, b Eatonville, Wash, June 13, 24; m 56; c 3. CHEMICAL ENGINEERING. *Educ:* Columbia Univ, BS, 49, MS, 50. *Prof Exp:* Chem engr, 50-55, res chem engr, 55-62, sr res chem engr, 62-77, GROUP LEADER, AM CYANAMID CO, 77- *Mem:* Am Chem Soc; Am Inst Chem Eng. *Res:* Process development; process design; process and economic evaluation; synthetic fiber process development. *Mailing Add:* Am Cyanamid Co 1937 W Main St Stanford CT 06901

KUROWSKI, GARY JOHN, b Fargo, NDak, Mar 22, 31; m 63; c 3. NUMERICAL ANALYSIS. *Educ:* Univ Minn, BS, 53, MS, 54; Carnegie Inst Technol, PhD(math), 59. *Prof Exp:* Res assoc math, Off Ord Res, Duke Univ, 59-63; from asst prof to assoc prof math, 63-72, dir comput ctr, 69-71, PROF MATH, UNIV CALIF, DAVIS, 72- *Mem:* Am Math Soc; Asn Comput Mach; Soc Indust & Appl Math. *Res:* Applied mathematics, especially discrete and semi-discrete analogues of the classic fields of analysis and their application to numerical analysis. *Mailing Add:* Dept of Math Univ of Calif Davis CA 95616

KURSHAN, JEROME, b Brooklyn, NY, Mar 10, 19; m 46; c 2. PHYSICS. *Educ:* Columbia Univ, AB, 39; Cornell Univ, PhD(physics), 43. *Prof Exp:* Asst physics, Columbia Univ, 39 & Cornell Univ, 39-43; res physicist, RCA Labs, 43-55, mgr employ & training, 55-59, mgr, Res Serv Lab, 59-66, mgr mkt, RCA Labs, 66-73, MGR ADMIN SERV, RCA LABS, RCA CORP, 73- *Concurrent Pos:* Instr, Rutgers Univ, 44. *Mem:* Am Phys Soc; Inst Elec & Electronics Engrs. *Res:* Ion sources; gated amplifiers; frequency modulated magnetrons; automatic frequency control oscillators; transistors; semiconductors physics; materials analysis; computer applications; research management; research administration. *Mailing Add:* RCA Labs Princeton NJ 08540

KURSS, HERBERT, b Brooklyn, NY, Mar 30, 24. MATHEMATICS. *Educ:* Cooper Union, BEE, 43; Polytech Inst Brooklyn, MEE, 52; NY Univ, PhD, 57. *Prof Exp:* Tech writer radar, Techlit Consult, Inc, 47; instr elec eng, US Merchant Marine Acad, 47-48; res assoc appl math, Microwave Res Inst, Polytech Inst Brooklyn, 48-54; res asst math, NY Univ, 54-57; res assoc appl math, Microwave Res Inst, Polytech Inst Brooklyn, 57-59, res asst prof, 59-62; assoc prof, 62-69, PROF MATH, ADELPHI UNIV, 69- *Mem:* Am Math Soc; Math Asn Am; Sigma Xi. *Res:* Problems associated with ordinary differential equations and with electromagnetic theory. *Mailing Add:* Dept of Math Adelphi Univ Garden City NY 11530

KURSTEDT, HAROLD ALBERT, JR, b Columbus, Ohio, Sept 15, 39; m 61; c 3. NUCLEAR ENGINEERING. *Educ:* Va Mil Inst, BS, 61; Univ Ill, Urbana, MS, 63, PhD(nuclear eng), 68. *Prof Exp:* Instr mech eng, Va Mil Inst, 61-62; res & develop coordr, Ballistic Res Labs, Aberdeen Proving Ground, Md, 66-68; asst prof nuclear eng, Col Eng, Ohio State Univ, 68-70; prog mgr, Fed Systs Div, Indust Nucleonics Corp, 70-76; ASSOC PROF MECH & NUCLEAR ENG, VA POLYTECH INST & STATE UNIV, 76- *Mem:* Am Soc Civil Eng; Am Soc Eng Educ; Am Nuclear Soc. *Res:* Nuclear reactor kinetics and heat transfer, particularly experimental and analytical techniques in pulsed thermal and fast reactors; nuclear instrumentation and control; nondestructive inspection. *Mailing Add:* Dept of Mech & Nuclear Eng VA Polytech Inst & State Univ Blacksburg VA 24061

KURSUNOGLU, BEHRAM N, b Bayburt, Turkey, Mar 14, 22; m 52; c 3. THEORETICAL PHYSICS. *Educ:* Univ Edinburgh, BSc, 49; Cambridge Univ, PhD, 52. *Prof Exp:* Res assoc, Cornell Univ, 52-54; vis prof physics, Miami Univ, 54-55; dean fac nuclear sci & technol, Mid E Tech Univ, Ankara, Turkey, 56-58; PROF PHYSICS, UNIV MIAMI, 58-, DIR CTR THEORET STUDIES, 65- *Concurrent Pos:* Adv, Turkish Gen Staff Atomic Matters, 56-58; mem, Turkish Atomic Energy Comn, 56-58; Turkish mem sci comt, NATO, 58; consult, Brit Atomic Energy Res Estab, 61 & Max Planck Inst Physics & Astrophys, 61; consult, Oak Ridge Nat Lab, 62-64, chmn, Annual High Energy Physics Conf, Fla, 64-; chmn, Annual Int Sci Forum, Energy, 77- *Mem:* Fel Am Phys Soc; Am Asn Physics Teachers. *Res:* Theoretical high energy, relativity and plasma physics. *Mailing Add:* Ctr for Theoret Studies Univ of Miami PO Box 249055 Coral Gables FL 33124

KURT, CARL EDWARD, b Muskogee, Okla, June 3, 43. CIVIL ENGINEERING, STRUCTURAL ENGINEERING. *Educ:* Okla State Univ, BS, 65, MS, 66, PhD(civil eng), 69. *Prof Exp:* Instr civil eng, Okla State Univ, 69; sr engr strength, McDonnell Douglas Astronaut Corp, 69-74; asst prof, 74-80, ASSOC PROF, DEPT CIVIL ENG, AUBURN UNIV, 80- *Mem:* Am Soc Civil Engrs; Nat Water Well Asn; Am Soc Testing & Mat. *Res:* Behavior of structural materials; structural analysis and stability; engineering properties of thermoplastic water well casings; hydraulic analysis and model studies. *Mailing Add:* Dept of Civil Eng Auburn Univ Auburn AL 36849

KURTENBACH, AELRED J(OSEPH), b Dimock, SDak, Jan 3, 34; m 60; c 5. ELECTRICAL ENGINEERING. *Educ:* SDak Sch Mines & Technol, BS, 61; Univ Nebr, MS, 62; Purdue Univ, PhD(elec eng), 68. *Prof Exp:* Instr elec eng, SDak State Univ, 62-65, asst prof, 65-69, assoc prof, 69-72; PRES, DAKTRONICS, INC, BROOKINGS, SDAK, 69- *Concurrent Pos:* Instr elec eng, Purdue Univ, 65-66. *Mem:* Inst Elec & Electronics Engrs. *Res:* Biomedical telemetry; pulse-code modulation telemetry. *Mailing Add:* Daktronics Inc PO Box 128 Brookings SD 57006

KURTH, RUDOLF, b Berlin, Ger, Dec 7, 17; m 44; c 1. MATHEMATICS. *Educ:* Univ Bern, DrPhil(astron, math, philos), 48. *Prof Exp:* Res worker astron, Univ Bern, 48-56 privatdozent, 51-56; from lectr to sr lectr, Manchester Univ, 56-60; sr lectr math, Univ Durham, 60-62; prof, Univ Ife, Nigeria, 62-63; vis prof, Mich State Univ, 63-64; prof, Ga Inst Technol, 64-69; prof math, Southern Ill Univ, Edwardsville, 69-80; RETIRED. *Concurrent Pos:* Sr res fel astron, St Andrews Univ, 52-53 & 54-55; vis prof, Univ Berlin, 55; consult, NSF, India, 67, 68. *Res:* Philosophy of mathematics; analysis, applied mathematics, statistics. *Mailing Add:* 1811 Cornell Ave Edwardsville IL 62025

KURTH, WILLIAM STEVEN, b Bowling Green, Ky, Feb 7, 51; c 2. SPACE PHYSICS, PLANETARY RADIO ASTRONOMY. *Educ:* Univ Iowa, BA, 73, MS, 75, PhD(physics), 79. *Prof Exp:* Res aide, 71-73, grad res asst, 73-79, res investr, 79, ASST RES SCIENTIST, DEPT PHYSICS & ASTRON, UNIV IOWA, 79- *Concurrent Pos:* Co-investr, Origin Plasmas Earths Neighborhood, Univ Iowa, 81-, Jupiter Data Anal Prog, 82- *Mem:* Am Geophys Union. *Res:* Plasma waves and wave-particle interactions in space plasmas in the magnetospheres of the Earth, Jupiter and Saturn as well as in the interplanetary medium. *Mailing Add:* Dept Physics & Astron Univ Iowa Iowa City IA 52242

KURTTI, TIMOTHY JOHN, b Minneapolis, Minn, Mar 8, 42; m 63. INSECT PATHOLOGY, INSECT PHYSIOLOGY. *Educ:* Univ Minn, BA, 65, PhD(entom), 74. *Prof Exp:* From jr scientist to asst scientist insect microbiol, 66-69, res asst, 69-70, res fel, 70-73, res assoc insect microbiol, Dept Entom, Fisheries & Wildlife, Univ Minn, St Paul, 73-77; scientist, Int Lab for Res on Animal Dis, Nairobi, Kenya, 77-80; ASST RES PROF MICROBIOL, WAKSMAN INST MICROBIOL, RUTGERS UNIV, 80- *Mem:* Tissue Cult Asn; Soc Invert Path; Entom Soc Am; Sigma Xi. *Res:* Insect microbiology; bovine and tick tissue culture; development physiology of insects; insect nutrition; biological calorimetry; theileriosis; intracellular parasitism; microbial control. *Mailing Add:* Rutgers Univ Waksman Inst Microbiol PO Box 759 Piscataway NJ 08900 Kenya

KURTZ, A PETER, b Staten Island, NY, June 2, 42; m 64; c 2. PESTICIDE CHEMISTRY. *Educ:* Fordham Univ, BS, 63; Columbia Univ, MA, 64, PhD(org chem), 68. *Prof Exp:* Res chemist, Letterman Army Inst Res, 69-71; res chemist, 71-78, RES SCIENTIST PESTICIDE CHEM, TECH CTR, UNION CARBIDE CORP, 78- *Mem:* Am Chem Soc. *Res:* Development of quantitative structure; activity relationships and application to the design of selectively toxic pesticide chemicals; computerizedc chemical/biological information storage and analysis systems. *Mailing Add:* Tech Ctr Union Carbide Corp PO Box 12014 Research Triangle Park NC 27709

KURTZ, ANTHONY DAVID, b New York, NY, May 3, 29; m 55; c 2. PHYSICAL METALLURGY. *Educ:* Mass Inst Technol, SB, 51, SM, 52, ScD(phys metall), 55. *Prof Exp:* Res asst, Mass Inst Technol, 51-54, staff mem, Lincoln Lab, 54-55; sr engr, Transistor Prod, Inc Div, Clevelite Corp, 56; supvr appl res, Semiconductor Div, Minneapolis-Honeywell Regulator Co, 56-59; dir res & develop, 59-66, PRES, KULITE SEMICONDUCTOR PROD, 66- *Honors & Awards:* Si Fluor Technol Award, Instrument Soc Am, 78. *Mem:* Am Soc Metals; Am Phys Soc; Inst Elec & Electronics Engrs. *Res:* Solid state physics and tranducer design; semiconductor devices and materials; diffusion in solids; imperfections in metals and semiconductors; experimental mechanics; stress analysis. *Mailing Add:* Kulite Semiconductor Prod 1025 Hoyt Ave Ridgefield NJ 07657

KURTZ, CLARK N, b Stillwater, Minn, Nov 24, 37; m 65; c 2. OPTICS. *Educ:* SDak Sch Mines & Technol, BS, 59; Univ Ill, MS, 63; Univ Rochester, PhD(elec eng), 67. *Prof Exp:* Design engr electronics, 59-62, sr res physicist, 66-72, res assoc optics, 72-79, LAB HEAD, RES LABS, EASTMAN KODAK CO, 79- *Honors & Awards:* Charles Ives Award, Soc Photog Scientists & Engrs, 72. *Mem:* Optical Soc Am; Am Inst Physics. *Res:* Physics of forming images on paper in copying; theory of light propagation in waveguides; design of optical screens and diffusers; optical disk; light waves. *Mailing Add:* Eastman Kodak Res Labs 343 State St Rochester NY 14650

KURTZ, DAVID ALLAN, b Evanston, Ill, Jan 31, 32. PESTICIDE CHEMISTRY. *Educ:* Knox Col, AB, 54; Pa State Univ, MS, 58, PhD(org chem), 60. *Prof Exp:* Instr gen chem, Pa State Univ, 59-60; sr chemist, HRB-Singer, Inc, 60-62; res assoc appl chem, Mat Res Lab, 62-66, asst prof pesticides anal, Pesticides Res Lab, 67-71, ANAL CHEMIST, PESTICIDES RES LAB, PA STATE UNIV, UNIVERSITY PARK, 71- *Concurrent Pos:* Co-leader coop regional proj NE-115 Pa Agr Exp Sta, 78- *Mem:* Am Chem Soc. *Res:* Methods of analysis for pesticides and herbicides; chemometric methods (use of statistical methods in trace residue analysis for pesticides and environmental compounds); neutron activation analysis of mercury in animal tissues. *Mailing Add:* Pesticides Res Lab Pa State Univ University Park PA 16802

KURTZ, EDWARD FRANK, b Claysburg, Pa, Apr 24, 26; m 49; c 7. NUCLEAR & METALLURGICAL ENGINEERING. *Educ:* Pa State Univ, BS, 47. *Prof Exp:* Engr, Harbison-Walker Refractories Co, Pa, 47; engr, Hanford Works, 47-62, engr, Vallecitos Nuclear Ctr, 62-66, mgr, Plutonium Lab, 66-71, mgr, Plutonium Fuel Develop Process Eng, 71-73, mgr, Advan Fuels Lab, Vallecitos Nuclear Ctr, 74-80, MGR, FUEL CYCLE & SPEC PROJ, GEN ELEC CO, 80- *Res:* Fuel fabrication and fabrication development on plutonium and its compounds, including refractory metals, oxide and cermet fuels and a variety of metal cladding materials. *Mailing Add:* Gen Elec Co PO Box 508 Sunnyvale CA 94086

KURTZ, EDWARD FULTON, JR, applied mechanics, mechanical engineering, see previous edition

KURTZ, EDWIN BERNARD, JR, b Wichita, Kans, Aug 11, 26; m 52; c 2. PLANT PHYSIOLOGY. *Educ:* Univ Ariz, BS, 48, MS, 49; Calif Inst Technol, PhD, 52. *Prof Exp:* Instr bot, Univ Ariz, 47, from asst prof to prof, 51-68, actg head dept, 54-55; prof biol & head dept, Kans State Teachers Col, 68-72; PROF LIFE SCI & CHMN DEPT, UNIV TEX PERMIAN BASIN, 72- *Mem:* AAAS; Am Soc Plant Physiol; Am Chem Soc; Bot Soc Am; Nat Sci Teachers Asn. *Res:* Science education. *Mailing Add:* Dept of Life Sci Univ of Tex of the Permian Basin Odessa TX 79762

KURTZ, GEORGE WILBUR, b Harrisburg, Pa, Dec 8, 28; m 53; c 3. ANALYTICAL CHEMISTRY. *Educ:* Pa State Univ, BS, 50, MS, 52, PhD(dairy sci), 54. *Prof Exp:* Res chemist, Swift & Co, 54; head flavor & phys chem lab, Armed Forces Qm Food & Container Inst, Chicago, 56-62; chemist, Dalare Assocs, 62-69; mgr qual control, 69-69, PLANT MGR, R P SCHERER NA, MONROE, NC, 79- *Mem:* Am Chem Soc; Inst Food Technol. *Res:* Analytical chemistry; food technology. *Mailing Add:* R P Scherer Corp 2021 E Roosevelt Blvd Box 847 Monroe NC 28110

KURTZ, HAROLD JOHN, b Brookings, SDak, Feb 18, 31; m 53; c 3. VETERINARY PATHOLOGY. *Educ:* SDak State Univ, BS & MS, 54; Univ Minn, DVM, 58, PhD(vet path), 66. *Prof Exp:* Instr vet surg, 60-61 & vet med, 61-62, fel vet path, 62-66, from asst prof to assoc prof, 66-74, PROF VET PATH, COL VET MED, UNIV MINN, ST PAUL, 74- *Mem:* Am Vet Med Asn; Am Col Vet Path; Int Cad Path. *Res:* Dissecting aortic rupture in turkeys; neuropathology and pathology of animal diseases; comparative pathology; edema disease of swine. *Mailing Add:* Dept of Vet Path Univ of Minn Col of Vet Med St Paul MN 55101

KURTZ, LAWRENCE ALFRED, b Providence, RI, Dec 29, 40. NUMERICAL ANALYSIS. *Educ:* Univ RI, BS, 62; Univ Conn, MS, 65; Univ Tenn, Knoxville, PhD(math), 69. *Prof Exp:* Engr, Eastman Kodak Co, 62-63; teaching asst math, Univ Conn, 63-65; teaching asst, Univ Tenn, Knoxville, 65, instr, 70; statist comput analyst, 71, asst prof, Hollins Col, 70-76; ASSOC PROF MATH, UNIV MONTEVALLO, 77- *Mem:* Am Math Soc; Soc Indust & Appl Math. *Res:* Computational fluid dynamics; numerical analysis of partial differential equations. *Mailing Add:* Dept of Math & Phys Montevallo AL 35115

KURTZ, LESTER TOUBY, b Howard Co, Ind, Nov 7, 14; m 40; c 2. AGRONOMY. *Educ:* Purdue Univ, BS, 38; Univ Ill, PhD(agron), 43. *Prof Exp:* Asst soil chemist, Dept Agron, Univ Ill, Urbana, 38-43, assoc, 43-44; instr US army spec training prog, 43-45, from asst prof to assoc prof, 44-50, prof soil fertil & fertilizers, Exp Sta, 50-82; RETIRED. *Concurrent Pos:* Guggenheim fel, soils lab, Agr Res Serv, USDA, 53-54; Fulbright fel, Waite Inst, SAustralia, 61-62 & soil & fertilizer br, Tenn Valley Authority, Ala, 68-69; Lady Davis fel, Soils & Fertilizer Div, Israel Inst Tech, Haifa, Israel. *Mem:* AAAS; fel Am Soc Agron; Am Chem Soc; Soil Sci Soc Am. *Res:* Soil chemistry and fertility; analytical chemistry; phosphate fixation in Illinois soils; fate of fertilizer nitrogen in soils as indicated by nitrogen 15; role of fertilizer in water pollution. *Mailing Add:* Dept of Agron Univ of Ill Urbana IL 61803

KURTZ, MARGOT, b Vohringen, Ger, Aug 30, 41; m 65; c 1. MEDICAL EDUCATION. *Educ:* Mich State Univ, BA, 72, MA, 73, PhD, 76. *Prof Exp:* Fac behav sci, Lansing Community Col, 74-76; coordr, 76-77, CO-DIR PRECEPTOR PROG, DEPT FAMILY MED, MICH STATE UNIV, 77-, CO-DIR PRECEPTOR & JR PARTNERSHIP PROGS, 80- *Res:* Educational and psychological aspects of clinical training; behavioral aspects of physician-patient relationships; processes in medical interviewing; psychological aspects of student personal development and relationship patterns while in medical school. *Mailing Add:* Dept of Family Med Mich State Univ East Lansing MI 48824

KURTZ, MARK EDWARD, b Trenton, Mo, Nov 8, 46; m 52, 71; c 2. WEED SCIENCE. *Educ:* Mo Valley Col, BS, 69; Miss State Univ, MS, 77, PhD(weed sci), 80. *Prof Exp:* ASST PLANT PHYSIOLOGIST, RES DEPT, DELTA BR, MISS AGR & FORESTRY EXP STA, MISS STATE UNIV, 80- *Concurrent Pos:* Adj asst prof, Dept Plant Path & Weed Sci, Miss State Univ, 81- *Mem:* Weed Sci Soc Am. *Res:* Soybean and cotton weed control, utilizing existing techniques and improvising new ideas to solve unanswered problems as they arise. *Mailing Add:* Box 197 Stonewall MS 38776

KURTZ, MYRA BERMAN, b New York, NY, July 20, 45; m 70; c 1. MICROBIOLOGY, GENETICS. *Educ:* Goucher Col, AB, 66; Harvard Univ, PhD(microbiol), 71. *Prof Exp:* Res assoc, State Univ NY, Albany, 71-72; assoc prof microbiol, Fed Univ Sao Carlos, Brazil, 72-74; res assoc, 75-76, ASST RES PROF, WAKSMAN INST MICROBIOL, RUTGERS UNIV, 76- *Mem:* Am Soc Microbiol; AAAS; Brit Mycol Soc. *Res:* Biochemical and genetic aspects of eukaryotic development; characterization of fungal mutants altered in sexual and asexual development. *Mailing Add:* Waksman Inst of Microbiol Rutgers Univ New Brunswick NJ 08854

KURTZ, PETER, JR, b Chicago, Ill, May 12, 27; m 50. CERAMIC ENGINEERING, THERMODYNAMICS. *Educ:* Univ Mo, Rolla, BS, 52, MS, 53; Univ Calif, Los Angeles, PhD(eng), 64. *Prof Exp:* Grad res engr, Univ Calif, Los Angeles, 53-55, jr res engr, 55-57, asst res engr, 57-58, assoc eng, 56-62, actg asst prof, 63-64, asst prof, 64-68; prof eng, 68-80, chmn, Div Sci, 71-80, PROF PHYSICS, BIOLA COL, 80- *Mem:* Am Asn Physics Teachers. *Res:* Mechanical properties of ceramic materials; thermodynamic properties of multicomponent polyphase systems. *Mailing Add:* Dept of Physics Biola Col 13800 Biola Ave La Mirada CA 90639

KURTZ, RICHARD BUNN, chemical engineering, see previous edition

KURTZ, RICHARD ROBERT, b Moose Jaw, Sask, Mar 20, 45; m 70; c 2. SYNTHETIC ORGANIC CHEMISTRY. *Educ:* Univ Calgary, BSc, 67; Mass Inst Technol, PhD(org chem), 71. *Prof Exp:* Assoc org chem, John C Sheehan Inst Res, 71-73; researcher, 73-80, RES HEAD, UPJOHN CO, 80- *Mem:* Am Chem Soc. *Res:* Pharmaceutical research and development; synthesis of heterocycles and prostaglandins. *Mailing Add:* Pharmaceut Res & Develop Div Upjohn Co Kalamazoo MI 49001

KURTZ, STANLEY MORTON, b Philadelphia, Pa, May 11, 26; m 57; c 2. PATHOLOGY. *Educ:* George Washington Univ, BS, 49, MS, 50, PhD(anat), 53; Univ Ala, MD, 58. *Prof Exp:* Instr anat, Bowman Gray Sch Med, Wake Forest Col, 52-54; instr anat, Med Sch, Univ Ala, 54-58; sr res fel path, Univ Pittsburgh, 58-61; assoc prof, Med Ctr, Duke Univ, 61-65; dir dept toxicol, Res Labs, Parke Davis & Co, 65-76; PROF PATH, MED UNIV SC, CHARLESTON & STAFF PATHOLOGIST, CHARLESTON VET ADMIN HOSP, 76- *Concurrent Pos:* Consult, Vet Admin Hosps, 61-65, Nat Acad Sci-Nat Res Coun, 72- & Nat Inst Drug Abuse, 74- *Mem:* AAAS; Am Soc Path & Bact; Am Soc Exp Path; Soc Toxicol. *Res:* Cytology; electron microscopy; development, structure and pathology of mammalian renal glomerulus. *Mailing Add:* Dept of Path Med Univ of SC Charleston SC 29401

KURTZ, STEVEN ROSS, b Washington, DC, Oct 3, 53; m 78. SOLID STATE PHYSICS. *Educ:* Bucknell Univ, BS, 75; Univ Ill, Urbana-Champaign, MS, 77, PhD(physics), 80. *Prof Exp:* MEM TECH STAFF, SANDIA NAT LAB, 80- *Mem:* Am Phys Soc. *Res:* Electron paramagnetic resonance, electron nuclear double resonance and electron-spin relaxation; theoretical electron-spin relaxation in disordered materials; photoconductivity and transport in disordered materials; prebreakdown and hot electron effects. *Mailing Add:* Div 5815 Sandia Nat Lab Albuquerque NM 87185

KURTZ, STEWART K, b Bryn Mawr, Pa, June 9, 31; m 51; c 4. ELECTROOPTICS. *Educ:* Ohio State Univ, BSc, 56, MSc, 57, PhD(physics), 60. *Prof Exp:* Staff scientist, Bell Tel Labs, Inc, 60-69; group dir explor res, Philips Labs Div, NAm Philips Corp, 69-80; WITH CLAIROL APPLIANCES, 80- *Mem:* Am Phys Soc; sr mem Inst Elec & Electronic Engrs; NY Acad Sci. *Res:* High resolution infrared molecular spectra; paramagnetic resonance, cross-relaxation; ferroelectrics, primarily optical and electrooptical properties; nonlinear optical materials; powder survey methods; second harmonic coefficients; Raman scattering; crystal growth; electro-crystallization; phase transitions; crystal chemistry. *Mailing Add:* Clairol Appliances 2 Blachley Rd Stamford CT 06902

KURTZ, THOMAS EUGENE, b Oak Park, Ill, Feb 22, 28; m 53, 74; c 3. COMPUTER SYSTEMS. *Educ:* Knox Col, BA, 50; Princeton Univ, PhD(math), 56. *Prof Exp:* From instr to assoc prof math, 56-66, dir, Comput Ctr, 59-75, dir, Off Acad Comput, 75-78, PROF MATH, DARTMOUTH COL, 66-, VCHMN PROG COMPUT INFO SCI, 80- *Concurrent Pos:* Consult, Vet Admin, White River Junction, Vt; mem Pierce panel, President's Sci Adv Coun Comput in Higher Educ, 65-67; chmn coun, EDUCOM, 73-74; chmn bd, NERComP, Inc, 74- *Honors & Awards:* Pioneer Award, Am Fed Info Processing Socs, 74. *Mem:* Am Statist Asn; Asn Comput Mach. *Res:* Computer languages; computer systems and their applications; computer use in education; statistics applications. *Mailing Add:* Dept of Math Dartmouth Col Hanover NH 03755

KURTZ, THOMAS GORDON, b Kansas City, Mo, July 14, 41; m 63; c 2. STOCHASTIC PROCESSES. *Educ:* Univ Mo-Columbia, BA, 63; Stanford Univ, MS, 65, PhD(math), 67. *Prof Exp:* Vis lectr math, 67-69, from asst prof to assoc prof, 69-75, PROF MATH, UNIV WIS-MADISON, 75- *Mem:* Math Asn Am; Soc Indust & Appl Math; Am Math Soc; Inst Math Statist. *Res:* Probability theory and stochastic processes; Markov processes; operator semigroups, particularly the relationship between Markov processes and operator semigroups; approximation for stochastic process. *Mailing Add:* Dept of Math Univ of Wis Madison WI 53706

KURTZ, VINCENT E, b Duluth, Minn, Apr 12, 26; m 53; c 5. PALEONTOLOGY, STRATIGRAPHY. *Educ:* Univ Minn, BA, 46, MS, 49; Univ Okla, PhD(geol), 60. *Prof Exp:* Geologist, Aurora Gasoline Co, Colo, 52-55; dist geologist, Kans, 56-58; from asst prof to assoc prof earth sci, 65-74, PROF GEOL, SOUTHWEST MO STATE COL, 74- *Mem:* Paleont Soc. *Res:* Late Cambrian and early Ordovician stratigraphy; paleontology and paleoecology of trilobites, inarticulate brachiopods and conodonts. *Mailing Add:* Dept of Geog & Geol Southwest Mo State Univ Springfield MO 65802

KURTZ, WILLIAM BOYCE, b Austin, Tex, July 15, 41; m 65; c 2. FOREST RESOURCE ECONOMICS. *Educ:* NMex State Univ, BS, 63, MS, 66; Univ Ariz, PhD(natural resource econ), 71. *Prof Exp:* Range conservationist, Soil Conserv Serv, USDA, 63-64; res assoc watershed mgt, Univ Ariz, 68-69; proj economist, Daniel Mann Johnson & Mendenhall, 69; sr economist, Voorhies, Trindle & Nelson, Orange County, 69-70; asst prof natural resources mgt, Calif Polytech State Univ, 70-75; assoc prof, 75-80, PROF FORESTRY, UNIV MO-COLUMBIA, 80- *Mem:* Sigma Xi; Soc Range Mgt; Soil Conserv Soc Am. *Res:* Multiple use economics of forest resources. *Mailing Add:* Forestry Fisheries & Wildlife Univ of Mo Columbia MO 65211

KURTZKE, JOHN F, b Brooklyn, NY, Sept 14, 26; m; c 7. NEUROLOGY, EPIDEMIOLOGY. *Educ:* St John's Univ, NY, BS, 48; Cornell Univ, MD, 52; Am Bd Psychiat & Neurol, dipl neurol, 58. *Prof Exp:* Intern, Kings County Hosp, 52-53; resident, Vet Admin Hosp, Bronx, 53-56; instr neurol, Jefferson Med Col, 58-61, asst neurologist, Hosp & Clin, 58-63, assoc clin neurol, Col, 61-63, asst prof, 63; clin assoc prof, 63-65, assoc prof, 65-68, PROF NEUROL & COMMUNITY MED, SCH MED, GEORGETOWN UNIV, 68- *Concurrent Pos:* Chief neurol serv, Vet Admin Hosp, Coatesville, Pa, 56-63, assoc chief staff res, 57-62; asst examr, Am Bd Psychiat & Neurol, 61-; consult neurol, Nat Naval Med Ctr, Bethesda, 66-; chief neurol serv, Vet Admin Med Ctr, Washington, DC, 63-; mem exec comt coop study of adrenocorticotropic hormone in multiple sclerosis, Nat Inst Neurol Dis & Blindness, 64-71; Vet Admin rep, Neurol Study Sect, Div Res Grant, 64-72; cor mem comn geog neurol, epidemiol & statist, World Fedn Neurol, 64-, mem med adv bd, Nat Multiple Sclerosis Soc, 66-; consult to Surgeon Gen, Dept Navy, 70-; mem int med adv bd, Int Fedn Multiple Sclerosis Soc, 72-; consult ad hoc comt spinal cord injury, Nat Inst Neurol Dis & Stroke, 73-76; mem epilepsy adv comt, NIH, 74-77; mem, task force on neurol serv, Joint Comn Neurol, 71-75, & work group on epidemiol, Nat Comn Multiple Sclerosis, 73; chmn work group on epidemiol, biostatist & population genetics, Comn for Control of Huntington's Dis, 76-77; med res prog specialist in neurol & neurobiol, VACO Res Serv, 77-80; liaison officer, US Navy Med Sch, Georgetown, 79- *Mem:* Fel AAAS; Am Neurol Asn; fel Am Col Physicians; fel Am Acad Neurol; Int Epidemiol Asn. *Res:* author of over 250 publications. *Mailing Add:* 7509 Salem Rd Falls Church VA 22043

KURTZMAN, CLETUS PAUL, b Mansfield, Ohio, July 19, 38; m 62; c 3. MYCOLOGY. *Educ:* Ohio Univ, BS, 60; Purdue Univ, MS, 62; WVa Univ, PhD(mycol), 67. *Prof Exp:* Microbiologist, 67-70, zymologist, 70-81, RES LEADER & HEAD AGR RES SERV CULTURE COLLECTION, NORTHERN REGIONAL RES LAB, USDA, 81- *Concurrent Pos:* Adj prof mycol, Ill State Univ, 81- *Mem:* Mycol Soc Am; Sigma Xi; Am Soc Microbiol; AAAS; US Fedn Cult Collections (vpres, 77-78, pres, 78-80). *Res:* Yeast taxonomy; genetic, molecular and physiological aspects of interspecific and intergeneric relationships. *Mailing Add:* USDA Northern Regional Res Ctr 1815 N University St Peoria IL 61604

KURTZMAN, RALPH HAROLD, JR, b Minneapolis, Minn, Feb 21, 33; m 55; c 2. BIOCHEMISTRY, MYCOLOGY. *Educ:* Univ Minn, BS, 55; Univ Wis, MS, 58, PhD(plant path biochem), 59. *Prof Exp:* Asst prof plant path, Univ RI, 59-62; asst prof biol, Univ Minn, 62-65; BIOCHEMIST, WESTERN REGIONAL RES LAB, USDA, 65- *Concurrent Pos:* NASA contract res with A H Brown & A O Dahl, Univ Minn, 63. *Mem:* Int Soc Mushroom Sci; Am Chem Soc; Am Soc Plant Physiol; Mycol Soc Am; Am Mushroom Inst. *Res:* Physiology of plant diseases, particularly Dutch elm disease; alkaloid metabolism of fungi; fungal decomposition of cellulose and lignin; mushroom production from wastes. *Mailing Add:* Western Regional Res Lab USDA 800 Buchanan St Albany CA 94710

KURUCZ, ROBERT LOUIS, b Columbus, Miss, Sept 7, 44. ASTROPHYSICS. *Educ:* Harvard Col, AB, 66, PhD(astron), 73. *Prof Exp:* Res fel, Harvard Col Observ, 73-74; PHYSICIST, SMITHSONIAN ASTROPHYS OBSERV, 74- *Mem:* Am Astron Soc; Int Astron Union. *Res:* Stellar atmospheres; solar physics; radiative transfer. *Mailing Add:* Smithsonian Astrophys Observ 60 Garden St Cambridge MA 02138

KURUP, VISWANATH PARAMESWAR, b Thattayil, India, Jan 20, 36; US citizen; m 62; c 3. MEDICAL MYCOLOGY, IMMUNOLOGY. *Educ:* Univ Poona, BS, 57, MS, 59; Univ Delhi, PhD(med mycol), 67. *Prof Exp:* Fel med mycol, Ohio State Univ, 68-70; microbiologist, St Anthony Hosp, Columbus, Ohio, 70-73; asst prof, Med Col Wis, 73-77; MICROBIOLOGIST MED MYCOL, VET ADMIN MED CTR, 73-; ASSOC PROF MED, MED COL WIS, 77- *Concurrent Pos:* Prin investr microbiol core, Pulmonary Hypersensitivity SCOR Prog, NIH, 73- & Vet Admin Merit Review Prog, 77- *Mem:* Am Soc Microbiol; Mycol Soc Am; Int Soc Human & Animal Mycol; Am Acad Allergy & Clin Immunol; Med Mycol Soc Am. *Res:* Isolation of antigens from pathogenic fungi; characterization of the antigens and development of immunological tests for the early diagnosis of mycoses. *Mailing Add:* Vet Admin Res Serv 151B 5000 W National Ave Milwaukee WI 53193

KURY, JOHN WILLIAM, b Kirkwood, Mo, Jan 31, 29; m 51; c 2. PHYSICAL CHEMISTRY, INORGANIC CHEMISTRY. *Educ:* St Louis Univ, BS, 50; Univ Calif, PhD(chem), 53. *Prof Exp:* RES CHEMIST, LAWRENCE LIVERMORE LAB, UNIV CALIF, 53- *Res:* Solution thermodynamics of metal fluorides; synthesis; fabrication, sensitivity and performance evaluation of conventional and high energy explosive formulations. *Mailing Add:* 3575 Blackhawk Rd Danville CA 94526

KURYLA, WILLIAM C, b Cuyahoga Falls, Ohio, Sept 3, 34; m 57; c 2. ORGANIC CHEMISTRY. *Educ:* Kent State Univ, BSc, 56; Univ Minn, MSc, 58, PhD(org chem), 60. *Prof Exp:* Microanalyst, Univ Minn, 56-59; res & develop chemist, Chem Div, 60-69, res scientist, Tech Ctr, 69-71, group leader, 71-73, mgr recruiting & univ rels, 73-77, technol mgr, Occup Health, Res & Develop Dept, Tech Ctr, 77-80, SR GROUP LEADER INDUST HYG SKILL CTR & CORP MGR APPL TOXICOLOGY SERV, UNION CARBIDE CORP, 80- *Concurrent Pos:* Adj prof, WVa State Col. *Mem:* Am Chem Soc; Am Inst Chem; Am Ind Hyg Asn ; Sigma Xi; NY Acad Sci. *Res:* Polyurethane chemistry and technology; ketene acetals and indole chemistry; radiochemical studies with polymers; textile and fiber chemicals; flame retardants; health effects of chemicals. *Mailing Add:* Tech Ctr 3005 Union Carbide Corp South Charleston WV 25303

KURYLO, MICHAEL JOHN, III, b Meriden, Conn, July 20, 45; m 66; c 4. STRATOSPHERIC OZONE DEPLETION. *Educ:* Boston Col, BS, 66; Catholic Univ Am, PhD(phys chem), 69. *Prof Exp:* Nat Res Coun res assoc, 69-71, RES CHEMIST, NAT BUR STANDARDS, 71- *Concurrent Pos:* Mem, Panel Lab Measurement & Data Eval, NASA, 78-; sci asst to dir, Nat Measurement Lab, Nat Bur Standards, 79-80. *Mem:* Am Chem Soc; Am Phys Soc; Interam Photochem Soc. *Res:* Rates and mechanisms of gas phase reaction of importance to stratospheric chemistry, tropospheric chemistry, and combustion processes; effects of internal reactant energy on reaction dynamics. *Mailing Add:* Ctr Chem Physics Chem Kinetics Div Nat Bur Standards Washington DC 20234

KURZ, JAMES ECKHARDT, b Louisville, Ky, Oct 8, 34; m 63; c 2. PHYSICAL CHEMISTRY, POLYMER CHEMISTRY. *Educ:* Centre Col, AB, 56; Duke Univ, MA, 58, PhD(phys chem), 61. *Prof Exp:* Sr res chemist, 61-66, sr res specialist, 66-75, SR GROUP LEADER, MONSANTO CO, 75- *Mem:* Am Chem Soc. *Res:* Characterization of polymers by dilute solution methods; column fractionation of polymers and gel permeation chromatography; physical, mechanical and thermal characterization of polymers and polymer structure; membrane structure and use in industrial processes. *Mailing Add:* Monsanto Co PO Box 12274 Durham NC 27709

KURZ, JOSEPH LOUIS, b St Louis, Mo, Dec 13, 33. PHYSICAL ORGANIC CHEMISTRY. *Educ:* Wash Univ, AB, 55, PhD(chem), 58. *Prof Exp:* Res fel, Harvard Univ, 58-60; res chemist, Cent Basic Res Lab, Esso Res & Eng Co, 60-64; from asst prof to assoc prof, 64-73, PROF CHEM, WASH UNIV, 73- *Concurrent Pos:* Vis prof, Wash Univ, 63-64. *Mem:* Am Chem Soc. *Res:* Mechanisms, kinetics and thermodynamics of reactions in solution; mechanisms of homogeneous catalysis; transition state structure. *Mailing Add:* Dept of Chem Wash Univ St Louis MO 63130

KURZ, MICHAEL E, b Detroit, Mich, Mar 5, 41; m 64; c 4. ORGANIC CHEMISTRY. *Educ:* St Mary's Col, BA, 63; Case Western Reserve Univ, PhD(chem), 67. *Prof Exp:* Instr & res assoc chem, Columbia Univ, 67-68; asst prof, 68-71, actg chmn dept, 74-75, assoc prof, 71-76, PROF CHEM, ILL STATE UNIV, 76- *Concurrent Pos:* Petrol Res Fund res grant, 69-72. *Mem:* Am Chem Soc. *Res:* Free radical aromatic substitution utilizing oxidative and photolytic methods of radical generation; oxidative aromatic substitutions; ozonolyses. *Mailing Add:* Dept of Chem Ill State Univ Normal IL 61761

KURZ, RICHARD J, b Springfield, Ill, Oct 10, 35; m 58. SPACE RESEARCH, INSTRUMENTATION. *Educ:* Univ Ill, BS, 57, MS, 58; Univ Calif, Berkeley, PhD(physics), 63. *Prof Exp:* Asst physics, Lawrence Radiation Lab, Univ Calif, 59-62, physicist, 62-64; NSF fel, LePrince-Ringuet Lab, Ecole Polytech, Paris, 64-65; physicist, Lawrence Radiation Lab, Univ Calif, Berkeley, 65-66; Nat Acad Sci res assoc, Goddard Space Flight Ctr, NASA, Md, 66-67, chief physics br, Planetary & Earth Sci Div, Manned Spacecraft Ctr, Houston, 67-72; ASST MGR, ADVAN SYSTS DEPT, TRW SYSTS GROUP, 72- *Mem:* Am Phys Soc. *Res:* Space research instrumentation development. *Mailing Add:* TRW Systs One Space Park Redondo Beach CA 90278

KURZ, RICHARD KARL, b New York, NY, Feb 4, 36; m 60; c 5. PHOTOGRAPHIC CHEMISTRY. *Educ:* St John Fisher Col, NY, BS, 57; Univ Ill, Champaign-Urbana, PhD(org chem), 61. *Prof Exp:* Res Chemist, 61-69, res assoc, 69-74, lab head, 74-81, SR LAB HEAD PHOTOG CHEM, RES LABS, EASTMAN KODAK CO, 81- *Mem:* Am Chem Soc; Soc Photog Scientists & Engrs. *Res:* Design and development of advanced photographic materials for use in radiography, graphic arts, micrographics and instrumentation recording applications. *Mailing Add:* Eastman Kodak Co Res Labs 1669 Lake Ave Rochester NY 14650

KURZ, WOLFGANG GEBHARD WALTER, b Innsbruck, Austria, June 9, 33; m 63; c 3. MICROBIOLOGY. *Educ:* Univ Vienna, PhD(microbiol, biochem), 58. *Prof Exp:* Res asst microbiol & biochem, Royal Inst Technol, Sweden, 55-63; fel, Prairie Regional Lab, Nat Res Coun Can, 63-65; res scientist, Tech Res Coun Sweden, 65-67; assoc res officer microbiol & fermentation technol, 67-73, SR RES OFFICER MICROBIOL & FERMENTATION TECHNOL, PRAIRIE REGIONAL LAB, NAT RES COUN CAN, 73-, HEAD, BIOTECHNOL SECT, 81- *Honors & Awards:* Can Soc Microbiologists Award, 79. *Mem:* Fel Chem Inst Can; Can Soc Microbiologists; Int Asn Plant Tissue Cult. *Res:* Biological dinitrogen fixation; continuous cultivation of microbes and plant cells; fermentation biology; enzymology; microbial physiology; process development; apparatus design; biosynthesis of secondary metabolites by microbes and plant cells. *Mailing Add:* Nat Res Coun of Can Prairie Regional Lab Saskatoon SK S7N 0W9 Can

KURZE, THEODORE, b Brooklyn, NY, May 18, 22; m 46; c 4. NEUROSURGERY. *Educ:* Wash Col, BS, 43; Long Island Col Med, MD, 47; Am Bd Neurol Surg, dipl, 56. *Prof Exp:* Intern, St Monica's Hosp, Phoenix, 47-48; resident neurosurg, Vet Admin Wadsworth Hosp, Los Angeles, 48-49; resident neurosurg, Los Angeles County Gen Hosp, 51-54; instr neurol surg, Med Ctr, Univ Calif, Los Angeles, 55-56; from instr to assoc prof, 56-57, PROF NEUROL SURG, SCH MED, UNIV SOUTHERN CALIF, 67-, CHMN DEPT, 63-; DIR NEUROL SURG, LOS ANGELES COUNTY-UNIV SOUTHERN CALIF MED CTR, 67- *Concurrent Pos:* Asst, Sch Med, Univ Southern Calif, 53-54; pvt pract, Calif, 56-61; head physician, Los Angeles County Gen Hosp, 61-65, chief neurol surg, 65-67; mem, Am Bd Neurol Surg, 68-74. *Mem:* Am Col Surgeons; Soc Neurol Surgeons; Am Asn Neurol Surgeons; Am Acad Neurol Surgeons; Cong Neurol Surg. *Res:* Microtecniques in neurological surgery; humoral response to cerebral injury; acoustic tumor surgery; biomedical ethics. *Mailing Add:* Dept of Neurol Surg Univ of Southern Calif Sch Med Los Angeles CA 90033

KURZEPA, HENRYKA JANINA, b Warsaw, Poland. MICROBIOLOGY, CANCER. *Educ:* Univ Warsaw, MSc, 53; Polish Acad Sci, PhD(microbiol, biochem, nutrit), 60. *Prof Exp:* Chief lab microbiol, State Inst Hyg, Dept Nutrit, Poland, 53-62 & Inst Food & Nutrit, 62-64; fac res microbiol, Cornell Univ, 65-71; res assoc, Boyce Thompson Inst Plant Res, NY, 71-72 & Hormel Inst, Univ Minn, 73-74; chief, Tissue Cult Lab, Vet Admin Hosp, Minneapolis, 74-77; head, Dept Biochem, Univ Minn, 74-77; ASST PROF, DEPT MICROBIOL & MOLECULAR GENETICS, UNIV CINCINNATI MED CTR, 78- *Concurrent Pos:* High sch prof, Warsaw, 52-53; prof, Sch Nursing, 59-60; fel, Grad Sch Nutrit, Cornell Univ, 61-62; adj, Inst Biochem & Biophys, Polish Acad Sci, 64-67; prof, Ithaca Neighborhood Col, 67-68. *Honors & Awards:* Annual Award, Ministry Health, Poland, 56. *Mem:* Am Soc Microbiol; Am Tissue Cult Asn. *Res:* Nutrition and metabolism of microorganisms; intestinal microflora; growth factors; sanitary conditions of the environment; mycoplasmas; arboviruses in insect tissue culture; chemical carcinogenesis in primary and low passages; tissue cultures. *Mailing Add:* Dept of Microbiol Univ of Cincinnati Med Ctr Cincinnati OH 45221

KURZHALS, PETER R(ALPH), b Berlin, Ger, Aug 20, 37; div. AEROSPACE ENGINEERING, INFORMATION SYSTEMS. *Educ:* Va Polytech Univ BS, 60, MS, 62, PhD(aerospace eng), 66; Harvard Univ, PMD, 73. *Prof Exp:* Aerospace engr, Space Sta Off, Langley Res Ctr, NASA, 60-62, head stability & control sect, 62-70, controls & performance br, 70, stability & control br, 70-71, chief guidance & control br, Hq Washington, DC, 71-73, dir, Guidance, Control & Info Systs Div, 74-76, dir, Electronics Div, 76-78, dir, Space Systs Div, 78-79, ASST DIR RES & TECHNOL, NASA GODDARD SPACE FLIGHT CTR, 79- *Concurrent Pos:* tech consult, Radio Tech Comn for Aeronaut, 74-79; mem guidance & control panel, Wash Opers Res & Mgt Sci Coun, 81- *Honors & Awards:* Inventions & Contrib Award, Langley Res Ctr, NASA, 65 & 67 & Special Serv Award, 67; Except Serv Medal, NASA, 76. *Mem:* Assoc fel Am Inst Aeronaut & Astronaut; Aerospace Group Res & Develop. *Res:* Aircraft and spacecraft guidance and control, sensing and data acquisition, data processing and transfer, mission operations, systems analysis, electronics, vehicle design. *Mailing Add:* Code 500 NASA Goddard Space Flight Ctr Greenbelt MD 20771

KURZWEG, FRANK TURNER, b Plaquemine, La, Aug 7, 17; m 56; c 2. SURGERY. *Educ:* Harvard Univ, SB, 38; Harvard Med Sch, MD, 42; Univ Minn, MS, 47. *Prof Exp:* Instr surg, Med Sch, Tulane Univ, 49-56; from assoc prof to prof, Med Sch, Univ Miami, 56-68; prof, Surg Div, Sch Med, La State Univ, Shreveport, 68-80, head dept & div, 68-76. *Mem:* Am Col Surgeons. *Res:* General, thoracic and vascular surgery. *Mailing Add:* 304 Acadian Pl Shreveport LA 71106

KURZWEG, ULRICH H(ERMANN), b Jena, Ger, Sept 16, 36; US citizen; m 63; c 1. FLUID MECHANICS, APPLIED MATHEMATICS. *Educ:* Univ Md, BS, 58; Princeton Univ, MA, 59, PhD(physics), 61. *Prof Exp:* Fulbright res grant appl math, Univ Freiburg, 61-62; res scientist physics, United Technol Res Labs, Conn, 62-64, sr theoret physicist, 64-68; assoc prof, 68-76, PROF ENG SCI, UNIV FLA, 76- *Concurrent Pos:* Adj asst & assoc prof, Hartford Grad Ctr, Rensselaer Polytech Inst, 63-68. *Mem:* AAAS; Am Phys Soc; Sigma Xi. *Res:* Hydrodynamic and hydromagnetic stability of rotating flows and of jets; thermal instability of electrically conducting fluids in cavities; molecular spectroscopy; two-phase magnetohydrodynamic flows; numerical solutions of partial differential equations; optics of solar concentrators. *Mailing Add:* Dept of Eng Sci Col of Eng Univ of Fla Gainesville FL 32611

KUSAK, LLOYD JAMES, b Dutton, Ont, June 23, 28; US citizen; m 63. MATHEMATICS, COMPUTER SCIENCES. *Educ:* Queen's Univ, Ont, BSc, 50; Cornell Univ, PhD(chem eng & math), 58. *Prof Exp:* Supvr tech comput, Am Oil Co, Ind, 54-62; chief systs analyst, Control Data Corp, 62-69; MGR DATA CTR, HEWLETT-PACKARD CO, SKOKIE, 69- *Concurrent Pos:* Lectr, Nat Eng Consortium, 73- *Mem:* Am Soc Qual Control (treas, 60); Asn Comput Mach; Data Processing Mgt Asn. *Res:* Development of mathematical models in petroleum refining; application of computers in real-time systems such as process control and communication systems. *Mailing Add:* 115 Stirrup Lane Burr Ridge IL 60521

KUSANO, KIYOSHI, b Nagasaki, Japan, Feb 1, 33; m 61. NEUROPHYSIOLOGY. *Educ:* Kumamoto Univ, BSc, 56; Kyushu Univ, DSc, 60. *Prof Exp:* Instr physiol, Med Sch, Kumamoto Univ, 56-59 & Tokyo Med & Dent Univ, 59-60; jr res zoologist, Univ Calif, Los Angeles, 60-61; res assoc neurol, Columbia Univ, 61-63; asst prof physiol, Tokyo Med & Dent Univ, 63-65; from asst prof to assoc prof psychiat, Med Sch, Ind Univ, 65-70; assoc prof, 70-73, PROF BIOL, ILL INST TECHNOL, 73- *Concurrent Pos:* Corp mem, Marine Biol Lab, 67; USPHS res grant, Med Sch, Ind Univ, 67-69, NSF grant, 68-70; USPHS res grant, Ill Inst Technol, 71-; mem, Physiol Study Sect, NIH, 79- *Mem:* Am Physiol Soc; Soc Gen Physiol; Soc Neurosci; Biophys Soc. *Res:* Synaptology; comparative neurophysiology. *Mailing Add:* Dept of Biol Ill Inst of Technol Chicago IL 60616

KUSCH, POLYKARP, b Ger, Jan 26, 11; nat US; m 35, 60; c 5. PHYSICS. *Educ:* Case Western Univ, BS; Univ Ill, MS, 33, PhD, 36. *Hon Degrees:* DSc, Case Western Reserve Univ, 56, Ohio State Univ, 59, Univ Ill & Colby Col, 61 & Gustavus Adolphus Col, 63. *Prof Exp:* Asst physics, Univ Ill, 31-36 & Univ Minn, 36-37; instr, Columbia Univ, 37-41; develop engr, Westinghouse Elec & Mfg Co, 41-42; res assoc, Div War Res, Columbia Univ, 42-44; mem tech staff, Bell Tel Labs, Inc, 44-46; from assoc prof to prof physics, Columbia Univ, 46-72, chmn dept, 49-52, exec dir radiation lab, 52-60, chmn dept physics, 60-63, vpres & dean fac, 69-70, exec vpres & provost, 70-71; EUGENE MCDERMOTT PROF PHYSICS, UNIV TEX, DALLAS, 72- *Concurrent Pos:* Fel, Ctr Advan Study in Behav Sci, 64-65. *Honors & Awards:* Nobel Prize in Physics, 55. *Mem:* Nat Acad Sci; Am Acad Arts & Sci; Am Phys Soc; Am Philos Soc; Am Asn Physics Teachers. *Res:* Atomic and molecular structure; molecular beams. *Mailing Add:* Univ of Tex at Dallas PO Box 688 Richardson TX 75080

KUSCHNER, MARVIN, b New York, NY, Aug 13, 19; m 48. PATHOLOGY. *Educ:* NY Univ, AB, 39, MD, 43. *Prof Exp:* Asst path, Col Med, NY Univ, 47-49; from instr to assoc prof, Col Physicians & Surgeons, Columbia Univ, 49-55; prof, Col Med, NY Univ, 55-70, dir labs, Univ Hosp, 68-70; PROF PATH & CHMN DEPT, HEALTH SCI CTR, STATE UNIV NY STONY BROOK, 70-, DEAN SCH MED, 75- *Concurrent Pos:* Asst pathologist, Bellevue Hosp, 49-54, actg dir path, 54-55, dir, 55-; consult pathologist in chg lung cancer res unit, Inst Environ Med, Med Ctr, NY Univ. *Mem:* Am Asn Path & Bact; Am Soc Exp Pathologists; Am Soc Clin Pathologists; Am Asn Cancer Res; Int Acad Path. *Res:* Pathology of cardiopulmonary diseases. *Mailing Add:* Dept of Path State Univ of NY Health Sci Ctr Stony Brook NY 11790

KUSHICK, JOSEPH N, b New York, NY, July 18, 48; m 70; c 1. CHEMICAL PHYSICS. *Educ:* Columbia Col, AB, 69; Columbia Univ, PhD(chem phys), 75. *Prof Exp:* Res assoc chem, Univ Chicago, 74-76; ASST PROF CHEM, AMHERST COL, 76- *Concurrent Pos:* Fel NSF, 76-78; vis scholar, Harvard Univ, 79-80; Camille and Henry Dreyfus teacher scholar grant, 80. *Honors & Awards:* L P Hammett Award, Columbia Univ, 73. *Mem:* Am Phys Soc; Am Chem Soc. *Res:* Time dependent statistical mechanics, computer simulation of liquids, proteins and polypeptides, molecular reorientation, vibrational relaxation and quantum rate processes. *Mailing Add:* Dept of Chem Amherst Col Amherst MA 01002

KUSHIDA, RAYMOND, chemical engineering, fluid mechanics, see previous edition

KUSHIDA, TOSHIMOTO, b Tokyo, Japan, Feb 13, 20; m 46; c 3. SOLID STATE PHYSICS. *Educ:* Hiroshima Univ, BSc, 44, ScD(physics), 56; Harvard Univ, MSc, 56. *Prof Exp:* Asst physics, Hiroshima Univ, 44-48, from instr to prof, 48-61; RES SCIENTIST, SCI LAB, FORD MOTOR CO, 61- *Concurrent Pos:* Res fel, Harvard Univ, 56-58. *Mem:* Fel Am Phys Soc; Phys Soc Japan; Inst Elec & Electronics Engrs. *Res:* Nuclear magnetic resonance; high pressure physics; the puli susceptibility of alkali metals as a function of pressure. *Mailing Add:* 22836 Nona Dearborn MI 48124

KUSHINSKY, STANLEY, b Brooklyn, NY, Sept 20, 30; div. BIOCHEMISTRY. *Educ:* City Col New York, BS, 51; Columbia Univ, MA, 52; Univ Boston, PhD(chem), 55; Nat Registry Clin Chem, dipl, 68. *Prof Exp:* Res asst, Worcester Found Exp Biol, 52-55; steroid chemist, Dept Surg, Sch Med, Univ Southern Calif, 55-57, res assoc, 57-58, adj asst prof surg & biochem, 58-62, asst prof, 62-64, asst prof biochem, 64-65; from assoc res biochemist to res biochemist, Dept Obstet & Gynec, Sch Med, Univ Calif, Los Angeles, 65-70; dir biochem res, Rees-Stealy Clin Res Found, 70-79; prin scientist, 79-81, DEPT HEAD, ANAL & METAB CHEM, SYNTEX RES, 81- *Concurrent Pos:* USPHS res career develop award, 65-70; adj prof chem, San Diego State Univ, 73-76. *Mem:* Fel AAAS; Am Chem Soc; Am Asn Clin Chem; Nat Acad Clin Biochem; Endocrine Soc. *Res:* Synthesis, isolation and metabolism of steroid hormones; enzyme kinetics; betaglucuronidase; gas chromatographic and radioimmunologic determination of steroids in blood and tissues; high performance liquid chromatography. *Mailing Add:* Syntex Res 3401 Hillview Ave Palo Alto CA 94304

KUSHMERICK, MARTIN JOSEPH, b Pa, May 21, 37; m 62; c 4. PHYSIOLOGY. *Educ:* Univ Scranton, BS, 58; Univ Pa, MD, 63, PhD(molecular biol), 66. *Prof Exp:* Asst prof biochem, Univ Pa, 67; staff assoc, Lab Phys Biol, Nat Inst Arthritis & Metab Dis, NIH, 67-69; hon res assoc & Brit-Am exchange fel, Am Heart Asn, Univ Col, Univ London, 69-70; asst prof, 70-76, ASSOC PROF PHYSIOL, HARVARD MED SCH, 76- *Mem:* Am Physiol Soc; AAAS; Biochem Soc Eng; Biophys Soc; Soc Gen Physiologists. *Res:* Muscle physiology; energetics, metabolism and their control; mechanism and control of contraction. *Mailing Add:* Dept of Physiol Harvard Med Sch 25 Shattuck St Boston MA 02115

KUSHNARYOV, VLADIMIR MICHAEL, b Odessa, USSR, Jan 2, 31; m 54; c 1. ELECTRON MICROSCOPY. *Educ:* 1st Moscow Med Inst, MD, 54; Acad Med Sci, USSR, PhD(microbiol), 61, DSc, 69. *Prof Exp:* Chief & lab prof, Moscow Inst Vaccines & Serim, 75-77; asst prof, 78-80, ASSOC PROF MED MICROBIOL, MED COL WIS, 80- *Concurrent Pos:* Lectr, Moscow Postgrad Med Sch, 60-77. *Mem:* AAAS; Am Soc Microbiol; NY Acad Sci. *Mailing Add:* 805 E Henery Clay 203 Milwaukee WI 53217

KUSHNER, ARTHUR SIMON, b New York, NY, May 9, 40; m 64. ORGANIC CHEMISTRY, PHOTOCHEMISTRY. *Educ:* Univ Evansville, BS, 62; Pa State Univ, PhD(org chem), 66; Cleveland State Univ, MBA, 78. *Prof Exp:* Fel chem, Univ Chicago, 66-68; asst prof, Cleveland State Univ, 68-74; supvr film chem sect, Photohorizons Div, Horizons Res, Inc, Cleveland, 74-75, mgr tech support serv, 75-76; group leader cooling water prod, Mogul Div, Dexter Corp, Chagrin Falls, 76-78, prod mgr, 78-79, sales mgr, 79-80; prod develop mgr, Woodhill Permatex Div, Loctite Corp, Cleveland, 80-81; MKT MGR, CHROMATIX, 81- *Concurrent Pos:* Dir, Joseph B Kushner Electroplating Sch, 78- *Mem:* Am Soc Testing & Mat; Am Soc Metals; Am Electroplaters Soc; Am Chem Soc; Sigma Xi. *Res:* Synthesis and reactions of bridged polycyclic systems; corrosion inhibition; treatment of cooling water; preparation of new corrosion inhibition materials; design and study of non-conventional imaging systems; photochemistry of free-radical film systems; corrosion inhibition; metal finishing and electroplating. *Mailing Add:* 732 Glencoe Ct Sunnyvale CA 94087

KUSHNER, DONN JEAN, b Lake Charles, La, Mar 29, 27; m 49; c 3. MICROBIAL BIOCHEMISTRY, MICROBIAL PHYSIOLOGY. *Educ:* Harvard Univ, SB, 48; McGill Univ, MSc, 50, PhD(biochem), 52. *Prof Exp:* Asst, Res Inst, Mont Gen Hosp, 52-53; Nat Found Infantile Paralysis fel, 53-54; res officer bact physiol & genetics, Forest Insect Lab, 54-61; assoc res officer, Nat Res Coun Can, 61-65; assoc prof, 65-67, PROF BIOL, UNIV OTTAWA, 67- *Concurrent Pos:* With Nat Inst Med Res, London, Eng, 58-59, Inst Pasteur, Paris, 72, MacDonald Col, 80 & Cornell Univ, 81; co-ed, Can J Microbiol. *Mem:* Am Soc Biol Chem; Am Soc Microbiol; Can Soc Microbiol (pres, 80-81); Brit Soc Gen Microbiol; Can Biochem Soc. *Res:* Physiology of halophilic and psychrophilic bacteria; action of microorganisms in natural environments on polymers and heavy metals; bacterial drug resistance. *Mailing Add:* Dept of Biol Univ of Ottawa Ottawa ON K1N 6N5 Can

KUSHNER, HAROLD J(OSEPH), b New York, NY, July 29, 33; m 60. MATHEMATICS, OPERATIONS RESEARCH. *Educ:* City Col New York, BSc, 55; Univ Wis, MSc, 56, PhD(elec eng), 58. *Prof Exp:* Staff mem, Lincoln Lab, Mass Inst Technol, 58-63 & Res Inst Advan Studies, Martin-Marietta Corp, Md, 63-64; PROF APPL MATH & ENG, BROWN UNIV, 64- *Mem:* Inst Math Statist; Soc Indust & Appl Math; Opers Res Soc Am; Inst Elec & Electronics Engrs. *Res:* Theoretical study of automatic control and communication systems, especially when random phenomenon are of some significance; applications of operations research methods to health systems; applied probability. *Mailing Add:* Dept of Appl Math & Eng Brown Univ Providence RI 02912

KUSHNER, HARVEY, b Philadelphia, Pa, Nov 2, 50; m 73; c 4. MATHEMATICAL BIOMEDICAL STATISTICS. *Educ:* Temple Univ, AB, 72, MA, 74, PhD(math), 78. *Prof Exp:* ASST PROF MATH & BIOSTATIST & SECT HEAD, DEPT PHYSIOL & BIOPHYSICS, DIV BIOMETRICS & COMPUT, HAHNEMANN MED COL, 78- *Concurrent Pos:* Adj asst prof, Dept Math, Temple Univ, 79- & Grad Sch, Med Col Pa, 80-81. *Mem:* Am Math Soc; Am Statist Asn. *Res:* Time series analysis; categorical data analysis. *Mailing Add:* Hahnemann Med Col 235 N Broad St Philadelphia PA 19102

KUSHNER, HARVEY D(AVID), b New York, NY, Dec 28, 30; m 51; c 3. OPERATIONS RESEARCH. *Educ:* Johns Hopkins Univ, BE, 51. *Prof Exp:* Engr, Mach Evals Group, Bur Ships, US Navy Dept, 51 & Performance & Sci Sect, 52-53; mem tech staff, Cent Res Lab, Melpar, Inc Div, Westinghouse Air Brake Co, 53-54 & Flight Simulator Dept, 54-55; res engr, 55-57, group leader, 57-59, prog dir, 59-61, vpres & dir, Eastern Div, 61-62, vpres & dir, Phys Systs Div, 63-64, dir, Govt & Indust Systs Div, 64-68, exec vpres, 62-69, vpres, Reliance Group, Inc, 71-77, pres, Disclosure, Inc, 72-77, PRES, ORI, INC, 69- *Concurrent Pos:* Consult, Appl Physics Lab, Johns Hopkins Univ, 57-58 & Nat Acad Sci Comt Undersea Warfare, 63-64. *Mem:* Opers Res Soc Am; Inst Mgt Sci; Am Inst Aeronaut & Astronaut; Am Soc Mech Engrs; fel NY Acad Sci. *Res:* Systems analysis. *Mailing Add:* ORI Inc 1400 Spring St Silver Spring MD 20910

KUSHNER, IRVING, b New York, NY, Jan 16, 29; m 55; c 3. RHEUMATOLOGY, MEDICINE. *Educ:* Columbia Univ, BA, 50; Washington Univ, MD, 54. *Prof Exp:* Intern med, New Haven Hosp, 54-55; asst resident, 2 & 4 med serv, Boston City Hosp, 57-58; demonstr med, Case Western Reserve Univ, 58-59, instr, 60-61, sr instr, 61-64, from asst prof to assoc prof, 64-73; prof, WVa Univ, 73-74; PROF MED, SCH MED, CASE WESTERN RESERVE UNIV, 74- *Concurrent Pos:* USPHS res fel, 58-59; Helen Hay Whitney Found res fel, 59-62; foreign fel, Inst Sci Res Cancer, France, 62-63. *Mem:* Am Col Physicians; Am Rheumatism Asn; Am Fedn Clin Res; Soc Exp Biol & Med; NY Acad Sci. *Res:* Acute phase reaction; C-reactive protein; ankylosing spondylates. *Mailing Add:* Dept of Med Cleveland Metrop Gen Hosp Cleveland OH 44109

KUSHNER, LAWRENCE MAURICE, b New York, NY, Sept 20, 24; m 72; c 2. PHYSICAL CHEMISTRY, SCIENCE ADMINISTRATION. *Educ:* Queens Col, BS, 45; Princeton Univ, AM, 47, PhD, 49. *Prof Exp:* Teaching asst, Princeton Univ, 47-48; staff mem, Nat Bur Standards, 48-56, chief metal physics sect, 56-61, chief metall div, 61-66, dep dir, Inst Appl Tech, 66-68, dir, Inst for Appl Technol, 68-69, dep dir, Bur, 69-73, actg dir, 72-73; comnr, Consumer Prod Safety Comn, 73-77; coordr policy develop, Nat Bur Standards, 77-80; SR STAFF SCIENTIST, MITRE CORP, 80- *Concurrent Pos:* Lectr chem, Am Univ, 52-60; mem ad hoc int group metal physics, Off Econ Coop & Develop, 61; fel, Sci & Technol Fel Prog, Dept Com, 64-65; mem, Md Gov Sci Adv Coun, 72-75; adj prof eng & pub policy, Carnegie-Mellon Univ, 81- *Honors & Awards:* Superior Accomplishment Award, Dept Com, 54, Gold Medal, 68; Meritorious Serv Award, Am Nat Standards Inst, 73. *Mem:* Fel AAAS; hon mem Am Soc Testing & Mat; Am Chem Soc; Am Phys Soc; Sigma Xi (pres, 76). *Res:* Physical chemistry of surface active agents; relationship between physical properties of materials and their molecular and crystal structures; defects in metal crystals. *Mailing Add:* 9528 Briar Glenn Way Gaithersburg MD 20879

KUSHNER, RICHARD ALLAN, physical chemistry, see previous edition

KUSHNER, SAMUEL, b Auburn, NY, Apr 25, 15; m 37; c 4. PHARMACEUTICAL CHEMISTRY. *Educ:* Univ Mich, BS, 39, MS, 40, PhD(chem), 42. *Prof Exp:* Res chemist, 42-44, group leader, 44-55, unit leader, 55-56, head dept med chem of infectious dis, 56-71, HEAD CHEM OF INFECTIOUS RES DIS SECT, LEDERLE LABS, AM CYANAMID CO, 71- *Mem:* AAAS; Am Chem Soc; NY Acad Sci. *Res:* Structure of penicillin; chemotherapy related to tropical diseases; tuberculosis and virus; structure and synthesis of antibiotics; antineoplastics. *Mailing Add:* 138 Highview Ave Nanuet NY 10954

KUSHNER, SIDNEY RALPH, b New York, NY, Dec 14, 43; c 1. MOLECULAR GENETICS, ENZYMOLOGY. *Educ:* Oberlin Col, BA, 65; Brandeis Univ, PhD(biochem), 70. *Prof Exp:* NIH fel molecular biol, Univ Calif, Berkeley, 70-71; NIH fel biochem, Med Sch, Stanford Univ, 71-73, from asst prof to assoc prof biochem, 73-80, assoc prof, 80-82, PROF GENETICS, UNIV GA, 82- *Concurrent Pos:* NIH res career develop award, 75; assoc ed, Gene, 80- *Mem:* Am Soc Microbiol; AAAS; Am Soc Biol Chemists; Genetics Soc. *Res:* Genetic control and enzymology of recombination and DNA repair; functional expression of eukaryotic DNA in prokaryotes; maintenance of eukaryotic DNA in prokaryotes. *Mailing Add:* Dept Molecular & Pop Genetics Univ of Ga Athens GA 30602

KUSHNICK, THEODORE, b Brooklyn, NY, Mar 29, 25; m 49; c 3. PEDIATRICS. *Educ:* Ohio State Univ, BS, 44, MS, 47; Harvard Med Sch, MD, 51. *Prof Exp:* Intern med, Boston City Hosp, 51-52; resident pediat, Boston Children's Med Ctr, 52-53, 54-55; clin res asst, Boston Children's Cancer Res Found, 55-56; pvt pract, NJ, 56-59; clin instr pediat, 58-59, from asst prof to assoc prof, 59-69, PROF PEDIAT, COL MED & DENT NJ, NEWARK, 69-, DIR DIV HUMAN GENETICS, 61- *Concurrent Pos:* Jr physician, Wrentham State Sch, Mass, 53; resident psychiat, Boston State Hosp, 53-54; clin instr, Harvard Med Sch, 55-56; cytogenetic consult, Nat Found March of Dimes Spec Birth Defects Treatment Ctr, Babies Hosp, Newark; Mead-Johnson res grant, 60-; NIH res grant, 61-63; Nat Found-March of Dimes Med Serv Prog Grants, 74-75 & 76-77. *Mem:* AAAS; Am Asn Ment Deficiency; fel Am Acad Pediat; Am Soc Human Genetics. *Res:* Clinical pediatrics; mental retardation; cytogenetics; bacteriology and infectious diseases; immunology. *Mailing Add:* NJ Med Sch 100 Bergen St Newark NJ 07103

KUSIAK, JOHN WARREN, biochemistry, see previous edition

KUSIC, GEORGE LARRY, JR, b Aliquippa, Pa, Aug 26, 35; m 69; c 1. CONTROL ENGINEERING, COMPUTER SCIENCE. *Educ:* Carnegie Inst Technol, BSEE, 57, MSEE, 66, PhDEE, 68. *Prof Exp:* Res engr, Sikorsky Aircraft Co, 57-59; elec develop engr, TRW Corp, 59-63; asst prof, 67-77, ASSOC PROF ELEC ENG & GRAD PROG COORDR, UNIV PITTSBURGH, 77- *Concurrent Pos:* NASA-Am Soc Eng Educ fac res fel, 69; sr Fulbright-Hays lect grant, Univ Belgrade, 70-71; consult, NSF-Agency Int Develop India Prog, 68; IBM Data Processing Div, 68 & Westinghouse Res Lab, 69-70. *Mailing Add:* Dept of Elec Eng Sch of Eng Univ of Pittsburgh Pittsburgh PA 15260

KUSIK, CHARLES LEMBIT, b New York, NY, Apr 24, 34. CHEMICAL ENGINEERING. *Educ:* Mass Inst Technol, BS, 56; NY Univ, DSc(chem eng), 61. *Prof Exp:* Scientist opers res, Mass Inst Technol, 61-62; scientist gas dynamics & task force mgr metal systs, Avco Corp, 63-64; SR STAFF MEM COM ASSESSMENTS, ARTHUR D LITTLE, INC, 64- *Mem:* Am Inst Chem Engrs; Am Chem Soc; Am Inst Mining, Metall & Petrol Engrs; Am Mgt Asn. *Res:* Energy assessments; environmental impact; process development; economics; commercial feasibility studies. *Mailing Add:* Arthur D Little Inc 20 Acorn Park Cambridge MA 02140

KUSKA, HENRY (ANTON), b Chicago, Ill, July 28, 37; m 64; c 3. PHYSICAL CHEMISTRY. *Educ:* Cornell Col, BA, 59; Mich State Univ, PhD(phys chem), 65. *Prof Exp:* Res assoc & res fel phys chem, Mich State Univ, 64-65; ASSOC PROF PHYS CHEM, UNIV AKRON, 65- *Mem:* Am Chem Soc. *Res:* Spectroscopy; nuclear magnetic resonance; electron spin resonance; electron-nuclear double resonance; infrared, visible ultraviolet. *Mailing Add:* Dept of Chem Univ of Akron Akron OH 44325

KUSKO, ALEXANDER, b New York, NY, Apr 4, 21; m 41; c 2. ELECTRICAL ENGINEERING. *Educ:* Purdue Univ, BS, 42; Mass Inst Technol, SM, 44, ScD, 51. *Prof Exp:* Asst, 42-44, from instr to assoc prof, 46-58, LECTR ELEC ENG, MASS INST TECHNOL, 58-; PRES, ALEXANDER KUSKO, INC, 56- *Mem:* Inst Elec & Electronics Engrs. *Res:* Energy conversion and control. *Mailing Add:* Alexander Kusko Inc 161 Highland Ave Needham Heights MA 02194

KUSLAN, LOUIS ISAAC, b New Haven, Conn, Feb 14, 22; m 47; c 2. HISTORY OF SCIENCE. *Educ:* Univ Conn, BS, 43; Yale Univ, MA, 49, PhD(sci educ), 54. *Prof Exp:* Instr high schs, Conn, 43-46; asst chem, Univ Conn, 46-47, instr, Waterbur Br, 47-49; from instr to asst prof sci, 50-56, assoc prof chem, 56-60, prof chem & chmn dept sci, 60-66, dean arts & sci, 66-78, PROF CHEM, CONN STATE COL, 78- *Concurrent Pos:* Fel chem, Yale Univ, 58-59, hist sci, 62-63. *Mem:* Am Chem Soc; Hist Sci Soc. *Res:* History of analytical and American chemistry; elementary science education; nineteenth century American chemistry. *Mailing Add:* Dept Chem Southern Conn State Col New Haven CT 06515

KUSPIRA, J, b Yorkton, Sask, Nov 20, 28; m 58; c 4. CYTOGENETICS. *Educ:* Univ Sask, BSc, 51, MSc, 52; Univ Alta, PhD(genetics), 55. *Prof Exp:* Asst cytogeneticist, 55-57, assoc res prof cytogenetics, 58-62, assoc prof, 62-70, PROF GENETICS, UNIV ALTA, 70-, ASSOC DEAN SCI, 72- *Mem:* Am Genetic Asn; Genetics Soc Can. *Res:* Cytogenetic analysis of tetraploid and hexaploid wheats. *Mailing Add:* Dept of Genetics Univ of Alta Edmonton AB T6G 2E1 Can

KUSSE, BRUCE RAYMOND, b Rochester, NY, Aug 10, 38. PLASMA PHYSICS. *Educ:* Mass Inst Technol, SB, 60, SM, 64, PhD(elec eng), 69. *Prof Exp:* Sr scientist, Eastern Sci & Technol Div, EG&G, 69-70; res assoc plasma physics, Res Lab Electronics, Mass Inst Technol, 70; res assoc, Lab Plasma Studies, 70-71, asst prof, 71-76, ASSOC PROF PLASMA PHYSICS, CORNELL UNIV, 76- *Mem:* Sigma Xi; Am Phys Soc. *Res:* Plasma physics--experimental studies of intense, relativistic beam-plasma interactions, particularly in toroidal geometry. *Mailing Add:* Dept of Appl & Eng Physics Cornell Univ Ithaca NY 14853

KUSSMAUL, KEITH, b Sterling, Ill, Apr 9, 39; m 65; c 4. STATISTICS. *Educ:* Univ Mich, BS, 60, MS, 61; NC State Univ, PhD(statist), 66. *Prof Exp:* Mathematician, Int Bus Mach Corp, 61-62; STATISTICIAN, WESTINGHOUSE ELEC CORP, 66- *Concurrent Pos:* Lectr indust eng, Univ Pittsburgh, 67-70. *Mem:* Am Statist Asn; Biomet Soc. *Res:* Design and analysis of industrial experiments; statistical methods; general linear hypothesis; general statistical consulting. *Mailing Add:* Math Dept Westinghouse Res & Develop Ctr Pittsburgh PA 15235

KUST, ROGER NAYLAND, b Berwyn, Ill, Apr 20, 35; m 57; c 2. INORGANIC CHEMISTRY, PHYSICAL CHEMISTRY. *Educ:* Purdue Univ, BS, 57; Iowa State Univ, PhD(fused salts), 63. *Prof Exp:* Asst prof inorg chem, Tex A&M Univ, 64-65 & Univ Utah, 65-71; sr inorg chemist,

Ledgemont Lab, Kennecott Copper Corp, 71-77, group leader chem, 77-78, sect head chem, 78-79; sr staff engr, 79-80, sect head, 80-81, MGR, MINERALS PROCESSING RES DIV, EXXON MINERALS CO, 81- *Mem:* AAAS; Am Chem Soc; Electrochem Soc; Am Acad Arts & Sci; Am Inst Chemists. *Res:* Acid-base reactions in fused salts; electrochemical investigations in nonaqueous media with emphasis on fused salts; chemistry of metallurgical processes. *Mailing Add:* 4 Tanglewood Ct Randolph NJ 07869

KUSTIN, KENNETH, b Bronx, NY, Jan 6, 34; m 56; c 3. INORGANIC CHEMISTRY, PHYSICAL CHEMISTRY. *Educ:* Queens Col, NY, BSc, 55; Univ Minn, Minneapolis, PhD(inorg chem), 59. *Prof Exp:* USPHS fel, Max Planck Inst Phys Chem, 59-61; from asst prof to assoc prof, 61-72, chmn dept, 74-77, PROF CHEM, BRANDEIS UNIV, 72- *Concurrent Pos:* Vis prof, Dept Pharmacol, Harvard Med Sch, 77-78; Fulbright lectr, 78. *Mem:* Am Chem Soc. *Res:* Inorganic biochemistry; oscillating reactions; fast reactions. *Mailing Add:* Dept of Chem Brandeis Univ Waltham MA 02254

KUSTOM, ROBERT L, b Chicago, Ill, July 11, 34. ION ACCELERATION & FOCUSING, POWER ELECTRONIC NETWORKS. *Educ:* Ill Inst Technol, BSEE, 56, MSEE, 58; Univ Wis-Madison, PhD(elec eng), 69. *Prof Exp:* Elec engr particle detect develop, 58-69, elec engr radio frequency separators & microwave discharge chambers, 69-71, group leader zero gradient synchrotron operations, 71-73, assoc div dir, Plasma Support Syst, Tokamaks & Accelerator Exp Area, 73-78, mgr accelerator syst intense pulsed neutron source, 78-79, div dir accelerator res & develop, 79-81, ASSOC PROJ DIR ELECTRON ACCELERATOR, ACCELERATOR RES FACIL DIV, ARGONNE NAT LAB, 81- *Concurrent Pos:* Vis scientist, Rutherford High Energy Lab, Didcot, UK, 70-71; Tokamak Fusion Test Reactor eng rev comt, Princeton Plasma Physics Lab, 75-77; vis prof, Elec & Comput Eng Dept, Univ Wis, Madison, 78-79 & 80-81, consult, Superconductive Energy Storage Group, 81. *Mem:* Inst Elec & Electronics Engrs; Nuclear Sci Soc; Indust Applications Soc; Plasma Sci Soc; Sigma Xi. *Res:* Development of ion acceleration, focussing, and detection techniques, and the electrodynamic interactions between ions and electromagnetic fields; theoretical and experimental development of superconductive energy storage and transfer techniques using power electronic circuits and electronic circuits and electrodynamic devices. *Mailing Add:* Argonne Nat Lab 9700 S Cass Ave Argonne IL 60439

KUSTU, SYDNEY GOVONS, b Baltimore, Md, Mar 18, 43. BACTERIOLOGY, GENETICS. *Educ:* Harvard Univ, BA, 63; Univ Calif, Davis, PhD(biochem), 70. *Prof Exp:* Asst prof, 74-80, ASSOC PROF BACT, UNIV CALIF, DAVIS, 80- *Mem:* AAAS; Am Soc Microbiol; Am Soc Biol Chemists. *Res:* Regulation of bacterial nitrogen metabolism. *Mailing Add:* Dept of Bact Univ of Calif Davis CA 95616

KUSUDA, TAMAMI, b Seattle, Wash, June 24, 25; m 55; c 3. MECHANICAL ENGINEERING. *Educ:* Univ Tokyo, BS, 47; Univ Wash, Seattle, MS, 52; Univ Minn, PhD(mech eng), 55. *Prof Exp:* Staff engr, Worthington Corp, 55-62; mech engr, 62-70, asst chief environ eng sect, 70-74, chief thermal eng sect, 74-78, CHIEF THERMAL ANAL PROG, NAT BUR STANDARDS, WASHINGTON, DC, 78- *Honors & Awards:* Wolverline Award, Am Soc Heating, Refrig & Air-Conditioning Engrs, 57; Silver Medal, Dept Com, 73; Crosby-Field Award, Am Soc Heating, Refrig & Air Conditioning Engrs, 76; Gold Medal, Dept Com, 80. *Mem:* Am Soc Mech Engrs; fel Am Soc Heating, Refrig & Air-Conditioning Engrs; hon mem Automated Procedure Eng Consult; AAAS. *Res:* Heat transfer and thermodynamics related to environmental science, such as air conditioning, heating, ventilating, refrigeration, ground heat exchange and psychrometrics; energy conservation; solar heating/cooling. *Mailing Add:* 4319 Rosedale Ave Bethesda MD 20814

KUSWA, GLENN WESLEY, b Milwaukee, Wis, Dec 11, 40; m 66; c 1. EXPERIMENTAL PHYSICS. *Educ:* Univ Wis-Madison, BS, 62, MS, 64, PhD(physics), 70. *Prof Exp:* Physicist, Sandia Labs, 70-74; physicist, Laser & Isotope Separation Technol Off, US Energy Res & Develop Admin, 74-76; MGR, PARTICLE BEAM FUSION RES DEPT, SANDIA LABS, 76- *Mem:* Am Phys Soc; AAAS; Sigma Xi. *Res:* Plasma guns; measurement of distribution functions; holographic interferometry; production of dense plasmas; electrical break-down in vacuum; interaction of electron and ion beams with matter; inertially driven fusion technology using lasers, ions, electron beams. *Mailing Add:* Sandia Labs Org 4240 Albuquerque NM 87185

KUSY, ROBERT PETER, b Worcester, Mass, Oct 19, 47; m 69; c 2. DENTAL RESEARCH, POLYMER SCIENCE. *Educ:* Worcester Polytech Inst, BS, 69; Drexel Univ, MS, 71, PhD(mat eng), 73. *Prof Exp:* Res asst mats, Dept Metall Eng, Drexel Univ, 69-72; res assoc, 72-74, asst prof oral biol, 74-79, ASSOC PROF ORTHOD, DEPT ORTHOD & DENT RES, DENT RES CTR, UNIV NC, 79- *Mem:* Am Soc Metals; Am Chem Soc. *Res:* Properties of dental and orthopaedic materials; fractography and fracture work energy of polymers; wear of dental restoratives in vivo; cleft palate research; thermal analysis and radiation properties of polymers. *Mailing Add:* Dent Res Ctr Univ of NC Chapel Hill NC 27514

KUSYK, CHRISTINE JOHANNA, genetics, biochemistry, see previous edition

KUTAL, CHARLES RONALD, b Chicago, Ill, Aug 9, 44; m 73. INORGANIC CHEMISTRY, PHOTOCHEMISTRY. *Educ:* Knox Col, Ill, AB, 65; Univ Ill, Urbana-Champaign, MS, 68, PhD(chem), 70. *Prof Exp:* Res assoc chem, Univ Southern Calif, 70-72; from instr to asst prof, 73-79, ASSOC PROF CHEM, UNIV GA, 79- *Concurrent Pos:* Res fel, Nat Res

Coun-Nat Acad Sci, 72-73. *Mem:* Am Chem Soc; AAAS; Sigma Xi; Int Solar Energy Soc. *Res:* Photochemical and photophysical investigations of transition metal and organometallic complexes in solution and the gas phase; development of solar energy storage system. *Mailing Add:* Dept of Chem Univ of Ga Athens GA 30602

KUTAS, MARTA, b Hungary, Sept 2, 49; US citizen. PSYCHOLOGY, PSYCHOPHYSIOLOGY. *Educ:* Oberlin Col, BA, 71; Univ Ill, Urbana-Champaign, MA, 74, PhD(biol psychol), 77. *Prof Exp:* Vis res assoc, Dept Psychol, Univ Ill, 77-78; res neuroscientist, 78-80, asst res neuroscientist II, 80-82, ASST RES NEUROSCIENTIST III, UNIV CALIF, SAN DIEGO, 82- *Mem:* Soc Psychophysiol Res. *Res:* Brain function, including recording and interpreting pattern of brain waves (event related potentials) from the scalp as humans try to comprehend the oral, written or pictorial world. *Mailing Add:* Dept Neurosci M-008 Sch Med Univ Calif San Diego CA 92093

KUTCHAI, HOWARD C, b Detroit, Mich, Feb 21, 42; div; c 1. PHYSIOLOGY, BIOCHEMISTRY. *Educ:* Univ Mich, BS, 63; Univ Calif, San Francisco, PhD(physiol), 67. *Prof Exp:* NIH trainee, Univ Mich, 67-69, fel, Univ Oslo, 69-70 & Johns Hopkins Univ, 70-72; asst prof, 72-76, assoc prof, 76-81, PROF PHYSIOL, SCH MED, UNIV VA, 81- *Mem:* AAAS; Am Physiol Soc; Biophys Soc; Soc Gen Physiol. *Res:* Development of sugar transport systems in chicken embryo heart cells; oxygen transport in red blood cells; lactate transport and metabolism in vascular smooth muscle; influence of membrane lipids on transport processes. *Mailing Add:* Dept of Physiol Univ of Va Charlottesville VA 22901

KUTCHES, ALEXANDER JOSEPH, b Montclair, NJ, June 23, 41; m 66; c 2. ANIMAL NUTRITION. *Educ:* Calif State Polytech Col, BS, 64; Clemson Univ, MS, 67; Ore State Univ, PhD(ruminant nutrit), 70. *Prof Exp:* Ga-Pac Corp grant nutrit, Wash State Univ, 70-71; biostatistician, Boehringer Ingelheim Ltd, 71-72; mgr, Food & Drug Res Labs, Inc, 72-74; DIR NUTRIT SERV, MOORMAN MFG CO CALIF, 74- *Mem:* Am Dairy Sci Asn; Am Soc Animal Sci. *Res:* Biopharmaceutical data services; clinical drug evaluation; data processing and analysis; product development and study initiation of new investigational drugs; consulting nutritionist, education of sales force, quality control, feed formulation and field research. *Mailing Add:* Moorman Mfg Co of Calif PO Box 1000 San Gabriel CA 91778

KUTIK, LEON, b New York, NY, Mar 6, 27; m 63; c 3. ORGANIC CHEMISTRY, TECHNICAL MANAGEMENT. *Educ:* City Col New York, BS, 49; Univ Chicago, MBA, 73. *Prof Exp:* Chemist, Clover Leaf Paint & Varnish Corp, 51-55; chemist, Cent Res Labs, Interchem Corp, 55-57, sr chemist, 57-59, group leader, 59, asst dept dir appl res finishes & adhesives, 59-63, prog mgr, 63-67, mgr graphic sci, 67-68; tech dir chem coatings, De Soto Inc, 68-70, mgr resin develop, Chem Coatings Div, 70-73, mgr indust res, 73-77, tech mgr construct coatings, 77-80; MGR MFG & TECH SERV, SHERWIN WILLIAMS CORP, 80- *Mem:* Am Chem Soc; Soc Paint Technol. *Res:* Organic coatings for metal, paper, fiberboard, plywood, wood and plastics; adhesives for packaging and structural applications; methods of application for industrial coatings; powder coatings. *Mailing Add:* Sherwin Williams Co 2325 Hollins Ferry Rd Baltimore MD 21230

KUTILEK, MICHAEL JOSEPH, b Baltimore, Md, July 1, 43; m 68; c 1. WILDLIFE ECOLOGY. *Educ:* San Diego State Univ, BS, 66, MS, 68; Mich State Univ, PhD(fisheries & wildlife), 75. *Prof Exp:* Res technician biol, Calif Dept Fish & Game, 65; wildlife biologist, Kenya Nat Parks, US Peace Corps, 69-71; asst prof, 75-80, ASSOC PROF BIOL, SAN JOSE STATE UNIV, 80- *Mem:* Wildlife Soc. *Res:* Foraging strategies of herbivorous large mammals of Africa particularly, grazing and browsing ungulates; ecological and evolutionary aspects of plant-herbivore interactions. *Mailing Add:* Dept of Biol San Jose State Univ San Jose CA 95192

KUTKUHN, JOSEPH HENRY, b Weehawken, NJ, Mar 28, 27; m 53; c 5. ECOLOGY, FISHERIES. *Educ:* Colo State Univ, BS, 53; Iowa State Univ, MS, 54, PhD(fishery mgt), 56. *Prof Exp:* Fishery biologist, Dept Fish & Game, Calif, 56-58; asst lab dir, Tex, 58-65, NC, 65-69, Mich, 72-75, DIR, GREAT LAKES FISHERY LAB, US FISH & WILDLIFE SERV, DEPT INTERIOR, 75- *Concurrent Pos:* Consult, UN Develop Prog, Food & Agr Orgn, Fishery Res & Develop Proj, Lima, Peru, 70-71. *Mem:* Am Fisheries Soc; Am Soc Limnol & Oceanog; Am Inst Fishery Res Biol; Am Inst Biol Sci; Sigma Xi. *Res:* Dynamics of exploited fish and shellfish resources. *Mailing Add:* Great Lakes Fishery Lab 1451 Green Rd Ann Arbor MI 48105

KUTLER, PAUL, aerodynamics, see previous edition

KUTNER, ABRAHAM, b Lynn, Mass, Mar 28, 19; m 47; c 3. ORGANIC POLYMER CHEMISTRY, PHOTOCHEMISTRY. *Educ:* Ohio State Univ, PhD(org chem), 50. *Prof Exp:* Res chemist, Schering Corp, 46-47; res chemist, 50-73, sr res chemist, 73-80, RES SCIENTIST, HERCULES INC, 80- *Mem:* Am Chem Soc. *Res:* Organic synthesis; polymers; polymer additives; stabilization; polymer reactions; photochemistry applications. *Mailing Add:* 2411 Heather Rd E Heatherbrooke Wilmington DE 19803

KUTNER, LEON JAY, b Camden, NJ, Mar 25, 28; m; c 2. MEDICAL MICROBIOLOGY. *Educ:* Temple Univ, AB, 49; Pa State Univ, MS, 50, PhD(bact), 53; Univ Pittsburgh, MD, 63. *Prof Exp:* Asst, Pa State Univ, 49-53; res assoc virol, Sloan-Kettering Inst Cancer Res, 56-59; intern, Second Med Div, Bellevue Hosp, New York, 63-64; asst prof microbiol in surg, Med Col, Cornell Univ, 64-73; asst prof path in residence, 73-77, ASSOC CLIN PROF PATH, UNIV CALIF, SAN DIEGO, 77-; CHIEF MICROBIOL LAB, LAB SERV, VET ADMIN HOSP, SAN DIEGO, 73- *Concurrent Pos:* Assoc scientist, Hosp Spec Surg, New York, 64-73. *Mem:* Am Soc Microbiol; NY Acad Sci. *Res:* Resistance to infectious disease. *Mailing Add:* Microbiol Lab Vet Admin Hosp Lab Serv San Diego CA 92161

KUTNEY, JAMES PETER, b Lamont, Alta, May 2, 32; m 53; c 2. ORGANIC CHEMISTRY. *Educ:* Univ Alta, BSc, 54; Univ Wis, MSc, 56; Wayne State Univ, PhD(org chem), 58. *Prof Exp:* Res fel org chem, Syntex Res Labs, Mex, 58-59; from instr to assoc prof, 59-66, PROF CHEM, UNIV BC, 66- *Concurrent Pos:* NATO scholar, Bonn, WGer, 65; vis prof, Japan Soc Prom Sci, 75. *Honors & Awards:* Merck, Sharp & Dohme Award, Chem Inst Can, 68. *Mem:* Am Chem Soc; The Chem Soc; fel Chem Inst Can; Swiss Chem Soc. *Res:* Chemistry, biosynthesis and biodegradation of natural products and related biologically active compounds, particularly synthesis, isolation and structure elucidation of alkaloids, steroids and terpenes. *Mailing Add:* Dept of Chem Univ of BC Vancouver BC V6T 1E1 Can

KUTSCH, H(OWARD) J(AMES), b Ft Wayne, Ind, Apr 11, 21; m 45; c 2. ENGINEERING, MATERIALS SCIENCE. *Educ:* Purdue Univ, BSAE, 48, MSE, 49, PhD(dynamics), 52. *Prof Exp:* Instr mech eng, Purdue Univ, 49-52; res engr, 52-57, sr res engr, 57-59, res supvr, 59-64, res assoc, Fabrics & Finishes Dept, 65-73, tech assoc, Elastomers Dept, 74-79, RES ASSOC, PLASTIC PROD DEPT, E I DU PONT DE NEMOURS & CO, INC, 79- *Mem:* Sigma Xi; Am Soc Mech Engrs; Soc Plastics Engrs; Soc Rheol; Am Inst Chem Engrs. *Res:* Polymer physics; new products and applications; elastomers. *Mailing Add:* Elastomers Dept E I du Pont de Nemours & Co Inc Wilmington DE 19898

KUTSCHA, NORMAN PAUL, b Irvington, NJ, Sept 24, 37; m 62; c 2. FOREST PRODUCTS. *Educ:* State Univ NY Col Forestry, Syracuse Univ, BS, 59, PhD(wood prod eng), 67; Univ Wis-Madison, MS, 61. *Prof Exp:* Forest prod technologist, US Forest Prod Lab, 59-62; asst prof wood prod eng, State Univ NY Col Forestry, Syracuse Univ, 67-68; asst prof wood technol, 68-73, assoc prof wood technol, Sch Forest Resources, Univ Maine, Orono, 73-77; SCIENTIST, WEYERHAEUSER CO, 77- *Concurrent Pos:* Partic, McIntire-Stennis Res Proj, Maine Agr Exp Sta, USDA, 69- *Mem:* Soc Wood Sci & Technol; Electron Micros Soc Am; Int Asn Wood Anat; Forest Prod Res Soc. *Res:* Light and electron microscopic studies of wood as a developing tissue in the growing tree and as a raw material for various products. *Mailing Add:* WTC 1B12 Weyerhaeuser Co Tacoma WA 98401

KUTSCHKE, KENNETH OTTO, b Kitchener, Ont, May 28, 26; m 57; c 4. PHOTOCHEMISTRY. *Educ:* Univ Western Ont, BSc, 48; Univ Rochester, PhD(phys chem), 51. *Prof Exp:* Can Ramsay fel, Univ Leeds, 51-52; RES OFFICER CHEM, NAT RES COUN CAN, 52- *Concurrent Pos:* Asst ed, Can J Chem, 68-70, ed, 71-78, asst ed, 79- *Mem:* Am Chem Soc; Chem Inst Can. *Res:* Kinetics of reactions of free radicals in gas phase; primary process in photochemistry of organic molecules. *Mailing Add:* Div of Chem Nat Res Coun of Can Ottawa ON K1A 0R6 Can

KUTSHER, GEORGE SAMUEL, b Reading, Pa, July 16, 21; wid; c 5. ANALYTICAL CHEMISTRY. *Educ:* Albright Col, BS, 47; Lehigh Univ, MS, 49. *Prof Exp:* Head res anal dept, Nitrogen Div, Allied Chem & Dye Corp, 49-58, supvr opers eng, Allied Chem Corp, 58-60, supvry res chemist, 60-69, sr engr, Gas Purification Dept, 69-81, SR PROCESS ENGR, SELEXOL DEPT, ALLIED CHEM CORP, MORRISTOWN, 81- *Mem:* Am Chem Soc. *Res:* Gas purification; selexol gas purification process. *Mailing Add:* 76 Woodland Rd Dover NJ 07801

KUTSKY, ROMAN JOSEPH, b Allentown, Pa, May 13, 22; m 47; c 3. BIOLOGY, CHEMISTRY. *Educ:* Princeton Univ, AB, 44; Univ Calif, MA, 49, PhD(zool), 53. *Prof Exp:* Asst physics, Princeton Univ, 44-46; asst zool, Univ Calif, 46-49, asst specialist plant path, 49-51, res fel biochem, Donner Lab, 53-57; res biochemist, Vet Admin Hosp, 57-67; assoc prof biol, Tex Woman's Univ, 67-73; prof life sci, Bishop Col, 73-77; chemist, Army Med Ctr, El Paso, 77-78; SUPVR & STAFF CHEMIST, BONNEVILLE POWER ADMIN, 78- *Concurrent Pos:* Consult, Microchem Specialties Co, 59; NASA res grant, 73-76. *Mem:* AAAS; Am Chem Soc; Tissue Cult Asn; NY Acad Sci; Am Inst Biol Sci. *Res:* Biochemical extractions of biologically active materials; cellular biochemistry and physiology; physical biochemistry; tissue culture growth and form; vitamins and hormones; continuous flow preparative electrophoresis; effects of antioxidants; hormones and vitamins in tissue culture. *Mailing Add:* 1800 Murton St Apt 261 Vancouver WA 98661

KUTTAB, SIMON HANNA, b Jerusalem, Palestine, Apr 17, 46; Jordan citizen; m 78. MEDICINAL CHEMISTRY. *Educ:* Am Univ Beirut, Lebanon, BSc, 68; Univ Kans, PhD(med chem), 74. *Prof Exp:* Asst res pharmacologist med chem, Univ Calif, Davis, 74-75 & Univ Calif, San Francisco, 75-76; asst prof med chem, Northeastern Univ, 76-81; ASST PROF CHEM, BIR-ZEIT UNIV, WEST BANK, ISRAEL, 81- *Concurrent Pos:* Prin investr, US Navy, 78-79; co-investr, NIH grant, Hormonal Anal, 78-81. *Mem:* Am Chem Soc; AAAS; Sigma Xi. *Res:* Drug metabolism and pharmacokinetics using advanced analytical techniques; design and synthesis of compounds of biological interest. *Mailing Add:* Dept Chem Box 14 Bir-Zeit Univ Bir-Zeit West Bank 02115 Isreal

KUTTER, ELIZABETH MARTIN, b Chicago, Ill, Aug 11, 39; m 80; c 2. MOLECULAR BIOLOGY. *Educ:* Univ Wash, BS, 62; Univ Rochester, PhD(biophys), 68. *Prof Exp:* Res assoc biol, Univ Va, 69-72, NSF res grant, 70-72; MEM FAC BIOPHYS, EVERGREEN STATE COL, 72- *Concurrent Pos:* res grants, NIH, 73-77 & 79-, mem, Adv Comt on Recombinant DNA Molecules, 75-79; mem, NSF Adv Comt Ethics & Values in Sci & Technol, 78-80; vis prof, Dept Biochem, Univ Calif, San Francisco, 78-79. *Mem:* Biochem Soc; Biophys Soc; AAAS; Am Soc Microbiol; Soc Nutrit Educ. *Res:* Biochemical developments during bacteriophage T4 infection of Escherichia coli, especially regulation of transcription; roles of 5-hydroxymethylcytosine in T4 DNA; nulceases in T4 infected Escherichia coli. *Mailing Add:* Dept Biophys Evergreen State Col Olympia WA 98505

KUTTNER, ROBERT EUGENE, b Queens, NY, Mar 10, 27; m 55, 76; c 3. BIOCHEMISTRY, PHYSIOLOGY. *Educ:* City Col New York, BS, 50; Univ Conn, PhD(biochem), 59. *Prof Exp:* Res technician, Brookhaven Nat Lab, 51-52; asst chem, Univ Conn, 52-54, res asst, 54-58; res assoc, Res Lab, Inst Living, 58-61; instr biochem, Sch Med, Creighton Univ, 61-64, res biochemist, 64-66; asst prof & res assoc obstet & gynec, Chicago Lying-In-Hosp, Univ Chicago, 66-70; res assoc, Electronic Lab, Stanford Univ, 71-72; assoc prof anthrop & chmn dept, Univ Southern Miss, 73-75; fel, Dept Physiol, La State Univ Med Ctr, 76-77; asst prof, 78-80, ASSOC PROF SURG & CHIEF, SURG RES LAB, CHICAGO MED SCH, NORTH CHICAGO VET ADMIN CTR, 81- *Mem:* Shock Soc; AAAS; NY Acad Sci; Soc Exp Biol & Med; Am Physiol Soc. *Res:* Neurochemistry; amino acids; enzymes; metabolic diseases; nutrition; reproductive biology; social biology; gluconeogenesis; pathophysiology of shock. *Mailing Add:* Surg Res Lab Vet Admin Med Ctr North Chicago IL 60064

KUTZ, FREDERICK WINFIELD, b Wilmington, Del, Sept 29, 39; m 63; c 2. ECOLOGY, MEDICAL ENTOMOLOGY. *Educ:* Univ Del, BS, 62, MS, 64; Purdue Univ, PhD(entom), 72. *Prof Exp:* Res fel & assoc entom, Univ Del, 62-64; res asst & instr, Purdue Univ, 66-69; entomologist & parasitologist, Insect Control & Res Inc, 69-72; ECOLOGIST, US ENVIRON PROTECTION AGENCY, 72- *Concurrent Pos:* Mem sci adv panel, Onchocerciasis Control Prog, WHO, 74-, monitoring panel, Fed Working Group Pest Mgr, 75-77 & subcomt, Comt Environ Carcinogens, Nat Cancer Inst, 76- *Mem:* Entom Soc Am; Am Soc Trop Med & Hyg; Am Mosquito Control Asn. *Res:* Arthropod-insect pest mangement, particularly of medical significance and pesticide residue monitoring activities in humans and ambient air. *Mailing Add:* 4967 Moonfall Way Columbia MD 21044

KUTZKO, PHILIP C, b Brooklyn, NY, Nov 24, 46; m 67; c 1. NUMBER THEORY. *Educ:* City Col New York, BA, 67; Univ Wis, MA, 68, PhD(math), 72. *Prof Exp:* Instr math, Univ Wis, Green Bay, 68-69, instr, Rock County Ctr, 69-72; instr, Princeton Univ, 72-74; asst prof, 74-77, assoc prof, 77-80, PROF MATH, UNIV IOWA, 80- *Mem:* Am Math Soc. *Res:* Representation theory of p-adic linear groups and applications to non-abelian classfield theory. *Mailing Add:* Div Math Sci Univ Iowa Iowa City IA 52240

KUTZMAN, RAYMOND STANLEY, b St Cloud, Minn, April 16, 49; m 74. TOXICOLOGY. *Educ:* St Cloud State Col, BA, 71; Univ Notre Dame, MS, 74; NC State Univ, PhD(zool), 77. *Prof Exp:* Res assoc, Chem Dept, 77-79, asst scientist, 79-81, ASSOC SCIENTIST, MED DEPT, BROOKHAVEN NAT LAB, 81- *Mem:* AAAS. *Res:* Biodistribution of xenobiotic agents after inhalation exposure; the relationship among structural, functional and compositional parameters in the lung after exposure of toxic agents; genetic disposition as an underlying factor in biochemical and physiological aspects of toxicity. *Mailing Add:* Med Dept Brookhaven Nat Lab Upton NY 11973

KUTZSCHER, EDGAR WALTER, b Leipzig, Ger, Mar 21, 06; nat US; m 45; c 2. PHYSICS. *Educ:* Univ Berlin, PhD(physics), 33, Dr phil habil(appl physics), 36. *Hon Degrees:* DrEng, Hannover Univ, 63. *Prof Exp:* Asst physics, Univ Berlin, 30-33 & Inst Technol, Berlin, 33; physicist, Dept Defense, Ger, 34-37; dir res, Electroacoust Co, Kiel, Ger, 37-45 & univ exten, Flensburg, Ger, 46-47; physicist infrared, US Navy, 47-51 & solid state physics, Santa Barbara Res Ctr, Calif, 51-53; head dept radiation sensors & technol, Lockheed Aircraft Corp, 54-72; CONSULT PHYSICIST, 72- *Concurrent Pos:* Asst prof, Inst Technol, Berlin, 37-45. *Honors & Awards:* Todt Prize, 44. *Mem:* Optical Soc Am. *Res:* Infrared physics and detectors. *Mailing Add:* 15450 Briarwood Dr Sherman Oaks CA 91403

KUWAHARA, STEVEN SADAO, b Lahaina, Hawaii, July 20, 40; m 73; c 2. BIOCHEMISTRY OF HEMOSTASIS, ANALYTICAL BIOCHEMISTRY. *Educ:* Cornell Univ, BS, 62; Univ Wis, MS, 65, PhD(biochem), 67. *Prof Exp:* Res assoc biochem, Univ Wash, 66-67; asst prof chem, Calif State Col, Long Beach, 67-71; asst res biologist, Dept Develop & Cell Biol, Univ Calif, Irvine, 71-73; biochemist & unit chief, 73-76, sect chief prod anal, 76-78, SECT CHIEF BIOCHEM & BIOASSAY, BUR DIS CONTROL & LAB SERVS, MICH DEPT PUB HEALTH, 78- *Concurrent Pos:* NIH spec res fel, Nat Inst Gen Med Sci, 71-73; adj res assoc, Dept Med, Mich State Univ, 81- *Mem:* NY Acad Sci; Am Chem Soc; Soc Exp Biol & Med; Am Fedn Clin Res; fel Am Inst Chemists. *Res:* Biochemistry of blood coagulation factors; biochemistry of platelet aggregation; analytical biochemistry. *Mailing Add:* Bur Dis Control & Lab Serv Mich Dept Pub Health Lansing MI 48909

KUWANA, THEODORE, b Idaho Falls, Idaho, Aug 3, 31. ANALYTICAL CHEMISTRY, ELECTROCHEMISTRY. *Educ:* Antioch Col, BS, 54; Cornell Univ, MS, 56; Univ Kans, PhD(anal chem), 59. *Prof Exp:* Res chemist, Aerojet-Gen Corp Div, Gen Tire & Rubber Co, 59; fel, Calif Inst Technol, 59-60; asst prof anal chem, Univ Calif, Riverside, 60-66; from assoc prof to prof, Case Western Reserve Univ, 66-71; PROF CHEM, OHIO STATE UNIV, 71- *Concurrent Pos:* Chmn, Gordon Res Conf Anal Chem, 64. *Mem:* AAAS; Am Chem Soc; Royal Soc Chem. *Res:* Organic electrode processes; photoelectrochemistry and electroluminescence. *Mailing Add:* Dept of Chem Ohio State Univ Columbus OH 43210

KUYATT, CHRIS ERNIE EARL, b Grand Island, Nebr, Nov 30, 30; m 49; c 4. ELECTRON OPTICS, ATOMIC PHYSICS. *Educ:* Univ Nebr, BS, 52, MS, 53, PhD(physics), 60. *Prof Exp:* Res assoc atomic physics, Univ Nebr, 59-60; physicist, 60-69, actg chief electron physics sect, 69-70, chief electron & optical physics sect, 70-73, chief surface & electron physics sect, 73-78, chief, Radiation Physics Div, 78-79, DIR, CTR RADIATION RES, NAT BUR STANDARDS, 79- *Honors & Awards:* US Dept Com Silver Medal, 64. *Mem:* Fel Am Phys Soc; AAAS; Sigma Xi. *Res:* Electron scattering; polarized electrons; electron monochromators; electron energy analyzers; optics. *Mailing Add:* Surface & Electron Physics Sect Nat Bur Standards Washington DC 20234

KUYPER, LEE FREDERICK, b Mitchell, SDak, Feb 28, 49; m 76; c 1. ORGANIC CHEMISTRY, MEDICINAL CHEMISTRY. *Educ:* Ouachita Univ, BS, 71; Univ Ark, PhD(org chem), 77. *Prof Exp:* Res assoc, Univ NC, 76-77; SR SCIENTIST, BURROUGHS WELLCOME CO, 77- *Mem:* Am Chem Soc. *Res:* Drug design and synthesis. *Mailing Add:* Burroughs Wellcome Co Research Triangle Park NC 27709

KUZAWA, MARY GRACE, b Springfield, Mass, Feb 11, 18. MATHEMATICS. *Educ:* St John's Univ, BA, 53; Fordham Univ, MA, 57; NY Univ, PhD(math educ), 66. *Prof Exp:* Chmn dept math physics, Nazareth Acad, 53-57; assoc prof, 57-70, PROF MATH PHYSICS, HOLY FAMILY COL, PA, 70-, CHMN DEPT MATH, 57- *Concurrent Pos:* NSF grants, Drexel Inst Technol, 67-68, Fla State Univ, 69, Vanderbilt Univ, 70 & Purdue Univ, 71. *Mem:* Math Asn Am; AAAS. *Res:* Mathematical analysis; history of mathematics. *Mailing Add:* Dept of Math Holy Family Col Philadelphia PA 19114

KUZEL, NORBERT R, b Angus, Minn, May 23, 23; m 49. ANALYTICAL CHEMISTRY, INSTRUMENTATION. *Educ:* NDak State Univ, BS, 48, MS, 49. *Prof Exp:* Anal chemist, 49-59, dept head anal develop, 59-63, sr anal chemist, 63-67, res scientist, 68-73, RES ASSOC, ELI LILLY & CO, 73- *Mem:* Am Chem Soc; Instrument Soc Am. *Res:* Development of analytical methods; residue analysis; laboratory and process automation and computerization. *Mailing Add:* Eli Lilly & Co 307 E McCarty St Indianapolis IN 46285

KUZMA, JAN WALDEMAR, b Warsaw, Poland, Apr 24, 36; US citizen; m 63; c 3. BIOSTATISTICS. *Educ:* Andrews Univ, BA, 59; Columbia Univ, MS, 61; Univ Mich, PhD(biostatist), 63. *Prof Exp:* Lectr biostatist & dir clin trials unit, Univ Calif, Los Angeles, 63-67; chmn dept biostatist, 67-73, PROF BIOSTATIST & CHMN DEPT BIOSTATIST & EPIDEMIOL, SCH HEALTH, LOMA LINDA UNIV, 73- *Concurrent Pos:* Consult biostatistician, Loma Linda Univ, 64-67. *Mem:* Am Statist Soc; Biomet Soc; Inst Math Statist; AAAS. *Res:* Cancer in Seventh-day Adventists; alcohol use during pregnancy; general statistical methodology. *Mailing Add:* Dept of Biostatist Sch of Health Loma Linda CA 92354

KUZMA, JOSEPH FRANCIS, b Austria, Mar 14, 15; US citizen; m 41; c 7. PATHOLOGY. *Educ:* Univ Ill, BS, 37, MD, 40; Marquette Univ, MS, 42. *Prof Exp:* From instr to prof, Marquette Univ, 46-74, dir dept, 53-69; prof path, 74-80, CLIN PROF PATH, MED COL WIS, 80- *Concurrent Pos:* Dir lab, Milwaukee Hosp, 43-47 & Milwaukee County Hosp, 47-54 & 64-69. *Mem:* Am Soc Clin Path; fel AMA; Am Asn Path & Bact; Am Col Physicians; Col Am Path. *Res:* Mammary tumors and diseases; sulfonamide reactions; experimental arthritis; kidney diseases; radioactive strontium; bone cancer. *Mailing Add:* 1115 Honey Creek Pkwy Wauwatosa WI 53213

KUZMAK, JOSEPH MILTON, b Man, Can, Mar 7, 22; m 42; c 3. PHYSICAL CHEMISTRY. *Educ:* Univ Man, BSc, 49, MSc, 50; McGill Univ, PhD(phys chem), 53. *Prof Exp:* Res officer, Nat Res Coun Can, 53-57; res chemist, Am Viscose Corp, Pa, 57-67; SR RES CHEMIST, ST REGIS PAPER CO, 67- *Mem:* Am Chem Soc; Tech Asn Pulp & Paper Indust. *Res:* Mechanism of moisture movement in porous materials; chemical modification of regenerated cellulose; chemical modification of pulp and paper. *Mailing Add:* 24 Collingswood Rd New City NY 10956

KUZMANOVIC, B(OGDAN) O(GNJAN), b Belgrade, Yugoslavia, July 16, 14; m 50; c 1. CIVIL ENGINEERING. *Educ:* Univ Belgrade, Dipl Eng, 37; Serbian Acad Sci, Dr Tech Sc, 56. *Prof Exp:* Asst designer bridges, Ministry Transp, Belgrade, 38-41, sr designer, 45-53; from asst prof to assoc prof struct, Univ Sarajevo, 53-58; Brit Coun & Gilchrist Ed Trust res fel, Sheffield Sci Sch, Yale, 58-59; prof, Univ Khartoum, 59-60, dean fac eng & head dept civil eng, 60-63, prof & head dept, 63-65; prof struct, Univ Kans, 65-81; SR STRUCT ENGR, BEISWENGER, HOCH & ASSOCS, MIAMI BEACH, FLA, 81- *Concurrent Pos:* Off Civil Defense res grant, 67. *Mem:* Fel Am Soc Civil Engrs; Int Asn Bridge & Struct Engrs. *Res:* Theory of elasticity and plasticity; plastic analysis and design of steel structures. *Mailing Add:* Beiswenger Hoch & Assocs 1190 NE 163rd St Miami Beach FL 33160

KUZNESOF, PAUL MARTIN, b Bronx, NY, Aug 13, 41; div; c 2. INORGANIC CHEMISTRY. *Educ:* Brown Univ, ScB, 63; Northwestern Univ, PhD, 67. *Prof Exp:* Fel inorg mat res div, Lawrence Radiation Lab, Univ Calif, 67-69; asst prof chem, San Francisco State Col, 69-70; prof chem, Univ Campinas, Brazil, 70-75; MEM STAFF, CHEM DIV, NAVAL RES LAB, 79-; ASSOC PROF, AGNES SCOTT COL, DECATUR, GA, 79- *Concurrent Pos:* Grant, FAPESP Res Found, Sao Paulo, 71; lectr, Univ Mich, 75-76; vis assoc prof, Trinity Col, Hartford, Conn, 76-78; grants, Res Corp, 77 & NSF, 81; vis scholar, Northwestern Univ, 82. *Mem:* Am Chem Soc; Sigma Xi. *Res:* Synthesis and electronic properties of boron-nitrogen compounds; hydrides of the lighter main group elements; electron donor-acceptor interactions; electroactive polymers. *Mailing Add:* Chem Dept Agnes Scott Col Decatur GA 30030

KVAAS, T(HORVALD) ARTHUR, b Des Moines, Iowa, Jan 8, 19; m 42; c 2. PHYSICS, ENGINEERING. *Educ:* Univ Calif, Los Angeles, BA, 40, MA, 42. *Prof Exp:* Phys sci res engr, Res Lab, Douglas Aircraft Co, 42-46, phys scientist, proj Rand, 46-48; proj engr, Rand Corp, 48-52; sect chief missiles adv design, Douglas Aircraft Co, 52-57; mgr, Synthesis Sect, Tech Mil Planning Oper, Gen Elec Co, 57-60, prof staff, 60-62, tech anal & appln oper, 62-63, mgr tech environ studies, tempo, ctr advan studies, 63-70; pres, ADCON Corp, 70-74; vpres & opers mgr, Moseley Assocs, 74-76; consult, 77; opers mgr, Cetec Broadcast Corp, 78-; CONSULT ACOUSTICS, 80- *Concurrent Pos:* Mem comt, Am Standards Asn Comt Acoust Terminology, 46-48; Am Rocket Soc rep, Cong Int Astronaut Fedn, Amsterdam, 58. *Mem:* Assoc fel Am Inst Aeronaut & Astronaut; Acoustical Soc Am. *Res:* Technological and environmental forecasting and planning with particular emphasis on future technologies, technical resources and their application to future human needs; corporate long range strategic business planning. *Mailing Add:* 933 Roble Lane Santa Barbara CA 93103

KVAM, DONALD CLARENCE, b Escanaba, Mich, Oct 20, 32; m 54; c 3. PHARMACOLOGY. *Educ:* Ferris State Col, BS, 54; Univ Wis, PhD(pharmacol), 60. *Prof Exp:* Sr pharmacologist, Mead Johnson & Co, 60-63, group leader pharmacol, 63-64; supvr biol res, 64-67, mgr biol res, 67-71, mgr pharmacol, 71-78, MGR CLIN PHARMACOL, RIKER LABS, MINN MINING & MFG CO, 78- *Concurrent Pos:* Lectr, Col Med Sci, Univ Minn. *Mem:* AAAS; NY Acad Sci; Am Soc Pharmacol & Exp Therapeut; Am Pharmaceut Asn; Acad Pharmaceut Sci. *Res:* Evaluation of agents for possible therapeutic utility. *Mailing Add:* Riker Labs Bldg 270-3A-01 3M Ctr St Paul MN 55101

KVARDA, ROBERT EDWARD, b Cleveland, Ohio, Mar 7, 29; m 66; c 2. APPLIED MATHEMATICS. *Educ:* Ohio State Univ, BSc, 53, MSc, 56; Ore State Univ, PhD(math), 65. *Prof Exp:* Electronics engr, Radio Corp Am, NJ, 53-54; res assoc physics, Ohio State Univ, 56-57; solid state physicist, Naval Electronics Lab Ctr, 57-60; res assoc math, Ore State Univ, 64-65; res physicist, Naval Electronics Lab Ctr, 65-69 & Naval Weapons Lab, 69-70, PHYSICIST, NAVAL OCEAN SYSTS CTR, 70- *Mem:* Am Phys Soc. *Res:* Naval communication systems; algebraic coding theory; information theory. *Mailing Add:* 6445 Mira Vista Lane San Diego CA 92120

KVEGLIS, ALBERT ANDREW, b Brooklyn, NY, Feb 10, 34; m 61; c 3. POLYMER CHEMISTRY, ORGANIC CHEMISTRY. *Educ:* Queens Col, NY, BS, 56; Stevens Inst Technol, MS, 65. *Prof Exp:* Sr res chemist polymers, Plastics Div, Allied Chem Corp, 56-71; res chemist polymers, Trimflex Div, Teleflex Corp, 71; methods develop, Biomed Sci, Inc, 71-72; GROUP LEADER, POLYMERS & VEHICLES, INMONT CORP, 72- *Mem:* Am Chem Soc. *Res:* Polymer synthesis and characterization, development of resins and vehicles for inks and coatings, synthesis of flame retardant monomers and additives for plastics, modification of polymers. *Mailing Add:* 6 Buckingham Circle Pine Brook NJ 07058

KVENBERG, JOHN EIDE, entomology, see previous edition

KVENVOLDEN, KEITH ARTHUR, b Cheyenne, Wyo, July 16, 30; m 59; c 2. ORGANIC GEOCHEMISTRY. *Educ:* Colo Sch Mines, GpE, 52; Stanford Univ, MS, 58, PhD(geol), 61. *Prof Exp:* Jr geologist, Socony Mobil Oil Co, Venezuela, 52-54, sr res technologist petrol geochem, Mobil Field Res Lab, Tex, 61-66; res scientist, Ames Res Ctr, NASA, Calif, 66-71, chief, Chem Evol Br, 71-74, chief, Planetary Biol Div, 74-75; GEOLOGIST, US GEOL SURV, 75- *Concurrent Pos:* Consult assoc prof geol, Stanford Univ, 67-73, consult prof, 73-; Chmn, Jodies Advisory Panel Organic Geochem, 74-80; mem, US Nat Comt Geochem, 80- *Mem:* Am Asn Petrol Geol; Geol Soc Am; Geochem Soc; Am Chem Soc; AAAS. *Res:* Organic geochemistry of modern and ancient sediments; petroleum geochemistry; environmental geochemistry; organic chemistry of meteorites; origin and evolution of life, geochemistry of amino acids. *Mailing Add:* US Geol Surv-Marine M/599 345 Middlefield Rd Menlo Park CA 94025

KVETKAS, MARILYN J, b Chicago, Ill, Nov 10, 28; m 56. FERMENTATIONS, BIOCHEMISTRY. *Educ:* Roosevelt Univ, BS, 51; Ill Inst Technol, MS, 59, PhD(microbiol, biochem), 69. *Prof Exp:* Res technician radiation chem, Argonne Nat Lab, Ill, 51-52, sci asst, 64-69; res technician microbiol, Food Res Inst, Chicago, 52-53; bacteriologist, Rosner-Hixson Lab, 53-59; res bacteriologist, Fleischmann Malting Co, 59-61 & Gen Foods Corp, 61-63; asst bacteriologist, Am Meat Inst Found, 63-64; res microbiologist, Int Minerals & Chem Corp, Ill, 69-73; sr res microbiologist, Microbics Oper, Beckman Instruments Inc, 73-75; sr res investr, 75-78, res scientist II, 78-81, GROUP LEADER II, G D SEARLE & CO, 81- *Mem:* Soc Indust Microbiol; Am Soc Microbiol. *Res:* Bacterial genetics; strain improvement; steroid transformations; fermentations; microbial enzymes; microbial physiology; bacteriophage and lysogeny. *Mailing Add:* G D Searle & Co Box 5110 Chicago IL 60680

KWAAN, HAU CHEONG, b Hong Kong, Sept 30, 31; US citizen; m 58; c 2. INTERNAL MEDICINE, HEMATOLOGY. *Educ:* Univ Hong Kong, MB & BS, 52, MD, 58; FRCP(E), 67; Am Bd Internal Med, cert internal med, 69, cert hemat, 74, cert med oncol, 79. *Prof Exp:* House physician, Univ Med Unit, Queen Mary Hosp, 52-53; sr clin asst med, Univ Hong Kong, 53-55, asst lectr, 56-59, lectr, 59-61; sr investr physiol, James F Mitchell Found, DC, 62-65; assoc prof, 66-72, PROF MED, MED SCH, NORTHWESTERN UNIV CHICAGO, 72- *Concurrent Pos:* China Med Bd NY fel pharmacol, 58-59; vis res fel, Col Physicians & Surgeons, Columbia Univ, 58-59; clin asst prof, Sch Med, Georgetown Univ, 64-65; mem coun thrombosis, Am Heart Asn, 64-; chief hemat sect, Vet Admin Lakeside Hosp, Chicago, 67-; attend physician, Northwestern Mem Hosp, Chicago, 69-; sr Fulbright travel scholar, 74. *Mem:* Fel Am Col Physicians; AMA; Am Physiol Soc; Am Soc Hemat; Am Fedn Clin Res. *Res:* Blood coagulation; fibrinolysis; thrombosis. *Mailing Add:* Dept of Med Northwestern Univ Med Sch Chicago IL 60611

KWAK, JAN C T, b Schagen, Neth, May 6, 42; m 65; c 3. PHYSICAL CHEMISTRY, ELECTROCHEMISTRY. *Educ:* Univ Amsterdam, MSc, 64, PhD, 67. *Prof Exp:* Res assoc molten salts, Neth Orgn Advan Pure Res, 64-68; res chemist, Sea Water Conversion Lab, Univ Calif, Berkeley, 68-70; asst prof, 70-77, ASSOC PROF CHEM, DALHOUSIE UNIV, 77- *Mem:* Am Chem Soc; Chem Inst Can. *Res:* Polyelectrolyte solutions; membrane transport; organic soils; biophysical chemistry; clay suspensions and flocculation studies; coal beneficiation; colloid chemistry. *Mailing Add:* Dept of Chem Dalhousie Univ Halifax NS B3H 3J5 Can

KWAK, NOWHAN, b Seoul, Korea, Sept 16, 28; US citizen; m 58; c 2. HIGH ENERGY PHYSICS. *Educ:* Seoul Nat Univ, BS, 52; Emory Univ, MS, 56; Univ Rochester, MA, 59; Tufts Univ, PhD(physics), 62. *Prof Exp:* Res assoc high energy physics, Tufts Univ, 62-65; from asst prof to assoc prof, 64-78, PROF PHYSICS & ASTRON, UNIV KANS, 78- *Concurrent Pos:* Vis scientist, Deutsches Elektronen-Synchrotron, WGer, 80-81. *Mem:* Am Phys Soc. *Res:* Experimental high energy physics. *Mailing Add:* Dept of Physics Univ of Kans Lawrence KS 66044

KWALWASSER, WILLIAM DAVID, b Bronx, NY, Aug 15, 44; m 68. ORGANIC CHEMISTRY. *Educ:* Harpur Col, State Univ NY Binghamton, BA, 65; Brandeis Univ, PhD(org chem), 71. *Prof Exp:* Nat Res Coun assoc org chem, Cambridge Air Force Res Labs, 70-71; chemist, Eco-Control, Inc,

72; assoc res eng chemist, AMP, Inc, 72-80; WITH RARITAN CTR, REVERE RES INC, 80- *Mem:* Am Chem Soc. *Res:* Organic photo- and semiconductivity; photochemistry of nitrogen containing heterocycles; the nature of polar-compound metal interactions. *Mailing Add:* Revere Res Inc Raritan Ctr 165 Fieldcrest Ave Edison NJ 08817

KWAN, JOHN YING-KUEN, b Hong Kong, Apr 5, 47; m 73; c 1. ASTROPHYSICS. *Educ:* Utah State Univ, BS, 69; Calif Inst Technol, PhD(physics), 72. *Prof Exp:* Res fel astrophys, Calif Inst Technol, 73 & Inst Advan Study, 73-74; asst prof astrophys, State Univ NY Stony Brook, 75-76; mem tech staff, Bell Labs, 76-80; ASSOC PROF ASTROPHYS, UNIV MASS, 81- *Mem:* Am Astron Soc; Inst Elec & Electronics Engrs. *Res:* Theoretical studies of astrophysical masers, interstellar molecular clouds, quasars. *Mailing Add:* Dept Physics & Astron Univ Mass Amherst MA 01003

KWAN, KING CHIU, b Hong Kong, Jan 14, 36. DRUG METABOLISM, PHARMACOKINETICS. *Educ:* Univ Mich, BS, 56, MS, 58, PhD(pharmaceut chem), 62. *Prof Exp:* Res chemist, R P Scherer Corp, 62-63; lectr pharm, Univ Mich, 63-64; sr investr, 64-79, EXEC DIR DRUG METAB, MERCK SHARP & DOHME RES LABS, 79- *Concurrent Pos:* Mem, Pharmacol Study Sect, NIH, 80-83. *Mem:* Am Pharmaceut Asn; Acad Pharmaceut Sci; NY Acad Sci; Am Soc Pharmacol & Exp Therapeuts; Int Soc Study Xenobiotics. *Res:* Pharmaceutical research and development; drug metabolism; pharmacokinetics; biopharmaceutics. *Mailing Add:* Merck Sharp & Dohme Res Labs West Point PA 19486

KWAN, PAUL WING-LING, b Hong Kong, Nov 7, 42; Brit citizen; m 77. CANCER, CELL BIOLOGY. *Educ:* Univ Md, BS, 66; Clark Univ, MA, 71, PhD(biol), 75. *Prof Exp:* Teaching asst biol, Dept of Biol, Clark Univ, 67-73; RES ASSOC DEPT OF PATH, SCH MED, TUFTS UNIV, 75-, INSTR HISTOL, DEPT ANAT, 77- *Mem:* AAAS. *Res:* Effects of hormones on tumor cells with special emphasis on the cell surface employing electron microscopy, freeze-fracture, Weibel morphometrics, digital analysis, tracer methods and cytochemistry; pathogenesis of benign prostatic hyperplasia and prostatic cancers in animal models. *Mailing Add:* Dept of Path 136 Harrison Ave Boston MA 02111

KWAN-GETT, CLIFFORD STANLEY, b Emmaville, NSW, Oct 14, 34; m 61; c 2. SURGERY. *Educ:* Univ Sydney, BSc, 54, BE, 56, MD, 63. *Prof Exp:* Engr, Australian Postmaster Gen Dept, 60-61; resident med off, Lanceston Gen Hosp, Tasmania, 64-66; asst res prof, 68-70, ASSOC RES PROF SURG, UNIV UTAH, 70- *Concurrent Pos:* Fel med, Cleveland Clin Found, 66-67; consult, Aerojet Gen Corp, Calif, 66-68. *Mem:* Am Soc Artificial Internal Organs; Biomed Eng Soc. *Res:* Developing total replacement artificial hearts to replace the irreparable human heart; use of artificial heart assist devices; development and use of artificial kidneys, especially for home use by patients. *Mailing Add:* Div Artificial Organs Bldg 518 Univ of Utah Salt Lake City UT 84112

KWART, HAROLD, b New York, NY, Sept 25, 16; m 41; c 4. PHYSICAL CHEMISTRY, ORGANIC CHEMISTRY. *Educ:* Brooklyn Col, AB, 37; Harvard Univ, PhD(chem), 48. *Prof Exp:* Mem staff, war res div, Manhattan Proj, Columbia Univ, 41-45; fel, Harvard Univ, 47-49; asst prof chem, Bryn Mawr Col, 49-51; from asst prof to prof, 51-65, H FLETCHER BROWN PROF CHEM, UNIV DEL, 65- *Concurrent Pos:* NSF sr fel, 60-61; Fulbright lectr, Nat Univ Mex, 65; lectr, Inst Chem, 70; Petrol Res Found int award, 66-67; vis prof, Univ Pisa, 66-67; Munich Tech Univ, 71 & Univ de Haute Alsace, Mulhouse, France, 80; Alexander von Humboldt Stiftung US sr scientist award, 81. *Mem:* Am Chem Soc; The Chem Soc. *Res:* Kinetics of chain reactions in solution, particularly polymerization; kinetics and mechanisms of chemical reactions; techniques and kinetic studies of thermolytic reactions; isotope effects; theoretical developments and measurements in the interests of reaction mechanism studies. *Mailing Add:* Dept of Chem Univ of Del Newark DE 19711

KWARTLER, CHARLES EDWARD, b Stanislau, Austria, Oct 5, 11; US citizen; m 41; c 3. ORGANIC CHEMISTRY. *Educ:* NY Univ, BS, 32, PhD(org chem), 36. *Prof Exp:* Microchem technician, NY Univ, 34-36, asst instr, 36-38; res chemist, Winthrop Chem Co, 39-43, dir pilot lab, 43-45, head process develop lab, Winthrop-Stearns, Inc, 45-51, chief chemist, Winthrop Prod, Inc, 47-51; dir res & develop, 51-56, vpres, 56-65, EXEC VPRES, GAMMA CHEM CO, 65-; CONSULT, ASHLAND CHEM CO, 76- *Concurrent Pos:* Mgr process develop, Ashland Chem Co, 69-71; asst to pres & tech coordr, Ashland Chem Co, 71-76; consult, Southland Corp, 78- *Mem:* Am Chem Soc. *Res:* Anesthetics; antimalarials; antiseptics; analgesics; antispasmodics; sulfanilamides; quaternary ammonium compounds; arsenicals; radiopaques; diuretics; synthetic sex hormones; organic antimony compounds; synthetic detergents; 8-hydroxyquinoline; synthetic herbicides and pecticides. *Mailing Add:* Southland Corp Alphano Rd Great Meadows NJ 07838

KWATNY, EUGENE MICHAEL, b Philadelphia, Pa, Oct 25, 43; m 66; c 2. BIOMEDICAL ENGINEERING. *Educ:* Drexel Univ, BS, 66, MS, 68, PhD(biomed eng), 71. *Prof Exp:* Biomed engr, Aerospace Crew Equipment Dept, US Naval Air Develop Ctr, 66-71; PRIN INVESTR VISUAL SYSTS & DIR COMPUT & INFO SCI, KRUSEN CTR RES & ENG & ASST PROF REHAB MED, SCH MED, TEMPLE UNIV, 71- *Concurrent Pos:* Adj asst prof visual sci & biomed eng, Pa Col Optom, 74- *Mem:* Inst Elec & Electronics Engrs. *Res:* Sensory aids for rehabilitation; bioelectric signal processing; computers in medicine and biology. *Mailing Add:* Krusen Ctr Res & Eng Temple Univ Sch of Med Philadelphia PA 19122

KWATRA, SUBHASH CHANDER, b India, Nov 12, 41; m 66; c 2. DIGITAL SATELLITE COMMUNICATIONS. *Educ:* Birla Inst Technol, BE, 62, MS, 70; Univ South Fla, PhD(elec eng), 75. *Prof Exp:* Lectr eng, Birla Inst Technol & Sci, 65-70; asst prof, 77-81, ASSOC PROF ENG, UNIV TOLEDO, 81- *Concurrent Pos:* Prin investr, Lewis Res Ctr, NASA, 79- *Mem:* Inst Elec & Electronics Engrs. *Res:* Digital signal processing. *Mailing Add:* Col Eng Dept Elec Eng Univ Toledo Toledo OH 43606

KWEI, TI-KANG, b Shanghai, China, Mar 19, 29; US citizen; m 54; c 3. POLYMER CHEMISTRY, PHYSICAL CHEMISTRY. *Educ:* Chiao Tung Univ, BS, 49; Univ Toronto, MASc, 54; Polytech Inst Brooklyn, PhD(chem), 58. *Prof Exp:* Polymer chemist, Stand Oil Co, Ind, 58-59; polymer chemist, Interchem Corp, 59-61, sr chemist, 61-63, group leader polymer chem, 63-65; MEM TECH STAFF, BELL LABS, 65- *Mem:* Am Chem Soc. *Res:* Thermodynamics of polymer mixtures; viscoelasticity and surface chemistry of polymers; transport phenomena in polymers. *Mailing Add:* 197 Old Forge Rd Murray Hill NJ 07974

KWENTUS, GERALD K(ENNETH), b St Louis, Mo, Jan 10, 37. CHEMICAL ENGINEERING. *Educ:* Wash Univ, BS, 60; Mass Inst Technol, PhD(chem eng), 67. *Prof Exp:* Sr res engr, Org Div, Monsanto Co, 66-70, res specialist, 70-75, sr res specialist, 75-80, SR RES GROUP LEADER, MONSANTO CHEM INTERMEDIATES CO, 80- *Mem:* Am Inst Chem Engrs. *Res:* Preparative chromatography; fractional distillation; chemical kinetics; heat transfer. *Mailing Add:* 9526 Pine Spray Ct St Louis MO 63126

KWIATEK, JACK, b Kansas City, Mo, Feb 9, 24; m 48; c 3. INDUSTRIAL ORGANIC CHEMISTRY. *Educ:* Univ Ill, BS, 44; Cornell Univ, PhD(chem), 50. *Prof Exp:* Org res chemist, M W Kellogg Co, 50-54; res assoc, Gen Elec Co, 54-58; SR RES ASSOC, US INDUST CHEM CO, 58- *Concurrent Pos:* Adj asst prof, Eve Col, Univ Cincinnati, 61-65; sr fel, Weizmann Inst Sci, 68-70. *Mem:* Am Chem Soc; Catalysis Soc. *Res:* Homogeneous and heterogeneous catalysis; hydrogenation; syngas reactions; oxidation; carbonylation; coordination compounds; organometallics; free radical reactions; organophosphorus compounds. *Mailing Add:* 3135 N Farmcrest Dr Cincinnati OH 45213

KWIRAM, ALVIN L, b Man, Can, Apr 28, 37; m 64; c 2. PHYSICAL CHEMISTRY, CHEMICAL PHYSICS. *Educ:* Walla Walla Col, BS(chem) & BA(physics), 58; Calif Inst Technol, PhD(chem), 62. *Prof Exp:* Instr & res assoc chem, Calif Inst Technol, 62-63; res assoc physics, Stanford Univ, 63-64; instr chem, Harvard, 64-67; lectr, 67-70; assoc prof, 70-75, PROF CHEM, UNIV WASH, 75-, CHMN DEPT, 77- *Concurrent Pos:* Mem, exec comt & secy-treas, div physical chem, Am Chem Soc, 76-, founding comt & bd dirs, Coun Chem Res, 80- *Mem:* Am Chem Soc; Am Phys Soc; Sigma Xi. *Res:* Magnetic resonance in solids and molecular crystals; electron-nuclear double resonance; optical detection of magnetic resonance; structure and dynamics in ground and excited states of molecules. *Mailing Add:* Dept of Chem Univ of Wash Seattle WA 98195

KWITOWSKI, PAUL THOMAS, b Buffalo, NY, Nov 14, 39; m 63; c 4. INORGANIC CHEMISTRY. *Educ:* Canisius Col, BS, 61; Univ Wis, PhD(inorg chem), 67. *Prof Exp:* Res chemist, Airco-Speer Res Labs, NY, 66-69; assoc prof, 69-80, PROF CHEM, NIAGARA COMMUNITY COL, 80-, CHMN DEPT PHYS SCI, 71- *Mem:* Am Chem Soc. *Res:* Gas chromatography; catalysis of organic reactions; halocarbon and organometallic chemistry; spectroscopy; chemistry of refractive compounds; chemical vapor deposition. *Mailing Add:* 215 Walton Dr Snyder NY 14226

KWITTER, KAREN BETH, b Brooklyn, NY, Mar 20, 51; m 79. GASEOUS NEBULAE. *Educ:* Wellesley Col, BA, 72; Univ Calif, Los Angeles, 74, PhD(astron), 79. *Prof Exp:* ASST PROF ASTRON, WILLIAMS COL, 79- *Concurrent Pos:* Harlow Shapley vis lectr, Am Astron Soc, 81- *Mem:* Am Astron Soc; Sigma Xi; Int Astron Union. *Res:* Gaseous nebulae in order to determine their chemical compositions and physical conditions, including nebulae around Wolf-Rayet stars and planetary nebulae. *Mailing Add:* Dept Physics & Astron Williams Col Williamstown MA 01267

KWOCK, LESTER, b San Francisco, Calif, June 21, 42; m 68; c 1. BIOCHEMISTRY, RADIATION BIOCHEMISTRY. *Educ:* San Jose State Univ, BS, 65; San Diego State Univ, MS, 68; Univ Calif, Santa Barbara, PhD(chem), 73. *Prof Exp:* Instr, 73-76, ASST PROF RADIATION BIOL, SCH MED, TUFTS UNIV, 76- *Concurrent Pos:* NIH fel, Sch Med, Tufts Univ & Tufts-New England Med Ctr, 74-76; Nat Cancer Inst grant, Tufts-New England Med Ctr, 76- *Mem:* Am Chem Soc; Radiation Res Soc; Sigma Xi; AAAS. *Res:* Membrane transport; effects of ionizing radiation on biological systems; radioprotectors and radiosensitizers for normal and neoplastic cells. *Mailing Add:* Dept of Therapeut Radiol 171 Harrison Ave Boston MA 02111

KWOK, CLYDE CHI KAI, b Shanghai, China, May 26, 37; m 62; c 1. MECHANICAL ENGINEERING. *Educ:* McGill Univ, BEng, 61, MEng, 62, PhD, 67. *Prof Exp:* Res asst mech eng, McGill Univ, 61-64; prin scientist, Aviation Elec Ltd, 64-69; assoc prof mech eng, 69-77, PROF ENG, SIR GEORGE WILLIAMS CAMPUS, CONCORDIA UNIV, 77- *Mem:* Am Soc Mech Engrs; Am Inst Aeronaut & Astronaut. *Res:* Research and development of basic fluidic devices particularly the design and analysis of vortex type devices; fluid control elements and systems. *Mailing Add:* Fac of Eng Sir Geo Williams Camp 1455 de Maisonneuve Blvd W Montreal PQ H3G 1M8 Can

KWOK, HOI S, b Hong Kong, China, Mar 1, 51; m 78; c 1. LASER SPECTROSCOPY, LASER-MATTER INTERACTION. *Educ:* Northwestern Univ, BS, 73; Harvard Univ, MS, 75, PhD(physics), 78. *Prof Exp:* Teaching fel physics, Harvard Univ, 77-78; res fel chem, Lawrence Berkeley Lab, Univ Calif, 78-80; ASST PROF ENG, STATE UNIV NY BUFFALO, 80- *Concurrent Pos:* Prin investr grants, NSF, US Dept Energy, 81-; sci adv, Photochem Res Assocs, 82- *Mem:* Am Phys Soc; Inst Elec & Electronics Engrs; Am Chem Soc; Optical Soc Am. *Res:* Picosecond laser spectroscopy of molecules and semiconductors; application of lasers to chemical and material processing and the generation of picosecond laser pulses. *Mailing Add:* Dept Elec & Comput Eng Bonner Hall State Univ NY Buffalo NY 14260

KWOK, SUN, b Hong Kong, Sept 15, 49; Can citizen; m 73. ASTRONOMY. *Educ:* McMaster Univ, BSc, 70; Univ Minn, Minneapolis, MS, 72, PhD(physics), 74. *Prof Exp:* Fel astron, Dept of Physics, Univ BC, 74-76; asst prof, Dept of Physics, Univ Minn, Duluth, 76-77; res assoc, Ctr Res Exp Space Sci, York Univ, 77-78; RES ASSOC ASTRON, HERZBERG INST ASTROPHYSICS, 78- *Concurrent Pos:* Course dir Atkinson Col, York Univ, 77-78. *Mem:* Am Astron Soc; Can Astron Soc; Int Astron Union. *Res:* Mass loss from late type stars; planetary nebulae; radio astronomy; symbiotic stars and navae; stellar evolution; interstellar molecules. *Mailing Add:* Herzberg Inst of Astrophysics Nat Res Coun of Can Ottawa ON K1A 0R6 Can

KWOK, WO KONG, b Hong Kong, Jan 13, 36; m 63. ORGANIC CHEMISTRY, POLYMER CHEMISTRY. *Educ:* Nat Taiwan Univ, BS, 58; E Tenn State Univ, MA, 63; Ill Inst Technol, PhD(phys org chem), 67. *Prof Exp:* Chemist, S China Bleaching & Dyeing Factory, 58-61; res chemist, Exp Sta, 66-79, sr res chemist, Kinston, 79-81, SR RES CHEMIST, CHESTNUT RUN, E I DU PONT DE NEMOURS & CO, INC, 81- *Mem:* Am Chem Soc. *Res:* Elimination reaction kinetics and mechanism; polymer degradation mechanism; nonwoven technology. *Mailing Add:* 2 Yorkridge Trail Hockessin DE 19707

KWOLEK, STEPHANIE LOUISE, b New Kensington, Pa, July 31, 23. POLYMER CHEMISTRY. *Educ:* Carnegie Inst Technol, BS, 46. *Hon Degrees:* DSc, Worcester Polytechnic Inst, 81. *Prof Exp:* Chemist, 46-59, from res chemist to sr res chemist, 59-74, RES ASSOC, TEXTILE FIBERS DEPT, PIONEERING RES LAB, EXP STA, E I DU PONT DE NEMOURS & CO, INC, 74- *Honors & Awards:* Publ Award, Am Chem Soc, 59; Howard N Potts Medal, Franklin Inst, 76; Mat Achievement Citation, Am Chem Soc Metals Eng, 78. *Mem:* Am Chem Soc; Sigma Xi; Am Inst Chem. *Res:* Condensation polymers; high temperature polymers; low temperature interfacial and solution polymerizations; high tenacity and high modulus fibers and films; mesomorphic polymers. *Mailing Add:* E I du Pont de Nemours & Co Inc Bldg 302 Exp Sta Wilmington DE 19898

KWOLEK, WILLIAM F, b Gary, Ind, Apr 2, 29; m 54; c 7. ENTOMOLOGY, STATISTICS. *Educ:* Purdue Univ, BS, 51; Iowa State Univ, MS, 53, PhD(entom, statist), 58. *Prof Exp:* Statistician, Lederle Labs Div, Am Cyanamid Co, 58-62; BIOMETRICIAN, SCI & EDUC ADMIN, AGR RES, USDA, 62- *Mem:* Entom Soc Am; Biomet Soc. *Res:* Applied statistics in chemistry and biology. *Mailing Add:* Northern Utilization Div USDA 1815 N University Peoria IL 61604

KWON, TAI HYUNG, b Yechon, Korea, Sept 15, 32; m 69; c 1. SOLID STATE PHYSICS. *Educ:* Univ Ga, BS, 63, MS, 65, PhD(physics), 67. *Prof Exp:* Res fel, Ga Inst Technol, 67-69; asst prof, 69-75, ASSOC PROF PHYSICS, UNIV MONTEVALLO, 75- *Concurrent Pos:* Frederick Gardner Cottrell Res Corp grant, 71- *Mem:* Am Phys Soc. *Res:* Statistical physics; spin dynamics; neutron scattering; Heisenberg system; magnetism; lattice dynamics; anharmonicity. *Mailing Add:* Dept of Physics Univ of Montevallo Montevallo AL 35115

KWON-CHUNG, KYUNG JOO, b Seoul, Korea, Oct 5, 33; m 58; c 3. MEDICAL MYCOLOGY. *Educ:* Ewha Womans Univ, Korea, BS, 56, MS, 58; Univ Wis, MS, 63, PhD(bact), 65. *Prof Exp:* Instr microbiol, Ewha Womans Univ, 59-61; res asst bact, Univ Wis, 61-65; RES MICROBIOLOGIST, NIH, 68- *Concurrent Pos:* Fel, Univ Wis, 65; vis fel med mycol, NIH, 66-68. *Mem:* Mycol Soc Am; Am Soc Microbiol; Med Mycol Soc of the Americas; Int Soc Human & Animal Mycol. *Res:* Morphology and genetics of fungi. *Mailing Add:* Rm 11N104 Bldg 10 Nat Insts of Health Bethesda MD 20014

KWONG, JOSEPH N(ENG) S(HUN), b Chung Won, China, Oct 28, 16; nat US; m 42; c 3. CHEMICAL ENGINEERING. *Educ:* Stanford Univ, BA, 37; Univ Mich, MS, 39; Univ Minn, PhD(chem eng), 42. *Prof Exp:* Chem engr, Minn Mining & Mfg Co, 42-44; chemist, Shell Develop Co, Calif, 44-47, chemist & res engr, 47-51; sr chemist, 51-60, RES SPECIALIST, MINN MINING & MFG CO, 60- *Mem:* Am Chem Soc; Am Inst Chem Engrs. *Res:* Process and resin development, design and evaluation; thermodynamics; polyethylene terephthalate polymer and film technology. *Mailing Add:* 1399 N Hamline Ave St Paul MN 55108

KWONG, MAN KAM, b Canton, China, Feb 2, 47; m 70; c 2. MATHEMATICS. *Educ:* Univ Hong Kong, BSc, 68; Univ Chicago, MSc, 70, PhD(math), 73. *Prof Exp:* Lectr math, Hong Kong Baptist Col, 73-75, Hong Kong Polytech, 75-77; asst prof, 77-80, ASSOC PROF MATH, NORTHERN ILL UNIV, 80- *Mem:* Sigma Xi; Am Math Soc. *Res:* Ordinary differential equations; functional analysis; inequalities. *Mailing Add:* Dept of Math Sci Northern Ill Univ DeKalb IL 60115

KWUN, KYUNG WHAN, b Seoul, Korea, Mar 7, 29; m 57; c 3. MATHEMATICS. *Educ:* Seoul Nat Univ, BS, 52; Univ Mich, MS, 54, PhD(math), 58. *Prof Exp:* Instr math, Univ Mich, 57-58; res assoc, Tulane Univ, 58-59; vis assoc prof, Seoul Nat Univ, 59-60, from instr to asst prof, 60-62; vis lectr, Fla State Univ, 62-64, assoc prof, 64-65; assoc prof, 65-66, PROF MATH, MICH STATE UNIV, 66- *Concurrent Pos:* Vis lectr, Univ Wis, 61-62; mem, Inst Advan Study, 64-65. *Mem:* Am Math Soc. *Res:* Topology, particularly theory of manifolds. *Mailing Add:* Dept of Math Mich State Univ East Lansing MI 48824

KYAME, GEORGE JOHN, b New Orleans, La, Dec 19, 10. TEXTILE PHYSICS, TEXTILE ENGINEERING. *Educ:* Tulane Univ, BS, 33, MS, 36. *Prof Exp:* Lab instr physics, Tulane Univ, 34-37; chemist, Celotex Corp, 38-41; physicist, 41-42; physicist & cotton technologist, Southern Regional Res Ctr, Sci & Educ Admin-Agr Res, USDA, 42-63, res physicist, 63-80; RETIRED. *Mem:* Am Phys Soc. *Res:* Allison magnetocaloric method of chemical analysis; design, development and evaluation of cotton textile processing and testing machinery; fabric structural design. *Mailing Add:* Southern Regional Res Ctr PO Box 19687 New Orleans LA 70179

KYAME, JOSEPH JOHN, b New Orleans, La, Mar 12, 24. MATHEMATICAL PHYSICS. *Educ:* Tulane Univ, BS, 44, MS, 45; Mass Inst Technol, PhD(physics), 48. *Prof Exp:* Asst & instr, 44-45, asst prof, 48-58, ASSOC PROF PHYSICS, TULANE UNIV, 58- *Mem:* Am Phys Soc. *Res:* Electromagnetic theory; piezoelectricity; thermodynamics. *Mailing Add:* Dept of Physics Tulane Univ New Orleans LA 70118

KYANKA, GEORGE HARRY, b Syracuse, NY, July 17, 41; m 66; c 2. MECHANICAL ENGINEERING, WOOD SCIENCE. *Educ:* Syracuse Univ, BS, 62, MS, 66, PhD(mech eng), 75. *Prof Exp:* Res engr gas turbines, Caterpillar Tractor Co, 62-64; res asst aero eng, Syracuse Univ, 64-66; asst prof mech tech, Onondaga Col, 67-68; asst prof, 68-73, assoc prof, 73-80, PROF WOOD ENG, COL ENVIRON SCI & FORESTRY, STATE UNIV NY, 80- *Concurrent Pos:* NSF res fel, Syracuse Univ, 67; proj dir, NSF, 70-73, 76- & Weyerhaeuser Corp, 78-; adj prof, Onondaga Col Archit, 70-; consult engr, M G Barzelay Assocs, 70-; dir, Educ Opportunity Prog in Forestry, 73-76. *Mem:* Am Soc Mech Engrs; Am Soc Testing & Mat; Soc Exp Stress Anal; Forest Prod Res Soc; Am Acad Mech. *Res:* Mechanical properties of wood and wood products; testing and design of wood products; professional responsibility and products liability in product design; wood in architecture and art. *Mailing Add:* Dept of Wood Prod Eng State Univ of NY Syracuse NY 13031

KYBA, EVAN PETER, b Canora, Sask, June 27, 40; m 62; c 1. ORGANIC CHEMISTRY. *Educ:* Univ Sask, BA, 62; Univ Ala, PhD(org chem), 71. *Prof Exp:* Teacher chem, Regina Col Inst, Sask, 62-65; Nat Res Coun Can fel, Univ Calif, Los Angeles, 71-72; asst prof, 72-78, ASSOC PROF CHEM, UNIV TEX, AUSTIN, 78- *Mem:* Am Chem Soc; The Chem Soc. *Res:* Reactive intermediates; organophosphorus chemistry; stereochemistry; synthesis of unusual small heterocycles and multiheteromacrocycles. *Mailing Add:* Dept of Chem Univ of Tex Austin TX 78712

KYBETT, BRIAN DAVID, b Oxford, Eng, May 10, 38; m 63. PHYSICAL CHEMISTRY. *Educ:* Univ Wales, BSc, 60, PhD(chem), 63. *Prof Exp:* Res assoc chem, Rice Univ, 63-65; from asst prof to assoc prof, 65-81, PROF CHEM & ASSOC DIR, ENERGY RES UNIT, UNIV REGINA, 81- *Mem:* Chem Inst Can; Royal Soc Chem. *Res:* Lattice energies; thermochemistry; reactivity of coal. *Mailing Add:* Dept of Chem Univ of Regina Regina SK S4S 0A2 Can

KYCIA, THADDEUS F, b Montreal, Que, Aug 10, 33; m 57; c 1. HIGH ENERGY PHYSICS. *Educ:* McGill Univ, BS, 54, MS, 55; Univ Calif, Berkeley, PhD(high energy physics), 59. *Prof Exp:* Res asst high energy physics, 59-61, from asst physicist to assoc physicist, 61-66, physicist, 66-72, SR PHYSICIST, BROOKHAVEN NAT LAB, 72- *Mem:* Fel Am Phys Soc. *Res:* Development of Cerenkov detectors; measurement of total cross sections; search for resonances; measurement of magnetic moment of hyperons; study of rare K meson decay. *Mailing Add:* Dept of Physics Brookhaven Nat Lab Upton NY 11973

KYDD, DAVID MITCHELL, b Jersey City, NJ, May 17, 03; m 29; c 1. MEDICINE, METABOLISM. *Educ:* Princeton Univ, BS, 24; Harvard Univ, MD, 28. *Prof Exp:* Sterling res fel, Yale Univ, 29, Sax res fel, 29-30, from instr to asst prof med, Sch Med, 30-34; asst prof, Albany Med Col, 36-47; assoc prof, Sch Med, Yale Univ, 47-52; from assoc prof to prof, 52-69, EMER PROF MED, STATE UNIV NY DOWNSTATE MED CTR, 70- *Concurrent Pos:* Assoc, Bassett Hosp, NY, 34-47. *Mem:* Am Soc Clin Invest; Harvey Soc; Soc Exp Biol & Med; Am Inst Nutrit. *Res:* Electrolyte disturbances; thyroid diseases. *Mailing Add:* 28 Fair St Cooperstown NY 13326

KYDD, GEORGE HERMAN, b Va, Aug 20, 20; m 44; c 3. CARDIOPULMONARY PHYSIOLOGY. *Educ:* Wva State Col, BS, 42; Ohio State Univ, MS, 50, PhD(physiol), 55. *Prof Exp:* Asst respiratory & circulatory physiol, Ohio State Univ, 48-55, asst instr, 52-53; physiologist, 55-62, res physiologist, Life Sci Div, Crew Systs Dept, 62-70, tech specialist, Systs Analysis & Eng Dept, 73-77, phys sci adminr, Crew Systs Dept, 73-77, planning, assessment & resources directorate, 77-80, PHYSIOLOGIST, DEPT PLANNING ASSESSMENT RESOURSES, NAVAL AIR DEVELOP CTR, 80- *Concurrent Pos:* Biophysicist, Civil Aeronaut Med Res Lab, 53-55; assoc, Univ Pa, 55- *Honors & Awards:* Fred A Hitchcock Award, Aerospace Physiologist Sect, Aerospace Med Asn, 72. *Mem:* Aerospace Med Asn; Am Physiol Soc. *Res:* Respiratory and circulatory physiology; aviation and space physiology and medicine. *Mailing Add:* Naval Air Develop Life Sci Div Warminster PA 18974

KYDD, PAUL HARRIMAN, b New Haven, Conn, Nov 25, 30; m 56; c 2. PHYSICAL CHEMISTRY, CHEMICAL ENGINEERING. *Educ:* Princeton Univ, AB, 52; Harvard Univ, MA, 53, PhD(phys chem), 56. *Prof Exp:* Fel phys chem, Harvard Univ, 56-57; phys chemist, Gen Elec Res Lab, 57-66; lectr, Harvard Univ, 59-60; mgr chem processes, Gen Elec Res & Develop Ctr, 66-75; V PRES TECHNOL, HYDROCARBON RES, INC, 75- *Mem:* AAAS; Sigma Xi; Am Inst Chem Eng. *Res:* Coal liquifaction, gasification; petroleum production and refining; gas turbines, power generation; renewable resources, chemical intermediates. *Mailing Add:* PO Box 6047 Lawrenceville NJ 08648

KYDES, ANDY STEVE, b Spilia, Greece, Jan 21, 45; US citizen; m; c 2. NUMERICAL ANALYSIS, ENERGY SYSTEMS ANALYSIS. *Educ:* Harvard Univ, AB, 68; State Univ NY, Stony Brook, MS, 73, PhD(numerical anal), 74. *Prof Exp:* Instr math & physics, Milton Acad, Mass, 68-71; asst prof math, State Univ NY, Stony Brook, 74-76; ENERGY SYST ANALYST, DEPT ENERGY & ENVIRON, BROOKHAVEN NAT LAB, 76- *Mem:* Oper Res Soc Am; Inst Mgt Sci. *Res:* Energy systems analysis; multi-criteria analysis; optimization. *Mailing Add:* 6353 12th Pl Arlington VA 22205

KYDONIEFS, ANASTASIOS D, b Athens, Greece, Mar 6, 28; m 53; c 2. APPLIED MATHEMATICS, CONTINUUM MECHANICS. *Educ:* Univ Nottingham, MSc, 65, PhD(theoret mech), 67. *Prof Exp:* Res fel theoret mech, Univ Nottingham, 67-69, sr res asst, 67-68; asst prof math, 68-73, ASSOC PROF MATH, LEHIGH UNIV, 73- *Res:* Finite elasticity and its applications to biomechanics. *Mailing Add:* Ctr for the Appln of Math Lehigh Univ Bethlehem PA 18015

KYHL, ROBERT LOUIS, b Omaha, Nebr, July 27, 17; m 43; c 1. ELECTRICAL ENGINEERING. *Educ:* Univ Chicago, SB, 37; Mass Inst Technol, PhD(physics), 47. *Prof Exp:* Asst physics, Univ Chicago, 40-41; res assoc radiation lab, Mass Inst Technol, 41-45, insulation lab, 45-47 & electronics res lab, 47-48; res assoc, Hansen Lab, Stanford Univ, 48-54 & res lab, Gen Elec Co, 54-56; assoc prof, 56-67, PROF ELEC ENG, MASS INST TECHNOL, 67- *Honors & Awards:* Baker Award, Inst Radio Eng, 58. *Mem:* Am Phys Soc; Inst Elec & Electronics Engrs. *Res:* Microwave spectroscopy and power tubes; electron accelerators; solid state masers. *Mailing Add:* Dept of Elec Eng Mass Inst of Technol Cambridge MA 02139

KYHOS, DONALD WILLIAM, b Los Angeles, Calif, Apr 10, 29; m 61; c 2. PLANT TAXONOMY, PLANT CYTOGENETICS. *Educ:* Whittier Col, AB, 51, MS, 56; Univ Calif, Los Angeles, PhD(bot), 64. *Prof Exp:* NIH fel biol, Stanford Univ, 64-65; from asst prof to assoc prof, 65-74, PROF BOT, UNIV CALIF, DAVIS, 74- *Concurrent Pos:* Australian Res Grant Comt fel, 72. *Mem:* Am Soc Plant Taxon; Bot Soc Am; Soc Study Evolution. *Res:* Plant systematics and evolutionary cytogenetics. *Mailing Add:* Dept of Bot Univ of Calif Davis CA 95616

KYKER, GARY STEPHEN, b Athens, Tenn, Jan 6, 42; m 73; c 1. INORGANIC CHEMISTRY, POLYMER CHEMISTRY. *Educ:* Tenn Wesleyan Col, BS, 64; Ohio State Univ, MS, 67, PhD(inorg chem), 69. *Prof Exp:* Res scientist, Cent Res Labs, Firestone Tire & Rubber Co, 69-74, sr res scientist, 74-79; mgr mat res, C R Indust, 79-82; SR POLYMER RES ASSOC, SCHLUMBERGER WELL SERV-ENG, 82- *Mem:* Am Chem Soc; Soc Automotive Engrs. *Res:* Synthesis and characterization of inorganic and organic polymers; preparation of catalyst for polymerization of inorganic and organic monomers; development and mechanical testing of polymeric composites; development of high-performance elastomer compounds. *Mailing Add:* Schlumberger Well-Serv-Eng 500 Gulf Freeway PO Box 2175 Houston TX 77001

KYLE, BENJAMIN G(AYLE), b Atlanta, Ga, Dec 4, 27; m 52; c 4. CHEMICAL ENGINEERING. *Educ:* Ga Inst Technol, BChE, 50; Univ Fla, MSE, 55, PhD(chem eng), 58. *Prof Exp:* From asst prof to assoc prof, 58-64, PROF CHEM ENG, KANS STATE UNIV, 64- *Mem:* Am Chem Soc; Am Inst Chem Engrs. *Res:* Thermodynamics; mass transfer. *Mailing Add:* Dept of Chem Eng Kans State Univ Manhattan KS 66506

KYLE, HERBERT LEE, b Monmouth, Ill, June 28, 30; m 60; c 1. ATMOSPHERIC PHYSICS. *Educ:* Univ Ariz, BS, 54; Univ NC, MS, 59, PhD(atomic physics), 64. *Prof Exp:* SPACE PHYSICIST, GODDARD SPACE FLIGHT CTR, NASA, 59- *Mem:* Am Phys Soc. *Res:* Atomic physics; remote sensing of the earth's atmosphere for cloud properties and cloud cover; atmospheric temperature and humidity profiles; wind vectors; minor constituents; radiative transfer theory and numerical analysis. *Mailing Add:* Code 931 Goddard Space Flight Ctr Greenbelt MD 20771

KYLE, JACK HIRAM, horticulture, see previous edition

KYLE, MARTIN LAWRENCE, b Akron, Ohio, Jan 2, 35; m 57; c 3. CHEMICAL ENGINEERING. *Educ:* Univ Notre Dame, BS, 56; Purdue Univ, MS, 61; Univ Chicago, MBA, 71. *Prof Exp:* Chem engr, E I du Pont de Nemours & Co, 56-57; chem engr, 60-78, ASST LAB DIR, ARGONNE NAT LAB, 78- *Mem:* Am Chem Soc. *Res:* Battery development; solar energy; coal technology. *Mailing Add:* Argonne Nat Lab 9700 S Cass Ave Argonne IL 60439

KYLE, NANSE RECTOR, chemical physics, see previous edition

KYLE, THOMAS GAIL, b Crawford, Okla, Sept 12, 36; m 58; c 2. CLOUD PHYSICS, MOLECULAR PHYSICS. *Educ:* Univ Okla, BS, 60, MS, 62; Univ Denver, PhD(physics), 65. *Prof Exp:* Res officer, Commonwealth Sci & Indust Res Orgn, Australia, 65-66; res physicist, Univ Denver, 66-71; scientist, Nat Ctr Atmospheric Res, 71-76; SCIENTIST, LOS ALAMOS NAT LAB, 76- *Concurrent Pos:* Vis prof, Clemson Univ, 81-82. *Mem:* Optical Soc Am; Sigma Xi. *Res:* High pressure physics; theoretical and experimental studies of infrared spectra; laser studies; studies of the composition and radiative properties of the atmosphere; weather modification. *Mailing Add:* 426 Connie Los Alamos NM 87544

KYLE, WENDELL H(ENRY), b Louisville, Ohio, June 8, 20; m 45; c 5. GENETICS. *Educ:* Iowa State Univ, BS, 43; Univ Wis, PhD(genetics), 49. *Prof Exp:* Asst genetics, Univ Wis, 45-48, proj assoc, 48-49; animal geneticist, US Sheep Exp Sta, Idaho, 49-57; asst nat coord, Regional Poultry Breeding Proj, Purdue Univ, 57-58, assoc prof univ & leader, Pioneering Res Lab Pop Genetics, USDA, 58-66; scientist adminstr, Div Res Grants, NIH, 66-78; RETIRED. *Mem:* AAAS; Am Inst Biol Sci; Biomet Soc; Genetics Soc Am. *Res:* Population genetics of Tribolium, mice, poultry and livestock; biometry. *Mailing Add:* Div of Res Grants NIH Room 222 Westwood Bldg Bethesda MD 20895

KYLSTRA, JOHANNES ARNOLD, b Manado, Neth EIndies, Nov 30, 25; m 56; c 2. MEDICINE, PHYSIOLOGY. *Educ:* Univ Leiden, MD, 58. *Prof Exp:* PROF PULMONARY & ALLERGY, DUKE UNIV, 72- *Honors & Awards:* Lockheed Award, Marine Technol Soc, 70. *Mem:* AAAS; Am Physiol Soc; Undersea Med Soc (pres, 73-74). *Res:* Liquid breathing and lung lavage. *Mailing Add:* Dept of Med Duke Univ Med Ctr Durham NC 27710

KYRALA, ALI, b New York, NY, Dec 14, 21; m 66; c 3. MATHEMATICAL PHYSICS, ASTROGEOPHYSICS. *Educ:* Mass Inst Technol, BSc, 47; Stanford Univ, MSc, 48; Harvard Univ, SM, 57; Vienna Tech Univ, DSc(physics), 60. *Prof Exp:* Instr math, Univ Santa Clara, 47-48 & Univ Mass, 51-53; mathematician & physicist, Lessells & Assocs, Mass, 53-58; math physicist, Goodyear Aerospace Corp, 58-60; staff scientist, semiconductor div, Motorola, Inc, 60-62; Fulbright prof & award math & physics, Univ Alexandria, 63-64; PROF PHYSICS, ARIZ STATE UNIV, 64- *Concurrent Pos:* Vis prof math, Am Univ Beirut & Univ Libanaise, 68-70 & Univ Petrol & Minerals, Dhahran/Saudi Arabia, 75-77. *Mem:* Am Phys Soc; Europ Phys Soc; Brit Interplanetary Soc; Am Astron Asn. *Res:* Theory of metal fatigue; continuum mechanics; partial differential and integral equations; microwaves; function theory; theoretical solid state physics; electro biophysics; sub-quantum theory; astrogeophysics; relativity; statistical physics; plasma physics; planetary sciences. *Mailing Add:* Dept of Physics Ariz State Univ Tempe AZ 85281

KYRALA, GEORGE AMINE, b Bhamdoun, Lebanon, Apr 20, 46; US citizen; m 73; c 1. ATOMIC PHYSICS, LASER FUSION & INTERACTIONS. *Educ:* Am Univ Beirut, BS, 67; Yale Univ, MPh, 69, PhD(physics), 74. *Prof Exp:* Fel physics, Joint Inst Lab Astrophysics, Univ Colo, 74-76; res assoc optics & physics, Optical Sci Ctr & Dept Physics, Univ Ariz, 76-78, res fel lasers & spectros, Dept Physics, 78-79; MEM STAFF, PHYSICS DIV, LOS ALAMOS NAT LAB, 79- *Concurrent Pos:* Lectr, Dept Physics, Univ Colo, 75; vis fac & consult, Al-Hazen Res Ctr, Baghdad, 75; Rockefeller fel, Am Univ Beirut, Lebanon, 66-67; Gibbs fel, Yale Univ, 67-68. *Mem:* Am Inst Phys; Arab Phys Soc. *Res:* Charge transfer in atomic collision; electron scattering from excited atoms; laser construction and use in ultra high resolution spectroscopy; laser fusion experiments and optics. *Mailing Add:* MS 545 Los Alamos Nat Lab Los Alamos NM 87545

KYRIAKOPOULOS, NICHOLAS, b Atalanti, Greece, Nov 14, 37; m 67; c 1. ELECTRICAL ENGINEERING, COMPUTER SCIENCE. *Educ:* George Washington Univ, BEE, 60, MS, 63, DSc, 68. *Prof Exp:* Electronic engr, Harry Diamond Labs, Dept Army, 60-62; aerospace engr, Goddard Space Flight Ctr, NASA, 62-64; instr elec eng, 64-66, asst prof, 66-70, ASSOC PROF ELEC ENG & COMPUT SCI, GEORGE WASHINGTON UNIV, 70- *Concurrent Pos:* NASA-Am Soc Eng Educ fac fel, Goddard Space Flight Ctr, NASA, 67-68; consult, Nat Biomed Res Found, 66-67, Howard Res Corp, 67 & RCA Serv Co, 67- *Mem:* Inst Elec & Electronics Engrs; Asn Comput Mach. *Res:* Computer-aided network analysis and design; system simulation; performance evaluation of space communication systems; radio frequency interference; network theory; logical design. *Mailing Add:* Dept of Elec Eng & Comput Sci George Washington Univ Washington DC 20052

KYRIAZIS, AIKATERINI A, b Thessaloniki, Greece; m 64; c 1. PATHOLOGY. *Educ:* Aristotelian Univ, Greece, MD, 62. *Prof Exp:* Resident path, Thomas Jefferson Univ, Philadelphia, 66-68; resident path, Univ Chicago, 68-70, John A Hartford fel, Dept Obstet & Gynec, 70-71, instr, 71-72; assoc dir path, Dept Path, Metaxas Mem Cancer Inst, Greece, 72-73; INSTR PATH, DEPT OBSTET & GYNEC, UNIV CHICAGO, 75- *Mem:* Royal Soc Health London; Reticuloendothelial Soc; Int Acad Path; NY Acad Sci. *Res:* Development of reticuloendothelial system in the human; factors influencing development of malignancies in female reproductive system, and early means of detection; embryology and tumor development. *Mailing Add:* 508 Williamsburg Rd Cincinnati OH 45215

KYRIAZIS, ANDREAS P, b Aigion, Greece, Jan 19, 32; m 65; c 1. PATHOLOGY, IMMUNOLOGY. *Educ:* Nat Univ Athens, MD, 57; Univ Thessaloniki, DrSci(path), 62; Jefferson Med Col, PhD(path), 68. *Prof Exp:* Resident path, Univ Thessaloniki, 60-64; attend pathologist, Piraeus Gen Hosp, Greece, 64; resident path, Jersey City Med Ctr, 65; res assoc, 68-70, asst prof path, Univ Chicago, 70-78; ASSOC PROF PATH, UNIV CINCINNATI, 78- *Concurrent Pos:* Vis scientist, Argonne Cancer Res Hosp, Univ Chicago, 68- *Mem:* Reticuloendothelial Soc; Am Soc Exp Pathologists; NY Acad Sci; Int Acad Path. *Res:* Immunopathology; immunological studies of malignant diseases; experimental tumor chemotherapy. *Mailing Add:* 508 Williamsburg Rd Cincinnati OH 45215

KYSER, DAVID SHELDON, b Houston, Tex, Aug 29, 36; m 59; c 3. EXPERIMENTAL SOLID STATE PHYSICS. *Educ:* Univ Tex, BS, 58 & 60, MA, 63, PhD(physics), 65. *Prof Exp:* Res assoc chem phys, Inst Study Metals, Univ Chicago, 64-66; PHYSICIST, NAVAL WEAPONS CTR, 66- *Mem:* Am Phys Soc. *Res:* Modulation of optical properties of semiconductors. *Mailing Add:* Michelson Lab Code 3813 Naval Weapons Ctr China Lake CA 93555

KYSER, FORREST DEWAYNE, b Shepherd, Mich, Feb 20, 13; m 38; c 2. PHYSICAL GEOGRAPHY, CULTURAL GEOGRAPHY. *Educ:* Cent Mich Univ, AB, 35; Univ Mich, AM, 39; Mich State Univ, PhD(geog), 68. *Prof Exp:* Asst instr geog, Mich State Univ, 64-65; from instr to assoc prof, 65-77, prof geog, 77-80, EMER PROF GEOG, CENT MICH UNIV, 80- *Mem:* Am Geog Soc; Asn Am Geog; Nat Coun Geog Educ. *Res:* Development of rural landscape under impact of twentieth century cultural changes. *Mailing Add:* Dept of Geog Cent Mich Univ Mt Pleasant MI 48858

KYSER, FRANKLIN A, b Chicago, Ill, Aug 8, 13; m 30; c 1. INTERNAL MEDICINE. *Educ:* Northwestern Univ, BS, 35, MD, 39; Univ Minn, MS, 41. *Prof Exp:* Asst prof, 50-59, ASSOC PROF INTERNAL MED, MED SCH, NORTHWESTERN UNIV, EVANSTON, 59- *Mem:* AMA; Am Heart Asn; Am Col Physicians; fel Am Col Cardiol. *Mailing Add:* 2500 Ridge Ave Evanston IL 60201

KYTE, JACK ERNST, b Pasadena, Calif, May 21, 47. BIOCHEMISTRY. *Educ:* Carleton Col, BA, 67; Harvard Univ, PhD(biochem), 72. *Prof Exp:* Damon Runyon Fund fel biochem, 72-74, ASST PROF BIOCHEM, UNIV CALIF, SAN DIEGO, 74- *Res:* Molecular structure of proteins which catalyze the transport of matter across biological membranes. *Mailing Add:* Dept of Chem D-006 Univ of Calif at San Diego La Jolla CA 92093

KYUNG, JAI HO, b Seoul, Korea, Dec 26, 47; m 73. ORGANIC CHEMISTRY. *Educ:* Seoul Nat Univ, BS, 69; Brown Univ, PhD(org chem), 75. *Prof Exp:* Res chemist, 74-76, SR RES CHEMIST, ASHLAND CHEM CO, 76- *Mem:* Am Chem Soc. *Res:* Synthesis of organic ligands for recovery of metals for mining industry and commercial development of solvent extraction of hydrometallurgy; homogeneous and heterogeneous catalysis of petrochemicals and industrial intermediate chemicals. *Mailing Add:* Ashland Chem Co PO Box 2219 Columbus OH 43216

L

LA, SUNG YUN, b Seoul, Korea, Sept 24, 36. PHYSICS. *Educ:* WVa Wesleyan Col, BS, 59; Univ Conn, MS, 62, PhD(physics), 64. *Prof Exp:* Res assoc appl physics, mat res lab, Pa State Univ, 65-68; ASSOC PROF PHYSICS & EARTH SCI, WILLIAM PATERSON COL NJ, 68- *Mem:* Am Phys Soc. *Res:* Theoretical studies of ionic crystals; defects investigated by electron spin resonance technique, cohesive energy and compressibility. *Mailing Add:* Dept of Physics William Paterson Col of NJ Wayne NJ 07470

LAAKSO, JOHN WILLIAM, b Minn, Jan 28, 15; m 41; c 4. BIOCHEMISTRY. *Educ:* Winona State Col, BS, 38; Mont State Col, MS, 49; Univ Minn, PhD(biochem), 56. *Prof Exp:* Teacher high schs, Minn, 38-42; instr math, Mont State Col, 46-47; from instr to assoc prof chem, St Cloud State Univ, 48-63, chmn dept, 66-73, prof chem, 63-80; RETIRED. *Mem:* Am Chem Soc. *Res:* Synthesis and biological assay of orotic acid analogs. *Mailing Add:* Dept of Chem St Cloud State Univ St Cloud MN 56301

LAALE, HANS W, b Copenhagen, Denmark, Apr 20, 35; Can citizen. EXPERIMENTAL EMBRYOLOGY, DEVELOPMENTAL BIOLOGY. *Educ:* Bob Jones Univ, BSc, 59; Univ Western Ont, MSc, 61; Univ Toronto, PhD(zool), 66. *Prof Exp:* Asst lectr biol, Hong Kong Baptist Col, 61-63; lectr, Chinese Univ Hong Kong, 66-67; asst prof, 67-74, ASSOC PROF ZOOL, UNIV MAN, 74- *Concurrent Pos:* Vis prof, Univ BC, 80- *Mem:* Can Soc Zoologists; NY Acad Sci; Sigma Xi. *Res:* Teleost embryology and teratology; In vitro fish embryo culture. *Mailing Add:* Dept Zool Univ Man Winnipeg MB R3T 2N2 Can

LAANE, JAAN, b Paide, Estonia, June 20, 42; US citizen; m 66; c 2. PHYSICAL CHEMISTRY, SPECTROSCOPY. *Educ:* Univ Ill, BS, Urbana, 64; Mass Inst Technol, PhD(chem), 67. *Prof Exp:* Asst prof chem, Tufts Univ, 67-68; asst prof, 68-72, assoc prof, 72-76, PROF CHEM, TEX A&M UNIV, 76-, CHMN, DIV PHYS & NUCLEAR CHEM, 77- *Concurrent Pos:* Vis prof, Univ Bayreuth, WGer, 79-80; Alexander von Humboldt award, 79. *Mem:* Am Chem Soc; Am Phys Soc; Soc Appl Spectros; Coblentz Soc. *Res:* Far-infrared spectroscopy of small ring compounds; potential energy functions; organometallic syntheses; infrared and raman spectroscopy; nitrogen-oxygen chemistry. *Mailing Add:* Dept of Chem Tex A&M Univ College Station TX 77843

LAASPERE, THOMAS, b T@:nnasilma, Estonia, Mar 17, 27; US citizen; m 55; c 3. RADIOPHYSICS. *Educ:* Univ Vt, BS, 56; Cornell Univ, MS, 58, PhD(commun eng), 60. *Prof Exp:* Res assoc radiophys, Cornell Univ, 60-61; asst prof, 61-64, assoc prof, 64-70, PROF ENG, THAYER SCH ENG, DARTMOUTH COL, 70- *Concurrent Pos:* Mem comn IV, US Nat Comt, Int Sci Radio Union, 64- *Mem:* Inst Elec & Electronics Engrs. *Res:* Scattering of radio waves in the troposphere and ionosphere; whistlers and other audio-frequency electromagnetic waves; space research; electric rates, load management. *Mailing Add:* Thayer Sch Dartmouth Col Hanover NH 03755

LAATSCH, RICHARD G, b Fairmont, Minn, July 14, 31; m 66; c 2. MATHEMATICAL ANALYSIS. *Educ:* Cent Mo State Col, BS, 53; Univ Mo, MA, 57; Okla State Univ, PhD(math), 62. *Prof Exp:* Instr math, Univ Tulsa, 57-60; asst prof, Okla State Univ, 62; from asst prof to assoc prof, 62-70, PROF MATH & ASST CHMN DEPT, MIAMI UNIV, 70- *Mem:* Am Math Soc; Math Asn Am. *Res:* Subadditive functions; topological vector spaces and cones of functions. *Mailing Add:* Dept of Math Miami Univ Oxford OH 45056

LABAHN, RAYMOND WILLIS, ionospheric physics, see previous edition

LABANA, SANTOKH SINGH, b Maritanda, India, Nov 15, 36; m 64. ORGANIC CHEMISTRY, POLYMER SCIENCE. *Educ:* Univ Panjab, India, BSc, 57, MSc, 59; Cornell Univ, PhD(org chem), 63. *Prof Exp:* Lectr chem, G H G Col, Sadhar, India, 58-60; res chemist, Univ Calif, Berkeley, 63-64; scientist, Xerox Corp, 64-67; prin scientist assoc, 67-70, staff scientist, 70-72, MGR POLYMER SCI DEPT, FORD MOTOR CO, 72- *Concurrent Pos:* Chmn coatings & films, Gordon Res Conf, 80 & Org Coatings & Plastics Chem Div, Am Chem Soc, 81; mem adv bd, J Coatings & Technol. *Mem:* Am Chem Soc. *Res:* Synthetic organic chemistry; polymer syntheses; mechanism of organic reactions; physical and thermal properties of polymers with special reference to network polymers; radiation induced polymerizations, coating and composites. *Mailing Add:* Eng & Res Staff Ford Motor Co PO Box 2053 Dearborn MI 48121

LABANAUSKAS, CHARLES KAZYS, b Upyna, Lithuania, Jan 3, 28; nat US. PLANT PHYSIOLOGY. *Educ:* Hohenheim Agr Univ, dipl, 47; Univ Ill, MS, 53, PhD, 55. *Prof Exp:* Asst horticulturist, 55-68, HORTICULTURIST, CITRUS RES CTR, UNIV CALIF, RIVERSIDE, 68-, PROF HORT SCI, COL NATURAL & AGR SCI, 68- *Concurrent Pos:* Lectr, Univ Calif, Riverside, 65-68. *Mem:* Am Soc Hort Sci. *Res:* Mineral metabolism in plants. *Mailing Add:* Dept of Botany & Plant Sci Univ of Calif Riverside CA 92521

LABANICK, GEORGE MICHAEL, b Passaic, NJ, Sept 27, 50; m 79; c 1. ZOOLOGY, HERPETOLOGY. *Educ:* Col William & Mary, BS, 72; Ind State Univ, MA, 74; Southern Ill Univ, PhD(zool), 78. *Prof Exp:* Asst prof biol, Emory & Henry Col, 78-79; ASST PROF BIOL, UNIV SC, SPARTANBURG, 79- *Mem:* Sigma Xi; Am Soc Ichthyologists & Herpetologists; Herpetologists' League; Soc Study Amphibians & Reptiles; Soc Study Evolution. *Res:* Mimicry and other defense mechanisms; salamander ecology and systematics. *Mailing Add:* Div Sci & Math Univ SC Spartanburg SC 29303

LABAR, MARTIN, b Radisson, Wis, May 15, 38. POPULATION BIOLOGY, BIOETHICS. *Educ:* Wis State Univ, Superior, BA, 58; Univ Wis, MS, 63, PhD(genetics, zool), 65. *Prof Exp:* Assoc prof, 64-66, PROF SCI, CENT WESLEYAN COL, 66-, CHMN DIV SCI, 64- *Mem:* Am Sci Affiliation; Ecol Soc Am; Soc Study Evolution. *Res:* Use of computer simulation in teaching population biology; bioethics. *Mailing Add:* Div of Sci Cent Wesleyan Col Central SC 29630

LA BAR, RICHARD GARY, b Plainfield, NJ, Oct 23, 39; m 62; c 3. CERAMIC SCIENCE. *Educ:* Rutgers Univ, BS, 65, PhD(ceramic sci), 69. *Prof Exp:* Supv engr res & develop, Carborundum Co, 69-73; sr engr res & develop, 73-74, group leader, 74-75, sect head, 75-78, MGR RES & DEVELOP, ALUMINUM CO AM, 78- *Mem:* Am Ceramic Soc; Brit Ceramic Soc; Sigma Xi. *Res:* Structural ceramics; fused-cast and bonded refractories; mechanisms of failure and performance criteria for refractories in the aluminum, glass and ceramic industries. *Mailing Add:* Alcoa Labs Alcoa Center PA 15069

LABARGE, ROBERT GORDON, b Buffalo, NY, July 11, 40. APPLIED CHEMISTRY, INDUSTRIAL CHEMISTRY. *Educ:* Univ Rochester, BS, 62; Carnegie-Mellon Univ, PhD(chem), 66. *Prof Exp:* Res chemist, Consumer Prod Dept, 66-73, dir acad educ, 73-75, RES SPECIALIST, DESIGNED PROD DEPT, DOW CHEM CO, 75- *Concurrent Pos:* Adj prof chem, Cent Mich Univ, 74. *Mem:* Am Chem Soc. *Res:* New product exploration and development. *Mailing Add:* Designed Prod Dept Dow Chem Co Midland MI 48640

LABARRE, ANTHONY E, JR, b New Orleans, La, July 18, 22; m 43, 77; c 2. MATHEMATICS. *Educ:* Tulane Univ, BE, 43, MS, 47; Univ Okla, PhD(math), 57. *Prof Exp:* Instr math, Tulane Univ, 46-48; asst prof, Univ Idaho, 48-50; instr, Univ Okla, 50-54 & Univ Wyo, 54-56; from asst prof to assoc prof, Univ Idaho, 56-61; chmn dept, 61-66, PROF MATH, CALIF STATE UNIV, FRESNO, 61- *Concurrent Pos:* Math Asn Am. *Res:* Functional analysis, differential geometry. *Mailing Add:* Dept of Math Calif State Univ Fresno CA 93740

LABARTHE, DARWIN RAYMOND, b Berkeley, Calif, Aug 5, 39. EPIDEMIOLOGY. *Educ:* Princeton Univ, AB, 61; Columbia Univ, MD, 65; Univ Calif, Berkeley, MPH, 67, PhD(epidemiol), 75. *Prof Exp:* Epidemiologist, Com Corps, Heart Dis & Stroke Control Prog, San Francisco, 67-69; dep chief & sr epidemiologist, Epidemiol Field & Training Sta, USPHS Heart Dis & Stroke Control Prog, San Francisco, 69-70; from assoc res epidemiologist to assoc prof epidemiol, Sch Pub Health, Univ Tex Health Sci Ctr, Houston, 70-73; consult epidemiol, dept med statist & epidemiol, Mayo Clin & Mayo Found, 74-77; PROF EPIDEMIOL, SCH PUB HEALTH, UNIV TEX, 77- *Concurrent Pos:* Dep dir, Coord Ctr, Hypertension Detection & Followup Prog, Nat Heart & Lung Inst, 71-73; consult, Task Force Automated Blood Pressure Devices, Nat Heart & Lung Inst, 73-74; consult, coord ctr, Hypertension Detection & Followup Prog, Nat Heart & Lung Inst, 74-; co-investr & co-dir, Study Incidence & Natural Hist Genital Tract Anomalies & Cancer in Offspring exposed in Utero to synthetic Estrogens, Nat Cancer Inst, 74-; chmn & dir, US Seminar in Cardiovasc Epidemiol, Int Heart Asn, 75-; dir design & anal, Baylor Col Med, 77-; dep dir, Beta-Blocker Heart Attack Trial Coord Ctr. *Mem:* Fel Am Heart Asn; fel Am Col Prev Med; Soc Epidemiol Res (pres, 72-73); Am Pub Health Asn; Int Soc Cardiol. *Res:* Epidemiology and prevention, especially of cardiovascular and other chronic conditions; drugs; intra-individual variability of blood pressure and other personal characteristics. *Mailing Add:* Univ Tex Health Sci Ctr Sch Pub Health PO Box 20186 Houston TX 77025

LABATE, SAMUEL, b Easton, Pa, Dec 19, 18; m 49; c 2. ACOUSTICS. *Educ:* Lafayette Col, AB, 40; Mass Inst Technol, MS, 48. *Prof Exp:* Asst instr math, Univ Pa, 40-41; engr, E I du Pont de Nemours & Co, 41-42; consult engr, Bolt & Beranek, 48-49, consult engr, 49-53, exec vpres, 53-69, pres, 69-76, DIR, BOLT BERANEK & NEWMAN, INC, 53-, CHMN BD, 76- *Mem:* Fel Acoust Soc Am; Acad Appl Sci. *Res:* Engineering; applied architectural and physical acoustics. *Mailing Add:* Bolt Beranek & Newman Inc 50 Moulton St Cambridge MA 02138

LABAVITCH, JOHN MARCUS, b Covington, Ky, Oct 15, 43. PLANT PHYSIOLOGY, BIOCHEMISTRY. *Educ:* Wabash Col, AB, 65; Stanford Univ, PhD(plant physiol), 73. *Prof Exp:* Instr biol, Wabash Col, 65-67; NIH fel biochem, Univ Colo, 72-76; asst pomologist, 76-80, ASSOC POMOLOGIST, UNIV CALIF, DAVIS, 80-, LECTR POMOL, 76- *Mem:* Am Soc Plant Physiologists; AAAS. *Res:* Cell wall metabolism of fruit. *Mailing Add:* Dept of Pomol Univ of Calif Davis CA 95616

L'ABBE, MAURICE, b Ottawa, Ont, May 20, 20; m 51; c 4. MATHEMATICS. *Educ:* Univ Montreal, BA, 42, LSc, 45; Princeton Univ, MA, 47, PhD(math), 51. *Prof Exp:* From asst prof to assoc prof math, 48-56, chmn dept math, 57-68, vdean fac sci, 64-68, PROF MATH, UNIV MONTREAL, 56-, VRECTOR RES, 68- *Concurrent Pos:* Can Govt res fel, Univ Paris, 52-53. *Mem:* Am Math Soc; Math Asn Am; Asn Symbolic Logic; Can Math Cong (pres, 67-69); Math Soc France. *Res:* Mathematical logic. *Mailing Add:* 5626 Canterbury Montreal PQ H3T 1S9 Can

LABBE, ROBERT FERDINAND, b Portland, Ore, Nov 12, 22; m 55; c 3. BIOCHEMISTRY, NUTRITION. *Educ:* Univ Portland, BS, 47; Ore State Col, MS, 49, PhD(biochem), 51. *Prof Exp:* AEC fel med sci, Col Physicians & Surgeons, Columbia Univ, 51-53; res instr, Med Sch, Univ Ore, 53-55, res asst prof, 55-57; res asst prof pediat & lectr biochem, 57-60, res assoc prof pediat, 60-68, prof pediat, 68-74, PROF LAB MED, MED SCH, UNIV WASH, 74-, HEAD, CLIN CHEM DIV, 80- *Concurrent Pos:* Vis asst prof, Inst Enzyme Res, Univ Wis, 56-57; vis researcher, Commonwealth Sci & Indust Res Orgn, Australia, 65; NIH spec fel, 65 & career develop award, 66-70. *Honors & Awards:* Ames Award, Am Asn Clin Chemists. *Mem:* Fel AAAS; Am Chem Soc; Am Soc Biol Chemists; Acad Clin Lab Physicians & Scientists; Am Asn Clin Chemists. *Res:* Heme biosynthesis; iron metabolism; related metabolic diseases and nutrition. *Mailing Add:* Dept of Lab Med Univ of Wash Seattle WA 98195

LABBE, RONALD GILBERT, b Berlin, NH, July 16, 46; m 78. MICROBIOLOGY. *Educ:* Univ NH, BA, 68; Univ Wis, MS, 70, PhD(bact), 76. *Prof Exp:* Res assoc microbiol, Food Res Inst, Univ Wis, 76; ASST PROF MICROBIOL, DEPT FOOD SCI & NUTRIT, UNIV MASS, 76- *Mem:* Sigma Xi; Int Asn Milk, Food & Environ Sanitarians; Am Soc Microbiol; Inst Food Technologists. *Res:* Clostridium perfringens food poisoning; recovery of bacterial spores from thermal injury. *Mailing Add:* Dept Food Sci & Nutrit Univ Mass Amherst MA 01003

LABBEE, MARCEL D, b Holyoke, Mass, Sept 6, 22; m; c 6. AGRICULTURAL CHEMISTRY, FOOD TECHNOLOGY. *Educ:* Univ Mass, BS, 49, MS, 50, PhD(food technol), 52. *Prof Exp:* Mem staff qual control, Old Deerfield Pickling Co, 51-52; MEM STAFF TECH SALES, ROHM AND HAAS CO, 52- *Res:* Peroxidase and its relation to off-flavors in food; enzymes; freezer jars; pickles. *Mailing Add:* Rohm & Haas Co 1389 Paddock Way Cherry Hill NJ 08034

LABBY, DANIEL HARVEY, b Portland, Ore, Sept 1, 14; m 40; c 3. MEDICINE, PSYCHIATRY. *Educ:* Reed Col, BA, 35; Univ Ore, MD, 39. *Prof Exp:* Intern, Johns Hopkins Hosp, 39-40; asst resident, New York Hosp, 43-44, chief resident & instr med, 44-45; asst, Rockefeller Inst & asst physician, Hosp, 45-47; asst clin prof med, 47-51, from assoc prof to prof, 51-71, chief div diabetes & metab dis, 51-70, PROF MED & PSYCHIAT, MED SCH, UNIV ORE, 71- *Concurrent Pos:* Fel med, Med Col, Cornell Univ & New York Hosp, 40-41; Brower traveling fel, 53; Commonwealth traveling fel, Univ Strasbourg, 60-61; trainee, Med Sch, Univ Pa, 71; instr, Med Col, Cornell Univ, 44-45; vis prof, Med Col Va, 58, Univ Strasbourg, 60-61 & Med Sch, Univ Colo, 64; assoc, Tavistock Inst & Clin, London, Eng, 72 & 78. *Mem:* Am Psychiat Asn; Am Soc Clin Invest; fel Am Col Physicians. *Mailing Add:* 5931 SW Hamilton Portland OR 97221

LABELLA, FRANK SEBASTIAN, b Middletown, Conn, Sept 23, 31; m 52; c 3. PHARMACOLOGY. *Educ:* Wesleyan Univ, BA, 52, MA, 54; Emory Univ, PhD(basic health sci), 57. *Prof Exp:* Asst biol, Wesleyan Univ, 52-54; asst physiol, Emory Univ, 54-55, asst histol, 55-57, instr physiol, 57-58; lectr pharmacol, 58-60, from asst prof to assoc prof, 60-67, PROF PHARMACOL & THERAPEUT, FAC MED, UNIV MAN, 67- *Concurrent Pos:* Am Heart Asn fel, Emory Univ, 57-58; Can Rheumatism & Arthritis Soc res fel, Univ Man, 58-61; estab investr, Am Heart Asn, 61-66, mem coun arteriosclerosis; career investr, Med Res Coun Can, 66-; mem, Manitoba Environ Res Comt; mem, Int Narcotics Res Conf. *Honors & Awards:* John J Abel Award, Am Soc Pharmacol & Exp Therapeut, 67; E W R Steacie Prize in Natural Sci, Can, 69. Pharmacol Soc Can; Can Biochem Soc; Endocrine Soc; AAAS; Can Asn Gerontol. *Res:* Cellular pharmacology and biochemistry; neurochemistry; aging; endocrine pharmacology; neuroendocrinology. *Mailing Add:* Dept of Pharmacol & Therapeut Univ of Man Fac of Med Winnipeg MB R3E 0W3 Can

LABELLE, EDWARD FRANCIS, b Worcester, Mass, Aug 11, 48; m 72; c 2. BIOCHEMISTRY. *Educ:* Col Holy Cross, AB, 70, MS, 70; Univ Mich, Ann Arbor, PhD(biochem), 74. *Prof Exp:* Fel biochem, Cornell Univ, 74-76; asst prof chem, West Ill Univ, 76-78; ASST PROF BIOCHEM, UNIV TEX MED BR, GALVESTON, 78- *Mem:* Am Chem Soc; AAAS. *Res:* Membrane biology; transport biochemistry. *Mailing Add:* Div Biochem Univ Tex Med Br Galveston TX 77550

LABEN, ROBERT COCHRANE, b Darien Center, NY, Nov 16, 20; m 46; c 4. GENETICS. *Educ:* Cornell Univ, BS, 42; Okla Agr & Mech Col, MS, 46; Univ Mo, PhD(animal breeding), 50. *Prof Exp:* Asst animal husb, Okla Agr & Mech Col, 46-47; asst dairy husb, Univ Mo, 47-49, asst instr, 49-50; instr animal husb & jr animal husbandman, 50-52, asst prof & asst animal husbandman, 52-58, assoc prof & assoc animal husbandman, 58-64, prof, animal husbandman & dir comput ctr, 64-69, dept vchmn, 78-82, PROF ANIMAL SCI & GENETICIST, EXP STA, UNIV CALIF, DAVIS, 69- *Mem:* Am Soc Animal Sci; Biomet Soc; Am Dairy Sci Asn; Am Genetic Asn. *Res:* Breeding and genetics of farm livestock. *Mailing Add:* Dept of Animal Sci Univ of Calif Davis CA 95616

LABER, LARRY JACKSON, b Lincoln, Vt, July 9, 37; m 63. PLANT PHYSIOLOGY. *Educ:* Univ Vt, BS, 59, MS, 61; Univ Chicago, PhD(bot), 67. *Prof Exp:* Asst prof, Pa State Univ, 65-66; NSF trainee, Univ Ga, 67-69; NIH trainee, Brandeis Univ, 69-70; asst prof, 70-76, ASSOC PROF BOT, UNIV MAINE, ORONO, 77- *Mem:* AAAS; Am Soc Plant Physiol; Japanese Soc Plant Physiol. *Res:* Choroplast development; photophosphorylation; carbon dioxide fixation. *Mailing Add:* Dept of Bot & Plant Path Univ of Maine Orono ME 04469

LABERGE, GENE L, b Ladysmith, Wis, Mar 15, 32; m 62; c 2. GEOLOGY. *Educ:* Univ Wis, BS, 58, MS, 59, PhD(geol), 63. *Prof Exp:* Sponsored res officer, Commonwealth Sci & Indust Res Orgn, Melbourne, Australia, 63-64; Nat Res Coun Can fel, Geol Surv Can, 64-65; from asst prof to assoc prof, 65-74, PROF GEOL, UNIV WIS-OSHKOSH, 74- *Concurrent Pos:* Mem staff, Wis Geol & Natural Hist Surv, 72- *Mem:* AAAS; Geol Soc Am; Soc Econ Geologists. *Res:* Origin of Precambrian iron formations; Precambrian geology and mineral deposits of Wisconsin. *Mailing Add:* Dept of Geol Univ Wis-Oshkosh Oshkosh WI 54901

LABERGE, WALLACE E, b Grafton, NDak, Feb 7, 27; m 58; c 3. ENTOMOLOGY. *Educ:* Univ NDak, BSc, 49, MS, 51; Univ Kans, PhD(entom), 55. *Prof Exp:* Asst cur, Snow Entom Mus & instr entom, Univ Kans, 54-55, asst prof, 55-56; asst prof zool, Iowa State Univ, 56-59; assoc prof entom, Univ Nebr, 59-65; assoc taxonomist, 65-67, TAXONOMIST, ILL NATURAL HIST SURV, 67-; PROF ENTOM, UNIV ILL, URBANA, 70- *Mem:* Entom Soc Am; Soc Study Evolution; Soc Syst Zool; Am Entom Soc. *Res:* Systematics of Hymenoptera, Apoidea and Braconidae. *Mailing Add:* Rm 287 Nat Resources Bldg Urbana IL 61801

LABES, MORTIMER MILTON, b Newton, Mass, Sept 9, 29; m 53; c 6. CHEMICAL PHYSICS. *Educ:* Harvard Univ, AB, 50; Mass Inst Technol, PhD, 54. *Prof Exp:* Asst, Mass Inst Technol, 51-54, res chemist, Sprague Elec Co, 54-57; sr res chemist, Franklin Inst, 57-59, sr staff chemist, 59-60, lab mgr, 60-61, tech dir chem div, 61-66; prof chem, Drexel Inst, 66-70; PROF CHEM, TEMPLE UNIV, 70- *Mem:* Am Chem Soc; Am Phys Soc; Sigma Xi. *Res:* Chemistry and physics of organic solid state; molecular complexes; liquid crystals; electronic properties of polymers. *Mailing Add:* Dept of Chem Temple Univ Philadelphia PA 19122

LABIANCA, DOMINICK A, b Brooklyn, NY, Feb 4, 43. ORGANIC CHEMISTRY, POLYMER CHEMISTRY. *Educ:* Polytech Inst Brooklyn, BS, 65; Univ Mich, PhD(chem), 69. *Prof Exp:* NSF fel org photochem, Calif Inst Technol, 69-70; res chemist, Res & Develop, Bound Brook Tech Ctr, Union Carbide Corp, 70-72; asst prof to assoc prof, New Sch Lib Arts, 72-80, ASSOC PROF, DEPT CHEM, BROOKLYN COL, CITY UNIV NEW YORK, 80- *Mem:* NY Acad Sci; Sigma Xi; Am Chem Soc; Nat Sci Teachers Asn. *Res:* Interdisciplinary teaching; drugs; environment. *Mailing Add:* 189 Ribbon St Franklin Square NY 11010

LABIANCA, FRANK MICHAEL, b Brooklyn, NY, Aug 17, 39; m 70; c 2. UNDERWATER ACOUSTICS, ACOUSTIC SIGNAL PROCESSING. *Educ:* Polytech Inst Brooklyn, BEE, 61, MS, 63, PhD(elec eng), 67. *Prof Exp:* Instr elec eng, Polytech Inst Brooklyn, 61-67; MEM TECH STAFF UNDERWATER ACOUST, BELL LABS INC, 67- *Mem:* Inst Elec & Electronic Engrs; Acoust Soc Am. *Res:* Propagation in surface ducts and underwater channel, scattering of sound from the ocean surface, radiation from cavitating propellers and the origins of ambient noise; adaptive array processing for underwater acoustic detection of signals in noise. *Mailing Add:* Bell Labs Inc Whippany NJ 07981

LABINGER, JAY ALAN, b Los Angeles, Calif, July 6, 47; m 70; c 1. INORGANIC CHEMISTRY, ORGANOMETALLIC CHEMISTRY. *Educ:* Harvey Mudd Col, BS, 68; Harvard Univ, PhD(chem), 74. *Prof Exp:* Res assoc chem, Princeton Univ, 73-74, instr, 74-75; asst prof chem, Univ Notre Dame, 75-81; SR RES CHEMIST, OCCIDENTIAL RES CORP, 81- *Concurrent Pos:* Assoc ed, Chem Reviews, 79-81. *Mem:* Am Chem Soc. *Res:* Synthetic and mechanistic organo-transition metal chemistry; activation of small molecules by transition metal complexes; homogeneous catalysis. *Mailing Add:* Occidential Res Corp PO Box 19601 Irvine CA 92713

LABISKY, RONALD FRANK, b Aberdeen, SDak, Jan 16, 34; m 58; c 2. WILDLIFE BIOLOGY, FISHERIES SCIENCE. *Educ:* SDak State Univ, BS, 55; Univ Wis, MS, 56, PhD(wildlife ecol-zool), 68. *Prof Exp:* Field asst game bird res, 56-57, from asst proj leader to proj leader, 57-59, from asst wildlife specialist to assoc wildlife specialist, 59-72, wildlife specialist, Ill State Natural Hist Surv, 72-76; act dir & asst dir, 76-78, PROF SCH FOREST RESOURCES & CONSERV, UNIV FLA, 76- *Concurrent Pos:* chmn, Nat Fish & Wildlife Resources Res Coun, 78- *Mem:* Am Fisheries Soc; Wildlife Soc; Am Ornith Union; Wilson Ornith Soc; Am Soc Mammal. *Res:* Ecology and physiology of gallinaceous game birds, doves and waterfowl; population ecology, social biology and spatial distribution of pheasants; ecological, ethological, physiological and nutritive factors influencing distribution and abundance of terrestrial and aquatic wildlife; biology and management of spiny lobsters and deep-water reef fishes. *Mailing Add:* Sch Forest Resources & Conserv Univ Fla Gainesville FL 32611

LA BONTE, ANTON EDWARD, b Minneapolis, Minn, May 6, 35; m 59. COMPUTER SCIENCE. *Educ:* Univ Minn, Minneapolis, BS, 57, MSEE, 60, PhD(elec eng), 66. *Prof Exp:* Instr elec eng, Univ Minn, Minneapolis, 59-62, res fel micromagnetics, 62-63, instr elec eng, 63-65; sr scientist, 66-69, mgr systs anal, Aerospace, Navigation & Space Systs, 69-75, SR ENG CONSULT, INFO SCI DIV, CONTROL DATA CORP, 75- *Mem:* Inst Elec & Electronics Eng; Am Phys Soc. *Res:* Application of computers to image processing and astronomy, especially coding techniques for digital images and automation of large-scale stellar proper motion survey. *Mailing Add:* 11 River Terrace Court Apt 104 Minneapolis MN 55414

LABOWS, JOHN NORBERT, JR, b Wilkes-Barre, Pa, June 27, 41; m 64; c 4. ORGANIC CHEMISTRY. *Educ:* Lafayette Col, BS, 63; Cornell Univ, PhD(org chem), 67. *Prof Exp:* Asst prof org chem, Wilkes Col, 67-70, assoc prof chem, 70-78; asst mem, 78-80, ASSOC MEM, MONELL CHEM SENSES CTR, UNIV PA, 80- *Concurrent Pos:* Nat Cancer Inst fel, Fels Res Inst, Temple Univ, 70-71. *Mem:* Am Chem Soc; Sigma Xi; Asn Chemoreception Sci. *Res:* Gas chromatography mass spectrometry analysis, role of microorganisms in odor production. *Mailing Add:* Monell Chem Senses Ctr 3500 Market St Philadelphia PA 19104

LA BRECQUE, GERMAIN C, medical entomology, see previous edition

LABREE, THEODORE ROBERT, b Lafayette, Ind, June 25, 31; m 51; c 2. BACTERIOLOGY, FOOD TECHNOLOGY. *Educ:* Purdue Univ, BS, 58, MS, 60. *Prof Exp:* Res asst food technol, Purdue Univ, 58-59; assoc bacteriologist, Mead Johnson & Co, 59-62, scientist bact, 62-65, mgr med admin, 65-73; TECH MGR, REGULATORY SERV, RIVIANA FOODS, INC, 73- *Mem:* Am Soc Microbiol; Inst Food Technologists. *Res:* Spore destruction of food spoilage organisms; new methods development; microbiology; government regulations, processing, packaging, labeling; good manufacturing practices regulations; low acid; sanitation; food plant; warehouse evaluation. *Mailing Add:* 9839 Canoga Ln Houston TX 77080

LABRIE, DAVID ANDRE, b Baltimore, Md, Mar 23, 37; m 62; c 2. MICROBIOLOGY, BIOCHEMICAL GENETICS. *Educ:* Bethany Col, WVa, AB, 61; NMex Highlands Univ, MS, 65; NC State Univ, PhD(microbiol), 68. *Prof Exp:* NIH fel, Univ Tex, Austin, 68-70; asst prof, 70-74, ASSOC PROF BIOL, W TEX STATE UNIV, 74- *Mem:* AAAS. *Res:* Microbiology genetics of antibiotic resistance and ultraviolet light. *Mailing Add:* Dept of Biol WTex State Univ Canyon TX 79015

LABRIE, FERNAND, b June 28, 37; Can citizen; m 63; c 4. ENDOCRINOLOGY, BIOCHEMISTRY. *Educ:* Laval Univ, BA, 57, MD, 62, PhD(endocrinol), 67; FRCP(C), 73. *Prof Exp:* From asst prof to assoc prof physiol, 66-73, HEAD LAB MOLECULAR ENDOCRINOL, HOSP CTR, LAVAL UNIV, 69-, PROF PHYSIOL, 73- *Concurrent Pos:* Med Res Coun Can fels, Laval Univ, 63-66, Univ Cambridge, 66-67, Univ Sussex, 67-68 & centennial fel, Lab Molecular Biol, Univ Cambridge, 68-69; Med Res Coun Can scholar, Laval Univ, 69-; Med Res Coun Can assoc, Laval Univ, 73-; dir molecular endocrinol, Med Res Coun Group, 73- *Mem:* Am Soc Biol Chemists; Am Physiol Soc; Endocrine Soc; Can Physiol Soc; Can Biochem Soc. *Res:* Mechanism of action of hypothalamic regulatory hormones in the anterior pituitary gland, mammalian messenger RNA; hormone dependent breast cancer; reproductive physiology and biochemistry; hormones and brain. *Mailing Add:* Ctr Hops de Univ Lavel 2705 Blvd Laurier Quebec PQ G1V 4G2 Can

LABROSSE, ELWOOD HENRY, b Mason, Mich, Oct 1, 21; m 47; c 3. BIOCHEMISTRY. *Educ:* Northwestern Univ, BS, 45, MS, 48, MD, 49; Univ Tex, PhD(biochem), 56. *Prof Exp:* Res scientist biochem, Univ Tex, 55-57; chief unit schizophrenia, NIMH, 57-63; res assoc prof surg & asst prof biochem, 64-78, ASSOC PROF PATH, SCH MED, UNIV MD, BALTIMORE, 78- *Concurrent Pos:* Eleanor Roosevelt Int Cancer fel, Inst Gustave Roussy, Villejuif, France, 63-64 & Nat Cancer Inst spec fel, 74-75; vis scientist, Inst Gustave Roussy, 73-74; asst res, Nat Inst Health & Med Res, Paris, 74-75. *Mem:* AAAS; Am Chem Soc; AMA; NY Acad Sci. *Res:* Metabolism of catechol amines and aromatic amino acid chemistry schizophrenia; cancer, neuroblastoma. *Mailing Add:* 9033 Sidehill Rd Elliott City MD 21043

LABUTE, JOHN PAUL, b Tecumseh, Ont, Feb 26, 38; m 61; c 3. MATHEMATICS. *Educ:* Univ Windsor, BSc, 60; Harvard Univ, MA, 61, PhD(math), 65. *Prof Exp:* Nat Res Coun Can res fel, Col France, 65-67; asst prof, 67-70, ASSOC PROF MATH, McGILL UNIV, 70- *Mem:* Can Math Cong; Am Math Soc. *Res:* Algebra and number theory. *Mailing Add:* Dept of Math McGill Univ PO Box 6070 Montreal PQ H3A 2K6 Can

LABUZA, THEODORE PETER, b Perth Amboy, NJ, Nov 10, 40; m 63; c 1. FOOD SCIENCE, PHYSICAL CHEMISTRY. *Educ:* Mass Inst Technol, SB, 62, PhD(food sci), 65. *Prof Exp:* From instr to assoc prof food eng, Mass Inst Technol, 65-71; assoc prof, 71-72, PROF FOOD TECHNOL, UNIV MINN, ST PAUL, 72- *Concurrent Pos:* Food processing consult. *Honors & Awards:* Samuel Cate Precott Res Award, Inst Food Technologists, 72. *Mem:* Fel Inst Food Technologists; Am Inst Chem Eng; Am Chem Soc. *Res:* Physical factors involved in autoxidation of food lipids and prediction of food storage life; stability of intermediate moisture foods; nutrient degradation in processing; kinetics of microbial death. *Mailing Add:* Dept Food Sci & Nutrit Univ Minn St Paul MN 55108

LACASCE, ELROY OSBORNE, JR, b Fryeburg, Maine, Jan 17, 23. ACOUSTICS. *Educ:* Bowdoin Col, AB, 43; Harvard Univ, AM, 51; Brown Univ, PhD(physics), 55. *Prof Exp:* Instr physics, Bowdoin Col, 43 & 47-49, instr math, 51; physicist, Naval Res Lab, 44; foreign serv officer, US Dept State, 45-46; teacher, High Sch, 46-47; asst, Brown Univ, 51-54; from instr to assoc prof physics, 54-69, PROF PHYSICS, BOWDOIN COL, 69-, CHMN DEPT, 77- *Concurrent Pos:* Res assoc, Yale Univ, 60-61; NSF fac fel, 60-61; vis investr, Woods Hole Oceanog Inst, 68-69, guest investr, 75-76. *Mem:* Acoust Soc Am; Am Asn Physics Teachers. *Res:* Ultrasonics and underwater sound. *Mailing Add:* Dept of Physics Bowdoin Col Brunswick ME 04011

LACEFIELD, GARRY DALE, b McHenry, Ky, Aug 22, 45; m 67; c 2. FORAGE PRODUCTION & MANAGEMENT. *Educ:* Western Ky Univ, BS, 70, MS, 71; Univ Mo, PhD(agron & physiol), 74. *Prof Exp:* Lab instr & instr plant sci, Western Ky Univ, 69-71; teaching asst, Univ Mo, 71-74; asst exten prof, 74-78, EXTEN FORAGE SPECIALIST, UNIV KY, 74-, ASSOC EXTEN PROF, 78- *Mem:* Am Soc Agron; Am Forage & Grassland Coun. *Res:* Development and implementation of improved practices in forage establishment, production and utilization. *Mailing Add:* Res & Educ Ctr PO Box 469 Princeton KY 42445

LACELLE, PAUL (LOUIS), b Syracuse, NY, July 4, 29; m 53; c 4. HEMATOLOGY, BIOPHYSICS. *Educ:* Houghton Col, BA, 51; Univ Rochester, MD, 59. *Prof Exp:* Intern & resident, Strong Mem Hosp, Univ Rochester, 59-62; from sr instr to assoc prof, 67-71, chmn dept, 71-77, PROF RADIATION BIOL & BIOPHYS, SCH MED, UNIV ROCHESTER, 71- *Concurrent Pos:* USAEC res fel, 63-65; USPHS spec fel, Univ Saarland, 65-66; Buswell fel, Sch Med, Univ Rochester, 66-67; NIH res grant, 70- *Mem:* Biophys Soc; Am Soc Hemat; Am Fedn Clin Res; Int Soc Hemat. *Res:* Hemolytic anemias; membrane biophysical properties of erythrocytes; microcirculation. *Mailing Add:* 601 Elmwood Ave Rochester NY 14642

LACEWELL, RONALD DALE, b Plainview, Tex, Apr 15, 40; m 62; c 3. RESOURCE ECONOMICS, PRODUCTION ECONOMICS. *Educ:* Tex Tech Univ, BS, 63, MS, 67; Okla State Univ, PhD(agr econ), 70. *Prof Exp:* Statistician, Bur Census, US Dept Commerce, 63-64; instr agr econ, Tex Tech Univ, 65-66; economist, Econ Res Serv, US Dept Agr, 67-70; asst prof, 70-73, assoc prof, 73-78, PROF AGR ECON, TEX A&M UNIV, 78- *Mem:* Am Agr Econ Asn. *Res:* Economics of water resources emphasizing agriculture; alternative energy sources and impacts of energy price adjustments; economics and environmental impacts of integrated pest management systems used for crop production. *Mailing Add:* Dept Agr Econ Tex A&M Univ College Station TX 77843

LACEY, BEATRICE CATES, b New York, NY, July 22, 19; m 38; c 2. PSYCHOPHYSIOLOGY. *Educ:* Cornell Univ, AB, 40; Antioch Col, MA, 58. *Prof Exp:* Instr psychol, Antioch Col, 56-63, asst prof, 63-68, assoc prof, 68-73, adj prof, 73-; co-prin investr, USPHS grant, 60-; assoc ed, Psychophysiol, 75-78; FELS PROF PSYCHIATRY, SCH MED, WRIGHT STATE UNIV, 77-, ACTG SCI DIR, FELS RES INST, 79- *Honors & Awards:* Distinguished Sci Contrib Award, Am Psychol Asn, 76. *Mem:* fel Soc Exp Psychologists; fel Acad Behav Med Res; Soc Psychophysiol Res (pres, (pres, 78-79); Soc Neurosci. *Res:* Psychophysiology of the autonomic nervous system. *Mailing Add:* Fels Res Inst Sch Med Wright State Univ 800 Livermore Yellow Springs OH 45387

LACEY, ELIZABETH PATTERSON, b Cleveland, Ohio. PLANT ECOLOGY. *Educ:* Univ Colo, BA, 69; Univ Mich, MS, 74, PhD(bot), 78. *Prof Exp:* ASST PROF BOT, UNIV NC, GREENSBORO, 78- *Mem:* Bot Soc Am; Brit Ecol Soc; Ecol Soc Am; Soc Study Evolution; Soc Int Plantarum Demographia. *Res:* Plant population biology; evolution of life history patterns. *Mailing Add:* Dept of Biol Univ of NC Greensboro NC 27412

LACEY, HOWARD ELTON, b Leakey, Tex, Feb 9, 37; m 58; c 4. MATHEMATICS. *Educ:* Abilene Christian Col, BA, 59, MA, 61; NMex State Univ, PhD(math), 63. *Prof Exp:* Asst prof math, Abilene Christian Col, 63-64 & Univ Tex, Austin, 64-67; res assoc, NASA Manned Spacecraft Ctr, 67-68; assoc prof, 68-73, vchmn dept, 75-77, PROF MATH, UNIV TEX, AUSTIN, 73-, MEM GRAD FAC, 68- *Concurrent Pos:* Res assoc, Inst Math, Polish Acad Sci, Warsaw, 72-73. *Mem:* Am Math Soc; Math Asn Am. *Res:* Functional analysis; classical Banach spaces. *Mailing Add:* Dept of Math Univ of Tex Austin TX 78712

LACEY, JOHN IRVING, b Chicago, Ill, Apr 11, 15; m 38; c 2. PSYCHOPHYSIOLOGY, NEUROPHYSIOLOGY. *Educ:* Cornell Univ, BA, 37, PhD(psychol), 41. *Prof Exp:* Instr psychol, Queens Col, NY, 41-42; res assoc, Antioch Col, 46-73, from assoc prof to prof psychophysiol & chmn dept, 48-77; sr scientist, 73-77, CHIEF SECT BEHAV PHYSIOL, FELS RES INST, 77-; FELS PROF PSYCHIAT & CHMN DEPT, SCH MED, WRIGHT STATE UNIV, 77- *Concurrent Pos:* Res assoc, Psychol Corp, 39-42; lectr, Ohio State Univ, 50 & sch med, Univ Louisville, 55; fel, Commonwealth Fund, 57-59; mem ment health, behav sci & exp psychol study sects, USPHS, 56-60, res career develop comt, 64-65; mem adv panel life sci facilities, NSF, 60-61; mem clin prog-proj rev comt, NIMH, 66-71, chmn, 70-71; adj prof, Antioch Col, 78-; mem bd sci counselors, Nat Inst Aging, 77-80. *Honors & Awards:* Award, Soc Psychophysiol Res, 70; Distinguished Sci Contrib Award, Am Psychol Asn, 76. *Mem:* Nat Acad Sci; fel Soc Exp Psychologists; Soc Neurosci; fel Acad Behav Med Res; Inst Elec & Electronics Engrs. *Res:* International brain research organization psychophysiology of the autonomic nervous system and psychomatic medicine; brain physiology and behavior. *Mailing Add:* Sect on Behav Physiol Wright State Univ Sch of Med Yellow Springs OH 45387

LACEY, RICHARD FREDERICK, b Vallejo, Calif, May 29, 31; m 71. MAGNETISM. *Educ:* Mass Inst Technol, SB, 52, PhD(physics), 59. *Prof Exp:* Sr engr, Sylvania Lighting Prod Co, 59-62; sr scientist, Am Sci & Eng Co, 62-63; sr physicist, Varian Assocs, 63-67; physicist, 67-69, STAFF SCIENTIST, HEWLETT-PACKARD LABS, 69- *Mem:* Inst Elec & Electronics Engrs; Am Phys Soc. *Res:* Atomic structure; radio-frequency spectroscopy; physical and quantum electronics. *Mailing Add:* Hewlett-Packard Labs 1651 Page Mill Rd Palo Alto CA 94304

LACEY, ROBERT EUGENE, b Kingfisher, Okla, Sept 7, 21; m 52; c 1. CHEMICAL ENGINEERING. *Educ:* Okla Agr & Mech Col, BS, 47, MS, 50. *Prof Exp:* Instr chem eng, Okla Agr & Mech Col, 47-50; res chem engr, Monsanto Co, 50-52; sr chem engr, 52-80, SR RES ADV, SOUTHERN RES INST, BIRMINGHAM, 80- *Mem:* Am Inst Chem Engrs; Am Chem Soc; AAAS. *Res:* Membrane processes; absorption refrigeration. *Mailing Add:* 3013B Massey Rd Birmingham AL 35216

LACH, JOHN LOUIS, b Blairmore, Alta, Feb 10, 27; nat US; m 53; c 4. PHYSICAL PHARMACY. *Educ:* Univ Alta, BSc, 50; Univ Wis, MS, 52, PhD(pharm), 54. *Prof Exp:* Instr pharm, Univ Wis, 54; from asst prof to assoc prof, 54-62, PROF PHARM, COL PHARM, UNIV IOWA, 62-, ASSOC DEAN, 72- *Honors & Awards:* Acad Pharmaceut Sci Res Achievement Award Pharmaceut, Am Pharmaceut Asn Found, 75. *Mem:* Am Chem Soc; Am Pharmaceut Asn. *Res:* Application of physical-chemical principles to pharmaceutical systems involving stability studies, complex formation, formulation and analytical techniques. *Mailing Add:* 18 Ridgewood Lane Iowa City IA 52240

LACH, JOSEPH T, b Chicago, Ill, May 12, 34; m 65. PHYSICS. *Educ:* Univ Chicago, AB, 53, MS, 56; Univ Calif, Berkeley, PhD(physics), 63. *Prof Exp:* Res assoc physics, Yale Univ, 63-65, asst prof, 66-69; chmn, Fermi Lab Physics Dept, 74-75, FERMI NAT ACCELERATOR LAB, 69- *Mem:* Am Phys Soc. *Res:* Elementary particle physics; physics electronic data processing. *Mailing Add:* 28 W 364 Indian Knoll Trail West Chicago IL 60185

LACHAINE, ANDRE RAYMOND JOSEPH, b Ottawa, Ont, Sept 22, 45; m 68; c 3. PHYSICS. *Educ:* Univ Ottawa, BSc Hons, 67, MSc, 70, PhD(physics), 76. *Prof Exp:* Instr physics, Univ NB, 76; ASST PROF PHYSICS, ROYAL MIL COL CAN, 76- *Concurrent Pos:* Investr contract, 77- *Res:* Electrical, magnetic and mechanical properties of type II high field superconductors. *Mailing Add:* Dept of Physics Royal Mil Col Kingston ON K7L 2W3 Can

LACHANCE, DENIS, b Quebec, Que, Feb 2, 39; m 64; c 3. FOREST PATHOLOGY. *Educ:* Laval Univ, BSc, 62; Univ Wis-Madison, PhD(phytopath), 66. *Prof Exp:* res scientist forest path, Laurentian Forest Res Ctr, 66-79, HEAD, FOREST INSECT & DIS SURV SECT, CAN FORESTRY SERV, 79- *Mem:* Can Phytopath Soc (secy-treas, 71-73); Can Inst Forestry; Int Soc Plant Path. *Res:* Decay of conifers; root diseases. *Mailing Add:* Laurentian Forest Res Ctr Can Forestry Serv PO Box 3800 Ste-Foy PQ G1V 4C7 Can

LACHANCE, JEAN PAUL, b Berthier, Que, Feb 4, 23; m 55; c 4. BIOLOGY. *Educ:* Levis Univ, BA, 45; Laval Univ, BSc, 49, PhD(biol), 53. *Prof Exp:* Dir med tech training lab, Laval Univ, 52-54, res asst inst physiol, Fac Med, 54-55; res asst biol, Univ Montreal, 55-56; Nuffield fel, Med Res Coun Radiopath Res Univ, Hammersmith Hosp, London, Eng, 56-57; Nat Res Coun Can fel, Univ Munich, 57-58; asst prof biochem, 58-61, asst prof biol, 61-65, ASSOC PROF BIOCHEM, UNIV MONTREAL, 65- *Mem:* Can Biochem Soc; Can Physiol Soc. *Res:* Fat metabolism in vivo and fatty acid biosynthesis; carboxylating enzymes. *Mailing Add:* Dept Biochem Univ Montreal 2900 Blvd Mt Royal Montreal PQ H3C 3V7 Can

LA CHANCE, LEO EMERY, b Brunswick, Maine, Mar, 1, 31; m 55; c 3. GENETICS. *Educ:* Univ Maine, AB, 53; NC State Col, MS, 55, PhD(genetics), 58. *Prof Exp:* Res assoc biol, Brookhaven Nat Lab, 58-60; insect geneticist, 60-63, proj leader, Insect Genetics & Radiation Biol Sect, Metab & Radiation Res Lab, Entom Res Div, Agr Res Serv, USDA, 63-69; sci officer & head, Insect Eradication & Pest Control Sect, Joint Food & Agr Orgn-Int Atomic Energy Agency, Austria, 69-71; proj leader, Insect Genetics & Radiation Biol Sect, 71-77, DIR, METAB & RADIATION RES LAB, AGR RES SERV, USDA, 77- *Mem:* AAAS; Genetics Soc Am; Radiation Res Soc; Entom Soc Am. *Res:* Insect genetics and radiation biology; genetic effect of chemical mutagens and chemical sterilization of insects; insect cytology and cytogenetic effects of radiation and chemicals; factors influencing chromosome aberrations and dominant lethal mutations induced by radiation and chemicals; insect reproduction. *Mailing Add:* Metab & Radiation Res Lab Agr Res Serv State Univ Sta Fargo ND 58102

LACHANCE, MURDOCK HENRY, b Detroit, Mich, Dec 12, 20; m 43; c 1. ELECTRO-OPTICS. *Educ:* Mich Technol Univ, BS, 42, MS, 47. *Prof Exp:* Prin phys metallurgist, Battelle Mem Inst, 47-57; sr res metallurgist, Whirlpool Res Labs, 57-62; SR SCIENTIST, XEROX ELECTRO-OPTICAL SYSTS, 62- *Concurrent Pos:* Flight instr, Purdue Aeronaut Corp, 42-44. *Mem:* Sigma Xi. *Res:* Corrosion of stainless steels; development of refractory alloys, controlled porosity tungsten for ion propulsion and semiconductors for Peltier cooling; failure mechanisms of alkali vapor lamps and of He-Cd and He-Ne lasers. *Mailing Add:* 260 S Chester Ave Pasadena CA 91106

LACHANCE, PAUL ALBERT, b St Johnsbury, Vt, June 5, 33; m 55; c 4. NUTRITION, FOOD SCIENCE. *Educ:* St Michael's Col, Vt, BSc, 55; Univ Ottawa, PhD(biol, nutrit), 60. *Prof Exp:* Res biologist, Aerospace Med Res Lab, Wright-Patterson AFB, Ohio, 60-63; coord flight food & nutrit, NASA Manned Spacecraft Ctr, 63-67; assoc prof food sci, 67-72, dir sch feeding effectiveness res proj, 69-72, PROF NUTRIT & FOOD SCI, RUTGERS UNIV, 72- *Concurrent Pos:* Lectr, Univ Dayton, 63. *Mem:* Inst Food Technolocists; Am Soc Clin Nutrit; Am Pub Health Asn; NY Acad Sci; Am Dietetic Asn. *Res:* Aerospace food and nutrition; metabolic role of vitamin A; nutritional aspects of food processing; amino acid fortification and micronutrient nutrification; school food service. *Mailing Add:* 34 Taylor Rd RD 4 Princeton NJ 08540

LACHAPELLE, BENOIT VINCENT, b Que, Jan 8, 30; m 53; c 3. APPLIED MATHEMATICS. *Educ:* Univ Montreal, BA, 51, BSc, 53. *Prof Exp:* Asst prof math, Univ Montreal, 56-64; appl math consult, SMA Inc, 64-78; SR ADV COMPUT SCI, GROUPE LAVALIN, 78- *Concurrent Pos:* Invited prof, Univ Montreal. *Mem:* Am Math Soc; Math Asn Am; Can Math Cong. *Res:* Complex analysis; numbers theory. *Mailing Add:* 5742 Plantagenet Montreal PQ H3S 2K3 Can

LACHAPELLE, EDWARD RANDLE, b Tacoma, Wash, May 31, 26; m 50; c 1. METEOROLOGY. *Educ:* Col Puget Sound, BS, 49. *Hon Degrees:* ScD, Col Puget Sound, 67. *Prof Exp:* Avalanche researcher, US Forest Serv, 57-72, sr scientist glaciol, 57-68, assoc prof geophys, 68-73, PROF GEOPHYS & ATMOSPHERIC SCI, UNIV WASH, 73- *Concurrent Pos:* Res assoc, Univ Colo, 73-75; vpres, Int Comn Snow & Ice. *Mem:* AAAS; Glaciol Soc (vpres). *Res:* Glaciology; snow physics; avalanche hazard forecasting and control. *Mailing Add:* Dept of Atmospheric Sci Univ of Wash Seattle WA 98105

LACHAPELLE, RENE CHARLES, b Joliette, Que, Jan 28, 30; US citizen; m 59; c 3. MEDICAL MICROBIOLOGY. *Educ:* Seminaire de Joliette, BA, 50; Univ Montreal, BSc, 53; Syracuse Univ, MS, 57, PhD(microbiol), 62. *Prof Exp:* Lab admin dir clin path, Syracuse Mem Hosp, 62-66; assoc prof biol, Univ Dayton, 66-74; CHAIRPERSON, DEPT MED TECHNOL, UNIV VT, 74- *Mem:* Sigma Xi; AAAS; Am Soc Med Tech; Am Soc Microbiol; Can Soc Microbiol. *Res:* Morphogenesis and serological properties of Candida albicans; monomine oxidase and serotonin in germfree animals; skin bacteria in long-term space flights; educational aspects of medical technology; coagglutination of streptococcal groups. *Mailing Add:* 302 Rowell Bldg Univ of Vt Burlington VT 05401

LACHENBRUCH, ARTHUR HEROLD, b New Rochelle, NY, Dec 7, 25; m 50; c 3. GEOPHYSICS. *Educ:* Johns Hopkins Univ, BA, 50; Harvard Univ, MA, 52, PhD(geophys), 58. *Prof Exp:* GEOPHYSICIST, US GEOL SURV, 51- *Concurrent Pos:* Vis prof, Dartmouth Col, 63. *Honors & Awards:* Kirk Bryan Award, Geol Soc Am, 63; US Geol Surv Meritorious Serv Award, 72; Dept Interior Distinguished Serv Award, 78. *Mem:* Nat Acad Sci; fel AAAS; fel Am Geophys Union; fel Royal Astron Asn; fel Arctic Inst N Am. *Res:* Solid earth geophysics; terrestrial heat flow; tectonophysics; permafrost. *Mailing Add:* Off of Earthquake Studies US Geol Surv 345 Middlefield Rd Menlo Park CA 94025

LACHENBRUCH, PETER ANTHONY, b Los Angeles, Calif, Feb 5, 37; m 62. BIOSTATISTICS. *Educ:* Univ Calif, Los Angeles, BA, 58, PhD(biostatist), 65; Lehigh Univ, MS, 61. *Prof Exp:* Asst math, Lehigh Univ, 58-59; programmer, Douglas Aircraft Co, 59-60; sr opers res analyst, Syst Develop Corp, 60-61; res scientist, Am Inst Res, 61-62; USPHS fel biostatist, Univ Calif, Los Angeles, 62-65; from asst prof to prof biostatist, 65-76; Univ NC, Chapel Hill, 75-76; PROF PREV MED, UNIV IOWA, 76- *Honors & Awards:* Mortimer Spiegelman Gold Medal Award, Am Pub Health Asn, 71. *Mem:* AAAS; fel Am Statist Asn; Biomet Soc; Am Pub Health Asn; Royal Statist Soc. *Res:* Discriminant analysis; Monte Carlo methods; computer analysis of data; survival analysis. *Mailing Add:* Dept of Prev Med Univ of Iowa Iowa City IA 52242

LACHER, ROBERT CHRISTOPHER, b Atlanta, Ga, Oct 14, 40. TOPOLOGY, APPLIED MATHEMATICS. *Educ:* Univ Ga, BS, 62, MA, 64, PhD(math), 66. *Prof Exp:* Asst prof math, Univ Calif, Los Angeles, 66-67; vis mem math, Inst Advan Study, 67-68; from asst prof to assoc prof, 68-75, PROF MATH, FLA STATE UNIV, 75- *Concurrent Pos:* Alfred P Sloan fel, 70-72; mem, Inst Advan Study, 72; NSF res grants, 72- *Mem:* AAAS; Sigma Xi; Am Math Soc. *Res:* Geometric topology; cell-like mappings and generalized manifolds; embedding problems; catastrophe theory. *Mailing Add:* Dept of Math Fla State Univ Tallahassee FL 32306

LACHIN, JOHN MARION, III, b New Orleans, La, July 4, 42. CLINICAL TRIALS. *Educ:* Tulane Univ, BS, 65; Univ Pittsburgh, ScD(biostatist), 72. *Prof Exp:* Actg chief statist & res, La State Dept Hosp, 67-69; statistician, Med Sch, Univ Pittsburgh, 69-72; epidemiologist & dir, Div Prog Info & Eval, Va, 72-73; asst res prof, 73-77, ASSOC RES PROF STATIST, GEORGE WASHINGTON UNIV, 77-, ASST DIR, BIOSTATIST CTR, 80- *Concurrent Pos:* Adj asst prof biometry, Va Commonwealth Univ, 72-73; mem, Serv Res & Epidemiol Studies Rev Comt, NIMH, 77-80, Gastrointestinal Drugs Adv Comt, Food & Drug Admin, 78-82, Data Monitoring Comt, Nat Coop Dialysis Study, 79-81, Opers Comt, Vet Admin Coop Study on Hypertension, 81-; dir, Biostatist Coord Ctr, Nat Coop Gallstone Study, 78-83, Lupus Nephritis Collab Study, 81- & Diabetes Control & Complications Trial, 82- *Mem:* Biomet Soc; Am Statist Asn; Soc Epidemiol Res; Soc Clin Trials. *Mailing Add:* Biostatist Ctr George Washington Univ Bethesda MD 20814

LACHMAN, IRWIN MORRIS, b New York, NY, Aug 2, 30; m 59; c 2. CERAMICS ENGINEERING. *Educ:* Rutgers Univ, BSc, 52; Ohio State Univ, MSc, 53, PhD(ceramic eng), 55. *Prof Exp:* Sr scientist ceramics, Thermo Mat, Inc, 57-58; staff mem, Sandia Corp, 58-60; RES ASSOC CERAMICS, CORNING GLASS WORKS, 60- *Mem:* AAAS; Am Ceramic Soc; Brit Ceramic Soc. *Res:* Mechanical and thermal properties of ceramics. *Mailing Add:* Corning Glass Works Sullivan Park Lab Corning NY 14830

LACHMAN, LEON, b Bronx, NY, Jan 29, 29; m 51; c 2. PHARMACY. *Educ:* Columbia Univ, BSc, 51, MSc, 53; Univ Wis, PhD, 56. *Hon Degrees:* Dr, Columbia Univ, 76. *Prof Exp:* Asst dir pharm, Res & Develop Div, Ciba Pharmaceut Co, NJ, 56-68, dir, 68-69; vpres develop & control, Endo Labs Inc, 69-79; SR VPRES SCI & TECHNOL, UNITED LAB INC, 79- *Concurrent Pos:* Vis scientist, Am Asn Cols Pharm; mem bd trustees, Col Pharm, Columbia Univ, 74-78. *Honors & Awards:* Indust Pharmaceut Technol Award, Acad Pharmaceut Sci, 70. *Mem:* Fel Acad Pharmaceut Sci; Parenteral Drug Asn (pres 81-). *Res:* Process and equipment design; research and development of pharmaceutical dosage forms; analytical research; quality control practices; medical research; regulatory affairs. *Mailing Add:* 138 Rolling Hill Rd Manhasset NY 11030

LACHMANN, ALFRED, b Ger, Apr 14, 15; nat US; m 46. PHYSICAL CHEMISTRY. *Educ:* Univ Geneva, ChE, 40, PhD(phys chem), 42. *Prof Exp:* Chemist, Fedn Migros Coops, Switz, 42-46; asst specialist, Dairy Indust Div, Univ Calif, 47-51; sr chemist, Stein, Hall & Co, Inc, 51-54; div head food prod develop, Am Sugar & Refining Co, 54-58; consult chemist, 59-64; asst tech dir, SuCrest Corp, 64-68; consult chemist & sr assoc, S M Cantor Assocs, 69-72; proj dir, UN Indust Develop Orgn, 72-75; technologist, Off Int Coop & Develop, USDA, Washington, DC, 75-81; CONSULT CHEMIST, 82- *Mem:* Am Chem Soc; Am Dairy Sci Asn; Am Inst Chem; Inst Food Technol; Soc Indust Chem. *Res:* Carbohydrate technology, proteins, fats, food ingredients, additives and their effect on nutrition and quality of foods; evaluation of food systems in developing and developed countries; domestic and foreign food legislation; technology transfer of food production and process. *Mailing Add:* 1407 Remington Rd Wynnewood PA 19096

LACHNER, ERNEST ALBERT, b New Castle, Pa, Apr 3, 15; m 39; c 4. SYSTEMATIC ICHTHYOLOGY. *Educ:* Pa State Teachers Col, Slippery Rock, BS, 37; Cornell Univ, PhD(ichthyol), 46. *Prof Exp:* Teacher high sch, Pa, 37-39; asst zool, Cornell Univ, 40-42; assoc prof fishery biol, Pa State Col, 47-49; assoc cur, 49-65, cur in charge, 65-66, SUPVR & CUR, DIV FISHES, NAT MUS NATURAL HIST, 66- *Concurrent Pos:* Guggenheim fel, 56 & 59. *Mem:* AAAS; Am Soc Ichthyol & Herpet (vpres, 54, pres-elect, 66, pres, 67); Am Fisheries Soc; Am Soc Limnol & Oceanog; Biol Soc Washington (vpres, 66, pres, 67). *Res:* Systematics and morphology of marine and fresh water fishes; ecology; life history of fishes. *Mailing Add:* Div of Fishes Nat Mus of Natural Hist Washington DC 20560

LACHS, GERARD, b Essen, Ger, Aug 2, 34; US citizen; m 57; c 2. ELECTRONICS. *Educ:* NY Univ, BS, 56; Univ Rochester, MS, 61; Syracuse Univ, PhD(elec eng), 64. *Prof Exp:* Asst engr, Sperry Gyroscope Co, 57-58; sr res staff mem commun, Gen Dynamics/Electronics, 58-61; instr elec eng, Syracuse Univ, 61-64; from asst prof to assoc prof, 64-74, PROF ELEC ENG, PA STATE UNIV, 74- *Mem:* Inst Elec & Electronics Engrs; Acoust Soc Am. *Res:* Quantum theory of laser beam communication systems; digital communication systems; coding of orthogonal wave shapes; audition and psycho-acoustics; bioengineering. *Mailing Add:* Dept of Elec Eng Pa State Univ University Park PA 16802

LACK, LEON, b New York, NY, Jan 7, 22; m 48; c 5. BIOCHEMISTRY. *Educ:* Brooklyn Col, AB, 43; Mich State Univ, MS, 48; Columbia Univ, PhD(biochem), 53. *Prof Exp:* Fel, Duke Univ, 53-55; from instr to asst prof pharmacol, Sch Med, Johns Hopkins Univ, 55-64; from asst prof to assoc prof, 65-71, PROF PHARMACOL, MED CTR, DUKE UNIV, 71-, CHIEF LAB MACROMOLECULAR PHARMACOL, 65- *Mem:* Am Soc Biol Chemists; Am Soc Pharmacol & Exp Therapeuts. *Res:* Metabolism of aromatic substances; intestinal active transport. *Mailing Add:* Lab of Molecular Pharmacol Duke Univ Med Ctr Durham NC 27706

LACKEY, CAROLYN JEAN, b Shelby, NC, Nov 24, 48. COMMUNITY NUTRITION. *Educ:* Univ NC, Greensboro, BSHE, 71; Univ Tenn, Knoxville, MS, 73, PhD(food sci), 74. *Prof Exp:* Asst prof foods & nutrit, Purdue Univ, 74-76; asst prof 76-80, ASSOC PROF COMMUNITY NUTRITION, MICH STATE UNIV, 80- *Concurrent Pos:* Proj dir nutrit educ grant, Mich Dept Educ, 78. *Mem:* Am Inst Nutrit; Soc Nutrit Educ; Inst Food Technologists. *Res:* Investigation of determinants of food behavior and food behavior modification; development, implementation and evaluation of food and nutrition education delivery systems. *Mailing Add:* Food Sci & Human Nutrit Mich State Univ East Lansing MI 48824

LACKEY, HOMER BAIRD, b Freewater, Ore, Nov 23, 20; m 42; c 3. APPLIED CHEMISTRY. *Educ:* Ore State Univ, BS, 47, MS, 48. *Prof Exp:* Asst, Ore State Univ, 47-48; res chemist, Cent Res Dept, 48-55, supvr prod res, Chem Prod Div, 55-68, mgr prod res, 68-80, MGR REGULATORY AFFAIRS, CHEM PROD DIV, CROWN ZELLERBACH CORP, 80- *Mem:* Am Chem Soc; Am Soc Test & Mat; Am Concrete Inst. *Res:* Forest byproduct utilization. *Mailing Add:* Chem Prod Div Crown Zellerbach Corp Camas WA 98607

LACKEY, JAMES ALDEN, b Glens Falls, NY, Nov 25, 38; m 61; c 2. MAMMALOGY. *Educ:* Cornell Univ, BS, 61; Calif State Univ, San Diego, MA, 67; Univ Mich, PhD(zool), 73. *Prof Exp:* ASST PROF ZOOL, NY STATE UNIV COL, OSWEGO, 73- *Mem:* Ecol Soc Am; Am Soc Mammalogists; Soc Study of Evolution; Sigma Xi; AAAS. *Res:* Reproduction, growth, development and population ecology of mammals. *Mailing Add:* Dept of Zool State Univ NY Oswego NY 13126

LACKEY, LAURENCE, US citizen. GEOMORPHOLOGY, ENGINEERING GEOLOGY. *Educ:* Principia Col, BS, 69; Univ Mich, PhD(geol), 74. *Prof Exp:* Asst prof geol, Mich State Univ, 74-75; asst prof geol, Memphis State Univ, 75-78; asst prof, 79-80, ASOC PROF & CHMN GEOL, PRINCIPIA COL, 81- *Concurrent Pos:* Dir, Tenn Earthquake Info Ctr, 77-78; consult eng geol, 75- & Off Energy Info Validation, US Dept Energy, 78; prin investr, US Nuclear Regulatory Comn Contract, 77-78; mem proposal rev panel, Inst Sci Equip Prof, NSF, 81. *Mem:* AAAS; Geol Soc Am; Am Quaternary Asn; Nat Asn Geol Teachers. *Res:* Computer applications in geology and quaternary geology. *Mailing Add:* Earth Sci Dept Principia Col Elsah IL 62028

LACKEY, ROBERT B, b Youngstown, Ohio, Feb 16, 32; m 61; c 3. ELECTRICAL ENGINEERING. *Educ:* Ohio State Univ, BEE & MSc, 54, PhD(elec eng), 61. *Prof Exp:* Res assoc control systs, Antenna Lab, 56-59, from instr to asst prof, 58-66, ASSOC PROF ELEC ENG, OHIO STATE UNIV, 66- *Concurrent Pos:* Specialist, NAm Rockwell Corp, 61- *Mem:* Am Soc Eng Educ. *Res:* Control systems; digital computer design; pattern recognition; information processing. *Mailing Add:* 264 Electronics Lab Ohio State Univ 2015 Neil Ave Columbus OH 43210

LACKEY, ROBERT SAMUEL, b Butler, Pa, June 13, 26; m 53; c 3. MECHANICAL ENGINEERING. *Educ:* Rensselaer Polytech Inst, BME, 46; Univ Pittsburgh, MS, 49. *Prof Exp:* Jr engr, Spec Prod Div, 46-51, fel engr, Air Arm Div, 51-55 & New Prod Labs, 55-61, FEL ENGR RES LABS, WESTINGHOUSE ELEC CORP, 61- *Mem:* Nat Soc Prof Engrs; Am Soc Mech Engrs. *Res:* Electromechanical development; gyroscopes and accelerometers; thermoelectric device development; heat transfer. *Mailing Add:* Westinghouse Elec Corp 1310 Beulah Rd Pittsburgh PA 15235

LACKEY, ROBERT T, b Kamloops, BC, May 18, 44; m 67; c 2. FISHERIES MANAGEMENT. *Educ:* Humboldt State Univ, BS, 67; Univ Maine, Orono, MS, 68; Colo State Univ, PhD(fisheries & wildlife), 71. *Prof Exp:* Asst prof, Va Polytech Inst & State Univ, 71-74, sect leader, Fisheries Sci, 71-72 & 75-77, assoc prof fisheries, 74-79; group leader, Nat Water Res Analysis Group, 79-81; RES BIOLOGIST, ENVIRON RES LAB, CORVALLIS, 81- *Concurrent Pos:* Res grants, Off Econ Opportunity & Celanese Corp, Va Polytech Inst & State Univ, 71-74, Off Water Resources Res, 72-77, US Nat Marine Fisheries Serv, 72-78, US Dept Agr, 73-78 & US Forest Serv, 75-78; consult, US Fish & Wildlife Serv, 74-76, Brandermill Corp, 74-75 & US Army Corps Engrs, 75-76; fish & wildlife adminr, US Fish & Wildlife Serv, 76-77; vis prof, George Mason Univ, 76-77. *Mem:* Inst Fishery Res Biologists; Am Fisheries Soc; Fisheries Soc Brit Isles; Wildlife Soc. *Res:* Fisheries management, including structure and management of aquatic renewable natural resources; systems analysis; environmetal assessment. *Mailing Add:* Environ Protection Agency 200 SW 35th St Corvallis OR 87333

LACKEY, WALTER JACKSON, b Shelby, NC, Feb 6, 40; m 61; c 2. CERAMICS & METALLURGICAL ENGINEERING. *Educ:* NC State Univ, BS(metall eng) & BS(ceramic eng), 61, MS, 63, PhD(ceramic eng), 70. *Prof Exp:* Res scientist, Battelle-Northwest Lab, 63-65; mat engr, Douglas Aircraft Corp, 65-66; res asst electronic ceramics, NC State Univ, 66-69; MEM RES STAFF, METALS & CERAMICS DIV, OAK RIDGE NAT LAB, 69- *Mem:* Am Ceramic Soc; Am Soc Metals; fel Am Ceramic Soc. *Res:* Fabrication, characterization and testing of nuclear fuels and waste forms; mechanisms and measurement of electrical conduction in ceramic insulators. *Mailing Add:* Metals & Ceramics Div PO Box X Oak Ridge TN 37830

LACKMAN, DAVID BUELL, b Plymouth, Conn, Dec 29, 11; m 47; c 4. BACTERIOLOGY, PUBLIC HEALTH. *Educ:* Univ Conn, BS, 33; Univ Pa, PhD(med bact), 37; Am Bd Med Microbiol, dipl pub health & med lab immunol. *Prof Exp:* Asst instr bact, Med Sch, Univ Pa, 33-37; instr, 37-39, assoc, 39-41; asst bacteriologist, USPHS, 41-46, from sr scientist to sci dir, Rocky Mountain Lab, Nat Inst Allergy & Infectious Dis, Mont, 46-67, dir microbiol lab, 67-71; adminr labs div, Mont State Dept Health & Environ Sci, 71-77; RETIRED. *Concurrent Pos:* Vis lectr, Mont State Univ, 52-77. *Mem:* Am Soc Microbiol; Asn Mil Surg US; fel Am Pub Health Asn; Am Asn Immunol; fel Am Acad Microbiol. *Res:* Serology of rickettsial and viral diseases; antigenic structure of bacteria and rickettsiae. *Mailing Add:* 1400 Winne Ave Helena MT 59601

LACKNER, HENRIETTE, b Vienna, Austria, Feb 27, 22; US citizen; m 49; c 3. HEMATOLOGY. *Educ:* Univ Leeds, MB & ChB, 45, MD, 48. *Prof Exp:* Jr lectr med, Univ Cape Town, 55-62; res assoc, 63-65, instr med, 65-67, from asst prof clin med to asst prof med, 67-75, ASSOC PROF CLIN MED, SCH MED, NY UNIV, 75- *Concurrent Pos:* Res asst, Groote Schuur Hosp, Cape Town, SAfrica, 55-62, asst physician, Arthritis Clin, 55-56, physician-in-chg & asst physician med outpatient clin, 56-62; res scientist, Am Nat Red Cross, 63-; clin asst vis physician, Bellevue Hosp, New York, 65-75, assoc vis physician, 75-; asst, Univ Hosp, 66-75, assoc med, 75- *Mem:* Soc Study Blood; Am Soc Hemat; Med Soc Ny. *Res:* Blood coagulation disorders and pathological fibrinolysis. *Mailing Add:* Dept of Med NY Univ Med Ctr New York NY 10016

LACKO, ANDRAS GYORGY, b Budapest, Hungary, Nov 10, 36; Can citizen; m 64; c 3. BIOCHEMISTRY, MICROBIOLOGY. *Educ:* Univ BC, BSA, 61, MSc, 63; Univ Wash, PhD(biochem), 68. *Prof Exp:* Res asst biochem, Univ Wash, 63-68; asst mem, Albert Einstein Med Ctr, 69-71; mem staff, 71-72, asst prof med, Med Sch, Temple Univ, 72-75; ASSOC PROF BIOCHEM, TEX COL OSTEOP MED, 75- *Concurrent Pos:* NIH fel, Albert Einstein Col Med, 68-69. *Mem:* Am Soc Biol Chem. *Res:* Structure and function of enzymes and lipo- proteins. *Mailing Add:* Dept Biochem Tex Col Osteop Med Ft Worth TX 76107

LACKS, SANFORD, b New York, NY, Jan 28, 34; m 59; c 3. GENETICS, BIOCHEMISTRY. *Educ:* Union Univ, NY, BS, 55; Rockefeller Univ, PhD, 60. *Prof Exp:* Instr biol, Harvard Univ, 60-61; from asst to assoc geneticist, 61-67, GENETICIST, BROOKHAVEN NAT LAB, 67- *Mem:* Am Soc Microbiol; Am Soc Biol Chem; Genetics Soc Am. *Res:* Microbial genetics; mechanism of bacterial transformation; function of enzymes acting on nucleic acids. *Mailing Add:* Biol Dept Brookhaven Nat Lab Upton NY 11973

LACKSONEN, JAMES W(ALTER), b Ashtabula, Ohio, Oct 17, 36; m 57; c 2. CHEMICAL ENGINEERING. *Educ:* Ohio State Univ, BChE & MSc, 59, PhD(chem eng), 64. *Prof Exp:* Res engr, Battelle Mem Inst, 60-65; proj engr, Pittsburgh Plate Glass Co, 65-66; sr develop engr chem-plastics div, Gen Tire & Rubber Co, Ohio, 66-67; asst prof, 67-80, ASSOC PROF CHEM ENG, UNIV TOLEDO, 80-, ASST DEAN, COL ENG, 71- *Mem:* AAAS; Am Inst Chem Engrs; Am Chem Soc; Electrochem Soc. *Res:* Kinetics and surface chemistry processes; fuel cells; transport of gases in microporous media; reactor design; reinforced plastics; foam; mass transfer. *Mailing Add:* 4758 S Crestridge Toledo OH 43623

LACOSS, RICHARD THADDEE, b Gardner, Mass, Aug 19, 37; m 60. ELECTRICAL ENGINEERING, GEOPHYSICS. *Educ:* Columbia Univ, AB, 59, BS, 60; Univ Calif, Berkeley, MS, 62, PhD(elec eng, info & control theory), 65. *Prof Exp:* Mem staff, 65-69, GROUP LEADER, LINCOLN LAB, MASS INST TECHNOL, 69- *Mem:* Inst Elec & Electronics Engrs; Sigma Xi. *Res:* Application of digital technology; statistics; information theory to problems in geophysics, especially solid earth problems; signal processing; underground nuclear test detection; system engineering; computer systems. *Mailing Add:* MIT Lincoln Lab PO Box 73 Lexington MA 02173

LACOSTE, RENE JOHN, b New York, NY, Feb 19, 27. ANALYTICAL CHEMISTRY, PESTICIDE CHEMISTRY. *Educ:* Rensselaer Polytech Inst, BS, 50; Univ Chicago, MS, 53. *Prof Exp:* Chemist, Am Dent Asn, 50-53; chemist, 53-68, sr chemist, 68-69, int registr agr & sanit chem, 69-75, regional regulatory mgr, 75-80, FOREIGN REGULATORY MGR AGR CHEM, ROHM AND HAAS CO, 80- *Mem:* AAAS; Am Chem Soc; Am Inst Chem; NY Acad Sci. *Res:* Physical and chemical methods of analysis; electrochemical analysis; separations of organic mixtures. *Mailing Add:* Park Dr Manor Lincoln Dr & Harvey St Philadelphia PA 19105

LACOUNT, ROBERT BRUCE, b Martinsburg, WVa, Sept 16, 35; m 64; c 2. ORGANIC CHEMISTRY. *Educ:* Shepherd Col, BS, 57; Univ Pittsburgh, MLitt, 62, PhD(org chem), 65. *Prof Exp:* Res assoc fundamental org chem, Mellon Inst, 58-65; from asst prof chem to prof & chmn dept chem, 65-71, PROF & CHMN DEPT CHEM & PHYSICS, WAYNESBURG COL, 71- *Concurrent Pos:* Res grant, Petrol Res Fund, 65-67; res chemist, US Bur Mines, 70-75 & Energy Res & Develop Admin, 75-77 & Dept Energy, 77- *Mem:* Am Chem Soc. *Res:* Synthetic organic chemistry; organic sulfur chemistry; production of low-sulfur fuels from coal. *Mailing Add:* Waynesburg Col Waynesburg PA 15370

LACROIX, GUY, b Que, Apr 10, 30; m 60; c 2. MARINE ECOLOGY. *Educ:* Laval Univ, BA, 52, LPh, 53; Univ Montreal, BSc, 57, MSc, 59, DSc, 68. *Prof Exp:* Zooplanktonologist, Grande Riviere Marine Biol Sta, Que, 58-68; asst prof, 68-71, assoc prof, 71-74, PROF BIOL OCEANOG, DEPT BIOL, LAVAL UNIV, 74- *Concurrent Pos:* Secy ed bd, Can Naturalist, 68-77; exec secy, Interuniv Group Oceanog Res, Que, 70-77; mem bd, Laval Univ, 74-77 & Sci Comt Oceanic Res, Can Nat Comt, 74-78. *Mem:* Marine Biol Asn UK; Am Soc Limnol & Oceanog; Plankton Soc Japan. *Res:* Zooplankton; invertebrate zoology; primary production; marine invertebrates. *Mailing Add:* Dept of Biol Laval Univ Ste-Foy Quebec PQ G1K 7P4 Can

LACROIX, JOSEPH DONALD, b Windsor, Ont, Apr 7, 25; nat US; m 51; c 3. BOTANY. *Educ:* Univ Western Ont, BA, 47; Univ Detroit, MS, 50; Purdue Univ, PhD(bot), 53. *Prof Exp:* Res asst mycol, Parke, Davis & Co, 51; from instr to assoc prof, 53-74, PROF BIOL, UNIV DETROIT, 74- *Concurrent Pos:* Kellogg fel, Univ Mich, 71-72. *Mem:* Bot Soc Am; Am Inst Biol Sci. *Res:* Scanning electron microscopy and electron probe analysis of silicification patterns in plant species; effects of gravity on plant tissue; radiosensitivity of higher plants. *Mailing Add:* Dept of Biol Univ of Detroit Detroit MI 48221

LACROIX, LUCIEN JOSEPH, b St Louis, Sask, May 14, 29; m 52; c 5. PLANT PHYSIOLOGY, HORTICULTURE. *Educ:* Univ Sask, BSA, 57, MSc, 58; Iowa State Univ, PhD(plant physiol), 61. *Prof Exp:* Technician field husb, Univ Sask, 54-57; res assoc plant sci, 61-63, from asst to assoc prof, 63-

72, PROF PLANT SCI, UNIV MAN, 72- *Mem:* Am Soc Plant Physiol; Can Soc Plant Physiol; Sigma Xi. *Res:* Potato tuberization; greenhouse research; winter hardiness. *Mailing Add:* Dept Plant Sci Univ Man Winnipeg MB R3T 2N2 Can

LACROIX, NORBERT HECTOR JOSEPH, b Sarsfield, Ont, Oct 26, 40; m 65; c 3. MATHEMATICS, BIOLOGICAL SCIENCES. *Educ:* Univ Ottawa, BSc, 62; Univ Notre Dame, PhD(math), 66. *Prof Exp:* Instr math, Univ Notre Dame, 62-66; from asst prof to assoc prof, 66-77, chmn dept, 70-77, PROF MATH, LAVAL UNIV, 77- *Mem:* Can Math Soc. *Res:* Organisational principles in developmental and sturctural biology; mathematical models. *Mailing Add:* Dept of Math Laval Univ Quebec PQ G1K 7P4 Can

LACY, ANN MATTHEWS, b Boston, Mass, May 29, 32. MICROBIAL GENETICS. *Educ:* Wellesley Col, BA, 53; Yale Univ, MS, 56, PhD(microbiol), 59. *Prof Exp:* Asst dept genetics, Carnegie Inst, 53-54; instr genetics, 59-61, asst prof, 61-67, assoc prof, 67-73, chmn dept biol sci, 69-72, PROF BIOL SCI, GOUCHER COL, 73- *Concurrent Pos:* Res fel, Glasgow Univ, 68-69. *Mem:* AAAS; Genetics Soc Am; Bot Soc Am; Am Inst Biol Sci; Sigma Xi. *Res:* Gene structure and function, and gene regulation in Neurospora crassa. *Mailing Add:* Dept of Biol Sci Goucher Col Towson MD 21204

LACY, GEORGE HOLCOMBE, b Washington, DC, Nov 13, 43; m 64; c 2. PHYTOPATHOLOGY, BACTERIAL GENETICS. *Educ:* Calif State Univ, Long Beach, BS, 66, MS, 71; Univ Calif, Riverside, PhD(phytopath), 75. *Prof Exp:* Lab technician qual control, Am Chem & Plastics Co, Stauffer Chem Co, Calif, 64-65; biol sci instr, US Peace Corps, Corozal Town, Brit Honduras, 66-68; scientist II soil microbiol, Jet Propulsion Lab, Calif Inst Technol, 69-71; res assoc plant path, Univ Wis-Madison, 75-77; asst plant pathologist, Conn Agr Exp Sta, 77-80; ASST PROF PLANT PATH, VA POLYTECH INST & STATE UNIV, 80- *Concurrent Pos:* NIH grant, 75-76, NSF grant, Univ Wis-Madison, 76-77. *Mem:* Am Phytopath Soc; Am Microbiol Soc. *Res:* Development of genetic systems among phytopathogenic bacteria to locate and study genetic determinants for pathogenicity and epidemiology and control of diseases of plants caused by prokaryotes. *Mailing Add:* Dept of Plant Path & Bot Box 1106 New Haven CT 06504

LACY, JULIA CAROLINE, b Detroit, Mich, July 10, 46. ENVIRONMENTAL BIOLOGY. *Educ:* Univ Mich, BA, 68, MS, 72. *Prof Exp:* Chief ecologist environ biol, Stearns Roger, Inc, 72-74; SR SCIENTIST BIOL ENVIRON BIOL, RADIAN CORP, 74- *Mem:* Ecol Soc Am; Am Inst Biol Sci; World Future Soc; Sigma Xi. *Res:* Policy analysis technology assessment with emphasis on energy resource use, particularly Texas lignite and analysis of policy complexes affecting resource development and commercialization of new technologies. *Mailing Add:* Radian Corp PO Box 9948 Austin TX 78766

LACY, LEWIS L, b Bluefield, WVa, Mar 25, 41; m 64; c 2. SOLID STATE PHYSICS, MATERIAL SCIENCE. *Educ:* Va Polytech Inst & State Univ, BS, 63, MS, 65; Univ Tenn, Knoxville, PhD(physics), 71. *Prof Exp:* Res assoc solid state physics, Los Alamos Sci Lab, 64; exp physicist, Nuclear & Plasma Physics Div, Space Sci Lab, Marshall Space Flight Ctr, NASA, 65-68, mat scientist appl physics, Space Sci Lab, 68-77, chief appl physics, Solid State Br, 77-80. *Honors & Awards:* Marshall Space Flight Ctr Dirs Commendation Award, NASA, 71 & NASA Manned Flight Awareness Award, 74; NASA Group Achievement Award, Johnson Space Flight Ctr, 76. *Mem:* Am Phys Soc; Am Inst Aeronaut & Astronaut. *Res:* Experimental solid state physics; low-temperature and superconducting material; solidification and crystal growth; containerless supercooling and low-gravity solidification. *Mailing Add:* 402 Rockmill Dr Southeast Huntsville AL 35803

LACY, MELVYN LEROY, b Henry, Nebr, Oct 24, 31; m 54; c 2. PLANT PATHOLOGY, SOIL MICROBIOLOGY. *Educ:* Univ Wyo, BS, 59, MS, 61; Ore State Univ, PhD(plant path), 64. *Prof Exp:* From asst prof to assoc prof, 71-78, PROF PLANT PATH, MICH STATE UNIV, 78- *Mem:* Am Phytopath Soc. *Res:* Soil-borne fungus diseases, survival of pathogens, inoculum potential and rhizosphere effects; soil fumigants and pesticides for disease control; epidemiology and disease management. *Mailing Add:* Dept of Bot & Plant Path Mich State Univ East Lansing MI 48823

LACY, PAUL ESTON, b Trinway, Ohio, Feb 7, 24; m 45; c 2. PATHOLOGY. *Educ:* Ohio State Univ, BA, 45, MSc & MD, 48; Univ Minn, PhD(path), 55. *Prof Exp:* Asst instr anat, Ohio State Univ, 44-48; intern, White Cross Hosp, Columbus, Ohio, 48-49; Nat Cancer Inst fel, Med Sch, Washington Univ, 55-56; from instr to assoc prof, 56-61, asst dean, 59-61, MALLINCKRODT PROF PATH & CHMN DEPT, MED SCH, WASHINGTON UNIV, 61- *Concurrent Pos:* Mem path B study sect, NIH, 61-66, chmn, 66-67; Banting mem lectr, Brit Diabetic Asn, 63; Eliott Proctor Joslin mem lectr, 66; mem adv comt res personnel, Am Cancer Soc, 66-70; mem basic sci adv comt, Nat Cystic Fibrosis Res Found, 67-69; Ninth Richard M Jaffe lectr, 69; Banting mem lectr & Rollin Turner Woodyatt mem lectr, 70; assoc ed, Diabetes, 73-; mem nat comn diabetes, NIH, 74-75 & mem nat adv environ health sci coun, 74-77. *Honors & Awards:* Mayo Found Achievement Award, 64; Banting Award, 70. *Mem:* Am Asn Anat; Am Soc Exp Path; Am Asn Path & Bact; Am Diabetes Asn; assoc mem Royal Soc Med. *Res:* Endocrine pathology; experimental diabetes. *Mailing Add:* Dept of Path Washington Univ Med Sch St Louis MO 63110

LACY, PETER D(EMPSEY), b Jacksonville, Fla, Dec 6, 20; m 50, 60; c 2. ELECTRONIC ENGINEERING. *Educ:* Univ Fla, BS, 42; Stanford Univ, MS, 47, PhD, 52. *Prof Exp:* Instr, Univ Fla, 42; asst, Stanford Univ, 46-49; consult, Varian Assocs, 49; engr, Hewlett-Packard Co, 50-60; CHMN BD, WILTRON CO, 60- *Mem:* Fel Inst Elec & Electronics Engrs; Sigma Xi. *Res:* Electron devices; microwave systems; automated measurement systems. *Mailing Add:* 825 E Middlefield Rd Mountain View CA 94043

LACY, W(ILLARD) C(ARLETON), b Waterville, Ohio, July 17, 16; m 40; c 6. GEOLOGICAL ENGINEERING. *Educ:* DePauw Univ, AB, 38; Univ Ill, MS, 40; Harvard Univ, PhD(geol), 50. *Prof Exp:* Geologist, Titanium Alloy Mfg Co, 42-43; petrologist, Cerro de Pasco Corp, 46-50, from asst chief to chief geologist, 50-55; prof geol, Univ Ariz, 55-64, prof mining & geol eng & head dept, 64-71; found chair geol, 72-81, EMER PROF GEOL, JAMES COOK UNIV, NORTH QUEENSLAND, 81- *Concurrent Pos:* Vis lectr, Harvard Univ, 53; Fulbright lectr, Univ Queensland, 67. *Mem:* Australian Inst Mining & Metall; fel Geol Soc Am; Soc Econ Geol; Am Inst Mining, Metall & Petrol Engrs; Australian Geol Soc. *Res:* Mining geology; localization of ore deposits; ground stabilization. *Mailing Add:* Dept of Geol James Cook Univ of N Queensland Townsville Queensland 4811 Australia

LACY, W(ILLIAM) J(OHN), b Meriden, Conn, May 26, 28; m 50; c 3. CHEMICAL ENGINEERING. *Educ:* Univ Conn, BS, 50. *Prof Exp:* Asst chemist & res assoc, NY Univ, 50-51; chemist & sr proj engr, Eng Res & Develop Labs, Va, 51-58; sr chemist, Oak Ridge Nat Lab, Tenn, 58-59; chief radiochemist, Off Civil Defense & Mobilization, 59-62, asst dir Posta Hack Res Div, Off Civil Defense, Washington, DC, 62-67; chief indust pollution control res & develop, Fed Water Pollution Control Admin, 67-71, dir, Appl Sci & Technol Div, 71-74, prin eng sci adv, 74-79, DIR, WATER, WASTE & HAZARDOUS MATERIAL RES, ENVIRON PROTECTION AGENCY, 79- *Concurrent Pos:* Partic sanit eng conf, Atomic Energy Comn, 52, 54 & 56, chmn adv comt spec weapons, 56-58; mem, Nat Adv Bd Water Decontamination, 54-56; lectr, numerous US univs; dep dir, US Deleg to USSR, 75, 76 & 78; head, US Deleg UN Environ Prog, Paris, 75 & 78; cochmn, Third Int Conf, Sorrento, Italy, 76; deleg, Tokyo Conf, 77; rep Environ Protection Agency, World Cong Berlin, 77; scientific dir, US Deleg to India, 78, Egypt, 79 & Italy, 81. *Mem:* AAAS; Am Chem Soc; Sigma Xi; Am Inst Chem Engrs; Am Acad Environ Engrs. *Res:* Industrial waste water treatment; radioactive water decontamination; reactor waste disposal problems; hazardous waste monitoring and disposal. *Mailing Add:* Off of Res & Develop Environ Protection Agency Washington DC 20460

LACY, WILLIAM WHITE, b Atlanta, Ga, Sept 18, 23; m 53; c 5. MEDICINE. *Educ:* Davidson Col, BS, 47; Harvard Med Sch, MD, 51. *Prof Exp:* Intern med, Sch Med, Johns Hopkins Univ, 51-52; asst resident, Duke Univ Hosp, 52-53 & Vanderbilt Univ Hosp, 53-54; from instr to asst prof, 54-73, ASSOC PROF MED, SCH MED, VANDERBILT UNIV, 73- *Concurrent Pos:* Am Heart Asn res fel, 57-61, estab investr, 61- *Res:* Metabolism in patients with cardiovascular and renal disease. *Mailing Add:* Dept of Med Vanderbilt Univ Sch of Med Nashville TN 37203

LAD, ROBERT AUGUSTIN, b Chicago, Ill, May 8, 19; m 44; c 9. CHEMISTRY. *Educ:* Univ Chicago, SB, 39, SM, 41, PhD(inorg chem), 46. *Prof Exp:* Asst, Nat Defense Res Comt, Univ Chicago, 42-46; aeronaut res scientist, Nat Adv Comt Aeronaut, Lewis Res Ctr, NASA, 46-59, chief, Mat Sci Br, 59-78; RETIRED. *Concurrent Pos:* Mem solid state sci panel, Nat Acad Sci-Nat Res Coun, 63- *Mem:* AAAS; Am Phys Soc; fel Am Inst Chem. *Res:* Physics and chemistry of surfaces; radiation chemistry; solid state physics. *Mailing Add:* 3114 W 159th St Cleveland OH 44111

LADA, ARNOLD, b New York, NY, May 26, 26; m 47; c 3. BIOCHEMISTRY, ORGANIC CHEMISTRY. *Educ:* Brooklyn Col, BS, 47; Georgetown Univ, MS, 51, PhD, 53. *Prof Exp:* Chemist, Glyco Prod Co, 47-48; biochemist, NIH, 49-50; res chemist, Food & Drug Admin, 50-54; biochemist, Toni Co Div, Gillette Co, 54-57; chief tech servs, Onyx Oil & Chem Co, 57-60, chief tech servs, Onyx Chem Corp, 60-65, GEN MGR, ONYX CHEM CO DIV, KEWANNEE INDUSTS INC, 65-, PRES, 74- *Mem:* AAAS; Am Chem Soc; Soc Cosmetic Chem; Chem Specialties Mfrs Asn; Cosmetics Toiletries Fragrances Asn. *Res:* Surface active agents; industrial applications; antimicrobial agents. *Mailing Add:* 6 Harbor Way Monmouth Beach NJ 07750

LADA, CHARLES JOSEPH, b Webster, Mass, Mar 18, 49. ASTRONOMY. *Educ:* Boston Univ, BA, 71; Harvard Univ, AM, 72, PhD(astron), 75. *Prof Exp:* Fel, Ctr Astrophysics, Harvard Col Observ & Smithsonian Astrophys Observ, 75-77; res fel, Harvard Univ, 77-78; Bart Bok fel astron, Steward Observ, 78-80, ASST PROF, UNIV ARIZ, 80- *Concurrent Pos:* Alfred P Sloan Found fel, 81- *Mem:* Am Astron Soc; Int Astron Union. *Res:* Formation of stars; interstellar chemistry and gas dynamics; structure and evolution of interstellar molecular clouds; structure and evolution of our galaxy. *Mailing Add:* Steward Observ Univ of Ariz Tucson AZ 85721

LADANYI, BRANKA MARIA, b Zagreb, Yugoslavia, Sept 7, 47; Can citizen; m 74. THEORETICAL CHEMISTRY. *Educ:* McGill Univ, BSc, 69; Yale Univ, MPhil, 71, PhD(chem), 73. *Prof Exp:* Vis asst prof chem, Univ Ill, Urbana, 74; res assoc chem, Yale Univ, 74-79; ASST PROF CHEM, COLO STATE UNIV, 79- *Mem:* Am Chem Soc; Am Phys Soc; AAAS. *Res:* Statistical mechanics of fluids; structure of molecular liquids; propagation and scattering of light in fluids; statistical mechanics of polymer solutions. *Mailing Add:* Dept Chem Colo State Univ Ft Collins CO 80523

LADANYI, BRANKO, b Zagreb, Yugoslavia, Dec 14, 22; Can citizen; m 46; c 3. GEOTECHNICAL ENGINEERING. *Educ:* Univ Zagreb, BEng, 47, Univ Louvain, PhD(civil eng), 59. *Prof Exp:* Design engr found & hydraul struct, Dept Transport, Zagreb, 47-52; asst prof soil mech & found eng, Univ Zagreb, 52-58; res engr soil mech, Belgian Geotech Inst, Ghent, 58-62; from assoc prof to prof geotech eng, Laval Univ, Que, 62-67; PROF ROCK MECH & PERMAFROST ENG, POLYTECH SCH, UNIV MONTREAL, HEAD, GEOTECH SECT, DEPT CIVIL ENG, 77- *Concurrent Pos:* Dir, Northern Eng Centre, 72- *Honors & Awards:* Que Sci Award, 74; Legget Goetechnical Award, 81. *Mem:* Eng Inst Can; Can Inst Metall; Am Soc Civil Engrs; Int Soc Rock Mech; fel Royal Soc Can. *Res:* Soil and rock mechanics; permafrost engineering. *Mailing Add:* Dept of Civil Eng Polytech Sch Univ Montreal Box 6079 Sta A Montreal PQ H3C 3A7 Can

LADAS, GERASIMOS, b Lixuri, Greece, Apr 25, 37; US citizen; m 65; c 2. DIFFERENTIAL EQUATIONS. *Educ:* Nat Univ Athens, BS, 61; MS, NY Univ, 66, PhD(math), 68. *Prof Exp:* Fel, NY Univ, 64-68; asst prof math, Fairfield Univ, 68-69; asst prof, 69-72, assoc prof, 72-75, chmn dept, 72-78, PROF MATH, UNIV RI, 75- *Mem:* Am Math Soc. *Res:* Ordinary, functional and abstract differential equations. *Mailing Add:* 80 Greenwood Dr Peace Dale RI 02879

LADD, ANTHONY THORNTON, b New York, NY, Aug 25, 20; m 56; c 2. INTERNAL MEDICINE. *Educ:* Cornell Univ, MD, 45. *Prof Exp:* Asst path, Med Col, Vanderbilt Univ, 45; from asst to instr, Med Col, Cornell Univ, 47-49; from intern to asst resident med, Presby Hosp, New York, 49-52; asst resident, Mary Imogene Bassett Hosp, Cooperstown, NY, 51; from instr to assoc prof med, State Univ NY Upstate Med Ctr, 52-70; chief med, Vet Admin Hosp, Charleston, 70-74; chief med & chief staff, County Hosp, 74-76, MED DIR, COUNTY HOSP, 76- PROF MED, MED UNIV SC, 70- *Concurrent Pos:* Chief hemat sect, Vet Admin Hosp, Syracuse, NY, 59-60, chief med serv, 60-70. *Res:* Experimental atherosclerosis; unsaturated fats; hematology; genetically controlled hemoglobin abnormalities. *Mailing Add:* County Hosp 326 Calhoun St Charleston SC 29401

LADD, CHARLES CUSHING, b Brooklyn, NY, Nov 23, 32; m 54; c 4. CIVIL ENGINEERING, SOIL MECHANICS. *Educ:* Bowdoin Col, AB, 55; Mass Inst Technol, SB, 55, MS, 57, ScD(soil eng), 61. *Prof Exp:* From instr to assoc prof, 57-70, PROF CIVIL ENG, MASS INST TECHNOL, 70- *Concurrent Pos:* Vis consult, Haley & Aldrich, Inc, 80- *Mem:* Am Soc Civil Engrs; Am Soc Testing & Mat; Am Soc Eng Educ; Nat Soc Prof Engrs. *Res:* Engineering properties of soils and soft ground construction as applied to civil engineering projects. *Mailing Add:* Rm 1-348 Dept of Civil Eng Mass Inst of Technol Cambridge MA 02139

LADD, HARRY STEPHEN, b St Louis, Mo, Jan 1, 99; m 34; c 2. GEOLOGY. *Educ:* Washington Univ, St Louis, AB, 22; Univ Iowa, MS, 24, PhD(geol), 25. *Prof Exp:* Asst geol, Univ Iowa, 22-25; asst prof geol, Univ Va, 26-29; paleontologist, Venezuela Gulf Oil Co, 29-31; pvt res, US Nat Mus, 31-33; res assoc geol, Univ Rochester, 33-35; assoc geologist, Nat Park Serv, 35-38, geologist, 38-40; assoc geologist, US Geol Surv, 40-41, geologist, 41-43, sr geologist, 44-45, prin geologist, Washington, DC, 45-69; RES ASSOC, US NAT MUS, SMITHSONIAN INST, 69- *Concurrent Pos:* Bishop Mus fel, Yale Univ, 25 & 28; mem staff, Oper Crossroads. *Honors & Awards:* Distinguished Serv Award, Dept Interior, 65; Paleont Soc Medal, 81. *Mem:* AAAS (vpres, 65); Paleont Soc (pres, 54); fel Geol Soc Am (vpres, 55); Am Asn Petrol Geol. *Res:* Tertiary paleontology and stratigraphy; geology of Pacific Islands; origin of coral reefs; tertiary mollusks of the Pacific. *Mailing Add:* 3905 Leland St Chevy Chase MD 20815

LADD, JOHN HERBERT, b Kewanee, Ill, Sept 6, 18; m 39; c 3. PHYSICAL CHEMISTRY, PHYSICS. *Educ:* Univ Ill, BS, 40, MS, 42, PhD(phys chem), 47. *Prof Exp:* Asst phys chem, Univ Ill, 40-42; sr chemist, 47-48, develop engr, 48, sr develop engr, 48-53, tech assoc, 53-57, sr develop proj engr, 57-69, RES ASSOC, EASTMAN KODAK CO, 69- *Concurrent Pos:* Instr, Univ Rochester, 49-51. *Mem:* Soc Motion Picture & TV Engrs; Inst Elec & Electronics Eng; Soc Photog Sci & Eng; Am Phys Soc. *Res:* Electron emission from metals; color photographic printers; color films in television; television test charts and standards; analog computers; digital equipment instrumentation, optical testing; digital hardward; photosensors; laser applications. *Mailing Add:* Physics Div Res Lab Bldg 81 Eastman Kodak Co Kodak Park Rochester NY 14650

LADD, KAYE VICTORIA, b Seattle, Wash, Aug 26, 41. INORGANIC CHEMISTRY, PHYSICAL CHEMISTRY. *Educ:* Reed Col, BA, 63; Brandeis Univ, MA, 65, PhD(inorg chem), 74. *Prof Exp:* Staff scientist chem biol, Tyco Labs Inc, 65-68; assoc prof chem, Suffolk Univ, 68-75; MEM FAC CHEM, EVERGREEN STATE COL, 75- *Concurrent Pos:* Consult, New Eng Aquarium, 70-75 & Corff & Shapiro, 77. *Mem:* Am Chem Soc; AAAS; Sci Inst Publ Info. *Res:* Environmental inorganic research, especially the transport of trace metals in metabolic process within and between organisms. *Mailing Add:* Dept of Chem Evergreen State Col Olympia WA 98505

LADD, SHELDON LANE, b Merced, Calif, Sept 21, 41; m 62; c 2. GENETICS, AGRONOMY. *Educ:* Calif State Univ, Fresno, BS, 63; Univ Calif, Davis, PhD(genetics), 66. *Prof Exp:* Captain asst chief forensic toxicol, US Air Force Sch Aerospace Med, 66-71; plant breeder sugarcane genetics, Dept Genetics & Path, Hawaiian Sugar Planters' Asn, 71-76; assoc prof, 76-80, PROF AGRON, COLO STATE UNIV, 80- *Concurrent Pos:* Dir, Asn Off Seed Certifying Agencies, exec dir, Colo Seed Growers Asn & head seed cert, State Colo, 76- *Mem:* Crop Sci Soc Am; Am Soc Agron. *Res:* Plant breeding of agronomic species; cell and tissue culture of agronomic and revegetation species; seed quality and vigor. *Mailing Add:* Dept of Agron Colo State Univ Ft Collins CO 80523

LADD, THYRIL LEONE, JR, b Albany, NY, Oct 10, 31; m 56; c 3. ENTOMOLOGY. *Educ:* State Univ NY, Albany, AB, 56, MA, 58; Cornell Univ, PhD(entom), 63. *Prof Exp:* Res entomologist, 62-69, RES LEADER, JAPANESE BEETLE RES LAB, AGR RES SERV, USDA, 69- *Concurrent Pos:* Adj prof entom, Ohio State Univ, 71- *Mem:* AAAS; Entom Soc Am; Am Entom Soc; Sigma Xi; Coun Agr Sci & Technol. *Res:* Effects of radiation and chemicals on insect reproduction; integrated insect control; insect responses to attractants and repellents; effects of insect feeding on plant yields; improved procedures for applications of insecticides. *Mailing Add:* Japanese Beetle Res Lab USDA Ohio Agr Res & Develop Ctr Wooster OH 44691

LADDE, GANGARAM SHIVLINGAPPA, b Jalkot, India, Mar 9, 40; US citizen; m 65; c 3. DIFFERENTIAL EQUATIONS, APPLIED SYSTEMS ANALYSIS. *Educ:* Marathwada Univ, BSc, 63, MSc, 65; Univ RI, PhD(math), 72. *Prof Exp:* Teaching asst math, Univ RI, 67-71, instr, 71-73; from asst prof to assoc prof math, State Univ NY, Potsdam, 73-80; PROF MATH, UNIV TEX, ARLINGTON, 80- *Concurrent Pos:* Fel, Univ Santa Clara, Calif, 74, res assoc, 81; grant-in-aid, Res Found, State Univ NY, Albany, 78-79; vis prof math, Univ Rome, Italy, 78 & Univ Tex, Arlington, 79-80; ed, Stochastic Anal & Applications. *Mem:* Am Math Soc; Indian Math Soc; Sigma Xi; Soc Indust & Appl Math. *Res:* Biomathematics; competitive analysis; differential games; deterministic analysis; mathematical modeling in biological, medical, physical, and social sciences; nonlinear boundary value problems; oscillation theory; stability theory; stochastic andlysis; systems analysis. *Mailing Add:* Dept Math Univ Tex Arlington TX 76019

LADE, ROBERT WALTER, b Fond du Lac, Wis, Apr 3, 35; m 56; c 4. SOLID STATE ELECTRONICS. *Educ:* Marquette Univ, BEE, 58, MS, 61; Carnegie Inst Technol, PhD(elec eng), 62. *Prof Exp:* Instr, Marquette Univ, 59-61 & Carnegie Inst Technol, 61-62; assoc prof, NC State Univ, 63-67; prof elec eng & chmn dept, Marquette Univ, 67-77; MEM STAFF, RWL ENG, FT MYERS, FLA, 77- *Concurrent Pos:* Engr, AC Spark Plug, Wis, 59-60. *Mem:* Inst Elec & Electronics Engrs. *Res:* Electrical properties of free and passivated semiconductor surfaces under the influence of high energy radiation fields; computer-aided circuit design. *Mailing Add:* RWL Eng PO Box 1401 Ft Myers FL 33902

LADELFE, PETER CARL, b Woburn, Mass, Feb 19, 43; m 78. PHYSICS, OPTICS. *Educ:* Clarkson Col Technol, BS, 68, MS, 71. *Prof Exp:* Sr physicist optical films, Spectrum Systs Div, Barnes Eng Co, 71-74; consult, Private Pract, 74-77; staff mem optical films, 78-79, SECT LEADER, COATINGS SECT, LOS ALAMOS NAT LAB, 79- *Mem:* Am Vacuum Soc; Optical Soc Am. *Res:* Design and development of optical interference filters including research in the materials science of producing optical films. *Mailing Add:* CMB-6 MS 770 Box 1663 Los Alamos NM 87545

LADEN, KARL, b Brooklyn, NY, Aug 10, 32; m 56; c 5. BIOCHEMISTRY. *Educ:* Univ Akton, BS, 54; Northwestern Univ, PhD(chem), 57. *Prof Exp:* Asst, Northwestern Univ, 54-57; res chemist, William Wrigley Jr Co, 57-58; res biochemist, Toni Co Div, 59-60, res supvr, 60-62, mgr biol res, 62-64, asst lab dir, Gillette Med Res Inst, 64-67, mgr biomed sci dept, Gillette Res Inst, 67-68, vpres biomed sci, Gillette Res Inst, Gillette Co, 68-76, pres, 71-76; V PRES RES & DEVELOP, CARTER PROD DIV, CARTER WALLACE, INC, 76- *Concurrent Pos:* Consult, Indust Bio-Test Labs, Inc, 55-57; lectr, Northwestern Univ, 58-64 & Am Univ, 64-65; ed, J Soc Cosmetic Chem, 67-71. *Mem:* Am Chem Soc; Soc Invest Dermat; Soc Cosmetic Chem (pres, 77). *Res:* Biochemistry and physiology of skin and hair. *Mailing Add:* Carter Prods Div Half Acre Rd Cranbury NJ 08512

LADENHEIM, HARRY, b Vienna, Austria, Oct 17, 32; US citizen; m 55; c 2. PROCESS & CATALYST DEVELOPMENT, REACTOR ENGINEERING. *Educ:* City Col New York, BS, 54; Polytech Inst Brooklyn, PhD(org polymer chem), 58. *Prof Exp:* Fel chem, Ill Inst Technol, 58-59; res chemist, Esso Res & Eng Co, 59-63; res chemist, Houdry Process & Chem Co, 63-70, sr res chemist, 70-76, sr develop engr, 76-79, prin res engr, Air Prods & Chem Inc, Marcus Hook, Pa, 79-81, SR PROCESS ENGR, AIR PRODS & CHEM INC, PAULSBORO, NJ, 82- *Mem:* Am Chem Soc. *Res:* Mechanisms in physical organic chemistry; exploratory and process study in petroleum technology; use of polymers as enzyme models; catalysis; catalytic chemistry. *Mailing Add:* 459 Levering Mill Rd Bala Cynwyd PA 19064

LADERMAN, A(RNOLD) J(OSEPH), b Pittsburgh, Pa, Apr 27, 30; m 59; c 2. FLUID MECHANICS, HEAT TRANSFER. *Educ:* Univ Calif, Berkeley, BS, 51, MS, 57, PhD(mech eng), 60. *Prof Exp:* Res engr mech eng, Mech Equip Unit, Boeing Co, 51-55; assoc res engr, Propulsion Dynamics Lab, Univ Calif, Berkeley, 57-65; supvr, Exp Fluid Mech Sect, 66-71, prin scientist, Fluid Mech Dept, 65-79, PRIN SCIENTIST, MECH ENG DEPT, AERONUTRONIC DIV, FORD AEROSPACE & COMMUN CORP, 79- *Concurrent Pos:* Lectr, Univ Calif, Berkeley, 60-61, 64; consult, Repub Aviation Co, NY, 62, Jet Propulsion Lab, Calif, 63-64 & Sandia Corp, 63-65. *Mem:* Am Inst Aeronaut & Astronaut; Combustion Inst; Sigma Xi. *Res:* Non steady gas dynamics of reactive media; shock and detonation wave phenomena; two phase flow; high power lasers; transition and turbulence in compressible boundary layers. *Mailing Add:* Advan Develop Oper Ford Aerospace & Commun Corp Ford Rd Newport Beach CA 92663

LADERMAN, JULIAN DAVID, b New York, NY, Oct 15, 48. MATHEMATICS, COMPUTER SCIENCE. *Educ:* NY Univ, BA, 70, MS, 72, PhD(comput sci), 76. *Prof Exp:* Instr, 73-77, ASST PROF MATH, LEHMAN COL, 77- *Concurrent Pos:* Consult, Systs Revisited, 78- *Mem:* Am Math Soc; Math Asn Am; Am Statist Asn. *Res:* Computational complexity; mathematical programming; statistics; game theory; probability; operations research; programming languages; numerical analysis. *Mailing Add:* Dept of Math Bedford Park Blvd W Bronx NY 10468

LADINSKY, HERBERT, b New York, NY, July 22, 35; m 67. PHARMACOLOGY. *Educ:* City Col New York, BS, 58; State Univ NY, PhD(pharmacol), 66. *Prof Exp:* Fel pharmacol, Royal Caroline Inst, Stockholm, 66-67 & Mario Negri Inst, 67-69; NIH fel, 66-68; LAB CHIEF, MARIO NEGRI INST, 69- *Mem:* Ital Pharmacol Soc. *Res:* Physiology and pharmacology of the cholinergic system. *Mailing Add:* Inst for Res in Pharmacol Mario Negri Inst Via Eritrea 62 Milan Italy

LADINSKY, JUDITH L, b Los Angeles, Calif, June 16, 38; m 61; c 2. CYTOLOGY, ENDOCRINOLOGY. *Educ:* Univ Mich, BS, 61; Univ Wis-Madison, MS, 64, PhD(reprod physiol), 68. *Prof Exp:* Med technologist, Clin Labs, St Mary's Hosp, Mich, 55-56; res asst, Dept Neuropath, Univ Mich, 56-58, Dept Anat, 58-60 & Dept Surg, 60-61; proj assoc, Dept Gynec-Obstet, 61-68, from instr to asst prof prev med, 68-74, ASSOC PROF PREV MED, SCH MED, UNIV WIS-MADISON, 75- *Mem:* Am Soc Cell Biol; NY Acad Sci; Tissue Cult Asn; Am Pub Health Asn; Asn Teachers Prev Med. *Res:* Cell kinetics of normal and neoplastic tissues; automated methods of cancer detection; endocrinology of tumors; community medicine; neonatology; health care delivery. *Mailing Add:* 300 Infirmary Dept Prev Med Med Sch Univ Wis Madison WI 53706

LADISCH, MICHAEL R, b Upper Darby, Pa, Jan 15, 50; m 75; c 1. BIOCHEMICAL ENGINEERING. *Educ:* Drexel Univ, BS, 73; Purdue Univ, MS, 74, PhD(chem eng), 77. *Prof Exp:* Res eng biochem, 77-78, asst prof, 78-81, GROUP LEADER RES & PROCESS ENG, LAB RENEWABLE RESOURCES, PURDUE UNIV, 78-, ASSOC PROF FOOD, AGR & CHEM ENG, 81- *Mem:* Am Chem Soc; Am Inst Chem Engrs; Am Soc Automotive Engrs. *Res:* Cellulose conversion; separations; enqyme and chemical kinetics. *Mailing Add:* Lab Renewable Resources Eng Potter Ctr Purdue Univ West Lafayette IN 47906

LADMAN, AARON JULIUS, b Jamaica, NY, July 3, 25; m 48; c 2. ANATOMY. *Educ:* NY Univ, AB, 47; Ind Univ, PhD(anat), 52. *Prof Exp:* Res fel anat, Harvard Med Sch, 52-55, assoc anat, 55-61; assoc prof, Med Units, Univ Tenn, 61-64; prof anat & chmn dept, Univ NMex, 64-81; DEAN, COL ALLIED HEALTH & PROF ANAT, HAHNEMANN MED COL & HOSP, PHILADELPHIA, 81- *Concurrent Pos:* USPHS career develop award, 62-64; mem res career award comt, Nat Inst Gen Med Sci, 67-71; ed, Anat Record, 68- *Mem:* Am Soc Cell Biol; Am Soc Zoologists; Endocrine Soc; Histochem Soc; Am Asn Anatomists (2nd vpres, 80-81 & 1st vpres, 81-82). *Res:* Cytochemistry; electron microscopy; endocrinology; experimental cytology; retina lung; tumor biology; scientific writing. *Mailing Add:* Hahnemann Med Col & Hosp 230 N Broad St Philadelphia PA 19102

LADNER, JANE ELLEN CRAWFORD, physical chemistry, molecular biology, see previous edition

LADNER, SIDNEY JULES, b Houston, Tex, Mar 12, 36; m 59; c 2. PHYSICAL CHEMISTRY. *Educ:* Univ Houston, BS, 59, PhD(phys chem), 65. *Prof Exp:* Fel chem, Univ NMex, 65-66; chemist, Shell Develop Co, Tex, 66-67; asst prof, 67-69, ASSOC PROF CHEM, HOUSTON BAPTIST UNIV, 69- *Mem:* Am Chem Soc. *Res:* Molecular spectroscopy; decay processes and the decay kinetics of molecules in excited electronic energy states; chemical education. *Mailing Add:* Dept of Chem Houston Baptist Univ 7502 Fondren Rd Houston TX 77074

LADO, FRED, b La Coruna, Spain, June 5, 38; US citizen; m 60; c 3. PHYSICS. *Educ:* Univ Fla, BS, 60, PhD(physics), 64. *Prof Exp:* Fel physics, Univ Fla, 64-65; staff mem, Los Alamos Sci Lab, 65-68; asst prof, 68-74, ASSOC PROF PHYSICS, NC STATE UNIV, 74- *Concurrent Pos:* Fulbright sr lectr, Spain, 71-72. *Mem:* Am Phys Soc. *Res:* Statistical mechanics; equilibrium and non-equilibrium theory of liquids; many-body problem. *Mailing Add:* Dept of Physics NC State Univ Raleigh NC 27607

LADOUCEUR, GILLES PIERRE, photogrammetry, forest ecology, see previous edition

LADSON, THOMAS ALVIN, b Hyattsville, Md, Sept 29, 17; m 48; c 2. VETERINARY MEDICINE. *Educ:* Univ Pa, VMD, 39. *Prof Exp:* Vet, 39-60; field rep, Livestock Sanit Serv, Md State Bd Agr, 60-62, dir, 62-73, head vet sci dept, Univ Md, College Park, 62-73; actg dir, Div Animal Indust, Md Dept Agr, 73-77, chief, 77-80. *Mem:* Am Vet Med Asn; US Animal Health Asn. *Res:* Large animal medicine; regulatory veterinary medicine. *Mailing Add:* Box 158 Sandy Spring MD 20860

LA DU, BERT NICHOLS, JR, b Lansing, Mich, Nov 13, 20; m 47; c 4. BIOCHEMICAL PHARMACOLOGY. *Educ:* Mich State Col, BS, 43; Univ Mich, MD, 45; Univ Calif, PhD(biochem), 52. *Prof Exp:* Intern, Rochester Gen Hosp, NY, 45-46; asst biochem, Mich State Col, 46-47 & Univ Calif, 47-50; from sr asst surgeon to med dir, NIH, 50-63; prof pharmacol & chmn dept, Med Sch, NY Univ, 63-74; chmn dept, 74-80, PROF PHARMACOL MED SCH, UNIV MICH, ANN ARBOR, 74- *Concurrent Pos:* Res assoc, Goldwater Mem Hosp Res Serv, NY Univ, 50-54, instr, Bellevue Med Ctr, 51-54. *Mem:* Am Soc Biol Chemists; Am Chem Soc; Am Soc Pharmacol & Exp Therapeut (pres, 78-79); Am Soc Human Genetics; NY Acad Sci (pres, 70). *Res:* Drug metabolism; metabolism of tyrosine; inborn errors of metabolism; pharmacogenetics. *Mailing Add:* Dept of Pharmacol Univ of Mich Med Sch Ann Arbor MI 48109

LADUKE, JOHN CARL, b Jackson, Mich, Nov 21, 50; m 73. SYSTEMATIC BIOLOGY. *Educ:* Tex Tech Univ, BS, 73, MS, 75; Ohio State Univ, PhD(bot), 80. *Prof Exp:* ASST PROF SYST BOT, UNIV NDAK, 80- *Honors & Awards:* Ralph E Alston Award, Bot Soc Am, 79. *Mem:* AAAS; Am Soc Plant Taxonomists; Bot Soc Am; Soc Syst Zool; Sigma Xi. *Res:* Plant systematics; chemosystematics; sphaeralcea section fendlerianae (malvacae) including gathering morphological, cytological and flavonoid chemical data. *Mailing Add:* Dept Biol Univ NDak Grand Forks ND 58202

LADWIG, HAROLD ALLEN, b Manilla, Iowa, May 11, 22; m 46; c 2. NEUROLOGY. *Educ:* Univ Iowa, MD, 47, BA, 52; Am Bd Psychiat & Neurol, dipl. *Prof Exp:* Clin instr neurol, Univ Minn, 50-53; from instr to asst prof, 54-66, ASSOC PROF NEUROL & PSYCHIAT, SCH MED, CREIGHTON UNIV, 66- *Concurrent Pos:* Dir electroencephalog lab, Creighton Mem St Joseph's Hosp, 54-, asst dir rehab ctr, 54-58, assoc dir, 58-64; attend physician, Vet Admin Hosp, 54-59, consult physician, 59-63; mem med staff, Nebr Children's Ther Ctr, 56-64; dir, Electroencephalog Lab, Children's Mem Hosp, 63-70 & Archbishop Bergan Mercy Hosp, 64- *Mem:* Am Electroencephalog Soc; AMA; Am Col Physicians; Am Cong Rehab Med; Am Acad Neurol. *Res:* Diagnostic neurology and rehabilitation of neurological patients; care of the aged; electroencephalography. *Mailing Add:* West Dodge Med Bldg 8300 Dodge St Suite 202 Omaha NE 68114

LADY, EDWARD RUSSELL, b West Reading, Pa, Nov 5, 26; m 50; c 3. MECHANICAL ENGINEERING, CRYOGENICS. *Educ:* Univ Louisville, BME, 47; Mass Inst Technol, SM, 49; Univ Mich, Ann Arbor, PhD(mech eng), 63. *Prof Exp:* Jr engr, Linde Div, Union Carbide Corp, 47-48 & Oak Ridge Nat Lab, 50; chief engr opers, Air Prod & Chem, Inc, 50-61; assoc prof mech eng, Univ Mich, 63-69; vis mem staff cryog, Los Alamos Sci Lab, 69-70; assoc prof, 70-77, PROF MECH ENG, UNIV MICH, ANN ARBOR, 77-,

DIR CONTINUING ENG EDUC, 80- *Concurrent Pos:* Mem bd, Cryog Eng Conf, Nat Acad Sci, 66-69. *Mem:* Am Soc Mech Engrs; Am Soc Heat, Refrig & Air-Conditioning Engrs. *Res:* Low heat flux boiling; liquid natural gas safety; cryogenic magnets. *Mailing Add:* Dept of Mech Eng Univ of Mich Ann Arbor MI 48104

LAEGREID, NILS, b Eidfjord, Norway, Mar 30, 24; nat US; m 61; c 3. ELECTRICAL ENGINEERING. *Educ:* Univ Minn, BEE, 55. *Prof Exp:* Engr, Minn, 55-57; sr scientist, Mech Div, Gen Mills, Inc, 57-61; mgr, Thin Film Res Electrocraft Corp, 61-64; res assoc, Univ Minn, 64-65; mem tech staff, Fairchild Semiconductor Res & Develop Lab, 65-68; mgr res, Veeco/Andar Corp, 68-71; STAFF ENGR, PAC NORTHWEST DIV, BATTELLE MEM INST, 71- *Mem:* Am Phys Soc; Am Vacuum Soc. *Res:* Semiconductor and optical thin films; multielectrode and radio frequency sputtering; plasma and surface physics; vacuum technology; material science related to optical components for high energy lasers. *Mailing Add:* Battelle Northwest Labs 231-Z Bldg 200-West Richland WA 99352

LAEMLE, LOIS K, b New York, NY, May 26, 41. DEVELOPMENTAL NEUROBIOLOGY, VISUAL SYSTEMS. *Educ:* City Univ New York, BS, 62; Columbia Univ, PhD(anat), 68. *Prof Exp:* Fel anat, Albert Einstein Col Med, 68; res fel neurosci, Rose F Kennedy Ctr Ment Retardation, 69-72; asst prof, 72-77, ASSOC PROF NEUROANAT & HISTOL, UNIV MED & DENT NJ, 77- *Mem:* Am Asn Anatomists; Soc Neurosci; Sigma Xi; NY Acad Sci. *Res:* Morphology and development of the central nervous system; fiber connections, neuronal maturation, and neurotransmitters in the visual system and midbrain Central Gray of man and other mammals. *Mailing Add:* Dept Anat Univ Med & Dent NJ Newark NJ 07103

LAEMMLE, JOSEPH THOMAS, b Louisville, Ky, Feb 7, 41; m 65; c 2. ORGANIC CHEMISTRY. *Educ:* Bellarmine Col, BA, 64; Ga Inst Technol, MS, 68, PhD(org chem), 71; Ga State Univ, MBA, 76. *Prof Exp:* From asst res chemist to asst, Ga Inst Technol, 67-73; asst prof chem, Kennesaw Col, 73-77; sr scientist, 77-80, staff scientist, 80-81, tech supvr, 81, SR TECH SUPVR, ALCOA LABS, 81- *Mem:* Am Chem Soc; Am Soc Fabrication Engrs; Sigma Xi. *Res:* Determination of the structure of organometallic compounds; lubricant testing and development; descriptions of organometallic reaction mechanisms and sterechemistry of additions with Ketones; metal working lubricants including formation, handling, reclamation and disposal. *Mailing Add:* Fabricating Tech Div Alcoa Tech Ctr Alcoa Lab Alcoa Ctr PA 15069

LAEMMLEN, FRANKLIN, b Reedley, Calif, Mar 8, 38; m 61; c 2. PLANT PATHOLOGY, ENTOMOLOGY. *Educ:* Univ Calif, Davis, BS, 60, PhD(plant path), 70; Purdue Univ, West Lafayette, MS, 67. *Prof Exp:* Res asst plant path, Univ Calif, Davis, 66-70; asst prof, Univ Hawaii, 70-72; asst prof, 72-76, ASSOC PROF PLANT PATH, MICH STATE UNIV, 76- *Concurrent Pos:* Assoc ed, Plant Dis Reporter, 74-77; vis colleague, Dept Plant Path, Univ Calif, Berkeley, 78-79. *Mem:* Sigma Xi; Am Phytopath Soc. *Res:* Extension plant pathology; ornamental plant diseases; plant disease diagnostic laboratory. *Mailing Add:* Univ Calif AG Extension Court House El Centro CA 92242

LAERM, JOSHUA, b Waynesboro, Pa, Sept 27, 42; m 81. FUNCTIONAL MORPHOLOGY. *Educ:* Pa State Univ, BA, 65; Univ Ill, MS, 72, PhD(zool), 76. *Prof Exp:* Asst prof, 76-81, ASSOC PROF ZOOL, UNIV GA, 81-, DIR, MUS NATURAL HIST, 78- *Mem:* AAAS; Soc Vert Paleont; Am Soc Mammalogists; Soc Study of Evolution; Am Soc Zoologists. *Res:* Evolution and functional morphology of vertebral column in fossil fishes; mammalian systematics; vertebrate natural history. *Mailing Add:* Dept Zool Univ Ga Athens GA 30602

LAESSIG, RONALD HAROLD, b Marshfield, Wis, Apr 4, 40; m 66; c 1. CLINICAL CHEMISTRY, PUBLIC HEALTH. *Educ:* Wis State Univ-Stevens Point, BS, 62; Univ Wis-Madison, PhD(anal chem), 65. *Prof Exp:* asst dir lab, 70-79, assoc prof, 71-76, PROF PREV MED & PATH, MED CTR, UNIV WIS-MADISON, 76-, CHIEF CHEM, STATE LAB HYG, 66-, DIR LAB, 79- *Concurrent Pos:* Mem, Inst Bd Anal Chem, 71-; chmn diagn prod comt, Food & Drug Admin, 72-; pres elect, Nat Comt Clin Lab Standards, 79-81. *Honors & Awards:* DIFCO Award, Am Pub Health Asn, 74. *Mem:* Am Asn Clin Chem; Am Chem Soc; Am Pub Health Asn. *Res:* Automation; multiphasic screening; computerization of laboratory operation. *Mailing Add:* State Lab Hyg 465 Henry Mall Univ of Wis Med Ctr Madison WI 53706

LAETSCH, THEODORE WILLIS, b St Louis, Mo, Jan 7, 40; m 61. MATHEMATICAL ANALYSIS. *Educ:* Washington Univ, St Louis, BS, 61; Mass Inst Technol, SM, 62; Calif Inst Technol, PhD(appl math), 68. *Prof Exp:* Asst prof physics, Col of Idaho, 62-65; asst prof math, Ill State Univ, 68-70; ASSOC PROF MATH, UNIV ARIZ, 71- & HEAD MATH DEPT, 78. *Concurrent Pos:* Nat Acad Sci-Nat Res Coun resident res associateship, Wright-Patterson AFB, Ohio, 70-71. *Mem:* Am Math Soc; Soc Indust & Appl Math. *Res:* Functional analysis in partially ordered spaces; boundary value problems for ordinary and partial differential equations. *Mailing Add:* Dept of Math Univ of Ariz Tucson AZ 85721

LAETSCH, WATSON MCMILLAN, b Bellingham, Wash, Jan 19, 33; m 58; c 2. BOTANY. *Educ:* Wabash Col, AB, 55; Stanford Univ, PhD(biol), 61. *Prof Exp:* Asst prof biol, State Univ NY, Stony Brook, 61-63; asst prof bot, 63-68, assoc prof, 68-71, assoc dir, Lawrence Hall Sci, 69-72, Dir Univ Bot Garden, 69-73; dir, Lawrence Hall Sci, 72-80, PROF BOT, UNIV CALIF, BERKELEY, 71-, VCHANCELLOR UNDERGRAD AFFAIRS, 80- *Concurrent Pos:* NSF sr fel, Univ Col, London, 68-69; mem bd dir, Asn Sci & Technol Ctrs, 73-; pres, Asn Sci-Tech Ctrs, 77-78. *Mem:* AAAS; Bot Soc Am; Am Soc Plant Physiol; Soc Develop Biol; Soc Exp Biol & Med. *Res:* Plant development; structure and function of the photosynthetic apparatus; science education. *Mailing Add:* Dept of Bot Univ of Calif Berkeley CA 94720

LAEVASTU, TAIVO, b Vihula, Estonia, Feb 26, 23; m 49; c 3. OCEANOGRAPHY, METEOROLOGY. *Educ:* Gothenburg & Lund, Fil Kand, 51; Univ Wash, Seattle, MS, 54; Univ Helsinki, PhD(oceanog), 61. *Prof Exp:* Fisheries officer, Swedish Migratory Fish Comt, 51-53; res assoc oceanog, Univ Wash, Seattle, 54-55; fisheries oceanogr, Food & Agr Orgn, UN, 55-62; assoc prof oceanog, Univ Hawaii, 62-64; res oceanogr, US Fleet Numerical Weather Facil, 64-71, chief oceanog div, Environ Prediction Res Facil, Naval Postgrad Sch, 71-76; ECOSYSTEM MODELING EXPERT, NAT OCEANIC & ATMOSPHERIC ADMIN, NAT MARINE FISHERIES SERV, 76- *Concurrent Pos:* UNESCO lectr, Bombay, India, 59; mem panel disposal radioactive waste into sea & fresh water, Int Atomic Energy Agency, 59-62; mem working group fisheries prob comn maritime meteorol, World Meteorol Orgn, 60-62; NSF & US Navy res grants, 62-64; mem, World Meteor Orgn/UNESCO Panel on Oceanic Water Balance, 72- & Sea Use Coun, Sci-Tech Bd, 71-76. *Honors & Awards:* Mil Oceanog Award, 69; US Naval Weather Serv Spec Award, 70. *Mem:* Am Geophys Union; Am Meteorol Soc. *Res:* Fisheries hydrography and oceanography; marine chemistry; sea-air interactions; oceanographic forecasting; numerical modeling in oceanography and meteorology; marine ecosystem modeling. *Mailing Add:* Nat Oceanic & Atomospheric Admin 2725 Montlake Blvd E Seattle WA 98112

LA FARGE, TIMOTHY, b New York, NY, Mar 14, 30; m 66; c 1. FOREST GENETICS. *Educ:* Univ Maine, BS, 64; Yale Univ, MF, 65; Mich State Univ, PhD(forestry), 71. *Prof Exp:* Assoc silviculturist, 65-68, assoc plant geneticist, 68-75, PLANT GENETICIST, FOREST GENETICS, FOREST SERV, SOUTHEASTERN FOREST EXP STA, 75- *Mem:* Soc Am Foresters; AAAS. *Res:* Hybridization of Pinus taeda and Pinus echinata to combine Pinus taeda's rapid growth rate with Pinus echinata's immunity to Cronartium quercuum various fusiform; breeding of Pinus taeda and Pinus elliottii. *Mailing Add:* 1918 Wood Valley Rd Macon GA 31211

LA FEHR, THOMAS ROBERT, b Los Angeles, Calif, Feb 6, 34; m 57; c 5. GEOPHYSICS. *Educ:* Univ Calif, Berkeley, AB, 58; Colo Sch Mines, MSc, 62; Stanford Univ, PhD(geophys), 64. *Prof Exp:* Geophysicist, US Geol Surv, 62-64; geophysicist, Geophys Assocs, Int, 64-66; vpres tech develop, GAI-GMX Inc, 66-67, dir tech develop, GAI-GMX Div, EG&G Inc, 67-69; assoc prof, 69-75, ADJ PROF GEOPHYS, COLO SCH MINES, 75-; PRES, EDCON, 75- *Concurrent Pos:* Lectr, Stanford Univ, 64; consult, GAI-GMS Div, EG&G, Inc, 69-70 & Explor Data Consult, 70- *Mem:* Hon mem Soc Explor Geophys; Am Asn Petrol Geol; Am Geophys Union. *Res:* Gravity and magnetic exploration; potential field theory; integrated seismic, gravity, well log data; borehole gravity. *Mailing Add:* 2428 Ward Dr Denver CO 80215

LAFERRIERE, ARTHUR L, b Willimantic, Conn, Dec 3, 33; m 55; c 3. ORGANIC CHEMISTRY, INORGANIC CHEMISTRY. *Educ:* Brown Univ, BS, 55; Rutgers Univ, MS, 58; Univ RI, PhD(chem), 60. *Prof Exp:* Res chemist, Minerals & Chem Corp, 56-58 & Am Cyanamid Co, 60-62; PROF CHEM, RI COL, 62- *Mem:* Am Chem Soc. *Res:* Inorganic solution chemistry; organic redox mechanisms. *Mailing Add:* Dept of Chem RI Col Providence RI 02908

LAFEVER, HOWARD N, b Hagerstown, Ind, May 13, 38; m 58; c 2. PLANT BREEDING, GENETICS. *Educ:* Purdue Univ, BS, 59, MS, 61, PhD(plant breeding & genetics), 63. *Prof Exp:* Instr bot, Wis State Univ, LaCrosse, 63; asst prof genetics, Purdue Univ, 63; res geneticist, Boll Weevil Res Lab, USDA, 63-65; asst prof, 65-71, prof genetics & plant breeding, 71-77, PROF AGRON, OHIO AGR RES & DEVELOP CTR, 77- *Concurrent Pos:* Prof, Ohio State Univ. *Honors & Awards:* Crops & Soils Award, Am Soc Agron, 77. *Mem:* Am Soc Agron; Crop Sci Soc Am. *Res:* Breeding new wheat varieties for distribution and production in midwest; genetic studies of wheat. *Mailing Add:* Dept of Agron Ohio Agr Res & Develop Ctr Wooster OH 44691

LAFF, ROBERT ALLAN, b North Platte, Nebr, Aug 20, 30; m 54; c 3. SOLID STATE PHYSICS. *Educ:* Calif Inst Technol, BS, 52; Univ Ill, MS, 54; Purdue Univ, PhD(physics), 60. *Prof Exp:* RES STAFF MEM, THOMAS J WATSON RES CTR, IBM CORP, 60- *Mem:* Am Phys Soc; Inst Elec & Electronics Engrs. *Res:* Transport and optical properties of semiconductors; physics and technology of semiconductor devices; acoustic physics. *Mailing Add:* Thomas J Watson Res Ctr IBM Corp Box 218 Yorktown Heights NY 10598

LAFFER, NORMAN CALLENDER, b Meadville, Pa, Nov 26, 07; m 43; c 4. BACTERIOLOGY. *Educ:* Allegheny Col, BS, 29; Univ Maine, MS, 32; Univ Ill, PhD(bact), 37. *Prof Exp:* Asst bact, Univ Maine, 29-30, instr, 30-31, asst, 31-32; asst, Univ Ill, 33-35; from instr to asst prof, Univ Ariz, 35-41; mem staff, Lederle Labs, Am Cyanamid Co, 41-42; assoc prof microbiol, 46-65, asst dean, Col Arts & Sci, 63-66, assoc dean, 66-74, prof, 65-78, ASSOC DEAN, COL ARTS & SCI, UNIV MD, COLLEGE PARK, 78- *Mem:* Am Soc Microbiol; fel Am Acad Microbiol. *Res:* Pathogenic fungi; yeasts. *Mailing Add:* 4603 Guilford Place College Park MD 20740

LAFFERTY, JAMES FRANCIS, b Pampa, Tex, Dec 23, 27; m 56; c 3. BIOMEDICAL ENGINEERING, MECHANICAL ENGINEERING. *Educ:* Univ Ky, BS, 51; Univ Southern Calif, MS, 57; Univ Mich, MS, 66, PhD(nuclear eng), 67. *Prof Exp:* Asst, Wenner-Gren Res Lab, Univ Ky, 54-55; mem tech staff, Hughes Aircraft Co, 55-57; asst prof nuclear eng, 57-62, assoc prof mech eng, 62-73, actg dir, Wenner-Gren Res Lab, 67-73, PROF MECH ENG & DIR, WENNERGREN RES LAB, UNIV KY, 73- *Concurrent Pos:* NSF fac fels, Univ Mich, 61-62 & 65-66. *Mem:* Orthop Res Soc; Am Soc Mech Eng. *Res:* Biomechanics of the skeletal and cardiovascular systems; response of biosystems to impact, vibration, acceleration and noise; development and application of biological probes. *Mailing Add:* Wenner-Gren Res Lab Univ of Ky Lexington KY 40506

LAFFERTY, JAMES M(ARTIN), b Battle Creek, Mich, Apr 27, 16; m 42; c 4. PHYSICAL ELECTRONICS, POWER ELECTRONICS. *Educ:* Univ Mich, BSE, 39, MS, 40, PhD(elec eng), 46. *Prof Exp:* Mem staff, Eastman Kodak Co, NY, 39; radio proximity fuse res, Carnegie Inst Technol, 41; res assoc, Gen Elec Co, 42-56, mgr plasma & vacuum physics br, 56-68, mgr gen physics lab, 68-72, mgr physics & elec eng lab, 72-74, mgr physics & electronic eng lab, 74-75, mgr electronic power conditioning & control lab, 75-78, mgr power electronics lab, Res & Develop Ctr, 78-81; CONSULT, 81- *Honors & Awards:* Naval Ord Develop Award, 46; Lamme Medalist, Inst Elec & Electronics Engrs, 79. *Mem:* Fel AAAS; fel Am Phys Soc; fel Inst Elec & Electronics Engrs; hon mem Am Vacuum Soc (past pres); Int Union Vacuum Sci & Technol (pres, 81-83). *Res:* Electrometer and microwave tubes; electron guns; lanthanum boride cathodes; color television picture tubes; gas discharge tubes; hot-cathode magnetron ionization gauge; triggered vacuum gap; vacuum switch; electric vehicles. *Mailing Add:* Gen Elec Res & Develop Ctr PO Box 43 Schenectady NY 12301

LAFFERTY, WALTER J, b Wilmington, Del, Feb 10, 34; m 58; c 6. PHYSICAL CHEMISTRY. *Educ:* Univ Del, BS, 56; Mass Inst Technol, PhD(phys chem), 61. *Prof Exp:* Res assoc, Johns Hopkins Univ, 61-62; CHEMIST, NAT BUR STANDARDS, 62- *Concurrent Pos:* Leverhulme vis fel, Univ Reading, 70-71. *Mem:* AAAS; Am Phys Soc. *Res:* Infrared and microwave spectroscopy. *Mailing Add:* Infrared Spectros Sect Nat Bur of Standards Washington DC 20234

LAFFIN, ROBERT JAMES, b New Haven, Conn, Apr 16, 27; m 51; c 4. MICROBIOLOGY. *Educ:* Yale Univ, BS, 49, PhD(microbiol), 55. *Prof Exp:* Instr microbiol, Womans Col, Univ NC, 53-55; from instr to assoc prof, Creighton Univ, 55-62; instr obstet & gynec, med sch, Tufts Univ, 62-64; asst prof, 64-67, assoc prof, 67-76, PROF MICROBIOL, ALBANY MED COL, 76- *Concurrent Pos:* Immunologist, St Margaret's Hosp, 62-64. *Res:* Study of Host immune responses to tumor-specific transplantation antigens; study of protein-protein interactions on metal-coated slides. *Mailing Add:* Dept of Microbiol Albany Med Col Albany NY 12208

LAFFLER, THOMAS G, b Detroit, Mich, May 10, 46; m 68; c 3. GENETICS. *Educ:* Mass Inst Technol, BS, 68; Univ Wash, PhD(genetics), 74. *Prof Exp:* Fel oncol, McArdle Lab Cancer Res, 74-78, res assoc, 78-80; ASST PROF MICROBIOL, MED & DENT SCHS, NORTHWESTERN UNIV, 80- *Mem:* Genetics Soc Am; Sigma Xi. *Res:* Study of molecular basis of cell cycle control using Physarum polycephalum as a lower enkorycote model; cell cycle mutants and the regulation of tubulin biosyntghesis and DNA replication. *Mailing Add:* Dept Microbiol Immunol Med & Dent Sch Northwestern Univ Chicago IL 60611

LA FLEUR, JAMES KEMBLE, b Los Angeles, Calif, Apr 23, 30; m 64; c 3. MECHANICAL ENGINEERING. *Educ:* Calif Inst Technol, BSME, 52. *Prof Exp:* Engr, AiResearch Mfg Co, 52-56; pres Kemsco Inc, 56-57, Dynamic Res Inc, 57-60 & LaFleur Corp, 60-65, chmn bd, 65-66; pres, Indust Cryogenics Inc, 66-75; CHMN, PRES & CHIEF EXEC OFFICER, GTI CORP, 75- *Mem:* Am Soc Mech Engrs; Cryogenic Soc Am; Int Solar Energy Soc; Int Asn Hydrogen Energy; Am Wind Energy Asn. *Res:* Applying knowledge gained in the development of normal turbo-machinery to the field of low temperature to develop new low temperature processes. *Mailing Add:* 4337 Talofa Ave Toluca Lake CA 91602

LAFLEUR, KERMIT STILLMAN, b Waterville, Maine, Feb 14, 15; m 39; c 1. TEXTILE CHEMISTRY, SOIL SCIENCE. *Educ:* Colby Col, BA, 37; Clemson Univ, MS, 64, PhD, 66. *Prof Exp:* Asst chemist, Wyandotte Worsted Co, Maine, 37-40, chief chemist, 40-46; chief chemist, Deering Milliken Maine Mills, 47-52; res chemist, Excelsior Mills, 52-56, tech supt, 56-58; group leader wool res, Deering Milliken Res Corp, 59-62, consult chemist, 62-66; res scientist, 66-67; assoc prof soil chem, Clemson Univ, 67-75, prof, 75-80; RETIRED. *Mem:* AAAS; Am Soc Agron; Soil Sci Soc Am. *Res:* Wool chemistry; soil chemistry. *Mailing Add:* 206 Hunter Ave Clemson SC 29631

LAFLEUR, LOUIS DWYNN, b Elton, La, Dec 28, 40; m 64; c 4. NONLINEAR ACOUSTICS, ULTRASONICS. *Educ:* Univ Southwestern La, BS, 62; Univ Houston, PhD(physics), 69. *Prof Exp:* Res scientist assoc, Defense Res Lab, Univ Tex, Austin, 64-65; aerospace technologist, Manned Spacecraft Ctr, NASA, 65-66; asst prof physics, Drury Col, 69-70; asst prof, 70-74, ASSOC PROF PHYSICS, UNIV SOUTHWESTERN LA, 74- *Mem:* Am Phys Soc; Am Asn Physics Teachers; Acoust Soc Am. *Res:* Nonlinear acoustics; ultrasonics; mossbauer spectroscopy; electroacoustics. *Mailing Add:* Dept of Physics Univ of Southwestern La Box 44210 Lafayette LA 70501

LAFLEUR, ROBERT GEORGE, b Albany, NY, Mar 31, 29; m 50; c 3. GEOMORPHOLOGY. *Educ:* Univ Rochester, AB, 50; Rensselaer Polytech Inst, MS, 53, PhD, 61. *Prof Exp:* Instr geol, 52-55, from asst prof to assoc prof stratig & paleont, 55-74, ASSOC PROF GEOMORPHOL, GLACIAL GEOL & WATER RESOURCES, RENSSELAER POLYTECH INST, 74- *Concurrent Pos:* Consult, NY State Educ Dept & US Geol Surv. *Mem:* Fel Geol Soc Am; Nat Asn Geol Teachers; Am Geophys Union; Arctic Inst NAm; Soc Econ Paleontologists & Mineralogists. *Res:* Sedimentology; glacial geology; photogeology. *Mailing Add:* Dept of Geol Rensselaer Polytech Inst Troy NY 12181

LAFON, EARL EDWARD, b Oklahoma City, Okla, Apr 24, 40; m 61. SOLID STATE PHYSICS. *Educ:* Univ Okla, BS, 62, MS, 64, PhD(physics), 67. *Prof Exp:* Adj asst prof physics & res assoc, Res Inst, Univ Okla, 67, NSF fel, 67-68; asst prof physics, 68-71, assoc prof, 71-74, PROF PHYSICS, OKLA STATE UNIV, 74- *Mem:* Am Phys Soc; Am Math Soc. *Res:* Electronic structure and band theory. *Mailing Add:* Dept of Physics Okla State Univ Stillwater OK 74074

LAFON, GUY MICHEL, b Bordeaux, France, June 5, 43. GEOCHEMISTRY. *Educ:* Paris Sch Mines, Civil Ing Mines, 64; Univ Alta, MSc, 65; Northwestern Univ, Ill, PhD(geol), 69. *Prof Exp:* Res Found fel, State Univ NY Binghamton, 69-70, asst prof geol, 70-72; asst prof geol, Johns Hopkins Univ, 72-80. *Mem:* Sigma Xi; AAAS; Geochem Soc; Soc Econ Paleont & Mineral. *Res:* Geochemistry of natural water systems; thermodynamic properties of brines; equilibrium models. *Mailing Add:* PO Box 2189 Houston TX 77001

LAFOND, ANDRE, b Montreal, Que, July 1, 20; m 46; c 3. FORESTRY. *Educ:* Jean-de-Brebeuf Col, BA, 42; Laval Univ, BA, 45, BASc, 46; Univ Wis, PhD, 51. *Prof Exp:* Forester, Que Forest Serv, 46-51; pres Res Found, 75, PROF FOREST ECOL & PHYSIOL, LAVAL UNIV, 51-, DEAN FAC FORESTRY, 71- *Concurrent Pos:* Consult, Que Northshore Paper Co, World Bank & Can Int Develop Agency. *Mem:* Can Soc Soil Sci; Can Soc Plant Physiol; French-Can Asn Advan Sci; Can Inst Forestry; Int Soc Soil Sci. *Res:* Forest ecology, particularly soil vegetation relationships; forest physiology, particularly mineral nutrition of trees and fertilization; forest management, particularly site classification. *Mailing Add:* 2071 Marie-Victorin St Nicolas PQ G0S 2Z0 Can

LA FOND, EUGENE CECIL, b Bridgport, Wash, Dec 4, 09; m 35; c 2. OCEANOGRAPHY. *Educ:* San Diego State Col, AB, 32; Andhra Univ, India, DSc, 56. *Prof Exp:* Asst, Scripps Inst, Univ Calif, 33-40, oceanogr, 40-47; prof oceanog, Andhra Univ, India, 52-53 & 55-56; specialist oceanog, US State Dept, 56-57; sr scientist, Atomic Submarine US Ship Skate, North Pole, 58; marine biologist, Scirpps Inst & Int Coop Admin, 60-61; chief scientist, US Prog Biol, Int Indian Ocean Exped, Woods Hole Oceanog Inst, 62-63; dep dir off oceanog & dep secy, Int Oceanog Comn, UNESCO, Paris, France, 63-64; supvry res oceanogr, Navy Electronics Lab, Naval Undersea Res & Develop Ctr, 64-68, sr scientist & consult oceanog, 68-73; SECY GEN, INT ASN PHYS SCI OCEAN, 70- *Mem:* AAAS; Am Soc Limnol & Oceanog (vpres, 54-55); Am Geophys Union; Sigma Xi (vpres, 65); Int Asn Phys Sci Ocean (secy, 70-). *Res:* Physical oceanography. *Mailing Add:* LaFond Oceanic Consult Box 7325 San Diego CA 92107

LAFONTAINE, JEAN-GABRIEL, b Sherbrooke, Que, Aug 4, 28; m 52; c 3. CELL BIOLOGY, ELECTRON MICROSCOPY. *Educ:* Laval Univ, Lic es Sci, 50; Univ Wis, MS, 52, PhD(zool), 54. *Prof Exp:* Res asst cytol, Sloan Kettering Inst, 54-56, Rockefeller Inst, 56-58 & Montreal Cancer Inst, 58-60; asst prof path, Med Sch, 60-64, assoc prof biol, 64-68, PROF BIOL, SCI FAC, LAVAL UNIV, 68- *Concurrent Pos:* Damon Runyon fel, 54-56. *Mem:* Am Soc Cell Biol; Can Soc Cell Biol. *Res:* Cytochemistry and ultrastructure of the cell nucleus. *Mailing Add:* Dept of Biol Fac of Sci Laval Univ Quebec G1K 7P4 Can

LAFORNARA, JOSEPH PHILIP, b Buffalo, NY, Dec 5, 42; m 67; c 2. CHEMISTRY, ENVIRONMENTAL SCIENCES. *Educ:* Canisius Col, BS, 64; Univ Fla, PhD(inorg chem), 70. *Prof Exp:* Res chemist, Edison Water Qual Lab, Fed Water Qual Admin, Dept Interior, 70-71; res chemist, Nat Environ Res Ctr, 71-75, res chemist, Oil & Hazardous Mat Spills Br, Indust Environ Res Lab, 75-78, PRES PHYS SCIENTIST, ENIRONON RESPONSE TEAM, US ENVIRON PROTECTION AGENCY, 78- *Concurrent Pos:* Tech adv, Hazardous Mat Adv Comt, Nat Res Coun-Nat Acad Sci, 71-; mem, Task Force for Nitrosamine Control & Task Force for Kepone Control, US Environ Protection Agency, 75-; chmn, Hazardous Mat Div, Am Soc Testing & Mat Comt, No F-20, Spill Control Syst, 78- *Mem:* Am Soc Testing & Mat; Am Chem Soc; Water Pollution Control Fedn. *Res:* Application of chemical technology to control of spills of hazardous materials; chemical analysis of inorganic and organic water and air pollutants; ultimate disposal of chemical wastes. *Mailing Add:* 27 Susan Dr Somerset NJ 08873

LAFOUNTAIN, JAMES ROBERT, JR, b Richmond, Va, Jan 8, 44; m 70; c 2. CELL BIOLOGY. *Educ:* Princeton Univ, AB, 66; State Univ NY, Albany, PhD(biol sci), 70. *Prof Exp:* Fel, Eidgenosstsche Technische Aochschrle, Switz, 71-72; asst prof, 72-77, ASSOC PROF BIOL SCI, STATE UNIV NY, BUFFALO, 77- *Mem:* Am Soc Cell Biol; Electron Micros Soc Am. *Res:* Physiology of cell division and cell motility. *Mailing Add:* Div Cell & Molecular Biol State Univ NY 657 Cooke Hall Buffalo NY 14260

LAFOUNTAIN, LESTER JAMES, JR, b Marinette, Wis, Sept 27, 42; m 64. GEOLOGY. *Educ:* Univ Wis, BS & MS, 64; Univ Colo, PhD(geol), 73. *Prof Exp:* Field geologist, US Steel Corp, 64; party chief geol, 65; geologist, Texaco Inc, 66; res assoc rock mech, Dept Geol, Univ NC, 71-74; asst proj geologist, 75-76, proj geologist, 76-77, chief geologist int oper, 78-79, GEN MGR, D'APPOLONIA GEOPHYS CORP, 80- *Mem:* Geol Soc Am; Am Geophys Union; AAAS; Sigma Xi; Am Soc Civil Engrs. *Res:* The mechanisms and physical aspects of rock dilation, stick slip and earthquake precursors; the tectonics of the mid-continent and its relationship to seismicity. *Mailing Add:* D'Appolonia Geophys Corp 10 Duff Rd Pittsburgh PA 15235

LAFRAMBOISE, JAMES GERALD, b Windsor, Ont, July 26, 38; m 62; c 2. PLASMA PHYSICS. *Educ:* Univ Windsor, BSc, 57; Univ Toronto, BASc, 59, MA, 60, PhD(aerospace studies), 66. *Prof Exp:* Asst prof math, Univ Windsor, 65-67; asst prof physics, 67-71, assoc prof, 71-77, PROF PHYSICS, YORK UNIV, 77- *Mem:* Can Asn Physicists; Am Geophys Union. *Res:* Electrodes in plasmas; transport problems in fluid flows. *Mailing Add:* Physics Dept York Univ 4700 Keele St Toronto ON M3J 1P3 Can

LAFRAMBOISE, MARC ALEXANDER, b Windsor, Ont, May 18, 15; m 49; c 2. MATHEMATICS. *Educ:* Univ Ottawa, BA, 42; Univ Mich, MA, 46, MSc, 49. *Prof Exp:* Prin & teacher pub & separate schs, Ont, 34-42; asst prof math, Assumption Col, 42-50; asst prof, 53-67, assoc prof math, Univ Detroit, 67-76. RETIRED. *Res:* Mathematics education. *Mailing Add:* 1477 Dufferin Place Windsor ON 48221 N8X 3K3 Can

LAFRANCHI, EDWARD ALVIN, b Petaluma, Calif, July 23, 28; m 54; c 3. ELECTRICAL ENGINEERING. *Educ:* Univ Santa Clara, BS, 50. *Prof Exp:* Opers engr, 53-56, design engr, 56-58, group leader, 58-66, div leader, 66-73, DEPT HEAD, DEPT ELECTRONICS ENG, LAWRENCE LIVERMORE LAB, 73- *Mem:* Inst Elec & Electronics Engrs. *Res:* Computer science and engineering; engineering management. *Mailing Add:* Dept of Electronics Eng Lawrence Livermore Lab Livermore CA 94550

LAFUSE, HARRY G, b Liberty, Ind, Jan 22, 30; m 54; c 1. ELECTRICAL ENGINEERING. *Educ:* Purdue Univ, BSEE, 57; Univ Ill, MSEE, 58, PhD, 62. *Prof Exp:* Instr elec eng, Univ Ill, 61-62; asst prof elec eng, Univ Notre Dame, 62-65, assoc prof, 65-81; ELEC ENGR, PHILLIPS ENG CO, 81- *Concurrent Pos:* Consult, Bendix Corp, 62-69 & McCarthy & Assocs, 70- *Mem:* Nat Soc Prof Engrs. *Res:* Electromagnetic field theory; network analysis and synthesis; high frequency transmission systems; microwave theory; heat pump control systems. *Mailing Add:* 1611 Tudor Lane Southbend IN 46614

LAGAKOS, STEPHEN WILLIAM, b Philadelphia, Pa, June 18, 46; m 68. BIOSTATISTICS. *Educ:* Carnegie-Mellon Univ, BS, 68; George Washington Univ, MPhil & PhD(math & statist), 72. *Prof Exp:* Math statistician, Naval Ord Sta, 68-70; statistician biostatist, Statist Lab, State Univ NY Buffalo, 72-80, asst prof statist sci, 73-80; ASSOC PROF, HARVARD SCH PUB HEALTH, 80- *Concurrent Pos:* Coord statistician, Working Party Ther Lung Cancer, 72-; protocol statistician, Eastern Coop Oncol Group, 72- *Mem:* Biomet Soc; Royal Statist Soc; Inst Math Statist; Int Asn Study Lung Cancer; Am Statist Asn. *Res:* The planning, design and analysis of clinical trials with particular emphasis on survival-type data. *Mailing Add:* Dept Biostatist Harvard Univ 677 Huntington Ave Boston MA 02115

LAGALLY, MAX GUNTER, b Darmstadt, Ger, May 23, 42; US citizen; m 69; c 3. MATERIALS SCIENCE, SURFACE PHYSICS. *Educ:* Pa State Univ, BS, 63; Univ Wis, MS, 65, PhD(physics), 68. *Prof Exp:* Vis fel physics, Fritz Haber Inst, Max Planck Soc, 68-69; instr physics & res assoc surface physics, 70-71, asst prof mat sci, 71-74, assoc prof, 74-77, PROF MAT SCI, UNIV WIS-MADISON, 77- *Concurrent Pos:* Sloan Found fel, 73-77; H I Romnes fel, 76-80. *Mem:* Fel Am Phys Soc; Am Inst Metall, Mining & Petrol Engrs; Electrochem Soc; Am Vacuum Soc; Am Soc Testing & Mat. *Res:* Crystallographic and electronic properties of surfaces, thin films, and interfaces; thin film deposition; characterization methods; diffraction; electron spectroscopy. *Mailing Add:* Dept Metall & Mineral Eng Univ Wis Madison WI 53706

LAGALLY, PAUL, b Munich, Ger, Aug 4, 11; US citizen; m 39; c 3. POLYMER CHEMISTRY. *Educ:* Dresden Tech Univ, BS, 35, MS, 37, PhD(chem), 39. *Prof Exp:* Chemist, Kaiser Wilhelm Inst, 39-40; group leader org chem, Rohm & Haas, Darmstadt, 40-45; dir org res, Paper Mills, Aschaffenburg, 46-52; dir org res, Linden Labs, Inc, 53-62, tech dir org chem, 62-66; res supvr, Naval Ship Res & Develop Ctr, 75-79; RETIRED. *Concurrent Pos:* Consult, Navy, 79- *Res:* Silicon organics; fluoro elastomers; surface chemistry of cellulose, glass and metals; polymerizations. *Mailing Add:* 1911 Dulany Place Annapolis MD 21401

LA GANGA, THOMAS S, b Caldwell, NJ, July 23, 27; m 75; c 5. ENDOCRINOLOGY, CLINICAL CHEMISTRY. *Educ:* Drew Univ, AB, 51; Rutgers Univ, MS, 66, PhD(animal sci), 67. *Prof Exp:* Clin chemist, Princeton Hosp, NJ, 67-69; asst dir endocrinol, 69-79, TECH COORDR, BIO-SCI LABS, 79- *Mem:* AAAS. *Res:* Improved methodology in chemical and biological hormone assays; endocrine physiology of the mammary gland; experimental hypertension; automated analytical systems; thyroid cancers and autoantibodies. *Mailing Add:* 7600 Tyrone Ave Van Nuys CA 91405

LAGANIS, DENO, b Detroit, Mich, July 17, 19; m 48; c 3. POLYMER CHEMISTRY, ORGANIC CHEMISTRY. *Educ:* Wayne State Univ, BS, 41. *Prof Exp:* Develop chemist rubber, US Rubber Co, 41-43; develop chemist plastics, Ford Motor Co, 43-45; group leader res & develop resins, Reichhold Chem Inc, 45-54; mgr plastics, Chem Compounding Co, 54-55; GROUP LEADER RES & DEVELOP RESINS, SCHENECTADY CHEM INC, 55- *Mem:* Am Chem Soc; Soc Mfg Engrs. *Res:* Polymer chemistry related to electrical insulation resins for surface coatings; unsaturated polyesters for various uses; polyurethanes for coatings and foams; epoxies as coatings and potting compounds; leveling resins for floor polishes. *Mailing Add:* 2331 Algonquin Rd Schenectady NY 12309

LAGANIS, EVAN DEAN, b Detroit, Mich, June 6, 53; m 77; c 1. ORGANOFLUORINE CHEMISTRY, CYCLOPHANE CHEMISTRY. *Educ:* State Univ NY, Geneseo, BA, 75; Dartmouth Col, PhD(org chem), 80. *Prof Exp:* Fel organometallic chem, Univ Ore, 79-81; RES CHEM ORGANOFLUORINE CHEM, E I DU PONT DE NEMOURS & CO INC, 81- *Mem:* Am Chem Soc. *Res:* The synthesis, chemistry, and properties of flourinated organosilicon compounds, novel cyclophones, and transition metal complexes of cyclophanes. *Mailing Add:* E I du Pont de Nemours Co Inc Exp Sta Bldg 328/208 Wilmington DE 19899

LAGARIAS, JEFFREY CLARK, b Pittsburgh, Pa, Nov 16, 49. MATHEMATICS. *Educ:* Mass Inst Technol, SB & SM, 72, PhD(math), 74. *Prof Exp:* MEM TECH STAFF, BELL TELEPHONE LABS, 74- *Concurrent Pos:* Vis asst prof, Univ Md, 78-79. *Mem:* Am Math Soc; Math Asn Am; Soc Indust & Appl Math. *Mailing Add:* Rm 2C-370 Bell Labs Murray Hill NJ 07974

LAGARIAS, JOHN S(AMUEL), b Rochester, NY, July 4, 21; m 47; c 3. PHYSICS, ELECTRONICS. *Educ:* Rensselaer Polytech Inst, BS, 48. *Prof Exp:* Engr, Res Dept, Westinghouse Elec Corp, 48-51; physicist, Koppers Co, Inc, Pa, 51-53, mgr, Precipitation Br, 53-56, mgr, Metal Prod Res, 56-61, mgr, Physics & Phys Chem Lab, 61-63; mgr, Res & Develop, Am Instrument Co, 63-65; vpres, Resources Res, Inc, Va, 65-66, exec vpres, 66-67, pres, 67-71; DIR ENVIRON QUAL, KAISER ENGRS INC, 71- *Concurrent Pos:* Conf chmn, 2nd Int Clean Air Cong, 70. *Mem:* Air Pollution Control Asn (pres, 68-69); Am Phys Soc; Inst Elec & Electronics Engrs; Am Acad Environ Engrs; Soc Mining Engrs/Am Inst Mining, Metall & Petrol Engrs. *Res:* Industrial gas cleaning equipment including electrostatic precipitators, bag filters, scrubbers and mechanical collectors; environmental controls. *Mailing Add:* Kaiser Engrs Inc PO Box 23210 Oakland CA 94623

LAGE, GARY LEE, b Hinsdale, Ill, Nov 11, 41; m 64; c 2. PHARMACOLOGY, TOXICOLOGY. *Educ:* Drake Univ, BS, 63; Univ Iowa, MS, 65, PhD(pharmacol), 67; Am Bd Toxicol, dipl, 80. *Prof Exp:* From asst prof to assoc prof pharmacol, Sch Pharm, Univ Kans, 67-73; assoc prof pharm, Univ Wis-Madison, 73-78; PROF TOXICOL & DIR TOXICOL PROGS, PHILADELPHIA COL PHARM & SCI, 78- *Concurrent Pos:* USPHS res career develop award, 75-80. *Mem:* Soc Toxicol; Am Pharmaceut Asn; AAAS; Am Soc Pharmacol & Exp Therapeut; Am Asn Col Pharm. *Res:* Study of drug distribution and metabolism in relation to drug toxicity, distribution and/or metabolism, especially cardiac glycosides. *Mailing Add:* Philadelphia Col Pharm & Sci 43rd St & Kingsessing Mall Philadelphia PA 19104

LAGERGREN, CARL ROBERT, b St Paul, Minn, Nov 21, 22; m 47; c 3. PHYSICS. *Educ:* State Col, Wash, BS, 44, MS, 49; Univ Minn, PhD(physics), 55. *Prof Exp:* Sr physicist, Hanford Atomic Prod Oper, Gen Elec Co, 55-65; mgr mass spectrometry, 65-68, RES ASSOC, RADIOL SCI DEPT, PAC NORTHWEST LABS, BATTELLE MEM INST, 68- *Mem:* Am Phys Soc. *Res:* Mass spectrometry; electron impact phenomena; isotopic abundances; surface ionization; ion optics. *Mailing Add:* 2110 Howell Ave Richland WA 99352

LAGERSTEDT, HARRY BERT, b Glen Ridge, NJ, Aug 2, 25; m 52; c 5. PLANT PHYSIOLOGY, HORTICULTURE. *Educ:* Ore State Univ, BS, 54, MS, 57; Tex A&M Univ, PhD(plant physiol), 65. *Prof Exp:* Instr, 57-60, asst prof, 60-67, ASSOC PROF HORT, ORE STATE UNIV, 67-; RES HORTICULTURIST, AGR RES SERV, 67- *Mem:* Am Soc Plant Physiol; Am Soc Hort Sci. *Res:* Plant growth regulators; nut crops. *Mailing Add:* Dept of Hort Ore State Univ Corvallis OR 97331

LAGERSTROM, JOHN E(MIL), b Galesburg, Ill, Dec 12, 22; m 47; c 3. ELECTRICAL ENGINEERING. *Educ:* Iowa State Univ, BS, 44, MS, 51, PhD(elec eng), 58. *Prof Exp:* Instr elec eng, Iowa State Univ, 46-49, from asst prof to prof, 49-66, res asst prof, A-C network anal, 50-57, asst to dean eng, 57-58, asst dean, 58-63, assoc dean, 63-66, actg dir tech inst, 60-62, actg head dept archit & archit eng, 62-64; dean eng, SDak State Univ, 66-71; chmn, Dept Elec Eng, 71-76, DIR ENG EXTEN, UNIV NEBR, LINCOLN, 76- *Concurrent Pos:* Consult, Winpower Mfg Co, Iowa, 56-59; adv to rector, Nat Univ Eng, Peru, Ford Found-Iowa State Univ contract, 64-66. *Mem:* Nat Soc Prof Eng; Inst Elec & Electronics Engrs. *Res:* Electrical machines; power transmission and distribution; power system protection; system stability; economic power system loading. *Mailing Add:* Dept of Elec Eng Univ of Nebr Lincoln NE 68588

LAGERSTROM, PACO (AXEL), b Oskarshamm, Sweden, Feb 24, 14; nat US. APPLIED MATHEMATICS. *Educ:* Stockholm Univ, MA, 35, PhD(philos), 39; Univ Münster, 37-38; Princeton Univ, PhD(math), 42. *Prof Exp:* Instr math, Princeton, 41-44; res aerodynamicist, Bell Aircraft Corp, 44-45 & Douglas Aircraft Co, Inc, 45-46; from asst prof to prof aeronaut, 47-67, prof, 67-81, EMER PROF APPL MATH, CALIF INST TECHNOL, 81- *Concurrent Pos:* Consult, Douglas Aircraft Co, Inc, 46-66; vis prof, Univ Paris, 60-61; Guggenheim grant & Fulbright lectr, 60-61; consult, TRW Inc, 66-68. *Mem:* Am Math Soc; Soc Indust & Appl Math. *Res:* Perturbation methods; applications of group theory; fluid dynamics. *Mailing Add:* Calif Inst of Technol 217-50 Pasadena CA 91125

LAGLER, KARL FRANK, b Rochester, NY, Nov 15, 12; m 41; c 3. FISHERIES, ZOOLOGY. *Educ:* Univ Rochester, AB, 34; Cornell Univ, MS, 36; Univ Mich, PhD(zool), 40. *Prof Exp:* Asst bot, Univ Rochester, 34-35; investr fish mgt, 37-39, from instr to asst prof zool, 39-50, res assoc, Lab Vert Biol, 45-49, from assoc prof to prof fisheries & zool, 50-72, chmn dept fisheries, 50-65, prof, 72-77, DISTINGUISHED NATURAL RESOURCES & ZOOL, UNIV MICH, ANN ARBOR, 77- *Concurrent Pos:* Leader, Mich Coop Fish Res Unit, Am Wildlife Inst, 37-40; res assoc, Inst Fish Res, Dept Conserv, Mich, 39- & Cranbrook Inst Sci, 40-41, 44-48 & 54; mem expeds, Upper Great Lakes, 45-49, Western Europe, 57, Alaska, 58 & SE Asia, 64-65 & 70; Billington lectr, 57; tech consult, Asn Fish Tackle Mfrs, 48-50; mem coun, Great Lakes Res Inst, 48-54 & 56-60; Guggenheim fel, 57-58; adv, US Opers Mission Kasetsart-Hawaii Univ Contract, Thailand, 64-65; consult, UN Food & Agr Orgn, UN Develop Prog & WHO, Africa & SAm, 65-; coordr African Lake projs, Food & Agr Orgn, UN, 66-67; dir, UN Mekong Basinwide Fishery Studies, Lao People's Democratic Republic, Thailand, Democratic Kampuchea & Vietnam, 74-76 & 78; consult, Bangladesh, 76-78, Morocco, Egypt & Repub SAfrica, 81. *Honors & Awards:* Gold Medal & Dipl, Fr Acad Agr, 61. *Mem:* Fel Int Inst Fishery Scientists (pres, 67-72); Am Soc Limnol & Oceanog; hon mem Am Fisheries Soc; fel Acad Zool; fel Am Inst Fishery Res Biol (pres, 64-65). *Res:* Fish predation; fishery biology, ecology and development including man-made lakes; fisheries and integrated water resource development; great lakes fishes. ecology; distribution and taxonomy of Great Lakes fishes; natural history. *Mailing Add:* Sch of Nat Resources Univ of Mich Ann Arbor MI 48109

LAGNESE, JOHN EDWARD, mathematics, see previous edition

LAGO, BARBARA (DRAKE), b Wheeling, WVa, Dec 18, 30; m 68. GENETICS. *Educ:* Univ Calif, BA, 52; Stanford Univ, PhD(biol), 59. *Prof Exp:* Res assoc biol, Stanford, 59-61; asst prof, San Jose State Col, 61-62; res assoc, Univ Calif, Berkeley, 62-63; asst prof, Univ Calif, Davis, 64-65; sr res microbiologist, 65-68, res fel, 68-72, sr res fel, 72-74, assoc dir, 74-80, Dir, 80-81, SR DIR, MERCK & CO INC, 81- *Mem:* Genetics Soc Am; Am Soc Microbiol. *Res:* Genetics of microorganisms; genetic control of metabolism and development. *Mailing Add:* Merck & Co Inc Rahway NJ 07065

LAGO, JAMES, b New York, NY, Nov 7, 21. CHEMICAL ENGINEERING. *Educ:* Polytech Inst Brooklyn, BChE, 44; Mass Inst Technol, MS, 47. *Prof Exp:* Asst, Manhattan Proj, 44-46; jr engr, 47-51, group leader chem eng, 51-57, sect mgr, 57-64, mgr, 64-69, dir chem eng res & develop, 69-79, VPRES PROCESS RES & DEVELOP, MERCK & CO INC, RAHWAY, 79- *Mem:* Am Chem Soc; Am Inst Chem Engrs; Soc Chem Indust. *Res:* Development of processes for the preparation of medicinals; design and startup of manufacturing facilities for the processes developed. *Mailing Add:* 2035 Winding Brook Way Westfield NJ 07090

LAGO, PAUL KEITH, b Worthington, Minn, June 24, 47; m 69; c 1. ENTOMOLOGY. *Educ:* Bemidji State Col, BA, 69, MA, 71; NDak State Univ, PhD(entom), 77. *Prof Exp:* ASST PROF BIOL, UNIV MISS, 76- *Mem:* Coleopterists Soc; Entom Soc Am; Inland Bird Banding Asn; Am Entom Soc; NAm Benthological Soc. *Res:* Insect taxonomy, principally coleoptera and aquatic insects; insect ecology. *Mailing Add:* Dept of Biol Univ of Miss University MS 38677

LAGOWSKI, JEANNE MUND, b St Louis, Mo, Nov 17, 29; m 54. ORGANIC CHEMISTRY. *Educ:* Bradley Univ, BS, 51, MS, 52; Univ Mich, PhD(org chem), 57. *Prof Exp:* Instr anal chem, Bradley Univ, 51-52; res chemist, Mich State Univ, 56-57; res fel phys org chem, Cambridge Univ, 57-59; assoc res scientist biochem genetics, 59-63, res scientist, 63-73, lectr zool, 73-74, asst dean, Div Gen & Comp Studies, 72-78, assoc prof zool, 74-81, asst dean, 78-81, ASSOC DEAN, COL NATURAL SCI & PROF ZOOL, UNIV TEX, AUSTIN, 81- *Concurrent Pos:* Res career develop award, NIH, 64-69; assoc, Danforth Found, 77- *Mem:* Am Chem Soc; Int Soc Heterocyclic Chemists. *Res:* Chemistry of nitrogen heterocycles; biochemical and genetic aspects of metabolism. *Mailing Add:* Dept of Zool Univ of Tex Austin TX 78712

LAGOWSKI, JOSEPH JOHN, b Chicago, Ill, June 8, 30; m 54. INORGANIC CHEMISTRY. *Educ:* Univ Ill, BS, 52; Univ Mich, MS, 54; Mich State Univ, PhD(inorg chem), 57; Cambridge Univ, PhD(inorg chem), 59. *Prof Exp:* From asst prof to assoc prof, 59-67, PROF CHEM, UNIV TEX, AUSTIN, 67- *Honors & Awards:* Piper Prof Award, Nat Chem Mfg Asn, 81. *Mem:* Am Chem Soc; The Chem Soc. *Res:* Liquid ammonia solutions; organometallic compounds; borazines and derivatives; electrochemistry; development of computer-based teaching methods; non-aqueous solution chemistry; metal atom reactions. *Mailing Add:* Dept Chem Univ Tex Austin TX 78712

LAGRANGE, WILLIAM SOMERS, b Ames, Iowa, Apr 23, 31; m 54; c 3. FOOD MICROBIOLOGY, DAIRY BACTERIOLOGY. *Educ:* Iowa State Univ, BS, 53, PhD(dairy bact), 59. *Prof Exp:* Exten technologist dairy mfg, Univ Ky, 59-62; EXTEN FOOD TECHNOLOGIST, IOWA STATE UNIV, 62- *Mem:* Int Asn Milk, Food & Environ Sanit; Inst Food Technol; Am Soc Microbiol; Am Dairy Sci Asn. *Res:* Dairy manufacturing quality control; dairy and foods microbiology; foods processing and control. *Mailing Add:* Dept of Food Technol Iowa State Univ Ames IA 50011

LAGREGA, MICHAEL DENNY, b Yonkers, NY, July 19, 44; m 70; c 2. HAZARDOUS WASTE MANAGEMENT, INDUSTRIAL WASTE TREATMENT. *Educ:* Manhattan Col, BE, 66; Syracuse Univ, MS, 71, PhD(environ eng), 72; Environ Engrs Intersoc, dipl, 75. *Prof Exp:* Proj mgr, O'Brien & Gere Engrs, Inc, NY, 66-72; asst prof environ eng, Drexel Univ, 72-74; asst prof, 74-78, ASSOC PROF CIVIL ENG, BUCKNELL UNIV, 78- *Concurrent Pos:* Staff consult, Buchart-Horn Engrs & Planners, 74-81; prin consult, Roy F Weston, Inc, 81- *Mem:* Water Pollution Control Fedn; Int Asn Water Pollution Res; Asn Environ Eng Prof; Am Soc Civil Engrs; Am Acad Environ Engrs. *Res:* Physical-chemical processes for water pollution control; management of hazardous wastes. *Mailing Add:* Dept of Civil Eng Bucknell Univ Lewisburg PA 17837

LAGRONE, ALFRED H(ALL), b De Berry, Tex, Sept 25, 12; m 55; c 4. ELECTRICAL ENGINEERING. *Educ:* Univ Tex, PhD(elec eng), 54. *Prof Exp:* Distribution engr elec power, San Antonio Pub Serv Co, 38-42; instr radar, Mass Inst Technol, 42-45; radio engr, 45-59, PROF ELEC ENG & DIR ANTENNAS & PROPAGATION LAB, UNIV TEX, AUSTIN, 59- *Honors & Awards:* Helt Mem Award, Inst Radio Engrs, 59. *Mem:* Inst Elec & Electronics Engrs. *Res:* Radio propagation and antennas. *Mailing Add:* Dept of Elec Eng Univ of Tex PO Box 7728 Austin TX 78712

LAGUAITE, JEANNETTE KATHERINE, b New Orleans, La, June 20, 12. SPEECH PATHOLOGY. *Educ:* Tulane Univ, BA, 37, MA, 40; La State Univ, PhD(speech), 52. *Prof Exp:* Teacher pub schs, La, 30-47, speech therapist, 47-52; prof speech path & audiol & dir, Speech & Hearing Ctr, 52-80, CLIN PROF OTOLARYNGOL & HEAD & NECK SURG, SCH MED, TULANE UNIV, 80- *Concurrent Pos:* Speech pathologist, La Eval Ctr for Except Children, 56; consult, Cleft Palate Team, State Dept Health Planning Coun, 71- *Honors & Awards:* John Robinson Award, La Speech & Hearing Asn, 70. *Mem:* Fel Am Speech & Hearing Asn; Am Soc Clin Hypnosis; Int Soc Clin & Exp Hypnosis; Int Asn Logopedics & Phonatrics; Am Cong Rehab Med. *Res:* Audiology; voice problems and esophageal speech; hereditary deafness. *Mailing Add:* Dept of Otolaryngol Tulane Univ Sch of Med New Orleans LA 70112

LAGUEUX, ROBERT, b Levis, Que, May 23, 16; m 47; c 7. ICHTHYOLOGY, LIMNOLOGY. *Educ:* Laval Univ, BA, 40, BS, 45; Univ Montreal, MSc, 50. *Prof Exp:* Biologist biol bur, Fish & Game Dept, Que, 45-47, biologist & dir, Tadoussac Salmon Hatchery, 47-60; asst dir, Wildlife Serv, Que, 60-62; prof ichthyol, limnol & fishery biol, Fac Sci, 62-72, secy, 72-80, ASST TO DIR, SCH GRAD STUDIES, LAVAL UNIV, 80- *Mem:* Fisheries Soc; French-Can Asn Adv Sci; Can Soc Wildlife & Fishery Biol. *Res:* Fishery science and conservation. *Mailing Add:* Sch of Grad Studies Laval Univ Quebec PQ G1K 7P4 Can

LAGUNOFF, DAVID, b New York, NY, Mar 14, 32; m 58; c 3. PATHOLOGY. *Educ:* Univ Chicago, MD, 57. *Prof Exp:* Asst microbiol, Univ Miami, 51-53; intern, San Francisco Hosp, Calif, 57-58; from instr to prof path, Univ Wash, 60-79; PROF & CHMN PATH, ST LOUIS UNIV, 79- *Concurrent Pos:* Nat Heart Inst fel path, Univ Wash, 58-59, USPHS trainee, 59-60; Nat Heart Inst spec fel physiol, Carlsberg Lab, Denmark, 62-64; Nat Cancer Inst spec fel path, Sir William Dunn Sch Exp Path, Oxford Univ, 69-70. *Mem:* Am Asn Path; Am Soc Cell Biol. *Res:* Mast cell structure and function; cell secretion; inflammation; pulmonary edema. *Mailing Add:* Dept Path Sch Med St Louis Univ St Louis MO 63104

LAGUROS, JOAKIM GEORGE, b Istanbul, Turkey, Feb 4, 24; US citizen; m 57; c 1. SOIL MECHANICS, HIGHWAY ENGINEERING. *Educ:* Robert Col, Istanbul, BS, 46; Iowa State Univ, MS, 55, PhD(soil mech), 62. *Prof Exp:* Asst engr, Naval Shipyard, Turkey, 48-51; instr civil eng, Robert Col, 51-54, asst prof, 56-59; res asst soils, Exp Sta, Iowa State Univ, 54-56, 59-62; asst prof soil mech, Univ Ohio, 62-63; assoc prof, 63-69, prof soils & hwys, 69-80, PROF CIVIL ENG & ENVIRON SCI, UNIV OKLA, 80- *Concurrent Pos:* Consult, Netherlands Harbor Works Co, Turkey, 52, Robert Col, 58 & McFadzen, Everly & Assocs, 61; mem physicochem phenomena soils comt, Hwy Res Bd, Nat Acad Sci-Nat Res Coun, 64-67. *Mem:* Am Soc Civil Engrs; Am Soc Eng Educ; Clay Minerals Soc. *Res:* Behavior of soils under load application; improvement of soil properties by admixtures; quality control of materials. *Mailing Add:* Dept of Civil Eng Univ of Okla Norman OK 73069

LAHA, RADHA GOVINDA, b Calcutta, India, Oct 1, 30; US citizen. ANALYTICAL MATHEMATICS, PURE MATHEMATICS. *Educ:* Univ Calcutta, BSc, 49, MSc, 51, PhD(math), 57. *Prof Exp:* Mem staff math, Res & Training Sch, Indian Statist Inst, Calcutta, 52-57, lectr, 57; Smith-Mundt-Fulbright fel, Cath Univ Am, 57-58, res asst prof, 58-60; reader, Div Theoret Res & Training, Indian Statist Inst, 60-61; vis res fel, Inst Statist, Univ Paris & Swiss Fed Inst Technol, 61-62; from asst prof to prof, Cath Univ Am, 62-72; PROF MATH, BOWLING GREEN STATE UNIV, 72- *Concurrent Pos:* Vis res fel, Mass Inst Technol, 68-69 & Inst Advan Study, Canberra, Australia, 80; vis mem, Inst Advan Study, Princeton, 74. *Mem:* Fel Inst Math Statist; Int Statist Inst; Am Math Soc. *Res:* Analytical and abstract probability; harmonic analysis and representation theory of groups; application of probability and analysis to number theory. *Mailing Add:* Dept of Math Bowling Green State Univ Bowling Green OH 43403

LAHAIE, IVAN JOSEPH, b Bay City, Mich, May 21, 54; m 80. ELECTROMAGNETIC IMAGING, OPTICAL IMAGING. *Educ:* Mich State Univ, BS, 76; Univ Mich, MS, 77, PhD(elec eng), 81. *Prof Exp:* Res asst, Radiation Lab, Univ Mich, 76-80; RES ENGR, ENVIRON RES INST MICH, 80- *Mem:* Inst Elec & Electronics Engrs; Sigma Xi. *Res:* Electromagnetic and optical imaging systems and radar systems; research and applications in inverse scattering for imaging systems. *Mailing Add:* Environ Res Inst Mich PO Box 8618 Ann Arbor MI 48107

LAHAM, QUENTIN NADIME, b Oshkosh, Wis, Feb 18, 27; m 50; c 3. HISTOLOGY, EMBRYOLOGY. *Educ:* Ripon Col, BA, 49; Marquette Univ, MS, 51; Univ Ottawa, PhD, 59. *Prof Exp:* Lectr gen biol, 51-54, from asst prof to assoc prof, 54-58, prof histol & embryol, 68-76, PROF BIOL, UNIV OTTAWA, 77-, CHMN BIOL 69- *Concurrent Pos:* Nuffield fel, 60-61. *Mem:* Teratology Soc; Soc Develop Biol; Can Soc Zoologists; Can Soc Cell Biol. *Res:* Ontogeny of enzyme systems during embryogenesis; influence of heavy metals on developing embryos. *Mailing Add:* Dept Biol Univ Ottawa Laurier Ave E Ottawa K1N 6N5 Can

LAHAM, SOUHEIL, b Port-au-Prince, Haiti, Apr 17, 26; m 55; c 2. INHALATION TOXICOLOGY, CANCER. *Educ:* Univ Haiti, BSc, 47; Univ Paris, PhD(toxicol), 54, dipl indust hyg, 55; Graz Univ, dipl microchem, 54; Am Bd Indust Hyg, dipl, 62. *Prof Exp:* Res assoc, Univ Paris, 56-58; guest scientist, 56-58, head biochem sect, Environ Health Directorate, 58-62, chief environ toxicol prog, Occup Health Div, 62-71, sr res scientist & consult, 62-79, HEAD INHALATION TOXICOL UNIT, ENVIRON HEALTH DIRECTORATE, CAN DEPT HEALTH & WELFARE, 79- *Concurrent Pos:* Guest scientist, Nat Res Coun Can, 56-58; vis prof, Univ Ottawa, 71-, Univ Quebec, 73-, Ohio State Univ, Columbus, 74-, Carleton Univ, 77- & Univ Calif, Berkeley, 81- *Mem:* Am Indust Hyg Asn; Pharmacol Soc Can; Europ Soc Toxicol; Soc Toxicol; AAAS. Toxicity and comparative metabolism of toxic and carcinogenic substances; structure-biological activity of toxic and carcinogenic chemicals; pulmonary clearance and inhalation toxicity of gases and vapors; telemetering techniques in cardiopulmonary physiology. *Res:* Inhalation toxicity and metabolism of toxic and carcinogenic substances; enviornal and occupational cancer; chemical carcinogenesis; neurotoxicology; peripheral neuropathy induced by industrial chemicals. *Mailing Add:* 249 Latchford Rd Ottawa ON K1Z 5W3 Can

LAHART, MARTIN JOSEPH, optical science, physics, see previous edition

LAHEY, JAMES FREDERICK, b Two Rivers, Wis, Mar 7, 21; m 43; c 2. PHYSICAL GEOGRAPHY, METEOROLOGY. *Educ:* Univ Wis, PhB, 43, MS, 49, PhD, 58. *Prof Exp:* Asst prof geog, Univ Ga, 50-53; res assoc meteorol, Univ Wis, 53-59; asst prof geog & meteorol, Univ Ohio, 59-61; from assoc prof to prof, Northern Ill Univ, 61-67; assoc prof, Univ Ill, Urbana, 67-71; prof meteorol, 71-80, PROF GEOG, ORE STATE UNIV, 71- *Concurrent Pos:* Vis assoc prof, Univ Calif, Berkeley, 65-66. *Mem:* Am Meteorol Soc; Asn Am Geog; Am Soc Photogram. *Res:* Long range weather forecasting; upper level windfield, cloud and smog climatology; ocean tidal and weather interrelationships. *Mailing Add:* Dept of Geog Ore State Univ Corvallis OR 97330

LAHEY, M EUGENE, b Ft Worth, Tex, Dec 28, 17; m 42; c 6. PEDIATRICS. *Educ:* Univ Tex, BA, 39; St Louis Univ, MD, 43. *Prof Exp:* Nat Res Coun fel med sci, Univ Utah, 44-45; asst prof pediat, 51-52; from asst prof to assoc prof, Univ Cincinnati, 52-58; head dept, 58-74, PROF PEDIAT, UNIV UTAH, 58- *Concurrent Pos:* Mem med adv bd, Leukemia Soc, 58- & hemat training grant comt, Nat Inst Arthritis & Metab Dis, 59-63; mem, Scope Panel, US Pharmacopeia, 60-; mem residency rev comt, AMA, 61-65, pres, 65-; res dir, Children's Hosp, East Bay, 64-65; vis prof, Children's Hosp, Honolulu. *Mem:* Am Soc Hemat; Am Pediat Soc; Soc Pediat Res. *Res:* Pediatric hematology. *Mailing Add:* Dept of Pediat Univ of Utah Med Ctr Salt Lake City UT 84132

LAHEY, RICHARD THOMAS, JR, b St Petersburg, Fla, Feb 20, 39; m 61; c 3. HEAT TRANSFER, FLUID MECHANICS. *Educ:* US Merchant Marine Acad, BS, 61; Rensselaer Polytech Inst, MS, 64; Columbia Univ, ME, 66; Stanford Univ, PhD(mech eng), 71. *Prof Exp:* Engr, Knolls Atomic Power Lab, 61-64; res assoc, Columbia Univ, 64-66; mgr core & safety develop, Nuclear Energy Div, Gen Elec, 66-75; MEM STAFF, RENSSELAER POLYTECH INST, 75- *Concurrent Pos:* Mem, Sci Adv Comt, EG&G Idaho Inc, 76-; mem advan code rev group & LOFT Rev Group, US Naval Res Ctr, 76-; comnr, Eng Manpower Comn, 81-; pres, R T Lahey Inc, 81- *Mem:* Fel Am Soc Mech Engrs; fel Am Nuclear Soc; Sigma Xi; NY Acad Sci; Am Asn Eng Educ. *Res:* Two-phase flow and boiling heat transfer technology; nuclear reactor thermal-hydraulics and safety. *Mailing Add:* Dept Nuclear Eng Rensselaer Polytech Inst Troy NY 12181

LAHIRI, SUKHAMAY, b Calcutta, India, Apr 1, 33; m 65. PHYSIOLOGY. *Educ:* Univ Calcutta, BSc, 51, MSc, 53, DPhil(physiol), 56; Oxford Univ, DPhil(physiol), 59. *Prof Exp:* Govt of WBengal scholar, Oxford Univ, 56-59; asst prof physiol, Presidency Col, Univ Calcutta, 59-65, hon lectr, Univ, 60-65; vis fel & asst prof, State Univ NY Downstate Med Ctr, 65-67; sr res assoc, Cardiovasc Inst, Michael Reese Hosp & Med Ctr, Chicago, Ill, 67-69; assoc prof environ physiol, 69-73, ASSOC PROF PHYSIOL, UNIV PA, 73- *Honors & Awards:* Premchand-Roychand Gold Medal, Univ Calcutta, 62. *Mem:* NY Acad Sci; Am Physiol Soc. *Res:* High altitude physiology; regulation and adaptation; gas exchange; chemoreceptors. *Mailing Add:* Dept of Physiol Univ of Pa Philadelphia PA 19104

LAHIRI, SYAMAL KUMAR, b Rangoon, Burma, Jan 1, 40; m 70. MATERIALS SCIENCE. *Educ:* Univ Calcutta, BE, 61; Univ Notre Dame, MS, 64; Northwestern Univ, PhD(mat sci), 69. *Prof Exp:* Sr asst, Defence Metall Res Lab, Govt of India, 61-62; RES STAFF MEM, T J WATSON RES CTR, IBM CORP, 68- *Concurrent Pos:* Vis scientist, Nat Phys Lab & Indian Inst Technol, New Delhi, India, 78-79. *Honors & Awards:* Outstanding Invention Award, IBM Corp, 76. *Mem:* Am Phys Soc; Am Vacuum Soc. *Res:* Thin film properties; fabrication of thin film devices; physical metallurgy; Josephson tunneling devices; packaging. *Mailing Add:* IBM Corp PO Box 218 Yorktown Heights NY 10598

LAHITA, ROBERT GEORGE, b Elizabeth, NJ, Dec 30, 45; m 71; c 2. IMMUNOLOGY, RHEUMATOLOGY. *Educ:* St Peter's Col, BS, 67; Thomas Jefferson Univ, MD, 73, PhD(microbiol), 73. *Prof Exp:* ASST PROF MED & PHARMACOL CORNELL MED COL, 80-; ASST PROF IMMUNOL, ROCKEFELLER UNIV, 80- *Concurrent Pos:* Lectr, Mt Sinai Med Ctr, 81-; consult, Medcom, 81-; mem exec bd, NY Arthritis Found, 82- *Mem:* Am Rheumatism Asn; Am Soc Microbiol; NY Acad Sci; Harvey Soc; AAAS. *Res:* Effect of sex steroids on immune response; disease systemic lupus erythematosus. *Mailing Add:* Rockefeller Univ 1230 York Ave New York NY 10021

LAHR, CHARLES DWIGHT, b Philadelphia, Pa, Feb 6, 45; m 69; c 3. MATHEMATICAL ANALYSIS. *Educ:* Temple Univ, BA, 66; Syracuse Univ, MA, 68, PhD(math), 71. *Prof Exp:* Mathematician, Bell Labs, 71-73; vis asst prof math, Savannah State Col, 73-74 & Amherst Col, 74-75; asst prof, 75-79, ASSOC PROF MATH, DARTMOUTH COL, 79-, ASSOC DEAN FAC SCI & DEAN GRAD STUDIES, 81- *Mem:* Am Math Soc; Sigma Xi; Math Asn Am. *Res:* Banach algebras, particularly convolution algebras in harmonic analysis. *Mailing Add:* Dept of Math Dartmouth Col Hanover NH 03755

LAHR, JOHN CLARK, b Indianapolis, Ind, Nov 11, 44; m 66, 78; c 2. SEISMOLOGY, TECTONICS. *Educ:* Rensselaer Polytech Inst, BS, 66; Columbia Univ, MS, 71, PhD(seismol), 75. *Prof Exp:* GEOPHYSICIST SEISMOL, US GEOL SURV, 71- *Mem:* Seismol Soc Am; Am Geophys Union. *Res:* Seismicity and tectonics of Alaska, especially as related to hazards assessment. *Mailing Add:* US Geol Surv 345 Middlefield Rd Menlo Park CA 94025

LAHTI, LESLIE ERWIN, b Floodwood, Minn, July 27, 32; m 56; c 3. CHEMICAL ENGINEERING. *Educ:* Tri State Col, BS, 54; Mich State Univ, MS, 58; Carnegie Inst Technol, PhD(chem eng), 64. *Prof Exp:* Glass technologist, Corning Glass Works, 55-57; develop engr, Ren Plastics, 57; assoc prof, Tri State Col, 58-60; asst prof chem eng, Purdue Univ, 63-67; assoc prof, 67-72, prof chem eng & chmn dept, 72-80, DEAN ENG, UNIV TOLEDO, 80- *Concurrent Pos:* consult, Am Oil, Great Lakes Chem, 67-69; Inland Chem Co, 70-, Stubbs, Overbeck, 79-81. *Mem:* Am Inst Chem Engrs; Am Chem Soc; Am Soc Eng Educ; Nat Soc Prof Engrs. *Res:* Fundamentals of nucleation and crystallization from solutions; polymerization processes. *Mailing Add:* Dept of Chem Eng Univ of Toledo Toledo OH 43615

LAI, CHING-SAN, b Taiwan, Nov 27, 46; m 71; c 2. CELL BIOPHYSICS, MEMBRANE BIOPHYSICS. *Educ:* Nat Taiwan Norm Univ, BS, 70; Univ Hawaii, PhD(biophysics), 78. *Prof Exp:* Fel biophysics, Univ Hawaii, 78; res assoc, 79-80, ASST PROF BIOPHYSICS, MED COL WIS, 81- *Mem:* Biophys Soc. *Res:* Free radical production in biological systems; membrane fluidity and oxygen uptake in mammalian cell systems, and receptor-hormone interactions in biological membranes by using electron spin resonance spectroscopy and related techniques. *Mailing Add:* Nat Biomed Electron Spin Resonance Ctr Med Col Wis 8701 Watertown Plank Rd Milwaukee WI 53226

LAI, CHINTU (VINCENT C), b Changhua, Formosa, Aug 5, 30; m 63; c 2. COMPUTATIONAL HYDRAULICS, HYDROMECHANICS. *Educ:* Taiwan Univ, BS, 54; Univ Iowa, MS, 57; Univ Mich, PhD(civil eng), 62. *Prof Exp:* Res hydraul engr, Washington, DC, 61-63, Ore, 63-65 & Arlington, Va, 65-73, HYDROLOGIST, WATER RESOURCES DIV, US GEOL SURV, RESTON, 73- *Mem:* Am Soc Civil Engrs; Asn Comput Mach; Int Asn Hydraul Res; Am Geophys Union. *Res:* Computational hydraulics-surface water problems; transient flows in closed and open conduits; numerical modelling and computer simulation of unsteady flows in rivers, estuaries, embayments, closed conduits and other areas in hydromechanics and hydrologic process. *Mailing Add:* US Geol Surv WRD NR Nat Ctr MS 430 Reston VA 22092

LAI, DAVID CHIN, b Beijing, China, Nov 11, 31; m 63; c 2. ELECTRICAL ENGINEERING. *Educ:* Taiwan Univ, BSEE, 54; Johns Hopkins Univ, DEng, 60. *Prof Exp:* Asst prof eng, Brown Univ, 60-62; assoc prof elec eng, Northeastern Univ, 62-65; assoc prof, 65-71, PROF ELEC ENG, UNIV VT, 71- *Concurrent Pos:* Vis prof elec eng, Stanford Univ, 71-75. *Mem:* Inst Elec & Electronics Engrs; Pattern Recognition Soc. *Res:* Signal processing; radar signals; pattern recognition; mini/micro computer applications; bioengineering problems. *Mailing Add:* Dept of Elec Eng Votey Bldg Univ of Vt Burlington VT 05405

LAI, DAVID YING FAT, b Honolulu, Hawaii, June 30, 31. PHYSICAL CHEMISTRY, SOLID STATE KINETICS. *Educ:* Univ Hawaii, BA, 53, MS, 55. *Prof Exp:* Res asst phys metall, Forrestal Res Ctr, Princeton, 58-59; RES CHEMIST, LAWRENCE LIVERMORE LAB, UNIV CALIF, 59- *Mem:* AAAS. *Res:* Mossbauer effects in alloys; diffusion in iron-alloys; aerosol and particle characterization. *Mailing Add:* Lawrence Livermore Lab Univ of Calif PO Box 808 Livermore CA 94550

LAI, FONG M, b Taiwan, Aug 17, 42; m 69; c 2. CARDIOVASCULAR PHARMACOLOGY. *Educ:* Taipei Med Col, BS, 66; Taiwan Univ, MS, 69; Med Col Va, PhD(pharmacol), 74. *Prof Exp:* Res fel, Roche Inst Molecular Biol, 74-76; GROUP LEADER & SR SCIENTIST, LEDERLE LABS, AM CYANAMID CO, 76- *Mem:* Am Soc Pharmacol & Exp Therapeut. *Res:* Mechanisms of the development of hypertension and how drugs lower the pressure. *Mailing Add:* Lederle Labs Am Cyanamid Co Pearl River NY 10965

LAI, FRANCIS MING-HUNG, physiology, biochemistry, see previous edition

LAI, JAI-LUE, b Taipei, Taiwan, Dec 9, 40; US citizen; m 68; c 2. ACOUSTICS, STRUCTURAL DYNAMICS. *Educ:* Nat Taiwan Univ, BS, 62; Polytech Inst Brooklyn, MSE, 66; Princeton Univ, PhD(mech eng), 69. *Prof Exp:* Engr satellite struct, RCA Corp, 67; sr scientist, 68-77, ENG SCI ASSOC, B F GOODRICH CO, 77- *Mem:* Sigma Xi; Am Inst Aeronaut & Astronaut; Acoust Soc Am. *Res:* Application of new material composite structure as new products or components. *Mailing Add:* B F Goodrich Co 500 S Main St Akron OH 44318

LAI, JUEY HONG, b Taipei, Taiwan, Dec 4, 36; US citizen; m 68; c 2. PHYSICAL CHEMISTRY, POLYMER CHEMISTRY. *Educ:* Nat Taiwan Univ, BS, 59; Univ Wash, MS, 63, PhD(phys chem), 69. *Prof Exp:* Res specialist polymer, Univ Minn, 69-73; prin res scientist polymer mat, 73-78, SR PRIN RES SCIENTIST POLYMER MAT, HONEYWELL CORP TECHNOL CTR, 78- *Mem:* Am Chem Soc; Sigma Xi. *Res:* Polymer materials for electronics; electron resists for electron beam microfabrication, polymer characterization and solid state chemistry. *Mailing Add:* Honeywell Corp Technol Ctr 10701 Lyndale Ave S Bloomington MN 55420

LAI, KAI SUN, b Hong Kong, China; US citizen. ENGINEERING. *Educ:* Pa State Univ, BSc, 59. *Prof Exp:* Engr, Aeorjet Gen Corp, 59-62; sr analyst, Atlantic Res Corp, 62-68; mgr, 68-80, sr scientist, 80-82, ENG SPECIALIST, TELEDYNE MCCORMICK SELPH, 82- *Res:* Combustion process and thermochemical analysis of solid fuels and additives, including boranes; propulsion for aerospace applications and use of explosives and pyrotechnics for safety applications. *Mailing Add:* 855 W Eighth St Gilroy CA 95020

LAI, KUO-YANN, b Miao-Li, Taiwan, Sept 13, 46; m 72. PHYSICAL CHEMISTRY, SURFACE SCIENCE. *Educ:* Cheng Kung Univ, Taiwan, BS, 69; Univ Tex, El Paso, MS, 74; Clarkson Col Technol, PhD(chem), 77. *Prof Exp:* Res chemist, 77-80, SR RES CHEMIST DETERGENTS, COLGATE-PALMOLIVE CO, 80- *Concurrent Pos:* Robert A Welch fel, 72-74; NSF fel, 74-77. *Mem:* Am Chem Soc; Am Oil Chemists Soc. *Res:* Adhesional wetting; scavenging of aerosols; detergents. *Mailing Add:* Res Ctr Colgate-Palmolive Co 909 River Rd Piscataway NJ 08854

LAI, KWAN WU, high energy physics, see previous edition

LAI, MICHAEL MING-CHIAO, b Tainan, Taiwan, Sept 8, 42; m 71; c 2. VIROLOGY, MOLECULAR BIOLOGY. *Educ:* Nat Taiwan Univ Col Med, MD, 68; Univ Calif, Berkeley, PhD(molecular biol), 73. *Prof Exp:* Med officer, Chinese Marine Corps, 68-69; postgrad molecular biologist, Univ Calif, Berkeley, 73; asst prof, 73-78, ASSOC PROF MICROBIOL, UNIV SOUTHERN CALIF SCH MED, 78- *Concurrent Pos:* Prin investr grants, Nat Cancer Inst & Am Cancer Soc, 73- & Nat Sci Found, 79- *Mem:* Am Soc Microbiol; Am Soc Virol. *Res:* Molecular biology of RNA tumor viruses and coronaviruses; mechanism of viral oncogenesis. *Mailing Add:* Dept of Microbiol 2025 Zonal Ave Los Angeles CA 90033

LAI, PING-YUEN, b Chai-yi, Taiwan, Apr 4, 30; m 59; c 2. PLANT PATHOLOGY, ENTOMOLOGY. *Educ:* Chung Hsing Univ, Taiwan, BS, 57; Wash State Univ, PhD(plant path), 67. *Prof Exp:* Sr specialist & sect chief plant protection, Taiwan Prov Food Bur, 59-63; res asst plant path, Wash State Univ, 63-66, sr sci aide, 66-67; USDA grant res assoc, Iowa State Univ, 67-68; chief plant pathologist, Res Dept, 68-73, sr plant pathologist, Standard

Fruit Co, 73-76; supt res, Castle & Cooke Inc, 76-80. *Mem:* Am Phytopath Soc; Am Inst Biol Sci. *Res:* Epidemiology and control of wheat, soybean and banana diseases; aerial application of fungicides. *Mailing Add:* 94-168-250 Anania Dr Mililani HI 96789

LAI, RALPH WEI-MEEN, b Tou-Lu, Taiwan, Dec 17, 36; US citizen; m 66; c 2. SURFACE CHEMISTRY, MINERAL SCIENCE & ENGINEERING. *Educ:* Cheng Kung Univ, Taiwan, BS, 59; SDak Sch Mines & Technol, MS, 64; Univ Calif, Berkeley, PhD(mineral & sci eng), 70. *Prof Exp:* Res scientist mat res, Cyprus Mines Corp, 69-72; mineral processing scientist process develop, Anglo-Am Clays Corp, 73-74; SR PROJ ENGR METALL ENG, KENNECOTT DEVELOP CTR, KENNECOTT COPPER CORP, 74- *Concurrent Pos:* Pres, Western Prospect Co, 78- *Mem:* Am Inst Mining, Metall & Petrol Engrs; Japan Inst Mining & Metall; Clay Minerals Soc. *Res:* Surface chemistry of oxide minerals. *Mailing Add:* 3239 Fairfield Rd Holladay UT 84117

LAI, SAN-CHENG, b Taiwan, China, Dec 8, 40; m 68. CHEMICAL ENGINEERING. *Educ:* Taiwan Univ, BS, 63; Univ Mo-Rolla, MS, 66, PhD(chem eng), 68. *Prof Exp:* Sr res engr, Am Potash & Chem Corp, 68-77; MEM TECH STAFF, ATOMICS INT, 77- *Mem:* Am Inst Chem Eng; Electrochem Soc; Am Chem Soc. *Res:* Electrodeposition of manganese dioxide; alkaline battery and magnesium can battery development; sodium chlorate and perchlorate process development; manganese metal process improvement; fluidized bed cell development. *Mailing Add:* 1478 Kingston Circle Westlake Village CA 91362

LAI, TZE LEUNG, b Hong Kong, June 28, 45; m 75. MATHEMATICS, STATISTICS. *Educ:* Univ Hong Kong, BA, 67; Columbia Univ, MA, 70, PhD(statist), 71. *Prof Exp:* From asst prof to assoc prof, 71-77, PROF STATIST, COLUMBIA UNIV, 77- *Concurrent Pos:* Vis assoc prof math, Univ Ill, Urbana-Champaign, 75-76; vis prof statist, Stanford Univ, 78-79. *Mem:* Am Statist Asn; fel Inst Math Statist; Sigma Xi. *Res:* Sequential methods in statistics; statistical quality control and clinical trials; time series analysis; limit theorems in probability; renewal theory and random walks; martingales and potential theory; system identification and control; cardiorespiratory physiology. *Mailing Add:* Dept of Math Statist Columbia Univ New York NY 10027

LAI, W(EI) MICHAEL, b Amoy, China, Nov 29, 31; US citizen; m 63; c 2. ENGINEERING MECHANICS. *Educ:* Nat Taiwan Univ, BS, 53; Univ Mich, Ann Arbor, MS, 59, PhD(eng mech), 62. *Prof Exp:* From asst to assoc prof, 61-77, PROF MECH, RENSSELAER POLYTECH INST, 78- *Mem:* Am Math Soc; Am Soc Mech Engrs; Am Soc Biomech. *Res:* Hydrodynamic stability; continuum mechanics; biomechanics. *Mailing Add:* 14 Bedford Dr Latham NY 12110

LAI, YUAN-ZONG, b Taiwan, Repub of China, Mar 11, 41; m 68; c 2. WOOD CHEMISTRY. *Educ:* Nat Taiwan Univ, BS, 63; Univ Wash, MS, 66 & 67, PhD(wood chem), 68. *Prof Exp:* From res asst to res assoc wood chem, Col Forest Resources, Univ Wash, 64-70; sr res assoc wood chem, Univ Mont, 70-75; asst prof wood chem, dept forestry, 75-77, ASSOC PROF FORESTRY, MICH TECHNOL UNIV, 77- *Mem:* Tech Asn Pulp & Paper Indust; Am Chem Soc; Sigma Xi. *Res:* Lignin, cellulose and extractive chemistry; thermal properties of wood components. *Mailing Add:* Dept of Forestry Mich Technol Univ Houghton MI 49931

LAI, YU-CHIN, b Feb 2, 49. POLYMER CHEMISTRY. *Educ:* Nat Tsing Hua Univ, Taiwan, BS, 71; Carnegie-Mellon Univ, MS, 75; Univ Fla, PhD(chem), 80. *Prof Exp:* Res assoc, Univ Mass, 80-81; RES CHEMIST POLYMER CHEM, CORP RES & DEVELOP, ALLIED CORP, 81- *Mem:* Am Chem Soc. *Res:* Synthesis of organic compounds: monomers and polymers; kinetics and mechanism of polymerization; structure-properties relationships in polymers. *Mailing Add:* Corp Res & Develop Allied Corp PO Box 1021 R Morristown NJ 07960

LAIBLE, CHARLES A, b Freeport, Ill, Jan 15, 36; m 59; c 4. GENETICS. *Educ:* Univ Ill, BS, 58, MS, 59; Univ Minn, PhD(genetics), 64. *Prof Exp:* Asst, Univ Ill, 58-59 & Univ Minn, 59-64; corn breeder, Funk Bros Seed Co, 64, mgr hybrid wheat dept, 64-67, MGR RES DATA & QUANT GENETICS, FUNK SEEDS INT, 67- *Mem:* Crop Sci Soc Am; Am Soc Agron; Soil Sci Soc Am; Am Genetics Asn. *Res:* Components of genetic variance for ear number; inheritance of ear number in four Zea Mays genotypes; genetic variance and selective value of ear number in corn; computer programming. *Mailing Add:* Funk Seeds Int Bloomington IL 61701

LAIBLE, JON MORSE, b Bloomington, Ill, July 25, 37; m 59; c 4. ALGEBRA. *Educ:* Univ Ill, Urbana, BS, 59, PhD(math), 67; Univ Minn, Minneapolis, MA, 61. *Prof Exp:* Asst prof math, Western Ill Univ, 61-64; from asst prof to assoc prof, 64-79, PROF MATH, EASTERN ILL UNIV, 79, DEAN, COL ARTS & SCI, 81- *Mem:* Am Math Soc; Math Asn Am; Sigma Xi. *Mailing Add:* Dept of Math Eastern Ill Univ Charleston IL 61920

LAIBLE, ROY C, b Boston, Mass, June 16, 24. POLYMER PHYSICS. *Educ:* Northeastern Univ, BS, 45; Boston Univ, MA, 48; Mass Inst Technol, PhD, 70. *Prof Exp:* Res assoc polymerization, Univ RI, 50-52; org chemist, Cent Intel Agency, 52-53; org chemist, 53-58, phys sci adminr, 58-63, physics scientist, 63-70, chief, Textile Res Sect, 70-76, CHIEF, POLYMERS & ORG MAT BR, US ARMY NATICK LABS, 76- *Concurrent Pos:* Secy of Army res & study fel viscoelastic properties polymers, Sweden & Scotland, 62-63. *Res:* Allyl polymerization; viscoelastic properties of fibrous and non-fibrous polymers; ballistic properties of polymers. *Mailing Add:* US Army Natick Res & Develop Command Kansas St Natick MA 01760

LAIBOWITZ, ROBERT (BENJAMIN), b Yonkers, NY, Mar 24, 37; m 58; c 3. APPLIED PHYSICS. *Educ:* Columbia Col, BA, 59; Columbia Univ, 60, MS, 63; Cornell Univ, PhD(appl physics), 67. *Prof Exp:* RES STAFF MEM, IBM RES CTR, 66- *Mem:* Am Phys Soc; fel Am Vacuum Soc. *Res:* Electrical and optical properties of materials; superconductivity. *Mailing Add:* IBM Res Ctr PO Box 218 Yorktown Heights NY 10598

LAIBSON, PETER R, b New York, NY, Dec 11, 33; m 63; c 1. OPHTHALMOLOGY. *Educ:* Univ Vt, BA, 55; State Univ NY Downstate Med Ctr, MD, 59; Am Bd Ophthal, dipl, 65. *Prof Exp:* NIH fel corneal dis, Retina Found & Mass Eye & Ear Infirmary, 64-65; ASSOC PROF OPHTHAL, SCH MED, TEMPLE UNIV, 66-; PROF OPHTHAL, SCH MED, THOMAS JEFFERSON UNIV, 73- *Concurrent Pos:* Attend surgeon & dir cornea serv, Wills Eye Hosp; consult lectr, US Naval Hosp, Philadelphia, 68-; mem ophthal staff, Lankenau Hosp, Philadelphia. *Mem:* Asn Res Ophthal; Am Acad Ophthal & Otolaryngol; AMA. *Res:* Corneal diseases and surgery of the cornea, particularly viral external diseases, herpes simplex and adenoviruses. *Mailing Add:* Wills Eye Hosp 1601 Spring Garden St Philadelphia PA 19130

LAIDERMAN, DONALD D, b Minneapolis, Minn, Feb 26, 26; m 48; c 3. CHEMISTRY. *Educ:* Univ Minn, BA, 48. *Prof Exp:* Chemist, Sherwin-Williams Co, 48-53; chemist, Toni Div, 53-60, mgr prod develop, 60-68, dir res, 68-71, VPRES RES & DEVELOP, TOILETRIES DIV, GILLETTE CO, 71- *Mem:* Fel Am Inst Chemists; Am Chem Soc; Soc Cosmetic Chem. *Res:* Cosmetic and paint chemistry; corrosion; detergents. *Mailing Add:* 189 Bristol Rd Wellesley MA 02106

LAIDLAW, HARRY HYDE, JR, b Houston, Tex, Apr 12, 07; m 46; c 1. APICULTURE. *Educ:* La State Univ, BS, 33, MS, 34; Univ Wis, PhD(entom, genetics), 39. *Prof Exp:* From minor sci helper to agent, USDA, 29-34 & 35-39; asst zool & entom, La State Univ, 33-34, asst exp sta, 34-35; prof biol sci, Oakland City Col, 39-41; apiarist, State Dept Agr & Indust, Ala, 41-42; entomologist hqs, 1st Army, New York, 46-47; asst prof entom & asst apiculturist, 47-53, assoc prof entom & assoc apiculturist, 53-59, prof entom & apiculturist, 59-74, prof genetics, 71-74, assoc dean col agr, 60-64, EMER PROF ENTOM, EXP STA, UNIV CALIF, DAVIS, 74- *Concurrent Pos:* Wis Alumni Res Found asst, Univ Wis, 37-39; NIH grant, Univ Calif, Davis, 63-66, NSF grant, 66-73. *Mem:* Fel AAAS; Genetics Soc Am; Am Soc Zool; Entom Soc Am; Am Soc Nat. *Res:* Genetics, breeding and anatomy of the honeybee; factors influencing the development of queen bees; artificial insemination of queen bees. *Mailing Add:* 761 Sycamore Lane Davis CA 95616

LAIDLAW, JOHN COLEMAN, b Toronto, Ont, Feb 28, 21; m 57; c 2. ENDOCRINOLOGY. *Educ:* Univ Toronto, BA, 42, MD, 44, MA, 47; Univ London, PhD(biochem), 50; FRCP(C), 55. *Prof Exp:* Jr intern, Toronto Gen Hosp, 44; demonstr biochem, Univ Toronto, 46-47; res fel biochem, Univ London, 47-50; sr intern med, Toronto Gen Hosp, 50-51; res fel, Harvard Med Sch, 51-53, instr, 53-54; assoc, 54-56, from asst prof to prof med, Univ Toronto, 56-75, dir inst med sci, 67-75; prof med & chmn dept, 75-81, DEAN, FAC HEALTH SCI, MCMASTER UNIV, 81- *Concurrent Pos:* Asst, Peter Bent Brigham Hosp, Boston, 51-53, jr assoc, 53-54; physician, Toronto Gen Hosp, 54-59, sr physician, 59-75. *Mem:* Endocrine Soc; Am Soc Clin Invest; Res; Can Soc Clin Invest (pres, 62); Can Soc Endocrinol & Metab. *Mailing Add:* Fac Health Sci McMaster Univ Hamilton ON L8N 3Z5 Can

LAIDLAW, WILLIAM GEORGE, b Wingham, Ont, Mar 13, 36; m 61; c 2. THEORETICAL CHEMISTRY. *Educ:* Univ Western Ont, BSc, 59; Calif Inst Technol, MSc, 61; Univ Alta, PhD(theoret chem), 63. *Prof Exp:* NATO fel, Math Inst, Univ Oxford, 64-65; from asst prof to assoc prof chem, 65-73, PROF CHEM, UNIV CALGARY, 73- *Concurrent Pos:* Vis prof, Univ Waterloo & Free Univ Brussels, 71-72. *Mem:* The Chem Soc. *Res:* Hydrodynamics; light-scattering from liquid crystals and systems near instabilities; molecular orbital calculations. *Mailing Add:* Dept of Chem Univ of Calgary Calgary AB T2N 1N4 Can

LAIDLER, KEITH JAMES, b Liverpool, Eng, Jan 3, 16; m 43; c 3. PHYSICAL CHEMISTRY. *Educ:* Oxford Univ, BA, 37, MA, 55, DSc, 56; Princeton Univ, PhD(phys chem), 40. *Prof Exp:* Res chemist, Nat Res Coun Can, 40-42; sci officer, Can Armaments Res & Develop Estab, 42-44, chief sci officer & supt phys & math wing, 44-46; from asst prof to assoc prof chem, Cath Univ Am, 46-55; chmn dept, 61-66, vdean fac pure & appl sci, 62-66, prof, 55-81, EMER PROF CHEM, UNIV OTTAWA, 81- *Concurrent Pos:* Commonwealth vis prof, Sussex Univ, 66-67. *Honors & Awards:* Queen's Jubilee Medal, 77. *Mem:* Royal Soc Chem; fel Royal Soc Can; fel Chem Inst Can. *Res:* Chemical kinetics of gas reactions; surface, solution and enzyme reactions; photochemistry. *Mailing Add:* Dept of Chem Univ of Ottawa Ottawa ON K1N 9B4 Can

LAI-FOOK, JOAN ELSA I-LING, b Port of Spain, Trinidad, Aug 3, 37. ZOOLOGY. *Educ:* Univ Col WI, BSc, 61; Western Reserve Univ, PhD(biol), 66. *Prof Exp:* Asst prof, 66-73, ASSOC PROF ZOOL, UNIV TORONTO, 73- *Mem:* Am Soc Cell Biol. *Res:* Fine structure of insect development and physiology. *Mailing Add:* Dept of Zool Univ of Toronto Toronto ON M5S 1A1 Can

LAIKEN, NORA DAWN, b Chicago, Ill, June 28, 46; m 67. MEDICAL PHYSIOLOGY, MEDICAL EDUCATION. *Educ:* Univ Chicago, BS, 67; Rockefeller Univ, PhD(life sci), 70. *Prof Exp:* USPHS fel & res assoc phys biochem, Inst Molecular Biol, Univ Ore, 70-71; USPHS fel & res assoc phys biochem, 71-72, sci curric adv physics, biol & chem, Adaptive Learning Prog, 72-73, lectr med, 74-76, asst prof, 76-80, DIR TUTORIAL PROG, UNIV CALIF, SAN DIEGO, 73-, ASST ADJ PROF MED, 80- *Concurrent Pos:* Mem test adv Asn Am Med Col, 74- *Res:* Development of innovative instructional materials and methods in the basic medical sciences, particularly in medical physiology and pharmacology. *Mailing Add:* Sch of Med M-006 Univ of Calif at San Diego LaJolla CA 92093

LAINE, RICHARD MASON, b San Fernando, Calif, Oct 31, 47. ORGANOMETALLIC CHEMISTRY. *Educ:* Calif State Univ, Northridge, BS, 69; Univ Southern Calif, PhD(chem), 73. *Prof Exp:* Fel chem, Univ Del, 73-74 & Dept Chem & Dept Chem & Nuclear Eng, Univ Calif, Santa Barbara, 74-76; fel chem, Stanford Res Inst, 76-77, PHYS INORG CHEMIST, SRI INT, 77- *Concurrent Pos:* Prin investr, NSF Chem Eng Grant, 78-79; proj leader, NIH Grant, 78-81. *Mem:* Am Chem Soc; Catalysis Soc; Sigma Xi. *Res:* Homogeneous catalysis of the water-gas shift reaction and the catalysis of related reactions wherein water serves as a source of hydrogen. *Mailing Add:* Stanford Res Inst Int 333 Ravenswood Ave Menlo Park CA 94025

LAINE, ROGER ALLAN, b Cloquet, Minn, Jan 28, 41. BIOCHEMISTRY. *Educ:* Univ Minn, Minneapolis, BA, 64; Rice Univ, Houston, PhD(biochem), 70. *Prof Exp:* Fel biochem, Mich State Univ, East Lansing, 70-72; fel pathobiol, Univ Wash, 72-74; asst prof, 75-78, ASSOC PROF BIOCHEM, COL MED, UNIV KY, 79- *Mem:* Am Chem Soc; Soc Complex Carbohydrates; Am Soc Mass Spectrometry; Am Soc Biol Chemists. *Res:* Biochemistry of cell membrane components; gas-liquid-chromatography and mass spectrometry in carbohydrate analysis. *Mailing Add:* Dept of Biochem Col of Med Univ of Ky Lexington KY 40506

LAING, CHARLES CORBETT, b Brooklyn, NY, Dec 24, 25; m 59; c 3. ECOLOGY. *Educ:* Univ Chicago, PhB, 50, PhD, 54. *Prof Exp:* Instr bot, Univ Tenn, 54-56; asst prof, Univ Wyo, 56-59 & Univ Nebr, Lincoln, 59-66; mem fac biol, 66-68, ASSOC PROF BIOL, OHIO NORTHERN UNIV, 68- *Mem:* Ecol Soc Am; Brit Ecol Soc. *Res:* Ecology of sand dunes; population ecology of dune grasses; grasslands. *Mailing Add:* Dept of Biol Ohio Northern Univ Ada OH 45810

LAING, FREDERICK M, b Barre, Vt, Nov 29, 19; m 43; c 2. PLANT PHYSIOLOGY. *Educ:* Univ Vt, BS, 51, MS, 53. *Prof Exp:* Res assoc, 53-77, exten assoc prof, 77-79, RES ASSOC PROF, STATE AGR COL, UNIV VT, 79- *Mem:* Bot Soc Am; Can Soc Plant Physiol; Am Soc Plant Physiol; Sigma Xi. *Res:* Growth, vigor and physiology of the sugar maple tree and factors involved in sap production; production of biomass for energy on marginal lands in Northeast. *Mailing Add:* Dept Vot Marsh Life Sci Bldg Univ Vt Burlington VT 05401

LAING, JOHN E, b Ottawa, Ont, Oct 17, 39; m 64; c 2. ENTOMOLOGY, ECOLOGY. *Educ:* Carleton Univ, BSc, 63, MSc, 64; Univ Calif, Berkeley, PhD(entom), 68. *Prof Exp:* Asst res entomologist & lectr, Div Biol Control, Univ Calif, Berkeley, 68-73; asst prof, 73-78, ASSOC PROF ENVIRON BIOL, UNIV GUELPH, 78- *Mem:* Entom Soc Can (secy, 78-81); Entom Soc Am; Ecol Soc Am; Int Asn Ecol; Int Orgn Biol Control. *Res:* Ecology of tetranychid mites; populations dynamics of arthropods; ecology and control of orchard pests; biological control of insect pests and weeds. *Mailing Add:* Dept of Environ Biol Univ of Guelph Guelph ON N1G 2W1 Can

LAING, PATRICK GOWANS, b Barnes, Eng, Nov 8, 23; US citizen; m 56; c 4. ORTHOPEDIC SURGERY. *Educ:* Univ Southampton, MB & BS, 40; FRCS, 48; FRCS(C), 54, Am Bd Orthop Surg, dipl, 60. *Prof Exp:* House surgeon, Kings Col Hosp, London, Eng, 45-46; registr orthop surg, Royal Hampshire County Hosp, Winchester, 46-47, gen & orthop surg, Queen Mary's Hosp, Sidcup, 48, orthop surg, Lewisham Hosp, London, 48-50 & Pembury Hosp, Kent, 50-52; sr registr, Bradford Hosp, Yorkshire, 52-54; chief resident surg, Vet Hosp, St John, NB, 54-55; assoc prof orthop surg, 56-63, CLIN PROF ORTHOP SURG, UNIV PITTSBURGH, 63-; CHIEF SERV, VET ADMIN HOSP, 56- *Concurrent Pos:* Fel cerebral palsy, Univ Pittsburgh, 55-56. *Mem:* Orthop Res Soc; Am Orthop Asn; Am Soc Testing & Mat; NY Acad Sci; Brit Orthop Asn. *Res:* Blood supply and the dynamics of circulation in bones and joints; metallurgy and engineering in orthopedics; radioisotopes in clinical orthopedics. *Mailing Add:* Aiken Med Bldg 532 S Aiken Ave Pittsburgh PA 15232

LAING, RONALD ALBERT, b Seattle, Wash, Dec 9, 33. BIOPHYSICS. *Educ:* Reed Col, BA, 56; Rice Univ, MA, 58, PhD(low temperature physics), 60. *Prof Exp:* Asst prof physics, Tulane Univ, 60-68; sr scientist, Space Sci Inc, 68-70; vis scientist, Univ Tokyo, 69-70; ASSOC PROF OPHTHAL, MED SCH, BOSTON UNIV, 70- *Concurrent Pos:* NSF sci fac fel, Harvard Univ, 65-66; NIH fel, Mass Inst Technol, 66-67; vis lectr, Univ Mass, Boston, 67-68; consult, Space Sci Inc, 67-68. *Mem:* Biophys Soc; Asn Res in Vision & Ophthalmol; Optical Soc Am; AAAS; Sigma Xi. *Res:* Ophthalmic biophysics; bioengineering. *Mailing Add:* 25 Maple St Lexington MA 02173

LAIPIS, PHILIP JAMES, b Charleston, SC, Apr 20, 44; m 70; c 2. MOLECULAR BIOLOGY, GENETICS. *Educ:* Calif Inst Technol, BS, 66; Stanford Univ, PhD(genetics), 72. *Prof Exp:* Nat Cancer Inst fel, Princeton Univ, 72-74; asst prof, 74-80, ASSOC PROF BIOCHEM, UNIV FLA, 80- *Concurrent Pos:* Vis scholar biochem, Harvard Univ, 81-82. *Mem:* AAAS; Am Soc Microbiol; Sigma Xi. *Res:* Gene organization and variation in mammalian mitochondrial DNA; mechanisms of maternal inheritance, mitochondrial amplification and embryonic distribution of mitochondria on mammals; gene organization and variation in mammalian mitochondrial DNA; virology. *Mailing Add:* Box J-245 J H M Health Ctr Univ of Fla Gainesville FL 32610

LAIR, ALAN VAN, b Anna, Tex, May 2, 48; m 78. MATHEMATICS. *Educ:* NTex State Univ, BA, 70; Tex Tech Univ, MS, 72, PhD(math), 76. *Prof Exp:* asst prof, 76-79, ASSOC PROF MATH, UNIV SDAK, 79- *Mem:* Am Math Soc; Math Asn Am; Sigma Xi. *Res:* Parabolic and elliptic partial differential equations. *Mailing Add:* Dept of Math Univ of SDak Vermillion SD 57069

LAIRD, ALAN D K, b Victoria, BC, Aug 8, 14; US citizen; m 41; c 3. MECHANICAL ENGINEERING. *Educ:* Univ BC, BASc, 40; Univ Calif, Berkeley, MS, 49, PhD(mech eng), 51. *Prof Exp:* Engr, Defense Industs, Ltd, Can, 41-45 & Leek & Co, 45-46; lectr mech eng, 48-51, from asst prof to prof mech eng, 51-80, dir Sea Water Conversion Lab, 68-80, EMER PROF MECH ENG, UNIV CALIF, BERKELEY, 80- *Mem:* Am Soc Mech Engrs; Water Supply Improv Asn. *Res:* Distillation desalination; wave and stream forces on cylinders; geothermal energy. *Mailing Add:* 6169 Etcheverry Hall Univ of Calif Berkeley CA 94720

LAIRD, CAMPBELL, b Ardrishaig, Scotland, June 17, 36; m 64; c 2. PHYSICAL METALLURGY. *Educ:* Cambridge Univ, BA, 59, MA, 63, PhD(metall), 63. *Prof Exp:* Res fel metall, Christ's Col, Cambridge Univ, 61-65; prin scientist, Sci Lab, Ford Motor Co, 63-68; prof metall, 68-80, PROF MATERIALS SCI & ENG, UNIV PA, 80- *Concurrent Pos:* Battelle vis prof, Ohio State Univ, 68- *Mem:* Am Inst Mining, Metall & Petrol Engrs; Am Soc Testing & Mat; Electron Micros Soc Am; Royal Inst Gt Brit; Brit Inst Metals. *Res:* Fracture of materials, especially by fatigue; super-conductivity; diffusional phase transformations; electron microscopy; cyclic stress-strain response of materials. *Mailing Add:* Lab for Res on Struct of Matter Univ of Pa 3231 Walnut Philadelphia PA 19104

LAIRD, CHARLES DAVID, b Portland, Ore, May 12, 39; m 61; c 3. CELL BIOLOGY. *Educ:* Univ Ore, BA, 61; Stanford Univ, PhD(genetics), 66. *Prof Exp:* NIH fel genetics, Univ Wash, 67-68; asst prof zool, Univ Tex, Austin, 68-71; assoc prof zool & adj assoc prof genetics, 71-75, PROF ZOOL & ADJ PROF GENETICS, UNIV WASH, 75- *Concurrent Pos:* Vis scholar, Cambridge Univ, 78-79; distinguished lectr, Univ Tex, Austin, 77. *Res:* Encoding the three dimensional structure of chromosomes; mechanisms of transcription control; chromosome structure and function. *Mailing Add:* Dept of Zool Univ of Wash NJ 15 Seattle WA 98195

LAIRD, CHRISTOPHER ELI, b Anniston, Ala, Nov 29, 42; m 66; c 2. NUCLEAR PHYSICS. *Educ:* Univ Ala, BS, 63, MS, 66, PhD(physics), 70. *Prof Exp:* From asst prof to assoc prof, 67-75, PROF PHYSICS, EASTERN KY UNIV, 75- *Concurrent Pos:* Fac res mem, Vanderbilt Univ, 69 & Argonne Nat Lab, 77-78; vis res prof, Univ Ky, 79-81. *Mem:* Am Phys Soc; Sigma Xi; Sci Res Soc. *Res:* Theoretical and experimental nuclear physics with primary emphasis in beta decay; atomic effects during beta decay; proton induced nuclear reactions; experimental measurement of proton-induced reaction cross-sections analysis of this data using various nuclear models. *Mailing Add:* Dept of Physics Moore 351 Eastern Ky Univ Richmond KY 40475

LAIRD, DONALD T(HOMAS), b Sykesville, Pa, Dec 12, 26; m 48; c 4. COMPUTER SCIENCE. *Educ:* Pa State Univ, BS, 46, PhD(physics), 55; Cornell Univ, MS, 51. *Prof Exp:* Asst physics, Cornell Univ, 46-49; res assoc, Ord Res Lab, 49-55, asst prof elec eng, 55-58, eng res, 58-61, assoc prof, 61-64, ASSOC PROF COMPUT SCI, PA STATE UNIV, 64-, DIR COMPUT CTR, 58- *Concurrent Pos:* Prog dir comput sci, NSF, 63-64. *Mem:* Soc Indust & Appl Math; Asn Comput Mach. *Res:* Computer programming systems including supervisors and language processors. *Mailing Add:* Comput Ctr Pa State Univ University Park PA 16802

LAIRD, HUGH EDWARD, II, b Phoenix, Ariz, Mar 30, 39; m 61; c 2. NEUROPHARMACOLOGY, NEUROCHEMISTRY. *Educ:* Univ Ariz, BS, 62, PhD(pharmacol), 74. *Prof Exp:* Res assoc, 69-70, teaching assoc, 71-73, instr, 73-74, asst prof, 74-80, ASSOC PROF PHARMACOL & TOXICOL, COL PHARM, UNIV ARIZ, 80-, ASST PROVOST GRAD STUDIES, GRAD COL, 81- *Concurrent Pos:* Teaching asst pharmeceut, Col Pharm, Univ Ariz, 68-70; consult, Ariz Poison Control Info Ctr, 74-79; prin investr, Nat Inst Neurol & Commun Dis & Stroke, 78-82. *Mem:* Acad Pharmaceut Sci; AAAS; Am Epilepsy; NY Acad Sci; Soc Neurosci. *Res:* Pathophysiology and treatment of convulsive seizure disorders with particular emphasis on the molecular function of neurotransmitter and neuromodulator systems in the genesis and propagation of seizure activity. *Mailing Add:* Grad Col Univ Ariz Tucson AZ 85721

LAIRD, MARSHALL, b Wellington, NZ, Jan 26, 23; m 49; c 2. PARASITOLOGY, MEDICAL ENTOMOLOGY. *Educ:* Univ NZ, BSc, 45, MSc, 47, PhD(zool), 49, DSc(zool), 54. *Prof Exp:* Entomologist, Royal NZ Air Force, 45-48, 50-54; lectr parasitol, Univ Malaya, 54-57; from asst prof to assoc prof, Macdonald Col, McGill Univ, 57-61; chief environ biol, WHO, Geneva, 61-67; prof biol & head dept, 67-72, RES PROF BIOL & DIR RES UNIT VECTOR PATH, MEM UNIV NFLD, 72- *Concurrent Pos:* Mem sci adv panel vector biol & control, WHO, 53-61 & 67-, mem sci adv panel & sci & tech comt, Onchocerciasis Control Prog, 74-, head, WHO Collab Ctr for Biol Control, Identification, Ecol & Safety Non-Target Organisms, 75-; Franklin lectr, Auburn Univ, 75. *Honors & Awards:* Hamilton Prize, Royal Soc NZ, 51; Res Medal, NZ Asn Sci Workers, 52. *Mem:* Fel Royal Soc Trop Med & Hyg; Soc Protozoologists; Soc Invert Path; Can Soc Zoologists; Am Soc Parasitologists. *Res:* Protozoology; blood parasitology; biting fly larval ecology; insect control relating to aviation. *Mailing Add:* Res Unit on Vector Path Mem Univ of Nfld St John's NF A1C 5S7 Can

LAIRD, REGGIE JAMES, b Bassfield, Miss, Feb 11, 20; m 57; c 3. SOIL SCIENCE. *Educ:* Miss State Col, BS, 40; Univ Wis, MS, 42; Univ Calif, PhD(soils), 52. *Prof Exp:* Asst agronomist, Exp Sta, Miss State Col, 46-49; from asst soil scientist to assoc soil scientist, 52-55, SOIL SCIENTIST, ROCKEFELLER FOUND, 56- *Mem:* Soil Sci Soc Am; Am Soc Agron; Int Soc Soil Sci. *Res:* Soil fertility and soil-plant-water relationships and agricultural development. *Mailing Add:* Londres 40 Mexico 6DF Mexico

LAIRD, WILSON MORROW, b Erie, Pa, Mar 4, 15; m 38; c 4. GEOLOGY. *Educ:* Muskingum Col, BA, 36; Univ NC, MA, 38; Univ Cincinnati, PhD(geol), 42. *Hon Degrees:* DSc, Muskingum Col, 64. *Prof Exp:* Asst geol, Univ NC, 36-38 & Univ Cincinnati, 38-40; from asst prof to prof, 40-69, EMER PROF GEOL, UNIV NDAK, 69-; DIR COMT EXPLOR, AM PETROL INST, 71-; CONSULT, 79- *Concurrent Pos:* State geologist, NDak, 41-69, state geologist emer, 69-; geologist, US Geol Surv, 44-48; consult geologist, 47-48; dir off oil & gas, Dept Interior, Washington, DC, 69-71. *Honors & Awards:* Am Asn Petrol Geol Pres Award, 48. *Mem:* Fel Geol Soc Am; Am Asn Petrol Geol; hon mem Asn Am State Geol (vpres, 48, pres, 50); Sigma Xi. *Res:* Stratigraphy of the upper Devonian and lower Mississippian of southwestern Pennsylvania and the northern Rockies; paleontology of brachiopods; physiography and glacial geology; oil conservation; petroleum and ground water geology; geomorphology. *Mailing Add:* 101 Spanish Oak Lane Kerrville TX 78028

LAISHES, BRIAN ANTHONY, b Ottawa, Ont, Apr 18, 47; m 69; c 2. CANCER. *Educ:* Carleton Univ, BS, 69; Univ BC, MS, 71, PhD(genetics), 74. *Prof Exp:* Res fel, Nat Cancer Inst Can, 74-77; ASST PROF ONCOL, McARDLE LAB, MED SCH, UNIV WIS, 78- *Mem:* Am Asn Cancer Res. *Res:* Sequential analysis of chemical carcinogenesis using chemically induced liver cancer as a laboratory model; biochemical interpretations of biological behavior of normal, premalignant and malignant animal cells in vitro and relationships to carcinogenesis in vivo. *Mailing Add:* McArdle Lab Cancer Res Univ of Wis Med Ctr Madison WI 53706

LAITIN, HOWARD N, b Brooklyn, NY, Nov 18, 31; m 61; c 3. SYSTEMS ANALYSIS & DESIGN. *Educ:* Brooklyn Col, BA, 52; Harvard Univ, MA, 53, PhD(statist, pub health & econ), 56. *Prof Exp:* Med economist, Hosp Coun Greater New York, 54-56; dir, Michael Saphier & Assoc, 56; proj dir, Army Med Serv, 57-59; sr economist, Rand Corp, 59-62; MGR PROG ANAL, HUGHES AIRCRAFT CO, 62- *Concurrent Pos:* Clin assoc prof pub health, Univ Calif, Los Angeles, 59-73; adj prof, Sch Eng, Univ Southern Calif, 66-; adv to various orgn & govt agencies. *Mem:* Am Econ Asn; Am Statist Asn; Inst Mgt Sci. *Res:* Technical analysis; military affairs; public health; solid and hazardous waste management; air pollution; transportation; safety; economic studies. *Mailing Add:* 4926 White Ct Torrance CA 90503

LAITINEN, HERBERT AUGUST, b Ottertail Co, Minn, Jan 27, 15; m 40; c 3. ANALYTICAL CHEMISTRY. *Educ:* Univ Minn, BCh, 36, PhD(phys chem), 40. *Prof Exp:* Asst phys chem, Univ Minn, 36-39; from instr to prof chem, 40-74, head div anal chem, 53-67, EMER PROF CHEM, UNIV ILL, URBANA, 74-; GRAD RES PROF, UNIV FLA, 74- *Concurrent Pos:* Guggenheim fel, 53, 62; Nat Acad Sci exchange visitor, Yugoslavia, 69. *Honors & Awards:* Fisher Award, 61; Synthetic Org Chem Mfrs Asn Award Environ Chem, 75. *Mem:* AAAS; Electrochem Soc; Am Chem Soc; hon mem Japan Soc Anal Chem; fel Royal Soc Chem. *Res:* Electrochemistry; polarography; amperometric titrations; diffusion; polarization of microelectrodes; fused salts; environmental science; surface chemistry. *Mailing Add:* Dept of Chem Univ of Fla Gainesville FL 32611

LAITY, DAVID SANFORD, b Mt Kisco, NY, Nov 20, 26; m 50; c 2. CHEMICAL ENGINEERING. *Educ:* Haverford Col, BA, 49; Mass Inst Technol, MS, 50; NY Univ, ScD(chem eng), 56. *Prof Exp:* Plant process engr & supvr, Eng Serv Div, E I du Pont de Nemours & Co, 50-59; supv res engr, Process Design Div, Chevron Res Co, 59-66, staff econ analyst, Comptroller's Anal Div, 67-69, asst proj mgr, Belg Refinery, 69-71, staff planner, Chevron Oil Europe, 71-73, MGR, PROCESS DESIGN DIV, CHEVRON RES CO, STANDARD OIL CO CALIF, 73- *Mem:* Am Inst Chem Eng. *Res:* Process engineering management in chemical and petroleum industries. *Mailing Add:* 96 Silverwood Dr Lafayette CA 95549

LAITY, JOHN LAWRENCE, b Helena, Mont, Feb 23, 42; m 64; c 2. INDUSTRIAL CHEMISTRY, PETROLEUM CHEMISTRY. *Educ:* Stanford Univ, BS, 64; Univ Wash, PhD(chem), 68. *Prof Exp:* CHEMIST & SUPVR, SHELL OIL CO, 68- *Mem:* Am Chem Soc. *Res:* Photochemical smog; automotive and engine research; combustion; gasoline and oil additives; compositions of fuels and solvents; exhaust emissions; catalysts; atmospheric reactions; air and water pollution; polymer chemistry. *Mailing Add:* Chem Div Shell Oil Co One Shell Plaza Houston TX 77001

LAITY, RICHARD WARREN, b Mt Kisco, NY, Sept 16, 28; m 51; c 5. ELECTROCHEMISTRY, PHYSICAL CHEMISTRY. *Educ:* Haverford Col, AB, 50, MS, 51; Iowa State Univ, PhD(phys chem), 55. *Prof Exp:* From instr to asst prof chem, Princeton Univ, 55-65; PROF CHEM, RUTGERS UNIV, NEW BRUNSWICK, 65- *Concurrent Pos:* Consult, Monsanto Res Corp, 59-69 & Standard Oil Co (Ohio), 60-68; AEC res contract, 60-71; Frontiers in Chem lectr, Cleveland, Ohio, 62; consult ed, Prentice-Hall, Inc, 62-68; chmn, Gordon Res Conf Molten Salts, 67-69; NSF res grant, 72. *Mem:* Am Chem Soc; Electrochem Soc; Sigma Xi. *Res:* Properties of molten salts; electrochemistry; irreversible thermodynamics; transport properties of extremely concentrated aqueous electrolytes. *Mailing Add:* Sch Chem Rutgers Univ New Brunswick NJ 08903

LAJOIE, JEAN, b Montreal, Que, Aug 6, 34; m 62; c 1. GEOLOGY. *Educ:* Univ Montreal, BSc, 58; McGill Univ, PhD(stratig, sedimentation), 62. *Prof Exp:* PROF SEDIMENTOLOGY, UNIV MONTREAL, 62- *Concurrent Pos:* Nat Res Coun Can grant, 64. *Mem:* Am Asn Petrol Geol; fel Geol Asn Can; Soc Econ Paleont & Mineral; Geol Soc France; Int Asn Sedimentol. *Res:* Cambro-Ordovician paleogeography in the Northern Appalachians. *Mailing Add:* Fac of Sci Dept of Geol Univ of Montreal Box 6128 Montreal PQ H3C 3J7 Can

LAJTAI, EMERY ZOLTAN, b Hungary, Oct 28, 34; Can citizen; m 59. GEOLOGY. *Educ:* Univ Toronto, BASc, 50, MASc, 61, PhD(Pleistocene geol), 66. *Prof Exp:* Soils engr, Subway Construct Br, Toronto Transit Comn, 61-63; eng geologist, H G Acres & Co Ltd, Ont, 63-65; vis lectr eng geol, 65-67, asst prof, 67-70, assoc prof eng geol & rock mech, 70-77, PROF GEOL, UNIV NB, 77- *Concurrent Pos:* Nat Res Coun Can res grants, 66-68, 71-74 & 74-77; Govt Can, Geol Surv grants, 67-68 & 71-72. *Mem:* Can Geotech Soc; Can Rock Mech Group. *Res:* Brittle fracture of rocks under compressive loading with application in structural and engineering geology. *Mailing Add:* Dept of Geol Univ of NB Fredericton NB E3B 5A3 Can

LAJTHA, ABEL, b Budapest, Hungary, Sept 22, 22; nat US; m 53; c 2. BIOCHEMISTRY. *Educ:* Eotvos Lorand Univ, Budapest, PhD(chem), 45. *Prof Exp:* Asst prof biochem, Eotvos Lorand Univ, 45-47; asst prof, Inst Muscle Res, Mass, 49-50; sr res scientist, NY State Psychiat Inst, 50-57, assoc res scientist, 57-62; prin res scientist, 62-66, DIR, NY STATE RES INST NEUROCHEM, 66-; PROF EXP PSYCHIAT, SCH MED, NY UNIV, 71- *Concurrent Pos:* Fel, Zool Sta, Italy, 47-48; res fel, Royal Inst Gt Brit, 48-49; asst prof, Col Physicians & Surgeons, Columbia Univ, 56-69. *Mem:* Int Brain Res Orgn; Am Soc Biol Chemists; Am Acad Neurol; Am Col Neuropsychopharmacol; Int Soc Neurochem. *Res:* Neurochemistry; amino acid and protein metabolism of the brain and the brain barrier system. *Mailing Add:* Ctr Neurochem Ward's Island New York NY 10035

LAKATOS, ANDRAS IMRE, b Budapest, Hungary, Aug 23, 37; US citizen; m 72; c 1. THIN FILM DEVICES, LIQUID CRYSTAL DISPLAYS. *Educ:* Alfred Univ, BS, 62, MS, 63; Cornell Univ, PhD(appl physics), 67. *Prof Exp:* Scientist photoelec properties displays, 66-78, MGR THIN FILM DEVICE AREA, WEBSTER RES CTR, XEROX, INC, 78- *Mem:* Inst Elec & Electronics Engrs; Soc Info Display; Am Phys Soc. *Res:* Development of thin film transistors for the addressing of one and two dimensional marking or display arrays. *Mailing Add:* 2137 Baird Rd Penfield NY 14526

LAKE, CHARLES RAYMOND, b Nashville, Tenn, July 6, 43; m 67; c 2. PSYCHOPHARMACOLOGY. *Educ:* Tulane Univ, BS, 65, MS, 66; Duke Univ, PhD(physiol & pharmacol), 71, MD, 72. *Prof Exp:* Resident psychiat, Duke Univ Med Ctr, 72-74; res assoc, 74-75, clin assoc, Lab Clin Sci, 75-77, attending physician, Sect Exp Therapeut, NIMH, 78-80; PROF PHARMACOL & PROF PSYCHIAT, UNIFORMED SERV UNIV HEALTH SCI, 80- *Concurrent Pos:* Psychiat consult, Nat Naval Med Ctr, Bethesda, Md, 80- *Mem:* Am Soc Pharmacol & Exp Therapeut; Soc Biol Psychiat; Am Soc Neurochem; Am Col Neuropsychopharmacol; Int Soc Hypertension. *Res:* Biogenic amine metabolism as related to neuropsychiatric disease and bloodpressure regulation; endorphins and neuropsychiatric disorders; endogenous opioid and catecholamine interrelationships. *Mailing Add:* Univ Health Sci 4301 Jones Bridge Rd Bethesda MD 20814

LAKE, JAMES ALBERT, b Nebr; m 67. MOLECULAR & CELL BIOLOGY. *Educ:* Univ Colo, BA, 63; Univ Wis, Madison, PhD(physics), 67. *Prof Exp:* Fel physics, Univ Wis, 67; NIH fel molecular biol, Mass Inst Technol, 67-68 & Children's Cancer Res Found, Mass, 68-70; res fel, Harvard Univ, 69-70; asst prof cell biol, Rockefeller Univ, 70-72; from asst prof to assoc prof cell biol, Med Sch, NY Univ, 72-76; PROF MOLECULAR BIOL, UNIV CALIF, LOS ANGELES, 76- *Honors & Awards:* Irma T Hirschl Found Award, 74; Burton Award, Electron Micros Soc Am, 75. *Mem:* AAAS; Biophys Soc; Electron Micros Soc Am; Cell Biol Soc; Am Soc X-ray Crystallog. *Res:* Molecular structure of biological molecules; ribosome function and structure; protein synthesis. *Mailing Add:* Molecular Biol Inst Univ of Calif Los Angeles CA 90024

LAKE, LORRAINE FRANCES, b St Louis, Mo, Feb 12, 18. ANATOMY, REHABILITATION MEDICINE. *Educ:* Wash Univ, BS, 50, MA, 54, PhD(anat), 62. *Prof Exp:* Instr phys ther, 49-54, instr anat & phys ther, 54-58, dir phys ther, 59-60, asst dir, 60-67, assoc dir, Irene Walter Johnson Inst Rehab, 67-79, asst prof, 68-80 EMER ASST PROF ANAT & PHYS THER, SCH MED, WASHINGTON UNIV, 80- *Concurrent Pos:* Assoc dir phys ther curric & chg clin training, Sch Med, Wash Univ, 58-63; Woodcock Mem lectr, Univ Calif, 59; consult, Surgeon Gen, US Air Force, 65-67 & birth defects treatment ctr, Nat Found, 65-69. *Res:* Normal and abnormal neuromuscular function; electromyocardiographic investigations of normal human movement; human teratology. *Mailing Add:* 7832 Delmar Blvd St Louis MO 63130

LAKE, ROBERT D, b Lansing, Mich, Sept 7, 30; m 64; c 2. POLYMER CHEMISTRY. *Educ:* Mich State Univ, BS, 52; Ind Univ, PhD(org chem), 56. *Prof Exp:* Am Petrol Inst fel, Northwestern Univ, 56-57; fel chem res, Mellon Inst, 57-60; scientist, 60-66, group mgr explor res, 66-72, SR SCIENTIST, RES DEPT, KOPPERS CO, INC, 72- *Mem:* Am Chem Soc. *Res:* Synthesis and properties of vinyl and condensation polymers; preparation and properties of unsaturated polyester resins; smoke and flammability behavior of polymers; development of thermoset polyester molding compounds. *Mailing Add:* Koppers Co Inc 440 College Park Dr Monroeville PA 15146

LAKE, ROBERT SAMUEL, b Wilkinsburg, Pa, Jan 23, 43. ANIMAL VIROLOGY, CELL BIOLOGY. *Educ:* Franklin & Marshall Col, BA, 64; Univ Del, MS, 67; Pa State Univ, PhD(microbiol), 70. *Prof Exp:* Res asst path, Dept Animal Sci, Univ Del, 64-67; staff fel virol, Lab Biol Viruses, Nat Inst Allergy & Infectious Dis, 70-73; group leader virol, Biosci Res, Dow Corning Corp, 73-75; SR RES ASSOC PATH, CHILDRENS HOSP AKRON, 75- *Mem:* Tissue Cult Asn; Am Soc Microbiol. *Res:* Characterization of in vitro mammalian bioassay systems for detection and quantitation of chemical carcinogens and mutagens. *Mailing Add:* 3920 S Turkey Foot Rd Akron OH 44319

LAKE, ROBIN BENJAMIN, b Warren, Ohio, Sept 8, 38; m 63; c 2. BIOMETRICS, BIOMEDICAL ENGINEERING. *Educ:* Rensselaer Polytech Inst, BEE, 60; Case Western Univ, PhD(biomed eng), 69; Harvard Univ, AM, 64. *Prof Exp:* Researcher cell biol & motor neuron degeneration, Harvard Univ, 62-65; researcher systs theory, Systs Res Ctr & Cybernet Systs Group, 65-69, res assoc biomed eng, 69, sr instr, Schs Med & Eng, 69-70, sr instr biomet, Sch Med, 70-72, dir, Biomet Comput Lab, 70-76, ASST PROF BIOMET & BIOMED ENG, SCH MED, CASE WESTERN RESERVE UNIV, 72-, DIR COMPUT APPLN TRAINING PROG, 73- *Concurrent Pos:* Consult comput mfr, 70-; prin scientist, Monolithic Systs Corp, 76- *Mem:* AAAS; Inst Elec & Electronics Engrs; Asn Comput Mach; Biomed Eng Soc. *Res:* Software systems; analysis and modelling of physiological systems; application of computers to clinical medicine; computer architecture; mathematical modelling of complex systems. *Mailing Add:* Dept Biometry Sch Med Case Western Reserve Univ Cleveland OH 44106

LAKEIN, RICHARD BRUCE, b Baltimore, Md, Mar 5, 41; m 64; c 2. MATHEMATICS. *Educ:* Yale Univ, BA, 62; Univ Md, MA, 64, PhD(math), 67. *Prof Exp:* Lectr math, Univ Md, 67-68; asst prof math, State Univ NY Buffalo, 68-74 & Erie Community Col, 74-75; MATHEMATICIAN, NAT SECURITY AGENCY, 75- *Mem:* Am Math Soc; Asn Comput Mach. *Res:* Number theory; computational mathematics. *Mailing Add:* 8711 Bunnell Dr Potomac MD 20854

LAKES, RODERIC STEPHEN, b New York, NY, Aug 10, 48; m 71. BIOPHYSICS, BIOMEDICAL ENGINEERING. *Educ:* Rensselaer Polytech Inst, BS, 69, PhD(physics, biophys), 75. *Prof Exp:* Res assoc appl sci, Yale Univ, 75-77; asst prof physics, Tuskegee Inst, 77-78; vis asst prof biomed eng, Rensselaer Polytech Inst, 78; ASST PROF BIOMED ENG, UNIV IOWA, 78- *Concurrent Pos:* NIH fel, Yale Univ, 75-77. *Mem:* Am Phys Soc; Orthop Res Soc; Sigma Xi. *Res:* Energy transfer processes in bone; bone biomechanics and bioelectricity; properties of piezoelectric solids. *Mailing Add:* Biomed Eng Prog Univ of Iowa Iowa City IA 52242

LAKEY, WILLIAM HALL, b Medicine Hat, Alta, Nov 12, 27; m 57; c 4. GENITO-URINARY SURGERY. *Educ:* Univ Alta, BSc, 49, MD, 53; FRCPS(C), 60. *Prof Exp:* PROF SURG, FAC MED, UNIV ALTA, 60-, DIR DIV UROL, UNIV HOSP, EDMONTON, 71- *Honors & Awards:* Surg Res Medal, Royal Col Physicians & Surgeons Can, 56. *Mem:* Fel Am Col Surg; Am Urol Asn; Can Urol Asn; Can Acad Genito-Urinary Surg; Am Asn Genito-Urinary Surg. *Res:* Renal transplantation; renal hypertension and use of diagnostic tests; kidney preservation. *Mailing Add:* 11-101 Clin Sci Bldg Univ Alta Edmonton AB T6G 2G3 Can

LAKI, KOLOMAN, b Szolnok, Hungary, Feb 1, 09; nat US; m 48; c 1. PHYSICAL BIOCHEMISTRY. *Educ:* Univ Szeged, PhD(org chem, biochem), 36. *Prof Exp:* Asst prof chem, Univ Szeged, 33-41, biochem & chem, 41-44; res prof, Inst Biochem, Budapest, 45-48; spec res fel phys biochem, 48-50, vis scientist, 50-52, sect chief, 53-63, CHIEF BIOPHYS CHEM LAB, NAT INST ARTHRITIS & METAB DIS, 63- *Concurrent Pos:* Rockefeller Found fel, Eng, 38-39; Prince Esterhazy Found fel, Hungary, 41-42; vis prof, Univ Leeds, 48. *Honors & Awards:* Kossuth Prize, Hungary, 48. *Mem:* Am Chem Soc; Hungarian Acad Sci. *Res:* Tissue metabolism; mechanisms of muscular contraction; chemistry and physical chemistry of proteins of blood coagulation; cancer immunology. *Mailing Add:* Bldg 4 Rm B1-10 NIH Bethesda MD 20014

LAKIN, WILFORD P(ORTER), chemical engineering, deceased

LAKOWICZ, JOSEPH RAYMOND, b Philadelphia, Pa, Mar 15, 48; m 70; c 1. BIOPHYSICS, BIOCHEMISTRY. *Educ:* La Salle Col, BA, 70; Univ Ill, Urbana, MS, 72, PhD(biochem), 73. *Prof Exp:* NATO fel biochem, Oxford Univ, 73-74; asst prof biochem, univ Minn, 75-80; ASST PROF, SCH MED, UNIV MD, 80- *Concurrent Pos:* Estab investr, Am Heart Asn, 77. *Mem:* AAAS; Am Chem Soc; Biophys Soc; Am Soc Photobiol. *Res:* Fluorescence spectroscopy; membrane transport of chlorinated hydrocarbons and carcinogens; rapid relaxation phenomena in biopolymers. *Mailing Add:* Dept Biol Chem Sch Med Univ Md Baltimore MD 21201

LAKRITZ, JULIAN, b Antwerp, Belg, Feb 13, 30; US citizen; c 2. ORGANIC CHEMISTRY. *Educ:* NY Univ, BA, 52; Univ Mich, MS, 54, PhD(org chem), 60. *Prof Exp:* Res chemist, Esso Res & Eng Co, 58-68; DIR RES & DEVELOP, AM PERMAC INC, GARDEN CITY, NY, 68- *Concurrent Pos:* Tech dir, Anscott-Signal Chem Co, 75- *Mem:* Am Chem Soc; Am Asn Textile Chem & Colorists. *Res:* Chemistry and technology for solvent processing of textiles. *Mailing Add:* 2 Livingston Ave Edison NJ 08817

LAKS, HILLEL, thoracic surgery, see previous edition

LAKSHMANAN, FLORENCE LAZICKI, b New York, NY, Nov 20, 28; m 52; c 5. BIOCHEMISTRY. *Educ:* Col Mt St Vincent, BS, 50; Univ Md, PhD(biochem), 58. *Prof Exp:* RES CHEMIST, NUTRIT INST, AGR RES SERV, USDA, BELTSVILLE, 58- *Concurrent Pos:* Res assoc, Dept Nutrit & Foods, Mass Inst Technol, 71-72. *Mem:* Am Chem Soc; Am Inst Nutrit; Sigma Xi. *Res:* Electrophoretic studies of proteins in blood and urine; nutrition and longevity; human amino acid requirements; protein-carbohydrate interrelationships; malnutrition; protein-mineral interactions. *Mailing Add:* Nutrit Inst Protein Nutrit Lab Agr Res Serv USDA Beltsville MD 20705

LAKSHMANAN, P R, b Jamshedpur, Bihar, India, Apr 28, 39. ORGANIC POLYMER CHEMISTRY. *Educ:* Univ Calcutta, BS, 58; Univ Bombay, BS, 61; NDak State Univ, MS, 63, PhD(polymers & coating), 66. *Prof Exp:* sect supvr, 66-80, RES CHEMIST PLASTICS & SR RES CHEMIST COATINGS & ADHESIVES, GULF OIL CHEM CO, 66-, DIR NEW PRODS RES & DEVELOP, 80- *Mem:* Am Chem Soc; Oil & Color Chemists Asn. *Res:* Relationship between structure and performance of adhesives and coatings; mechanism of adhesion, polymer blends and alloys. *Mailing Add:* Gulf Oil Chem Co Houston Lab PO Box 79070 Houston TX 77079

LAKSHMANAN, VAIKUNTAM IYER, b Pazhaya Kayal, Madras, India, July 10, 40; m 68. METALLURGICAL CHEMISTRY, HYDROMETALLURGY. *Educ:* Univ Bombay, BSc, 61, MSc, 63, PhD(chem), 68. *Prof Exp:* Chief chemist, H&R Johnson India (PVT) Ltd, 68-69; res fel minerals eng, Univ Birmingham, 69-72, lectr, 72-75; fel metall chem sect, CANMET, Dept Energy, Mines & Resources, Ottawa, 75-76; assoc scientist extractive metall sect, Noranda Res Ctr, Montreal, 76-77; RES CHEMIST, ELDORADO NUCLEAR LTD, 77- *Honors & Awards:* Bosworth Smith Inst Award, Brit Inst Mining & Metall, 74. *Mem:* Metall Soc; Royal Inst Chem; Brit Inst Mining & Metall; Soc Chem Indust; Can Inst Mining & Metall. *Res:* Solution chemistry; solution treatment precipitation; solvent extraction; ion exchange; treatment of effluents; radiotracer studies. *Mailing Add:* Res & Develop Div 400-255 Albert St Ottawa K1P 6A9 Can

LAKSHMIKANTHAM, VANGIPURAM, b Hyderabad, India, Aug 8, 26; m 42; c 3. MATHEMATICS. *Educ:* Osmania Univ, India, PhD(math), 59. *Prof Exp:* Res assoc math, Univ Calif, Los Angeles, 60-61; vis mem, Math Res Ctr, Univ Wis-Madison, 61-62; vis mem, Res Inst Advan Study, 62-63; assoc prof, Univ Alta, 63-64; prof & chmn dept, Marathwada Univ, India, 64-66; prof & chmn dept, Univ RI, 66-73; PROF MATH & CHMN DEPT, UNIV TEX, ARLINGTON, 73- *Concurrent Pos:* Ed, Nonlinear Anal; assoc ed, Jour Math Anal & Applns, Applicable Anal, Appl Math & Comput & Jour Math & Phys Sci. *Mem:* Am Math Soc; Indian Math Soc; Indian Nat Acad Sci; Soc Indust & Appl Math. *Res:* Differential inequalities; theory and applications, including stability theory by Liapunov's second method; nonlinear analysis. *Mailing Add:* Dept of Math Univ of Tex Arlington TX 76010

LAKSHMINARAYANA, B, b Shimoga, India, Feb 15, 35; m 65; c 2. AEROSPACE & MECHANICAL ENGINEERING. *Educ:* Univ Mysore, BE, 58; Univ Liverpool, PhD(mech eng), 63, DEng, 82. *Prof Exp:* Asst engr, Kolar Gold Fields, India, 58-60; from asst prof to assoc prof, 63-74, PROF AEROSPACE ENG, PA STATE UNIV, 74- & DIR COMPUTATIONAL FLUID DYNAMIC STUDIES, 80- *Concurrent Pos:* Consult, Pratt & Whitney Aircraft, 72-, Garret Turbine Engine, 80- *Honors & Awards:* Henry R Worthington Prize, 77. *Mem:* Am Soc Mech Engrs; assoc fel Am Inst Aeronaut & Astronaut; Sigma Xi; Am Soc Eng Educ; AAAS. *Res:* Three dimensional inviscid and viscid flow through rotor; rotor wake flow; rotor end wall flows; unsteady flow; transonic flow and acoustics of turbomachinery; aircraft and space propulsion; fluid mechanics; computational fluid dynamics. *Mailing Add:* Dept of Aerospace Eng Pa State Univ University Park PA 16802

LAKSHMINARAYANA, J S S, b Penumantra, India, Sept 22, 31; m 60; c 2. PHYCOLOGY, WATER POLLUTION. *Educ:* Andhra Univ, India, BSc, 52; Banaras Hindu Univ, MSc, 54, PhD(bot), 60. *Prof Exp:* Lectr bot, Banaras Hindu Univ, 55; scientist & head biol, Cent Pub Health Eng Res Inst, India, 59-70; assoc prof biol, 70-80, PROF, DEPT BIOL, UNIV MONCTON, 80- *Concurrent Pos:* Fr Govt fel, ASTEF, Paris, 65-66; lectr, Visvesvaraya Regional Col Eng, India, 66-69; fel, Mem Univ Nfld, 70. *Mem:* AAAS; Marine Biol Asn UK; Ecol Soc Am; Can Soc Microbiol; Int Phycol Soc. *Res:* Algology, limnology and oceanography in relation to pollution; biological treatment of waste waters; primary productivity in relation to fishery development. *Mailing Add:* Dept of Biol Univ of Moncton Moncton NB E1A 3E9 Can

LAKSHMINARAYANAN, KRISHNAIYER, b Bikshandarkoil, India, July 5, 24; m 60; c 2. BIOCHEMISTRY, INDUSTRIAL MICROBIOLOGY. *Educ:* Univ Madras, BSc, 45, MSc, 50, PhD(biochem), 55. *Prof Exp:* Jr chemist, King Inst Prev Med, India, 45-47, biochemist, Stanley Hosp, Madras, 50-51; asst prof microbiol, Birla Col, Pilani, 52; Imp Chem Industs fel, Nat Inst Sci India, 55-56; Nat Res Coun Can fel, Univ Manitoba, 56-58; Sci & Indust Res, Govt India, 59-60; plant biochemist, Cent Bot Lab, Allahabad, 60-61; res scientist indust microbiol, John Labatt Ltd, 61-62, sr res scientist, 62-63, proj leader, 63-67, sr indust enzymologist, Dawe's Fermentation Prod, Inc, 67-69, dir fermentation develop, 69-71, res & develop, 71; mgr process develop, Searle Biochemics, Div G D Searle & Co, 71-75; PRES, BIO-TECH INC, BENSENVILLE, ILL, 75- *Concurrent Pos:* Hon lectr, Univ Western Ont, 64- *Mem:* Fel Chem Inst Can; fel Royal Inst Chemists. *Res:* Microbial enzymology; plant biochemistry; toxicology; immunology; chromatography; microtechniques; industrial fermentations; enzyme production; immobilization. *Mailing Add:* 1310 N Belmont Ave Arlington Heights IL 60004

LAKSO, ALAN NEIL, b Auburn, Calif, Jan 3, 48. POMOLOGY, PLANT PHYSIOLOGY. *Educ:* Univ Calif, Davis, BS, 70, PhD(plant physiol), 73. *Prof Exp:* asst prof pomol, 73-80, ASSOC PROF POMOL & VITICULT DEPT, NY STATE AGR EXP STA, CORNELL UNIV, 80- *Mem:* Am Soc Plant Physiologists; Am Soc Hort Sci; Am Soc Enologists; Sigma Xi. *Res:* Pruning and training in apple pertaining to tree and orchard productivity and mechanical harvest; plant-environment interaction and fruiting. *Mailing Add:* Dept of Pomol & Viticult NY State Agr Exp Sta Geneva NY 14456

LAL, DEVENDRA, b Banaras, India, Feb 14, 29; m 55. NUCLEAR PHYSICS, GEOCHEMISTRY. *Educ:* Banaras Hindu Univ, BSc, 47, MSc, 49; Univ Bombay, PhD(physics), 58. *Hon Degrees:* Hon DSc, Banaras Hindu Univ, Varanasi. *Prof Exp:* Res asst, Tata Inst Fundamental Res, India, 50-53, fel, 57-60, prof, 63-67; PROF OCEANOG, SCRIPPS INST OCEANOG, UNIV CALIF, SAN DIEGO, 67- *Concurrent Pos:* Pres, Int Asn Phys Sci Oceans, 80-84; pres, Indian Geophys Union, 81-82; sr prof, Tata Inst Fundamental Res, India, 69-72; mem, Sci Adv Comt to Cabinet, Govt India, 81-82; foreign secy, Indian Nat Sci Acad; vpres, Indian Acad Sci; mem joint sci comt, India-US Joint Comn Sci & Technol. *Honors & Awards:* Krishnan Medal Award, 65; Bhatnagar Award, Coun Sci & Indust Res, Govt of India, 67; Padma Shri, Govt of India, 71. *Mem:* Foreign assoc Nat Acad Sci; fel Indian Acad Sci. *Res:* Cosmic rays; astrophysics; meteoritics; oceanography; meteorology; hydrology. *Mailing Add:* GRD A-020 Scripps Inst of Oceanog La Jolla CA 92093

LAL, JOGINDER, b Amritsar, India, July 2, 23; nat US; m 51; c 2. POLYMER CHEMISTRY. *Educ:* Punjab Univ, India, BSc, 44, MSc, 46; Polytech Inst Brooklyn, MS, 49, PhD, 51. *Prof Exp:* Prof chem, Jain Col, Ambala, India, 45-47 & Hindu Col Amritsar, 51-52; head polymer res, H D Justi & Son, Inc, Pa, 52-56; res scientist, Res Div, 56-67, sect head, 67-75, MGR POLYMER RES, GOODYEAR TIRE & RUBBER CO, 75- *Concurrent Pos:* Mem adv bd, J Polymer Sci; mem adv comt, Chem Technol Prog, Univ Akron; vchmn, Gordon Res Conf, 82, Chmn, 83. *Honors & Awards:* Gold Medal, Hindu Col Amritsar, 41; Distinguished Serv Award, Akron Sect, Am Chem Soc, 76; Akron Summit Polymer Conf Award, 76. *Mem:* Am Chem Soc. *Res:* Dental prosthetic materials; stereoregular polymers; mechanism of polymerization catalysts; chemical reactions of polymers; block copolymers; coatings; relationship between structure and properties of polymers; vulcanization; monomer synthesis; Hexsyn rubber. *Mailing Add:* Elastomer & Chem Res Goodyear Tire & Rubber Co Akron OH 44316

LAL, MANOHAR, b Lakki Marwat, India, Apr 11, 34; m 63; c 3. ENGINEERING SYSTEM MODELS, MATHEMATICAL PHYSICS. *Educ:* Allahabad Univ India, BSc, 55; Indian Inst Sci, DIISc, 58; Univ Ill, Urbana, MS, 61, PhD(elec eng), 63. *Prof Exp:* Lectr electronics & commun, Univ Roorkee, India, 58-60, asst prof to prof, 63-74; prof elec eng, Wichita State Univ, 74-78; sr res scientist math physics, 78-80, SR STAFF SCIENTIST PRODUCTION RESEARCH, RES CTR, AMOCO PROD CO, 80- *Concurrent Pos:* Khosla res award, Univ Roorkee, India, 71; vis res prof, Coord Sci Lab, Univ Ill & Elec Eng & Comput Sci Dept, Univ Santa Clara, 75; adj prof, Univ Tulsa, 81. *Mem:* Inst Elec & Electronics Engrs. *Res:* Engineering systems modeling and control, fluid mechanics, drilling and production, research in petroleum, fluid flow and wave propagation in earth models and digital signal processing. *Mailing Add:* AMOCO Prod Co Res Ctr PO Box 591 Tulsa OK 74133

LAL, MOHAN, b Dharmkot, Punjab, May 8, 32; Can citizen; m 64. MATHEMATICS. *Educ:* D M Col, Punjab, India, BA, 52; Aligarh Muslim Univ, MSc, 55; Univ BC, PhD(nuclear physics), 62. *Prof Exp:* Lectr physics, D A V Col, Punjab, India, 55-57; res asst, Univ BC, 57-61; res assoc, Univ Alta, 62-63; asst prof math & physics, Mt Allison Univ, 63-64; from asst prof to assoc prof math, 64-75, PROF MATH, MEM UNIV NFLD, 75- *Concurrent Pos:* Comput specialist, Fed & Prov Land Inventory Studies, Dept Mines & Natural Resources, Can, 67. *Mem:* Can Math Cong. *Res:* Numerical analysis; applied mathematics and elementary number theory. *Mailing Add:* Dept of Math Mem Univ Nfld St John's NF A1C 5S7 Can

LAL, RAVINDRA BEHARI, b Agra, India, Oct 5, 35; m 62; c 1. PHYSICS. *Educ:* Agra Univ, BSc, 55, MSc, 58, PhD(physics), 63. *Prof Exp:* Lectr physics, REI Col, Agra Univ, 58-59 & Delhi Polytech, 63-64; Nat Acad Sci-Nat Res Coun resident res assoc, Marshall Space Flight Ctr, NASA, 64-67; asst prof, Indian Inst Technol, Delhi, 68-70; sr res assoc, Univ Ala, Huntsville, 71-73; asst prof physics, Paine Col, 73-75; assoc prof, 75-79, PROF PHYSICS, ALA A&M UNIV, 79- *Mem:* Am Phys Soc; Sigma Xi; Am Asn Crystal Growth. *Res:* solid state physics; crystal growth and characterization of materials; magnetic and electrical properties of II-VI and III-V compounds; infra-red detector materials; manufacturing in space. *Mailing Add:* Dept Physics Ala A&M Univ PO Box 71 Normal AL 35762

LAL, SAMARTHJI, b London, Eng, Mar 23, 38; Can citizen; m 74; c 1. NEUROPSYCHIATRY. *Educ:* Univ London, MB, BS, 62; McGill Univ, dipl psychiat, 67; FRCP(C), 70; Am Bd Psychiat & Neurol, 78. *Prof Exp:* Med Res Coun Can res fel psychiat, 67-71; chief consultation serv, Montreal Gen Hosp, 71-75, assoc psychiatrist, 74-78; asst prof psychiat, 73-76, ASSOC PROF PSYCHIAT, MCGILL UNIV, 76-; DIR CLIN & BASIC RES PSYCHIAT, MONTREAL GEN HOSP, 75-, SR PSYCHIATRIST, 78- *Concurrent Pos:* Consult psychiatrist, Queen Mary Vet Hosp, 71-78; staff psychiatrist, Montreal Gen Hosp, 71-, consult, Psychiat Consultation Serv, 75-; staff psychiatrist, Douglas Hosp, 77-, bd dirs, Res Ctr, 80- *Mem:* Can Soc Clin Invest; Can Psychiat Asn; fel Am Psychiat Asn; fel Can Col Neuropsychopharmacol; Soc Biol Psychiat. *Res:* Monoaminergic mechanisms in anterior pituitary secretion and in neurological and psychiatric disorders; drug-induced sterotyped behavior in the rat. *Mailing Add:* Montreal Gen Hosp Dept Psychiat 1650 Cedar Ave Montreal PQ H3G 1A4 Can

LALA, PEEYUSH KANTI, b Chittagong, Bangladesh, Nov 1, 34; m 62; c 2. CANCER, CELL BIOLOGY. *Educ:* Univ Calcutta, MB, BS, 57, PhD(med biophysics), 62. *Prof Exp:* Demonstr path, Calcutta Med Col, 59-60; demonstr path & hemat, NRS Med Col, 61-62; res assoc biol & med res, Argonne Nat Lab, 63-64; res scientist, Radiobiol Lab, Univ Calif, San Francisco, 64-66; res assoc biol & health physics, Chalk River Nuclear Labs, Atomic Energy Can Ltd, 67-68; from asst prof to assoc prof, 68-77, PROF ANAT, McGILL UNIV, 77- *Concurrent Pos:* Fulbright travel scholar, 62; res dir, Med Res Coun Can grant, 68 & Nat Cancer Inst Can grant, 69; USPHS grant, 75; vis prof, Melbourne Univ, 77-78. *Mem:* Am Soc Cell Biol; Am Asn Cancer Res; Int Soc Exp Hemat; Can Soc Cell Biol; Am Asn Anat. *Res:* Studies on cell population kinetics during normal hematopoiesis and human leukemias; host-tumor cell interactions in vivo; control mechanisms in tumor growth; tumor and feto-placental immuno-biology. *Mailing Add:* Dept of Anat McGill Univ Montreal PQ H3A 2B2 Can

LALANCETTE, JEAN-MARC, b Drummondville, Que, Apr 21, 34; m 59; c 3. INORGANIC CHEMISTRY, ENVIRONMENTAL CHEMISTRY. *Educ:* Univ Montreal, BSc, 57, MSc, 58, PhD(chem), 61. *Prof Exp:* From asst prof to prof chem, Univ Sherbrooke, 60-80; MEM STAFF, NAT ASBESTOS SOC, 80- *Mem:* Chem Inst Can. *Res:* Organometallic chemistry; chemistry of graphite intercalates, both catalytic and synthetic properties; photochemical reactions; use of natural materials for protection of environment; peat moss. *Mailing Add:* Soc Nat De L'Amiante 4125 Rue Garlock Sherbrooke PQ J1L 1W9 Can

LALANCETTE, ROGER A, b Springfield, Mass, July 30, 39; m 67. ANALYTICAL CHEMISTRY, CRYSTALLOGRAPHY. *Educ:* Am Int Col, BA, 61; Fordham Univ, PhD(anal chem), 67. *Prof Exp:* Res fel, Brookhaven Nat Lab, 66-67; res chemist photopolymerization, Photo Prod Dept, E I du Pont de Nemours & Co, Inc, NJ, 67-69; asst prof anal chem, 69-76, ASSOC PROF CHEM, RUTGERS UNIV, NEWARK, 76- *Res:* Preparation and structural studies, magnetic susceptibility, x-ray powder and single crystal analysis, thermal stability of chelates of rare-earth and transition metals. *Mailing Add:* Dept of Chem Rutgers Univ Newark NJ 07102

LALAS, DEMETRIUS P, b Athens, Greece, Sept 28, 42; m 67; c 2. DYNAMIC METEOROLOGY, ENVIRONMENTAL FLUID DYNAMICS. *Educ:* Hamilton Col, AB, 62; Cornell Univ, MAeroE, 65, PhD(Aerospace), 68. *Prof Exp:* Asst prof, Dept Eng Mech & Dept Mech Eng, 68-73, assoc prof, 73-79, PROF, DEPT MECH ENG, WAYNE STATE UNIV, 79- *Concurrent Pos:* Vis fel, Coop Inst Res Environ Eng, Univ Colo, 73-74, consult, 74-75; assoc prof, Dept Meteorol, Univ Athens, Greece, 76-77, prof & chmn dept & dir, Meteorol Inst, 79- *Mem:* Am Meteorol Soc; Am Geophys Union; Greek Meteorol Soc. *Res:* Dynamics of micro and mesoscale wave dynamics, their excitation, stability and properties; physics and dynamics of two phase flows in the atmosphere and the laboratory; solar and wind energy; air pollution modelling; computational fluid mechanics. *Mailing Add:* Dept of Mech Eng Wayne State Univ Detroit MI 48202

LALCHANDANI, ATAM PRAKASH, b India, Oct 20, 43; US citizen; m 75; c 1. OPERATIONS RESEARCH, PLANNING. *Educ:* Indian Inst Technol, Bombay, BTech, 63; Cornell Univ, MS, 66, PhD(oper res), 67. *Prof Exp:* Sr oper res analyst, Procter & Gamble, 67-69; dir appl syst, Optimum Systs Inc, Santa Clara, Calif, 69-73; dir indust serv, Control Anal Corp, 73-77; dir planning & anal, Nat Semiconductor Corp, 77-81; TREAS, NAT ADV SYSTS, 81- *Concurrent Pos:* Vis lectr, Grad Sch Bus, Univ Santa Clara, 69-77, Univ Cincinnati, 69 & Xavier Univ, Ohio, 69. *Mem:* Opers Res Soc Am; Inst Mgt Sci; Planning Execs Inst. *Res:* finance. *Mailing Add:* 800 E Middlefield Nat Adv Systs Mountain View CA 94040

LALEZARI, PARVIZ, b Hamadan, Iran, Aug 17, 31; m 58; c 2. MEDICINE, PHYSIOLOGY. *Educ:* Univ Teheran, MD, 54. *Prof Exp:* from asst prof to assoc prof med, 67-79, PROF MED, ALBERT EINSTEIN COL MED, 79-; DIR IMMUNOHEMAT & BLOOD BANK, MONTEFIORE HOSP & MED CTR, 60- *Concurrent Pos:* City New York Res Coun res grant, 60-64; NIH res grant, 65- *Mem:* Am Soc Hemat; Am Soc Clin Invest; Am Asn Immunol. *Res:* Leukocyte immunology; red cell immunology and autoimmune diseases. *Mailing Add:* Montefiore Hosp & Med Ctr 111 E 210th St Bronx NY 10467

LALIBERTE, GARLAND E, b Walkerburn, Manitoba, Dec 28, 36; m 59; c 2. AGRICULTURAL ENGINEERING. *Educ:* Univ Sask, BEng, 56, MSc, 61; Colo State Univ, PhD(agr eng), 66. *Prof Exp:* Engr, Can Dept Agr, 56-61, res scientist, 61-67; assoc prof, 67-69, PROF AGR ENG & HEAD DEPT, UNIV MANITOBA, 69- *Honors & Awards:* Maple Leaf Award, Can Soc Agr Eng, 81. *Mem:* Am Soc Agr Engrs; Can Soc Agr Eng (pres, 78-79); Can Coun Prof Engrs; Am Soc Eng Educ; Sigma Xi. *Res:* Drainage engineering, modeling transient and steady-state flow problems in such saturated and partially saturated porous media as agricultural soils. *Mailing Add:* Dept of Agr Eng Univ of Manitoba Winnipeg MB R3T 2N2 Can

LALIBERTE, LAURENT HECTOR, b Ottawa, Ont, Can, Nov 7, 43; m 66; c 2. ELECTROCHEMISTRY, CORROSION. *Educ:* Univ Ottawa, BSc, 66, PhD(chem), 69. *Prof Exp:* Fel chem, Univ Ottawa, 69-71; scientist corrosion, Pulp & Paper Res Inst Can, 71-78; sr res assoc, 78-79, GROUP MGR, INT PAPER CO, 79- *Honors & Awards:* Weldon Medal, Can Pulp & Paper Asn. *Mem:* Nat Asn Corrosion Engrs; Tech Asn Pulp & Paper Indust. *Res:* Corrosion of materials used in pulp and paper industry process equipment. *Mailing Add:* Int Paper Co PO Box 2787 Mobile AL 36601

LALICH, JOSEPH JOHN, b Slunj, Yugoslavia, Nov 23, 09; nat US; m 41. PATHOLOGY. *Educ:* Univ Wis, BS, 33, MS, 36, MD, 37. *Prof Exp:* Fel exp med, Univ Kans, 38-42; from instr to assoc prof, 46-56, PROF PATH, MED SCH, UNIV WIS-MADISON, 56- *Mem:* AAAS; fel Soc Exp Biol & Med. *Res:* Hemorrhagic and traumatic shock; hemostasis; coagulation; hemoglobinuric nephrosis; experimental lathyrism; myocardial necrosis after allylamine ingestion; monocrotaline induced cor pulmonale. *Mailing Add:* Dept of Path Univ of Wis Med Sch Madison WI 53705

LALICH, MICHAEL JOHN, b Iron Mountain, Mich, June 16, 43; m 66; c 2. METALLURGICAL ENGINEERING. *Educ:* Mich Technol Univ, BS, 65, MS, 66; Univ Wis, PhD(metal eng), 72. *Prof Exp:* Res metallurgist, Mining & Metals Div, Union Carbide Corp, 66-69; teaching assoc metall, Mich Technol Univ, 69-71; sr res metallurgist, 72-74, res assoc ferrous metall, 74-76, mgr foundry res & develop metals casting, 76-77, DIR RES FERROALLOYS, FOOTE MINERAL CO, 77- *Honors & Awards:* Howard Taylor Award, Am Foundrymen's Soc, 76. *Mem:* Am Foundrymen's Soc; Ductile Iron Soc; Am Soc Metals; Am Inst Mining, Metall & Petrol Engrs. *Res:* Alloy additives to cast irons and steels, with particular research on gray, ductile and compacted graphite cast irons. *Mailing Add:* Foote Mineral Co Rte 100 Exton PA 19341

LALL, ABNER BISHAMBER, b Barielly, UP NIndia, Jan 28, 33; m 68; c 1. ELECTROPHYSIOLOGY, SENSORY PHYSIOLOGY. *Educ:* Univ Delhi, BSc, 54; Boston Univ, STB, 59; Syracuse Univ, MS, 62; Univ Md, PhD(zool), 71. *Prof Exp:* Investr, Eye Res Found Bethesda, 69-72; asst prof neurophysiol & comp physiol, City Col City Univ NY, 72-74; fel neurphysiol, Johns Hopkins Univ Sch Med, 74-75; sr assoc, Howard Univ Col Med, 76-77; asst prof, Skidmore Col, 77-78; sr assoc, Howard Univ Col Med, 78-79; RES SCIENTIST, JOHNS HOPKINS UNIV, MCCOLLUM PRATT INST & DEPT OF BIOL, 79- *Mem:* Asn Res Vision & Opthal; Am Soc Zoologists; AAAS. *Res:* Sensory mechanisms of vision and neural mechanisms ethologically significant behavior among anthropods, Limulus and amphibians. *Mailing Add:* McCollum-Pratt Inst & Dept Biol John Hopkins Univ Baltimore MD 21218

LALL, BHAGIRATH, b Sargodha, India, Feb 4, 39; Can citizen; m 70; c 1. CIVIL ENGINEERING, TRANSPORTATION ENGINEERING. *Educ:* Panjab Univ, India, BSc, 61; Univ Roorkee, ME, 64; Univ Birmingham, PhD(transp), 69. *Prof Exp:* Teaching fel hwy, Univ Roorkee, 61-64; asst prof & lectr civil eng, Indian Inst Technol, Delhi, 64-75; assoc prof, Univ Manitoba, 75-77; ASSOC PROF CIVIL ENG, PORTLAND STATE UNIV, 77- *Mem:* Nat Soc Prof Engrs; Nat Soc Prof Engrs; Am Soc Eng Educ; Sigma Xi. *Res:* Urban transportation; transportation planning and systems; pavement design; highway and traffic engineering; highway materials and construction; highway capacity and geometric design. *Mailing Add:* Div Eng Portland State Univ Box 751 Portland OR 97207

LALL, SANTOSH PRAKASH, b Motihari, Bihar, India, Sept 8, 44; Can citizen; m 74; c 4. NUTRITIONAL BIOCHEMISTRY. *Educ:* Allahabad Univ, BSc, 64; Univ Guelph, MSc, 68, PhD(nutrit), 73. *Prof Exp:* Res asst animal nutrit, Allahabad Agr Inst, 64-65; RES SCIENTIST FISH NUTRIT, HALIFAX LAB, 74- *Concurrent Pos:* Res asst, Nutrit Dept, Univ Guelph, 68, fel, 73. *Mem:* Nutrit Soc Can; Nutrit Today Soc. *Res:* Nutrient requirements of salmonids in fresh water and sea water. *Mailing Add:* Fisheries & Environ Sci Div PO Box 550 Halifax NS B3J 2S7 Can

LALLEY, PETER AUSTIN, b Lackawanna, NY, Feb 19, 40; m 67; c 3. HUMAN GENETICS, BIOCHEMICAL GENETICS. *Educ:* Siena Col, BS, 61; Cath Univ Am, MS, 69; State Univ NY Buffalo, PhD(human genetics), 74. *Prof Exp:* Fel human genetics, Roswell Park Mem Inst, 74-75; mem staff biochem genetics, Nat Cancer Inst, Vet Admin Oncol Br, 75-77; SR INVESTR BIOCHEM GENETICS, BIOL DIV, OAK RIDGE NAT LAB, 77- *Concurrent Pos:* Mem, Int Comt Human Gene Mapping, 75-; contract, genetic basis of mutagenesis & carcinogenesis, Dept of Energy, 78- *Mem:* AAAS; Am Soc Human Genetics; Genetics Soc Am. *Res:* Comparative genetics; gene mapping; somatic cell hybrids; genetics of carcinogenesis; mutagenesis; genetics of inherited diseases. *Mailing Add:* Biol Div Oak Ridge Nat Lab Oak Ridge TN 37830

LALLEY, PETER MICHAEL, b Scranton, Pa, Jan 21, 40; m 63; c 4. NEUROPHYSIOLOGY, NEUROPHARMACOLOGY. *Educ:* Philadelphia Col Pharm & Sci, BSc, 63, MSc, 65, PhD(pharmacol), 70. *Prof Exp:* Fel neuropharmacol, Sch Med, Univ Pittsburgh, 70-73, lectr neurosci pharmacol, 72-73, asst prof, 73-74; asst prof pharmacol, Col Med, Univ Fla, 74-76; asst prof, 76-80, ASSOC PROF PHYSIOL, SCH MED, UNIV WIS-MADISON, 80- *Concurrent Pos:* Consult, US Pharmacopoeia & Dispensing Info. *Mem:* Soc Neurosci; Sigma Xi; Am Physiol Soc; AAAS; Am Pharmaceut Asn. *Res:* Identifying the neurotransmitters in the brainstem and spinal cord under which control respiration and blood pressure, and determining the conditions under which they are operative. *Mailing Add:* Dept Physiol Ctr Health Sci Univ Wis 1300 University Ave Madison WI 53706

LALLI, ANTHONY, b Akron, Ohio, June 17, 30; m 55; c 2. ROENTGENOLOGY. *Educ:* Hiram Col, BA, 51; Univ Chicago, MD, 54. *Prof Exp:* Intern med, Toronto Gen Hosp & Hosp Sick Children, 54-55; gen pract, 55-57; resident radiol, Univ Chicago, 57-60; pvt pract, 60-63; from instr to asst prof, 63-68, ASSOC PROF RADIOL, UNIV MICH, ANN ARBOR, 68-; HEAD CLIN RADIOL, CLEVELAND CLIN, 69- *Concurrent Pos:* Asn Univ Radiologists travel grant, Karolinska Inst, Sweden, 65-66. *Res:* Uroradiology. *Mailing Add:* Cleveland Clin Dept of Radiol 9500 Euclid Ave Cleveland OH 44106

LALLI, CAROL MARIE, b Toledo, Ohio, Dec 5, 38. MARINE BIOLOGY. *Educ:* Bowling Green State Univ, BS & BEd, 60, MA, 62; Univ Wash, PhD(zool), 67. *Prof Exp:* Lectr zool, McGill Univ, 68-69; from asst prof to assoc prof marine sci, 69-79; RES ASSOC, UNIV BC, 80- *Mem:* Am Soc Zool; Can Soc Zool; Marine Biol Asn UK. *Res:* Ecological studies of planktonic and benthonic gastropod molluscs. *Mailing Add:* 2407 W 5th Ave Vancouver BC V6K 1S7 Can

LALLY, PHILIP M(ARSHALL), b New York, NY, Sept 30, 25; m 47; c 3. ELECTRICAL ENGINEERING. *Educ:* Mass Inst Technol, SB, 48, SM, 49. *Prof Exp:* Asst elec eng, Mass Inst Technol, 48-49; engr, Electron Tube Dept, Sperry Gyroscope Co, 49-54, sr engr, 54-55, eng sect head, 55-57, eng supvr res & develop, Electronic Tube Div, Sperry-Rand Corp, 57-59, eng dept head, 59-60, asst prod eng supt, 60, prod eng mgr, 60-64, mgr res & advan devices, 64-68; MGR ENG, LOW POWER PROD LINE, TELEDYNE MEC, 68- *Concurrent Pos:* Lectr, Adelphi Col, 55-56 & Univ Fla, 58-59. *Mem:* Inst Elec & Electronics Eng. *Res:* Microwave vacuum tubes, especially traveling wave tubes and klystrons. *Mailing Add:* Teledyne Mec 3165 Porter Dr Palo Alto CA 94304

LALLY, VINCENT EDWARD, b Brookline, Mass, Oct 13, 22; m 53; c 3. METEOROLOGY, ELECTRONICS. *Educ:* Univ Chicago, BS, 44; Mass Inst Technol, BS, 48, MS, 49. *Prof Exp:* Engr, Bendix-Friez, Md, 49-51; chief meteorol instrument sect, Air Force Cambridge Res Labs, 51-58; res mgr, Tele-Dynamics Div, Am Bosch Arma Corp, 58-61; PROG HEAD, NAT CTR ATMOSPHERIC RES, 61-, COMT ON SPACE RES, 65- *Mem:* AAAS; fel Am Meteorol Soc; Sigma Xi. *Res:* Meteorological instruments and measurement systems. *Mailing Add:* 4330 Comanche Dr Boulder CO 80303

LALONDE, ROBERT THOMAS, b Bemidji, Minn, May 7, 31; m 57; c 7. ORGANIC CHEMISTRY. *Educ:* St John's Univ, Minn, BA, 53; Univ Colo, PhD, 57. *Prof Exp:* Sr res engr chem, Jet Propulsion Lab, Calif Inst Technol, 57-58; res assoc, Univ Ill, 58-59; from asst prof to assoc prof chem, 59-68, PROF CHEM, STATE UNIV NY COL ENVIRON SCI & FORESTRY, 68- *Concurrent Pos:* NIH fel, 65-66, Fed Rep Ger Exchange, 80. *Mem:* Am Chem Soc. *Res:* Chemistry of natural products; stereochemistry; chemistry of alkaloids, terpenoids, steroids and fatty acid derivatives. *Mailing Add:* Dept of Chem State Univ of NY Col of Environ Sci & Forestry Syracuse NY 13210

LALOS, GEORGE THEODORE, b Harrisburg, Pa, June 5, 25; m 57; c 3. PHYSICS. *Educ:* Rensselaer Polytech Inst, BAeE, 46; Cath Univ Am, MS, 51. *Prof Exp:* Physicist, Nat Bur Standards, 47-53; PHYSICIST, US NAVAL ORD LAB, 53- *Mem:* Am Phys Soc; Soc Appl Spectros. *Res:* Spectroscopy of flames; high gas temperature measurement; pressure effects on spectral lines; hot dense gas emission spectra; chemical and high energy lasers. *Mailing Add:* Advan Chem Div US Naval Ord Lab 323-309 White Oak MD 20910

LAM, CHAN FUN, b Kwantung, China, Oct 23, 43; m 70; c 2. BIOMEDICAL ENGINEERING. *Educ:* Calif Polytech State Univ, BS, 65; Clemson Univ, MS, 67, PhD(elec & comp eng), 70. *Prof Exp:* Res asst, Grad Inst Technol, Univ Ark, 65-66; res asst comp anal, Clemson Univ, 66-70; dir, Opers & Chief Prog, 71-72, asst prof biomed eng, 70-75, assoc prof, 75-80, dir time share & hybrid comput systs, 76-80, PROF BIOMET, MED UNIV SC, 80-, DIR, BIOMET COMPUT CTR, 79- *Mem:* Sigma Xi; Inst Elec & Electronics Engrs; Pattern Recognition Soc; Soc Comput Simulation; Soc Math Biol. *Mailing Add:* Dept of Biomet Med Univ of SC Charleston SC 29425

LAM, DANIEL J, b Hong Kong, Dec 30, 30; m 59; c 3. PHYSICAL METALLURGY & CHEMISTRY. *Educ:* Rensselaer Polytech Inst, BMetE, 56, MMetE, 58, PhD(phys metall), 60. *Prof Exp:* Res assoc metall, Rensselaer Polytech Inst, 56-58, instr, 58-60; asst metallurgist, 60-66, assoc metallurgist, 66-72, metallurgist, 72-74, SR SCIENTIST, ARGONNE NAT LAB, 74-, GROUP LEADER, 78- *Mem:* AAAS; Am Phys Soc; Am Inst Mining, Metall & Petrol Engrs. *Res:* Electronic structure and related physical and chemical properties of actinide metals, alloys and compounds. *Mailing Add:* Mat Sci Div Argonne Nat Lab 9700 S Cass Ave Argonne IL 60439

LAM, FUK LUEN, b Hong Kong, Nov 7, 37; US citizen; m 68; c 2. CHEMISTRY. *Educ:* Univ SC, PhD(org chem), 66. *Prof Exp:* Fel chem, Mass Inst Technol, 66-67; Brandeis Univ, 68-69; res assoc, 70-75, ASSOC CHEM ONCOGENESIS, SLOAN-KETTERING INST, 75- *Mem:* Am Chem Soc. *Res:* Photochemistry and chemical reactions. *Mailing Add:* 92 Westminster Rd Chatham NJ 07928

LAM, GABRIEL KIT YING, b Hong Kong, Jan 1, 47; m 74; c 3. RADIATION BIOPHYSICS, CANCER RADIOTHERAPY. *Educ:* Univ Hong Kong, BSc, 70; Univ Western Ont, MSc, 71; Univ Toronto, PhD(biophysics), 74. *Prof Exp:* STAFF BIOPHYSICIST, BC CANCER RES CTR, 76- *Concurrent Pos:* Hon asst prof, Univ BC, 81- *Mem:* Radiation Res Soc; Am Asn Physicists Med. *Res:* Biophysical studies in the use of gamma meson radiation for cancer radiotherapy; statistical analysis of radionological data for extraction of relative biological effectiveness. *Mailing Add:* BC Cancer Res Ctr 601 W 10th Ave Vancouver BC V5Z 1L3 Can

LAM, GILBERT NIM-CAR, b Shanghai, China, Nov 10, 51. PHARMACOKINETICS, DRUG METABOLISM. *Educ:* State Univ NY Buffalo, BS, 76; Univ Ill, PhD(pharm), 81. *Prof Exp:* RES BIOCHEMIST, E I DUPONT DE NEMOURS & CO, INC, 81- *Mem:* Am Pharmaceut Asn. *Res:* Pharmacokinetics; biopharmaceutics; drug metabolism and analytical methodology of pharmaceuticals. *Mailing Add:* 708 D Village Circle Newark DE 19713

LAM, GOW THUE, microbiology, see previous edition

LAM, HARRY CHI-SING, b Hong Kong, Nov 10, 36. THEORETICAL HIGH ENERGY PHYSICS. *Educ:* McGill Univ, BSc, 58; Mass Inst Technol, PhD(physics), 63. *Prof Exp:* Res assoc physics, Univ Md, 63-65; from asst prof to assoc prof, 65-75, chmn dept, 76-80, PROF PHYSICS, MCGILL UNIV, 75- *Concurrent Pos:* Asst ed, Can J Physics, 73- *Mem:* Am Phys Soc; Can Asn Physicists. *Res:* Quantum field theory; particle theory. *Mailing Add:* Dept of Physics McGill Univ Montreal PQ H3A 2T6 Can

LAM, HING-YAT PETER, Can citizen. BIOCHEMISTRY. *Educ:* Chinese Univ, Hong Kong, BSc, 69; Univ Wis-Madison, PhD(biochem), 74. *Prof Exp:* Fel, 74-78, ASST PROF, DEPT MED, UNIV MANITOBA, 78- *Concurrent Pos:* Sr investr, Manitoba Inst Cell Biol, 78- *Res:* Organic syntheses of antitumor drugs; mechanism of drug action; tumor biochemistry. *Mailing Add:* Manitoba Inst Cell Biol 100 Olivia St Winnipeg MB R3E 0V9 Can

LAM, HING-YEE, b Macao, June 24, 49; m 74. MAGNETIC ALLOYS, MATERIALS SCIENCE. *Educ:* Fu-Jen Catholic Univ, BSc, 73; Lakehead Univ, MSc, 76; Univ Toronto, PhD(physics), 81. *Prof Exp:* Fel, Dept Physics, Univ Toronto, 80-82; ENG ANALYST, MULTIPLE ACCESS DIV, CAN SYSTS GROUP, 82- *Mem:* Optical Soc Am. *Res:* Magnetisation studies of intermatellic compounds using neutron diffraction and mossbauer spectroscopy. *Mailing Add:* 285 Elmwood Ave Richmond Hill ON L4C 1L5 Can

LAM, JOHN LING-YEE, b Hong Kong, May 28, 40; US citizen. CLASSICAL & QUANTUM ELECTRODYNAMICS. *Educ:* Rice Univ, BA, 62; Calif Inst Technol, PhD(physics), 67. *Prof Exp:* Res fel, Calif Inst Technol, 66-68; Univ Miami, 68-69; Max Planck Inst Physics & Astrophysics, Munich, 71-73; sr res physicist, Dikewood Corp, 74-81; SR RES PHYSICIST, NORTHROP CORP, 81- *Mem:* Am Phys Soc. *Res:* Interaction between radiation and matter in both the classical and quantum regimes, and in both the microscopoic and macroscopic aspects. *Mailing Add:* Apt 26 1025 2nd St Santa Monica CA 90403

LAM, KAI SHUE, b Hong Kong, Feb 22, 49. PHYSICS, CHEMICAL PHYSICS. *Educ:* Univ Calif, Berkeley, AB, 70; Mass Inst Technol, PhD(physics), 76. *Prof Exp:* Fel & instr chem physics, 76-80, SR RES ASSOC CHEM PHYSICS, DEPT CHEM, UNIV ROCHESTER, 80- *Mem:* Am Phys Soc; Sigma Xi. *Res:* Atomic and molecular collision physics; atom-surface collisions; interaction of collision systems with laser radiation; spectral line broadening. *Mailing Add:* Dept of Chem Univ of Rochester Rochester NY 14627

LAM, KWOK-WAI, b Kowloon, Hong Kong, Sept 21, 35; m 61; c 2. BIOCHEMISTRY. *Educ:* ETex Baptist Col, BS, 57; Univ Pittsburgh, PhD(biochem), 63. *Prof Exp:* Nat Inst Child Health & Human Develop fel enzymol & geront, 63-65, assoc, 65-66; assoc enzymol, Retina Found, Boston, 66-73; res assoc prof biochem, 73-81, RES PROF OPHTHAL, ALBANY MED COL, 81- *Concurrent Pos:* NIH career develop award, 67; asst prof biochem, Sch Med, Boston Univ, 70-73. *Mem:* Nat Acad Clin Biochem; Am Chem Soc; Asn Res Vision & Ophthal; Fedn Am Socs Exp Biol; Nat Registry Clin Chem. *Res:* Mechanism of oxidative phosphorylation; clinical enzymology. *Mailing Add:* Dept of Biochem Albany Med Col Albany NY 12208

LAM, LEO KONGSUI, b Hong Kong, Sept 12, 46. ATOMIC PHYSICS, CHEMICAL PHYSICS. *Educ:* Univ Hong Kong, BSc, 69; Columbia Univ, MA, 70, PhD(physics), 75. *Prof Exp:* Res assoc physics, Joint Inst Lab Astrophys, Univ Col, 75-77; res asst prof physics, Univ Mo-Rolla, 77-79; mem fac, Univ Southern Calif, 79-81; MEM TECH STAFF, GUIDANCE & CONTROL SYSTEMS DIV, LITTON INDUSTS, INC, 81- *Concurrent Pos:* Guest worker physics, Boulder Labs, Nat Bur Standards, 75-77. *Mem:* Am Phys Soc; Sigma Xi. *Res:* Atomic, molecular and chemical physics; optical double resonance spectroscopy; laser spectroscopy; atom- molecule kinetics; low temperature plasma. *Mailing Add:* Dept of Physics Univ of Southern Calif Los Angeles CA 90007

LAM, NGHI QUOC, b Vietnam, Oct 4, 45; US citizen; m 69; c 3. METAL PHYSICS. *Educ:* Laval Univ, BS, 68; McMaster Univ, PhD(mat sci), 71. *Prof Exp:* Fel metal physics, 71-74, asst scientist, 74-77, SCIENTIST METAL PHYSICS & RADIATION EFFECTS, ARGONNE NAT LAB, 77- *Concurrent Pos:* Adj assoc prof, Div Med Physics & Bioeng, Chicago Med Sch, 76-81; guest scientist, Ctr Nuclear Studies, Saclay, France, 79-80. *Mem:* Am Phys Soc; Mat Res Soc; AAAS. *Res:* Radiation effects; atomic defects; diffusion; nonequilibrium segregation; phase transformation; sputtering; ion implantation; electron microscopy; computer modeling and simulations. *Mailing Add:* Mat Sci Div Argonne Nat Lab Argonne IL 60439

LAM, PING-FUN, b Hong Kong, Dec 16, 38. MATHEMATICS. *Educ:* Wash State Univ, BA, 62; Yale Univ, MA, 65, PhD(math), 67. *Prof Exp:* From instr to asst prof math, Wesleyan Univ, 66-69; asst prof, 69-71, ASSOC PROF MATH, UNIV MO-COLUMBIA, 71- *Concurrent Pos:* Asst, Sch Math, Inst Advan Study, 71-72. *Mem:* Am Math Soc. *Res:* Topological dynamics; Morse theory. *Mailing Add:* Dept of Math Univ of Mo Columbia MO 65201

LAM, RONALD KA-WEI, b Hong Kong, Mar 3, 41; US citizen. OCEANOGRAPHY. *Educ:* Mass Inst Technol, SB, 63; Stanford Univ, MS, 65; Scripps Inst Oceanog, PhD(oceanog), 71. *Prof Exp:* Oceanogr, Scripps Inst Oceanog, 71-73; res assoc oceanog, Univ Wash, 73-80. *Mem:* Sigma Xi; The Coastal Soc. *Res:* Fjord dynamics; models of marine primary and secondary production. *Mailing Add:* 5308 S Hudson Seattle WA 98118

LAM, SAU-HAI, b Macao, Dec 18, 30; m 59. AERONAUTICAL ENGINEERING. *Educ:* Rensselaer Polytech Inst, BAeroEng, 54; Princeton Univ, PhD(aeronaut eng), 58. *Prof Exp:* Asst, Princeton Univ, 56-58, res assoc, 58-59; asst prof, Cornell Univ, 59-60; from asst prof to assoc prof, 60-67, PROF AERONAUT ENG, PRINCETON UNIV, PRINCETON, 67- *Mem:* Am Inst Aeronaut & Astronaut; Am Phys Soc. *Res:* Theoretical gas dynamics; boundary layer theory; ionized gas flows. *Mailing Add:* Dept of Aeronaut Eng Sch of Eng Princeton Univ Princeton NJ 08540

LAM, SHEUNG TSING, b Hong Kong, Dec 11, 34; Can citizen. NUCLEAR PHYSICS. *Educ:* Univ Hong Kong, BSc, 59; Univ Ottawa, MSc, 62; Univ Alta, PhD(physics), 67. *Prof Exp:* Demonstr physics, Univ Hong Kong, 59-60; Can Nat Coun fel & res assoc nuclear physics, Univ Toronto, 67-70; asst prof nuclear physics, Univ Va, 70-72; STAFF PHYSICIST & SAFETY OFFICER, NUCLEAR RES CTR, UNIV ALTA, 72- *Concurrent Pos:* Attached staff mem, Chalk River Nuclear Labs, Atomic Energy Can Ltd, 67-70; Frederick Gardner Cottrell Res Corp grant, 71-72. *Mem:* Am Phys Soc. *Res:* Nuclear structure studies using electrostatic accelerators and fast neutron induced fission studies; neutron-nucleus scattering and analysis using optical potentials. *Mailing Add:* Nuclear Res Ctr Univ of Alta Edmonton AB T6G 2N5 Can

LAM, STANLEY K, b Hong Kong; Brit citizen. SEPARATION SCIENCE, CLINICAL CHEMISTRY. *Educ:* Sacramento City Col, AA, 72; Calif State Univ, BA, 74; State Univ NY, Buffalo, PhD(chem), 81. *Prof Exp:* INSTR CLIN CHEM, ALBERT EINSTEIN COL MED, 78- *Mem:* Am Chem Soc; Am Asn Clin Chem. *Res:* Chromatographic methods for the monitoring of therapeutic agents and development of chromatographic techniques. *Mailing Add:* Dept of Lab Med 1300 Morris Park Ave Bronx NY 18461

LAM, TENNY N(ICOLAS), b Hong Kong, Nov 28, 40; m 66; c 1. TRANSPORTATION ENGINEERING, OPERATIONS RESEARCH. *Educ:* Univ Calif, Berkeley, BS, 63, MEng, 64, DEng(transp sci), 67. *Prof Exp:* Asst prof civil eng, Univ Mo-Columbia, 66-68; sr res engr, Dept Theoret Physics, Gen Motors Res Labs, 68-74; assoc prof, 74-80, PROF CIVIL ENG, UNIV CALIF, DAVIS, 80- *Concurrent Pos:* Assoc ed, Transp Sci, 74-77 & 80-; mem, Transp Res Forum & Transp Res Bd. *Mem:* Opers Res Soc Am; Am Soc Civil Engrs. *Res:* Traffic flow theory; transportation systems planning and analysis. *Mailing Add:* Dept of Civil Eng Univ of Calif Davis CA 95616

LAM, TSIT-YUEN, b Hong Kong, Feb 6, 42; m 70. ALGEBRA. *Educ:* Hong Kong Univ, BA, 63; Columbia Univ, PhD(math), 67. *Prof Exp:* Fel math, Univ Ill, Urbana, 67; instr, Univ Chicago, 67-68; lectr, 68-69, asst prof, 69-72, assoc prof, 72-77, chmn dept, 75 & 80-81, Miller prof, 78-79, PROF MATH, UNIV CALIF, BERKELEY, 77- *Concurrent Pos:* Alfred P Sloan Found fel, 72-74; Guggenheim Fel, 81-82. *Mem:* Am Math Soc. *Res:* Finite groups and group representation theory; quadratic forms. *Mailing Add:* Dept Math Univ Calif Berkeley CA 94720

LAM, VINH-TE, b Saigon, SVietnam, Dec 12, 39; Can citizen. PHYSICAL CHEMISTRY. *Educ:* Univ Montreal, BSc, 62, PhD(phys chem), 67. *Prof Exp:* Prof org chem, Col St Laurent, 66-67; fel, Nat Res Coun Can, 67-69; lectr phys chem & Nat Res Coun Can grant, Univ Sherbrooke, 69-72; PROF CHEM, COL BOIS-DE-BOULOGNE, 72- *Mem:* Am Chem Soc; Chem Inst Can. *Res:* Thermodynamics; thermochemistry; static and dynamic microcalorimetry; critical phenomena; surface and polymer chemistry; molecular interactions; structure of liquids and solutions. *Mailing Add:* 6728 Chateaubriand Montreal PQ #H2S 2N8 Can

LAM, YIU-KUEN TONY, b Hong Kong, June 5, 47; US citizen; m 77; c 2. ORGANIC CHEMISTRY. *Educ:* Chinese Univ, Hong Kong, BSc, 71; Univ NB, PhD(org chem), 74. *Prof Exp:* Res assoc, Univ Tex, Austin, 75-77; asst prof, Univ Alta, 77-79; SR RES CHEMIST, MERCK & CO, INC, 79- *Mem:* AAAS; Am Chem Soc. *Res:* Discovery and chemistry of novel biologically interesting principles from microbial, herbal and animal sources. *Mailing Add:* PO Box 2000 Rahway NJ 07065

LAMANNA, CARL, b Brooklyn, NY, Dec 1, 16; m 42; c 2. MICROBIOLOGY, TOXICOLOGY. *Educ:* Cornell Univ, BS, 36, MS, 37, PhD(bact), 39. *Prof Exp:* Asst bact, Cornell Univ, 36-39; instr bact & pub health, State Col Wash, 40-41; instr bact, Ore State Col, 41-42; instr bact, Sch Med, La State Univ, 42-44; consult biologist, Fed Security Agency, 44; bacteriologist, Chem Corps, US War Dept, 45-48; from asst prof to assoc prof, Sch Hyg & Pub Health, Johns Hopkins Univ, 48-57; sci dir, Naval Biol Lab, Univ Calif, 57-61; dep & adv life sci div, Off Chief for Res & Develop, Dept Army, 61-74; ASSOC DIR PHARMACEUT RES & TESTING, FOOD & DRUG ADMIN, DEPT HEALTH, EDUC & WELFARE, 75- *Concurrent Pos:* WHO vis prof, Inst Hyg, Philippines, 54-55. *Mem:* AAAS; Am Soc Microbiol; Soc Exp Biol & Med; Am Acad Microbiol; NY Acad Sci. *Res:* Botulism; nature of bacterial neurotoxin; spore-forming bacteria; toxicology. *Mailing Add:* 3812 37th St N Arlington VA 22207

LAMANNA, JOSEPH CHARLES, b Bronxville, NY, July 12, 49; m 71; c 1. NEUROSCIENCES. *Educ:* Georgetown Univ, BS, 71; Duke Univ, PhD(physiol), 75. *Prof Exp:* NIH fel & res assoc physiol, Duke Univ Med Ctr, 75-77; asst prof, 77-80, ASSOC PROF NEUROL, DEPT NEUROL & PHYSIOL/BIOPHYS, MED SCH, UNIV MIAMI, 80- *Mem:* Am Physiol Soc; Optical Soc Am; Int Soc Oxygen Transp Tissues; Soc Neurosci. *Res:* Determining the role of oxygen and oxidative energy metabolism in the function of the central nervous system in mammals, utilizing optical monitoring techniques. *Mailing Add:* Dept of Neurol D4-5 Univ of Miami Med Sch Box 016960 Miami FL 33101

LA MANTIA, CHARLES R, b New York, NY, June 12, 39; m 61; c 2. CHEMICAL ENGINEERING. *Educ:* Columbia Univ, BA, 60, BS, 61, MS, 63, ScD(chem eng), 65. *Prof Exp:* Res & develop proj off, Defense Atomic Support Agency, 65-67; vpres chem & metall eng, Arthur D Little Inc, Cambridge, 67-81; PRES, KOCH PROCESS SYSTS INC, WESTBOROUGH, MASS, 81- *Concurrent Pos:* Mem staff, Charles F Bonilla & Assocs, 65. *Mem:* Am Inst Chem Engrs; Am Chem Soc. *Res:* Chemical process design, analysis and development; air pollution control. *Mailing Add:* 3 Goodwin Rd Lexington MA 02173

LA MAR, GERD NEUSTADTER, b Brasov, Romania, Dec 21, 37; US citizen; m 64; c 2. STRUCTURAL CHEMISTRY. *Educ:* Lehigh Univ, BS, 60; Princeton Univ, PhD(chem), 64. *Prof Exp:* NSF fel, 64-66; NATO fel, 66-67; res chemist, Shell Develop Co, 67-70; from asst prof to assoc prof, 71-74, PROF CHEM, UNIV CALIF, DAVIS, 74- *Concurrent Pos:* Fel, Alfred P Sloan Found, 72, John Simon Guggenheim Mem Found, 75. *Mem:* Am Chem Soc. *Res:* The use of magnetic resonance spectroscopy as a tool for elucidating structure-function relationships in metallo-enzymes and their model complexes. *Mailing Add:* Dept of Chem Univ of Calif Davis CA 95616

LAMAR, JULE K, b Birmingham, Ala, Dec 5, 09; m 39; c 2. TOXICOLOGY. *Educ:* Birmingham-Southern Col, BS, 31; Univ Chicago, PhD(zool), 38. *Prof Exp:* Asst instr biol, Birmingham-Southern Col, 31-33, instr, 33-34; asst zool, Univ Chicago, 34-38; Nat Comt Maternal Health fel, Carnegie Lab Embryol, 38-40; instr obstet & gynec, Med Sch, Univ Tex, 40-43, from asst prof to assoc prof, 43-64; physiologist, Div Toxicol Eval, Bur Sci, 64-66, pharmacologist, Bur Med, 66-67, supvry pharmacologist, 67-70, pharmacologist, 70-74, RES COORDR NEW DRUG EVAL, BUR DRUGS, US FOOD & DRUG ADMIN, 74- *Mem:* Environ Mutagen Soc; Assoc Am Soc Zool; assoc Soc Exp Biol & Med; Soc Toxicol. *Res:* Sperm migration and purification; hormone assays; pregnancy testing; cancer and hormones; drug actions and toxicology; adverse effects on reproduction; mutagenicity testing; carcinogenicity testing. *Mailing Add:* US Food & Drug Admin Bur Drugs 5600 Fishers Lane Rockville MD 20857

LAMAR, PERCIE LEE, III, b Lambert, Miss, Oct 3, 41; m 64; c 1. FOOD SCIENCES & TECHNOLOGY. *Educ:* Tex A&M Univ, BS, 63, PhD(food sci), 72; Miss State Univ, MS, 64. *Prof Exp:* Food technologist, Rivianis Foods, Houston, Tex, 67-70; head, Food Sci Dept, Syntex Resources, Palo Alto, Calif, 73-77; prin scientist, Frito Lay, Dallas, Tex, 77-80; DIR RES & DEVELOP, TOM'S FOODS LTD, GEN MILLS CORP, COLUMBUS, GA, 80- *Concurrent Pos:* Vchmn, Ga Inst Human Nutrit Bd, 80- *Mem:* Inst Food Technologists; Am Asn Cereal Chemists; NY Acad Sci. *Res:* New snack foods from fortified products to unique processing systems; development of low residue diet for special dietary fooods in hospitals. *Mailing Add:* Tom's Foods Ltd Gen Mills Corp 900 Eighth St Columbus GA 31902

LAMARCA, MICHAEL JAMES, b Jamestown, NY, June 4, 31; m 54; c 3. DEVELOPMENTAL BIOLOGY. *Educ:* State Univ NY Albany, AB, 53; Cornell Univ, PhD(zool), 61. *Prof Exp:* Instr zool, Rutgers Univ, 61-63, asst prof, 63-65; from asst prof to assoc prof biol, 65-76, chmn dept, 70-74, PROF BIOL, LAWRENCE UNIV, 76- *Concurrent Pos:* NSF res grant, 63-65; resident dir, Assoc Cols Midwest Argonne Semester Prog, Argonne Nat Lab, 68-69; NSF sci fac fel biol sci, Purdue Univ, 71-72; vis lectr biol chem, Harvard Med Sch, 77-78. *Res:* RNA and protein synthesis in echinoderm, amphibian, and mammalian development. *Mailing Add:* Dept of Biol Lawrence Univ Appleton WI 54911

LAMARCHE, J L GILLES, b Montreal, Que, May 31, 27. PHYSICS. *Educ:* Univ Montreal, BSc, 50; Univ BC, MA, 53, PhD(physics), 57. *Prof Exp:* From asst prof to assoc prof, 57-70, PROF PHYSICS, UNIV OTTAWA, 70- *Mem:* Am Phys Soc; Am Asn Physics Teachers; Can Asn Physicists. *Res:* Low temperature physics; adiabatic demagnetization; nuclear magnetism. *Mailing Add:* Dept of Physics Univ of Ottawa Ottawa ON K1H 5T1 Can

LAMARCHE, PAUL H, b Boston, Mass, Sept 5, 29; m 52; c 5. GENETICS, PEDIATRICS. *Educ:* Boston Col, BS, 56; Boston Univ, MD, 60; Mass Inst Technol, ScM, 74. *Prof Exp:* Res assoc path & dir genetics lab, RI Hosp, 63-75, med dir, Birth Defects Ctr, 65-75, med dir child develop ctr, 66-75, assoc physician-in-chief pediat, 69-75; PROF GENETICS, UNIV MAINE, ORONO, 74-; CHIEF PEDIAT & GENETICS, EASTERN MAINE MED CTR, BANGOR, 74- *Concurrent Pos:* Asst pediatrician, Providence Lying-In Hosp, 63-74, consult, 66-74; prin investr Nat Cancer Inst grant, 64-69; prof pediat, Sch Med, Tufts Univ, 81; consult, Child Study Ctr, Brown Univ, 67-74. *Mem:* AAAS; Genetics Soc Am; Tissue Cult Asn. *Res:* Genetics and cytogenetics of teratogenesis and oncogenesis; electron microscopy of fine structure of somatic cellular phenotypes normal and abnormal in the human. *Mailing Add:* 489 State St Bangor ME 04401

LAMARCHE, VALMORE CHARLES, JR, b Hurley, Wis, Aug 27, 37; m 57; c 4. GEOLOGY. *Educ:* Univ Calif, Berkeley, BA, 60; Harvard Univ, MA, 62, PhD(geol), 64. *Prof Exp:* Geologist, US Geol Surv, 62-67, hydrologist, 67; res assoc, 67-69, assoc prof dendrochronol, 69-74, PROF DENDROCHRONOL, UNIV ARIZ, 74- *Mem:* AAAS; Geol Soc Am; Ecol Soc Am; Int Asn Quaternary Res. *Res:* Geomorphology; hydrology; applications of tree-ring studies to geological problems; paleoclimatology; dendrochronology. *Mailing Add:* Lab for Tree-Ring Res Univ of Ariz Tucson AZ 85721

LAMARSH, JOHN R(AYMOND), b Hartford, Conn, Mar 12, 28; m 58; c 1. NUCLEAR ENGINEERING. *Educ:* Mass Inst Technol, SB, 48, PhD(physics), 52. *Prof Exp:* Group leader aircraft nuclear propulsion, Pratt & Whitney Div, United Aircraft Corp, 52-53; asst prof physics, Univ Ky, 53-54; assoc physicist, Brookhaven Nat Lab, 54-56; asst prof physics, NY Univ, 56-57; asst prof eng physics, Cornell Univ, 57-62; assoc prof, nuclear eng, NY Univ, 62-66, prof & chmn dept, 67-73; PROF NUCLEAR ENG & HEAD DEPT, POLYTECH INST NEW YORK, 73- *Concurrent Pos:* Adj asst prof, Univ Conn, 52-53; consult, Twp Lower Alloways Creek, NJ, 74-, Cong Res Serv, Libr Cong, US Gen Acct Off & US Off Technol Assessment, 76- *Mem:* Fel Am Nuclear Soc (vchmn, chmn educ div, 77-79); Am Soc Eng Educ; Am Phys Soc. *Res:* Nuclear reactor theory; nuclear weapons effects, nuclear weapons proliferation. *Mailing Add:* 68 N Chatsworth Ave Larchmont NY 10538

LAMARTINE, BRUCE CARVELL, b Richmond, Ind, Oct 3, 46; m 71; c 2. PHYSICAL CHEMISTRY, SURFACE PHYSICS. *Educ:* New Col, BA, 67; Case Western Reserve Univ, MS, 70, PhD(chem), 78. *Prof Exp:* Fel phys chem, Case Western Reserve Univ, 68-70; intercontinental ballistic missile crew comdr, US Air Force Strategic Air Command, 72-76; GROUP RES DIR SURFACE PHYSICS, US AIR FORCE MAT LAB, 76- *Concurrent Pos:* Surface anal consult, US Air Force Space & Missile Systs Orgn, 77- *Res:* Analysis of cathode activation and end of life by auger electron spectroscopy, x-ray photoelectron spectroscopy, scanning auger microprobe, secondary ion mass spectrometry and regional gas analysis; diffusion of spherical molecules in hydrogen bonding solvents. *Mailing Add:* Air Force Mat Lab AFML/MBM Bldg 32 Rm 214 Wright-Patterson AFB OH 45433

LAMATTINA, JOHN LAWRENCE, b Brooklyn, NY, Jan 22, 50; m 71; c 2. ORGANIC CHEMISTRY, MEDICINAL CHEMISTRY. *Educ:* Boston Col, BS, 71; Univ NH, PhD(chem), 75. *Prof Exp:* RES SCIENTIST MED CHEM, PFIZER INC, 77- *Concurrent Pos:* NIH fel, Princeton Univ, 75-77. *Mem:* Am Chem Soc. *Res:* Design and synthesis of compounds which possess intriguing biological properties. *Mailing Add:* Pfizer Inc Eastern Point Rd Groton CT 06340

LAMAZE, GEORGE PAUL, b Algiers, Algeria, Jan 15, 45; US citizen; m 65; c 2. EXPERIMENTAL NUCLEAR PHYSICS. *Educ:* Fla State Univ, BA, 65; Duke Univ, PhD(physics), 72. *Prof Exp:* PHYSICIST NEUTRON STAND, NAT BUR STAND, 72- *Concurrent Pos:* Sci asst to Rep George Brown, Calif, 78-79. *Mem:* Am Phys Soc; Am Soc Testing & Mat; AAAS. *Res:* Measurement of standard neutron reaction cross sections, standard neutron fields, and neutron source strengths. *Mailing Add:* Nat Bur of Stand Bldg 245 B102 Washington DC 20234

LAMB, ALBERT R, JR, b New York, NY, Dec 3, 13; m 42; c 4. MEDICINE. *Educ:* Yale Univ, BA, 35; Columbia Univ, MD, 40. *Prof Exp:* Instr to asst med, Columbia Univ, 46-54, asst prof clin med, 54-61, assoc prof clin med, 61-79; RETIRED. *Concurrent Pos:* Dir student health serv, Col Physicians & Surgeons, Columbia Univ, 46-74; consult, Englewood Hosp, NJ, 55-79. *Mem:* AMA. *Res:* Internal medicine. *Mailing Add:* Columbia-Presby Med Ctr 161 Ft Washington Ave New York NY 10032

LAMB, DAVID E(RNEST), b Pampa, Tex, Apr 6, 32; m 56; c 5. CHEMICAL ENGINEERING, COMPUTER SCIENCE. *Educ:* Yale Univ, BE, 53; Princeton Univ, MS, 54, PhD(chem eng), 62. *Prof Exp:* Instr chem eng, Princeton Univ, 56; res engr, Sun Oil Co, Pa, 57; asst prof chem eng, 58-63, assoc prof & dir comput ctr, 63-65, PROF CHEM ENG, STATIST & COMPUT SCI & CHMN DEPT STATIST & COMPUT SCI, UNIV DEL, 65- *Concurrent Pos:* Consult, Sun Oil Co, 57-, Ethyl Corp, 60 & Prentice-Hall, Inc, 60-; mem theory comt, Am Automatic Control Coun, 61-; mem steering comt, Simulation Coun, 65-; mem adv comt, Off Comput Activities, NSF, 68-71. *Mem:* Asn Comput Mach; Simulation Coun. *Res:* Continuous and discrete system simulation; computer graphics. *Mailing Add:* 708 Nottingham Rd Wilmington DE 19805

LAMB, DENNIS, b Chicago, Ill, Feb 3, 41. CLOUD PHYSICS. *Educ:* Kalamazoo Col, BA, 63; Univ Wash, PhD(atmospheric sci), 70. *Prof Exp:* Gen physicist data assessment, Naval Weapons Ctr, China Lake, Calif, 63-65; NATO res assoc meteorol, Univ Frankfurt, 71-72; from asst to assoc prof, 72-79, RES PROF, ATMOSPHERIC SCI CTR, DESERT RES INST, UNIV NEV, RENO, 79- *Mem:* Am Meteorol Soc; Sigma Xi. *Res:* Nucleation and growth of solids from the liquid and vapor phases; formation of cloud nuclei; cloud physics/weather modification; atmospheric chemistry. *Mailing Add:* Atmospheric Sci Ctr Desert Res Inst Univ of Nev Reno NV 89507

LAMB, DONALD JOSEPH, b Pittsburgh, Pa, Oct 29, 31; m 56; c 2. PHARMACY. *Educ:* Ohio State Univ, BSc, 54, MSc, 55, PhD(pharm), 60. *Prof Exp:* Res assoc pharmaceut res & develop, 60-65, res head, 65-70, RES MGR PHARMACEUT RES & DEVELOP, UPJOHN CO, 70- *Mem:* Am Pharmaceut Asn; Am Acad Pharmaceut Sci; Am Chem Soc. *Res:* Design and evaluation of drug dosage forms, including design and evaluation of drugs to fit specific dosage forms. *Mailing Add:* Upjohn Co 7171 Portage Rd Kalamazoo MI 49001

LAMB, DONALD QUINCY, JR, b Manhattan, Kans, June 30, 45; m 78. ASTROPHYSICS. *Educ:* Rice Univ, BA, 67; Univ Liverpool, MSc, 69; Univ Rochester, PhD(physics), 74. *Prof Exp:* Res asst prof physics, Univ Ill, 73-75, asst prof, 75-77, assoc prof, 77-79, prof, 79-80; res assoc, 79-80, PHYSICIST, SMITHSONIAN CTR ASTROPHYS, HARVARD UNIV, 80- *Concurrent Pos:* Vis assoc prof physics, Mass Inst Technol, 78-79; John Simon Guggenheim Mem fel, 78-79; proj coordr astrophysics, Comt US-USSR Coop Physics, Nat Acad Sci, 78-; trustee, Aspen Ctr Physics, 81-; lectr astron, Harvard Univ. *Mem:* Am Phys Soc; Am Astron Soc; fel Royal Astron Soc; Brit Inst Physics; Europ Phys Soc. *Res:* Evolution and structure of white dwarfs and neutron stars; physics of compact x-ray and gamma-ray sources, supernovae and cataclysmic variables; properties of matter at high densities. *Mailing Add:* Smithsonian Ctr Astrophys Harvard Univ 60 Garden St Cambridge MA 02138

LAMB, DONALD R(OY), b Yuma, Colo, May 6, 23; m 43; c 3. CIVIL ENGINEERING. *Educ:* Hastings Col, BA, 47; Univ Wyo, BS, 51, MS, 53, CE, 58; Purdue Univ, PhD, 62. *Prof Exp:* Supt high schs, Nebr, 46-47, coach, 47-49; from supply instr to assoc prof civil eng, 51-70, PROF CIVIL ENG & HEAD DEPT, UNIV WYO, 70- *Mem:* Am Soc Eng Educ; Am Soc Civil Engrs; Nat Soc Prof Engrs. *Res:* Use of radioisotopes in the study of portland cement, asphalt concrete and soils; portland cement concrete and associated aggregates; transportation; recreational engineering; engineering geology. *Mailing Add:* Dept of Civil & Archit Eng Box 3295 University Sta Laramie WY 82070

LAMB, FRANK D(OUGLAS), b Williams, Ariz, June 14, 10; m 37; c 3. METALLURGY, MINING. *Educ:* Univ Ariz, BS, 33, MS, 34. *Prof Exp:* Metallurgist, Ariz Consol Mining Co, 33-34; jr assayer, US Assay Off, 34-35; metallurgist, SAm Develop Co, 35-37, asst supt mining, 37-40; asst res metallurgist, US Bur Mines, 40-42, assoc metallurgist, 42-43, sr metallurgist, 43-54, asst chief div minerals, 54-59, res dir, 59-67, dep asst dir, 67-72; RETIRED. *Mem:* Am Inst Mining, Metall & Petrol Engrs. *Res:* Mineral dressing; extractive and process metallurgy. *Mailing Add:* 7 Fleming Ct Palm Coast FL 32037

LAMB, FRANK WYMAN, b Akiak, Alaska, Aug 17, 18. PHYSICAL CHEMISTRY, OPERATIONS RESEARCH. *Educ:* Univ Wash, BS, 39, PhD(phys chem), 43. *Prof Exp:* Carnegie Inst fel, Northwestern Univ, 46; opers res, US Navy Proj, Div Indust Coop, Mass Inst Technol, 47-56; CONSULT SCIENTIST, LOCKHEED AIRCRAFT CORP, 56- *Mem:* Am Chem Soc; Opers Res Soc Am. *Res:* Compressibility and specific heat of aqueous solutions; operations research. *Mailing Add:* Dept 80 82 Bldg 154 Lockheed Aircraft Sunnyvale CA 94086

LAMB, FREDERICK KEITHLEY, b Manhattan, Kans, June 30, 45; m 71. THEORETICAL PHYSICS. *Educ:* Calif Inst Technol, BS, 67; Oxford Univ, DPhil(theoret physics), physics), 70. *Prof Exp:* Instr & res assoc, 70-72, asst prof, 72-75, assoc prof, 75-78, PROF PHYSICS, UNIV ILL, URBANA, 78- *Concurrent Pos:* Fel physics, Magdalen Col, Oxford Univ, 70-72; assoc, Ctr Advan Study, Univ Ill, Urbana, 73-74; res fel, Alfred P Sloan Found, 74- *Mem:* Am Phys Soc; Am Astron Soc; fel Royal Astron Soc. *Res:* White dwarfs, neutron stars, and black holes; plasma theory and applications to pulsars and cosmic X-ray sources; the interaction of radiation with matter. *Mailing Add:* Dept of Physics Univ of Ill Urbana IL 61801

LAMB, GEORGE ALEXANDER, b Glens Falls, NY, Sept 25, 34; m 56; c 3. PEDIATRICS, INFECTIOUS DISEASES. *Educ:* Swarthmore Col, BS, 55; State Univ NY Upstate Med Ctr, MD, 59. *Prof Exp:* Intern pediat, State Univ NY Upstate Med Ctr, 59-60, resident, 60-62, from asst prof to assoc prof, 64-72; assoc prof prev & social med, Harvard Med Sch, 72-79; PROF PEDIAT, BOSTON UNIV SCH MED, 79- *Concurrent Pos:* Fel infectious dis, 64- *Res:* Infectious diseases of children, especially the epidemiology of respiratory illnesses; community child health. *Mailing Add:* Boston Dept Health & Hosp 818 Harrison Ave Boston MA 02118

LAMB, GEORGE LAWRENCE, JR, b Norwood, Mass, Apr 28, 31; m 59; c 4. PHYSICS. *Educ:* Boston Col, BS, 53, MS, 54; Mass Inst Technol, PhD(physics), 58. *Prof Exp:* Staff mem, Los Alamos Sci Lab, 58-63; physicist, United Aircraft Res Labs, Conn, 63-74; fac mem, 74-80, PROF MATH & PROF OPTICAL SCI, UNIV ARIZ, 80- *Mem:* Am Phys Soc. *Res:* Nonlinear waves and solitons; wave propagation. *Mailing Add:* Dept of Math & Optical Sci Ctr Univ of Ariz Tucson AZ 85721

LAMB, GEORGE MARION, b Little Rock, Ark, Dec 23, 28; m 53; c 2. MICROPALEONTOLOGY, STRATIGRAPHY. *Educ:* Emory Univ, BA, 50, MS, 54; Univ Colo, Boulder, PhD(geol), 64. *Prof Exp:* Geologist, Standard Oil Calif, Inc, 55-61; PROF GEOL & CHMN DEPT, UNIV SOUTH ALA, 64- *Mem:* Am Asn Petrol Geol; Geol Soc Am. *Res:* Ecology and paleoecology of Foraminifera; biostratigraphic relationships; groundwater and environmental geology. *Mailing Add:* Dept of Geol Univ of SAla Mobile AL 36608

LAMB, H RICHARD, b Philadelphia, Pa, Sept 18, 29; m 69; c 3. PSYCHIATRY. *Educ:* Univ Pa, BA, 50; Yale Univ, MD, 54. *Prof Exp:* Chief rehab serv, San Mateo County Ment Health Serv, 60-76; assoc prof, 76-80, PROF PSYCHIAT, SCH MED, UNIV SOUTHERN CALIF, 80- *Concurrent Pos:* Consult, NIMH, 75-; ed-in-chief, New Directions Ment Health Serv J, 78-; mem comt rehab, Am Psychiat Asn, 78- *Mem:* Am Psychiat Asn. *Res:* Social and community psychiatry and community mental health with a major focus on the long-term severely disabled psychiatric patient in the community. *Mailing Add:* Dept Psychiat Univ Southern Calif Sch Med Los Angeles CA 90033

LAMB, J(AMIE) PARKER, JR, b Boligee, Ala, Sept 21, 33; m 55; c 2. MECHANICAL & AEROSPACE ENGINEERING. *Educ:* Auburn Univ, BS, 54; Univ Ill, MS, 58, PhD(mech eng), 61. *Prof Exp:* Proj engr, Flight Control Lab, Wright Air Develop Ctr, Ohio, 55-57; asst prof eng mech, Univ NC, Raleigh, 61-63; from asst prof to assoc prof, 63-70, chmn dept, 70-76, prof mech eng, 70-81, assoc dean, Col Eng, 76-81, ERNEST COCKRELL JR MEM PROF & CHMN AEROSPACE ENG, UNIV TEX, AUSTIN, 81- *Concurrent Pos:* Consult, ARO, Inc, Tenn, 63-65, Tracor, Inc, Tex, 65-67, NASA, Ala, 69-70, Vought Aerospace Corp, Tex, 69-70 & Mobil Oil Corp, Tex, 77-78; assoc tech ed, J Fluids Eng, 76-79. *Honors & Awards:* Founders Award, Am Soc Mech Engrs, 75; Centennial Award, Am Soc Mech Engrs, 80. *Mem:* Fel Am Soc Mech Engrs; assoc fel Am Inst Aeronaut & Astronaut; Am Soc Eng Educ. *Res:* Heat transfer and fluid mechanics in separated flow regions; compressible turbulent boundary layers; heat, mass and momentum transfers in free turbulent jets; energy conversion processes for low temperature sources. *Mailing Add:* Dept Aerospace Eng Univ of Tex Austin TX 78712

LAMB, JAMES C(HRISTIAN), III, b Warsaw, Va, Aug 20, 24. SCIENCE EDUCATION, RESEARCH ADMINISTRATION. *Educ:* Va Mil Inst, BS, 47; Mass Inst Technol, SM, 48, SE, 52, ScD(sanit eng), 53; Environ Engrs Intersoc Bd, dipl. *Prof Exp:* Instr civil eng, Va Mil Inst, 48-50; asst sanit eng, Mass Inst Technol, 51-53, res assoc, 53-55; sanit engr, Am Cyanamid Co, 55-59; assoc prof, 59-65, PROF SANIT ENG, UNIV NC, CHAPEL HILL, 65- *Concurrent Pos:* Consult engr, 48-50, 52-55, 59-; lectr, Washington & Lee Univ, 49-50 & Exten Div, State Dept Educ, Mass, 51-52; adj prof, Newark Col Eng, 56-59; Judge, US Nuclear Regulatory Comn, 74- *Mem:* Am Soc Civil Engrs; Am Water Works Asn; Water Pollution Control Fedn. *Res:* Industrial wastes; sewage treatment; water supply; saline water conversion; corrosion; stream pollution; refuse disposal; steam pollution, regulatory controls and standards; civil engineering. *Mailing Add:* Dept of Environ Sci & Eng Univ of NC Chapel Hill NC 27514

LAMB, JAMES FRANCIS, b Denton, Tex, Oct 3, 37; m 58; c 2. NUCLEAR MEDICINE, NUCLEAR CHEMISTRY. *Educ:* NTex State Univ, BS, 60, MS, 61; Univ Calif, Berkeley, PhD(chem), 69. *Prof Exp:* Res chemist, Lawrence Radiation Lab, Univ Calif, 69-70; prin radiochemist, 70-74, assoc dir, 74-81, DIR RES & DEVELOP, MEDI-PHYSICS, INC, 81- *Mem:* Am Chem Soc; Soc Nuclear Med; AAAS. *Res:* Nuclear chemistry in nuclear medical and radiopharmaceutical applications. *Mailing Add:* Medi-Physics Inc PO Box 8684 Emeryville CA 94608

LAMB, JAMES L, b Los Angeles, Calif, Jan 17, 25; m 45; c 2. MICROPALEONTOLOGY. *Educ:* Univ Southern Calif, BS, 53. *Prof Exp:* Paleontologist, Richfield Oil Corp, 53-57 & Creole Petrol Corp, 57-64; paleontologist, Exxon Prod Res Co, 64-81; CONSULT, 81- *Mem:* Soc Econ Paleont & Mineral; Am Asn Petrol Geologists; Venezuelan Asn Geol, Mining & Petrol. *Res:* Historical geology and paleontology; geologic distribution of planktonic foraminifera; tertiary microfossils; Pleistocene epoch. *Mailing Add:* 7600 Highmeadow Apt 54 Houston TX 77063

LAMB, JOHN H(ENRY), JR, b Memphis, Tenn, Sept 30, 31; m 54; c 3. CIVIL ENGINEERING, SOIL MECHANICS. *Educ:* Univ Ill, BSCE, 56, MSCE, 59, PhD(soil mech, found eng), 63. *Prof Exp:* Asst struct dynamics, Univ Ill, 56-58, instr, 58-62; ASSOC PROF CIVIL ENG, WAYNE STATE UNIV, 62- *Mem:* Am Soc Civil Engrs; Am Soc Testing & Mat; Am Soc Eng Educ; Int Soc Soil Mech & Found Engrs. *Res:* Foundation engineering; static and dynamic soil-structure interaction and the determining of soil properties that influence it; development of gelatin models for the study of these problems; construction management. *Mailing Add:* Dept of Civil Eng Col of Eng Wayne State Univ Detroit MI 48202

LAMB, LAWRENCE EDWARD, b Fredonia, Kans, Oct 13, 26. MEDICINE. *Educ:* Univ Kans, MD, 49; Am Bd Internal Med, dipl, 58. *Prof Exp:* Intern, Med Ctr, Univ Kans, 49-50, resident internal med, 50-51; chief, Cardiovasc & Renal Sect, Sheppard AFB Hosp, 51-53; asst, Emory Univ, 54; dir cardiol, Dept Internal Med, Sch Aviation Med, Randolph AFB, Tex, 55-57, chief dept, 57-58, prof internal med & chief dept, Sch Aviation Med, Brooks AFB Aerospace Med Ctr, 58-61, dir consult serv, 59-61, chief, Aerospace Med Sci Div, US Air Force Sch Aerospace Med, 61-66; prof med, Col Med, Baylor Univ, 66-71; SYNDICATED MED COLUMNIST, NEWSPAPER ENTERPRISE ASN, 71- *Concurrent Pos:* Teaching fel, Emory Univ, 53; Am Heart Asn res fel, Geneva, Switz, 54-55; mem conf electrocardiog probs in aviation, Royal Can Air Force, 56; lectr, St Thomas, Manila, 57, Med Sch, Stanford Univ, 58 & Life Sci Div, Nat Acad Sci, 58; fel coun epidemiol, Am Heart Asn; consult, Mercury Proj, NASA, 60, consult to dir life sci, 65-; consult, President's Coun Phys Fitness & Sports, 62- *Honors & Awards:* Tuttle Award, Civil Aviation Med Asn, 59; Distinguished Civilian Serv Award, Dept Defense, 62; Meritorious Civilian Serv Award, Dept Air Force, 66. *Mem:* Fel Aerospace Med Asn; fel Am Col Chest Physicians; fel Am Col Cardiol; fel Am Col Physicians; fel Am Soc Clin Pharmacol & Chemother. *Res:* Myocardial infarction; cardiology; stresses and effects of influence of space flight on cardiovascular system; results of vectorcardiograms and electrocardiograms. *Mailing Add:* 135 Downing Dr San Antonio TX 78209

LAMB, MINA MARIE WOLF, b Sagerton, Tex, Aug 14, 10; m 41; c 1. NUTRITION. *Educ:* Tex Tech Col, BA, 32, MS, 37; Columbia Univ, PhD(nutrit, chem), 42. *Prof Exp:* Teacher, elem & high sch, 33-35; teacher & res worker food & nutrit, 35-37; from lab asst to prof, 40-69, Margaret W Weeks distinguished prof, 69-75, head dept food & nutrit, 55-69, lectr & adv foreign students, 60-71, EMER PROF FOOD & NUTRIT, TEX TECH UNIV, 75- *Honors & Awards:* Piper Award, 65. *Mem:* AAAS; Am Dietetic Asn; Am Home Econ Asn; Am Pub Health Asn; Am Inst Nutrit. *Res:* Basal metabolism of college girls and children of various ages older than two years; needs of children and adults; dietary studies of children, college girls and families; animal feeding work with albino rats determining growth and reproduction responses to various diets and foods. *Mailing Add:* 6002 W 34th St Lubbock TX 79407

LAMB, NEVEN P, b New York, NY, May 18, 32; m 57; c 2. BIOLOGICAL ANTHROPOLOGY. *Educ:* Pa State Univ, BA, 54; Univ Ariz, PhD(anthrop), 69. *Prof Exp:* Res asst morphogenetics, Jackson Mem Lab, Maine, 60-61; from asst prof to assoc prof anthrop, Portland State Univ, 65-73; ASSOC PROF ANTHROP, TEX TECH UNIV, 73- *Concurrent Pos:* Vis prof, Univ Ariz, 71-72; prin investr, NIH, 74-76; proj dir curric improvement, NSF, 78-81. *Mem:* AAAS; fel Am Asn Anthropologists; Am Asn Phys Anthropologists; Sigma Xi. *Res:* Human evolution; population biology; mating patterns and genetic systems; anthropometry of North American Indians; socio-cultural and biological aspects of mate selection among Papago Indians. *Mailing Add:* Dept of Anthrop Tex Tech Univ Lubbock TX 79409

LAMB, RICHARD C, b Lexington, Ky, Sept 8, 33; m 59; c 4. GAMMA RAY ASTRONOMY, ELEMENTARY PARTICLE PHYSICS. *Educ:* Mass Inst Technol, BS, 55; Univ Ky, PhD(physics), 63. *Prof Exp:* Asst scientist, Argonne Nat Lab, 63-67; assoc prof physics, 67-72, PROF PHYSICS, IOWA

STATE UNIV, 72- *Concurrent Pos:* Vis scientist, NASA-Goddard Space Flight Ctr, 75-76. *Mem:* Am Phys Soc; Am Astron Soc. *Res:* Very high energy gamma ray astronomy using the atmospheric Cerenkov technique; identification of gamma ray sources. *Mailing Add:* Dept of Physics Iowa State Univ Ames IA 50010

LAMB, ROBERT ANDREW, b London, Eng, Sept 26, 50; m 76. VIROLOGY, MOLECULAR BIOLOGY. *Educ:* Univ Birmingham, BSc, 71; Univ Cambridge, PhD(virol), 74. *Prof Exp:* Res assoc 74-77, ASST PROF VIROL, ROCKEFELLER UNIV, 77- *Concurrent Pos:* Fulbright-Hays travel award, Med Res Coun, 71-74; assoc ed, Virology, 80- *Honors & Awards:* Irma T Hirschl Career Scientist Award, 78; Phoebe Weinstein Award for Negative Strand Virus Res, 1980. *Mem:* Harvey Soc; Am Soc Microbiol; Biochem Soc; Soc Gen Microbiol; Am Soc Virol. *Res:* Virology; replication of influenza virus and paramyxoviruses: RNA processing and gene expression and regulation. *Mailing Add:* Dept Virol 1230 York Ave New York NY 10021

LAMB, ROBERT CARDON, b Logan, Utah, Jan 8, 33; m 53; c 5. DAIRY SCIENCE. *Educ:* Utah State Univ, BS, 56; Mich State Univ, MS, 59, PhD(dairy cattle breeding), 62. *Prof Exp:* Instr dairy sci, Mich State Univ, 58-60; asst prof, Utah State Univ, 61-64; res dairy husbandman, 64-72, RES LEADER, AGR RES SERV, USDA, 72- *Mem:* Am Dairy Sci Asn. *Res:* Use of incomplete records in dairy cattle selection; genetics by nutrition interactions; inheritance of abnormalities in livestock; feed utilization efficiency in dairy cattle; dairy herd management; exercise for dairy cows. *Mailing Add:* Dept Animal Dairy & Vet Sci Utah State Univ Logan UT 84322

LAMB, ROBERT CHARLES, b Union Co, SC, Sept 28, 28; m 50; c 2. ORGANIC CHEMISTRY. *Educ:* Presby Col, SC, BS, 48; Univ Ga, MS, 55; Univ SC, PhD(chem), 58. *Prof Exp:* Instr chem, Presby Col, SC, 50-51; asst prof, Univ Ga, 58-66; assoc prof & chmn dept, Augusta Col, 66; chmn dept, 66-77, PROF CHEM, EAST CAROLINA UNIV, 66- *Mem:* Am Chem Soc. *Res:* Organic peroxides; free radicals in solution; chemical kinetics. *Mailing Add:* Dept Chem ECarolina Univ PO Box 2787 Greenville NC 27834

LAMB, ROBERT CONSAY, b Saskatoon, Sask, May 11, 19; nat US; m 49; c 3. POMOLOGY. *Educ:* Univ Sask, BSA, 41; Univ Minn, MS, 47, PhD(hort), 54. *Prof Exp:* Asst hort, Univ Minn, 46-48; asst prof pomol, 48-55, ASSOC PROF POMOL, NY STATE COL AGR & LIFE SCI, CORNELL UNIV, 55- *Concurrent Pos:* Orgn Europ Econ Coop sr vis fel sci, John Innes Inst, Eng, 62. *Mem:* Am Soc Hort Sci; Int Soc Hort Sci; Can Soc Hort Sci; Am Pomol Soc (pres, 80-82). *Res:* Breeding peaches, apricots, pears and apples. *Mailing Add:* NY State Agr Exp Sta Geneva NY 14456

LAMB, ROBERT EDWARD, b Sharon, Pa, July 12, 45; m 73. ANALYTICAL CHEMISTRY. *Educ:* St Louis Univ, AB, 69, BS, 70; Univ Ill, MS, 74, PhD(anal chem), 75. *Prof Exp:* Lectr anal chem, Sch Chem Sci, Univ Ill, 75; asst prof chem, Southern Methodist Univ, 75-78; asst prof chem, 78-80, ASSOC PROF CHEM, OHIO NORTHERN UNIV, 80- *Mem:* Am Chem Soc. *Res:* Pulse polarography and stripping analysis; ion-selective electrodes; analysis of trace metal complexes; environmental applications of analytical techniques. *Mailing Add:* Dept of Chem Ohio Northern Univ Ada OH 45810

LAMB, ROBERT W, organic chemistry, physical chemistry, see previous edition

LAMB, SANDRA INA, b New York, NY, Apr 20, 31; m 50; c 4. ORGANIC CHEMISTRY, ENVIRONMENTAL CHEMISTRY. *Educ:* Univ Calif, Los Angeles, BS, 54, PhD(phys org chem), 59. *Prof Exp:* Instr chem, Santa Monica City Col, fall 59; asst prof, San Fernando Valley State Col, 60-61; instr, Exten Div, Univ Calif, 61-69; from asst prof to assoc prof chem, 69-76, Mt St Mary's Col, Calif, 71-76, chmn dept phys sci & math, 69-75; LECTR CHEM, UNIV CALIF, LOS ANGELES, 76- *Concurrent Pos:* Asst res pharmacologist, Med Univ Calif, 66-, lectr, 70. *Mem:* AAAS; Am Chem Soc. *Res:* Analytical applications of gas chromatography in chemistry and medicine with special interest in analysis of acetylcholine and various cholinergic agents; mechanism of action of muscarinic agents; analytical applications of gas chromatography and ion chromatography air pollution; synthesis of small ring compounds. *Mailing Add:* Dept of Chem Univ of Calif Los Angeles CA 90024

LAMB, STEVE CHARLES, b St Louis, Mo, June 3, 48; m 70; c 3. BIOCHEMISTRY, MICROBIOLOGY. *Educ:* Univ Mo-Rolla, BS, 70; Univ Wis-Madison, PhD(biochem), 74. *Prof Exp:* Res microbiologist biochem, Archer Daniels Midland Co, 74-76; res biochemist microbiol, Air Prod & Chem Inc, 76-82; RES SCIENTIST, G D SEARLE & CO, 82- *Mem:* AAAS. *Res:* Growth and metabolism of microorganisms batch and continuous culture; product formation kinetics; industrial microbiology; fermentations; microbial enzymes; steroid transformations; microbial physiology. *Mailing Add:* G D Searle & Co Box 5110 Chicago IL 60680

LAMB, WALTER ROBERT, b Weiser, Idaho, Sept 26, 22; m 46; c 1. PHYSICS. *Educ:* Univ Calif, AB, 48. *Prof Exp:* Physicist, US Naval Radiol Defense Lab, 48-59; solid state physicist, Res & Develop Dept, Raytheon Semiconductor Co, 59-63, Fairchild Semiconductor, 63-64 & Union Carbide Corp, 64-65; mgr advan processing, Stewart-Warner Microcircuits, 65-68; physicist, Fairchild Semiconductor Corp, 68-71; physicist, Raytheon Co, 71-77; PHYSICIST, FAIRCHILD SEMICONDUCTOR CORP, 78- *Mem:* AAAS; Am Phys Soc. *Res:* Solid state, nuclear, atomic, optical, luminescent, thermodynamic and gravitational phenomena. *Mailing Add:* 148 Jacinto Way Sunnyvale CA 94086

LAMB, WILLIAM BOLITHO, b Chicago, Ill, May 6, 37; m 61; c 2. CHEMICAL ENGINEERING. *Educ:* Princeton Univ, BSE, 58; Univ Del, MChE, 63, PhD(chem eng), 65. *Prof Exp:* Res engr, 65-68, res suprv, 68-69, group mgr, 69-75, tech supt, Film Dept, 75-78, planning mgr, 79-80, PROD MGR, POLYMER PROD DEPT, E I DU PONT DE NEMOURS & CO,

INC, 80- *Mem:* Am Inst Chem Eng. *Res:* Mass transfer in gas-liquid systems; polymer rheology; extrusion and processing of polymers for packaging film applications; fluoropolymers. *Mailing Add:* 4 Sorrel Dr Surrey Park Wilmington DE 19803

LAMB, WILLIS EUGENE, JR, b Los Angeles, Calif, July 12, 13; m. QUANTUM MECHANICS, ATOMIC PHYSICS. *Educ:* Univ Calif, BS, 34, PhD(physics), 38; Oxford Univ, MA, 56; Yale Univ, MA, 61. *Hon Degrees:* ScD, Univ Pa, 54; LHD, Yeshiva Univ, 65; ScD, Gustavus Adolphus Col, 75. *Prof Exp:* Asst physics, Univ Calif, 34-35, 36-37; instr, Columbia Univ, 38-43, assoc, 43-45, from asst prof to prof physics, 45-52; prof, Stanford Univ, 51-56; Wykeham prof & fel, New Col, Oxford Univ, 56-62; Henry Ford II prof, Yale Univ, 62-72, Josiah Willard Gibbs prof, 72-74; PROF PHYSICS & OPTICAL SCI, UNIV ARIZ, 74- *Concurrent Pos:* Mem staff, Radiation Lab, Columbia Univ, 43-52; Loeb lectr, Harvard Univ, 53-54; Guggenheim fel, 60-61; consult, Philips Labs, Inc, NASA, Bell Tel Labs & Perkin-Elmer Corp. *Honors & Awards:* Rumford Medal, Am Acad Arts & Sci, 53; Nobel Prize Physics, 55; Award, Res Corp, 55. *Mem:* Nat Acad Sci; fel Am Phys Soc; hon mem NY Acad Sci; hon fel Brit Inst Physics; hon fel Royal Soc Edinburgh. *Res:* Theoretical physics; atomic and nuclear structure; microwave spectroscopy; fine structure of hydrogen and helium; magnetron oscillators; statistical mechanics; masers and lasers. *Mailing Add:* Dept of Physics Univ of Ariz Tucson AZ 85721

LAMBA, RAM SARUP, b Calcutta, India, Dec 29, 41; US citizen; m 69; c 2. INORGANIC CHEMISTRY, ORGANIC CHEMISTRY. *Educ:* Delhi Univ, India, BSc, 62, MSc, 64; ETex State Univ, DEd(inorg chem, educ), 73. *Prof Exp:* Res asst, Indian Inst Petrol, Dehradun, India, 64-65; chemist & supt dyeing & finishing, Beaunit Corp of NC, Humacao, PR, 68-69; instr chem, 69-70, asst prof & chmn dept, 70-71, chmn dept natural sci, 73-77, ASSOC PROF CHEM, MATH & PHYSICS, INTER AM UNIV PR, 73-, DEAN ACAD AFFAIRS, 77- *Mem:* Royal Inst Chem; Am Chem Soc; The Chem Soc; fel Inst Educ Leadership. *Res:* To develop innovative methods in the teaching of college chemistry and to integrate with biological sciences; synthesis and study of chromium (III), complexes. *Mailing Add:* Off of Dean Acad Affairs Inter Am Univ PO Box 1293 Hato Rey PR 00919

LAMBA, SURENDAR SINGH, b India, Mar 3, 36; m 67; c 1. PHARMACY, PHARMACOGNOSY. *Educ:* Agra Univ, BSc, 54; Univ Rajasthan, BPharm, 57; Panjab Univ, India, MPharm, 60; Univ Nebr, MS, 63; Univ Colo, PhD(pharmacog), 66. *Prof Exp:* Assoc prof, 66-67, PROF PHARMACOG, FLA A&M UNIV, 67- *Honors & Awards:* Lederle Fac Award, 75. *Mem:* Am Pharmaceut Asn; Acad Pharmaceut Sci; NY Acad Sci; Am Soc Pharmacog. *Res:* Tissue culture studies; effects of growth retardants on growth and alkaloid biosynthesis; phytochemical investigation of some members of Papaveraceae; microbial transformation of Nucleosides. *Mailing Add:* Dept of Pharm-Pharmacog Fla A&M Univ Tallahassee FL 32307

LAMBDIN, MORRIS ARTHUR, pediatrics, see previous edition

LAMBDIN, PARIS LEE, b St Charles, Va, Oct 13, 41; m 64; c 2. ENTOMOLOGY. *Educ:* Lincoln Mem Univ, BA, 64; Va Polytech Inst & State Univ, MS, 72, PhD(entom), 74. *Prof Exp:* Teacher biol, Bassett High Sch, 64-66; ASSOC PROF ENTOM, DEPT ENTOM & PLANT PATHOL, UNIV TENN, 74- *Mem:* Entom Soc Am. *Res:* Systematics of species in the superfamily Coccoidea; biological control of vegetable insect pests. *Mailing Add:* Dept Agr Biol Univ Tenn Knoxville TN 37916

LAMBE, EDWARD DIXON, b Prince Rupert, BC, July 25, 24; m 50; c 4. PHYSICS. *Educ:* Univ BC, BASc, 48, MASc, 49; Princeton Univ, PhD(physics), 59. *Prof Exp:* Asst prof physics, Washington Univ, 56-61; assoc prof, 61-65, asst vchancellor, 66-70, dir, Instructional Resources Ctr, 67-74, PROF PHYSICS, STATE UNIV NY STONY BROOK, 65- *Concurrent Pos:* Exec secy, Comn Col Physics, 62-64, secy, 64-68. *Mem:* Am Asn Physics Teachers. *Res:* Electron and nuclear magnetic resonance; beta and gamma ray polarization; learning processes in physics. *Mailing Add:* Dept of Physics State Univ of NY Stony Brook NY 11794

LAMBE, JOHN JOSEPH, b Cork, Ireland, Dec 1, 26; US citizen; m 50; c 2. SOLID STATE PHYSICS. *Educ:* Univ Mich, BSE, 48, MS, 50; Univ Md, PhD(physics), 54. *Prof Exp:* Res physics, Airborne Instruments Lab, 48-51; physicist solid state physics, Naval Res Lab, 51-56; physicist microwave res, Univ Mich 56-59; STAFF SCIENTIST SOLID STATE PHYSICS, FORD MOTOR CO, 59- *Mem:* Fel Am Phys Soc. *Res:* Solid state physics; magnetic resonance; luminescence; super conductivity; electron tunneling. *Mailing Add:* Ford Motor Co Box 2053 Dearborn MI 48121

LAMBE, ROBERT CARL, b Minneapolis, Minn, Nov 25, 27; m 50; c 2. PLANT PATHOLOGY. *Educ:* Univ Southern Calif, AB, 52; Univ Calif, MS, 55; Ore State Col, PhD(plant path), 60. *Prof Exp:* Jr plant pathologist, Ore State Univ, 58-60; plant pathologist, Area Exten, Tex A&M Univ, 60-63; exten plant pathologist, Iowa State Univ, 63-67; ASSOC PROF PLANT PATH, VA POLYTECH INST & STATE UNIV, 67- *Res:* Fungicides and extension plant pathology. *Mailing Add:* Dept of Plant Path Va Polytech Inst & State Univ Blacksburg VA 24061

LAMBE, T(HOMAS) WILLIAM, b Raleigh, NC, Nov 28, 20; m 47. CIVIL ENGINEERING. *Educ:* NC State Col, BCE, 42; Mass Inst Technol, SM, 44, ScD(soil mech), 48. *Prof Exp:* Struct detailer, Am Bridge Co, Pa, 42; party chief, Olsen Consult Eng, 42; instr civil eng, Univ NH, 42-43; civil engr, US Navy, 43, Standard Oil Co, Calif, 44 & Dames & Moore, 44-45; from instr to assoc prof soils, 45-58, dir, Soil Stabilization Lab, 50-58, prof civil eng, 58-69, Edmund K Turner prof civil eng, 69-80, head, Soil Mech Div, 58-80, EMER EDMUND K TURNER PROF CIVIL ENG, MASS INST TECHNOL, 80- *Concurrent Pos:* Consult soil projs. *Mem:* Nat Acad Eng; Am Soc Civil Engrs. *Res:* Soil testing, stabilization and mineralogy; soil engineering; earth and rock dams. *Mailing Add:* 40 Elm St East Popperell MA 01437

LAMBE, THOMAS ANTHONY, b Victoria, BC, Dec 27, 30; m 64. OPERATIONS RESEARCH, ENGINEERING SCIENCE. *Educ:* Univ BC, BASc, 52; Stanford Univ, MSc, 58, PhD(eng sci), 68. *Prof Exp:* Engr, Can Westinghouse, 52-54; res engr, BC Res Coun, 54-57, proj leader opers res, 58-65; assoc prof indust eng, Univ Toronto, 68-74; ASSOC PROF, SCH PUB ADMIN, UNIV VICTORIA, 74- *Mem:* Can Oper Res Soc; Opers Res Soc Am. *Res:* Economic analysis of engineering systems, particularly the transportation and natural resource industries; decision theory and individual choice behavior. *Mailing Add:* Sch of Pub Admin Univ of Victoria Victoria BC V8W 2Y2 Can

LAMBEK, JOACHIM, b Leipzig, Ger, Dec 5, 22; nat Can; m 48; c 3. MATHEMATICS. *Educ:* McGill Univ, BSc, 46, MSc, 47, PhD, 51. *Prof Exp:* Assoc prof math, 54-63, PROF MATH, McGILL UNIV, 63- *Concurrent Pos:* Mem, Inst Advan Study, 59-60. *Mem:* Am Math Soc; Math Asn Am; Can Math Cong. *Res:* Algebra. *Mailing Add:* Dept of Math McGill Univ Montreal PQ H3A 2T6 Can

LAMBERD, WILLIAM GORDON, b Wales, Oct 29, 21; Can citizen; m 53; c 3. PSYCHIATRY. *Educ:* Univ Liverpool, MB, ChB, 52; Univ Man, MSc, 57; CRCP(C), 57. *Prof Exp:* Clin dir psychiat, Hosp Ment Dis, Selkirk, Man, 58-60; chief psychiat, Can Dept Vet Affairs Hosp, Winnipeg, 60-69; clin dir dept psychiat, Health Sci Centre, 69-75, PROF PSYCHIAT, UNIV MAN, 69-, COORDR UNDERGRAD EDUC, DEPT PSYCHIAT, HEALTH SCI CENTRE, 75- *Concurrent Pos:* Am Psychiat Asn spec fel, Mayo Found, Univ Minn, 57-58; consult, Can Pensions Bd, 68-; Royal Can Air Force, 70- & Dept Civil Aviation Med, 72-; mem rev bd, Govt Man, 69- *Res:* Psychotherapy, group therapy. *Mailing Add:* Dept of Psychiat Univ of Man Health Sci Centre Winnipeg MB R3T 2N2 Can

LAMBERG, STANLEY LAWRENCE, b Brooklyn, NY, Oct 2, 33; m 63; c 2. HEMATOLOGY, HISTOLOGY. *Educ:* Brooklyn Col, BS, 55; Oberlin Col, MA, 57; Tufts Univ, MS, 62; NY Univ, PhD(biol), 68. *Prof Exp:* Teaching asst biol, Oberlin Col, 55-57; chief technician biochem, Sch Med, Cornell Univ, 57-58; res fel, Sch Med, Tufts Univ, 58-61; Nat Inst Dent Res fel, Col Dent, NY Univ, 61-66; lectr biol, City Col New York, 66-67; asst prof biol, Conolly Col, Long Island Univ, 67-70; from asst prof to assoc prof, 70-75, PROF MED LAB TECHNOL, STATE UNIV NY AGR & TECH COL FARMINGDALE, 75- *Concurrent Pos:* Asst res scientist, Guggenheim Inst Dent Res, NY Univ, 68-69; adj asst prof, Conolly Col, Long Island Univ, 70-73; adj assoc prof, 73-75; adj instr, Suffolk County Comt Col, 81- *Honors & Awards:* Founder's Day Award, NY Univ, 69. *Mem:* AAAS; NY Acad Sci; Sigma Xi; AAAS. *Res:* Mitochondrial phosphorylation reactions during embryonic development; effect of ultraviolet irradiation and various inhibitors and uncoupling reagents on mitochondrial phosphorylation reactions. *Mailing Add:* Dept of Med Lab Technol State Univ NY Agr & Tech Col Farmingdale NY 11735

LAMBERSON, HAROLD VINCENT, b Albany, NY, July 29, 45. MEDICINE. *Educ:* Union Col, Schenectady, NY, BS, 67, MS, 69; Albany Med Col, MD & PhD, 75. *Prof Exp:* asst prof path, asst dir clin path & dir, Diagnostic Virol Lab & Microbiol Sect, Upstate Med Ctr, State Univ NY, 78-82, actg dir, Clin Immunol Sect, 80-81; actg dir, 82, DIR, AM RED CROSS BLOOD SERV, 82- *Mem:* Am Soc Clin Pathologists; Am Soc Microbiol. *Res:* Rapid laboratory diagnosis of infectious diseases; transfusion related viral infections; investigation of in vitro lymphocyte function in leukemia. *Mailing Add:* Am Red Cross Blood Serv Syracuse NY 13202

LAMBERT, BRIAN KERRY, b Spokane, Wash, Nov 21, 41; m 63; c 2. INDUSTRIAL ENGINEERING. *Educ:* Tex Tech Col, BS, 64, MS, 66, PhD(indust eng), 67. *Prof Exp:* Asst prof, 67-71, ASSOC PROF INDUST ENG, TEX TECH UNIV, 71- *Mem:* Soc Mfg Engrs; Inst Indust Engrs; Am Soc Eng Educ. *Res:* Manufacturing research and development, specifically machining operations research and systems analysis, specifically reliability. *Mailing Add:* Dept of Indust Eng Tex Tech Univ Lubbock TX 79409

LAMBERT, CHARLES CALVIN, b Rockford, Ill, Apr 10, 35; m 65; c 2. DEVELOPMENTAL BIOLOGY, REPRODUCTIVE BIOLOGY. *Educ:* San Diego State Univ, BA, 64, MS, 66; Univ Wash, PhD(zool), 70. *Prof Exp:* NIH traineeship, Univ Wash, 70; asst prof zool, 70-74, assoc prof, 74-79, PROF ZOOL, CALIF STATE UNIV, FULLERTON, 79- *Mem:* Am Soc Zoologists; Soc Develop Biol; AAAS. *Res:* Development and physiology of marine invertebrates. *Mailing Add:* Dept of Biol Calif State Univ Fullerton CA 92634

LAMBERT, EDWARD HOWARD, b Minneapolis, Minn, Aug 30, 15; m 40, 75. MEDICAL PHYSIOLOGY. *Educ:* Univ Ill, BS, 36, MS, 38, MD, 39, PhD(physiol), 44. *Prof Exp:* Instr med technol, Herzl Jr Col, 41-42; assoc med, Off Sci Res & Develop, Col Med, Univ Ill, 42-43; res asst, 43-45, from instr to prof physiol, 45-58, prof physiol, Mayo Grad Sch Med, Univ Minn, 58-73, PROF PHYSIOL & NEUROL, MAYO MED SCH, 73- *Concurrent Pos:* Consult, Mayo Clin, 45-; mem pub adv group, NIH; prin investr, NIH grant, 81- *Honors & Awards:* Presidential Cert Merit, 47; Tuttle Award, Aerospace Med Asn, 52. *Mem:* Am Acad Neurol; Soc Neurosci; Am Physiol Soc; Aerospace Med Asn; Am Asn Electromyography & Electrodiag (pres, 58). *Res:* Neurophysiology; neuromuscular disorders in man; electromyography; neuromuscular transmission. *Mailing Add:* Dept of Physiol & Biophys Mayo Med Sch Rochester MN 55901

LAMBERT, FRANCIS LINCOLN, b Staunton, Va, Oct 8, 23; m 67. PHYSIOLOGY. *Educ:* George Washington Univ, BS, 49, MS, 51; Harvard Univ, PhD(biol), 58. *Prof Exp:* Instr zool, George Washington Univ, 52-55; asst prof biol, 55-61, assoc prof physiol & biophys, 61-80, PROF & CHMN BIOL SCI, UNION COL, NY, 80- *Concurrent Pos:* Jacques Loeb assoc marine biol, Rockefeller Inst, 60-61. *Mem:* AAAS; Am Soc Zool. *Res:* Invertebrate physiology; cellular neurophysiology. *Mailing Add:* Dept of Biol Sci Union Col Schenectady NY 12308

LAMBERT, FRANK LEWIS, b Minneapolis, Minn, July 10, 18; m 43. ORGANIC CHEMISTRY. *Educ:* Harvard Univ, BA, 39; Univ Chicago, PhD(org chem), 42. *Prof Exp:* Res & develop chemist, Edwal Labs, Ill, 42-43, develop chemist, 43-44, head develop dept, 46-47; instr chem, Univ Calif, Los Angeles, 47-48; from asst prof to prof chem, Occidental Col, 48-80. *Concurrent Pos:* NSF fac fel, 57-58, 70-71. *Mem:* Am Chem Soc. *Res:* Polarography of organic halogenation compounds; halogenation of organic compounds. *Mailing Add:* 1105 Olancha Dr Los Angeles CA 90065

LAMBERT, GEORGE, b Etobicoke, Ont, Oct 8, 23; US citizen; m 48; c 3. VETERINARY MICROBIOLOGY. *Educ:* Univ Guelph, DVM, 47; Iowa State Univ, MS, 66. *Prof Exp:* Instr vet path, Ont Vet Col, Univ Guelph, 47-48; asst prof, WVa Univ, 48-50; coop agt, Univ Wis & USDA, 50-53; asst state vet epidemiol, Va Dept Agr, 53-57; res vet bact, Nat Animal Dis Lab, 57-65, res virol, 65-67; asst dir biol dept, Diamond Labs, Inc, 67-70; chief virol res lab, 70-75, asst dir, 75-80, ASSOC DIR, NAT ANIMAL DIS CTR, 80- *Mem:* Am Vet Med Asn; US Animal Health Asn; Conf Res Workers Animal Dis. *Res:* Administration of animal disease research. *Mailing Add:* Nat Animal Dis Ctr Box 70 Ames IA 50010

LAMBERT, GLENN FREDERICK, b Columbus, Ohio, Nov 21, 18; m 45; c 2. BIOCHEMISTRY. *Educ:* DePauw Univ, AB, 40, Univ Ill, PhD(biochem), 44. *Prof Exp:* Spec res asst, Univ Ill, 45-46; res chemist, 46-60, sr res pharmacologist, 61-73, SR RES CHEMIST, ABBOTT LABS, 73- *Concurrent Pos:* Mem coun arteriosclerosis & coun thrombosis, Am Heart Asn. *Mem:* Am Chem Soc. *Res:* Biochemistry and nutrition of amino acids; fat emulsions for intravenous therapy; atherosclerosis; thrombolytic drugs; high pressure liquid chromatography separation and analysis of peptides. *Mailing Add:* Anal Res Dept Abbott Labs North Chicago IL 60064

LAMBERT, HELEN HAYNES, b Baton Rouge, La, July 25, 39; div; c 2. ENDOCRINOLOGY. *Educ:* Wellesley Col, BA, 61; Univ NH, MS, 63, PhD(zool), 69. *Prof Exp:* Instr zool, Univ NH, 67-68; asst prof biol, Simmons Col, 69-70; asst prof, 70-80, ASSOC PROF BIOL, NORTHEASTERN UNIV, 80- *Mem:* AAAS; Sigma Xi; Am Inst Biol Sci; Am Soc Zool. *Res:* Effect of lighting on reproduction; environmental factors affecting sexual behavior; neuroendocrine mechanisms of ovulation; sex determination and development of sex differences. *Mailing Add:* Dept of Biol Northeastern Univ Boston MA 02115

LAMBERT, HOWARD W, b Oakland, Calif, Aug 2, 37; m 57; c 3. TOPOLOGY. *Educ:* Univ Calif, Berkeley, BA, 60; Iowa State Univ, MS, 61; Univ Utah, PhD(math), 66. *Prof Exp:* Asst prof, 66-71, assoc prof, 71-78, prof math, Univ Iowa, 78-80; PROF MATH, WESTERN NMEX UNIV, 80- *Mem:* Am Math Soc; Math Asn Am; Am Asn Univ Professors; Soc Indust & Appl Math. *Res:* Upper semi-continuous decompositions of topological spaces, 3-manifolds. *Mailing Add:* Dept of Math Western NMex Univ Silver City NM 88061

LAMBERT, JACK LEEPER, b Pittsburg, Kans, Mar 2, 18; m 43; c 4. ANALYTICAL CHEMISTRY, INORGANIC CHEMISTRY. *Educ:* Kans State Teachers Col, Pittsburg, BA & MS, 47; Okla State Univ, PhD(chem), 50. *Prof Exp:* Instr chem, Kans State Teachers Col, Pittsburg, 47-48; asst, Okla State Univ, 48-50; from instr to assoc prof, 50-65, PROF CHEM, KANS STATE UNIV, 65- *Concurrent Pos:* Assoc prog dir, NSF, Washington, DC, 65-66. *Mem:* Am Chem Soc; Sigma Xi. *Res:* Methods research in analytical chemistry; reagents for trace analysis in air, water and blood; insoluble, demand-type disinfectants for water. *Mailing Add:* Dept of Chem Kans State Univ Manhattan KS 66506

LAMBERT, JAMES LEBEAU, b Sanford, Fla, Feb 11, 34. ORGANIC CHEMISTRY, BIOCHEMISTRY. *Educ:* Spring Hill Col, BS, 59; Johns Hopkins Univ, PhD(chem), 63. *Prof Exp:* From asst prof to assoc prof, 68-79, PROF CHEM, SPRING HILL COL, 79- *Mem:* AAAS; Am Chem Soc. *Res:* Mechanisms of organic reactions; carbanions. *Mailing Add:* Dept of Chem Spring Hill Col Mobile AL 36608

LAMBERT, JAMES MORRISON, b Chicago, Ill, Feb 18, 28; m 53; c 3. NUCLEAR PHYSICS. *Educ:* Johns Hopkins Univ, BA, 55, PhD(physics), 61. *Prof Exp:* Instr physics, Johns Hopkins Univ, 60-61; asst prof, Univ Mich, 61-63; from asst prof to assoc prof, 64-74, PROF PHYSICS, GEORGETOWN UNIV, 74- *Concurrent Pos:* Res consult, Naval Res Lab, 66- *Mem:* Am Phys Soc; AAAS. *Res:* Experimental medium energy nuclear physics; nuclear reaction studies using particle accelerators; experimental surface physics. *Mailing Add:* Dept Physics Georgetown Univ Washington DC 20007

LAMBERT, JEAN WILLIAM, b Ewing, Nebr, June 10, 14; m 43; c 2. AGRONOMY. *Educ:* Univ Nebr, BS, 40; Ohio State Univ, MS, 42, PhD(agron), 45. *Prof Exp:* Instr agron, Ohio State Univ, 43-45; from asst prof to assoc prof agron & plant genetics, 46-59, PROF AGRON & PLANT GENETICS, UNIV MINN, ST PAUL, 59- *Concurrent Pos:* Consult, Am Soybean Asn, 63; Food & Agr Orgn, Hungary, 75; US Info Agency, Romania, 76; Agr Corp Am, USSR, 79 & Food & Agr Orgn, Poland, 80; res consult, Chilean Agr Prog, Rockefeller Found, 64; partic, vis scientist prog, Am Soc Agron; tech ed, Agron J, 71-73. *Mem:* Fel Am Soc Agron; Am Soybean Asn. *Res:* Bromegrass cultural research; varietal improvement in barley and soybeans; barley and soybean genetics. *Mailing Add:* Dept Agron & Plant Genetics Univ Minn 1509 Gortner Ave St Paul MN 55108

LAMBERT, JERRY ROY, b Benton, Ill, Sept 16, 36; m 55; c 3. AGRICULTURAL ENGINEERING. *Educ:* Univ Fla, BAgrE, 58, MS, 62; NC State Col, PhD(agr eng), 64. *Prof Exp:* Design eng trainee, Soil Conserv Serv, USDA, 58-60; from asst prof to assoc prof, 64-72, PROF AGR ENG, CLEMSON UNIV, 72- *Mem:* Am Soc Eng Educ; Am Soc Agr Engrs. *Res:* Hydrology; water relations of plants; evapotranspiration; water movement in soils; simulation of agricultural systems; microcomputer applications to agriculture. *Mailing Add:* Dept of Agr Eng Clemson Univ Clemson SC 29631

LAMBERT, JOHN B(OYD), b Billings, Mont, July 5, 29; m 53, 58; c 6. CHEMICAL ENGINEERING. *Educ:* Princeton Univ, BS, 51; Univ Wis, PhD(chem eng), 56. *Prof Exp:* Res engr, Indust & Biochem Dept, E I du Pont de Nemours & Co, 56-63, sr res engr, Pigments Dept, Del, 63-68; mkt mgr, Fansteel, Inc, 68-70, plant mgr, 70-71, tech mgr, 72-73, MGR MFG ENG, VR/WESSON, DIV FANSTEEL, INC, 73- *Mem:* Am Chem Soc; Am Inst Chem Engrs; Electrochem Soc. *Res:* Inorganic colloid chemistry, physical metallurgy, powder metallurgy, surface chemistry, drying, machining and metal cutting, ceramic cutting tools. *Mailing Add:* c/o VR/Wesson 800 Market St Waukegan IL 60085

LAMBERT, JOSEPH B, b Ft Sheridan, Ill, July 4, 40; m 67; c 3. ORGANIC CHEMISTRY. *Educ:* Yale Univ, BS, 62; Calif Inst Technol, PhD(nuclear magnetic resonance spectros), 65. *Prof Exp:* From asst prof to assoc prof, 65-74, PROF CHEM, NORTHWESTERN UNIV, 74- *Concurrent Pos:* Alfred P Sloan Found fel, 68-70; Guggenheim fel, 73; Japan Soc Prom Sci fel, 78; vis scholar, Polish Acad Sci, 81. *Honors & Awards:* Eastman Kodak Award, 65; Nat Fresenius Award, 76. *Mem:* Fel AAAS; Sigma Xi; Am Chem Soc; The Chem Soc; fel Brit Interplanetary Soc. *Res:* Nuclear magnetic resonance spectroscopy, conformational analysis, organic reaction mechanisms, applications of analytical chemistry to archaeology. *Mailing Add:* Dept of Chem Northwestern Univ Evanston IL 60201

LAMBERT, JOSEPH MICHAEL, b Philadelphia, Pa, Nov 19, 42; m 73; c 2. APPROXIMATION THEORY, NUMERICAL METHODS. *Educ:* Drexel Univ, BS, 65; Cornell Univ, MA, 67; Purdue Univ, PhD(math), 70. *Prof Exp:* from asst prof to assoc prof math, 70-81, asst dean, Col Sci, 79-82, actg head, 80-82, ASSOC PROF & DEPT HEAD COMPUT SCI, PA STATE UNIV, 82- *Concurrent Pos:* Vis assoc prof math, Univ Tenn, Knoxville, 77-78. *Mem:* Am Math Soc; Asn Comput Mach; Math Asn Am. *Res:* Functional analysis; approximation theory; numerical analysis. *Mailing Add:* Pa State Univ University Park PA 16802

LAMBERT, JOSEPH PARKER, b Bronte, Tex, Oct 6, 21; m 45; c 4. DENTISTRY. *Educ:* Baylor Univ, DDS, 52. *Prof Exp:* Instr, 52-56, PROF PROSTHETICS & CHMN DEPT, COL DENT, BAYLOR UNIV, 56- *Mem:* Am Dent Asn. *Mailing Add:* Dept of Prosthetics Baylor Univ Col of Dent Dallas TX 75246

LAMBERT, LLOYD MILTON, JR, b Olympia, Wash, May 10, 29; m 52; c 3. SOLID STATE PHYSICS. *Educ:* US Naval Acad, BS, 52; Univ Calif, MS, 58, MA, 63, PhD(physics), 64. *Prof Exp:* Res engr, Sperry Gyroscope Co, 57; assoc elec eng, Univ Calif, 58; res engr & mgr phys electronics dept, Aeronutronic Div, Ford Motor Co, 58-63; staff scientist, Aerospace Corp, 63-65; assoc prof elec eng, 65-71, prof 71-77, PROF & CHMN, PHYSICS DEPT, UNIV VT, 77- *Concurrent Pos:* Res fel, Norges Teknisk-Naturvitenskaplige Forskningsrad, 71-72, sr fel, 77-78; Nat Acad Sci exchange, Rumania, 77 & USSR, 77. *Mem:* Am Phys Soc. *Res:* Solid state devices; magnetic storage devices; semiconductors; low temperature research; thin film devices; optical properties of solids; transport properties of semiconductors. *Mailing Add:* Dept Physics Univ of Vt Burlington VT 05401

LAMBERT, MARY PULLIAM, b Birmingham, Ala, Apr 27, 44; m 67; c 3. BIOCHEMISTRY. *Educ:* Birmingham-Southern Col, BS, 66; Northwestern Univ, PhD(biochem), 71. *Prof Exp:* Instr biochem, 70-72, FEL REPRODUCTIVE BIOL, NORTHWESTERN UNIV, ILL, 81- *Mem:* Sigma Xi. *Res:* Control mechanisms; bacterial enzyme function; cell wall biosynthesis; enzyme kinetics. *Mailing Add:* Dept Neurobiol & Physiol Northwestern Univ Evanston IL 60201

LAMBERT, MAURICE C, b Roosevelt, Utah, Apr 14, 18; m 42; c 5. PHYSICAL CHEMISTRY. *Educ:* Brigham Young Univ, BS, 39, MA, 41. *Prof Exp:* Assoc chemist, Indust Lab, Mare Island Naval Shipyard, 41-46; chemist, Hanford Atomic Prod Oper, 48-64; sr chemist, Gen Elec Co, 64; sr res scientist, Battelle Northwest Labs, 65-70; sr res scientist, Westinghouse Hanford Co, 70-82; RETIRED. *Mem:* Am Chem Soc; Soc Appl Spectros. *Res:* X-ray spectrometry, absorptiometry and diffraction; atomic absorption and flame emission spectrometry; separations of trace elements; gas-solid reactions; properties of inorganic oxides; fused salt studies; surface analysis by electron spectroscopy; automation of analytical techniques. *Mailing Add:* 1617 Hains Ave Richland WA 99352

LAMBERT, MAURICE REED, b Fillmore, Utah, July 13, 20; m 50; c 5. ANIMAL NUTRITION. *Educ:* Utah State Univ, BS, 48, MS, 49; Iowa State Univ, PhD(animal nutrit), 53. *Prof Exp:* From instr to asst prof animal nutrit, Iowa State Univ, 52-57; mgr animal nutrit res, Western Condensing Co, 57-65, mgr animal nutrit res, Foremost-McKesson Inc, 65-71, mgr nutrit, 71-79, SR RES SCIENTIST-NUTRIT, FOREMOST MCKESSON CO, 79- *Res:* Fat and carbohydrate metabolism of the calf, pig and chicken; lipid deficiency of the calf; human nutrition. *Mailing Add:* Foremost McKesson Co Res & Develop Ctr PO Box 2277 Dublin CA 94566

LAMBERT, PAUL DUDLEY, public health administration, see previous edition

LAMBERT, PAUL WAYNE, b Ft Worth, Tex, Oct 27, 37; m 59; c 1. GEOMORPHOLOGY, QUATERNARY GEOLOGY. *Educ:* Tex Tech Col, BA, 59; Univ NMex, MS, 61, PhD(geol), 68. *Prof Exp:* Geologist, Texaco Inc, NMex, 61-62; asst prof geol, Cent Mo State Col, 65-68; assoc prof, WTex State Univ, 68-70; geologist, Dept Prehist, Nat Inst Anthrop & Hist, Mex, 72-73; geologist, US Geol Surv, 73-81; ASSOC PROF GEOL, WEST TEX STATE UNIV, 81- *Concurrent Pos:* Res grants, Geol Soc Am & Sigma Xi, 68-69 & NSF, 69-70. *Mem:* Geol Soc Am; Am Quaternary Asn; Soc Am Archaeol; Asn Am Geograpghers. *Res:* Photographic monitoring of geomorphic processes and vegetation change in arid regions in southwest USA and Mexico; photographic documentation of physical and cultural geographic features in remote areas of Mexico. *Mailing Add:* Dept Geosci West Tex State Univ Canyon TX 79016

LAMBERT, PETER FRANCIS, b New Haven, Conn, Sept 26, 39; m 63; c 1. ELECTRICAL ENGINEERING. *Educ:* Yale Univ, BE, 61, ME, 62, DE, 68. *Prof Exp:* Sr develop engr, Aerojet-Gen Corp, Calif, 63-64; MEM TECH STAFF, BELL LABS, 67- *Mem:* Inst Elec & Electronics Engrs. *Res:* Pattern recognition; artificial intelligence for automation of complex information/decision tasks. *Mailing Add:* Bell Labs Naperville Rd Naperville IL 60540

LAMBERT, REGINALD MAX, b Delta, Ohio, Feb 25, 26; m 52; c 3. BACTERIOLOGY, IMMUNOLOGY. *Educ:* Butler Univ, BA, 50; Univ Buffalo, MA, 52, PhD(bact, immunol), 55. *Prof Exp:* Asst bact & immunol, Sch Med, State Univ NY Buffalo, 51-55, instr, 55-57, assoc, 57-59, asst prof, 59-64; asst prof path, Col Med, Univ Fla, 64-67; assoc dir, Blood Group Res Unit, 55-64 & 67-76, ASSOC PROF MICROBIOL, SCH MED, STATE UNIV NY BUFFALO, 67- *Concurrent Pos:* Consult, E J Meyer Mem Hosp, Buffalo, 58, 60-63 & 67- & Buffalo Gen Hosp, 63-64; dir blood bank, Shands Teaching Hosp, Univ Fla, 64-67; dir, Buffalo Regional Red Cross Bldg Prog, 73- *Mem:* AAAS; Am Soc Microbiol; Int Soc Blood Transfusion; Int Soc Hemat. *Res:* Blood groups; immunohematology; transfusion genetics. *Mailing Add:* Dept of Microbiol Sch of Med State Univ of NY Buffalo NY 14214

LAMBERT, RICHARD BOWLES, JR, b Clinton, Mass, Apr 20, 39; m 64. PHYSICAL OCEANOGRAPHY. *Educ:* Lehigh Univ, AB, 61; Brown Univ, ScM, 64, PhD(physics), 66. *Prof Exp:* Fulbright fel, aerodyn, Munich Tech, 66-67; from asst prof to assoc prof oceanog, Univ RI, 67-75; prog dir phys oceanog, NSF, 75-77; RES OCEANOGR, SCI APPLICATIONS, INC, 77-, MGR, OCEAN PHYSICS DIV, 79-, ASST VPRES, 80- *Mem:* AAAS; Am Geophys Union. *Res:* Hydrodynamic stability; oceanic turbulence; diffusion energy transfer; air-sea interaction. *Mailing Add:* Ocean Sci Div Sci Appln Inc 8400 Westpark Dr McLean VA 22101

LAMBERT, RICHARD H(OLLAND), b Tyngsboro, Mass, May 20, 10; m 36, 69; c 2. METALLURGY, MATERIALS SCIENCE. *Educ:* US Naval Acad, BS, 32. *Prof Exp:* Officer in charge metall & testing br, Naval Gun Factory, US Navy, 44-46 & welding & metall br, Bur Ships, 46-51, shop supt, Philadelphia Naval Shipyard, 51-54, inspector naval mat, Mass, 54-56, asst dir field serv div, Off Naval Mat, 56-57, dir res & develop div, Bur Ships, 57; assoc prof metall & mat sci, asst head dept & assoc dir metals res lab, 57-78, EMER ASSOC PROF METALL & MAT SCI, CARNEGIE-MELLON UNIV, 78- *Honors & Awards:* A V deForest Award, Am Soc Nondestruct Testing, 61, Gold Medal, 66. *Mem:* Am Soc Metals; Am Soc Naval Engrs; Am Soc Nondestruct Testing; Am Inst Mining, Metall & Petrol Engrs; Am Soc Eng Educ. *Res:* Nondestructive testing techniques; research administration; welding metallurgy. *Mailing Add:* 598 Dorseyville Rd Pittsburgh PA 15238

LAMBERT, RICHARD ST JOHN, b Trowbridge, Eng, Nov 11, 28; m 52; c 6. PETROLOGY, GEOCHEMISTRY. *Educ:* Univ Cambridge, BA, 52, PhD(petrol), 55, MA, 56; Oxford Univ, MA, 56. *Prof Exp:* Asst lectr geol, Univ Leeds, 55-56; lectr, Oxford Univ, 56-70; PROF GEOL & CHMN DEPT, UNIV ALTA, 70- *Concurrent Pos:* Vis prof, Univ Alta, 63-64; fels, Iffley Col, Oxford Univ, 65-66 & Wolfson Col, 66-70. *Mem:* Geol Soc London; Geol Asn Can; Am Geophys Union; Geochem Soc; Mineral Soc Gt Brit & Ireland. *Res:* Mineralogy, petrology, geochemistry and isotope geology of medium to high grade metamorphic rocks; theory of metamorphic processes; thermal history of the earth; geological time-scale. *Mailing Add:* Dept of Geol Univ of Alta Edmonton AB T6G 2E3 Can

LAMBERT, ROBERT F, b Warroad, Minn, Mar 14, 24; m 51; c 3. ELECTRICAL ENGINEERING, ACOUSTICS. *Educ:* Univ Minn, BEE, 48, MS, 49, PhD, 53. *Prof Exp:* Asst elec eng, 48-49, from instr to assoc prof, 49-59, assoc dean, Inst Technol, 67-68, PROF ELEC ENG, UNIV MINN, MINNEAPOLIS, 59- *Concurrent Pos:* Vis asst prof, Mass Inst Technol, 53-55; vis scientist, III Phys Inst, Univ Goettingen, Ger, 64 & NASA Langley Res Ctr, Hampton, Va, 79; acoust consult. *Mem:* Am Soc Eng Educ; fel Acoust Soc Am; fel Inst Elec & Electronics Engrs. *Res:* Signal analysis including random processes and noise; acoustics including flow ducts, wave filters, porous materials, wave propagation, noise control; communication technology including ink jet printing, ultrasonic scanning, speech and electro-acoustics; random processes. *Mailing Add:* Dept Elec Eng Inst Technol Univ Minn Minneapolis MN 55455

LAMBERT, ROBERT HENRY, b Bayshore, NY, Nov 3, 30; div; c 2. ATOMIC PHYSICS. *Educ:* St Lawrence Univ, BS, 52; Harvard Univ, MS, 54, PhD(physics), 63. *Prof Exp:* Instr physics, Univ NH, 55-57; asst, Harvard Univ, 57-60; from asst prof to assoc prof, 61-68, PROF PHYSICS, UNIV NH, 68- *Concurrent Pos:* Cent Univ res grants, Univ NH, 62-63, 65-66; NSF grant, 65-67, 67-71. *Mem:* Am Phys Soc. *Res:* Measurement of hyperfine structure using optical pumping. *Mailing Add:* Dept of Physics De Meritt Hall Univ of NH Durham NH 03824

LAMBERT, ROBERT J, b Dubuque, Iowa, Dec 23, 21; m 42; c 2. MATHEMATICS. *Educ:* Drake Univ, BA, 43; Iowa State Univ, MS, 48, PhD(math), 51. *Prof Exp:* Instr math, Drake Univ, 43-44; instr, Iowa State Univ, 46-51; mathematician, Nat Security Agency, 51-53; from asst prof to assoc prof math, Univ, 53-64, sr mathematician, Ames Lab, 64-78, PROF MATH & COMPUT SCI, COMPUT CTR, IOWA STATE UNIV, 64-, ASSOC DIR, 78- *Concurrent Pos:* Consult, Nat Security Agency & Collins Radio Co. *Mem:* Am Math Soc; Math Asn Am; Soc Indust & Appl Math. *Res:* Matrix theory; finite fields; numerical analysis; partial differential equations; ordinary differential equations; development of numerical software packages for solving differential equations, linear systems and eigensystems. *Mailing Add:* 3301 Ross Rd Ames IA 50010

LAMBERT, ROBERT JOHN, b Faribault, Minn, Mar 14, 27. PLANT GENETICS. *Educ:* Univ Minn, BS, 52, MS, 58; Univ Ill, PhD(plant breeding, genetics), 63. *Prof Exp:* Res asst plant breeding & genetics, Univ Minn, 56-58; from res asst to res assoc, 58-64, from instr to assoc prof, 64-76, PROF PLANT BREEDING & GENETICS, UNIV ILL, URBANA, 76-

Concurrent Pos: Supvr world collection of maize mutants, Maize Genetics Coop. Mem: AAAS; Crop Sci Soc Am; Genetics Soc Am; Am Asn Cereal Chemists. Res: Investigations of plant geometry of maize and breeding in high yield environment; selection and development of modified protein maize strains. Mailing Add: S-118 Turner Hall Dept of Agron Univ of Ill Urbana IL 61822

LAMBERT, ROGER GAYLE, b Minneapolis, Minn, Jan 22, 30; m 56; c 3. PLANT PHYSIOLOGY. Educ: Univ Minn, BS, 53, MS, 57, PhD(plant physiol), 61. Prof Exp: Instr plant physiol, Univ Minn, 57-61; asst prof plant physiol & path, 61-64, from actg head to head dept biol, 63-66, assoc prof plant physiol, 64-68, PROF PLANT PHYSIOL, UNIV LOUISVILLE, 68- Concurrent Pos: Fel bot & plant path, Potato Virus Lab, Colo State Univ, 70-71. Mem: AAAS; Am Soc Plant Physiol; Am Asn Univ Profs; Sigma Xi. Res: Plant competition and trophic structure of ecosystems. Mailing Add: Dept of Biol Univ of Louisville Louisville KY 40208

LAMBERT, ROGERS FRANKLIN, b Kamas, Utah, July 12, 29; m 51; c 4. ORGANIC CHEMISTRY. Educ: Brigham Young Univ, BS, 53; Purdue Univ, PhD(org chem), 58. Prof Exp: Chemist, US Bur Mines, 53; res chemist, Ethyl Corp, 58-61; res supvr, Thiokol Chem Corp, 61-65; PROF CHEM, RADFORD COL, 65- Mem: Am Chem Soc. Res: Polymers; chemical reductions; transition metal carbonyls; reactions of heterocyclics. Mailing Add: Dept of Chem Radford Col Box 5795 Radford VA 24142

LAMBERT, RONALD, b Brooklyn, NY, Mar 16, 39. PHOTOGRAPHIC CHEMISTRY. Educ: Columbia Univ, BS, 62; Univ Ill, MS, 64, PhD(flavin analog), 67. Prof Exp: Asst org chem, Univ Ill, 62-67; scientist, 67-70, sr scientist, 70-76, RES ASSOC, POLAROID CORP, 76- Mem: Am Chem Soc. Mailing Add: Polaroid Corp Res Lab 1265 Main St Waltham MA 01778

LAMBERT, ROYCE LEONE, b Coatesville, Ind, Nov 3, 33; m 53; c 3. SOILS, AGRONOMY. Educ: Purdue Univ, Lafayette, BS, 64, MS, 66, PhD(soil physics), 70. Prof Exp: ASSOC PROF SOILS, CALIF POLYTECH STATE UNIV, SAN LUIS OBISPO, 69- Concurrent Pos: Soil conservationist, Nat Park Serv, 71. Mem: Am Soc Agron; Soil Sci Soc Am; Soil Conserv Soc Am. Res: Soil management. Mailing Add: Dept of Soil Sci Calif Polytech State Univ San Luis Obispo CA 94307

LAMBERT, SHELDON MARVIN, b Cleveland, Ohio, Sept 27, 30; m 53; c 3. PHYSICAL CHEMISTRY. Educ: Ohio State Univ, BSc, 53, PhD(chem), 57. Prof Exp: Fel chem, Ohio State Univ, 58; chemist, Shell Develop Co, 58-66, supvr phys & anal chem, 66-70, mgr info servs, Shell Chem Co, 70-71, mem staff chem econ, 71-74, mgr energy econ & forecasting, Shell Oil Co, 74-77, mgr energy planning & econ, 77-81; SR VPRES, CORP PLANNING, LTV CORP, 81- Concurrent Pos: Consult, Ore State Univ, 65-; adv bd, Energy Inst & Univ Tex, Austin, 81- Mem: Am Chem Soc. Res: Chemistry of complex ions in solution; polyphosphate solution equilibria; instrumental methods of analysis; liquid-liquid chromatography; correlations of biological activity and chemical structure; movement and sorption of chemicals in soil. Mailing Add: 1415 Castle Rock Rd Houston TX 77090

LAMBERT, VERNON L, b Dover, Ohio, Aug 22, 26; m 49; c 3. SOLID STATE PHYSICS, ELECTRICAL ENGINEERING. Educ: Univ Cincinnati, EE, 48, MS, 50, PhD(physics), 64. Prof Exp: Elec engr, Radio Corp Am, NJ, 50-52 & Farnsworth Corp, Ind, 52-56; staff engr, 56-60, SR STAFF ENGR, ELECTRONICS DIV, AVCO CORP, 64- Mem: Electrochem Soc; Nat Soc Prof Engrs; Am Phys Soc. Res: Semiconductors and semiconducting compounds; surface effects, treatment and diffusion; insulators; lattice effects; internal fields. Mailing Add: 7199 Juniperview Cincinnati OH 45243

LAMBERT, WALTER PAUL, b Glendale, WVa, Sept 25, 44; m 72. CIVIL ENGINEERING. Educ: Univ Cincinnati, BS, 67, MS, 69; Univ Tex, Austin, PhD(civil eng), 75. Prof Exp: Fel, Univ Tex, Austin, 72-75; res area mgr, Med Bioeng Res & Develop Lab, US Army, Ft Detrick, 75-77, environ eng staff officer, Hq, US Army Med Res & Develop Command, 77-81; MGR, RES & DEVELOP, ROY F WESTON, INC, 81- Concurrent Pos: Lectr, Hood Col, 79-81. Honors & Awards: Medal, Int Ozone Inst, 77. Mem: Am Water Works Asn; Water Pollution Control Fedn; Soc Am Military Engrs; Am Defense Preparedness Asn; Am Soc Testing & Mat. Res: Mathematical modeling of water resource systems; wastewater reuse; research management decision theory; human factors engineering; hazardous materials; decontamination of contaminated soils and sediments. Mailing Add: 346 Washington Ave Phoenixville PA 19460

LAMBERT, WILLIAM M, JR, b Wausau, Wis, Apr 6, 36. MATHEMATICS. Educ: Univ Wis, BA, 58; Univ Calif, Los Angeles, MA, 59, PhD(math), 65. Prof Exp: Teaching asst math, Univ Wis, 57-58; teaching asst, Univ Calif, Los Angeles, 59-60, res asst, 60-63; from asst prof to assoc prof, Loyola Univ, Calif, 63-69; assoc prof, Univ Detroit, 69-74; PROF, DEPT MATH, UNIV COSTA RICA, 74- Mem: Am Math Soc; Math Asn Am; Asn Symbolic Logic. Res: Effective processes of general algebraic structures; metamathematics of algebra. Mailing Add: Dept of Math Univ of Costa Rica San Jose Costa Rica

LAMBERTI, JOSEPH W, b Toronto, Ont, Dec 20, 29; m 55; c 6. PSYCHIATRY. Educ: Univ Ottawa, MD, 54; Royal Col Physicians & Surgeons Can, cert psychiat, 61. Prof Exp: Asst psychiatrist, Winnipeg Psychiat Inst, 60-61, sr psychiatrist, 61-63; asst prof, 63-69, ASSOC PROF PSYCHIAT, MED CTR, UNIV MO-COLUMBIA, 69- Concurrent Pos: Dir consult serv & lectr, Med Ctr, Univ Mo, 63-67; consult, Peace Corps, 64- & Univ Press, 65- Mem: Am Psychiat Asn; cor mem Can Psychiat Asn. Res: Treatment of common sexual disorders; study of antisocial behavior; study of affective disorders. Mailing Add: Dept of Psychiat Univ of Mo Med Ctr Columbia MO 65201

LAMBERTS, AUSTIN E, b East Saugatuck, Mich, Nov 30, 14; div; c 4. MARINE ZOOLOGY, NEUROSURGERY. Educ: Calvin Col, AB, 36; Univ Mich, Ann Arbor, MD, 41, MS, 50; Am Bd Neurosurg, dipl, 52; Univ Hawaii, PhD(marine zool), 73. Prof Exp: Resident & instr neurosurg, Univ Mich, 45-50; pvt pract neurosurg, St Mary's Hosp, Grand Rapids, 50-68; teaching asst marine zool, Univ Hawaii, 69-73; INDEPENDENT RES, REEF ECOL, 73- Concurrent Pos: Consult neurosurg, St Mary's Hosp, Grand Rapids, 50-76. Honors & Awards: Res grant, Nat Geog Soc, 74 & 78, Nat Sci Asn, 76. Mem: Paleont Res Inst; Am Asn Neurosurgeons; Cong Neurosurgeons; Am Med Asn. Res: Study of natural life cycles of reef corals and unexplained coral kills; coral growth using the dye alizarin; effects of pesticides on coral growth; collecting and identification of modern Pacific reef corals. Mailing Add: 1520 Leffingwell NE Grand Rapids MI 49505

LAMBERTS, BURTON LEE, b Fremont, Mich, Oct 24, 19; m 60; c 2. BIOCHEMISTRY. Educ: Calvin Col, BS, 49; Mich State Univ, PhD(chem), 58. Prof Exp: Chemist, Northern Regional Res Lab, Ill, 51-54; asst chem, Mich State Univ, 55-58, instr, 58-60; CHIEF BIOCHEMIST, DENT RES FACIL, NAVAL DENT RES INST, 60- Mem: Am Chem Soc; Int Asn Dent Res. Res: Dental caries; salivary gland secretions; products of oral microorganisms. Mailing Add: Biochem Div Naval Dent Res Inst USN Base Great Lakes IL 60088

LAMBERTS, ROBERT L, b Fremont, Mich, Sept 8, 26; m 51; c 6. PHOTOGRAPHIC OPTICS, PHYSICAL OPTICS. Educ: Calvin Col, AB, 49; Univ Mich, MS, 51; Univ Rochester, PhD(optics), 69. Prof Exp: Res assoc, 51-80, SR RES ASSOC, KODAK RES LABS, EASTMAN KODAK CO, 80- Mem: Fel Optical Soc Am; Soc Photog Sci & Eng; Soc Photographic Instrumentation Engrs. Res: Image structure of optical systems and photographic emulsions; physical optics. Mailing Add: Res Labs Eastman Kodak Co Rochester NY 14650

LAMBERTSEN, CHRISTIAN JAMES, b Westfield, NJ, May 15, 17; m 44; c 4. PHARMACOLOGY. Educ: Rutgers Univ, BS, 39; Univ Pa, MD, 43. Prof Exp: Intern, Hosp Univ Pa, 43; from instr to assoc prof, 46-53, PROF PHARMACOL, SCH MED, UNIV PA, 53-, PROF EXP THERAPEUT, 62-, PROF MED, UNIV HOSP, 78-, DIR INST ENVIRON MED, 70- Concurrent Pos: Markle scholar, 48-53; vis res assoc prof, Univ Col, London, 51-52; consult, US Army Chem Ctr, 55-59; consult & lectr, Off Surgeon Gen, US Navy, 57-60; consult neuropharmacol, Del State Hosp, 57-61; consult, Sci Adv Bd, US Air Force, 59-61. Mem adv panel med sci, Off Secy Defense; mem comt undersea warfare & comt naval med res, Nat Res Coun, 53- & panel underwater swimmers, 53-56; mem panel shipboard & submarine med, Off Secy Defense Res Develop Bd, 50-53; basic sci secy, Nat Bd Med Exam, 54-, mem pharmacol comt, 54-55; chmn man in space comt, Space Sci Bd, Nat Acad Sci, 60-62, consult, 62-; mem, US Oceanogr Adv Bd, 70-; mem comt undersea physiol & med, Nat Res Coun, 72- & comt hyperbaric oxygenation; chmn comt manned undersea activity, Off Secy Navy; assoc med, Univ Hosp, Univ Pa, 48-77. Honors & Awards: Meritorious Pub Serv Citation, US Navy, 70; Distinguished Pub Serv Medal, US Govt, 72. Mem: Fel Am Soc Clin Pharmacol & Therapeut; Am Physiol Soc (pres, 54-55); Am Soc Clin Invest; Am Soc Pharmacol & Exp Therapeut. Res: Respiratory physiology and pharmacology; aerospace and diving medicine; breathing apparatus for underwater swimmers. Mailing Add: Dept of Pharmacol Univ of Pa Philadelphia PA 19104

LAMBERTSON, WINGATE A(UGUSTUS), b Rich Square, NC, June 29, 20; m 46; c 3. CERAMICS. Educ: NC State Col, BS, 41; Rutgers Univ, MS, 48, PhD(ceramics), 49. Prof Exp: Engr, Mex Refractories Co, 45-46; res assoc, Metall Div, Argonne Nat Lab, 49-53; prof silicate technol, Inst Silicate Res, Univ Toledo, 53-55; from asst to mgr, Eng Res Br, Res & Develop Div, Carborundum Co, 55-60; mgr, Appl Res Br, 60-63; mgr, Mat Br, Spindletop Res, Inc, 63-64, mgr, Phys Sci Div, 64-66; exec dir, Ky Sci & Technol Comn, 66-69; pres, Solvex Corp, Louisville, 69-74; pres, Watersol Yarns, 74-76; PRES, INVENTIVE IDEAS, 76-; MGR QUAL CONTROL, CONFEDERATE PLASTICS, 81- Mem: Am Chem Soc; Am Ceramic Soc; Sigma Xi; Am Soc Metals. Res: High temperature ceramic materials; specialty thread; quality control. Mailing Add: 420 Chinoe Rd Lexington KY 40502

LAMBETH, DAVID N, b Carthage, Mo, Mar 18, 47; m 69; c 1. MAGNETISM. Educ: Univ Mo-Columbia, BS, 69; Mass Inst Technol, PhD(physics), 73. Prof Exp: SR RES PHYSICIST, EASTMAN KODAK CO, 73- Mem: Inst Elec & Electronic Engrs; Magnetics Soc. Res: Magnetism and magneto-optics of thin film materials. Mailing Add: Eastman Kodak Bldg 81 Kodak Park Rochester NY 14650

LAMBETH, DAVID ODUS, b Carthage, Mo, June 16, 41; m 62; c 2. BIOCHEMISTRY, ORGANIC CHEMISTRY. Educ: Univ Mo-Columbia, BSEd, 62; Purdue Univ, MS, 67; Univ Wis-Madison, PhD(biochem), 71. Prof Exp: Instr chem, Columbia Pub Schs, 62-67; NIH fel biochem, Univ Mich, 71-73; asst prof chem, Univ SFla, 73-77; asst prof, 77-79, ASSOC PROF BIOCHEM, SCH MED, UNIV NDAK, 79- Mem: Sigma Xi; Am Chem Soc; Am Soc Biol Chemists. Res: Chemistry and biochemistry of sulfides and thiols; enzymology; metabolism of iron in biological systems. Mailing Add: Dept of Biochem Univ of NDak Grand Forks ND 58201

LAMBETH, VICTOR NEAL, b Sarcoxie, Mo, July 5, 20; m 46; c 2. VEGETABLE CROPS, TOMATO BREEDING. Educ: Univ Mo, BS, 42, MA, 48, PhD(hort), 50. Prof Exp: Asst instr, 39-42, from asst prof to assoc prof, 50-59, PROF HORT, UNIV MO-COLUMBIA, 59- Concurrent Pos: NSF vis prof, Thialand, 81. Mem: AAAS; Am Soc Plant Physiol; fel Am Soc Hort Sci; Sigma Xi. Res: Soil fertility and plant nutrition; raw product quality; vegetable breeding; water relationships; post harvest physiology. Mailing Add: 1-40 New Agr Bldg Univ of Mo Columbia MO 65211

LAMBIE, MARGARET B MCCLEMENTS, computer science, power engineering, see previous edition

LAMBOOY, JOHN PETER, b Kalamazoo, Mich, Dec 6, 14; m 42; c 4. BIOCHEMISTRY. *Educ:* Kalamazoo Col, AB, 37, MS, 38; Univ Ill, MA, 39; Univ Rochester, PhD(physiol chem), 42. *Prof Exp:* From instr to assoc prof physiol, Univ Rochester, 46-63; prof chem pharmacol & sect head biochem pharmacol, Eppley Inst Cancer Res, Col Med, Univ Nebr, 63-68, prof biochem, 64-69; assoc dean grad sch, Baltimore Campuses, 69-71, prof biol chem, Sch Med, 69-74, dean grad studies & res, 71-74, PROF BIOCHEM & CHMN DEPT, SCH DENT, UNIV MD, BALTIMORE, 74- *Mem:* Fel AAAS; Am Chem Soc; Am Soc Biol Chem; Am Physiol Soc; Soc Exp Biol & Med. *Res:* Synthesis and biological acitivity of vitamin analogs, amino acid analogs, anesthetics, sympathomimetic amines, bacteriostatic agents, carcinolytic agents and carcinogenic agents. *Mailing Add:* Dept of Biochem Univ of Md Sch of Dent Baltimore MD 21201

LAMBORG, MARVIN, b Philadelphia, Pa, Aug 13, 27; m 56; c 1. BIOCHEMISTRY. *Educ:* Univ Rochester, BS, 51; Johns Hopkins Univ, PhD(biol), 58. *Prof Exp:* Jr instr biol, McCoy Col, Johns Hopkins Univ, 55-56; res fel biochem, Mass Gen Hosp, 58-65; investr, 65-69, chief cell specialization br, 69-72, MGR ENHANCEMENT PLANT PRODUCTIVITY MISSION, C F KETTERING RES LAB 72-; ADJ FAC, ANTIOCH COL,72- *Concurrent Pos:* Res fel,Harvard Univ,60-65; consult, Am Cancer Soc, 62-65 & UN Develop Prog, 81- *Mem:* Am Chem Soc; Am Soc Biol Chemists; AAAS; Am Soc Cell Biologists. *Res:* Cell biology of nitrogen fixation in legumes and microorganisms. *Mailing Add:* C F Kettering Res Labs Yellow Springs OH 45387

LAMBORN, BJORN N A, b Stockholm, Sweden, Apr 2, 37. PLASMA PHYSICS. *Educ:* Univ Calif, Berkeley, AB, 58, MA, 60; Univ Fla, PhD(physics, math), 62. *Prof Exp:* Instr physics, Univ Miami, 63; res physicist, Inst Plasmaphysik, GmbH, Munich, Ger, 63-65; from asst prof to assoc prof physics, 65-75, chmn dept, 70-73, PROF PHYSICS, FLA ATLANTIC UNIV, 75-, CHMN DEPT, 79- *Mem:* Am Phys Soc. *Res:* Theoretical plasma physics; wave interaction in relativistic plasmas; nonadiabatic particle motion; diffusion; nonlinear wave coupling. *Mailing Add:* Dept of Physics Fla Atlantic Univ Boca Raton FL 33431

LAMBORN, CALVIN RAY, b Laketown, Utah, Dec 28, 33; m 62; c 5. PLANT VIROLOGY, PLANT BREEDING. *Educ:* Univ Utah, BS, 62; Utah State Univ, MS, 64, PhD(plant virol), 69. *Prof Exp:* Res asst plant virol, Utah State Univ, 62-68; asst res dir pea & bean res lab, 68-73, DIR RES, PEA & BEAN RES LAB, GALLATIN VALLEY SEED CO, 73- *Mem:* Am Phytopath Soc. *Res:* Biological assay of tobacco mosaic virus; breeding pea and bean varieties and research related to the seed industry. *Mailing Add:* Gallatin Valley Seed Co PO Box 167 Twin Falls ID 83301

LAMBRECHT, RICHARD MERLE, b Salem, Ore, Apr 8, 43; m 64; c 3. PHYSICAL CHEMISTRY, NUCLEAR MEDICINE. *Educ:* Ore State Univ, BS, 65; Univ Nebr, PhD(phys chem), 69. *Prof Exp:* Res assoc chem, 69-70, assoc, 70-74, CHEMIST, BROOKHAVEN NAT LAB, 74- *Concurrent Pos:* Consult, Capintec, Inc, 75-; ed, J Radioanalytical Chem, 78- *Mem:* Soc Nuclear Med; Europ Soc Nuclear Med; Am Chem Soc. *Res:* Radiopharmaceutical chemistry and nuclear medicine with emphasis on accelerator production and use of short-lived radionuclides; positron emission tomography; exotic atoms; chemical effects of nuclear transformation. *Mailing Add:* Dept of Chem Brookhaven Nat Lab Upton NY 11973

LAMBREMONT, EDWARD NELSON, b New Orleans, La, July 29, 28; m 81; c 4. ENTOMOLOGY, NUCLEAR SCIENCE. *Educ:* Tulane Univ, BS, 49, MS, 51; Ohio State Univ, PhD(entom), 58. *Prof Exp:* Asst zool, Tulane Univ, 48-51; asst entom, Ohio State Univ, 54-56; entomologist, Insect Physiol, Entom Res Div, Agr Res Serv, USDA, La, 58-66; assoc prof nuclear sci, 66-74, PROF NUCLEAR SCI & DIR NUCLEAR SCI CTR, LA STATE UNIV, BATON ROUGE, 74- *Concurrent Pos:* Vis scientist, Oak Ridge Assoc Univs, Med & Health Sci Div, 77-; consult nuclear sci & technol, pub info & radiation safety. *Mem:* AAAS; Entom Soc Am; Am Oil Chem Soc; Sigma Xi. *Res:* Physiology and biochemistry of insects, especially lipid metabolism, synthesis and utilization of fatty acids and other lipids; radiotracer and nuclear science methodology as applied to biological problems; insect radiation biology and physiology of tumorous tissues. *Mailing Add:* Nuclear Sci Ctr La State Univ Baton Rouge LA 70803

LAMBROPOULOS, HECTOR DEMETRIOS, b Athens, Greece, July 8, 42; nat US; m 69; c 1. PHYSICAL CHEMISTRY, CHEMICAL ENGINEERING. *Educ:* Nat Tech Univ, Athens, dipl(chem eng), 65; Brown Univ, PhD(chem), 78. *Prof Exp:* Field engr tech sales, Mobil Oil, Greece, 69-72; proj engr thin film technol microelectronics, Datel Systs Inc, 76-79; proj mgr develop thin film magnetic devices, Digital Equip Corp, Maynard, Mass, 79-81; STAFF ENGR DEVELOP THIN FILM MAT & PROCESSES, IBM CORP, 82- *Mem:* Am Phys Soc; Tech Chamber Greece; Am Vacuum Soc. *Res:* Molecular beams; electron beams; surface ionization; thin metallic films. *Mailing Add:* IBM Corp E09-015 5600 Cottle Rd San Jose CA 95193

LAMBROPOULOS, PETER POULOS, b Tripolis, Greece, Oct 5, 35; US citizen. THEORETICAL PHYSICS. *Educ:* Athens Tech Univ, dipl, 58; Univ Mich, MSE, 62, MS, 63, PhD(nuclear sci), 65. *Prof Exp:* Engr, Orgn Telecommun, Greece, 59-60; sr physicist, Bendix Res Lab, Mich, 65-67; asst physicist, Argonne Nat Lab, Ill, 67-72; vis fel, Joint Inst Lab Astrophys, 72-73; from asst to assoc prof, Tex A&M Univ, 73-75; assoc prof, 75-80, PROF PHYSICS, UNIV SOUTHERN CALIF, 80-, CO-CHMN DEPT, 81- *Mem:* AAAS; Am Phys Soc; Fedn Am Scientists. *Res:* Atomic physics; interaction of radiation with matter; quantum optics; strong electromagnetic fields. *Mailing Add:* Dept of Physics Univ of Southern Calif Los Angeles CA 90007

LAMBSON, ROGER O, b Provo, Utah, Feb 5, 39; m 59; c 3. ANATOMY. *Educ:* Univ Mont, BA, 61; Tulane Univ, PhD(anat), 65. *Prof Exp:* From instr to assoc prof, 65-80, assoc dean student affairs & dir admis, 71-75, assoc dean acad affairs, 75-76, PROF ANAT, COL MED, UNIV KY, 80-, ASSOC DEAN BASIC SCI, 76- *Mem:* AAAS; Electron Micros Soc Am; Soc Study Reproduction; Am Asn Anatomists. *Res:* Electron microscopic visualization of placental transport; ultrastructure of lung. *Mailing Add:* Dept of Anat Univ of Ky Col of Med Lexington KY 40506

LAMBUTH, ALAN LETCHER, b Seattle, Wash, Jan 5, 23; m 44; c 4. ADHESIVE TECHNOLOGY, WOOD UTILIZATION. *Educ:* Univ Wash, BS, 47. *Prof Exp:* Res chemist, Western Div, Monsanto Co, 47-57, res group leader, Plastics Div, 58-68; asst mgr mfg tech serv, 69-70, mgr prod develop, 71-76, mgr res & develop, 77-81, MGR PROD & PROCESS DEVELOP, TIMBER & WOOD PROD DIV, BOISE CASCADE CORP, 82- *Mem:* Forest Prod Res Soc; Am Chem Soc; Am Inst Timber Construct; Am Soc Testing & Mat; Int Union Forestry Res Orgn. *Res:* Adhesive technology and innovation; wood resource utilization; wood product development; chemical utilization of biomass. *Mailing Add:* 7240 Cascade Dr Boise ID 83704

LAMDEN, MERTON PHILIP, b Boston, Mass, Sept 7, 19; m 42; c 2. BIOCHEMISTRY. *Educ:* Univ Mass, BS, 41; Mass Inst Technol, PhD(food technol), 47. *Prof Exp:* Asst, Mass Inst Technol, 41-42, mem res staff, Food Technol Labs, 43-44; from asst prof to assoc prof, 47-72, PROF BIOCHEM, COL MED, UNIV VT, 72- *Concurrent Pos:* Commonwealth Fund fel & NSF-Orgn Europ Econ Coop sr vis fel, Univ Col, Univ London, 61-62; vis res biochem, Dept Food Sci & Technol, Univ Calif, Davis, 75. *Mem:* AAAS; Am Chem Soc; Am Inst Nutrit; Brit Biochem Soc. *Res:* Vitamin content and retention in foods; nutritional status of humans; biochemical studies on ascorbic and oxalic acids; role of ascorbic acid in metabolism. *Mailing Add:* Dept of Biochem Univ of Vt Col of Med Burlington VT 05401

LAMDIN, EZRA, b Cleveland, Ohio, Nov 25, 23; m; c 3. MEDICINE, PHYSIOLOGY. *Educ:* Harvard Univ, AB, 47, MD, 51; Am Bd Internal Med, dipl, 58. *Prof Exp:* Intern med, Harvard Med Serv, Boston City Hosp, 51-52, asst resident, 52-53; USPHS fel, Sch Med, Yale Univ, 53-55; asst, Sch Med, Boston Univ, 55-56, instr, 56-58; clin instr, Sch Med, Tufts Univ, 58-60; res fel biochem, Brandeis Univ, 61-62; asst prof med & physiol, Col Med, Univ Cincinnati, 62-67; assoc prof med, Sch Med, Univ Pittsburgh, 67-69; asst med dir, Am Heart Asn, 69-73, dir div sci affairs, 73-75; asst med dir, 75-77, ASSOC MED DIR, AYERST LABS, 77- *Concurrent Pos:* Teaching fel med, Harvard Med Sch, 52-53; resident, Vet Admin Hosp, Boston, 55-56, staff physician, 56-60, clin investr, 58-60; clin & res fel med, Mass Gen Hosp, Boston, 58-59; res collabr, Med Res Dept, Brookhaven Nat Lab, 63-69; chief med serv, Vet Admin Hosp, Pittsburgh, 67-69; adj assoc prof physiol, Mt Sinai Sch Med, 69- *Mem:* AAAS; Am Fedn Clin Res; Am Soc Cell Biol; Am Heart Asn; Am Soc Clin Pharmacol & Therapeut. *Res:* Renal physiology and disease; biochemical aspects of membrane phenomena and active transport; intermediary metabolism; diabetes and obesity; mechanism of hormone action; clinical pharmacology. *Mailing Add:* Ayerst Labs 685 Third Ave New York NY 10017

LAME, EDWIN LEVER, b Evanston, Ill, Feb 23, 04; m 40; c 2. RADIOLOGY. *Educ:* Mass Inst Technol, BS, 26; Univ Pa, MD, 33; Am Bd Internal Med, dipl, 45; Am Bd Radiol, dipl, 45. *Prof Exp:* Asst med, Sch Med, Univ Pa, 36-42, asst radiol, 42-47; dir radiol, Presby Hosp, 47-66; chief radiol, Vet Admin Hosp, Coatesville, 66-77; RETIRED. *Concurrent Pos:* Fel internal med & chest dis, physician & asst to dir, Dept Res Respiratory Dis, Germantown Hosp, 36-42; asst physician, Pa Hosp, 37-43; asst pediatrist & chief chest clin, Children's Hosp, 38-45; fel radiol, Hosp Univ Pa, 42-45; chief radiol, Jeanes Hosp, 45-48, consult, 48-60; assoc prof clin radiol, Sch Med & asst prof radiol, Grad Sch Med, Univ Pa, 57-66. *Mem:* Radiol Soc NAm; Am Roentgen Ray Soc; AMA; fel Am Col Physicians; fel Am Col Radiol. *Res:* Pulmonary radiologic interpretation; pelvic and vertebral osteomyelitis arising from the urinary tract; cholecystitis; clinical and radiologic criteria; gastrointestinal barium; protection and dose reduction in diagnostic radiology; radiologic signs of preclinical heart failure. *Mailing Add:* 29 W Sunset Ave Philadelphia PA 19118

LAMEIRO, GERARD FRANCIS, b Paterson, NJ, Oct 3, 49. ENERGY SIMULATIONS, ENERGY POLICY FORMULATION. *Educ:* Colo State Univ, BS, 71, MS, 73, PhD(mech eng), 77. *Prof Exp:* NSF fel solar energy, Solar Energy Appln Lab, Colo Energy Res Inst fel, Colo State Univ, 74-76 & 77, sr scientist, 77-78; ASST PROF MGT SCI & INFO SYSTS, COLO STATE UNIV, 78- *Concurrent Pos:* Instr solar energy, Univ Colo, 76-78; consult, Solar Energy Res Inst, 78. *Mem:* Asn Energy Engrs (pres-elect, 79, pres, 80); Asn Comput Mach. *Res:* Computer science techniques applied to the solution of real world problems; solar energy, especially space heating active and passive; national energy policy work; simulation models. *Mailing Add:* Dept of Mgt Sci & Info Systs Colo State Univ Ft Collins CO 80523

LAMENSDORF, DAVID, b NY, Nov 22, 37. ELECTRICAL ENGINEERING. *Educ:* Cornell Univ, BEE, 60; Harvard Univ, SM, 61, PhD(appl physics), 67. *Prof Exp:* MEM TECH STAFF, SPERRY RES CTR, 67- *Concurrent Pos:* Res assoc, Univ Col London, 72-73. *Mem:* AAAS; sr mem Inst Elec & Electronics Engrs; Sigma Xi. *Res:* Electromagnetic theory; transient analysis of antennas; microwave antennas, networks and electronics. *Mailing Add:* Sperry Corp Res Ctr 100 N Rd Sudbury MA 01776

LAMEY, STEVEN CHARLES, b Lock Haven, Pa, Mar 5, 44; m 70. ANALYTICAL CHEMISTRY, ORGANIC CHEMISTRY. *Educ:* Lock Haven State Col, BA, 68; WVa Univ, MS, 73, PhD(anal chem), 75. *Prof Exp:* Res chemist organic synthesis, Am Aniline Corp, 68-70; RES CHEMIST ENERGY RES, MORGANTOWN ENERGY TECHNOL CTR, 75- *Mem:* Am Chem Soc; AAAS; Coblentz Soc; Sigma Xi. *Res:* Characterization of coal tars; organic composition of shale; instrument development for coal characterization; alkali corrosion; characterization of coal combustion products. *Mailing Add:* Morgantown Energy Technol Ctr Collins Ferry Rd Morgantown WV 26505

LAMIE, EDWARD LOUIS, b Kingsley, Mich, Aug 27, 41; m 60; c 3. COMPUTER SCIENCE. *Educ:* San Diego State Univ, AB, 69; Univ Southern Calif, MS, 71; Mich State Univ, PhD(comput sci), 74. *Prof Exp:* Mem tech staff, Rockwell Int, 69-71; assoc prof, 71-80, PROF COMPUT SCI & CHMN DEPT, CENT MICH UNIV, 80- *Mem:* Asn Comput Mach. *Res:* Database systems; discrete simulation; artificial intelligence. *Mailing Add:* Dept of Comput Sci Cent Mich Univ Mt Pleasant MI 48859

LAMM, AUGUST UNO, b Goteborg, Sweden, May 22, 04; US citizen. TRANSDUCTOR. *Educ:* Royal Inst Technol, Sweden, MA, 27, PhD(elec eng), 43. *Hon Degrees:* Dr, Danish Inst Technol, 65. *Prof Exp:* Mgr, Rectifier Dept, ASEA AB, 29-39, head, Static Convertor & High Voltage Switchgear Dept & Labs, 39-55, head, Nuclear Dept, 55-59, dir electrotech design & res & develop, 59-61, consult to pres, 61-69; RETIRED. *Concurrent Pos:* Mem bd dirs, Atomic Energy Co, Sweden, 56-59. *Honors & Awards:* Gold Medal, Swed Royal Acad Eng Sci, 39; Lamme Medal, Inst Elec & Electronics Engrs, 65; Howard N Potts Award, Franklin Inst, Philadelphia, 81. *Mem:* Nat Acad Eng; Royal Soc Sci; Royal Acad Sci Sweden; Royal Acad Eng Sci; fel Inst Elec & Electronics Engrs. *Res:* Invented and led development of mercury arc valves and basic systems engineering for high voltage direct current transmission; developed theory for and led development of transductor (magnetic amplifier). *Mailing Add:* 365 Mosely Rd Hillsborough CA 94010

LAMM, FOSTER PHILIP, b Whittier, Calif, April 18, 50; m 77; c 2. POLYMER CHEMISTRY. *Educ:* Univ Calif, San Diego, BA, 72; Wesleyan Univ, PhD(chem), 79. *Prof Exp:* RES SCIENTIST, UNITED TECHNOLOGIES RES CTR, 79- *Mem:* Am Chem Soc; Soc Mfg Engrs. *Res:* Chemistry and processing of high performance adhesives; new materials and processing techniques for electrical insulating; organic materials failure analysis. *Mailing Add:* United Technologies Res Ctr MS22 East Hartford CT 06108

LAMM, MICHAEL EMANUEL, b Brooklyn, NY, May 19, 34; m 61; c 2. IMMUNOLOGY, PATHOLOGY. *Educ:* Univ Rochester, MD, 59; Western Reserve Univ, MS, 62; Am Bd Path, dipl, 65. *Prof Exp:* From intern to resident path, Univ Hosps, Cleveland, Ohio, 59-62; res assoc chem, NIH, 62-64; from asst prof to assoc prof path, Sch Med, NY Univ, 64-73, prof, 73-81; PROF & CHMN PATH, CASE WESTERN RESERVE UNIV, 81- *Mem:* NY Acad Sci; Am Soc Biol Chemists; Soc Exp Biol & Med; Am Asn Immunol; Am Asn Pathologists. *Res:* Mucosal immunity; immuno pathology. *Mailing Add:* Inst Path Case Western Reserve Univ Cleveland OH 44106

LAMM, WARREN DENNIS, b West Reading, Pa, Jan 27, 47; m 71; c 1. BEEF CATTLE MANAGEMENT. *Educ:* Delaware Valley Col Sci & Agr, BS, 69; Iowa State Univ, MS, 72; Univ Nebr, PhD(ruminant nutrit), 76. *Prof Exp:* Exten agt, Exten Serv, Colo State Univ, 72-73; asst prof beef cattle nutrit & eval, Va Polytech Inst & State Univ, 76-81; EXTEN BEEF SPECIALIST, DEPT ANIMAL SCI, COLO STATE UNIV, 81- *Mem:* Am Soc Animal Sci; Am Forage & Grassland Coun; Coun Agr Sci & Technol. *Res:* Beef nutrition and management; energetic efficiency; protein utilization; use of underutilized feedstuffs and animal waste refeeding. *Mailing Add:* Dept Animal Sci Rm 108A Colo State Univ Ft Collins CO 80523

LAMOLA, ANGELO ANTHONY, b Newark, NJ, Aug 12, 40; m 63; c 2. PHOTOBIOLOGY, PHOTOCHEMISTRY. *Educ:* Mass Inst Technol, BS, 61; Calif Inst Technol, PhD(chem), 65. *Prof Exp:* Asst prof chem, Univ Notre Dame, 64-66; mem res staff, 66-80, HEAD, MOLECULAR BIOPHYS RES DEPT, BELL LABS, 80- *Concurrent Pos:* Mem photobiol comt, Nat Res Coun-Nat Acad Sci; ed, Molecular Photochem; adj prof, Dept Dermat, Columbia Col Physicians & Surgeons, 75-; mem study sect biophys & biophys chem, NIH, 78- *Honors & Awards:* Baekeland Award, Am Chem Soc, 77; Welch Found lectr, 78; Snider Found lectr, Univ Toronto, 81. *Mem:* AAAS; Am Chem Soc; Am Soc Photobiol (pres, 76-77); Biophys Soc. *Res:* Molecular photobiology; molecular biophysics; medical applications of fluorescence. *Mailing Add:* Bell Labs Murray Hill NJ 07974

LAMON, EDDIE WILLIAM, b Yuba City, Calif, Aug 30, 39; c 2. CANCER, IMMUNOLOGY. *Educ:* Univ NAla, BS, 61; Med Col Ala, MD, 69; Karolinska Inst, Sweden, DSc, 74. *Prof Exp:* Asst biologist, Southern Res Inst, 64-65; from intern surg to resident gen surg, Univ Ala Sch Med, 69-71; from asst prof to assoc prof, 74-79, PROF SURG & MICROBIOL, UNIV ALA, BIRMINGHAM, 79- *Concurrent Pos:* Guest investr, Karolinska Inst, Sweden, 71-74; mem, Comt Cancer Immunodiagnosis, Nat Cancer Inst, Div Cancer Biol & Diag, 76-77; Nat Cancer Inst res career develop award, 75. *Mem:* Am Asn Univ Professors; Am Asn Immunologists; AAAS; Sigma Xi; NY Acad Sci. *Res:* Studies of the immune response to virus induced tumors with emphasis on the interactions of antibodies and lymphocytes in tumor cell destruction. *Mailing Add:* Dept of Surg Univ Sta Univ of Ala Birmingham AL 35294

LAMONDE, ANDRE M, b St Lambert, Que, Oct 5, 36; m 66. PHARMACY. *Educ:* Univ Montreal, BPharm, 61; Purdue Univ, MSc, 63, PhD(indust pharm), 65. *Prof Exp:* Asst prof pharm, Univ Montreal, 65-68; regulatory affairs coordr, Med Div, 68-70, qual control mgr, 70-72, QUAL CONTROL DIR, SYNTEX LTD, 72- *Res:* Basic pharmaceutics and pharmaceutical analysis. *Mailing Add:* 151 Anselme Lavigne Blvd Roxboro PQ H9A 1P4 Can

LAMONDS, H(AROLD) A(UGUSTUS), b Greensboro, NC, Aug 22, 24; m 45; c 2. NUCLEAR ENGINEERING, ENGINEERING PHYSICS. *Educ:* NC State Univ, BS, 53, MS, 54, PhD(eng physics), 58. *Prof Exp:* Reactor instrumentation supvr, NC State Univ, 52-57, reactor proj dir, 57-60, coordr nuclear eng, 60-61, head, Dept Nuclear Eng, 61-63; head reactor subsysts, Integration Dept, Aerojet Gen Corp, 63-64; head spec projs group, EG&G Inc, 64-69, sr sci exec, 69-70, chief scientist, Santa Barbara Div, 70-74; gen mgr, Orion Sci Corp, 74-76; prin scientist, IRT Corp, 76-77; MGR NV PROGS, ENERGY MEASUREMENTS GROUP, EG&G INC, 77- *Concurrent Pos:* Consult, Atomic Energy Comn/Nat Res Coun, 56- & Nat Res Coun-Nat Acad Sci; mem adv comt, Radiation Physics Div, Nat Bur Standards, 59-65; mem prog steering comt, Nuclear Eng & Sci Cong, 59. *Mem:* Am Nuclear Soc; Inst Elec & Electronics Engrs. *Res:* Nuclear and engineering physics. *Mailing Add:* EG&G Inc 130 Robin Hill Rd Goleta CA 93017

LAMONT, GARY BYRON, b St Paul, Minn, Feb 14, 39; m 66; c 3. CONTROL ENGINEERING, COMPUTER SCIENCE. *Educ:* Univ Minn, BPhysics, 61, MSEE, 67, PhD(control sci), 70. *Prof Exp:* Develop engr, Honeywell Inc, 61-65, systs analyst, 65-67; from asst prof to assoc prof, 70-80, PROF ELEC ENG, AIR FORCE INST TECHNOL, 80- *Mem:* Inst Elec & Electronics Engrs; Am Soc Eng Educ; Asn Comput Mach. *Res:* Control estimation theory; applications of small computers; computer structures; data base systems; operating systems. *Mailing Add:* Dept of Elec Eng Wright-Patterson AFB Dayton OH 45433

LAMONT, JOHN THOMAS, b Lockport, NY, Oct 2, 38; m 64; c 3. MEDICINE, GASTROENTEROLOGY. *Educ:* Canisius Col, BS, 60; Univ Rochester, MD, 65. *Prof Exp:* Fel, Mass Gen Hosp, 71-73; instr, Harvard Med Sch, 73-75, asst prof med, 75-80; ASSOC PROF, SCH MED & CHIEF GASTROENTEROL, UNIV HOSP, BOSTON UNIV, 80- *Concurrent Pos:* Consult gastroenterologist, Peter Bent Brigham Hosp, Boston Hosp Women & W Roxbury Vet Admin Hosp, 75-80 & Univ & Boston City Hosp, 80-; NIH career investr award, 75; res grants, Am Cancer Soc & Nat Found for Ileitis Colitis, 77-78. *Mem:* Am Soc Clin Res; Am Gastroenterol Soc; Am Soc Study Liver Dis. *Res:* Structure and function of colonic glycoproteins; biochemistry of intestinal tract in health and disease; colon cancer; gallstones, ulcer. *Mailing Add:* Div of Gastroenterol Univ Hosp Boston MA 02118

LAMONT, JOHN W(ILLIAM), b Cape Girardeau, Mo, Mar 7, 42; m 68. ELECTRICAL ENGINEERING, COMPUTER SCIENCE. *Educ:* Univ Mo-Rolla, BSEE, 64; Univ Mo-Columbia, MSEE, 66, PhD, 70. *Prof Exp:* Instr elec eng, Univ Mo-Columbia, 66-70; asst prof, Univ Southern Calif, 70-73; asst prof, dept elec eng, Univ Tex, Austin, 73-77; PROJ MGR, ELEC POWER RES INST, 77- *Mem:* Nat Soc Prof Engrs; Inst Elec & Electronics Engrs. *Res:* Application of computers to power systems. *Mailing Add:* Elec Power Res Inst PO Box 10412 Palo Alto CA 78712

LAMONT, PATRICK JOHN COLL, b Dublin, Ireland, Aug 29, 36. ALGEBRA, NUMBER THEORY. *Educ:* Glasgow Univ, BSc, 58, PhD(math), 62. *Prof Exp:* Asst lectr math, Royal Col Sci & Technol, Scotland, 61-62; Dept Sci & Indust Res traveling fel, State Univ Utrecht & Univs Gottingen & Munich, 62-64; lectr pure math, Univ Birmingham, 64-70; assoc prof math, St Mary's Col, Ind, 70-74; chmn, Deep Springs Col, California, 74-76; asst prof math, Monmouth Col, Ill, 76-79; ASST PROF QUANT INFO SCI, WESTERN ILL UNIV, 79- *Concurrent Pos:* Asst prof, Univ Notre Dame, 66-68. *Mem:* Am Math Soc; London Math Soc. *Res:* Arithmetic theory of nonassociative algebras and computing. *Mailing Add:* Quant Info Dept Western Ill Univ Macomb IL 61455

LAMOREAUX, PHILIP ELMER, b Chardon, Ohio, May 12, 20; m 43; c 3. GEOLOGY, HYDROLOGY. *Educ:* Denison Univ, BA, 43, DSc; Univ Ala, MA, 49. *Prof Exp:* Jr geologist, US Geol Surv, 43-45, asst geologist, 45-47, dist geologist, 47-48, div hydrologist, 58-59, chief groundwater br, 59-61; state geologist & oil & gas supvr, Geol Surv Ala, 61-77; PROF GEOL, UNIV ALA, TUSCALOOSA, 66- *Concurrent Pos:* Lectr, Univ Ala, Tuscaloosa, 48-59, assoc prof, 61-66; consult, Egypt, 53, 59, 61, 63-64, 65, Thailand, 54, 61, Philippines, 61, Surinam, 63, Mauritania, Africa, Senegal & Colombia, 64; pres, P E LaMoreaux & Assocs, Consult Geologists, 77- *Mem:* Int Union Geod & Geophys; Geol Soc Am; Soc Econ Geol; Am Asn Petrol Geologists; Am Inst Mining, Metall & Petrol Eng. *Res:* Groundwater geology; fluoride in groundwater; stratigraphy of Gulf Coastal Plain; hydrogeology of Karst areas. *Mailing Add:* PO Box 2310 Tuscaloosa AL 35403

LA MORI, PHILLIP NOEL, b Anaheim, Calif, Dec 9, 33; c 2. GEOPHYSICS. *Educ:* Univ Calif, Los Angeles, BS, 56, MA, 62; Northwestern Univ, PhD(mat sci), 67. *Prof Exp:* Res asst geol, Univ Calif, Los Angeles, 56-60; res chemist, Gen Chem Res Lab, Allied Chem Corp, 60-62; high pressure scientist, Northwestern Univ, 62-67; sr geophysicist, Battelle Mem Inst, 67-75; proj mgr geothermal energy, Elec Power Res Inst, 75-78; MGR, GEOTHERMAL RES, OCCIDENTAL RES CORP, 78- *Mem:* AAAS; Am Geophys Union; Geothermal Resources Coun (vpres, 75-78, secy-treas, 78). *Res:* Solid earth geophysics; equation of state of geologic materials; effect of pressure and temperature on materials; high pressure calibration standards; geothermal energy, program planning and project management in research and development of utilization of geothermal energy; resource assessment. *Mailing Add:* Occidental Res Corp PO Box 19601 Irvine CA 92713

LAMORTE, MICHAEL FRANCIS, b Altoona, Pa, Feb 20, 26; m 57; c 3. SOLID STATE ELECTRONICS, ELECTRICAL ENGINEERING. *Educ:* Va Polytech Inst & State Univ, BS, 50; Polytech Inst New York, MEE, 51. *Prof Exp:* Mgr solid state, RCA Corp, 59-67; pres solid state, Laser Diode Labs, 67-69; pres comput, Mathatronics Corp, 70-71; gen mgr med, Diamondhead Corp, 71-72; pres electronics, Princeton Synergestek Prod, 72-76; SR ENGR SOLID STATE, RES TRIANGLE INST, 76- *Concurrent Pos:* Fel engr, Westinghouse Elec Corp, 55-59; solid state physicist, Fort Monmouth, 52-55. *Honors & Awards:* Eng Achievement Award, RCA Corp, 60. *Mem:* Inst Elec & Electronics Engrs; Am Inst Physics; AAAS. *Res:* Semiconductor device physics; properties of materials; device design; device and material technology; special research interest in application of III-IV materials to electrooptical, microwave and logic devices. *Mailing Add:* Timberly Dr Box 222 Rte 7 Durham NC 27707

LAMOTTE, CAROLE CHOATE, b Washington, DC, May 15, 47; m 70; c 1. NEUROANATOMY, NEUROPHYSIOLOGY. *Educ:* Univ Okla, BS, 67; Georgetown Univ, MS, 69; Johns Hopkins Univ, PhD(physiol), 72. *Prof Exp:* NIH fel anat, Sch Med, Johns Hopkins Univ, 72-74, Inst res grant & instr anat, Sch Med, 74-75, asst prof anat, Sch Med, Johns Hopkins Univ, 75-77;

res assoc neurosurg, 77-78, ASST PROF NEUROANAT & NEUROSURG, SCH MED, YALE UNIV, 78- Concurrent Pos: NIH grant, 78- Mem: Am Asn Anatomists. Res: Anatomy and physiology of pain and temperature sensation. Mailing Add: Neurol Surg Sect Yale Univ Sch Med New Haven CT 06510

LAMOTTE, CLIFFORD ELTON, b Alpine, Tex, June 24, 30; m 74; c 2. PLANT PHYSIOLOGY. Educ: Tex A&M Univ, BS, 53; Univ Wis, PhD(bot), 60. Prof Exp: Res assoc biol, Princeton Univ, 60-61; from instr to asst prof, Boston Univ, 61-66; assoc prof bot & plant path, 66-80, PROF BOT, IOWA STATE UNIV, 80- Concurrent Pos: Fac leave Univ Col Wales, UK, 74-75. Mem: Bot Soc Am; AAAS; Am Soc Plant Physiol. Res: Hormonal regulation of development and orientation in plants; plant morphogenesis using tissue culture methods; growth and development in plants. Mailing Add: Dept Bot Iowa State Univ Ames IA 50011

LAMOTTE, LOUIS COSSITT, JR, b Clinton, SC, Jan 21, 28; m 48; c 5. MICROBIOLOGY, EPIDEMIOLOGY. Educ: Duke Univ, AB, 48; Univ NC, MSPH, 51; Johns Hopkins Univ, ScD(virol, entom), 58. Prof Exp: Bacteriologist, State Bd Health, NC, 48-51; virologist, Chem Corps, US Dept Army, 51-58; chief virus invests unit, Dis Ecol Sect, Tech Br, Nat Commun Dis Ctr, 58-65, asst chief, Dis Ecol Sect, Nat Ctr Disease Control, 65-66, chief community studies, Pesticides Prog, Ga, 66-69, dep chief, 69-70, chief, Microbiol Br, Lab Div, 70-72, DIR, LICENSURE & PROFICIENCY TESTING DIV, BUR LABS, CTR DIS CONTROL, 72- Concurrent Pos: Mem grad fac, Colo State Univ, 59-66; adj prof, Ga State Univ, 71- Mem: AAAS; Sigma Xi; Am Soc Trop Med & Hyg; Am Pub Health Asn; Am Soc Microbiol. Res: Epidemiology of arthropod-borne viruses; virology; bacteriology, parasitology and epidemiology of infectious diseases. Mailing Add: Licensure & Proficiency Testing Div Ctr Dis Control 1600 Clifton Rd Atlanta GA 30333

LAMOTTE, ROBERT HILL, b Washington, DC, Nov 4, 40; m 70. NEUROSCIENCES. Educ: Trinity Col, BS, 63; Kans State Univ, PhD(psychol), 68. Prof Exp: Fel neurophysiol, 68-70, instr, 70-73, asst prof neurophysiol, Sch Med & asst prof psychol, Johns Hopkins Univ, 73-77; ASSOC PROF ANESTHESIOL & PHYSIOL, MED SCH, YALE UNIV, 77- Mem: Soc Neurosci; AAAS. Res: Neurophysiology and psychophysics of somesthesis. Mailing Add: Dept of Anesthesiol 333 Cedar St New Haven CT 06510

LAMOUREUX, CHARLES HARRINGTON, b West Greenwich, RI, Sept 14, 33; m 54; c 2. BOTANY. Educ: Univ RI, BS, 53; Univ Hawaii, MS, 55; Univ Calif, Davis, PhD(bot), 61. Prof Exp: Asst bot, Univ Hawaii, 53-55; jr plant pathologist, Calif State Dept Agr, 55; asst bot, Univ Calif, Davis, 55-59; from asst prof to assoc prof, 59-71, PROF BOT, UNIV HAWAII, 71- Concurrent Pos: Hon assoc, Bernice P Bishop Mus, 62-; guest scientist, Nat Biol Inst Indonesia, 72-73, 79-80. Mem: AAAS; Sigma Xi; Bot Soc Am. Res: Plant morphology; phenology; island biology; pterridology. Mailing Add: 3190 Maile Way Honolulu HI 96822

LAMOUREUX, GERALD LEE, b Bottineau, NDak, Apr 13, 39; m 69. BIOCHEMISTRY. Educ: Minot State Col, BS, 61; NDak State Univ, PhD(chem), 66. Prof Exp: RES CHEMIST, METAB & RADIATION RES LAB, SCI & EDUC ADMIN, AGR RES, USDA, 66- Concurrent Pos: Adj prof, NDak State Univ, 74- Mem: Am Chem Soc; Sigma Xi. Res: Elucidation of metabolic pathways utilized by plants and animals in the metabolism of herbicides, insecticides and other exenobiotics; glutathione-S-transferase mediated reactions; isolation and identification of natural products. Mailing Add: USDA Metab & Radiation Res Lab State Univ Sta Fargo ND 58105

LAMOUREUX, GILLES, b Marieville, Que, Mar 2, 34; c 5. MEDICINE, IMMUNOLOGY. Educ: St Mary's Col, BA, 56; Univ Montreal, MD, 61, MSc, 63, PhD(immunol), 67. Prof Exp: HEAD IMMUNODIAG LAB, INST ARMAND FRAPPIER, 67-; ASST PROF IMMUNOL, UNIV MONTREAL, 68- Concurrent Pos: Fel, Walter & Eliza Hall Inst Med Res, Melbourne, Australia; Multiple Sclerosis Soc Can grant. Mem: Can Soc Immunol; Fr Soc Immunol; Transplantation Soc. Res: Immune studies in multiple sclerosis and experimental allergic encephalomyelitis; mechanism of action of lymphocytes in specific cell-mediated immunity; stimulation and immunosuppression; practical aspect in autoimmune diseases, transplantation and cancer; genetic control of natural resistance in multiple sclerosis and normal population. Mailing Add: Inst Armand Frappier PO Box 100 Laval-del Rapides Laval PQ H7N 4Z3 Can

LAMP, GEORGE EMMETT, JR, b Richland Twp, Iowa, Nov 24, 33; m 57; c 1. INDUSTRIAL ENGINEERING. Educ: Iowa State Univ, BS, 60, MS, 64, PhD(eng valuation), 68. Prof Exp: From instr to asst prof, 60-73, ASSOC PROF INDUST ENG, IOWA STATE UNIV, 73- Mem: Am Inst Indust Engrs; Am Soc Eng Educ; Am Gas Asn. Res: Engineering valuation; depreciation; life analysis of property; engineering economy. Mailing Add: Dept of Indust Eng Marston Hall Iowa State Univ Ames IA 50011

LAMP, HERBERT F, b Davenport, Iowa, Aug 6, 19; m 47; c 6. PLANT ECOLOGY. Educ: Chicago Teacher Col, BEd, 41; Univ Chicago, SM, 47, PhD(bot), 51. Prof Exp: Instr bot, Fla State Univ, 47-50; teacher biol, Ill Teachers Col Chicago-South, 50-59, from assoc prof to prof, 59-64, chmn dept natural sci, 56-64; prof biol, 64-66, PROF BIOL SCI & CHMN DEPT, NORTHEASTERN ILL UNIV, 66- Concurrent Pos: Res assoc, Univ Chicago, 52-56. Mem: Bot Soc Am; Ecol Soc Am. Res: Physiological ecology of range grasses; bromus inermis leyss; prairie ecology; commmunity ecology. Mailing Add: Dept of Biol Northeastern Ill Univ Chicago IL 60625

LAMP, WILLIAM OWEN, b Omaha, Nebr, June 19, 51; m 73; c 2. POPULATION ECOLOGY, BIOLOGICAL CONTROL. Educ: Ohio State Univ, MS, 76; Univ Nebr, BS, 72, PhD(entom), 80. Prof Exp: RES ASSOC, ILL NATURAL HIST SURV, 80- Mem: Entom Soc Am; Ecol Soc Am; Weed Sci Soc Am. Res: Weed-insect interactions including studies of biological control of weeds using imported or indigenous weed-feeding insects, and the influence of background weedy vegetation on insect pest populations in crops. Mailing Add: Ill Natural Hist Surv 607 E Peabody Champaign IL 61820

LAMPE, FREDERICK WALTER, b Chicago, Ill, Jan 5, 27; m 49; c 5. PHYSICAL CHEMISTRY. Educ: Mich State Col, BS, 50; Columbia Univ, AM, 51, PhD(chem), 53. Prof Exp: Asst chem, Columbia Univ, 50-53; res chemist, Humble Oil & Refining Co, 53-56, sr res chemist, 56-60, res specialist, 60; assoc prof chem, 60-65, PROF CHEM, PA STATE UNIV, 65- Concurrent Pos: Consult, Socony Mobil Oil Co, 61-69, Sci Res Instruments Corp, 67-77 & W H Johnston Labs, Inc, 60-67; NSF sr fel & guest prof, Univ Freiburg, 66-67; Alexander von Humboldt Found US sr scientist award, 73-74. Mem: AAAS; Am Chem Soc; fel Am Phys Soc; Royal Soc Chem. Res: Photochemistry; radiation chemistry; reactions of free radicals and of gaseous ions; mass spectrometry. Mailing Add: 542 Ridge Ave State College PA 16801

LAMPE, KENNETH FRANCIS, b Dubuque, Iowa, Dec 3, 28; m 49; c 1. PHARMACOLOGY. Educ: Univ Iowa, BA, 49, MS, 51, PhD(pharm), 53. Prof Exp: Instr chem, Mont State Col, 49-50; instr pharm, Univ Iowa, 53; from asst prof to assoc prof pharmacol, Sch Med, Univ Miami, 54-67, prof pharmacol & anesthesiol, 67-81; SR SCIENTIST, AM MED ASN, 81- Concurrent Pos: Fel, Yale Univ, 53-54. Mem: Am Chem Soc; Am Acad Clin Toxicol. Res: Chemical constitution and biological activity; neuropharmacology. Mailing Add: Div Drug Am Med Asn 535 N Dearborn St Chicago IL 60610

LAMPEN, J OLIVER, b Holland, Mich, Feb 26, 18; m 44; c 3. MICROBIOLOGY. Educ: Hope Col, AB, 39; Univ Wis, MS, 41, PhD(biochem), 43. Hon Degrees: LHD, Hope Col, 74. Prof Exp: Biochemist, Am Cyanamid Co, 43-46; res assoc, Med Sch, Washington Univ, 46-47, instr biochem, 47-48; asst prof biol chem, 48-49; assoc prof microbiol, Sch Med, Western Reserve Univ, 49-53; dir div biochem res, Squibb Inst Med Res, Olin Mathieson Chem Corp, 53-58; dir, Waksman Inst, 58-80, PROF MICROBIOL, RUTGERS UNIV, 80- Honors & Awards: Lilly Award, 52. Mem: AAAS; Am Soc Microbiol; Am Soc Biol Chemists; Am Acad Microbiol; Brit Biochem Soc. Res: Secretion of enzymes by microorganisms; site of exoenzyme formation, mechanism of secretion, control of synthesis; antibiotics and cell membrane. Mailing Add: Waksman Inst of Microbiol Rutgers Univ New Brunswick NJ 08903

LAMPERTI, ALBERT A, b Bronx, NY, Oct 24, 47; m 72; c 1. NEUROENDOCRINOLOGY. Educ: Manhattan Col, BS, 69; Univ Cincinnati, PhD(anat), 73. Prof Exp: ASST PROF ANAT, COL MED, UNIV CINCINNATI, 73- Mem: AAAS; Am Asn Anatomists; Soc Study Reprod; Sigma Xi. Res: Reproductive neuroendocrinology; heavy metals. Mailing Add: Col of Med Dept of Anat 231 Bethesda St Cincinnati OH 45267

LAMPERTI, JOHN WILLIAMS, b Montclair, NJ, Dec 20, 32; m 57; c 4. MATHEMATICS. Educ: Haverford Col, BS, 53; Calif Inst Technol, PhD(math), 57. Prof Exp: From instr to asst prof math, Stanford Univ, 57-61; vis instr math, Dartmouth Col, 61-62; res assoc, Rockefeller Inst, 62-63; assoc prof, 63-68, PROF MATH, DARTMOUTH COL, 68- Concurrent Pos: Sci exchange visitor, USSR, 70; vis prof, Aarhus Univ, 72-73; consult, Am Friends Serv Comt, 80. Mem: Fedn Am Scientists; fel Inst Math Statist. Res: Probability theory, particularly properties of stochastic processes, especially limit theorems for Markov processes. Mailing Add: Dept of Math Dartmouth Col Hanover NH 03755

LAMPI, RAUNO ANDREW, b Gardner, Mass, Aug 12, 29; m 51; c 4. FOOD TECHNOLOGY. Educ: Univ Mass, BS, 51, MS, 55, PhD(food technol), 57. Prof Exp: Res instr food technol, Univ Mass, 53-57; tech dir food processing, New Eng Appl Prod Co, 59-62; mgr, Food Technol Sect, Cent Eng Labs, FMC Corp, 62-66; packaging technologist, Container Div, Natick Labs, 66-67, res phys scientist, Packaging Div, 67-69, chief systs develop br, Packaging Div, 69-76, CHIEF, FOOD SYSTS EQUIP DIV, NATICK RES & DEVELOP LABS, US ARMY, 76- Concurrent Pos: Asst mgr indust instrumentation, Food Div, Foxboro Co, 57-59. Honors & Awards: Rohland Isker Award, Res & Develop Assocs, 69. Res: Development of continuous applesauce and juice processes; stability characteristics of freeze dried foods; thermal processing of foods in flexible packages; development of food service equipment. Mailing Add: Food Systs Equip Div FEL Res & Develop Labs Natick MA 01760

LAMPIDIS, THEODORE JAMES, b New York, NY, June 10, 43; m 69. MICROBIOLOGY, CELL BIOLOGY. Educ: Brooklyn Col, BS, 65; NY Univ, MS, 69; Univ Miami, PhD(microbiol), 74. Prof Exp: Med res technician med microbiol, Sch Med, NY Univ, 65-67; NIH fel, 69-74; NAT INST AGING RES FEL PHYSIOL, SCH PUB HEALTH, HARVARD UNIV, 74- Mem: Am Soc Microbiol. Res: DNA repair in post-mitotic cells; beating myocardial cell cultures in vitro as a model for assaying effects on cellular function in non-dividing cells; various physical and chemical agents, particulary adriamycin and related anthracyclines. Mailing Add: 400 Brooklin Ave Roxbury MA 02215

LAMPKIN-ASAM, JULIA MCCAIN, b Tuscaloosa, Ala, Feb 27, 31; m 71. ONCOLOGY, PHYSIOLOGY. Educ: Univ Ala, BS, 52; George Washington Univ, MS, 54, PhD(oncol, physiol), 58. Prof Exp: Med asst, Med Div, Civil Aeronaut Admin, Washington, DC, 55-56; res instr endocrinol cancer res, Univ Miami, 58-62; vis scientist, Univ Okla, 62-63; dir cancer res, Appl Res Lab, Inc, Fla, 63-65, Miami Serpentarium Cancer Res Lab, 65-66 & Lampkin-Hibbard Cancer Inst, Inc, Miami, 65-71; DIR CANCER RES, LAMPKIN-ASAM CANCER INST, INC, 71- Concurrent Pos: Cancer Chemother Nat Serv Ctr contract, Univ Miami, 58-62, Am Cancer Soc instnl grant, 61-62; USPHS spec travel grant, Univ Wis, 61; Am Cancer Soc instnl grant, Univ Okla, 62-63; Am Cancer Soc grant, Appl Res Lab, 63-65, Miami Serpentarium & Lampkin-Hibbard Cancer Inst, Inc, 65-66; teacher exten div,

Univ Tampa, Homestead AFB, 71. *Mem:* Am Asn Cancer Res. *Res:* Developer of p1798 model lymphoma systems in mice; chemotherapy; carcinogenesis; biochemistry; endocrinology; pharmacology; immunology; genetics; radioactive tracers; methods of obtaining anti-lymphoma antibodies. *Mailing Add:* Lampkin-Asam Cancer Inst Inc PO Box 6212 Ft Myers FL 33901

LAMPKY, JAMES ROBERT, b Battle Creek, Mich, June 19, 27; m 50, 71; c 6. MICROBIOLOGY. *Educ:* Eastern Mich Univ, BS, 59; Univ Mo, MA, 61, PhD(microbiol), 66. *Prof Exp:* From instr to asst prof bact, Wis State Univ, 63-66; asst prof, 66-70, assoc prof, 70-76, PROF BACT, CENT MICH UNIV, 76-. *Mem:* Am Soc Microbiol; Soc Indust Microbiologists; Mycol Soc Am. *Res:* Cellulolytic fruiting myxobacteria of the genus Polyangium with emphasis on morphology and ultrastructure. *Mailing Add:* Dept of Biol Cent Mich Univ Mt Pleasant MI 48858

LAMPMAN, GARY MARSHALL, b South Gate, Calif, Oct 8, 37; m 71; c 2. ORGANIC CHEMISTRY. *Educ:* Univ Calif, Los Angeles, BS, 59; Univ Wash, PhD(chem), 64. *Prof Exp:* From asst prof to assoc prof, 64-73, PROF CHEM, WESTERN WASH UNIV, 73-. *Mem:* Am Chem Soc. *Res:* Conformational analysis in small ring compounds; synthesis and reactions of strained compounds; organometallic chemistry. *Mailing Add:* Dept of Chem Western Wash Univ Bellingham WA 98225

LAMPORT, DEREK THOMAS ANTHONY, b Brighton, Eng, Dec 1, 33; m 63; c 5. BIOCHEMISTRY. *Educ:* Univ Cambridge, BA, 58, PhD(biochem), 63. *Prof Exp:* Staff scientist, Res Inst Advan Studies, Martin County, Md, 61-64; from asst prof to assoc prof biochem, 64-74, PROF BIOCHEM, ERDA PLANT RES LAB, MICH STATE UNIV, 74-. *Mem:* Am Chem Soc. *Res:* Plant cell wall proteins. *Mailing Add:* ERDA Plant Res Lab Mich State Univ East Lansing MI 48824

LAMPORT, JAMES EVERETT, b Seligman, Ariz, Nov 8, 21; m 45; c 5. COSMIC RAY PHYSICS. *Educ:* Ill Inst Technol, BS, 50. *Prof Exp:* Asst technologist, Sinclair Res Labs, Inc, 50-51; res physicist, Armour Res Found, Ill Inst Technol, 51-57; asst dir syst develop, Labs Appl Sci, 57-64, TECH SERV MGR, LAB ASTROPHYS & SPACE RES, UNIV CHICAGO, 64-. *Honors & Awards:* NASA Pub Serv Award, 75. *Res:* Spectroscopy; infrared detection systems; cosmic ray measurement systems for space vehicles; cosmic ray instrumentation for space flight. *Mailing Add:* 700 Bruce Lane Glenwood IL 60425

LAMPRECH, EARL DUWAIN, food science, see previous edition

LAMPSON, BUTLER WRIGHT, b Washington, DC, Dec 23, 43; m 67; c 1. COMPUTER SCIENCE. *Educ:* Harvard Univ, AB, 64; Univ Calif, Berkeley, PhD(comput sci), 67. *Prof Exp:* From asst prof to assoc prof comput sci, Univ Calif, Berkeley, 67-71; res fel, 71-80, SR RES FEL, XEROX PALO ALTO RES CTR, 80-. *Concurrent Pos:* Dir syst develop, Berkeley Comput Corp, 69-71. *Mem:* Asn Comput Mach. *Res:* Programming languages and operating systems. *Mailing Add:* Xerox Palo Alto Res Ctr 3333 Coyote Hill Rd Palo Alto CA 94304

LAMPSON, FRANCIS KEITH, b Minneapolis, Minn, Aug 7, 24; m 45; c 4. METALLURGICAL ENGINEERING, MATERIALS ENGINEERING. *Educ:* Univ Ill, BS, 49. *Prof Exp:* Jr metallurgist, NEPA Div, Fairchild Eng & Air Corp, 49-51; exp metallurgist, Allison Div, Gen Motors Corp, 51-54; group leader, Mat & Processing, Marquardt Co, Van Nuys, Calif, 54-57; Pacific Coast area tech rep, Allegheny-Ludlum Steel Corp, Los Angeles, 57-65; DIR MAT ENGRS, MARQUARDT CO, DIV CCI CORP, 65-. *Concurrent Pos:* Pres, F K Lampson Assocs, 74-. *Mem:* Am Soc Metals; Soc Aerospace Mat Process Engrs; Am Soc Testing Mats; Am Inst Mining Engrs. *Res:* Propulsion technology materials; ferrous and super alloy materials; refractory materials and related disilicide coatings; biomedical materials. *Mailing Add:* Marquardt Corp 16555 Saticoy St Van Nuys CA 91409

LAMPSON, GEORGE PETER, b Colman, SDak, June 12, 19; m 48; c 3. BIOCHEMISTRY. *Educ:* SDak State Univ, BS, 42; Univ Wis, MS, 50. *Prof Exp:* Res assoc biochem, Ortho Pharmaceut Corp, 50-59; SR RES BIOCHEMIST, DEPT VIRUS & CELL BIOL, MERCK INST THERAPEUT RES, 59-. *Mem:* NY Acad Sci; Am Chem Soc; Am Soc Biol Chemists. *Res:* Purification and characterization of chicken embryo interferon as a low molecular protein; synthetic and natural double-stranded RNA as inducers of inderferon and host resistance; virus chemistry. *Mailing Add:* Dept of Virus & Cell Biol Merck Inst for Therapeut Res West Point PA 19486

LAMPTON, MICHAEL LOGAN, b Williamsport, Pa, Mar 1, 41. X-RAY ASTRONOMY. *Educ:* Calif Inst Technol, BS, 62; Univ Calif, Berkeley, PhD(physics), 67. *Prof Exp:* ASST RES PHYSICIST, SPACE SCI LAB, UNIV CALIF, BERKELEY, 67-. *Concurrent Pos:* NSF fel, Univ Calif, Berkeley, 68-69. *Mem:* Am Geophys Union; Am Astron Soc. *Res:* Ultraviolet astronomy. *Mailing Add:* Space Sci Lab Univ of Calif Berkeley CA 94720

LAMSON, BALDWIN GAYLORD, b Berkeley, Calif, May 20, 16; m 42; c 4. PATHOLOGY. *Educ:* Univ Calif, AB, 38; Univ Rochester, MD, 44. *Prof Exp:* Asst path, Sch Med & Dent, Univ Rochester, 44-45; asst, Sch Med, Emory Univ, 45-46; clin instr exp oncol, Sch Med, Univ Calif, 48-49; from asst prof to assoc prof, 51-61, assoc dean, Sch Med, 65-66, dir univ hosps & clins, 66-80, asst chancellor health sci, 77-80, PROF PATH, SCH MED, UNIV CALIF, LOS ANGELES, 62-, VPRES FINANCIAL & BUS MGT, 80-. *Concurrent Pos:* AEC & Nat Res Coun fel, Med Sch, Univ Calif, 48-49; fel, Sch Med & Dent, Univ Rochester, 49. *Res:* Automation in hospital management. *Mailing Add:* Director's Off Univ of Calif Hosp & Clins Los Angeles CA 90024

LAMUTH, HENRY LEWIS, b Painesville, Ohio, Apr 15, 42; m 69; c 2. APPLIED PHYSICS, ELECTRICAL ENGINEERING. *Educ:* Ohio State Univ, BS, 66, PhD(physics), 70. *Prof Exp:* Assoc res physicist optics, Willow Run Labs, Inst Sci & Technol, Univ Mich, 70-72; mem tech staff electro-optics, Orlando Div, Martin Marietta Aerospace, 72-74; MGR, SENSORS, ELECTRONICS & CONTROLS GROUP, COLUMBUS LABS, BATTELLE MEM INST, 74-. *Mem:* AAAS; Am Phys Soc; Sigma Xi. *Res:* Electro-optics, infrared, radar sensors and sensing; missile systems; atmospheric transmission; fiber and integrated optics; communication systems and techniques with optical radiation; electronic control systems; analog-digital electronic systems. *Mailing Add:* Columbus Labs Battelle Mem Inst 505 King Ave Columbus OH 43201

LAMY, FRANCOIS, biochemistry, see previous edition

LAMY, PETER PAUL, b Breslau, Ger, Dec 14, 25; US citizen; m 51; c 3. BIOPHARMACEUTICS, CLINICAL PHARMACY. *Educ:* Philadelphia Col Pharm & Sci, BSc, 56, MSc, 58, PhD(biopharmaceut), 64. *Prof Exp:* Instr pharm, Philadelphia Col Pharm & Sci, 56-63; assoc prof, Sch Pharm, 67-72, prof, Dept Social & Prev Med, Sch Med, 72-78, PROF PHARM, SCH PHARM UNIV MD, BALTIMORE, 72-, DIR INSTNL PHARM PROGS, 68-. *Concurrent Pos:* Asst to dir pharm, Jefferson Med Col, 59-62; instr, Woman's Hosp, Philadelphia, 60-62; lectr, Sch Nursing, Cath Univ Am; consult, USPHS Hosp, 66-72; Levindale Hebrew Geriat Ctr & Hosp, Baltimore, 72-, John L Deaton Med Ctr, Baltimore, 73-, Vet Admin Hosps, Baltimore & Washington, DC; Am Asn Cols Pharm vis scientist, 68-72; consult geriat & gerontology; vchmn, Univ Md at Baltimore task force on aging; ed, Contemp Pharm Pract, 78-; mem, Nat Aging Res Planning Panel, 81-. *Mem:* fel AAAS; fel Am Col Clin Pharmacol; Acad Pharmaceut Sci; Am Soc Clin Pharmacol Therapeut; Sigma Xi. *Res:* Drug transport mechanisms in vivo and in vitro; drug interactions; drug equivalencies and efficiencies. *Mailing Add:* Univ of Md Sch of Pharm 636 W Lombard St Baltimore MD 21201

LAN, CHUAN-TAU EDWARD, b Taiwan, China, Apr 21, 35; US citizen; m 61; c 3. ENGINEERING MECHANICS, CIVIL ENGINEERING. *Educ:* Nat Taiwan Univ, BS, 58; Univ Minn, MS, 63; NY Univ, PhD(aeronaut), 68. *Prof Exp:* Asst civil engr hydraul, Bd Water Supply, New York, 63-65; assoc res scientist aeronaut, Aerospace Labs, NY Univ, 68; from asst prof to assoc prof, 68-78, PROF AERONAUT, UNIV KANS, 78-. *Concurrent Pos:* Consult, Roskam Aviation & Eng Corp, 76; reviewer, J Aircraft, 75-; consult, Aeronaut Res Lab, Taiwan, 77-; prin investr, NASA Langley Res Ctr, 73-. *Mem:* Am Inst Aeronaut & Astronaut. *Res:* Steady and unsteady aerodynamics. *Mailing Add:* Dept Aerospace Eng Univ Kans Lawrence KS 66045

LAN, SHIH-JUNG, drug metabolism, see previous edition

LANA, EDWARD PETER, b Duluth, Minn, Oct 17, 14; m 42; c 3. HORTICULTURE. *Educ:* Univ Minn, BS, 40, MS, 43; PhD, 48. *Prof Exp:* Canning crops res, Fairmont Canning Co, Minn, 43-47; asst prof hort, Iowa State Univ, 47-56; prof & chmn dept, 56-81, EMER PROF HORT, NDAK STATE UNIV, 81-. *Mem:* Am Soc Hort Sci. *Res:* Crop breeding; cultural studies. *Mailing Add:* Dept of Hort NDak State Univ Fargo ND 58102

LANCASTER, DOUGLAS, b Fargo, NDak, Mar 30, 29; m 62; c 1. ORNITHOLOGY. *Educ:* Carleton Col, BA, 50; La State Univ, PhD(zool), 60. *Prof Exp:* Asst prof zool, Northwestern State Col, La, 60-62; Frank M Chapman res fel ornith, Am Mus Natural Hist, 62-64; asst dir lab ornith, 64-73, DIR LAB ORNITH, CORNELL UNIV, 73-. *Concurrent Pos:* NSF grant, 66-68. *Mem:* Cooper Ornith Soc; Am Ornith Union; Am Soc Zool; Soc Study Evolution; Animal Behav Soc. *Res:* Tropical new world ornithology, especially general biology of family Tinamidae; comparative behavior and ecology of the family Ardeidae. *Mailing Add:* 1601 Dryden-Ithaca Rd Freeville NY 13068

LANCASTER, GEORGE MAURICE, b Penrith, Eng, July 18, 34; m 64; c 2. DIFFERENTIAL GEOMETRY. *Educ:* Univ Liverpool, BSc, 56; Univ Sask, PhD(math), 67. *Prof Exp:* Res analyst, Weapons Res Div, A V Roe & Co Ltd, Woodford, Eng, 56-58; opers res analyst, Northern Elec Co Ltd, Montreal, 58-60; lectr math, Royal Roads Mil Col, 60-64; asst prof, Univ Sask, 67-70; assoc prof, 70-78, PROF MATH, ROYAL ROADS MIL COL, 78-, HEAD DEPT, 70-. *Concurrent Pos:* Nat Res Coun Can grant, Univ Sask, 68-70; spec lectr, Univ Victoria, 71. *Mem:* Am Math Soc; Can Math Cong. *Res:* Differential geometry; imbedding of Riemannian manifolds. *Mailing Add:* Dept of Math Royal Roads Mil Col Victoria BC V0S 1B0 Can

LANCASTER, JAMES D, b Randolph, Miss, June 11, 19; m 42; c 3. AGRONOMY. *Educ:* Miss State Col, BS, 47, MS, 48; Univ Wis, PhD, 54. *Prof Exp:* Asst agronomist, Exp Sta. & asst prof agron, 51-57, AGRONOMIST, EXP STA & PROF AGRON, MISS STATE UNIV, 57-. *Mem:* Am Soc Agron; Soil Sci Soc Am; AAAS. *Res:* Soil fertility and testing; fertilizer evaluation; crop fertilization. *Mailing Add:* Dept Agron Miss State Univ Mississippi State MS 39762

LANCASTER, JESSIE LEONARD, JR, b Horatio, Ark, Jan 26, 23; m 46; c 4. ENTOMOLOGY. *Educ:* Univ Ark, BSA, 47; Cornell Univ, PhD(econ entom), 51. *Prof Exp:* Asst, Cornell Univ, 47-51; from asst prof to assoc prof entom, 51-60; PROF ENTOM, UNIV ARK, FAYETTEVILLE, 60-. *Concurrent Pos:* NIH spec res fel, Rocky Mountain Lab, 63-64. *Mem:* Entom Soc Am. *Res:* Medical veterinary entomology and mosquito control. *Mailing Add:* Rte 9 Old Wire Rd N Fayetteville AR 72701

LANCASTER, JOHN, b Bolton, Miss, Aug 30, 37; m 64. MICROBIAL GENETICS. *Educ:* Miss State Univ, BS, 59, MS, 61; Univ Tex, PhD(microbiol), 64. *Prof Exp:* NIH trainee, Univ Tex, 63-64; asst prof microbiol, 64-68, ASSOC PROF MICROBIOL, UNIV OKLA, 68-. *Concurrent Pos:* NIH grant, 66. *Mem:* AAAS; Am Soc Microbiol. *Res:* Mechanism of conjugation in Escherichia coli. *Mailing Add:* Dept of Bot & Microbiol Univ of Okla Norman OK 73019

LANCASTER, JOHN EDGAR, b Newell, WVa, Mar 18, 21; m 56; c 3. PHYSICAL CHEMISTRY. *Educ:* Duquesne Univ, BS, 42; Univ Minn, PhD(chem), 51. *Prof Exp:* Chemist, Chem Warfare Serv, 42-44; PHYS CHEMIST & INFRARED SPECTROSCOPIST, AM CYANAMID CO, 52- *Mem:* Am Chem Soc; Am Phys Soc. *Res:* Infrared spectroscopy; molecular vibrations; magnetic resonance. *Mailing Add:* 41 Old Orchard Rd Riverside CT 06878

LANCASTER, MALCOLM, b Amarillo, Tex, July 28, 31; m 59; c 4. AEROSPACE MEDICINE, CARDIOLOGY. *Educ:* Univ Tex Southwestern Med Sch, MD, 56; Univ Colo, Denver, MS, 60. *Prof Exp:* Chief med serv, 48th Tactical Hosp, Royal Air Force, Lakenheath, Eng, 60-63; chief cardiopulmonary serv & chmn dept med, US Air Force Hosp, Wright-Patterson AFB, 65-66; chief internal med br, Sch Aerospace Med, Brooks AFB, Tex, 66-73, chief clin sci div, 72-78; chief med serv & clin dir, San Antonio State Chest Hosp, 78-81; CONSULT CARDIOLOGIST, SCI SYSTS, INC, CAMBRIDGE, MASS, 81- *Concurrent Pos:* Prof clin med, Med Sch, Univ Tex, San Antonio, 72- *Honors & Awards:* Casimir Funk Award, Asn Mil Surgeons US, 71; USAF Res & Develop Award, 71; John Jeffries Award, Am Inst Aeronaut & Astronaut, 74; Arnold D Tuttle Award, Aerospace Med Asn, 75. *Mem:* Fel Aerospace Med Asn; fel Am Col Cardiol; fel Am Col Physicians; Am Heart Asn; fel Am Col Prev Med. *Res:* Medical aspects of aerospace operations; cardiovascular disease epidemiology; computers and electrocardiography. *Mailing Add:* 101 Hibiscus San Antonio TX 78213

LANCASTER, OTIS EWING, b Pleasant Hill, Mo, Jan 28, 09; m 42; c 5. AERONAUTICAL ENGINEERING, MATHEMATICS. *Educ:* Cent Mo State Teachers Col, 29; Univ Mo, MA, 34; Harvard Univ, PhD(math), 37; Calif Inst Technol, AeroE, 45. *Prof Exp:* Teacher, Oak Grove High Sch, Mo, 29-30 & Independence Jr High Sch, Mo, 30-33; instr & tutor math, Harvard Univ, 36-37; from instr to asst prof, Univ Md, 37-42; head appl math br, Res Div, Bur Aeronaut, Navy Dept, Washington, DC, 46-54, asst dir, 54; mem planning staff, Internal Revenue Serv, 54-55; dir statist & econ staff, Bur Finance, Post Off Dept, 55-57; George Westinghouse prof eng educ, 57-75, assoc dean eng, 67-75, EMER DEAN, PA STATE UNIV, UNIVERSITY PARK, 75- *Concurrent Pos:* Consult, NASA-Univ rels; chief math & statist, Interstate Com Comn, 76-80. *Mem:* Am Soc Eng Educ (pres, 77-78); Math Asn Am; assoc fel Am Inst Aeronaut & Astronaut; Inst Math Statist; Am Soc Mech Engrs. *Res:* Engineering education; aircraft propulsion; statistics; improvement of teaching. *Mailing Add:* 268 Ellen Ave State College PA 16801

LANCE, GEORGE M(ILWARD), b Youngstown, Ohio, Dec 4, 28; m 64; c 5. MECHANICAL ELECTRICAL ENGINEERING. *Educ:* Case Inst Technol, BS, 52, MS, 54. *Prof Exp:* Instr eng, Case Inst Technol, 52-54; res engr, TRW, Inc, 54-56; lectr mech eng, Univ Wash, St Louis, 56-60; sr systs engr, Moog Servocontrols, Inc, 60-61; from asst prof to assoc prof, 61-70, assoc dean undergrad progs & student affairs, 74-79, PROF MECH ENG, UNIV IOWA, 70-, CHMN ENG PROG, 79- *Mem:* Am Soc Mech Engrs; Am Soc Eng Educ; Inst Elec & Electronics Engrs. *Res:* Theory of automatic control; hydraulic servosystems; system design. *Mailing Add:* Col Eng Univ Iowa Iowa City IA 52240

LANCE, JOHN FRANKLIN, b Vaughn, NMex, May 21, 16; m 42; c 2. GEOLOGY. *Educ:* Col Mines & Metal, Univ Tex, BA, 37; Calif Inst Technol, MS, 46, PhD(paleont, petrog), 49. *Prof Exp:* Asst prof geol, Whittier Col, 48-50; from asst prof to prof paleont, Univ Ariz, 50-67; staff assoc, Div Inst Prog, 63-65 & 67-70, exec asst div environ sci, 71-75, PROG DIR GEOL, NSF, 75- *Concurrent Pos:* Geologist, US Geol Surv, 52-63. *Mem:* Geol Soc Am; Paleont Soc; Soc Vert Paleontologists; Soc Study Evolution. *Res:* Pliocene and Pleistocene mammalian fossils. *Mailing Add:* 3800 N Fairfax Dr Apt 210 Arlington VA 22203

LANCE, R(ICHARD) H, b Geneva, Ill, Nov 29, 31; m 53; c 3. MECHANICS. *Educ:* Univ Ill, Urbana, BSME, 54; Ill Inst Technol, MSME, 57; Brown Univ, PhD(solid mech), 62. *Prof Exp:* Test engr, Minneapolis Honeywell Regulator Co, 54; mech engr, Ingersoll Milling Mach Co, Ill, 57-58; res assoc, Brown Univ, 62; asst prof, 62-67, assoc prof, 67-81, dean eng, 74-80, PROF THEORET & APPL MECH, CORNELL UNIV, 81- *Concurrent Pos:* Lectr, Int Bus Mach Corp, NY, 66; sr scientist, Hughes Aircraft Co, 80-81. *Res:* Mechanical behavior of solids; engineering structural mechanics; plasticity; numerical methods in engineering. *Mailing Add:* Col of Eng Cornell Univ Thurston Hall Ithaca NY 14853

LANCE, VALENTINE A, b London, Eng, Feb 14, 40; m 74. REPRODUCTIVE PHYSIOLOGY, COMPARATIVE ENDOCRINOLOGY. *Educ:* Long Island Univ, BS, 66; Col William & Mary, MA, 68; Univ Hong Kong, PhD(zool), 74. *Prof Exp:* Demonstr zool, Univ Hong Kong, 68-74; res assoc endocrinol, Boston Univ, 74-78; ASST PROF PHYSIOL, LA STATE UNIV, 78- *Mem:* Endocrine Soc; Soc Study Reproduction; Am Soc Zoologists; Soc Study Amphibians & Reptiles. *Res:* Evolution of the endocrine system; evolution of pituitary control of gonadal steroidogenesis; role of hypothalamic hormones and related reptiles in non-mammalian vertebrates. *Mailing Add:* Dept of Zool & Physiol La State Univ Baton Rouge LA 70803

LANCEFIELD, REBECCA CRAIGHILL, bacteriology, deceased

LANCET, MICHAEL SAVAGE, b Detroit, Mich, Dec 11, 44; m 69; c 1. PHYSICAL CHEMISTRY, CHEMICAL ENGINEERING. *Educ:* Rose Hulman Inst Technol, BS, 66; Univ Chicago, MS, 71, PhD(nuclear chem), 72. *Prof Exp:* Res assoc nuclear cosmo chem, Carnegie-Mellon Univ, 72-74; RES SCIENTIST COAL CONVERSION RES, CONOCO COAL DEVELOP CO, 74- *Concurrent Pos:* Fel, Carnegie-Mellon Univ, 72-74. *Mem:* AAAS; Am Chem Soc; Geochem Soc; Meteroritical Soc. *Res:* Conversion of coal to substitute natural gas and synthetic liquids; utilization of all other forms of energy. *Mailing Add:* Conoco Coal Develop Co Res Div Library PA 15129

LANCHANTIN, GERARD FRANCIS, b Detroit, Mich, Mar 27, 29; m 55; c 5. BIOCHEMISTRY. *Educ:* Seton Hall Univ, BS, 50; Univ Wyo, MS, 51; Univ Southern Calif, PhD(biochem), 54. *Prof Exp:* Res assoc, 54-55, from asst prof to assoc prof, 57-69, ADJ PROF BIOCHEM, SCH MED, UNIV SOUTHERN CALIF, 69-; DIR BIOCHEM, ST JOSEPH MED CTR, 74- *Concurrent Pos:* Consult, Los Angeles County Gen Hosp, 57-; chief biochem dept, Cedars-Sinai Med Ctr, 57-74. *Honors & Awards:* Chaney Award Clin Chem, 81. *Mem:* Fel AAAS; Am Asn Clin Chem; Am Chem Soc; Am Soc Hemat; Am Soc Biol Chemists. *Res:* Clinical biochemistry; blood coagulation. *Mailing Add:* Dept of Biochem Div of Labs St Joseph Med Ctr Burbank CA 91505

LANCIANI, CARMINE ANDREW, b Leominster, Mass, May 16, 41; m 64; c 2. ECOLOGY. *Educ:* Cornell Univ, BS, 63, PhD, 68. *Prof Exp:* Interim asst prof zool, 68-70, asst prof zool & biol sci, 70-73, assoc prof zool, 73-80, PROF ZOOL, UNIV FLA, 80- *Mem:* Ecol Soc Am; Entom Soc Am; Am Soc Limnol & Oceanog; Soc Study Evolution. *Res:* Population ecology of aquatic organisms, particularly life cycles, growth, reproduction and competition of parasitic water mites; effect of parasitism on host ecology. *Mailing Add:* Dept of Zool Univ of Fla Gainesville FL 32611

LAND, CECIL E(LVIN), b Lebanon, Mo, Jan 8, 26; m 47; c 2. ELECTRONICS ENGINEERING, SOLID STATE PHYSICS. *Educ:* Okla State Univ, BS, 49. *Hon Degrees:* DSc, Okla Christian Col, 78. *Prof Exp:* Prof engr, Electronics Div, Westinghouse Elec Corp, Md, 49-56; STAFF MEM, SOLID STATE DEVICE PHYSICS DIV, SANDIA NAT LABS, 56- *Honors & Awards:* Nat Soc Prof Engrs Award, 73; Frances Rice Darne Mem Award, Soc Info Display, 76. *Mem:* Fel Soc Info Display; fel Inst Elec & Electronics Engrs; Am Phys Soc; fel Am Ceramics Soc; Optical Soc Am. *Res:* Ferroelectric ceramic electrooptic and piezoelectric materials and devices. *Mailing Add:* Solid State Device Physics Div 5112 Sandia Nat Labs Albuquerque NM 87185

LAND, CHARLES EVEN, b San Francisco, Calif, July 13, 37; m 60; c 1. STATISTICS. *Educ:* Univ Ore, BA, 59; Univ Chicago, MA, 64, PhD(statist), 68. *Prof Exp:* Res assoc statist, Atomic Bomb Casualty Comn, Nat Acad Sci, 66-68; asst prof, Ore State Univ, 68-73; res assoc statist, Atomic Bomb Casualty Comn & Radiation Effects Res Found, 73-75; expert math statistician, Biometry Br, 75-77, HEALTH STATISTICIAN, ENVIRON EPIDEMIOL BR, NAT CANCER INST, 77- *Mem:* Radiation Res Soc; Inst Math Statist; Am Statist Asn; Biomet Soc. *Res:* Mathematical statistics; inference problems associated with transformations of data; radiation carcinogenesis in human populations; epidemiology; biometry. *Mailing Add:* Environ Epidemiol Br Nat Cancer Inst Bethesda MD 20014

LAND, DAVID JOHN, b Boston, Mass, Feb 15, 39. ATOMIC & MOLECULAR PHYSICS, OPTICS. *Educ:* Boston Col, BS, 59; Brown Univ, PhD(physics), 66. *Prof Exp:* Res asst physics, Brown Univ, 59-66; Nat Acad Sci res assoc, 66-68, RES PHYSICIST, NAVAL SURFACE WEAPONS CTR, 68- *Mem:* Am Phys Soc. *Res:* Atomic collision physics; effects of meteorology on optical systems. *Mailing Add:* Nuclear Br Naval Surface Weapons Ctr Silver Spring MD 20910

LAND, EDWIN HERBERT, b Bridgeport, Conn, May 7, 09; m; c 2. PHYSICS. *Hon Degrees:* ScD, Tufts Col, 47, Polytech Inst Brooklyn, 52, Colby Col, 55, Harvard Univ, 57, Northeastern Univ, 59, Yale Univ, 66, Columbia Univ, 67, Loyola Univ, 70 & NY Univ, 73; LLD, Bates Col, 53, Wash Univ, 66 & Univ Mass, 67; LHD, Williams Col, 68. *Prof Exp:* FOUNDER, CHMN BD & DIR RES, POLAROID CORP, 37- *Concurrent Pos:* Vis prof, Mass Inst Technol, 56-; mem, President's Sci Adv Comt, 57-59, consult-at-large, 60-73; mem, Nat Comn Technol, Automation & Econ Progress, 64-66; mem, Carnegie Comn Educ TV, 66-67; William James lectr psychol, Harvard Univ, 66-67, Morris Loeb lectr physics, 74; mem bd trustees, Ford Found, 67- *Honors & Awards:* Hood Medal, Royal Photog Soc Gt Brit, 35, Progress Medal, 57; Cresson Medal, Franklin Inst, 37, Potts Medal, 56 & Vermilye Medal, 74; John Scott Medal & Award, Philadelphia City Trusts, 38; Rumford Medal, Am Acad Arts & Sci, 45; Holley Medal, Am Soc Mech Engrs, 48; Duddell Medal, Phys Soc Gt Brit, 49; Progress Medal, Soc Photog Scientists & Engrs, 55; Progress Medal, Photog Soc Am, 60; Golden Soc Medal, Photog Soc Vienna, 61; Proctor Award, Sci Res Soc Am, 63; Presidential Medal of Freedom, 63; Indust Res Inst Medal, 65; Albert A Michelson Award, 66; Diesel Medal in Gold, Ger Asn Inventors, 66; Frederick Ives Medal, Optical Soc Am, 67. *Mem:* Nat Acad Sci; Nat Acad Eng; fel Am Acad Arts & Sci (pres, 51-53); Am Philos Soc; hon mem Optical Soc Am. *Res:* Light polarization; synthetic polarizers; three-dimensional presentation; one-step photography and associated photochemical mechanisms; vision and color vision. *Mailing Add:* Polaroid Corp 730 Main St Cambridge MA 02138

LAND, GEOFFREY ALLISON, b Jeannette, Pa, July 9, 42; m 66; C 4. MEDICAL MYCOLOGY, MEDICAL MICROBIOLOGY. *Educ:* Univ Tex, Arlington, BSc, 68; Tex Christian Univ, MSc, 70; Tulane Univ, PhD(med mycol), 73. *Prof Exp:* Inhalation therapist, Baylor Univ Med Ctr, Dallas, 66-68; teaching asst microbiol, Tex Christian Univ, 68-70; chmn & dir med mycol, Wadley Inst Molecular Med, 74-79; dir mycol & assoc dir microbiol, Univ Cinn Med Ctr, 79-81; DIR MICROBIOL & IMMUNOL, METHODIST HOSP, 81- *Concurrent Pos:* Vis asst prof, NC Cent Univ, 73-74; instr & lectr, Tex Soc Clin Microbiologists, 74- & NTex Soc Med Technologists, 75-; vis scientist, Dept Virol, Cent Pub Health Lab State Serum Inst, Helsinki, 75; adj prof biol & chem, NTex State Univ, 75-; assoc ed, J Oncol & Hematol, 75-79; adj assoc prof biol, Tex Christian Univ, 81-; consult, Clin Microbiol Labs, Univ Tex Health Sci Ctr, Dallas, 81- *Mem:* Am Soc Microbiol; Med Mycol Soc Am; Int Soc Human & Animal Mycol. *Res:* The molecular basis and early diagnosis of fungal infections in the compromised host; production of the antiviral interferon and its possible chemotherapeutic role for treating viral diseases. *Mailing Add:* Dept of Mycol Wadley Inst of Molecular Med Dallas TX 75235

LAND, LYNTON S, b Baltimore, Md, Dec 30, 40. GEOLOGY, GEOCHEMISTRY. *Educ:* Johns Hopkins Univ, AB, 62, MA, 63; Lehigh Univ, PhD(geol), 66. *Prof Exp:* Res fel geol, Calif Inst Technol, 66-67; asst prof, 67-77, PROF GEOL, UNIV TEX, AUSTIN, 77- *Mem:* Soc Econ Paleontologists & Mineralogists; Int Asn Sedimentol. *Res:* Sedimentology; carbonate sedimentation; diagenesis; sedimentary geochemistry; stable isotope geochemistry. *Mailing Add:* Dept of Geol Univ of Tex Austin TX 78712

LAND, PAUL COURTNEY, b Richmond, Va, Feb 5, 47; m 77; c 1. ANESTHESIOLOGY. *Educ:* Randolph-Macon Col, BS, 69; Med Col, Va, MD, 73; Univ Toronto, MSc, 78. *Prof Exp:* ASST PROF ANESTHESIOL, MED SCH, NORTHWESTERN UNIV, 77- *Mem:* Int Anesthesia Res Soc. *Res:* Anesthetic metabolism and toxicity anesthetic mechanisms. *Mailing Add:* Dept of Anesthesia 303 E Chicago Ave Chicago IL 60611

LAND, PETER L, b Leasburg, Mo, Nov 20, 29; m 66; c 3. SOLID STATE PHYSICS, CERAMICS. *Educ:* Univ Mo, BS, 58, MS, 60, PhD(physics), 64. *Prof Exp:* Res scientist, Metall & Ceramics Lab, Aerospace Res Labs, 74-75, RES SCIENTIST, LASER HARDENED MAT BR, AIR FORCE MAT LABS, WRIGHT-PATTERSON AFB, 75- *Mem:* Am Phys Soc. *Res:* New or improved optical materials; optical properties of solids; laser effects on materials. *Mailing Add:* 1565 Woods Dr Dayton OH 45432

LAND, ROBERT H, b Portland, Maine, Sept 17, 24. NUCLEAR PHYSICS. *Educ:* Univ Maine, BS, 49; Mass Inst Technol, PhD(nuclear physics), 57. *Prof Exp:* Asst physicist, 56-60, ASSOC PHYSICIST, ARGONNE NAT LAB, 60- *Mem:* Am Phys Soc; Am Nuclear Soc; Asn Comput Mach. *Res:* Photoproduction of charged pi-mesons from deuterium; reactor neutron diffusion theory; molecular physics and solid state physics calculations using digital computers. *Mailing Add:* Argonne Nat Lab Chem Eng Div 9700 S Cass Ave Argonne IL 60439

LAND, WILLIAM EVERETT, b Baltimore, Md, Aug 23, 08; m 42. PHYSICAL CHEMISTRY. *Educ:* Johns Hopkins Univ, BS, 28, PhD(phys chem), 33. *Prof Exp:* Chemist, Devoe & Raynolds Co, 28-29; instr chem, Emory Univ, 33-37; asst dir res, Glidden Co, 37-42; dep head high explosives sect, Bur Ord, 42-51, head high explosives res & develop, 51-60, div engr, Mines & Explosives Div, Bur Naval Weapons, 60-65, asst dir, Mine Warfare Proj Off, 65-66, div engr, Mine Warfare Div, Naval Ord Systs Command, 66-68, CONSULT NAVAL ORD SYSTS COMMAND, BUR NAVAL WEAPONS, NAVY DEPT, 68- *Concurrent Pos:* Mem ammunition & high explosives panel, Res & Develop Bd, 48-51, chmn, 51-53; US leader explosives panel, Tripartite Tech Coop Prog, 61-65. *Mem:* Am Chem Soc. *Res:* Adsorption; catalysis; titanium pigments; microscopy; chemical engineering; ordnance engineering. *Mailing Add:* 9200 Beech Hill Dr Bethesda MD 20817

LANDAHL, HERBERT DANIEL, b Fancheng, China, Apr 23, 13; US citizen; m 40; c 3. MATHEMATICAL BIOLOGY. *Educ:* St Olaf Col, AB, 34; Univ Chicago, SM, 36, PhD(math biophys), 41. *Prof Exp:* Asst, Psychomet Lab, Univ Chicago, 37-38, asst math biophys, Dept Physiol, 39-42, res assoc, 42-45, asst prof, 45-48, from assoc prof to prof math biol, 48-58, prof biophys, 64-68, secy comt math biol, 48-64, actg chmn, 64-68; prof, 68-80, EMER PROF BIOPHYS & BIOMATH, UNIV CALIF, SAN FRANCISCO, 80- *Concurrent Pos:* Res career award, NIH, 62-68; chief ed, Bull Math Biol, 73-81. *Mem:* Biomet Soc; Biophys Soc; Soc Math Biol (vpres, 72-82, pres, 82-). *Res:* Mathematical biophysics of cell division, nerve excitation and central nervous system; removal of aerosols and vapors by the human respiratory tract; biological effects of radiation; population interaction; biological periodicities; insulin production and release mechanisms. *Mailing Add:* Dept of Biochem & Biophys Univ of Calif San Francisco CA 94122

LANDAU, BARBARA RUTH, b Pierre, SDak, Apr 28, 23. PHYSIOLOGY. *Educ:* Univ Wis, BS, 45, MS, 49, PhD, 56. *Prof Exp:* Instr phys educ, Rockford Col, 45-47; instr physiol, Mt Holyoke Col, 49-51; instr, St Louis Univ, 56-59; from instr to asst prof, Univ Wis, 59-62; asst prof zool, Univ Idaho, 62-64; asst prof physiol, biophys & biol struct, 64-72, ASSOC PROF PHYSIOL, BIOPHYS & BIOL STRUCT, UNIV WASH, 72- *Mem:* AAAS; Am Physiol Soc. *Res:* Neural aspects of temperature regulation, hibernation, cell activity at reduced temperature; author of textbooks of anatomy and physiology. *Mailing Add:* Dept of Physiol & Biophys Univ of Wash Seattle WA 98195

LANDAU, BERNARD ROBERT, b Newark, NJ, June 24, 26; m 56; c 3. MEDICINE, BIOCHEMISTRY. *Educ:* Mass Inst Technol, SB, 47; Harvard Univ, MA, 49, PhD(chem), 50; Harvard Med Sch, MD, 54. *Prof Exp:* Med house officer, Peter Bent Brigham Hosp, Boston, Mass, 54-55, sr res physician, 58-59; asst prof biochem & from asst prof to assoc prof med, Case Western Reserve Univ, 59-67; dir dept biochem, Merck Inst Therapeut Res, 67-69; prof pharmacol, 70-78, PROF MED, CASE WESTERN RESERVE UNIV, 69-, PROF BIOCHEM, 79- *Concurrent Pos:* Clin assoc, Nat Cancer Inst, 55-57; USPHS res fel biochem, Harvard Med Sch, 57-58, tutor, 57-59; estab investr, Am Heart Asn, 59-64. *Mem:* Endocrine Soc; Soc Biol Chem; Am Physiol Soc; Asn Am Physicians; Am Diabetes Asn. *Res:* Carbohydrate metabolism; endocrinology; diabetes mellitus. *Mailing Add:* 19501 S Woodland Rd Cleveland OH 44102

LANDAU, BURTON JOSEPH, b Boston, Mass, May 6, 33; m 57; c 2. MICROBIOLOGY, VIROLOGY. *Educ:* Boston Univ, AB, 54; Univ NH, MS, 57; Univ Mich, PhD(microbiol), 67. *Prof Exp:* Sr res virologist, Merck Inst Therapeut Res, Merck, Inc, 64-65; res assoc microbiol, Univ Mich, 65-67; sr instr, 67-69, asst prof, 69-74, ASSOC PROF MICROBIOL, HAHNEMANN MED COL, 74- *Mem:* Am Soc Microbiol; Soc Gen Microbiol; Tissue Culture Asn. *Res:* Use of differentiating cell cultures to grow viruses with restricted host ranges; virus-host cell interactions leading to virus induced transformation. *Mailing Add:* Dept of Microbiol & Immunol Hahnemann Med Col Philadelphia PA 19102

LANDAU, DAVID PAUL, b St Louis, Mo, June 22, 41; m 66; c 2. MAGNETISM, STATISTICAL MECHANICS. *Educ:* Princeton Univ, BA, 63; Yale Univ, MS, 65, PhD(physics), 67. *Prof Exp:* Asst res physics, Nat Ctr Sci Res, Grenoble, France, 67-68; lectr eng & appl sci, Yale Univ, 68-69; from asst prof to assoc prof, 69-78, PROF PHYSICS, UNIV GA, 78- *Concurrent Pos:* Guest scientist, KFA Jülich, WGer, 74; Alexander von Humboldt fel, Univ Saarland, 75. *Mem:* Fel Am Phys Soc; Sigma Xi. *Res:* Critical phenomena associated with phase transitions; properties of magnetic solids. *Mailing Add:* Dept Physics Univ Ga Athens GA 30602

LANDAU, EDWARD FREDERICK, b New York, NY, Jan 25, 16; m 46, 76; c 2. ORGANIC CHEMISTRY, TEXTILE CHEMISTRY. *Educ:* City Col New York, BS, 38; Polytech Inst Brooklyn, MS, 42, PhD(org chem), 45. *Prof Exp:* Clin chemist, Hosp Holy Family, NY, 38-41; develop & res chemist, Nopco Chem Co, NJ, 41-44; res chemist, Celanese Corp Am, 45-49; lab dir, United Merchants Labs, Inc, 49-57; prod appln mgr, Cent Res Lab, 58-60, mgr mkt eval, Plastics Div, 60-68, mgr res strategy, 68-70, mgr res planning & admin, 70-72, dir res planning & admin, 72-77, assoc dir res-admin & polymer sci, 77-79, ASST TO VPRES RES, ALLIED CHEM CORP, 79- *Concurrent Pos:* Instr, Polytech Inst Brooklyn, 42-52; adj prof, Fairleigh Dickenson Univ. *Mem:* Am Chem Soc; Chem Mkt Res Asn; Com Develop Asn; Indust Res Inst. *Res:* Synthetic resins, plastics and fibers; market research and evaluations; research planning, evaluation and administration; research management; polymer science. *Mailing Add:* 4 N Cobane Terr West Orange NJ 07052

LANDAU, EMANUEL, b New York, NY, Nov 28, 19; m 48; c 2. EPIDEMIOLOGY, BIOSTATISTICS. *Educ:* City Col New York, BA, 39; Am Univ, PhD(econ), 66. *Prof Exp:* Bus economist, Econ Date Anal Br, Off Price Admin, 41-42 & 46-47; chief, Family Statist Sect, Bur Census, 48-56; mem staff, Calif State Dept Pub Health, 57-59; chief, Biomet Sect, Div Air Pollution, USPHS, 59-62; head, Lab & Clin Trials Sect, Nat Cancer Inst, 62-64; statist adv, Nat Air Pollution Control Admin, 65-69; epidemiologist, Adminr Res & Develop, Environ Health Serv, 69-71; epidemiologist, Adminr Res & Monitoring, Environ Protection Agency, 71; chief, Epidemiol Studies Br, Bur Radiol Health, Food & Drug Admin, USPHS, 71-75; PROJ DIR, AM PUB HEALTH ASN, 75- *Concurrent Pos:* Mem, Career Serv Bd Math & Statist, Dept Health, Educ & Welfare, 65-69; mem, Comt Long-term Training Outside Serv, USPHS, 66-68; adv air qual criteria, WHO, Switz, 67; mem, Study Lung Cancer Among Uranium Miners, USPHS, 67; adv air qual criteria, Karolinska Inst, Sweden, 68; Nat Air Control Admin tech liaison rep, Adv Comt Toxicol, Nat Acad Sci, 68-69; adv, Dept Transp, 72-74; assoc ed, J Air Pollution Control Asn, 72 & J Clin Data & Anal, 74-; consult, Bur Radiol Health, Food & Drug Admin, 75- *Honors & Awards:* Superior Serv Award, Dept Health, Educ & Welfare, 63. *Mem:* Fel Am Pub Health Asn; fel Royal Soc Health; Air Pollution Control Asn; Am Statist Asn; Soc Occup & Environ Health. *Res:* Problems of environmental health; public health statistics; chronic disease epidemiology. *Mailing Add:* Am Pub Health Asn 1015 15th St NW Washington DC 20005

LANDAU, HENRY J, b Lwow, Poland, Feb 11, 31; nat US; m 60; c 2. MATHEMATICS. *Educ:* Harvard Univ, AB, 53, AM, 55, PhD(math), 57. *Prof Exp:* MEM TECH STAFF, BELL TEL LABS, 57- *Concurrent Pos:* NSF fel, Inst Advan Study, 59-60, 67. *Mem:* Am Math Soc. *Res:* Fourier analysis; signal theory. *Mailing Add:* Bell Tel Labs Murray Hill NJ 07971

LANDAU, JOSEPH VICTOR, b New York, NY, Jan 9, 28; m 50; c 3. MOLECULAR BIOLOGY. *Educ:* City Col New York, BS, 47; NY Univ, MSc, 49, PhD, 53. *Prof Exp:* USPHS asst, NY Univ, 49-51; USPHS res asst, Naples Zool Sta, Italy, 52; Runyon Cancer Res fel, NY Univ, 52-55; instr physiol, Russell Sage Col, 56-57; res assoc oncol, Albany Med Col, Union, 57-66; PROF BIOL & HEAD ACCELERATED BIOMED PROG, RENSSELAER POLYTECH INST, 67-, CHMN DEPT BIOL, 72- *Concurrent Pos:* Chief biol sect, Basic Sci Res Lab, Vet Admin Hosp, Albany, 57-66; adj assoc prof, Rennselaer Polytech Inst, 64-67. *Mem:* Am Soc Cell Biol; Biophys Soc; Am Inst Biol Sci; Am Soc Microbiol. *Res:* Protein and nucleic acid synthesis; barobiology; contractility. *Mailing Add:* Dept of Biol Rensselaer Polytech Inst Troy NY 12181

LANDAU, JOSEPH WHITE, b Buffalo, NY, May 23, 30; m 64; c 5. MEDICINE, DERMATOLOGY. *Educ:* Cornell Univ, BA, 51, MD, 55; Am Bd Pediat, dipl, 62; Am Bd Dermat, dipl, 65, cert dermatopath, 75. *Prof Exp:* Intern, Gen Hosp, Buffalo, 55-56; resident pediat, Children's Hosp, Buffalo, 56, Children's Hosp, Boston, Mass, 59-60 & Med Ctr, Univ Calif, Los Angeles, 60-61; asst res dermatologist, 64, from asst prof to assoc prof med & dermat, 64-74, ASSOC CLIN PROF MED DERMAT, MED CTR, UNIV CALIF, LOS ANGELES, 74-, ATTEND PHYSICIAN, STUDENT HEALTH SERV, 65- *Concurrent Pos:* USPHS fel hemat, Children's Hosp, Los Angeles, 61-62 & fel mycol, Med Ctr, Univ Calif, Los Angeles, 62-63; attend physician, Wadsworth Vet Admin Hosp, 66- *Mem:* Am Acad Dermat; Soc Invest Dermat. *Res:* Host-parasite relationships in mycology; genodermatoses. *Mailing Add:* Suite 106 Med Arts Bldg 2200 Santa Monica Blvd Santa Monica CA 90404

LANDAU, RALPH, b Philadelphia, Pa, May 19, 16; m 40; c 1. CHEMICAL ENGINEERING. *Educ:* Univ Pa, BS, 37; Mass Inst Technol, ScD(chem eng), 41. *Prof Exp:* Asst chem eng, Mass Inst Technol, 38-41; process develop engr, M W Kellogg Co, 41-43; head, Chem Dept, Kellex Corp, 43-45; process develop engr, M W Kellogg Co, 46; exec vpres, Sci Design Co, Inc, 46-63; pres, Halcon Int, Inc, 63-75, chmn, 75-81, CHMN, HALCON SD GROUP, INC, 81- *Concurrent Pos:* Dir, Aluminum Co Am, 77-; adj prof mgt, tech & soc, Univ Pa, 77- *Honors & Awards:* Petrochem & Petrol Div Award, Am Inst Chem Engrs, 73; Chem Indust Medal, Soc Chem Indust, 73; Winthrop-Sears Medal, Chem Indust Asn, 77; Award, Newcomen Soc NAm, 78; Award, Asn Consult Chemists & Chem Engrs, 78; Perkin Medal, 81. *Mem:* Nat Acad Eng (vpres, 81-); fel Am Inst Chem Engrs; fel NY Acad Sci; Am Chem Soc; Dirs Indust Res. *Res:* Commercial and technical research, development and manufacture in chemical process industries; international operations of chemical industry; economics of technology and public policy implications. *Mailing Add:* Halcon SD Group Inc 2 Park Ave New York NY 10016

LANDAU, RICHARD LOUIS, b St Louis, Mo, Aug 8, 16; m 43; c 3. ENDOCRINOLOGY. *Educ:* Wash Univ, BS & MD, 40. *Prof Exp:* From asst prof to assoc prof, 48-59, PROF MED, UNIV CHICAGO, 59- *Concurrent Pos:* Ed, Perspectives in Biol & Med, 73- *Mem:* Am Soc Clin Invest; Endocrine Soc; AMA; Cent Soc Clin Res. *Res:* Hormonal regulation of growth processes; reproductive endocrinology; metabolic influence of progesterone; effect of steroid hormones on electrolyte metabolism. *Mailing Add:* 950 E 59th St Chicago IL 60637

LANDAU, RONALD WOLF, plasma physics, see previous edition

LANDAU, WILLIAM, b Jersey City, NJ, July 3, 27; m 63; c 2. MICROBIOLOGY. *Educ:* Univ Conn, BA, 49; Yale Univ, MS, 51; Univ Pa, PhD(pub health, prev med), 58. *Prof Exp:* Res assoc biochem, Roswell Park Mem Inst, 58-61; assoc dir microbiol dept, Presby-St Luke's Hosp, 61-74; asst prof, 62-74, ASSOC PROF BACT, RUSH MED CTR, 74-; ASSOC SCIENTIST, PRESBY-ST LUKE'S HOSP, CHICAGO, 74- *Mem:* Am Soc Microbiol; NY Acad Sci. *Res:* Clinical bacteriology. *Mailing Add:* Microbiol Dept Rush Med Ctr 1753 W Congress Pkwy Chicago IL 60612

LANDAU, WILLIAM M, b St Louis, Mo, Oct 10, 24; m 47; c 4. NEUROLOGY, NEUROPHYSIOLOGY. *Educ:* Washington Univ, MD, 47. *Prof Exp:* From instr to assoc prof, 52-63, PROF NEUROL, SCH MED, WASHINGTON UNIV, 63-, HEAD DEPT, 70-, CO-HEAD DEPT NEUROL & NEUROL SURG, 75- *Concurrent Pos:* Sr asst surgeon & neurophysiologist, NIMH & Nat Inst Neurol Dis & Blindness, 52-54; vis prof, Univ Munich, 63; pres, Am Bd Psychiat & Neurol, 75; chmn, Nat Comt Res Neurol & Commun Disorders, 80- *Mem:* Am Physiol Soc; Am Electroencephalog Soc; Am Neurol Asn (pres, 77); Asn Univ Profs Neurol (pres, 78); Am Acad Neurol. *Res:* Sensory and motor systems. *Mailing Add:* 660 S Euclid Ave St Louis MO 63110

LANDAUER, JOSEPH K, b Highland Park, Ill, June 9, 27; m 51; c 2. PHYSICS. *Educ:* Univ Chicago, MS, 51, PhD(physics), 54. *Prof Exp:* Physicist, Snow, Ice & Permafrost Res Estab, US Army Corps Engrs, Ill, 53-58; asst assoc dir arms control, 78-81, PHYSICIST, LAWRENCE LIVERMORE LAB, UNIV CALIF, 58-, DEP DIR, SPEC PROJS DIV, 81- *Concurrent Pos:* Asst to dep asst secy defense, Dept Defense, 75-76; Dept Energy rep to Conf of Comt on Disarmament, 70-75; Rep to comprehensive test ban negotiations, 77-80. *Mem:* Am Phys Soc. *Res:* Rheology of snow and ice; hydrodynamics; neutronics. *Mailing Add:* 241 La Questa Dr Danville CA 94526

LANDAUER, MICHAEL ROBERT, b New York, NY, Sept 24, 46. ANIMAL BEHAVIOR. *Educ:* Rutgers Univ, BS, 68; Univ Ill, Urbana, MS, 70, PhD(biopsychol), 75. *Prof Exp:* Res assoc psychol, Beaver Col, 74-76; vis asst prof biol, Barnard Col, Columbia Univ, 76-79; fel toxicol & pharmacol, 79-82, RES ASSOC PHARMACOL, MED COL VA, VA COMMONWEALTH UNIV, 82- *Concurrent Pos:* Lectr, Philadelphia Zoo, 76; grant, NIMH, 79. *Mem:* AAAS; Animal Behavior Soc; Am Soc Zoologists; Psychonomic Soc. *Res:* Hormonal determinants of reproductive behavior; psychopharmacology; behavioral toxicology; olfactory communication in humans and rodents. *Mailing Add:* Dept Pharmacol Box 613 Med Col Va Va Commonwealth Univ Richmond VA 23298

LANDAUER, ROLF WILLIAM, b Stuttgart, Ger, Feb 4, 27; nat US; m 50; c 3. SOLID STATE PHYSICS, COMPUTER TECHNOLOGY. *Educ:* Harvard Univ, SB, 45, AM, 47, PhD(physics), 50. *Prof Exp:* Physicist, Lewis Lab, Nat Adv Comt Aeronaut, 50-52; physicist, 52-61, dir phys sci, 61-66, asst dir res, 66-69, IBM FEL, THOMAS J WATSON RES CTR, IBM CORP, 69- *Mem:* Nat Acad Eng; fel Am Phys Soc; fel Inst Elec & Electronics Eng. *Mailing Add:* Thomas J Watson Res Ctr IBM Corp PO Box 218 Yorktown Heights NY 10598

LANDAUER, WALTER I(SFRIED), b Urspringen, Ger, June 12, 25; US citizen. COMPUTER & INFORMATION SCIENCE. *Educ:* Israel Inst Technol, BS, 54; Univ Pa, MS, 58, PhD(elec eng), 62. *Prof Exp:* Res engr, Radio Corp Am, NJ, 55-56; instr elec eng, Univ Pa, 56-60, res assoc, 60-63; mem tech staff, Comput Systs, Comput Command & Control Co, 63-76; SR COMPUT SCI, COMPUT SCI CORP, 76- *Mem:* Inst Elec & Electronics Engrs. *Res:* Associative and multi-program memory organization; logical design of computer circuits; many-valued and probabilistic logic; theory of automata. *Mailing Add:* Comput Sci Corp 6565 Arlington Blvd Falls Church VA 22042

LANDAW, STEPHEN ARTHUR, b Paterson, NJ, June 20, 36; c 2. INTERNAL MEDICINE, HEMATOLOGY. *Educ:* Univ Wis-Madison, BS, 57; George Washington Univ, MD, 59; Univ Calif, Berkeley, PhD(med physics), 69; Am Bd Internal Med, dipl, 72, cert hemat, 72, cert med oncol, 75; Am Bd Nuclear Med, dipl, 72. *Prof Exp:* Intern, Mt Sinai Hosp, NY, 59-60, asst resident internal med, 60-61; NIH fel med & hemat, Med Col Va, 62-63; Nat Heart Inst fel med physics, Donner Lab, Univ Calif, Berkeley, 63-70; asst physician, Donner Lab, Univ Calif, Berkeley, 70-73, lectr med physics, Univ, 70-72; assoc prof med & radiol, 73-78, PROF MED, STATE UNIV NY UPSTATE MED CTR, 78- *Concurrent Pos:* Attend staff physician, Alameda County Hosp, Oakland, Calif, 69-73; chief isotope lab, 71-73; Nat Heart & Lung Inst career develop award, 70-73; assoc chief staff res, Vet Admin Hosp, Syracuse, NY, 73-; mem attend staff med, Vet Admin Hosp, Univ Hosp & Crouse-Irving Mem Hosp, 73- *Mem:* Fel Am Col Physicians; Am Soc Hemat; Am Fedn Clin Res; Soc Nuclear Med; Soc Exp Biol & Med. *Res:* Red cell membrane studies; quantitative red blood cell kinetics; polycythemic disorders. *Mailing Add:* Vet Admin Hosp Irving Ave & University Pl Syracuse NY 13210

LANDBORG, RICHARD JOHN, b Manchester, Iowa, May 13, 33; m 55; c 4. CHEMISTRY, SCIENCE EDUCATION. *Educ:* Luther Col, Iowa, BA, 55; Univ Iowa, MS, 57, PhD(chem), 59. *Prof Exp:* Part-time instr chem, Cornell Col, 57-58; asst prof, 59-63, chmn dept, 65-67, ASSOC PROF

CHEM, AUGUSTANA COL, SDAK, 63- *Concurrent Pos:* Fulbright exchange prof, Univ Santa Maria Antigua, Panama, 67. *Mem:* AAAS; Am Chem Soc. *Res:* Chemistry of diazomethane particularly the addition cyclization reactions with activated olefinic systems. *Mailing Add:* Dept of Chem Augustana Col Sioux Falls SD 57102

LANDE, ALEXANDER, b Hilversum, Netherlands, Jan 5, 36; US citizen. THEORETICAL NUCLEAR PHYSICS. *Educ:* Cornell Univ, BA, 57; Mass Inst Technol, PhD(theoret physics), 64. *Prof Exp:* Instr, Palmer Phys Lab, Princeton Univ, 63-66; NSF fel, Niels Bohr Inst, 66-68, asst prof, 68-70; vis assoc prof, Nordic Inst Theoret Atomic Physics, 70-72; assoc prof, 72-80, PROF PHYSICS, INST THEORET PHYSICS, STATE UNIV GRONINGEN, 80- *Concurrent Pos:* Chmn, Inst Theoret Physics, 76. *Mem:* Am Phys Soc; Europ Phys Soc; Netherlands Phys Soc. *Res:* Theoretical nuclear structure. *Mailing Add:* Inst for Theoret Physics PO Box 800-WSN Groningen Netherlands

LANDE, KENNETH, b Vienna, Austria, June 5, 32; nat US. ASTROPHYSICS, ELEMENTARY PARTICLE PHYSICS. *Educ:* Columbia Univ, AB, 53, AM, 55, PhD(physics), 58. *Prof Exp:* Asst physics, Columbia Univ, 54-57; from instr to assoc prof, 59-74, PROF PHYSICS, UNIV PA, 74- *Mem:* Am Phys Soc. *Res:* Meson, nuclear and neutrino physics. *Mailing Add:* Dept of Physics Univ of Pa Philadelphia PA 19104

LANDE, RUSSELL SCOTT, b Jackson, Miss, Aug 10, 51. POPULATION GENETICS, EVOLUTION. *Educ:* Univ Calif, Irvine, BS, 72; Harvard Univ, PhD(biol), 76. *Prof Exp:* Fel genetics, Univ Wis-Madison, 76-78; ASST PROF BIOPHYS & THEORET BIOL, UNIV CHICAGO, 78- *Res:* Population genetics and evolution, especially of quantitative characters and chromosomal rearrangements. *Mailing Add:* Dept of Biophys & Theoret Biol 920 E 58th St Chicago IL 60637

LANDE, SAUL, b Philadelphia, Pa, Aug 7, 30; m 54; c 4. BIOCHEMISTRY, ORGANIC CHEMISTRY. *Educ:* Ursinus Col, BS, 48; Univ Pittsburgh, PhD(biochem), 60. *Prof Exp:* Sr res chemist, Squibb Res Inst, 61-63; assoc prof biochem in med, 63-76, ASSOC CLIN PROF DERMAT, SCH MED, YALE UNIV, 77- *Mem:* Am Chem Soc. *Res:* Chemistry of biologically active peptides. *Mailing Add:* Dept of Dermat Yale Univ Sch of Med New Haven CT 06511

LANDE, SHELDON SIDNEY, b Chicago, Ill, July 16, 41; m 64; c 1. ENVIRONMENTAL CHEMISTRY. *Educ:* Ill Inst Technol, BS, 62; Mich State Univ, PhD(chem), 66. *Prof Exp:* Multiple fel petrol, Mellon Inst, 68-70; res chemist, Gulf Res & Develop Co, 70-71; res assoc water chem, Grad Sch Pub Health, Univ Pittsburgh, 71-72; pub health adminr, Allegheny County Health Dept, Pa, 72-75; res assoc, Syracuse Univ Res Corp, 75-79; ENVIRON SPECIALIST, 3M CO, 79- *Mem:* Am Chem Soc. *Res:* Fate of organic substances in soil and water; analysis of organic chemicals in the environment; treatment of hazardous waste, waste-water and landfill leachate. *Mailing Add:* Environ Lab 3M Co PO box 33331 St Paul MN 55133

LANDEFELD, THOMAS DALE, b Columbus, Ohio, Mar 24, 47; m 65; c 2. REPRODUCTIVE ENDOCRINOLOGY, BIOCHEMISTRY. *Educ:* Marietta Col, AB, 69; Univ Wis-Madison, BS & PhD(reproductive endocrinol), 73. *Prof Exp:* Fel endocrinol div, Med Col, Cornell Univ, 73-74; fel obstet & gynec dept, Sch Med, Washington Univ, 74-76; res assoc, 76-77, sr res assoc, 77-78, ASST RES SCIENTIST DEPT PATH, UNIV MICH, ANN ARBOR, 78- *Concurrent Pos:* Prin investr, NIH res grant, Univ Mich, 78-81, co-investr, 79-82. *Mem:* Endocrine Soc; Soc Study Reproduction; Sigma Xi; NY Acad Sci; Am Soc Biol Chemists. *Res:* Pituitary gonadotropins; isolation, purification, and biochemical characterization; mechanisms and control of biosynthesis; mRNA purification and translation; gene expression and regulation; recombinant DNA and cloning. *Mailing Add:* Dept of Path Univ of Mich Ann Arbor MI 48109

LANDEL, AURORA MAMAUAG, b Manila, Philippines, Feb 12, 26; m 53; c 6. BIOCHEMISTRY. *Educ:* Univ Philippines, BS, 49; Univ Wis-Madison, MS, 51, PhD(biochem), 55. *Prof Exp:* Instr org chem, Univ Philippines, 49-50; instr org chem & math, Far Eastern Univ, 49-50; res fel chem, Calif Inst Technol, 68-71, sr res fel biomed eng, 73-79; RES SCIENTIST, CITY HOPE NAT MED CTR, 79- *Mem:* Am Chem Soc; Sigma Xi. *Res:* Preparation of fluorescent tracers in studies of capillary permeability; lipoprotein and lipoprotein lipase studies by means of fluorchromes; studies on lipoprotein metabolism as related to metabolic disorders; assessment of nutritional support of post-operation cancer patients; studies on appetite. *Mailing Add:* Dept Clin Nutrit City Hope Nat Med Ctr Duarte CA 91010

LANDEL, ROBERT FRANKLIN, b Pendleton, NY, Oct 10, 25; m 53; c 6. PHYSICAL CHEMISTRY, RHEOLOGY. *Educ:* Univ Buffalo, BA, 50, MA, 51; Univ Wis, PhD(phys chem), 54. *Prof Exp:* Res assoc, Univ Wis, 54-55; sr res engr, 55-59, chief solid propellant chem sect, 59-61, chief polymer res sect, 61-65, MGR ENERGY & MAT RES SECT, JET PROPULSION LAB, CALIF INST TECHNOL, 75- *Concurrent Pos:* Sr res fel, Calif Inst Technol, 65-69; sr Fulbright fel, Italy, 71-72; sr fel, Ctr Res Macromolecules, France, 72. *Mem:* Am Phys Soc; Am Chem Soc; Soc Rheol. *Res:* Mechanical properties of high polymers. *Mailing Add:* 1027 Sunmore Ln Altadena CA 91001

LANDER, HORACE N(ORMAN), b Cambridge, Mass, May 28, 23; m 43; c 5. METALLURGY. *Educ:* Mass Inst Technol, BS, 51, ScD(metall), 55. *Prof Exp:* Group leader metall, Metal Hydrides, Inc, 54-55; supvr process metall, Jones & Laughlin Steel Corp, 56-60; asst dir res & develop, Youngstown Sheet & Tube Co, 60-62, dir, 62-70; vpres res & develop, Molybdenum & Specialty Metals Div, 70-75, SR VPRES RES & DEVELOP, AM METAL CLIMAX, INC, GREENWICH, 75- *Honors & Awards:* Hunt Award, Am Inst Mining, Metall & Petrol Engrs, 59. *Mem:* Am Soc Metals; Am Inst Mining, Metall & Petrol Engrs; Am Iron & Steel Inst. *Res:* Physical chemistry of metals; industrial research administration; coordination of process and product development programs with management and market objectives. *Mailing Add:* 18 Pilgrim Lane Weston CT 06880

LANDER, JAMES FRENCH, b Bristol, Va, Aug 24, 31; m 60; c 3. GEOPHYSICS, SEISMOLOGY. *Educ:* Pa State Univ, BS, 58; Am Univ, MS, 62, MA, 68. *Prof Exp:* Geophysicist, US Coast & Geod Surv, Nat Oceanic & Atmospheric Admin, 58-62, chief seismol invests sect, 62-63, chief seismol invests br, Environ Res Labs, 63-73, chief, Nat Earthquake Info Ctr, 66-73; DEP DIR, NAT GEOPHYS & SOLAR-TERRESTRIAL DATA CTR, 73- *Concurrent Pos:* With Exec Off of President, Off Emergency Preparedness, 70-71; dir, World Data Ctr-A Solid Earth Geophys, 73- *Mem:* AAAS; Seismol Soc Am; Am Geophys Union; Sigma Xi. *Res:* Seismicity, earthquake intensity, earthquake engineering, strong motion seismology, volcanology, marine geology and geophysics, geomagnitism, geothermics, geodynamics, disaster studies, natural hazard risks, digital data bases, seismic reflections, computer graphics. *Mailing Add:* NOAA/EDS Nat Geophys & Solar Terrestrial Data Ctr Boulder CO 80302

LANDER, RICHARD LEON, b Oakland, Calif, Apr 23, 28; Div; c 3. PHYSICS. *Educ:* Univ Calif, Berkeley, BA, 50, PhD(physics), 58; Ohio State Univ, MA, 51. *Prof Exp:* Staff physicist, Lawrence Radiation Lab, Univ Calif, 58-60; res specialist nuclear physics, Boeing Co, 60-61; assoc res physicist, Univ Calif, San Diego, 61-66; assoc prof physics, 66-70, assoc dean res, Grad Div, 70-73, PROF PHYSICS, UNIV CALIF, DAVIS, 70- *Concurrent Pos:* Vis scientist, Europ Orgn Nuclear Res, Switz, 66-67. *Mem:* AAAS; Am Phys Soc. *Res:* Experimental elementary particle physics. *Mailing Add:* Dept of Physics Univ of Calif Davis CA 95616

LANDERL, HAROLD PAUL, b Pittsburgh, Pa, Apr 26, 22; m 44; c 3. ORGANIC CHEMISTRY. *Educ:* Carnegie Inst Technol, BS, 43, MS, 47, DSc(chem), 48. *Prof Exp:* Asst, Nat Defense Res Comt, Calif Inst Technol, 44-46; res chemist, Jackson Lab, 48-54, supvr res & develop, Tech Lab, 54-60, head textile dye appln div, 60-70, asst dir dyes & chem tech lab, 70-72, tech mgr dyes & chem, Belg, 72-76, tech mgr dyes, Chem, Dyes & Pigments Dept, 76-80, STAFF CONSULT, EMPLOYEE RELATIONS DEPT, E I DU PONT DE NEMOURS & CO, INC, 80- *Mem:* Am Chem Soc; Am Asn Textile Chemists & Colorists. *Res:* Application of dyes to fibers. *Mailing Add:* 1503 Fresno Rd Wilmington DE 19803

LANDERS, EARL JAMES, b Greybull, Wyo, Dec 17, 21; m 51; c 2. INVERTEBRATE ZOOLOGY. *Educ:* Univ Wyo, AB, 50, MS, 52; NY Univ, PhD(zool), 58. *Prof Exp:* Instr zool, Univ Wyo, 55-56; from asst prof to assoc prof biol sci, Tex Western Col, 56-60, actg chmn dept, 59-60; assoc prof zool, 60-70, PROF ZOOL, ARIZ STATE UNIV, 70- *Mem:* AAAS; Am Soc Parasitol. *Res:* Parasitic protozoa life cycles; transmembrane electrolyte transport. *Mailing Add:* Dept of Zool Ariz State Univ Tempe AZ 85281

LANDERS, JAMES WALTER, b Norfolk, Nebr, Oct 19, 27; m 52; c 3. PATHOLOGY. *Educ:* Univ Nebr, MD, 53. *Prof Exp:* Assoc prof, 62-80, CLIN PROF PATH, SCH MED, WAYNE STATE UNIV, 80- *Concurrent Pos:* Assoc pathologist, William Beaumont Hosp, Royal Oak, Mich, 64-68 & St John Hosp, Detroit, 68- *Mem:* Am Soc Clin Path; Col Am Path; Int Acad Path. *Res:* Neuropathology. *Mailing Add:* 1507 Sunningdale Grosse Pointe MI 48236

LANDERS, JOHN HERBERT, JR, b Stockton, Mo, Jan 24, 21; m 43; c 3. ANIMAL NUTRITION. *Educ:* Univ Mo, BS, 42, MS, 50; Kans State Univ, PhD(animal nutrit), 66. *Prof Exp:* County agent agr, Univ Mo, 45-49, instr animal sci, 49-50; from asst prof to prof & exten animal scientist, 50-77, EMER PROF, ORE STATE UNIV, 77- *Mem:* Am Romney Sheep Breeders Asn (secy); Am Soc Animal Sci. *Res:* Counseling and advising livestock growers in more efficient production of meat and fiber. *Mailing Add:* 4375 NE Weslinn Dr Corvallis OR 97333

LANDERS, KENNETH EARL, b Leighton, Ala, Aug 31, 33; m 52; c 3. PLANT PHYSIOLOGY. *Educ:* Florence State Col, BS, 60; Auburn Univ, MS, 63, PhD(bot, zool), 66. *Prof Exp:* Inspector, Reynolds Metals Co, Ala, 52-54, 56-60; res asst bot & plant path, Auburn Univ, 60-61, instr, 62-63; assoc prof biol, 66-71, PROF BIOL, JACKSONVILLE STATE UNIV, 71-, HEAD DEPT, 73- *Mem:* Ecol Soc Am; Am Phytopath Soc. *Res:* Ecology. *Mailing Add:* Dept of Biol Jacksonville State Univ Jacksonville AL 36265

LANDERS, ROGER Q, JR, b Menard, Tex, July 23, 32; m 54; c 2. PLANT ECOLOGY, RANGE MANAGEMENT. *Educ:* Tex A&M Univ, BS, 54, MS, 55; Univ Calif, Berkeley, PhD(bot), 62. *Prof Exp:* From asst prof to assoc prof plant ecol, Iowa State Univ, 62-71, prof, 71-79; EXTEN RANGE SPECIALIST, TEX A&M UNIV SYST, 79- *Mem:* Ecol Soc Am; Soil Conserv Soc Am; Soc Range Mgt. *Res:* Grasslands; prescribed burning management of grazing land by chemical, mechanical and biological methods; prescribed burning to control undesirable brush and cactus and enhance productivity of desirable forage species for livestock and wildlife. *Mailing Add:* Res & Exten Ctr Tex A&M Univ Syst Rt 2 Box 950 San Angelo TX 76901

LANDES, CHESTER GREY, b Lowell, Ind, Dec 22, 03; m 34; c 3. CELLULOSE & PAPER CHEMISTRY. *Educ:* Ohio State Univ, BS, 26. *Prof Exp:* Chem engr, Mead Corp, Tenn & Ohio, 26-34; supt, Fitchburg Paper Co, Mass, 34-36; sr group leader chem, Am Cyanamid Co, 36-58; tech dir, Wica Chem, Inc, 59-60; assoc prof, 60-72, EMER ASSOC PROF WOOD & PAPER SCI, NC STATE UNIV, 72- *Concurrent Pos:* Paper chem consult, 60- *Mem:* Am Chem Soc; Tech Asn Pulp & Paper Indust; Tech Asn Graphic Arts; Am Asn Textile Chemists & Colorists. *Res:* Paper sizing materials; wet strength and dry strength resins for paper; paper coating raw materials and additives; retention and drainage aids for paper making; pulp and paper chemicals and resins in general. *Mailing Add:* PO Box 968 Skyland Asheville NC 28776

LANDES, HUGH S(TEVENSON), b Waynesboro, Va, July 4, 24; m 46; c 1. PHYSICS, ELECTRICAL ENGINEERING. *Educ:* Univ Va, BEE, 53, PhD(physics), 56. *Prof Exp:* Asst prof physics, Univ SC, 56-57; asst prof elec eng, 57-60, ASSOC PROF ELEC ENG, UNIV VA, 60- *Mem:* Nat Soc Prof Engrs; Am Asn Physics Teachers; Inst Elec & Electronics Engrs. *Res:* Electric circuit theory; electromagnetic field theory; microwave devices; ferrite phenomena. *Mailing Add:* Dept of Elec Eng Univ of Va Charlottesville VA 22902

LANDES, ROBERT CARL, b Philadelphia, Pa, Nov 2, 32. NEUROPHARMACOLOGY, NEUROPHYSIOLOGY. *Educ:* Bluffton Col, AB, 54; Univ Ala, MS, 60; Tulane Univ, PhD(pharmacol), 67. *Prof Exp:* Res assoc, G D Searle & Co, 60-64; res pharmacologist, Imp Chem Indust, 67-77; supvr pharmacol, 77-78, prin scientist, 78-79, assoc dir clin res, 79-82, SR SCIENTIST, ADRIA LABS, INC, 82- *Concurrent Pos:* Adj assoc prof, Dept Pharmacol, Ohio State Univ, 77- *Mem:* Soc Neurosci; Am Soc Clin Pharmacol & Therapeut; Am Acad Cerebral Palsy. *Res:* Pharmaceutical research and development, especially motor disorders such as epilepsy and spasticity. *Mailing Add:* Adria Res Lab Box 16529 Columbus OH 43216

LANDESBERG, JOSEPH MARVIN, b New York, NY, Apr 21, 39; m 64; c 2. ORGANIC CHEMISTRY. *Educ:* Rutgers Univ, BS, 60; Harvard Univ, MA, 62, PhD(chem), 65. *Prof Exp:* NIH res fel, Columbia Univ, 64-66; asst prof, Univ, 66-70, assoc prof, 70-75, PROF CHEM, GRAD SCH ARTS & SCI, ADELPHI UNIV, 75- *Mem:* AAAS; Am Chem Soc; The Chem Soc; Am Asn Univ Prof. *Res:* Heterocyclic chemistry; synthetic applications of organometallic compounds; synthesis of strained, small-membered rings. *Mailing Add:* Dept of Chem Adelphi Univ Garden City NY 11530

LANDESMAN, EDWARD MILTON, b Brooklyn, NY, Mar 19, 38. MATHEMATICS. *Educ:* Univ Calif, Los Angeles, BA, 60, MA, 61, PhD(math), 65. *Prof Exp:* Asst prof in residence math, Univ Calif, Los Angeles, 65-66; asst prof, Univ Calif, Santa Cruz, 66-68; asst prof, Univ Calif, Los Angeles, 68-69; asst prof, 69-71, assoc prof, 71-80, PROF MATH, CROWN COL, UNIV CALIF, SANTA CRUZ, 80- *Concurrent Pos:* Air Force Off Sci Res grant, Univ Calif, Santa Cruz, 70-71. *Mem:* AAAS; Am Math Soc; Math Asn Am. *Res:* Partial differential equations; combinatorial theory; calculus. *Mailing Add:* Dept Math Crown Col Univ of Calif Santa Cruz CA 95064

LANDESMAN, HERBERT, b Newark, NJ, Apr 22, 27; m 53; c 2. INORGANIC CHEMISTRY. *Educ:* Harvard Univ, BS, 48; Purdue Univ, PhD(chem), 51. *Prof Exp:* Res chemist, Naval Ord Test Sta, 51-52, Olin Mathieson Chem Corp, 52-59 & Nat Eng Sci Co, 59-66; chem consult, West Precipitation Group, Joy Mfg Co, 66-68; vpres, Environ Resources, Inc, 68-69; PROF CHEM, LOS ANGELES SOUTHWEST COL, 69- *Mem:* Air Pollution Control Asn; Am Chem Soc. *Res:* Organosilicon chemistry; chemistry of boron hydrides; fire extinguishants; fluorocarbons; hazards analysis; air and water pollution. *Mailing Add:* Dept of Chem Los Angeles Southwest Col Los Angeles CA 90047

LANDESMAN, RICHARD, b Brooklyn, NY, Jan 30, 40. DEVELOPMENTAL BIOLOGY. *Educ:* NY Univ, BA, 61, MS, 63; Univ BC, PhD(zool), 66. *Prof Exp:* NIH fel biol, Mass Inst Technol, 66-69; ASSOC PROF ZOOL, UNIV VT, 69- *Mem:* Soc Develop Biol. *Res:* Cellular and molecular basis of limb regeneration; fracture healing in the newt. *Mailing Add:* Dept of Zool Univ of Vt Burlington VT 05405

LANDGRAF, RONALD WILLIAM, b Freeport, Ill, Mar 7, 39; m 62; c 2. FATIGUE, FRACTURE. *Educ:* Carnegie Inst Technol, BS, 61; Univ Ill, Urbana, MS, 66, PhD(theoret & appl mech), 68. *Prof Exp:* Mat engr, Micro Switch Div, Honeywell, Inc, 61-65; res assoc theoret & appl mech, Univ Ill, Urbana, 66-68; res scientist, Sci Res Staff, 68-77, mem eng & res staff, 77-79, STAFF SCIENTIST, ENG & RES STAFF, FORD MOTOR CO, 79- *Concurrent Pos:* Assoc ed, Fatigue of Eng, Mat & Struct, 79- *Mem:* Am Soc Metals; Am Inst Mining, Metall & Petrol Engrs; Am Soc Testing & Mat; Soc Automotive Engrs. *Res:* Cyclic deformation and fracture behavior of metals and alloys; influence of metallurgical structure on fatigue crack initiation and propagation; development of fatigue design procedures. *Mailing Add:* Eng & Res Staff Ford Motor Co PO Box 2053 Dearborn MI 48121

LANDGRAF, WILLIAM CHARLES, b Elizabeth, NJ, Jan 10, 28; m 53; c 3. PHARMACEUTICAL CHEMISTRY, SOFTWARE SYSTEMS. *Educ:* Seton Hall Univ, BS, 50; Stanford Univ, PhD(chem), 59; Univ Santa Clara, MBA, 75. *Prof Exp:* Sr scientist chem, Lockheed Res Labs, Lockheed Missile Systs Div, 58-61; proj leader & lab supt, Ampex Corp, 61-63; mgr & res scientist, Varian Assocs, Calif, 63-70; MGR, SYNTEX LABS, 70- *Mem:* Am Chem Soc; Am Pharmaceut Asn. *Res:* Physical, biophysical and organic chemistry; kinetics; computer assisted experimentation; analytical chemistry; physical organic chemistry. *Mailing Add:* 3401 Hillview Ave Palo Alto CA 94304

LANDGREBE, ALBERT R, b New Rochelle, NY, Mar 4, 33; m 58; c 2. CHEMISTRY. *Educ:* Fordham Univ, BS, 57; Univ Md, PhD(chem), 64. *Prof Exp:* Inorg chemist, USDA, 60-63; radiochemist, Nat Bur Standards, Md, 63-68; chemist & chmn comt sci & tech symposia, AEC, 68-75; BR CHIEF CHEM STORAGE, ENERGY RES & DEVELOP ADMIN, 75- *Mem:* AAAS; Soc Nuclear Med; Sigma Xi; Am Chem Soc. *Res:* Use of radioisotopes in analytical and inorganic chemistry; radio chromatographic methods; substoichiometric radioisotopic dilution analysis; removal of radioisotopes from milk; activation analysis; trace and micro analysis. *Mailing Add:* Almar Res Lab 3201 Dunnington Rd Beltsville MD 20705

LANDGREBE, DAVID ALLEN, b Huntingburg, Ind, Apr 12, 34; m 59; c 1. ELECTRICAL ENGINEERING. *Educ:* Purdue Univ, BSEE, 56, MSEE, 58, PhD(elec eng), 62. *Prof Exp:* From asst prof to assoc prof, 62-70, dir, Lab Applications Remote Sensing, 69-81 PROF ELEC ENG, PURDUE UNIV, 70-, ASSOC DEAN ENG & DIR, ENG EXP STA, 81- *Concurrent Pos:* Consult, Earlham Col, 63 & Douglas Aircraft Co, 64-70. *Honors & Awards:* Except Sci Achievement Medal, NASA, 73. *Mem:* Fel Inst Elec & Electronics Engrs; Am Soc Eng Educ; AAAS. *Res:* Representation and analysis of signals; data processing. *Mailing Add:* Assoc Dean Eng Purdue Univ West Lafayette IN 47907

LANDGREBE, JOHN A, b San Francisco, Calif, May 6, 37; m 61; c 2. ORGANIC CHEMISTRY. *Educ:* Univ Calif, Berkeley, BS, 59; Univ Ill, Urbana, PhD(org chem), 62. *Prof Exp:* From asst prof to assoc prof, 62-71, assoc chmn, 67-70, chmn, 70-80, PROF CHEM, UNIV KANS, 71- *Mem:* Am Chem Soc; The Chem Soc. *Res:* Organic reaction mechanisms; small ring compounds; carbine intermediates; reactions of carbonylides. *Mailing Add:* Dept of Chem Univ of Kans Lawrence KS 66044

LANDGREN, CRAIG RANDALL, b St Paul, Minn, Dec 20, 47. PLANT TISSUE CULTURE, PLANT DEVELOPMENT. *Educ:* Albion Col, BA, 69; Harvard Univ, MA, 70, PhD(biol), 74. *Prof Exp:* Asst prof, George Mason Univ, 74-77; vis asst prof, Univ Ore, 76-77; ASST PROF BIOL, MIDDLEBURY COL, 77- *Concurrent Pos:* Res grant, George Mason Found, 75-76; res assoc, Univ Ore, 78, 79, 80 & 81; vis scientist, US-USSR Nat Acad Sci Exchange Prog, 80. *Mem:* Scand Soc Plant Physiol; Sigma Xi. *Res:* Studies in the culture and differentiation of isolated plant cells and plant cell protoplasts; electron microscopy; genetic engineering through organelle transplantation and cell fusion. *Mailing Add:* Dept of Biol Middlebury Col Middlebury VT 05753

LANDGREN, JOHN JEFFREY, b St Paul, Minn, Nov 16, 47; m 77. MATHEMATICS, FUNCTIONAL ANALYSIS. *Educ:* Univ Minn, BS, 69, MS, 71, PhD(math), 76. *Prof Exp:* Vis asst prof math, Ga Inst Technol, 76-78; asst prof math, Univ Tenn, 78-80; RES SCIENTIST, GA INST TECHNOL, 80- *Mem:* Sigma Xi; Soc Indust & Appl Math. *Res:* Functional analysis, in particular, essentially self-adjoint operators; these operators are typically partial differential equations from quantum mechanics. *Mailing Add:* Eng Exp Sta Ga Inst Technol Atlanta GA 30332

LANDING, BENJAMIN HARRISON, b Buffalo, NY, Sept 11, 20; m 49; c 4. PATHOLOGY. *Educ:* Harvard Univ, AB, 42; Harvard Med Sch, MD, 45. *Prof Exp:* Intern, Children's Hosp, Boston, 45-46; res pathologist, Children's Med Ctr, Boston, 48-50, asst pathologist, 50-52, assoc pathologist, 52-53; from asst to instr & assoc path, Harvard Med Sch, 48-53; from asst prof to assoc prof path & pediat, Col Med, Univ Cincinnati, 53-61; prof path & pediat, 61-76, WINZER PROF PATH & PEDIAT, UNIV SOUTHERN CALIF, 76-; PATHOLOGISTINCHIEF & DIR LABS, CHILDREN'S HOSP, LOS ANGELES, 61- *Concurrent Pos:* Res pathologist, Free Hosp for Women & Boston Lying-In-Hosp, 49; dir pathologist, Children's Hosp & Res Found, Cincinnati, 53-61. *Mem:* Histochem Soc; Endocrine Soc; Am Asn Path & Bact (asst secy, 53-57); Int Acad Path. *Res:* Histochemistry of endocrine and metabolic diseases; pediatric pathology. *Mailing Add:* Children's Hosp 4650 Sunset Blvd Los Angeles CA 90027

LANDIS, ABRAHAM L, b New York, NY, May 25, 28; m 57; c 2. CHEMISTRY. *Educ:* City Col New York, BS, 51; Univ Kans, PhD(chem), 55. *Prof Exp:* Asst chem, Univ Kans, 51-55; aeronaut res scientist, Nat Adv Comt Aeronaut, 55-56; sr res chemist, Atomics Int Div, NAm Rockwell, Inc, 56-61; sr staff chemist, 61-80, SR SCIENTIST, HUGHES AIRCRAFT CO, CULVER CITY, 61- *Mem:* Am Chem Soc; Sigma Xi; Am Inst Chem. *Res:* High temperature polymers; polymer chemistry; vacuum technology; organic synthesis; organometallic polymers; aerospace materials. *Mailing Add:* 10935 Canby Ave Northridge CA 91326

LANDIS, CHARLES WALTER, b Logansport, Ind, Sept 16, 20; m 53; c 2. PSYCHIATRY. *Educ:* DePauw Univ, AB, 42; Ind Univ, MD, 51. *Prof Exp:* Instr psychiat, Sch Med & dir, Riley Child Guid Clin, Ind Univ, 56-58; med dir, Milwaukee County Hosp Ment Dis, 58; from asst prof to assoc prof psychiat, Med Col Wis, 64-71; MED DIR & CHIEF STAFF, ST MARY'S HILL HOSP, 71- *Concurrent Pos:* Consult, Ind State Hosps, 56-58; dir ment health, Milwaukee County Insts & Depts, 58-71; consult, NIMH, 64-66; clin prof psychiat & social welfare, Univ Wis, 65-69; deleg, White House Conf Aging, 71. *Mem:* AMA; Am Psychiat Asn; Am Col Psychiat. *Res:* Public and private mental health services. *Mailing Add:* St Mary's Hill Hosp 2350 N Lake Dr Milwaukee WI 53211

LANDIS, E K, b Pulaski, Va, June 17, 30; m 65; c 1. CHEMICAL ENGINEERING. *Educ:* Va Polytech Inst, BS, 54; Univ Va, MChE, 55; Carnegie Inst Technol, PhD(chem eng), 59. *Prof Exp:* From asst prof to assoc prof, 59-65, PROF CHEM ENG, UNIV ALA, TUSCALOOSA, 65- *Concurrent Pos:* Consult, US Army Missile Command, 61- & US Bur Mines, 62-; Ford Found prof, Carnegie Inst Technol, 64. *Mem:* Am Inst Chem Engrs; Am Soc Eng Educ. *Res:* Combustion instability; thermodynamics of solution; mass transfer in fixed beds; mass and energy transfer across living cell walls. *Mailing Add:* Col of Eng Univ of Ala Tuscaloosa University AL 35486

LANDIS, EDWARD EVERETT, b Marion, Kans, June 15, 07; m 34; c 2. PSYCHIATRY. *Educ:* NCent Col, Ill, BA, 28; Northwestern Univ, MD, 34; Am Bd Psychiat & Neurol, dipl, 46. *Prof Exp:* Nat Comt Ment Hyg fel child psychiat, Louisville Ment Hyg Clin, 37-38; instr, 38-39, from asst prof to prof psychiat, 41-75, actg chmn dept, 73, vchmn dept, 74-75, PROF EMER PSYCHIAT, SCH MED, UNIV LOUISVILLE, 75- *Concurrent Pos:* Rockefeller fel neurol & res, Johnson Found, Univ Pa, 39-40; founder & dir dept electroencephalog, Sch Med, Univ Louisville & Dept Psychiat, Louisville & Jefferson County Children's Home, 40-47, mem gov bd, 51-; clin dir psychiat, Louisville Gen Hosp, 42-45, med dir outpatient clin, 45-49; asst dir psychiat, Louisville Ment Hyg Clin, 42-51 & Norton Mem Infirmary, 45-; med dir psychiat, Norton Psychiat Clin, 49-75; psychiat consult, Louisville Vet Admin, Kosair Crippled Children's, Jewish & Our Lady of Peace Hosps. *Mem:* Fel Am Col Physician; fel Am Psychiat Asn; Am Acad Child Psychiat; AMA. *Res:* Grantham type pre-frontal lobotomy; D-Lysergic acid diethylamide; vitamin B-complex in alcohol addiction. *Mailing Add:* Rte 2 Box 77 Anchorage KY 40223

LANDIS, EUGENE MARKLEY, b New Hope, Pa, Apr 4, 01; m 34; c 1. PHYSIOLOGY, MEDICINE. *Educ:* Univ Pa, BS, 22, MS, 24, MD, 26, PhD, 27. *Hon Degrees:* MS, Yale Univ, AM, Harvard Univ, 43. *Prof Exp:* Asst zool, Univ Pa, 20-21, asst instr, 21-22; fel, Nat Res Coun, 26-27; intern, Hosp Univ Pa, 27-29; fel, Guggenheim Mem Found, 29-31; assoc med, Univ Pa, 31-35, res assoc, 32-39, asst prof, 35-39; prof internal med & head dept, Univ Va, 39-43; George Higginson prof physiol, 43-67, chmn div med sci, Fac Arts & Sci, 49-52, EMER PROF PHYSIOL, HARVARD MED SCH, 67- *Concurrent Pos:* Secy comt aviation med, Nat Res Coun, 40-46, chmn subcomt acceleration, 41-46; mem sci adv coun, Life Ins Med Res Fund, 45-51, chmn, 51; mem panel physiol, Res & Develop Bd, 48-51, chmn, 51; spec lectr, Univ London, 52; consult, AEC, 52; Graves lectr, Ind Univ, 53; consult, Vet Admin, 56-59; ed, Circulation Res, Am Heart Asn, 62-66; adj prof, Lehigh Univ, 67-72. *Honors & Awards:* Phillips Medal, Am Col Physicians, 36; Gold Heart Award, Am Heart Asn, 66. *Mem:* Nat Acad Sci; Am Soc Clin Invest (secy, 38-42, pres, 42); Am Physiol Soc (pres, 52); hon mem Harvey Soc; fel Am Col Physicians. *Res:* Physiology of circulation, particularly blood capillaries; hypertension; kidney disease; edema. *Mailing Add:* 1547 Silver Creek Dr Hellertown PA 18055

LANDIS, FRED, b Munich, Ger, Mar 21, 23; nat US; m 51; c 3. MECHANICAL ENGINEERING. *Educ:* McGill Univ, BE, 45; Mass Inst Technol, SM, 49, ScD(mech eng), 50. *Prof Exp:* Design engr, Can Vickers, Ltd, 45-47; asst, Mass Inst Technol, 48-50; asst prof mech eng, Stanford Univ, 50-52; thermodyn res engr, Northrop Aircraft, Inc, 52-53; from asst prof to prof mech eng, NY Univ, 61-73, chmn dept, 63-73; prof & dean Intercampus Progs, Polytech Inst New York, 73-74; DEAN, COL ENG & APPL SCI, UNIV WIS-MILWAUKEE, 74- *Concurrent Pos:* Mem, New York State Comn on Primary & Secondary Educ, 71; staff consult, Pratt & Whitney Aircraft, 57- *Mem:* Fel Am Soc Mech Engrs; assoc fel Am Inst Aeronaut & Astronaut; Am Soc Eng Educ. *Res:* Thermodynamics; fluid mechanics; heat transfer; manpower economics. *Mailing Add:* Col Eng & Appl Sci Univ Wis Milwaukee WI 53201

LANDIS, G(IVEN) A(RNOLD), metallurgical engineering, deceased

LANDIS, JAMES NOBLE, b Champaign, Ill, Aug 18, 99; m 22; c 3. MECHANICAL ENGINEERING. *Educ:* Univ Mich, BSME, 22. *Prof Exp:* Mech engr, Brooklyn Edison Co, 23-38; mgr contract control, inspection dept & asst mech engr, Consol Edison Co, NY, 38-48; chief power engr, 48-52, vpres, 53-64, exec consult, 64-69, CONSULT, BECHTEL CORP, SAN FRANCISCO, 69- *Honors & Awards:* James N Landis Award. *Mem:* Nat Acad Eng; hon mem & fel Am Soc Mech Engrs (past pres); fel Am Nuclear Soc; Sigma Xi. *Mailing Add:* 2701 Golden Rain Rd Walnut Creek CA 94595

LANDIS, PHILLIP SHERWOOD, b York, Pa, July 29, 22; m 44; c 2. ORGANIC CHEMISTRY. *Educ:* Franklin & Marshall Col, BS, 43; Univ Ky, MS, 47; Northwestern Univ, PhD(chem), 58. *Prof Exp:* Chemist, Cities Serv Refining Corp, 43-45; res chemist, Mobil Oil Corp, 47-63, res assoc, 63-66, sr res assoc, 66-69, MGR PROD RES GROUP, MOBIL RES & DEVELOP CORP, 69- *Concurrent Pos:* Adj prof, Glassboro State Col, 81- *Mem:* Am Chem Soc. *Res:* Mechanisms and kinetics of organic reactions; pyrolysis of organic compounds; organo-sulfur compounds; petrochemicals; radical reactions. *Mailing Add:* Mobil Res & Develop Corp Paulsboro NJ 08066

LANDIS, STORY CLELAND, b New York, NY, May 14, 45; m 69. NEUROBIOLOGY. *Educ:* Wellesley Col, BA, 67; Harvard Univ, MA, 70, PhD(biol), 73. *Prof Exp:* NIH fel neuropath, 73-75, RES FEL NEUROBIOL, HARVARD MED SCH, 75-, INSTR, 80- *Mem:* Am Asn Anatomists; Soc Neurosci; Am Soc Cell Biol. *Res:* Developmental neurobiology; cell biology. *Mailing Add:* Dept of Neurobiol Harvard Med Sch Boston MA 02115

LANDIS, VINCENT J, b Minneapolis, Minn, Oct 27, 28; m 50; c 6. INORGANIC CHEMISTRY. *Educ:* Wash State Univ, BS, 50; Univ Minn, PhD(inorg chem), 57. *Prof Exp:* From instr to assoc prof, 54-65, PROF CHEM, SAN DIEGO STATE UNIV, 65- *Concurrent Pos:* Richland fac fel, Univ Wash, 64-65. *Mem:* Am Chem Soc. *Res:* Metal coordination compounds; radiochemistry. *Mailing Add:* Dept of Chem San Diego State Univ San Diego CA 92182

LANDMAN, ALFRED, b Vienna, Austria, June 29, 33; US citizen. ATOMIC PHYSICS. *Educ:* Univ Pa, AB, 54; Columbia Univ, PhD(physics), 63. *Prof Exp:* Lectr physics, Brooklyn Col, 59-62; res assoc, Columbia Univ, 63; res assoc chem physics, Inst Study Metals, Univ Chicago, 63-64; res engr physics, Gen Tel & Electronics Labs, 65-66, adv res engr, 66-67; physicist, NASA Electronics Res Ctr, 67-70; GEN ENGR, TRANSP SYSTS CTR, US DEPT TRANSP, 70- *Mem:* Am Phys Soc. *Res:* Spectroscopy; optical pumping; gas laser molecular stark effect; synthetic fuels. *Mailing Add:* 29 Tyler Rd Lexington MA 02173

LANDMAN, DONALD ALAN, b New York, NY, Apr 23, 38; m 70; c 2. SOLAR PHYSICS, ATOMIC PHYSICS. *Educ:* Columbia Univ, AB, 59, MA, 61, PhD(physics), 65. *Prof Exp:* Asst prof physics, NY Univ, Bronx, 65-69; res scientist, Cornell Aeronaut Lab, Buffalo, 70 & Advan Res Instrument Systs Inc, 71; assoc astronomer, 72-79, ASTRONOMER SOLAR PHYSICS, INST ASTRON, UNIV HAWAII, 79- *Mem:* Am Astron Soc; Am Phys Soc; Int Astron Union. *Res:* Application of theoretical and experimental atomic physics to astrophysical problems, especially in the area of solar physics research; development of modern astrophysical instrumentation. *Mailing Add:* Inst Astron Univ Hawaii 2680 Woodlawn Dr Honolulu HI 96822

LANDMAN, OTTO ERNEST, b Mannheim, Ger, Feb 15, 25; nat US; m 48; c 3. MICROBIAL GENETICS. *Educ:* Queens Col, BS, 47; Yale Univ, MS, 48, PhD(microbiol), 51. *Prof Exp:* USPHS fel, Calif Inst Technol, 51-52; res assoc bact, Univ Ill, 53-56; chief microbial genetics br, US Army Biol Labs, Ft Detrick, 56-61, sr investr, 61-63; assoc prof biol, 63-66, PROF BIOL, GEORGETOWN UNIV, 66- *Concurrent Pos:* NIH spec fel, Ctr Molecular Genetics, Nat Ctr Sci Res, Gif-Sur-Yvette, France, 68-69; vis investr, Nat Inst Med Res, Mill Hill, London, 75-76. *Mem:* AAAS; Am Soc Microbiol; Genetics Soc Am. *Res:* Protoplasts and L forms of bacteria; cell division; wall biosynthesis and transformation in bacteria; phage infection of protoplasts; gene expression in dicaryotic bacterial system. *Mailing Add:* Dept of Biol Georgetown Univ Washington DC 20057

LANDMANN, WENDELL AUGUST, b Waterloo, Ill, Dec 29, 19; m 44; c 2. BIOCHEMISTRY. *Educ:* Univ Ill, BS, 41; Purdue Univ, MS, 44, PhD(biochem), 51. *Prof Exp:* Chemist, US Naval Res Lab, 43-46; asst chem, Purdue Univ, 46-51; res chemist, Armour & Co, 51-55; assoc biochem, Argonne Nat Lab, 55-57; chief div anal & phys chem, Am Meat Inst Found, Ill, 57-64; prof animal sci, biochem & nutrit, 64-70, King Ranch chair, 64-72, PROF BIOCHEM & BIOPHYS, TEX A&M UNIV, 70-, PROF ANIMAL SCI & FOOD SCI, 78- *Mem:* AAAS; Am Chem Soc; Inst Food Technol; Am Meat Sci Asn; Am Inst Nutrit. *Res:* Lysosomal enzymes; human nutrition; protein chemistry; chemistry of muscle tissues; nutrient bioavailability. *Mailing Add:* Dept Animal Sci Tex A&M Univ College Station TX 77843

LANDO, BARBARA ANN, b Elizabeth, NJ, Dec 7, 40; m 65. ALGEBRA. *Educ:* Georgian Court Col, BA, 62; Rutgers Univ, New Brunswick, MS, 64, PhD(math), 69. *Prof Exp:* Instr math, Douglass Col, Rutgers Univ, New Brunswick, 69; asst prof, 69-73, ASSOC PROF MATH, UNIV ALASKA, FAIRBANKS, 73- *Mem:* Am Math Soc; Math Asn Am; Inst Elec & Electronics Engrs; Asn Comput Mach. *Res:* Differential algebra. *Mailing Add:* Dept of Math Univ of Alaska Fairbanks AK 99701

LANDO, JEROME B, b Brooklyn, NY, May 23, 32; m 62; c 2. POLYMER SCIENCE. *Educ:* Cornell Univ, BA, 53; Polytech Inst Brooklyn, PhD(chem), 63. *Prof Exp:* Fel, Polytech Inst Brooklyn, 63; res chemist, Camille Dreyfus Lab, Res Triangle Inst, 63-65; asst prof polymer sci & eng, 65-68, assoc prof macromolecular sci, 68-74, PROF & CHMN MACROMOLECULAR SCI, CASE WESTERN RESERVE UNIV, 74- *Concurrent Pos:* Humboldt Found Sr Am Scientist Award, 74; vis prof, Univ Mainz, 74. *Mem:* Am Chem Soc; Am Crystallog Asn; Am Phys Soc. *Res:* Polymer physical chemistry; solid state reactions, especially polymerization reactions and polymer crystal structure. *Mailing Add:* Dept of Macromolecular Sci Case Western Reserve Univ Cleveland OH 44106

LANDOLL, LEO MICHAEL, b Cleveland, Ohio, Oct 11, 50; m 71; c 2. POLYMER CHEMISTRY. *Educ:* Kent State Univ, BA, 70; Univ Del, MBA, 82; Univ Akron, PhD(polymer sci), 75. *Prof Exp:* res chemist, 74-79, SR RES CHEMIST POLYMER SYNTHESIS, HERCULES INC, 79- *Mem:* Am Chem Soc. *Res:* Polymer synthesis related to thermoplastic and thermoset systems, fibers, property correlations; synthesis and structure property relations of natural and synthetic water soluble polymers; steric stabilization of particles in suspension. *Mailing Add:* Hercules Res Ctr Hercules Inc Wilmington DE 19808

LANDOLT, ARLO UDELL, b Highland, Ill, Sept 29, 35; m 66; c 5. ASTRONOMY. *Educ:* Miami Univ, BA, 55; Ind Univ, MA, 60, PhD(astron), 62. *Prof Exp:* Scientist aurora & airglow, US Int Geophys Year Comt, 56-58; from asst prof to assoc prof physics & astron, 62-68, PROF PHYSICS & ASTRON, LA STATE UNIV, BATON ROUGE, 68-, DIR OBSERV, 70- *Concurrent Pos:* Mem first wintering-over party, Int Geophys Year Amundson-Scott S Pole Sta, Antarctica, 57; Grad Res Coun res grants, La State Univ, Baton Rouge, 64-76; res grants, NSF, 64-77 & Res Corp, 65 & NASA, 65-67; Air Force Off Sci Res, grants, 77-82; prog dir, NSF, Washington, DC, 75-76; guest investr, Dyer Observ, Vanderbilt Univ, Goethe Link Observ, Ind Univ, Kitt Peak Nat Observ, Cerro Tololo Inter-Am Observ, La Serena, Chile. *Mem:* AAAS; Int Astron Union; Am Astron Soc (pres, 80); Royal Astron Soc; Am Polar Soc. *Res:* Photographic and photoelectric narrow band phoeoelectric and spectroscopic investigations of star clusters, variable stars, and eclipsing binaries; standard photometric systems; variable stars; galactic structure. *Mailing Add:* Dept of Physics & Astron La State Univ Baton Rouge LA 70803

LANDOLT, JACK PETER, b Zurich, Switz, Mar 17, 34; Can citizen; m 64; c 5. SPATIAL DISORIENTATION, BIODYNAMICS. *Educ:* Univ Ottawa, BASc, 59, MSc, 62; Iowa State Univ Sci & Technol, PhD(elec eng), 68. *Prof Exp:* Defence scientist oper res, Can Army Oper Res Estab, 61-65; defence scientist vestibular physiol, 68-75, group head motion sickness biodynamics, 75-76, sect head disorientation biodynamics, 76-80, SECT HEAD BIOPHYS, DEFENCE & CIVIL INST ENVIRON MED, 80- *Concurrent Pos:* mem, Can Adv Comt, Int Standardization Org, 77-, Aerospace Med Panel, Adv Group, Aerospace Res & Develop, NATO, 78- *Mem:* Soc Neurosci; Can Med & Biol Engrs Soc; Barany Soc. *Res:* Neurobiology of peripheral vestibular apparatus; inner ear problems in diving; vestibular-visual interactions in visual cortex; role of efferent vestibular pathways in pilot orientation; impact protection of the human; author or coauthor of over 50 publications. *Mailing Add:* Defence & Civil Inst Environ Med 1133 Sheppard Ave W Downsview ON M3M 3B9 Can

LANDOLT, MARSHA LAMERLE, b Houston, Tex, Jan 19, 48. FISH PATHOLOGY, TOXICOLOGY. *Educ:* Baylor Univ, BS, 69; Univ Okla, MS, 70; George Washington Univ, PhD(path), 76. *Prof Exp:* Asst prof, 75-79, ASSOC PROF FISHERIES, SCH FISHERIES, UNIV WASH, 79-, ASST DIR, 80- *Concurrent Pos:* Histopathologist, Eastern Fish Dis Lab, US Dept Interior, Leetown, WVa, 70-74; path clerk, Dept Animal Health, Nat Zool Park, Smithsonian Inst, Washington, DC, 74-75. *Mem:* NY Acad Sci; Soc Invertebrate Path; Am Fish Soc; Wildlife Dis Asn; Nat Shellfish Asn. *Res:* Development of in vitro test systems for use in poikilothermic toxicological research; wildlife pathology. *Mailing Add:* Sch Fisheries Univ Wash Seattle WA 98195

LANDOLT, PAUL ALBERT, b Shubert, Nebr, July 10, 12; m 35; c 1. PHYSIOLOGY. *Educ:* Nebr State Teachers Col, Peru, BA, 33; Univ Nebr, MS, 51, PhD(zool, physiol), 60. *Prof Exp:* Teacher, High Schs, Nebr, 36-42; field dir mil welfare, Am Red Cross, Mariannas Islands, 42-46; instr biol sci, Scottsbluff Jr Col, Nebr, 46-53; from instr to assoc prof physiol, 53-74, prof physiol, 74-77, EMER PHYSIOL, UNIV NEBR, LINCOLN, 77- *Concurrent Pos:* Instr, Southeast Community Col, Lincoln, 77- *Mem:* AAAS; Am Soc Cell Biol; Am Soc Zool; Tissue Cult Asn. *Res:* Vertebrate physiology; tissue culture; problems related to effects of air pollutants on lung tissue. *Mailing Add:* Sch of Life Sci Univ of Nebr Lincoln NE 68588

LANDOLT, ROBERT GEORGE, b Houston, Tex, Apr 4, 39; m 62; c 3. ORGANIC CHEMISTRY. *Educ:* Austin Col, BA, 61; Univ Tex, PhD(org chem), 65. *Prof Exp:* Res assoc org chem, Univ Ill, 65-67; asst prof org chem, Muskingum Col, 67-71, chmn dept, 71-74, assoc prof, 71-80; sr scientist, Radian Corp, 80-81; ASSOC PROF & CHMN, CHEM DEPT, TEX WESLEYAN COL, 81- *Concurrent Pos:* Resident consult, Columbus Labs, Battelle Mem Inst, 74-75. *Mem:* AAAS; Am Asn Univ Prof; Am Chem Soc. *Res:* Abnormal claisen rearrangement and reactions in aprotic polar solvents; nitroso aromatic compounds; oxidation of coal and coal model compounds; computer assisted information retrieval; origin of organic pollutants in water. *Mailing Add:* Dept Chem Texas Wesleyan Col Ft Worth TX 76105

LANDOLT, ROBERT RAYMOND, b Sherman, Tex, May 11, 37; m 70; c 3. BIONUCLEONICS. *Educ:* Austin Col, BA, 59; Univ Kans, MS, 61; Purdue Univ, PhD(bionucleonics), 68. *Prof Exp:* Reactor health physicist, Phillips Petrol Co, Idaho, 61-64; from instr to assoc prof, 64-81, PROF BIONUCLEONICS, PURDUE UNIV, WEST LAFAYETTE, IND, 81- *Mem:* Health Physics Soc. *Res:* Effects of ionizing radiation on prostaglandins in tumors; measurement of neutron doses using threshold detectors; activation analysis with isotopic nutron sources. *Mailing Add:* Dept of Bionucleonics Purdue Univ West Lafayette IN 47906

LANDON, DONALD OMAR, b Champaign, Ill, Apr 19, 26; m 46. PHYSICS, CHEMISTRY. *Prof Exp:* Asst chemist, Armour Res Found, Ill Inst Technol, 49-54; group leader instrument anal, Sperry Gyroscope Co, 54-58; dir res, 58-69, vpres res, Spex Industs, Inc, 69-76; dir res & develop, 76-81, SPEC PROJ MGR, TRACOR ANAL, INSTRUMENTS SA, INC, 81- *Concurrent Pos:* Consult, Wall St Authority, 55- *Mem:* AAAS; Soc Appl Spectros; Optical Soc Am. *Res:* Instrumentation for optical spectroscopy, particularly vacuum ultraviolet spectrometers and Raman instrumentation. *Mailing Add:* 6 Robin Rd Warren NJ 07060

LANDON, ERWIN JACOB, b Cleveland, Ohio, Jan 22, 25; m 65. BIOCHEMISTRY. *Educ:* Univ Chicago, BS, 45, MD, 48; Univ Calif, PhD(biochem), 53. *Prof Exp:* Intern, Harper Hosp, Detroit, Mich, 48-49; asst prof, 59-67, ASSOC PROF PHARMACOL, SCH MED, VANDERBILT UNIV, 67- *Concurrent Pos:* Sr res fel pharmacol, Sch Med, Yale Univ, 57-59. *Mem:* Am Chem Soc; Am Soc Pharmacol & Exp Therapeut. *Res:* Biochemistry of renal transport; cell calcium regulation. *Mailing Add:* Dept of Pharmacol Vanderbilt Univ Nashville TN 37203

LANDON, JOHN CAMPBELL, b Hornell, NY, Jan 3, 37; m 58; c 4. VIROLOGY, CANCER. *Educ:* Alfred Univ, AB, 59; George Washington Univ, MS, 62, PhD(biol), 67. *Prof Exp:* Biologist, Nat Cancer Inst, 60-65; head virol, Litton Bionetics, Inc, 65-68, dir dept virol & cell biol, 68-71, dir spec prog develop, 71-72, dir sci, Frederick Cancer Res Ctr, 72-75; PRES, MASON RES INST, 75- *Mem:* AAAS; Tissue Cult Asn; Am Soc Cell Biol; NY Acad Sci; Am Soc Microbiol. *Res:* Viral oncology; tissue culture; general human and simian virology; cell biology; environmental biology. *Mailing Add:* 8213 Raymond Ln Potomac MD 20854

LANDON, ROBERT E, b Chicago, Ill, June 1, 05; m 35. GEOLOGY. *Educ:* Univ Chicago, SB, 26, PhD(geol), 29. *Prof Exp:* Instr, YMCA Col, 28-29; geologist, Anaconda Copper Mining Co, 29-30; asst geologist, US Geol Surv, 30-31; instr geol, Colo Col, 31-33; consult mining geologist, 33-39; sr mining securities analyst, US Securities & Exchange Comn, 40-45; geologist, Mobil Oil Corp, NY, 45-70; geol consult, 70-81; RETIRED. *Mem:* Fel Geol Soc Am; Am Asn Petrol Geol. *Mailing Add:* 3460 S Race St Englewood CO 80110

LANDOR, JOHN HENRY, b Canton, Ohio, Sept 30, 27; m 53; c 6. SURGERY. *Educ:* Univ Chicago, PhB, 48, MD, 53. *Prof Exp:* Instr surg, Sch Med, Univ Chicago, 58; from instr to prof, Sch Med, Univ Mo-Columbia, 59-69; prof, Col Med, Univ Fla, 69-72; PROF & CHIEF GEN SURG, COL MED & DENT NJ, RUTGERS MED SCH, 72-; CHIEF DEPT SURG, RARITAN VALLEY HOSP, GREEN BROOK, 73- *Concurrent Pos:* Commonwealth Found fel, Royal Postgrad Med Sch, London, 66-67. *Mem:* Am Col Surgeons; Soc Univ Surgeons; Am Gastroenterol Asn; Soc Surg Alimentary Tract; Int Soc Surgeons. *Res:* Physiology of the stomach. *Mailing Add:* Dept of Surg Col Med & Dent NJ Rutgers Med Sch Piscataway NJ 08854

LANDOVITZ, LEON FRED, theoretical physics, see previous edition

LANDOWNE, DAVID, b Chicago, Ill, Dec 26, 42; m 66; c 2. PHYSIOLOGY, BIOPHYSICS. *Educ:* Mass Inst Technol, BS, 63; Harvard Univ, PhD(physiol), 68. *Prof Exp:* Res assoc pharmacol, Sch Med, Yale Univ, 68-70, 71-72; asst prof physiol, 72-75, ASSOC PROF PHYSIOL, SCH MED, UNIV MIAMI, 75- *Concurrent Pos:* Grass Found fel, 70; NSF fel, Univ London, 70-71. *Mem:* Biophys Soc; Soc Gen Physiol. *Res:* Excitable membranes; ion movements and optical methods. *Mailing Add:* Dept of Physiol & Biophys Univ Miami Sch Med PO Box 016430 Miami FL 33101

LANDOWNE, MILTON, b New York, NY, Nov 19, 12; m 41; c 5. INTERNAL MEDICINE, CIRCULATORY PHSIOLOGY. *Educ:* City Col New York, BS, 32; Harvard Univ, MD, 36. *Prof Exp:* Intern, Mt Sinai Hosp, New York, 36-39; Libman fel, Michael Reese Hosp, Chicago, 39-41; instr, Univ Chicago, 41-46, asst prof med, 46-48; chief cardiovasc res unit, Vet Admin Hosp, 48-49; assoc chief geront sect, Nat Heart Inst, 49-57; med dir, Levindale Hebrew Home & Infirmary, Baltimore, Md, 57-65; dir med lab, 65-76, MED ADV, US ARMY RES INST ENVIRON MED, 76- *Concurrent Pos:* Asst prof, Johns Hopkins Univ, 55-65; head div cardiol & chronic dis, Sinai Hosp, Baltimore, 58-65; asst clin prof, Harvard Univ, 65-74. *Mem:* AAAS; Am Soc Clin Invest; Am Physiol Soc; Soc Exp Biol & Med; Am Heart Asn. *Res:* Disorders of the circulation; biology aging; clinical medicine; physiology of blood and circulation; metabolic and renal diseases; environmental medicine. *Mailing Add:* US Army Res Inst of Environ Med Natick MA 01760

LANDRETH, RONALD RAY, b Mattoon, Ill, June 15, 49; m 71; c 2. ENVIRONMENTAL CHEMISTRY. *Educ:* Northwestern Univ, BA, 71; Pa State Univ, PhD(chem), 75. *Prof Exp:* Res fel chem, Pa State Univ, 72-75; res engr, 75-79, SR RES ENG ENVIRON CHEM, INLAND STEEL CO, 79- *Mem:* Air Pollution Control Asn; Am Chem Soc. *Res:* Characterization and control of air pollutants in an industrial area. *Mailing Add:* Inland Steel Res Labs 3001 E Columbus Dr E Chicago IN 46312

LANDROCK, ARTHUR HAROLD, b New York, NY, May 19, 19; m 42; c 6. PLASTICS, MATERIALS ENGINEERING. *Educ:* Queens Col, BS, 41; Boston Univ, AM, 50. *Prof Exp:* Chemist packaging res, Paper Containers Div, Continental Can Co, 45-47; res asst & tech asst food packaging, Mass Inst Technol, 47-53; sr food packaging scientist, Film Div, Olin Mathieson Chem Corp, 53-55, sr res chemist, viscose res, Gen Res Orgn, 55-56; prod standards mgr, M&M'S Candies, Div Food Mfrs, 56-60; PACKAGING TECHNOLOGIST, PLASTICS TECH EVAL CTR, ARMAMENT RES & DEVELOP COMMAND, US ARMY, 61- *Concurrent Pos:* US deleg & mem tech group, Int Orgn Standardization, 77- *Honors & Awards:* Am Soc Testing & Mat Award, 77. *Mem:* Am Soc Testing & Mat; Int Orgn Standardization; Soc Advan Mat & Process Eng; Sigma Xi. *Res:* Collecting, evaluating and disseminating technical information in packaging, adhesive bonding, powder coatings, cryogenic properties, cellular plastics, flammability, and specifications in plastics and adhesives; plastics terminology. *Mailing Add:* Plastics Tech Evaluation Ctr Bldg 351-N Dover NJ 07801

LANDRUM, BILLY FRANK, b Atlanta, Ga, June 7, 20; m 48; c 3. ORGANIC CHEMISTRY, POLYMER CHEMISTRY. *Educ:* Emory Univ, AB, 47, MS, 49, PhD(chem), 50. *Prof Exp:* Res chemist polymer chem, M W Kellogg Co, 50-53, res supvr pilot plant, 53-57; head polymer sect, Minn Mining & Mfg Co, 57-62; mgr advan projs, FMC Corp, NJ, 62-66; staff scientist, Whittaker Corp, 66-67; staff scientist, Com Develop Dept, 67-74, mgr, Mkt Develop, Plastics & Additives Div, 74-78, TECH SERV MGR, COMPUT MAT DEPT, CIBA-GEIGY CORP, 81- *Mem:* Am Chem Soc; Sigma Xi; Soc Advan Mat & Processing Eng. *Res:* Organo-metallic reactions; polymers; fluorocarbons; urethanes; coal and coke; activated carbon; composite materials. *Mailing Add:* 8661 Anchorage Dr Huntington Beach CA 92646

LANDRUM, BOBBY L, b Taylor, Tex, Jan 18, 32; m 51; c 4. PHYSICS, MATHEMATICS. *Educ:* Tex A&M Univ, BS, 53, MS, 54, PhD(physics), 59. *Prof Exp:* Chief new detection tech sect, Wright-Patterson AFB, Ohio, 60-61; from res scientist to dir appl res, Northrop Corp, 61-69, chief engr, Electro-Optical Dept, Systs Labs, 69-72, dir advan sensors & displays, 72-74; MEM STAFF, MARTIN MARIETTA CORP, ORLANDO, 74- *Mem:* Am Phys Soc. *Res:* Applied research for military and scientific purposes; technical program management of electrooptical sensors and instruments. *Mailing Add:* Trout Rd Box 48JM Winter Garden FL 32787

LANDRUM, RALPH AVERY, JR, b Memphis, Tenn, Oct 2, 26; m 49; c 3. GEOPHYSICS. *Educ:* Rice Univ, BS, 49; Univ Tulsa, MS, 64. *Prof Exp:* Asst seismic observer, Amerada Petrol Corp, 49-51; res seismic observer, Stanolind Oil & Gas Co, 51-56; res engr, Pan Am Petrol Corp, 56-63, staff res engr, 63-67, staff res scientist, 67-71; res assoc, Res Ctr, Amoco Prod Co, 71-74; SR RES GEOPHYSICIST, WESTERN GEOPHYS CO AM, 74- *Mem:* Am Soc Explor Geophys; Inst Elec & Electronic Eng; Europ Asn Explor Geophys. *Res:* Exploration geophysics; design of seismic instrumentation; mathematics of seismic data processing. *Mailing Add:* PO Box 2469 Houston TX 77001

LANDRY, EDWARD F, b Cambridge, Mass, Jan 9, 47; m 71. MOLECULAR GENETICS. *Educ:* State Col Boston, BA, 68; Univ NH, PhD(microbiol), 75. *Prof Exp:* Fel molecular genetics, Sch Med & Dent, Univ Rochester, 75-76; MEM STAFF, DEPT ATMOSPHERE, BROOKHAVEN NAT LAB, 76- *Mem:* Am Soc Microbiol. *Res:* Study of control mechanisms in the translation of bacteriophage T4; studies center around the ribosome and its factors and proteins. *Mailing Add:* Dept of Atmosphere Brookhaven Nat Lab Upton NY 11973

LANDRY, FERNAND, b Levis, PQ, Can, Jan 13, 30; m 55; c 4. EXERCISE PHYSIOLOGY. *Educ:* Univ Ottawa, BSc, 54; Univ Ill, Urbana, MS, 55, PhD(phys educ exercise physiol), 68. *Prof Exp:* From teacher-researcher, phys educ to dept head, Univ Ottawa, 55-68; dept head phys activ sci, 68-81, HEAD PHYS ACTIV SCI LAB, LAVAL UNIV, 81- *Honors & Awards:* Medal, Que Govt, 74. *Mem:* Can Asn Sport Sci (pres, 71-72); Int Coun Sport & Phys Educ (vpres, NAm, 72-); Corp Int Cong Phys Activ Sci (pres, 74-78); Am Col Sports Med. *Res:* Short-term and chronic effects of physical activity and sports; use of physical activity in the prevention of and/or rehabilitation from generative diseases; causes of variations in susceptibility sensitivity to training stimuli; trainability of aerobic and anaerobic cafacitus; effects of training in patients with prosthetic aortic valves. *Mailing Add:* Dept of Phys Activ Sci Laval Univ Quebec PQ G1K 7P4 Can

LANDRY, MICHAEL RAYMOND, b Berlin, NH, Apr 16, 48; m 72; c 2. MARINE ZOOPLANKTON ECOLOGY. *Educ:* Univ Calif, Santa Barbara, BA, 70; Univ Wash, PhD(oceanog), 76. *Prof Exp:* Res biologist, Scripps Inst Oceanog, Univ Calif, San Diego, 76-78; RES ASST PROF BIOL OEANOG, SCH OCEANOG, UNIV WASH, 78- *Mem:* Am Soc Limnol & Oceanog; Western Soc Naturalists. *Res:* Feeding ecology and population dynamics of marine zooplankton; marine ecosystem research and modeling. *Mailing Add:* Sch Oceanog WB-10 Univ Wash Seattle WA 98195

LANDRY, PRESTON MYLES, b New Orleans, La, Apr 14, 30; m 53; c 4. OPERATIONS RESEARCH. *Educ:* Southeastern La Col, BS, 52; Univ Miss, MA, 57. *Prof Exp:* Assoc mathematician, Vitro Corp Am, 53-54; mathematician, 56-58; supvry mathematician, Air Proving Ground Ctr, 58-59, mathematician, 59-65, chief anal br, Math Serv Lab, 65-66, chief systs div, Directorate Sci Staff, Dept Chief Staff Eval, Ninth Aerospace Defense Div, Ent AFB, 66-68, asst dir, Directorate Sci Appln, 14th Aerospace Force, 68-

73, OPERS ANALYST, AEROSPACE DEFENSE COMMAND, US AIR FORCE, 73- *Concurrent Pos:* Mem, Electronic Trajectory Measurements Group. *Res:* Data reduction and analysis related to weapons system evaluation; electromagnetic propagation; Space-track system; characteristics and projections of earth satellite population. *Mailing Add:* 1123 N Meade Ave Colorado Springs CO 80909

LANDRY, RICHARD GEORGES, b Manchester, NH, Nov 7, 42; m 66; c 3. APPLIED STATISTICS. *Educ:* Oblate Col, BA, 64; Boston Col, MEd, 67, PhD(res & statist), 70. *Prof Exp:* Asst prof, 69-73, assoc prof measurement & statist, 70-80, PROF, CTR TEACHING & LEARNING, UNIV NDAK, 80- *Concurrent Pos:* Eval auditor, numerous ESEA Title III Projs, 70-; eval consult, Grand Rapids Sch Dist, Minn, 73-; res coordr, Nat Inst Educ Proj, Univ N Dak, 73- *Mem:* Am Asn Univ Prof; Am Educ Res Asn; Am Statist Asn; Nat Coun Measurement Educ. *Res:* Applied educational statistics; educational measurement and evaluation in affective domain; foreign language learning and creativity. *Mailing Add:* Ctr Teaching & Learning Univ of N Dak Grand Forks ND 58201

LANDRY, STUART OMER, JR, b New Orleans, La, Sept 30, 24; m 50; c 2. ZOOLOGY. *Educ:* Harvard Univ, BS, 49; Univ Calif, PhD(zool), 54. *Prof Exp:* Curatorial asst, Mus Vert Zool, Calif, 50-52; asst zool, Univ Calif, 52-53, assoc, 53-54; from instr to asst prof anat, Univ Mo, 54-59; assoc prof biol & chmn dept, La State Univ, 59-63; actg dean grad sch, 66-68, PROF BIOL, STATE UNIV NY BINGHAMTON, 63- *Mem:* AAAS; Soc Syst Zool; Am Soc Mammal; Am Asn Anat; Am Soc Zoologists. *Res:* Comparative anatomy and classification of mammals; functional anatomy of mammals. *Mailing Add:* Dept of Biol State Univ NY Binghamton NY 13901

LANDS, WILLIAM EDWARD MITCHELL, b Chillicothe, Mo, July 22, 30; c 4. BIOCHEMISTRY. *Educ:* Univ Mich, Ann Arbor, BS, 51; Univ Ill, PhD(biol chem), 54. *Prof Exp:* NSF fel, Calif Inst Technol, 54-55; from instr to assoc prof chem, Univ Mich, Ann Arbor, 55-67, prof, 67-80; PROF & HEAD BIOCHEM, UNIV ILL MED CTR, 80- *Concurrent Pos:* Chmn subcomt biochem nomenclature, Nat Acad Sci, 62-64; Danforth Assoc, 66-; ed, Can J 72-78; ed, Arch Biochem & Biophys, Life Sci & Prostaglandins & Med, 78- *Honors & Awards:* Gold Medal Bond Award, Am Oil Chemists Soc, 65; Glycerine Res Award, 69. *Mem:* AAAS; Am Chem Soc; Am Soc Biol Chemists; Am Oil Chemists Soc. *Res:* Metabolism of glycerides and long-chain aliphatic acids and aldehydes; formation of membranes and regulation of membrane function; prostaglandin biochemistry and control of its biosynthesis. *Mailing Add:* Dept Biol Chem Univ Ill Med Ctr Chicago IL 60612

LANDSBAUM, ELLIS M(ERLE), b Chicago, Ill, Feb 28, 25; m 52; c 2. CHEMICAL ENGINEERING. *Educ:* Ill Inst Technol, BSc, 49; Northwestern Univ, MSc, 53, PhD(chem eng), 55; Univ Calif, Los Angeles, cert nuclear tech, 67, cert bus mgt, 72. *Prof Exp:* Jr engr, Socony Oil Co, 49-51; res group supvr, Jet Propulsion Lab, Calif Inst Technol, 55-61; SECT MGR, PROPULSION DEPT, AEROSPACE CORP, 61- *Mem:* Am Chem Soc; Am Inst Aeronaut & Astronaut; Combustion Inst. *Res:* Solid propellant rockets; combustion; nozzles; system analysis. *Mailing Add:* 518 N Alta Dr Beverly Hills CA 90210

LANDSBERG, ARNE, b Des Moines, Iowa, June 10, 33; c 2. CHEMICAL ENGINEERING. *Educ:* Univ Colo, BS, 55; Ore State Univ, PhD(chem eng), 64. *Prof Exp:* Chem engr, US Bur Mines, 61-64; peace corps vol for prof, Chem Eng Prog, Costa Rica, 64-66; CHEM RES ENGR, US BUR MINES, ALBANY, 66- *Mem:* Sigma Xi; Am Chem Soc. *Res:* Chemical kinetics of gas-solid reactions; vapor-solid equilibrium. *Mailing Add:* 1430 NW Greenwood Pl Corvallis OR 97330

LANDSBERG, HELMUT ERICH, b Frankfurt-am-Main, Ger, Feb 9, 06; nat US; m. CLIMATOLOGY. *Educ:* Univ Frankfurt, PhD(geophys, meteorol), 30. *Prof Exp:* Asst seismol & climatol, Inst Meteorol & Geophys, Univ Frankfurt, 30-31; supvr res seismol & meteorol, Taunus Observ, Ger, 31-34; from instr to asst prof geophys, Pa State Col, 34-41; assoc prof meteorol, Univ Chicago, 41-43, res assoc indust climatol, 45-46; chief sect indust climatol, US Weather Bur, Wash, 46; dep exec dir comt geophys sci, Res & Develop Bd, 46-48, exec dir comt geophys & geog, 48-51; dir geophys res directorate, Air Force Cambridge Res Ctr, 51-54; dir off climat, US Weather Bur, 54-65, dir environ data serv, Environ Sci Serv Admin, 65-66; actg dir, 74-76, EMER RES PROF, INST FLUID DYNAMICS & APPL MATH, UNIV MD, COLLEGE PARK, 76- *Concurrent Pos:* Vis prof, Inst Fluid Dynamics & Appl Math, Univ Md, College Park, 64-67; pres comn spec applns meteorol & climatol, World Meteorol Orgn, 69-78; mem, Nat Adv Comt Oceans & Atmosphere, 75-77. *Honors & Awards:* Award Bioclimat, Am Meteorol Soc, 64, Brooks Award, 72; Bowie Med, Am Geophys Union, 78; Int Meteorol Org Prize, 79; Wegener Medal, Ger Meteorol Soc, 80. *Mem:* Nat Acad Eng; AAAS; Am Meteorol Soc (vpres, 63-64); Meteoritical Soc; Am Geophys Union (vpres, 66-68, pres, 68-70). *Res:* Microclimatology; urban climatology; bioclimatology; aerosol; meteorology; seismology. *Mailing Add:* Inst Phys Sci & Tech Univ Md College Park MD 20742

LANDSBERGER, FRANK ROBBERT, b Amsterdam, Netherlands, Aug 10, 43; US citizen; m 65. PHYSICAL BIOCHEMISTRY, VIROLOGY. *Educ:* Cornell Univ, BA, 64; Brown Univ, PhD(physics), 70. *Prof Exp:* Res asst physics, Brown Univ, 64-69; res fel biochem, Div Endocrinol, Sloan-Kettering Inst Cancer Res, 69-71; asst prof chem, Ind Univ, Bloomington, 71-74; asst prof, 74-80, ASSOC PROF & ANDREW W MELLON FOUND FEL, ROCKEFELLER UNIV, 80- *Mem:* AAAS; Biophys Soc; fel NY Acad Sci; Am Soc Microbiol; Am Chem Soc. *Res:* Use of physical biochemical studies of the structure and function of biological and model membranes with emphasis on enveloped viruses and their interaction with cell surfaces. *Mailing Add:* Rockefeller Univ New York NY 10021

LANDSHOFF, ROLF, b Berlin, Ger, Nov 30, 11; nat US; m 41; c 4. MATHEMATICAL PHYSICS. *Educ:* Berlin Tech Inst, DrIng, 36; Univ Minn, PhD(theoret physics), 38. *Prof Exp:* Asst physics, Univ Minn, 36-40; prof, Col St Thomas, 40-44; scientist, Los Alamos Sci Lab, 44-56; sr mem, Lockheed Palo Alto Res Lab, 56-76; CONSULT, 77- *Concurrent Pos:* Vis lectr, Weizmann Inst, 63-64. *Mem:* Fel Am Phys Soc. *Res:* Atomic physics; hydrodynamics; statistical mechanics. *Mailing Add:* 525 E Crescent Dr Palo Alto CA 94301

LANDSMAN, DOUGLAS ANDERSON, b Dundee, Scotland, May 31, 29; m 57; c 4. PHYSICAL CHEMISTRY. *Educ:* Univ St Andrews, BSc, 49, Hons, 50, PhD(thermodynamics), 57. *Prof Exp:* Sr sci officer, Chem Div, Atomic Weapon Res Estab, UK Atomic Energy Authority, Eng, 53-57; Nat Res Coun Can fel, 57-58; Harwell sr fel, Chem Div, Atomic Energy Res Estab, UK Atomic Energy Authority, Eng, 58-60, prin sci officer, 60-65; res supvr, Mat Eng Res Lab, Pratt & Whitney Aircraft Div, Middletown, 65-72, SR PROJ ENGR, FUEL CELL FACILITY, POWER SYST DIV, UNITED TECHNOL CORP, 72- *Mem:* Fel Royal Inst Chem. *Res:* Thermodynamics of ionization in aqueous solutions; chemistry of the hydrogen isotopes; isotope separation; gas chromatography; chemonuclear reactors; energy conversion; fuel cells. *Mailing Add:* 1088 N Main St West Hartford CT 06117

LANDSTREET, JOHN DARLINGTON, b Philadelphia, Pa, Mar 13, 40; m 72; c 2. ASTROPHYSICS. *Educ:* Reed Col, BA, 62; Columbia Univ, MA, 63, PhD(physics), 66. *Prof Exp:* Instr physics, Mt Holyoke Col, 65-66, asst prof, 66-67; res assoc astron, Columbia Univ, 67-70, asst prof, 70; asst prof, 70-72, assoc prof, 72-76, PROF ASTRON, UNIV WESTERN ONT, 76- *Concurrent Pos:* Mem, Grant Selection Comt for Space & Astron, Natural Sci & Eng Res Coun Can, 80-83; mem sci adv comt, Can Ctr Space Sci, 81-83; mem sci adv coun, Can-France-Hawaii Telescope Corp, 80-83, vchmn, 81, chmn, 82-83. *Mem:* Am Astron Soc; Can Astron Soc; Royal Astron Soc; Int Astron Union. *Res:* Observation of circular and linear polarization in stars and extra-galactic objects, especially white dwarfs; observation of stellar magnetism. *Mailing Add:* Dept of Astron Univ of Western Ont London ON N6A 3K7 Can

LANDSTROM, D(ONALD) KARL, b Portland, Ore, Oct 12, 37. SOLAR PHYSICS, MATERIALS SCIENCE. *Educ:* Mass Inst Technol, BS, 59. *Prof Exp:* Supvr electron micros, Goodyear Atomic Corp, 59-63; res engr mat environ, NAm Aviation, 63-65; prin res scientist solar mat anal, 65-80, PROJ MGR, ENERGY & THERMAL TECHNOL, COLUMBUS LABS, BATTELE MEM INST, 80- *Mem:* AAAS; Int Solar Energy Soc; Electron Micros Soc Am; Am Soc Metals; Electron Microprobe Soc Am. *Res:* Solar energy; environmental impact analysis; thermal analysis; materials research; physical and chemical analysis; electron microscopy; electron probe analysis; nuclear waste; energy and environmental systems; agricultural controlled environment system. *Mailing Add:* Battelle Mem Inst 505 King Ave Columbus OH 43201

LANDT, JAMES FREDERICK, b Anniston, Ala, Jan 4, 26; m 50; c 2. BIOLOGY. *Educ:* Howard Col, AB, 50; Emory Univ, MS, 54, PhD(biol), 61. *Prof Exp:* Parasitologist, US Army Med Lab, Ga, 54; instr biol, 54-57, asst prof, 60-63, assoc prof, 63-74, chmn, Div Sci & Math, 67-74, PROF BIOL & HEAD DEPT, OXFORD COL, EMORY UNIV, 74- *Concurrent Pos:* Assoc prof, Univ Ala, 63-65. *Mem:* AAAS; Am Soc Parasitol; Am Soc Zoologists. *Res:* Host-parasite relationships; biochemistry of parasites. *Mailing Add:* Dept of Biol Oxford Col Emory Univ Oxford GA 30267

LANDUCCI, LAWRENCE L, b St Paul, Minn, May 20, 39; m 69; c 3. ORGANIC CHEMISTRY, NUCLEAR MAGNETIC RESOURCES. *Educ:* Univ Minn, BS, 62, PhD(org chem), 67. *Prof Exp:* RES CHEMIST, US FOREST PROD LAB, 67- *Mem:* Am Chem Soc. *Res:* Lignin and lignin model compound chemistry; methods of lignin degradation; mechanism of anthraquinone pulping; carbon 13 Nuclear Magnetic Resonance characterization of lignin and reaction products. *Mailing Add:* US Forest Prod Lab N Walnut St Madison WI 53705

LANDWEBER, LAWRENCE H, b New York, NY, Nov 29, 42; m 66. COMPUTER SCIENCE. *Educ:* Brooklyn Col, BS, 63; Purdue Univ, MS & PhD(comput sci), 66. *Prof Exp:* From asst prof to assoc prof, 67-77, PROF COMPUT SCI & CHMN DEPT, UNIV WIS-MADISON, 77- *Mem:* Am Math Soc; Asn Comput Mach. *Res:* Theoretical computer science; computer networks; computer conferencing and mail. *Mailing Add:* Dept of Comput Sci 1210 W Dayton Univ of Wis Madison WI 53706

LANDWEBER, PETER STEVEN, b Washington, DC, Aug 17, 40; m 64; c 2. MATHEMATICS. *Educ:* Univ Iowa, BA, 60; Harvard Univ, MA, 61, PhD(math), 65. *Prof Exp:* Asst prof math, Univ Va, 65-68; asst prof, Yale Univ, 68-70; assoc prof, 70-74, PROF MATH, RUTGERS UNIV, NEW BRUNSWICK, 74- *Concurrent Pos:* Mem sch math, Inst Advan Study, 67-68; NATO fel, Univ Cambridge, 74-75. *Mem:* Am Math Soc. *Res:* Cobordism theory of differential manifolds. *Mailing Add:* Dept of Math Rutgers Univ New Brunswick NJ 08903

LANDY, ARTHUR H, b Philadelphia, Pa, Mar 17, 39; m 65; c 2. BIOCHEMICAL GENETICS, GENE REGULATION. *Educ:* Amherst Col, BA, 61; Univ Ill, PhD(microbiol & biochem), 65. *Prof Exp:* Res fel biochem genetics, Med Res Coun Lab Molecular Biol, Cambridge, Eng, 66-68; asst prof, 68-74, assoc prof, 75-77, PROF MED SCI, BROWN UNIV, 78- *Concurrent Pos:* NATO fel, 66-67; fel, Am Cancer Soc, 68 , fac res assoc, 75-81, mem adv bd, 78-; assoc ed, Cell, 79-; mem recombinant DNA adv comt, NIH, 81-; chmn nucleic acids, Gordon Res Conf, 83. *Mem:* Am Soc Microbiol; Am Soc Biol Chemists. *Res:* Gene structure and regulation in prokaryotes and eukaryotes; organization of eukaryote genes; mechanisms of site-specific recombination. *Mailing Add:* Div of Biol & Med Med G Brown Univ Providence RI 02912

LANDY, RICHARD ALLEN, b Clearfield, Pa, Sept 23, 31; m 59; c 2. MINERALOGY. *Educ:* Mass Inst Technol, SB, 53; Pa State Univ, MS, 55, PhD(mineral), 61. *Prof Exp:* Supvr engr, Bonded Abrasives Div, Carborundum Co, 60-62; group leader, Basic Inc, 62-63, mgr qual assurance, 63-65; asst prof geol, Allegheny Col, 65-67; mineralogist, 67-70, DIR RES, NAM REFRACTORIES CO, 70- *Mem:* Am Crystallog Asn; Am Soc Qual Control; Soc Appl Spectros. *Res:* Quality control; statistical applications to sampling problems in geology and ceramic industry; quantitative analysis of inorganic chemistry systems by means of x-ray diffraction analysis and other instrumental techniques. *Mailing Add:* 105 Pauline Dr W Clearfield PA 16830

LANDZBERG, ABRAHAM H(AROLD), b New York, NY, Sept 10, 29; m 55; c 3. SEMICONDUCTOR PROCESS ENGINEERING. *Educ:* NY Univ, BSME, 51; Princeton Univ, MSE, 53. *Prof Exp:* Develop engr, Gen Elec Co, 52-59; dept mgr appl mech, Res Div, 59-65, dept mgr integrated circuits, Components Div, 65-70, sr engr, 70-71, advan mfg mgr, 71-76, SEMICONDUCTOR PROCESS ENG MGR, IBM CORP, 76- *Res:* Physics of failure of integrated circuits; mechanical properties of materials; applied mechanics, application to electronic computer components; turbines; electrical machinery; manufacturing systems and processes for integrated circuits; electronic component packaging engineering. *Mailing Add:* 685 Fieldstone Ct Yorktown Heights NY 10598

LANE, ALEXANDER Z, b Detroit, Mich, July 22, 29; m 56. BIOCHEMISTRY, MEDICINE. *Educ:* Univ Detroit, BS, 50; Wayne State Univ, PhD(biochem), 54, MD, 58. *Prof Exp:* Intern med, Bon Secours Hosp, Grosse Pointe, Mich, 58-59; clin investr, Parke Davis & Co, Mich, 60-62, dir clin pharmacol, 62-66; dir med res, 66-70, vpres & med dir, Bristol Labs, 70-77; sr vpres res oper, 76-77, PRES PHARMACEUT RES DIV, SHERING-PLOUGH CORP, 77- *Concurrent Pos:* Nat Cancer Inst fel occup med, Wayne State Univ, 59-60; lectr, Univ Mich, 65-66. *Mem:* Fel Am Soc Clin Pharmacol & Therapeut; Am Chem Soc; Am Soc Microbiol. *Res:* Correlation of animal and clinical pharmacological data; experimental design of clinical studies; analysis, performance and interpretation of clinical chemical tests; antibiotics; cancer chemotherapy; narcotic antagonists. *Mailing Add:* Schering-Plough Corp 60 E Orange St Bloomfield NJ 07003

LANE, ALFRED GLEN, b Stoutland, Mo, Aug 21, 32; m 57; c 2. ANIMAL NUTRITION. *Educ:* Univ Mo, BS, 59, MS, 60, PhD(animal nutrit), 65. *Prof Exp:* Instr voc agr, Parkersburg Community Sch, Iowa, 60-63; asst dairy husb, Univ Mo-Columbia, 63-65, asst prof, 65-70; mgr diary res, Allied Mills, Inc, 70-77; PVT CONSULT, 77- *Mem:* Am Dairy Sci Asn; Am Soc Animal Sci. *Res:* Ruminant nutrition; physiology. *Mailing Add:* PO Box 5 Montreal MO 65591

LANE, ARDELLE CATHERINE, b Port Angeles, Wash, Mar 8, 22; m 67. PHYSIOLOGY. *Educ:* Seattle Pac Col, BS, 44; Northwestern Univ, MS, 47; Univ Ill, PhD(physiol), 54. *Prof Exp:* From instr to assoc prof physiol, 52-64, PROF PHYSIOL, DENT SCH, NORTHWESTERN UNIV, 64- *Mem:* Am Physiol Soc. *Res:* Controlling mechanisms of gastric secretion. *Mailing Add:* Dept of Physiol Northwestern Univ Dent Sch Chicago IL 60611

LANE, BENNIE RAY, b Deming, NMex, July 2, 35; m 56; c 4. MATHEMATICS. *Educ:* Colo State Col, BA, 56, MA, 57; George Peabody Col, PhD(math), 62. *Prof Exp:* Asst prof math, Univ Chattanooga, 59-61; instr appl math, Vanderbilt Univ, 61-62; asst prof math, Colo State Col, 62-63; from asst prof to assoc prof, George Peabody Col, 63-66; chmn dept, 66-78, PROF MATH, EASTERN KY UNIV, 66- *Mem:* Am Math Asn. *Res:* Mathematics education; teaching mathematics by television; abstract algebra; programmed instruction. *Mailing Add:* Dept of Math Eastern Ky Univ Richmond KY 40475

LANE, BERNARD OWEN, b Greensboro, NC, Oct 5, 25; m 51. INVERTEBRATE PALEONTOLOGY. *Educ:* Univ NC, BS, 50; Brown Univ, MSc, 55; Univ Southern Calif, PhD(geol), 60. *Prof Exp:* Lectr geol, Univ Nev, 59-60 & 61-62; from asst prof to assoc prof, 62-72, PROF GEOL, CALIF STATE POLYTECH UNIV, POMONA, 72- *Concurrent Pos:* Consult, Earth Sci Curriculum Proj, 65-66. *Mem:* Paleont Soc; Nat Asn Geol Teachers. *Res:* Paleontology and stratigraphy of the early Pennsylvanian in the cordilleran region of North America. *Mailing Add:* Dept of Earth Sci Calif State Polytech Univ Pomona CA 91768

LANE, BERNARD PAUL, b Brooklyn, NY, June 27, 38; m 62; c 3. PATHOLOGY. *Educ:* Brown Univ, AB, 59; NY Univ, MD, 63. *Prof Exp:* NIH trainee exp path, Sch Med, NY Univ, 65-66, from asst prof to assoc prof path, 66-71; assoc prof, 71-76, PROF PATH, HEALTH SCI CTR, STATE UNIV NY STONY BROOK, 76- *Concurrent Pos:* Attend pathologist, Bellevue & NY Univ Hosps, 69-71; attend pathologist, Vet Admin Hosp, Northport, NY, 71- & Stony Brook Univ Hosp, 79-; vis scientist, Armed Forces Inst Path, 71; chief cell injury labs, Armed Forces Inst Path. *Mem:* Am Soc Cell Biol; Int Acad Path; Am Asn Path; Am Soc Clin Path; Am Asn Cancer Res. *Res:* Experimental pathology; electron microscopy; cellular injury; chemical carcinogenesis. *Mailing Add:* Dept of Path State Univ of NY Health Sci Ctr Stony Brook NY 11790

LANE, BYRON GEORGE, b Toronto, Ont, May 16, 33; m 61. BIOCHEMISTRY. *Educ:* Univ Toronto, BA, 56, PhD(biochem), 59. *Prof Exp:* Jr res asst biochem, Med Ctr, Univ Calif, San Francisco, 59-60; res assoc, Rockefeller Inst, 60-61; asst prof, Univ Alta, 61-63, assoc prof, 64-68; PROF BIOCHEM, UNIV TORONTO, 68- *Mem:* Am Soc Biol Chemists. *Res:* Biochemistry of ribonucleates and chemical biology of wheat emkbryos. *Mailing Add:* Dept of Biochem Univ of Toronto Toronto ON M5S 1A8 Can

LANE, CARL LEATON, b Raleigh, NC, Feb 11, 28; m 52; c 1. FOREST SOILS. *Educ:* NC State Univ, BS, 52, MS, 61; Purdue Univ, PhD(forest soil microbiol), 68. *Prof Exp:* Forest mgr, State Hosp Butner, NC, 52-59; asst prof forestry, 60-70, assoc prof, 70-75, PROF FORESTRY, CLEMSON UNIV, 75- *Mem:* Soc Am Foresters. *Res:* Forest soils microbiology; forest soil tree disease relationships; nitrogen fixation; effluent truisation. *Mailing Add:* Dept of Forestry Clemson Univ Clemson SC 29631

LANE, CHARLES A, b Wichita, Kans, Nov 18, 32. ORGANIC CHEMISTRY. *Educ:* Univ Okla, BS, 54; Yale Univ, MS, 59; Univ Calif, PhD(chem), 63. *Prof Exp:* Org chemist, Lederle Labs, Am Cyanamid Co, 56-58; asst prof org chem, Univ Nigeria, 61-63; asst prof, Univ Calif, 63-64; asst prof, 64-73, ASSOC PROF ORG CHEM, UNIV TENN, KNOXVILLE, 73- *Mem:* AAAS. *Res:* Theoretical organic chemistry. *Mailing Add:* Dept of Chem Univ of Tenn Knoxville TN 37916

LANE, CHARLES EDWARD, b Riverton, Wyo, Dec 17, 09; m 31; c 2. ZOOLOGY. *Educ:* Univ Wis, AB, 31, MA, 33, PhD(physiol, zool), 35. *Prof Exp:* Asst zool, Univ Wis, 31-36; from asst prof to assoc prof, Univ Wichita, 36-42; marine biologist, Borden Co, 45-49; from assoc prof to prof marine sci, 49-74, EMER PROF MARINE SCI, UNIV MIAMI, 74- *Mem:* AAAS; Am Physiol Soc; Soc Exp Biol & Med; Int Soc Toxicol. *Res:* General marine biology. *Mailing Add:* PO Box 3512 Beach Sta Vero Beach FL 32960

LANE, CONSTANCE A, b Rockport, Maine, Jan 7, 24. POLYMER CHEMISTRY, COATINGS CHEMISTRY. *Educ:* Bates Col, BS, 46. *Prof Exp:* Jr chemist, 46-51, intermediate chemist, 51-61, sr chemist, 61-66, group leader plastics res, 66-76, GROUP LEADER COATINGS RES, ROHM AND HAAS CO, 76- *Mem:* Am Chem Soc; Am Inst Chem. *Res:* Synthesis of polymeric intermediates for coatings. *Mailing Add:* Rohm & Haas Co Norristown Rd Spring House PA 19477

LANE, DONALD WILSON, b Fayetteville, Tenn, June 23, 34; m 60; c 3. PETROLEUM GEOLOGY. *Educ:* Dartmouth Col, BA, 56; Univ Ill, MS, 58; Rice Univ, PhD(geol), 61. *Prof Exp:* Geologist, Tenneco Oil Co, 61-70; regional geologist, Royal Resources Corp, 70; staff geologist, Geol Surv Wyo, 70-73; mgr exp geol & Rocky Mountain area, 73-76; MEM STAFF, MICH-WIS PIPELINE CO, 77- *Concurrent Pos:* Consult geologist, 76-77. *Mem:* Am Asn Petrol Geol; Soc Econ Paleont & Mineral; Geol Soc Am. *Res:* Lower Paleozoic stratigraphy and hydrocarbon potential of the northeastern United States; Wyoming stratigraphy and stratigraphic resources; Lower Cretaceous stratigraphy of northwestern Colorado. *Mailing Add:* Mich-Wis Pipeline Co 5051 Westheimer Houston TX 77027

LANE, EDWIN DAVID, b Vancouver, BC, May 9, 34; m 58; c 2. FISH CULTURE, FISH ECOLOGY. *Educ:* Univ BC, BSc, 59, MSc, 62; Univ Tex, PhD(zool), 66. *Prof Exp:* Staff mem, Fisheries Invest Off, NZ Marine Dept, 62-63; res scientist, Res Br, Ont Dept Land & Forest, 66-68; assoc prof zool, Calif State Univ, Long Beach, 68-74, res grant, 68-69 & 71-74; head coop res, Can Wildlife Serv, Can Dept Environ, 74-79; COORDR, FISH CULTURE DEPT, MALASPINA COL, NANAIMO, BC, 79- *Concurrent Pos:* Fisheries expert, Food & Agr Orgn, 67- *Mem:* Can Soc Zoologists; NZ Limnol Soc; Am Fish Soc. *Res:* Salmonid culture especially feeding; ecology of fishes, especially in streams, estuaries and coastal bay systems; environmental impact of development, especially in the North. *Mailing Add:* Can Wildlife Serv 1000-9942 108th St Edmonton AB T5K 2J5 Can

LANE, ERIC TRENT, b Baton Rouge, La, Aug 30, 38; c 2. THEORETICAL PHYSICS. *Educ:* La State Univ, BS, 60; Rice Univ, MA, 63, PhD(physics), 67. *Prof Exp:* Vis lectr physics, La State Univ, New Orleans, 63-65; assoc prof, 67-77, PROF PHYSICS, UNIV TENN, CHATTANOOGA, 77- *Concurrent Pos:* NSF grant, microcomput course develop. *Mem:* Am Phys Soc; Am Asn Physics Teachers; Soc Gen Systs Res. *Res:* Microcomputer applications and interfacing systems research applied to improvement of teaching and human relationships. *Mailing Add:* Univ Tenn Chattanooga TN 37403

LANE, ERNEST PAUL, b Greene Co, Tenn, Nov 14, 33; m 61; c 2. TOPOLOGY. *Educ:* Berea Col, BA, 55; Univ Tenn, MA, 57; Purdue Univ, PhD(math), 65. *Prof Exp:* Programmer, Army Ballistic Missile Agency, Ala, 57-58; instr math, Berea Col, 58-60; asst prof, Va Polytech Inst, 65-70; assoc prof, 70-75, PROF MATH, APPALACHIAN STATE UNIV, 75- *Mem:* Math Asn Am; Am Math Soc. *Res:* Abstract spaces; metrization; real-valued functions on abstract spaces. *Mailing Add:* Dept of Math Appalachian State Univ Boone NC 28607

LANE, FORREST EUGENE, b Enola, Ark, June 24, 34; m 54; c 5. PLANT PHYSIOLOGY, PLANT BIOCHEMISTRY. *Educ:* Univ Ark, BA, 56, MEd, 59, MS, 63; Univ Okla, PhD(plant physiol), 65. *Prof Exp:* Teacher, Hall High Sch, Ark, 57-58; instr biol, Univ Ark, 58-63; asst prof biol, Kans State Col Pittsburg, 65-67; asst prof, Dept Bot & Bact, 67-69, ASSOC PROF BOT & BACT, UNIV ARK, FAYETTEVILLE, 69- *Concurrent Pos:* NSF fel, 63-65. *Mem:* Sigma Xi; Am Soc Plant Physiol; Scand Soc Plant Physiol; Bot Soc Am; Phytochem Soc NAm. *Res:* Dormancy in plant structures such as seeds, fruits, tubers and buds; relationship between dormancy and plant phenolics; enzymes associated with hormone control and plant growth. *Mailing Add:* Hwy 16W Fayetteville AR 72701

LANE, FRANK, b New York, NY, Dec 21, 23; m 45; c 1. AEROSPACE ENGINEERING, APPLIED MECHANICS. *Educ:* Univ Mich, BS, 44; Stevens Inst Technol, MS, 48; NY Univ, ScD(aeronaut eng), 54. *Prof Exp:* Asst & assoc prof underwater ord res, Ord Res Lab, Pa State Univ, 48-51; res assoc aerospace eng, NY Univ, 53-54, res assoc prof, 54-56; sr scientist aerospace eng & appl mech, Gen Appl Sci Labs, 56-60, sci supvr, 60-65, tech asst to pres, 65-67, chief scientist, 67-71, vpres, 69-71; CHIEF SCIENTIST & V PRES, KLD ASSOCS INC, 71- *Concurrent Pos:* Mem hydroballistics adv comt, Bur Ord, 50-51; adj assoc prof, NY Univ, 56-65; mem panel aeroelasticity & struct dynamics, Bur Naval Weapons Adv Comt Aeroballistics, 63-65. *Mem:* Am Inst Aeronaut & Astronaut. *Res:* Aeroelasticity; structural dynamics; aerodynamics and hydrodynamics; wave propagation; aerodynamic noise. *Mailing Add:* KLD Assocs Inc 300 Broadway Huntington Station NY 11746

LANE, GARY (THOMAS), b Center, Ky, Nov 8, 41; m 63; c 3. ANIMAL NUTRITION, BIOCHEMISTRY. *Educ:* Berea Col, BS, 63; Purdue Univ, West Lafayette, MS, 65, PhD(animal nutrit), 68. *Prof Exp:* Res asst animal nutrit, Purdue Univ, West Lafayette, 63-67; asst prof, 67-73, assoc prof animal nutrit, Tex A&M Univ, 73-77; ASSOC EXTEN PROF DAIRY, UNIV KY, 77- *Mem:* Am Dairy Sci Asn; Am Soc Animal Sci. *Res:* Ration additives for ruminants; ration and its relation to milk composition and yield; mechanisms of milk synthesis; chemical preservation of high-moisture grain. *Mailing Add:* Dept of Animal Sci Univ Ky Lexington KY 40506

LANE, GEORGE ASHEL, b Norman, Okla, May 9, 30; m 52. PHYSICAL CHEMISTRY, APPLIED CHEMISTRY. *Educ:* Grinnell Col, AB, 52; Northwestern Univ, PhD(phys chem), 55. *Prof Exp:* Asst chem, Grinnell Col, 51-52; asst, Northwestern Univ, 52-55; spec projs chemist, 55-56, staff asst, 56-58, chemist, 58-63, proj leader, 63-66, sr res chemist, 66-69, res specialist, 69-73, sr res specialist, 73-80, RES ASSOC, DOW CHEM USA, 80- *Honors & Awards:* IR-100 Award, 80. *Mem:* AAAS; Am Chem Soc; Int Solar Energy Soc; Sigma Xi. *Res:* Solar energy; energy storage; oxygen isotope effects; trout ecology; auto crash protection; rocket propellant testing and evaluation; pyrotechnics. *Mailing Add:* 3802 Wintergreen Dr Midland MI 48640

LANE, GEORGE H, b Milford, NH, Feb 19, 24; m 48; c 2. PHYSICS. *Educ:* Amherst Col, BA, 47; Yale Univ, MS, 49; Univ Conn, PhD(physics), 61. *Prof Exp:* Asst instr physics, Univ Conn, Hartford Br, 49-51; instr, Franklin & Marshall Col, 54-57, asst prof, 57-60; from asst prof to assoc prof, 60-66, dir grad studies, 68-75, head dept, 62-79, PROF PHYSICS, NORWICH UNIV, 66-, DIR GRAD STUDIES, 79- *Mem:* AAAS; Am Phys Soc; Am Asn Physics Teachers. *Res:* Atomic collisions; mass spectrometry. *Mailing Add:* Dept of Physics Norwich Univ Northfield VT 05663

LANE, HAROLD RICHARD, b Danville, Ill, Mar 7, 42; m 68. PALEONTOLOGY, STRATIGRAPHY. *Educ:* Univ Ill, Urbana, BS, 64; Univ Iowa, MS, 66, PhD(geol), 69. *Prof Exp:* SR RES SCIENTIST, RES CTR, AMOCO PROD CO, 68- *Mem:* Brit Palaeont Asn; Int Palaeont Asn; Soc Econ Paleont & Mineral. *Res:* The evolution, biostratigraphy and systematic paleontology of the microfossils, conodonts, especially in Devonian through Middle Pennsylvanian strata of North America. *Mailing Add:* Amoco Prod Co Res Ctr PO Box 591 Tulsa OK 74102

LANE, HARRY CLEBURNE, plant physiology, see previous edition

LANE, JAMES A(RTHUR), nuclear engineering, deceased

LANE, JAMES DALE, b Las Cruces, NMex, Aug 28, 37; m 58. VERTEBRATE ZOOLOGY. *Educ:* NMex State Univ, BS, 59, MS, 62; Univ Ariz, PhD(zool), 65. *Prof Exp:* Asst biol, NMex State Univ, 59-62; asst zool, Univ Ariz, 62-65, asst geochronology, 65; asst prof biol, 65-70, PROF ZOOL, McNEESE STATE UNIV, 70- *Mem:* AAAS; Soc Syst Zool; Am Soc Mammal; Soc Vert Paleont; Am Inst Biol Sci. *Res:* Ecology and systematics of various mammalians taxons, especially rodents. *Mailing Add:* Dept of Biol McNeese State Univ Lake Charles LA 70601

LANE, JOSEPH ROBERT, b Chicago, Ill, Mar 3, 17; m 49. PHYSICAL METALLURGY, METALLURGICAL ENGINEERING. *Educ:* Univ Ill, BS, 43; Mass Inst Technol, ScD(metall), 50. *Prof Exp:* Metallurgist, Univ Chicago, Metall Lab, 43-45; res asst, Mass Inst Technol, 45-50; br head, Naval Res Lab, 50-55; STAFF METALLURGIST, NAT MAT ADV BD, NAT ACAD SCI, 55- *Mem:* Fel Am Soc Metals; Soc Mfg Engrs; Am Inst Mining, Metall & Petrol Engrs; Soc Advan Mat & Process Eng. *Res:* Superalloys; refractory metals. *Mailing Add:* Nat Mat Adv Bd 2101 Constitution Ave Washington DC 20418

LANE, KEITH ALDRICH, b Gridley, Kans, Nov 11, 21; m 45; c 2. ANALYTICAL CHEMISTRY. *Educ:* Oglethorpe Univ, AB, 42, MA, 43. *Prof Exp:* Chemist, Mutual Chem Co Am, 43-51, group leader anal res, 51-58; chemist, Solvay Process Div, 58-64, group leader anal res, 64-70, ENVIRON CHEMIST, INDUST CHEMS DIV, ALLIED CHEM CORP CORP, 70- *Mem:* Am Chem Soc. *Res:* All phases of chromium chemistry; organic and inorganic analytical method development; environmental studies and pollution control. *Mailing Add:* 122 Royal Rd Liverpool NY 13088

LANE, LEONARD JAMES, b Tucson, Ariz, Apr 25, 45; m 64; c 2. HYDROLOGY. *Educ:* Univ Ariz, BS, 70, MS, 72; Colo State Univ, PhD(civil eng), 75. *Prof Exp:* HYDROLOGIST, USDA, 70- *Concurrent Pos:* Fac affil civil eng, Colo State Univ, 73-74. *Mem:* Am Geophys Union; Am Soc Civil Engrs; Am Water Resources Asn; Brit Geomorphol Res Group. *Res:* Hydrology of semiarid regions; runoff and sediment simulation models incorporating geomorphic features and geomorphic thresholds; prediction of runoff and sediment production. *Mailing Add:* US Dept of Agr 442 E Seventh St Tucson AZ 85705

LANE, LESLIE CARL, b Stamford, Conn, Apr 5, 42; m 66, 77; c 2. PLANT VIROLOGY. *Educ:* Univ Wis, BS, 65, PhD(biochem), 71. *Prof Exp:* Fel virol, John Innes Inst, Norwich, Eng, 71-73; fel virol, 73-75, asst prof, 75-81, ASSOC PROF PLANT PATH, UNIV NEBR-LINCOLN, 81- *Mem:* Am Phytopath Soc; Electrophoresis Soc. *Res:* Structure and replication of plant viruses; virus directed protein and nucleic acid synthesis; virus-host interactions; gel electrophoretic spearations; fluorescence detection methods. *Mailing Add:* Dept Plant Path Univ Nebr Lincoln NE 68583

LANE, MALCOLM DANIEL, b Chicago, Ill, Aug 10, 30; m 51; c 2. BIOCHEMISTRY. *Educ:* Iowa State Univ, BS, 51, MS, 53; Univ Ill, PhD, 56. *Prof Exp:* Res asst, Iowa State Univ, 51-53; assoc prof biochem & nutrit, Va Polytech Inst, 56-62, prof, 62-64; assoc prof biochem, Sch Med, NY Univ, 64-69, prof, 69-70; prof physiol chem, 70-78, DELAMAR PROF PHYSIOL CHEM & CHMN DEPT, SCH MED, JOHNS HOPKINS UNIV, 78- *Concurrent Pos:* Sr fel, Max Planck Inst Cell Chem, 62-63; mem biochem study sect, NIH, 70- *Honors & Awards:* Mead Johnson Award, Am Inst Nutrit, 66. *Mem:* AAAS; Am Chem Soc; Am Soc Biol Chem; Am Inst Nutrit; Harvey Soc. *Res:* Enzymology regulation of enzyme activity; enzymatic carboxylation; fatty acid and carbohydrate metabolism; cholesterol biosynthesis; lipogenic differentiation; very low density lipoprotein synthesis and secretion. *Mailing Add:* Dept of Physiol Chem Johns Hopkins Univ Sch of Med Baltimore MD 21205

LANE, MEREDITH ANNE, b Mesa, Ariz, Aug 4, 51; m 74. SYSTEMATICS, EVOLUTION. *Educ:* Ariz State Univ, BS, 74, MS, 76; Univ Tex, PhD(bot), 80. *Prof Exp:* ASST PROF BOT, DEPT BIOL, UNIV COLO, BOULDER, 80- *Concurrent Pos:* Vis asst prof, Dept Bot, Univ Tex, 82. *Mem:* Int Asn Plant Taxon; Am Soc Plant Taxonomists; Bot Soc Am; AAAS. *Res:* Angiosperm systematics, specifically of southwestern American and Mexican Compositae (Astereae), using cytotaxonomic, ecogeographic, scanning electron microscopic, biogeographic and cladistic techniques; pollination biology of Compositae, especially micromorphological pollinator cues. *Mailing Add:* Dept EPO Biol Univ Colo Boulder CO 80309

LANE, MONTAGUE, b New York, NY, Aug 28, 29; m 57. CLINICAL PHARMACOLOGY, THERAPEUTICS. *Educ:* NY Univ, BA, 47; Chicago Med Sch, MB, 52, MD, 53; Georgetown Univ, MS 57. *Prof Exp:* Res assoc radiobiol, Cancer Res Lab, City New York, 47-48; res assoc oncol, Chicago Med Sch, 50-52; intern med, Jewish Hosp Brooklyn, NY, 52-53, asst res, 53-54; clin assoc pharmacol, Nat Cancer Inst, 54-56; asst resident med, USPHS, Rochester, 56-57; investr clin pharmacol, Nat Cancer Inst, 57-60; from asst prof to assoc prof, 60-67, PROF PHARMACOL & MED, BAYLOR COL MED, 67-, HEAD DIV CLIN ONCOL, 69- *Concurrent Pos:* Instr, Sch Med, George Washington Univ, 57-60; consult, Vet Admin Hosp, 63-; mem pharmacol & therapeut study sect, Nat Cancer Inst, 66-69, consult chemother study sect, mem nat new agents & spec Krebiozen rev comts & ad hoc pharmacol adv comt, Colo-Rectal Task Force, mem cancer clin invests rev comt, 73-; mem subcomt med oncol, Am Bd Internal Med. *Mem:* Am Soc Hemat; Am Soc Pharmacol & Exp Therapeut; Soc Exp Biol & Med; Am Asn Cancer Res; Am Soc Clin Pharmacol & Therapeut (pres, 71-72). *Res:* Cancer chemotherapy alkylating agents; antimetabolites; riboflavin deficiency; drug screening; ferro-kinetics; internal medicine. *Mailing Add:* Baylor Col of Med 1200 Moursund Houston TX 77030

LANE, NANCY JANE, b Halifax, NS, Nov 23, 36; m 69; c 2. DEVELOPMENTAL CELL BIOLOGY, NEUROBIOLOGY. *Educ:* Dalhousie Univ, BSc, 58, MSc, 60; Oxford Univ, DPhil(cytol), 63; Cambridge Univ, PhD, 68. *Hon Degrees:* ScD, Cambridge Univ, 81. *Prof Exp:* Res asst prof path, Albert Einstein Col Med, 64-65; res staff biologist, Yale Univ, 65-68; PRIN SCI OFFICER & HEAD ELECTRON MICROS, AGR RES COUN RES UNIT INVERT CHEM & PHYSIOL, DEPT ZOOL, CAMBRIDGE UNIV, 68- *Concurrent Pos:* Res fel, Girton Col, Cambridge Univ, 68-70, off fel & lectr cell biol, 70-, grad tutor, 75- *Mem:* AAAS; Am Soc Cell Biol; Brit Soc Cell Biol; Soc Exp Biol & Med; fel Royal Micros Soc. *Res:* Freeze-fracture and tracer analysis of invertebrate central nervous system; experimental and cytological studies on neuropile and neurosecretory systems in invertebrates; enzyme cytochemistry and freeze fracture studies of invertebrate cells; accessibility of nervous systems to tracer molecules; development of junctions in arthropod tissues; receptor structure and localization by ligand binding. *Mailing Add:* Agr Res Coun Res Unit Dept Zool Downing St Cambridge CB2 3EJ England

LANE, NEAL F, b Oklahoma City, Okla, Aug 22, 38; m 60; c 2. ATOMIC PHYSICS. *Educ:* Univ Okla, BSc, 60, MS, 62, PhD(physics), 64. *Prof Exp:* NSF res fel physics, Queen's Univ, Belfast, 64-65; vis fel, Joint Inst Lab Astrophys, Univ Colo, 65-66; from asst prof to assoc prof, 66-72, chmn dept, 77-82, PROF PHYSICS, RICE UNIV, 72-, PROF SPACE PHYSICS & ASTRON, 77- *Concurrent Pos:* Alfred P Sloan res fel, 67-73; vis fel, Joint Inst Lab Astrophys, Univ Colo, 75-76; dir, Phys Div, NSF, 79-80, mem advisory comt, 78-82; chmn evaluation panel, Joint Inst Lab Astrophys, Nat Res Coun, Nat Acad Sci. *Mem:* Fel Am Phys Soc; fel AAAS; Am Assoc Phys Teachers; Sigma Xi. *Res:* Theoretical studies of electron-atom and electron molecule elastic and inelastic collision processes; theoretical investigation of atom-atom collision processes. *Mailing Add:* Dept of Physics Rice Univ Houston TX 77001

LANE, NORMAN GARY, b French Lick, Ind, Feb 19, 30; m 58; c 3. PALEONTOLOGY. *Educ:* Oberlin Col, AB, 52; Univ Kans, MS, 54, PhD(geol), 58. *Prof Exp:* From asst prof to prof geol, Univ Calif, Los Angeles, 58-73; PROF PALEONT, IND UNIV, BLOOMINGTON, 73- *Concurrent Pos:* Fulbright scholar, Univ Tasmania, 55-56; Fulbright prof, Trinity Col, Dublin, 71-72; res assoc paleont, Smithsonian Inst, 71- *Mem:* Paleont Soc; Soc Econ Paleontologists & Mineralogists; Soc Vert Paleont. *Res:* Functional morphology and community relations of fossil crinoids. *Mailing Add:* Dept of Geol Ind Univ Bloomington IN 47401

LANE, RAYMOND OSCAR, b Asbury Park, NJ, Sept 25, 24; m 49; c 3. NUCLEAR PHYSICS. *Educ:* Iowa State Univ, PhD(physics), 53. *Prof Exp:* Res asst, Inst Atomic Res, Iowa State Col, 49-53; assoc physicist, Argonne Nat Lab, 53-66; prof physics, 66-74, DISTINGUISHED PROF PHYSICS, OHIO UNIV, 74- *Mem:* Am Phys Soc. *Res:* Penetration of electrons in matter; beta ray spectroscopy; neutron scattering; neutron polarization; nuclear structure. *Mailing Add:* Dept of Physics Ohio Univ Athens OH 45701

LANE, RICHARD DURELLE, b Detroit, Mich, May 14, 53; m 75; c 1. TUMOR IMMUNOLOGY. *Educ:* Bowling Green State Univ, BS, 75; Med Col Va, PhD(anat), 80. *Prof Exp:* NIH res technician, 75-76, INSTR, DEPT ANAT, MED COL OHIO, 80- *Mem:* Sigma Xi. *Res:* Investigating neoplastic cell produced factors which influence tumoricidal macrophages; production of monoclonal antibodies to these tumor produced factors; examining the influence of chemotherapuetic drugs upon macrophages; investigating non-pancreatic sources of insulin production. *Mailing Add:* Dept Anat Med Col Ohio CS #10008 Toledo OH 43699

LANE, RICHARD L, b Franklinville, NY, Mar 11, 35; m 58; c 4. CERAMICS, PHYSICAL CHEMISTRY. *Educ:* State Univ NY, Alfred, BS, 57, PhD(ceramic sci), 62. *Prof Exp:* Res scientist, Appl Res Lab, Xerox Corp, 62-65, Fundamental Res Lab, 65-68; proj leader, Hamco Mach & Electronics Corp, 68-70, mgr res & develop, 70-74, dir eng, Hamco Div, 74-78, DIR, TECHNOL CTR, KAYEX CORP, 78- *Mem:* Am Ceramic Soc; Am Inst Ceramic Engrs; Electrochem Soc. *Res:* Physics of glass, electrical and optical properties; chemistry of glass, surface properties and reactions, high temperature reactions and crystal-glass interactions; chemical and physical properties of crystalline ceramic materials; semiconductor materials processing; crystal growth; abrasive machining. *Mailing Add:* Hamco Div Kayex Corp 1000 Millstead Way Rochester NY 14624

LANE, RICHARD NEIL, b Richmond, Va, Sept 1, 44. MATHEMATICS, ELECTRICAL ENGINEERING. *Educ:* Calif Inst Technol, BS, 65, PhD(math), 68. *Prof Exp:* Mem prof staff math, Gen Elec Co, 68-69; sr scientist, Systs Applns, Inc, 69-70, dir commun studies, 70-75; CONSULT, 75- *Mem:* Am Math Soc; Inst Elec & Electronics Engrs. *Res:* Systems analysis and modeling of cost and performance of communications systems, especially mobile radio and common carrier systems. *Mailing Add:* 4925 River Rd Washington DC 20016

LANE, ROBERT HAROLD, b Tampa, Fla, Sept 4, 44. BIOINORGANIC CHEMISTRY, INORGANIC CHEMISTRY. *Educ:* Univ NC, BS, 66; Univ Fla, PhD(chem), 71. *Prof Exp:* Assoc phys biochem, Ore Grad Ctr, 71-72, sr res fel, 73; instr, Univ Ga, 73-75, asst prof chem, 75-80; SR RES CHEMIST, OCCIDENTAL RES CORP, 80- *Concurrent Pos:* NIH fel, Ore Grad Ctr, 73. *Mem:* Am Chem Soc. *Res:* Theoretical and experimental aspects of transition metal electron transfer in multinuclear systems; highly dispersed metal species on ordered supports. *Mailing Add:* Dept of Chem Univ of Ga Athens GA 30602

LANE, ROBERT K, b Brandon, Man, Feb 7, 37; m; c 1. ENVIRONMENTAL MANAGEMENT. *Educ:* Brandon Col, BSc, 57; Ore State Univ, MS, 62, PhD(phys oceanog), 65. *Prof Exp:* Meteorol officer, Meteorol Br, Dept Transport, Can, 57-58; asst scientist, Pac Oceanog Group, Fisheries Res Bd Can, 59-61; instr oceanog, Ore State Univ, 63-65; res scientist, Marine Sci Br, Dept Energy, Mines & Resources, Can, 65-67; head phys limnol sec, Great Lakes Div, Inland Waters Br, Dept Environ, Can, 67-72, head lake resources sudiv, Lakes Div, 72-73, chief sci opers div, Can Ctr Inland Waters, 73-75, policy & prog develop off, Western & Northern Region, Environ Mgt Serv, 75-79; dir, Water Resources Proj, Can West Found, 79-81; SR ADV CORP AFFAIRS, DEPT ENVIRON CAN, EDMONTON, 81- *Concurrent Pos:* Mem subcomt hydrol, Nat Res Coun, 68- *Honors & Awards:* Can Centennial Medal, 68. *Mem:* Am Soc Limnol & Oceanog; Am Geophys Union; Royal Meteorol Soc; Int Asn Gt Lakes Res (pres, 74-75); Am Meteorol Soc. *Res:* Physical oceanography and limnology, especially heat and radiation exchange; remote sensing. *Mailing Add:* Dept Environ Environ Mgt Serv 901 9942-108 St 901 9942-108th St Edmonton AB T5K 2J5 Can

LANE, ROBERT SIDNEY, b Worcester, Mass, Mar 7, 44; m 68. MEDICAL ENTOMOLOGY, VETERINARY ENTOMOLOGY. *Educ:* Univ Calif, Berkeley, BA, 66, PhD(entom), 74; San Francisco State Col, MA, 69. *Prof Exp:* Asst pub health biologist, Vector Biol & Control Sect, State Dept Health, Calif, 74-77, assoc pub health biologist, 77-79; ASSOC SPECIALIST, DEPT ENTOM SCI, UNIV CALIF, BERKELEY, 80- *Concurrent Pos:* Lectr, Biol Dept, San Francisco State Univ, 79-80. *Mem:* Entom Soc Am; Wildlife Dis Asn; Am Soc Trop Med & Hyg; Soc Vector Ecologists. *Res:* Biosystematics of Tabanidae and Rhagionidae (Diptera); ecology of tick-borne diseases. *Mailing Add:* Dept Entom Sci Univ Calif Berkeley CA 94720

LANE, RONALD PATON, b Jackson, Ga, Oct 11, 37; m 61; c 2. HORTICULTURE, PLANT BREEDING. *Educ:* Univ Ga, BSA, 63, MS, 65; Mich State Univ, PhD(hort), 68. *Prof Exp:* ASST HORTICULTURIST, GA STA, COL AGR, UNIV GA, 68- *Mem:* Am Soc Hort Sci. *Res:* Grape and bramble breeding. *Mailing Add:* Dept of Hort Ga Exp Sta Experiment GA 30212

LANE, STEPHEN MARK, b Scott Air Force Base, Ill, Nov 22, 48. PHYSICS. *Educ:* San Jose State Univ, BA, 71; Univ Calif, Davis, MS, 73, PhD(appl sci), 79. *Prof Exp:* PHYSICIST, LASER FUSION, LAWRENCE LIVERMORE LAB, 78- *Mem:* Am Phys Soc. *Res:* Atomic and nuclear spectroscopy as applied to laser fusion research. *Mailing Add:* Lawrence Livermore Lab PO Box 808 Livermore CA 94550

LANE, WALLACE, b Chicago, Ill, Aug 31, 11; m 38; c 2. PREVENTIVE MEDICINE. *Educ:* Univ Kans, AB, 33, MA, 35, MD, 39; Johns Hopkins Univ, MPH, 51. *Prof Exp:* Staff physician student health serv, Univ Kans, 46-48, clin assoc prof med & microbiol, 52-56; dir Bi-County Health Dept, Kans, 48-52; dir, Div Adult Health, Seattle-King County Health Dept, 56-58; chief div, Wash State Dept Pub Health, 58-68, dir, 68-73; RETIRED. *Concurrent Pos:* Dir, Health Dept, Kansas City, Kans, 52-56; lectr, Sch Med, Univ Kans, 55-56; clin assoc prof prev med, Univ Wash, 57-73. *Mem:* AAAS; AMA; Am Pub Health Asn; Sigma Xi. *Res:* Role of behavioral science in medicine and public health. *Mailing Add:* 1817 Governor Stevens Ave Olympia WA 98501

LANE, WILLIAM DAVID, plant breeding, see previous edition

LANE, WILLIAM JAMES, b Zanesville, Ohio, Dec 5, 25; m 50; c 3. ANALYTICAL CHEMISTRY. *Educ:* Denison Univ, BA, 47; Miami Univ, MS, 53; Iowa State Univ, PhD(chem), 57. *Prof Exp:* Asst chemist, AEC, Mound Lab, Monsanto Chem Co, 48-51; res asst anal chem, Ames Lab, Iowa State Univ, 52-57; anal chemist, Columbia-Southern Chem Corp, Pittsburgh Plate Glass Co, 57-60, anal group supvr, 60-64, res anal chemist, Chem Div, 64-69; res coordr anal chem, Universal Oil Prod Co, 69-74, group leader anal chem res & develop, 74-78, lab supvr, Spectroscopy & anal res, 78-81, LAB SUPVR, ANAL RES & SCHEDULING, UOP, INC, 81- . *Mem:* Am Chem Soc. *Res:* General wet chemical analysis; polarography; chromatography; spectrophotometry. *Mailing Add:* 444 W Norman Ct Des Plaines IL 60016

LANE, WYMAN CURTIS, b Cleveland, Ohio, Jan 19, 36; m 63; c 1. METALLURGY, ELECTRON MICROSCOPY. *Educ:* Ohio State Univ, BMetE, 67. *Prof Exp:* Res engr corrosion, Columbus Labs, Battelle Mem Inst, 67-71; dir appln lab, Etec Corp, 71-75; METALL CONSULT, 75- *Concurrent Pos:* Consult, Lane Assocs, 75- *Res:* Scanning electron microscopy; metallurgy. *Mailing Add:* 5324 Selma Ave Fremont CA 94536

LANEWALA, MOHAMMED A, b Dohad, India; m 68. CHEMICAL ENGINEERING. *Educ:* Univ Calcutta, BSc, 56, MSc, 59; Univ Toronto, MASc, 61; NY Univ, PhD(chem eng), 67. *Prof Exp:* Develop engr, Molecular Sieve Dept, Linde Div, 67-69, proj leader, Eastview, 69-77, COMPUT TECH COORDR, UNION CARBIDE CORP, 77- *Mem:* Assoc Am Inst Chem Engrs; Am Soc Testing & Mat; Instrument Soc Am. *Res:* Catalysis; adsorption; petroleum processes; computer technology. *Mailing Add:* 5909 Ole Mill Rd Mobile AL 36609

LANEY, BILLIE EUGENE, b Joplin, Mo, Aug 27, 35; m 69; c 5. THEORETICAL PHYSICS. *Educ:* Univ Tulsa, BS, 60; NMex State Univ, MS, 62, PhD(physics), 64. *Prof Exp:* Sr res physicist oil explor, Schlumberger Res & Develop Labs, 64-66; sr res physicist space physics, NAm Rockwell, Inc, 66-68; chief scientist nuclear weapons, Braddock, Dunn & MacDonald, Inc, 68-71; prin res physicist, Cornell Aeronaut Labs, 71-73; vpres opers comput aided design, R/M Systs, Inc, 73-76; PRES ENERGY CONVERSION, EX-CAL, INC, 76- *Concurrent Pos:* Consult, Cities Serv Res & Develop Labs, 60-62, Calspan Corp, 73-, Sci Appl, Inc, 74-, EG&G, Inc, 74- & BDM Corp, 75-; tech referee, Am Phys Soc, 76- *Mem:* Am Phys Soc; Am Inst Aeronaut & Astronaut; Am Soc Testing & Mat. *Res:* Product oriented research in energy conversion mechanisms, electromagnetic interactions, thermodynamic heat transfer, seismic wave propagation, radiation transfer and gas dynamics, for application to the design of biomedical instrumentation, micrographics, and underground nuclear test equipment. *Mailing Add:* 13425 Cedarbrook NE Albuquerque NM 87111

LANFORD, OSCAR E, III, b New York, NY, Jan 6, 40; m 61; c 1. MATHEMATICAL PHYSICS. *Educ:* Wesleyan Univ, BA, 60; Princeton Univ, MA, 62, PhD(physics), 66. *Prof Exp:* Instr math, Princeton Univ, 65-66; asst prof, Univ Calif, Berkeley, 66-67; vis prof physics, Inst Advan Sci Studies, 67-68; asst prof math, 68-70, assoc prof, 70-75, PROF MATH, UNIV CALIF, BERKELEY, 75- *Concurrent Pos:* Alfred Sloan Found res fel, 69-71; mem, Inst Advan Studies, 70; exchange prof, Univ Aix Marseille, 71. *Res:* Mathematical physics, especially statistical mechanics and quantum field theory. *Mailing Add:* Dept of Math Univ of Calif Berkeley CA 94720

LANFORD, WILLIAM ARMISTEAD, b Albany, NY, Nov 15, 44; m 66; c 3. NUCLEAR PHYSICS, MATERIALS SCIENCE. *Educ:* Univ Rochester, BS, 66, PhD(physics), 72. *Prof Exp:* Res assoc, Mich State Univ, 71-72, asst prof, 72-73; from asst prof to assoc prof physics, Yale Univ, 78-79; ASSOC PROF PHYSICS, STATE UNIV NY, ALBANY, 79- *Mem:* Am Ceramic Soc; NY Acad Sci; Mat Res Soc. *Res:* Glass surfaces; reaction between water and glass; hydrogen in solids; effects of sea-level cosmic rays on microelectronics; storage of ultracold neutrons; nuclear reaction analysis of hydrogen in metals; nuclear structure; beta-decay and solar neutrinos; archaeometry. *Mailing Add:* Dept of Physics State Univ NY Albany NY 12203

LANG, ANTON, b Petersburg, Russia, Jan 18, 13; nat US; m 46; c 3. DEVELOPMENTAL PLANT BIOLOGY, PHYSIOLOGY. *Educ:* Univ Berlin, Dr Nat Sci, 39. *Hon Degrees:* LLD, Univ Glasgow, UK, 81. *Prof Exp:* Sci asst plant physiol, Max-Planck Inst Biol, Ger, 39-49; res assoc genetics, McGill Univ, 49; vis prof genetics & agron, Agr & Mech Col Tex, 50; from res fel to sr res fel plant physiol, Calif Inst Technol, 50-52; from asst prof to assoc prof bot, Univ Calif, Los Angeles, 52-59; prof biol, Calif Inst Technol, 59-65; dir, Mich State Univ/Dept of Energy Plant Res Lab, 65-78, PROF, MICH STATE UNIV/DEPT ENERGY PLANT RES LAB & PROF BOT & PLANT PATH, 78- *Concurrent Pos:* Lady Davis Found Can fel, 49; NSF sr fel, Max-Planck Inst Biol, Ger & Hebrew Univ, Israel, 58-59; consult develop biol prog, NSF, 60-64, consult, adv comt biol & med sci, 68-70; partic sci exchange prog, Nat Acad Sci-Acad Sci, USSR, 63, 68 & 75-76; trustee, Argonne Univs Asn, 65-69; chmn comt effects on herbicides in Vietnam, Nat Acad Sci-Nat Res Coun, 72-74; Hon vpres, XII Int Bot Cong, Leningrad, 75; mem, Comt USSR & Eastern Europe, Nat Acad Sci, 64-67 & 77-78; mem, Pres Comt, Nat Medal Sci, 76-79. *Honors & Awards:* Sr Scientist Award, Sigma Xi & Mich State Univ, 69; Stephen Hales Price & Charles Reid Barnes Life Mem Award, Am Soc Plant Physiologists, 76. *Mem:* Nat Acad Sci; fel AAAS; Am Acad Arts & Sci; Leopoldina Acad Naturalists; Am Soc Plant Physiol (vpres, 63, pres, 71). *Res:* Physiology of flowering; plant hormone physiology. *Mailing Add:* Mich State Univ Dept Energy Plant Res Lab East Lansing MI 48824

LANG, BRUCE Z, b St Joseph, Mo, May 31, 37; m 59; c 1. PARASITOLOGY, IMMUNOLOGY. *Educ:* Chico State Col, BS, 60; Univ NC, Chapel Hill, 61, PhD(parasitol), 66. *Prof Exp:* Vis asst prof zool, Univ Okla, 66-67; from asst prof to assoc prof biol, 67-74, PROF BIOL, EASTERN WASH UNIV, 74-, CHMN DEPT, 78- *Concurrent Pos:* NIH fel zool, Univ Okla, 66-67; NSF grants, 69-72. *Mem:* AAAS; Am Soc Parasitol; Am Soc Zoologists; Am Soc Trop Med & Hyg; Am Inst Biol Sci. *Res:* Host-parasite relationships; ecology of parasitism; ecology of fresh-water gastropod molluscs. *Mailing Add:* Dept of Biol Eastern Washington Univ Cheney WA 99004

LANG, CALVIN ALLEN, b Portland, Ore, June 13, 25; m 49; c 4. GERONTOLOGY, NUTRITION. *Educ:* Princeton Univ, AB, 47; Johns Hopkins Univ, ScD(biochem), 54. *Prof Exp:* Res collabr, Brookhaven Nat Labs, 49-51; asst scientist insect biochem, Conn Agr Exp Sta, 54-56; res assoc, Sch Hyg & Pub Health, Johns Hopkins Univ, 56-59; from asst prof to assoc prof, 59-72, dirbiomed aging res prog, 71-74, PROF BIOCHEM, SCH MED, UNIV LOUISVILLE, 72- *Concurrent Pos:* Fel, Sch Hyg & Pub Health & McCollum-Pratt Inst, Johns Hopkins Univ, 56-59; NIH fel, 57-59 & res career develop award, 67-72. *Mem:* Am Soc Biol Chem; Am Inst Nutrit; Soc Exp Biol & Med; fel Geront Soc (vpres, 71). *Res:* Biochemistry of growth and aging; insect and nutritional biochemistry; glutathione detoxification and aging. *Mailing Add:* Dept Biochem Univ of Louisville Sch of Med Louisville KY 40292

LANG, CONRAD MARVIN, b Chicago, Ill, July 1, 39; m 61; c 3. PHYSICAL CHEMISTRY. *Educ:* Elmhurst Col, BS, 61; Univ Wis-Madison, MS, 64; Univ Wyo, PhD(chem), 70. *Prof Exp:* Teaching asst chem, Univ Wis-Madison, 61-63, res asst, 63-64; from instr to assoc prof, 64-78, PROF CHEM, UNIV WIS-STEVENS POINT, 78- *Concurrent Pos:* Consult, Crowns, Merklin, Midthun & Hill, Attorneys at Law, 70-; NSF res grant, Univ Wis-Stevens Point, 71-73. *Mem:* Am Chem Soc. *Res:* Application of electron spin resonance to molecular structure and biological molecules; semiempirical quantum chemical calculations on systems of biological interest; physiochemical aspects of vision; macromolecular structure of binary fluids. *Mailing Add:* Dept of Chem Univ of Wis Stevens Point WI 54481

LANG, DAVID (VERN), b Wilmar, Minn, July 11, 43; m 68; c 3. SEMICONDUCTORS, PHYSICS. *Educ:* Concordia Col, Moorhead, Minn, BA, 65; Univ Wis-Madison, PhD(physics), 69. *Prof Exp:* Res assoc physics, Univ Ill, Urbana, 69-70, res asst prof, 70-72; mem tech staff, 72-81, HEAD, SEMICONDUCTOR ELECTRONICS RES DEPT, BELL LABS, 81- *Mem:* Am Phys Soc. *Res:* Capacitance spectroscopy; defects in III-V semiconductors; recombination enhanced solid state defect reactions; radiation damage in semiconductors; gap states in amorphous semiconductors. *Mailing Add:* Bell Labs Murray Hill NJ 07974

LANG, DENNIS ROBERT, b Albany, NY, May 7, 44. CELL PHYSIOLOGY. *Educ:* Syracuse Univ, BS, 66, PhD(microbiol), 71. *Prof Exp:* Fel biochem, Cornell Univ, 71-73; ASST PROF MICROBIOL, SCH MED, UNIV CINCINNATI, 73- *Mem:* Am Soc Microbiol; Sigma Xi; Tissue Cult Asn. *Res:* Role of the magnesium stimulated adenosine triphosphatase in membrane bioenergetics of bacteria; chemical carcinogenesis and mutagenesis in mammalian cells. *Mailing Add:* Dept of Microbiol Sch of Med Univ of Cincinnati Cincinnati OH 45267

LANG, DIMITRIJ ADOLF, b Berlin, Ger, Aug 30, 26; m 59; c 2. BIOPHYSICS, MOLECULAR BIOLOGY. *Educ:* Univ Frankfurt, MS, 53, PhD(biophys), 59. *Prof Exp:* Res asst biophys, Max Planck Inst Biophys, 53-58 & Hyg Inst, Univ Frankfurt, 58-65; from asst prof to assoc prof biol, 65-72, PROF BIOL, UNIV TEX, DALLAS, 72- *Concurrent Pos:* NIH res career develop awards, 67-71 & 72-76. *Mem:* Electron Micros Soc Am; Biophys Soc. *Res:* Electronics; physics of ionizing radiations; high-output x-ray machines; standard dosimetry of x-rays; electron microscopy of bacteria, viruses and nucleic acids; physical chemistry of nucleic acids. *Mailing Add:* Univ Tex Dallas Biol Prog FO 3-1 PO Box 688 Richardson TX 75080

LANG, ENID ASHER, b Los Angeles, Calif, Aug 28, 44; m 69; c 2. PSYCHIATRY. *Educ:* Radcliffe Col, AB, 66; Univ Southern Calif, MD, 70; Columbia Univ, MS, 74. *Prof Exp:* Med intern, Beth Israel Hosp, New York, 71-72; resident psychiat, Columbia Psychiat Inst, 72-74; res fel, Columbia Univ Health Serv, 74-75; fac mem psychiat, Sch Med, NY Univ, 75-80; FAC MEM PSYCHIAT, MT SINAI SCH MED, NY, 81- *Concurrent Pos:* Dir, Group Psychiat & Training Psychiat Residents, Bellevue Hosp, Sch Med, NY Univ, 75-, dir, Socialization Prog Psychiat Outpatients, 75- *Mem:* Am Psychiat Asn; NY Acad Sci; Am Women's Med Asn. *Res:* A longitudinal comparative study of treatment-outcome of discharged psychiatric outpatients who receive group therapy with medication versus individual therapy with medication only. *Mailing Add:* 10 Innes Rd Scarsdale NY 10583

LANG, ERICH KARL, b Vienna, Austria, Dec 7, 29; US citizen; m 56; c 2. RADIOLOGY. *Educ:* Columbia Univ, MS, 51; Univ Vienna, MD, 53. *Prof Exp:* Assoc radiol, Johns Hopkins Hosp & Univ, 56-59, assoc radiologist, 59-61; radiologist, Methodist Hosp, Indianapolis, Ind, 61-67; prof radiol & chmn dept, Sch Med, La State Univ, Shreveport, 67-76; PROF RADIOL & CHMN DEPT, SCH MED, LA STATE UNIV, NEW ORLEANS, 76-; PROF RADIOL, SCH MED, TULANE UNIV, 76- *Mem:* AMA; Radiol Soc NAm; Soc Nuclear Med; Am Col Radiol; Am Col Chest Physicians. *Res:* Diagnostic, vascular roentgenographic examinations; diagnostic roentgenographic evaluation of tumors and tumor diagnosis. *Mailing Add:* Dept of Radiol La State Univ Med Ctr New Orleans LA 70110

LANG, FRANK ALEXANDER, b Olympia, Wash, May 14, 37; m 59; c 2. SYSTEMATIC BOTANY. *Educ:* Ore State Univ, BS, 59; Univ Wash, MS, 61; Univ BC, PhD(bot), 65. *Prof Exp:* Asst prof biol, Whitman Col, 65-66; asst prof, 66-71, assoc prof, 71-77, PROF BIOL, SOUTHERN ORE STATE COL, 77-, CHMN DEPT, 76- *Mem:* Am Soc Plant Taxon; Int Asn Plant Taxon. *Res:* Biosystematics and cytotaxonomy of vascular plants; flora of the Siskiyou Mountains. *Mailing Add:* Dept of Biol Southern Ore State Col Ashland OR 97520

LANG, FRANK THEODORE, b New York, NY, Jan 25, 38; m 63; c 3. PHYSICAL CHEMISTRY. *Educ:* St Francis Col, NY, BS, 59; Rensselaer Polytech Inst, PhD(phys chem), 64. *Prof Exp:* Res assoc photochem, Univ Sheffield, 64-65; res assoc-instr energy transfer, Univ NC, Chapel Hill, 65-67; chmn dept chem, 70-73, assoc prof phys chem, 67-80, PROF CHEM, FAIRLEIGH DICKINSON UNIV, FLORHAM-MADISON, 80- *Mem:* Am Chem Soc. *Res:* Charge transfer complexes; flash photolysis; low temperature photochemistry; energy transfer processes; luminescene studies. *Mailing Add:* Dept of Chem Fairleigh Dickson Univ Madison NJ 07940

LANG, FREDERICK, neurobiology, invertebrate zoology, deceased

LANG, GEORGE E, JR, b Chicago, Ill, June 29, 42; m 68; c 1. TOPOLOGY. *Educ:* Loyola Univ Chicago, BS, 64; Univ Dayton, MS, 66; Purdue Univ, PhD(math), 70. *Prof Exp:* Teaching asst, Univ Dayton, 64-66 & Purdue Univ, 67-69; ASSOC PROF MATH, FAIRFIELD UNIV, 70- *Mem:* Am Math Soc; Math Asn Am; Am Asn Univ Profs. *Res:* Homotopy theory; subgroups of homotopy groups; direct limits of CW complexes with an eye to group theoretic applications. *Mailing Add:* Dept Math Fairfield Univ Fairfield CT 06430

LANG, GERALD EDWARD, b Chicago, Ill, Mar 1, 45; m 73; c 1. PLANT ECOLOGY. *Educ:* Western Ill Univ, BS, 67; Univ Wyo, MS, 69; Rutgers Univ, PhD(bot), 73. *Prof Exp:* Res instr terrestrial ecol, Dartmouth Col, 73-76; asst prof, 76-80, ASSOC PROF BIOL, WVA UNIV, 80- *Concurrent Pos:* NSF res grants, 74-76, 76-79, 77 & 79-82; Army Corps Engrs res contract, 79-82. *Mem:* AAAS; Brit Ecol Soc; Ecol Soc Am. *Res:* Vegetation patterns and biogeochemical processes in high-elevation wetland ecosystems in the Appalachian Mountains; decomposition rates for leaf and wood litter; concomitant elemental mineralization patterns in forest ecosystems. *Mailing Add:* Dept Biol WVa Univ Morgantown WV 26506

LANG, GERHARD HERBERT, b Neunkirchen, WGer, Jan 6, 27; Can citizen; m 59; c 2. MEDICAL MICROBIOLOGY, VETERINARY MEDICINE. *Educ:* Univ Lyons, France, DVM, 55; Pasteur Inst, Paris, cert bact, 55; Univ Toronto, MVSc, 62. *Prof Exp:* Assoc vet, Beauquesne, France, 55-57; asst prof, 61-74, ASSOC PROF VET VIROL, ONT VET COL, UNIV GUELPH, 74- *Concurrent Pos:* Animal health expert virol, Food & Agr Orgn, Rome, 71-73. *Mem:* Am Asn Avian Pathologists; World Vet Poultry Asn; Can Soc Microbiologists. *Res:* Animal and human virus infections, their diagnosis and control; medical and veterinary microbiology. *Mailing Add:* Dept Vet Microbiol & Immunol Univ Guelph Guelph N1G 2W1 Can

LANG, GERHARD PAUL, b Omaha, Nebr, Feb 20, 17; m 44; c 4. INORGANIC CHEMISTRY. *Educ:* Valparaiso Univ, BA, 43; Wash Univ, MA, 55. *Prof Exp:* Chemist, Visking Corp, 44-45; chemist, Uranium Div, Mallinckrodt Chem Works, 46-64; res chemist, Emerson Elec Mfg Co, 64-66; SR ENGR, McDONNELL DOUGLAS CORP, 66- *Mem:* Am Chem Soc. *Res:* Uranium chemistry; liquid-liquid extraction; radiochemistry; aerospace chemistry. *Mailing Add:* 7430 Hiawatha Richmond Heights MO 63117

LANG, HARRY GEORGE, b Pittsburgh, Pa, June 2, 47; m 73. PHYSICS. *Educ:* Bethany Col, WVa, BS, 69; Rochester Inst Technol, MS, 74; Univ Rochester, EdD, 79. *Prof Exp:* asst prof, 70-80, PROF PHYSICS, ROCHESTER INST TECHNOL, NAT TECH INST DEAF, 80- *Concurrent Pos:* Consult, Proj Handicapped Sci, AAAS, 78-; Res Better Sch, Inc & Am Printing House for Blind; vis assoc prof, Univ Rochester, 81-; ed, Testing Phys Handicapped Students in Sci. *Mem:* Nat Sci Teachers Asn; AAAS; Am Educ Res Asn; Nat Asn Res Sci Teaching. *Res:* Test measurement theory; criterion referenced measurement; science curriculum research for handicapped students; digital computer analysis and synthesis of speech. *Mailing Add:* Nat Tech Inst for the Deaf 1 Lomb Mem Dr Rochester NY 14623

LANG, HELGA M (SISTER THERESE), b York, Pa, Dec 2, 28. BIOCHEMISTRY. *Educ:* Duquesne Univ, BS, 50; Univ Iowa, MS, 52; Marquette Univ, PhD(biochem), 71. *Prof Exp:* Res asst, Inst Cancer Res, Philadelphia, 52-54 & McCollum Pratt Inst, Johns Hopkins Univ, 54-56; instr biol, Nazareth Col Rochester, 56-59; instr chem, St Agnes High Sch, 59-67; asst prof, 71-77, ASSOC PROF & HEAD CHMN CHEM, NAZARETH COL, ROCHESTER, 77- *Concurrent Pos:* Fels, Sch Med, Univ Rochester, 71-72, Cornell Univ, 73 & Max Planck Inst WGer, 75 & 76-77. *Mem:* Am Chem Soc; AAAS; Nat Sci Teachers Asn; Sigma Xi. *Res:* Enzyme kinetic studies of pepsin; primary structure studies of collagen. *Mailing Add:* Nazareth Col of Rochester 4245 E Ave Rochester NY 14610

LANG, JAMES FREDERICK, b Dayton, Ohio, Mar 19, 31; m 58; c 2. DRUG METABOLISM. *Educ:* Univ Cincinnati, BS, 58, MS, 70. *Prof Exp:* Res asst toxicol & drug metab, Christ Hosp Inst Med Res, Subsid Elizabeth Gamble Deaconess Home Asn, 58-63; from res asst biochem to biochemist, 63-72, SECT HEAD DRUG METAB, MERRELL RES CTR, MERRELL DOW PHARMACEUTICALS INC, 72- *Mem:* Am Chem Soc. *Res:* Isolation and identification of drug metabolites, pharmacokinetics; development and application of analytical methods for trace analysis of drug residues in biological media. *Mailing Add:* Merrell Res Ctr 2110 E Galbraith Rd Cincinnati OH 45215

LANG, JOHN CALVIN, JR, b Montclair NJ, May 6, 42; m 66; c 1. PHYSICAL CHEMISTRY. *Educ:* Wesleyan Univ, BA, 64; Cornell Univ, MS, 68, PhD(chem), 72. *Prof Exp:* Fels, Cornell Univ, 72 & 73-75, Univ Reading, Eng, 72-73; RES SCIENTIST PHYS CHEM, PROCTER & GAMBLE CO, 75- *Mem:* Am Phys Soc; Sigma Xi; Am Chem Soc. *Res:* Phase equilibria; phase transitions; critical phenomena; thermodyamics of aqueous solutions; magnetic resonance; light scattering; surfactant and colloid physical chemistry. *Mailing Add:* 9750 Winton Hills Lane Cincinnati OH 45215

LANG, JOSEPH EDWARD, b Covington, Ky, Aug 10, 42. THEORETICAL PHYSICS. *Educ:* Thomas More Col, AB, 64; Univ Ill, MS, 65, PhD(physics), 70. *Prof Exp:* NSF fel, Lawrence Radiation Lab, Univ Calif, Berkeley, 70-71; asst prof physics, 71-80, ASSOC PROF PHYSICS, THOMAS MORE COL, 80- *Concurrent Pos:* Vis scientist, Air Force Mat Lab, Wright-Patterson AFB, 78-79. *Mem:* Am Phys Soc; Am Asn Physics Teachers, Sigma Xi. *Res:* Elementary particle physics; magnetic anisotropy; computers in education. *Mailing Add:* Dept of Physics Thomas More Col Ft Mitchell KY 41017

LANG, JOSEPH HERMAN, b New York, NY, Oct 31, 23. BIOCHEMISTRY. *Educ:* Univ Calif, Los Angeles, BS, 45; Fla State Univ, PhD(biochem), 57. *Prof Exp:* Res assoc biochem, Grad Sch Pub Health, Univ Pittsburgh, 57-63, asst res prof radiol, Sch Med, 63-68; assoc res biochemist & radiologist, 68-74, RES BIOCHEMIST & RADIOLOGIST, SCH MED, UNIV CALIF, SAN DIEGO, 74- *Mem:* AAAS. *Res:* Physical chemistry of proteins; protein binding; pharmacology of radiopaque compounds; activation systems of blood plasma. *Mailing Add:* Radiol Res S-004 Univ of Calif San Diego La Jolla CA 92093

LANG, KENNETH LYLE, b Cuba City, Wis, Apr 12, 36; m 61; c 1. FRESHWATER ECOLOGY. *Educ:* Iowa State Col, BS, 59; Univ Iowa, MS, 66, PhD(zool), 70. *Prof Exp:* Assoc prof biol, 70-77, ASSOC PROF ZOOL, HUMBOLDT STATE UNIV, 77- *Mem:* Am Soc Zool; Am Soc Limnol & Oceanog. *Res:* Freshwater zooplankton populations; dispersion patterns and species diversity of benthic and planktonic Cladoceran assemblages. *Mailing Add:* Dept of Biol Humboldt State Univ Arcata CA 95521

LANG, LAWRENCE GEORGE, b Pittsburgh, Pa, Mar 25, 31; m 53; c 2. SOLID STATE PHYSICS. *Educ:* Carnegie Inst Technol, BS, 52, MS, 53, PhD(physics), 57. *Prof Exp:* Res physicist, Carnegie Inst Technol, 56-57; eng specialist, Philco Corp, 57-58; res physicist, Carnegie Inst Technol, 58-60, asst prof physics, 60-64; res physicist, Atomic Energy Res Estab, Eng, 63-65; assoc prof physics, Carnegie Inst Technol, 64-66; res physicist, Atomic Energy Res Estab, Eng, 66-73; PROF PHYSICS, PA STATE UNIV, 73- *Concurrent Pos:* Nat Acad Sci-Nat Res Coun fel, 63-64. *Mem:* Am Phys Soc. *Res:* Angular correlation of radiation from positron annihilation in solids; Mossbauer effect in compounds; paramagnetic and diamagnetic salts; biological macromolecules. *Mailing Add:* Dept of Physics Davey Bldg Pa State Univ University Park PA 16802

LANG, MICHAEL ALAN, physiology, biophysics, see previous edition

LANG, NEIL CHARLES, b Montreal, Que, Jan 24, 48; US citizen. CHEMICAL PHYSICS. *Educ:* McGill Univ, BSc, 68; Mass Inst Technol, PhD(phys chem), 74. *Prof Exp:* CHEMIST, LASER PROG, LAWRENCE LIVERMORE LAB, 76- *Concurrent Pos:* Fel, Nat Res Coun Can, 74-76. *Mem:* Am Phys Soc; Sigma Xi. *Res:* Chemical physics, reaction dynamics and energy transfer processes in gas phase collisions; applications in laser technology and isotope enrichment. *Mailing Add:* Lawrence Livermore Lab Mail Stop L-468 Livermore CA 94550

LANG, NORMA JEAN, b Memphis, Tenn, July 25, 31. PHYCOLOGY. *Educ:* Ohio State Univ, BS, 52, MA, 58; Ind Univ, PhD(bot), 62. *Prof Exp:* NIH res fel algae, Univ Tex, 62-63; from asst prof to assoc prof bot, 63-74, PROF BOT, UNIV CALIF, DAVIS, 74- *Concurrent Pos:* NSF res grant, 65-67; Guggenheim fel, Westfield Col, London, 69-70. *Mem:* Phycol Soc Am (treas, 71-73, vpres, 74, pres, 75); Brit Phycol Soc; Electron Micros Soc Am; Int Phycol Soc; Bot Soc Am. *Res:* Electron microscopic studies of cellular structure in unicellular green algae, colonial green algae and blue-green algae, especially differentiation of heterocysts; desiccation survival and development of colonial form. *Mailing Add:* Dept of Bot Univ of Calif Davis CA 95616

LANG, NORTON DAVID, b Chicago, Ill, July 5, 40; m 69; c 2. THEORETICAL SOLID STATE PHYSICS, SURFACE PHYSICS. *Educ:* Harvard Univ, AB, 62, AM, 65, PhD(physics), 68. *Prof Exp:* Asst res physicist, Univ Calif, San Diego, 67-69; STAFF MEM, IBM CORP, 69- *Concurrent Pos:* Assoc ed, Phys Review Letters, 80- *Honors & Awards:* Davisson-Germer Prize, Am Phys Soc, 77. *Mem:* Fel NY Acad Sci; fel Am Phys Soc. *Res:* Solid state physics. *Mailing Add:* IBM Res Ctr Yorktown Heights NY 10598

LANG, PETER MICHAEL, b Vienna, Austria, Sept 3, 30; US citizen. CHEMICAL & NUCLEAR ENGINEERING. *Educ:* Mass Inst Technol, SB, 51, SM, 52, ScD(chem eng), 55. *Prof Exp:* Res asst chem eng, Mass Inst Technol, 52-53 & 54-55; chem engr, Shell Develop Co, 55-56; nuclear engr, ACF Industs, 56-59 & Allis-Chalmers Mfg Co, 59-66; staff consult, NUS Corp, 66-73; div mgr, Aerojet Nuclear Co, 73-77; BR CHIEF, DEPT ENERGY, 77- *Concurrent Pos:* Lectr, Univ Md, 60; vis scientist, Swiss Fed Inst Reactor Res, 62-64. *Mem:* Am Nuclear Soc. *Res:* Development and demonstration of nuclear power plant improvements, design, economics, safety and operation of nuclear plants; nuclear fuel improvements. *Mailing Add:* US Dept Energy Washington DC 20545

LANG, PHILIP CHARLES, b Jamestown, NY, Nov 16, 34; m 55; c 3. ORGANIC CHEMISTRY. *Educ:* Allegheny Col, BS, 57; Ohio Univ, MS, 59; Rensselaer Polytech Inst, PhD(org chem), 66. *Prof Exp:* Res chemist, Diamond Alkali Co, 59-62; assoc res chemist, Sterling Winthrop Res Inst, 62-67; res chemist, GAF Corp, 67-73; RES CHEMIST, TOMS RIVER CHEM CORP, 73- *Mem:* Am Chem Soc. *Res:* Synthetic medicinal chemistry; heterocyclic and acteylene compounds; aromatics and synthetic dyes. *Mailing Add:* Toms River Chem Co Box 71 Toms River NJ 08753

LANG, RAYMOND W, b Syracuse, NY, Aug 1, 30; m 53; c 5. IMMUNOLOGY. *Educ:* LeMoyne Col, NY, BS, 52; Mich State Univ, MS, 57; PhD(microbiol), 59. *Prof Exp:* Asst prof microbiol, St John's Univ, NY, 59-62; fel bact & immunol, Sch Med, State Univ NY Buffalo, 62-63; from instr to asst prof bact & immunol, 63-68; assoc prof, 68-72, PROF MED MICROBIOL, COL MED, OHIO STATE UNIV, 72- *Concurrent Pos:* Consult urol res sect, Millard Fillmore Hosp, 64-66; consult training prog, Nat Inst Dent Res, 72-75. *Mem:* AAAS; Am Soc Microbiol. *Res:* Immunochemistry of tissue antigens; transplantation; autoimmunity. *Mailing Add:* Dept of Med Microbiol Ohio State Univ Col of Med Columbus OH 43210

LANG, RICHARD CHARLES, b Boston, Mass, Nov 24, 50; m 74. ENGINEERING ECONOMICS. *Educ:* Univ Calif, Berkeley, BS, 72; Stanford Univ, MS, 74. *Prof Exp:* Assoc engr, Lockheed Missiles & Space Corp, 72-74; mem tech staff, Pres Off Res & Develop Planning, Elec Power Res Inst, 74-76; spec consult, Calif Energy Comn, 76-77, energy fuels specialist, 77-82; PROJ ENGR, KAISER ENGRS POWER GROUP, KAISER ALUMINUM & CHEM CORP, 82- *Concurrent Pos:* Energy consult, 77- *Mem:* Inst Elec & Electronics Engrs; Forest Prod Res Soc. *Res:* Alternative energy technologies with emphasis on gasification, tests of solid fuels and economic and feasibility analysis of biomass, fuel cell, and cogeneration systems. *Mailing Add:* Kaiser Engrs Power Group 300 Lakeside Dr PO Box 23210 Oakland CA 94623

LANG, ROBERT JOSEPH, b New York, NY, Oct 8, 30; m; c 2. FUELS SCIENCE. *Educ:* Columbia Univ, BS, 52, MS, 53. *Prof Exp:* Res engr combustion, Standard Oil Develop Co, 53-64; sr res engr petrol fuels, Esso Res & Eng Co, 64-71; res assoc automotive air pollution, Prod Res Lab, 71-77, sr res assoc coal conversion, Coal Res Lab, 77-80, SCI ADVISOR, SHALE & EXPLOR RES LAB, EXXON RES & ENG CO, 80- *Res:* Coal gasification; automotive air pollution; atomization and combustion; catalysis in fuels science. *Mailing Add:* Exxon Res & Eng Co PO Box 4255 Baytown TX 77520

LANG, ROBERT LEE, b Ely, Mo, Apr 8, 13; m 38; c 4. AGRONOMY. *Educ:* Univ Wyo, BS, 36, MS, 41; Univ Nebr, PhD, 55. *Prof Exp:* From instr to assoc prof agron, 36-55, head, Plant Sci Div, 61-70, prof range mgt, 55-78, EMER PROF, UNIV WYO, 78- *Mem:* Soc Range Mgt. *Res:* Range and pasture management and improvement. *Mailing Add:* Univ of Wyo Col of Agr Univ Sta Box 3354 Laramie WY 82071

LANG, ROBERT PHILLIP, b Chicago, Ill, June 15, 32. PHYSICAL CHEMISTRY. *Educ:* Univ Ill, BS, 55; Univ Chicago, MS, 60, PhD(phys chem), 62. *Prof Exp:* From instr to assoc prof 62-74, PROF CHEM, QUINCY COL, 74-, CHMN DEPT, 71- *Concurrent Pos:* NSF res grant, 65-68 & 70-72. *Mem:* AAAS; Am Chem Soc; Am Asn Physics Teachers. *Res:* Thermodynamic and electronic spectral characteristics of molecular complexes of iodine; amino acid sequences in enzymes. *Mailing Add:* Dept Chem Quincy Col Quincy IL 62301

LANG, SOLOMON MAX, b Jersey City, NJ, Nov 21, 25; m 49; c 3. HYDROLOGY. *Educ:* Newark Col Eng, BS, 49. *Prof Exp:* Hydraul engr, 49-67, supv hydrologist & chief reports sect, Water Resources Div, 67-69, hydrologist & prin asst, Off Asst Chief Hydrologist for Sci Publ & Data Mgt, Washington, DC, 69-73, dep asst chief hydrologist for sci publ & data mgt, 73-80, COORDR ENERGY HYDROL PROG, WATER RESOURCES DIV, US GEOL SURV, 80- *Concurrent Pos:* Mem comt X3L8 data representations, Am Nat Standards Inst, 73-81; dep mem, US Bd Geog Names, 75-; mem, Joint Comt Nat Soc Metrication Water Resources, 78- *Mem:* Am Water Works Asn; Am Geophys Union. *Res:* Management and coordination of energy hydrology studies (coal and oil shale); selection, review and support of field and laboratory projects. *Mailing Add:* Water Resources Div US Geol Surv 440 Nat Ctr Reston VA 22092

LANG, STANLEY ALBERT, JR, b Cleveland, Ohio, Mar 30, 44. ORGANIC CHEMISTRY. *Educ:* John Carroll Univ, BS, 66; Brown Univ, PhD(org chem), 70. *Prof Exp:* Res fel, Ohio State Univ, 70, Nat Cancer Inst fel, 71; res chemist, Lederle Labs, 72-74, group leader, Info Dis Therapy Sect, 74-77, group leader, 77-80, HEAD CHEM DEPT, INFECTIOUS DIS THERAPY SECT, MED RES DIV, AM CYANAMID INC, 80- *Mem:* Am Chem Soc. *Res:* Synthetic organic chemistry; medicinal drugs; antibiotics, anticancer agents; immunoregulants. *Mailing Add:* Med Res Div Am Cyanamid Co Lederle Labs Pearl River NY 10965

LANG, THOMAS G(LENN), b San Jose, Calif, July 28, 28; m 62; c 2. MECHANICAL ENGINEERING. *Educ:* Calif Inst Technol, BS, 48 & 50; Univ Southern Calif, MS, 53; Pa State Univ, PhD(aerospace eng), 68. *Prof Exp:* Operator, Southern Calif Coop Wind Tunnel, 48-49; stress analyst, NAm Aviation, Inc, 50-51; designer, US Naval Ord Test Sta, 51-52, hydrodynamicist, 52-58, head oceanic res group, 58-61, head hydrodyn res group, 61-66; US Naval Ord Test Sta scholar, Pa State Univ, 66-68; tech consult, Ocean Technol Dept, Naval Undersea Warfare Ctr, 68; head advan design, Systs Anal Group, Naval Undersea Ctr & Naval Ocean Systs Ctr, 68-70, head advan concepts group, 70-73, head, Advan Concepts Div, 73-78; RETIRED. *Concurrent Pos:* Consult, 78-79; pres Semi-Submerged Ship Co, 79- *Mem:* Am Inst Aeronaut & Astronaut; Marine Technol Soc; Soc Naval Architects & Marine Engrs. *Res:* Hydrodynamics, especially stability and control, propulsion, boundary layer control, vented hydrofoils, sea animal hydrodynamics, polymer additives for drag reduction; semisubmerged ship design. *Mailing Add:* 417 Loma Larga Dr Solana Beach CA 92075

LANG, WILLIAM HARRY, b Etna, Pa, Mar 29, 18; m 46; c 2. PETROLEUM CHEMISTRY, FUEL SCIENCE. *Educ:* Grove City Col, BS, 40. *Prof Exp:* Sr res chemist, Cent Res Div, Mobil Res & Develop Corp, 40-81; RETIRED. *Mem:* Am Chem Soc; Catalysis Soc. *Res:* Development of new and alternate fuels and energy sources to use as a petroleum substitute. *Mailing Add:* Box 186 RR 2 Johnny Brook Rd Richmond VT 05477

LANG, WILLIAM WARNER, b Boston, Mass, Aug 9, 26; m 54; c 1. ACOUSTICAL ENGINEERING, NOISE CONTROL ENGINEERING. *Educ:* Iowa State Univ, BS, 46, PhD(physics), 58; Mass Inst Technol, SM, 49. *Prof Exp:* Acoustical engr, Bolt, Beranek & Newman, Inc, 49-51; instr physics, US Naval Post-Grad Sch, 51-55; spec engr, E I du Pont de Nemours & Co, 55-57; adv physicist, 58-64, sr physicist & mgr acoust lab, 64-75, PROG MGR ACOUSTICS TECHNOL, IBM CORP, 75- *Concurrent Pos:* Mem eval panel, Mech Div, Nat Bur Standards, 74-75, chmn, 75-76; adj prof physics, Vassar Col, 79- *Honors & Awards:* Achievement Award, Inst Elec & Electronics Engr Group Audio & Electroacoustics, 72. *Mem:* Nat Acad Eng; AAAS; Inst Noise Control Eng (pres, 78); fel Acoust Soc Am; fel Inst Elec & Electronics Engr; fel Audio Eng Soc. *Res:* Physical acoustics; effects and control of noise; theory and design of acoustical materials. *Mailing Add:* 29 Hornbeck Ridge Poughkeepsie NY 12603

LANGACKER, PAUL GEORGE, b Evanston, Ill, July 14, 46. THEORETICAL PHYSICS, ELEMENTARY PARTICLE PHYSICS. *Educ:* Mass Inst Technol, BS, 68; Univ Calif, Berkeley, MA, 69, PhD(physics), 72. *Prof Exp:* Res assoc, Rockefeller Univ, 72-74; res assoc, 74-75, asst prof, 75-81, ASSOC PROF DEPT PHYSICS, UNIV PA, 81- *Mem:* Am Phys Soc. *Res:* Theoretical elementary particle physics. *Mailing Add:* Dept of Physics Univ of Pa Philadelphia PA 19174

LANGAGER, BRUCE ALLEN, b Willmar, Minn, Jan 17, 42; m 64; c 2. POLYMER CHEMISTRY. *Educ:* Augsburg Col, BA, 64; Univ Minn, Minneapolis, PhD(org chem), 68. *Prof Exp:* Sr res chemist, 68-74, res specialist, 74-78, TECH SUPVR, 3M CO, 78- *Mem:* Sigma Xi. *Res:* Life sciences; surface chemistry. *Mailing Add:* Bldg Serv & Cleaning Prod Div/3M 3M Center St Paul MN 55101

LANGAN, THOMAS AUGUSTINE, b Providence, RI, July 25, 30; m 60; c 2. BIOCHEMISTRY. *Educ:* Fordham Univ, BS, 52; Johns Hopkins Univ, PhD(biochem), 59. *Prof Exp:* Mem res staff, Med Nobel Inst, Stockholm, Sweden, 59-60; guest investr biochem, Rockefeller Inst, 60-61; mem res staff, Wenner-Gren Inst, Stockholm, Sweden, 61-62; res assoc biochem, Rockefeller Inst, 62-65; staff scientist, C F Kettering Res Lab, 65-67, investr, 67-70, sr investr, 70-71; ASSOC PROF PHARMACOL, MED SCH, UNIV COLO, DENVER, 71- *Concurrent Pos:* NSF fel, 59-62; from asst prof to assoc prof, Antioch Col, 67-71. *Mem:* Am Soc Biol Chemists; Am Soc Cell Biol. *Res:* Metabolism and function of histones and nuclear phosphoproteins; control of histone phosphorylation by cyclic adenosine monophosphate; regulation of nucleic acid synthesis in eukaryotes. *Mailing Add:* Dept of Pharmacol Univ of Colo Med Ctr Denver CO 80262

LANGAN, WILLIAM BERNARD, b Wayne Co, Pa, Oct 31, 13; m 57; c 2. PHYSIOLOGY. *Educ:* Univ Scranton, BS, 36; Columbia Univ, MA, 37 & 44; Fordham Univ, PhD(zool), 42. *Prof Exp:* Asst sci, Teachers Col, Columbia Univ, 36-37; asst biol, Fordham Univ, 40-42; instr physiol, New York Med Col, 42-47, assoc, 47-50, asst prof prof, 50-60, asst prof pharmacol, 58-60; sect head physiol, Food & Drug Res Labs, Inc, 60-61; NIH spec fel, State Univ NY Downstate Med Ctr, 61-62, asst prof, 62-63; assoc prof biol, 63-80, ASST TO DIR RES, VILLANOVA UNIV, 81- *Concurrent Pos:* Lectr, Hunter Col, 60-62; consult, Food & Drug Res Labs, Inc, 61-63; training prog partic, Int Lab Genetics & Biophys, Italy, 65; vis prof, Dept Pharmacol, Thomas Jefferson Med Col, Philadelphia, 80- *Mem:* Fel AAAS; Harvey Soc; Endocrine Soc; Am Soc Zool; NY Acad Sci. *Res:* Steroids and cardiac electrophysiology; steroids and ovulation in sub-mammalian species; mechanism of hormone action at the cellular level. *Mailing Add:* Dept of Biol Villanova Univ Villanova PA 19085

LANGBEIN, WALTER, b Newark, NJ, Oct 17, 07; m 39; c 2. HYDROLOGY. *Educ:* Cooper Union, BS, 31. *Prof Exp:* Construct engr, Rosoff Construct Co, NY, 31-35; hydraul engr, US Geol Surv, NY, 35-36, hydrologist, 36-75; RETIRED. *Concurrent Pos:* Ed, Water Resources Res, 65- *Honors & Awards:* Distinguished Serv Award, US Dept Interior, 58. *Mem:* Nat Acad Sci; Geol Soc Am; Am Soc Civil Eng; Am Geophys Union; Int Asn Hydrol (vpres, 63-67). *Res:* Rivers; lakes; climatology. *Mailing Add:* 4452 N 38th St Arlington VA 22207

LANGDALE, GEORGE WILFRED, b Walterboro, SC, Sept 14, 30; m 55. SOIL FERTILITY, CONSERVATION TILLAGE. *Educ:* Clemson Univ, BS, 57, MS, 61; Univ Ga, PhD(soil sci), 69. *Prof Exp:* Soil scientist, SC Exp Sta, 57-63, res soil scientist, Southeast Tidewater Exp Sta, Ga, 66-68, res soil scientist, Rio Grande Soil & Water Res Ctr, Tex, 68-71, RES SOIL SCIENTIST, SOUTHERN PIEDMONT CONSERV RES CTR, AGR RES SERV, USDA, 71- *Mem:* Am Soc Agron; Soil Sci Soc Am; Soil Conserv Soc Am. *Res:* Soil-water-plant interactions, with respect to optimizing food and fiber production; environmental quality, minimum tillage, salinity and drainage, plant nutrition, and conservation of soil and water resources of the humid east. *Mailing Add:* Southern Piedmont Conserv Res Ctr USDA PO Box 555 Watkinsville GA 30677

LANGDELL, ROBERT DANA, b Pomona, Calif, Mar 14, 24; m 48; c 2. PATHOLOGY. *Educ:* George Washington Univ, MD, 48. *Prof Exp:* Intern, Henry Ford Hosp, Detroit, Mich, 48-49; fel path, Sch Med, Univ NC, Chapel Hill, 49-51, from instr to assoc prof, 51-64, PROF PATH, SCH MED, UNIV NC, CHAPEL HILL, 64- *Concurrent Pos:* USPHS sr res fel, 56-62 & career develop award, 62-67; mem hemat study sect, USPHS, 67-70; ed-in-chief, Transfusion, 72; pres, Am Asn Blood Banks, 73-74; mem panel rev blood & blood derivatives, Food & Drug Admin, 75. *Mem:* Am Asn Path; AMA; Am Soc Clin Path; Col Am Path. *Res:* Hematologic pathology; physiology of blood coagulation; hemorrhagic disorders. *Mailing Add:* Dept of Path Univ of NC Sch of Med Chapel Hill NC 27514

LANGDON, ALLAN BRUCE, b Edmonton, Alta, Dec 14, 41; m 66; c 2. PLASMA THEORY, COMPUTATIONAL PHYSICS. *Educ:* Univ Man, BSc, 63; Princeton Univ, PhD(astrophys), 69. *Prof Exp:* Actg asst prof elec eng, Univ Calif, Berkeley, 67-69; STAFF PHYSICIST, LAWRENCE LIVERMORE LAB, 70- *Concurrent Pos:* Lectr elec eng, Univ Calif, Berkeley, 69-73 & 81-; affil mem, Ctr Plasma Physics & Fusion Eng, Univ Calif, Los Angeles, 77- *Mem:* Fel Am Phys Soc; Sigma Xi; Can Asn Physicists; Asn Comput Mach. *Res:* Plasma theory; computational physics; computer simulation of plasmas; numerical analysis. *Mailing Add:* L-477 Lawrence Livermore Lab Box 808 Livermore CA 94550

LANGDON, EDWARD ALLEN, b Los Angeles, Calif, Feb 9, 22. MEDICINE, RADIOLOGY. *Educ:* Western Reserve Univ, BS, 42; Univ Mich, MD, 45. *Prof Exp:* From asst prof to assoc prof, 59-70, prof radiol, Chief Raiother Div & asst dean student affairs, 70-78, PROF RADIOL ONCOL, VCHMN, DEPT RADIOL ONCOL & ASST DEAN STUDENT AFFAIRS, SCH MED, UNIV CALIF, LOS ANGELES, 70- *Mem:* AMA; Am Col Radiol; Radiol Soc NAm; Soc Nuclear Med; Asn Univ Radiol. *Res:* Radiation therapy. *Mailing Add:* Dept of Radiol Radio Ther Div Univ of Calif Med Ctr Los Angeles CA 90024

LANGDON, GLEN GEORGE, JR, b Morristown, NJ, June 30, 36; m 63; c 1. COMPUTER ENGINEERING, COMPUTER SCIENCE. *Educ:* Wash State Univ, BSEE, 57; Univ Pittsburgh, MSEE, 63; Syracuse Univ, PhD(elec engr), 68. *Prof Exp:* Engr, Westinghouse Elec Corp, 60-63; engr, 63-73, RES STAFF COMPUT SCI, IBM CORP, 74- *Concurrent Pos:* Lectr, Syracuse Univ, NY, 68-69; vis prof, Univ Sao Paulo, Brazil, 71-72; lectr, Univ Santa Clara, 75-78. *Mem:* Inst Elec & Electronic Engrs; Asn Comput Mach. *Res:* Computer and logic design; image compression and processing. *Mailing Add:* 6772 Hampton Dr San Jose CA 95120

LANGDON, HERBERT LINCOLN, b Malone, NY, July 7, 35; m 72. GROSS ANATOMY, DEVELOPMENTAL ANATOMY. *Educ:* St Lawrence Univ, BS, 57; Univ Mo, MA, 63; Univ Miami, PhD(biol struct), 72. *Prof Exp:* Asst prof biol, Miami-Dade Community Col, 65-68; asst prof anat, 72-78, ASSOC PROF ANAT, SCH DENT MED, UNIV PITTSBURGH, 78- *Concurrent Pos:* Coordr lab sci, Cleft Palate Ctr, Univ Pittsburgh, 76. *Mem:* Am Cleft Palate Asn; Sigma Xi; Am Asn Anatomists; Soc Craniofacial Genetics. *Res:* Normal and abnormal morphology and development of human tongue and velopharyngeal mechanism. *Mailing Add:* Univ Pittsburgh 620 Salk Hall Pittsburgh PA 15261

LANGDON, KENNETH R, b Cache, Okla, Aug 20, 28; m 61; c 3. PLANT TAXONOMY. *Educ:* Okla State Univ, BS, 58, MS, 60; Univ Fla, PhD(plant path, nematol, bot), 63. *Prof Exp:* NEMATOLOGIST & BOTANIST, DIV PLANT INDUST, FLA DEPT AGR & CONSUMER SERV, 63- *Mem:* Soc Europ Nematologist; Int Asn Plant Taxon; Am Soc Plant Taxonomists; Soc Europ Nematologies. *Res:* Plant systematics. *Mailing Add:* Fla Dept Agr & Consumer Serv Box 1269 Div Plant Indust Gainesville FL 32602

LANGDON, ROBERT GODWIN, b Dallas, Tex, Jan 18, 23; m 45; c 4. BIOCHEMISTRY. *Educ:* Univ Chicago, MD, 45, PhD(biochem), 53. *Prof Exp:* From instr to prof physiol chem, Sch Med, Johns Hopkins Univ, 53-67; prof biochem & chmn dept, Col Med, Univ Fla, 67-69; PROF BIOCHEM, UNIV VA, 69-, CHMN DEPT, 77- *Concurrent Pos:* USPHS fel, Univ Chicago, 51-53; Lederle award, 54-57. *Mem:* Am Soc Biol Chemists; Am Chem Soc. *Res:* Membrane biochemistry; glucose transport; mechanism of hormone action. *Mailing Add:* Dept of Biochem Univ of Va Charlottesville VA 22901

LANGDON, WARREN R, b Schenectady, NY, Dec 17, 21; m 49; c 4. NUCLEAR ENGINEERING. *Educ:* State Col Wash, BS, 43; Union Col, MS, 58. *Prof Exp:* Develop engr, Gen Eng Lab, 43-54, radiation effects engr, 54-61, proj engr, Res & Develop Ctr, NY, 61-67, proj engr weapons effects prof off, Reentry Systs Dept, Pa, 67-68, tech consult, 68-71, INSTRUMENTATION ENGR, REENTRY SYSTS DIV, GEN ELEC CO, 71- *Mem:* Am Soc Mech Engrs; Nat Soc Prof Engrs. *Res:* Development and project engineering, chiefly in the fields of particle accelerators and measurements of plasma properties; development of instrumentation for reentry vehicles. *Mailing Add:* Gen Elec Co PO Box 8661 Philadelphia PA 19101

LANGDON, WILLIAM KEITH, b Hubbardston, Mich, May 8, 16; m 40; c 4. ORGANIC CHEMISTRY. *Educ:* Mich State Univ, BS, 38, MS, 40. *Prof Exp:* Res chemist, Chrysler Corp, 39-43; res chemist, Wyandotte Chem Corp, 43-69, RES SUPVR ORG CHEM, BASF WYANDOTTE CORP, 69- *Mem:* Am Chem Soc; Sigma Xi. *Res:* New organic chemical synthesis including heterocyclic nitrogen compounds, surfactants, acetals, epoxides and plastic intermediates. *Mailing Add:* 22247 W River Rd Grosse Ile MI 48138

LANGDON, WILLIAM MONDENG, b LaGrange, Ill, Aug 18, 14; m 42, 71; c 4. CHEMICAL ENGINEERING. *Educ:* Univ Ill, BS, 35, MS, 39, PhD(chem eng), 41. *Prof Exp:* Testing engr & metallurgist, Int Harvester Co, Ill, 35-37; asst chem & chem eng, Univ Ill, 37-41, asst prof chem eng, 43-46; res chem engr, Standard Oil Develop Co, NJ, 41-42; st mat engr, War Prod Bd, Wash, 43-45; assoc prof chem eng, Rensselaer Polytech Inst, 46-48; assoc dir res, Graham Crowley & Assocs, Inc, 48-55; sr engr, IIT Res Inst, 55-69, prof, 69-79, EMER PROF CHEM ENG, ILL INST TECHNOL, 79- *Mem:* AAAS; Am Chem Soc; Am Vacuum Soc; Am Inst Chem Engrs. *Res:* Column operation; vapor-liquid equilibrium; azeo and extractive distillation; synthetic organic chemical manufacturing; environmental control and design. *Mailing Add:* Dept of Chem Eng Ill Inst of Technol Chicago IL 60616

LANGE, BARRY CLIFFORD, b Philadelphia, Pa, June 14, 52; m 74; c 2. PROCESS RESEARCH, PLANT DESIGN. *Educ:* Stevens Inst Technol, BS, 74; Pa State Univ, PhD(chem), 79. *Prof Exp:* CHEMIST, ROHM AND HAAS CO, 80- *Mem:* Am Chem Soc. *Res:* Chemical process research, involving synthesis of organic compounds, kinetics and mechanisms of organic reactions; synthesis of penicillin and cephalosporin analogs and other antibiotics; physical organic chemistry involving enolate alkylation. *Mailing Add:* Res Labs Rohm and Haas Co PO Box 219 Bristol PA 19007

LANGE, BRUCE AINSWORTH, b Springfield, Mass, Aug 3, 48; m 77; c 2. CHEMISTRY OF SURFACES, CEMENT CHEMISTRY. *Educ:* Lowell Technol Inst, BS, 70; Univ NH, PhD(chem), 74. *Prof Exp:* Fel chem, Northwestern Univ, 74-75; Univ Cincinnati, 75-76; res chemist, Nat Inst Occup Safety & Health, Cincinnati, Ohio, 76-79; GROUP LEADER CHEM, W R GRACE & CO, CAMBRIDGE, MASS, 79- *Mem:* Am Ceramic Soc. *Res:* X-ray crystallography; inorganic synthesis; radiopharmaceuticals; development of analytical methods for hazardous materials; surface chemistry; cement chemistry; comminution of minerals; process design; computer modelling. *Mailing Add:* W R Grace & Co 62 Whittemore Ave Cambridge MA 02140

LANGE, CHARLES FORD, b Chicago, Ill, Feb 16, 29; m 53; c 3. BIOCHEMISTRY, IMMUNOLOGY. *Educ:* Roosevelt Univ, BS, 51, MS, 53; Univ Ill, PhD(biochem), 59; Am Bd Med Lab Immunol, dipl, 81. *Prof Exp:* Res assoc biochem, Univ Ill, 60-61; res assoc, Hektoen Inst Med Res, Cook County Hosp, 61-63; head phys chem, 63-69; assoc prof microbiol, 70-75, PROF MICROBIOL, STRITCH SCH MED, LOYOLA UNIV, 75- *Concurrent Pos:* Consult immunologist, Hines Vet Admin Hosp, 75- *Mem:* Am Chem Soc; Brit Biochem Soc; Transplantation Soc; Am Soc Microbiol; Am Asn Immunol. *Res:* Urinary glycoproteins; immunochemistry of streptococcal related glomerulonephritis; streptococcal M-proteins; transplantation antigens; immunology of aging. *Mailing Add:* Dept Microbiol Stritch Sch Med Loyola Univ Maywood IL 60153

LANGE, CHARLES GENE, b Chattanooga, Tenn, Mar 30, 42; m 63; c 3. APPLIED MATHEMATICS. *Educ:* Tri-State Col, BS, 63; Case Inst Technol, MS, 65; Mass Inst Technol, PhD(appl math), 68. *Prof Exp:* Asst prof, 68-75, ASSOC PROF MATH, UNIV CALIF, LOS ANGELES, 75- *Mem:* Soc Indust & Appl Math; Am Math Soc. *Res:* Nonlinear random processes; singular perturbation techniques; nonlinear stability theory; elasticity; wave propagation. *Mailing Add:* Dept of Math Univ of Calif Los Angeles CA 90024

LANGE, CHRISTOPHER STEPHEN, b Chicago, Ill, Feb 11, 40; m 64, 73; c 2. RADIOBIOLOGY, BIOPHYSICS. *Educ:* Mass Inst Technol, BS, 61; Oxford Univ, DPhil(radiation biol), 68. *Prof Exp:* Res asst radiation biol, Churchill Hosp, Headington, Eng, 61-62; from res officer to sr res officer,

Paterson Labs, Christie Hosp & Holt Radium Inst, Univ Manchester, 62-69; ASST PROF RADIOL, RADIATION BIOL & BIOPHYS, SCH MED & DENT, UNIV ROCHESTER, 69- *Concurrent Pos:* NIH cancer res career develop award, 72-77; vis prof chem, Univ Calif, San Diego, 75-76. *Mem:* Brit Asn Radiation Res; Radiation Res Soc; Biophys Soc. *Res:* Induction and repair of radiation injury at the molecular, cellular and organismal levels; DNA structure in the chromosomes of eukaryotes; the cellular basis of aging; metabolic requirements for cell cycle progression; mechanisms of differentiation control in the organism. *Mailing Add:* 552 Greenleaf Meadows Rochester NY 14612

LANGE, FREDERICK F, materials science, see previous edition

LANGE, GAIL LAURA, b Chicago, Ill, June 28, 46. ALGEBRA. *Educ:* Univ Md, BS, 67; Univ NH, MS, 69, PhD(math), 75. *Prof Exp:* Instr math, Univ Maine, Farmington, 72-75, asst prof, 75-80. *Mem:* Am Math Soc; Math Asn Am. *Res:* Investigation of which finite p-groups can be the Frattini subgroup of finite p-groups. *Mailing Add:* Shaw Hill Rd RFD 1 Box 1203 Farmington ME 04938

LANGE, GORDON DAVID, b Douglas, Ariz, Jan 15, 36; c 3. NEUROPHYSIOLOGY, BIOLOGICAL OCEANOGRAPHY. *Educ:* Calif Inst Technol, BS, 58; Rockefeller Univ, PhD(biophys), 65. *Prof Exp:* Res assoc biophys, Rockefeller Univ, 65-68; asst res neuroscientist, 66-68, asst prof, 68-74, ASSOC PROF NEUROSCI, UNIV CALIF, SAN DIEGO, 74- *Mem:* Soc Neurosci; NY Acad Sci; Sigma Xi. *Res:* Neurophysiology of sensory systems; studies of the dynamics of interactions among nerve cells; mathematical and computer models of interactions of organisms. *Mailing Add:* Dept of Neurosci Univ Calif A-012 La Jolla CA 92093

LANGE, GORDON LLOYD, b Edmonton, Alta, Mar 1, 37; m 64; c 2. ORGANIC CHEMISTRY. *Educ:* Univ Alta, BSc, 59; Univ Calif, Berkeley, PhD(org chem), 63. *Prof Exp:* Res chemist, Procter & Gamble Co, 62-65; lectr org chem, Univ Western Ont, 65-67; asst prof chem, 67-73, ASSOC PROF CHEM, UNIV GUELPH, 73- *Mem:* Am Chem Soc; Chem Inst Can. *Res:* Synthesis of natural products and compounds with biological activity. *Mailing Add:* Dept of Chem Univ of Guelph Guelph ON N1G 2W1 Can

LANGE, HOWARD BARKER, JR, b Pittsburgh, Pa, Nov 6, 40. CHEMICAL ENGINEERING. *Educ:* Lehigh Univ, BS, 62, MS, 67, PhD(chem eng), 69. *Prof Exp:* Res engr, 69-77, GROUP SUPVR, RES DIV, BABCOCK & WILCOX CO, 77- *Mem:* Am Inst Chem Eng. *Res:* Mathematical modeling; pulping chemical recovery; air pollution control combustion sources. *Mailing Add:* Babcock & Wilcox Co 1562 Beeson Alliance OH 44601

LANGE, IAN M, b New York, NY, Nov 11, 40. GEOLOGY, GEOCHEMISTRY. *Educ:* Dartmouth Col, BA, 62, MA, 64; Univ Wash, PhD(geol), 68. *Prof Exp:* Asst prof geol, Fresno State Col, 68-73; assoc prof, 73-77, PROF GEOL, UNIV MONT, 77- *Mem:* Geochem Soc; Geol Soc Am. *Res:* Isotope geology, economic geology. *Mailing Add:* Dept of Geol Univ of Mont Missoula MT 59812

LANGE, JAMES NEIL, JR, b Bridgeport, Conn, May 4, 38; m 58; c 1. PHYSICS. *Educ:* Pa State Univ, PhD(physics), 64. *Prof Exp:* From asst prof to assoc prof, 65-71, PROF PHYSICS, OKLA STATE UNIV, 71- *Concurrent Pos:* Sr vis fel, Univ Nottingham, 76; vis prof, Univ Mex, 78. *Mem:* Am Phys Soc; Acoust Soc Am. *Res:* Low temperature solid state physics; physical acoustics and superconductivity; acoustics; geophysics. *Mailing Add:* Dept of Physics Okla State Univ Stillwater OK 74074

LANGE, KLAUS ROBERT, b Berlin, Ger, Jan 15, 30; US citizen; m 51; c 2. PHYSICAL CHEMISTRY, SURFACE CHEMISTRY. *Educ:* Univ Pa, AB, 52; Univ Del, MS, 54, PhD(phys chem), 56. *Prof Exp:* Res chemist, Atlantic Refining Co, 55-59; sr res chemist, Philadelphia Quartz Co, 59-67, res assoc, 67-69; lab mgr, Betz Lab Inc, 69-74; TECH DIR, QUAKER CHEM CORP, 75- *Concurrent Pos:* Mem bd dir, Chem Data Systs, 70-75. *Mem:* Am Chem Soc. *Res:* Physical adsorption; heterogeneous catalysis; surface chemistry of silica and related solids; silicate solutions, fundamental properties; colloidal suspensions; detergency; pollution control; polymer applications; lignin and paper chemistry. *Mailing Add:* Quaker Chem Co Conshohocken PA 19428

LANGE, KURT, b Berlin, Ger, Oct 31, 06; nat US; m 36; c 2. INTERNAL MEDICINE, NEPHROLOGY. *Educ:* Univ Berlin, MD, 30. *Prof Exp:* Instr med, Univ Berlin, 31-33; from instr to assoc prof, 40-64, dir med & pediat renal serv, 55-77, PROF MED & PEDIAT, NEW YORK MED COL, 64- *Concurrent Pos:* Vis physician, Metrop & Bird S Coler Hosps, 54-; attend physician, Flower & Fifth Ave Hosps, 54-78; consult physician, Chenango Mem Hosp, Norwich, NY, 66- & Horton Mem Hosp, Middletown; consult artificial kidney-uremia prog, 71-75; consult, Nat Med Libr; vchmn, Int Comt Nomenclature & Nosology of Renal Dis; consult physician, Lenox Hill Hosp, 77- *Honors & Awards:* Bronze Medal, AMA, 46; Hektoen Gold Medal, AMA, 66; Franz Vollhard Medal, 76; Lester Honig Award, NY Kidney Found. *Mem:* Fel AMA; fel Am Col Physicians; fel Am Col Cardiol; sr mem Am Fedn Clin Res; fel NY Acad Sci. *Res:* Renal and vascular diseases; immunology. *Mailing Add:* Lenox Hill Hosp 100 E 77th St New York NY 10021

LANGE, LEO JEROME, b New Rockford, NDak, Aug 29, 28; m 55; c 4. MATHEMATICS. *Educ:* Regis Col, Colo, BS, 52; Univ Colo, MA, 56, PhD(math), 60. *Prof Exp:* Instr math, Univ Colo, 52-56, asst, 58-60; mathematician, Boulder Labs, Nat Bur Standards, 56-60; asst prof, 60-65, ASSOC PROF MATH, UNIV MO-COLUMBIA, 65- *Mem:* Math Asn Am; Am Math Soc. *Res:* Continued fractions. *Mailing Add:* Dept of Math Univ of Mo Columbia MO 65201

LANGE, LESTER HENRY, b Concordia, Mo, Jan 2, 24; m 47, 62; c 5. MATHEMATICS. *Educ:* Valparaiso Univ, AB, 48; Stanford Univ, MS, 50; Univ Notre Dame, PhD, 60. *Prof Exp:* Instr math, Valparaiso Univ, 50-53, asst prof, 54-56; instr, Univ Notre Dame, 56-57 & 59-60; from asst prof to prof, 60-70, actg head dept, 61-62, chmn dept, 62-70, DEAN SCH SCI, SAN JOSE STATE UNIV, 70- *Honors & Awards:* L R Ford Sr Award, Math Asn Am, 72. *Mem:* AAAS; Math Asn Am; London Math Soc; Nat Coun Teachers Math. *Res:* Complex variable; topology. *Mailing Add:* Sch of Sci San Jose State Univ San Jose CA 95192

LANGE, ROBERT CARL, b Stoneham, Mass, Aug 26, 35; m 59; c 2. NUCLEAR MEDICINE, RADIOLOGICAL PHYSICS. *Educ:* Northeastern Univ, BS, 57; Mass Inst Technol, PhD(chem), 62. *Prof Exp:* Group leader physics, Monsanto Res Corp, 62-69; asst prof, 69-76, ASSOC PROF RADIOL PHYSICS, SCH MED, YALE UNIV, 76- *Concurrent Pos:* Consult, Stamford Hosp, 71- & R J Schulz Assocs, 73- tech dir nuclear med, Yale New Haven Hosp, 69- *Mem:* AAAS; Am Chem Soc; Am Phys Soc; Soc Nuclear Med. *Res:* New radioisotopes for nuclear medicine; radiopharmaceutals; computer applications to medicine. *Mailing Add:* Dept Radiol Sect Nuclear Med Sch Med Yale Univ New Haven CT 06510

LANGE, ROBERT DALE, b Redwood Falls, Minn, Jan 24, 20; m 44; c 2. HEMATOLOGY. *Educ:* Macalester Col, AB, 41; Wash Univ, MD, 44. *Prof Exp:* Dir, St Louis Regional Blood Ctr, 48-51; instr med, Washington Univ, 51-53; instr clin med, Univ Minn, 53-54; asst prof med, Washington Univ, 56-61; chief physician, Vet Admin Hosp, 61-62; assoc prof med, Med Col, Univ Ga, 62-65; dir, 77-81, chmn dept, 78-81, RES PROF, MEM RES CTR, UNIV TENN, KNOXVILLE, 65-, PROF, DEPT MED BIOL, 78- *Concurrent Pos:* Consult, Milledgeville State Hosp & Vet Admin Hosp, Augusta, Ga; hematologist, Atomic Bomb Casualty Comn, 51-53. *Mem:* Am Soc Hemat; Am Fedn Clin Res; fel Am Col Physicians; fel Int Soc Hemat. *Res:* Internal medicine. *Mailing Add:* Univ of Tenn Mem Res Ctr 1924 Alcoa Hwy Knoxville TN 37920

LANGE, ROBERT ECHLIN, JR, b Janesville, Wis; m 70. WILDLIFE DISEASES, WILDLIFE DISEASE PREVENTION. *Educ:* Colo State Univ, BS, 68, 70, MS, 73, DVM, 74. *Prof Exp:* Wildlife vet wildlife dis, NMex Dept Game & Fish, 74-80; adj prof wildlife dis, NMex State Univ, 78-80; FIELD DIAGNOSTICIAN, NAT WILDLIFE HEALTH LAB, 80- *Concurrent Pos:* Wildlife dis consult, Colo Wild Animal Dis Ctr, 72-74; adj prof biol dept, NMex Highlands Univ, 75-77. *Mem:* Wild Animal Dis Asn; Am Vet Med Asn; Wildlife Soc; Am Asn Wildlife Veterinarians (secy tres, 81-). *Res:* Investigation into the game management implications of wildlife diseases in elk, Rocky Mountain bighorn sheep and other mammals; wildlife disease management in migratory waterfowl; mammals and wildlife disease prevention. *Mailing Add:* Nat Wildlife Health Lab 6006 Schroeder Rd Madison WI 53706

LANGE, ROLF, b E Wuppertal, Ger, Feb 9, 32; US citizen. ATMOSPHERIC SCIENCE, PHYSICS. *Educ:* Univ Calif, Los Angeles, BA, 62; Univ Calif, Davis, MS, 72. *Prof Exp:* Jr physicist numerical modeling, Lawrence Livermore Lab, 62-68; physicist rock mech, Physics Int, 68-71; PHYSICIST ATMOSPHERIC SCI, LAWRENCE LIVERMORE NAT LAB, 71- *Res:* Numerical modeling of atmospheric transport and turbulent diffusion; study of air pollution; development of numerical air pollution models for the atmospheric boundary layer. *Mailing Add:* Lawrence Livermore Nat Lab PO Box 808 Livermore CA 94550

LANGE, WILLIAM HARRY, JR, b San Francisco, Calif, Sept 2, 12; m 37, 69; c 3. ENTOMOLOGY. *Educ:* Univ Calif, BS, 33, MS, 34, PhD(entom), 41. *Prof Exp:* Sci aide forest entom, Bur Entom & Plant Quarantine, USDA, 34-35; asst, Univ, 35-36, assoc, 36-43, jr entomologist, Exp Sta, 43-47, asst entomologist, 47-55, assoc prof entom & assoc entomologist, 55-57, ENTOMOLOGIST, EXP STA & PROF ENTOM, UNIV CALIF, DAVIS, 57- *Concurrent Pos:* Field assoc, Nat Res Coun, 47-48. *Honors & Awards:* C W Woodworth Award, 78. *Mem:* Entom Soc Am; Am Entom Soc; NY Acad Sci; Can Entom Soc; Am Soc Naturalists. *Res:* Biosystematics of Lepidoptera and Aphidoidea; integrated pest management of vegetable and field crop insects; mites and mollusks. *Mailing Add:* Dept of Entom Univ of Calif Davis CA 95616

LANGE, WILLIAM JAMES, b Sandusky, Ohio, Jan 20, 30; m 51; c 4. SURFACE PHYSICS. *Educ:* Oberlin Col, AB, 51; Mass Inst Technol, PhD(physics), 56. *Prof Exp:* Asst phys electronics, Mass Inst Technol, 51-56; physicist, 56-64, MGR VACUUM PHYSICS, RES LABS, WESTINGHOUSE ELEC CORP, 64- *Mem:* Am Phys Soc; Am Soc Mass Spectrometry; Am Vacuum Soc. *Res:* Ultrahigh vacuum; interaction of gases with surfaces. *Mailing Add:* Westinghouse Res Lab Beulah Rd Pittsburgh PA 15235

LANGE, WINTHROP EVERETT, b Appleton, Wis, Sept 22, 25; m 48; c 2. PHARMACY. *Educ:* Univ Wis, BS, 52, MS, 53, PhD(pharm, chem), 55. *Prof Exp:* Asst pharm, Univ Wis, 52-54; asst prof, SDak State Col, 55-58; from asst prof to assoc prof, Mass Col Pharm, 58-66, prof & chmn dept, 66-68; dir labs, 68-74, VPRES, INT DIR TECH SERV, PURDUE FREDERICK CO, 74- *Concurrent Pos:* Adj prof, A&M Schwartz Col Pharm & Health Sci, 78- *Mem:* Am Chem Soc; Am Pharmaceut Asn; Soc Cosmetic Chem; Acad Pharmaceut Sci; Int Fedn Socs Cosmetic Chem (pres, 76-77). *Res:* Synthesis of metal chelates as pro-drugs; pharmaceutical analysis. *Mailing Add:* Purdue Frederick Co 50 Washington St Norwalk CT 06856

LANGEBARTEL, RAY GARTNER, b Quincy, Ill, Apr 27, 21; m 45; c 4. MATHEMATICS, ASTRONOMY. *Educ:* Univ Ill, AB, 42, AM, 43, PhD(math), 48. *Prof Exp:* Asst math, 46-48, from instr to assoc prof, 48-70, PROF MATH, UNIV ILL, URBANA, 70- *Concurrent Pos:* Vis res assoc, Stockholm Observ, 50-51. *Res:* Function theory; stellar dynamics. *Mailing Add:* Dept of Math Univ of Ill Urbana IL 61801

LANGEL, ROBERT ALLAN, b Pittsburgh, Pa, May 25, 37; m 59; c 3. GEOPHYSICS. *Educ:* Wheaton Col, AB, 59; Univ Md, College Park, MS, 71, PhD(physics), 73. *Prof Exp:* Physicist, Optics Br, US Naval Res Lab, 59-62; physicist, Commun Br, 62-63, Fields & Plasmas Br, 63-74, GEOPHYSICIST GEOMAGNETISM, GEOPHYS BR, GODDARD SPACE FLIGHT CTR, NASA, 74- *Concurrent Pos:* Proj scientist for Magsat Spacecraft. *Mem:* Am Geophys Union. *Res:* Utilization of surface and near-earth satellite magnetic field measurements to study lithospheric magnetic anomalies, upper mantle conductivity and core-mantle processes; derivation of geomagnetic field models. *Mailing Add:* Code 922 Goddard Space Flight Ctr Greenbelt MD 20771

LANGELAND, KAARE, b Saltdal, Norway, Nov 3, 16. DENTAL MATERIALS, EXPERIMENTAL PATHOLOGY. *Educ:* Vet Col Norway, grad, 38; Norweg State Dent Sch, DDS, 42; Univ Oslo, PhD, 57. *Prof Exp:* asst, Dent Diag Dept, Gaustad Hosp, 42-52; res assoc, Norweg Inst Dent Res, 52-63; assoc prof oral histol & chmn dept, univ & proj dir, Minn Mining & Mfg, State Univ NY Buffalo, 63, prof oral biol, 64-69; prof gen dent, 69-71, PROF ENDODONT & CHMN DEPT, SCH DENT MED, UNIV CONN, 71- *Concurrent Pos:* USPHS grants, Res Found, State Univ NY Buffalo, 63; 3M grant, 63-69; USPHS grants, 63-68, 69-70 & 77-79; Serco grant, 66-67; Univ Conn Res Found grants, 70-73 & 76-77; Off Naval Res Contract, 71-77; teacher, Norweg State Dent Sch, 48-49; ed, Scand Dent J, 57-63; vis lectr, Boston Univ; vchmn comn dent res, Int Dent Fedn, chmn working group biol testing dent mat; mem coun standardization dent mats & devices, Am Mat Standardization Inst; Norweg state rep, Inter-Nordic Comt Planning Nordic Bur Standards Dept Mat, 61-62; mem working group dent terminology, Int Orgn Standardization, 65. *Honors & Awards:* Badge of Honor in Silver & Prize, Norweg Dent Asn, 59. *Mem:* Norweg Dent Asn; hon mem Dent Asn SAfrica; hon mem Dent Asn South Rhodesia; hon mem SAfrican Prosthodont Soc; cor mem Finnish Dent Soc. *Res:* Experimental pathology regarding biomaterials; evaluation of the biologic properties of methods; devices, and materials used in dentistry before they are released for general use. *Mailing Add:* Sch of Dent Med Univ of Conn Health Ctr Farmington CT 06032

LANGELAND, WILLIAM ENBERG, b Massillon, Ohio, July 5, 23; m 74. ORGANIC CHEMISTRY. *Educ:* Hobart Col, BA, 44; Rochester Univ, PhD(chem), 50. *Prof Exp:* Res assoc, NY State Agr Exp Sta, 46; asst, Rochester Univ, 47-49; asst prof chem, St Lawrence Univ, 50-52; Cottrell res grant, 52; res chemist, Pa Salt Mfg Co, 52-54, develop chemist, 54-56, sr develop rep, 56-58; proj coordr, 58-62, dir proj coord div, 63-77, DIR LAB COORD, WYETH LABS, INC, 77- *Mem:* AAAS; Am Chem Soc; Am Inst Chemists; NY Acad Sci. *Res:* Heterocyclic nitrogen compounds; pseudoaromaticity in polycyclic materials; vapor phase reactions of amines; correlation of biological activity with chemical structure; research administration. *Mailing Add:* Wyeth Labs Inc King of Prussia Rd Radnor PA 19807

LANGENAU, EDWARD E, JR, b Brooklyn, NY, Oct 28, 46; m 69; c 2. WILDLIFE BIOLOGY, PSYCHOLOGY. *Educ:* Rensselaer Polytech Inst, BS, 68; Mich State Univ, MS, 73, PhD(wildlife mgt), 76; Mich State Univ, MPA, 81. *Prof Exp:* WILDLIFE RES BIOLOGIST, STATE MICH, 74- *Mem:* Soc Am Foresters; Wildlife Soc. *Res:* Public behavior; white-tailed deer behavior; forest recreation; attitude toward clearcutting; hunter behavior; natural resource policy analysis; public administration. *Mailing Add:* 3980 Willow Ridge Dr Holt MI 48842

LANGENBERG, DONALD NEWTON, b Devils Lake, NDak, Mar 17, 32; m 53; c 4. SOLID STATE PHYSICS. *Educ:* Iowa State Univ, BS, 53; Univ Calif, Los Angeles, MS, 55, Berkeley, PhD(physics), 59. *Hon Degrees:* MA, Univ Pa, 71. *Prof Exp:* Actg instr physics, Univ Calif, Berkeley, 58-59; NSF fel, 59-60; from asst prof to assoc prof, 60-67, dir lab res struct matter, 72-74, vprovost grad studies & res, 74-79, PROF PHYSICS, UNIV PA, 67-, PROF ELEC ENG & SCI, 76- *Concurrent Pos:* Sloan Found fel, 62-64; Guggenheim Found fel, 66-67; assoc prof, Advan Normal Sch, Univ Paris, 66-67; distinguished vis scientist, Mich State Univ, 69; mem, Nat Acad Sci-Nat Acad Eng-Nat Res Coun Panel Adv to Cryogenics Div, Nat Bur Standards, 69-70, chmn, 70-75; mem, Comn I, Int Union Radio Sci, 69-; vis prof, Calif Inst Technol, 71; guest researcher, Cent Inst Low Temperature Study, Bayer Acad Sci & Tech Univ Munich, 74; mem, Adv Comt Res, NSF, 74-77, Coun Govt Relations & chmn, Adv Coun, 77-80, dep dir, NSF, 80-; trustee, Assoc Univs, Inc, 75-80; mem, Nat Comn Res, 78-80. *Honors & Awards:* John Price Wetherill Medal, Franklin Inst, 75. *Mem:* Fel AAAS; fel Am Phys Soc. *Res:* Cyclotron resonance and Fermi surface studies in metals and semiconductors; tunneling and Josephson effects in superconductors; precision measurement and fundamental physical constants; low temperature physics; nonequilibrium phenomena in superconductors. *Mailing Add:* Dept of Physics Univ of Pa Philadelphia PA 19104

LANGENBERG, F(REDERICK) C(HARLES), b New York, NY, July 1, 27; m 53; c 2. METALLURGICAL ENGINEERING. *Educ:* Lehigh Univ, BS, 50, MS, 51; Pa State Univ, PhD(metall eng), 55. *Prof Exp:* Engr, US Steel Corp, 51-53; vis fel, Mass Inst Technol, 55-56; supvr pyrometall, Crucible Steel Co Am, 56-58, mat & process eng, Primary Opers, 58, chief develop metallurgist, Opers, 59, mgr process res, 59-63, asst dir process res & develop, 63-64, dir, 64-65, dir tech, 65-67, vpres, Tech, 67-68, vpres res, Develop & Eng, 68; pres, Trent Tube Div, Colt Industs, Wis, 68-70; pres, Jessop Steel Co, 70-75; pres, Am Iron & Steel Inst, 75-79; PRES, INTERLAKE, INC, 79- *Mem:* Am Soc Metals; Am Chem Soc; Am Inst Mining, Metall & Petrol Eng; Am Iron & Steel Inst; Brit Iron & Steel Inst. *Res:* Process research and development in the smelting, melting, casting and processing of ferrous base materials; management of research and development. *Mailing Add:* c/o Interlake Inc 2015 Spring Rd Oak Brook IL 60521

LANGENBERG, PATRICIA WARRINGTON, b Des Moines, Iowa, Sept 10, 31; m 53; c 4. STATISTICS. *Educ:* Iowa State Univ, BS, 53; Temple Univ MA, 75, PhD(math), 78. *Prof Exp:* Instr math, LaSalle Col, 75-78, asst prof, 78-80; ASST PROF STATIST, TEMPLE UNIV, 80- *Mem:* Am Statist Asn; Biomet Soc; Asn Women Math; Am Asn Univ Professors; Inst Math Statist. *Res:* Clinical trials; biostatistics; mathematical statistics. *Mailing Add:* Dept Statist Sch Bus Admin Temple Univ Philadelphia PA 19122

LANGENBERG, WILLEM G, b Djombang, Indonesia, Apr 16, 28; US citizen; m 55; c 3. PLANT PATHOLOGY, PLANT VIROLOGY. *Educ:* Calif State Col Long Beach, BS, 63; Univ Calif, Berkeley, PhD(plant path), 67. *Prof Exp:* RES PLANT PATHOLOGIST, AGR RES SERV, USDA, 67-; assoc prof plant path, 67-80, PROF, LIFE SCI DEPT, UNIV NEBR-LINCOLN, 80- *Mem:* Am Phytopath Soc. *Res:* Study of plant-virus-vector relationships with labeled antibodies or viruses; light and electron microscopy radioautography. *Mailing Add:* Dept of Life Sci Univ of Nebr Lincoln NE 68588

LANGENDORF, RICHARD, b Prague, Czech, July 11, 08; US citizen; m 44; c 3. CARDIOLOGY. *Educ:* Ger Univ Prague, MD, 32. *Prof Exp:* RES ASSOC CARDIOL, CARDIOVASC INST, MICHAEL REESE HOSP, 39- *Concurrent Pos:* Mem sci coun, Am Heart Asn, 48; Malcolm Rogers lectr, Univ Wis, 59; mem, Nat Conf Cardiovasc Dis, Washington, DC, 64; prof lectr, Univ Chicago, 66-73, clin prof med, 73- *Honors & Awards:* Distinguished Serv Award of the Med Alumni Asn, Univ of Chicago, 74; Gifted Teacher Award, Am Col of Cardiol, 75; Distinguished Alumnus Award of the Alumni Asn, Michael Reese Med Ctr, 77. *Mem:* Soc Exp Biol & Med; Am Col Physicians; NY Acad Med. *Res:* Electrocardiography, especially interpretation of complex arrhythmias. *Mailing Add:* 111 N Wabash Ave Chicago IL 60602

LANGENHEIM, JEAN HARMON, b Homer, La, Sept 5, 25. PLANT ECOLOGY & EVOLUTION. *Educ:* Univ Tulsa, BS, 46; Univ Minn, MS, 49, PhD(bot, geol), 53. *Prof Exp:* investr, Nat Geol Serv, Colombia, 53; res assoc, Univ Calif, Berkeley, 54-59; teaching assoc, Univ Ill, 59-62; Asn Univ Women fel, Harvard Univ, 62-63; res assoc, Bot Mus, 63-66; from asst prof to assoc prof biol, 66-73, PROF BIOL, UNIV CALIF, SANTA CRUZ, 73- *Concurrent Pos:* Mem teaching staff & bd trustees, Rocky Mountain Biol Lab, 54-65; lectr, Mills Col, 55-56; from instr to asst prof, San Francisco Col Women, 56-59; scholar, Radcliffe Inst Independent Study, 63-64. *Mem:* AAAS; Bot Soc Am; Ecol Soc Am (vpres, 80-); Soc Study Evolution; Asn Tropical Biol. *Res:* Paleoecological studies of amber; evolutionary and physio-ecological studies of tropical resin-producing and other terpene-producing plants; concepts of ecology; plants and human affairs. *Mailing Add:* Div of Natural Sci Univ of Calif Santa Cruz CA 95064

LANGENHEIM, RALPH LOUIS, JR, b Cincinnati, Ohio, May 26, 22; m 46, 62, 70; c 2. PALEONTOLOGY, STRATIGRAPHY. *Educ:* Univ Tulsa, BS, 43; Univ Colo, MS, 47; Univ Minn, PhD(geol), 51. *Prof Exp:* Asst prof geol, Coe Col, 50-52; asst prof paleont, Univ Calif, 52-59; from asst prof to assoc prof, 59-67, PROF GEOL, UNIV ILL, URBANA, 67- *Concurrent Pos:* Foreign expert, Inst Geol Nac, Colombia, 53; adv, Geol Surv Can, 57 & Cent Geol Surv, Repub China, 81; foreign assoc, Geol Surv Iran, 73; partner, Lanman Assocs, Consult Geologists, 74- *Mem:* AAAS; Geol Soc Am; Paleont Soc (secy, 62-70); Am Asn Petrol Geol; Soc Econ Paleont & Mineral. *Res:* Invertebrate paleontology and stratigraphy; Paleozoic of western and central North America; Tertiary of southern Mexico; Permian and Carboniferous of Iran; petroleum and energy geology. *Mailing Add:* Dept of Geol Univ of Ill Urbana IL 61801

LANGENHOP, CARL ERIC, b Richmond, Va, Dec 20, 22; m 46. MATHEMATICS. *Educ:* Univ Louisville, BA, 43; Iowa State Col, MS, 45, PhD(math), 48. *Prof Exp:* Instr math, Iowa State Col, 46-48; res asst, Princeton Univ, 48-49; asst prof, Iowa State Univ, 49-51 & 52-53, from assoc prof to prof, 53-60; dir res, Mathematica Div, Mkt Res Corp Am, 60-61; prof math, Southern Ill Univ, 61-67 & Univ Ky, 67-70; PROF MATH, SOUTHERN ILL UNIV, 70- *Concurrent Pos:* Res assoc, Princeton Univ, 51-52. *Mem:* Am Math Soc; Math Asn Am; Soc Indust & Appl Math. *Res:* Matrix theory; control theory. *Mailing Add:* Dept of Math Southern Ill Univ Carbondale IL 62901

LANGER, ARTHUR M, b New York, NY, Feb 18, 36; m 62; c 2. MINERALOGY, ENVIRONMENTAL SCIENCES. *Educ:* Hunter Col, BA, 56; Columbia Univ, MA, 62, PhD(mineral), 65. *Prof Exp:* Res assoc mineral, Columbia, 62-65; res assoc environ sci, Mt Sinai Hosp, 65-66, asst prof mineral, 66-68, ASSOC PROF MINERAL, MT SINAI SCH MED, 68-, ASSOC PROF COMMUNITY MED, 74- *Concurrent Pos:* Adj assoc prof, Queens Col, NY, 68-70. *Mem:* AAAS; Geol Soc Am; Electron Probe Anal Soc Am; Geochem Soc; Mineral Soc Am. *Res:* Metamorphic and igneous petrology; clay mineralogy; secondary mineralization; instrumentation; microparticulate identification, analysis and interaction in the human environment. *Mailing Add:* Environ Sci Lab Mt Sinai Sch of Med New York NY 10029

LANGER, ARTHUR WALTER, JR, b Manchester, NH, May 17, 23; m 45; c 2. SYNTHETIC INORGANIC CHEMISTRY, ORGANOMETALLIC CHEMISTRY. *Educ:* Univ NH, BS, 44, MS, 47; Ohio State Univ, PhD(chem), 51. *Prof Exp:* Instr, Univ NH, 47; res assoc, Ohio State Univ, 50-51; res chemist, Standard Oil Develop Co, 51-56, res asst sect head, Esso Labs, 56-57, sect head, Esso Res & Eng Co, 57-59, res assoc, 59-64, sr res assoc, 64-67, assoc sci adv, 67-69, SCI ADV, EXXON RES & ENG CO, 69- *Mem:* Am Chem Soc. *Res:* Petrochemicals; polymerization; petroleum processing; polyolefin catalysis. *Mailing Add:* Oakwood Rd Watchung NJ 07060

LANGER, DIETRICH WILHELM JOSEF, b Berlin, Ger, Aug 13, 30; US citizen; m 61; c 4. SOLID STATE PHYSICS. *Educ:* Tech Univ Berlin, MS, 57, PhD(physics), 60. *Prof Exp:* From res physicist, to sr res physicist, 57-65, GROUP LEADER, ELECTRONIC PROPERTIES, SEMICONDUCTORS GROUP, AEROSPACE RES LABS, WRIGHT-PATTERSON AIR FORCE BASE, 65- *Concurrent Pos:* Eve lectr, Univ Dayton, 59-60; grant, Ecole Normale Superieure, Paris, 64-65; adv, Max Planck Inst Solid State Study, 72-73; fel Indust Col Armed Forces, 75-76. *Mem:* Fel Am Phys Soc. *Res:* Optical, electronic and electrooptical properties of semiconductors; high pressure, optical and electron spectroscopy; materials research; research and development administration. *Mailing Add:* Air Force Wright Aeronaut Labs Wright-Patterson AFB Dayton OH 45433

LANGER, GLENN A, b Nyack, NY, May 5, 28; m 54; c 1. MEDICINE. *Educ:* Colgate Univ, BA, 50; Columbia Univ, MD, 54. *Prof Exp:* Intern, Mass Gen Hosp, 54-55; asst res, Columbia-Presby Med Ctr, 57-58; sr resident, Mass Gen Hosp, 59-60; clin instr, Los Angeles County Cardiovasc Res Lab & Med Ctr, Univ Calif, Los Angeles, 60-62; asst prof med, Columbia Univ, 63-66; assoc prof, 66-69, PROF MED & PHYSIOL, MED CTR, UNIV CALIF, LOS ANGELES, 69-, ASSOC DIR CARDIOVASC RES LAB, 66-, VCHMN DEPT PHYSIOL, 67-, CASTERA PROF CARDIOL, 78- *Concurrent Pos:* Chmn exec comt, Basic Sci Coun & bd dirs, Am Heart Asn, 76-78; Griffith vis prof cardiol, 79; Macy fac scholar, 79-80. *Mem:* Am Heart Asn; Am Physiol Soc; Am Soc Clin Invest; Am Asn Physicians; Soc Gen Physiologists. *Res:* Myocardial physiology and metabolism. *Mailing Add:* Cardiovasc Res Lab Univ of Calif Med Ctr Los Angeles CA 90024

LANGER, HORST GÜNTER, b Breslau, Ger, Dec 29, 27; US citizen; m 55; c 2. INORGANIC CHEMISTRY. *Educ:* Brunswick Tech Univ, Dipl, 54, Dr rer nat(chem), 56. *Prof Exp:* Asst inorg anal chem, Brunswick Tech Univ, 51-56; res assoc inorg chem, Univ Ind, 56-58; res chemist, 58-64, sr res chemist, 64-68, ASSOC SCIENTIST, DOW CHEM USA, 68- *Mem:* Am Chem Soc; Am Soc Mass Spectrometry; Int Confedn Thermal Anal; NAm Thermal Anal Soc; Ger Chem Soc. *Res:* Analytical, dental and organometallic chemistry; mass spectrometry; thermal analysis; fire retardants; catalysts. *Mailing Add:* PO Box 400 Cor Rice Commonwealth Rd Rt 30 Wayland MA 01778

LANGER, JAMES STEPHEN, b Pittsburgh, Pa, Sept 21, 34; m 58; c 3. STATISTICAL MECHANICS. *Educ:* Carnegie Inst Technol, BS, 55; Univ Birmingham, PhD, 58. *Prof Exp:* Instr, 58-64, assoc prof, 64-67, assoc dean, Mellon Inst Sci, 71-74, PROF PHYSICS, CARNEGIE-MELLON UNIV, 67- *Concurrent Pos:* Vis assoc prof, Cornell Univ, 66-67; Guggenheim fel, Harvard Univ, 74-75. *Mem:* Fel Am Phys Soc. *Res:* Theoretical solid state physics; kinetics of phase transformations. *Mailing Add:* Dept of Physics Carnegie-Mellon Univ Pittsburgh PA 15213

LANGER, LAWRENCE MARVIN, b New York, NY, Dec 22, 13; m 36. NUCLEAR PHYSICS. *Educ:* NY Univ, BS, 34, MS, 35, PhD(physics), 38. *Prof Exp:* Asst physics, NY Univ, 34-38; from instr to assoc prof, 38-52, actg chmn dept, 61-62 & 65-66, chmn, 66-73, PROF PHYSICS, IND UNIV, BLOOMINGTON, 52- *Concurrent Pos:* Res assoc, Radiation Lab, Mass Inst Technol, 41-42; alternate group leader, Los Alamos Atomic Bomb Proj, 43-45; sci consult, US War Dept, 45; expert consult, AEC, 48-74, US Energy Res & Develop Admin, 74-; consult & observer, Greenhouse Atomic Bomb Tests, Marshall Islands, 51; adv consult, Nat Res Coun, 57-60; dir, Off Naval Res & NSF res nuclear spectros, 63-; adv consult, Nuclear Data Proj, Nat Acad Sci-Nat Res Coun. *Mem:* AAAS; fel Am Phys Soc. *Res:* Nuclear physics; artificial and natural radioactivity; beta ray spectra; neutron scattering; D-D reaction; beta and gamma coincidence measurements; Cockroft-Walton accelerator; Geiger Counter; cyclotron; counting equipment; microwave radar; underwater sound; ballistics; nuclear spectroscopy and nuclear weapons; double beta decay; mass of the neutrino; shapes of the allowed and forbidden beta spectra. *Mailing Add:* Dept of Physics Ind Univ Bloomington IN 47401

LANGER, ROBERT SAMUEL, b Aug 29, 48; US citizen. BIOENGINEERING, BIOMEDICAL SCIENCE. *Educ:* Cornell Univ, BS, 70; Mass Inst Technol, ScD, 74. *Prof Exp:* RES ASSOC SURG, BOSTON CHILDREN'S HOSP, 74-; asst prof, 78-81, ASSOC PROF, DEPT NUTRIT & FOOD SCI, MASS INST TECHNOL, 81- *Concurrent Pos:* Vis asst prof nutrit & food sci, Mass Inst Technol, 77-78. *Mem:* Am Chem Soc; Am Inst Chem Engrs; Sigma Xi. *Res:* Polymer drug delivery systems; tumor neovascularization; application of enzymes in medicine. *Mailing Add:* Dept Nutrit & Food Sci Mass Inst Technol Cambridge MA 02139

LANGER, SIDNEY, b New York, NY, Dec 15, 25; c 1. PHYSICAL CHEMISTRY. *Educ:* NY Univ, AB, 49; Ill Inst Technol, PhD(chem), 55. *Prof Exp:* Chemist, Oak Ridge Nat Lab, 54-60; mem res staff, Gen Atomic Div, Gen Dynamics Corp, 60-69, group leader, Nuclear Fuels Group, Res & Develop Div, Gulf Gen Atomic, 69-71, mgr gas-cooled fast breeder reactor fuels, 77-81, GROUP LEADER FUELS & MAT DEVELOP, GAS-COOLED FAST REACTOR PROJECT, GEN ATOMIC CO, 71-, MEM SR RES STAFF, 69- *Mem:* AAAS; Sigma Xi; Am Chem Soc; fel Am Nuclear Soc. *Res:* Nuclear reactor chemistry; physical chemistry and thermodynamics of high temperature systems; phase equilibria; fission product behavior in fuels; fission product release; fuel processing and reprocessing. *Mailing Add:* Gen Atomic Co PO Box 81608 San Diego CA 92138

LANGER, WILLIAM DAVID, b New York, NY, Sept 28, 42. ASTROPHYSICS, PHYSICS. *Educ:* NY Univ, BS, 64; Yale Univ, MS, 65, PhD(physics), 68. *Prof Exp:* Assoc fel astrophys, Goddard Inst Space Studies, NASA, 68-70; NSF NATO fel physics, Niels Bohr Inst, Copenhagen, Denmark, 70-71; res asst prof astrophys, NY Univ, 71-76; asst prof, Univ Pa, 76-78; assoc prof astron, Univ Mass, 78-80; RES PHYSICIST, PLASMA PHYSICS LAB, PRINCETON UNIV, 80- *Concurrent Pos:* Res assoc astrophys, Goddard Inst Space Studies, NASA, 74-76; consult radio astron, Bell Tel Labs, 76-81. *Mem:* AAAS; Am Astron Soc; Am Phys Soc; Sigma Xi. *Res:* plasma physics. *Mailing Add:* Princeton Univ PO Box 451 Princeton NJ 08544

LANGERMAN, NEAL RICHARD, b Philadelphia, Pa, Mar 11, 43. PHYSICAL BIOCHEMISTRY. *Educ:* Franklin & Marshall Col, AB, 65; Northwestern Univ, PhD(chem), 69. *Prof Exp:* NIH fel chem, Yale Univ, 69-70; asst prof biochem, Sch Med, Tufts Univ, 70-75; asst prof, 75-77, ASSOC PROF CHEM, UTAH STATE UNIV, 77- *Mem:* Am Soc Biol Chemists; Biophys Soc; Calorimetry Soc; Undersea Med Soc. *Res:* Thermodynamic studies of protein reactions, especially flavin-flavoprotein interactions; microcalorimetry; fluorescence spectroscopy; analytical ultracentrifugation; chemical safety; management of hazardous waste; chemical resource recovery. *Mailing Add:* Dept of Chem Utah State Univ Logan UT 84322

LANGFELDER, LEONARD JAY, b Lynbrook, NY, Feb 5, 33; m 55; c 3. GEOTECHNICAL & COASTAL ENGINEERING. *Educ:* Univ Fla, BSCE, 59, MSE, 60; Univ Ill, PhD(civil eng), 64. *Prof Exp:* Res assoc coastal eng, Univ Fla, 60-62; vis lectr civil eng, Univ Ill, 64; from asst prof to prof civil eng, 69-78, PROF MARINE SCI & ENG & HEAD DEPT, NC STATE UNIV, 78-, DIR CTR MARINE & COASTAL STUDIES, 69- *Concurrent Pos:* Mem soils, geol & found cmt, Hwy Res Bd, Nat Acad Sci-Nat Res Coun, 65- *Mem:* Am Soc Civil Engrs. *Res:* Soil properties, principally shear strength and compaction properties of cohesive soils; improved foundation engineering principles; coastal processes. *Mailing Add:* Dept of Marine Sci & Eng NC State Univ Raleigh NC 27650

LANGFITT, THOMAS WILLIAM, b Clarksburg, WVa, Apr 20, 27; m 53; c 3. NEUROSURGERY. *Educ:* Princeton Univ, AB, 49; Johns Hopkins Univ, MD, 53. *Prof Exp:* Intern gen surg, Johns Hopkins Univ Hosp, 53-54; asst resident, Vanderbilt Univ Hosp, 54-55; from asst resident to chief resident neurosurg, Johns Hopkins Univ Hosp, 57-61; assoc, 61-63, from asst prof to assoc prof, 63-68, CHARLES FRAZIER PROF NEUROSURG, MED SCH, UNIV PA, 68-, HEAD DEPT, UNIV HOSP, 68-, VPRES HEALTH AFFAIRS, UNIV, 74- *Concurrent Pos:* Res fel, Johns Hopkins Univ Hosp, 57-60; contractor, US Army Chem Corp, 57-; head sect neurosurg, Pa Hosp, 61-68. *Mem:* Inst Med-Nat Acad Sci; Cong Neurol Surg; Am Col Surgeons; Am Asn Neurol Surg; AMA. *Res:* Pathophysiology and metabolism in acute brain injuries. *Mailing Add:* Div of Neurosurg Univ of Pa Med Sch Philadelphia PA 19104

LANGFORD, ARTHUR NICOL, b Ingersoll, Ont, July 30, 10; m 38, 76; c 3. GENERAL BOTANY TEACHER. *Educ:* Queen's Univ, Ont, BA, 31; Univ Toronto, MA, 33, PhD(plant path, genetics), 36. *Prof Exp:* Asst bot, Univ Toronto, 33-36, bact, 37; lectr, Bishops Univ, 38-45, from asst prof to prof biol, 46-78, emer prof, 78-81; RETIRED. *Concurrent Pos:* Head dept biol, Bishops Univ, 51-71, chmn dept, 71-75; co-operant, Ctr for Info on Am, Swaziland, S Africa, 76- *Res:* Plant ecology of forests and peat bogs; gradient analysis. *Mailing Add:* 41 Clough Ave Lennoxville PQ J1M 1W4 Can

LANGFORD, COOPER HAROLD, III, b Ann Arbor, Mich, Oct 14, 34; m 59. PHYSICAL INORGANIC CHEMISTRY. *Educ:* Harvard Univ, AB, 56; Northwestern l)niv, PhD(chem), 59. *Prof Exp:* NSF fel, Univ Col, London, 59-60; instr chem, Amherst Col, 60-61, from asst prof to assoc prof, 61-67; assoc prof chem, Carleton Univ, 67-70, prof, 70-80; PROF CHEM & CHMN DEPT, CONCORDIA UNIV, 80- *Concurrent Pos:* Vis asst prof, Columbia Univ, 64; Alfred P Sloan Found fel, 68-70; consult, Inland Waters Directorate, Can, 73; consult, Nat Health & Welfare Can, 77; mem, Chem Grants Comt, Nat Res Coun Can, 75-78 & chmn, 77-78. *Mem:* fel AAAS; Am Chem Soc; The Chem Soc; fel Chem Inst Can. *Res:* Applications to energy problems; inorganic photochemistry; kinetics in analysis; solution physical chemistry. *Mailing Add:* Dept of Chem Concordia Univ Montreal PQ H3G 1M8 Can

LANGFORD, DAVID, b New York, NY, May 6, 34; div; c 2. MECHANICAL ENGINEERING, NUCLEAR ENGINEERING. *Educ:* NY Univ, BS, 56, MS, 57; Ill Inst Technol, MS, 59; Rensselaer Polytech Inst, DEngSc, 65. *Prof Exp:* From asst physicist to assoc physicist, IIT Res Inst, 57-59; from sr anal engr to asst proj engr, Pratt & Whitney Aircraft, United Aircraft Corp, 59-66; from asst prof to assoc prof mech eng, Drexel Univ, 66-72; REGIONAL RADIATION/NOISE REP, US ENVIRON PROTECTION AGENCY, 72- *Mem:* AAAS; Am Phys Soc; Am Nuclear Soc; Am Soc Mech Eng; NY Acad Sci. *Res:* Psychology and education of engineers; nuclear engineering; plasma physics and magnetohydrodynamics; superconductivity; conduction heat transfer; fluid flow; environmental science. *Mailing Add:* US Environ Protection Agency Philadelphia PA 19106

LANGFORD, EDGAR VERDEN, b Parry Sound, Ont, Can, Apr 27, 21; m 44; c 4. VETERINARY BACTERIOLOGY. *Educ:* Mem, Royal Col Vet Surgeons, Univ Toronto, DVM, VS, 49, DVPH, 50. *Prof Exp:* Vet surgeon diag & res, Can Dept Agr, 50-56; animal pathologist, BC Dept of Agr, 56-67; res sci diag, Can Dept Agr, 67-80; RETIRED. *Mem:* Am Soc Microbiol; Can Soc Microbiologists; Can Vet Med Asn; Int Soc Mycoplasmologists; Brit Vet Asn. *Res:* Mycoplasma relationship to disease in the ruminant; incidence of infection in the systems of the ruminant; serological response of the host; development of diagnostic serological methods; pathogenicity of Mycoplasma. *Mailing Add:* 1024 13th St S Lethbridge AB T1K 1S5 Can

LANGFORD, ERIC SIDDON, b New York, NY, May 23, 38; m 59; c 1. MATHEMATICS. *Educ:* Mass Inst Technol, SB, 59; Rutgers Univ, MS, 60, PhD(math), 63. *Prof Exp:* Res specialist, Autonetics Div, NAm Rockwell, 63-64; asst prof math, Naval Postgrad Sch, 64-69; assoc prof math, Univ Maine, Orono, 69-77, prof, 77-82; PROF MATH, CALIF STATE UNIV, CHICO, 82- *Concurrent Pos:* Vis assoc, Daniel H Wagner, Assocs, 66; collab ed, Am Math Monthly, 69-71; assoc ed, 71-75; vis assoc prof math, Calif Inst Technol, 72-73; vis scholar, Univ Calif, Berkeley, 76; vis distinguished prof math, Calif Polytech State Univ, San Luis Obispo, 77-78. *Honors & Awards:* L R Ford Award, Math Asn Am, 71. *Mem:* Am Math Soc. *Res:* Geometrical aspects of Banach spaces; Riesz spaces. *Mailing Add:* Dept Math Calif State Univ Chico CA 95929

LANGFORD, ERNEST ROBERT, preventive medicine, public health, see previous edition

LANGFORD, FLORENCE, b Celina, Tex, Sept 20, 12. NUTRITION. *Educ:* Tex Woman's Univ, BS, 32, MA, 38; Iowa State Univ, PhD(nutrit), 60. *Prof Exp:* High sch teacher, Tex, 32-34; teacher home econ, Kilgore Jr Col, 35-37; instr nutrit & home mgt, Univ Tenn, 38-41; from asst prof to assoc prof, 42-61, actg dean, 70-72, PROF FOOD & NUTRIT, TEX WOMAN'S UNIV, 62- *Mem:* Am Chem Soc; Am Dietetic Asn; Am Home Econ Asn; Am Pub Health Asn; Int Fedn Home Econ. *Res:* Food and nutrition; human nutrition; energy metabolism. *Mailing Add:* Dept of Food & Nutrit Tex Woman's Univ Denton TX 76204

LANGFORD, FRED F, b Toronto, Ont, Dec 19, 29; m 53; c 3. ECONOMIC GEOLOGY. *Educ:* Univ Toronto, BA, 53; Queen's Univ, Ont, MA, 55; Princeton Univ, PhD(geol), 60. *Prof Exp:* Geologist, Imp Oil Co, 53-54; geologist, Ont Dept Mines, 54-57; assoc prof geol, Univ Kans, 58-62; assoc prof, 62-71, PROF GEOL SCI, UNIV SASK, 71- *Mem:* Mineral Asn Can; Geol Asn Can. *Res:* Economic geology; Precambrian geology; engineering geology. *Mailing Add:* Dept of Geol Sci Univ of Sask Saskatoon SK S7N 0W0 Can

LANGFORD, GEORGE, b Chicago, Ill, Dec 26, 36; m 68; c 2. PHYSICAL & MECHANICAL METALLURGY. *Educ:* Mass Inst Technol, SB, 59, ScD(metall), 66. *Prof Exp:* Instr metall, Mass Inst Technol, 60-62; scientist, Edgar C Bain Lab Fundamental Res, US Steel Corp, Pa, 66-71; res specialist, Monsanto, Chemstrand Res Ctr, Inc, Durham, 72-75; ASSOC PROF MAT ENG, DREXEL UNIV, 75- *Mem:* AAAS; Am Soc Metals; Am Inst Mining, Metall & Petrol Engrs. *Res:* Optical and electron metallography of heavily deformed metals and theory of their strain hardening; wire drawing; steel casting by diffusion solidification and liquid infiltration. *Mailing Add:* Dept of Mat Eng Drexel Univ Philadelphia PA 19104

LANGFORD, GEORGE MALCOLM, b Halif, NC, Aug 26, 44; m 68; c 3. CELL BIOLOGY, MICROTUBULES. *Educ:* Fayetteville State Univ, BS, 66; Ill Inst Technol, MS, 69, PhD(cell biol), 71. *Prof Exp:* Fel biophys cytol, Univ Pa, 71-73; asst prof cell biol, Univ Mass, 73-76, Col Med, Howard Univ, 77-79; ASSOC PROF CELL BIOL, SCH MED, UNIV NC, CHAPEL HILL, 79- *Concurrent Pos:* NIH fel, 71-73; Macy fel, Marine Biol Lab, 76 & 77, Steps fel, 78; consult, NIH, 81-, Marine Biol Lab, 82- *Mem:* AAAS; Am Soc Cell Biol; Sigma Xi. *Res:* Organization of the cytoplasmic matrix and the structure and function of microtubules; wave propagation in the microtubular axostyle; properties of axonal and dendritic microtubules. *Mailing Add:* Dept Physiol Sch Med Univ NC Chapel Hill NC 27514

LANGFORD, GEORGE SHEALY, b Blythewood, SC, Mar 9, 01; m 26; c 2. ENTOMOLOGY. *Educ:* Clemson Col, BS, 21; Univ Md, MS, 24; Ohio State Univ, PhD(entom), 29. *Prof Exp:* Teacher pub schs, NC, 21-22; asst entom, Univ Md, 22-24; dep state entomologist, Colo, 24-27; asst zool, Ohio State Univ, 27-28 & Ohio Exp Sta, 28-29; from assoc prof to prof entom, Univ Md, College Park, 29-71; actg dir, State Bd Agr Progs, 71-72; ENTOM CONSULT, 72- *Concurrent Pos:* Ed, Entoma, 44-54; pres, Eastern Plant Bd, 55; state entomologist, 56-71. *Mem:* Entom Soc Am; Am Mosquito Control Asn. *Res:* Economic and applied entomology. *Mailing Add:* 4606 Hartwick Rd College Park MD 20740

LANGFORD, HERBERT GAINES, b Columbia, SC, Apr 22, 22; m 50; c 4. INTERNAL MEDICINE, PHYSIOLOGY. *Educ:* Univ SC, BS, 42; Med Col Va, MD, 45. *Prof Exp:* Jr res asst, Med Col Va, 48-49, res asst neurophysiol, 49-50, assoc med & res assoc neurol sci, 52-55; asst res, Osler Med Serv, Johns Hopkins Hosp, 50-52; from asst prof to assoc prof med, 55-64, from asst prof to assoc prof physiol, 61-71, chief endocrine & hypertension div, 58-64, actg chmn dept med, 63-65; PROF MED, MED SCH, UNIV MISS, 64-, PROF PHYSIOL, 71- *Concurrent Pos:* Chmn steering comt, Hypertension Detection & Follow-up Prog, Nat Heart, Lung & Blood Inst. *Mem:* Am Fedn Clin Res; Am Soc Clin Invest; Am Physiol Soc; Soc Exp Biol & Med. *Res:* Endocrine control of blood pressure; pre-eclampsia; epidemiology and hypertension. *Mailing Add:* Dept of Med Univ of Miss Sch of Med Jackson MS 39216

LANGFORD, PAUL BROOKS, b Lockesburg, Ark, Aug 11, 30; m 59; c 1. PHYSICAL ORGANIC CHEMISTRY. *Educ:* Okla State Univ, BS, 52, MS, 54; Ga Inst Technol, PhD(chem), 62. *Prof Exp:* Instr chem, Ga Inst Technol, 56-62; from asst prof to assoc prof, 62-70, PROF CHEM, DAVID LIPSCOMB COL, 70-, CHMN DEPT, 80- *Mem:* Am Chem Soc. *Res:* Rates and mechanisms of reactions of organic halogen compounds; charge transfer complex compounds. *Mailing Add:* Dept of Chem David Lipscomb Col Nashville TN 37203

LANGFORD, R(OBERT) C(HARLES), b Portsmouth, Eng, Oct 6, 21; US citizen; m 45; c 1. ELECTRONIC ENGINEERING. *Educ:* Univ London, BS, 43, PhD(elec eng), 51. *Prof Exp:* Engr instrumentation, Sangamo Weston Instruments, 43-52, dir eng, Weston Instruments, 52-61; dir guid & control res, Aerospace Res Ctr, Gen Precision, Inc, 61-65; asst dir guid & control res, Electronics Res Ctr, NASA, 65-68; spec asst to pres, Gen Precision, Inc, Aerospace Group, 68-69, vpres & dir progs mgt, Kearfott Div, 69-71; PRES, BERTEA CORP, 71- *Concurrent Pos:* Swan res fel; mem res adv comt commun, instrumentation & data processing, NASA, 63-64, res comt guid & control, 64- *Mem:* Assoc fel Am Inst Aeronaut & Astronaut; sr mem Inst Elec & Electronics Engrs; Am Nuclear Soc; Brit Inst Elec & Electronics Engrs. *Res:* Guidance and control of aerospace vehicles, inertial and stellar; strapdown systems; computers and computation; displays; celestial mechanics; instrumentation; electronic and electrical microminiaturization research. *Mailing Add:* Bertea Corp 18001 Von Karman Ave Irvine CA 92677

LANGFORD, ROBERT BRUCE, b San Francisco, Calif, Mar 7, 19; m 57. ORGANIC CHEMISTRY. *Educ:* Univ Calif, Los Angeles, BS, 48; Univ Southern Calif, MS, 63, PhD, 72. *Prof Exp:* Chemist petrol anal, Southern Pac Co, 49-54; res chemist pesticides, Stauffer Chem Co, 54-58; lab mgr org synthesis, Cyclo Chem Corp, 58-61; teacher chem, Los Angeles City Schs, 61-64; from instr to assoc prof, 64-73, chmn dept, 68-74, PROF CHEM, EAST LOS ANGELES COL, 73- *Mem:* AAAS; Am Chem Soc. *Res:* Organic synthesis; sulfur compounds; photochemistry. *Mailing Add:* 644 Haverkamp Dr Glendale CA 91206

LANGFORD, RUSSELL HAL, b North Platte, Nebr, Nov 14, 25; m 46; c 4. HYDROLOGY, ENVIRONMENTAL CHEMISTRY. *Educ:* Univ Nebr, BSc, 49. *Prof Exp:* Hydrologist, US Geol Surv, 49-66, asst chief, Off Water Data Coord, 66-68, chief, Off Water Data Coord, 68-80, ASSOC CHIEF

HYDROLOGIST, US GEOL SURV, 80- Concurrent Pos: Mem, Int Souris-Red River Eng Bd, Int Joint Comn US & Can; alt chmn, US Nat Comt Sci Hydrol; US mem comn hydrol, World Meteorol Orgn. Mem: Am Chem Soc; Am Water Works Asn; Am Geophys Union; Water Pollution Control Fedn; AAAS. Res: Water chemistry; geochemistry. Mailing Add: US Geol Surv 408 Nat Ctr Reston VA 22092

LANGFORD, WALTER ROBERT, agronomy, see previous edition

LANGHAAR, HENRY LOUIS, b Bristol, Conn, Oct 14, 09; m 37; c 3. APPLIED MECHANICS. Educ: Lehigh Univ, BS, 31, MS, 33, PhD(math), 40. Prof Exp: Test engr, Ingersoll Rand Co, NJ, 33-36; seismographer, Carter Oil Co, 36-37; instr math, Purdue Univ, 40-41; struct engr, Consol-Vultee Aircraft Corp, 41-47; from assoc prof to prof, 47-78, EMER PROF THEORET & APPL MECH, UNIV ILL, URBANA, 78- Honors & Awards: Von Karman Medal, Am Soc Civil Engrs. Mem: AAAS; fel Am Soc Mech Eng. Res: Stress analysis; elasticity and buckling theories; theory of plates and shells; dimensional analysis and model theory. Mailing Add: Dept of Theoret & Appl Mech Univ of Ill Urbana IL 61801

LANGHAM, ROBERT FRED, b Grand Ledge, Mich, Jan 31, 12; m 37; c 4. PATHOLOGY. Educ: Calvin Col, AB, 35; Mich State Univ, MS, 37, DVM, 42, PhD, 50. Prof Exp: From instr to assoc prof, 38-51, actg chmn, Dept Path, Col Vet Med, 73-75, PROF VET PATH, MICH STATE UNIV, 51- Mem: Am Vet Med Asn; Am Col Vet Path; Conf Res Workers Animal Dis; Int Acad Path. Res: Leptospirosis; neoplasms and joint disease in animals. Mailing Add: Col of Vet Med Mich State Univ 539A E Ice Hall East Lansing MI 48824

LANGHANS, ROBERT W, b Flushing, NY, Dec 29, 29; m 52; c 3. FLORICULTURE. Educ: Rutgers Univ, BS, 52; Cornell Univ, MS, 54, PhD(floricult), 56. Prof Exp: From asst prof to assoc prof, 56-68, PROF FLORICULT, CORNELL UNIV, 68- Honors & Awards: Blauvelt Award, 55; Kenneth Post Award, Am Soc Hort Sci, 65. Mem: Am Soc Hort Sci; Am Soc Plant Physiol; Int Soc Hort Sci. Res: Effects of photoperiod and temperature on growth and flowering. Mailing Add: Dept of Hort Cornell Univ Col of Agr Ithaca NY 14853

LANGHEINRICH, ARMIN P(AUL), b Planitz, Ger, Sept 1, 26; US citizen; m 49; c 3. CHEMISTRY, FUEL ENGINEERING. Educ: Univ Utah, BS, 58, MA, 63. Prof Exp: Asst chemist, Utah Cooper Div, 59, jr scientist, Res Ctr, Western Mining Div, 59-62, from asst scientist to scientist, 62-71, sr scientist, Res Dept, Metal Mining Div, 71-79, MGR, TECH & ADMIN SERV, KENNECOTT MINERALS CO, 79- Concurrent Pos: Spec instr chem, Salt Lake Ctr Continuing Educ, Brigham Young Univ, 63-77. Mem: Am Chem Soc; Am Soc Testing & Mat (secy, 77-). Res: Application of x-ray fluorescence techniques to laboratory and on-stream analyses; energy dispersion x-ray analysis with conventional and radioisotope excitation; optical emission spectroscopy applied to geochemical samples and to refined copper; development of high purity copper standards; environmental analysis. Mailing Add: 230 M St Salt Lake City UT 84103

LANGHOFF, CHARLES ANDERSON, b New Orleans, La, June 27, 47; m 73; c 2. CHEMICAL PHYSICS. Educ: Tulane Univ, BS, 69; Calif Inst Technol, PhD(chem), 74. Prof Exp: Fel chem, IBM Res Lab, San Jose, 73-75; ASST PROF CHEM, ILL INST TECHNOL, 75- Concurrent Pos: IBM Res Corp grant, 77-78. Mem: Am Chem Soc; Am Phys Soc. Res: Picosecond spectroscopy; dynamic of liquids; theory of radiationless transitions. Mailing Add: Dept of Chem Ill Inst of Technol Chicago IL 60616

LANGHOFF, PETER WOLFGANG, b New York, NY, Jan 19, 37; m 62; c 3. THEORETICAL CHEMISTRY. Educ: Univ Hofstra, BS, 58; State Univ NY Buffalo, PhD(physics), 65. Prof Exp: Physicist, Cornell Aeronaut Labs, Inc, Cornell Univ, 62-65; fel, Harvard Univ, 67-69; from asst prof to assoc prof, 69-77, PROF CHEM, IND UNIV, BLOOMINGTON, 77- Concurrent Pos: Vis prof, Univ Colo, Boulder, 76 & Univ Paris, Orsay, 81. Mem: Am Phys Soc. Res: Atomic and molecular physics; interaction of radiation and matter; atomic and molecular structure; molecular photoionization. Mailing Add: Dept of Chem Ind Univ Bloomington IN 47401

LANGILLE, ALAN RALPH, b Amherst, NS, Apr 2, 38; m 67; c 1. CROP PHYSIOLOGY. Educ: McGill Univ, BS, 60; Univ Vt, MS, 62; Pa State Univ, PhD(agron), 67. Prof Exp: Asst prof agron, 67-73, assoc prof, 73-79, PROF AGRON & BOT, UNIV MAINE, ORONO, 79- Concurrent Pos: Maine State Hwy Comn grant, Univ Maine, Orono, 71-73. Mem: Am Soc Agron; Am Soc Hort Sci; Am Inst Biol Sci; Potato Asn Am. Res: Hormonal control of tuber initiation and subsequent growth in the potato; growth regulator physiology; salt tolerance in conifers. Mailing Add: Dept Plant & Soil Sci Univ Maine Orono ME 04473

LANGILLE, ROBERT C(ARDEN), b Yarmouth, NS, Apr 22, 15; m 52; c 3. ELECTRONICS. Educ: St Francis Xavier Univ, Can, BSc, 37; Dalhousie Univ, MSc, 40; Univ Toronto, PhD(phys chem), 44. Prof Exp: Res officer, Can Army Oper Res Group, 44-46; from sci officer to supt electronics lab, 47-69, DIR GEN, COMMUN RES CTR, DEPT COMMUN, TELECOMMUN ESTAB, DEFENCE RES BD CAN, 69- Mem: Int Union Radio Sci; Inst Elec & Electronics Engrs; Arctic Inst N Am; Royal Meteorol Soc; Can Asn Physicists. Res: Solid state physics; general electronics; space research; tropospheric radio propagation. Mailing Add: 1875 Ferncroft Crescent Ottawa ON K1H 7B5 Can

LANGLAND, BARBARA JUNE, b Reedley, Calif, June 24, 49; m 68; c 2. MAGNETIC RECORDING, EQUALIZATION. Educ: Univ Calif, Davis, BS, 71; Univ Colo, Boulder, MS, 73. Prof Exp: Assoc engr spectral estimates, IBM, 73-75; engr lab automation, Lawrence Livermore Lab, 75-77; STAFF MEM MAGNETICS, IBM, 78- Concurrent Pos: Consult, 76-78. Mem: Inst Elec & Electronics Engrs. Res: Appropriate material properties and recording head structure for perpendicular magnetic recording; signal processing issues resulting from the perpendicular recording system. Mailing Add: 650 Mindy Way San Jose CA 95123

LANGLAND, OLAF ELMER, b Madrid, Iowa, May 30, 25; m 56, 75; c 2. RADIOLOGY, DENTISTRY. Educ: Univ Iowa, DDS, 52, MS, 61; Am Bd Oral & Maxillo-Facial Radiol, dipl, 81. Prof Exp: From instr to assoc prof oral diag & radiol, Col Dent, Univ Iowa, 59-69, head dept, 64-69; prof oral diag-med-radiol & head dept, Sch Dent, La State Univ, New Orleans, 69-75; PROF DIAG & ROENTGENOL, SCH DENT, UNIV TEX HEALTH SCI CTR, SAN ANTONIO, 75-, PROF DEPT RADIOL, SCH MED, 80- Concurrent Pos: USPHS grant, Col Dent, Univ Iowa, 64-66; consult, Wilford Hall US Air Force Hosp, Lackland, Tex, 68-71; mem subcomt proposed dent x-ray mach, Am Nat Standards Inst, 68-74; staff dentist, Charity Hosp, New Orleans, 69-75. Mem: Fel Am Col Dent; Am Acad Dent Radiol (vpres, 81); Orgn Teachers Oral Diag (pres, 73); Am Asn Dent Schs; Int Asn Oral & Maxillo-Facial Radiol. Res: Panoramic radiography; educational research in dentistry; clinical research in oral manifestations of systemic disease; application of modern intensifying screens in diagnostic radiology. Mailing Add: Dept Diag & Roentgenol Sch Dent Univ of Tex Health Sci Ctr San Antonio TX 78284

LANGLANDS, ROBERT P, b New Westminster, BC, Oct 6, 36; m 56; c 4. MATHEMATICS. Educ: Univ BC, BA, 57, MA, 58; Yale Univ, PhD(math), 60. Prof Exp: Instr math, Princeton Univ, 60-61, lectr, 61-62, from asst prof to assoc prof, 62-67; prof math, Yale Univ, 67-72; PROF MATH, INST ADVAN STUDY, 72- Concurrent Pos: Mem, Inst Advan Study, 62-63; Miller fel, Univ Calif, Berkeley, 64-65; Sloan fel, 64-66. Res: Group representations; automorphic forms. Mailing Add: Inst for Advan Study Princeton NJ 08540

LANGLEBEN, MANUEL PHILLIP, b Poland, Apr 9, 24; nat Can; m 48; c 3. GLACIOLOGY, MICROMETEOROLOGY. Educ: McGill Univ, BSc, 49, MSc, 50, PhD(physics), 53. Prof Exp: Res atmospheric physics, 53-57, lectr, 57-59, from asst prof to assoc prof, 59-69, dir, McGill Ctr Northern Studies & Res, 77-80, PROF PHYSICS, MCGILL UNIV, 69- Mem: Can Asn Physicists; Royal Meteorol Soc; Glaciol Soc; Am Geophys Union. Res: Physics of ice; sea ice; ice drift. Mailing Add: Rutherford Physics Bldg 3600 University St Montreal PQ H3A 2T8 Can

LANGLER, JAMES EDWARD, b Oakland, Calif, Oct 27, 36; m 63; c 2. FOOD SCIENCE. Educ: Univ Calif, Berkeley, BS, 59; Ore State Univ, MS, 64, PhD(food sci), 66. Prof Exp: Lab technician biochem, Univ Calif, Berkeley, 59-61; res asst food sci, Ore State Univ, 61-66, asst prof, Seafoods Lab, 66-69; dir food res, Woodstock Res Ctr, Morton Salt Div, Morton Norwich Prod, Inc, 69-79; RES MGR, NEW PROD DEVELOP, CORP RES & DEVELOP, LAND O'LAKES, INC, 79- Mem: Am Chem Soc; Inst Food Technologists; Am Oil Chemists Soc. Res: Chemistry and biochemistry of marine biological systems as they are related to food; lipid deterioration; flavor chemistry; diary products; new product development. Mailing Add: Morton Salt Co Div 1275 Lake Ave Woodstock IL 60098

LANGLEY, G R, b Sydney, NS, Oct 6, 31; m; c 3. INTERNAL MEDICINE, HEMATOLOGY. Educ: Mt Allison Univ, BA, 52; Dalhousie Univ, MD, 57; FRCP(C), 61. Prof Exp: Asst resident internal med, Victoria Gen Hosp & Totonto Gen Hosp, 57-60; J Arthur Haatz fel hemat, Univ Melbourne, 60-61; Med Res Coun Can fel, Sch Med & Dent, Univ Rochester, 61-62 & Dalhousie Univ, 63; lectr internal med, 63-64, from asst prof to assoc prof med, 64-68, PROF MED, DALHOUSIE UNIV, 68-, HEAD DEPT, 74- Concurrent Pos: John & Mary R Markle scholar med, 63-68; consult, Armed Forces Hosp, Halifax, 64-; head dept med, Camp Hill Hosp, 69-74; head dept med, Victoria Gen Hosp, 74- Honors & Awards: Queens Jubilee Medal, 77. Mem: Fel Am Col Physicians; Can Soc Clin Invest; Can Med Asn. Res: Hematological oncology. Mailing Add: Dept of Med Victoria Gen Hosp Halifax NS B3H 2Y9 Can

LANGLEY, KENNETH HALL, b Ft Collins, Colo, Sept 1, 35; m 59; c 2. BIOPHYSICS. Educ: Mass Inst Technol, SB, 58; Univ Calif, Berkeley, PhD(physics), 66. Prof Exp: Actg asst prof & res assoc physics, Univ Calif, Berkeley, 66; asst prof, 66-73, ASSOC PROF PHYSICS, UNIV MASS, AMHERST, 73- Mem: Am Phys Soc; AAAS. Res: Experimental solid state physics; dynamic nuclear orientation; light scattering from critical point fluids macromolecules; biological systems. Mailing Add: Dept of Physics & Astron Univ of Mass Amherst MA 01002

LANGLEY, MAURICE N(ATHAN), b Dorchester, Nebr, July 6, 13; m 39; c 3. AGRICULTURAL ENGINEERING. Educ: Colo Agr & Mech Col, BS, 39. Prof Exp: Soil surveyor, Agr Exp Sta, Colo State Col, 39-40; jr soil surveyor, Soil Conserv Serv, USDA, Tex, 40-42, asst soil technologist & chief land classification div, 46-48, land use specialist & head land use & settlement div, 49-56, agr engr & chief opers div, 56-59, hydraul engr, Land & Water Br, 59-60, chief, Irrig Br, 60-62, asst chief div irrig & land use, 62-64, chief water & land, 64-73; VPRES, BOOKMAN-EDMONSTON ENG, INC, 73- Concurrent Pos: Pres, US Comt Irrig, Drainage & Flood Control, 70, 71 & 72; US nat chmn, Int Comn Irrig & Drainage, vpres, 74, 75 & 76. Honors & Awards: Meritorious Serv Award, US Bur Reclamation, 56 & 69. Mem: Am Soc Agr Engrs; Soil Sci Soc Am; Am Soc Agron; Int Water Resources Asn; Am Water Works Asn. Res: Land and water resources development and administration. Mailing Add: Bookman-Edmonston Eng Inc 702 World Ctr 918 16th St NW Washington DC 20006

LANGLEY, NEAL ROGER, b Sumas, Wash, July 27, 39. POLYMER CHEMISTRY. Educ: Univ Wash, BS, 61; Univ Wis, PhD(chem), 68. Prof Exp: Sr res scientist, Pac Northwest Lab, Battelle Mem Inst, 67-68; chemist, 68-80, ASSOC RES SCIENTIST, DOW CORNING CORP, 80- Mem: Am Chem Soc. Res: Viscoelastic properties of cross-linked polymers; mechanical property-structure relations of silicone elastomers; statistical analysis of cured polymer networks. Mailing Add: Res Dept Dow Corning Corp Midland MI 48640

LANGLEY, ROBERT ARCHIE, b Athens, Ga, Oct 21, 37; div; c 3. SOLID STATE PHYSICS. *Educ:* Ga Inst Technol, BS, 59, MS, 60, PhD(physics), 63. *Prof Exp:* Asst physics, Ga Inst Technol, 59-63; physicist, Air Force Cambridge Res Labs, 63-65 & Oak Ridge Nat Lab, 66-68; staff mem, Sandia Corp, 68-78; prog coordr, Oak Ridge Nat Lab, 78-80; prog coordr, Int Atomic Energy Agency, 80-81; PROG COORDR, OAK RIDGE NAT LAB, 81- *Mem:* Am Phys Soc; Am Nuclear Soc; Am Vacuum Soc; Health Physics Soc. *Res:* Plasma-wall interactions in controlled fusion devices; ion implantation; hydrogen and helium migration in metals; surface physics; ion backscattering; nuclear microanalysis. *Mailing Add:* Fusion Energy Div Oak Ridge Nat Lab Oak Ridge TN 37830

LANGLEY, ROBERT CHARLES, b NJ, Apr 11, 25; m 54; c 1. ORGANIC CHEMISTRY. *Educ:* St Peters Col, BS, 49. *Prof Exp:* Chemist, E I du Pont de Nemours & Co, 50-54; res dir, Hanovia Div, 54-62, SECT HEAD, RES & DEVELOP DIV, ENGELHARD INDUSTS, INC, 62- *Mem:* Am Chem Soc; Am Ceramic Soc. *Res:* Organic compounds of metals; thin films; gas purification. *Mailing Add:* 214 Old Forge Rd Millington NJ 07946

LANGLOIS, BRUCE EDWARD, b Berlin, NH, Sept 16, 37; m 60; c 2. FOOD MICROBIOLOGY. *Educ:* Univ NH, BS, 59; Purdue Univ, PhD(dairy microbiol), 62. *Prof Exp:* Asst prof dairy, Purdue Univ, 62-64; from asst prof to assoc prof dairy sci, 64-74, PROF ANIMAL SCI, UNIV KY, 74- *Mem:* Am Soc Microbiol; Am Meat Sci Asn; Int Asn Milk, Food & Environ Sanit; Sigma Xi. *Res:* Effects of pesticides on physical and biological properties of foods; transferable drug resistance in farm animals; microflora of dairy and meat products. *Mailing Add:* Dept of Animal Sci Univ of Ky Lexington KY 40506

LANGLOIS, GORDON ELLERBY, b Burley, Idaho, Aug 30, 18; m 44; c 3. PHYSICAL CHEMISTRY. *Educ:* Northwestern Univ, BS, 42; Univ Calif, PhD(phys chem), 52. *Prof Exp:* Sr res chemist, Calif Res Corp, Chevron Res Co, 43-69, sr res chemist, 69-73, mgr, Synthetic Fuels Div, 73-78. *Mem:* Am Chem Soc. *Res:* Catalytic reactions of hydrocarbons, as polymerization, alkylation and isomerization; synthetic fuels technology. *Mailing Add:* 15 Doral Dr Moraga CA 94556

LANGLOIS, WILLIAM EDWIN, b Providence, RI, Oct 23, 33; m 54; c 2. HYDRODYNAMICS. *Educ:* Univ Notre Dame, ScB, 53; Brown Univ, PhD(appl math), 57. *Prof Exp:* Res engr, Polychem Dept, E I du Pont de Nemours & Co, 56-59; STAFF MEM, SAN JOSE RES LAB, IBM CORP, 59- *Concurrent Pos:* Lectr, Univ Del, 56-58 & Univ Santa Clara, 61-69; vis prof, Univ Notre Dame, 70-71. *Res:* Theory of viscous and viscoelastic fluid flow. *Mailing Add:* San Jose Res Lab IBM Corp San Jose CA 95193

LANGLYKKE, ASGER FUNDER, b Pleasant Prairie, Wis, July 17, 09; m 39; c 4. MICROBIOLOGY. *Educ:* Univ Wis, BS, 31, MS, 34, PhD(biochem), 36. *Hon Degrees:* ScD, Trinity Col, 65. *Prof Exp:* Foreman, Proctor & Gamble Co, Ill, 31-32; asst, Univ Wis, 32-36, Dow fel, 36-37; res chemist, Hiram Walker & Sons, Inc, 37-40; supt butyl alcohol plant, Cent Lafayette, PR, 40-43; div head, Northern Regional Res Lab, USDA, Ill, 43 & 45-47; chief pilot plant div & chief tech officer, Chem Warfare Serv, Md & Ind, 43-45; dir, Microbiol Develop, E R Squibb & Sons, 47-49, dir res & develop labs, 49-64, vpres, 64-68; proj mgr, Frederick Cancer Res Ctr, 74-77, consult, 77-80; EXEC STAFF SCIENTIST, GENEX CORP, 79- *Concurrent Pos:* Consult, Res & Develop Bd, US Army, 45-53 & Chem Corp, 53-66; off dir, Defense Res & Eng, 60-63; mem, Comdt Agr Sci, USDA, 64-68; Adv Bd Res & Grad Educ, Rutgers Univ & Sci Adv Comt, Rutgers Inst Microbiol, 64-68; vpres, Appl Chem Div Comt, Int Union Pure & Appl Chem, 77-81; adj prof, Rutgers Univ, 68-74. *Honors & Awards:* Barnett Cohen Award, Am Soc Microbiol, 78. *Mem:* Fel AAAS; fel NY Acad Sci; Emer Mem Biochem Soc UK; Am Inst Chem Engrs; Am Soc Microbiol. *Res:* Fermentation processes for antibiotics steroids, industrial and pharmaceutical chemicals; biochemical engineering. *Mailing Add:* Genex Corp 6110 Exec Blvd Rockville MD 20852

LANGMAN, JAN, medicine, deceased

LANGMUIR, DAVID BULKELEY, b Los Angeles, Calif, Dec 14, 08; m 42; c 3. PHYSICS. *Educ:* Yale Univ, BS, 31; Mass Inst Technol, ScD(physics), 35. *Prof Exp:* Res physicist, Radio Corp Am Mfg Co, NJ, 35-41; liaison officer, Off Sci Res & Develop, Washington, DC & London, 41-45; secy, Guided Missiles Comt, Joint Chiefs of Staff, Washington, DC, 45-46; dir planning div, Res & Develop Bd, 46-48; exec officer, Prog Coun, AEC, 48-50, liaison officer, Chalk River, 50-54; mem tech staff, Ramo-Wooldridge Corp, 54-56, dir res lab, Ramo-Wooldridge Div, Thompson Ramo Wooldridge Corp, 56-60 & TRW Space Technol Labs, 60-65, dir, Phys Res Ctr, TRW Systs, Calif, 65-70, dir res planning, 70-73; RES CONSULT, 73- *Concurrent Pos:* Prof lectr, George Washington Univ, 48-50; mem sci adv group, Off Aerospace Res, US Air Force, 63-70; chmn, 69-70; chmn, Joint Workshop Indust Innovation, Nat Acad Sci, Taiwan, 75. *Mem:* Fel Am Phys Soc; fel Inst Elec & Electronics Engrs; Am Inst Aeronaut & Astronaut. *Res:* Thermionics; television light valves; high frequency tubes; diffusion in metals; ionic propulsion. *Mailing Add:* 350 21st St Santa Monica CA 90402

LANGMUIR, DONALD, b Nashua, NH, Apr 5, 34; c 2. GEOCHEMISTRY. *Educ:* Harvard Univ, AB, 56, MA, 61, PhD(geol sci), 65. *Prof Exp:* Geochemist, Water Resources Div, US Geol Surv, 64-66; lectr water resources, Rutgers Univ, 66-67; from asst prof to prof geochem, Pa State Univ, University Park, 67-78; PROF GEOCHEM, COLO SCH OF MINES, 78- *Concurrent Pos:* Adj prof geochem, Desert Res Inst, Univ Nev, Reno, 74-75; assoc ed, Geochim Cosmochim Acta, 75-80; pres, Hydrochem Systs Corp, 79-; vis prof inorg chem, Univ Sidney, Australia, 80; dir, Earth Search, Inc, 81- *Mem:* AAAS; Am Chem Soc; Am Geophys Union; Soc Environ Geochem & Health; Geochem Soc. *Res:* Geochemistry of subsurface waters; thermodynamic properties of minerals and dissolved species in water; absorption of dissolved metal species on geological materials; geochemistry of exploration for ore deposits, of solution mining, and of groundwater pollution and restoration. *Mailing Add:* Dept of Chem & Geochem Colo Sch of Mines Golden CO 16802

LANGMUIR, MARGARET ELIZABETH LANG, b Chicago, Ill, Nov 11, 35; m 62; c 2. PHYSICAL CHEMISTRY, PHOTOCHEMISTRY. *Educ:* Culver-Stockton Col, BA, 56; Purdue Univ, PhD(chem), 63. *Prof Exp:* Instr anal & inorg chem, Wellesley Col, 60-63; phys chemist, Pioneering Res Div, US Army Natrick Labs, 63-69; consult, 69-74; res assoc, Northeastern Univ, 76-78; SR SCIENTIST, 78- *Mem:* AAAS; Am Chem Soc; Electrochem Soc; Sigma Xi. *Res:* Organic photochemistry; acidity functions; flash photolysis; fast reaction mechanisms; excited state proton transfer; fluorescence, phosphorescence and charge transfer spectra; electrochemistry; implantable electrodes; isomerization; semiconductor electrochemistry; photoelectrochemical cells; solar cells. *Mailing Add:* 9 Bent Brook Rd Sudbury MA 01776

LANGMUIR, ROBERT VOSE, b White Plains, NY, Dec 20, 12; m 39; c 2. PHYSICS. *Educ:* Harvard Univ, AB, 35; Calif Inst Technol, PhD(physics), 43. *Prof Exp:* Physicist, Consol Eng Corp, Calif, 39-42 & Gen Elec Co, 42-48; sr res fel, 48-50, asst prof physics, 50-52, assoc prof elec eng, 52-57, prof, 57-80, EMER PROF ELEC ENG, CALIF INST TECHNOL, 80- *Concurrent Pos:* Consult, TRW, Inc, 57- *Mem:* Am Phys Soc; Inst Elec & Electronics Eng. *Res:* Mass spectroscopy; synchrotrons; secondary emission cathode in magnetrons; starting of synchrotrons. *Mailing Add:* Dept of Elec Eng Calif Inst of Technol Pasadena CA 91125

LANGNER, GERALD CONRAD, b Austin, Minn, Feb 13, 44; m 73; c 1. PHYSICS. *Educ:* St John's Univ, BA, 66; NDak State Univ, MA, 68. *Prof Exp:* Physicist control syst eng, US Navy, 68-69; scientist II physics, Albuquerque Div, EG&G Inc, 69-73; MEM STAFF NONDESTRUCTIVE TESTING, LOS ALAMOS NAT LAB, 74- *Mem:* Am Soc Nondestructive Testing; Am Phys Soc. *Mailing Add:* Los Alamos Nat Lab PO Box 1663 MS 912 Los Alamos NM 87545

LANGNER, RALPH ROLLAND, b Alta, Iowa, June 24, 25; m 48; c 5. ENVIRONMENTAL CHEMISTRY. *Educ:* Univ Iowa, BA, 50, MS, 52, PhD(biochem), 53; Am Bd Indust Hyg, cert, 75. *Prof Exp:* Asst, Univ Iowa, 51-53; instr biochem, Univ Tex, 53-56; indust hygienist, 56-60, res specialist, 60-72, mgr indust hyg, 72-75, dir, 75-78, tech specialist, Indust Hyg Lab, 78-80, TECH SPECIALIST, CORP MED DEPT, DOW CHEM CO, 80- *Mem:* AAAS; Am Chem Soc; NY Acad Sci; Am Indust Hyg Asn; Soc Occup & Environ Health. *Res:* Environmental health and ecology. *Mailing Add:* Dow Chem Co 2030 Dow Ctr Midland MI 48640

LANGNER, RONALD O, b Chicago, Ill, May 10, 40; m 63; c 2. BIOCHEMICAL PHARMACOLOGY. *Educ:* Blackburn Col, BA, 62; Univ RI, MS, 66, PhD(pharmacol), 69. *Prof Exp:* ASSOC PROF PHARMACOL, UNIV CONN, 69- *Res:* Metabolism of collagen and its relationship to experimental atherosclerosis. *Mailing Add:* Dept of Pharmacol Univ of Conn Storrs CT 06268

LANGNER, THOMAS S, b New York, NY, Jan 1, 24; m 53; c 5. PSYCHIATRY, EPIDEMIOLOGY. *Educ:* Harvard Col, AB, 48; Columbia Univ, PhD(sociol), 54. *Prof Exp:* Res assoc pub health, Cornell Univ, 52-53, res assoc psychiat, 53-56, asst prof sociol, 56-63, res assoc anthrop & sociol, 58-63; asst prof psychiat & sociol, Sch Med, NY Univ, 63-66, res assoc & prof psychiat, 66-69; prof epidemiol, 69-77, PROF CLIN PSYCHIAT EPIDEMIOL, SCH PUB HEALTH, COLUMBIA UNIV, 77- *Concurrent Pos:* Health Res Coun New York career scientist award, 63-72; NIMH res scientist award, 72-81; mem epidemiol studies rev comt, NIMH, 72-75. *Mem:* Fel Am Sociol Asn; fel Am Pub Health Asn. *Res:* Psychopathology of children; family and its effect on child behavior; value systems; class and ethnic differences in behavior; environmental stress and effect on strain in individual cross-cultural studies. *Mailing Add:* Columbia Univ Sch of Pub Health New York NY 10032

LANGONE, JOHN JOSEPH, b Cambridge, Mass, Aug 20, 44; m 67; c 2. BIO-ORGANIC CHEMISTRY. *Educ:* Boston Col, BS, 66; Boston Univ, PhD(org chem), 72. *Prof Exp:* Fel org chem, Boston Univ, 71-72; sr res assoc biochem, Brandeis Univ, 72-75; STAFF FEL IMMUNOCHEM, NAT CANCER INST, 75- *Mem:* Am Chem Soc; Am Soc Biol Chemists. *Res:* Immunopharmacology and immunochemistry of biologically active compounds; cancer immunochemistry. *Mailing Add:* Dept of Health Educ & Welfare NIH Bldg 37 Rm 2B13 Bethesda MD 20205

LANGRANA, NOSHIR A, b Bombay, India, Oct 1, 46; US citizen; m 72; c 1. COMPUTER AIDED DESIGN, BIOMECHANICS. *Educ:* Univ Bombay, India, BE, 68; Cornell Univ, MS, 71, PhD(mech eng), 75. *Prof Exp:* Asst prof, 76-82, ASSOC PROF MECH DESIGN, COL ENG, RUTGERS UNIV, 82- *Concurrent Pos:* Adj asst prof surg, NJ Med Sch, 81- *Honors & Awards:* Ralph R Teetor Award, Soc Automotive Engrs, 77. *Mem:* Am Soc Mech Engrs; Am Soc Eng Educ; Orthopaedic Res Soc; Sigma Xi. *Res:* Application of mechanical engineering to solve problems in biomechanics, such as kinematics of joints, low back mechanics and spinal fusion and to develop new materials and devices for medical use. *Mailing Add:* Rutgers Univ PO Box 909 Piscataway NJ 08854

LANGRETH, DAVID CHAPMAN, b Greenwich, Conn, May 22, 37; m 66; c 2. THEORETICAL CONDENSED MATTER PHYSICS. *Educ:* Yale Univ, BS, 59; Univ Ill, MS, 61, PhD(physics), 64. *Prof Exp:* Res assoc physics, Univ Chicago, 64-65 & Cornell Univ, 65-67; from asst prof to assoc prof, 67-74, assoc chmn dept & dir grad progs, 70-73, PROF PHYSICS, RUTGERS UNIV, NEW BRUNSWICK, 74- *Concurrent Pos:* Rutgers Res Coun fel, Univ Calif, San Diego, 73-74; guest prof, Nordita, Copenhagen, 75-76; prin investr, NSF grants, 69- *Mem:* AAAS; Am Phys Soc. *Res:* Theoretical solid state physics, specializing in the many body problem. *Mailing Add:* Dept of Physics Rutgers Univ New Brunswick NJ 08903

LANGRIDGE, ROBERT, b Essex, Eng, Oct 26, 33; m 60; c 2. MOLECULAR BIOLOGY. *Educ:* Univ London, BSc, 54, PhD(crystallog), 57. *Prof Exp:* Res fel biophys, Yale Univ, 57-59; res assoc biophys, Mass Inst Technol, 59-61 & Children's Hosp, Med Ctr, Boston Univ, 61-66; res assoc, Harvard Univ, 63-64, lectr, 64-66; prof biophys & info sci, Univ Chicago, 66-68; prof biochem, Princeton Univ, 68-76; PROF PHARMACOL, CHEM, BIOCHEM & BIOPHYSICS, UNIV CALIF, SAN FRANCISCO, 76- *Mem:* AAAS; Biophys Soc; Am Crystallog Asn. *Res:* X-ray diffraction and physical-chemical studies of the structures of biological macromolecules, particularly nucleic acids, nucleoproteins, viruses and ribosomes; applications of high speed digital computers. *Mailing Add:* 926 Med Sci Bldg Univ of Calif San Francisco CA 94143

LANGRIDGE, WILLIAM HENRY RUSSELL, b New York, NY, Jan 30, 38; m 60; c 1. VIROLOGY, DEVELOPMENTAL BIOLOGY. *Educ:* Univ Ill, Urbana, BS, 62, MS, 64; Univ Mass, PhD(biochem), 74. *Prof Exp:* NIH FEL VIROL, BOYCE THOMPSON INST, ITHACA, NY, 74- *Mem:* AAAS; Soc Invert Path; Am Soc Microbiol; Sigma Xi. *Res:* Metabolism of baculoviruses and vertebrate and insect poxviruses; the mechanism of infection and the structure of the virus genome and virus protein; plant molecular biology. *Mailing Add:* 209 Eastern Heights Dr Ithaca NY 14853

LANGSAM, MICHAEL, b Brooklyn, NY, Nov 4, 38; m 62; c 3. POLYMER CHEMISTRY. *Educ:* Rensselaer Polytech Inst, BS, 59; Polytech Inst Brooklyn, PhD(polymer sci), 64. *Prof Exp:* Res chemist polymer, BF Goodrich Lab, Brecksville, Ohio, 64-67; sr res chemist, 67-75, MGR POLYMER PROCESS DEVELOP, AIR PROD & CHEM, INC, 75- *Mem:* Sigma Xi. *Res:* Polymer synthesis, rheology, polymer kinetics, and particle morphology. *Mailing Add:* Air Prod & Chem Box 538 Allentown PA 18105

LANGSDORF, ALEXANDER, JR, b St Louis, Mo, May 30, 12; m 41; c 2. NUCLEAR PHYSICS. *Educ:* Washington Univ, AB, 32; Mass Inst Technol, PhD(physics), 37. *Prof Exp:* Nat Res Found fel, Univ Calif, 38; instr physics, Washington Univ, 39-43; physicist, 43-45, sr physicist, 45-77, CONSULT, ARGONNE NAT LAB, 77- *Concurrent Pos:* Asst physicist, Mallinckrodt Inst Radiol, 39-43; vis scientist, Atomic Energy Res Estab 59-60; assoc ed, Appl Physics Letters. *Mem:* Fel Am Phys Soc. *Res:* Neutron cross-section and polarization measurements; cyclotron, electrostatic and dynamitron construction, design and operation; theory of design of experiments; corona studies; diffusion cloud chamber. *Mailing Add:* RR 3 Box 228 Meacham Rd Schaumburg IL 60172

LANGSDORF, WILLIAM PHILIP, b Cambridge, Ohio, Apr 6, 19; m 41; c 1. PHYSICAL ORGANIC CHEMISTRY. *Educ:* Ohio State Univ, BSc, 41; Mass Inst Technol, PhD(chem), 49. *Prof Exp:* Res chemist, Indust & Biochem Dept, E I du Pont de Nemours & Co, 49-62, res assoc, 62-79; RETIRED. *Mem:* Am Chem Soc; Sigma Xi. *Res:* Organic reactions; mechanism of organic reactions; kinetics. *Mailing Add:* 2407 Rambler Rd Graylyn Crest Wilmington DE 19810

LANGSETH, MARCUS G, b Lebanon, Tenn, Nov 24, 32; m 63. GEOPHYSICS, OCEANOGRAPHY. *Educ:* Waynesburg Col, BS, 54; Columbia Univ, PhD(geol), 64. *Prof Exp:* SR RES ASSOC GEOPHYS, LAMONT-DOHERTY GEOL OBSERV, COLUMBIA UNIV, 58- *Concurrent Pos:* Adj prof, Columbia Univ. *Mem:* AAAS; Am Geophys Union; Geol Soc Am. *Res:* Terrestrial heat flow; lunar heat flow; oceanographic instrumentation; submarine geology. *Mailing Add:* Lamont-Doherty Geol Observ Palisades NY 10964

LANGSETH, ROLLIN EDWARD, b St Paul, Minn, Apr 13, 40; m 66; c 2. ELECTRICAL ENGINEERING, MATHEMATICS. *Educ:* Univ Minn, Minneapolis, BS, 62, MSEE, 65, PhD(elec eng), 68. *Prof Exp:* mem tech staff, Bell Tel Labs, 68-80; DIST MGR, AM TEL & TEL CO, 81- *Mem:* Inst Elec & Electronics Engrs. *Res:* Communication in multipath propagation media; diversity systems; effects of noise and interference; data networks; satellite systems. *Mailing Add:* 5 Brookside Dr Colts Neck NJ 07722

LANGSJOEN, ARNE NELS, b Dalton, Minn, Apr 6, 19; m 43; c 3. ORGANIC CHEMISTRY. *Educ:* Gustavus Adolphus Col, BA, 42; Univ Iowa, MS, 43, PhD, 49. *Prof Exp:* From asst prof to assoc prof, 48-56, chmn dept, 56-66, PROF CHEM, GUSTAVUS ADOLPHUS COL, 56- *Concurrent Pos:* NSF res fel, Uppsala & Royal Inst Technol, Sweden, 58-59; vis prof chem, Tughai Univ, Taichung, Taiwan, 69-70. *Mem:* Am Chem Soc. *Res:* Biological chemistry. *Mailing Add:* Dept of Chem Gustavus Adolphus Col St Peter MN 56082

LANGSJOEN, PER HARALD, b Fergus Falls, Minn, Aug 9, 21; m 45; c 5. MEDICINE, CARDIOLOGY. *Educ:* Gustavus Adolphus Col, AB, 43; Univ Minn, Minneapolis, MB, 50, MD, 51. *Prof Exp:* Intern & residency internal med, Letterman Army Hosp, San Francisco, Calif, 50-54; staff physician, Coco Solo Hosp, Cristobal, CZ, 54-56; resident cardiol, Fitzsimmons Army Hosp, Denver, Colo, 56-58; chief cardiovasc serv, Wm Beaumont Gen Hosp, El Paso, Tex, 58-60; chief cardiovasc serv, Scott & White Clin, 60-75; CLIN PROF, COL MED, TEX A&M UNIV, 75- *Concurrent Pos:* Fel coun clin cardiol, Am Heart Asn, 65-; consult, US Army Hosp, Ft Hood, Tex, 61-75 & Vet Admin Hosp, Temple, 61-75. *Mem:* Fel Am Col Physicians; fel Am Col Cardiol. *Res:* Rheologic aspects of the circulatory system in health and in disease states. *Mailing Add:* Col Med Tex A&M Univ College Station TX 77843

LANGSLEY, DONALD GENE, b Topeka, Kans, Oct 5, 25; m 55; c 3. PSYCHIATRY, PSYCHOANALYSIS. *Educ:* State Univ NY Albany, AB, 49; Univ Rochester, MD, 53. *Prof Exp:* Intern, USPHS Hosp, San Francisco, 53-54; resident psychiat, Langley Porter Clin, Sch Med, Univ Calif, San Francisco, 54-59, NIMH career teacher award psychiat, 59-61; from asst to assoc prof psychiat, Sch Med, Univ Colo, 61-68; prof psychiat & chmn dept, Sch Med, Univ Calif, Davis, 68-77; prof psychiat & chmn dept, Sch Med, Univ Cincinnati, 77-81; EXEC VPRES, AM BD MED SPECIALTIES, 81-

Concurrent Pos: Dir inpatient serv, Colo Psychiat Hosp, Denver, 61-68; dir ment health serv, Sacramento Med Ctr, Univ Calif, Davis, 68-73; mem psychiat training comt, NIMH, 71-75, mem psychiat test comt, Nat Bd Med Examr, 72-76; chief staff, Sacramento Med Ctr, 74-75; chmn dept defense select comt psychiat care eval, NIMH, 75-78; dir, Am Bd Psychiat & Neurol, 75-80. *Mem:* Am Psychiat Asn (vpres, 77-79, pres, 80-81); Am Psychoanal Asn; AMA. *Res:* Family crisis therapy; evaluation of therapy, medical education and psychiatric education. *Mailing Add:* Am Bd Med Specialties 1603 Orrington Ave Evanston IL 60201

LANGSTON, CLARENCE WALTER, b Gainesville, Tex, July 4, 24; m 48; c 2. MICROBIOLOGY. *Educ:* Southern Methodist Univ, BS, 49; North Texas State Univ, MA, 51; Univ Wis, PhD(bact), 55. *Prof Exp:* Bacteriologist, Kraft Foods Co, 50-51; asst, Univ Wis, 51-54; bacteriologist, Dairy Cattle Res Br, Agr Res Serv, USDA, 54-62; chief virus & rickettsial div, Directorate Biol Opers, Pine Bluff Arsenal, US Army, Ark, 62-66; head bact sect, Midwest Res Inst,66-71;PRES,LANGSTON LABS,INC,KANS & PR,71- *Mem:*Am Acad Microb; Am Soc Microbiol; Soc Indust Microbiol. *Res:* Dairy and food bacteriology; microbiology and chemistry of fermentations; physiology of bacteria; taxonomy and nomenclature of bacteria; research development and production of viruses and rickettsiae. *Mailing Add:* Langston Labs Inc 2005-W103 tr Leawood KS 66206

LANGSTON, DAVE THOMAS, b Chickasha, Okla, Apr 19, 45; m 65; c 4. ENTOMOLOGY. *Educ:* Southwestern Okla State Univ, BS, 67; Okla State Univ, MS, 70; Univ Ariz, PhD(entom), 74. *Prof Exp:* Res asst, Okla State Univ, 67-70; res assoc, 70-74, ASSOC PROF ENTOM, UNIV ARIZ, 80-, EXTEN SPECIALIST ENTOM, 74- *Mem:* Entom Soc Am. *Res:* Insect management as it influences production agriculture, specifically those insects which are economically important in the Southwestern United States. *Mailing Add:* 4341 E Broadway Rd Phoenix AZ 85040

LANGSTON, HIRAM THOMAS, b Rio de Janeiro, Brazil, Jan 12, 12; US citizen; m 41; c 3. THORACIC SURGERY. *Educ:* Univ Louisville, AB, 30, MD, 34; Univ Mich, MS, 41; Am Bd Surg, dipl, 42; Am Bd Thoracic Surg, dipl, 48. *Prof Exp:* Intern, Garfield Mem Hosp, Washington, DC, 34-35, resident path, 35-37; from asst resident to resident surg, Univ Mich Hosp, 37-39, resident thoracic surg, 39-40, instr, Univ, 40-41; assoc surg, Med Sch, Northwestern Univ, Ill, 41-42, asst prof, 46-48; assoc prof, Col Med, Wayne State Univ, 48-52; prof surg, 52-78, clinical prof, 78-80, EMER PROF, COL MED, UNIV ILL, 80- *Concurrent Pos:* Chief surgeon, Chicago State Tuberc Sanitarium, State Dept Pub Health, 52-71; mem staff, Grant & St Joseph's Hosps, 52- *Mem:* Am Thoracic Soc; Am Asn Thoracic Surg (secy, 56-61, vpres, 68-69, pres, 69-70); fel Am Col Surg; Soc Thoracic Surgeons; Am Surg Asn. *Res:* Surgery for diseases of the chest; tuberculosis and cancer of the lung. *Mailing Add:* 2913 N Commonwealth Ave Chicago IL 60657

LANGSTON, JAMES HORACE, b Garrison, Tex, Oct 8, 17. ORGANIC CHEMISTRY. *Educ:* Stephen F Austin State Col, BA, 37; Univ NC, MA, 39, PhD(org chem), 41. *Prof Exp:* Asst chem, Univ NC, 37-40; res chemist, Columbia Chem Div, Pittsburgh Plate Glass Co, 41-46; from assoc prof to prof textile chem & dyeing, Clemson Col, 46-58; head dept chem, 58-78, chmn div natural sci & math, 68-72, PROF CHEM,SAMFORD UNIV, 58- *Concurrent Pos:* Fulbright lectr, Cent Univ & Nat Polytech Sch, Ecuador, 59-60, Fulbright lectr & res consult, Nat Univ Honduras, 67-68. *Mem:* Am Chem Soc; fel Am Inst Chemists. *Res:* Drugs; polymers; plastics; plasticizers; catalysis; fibers; textile finishing materials; sulfone formation. *Mailing Add:* Dept of Chem Samford Univ Birmingham AL 35229

LANGSTON, JIMMY BYRD, b Shelby, Miss, Apr 10, 27; m 72; c 2. PHYSIOLOGY, PHARMACOLOGY. *Educ:* Delta State Col, BS, 49; Univ Miss, Jackson, MS, 58, PhD(physiol), 59. *Prof Exp:* From instr to asst prof physiol, Med Ctr, Univ Miss, Jackson, 60-64; sect head toxicol, Alcon Labs, Inc, 64-65; dir urol, 65-72; res scientist, ALZA Res, 73-77; DIR TOXICOL, COOPER LABS, INC, 77- *Concurrent Pos:* NIH fel, Univ Miss 59-60; spec NIH fel, Univ Gothenburg, 62-63; NIH develop award, Med Ctr, Univ Miss, 63-64. *Mem:* Am Physiol Soc. *Res:* Renal physiology; cardiovascular physiology; ocular pharmacology; pharmaceutical toxicology. *Mailing Add:* Cooper Labs Inc 455 E Middlefield Rd Mountain View CA 94943

LANGSTON, WANN, JR, b Oklahoma City, Okla, July 10, 21; m 46; c 2. VERTEBRATE PALEONTOLOGY. *Educ:* Univ Okla, BS, 43, MS, 47; Univ Calif, PhD(paleont), 51. *Prof Exp:* Instr geol, Tex Tech Col, 46-48; preparator, Mus Paleont, Univ Calif, 49-54, lectr, 51-52; vert paleontologist, Nat Mus Can, 54-62; RES SCIENTIST, TEX MEM MUS, 62-, DIR VERTEBRATE PALEONT LAB, 69-; PROF DEPT GEOL SCI, UNIV TEX, AUSTIN, 75- *Concurrent Pos:* Res assoc, Cleveland Mus Natural Hist, 74- *Mem:* Geol Soc Am; Soc Vert Paleont (vpres, 73-74, pres, 74-75); Am Soc Icthyol & Herpet; Am Asn Petrol Geologists. *Res:* Fossil amphibians and reptiles. *Mailing Add:* 4001 Rockledge Dr Austin TX 78731

LANGSTROTH, GEORGE FORBES OTTY, b Montreal, Que, July 13, 36; m 60; c 2. PHYSICS. *Educ:* Univ Alta, BSc, 57; Dalhousie Univ, MSc, 59; Univ London, PhD(physics), 62. *Prof Exp:* Res assoc physics, 62-63, from asst prof to assoc prof, 67-69, asst dean grad studies, 67-68, actg dean, 68-69, dean, 69-72, PROF PHYSICS, DALHOUSIE UNIV, 69- *Concurrent Pos:* Mem, Defence Res Bd Can, 71-77. *Mem:* Can Asn Physicists. *Res:* Microwave breakdown in gases; ions in afterglows; positron annihilation; optical properties of metals. *Mailing Add:* 304 Bedford Hwy Halifax NS B3M 2K8 Can

LANGVARDT, PATRICK WILLIAM, b Dodge City, Kans, Mar 20, 50. ANALYTICAL CHEMISTRY. *Educ:* Kans State Teachers Col, BS, 72; Purdue Univ, MS, 74. *Prof Exp:* PROJ LEADER ANAL CHEM, DOW CHEM CO, 74- *Res:* Environmental analytical chemistry; metabolite identification; analytical toxicology. *Mailing Add:* 616 E Grove Midland MI 48640

LANGWAY, CHESTER CHARLES, JR, b Worcester, Mass, Aug 15, 29; m 59; c 4. GEOLOGY. *Educ:* Boston Univ, AB, 55, MA, 56; Univ Mich, PhD(geol, glaciol), 65. *Prof Exp:* Res geologist, US Army Snow, Ice & Permafrost Res Estab, 56-59; res assoc properties of snow & ice, Res Inst, Univ Mich, 59-61; res glaciologist, US Army Cold Regions Res & Eng Lab, 61-65, chief snow & ice br, 66-77; PROF GEOL SCI & CHMN DEPT, STATE UNIV NY BUFFALO, 77- *Concurrent Pos:* Mem panel glaciol, Comt Polar Res, Nat Acad Sci, 69-75, secy, Int Comt Ice Core Studies; chmn dept geol sci, State Univ NY Buffalo, 75- *Mem:* AAAS; fel Geol Soc Am; Am Geophys Union; Am Polar Soc; fel Arctic Inst NAm. *Res:* Basic and applied research related to the properties of snow and ice, including field and laboratory techniques of analyzing shallow and deep ice cores for stratigraphy and age dating; isotopic and ionic constituents, terrestrial and extraterrestrial inclusions. *Mailing Add:* Dept of Geol Sci 4240 Ridge Lea Rd Amherst NY 14226

LANGWIG, JOHN EDWARD, b Albany, NY, Mar 5, 24; m 46; c 1. FOREST PRODUCTS, WOOD SCIENCE. *Educ:* Univ Mich, Ann Arbor, BS, 48; State Univ NY Col Forestry, Syracuse Univ, MS, 68, PhD(wood sci), 71. *Prof Exp:* Instr wood prod eng, State Univ NY Col Forestry, Syracuse Univ, 69-70; from asst prof to assoc prof, 71-75, chmn, Dept Forestry, 75-81, PROF WOOD SCI, OKLA STATE UNIV, 75-, EXTEN PROF WOOD PROD SCI, 81- *Mem:* Soc Wood Sci & Technol; Forest Prod Res Soc; Soc Am Foresters; Sigma Xi. *Res:* Neutron activation analysis of trace elements in wood and effects on physical properties; physical properties of wood-polymer composites. *Mailing Add:* Dept of Forestry Okla State Univ Stillwater OK 74078

LANGWORTHY, HAROLD FREDERICK, b White Plains, NY, Aug 1, 40; m 65; c 3. MATHEMATICS, OPTICS. *Educ:* Rensselaer Polytech Inst, BS, 62; Univ Minn, PhD(math), 70. *Prof Exp:* Res assoc, Res Labs, 67-79, lab head, 79-80, ASST DIR, PHYSICS DIV, EASTMAN KODAK CO, ROCHESTER, 81- *Mem:* Optical Soc Am. *Res:* Mathematical optics; rheology. *Mailing Add:* 732 Hightower Way Webster NY 14580

LANGWORTHY, JAMES BRIAN, b Billings, Mont, Feb 18, 34; m 65; c 2. NUCLEAR PHYSICS, MATHEMATICAL PHYSICS. *Educ:* Univ Colo, BS, 56; Univ Md, MS, 66. *Prof Exp:* Physicist math physics, Radiation Div, 59-69, res physicist particle transport, Theory Br, Nuclear Physics Div, 69-76, RES PHYSICIST RADIATION DAMAGE, RADIATION SURVIVABILITY & DETECTION BR, CONDENSED MATTER & SCI DIV, NAVAL RES LAB, 76- *Mem:* Am Phys Soc; AAAS; Sigma Xi. *Res:* Radiation damage, hardening and shielding; energetic particle transport by Monte Carlo computer codes. *Mailing Add:* Code 6611 Naval Res Lab Washington DC 20375

LANGWORTHY, THOMAS ALLAN, b Oak Park, Ill, Aug 7, 43; m 65; c 2. MICROBIAL PHYSIOLOGY. *Educ:* Grinnell Col, AB, 65; Univ Kans, PhD(microbiol), 71. *Prof Exp:* Res assoc, 71-72, asst prof, 72-77, assoc prof, 77-82, PROF MICROBIOL, UNIV SD, 82- *Mem:* Am Soc Microbiol; AAAS; Am Acad Microbiol; Int Orgn Mycoplasmology. *Res:* Structure and function of the membranes and cell surfaces of bacteria from extreme environments, mycoplasmas, archaebacteria and cellular evolution. *Mailing Add:* Dept of Microbiol Sch of Med Univ of SD Vermillion SD 57069

LANGWORTHY, WILLIAM CLAYTON, b Watertown, NY, Sept 3, 36; m 58; c 2. ORGANIC CHEMISTRY, ENVIRONMENTAL CHEMISTRY. *Educ:* Tufts Univ, BSChem, 58; Univ Calif, Berkeley, PhD(org chem), 62. *Prof Exp:* NIH fel chem, Mass Inst Technol, 61-62; asst prof, Alaska Methodist Univ, 62-65; from asst prof to prof chem, Calif State Col, Fullerton, 65-73; prof chem & head dept, 73-76, DEAN SCH SCI & MATH, CALIF POLYTECH STATE UNIV, SAN LUIS OBISPO, 76- *Concurrent Pos:* Assoc dean, Sch Letters, Arts & Sci, Calif State Col, Fullerton, 70-73, dir environ studies prog, 70-72. *Mem:* AAAS; Am Chem Soc; Sigma Xi. *Res:* Physical organic chemistry; organic reactions in liquid ammonia; environmental chemistry, especially analysis and effects of trace pollutants. *Mailing Add:* Sch of Sci & Math Calif State Polytech Univ San Luis Obispo CA 93407

LANHAM, URLESS NORTON, b Grainfield, Kans, Oct 17, 18; m 45; c 3. ENTOMOLOGY. *Educ:* Univ Colo, BA, 40; Univ Calif, Berkeley, PhD(entom), 48. *Prof Exp:* Asst zool, Univ Calif, Los Angeles, 40-41, biol, Scripps Inst, 41-42, entom, 47-48; from instr to asst prof zool, Univ Mich, 48-56, res asst & consult, NSF Proj Insect Ecol, 56-61; vis cur entom, 61-62, assoc cur, 62-73, CUR ENTOM & PROF NATURAL HIST, UNIV COLO MUS, BOULDER, 73- *Concurrent Pos:* Consult, Biol Sci Curriculum Study, Univ Colo, Boulder, 63-66, lectr, Inst Develop Biol, 66-67, asst prof biophys, 68-71; adv ed, Columbia Univ Press, 64-72; assoc prof, Div Natural Sci, Monteith Col, Wayne State Univ, 59-61; consult, Smithsonian Inst, 67. *Res:* Faunistics and systematics of Colorado Apoidea, especially of the genus Andrena. *Mailing Add:* Univ Colo Mus Boulder CO 80309

LANIER, GERALD NORMAN, b Alamosa, Colo, Dec 9, 37; m 62; c 2. FOREST ENTOMOLOGY. *Educ:* Univ Calif, Berkeley, BSc, 60, MSc, 65, PhD(entom), 67. *Prof Exp:* Forester, US Forest Serv, 60-64; res scientist, Can Dept Forestry, 67-70; from asst prof to assoc prof, 70-78, PROF ENTOM, STATE UNIV NY COL ENVIRON SCI & FORESTRY, 78- *Mem:* AAAS; Entom Soc Am; Entom Soc Can. *Res:* Pheromones in bark beetles; intergraded control of Dutch elm disease; biosystematics; karyology; management of forest insects, ecological impact of forest insects. *Mailing Add:* Dept of Forest & Environ Biol State Univ NY Syracuse NY 13210

LANIER, ROBERT GEORGE, b Chicago, Ill, Oct 27, 40; m 69; c 2. NUCLEAR PHYSICS. *Educ:* Lewis Col, BS, 62; Fla State Univ, PhD(nuclear chem), 68. *Prof Exp:* US AEC fel, Chem Div, Oak Ridge Nat Lab, 67-69; fel, 69-71, STAFF MEM, NUCLEAR CHEM DIV, LAWRENCE LIVERMORE NAT LAB, UNIV CALIF, 71- *Mem:* AAAS; Am Phys Soc. *Res:* Experimental low energy nuclear structure studies; charged-particle reaction spectroscopy and in-beam gamma ray spectroscopy. *Mailing Add:* Nuclear Chem Div L 232 Lawrence Livermore Nat Lab Univ Calif Livermore CA 94550

LANING, STEPHEN HENRY, b Albany, NY, Oct 18, 18; m 46; c 2. ANALYTICAL CHEMISTRY. *Educ:* Union Col, NY, BS, 41; Rutgers Univ, PhD(phys chem), 47. *Prof Exp:* Asst, Rutgers Univ, 41-44, instr, 45-46; res chemist, Chem Div, Pittsburg Plate Glass Co, 47-61, supvr res & tech serv, 61-67, SUPVR RES & TECH SERV, PPG INDUSTS, INC, 67- *Honors & Awards:* Hon Award, Pittsburgh Plate Glass Co, 62. *Mem:* Am Chem Soc. *Res:* Development of methods for x-ray analysis of glass, silica and titania pigments, minerals, cements and other types of materials. *Mailing Add:* PPG Industs Inc PO Box 31 Barberton OH 44203

LANKFORD, CHARLES ELY, b DeValls Bluff, Ark, Mar 22, 12; m 42; c 2. BACTERIOLOGY. *Educ:* Univ Tex, BA, 35, PhD(bact), 48; Univ Wis, MA, 43. *Prof Exp:* Instr bact, Univ Tex, 35-37; bacteriologist, State Dept Health Labs, Tex, 39-40; instr bact, Med Br, 40-45, asst prof med bact, 45-48, assoc prof, 48-49, assoc prof gen bact & pub health bact, 49-55, PROF PUB HEALTH BACT & MICROBIOL, UNIV TEX, AUSTIN, 55-, DIR LAB MED BACT, 52- *Mem:* AAAS; Soc Exp Biol & Med; Am Soc Microbiol; Am Acad Microbiol; NY Acad Sci. *Res:* Host-parasite biology; cell division control mechanisms; nutritional studies of bacteria; drug resistance of microorganisms; bacterial variation; biology and physiology of Vibrio cholera and Brucella. *Mailing Add:* Dept of Microbiol Univ of Tex Austin TX 78712

LANKFORD, J(OHN) L(LEWELLYN), b Hampton, Va, Sept 13, 20; m 45; c 2. AERODYNAMICS. *Educ:* Va Polytech Inst, BS, 42. *Prof Exp:* Aeronaut res scientist, Nat Adv Comt Aeronaut, 45-53; res engr, Cent Res Lab, Melpar, 53-54; head gas dynamics, Exp Inc, 54-58; aeronaut res engr, Naval Ord Lab, 58-62; chief adv studies flight systs, Lunar Studies, NASA, 62-64; actg chief, Missile Dynamics Div, Naval Ord Lab, 64-65, prin investr & mgr rain erosion & hypersonic reentry mat, Naval Surface Weapons Ctr, White Oak, Md, 65-70, consult & prog mgr, US Navy, 70-75; RETIRED. *Concurrent Pos:* Consult, Bur Weapons, US Navy, 64-75; consult energy & heat transfer, 76-; lectr eng & career coun, 76-; assoc staff & consult energy prog, Univ Md, 79-80; lectr, Montgomery Col, 78- *Honors & Awards:* Navy Meritorious Award, 61 & 70. *Mem:* Assoc fel Am Inst Aeronaut & Astronaut. *Res:* Supersonics; hypersonics; propulsion aerodynamics; inlets; aeroballistics. *Mailing Add:* 1717 Marymont Rd Silver Spring MD 20906

LANKFORD, W(ILLIAM) T(HOMAS), JR, b Rockwood, Tenn, Nov 1, 19; m 44; c 4. METALLURGY. *Educ:* Carnegie Inst Technol, BS, 41, DSc(metall), 45. *Prof Exp:* Asst metall, Carnegie Inst Technol, 41-43, res metallurgist, 43-45; res metallurgist, Pa State Col, 45; develop engr & res assoc, Carnegie-Ill Steel Corp, 45-50; develop engr & res assoc, 50-60, chief sheet prod div, Appl Res Lab, 60-63, asst dir, 63-67, mgr steel processing, 67-75, assoc dir, 75-81, DIR RES PLANNING, RES LAB, US STEEL CORP, 81- *Concurrent Pos:* Howe Mem lectr, Am Inst Mining, Metall & Petrol Engrs, 72. *Honors & Awards:* Richard L Templin Award, Am Soc Testing & Mat, 49, Charles B Dudley Medal, 59. *Mem:* Fel Am Soc Metals; fel Am Soc Mech Engrs; AAAS; Am Inst Mining, Metall & Petrol Engrs; fel Metall Soc. *Res:* Physical metallurgy, particularly phases dealing with plastic flow and fracture of metals; process metallurgy; continuous casting. *Mailing Add:* US Steel Corp 600 Grant St Pittsburgh PA 15230

LANKFORD, WILLIAM FLEET, b Charlottesville, Va, Jan 9, 38. NUCLEAR & SOLID STATE PHYSICS. *Educ:* Univ Va, BA, 60; Univ SC, MS, 64, PhD(physics), 69. *Prof Exp:* Instr physics, Univ NC, Greensboro, 62-63; fel, Col William & Mary, 69; from asst prof to assoc prof, 59-78, PROF PHYSICS, GEORGE MASON UNIV, 78- *Mem:* Am Inst Physics. *Res:* Experimental solid state research. *Mailing Add:* Dept of Physics George Mason Univ Fairfax VA 22030

LANKS, KARL WILLIAM, b Philadelphia, Pa, Nov 1, 42. PATHOLOGY, MOLECULAR BIOLOGY. *Educ:* Pa State Univ, BS, 63; Temple Univ, MD, 67; Columbia Univ, PhD(path), 71. *Prof Exp:* Intern, Columbia-Presby Hosp, 67-68; instr path, Columbia Univ, 71-72; asst prof, 74-79, ASSOC PROF PATH, STATE UNIV NY DOWNSTATE MED CTR, 79- *Concurrent Pos:* NIH res fel, Dept Chem, Harvard Univ, 71-72. *Mem:* Am Soc Biol Chemists; Am Soc Exp Path; Am Soc Cell Biol; Biophys Soc. *Res:* Structure and metabolism of messenger ribonucleic acids; mechanism of cell attachment; regulation of protein and RNA messenger synthesis in cultured cells; structure and function of syndromin. *Mailing Add:* 450 Clarkson Ave Brooklyn NY 11203

LANMAN, ROBERT CHARLES, b Bemidji, Minn, Oct 2, 30; m 57; c 4. BIOCHEMICAL PHARMACOLOGY, TOXICOLOGY. *Educ:* Univ Minn, BS, 56, PhD(pharmacol), 67. *Prof Exp:* Teaching asst, Col Pharm, Univ Minn, 58-59; pharmacologist, Sect Biochem Drug Action, Lab Chem Pharmacol, Nat Heart Inst, 62-66; assoc prof, 66-81, PROF PHARMACOL & MED, UNIV MO-KANSAS CITY, 81- *Mem:* AAAS; Am Asn Cols Pharm; Am Soc Pharmacol & Exp Therapeut; Fedn Am Socs Exp Biol; Found Advan Educ Sci. *Res:* Passage of drugs across body membranes; mechanism of active transport, drug absorption, distribution, metabolism and excretion. *Mailing Add:* 8202 W72nd St Overland Park KS 66204

LANN, JOSEPH SIDNEY, b Washington, DC, Sept 16, 17; m 45; c 3. ORGANIC CHEMISTRY. *Educ:* Univ Md, BS, 37, PhD(org chem), 41. *Prof Exp:* Res chemist, Jackson Lab, E I du Pont de Nemours & Co Inc, 46-54, dir, Freon Prod Lab, 54-64, asst mgr new prod & mkt develop, Freon Prod Div, 64-65, asst dist mgr, 65-68, mgr develop prod, Freon Prod Div, 68-80; RETIRED. *Mem:* Am Chem Soc. *Res:* Surface active agents and neoprene; organic compounds; fluorinated hydrocarbons. *Mailing Add:* 608 Haverhill Rd Sharpley Wilmington DE 19803

LANN, LEONARD I, b New London, Conn, Apr 12, 28; m 54; c 2. MECHANICAL ENGINEERING. *Educ:* Mass Inst Technol, BS, 50; Drexel Inst Technol, MS, 64. *Prof Exp:* Tech mgt aerospace, Martin Co, 57-65; qual & reliability mgt, Unmanned Space Probes, NASA, 65-66, tech mgt, Apollo Appln Prog, 66-68; br chief, Urban Network Br, res & develop, Fed Hwy Admin, 68-70; asst plans & progs res & develop, 70-79, CHIEF EXEC OFFICER RES & DEVELOP, NAT HWY TRAFFIC SAFETY ADMIN, 79- *Res:* Automotive safety; traffic control in urban networks; operations research; reliability engineering; technical administration. *Mailing Add:* 3426 Janvale Rd Baltimore MD 21207

LANNER, RONALD MARTIN, b Brooklyn, NY, Nov 12, 30; m 57; c 2. FOREST GENETICS, TREE PHYSIOLOGY. *Educ:* Syracuse Univ, BS, 52, MF, 58; Univ Minn, Minneapolis, PhD(forestry), 68. *Prof Exp:* Res forester, Pac Southwest Forest & Range Exp Sta, US Forest Serv, 58-64; ASSOC PROF FOREST GENETICS & DENDROL, UTAH STATE UNIV, 67- *Concurrent Pos:* Consult, Forestry Proj, Food & Agr Orgn, UN, Taiwan, 69; res fel, Univ Fla, 73-74. *Mem:* AAAS; Soc Am Foresters. *Res:* Morphogenesis and growth of woody p)ants; evolution and ecology of pines with bird-dispersed seeds. *Mailing Add:* Dept Forest Sci Utah State Univ Logan UT 84321

LANNERS, H NORBERT, b Volkmarsen, Ger, June 23, 43; m 73. ELECTORN MICROSCOPY. *Educ:* Univ Tubingen, Ger, Dr rer nat, 73. *Prof Exp:* Fel, Rockefeller Univ, 73-76; res assoc, Cornell Univ Med Col, 76-80; ASST PROF, ROCKEFELLER UNIV, 80- *Concurrent Pos:* Vis scientist, Agr Exp Sta, Univ Puerto Rico, 76; adj res assoc, Rockefeller Univ, 76-79. *Mem:* Soc Protozoologists; Electron Microscopic Soc Am. *Res:* Cultivation of human malaria parasites. *Mailing Add:* Dept Biol Rockefeller Univ 1230 York Ave New York NY 10021

LANNERT, KENT PHILIP, b Belleville, Ill, Nov 29, 44; m 70; c 2. INDUSTRIAL ORGANIC CHEMISTRY. *Educ:* Southern Ill Univ, Carbondale, BA, 66; Vanderbilt Univ, PhD(chem), 69. *Prof Exp:* Res chemist, 69-72, res specialist, 72-76, SR RES SPECIALIST, MONSANTO CO, 76- *Mem:* Am Chem Soc. *Res:* Organic synthesis; chelation; synthesis of chelants and other detergent related chemicals. *Mailing Add:* Monsanto Co 800 N Lindbergh Blvd St Louis MO 63166

LANNIN, JEFFREY S, b New York, NY, Aug 21, 40; m 71; c 1. SOLID STATE PHYSICS, MATERIALS SCIENCE. *Educ:* Purdue Univ, BS, 62; Univ Ill, Urbana, MS, 64; Stanford Univ, PhD(solid state physics), 71. *Prof Exp:* Physicist thin films, Fairchild Semiconductor Res Lab, 66-67 & semiconductor physics, Lockheed Palo Alto Res Labs, 67-68; staff physicist raman scattering, Max-Planck Inst Solid State Res, 71-74; vis scientist optical properties, Argonne Nat Lab, 74-75; vis asst prof mat sci, Univ Del, 75-76; asst prof, 76-81, ASSOC PROF PHYSICS, PA STATE UNIV, 81- *Concurrent Pos:* Consult, Lockheed Palo Alto Res Lab, 68-71. *Mem:* Am Phys Soc; Sigma Xi; Am Vacuum Soc. *Res:* Raman scattering in ordered and disordered solids; amorphous materials; thin film physics. *Mailing Add:* Dept of Physics Pa State Univ University Park PA 16802

LANNING, DAVID D(AYTON), b Baker, Ore, Mar 30, 28; m 50; c 3. NUCLEAR ENGINEERING. *Educ:* Univ Ore, BA, 51; Mass Inst Technol, PhD(nuclear eng), 63. *Prof Exp:* Physicist, Hanford Atomic Prod Oper, Gen Elec Co, 51-57; res assoc & reactor supt, Mass Inst Technol, 57-62, asst prof nuclear eng, 62-64, assoc prof, 64-65, asst dir res reactor, 62-65; unit mgr reactor physics, Battelle-Northwest, 65-66, sect mgr, 66-69; PROF NUCLEAR ENG, MASS INST TECHNOL, 69- *Concurrent Pos:* Consult, Stone & Webster Eng Corp, Agronne Nat Lab, 77-78, Boston Edison Co; mem, Monticello Nuclear Power Reactor Safety Audit Comt. *Mem:* Am Nuclear Soc. *Res:* Nuclear engineering education; design, safety, control and operation of nuclear reactor systems. *Mailing Add:* Dept Nuclear Eng Mass Inst Technol Cambridge MA 02139

LANNING, FRANCIS CHOWING, b Denver, Colo, Jan 5, 08; m 34; c 2. CHEMISTRY. *Educ:* Univ Denver, BS, 30, MS, 31; Univ Minn, PhD(phys chem), 36. *Prof Exp:* Asst, Univ Denver, 30-31; anal chemist, Minn State Hwy Dept, 36-42; from instr to prof, 42-78, EMER PROF CHEM, KANS STATE UNIV, 78- *Mem:* Am Chem Soc; Sigma Xi; Am Soc Hort Sci. *Res:* Organosilicon compounds; silicon and other minerals in plants; chemical composition of limestones. *Mailing Add:* Dept of Chem Kans State Univ Manhattan KS 66506

LANNING, WILLIAM CLARENCE, b Boicourt, Kans, Dec 9, 13; m 36; c 3. PHYSICAL CHEMISTRY. *Educ:* Sterling Col, AB, 34; Univ Kans, AM, 36, PhD(chem), 38. *Prof Exp:* Asst instr chem, Univ Kans, 35-38; res chemist & sect mgr, Naval Res Lab, 38-45; res chemist, Phillips Petrol Co, 46-73, sect mgr, 57-73; res chemist, Bartlesville Energy Res Ctr, ERDA, 74-80; RETIRED. *Mem:* Am Chem Soc; Sigma Xi. *Res:* Non-aqueous solutions; inorganic preparations; catalytic hydrocarbon and petroleum processes; fundamentals of crude oil production; refining of synthetic crude oils. *Mailing Add:* 1609 Dewey Ave Bartlesville OK 74003

L'ANNUNZIATA, MICHAEL FRANK, b Springfield, Mass, Oct 14, 43; m 73; c 3. SCIENCE EDUCATION, AGRICULTURAL BIOCHEMISTRY. *Educ:* St Edward's Univ, BS, 65; Univ Ariz, MS, 67, PhD(agr chem & soils), 70. *Prof Exp:* Res chemist herbicides, Amchem Prods, Inc, 71-72; res assoc, Univ Ariz, 72-73; prof & res investr, Univ Chapingo, Mex, 73-75; res investr, Nat Inst Nuclear Energy, Mex, 75-77; assoc officer, 77-80, SECOND OFFICER, INT ATOMIC ENERGY AGENCY, VIENNA, 80- *Concurrent Pos:* Consult health veg, Caborca, Mex, 72; consult, Govt Nicaragua, 78, Costa Rica, 78 & 80, Guatemala, 79, Colombia, 79, Panama & Uruguay, 80; consult & lectr, Atomic Energy Comn, Quito, Ecuador, 78; vis lectr, Timiryazev Agr Acad, Moscow, Inst Nuclear Appln Vet Sci, Turkey & Univ Guanajuato, Mex, 81. *Mem:* Am Chem Soc; Soil Sci Soc Am; Am Soc Agron; Int Soc Soil Sci. *Res:* Nuclear techniques in the agricultural and biological sciences; soil and plant biochemistry; liquid scintillation and Cherenkov counting of radioisotope tracers; use of isotopes in the elucidation of biochemical pathways and mechanisms. *Mailing Add:* Int Atomic Energy Agency Wagramerstrasse 5 PO Box 200 A-1400 Vienna Austria

LANNUS, ARVO, chemical engineering, energy engineering, see previous edition

LANNUTTI, JOSEPH EDWARD, b Cedar Hollow, Pa, May 4, 26; m 54; c 3. EXPERIMENTAL HIGH ENERGY PHYSICS. *Educ:* Pa State Univ, BS, 50; Univ Pa, MS, 53; Univ Calif, PhD(physics), 57. *Prof Exp:* Admin asst, Pa RR, 43-47; asst, Univ Pa, 51-52; physicist, NAm Aviation Inc, 52-53; asst, Univ Calif, 54-57; from asst prof to assoc prof, 57-64, PROF PHYSICS, FLA STATE UNIV, 64- *Concurrent Pos:* Physicist, Lawrence Radiation Lab, Univ Calif, 59-60; consult, Oak Ridge Nat Lab. *Mem:* Am Phys Soc. *Res:* Physics of elementary particles. *Mailing Add:* Dept of Physics Fla State Univ Tallahasee FL 32306

LANOU, ROBERT EUGENE, JR, b Burlington, Vt, Feb 13, 28; m 60; c 4. EXPERIMENTAL PHYSICS. *Educ:* Worcester Polytech Univ, BS, 52; Yale Univ, PhD(physics), 57. *Prof Exp:* Physicist, Lawrence Radiation Lab, Univ Calif, 57-59; mem fac, 59-66, PROF PHYSICS, BROWN UNIV, 66- *Concurrent Pos:* Chmn, High Energy Discussion Group, Brookhaven Nat Lab, 81-83; consult, Brookhaven Nat Lab. *Mem:* AAAS; fel Am Phys Soc. *Res:* Elementary particle physics. *Mailing Add:* Dept of Physics Brown Univ Providence RI 02912

LA NOUE, KATHRYN F, b Camden, NJ, Dec 21, 34; m 76; c 4. BIOCHEMISTRY, CELL PHYSIOLOGY. *Educ:* Bryn Mawr Col, AB, 56; Yale Univ, PhD(biochem), 60. *Prof Exp:* Res chemist, US Army Surg Res Unit, 61-67; NIH fel, Johnson Res Found, Sch Med, Univ Pa, 68-70; res assoc, Johnson Res Found, Sch Med, Univ Pa, 70, asst prof, 71-74; assoc prof, 74-81, PROF PHYSIOL, MILTON S HERSHEY MED CTR, PA STATE UNIV, 81- *Concurrent Pos:* Dr W D Stroud estab investr, Am Heart Asn, 71-76. *Mem:* AAAS; Am Chem Soc; Am Soc Biol Sci; Biophys Soc. *Res:* Interaction of riboflavin with various aromatic compounds, mechanism of interaction of riboflavin with protein; metabolic effects of endotoxic shock; control of mitochondrial metabolism; membrane transport mechanisms. *Mailing Add:* Dept of Physiol Milton S Hershey Med Ctr Hershey PA 17033

LANOUX, SIGRED BOYD, b New Orleans, La, Nov 1, 31; m 54; c 2. INORGANIC CHEMISTRY. *Educ:* Southwestern La Univ, BS, 57; Tulane Univ, PhD(inorg chem), 62. *Prof Exp:* Res assoc, Univ Ill, Urbana, 61-62; res chemist, Textile Fibers Dept, E I du Pont de Nemours & Co, 62-66; from asst prof to assoc prof, 66-74, PROF CHEM, UNIV SOUTHWESTERN LA, 74-, HEAD DEPT CHEM, 72- *Mem:* Am Chem Soc. *Res:* Phosphonitrile chemistry. *Mailing Add:* 104 Ridgewood Lafayette LA 70506

LANPHERE, MARVIN ALDER, b Spokane, Wash, Sept 29, 33; m 61; c 3. GEOLOGY, GEOCHEMISTRY. *Educ:* Mont Sch Mines, BS, 55; Calif Inst Technol, MS, 56, PhD(geol), 62. *Prof Exp:* Geologist, US Geol Surv, Calif, 62-67, dep asst chief geologist, Washington, DC, 67-69, RES GEOLOGIST, US GEOL SURV, CALIF, 69- *Concurrent Pos:* Vis prof, Stanford Univ, 72; vis fel, Australian Nat Univ, 75-76. *Mem:* Geol Soc Am; Am Geophys Union. *Res:* Geochronology, application of techniques of radioactive age determination of rocks and minerals to geological problems; isotope tracer studies of geological processes. *Mailing Add:* US Geol Surv 345 Middlefield Rd Menlo Park CA 94025

LANPHIER, EDWARD HOWELL, b Madison, Wis, May 29, 22; m 78. MEDICINE, ENVIRONMENTAL PHYSIOLOGY. *Educ:* Univ Wis, BS, 46; Univ Ill, MS & MD, 49; MDiv, Nashotah House, 76. *Prof Exp:* Am Col Physicians res fel physiol, Grad Sch Med, Univ Pa, 50-51; asst med officer & physiologist, Exp Diving Unit, US Navy, 52-58, diving med officer, Eniwetok Proving Ground, 58, med officer, Under-water Demolition Team, Norfolk, Va, 58-59; from asst prof to assoc prof physiol, Sch Med, State Univ NY, Buffalo, 59-73; SR SCIENTIST PREV MED, UNIV WIS-MADISON, 76-, ASST DIR RES, THE BIOTRON, 78- *Mem:* Am Physiol Soc; Aerospace Med Asn; Am Col Sports Med; Am Thoracic Soc; Undersea Med Soc. *Res:* Respiratory physiology; submarine and diving medicine; physiological problems of exposure to increased pressure; hyperbaric medicine. *Mailing Add:* Biotron 2115 Observatory Dr Madison WI 53706

LANSBURY, PETER THOMAS, b Vienna, Austria, Feb 24, 33; US citizen; m 57; c 3. ORGANIC CHEMISTRY. *Educ:* Pa State Univ, BS, 53; Northwestern Univ, PhD(chem), 56. *Prof Exp:* Res scientist chem, E I du Pont de Nemours & Co, Inc, 56-58; lectr org chem, Univ Del, 58-59; from asst prof to assoc prof, 59-65, PROF CHEM, STATE UNIV NY BUFFALO, 65- *Concurrent Pos:* Prin investr, NSF res grants, 60-; vis prof chem, Univ Ill, Urbana, 63-64; fel, Alfred P Sloan Found, 63-67; consult, Hooker Chem Corp, 65-74; res award, Ciba-Geigy Corp, 73-74. *Mem:* Am Chem Soc; Sigma Xi. *Mailing Add:* Dept of Chem 357 Acheson Hall Buffalo NY 14214

LANSDELL, HERBERT CHARLES, b Montreal, Que, Dec 22, 22; US citizen; m 63; c 2. NEUROPSYCHOLOGY, PHYSIOLOGICAL PSYCHOLOGY. *Educ:* Sir George Williams Eve Col, BSc, 44; McGill Univ, PhD(psychol), 50. *Prof Exp:* Asst prof psychol, McGill Univ, 49-50; defense res sci officer, Defense Res Med Labs, 50-54; asst prof psychol, Univ Buffalo, 54-58; res supvr, 58-70, HEALTH SCI ADMINR, NAT INST NEUROL & COMMUN DIS & STROKE, 70- *Mem:* Fel Am Psychol Asn; AAAS; Soc Neurosci; Psychomet Soc; Eastern Psychol Asn. *Res:* Statistical analysis of psychological test results obtained from neurological patients to investigate brain function, especially hemispheric and sex differences; test construction. *Mailing Add:* Fed Bldg Rm 916 Nat Inst Health Bethesda MD 20205

LANSDOWN, A(LLEN) M(AURICE), b Winnipeg, Manitoba, Sept 7, 39; m 61; c 3. CIVIL & STRUCTURAL ENGINEERING. *Educ:* Univ Manitoba, BSc, 61; Southampton Univ, PhD(struct), 64. *Prof Exp:* Nat Res Coun Can fel, 64-65; asst prof, 65-67, head dept, 67-73, assoc prof, 67-69, PROF CIVIL ENG, UNIV MAN, 69- *Concurrent Pos:* Mem, Defence Res Bd, 73-; provost, Univ Col, 78-81. *Mem:* Eng Inst Can; fel Royal Soc Arts, London. *Res:* Housing in small remote northern communities: self-help, sweat-equity and house performance; railway transportation in Canada: relationship of capital expenditures to technical operation. *Mailing Add:* Civil Eng Dept Fac Eng Univ Man Winnipeg MB R3T 2N2 Can

LANSDOWN, WILLIAM D(EE), b Pueblo, Colo, Oct 25, 24; m 56; c 2. ELECTRICAL ENGINEERING. *Educ:* Calif Inst Technol, BS, 50, MS, 51; Univ Kans, PhD(elec eng), 64. *Prof Exp:* Res engr Midwest Res Inst, 51-54; instr elec eng, Univ Kans, 54-62; from asst prof to assoc prof elec eng, Univ Denver, 63-75; secy, 74-79, TREAS, DENCOR INC, 74-, VPRES, 79- *Concurrent Pos:* Consult, IBM Corp, 66-71. *Mem:* Inst Elec & Electronics Engrs. *Res:* Digital computers and digital systems, electric power demand controllers, electric power usage studies. *Mailing Add:* Dencor Inc 2750 S Shoshone St Englewood CO 80110

LANSFORD, EDWIN MYERS, JR, b Houston, Tex, June 26, 23; m 50; c 3. BIOCHEMISTRY. *Educ:* Univ Calif, Los Angeles, BA, 46; Univ Tex, MA, 51, PhD(biochem), 51. *Prof Exp:* Fel, Univ Ill, 51-52; fel, Univ Tex, 52-53, instr chem, 56-57, res scientist, Clayton Found Biochem Inst, 53-67; PROF BIOCHEM, SOUTHWESTERN UNIV, TEX, 67- *Mem:* Am Chem Soc. *Res:* Microbial intermediary metabolism; amino acid activating enzymes; metabolic effects of alcohol; single carbon unit metabolism and its control. *Mailing Add:* Dept of Biol Southwestern Univ Georgetown TX 78626

LANSING, ALLAN M, b St Catherines, Ont, Sept 12, 29; m 51; c 3. CARDIOVASCULAR SURGERY. *Educ:* Univ Western Ont, MD, 53, PhD(physiol), 57; FRCS(C), 59. *Prof Exp:* Nat Res Coun Can scholar, Univ Western Ont, 55-57; asst prof surg & physiol, Fac Med, Univ Western Ont, 61-63; assoc prof, 63-69, chief sect cardiovasc surg, 69-74, prof surg, 69-80, PROF SURG THORACIC & CARDIOVASC, SCH MED, UNIV LOUISVILLE, 80- *Concurrent Pos:* Markle scholar med sci, 61- *Mem:* Fel Am Col Surg; fel Am Col Cardiol; Soc Univ Surg. *Res:* Cardiovascular physiology and shock; pulmonary atelectasis; renal transplantation; open heart surgery. *Mailing Add:* 718 Medical Towers Louisville KY 40202

LANSING, DONALD LEONARD, b Poughkeepsie, NY, Aug 12, 34; m 56; c 3. ACOUSTICS. *Educ:* Union Col, BS, 56; Va Polytech Inst & State Univ, MS, 63. *Prof Exp:* Res scientist math, 56-69, sect head theoret acoust, 69-74, BR HEAD AEROACOUST, NASA LANGLEY RES CTR, 74- *Mem:* Acoust Soc Am; Am Inst Aeronaut & Astronaut; AAAS. *Res:* Duct acoustics; aeroacoustics. *Mailing Add:* NASA Langley Res Ctr Mail Stop 460 Hampton VA 23665

LANSING, NEAL F(ISK), JR, b Oakland, Calif, Nov 16, 16; m 43; c 3. ENERGY, ENVIRONMENTAL SCIENCE. *Educ:* Pomona Col, BA, 38; Calif State Univ, Dominquez Hills, MS, 77. *Prof Exp:* Develop engr, Res Div, Elliott Co, Pa, 46-47; sr physicist, Reactor Tech Div, Oak Ridge Nat Lab, 47-55; head, Res Reactors Sect, Atomic Energy Div, Am Radiator & Standard Sanit Corp, 55-57, mgr, Atomic Energy Serv, Foreign Div, 57-59, supvr, Res Reactors Sect, Adv Technol Labs, 59-61; sr staff engr, Space Technol Labs, TRW, Inc, 61-63, prod line mgr, Mech Div, 63-65, prod line mgr, Adv Systs Lab, 66, sr staff engr, Adv Systs Lab, TRW Systs Group, 66, proj mgr urban progs group, 66-72; ENERGY & ENVIRON PLANNING CONSULT, 72- *Concurrent Pos:* Environ Protection Agency fel, Environ Mgt Inst, Univ Southern Calif, 73; consult, Southern Calif Asn Govts, 73- & Elec Power Res Inst, 74- *Mem:* Am Phys Soc; Am Nuclear Soc; Am Soc Chem Engrs; Int Solar Energy Soc; AAAS. *Res:* Heat transmission and fluid dynamics; design and development of community analysis systems for resource management in local government; technology transfer and applications; research planning; solar energy power plants; regional transportation energy and air quality planning; preparation of environmental documents. *Mailing Add:* 3116 Carolwood Lane Torrance CA 90505

LANSINGER, JOHN MARCUS, b July 20, 32; US citizen; m 53; c 2. GEOPHYSICS, IONOSPHERIC PHYSICS. *Educ:* Lewis & Clark Col, BS, 54; Univ Alaska, MS, 56. *Prof Exp:* Instr geophys, Univ Alaska, 56-57; sr engr, Philco Corp, 57-59; staff assoc, Boeing Sci Res Labs, Northwest Environ Technol Labs, Inc, 59-69, vpres, 69-76; STAFF MEM, PHYS DYNAMICS INC, 76- *Mem:* Am Geophys Union; Inst Elec & Electronics Engrs; Air Pollution Control Asn; Am Phys Soc. *Res:* Environmental sciences; ionospheric research; atmospheric propagation at optical wavelengths. *Mailing Add:* Phys Dynamics Inc PO Box 3027 Bellevue WA 98009

LANSKI, CHARLES PHILIP, b Chicago, Ill, Oct 19, 43. MATHEMATICS. *Educ:* Univ Chicago, SB, 65, SM, 66, PhD(math), 69. *Prof Exp:* Asst prof, 69-74, ASSOC PROF MATH, UNIV SOUTHERN CALIF, 74- *Concurrent Pos:* NSF grant, 71-73. *Mem:* Am Math Soc. *Res:* Noncommutative ring theory. *Mailing Add:* Dept of Math Univ of Southern Calif Los Angeles CA 90007

LANSON, HERMAN JAY, b Utica, NY, Feb 22, 13; m 35; c 3. ORGANIC CHEMISTRY. *Educ:* Syracuse Univ, BS, 34, MS, 36; Polytech Inst New York, PhD(org chem), 45. *Prof Exp:* Org res chemist, Nuodex Prod Co, Inc, NJ, 36-40; res chemist, HD Roosen Co, NY, 40-43; chief chemist, Crown Oil Co Prod Corp, 43-45; supvr, Vehicle Res & Prod, Grand Rapids Varnish Corp, 45-50; supvr, resin & plasticizer develop, Chem Mat Dept, Gen Elec Co, 50-57; vpres & tech dir, US Vehicle & Chem Co, 57-61; pres & res dir, Lanson Chem Corp, 61-70, pres & res dir, Washburn Lanson Corp, 70-75; PRES & RES DIR, LANCHEM CORP, 75- *Concurrent Pos:* Lectr, Washington Univ, Roosevelt Univ, Chicago, Univ Houston, Univ Mo & St Louis Univ. *Mem:* Am Oil Chem Soc; Soc Plastics Engrs; fel Am Inst Chemists; Am Chem Soc. *Res:* Synthetic resins; drying oils; protective coatings; electrical insulation materials; development of water-soluble polymers, synthetic latexes, synthetic resins for electrical insulation. *Mailing Add:* 12020 Gardengate Dr St Louis MO 63141

LANTER, ROBERT JACKSON, b Middletown, Ohio, Nov 9, 14; m 47; c 2. PHYSICS, NUCLEAR WEAPON ENGINEERING. *Educ:* Univ Utah, BA, 42; Univ NMex, MS, 57. *Prof Exp:* Alt group leader physics, 46-48, STAFF MEM PHYSICS & ENG, LOS ALAMOS NAT LAB, UNIV CALIF, 49- *Mem:* Am Phys Soc; AAAS. *Res:* Neutron production and detection; developed 1-meter diameter liquid scintillation counter for detection of bursts of fewer than 100 neutrons; helped develop D-T pulsed neutron sources; silver counter for detecting and counting deutron-deutron reaction and deutrium-tritium reaction neutrons. *Mailing Add:* Los Alamos Nat Lab PO Box 1663 Los Alamos NM 87545

LANTERMAN, ELMA, b Elkhart, Ill, Jan 25, 17. ANALYTICAL CHEMISTRY. *Educ:* Univ Ill, BS, 40; Ind Univ, MA, 48, PhD(anal chem), 51. *Prof Exp:* Chem technician, Mayo Clin, 41-42; chemist, Devoe & Raynolds Co, 42-43 & Metal & Thermit Corp, 43-46; asst, Univ Ind, 46-51; asst prof physics, NC State Col, 51-53; supvr, Metall Groups, Indianapolis Naval Ord Plant, 53-55; sr res chemist, Am Can Co, 55-59; sr res chemist, Borg-Warner Corp, 59-61, scientist, 61-63, mgr anal chem, 63-74, staff scientist, res ctr, 74-82; RETIRED. *Concurrent Pos:* Comnr, Environ Comn, Des Plaines, Ill, 74-79. *Mem:* Am Chem Soc; Electron Micros Soc Am; Am Crystallog Asn; Soc Appl Spectros (treas, 70-74). *Res:* X-ray diffraction and spectroscopy; electron microscopy; technology forecasting. *Mailing Add:* Res Ctr Borg-Warner Corp Des Plaines IL 60018

LANTERO, ORESTE JOHN, JR, b Chicago, Ill, Aug 26, 42; m 67; c 2. BIOCHEMISTRY, ORGANIC CHEMISTRY. *Educ:* Purdue Univ, BS, 64; NDak State Univ, PhD(biochem), 71. *Prof Exp:* Res fel, Merrell Nat Lab, 71-73; RES SCIENTIST BIOCHEM, MILES LABS, INC, 73- *Mem:* AAAS. *Res:* Isolation and characterization of enzymes; preparation and characterization of immobilized enzymes. *Mailing Add:* Miles Labs Inc 1127 Myrtle St Elkhart IN 46514

LANTHIER, ANDRE, b Montreal, Que, Apr 13, 28; m 56; c 3. MEDICINE, BIOCHEMISTRY. *Educ:* Univ Montreal, BA, 47, MD, 53; FRCPS(C), 58. *Prof Exp:* Resident med, Notre Dame Hosp, Montreal, Que, 52-55; asst, Peter Bent Brigham Hosp, Boston, 55-57; clin instr, 57-58, from asst prof to assoc prof, 59-68, PROF MED & CHMN DEPT, UNIV MONTREAL, 68- *Concurrent Pos:* Res fel, Harvard Med Sch, 55-57; asst physician, Notre-Dame Hosp, 57-64, sr physician, 64-, dir endocrinol lab, 58- *Mem:* Endocrine Soc; Am Fedn Clin Res; NY Acad Sci; fel Am Col Physicians; Can Soc Clin Invest. *Res:* Ovarian steroid biosynthesis; biosynthesis and physiological effects of 18-hydroxylated corticosteroids; mechanism of ovulation. *Mailing Add:* Notre Dame Hosp 1560 Sherbrooke St E Montreal PQ H2L 4K8 Can

LANTOS, P(ETER) R(ICHARD), b Budapest, Hungary, July 18, 24; nat US; m 47; c 4. CHEMICAL ENGINEERING. *Educ:* Cornell Univ, BChE, 45, PhD(chem eng), 50. *Prof Exp:* Develop chemist, Gen Elec Co, 46-47; res engr, E I du Pont de Nemours & Co, 50-55, res supvr, 55-60; mgr appln & prod develop, Celanese Plastics Co, 61-63, mgr res & develop, 64-69; dir develop, Sun Chem Corp, 69-70, vpres res & develop, 70-75; gen mgr, Plastics Div, Rhodia Inc, 75; dir res & develop, Arco Polymers, Inc, 76-77, vpres, 78-79; PRES, TARGET GROUP, INC, 80- *Mem:* Asn Consult Chemists & Chem Engrs; Am Chem Soc; Am Inst Chem Engrs; Plastic Inst Am; Soc Plastics Engrs. *Res:* Polymers; plastics; fibers. *Mailing Add:* 1000 Harston Lane Target Group Inc Philadelphia PA 19118

LANYI, JANOS K, b Budapest, Hungary, June 5, 37; US citizen; m 62; c 3. BIOCHEMISTRY. *Educ:* Stanford Univ, BS, 59; Harvard Univ, MA, 61, PhD(biochem), 63. *Prof Exp:* NIH fel genetics, sch med, Stanford Univ, 63-65; Nat Acad Sci-Nat Res Coun res assoc biochem, 65-66; res scientist, Planetary Biol Div, Ames Res Ctr, NASA, 66-80; PROF PHYSIOL & BIOPHYS, UNIV CALIF, IRVINE, 80- *Honors & Awards:* Except Sci Achievement Medal, NASA, 77; H Julian Allen Award, 78. *Mem:* Am Soc Microbiol; Biophys Soc; Am Soc Biol Chem. *Res:* Physical chemistry of proteins; structure and function of enzymes and membranes in halophilic microorganisms; bacteriorhodopsin, electron transport system and ion carriers; energetics and mechanism of amino acid transport. *Mailing Add:* Dept Physiol & Biophys Univ Calif Irvine CA 92717

LANYON, HUBERT PETER DAVID, b Halesowen, Eng, June 25, 36; m 62; c 3. SOLID STATE PHYSICS. *Educ:* Cambridge Univ, BA, 58, MA, 62; Leicester Univ, PhD(physics), 61. *Prof Exp:* Res demonstr physics, Leicester Univ, 58-61; res assoc elec eng, Univ Ill, Urbana, 61-63; mem tech staff, RCA Labs, 63-66; assoc prof elec eng, Carnegie Inst Technol, 66-67; assoc prof, 67-77, PROF ELEC ENG, WORCESTER POLYTECH INST, 77- *Mem:* Am Phys Soc. *Res:* Photoconductivity; surface physics. *Mailing Add:* Dept of Elec Eng Worcester Polytech Inst Worcester MA 01609

LANYON, WESLEY EDWIN, b Norwalk, Conn, June 10, 26; m 51; c 2. ORNITHOLOGY. *Educ:* Cornell Univ, AB, 50; Univ Wis, MS, 51, PhD(zool), 55|. *Prof Exp:* Instr zool, Univ Ariz, 55-56; asst prof, Miami Univ, 56-57; asst cur, 57-63, assoc cur, 63-67, CUR, AM MUS NATURAL HIST, 67- *Concurrent Pos:* Res dir, Kalbfleisch Field Res Sta, Am Mus Natural Hist, Huntington, 58-80; adj prof, City Univ New York, 68- *Honors & Awards:* Brewster Award, Amer Ornith Union, 68. *Mem:* Amer Ornith Union (pres, 76-78); Cooper Ornith Soc; Wilson Ornith Soc; Soc Syst Zool; Soc Study Evolution. *Res:* Application of compararive behavior and ecology of closely related populations of birds to avian systematics, especially vocalizations in avian taxonomy; use of morphology in the systematics of higher categories of birds. *Mailing Add:* Dept of Ornith Am Mus of Natural Hist New York NY 10024

LANZA, GIOVANNI, b Trieste, Italy, Aug 5, 26; m 50; c 4. PHYSICS. *Educ:* Univ Trieste, PhD, 50. *Prof Exp:* Asst prof quantum theory, Univ Trieste, 50-52; prof, Univ Cagliari, Univ Sardinia & Univ Padua, 52-54; vis physicist nuclear physics, Mass Inst Technol, 54-55; res fel, Harvard Univ, 55-58; assoc prof, 58-60, PROF PHYSICS, NORTHEASTERN UNIV, 60- *Concurrent Pos:* Fulbright & Smith Mundt scholars, 54; consult, Lab Electronics, Inc, 58- & Saunders Assocs, 63- *Mem:* Ital Phys Soc. *Res:* Magnetohydrodynamics; plasma physics; energy conversion techniques; nuclear physics; physics of upper atmosphere. *Mailing Add:* Dept of Physics Northeastern Univ Boston MA 02115

LANZA, GUY ROBERT, b Englewood, NJ, Jan 27, 39; m 68; c 2. AQUATIC ECOLOGY. *Educ:* Fairleigh Dickinson Univ, BS, 61; Univ Ky, MS, 69; Va Polytech Inst & State Univ, PhD(zool), 72. *Prof Exp:* Res biologist, Merck Inst Therapeut Res, 63-69; aquatic ecologist, Smithsonian Inst, 71-73 & NY Univ, 73-75; AQUATIC ECOLOGIST, UNIV TEX, DALLAS, 75-, ASSOC PROF ENVIRON SCI, 75- *Concurrent Pos:* Consult ecologist, Int Ctr Med

Res & Training, Malaysia, 72-73; asst dir, Aquatic ecol prog, NY Univ Med Ctr, 73-75; subcomt partic, Nat Comn Water Qual, 75. *Mem:* AAAS; Water Pollution Control Fedn. *Res:* Structure and function of aquatic ecosystems; pollution ecology and the environmental physiology and energetics of aquatic organisms. *Mailing Add:* Environ Sci Prog Univ of Tex Dallas Box 688 Richardson TX 75080

LANZA, JANET, evolutionary ecology, population biology, see previous edition

LANZA, RICHARD CHARLES, b New York, NY, Apr 28, 39; m 63. PHYSICS. *Educ:* Princeton Univ, AB, 59; Univ Pa, MS, 61, PhD(physics), 66. *Prof Exp:* Res assoc physics, 66-68, asst prof, 68-74, MEM RES STAFF, MASS INST TECHNOL, 74- *Concurrent Pos:* Assoc radiol, Harvard Med Sch & Peter Bent Brigham Hosp, 74-; res fel, Mass Gen Hosp, 75-76. *Mem:* AAAS; Inst Elec & Electronics Engrs; Am Phys Soc. *Res:* Experimental particle physics, nuclear and electronic instrumentation, medical instrumentation, especially in radiology and nuclear medicine. *Mailing Add:* Lab for Nuclear Sci Mass Inst of Technol Cambridge MA 02139

LANZANO, BERNADINE CLARE, b Stanberry, Mo, Oct 29, 33; m 57. COMPUTER SCIENCE, MATHEMATICS. *Educ:* Benedictine Col, BS, 55. *Prof Exp:* Mathematician, Lockheed Corp, 56-57; SR STAFF ENGR COMPUT SCI, TRW SYSTS GROUP, 57- *Mem:* Math Asn Am; Soc Indust & Appl Math. *Res:* Design and development of computer software in the areas of trajectory analysis, optimization, targeting, and in the fields of information processing of financial and scientific data. *Mailing Add:* 8614 Pappas Way Annandale VA 22003

LANZANO, PAOLO, b Cairo, Egypt, Nov 29, 23; nat US; m 57. APPLIED MATHEMATICS, SPACE PHYSICS. *Educ:* Univ Rome, BS, 42, PhD(math), 45. *Prof Exp:* Asst prof math, Univ Rome, 46-49 & St Louis Univ, 50-56; design specialist, Douglas Aircraft Co, Calif, 56-58; mem tech staff, Space Tech Labs, Calif, 58-60; res scientist, Nortronics Div, Northrop Corp, 60-61; prin scientist, Space & Info Systs Div, NAm Aviation, 61-71; assoc prof math, Nicholls State Univ, 71-72; head math res ctr, 72-76, SR RES SCIENTIST, NAVAL RES LAB, 76- *Concurrent Pos:* Fel, Inst Advan Studies, Univ Rome, 46-48. *Mem:* Am Math Soc; Am Geophys Union; Am Astronaut Soc; Soc Indust & Appl Math; Am Inst Aeronaut & Astronaut. *Res:* Celestial mechanics; theory of relativity; Riemannian geometry; space physics; geodesy. *Mailing Add:* 8614 Pappas Way Annandale VA 22003

LANZEROTTI, LOUIS JOHN, b Carlinville, Ill, Apr 16, 38; m 65; c 2. GEOPHYSICS, SPACE PHYSICS. *Educ:* Univ Ill, BS, 60; Harvard Univ, AM, 63, PhD(physics), 65. *Prof Exp:* Fel, 65-67, MEM TECH STAFF, BELL LABS, 67- *Concurrent Pos:* Mem, Space Sci Adv Comt, NASA, 75-79 & Space Sci Bd, Nat Acad Sci, 79-; adj prof, Univ Fla, 78- *Mem:* Fel AAAS; fel Am Phys Soc; Am Geophys Union; Inst Elec & Electronics Engrs; Soc Terrestial Magnegtism & Elec Japan. *Res:* Particles and fields in planetary magnetospheres; solar cosmic ray composition and propagation; ionosphere-magnetosphere coupling; planetary magnetospheres; geomagnetic depth sounding. *Mailing Add:* Bell Labs Murray Hill NJ 07974

LANZEROTTI, MARY YVONNE DEWOLF, b Phoenix, Ariz, Nov 7, 38; m 65; c 2. PHYSICAL CHEMISTRY. *Educ:* Univ Calif, Berkeley, BS, 60; Harvard Univ, PhD(phys chem), 65. *Prof Exp:* Chemist, US Naval Ord Test Sta, 60; asst, Harvard Univ, 60-64; res chemist, Mithras Inc, Mass, 64-65; RES PHYSICAL SCIENTIST, ENERGETIC MAT DIV, US ARMY ARMAMENT RES & DEVELOP COMMAND, 65- *Mem:* AAAS; Am Chem Soc; Am Phys Soc; Am Soc Mech Engrs; Am Soc Lubrication Engrs. *Res:* Gas dynamic lasers; chemical lasers; explosive product lasers; mechanical sensitivity of energetic materials; tribology; mechanical behavior of materials under high acceleration. *Mailing Add:* Energetic Mat Div US Army Armament R&D Command Dover NJ 07801

LANZI, LAWRENCE HERMAN, b Chicago, Ill, Apr 8, 21; m 47; c 2. PHYSICS, MEDICAL PHYSICS. *Educ:* Northwestern Univ, BS, 43; Univ Ill, MS, 47, PhD(physics), 51; Am Bd Health Physics, dipl; Am Bd Radiol, dipl. *Prof Exp:* Asst, Dearborn Observ, Ill, 41-42; asst, Northwestern Univ, 42-43; asst, Univ Chicago, 44; jr scientist, Los Alamos Sci Lab, 44-45; asst, Univ Ill, 46-50; assoc physicist, Argonne Nat Lab, 51; sr physicist, 51-55, from asst prof to assoc prof, Dept Radiol, Sch Med, 55-68, prof med physics, div biol sci, 68-80, EMER PROF, DIV BIOL SCI, PRITZKER SCH MED & FRANKLIN MCLEAN MEM RES INST, UNIV CHICAGO, 80-; PROF MED PHYSICS, RUSH UNIV, RUSH-PRESBY ST LUKE'S MED CTR, CHICAGO, 80- *Concurrent Pos:* With Argonne Cancer Res Hosp, 51-; first officer, Int Atomic Energy Comn, Vienna, Austria, 67-68; bd mem, Am Int Sch, Vienna, 67-68; mem Nat Coun Radiation Protection, 67 & US Nat Comt Med Physics, 70-; chmn Radiation Protection Adv Coun, State of Ill, 71-; mem tech adv panel, Los Alamos Meson Physics Facil, Los Alamos, NMex & steering comt, radiol physics ctr, Univ Tex M D Anderson Hosp & Tumor Inst; consult, Int Atomic Energy Agency, Vienna, Hines Vet Admin Hosp, Ill, NIH & WHO, Geneva; consult radiation dosimetry prob, India, 73, Turkey, 75, Saudia Arabia, 75, Iran, 76, Israel, 77, Ghana, 78, Thailand, 79 & Nigeria, 81; chmn, Comn Accreditation Educ Progs Med Physicists. *Honors & Awards:* Coolidge Award, Am Asn Physicists Med, 78. *Mem:* AAAS; Asn Med Physicists India; Brit Hosp Physicists' Asn; Am Asn Physicists in Med (past pres); Radiol Soc NAm. *Res:* Accelerators; radiation as applied to medicine; radiation physics; high energy x-rays and electrons; isotopes in medicine; nuclear reactors; health physics; radiation dosimetry. *Mailing Add:* Rush-Presby St Luke's Med Ctr 1750 W Congress Parkway Chicago IL 60612

LANZILOTTA, RAYMOND PHILIP, b Camden, NJ, Sept 26, 42; m 65; c 1. MICROBIOLOGY. *Educ:* Rutgers Univ, BA, 64, MS, 67, PhD(biochem, microbiol), 68. *Prof Exp:* Instr microbiol, Sch Med, Temple Univ, 68-70; microbial chemist, Syntex Res Div, Palo Alto, 70-77; dept head, 77-80, VPRES RES & DEVELOP, NOVO LABS, INC, 80- *Mem:* Am Soc Microbiol; Am Chem Soc; Soc Indust Microbiol. *Res:* Microbial transformations of organic substrates; fermentation technology; enzyme technology. *Mailing Add:* 179 Grumman Ave Norwalk CT 06851

LANZKOWSKY, PHILIP, b Cape Town, SAfrica, Mar 17, 32; m 55; c 5. PEDIATRICS, HEMATOLOGY. *Educ:* Univ Cape Town, MB ChB, 54, MD, 59; Royal Col Physicians & Surgeons, dipl child health, 60; Am Bd Pediat, dipl, 66, cert pediat hematol-oncol, 75; FRCP(E), 73. *Prof Exp:* From intern to sr intern, Groote Schuur Hosp, Univ Cape Town, 55-56; gen pract, 56-57; from registr to sr registr, Red Cross War Mem Children's Hosp, 57-60, consult pediatrician & pediat hematologist, 63-65; asst prof pediat, New York Hosp-Cornell Med Ctr, 65-67, assoc prof, 67-70; PROF PEDIAT, STATE UNIV NY STONY BROOK, 70- *Concurrent Pos:* Dr C L Herman res grants, 58 & 64; Cecil John Adams mem traveling fel & Hill-Pattison-Struthers bursary, 60; Benger Labs traveling grant, 61; registr pediat unit, St Mary's Hosp Med Sch, Univ London, 61; clin & res fel pediat hemat, Duke Univ, 61-62; res fel, Col Med, Univ Utah, 62-63; lectr, Univ Cape Town, 63-65; dir pediat hemat, New York Hosp-Cornell Med Ctr, 65-70; pediatrician-in-chief, chmn pediat & chief pediat hemat, Long Island Jewish-Hillside Med Ctr, 70-; pediatrician-in-chief, Queens Hosp Ctr, 70-; mem pediat adv comt NY City Dept Health, 70-73. *Honors & Awards:* Joseph Arenow Prize, 59. *Mem:* Am Soc Hemat; Am Acad Pediat; Am Soc Clin Oncol; Am Asn Cancer Res; Am Pediat Soc. *Res:* Nutritional anemias in children, especially iron, folate and protein deficiency; pediatric oncology. *Mailing Add:* Dept of Pediat Long Island Jewish-Hillside Med Ctr New Hyde Park NY 11040

LANZKRON, R(OLF) W(OLFGANG), b Hamburg, Ger, Dec 9, 29; nat US; m 61; c 2. ELECTRICAL ENGINEERING. *Educ:* Milwaukee Sch Eng, BS, 54; Univ Wis, MS, 55, PhD, 56. *Prof Exp:* Asst, Univ Wis, 55-56; asst res & develop, Univac Div, Sperry Rand Corp, 56-57; design engr, Martin Co, 57-62; chief flight projs, Div, Apollo, NASA, 62-68; prog mgr, Fed Aviation Admin Display Systs, 68-73, prog mgr Air Force AN-TPN/10 Prog, 73-78, opers mgr graphic oper, 78-81, GRAPHIC SYSTS MGR, RAYTHEON CO, 81- *Honors & Awards:* Outstanding Achievement Award, NASA, 64. *Mem:* Am Inst Aeronaut & Astronaut; Sigma Xi; Math Asn Am; Inst Elec & Electronics Engrs; Nat Soc Prof Engrs. *Res:* Guidance and control of ballistic missiles and space vehicles; digital and analog computer design and usage and ground systems engineering; flight vehicle integration. *Mailing Add:* 35 Gardner Rd Brookline MA 02146

LANZL, GEORGE FRANK, b Chicago, Ill, Aug 9, 18; m 42; c 2. PHYSICAL CHEMISTRY. *Educ:* De Pauw Univ, BS, 40; Northwestern Univ, PhD(chem), 46. *Prof Exp:* Instr chem, Northwestern Univ, 40-44; mem staff, 44-51, res mgr, 51-57, dir dacron res lab, 57-60, DIR, PIONEERING RES DIV, TEXTILE FIBERS DEPT, E I DU PONT DE NEMOURS & CO, 60- *Mem:* Am Chem Soc; Am Phys Soc. *Res:* Physical chemistry of polymers; fiber physics and processing. *Mailing Add:* 409 Crest Rd Wilmington DE 19803

LANZONI, VINCENT, b Kingston, Mass, Feb 23, 28; m 60; c 3. PHARMACOLOGY, CLINICAL MEDICINE. *Educ:* Tufts Univ, PhD(pharmacol), 53; Boston Univ, MD, 60. *Prof Exp:* Instr pharmacol, Sch Med, Tufts Univ, 53-54; from intern to resident, Boston City Hosp, 60-63; asst prof pharmacol & instr med, 63-66, assoc prof pharmacol & med, 66-73, assoc dean sch med, 69-75, prof pharmacol, Sch Med, Boston Univ, 73-75; DEAN & PROF MED, NJ MED SCH, 75- *Concurrent Pos:* Res fel, NIH, 53-54; fel med, Boston City Hosp. *Res:* Cardiovascular pharmacology. *Mailing Add:* 100 Bergen St Newark NJ 07103

LAO, BINNEG YANBING, b Szechwan, China, Feb 25, 45; US citizen; m 70; c 2. SOLID STATE PHYSICS, APPLIED PHYSICS. *Educ:* Univ Calif, Los Angeles, BS, 67; Princeton Univ, MA, 69, PhD(physics), 71. *Prof Exp:* NSF fel solid state physics, Ctr Theoret Physics, Univ Md, 71-73; sr res physicist instrumentation, Eastern Div Res Labs, Dow Chem Co, 73-76; prin physicist appl physics, Bendix Res Labs, Bendix Corp, 76-80; SR STAFF SCIENTIST, MAGNAVOX ADV PROD & SYST CO, 80- *Mem:* Am Phys Soc; Sigma Xi. *Res:* Surface acoustic wave devices and gallium arsenide integrated circuits; sensors and solid state devices; analytical instrument development; optical and dielectrical properties of matter; nonlinear and excitonic effects in semiconductors. *Mailing Add:* 3449 Coolheights South Palos Verdes CA 90274

LAO, ROBERT CHANG-CHUN, b Shanghai, China, Apr 15, 34; Can citizen; m 69. ANALYTICAL CHEMISTRY, INDUSTRIAL HYGIENE. *Educ:* Nat Taiwan Univ, BSc, 58; Univ Denver, PhD(chem), 66. *Prof Exp:* Res fel chem, Johns Hopkins Univ, 66-67 & Nat Res Coun Can, 67-69; res chemist indust hyg, Nat Health & Welfare, Can, 69-72; RES SCIENTIST & SECT HEAD, ENVIRON CAN, 72- *Concurrent Pos:* Proj investr, Int Agency Res Cancer, WHO, 73-76. *Mem:* Am Soc Mass Spectrometry; Sigma Xi. *Res:* Mass spectrometry; chromatography; instrumentation; physical and chemical analytical methodology and their applications to environmental pollution. *Mailing Add:* 80 Delong Dr Ottawa ON L1K 7E3 Can

LAO, YAN-JEONG, b Nanking, China, Feb 5, 36; US citizen; m 65; c 2. CHEMICAL ENGINEERING, ENVIRONMENTAL HEALTH. *Educ:* Nat Taiwan Univ, BS, 58; Univ Mich, MS, 62; PhD(chem eng), 69. *Prof Exp:* Res engr chem eng, E I du Pont de Nemours & Co, Inc, 69-71; sr engr, Monsanto Co, 72-73; from asst prof to assoc prof, 73-81, PROF ENVIRON HEALTH, EAST CAROLINA UNIV, 81- *Concurrent Pos:* Bd mem, Eastern Lung Asn, 77-79. *Mem:* Nat Environ Health Asn; Am Indust Hyg Asn; Sigma Xi. *Res:* Monitoring and analyzing environmental pollutants, the study of their effects and health related problems. *Mailing Add:* Dept of Environ Health E Carolina Univ Greenville NC 27834

LAPALME, DONALD WILLIAM, b Woonsocket, RI, July 27, 37; m 61; c 4. PHOTOGRAPHIC ENGINEERING, PHYSICAL CHEMISTRY. *Educ:* St John's Univ NY, BS, 59, MS, 61, PhD(chem), 68. *Prof Exp:* Sr res chemist photo eng, Photo Div, 67-72, sr prod engr, 72-74, prod mgr reprographics, 74-76, tech dir process eng, Res & Develop, 76-78, plant mgr prod, Photo Div, 78-81, VPRES & DIR MFG, BLDG MAT GROUP, GAF CORP, 81- *Mem:* Soc Photographic Scientists & Engrs (pres, 73-74); Am Chem Soc. *Res:* Photographic science. *Mailing Add:* GAF Corp 140 W 51st St New York NY 10020

LAPE, HARLAN EDWIN, b Troy, NY, June 22, 28; m; c 2. PHARMACOLOGY, PHYSIOLOGY. *Educ:* Siena Col, BS, 50; Boston Univ, MS, 52. *Prof Exp:* GROUP LEADER CARDIOVASC HYPERTENSION, STERLING-WINTHROP RES INST, 52- *Res:* Antihypertensive, cardiovascular fields of medical research. *Mailing Add:* Sterling-Winthrop Res Inst Columbia Turnpike Rensselaer NY 12144

LAPERRIERE, JACQUELINE DOYLE, b Northampton, Mass, Dec 31, 42; div; c 2. AQUATIC FISHERIES. *Educ:* Univ Mass, BS, 64; Iowa State Univ, MS, 71, PhD(water resources), 81. *Prof Exp:* Water resource technician, 71-72, res biologist, 72-73, aquatic biologist, 73-74, instr water resources, 74-79, asst prof, Inst Water Resources, 79-80, ASST LEADER, ALASKA COOP FISHERY RES UNIT & AFFIL ASST PROF WATER RESOURCES, INST WATER RESOURCES, UNIV ALASKA, 80- *Concurrent Pos:* Andrew W Mellon Found travel grant, 80. *Mem:* Am Fisheries Soc; Am Soc Limnol & Oceanog; Int Asn Limnol; NAm Benthol Soc; NAm Lake Mgt Soc. *Res:* Stream ecology, primary and secondary production, water quality and effects of development; limnology of subarctic lakes, thermal regime, chemical cycling and production; culture and toxicity testing of Alaskan fishes. *Mailing Add:* PO Box 81547 College AK 99708

LAPEYRE, GERALD J, b Riverton, Wyo, Jan 3, 34; m 60; c 3. SOLID STATE PHYSICS, SURFACE PHYSICS. *Educ:* Univ Notre Dame, BS, 56; Univ Mo, MA, 58, PhD(physics), 62. *Prof Exp:* From asst prof, to assoc prof physics, 62-74, PROF PHYSICS, MONT STATE UNIV, 74- *Mem:* Fel Am Phys Soc; Am Asn Physics Teachers; Am Vacuum Soc. *Res:* Solid state physics surface science with emphasis on synchrotron photoemission and electronic structure. *Mailing Add:* Dept of Physics Mont State Univ Bozeman MT 59715

LAPHAM, LOWELL WINSHIP, b New Hampton, Iowa, Mar 20, 22; m 45; c 4. NEUROPATHOLOGY. *Educ:* Oberlin Col, BA, 43; Harvard Med Sch, MD, 48. *Prof Exp:* Sr instr path, Western Reserve Univ, 55-57, from asst prof to assoc prof, 57-64; assoc prof path, 64-69, PROF NEUROPATH, MED CTR, UNIV ROCHESTER, 69- *Concurrent Pos:* Nat Multiple Sclerosis Soc fel cytochem, Western Reserve Univ, 56-58. *Mem:* AAAS; Am Asn Neuropath; Am Asn Path; Am Acad Neurol. *Res:* Studies of developmental diseases of nervous system; brain tumors; nature and function of glia; effects of environmental substances on nervous system. *Mailing Add:* Dept of Path Univ of Rochester Med Ctr Rochester NY 14642

LAPIDES, JACK, b Rochester, NY, Nov 27, 14; m 48. UROLOGY. *Educ:* Univ Mich, BA, 36, MA, 38, MD, 41. *Prof Exp:* USPHS fel, Nat Cancer Inst, 48-50; from instr to assoc prof, 50-64, PROF SURG, MED SCH, UNIV MICH, ANN ARBOR, 64-, HEAD SECT UROL, 68- *Concurrent Pos:* Rockefeller res assoc, 36-38; assoc physician surg, Wayne County Gen Hosp, 50-81, chief sect urol, 58- & Vet Admin Hosp, Ann Arbor, 54-; mem comt genito-urinary systs, Nat Acad Sci-Nat Res Coun, 66-70. *Mem:* AMA; Am Urol Asn; fel Am Col Surg; Am Asn Genito-Urinary Surg. *Res:* Renal, ureteral and bladder physiology; fluid and electrolyte balance; urinary incontinence; urinary infection. *Mailing Add:* 1405 EAnn St Ann Arbor MI 48109

LAPIDUS, ARNOLD, b Brooklyn, NY, Nov 6, 33; m 52. MATHEMATICS. *Educ:* Brooklyn Col, BS, 56; NY Univ, MS, 60, PhD(math), 67. *Prof Exp:* Asst math, Courant Inst, NY Univ, 58-60, asst res scientist, AEC comput facility, 61-65, assoc res scientist, 61-68; math analyst, Comput Applns Inc-NASA, 68-69, sci prog mgr, 69-71; asst prof math, 71-76, ASSOC PROF QUANT ANAL, FAIRLEIGH DICKINSON UNIV, 77- *Mem:* Soc Indust & Appl Math; Math Asn Am; Am Math Soc. *Res:* Partial and ordinary differential equations; Monte Carlo methods; scientific programming; artificial intelligence; tedious algebra by computer; fluid dynamics by computer; shock calculations; numerical methods and analysis; linear programming. *Mailing Add:* Dept of Quant Anal Fairleigh Dickinson Univ Teaneck NJ 07666

LAPIDUS, HERBERT, b New York, NY, Aug 10, 31; m 52; c 2. PHARMACY, PHARMACOLOGY. *Educ:* Columbia Univ, BS, 53, MS, 55; Rutgers Univ, PhD(pharm), 68. *Prof Exp:* Proj leader, Julius Schmid Co, 57-60; proj leader pharm, Bristol-Myers Co, 60-63, group leader, 63-67, dept head, 67-70; tech dir, 70-77, VPRES RES & DEVELOP, COMBE INC, 77- *Mem:* Am Chem Soc; Sigma Xi; Soc Cosmetic Chemists; NY Acad Sci; Am Soc Clin Pharmacol & Therapeut. *Res:* Development of pharmaceutical dosage forms, especially sustained release medication, biopharmaceutics and percutaneous absorption. *Mailing Add:* Combe Inc 1101 Westchester Ave White Plains NY 10604

LAPIDUS, IVAN RICHARD, b Brooklyn, NY, Apr 7, 35; m 59; c 3. MOLECULAR BIOPHYSICS, BIOMATHEMATICS. *Educ:* Univ Chicago, AB, 55, BS, 56, MS, 57; Columbia Univ, PhD(physics), 63. *Prof Exp:* Lectr physics, City Col, New York, 59-60; asst prof, 63-68, assoc prof, 68-80, PROF PHYSICS, STEVENS INST TECHNOL, 80- *Concurrent Pos:* Res grants, Stevens Inst Technol, 65, 68 & 71; NASA fac fel, 66; vis assoc prof, Inst Cancer Res, Columbia Univ, 69; vis fel biochem sci, Princeton Univ, 70-71; vis sr scientist, Pace Univ, 79; vis fel, Calif Inst Technol, 80 & 81. *Mem:* AAAS; Am Phys Soc; Am Asn Physics Teachers; Am Inst Biol Sci; Am Soc Microbiol. *Res:* Modility and chemoreception in microorganisms; cell cycle in bacteria; secondary structure of RNA. *Mailing Add:* Dept of Physics Stevens Inst of Technol Hoboken NJ 07030

LA PIDUS, JULES BENJAMIN, b Chicago, Ill, May 1, 31; m 54; c 2. MEDICINAL CHEMISTRY. *Educ:* Univ Ill, BS, 54; Univ Wis, MS, 57, PhD(pharmaceut chem), 58. *Prof Exp:* From asst prof to assoc prof, 58-67, assoc dean res, Grad Sch, 72-74, PROF MED CHEM, OHIO STATE UNIV, 67-, VPROVOST RES & DEAN, GRAD SCH, 74- *Concurrent Pos:* Consult, Pharmacol & Toxicol Training Grants Comt, Nat Inst Gen Med Sci, NIH, 65-67, Prog Comt, 71-75. *Mem:* Am Chem Soc; AAAS. *Res:* Structure-action relationships; autonomic pharmacology. *Mailing Add:* Ohio State Univ 230 N Oval Mall Number 250 Columbus OH 43210

LAPIDUS, LEON, chemical engineering, deceased

LAPIDUS, MICHEL LAURENT, b Casablanca, Morocco, July 4, 56. FUNCTIONAL ANALYSIS, MATHEMATICAL PHYSICS. *Educ:* Univ Pierre-Marie-Curie, Paris VI, MS, 77, DEA, 78, Dr(math). 80. *Prof Exp:* Res assoc, math, Rectorat de Paris, Inst of Pure math, Univ Paris VI, 78-80; Georges Lurcy fel math, Univ Calif, Berkeley, 79-80; ASST PROF MATH, UNIV SOUTHERN CALIF, LOS ANGELES, 80- *Mem:* Am Math Soc; Math Asn Am. *Res:* Mathematical research in linear and nonlinear functional analysis and in mathematical physics; study of the Trotter-Lie formula and modification of the Feynman integral. *Mailing Add:* Dept Math Univ Southern Calif Los Angeles CA 90007

LAPIDUS, MILTON, b New York, NY, May 8, 22; m 58; c 2. BIOCHEMISTRY. *Educ:* Univ Wis, BS, 48, MS, 53, PhD(biochem), 56. *Prof Exp:* Res chemist, Abbott Labs, 48-51; sr fel, Eastern Regional Res Lab, USDA, 56-59; SR BIOCHEMIST, WYETH LABS, INC, 59- *Mem:* AAAS; Am Chem Soc. *Res:* Isolation of vitamin B12b; microbiological transformation of steroids; chromatographic purification of viruses; prostaglandin biosynthesis and isolation; synthesis of penicillins and sweeteners; synthesis of peptides, complement inhibitors. *Mailing Add:* 412 Yorkshire Way Rosemont PA 19010

LAPIER, R(AE) THEODORE, b Montgomery, Vt, July 13, 23; m 49; c 3. CHEMICAL ENGINEERING. *Educ:* Mass Inst Technol, SB, 47. *Prof Exp:* Chem engr, 47-53, supvr prod, 53-61, DIR ADMIN & PLANNING RES & DEVELOP, COLGATE-PALMOLIVE CO, 61- *Mem:* Am Inst Chem Engrs. *Res:* Automation of operations and processes; management of technical personnel; long range planning of research and development. *Mailing Add:* Res & Develop Ctr 909 River Rd Piscataway NJ 08854

LAPIERRE, WALTER A(LFRED), b Jamaica, NY, Aug 9, 10; m 60; c 4. ELECTRICAL & MECHANICAL ENGINEERING. *Educ:* Polytech Inst Brooklyn, MEE, 36. *Prof Exp:* Tutor elec eng, City Col New York, 37-40; asst, Columbia Univ, 40-41, instr, 41-46, asst prof, 46-56; prof elec eng, Webb Inst Naval Archit, 56-60; chief res engr, Electro Dynamic Div, Gen Dynamics Corp, 61-65, mgr res & develop, 65-67; chief eng serv, Diehl Div, Singer Co, 67-70; CONSULT ENGR, 70- *Concurrent Pos:* Engr spec proj, NY Naval Ship Yard, 56-61. *Mem:* Inst Elec & Electronics Engrs; Nat Soc Prof Engrs. *Res:* Mechanical vibrations; instrumentation; electric power systems; physics; engineering investigations; electrical machine design; analysis by computer; general engineering. *Mailing Add:* 133 W Dudley Ave Westfield NJ 07090

LAPIERRE, YVON DENIS, b Bonnyville, Alta, Oct 19, 36; m 60; c 3. PHARMACOLOGY. *Educ:* Ottawa Univ, BA, 57, MD, 61; Univ Montreal, MSc, 70. *Prof Exp:* Lectr, 70-73, asst prof, 73-76, assoc prof, 76-81, PROF PSYCHIAT & PHARMACOL, OTTAWA UNIV, 81- *Concurrent Pos:* Sci dir psychiat, Pierre Janet Hosp, Que, 70-76; dir psychopharmacol, Ottawa Gen Hosp, 76-79; chmn, Expert Standing Comt Psychotrop Drugs, 82; dir res & psychiat, Royal Ottawa Hosp, 79-, dir outpatient clin, 80- *Honors & Awards:* Tait-MacKenzie Medal, Ottawa Acad Med, 80. *Mem:* Can Col Neuropsychopharmacol; fel Royal Col Physicians & Surgeons Can; Soc Biol Psychiat. *Res:* Drugs used in the treatment of psychiatric disorders plus biochemical clinical and electrophysiological research in the underlying biological factors contributing to mental illness. *Mailing Add:* Royal Ottawa Hosp 1145 Carling Ave Ottawa ON K1Z 7K4 Can

LAPIETRA, JOSEPH RICHARD, b New York, NY, July 20, 32. PHYSICAL CHEMISTRY, THERMODYNAMICS. *Educ:* Marist Col, BA, 54; Cath Univ Am, PhD(chem), 61. *Prof Exp:* Teacher high sch, NY, 54-56; instr chem, Cath Univ Am, 60-61; from asst prof to assoc prof, 64-77, acad dean, 69-75, PROF CHEM, MARIST COL, 77- *Res:* Chemistry of transition metal complexes; thermochemistry; history of science; electrochemistry. *Mailing Add:* Marist Col Poughkeepsie NY 12601

LAPIN, A I E, b Montreal, Que, May 13, 38; m 64. ELECTRICAL ENGINEERING. *Educ:* McGill Univ, BEng, 60; Univ Sheffield, PhD(elec eng), 63. *Prof Exp:* Mem tech staff, Bell Tel Labs Inc, 63-70; DESIGN SPECIALIST, GEN DYNAMICS CORP, 70- *Mem:* Inst Elec & Electronics Engrs. *Res:* Microwave diode and transistor circuitry; microwave systems for tactical missiles. *Mailing Add:* Gen Dynamics Corp PO Box 2507 Pomona CA 91766

LAPIN, ABRAHAM, b Cairo, Egypt, Sept 30, 23; US citizen; m 50; c 2. CHEMICAL ENGINEERING, MATHEMATICS. *Educ:* Univ Mich, BScE(chem eng) & BScE(math), 49; Polytech Inst Brooklyn, MSc, 55; Lehigh Univ, PhD(chem eng), 63. *Prof Exp:* Asst port engr, Am Israeli Shipping Co, Inc, 49-51; sales mgr, Dapor Trading Co, Inc, 51-52; mat engr, US Corps Eng, 53; chem engr, Mineral Beneficiation Lab, Columbia Univ, 54; chem engr, Air Prod & Chem, Inc, 55-57, proj engr, 57-59, group leader, 59-63, sect mgr cryogenic eng res & develop, 63-75; RETIRED. *Concurrent Pos:* Lectr, Pa State Univ, 61 & Lehigh Univ, 64. *Mem:* Am Chem Soc; Am Inst Chem Engrs; Am Inst Chemists; Am Soc Heating, Refrig & Air-Conditioning Eng; Am Soc Testing & Mat. *Res:* Cryogenic engineering; low temperature separation; distillation; heat transfer; insulation; fluid flow. *Mailing Add:* 2737 Saxon St Allentown PA 18103

LAPIN, DAVID MARVIN, b New York, Apr 12, 39; m 67; c 2. BIOLOGY. *Educ:* NY Univ, BA, 60, MS, 63, PhD(biol), 68. *Prof Exp:* From instr to assoc prof biol, 66-76, PROF BIOL SCI, CHMN DEPT, FAIRLEIGH DICKINSON UNIV, 76- *Concurrent Pos:* Grants in aid, Fairleigh Dickinson Univ, 68-72. *Mem:* AAAS; Am Soc Hemat. *Res:* Kinetics of hematopoiesis; humoral regulation of hematopoiesis. *Mailing Add:* Dept of Biol Fairleigh Dickinson Univ Teaneck NJ 07666

LAPIN, ELLIS E, b Chicago, Ill, Feb 21, 17; m 44; c 2. AERONAUTICS, MECHANICAL ENGINEERING. *Educ:* Drexel Inst Technol, BSME, 39; Calif Inst Technol, MSAe, 40, AeE, 41. *Prof Exp:* Asst aeronaut, Calif Inst Technol, 39-41; aerodyn engr, Douglas Aircraft Co, Inc, 41-52, chief group engr, 52-59; proj engr space vehicles, Aerojet Gen Corp, 59-61; proposals dir, Space-Gen Corp, 61-62; prog dir satellite vehicles, Satellite Systs Div, Aerospace Corp, 62-65, group prog dir, 65-78, prin engr & staff group vpres, 78-79; RETIRED. *Concurrent Pos:* Aerospace Corp fel, 75; res assoc, Calif Inst Technol, 75-76; prin investr, Dept Energy, 77-78. *Mem:* AAAS; Am Inst Aeronaut & Astronaut; Am Astronaut Soc. *Res:* Aerodynamic problems of supersonic flows; development and application of aerodynamic theory; engineering design of earth satellites; windmill design; alternative energy sources. *Mailing Add:* 5939 Chariton Ave Los Angeles CA 90056

LAPIN, EVELYN P, b Montreal, Que, Aug 29, 33; m; c 3. NEUROCHEMISTRY, ENZYMOLOGY. *Educ:* McGill Univ, BSc, 54, PhD(biochem), 57. *Prof Exp:* Am Cancer Soc fel, Albert Einstein Col Med, 57-59; instr math & chem, Herzliah Acad, 62-65; lectr biochem, McGill Univ, 65-66; NIH fel, Mt Sinai Sch Med, 70-73; instr neurochem, 74-81, RES ASST PROF, MT SINAI SCH MED, 81- *Concurrent Pos:* Lectr, Queen's Col, NY, 73-; vis asst prof, Stern Col Women, Yeshiva Univ, NY; vis assoc prof, Columbia Univ. *Mem:* Brit Biochem Soc; Am Soc Neurochem; Can Fedn Univ Women. *Res:* Subcellular compartmentalization of respiratory activity and energy metabolism; protein and lipid chemistry of nervous system, localization, separation and identification and function; biochemical mechanisms of hydrocarbon neurotoxins in central and distal axonopathy. *Mailing Add:* Dept of Neurol Mt Sinai Sch of Med New York NY 10029

LAPKIN, MILTON, b New York, NY, July 29, 29; m 64; c 3. POLYMER CHEMISTRY. *Educ:* Polytech Inst New York, BS, 51, PhD(org chem), 55. *Prof Exp:* Group leader, Olin Corp, 55-59, sect leader, 59-60, dir res, 69-73; DIR RES, BEATRICE FOODS, POLYVINYL CHEM INDUST, 73- *Mem:* Am Chem Soc; AAAS; Am Inst Chem; Fedn Soc for Coating Technol. *Res:* Free radical polymerization; polyvinly chloride; acrylic and methacyclic polymers; epoxies; prophyline oxide; ethylene oxide; oxzalylatim. *Mailing Add:* 12 Darvell Dr Sadbury MA 01776

LAPLANCHE, LAURINE A see Grapham, Laurine LaPlanche

LAPLAZA, MIGUEL LUIS, b Zaragoza, Spain, Mar 20, 38; m 69; c 4. MATHEMATICS. *Educ:* Univ Barcelona, MD, 60; Univ Madrid, PhD(math), 65. *Prof Exp:* Instr math, Univ Barcelona, 60-61; from asst prof to assoc prof, Univ Madrid, 60-66; assoc prof math, 67-76, PROF MATH, UNIV PR, MAYAGUEZ, 76- *Mem:* Am Math Soc; Math Asn Am. *Res:* Category theory. *Mailing Add:* 14-M-7-B Terrace Mayaguez PR 00708

LA POINTE, JOSEPH L, b Harvey, Ill, Sept 7, 34; m 54, 66; c 3. ZOOLOGY. *Educ:* Portland State Col, BA, 60; Univ Calif, Berkeley, PhD(zool), 66. *Prof Exp:* Assoc instr zool, Univ Calif, Berkeley, 64-66; Nat Inst Child Health & Human Develop fel, 66-68; asst prof, 68-71, assoc prof biol, 71-80, PROF ENDOCRINOL, NMEX STATE UNIV, 80- *Concurrent Pos:* NIH res grant, 72-73. *Mem:* Am Soc Ichthyol & Herpet; Am Soc Zool; Brit Soc Endocrinol; Europ Soc Comp Endocrinol. *Res:* Effect of perietal eye on circadian rhythms in lizards; thermoregulation in antusiid lizards; ultrastructure of reptilian pituitary; physiology of neurohypophysial hormones in lower vertebrates; fat mobilization in lizards. *Mailing Add:* Dept of Biol NMex State Univ Las Cruces NM 88003

LAPOINTE, LEONARD LYELL, b Iron Mountain, Mich, June 28, 39; m 63; c 2. SPEECH PATHOLOGY. *Educ:* Mich State Univ, BA, 61; Univ Colo, MA, 66, PhD(speech path), 69. *Prof Exp:* Dir speech path commun dis, Bd Educ, Menasha, Wis, 61-64; speech pathologist, Gen Rose Mem Hosp, 66; asst prof phonetics, Univ Colo, Denver, 68-69; COORDR & INSTR AUDIOL & SPEECH PATH, VET ADMIN MED CTR, GAINESVILLE, 69-, RES INVESTR SPEECH SCI, 71- *Concurrent Pos:* Fel neurogenic commun dis, Vet Admin Hosp, Denver, 68-69; adj prof commun dis, Univ Fla, 69-, mem res fac neuroling, Ctr Neurol-Behav Ling Res, 74- *Honors & Awards:* Award, Sci Exhib, XV World Cong Logopedics & Phoniatrics, 71. *Mem:* Acad Aphasia; fel Am Speech & Hearing Asn; Int Asn Logopedics & Phoniatrics; Int Neuropsychol Soc; Am Cleft Palate Asn. *Res:* Development of measurement strategies of human oral sensation-perception; oral physiology and neurolinguistics; diagnosis and treatment strategies in aphasia and related neurogenic communication impairments. *Mailing Add:* Audiol & Speech Path Serv Vet Admin Med Ctr Gainesville FL 32602

LAPONSKY, ALFRED BAER, b Cleveland, Ohio, Nov 24, 21; m 57; c 2. PHYSICAL ELECTRONICS. *Educ:* Lehigh Univ, BS, 43, MS, 47, PhD(physics), 51. *Prof Exp:* Instr physics, Lehigh Univ, 47-51; physicist electron physics, Res Lab, Gen Elec Co, 51-63; assoc prof elec eng, Univ Minn, Minneapolis, 63-66; FEL ENGR, INDUST & GOVT TUBE DIV, WESTINGHOUSE ELEC CORP, 66- *Mem:* Am Phys Soc. *Res:* Electron physics; electro-optics; image sensing and display techniques. *Mailing Add:* Westinghouse Elec Corp Indust & Govt Tube Div Horseheads NY 14845

LAPORTE, LEO FREDERIC, b Englewood, NJ, July 30, 33; m 56; c 2. GEOLOGY. *Educ:* Columbia Univ, AB, 56, PhD(geol), 60. *Prof Exp:* From instr to prof geol, Brown Univ, 59-71; dean natural sci, 75-76, PROF EARTH SCI, UNIV CALIF, SANTA CRUZ, 71- *Concurrent Pos:* Vis prof, Yale Univ, 64- *Mem:* AAAS; Am Asn Petrol Geologists; Geol Soc Am; Soc Econ Paleont & Mineral; Paleont Soc. *Res:* Paleoecology and environmental stratigraphy; history and evolution of life. *Mailing Add:* Div of Natural Sci Univ of Calif Santa Cruz CA 95064

LAPORTE, RONALD E, b Buffalo, NY, May 29, 49; m 71. EPIDEMIOLOGY. *Educ:* Univ Buffalo, BA, 71; Univ Pittsburgh, MS, 73, PhD(psychol), 76. *Prof Exp:* EPIDEMIOLOGIST, DEPT EPIDEMIOL, UNIV PITTSBURGH, 78- *Concurrent Pos:* Fel epidemiol, Univ Pittsburgh, 76- *Mem:* AAAS; Soc Epidemiol Res; Am Psychol Asn. *Res:* Chronic disease epidemiology; investigating possible protective factors of coronary heart disease and diabetes epidemeology. *Mailing Add:* Dept of Epidemiol Univ of Pittsburgh Pittsburgh PA 15261

LAPOSA, JOSEPH DAVID, b St Louis, Mo, July 21, 38; m 68; c 3. PHYSICAL CHEMISTRY. *Educ:* St Louis Univ, BS, 60; Univ Chicago, MS, 62; Loyola Univ, Ill, PhD(chem), 65. *Prof Exp:* NIH fel chem, Cornell Univ, 65-67; asst prof, 67-73, ASSOC PROF CHEM, McMASTER UNIV, 73- *Mem:* Am Phys Soc. *Res:* Molecular luminescence. *Mailing Add:* Dept Chem McMaster Univ Hamilton ON L3S 4L8 Can

LAPP, H(ERBERT) M(ELBOURNE), b Alameda, Sask, Feb 2, 22; m 50; c 3. AGRICULTURAL ENGINEERING. *Educ:* Univ Sask, BE, 49; Univ Minn, MS, 62. *Prof Exp:* With water develop, Prairie Farm Rehab Admin, Dominion Govt Can, 49-51; exten engr, Manitoba Dept Agr, 51-53; from asst prof to assoc prof, 53-70, head dept, 58-67, PROF AGR ENG, UNIV MANITOBA, 70- *Concurrent Pos:* Colombo plan adv, Khon Kaen Univ, Thailand, 65-67; local prog head develop grad studies in agr eng for Latin Am region, Nat Agrarian Univ, Peru, 67-70; consult, Can Int Develop Agency, Nigeria, 73 & 76, F F Co, Consult Engrs, Vancouver, Honduras, 74 & Int Bank Reconstruct & Develop, Philippines, 76, Pakistan, 77. *Mem:* Fel Can Soc Agr Eng (pres, 75-76); Am Soc Agr Engrs; Agr Inst Can. *Res:* Farm structure; soil and water. *Mailing Add:* Dept of Agr Eng Univ of Manitoba Winnipeg MB R3T 2N2 Can

LAPP, M(ARSHALL), b Buffalo, NY, Aug 20, 32; m 58, 80; c 2. LASER GAS DIAGNOSTICS, LIGHT SCATTERING. *Educ:* Cornell Univ, BEngPhys, 55; Calif Inst Technol, PhD(eng sci), 60. *Prof Exp:* Physicist, Corp Res & Develop, 60-80, ACTG MGR, COMBUSTION UNIT, GEN ELEC CO, 81- *Concurrent Pos:* Sci Res coun sr vis fel, Sch Physics, Univ Newcastle, 68-69. *Mem:* AAAS; fel Am Phys Soc; fel Optical Soc Am; Am Inst Aeronaut & Astronaut; fel Brit Inst Physics. *Res:* Optical diagnostics of flames; laser Raman spectroscopy; radiative properties of metal vapors and gases; optical diagnostics of gases and surfaces; atomic and molecular physics; physics of fluids. *Mailing Add:* Gen Elec Res & Develop Ctr PO Box 8 Bldg K-1 Schenectady NY 12301

LAPP, MARTIN STANLEY, b Toronto, Ont. NUMERICAL TAXONOMY, COMPUTER SIMULATION. *Educ:* York Univ, BSc, 69, MSc, 72; Univ Alta, PhD(plant path), 77. *Prof Exp:* Res assoc, 77-80, RES OFFICER NUMERICAL TAXON, NAT RES COUN CAN, 80- *Mem:* Can Phytopath Soc; Can Bot Asn. *Res:* Numerical taxonomy of conifers using the leaf-oil terpene patterns; preinfection phase of the life cycle of leaf pathogens. *Mailing Add:* Nat Res Coun Can 110 Gymnasium Rd Saskatoon SK S7N 0W9 Can

LAPP, NEIL ARDEN, b Bloomington, Ill, Dec 7, 42; m 67; c 2. PLANT PATHOLOGY, NEMATOLOGY. *Educ:* Goshen Col, BA, 64; WVa Univ, MS, 67; NC State Univ, PhD(plant path), 70. *Prof Exp:* plant pathologist, Plant Protection Div, NC Dept Agr, 71-81; FIELD DEVELOP FEL, MERCK & CO, 81- *Concurrent Pos:* Adj asst prof plant path, NC State Univ, 71-77, adj assoc prof, 77- *Mem:* Am Phytopath Soc; Soc Nematologists. *Res:* Plant disease and nematode survey and detection; chemical control. *Mailing Add:* Merck & Co 7208 Madiera Ct Raleigh NC 27609

LAPP, P(HILIP) A(LEXANDER), b Toronto, Ont, May 12, 28; m 52; c 3. REMOTE SENSING. *Educ:* Univ Toronto, BASc, 50; Mass Inst Technol, SM, 51, ScD(instrumentation), 54. *Prof Exp:* Instr aeronaut eng, Mass Inst Technol, 52-53, res assoc, 53-54; systs eng, DeHavilland Aircraft Can Ltd, 54-56, proj engr, Guided Missile Div, 55-60, chief engr, Spec Prod & Appl Res Div, 60-65, dir tech opers, 65-68; sr vpres, Spar Aerospace Prod Ltd, 68-69; PRES, PHILIP A LAPP LTD, 69- *Concurrent Pos:* Chmn working group sensors, Can Ctr Remote Sensing, 70-76; mem, Can Accreditation Bd, 71-75; mem, Bd Govs, York Univ, 80- *Mem:* Am Inst Aeroanut & Astronaut; Inst Elec & Electronics Engrs; Can Aeronaut & Space Inst; Can Res Mgt Asn. *Res:* Dynamics of vehicles; guidance and control of missiles and aircraft; military and industrial instrumentation and automatic control; educational planning and research on public policy; remote sensing applied to resource management and environmental monitoring. *Mailing Add:* Philip A Lapp Ltd 14a Hazelton Toronto ON M5R 2E2 Can

LAPP, THOMAS WILLIAM, b Joliet, Ill, Oct 6, 37; m 61. ENVIRONMENTAL CHEMISTRY, INDUSTRIAL CHEMISTRY. *Educ:* Coe Col, BA, 59; Kans State Univ, MS, 61, PhD(inorg chem), 63. *Prof Exp:* Fel radiation chem, NAm Aviation Sci Ctr, 63-64; asst prof nuclear chem, Univ WVa, 64-66; assoc chemist, Midwest Res Inst, Mo, 66-69; mem staff, Univ Mo-Kansas City, 70-74; assoc chemist, 74-77, SR CHEM, MIDWEST RES INST, MO, 77- *Res:* Production and utilization of industrial chemicals suspected of possessing toxic properties; mechanisms whereby such materials are introduced to the environment, quantities introduced, and subsequent reactions in the environment. *Mailing Add:* Midwest Res Inst 425 Volker Blvd Kansas City MO 64110

LAPPAS, LEWIS CHRISTOPHER, b Lynn, Mass, May 14, 21; m 49; c 3. PHARMACEUTICAL CHEMISTRY. *Educ:* Mass Col Pharm, BS, 43, MS, 48; Purdue Univ, PhD(pharmaceut chem), 51. *Prof Exp:* RES SCIENTIST, ELI LILLY & CO, 51- *Mem:* Am Chem Soc; Am Pharmaceut Asn. *Res:* Drug encapsulation processes; basic gelatin research as applied to capsular forms; study pf filmogens as drug release mechanisms; stabilization of drugs and drug forms; pharmaceutical aspects of drug absorption; investigation of new antimicrobials in drug and cosmetic formulations. *Mailing Add:* 12936 Pepper Mill Ct Carmel IN 46032

LAPPIN, GERALD R, b Caro, Mich, Apr 14, 19; m 45; c 2. CHEMISTRY. *Educ:* Alma Col, BS, 41; Northwestern Univ, PhD(org chem), 46. *Prof Exp:* Asst, Northwestern Univ, 41-43, interim instr chem, 44, asst, 44-46; asst prof, Antioch Col, 46-49 & Univ Ariz, 49-51; sr res chemist, 51-69, RES ASSOC, TENN EASTMAN CO DIV, EASTMAN KODAK CO, 69- *Concurrent Pos:* Consult, Vernay Labs, Ohio, 46-49. *Mem:* Am Chem Soc. *Res:* Additives for foods; plastics and petroleum products; chemistry of polyesters; technology forecasting as applied to research and development planning. *Mailing Add:* 4047 Skyland Dr Kingsport TN 37664

LAPPLE, CHARLES E, b New York, NY, Feb 11, 16; m 41; c 2. CHEMICAL ENGINEERING. *Educ:* Columbia Univ, BS, 36, ChE, 37. *Prof Exp:* Chem engr, E I du Pont de Nemours & Co, 37-45, process engr, 45-46, chem engr, 46-48, res proj eng, 48-50; assoc prof chem eng, Ohio State Univ, 50-55; sr scientist, SRI Int, 55-79; CONSULT, 79- *Concurrent Pos:* Lectr, Columbia Univ, 41-48 & Univ Del, 48-50; indust consult, 50-; consult, USPHS, 61-66 & US Dept Interior, 66- *Mem:* Am Chem Soc; Am Inst Chem Engrs. *Res:* Fluid mechanics; heat transfer; dust and mist collection; particle dynamics; aerosols; atmospheric pollution abatement; fine particle technology. *Mailing Add:* 13691 Old Altos Rd Los Altos Hills CA 94022

LAPPLE, WALTER C(HRISTIAN), b Mt Vernon, NY, Apr 8, 21; m 45; c 2. CHEMICAL ENGINEERING. *Educ:* Cooper Union, BS, 43; Univ Kans, MS, 57. *Prof Exp:* Indust engr, E I du Pont de Nemours & Co, 43-46; res chem engr, Varcum Chem Corp, 46-47; chem engr, Dorr Co, 47-51; sr chem engr, Midwest Res Inst, 51-52, head process sect, Chem Eng Dept, 52-54, asst mgr, 54-57; sr chem engr, Oliver Iron Mining Div, US Steel Corp, 57-59 & FMC Corp, 60-65; SR CHEM ENGR, BABCOCK & WILCOX CO, 65- *Mem:* Am Inst Chem Engrs; Am Chem Soc. *Res:* Chemical processing; metallurgical operations; industrial waste abatement; fluidized bed technology, fundamentals, drying and high temperature reactions. *Mailing Add:* 3505 Mountview Ave Alliance OH 44601

LAPPORTE, SEYMOUR JEROME, b Chicago, Ill, Mar 26, 30; m 64; c 2. ORGANIC CHEMISTRY, PETROLEUM CHEMISTRY. *Educ:* Univ Chicago, MS, 53; Univ Calif, Los Angeles, PhD(chem), 57. *Prof Exp:* Asst, Univ Calif, Los Angeles, 53-56; sr res assoc, Chevron Res Co, 56-74, MGR, PIONEERING DIV, CHEVRON RES CO, 74-, SR RES SCIENTIST, 80- *Concurrent Pos:* Teacher, Exten, Univ Calif, 60-; vis scholar, Stanford Univ, 68-69. *Mem:* Am Chem Soc; The Chem Soc. *Res:* Organic reaction mechanisms; organometallics; oxidation; transition metal chemistry; homogenous catalysis; ultraviolet stabilization. *Mailing Add:* 107 Ardith Dr Orinda CA 94563

LA PRADE, KERBY EUGENE, b Grand Saline, Tex, Feb 12, 28; div; c 1. GEOLOGY. *Educ:* Tex Tech Univ, BS, 51, MS, 54, PhD(geol), 69. *Prof Exp:* Geophysicist, Texaco, Inc, 53-55; geologist, Phillips Petrol Co, 55-63; from instr to teaching asst gen geol, Tex Tech Univ, 63-67; PROF EARTH SCI, E TEX STATE UNIV, 67- *Concurrent Pos:* Res assoc NSF-Tex Tech Univ Antarctic Exped, 64-65; leader and chief scientist NSF-Tex Tech Univ Antarctic Exped, 68-69; fac res grant geol, E Tex State Univ, 69-70; Am Geol Inst field geol, Spain, 71. *Honors & Awards:* Antarctic Serv Medal, US Govt, 69. *Mem:* Am Asn Petrol Geologists; Geol Soc Am. *Res:* Structure, stratigraphy and sedimentation of Antarctica and the southwestern United States. *Mailing Add:* Dept of Earth Sci ETex State Univ Commerce TX 75428

LA PRADE, MARIE DOUGLAS, b Jerome, Ariz, Aug 21, 42; m 63. STRUCTURAL CHEMISTRY, INORGANIC CHEMISTRY. *Educ:* Univ Mich, BSc, 64; Univ Vt, MS, 67; Mass Inst Technol, PhD(chem), 70. *Prof Exp:* Res assoc chem, Mass Inst Technol, 69-73; asst prof chem, Nasson Col, 73-78; vis prof chem, Clemson Univ, 78-81; VIS PROF CHEM, RUTGERS UNIV, 81- *Concurrent Pos:* Vis res assoc chem, Univ NH, 76-78. *Mem:* Am Crystallog Asn; Am Asn Univ Prof. *Res:* Single crystal x-ray diffraction applied to inorganic and organometallic molecules. *Mailing Add:* Dept of Chem Rutgers Univ New Brunswick NJ 08903

LAPRADE, MARY HODGE, b Oakland, Calif, Feb 6, 29; m 58; c 2. ZOOLOGY. *Educ:* Wilson Col, AB, 51; Radcliffe Col, AM, 52, PhD(biol), 58. *Prof Exp:* Instr biol, Simmons Col, 52-55; instr zool, 58-60 & 64-65, LECTR BIOL SCI, SMITH COL, 65-, DIR, CLARK SCI CTR, 73- *Concurrent Pos:* Instr, NSF In-Serv Inst High Sch Biol Teachers, 65-66. *Mem:* Sigma Xi. *Res:* Growth and regeneration, particularly in crustaceans; fine structure of endocrine organs in crustaceans. *Mailing Add:* Dept of Biol Sci Smith Col Northampton MA 01063

LAPSLEY, ALWYN COWLES, b Albemarle Co, Va, Mar 12, 20. PHYSICS. *Educ:* Univ Va, BEE, 41, MS, 44, PhD(physics), 47. *Prof Exp:* Instr physics, Univ Va, 41-43, asst, Manhattan Proj & Navy Fire Control, 43-46; sr physicist, Photo Prod Dept, E I du Pont de Nemours & Co, 47-51, res engr, Atomic Energy Div, 51-60; lectr nuclear eng, 60-77, SR SCIENTIST, REACTOR FACIL, SCH ENG & APPL SCI, UNIV VA, 60-, RES ASSOC PROF, NUCLEAR ENG, 77- *Mem:* Am Phys Soc; Am Nuclear Soc. *Res:* Mechanics; physical optics; Kerr effect with high frequency fields; nuclear physics; ion chambers; reactor kinetics; isotope separation. *Mailing Add:* Reactor Facil Univ of Va Sch of Eng & Appl Sci Charlottesville VA 22901

LAPUCK, JACK LESTER, b Jamaica Plain, Mass, Aug 28, 24; m 48; c 3. FOOD CHEMISTRY, BACTERIOLOGY. *Educ:* Northeastern Univ, BS, 46; Univ Mass, MS, 49; Calvin Coolidge Col, DSc(sci educ), 60. *Prof Exp:* Food sanitarian, Montgomery County Health Dept, Md, 50-51; food chemist, Food & Drug Res Labs, NY, 51; chemist, Waltham Labs, Inc, 51-55, lab dir & vpres, 55-66; OWNER & MGR, LAPUCK LABS, 66- *Concurrent Pos:* Instr, Univ Exten, Mass Dept Educ, 55-; instr, Boston State Col. *Mem:* AAAS; Am Chem Soc; Am Soc Microbiol; Inst Food Technologists; Am Pub Health Asn. *Res:* Food technology; microbiology; analytical chemistry. *Mailing Add:* 50 Hunt St Watertown MA 02172

LA QUE, F(RANCIS) L(AURENCE), b Gananoque, Ont, July 21, 04; nat US; m 30; c 2. METALLURGICAL ENGINEERING. *Educ:* Queen's Univ, Ont, BSc, 27, LLD, 64. *Prof Exp:* Foreman in charge refining cobalt oxide, Deloro Smelting & Refining Co, Can, 27; from metallurgist to vpres & mgr develop & res div, Int Nickel Co, Inc, NY, 27-62, vpres, Exec Dept, 62-69, spec asst to pres, Int Nickel Co Can, Ltd, 65-69; pres, Am Nat Standards Inst, 70-71; pres, Int Orgn Standardization, 71-73; GOVT & INDUST CONSULT, 73- *Concurrent Pos:* Vchmn, Welding Res Coun; sr lectr, Scripps Inst Oceanog, 70-76. *Honors & Awards:* Speller Award, Nat Asn Corrosion Eng, 49; Acheson Medal, Electrochem Soc, 68. *Mem:* Soc Naval Archit & Marine Eng; Electrochem Soc (pres, 62); Am Soc Testing & Mat (pres, 59); Am Chem Soc; Nat Asn Corrosion Eng (pres, 49). *Res:* Corrosion of metals and alloys; standardization; ocean mining. *Mailing Add:* 1850 Ontario St Kingston ON 07044 K7L 2Y7 Can

LAQUER, HENRY L, b Frankfurt-am-Main, Ger, Nov 28, 19; nat US; m 47; c 4. CRYOGENICS, SYSTEMS ANALYSIS. *Educ:* Temple Univ, AB, 43; Princeton Univ, MA, 45, PhD(phys chem), 47. *Prof Exp:* Res chemist, Ladox Labs, Pa, 46; mem staff, Los Alamos Sci Lab, Univ Calif, 47-77; CONSULT, 77- *Concurrent Pos:* Adj prof, Los Alamos Residence Ctr, Univ NMex, 70-73. *Mem:* Am Phys Soc. *Res:* High magnetic fields; applied superconductivity; dielectric studies; elastic properties of metals; cryogenics. *Mailing Add:* Rte 1 Box 445 Espanola NM 87532

LARA-BRAUD, CAROLYN WEATHERSBEE, b Waco, Tex, Jan 4, 40; m 70. BIOCHEMISTRY. *Educ:* Univ Tex, Austin, BA, 62, PhD(chem), 69. *Prof Exp:* Res assoc biochem, Clayton Found Biochem Inst & lectr home econ, Nutrit Div, Univ Tex, Austin, 71-73; asst res scientist biochem 73-75, asst prof, 75-80, ASSOC PROF HOME ECON, UNIV IOWA, 80- *Mem:* AAAS; Am Chem Soc; Sigma Xi, Inst Food Technol; Am Home Econ Asn. *Res:* Intermediary metabolism; regulation of inducible enzyme systems. *Mailing Add:* Dept of Home Econ Univ of Iowa Iowa City IA 52242

LARACH, SIMON, b Brooklyn, NY, Apr 21, 22; m 48; c 2. PHYSICAL INORGANIC CHEMISTRY, SOLID STATE CHEMISTRY. *Educ:* City Col New York, BS, 43; Princeton Univ, MA, 51, PhD(chem), 54. *Prof Exp:* Res chemist, Third Res Div, Goldwater Hosp, Col Med, NY Univ, 43 & 46; res chemist luminescence & solid state, David Sarnoff Res Ctr, Radio Corp Am, 46-59, head photoelectronic, magnetic & dielec res, 59-61, assoc lab dir, 61-67, overseas fel, 69, FEL, DAVID SARNOFF RES CTR, RCA CORP, 67- *Concurrent Pos:* Vis fel, Princeton Univ, 67-68; Indust Res Inst-Am Chem Soc liaison lectr, 68; vis prof, Hebrew Univ Jerusalem, 69-70, adj prof, 71-73; UN consult, UNESCO Div Tech Educ & Res, 71; prin lectr, NATO Adv Study Inst, Norway, 72; vis prof, Swiss Fed Inst Technol, 72; vis prof, Princeton Univ, 73; div ed electronics, J Electrochem Soc; res prof radiol, Hahnemann Med Col & Hosp, 74-; adj prof radiol, Col Physicians & Surgeons, Columbia Univ, 78- *Mem:* Am Chem Soc; fel Am Phys Soc; fel Am Inst Chem; Electrochem Soc. *Res:* Synthesis and properties of electronically-active solids; medical ultrasound. *Mailing Add:* 139 Sycamore Rd Princeton NJ 08540

LARAGH, JOHN HENRY, b Yonkers, NY, Nov 18, 24; m 74; c 3. PHYSIOLOGY, MEDICINE. *Educ:* Cornell Univ, MD, 48. *Prof Exp:* Intern med, Presby Hosp, New York, 48-49, asst resident, 49-50, asst, 50-55, instr, 55-57, assoc, 57-59, from asst prof to prof clin med, Col Physicians & Surgeons, Columbia Univ, 67-75; HILDA ALTSCHUL MASTER PROF MED, MED COL, CORNELL UNIV, 75-, DIR CARDIOVASC CTR, NY HOSP-CORNELL MED CTR, 75- *Concurrent Pos:* Nat Heart Inst trainee, 50-51; asst physician, Presby Hosp, New York, 50-54, from asst attend physician to assoc attend physician, 54-69, attend physician, 69-75, vchmn in chg med affairs, Bd Trustees, 74; NY Heart Asn res fel, 51-52; mem med adv bd, Coun High Blood Pressure Res, Am Heart Asn, 61, chmn, 68-72; consult cardiovasc study sect, USPHS, 64-68 & heart prog proj A, 67-72; dir, Hypertension Ctr & Nephrol Div, Columbia-Presby Med Ctr, 71-75; mem policy adv bd, Hypertension Detection & Follow-Up Prog, Nat Heart & Lung Inst, 71-, mem bd sci coun, 74-; mem adv bd, Am Soc Contemporary Med & Surg, 74. *Honors & Awards:* Stouffer Prize Med Res, 69. *Mem:* Am Soc Clin Invest; fel Am Col Physicians; Am Soc Nephrol; assoc Harvey Soc; Asn Am Physicians. *Res:* Cardiovascular and renal diseases; endocrinology. *Mailing Add:* New York Hosp-Cornell Med Ctr 525 E68th St New York NY 10021

LARAMORE, GEORGE ERNEST, b Ottawa, Ill, Nov 5, 43; m 64; c 1. PHYSICS, MEDICINE. *Educ:* Purdue Univ, BS, 65; Univ Ill, Urbana, MS, 66, PhD(physics), 69; Univ Miami, MD, 76. *Prof Exp:* NSF fel, Univ Ill, Urbana, 69-70, res assoc physics, 70-71; res physicist, Sandia Labs, 71-75; ASST PROF, DEPT RADIATION ONCOL, UNIV WASH, 78- *Mem:* Am Phys Soc; Am Vacuum Soc; AMA. *Res:* Theory of low-energy electron diffraction; fast neutron radiotherapy for human malignancies; interaction of fast electrons with solids. *Mailing Add:* 19003 Sunnyside Ave N Seattle WA 98133

LARCHER, HEINRICH, b Telfs, Austria, Dec 1, 25; nat US; m 64; c 2. PURE MATHEMATICS. *Educ:* Univ Innsbruck, Dr phil(math), 50. *Prof Exp:* Teacher pub sch, Eng, 50-51; master math, Seaford Col, 51-53; prof, Inst Montana, Switz, 54-56; from instr to asst prof, Mich State Univ, 56-64; MEM STAFF, UNIV MD, MUNICH, 64- *Mem:* Am Math Soc. *Res:* Orthogonal functions in two variables; theory of functions of a complex variable; theory of numbers. *Mailing Add:* Univ of Md Munich Campus APO New York 09407 Germany, Federal Republic of

L'ARCHEVEQUE, REAL VIATEUR, b Montreal, Que. NUCLEAR ENGINEERING, ELECTRONICS. *Educ:* Polytech Inst, Montreal, BSc, 60; Univ London, PhD(electronics), 64. *Prof Exp:* Head, Electronics Br, Atomic Energy of Can Ltd, 65-77; asst to pres, 77-80, PRES, CANATOM, 80- *Res:* Hybrid microelectronics; thick film microcircuits; nuclear instruments development and design; on-line computer data acquisition systems development. *Mailing Add:* Canatom 740 Notre-Dame St W Montreal PQ H3C 3X6 Can

LARCOM, LYNDON LYLE, b Olean, NY, Apr 11, 40. BIOPHYSICS, MOLECULAR BIOLOGY. *Educ:* Carnegie-Mellon Univ, BS, 62; Univ Pittsburgh, MS, 65, PhD(biophysics), 68. *Prof Exp:* NIH fel chem, Univ Pittsburgh, 68-70, res assoc, 70-72; asst prof, 72-77, assoc prof, 77-81, PROF PHYSICS & MICROBIOL, CLEMSON UNIV, 81- *Mem:* Biophys Soc; Am Soc Photobiol; Am Soc Microbiol; Am Chem Soc. *Res:* Mechanisms of DNA damage and repair; the biophysical properties of nucleic acids; molecular quantum mechanics; DNA-protein interactions; virus structure. *Mailing Add:* Dept of Physics Clemson Univ Clemson SC 29631

LARD, EDWIN WEBSTER, b Ala, July 17, 21; m 45; c 4. ANALYTICAL CHEMISTRY. *Educ:* Ark State Col, BS, 49; Memphis State Univ, MA, 61. *Prof Exp:* Chemist, Ethyl Corp, 49-52 & Chemstrand Corp, 52-54; sr chemist, Nitrogen Prod Div, W R Grace & Co, Tenn, 54-62, res supvr, Res Div, Clarksville, Md, 62-74; CHEM ENGR, NAVAL SEA SYSTS COMMAND, WASHINGTON, DC, 74- *Mem:* Am Chem Soc. *Res:* Trace gas analysis with infrared; separation and determination of argo, oxygen and nitrogen by chromatography; trace analysis of acetylene, methane, carbon monoxide and carbon dioxide; synthesis of aryl dimethyl sulfonium chloride compounds; chemical warfare agents; unsaturates in auto emissions; water energy conservation on naval ships. *Mailing Add:* 12703 Beaverdale Lane Bowie MD 20715

LARDNER, ROBIN WILLMOTT, b Leicester, Eng, Feb 9, 38; m 58, 79; c 4. APPLIED MATHEMATICS, MECHANICS. *Educ:* Cambridge Univ, BA, 59, PhD(appl math), 63. *Prof Exp:* Res assoc physics, Columbia Univ, 61-63; NATO fel appl math & theoret physics, Peterhouse Col, Cambridge Univ, 63-65; lectr math & physics, Univ East Anglia, 65-67; assoc prof, 67-70, chmn dept, 71-73, PROF MATH, SIMON FRASER UNIV, 70- *Res:* Solid mechanics, particularly dislocation theory and fracture; nonlinear vibrations of continuous media; asymptotic solutions of nonlinear partial differential equations. *Mailing Add:* Dept of Math Simon Fraser Univ Burnaby BC V5A 1S6 Can

LARDNER, THOMAS JOSEPH, b New York, NY, July 19, 38; m 64; c 3. ENGINEERING MECHANICS. *Educ:* Polytech Inst Brooklyn, BAeroE, 58, MS, 59, PhD(appl mech), 61. *Prof Exp:* Res assoc appl mech, Polytech Inst Brooklyn, 59-61; res engr, Jet Propulsion Lab, Calif Inst Technol, 62-63; instr math, Mass Inst Technol, 63-67, asst prof appl math, 67-70, assoc prof mech eng, 70-73; prof theoret & appl mech, Univ Ill, Urbana, 73-78; PROF CIVIL ENG, UNIV MASS, 78- *Concurrent Pos:* Fulbright lectr, Univ Nepal, 65-66; consult, Adelphi Res Ctr, Polytech Inst Brooklyn & Jet Propulsion Lab, Calif Inst Technol. *Mem:* Am Soc Mech Eng; Soc Indust & Appl Math; Am Soc Eng Educ. *Res:* Applied mathematics and mechanics in heat transfer, thermoelasticity, spacecraft temperature control and shell theory; applied solid mechanics. *Mailing Add:* 175 Amity St Amherst MA 01002

LARDY, HENRY ARNOLD, b Roslyn, SDak, Aug 19, 17; m 43; c 4. BIOCHEMISTRY. *Educ:* SDak State Univ, BS, 39; Univ Wis, MS, 41, PhD(biochem), 43. *Hon Degrees:* DSc, SDak State Univ, 78. *Prof Exp:* Fel, Nat Res Coun, Banting Inst, Univ Toronto, 44-45; from asst prof to prof, 45-66, VILAS PROF BIOL SCI, UNIV WIS-MADISON, 66-, CHMN, RES DEPT, ENZYME INST, 50- *Honors & Awards:* Neuberg Medal, 56; Lewis Award, Am Chem Soc, 49; Wolf Found Award Agr, 81. *Mem:* Nat Acad Sci; Am Philos Soc; Am Chem Soc; Am Soc Biol Chem (pres, 64); Am Acad Arts & Sci. *Res:* Enzymes; intermediary metabolism; hormones. *Mailing Add:* Enzyme Inst Univ of Wis-Madison Madison WI 53706

LARDY, LAWRENCE JAMES, b Sentinel Butte, NDak, Aug 23, 34; m 56; c 2. NUMERICAL ANALYSIS. *Educ:* NDak State Col, Dickinson, BS, 57; Univ NDak, MS, 59; Univ Minn, PhD(math), 64. *Prof Exp:* Instr math, Univ NDak, 59-60 & Univ Minn, 62-64; from asst prof to assoc prof, 64-74, PROF MATH, SYRACUSE UNIV, 74- *Concurrent Pos:* Res fel, Yale Univ, 67-68; vis assoc prof, Univ Md, 73-74. *Mem:* Soc Indust & Appl Math; Math Asn Am; Am Math Soc. *Res:* Functional analysis. *Mailing Add:* Dept of Math Syracuse Univ Syracuse NY 13210

LAREW, H(IRAM) GORDON, b Independence, WVa, June 5, 22; m 46; c 3. CIVIL ENGINEERING, SOIL MECHANICS. *Educ:* Univ WVa, BS, 44; Purdue Univ, MS, 51, PhD, 60. *Prof Exp:* Jr engr, NY Cent Syst, 46; instr civil eng, Purdue Univ, 47-56; assoc prof, 56-64, PROF CIVIL ENG, UNIV VA, 64- *Concurrent Pos:* Consult, 54- *Mem:* Am Soc Civil Engrs; Am Soc Eng Educ; Am Arbitration Asn. *Res:* Utilization of solid wastes; the effects of repeated loads upon soils; soil strength; earth dams; blast damage. *Mailing Add:* 2500 Hillwood Pl Charlottesville VA 22901

LARGE, ALFRED MCKEE, b Listowel, Ont, Mar 7, 12; nat US; m 43; c 1. SURGERY. *Educ:* Univ Toronto, BA, 33, MD, 36. *Prof Exp:* Instr surg, Sch Med, Washington Univ, 43-44; asst prof, 46-62, ASSOC PROF CLIN SURG, COL MED, WAYNE STATE UNIV, 62- *Concurrent Pos:* Attend surgeon, St John Hosp, Ben Secours Hosp & Cottage Hosp; pvt pract. *Mem:* AMA. *Res:* Clinical surgery. *Mailing Add:* 21331 Kelly Rd East Detroit MI 48021

LARGE, RICHARD L, b Rochester, Ind, June 9, 40; m 62; c 3. SOIL SCIENCE, AGRONOMY. *Educ:* Purdue Univ, BSc, 62; Okla State Univ, MSc, 66; Ohio State Univ, PhD(soil sci), 69. *Prof Exp:* Agronomist, US Testing Co, Inc, 69-71; VPRES, A&L AGR LABS, INC, 71- *Mem:* Soil Sci Soc; Am Soc Agron; Coun Agr Sci & Technol. *Res:* Soil fertility; crop nutrition; land application of sludge. *Mailing Add:* A&L Agr Labs Inc 2176 Dunn Ave Memphis TN 37114

LARGE, ROBERT F, analytical chemistry, photographic science, see previous edition

LARGENT, DAVID LEE, b San Francisco, Calif, Oct 30, 37; m 70. MYCOLOGY. *Educ:* San Francisco State Col, BA, 60, MA, 63; Univ Wash, PhD(bot), 68. *Prof Exp:* Instr bot, Foothills Jr Col, 63; instr bot & biol, Phoenix Jr Col, 63-64; asst prof bot, 68-74, assoc prof, 74-77, PROF BOT, HUMBOLDT STATE COL, 77- *Mem:* Am Soc Plant Taxon; Mycol Soc Am; Am Bryol & Lichenological Soc. *Res:* Taxonomy and ecology of the Rhodophylloid fungi on the Pacific coastal states of America; cryptogamic botany. *Mailing Add:* Dept of Biol Humboldt State Col Arcata CA 95521

LARGENT, MAX DALE, b Winchester, Va, Feb 28, 23; m 54; c 2. DENTISTRY. *Educ:* Med Col Va, DDS, 50. *Prof Exp:* Instr pedodontics, Med Col Va, 52-56, from asst prof to prof, 56-72; ASSOC DEAN, BAYLOR COL DENT, 72- *Concurrent Pos:* Chmn dept pedodontics, Med Col Va, 69-72, dir postgrad pedodontics, 57-69. *Mem:* Am Dent Asn; Am Asn Dent Schs; fel Am Col Dent. *Mailing Add:* Baylor Col of Dent 3302 Gaston Ave Dallas TX 75246

LARGMAN, THEODORE, b Philadelphia, Pa, Nov 16, 23; m 59; c 4. ORGANIC CHEMISTRY. *Educ:* Temple Univ, AB, 48; Ind Univ, PhD(org chem), 52. *Prof Exp:* Sr res chemist, Nitrogen Div, 62-66, scientist, Cent Res Labs, 66-68, RES GROUP LEADER, CORP CHEM RES LAB, ALLIED CHEM CORP, 68-, RES ASSOC, 81- *Res:* Organic synthesis; fine chemicals; ozone reactions; design of micro-pilot plants; agricultural pesticides; flame retardant chemicals and polymers; uranium extraction; polymer adhesion. *Mailing Add:* 7 Upper Field Rd Morristown NJ 07960

LARI, ROBERT JOSEPH, b Aurora, Ill. PHYSICS. *Educ:* St Procopius Col, BS, 53; Univ Notre Dame, MS, 55. *Prof Exp:* Instr physics, St Procopius Col, 57-61; PHYSICIST, ARGONNE NAT LAB, 61- *Mem:* Am Asn Physics Teachers; Asn Comput Mach. *Res:* Particle accelerator research and development. *Mailing Add:* Argonne Nat Lab 360 9700 S Cass Ave Argonne IL 60439

LARIMER, JAMES LYNN, b Washington Co, Tenn, Jan 7, 32. NEUROBIOLOGY. *Educ:* ETenn State Univ, BS, 53; Univ Va, MA, 54; Duke Univ, PhD, 59. *Prof Exp:* From asst prof to assoc prof, 59-68, actg chmn dept, 73-74, PROF ZOOL, UNIV TEX, AUSTIN, 68- *Concurrent Pos:* Guggenheim fel, Stanford Univ, 67-68; mem, Physiol Study Sect, NIH, 72-76. *Mem:* Soc Neurosci; Am Physiol Soc; Sigma Xi; Am Soc Zoologists. *Res:* Comparative physiology; behavior and neurophysiology of invertebrates. *Mailing Add:* Dept of Zool Univ of Tex Austin TX 78712

LARIMER, JOHN WILLIAM, b Pittsburgh, Pa, Sept 4, 39; m 65; c 2. GEOCHEMISTRY. *Educ:* Lehigh Univ, BA, 62, MS, 63, PhD(geol), 66. *Prof Exp:* NASA-AEC res assoc geochem, Enrico Fermi Inst, Univ Chicago, 66-69; from asst prof, to assoc prof, 74-77, PROF GEOL, ARIZ STATE UNIV, 77- *Mem:* AAAS; Geochem Soc; Am Geophys Union; Meteoritical Soc; Sigma Xi. *Res:* Cosmochemistry; mineralogy and composition of meteorites. *Mailing Add:* Dept of Geol Ariz State Univ Tempe AZ 85281

LARIMORE, RICHARD WELDON, b Rogers, Ark, Feb 10, 23; m 47; c 3. FISH BIOLOGY. *Educ:* Univ Ark, BS, 46; Univ Ill, MS, 47; Univ Mich, PhD(zool), 50. *Prof Exp:* Asst aquatic biol, 46-54, assoc, 54-58, prof zool, 70-76, AQUATIC BIOLOGIST, ILL STATE NATURAL HIST SURV, 58-, PROF ENVIRON ENG, UNIV ILL, URBANA, 69- *Concurrent Pos:* Fishery expert, Food & Agr Orgn, 63-64 & 72-73; sr lectr, Fulbright Comn, 80. *Honors & Awards:* Fisheries Pub Award, Wildlife Soc, 57; Am Fisheries Soc Award, 60. *Mem:* Am Inst Biol Sci; Am Soc Limnol & Oceanog; Am Soc Ichthyol & Herpet; Am Fisheries Soc; Am Inst Fishery Res Biol. *Res:* Ecology of stream and reservoir fishes; dynamics of cooling lakes; utilization of tropical aquatic resources. *Mailing Add:* Natural Hist Surv Champaign IL 61820

LARIS, PHILIP CHARLES, b Perth Amboy, NJ, Sept 5, 31; m 56; c 4. PHYSIOLOGY. *Educ:* Rutgers Univ, BS, 52; Princeton Univ, MA, 54, PhD(physiol), 56. *Prof Exp:* Instr biol, Univ Calif, 56-58, from asst prof to assoc prof, 58-65; assoc prof, Franklin & Marshall Col, 65-66; assoc prof, 66-75, PROF BIOL, UNIV CALIF, SANTA BARBARA, 75- *Mem:* Am Physiol Soc; Soc Gen Physiol. *Res:* Cell permeability membrane potentials; amino acid and ion transport. *Mailing Add:* Dept of Biol Sci Univ of Calif Santa Barbara CA 93106

LARK, CYNTHIA ANN, b Shawnee, Okla, Dec 31, 28; m 51; c 4. MICROBIOLOGY. *Educ:* Mt Holyoke Col, BA, 50; St Louis Univ, PhD, 62. *Prof Exp:* Lab technician, Carnegie Inst, 50-51 & Sloan-Kettering Inst Cancer Res, 51-53; res asst, Univ Geneva, 55-56 & St Louis Univ, 59-62; NIH fel, Washington Univ, 62-63; asst prof microbiol, Kans State Univ, 63-70; assoc res prof biochem, 70-72, ASSOC PROF BIOL, UNIV UTAH, 72- *Res:* Microbial genetics; molecular biol; DNA reproducing bacteria. *Mailing Add:* 3605 Mill Circle Salt Lake City UT 84109

LARK, KARL GORDON, b Lafayette, Ind, Dec 13, 30; m 51; c 4. MOLECULAR BIOLOGY, GENETICS. *Educ:* Univ Chicago, PhB, 49; NY Univ, PhD(microbiol), 53. *Prof Exp:* Am Cancer Soc res fel, Statenserum Inst, Denmark, 53-55; Nat Found res fel, Biophys Lab, Univ Geneva, 55-56; instr microbiol, Sch Med, St Louis Univ, 56-57, sr instr, 57-58, from asst prof to assoc prof, 58-63; prof, Kans State Univ, 63-70; chmn dept, 70-77, PROF BIOL, UNIV UTAH, 77- *Concurrent Pos:* Nat Inst Gen Med Sci career develop award, 63-70; mem, Genetics Panel, NSF, 66-69; consult, Eli Lilly & Co, 68-74; mem Genetics Study Sect, NIH, 71-75; ad hoc mem, Nat Inst Gen Med Sci Coun, 78-79, mem, 79- *Mem:* Biophys Soc; Am Soc Cell Biol; Am Soc Biol Chem; Am Soc Microbiol. *Res:* Cell growth and division; DNA replication and segregation in bacteria and eucaryotes; plant genetics and tissue culture. *Mailing Add:* Dept of Biol Univ Utah Salt Lake City UT 84112

LARK, NEIL LAVERN, b Baker, Ore, Sept 10, 34; m 58; c 2. NUCLEAR PHYSICS. *Educ:* Chico State Col, AB, 55; Cornell Univ, PhD(phys chem), 60. *Prof Exp:* Res asst, Los Alamos Sci Lab, 55-56; res asst, Brookhaven Nat Lab, 57, jr res assoc, 58-59, res assoc, 60-61; NATO fel, Inst Nuclear Res, Amsterdam, Netherlands, 61-62, res assoc, 62; from asst prof to prof natural sci, Raymond Col, 62-75, PROF PHYSICS, UNIV PAC, 75- *Concurrent Pos:* Res asst, Univ NMex, 54; consult & res collabr, Los Alamos Sci Lab, 69; Ford Found fel & Fulbright grantee, Niels Bohr Inst, Copenhagen, Denmark, 67-68; NSF lectr, Tex A&M Univ, 70; res collabr, Brookhaven Nat Lab, 71-72, vis physicist, 75; vis fel, Australian Nat Univ, 76. *Mem:* Am Phys Soc; Am Asn Physics Teachers. *Res:* Nuclear spectroscopy; teaching of physics and chemistry. *Mailing Add:* Dept of Physics Univ of the Pacific Stockton CA 95211

LARKE, R(OBERT) P(ETER) BRYCE, b Blairmore, Alta, Nov 14, 36; m 60; c 3. VIROLOGY, INFECTIOUS DISEASES. *Educ:* Queen's Univ, Ont, MD & CM, 60; Univ Toronto, DClSc, 66. *Prof Exp:* Intern, St Michael's Hosp, Toronto, Ont, 60-61; resident pediat, Hosp for Sick Children, Toronto, Ont, 61-62, res fel virol, Res Inst, 62-66; instr prev med, Sch Med, Case Western Reserve Univ, 66-68, sr instr, 68; asst prof pediat, McMaster Univ,

69-72, assoc prof pediat & path, 72-75; assoc prof pediat, 75-76, PROF PEDIAT, UNIV ALTA, 76-, CHIEF, DIV DIAG VIROL, PROVINCIAL LAB PUB HEALTH, 75-, HON PROF MED, DIV INFECTIOUS DIS, 77- Concurrent Pos: Fel Microbiol, Sch Hyg, Univ Toronto, 63-66; Med Res Coun Can res fel, 64-66; asst prof path, McMaster Univ, 71-72; dir virol lab, St Joseph's Hosp, Hamilton, 71-75. Honors & Awards: Parkin Prize, Royal Col Physicians, Edinburgh, 66. Mem: Am Soc Microbiol; Am Pediat Soc; Infectious Dis Soc Am; Soc Pediat Res; Can Paediat Soc. Res: Clinical virology and infectious diseases of children and adults; mechanisms of host resistance to viral infections; interaction between viruses and blood platelets; epidemiology of viral infections. Mailing Add: Dept of Pediat Univ of Alta Edmonton AB T6G 2G3 Can

LARKIN, B(ERT) K(ENNETH), b Kansas City, Mo, Jan 9, 32; m; c 3. CHEMICAL ENGINEERING. Educ: Univ Kans, BS, 53, MS, 54; Univ Mich, PhD(chem eng), 57. Prof Exp: Res engr, Denver Res Ctr, Ohio Oil Co, 57-63; design engr, Martin-Marietta Co, 63-67; DIR SYSTS ANAL, AEROSPACE CORP, 67- Res: Radiant energy transfer; systems analysis; propulsion; fluid flow; numerical analysis. Mailing Add: Iuan A Getting Lab Aerospace Corp PO Box 92957 Los Angeles CA 90009

LARKIN, DAVID, b London, Eng, Oct 6, 41. ELECTROCHEMISTRY. Educ: Loughborough Univ Technol, BTech, 65, PhD(electrochem), 68; Royal Inst Chem, ARIC, 70. Prof Exp: Asst prof chem, Fla Technol Univ, 72-73; asst prof, 73-80, ASSOC PROF CHEM, TOWSON STATE UNIV, 80- Mem: Am Chem Soc; The Chem Soc. Res: Study of electro kinetics at solid metal electrodes. Mailing Add: Dept of Chem Towson State Col Baltimore MD 21204

LARKIN, EDWARD CHARLES, b Waltham, Mass, Aug 7, 37; m 65; c 2. HEMTOLOGY. Educ: Harvard Col, AB, 59; Yale Univ Sch Med, MD, 63. Prof Exp: Asst prof med, Univ Tex Med Br, 70-74, assoc prof, 74-75; assoc prof med, 75-81, PROF MED, UNIV CALIF, DAVIS, 81- Concurrent Pos: Chief hematol oncol, Marinez Va Hosp, 75- Mem: Am Soc Hematol; Int Soc Hematol; Am Col Physicians; Western Soc Clin Res. Mailing Add: 2560 San Miguel Dr Walnut Creek CA 94596

LARKIN, EDWARD P, b Watertown, Mass, Sept 27, 20; m 49; c 3. FOOD MICROBIOLOGY, VIROLOGY. Educ: Mass State Col, BS, 46; Univ Mass, MS, 48, PhD(bact), 54. Hon Degrees: Hon BS, Mass State Col, 43. Prof Exp: Instr bact, Univ Mass, 48-54, asst prof, 54-61; adminr, & assoc mem virol, Inst Med Res, NJ, 61-68; asst prof viral oncol, Sch Vet Med, Univ Pa, 68-70; CHIEF VIROL BR, BUR FOODS, FOOD & DRUG ADMIN, 70- Concurrent Pos: Vis assoc, Univ Pa, 61-65; Leukemia Soc scholar, 65-70. Mem: Am Soc Microbiol; Sigma Xi; Int Asn Comp Res on Leukemia & Related Dis (secy, 69-71). Res: Food virology; physical characterization of viruses; kinetic studies of physical and chemical inactivation of viruses. Mailing Add: Virol Br Div Microbiol Bur Foods Food & Drug Admin 1090 Tusculum Ave Cincinnati OH 45226

LARKIN, FRANCES ANN, b Ohio, Jan 16, 30. NUTRITION. Educ: Ohio State Univ, BS, 52; Univ Minn, Minneapolis, MS, 58; Cornell Univ, PhD(educ), 67. Prof Exp: Clin dietitian, St Luke's Hosp, Cleveland, Ohio, 53-57; assoc prof nutrition, Long Beach State Col, 58-61; adv, Col Home Econ, Dacca, Bangladesh, 61-64; assoc prof, 68-80, PROF NUTRIT SCI, SCH PUB HEALTH, UNIV MICH, ANN ARBOR, 80- Mem: Am Dietetic Asn; Am Pub Health Asn. Res: Food consumption studies; nutrition education techniques; social correlates of food consumption. Mailing Add: 1343 Ardmoor Ave Ann Arbor MI 48103

LARKIN, JEANNE HOLDEN, b Chicago, Ill, Jan 19, 31; m 57; c 1. DEVELOPMENTAL BIOLOGY. Educ: Univ Ill, BEd, 52, MS, 53; Univ Mich, PhD(zool), 58. Prof Exp: Instr zool, Univ Mich, 57-58 & Duke Univ, 58-61; asst prof, 66-70, ASSOC PROF ZOOL, WESTERN ILL UNIV, 71- Mem: Soc Develop Biol; Am Soc Zoologists; Am Inst Biol Sci. Res: Homotransplantation, especially differentiation of first and second set of testicular grafts and antigen-antibody reactions; sex differentiation in fish; gut associated lymphod tissue. Mailing Add: 913 Jamie Lane Macomb IL 61455

LARKIN, JOHN MICHAEL, b York, Maine, Aug 11, 37; m 65; c 3. ORGANIC CHEMISTRY. Educ: Univ Nebr, Lincoln, BS, 59; Univ Colo, Boulder, MS, 63, PhD(org chem), 65. Prof Exp: Chemist, Qual Water Br, US Geol Surv, Nebr, 59-60; from chemist to sr chemist, Texaco Inc, Beacon, 65-70, res chemist, 70-74, sr res chemist, 74-76; SR PROJ CHEMIST, JEFFERSON CHEM CO, AUSTIN, 76- Mem: Am Chem Soc. Res: Organic synthesis; structure elucidation; reaction mechanisms; organic nitrogen compounds; free radical rearrangements; steroidal heterocycles; air pollution; lubricant additive synthesis; chemicals from synthesis gas. Mailing Add: 12414 Dorsett Rd Austin TX 78759

LARKIN, JOHN MONTAGUE, b Philadelphia, Pa, Apr 7, 36; m 62; c 2. MICROBIAL PHYSIOLOGY, MICROBIAL ECOLOGY. Educ: Ariz State Univ, BS, 61, MS, 63; Wash State Univ, PhD(microbiol), 67. Prof Exp: Asst microbiol, Ariz State Univ, 61-63 & Wash State Univ, 63-67; asst prof, 67-71, assoc prof, 71-81, PROF MICROBIOL, LA STATE UNIV, BATON ROUGE, 81- Mem: AAAS; Am Soc Microbiol; Soc Appl Microbiol; Can Soc Microbiol. Res: bacterial taxonomy; biology of gliding bacteria; filamentous sulfur bacteria. Mailing Add: Dept Microbiol La State Univ Baton Rouge LA 70803

LARKIN, K(ENNETH) T(RENT), b Fowler, Colo, Nov 11, 20; m 46; c 2. ELECTRICAL ENGINEERING. Educ: Southern Methodist Univ, BS, 43. Prof Exp: Jr engr, Lone Star Gas Co, 39-42; instr radio eng, Southern Methodist Univ, 42-43; scientist, US Naval Res Lab, DC, 43-45; mgr receiver & indicators br, Raytheon Mfg Co, 46-55; dept mgr radar & radar develop, Santa Barbara Labs, 55-56; mgr telecommun dept, Lockheed Missiles & Space Co, 56-57, mgr electronics div, 57-58, assoc dir electronics res & develop, 58-62, assoc dir eng electronics, 62-63, asst dir eng, Res &

Develop Div, 63, dir, 63-65, dir info systs, 65-71; PRES, TECHNICON MED INFO SYSTS CORP, 71- Mem: Sr mem Inst Elec & Electronics Engrs. Res: Computer systems, especially as applied to health care. Mailing Add: 215 Golden Hills Dr Portola Valley CA 94025

LARKIN, LAWRENCE A(LBERT), b Kansas City, Mo, Jan 5, 37; m 60. FINITE ELEMENT ANALYSIS, ELASTO-PLASTIC FLOW. Educ: Univ Kans, BS, 62, MS, 64; Univ Kans, MS, 60, PhD(civil eng), 64. Prof Exp: Asst prof civil eng, State Univ NY Buffalo, 64-69; res scientist, 70-74, CONSULT ENGR, DATA SYSTS DIV, A O SMITH CORP, 74- Mem: Am Soc Civil Engrs. Res: Development of finite element computer codes; finite element computation of elasto-plastic response of vehicle structures during crash conditions. Mailing Add: Dept 9218 Box 584 A O Smith Corp Milwaukee WI 53201

LARKIN, LYNN HAYDOCK, b Highland Co, Ohio, Jan 29, 34; c 2. ANATOMY, REPRODUCTIVE BIOLOGY. Educ: Otterbein Col, BS, 56; Univ Colo, PhD(anat), 67. Prof Exp: Instr anat, Sch Med, Univ Colo, 66-67, res assoc molecular, cellular & develop biol, 67-68; asst prof anat, 68-73, assoc prof, 73-79, PROF ANAT, COL MED, UNIV FLA, 79- Res: Role of relaxin in pregnancy and parturition. Mailing Add: Dept Anat Box J235 Col Med Univ Fla Gainesville FL 32610

LARKIN, PETER ANTHONY, b Auckland, NZ, Dec 11, 24; m 48; c 5. FISHERIES. Educ: Univ Sask, BA, 45, MA, 46; Oxford Univ, DPhil, 48. Prof Exp: Chief fisheries biologist, Game Comn, BC, 48-55; dir inst fisheries & prof zool, Univ BC, 55-63; dir biol sta, Fisheries Res Bd Can, BC, 63-66; dir inst fisheries, 66-69, prof zool, 66-75, actg head dept, 69-70, prof, Inst Animal Resource Ecol, 69-75, head dept zool, 72-75, DEAN FAC GRAD STUDIES, UNIV BC, 75-, PROF INST ANIMAL RESOURCES EDUC, 77- Concurrent Pos: Nuffield Found fel, 61-62; mem, Sci Coun Can, 71-; mem Can nat comt, Spec Comt on Probs of Environ, 71-; mem, Fisheries Res Bd Can, 72-; mem adv comt sci criteria environ qual, Nat Res Coun Can, 75- Honors & Awards: Can Centennial Medal, 67. Mem: Am Fisheries Soc; Can Nature Fedn; Can Soc Environ Biologists; Can Soc Zoologists (pres, 72). Res: Population studies in fisheries biology. Mailing Add: Inst Animal Resource Ecol Univ of BC Vancouver BC V6T 1W5 Can

LARKIN, ROBERT HAYDEN, b New York, NY, Mar 26, 46; m 67; c 4. ANALYTICAL CHEMISTRY. Educ: Providence Col, BS, 68; Univ Mass, PhD(phys chem), 72. Prof Exp: Res assoc chem, Mass Inst Technol, 72-73; res chemist, 73-79, SECT MGR ANAL RES, ROHM AND HAAS CO, 79- Mem: Am Chem Soc. Res: Development of analytical methods, particularly separation methods, for the analysis of a wide variety of industrial products and/or processes. Mailing Add: Rohm & Haas Co Spring House Res Labs Spring House PA 19477

LARKIN, WILLIAM (JOSEPH), b Morristown, NJ, Aug 18, 18; m 49; c 1. NUCLEAR ENGINEERING, ENGINEERING MANAGEMENT. Educ: Mass Inst Technol, BS & MS, 49; Univ Tenn, MS, 56. Prof Exp: Design draftsman, Ford Instrument Co, NY, 42; mech engr, Los Alamos Sci Lab, 44-46; asst dir eng sch, Mass Inst Technol, 49-50; engr, US AEC, 50-55, chief, Reactor Projs Br, 55-66, actg dir, Reactor Div, 66-69, dir off nuclear & criticality safety, 69-70, dir off safety, 70-73, chief uranium enrichment expansion proj br, US AEC/US Energy Res Develop Admin, 73-76, dir planning, anal, control & reports div, US Dept Energy, 77-78; CONSULT ENGR, 78- Mem: Am Nuclear Soc; NY Acad Sci; Nat Soc Prof Engrs. Res: Uranium enrichment plant engineering; construction project planning and management control. Mailing Add: 110 Nebraska Ave Oak Ridge TN 37830

LARKINS, BRIAN ALLEN, b Bellville, Kans, Aug 12, 46; m 69; c 2. PLANT PHYSIOLOGY, PLANT BIOCHEMISTRY. Educ: Univ Nebr, BSEd, 69, PhD(bot), 74. Prof Exp: Res assoc biochem genetics, 75-76, asst prof, 76-79, ASSOC PROF PLANT PHYSIOL, PURDUE UNIV, 79- Mem: Am Soc Plant Physiologists; AAAS; Sigma Xi. Res: Protein and nucleic acid biosynthesis; seed storage protein metabolism; regulation of gene activity during seed formation. Mailing Add: Dept of Bot & Plant Path Purdue Univ West Lafayette IN 47907

LARKINS, HERBERT ANTHONY, b Baltimore, Md, Oct 11, 34; m 58; c 2. FISHERY BIOLOGY, POPULATION DYNAMICS. Educ: Mich State Univ, BS, 56. Prof Exp: Res asst radiation biol, Univ Wash, 56-57; hydrographic officer, US Navy Hydrographic Off, 57-61; res biologist high seas salmon, Bur Com Fisheries, US Dept Interior, 61-65, invest chief groundfish, 65-71; dep div dir fishery mgt, 73-78; div dir fishery mgt, 79-80, NORTHWEST REGIONAL DIR, US NAT MARINE FISHERIES SERV, NAT OCEANIC & ATMOSPHERIC ADMIN, 80- Concurrent Pos: Tech adv, US deleg, UN Seabed Comt, 71-73 & NPac Fishery Mgt Coun, 77-; mem, Sci Comt, Pac Fishery Mgt Coun, 77- Mem: Am Fisheries Soc; Am Inst Fishery Res Biologist; Int Acad Fishery Scientist. Res: Fishery management strategy; effects of fishing on fishery resources; fish population dynamics. Mailing Add: NW Regional Off Nat Marine Fish Serv 7600 Sandpoint Way NE Seattle WA 98115

LARKINS, THOMAS HASSELL, JR, b Dickson, Tenn, Mar 1, 39; m 60; c 3. INORGANIC CHEMISTRY. Educ: Austin Peay State Col, BS, 60; Vanderbilt Univ, MA, 62, PhD(chem), 63. Prof Exp: Sr res chemist, Tenn Eastman Co, 63-80, RES ASSOC, EASTMAN CHEM DIV, EASTMAN KODAK CO, 80- Mem: Am Chem Soc. Res: Coordination chemistry; catalysis; coal gasification; chemicals from coal. Mailing Add: 4408 Beechcliff Dr Kingsport TN 37664

LARKY, ARTHUR I(RVING), b Bound Brook, NJ, Feb 27, 31; m 81; c 6. ELECTRICAL ENGINEERING, COMPUTER SCIENCE. Educ: Lehigh Univ, BS, 52; Princeton Univ, MS, 53; Stanford Univ, PhD(elec eng), 57. Prof Exp: Res asst prof elec eng, 56-60, assoc prof, 60-64, PROF ELEC & COMPUT ENG, LEHIGH UNIV, 64- Concurrent Pos: Consult, Bell Tel Labs, 61- & Univac Div, Sperry Rand Corp, 70-72. Mem: Inst Elec & Electronics Engrs. Res: Computer design; automated testing. Mailing Add: Dept Elec Eng Lehigh Univ 310 Packard Bldg 19 Bethlehem PA 18015

LARMIE, WALTER ESMOND, b Smithfield, RI, Sept 6, 20; m 43; c 3. FLORICULTURE. *Educ:* Univ RI, BS, 49, MS, 54. *Prof Exp:* From asst prof to assoc prof, 49-72, PROF HORT & CHMN DEPT PLANT & SOIL SCI, UNIV RI, 72- *Mem:* Am Soc Hort Sci; Am Hort Soc; Nat Coun Ther Rehab through Hort; Soc Am Florists; Bedding Plants, Inc. *Res:* Storage of flowers and plants; weed control; growth regulators; propagation and culture of poinsettias. *Mailing Add:* Red Wing Park West Kingston RI 02892

LARMORE, LAWRENCE LOUIS, b Washington, DC, Nov 23, 41; m 64; c 2. MATHEMATICS. *Educ:* Tulane Univ, BS, 61; Northwestern Univ, PhD(math), 65. *Prof Exp:* Asst prof math, Univ Ill, Chicago Circle, 65-68 & Occidental Col, 68-70; assoc prof, 70-77, PROF MATH, CALIF STATE COL, DOMINGUEZ HILLS, 77- *Mem:* Am Math Soc. *Res:* Algebraic topology; obstruction theory; classification of liftings, embeddings and immersions; twisted extraordinary cohomology. *Mailing Add:* Dept of Math Calif State Col at Dominguez Hills Dominguez Hills CA 90747

LARNER, JOSEPH, b Brest-Litovsk, Poland, Jan 9, 21; nat US; m 47; c 3. BIOCHEMISTRY, PHARMACOLOGY. *Educ:* Univ Mich, BA, 42; Columbia Univ, MD, 45; Univ Ill, MS, 49; Wash Univ, PhD(biochem), 51. *Prof Exp:* Instr biochem, Wash Univ, 51-53; asst prof, Noyes Lab Chem, Univ Ill, 53-57; from assoc prof to prof pharmacol, Sch Med, Western Reserve Univ, 57-65; Hill prof metab enzym, Col Med Sci, Univ Minn, Minneapolis, 65-69; PROF PHARMACOL & CHMN DEPT, SCH MED, UNIV VA, 69- *Concurrent Pos:* Travel award, Int Cong Biochem, 55; NIH res career award, 63-64; Commonwealth Fund fel, Lab Molecular Biol, Cambridge Univ, 63-64; mem metab study sect, NIH, 62-66, mem training comt, Nat Inst Arthritis & Metab Dis, 66; mem subcomt enzymes, Nat Res Coun-Nat Acad Sci, 64-; mem rev bd, Am Cancer Soc, 70-74. *Honors & Awards:* Alumni Prof Pharmacol, Univ Va, 73. *Mem:* Am Chem Soc; Am Soc Biol Chemists; fel Royal Col Med; Am Soc Pharmacol & Exp Therapeut. *Res:* Enzymatic aspects of intermediary carbohydrate metabolism, genetic and hormonal control. *Mailing Add:* Dept of Pharmacol Univ of Va Sch of Med Charlottesville VA 22903

LARNER, KENNETH LEE, b Chicago, Ill, Nov 1, 38; m 76; c 2. EXPLORATION GEOPHYSICS. *Educ:* Colo Sch Mines, GpE, 60; Mass Inst Technol, PhD(geophys), 70. *Prof Exp:* Res scientist image enhancement, EG&G, Inc, 67-69; sr res geophysicist, 70-74, mgr res & develop explor geophys, 75-80, VPRES RES & DEVELOP, WESTERN GEOPHYS CO, 80- *Concurrent Pos:* Lectr geophysics, Univ Houston, 73-74. *Mem:* Soc Explor Geophysicists; Seismol Soc Am; Europ Asn Explor Geophysicists; Sigma Xi. *Res:* Seismic signal enhancement and wave propagation; estimation of geophysical parameters from seismic measurements. *Mailing Add:* Western Geophys Co PO Box 2469 Houston TX 77001

LARNEY, VIOLET HACHMEISTER, b Chicago, Ill, May 19, 20; m 50. MATHEMATICS. *Educ:* Ill State Univ, BEd, 41; Univ Ill, AM, 42; Univ Wis, PhD(math), 50. *Prof Exp:* Teacher high sch, Ill, 42-44; asst math, Univ Wis, 44-48, instr, Exten Div, 48-50; asst prof, Kans State Univ, 50-52; assoc prof, 52-59, PROF MATH, STATE UNIV NY, ALBANY, 59- *Mem:* Math Asn Am; Am Math Soc. *Res:* Abstract algebra. *Mailing Add:* Dept of Math State Univ of NY Albany NY 12222

LARNTZ, KINLEY, b Coshocton, Ohio, Oct 2, 45; m 65; c 3. APPLIED STATISTICS, MATHEMATICAL STATISTICS. *Educ:* Dartmouth Col, AB, 67; Univ Chicago, PhD(statist), 71. *Prof Exp:* ASSOC PROF APPL STATIST, UNIV MINN, ST PAUL, 71- *Mem:* Am Statist Asn; Royal Statist Soc; Biomet Soc; Inst Math Statist. *Res:* Analysis of qualitative data; comparison of small sample distributions for chi-square goodness-of-fit statistics; data analysis applied statistical methods. *Mailing Add:* Dept of Appl Statist Univ of Minn St Paul MN 55108

LAROCCA, ANTHONY JOSEPH, b New Orleans, La, May 15, 23; m 54; c 6. PHYSICS, ELECTRICAL ENGINEERING. *Educ:* Tulane Univ, BS in EE, 49; Univ Mich, MS, 52. *Prof Exp:* Res asst physics, Tulane Univ, 49-51; res asst, Inst Sci & Technol, Univ Mich, Ann Arbor, 56-58, res assoc, 58-60, from assoc res physicist to res physicist, 60-73; RES PHYSICIST, ENVIRON RES INST MICH, 73- *Concurrent Pos:* Adj prof, Univ Mich, 73- *Mem:* AAAS; Optical Soc Am. *Res:* Infrared and optical technology; radiation phenomena; propagation and attenuation; techniques of measurement of radiation; design and use of electrooptical devices; standards of radiation; study of techniques of remote sensing of environment. *Mailing Add:* 2600 Englave Ann Arbor MI 48103

LA ROCCA, JOSEPH PAUL, b La Junta, Colo, July 5, 20; m 47; c 4. MEDICINAL CHEMISTRY. *Educ:* Univ Colo, BS, 42; Univ NC, MS, 44; Univ Md, PhD(pharmaceut chem), 48. *Prof Exp:* Res chemist, Naval Res Lab, 47-49; assoc prof, 49-50, PROF PHARM, UNIV GA, 50-, HEAD DEPT MEDICINAL CHEM, 70- *Mem:* Am Chem Soc; Am Pharmaceut Asn. *Res:* Synthetic sedative-hypnotics; anticonvulsant compounds; chemotherapy of cancer. *Mailing Add:* 115 Fortson Circle Athens GA 30601

LAROCHELLE, JACQUES, b Quebec, Can, Sept 4, 46; m 72; c 2. ANIMAL PHYSIOLOGY, CELL PHYSIOLOGY. *Educ:* Laval Univ, BA, 66, BSc, 71, DSc(physiol), 76. *Prof Exp:* Lectr physiol, Laval Univ, 74-75; Que Ministry Educ fel & vis scholar zool, Duke Univ, 76; asst prof, 77-80, ASSOC PROF PHYSIOL, LAVAL UNIV, 80- *Res:* Cell and whole animal reactions to water stresses induced by osmotic and/or thermal changes in the environment. *Mailing Add:* Dept Biol Laval Univ Quebec PQ G1K 7P4 Can

LA ROCHELLE, JOHN HART, b Longmeadow, Mass, Aug 17, 24; m 48; c 4. PHYSICAL CHEMISTRY. *Educ:* Univ Mass, BS, 48; Northeastern Univ, MS, 50; Univ Mich, PhD(chem), 55. *Prof Exp:* Res chemist, Shell Chem Co, 55-60, sr res chemist, 60-68, res supvr, 68-72, res supvr, 72-74, STAFF CHEMIST, GEISMAR PLANT, SHELL CHEM CO, 74- *Mem:* AAAS; Am Inst Chemists. *Res:* Dielectric polarization of gases. *Mailing Add:* Shell Chem Co Box 500 Geismar LA 70734

LAROCK, BRUCE E, b Berkeley, Calif, Dec 24, 40; m 68; c 2. CIVIL ENGINEERING, HYDRODYNAMICS. *Educ:* Stanford Univ, BS, 62, MS, 63, PhD(civil eng), 66. *Prof Exp:* Asst prof civil eng, 66-72, assoc prof, 72-79, PROF CIVIL ENG, UNIV CALIF, DAVIS, 79- *Mem:* Am Soc Civil Engrs. *Res:* Hydraulics and fluid mechanics; finite element methods. *Mailing Add:* Dept of Civil Eng Univ of Calif Davis CA 95616

LAROCK, RICHARD CRAIG, b Berkeley, Calif, Nov 16, 44. ORGANIC CHEMISTRY. *Educ:* Univ Calif, Davis, BS, 67; Purdue Univ, PhD(chem), 72. *Prof Exp:* NSF fel chem, Harvard Univ, 71-72; from instr to asst prof, 72-78, ASSOC PROF CHEM, IOWA STATE UNIV, 78- *Concurrent Pos:* Du Pont Young fac scholar, Du Pont Chem Co, 75-76; A P Sloan fel, 77-79. *Mem:* Am Chem Soc; The Chem Soc; Sigma Xi. *Res:* Synthesis of biologically active compounds; new synthetic methods; organometallic and hetrocyclic chemistry. *Mailing Add:* Dept of Chem Iowa State Univ Ames IA 50011

LA ROCQUE, JOSEPH ALFRED AURELE, b Ottawa, Ont, Apr 26, 09; m 40. GEOLOGY. *Educ:* Univ Ottawa, Can, BA, 45; Univ Mich, MSc, 47, PhD(geol), 48. *Prof Exp:* Asst, Mus Zool, Univ Mich, 45-48; from asst prof to prof, 48-76, EMER PROF GEOL, OHIO STATE UNIV, 76- *Mem:* Paleont Soc; Am Asn Petrol Geologists. *Res:* Fossil Molusca; paleoecology; history of geology. *Mailing Add:* Dept of Geol & Mineral Ohio State Univ Columbus OH 43210

LAROS, GERALD SNYDER, II, b Los Angeles, Calif, July 19, 30; m 58; c 3. ORTHOPEDIC SURGERY. *Educ:* Northwestern Univ, BS, 52, MD, 55; Univ Iowa, MS, 70. *Prof Exp:* Orthop resident, Vet Admin Hosp, Hines, Ill, 56-60 & Shriners Hosp, Honolulu, Hawaii, 60-61; pvt pract, 61-68; NIH fel, Univ Iowa, 68-70, asst prof orthop surg, 70-71; assoc prof, Univ Ark, 71-73; PROF SURG & CHMN SECT ORTHOP SURG, UNIV CHICAGO, 73- *Concurrent Pos:* Mem & secy-treas, Am Bd Orthop Surg, 81- *Mem:* Am Acad Orthop Surg; Orthop Res Soc; Am Col Surgeons; Am Orthop Asn. *Res:* Electromicroscopy of bone tendon and ligaments. *Mailing Add:* Sect of Orthop Univ of Chicago Hosps & Clins Chicago IL 60637

LA ROSA, RICHARD THOMAS, b Brooklyn, NY, July 26, 37; m 62; c 2. PHARMACOLOGY, PHARMACY. *Educ:* St John's Univ, BS, 61, MS, 63; State Univ NY Buffalo, PhD(pharmacol), 68. *Prof Exp:* Control pharmacologist, Parke, Davis & Co, 68-74; sect head pharmacol, Colgate-Palmolive Co, 74-80; WITH AM CYANAMID CO, 80- *Concurrent Pos:* Adj assoc prof pharmacol, St John's Univ, 75- *Honors & Awards:* President's Award, Colgate-Palmolive Co, 75. *Mem:* NY Acad Sci; Am Asn Lab Animal Sci. *Res:* Dermatopharmacology; toxicology. *Mailing Add:* Am Cyanamid Co 697 Rte 46 Clifton NJ 07015

LAROSE, ROGER, b Montreal, Que, July 28, 10; m 36, 61; c 1. PHARMACY. *Educ:* Univ Montreal, BSP, 32, Lic sci, 34. *Prof Exp:* lectr pharm, Univ Montreal, 34-50, assoc prof, 50-60, dean fac pharm, 60-65, mem bd gov, 65-67, spec counr to rector, 68-69, vice rector admin, 69-79; PRES, ST LUC HOSPITAL, MONTREAL, 79- *Concurrent Pos:* Adminr, Mt Royal Chem Ltd, 58-72; mem exec admin coun, Pharm Exam Bd Can, 64; mem, Sci Coun Can, 66-71; pres, Ciba Co Ltd, 68-71 & Ciba-Geigy Can Ltd, 71-74, dep chmn bd, 73-78, chmn bd, 78-; mem, Nat Comn Pharmaceut Serv in Can & WHO Coun Experts Pharm; dir, Inst Diag & Clin Res Montreal; hon mem, Can Conf; mem, Can Nat Bank, 69-80, mem exec comt & vchmn bd, 74-; officer, Order of Can, 73; gov, Can Bankers Inst, 73-81; chmn bd, Yvon Fournier Ltd, 78- *Mem:* Pharm Soc Gt Brit; Fr Acad Pharmaceut Sci. *Res:* Teaching and administration. *Mailing Add:* Le Tournesol #404-205 Ch De La Cote Ste Catherine Montreal PQ H2V 2A9 Can

LAROW, EDWARD J, b Albany, NY, Dec 22, 37; m 63; c 4. AQUATIC ECOLOGY, INVERTEBRATE ZOOLOGY. *Educ:* Siena Col, BS, 60; Kans State Univ, MS, 65; Rutgers Univ, PhD(zool), 68. *Prof Exp:* From asst prof to assoc prof, 68-74, chmn dept, 71-80, PROF BIOL, SIENA COL, NY, 74- *Concurrent Pos:* Nat Res Coun Int Biol Prog grant, 70-74; vis lectr, State Univ NY Albany, 70-75 & Col Environ Sci & Forestry, 76- *Mem:* Ecol Soc Am; Am Soc Limnol & Oceanog; Am Inst Biol Sci; Int Soc Limnol. *Res:* Biological rhythms and their role in the vertical migration of zooplankton; remineralization and respiration in zooplankton; secondary production of zooplankton. *Mailing Add:* Dept of Biol Siena Col Loudonville NY 12211

LARRABEE, ALLAN ROGER, b Flushing, NY, Feb 24, 35; m 60; c 2. BIOCHEMISTRY. *Educ:* Bucknell Univ, BS, 57; Mass Inst Technol, PhD, 62. *Prof Exp:* Staff fel biosynthesis of fatty acids, NIH, 64-66; asst prof chem, Univ Ore, 66-72; assoc prof, 72-80, PROF CHEM, MEMPHIS STATE UNIV, 80- *Concurrent Pos:* NIH res grant, 67-70; NSF res grant, 70-75. *Mem:* Am Soc Biol Chemists. *Res:* Role of vitamin B-12, folic acid and pantothenate as coenzymes; biosynthesis of fatty acis; multienzyme complexes; protein turnover. *Mailing Add:* Dept of Chem Memphis State Univ Memphis TN 38152

LARRABEE, CLIFFORD EVERETT, b Springfield, Mass, June 17, 22; m 45; c 3. ORGANIC CHEMISTRY. *Educ:* Bates Col, BS, 44; Univ Rochester, PhD(org chem), 49. *Prof Exp:* Res chemist, Gen Aniline & Film Corp, 49-52; RES CHEMIST, PFIZER, INC, 52- *Mem:* Am Chem Soc. *Res:* Synthetic organic chemistry. *Mailing Add:* 362 Boston Post Rd East Lyme CT 06333

LARRABEE, GRAYDON B, b Sherbrooke, Que, Oct 2, 32; US citizen; m 54; c 2. RADIOCHEMISTRY. *Educ:* Bishop's Univ, Can, BSc, 53; McMaster Univ, MSc, 54. *Prof Exp:* Radiochemist, Atomic Energy Can Ltd, 54-56; analyst, Can Westinghouse, 56-59; HEAD RES BR, MAT SCI LAB, TEX INSTRUMENTS, INC, 59- *Mem:* Soc Appl Spectros; Electrochem Soc. *Res:* Materials characterization; solid state chemistry. *Mailing Add:* Mat Sci Lab MS 147 Tex Instruments Inc PO Box 225936 Dallas TX 75265

LARRABEE, MARTIN GLOVER, b Boston, Mass, Jan 25, 10; m 32, 44; c 2. NEUROCHEMISTRY, NEUROPHYSIOLOGY. *Educ:* Harvard Univ, AB, 32; Univ Pa, PhD(biophys), 37. *Hon Degrees:* MD, Univ Lausanne, 74. *Prof Exp:* Asst, Univ Pa, 34-35, fel med physics, 37-40; asst prof physiol, Med Col, Cornell Univ, 40-41; fel, Johnson Found, Univ Pa, 41-42, assoc, 42-43, from asst prof to assoc prof biophys, 43-48; assoc prof, 49-63, PROF BIOPHYS, JOHNS HOPKINS UNIV, 63- *Mem:* Nat Acad Sci; Am Physiol Soc; Am Soc Neurochem; Int Soc Neurochem; Soc Neurosci (treas, 72-75). *Res:* Metabolism in relation to physiological function and embryological development in sympathetic ganglia. *Mailing Add:* Dept of Biophys Johns Hopkins Univ Baltimore MD 21218

LARRABEE, R(OBERT) D(EAN), b Flushing, NY, Nov 29, 31; m 53; c 2. ELECTRICAL ENGINEERING, PHYSICS. *Educ:* Bucknell Univ, BS & MS, 53; Mass Inst Technol, SM, 55, ScD(physics), 57; Rider Col, MBA, 76. *Prof Exp:* Res engr, David Sarnoff Res Ctr, RCA Corp, 57-71, develop engr, RCA Advan Technol Lab, 72-76; physicist, 76-81, GROUP LEADER, NAT BUR STANDARDS, 81- *Concurrent Pos:* Mem adj fac, Univ Md, 82. *Mem:* AAAS; sr mem Inst Elec & Electronics Engrs; Am Phys Soc. *Res:* Semiconductor materials and devices; solid-state plasma physics; semiconductor microwave oscillators and amplifiers; infrared physics and detectors; characterization of semiconductor materials; Hall, photo response, and deep-level transient spectroscopy measurement techniques. *Mailing Add:* Nat Bur Standards Rm A-331 Bldg 225 Washington DC 20234

LARRABEE, RICHARD BRIAN, b Sacramento, Calif, Apr 29, 40; c 2. ORGANIC CHEMISTRY. *Educ:* Univ Santa Clara, BS, 61; Univ Chicago, MS & PhD(chem), 67. *Prof Exp:* NIH fel, Ohio State Univ, 66-67; STAFF MEM CHEM, IBM CORP, 67- *Mem:* AAAS; Am Chem Soc. *Res:* Materials science; magnetic disk technology. *Mailing Add:* IBM Corp 5600 Cottle Rd San Jose CA 95193

LARRAIN, JOSE MIGUEL, b Talca, Chile, Mar 29, 44; m 71. TRANSPORT PHENOMENA, THERMODYNAMICS. *Educ:* Columbia Univ, MS, 67, DEngSc(chem eng), 73. *Prof Exp:* Asst prof mineral eng, Henry Krumb Sch Mines, Columbia Univ, 73-77, assoc prof, 77-80; SR ENGR, EXXON MINERALS CO, 80- *Concurrent Pos:* NSF investr grants, 73-78; chem metall grants, Int Nickel Co, 75-78. *Mem:* Am Chem Soc; Instrument Soc Am; Am Inst Mining, Metall & Petrol Engrs. *Res:* Concentrates in extractive metallurgy of non-ferrous metals and the application of the fundamental principles of heat and mass transfer to the minerals industries. *Mailing Add:* 224 Park Ave Exxon Minerals Co Florham Park NJ 07932

LARROWE, BOYD T, b Merriam, Kans, May 6, 23; m 59; c 4. ELECTRICAL ENGINEERING. *Educ:* Univ Kans, BS, 50; Univ Ill, MS, 51. *Prof Exp:* Mem staff digital comput design, Univ Ill, 50-51; res assoc, Univ Mich, 52-57; sr engr, Strand Eng Co, 57-62; chief engr, Comput Displays, Burroughs Corp Labs, Mich, 62-64; res engr, Inst Sci Technol, Univ Mich, 64-73; RES ENGR, ENVIRON RES INST MICH, 73- *Mem:* Inst Elec & Electronics Engrs. *Res:* Digital computer design; automatic radar image interpretation; display techniques; real time electronic processor design for synthetic aperture radar. *Mailing Add:* 6585 Hack Rd Clinton MI 49236

LARROWE, VERNON L, b Galax, Va, Feb 21, 21; m 66; c 1. ELECTRICAL ENGINEERING. *Educ:* Univ Kans, BS, 50; Univ Ill, MS, 51; Univ Mich, PhD(elec eng), 64. *Prof Exp:* Asst elec eng, Univ Ill, 50-51; res assoc, Inst Sci & Technol, Univ Mich, Ann Arbor, 51-53, assoc res engr, 53-57, head analog comput lab, 53-65, res engr, Inst, 57-65, res engr, Infrared & Optics Lab, Willow Run Labs, 65-73; RES ENGR, ENVIRON RES INST OF MICH, 73- *Mem:* Inst Elec & Electronics Engrs; Soc Comput Simulation; Soc Photo & Instrumentation Engrs; AAAS; NY Acad Sci. *Res:* Application of electronic analog computers; data processing; information theory; remote sensing; automatic pattern recognition; high density digital recording. *Mailing Add:* Environ Res Inst Mich Box 8618 Ann Arbor MI 48107

LARRY, JOHN ROBERT, b Mt Clare, WVa, Nov 13, 39; m 63; c 3. PHYSICAL CHEMISTRY. *Educ:* WVa Univ, BS, 61; Ohio State Univ, PhD(chem), 66. *Prof Exp:* Res chemist, 66-74, sr res chemist, 74-76, res supervr, 77-81, RES MGR, PHOTO PROD DEPT, ELECTRONIC PROD DIV, E I DU PONT DE NEMOURS & CO, INC, NIAGARA FALLS, 81- *Mem:* Am Chem Soc; Int Soc Hybrid Microelectronics. *Res:* Charge transfer and molecular complexes; ultracentrifugation; emulsion polymerization; colloid chemistry; rheology; solid state conductors; solid state resistors; multilayer capacitors. *Mailing Add:* 396 Dansworth Rd Youngstown NY 14174

LARSEN, ARNOLD LEWIS, b Audubon, Iowa, Sept 7, 27; m 50; c 2. BOTANY, AGRONOMY. *Educ:* Univ Iowa, BA, 50; Iowa State Univ, MS, 61, PhD(econ bot), 63. *Prof Exp:* Farmer, Audobon County, Iowa, 53-57; from assoc to res asst bot, Seed Lab, Iowa State Univ, 57-63; botanist, Field Crops & Animal Prod Seed Res Lab, Agr Res Serv, USDA, 63-70; RES ASSOC PROF SEED TECHNOL, COLO STATE UNIV, 70-, DIR, COLO SEED LAB, 70- *Mem:* Am Soc Agron; Crop Sci Soc Am; Asn Off Seed Analysts; Coun Agr Sci & Technol. *Res:* Developmental procedures for determining quality of seeds. *Mailing Add:* E-10 Plant Sci Colo State Univ Ft Collins CO 80523

LARSEN, AUBREY ARNOLD, b Rockford, Ill, Sept 27, 19; m 43; c 5. MEDICINAL CHEMISTRY. *Educ:* Antioch Col, BS, 43; Mich State Col, MS, 44; Cornell Univ, PhD(org chem), 46. *Prof Exp:* Mem staff, Sterling-Winthrop Res Inst, 46-60; asst dir org chem, Mead Johnson & Co, Ind, 60-63, dir chem res, 63-67, vpres phys sci, 67-70; vpres & sci dir, Bristol-Myers Int, 70-75; VPRES RES & DEVELOP, MEAD JOHNSON & CO, 75- *Mem:* AAAS; NY Acad Sci; Am Chem Soc. *Res:* Pharmaceutical and nutritional research and development. *Mailing Add:* Mead Johnson & Co 2404 Pennsylvania St Evansville IN 47721

LARSEN, AUSTIN ELLIS, b Provo, Utah, Nov 1, 23; m 45; c 4. VETERINARY MEDICINE, MICROBIOLOGY. *Educ:* Wash State Univ, BS, 48, DVM, 49; Univ Utah, MS, 56, PhD(microbiol), 69. *Prof Exp:* Vet pvt pract, Utah, 49-68; clin instr microbiol, 61-68, asst prof microbiol, 68-80, ASSOC PROF CELLUAR, VIRAL & MOLLECULAR VIROL, COL MED, UNIV UTAH, 80-, DIR VIVARIUM, 68- *Concurrent Pos:* Vet & dir res lab, Fur Breeders Agr Coop Lab, 52-68, consult vet, 68-; consult, Schering Corp, 63-; non-med med asst res, Vet Admin, 69-; mem, Adv Comt Fur Farmers Res Inst; mem, Health Task Force of Utah. *Mem:* Am Soc Microbiol; Am Soc Exp Path; Am Soc Lab Animal Pract; Sigma Xi. *Res:* Slow virus research. *Mailing Add:* Dept of Microbiol Univ of Utah Salt Lake City UT 84112

LARSEN, CHARLES MCLOUD, b Staten Island, NY, Dec 6, 24; m 48; c 4. MATHEMATICS. *Educ:* Cornell Univ, AB, 45, AM, 50; Stanford Univ, PhD(educ), 60. *Prof Exp:* From instr to assoc prof, 54-67, PROF MATH, SAN JOSE STATE UNIV, 67- *Mem:* Math Asn Am; Soc Indust & Appl Math. *Res:* History of mathematics; mathematics education. *Mailing Add:* Dept of Math San Jose State Univ San Jose CA 95192

LARSEN, DAVID M, b Hawthorne, NJ, Mar 8, 36; m 58; c 3. THEORETICAL PHYSICS. *Educ:* Mass Inst Technol, SB, 57, PhD(physics), 62. *Prof Exp:* Nat Res Coun-Nat Bur Standards fel physics, Nat Bur Standards, Washington, DC, 62-64; staff physicist, Lincoln Lab, 64-76, STAFF PHYSICIST, FRANCIS BITTER NAT MAGNET LAB, MASS INST TECHNOL, 76- *Mem:* Fel Am Phys Soc. *Res:* Impurities in semiconductors; polaron theory. *Mailing Add:* Francis Bitter Nat Magnet Lab Bldg NW 14 Cambridge MA 02139

LARSEN, DAVID W, b Chicago, Ill, Feb 21, 36; m 63. PHYSICAL CHEMISTRY. *Educ:* Dana Col, BA, 58; Northwestern Univ, PhD(phys chem), 63. *Prof Exp:* Res assoc nuclear magnetic resonance spectros, Washington Univ, 63-64; asst prof, 64-66, assoc prof chem, 66-80, PROF, UNIV MO-ST LOUIS, 80- *Mem:* Am Chem Soc. *Res:* Nuclear magnetic resonance spectroscopy; exchange reactions of Lewis acids and bases in non-aqueous media; ionic interactions in aqueous media. *Mailing Add:* Dept of Chem Univ of Mo-St Louis St Louis MO 63121

LARSEN, DON HYRUM, b Provo, Utah, Sept 22, 17; m 41; c 3. INDUSTRIAL MICROBIOL, MEDICAL MICROBIOLOGY. *Educ:* Brigham Young Univ, BS, 40; Univ Nebr, MA, 42; Univ Utah, PhD, 50. *Prof Exp:* Bacteriologist, Commercial Solvents Co, Inc, 43-46; instr bact, Univ Utah, 47-50; asst prof, Univ Nebr, 50-52; from asst prof to assoc prof, 52-60, chmn dept, 55-60 & 65-72, PROF BACT, BRIGHAM YOUNG UNIV, 60- *Concurrent Pos:* Res assoc, Naval Biol Lab, Calif, 60-61; consult, Vitamins Inc, 74- *Mem:* AAAS; Am Soc Microbiol; Soc Indust Microbiol; Soc Appl Microbiol. *Res:* Microbial physiology; pathogenic microbiology; ergosterol production by yeasts; single cell protein from waste materials. *Mailing Add:* 893 Widtsoe Bldg Brigham Young Univ Provo UT 84602

LARSEN, EARL GEORGE, b Milltown, Wis, Oct 11, 21. BIOCHEMISTRY. *Educ:* Univ Wis, BS, 43, MS, 44; Wayne State Univ, PhD(biochem), 53. *Prof Exp:* Res chemist biochem, Armour Res Labs, Ill Inst Technol, 44-46; res chemist, Carnation Res Labs, Wis, 46-48; chief biochemist, Vet Admin Hosp, Dearborn, 48-; res assoc, Col Med, Wayne State Univ, 53-55; ASSOC PROF BIOCHEM, SCH MED, UNIV OKLA, 55- *Mem:* AAAS. *Res:* Chemistry and biosynthesis of porphyrins and heme-enzymes; physical biochemistry; chemical origins and evolution of life; chemical basis and mechanisms of the mind. *Mailing Add:* 1601 NW 43rd Oklahoma City OK 73118

LARSEN, EDWARD WILLIAM, b Flushing, NY, Nov 12, 44; m 74. APPLIED MATHEMATICS. *Educ:* Rensselaer Polytech Inst, BS, 66, PhD(math), 71. *Prof Exp:* Asst prof math, NY Univ, 71-76; assoc prof, Univ Del, 76-77; MEM STAFF MATH, LOS ALAMOS NAT LAB, 77- *Concurrent Pos:* Ed, Transport Theory & Statist Physics, 75- & J Appl Math, 76- *Mem:* Soc Indust & Appl Math; Am Nuclear Soc. *Res:* Asymptotic expansions; spectral theory; numerical analysis; transport theory. *Mailing Add:* Los Alamos Nat Lab PO Box 1663 MS 269 Los Alamos NM 87545

LARSEN, EDWIN MERRITT, b Milwaukee, Wis, July 12, 15; m 46; c 3. INORGANIC CHEMISTRY. *Educ:* Univ Wis, BS, 37; Ohio State Univ, PhD(chem), 42. *Prof Exp:* Chemist, Rohm and Haas, Pa, 37-38; asst chem, Ohio State Univ, 38-42; instr, Univ Wis, 42-43; group leader, Manhattan Dist Proj, Monsanto Chem Co, Ohio, 43-46; from asst prof to assoc prof, 46-58, PROF CHEM, UNIV WIS-MADISON, 58-, ASSOC CHMN DEPT, 77- *Concurrent Pos:* Vis prof, Univ Fla, 58; Fulbright lectr, Inst Inorg Chem, Vienna Tech Inst, 66-67. *Mem:* AAAS; Am Chem Soc. *Res:* Chemistry of the transitional elements; reduced states; solid state chemical and physical properties. *Mailing Add:* Dept Chem Univ Wis Madison WI 53706

LARSEN, ERIC RUSSELL, b Port Angeles, Wash, July 7, 28; m 51; c 4. ORGANIC CHEMISTRY. *Educ:* Univ Wash, BS, 50; Univ Colo, PhD(org chem), 54. *Prof Exp:* Res chemist, Chem Eng Lab, 56-59, proj leader, 59-62, sr res chemist, 62-64, group leader, Halogens Res Lab, 64-68, assoc res scientist, 68-74, RES SCIENTIST, HALOGENS RES LAB, DOW CHEM CO, 74- *Mem:* AAAS; Am Chem Soc. *Res:* Primary research in bromine and fluorine chemistry; flammability of organic compounds, inluding polymers and in the mechanism of flame suppression; fire research, especially flame retardancy in plastics. *Mailing Add:* Dow Chem Co Res & Develop 2020 Bldg Midland MI 48640

LARSEN, FENTON E, b Preston, Idaho, Mar 22, 34; m 54; c 4. HORTICULTURE. *Educ:* Utah State Univ, BS, 56; Mich State Univ, PhD(hort), 59. *Prof Exp:* From asst horticulturist to assoc horticulturist, 59-73, PROF & HORTICULTURIST, WASH STATE UNIV, 73- *Concurrent Pos:* Vis prof, Univ Jordan, Amman, 79; consult, Costa Rica, 79. *Mem:* Am Soc Hort Sci; Am Pomol Soc; Int Plant Propagators Soc. *Res:* Pomology; propagation; rootstocks; leaf abscission of nursery stock. *Mailing Add:* Dept of Hort Wash State Univ Pullman WA 99163

LARSEN, FREDERICK DUANE, b St Johnsbury, Vt, Mar 20, 30; m 52; c 4. GEOMORPHOLOGY. *Educ:* Middlebury Col, BA, 52; Boston Univ, MA, 60; Univ Mass, PhD(geol), 72. *Prof Exp:* From instr to asst prof, 57-64, assoc prof geol, 64-80, PROF, NORWICH UNIV, 80- *Concurrent Pos:* US Geol Surv, 68- *Mem:* AAAS; Geol Soc Am; Glaciol Soc. *Res:* Glacial geology; deglaciation of Muir Inlet, Alaska; glacial geology of central Vermont and Mount Tom Quadrangle, Massachusetts. *Mailing Add:* 9 Slate Ave Northfield VT 05663

LARSEN, HAROLD CECIL, b Granite, Utah, June 15, 18; m 56; c 3. AERODYNAMICS, ASTRODYNAMICS. *Educ:* Univ Utah, BSc, 41; Calif Inst Technol, MSc, 46, AE, 55. *Prof Exp:* Prod engr, Lockheed Aircraft Corp, Calif, 41; from asst prof to assoc prof aerodyn, 46-56, PROF AERODYN & HEAD DEPT, US AIR FORCE INST TECHNOL, 56- *Mem:* Am Inst Aeronaut & Astronaut. *Res:* Wind energy conversion; vortex theory of the cyclogiro and application to vertical axis wind turbine; Giro mill and Madaras rotor. *Mailing Add:* US Air Force Inst Technol Wright-Patterson AFB Dayton OH 45433

LARSEN, HARRY STITES, b Pittsburgh, Pa, Aug 12, 27; m 56; c 3. FORESTRY. *Educ:* Rutgers Univ, BS, 50; Mich State Univ, MS, 53; Duke Univ, PhD, 63. *Prof Exp:* Forester, Southern Timber Mgt Serv, 53-56; asst prof, 59-71, assoc prof silvicult, Dept Forestry, 71-80, ASSOC PROF FORESTRY, AUBURN UNIV, 80- *Mem:* Ecol Soc Am; Soc Am Foresters. *Res:* Tree physiology and silvics. *Mailing Add:* Dept of Forestry Auburn Univ Auburn AL 36830

LARSEN, HOWARD JAMES, b Duluth, Minn, Jan 21, 25; m 46; c 2. DAIRY NUTRITION. *Educ:* Univ Wis, BS, 50; Iowa State Col, MS, 52, PhD(dairy husb), 53. *Prof Exp:* Assoc & instr dairy husb, Iowa State Col, 54-55; from asst prof to assoc prof, 55-57, PROF DAIRY SCI, MARSHFIELD EXP STA, UNIV WIS, 75- *Concurrent Pos:* Consult, US Feed Grains Coun, 81. *Mem:* Fel AAAS; Coun Agr Sci & Technol; Am Soc Animal Sci; Am Dairy Sci Asn; Sigma Xi. *Res:* Forage utilization by dairy cattle; forage and concentrate preservation and utilization by dairy cattle; environmental studies with ruminants. *Mailing Add:* Univ of Wis Marshfield Exp Sta Rte 2 Marshfield WI 54449

LARSEN, HOWLAND AIKENS, b Seattle, Wash, June 29, 28; m 62; c 6. CHEMICAL ENGINEERING. *Educ:* Mass Inst Technol, SB, 50; Univ Ill, MS, 51, PhD(chem eng), 57. *Prof Exp:* Jr engr, Shell Develop Co, 51-53; res engr, 57-64, sr res engr, 64-66, res supvr, 67-68, sr supvr, Fluorocarbons Div, 69-80, RES ASSOC, PLASTICS PROD DEPT, E I DU PONT DE NEMOURS & CO, INC, 80- *Mem:* Am Chem Soc. *Res:* Thermoplastics; irreversible chemical effects of high pressure and shear. *Mailing Add:* E I Du Pont de Nemours & Co Washington Lab PO Box 1217 Parkersburg WV 26101

LARSEN, JAMES ARTHUR, b Rhinelander, Wis, Mar 14, 21; m 68; c 4. PLANT ECOLOGY. *Educ:* Univ Wis-Madison, BS, 46, MS, 56, PhD(ecol), 68. *Prof Exp:* SCI ED, UNIV WIS-MADISON, 56- *Mem:* Ecol Soc Am; Bot Soc Am; Arctic Inst NAm; Nat Asn Sci Writers; Am Meteorol Soc. *Res:* Arctic ecology and bioclimatology; ecologico-economic studies of northern lands; arctic botany; problems of scientific communication and of public information on science. *Mailing Add:* 1215 WARF Bldg Univ Wis-Madison Madison WI 53706

LARSEN, JAMES BOUTON, b Detroit, Mich, July 28, 41; m 64; c 2. COMPARATIVE PHYSIOLOGY, BIOCHEMISTRY. *Educ:* Kalamazoo Col, BA, 63; Univ Miami, MS, 66, PhD(marine biol), 68. *Prof Exp:* Fel biochem, Colo State Univ, 67-68; asst prof biol, Hamline Univ, 68-73; asst prof, 73-76, ASSOC PROF BIOL, UNIV SOUTHERN MISS, 76- *Mem:* AAAS; Sigma Xi; NY Acad Sci; Am Soc Zoologists. *Res:* Physiology, toxicology and biochemistry of coelenterate toxins; teleost endocrine systems; physiological effects of mycotoxins. *Mailing Add:* Dept Biol Univ Southern Miss Southern Sta Box 9236 Hattiesburg MS 39401

LARSEN, JAMES VICTOR, b Salt Lake City, Utah, June 16, 42; m 66. CHEMICAL & MATERIALS ENGINEERING. *Educ:* Univ Utah, BS, 67; Univ Md, College Park, MS, 69, PhD(chem eng), 71. *Prof Exp:* Chem engr, US Naval Ord Lab, 67-71; sales mgr, Eimco Div, 71-73, gen mgr, Eimcomet Plastics, 73-76, gen mgr extractor opers, Eimco PMD, 76-77, PRES MOLDED PROD DIV, ENVIROTECH CORP, 77- *Mem:* Am Inst Chem Engrs; Am Inst Mining Engrs. *Res:* Nonmetallic materials; carbon fiber composites; plastics. *Mailing Add:* Molded Prod Div Envirotech Corp PO Box 300 Salt Lake City UT 84110

LARSEN, JOHN ELBERT, b Watseka, Ill, Feb 7, 19; m 47; c 2. HORTICULTURE. *Educ:* Purdue Univ, BS, 42, MS, 46, PhD(hort), 57. *Prof Exp:* Agronomist, Stokeley-Van Camp, Inc, 46-51; asst hort, Purdue Univ, 51-55; horticulturist, J W Davis Co, 57-61; horticulturist, Agr Exten Serv, 61-76, ASSOC PROF HORT, TEX A&M UNIV, 70-, PLANT NUTRIT SPECIALIST GREENHOUSE VEG PROD, AGR EXTEN SERV, 76- *Mem:* Am Soc Hort Sci; Int Soc Soilless Culture. *Res:* Mineral nutrition and production of glasshouse vegetables. *Mailing Add:* Agr Exten Serv Tex A&M Univ College Station TX 77843

LARSEN, JOHN HERBERT, JR, b Tacoma, Wash, July 20, 29; m 51; c 2. VERTEBRATE ZOOLOGY. *Educ:* Univ Wash, BA, 55, MS, 58, PhD(zool), 63. *Prof Exp:* Instr embryol, Univ Wash, 60; instr biol, Univ Puget Sound, 60-61; asst cur & instr zool, Univ Wash, 61-62, NIH res fel, 63-64, USPHS sr fel electron micros, 64-65; from asst prof to assoc prof, 65-75, PROF ZOOL, WASH STATE UNIV, 75-, CHMN DEPT, 78- *Mem:* Am Inst Biol Sci; Am Soc Zoologists; Sigma Xi; Soc Syst Zool; Am Soc Ichthyologists & Herpetologists. *Res:* Evolution and functional morphology of feeding systems in amphibians; implications of neoteny to urodele evolution; mechanisms of ovulation in lower vertebrates. *Mailing Add:* Dept of Zool Wash State Univ Pullman WA 99164

LARSEN, JOHN W, b Hartford, Conn, Oct 30, 40; c 2. ORGANIC CHEMISTRY, PHYSICAL CHEMISTRY. *Educ:* Tufts Univ, BS, 62; Purdue Univ, PhD(chem), 67. *Prof Exp:* Res fel chem, Univ Pittsburgh, 66-68; from asst prof to assoc prof, 68-78, PROF CHEM, UNIV TENN, KNOXVILLE, 78-; PROF CHEM DIV, OAK RIDGE NAT LAB, 76- *Mem:* AAAS; Am Chem Soc; The Chem Soc. *Res:* Coal chemistry; thermodynamics of organic intermediates; chemistry in strong acid solutions and molten salts; solvent-solute interactions. *Mailing Add:* Dept of Chem Univ of Tenn Knoxville TN 37916

LARSEN, JOSEPH REUBEN, b Ogden, Utah, May 21, 27; m 48; c 3. INSECT PHYSIOLOGY. *Educ:* Univ Utah, BS, 50, MS, 52; Johns Hopkins Univ, ScD(med entom), 58. *Prof Exp:* Asst biol, Univ Utah, 50-52; entomologist, US Army Chem Corps, 52-54; res assoc zool, Univ Pa, 58-62; asst prof, Univ Wyo, 62-63; from assoc prof to prof & head dept entom, 63-75, DIR SCH LIFE SCI, UNIV ILL, URBANA, 75- *Concurrent Pos:* John R Emens distinguished professorship, Ball State Univ, Muncie, Ind, 80. *Mem:* Fel AAAS; Entom Soc Am; Am Soc Zoologists; Electron Micros Soc Am; Am Physiol Soc. *Res:* Endocrine relationships in insects; insect histology; microanatomy and physiology of insect sensory receptors and insect nervous system. *Mailing Add:* Sch of Life Sci Univ of Ill Urbana IL 61801

LARSEN, KENNETH MARTIN, b Ogden, Utah, June 26, 27; m 55; c 9. APPLIED MATHEMATICS. *Educ:* Univ Utah, BA, 50; Brigham Young Univ, MA, 56; Univ Calif, Los Angeles, PhD(math), 64. *Prof Exp:* Teaching asst math, Brigham Young Univ, 54-55 & Univ Calif, Los Angeles, 56-60; from asst prof to assoc prof, 60-75, PROF MATH, BRIGHAM YOUNG UNIV, 75- *Mem:* Sigma Xi; Math Asn Am; Soc Indust & Appl Math. *Res:* Numerical analysis; ordinary and partial differential equations; plasma confinement and stability. *Mailing Add:* 292 TMCB Dept of Math Brigham Young Univ Provo UT 84602

LARSEN, LAWRENCE HAROLD, b Staten Island, NY, July 22, 39; m 69; c 1. OCEANOGRAPHY, HYDRODYNAMICS. *Educ:* Stevens Inst Technol, BS, 61; Johns Hopkins Univ, PhD(hydrodyn), 65. *Prof Exp:* NSF fel meteorol, Univ Oslo, 65-66; vis res asst prof, Johns Hopkins Univ, 66-67; res asst prof, 67-71, RES ASSOC PROF OCEANOG, UNIV WASH, 71- *Concurrent Pos:* Prog dir phys & chem oceanog, NSF, 72-73. *Mem:* Am Meteorol Soc; Am Geophys Union. *Res:* Physical oceanography; wave motion; estuaries; sediment dynamics. *Mailing Add:* Rm 22A Dept of Oceanog Univ of Wash Seattle WA 98105

LARSEN, LELAND MALVERN, b Blair, Nebr, Aug 20, 15; m 40; c 3. ALGEBRA. *Educ:* Dana Col, BA, 41; Univ Nebr, MA, 48, PhD, 67. *Prof Exp:* Pub sch teacher, Nebr, 36-41, supt schs, 41-43; instr, Univ Nebr, 43-44; assoc prof, 48-67, head dept, 67-80, PROF MATH, KEARNEY STATE COL, 67- *Mem:* Math Asn Am; Nat Coun Teachers Math. *Res:* Theory of fields; various algorithms. *Mailing Add:* Dept of Math Kearney State Col Kearney NE 68847

LARSEN, LLOYD DON, b Terre Haute, Ind, Sept 13, 44; m 69; c 6. FOOD MICROBIOLOGY. *Educ:* Brigham Young Univ, BS, 69, MS, 74; Univ Minn, PhD(food microbiol), 79. *Prof Exp:* SR SCIENTIST, CARNATION RES LAB, 79- *Mem:* Am Soc Microbiol; Inst Food Technol. *Res:* Plasmids in industrial microorganisms including group N streptococci; improving fermentations via biotechnology; development of substitute dairy products. *Mailing Add:* Carnation Res Lab 8015 Van Nuys Blvd Van Nuys CA 91412

LARSEN, LYNN ALVIN, b Grand Forks, NDak, Aug 2, 43; m 66; c 2. NUTRITION. *Educ:* Univ NDak, BS, 65; Univ Wash, PhD(inorg chem), 71. *Prof Exp:* Res assoc, Div Nephrology, Dept Med, Univ Wash, 71-77; chemist, Safe Rev Br, Div Food & Color Additives, 77-78, consumer safety officer, 78-81, ASSOC DIR PROG DEVELOP, DIV NUTRIT, BUR FOODS, FOOD & DRUG ADMIN, 81- *Concurrent Pos:* Wash State Heart Asn fel, Div Nephrology, Dept Med, Univ Wash, 72-74; instr, Prog Educ Gifted, Dept Health & Human Serv, 79. *Mem:* Am Chem Soc; AAAS. *Mailing Add:* Div Nutrit Food & Drug Admin HFF-262 200 C St SW Washington DC 20204

LARSEN, MARLIN LEE, b Grand Island, Nebr, Nov 22, 42; m 64; c 3. CLINICAL CHEMISTRY. *Educ:* Kearney State Col, BS, 64; Wash State Univ, PhD(chem), 68. *Prof Exp:* DIR RES & DEVELOP, ICN MED LABS, INC, 68- *Mem:* Am Asn Clin Chemists; Asn Advan Med Instrumentation; Am Chem Soc. *Res:* Automation and methodology research of medical laboratory procedures. *Mailing Add:* ICN Med Labs Inc Box 3932 Portland OR 97208

LARSEN, MAX DEAN, b Pratt, Kans, Jan 23, 41; m 62. ALGEBRA. *Educ:* Kans State Teachers Col, BA, 61; Univ Kans, MA, 63, PhD(math), 66. *Prof Exp:* From asst prof to assoc prof, 66-73, dean, Col Arts & Sci, 74-82, PROF MATH, UNIV NEBR-LINCOLN, 73- *Concurrent Pos:* NSF res grant, 68-70. *Mem:* Am Math Soc; Math Asn Am; Nat Coun Teachers Math. *Res:* Extension of integral domain concepts to general commutative rings, particularly valuation theory and Prüfer rings; module theory over commutative rings. *Mailing Add:* Dept of Math Univ of Nebr Lincoln NE 68508

LARSEN, MICHAEL JOHN, b London, Eng, Apr 27, 38; m 70; c 2. MYCOLOGY, FOREST PATHOLOGY. *Educ:* Syracuse Univ, BSc, 60; State Univ NY, MSc, 63, PhD(mycol pathol), 67. *Prof Exp:* Res scientist, Can Forestry Serv, 66-70; RES SCIENTIST, US FOREST SERV, USDA, 70- *Concurrent Pos:* Adj assoc prof, Univ Wis-Madison, 71- & Mich Technol Univ, 78- *Mem:* Mycol Soc Am; Am Phytopathol Soc; Int Asn Plant Taxon & Nomeclature; Int Mycol Soc. *Res:* Speciation, taxonomy, physiology of North American wood inhabiting fungi and their ecological roles in forest ecosystems. *Mailing Add:* Ctr Forest Mycol Res Forest Serv USDA Pinchot Dr Madison WI 53705

LARSEN, PETER FOSTER, b Mt Kisco, NY. BIOLOGICAL OCEANOGRAPHY. *Educ:* Univ Conn, BA, 67, MS, 69; Col William & Mary, PhD(marine sci), 74. *Prof Exp:* Lectr chem, Norwalk Community Col, 68-70; res asst marine biol, Va Inst Marine Sci, 70-72, asst marine scientist ecol, 72-73; state oceanogr, Maine Dept Marine Resources, 73-76; res scientist, 76-77, SR RES SCIENTIST, BIGELOW LAB OCEAN SCI, 77- *Concurrent Pos:* Pres, Coastal Sci, 73-; consult, Res Inst Gulf Maine, 73- & Bigelow Lab Ocean Sci, 75-76. *Mem:* New England Estuarine Res Soc (secy-treas, 80-82); Ecol Soc Am; Estuarine & Brackish-Water Sci Asn; Atlantic Estuarine Res Soc. *Res:* The documentation of benthic community structure and function in the estuarine and marine environments of the Gulf of Maine region; environmental consequences of tidal power developments. *Mailing Add:* Bigelow Lab Ocean Sci West Boothbay Harbor ME 04575

LARSEN, PHILIP O, b Audubon Co, Iowa, Dec 1, 40; m 61; c 3. PLANT PATHOLOGY. *Educ:* Iowa State Univ, BS, 63; Univ Ariz, MS, 67, PhD(plant path), 69. *Prof Exp:* Asst prof plant path, 69-73, assoc prof, 73-76, assoc prof, 76-81, PROF BOT, OHIO STATE UNIV, 81- *Mem:* Am Phytopath Soc. *Res:* Diseases of turf grasses. *Mailing Add:* Dept of Plant Path Ohio State Univ Columbus OH 43210

LARSEN, RALPH IRVING, b Corvallis, Ore, Nov 26, 28; m 50; c 4. ENVIRONMENTAL ENGINEERING. *Educ:* Ore State Univ, BS, 50; Harvard Univ, MS, 55, PhD(air pollution, indust hyg), 57. *Prof Exp:* Sanit engr, Div Water Pollution Control, USPHS, 50-54, chief tech serv, State & Community Serv Sect, Nat Air Pollution Control Admin, 57-61, chief biomet sect, field studies br, 63-65, asst chief br, 65-67, res engr, Off Criteria & Standards, 67-71; environ res engr, Environ Appln Br, 71-80, ENVIRON RES ENGR, OPERATIONS, METEOROL & ASSESSMENT DIV, ENVIRON SCI RES LAB, US ENVIRON PROTECTION AGENCY, 80- *Concurrent Pos:* Lectr, adj fac, Inst Air Pollution Training, Environ Protection Agency, 69-; mem, Conf Fed Environ Engrs. *Mem:* Air Pollution Control Asn; Sigma Xi. *Res:* Studies on the concentration, effects and control of air pollution; mathematical modeling; computer analyses; statistical analyses. *Mailing Add:* Environ Res Ctr Environ Protection Agency MD-80 Research Triangle Park NC 27711

LARSEN, ROBERT PAUL, b Vineyard, Utah, Dec 1, 26; m 48; c 4. HORTICULTURE. *Educ:* Utah State Univ, BS, 50; Kans State Univ, MS, 51; Mich State Univ, PhD(hort), 55. *Prof Exp:* From asst prof to prof hort, Mich State Univ, 55-68; SUPT TREE FRUIT RES CTR, WASH STATE UNIV, 68- *Mem:* Fel Am Soc Hort Sci (pres, 75); Int Soc Hort Sci. *Res:* Physiology, nutrition and management of tree fruit crops. *Mailing Add:* Tree Fruit Res Ctr Wash State Univ Wenatchee WA 98801

LARSEN, ROBERT PETER, b Kalamazoo, Mich, Jan 1, 21; m 48; c 2. PHYSICAL CHEMISTRY. *Educ:* Kalamazoo Col, AB, 42; Brown Univ, PhD(chem), 48. *Prof Exp:* Instr phys chem, Brown Univ, 44-46; instr anal chem, Amherst Col, 47-48; asst prof phys chem, Ohio Wesleyan Univ, 48-51; assoc chemist & anal group leader, 51-73, GROUP LEADER, METAB & ENVIRON BEHAVIOR PLUTONIUM, RADIOL & ENVIRON RES DIV, ARGONNE NAT LAB, 73- *Mem:* Am Chem Soc. *Res:* Inorganic analytical chemistry in reactor fuel process development; uranium and plutonium analysis and the measurement of fission yields; metabolism of plutonium and other actinide elements in mammals, the behavior of these elements in the environment, and their determination in materials of biological and environmental origin. *Mailing Add:* Radiol & Environ Res Div Argonne Nat Lab Argonne IL 60439

LARSEN, RONALD JOHN, b Chicago, Ill, Jan 1, 37; m 62. MATHEMATICAL ANALYSIS. *Educ:* Mich State Univ, BS, 57, MS, 59; Stanford Univ, PhD(math), 64. *Prof Exp:* Instr math, Yale Univ, 63-65; asst prof, Cowell Col, Univ Calif, Santa Cruz, 65-70; assoc prof math, Wesleyan Univ, 70-75; vis assoc prof, State Univ NY Binghamton, 75-76 & State Univ NY Albany, 76-77; adj assoc prof, Clarkson Col Technol, 77-78. *Concurrent Pos:* Fulbright-Hays advan res grant, Univ Oslo, 68-69, vis asst, 73-74; Fulbright-Hays travel award to Norway, 73-74. *Mem:* Am Math Soc; Math Asn Am; Norweg Math Soc. *Mailing Add:* RD 4 Canton NY 13617

LARSEN, RUSSELL D, b Muskegon, Mich, June 6, 36; m 58; c 2. CHEMICAL PHYSICS, STATISTICS. *Educ:* Kalamazoo Col, BA, 57; Kent State Univ, PhD(chem), 64. *Prof Exp:* Teaching asst chem, Univ Cincinnati, 58-60; asst instr, Kent State Univ, 64; res assoc, Princeton Univ, 64-65; Robert A Welch fel, Rice Univ, 65-66; asst prof, Ill Inst Technol, 66-72; asst prof chem, Tex A&M Univ, 72-76; actg assoc prof, Dept Chem, Univ Nev, Reno, 76-77; ASSOC PROF, DEPT CHEM, UNIV MICH, 77- *Mem:* Am Chem Soc; Am Phys Soc; Am Statist Asn. *Res:* Chemical and biomedical signal processing; spectral analysis; Walsh functions; spline representations; zero-based signed representations. *Mailing Add:* Dept of Chem Univ of Mich Ann Arbor MI 48109

LARSEN, SIGURD YVES, b Brussels, Belg, Aug 14, 33; US citizen. THEORETICAL PHYSICS. *Educ:* Columbia Univ, AB, 54, MA, 56, PhD(physics), 62. *Prof Exp:* Asst physics, Columbia Univ, 54-57 & 60-62; consult, Nat Bur Standards, 62; Nat Acad Sci-Nat Res Coun assoc, 62-63, physicist, Washington, DC, 63-68; assoc prof, 68-75, PROF PHYSICS & CHMN DEPT, TEMPLE UNIV, 75- *Concurrent Pos:* Consult, Los Alamos Sci Lab, 64, Lawrence Radiation Lab, 67-72 & Nat Bur Standards, 68-71; mem panel quantum fluids, Int Union Pure & Appl Chem, 66-; vis prof, Mex Inst Petrol, 71-72 & Nat Univ Mex, 72. *Mem:* Am Phys Soc; Ital Phys Soc; Sigma Xi. *Res:* Statistical physics; quantum theory; numerical analysis. *Mailing Add:* Dept of Physics Temple Univ Philadelphia PA 19122

LARSEN, STEVEN H, b Bringham City, Utah, Aug 28, 44; m 68; c 4. EUKARYOTIC GENE EXPRESSION, CLONING. *Educ:* Utah State Univ, BA, 68, MS, 70; Univ Wis, PhD(biochem), 74. *Prof Exp:* Teaching asst chem & physics, Utah State Univ, 66-70; trainee biochem, Univ Wis, 70-74, fel genetics, 74-75; fel microbiol, John Hopkins Univ Sch Med, 75-79, instr, 77; ASST PROF MICROBIOL, IND UNIV SCH MED, 79- *Concurrent Pos:* Consult, Human Amylase Cloning Group, Dept Genetics, Ind Univ, 80- *Mem:* Am Soc Microbiol; AAAS. *Res:* Development of eukaryotic cloning vectors; determination of the utility of mouse adenovirus as an animal vector. *Mailing Add:* Dept Microbiol & Immunol Ind Univ Sch Med 1100 W Wash St Indianapolis IN 46223

LARSEN, TED LEROY, b Jerome, Idaho, Mar 18, 35; m 57; c 2. PHYSICS, SEMICONDUCTORS. *Educ:* Univ Calif, Berkeley, BS, 61, MS, 62; Stanford Univ, PhD(mat sci), 70. *Prof Exp:* Mem tech staff, Hewlett-Packard Co, 62-65, res & develop group leader, 68-71, res & develop sect mgr semiconductors, 71-79; DIR RES & DEVELOP, ENG OPTOELECTRONICS DIV, GEN INSTRUMENT CORP, 79- *Mem:* Electrochem Soc. *Res:* III-V compound materials and devices for optoelectronic and microwave applications, including single crystal and epitaxial growth, crystalline defects, impurity diffusion and minority carrier recombination processes; III-IV and silicon device and product development including led lamps and displays and optocouplers. *Mailing Add:* 1099 Los Robles Ave Palo Alto CA 94306

LARSEN, WAYNE AMMON, b Waynesboro, Va, Apr 2, 39; m 64; c 3. STATISTICS. *Educ:* Brigham Young Univ, BS, 61; Va Polytech Inst, PhD(statist), 68. *Prof Exp:* Statistician, Hercules Powder Co, Utah, 61-63; mem tech staff data anal, Bell Tel Labs, NJ, 67-69, supvr data anal, 69-75; SR SCIENTIST, EYRING RES INST, 75- *Mem:* Am Statist Asn. *Res:* Methodology of data analysis. *Mailing Add:* 945 S Austin Ave Orem UT 84057

LARSEN, WESLEY P, b Twin Falls, Idaho, July 29, 16; m 42; c 4. ZOOLOGY. *Educ:* Univ Utah, BS, 40, MS, 52, PhD(zool), 60. *Prof Exp:* Instr biol, Carbon Col, Univ Utah, 48-58, dir sci, 58-60; from assoc prof to prof, Col Southern Utah, Utah State Univ, 60-65; assoc prog dir pre-col sci educ, NSF, 66-67, eval panelist, 65; dean, Sch Sci, 67-71, PROF BIOL, SOUTHERN UTAH STATE COL, 67- *Concurrent Pos:* NSF fac fel sci, 58-59; prin investr, AEC res contract, 61-65; dir resource personnel workshop, NSF, 72-73, asst dir, Indust Sci Educ Proj, 75-77; assoc, Danforth Found, 78-86. *Mem:* AAAS; Am Soc Zoologists; Entom Soc Am; Am Nature Study Soc. *Res:* Insect tissue and organ culture; radiation biology; cryobiology. *Mailing Add:* Sch of Sci Southern Utah State Col Cedar City UT 84720

LARSEN, WILLIAM L(AWRENCE), b Crookston, Minn, July 16, 26; m 54; c 2. CORROSION, FAILURE ANALYSIS. *Educ:* Marquette Univ, BME, 48; Ohio State Univ, MS, 50, PhD(metall eng), 56. *Prof Exp:* Res assoc metall eng, Ohio State Univ, 51-56; res metallurgist, E I du Pont de Nemours & Co, 56-58; asst prof mech eng & chem, 58-62, assoc metallurgist, Ames Lab, 58-62, metallurgist, 62-69, assoc prof metall, Univ, 69-73, PROF METALL, IOWA STATE UNIV, 73- *Concurrent Pos:* Consult mat design, mat failure & educ progs for superior students. *Mem:* Am Soc Metals; Am Inst Mining, Metall & Petrol Engrs; Nat Asn Corrosion Engrs; Am Soc Eng Educ; Am Soc Testing & Mat. *Res:* Metallurgical engineering design and failure analysis; expert witness-product liability. *Mailing Add:* Dept of Mat Sci & Eng Iowa State Univ Ames IA 50011

LARSEN-BASSE, JORN, b Maribo, Denmark, Oct 14, 34; US citizen; m 59; c 1. MATERIALS SCIENCE, CORROSION. *Educ:* Tech Univ Denmark, MS, 58, PhD(metall), 61. *Prof Exp:* Actg asst prof metall, Tech Univ Denmark, 59-61; researcher, Soderfors Bruk, Sweden, 61-62; res assoc mat sci, Stanford Univ, 63; asst prof, San Jose State Col, 63-64; asst prof mech eng, 64-70, PROF MECH ENG, UNIV HAWAII, 70-, CHMN DEPT, 76- *Concurrent Pos:* Ford Found resident indust, 68-69; hon vis prof, Univ New South Wales, 71. *Mem:* Am Inst Mining, Metall & Petrol Engrs; Nat Asn Corrosion Engrs. *Res:* Abrasion resistance of metals; corrosion in marine and volcanic environments. *Mailing Add:* Dept of Mech Eng Univ of Hawaii 2540 Dole St Honolulu HI 96822

LARSH, HOWARD WILLIAM, b East St Louis, Ill, May 29, 14; m 38; c 1. MEDICAL MYCOLOGY. *Educ:* McKendree Col, BA, 36; Univ Ill, MS, 38, PhD, 41. *Prof Exp:* Asst bot, Univ Ill, 38-41; instr, Dept Bot & Bact, Univ Okla, 41-42; plant pathologist, Bur Plant Indust, Soils & Agr Eng, USDA, 43-45; assoc prof bact, med, mycol & plant path, 45-48, chmn, Dept Plant Sci, 45-62, chmn, Dept Microbiol & Bot, 66-76, PROF PLANT SCI, UNIV OKLA, 48-, RES PROF, 62- *Concurrent Pos:* Spec consult, McKnight State Tuberc Hosp & Nat Communicable Disease Ctr, USPHS, 50-; med mycologist consult & co-dir lab, Mo State Chest Hosp, Mt Vernon, 55-; dir labs, 77; consult, Manned Spacecraft Ctr, NASA; res reviewer immunol & infectious diseases comt, Vet Admin Hosp, Oklahoma City, 72; cert bioanal lab dir, Am Bd Bioanal, 74-; ed rev bd, J Clin Microbiol, 74-; ed-in-chief, Sabouraudia, 75-79. *Mem:* Fel AAAS; fel Am Pub Health Asn; fel Am Acad Microbiol; Bot Soc Am; Mycol Soc Am. *Res:* Medical mycosis; systemic mycoses; histoplasmosis; cryptococcosis. *Mailing Add:* Dept of Bot & Microbiol Univ of Okla Norman OK 73069

LARSH, JOHN E, JR, b East St Louis, Ill, Oct 3, 17; m 39; c 3. MEDICAL PARASITOLOGY. *Educ:* Univ Ill, AB, 39, MS, 40; Johns Hopkins Univ, ScD(parasitol), 43; Am Bd Med Microbiol, dipl, 63. *Prof Exp:* From instr to assoc prof parasitol, Sch Pub Health, 43-47, asst dean acad progs, 64-70, actg dean sch pharm, 65-66, assoc dean acad progs, Sch Pub Health, 71-76, PROF PARASITOL & HEAD DEPT, SCH PUB HEALTH & SCH MED, UNIV NC, CHAPEL HILL, 47- *Concurrent Pos:* Assoc, Sch Med, Duke Univ, 43, assoc prof, 57-58, prof parasitol, 59-; consult, Nat Univ Eng, Peru, 56, Dept Health, Educ & Welfare, USPHS, Bur State Serv, 64-66 & Bur Health Manpower, 66-68; mem trop med & parasitol study sect, Div Res Grants, NIH, 69-73, chmn, 71-73; pres, Int Comn Trichinellosis, 72-76. *Honors & Awards:* Order of Carlos Finlay, Cuban Acad Sci, 58. *Mem:* Fel AAAS; Am Soc Trop Med & Hyg (secy-treas, 53-56, vpres, 63-64, pres, 65-66); Am Soc Parasitologists; Am Pub Health Asn; Am Acad Microbiol. *Res:* Immunity to Trichinella; host-parasite relations. *Mailing Add:* Dept of Parasitol Bldg 201H Chapel Hill NC 27514

LARSON, ALLAN BENNETT, b Chicago, Ill, Feb 9, 43; m 71; c 1. INDUSTRIAL PHARMACY, COSMETIC CHEMISTRY. *Educ:* Drake Univ, BS, 66; Univ Wis, MS, 69; Purdue Univ, PhD(phys & indust pharm), 72. *Prof Exp:* Sr res pharmacist, Dorsey Labs Div, Sandoz-Wander Inc, 72-76; sr pharmaceut scientist, 76-77, GROUP LEADER, VICK DIVS RES & DEVELOP, RICHARDSON-MERRELL INC, 77- *Mem:* Am Pharmaceut Asn; Acad Pharmaceut Sci; Am Soc Cosmetic Chemists. *Res:* Pharmaceutical and skin care product development and stability, preformulation, uniformity of mixing, scale-up technology, process improvements. *Mailing Add:* 16 Harstrom Pl Rowayton CT 06853

LARSON, ANDREW HESSLER, b Peru, Ill, Sept 14, 31; m 55; c 3. METALLURGY. *Educ:* Mo Sch Mines, BS, 53, MS, 54; Univ Mo, PhD(metall), 59. *Prof Exp:* From asst prof to assoc prof metall eng, Mo Sch Mines, 59-63; from assoc prof to prof, Colo Sch Mines, 63-68; sr res metallurgist, Bunker Hill Co, 68-69, mgr res & develop, 69-78; DIR PROD DEVELOP & ENG, METALS DIV, GOULD INC, 78- *Concurrent Pos:* Ford Found Prog prod specialist, Tex Div, Dow Chem Co, 66-67. *Mem:* Am Soc Metals; Am Inst Mining, Metall & Petrol Engrs. *Res:* High temperature thermodynamic and kinetic studies of metallurgical systems involving the extraction and refining of metals. *Mailing Add:* Prod Develop & Eng Metals Div Gould Inc PO Box 43484 St Paul MN 55164

LARSON, BENNETT CHARLES, b Buffalo, NDak, Oct 9, 41; m 69; c 2. CRYSTAL DEFECTS, LASER ANNEALING. *Educ:* Concordia Col, BA, 63; Univ NDak, MS, 65; Univ Mo, PhD(physics), 70. *Prof Exp:* Physicist, 69-79, GROUP LEADER, SOLID STATE DIV, OAK RIDGE NAT LAB, 80- *Mem:* Am Phys Soc; Am Crystallog Asn; Mat Res Soc. *Res:* X-ray diffraction study of intrinsic and induced defects in crystalline solids using diffuse scattering; x-ray diffraction study of pulsed-laser annealing. *Mailing Add:* Solid State Div Oak Ridge Nat Lab Oak Ridge TN 37830

LARSON, BRUCE LINDER, b Minneapolis, Minn, June 24, 27; m 54; c 3. BIOCHEMISTRY, NUTRITION. *Educ:* Univ Minn, BS, 48, PhD(biochem), 51. *Prof Exp:* Asst, Univ Minn, 48-51; from instr to assoc prof, 51-66, PROF BIOL CHEM, UNIV ILL, URBANA, 66-, MEM STAFF, NUTRIT SCI FAC, 72- *Concurrent Pos:* Fulbright lectr, Arg, 65. *Honors & Awards:* Am Chem Soc Award, 66. *Mem:* AAAS; Am Chem Soc; Am Soc Biol Chemists; Am Dairy Sci Asn. *Res:* Lactation and mammary gland metabolism in the formation of mammary secretions, including origin and transport of precursors, synthesis and cellular ejection of products and biological significance of colostrum and milk; lactation. *Mailing Add:* Dept Dairy Sci 328 Animal Sci Lab Univ Ill 1207 W Gregory Dr Urbana IL 61801

LARSON, CHARLES CONRAD, b Pettibone, NDak, Nov 17, 14; m 58; c 2. FORESTRY ADMINISTRATION. *Educ:* Univ Minn, BS, 40; Univ Vt, MS, 43; Inst Pub Admin, NY, cert, 50; State Univ NY Col Forestry, Syracuse Univ, PhD(forestry admin), 52. *Prof Exp:* Summer res asst, Lake States Forest Exp Sta, 40-41; asst forest supvr, Crossett Lumber Co, Ark, 44; res & state exten forester, Univ Vt, 44-47; res assoc, Inst Pub Admin, NY, 48-49; forest economist & res assoc forestry, 50-58, assoc prof, 59-61, dean, Sch Environ & Resource Mgt, 71-79 PROF WORLD FORESTRY, COL ENVIRON SCI & FORESTRY, STATE UNIV NY, 61-, DIR INT FORESTRY, 64-, PROF FORESTRY, 79- *Concurrent Pos:* Ford Found oversease res fel, 54-; consult, Syracuse Univ Res Inst, 57-59; vis prof & proj leader, AID-State Univ NY Res Found Assistance Contract, Col Forestry, Univ Philippines, 59-62; mem bd dirs, Orgn Trop Studies, 71-; chmn educ comn, Int Union Socs Foresters, 71-79. *Mem:* Soc Am Foresters; Int Soc Trop Foresters (pres, 79-81). *Res:* Forestry administration, policy and economics; tropical vegetation; world forestry development with emphasis on the tropics; range management. *Mailing Add:* Sch Forestry Col Environ Sci & Forestry State Univ NY Syracuse NY 13210

LARSON, CHARLES FRED, b Gary, Ind, Nov 27, 36; m 59; c 2. MECHANICAL ENGINEERING, WELDING METALLURGY. *Educ:* Purdue Univ, BS, 58; Fairleigh Dickinson Univ, Rutherford, MBA, 73. *Prof Exp:* Proj engr, Combustion Eng, Inc, 58-60; asst dir, Welding Res Coun, 60-75; EXEC DIR, INDUST RES INST, INC, 75- *Concurrent Pos:* Secy, Indust Res Inst Res Corp, 75- *Mem:* AAAS; Am Soc Mech Engrs; Soc Res Adminr. *Res:* Pressure vessels; fatigue of welded structures; fracture toughness of metals; non-destructive examination; heavy-section steels; research management. *Mailing Add:* Indust Res Inst Inc 100 Park Ave New York NY 10017

LARSON, CLARENCE EDWARD, b Cloquet, Minn, Sept 20, 09; m 34, 57; c 3. PHYSICAL CHEMISTRY. *Educ:* Univ Minn, BS, 32; Univ Calif, PhD(chem), 36. *Prof Exp:* Instr chem, Univ Calif, 32-36; res assoc, Mt Zion Res Found, Calif, 36-37; assoc prof chem, Col of the Pac, 37-39, prof & head dept, 39-40; chief anal sect, Radiation Lab, Univ Calif, 40-43; head tech staff, Electromagnetic Plant, Carbide & Carbon Chem Co Div, Union Carbide Corp, 43-46, dir res & develop, 46-49, supt, 49-50, dir, Oak Ridge Nat Lab, 50-55, vpres chg res, Nat Carbon Co Div, 55-59, assoc mgr res admin, 59-61, vpres, Union Carbide Nuclear Co Div, 61-64; ENERGY CONSULT, SYSTS CONTROL, INC, 64-; COMNR, ENERGY RES & DEVELOP ADMIN, WASHINGTON, DC, 69- *Concurrent Pos:* Am Nuclear Soc fel, 62; mem bd dirs, Oak Ridge Inst Nuclear Studies, 63-65; pres, Nuclear Div, Union Carbide Co, Tenn, 65-69; deleg, UN Conf Peaceful Uses of Atomic Energy. *Mem:* Nat Acad Eng; AAAS; Am Chem Soc; fel Am Inst Chemists; Am Nuclear Soc. *Res:* Inorganic chemistry of biological systems; separation methods for isotopes; radiochemistry; analytical methods; uranium chemistry; colloids; chemical separation methods. *Mailing Add:* 6514 Bradley Blvd Bethesda MD 20034

LARSON, CURTIS L(UVERNE), b Cottonwood, Minn, Oct 10, 20; m 44; c 3. AGRICULTURAL & CIVIL ENGINEERING. *Educ:* Univ Minn, BAgrE, 43, MS, 49; Stanford Univ, PhD(civil eng), 65. *Prof Exp:* From instr to assoc prof agr eng, 48-65, PROF AGR ENG, INST AGR, UNIV MINN, ST PAUL, 65- *Concurrent Pos:* Water mgt consult, Colombia, 72-73, Nicaragua, 75, Chile, 76 & Panama, 78. *Mem:* Am Soc Agr Engrs; Am Geophys Union; Am Water Resources Asn; Soil Conserv Soc Am. *Res:* Surface water hydrology; watershed modeling; erosion control; water resources. *Mailing Add:* Dept of Agr Eng Univ of Minn St Paul MN 55108

LARSON, DANIEL A, b Jersey City, NJ, July 7, 23; m 51; c 3. ATOMIC PHYSICS. *Educ:* St Peter's Col, NJ, BS, 44; Stevens Inst Technol, MS, 56. *Prof Exp:* Trainee physics, Schenectady Res Lab, Gen Elec Co, 47-48, physicist, Nela Park Lamp Div, 48-52; from assoc res engr to sr res engr, 52-65, ENGR FEL RES, LAMP DIV, WESTINGHOUSE ELEC CORP, 65- *Mem:* AAAS; Illum Eng Soc; Optical Soc Am. *Res:* Low pressure discharges in metal vapor; fluorescent lamp discharges; high pressure discharges in mercury metal and metal iodides in high pressure discharges; optical pumps for lasers; high pressure sodium lamp discharges. *Mailing Add:* Westinghouse Lamp Div Dept 8015.2 One Westinghouse Plaza Bloomfield NJ 07003

LARSON, DANIEL JOHN, b Minneapolis, Minn, Nov 8, 44; m 66; c 2. LASER SPECTROSCOPY, NEGATIVE IONS. *Educ:* St Olaf Col, Northfield, Minn, BA, 66; Harvard Univ, Cambridge, Mass, MA, 67, PhD(physics), 71. *Prof Exp:* Asst prof physics, Harvard Univ, 70-75, assoc prof, 75-78; ASSOC PROF PHYSICS, UNIV VA, 78- *Mem:* Am Phys Soc. *Res:* High resolution optical and microwave spectroscopy of atoms and ions, especially negative ions, using tunable lasers and atom and ion storage techniques. *Mailing Add:* Dept Physics Univ Va Charlottesville VA 22901

LARSON, DANIEL LEWIS, b Sioux City, Iowa, Nov 28, 21; m 55; c 4. MEDICINE. *Educ:* Columbia Univ, MD, 46; Am Bd Internal Med, dipl. *Prof Exp:* Intern med, Columbia-Presby Hosp, 46-47, resident, 47-50; instr, 50-52, assoc, 52-53 & 55-57, ASST PROF MED, COL PHYSICIANS & SURGEONS, COLUMBIA UNIV, 57- *Concurrent Pos:* Markle scholar, 50-53 & 55-57; dir prof affairs, St Barnabas Hosp, 65-81. *Mem:* AAAS; Harvey Soc; Soc Exp Biol & Med; AMA; Am Asn Immunol. *Res:* Immunochemistry; rheumatic fever, systemic lupus erythematosus; connective tissue disease. *Mailing Add:* St Barnabas Hosp Third Ave Bronx NY 10457

LARSON, DAVID L, immunology, biochemistry, see previous edition

LARSON, DENIS WAYNE, b Prince Albert, Sask, Dec 2, 38; m 62; c 4. PHYSICAL CHEMISTRY. *Educ:* Univ Sask, BA, 61, MA, 62; Univ Toronto, PhD(inorg chem), 65. *Prof Exp:* Mem res staff, Can Forces Inst Aviation Med, 65-68; asst prof, 68-71, ASSOC PROF CHEM, UNIV REGINA, 71- *Concurrent Pos:* Asst to dean, Fac Grad Studies & Res, Univ Regina, 73-79. *Mem:* Chem Inst Can. *Mailing Add:* Dept of Chem Univ of Regina Regina SK S4S 0A2 Can

LARSON, DONALD ALFRED, b Chicago, Ill, Sept 15, 30; m 53; c 3. BOTANY. *Educ:* Wheaton Col, Ill, BS, 53; Univ Ill, MS, 55, PhD(bot), 59. *Prof Exp:* Assoc prof bot, Univ Tex, Austin, 59-69, prof & dir health prof, 69-73; PROF BIOL & ASSOC VPRES HEALTH SCI, STATE UNIV NY BUFFALO, 73- *Mem:* Bot Soc Am; Am Soc Cell Biologists. *Res:* Electron microscopy; cytology; palynology; taxonomic uses; paleobotany. *Mailing Add:* Edgar Beck Hall State Univ NY Buffalo NY 14214

LARSON, DONALD CLAYTON, b Wadena, Minn, Jan 29, 34; m 60; c 3. SOLID STATE PHYSICS. *Educ:* Univ Wash, BS, 56; Harvard Univ, SM, 57, PhD(appl physics), 62. *Prof Exp:* Asst prof physics, Univ Va, 62-67; ASSOC PROF PHYSICS, DREXEL UNIV, 67- *Mem:* Am Phys Soc; Int Solar Energy Soc; Am Soc Testing & Mat. *Res:* Electrical properties of metallic, organic and amorphous semiconducting films; biomechanics; solar energy; insulation studies. *Mailing Add:* Dept of Physics Drexel Univ Philadelphia PA 19104

LARSON, DONALD W, b Avoca Minn, Aug 7, 40; m 62; c 3. AGRICULTURAL ECONOMICS. *Educ:* SDak State Univ, BS, 62; Mich State Univ, MS, 64, PhD(agr econ), 68. *Prof Exp:* Asst prof agr econ, Mich State Univ, 68-70; asst prof, 70-76, ASSOC PROF AGR ECON, OHIO STATE UNIV, 76- *Concurrent Pos:* Mkt consult, 73, Loan consult, US AID, 74; mkt & price policy consult, World Bank, 78. *Mem:* Am Agr Econ Asn; Int Asn Agr Economists; Brazilian Agr Econ Asn. *Res:* Grain marketing and transportation systems, marketing and market policy in developing countries. *Mailing Add:* Ohio State Univ Dept of Agr Econ Columbus OH 43210

LARSON, DUANE L, b Stoughton, Wis, June 19, 28; m 58; c 3. PLASTIC SURGERY, SURGERY. *Educ:* Univ Wis, BS, 51, MD, 54; Am Bd Surg, dipl, 62; Am Bd Plastic Surg, dipl, 65. *Prof Exp:* Intern, Med Col Va, 54-55; gen surg resident, Univ Wis, 55-57 & 59-61; plastic surg resident, 61-64, asst prof, 64-68, assoc prof, 69-73, PROF PLASTIC SURG, UNIV TEX MED BR GALVESTON, 73-; CHIEF SURGEON, SHRINERS BURNS INST, 65- *Mem:* AAAS; Am Col Surg; Am Fedn Clin Res; Plastic Surg Res Coun; Am Soc Head & Neck Surg. *Res:* Lymphatics; burns. *Mailing Add:* Shriners Burns Inst Galveston TX 77550

LARSON, EDWARD RICHARD, geology, see previous edition

LARSON, EDWARD WILLIAM, JR, b New Haven, Conn, Apr 17, 23; m 52; c 2. STRUCTURAL ENGINEERING. *Educ:* Ind Technol Col, BSCE, 43; Northwestern Univ, MS, 48, PhD(civil eng), 53. *Prof Exp:* Jr engr, Bur Ships, US Dept Navy, 43-44, physicist, David Taylor Model Basin, 44-46; res assoc struct, Northwestern Univ, 49-52, instr struct eng, 52-53; engr, Hughes Tool Co, Calif, 53-55; res engr, Lockheed Aircraft Corp, 55-57; supvr stress anal, 57-62, group leader dynamic sci, 62-63, sect chief & mgr turbomach, 63-69, mgr tech specialties, 69-75, assoc chief engr, 75-79, DIR, DESIGN TECHNOL, ROCKETDYNE DIV, ROCKWELL INT, 79- *Concurrent Pos:* Lectr, Univ Calif, Los Angeles, 53-64. *Mem:* Soc Exp Stress Anal; Am Inst Aeronaut & Astronaut. *Res:* Failure investigation of engine components under actual operating conditions and structural behavior of liquid rocket engines to transient, steady state and flow-induced vibrations. *Mailing Add:* 18621 Ringling Tarzana CA 91356

LARSON, EDWIN E, b Los Angeles, Calif, Jan 5, 31. GEOPHYSICS, GEOLOGY. *Educ:* Univ Calif, Los Angeles, BA, 54, MA, 58; Univ Colo, PhD(geol), 65. *Prof Exp:* Explor geologist, Humble Oil & Refining Co, 57-60; NSF fel, 65-66; from asst prof to assoc prof, 66-75, PROF GEOL SCI, UNIV COLO, BOULDER, 75- *Mem:* AAAS; Geol Soc Am; Am Geophys Union. *Res:* Investigation of rock magnetic properties; paleomagnetism and its application to the solution of geological problems; lunar magnetism. *Mailing Add:* Dept of Geol Univ of Colo Boulder CO 80309

LARSON, EDYTHE MARIE, b New York, NY, Mar 23, 22. BACTERIOLOGY. *Educ:* Wagner Col, BS, 44; NY Univ, MA, 46, PhD, 57. *Prof Exp:* From asst prof to assoc prof bact, 46-61, PROF BACT & HEALTH SCI, 61-, CHMN DEPT & COORDR ALLIED HEALTH CAREERS, 71-; BACTERIOLOGIST, PKWY HOSP, 44- *Concurrent Pos:* Lectr, Hunter Col, 49-51; instr, NY Univ, 55-56. *Mem:* Fel AAAS; Am Soc Microbiol; fel Am Pub Health Asn; Nat Sci Teachers Asn; Royal Soc Health. *Res:* General bacteriology; marine microbiology. *Mailing Add:* Dept Bact & Pub Health Wagner Col Staten Island NY 10301

LARSON, EVERETT GERALD, b Logan, Utah, Nov 12, 35; m 63; c 4. SOLID STATE PHYSICS, MOLECULAR PHYSICS. *Educ:* Mass Inst Technol, SB, 57, SM, 59, PhD(electron correlation), 64. *Prof Exp:* Asst, Mass Inst Technol & mem staff, Lincoln Labs, 57-64; asst prof physics, Brigham Young Univ, 64-68; vis asst prof chem, Univ Ga, 68-69; assoc prof, 69-75, PROF PHYSICS, BRIGHAM YOUNG UNIV, 75- *Mem:* Am Phys Soc. *Res:* Atomic molecular and solid state theory; correlation effects; cooperative phenomena; theory of irreversible processes. *Mailing Add:* Dept of Physics & Astron Brigham Young Univ Provo UT 84601

LARSON, FRANK CLARK, b Columbus, Nebr, Jan 17, 20; m 48; c 3. MEDICINE. *Educ:* Nebr State Teachers Col, AB, 41; Univ Nebr, MD, 44; Am Bd Internal Med, dipl. *Prof Exp:* Instr, 50-51, asst clin prof, 51-56, from asst prof to assoc prof, 56-63, PROF MED & PATH, UNIV WIS-MADISON, 63-, DIR CLIN LABS, HOSP, 58- *Concurrent Pos:* Asst chief med & tuberc serv, Vet Admin Hosp, Madison, 51-56, chief invest med serv, 52-56. *Mem:* Endocrine Soc; Am Col Physicians; Cent Soc Clin Res. *Res:* Thyroid metabolism. *Mailing Add:* 600 Highland Ave Madison WI 53706

LARSON, FRANK R, b Medford, Mass, June 7, 24; m; c 4. ENGINEERING & MATERIALS SCIENCE. *Educ:* Tufts Univ, BS, 45; Brown Univ, PhD, 71. *Prof Exp:* Engr, Gen Elec Co, 47-51; CHIEF METALS DIV, ARMY MAT & MECH RES CTR, 51- *Concurrent Pos:* Lectr, Am Soc Metals. *Honors & Awards:* Charles A Coffin Award, Gen Elec Co; Meritorious Civilian Serv Award, US Dept Army, 68. *Mem:* Am Soc Metals; Am Soc Testing & Mat; Am Inst Mining, Metall & Petrol Engrs; Brit Inst Metals. *Res:* Mechanical metallurgy; metals deformation; plastic flow; flow and fracture and effects of anisotropy on mechanical behavior of metals and alloys. *Mailing Add:* Dept of the Army Mat & Mech Res Ctr Watertown MA 02172

LARSON, FREDERIC ROGER, b Los Angeles, Calif, Mar 26, 42; m 74; c 1. FOREST MANAGEMENT, SYSTEMS ANALYSIS. *Educ:* Northern Ariz Univ, BSF, 66, MS, 68; Colo State Univ, PhD(forestry), 75. *Prof Exp:* Forester, Nez Perce Nat Forest, 66-67, res forester, Rocky Mountain Forest & Range Exp Sta, 67-78, RES FORESTER, PAC NORTHWEST FOREST & RANGE EXP STA, US FOREST SERV, 79- *Concurrent Pos:* Prof, Northern Ariz Univ Forestry Sch, 71-72, adj prof, 75-78. *Mem:* Soc Am Foresters; Am Soc Photogram; Soc Range Mgt; Wildlife Soc. *Res:* Quantifying and simulating growth and management of southwestern coniferous forests; computer simulation models ecosystems; forest multi-resource inventories. *Mailing Add:* Forest Sci Lab Suite 106 2221 E Northern Lights Anchorage AK 99504

LARSON, GARY EUGENE, b Jersey Shore, Pa, Aug 10, 36; m 60; c 2. BOTANY, BIOPHYSICS. *Educ:* State Univ NY Albany, BS, 58, MS, 60; Rutgers Univ, PhD(bot), 64. *Prof Exp:* Asst bot, Rutgers Univ, 61-62, instr biol, Douglass Col, 62-64; asst prof, 64-66, assoc prof, 66-81, chmn dept, 68-81, PROF BOT, BETHANY COL, WVA, 81-, DIR HEALTH SCI PROG, 81- *Concurrent Pos:* WVa Heart Asn grant, 67-68; teacher & dir, Col Educ Prog, WVa Penitentiary, 68-78; Peace Corps sci curric adv, Gambian Govt, 70-71; dir, Nat Defense Educ Act Title I Proj, 72-73; exec dir, Brooke-Hancock Comprehensive Health Planning Asn, 74-75; vis Fulbright Lectr, Dept Biol, Univ Ile, Nigeria, 77-78; AAAS rep to West African Sci Asn meeting, Lome, Togo, 79. *Mem:* Fel AAAS; Sigma Xi; Am Inst Biol Sci; Audubon Soc. *Res:* Bioelectric potentials surrounding the roots of plants; computer aided instruction; audio-tutorial education. *Mailing Add:* Dept Biol Bethany Col Bethany WV 26032

LARSON, GEORGE H(ERBERT), b Lindsborg, Kans, Jan 28, 15; m 41; c 1. AGRICULTURAL ENGINEERING. *Educ:* Kans State Univ, BS, 39, MS, 40; Mich State Univ, PhD, 55. *Prof Exp:* Asst, Kans State Univ, 39-40; asst instr agr eng, Univ Wis, 40-42; instr, Panhandle Agr & Mech Col, 42; jr instr, US Dept Navy, 42-43; assoc prof agr eng, 46-50, head dept, 56-70, PROF AGR ENG, KANS STATE UNIV, 50- *Concurrent Pos:* Proj & proj leader agr eng, Nebr Mission, USAID, Bogota, Colombia, 70-72; prof agr eng & head dept agron with Kans State Univ Proj, USAID, Ahmadu Bello Univ, Nigeria, 72-74; consult with Kans State Univ Proj, USAID, Central Luzon State Univ, Philippines, 78-80. *Mem:* Am Soc Agr Engrs; Am Soc Eng Educ. *Res:* Utilizing liquefied petroleum gas for weed control by flaming; power and machinery, utilizing liquefied petroleum gas in tractors; operating costs of field machinery; agricultural mechanization in developing countries. *Mailing Add:* Dept of Agr Eng Kans State Univ Manhattan KS 66502

LARSON, GERALD WILLIS, b Halstad, Minn, Nov 21, 23; m 60. ORGANIC CHEMISTRY. *Educ:* Univ Minn, BChem, 49; Carnegie Inst Technol, PhD(chem), 53. *Prof Exp:* Chemist, E I du Pont de Nemours & Co, 53-55; CHEMIST, 3M CO, ST PAUL, 55- *Res:* Polymers; photochemistry. *Mailing Add:* Printing Prod Div Bldg 235 3M Co St Paul MN 55101

LARSON, GUSTAV OLOF, b Cedar City, Utah, Dec 24, 26; m 55; c 4. ORGANIC CHEMISTRY. *Educ:* Univ Utah, BS, 48, MA, 51; Wash State Univ, PhD, 59. *Prof Exp:* Asst prof chem, Utah State Univ, 57-62; assoc prof & Lead dept, Westminster Col, Utah, 62-65; NSF fac fel, Univ Colo, 65-66; assoc prof, 66-71, PROF CHEM, FERRIS STATE COL, 71- *Mem:* AAAS; Am Chem Soc. *Res:* Organic reaction mechanisms; stereochemistry; teaching aids, including patents on paper steromodels and pK-pH calculator. *Mailing Add:* Dept of Phys Sci Ferris State Col Big Rapids MI 49307

LARSON, HAROLD JOSEPH, b Eagle Grove, Iowa, Nov 16, 34; m 62; c 4. MATHEMATICAL STATISTICS. *Educ:* Iowa State Univ, BS, 56, MS, 57, PhD(math, statist), 60. *Prof Exp:* Instr statist, Iowa State Univ, 59-60; math statistician, Stanford Res Inst, 60-62; prof opers anal, 62-80, PROF OPERS RES & STATIST, NAVAL POSTGRAD SCH, 80- *Concurrent Pos:* Consult, Autonetics Div, NAm Aviation, Inc, 63-64, Data Dynamics, Inc, 65-67 & Field Res Corp, 65-69; Fulbright prof, Univ Sao Paulo, 70-71. *Mem:* Am Statist Asn. *Res:* Probability theory; general statistical methods. *Mailing Add:* Dept of Opers Anal Naval Postgrad Sch Monterey CA 93940

LARSON, HAROLD OLAF, b Port Wing, Wis, May 27, 21. ORGANIC CHEMISTRY. *Educ:* Univ Wis, BS, 43; Purdue Univ, MS, 47; Harvard Univ, PhD, 50. *Prof Exp:* Navigator, Pan Am Airways, 44-45; chemist, Hercules Powder Co, 50-54; res fel chem, Harvard Univ, 54-55; asst prof, Univ WVa, 55-57; res fel, Purdue Univ, 57-58; from asst prof to assoc prof, 58-72, PROF CHEM, UNIV HAWAII, 72- *Mem:* Am Chem Soc; The Chem Soc. *Mailing Add:* Dept of Chem Univ of Hawaii Honolulu HI 96822

LARSON, HAROLD PHILLIP, b Hartford, Conn, July 13, 38; m 60; c 2. ASTRONOMY. *Educ:* Bates Col, BS, 60; Purdue Univ, MS, 63, PhD(physics), 67. *Prof Exp:* Res assoc physics, Purdue Univ, 67-68; fel, Aime-Cotton Lab, Nat Ctr Sci Res, France, 68-69; asst prof, 69-71, assoc prof astron, 71-76, ASSOC RES PROF, LUNAR & PLANETARY LAB, UNIV ARIZ, 76-, ASSOC ASTONR, STEWARD OBSERV, 80- *Mem:* Am Astron Soc. *Res:* Infrared astronomy of planetary atmospheres and surfaces. *Mailing Add:* Lunar & Planetary Lab Univ of Ariz Tucson AZ 85721

LARSON, HAROLD RICHARD, metallurgy, see previous edition

LARSON, HAROLD VINCENT, b Portland, Ore, Dec 15, 24; m 48; c 5. HEALTH PHYSICS. *Educ:* Ore State Col, BS, 50, MS, 57; Am Bd Health Physics, cert. *Prof Exp:* Physicist health physics, Gen Elec Co, 52-65; sr develop engr, Radiation Protection Dept, 65-68, mgr radiation protection dept, 68-70, mgr radiation standards & eng sect, 70-71, mgr personnel dosimetry sect, 71-72, mgr environ evaluations sect, 72-74, MGR OCCUP & ENVIRON SAFETY DEPT, BATTELLE MEM INST, 74- *Mem:* Am Phys Soc; Health Physics Soc; Radiation Res Soc; Am Asn Physicists in Med; Am Nuclear Soc. *Res:* Atomic and nuclear physics as applied to radiological and health physics. *Mailing Add:* 904 Cottonwood Ave Richland WA 99352

LARSON, HUGO R, b Gary, Ind, Jan 21, 25; m 49; c 4. PHYSICAL METALLURGY, MELTING PRACTICE. *Educ:* Pa State Univ, BS, 47, MS, 49; Mass Inst Technol, ScD, 51. *Prof Exp:* Res metallurgist, 52-64, tech dir, 64-70, DIR METALL RES, ABEX CORP, 70- *Mem:* Am Soc Metals; Am Soc Testing & Mat; Am Foundrymens Soc. *Res:* Metallurgical research in abrasion and heat resistant alloys, low alloy-high strength steels and railroad products (wheels, brake shoes, and trackwork). *Mailing Add:* 12 Rumopock Ct Mahwah NJ 07430

LARSON, INGEMAR W, b Clarissa, Minn, Dec 4, 28; m 62. ZOOLOGY, PARASITOLOGY. *Educ:* Concordia Col, Moorhead, Minn, AB, 51; Kans State Univ, MS, 57, PhD(parasitol), 63. *Prof Exp:* Instr biol, Concordia Col, 51-52; asst zool, Kans State Univ, 55-57; asst parasitol, Biol Sta, Univ Mich, 57; instr zool, Kans State Univ, 57-62, asst zool, 62-63; res assoc, Ore State Univ, 63-66; from asst prof to assoc prof, 66-77, PROF BIOL & DEPT CHMN, AUGUSTANA COL, ILL, 77- *Mem:* Am Soc Parasitologists; Am Micros Soc; Sigma Xi. *Res:* Parasitic protozoa; floodplain insects. *Mailing Add:* Dept Biol Augustana Col Rock Island IL 61201

LARSON, JAY REINHOLD, b Urbana, Ill, Dec 6, 32; m 58; c 4. MECHANICAL & NUCLEAR ENGINEERING. *Educ:* Univ Ill, Urbana, BS, 55; Univ Wash, MS, 60; Purdue Univ, PhD(mech eng), 64. *Prof Exp:* Engr, Gen Elec Co, 60-61; assoc scientist, Aerojet Nuclear Co, 64-77; SCIENTIST & ENG SUPVR, EG&G IDAHO INC, 77- *Concurrent Pos:* Affil prof, Univ Idaho. *Mem:* Am Soc Mech Eng; Nat Soc Prof Eng. *Res:* Heat transfer; nuclear reactor safety research. *Mailing Add:* 1033 E 25 St Idaho Falls ID 83401

LARSON, JERRY KING, b Willmar, Minn, May 15, 41; m 64; c 2. CLINICAL PHARMACOLOGY. *Educ:* Macalester Col, BA, 63; Mass Inst Technol, PhD(org chem), 67. *Prof Exp:* Res chemist, Chas Pfizer & Co, Inc, 67-70; asst to dir clin res, 70-76, MGR CLIN SCI SERV, PFIZER CENT RES, PFIZER INC, 76- *Mem:* Am Chem Soc. *Res:* Clinical trials with new potential drug candidates, particularly the administration and monitoring of such trials. *Mailing Add:* Pfizer Inc Groton CT 06340

LARSON, JOHN GRANT, b Galesburg, Ill, Aug 17, 33; m 59; c 2. CATALYSIS, SURFACE SCIENCE. *Educ:* Bradley Univ, BS, 55; Univ Ill, Urbana, PhD(phys chem), 62. *Prof Exp:* Proj officer, Mat Lab, Wright Field, US Air Force, 55-57; fel, Mellon Inst, 61-64; group leader, Gulf Res & Develop Co, 64-66; supvr chem physics sect, 66-69, dir, 70-73; HEAD PHYS CHEM DEPT, GEN MOTORS RES LABS, 73- *Mem:* Catalysis Soc; Am Chem Soc; Sigma Xi. *Res:* Catalysis, both oxide and supported metals especially for emission control; combustion chemistry; surface chemistry; analytical petroleum chemistry; molecular spectroscopy, especially mass spectroscopy. *Mailing Add:* Phys Chem Dept Gen Motors Res Labs Warren MI 48090

LARSON, JOSEPH STANLEY, b Stoneham, Mass, June 23, 33; m 58; c 2. WILDLIFE BIOLOGY. *Educ:* Univ Mass, BS, 56, MA, 58; Va Polytech Inst, PhD(zool), 66. *Prof Exp:* Exec secy, Wildlife Conserv Inc, Mass, 58-59; state ornithologist & asst to dir, Mass Div Fisheries & Game, 59-60; head conserv educ div, Natural Resources Inst, Univ Md, 60-62, res asst prof wildlife, 65-67; adj asst prof wildlife biol & asst unit leader, Mass Coop Wildlife Res Unit, 67-69, assoc prof, 69-77, PROF, DEPT FORESTRY & WILDLIFE MGT, UNIV MASS, AMHERST, 77-, CHMN DEPT, 80- *Concurrent Pos:* Consult wetland mgt to var pub & pvt agencies; exec chmn, Nat Wetlands Tech Coun, 77- *Mem:* AAAS; Wildlife Soc; Ecol Soc Am; Animal Behav Soc; Am Soc Mammal. *Res:* Wetland ecology and management; beaver behavior. *Mailing Add:* Dept of Forestry & Wildlife Mgt Univ of Mass Amherst MA 01003

LARSON, KENNETH ALLEN, b Havre, Mont, July 6, 35; m 61; c 4. IMMUNOLOGY, VETERINARY MEDICINE. *Educ:* Wash State Univ, DVM, 61, MS, 65, PhD(immunol), 66. *Prof Exp:* Vet pvt pract, Mont, 61-63; asst prof vet med, Colo State Univ, 66-69, assoc prof vet med & microbiol, 69-76; PRES, ELARS BIORES LABS INC, 76- *Mem:* AAAS; Am Soc Microbiol; Am Vet Med Asn. *Res:* Immunology of tumors in animals. *Mailing Add:* 1305 Teakwood Dr Ft Collins CO 80521

LARSON, KENNETH BLAINE, b Mesa, Ariz, Jan 16, 30; m 58; c 4. BIOPHYSICS, BIOMATHEMATICS. *Educ:* Colo Sch Mines, MetE, 51; Mass Inst Technol, SM, 54 & 58, PhD(metall & physics), 64. *Prof Exp:* Instr & res asst metall, Mass Inst Technol, 51-53; staff mem, Engr Res & Develop Labs, US Army, Ft Belvoir, Va, 54 & White Sands Proving Ground, NMex, 54-55; res asst metall, Mass Inst Technol, 58-64; staff mem, Gen Atomic Div, Gen Dynamics Corp, Calif, 64-65; res staff, Cent Res Dept, Monsanto Co, 65-70; INSTR BIOMED ENG & RES ASSOC, BIOMED COMPUT LAB, SCH MED, WASHINGTON UNIV, 70- *Concurrent Pos:* Consult, NIH, 78- *Mem:* AAAS. *Res:* Ion-exchange resins; diffusion in liquid metals; measurement of thermal diffusivity and heat capacity of thin films; experimental design and statistics; structure of liquids; semiconductor crystal growth; mathematical modeling in physiology; tracer kinetics; biomedical engineering; physics of cancer radiotherapy. *Mailing Add:* 12855 Kent Manor St Louis MO 63131

LARSON, KENNETH CURTIS, b Madison, Wis, July 7, 40; m 64; c 2. PAPER CHEMISTRY, WOOD CHEMISTRY. *Educ:* Calif Inst Technol, BS, 62; Lawrence Univ, MS, 64, PhD(wood chem), 67. *Prof Exp:* Sci specialist res & develop, 67-74, sci assoc, 74-77, proj head, 77-80, Mgr Res & Develop, 80-81, DIR RES & DEVELOP, SCOTT PAPER CO, PHILADELPHIA, 81- *Mem:* Tech Asn Pulp & Paper Indust; Am Chem Soc. *Res:* Catalysis; colloid and surface chemistry of wood pulp fibers; product and process development. *Mailing Add:* Scott Paper Co Scott Plaza 3 Philadelphia PA 19113

LARSON, LARRY LEE, b Horton, Kans, Nov 18, 39; m 63; c 2. REPRODUCTIVE PHYSIOLOGY. *Educ:* Kans State Univ, BS, 62, MS, 65, PhD(animal breeding), 68. *Prof Exp:* NIH fel, Cornell Univ, 68-70, asst prof reproductive physiol, 70-72; asst prof, 72-77, ASSOC PROF REPRODUCTIVE PHYSIOL, UNIV NEBR-LINCOLN, 77- *Mem:* Soc Study Reproduction; Brit Soc Study Fertil; Am Soc Animal Sci; Am Dairy Sci Asn. *Res:* Estrus control and determination; conception failures; management factors to improve reproductive performance. *Mailing Add:* Dept of Animal Sci Univ of Nebr Lincoln NE 68503

LARSON, LAURENCE ARTHUR, b Cleveland, Ohio, Mar 17, 30; m 56; c 2. PLANT PHYSIOLOGY, BIOLOGY EDUCATION. *Educ:* Ohio Univ, BS, 56; Univ Tenn, MS, 59; Purdue Univ, PhD(amino acid metab), 63. *Prof Exp:* Phys oceanogr, US Navy Hydrographic Off, 56-57; instr bot, Univ Tenn, 59; from asst prof to assoc prof, 63-75, PROF BOT, OHIO UNIV, 75- *Mem:* Am Inst Biol Sci; Asn Am Biol Teachers. *Res:* Germination physiology. *Mailing Add:* Dept of Bot Ohio Univ Col Arts & Sci Athens OH 45701

LARSON, LAWRENCE T, b Waukegan, Ill, Dec 3, 30; m 57; c 3. ECONOMIC GEOLOGY, MINERALOGY. *Educ:* Univ Ill, BS, 57; Univ Wis, MS, 59, PhD(geol), 62. *Prof Exp:* From asst prof to prof geol, Univ Tenn, Knoxville, 61-75; PROF GEOL & CHMN DEPT, MACKAY SCH MINES, UNIV NEV, RENO, 75- *Concurrent Pos:* Consult, Oak Ridge Nat Lab, 63-69 & mining firms, 68-, United Nations Develop Prog, WHO & US Dept Energy; partner, Appl Explor Concepts, 72-79. *Mem:* Geol Soc Am; Can Inst Mining & Metall; Am Inst Mining, Metall & Petrol Engrs; Soc Econ Geologists. *Res:* Manganese mineralogy and ore deposits; ore microscopy; uranium mineralization in Great Basin; geologic thermometry; ceramic and high alumina clay deposits; applied geochemistry and gold exploration. *Mailing Add:* Dept of Geol Sci Univ of Nev Mackay Sch of Mines Reno NV 89507

LARSON, LEE EDWARD, b Bristol, Conn, Dec 2, 37; m 63; c 1. PHYSICS. *Educ:* Univ NH, PhD(ionospheric physics), 67. *Prof Exp:* Instr physics, Allegheny Col, 61-63; from asst prof to assoc prof, 66-78, PROF PHYSICS, DENISON UNIV, 78- *Mem:* Am Asn Physics Teachers; Am Geophys Union. *Res:* High resolution molecular spectroscopy. *Mailing Add:* Dept of Physics Denison Univ Granville OH 43023

LARSON, LESTER LEROY, b Amherst Junction, Wis, Feb 12, 23; m 51; c 3. VETERINARY MEDICINE. *Educ:* Univ Minn, BS, 50, DVM & MS, 53, PhD(vet med), 57; Am Col Theriogenologists, dipl, 70. *Prof Exp:* Vet, 53-54; from instr to asst prof vet med, Univ Minn, 54-58; assoc vet, 58-73, VET & HEAD VET DEPT, AM BREEDERS SERV, 74- *Concurrent Pos:* Chmn comt exam, Am Col Theriogenologists, 73; guest lectr genital path in the bull, Univ Venezuela, 78. *Mem:* Am Vet Med Asn; US Animal Health Asn. *Res:* Neuroanatomical and neurophysiological aspects of reproductive process-male; surgical technique for anesthesia of penis-bull; control of venereal diseases of cattle through artificial insemination; actuarial studies of bull under conditions of an artificial insemination center. *Mailing Add:* 2102 Brentwood Pkwy Madison WI 53704

LARSON, LESTER MIKKEL, b Devils Lake, NDak, Aug 2, 18; m 43; c 3. CHEMISTRY. *Educ:* Lawrence Col, BA, 40; Univ Wis, MS, 50, PhD(biochem), 51. *Prof Exp:* Chemist, Abbott Labs, 41-48; instr biochem, Univ Wis, 51-52; biochemist, E I du Pont de Nemours & Co, 52-64; assoc prof, 65-69, PROF CHEM, DEL STATE COL, 69- *Concurrent Pos:* Pres, Larson Corp. *Mem:* Am Chem Soc; Am Inst Chem. *Res:* Arsenicals; antibiotics; polymers; separations. *Mailing Add:* Dept of Chem Del State Col Dover DE 19901

LARSON, M(ILTON) B(YRD), b Portland, Ore, July 3, 27; m 50; c 4. MECHANICAL ENGINEERING. *Educ:* Ore State Univ, BS, 50, MS, 55; Yale Univ, MEng, 51; Stanford Univ, PhD(mech eng), 61. *Prof Exp:* From instr to assoc prof mech eng, Ore State Univ, 52-64; dean eng, Univ NDak, 64-68; PROF MECH ENG, ORE STATE UNIV, 69- *Concurrent Pos:* Ford Found resident, Washington Works, E I du Pont de Nemours & Co, 68-69. *Mem:* Am Soc Mech Engrs; Am Soc Eng Educ. *Res:* Heat transfer. *Mailing Add:* Dept of Mech Eng Ore State Univ Corvallis OR 97331

LARSON, M JOAN, b Dayton, Ohio, June 29, 42; m 81. DENTISTRY. *Educ:* Univ Nebr, Omaha, BA, 64; Univ Ill, Urbana-Champaign, PhD(zool), 71; Case Western Reserve Univ, DDS, 78. *Prof Exp:* Asst prof biol, Kenyon Col, 71-74; gen pract dent resident, Kansas City Vet Admin Med Ctr, 78-79. *Mem:* Am Dent Asn. *Res:* Analyses of variation in odontometric traits of rodents. *Mailing Add:* 4620 Redfield Ct Apt 1-13 St Louis MO 63121

LARSON, MAURICE A(LLEN), b Iowa, July 19, 27; m 53; c 3. CHEMICAL ENGINEERING. *Educ:* Iowa State Univ, BS, 51, PhD(chem eng), 58. *Prof Exp:* Chem engr res & develop, Dow Corning Corp, 51-52, chem engr prod, 53-54; res asst chem eng, 54-55, instr & res assoc, 55-58, from asst prof to prof, 58-77, DISTINGUISHED PROF CHEM ENG, IOWA STATE UNIV, 77-, CHMN DEPT, 78- *Concurrent Pos:* NSF sci fac fel, Stanford Univ, 65-66; Shell vis prof, Univ Col, Univ London, 71-72; vis prof, Univ Queensland, 81. *Mem:* Am Chem Soc; Am Soc Eng Educ; Am Inst Chem Engrs. *Res:* Process dynamics and control; crystallization; analysis of particulate system; fertilizer technology. *Mailing Add:* Dept of Chem Eng Iowa State Univ Ames IA 50011

LARSON, MERLYN MILFRED, b Story City, Iowa, Sept 11, 28; m 54; c 6. FOREST PHYSIOLOGY. *Educ:* Colo State Univ, BS, 54; Univ Wash, MF, 58, PhD, 62. *Prof Exp:* Jr forester, US Forest Serv, 55, res forester, Rocky Mountain Forest & Range Exp Sta, 55-64, forest physiologist, 64-66; assoc prof silvicult, 66-70, PROF FORESTRY, OHIO AGR RES & DEVELOP CTR, 70-; PROF NATURAL RESOURCES, OHIO STATE UNIV, 70- *Concurrent Pos:* Asst, Univ Wash, 58-59. *Mem:* Soc Am Foresters. *Res:* Forest regeneration; tree physiology. *Mailing Add:* Dept of Forestry Ohio Agr Res & Develop Ctr Wooster OH 44691

LARSON, NANCY MARIE, b Dickinson, ND, Sept 30, 46; m 68. THEORETICAL PHYSICS. *Educ:* Mich State Univ, BS, 67, MS, 69, PhD(theoret physics), 72. *Prof Exp:* COMPUT SCI SPECIALIST PHYSICS, OAK RIDGE NAT LAB, NUCLEAR DIV, UNION CARBIDE CORP, 72- *Mem:* Am Phys Soc; Pattern Recognition Soc. *Res:* Computer modeling of environmental transport; nuclear structure theory; pattern recognition applied to chemical and biological data. *Mailing Add:* Comput Sci Div Oak Ridge Nat Lab Oak Ridge TN 37830

LARSON, NORA LEONA, b Fillmore Co, Minn, Sept 19, 01. BACTERIOLOGY. *Educ:* St Olaf Col, BA, 23; Univ Minn, MS, 33, PhD(bact), 47. *Prof Exp:* Tech asst clin bact, Mayo Clin, 24-36; bacteriologist, Lahey Clin, Boston, 36-39; asst res bact, Mayo Clin, 39-41; bacteriologist, Lahey Clin, Boston, 41-43; asst bact, Univ Minn, 44-46; bacteriologist, Takamine Labs, Inc, 46-49; res fel, Hormel Inst, Univ Minn, 50-56, asst prof, 56-60; assoc prof, 60-72, EMER ASSOC PROF BIOL, ST OLAF COL, 72- *Mem:* AAAS; Am Soc Microbiol; Am Inst Biol Sci; NY Acad Sci. *Res:* Lipids of Enterobacter cloacae; effect of chlortetracycline on intestinal microorganisms of young swine. *Mailing Add:* 1110 W First St Northfield MN 55057

LARSON, OMER R, b Roseau, Minn, Dec 1, 31; m 60; c 4. PARASITOLOGY. *Educ:* Univ NDak, BA, 54; Univ Minn, MS, 60 PhD(fish parasites), 63. *Prof Exp:* Instr biol, Minot State Col, 63-64; fr[illegible]st prof to assoc prof, 64-76, actg chmn dept, 66-67, assoc dean arts & sci, [illegible]-70 & 75-76, chmn dept, 78-80, PROF BIOL, UNIV NDAK, 76- *Mem:* Am Soc Parasitologists; Wildlife Disease Asn. *Res:* Helminth life cycles; parasites and diseases of fish; biogeography of fleas. *Mailing Add:* Dept Biol Univ NDak Grand Forks ND 58202

LARSON, PAUL STANLEY, b Cannon Falls, Minn, June 9, 07; m 36; c 1. PHARMACOLOGY. *Educ:* Univ Calif, AB, 30, PhD(physiol), 34. *Prof Exp:* Instr physiol, Sch Med, Georgetown Univ, 34-39; assoc physiol & pharmacol, Med Col Va, 40; lectr pharmacol, Col Med, Wayne Univ, 40-41; res assoc, 41-46, from assoc prof to prof, 46-63, chmn, Dept Pharmacol, 55-72, chmn dept, 55-75, HAAG PROF RES PHARMACOL, MED COL VA, 63- *Mem:* Am Physiol Soc; Am Soc Pharmacol & Exp Therapeut; Am Chem Soc; Soc Toxicol (pres, 63-64); NY Acad Sci. *Res:* Protein and purine metabolism; water balance; potassium metabolism; anti-spasmodics; biological actions of nicotine; chemical nature of irritants; toxicology. *Mailing Add:* Dept of Pharmacol Med Col of Va Richmond VA 23298

LARSON, PHILIP RODNEY, b North Branch, Minn, Nov 26, 23; m 48; c 2. FOREST PHYSIOLOGY, WOOD ANATOMY. *Educ:* Univ Minn, BS, 49, MS, 52; Yale Univ, PhD(forestry), 57. *Prof Exp:* Res forester, Fla, 52-54, plant physiologist, Lake States Forest Exp Sta, 56-62, LEADER PHYSIOL WOOD FORMATION, PIONEERING RES UNIT, N CENT FOREST EXP STA, US FOREST SERV, 62- *Honors & Awards:* Distinguished Serv Award, USDA, 75; Barrington Moore Biol Res Award, Soc Am Foresters, 75; New York Bot Garden Award, Bot Soc Am, 77. *Mem:* Am Soc Plant Physiologists; Soc Am Foresters; fel Int Acad Wood Sci; Bot Soc Am; Int Asn Wood Anatomists. *Res:* Wood formation; vascular anatomy; physiology of growth and development. *Mailing Add:* Pioneering Res Unit NCent Forest Exp Sta Box 898 Rhinelander WI 54501

LARSON, RACHEL HARRIS (MRS JOHN WATSON HENRY), b Wake Forest, NC, Aug 1, 13; m 56, 71; c 3. DENTAL RESEARCH. *Educ:* Appalachian State Univ, BS, 40; Georgetown Univ, MS, 49, PhD(biochem), 58. *Prof Exp:* Teacher, High Sch, Ga, 40-41 & NC, 41-42; chemist, Lab Indust Hyg Res, NIH, 42-48, res chemist, Nat Inst Dent Res, 48-76, chief, Prev Methods Develop Sect, Nat Caries Prog, 72-76; CONSULT, VET ADMIN, WASHINGTON, DC, 77- *Concurrent Pos:* Vis scientist, Royal Dent Col, Denmark, 70-71. *Mem:* Am Inst Nutrit; Int Asn Dent Res. *Res:* In vivo studies of caries inhibitory effects of trace elements in the rat. *Mailing Add:* 9301 Fernwood Rd Bethesda MD 20817

LARSON, REGINALD EINAR, b Milo, Maine, July 27, 34; m 66; c 1. AIR MASS TRACERS, NUCLEAR SPECTROSCOPY. *Educ:* Univ Maine, BS, 55; Univ Md, MS, 66. *Prof Exp:* RES PHYSICIST, NAVAL RES LAB, 59- *Mem:* Am Phys Soc; Am Meterol Soc; Am Geophys Union; Sigma Xi. *Res:* Nuclear physics; atmospheric physics research; author or coauthor of over 80 publications. *Mailing Add:* 1106 Montezuma Ft Washington MD 20746

LARSON, RICHARD ALLEN, b Minot, NDak, July 9, 41; m 63; c 2. ENVIRONMENTAL ORGANIC CHEMISTRY. *Educ:* Univ Minn, Minneapolis, BA, 63; Univ Ill, Urbana, PhD(org chem), 68. *Prof Exp:* USPHS fels, Univ Liverpool, 68-69 & Cambridge Univ, 69-70; res assoc bot, Univ Tex, Austin, 70-72; asst cur, Stroud Water Res Ctr, Acad Natural Sci Philadelphia, 72-79; ASST PROF ENVIRON RES LAB, UNIV ILL, URBANA, 79- *Concurrent Pos:* Spec lectr, Univ Pa, 73-74. *Mem:* Phytochem Soc NAm; Am Chem Soc; The Chem Soc. *Res:* Natural products; phytochemistry; aquatic chemical ecology. *Mailing Add:* 304 Environ Res Lab Univ Ill Urbana IL 61801

LARSON, RICHARD BONDO, b Toronto, Ont, Jan 15, 41. ASTROPHYSICS. *Educ:* Univ Toronto, BSc, 62, MA, 63; Calif Inst Technol, PhD(astron), 68. *Prof Exp:* from asst prof to assoc prof, 68-75, PROF ASTRON, YALE UNIV, 75- *Mem:* Int Astron Union; Am Astron Soc; Royal Astron Soc Can; Royal Astron Soc; Sigma Xi. *Res:* Theoretical studies of star formation and early stellar evolution; stellar dynamics, formation and evolution of galaxies. *Mailing Add:* Dept Astron Yale Univ Box 6666 Palisades NY 06511

LARSON, RICHARD GUSTAVUS, b Pittsburgh, Pa, May 16, 40; div; c 3. MATHEMATICS. *Educ:* Univ Pa, AB, 61; Univ Chicago, MS, 62, PhD(math), 65. *Prof Exp:* Instr math, Mass Inst Technol, 65-67; from asst prof to assoc prof, 67-77, PROF MATH, UNIV ILL, CHICAGO CIRCLE, 77- *Mem:* Am Math Soc; Asn Comput Mach; Math Asn Am; Soc Indust & Appl Math. *Res:* Algebraic and arithmetic structure of Hopf algebras; applications of Hopf algebras to algebra; computational problems of algebra; computer science. *Mailing Add:* Dept of Math Univ of Ill at Chicago Circle Chicago IL 60680

LARSON, RICHARD I, b Chicago, Ill, Dec 29, 37; m 61; c 3. CHEMICAL ENGINEERING. *Educ:* Northwestern Univ, BSchE, 60; Cornell Univ, MChE, 63; Rensselaer Polytech Inst, PhD(chem eng), 69. *Prof Exp:* Engr, Knolls Automic Power Lab, Gen Elec Co, 63-66; consult, Atomic Energy Comn, 66-68; proj engr, Knolls Atomic Power Lab, Schenectady, 68-77, PRIN ENGR, NUCLEAR FUEL DEPT, GEN ELEC CO, 75- *Honors & Awards:* Award, Knolls Atomic Power Lab, 64. *Mem:* Am Inst Chem Eng; Am Chem Soc; Am Nuclear Soc. *Res:* Turbulent flow-heat and mass transfer; colloidal chemistry; numerical solution; ordinary and partial differential equations; system analysis. *Mailing Add:* 417 Pettigrew Wilmington NC 28401

LARSON, ROBERT ELOF, b Spokane, Wash, Oct 9, 32; m 57; c 3. PHARMACOLOGY, TOXICOLOGY. *Educ:* Wash State Univ, BS, & BPharm, 57, MS, 62; Univ Iowa, PhD(pharmacol), 64. *Prof Exp:* Pharmacist, Manito Pharm, Wash, 57-59; staff fel toxicol, Nat Cancer Inst, 64-65; from asst prof to assoc prof, 65-76, chmn dept, 70-76, PROF PHARMACOL & TOXICOL, SCH PHARM, ORE STATE UNIV, 76- *Mem:* Am Soc Toxicol; Am Soc Pharmacol & Exp Therapeut; Soc Exp Biol Med. *Res:* Hepatotoxicity and nephrotoxicity of halogenated hydrocarbons; toxicity of nitrosoureas. *Mailing Add:* Dept of Pharmacol & Toxicol Ore State Univ Sch of Pharm Corvallis OR 97331

LARSON, ROBERT W(ALLACE), b Oak Park, Ill, Nov 17, 32; m 60; c 1. FOOD SCIENCE. *Educ:* Augustana Col, Ill, AB, 55; Univ Ill, MS, 60, PhD(food sci), 62. *Prof Exp:* Assoc res food technologist, Tectrol Div, Whirlpool Corp, 62-64; res food scientist, Life Support Dept, 64-69, sr res food scientist, Life Support Systs Group, 69-77; MEM STAFF, GEN FOODS CORP, 77- *Mem:* Inst Food Technol. *Res:* Freeze drying as a method of food preservation; post harvest physiology of fruit, vegetables and flowers; food development for Skylab space program; development of aerospace foods, compressed foods, rehydratable foods, and edible coatings. *Mailing Add:* Gen Foods Corp 250 North St T-32-1 White Plains NY 10625

LARSON, ROLAND EDWIN, b Ft Lewis, Wash, Oct 31, 41; m 60; c 2. MATHEMATICS. *Educ:* Lewis & Clark Col, BS, 66; Univ Colo, Boulder, MA, 68, PhD(math), 70. *Prof Exp:* Asst prof, 70-75, ASSOC PROF MATH, BEHREND COL, PA STATE UNIV, 75- *Mem:* Am Math Soc; Math Asn Am; Nat Coun Teachers Math. *Mailing Add:* Dept of Math Behrend Col Pa State Univ Erie PA 16563

LARSON, ROY AXEL, b Cloquet, Minn, Feb 5, 31; m 53; c 4. HORTICULTURE. *Educ:* Univ Minn, BS, 53, MS, 57; Cornell Univ, PhD(floricult), 61. *Prof Exp:* Assoc prof, 61-69, PROF HORT, NC STATE UNIV, 69- *Mem:* Am Soc Hort Sci. *Res:* Floriculture, particularly investigations on effects of environment and regulators on flowering and plant growth. *Mailing Add:* Dept of Hort Sci NC State Univ Raleigh NC 27607

LARSON, RUBY ILA, b Hatfield, Sask, Can, May 30, 14. CYTOGENETICS. *Educ:* Univ Sask, BS, 42 & 43, MA, 45; Univ Mo, PhD(genetics), 52. *Prof Exp:* Cytogeneticist, Cereal Div, Dom Exp Sta, Sask, 45-48; cytogeneticist, Sci Serv Lab, 48-59, CYTOGENETICIST, RES STA, CAN DEPT AGR, 59- *Res:* Wheat cytogenetics. *Mailing Add:* 2503 12 Ave S Lethbridge AB T1K 0P4 Can

LARSON, RUSSELL E(LMER), b Farmington, Minn, Oct 3, 17; m 41; c 2. AGRICULTURAL ENGINEERING. *Educ:* Univ Minn, BS, 48, MS, 59. *Prof Exp:* Proj leader & agr engr, Weed Control Equip Proj, Sci & Educ Admin, USDA, Minn, 48-52, proj leader, coordr & agr engr, Mo, 52-57, proj leader & agr engr, Dairy Labor Reduction Proj, Minn, 57-61, res invest leader, farmstead eng, 61-72, res leader livestock waste mgt, Agr Eng Res Div, 72-; prof, 73-79, EMER PROF AGR ENG, UNIV MINN, ST PAUL, 79- *Concurrent Pos:* Assoc prof agr eng, Univ Minn, St Paul, 67-72. *Mem:* Am Soc Agr Engrs. *Res:* Farmstead layout; farm animal waste management. *Mailing Add:* Agr Eng Bldg Univ of Minn Inst of Agr St Paul MN 55101

LARSON, RUSSELL EDWARD, b Minneapolis, Minn, Jan 2, 17; m 39; c 3. AGRICULTURAL EDUCATION, ACADEMIC ADMINISTRATION. *Educ:* Univ Minn, BS, 39, MS, 40, PhD(genetics, plant breeding), 42. *Prof Exp:* Asst hort, Univ Minn, 39-41; asst res prof agron & asst agronomist, Exp Sta, RI State Col, 41-44; asst prof veg gardening, 44-45, assoc prof plant breeding, 45-47, head dept hort, 52-61, dir agr & home econ exten, 61-63, dean & dir, Col Agr, 63-74, provost, 72-77, prof, 47-77, EMER PROVOST, EMER DEAN & EMER PROF HORT, PA STATE UNIV, UNIVERSITY PARK, 77-; CONSULT AGR, 77- *Concurrent Pos:* Sci aide, Mex Agr Prog, Rockefeller Found, 60; chmn comn educ agr & natural resources, Nat Acad Sci-Nat Res Coun, 66- *Honors & Awards:* Vaughan Award, Am Soc Hort Sci, 48. *Mem:* AAAS; Am Soc Hort Sci; Genetics Soc Am; Am Genetics Asn. *Res:* Administration of agricultural research development and education. *Mailing Add:* 206 Acad Projs Bldg Pa State Univ University Park PA 16802

LARSON, RUSSELL L, b Bridgewater, SDak, Dec 9, 28; m 64. BIOCHEMISTRY. *Educ:* SDak State Univ, BS, 57, MS, 59; Univ Ill, PhD(biochem), 62. *Prof Exp:* Fel microbiol, Ore State Univ, 62-64; RES CHEMIST, USDA, UNIV MO-COLUMBIA, 65- *Mem:* Am Chem Soc; Phytochem Soc NAm; Am Soc Plant Physiol. *Res:* Metabolic processes in microorganisms; alteration in metabolic processes in maize as a result of alteration in the genetic systems in maize. *Mailing Add:* 304 Curtis Hall USDA Univ of Mo Columbia MO 65211

LARSON, SANFORD J, b Chicago, Ill, Apr 9, 29; m 57; c 3. NEUROANATOMY, NEUROSURGERY. *Educ:* Wheaton Col, Ill, BA, 50; Northwestern Univ, MD, 54, PhD(anat), 62. *Prof Exp:* Resident neurosurg, Northwestern Univ, 55-57 & 59-61; USPHS res fel, 61-62; dir neurosurg educ, Cook County Hosp, Chicago, 62-63; assoc prof, 63-68, PROF NEUROSURG, MED COL WIS, 68-, CHMN DEPT, 63- *Concurrent Pos:* Chief neurosurg, Vet Admin Hosp, Wood, Wis, Milwaukee County Gen Hosp & Froedtert Mem Lutheran Hosp; consult, Milwaukee Lutheran, Columbia & Milwaukee Children's Hosps, Wis & Shriners Hosps Crippled Children, Chicago, Ill. *Mem:* Biophys Soc; Soc Univ Surg; Am Asn Neurol Surg; Am Col Surg; Soc Neurol Surgeons. *Res:* Neurophysiology; neurological surgery. *Mailing Add:* Dept of Neurosurg Med Col of Wis Milwaukee WI 53226

LARSON, THOMAS E, b Waupaca, Wis, Apr 13, 26; m 49; c 3. PHYSICAL CHEMISTRY, ORGANIC CHEMISTRY. *Educ:* Lewis & Clark Col, BA, 50; Johns Hopkins Univ, MA, 51, PhD(phys chem), 56. *Prof Exp:* Jr instr chem, Johns Hopkins Univ, 50-53, res asst, Inst Coop Res, 53-56; staff mem, 56-75, ALT GROUP LEADER WX-2, LOS ALAMOS NAT LAB, 75- *Mem:* Am Chem Soc. *Res:* Kinetics of exchange reactions in boron hydrides; sensitivity of explosives to various stimuli; radioactive materials. *Mailing Add:* Los Alamos Nat Lab Box 1663 Los Alamos NM 87544

LARSON, THURSTON E, b Chicago, Ill, Mar 3, 10; m 38; c 2. CHEMISTRY. *Educ:* Univ Ill, BS, 32, PhD(chem), 37. *Prof Exp:* From asst chemist to chemist, 32-47, head chem sect, 47-56, head & asst chief chem sect, 57-78, EMER PRIN SCIENTIST, ILL STATE WATER SURV, 78-; PROF SANIT ENG, UNIV ILL, URBANA, 61- *Mem:* Nat Acad Eng; Fel AAAS; Water Pollution Control Fedn; hon mem Am Water Works Asn; Nat Asn Corrosion Engrs. *Res:* Corrosion; water treatment; water quality; analytical; corrosion; environmental pollution. *Mailing Add:* Chem Sect Ill State Water Surv Box 232 Urbana IL 61801

LARSON, VAUGHN LEROY, b Mondovi, Wis, Feb 21, 31; m 61; c 1. VETERINARY MEDICINE. *Educ:* Univ Minn, BS, 58, DVM, 60, PhD(vet med), 68. *Prof Exp:* Veterinarian, 60-61; fel bovine leukemia, Univ Minn, 61-68; med scientist animal res, Brookhaven Nat Lab, 68; from asst prof to assoc prof, 68-74, PROF VET MED, UNIV MINN, ST PAUL, 74- *Mem:* Am Vet Med Asn; Am Asn Practitioners; Int Leukemia Res Asn; Sigma Xi. *Res:* Transmission and pathogenesis studies on bovine leukemia; clinical, pathological and therapeutic studies on chronic obstructive pulmonary disease in the equine. *Mailing Add:* Vet Teaching Hosp Univ of Minn St Paul MN 55101

LARSON, VERNON C, b Stambough, Mich, Apr 8, 23; m 46; c 3. AGRICULTURE, ACADEMIC ADMINISTRATION. *Educ:* Mich State Univ, BS, 47, MS, 50, EdD(educ admin), 54. *Prof Exp:* From asst prof to assoc prof dairy & asst to dean, Mich State Univ, 47-59; prof agr & asst dean, Am Univ, Beirut, 59-62; prof dairy agr & dir int agr prog, Kans State Univ, 62-65; prof agr sci & dean agr, Ahmadu Bello Univ, Nigeria & chief party, AID & Kans State Univ Team in Nigeria, 66-68; dir int agr progs, Kans State Univ, 68-70; chief party, AID & Kans State Univ Team in India, 70-72; DIR INT AGR PROGS, KANS STATE UNIV, 72- *Concurrent Pos:* AID consult, Jordan, 60; Cyprus & Sudan, 61; Kenya, 68; Colombia, 69; Philippines, 77; Paraguay, 78 & Peru, 78. *Mem:* AAAS. *Res:* Agricultural education. *Mailing Add:* Int Agr Progs Waters Hall 14 Kans State Univ Manhattan KS 66506

LARSON, VINCENT H(ENNIX), b Clinton, Minn, Feb 23, 17; m 55. MECHANICAL ENGINEERING. *Educ:* Univ Minn, BS, 51, ME, 64, PhD(mech eng), 65. *Prof Exp:* Proj engr, Research, Inc, Minn, 54-58, chief anal engr, 58-63; assoc prof mech eng & astronaut sci, Northwestern Univ, 65-72; PROF MECH ENG & CHMN DEPT, CLEVELAND STATE UNIV, 72- *Mem:* Am Inst Aeronaut & Astronaut; Am Soc Mech Engrs; NY Acad Sci; Am Asn Univ Prof; Am Soc Eng Educ. *Res:* Control system theory and practice; systems engineering; conception; analysis, evaluation, synthesis and optimization of mechanical and electromechanical systems; transportation engineering. *Mailing Add:* Dept of Mech Eng Fenn Col of Eng Cleveland OH 44115

LARSON, VIVIAN M, b Erie, NDak, Oct 3, 31. VIROLOGY. *Educ:* NDak State Col, BS, 53; Univ Mich, MPH, 58, PhD(virol), 63. *Prof Exp:* Bacteriologist, Detroit Dept Health Labs, Mich, 53-59; from res fel to sr res fel virol, 63-71, dir, NIH Virus Lab, 71-80, DIR, HERPES VIRUS RES & VACCINE DEVELOP, MERCK SHARP & DOHME RES LABS, 80- *Mem:* Am Soc Microbiol; Am Acad Microbiol; AAAS. *Res:* Cell biology; immunology; tumor viruses; viral biochemistry; herpes virus and leukemia virus subunit vaccines. *Mailing Add:* Merck Sharp & Dohme Res Labs West Point PA 19486

LARSON, WILBUR JOHN, b Rockford, Ill, Nov 19, 21; m 45; c 3. ANALYTICAL CHEMISTRY. *Educ:* Augustana Col, Ill, BA, 46; Univ Wis, MS, 48, PhD, 51. *Prof Exp:* Chemist, Mallinckrodt Chem Works, 51-57, head anal develop lab, 57-63, asst dir qual control, 64-72; RES ASSOC, MALLINCKRODT INC, 72- *Mem:* Am Chem Soc; Sigma Xi. *Res:* Trace analysis; quality control; electronic grade chemicals; reagent chemicals. *Mailing Add:* Mallinckrodt Inc 3600 N Second St St Louis MO 63147

LARSON, WILBUR S, b Downing, Wis, Jan 28, 23; m 53; c 1. INORGANIC CHEMISTRY, ANALYTICAL CHEMISTRY. *Educ:* Wis State Univ, River Falls, BS, 45; Univ Wyo, MS, 58, PhD(inorg chem), 64. *Prof Exp:* Teacher high schs, Wis, 44-55; asst gen chem, Univ Wyo, 55-63; assoc prof, 63-76, PROF CHEM, UNIV WIS-OSHKOSH, 76- *Mem:* Am Chem Soc. *Res:* Colorimetric sulfide, sulfite and thiosulfate analysis; stability of antimony addition compounds; equilibrium exchange mechanisms of metallic sulfides; mechanism studies of antimony pentachloride. *Mailing Add:* Dept of Chem Univ of Wis-Oshkosh Oshkosh WI 54901

LARSON, WILLIAM EARL, b Creston, Nebr, Aug 7, 21; m 47; c 4. SOIL SCIENCE. *Educ:* Univ Nebr, BS, 44, MS, 46; Iowa State Univ, PhD, 49. *Prof Exp:* Asst prof agron, Iowa State Univ, 49-50; soil scientist, USDA, Mont State Col, 51-54; from assoc prof to prof soils, Iowa State Univ, 54-67; PROF SOIL SCI, UNIV MINN, ST PAUL, 67- *Concurrent Pos:* Soil scientist, USDA, Iowa State Univ, 54-67; vis prof, Univ Ill, 60 & Univ Minn, 63; Fulbright scholar, Australia, 65-66. *Honors & Awards:* Soil Sci Award, Am Soc Agron. *Mem:* Fel AAAS; fel Am Soc Agron; fel Soil Sci Soc Am; Int Soc Soil Sci; fel Soil Conserv Soc Am. *Res:* Soil structure and mechanics; water infiltration; nutrient interrelations in plants; crop response to soil moisture levels and soil temperature; tillage requirements of crops; utilization of sewage wastes on land. *Mailing Add:* 201 Soil Sci Bldg Univ Minn St Paul MN 55108

LARTER, EDWARD NATHAN, b Can, Feb 13, 23; m 45; c 3. GENTICS, PLANT BREEDING. *Educ:* Univ Alta, BSc, 51, MSc, 52; State Col Wash, PhD(genetics, plant breeding), 54. *Prof Exp:* Assoc prof genetics & plant breeding, Univ Sask, 54-69; ROSNER RES CHAIR PROF PLANT SCI & DIR TRITICALE RES PROG, UNIV MAN, 69- *Mem:* Genetics Soc Can; Can Soc Agron; Agr Inst Can. *Res:* Plant breeding and cytogenetics of barley and related species. *Mailing Add:* Dept Plant Sci Univ Man Winnipeg MB R3T 2N2 Can

LARTIGUE, DONALD JOSEPH, b Baton Rouge, La, Sept 7, 34; m 62; c 2. BIOCHEMISTRY, ENZYMOLOGY. *Educ:* La State Univ, BS, 57, MS, 59, PhD(biochem), 65. *Prof Exp:* Analyst, US Food & Drug Admin, 59-60; marine biologist, Marine Lab, Univ Miami, 60; biochemist, USPHS Hosp, Carville, La, 60-62; asst biochem, La State Univ, 62-63, assoc, 63-65; biochemist, R J Reynolds Tobacco Co, NC, 65-70; sr clin biochemist, J T Baker Chem Co, 70-71; sr res biochemist, Corning Glass Works, 71-74; clin chemist, Ochsner Clinic, 74-76; CLIN CHEMIST, SOUTHERN BAPTIST HOSP, 76- *Concurrent Pos:* Vis prof, Wake Forest Univ, 68. *Mem:* AAAS; Sigma Xi; Am Asn Clin Chemists. *Res:* Clinical chemistry; industrial enzymology; immobilized enzymes. *Mailing Add:* Dept of Path 2700 Napoleon Ave New Orleans LA 70115

LARUE, JAMES ARTHUR, b Rivesville, WVa, Apr 24, 23; m 47; c 2. MATHEMATICS. *Educ:* WVa Univ, AB, 48, MS, 49; Univ Pittsburgh, PhD(math), 61. *Prof Exp:* Asst prof math, Morris Harvey Col, 49-54; asst prof, 54-65; PROF MATH & CHMN DEPT, FAIRMONT STATE COL, 65- *Res:* Mathematical analysis; divergent series. *Mailing Add:* Dept of Math Fairmont State Col Fairmont WV 26554

LA RUE, JERROLD A, b San Bernardino, Calif, June 22, 23; m 46; c 2. METEOROLOGY. *Educ:* Univ Calif, Los Angeles, BA, 48. *Prof Exp:* Gen meteorologist, US Weather Bur, Nat Weather Serv, 51-55; forecast meteorologist, 55-57, meteorologist proj analyst, 57-60, quant precipitation meteorologist, 60-64, sect supvr meteorol, 64-68, br chief, 68-69, meteorologist in chg, Weather Serv Off, Washington, DC, 69-80; RETIRED. *Mem:* Am Meteorol Soc; Nat Weather Asn. *Res:* Objective methods adapted to operational metoeorology. *Mailing Add:* World Weather Bldg Marlow Heights MD 20233

LARUE, ROBERT D(EAN), b Meridian, Idaho, June 4, 22; m 46; c 3. COMPUTER GRAPHICS, COMPUTER AIDED DESIGN. *Educ:* Univ Idaho, BS, 44 & 49, MS, 51. *Prof Exp:* Engr, Amalgamated Sugar Co, Idaho, 46-48; instr civil eng, Univ Idaho, 51-52; asst prof mech eng, SDak Sch Mines & Technol, 52-54 & Colo State Univ, 54-58, from assoc prof to prof, 58-65; assoc prof, 65-71, PROF ENG GRAPHICS, OHIO STATE UNIV, 71-

Honors & Awards: Award, Am Soc Eng Educ, 56. *Mem:* Am Soc Eng Educ. *Res:* Improvement of educational methods and text material in area of engineering design. *Mailing Add:* Dept of Eng Graphics Ohio State Univ Columbus OH 43210

LARUE, THOMAS A, b Winnipeg, Man, May 1, 35; m 58; c 4. BIOCHEMISTRY. *Educ:* Univ Man, BSc, 56, MSc, 58; Univ Iowa, PhD(biochem), 62. *Prof Exp:* From asst res officer to sr res officer, 62-78, Nat Res Coun Can; BIOCHEMIST, BOYCE THOMPSON INST PLANT RES, CORNELL UNIV, 78- *Mem:* Am Soc Plant Physiologists; Can Soc Microbiol; Sigma Xi. *Res:* Analytical biochemistry; plant tissue culture; nitrogen fixation. *Mailing Add:* Boyce Thompson Inst Tower Rd Ithaca NY 14853

LARY, EDMUND C, b Biddeford, Maine, Apr 20, 35; m 56; c 4. FLUID MECHANICS, ELECTROMAGNETICS. *Educ:* Brown Univ, ScB, 57; Cornell Univ, PhD(magnetohydrodyn), 60. *Prof Exp:* Prin scientist magnetohydrodyn, Res Labs, United Aircraft Corp, 59-66, sr theoret physicist, 66-67, asst to dir res, 67-71; MEM CENT TECH STAFF, AMF, INC, 71- *Concurrent Pos:* From adj asst prof to adj prof, Rensselaer Polytech Inst, 60-71; NSF fel, Inst Plasma Physics, Utrecht, Netherlands, 64-65; from vis asst prof to vis prof, Trinity Col, 64-71. *Res:* Engineering applications of fluid mechanics; plasma physics; laser physics. *Mailing Add:* 17 Revere Dr Stamford CT 06902

LASAGA, ANTONIO C, b Havana, Cuba, Dec 17, 49; US citizen; m 73; c 2. GEOCHEMISTRY, PHYSICAL CHEMISTRY. *Educ:* Princeton Univ, BA, 71; Harvard Univ, MS, 73, PhD(chem physics), 76. *Prof Exp:* Res assoc chem, Harvard Univ, 73-76, lectr chem & geol, 76-77; asst prof, 77-80, ASSOC PROF GEOCHEM, PA STATE UNIV, 80- *Concurrent Pos:* NSF prin investr, 78-80; vis assoc prof, Yale Univ, 81. *Honors & Awards:* F W Clarke Medal, Geochem Soc, 79. *Mem:* Geochem Soc; Am Geophys Union. *Res:* Kinetics and thermodynamics of geochemical processes, particularly modeling diagenetic reactions in the oceans; geochemical cycles; diffusion in silicates; non-equilibrium aspects of geothermometry; quantum mechanics of bonding in silicates; crystal growth from melts. *Mailing Add:* Dept of Geosci 210 Deike University Park PA 16802

LASAGNA, LOUIS (CESARE), b New York, NY, Feb 22, 23; m 46; c 7. PHARMACOLOGY. *Educ:* Rutgers Univ, BS, 43; Columbia Univ, MD, 47. *Prof Exp:* Asst & instr pharmacol, Sch Med, Johns Hopkins Univ, 50-52, from asst prof to assoc prof med & from asst prof to assoc prof pharmacol & exp therapeut, 54-70; PROF PHARMACOL, TOXICOL & MED, UNIV ROCHESTER, 70- *Concurrent Pos:* Vis physician, Columbia Res Serv, Goldwater Mem Hosp, 51, 53 & 54; clin & res fel, Mass Gen Hosp, 52-54; lectr, Sch Med, Boston Univ, 52-54; res assoc, Harvard Univ, 53-54. *Mem:* Inst Med; Asn Am Physicians; Am Soc Pharmacol & Exp Therapeut; Am Soc Clin Invest; Am Fedn Clin Res. *Res:* Hypnotics; analgesics; psychological responses to drugs; placebos; clinical trials; prescribing patterns. *Mailing Add:* Dept of Pharmacol Univ of Rochester Sch of Med Rochester NY 14642

LASALA, EDWARD FRANCIS, b Lynn, Mass, June 15, 28; m 53; c 5. PHARMACEUTICAL CHEMISTRY, ORGANIC CHEMISTRY. *Educ:* Mass Col Pharm, BS, 53, MS, 55, PhD(pharmaceut chem), 58. *Prof Exp:* From instr to asst prof, 58-67, assoc prof, 67-77, PROF CHEM & CHMN DEPT, MASS COL PHARM, 77- *Mem:* Am Chem Soc; Am Pharmaceut Asn. *Res:* Synthesis and biological studies of medicinal agents, chiefly analgesics and antiradiation agents. *Mailing Add:* Dept of Chem Mass Col of Pharm Boston MA 02115

LA SALLE, GERALD, b Ile du Calumet, Que, Dec 2, 15; m 41; c 9. MEDICAL ADMINISTRATION. *Educ:* Univ Montreal, BA, 35; Laval Univ, MD, 40; Univ Toronto, DHA, 51. *Prof Exp:* Asst dir, Royal Victoria Hosp, 50-52; dir, Univ Montreal Hosp, 52-56, dir & prof hosp admin, Inst Sup d'Admin Hosp, 56-60; exec dir, Col Physicians & Surgeons, Ont, 60-64; dean & dir med ctr, 64-68, VPRES IN CHG MED AFFAIRS, UNIV SHERBROOKE, 68- *Concurrent Pos:* Trustee, Can Hosp Asn, 52-54 & Can Asn Hosp Accreditation, 52-54; exec dir, Montreal Hosp Coun, 52-58 & Que Hosp Asn, 56-60; dir, Les Artisans' Coopvie; mem, State Comn Hosps, 54-58, Royal Comn Hosp Prob, 59-60 & Med Coun Can, 62-64; vpres, Unity Bank Can; dir, Sandoz Ltd, Exec Fund Can, Exec Int Investment Ltd & Pony Sporting Goods; comnr, Can Pension Comn, Dept Vet Affairs, Ottawa, 78-80. *Mem:* Can Med Asn. *Res:* Social aspects of medical care. *Mailing Add:* 10 Driveway Sherbrooke ON K2P 1C7 Can

LASALLE, JOSEPH PIERRE, b State College, Pa, May 28, 16; m 42; c 2. DYNAMICAL SYSTEMS. *Educ:* La State Univ, BS, 37; Calif Inst Technol, PhD(math), 41. *Prof Exp:* Instr math, Univ Tex, 41-42 & Radar Sch, Mass Inst Technol, 42-43; mathematician, Design Div, Frankford Arsenal, 43-44 Cornell Univ & Stromberg-Carlson Co, NY, 44-46; from asst prof to prof math, Univ Notre Dame, 46-58; assoc dir math ctr, Res Inst Advan Study, 58-64; chmn, Div Appl Math, 68-75, prof & dir, Lefschetz Ctr Dynamical Systs, 64-80, EMER PROF APPL MATH, BROWN UNIV, 80- *Concurrent Pos:* Vis res assoc, Princeton Univ, 43-44, asst prof & res assoc, 47-49; res assoc, Cornell Univ, 44-46; sci adv, US Naval Forces, Ger, 50-52; Guggenheim Found fel, 75-76. *Honors & Awards:* Chauvenet Prize, Math Asn Am, 65. *Mem:* Fel AAAS; Soc Indust & Appl Math (pres, 63); fel Am Acad Mech; Am Math Soc; Math Asn Am. *Res:* Differential equations; theory of stability; control theory. *Mailing Add:* Div of Appl Math Brown Univ Providence RI 02912

LASALLE, PIERRE, b Que, July 17, 31; m 67. GEOMORPHOLOGY. *Educ:* Univ Montreal, BA, 52, BSc, 59; McGill Univ, MSc, 62; State Univ Leiden, PhD(geol), 66. *Prof Exp:* GEOLOGIST, QUE DEPT NATURAL RESOURCES, 66- *Mem:* AAAS; Geol Soc Am; Geol Asn Can; Geol Soc France. *Mailing Add:* Que Dept of Natural Resources 1620 Blvd de l'Entente Quebec PQ G1S 4N6 Can

LASATER, HERBERT ALAN, b Paris, Tenn, Sept 11, 31; m 59; c 2. MATHEMATICAL STATISTICS, APPLIED STATISTICS. *Educ:* Univ Tenn, BS, 57, MS, 62; Rutgers Univ, PhD(statist), 69. *Prof Exp:* Instr statist, Univ Tenn, Knoxville, 57-58; assoc statistician, Nuclear Div, Union Carbide Corp, 58-62; asst prof, 62-65 & 68-71, ASSOC PROF STATIST, UNIV TENN, KNOXVILLE, 71- *Concurrent Pos:* Lectr statist, Univ Tenn, 59-62; ed, J Qual Technol, 71-74. *Mem:* Am Statist Asn; fel Am Soc Qual Control; Sigma Xi. *Res:* Statistical quality control techniques. *Mailing Add:* Dept Statist Univ Tenn Knoxville TN 37916

LASCA, NORMAN P, JR, b Detroit, Mich, Oct 20, 34; m 65. QUATERNARY GEOLOGY, GEOMORPHOLOGY. *Educ:* Brown Univ, AB, 57; Univ Mich, MS, 61, PhD(geol), 65. *Prof Exp:* Res asst geol, Univ Mich, 60-61, teaching fel, 61-65; NATO res fel, Inst Geol, Univ Oslo, 65-66; asst proff, 66-71, assoc prof geol, 71-76, asst to chancellor, 75-77, assoc dean grad sch, 77-80, chmn dept, 80-81, PROF GEOL SCI, UNIV WIS-MILWAUKEE, 76-, ACTG VCHANCELLOR, 81- *Concurrent Pos:* Assoc scientist, 71-76, sr scientist, Ctr Great Lakes Studies, Univ Wis-Milwaukee, 76-; fel acad admin, Am Coun Educ, 74-75. *Mem:* fel Geol Soc Am; Am Asn Quaternary Res; Int Asn Quaternary Res; Glaciol Soc; Swedish Soc Anthrop & Geog. *Res:* Glacial geology and geomorphology of polar regions; river and lake ice formation and processes; Glacial-Pleistocene geology in Wisconsin. *Mailing Add:* Dept of Geol Sci Univ of Wis Milwaukee WI 53201

LASCELLES, JUNE, b Sydney, Australia, Jan 23, 24. MICROBIOLOGY, BIOCHEMISTRY. *Educ:* Univ Sydney, BSc, 44, MSc, 47; Oxford Univ, DPhil(microbial biochem), 52. *Prof Exp:* Mem external sci staff, Med Res Coun, Eng, 53-60; lectr microbial biochem, Oxford Univ, 60-65; PROF BACT, UNIV CALIF, LOS ANGELES, 65- *Concurrent Pos:* Rockefeller fel, 56-57; consult panel microbial chem, NIH, 73-77; ed, J Bact, 80- *Mem:* Am Soc Microbiol; Am Soc Biol Chemists; Brit Biochem Soc; Brit Soc Gen Microbiol. *Res:* Biochemistry of microorganisms; tetrapyrrole synthesis and regulation; bacterial photosynthesis. *Mailing Add:* Dept of Bact Univ of Calif Los Angeles CA 90024

LASCHEVER, NORMAN LEWIS, b Hartford, Conn, July 27, 18; m 42; c 4. ELECTRICAL ENGINEERING. *Educ:* Mass Inst Technol, BS, 40; Northeastern Univ, MSEE, 70. *Prof Exp:* Sect chief airborne commun & navig hq, Air Tech Command, Wright-Patterson AFB, Ohio, 46-55; asst dir res eng, Lab Electronics, Mass, 55-62; mgr radar eng, 62-71, chief engr, Aerospace Systs Div, 71-76, PRIN SCIENTIST, AUTOMATED SYSTS DIV, RCA CORP, 76- *Mem:* Sr mem Inst Elec & Electronics Engr; Sigma Xi. *Res:* Instrumentation of aircraft dynamics; development of aircraft communication and navigation equipment, airborne Doppler navigators and aerospace radar and transponder equipment. *Mailing Add:* Automated Systs Div Box 588 Burlington MA 01803

LASDAY, ALBERT HENRY, b Pittsburgh, Pa, Apr 8, 20; m 42; c 2. ENVIRONMENTAL MANAGEMENT. *Educ:* Univ Pittsburgh, BS, 41; Harvard Univ, MA, 47; Carnegie Inst Technol, DSc(physics), 51. *Prof Exp:* Engr, Carnegie Inst Technol, 47-50; physicist, Preston Labs, 51-55; dir res, Houze Glass Corp, 55-58; pres, A H Lasday Co, 58-63; proj mgr, Micarta Div, Westinghouse Elec Corp, SC, 63-65; group leader mat develop, Texaco Exp, Inc, 65-68; supvr res, Richmond Res Labs, 68-71, COORDR, ENVIRON PROTECTION DEPT, TEXACO INC, 71- *Concurrent Pos:* Consult, Res & Develop Bd, Off Secy Defense, 51. *Mem:* Am Phys Soc; Sigma Xi; Mfg Chemists Asn; AAAS; NY Acad Sci. *Res:* Air and water conservation; water pollution control for petroleum and petrochemical waste effluents. *Mailing Add:* 37 King Dr Poughkeepsie NY 12603

LASDON, LEON, operations research, see previous edition

LASEK, RAYMOND J, b Chicago, Ill, Nov 25, 40; m 64; c 3. NEUROBIOLOGY. *Educ:* Utica Col, BA, 61; State Univ NY, PhD(anat), 67. *Prof Exp:* NIH res fel neuropath, McLean Hosp, Harvard Med Sch, 66-68 & neurobiol, Univ Calif, San Diego, 68-69; asst prof, 69-73, assoc prof, 74-78, PROF ANAT, CASE WESTERN RESERVE UNIV, 79- *Res:* Axonal transport; regulation of growth and differentiation in neurons; evolutionary neurobiology. *Mailing Add:* Med Ctr Case Western Reserve Univ Cleveland OH 44106

LASERSON, GREGORY, b Vienna, Austria, Mar 17, 23; nat US; m 44; c 2. MECHANICAL ENGINEERING. *Educ:* Columbia Univ, BS, 44, MS, 45, PhD(mech eng), 49. *Prof Exp:* Asst mech eng, Columbia Univ, 42-45, asst temperature measurement, 44-46; stress analyst chem process equip, Chem Construct Corp, 46-49; res engr instrumentation, E I du Pont de Nemours & Co, 49-53, res proj engr, 53, engr eng res & develop, Nuclear Develop Assoc, 53, sect leader, 54-56, supvr cost & budget dept, 57, supvr develop & appln, 58-60; asst mgr mech develop lab, Am Mach & Foundry Co, 60-63, dir res, 63-64, mgr mech develop lab, 64-66, dir eng, 66-67, vpres tech opers, 67-76, EXEC V PRES & DIR RES, RES & DEVELOP DIV, SEALECTRO CORP, 76- *Mem:* Sigma Xi. *Res:* Automatic machinery. *Mailing Add:* Res & Develop Div 225 Hoyt St Mamaroneck NY 10543

LASETER, JOHN LUTHER, b Houston, Tex, Sept 9, 37; m 69; c 2. BIOCHEMISTRY. *Educ:* Univ Houston, BS, 59, MS, 62, PhD(biochem), 68. *Prof Exp:* Instr biol, Univ Houston, 59-60; asst prof, Sacred Heart Col, Houston, 61-64; dir chem res, Teledyne, Inc, 64-65; instr biol, Univ Houston, 65-66, NASA fel biophys, 68-69; asst prof, 69-70, assoc prof biol sci & chmn dept, La State Univ, New Orleans, 70-77; PROF BIOL SCI, UNIV NEW ORLEANS, 77-, DIR CTR BIO-ORG STUDIES, 77- *Concurrent Pos:* Pres, J L Laseter & Assocs, Inc, 66-; Res Corp & New Orleans Cancer Soc grants, La State Univ, New Orleans, 70-71, NASA res grant, 70-72. *Mem:* AAAS; Am Chem Soc; Am Soc Mass Spectrometry; NY Acad Sci; Am Oil Chem Soc. *Res:* Lipid biochemistry; analytical biochemistry and mass spectrometry; control mechanisms in steroid metabolism. *Mailing Add:* Ctr for Bio-Org Studies Univ of New Orleans New Orleans LA 70122

LA SEUR, NOEL EDWIN, b Stanhope, Iowa, June 25, 22; m 44; c 3. METEOROLOGY. *Educ:* Univ Chicago, SB, 47, SM, 49, PhD(meteorol), 53. *Prof Exp:* From asst to instr, Univ Chicago, 48-52; asst prof, 53-56, assoc prof, 56-58, PROF METEOROL, FLA STATE UNIV, 58- *Mem:* AAAS; Am Meteorol Soc; Am Geophys Union; Royal Meteorol Soc. *Res:* Synoptic meteorology of temperature and tropical latitudes. *Mailing Add:* Dept of Meteorol Fla State Univ Tallahassee FL 32306

LASFARGUES, ETIENNE YVES, b Milhars, France, May 5, 16; nat US; m 50; c 2. MICROBIOLOGY, ONCOLOGY. *Educ:* Univ Paris, BS, 35, DVM, 41. *Prof Exp:* Roux Found res fel microbiol, Pasteur Inst, France, 42-44, asst virol, 44-47, head lab virol, 50-55; Am Cancer Soc res fel cytol, Inst Cancer Res, Pa, 47-50; assoc microbiol, Col Physicians & Surgeons, Columbia Univ, 55-59, asst prof, 59-66; assoc mem, Dept Cytol Biophys, Inst Med Res, 66-77, head, Dept Tumor Cell Biol, 77-82. *Concurrent Pos:* Mem, Breast Cancer Task Force Comt, Nat Cancer Inst, 79-82. *Honors & Awards:* Jensen Prize, Fr Acad Med, 46; Silver & Bronze Medal, Pasteur Inst, 69. *Mem:* AAAS; Am Soc Cell Biologists; Tissue Cult Asn; Int Soc Cell Biologists; Am Asn Cancer Res. *Res:* Viral oncology; cell transformation; cytogenetics. *Mailing Add:* Dept of Tumor Cell Biol Inst for Med Res Copewood St Camden NJ 08103

LASH, JAMES (JAY) W, b Chicago, Ill, Oct 24, 29; m 55; c 1. DEVELOPMENTAL BIOLOGY, ANATOMY. *Educ:* Univ Chicago, PhD(zool), 55. *Hon Degrees:* MA, Univ Pa, 71. *Prof Exp:* Nat Cancer Inst, Univ Pa, 55-57, instr, 57-59, assoc, 59-61, from asst prof to assoc prof, 61-69, PROF ANAT, SCH MED, UNIV PA, 69- *Concurrent Pos:* Helen Hay Whitney Found fel, 58-61; estab investr, Helen Hay Whitney Found, 61-66; NIH career develop award, 66-70; mem maternal & child health res comt, Nat Inst Child Health & Human Develop, 71-75, nat adv comt, 77-80, nat adv coun, 76-80 & bd sci counrs, 81-; mem sci adv comt, Ctr Oral Health Res, Univ Pa, 73-76; mem nat adv comt, Primate Res Ctr, Davis, Calif, 73-80. *Mem:* Soc Cell Biol; Soc Develop Biol. *Res:* Developmental biology; tissue interactions during chondrogenesis; Ascidian embryology. *Mailing Add:* Dept of Anat Univ of Pa Sch of Med Philadelphia PA 19104

LASHEEN, ALY M, b Cairo, Egypt, Dec 27, 19; nat US; m 54; c 3. PLANT PHYSIOLOGY, HORTICULTURE. *Educ:* Cairo Univ, BS, 42; Univ Calif, Los Angeles, 49; Agr & Mech Col Tex, PhD(plant physiol, hort), 54. *Prof Exp:* Asst hort, Agr & Mech Col Tex, 50-53, res assoc plant physiol, 54-55; jr plant pathologist, Wash State Univ, 55-57, asst prof hort, 57-61; assoc prof plant physiol, AID Contract-Univ Ky, Indonesia, 61-65, prof, 65-67, prof hort, 67-77; PROF HORT, AID CONTRACT-UNIV MINN, 77- *Concurrent Pos:* Hort adv & chief party, Univ Minn proj, Morocco, 70- *Mem:* Am Soc Hort Sci; Am Soc Plant Physiol. *Res:* Chemical analysis of macro and micro elements in plants; biochemical analysis of sugars and amino, organic and nucleic acids in plants; dormancy in seeds; effects of additives on plants; cold hardiness in plants; nature of dwarfing in apples. *Mailing Add:* Dept Hort Univ Minn St Paul MN 55108

LASHEN, EDWARD S, b New York, NY, Aug 11, 34; m 57; c 3. MICROBIOLOGY. *Educ:* Brooklyn Col, BS, 56; Rutgers Univ, MS, 62, PhD(microbiol), 65. *Prof Exp:* Res asst blood res, Jewish Chronic Disease Hosp Brooklyn, NY, 56-57; res asst hemat & pharmacol, Wallace Labs Div, Carter Prod, Inc, 57-61; sr microbiologist, 64-75, head proj leader biocides, 75-81, RES SECT MGR BIOCIDES, RES LABS, ROHM AND HAAS CO, 81- *Mem:* Am Soc Testing & Mat; Am Soc Microbiol; Soc Indust Microbiol. *Res:* Microbial transformation of thiourea and substituted thioureas; biodegradation of surfactants by sewage sludge and river water microflora; broad spectrum anti-microbial agents for application as industrial biocides. *Mailing Add:* Rohm and Haas Res Labs Spring House PA 19477

LASHER, GORDON (JEWETT), b Denver, Colo, Feb 1, 26; m 53; c 3. ASTROPHYSICS. *Educ:* Rensselaer Polytech Inst, BS, 49; Cornell Univ, PhD(theoret physics), 54. *Prof Exp:* Staff physicist, Lawrence Radiation Lab, Univ Calif, 53-55; assoc physicist, 55-56, PROJ PHYSICIST, RES LAB, IBM CORP, 56- *Concurrent Pos:* Vis prof, Cornell Univ, 69-70; vis scholar, Stanford Univ, 80. *Mem:* Am Phys Soc; Am Astron Soc. *Res:* Applied mathematics with computer applications; solid state physics; superconductivity; theory of liquid crystals; general relativity; cosmology; theory of supernovae; lattice gauge theory. *Mailing Add:* IBM-Watson Res Ctr Yorktown Heights NY 10598

LASHINSKY, HERBERT, physics, see previous edition

LASHLEY, GERALD ERNEST, b Johnstown, Pa, Sept 26, 35; m 55; c 3. NUMERICAL ANALYSES. *Educ:* Eastern Nazarene Col, BS, 57; Boston Univ, AM, 61; Boston Univ, EdD(math educ), 69. *Prof Exp:* High sch teacher, Mass, 58-63; assoc prof math, Eastern Nazarene Col, 64-72, chmn dept, 70-72; chmn div natural sci, 72-76, dir, Acad Comput Ctr, 77-80, PROF COMPUTER SCI & MATH, MT VERNON NAZARENE COL, 80- *Concurrent Pos:* Dir & instr, NSF In-Serv Inst Secondary Teachers, 64-72. *Mem:* Asn Comput Mach; Math Asn Am. *Mailing Add:* Mt Vernon Nazarene Col Mt Vernon OH 43050

LASHMET, PETER K(ERNS), b Ann Arbor, Mich, Aug 28, 29; m 56; c 5. CHEMICAL ENGINEERING. *Educ:* Univ Mich, BSE(chem eng) & BSE(math), 51, MSE, 52; Univ Del, PhD(chem eng), 62. *Prof Exp:* Process design engr, M W Kellogg Co, 52-53; from chem engr to sr chem engr, Air Prod & Chem, Inc, 58-60, mgr cryostat eng, 60-62, sr cryogenic specialist, 62-65; ASSOC PROF CHEM ENG, RENSSELAER POLYTECH INST, 65-, DEPT EXEC OFFICER, 77- *Mem:* Am Chem Soc; Am Inst Chem Engrs. *Res:* Catalytic properties of ion exchange resins; cryogenic refrigeration processes; miniature and compact heat exchangers; heat exchanger dynamics; computer simulation of chemical processes; chemical separation processes. *Mailing Add:* Dept of Chem & Environ Eng Rensselaer Polytech Inst Troy NY 12181

LASHMORE, DAVID S, b Hempstead, NY, July 9, 46; m 70; c 2. MATERIALS SCIENCE, PHYSICAL METALLURGY. *Educ:* Univ Fla, BS, 69; Mich Technol Univ, MS, 70; Univ Va, PhD(mat sci), 77. *Prof Exp:* Res assoc metallurgist coatings, 77-79, GROUP LEADER ELECTRODEPOSITED COATINGS, NAT BUR STANDARDS, 79- *Concurrent Pos:* Consult, B-08 Comt Aluminum Coatings, Am Soc Testing & Mat, 78- *Mem:* Sigma Xi; Am Soc Metals; Am Electroplaters; Am Soc Testing & Mat; Am Soc Mech Engrs. *Res:* Surface and interface properties; transmission electron microscopy; diffraction; electrocrystallization; anodizing. *Mailing Add:* Sect 561 Dept of Commerce Washington DC 20234

LASHOF, JOYCE COHEN, b Philadelphia, Pa, Mar 27, 26; m 50; c 3. MEDICINE. *Educ:* Duke Univ, AB, 46. *Prof Exp:* Intern, Bronx Hosp, New York, 50-51, asst resident med, 51-52; asst resident med, Montefiore Hosp, 52-53; Nat Found Infantile Paralysis fel, Yale Univ, 53-54; asst med & physician, Student Health Serv, Univ Chicago, 54-56, from instr to asst prof, Sch Med, 56-60; dir sect prev med & clin labs, Rush-Presby-St Luke's Med Ctr, 61-66, dir sect community med, 66-72, chmn dept prev med, 72-73; dir, Dept Pub Health, State of Ill, 73-77; dep asst secy health progs, Dept HEW, 77-78; asst dir, Off Technol Assessment, US Congress, 78-81; DEAN, SCH PUB HEALTH, UNIV CALIF, BERKELEY, 82- *Concurrent Pos:* Staff physician, Union Health Serv, Inc, 60-61; asst attend physician, Presby-St Luke's Hosp, 60-61, assoc attend physician, 61-; clin asst prof med, Sch Med, Univ Ill, 61-64, assoc prof prev med, 64-71; prof prev med, Rush Med Col, 71-77. *Res:* Internal medicine; medical care. *Mailing Add:* Sch Pub Health Univ Calif Berkeley CA 94720

LASHOF, RICHARD KENNETH, b Philadelphia, Pa, Nov 9, 22; m 50; c 3. MATHEMATICS. *Educ:* Univ Pa, BS, 43; Columbia Univ, PhD(math), 54. *Prof Exp:* From instr to assoc prof, 54-64, chmn dept, 67-70, PROF MATH, UNIV CHICAGO, 64- *Concurrent Pos:* NSF fel, 60-61; mem-at-large, Nat Res Coun. *Mem:* Am Math Soc. *Res:* Algebraic topology; differential geometry. *Mailing Add:* Dept of Math Univ of Chicago Chicago IL 60637

LASHOF, THEODORE WILLIAM, b Philadelphia, Pa, June 27, 18; m 50; c 3. PHYSICS. *Educ:* Univ Pa, BS, 39, PhD(physics), 42. *Prof Exp:* Mem staff, Radiation Lab, Mass Inst Technol, 42-45; from instr to asst prof physics, Reed Col, 45-49; assoc prof, Mich Col Mining & Technol, 49-50; physicist, Mass Sect, 50-54, paper sect, 54-62, appl polymer standards sect, 62-64 & eval criteria sect, 64-67, actg chief paper standards sect, 67-70, chief performance criteria sect, 70-74, prog mgr lab performance, 74-78, res assoc, 78-81, MEM STAFF, NAT BUR STANDARDS, 81- *Concurrent Pos:* consult standards develop & statist methods in lab performance. *Honors & Awards:* Testing Div Medal, Tech Asn Pulp & Paper Indust, 72; Award of Merit, Am Soc Testing & Mat, 75; US Dept of Com Silver Medal, 77. *Mem:* Fel Am Soc Testing & Mat; fel Tech Asn Pulp & Paper Indust. *Res:* Physical properties of paper; interlaboratory standardization; consumer product performance and safety; testing laboratory evaluation. *Mailing Add:* B154 Technol Bldg Nat Bur Standards Washington DC 20234

LASHOMB, JAMES HAROLD, b Potsdam, NY, Oct 25, 42; m 69; c 1. ENTOMOLOGY. *Educ:* Cornell Univ, BS, 70; Univ Md, College Park, MS, 73, PhD(entom), 75. *Prof Exp:* Res assoc entom, Miss State Univ, 75-78; ASST PROF ENTOM, RUTGERS UNIV, 78- *Mem:* AAAS; Entom Soc Am; Ecol Soc Am. *Res:* Sampling of insect populations and antural enemies; parasitic insect distribution within plants and parasitic insect biology. *Mailing Add:* Dept of Entom PO Box 231 New Brunswick NJ 08903

LASINSKI, BARBARA FORMAN, b New York, NY, Nov 28, 41; m 71; c 1. PLASMA PHYSICS. *Educ:* Barnard Col, BA, 62; Univ Rochester, PhD(physics), 68. *Prof Exp:* Res assoc high energy physics, Enrico Fermi Inst, Univ Chicago, 68-71; PHYSICIST PLASMA PHYSICS, LAWRENCE LIVERMORE LAB, 72- *Mem:* Am Phys Soc. *Res:* Computational simulation of plasmas; laser-plasma interactions; computational physics. *Mailing Add:* L-477 Lawrence Livermore Lab Livermore CA 94550

LASKA, EUGENE, b New York, NY, Mar 17, 38; m 59; c 3. MATHEMATICS, STATISTICS. *Educ:* City Col New York, BS, 59; NY Univ, MS, 61, PhD(math), 63. *Prof Exp:* Asst res scientist, Comput Lab, Res Div, NY Univ, 59-61, res assoc math, Courant Inst Math Sci, 61-62; systs engr, Int Bus Mach Corp, NJ, 62-63; DIR INFO SCI DIV, ROCKLAND RES INST, ORANGEBURG, NY, 63-; RES PROF PSYCHIAT, NY UNIV MED CTR, 79- *Concurrent Pos:* NIMH grants, 67-78; consult comput in psychiat, USSR, Israel, Italy, Iran, Peru & Indonesia, 68; mem comput & biomath sci study sect, NIH, 72-76; assoc comnr inter-off coord coun, NY State Dept Ment Hyg, 80. *Mem:* Fel AAAS; Inst Math Statist; Am Statist Asn; Soc Indust & Appl Math; Biomet Soc. *Res:* Mathematical statistics, including estimation theory; applied statistics, including biostatistics and clinical trial methodology. *Mailing Add:* 34 Dante St Larchmont NY 10538

LASKAR, AMULYA LAL, b Dacca, India, June 11, 31; m 62; c 2. PHYSICS. *Educ:* SN Col, India, BS, 50; Univ Calcutta, MS, 52; Inst Elec Engrs, Gt Brit, grad, 58; Univ Ill, Urbana, PhD(physics), 60. *Prof Exp:* Lectr physics, Indian Inst Technol, Kharagpur, 53-60, asst prof, 60-65; sr fel & sr res assoc, Univ NC, Chapel Hill, 65-68; assoc prof, 68-75, PROF PHYSICS, CLEMSON UNIV, 75- *Concurrent Pos:* Vis res scientist, Picatinny Arsenal, NJ, 69 & Argonne Nat Lab, Ill, 70; Res Corp grant, 71-74; Army Res Off-Durham grant, 72-78; guest scientist, Saclay Nuclear Res Ctr, Saclay, France, 75-76. *Mem:* Am Phys Soc; Indian Phys Soc. *Res:* Solid state physics, especially transport phenomena; defect structures and their role on the physical properties in various solids, especially ionic and semiconductors. *Mailing Add:* Dept of Physics Clemson Univ Clemson SC 29631

LASKAR, RENU CHAKRAVARTI, b Bhagalpur, India, Aug 8, 30; m 62; c 2. MATHEMATICS. *Educ:* Univ Bihar, BS, 54; Univ Bhagalpur, MS, 57; Univ Ill, Urbana, PhD(group theory), 62. *Prof Exp:* Lectr math, Ranchi Women's Col, India, 57-59; lectr, Indian Inst Technol, Kharagpur, 62-65; fel, Univ NC, Chapel Hill, 65-68; assoc prof, 68-76, PROF MATH, CLEMSON UNIV, 76-

Concurrent Pos: Guest mathematician, Univ Paris, 75-76. *Mem:* Am Math Soc; Math Asn Am. *Res:* Group theory; combinatorial mathematics, especially graph theory. *Mailing Add:* Dept of Math Clemson Univ Clemson SC 29631

LASKARIS, TRIFON EVANGELOS, b Cairo, Egypt, Jan 4, 44; US citizen; m 71; c 2. MECHANICAL ENGINEERING, ELECTRICAL ENGINEERING. *Educ:* Nat Tech Univ Athens, BS, 66; Rensselaer Polytech Inst, MS, 71, PhD(mech eng), 74. *Prof Exp:* Mech engr advan eng, Large Steam-Turbine Generator Dept, 67-73, cryog br, Power Generation & Propulsion Lab, 73-77, MGR ROTATING MACH, POWER SYSTS LAB, GEN ELEC CO, 77- *Honors & Awards:* Silver Patent Award, Corp Res & Develop, Gen Elec Co; IR-100 Award, Indust Res Mag, 77. *Mem:* Greek Chamber Engrs. *Res:* Superconductivity; cryogenics; computational fluid dynamics; rotating machinery; intense magnetic fields. *Mailing Add:* 918 Randall Rd Schenectady NY 12309

LASKER, BARRY MICHAEL, b Hartford, Conn, Aug 12, 39; m 70; c 1. ASTROPHYSICS. *Educ:* Yale Univ, BS, 61; Princeton Univ, MA, 63, PhD(astrophys sci), 64. *Prof Exp:* NSF fel, Mt Wilson & Palomar Observ, 65-67; asst prof astron, Univ Mich, 67-69; staff astronr, Cerro Tololo Interam Observ, Chile, 69-81; MEM STAFF, SPACE TELESCOPE SCI INST, 81- *Mem:* Am Astron Soc. *Res:* Supernova remnants; the interstellar medium in galaxies; extragalactic astronomy and cosmology; ultrashort period stellar oscillations; astronomical instrumentation. *Mailing Add:* Space Telescope Sci Inst Homewood Campus Baltimore MD 21218

LASKER, GABRIEL (WARD), b Huntington, Eng, Apr 29, 12; US citizen; m 49; c 3. HUMAN ANATOMY, BIOLOGICAL ANTHROPOLOGY. *Educ:* Univ Mich, AB, 34; Harvard Univ, MA, 41, PhD(phys anthrop), 45. *Prof Exp:* From instr to assoc prof, 46-64, PROF ANAT, SCH MED, WAYNE STATE UNIV, 64- *Concurrent Pos:* Viking Fund grant, Paracho, Michoacan, Mex, 48; ed, Human Biol, 53-; mem staff, Dept Anthrop, Univ Wis, 54-55; Fulbright fel, Peru, 57-58. *Mem:* Fel AAAS (vpres, 68); Am Asn Phys Anthrop (secy-treas, 46-50, vpres, 60-62, pres, 63-65); Am Asn Anat; fel Am Anthrop Asn; hon life mem Soc Study Human Biol. *Res:* Human genetics; physical anthropology; physical characteristics of Chinese, Mexicans and Peruvians; demographic aspects of human biology. *Mailing Add:* Dept of Anat Wayne State Univ Sch of Med Detroit MI 48201

LASKER, GEORGE ERIC, b Prague, Czech; Can citizen. INFORMATION SCIENCES, PSYCHOLOGY. *Educ:* Prague Tech Univ, EC, 57; Charles Univ, Prague, DP, 61. *Prof Exp:* Asst prof math, Univ Sask, 65-66; assoc prof comput sci, Univ Man, 66-68; PROF COMPUT SCI, UNIV WINDSOR, 68- *Concurrent Pos:* Nat Res Coun Can grant, Univ Man, 66-68; ed bd, Int J Gen Systs, 74-; vis scholar, Dept Comput & Commun Sci, Univ Mich, Ann Arbor, 74-; pres, Int Cong Appl Systs Res & Cybernet, 80- *Mem:* Can Comput Sci Asn; World Orgn Gen Systs & Cybernet; NY Acad Sci. *Res:* Diagnostic methodology; pattern recognition techniques; threshold logic; automata; systems interaction; simulation models; behavioral prediction; computer controlled conditioning; mathematical psychology; forecasting methodology; computer applications; psychotronics; psychocybernetics; quality of life; educational systems. *Mailing Add:* Sch of Comput Sci Univ Windsor Windsor ON N9B 3P4 Can

LASKER, HOWARD ROBERT, b New York, NY, Feb 8, 52. MARINE BENTHIC ECOLOGY, ECOLOGY OF CORALS. *Educ:* Univ Rochester, BS, 72, MS, 73; Univ Chicago, PhD(geophys sci), 78. *Prof Exp:* Fel, Rosenstiel Sch Marine & Atmospheric Sci, Univ Miami, 78-79; ASST PROF BIOL SCI, STATE UNIV NY, BUFFALO, 79- *Mem:* AAAS; Am Soc Limnol & Oceanog; Sigma Xi. *Res:* Ecology of corals and coral reefs; physiological ecology of algal-coelenterate symbioses; population biology of asexual reproduction in benthic invertebrates. *Mailing Add:* Dept Biol Sci State Univ NY Buffalo NY 14260

LASKER, REUBEN, b Brooklyn, NY, Dec 1, 29; m 52; c 2. COMPARATIVE PHYSIOLOGY. *Educ:* Univ Miami, BS, 50, MS, 52; Stanford Univ, PhD(biol), 56. *Prof Exp:* Rockefeller Found res fel marine biol, Scripps Inst, Univ Calif, 56-57; instr biol, Compton Dist Jr Col, 57-58; physiologist, Bur Commercial Fisheries, US Fish & Wildlife Serv, 58-70, asst dir, Fishery-Oceanog Ctr, 68-70, PHYSIOLOGIST, 70-, CHIEF, COASTAL FISHERIES RES DIV, SOUTHWEST FISHERIES CTR, NAT MARINE FISHERIES SERV, 78- *Concurrent Pos:* Assoc prof in residence, Univ Calif, San Diego, 67-74; adj prof marine biol, Scripps Inst Oceanog, 74-; res fel natural hist, Aberdeen Univ, 66-67; ed, Fishery Bull, 70-75. *Honors & Awards:* Gold Medal Award, US Dept Com, 74. *Mem:* Fel AAAS; Am Soc Limnol & Oceanog; Soc Gen Physiol; Am Soc Zoologists; Marine Biol Asn UK. *Res:* Nutrition, biochemistry and general physiology of marine organisms. *Mailing Add:* Southwest Fisheries Ctr Nat Marine Fisheries Serv La Jolla CA 92038

LASKER, SIGMUND E, b New York, NY, Sept 5, 23; m 65; c 1. PHYSICAL CHEMISTRY. *Educ:* Brooklyn Col, BS, 49; NY Univ, MS, 51; Stevens Inst Technol, PhD(phys chem), 65. *Prof Exp:* Res assoc surg, NY Med Col, 57-60, asst instr biochem, 58-60; res assoc phys chem, Stevens Inst Technol, 60-66; asst prof biophys, 66-72, asst prof pharmacol, 72-75, ASSOC PROF MED (RES), NY MED COL, 75- *Mem:* AAAS; Am Inst Chemists; Am Chem Soc; NY Acad Sci; Am Heart Asn. *Res:* Solution properties of biological macromolecules; polyelectrolytes; experimental thermal injuries; anticoagulants. *Mailing Add:* Dept of Med NY Med Col New York NY 10029

LASKI, BERNARD, b Ont, Nov 11, 15; m 47; c 2. PEDIATRICS, HEMATOLOGY. *Educ:* Univ Toronto, MD, 39, FRCP(C), 49; Am Acad Pediat, FAAP, 79. *Prof Exp:* PROF PEDIAT, UNIV TORONTO, 77- *Concurrent Pos:* Chieff Pediat, Mt Sinai Hosp, 54-; sr physician, Hosp for Sick Children, 79- *Mem:* Am Pediat Soc; Am Soc Pediat Res; Can Pediat Soc; Am Soc Hemat; Am Acad Pediat. *Mailing Add:* 99 Avenue Rd Toronto ON M5S 2R8 Can

LASKIN, ALLEN I, b Brooklyn, NY, Dec 7, 28; m 54, 73; c 2. MICROBIOLOGY. *Educ:* City Col New York, BS, 50; Univ Tex, MA, 52, PhD, 56. *Prof Exp:* Res scientist, Univ Tex, 53-55; sr res microbiologist, Squibb Inst Med Res, 55-64, res supvr microbiol, 64-67, asst dir microbiol, 67-69; res assoc, 69-74, HEAD BIOSCI RES, EXXON RES & ENG CO, 71-, SR RES ASSOC, 74- *Concurrent Pos:* Found microbiol lect, Am Soc Microbiol, 72. *Honors & Awards:* I M Lewis Award, Am Soc Microbiol, 77; Selman A Waksman hon lectr, Theobald Smith Soc, 74. *Mem:* Soc Indust Microbiol (pres, 78-79); Am Soc Microbiol; Am Chem Soc; fel Am Acad Microbiol; fel NY Acad Sci. *Res:* Cell-free protein synthesis; mode of action of antibiotics; mechanisms of bacterial resistance to antibiotics; microbial transformations of steroids; petroleum microbiology; microbial enzymes; transformations of hydrocarbons and related compounds. *Mailing Add:* Exxon Res & Eng Co PO Box 45 Linden NJ 07036

LASKIN, DANIEL M, b New York, NY, Sept 3, 24; m 45; c 3. ORAL SURGERY, MAXILLOFACIAL SURGERY. *Educ:* Ind Univ, BS & DDS, 47; Univ Ill, MS, 51; Am Bd Oral & Maxillofacial Surg, dipl. *Prof Exp:* Intern oral surg, Jersey City Med Ctr, 47-48; clin asst, 49-50, res asst, 50-51, from instr to assoc prof, 51-60, PROF ORAL & MAXILLOFACIAL SURG, COL DENT, UNIV ILL MED CTR, 60-, HEAD DEPT ORAL & MAXILLOFACIAL SURG, 73-, DIR, TEMPOROMANDIBULAR JOINT & FACIAL PAIN RES CTR, 61- *Concurrent Pos:* Resident, Cook County Hosp, 50-51, chmn dept oral surg, 67-77, dep chmn, 77-; attend oral surg, Hosps, 52-; clin prof, Col Med, Univ Ill, Chicago, 58-, head dept dent, Hosps, 70-; ed, Am Asn Oral Maxillofacial & Surgeons Forum & J Oral & Maxillofacial Surg. *Honors & Awards:* Res Recognition Award, Am Asn Oral & Maxillofacial Surgeons, 78; W Harry Archer Award, 81. *Mem:* Sigma Xi; Int Asn Dent Res; Soc Exp Biol & Med; Am Soc Exp Path; AAAS. *Res:* Temporomandibular joint; metabolism of bone and cartilage; sutural growth; calcification and resorption of bone. *Mailing Add:* Dept Oral & Maxillofacial Surg Univ of Ill at the Med Ctr Chicago IL 60612

LASKOWSKI, LEONARD FRANCIS, JR, b Milwaukee, Wis, Nov 16, 19; m 46; c 3. MEDICAL MICROBIOLOGY, CLINICAL MICROBIOLOGY. *Educ:* Marquette Univ, BS, 41, MS, 48; St Louis Univ, PhD(med bact), 51; Am Bd Med Microbiol, dipl. *Prof Exp:* Instr bact, 46-48 & 51-53, sr instr, 53-54, asst prof microbiol, 54-57, from asst prof to assoc prof path, 57-69, PROF PATH, SCH MED, ST LOUIS UNIV, 69-, ASSOC PROF INTERNAL MED, 77- *Concurrent Pos:* China Med Bd fel, Latin Am, 57; fel trop med, La State Univ, 57; consult, St Mary's Group Hosp, 57-; attend, Vet Admin Hosp, health & tech training coordr, Latin Am Peace Corps Projs, 62-66; dir clin microbiol sect, St Louis Univ Hosps, 65; consult clin microbiol, John Cochran Vet Hosp, 66-; St Elizabeth's Hosp, Belleville, Ill, 68- & St Louis County Hosp, 69-; referee mycol, USPHS Commun Dis Ctr Prog for Testing Clin Diag Labs, 68-; consult, Jefferson Barracks, Vet Hosp, 72-; Mogul Diag Div, Mogul Corp, 72-79; St Francis Hosp, 74-77; St Elizabeth's Hosp, Granite City, Ill, 78- & St Louis County & City Med Examr, 78- *Mem:* AAAS; Am Soc Microbiol; NY Acad Sci; fel Am Acad Microbiol; Med Mycol Soc Americas. *Res:* Mechanism of intracellular parasitism; mechanism of action of therapeutic compounds. *Mailing Add:* Dept of Path St Louis Univ Sch of Med St Louis MO 63103

LASKOWSKI, MICHAEL, biochemistry, deceased

LASKOWSKI, MICHAEL, JR, b Warsaw, Poland, Mar 13, 30; nat US; m 57; c 2. BIOCHEMISTRY. *Educ:* Lawrence Col, BS, 50; Cornell Univ, PhD(phys chem), 54. *Prof Exp:* Asst chem, Cornell Univ, 50-52, USPHS fel, 52-56, instr, 56-57; from asst prof to assoc prof, 57-65, PROF CHEM, PURDUE UNIV, 65- *Concurrent Pos:* Chmn, Gordon Res Conf Physics & Phys Chem Biopolymers, 66; mem, Biophys & Biophys Chem Study Sect, NIH, 67-71. *Honors & Awards:* McCoy Award, Purdue Univ, 75; Alfred Jurzykowski Found Award, 77. *Mem:* AAAS; Am Chem Soc (treas, Biol Chem Div, 82-); Am Soc Biol Chemists; Polish Inst Arts & Sci Am; AAAS. *Res:* Protein chemistry; role of individual amino acid residues in proteinase inhibitor-proteinase interaction; evolution; proteolytic enzymes and their inhibitors. *Mailing Add:* Dept of Chem Purdue Univ Lafayette IN 47907

LASKOWSKI, MICHAEL BERNARD, b Chicago, Ill, Apr 20, 43; m 65; c 4. NEUROPHYSIOLOGY, NEUROANATOMY. *Educ:* Loyola Univ, BS, 66; Univ Okla, PhD(physiol), 70. *Prof Exp:* Muscular Dystrophy Asn fel, Northwestern Univ, 70-71; res assoc, 71-72, instr, 72-74, asst prof pharmacol, Vanderbilt Univ, 74-76; ASST PROF PHYSIOL, ST LOUIS UNIV, 76- *Honors & Awards:* Career Develop Award, Andrew Mellon Found, 74. *Mem:* Am Physiol Soc. *Res:* Electrophysiology; electron microscopy. *Mailing Add:* Dept of Physiol 1402 S Grand Blvd St Louis MO 63104

LASKY, ELAINE ZELIGSON, speech pathology, audiology, see previous edition

LASKY, JACK SAMUEL, b New York, NY, Mar 14, 30; m 52; c 2. ORGANIC CHEMISTRY, POLYMER CHEMISTRY. *Educ:* City Col New York, BS, 51; Univ Md, PhD(chem), 55. *Prof Exp:* Res chemist, US Rubber Co, 55-69; dir polymer res, 69-70, vpres res, 70-76, VPRES RES & ENG, OKONITE CO, 76- *Mem:* Am Chem Soc; Inst Elec & Electronics Engrs; Power Eng Soc. *Res:* Synthetic polymers; rubber; plastics; stereospecific polymerization; heterogeneous catalysis; kinetics of reactions; electrical insulating and covering materials. *Mailing Add:* 29 Newman Ave Verona NJ 07044

LASLETT, LAWRENCE JACKSON, b Boston, Mass, Jan 12, 13; m 39; c 3. PHYSICS. *Educ:* Calif Inst Technol, BS, 33; Univ Calif, PhD(physics), 37. *Prof Exp:* Rockefeller Found fel, Inst Theoret Physics, Copenhagen Univ, 37-38, Oersted fel, 38; instr physics, Univ Mich, 39 & Ind Univ, 39-42; mem staff, Radiation Lab, Mass Inst Technol, 41-45; from asst prof to prof physics, Iowa State Univ, 46-63; STAFF MEM, THEORET PHYSICS DIV & ACCELERATOR THEORY GROUP, LAWRENCE BERKELEY LAB, UNIV CALIF, 63- *Concurrent Pos:* Head nuclear physics br & consult, Off Naval Res, DC, 52-53, sci liaison officer, London Br, 60-61; vis res prof, Univ Ill, 55-56 & Univ Wis, 56-57; head high energy physics br, US AEC, 61-63; lectr physics, Univ Calif, 65-67. *Mem:* AAAS; fel Am Phys Soc. *Res:* Accelerator theory and design; beta-ray spectra; electron and gamma-ray spectra; photonuclear research. *Mailing Add:* Accelerator Theory Group Lawrence Berkeley Lab Berkeley CA 94720

LASLEY, BETTY JEAN, b Winston-Salem, NC, July 10, 27. MICROBIOLOGY. *Educ:* Drew Univ, AB, 49; Rutgers Univ, MS, 53; NY Univ, PhD, 68. *Prof Exp:* Sr med technologist, Path Lab, NJ State Hosp, Greystone Park, 49-51; assoc investr chem microbiol, Warner Chilcott Res Labs Div, Warner-Lambert Co, 53-56; asst physiol, Med Col, NY Univ, 56; asst leukemia div, Sloan-Kettering Inst Cancer Res, 56-57; asst abstractor, Am Cyanamid Co, 57-58; asst metab & endocrinol, Med Ctr, 58-70, res assoc, 70-74, INSTR, MED CTR, NY HOSP, CORNELL UNIV, 74- *Mem:* NY Acad Sci. *Res:* Metabolism; immunobiology and endocrinology. *Mailing Add:* Payne Whitney Cornell Med Ctr NY Hosp 525 E 68th St New York NY 10021

LASLEY, BILL LEE, b Ottumwa, Iowa, June 4, 41. REPRODUCTIVE PHYSIOLOGY. *Educ:* Calif State Univ, Chico, BA, 63; Univ Calif, Davis, PhD(physiol), 72. *Prof Exp:* Teacher math & sci, Roseville Union High Sch, 64-67; fel reproductive biol, Rockefeller Found, 72-75; RES ENDOCRINOLOGIST, SAN DIEGO ZOOL GARDEN, 75- *Mem:* Endocrin Soc; Soc Gynecol Invest; Soc Study Reproduction. *Res:* Reproductive endocrinology with emphasis on comparative studies. *Mailing Add:* San Diego Zool Res Dept PO Box 551 San Diego CA 92112

LASLEY, JOHN FOSTER, b Liberal, Mo, Jan 26, 13; m 40; c 1. ANIMAL BREEDING. *Educ:* Univ Mo, BSA, 38, AM, 40, PhD(physiol reprod), 43. *Prof Exp:* Asst animal husb, Univ Mo, 38-43; agr exten agent & supvr agr & stock raising, US Indian Serv, 43-49, PROF ANIMAL HUSB, UNIV MO-COLUMBIA, 49- *Concurrent Pos:* Mem, Gov Sci Adv Comts, Mo. *Mem:* AAAS; Am Soc Animal Sci; Am Genetic Asn. *Res:* Physiology of spermatozoa; breeding problems of range cattle; staining method for differentiation of live and dead spermatozoa; improvement of beef cattle through selection and crossing. *Mailing Add:* 2207 Bushnell Dr Columbia MO 65201

LASMAN, LONNIE LOUIS, statistics, see previous edition

LASS, NORMAN JAY, b New York, NY, Sept 20, 43; m 67; c 2. SPEECH PATHOLOGY, AUDIOLOGY. *Educ:* Brooklyn Col, City Univ NY, BA, 65; Purdue Univ, MS, 66, PhD(speech & hearing sci), 68. *Prof Exp:* Res fel, Bur Child Res, Univ Kans Med Ctr, Kansas City, 68-69; asst prof, 69-73, assoc prof, 73-77, PROF SPEECH & HEARING SCI, WVA UNIV, 77-, DIR, SPEECH & HEARING SCI LAB, 69-, CHMN, DEPT SPEECH PATH & AUDIOL, 74- *Concurrent Pos:* Consult speech path, Audiol & Speech Path Serv, Vet Admin Med Ctr, Martinsburg, WVa, 75- *Mem:* Am Speech-Lang-Hearing Asn; Acoust Soc Am; Am Asn Phonetic Sci; Int Soc Phonetic Sci; Am Cleft Palate Asn. *Res:* Determination of acoustic and perceptual cues in speaker race, sex, height, weight and age by listeners; sex differences in speech rate production and perception; usefulness of time-expanded speech; listener attitudes toward vocal characteristics and communicative disorders. *Mailing Add:* Dept of Speech Path & Audiol WVa Univ Morgantown WV 26506

LASSEN, LAURENCE E, b Milwaukee, Wis, Dec 16, 32; m 59; c 2. FORESTRY. *Educ:* Iowa State Univ, BS, 54, MS, 58; Univ Mich, PhD(forestry), 67. *Prof Exp:* Res forest prod technologist, Forest Prod Lab, Wis, 58-67, proj leader, 67-71; staff asst res admin, 71-72, chief forest prod technol res, Washington, DC, 72-74, dep dir, 74-76, DIR, SOUTHERN FOREST EXP STA, US FOREST SERV, 76- *Mem:* Soc Am Foresters. *Res:* Forestry research. *Mailing Add:* Southern Forest Exp Sta US Forest Serv 701 Loyola Ave New Orleans LA 70113

LASSER, ELLIOTT CHARLES, b Buffalo, NY, Nov 30, 22; m 44; c 4. MEDICINE, RADIOLOGY. *Educ:* Harvard Univ, BS, 43; Univ Buffalo, MD, 46; Univ Minn, MS, 53. *Prof Exp:* Instr radiol, Grad Sch Med, Univ Minn, 52-53; assoc, Sch Med, Univ Buffalo, 53-54, asst prof, 54-56; prof & chmn dept, Sch Med, Univ Pittsburgh, 56-68; chmn dept, 68-77, PROF RADIOL, SCH MED, UNIV CALIF, SAN DIEGO, 68- *Concurrent Pos:* Consult, Vet Admin Hosp, Pittsburgh, Pa, 57-68. *Mem:* AAAS; Radiol Soc NAm; AMA; Am Col Radiol. *Res:* Radiology of the vascular system. *Mailing Add:* 8081 Calle Del Cielo La Jolla CA 92037

LASSER, HOWARD GILBERT, b New York, NY, Nov 24, 26; m 50; c 3. CHEMICAL ENGINEERING, ELECTROCHEMISTRY. *Educ:* Lehigh Univ, BS, 50; Columbia Univ, ChemE, 51. *Hon Degrees:* Dr Ing, Darmstadt Polytech Inst, Ger, 56. *Prof Exp:* Chem engr indust gases, Eng Res & Develop Labs, Army Corps Engrs, 51-53, cryog, Bur Ships, Dept Navy, 53-55, metal prod, Gen Serv Admin, 55-56, metallic & org coatings, Eng Res & Develop Ctr, Army Corps Engrs, 56-68 & electrochem, Electronics Command, 68-73; MAT ENG CONSULT COATINGS & ELECTROCHEM, NAVAL FACIL ENG COMMAND, DEPT NAVY, 73- *Concurrent Pos:* Chmn, Coatings Comt, Dept Defense, 74- *Honors & Awards:* Sci Res Award, Sigma Xi, 68. *Mem:* Fel Oil & Colour Chemists Asn; Am Electroplaters Soc; Am Inst Chem Engrs; fel Am Inst Chemists; fel AAAS. *Res:* Corrosion prevention through the use of metallic and organic coatings; development of anodic films on aluminum; transport theory as related to corrosion processes. *Mailing Add:* Mat Res Consults 5912 Camberly Ave Springfield VA 22150

LASSER, MARVIN ELLIOTT, b Brooklyn, NY, Feb 9, 26; m 54; c 2. SOLID STATE PHYSICS. *Educ:* Brooklyn Col, AB, 49; Syracuse Univ, MS, 51, PhD(physics), 54. *Prof Exp:* Res assoc physics, Syracuse Univ, 49-54; proj scientist, Philco Corp, 54-56, sect head, 56-57, mgr res sect, 57-63, asst dir physics lab, 63-64, dir appl res lab, 64-66; chief scientist, US Dept Army, 66-77, exec dir, Army Sci Adv Panel, 70-77, DIR, ARMY RES, 74- *Concurrent Pos:* Mem comt, Int Conf Semiconductors, NY, 58; mem, Int Conf

Photoconductivity, 61; consult, US Army Electronics Command & adv comt optical commun & tracking, instrumentation & data processing, NASA, 66; adv, Electronics & Aerospace Systs Conf; sr adv, Asn Old Crows (EW countermeasures). *Mem:* Fel Am Phys Soc. *Res:* Photoconductivity; optical and surface properties; metallurgy and measurements of electrical characteristics; lasers; electrooptics; semiconductor devices. *Mailing Add:* Off Dep Chief Staff Res Dev & Acq Rm 3E 360 The Pentagon Washington DC 20310

LASSETER, KENNETH CARLYLE, b Jacksonville, Fla, Aug 12, 42; m 63; c 2. CLINICAL PHARMACOLOGY, INTERNAL MEDICINE. *Educ:* Stetson Univ, BS, 63; Univ Fla, MD, 67. *Prof Exp:* From intern to resident med, Univ Ky Hosp, 67-69, USPHS fel cardiol, 69-70; fel clin pharmacol, 70-71, asst prof, 71-74, assoc prof pharmacol & med, 74-81, CLIN ASSOC PROF PHARMACOL, UNIV MIAMI, 81-; VPRES & MED DIR, CLIN PHARMACOL ASSOC, INC, 81- *Concurrent Pos:* Attend physician, Jackson Mem Hosp, 71- *Honors & Awards:* Res Award, Interstate Postgrad Med Asn, 74. *Mem:* Am Soc Pharmacol & Exp Therapeut; Am Soc Clin Pharmacol & Therapeut; Am Col Physicians; Am Col Clin Pharmacol; Sigma Xi. *Res:* Cardiovascular pharmacology. *Mailing Add:* Clin Pharmacol Assoc Inc 2060 NW 22 Ave Miami FL 33142

LASSETTER, JOHN STUART, b Jackson, Miss, Jan 7, 44; m 65; c 2. BOTANY. *Educ:* Miss Col, BS, 66; Univ Miss, MS, 68; Iowa State Univ, PhD(plant taxon), 72. *Prof Exp:* Asst prof, 73-77, ASSOC PROF BOT, EASTERN KY UNIV, 73- *Concurrent Pos:* Res assoc, Surface Mine Pollution Abatement & Land Use Impact Invest proj, 74-75 & Ky River Palisades Proj, 78-79. *Mem:* Am Soc Plant Taxonomists; Int Asn Plant Taxon; Sigma Xi. *Res:* Biosystematics of North American Vicia, local Kentucky flora. *Mailing Add:* Dept of Biol Sci Eastern Ky Univ Richmond KY 40475

LASSETTRE, EDWIN NICHOLS, b Monroe Co, Ga, Oct 26, 11; m 33, 51; c 2. CHEMICAL PHYSICS. *Educ:* Mont State Col, BSc, 33; Calif Inst Technol, PhD(chem), 38. *Hon Degrees:* DTech, Royal Inst Technol, Stockholm, 77. *Prof Exp:* Instr chem, Ohio State Univ, 37-40, asst prof, 40-54, group leader & res scientist, Manhattan Proj, SAM Labs, Columbia Univ, 44 & Union Carbide & Carbon Chem Corp, 45; assoc prof chem, Ohio State Univ, 46-49, prof, 50-62; staff fel, Mellon Inst Sci, 62-74, dir ctr spec studies, 71-73, prof, 67-74, univ prof chem physics, 74-77, EMER UNIV PROF CHEM PHYSICS, CARNEGIE-MELLON UNIV, 77- *Concurrent Pos:* Consult, Oak Ridge Gaseous Diffusion Plant, Union Carbide Nuclear Co, 54-64. *Mem:* Am Chem Soc; fel Am Phys Soc; Optical Soc Am. *Res:* Elastic and inelastic electron scattering by molecular gases; electron impact spectroscopy; theoretical chemistry. *Mailing Add:* Dept of Chem 4400 Fifth Ave Carnegie-Mellon Univ Pittsburgh PA 15213

LASSILA, KENNETH EINO, b Hancock, Mich, Apr 27, 34; div. HIGH ENERGY PHYSICS, THEORETICAL NUCLEAR PHYSICS. *Educ:* Univ Wyo, BS, 56; Yale Univ, MS, 59, PhD(theoret physics), 61. *Prof Exp:* Res assoc theoret physics, Case Inst Technol, 61-63; asst prof physics, Iowa State Univ, 63-64; sr res assoc, Res Inst Theoret Physics, Univ Helsinki, 64-66; res assoc, Stanford Univ, 66; from asst prof to assoc prof physics, 66-69, PROF PHYSICS, IOWA STATE UNIV, 69- *Concurrent Pos:* Fulbright res fel, Res Inst Theoret Physics, Univ Helsinki, 65; prof, Nordic Inst Theoret Atomic Physics, 72; Fulbright lectr, Univ Oulu, Finland & Univ Oslo, Norway, 73, Fermi Nat Accelerator Lab, 80-81. *Mem:* AAAS; fel Am Phys Soc. *Res:* Nucleon-nucleon interaction; radiation theory; elementary particle interactions. *Mailing Add:* Dept of Physics Iowa State Univ Ames IA 50010

LASSITER, CHARLES ALBERT, b Murray, Ky, Feb 20, 27; m 46; c 2. ANIMAL SCIENCE. *Educ:* Univ Ky, BS, 49, MS, 50; Mich State Univ, PhD, 52. *Prof Exp:* From asst prof to assoc prof dairy sci, Univ Ky, 52-55; assoc prof, Mich State Univ, 56-59, prof dairy sci & chmn dept, 59-76; PROF ANIMAL SCI & HEAD DEPT, NC STATE UNIV, 76- *Mem:* Am Soc Animal Sci; Am Dairy Sci Asn. *Res:* Dairy cattle nutrition, especially pasture and forage studies dealing with more applied aspects; nutritional problems of young dairy calves. *Mailing Add:* Dept of Animal Sci NC State Univ Raleigh NC 27650

LASSITER, JAMES WILLIAM, b Covington, Ga, May 28, 20; m 47; c 2. ANIMAL NUTRITION. *Educ:* Univ Ga, BSA, 41, MSA, 52; Univ Ill, PhD, 55. *Prof Exp:* Asst, Univ Ill, 52-54; asst prof animal husb, 54-61, assoc prof animal sci, 61-70, PROF ANIMAL SCI, UNIV GA, 70- *Concurrent Pos:* Gold Kist study & res grant, Cambridge & Aberdeen Univs, 72; mem manganese panel, Comt Biol Effects of Atmospheric Pollutants, Nat Acad Sci. *Mem:* Am Inst Nutrit; Am Soc Animal Sci; Am Dairy Sci Asn; Soc Environ Chem & Health; Coun Agr Sci & Technol. *Res:* Protein requirements of swine; effects of antibiotics in swine; factors influencing body composition; interrelationships of nutrients; ruminant nutrition; mineral nutrition of animals; metabolism of mineral elements by animals. *Mailing Add:* Dept of Animal & Dairy Sci Univ of Ga Athens GA 30602

LASSITER, RAY ROBERTS, b Hertford Co, NC, Apr 8, 37; m 60; c 2. ECOLOGY, ENVIRONMENTAL SCIENCE. *Educ:* NC State Col, BS, 59, MS, 62; NC State Univ, PhD(animal ecol), 71. *Prof Exp:* Instr biol, Campbell Col, NC, 62-63; asst statistician quant ecol, NC State Univ, 63-67; systs analyst environ statist, Pollution Surveillance Br, SE Water Lab, Environ Protection Agency, 67-70, biol statistician environ sci, Freshwater Ecosysts Br, 70-75; chief environ systs, Br Environ Sci, Athens Environ Res Lab, Environ Protection Agency, 75-81; RESIDENT RES SCIENTIST, INST ECOL, UNIV GA, 81- *Concurrent Pos:* Mem, Inst Ecol, Univ Ga, 77-; res grant, Environ Protection Agency, 81. *Mem:* Sigma Xi; AAAS; Am Inst Biol Sci; Am Soc Limnol & Oceanog. *Res:* Quantitative ecology; population and community dynamics; experimental ecology using laboratory ecosystems; mathematical modeling of ecosystem processes; fate of toxic chemicals in aquatic ecosystems; predicting effects of toxic chemicals on aquatic ecosystem functions. *Mailing Add:* Athens Environ Res Lab Col Sta Rd Athens GA 30605

LASSITER, WILLIAM EDMUND, b Wilmington, NC, July 21, 27; m 56; c 4. PHYSIOLOGY, NEPHROLOGY. *Educ:* Harvard Univ, AB, 50, MD, 54. *Prof Exp:* Intern & asst resident med, Mass Gen Hosp, Boston, 54-56; sr asst resident, NC Mem Hosp, 56-57; Donner res fel, Mass Gen Hosp, Boston, 57-58; Life Ins Med Res Fund fel, Univ NC, Chapel Hill, 58-60; from instr to assoc prof, 60-70, PROF MED, SCH MED, UNIV NC, CHAPEL HILL, 70- *Concurrent Pos:* Estab investr, Am Heart Asn, 62-67, mem coun clin cardiol & coun kidney in cardiovasc dis, 71-; vis investr, Physiol Inst, Berlin, 63-64; Markle scholar, 63-68; Nat Inst Arthritis & Metab Dis career develop award, 67-72; mem cardiovasc & pulmonary res A study sect, NIH, 69-73 & gen med B study sect, 78-82; sect ed, Renal & Electrolyte Physiol, Am J Physiol & J Appl Physiol, 74-76; co-dir NIH surv res needs nephrol & urol, 74-78. *Mem:* AAAS; Am Soc Clin Invest; Am Physiol Soc; fel Am Col Physicians; Am Soc Nephrol. *Res:* Micropuncture studies of mammalian kidney function; tubular transport processes in mammalian kidney; calcium and phosphorus metabolism. *Mailing Add:* Dept of Med Univ of NC Sch of Med Chapel Hill NC 27514

LASSITER, WILLIAM STONE, b Spring Hope, NC, July 7, 39; m 71; c 2. ENGINEERING MANAGEMENT, NOISE AND POLLUTION CONTROL. *Educ:* NC State Univ, BS, 61, PhD(mech eng), 71; Col William & Mary, MS, 68, MBA, 73. *Prof Exp:* Facil Engr, 63-65, mat engr, 65-70, pollution sensing res, 70-75, ENG MGR ACOUST FLUID ANAL, LANGLEY RES CTR, NASA, 76- *Concurrent Pos:* Adj instr, George Washington Univ, Christopher Newport Col & Golden Gate Univ. *Mem:* Am Soc Mech Engrs. *Res:* Noise control; pollution sensing. *Mailing Add:* Langley Res Ctr NASA Mail Stop 431 Hampton VA 23665

LASSLO, ANDREW, b Mukacevo, Czech, Aug 24, 22; nat US; m 55; c 1. MEDICINAL CHEMISTRY. *Educ:* Univ Ill, MSc, 48, PhD(pharmaceut chem), 52, MSLS, 61. *Prof Exp:* Asst chem, Univ Ill, 47-51; res chemist, Org Chem Div, Monsanto Chem Co, 52-54; asst prof med chem, Emory Univ, 54-60; PROF MED CHEM & CHMN DEPT, COL PHARM, HEALTH SCI CTR, UNIV TENN, MEMPHIS, 60- *Concurrent Pos:* Dir postgrad training prog for sci librn, Nat Libr Med, 66-72; dir postgrad training prog org med chem, US Food & Drug Admin, 71; producer & moderator TV and radio series, Health Care Perspectives, 76-78; prin investr, Gustavus & Louise Pfeiffer Res Found, 81- *Mem:* Fel AAAS; fel Am Inst Chemists; sr mem Am Chem Soc; Am Soc Pharmacol & Exp Therapeut; Am Pharmaceut Asn. *Res:* Synthesis and study of compounds with pharmacodynamic potentialities; exploration of relationships between the molecular constitution of synthetic entities and their biodynamic response; processing and coordination of scientific and technical information. *Mailing Add:* Dept Med Chem Col Pharm Univ Tenn Ctr Health Sci Memphis TN 38163

LAST, ARTHUR W(ILLIAM), b Salt Lake City, Utah, Apr 5, 18; m 43; c 6. METALLURGICAL ENGINEERING. *Educ:* Univ Utah, BS, 47, MS, 48, PhD(metall eng), 50. *Prof Exp:* Metallurgist, US Bur Mines, 50-52; DEPT MGR, METAL MINING DIV RES CTR, KENNECOTT COPPER CORP, 52- *Mem:* Am Inst Mining, Metall & Petrol Engrs; Am Inst Mech Engrs. *Res:* Theory and practice of mineral flotation; mineral processing; flotation recovery of sulfide minerals. *Mailing Add:* 1828 Redondo Ave Salt Lake City UT 84108

LAST, JEROLD ALAN, b New York, NY, June 5, 40; m 75; c 3. BIOCHEMISTRY, INHALATION TOXICOLOGY. *Educ:* Univ Wis, BS, 59, MS, 61; Ohio State Univ, PhD(biochem), 65. *Prof Exp:* Biochemist, Corn Prod Co, Ill, 61-62; sr res scientist, Squibb Inst Med Res, NJ, 67-69 & Rockefeller Univ, 69-70; asst managing ed, Proc Nat Acad Sci, USA, 70-71, managing ed, 71-73; consult, NIH, 71-73; res assoc, Dept Biochem & Molecular Biol, Harvard Univ, 73-76; asst prof, 76-79, ASSOC PROF, DEPT INTERNAL MED, PULMONARY SECT, MED CTR, UNIV CALIF, DAVIS, 79- *Concurrent Pos:* Am Cancer Soc fel biochem, Med Sch, NY Univ, 66-67. *Honors & Awards:* Frank R Blood Award, Soc Toxicol, 80. *Mem:* Am Soc Biol Chem; Am Fedn Clin Res; Brit Biochem Soc; Soc Toxicol. *Res:* Antibiotics biosynthesis and mechanism of action; lung disease; protein biosynthesis; nucleic acids; collagen biosynthesis; mucus glycoproteins; lung biochemistry; pulmonary fibrosis; health effects of air pollutants. *Mailing Add:* Sect Pulmonary Med Univ Calif Davis CA 95616

LAST, JOHN MURRAY, b Tailem Bend, Australia, Sept 22, 26; m 57; c 3. EPIDEMIOLOGY. *Educ:* Univ Adelaide, MB & BS, 49, MD, 68; Univ Sydney, DPH, 60. *Prof Exp:* Australian Postgrad Med Found fel, Social Med Res Unit, Med Res Coun UK, 61-62; lectr pub health, Univ Sydney, 62-63; asst prof epidemiol, Univ Vt, 63-64; sr lectr social med, Univ Edinburgh, 65-69; PROF EPIDEMIOL & COMMUNITY MED & CHMN DEPT, UNIV OTTAWA, 70- *Concurrent Pos:* Mem, Nat Health Grant Rev Comt, 70- & Epidemiol Study Sect, NIH, 72-; consult med educ, WHO, 72-73, 74 & 76. *Mem:* Int Asn Epidemiol; fel Am Pub Health Asn; fel Royal Australasian Col Physicians; fel Am Col Prev Med. *Res:* Medical care and education; cancer epidemiology; environmental health. *Mailing Add:* Fac Health Sci Univ Ottawa Ottawa ON K1N 9A9 Can

LASTER, DANNY BRUCE, b Scotts Hill, Tenn, Nov 29, 42; m 60; c 2. ANIMAL SCIENCES. *Educ:* Univ Tenn, Knoxville, BS, 63; Univ Ky, Lexington, MS, 64; Okla State Univ, PhD(animal breeding), 70. *Prof Exp:* Res specialist, Univ Ky, Lexington, 65-68; asst prof endocrin res, Iowa State Univ, 70-71; res leader, Reproduction Res Unit, Clay Ctr, Nebr, 71-78, NAT RES PROF LEADER, BEEF & SHEEP, AGR RES SERV, NAT PARK SERV, USDA, 81- *Concurrent Pos:* Assoc prof, Univ Nebr, 71-78. *Mem:* Am Soc Animal Sci; Soc Study Reproduction; Soc Study Fertility. *Res:* Twinning, dystocia and embryonic mortality in beef cattle. *Mailing Add:* Agr Res Serv Nat Park Serv USDA PO Box 166 Clay Center NE 68933

LASTER, HOWARD JOSEPH, b Jersey City, NJ, Mar 13, 30; m 52; c 4. COSMIC RAY PHYSICS. *Educ:* Harvard Univ, AB, 51; Cornell Univ, PhD(theoret physics), 57. *Prof Exp:* Asst physics, Cornell Univ, 51-56; from asst prof to prof physics, Univ Md, College Park, 56-77, chmn dept physics

& astron, 65-75; PROF PHYSICS & DEAN COL LIB ARTS, UNIV IOWA, 77- *Concurrent Pos:* Instr, Wells Col, 53-54; mem adv comn UNESCO sci prog, Nat Acad Sci; mem bd dirs, Atlantic Res Corp, 72-; chmn, Gov Sci Adv Coun, Md, 73-75; vis prog assoc, Div Int Progs, NSF, 75-76; mem, Gov Sci Adv Coun, Iowa 80- *Mem:* AAAS; Am Phys Soc; Am Asn Physics Teachers; Am Astron Soc; Royal Astron Soc. *Res:* Cosmic ray theory; astrophysics; space theory; origins and propagation of cosmic rays; interplanetary modulation of cosmic rays; science education. *Mailing Add:* Col of Lib Arts Univ of Iowa Iowa City IA 52242

LASTER, LEONARD, b New York, NY, Aug 25, 28; m 56; c 3. MEDICINE, SCIENCE POLICY. *Educ:* Harvard Univ, AB, 49, MD, 50; Am Bd Internal Med, dipl, 61; Am Bd Gastroenterol, dipl, 66. *Prof Exp:* From intern to resident med, Mass Gen Hosp, 50-53; vis investr purine metab, Pub Health Res Inst, New York, Inc, 53-54; sr clin investr, Nat Inst Arthritis & Metab Dis, 54-58; chief sect gastroenterol, Metab Dis Br, Nat Inst Arthritis & Metab Dis, 59-69; staff mem, Off Sci & Technol, Exec Off of President, 69-71, asst dir human resources, 71-74; vpres acad & clin affairs & dean, Col Med, State Univ NY Downstate Med Ctr, 74-78; PROF MED, SCH MED & PRES, ORE HEALTH SCI UNIV, 78- *Concurrent Pos:* Res fel gastroenterol, Mass Mem Hosps, 58-59; clin instr, Sch Med, George Washington Univ, 55-58; prof lectr, 66- *Mem:* Am Soc Biol Chemists; Am Fedn Clin Res; Am Gastroenterol Asn; Am Col Physicians; Am Soc Clin Invest. *Res:* Biochemical aspects of human disease; inborn errors of metabolism; disturbances of the gastrointestinal tract. *Mailing Add:* 3181 S W Sam Jackson Park Rd Ore Health Sci Univ Portland OR 97201

LASTER, MARION LOGAN, entomology, see previous edition

LASTER, RICHARD, b Vienna, Austria, Nov 10, 23; nat US; m 48; c 2. CHEMICAL ENGINEERING. *Educ:* Polytech Inst Brooklyn, BChE, 43. *Prof Exp:* Asst lab dir eng res & develop, Cent Labs, 44-54, res mgr, Walter Baker Div, 54-58, mgr mfg & eng, Franklin Baker Div, 58-60, oper mgr, 60-62, oper mgr, Atlantic Gelatin Div, 62-64, oper mgr res & new prod develop, Jello Div, 64-67, dir corp qual assurance, 67, opers mgr, Maxwell House Coffee Div, 67-69, asst gen mgr corp, 69-71, vpres corp & pres, Maxwell House Coffee Div, 71-72, group vpres coffee & food serv, 72-74, EXEC VPRES & DIR, GEN FOODS CORP, 74- *Honors & Awards:* Food & Bioeng Award, Am Inst Chem Engrs, 72. *Mem:* AAAS; Am Chem Soc; Am Inst Chem Engrs. *Res:* Chemical engineering research as applied to food processing; spray drying; atomization and leaching; chemistry of fats and oils; chocolate processing. *Mailing Add:* Gen Foods Corp 250 North St White Plains NY 10625

LASTER, STANLEY JERRAL, geophysics, see previous edition

LASTER, WILLIAM RUSSELL, JR, b Ala, Oct 20, 26; m 61; c 1. VETERINARY MEDICINE. *Educ:* Auburn Univ, DVM, 51. *Prof Exp:* Virologist, 51-56, head cancer screening sect, 56-66, HEAD CANCER SCREENING DIV, SOUTHERN RES INST, 66- *Mem:* Am Asn Cancer Res. *Res:* Cancer chemotherapy. *Mailing Add:* Cancer Scrn Div Southern Res Inst PO Box 3307-A Birmingham AL 35255

LASTHUYSEN, WILLEM, b Netherlands, July 18, 10; nat US; m 59. ORGANIC CHEMISTRY. *Educ:* Univ Bonn, MS, 32. *Prof Exp:* Chemist, Indonesia, 32-34; chemist & tech salesman, Netherlands, 34-40; res chemist, NV Chem Works, 40-45; res dir, Great Atlantic & Pac Tea Co, NY, 47-52; chief chemist, Dodge & Olcott, Inc, 52-55; res dir, Colgate-Palmolive Co, NJ, 55-57; tech dir, Rhodia, Inc, 57-64; vpres & tech dir, Firmenich, Inc, NY, 64-66; PRES, FLAVOR RES LABS, 66- *Concurrent Pos:* Lectr, Brookdale Col, Columbia & Rutgers Univs, 50-; indust consult. *Mem:* Am Chem Soc; Inst Food Technologists; Soc Flavor Chemists. *Res:* Essential oils; aromatic chemicals; pharmaceuticals; food, beverage and feed problems; flavors and nutrition; tobacco. *Mailing Add:* 318 Ocean Blvd Atlantic Highlands NJ 07716

LASTOVICA, J(OHN) E(UGENE), JR, chemical engineering, see previous edition

LASURE, LINDA LEE, b Bartlesville, Okla, Nov 23, 46. MICROBIAL GENETICS. *Educ:* St Cloud State Col, BS, 68; Syracuse Univ & State Univ NY, PhD(genetics), 73. *Prof Exp:* Res fel, New York Bot Garden, 72-74; res scientist microbiol, 74-79, sr res scientist, 79-80, SUPV MUTATION & SCREENING, MILES LABS INC, 80- *Mem:* Sigma Xi; AAAS; Genetics Soc Am; Am Soc Microbiol; Mycol Soc Am. *Res:* Studies of mutagenesis, inheritance, and physiological control of sexual reproduction in the lower fungi, fungal spore germination, and selection of strains of fungi with improved yields of enzymes and organic acids. *Mailing Add:* Dept of Biosynthesis Res Miles Labs Inc Elkhart IN 46515

LASWELL, TROY JAMES, b Ottawa, Ky, Nov 12, 20; m 43; c 1. GEOLOGY. *Educ:* Berea Col, AB, 42; Oberlin Col, AM, 48; Univ Mo, PhD(geol), 53. *Prof Exp:* Instr geol, Univ Mo, 48-53; from asst prof to assoc prof, Washington & Lee Univ, 53-57; from assoc prof to prof, La Polytech Inst, 57-62; PROF GEOL & GEOG & HEAD DEPT, MISS STATE UNIV, 62- *Mem:* Geol Soc Am; Am Asn Petrol Geologists; Am Asn Geol Teachers; Sigma Xi. *Res:* Stratigraphy; sedimentation. *Mailing Add:* PO Box 824 Mississippi State MS 39762

LASZEWSKI, RONALD M, b Chicago, Ill, June 22, 47. EXPERIMENTAL NUCLEAR PHYSICS. *Educ:* Univ Ill, Urbana, BS, 69, MS, 72, PhD(physics), 75. *Prof Exp:* Res assoc physics, Argonne Nat Lab, 75-78; RES ASST PROF PHYSICS, UNIV ILL, URBANA, 78- *Mem:* Am Phys Soc. *Res:* Photonuclear physics and medium energy physics. *Mailing Add:* Dept of Physics Univ of Ill Urbana IL 61801

LASZLO, JOHN, b Cologne, Ger, May 28, 31; US citizen; m 62; c 3. MEDICINE, BIOCHEMISTRY. *Educ:* Columbia Univ, AB, 52; Harvard Med Sch, MD, 55; Am Bd Internal Med, dipl, 63. *Prof Exp:* Intern, Univ Chicago Clins, 55-56; clin assoc clin chemother, Nat Cancer Inst, 56-58; USPHS fel cytochem, Nat Cancer Inst, 58; resident med, 59-60, from asst prof to assoc prof, 62-70, PROF MED, DUKE UNIV, 70- *Concurrent Pos:* Chief hemat sect, Vet Admin Hosp, Durham, 63-68, chief med serv, 68-73; mem pharmacol study sect, Nat Cancer Inst, 70-74. *Mem:* Am Soc Hemat; Am Asn Cancer Res; fel Am Col Physicians; Asn Am Physicians. *Res:* Nucleic acids; leukemia. *Mailing Add:* Dept of Med Duke Univ Med Ctr Durham NC 27706

LASZLO, TIBOR S, b Oraviczafalu, Hungary, Apr 25, 12; US citizen. INDUSTRIAL CHEMISTRY. *Educ:* Royal Hungarian Univ Technol & Econ Sci, DSc(chem eng), 35. *Prof Exp:* Res & develop engr oil industs, Hungary, 35-48; asst dir inorg high temperature chem, Fordham Univ, 48-51, process engr res dept, Calif Tex Oil Co, 51-53; dir high temperature lab, Fordham Univ, 53-57; proj specialist high temperature ceramics, Wright Aeronaut Div, Curtiss Wright Corp, 57-58; prin staff scientist, High Temperature Inorg Lab, Res & Adv Develop Div, Avco Corp, 58-65, sr consult scientist, 65-66; prin scientist, Res Ctr, Philip Morris, Inc, 66-77; CONSULT, 77- *Concurrent Pos:* Consult specialist, 53-57; NSF grant, 55-57; foreign ed, La Revue des Hautes Temperatures et des Refractaires, 65-; mem bd gov & symp dir, Int Microwave Power Inst. *Mem:* Solar Energy Soc; Am Soc Testing & Mat. *Res:* Petroleum and vegetable oil processing; high temperature generation; solar furnaces; high refractory compounds; solar radiation simulation; temperature control coatings; thermal radiation measurements; microwave industrial technology; cellulose-water bond. *Mailing Add:* 4600 S Four Mile Dr 226 Arlington VA 22204

LATA, GENE FREDERICK, b New York, NY, May 17, 22; m 51; c 5. BIOCHEMISTRY. *Educ:* City Col New York, BS, 42; Univ Ill, MS, 48, PhD(biochem), 50. *Prof Exp:* Jr chemist, Gen Foods Corp, 42, chemist, 46; asst chem, Univ Ill, 47, asst biochem, 48-50; from instr to asst prof, 50-62, fel med, 65-66, ASSOC PROF BIOCHEM, UNIV IOWA, 62- *Concurrent Pos:* Vis lectr, Huntington Labs, Harvard Med Sch, 65-66; consult, Am Dent Asn. *Mem:* Fel AAAS; Am Chem Soc; Am Soc Biol Chemists; NY Acad Sci. *Res:* Peroxisomal enzymes and their control; hormonal control of enzyme actions; steroid interactions and transport; aging and steroid hormone dynamics; angiogenesis factors. *Mailing Add:* Dept of Biochem Univ of Iowa Iowa City IA 52242

LATCH, DANA MAY, b New York, NY, Aug 29, 43; c 1. ALGEBRA, TOPOLOGY. *Educ:* Harpur Col, BA, 65; Queens Col, NY, MA, 67; City Univ New York, PhD(math), 71. *Prof Exp:* Teaching asst math, Queens Col, NY, 65-66, lectr, 66-67; asst prof, Douglass Col, Rutgers Univ, 71-74 & Lawrence Univ, 74-76; asst prof, 76-79, ASSOC PROF MATH, NC STATE UNIV, 79- *Concurrent Pos:* NSF res grant, Rutgers Univ, 72-73 & NC State Univ, 78-80 & 81-83; Carnegie Found fac develop award, Lawrence Univ, 75; study grant, Ger Acad Exchange Serv, Univ Konstanz, Ger, 78; vis prof math, Universitat Konstanz, Ger, 79; vis scholar comput sci, Univ NC, Chapel Hill, 82; Alexander von Humboldt res fel, Munich, Fed Repub Ger, 83. *Mem:* Am Math Soc; Asn Women Math. *Res:* Algebraic topology of small categories; applications of category theory to the theory of program behaviors; applications of categorical methods to homotopy theory and the theory of localizations. *Mailing Add:* Dept of Math NC State Univ Raleigh NC 27650

LATEEF, ABDUL BARI, b Lyallpur, Pakistan, Apr 4, 39; m 70. FORENSIC SCIENCE, CHEMISTRY. *Educ:* Punjab Univ, Pakistan, BS, 59, MS, 61; Univ Newcastle, PhD(chem), 66. *Prof Exp:* Nat Res Coun Can fel, Univ Calgary, 66-69; from instr to asst prof chem, 69-71, asst prof forensic sci, 71-75, ASSOC PROF FORENSIC SCI, YOUNGSTOWN STATE UNIV, 76- *Mem:* Am Acad Forensic Sci; Am Chem Soc; Forensic Soc, London; Acad Criminal Justice; Sigma Xi. *Res:* Spectroscopic and chromatographic analytical techniques in forensic science; role of forensic science in criminal justice system. *Mailing Add:* Dept of Criminal Justice Youngstown State Univ Youngstown OH 44503

LATHAM, ALLEN, JR, b Norwich, Conn, May 23, 08; m 33; c 4. ENGINEERING. *Educ:* Mass Inst Technol, BS, 30. *Prof Exp:* Jr engr, E I du Pont de Nemours & Co, WVa, 30-35; chief engr, Polaroid Corp, Mass, 36-41; sr mech engr, Arthur D Little, Inc, 41-51, vpres, 51-59, sr engr, 59-67; pres, 500 Inc, 67-68; PRES, HAEMONETICS CORP, 68-, CHMN BD, 72- *Concurrent Pos:* Chmn bd, Cryogenic Technol, 68-72. *Mem:* Am Soc Mech Engrs; Am Inst Chem Engrs. *Res:* Cryogenics; blood processing. *Mailing Add:* Haemonetics Corp 400 Wood Rd Braintree MA 02184

LATHAM, ARCHIE J, b Blackfoot, Idaho, June 26, 26; m 63; c 3. PLANT PATHOLOGY, MYCOLOGY. *Educ:* Idaho State Col, BS, 56; Univ Idaho, MS, 59; Univ Ill, PhD(plant path), 61. *Prof Exp:* Ranger, Yellowstone Park, Wyo, 56; res asst plant path, Univ Idaho, 56-58 & Univ Ill, 58-61; res biologist, Gulf Res & Develop Co, Kans, 61-67; asst prof bot & plant path, Auburn Univ, 67-78, assoc prof, 78-80. *Mem:* Am Phytopath Soc; Mycol Soc Am. *Res:* Fruit and nut diseases. *Mailing Add:* 310 Flowers Circle Auburn AL 36830

LATHAM, DAVID WINSLOW, b Boston, Mass, Mar 19, 40; m 60; c 5. ASTRONOMY. *Educ:* Mass Inst Technol, BS, 61; Harvard Univ, MA, 65, PhD(astron), 70. *Prof Exp:* ASTRONOMER, SMITHSONIAN ASTROPHYS OBSERV, 65-; LECTR ASTRON, HARVARD UNIV, 71- *Mem:* Am Astron Soc; Soc Photog Scientist & Engrs; Royal Astron Soc. *Res:* Stellar spectroscopy; stellar chemical abundances and nucleosynthesis; detection of light at low levels. *Mailing Add:* Ctr for Astrophys 60 Garden St Cambridge MA 02138

LATHAM, DEWITT ROBERT, b Chugwater, Wyo, Oct 26, 28; m 55; c 2. PETROLEUM CHEMISTRY. *Educ:* Univ Wyo, BS, 50. *Prof Exp:* Anal chemist, Rocky Mountain Arsenal, US Army Chem Corps, Colo, 52-54; chemist, Laramie Energy Res Ctr, US Bur Mines, 54-60, res chemist, 60-64,

PROJ LEADER LARAMIE ENERGY TECH CTR, DEPT ENERGY, 64- *Mem:* Am Chem Soc; Sigma Xi. *Res:* Nitrogen and oxygen compounds in petroleum; development of methods of analysis for petroleum shale, oil and coal liquids; separation and characterization of fossil fuel energy sources. *Mailing Add:* Laramie Energy Tech Ctr PO Box 3395 Laramie WY 82070

LATHAM, DON JAY, b Lewiston, Idaho, Dec 21, 38; m 60; c 3. ATMOSPHERIC SCIENCES. *Educ:* Pomona Col, BA, 60; NMex Inst Mining & Technol, MS, 64, PhD, 68. *Prof Exp:* Res asst, NMex Inst Mining & Technol, 61-67; sr res scientist, Rosenstiel Sch Marine & Atmospheric Sci, Univ Miami, 67-68, asst prof atmospheric sci, 68-72, assoc prof, 72-75; RES METEOROLOGIST & PHYSICIST, NORTHERN FOREST FIRE LAB, 75- *Concurrent Pos:* NSF grants, Univ Miami, 69-75; fac affil, Univ Mont, 75-; mem, Atmospheric Elec Comt, Am Meteorol Soc, 81. *Mem:* Am Meteorol Soc; Am Geophys Union. *Res:* Atmospheric electricity; radar meteorology. *Mailing Add:* Northern Forest Fire Lab Drawer G Missoula MT 59806

LATHAM, GARY V, b Conneautville, Pa, Sept 2, 35; m 71; c 1. GEOPHYSICS. *Educ:* Pa State Univ, BS, 58; Columbia Univ, PhD(geophys), 65. *Prof Exp:* Sr res scientist, Columbia Univ, 66-71; PROF GEOPHYS, UNIV TEX, 72-, ASSOC DIR GEOPHYS LAB, MARINE SCI INST, 75- *Concurrent Pos:* Prin investr, Apollo Lunar Seismic Exp, 68-; trustee, Palisades Geophys Inst, 71-; consult, NASA, 72- *Honors & Awards:* Medal for Except Sci Achievement, NASA, 71 & Expert, 73. *Mem:* AAAS; Soc Explor Geophysicists; Seismol Soc Am; Am Geophys Union; Am Soc Oceanog. *Res:* Seismic experiments on the moon and Mars, Apollo and Viking; seismic and land deformation studies in Central America; ocean bottom seismic stations. *Mailing Add:* 700 The Strand Galveston TX 77550

LATHAM, MICHAEL CHARLES, b Kilosa, Tanzania, May 6, 28; m 74; c 2. NUTRITION, TROPICAL PUBLIC HEALTH. *Educ:* Univ Dublin, BA, 49, MB, BCh & BAO, 52; Univ London, DTM&H, 58; Harvard Univ, MPH, 65. *Prof Exp:* House surgeon, High Wycombe Hosp, Buckinghamshire, Eng, 52-53; rotating physician, Methodist Hosp, Los Angeles, 53-54; sr house officer, NMiddlesex Hosp, London, 54-55; med officer, Tanzania Ministry of Health, 55-64, dir nutrit unit, 62-64; res assoc & asst prof nutrit, Harvard Univ, 64-68; PROF INT NUTRIT & DIR, PROG INT NUTRIT, DIV NUTRIT SCI, CORNELL UNIV, 68- *Concurrent Pos:* Vis exchange fel, Methodist Hosp, Los Angeles, 53-54; contrib ed, Nutrit Rev, 68-74; chmn panel, White House Conf Food, Nutrit & Health & vchmn panel, Follow-Up Conf, 69-71; consult, WHO, Manila, 70 & UN Food & Agr Orgn, 64 & Zambia, 70; mem, Nat Acad Sci-Nat Res Coun Int Nutrit Comt, 70-76; UNICEF consult, Thailand & Malaysia, 73; fel, Fac Community Med, Univ London, 73; mem exec comt pest control, Nat Acad Sci, 73-; mem expert adv panel nutrit, WHO, 74-; vis prof, Univ Nairobi, Kenya, 74-75; World Bank consult, Indonesia, 75; US AID consult, Guyana, 77 & 78; mem comt nutrit & infections, Nat Acad Sci, 78- *Honors & Awards:* Officer of the Order of the Brit Empire, 65; Food Cycle Trophy Award, Ministry Health, Tanzania, 78. *Mem:* Am Inst Nutrit; Brit Nutrit Soc; Am Soc Clin Nutrit; fel Royal Soc Trop Med & Hyg; fel Am Pub Health Asn. *Res:* International nutrition problems; nutrition and health of low income populations; xerophthalmia; infant feeding practices; nutrition and intellectual development; protein-calorie malnutrition of children; evaluation of applied nutrition programs; lactose intolerance; nutritional surveillance; energy expenditure. *Mailing Add:* Div of Nutrit Sci Cornell Univ Ithaca NY 14853

LATHAM, PATRICIA SUZANNE, b Annapolis, Md, Aug 22, 46. HEPATOLOGY. *Educ:* Simmons Col, BS, 68; Sch Med, Univ Southern Calif, MD, 72. *Prof Exp:* ASST PROF MED & PATH, UNIV MD HOSP & BALTIMORE VET ADMIN HOSP, 81- *Mem:* Am Asn Study Liver Dis; Am Gastroenterol Asn. *Res:* Investigation of liver diseases with emphasis on structure and function. *Mailing Add:* 629 Colorado Ave Baltimore MD 21210

LATHAM, ROGER ALAN, b Parsons, WVa, July 6, 39; m 66; c 2. POLYMER CHEMISTRY. *Educ:* Harvard Univ, AB, 61; Mass Inst Technol, PhD(org chem), 66. *Prof Exp:* SR RES CHEMIST, E I DU PONT DE NEMOURS & CO, INC, 66- *Res:* Development of engineering plastics. *Mailing Add:* E I du Pont de Nemours & Co Inc PO Box 1217 Parkersburg WV 26101

LATHAM, ROSS, JR, b Chicago, Ill, Dec 18, 32; m 61; c 2. INORGANIC CHEMISTRY. *Educ:* Principia Col, BS, 55; Univ Ill, MS, 57, PhD(inorg chem), 61. *Prof Exp:* Instr chem, Lafayette Col, 59-60; chemist, Esso Res & Eng Co, NJ, 61-66; assoc prof, 66-72, PROF CHEM, ADRIAN COL, 72- *Res:* Titanium alkoxide-halide chemistry. *Mailing Add:* 434 Westwood Dr W Adrian MI 49221

LATHEM, WILLOUGHBY, b Atlanta, Ga, Oct 9, 23; m 51; c 5. MEDICINE. *Educ:* Emory Univ, BS, 44, MD, 46; Am Bd Internal Med, dipl, 54. *Prof Exp:* Asst med, Col Physicians & Surgeons, Columbia Univ, 52-53; asst clin prof, Yale Univ, 53-56; from asst prof to assoc prof, Sch Med, Univ Pittsburgh, 56-64; sci rep, Off Int Res, NIH, Eng, 62-66; dep dir biomed sci, Rockefeller Found, 66-72, assoc dir health sci, 72-78, regional officer, Asia, Bangkok & Thailand, 75-77, field staff, Salvador, Bahia & Brazil, 78-80; VPRES & MED DIR, STERLING INT GROUP, STERLING DRUG INC, 80- *Concurrent Pos:* Hon res assoc, Univ Col, Univ London, 62-65; vis prof, Mt Sinai Sch Med, 80. *Mem:* Am Soc Clin Invest; Harvey Soc; Am Fedn Clin Res. *Res:* International health. *Mailing Add:* Sterling Drug Inc 90 Park Ave New York NY 10016

LATHROP, ARTHUR LAVERN, b Kittitas, Wash, Nov 21, 18; m 46. PHYSICS. *Educ:* Wash State Univ, BS, 43, Univ Ill, MS, 46; Rice Univ, PhD(physics), 52. *Prof Exp:* Instr physics, Wash State Univ, 43-44; physicist, Ames Aeronaut Lab, Moffett Field, Calif, 44-45; instr physics, Univ Tulsa, 47-49; res engr, Boeing Airplane Co, Wash, 52-53; res asst physics, Inst Paper Chem, Lawrence, 53-58, res assoc, 58-65; from asst prof to assoc prof, 65-71, PROF PHYSICS, WESTERN ILL UNIV, 71- *Concurrent Pos:* Res Corp grant. *Mem:* Am Asn Physics Teachers. *Res:* Superconductivity; physical properties of paper; radiative transfer theory. *Mailing Add:* 700 Auburn Dr Macomb IL 61455

LATHROP, EARL WESLEY, b Oakley, Kans, Mar 1, 24; m 49; c 1. SYSTEMATIC BOTANY. *Educ:* Walla Walla Col, BA, 50, MA, 52; Univ Kans, PhD(bot), 57. *Prof Exp:* Instr biol, Can Union Col, 52-54; assoc prof bot, La Sierra Col, 57-64; assoc prof biol, 64-80, PROF BIOL, LOMA LINDA UNIV, 80- *Mem:* Am Range Mgt Soc. *Res:* Floristics. *Mailing Add:* 11740 Valiant St Riverside CA 92505

LATHROP, JAY WALLACE, b Bangor, Maine, Sept 6, 27; m 48; c 4. SOLID STATE PHYSICS, ELECTRICAL ENGINEERING. *Educ:* Mass Inst Technol, BS, 48, MS, 49, PhD(physics), 52. *Prof Exp:* Electronic scientist, Nat Bur Standards, 52-58; mgr advan technol, Semiconductor Components Div, Tex Instruments Inc, 58-68; PROF ELEC ENG, CLEMSON UNIV, 68- *Mem:* Fel Inst Elec & Electronics Engrs. *Res:* Microelectronics; integrated circuits; solar cells; semiconductor devices. *Mailing Add:* Dept of Elec Eng Clemson Univ Clemson SC 29631

LATHROP, JOHN DOUGLASS, astrophysics, cosmology, see previous edition

LATHROP, KATHERINE AUSTIN, b Lawton, Okla, June 16, 15; m 38; c 5. NUCLEAR MEDICINE. *Educ:* Okla State Univ, BS, 36 & 39, MS, 39. *Prof Exp:* Asst, Univ Wyo, 42-44; jr chemist, Biomed Div, Manhattan Proj Metall Lab, 45-47; assoc biochemist, Argonne Nat Lab, 47-54, assoc prof radiol, Univ Chicago, 67-78, RES ASSOC, FRANKLIN McLEAN MEM RES INST, 54-, PROF RADIOL, UNIV CHICAGO, 78- *Concurrent Pos:* Mem comt nuclear med, Am Nat Standards Inst; adv comt radiopharmaceut, US Pharmacopeia; from instr to asst prof, Univ Chicago, 54-67; mem med internal radiation dose comt, Soc Nuclear Med, 67-, chmn, 77- *Mem:* AAAS; Radiation Res Soc; NY Acad Sci; Soc Nuclear Med; Sigma Xi. *Res:* Development of radionuclides for diagnostic and therapeutic purposes, including their production, purification and incorporation into various chemical forms; biological behavior and dosimetry in laboratory animals and humans. *Mailing Add:* Univ Chicago & F M Mem Res Inst 950 E 59th St Box 420 Chicago IL 60637

LATHROP, KAYE DON, b Bryan, Ohio, Oct 8, 32; m 57; c 2. COMPUTER SCIENCE. *Educ:* US Mil Acad, BS, 55; Calif Inst Technol, MS, 59, PhD(mech eng, physics), 62. *Prof Exp:* Staff mem reactor math, Los Alamos Sci Lab, 62-67; staff mem & group leader reactor physics methods develop, Nuclear Anal & Reactor Physics Dept, Gen Atomic Div, Gen Dynamics Corp, 67-68; T-1 alt group leader, 68-72, T-1 group leader, 72-75, T-div asst div leader, 73-75, assoc div leader nuclear safeguards, Reactor Safety & Technol Div, 75-77, alt div leader, Energy Div, 77-78, div leader, Comput Sci & Serv Div, 78-79, ASSOC DIR ENG SCI, LOS ALAMOS NAT LAB, 79- *Concurrent Pos:* Vis prof, Univ NMex, 64-65, adj prof, 66-67; mem, US Energy Res & Develop Admin Adv Comt for Reactor Physics, 73- *Honors & Awards:* E O Lawrence Mem Award, 76. *Mem:* Fel Am Nuclear Soc (treas, 77-79); Am Phys Soc. *Res:* Analytic and numerical solutions of equations of neutron and photon transport; reactor safety; computer systems and communications. *Mailing Add:* MS-145 Los Alamos Nat Lab PO Box 1663 Los Alamos NM 87545

LATHROP, RICHARD C(HARLES), b Wauwatosa, Wis, Sept 6, 24; m 56. ELECTRICAL & AERONAUTICAL ENGINEERING. *Educ:* Univ Wis, BS, 48, MS, 50, PhD(elec eng), 51. *Prof Exp:* Res asst, Univ Wis, 51; proj engr, Wright Air Develop Ctr, US Air Force, 51-55, staff mem Test Pilot Sch, 55-59, commandant, 59-61, assoc prof elec eng, US Air Force Acad, 61-65, prof & head dept, Pakistan Air Force Col Aeronaut Eng, 65-67, pilot, Fourth Air Commando Squadron, 67-68, exec officer, Cent Inertial Guide Test Facil, Air Force Missile Develop Ctr, Holloman AFB, NMex, 68-70, tech dir, Air Force Flight Test Ctr, 71-74; CONSULT ENGR, 74- *Mem:* Sr mem Inst Elec & Electronics Engrs; assoc fel Am Inst Aeronaut & Astronaut; sr mem Simulation Coun. *Res:* Analog and digital computers; automatic controls; aircraft flight testing; aircraft dynamics; microcomputers. *Mailing Add:* PO Box 53 Edwards CA 93523

LATHWELL, DOUGLAS J, b Mich, Mar 28, 22; m 48; c 3. SOIL SCIENCE. *Educ:* Mich State Univ, BS, 47; Ohio State Univ, PhD(soil sci), 50. *Prof Exp:* From asst prof to assoc prof, 50-61, PROF SOIL SCI, CORNELL UNIV, 61- *Concurrent Pos:* Fulbright res scholar, Neth, 64. *Mem:* Soil Sci Soc Am; Am Soc Agron; Am Soc Plant Physiol; Int Soc Soil Sci. *Res:* Soil fertility; plant nutrition. *Mailing Add:* 130 Northview Rd Ithaca NY 14850

LATIES, ALAN M, b Beverly, Mass, Feb 8, 31; m; c 2. OPHTHALMOLOGY. *Educ:* Harvard Col, AB, 54; Baylor Univ, MD, 59; Am Bd Ophthal, dipl, 65. *Prof Exp:* Intern, Mt Sinai Hosp, New York, 59-60; resident ophthal, Hosp Univ Pa, 60-63, instr, 63-64, assoc, 64-66, asst prof, 66-70, GIVEN PROF OPHTHAL, MED SCH, UNIV PA, 70- *Concurrent Pos:* NIH trainee, 61-63, spec fel, 63-64; assoc ophthal, Children's Hosp Philadelphia, 63-; asst attend physician, Philadelphia Gen Hosp, 63-; attend ophthal, Vet Admin Hosp, 63-; mem vision res & training comt, Nat Eye Inst. *Honors & Awards:* Res to Prevent Blindness Professorship Award, 64; Friedenwald Award for Res in Ophthal, 72. *Mem:* AMA; Asn Res Vision & Ophthal; Histochem Soc; Am Asn Anat; Am Acad Ophthal & Otolaryngol. *Res:* Histochemistry; visual pathways. *Mailing Add:* Scheie Eye Inst Univ of Pa Med Ctr Philadelphia PA 19104

LATIES, GEORGE GLUSHANOK, b Sevastopol, Russia, Jan 17, 20; US citizen; m 47. PLANT PHYSIOLOGY. *Educ:* Cornell Univ, BS, 41; Univ Minn, MS, 42; Univ Calif, PhD(plant physiol), 47. *Prof Exp:* Asst, Div Plant Nutrit, Univ Calif, 42-43, sr asst, 43-47; res fel biol, Calif Inst Technol, 47-50, sr res fel, 50-52 & 55-58; asst prof bot, Univ Mich, 52-55; plant physiologist, Exp Sta & assoc prof hort sci, Univ, 59-63, PROF PLANT PHYSIOL, DEPT BIOL, UNIV CALIF, LOS ANGELES, 63- *Concurrent Pos:* Rockefeller Found fel, Sheffield & Cambridge Univs, 49-50; res botanist, Univ Mich, 52-55; mem physiol chem study sect, USPHS, 63-65; Guggenheim fel, Commonwealth Sci & Indust Res Orgn, Australia, 66-67. *Mem:* AAAS; Am Soc Plant Physiol (vpres, 64-65); Bot Soc Am; Scand Soc Plant Physiol. *Res:*

Respiratory regulatory mechanisms and respiratory pathways in plant tissues; permeability and salt transport; biochemical aspects of growth and development. *Mailing Add:* Dept of Biol 2203 Life Sci Bldg Univ of Calif Los Angeles CA 90024

LATIES, VICTOR GREGORY, b Racine, Wis, Feb 2, 26; m 56; c 3. PSYCHOPHARMACOLOGY. *Educ:* Tufts Univ, AB, 49; Univ Rochester, PhD(psychol), 54. *Prof Exp:* Res assoc, Univ Rochester, 53-54; teaching intern, Brown Univ, 54-55; from instr to asst prof, Sch Med, Johns Hopkins Univ, 55-65; assoc prof radiation biol, biophys, pharmacol & psychol, 65-71, PROF RADIATION BIOL, BIOPHYS, PHARMACOL & PSYCHOL, UNIV ROCHESTER, 71- *Concurrent Pos:* Mem preclin psychopharmacol res rev comt, NIMH, 67-71; ed, J Exp Anal Behav, 73-77; mem, Nat Acad Sci-Nat Res Coun Panel on Carbon Monoxide, 73-77, mem bd toxicol & environ health hazards, 77-80; mem, Sci Review Panel Health Res, Environ Protection Agency, 81- *Mem:* Am Psychol Asn; Am Soc Pharmacol & Exp Therapeut; Behav Pharmacol Soc (pres, 66-68); Soc Neurosci; Psychonomic Soc. *Res:* Behavioral pharmacology; experimental analysis of behavior. *Mailing Add:* Dept of Radiation Biol & Biophys Univ of Rochester Sch Med & Dent Rochester NY 14642

LATIMER, CLINTON NARATH, b New York, NY, Aug 30, 24; m 56; c 3. NEUROPHYSIOLOGY. *Educ:* Columbia Univ, AB, 48; Syracuse Univ, PhD(physiol), 56. *Prof Exp:* Group leader neuroharmacol, Am Cyanamid Co, 58-76, study dir toxicol, Lederle Labs Div, 76-80; DIR DRUG SAFETY EVAL, PHARMACEUT DIV, PENNWALT CORP, 80- *Concurrent Pos:* Nat Inst Neurol Dis & Blindness res fel neurophysiol, Univ Wash, 56-58. *Mem:* AAAS; Am Soc Pharmacol & Exp Therapeut; Soc Neurosci; Am Physiol Soc; Am Col Toxicol. *Res:* Neuropharmacology; function of the central nervous system as delineated by extra and intracellular recordings of neuronal activity under influence of drugs and in control states; psychopharmacology; safety evaluation of all classes of compounds; physiologic toxicology; long-term alteration of function by drugs; computer applications; research administration, toxicology, pathology, drug safety evaluation. *Mailing Add:* Drug Safety Eval Pennwalt Pharmaceut 755 Jefferson Rd Rochester NY 14623

LATIMER, DONALD ANDREW, physical organic chemistry, biochemistry, see previous edition

LATIMER, HOWARD LEROY, b Seattle, Wash, July 18, 29; m 57; c 4. PLANT GENETICS, PLANT ECOLOGY. *Educ:* Wash State Univ, BS, 51, MS, 55; Claremont Cols, PhD(bot), 59. *Prof Exp:* From asst prof to assoc prof, 58-68, PROF BIOL, CALIF STATE UNIV, FRESNO, 68- *Mem:* Soc Study Evolution; Ecol Soc Am. *Res:* Gene ecology of plant populations and the impact of man on natural ecosystems. *Mailing Add:* Dept of Biol Calif State Univ Fresno CA 93740

LATIMER, PAUL HENRY, b New Orleans, La, Nov 25, 25; m 52; c 3. BIOPHYSICS. *Educ:* Univ Ill, MS, 50, PhD(biophys), 56. *Prof Exp:* Instr physics, Col William & Mary, 50-51; asst bot, Univ Ill, 53-56; res fel plant biol, Carnegie Inst Technol, 56-57; asst prof physics, Vanderbilt Univ, 57-62; assoc prof, 62-71, PROF PHYSICS, AUBURN UNIV, 71- *Concurrent Pos:* Investr, Howard Hughes Med Inst, 57-62; consult, Southern Res Inst, Birmingham, 76; contractor, US Army, 77. *Mem:* Biophys Soc; Am Phys Soc; Optical Soc Am. *Res:* Light scattering; biological optics; fluorescence; photosynthesis. *Mailing Add:* Dept of Physics Auburn Univ Auburn AL 36849

LATIMER, STEVE B, biochemistry, organic chemistry, see previous edition

LATORELLA, A HENRY, b Winthrop, Mass, Mar 12, 40; m 64; c 2. GENETICS, ALGOLOGY. *Educ:* Boston Col, BS, 61, MS, 64; Univ Maine, Orono, PhD(zool, genetics), 71. *Prof Exp:* Asst prof biol, Salem State Col, 66-68; ASSOC PROF BIOL, STATE UNIV NY COL GENESEO, 70- *Mem:* Am Genetic Asn; Phycol Soc Am; AAAS; Genetics Soc Am. *Res:* Algal genetics and physiology; regulation of DNA replication and genetics and biochemistry of salinity adaptation by phytoflagellates. *Mailing Add:* Dept of Biol State Univ NY Col Geneseo NY 14454

LATORRE, DONALD RUTLEDGE, b Charleston, SC, May 4, 38; m 60; c 2. MATHEMATICS. *Educ:* Wofford Col, BS, 60; Univ Tenn, MA, 62, PhD(math), 64. *Prof Exp:* Asst prof math, Univ Tenn, 67; from asst prof to assoc prof, 67-76, PROF MATH, CLEMSON UNIV, 76- *Mem:* Am Math Soc; Math Asn Am. *Res:* Abstract algebra, especially semigroups. *Mailing Add:* Dept of Math Sci Clemson Univ Clemson SC 29631

LATORRE, V(ICTOR) R(OBERT), b Brooklyn, NY, Nov 17, 31; m 57; c 2. ELECTRICAL ENGINEERING. *Educ:* Univ Ariz, BSEE, 56, MS, 57, PhD(elec eng), 60. *Prof Exp:* From instr to asst prof elec eng, Univ Ariz, 57-61; res specialist commun systs, Boeing Co, Wash, 61-64; asst prof elec eng, Univ Calif, Davis, 64-67; electronics engr, Lawrence Livermore Lab, 67-72, ASSOC DIV HEAD, ELECTRONIC ENG DEPT, LAWRENCE LIVERMORE LAB, UNIV CALIF, LIVERMORE, 72- *Concurrent Pos:* Sr res engr, Frederick Res Corp, Ariz, 60-61; lectr, Seattle Univ, 62. *Mem:* Sr mem Inst Elec & Electronics Engrs; Am Soc Eng Educ; Sigma Xi; NY Acad Sci. *Res:* Biotelemetry systems; meteoric and tropospheric scatter propagation; design and statistical analysis of secure and jam-resistant communication systems; transportation systems research. *Mailing Add:* Lawrence Livermore Lab Univ of Calif Box 808 Livermore CA 94550

LATOUR, PIERRE RICHARD, b Buffalo, NY, Apr 15, 40; m 62; c 2. CHEMICAL ENGINEERING, AUTOMATIC CONTROL. *Educ:* Va Polytech Inst, BSChE, 62; Purdue Univ, MS, 64, PhD(chem eng), 66. *Prof Exp:* Coop student, E I du Pont de Nemours & Co, NC, 58-61; res engr, math group, Houston Res Lab, Shell Oil Co, Tex, 66, comput control group, 66-67; mathematician, Theory & Anal Off, Manned Spacecraft Ctr, NASA, Houston, 67, tech asst to chief, Simulation Br, 67-68; br Shell Oil Co, NY, chief & sr engr, head off mfg, Technol Dept, 69; mgr process control eng,

Davis Comput Systs, Inc, NY & Tex, 70 & Biles & Assocs, Inc, 71-77; CONSULT ENGR & V PRES, SETPOINT, INC, 77- *Concurrent Pos:* Lectr, Purdue Univ, 66, Houston Res Lab, Shell Oil Co, 66, 67, Univ Houston, 68, Lehigh Univ, 69 & Univ Calif, Santa Barbara, 80, 81. *Mem:* Am Chem Soc; Am Inst Chem Engrs; Instrument Soc Am. *Res:* Automatic process control; applied mathematics; digital computation; crude oil distillation; computer control of petroleum refining; cracking; simulation; process dynamics; plant economics; optimization; process engineering; computer control justification. *Mailing Add:* 1503 Briarpark Dr Houston TX 77042

LATOUR, ROGER, b Gravelbourg, Sask, Mar 20, 30; m 58; c 2. PHYSIOLOGY. *Educ:* Univ Montreal, BPharm, 54; Univ Paris, DPharm, 57. *Prof Exp:* Asst prof physiol, Fac Med, Univ Montreal, 57-67; clin coordr, Med Div, 67-70, DIR SCI AFFAIRS, SYNTEX LTD, 70- *Mem:* NY Acad Sci; Pharmacol Soc Can; Can Asn Res Toxicol; Int Pharmaceut Fedn. *Res:* Neurophysiology; clinical research in contraceptive field and with anti-inflammatory agents. *Mailing Add:* Syntex Ltd 8255 Mountain Sights Ave Montreal PQ H4P 2B5 Can

LATOURETTE, HAROLD KENNETH, b Seattle, Wash, Apr 10, 24; m 44; c 4. ORGANIC CHEMISTRY. *Educ:* Whitman Col, AB, 47; Univ Wash, PhD(chem), 51. *Prof Exp:* Res assoc, Univ Wash, 48-51; res chemist, Westvaco Chem Div, FMC Corp, WVa, 51-54, dir pioneering res, Westvaco Chlor-Alkali Div, 54-56, supvr org res, Cent Res Labs, NJ, 56-57, mgr org res & develop, Becco Chem Div, NY, 57-58, mgr org chem res, Inorg Chem Div, 58-62, Europ tech dir, Chem Div & vpres, FMC Chem, SA, Switz, 62-65, mgr planning & eval, Cent Res Dept, 65-72, mgr eval, Chem Group, 72-76, ENVIRON MGR TOXIC SUBSTANCES, FMC CORP, 77- *Mem:* AAAS; Sigma Xi; Am Chem Soc. *Res:* Organic reaction mechanisms; aromatic substitution; peroxides; epoxides; isocyanates; phosphorus and sulfur organics; halogenation; industrial processes. *Mailing Add:* FMC Corp 2000 Market St Philadelphia PA 19103

LATOURETTE, HOWARD BENNETT, b Detroit, Mich, Aug 26, 18; m 42; c 4. RADIOLOGY. *Educ:* Oberlin Col, AB, 40; Univ Mich, MD, 43. *Prof Exp:* From instr to assoc prof radiol, Univ Mich, 49-59; prof radiol, Col Med, Univ Iowa, 59-80, head radiation ther, 78-80. *Concurrent Pos:* Mem staff radiation ther sect, Univ Hosps, Univ Iowa. *Mem:* AAAS; Radiol Soc NAm. *Res:* Clinical use of radiation in treatment of cancer and resulting survival studies; tumor registry organization and function alteration of radiosensitivity of tumors. *Mailing Add:* 815 W Park Rd Iowa City IA 52240

LA TOURRETTE, JAMES THOMAS, b Miami, Ariz, Dec 26, 31; m 55; c 4. PHYSICS. *Educ:* Calif Inst Technol, BS, 53; Harvard Univ, MA, 54, PhD(physics), 58. *Prof Exp:* Res fel physics, Harvard Univ, 57-58, lectr, 58-59; NSF fel, Univ Bonn, 59-60; physicist, Gen Elec Res Lab, 60-62; sr supvry scientist, TRG, Inc Div, Control Data Corp, 62-66, sect head gas laser, 66-67; PROF ELECTROPHYS, POLYTECH INST NEW YORK, 67- *Mem:* AAAS; Am Phys Soc; Inst Elec & Electronics Engrs. *Res:* Gas laser research and applications; saturated resonance spectroscopy and laser frequency stabilization. *Mailing Add:* Polytech Inst New York Route 110 Farmingdale NY 11735

LATSCHAR, CARL ERNEST, b Newton, Kans, May 24, 19; m 41; c 5. PHYSICAL CHEMISTRY. *Educ:* Kans State Univ, BS, 41, MS, 47; Univ Wis, PhD(phys chem), 50. *Prof Exp:* Res chemist, 50-62, SR RES CHEMIST, E I DU PONT DE NEMOURS & CO, INC, 62- *Mem:* Am Chem Soc. *Res:* Textile fiber process and product development. *Mailing Add:* 2905 Ginger Rd Kinston NC 28501

LATSHAW, DAVID RODNEY, b Allentown, Pa, Nov 4, 39; m 71; c 2. ANALYTICAL CHEMISTRY, TECHNICAL MANAGEMENT. *Educ:* Muhlenberg Col, BS, 61; Lehigh Univ, MS, 63, PhD(chem), 66. *Prof Exp:* Res asst, Lehigh Univ, 63-66; res chemist, 66-69, group leader, 69-80, MGR, ANAL SERV, ALLENTOWN LABS, AIR PROD & CHEM INC, 80- *Mem:* Am Chem Soc; Sigma Xi. *Res:* Gas chromatography; infrared spectroscopy; atomic absorption. *Mailing Add:* 944 Belford Rd Allentown PA 18103

LATTA, BRUCE MCKEE, b Oil City, Pa, Dec 31, 40; m 68; c 1. PHYSICAL ORGANIC CHEMISTRY. *Educ:* Muskingum Col, BS, 62; Univ Calif, Irvine, PhD(phys chem), 67. *Prof Exp:* Res chemist, Film Dept, E I du Pont de Nemours & Co, Inc, 67-70; res assoc textile finishing, Garfield, NJ, 70-74, mgr explor res, 74-77, mgr, Indust Prod Dept, 77-81, DIR, INDUST PROD DEPT, J P STEVENS & CO, INC, GREENVILLE, SC, 81- *Mem:* AAAS; Am Chem Soc; Sigma Xi; Am Inst Chemists. *Res:* Molecular structure-property relationships; morphological modifications of polymer films and fibers and effects on properties; chemical modification of textile fiber surfaces; textile finishing and dyeing. *Mailing Add:* 102 Shady Creek Ct Greer SC 29651

LATTA, GORDON, b Vancouver, BC, Mar 8, 23; m 45; c 3. MATHEMATICS. *Educ:* Calif Inst Technol, PhD(math), 51. *Prof Exp:* Lectr math, Univ BC, 47-48; asst, Calif Inst Technol, 48-51; Fine instr math & hydrodyn, Princeton Univ, 51-52; asst prof, Univ BC, 52-53; from asst prof to prof math, Stanford Univ, 53-67; prof math, Univ Va, 67-81; PROF MATH, NAVAL POSTGRAD SCH, 81- *Res:* Singular perturbation problems for differential equations; linear integral equations and Wiener-Hopf techniques. *Mailing Add:* 125 Surf Way Apt 427 Monterey CA 93940

LATTA, HARRISON, b Los Angeles, Calif, Apr 5, 18; m 41; c 4. PATHOLOGY, BIOPHYSICS. *Educ:* Univ Calif, Los Angeles, AB, 40; Johns Hopkins Univ, MD, 43. *Prof Exp:* Intern, Church Home & Hosp, Md, 44; from asst resident to resident path, Johns Hopkins Hosp, 44-46, instr, Johns Hopkins Univ, 45-46; res assoc biol, Mass Inst Technol, 49-51; asst prof path, Sch Med, Case Western Reserve Univ, 51-54; assoc prof, 54-60, PROF PATH, SCH MED, UNIV CALIF, LOS ANGELES, 60- *Concurrent Pos:* Res fel, Children's Hosp, Boston & Harvard Med Sch, 48-49. *Mem:* AAAS; Electron Micros Soc Am; Am Soc Cell Biol; Am Soc Exp Path; Am Asn Path

& Bact. *Res:* Foreign protein behavior and hypersensitivity; mechanisms of hemolysis and of cytologic injury; tissue culture and electron microscopy; ultrastructure and diseases of the kidney. *Mailing Add:* Dept of Path Ctr for Health Sci Univ of Calif Sch of Med Los Angeles CA 90024

LATTA, JOHN NEAL, b Ottumwa, Iowa, Apr 11, 44; m 66; c 2. OPTICS, ELECTRICAL ENGINEERING. *Educ:* Brigham Young Univ, BES, 66; Univ Kans, MS, 69, PhD(elec eng), 71. *Prof Exp:* Mem tech staff holography, RCA Labs, NJ, 67; res asst optics, Ctr Res Eng Sci, Univ Kans, 67-68; mem tech staff holography, Bell Tel Labs, NJ, 69; res engr, Radar & Optics Lab, Univ Mich, Ann Arbor, 69-73; sr res engr, Environ Res Inst Mich, 73-77; SR STAFF SCIENTIST, SCI APPLNS, INC, 77- *Mem:* Inst Elec & Electronics Engrs; Optical Soc Am; Brit Comput Soc; Soc Info Display; Sigma Xi. *Res:* Digital image processing; visual displays; system engineering; digital system architecture; software engineering; holography; optical design. *Mailing Add:* PO Box 1297 Arlington VA 22210

LATTA, WILLIAM CARL, b Niagara Falls, NY, May 18, 25; m 50; c 5. FISH BIOLOGY. *Educ:* Cornell Univ, BS, 50; Univ Okla, MS, 52; Univ Mich, PhD(fishery biol), 57. *Prof Exp:* Aquatic biologist, State Conserv Dept, NY, 50; in-chg, Inst Fisheries Res, 66-76, FISHERY BIOLOGIST, INST FISHERIES RES, STATE DEPT NATURAL RESOURCES, MICH, 55-, CHIEF RES SECT, FISHERIES DIV, 76- *Concurrent Pos:* Adj prof fisheries & wildlife, Sch Natural Resources, Univ Mich, Ann Arbor, 73- *Mem:* Am Fisheries Soc; Am Soc Ichthyol & Herpet; Wildlife Soc; Ecol Soc Am; Am Inst Fishery Res Biologists. *Res:* Fish population dynamics; management of freshwater fisheries. *Mailing Add:* Inst for Fisheries Res Univ Mus Annex Ann Arbor MI 48109

LATTER, ALBERT L, b Kokomo, Ind, Oct 17, 20; m 49; c 2. THEORETICAL PHYSICS. *Educ:* Univ Calif, Los Angeles, BA, 41, PhD(physics), 51. *Prof Exp:* Staff physicist radiation lab, Univ Calif, 41-46; staff physicist, Rand Corp, 52-60, head physics dept, 60-71; PRES, R&D ASSOCS, 71- *Concurrent Pos:* Mem Air Force Sci Adv Bd, 56-72, chmn nuclear panel, 63-67; mem US sci deleg to test ban negotiations, Geneva, 59; mem adv group, Ballistic Systs Div, 61-67; mem sci adv group on effects, Defense Nuclear Agency, 64-; mem adv group, Space & Missile Systs Orgn, 66-; mem Defense Sci Bd, 67-70, chmn penetration panel, 66-68, mem vulnerability task force, 66-, chmn strategic task force, 69-72, mem net assessment task force, 71-72; mem sci adv group, Joint Strategic Target Planning Staff, 68-72. *Res:* Nuclear physics; quantum mechanics; nuclear weapons design and effects; strategic weapons systems. *Mailing Add:* R&D Assocs PO Box 9695 Marina del Rey CA 90291

LATTER, RICHARD, b Chicago, Ill, Feb 20, 23; m 62; c 4. THEORETICAL PHYSICS. *Educ:* Calif Inst Technol, BS, 42, PhD(theoret physics), 49. *Prof Exp:* Physicist, Rand Corp, 49-56, chief physics div, 56-60, mem res coun, 60-71; VPRES, R&D ASSOCS, 71- *Concurrent Pos:* Lectr, Calif Inst Technol, 55-57; adv, AEC, 58-71 & Dept Defense, 58- *Honors & Awards:* E O Lawrence Award. *Mem:* Am Phys Soc. *Res:* Solid state, atomic, and nuclear physics; hydrodynamics. *Mailing Add:* 1401 Wilson Blvd Suite 500 Arlington VA 22209

LATTERELL, FRANCES MEEHAN, b Kansas City, Mo, Dec 21, 20; m 51. PLANT PATHOLOGY. *Educ:* Univ Kansas City, BA, 42; Iowa State Col, MS, 47, PhD, 50. *Prof Exp:* Seed analyst, Iowa State Univ, 42-44; res assoc cereal path, State Agr Exp Sta, Iowa, 45-49; res plant pathologist, US Dept Army, 49-71; RES PLANT PATHOLOGIST, PLANT DIS RES, USDA-AGR RES SERV, FREDERICK, MD, 71- *Concurrent Pos:* Consult, Cent Am small farmers prog, 79-80; team leader, US-Mex coop proj, dis corn & beans, 80. *Honors & Awards:* Ruth Allen Award, Amer Phytopath Soc, 73. *Mem:* Am Phytopath Soc; Am Inst Biol Sci; Mycol Soc Am. *Res:* Cereal crop pathology; rice blast; Helminthosporium diseases; fungal diseases of corn. *Mailing Add:* Plant Dis Res USDA Box 1209 Frederick MD 21701

LATTERELL, JOSEPH J, b St Cloud, Minn, Nov 2, 32; m 64; c 4. ANALYTICAL CHEMISTRY. *Educ:* St John's Univ, Minn, BA, 59; Purdue Univ, MS, 62; Univ Colo, PhD(anal chem), 64. *Prof Exp:* Instr anal chem, Univ Wis, 64; asst prof, John Carroll Univ, 64-67; from asst prof to assoc prof, 67-78, PROF ANAL CHEM, UNIV MINN, MORRIS, 78- *Mem:* Am Chem Soc. *Res:* Separation of amines by ligand exchange; chemical analyses of the bottom deposits of Minnesota lakes; removal of dissolved phosphate from lake water by bottom deposits; land application of sewage wastewater and sewage sludge. *Mailing Add:* Dept of Chem Univ of Minn Morris MN 56267

LATTERELL, RICHARD L, b Paynesville, Minn, Mar 14, 28; m 51. GENETICS. *Educ:* Univ Minn, Duluth, BA, 50; Pa State Univ, MS, 55; Cornell Univ, PhD(genetics), 58. *Prof Exp:* Nat Cancer Inst fel genetics, Brookhaven Nat Lab, 58-60; geneticist, Div Radiation & Organisms, Smithsonian Inst, 60-63; geneticist, Union Carbide Res Inst, 63-68; ASSOC PROF BIOL SHEPHERD COL, 68- *Concurrent Pos:* Vis assoc prof agron, Colo State Univ, 79-80. *Mem:* Genetics Soc Am; Bot Soc Am; Sigma Xi; Am Inst Biol Sci. *Res:* Radiation genetics of maize; space biology; stress tolerance of higher plants; plant cytogenetics; ecology; evolution. *Mailing Add:* Dept of Biol Shepherd Col Shepherdstown WV 25443

LATTES, RAFFAELE, b Italy, May 22, 10; nat US; m 36; c 2. MEDICINE. *Educ:* Univ Turin, MD, 33; Columbia Univ, MedSciD, 46. *Prof Exp:* Asst gen surg, Univ Turin, 34-38; instr path, Woman's Med Col Pa, 41-43; instr surg & surg path, 43-46, asst prof path, Postgrad Hosp, 46-48, asst prof, 48-51, prof surg path, 51-78, EMER PROF SURG PATH, COL PHYSICIANS & SURGEONS, COLUMBIA UNIV, 78-; SR CONSULT SURG PATH, NY PRESBY HOSP, 78- *Concurrent Pos:* Consult, US First Army, Roswell Park Mem Inst, Knickerbocker Hosp, NY, Roosevelt Hosp, St Lukes Hosp, Hosp Joint Dis & Vet Admin Hosp. *Mem:* Harvey Soc; Am Asn Path & Bact; Am Asn Cancer Res; Col Am Path; Asn Am Med Cols. *Res:* Surgical pathology. *Mailing Add:* Col of Physicians & Surgeons Columbia Univ New York NY 10032

LATTIMER, JAMES MICHAEL, b Marion, Ind, Apr 12, 50. ASTROPHYSICS, COSMOCHEMISTRY. *Educ:* Univ Notre Dame, BS, 72; Univ Tex, Austin, PhD(astron), 76. *Prof Exp:* Res assoc, Univ Chicago, 76; res assoc astron, Univ Ill, Urbana-Champaign, 76-79; ASST PROF, STATE UNIV NY, STONY BROOK, 79- *Concurrent Pos:* Alfred P Sloan res fel, 82-84. *Mem:* Am Astron Soc; Int Astron Union. *Res:* Supernovae; neutron stars; equation of state at high densities and temperatures; meteoritics; formation of the solar system; grain formation in novae and supernovae; nuclear physics. *Mailing Add:* Dept Earth & Space Sci State Univ NY Stony Brook NY 11794

LATTIMER, ROBERT PHILLIPS, b Kansas City, Mo, Feb 2, 45. ANALYTICAL CHEMISTRY, PHYSICAL CHEMISTRY. *Educ:* Univ Mo-Columbia, BS, 67; Univ Kans, PhD(chem), 71. *Prof Exp:* Fel chem, Univ Mich, Ann Arbor, 71-74; SR RES CHEMIST ANAL CHEM, B F GOODRICH CO, 74- *Concurrent Pos:* Lectr chem, John Carroll Univ, 78- *Mem:* Am Chem Soc; Am Soc Mass Spectrometry. *Res:* Field desorption mass spectroscopy; trace environmental analysis; thermal degradation of polymers. *Mailing Add:* B F Goodrich Res & Develop Ctr 9921 Brecksville Rd Brecksville OH 44141

LATTIN, DANNY LEE, b Smith Center, Kans, Jan 9, 42; m 61; c 2. MEDICINAL CHEMISTRY. *Educ:* Univ Kans, BS, 65; Univ Minn, Minneapolis, PhD(med chem), 70. *Prof Exp:* Asst prof med chem, 70-75, assoc prof, 75-80, PROF MED CHEM, COL PHARM, UNIV ARK, MED SCI CAMPUS, LITTLE ROCK, 80- *Mem:* Am Chem Soc; Am Asn Cols Pharm. *Res:* Synthesis of new organic medicinal agents; study of stereochemical properties of drug receptors; synthesis of novel opiate antagonists. *Mailing Add:* Dept of Med Chem Col of Pharm Univ Ark Med Sci Campus Little Rock AR 72205

LATTIN, JOHN D, b Chicago, Ill, July 27, 27; m 53; c 3. ENTOMOLOGY. *Educ:* Iowa State Univ, BS, 50; Univ Kans, MA, 51; Univ Calif, Berkeley, PhD(entom), 64. *Prof Exp:* Aquatic entomologist, Dept Limnol, Acad Natural Hist, Philadelphia, 51; jr vector control specialist, Bur Vector Control, Calif Dept Pub Health, 54-55; asst entomologist, Agr Exp Sta, 55-61, from instr to assoc prof, 55-68, asst dean sci, 67-73, PROF ENTOM, ORE STATE UNIV, 68- *Concurrent Pos:* Cur, Syst Entom Lab, Ore State, 61-66 & 74-; NSF fac fel, Univ Wageningen, 65-66; consult, USDA, 81-82. *Honors & Awards:* Loyd Carter Award, Ore State Univ, 61. *Mem:* Entom Soc Am; Soc Syst Zool. *Res:* Systematics of the Pentatomoidea, Leptopododoidea and Miridae; origin, distribution and phylogeny of the Heteroptera; evolution and zoogeography of the insecta; aquatic entomology; scientific education; education of talented students; introduced insects; applied systematic entomology. *Mailing Add:* Dept of Entom Ore State Univ Corvallis OR 97331

LATTMAN, EATON EDWARD, b Chicago, Ill, May 15, 40; m 66. MOLECULAR BIOPHYSICS. *Educ:* Harvard Col, BA, 62; Johns Hopkins Univ, 69. *Prof Exp:* NIH fel biophysics, Johns Hopkins Univ, 69-70, res scientist, 70-73; fel, Max Planck Inst Biochem, 74; NIH fel biophys, Brandeis Univ, 74-76; ASST PROF BIOPHYS, SCH MED, JOHNS HOPKINS UNIV, 76- *Mem:* Am Phys Soc; Am Crystallog Asn. *Res:* Determination of the three-dimensional structure of biological macromolecules by x-ray diffraction and|or electron microscopy; globins, muscle proteins and viruses. *Mailing Add:* Dept of Biophys Johns Hopkins Univ Med Sch Baltimore MD 21205

LATTMAN, LAURENCE HAROLD, b New York, NY, Nov 30, 23; m 46; c 2. GEOLOGY. *Educ:* City Col New York, BChE, 48; Univ Cincinnati, MS, 51, PhD(geol), 53. *Prof Exp:* Instr geol, Univ Cincinnati, 51 & Univ Mich, 52-53; photogeologist, Gulf Oil Corp, 53-56, asst head photogeol sect, 56-57; from asst prof to prof geomorphol, Pa State Univ, 57-70; prof geol & head dept, Univ Cincinnati, 70-75; DEAN COL MINES & MINERAL INDUST & COL ENG, UNIV UTAH, 75- *Concurrent Pos:* Mem, Nat Res Coun, 59-62. *Honors & Awards:* Fulbright lectr, Moscow State Univ, 75. *Mem:* Fel Geol Soc Am; Am Soc Photogram; Am Asn Petrol Geologists. *Res:* Remote sensing of environment; geomorphology; fracture analysis on aerial photographs. *Mailing Add:* 209 Mineral Sci Univ of Utah Salt Lake City UT 84112

LATTUADA, CHARLES P, b Danville, Ill, May 8, 33; m 55, 79; c 4. BACTERIOLOGY. *Educ:* Ind State Univ, BS, 56; Univ Wis, MS, 58, PhD(bact), 63. *Prof Exp:* Instr bact, Univ Wis, 58-59; consult microbiol, Res Prod Corp, Wis, 59-61; bacteriologist, Wis Alumni Res Found, 61-64; consult, A R Schmidt Co, Inc, 62-64, dir res, 64-69; dir germ-free res, ARS/Sprague-Dawley Div, 69-74, Mogul Corp, gen mgr microbiol lab, 68-74, vpres, Gibco Diag Div, 74-76; vpres, Harlan Industs, Inc, 77-81; DIR, BIO-TROL, INC, 77-; EXEC VPRES, GRANITE DIAGNOSTICS, INC, 81- *Concurrent Pos:* Vpres & mgr, A R S Serum Co, Inc, 62-68. *Mem:* Am Soc Microbiol; Am Asn Lab Animal Sci; Asn Microbiol Media Mfrs; Asn Gnotobiotics; NY Acad Sci. *Res:* Dairy and food industries; botulinum food poisoning; derivation of new strains of germfree animals and their maintenance and associated technology; intestinal flora of laboratory animals; process, development and management of microbiological culture media manufacture. *Mailing Add:* Granite Diag Inc PO Box 908 Burlington NC 27215

LATZ, ARJE, b Lithuania, July 1, 27; US citizen; m 60; c 1. PSYCHOPHARMACOLOGY. *Educ:* Univ Maine, BA, 58; Boston Univ, MA, 60, PhD(psychol), 63. *Prof Exp:* Res assoc, 63-67, asst prof, 67-71, ASSOC PROF PSYCHOPHARMACOL, SCH MED, BOSTON UNIV, 71- *Concurrent Pos:* NIH fel, 63-65; Boston Med Found fel, 65-67; consult ed, Psychopharmacologia, 69- *Res:* Effects of amphetamine on behavior differentially maintained by excitatory or inhibitory processes; the effects of morphine and morphine antagonists on the cortical EEG of free moving rats. *Mailing Add:* Dept of Psychiat Boston Univ Sch of Med Boston MA 02118

LATZ, HOWARD W, b Rochester, NY, Jan 9, 33; m 53; c 3. ANALYTICAL CHEMISTRY. *Educ:* Rochester Inst Technol, BS, 59; Univ Fla, MS, 61, PhD(chem), 63. *Prof Exp:* Res specialist, Union Carbide Corp, 63-66; assoc prof, 66-74, PROF ANAL CHEM, OHIO UNIV, 74- *Mem:* Am Chem Soc. *Res:* Luminescence methods of analysis; electrophoresis of organic ions; analytical applications of dye lasers. *Mailing Add:* Dept of Chem Ohio Univ Athens OH 45701

LAU, DERICK HON-MAN, pharmacology, toxicology, see previous edition

LAU, FRANCIS YOU KING, b Honolulu, Hawaii, Jan 5, 24; m 48; c 4. MEDICINE. *Educ:* Loma Linda Univ, MD, 47. *Prof Exp:* From clin instr to clin asst prof med, Loma Linda Univ, 54-59; asst prof, Sch Med, Univ Calif, San Francisco, 59-60; assoc prof, 60-72, PROF MED, LOMA LINDA UNIV, 72-; CLIN PROF MED & RADIOL, SCH MED, UNIV SOUTHERN CALIF, 79- *Concurrent Pos:* Assoc prof med, Univ Southern Calif, 64-70; mem attend staff & chief, Adult Cardiovasc Catheterization Lab, Los Angeles County-Univ Southern Calif Med Ctr, 65-79, chief cardiol, 70-79; consult, Vet Admin & Glendale Hosps; fel coun clin cardiol, Am Heart Asn. *Mem:* Fel Am Col Cardiol; fel Am Col Physicians. *Res:* Cardiology; cardiac catheterization, arrhythmias and pacemakers; artificial heart-lung preparations. *Mailing Add:* 1720 Brooklyn Ave #1231 Los Angeles CA 90033

LAU, KENNETH W, b Lamoure, NDak, Nov 27, 41; m 63; c 1. CHEMISTRY. *Educ:* Univ NDak, BS, 63, PhD(chem), 69; Univ Sask, Regina, MSc, 68. *Prof Exp:* Chemist, Rock Island Arsenal Lab, US Army, 63-64; res chemist, 69-73, develop supvr, Film Dept, Richmond, Va, 73-76, area supt-tech, Plastic Prod & Resins Dept, 76-79, MKT MGR, FLUOROPOLYMERS DIV, E I DU PONT DE NEMOURS & CO, INC, 79- *Mem:* Am Chem Soc; Sigma Xi. *Res:* Ylid chemistry; new packaging films and packaging methods. *Mailing Add:* E I du Pont de Nemours & Co Inc 1007 Market St Wilmington DE 19898

LAU, KREISLER S Y, US citizen. ORGANIC CHEMISTRY. *Educ:* Univ Iowa, PhD(org chem), 76. *Prof Exp:* Res fel, Inst Org Chem, Univ Lausanne, Switz, 76-77; vis res scientist, Mat Lab, Wright-Patterson AFB, 77-78; TECH SUPVR RES & PROG MGR, TECHNOL SUPPORT DIV, HUGHES AIRCRAFT CO, 78- *Mem:* Am Chem Soc; Sigma Xi. *Res:* Organic synthesis; organometallic reagents in organic synthesis; thermally stable heteroaromatic polymers and oligomers; high performance fluoropolymers. *Mailing Add:* Technol Support Div Hughes Aircraft Co Culver City CA 90230

LAU, L(EUNG KU) STEPHEN, b Shanghai, China, Sept 9, 29; US citizen; m 59; c 3. HYDROLOGY, HYDRAULIC & SANITARY ENGINEERING. *Educ:* Univ Calif, Berkeley, BS, 53, MS, 55, PhD(hydraul & sanit eng), 59. *Prof Exp:* Res engr sea water intrusion, Univ Calif, Berkeley, 53-54 & ground water pollution, 55-56; from asst prof to assoc prof, 59-67, assoc dir water resources res ctr, 64-70, actg dir, 70, PROF CIVIL ENG, UNIV HAWAII, 67-, DIR WATER RESOURCES RES CTR, 71- *Concurrent Pos:* Ground water consult, Honolulu Bd Water Supply, 60-64; dir, US Pub Health Serv training grant, Univ Hawaii, 64-65; vis assoc prof, Univ Calif, Berkeley, 65-66; Fulbright vis prof, Univ Malaya, 73-74; adj res assoc, East-West Ctr, 80-81; consult, Univ Guam, 72 & 75, World Health Orgn, 74, AMAX, 78, World Bank, 78 & UN, 81. *Mem:* AAAS; Am Geophys Union; Am Soc Civil Engrs; Water Pollution Control Fedn. *Res:* Water reuse; water pollution assessment; hydrologic evaluation of water resources; flood computations; water resources research administration; water resources policies; hydrology and water resources of the Hawaiian Islands. *Mailing Add:* Water Resources Res Ctr Univ of Hawaii Honolulu HI 96822

LAU, NORMAN EUGENE, b Harvey, Ill, July 8, 30; m; c 1. ENVIRONMENTAL MANAGEMENT. *Educ:* Colo State Univ, BS, 53, MS, 55; Rutgers Univ, PhD(entom), 58. *Prof Exp:* Entomologist, NJ Dept Agr, 58-60, Ratner Pest Control, 61-63 & Hooker Chem Corp, 63-65; assoc prof entom, 65-70, PROF ENTOM, VA POLYTECH INST & STATE UNIV, 70-, EXTEN COORDR CHEM, DRUGS & PESTICIDES, COOP EXTEN SERV, 65- *Concurrent Pos:* Pvt consult, 65- *Mem:* Am Soc Agr Consults; Entom Soc Am; Sigma Xi. *Res:* Applied science and administration in fields of entomology, plant pathology and botany. *Mailing Add:* 17 Laurel Dr Blacksburg VA 24060

LAU, PHILIP T S, b Kuala Lumpur, Malaysia, Feb 13, 35; US citizen; m 59; c 3. ORGANIC CHEMISTRY. *Educ:* Alfred Univ, BS, 58; Syracuse Univ, PhD(org chem), 62. *Prof Exp:* Fel & res assoc chem, Univ Calif, Berkeley, 62-63; sr res chemist, 63-68, res assoc, 68-79, SR RES ASSOC, COLOR PHOTOG DIV, RES LABS, EASTMAN KODAK CO, 79- *Mem:* Am Chem Soc. *Res:* New synthetic methodologies to novel heterocyclic aliphatic and aromatic compounds; regioselective and regiospecific reactions photographic developers, couplers, stabilizers and dyes. *Mailing Add:* Color Photog Div Eastman Kodak Res Labs Rochester NY 14650

LAU, RICHARD LEWIS, b Kansas City, Mo, Sept 30, 41. APPLIED MATHEMATICS. *Educ:* Yale Univ, BA, 63, PhD(math), 67. *Prof Exp:* Fel math, Calif Inst Technol, 67-69; MATHEMATICIAN, OFF NAVAL RES, US DEPT NAVY, 69- *Mem:* Soc Indust & Appl Math. *Res:* Partial differential equations, numerical analysis and computer architecture. *Mailing Add:* Off of Naval Res Dept of Navy 1030 E Green St Pasadena CA 91106

LAU, ROLAND, b China, May 5, 43; US citizen; m 67; c 1. ORGANIC CHEMISTRY. *Educ:* Wayne State Univ, BA, 65; Purdue Univ, PhD(chem), 72. *Prof Exp:* Clin chemist, Henry Ford Hosp, 65-66; res chemist, Ash-Stevens, Inc, 65-66; fel, Syntex Res Div, Syntex Corp, 72-73; res investr org chem, E R Squibb, Inc, 73-77, sr res investr, 77-80; MGR PHARMACEUT CHEM, HARDWICKE CHEM CO, SUBSID ETHYL CORP, 80- *Mem:* Am Chem Soc. *Res:* Commercial developments of medicinal agents. *Mailing Add:* Hardwicke Chem Co Ethyl Corp Box 50A Elgin SC 29045

LAU, S S, b Chungking, China, July 31, 41; US citizen. ELECTRONICS ENGINEERING. *Educ:* Univ Calif, Berkeley, BS, 64, MS, 66, PhD, 69. *Prof Exp:* Mem staff, Bell Labs, 69-72; mem staff, Calif Inst Technol, 72-80; PROF MICROELECTRONICS, UNIV CALIF, SAN DIEGO, 80- *Mem:* Bohmische Phys Soc. *Res:* Metal semiconductor interactions; ion-beam processes; Rutherford backscattering spectrometry; electronic materials. *Mailing Add:* Dept Elec Eng & Comput Sci Univ Calif San Diego La Jolla CA 92093

LAU, YIU-WA AUGUST, b Aug 22, 48; US citizen. MATHEMATICS. *Educ:* Univ Houston, BS & MS, 68, PhD(math), 71. *Prof Exp:* Asst prof math, NTex State Univ, 71-77, assoc prof, 77-80; MEM STAFF, JOHNSON SPACE CTR, NASA, 80- *Mem:* Am Math Soc. *Res:* Topological semigroups; topology. *Mailing Add:* Johnson Space Ctr NASA Houston TX 77058

LAUB, RICHARD J, b San Francisco, Calif, Aug 4, 45. NON-ELECTROLYTE SOLUTIONS THEORIES. *Educ:* Regis Col, BS, 67; Univ Calif, Los Angeles, MS, 71; Univ Hawaii, PhD(chem), 74. *Prof Exp:* Res fel chem, UK Sci Res Coun, Univ Col Swansea, Wales, 74-78; ASST PROF CHEM, OHIO STATE UNIV, 78- *Mem:* Am Chem Soc; Sigma Xi; Royal Soc Chem. *Res:* Separations science, analytical and physicochemical applications of gas and liquid chromatography; physical chemistry; mass spectrometry. *Mailing Add:* Dept Chem Ohio State Univ 140 W 18th Ave Columbus OH 43210

LAUB, RICHARD STEVEN, b Brooklyn, NY, Nov, 15, 45; m 74; c 1. PALEONTOLOGY, SEDIMENTOLOGY. *Educ:* Queen's Col, NY, BA, 66; Cornell Univ, MS, 68; Univ Cincinnati, PhD(paleont), 76. *Prof Exp:* CUR GEOL, BUFFALO MUS SCI, 73- *Concurrent Pos:* Supvr, Morse Creek Fossil Salvage Proj, 76; adj fac, Empire State Col, 76-78; corresp, Fossile Cnidaria Newsletter, 76-; adj fac geol, State Univ NY Buffalo, 77-; mem, Distinguished Lectureship Comt, Buffalo Soc Natural Sci, 78- *Mem:* Paleont Soc; Paleont Asn; Am Asn Petrol Geologists; Sigma Xi; Paleont Res Inst. *Res:* Early Paleozoic corals, their systematics, morphology, ecology and distribution; axial torsion in rugose corals; systematics and biology of auloporid tabulate corals. *Mailing Add:* 185 Pleasant Ave Hamburg NY 14075

LAUBACH, GERALD DAVID, b Bethlehem, Pa, Jan 21, 26; m 53; c 3. ORGANIC CHEMISTRY. *Educ:* Univ Pa, AB, 47; Mass Inst Technol, PhD(chem), 50. *Prof Exp:* Res chemist, Chas Pfizer & Co, Inc, 50-54, res supvr, 54-59, mgr med prod sect, 59-61, dir med chem res, 61-63, group dir med prod res, 63-64, vpres med prod res & develop, 64-68, vpres & dir, 68-69, pres, Pfizer Pharmaceut, 69-71, exec vpres, 71-72, PRES, PFIZER INC, 72- *Mem:* AAAS; Am Chem Soc; NY Acad Sci. *Res:* Medicinal chemistry; steroids. *Mailing Add:* Pfizer Inc 235 E 42nd St New York NY 10017

LAUBER, JEAN KAUTZ, b Seattle, Wash, Aug 30, 26; m 56; c 3. ZOOLOGY, PHYSIOLOGY. *Educ:* Whitman Col, BA, 48; Washington Univ, MA, 51; Univ NMex, PhD(zool), 59. *Prof Exp:* Sr lab technician electron micros, Sch Med, Univ Wash, 51-53, res assoc, 53-56; instr zool, Univ Idaho, 58-60, asst prof, 60-62; asst prof, Wash State Univ, 62-65; from asst prof to assoc prof, 65-76, hon assoc prof ophthal, 75-76, PROF ZOOL, HON PROF OPHTHAL & ASSOC V PRES ACAD, UNIV ALTA, 76- *Mem:* AAAS; Am Soc Zool; Am Physiol Soc; Soc Exp Biol & Med; Electron Micros Soc Am. *Res:* Endocrine physiology; photobiology; ophthalmology; electron microscopy; embryology. *Mailing Add:* Dept of Zool Univ of Alta Edmonton AB T6G 2E9 Can

LAUBER, THORNTON STUART, b Cornwall, Ont, Jan 5, 24; US citizen; m 56; c 4. ELECTRIC POWER ENGINEERING. *Educ:* Cornell Univ, BSEE, 44; Ill Inst Technol, MSEE, 51; Univ Pa, PhD(elec eng), 64. *Prof Exp:* Engr, Commonwealth Serv, Inc, Mich, 46-50; develop engr, Large Power Transformer Dept, Gen Elec Co, 51-58, sr anal engr, Power Circuit Breaker Dept, 58-69; PROF ELEC POWER ENG, RENSSELAER POLYTECH INST, 69-, S B CRARY PROF ENG, 70- *Concurrent Pos:* Consult, Gen Elec Co & Hydro-Quebec; comt mem, Am Nat Standards Inst; mem, Int Conf Large High Voltage Elec Systs, 72. *Mem:* Sr mem Inst Elec & Electronics Engrs; Am Soc Mech Engrs; Sigma Xi; Am Asn Univ Professors. *Res:* Electric power engineering; traveling waves on multiphase transmission lines; power system transients; electromagnetic field theory. *Mailing Add:* Dept of Eng Rensselaer Polytech Inst Troy NY 12181

LAU-CAM, CESAR A, b Lima, Peru, Nov 24, 40; m 67; c 2. PHARMACOGNOSY, PHYTOCHEMISTRY. *Educ:* San Marcos Univ, Lima, BS, 63; Univ RI, MS, 66, PhD(pharmacog), 69. *Prof Exp:* Instr pharm bot, San Marcos Univ, Lima, 62-63; lab instr pharmacog, Univ RI, 67; asst prof phytochem, 69-73, assoc prof phytochem, 73-80, PROF PHARMACOG, DEPT PHARMACEUT SCI, COL PHARM & ALLIED HEALTH PROFESSIONS, ST JOHN'S UNIV, NY, 80- *Concurrent Pos:* Sci adv, US Food & Drug Admin, 79- *Mem:* AAAS; Am Soc Pharmacog; Am Pharmaceut Asn; Phytochem Soc NAm; NY Acad Sci. *Res:* Alkaloids; terpenes; phytosterols; phenolic compounds; chemotaxonomy; analytical methods applied to natural products; clinical chemistry; phytochemical screenings for pharmacologically active compounds; toxicology; pharmaceutical analysis. *Mailing Add:* Dept Pharmaceut Sci St John's Univ Col Pharm & Allied Health Prof Jamaica NY 11439

LAUCHLE, GERALD CLYDE, b Williamsport, Pa, Sept 20, 45; m 71; c 2. FLUIDS ENGINEERING, ACOUSTICS. *Educ:* Pa State Univ, BS, 68, MS, 70, PhD(eng acoust), 74. *Prof Exp:* From res asst to res assoc, 68-79, SR RES ASSOC, APPL RES LAB, PA STATE UNIV, 79- *Mem:* Acoust Soc Am. *Res:* Basic and applied research on the noise generated by fluid flow and general underwater fluid mechanics and acoustics. *Mailing Add:* Appl Res Lab PO Box 30 State College PA 16801

LAUCK, DAVID R, b Alton, Ill, June 6, 30; m 53; c 2. ENTOMOLOGY. *Educ:* Univ Ill, BS, 55, MS, 58, PhD(entom), 61. *Prof Exp:* Cur invert entom, Chicago Acad Sci, 59-61; from asst prof to assoc prof, 61-70, chmn div biol sci, 66-72, PROF ZOOL HUMBOLDT STATE UNIV, 70- *Mem:* Entom Soc Am; Entom Soc Can. *Res:* Aquatic and forest entomology. *Mailing Add:* Div of Biol Sci Humboldt State Univ Arcata CA 95521

LAUCK, FRANCIS W, b Madison, Wis, Oct 4, 18; m 40; c 4. MECHANICAL & CHEMICAL ENGINEERING. *Educ:* Univ Wis, BS, 40, MS, 52. *Prof Exp:* Engr, A O Smith Corp, Wis, 40-46, lab supvr electrodes, 46-49, lab supvr appliance, 50-53, plant engr, 53-54, proj engr, 54-59, res scientist, 59-62, res scientist govt contracts, 62-63; from asst prof to assoc prof thermodyn & eng anal, Univ Nebr, Lincoln, 64-74; CHIEF ENGR, R J G ENG, INC, 74- *Mem:* Am Soc Mech Engrs. *Res:* Energy conversion; engineering analysis; mobile structures. *Mailing Add:* R J G Eng Inc PO Box 6426 Lincoln NE 68506

LAUD, PURUSHOTTAM WAMAN, b Bombay, India, Nov 25, 48. MATHEMATICAL STATISTICS, APPLIED PROBABILITY. *Educ:* Bombay Univ, BSc, 69; Lamar Univ, MS, 71; Univ Mo-Columbia, MA, 73, PhD(statist), 77. *Prof Exp:* asst prof statist, 77-80, ASST PROF MATH, NORTHERN ILL UNIV, 80- *Mem:* Inst Math Statist. *Res:* Bayesian nonparametric inference; reliability theory; stochastic processes. *Mailing Add:* Dept of Math Sci Northern Ill Univ De Kalb IL 60115

LAUDE, HORTON MEYER, b Beaumont, Tex, Feb 25, 15; m 46; c 2. AGRONOMY, BOTANY. *Educ:* Kans State Univ, BS, 37; Univ Chicago, PhD(bot), 41. *Prof Exp:* Agent, USDA, Univ Chicago, 40-41; asst prof agron & asst agronomist, 46-52, assoc prof & assoc agronomist, 52-58, prof & agronomist, 58-81, EMER PROF AGRON, EXP STA, UNIV CALIF, DAVIS, 81- *Mem:* Fel Am Soc Agron; Am Soc Plant Physiol; Soc Range Mgt; Crop Sci Soc Am. *Res:* Physiology and ecology of dry range plants, irrigated forages and cereals; plant growth substances; seed production; resistance to environmental stresses of heat, cold and drought. *Mailing Add:* Dept of Agron & Range Sci Univ of Calif Davis CA 95616

LAUDEL, ARTHUR, JR, b Waterloo, Iowa, Sept 23, 22; m 51; c 3. ELECTRICAL ENGINEERING. *Educ:* Univ Kans, BS, 42. *Prof Exp:* Elec engr, Gen Elec Co, 42-44; owner, Laudel Home Bldg Co, 46-48; prof engr, J F Pritchard & Co, 48-55; head elec eng sect, Midwest Res Inst, 55-63; HEAD THIN FILM LAB, BENDIX CORP, 63- *Mem:* Inst Elec & Electronics Engrs; Vacuum Soc. *Res:* Instrumentation; electronic controls; nonlinear magnetic devices for power applications; variable-speed constant-frequency generators; ceramics and ceramics machining; microelectronics; thin films; ion beams. *Mailing Add:* 9630 High Dr Melrose MO 94108

LAUDENSLAGER, JAMES BISHOP, b Harrisburg, Pa, June 8, 45. CHEMICAL PHYSICS. *Educ:* Temple Univ, AB, 67; Univ Calif, Santa Barbara, PhD(phys chem), 71. *Prof Exp:* Res assoc space sci, 71-73, SR RES SCI CHEM PHYSICS, JET PROPULSION LAB, 73- *Mem:* Am Phys Soc. *Res:* Fundamental properties of charge transfer and metastable rare gas reactions in the gas phase for use in laser development and mass spectrometry. *Mailing Add:* Jet Propulsion Lab 4800 Oak Grove Dr Pasadena CA 91103

LAUDENSLAGER, MARK LEROY, b Charlotte, NC, May 13, 47; m 69; c 1. BEHAVIORAL IMMUNOLOGY, PHYSIOLOGICAL PSYCHOLOGY. *Educ:* Univ NC, AB, 69; Univ Calif, Santa Barbara, PhD(psychol), 75. *Prof Exp:* Teaching asst introductory psychol, Univ Calif, Santa Barbara, 70-71, res asst neuropsychol, 71-72, teaching asst physiol psychol, 73, lectr, 74; NIMH fel, Scripps Inst Oceanog, 75-77; asst res psychologist, Univ Calif, Santa Barbara, 77-80; LECTR, DENVER UNIV, 81- *Concurrent Pos:* NIMH fel, Health Sci Ctr, Univ Colo, 80. *Mem:* Am Ornith Union; Am Soc Mammalogists; AAAS; Am Physiol Soc; Soc Neurosci. *Res:* Hypothalamic and hormonal factors influencing autonomic and behavioral thermoregulatory responses in mammals, reptiles and birds; effects of stress and affective disorders on various aspects of immunocompetence. *Mailing Add:* Dept Psychol Denver Univ Denver CO 80208

LAUDERDALE, JAMES W, JR, b Washington, DC, Dec 21, 37; m 62; c 3. REPRODUCTIVE PHYSIOLOGY, ENDOCRINOLOGY. *Educ:* Auburn Univ, BS, 62; Univ Wis, MS, 64, PhD(reproductive physiol, endocrinol), 68. *Prof Exp:* SCIENTIST, UPJOHN CO, 67- *Mem:* Am Soc Animal Sci; Soc Study Reproduction. *Res:* Reproductive and endocrinological function of large and small animals. *Mailing Add:* Upjohn Co 7000 Portage Rd Kalamazoo MI 49001

LAUDERDALE, ROBERT A(MIS), JR, b Harriman, Tenn, July 27, 22; m 48; c 1. SANITARY ENGINEERING. *Educ:* Univ Tenn, BS, 44, MS, 48; Mass Inst Technol, PhD(sanit eng), 58. *Prof Exp:* Jr chem engr, Tenn Valley Authority, 44-45; assoc health physicist, Oak Ridge Nat Lab, 48-52; res assoc sanit eng, Mass Inst Technol, 52-58, asst prof, 57-58; PROF CIVIL ENG, UNIV KY, 58-, DIR WATER RESOURCES INST, 65- *Mem:* Am Chem Soc; Water Pollution Control Fedn. *Res:* Industrial and radioactive waste treatment. *Mailing Add:* Dept of Civil Eng Univ of Ky Lexington KY 40506

LAUDISE, ROBERT ALFRED, b Amsterdam, NY, Sept 2, 30; m 57; c 5. SOLID STATE CHEMISTRY. *Educ:* Union Univ, NY, BS, 52; Mass Inst Technol, PhD(inorg chem), 56. *Prof Exp:* Mem tech staff, 56-60, head, Crystal Chem Res Dept, 60-73, asst dir mat res, 73-76, dir mat res, 76-79, DIR PHYSICS & INORGCHEM RES, BELL LABS, 80- *Concurrent Pos:* Consult, President's Sci Adv Comt, 60-70; panel mem mat adv bd, Nat Acad Sci, 65-70; vis comt, Nat Bur Standards, 68-75, mat sci, Mass Inst Technol, 80-; ed, J Crystal Growth, 70- *Honors & Awards:* Sawyer Award, Conf Frequency Control, 74. *Mem:* Am Asn Crystal Growth (pres, 68-75); Int Orgn Crystal Growth (pres, 77-); fel Mineral Soc Am; Am Ceramic Soc; Am Chem Soc. *Res:* Materials research; crystal growth; hydrothermal chemistry; quartz; ferroelectrics; non-linear optical materials; magnetic materials. *Mailing Add:* 65 Lenape Lane Berkeley Heights NJ 07922

LAUDON, THOMAS S, b Sac City, Iowa, June 14, 32; m 56; c 5. SEDIMENTARY PETROLOGY, GRAVITY. *Educ:* Univ Wis, BSc, 55, MSc, 57, PhD(geol), 63. *Prof Exp:* Chmn dept geol, 69-72, PROF GEOL, UNIV WIS-OSHKOSH, 63- *Concurrent Pos:* NSF res grants, 62-67 & 70-71; consult geol & geophys, 79- *Mem:* Sigma Xi; Geol Soc Am; Am Asn Petrol Geologists; Am Geophys Union. *Res:* Geologic exploration of Antarctica; gravity, tectonics and sedimentation in modern and ancient mobile belts. *Mailing Add:* Dept of Geol Univ of Wis Oshkosh WI 54901

LAUENROTH, WILLIAM KARL, b Carthage, Mo, July 31, 45; m. PLANT ECOLOGY. *Educ:* Humboldt State Col, BS, 68; NDak State Univ, MS, 70; Colo State Univ, PhD(plant ecol), 73. *Prof Exp:* sr res ecologist, Nat Resource Ecol Lab, 75-81, ASSOC PROF, RANGE SCI DEPT, COLO STATE UNIV, 81- *Mem:* Ecol Soc Am; Soc Range Mgt; Bot Soc Am. *Res:* Primary production and water relations of native plant communities, particularly temperate grasslands; ecosystem analysis of natural and agricultural ecosystems including situational modelling. *Mailing Add:* Nat Resource Ecol Lab Colo State Univ Ft Collins CO 80521

LAUER, B(YRON) E(LMER), b Glencoe, Okla, Apr 14, 07; m 31; c 1. SCIENCE EDUCATION, CHEMICAL ENGINEERING. *Educ:* Ore State Univ, BS, 47; Univ Minn, MS, 29, PhD(chem eng), 31. *Prof Exp:* Asst instr, Univ Minn, 27-31; res chem engr, Northern Paper Mills, 31-34 & Crown-Zellerbach Corp, 34-35; from asst prof to prof chem eng, NC State Univ, 35-42; prof, 46-75, head dept, 47-61, EMER PROF CHEM ENG, UNIV COLO, BOULDER, 75- *Concurrent Pos:* Consult, Nat Bur Standards, 61-64, PEC Corp, 64-65 & Interam Transp, 68-; ed televized higher educ, Assoc Western Univs, Inc, 75- *Mem:* Am Chem Soc; Am Soc Eng Educ; Tech Asn Pulp & Paper Indust; Am Inst Chem Engrs. *Res:* Pulp and paper; testing methods; heat transfer; oil shale retorting; information storage and retrieval. *Mailing Add:* 546 14th St Boulder CO 80302

LAUER, DAVID ALLAN, b Creston, Iowa, Sept 25, 44; m 64; c 2. SOIL SCIENCE, AGRONOMY. *Educ:* Iowa State Univ, BS, 66; Colo State Univ, MS, 69, PhD(soil sci), 71. *Prof Exp:* Res assoc agron, Cornell Univ, 71-75; asst prof, Univ Ga, 75-76; RES SOIL SCIENTIST, AGR RES, USDA, 76- *Mem:* Am Soc Agron; Crop Sci Soc; Soil Sci Soc; AAAS. *Res:* Application of soil chemical and plant physiological principles to management of crop production systems with emphasis on plant nutrition. *Mailing Add:* Irrigated Agr Res & Exten Ctr PO Box 30 Prosser WA 99350

LAUER, DOLOR JOHN, b St Paul, Minn, July 8, 12; m 40; c 7. INDUSTRIAL MEDICINE, TOXICOLOGY. *Educ:* Univ Minn, BS & MB, 37, MD, 38; Univ Pittsburgh, IMD, 50; Am Bd Prev Med, dipl, 51. *Prof Exp:* Kemper fel, Univ Pittsburgh, 46-47; from instr to asst prof indust med, Col Med, Univ Cincinnati, 48-51; asst prof occup med, Kettering Lab, 48-51; asst prof indust med, Sch Med, Univ Pittsburgh, 51-55, clin assoc prof, 55-60; med dir, 60-77, CONSULT, INT TEL & TEL CORP, 78- *Concurrent Pos:* Med dir, Jones & Laughlin Steel Corp, 51-60; clin assoc prof occup med, Postgrad Med Sch, NY Univ, 60-; trustee, Nat Health Coun; mem Permanent Comn & Int Asn Occup Health; del, Int Conf Health & Health Educ; mem, Am Bd Prev Med, 71-77. *Honors & Awards:* Kehoe Award, Am Acad Occup Med, 77. *Mem:* AMA; Am Acad Occup Med; fel Am Pub Health Asn; Am Col Prev Med (pres, 63-64). *Res:* Toxicology of selenium related to occupational uses; observations on epidemiology and various drugs in the treatment of lead intoxication. *Mailing Add:* Med Dept Int Tel & Tel Corp 320 Park Ave New York NY 10022

LAUER, EUGENE JOHN, b Red Bluff, Calif, Apr 11, 20; m 48; c 5. PLASMA PHYSICS. *Educ:* Univ Calif, BS, 42, PhD(physics), 51. *Prof Exp:* Asst physics, 46-51, PHYSICIST, LAWRENCE LIVERMORE LAB, UNIV CALIF, 51- *Mem:* Am Phys Soc. *Res:* Discharge through gases; particle accelerator design; nuclear and plasma physics; controlled thermonuclear energy; relativistic beams. *Mailing Add:* 2221 Martin Ave Pleasanton CA 94566

LAUER, FLORIAN ISIDORE, b Richmond, Minn, Sept 13, 28; m 55; c 3. HORTICULTURE. *Educ:* Univ Minn, BS, 51, PhD, 57. *Prof Exp:* From asst prof to assoc prof, 59-66, PROF POTATO BREEDING, UNIV MINN, ST PAUL, 66- *Mem:* Am Soc Hort Sci; Potato Asn Am. *Res:* Potato breeding and genetics. *Mailing Add:* Dept of Hort Inst of Agr Univ of Minn St Paul MN 55101

LAUER, G NICHOLAS, b Mt Pleasant, Mich, Sept 14, 44; m 71; c 2. STATISTICS, COMPUTER SCIENCE. *Educ:* Cent Mich Univ, BS, 67; Iowa State Univ, MS, 69, PhD(statist), 71. *Prof Exp:* Sr statistician, Owens-Ill Inc, 71-80; MGR, MATH DEPT, DURKEE FOODS DIV, SCM CORP, 80- *Mem:* Am Statist Asn; Sigma Xi. *Res:* Regression; quality control. *Mailing Add:* Durkee Foods Div SCM Corp 16651 Sprague Rd Strongsville OH 44136

LAUER, GEORGE, b Vienna, Austria, Feb 18, 36; US citizen; wid; c 2. PHYSICAL CHEMISTRY. *Educ:* Univ Calif, Los Angeles, BS, 61; Calif Inst Technol, PhD(chem), 67. *Prof Exp:* Staff assoc, Sci Ctr, NAm Rockwell Corp, 62-66, mem tech staff, 66-71, group leader, Measurement Sci, 71-72, dir air qual monitoring res, 72-75, mgr environ res & technol, 76-78, DIR ENVIRON MONITORING & SERV CTR, ROCKWELL INT SCI CTR, 78- *Mem:* AAAS; Am Chem Soc; Air Pollution Control Asn Am; Am Meteorol Soc. *Res:* Development of chronocoulometric techniques in electrochemistry; study of electroactive adsorbed species at electrodes; development of computer controlled instrumentation; instrumental methods in air pollution monitoring; air quality simulation modeling; environmental assessment. *Mailing Add:* 23119 Gainford Woodland Hills CA 91364

LAUER, GERALD J, b Montgomery City, Mo, Oct 18, 34; m 63. AQUATIC ECOLOGY, LIMNOLOGY. *Educ:* Quincy Col, BS, 56; Univ Wash, MS, 59, PhD(zool), 63. *Prof Exp:* Lab aide limnol, Quincy Col, 54-56; asst, Univ Wash, 56-59; teacher high sch, Mo, 59-60; staff biologist, USPHS, 60-62, prin biologist, Southeast Water Lab, 63-66, chief training br, 66; leader, Fisheries Coop Unit & assoc prof fisheries & limnol res, Ohio State Univ, 66-67; assoc cur limnol dept, Acad Natural Sci, Philadelphia, 67-69; asst dir, Lab Environ Studies, Med Ctr, NY Univ, 69-75; SR SCIENTIST & VPRES, ECOL ANALYSTS, INC, 75- *Concurrent Pos:* Adj assoc prof biol, NY Univ, 70- *Mem:* AAAS; Am Soc Limnol & Oceanog; Am Fisheries Soc; Am Littoral Soc; Ecol Soc Am. *Res:* Population dynamics and community diversity of aquatic organisms; effects of pollutants and other environmental stresses on aquatic life. *Mailing Add:* 25 Mine Rd Monroe NY 10950

LAUER, JAMES LOTHAR, b Vienna, Austria, Aug 2, 20; nat US; m 55. MATERIALS SCIENCE. *Educ:* Temple Univ, AB, 42, MA, 44; Univ Pa, PhD(physics), 48. *Prof Exp:* Asst instr org chem, Temple Univ, 42-44; phys chemist, Sun Oil Co, 44-45, res physicist, 47-54, sr physicist, 54-58, res assoc, 58-62, res scientist, 62-77; RES PROF MECH ENG, RENSSELAER POLYTECH INST, 78- *Concurrent Pos:* Lectr, Univ Del, 52-56; asst prof, Univ Pa, 52-54; fel aerospace eng, Univ Calif, San Diego, 64-65; prin investr, Air Force Off Sci Res & NASA-Lewis Res Ctr, 73- & Off Naval Res, 78-; lectr, Coblentz, 78; lectr friction & lubrication, Gordon Res Conf, 82. *Mem:* Am Chem Soc; Am Phys Soc; Soc Appl Spectros; Optical Soc Am; Spectros Soc Can. *Res:* Fourier spectroscopy; Raman and infrared spectroscopy; refraction and dispersion; theory of molecular structure; mathematical physics; x-ray spectra of polymers; combustion; shock waves in gases; adsorption and desorption; applications of molecular, mainly infrared emission, spectroscopy to problems of lubrication; optical methods of non-contacting surface analysis. *Mailing Add:* 7 Northeast Lane Ballston Lake NY 12019

LAUER, ROBERT B, b York, Pa, Mar 9, 42; m 60; c 3. MATERIALS SCIENCE, SOLID STATE SCIENCE. *Educ:* Franklin & Marshall Col, AB, 64; Univ Del, MS, 66, PhD(physics), 70. *Prof Exp:* Sr physicist, Itek Corp, 69-74; mem tech staff, 74-81, ACTG TECH MGR, GTE LABS, 81- *Mem:* Am Phys Soc; Sigma Xi. *Res:* Luminescence and photoconductivity of semiconductors, semi-insulators and insulators; defect structure of solids; materials preparation; liquid phase epitaxial growth; semiconductor lasers; high radiance light emitting diodes; photodetectors. *Mailing Add:* GTE Labs 40 Sylvan Rd Waltham MA 02154

LAUER, RUDOLPH FRANK, b Vienna, Austria, Aug 28, 48; US citizen. PHARMACEUTICAL CHEMISTRY. *Educ:* Polytech Inst Brooklyn, BS, 70; Mass Inst Technol, PhD(org chem), 74. *Prof Exp:* SR SCIENTIST PHARMACEUT CHEM, HOFFMANN-LaROCHE INC, 74- *Mem:* Am Chem Soc. *Res:* The synthesis of new and potentially useful pharmaceutical agents. *Mailing Add:* Hoffmann-LaRoche Inc Nutley NJ 07110

LAUERMAN, LLOYD HERMAN, JR, b Everett, Wash, Feb 5, 33; m 55; c 3. VETERINARY MICROBIOLOGY, VETERINARY IMMUNOLOGY. *Educ:* Wash State Univ, BA, 56, DVM, 58; Univ Wis, MS, 59, PhD, 68; Am Col Vet Microbiol, dipl, 74. *Prof Exp:* Res asst vet med, Univ Wis, 58-60, proj asst, 60-63; res dir vet biol, Biol Specialties Corp, 63-68; Colo State Univ-AID prof microbiol, Univ Nairobi, 68-72; assoc prof, Colo State Univ, 72-81, head bact sect, Diag Lab, Dept Path, 73-81; VET, DIAG LAB & HEAD, MICRO SECT, STATE ALA, 81- *Concurrent Pos:* Vis assoc prof microbiol, Sch Dent, Univ Colo, Denver, 74-75. *Mem:* Am Soc Microbiologists; Am Asn Vet Lab Diagnosticians; Am Vet Med Asn; US Am Health Asn; Am Asn Vet Immunol. *Res:* Diagnosis and prevention of infectious diseases of animals; research and development of laboratory diagnostic techniques and animal vaccines. *Mailing Add:* Vet Diag Lab 2115 Main Daplne Mobile AL 36617

LAUF, PETER KURT, b Wuerzburg, Ger, Sept 25, 33; US citizen. PHYSIOLOGY, IMMUNOLOGY. *Educ:* Univ Freiburg, MD, 60. *Prof Exp:* Res assoc path, Inst Path, Univ Freiburg, 60-62; res fel biochem, Max Planck Inst Immunobiol, Freiburg, 62-64; res assoc path, Inst Path, Univ Marburg, Ger, 64; res assoc biochem, Child Res Ctr Mich, Detroit, 65-67; asst prof biochem, Wayne State Univ, 66-67; from asst prof to assoc prof physiol, 68-77, asst prof immunol, 70-80, PROF PHYSIOL, DUKE UNIV MED CTR, 78- *Concurrent Pos:* NIH res career develop award, 71-75. *Mem:* Soc Gen Physiol; Am Soc Hematol; Biophys Soc; Am Soc Immunol; Am Soc Physiol. *Res:* Membrane physiology; active and passive action transport processes in erythrocytes; modulation of membrane transport processes by immunological reactions; isolation and identification of membrane transport proteins and functionally associated surface antigens. *Mailing Add:* Dept Physiol Duke Univ Med Ctr Box 3709 Durham NC 27710

LAUFER, ALLAN HENRY, b New York, NY, Mar 27, 36; m 59; c 2. PHOTOCHEMISTRY, CHEMICAL KINETICS. *Educ:* NY Univ, BA, 56; Lehigh Univ, MS, 58, PhD(phys chem), 62. *Prof Exp:* Res chemist, Gulf Res & Develop Co, 62-64; RES CHEMIST, NAT BUR STANDARDS, 64- *Mem:* AAAS; Am Chem Soc; Am Phys Soc; Sigma Xi. *Res:* Vacuum ultraviolet photochemistry; gas phase radical reactions and kinetics; properties of materials in the vacuum ultraviolet region; chemistry of excited states; fluorescence. *Mailing Add:* Div 542 Nat Bur Standards Washington DC 20234

LAUFER, DANIEL A, b Affula, Israel, May 30, 38; US citizen; m 68. ORGANIC CHEMISTRY. *Educ:* Mass Inst Technol, BS, 59; Brandeis Univ, PhD(org chem), 64. *Prof Exp:* Res assoc org chem, Columbia Univ, 63-64; res fel biol chem, Harvard Med Sch, 64-66; asst prof, 66-72, ASSOC PROF CHEM, UNIV MASS, BOSTON, 72- *Concurrent Pos:* NIH trainee, 65-66, res grant, 67-70. *Mem:* Am Chem Soc. *Res:* Mechanism of organic reactions; peptide synthesis; protein conformation; enzymic activity. *Mailing Add:* Dept of Chem Univ of Mass Boston MA 02116

LAUFER, HANS, b Ger, Oct 18, 29; nat US; m 53; c 3. DEVELOPMENTAL BIOLOGY. *Educ:* City Col New York, BS, 52; Brooklyn Col, MA, 54; Cornell Univ, PhD(zool), 58. *Prof Exp:* Asst, Cornell Univ, 55-57; Nat Res Coun fel embryol, Carnegie Inst, 57-59; asst prof biol, Johns Hopkins Univ, 59-65; assoc prof biol, 65-72, PROF BIOL, UNIV CONN, 72- *Concurrent Pos:* Vis scholar, Case Western Reserve Univ, 62; Lalor fel, Marine Biol Lab, Woods Hole, Mass, 62-63, staff embryol course, 67-72, trustee mem, Corp Marine Biol Lab, 78-, mem exec comt, 79-80; assoc ed, J Exp Zool, 69-73; mem nat bd on grad educ, Conf Bd Assoc Res Couns, 71-75; vis prof, Karolinska Inst, Stockholm, 72 & Yale Univ, 80; NATO fel rev panel, NSF, 74 & 76; partic, Nat Acad Sci-Czech Acad Sci Exchange Prog, 74 & 77. *Honors & Awards:* Rosenstiel vis scholar, Brandeis Univ, 73; hon prof, Charles Univ, Prague, 74. *Mem:* Fel Am Soc Zoologists; Soc Develop Biol; Am Soc Cell Biol; Tissue Culture Asn; AAAS. *Res:* Developmental physiology and biochemistry; molecular interactions in development; proteins and enzymes in ontogeny, regeneration and metamorphosis; chromosomal puffing in Diptera; gene action as related to development. *Mailing Add:* Biol Sci Group U-42 Univ of Conn Storrs CT 06268

LAUFER, JOHN, b Hungary, Sept 22, 21; nat US; m 49; c 2. AERODYNAMICS. *Educ:* La State Univ, BS, 42; Calif Inst Technol, MS, 43, AE, 44, PhD(aeronaut), 48. *Prof Exp:* Res engr, Calif Inst Technol, 44-48, fel, 48-49; physicist, Nat Bur Standards, 49-52; sr res engr, Jet Propulsion Lab, Calif Inst Technol, 52-58, chief gas dynamic sect, 58-64; PROF AEROSPACE ENG & CHMN DEPT, UNIV SOUTHERN CALIF, 64- *Concurrent Pos:* Guggenheim & Fulbright fel, Turin Polytech Inst, Italy, 58-59; consult, Rand Corp, Aerospace Corp & McDonnell Douglas Astronaut Co. *Mem:* Fel Am Inst Aeronaut & Astronaut; fel Am Phys Soc; Nat Acad Eng. *Res:* Fluid mechanics; turbulence. *Mailing Add:* Univ Southern Calif Dept Aerospace Eng-OHE 300 Los Angeles CA 90007

LAUFER, ROBERT J, b Pittsburgh, Pa, May 10, 32; m 67; c 2. ORGANIC CHEMISTRY. *Educ:* Carnegie Inst Technol, BS, 53, MS, 56, PhD(org chem), 58. *Prof Exp:* Proj supvr res div, Consol Coal Co, 58-68; proj leader, Int Flavors & Fragrances Inc, 68-69, assoc dir fragrance res, 69-72, dir, 72-75; dir aromatic technol, 75-77, corp dir res & develop, 77-78, vpres aromatics, 79-80, vpres & gen mgr, Orbis Prod Div, 80-81, VPRES CORP PLANNING, NORDA, INC, 81- *Mem:* AAAS; Am Chem Soc; fel Am Inst Chemists. *Res:* Research management; aroma chemicals; terpenoids; fragrance applications research. *Mailing Add:* 6 Greenhill Rd Colts Neck NJ 07722

LAUFERSWEILER, JOSEPH DANIEL, b Columbus, Ohio, Aug 13, 30; m 59; c 2. ECOLOGY, BOTANY. *Educ:* Univ Notre Dame, BS, 52; Ohio State Univ, MSc, 54, PhD(ecol), 60. *Prof Exp:* Instr bot & ecol, Ohio State Univ, 59-61; asst prof biol, Drake Univ, 61-63; asst prof, 63-77, ASSOC PROF BIOL, UNIV DAYTON, 77- *Concurrent Pos:* Bus mgr, Ohio J Sci, 74- *Mem:* AAAS; Ecol Soc Am; Am Inst Biol Sci. *Res:* Reproduction of plant communities; distribution of original vegetation and its influence on man. *Mailing Add:* Dept of Biol Univ of Dayton Dayton OH 45469

LAUFF, GEORGE HOWARD, b Milan, Mich, Mar 23, 27. LIMNOLOGY, ZOOLOGY. *Educ:* Mich State Univ, BS, 49, MS, 51; Cornell Univ, PhD(limnol, zool), 53. *Prof Exp:* Fisheries res technician, Mich State Dept Conserv, 50; asst phycol, Point Barrow, Alaska, 51; biol asst, Cornell Univ, 51-52, zool, 52-53; instr, Univ Mich, 53-57, from asst prof to assoc prof, 57-62; res coordr, Sapelo Island Res Found, Ga, 62-64; PROF ZOOL, FISHERIES & WILDLIFE & DIR, W K KELLOGG BIOL STA, MICH STATE UNIV, 64- *Concurrent Pos:* Res assoc, Great Lakes Res Inst, 54-59, Oak Ridge Inst Nuclear Studies & Oak Ridge Nat Lab, 60; assoc prof & dir marine inst, Univ Ga, 60-62. *Mem:* AAAS; Am Inst Biol Sci; Am Soc Limnol & Oceanog (treas, 58-61, secy, 58-64, 67-70, vpres, 71-72, pres, 72-73); Ecol Soc Am; Int Asn Theoret & Appl Limnol. *Mailing Add:* W K Kellogg Biol Sta Mich State Univ Hickory Corners MI 49060

LAUFFENBURGER, JAMES C, b Buffalo, NY, Aug 23, 38; m 61; c 5. SOLID STATE PHYSICS. *Educ:* Canisius Col, BS, 60; Univ Notre Dame, PhD(solid state physics), 65. *Prof Exp:* Asst prof, 64-72, ASSOC PROF PHYSICS, CANISIUS COL, 72- *Mem:* Sigma Xi; Am Asn Physics Teachers. *Res:* X-rays. *Mailing Add:* 1337 N French Rd North Tonawanda NY 14120

LAUFFER, DONALD EUGENE, b Lebanon, Pa, July 29, 40; m 64; c 3. PHYSICS. *Educ:* Ohio State Univ, BS, 64, PhD(physics), 68. *Prof Exp:* SR RES PHYSICIST, PHILLIPS PETROL CO, 68- *Mem:* Am Phys Soc; Inst Elec & Electronics Engrs; Soc Explor Geophysicists. *Res:* Geophysics; wave propagation and signal processing. *Mailing Add:* Phillips Petrol Co PRC 177 GB Bartlesville OK 74004

LAUFFER, MAX AUGUSTUS, JR, b Middletown, Pa, Sept 2, 14; m 36, 64; c 4. BIOPHYSICS. *Educ:* Pa State Univ, BS, 33, MS, 34; Univ Minn, PhD(biochem), 37. *Prof Exp:* Asst, Univ Minn, 35-36, instr biochem, 36-37; fel plant path, Rockefeller Inst, 37-38, asst, 38-41, assoc, 41-44; assoc res prof, 44-47, res prof physics & physiol chem, 47-49, chmn dept physics, 47-48, prof biophys, 49-63, head dept, 49-56 & chmn dept, 63-67, assoc dean res in natural sci, 53-54, dean div natural sci, 56-63, chmn dept biophys & microbiol, 71-76, ANDREW MELLON PROF BIOPHYS, UNIV PITTSBURGH, 63- *Concurrent Pos:* Spec lectr, Stanford Univ, 41; prin investr, Comt Med Res, 44-46; Priestley lectr, Pa State Univ, 46; Gehrmann lectr, Univ Ill, 51; vis prof, Theodor Kocher Inst, Bern Univ, 52, Max Planck Inst Virus Res, Tübingen, 65-66 & Univ Philippines, 67; mem Nat Res Coun comn macromolecules, 47-53, mem panel virol & immunol, sect biol, comt growth, 53-56; mem sci adv comt, Boyce Thompson Inst Plant Res Inc, 53-; co-ed, Adv Virus Res, 53-; mem prog proj comt, Nat Inst Gen Med Sci, 61-63, chmn, 62-63, mem adv coun, 63-67; mem sci adv bd, Delta Regional Primate Res Ctr, Tulane Univ, 64-67; ed, Biophys J, 69-73. *Honors & Awards:* Award, Eli Lilly & Co, 45; Pittsburgh Award, Am Chem Soc, 58. *Mem:* Am Chem Soc; Am Soc Biol Chemists; Biophys Soc (pres elect, 60, pres, 61); Soc Exp Biol & Med; Fedn Am Sci. *Res:* Electrokinetics; ultracentrifugation; viscometry; biophysics of viruses; kinetics of virus disintegration; size and shape of macromolecules; polymerization of virus protein; hydration of proteins; entropy-driven processes in biology. *Mailing Add:* 327 Clapp Hall Univ of Pittsburgh Pittsburgh PA 15260

LAUFMAN, HAROLD, b Milwaukee, Wis, Jan 6, 12; m 40; c 2. SURGERY. *Educ:* Univ Chicago, BS, 32, Rush Med Col, MD, 37; Northwestern Univ, MS, 46, PhD(surg), 48; Am Bd Surg, dipl. *Prof Exp:* From clin asst to prof surg, Med Sch, Northwestern Univ, 40-65; prof, 65-77, EMER PROF SURG, ALBERT EINSTEIN COL MED, 77-; PROF LECTR SURG, MT SINAI SCH MED, 79- *Concurrent Pos:* Assoc attend surgeon, Cook County Hosp, 46-48; attend, Hines Vet Admin Hosp, 48-50; adj attend, Michael Reese Hosp, Chicago, 48-54; attend, Passavant Mem & Vet Admin Res Hosps, 54-65; James IV traveling prof, Israel, 62; dir, Inst Surg Studies, Montefiore Hosp, 65-81, emer dir, 81- *Mem:* Am Surg Asn; Soc Vascular Surg; fel Am Col Surg; Am Med Writers Asn (pres, 69); Asn Advan Med Instrumentation (pres, 74-75). *Res:* Surgical physiology, especially mesenteric and peripheral vascular diseases; surgical design and facilities engineering. *Mailing Add:* Inst Surg Studies Montefiore Hosp Bronx NY 10467

LAUG, GEORGE MILTON, b Ossining, NY, Feb 23, 23; m 48; c 1. BIOLOGY. *Educ:* Syracuse Univ, BS, 47, MS, 48, PhD(sci educ), 60. *Prof Exp:* Instr sci educ & genetics, Syracuse Univ, 48-49; asst prof sci, 49-60, PROF BIOL, STATE UNIV NY COL BUFFALO, 60- *Mem:* AAAS; Nat Asn Biol Teachers. *Res:* Environmental biology; ecology; genetics; successional replacement of elms which have died in natural communities as a result of the Dutch elm disease. *Mailing Add:* 4485 E Overlook Dr Williamsville NY 14221

LAUGHLIN, ALEXANDER WILLIAM, b Hot Springs, Ark, Nov 9, 36; m 69; c 3. GEOCHEMISTRY, ECONOMIC GEOLOGY. *Educ:* Mich Technol Univ, BSc, 58; Univ Ariz, MSc, 60, PhD(geol), 69. *Prof Exp:* Res assoc isotope geochem, Univ Ariz, 66-69; res assoc geol, Univ NMex, 69-70; from asst prof to assoc prof, Kent State Univ, 70-74; mem staff, 74-78, group leader, 78-80, MEM STAFF, LOS ALAMOS NAT LAB, 80- *Concurrent Pos:* Adj prof, Univ NMex, 75. *Mem:* Geochem Soc; Am Geophys Union; Int Asn Geochem & Cosmochem; Geol Soc Am. *Res:* Geochronology; trace element geochemistry; origin of ultramafic inclusions and basalts; economic geology; geothermal energy extraction from dry hot rock, geothermal exploration techniques, petrology of pre-Cambrian rocks. *Mailing Add:* ESS-2 MS983 Los Alamos Nat Lab Univ of Calif Los Alamos NM 87545

LAUGHLIN, ALICE, b Malone, NY, Feb 19, 18. BIOCHEMISTRY, ANALYTICAL CHEMISTRY. *Educ:* St Joseph Col, Conn, BS, 49; Univ Vt, MS, 54; Columbia Univ, EdD(col sci teaching), 65. *Prof Exp:* Lab technician, Clin Lab, Staten Island Hosp, 49-50; teaching asst biochem, Univ Vt, 50-52; asst biochemist, Vt State Agr Exp Sta, 52-56; res chemist, Nat Biscuit Co, 56-57; res asst hemat & chemother, Columbia-Presby Med Ctr, Columbia Univ, 57-61; sci instr, Sch Nursing, St Michael Hosp, 61-62; from asst prof sci to assoc prof chem, 62-74, chmn dept, 69-70, PROF CHEM, JERSEY CITY STATE COL, 74- *Concurrent Pos:* Resource mem long range planning bd, Sch Nursing, St Francis Hosp, 63-; consult, NSF meeting on chem curric in jr cols, Rutgers Univ, 69. *Mem:* Am Chem Soc; Am Asn Higher Educ; fel Am Inst Chemists; NY Acad Sci; Am Microchem Soc. *Res:* Human nutrition; science education. *Mailing Add:* 1225 76th St 8C North Bergen NJ 07047

LAUGHLIN, DAVID EUGENE, b Philadelphia, Pa, July 15, 47; m 71; c 4. PHYSICAL METALLURGY, ELECTRON MICROSCOPY. *Educ:* Drexel Univ, BSc, 69; Mass Inst Technol, PhD(metall), 73. *Prof Exp:* Res assoc, Nat Bur Standards, 73-74; asst prof, 74-78, ASSOC PROF METALL, CARNEGIE-MELLON UNIV, 78- *Concurrent Pos:* Pres, Trinity Christian Sch Bd Dirs, 78-; chmn, Metals Topic Area Team, Educ Modules in Mat Sci & Eng, 78-80; consult, 80- *Mem:* Am Soc Metals; Am Inst Mining, Metall & Petrol Engrs; Am Soc Eng Educ; Am Sci Affil. *Res:* X-ray diffraction; innovative teaching; phase transformations; differential scanning calorimetry; electron microscopy. *Mailing Add:* Dept of Metall & Mat Sci Carnegie-Mellon Univ Pittsburgh PA 15213

LAUGHLIN, ETHELREDA R, b Cleveland, Ohio, Nov 13, 22; m 51; c 1. BIOCHEMISTRY, SCIENCE EDUCATION. *Educ:* Case Western Reserve Univ, AB, 42, MS, 44, PhD(sci educ), 62. *Prof Exp:* Instr chem, anat & physiol, St John Col, 49-51; teacher high sch, Ohio, 53-62; assoc prof sci educ & org chem, Ferris State Col, 62-63; instr chem, 63-65, HEAD DEPT SCI, CUYAHOGA COMMUNITY COL, WESTERN CAMPUS, 65-, PROF CHEM, 68- *Concurrent Pos:* Vis prof biochem, Case Western Reserve Univ, 70-71. *Mem:* Nat Educ Asn; Am Chem Soc; Audubon Soc; Sigma Xi; Sierra Club. *Mailing Add:* 6486 State Rd 12 Parma OH 44134

LAUGHLIN, HAROLD EMERSON, b Tulsa, Okla, Feb 11, 32; m 52; c 3. ANIMAL ECOLOGY, HERPETOLOGY. *Educ:* Univ Tulsa, BSc, 55; Univ Tex, MA, 58, PhD(zool), 66. *Prof Exp:* Asst prof biol, Southeastern State Col, 61-63; DIR, HEARD NATURAL SCI MUS & WILDLIFE SANCTUARY, 66- *Mem:* Am Soc Ichthyol & Herpet. *Res:* Interspecific lizard ecology; vertebrate population dynamics; vertebrate dietary studies. *Mailing Add:* Heard Mus Rte 6 Box 22 McKinney TX 75069

LAUGHLIN, JAMES STANLEY, b Guilford, Mo, Sept 23, 36; m 60; c 2. STATISTICS, OPERATIONS RESEARCH. *Educ:* Northwest Mo State Univ, BS, 58; Univ Northern Colo, MA, 61; Univ Denver, PhD(higher educ, math), 68. *Prof Exp:* Teacher chem & math, Grand Community Schs, Boxholm, Iowa, 58-59; teacher math, Denver Pub Schs, Colo, 59-67, res asst, 67-68; assoc prof math, Kans State Teachers Col, 68-75, dir instnl studies, 70-75; DIR INSTNL RES, IDAHO STATE UNIV, 75- *Concurrent Pos:* Kans State Dept Educ grant, 69-70. *Mem:* Asn Instnl Res; Am Educ Res Asn. *Res:* Higher education research in college management. *Mailing Add:* Idaho State Univ Pocatello ID 83201

LAUGHLIN, JOHN SETH, b Canton, Mo, Jan 26, 18; m 79; c 3. MEDICAL PHYSICS. *Educ:* Willamette Univ, AB, 40; Haverford Col, MS, 42; Univ Ill, PhD(physics), 47. *Hon Degrees:* DSc, Willamette Univ, 68. *Prof Exp:* Asst, Haverford Col, 40-42; asst, Univ Ill, 42-44, res assoc, Off Sci Res & Develop, 44-45, asst, 45-46; asst prof spec res, 46-48, asst prof radiol, Col Med, 48-51, assoc prof, 51-52; assoc prof biophys, 52-55, PROF BIOPHYS, SLOAN-KETTERING DIV, MED COL, CORNELL UNIV, 55-; CHIEF DIV BIOPHYS, SLOAN-KETTERING INST CANCER RES, 52-, VPRES, 66- *Concurrent Pos:* Attend physicist & chmn dept med physics, Mem Hosp, 52- *Mem:* Radiol Soc NAm; Radiation Res Soc (pres, 70-71); Soc Nuclear Med; Am Asn Physicists in Med (pres, 64-65); Health Physics Soc (pres, 60-61). *Res:* Neutron-proton and neutron-deutron interaction; high pressure cloud chamber design; interaction of high energy electrons with nuclei; application of betatron to medical therapy; radiation dosimetry; high energy gamma ray scanning; development of digital and computer controlled scanning; isotope metabolic studies. *Mailing Add:* Div of Biophys 444 E 68th St Mem Sloan-Kettering Cancer Ctr New York NY 10021

LAUGHLIN, R(OBERT) G(ARDINER) W(ILLIS), b London, Eng, Oct 11, 42; m 67. CHEMICAL ENGINEERING. *Educ:* Univ Col, Univ London, BSc, 64, PhD(chem eng), 67. *Prof Exp:* ASST DIR, DEPT ENVIRON CHEM, ONT RES FOUND, 67- *Mem:* Can Soc Chem Eng. *Res:* Environmental engineering; air pollution; spontaneous combustion phenomena; industrial and municipal solid waste utilization; industrial waste treatment; biomass to energy conversion systems; energy from waste systems; biotechnology. *Mailing Add:* Dept Environ Chem Ont Res Found Sheridan Park Mississauga ON L5K 1B3 Can

LAUGHLIN, ROBERT GENE, b Sullivan, Ind, Aug 9, 30; div; c 2. PHYSICAL ORGANIC CHEMISTRY. *Educ:* Purdue Univ, BS, 51; Cornell Univ, PhD(org chem), 55. *Prof Exp:* Fel org chem, Hickrill Res Labs, NY, 55-56; res chemist, 56-68, SECT HEAD, MIAMI VALLEY LABS, PROCTER & GAMBLE CO, 68- *Mem:* AAAS; Royal Soc Chem; Am Chem Soc. *Res:* Synthesis phase equilibria, and colloid science of molecules; the correlation of surfactant molecular structure with solubility phase equilibria, and other physical properties; synthesis of aliphatic organophosphorus compounds; chemistry of positive-halogen compounds; synthesis of organophosphorus and organosulfur compounds. *Mailing Add:* Procter & Gamble Co Miami Valley Labs Cincinnati OH 45247

LAUGHLIN, WILLIAM SCEVA, b Canton, Mo, Aug 26, 19; m 44; c 2. PHYSICAL ANTHROPOLOGY. *Educ:* Willamette Univ, BA, 41; Haverford Col, MA, 42; Harvard Univ, AM, 48, PhD(anthrop), 49. *Hon Degrees:* DSc, Willamette Univ, 68. *Prof Exp:* Asst anthrop, Harvard Univ, 47-48; asst prof, Univ Ore, 49-53, assoc prof, 53-55; from assoc prof to prof, Univ Wis, 55-69, chmn dept, 60-62; PROF BIOBEHAV SCI & ANTHROP, UNIV CONN, 69- *Concurrent Pos:* Ed, J Am Asn Phys Anthrop, 58-63; mem anthrop study sect, Nat Res Coun, 59-62; fel, Ctr Advan Study Behav Sci, Stanford Univ, 64-65. *Mem:* AAAS; fel Am Soc Human Genetics; Soc Am Archaeol; Am Asn Phys Anthrop; Am Anthrop Asn. *Res:* Population genetics; blood group genetics and skeletal history of human isolates, Indians and Eskimo-Aleut stock; skeletal analysis of Eskimos and Indians; peoplory of New World from Siberia. *Mailing Add:* Univ of Conn Storrs CT 06208

LAUGHLIN, WINSTON MEANS, b Fountain, Minn, May 2, 17; m 47; c 4. SOIL SCIENCE. *Educ:* Univ Minn, BS, 41; Mich State Univ, MS, 47, PhD(soil sci), 49. *Prof Exp:* Soil surveyor, Univ Minn, 40-41; asst, Mich State Univ, 41-42; SOIL SCIENTIST, ALASKA AGR EXP STA, 49- *Mem:* AAAS; Am Soc Agron; Soil Sci Soc Am; Am Sci Affil; Int Soc Soil Sci. *Res:* Soil fertility, chemistry and classification with emphasis on Arctic conditions. *Mailing Add:* Agr Res Serv USDA Box AE Palmer AK 99645

LAUGHNAN, JOHN RAPHAEL, b Spring Green, Wis, Sept 27, 19; m 42; c 3. GENETICS. *Educ:* Univ Wis, BS, 42; Univ Mo, PhD(genetics), 46. *Prof Exp:* Asst prof biol, Princeton Univ, 47-48; asst prof bot, Univ Ill, 48-51, assoc prof, 51-54; prof field crops, Univ Mo, 54-55; prof bot & chmn dept, 55-59, head dept bot, 63-65, PROF BOT & PLANT GENETICS, UNIV ILL, URBANA, 59- *Concurrent Pos:* Gosney fel, Calif Inst Technol, 48; Guggenheim fel, 60-61. *Mem:* Genetics Soc Am; Bot Soc Am; Am Soc Naturalists. *Res:* Functional genetics; fine structure and recombination in maize and Drosophila; intrachromosomal recombination mechanisms; development of sweet corn carrying sh2 gene. *Mailing Add:* Dept of Bot Univ of Ill Urbana IL 61801

LAUGHNER, WILLIAM JAMES, JR, b Wickliffe, Ohio, Oct 22, 43; m 68; c 3. GENETICS, MOLECULAR BIOLOGY. *Educ:* Thiel Col, BA, 65; Ind Univ, Bloomington, PhD(genetics & bot), 70. *Prof Exp:* ASSOC PROF BIOL, HIRAM COL, 70- *Concurrent Pos:* Assoc, Dept Med Genetics, Med Sch, Ind Univ, 74-75. *Mem:* Genetics Soc Am. *Res:* Heterosis in plants based on enzyme unit interactions. *Mailing Add:* Dept of Biol Hiram Col Hiram OH 44234

LAUGHON, ROBERT BUSH, b Greensboro, NC, Apr 20, 34. GEOLOGY. *Educ:* Colo Col, BA, 60; Univ Colo, Boulder, MS, 63; Univ Ariz, PhD(geol), 70. *Prof Exp:* Geologist, US Geol Surv, 62-63 & Anaconda Co, 64-65; instr, Univ Ariz, 66-67; geologist, Manned Spacecraft Ctr, NASA, 67-76; proj mgr, Nuclear Div, Union Carbide Corp, 76-78; mgr, Geol Explor Dept, 78-81, DEP MGR & CHIEF GEOLOGIST, SITE EXPLOR DEPT, OFF NUCLEAR WASTE ISOLATION, PROJ MGT DIV, BATTELLE MEM INST, 81- *Concurrent Pos:* Lectr, Moody Col, Tex A&M Univ, 74. *Mem:* Geol Soc Am; Mineral Soc Am. *Res:* Mineralogy; structural crystallography. *Mailing Add:* Proj Mgt Div 505 King Ave Columbus OH 43201

LAUGHTON, PAUL MACDONELL, b Toronto, Ont, Sept 8, 23; m 46; c 4. ORGANIC CHEMISTRY. *Educ:* Univ Toronto, BA, 45; Dalhousie Univ, MSc, 47; Univ Wis, PhD(chem), 50. *Prof Exp:* Res assoc, Univ Wis, 50; Nat Res Coun Can fel, Dalhousie Univ, 50-51; from asst prof to assoc prof chem, 51-65, PROF CHEM, CARLETON UNIV, 65- *Concurrent Pos:* Vis prof, Stanford Univ, 62 & Kings Col, London, 72-73; Am Chem Soc-Petrol Res Fund fel, Univ Calif, Berkeley, 62-63. *Mem:* Am Chem Soc; fel Chem Inst Can; The Chem Soc; Sigma Xi. *Res:* Mechanism studies; isotope effects. *Mailing Add:* Dept Chem Carleton Univ Ottawa ON K1S 5B6 Can

LAUKHUF, WALDEN LOUIS SHELBURNE, b Maysville, Ky, July 25, 43; m 67; c 1. CHEMICAL ENGINEERING. *Educ:* Univ Louisville, BSChE, 66, MSChE, 67, PhD(chem eng), 69. *Prof Exp:* Engr, Humble Oil & Refining Co, 69; US Air Force, 69-73, proj engr, Air Force Rocket Propulsion Lab, 69-71, develop eng specialist, Air Force Mat Lab, 71-73; asst prof chem eng, 73-77, ASSOC PROF CHEM ENG, UNIV LOUISVILLE, 77- *Honors & Awards:* Air Force Systs Command Cert of Merit, 71. *Mem:* Am Inst Chem Engrs; Am Chem Soc; Am Soc Eng Educ. *Res:* Adsorption; kinetics; mass transfer and thermodynamics; coal gasification; energy. *Mailing Add:* 14104 Tree Crest Ct Louisville KY 40223

LAUKONIS, JOSEPH VAINYS, b Mich, Apr 1, 25; m 54. PHYSICS. *Educ:* Univ Detroit, BS, 51; Univ Cincinnati, PhD, 57. *Prof Exp:* SR RES PHYSICIST, GEN MOTORS CORP, 57- *Res:* Iron whiskers; metal surfaces; high temperature oxidation; formability of sheet metals; electron microscopy; ultrahigh vacuums; oxidation-reduction catalysts. *Mailing Add:* Gen Motors Tech Ctr Mound Rd & 12 Mile Warren MI 48092

LAUKS, IMANTS RUDOLF, b Bradford, Eng, Aug 12, 52; m 77. SOLID STATE ELECTRONICS, CHEMICAL ELECTRONICS. *Educ:* London Univ, BSc, 73, PhD(elec eng), 77; ARCS, 73; Imp Col, dipl, 77. *Prof Exp:* Fel, 77-78, res investr, 78-79, ASST PROF ELEC ENG, MOORE SCH ELEC ENG & SCI, UNIV PA, 79- *Res:* Chemical electronics research which includes a specialization in semiconductor chemical sensors, and high resolution photolithography. *Mailing Add:* 10 Uranus Rd Sewell NJ 08080

LAUL, JAGDISH CHANDER, b India, Sept 1, 39; m 70; c 3. GEOCHEMISTRY, COSMOCHEMISTRY. *Educ:* Punjab Univ, India, BS, 59; Purdue Univ, MS, & PhD(radio geochem), 69. *Prof Exp:* Res assoc, Enrico Fermi Inst, Univ Chicago, 69-71 & Radiation Ctr, Ore State Univ, 71-75; SR RES SCIENTIST CHEM, PHYS SCI DEPT, PAC NORTHWEST DIV, BATTELLE MEM INST, 72- *Honors & Awards:* Group Achievement Award, NASA, 73. *Mem:* Am Chem Soc; Geochem Soc; Meteoritical Soc. *Res:* Studies of trace elements and their implications in lunar, meteorite, terrestrial, environmental, nuclear waste and fossile fuel samples; development of radioanalytical methods and instrumentation in neutron activation area. *Mailing Add:* Dept of Phys Sci Box 999 Richland WA 00352

LAULAINEN, NELS STEPHEN, b Longview, Wash, Oct 22, 41; wid; c 3. ATMOSPHERIC SCIENCE. *Educ:* Univ Wash, BS, 63, MS, 65, PhD(physics), 68. *Prof Exp:* Res scientist physics, First Phys Inst, Heidelberg Univ, 68-70; res assoc med physics, Med Radiation Physics & Radiol, Univ Wash, 70-71, res assoc geophys & astron, Geophys Prog, 71-74; SR RES SCIENTIST, ATMOSPHERIC SCI, BATTELLE-PAC NORTHWEST LABS, 74- *Concurrent Pos:* Res scientist, Fulbright Travel Stipend, 68-70; lectr physics, Univ Wash, 72-74; tech adv, US Environ Protection Agency, Washington, DC, 81-82. *Mem:* Am Phys Soc; Sigma Xi; Am Geophys Union. *Res:* Atmospheric aerosol physics; solar radiation and its interaction with atmospheric constituents; atmospheric pollutant transformation and removal processes; climate effects of energy production. *Mailing Add:* Battelle-Northwest Labs Atmospheric Sci Richland WA 99352

LAUNCHBAUGH, JOHN L, JR, b Sheridan Co, Kans, Nov 8, 22; m 46; c 2. PLANT ECOLOGY. *Educ:* Ft Hays State Univ, AB, 47, MS, 48; Tex A&M Univ, PhD(range mgt), 52. *Prof Exp:* Instr bot, Ft Hays State Univ, 48-49; asst range mgt, Dept Range & Forestry, Tex A&M Univ, 49-52; asst res specialist, Sch Forestry, Univ Calif, Berkeley, 52-55; assoc prof, 55-67, PROF RANGE MGT, FT HAYS BR, AGR EXP STA, KANS STATE UNIV, 67- *Mem:* Soc Range Mgt. *Res:* Grassland succession; grazing management; range reseeding. *Mailing Add:* Ft Hays Br Exp Sta Kans State Univ Hays KS 67601

LAUNDRE, JOHN WILLIAM, b Green Bay, Wis, Jan 30, 49; m 73. WILDLIFE BEHAVIOR, ECOLOGY. *Educ:* Univ Wis, Green Bay, BSc, 71; Northern Mich Univ, MA, 74; Idaho State Univ, PhD(ecol), 79. *Prof Exp:* Instr anat, Northeat Wis Tech & Voc Inst, 74-76; ASST PROF ECOL, SOUTHWEST STATE UNIV, 79- *Mem:* Wildlife Soc; Animal Behav Soc; Am Soc Mammalogist; Sigma Xi. *Res:* Ecology and behavior of mammals, including coyotes, deer, cats and small mammals. *Mailing Add:* Dept Biol Southwest State Univ Marshall MN 56258

LAUNER, PHILIP JULES, b Philadelphia, Pa, Nov 20, 22; m 47; c 3. ANALYTICAL CHEMISTRY. *Educ:* Drew Univ, AB, 43; Columbia Univ, MA, 47. *Prof Exp:* Teaching asst quant anal, Columbia Univ, 47-48; proj chemist petrol chem, Res Dept, Standard Oil Co (Ind), 48-55; specialist spectros, Silicone Prod Dept, Gen Elec Co, 55-72; PRES, LAB FOR MATS INC, 73- *Concurrent Pos:* Consult, Lazare Kaplan & Sons Inc, 75- *Mem:* Am Chem Soc; Coblentz Soc; Soc Appl Spectros; fel Am Inst Chemists. *Res:* Infrared spectroscopy; silicone technology; analysis of urinary tract calculi; identification of industrial materials. *Mailing Add:* Lab For Mats Inc PO Box 14 Burnt Hills NY 12027

LAUPUS, WILLIAM E, b Seymour, Ind, May 25, 21; m 48; c 4. MEDICINE. *Educ:* Yale Univ, BS, 43, MD, 45. *Prof Exp:* Instr pediat, Med Col, Cornell Univ, 50-52; from asst prof to prof, Med Col Ga, 59-63; prof pediat & chmn dept, Med Col Va, 63-75; DEAN SCH MED, EAST CAROLINA UNIV, 75- *Mem:* Fel Am Acad Pediat; Am Fedn Clin Res; AMA; Am Pediat Soc. *Res:* Pediatric medicine. *Mailing Add:* Sch of Med Med Col of Va Richmond VA 23219

LAURANCE, NEAL L, b Winsted, Minn, Aug 19, 32; m 53; c 4. COMPUTER SCIENCE. *Educ:* Marquette Univ, BS, 54, MS, 55; Univ Ill, PhD(physics), 60. *Prof Exp:* Res scientist, Sci Lab, 60-73; mgr, Control Systs Dept, 73-79, MGR ANAL SCI, ENG & RES STAFF, FORD MOTOR CO, 79- *Mem:* AAAS; Am Phys Soc; Asn Comput Mach; Inst Elec & Electronics Eng. *Res:* Computer languages; time-sharing systems; simulation systems; computer design; real-time systems; micro processor systems. *Mailing Add:* Eng & Res Staff Ford Motor Co Dearborn MI 48121

LAURENCE, GEOFFREY CAMERON, b Quincy, Mass, Mar, 24, 43; div; c 2. FISH BIOLOGY, ECOLOGICAL MODELLING. *Educ:* Univ Maine, BA, 65; Fla State Univ, MS, 67; Cornell Univ, PhD(fishery sci), 71. *Prof Exp:* Asst biol, Fla State Univ, 65-67; res asst fishery sci, Cornell Univ, 67-70; fishery biologist, Bur Sport Fisheries & Wildlife, 70-72; SUPVRY FISHERY BIOLOGIST, NAT MARINE FISHERIES SERV, NAT OCEANIC ATMOSPHERIC ADMIN, 72- *Mem:* Am Fisheries Soc; Am Inst Fishery Res Biologists; Am Soc Limnol & Oceanog; Sigma Xi. *Res:* Larval fish ecology and physiology as they pertain to growth and survival; ecological and mathematical modelling of larval survival in relation to stock-recruitment problems in fishery management; biological oceanography. *Mailing Add:* Narragansett Lab Nat Marine Fisheries Serv Narragansett RI 02882

LAURENCE, KENNETH ALLEN, b Cleveland, Ohio, Nov 4, 28; m 49. MICROBIOLOGY. *Educ:* Marietta Col, AB, 51; Univ Iowa, MS, 53, PhD, 56. *Prof Exp:* NIH fel immunol, Univ Iowa, 56-57; instr microbiol & immunol, Med Col, Cornell Univ, 57-59, asst prof, 59-60; asst med dir, 60-68, ASSOC DIR BIOMED DIV, POP COUN, INC, 68- *Concurrent Pos:* Ford Found consult physiol reprod, Egyptian Univs Prog, 66-67 & 70-; ed bd, J Fertil & Sterility, 71-; proj specialist, Ford Found, Cairo, Egypt, 73-74. *Mem:* AAAS; Am Soc Microbiol; Soc Study Reprod; Int Soc Res Reprod; Am Fertil Soc. *Res:* Physiology of reproduction; immunology; parasitology; medical bacteriology; immunologic studies of the reproductive processes. *Mailing Add:* Biomed Div York Ave & 66th St Pop Coun Inc Rockefeller Univ New York NY 10021

LAURENCE, MARIA (MAHER), b Lenox, Pa, July 16, 97. BOTANY. *Educ:* Marywood Col, BS, 26; Villanova Col, MS, 40; Fordham Univ, PhD(biol), 46. *Prof Exp:* Teacher chem & physics, Laurel Hill Acad, 32-38; from asst prof to assoc prof biol sci, Marywood Col, 38-56, prof 56-79. *Mem:* AAAS; Nat Asn Biol Teachers; Phycol Soc Am; Bot Soc Am. *Res:* Effect of environmental factors on growth of algae. *Mailing Add:* Dept of Sci Marywood Col Scranton PA 18509

LAURENCE, ROBERT L(IONEL), b West Warwick, RI, July 13, 36; m 59; c 3. CHEMICAL ENGINEERING, POLYMER SCIENCE. *Educ:* Mass Inst Technol, BS, 57; Univ RI, MS, 60; Northwestern Univ, PhD(chem eng), 65. *Prof Exp:* Res engr, Elec Boat Div, Gen Dynamics Corp, Conn, 57-58; engr, Eng Res Lab, E I du Pont de Nemours & Co, Del, 60-61, engr, Elastomers Dept, Tex, 61-63; asst prof chem eng, Johns Hopkins Univ, 65-68; assoc prof chem eng & polymer sci & eng, 68-73, PROF CHEM ENG, POLYMER SCI & ENG, UNIV MASS, AMHERST, 73- *Concurrent Pos:* Vis prof, Imp Col Sci & Technol, 74-75 & Universidad Nac del Sur, Bahia Blanca, Arg, 78. *Mem:* Soc Rheology; Am Inst Chem Eng; Am Soc Eng Educ; Am Chem Soc. *Res:* Fluid mechanics-hydrodynamic stability; polymerization reaction engineering; diffusion in polymers; polymer processing. *Mailing Add:* Dept of Chem Eng Univ of Mass Amherst MA 01002

LAURENCOT, HENRY JULES, JR, b Brooklyn, NY, Dec 14, 29; m 61; c 4. DRUG METABOLISM. *Educ:* St Peter's Col, NJ, BS, 51; Fordham Univ, MS, 55, PhD(biol), 65. *Prof Exp:* Asst plant physiologist, Boyce Thompson Inst Plant Res, Inc, 57-66; SR BIOCHEMIST, HOFFMANN-LA ROCHE, INC, 66- *Mem:* Am Soc Pharmacol & Exp Therapeut; NY Acad Sci. *Res:* In vivo and in vitro metabolic studies of radioactive experimental drugs. *Mailing Add:* Hoffmann-La Roche Inc Kingsland St Nutley NJ 07110

LAURENDEAU, NORMAND MAURICE, b Lewiston, Maine, Aug 16, 44; m 72; c 2. MECHANICAL ENGINEERING, PHYSICAL CHEMISTRY. *Educ:* Univ Notre Dame, BS, 66; Princeton Univ, MSE, 68; Univ Calif, Berkeley, PhD(mech eng), 72. *Prof Exp:* From asst prof to assoc prof, 72-82, PROF MECH ENG, PURDUE UNIV, 82- *Concurrent Pos:* Res engr, Arthur D Little, Inc, 80-81; consult, Ind Energy Develop Bd, 81-; dir, Coal Res Ctr, Purdue Univ, 81- *Mem:* Am Soc Mech Engrs; Am Chem Soc; Combustion Inst; Am Soc Eng Educ. *Res:* Combustion; chemical kinetics; coal combustion and gasification; combustion diagnostics; air pollution; heterogeneous char reactions. *Mailing Add:* Sch of Mech Eng Purdue Univ West Lafayette IN 47907

LAURENSON, RAE DUNCAN, b Lerwick, Scotland, Sept 10, 22; m 53; c 3. ANATOMY, MEDICAL EDUCATION. *Educ:* Univ Aberdeen, MB & Chb, 53, MD, 63. *Prof Exp:* Lectr anat, Univ Aberdeen, 54-57; asst prof, Queen's Univ, Ont, 57-63; from assoc prof to prof anat, Univ Alta, 68-74; COORDR MED INSTRNL RESOURCES, FAC MED, UNIV CALGARY, 74- *Concurrent Pos:* Dir health sci AV educ, Health Sci Ctr, Univ Alta, 69-74. *Res:* Communications; health sciences AV education. *Mailing Add:* 2212 12th Ave NW Calgary AB T2N 1K2 Can

LAURENSON, ROBERT MARK, b Pittsburgh, Pa, Oct 25, 38; m 61; c 2. MECHANICAL ENGINEERING. *Educ:* Mo Sch Mines, BS, 61; Univ Mich, Ann Arbor, MSE, 62; Ga Inst Technol, PhD(mech eng), 69. *Prof Exp:* Dynamics engr, McDonnell Aircraft Co, 62-64; sr dynamics engr, McDonnell Douglas Corp, 68-71; group dynamics engr, 71-74; staff engr, 74-75, TECH SPECIALIST, McDONNELL DOUGLAS CORP, 75- *Concurrent Pos:* Lectr, Dept Eng Mech, St Louis Univ, 69-71. *Honors & Awards:* Award, McDonnell Douglas Astronaut Co, McDonnell Douglas Corp, 71. *Mem:* Am Inst Aeronaut & Astronaut; Am Soc Mech Engrs. *Res:* Vibrations of structures and machine elements; response of elastic and flexible structures to transient loadings. *Mailing Add:* McDonnell Douglas Corp PO Box 516 St Louis MO 63166

LAURENT, ANDRE GILBERT (LOUIS), b Paris, France, July 13, 21; nat US; m 45, 70; c 5. MATHEMATICAL STATISTICS. *Educ:* Univ Paris, BA & BSc, 38, statistician economist dipl, 46; Univ Lyon, MSc, 42; Superior Nat Sch Mines, Saint-Etienne, PhD(math eng), 44. *Prof Exp:* Adminr & head prices sect, Nat Inst Statist & Econ, France, 46-54; from instr to asst prof statist, Mich State Univ, 54-57; assoc prof math statist, 57-63, PROF MATH STATIST, WAYNE STATE UNIV, 63- *Concurrent Pos:* Adj prof inst statist, Univ Paris, 52-54; Rockefeller Award fel comt statist, Univ Chicago, 53-54;

prof fac law, Royal Univ Khmere, Cambodia, 63-65; statist adv, Cambodian Govt for Asia Found, 63-65. *Mem:* Fel Am Statist Asn; Inst Math Statist; Am Acad Relig. *Res:* Mathematical statistics; foundations of statistics; statistical multivariate analysis; theory of meaning. *Mailing Add:* 10230 Dartmouth Oak Park MI 48237

LAURENT, ROGER, b Geneva, Switz, June 23, 38; m 62; c 2. GEOLOGY. *Educ:* Univ Geneva, Lic es sci, 62, Ing Geol, 64, Dr es Sci(geol & mineral sci), 67. *Prof Exp:* Asst mineral, Univ Geneva, 63-65, res asst geochronology for Sci Res Nat Corp of Switz, 65-67; asst prof mineral & petrog, Middlebury Col, 67-71; adj prof, 71-73, assoc prof, 73-79, PROF PETROL, LAVAL UNIV, 79- *Concurrent Pos:* Vis prof, Univ Nancy, France, 80. *Mem:* Fel Geol Asn Can; Swiss Soc Mineral & Petrog; Swiss Geol Soc; fel Geol Soc Am. *Res:* Study of ophiolites and asbestos in the field and in the labs by petrography; petrology; geochronometric determinations and geochemical studies. *Mailing Add:* Dept Geol Laval Univ Quebec PQ C1K 7P4 Can

LAURENT, SEBASTIAN MARC, b Wallace, La, Jan 21, 26; m 49; c 7. CATALYSIS, ZEOLITE SCIENCE. *Educ:* Loyola Univ, La, BS, 49. *Prof Exp:* Res physicist catalysis, Esso Res Labs, Humble Oil & Refining Co, 57-67; res physicist, 67-77, sr res physicist mat sci, 77-80, SR RES PHYSICIST, ZEOLITE APPL RES, ETHYL CORP, 80- *Mem:* Catalysis Soc; Int Zeolite Asn. *Res:* Zeolites; scanning electron microscopy; x-ray crystallography; x-ray fluorescence spectroscopy; adsorption; ion exchange; animal science research. *Mailing Add:* Ethyl Corp PO Box 341 Baton Rouge LA 70821

LAURENZI, BERNARD JOHN, b Philadelphia, Pa, Dec 23, 38. CHEMICAL PHYSICS. *Educ:* St Joseph's Col, Pa, BS, 60; Univ Pa, PhD(chem), 65. *Prof Exp:* Res chemist, Rohm & Haas Chem Co, 60-61; NSF fel, Pa State Univ, 65-66; asst prof chem, Univ Tenn, Knoxville, 66-68 & Bryn Mawr Col, 68-69; asst prof, 69-71, ASSOC PROF CHEM, STATE UNIV NY ALBANY, 71- *Mem:* Am Chem Soc; Am Phys Soc. *Res:* Quantum chemistry; use of Green's functions in atomic and molecular calculations; properties of isoelectronic molecules. *Mailing Add:* Dept Chem State Univ NY Albany NY 12222

LAURENZI, GUSTAVE, b Orange, NJ, July 19, 26; m; c 2. MEDICINE. *Educ:* NY Univ, BA, 49; Georgetown Univ, MD, 53; Am Bd Internal Med, dipl; Am Bd Pulmonary Dis, dipl. *Prof Exp:* Intern path, Mallory Inst Path, Boston City Hosp, 53-54; intern med, Yale Med Serv, Grace-New Haven Hosp, Conn, 54-55; asst resident, Columbia Med Serv, Bellevue Hosp, NY, 55-56; chief resident physician chest serv, Bellevue Med Ctr, 58-59; asst prof med & dir div respiratory dis, NJ Col Med & Dent, 60-63, assoc prof med, 63-68; assoc prof, 70-75, PROF MED, SCH MED, TUFTS UNIV, 75- *Concurrent Pos:* Res fel, Cardiopulmonary Lab, Columbia-Presby Med Ctr, 56-57; USPHS res fel, 57-58; Nat Found training fel, Am Trudeau Soc, 58-59; Channing res fel bact & immunol, Mallory Inst Path, Harvard Univ & res fel, Am Thoracic Soc, 59-60; Am Thoracic Soc Edward L Trudeau fel, 62-64; consult, Harvard Med Serv, Boston City Hosp, 59-60; chief med, St Vincent Hosp, Worcester, Mass, 68-; dir respiratory care serv, Newton-Wellesley Hosp. *Mem:* Fel Am Col Physicians; Am Thoracic Soc; Am Fedn Clin Res. *Res:* Chest disease; chronic bronchitis and pulmonary emphysema. *Mailing Add:* Newton-Wellesley Hosp 2000 Washington St Newton Lower Falls MA 01778

LAURIE, JOHN SEWALL, b Gloucester, Mass, May 30, 25. EXPERIMENTAL BIOLOGY. *Educ:* Ore State Univ, BS, 50; Johns Hopkins Univ, ScD, 56. *Prof Exp:* Res fel parasite physiol, Inst Parasitol, McGill Univ, 56-57; instr zool, Tulane Univ, 57-59; asst prof exp biol, Univ Utah, 59-62; mem staff water pollution study, USPHS, 62-63; assoc prof biol, 63-80, PROF BIOL, EAST CAROLINA UNIV, 80- *Mem:* Am Soc Parasitol; Wildlife Dis Asn; Am Soc Zoologists; Sigma Xi. *Res:* Physiology of parasites; physiology, ultrastructure and ecology of helminth parasites. *Mailing Add:* Dept of Biol E Carolina Univ Greenville NC 27834

LAURIE, VICTOR WILLIAM, b Columbia, SC, June 1, 35; m 65; c 2. PHYSICAL CHEMISTRY. *Educ:* Univ SC, BS, 54; Harvard Univ, AM, 56, PhD(chem), 58. *Prof Exp:* Fel, Nat Res Coun-Nat Bur Standards, 57-59; NSF fel, Univ Calif, 59-60; asst prof chem, Stanford Univ, 60-66; assoc prof chem, Princeton Univ, 66-71, prof, 71-80. *Concurrent Pos:* Alfred P Sloan fel, 63-67; John S Guggenheim fel, 70. *Mem:* Sigma Xi; AAAS; Am Chem Soc; Am Phys Soc. *Res:* Molecular spectroscopy and structure. *Mailing Add:* 109 Kingsway Commons Princeton NJ 08540

LAURIENTE, MIKE, b Trail, BC, June 26, 22; US citizen; m 56; c 1. METALLURGY, PHYSICS. *Educ:* Mich Technol Univ, BS, 43, MS, 47; Johns Hopkins Univ, DrEng, 55. *Prof Exp:* Metallurgist, Int Harvester Co, Ill, 47-49; res staff asst metal physics, Johns Hopkins Univ, 49-55; fel engr, Aerospace Div, Westinghouse Elec Corp, Md, 56-62, adv engr, 62-71; mem staff, 71-76, PROG MGR, OFF SYSTS ENG, US DEPT TRANSP, WASHINGTON, DC, 76- *Concurrent Pos:* Consult, Ballistics Res Lab, Ord Dept, US Army, Aberdeen Proving Ground, 51-55. *Mem:* Am Phys Soc; fel Am Soc Metals. *Res:* Magnetic thin films; active and passive electronic devices; radiation damage; electrical insulation; magnetic anisotropic metals; technological advances having application to transportation safety and security. *Mailing Add:* White Gate Rd Clarksville MD 21029

LAURILA, SIMO HEIKKI, b Tampere, Finland, Jan 15, 20; m 46; c 5. GEODESY. *Educ:* Inst Technol, Finland, BSc, 46, MSc, 48, PhD(electronic surv, photogram), 53, LLSc, 56. *Prof Exp:* Surveyor, Finnish Govt, 46-48; res assoc photogram, Hq Staff, Finnish Defense Forces, 48-52; geodesist, Finnish Geod Inst, 53; res assoc electronic surv, Res Found, Ohio State Univ, 53-56, assoc prof geod, 56-59, assoc prof & res assoc, 60-62, prof photogram, 62-66; chmn dept geosci, 69-73, PROF GEOD SCI, UNIV HAWAII, 66-, HEAD GEOD DIV, HAWAII INST GEOPHYS, 66- *Concurrent Pos:* Sr sci ed, Finnish Broadcasting Corp, 60; Fulbright-Hays sr scholar, Finland, 73; UN expert Sri Lanka, 72, 74. *Honors & Awards:* Found Advan Technol Award,

Finland, 60; Kaarina & W A Heiskanen Award, Ohio State Univ, 65. *Mem:* Am Geophys Union. *Res:* Applications of electronics in geodesy photogrammetry and navigation. *Mailing Add:* Dept of Geol & Geophys Univ of Hawaii Honolulu HI 96822

LAURIN, ANDRE FREDERIC, b Ste Anne de Bellevue, Que, Jan 18, 29; m; c 3. PETROLOGY, STRUCTURAL GEOLOGY. *Educ:* Univ Montreal, BSc, 51; McGill Univ, MSc, 54; Laval Univ, DSc(petrol), 57. *Prof Exp:* Geologist, Que Dept Natural Resources, 56-65, regional geologist, Grenville, 65-69, dir mineral deposits serv, 69-71, dir geol serv, 71-78, gen dir geol & mineral res, 78-80, ASST DEP MINISTER, QUE DEPT NATURAL RESOURCES, 80- *Concurrent Pos:* Lectr tour numerous univs, France & Ger, 68. *Mem:* Fel Geol Soc Am; Geol Asn Can; Can Inst Mining & Metall; NY Acad Sci. *Res:* Mapping and supervision of the mapping of the Grenville geological province, Quebec on a regional scale. *Mailing Add:* 2011 Chapdelaine St Ste Foy PQ G1V 1M4 Can

LAURIN, DEAN GORDON, b Kalamazoo, Mich, Oct 18, 38; m 64; c 2. ENGINEERING, CHEMISTRY. *Educ:* Univ Mich, Ann Arbor, BS & BSE, 62, MSE, 64, PhD(chem eng), 67. *Prof Exp:* Inst Sci & Technol fel, Univ Mich, Ann Arbor, 67-68; res specialist, Monsanto Co, 68-70; SR BIOMED ENGR, BAXTER-TRAVENOL LABS, 71- *Mem:* Soc Plastics Engrs; Am Chem Soc; World Future Soc; Am Inst Chem Eng. *Res:* Polymer synthesis and development; organic electrochemistry; electroanalytical chemistry; biocompatible plastics and rubbers; thermoplastic elastomers; polymer alloys. *Mailing Add:* Baxter-Travenol Labs PO Box 490 Round Lake IL 60073

LAURIN, PUSHPAMALA, b Bangalore City, India; US citizen; m 64; c 2. ELECTROMAGNETISM. *Educ:* Gujarat Univ, India, BSc, 56; Karnatak Univ, India, MSc, 58; Univ Mich, Ann Arbor, MSE, 62, PhD(physics), 67. *Prof Exp:* Jr sci asst, Nat Sugar Inst, Kanpur, India, 58-59; sales engr, Toshniwal Bros, Bombay, 59-60; res asst meteorol, Univ Mich, Ann Arbor, 61-62, asst res physicist, Radiation Lab, 62-67; asst prof math, Eastern Mich Univ, 67-68; res scientist physics, McDonnell-Douglas Corp, Mo, 68-69; lectr elec eng & physics, Southern Ill Univ, 70-71; instr electronics & physics, Harper Col, 71-76; DIR INFO RESOURCES, GOULD INC, ROLLING MEADOWS, ILL, 76- *Mem:* Inst Elec & Electronics Engrs. *Res:* Electromagnetic interactions. *Mailing Add:* 40 Gould Ctr Info Ctr Gould Inc Rolling Meadows IL 60008

LAURITZEN, PETER O, b Valparaiso, Ind, Feb 14, 35; m 63; c 2. ELECTRICAL ENGINEERING. *Educ:* Calif Inst Technol, BS, 56; Stanford Univ, MS, 58, PhD(elec eng), 61. *Prof Exp:* Mem tech staff, Fairchild Semiconductor Div, 61-65; from asst prof to assoc prof elec eng, 65-73, PROF ELEC ENG, UNIV WASH, 73- *Concurrent Pos:* Adj prof social mgt technol, Univ Wash, 77-; eng mgr, Avtech Corp, 79-80. *Mem:* Inst Elec & Electronics Engrs; Am Soc Eng Educ; AAAS. *Res:* Semiconductor devices and instrumentation; power electronics. *Mailing Add:* Dept of Elec Eng Univ of Wash Seattle WA 98195

LAURMANN, JOHN ALFRED, b Cambridge, Eng, Aug 8, 26; nat US; m 57; c 2. FLUID DYNAMICS. *Educ:* Cambridge Univ, BA, 47, MA, 51; Cranfield Univ, MSc, 51; Univ Calif, PhD(eng sci), 58. *Prof Exp:* Asst res engr, Univ Calif, 53-58; head aerodyn res, Space Technol Labs, Inc, 58-59; aeronaut res scientist, NASA, 59-60; staff scientist, Lockheed Missile & Space Co, 60-63; tech staff mem, Gen Res Corp, 63-69; staff mem, Inst Defense Anal, 69-70; sr staff mem, Nat Acad Sci, Washington, DC, 70-74; consult scientist, 75-76; SR RES ASSOC, DEPT MECH ENG, STANFORD UNIV, 76- *Concurrent Pos:* Lectr, Univ Calif, 55-58, San Jose State Col, 60 & Calif Exten Div, 60-63. *Mem:* Am Phys Soc; Am Geophys Union; Am Meteorol Soc; AAAS; Sigma Xi. *Res:* Environmental sciences; climatology; fluids; science administration. *Mailing Add:* Div of Applied Mech Stanford Univ Stanford CA 94305

LAURO, GABRIEL JOSEPH, b New York, NY, Oct 26, 30; m 58; c 2. FOOD SCIENCE, MICROBIOLOGY. *Educ:* NY Univ, AB, 52; Univ Idaho, MS, 55; Rutgers Univ, PhD(food sci), 60. *Prof Exp:* Microbiologist, Sixth Army Med Lab, Calif, 55-57; food scientist new prod develop, Lever Bros & Co, 60-63, food microbiologist, 63-65, asst new prod coord, 65-67; mgr new prod & Pkg coord, Thomas J Lipton, Inc, 67-69; dir res & develop, Roman Prod Corp, NJ, 69-71, vpres res & develop, 71-72; assoc res dir prod develop, Hunt-Wesson Foods Inc, 72-82; PRES, LA MONDE LTD, 82- *Mem:* Am Soc Microbiol; Inst Food Technologists. *Res:* Microbiology of foods and food processes; new product development and marketing; treponema pallidum immobilization test. *Mailing Add:* La Monde Ltd 424 W Commonwealth Suite 140 Fullerton CA 92632

LAURS, ROBERT MICHAEL, b Oregon City, Ore, Jan 27, 39; m 63; c 2. OCEANOGRAPHY, FISHERIES. *Educ:* Ore State Univ, BS, 61, MS, 63, PhD(oceanog), 67. *Prof Exp:* OCEANOGR, SOUTHWEST FISHERIES CTR, LA JOLLA LAB, NAT MARINE FISHERIES SERV, 67- *Concurrent Pos:* sci adv, Am Fisherman's Res Found, 71-; sci subgroup, Intergovernment Oceanog Comn, Intergrated Global Ocean Sta Syst, 81- *Mem:* AAAS; Marine Biol Asn UK; Am Soc Limnol & Oceanog; Am Inst Fishery Res Biologists; Eastern Pac Oceanic Conf. *Res:* Fishery forecasting; environmental conditions affecting the distribution and abundance of tunas; albacore tuna ecology; vertical distribution and migration of micronektonic organisms. *Mailing Add:* La Jolla Lab PO Box 271 Nat Marine Fisheries Serv La Jolla CA 92037

LAURSEN, E(MMETT) M(ORTON), b Fairmount, NDak, Jan 24, 19; m 51; c 3. HYDRAULIC ENGINEERING. *Educ:* Univ Minn, BCE, 41; Univ Iowa, PhD(mech, hydraul), 58. *Prof Exp:* Asst, St Anthony Falls Hydraul Lab, Minn, 41-42, asst scientist, 45; jr engr, Al Johnson Construct Co, 42-43; asst, Inst Hydraul Res, Univ Iowa, 45-47, res assoc, 47-48, res engr, 48-58; assoc prof civil eng, Mich State Univ, 58-62; head dept, 62-68, PROF CIVIL ENG, UNIV ARIZ, 62- *Honors & Awards:* Hilgard Prize, Am Soc Civil Engrs, 59, Res Prize, 61. *Mem:* Am Soc Civil Engrs; Am Geophys Union; Int Asn Hydraul Res. *Res:* Sediment transportation; fluid mechanics and its applications. *Mailing Add:* Dept of Civil Eng Univ of Ariz Tucson AZ 85721

LAURSEN, GARY A, b Seattle, Wash, Aug 13, 42; m 63; c 2. MYCOLOGY, ARCTIC ECOLOGY. *Educ:* Western Wash Univ, BA, 65; Univ Mont, MST, 70; Va Polytech Inst & State Univ, PhD(bot/mycol), 75. *Prof Exp:* Biol instr, Toppenish, Wash, Sch Dist, 65-71; res asst mycol, Va Polytech Inst & State Univ, 71-75, res assoc, 75-76; asst dir sci, Naval Arctic Res Lab, Univ Alaska, 76-80; proj officer cold prog, Off Naval Res, Arlington, 80-82. *Concurrent Pos:* actg tech dir admin & sci, Naval Arctic Res Lab, Univ Alaska, 76-77, prin investr, Animal Res Facil, 76- & Remote Sensing Prog, 77-78. *Honors & Awards:* Sigma Xi Res Award, Va Polytech Inst & State Univ, 77. *Mem:* Mycol Soc Am. *Res:* Systematic and ecological treatments of Arctic, Alpine and Meratime tundra fleshy fungi, their role and significance within these environmentally harsh ecosystems. *Mailing Add:* Cold Prof Off Naval Res 800 N Quincy St Arlington VA 22217

LAURSEN, PAUL HERBERT, b Ord, Nebr, Mar 28, 29; m 59; c 2. ORGANIC CHEMISTRY. *Educ:* Dana Col, BA, 54; Ore State Univ, PhD(org chem), 61. *Prof Exp:* From asst prof to assoc prof chem, 59-64, academic dean, 76-78, PROF CHEM, NEBR WESLEYAN UNIV, 64-, PROVOST, 78- *Concurrent Pos:* NSF sci fac fel, Univ Calif, Los Angeles, 67-68. *Mem:* AAAS; Am Chem Soc. *Res:* Synthesis of nitrogen heterocycles; identification of natural products. *Mailing Add:* Nebr Wesleyan Univ Lincoln NE 68504

LAURSEN, RICHARD ALLAN, b Normal, Ill, May 1, 38; m 71; c 2. BIO-ORGANIC CHEMISTRY. *Educ:* Univ Calif, Berkeley, BS, 61; Univ Ill, PhD(chem), 64. *Prof Exp:* NIH fel, Harvard Univ, 64-66; from asst prof to assoc prof chem, 66-76, PROF CHEM, BOSTON UNIV, 76- *Concurrent Pos:* NIH res career develop award, 69-74; guest scientist, Max Planck Inst Molecular Genetics, 71; Alfred P Sloan fel, 72-74; mem sci adv comt on clin invest, Am Cancer Soc, 75-79. *Mem:* AAAS; Am Chem Soc; Am Soc Biol Chemists. *Res:* Development of new methods for protein sequence analysis; sequence studies on elongation factors Tu and other proteins; structure and function of human plasmin. *Mailing Add:* Dept of Chem Boston Univ Boston MA 02215

LAUSCH, ROBERT NAGLE, b Chambersburg, Pa, Feb 22, 38; m 68; c 2. IMMUNOBIOLOGY. *Educ:* Muhlenberg Col, BS, 60; Pa State Univ, MS, 62; Univ Fla, PhD(microbiol), 66. *Prof Exp:* Fel virol, Baylor Col Med, 66-69; asst prof, 69-75, assoc prof microbiol, Col Med, Pa State Univ, 75-77; ASSOC PROF MICROBIOL & IMMUNOL, COL MED, UNIV S ALA, 77- *Mem:* Am Soc Microbiol; Am Asn Cancer Res; Am Asn Immunologists. *Res:* Vitus immunology; study of the host immune response to membrane antigens found on the surface of virus infected cells and how such cells may escape immune destruction. *Mailing Add:* Dept of Microbiol & Immunol Col Med Univ SAla Mobile AL 36688

LAUSH, GEORGE, b Barrackville, WVa, Sept 17, 21; m 56. MATHEMATICS. *Educ:* Univ Pittsburgh, BS, 43; Cornell Univ, PhD, 49. *Prof Exp:* Asst chem, Univ Pittsburgh, 43-44; res assoc, Manhattan Dist, Univ Rochester, 44-46; asst math, Cornell Univ, 46-49; from asst prof to assoc prof, 49-62, PROF MATH, UNIV PITTSBURGH, 62- *Mem:* Am Math Soc; Math Asn Am. *Res:* Infinite series; real functions; functional analysis. *Mailing Add:* Dept of Math Univ of Pittsburgh Pittsburgh PA 15260

LAUSHEY, LOUIS M(CNEAL), b Columbia, Pa, May 13, 17; m 49. CIVIL ENGINEERING. *Educ:* Pa State Univ, BS, 42; Carnegie Inst Technol, MS, 47, DSc, 51. *Prof Exp:* Struct draftsman, Am Bridge Co, NJ, 42; instr civil eng, Carnegie Inst Technol, 42-44, 46-48, from asst prof to assoc prof, 48-54; prof & head dept, Norwich Univ, 54-58; WILLIAM THOMS PROF CIVIL ENG & HEAD DEPT, UNIV CINCINNATI, 58- *Concurrent Pos:* Former partner, D'Appolonia, Laushey & Peck, Consult Engrs; consult to govt & industs. *Mem:* Am Soc Civil Engrs; Soc Am Mil Engrs; Am Soc Eng Educ; Am Geophys Union; Int Asn Hydraul Res. *Res:* Fluid mechanics; structural design and analysis. *Mailing Add:* Dept of Civil & Environ Eng Univ of Cincinnati Cincinnati OH 45221

LAUSON, HENRY DUMKE, b New Holstein, Wis, Aug 20, 12; m 77. PHYSIOLOGY. *Educ:* Univ Wis, BS, 36, PhD(physiol), 39, MD, 40. *Prof Exp:* Asst med, Univ Wis, 36-39; intern, Univ Kans Hosps, 40-41; asst resident med, Henry Ford Hosp, 41-42; Off Sci Res & Develop fel physiol & med, Col Med, NY Univ, 42-43, instr physiol, 43-46; assoc & assoc physician, Rockefeller Inst, 46-50; assoc prof physiol in pediat, Med Col, Cornell Univ, 50-55; chmn dept, 55-78, prof physiol, 55-78, EMER PROF PHYSIOL & BIOPHYSICS, ALBERT EINSTEIN COL MED, 78- *Concurrent Pos:* Assoc prof physiol, Med Col, Cornell Univ, 51-55; consult prog-proj comt, Nat Inst Arthritis & Metab Dis, 61-65. *Mem:* Am Physiol Soc; Am Soc Exp Biol & Med; Am Soc Clin Invest; Harvey Soc (secy, 52-55); Am Fed Clin Res. *Res:* Pituitary-ovary interrelations; blood pressure in human right heart; renal physiology; nephrotic syndrome; metabolism of antidiuretic hormone. *Mailing Add:* Leather Hill Rd RR1 Box 496 Wingdale NY 12594

LAUTENBERGER, WILLIAM J, b Flushing, NY, Mar 11, 43; m 67; c 2. APPLIED STATISTICS, PHYSICAL CHEMISTRY. *Educ:* Muhlenberg Col, BS, 64; Univ Pa, PhD(phys chem), 67. *Prof Exp:* Res chemist, Dye Div, Org Chem & Res & Develop Dept, Jackson Labs, NJ, 67-71, res chemist, Org Chem Dept, Exp Sta, Wilmington, 71-74, statist prog consult, 74-78, DEVELOP SPECIALIST, INDUST HYG, DU PONT FABRICS & FINISHES DEPT, APPL TECHNOL DIV, E I DU PONT DE NEMOURS & CO, WILMINGTON, 78- *Mem:* Am Chem Soc; Sigma Xi. *Res:* Reaction mechanisms; photochemistry; heterogeneous catalysis; mechanisms of dyeing; emulsion science; solid-solid adsorption; consulting in design and analysis of experiments; air sampling; gas diffusion mechanisms; gas adsorption, desorption phenomena. *Mailing Add:* 514 B S Randolph St Philadelphia PA 19147

LAUTENSCHLAEGER, FRIEDRICH KARL, b Gefell, Ger, June 27, 34; m 60; c 2. ORGANIC CHEMISTRY. *Educ:* Univ Heidelberg, BA, 56; Univ Toronto, MA, 60. *Prof Exp:* Res asst org chem, Univ Toronto, 57-59; res chemist, NAm Res Centre, Dunlop Co, Ltd, 61-72, GROUP LEADER, DUNLOP RES CENTRE, 72- *Mem:* Chem Inst Can; Am Chem Soc. *Res:* Stereochemistry of organic compounds; synthesis of small ring compounds; organic sulfur chemistry; reactive intermediates; vulcanization chemistry and physics. *Mailing Add:* Dunlop Res Centre Sheridan Park ON L5K 1X1 Can

LAUTENSCHLAGER, EUGENE PAUL, b Chicago, Ill, Apr 5, 37; m 61; c 1. BIOMATERIALS. *Educ:* Ill Inst Technol, BS, 58; Northwestern Univ, MS, 60, PhD(mat sci), 66. *Prof Exp:* Res metallurgist, Allis-Chalmers Mfg Co, 60-62; from asst prof to assoc prof, 66-74, PROF BIOL MAT, NORTHWESTERN UNIV, 74- *Concurrent Pos:* NIH career develop award, 71-75; consult, Bioeng Comt, Am Acad Orthop Surgeons, 73-81. *Mem:* Am Soc Testing & Mat; Am Inst Mining, Metall & Petrol Eng; Int Asn Dent Res. *Res:* Biological and dental materials; medical implant materials; kinetics of cementing media for implant stabilization; x-radiopacity; computer assisted instruction. *Mailing Add:* Dept of Biol Mat Northwestern Univ 311 E Chicago Chicago IL 60611

LAUTENSCHLAGER, HERMAN KENNETH, b Ohio, June 5, 18; m 42; c 3. GEOLOGY. *Educ:* Miami Univ, Ohio, AB, 42; Ohio State Univ, PhD(geol), 52. *Prof Exp:* Asst dept geol, Miami Univ, Ohio, 39-42; geologist, Ohio Fuel Gas Co, 45-48; asst dept geol, Ohio State Univ, 49-51; geologist, Standard Oil Co, Calif, 52-58; PROF GEOL, BAKERSFIELD COL, 58-, CHMN DEPT PHYS SCI, 67- *Concurrent Pos:* Vis prof, Ohio State Univ, 61-71. *Mem:* Geol Soc Am; Soc Econ Paleontologists & Mineralogists; Am Soc Testing & Mat; Am Asn Petrol Geologists; Nat Asn Geol Teachers. *Res:* Geology of Pavant Range of Utah, central coast ranges and San Joaquin Valley of California and Colorado plateaus. *Mailing Add:* 1801 Panorama Dr Bakersfield CA 93305

LAUTER, FELIX H, b Somerville, NJ, Feb 12, 19; m; c 1. PARASITOLOGY. *Educ:* Southwestern Col, Kans, BA, 50; La State Univ, MS, 52, PhD(parasitol), 59. *Prof Exp:* Asst prof Biol, Birmingham-Southern Col, 55-57; assoc prof & chmn dept, Ill Col, 58-61; ASSOC PROF PARASITOL & HISTOL, UNIV SC, 61- *Mem:* Am Soc Zoologists; Am Soc Parasitol. *Res:* Hemoflagellates and intestinal flagellates from anuran hosts; electron microscope studies in parasitology. *Mailing Add:* 1306 Glenhaven Dr Columbia SC 29205

LAUTERBACH, GEORGE ERVIN, b Bushnell, Ill, June 13, 27; m 49; c 5. PHYSICAL CHEMISTRY. *Educ:* Monmouth Col, BS, 49; Bradley Univ, MS, 53; Purdue Univ, PhD(biochem), 58. *Prof Exp:* Chemist, Starch & Dextrose Div, Northern Regional Res Lab, 49-53; res org chemist, Paper Lab, Kimberly Clark Corp, 57-65 & Pioneering & Advan Develop Lab, 65; assoc prof chem & res assoc, Div Natural Mat & Systs, Inst Paper Chem, 65-78; MGR NEW PRODS RES & DEVELOP, MARINE COLLOIDS INC, 78- *Mem:* Am Chem Soc; Tech Asn Pulp & Paper Indust; Am Asn Cereal Chemists. *Res:* Polysaccharide chemistry; enzymic and chemical modification of starch; high temperature starch cooking; hemicelluloses; starch in paper coatings; top sizes and internal sizing of paper products. *Mailing Add:* Marine Colloids Inc PO Box 213 Thomaston ME 04841

LAUTERBACH, JOHN HARVEY, b Jersey City, NJ, Apr 2, 44; div. CARBOHYDRATE CHEMISTRY, ANALYTICAL CHEMISTRY. *Educ:* Worcester Polytech Inst, BS, 66; Ohio State Univ, MSc, 68, PhD(chem), 70. *Prof Exp:* Asst anal chem, Ohio State Univ, 66-67; chief asst, 67-68 & org chem, 68-69, res assoc, 70-; chemist anal chem, Union Carbide Chem & Plastics Co, 70-71; proj supvr, Cent Tech Eval, Nat Starch & Chem Corp, 71-73, mgr, 74-78; mgr chem, Pillsbury Co, 78-79; dir chem, Prof Serv Indust, Inc, 79-80; ANALYTICAL RES DIV HEAD, BROWN & WILLIAMSON TOBACCO CORP, 80- *Concurrent Pos:* Chmn, Environ Comn, Borough Raritan, NJ, 76-78. *Mem:* Am Chem Soc; fel Am Inst Chemists; The Chem Soc; Sigma Xi; Am Soc Testing & Mat. *Res:* Polysaccharide chemistry, particularly structure determinations and modifications; high performance liquid chromatograph, and nuclear magnetic resonance spectroscopy; new techniques for managing service departments in research and development organizations. *Mailing Add:* Brown & Williamson PO Box 35090 Louisville KY 40232

LAUTERBACH, RICHARD THOMAS, b Rochester, Pa, Dec 29, 46; m 69; c 1. POLYMER CHEMISTRY, ORGANIC CHEMISTRY. *Educ:* Johns Hopkins Univ, BS, 68; Northwestern Univ, PhD(chem), 75. *Prof Exp:* group leader water soluble polymers, Daubert Chem Co, 75-80, group leader protective coatings, 80-81; GROUP LEADER, OIL FIELD SERVS, RICHARDSON CO, 81- *Mem:* Am Chem Soc; Soc Cosmetic Chem. *Res:* Water soluble polymers for wastewater treatment and paper production additives; corrosion preventive coatings. *Mailing Add:* 2701 Lake St Richardson Co Melrose Park IL 60160

LAUTERBUR, PAUL CHRISTIAN, b Sidney, Ohio, May 6, 29; m 58; c 2. PHYSICAL CHEMISTRY, MEDICAL IMAGING. *Educ:* Case Inst, BS, 51; Univ Pittsburgh, PhD(chem), 62. *Prof Exp:* Res asst, Mellon Inst, 51-52, res assoc, 52-53, jr fel, 53, fel, 55-63; assoc prof chem, 63-69, PROF CHEM, STATE UNIV NY STONY BROOK, 69-, RES PROF RADIOL, 78- *Concurrent Pos:* Ed, Magnetic Resonance in Med, 82- *Mem:* AAAS; Am Chem Soc; Am Phys Soc; Soc Magnetic Resonance Med (pres, 81). *Res:* Nuclear magnetic resonance studies of structure and properties of molecules, crystals and biological systems; imaging by magnetic resonance zeugmatography, including biological and medical applications. *Mailing Add:* Dept Chem State Univ NY Stony Brook NY 11794

LAUTT, WILFRED WAYNE, b Lethbridge, Alta, Can, June 29, 46; m 68; c 2. LIVER FUNCTIONS, HEPATIC CIRCULATION. *Educ:* Univ Alta, BSc, 68; Univ Man, MSc, 70, PhD(pharmacol), 72. *Prof Exp:* Med Res Coun Can fel toxicol, Univ Montreal, 72-74; asst prof & res scholar, 74-78, ASSOC

PROF PHYSIOL, CAN LIVER FOUND, UNIV SASK, 78- *Mem:* Microcirculatory Soc; Can Physiol Soc. *Res:* Peripheral vascular physiology and hepatic physiology, pharmacology and toxicology; vascular and metabolic consequences of autonomic nerve activity in the liver; local control of intestinal and hepatic blood flow. *Mailing Add:* Dept of Physiol Col of Med Univ of Sask Saskatoon SK S7N 0N0 Can

LAUTZ, WILLIAM, b New York, NY, Nov 17, 17; m 49. PLANT PATHOLOGY, AIR POLLUTION. *Educ:* Yale Univ, BS, 40; Cornell Univ, MS, 50. *Prof Exp:* Plant pathologist, USDA, 51-57, nematologist, Fla, 57-60, plant pest control inspector, 60-63, plant patholgist, 63-81; RETIRED. *Mem:* Nature Conservancy; Am Forestry Asn. *Res:* Plant pathology including breeding for disease resistance; plant nematology including chemical control of nematodes. *Mailing Add:* 101 S Sproul Rd Broomall PA 19008

LAUTZENHEISER, CLARENCE ERIC, b Lincoln, Nebr, May 21, 21; m 48; c 3. METALLURGY. *Educ:* Mass Inst Technol, BS, 52. *Prof Exp:* Res engr, Dow Chem Co, 52-53, maintenance engr, 52-60, maintenance specialist, 60-62; sr res engr, 62-67, mgr metall eng, 67-69, from asst dir to dir spec eng serv, 69-74, VPRES QUAL ASSURANCE SYSTS & ENG DIV, SOUTHWEST RES INST, 74- *Concurrent Pos:* Consult reliability & qual assurance div, NASA, 65-67. *Mem:* Am Soc Metals; Am Soc Nondestructive Testing (pres, 75-76); Am Welding Soc; Am Soc Mech Engrs; Nat Asn Corrosion Engrs. *Res:* New methods of magnesium production; corrosion; failure analysis; welding; nondestructive inspection in petrochemical industry fabrication quality control and in-service inspection of nuclear reactor power systems. *Mailing Add:* Southwest Res Inst 6220 Culebra Rd San Antonio TX 78284

LAUVER, DEAN C, b Warren, Pa, June 8, 20; m 46; c 3. MECHANICAL ENGINEERING. *Educ:* Pa State Univ, BS, 42. *Prof Exp:* Jr engr, Mesta Mach Co, Pa, 42; stress analyst, Air Frame Design Div, Bur Aeronaut, Dept Navy, 46-49, head struct design & anal unit, 49-57, tech asst & asst head contract struct design sect, 57-59, air craft & missile specialist, Chief of Naval Opers, 59-61; chief struct & mat br, Fed Aviation Agency, 61-62; tech dir air progs, 62-67, DEP ASST CHIEF TECHNOL, OFF NAVAL RES, 67- *Concurrent Pos:* Mem Fed Aviation Agency-Air Force-NASA working groups supersonic transport res progs & Fed Aviation Agency rep on NASA screening comt on mat, 62; Off Naval Res mem Dept Defense res & eng panel supporting res & technol, Aeronaut & Astronaut Coord Bd, 66- *Mem:* Am Inst Aeronaut & Astronaut. *Res:* Naval vehicle and weapon research and technology, including sensors, electronics, acoustics and operational analysis. *Mailing Add:* 6538 Cedarwood Ct Falls Church VA 22041

LAUVER, MILTON RENICK, b Springfield, Ohio, Sept 14, 20; m 48; c 4. PLASMA PHYSICS. *Educ:* Wittenberg Col, AB, 42; Western Reserve Univ, MS, 44, PhD(phys chem), 48. *Prof Exp:* Res chemist, Westvaco Div, Food Mach & Chem Corp, 48-53; res chemist chromium chem div, Diamond Alkali Co, 53-58; RES CHEMIST, LEWIS RES CTR, NASA, 58- *Mem:* Electrochem Soc; Am Chem Soc. *Res:* Gas dynamics; nuclear fusion plasmas; electrochemistry and phosphoric acid fuel cell technology. *Mailing Add:* 28385 Holly Dr North Olmsted OH 44070

LAUVER, RICHARD WILLIAM, b Monmouth, Ill, Mar 15, 43; m 72. PHYSICAL CHEMISTRY. *Educ:* Knox Col, AB, 65; Univ Ill, Urbana, PhD(chem), 70. *Prof Exp:* Nat Res Coun res assoc, 72-74, RES CHEMIST, LEWIS RES CTR, NASA, 74- *Mem:* Am Chem Soc; Soc Adv Mat & Process Eng; Soc Plastic Eng; Coblentz Soc. *Res:* Physical and chemical characterization of polymer materials. *Mailing Add:* 20090 Carolyn Ave Rocky River OH 44116

LAUX, DAVID CHARLES, b Sarver, Pa, Jan 1 45; m 70; c 1. IMMUNOLOGY, ONCOLOGY. *Educ:* Washington & Jefferson Col, BA, 66; Miami Univ, MS, 68; Univ Ariz, PhD(microbiol), 71. *Prof Exp:* Fel immunol, Dept Microbiol, Sch Med, Pa State Univ, 71-73; ASSOC PROF IMMUNOL, DEPT MICROBIOL, UNIV RI, 73- *Concurrent Pos:* Res grant, Nat Cancer Inst, 74, 78 & 80. *Mem:* Am Asn Cancer Res; Am Soc Microbiol. *Res:* Investigation of factors responsible for tumor mediated suppression of cellular immune reactivity; molecular basis of large intestine colonization; T-lymphocyte mediated cytotoxicity. *Mailing Add:* Dept of Microbiol 318 Morrill Hall Univ of RI Kingston RI 02881

LAUZAU, WILBUR R, inorganic chemistry, physical chemistry, see previous edition

LAUZON, RODRIGUE VINCENT, b Ottawa, Ont, Oct 24, 37; US citizen; m 65; c 2. COLLOID SCIENCE, POLYMER SCIENCE. *Educ:* Univ Toronto, BA, 60; Univ Conn, MS, 62; Clarkson Col Technol, PhD(colloid chem), 71. *Prof Exp:* Res specialist latex, Dow Chem Co, 70-74; res assoc colloid chem, Celanese Res Co, 74-75; dir, latex res & develop, Dart Industs, 75-78; SR RES SCIENTIST COLLOID, NL BAROID, NL INDUSTS, INC, 78- *Mem:* Am Chem Soc; Trade Asn Pulp & Paper Indust; Soc Petrol Engrs; Inst Colloid & Surface Sci. *Res:* Inorganic colloids; clays, oxides, halides; polymeric colloids: latexes, water-soluble polymers, natural polymers; rheology of disperse systems; drilling muds; foams and emulsions; coagulation; adsorption from solution; electrokinetics. *Mailing Add:* 206 Lakeshore Dr Seabrook TX 77586

LAVAGNINO, EDWARD RALPH, b Fall River, Mass, Apr 3, 30; m 58; c 4. ORGANIC CHEMISTRY. *Educ:* Southeastern Mass Technol Inst, BS, 52; Univ Mass, MS, 55. *Prof Exp:* Assoc sr org chemist, 54-68, sr org chemist, 68-75, RES SCIENTIST, CHEM RES DIV, ELI LILLY & CO, 75- *Mem:* Am Chem Soc. *Res:* Preparative organic chemistry; hydrogenation and high pressure reactions. *Mailing Add:* Chem Res Div Eli Lilly & Co 307 E McCarty St Indianapolis IN 46206

LAVAIL, JENNIFER HART, b Evansville, Ind, Apr 2, 43; m 70; c 2. NEUROANATOMY, NEUROEMBRYOLOGY. *Educ:* Trinity Col, DC, BA, 65; Univ Wis, PhD(anat), 70. *Prof Exp:* From instr to asst prof neuropath, Harvard Med Sch, 73-76; ASSOC PROF ANAT, UNIV CALIF, SAN FRANCISCO, 76- *Concurrent Pos:* Vis fel anat, Sch Med, Washington Univ, 68-69, res fel, 69-70; Nat Inst Neurol Dis & Stroke res fel neuropath, Harvard Med Sch, 70-73, spec fel, 73-76; Alfred P Sloan fel, 76-79. *Mem:* Am Asn Anatomists; Soc Neurosci. *Res:* Development of the central nervous system; anterograde and retrograde axonal transport. *Mailing Add:* Dept Anat Univ Calif San Francisco CA 94143

LAVAIL, MATTHEW MAURICE, b Abilene, Tex, Jan 7, 43; m 70. NEUROSCIENCES, CELL BIOLOGY. *Educ:* NTex State Univ, BA, 65; Univ Tex Med Br, PhD(anat), 69. *Prof Exp:* Res fel, Harvard Med Sch, 69-73, asst prof neuropath, 73-76; actg chmn, 81-82, ASSOC PROF ANAT, MED SCH, UNIV CALIF, SAN FRANCISCO, 76- *Concurrent Pos:* NatEye Inst fel neuropath, Harvard Med Sch, 70-73; res assoc neurosci, Children's Hosp Med Ctr, 73-76; Nat Eye Inst res career develop award, 74-79. *Honors & Awards:* Res Award, Sigma Xi, 70; Fight for Sight Citation, 75; Sundial Award, Retina Found, 76; Friedenwald Award, Asn Res Vision & Ophthal, 81. *Mem:* Asn Res Vision & Ophthal; Soc Cell Biol; AAAS; Am Asn Anat; Soc Neurosci. *Res:* Photoreceptor-pigment epithelial cell interactions; retinal development; inherited retinal degeneration; neuroembryology; retrograde axonal transport. *Mailing Add:* Dept of Anat Univ of Calif San Francisco CA 94143

LAVAL, WILLIAM NORRIS, b Seattle, Wash, Jan 27, 22; m 63; c 2. GEOLOGY. *Educ:* Univ Wash, BS, 43, MS, 48, PhD(geol), 56. *Prof Exp:* Field asst, US Geol Surv, 42, geologist, 43-45 & 48-49; geologist, Corps Eng, US Army, 49-51; resident geologist, Yale Dam, Ebasco Serv, Inc, Wash, 51-53; asst prof geol, Colo State Univ, 56-60; assoc prof geol & geol eng, SDak Sch Mines & Technol, 60-62; chmn div natural sci, 63-75, PROF GEOL & EARTH SCI, LEWIS-CLARK STATE COL, 63- *Concurrent Pos:* Consult, 54-56 & 62-63. *Mem:* Fel Geol Soc Am. *Res:* Stratigraphy, structure and petrology of Columbia Plateau; environmental geology; earth sciences teaching. *Mailing Add:* Lewis-Clark State Col Lewiston ID 83501

LAVALLE, PLACIDO DOMINICK, b New York, NY, May 13, 37; m 58; c 3. GEOMORPHOLOGY. *Educ:* Columbia Univ, BA, 59; Univ Southern Ill, MA, 61; Univ Iowa, PhD(geog), 65. *Prof Exp:* Res asst geog, Univ Iowa, 62-63; asst prof, Univ Calif, Los Angeles, 64-67 & Univ Ill, Urbana, 67-69; ASSOC PROF GEOG, UNIV WINDSOR, 69- *Mem:* AAAS; Asn Am Geogrs; Am Geophys Union; Nat Speleol Soc. *Res:* Soil geography; quantative analysis of karst geomorphology in Kentucky and Puerto Rico; spatial patterns of soil toxin distribution in Lebec, California; application of remote sensors in environmental research. *Mailing Add:* Dept of Geog Univ of Windsor Windsor ON N9B 3P4 Can

LAVALLEE, DAVID KENNETH, b Malone, NY, Oct 1, 45; m 71; c 2. INORGANIC CHEMISTRY, BIOLOGICAL CHEMISTRY. *Educ:* St Bonaventure Univ, BS, 67; Univ Chicago, SM, 68, PhD(inorg chem), 71. *Prof Exp:* USPHS fel, Dept Anat, Univ Chicago, 71-72; asst prof chem, Colo State Univ, 72-78; ASSOC PROF CHEM, HUNTER COL, 78- *Concurrent Pos:* Vis scientist, Argonne Nat Lab, 71-72; mem grad fac biochem & chem, City Univ New York, 78-; res collabr, Brookhaven Nat Lab, 79- *Mem:* Am Chem Soc; AAAS; Sigma Xi; NY Acad Sci. *Res:* Synthesis, spectroscopy, reaction mechanisms and structural chemistry of metalloporphyrins; electron transfer reaction mechanisms; nuclear magnetic resonance spectroscopy of coordination compounds. *Mailing Add:* Dept of Chem 695 Park Ave New York NY 10021

LAVALLEE, LORRAINE DORIS, b Holyoke, Mass, May 31, 31. MATHEMATICS. *Educ:* Mt Holyoke Col, AB, 53; Univ Mass, MA, 55; Univ Mich, PhD(math), 62. *Prof Exp:* Instr, 59-60, asst prof, 60-70, assoc head, Dept Math & Statist, 71-72, ASSOC PROF MATH, UNIV MASS, AMHERST, 70- *Mem:* Am Math Soc; Asn Women in Math; Math Asn Am. *Res:* General topology. *Mailing Add:* Dept of Math & Statist Univ of Mass Amherst MA 01003

LA VALLEE, WILLIAM ALFRED, pulp & paper technology, see previous edition

LAVANCHY, ANDRE C(HRISTIAN), b Switz, Nov 17, 22; nat US; m 53; c 3. MECHANICAL ENGINEERING. *Educ:* Swiss Fed Inst Technol, ME, 46. *Prof Exp:* Design & test engr, Brown & Boveri, Switz, 46-49; res engr, Sharples Res Labs, 50-55, chief anal engr, 56-65, MGR CENTRIFUGE DEVELOP, PENNWALT CORP, 65- *Concurrent Pos:* Design engr, Am Viscose Corp, 55. *Mem:* Am Soc Mech Engrs. *Res:* Stress and vibration analysis; applied dynamics; powder technology; liquid-liquid and solid-liquid separation; fluid flow; aerodynamics; thermodynamics. *Mailing Add:* Sharples Stokes Div Pennwalt Corp 955 Mearns Rd Warminster PA 18974

LAVANISH, JEROME MICHAEL, b Cleveland, Ohio, Mar 10, 40; m 65. ORGANIC CHEMISTRY. *Educ:* Case Inst Technol, BS, 62; Yale Univ, MS, 63, PhD(chem), 66. *Prof Exp:* Sr res chemist, 66-80, SR RES ASSOC, PPG INDUSTS, 80- *Mem:* Am Chem Soc; Sigma Xi; NY Acad Sci. *Res:* Synthetic organic chemistry; synthesis and action of herbicides and plant growth regulators. *Mailing Add:* Chem Div PPG Indust PO Box 31 Barberton OH 44203

LAVAPPA, KANTHARAJAPURA S, b India, Mar 8, 38; m 68; c 3. BIOLOGY. *Educ:* Univ Mysore, BSc, 59, MSc, 60; Boston Univ, PhD(biol), 68. *Prof Exp:* Lectr zool, Univ Mysore, 60-62; sci officer, Ministry of Sci Res, Govt India, 63-64; res asst, Children's Cancer Res Found, Boston, Mass, 65-68, fel, Lab Cytogenetics, 68-70; res assoc path, Children's Hosp Med Ctr, Boston, 70-72; asst prof pharmacol, Med Sch, Case Western Reserve Univ, 72-74; res assoc, Am Type Cult Collection, 74-79; biologist, 79-81, TOXICOLOGIST, US ENVIRON PROTECTION AGENCY, 81-

Concurrent Pos: Nat Found-March of Dimes Basil O'Connor starter res grant, 73-74; ed reviewer, Lab Animal Sci, 73 & Can J Genetics & Cytol, 74; vis fac, Alton Jones Cell Sci Ctr, 77-78. *Mem:* Environ Mutagen Soc; Tissue Cult Asn. *Res:* In vivo and in vitro human and mammalian cytogenetics; environmental mutagenesis, teratogenesis and carcinogenesis. *Mailing Add:* Off Health & Environ Assessment RD-689 Environ Protection Agency 401 M St SW Washington DC 20852

LAVE, ROY E(LLIS), JR, b Homewood, Ill, Sept 23, 35; m 60; c 2. INDUSTRIAL ENGINEERING, OPERATIONS RESEARCH. *Educ:* Univ Mich, BS & MBA, 58, MS, 60; Stanford Univ, PhD(indust eng), 65. *Prof Exp:* Asst opers res, Univ Mich, 57-60; asst prof indust eng, Stanford Univ, 62-68, assoc prof & assoc chmn dept, 68-72; DIR & CHMN BD, SYSTAN, INC, 66- *Concurrent Pos:* Consult, Rand Corp, 61-65, Coun Int Prog Mgt, 63, Agency Int Develop, 65-67 & Ford Found, 66; assoc prof eng-econ systs & dir fed internships & interdisciplinary projs, Stanford Univ, 67-68; consult, Inter-Am Develop Bank, 68-72 & Unido, 68-70; dir, Phoenix Housing Develop Corp, 69-77 & Consumer Alliance, 71-73. *Honors & Awards:* Outstanding Young Fac, Am Soc Eng Educ, 71. *Mem:* Opers Res Soc Am; Inst Mgt Sci; Am Inst Indust Engrs. *Res:* Systems analysis in international development planning; managements control systems; national and urban transportation planning; decision budgeting; information systems design. *Mailing Add:* Systan Inc PO Box U Los Altos CA 94022

LAVEGLIA, JAMES GARY, b Cleveland, Ohio, May 8, 47; m 68; c 3. ENTOMOLOGY. *Educ:* Bowling Green State Univ, BS, 69, MA, 70; Iowa State Univ, PhD(entom), 75. *Prof Exp:* Res assoc entom, Iowa State Univ, 72-76; sr toxicologist, Monsanto Co, 76-78; DIR DEPT PREP, INT RES DEVELOP CORP, 78- *Mem:* Entom Soc Am; Sigma Xi. *Res:* The interaction of insecticides with soil, including their effect on soil microorganisms, as well as their breakdown in the soil. *Mailing Add:* Int Res & Develop Corp Mattawan MI 49071

LAVELLE, FAITH WILSON, b St Johnsbury, Vt, Mar 14, 21; m 47; c 1. HISTOLOGY, NEUROEMBRYOLOGY. *Educ:* Mt Holyoke Col, BA, 43, MA, 45; Johns Hopkins Univ, PhD(biol), 49. *Prof Exp:* Lab instr zool, Mt Holyoke Col, 43-45; admin asst zool, Univ Pa, 48-51, instr anat, Med Sch, 51-52; lectr, Univ Ill Col Med, 52-53, instr, 53-55, res assoc anat, 55-70; asst prof, 70-76, ASSOC PROF ANAT, STRITCH SCH MED, LOYOLA UNIV CHICAGO, 76- *Concurrent Pos:* USPHS res grant, Univ Ill Col Med, 53-70. *Mem:* Am Asn Anat; Soc Neurosci; Sigma Xi. *Res:* Experimental alteration of development of nerve cells; proteins in neural development. *Mailing Add:* Dept of Anat Loyola Univ Med Ctr Maywood IL 60153

LAVELLE, GEORGE ARTHUR, b Fargo, NDak, Nov 29, 21; m 47; c 1. NEUROANATOMY. *Educ:* Univ Wash, BS, 46; Johns Hopkins Univ, MA, 48; Univ Pa, PhD(anat), 51. *Prof Exp:* Asst zool, Univ Wash, 44-46; jr instr biol, Johns Hopkins Univ, 46-48; asst instr anat, Sch Med, Univ Pa, 48-51; from instr to assoc prof, 52-65, PROF ANAT, UNIV ILL COL MED, 65- *Concurrent Pos:* USPHS fel, Univ Pa, 51-52; USPHS-NIH res grant, Univ Ill, 53-70; vis prof dept anat & brain res inst & Guggenheim fel, Univ Calif, Los Angeles, 68-69. *Mem:* AAAS; Am Asn Anat; Biol Stain Comn (pres, 81-); Soc Develop Biol; Am Soc Cell Biol. *Res:* Neurocytology; cytological development of nerve cells; experimental alteration of development of nerve cells. *Mailing Add:* Dept of Anat Univ of Ill Col of Med Chicago IL 60612

LAVELLE, GEORGE CARTWRIGHT, b Minneapolis, Minn, Dec 1, 37; m 66; c 4. TOXICOLOGY. *Educ:* St Johns Univ, Minn, BA, 59; Univ Notre Dame, PhD(microbiol), 67. *Prof Exp:* Res assoc, Sch Hyg & Pub Health, Johns Hopkins Univ, 67-69; sr staff fel NIH, 69-73; res scientist virol, Oak Ridge Nat Lab, 73-79; DIR, TECH SERV, HILL TOP RES, INC, 80- *Concurrent Pos:* Mem fac, Univ Tenn-Oak Ridge Grad Sch Biomed Sci, 75-79. *Mem:* Environ Mutagen Soc; Am Soc Microbiol. *Res:* Genetic toxicology, especially in vitro carcinogenesis, mutagenesis, cytogenetics, as applied to environmental and industrial toxicology and product safety. *Mailing Add:* Hill Top Res Inc PO Box 42501 Cincinnati OH 45242

LAVELLE, JAMES W, b Lamar, Colo, Aug 11, 30; m 50; c 3. LIMNOLOGY. *Educ:* Abilene Christian Col, BS, 53; Univ Tex, MA, 55, PhD(stream biol), 68. *Prof Exp:* Instr biol, Abilene Christian Col, 55-56; PROF BIOL, UNIV SOUTHERN COLO, 56- *Res:* Primary and secondary productivity of the upper Arkansas River; stream biology and limnology. *Mailing Add:* Dept of Life Sci Univ of Southern Colo Pueblo CO 81001

LAVELLE, JOHN WILLIAM, b Sacramento, Calif, Apr 26, 43; m 71. GEOLOGICAL OCEANOGRAPHY, PHYSICAL OCEANOGRAPHY. *Educ:* Univ Calif, Berkeley, BA, 65; Univ Calif, San Diego, MS, 68, PhD(physics), 71. *Prof Exp:* Marine geophysicist, 72-73, geol oceanogr, Environ Res Labs, Miami, 73-76, GEOL OCEANOGR, PAC MARINE ENVIRON LAB, NAT OCEANOG & ATMOSPHERIC ADMIN, 76- *Mem:* Am Geophys Union; Am Phys Soc. *Res:* Experimental and theoretical studies of sediment movement and bed forms in marine environments. *Mailing Add:* Pac Marine Environ Lab 3711 15th Ave NE Seattle WA 98105

LAVENDEL, HENRY W, b Warsaw, Poland, Apr 23, 19; m 51; c 2. CHEMICAL ENGINEERING, METALLURGY. *Educ:* Univ MIlan, PhD(indust chem), 51. *Prof Exp:* Res scientist powder metall, Am Electro Metal Co, NY, 52-55; res assoc, Sintercast Corp, 55-57; assoc chem engr, Argonne Nat Lab, 57-60; SR STAFF SCIENTIST, PALO ALTO RES LABS, LOCKHEED MISSILES & SPACE CO, LOCKHEED AIRCRAFT CO, 61- *Mem:* Sigma Xi; Am Inst Mining, Metall & Petrol Engrs; Am Soc Metals; Am Chem Soc. *Res:* Research and development in the field of high temperature materials. *Mailing Add:* Lockheed Missiles & Space Co Palo Alto Res Labs 3251 Hanover Palo Alto CA 94304

LAVENDER, DENIS PETER, b Seattle, Wash, Oct 13, 26; m 57. PLANT PHYSIOLOGY. *Educ:* Univ Wash, BS, 49; Ore State Univ, MSc, 58, PhD, 62. *Prof Exp:* Res asst, Ore State Bd Forestry, 50-57, in chg forest physiol, Forest Res Ctr, 57-63; assoc prof, Ore Forest Res Lab, 63-70, PROF FOREST PHYSIOL, SCH FORESTRY, ORE STATE UNIV, 70- *Res:* Development of hardy coniferous seedlings; nutrition of second growth Douglas fir stands; reduction of the juvenile period of conifers; dormancy in Douglas fir seedlings and conifers; mineral nutrition and precocious flowering in conifers. *Mailing Add:* Sch of Forestry Ore State Univ Corvallis OR 97331

LAVENDER, DEWITT EARL, b Jackson Co, Ga, Nov 9, 38; m 58; c 3. MATHEMATICS, STATISTICS. *Educ:* Univ Ga, BS, 62, MA, 63, PhD(math, statist), 66. *Prof Exp:* Asst prof math, 66-68, ASSOC PROF MATH, GA SOUTHERN COL, 68-, HEAD DEPT, 70- *Mem:* Am Math Soc; Math Asn Am; Inst Math Statist. *Res:* Mathematical statistics. *Mailing Add:* Dept of Math Ga Southern Col Statesboro GA 30458

LAVENDER, JOHN FRANCIS, b Nov 16, 29; US citizen; m 69; c 3. VIROLOGY, MICROBIOLOGY. *Educ:* Drake Univ, BA, 51; Univ Ill, Champaign, MS, 53; Univ Calif, Los Angeles, PhD(infectious dis), 62. *Prof Exp:* NIMH fel virol, Univ Calif, Los Angeles, 62-63; sr virologist, 64-72, RES VIROLOGIST, ELI LILLY & CO, 72- *Mem:* Am Soc Microbiol; Sigma Xi; NY Acad Sci. *Res:* Psychological stress and viral disease resistance; drugs and the entry of viruses across the blood brain barrier; development of parainfluenza, rabies, canine distemper and measles vaccines; Herpes Simplex vaccines types 1 and 2; chemotherapy of virus diseases. *Mailing Add:* Dept MC 539 Virus Chemother Eli Lilly & Co Indianapolis IN 46206

LAVER, MURRAY LANE, b Warkworth, Ont, Mar 7, 32; m 63; c 2. ORGANIC CHEMISTRY. *Educ:* Ont Agr Col, BScA, 55; Ohio State Univ, PhD(org chem), 59. *Prof Exp:* Res chemist food sci, Westreco Co, 59-63; res chemist wood sci, Rayonier Can, Inc, 63; res scientist, Weyerhaeuser Co, 64-66, prof specialist res div, 66-68; res instr chem, Univ Wash, 68-69; ASSOC PROF FOREST PRODS CHEM, ORE STATE UNIV, 69- *Concurrent Pos:* Vis lectr biol chem, Harvard Univ, 77-78. *Mem:* Am Chem Soc. *Res:* Pulp and paper, carbohydrate, food and wood chemistry. *Mailing Add:* Sch of Forestry Ore State Univ Corvallis OR 97331

LAVERDIERE, MARC RICHARD, b Coaticook, Que, May 28, 46; m 69; c 3. CLAY MINERALOGY, SOIL CHEMISTRY. *Educ:* Laval Univ, BSc, 69, MSc, 71; Cornell Univ, PhD(agron), 76. *Prof Exp:* Res off pedogenesis, 71-73, RES SCIENTIST CLAY MINERAL, CAN DEPT AGR, 76- *Concurrent Pos:* Guest lectr, Fac Agr, Alimentation Dept Soils, Laval Univ, 77. *Mem:* Clays & Clay Minerals Soc; Am Soc Agron; Soil Sci Soc Am; Can Soil Sci Soc. *Res:* Nature and distribution of components responsible of cation and anion exchange capacities in soils of various texture; influence of drainage on specific soil properties; hydraulic conductivity; organic matter migration; evolution of clay minerals. *Mailing Add:* Can Dept of Agr Soils Sect 2560 Boul Hochelaga Ste-Foy PQ G1V 2J3 Can

LAVERELL, WILLIAM DAVID, mathematics, see previous edition

LAVERTY, JOHN JOSEPH, b Chicago, Ill, May 27, 38; m 67; c 2. ORGANIC CHEMISTRY. *Educ:* Eastern Ill Univ, BS, 64; Univ Ariz, MS, 66. *Prof Exp:* Res chemist, 66-71, assoc sr res chemist, 71-78, sr res chemist, 78-81, STAFF RES SCIENTIST, POLYMER DEPT, GEN MOTORS RES LABS, 81- *Mem:* Am Chem Soc. *Res:* Monomer and polymer synthesis; structure and property relationship of block and graft copolymers; polyurethanes. *Mailing Add:* Gen Motors Res Labs 12 Mile & Mound Rd Warren MI 48090

LAVERTY, WILLIAM F(INLEY), b Pasadena, Calif, Aug 3, 35; m 62; c 3. MECHANICAL ENGINEERING. *Educ:* Univ Calif, Los Angeles, BS, 57; Mass Inst Technol, MS, 58, ScD(mech eng), 64. *Prof Exp:* Anal engr, Pratt & Whitney Aircraft, 58-60, sr anal engr, 60-61; asst prof mech eng, Carnegie Inst Technol, 64-69; sr asst proj engr, 69-73, proj engr, 73-81, SR STAFF COM PROD DIV, PRATT & WHITNEY AIRCRAFT DIV, UNITED TECHNOLOGIES CORP, 73- *Concurrent Pos:* NSF res grant, 66-67. *Mem:* Am Soc Mech Engrs. *Res:* Heat transfer; fluid mechanics; two phase flow; wear mechanics; lubrication systems. *Mailing Add:* Pratt & Whitney Aircraft CPD 400 Main St East Hartford CT 06033

LAVERY, BERNARD JAMES, b New York, NY, Sept 7, 40; m 62; c 3. PHYSICAL CHEMISTRY. *Educ:* Mt St Mary's Col, BS, 62; Pa State Univ, PhD, 67. *Prof Exp:* RES CHEMIST, E I DU PONT DE NEMOURS & CO, INC, 66- *Res:* Nuclear magnetic resonance; liquid crystals; polymer solution rheology; textile fiber end-use research and product development; floor covering market development; apparel fibers technical service; industrial fibers direct marketing; technical marketing management. *Mailing Add:* Textile Fibers Dept E I du Pont de Nemours & Co Inc Wilmington DE 19898

LAVI, ABRAHIM, b Iran, Jan 12, 34; US citizen; m 59; c 2. ELECTRICAL ENGINEERING, COMPUTER SCIENCE. *Educ:* Purdue Univ, BScEE, 57; Carnegie Inst Technol, MS, 58, PhD(elec eng), 59. *Prof Exp:* Res asst, 57, from asst prof to assoc prof elec eng, 59-68, PROF ELEC ENG, CARNEGIE-MELLON UNIV, 68- *Concurrent Pos:* Consult, Graphic Arts Technol Found, Pa; mem staff, Dept Energy, Washington, DC, 76-78. *Mem:* Sr mem Inst Elec & Electronics Engrs; Marine Technol Soc; Int Solar Energy Soc. *Res:* System modelling and optimization; low temperature difference energy conversion; control and instrumentation. *Mailing Add:* Carnegie-Mellon Univ Pittsburgh PA 15213

LA VIA, MARIANO FRANCIS, b Rome, Italy, Jan 29, 26; nat US; m 59; c 7. PATHOLOGY. *Educ:* Univ Messina, MD, 49. *Prof Exp:* Asst gen path, Univ Palermo, 50-52; asst path, Univ Chicago, 52-57, instr anat, 57-60; from asst prof to assoc prof, Sch Med, Univ Colo, Denver, 60-68; prof, Bowman Gray Sch Med, 68-71; PROF PATH, SCH MED, EMORY UNIV, 71- *Mem:* Sigma Xi; Am Asn Immunol; Am Soc Exp Path; Am Soc Cell Biol; Soc Exp Biol & Med. *Res:* Cellular and biochemical mechanism of antibody production. *Mailing Add:* Dept of Path Emory Univ Sch of Med Atlanta GA 30322

LAVIER, EUGENE CLARK, b Ogdensburg, NY, Dec 26, 15; m 41; c 3. PHYSICS. *Educ:* US Air Force Inst Technol, BSc, 50; Johns Hopkins Univ, PhD(physics), 53. *Prof Exp:* Chief radiation br, Weapons Effects Div, Armed Forces Spec Weapons Proj, 53-57, dep comdr opers, Air Force Off Sci Res, 57-59, dep dir res vehicles & instrumentation, Air Res & Develop Command, 59-60, dir anal, 60-61; mgr res div, Nat Co, 61-65; mgr optical signal processing br, Perkin-Elmer Corp, 65-66; asst dir res & develop, Page Commun Engrs, 66-70; prin scientist, Northrop Corp Labs, 70-71; dir vulnerability, Defense Nuclear Agency, 71-77; RETIRED. *Res:* Physical sciences. *Mailing Add:* 7850 S Tropical Trail Merritt Island FL 32952

LAVIETES, BEVERLY BLATT, developmental biology, oncology, see previous edition

LAVIGNE, ANDRE ANDRE, b Manchester, NH, Sept 6, 32; m 53; c 3. ORGANIC CHEMISTRY. *Educ:* St Anselm's Col, BA, 58; Univ NH, MS, 60; Lowell Tech Inst, PhD(org chem), 64. *Prof Exp:* Head chemist, Sylvania Elec Co, 60-61; asst prof, 63-70, ASSOC PROF CHEM, ST ANSELM'S COL, 70-, DIR, INST RES & SERVS, 71- *Concurrent Pos:* Nat Defense Ed Act lectr adv high sch srs, 66; consult water pollution study, Merrimack River, Pub Serv Co, NH, 67-70; surv analyst effectiveness educ progs relevant to small town planning bd, 67-; dir, Water Resources Bd, State NH, 75- *Mem:* Am Chem Soc; NY Acad Sci. *Res:* Interaction of organocadmium reagents on various substituted phthalides; action of halogermanes on cyclic ethers. *Mailing Add:* Dept of Chem St Anselm's Col Manchester NH 03102

LAVIGNE, DAVID M, b Watford, England, Mar 18, 46; Can citizen; m 68; c 3. ZOOLOGY. *Educ:* Univ Western Ont, BSc, 68; Univ Guelph, MSc, 71, PhD(zool), 73. *Prof Exp:* Asst prof, 73-79, ASSOC PROF ZOOL, UNIV GUELPH, 79- *Concurrent Pos:* Mem, Comt Marine Mammals, Int Union Conserv Nature & Natural Resources, 77-; vis scientist, Brit Antarctic Surv, Cambridge, UK, 80-81. *Mem:* Can Soc Zoologists. *Res:* Population ecology of marine mammals, in particular of the harp seal; Phoca groenlandica; ecological energetics and life history parameters of mammalian populations. *Mailing Add:* Dept Zool Univ Guelph Guelph ON N1G 2W1 Can

LAVIGNE, ROBERT JAMES, b Herkimer, NY, May 30, 30; m 76; c 4. ENTOMOLOGY. *Educ:* Am Int Col, BA, 52; Univ Mass, MS, 58, PhD(entom), 61. *Prof Exp:* Res instr entom, Univ Mass, 56-59; from asst prof to assoc prof, 59-71, PROF ENTOM, UNIV WYO, 71- *Mem:* Entom Soc Am; Animal Behav Soc; Pan-Pac Entom Soc; Soc Range Mgt; Soc Am Acridiol. *Res:* Insect taxonomy, especially Diptera; insect behavior, especially robber flies, Asilidae, and horse flies, Tabanidae; environmental entomology; biocontrol of weeds; forest entomology; rangeland entomology. *Mailing Add:* Box 3354 University Sta Laramie WY 82070

LAVIK, PAUL SOPHUS, b Camrose, Alta, Feb 11, 15; US citizen; m 41; c 4. BIOCHEMISTRY. *Educ:* St Olaf Col, AB, 37; Univ Wis, MS, 41, PhD(biol chem), 43; Western Reserve Univ, MD, 59. *Prof Exp:* Instr biochem, Sch Med, La State Univ, 43; from instr to asst prof, Baylor Col Med, 43-47; asst prof biochem, 47-52, assoc prof, 52-70, ASSOC CLIN PROF RADIOL, SCH MED, CASE WESTERN RESERVE UNIV, 70- *Concurrent Pos:* Staff physician radiotherapy, Cleveland Clin, 74-81, emergency clin, 81-; pres, Radiation Therapy Consults, 82- *Mem:* Am Soc Biol Chemists; Radiation Res Soc; Am Asn Cancer Res; Am Soc Therapeut Radiologists; Am Col Radiol. *Res:* Nucleic acid metabolism; radiation biochemistry; radiation therapy. *Mailing Add:* Dept of Radiol Case Western Reserve Univ Cleveland OH 44106

LAVILLA, ROBERT E, b New York, NY, May 8, 26. PHYSICAL CHEMISTRY. *Educ:* Bethany Col, BS, 53; Cornell Univ, PhD(phys chem), 60. *Prof Exp:* RES CHEMIST, NAT BUR STANDARDS, 60- *Concurrent Pos:* Nat Res Coun-Nat Bur Standards fel, 60-61. *Mem:* Am Phys Soc. *Res:* Electron diffraction of solids and gases; optical properties of materials; x-ray absorption and emission. *Mailing Add:* Nat Bur of Standards Washington DC 20234

LAVIN, EDWARD, b Springfield, Mass, Jan 6, 16; m 48; c 3. POLYMER CHEMISTRY. *Educ:* Univ Mass, BS, 36; Tufts Col, MS, 37. *Prof Exp:* Res chemist, Shawinigan Resins Corp, 38-53, group leader, 53-56, sect leader, 56-60, dir appln res, 60-63, res mgr, 63-65; mgr res, 65-76, MGT TECHNOL, MONSANTO CO, 76- *Concurrent Pos:* Monsanto Acad Award, Harvard Univ, 49-50. *Mem:* AAAS; Am Chem Soc; Inst Elec & Electronics Eng; Soc Aerospace Mat & Process Eng. *Res:* Vinyl high polymers; polyvinyl acetal resins; polyimides; adhesives; reprographic polymer coating. *Mailing Add:* Monsanto Co Bircham Bend Plant Springfield MA 01151

LAVIN, PETER MASLAND, b Philadelphia, Pa, Apr 16, 35; m 58; c 2. GEOPHYSICS. *Educ:* Princeton Univ, BSE, 57; Pa State Univ, PhD(geophys), 62. *Prof Exp:* From instr to asst prof, 60-71, ASSOC PROF GEOPHYS, PA STATE UNIV, 71- *Mem:* Soc Explor Geophys; Am Geophys Union. *Res:* Exploration geophysics with emphasis on gravity and magnetic interpretation; time-series analysis; crustal structure and tectonic history. *Mailing Add:* Dept Geosci 443 Deike Bldg Pa State Univ University Park PA 16802

LAVIN, PHILIP TODD, b Rochester, NY, Nov 21, 46. BIOSTATISTICS. *Educ:* Univ Rochester, AB, 68; Brown Univ, PhD(appl math), 72. *Prof Exp:* Res asst prof appl math, Brown Univ, 72-74; res asst prof biostatist, State Univ NY, Buffalo, 74-81; asst prof, 77-81, ASSOC PROF BIOSTATIST, HARVARD SCH PUB HEALTH, 81- *Concurrent Pos:* biostatistician, US deleg Japan, Sci Exchange Comt Gastric Oncol, Nat Cancer Inst, 75; protocol statistician, Eastern Coop Oncol Group, 74-; coord statistician, Eastern Coop Oncol Group, 76-78; biostatistician, Sidney Farber Cancer Inst, 77-; pres, Frontier Sci Assocs, 79-; group statistician, Nat Infertility Study Group, 80- *Mem:* Am Statist Asn; Biomet Soc; Pattern Recognition Soc. *Res:* Biometry; clinical trials; pattern analysis; experimental design; statistical computing; health care evaluation policy science; standardization. *Mailing Add:* Sidney Farber Cancer Inst 44 Binney St Boston MA 02115

LAVINE, JAMES PHILIP, b Syracuse, NY, Dec 3, 44; m 71; c 1. THEORETICAL PHYSICS, COMPUTATIONAL PHYSICS. *Educ:* Mass Inst Technol, BS, 66; Univ Md, PhD(physics), 71. *Prof Exp:* Res assoc physics, Univ Liege, 71-73; res asst prof, Laval Univ, 73-74; res assoc physics, Univ Rochester, 74-76; PHYSICIST, EASTMAN KODAK CO, 76- *Mem:* Am Phys Soc; Soc Indust & Appl Math. *Res:* Semiconductor device modeling; optical properties of solids; transport in solids; numerical analysis. *Mailing Add:* Res Labs Bldg 81 Eastman Kodak Co Rochester NY 14650

LAVINE, LEROY S, b Jersey City, NJ, Oct 28, 18; m 46; c 2. ORTHOPEDIC SURGERY. *Educ:* NY Univ, AB, 40, MD, 43; Am Bd Orthop Surg, dipl, 55. *Prof Exp:* Res instr orthop surg, Col Med, Ind Univ, 51-52; from instr to prof, 65-80, EMER PROF ORTHOP SURG, COL MED, STATE UNIV NY DOWNSTATE MED CTR, 80- *Concurrent Pos:* Consult, Am Mus Natural Hist, 55- & Brooklyn Vet Admin Hosp, 65-; attend orthop surgeon, Long Island Jewish Hosp, 57-; vis surgeon, Kings County Hosp, 65-; adj prof biol, Grad Sch, NY Univ, 66-; clin prof, Med Sch, State Univ NY Stony Brook, 72- *Mem:* Fel Am Col Surg; Am Asn Phys Anthrop; fel Am Acad Orthop Surg; fel NY Acad Sci; fel NY Acad Med. *Res:* Bone growth and metabolism and mechanisms of calcification; clinical research in bone healing and nerve root compression syndromes; physical properties of and piezoelectricity in bone; electrical enhancement of bone growth. *Mailing Add:* 1300 Union Turnpike New Hyde Park NY 11040

LAVINE, RICHARD BENGT, b Philadelphia, Pa, June 27, 38; m 65; c 1. MATHEMATICAL ANALYSIS. *Educ:* Princeton Univ, AB, 61; Mass Inst Technol, PhD(math), 65. *Prof Exp:* Instr math, Aarhus Univ, 65-66; asst prof, Cornell Univ, 66-71; vis prof, Inst Theoret Physics, Univ Geneva, 71; mem staff, Inst Advan Study, 71-72; assoc prof, 72-76, PROF MATH, UNIV ROCHESTER, 76- *Mem:* Am Math Soc. *Res:* Mathematics of quantum mechanics; functional analysis. *Mailing Add:* 360 Rockingham St Rochester NY 14620

LAVINE, ROBERT ALAN, b Chicago, Ill, Feb 18, 41. NEUROPHYSIOLOGY, PSYCHOLOGY. *Educ:* Univ Chicago, BS, 62, PhD(physiol), 69. *Prof Exp:* From instr to asst prof, 69-75, PROF PHYSIOL, SCH MED, GEORGE WASHINGTON UNIV, 75- *Concurrent Pos:* NIH fel, George Washington Univ, 69-70. *Res:* Neuron discharge patterns and averaged evoked potentials in audition; human psychophysiology using computer analysis, averaged evoked potentials; evolution and modification of behavior. *Mailing Add:* Dept of Physiol George Washington Univ Med Ctr Washington DC 20005

LAVIOLETTE, FRANCIS A, b Bellingham, Wash, Nov 22, 19; m 46; c 2. PLANT PATHOLOGY. *Educ:* Purdue Univ, BS, 53, MS, 56. *Prof Exp:* Res asst plant path, 55-56, from instr to asst prof, 56-71, ASSOC PROF PLANT PATH, PURDUE UNIV, 71- *Concurrent Pos:* Consult, Ind Crop Improv Asn, 67-71. *Mem:* Am Phytopath Soc; Am Inst Biol Sci. *Res:* Host relationships and methods of control of diseases of soybeans and diseases of forage crops. *Mailing Add:* Dept of Bot & Plant Path Lilly Hall Life Sci Purdue Univ West Lafayette IN 47906

LA VIOLETTE, PAUL ESTRONZA, b New York, NY, Apr 11, 30; m 75; c 2. SATELLITE OCEANOGRAPHY. *Educ:* Univ Ill, BS, 52. *Prof Exp:* Oceanogr descriptive oceanog, Naval Oceanogr Off, 60-76, OCEANOGR REMOTE SENSING, NAVAL OCEAN RES & DEVELOP ACTIVITY, 76- *Concurrent Pos:* Prin investr, Little Window II, US & Mex Ocean Exp, 71, Sahara Upwelling Explor, US & Spain Ocean Exp, 73 & Grand Banks Explor, US & Can Ocean Exp, 79-80. *Mem:* Am Geophys Union; AAAS; Marine Technol Soc; Res Soc Am. *Res:* Basic and applied research in satellite oceanography. *Mailing Add:* Naval Ocean Res & Develop Activity Code 335 Nat Space Tech Lab Station MS 39529

LAVKULICH, LESLIE MICHAEL, b Coaldale, Alta, Apr 28, 39; m 62; c 2. SOIL SCIENCE. *Educ:* Univ Alta, BSc, 61, MSc, 63; Cornell Univ, PhD(soil sci), 67. *Prof Exp:* From asst prof to assoc prof, 66-75, PROF SOIL SCI, UNIV BC, 75-, HEAD DEPT, 80- *Mem:* Am Soc Agron; Can Agr Res Coun; Am Soc Soil Sci; Can Soc Soil Sci (pres, 80-81); Int Soc Soil Sci. *Res:* Soil genesis and classification; weathering of minerals; soil clay mineralogy; soil-plant relationships; mine waste characterization; resource allocation. *Mailing Add:* Dept of Soil Sci Univ of BC Vancouver BC V6T 2A2 Can

LAVOIE, ALVIN CHARLES, b Fall River, Mass, Jan 26, 56. EMULSION POLYMERIZATION, ACRYLATES. *Educ:* Southeastern Mass Univ, BS, 77; Univ Wis-Madison, PhD(org chem), 82. *Prof Exp:* SR SCIENTIST, ROHM AND HAAS CO, 81- *Mem:* Am Chem Soc; AAAS. *Res:* Utilization of vinyl sulfides as enolonium equivilants in organic synthesis; applications of organosulfer intermediates in organic synthesis; emulsion polymerization of acrylates. *Mailing Add:* Rohm and Haas Co Morristown & McKeon Rd Springhouse PA 19477

LAVOIE, EDMOND J, b New York, NY, Jan 11, 50; m 71. BIOCHEMISTRY, SYNTHETIC ORGANIC & NATURAL PRODUCTS CHEMISTRY. *Educ:* Fordham Univ, BS, 71; State Univ NY, Buffalo, PhD(med chem), 75. *Prof Exp:* Res assoc, 75-76, assoc, 76-79, HEAD SECT METAB BIOCHEM, DIV ENVIRON CARCINOGENESIS, AM HEALTH FOUND, 77-, ASSOC MEM, 80- *Concurrent Pos:* Asst res prof, Dept Urol, NY Med Col. *Mem:* Am Chem Soc; Am Asn Cancer Res; Environ Mutagen Soc. *Res:* Experimental and environmental carcinogenesis; environmental sciences; tobacco sciences. *Mailing Add:* Am Health Found Valhalla NY 10595

LAVOIE, MARCEL ELPHEGE, b Manchester, NH, July 16, 17; m 42; c 2. ZOOLOGY. *Educ:* St Anselm's Col, BA, 40; Univ NH, MS, 52; Syracuse Univ, PhD(zool), 56. *Prof Exp:* Instr chem, St Anselm's Col, 46-47; instr biol, Univ NH, 50-52; lectr zool, Syracuse Univ, 52-55; asst prof, 55-61, ASSOC PROF ZOOL, UNIV NH, 61- *Res:* Mammalian anatomy and physiology. *Mailing Add:* Dept Zool Univ NH Durham NH 03824

LAVOIE, RONALD LEONARD, b Manchester, NH, Apr 21, 33; m 59; c 2. METEOROLOGY. *Educ:* Univ NH, BA, 54; Fla State Univ, MS, 56; Pa State Univ, PhD, 68. *Prof Exp:* Chief observer, Mt Wash Observ, 57-59; asst prof meteorol, Univ Hawaii, 59-68; assoc prof, Pa State Univ, 68-72; assoc dir meteorol prog, NSF, 72-73; dir, Environ Modification Off, 73-79, DIR, ATMOSPHERIC PROGS OFF RES DEVELOP, NAT OCEANIC & APMOSPHERIC ADMIN, 79- *Concurrent Pos:* NSF sci fac fel, 63-64. *Mem:* AAAS; Am Meteorol Soc; Am Geophys Union. *Res:* Cloud physics and weather modification; numerical modeling on the mesoscale; tropical meteorology. *Mailing Add:* Nat Oceanic & Atmospheric Admin 6010 Exec Blvd Rockville MD 20852

LAVOIE, VICTORIN, b Petite Riviere, Que, Apr 8, 28; m 58; c 4. PLANT ECOLOGY. *Educ:* Laval Univ, BS, 53; Univ Montreal, MSc, 57; Univ Madrid, DSc(natural sci), 59. *Prof Exp:* Res officer ecol, Que Dept Agr, 60-62, chief admin div, 62-65; dean fac agr & food sci, 71-79, PROF PLANT ECOL, LAVAL UNIV, 65- *Res:* Classification of plants in flood plain in New Jersey; ecological study of pine stands in the Sierra de Guadarrama in Spain; blueberries; sugar maple stands. *Mailing Add:* Fac of Agr & Food Sci Laval Univ Quebec PQ G1K 7P4 Can

LAVY, TERRY LEE, b Greenville, Ohio, Feb 9, 36; m 55; c 3. WEED SCIENCE, SOIL CHEMISTRY. *Educ:* Ohio State Univ, BS, 58, MS, 59; Purdue Univ, PhD(plant nutrit), 62. *Prof Exp:* Lab supvr soil chem classification, Ohio State Univ, 58-59; from asst prof to prof agron, Univ Nebr-Lincoln, 62-78; DIR, PESTICIDE RESIDUE LAB, UNIV ARK, 78- *Mem:* Weed Sci Soc Am; Am Soc Agron. *Res:* Factors affecting the mobility and degradation of pesticides in the soil profile; evaluating exposure of pesticide applicators. *Mailing Add:* Dept of Agron Altheimer Lab Univ of Ark Fayetteville AR 72701

LAW, ALBERT G(ILES), b Ottawa, Ill, July 1, 31; m 54; c 4. CIVIL ENGINEERING, HYDROLOGY. *Educ:* Univ Ill, Urbana, BS, 54; Univ Wis, MS, 60, PhD(civil eng), 65. *Prof Exp:* Design engr, Warzyn Eng Co, Wis, 56-58; instr civil eng, Univ Wis, 58-62; from asst prof to assoc prof civil eng, Clemson Univ, 62-77; MGR HYDROL SCI, ROCKWELL HANFORD OPERS, 77- *Concurrent Pos:* Vis assoc prof, Colo State Univ, 71-72; dir water resources engr, Clemson Univ & consult, US Geol Surv, 75-77. *Mem:* Nat Water Well Asn; Soc Mining Engrs; Am Soc Civil Engrs; Am Geophys Union; Am Water Resources Asn. *Res:* Ground water hydrology, ground water flow, radioactive waste disposal. *Mailing Add:* Rockwell Hanford Opers PO Box 800 Richland WA 99352

LAW, AMY STAUBER, b Philadelphia, Pa, June 26, 38; m 65. CLINICAL BIOCHEMISTRY. *Educ:* Mt Holyoke Col, AB, 59; Univ Del, MS, 63, PhD(biochem), 69. *Prof Exp:* Res chemist, AviSun Corp, 61-65; chief lab sect, Meat Inspection Div, Del State Bd Agr, 68-69; CLIN BIOCHEMIST, WILMINGTON MED CTR, 69- *Mem:* AAAS; Am Chem Soc; Am Asn Clin Chemists; Asn Women Sci; Sigma Xi. *Res:* Fetal and neonatal medicine; development of clinical methods with special application to fetal and neonatal patients; endocrine assays for clinical application; clinical applications of protein biochemistry; hemoglobinopathies. *Mailing Add:* Res Lab Mem Div Wilmington Med Ctr PO Box 1548 Wilmington DE 19899

LAW, CECIL E, b Vancouver, BC, Nov 27, 22; m 45; c 6. OPERATIONS RESEARCH. *Educ:* Univ BC, BA, 50. *Prof Exp:* Head animal field exp sect, Suffield Exp Sta, Defence Res Bd, 51, head arctic oper res sect, Defence Res Northern Lab, 51-54, head weapons effects & field trials sect, Can Army Oper Res Estab, 55-58, head oper gaming & tactics sect, 58-60; supvr opers res, Can Industs Ltd, 60-61, opers res mgr, 61-62; sr opers res analyst, Can Nat Rwy, 62-64, coordr opers anal, 64-66; PROF OPERS RES, SCH BUS, QUEEN'S UNIV, ONT, 66-, PROF COMPUT SCI, 69-, EXEC DIR, CAN INST GUIDED GROUND TRANSPORT, 71- *Concurrent Pos:* Lectr, Exten Dept, McGill Univ, 64-66. *Mem:* Opers Res Soc Am; Wildlife Soc; Am Inst Indust Eng; Can Soc Wildlife & Fishery Biol; Can Opers Res Soc (vpres, 66, pres, 67). *Res:* Wildlife ecology and population dynamics, particularly Arctic; operations research, especially military and civil operational gaming and simulation; theoretical and applied critical path analysis and program evaluation and review technique; transportation research. *Mailing Add:* Can Inst Guided Ground Transport Queen's Univ Kingston ON K7L 3W6 Can

LAW, DAVID H, b Milwaukee, Wis, July 24, 27; m 49; c 5. INTERNAL MEDICINE, GASTROENTEROLOGY. *Educ:* Cornell Univ, AB, 50, MD, 54. *Prof Exp:* Intern med, NY Hosp, 54-55, asst resident, 55-57, asst physician to outpatients, 57-58, physician to out-patients & dir personnel health serv, 58-60; med dir out-patient dept & chief div gastroenterol, Vanderbilt Univ Hosp, 60-69; PROF MED, SCH MED, UNIV N MEX, 69-; CHIEF MED SERV, ALBUQUERQUE VET ADMIN HOSP, 69- *Concurrent Pos:* NIH fel, Nat Cancer Inst, 57-58; spec consult interdept comt nutrit for nat defense, NIH, 62-63; attend physician, Thayer Vet Admin Hosp, 62-69. *Mem:* Fel Am Col Physicians; Am Fedn Clin Res; Am Soc Clin Nutrit; Am Gastroenterol Asn; Am Inst Nutrit. *Res:* Inflammatory bowel disease; malabsorption; gastric secretion; medical care; nutrition; out-patient clinics; delivery of health care. *Mailing Add:* Dept of Med Univ of NMex Sch of Med Albuquerque NM 87106

LAW, FRANCIS C P, b Hong Kong, Oct 12, 41; Can citizen; m 80; c 1. DRUG METABOLIOSM, TOXICOLOGY. *Educ:* Univ Alta, BS, 66, MS, 69; Univ Mich, PhD(drug metab), 72. *Prof Exp:* Vis fel, Nat Inst Environ Health Sci, 72-75; asst prof, 75-81, ASSOC PROF DRUG METAB & TOXICOL, COL PHARM, DALHOUSIE UNIV, 81- *Mem:* Pharmacol Soc Can; Soc Toxicol Can; Am Soc Pharmacol & Exp Therapeut. *Res:* Disposition, metabolism and toxicity of drugs; environmental pollutants and other chemicals in living organisms including man. *Mailing Add:* Col Pharm Dalhousie Univ Halifax NS B3H 3J5 Can

LAW, GEORGE ROBERT JOHN, b Vermilion, Alta, June 4, 28; US citizen; m 50; c 2. POULTRY GENETICS. *Educ:* Univ BC, BSA, 50; Wash State Univ, MS, 57; Univ Calif, Davis, PhD(genetics), 61. *Prof Exp:* Immuno-geneticist, Hy-Line Int, Pioneer Hi-Bred Int Inc, 61-72; assoc prof animal sci, 73-78, asst to dean, Col Agr Sci, 78-81, COUNR, DIV CONTINUING EDUC, COLO STATE UNIV, 81- *Mem:* Genetics Asn Am; Poultry Sci Asn. *Res:* Immuno-genetic studies of turkeys and chickens including blood type variation, serum protein, egg white protein and isozyme polymorphism; teaching, research and application of studies to breeding of poultry. *Mailing Add:* Col of Agr Sci Colo State Univ Ft Collins CO 80523

LAW, HAROLD BELL, b Douds, Iowa, Sept 7, 11, M 42; c 3. PHYSICS. *Educ:* Kent State Univ, BS, 34; Ohio State Univ, MS, 36, PhD(physics), 41. *Prof Exp:* Asst physics dept, Ohio State Univ, 38-41; physicist, RCA Labs, 41-62, dir mat & display device lab, Picture Tube Div, RCA Corp, 62-75, staff adv, 75-76; RETIRED. *Honors & Awards:* TV Broadcasters Asn Medal, 46; Zworkin Prize, 55; David Sarnoff Outstanding Achievement Award, RCA, 61; consumer electronics Group Award, Inst Elec & Electronics Eng, 66; Francis Rice Darne Mem Award, Soc Info Display, 75; Lamme Medal, Inst Elec & Electronics Engrs, 75. *Mem:* Am Phys Soc; fel Inst Elec & Electronics Eng; fel Soc Info Display. *Res:* Color television kinescopes. *Mailing Add:* 145 Van Dyke Rd Hopewell NJ 08525

LAW, HSIANG-YI DAVID, b Hong Kong, Feb 12, 49; US citizen; m 73. ELECTRICAL ENGINEERING, APPLIED PHYSICS. *Educ:* Univ Wash, BSEE, 72; Cornell Univ, MSEE, 75, PhD(elec eng), 77. *Prof Exp:* Mem tech staff, Sci Ctr, Rockwell Int Corp, 77-80; MGR, SEMICONDUCTOR DEVICE LAB, TECHNOL RES CTR, TRW INC, 80- *Mem:* Inst Elec & Electronics Engrs; Am Phys Soc. *Res:* III-V alloys material study; avalanche photodiodes; double heterostructure lasers; integrated optoelectronic devices; ionization coefficients of III-V materials; ion implantation, anodic oxidation and other surface passivation methods. *Mailing Add:* 29014 W Saddlebrook Dr Agoura CA 91301

LAW, JAMES PIERCE, JR, b Atlanta, Tex, Aug 4, 16; m 41; c 1. WATER POLLUTION. *Educ:* Univ Tex, BS, 39; Southern Methodist Univ, MS, 61; Tex A&M Univ, PhD(soil physics), 65. *Prof Exp:* Chemist, Convair Div, Gen Dynamics Corp, Tex, 56-61; res asst, Agr Exp Sta, Tex A&M Univ, 61-65; soil scientist, 65-67, res soil scientist, 67-73, SUPVRY SOIL SCIENTIST, ROBERT S KERR ENVIRON RES LAB, OFF RES & DEVELOP, ENVIRON PROTECTION AGENCY, 73- *Mem:* Am Soc Agron; Soil Sci Soc Am; Int Soc Soil Sci; Am Soc Agr Eng. *Res:* Water pollution problems of irrigation return flows; soil and plant systems for treating wastewaters such as cannery, sewage effluents and animal wastes. *Mailing Add:* Robert S Kerr Environ Res Lab PO Box 1198 Ada OK 74820

LAW, JIMMY, b Seremban, Malaysia, Sept 23, 42; m 69. THEORETICAL PHYSICS. *Educ:* Univ London, BSc, 63, PhD(physics), 68. *Prof Exp:* Teaching fel physics, McMaster Univ, 66-69; asst prof, 69-74, ASSOC PROF PHYSICS, UNIV GUELPH, 74- *Mem:* Brit Inst Physics; Can Asn Physicists. *Res:* Theoretical calculations in nuclear and hypernuclear physics; inner shell vacancy creation mechanisms in atomic physics. *Mailing Add:* Dept of Physics Univ of Guelph Guelph ON N1G 2W1 Can

LAW, JOHN, b Cleveland, Ohio, Dec 8, 30; m 53; c 4. POWER SYSTEMS, ELECTRIC MACHINERY. *Educ:* Case Inst Technol, BS, 57; Univ Wis-Madison, MS, 60, PhD(elec eng), 62. *Prof Exp:* Instr, Univ Wis, 57-61; assoc prof elec eng, Mont State Univ, 62-63; sr elec engr, Carrier Corp, 63-65, chief engr, 65-74, sr staff engr, 74; assoc prof, 75-79, PROF ELEC ENGR, UNIV IDAHO, 79- *Concurrent Pos:* Vis assoc prof elec eng, Bogazici Univ, Turkey, 74-75; NSF fel, Elec Power Res Inst, 78; vis engr, Eng Soc Comn Energy, 79; vis prof elec eng, Wash State Univ, 80; planning engr, Idaho Power Co, 81; engr, Idaho Nat Eng Lab, 77; consult, Idaho Power Co, 76; mem, Fac Improvement Comt, NSF, 78. *Mem:* Inst Elec & Electronics Engrs; Nat Soc Prof Engrs. *Res:* Computer methods in power systems analysis; response of AC servomotors with nonsinusoinal and discontinuous impedance source voltage. *Mailing Add:* Elec Eng Dept Univ Idaho Moscow ID 83843

LAW, JOHN HAROLD, b Cleveland, Ohio, Feb 27, 31; m 56. BIOCHEMISTRY. *Educ:* Case Inst Technol, BS, 53; Univ Ill, PhD(chem), 57. *Prof Exp:* Res fel, Harvard Univ, 57-58; instr chem, Northwestern Univ, 58-59; from instr to asst prof, Harvard Univ, 59-65; PROF BIOCHEM, UNIV CHICAGO, 65-, PROF CHEM, 67- *Mem:* Am Chem Soc; Am Soc Biol Chemists. *Res:* Insect biochemistry; lipid metabolism; enzymology. *Mailing Add:* Dept of Biochem Univ of Chicago 920 E 58th St Chicago IL 60637

LAW, LLOYD WILLIAM, b Ford City, Pa, Oct 28, 10; m 42; c 2. ONCOLOGY. *Educ:* Univ Ill, BS, 31; Harvard Univ, AM, 35, PhD(biol), 37. *Prof Exp:* Instr high sch, Ill, 31-33; asst, Harvard Univ, 36-37; res assoc, Stanford Univ, 37-38; Finney-Howell med res fel physiol genetics, Jackson Mem Lab, 38-41, Commonwealth Fund fel cancer res, 41-42; sci dir, Jackson Mem Lab, 46-47; sr geneticist, 47-54, mem sci directorate, 71-80, SCIENTIST DIR, NAT CANCER INST, 54-, CHIEF, LAB CELL BIOL, 71- *Concurrent Pos:* Harvard Univ Parker fel, Stanford Univ, 37-38; trustee, Jackson Mem Lab, 47-; mem study sect cancer chemother, NIH, 56-59, drug eval panel, Nat Serv Ctr, 56-59, sci adv bd, Roswell Park Mem Inst, 57-, adv bd, Children's Cancer Found, expert adv panel cancer, WHO, 60- & adv sci bd, Hektoen Inst Chicago, 64-; mem, US Nat Comt, Int Union Against Cancer, 68-72 & 72- *Honors & Awards:* A F Rosenthal Award, AAAS, 58; G H A Clowes Award, Am Asn Cancer Res, 65; Meritorious Serv Award, USPHS, 65, Distinguished Serv Award, 69; Alexander Pascoli Prize, Univ Perugia, 69; G B Mider Lect Award, 70. *Mem:* Am Soc Exp Path; Am Asn Cancer Res (pres, 68-69); Transplantation Soc; Soc Exp Biol & Med; Soc Exp Leukemia. *Res:* Genetics; factors affecting development of leukemia and breast tumors; immunogenetics of the mouse; tumor immunology; chemotherapy of neoplasms. *Mailing Add:* Lab Cell Biol Nat Cancer Inst Bethesda MD 20014

LAW, MARGARET ELIZABETH, b Birmingham, Eng, May 6, 34; m 57. EXPERIMENTAL HIGH ENERGY PHYSICS. *Educ:* Univ Birmingham, Eng, BSc, 55, PhD(high energy physics), 58. *Prof Exp:* Nat Res Coun fel nuclear physics, McMaster Univ, 58-60; res fel, 61-67, res assoc, 67-71, sr res assoc high energy physics, 71-78, lectr, 72-78, REGISTR, FAC ARTS & SCI, HARVARD UNIV, 78- *Mem:* Am Phys Soc; Brit Inst Physics. *Res:* Experimental research in strong interactions. *Mailing Add:* Registr Off Harvard Univ Cambridge MA 02138

LAW, MARTHA LIAO, b Leeds, Eng, Feb 9, 48; US citizen; m 72. SOMATIC CELL GENETICS, RECOMBINANT DNA. *Educ:* Bryn Mawr Col, BA, 70; Univ Pa, PhD(chem), 74. *Prof Exp:* Fel chem, Univ Denver, 74-75; fel, 75-79, INST FEL GENETICS, HEALTH SCI CTR, ELEANOR ROOSEVELT INST CANCER RES, UNIV COLO, 79- *Concurrent Pos:* Am res scholar, Comt Scholarly Commun with People's Republic China, Nat Acad Sci, 81-82; NIH fel, 76-79. *Mem:* Am Cell Biol; Am Soc Human Genetics; AAAS. *Res:* Human gene mapping using chinese hamster/human cell hybrids; using recombinant DNA techniques to obtain DNA markers from specific human chromosome. *Mailing Add:* Eleanor Roosevelt Inst Cancer Res B129 4200 E 9th Ave Denver CO 80262

LAW, PAUL ARTHUR, b Lowell, Mass, Sept 19, 34; m 60, 81; c 4. CLINICAL CHEMISTRY. *Educ:* Lowell Technol Inst, BS, 56; Mich State Univ, PhD(org chem), 62. *Prof Exp:* Res chemist, Dow Corning Corp, 56-58; fel polypeptide synthesis, Fla State Univ, 62-63; sr res chemist, 63-69, tech assoc, 69-78, gen supvr, 78-80, ASST SUPT MED PROD, EASTMAN KODAK CO, 80- *Mem:* Am Asn Clin Chemists. *Res:* Color photographic chemistry. *Mailing Add:* Eastman Kodak Co 343 State St Rochester NY 14650

LAW, PETER KOI, b Chengsha, China, Feb 25, 46; Chinese & Can citizen; m 73; c 1. NEUROMUSCULAR ELECTROPHYSIOLOGY. *Educ:* McGill Univ, BSc, 68; Univ Toronto, MSc, 69, PhD(neurophysiol), 72. *Prof Exp:* Fel, Med Ctr, McMaster Univ, 72-75; ASST PROF NEUROL, SCH MED, VANDERBILT UNIV, 75- *Concurrent Pos:* Sr investr, Jerry Lewis Neuromuscular Dis Res Ctr, Nashville, Tenn, 75-; electromyography consult, Vanderbilt Univ Hosp, Nashville, 75- & St Thomas Hosp, 75-; Muscular Dystrophy Asn Can fel, 72-75; Muscular Dystrophy Asn res grant, 75-, Vanderbilt Univ Res Coun res grant, 75-; NIH res grant, 78-79; NSF res grant, 79-82. *Mem:* Asn Am Med Cols; AAAS; NY Acad Sci; Soc Neurosci; Can Soc Neurosci. *Res:* Developmental membrane biophysics; motor-unit electrophysiology; muscular dystrophy; myogenesis and muscle regeneration; genetic complementation and therapy; acupuncture analgesia. *Mailing Add:* Dept of Neurol Vanderbilt Univ Nashville TN 37232

LAW, WILLIAM BROUGH, b Elko, Nev, Oct 11, 32; m 56; c 3. PLASMA PHYSICS. *Educ:* Univ Nev, BSc, 54; Ohio State Univ, PhD(nuclear physics), 60. *Prof Exp:* Physicist, Armour Res Found, 60; staff mem, Sandia Lab, 60-65; asst prof, 65-68, ASSOC PROF PHYSICS, COLO SCH MINES, 68- *Res:* Gamma ray spectroscopy; accelerator physics. *Mailing Add:* Dept of Physics Colo Sch of Mines Golden CO 80401

LAWFORD, GEORGE ROSS, b Toronto, Ont, Feb 27, 41; m 66. BIOCHEMISTRY, CELL BIOLOGY. *Educ:* Univ Toronto, BSc, 63, PhD(biochem), 66. *Prof Exp:* Can Med Res Coun fel, 66-68; asst prof biochem, McMaster Univ, 68-73; mem staff, 73-77, TECH DIR & GEN MGR, WESTON RES CTR, 77- *Mem:* Can Biochem Soc; Brit Biochem Soc. *Res:* Functional significance of interactions between subcellular components; regulation of protein biosynthesis and the adenyl cyclase system; food chemistry; fermentation. *Mailing Add:* Weston Res Ctr 1047 Yonge St Toronto ON M4W 2L3 Can

LAWING, WILLIAM DENNIS, b Charlotte, NC, Mar 29, 35; m 57; c 3. STATISTICS. *Educ:* NC State Col, BS, 57, MS, 59; Iowa State Univ, PhD(statist), 65. *Prof Exp:* Statistician, Res Triangle Inst, 65-69; ASSOC PROF INDUST & EXP STATIST, UNIV RI, 69- *Concurrent Pos:* Adj prof, Duke Univ, 66-67; vis lectr, Iowa State Univ, 67-68; adj assoc prof, NC State Univ, 68-69. *Mem:* Inst Math Statist; Am Statist Asn; Math Asn Am. *Res:* Industrial applications of statistics; quality control; operations research; sequential analysis; decision theory; survey sampling. *Mailing Add:* Dept Comput Sci & Ext Statist Univ of RI Kingston RI 02881

LAWLER, ADRIAN RUSSELL, b Etowah, Tenn, Nov 25, 40; m 62; c 2. AQUACULTURE, TOXICOLOGY. *Educ:* Univ Rochester, AB, 62; Col William & Mary, Va, MS, 64, PhD(marine biol), 71. *Prof Exp:* NSF summer student, Va Inst Marine Sci, 62, grad asst, 62-71; fel, 71-73, assoc marine biologist, 73-75, MARINE BIOLOGIST, GULF COAST RES LAB, 75-, CO-CHMN TOXICOL PROG & HEAD EXP ORGANISM CULTURE, 76- *Concurrent Pos:* Consult, Nat Aquaculture Info Syst, 75- *Res:* Culture of marine and freshwater organisms, birds and mammals for experimentation; toxicity testing; external parasites of marine and freshwater fishes; larval fish development. *Mailing Add:* Gulf Coast Res Lab East Beach Ocean Springs MS 39564

LAWLER, EUGENE L(EIGHTON), b New York, NY, July 28, 33; d; m 80; c 2. APPLIED MATHEMATICS, COMPUTER SCIENCE. *Educ:* Fla State Univ, BS, 54; Harvard Univ, AM, 57, PhD(appl math), 63. *Prof Exp:* Sr elec engr, Sylvania Elec Prod Co, Mass, 59-62; from asst prof to prof elec eng, Univ Mich, 62-70; PROF COMPUT SCI, UNIV CALIF, BERKELEY, 71- *Mem:* Asn Comput Mach; Soc Indust & Appl Math; Inst Mgt Sci. *Res:* Combinatorial optimization; complexity of computations. *Mailing Add:* Dept of Elec Eng & Comput Sci Univ of Calif 591 Evans Berkeley CA 94720

LAWLER, GEORGE HERBERT, b Kingston, Ont, June 13, 23; m 47; c 5. FISHERIES. *Educ:* Queen's Univ Ont, BA, 46; Univ Western Ont, MSc, 48; Univ Toronto, PhD, 59. *Prof Exp:* Demonstr, Zool Lab, Queen's Univ Ont, 44-46 & Univ Western Ont, 46-48; assoc div ichthyol, Royal Ont Mus Zool, 48-50; asst scientist, Fisheries Res Bd, Man, 50-57, assoc scientist, Ont, 57-

61, sr scientist, Man, 60-72, from asst dir to dir, Freshwater Inst, 72-74, GEN DIR, WESTERN REGION, DEPT FISHERIES & OCEANS, SERV, 74- *Concurrent Pos:* Hon prof, Dept Zool, Univ Man, 68-77. *Mem:* Am Fisheries Soc; Am Inst Fishery Res Biol; Int Asn Great Lakes Res; Int Asn Theoret & Appl Limnol. *Res:* Population dynamics; parasitology and taxonomy of fishes. *Mailing Add:* Freshwater Inst 501 University Crescent Winnipeg MB R3T 2N6 Can

LAWLER, JAMES HENRY LAWRENCE, b Detroit, Mich, Jan 31, 36; m 64; c 7. CHEMICAL ENGINEERING. *Educ:* Univ Louisville, BChE, 59, ME, 72; Brigham Young Univ, MS, 66; Univ Utah, ME & PhD(chem eng), 69. *Prof Exp:* Radio engr, Louisville Free Pub Libr, 52-54, radio sta WKLO, 57-58 & WKYW, 58-59; engr, Wright Patterson AFB, 59-62 & Boeing Co, 62-65; asst prof chem, Dixie Col, 69-73; head nuclear eng technol, Trident Technol Col, SC, 73-77; chmn chem technol, Univ Dayton, 77-80; MEM STAFF, ROCKWELL HANFORD OPER, 80- *Concurrent Pos:* Atomic Energy Comn fel, Kans State Univ, 72. *Mem:* Am Inst Chem Eng; Am Chem Soc. *Res:* Materials; cyclic history; socio-mathematics; quantization of space-time; unified theory of gravity, strong and weak nuclear forces, electromagnetic forces, proton theory. *Mailing Add:* 4068 Ironton Dr W Richland WA 99352

LAWLER, JOHN PATRICK, b Brooklyn, NY, Jan 30, 34; m 57; c 7. SANITARY ENGINEERING, MATHEMATICS. *Educ:* Manhattan Col, BCE, 55; NY Univ, MCE, 58; Univ Wis, PhD(sanit eng), 60. *Prof Exp:* Civil engr, F G Davidson, Inc, NY, 55-56; instr civil eng, Manhattan Col, 56-58; asst prof, Rutgers Univ, 60-65; partner, Quirk, Lawler & Matusky Engrs, 65-77; PARTNER, LAWLER, MATUSKY & SKELLY ENGRS, 77- *Concurrent Pos:* Consult, Humble Oil & Refining Co, NJ, 61-62; vis assoc prof, Manhattan Col, 63-; lectr summer inst stream anal, 64-66; assoc, Cosulich & Quirk, Water Resources Engrs, 64-65; lectr summer inst water resources, Clemson Univ, 65 & 66. *Mem:* Am Soc Civil Engrs; Water Pollution Control Fedn. *Res:* Mathematical analysis of the transport processes and reaction kinetics associated with stream and estuarine pollution; water resources systems; water and waste treatment operations. *Mailing Add:* Lawler Matusky & Skelly Engrs One Blue Hill Plaza Pearl River NY 10965

LAWLER, JOSEPH CHRISTOPHER, b Lynn, Mass, May 3, 20; div; c 3. ENVIRONMENTAL ENGINEERING, CIVIL ENGINEERING. *Educ:* Northeastern Univ, BS, 43; Harvard Univ, MS, 47; Am Acad Environ Engrs, dipl, 63. *Hon Degrees:* Dr Eng, Northeastern Univ, 72. *Prof Exp:* Officer, Civil Eng Corps, US Navy, 44-46; proj eng, Camp Dresser & McKee, 47-52, pres, Camp Dresser & McKee Int, Inc, 68-76, pres, Camp Dresser & McKee, 70-77, CHIEF EXEC OFFICER, CAMP DRESSER & MCKEE, 78-, CHMN BD, 70-, PARTNER, 52- *Honors & Awards:* Prof Engrs in Pvt Pract Award, Nat Soc Prof Engrs, 77. *Mem:* Nat Acad Eng; Am Consult Engrs Coun; Nat Coun Prof Serv Firms, (pres, 76). *Res:* General areas of water development, transmission, treatment and distribution; wastewater collection, treatment, reuse and reclamation; hydraulic engineering. *Mailing Add:* Camp Dresser & McKee Inc One Center Plaza Boston MA 02108

LAWLER, MARTIN TIMOTHY, b Rochester, Minn, Apr 6, 37; m 59; c 3. FLUID MECHANICS, HEAT TRANSFER. *Educ:* Milwaukee Sch Eng, BS, 61; Case Inst Technol, MS, 65, PhD(eng), 67. *Prof Exp:* Instr mech eng & physics, Milwaukee Sch Eng, 59-61; res asst, Fluid, Thermal & Aerospace Sci, Case Inst Technol, 64-67; prin res scientist, Corp Res Ctr, Honeywell Inc, Minn, 67-70; vpres, Swenberg Eng Inc, 70-72; MANAGING PARTNER, LAWLER, SWENBERG & ASSOCS, 72- *Mem:* Am Soc Mech Engrs; Nat Soc Prof Engrs; Am Soc Heating, Refrig & Air Conditioning Engrs; Sigma Xi. *Res:* Fluid-particle and two-phase flows; heat transfer; solar systems, energy consumption and conservation. *Mailing Add:* 5491 Scioto Darby Rd Hilliard OH 43026

LAWLER, RONALD GEORGE, b Centralia, Wash, May 19, 38. PHYSICAL ORGANIC CHEMISTRY. *Educ:* Calif Inst Technol, BS, 60; Univ Calif, Berkeley, PhD(chem), 64. *Prof Exp:* Res assoc chem, Columbia Univ, 63-65; from asst prof to assoc prof, 65-73, PROF CHEM, BROWN UNIV, 73- *Concurrent Pos:* NSF fel, 63-64; Alfred P Sloan res fel, 70-71. *Mem:* Am Chem Soc. *Res:* Theoretical organic chemistry; electron and nuclear magnetic resonance; chemistry of free radicals and radical ions; radiation chemistry. *Mailing Add:* Dept of Chem Brown Univ Providence RI 02912

LAWLESS, EDWARD WILLIAM, b Jacksonville, Ill, Apr 9, 31; m 59; c 6. TECHNICAL MANAGEMENT, PHYSICAL INORGANIC CHEMISTRY. *Educ:* Ill Col, AB, 53; Univ Mo, PhD(phys chem), 60. *Hon Degrees:* DSc, Ill Col, 79. *Prof Exp:* Assoc chemist, 59-64, sr chemist, 64-66, prin chemist, 66-73, HEAD, TECHNOL ASSESSMENT SECT, MIDWEST RES INST, 73- *Mem:* AAAS; Am Chem Soc; World Future Soc; Soc Risk Anal; Int Asn Impact Assessment. *Res:* Technology forecast, risk assessment and societal effects analysis; environmental chemistry and pollution control; evaluation of health and environmental hazards of industrial, consumer product and agricultural chemicals; chemistry of pesticides, fluorine, metal hydrides; correlations of chemical structures with properties; analysis of agricultural innovation; chemical kinetics. *Mailing Add:* Ctr Technoeconomic Anal Midwest Res Inst 425 Volker Blvd Kansas City MO 64110

LAWLESS, GREGORY BENEDICT, b Covington, Va, Jan 5, 40; m 66; c 2. PHARMACEUTICAL CHEMISTRY. *Educ:* Fordham Univ, BS, 62; St Johns Univ NY, MS, 65; Temple Univ, PhD(pharmaceut chem), 69. *Prof Exp:* Tech rep, 69-71; regional sales mgr, 71-73, nat sales mgr, 73-74, mkt mgr, Instrument Prod, Sci & Process Div, 74-77, bus develop mgr, Riston Prod Div, 77-78, dir, Electronic Mat Div, 78-79, exec vpres, Endo Labs, Inc, 79-81, DIR, DEPT PLANS DIV, E I DU PONT DE NEMOURS & CO, INC, 81- *Mem:* Am Chem Soc. *Res:* Strategic planning for photo products department. *Mailing Add:* Photo Prod Dept E I du Pont de Nemours & Co Inc Wilmington DE 19898

LAWLESS, JAMES GEORGE, b Brooklyn, NY, Aug 18, 42; m 66; c 1. ANALYTICAL CHEMISTRY. *Educ:* Lafayette Col, BS, 64; Purdue Univ, MS, 66; Kans State Univ, PhD(chem), 69. *Prof Exp:* RES SCIENTIST MASS SPECTROMETRY, AMES RES CTR, NASA, 69- *Concurrent Pos:* Co-investr returned lunar samples, NASA, 70- *Mem:* Am Soc Mass Spectrometry; Geochem Soc; Meteoritic Soc. *Res:* Mass spectrometry of organic compounds; analysis of lunar samples and meteorites for carbon compounds. *Mailing Add:* Ames Res Ctr NASA Moffet Field CA 94035

LAWLESS, KENNETH ROBERT, b Key West, Fla, Aug 21, 22; m 52; c 4. MATERIALS SCIENCE. *Educ:* Lynchburg Col, BS, 46; Univ Va, PhD(chem), 51. *Prof Exp:* Fulbright fel, Univ Norway, 51-52; res assoc chem, Univ Va, 52-60, from asst prof to assoc prof, 60-68, prof mat sci, 68-80, chmn dept, 76-80. *Mem:* Electron Micros Soc Am; Am Crystallog Asn; Int Asn Dent Res; Inst Mining, Metall & Petrol Engrs; Microbeam Anal Soc. *Res:* Chemistry and physics of solids and surfaces; x-ray diffraction; electron diffraction and electron microscopy. *Mailing Add:* Montvue Dr Charlottesville VA 22901

LAWLESS, PHILIP AUSTIN, b Tulsa, Okla, June 7, 43; m 72; c 2. ENGINEERING PHYSICS. *Educ:* Rice Univ, BA, 65; Duke Univ, PhD(physics), 74. *Prof Exp:* PHYSICIST, RES TRIANGLE INST, 74- *Res:* Theoretical and experimental investigations of electrostatic precipitatiors for particulate control. *Mailing Add:* PO Box 12194 Res Triangle Park NC 27709

LAWLESS, WILLIAM N, b Denver, Colo, Sept 15, 36; m 57; c 3. SOLID STATE PHYSICS. *Educ:* Colo Sch Mines, EMet, 59; Rensselaer Polytech Inst, PhD(physics), 64. *Prof Exp:* Fel solid state physics, Swiss Fed Inst Technol, 64-66; sr res phyicist, Res & Develop Labs, Corning Glass Works, 66-68, res assoc physics, 69-80; WITH LAKE SHORE CRYOTRONICS, INC, 80- *Concurrent Pos:* Guest worker, Cryogenics Div, Nat Bur Stand, Boulder, 73-75. *Mem:* AAAS; Am Inst Physics; Cryogenic Soc Am. *Res:* Ferroelectricity; doped alkali halides; glass-ceramic technology. *Mailing Add:* 64 E Walnut St Lake Shore Crytronics Inc Westerville OH 43081

LAWLEY, ALAN, b Birmingham, Eng, Aug 29, 33; m 60; c 3. METALLURGY, MATERIALS SCIENCE. *Educ:* Univ Birmingham, BSc, 55, PhD(phys metall), 58. *Prof Exp:* Res assoc metall, Univ Pa, 58-61; lab mgr phys metall, Res Labs, Franklin Inst, Pa, 61-66; assoc prof metall eng, 66-69, chmn, Mat Eng Dept, 69-78, PROF METALL ENG, DREXEL UNIV, 79- *Mem:* Am Inst Mining, Metall & Petrol Engrs; fel Am Soc Metals; Am Soc Eng Educ; Am Powder Metall Inst; Metall Soc (pres, 82). *Res:* Powder metallurgy; composite materials; deformation processing. *Mailing Add:* Dept of Mat Eng Drexel Univ Philadelphia PA 19104

LAWLOR, IGNATIUS E, electrical & electronic engineering, deceased

LAWRASON, F DOUGLAS, b St Paul, Minn, July 30, 19; m 44; c 3. INTERNAL MEDICINE. *Educ:* Univ Minn, BA, 41, MA & MD, 44. *Prof Exp:* Instr anat, Med Sch, Univ Minn, 41-43; from intern to resident, Sch Med, Yale Univ, 44-49, from instr to asst prof med, 49-50; prof assoc, Nat Res Coun, 50-53; asst prof & asst dean, Sch Med, Univ NC, 53-55; prof internal med, provost med affairs & dean med ctr, Univ Ark, 55-61; exec dir med res, Merck Sharp & Dohme Res Labs, Pa, 61-66, vpres med res, 66-69; prof internal med, Univ Tex Health Sci Ctr Dallas, 69-73, assoc dean acad affairs, 69-72, dean, 72-73; sr vpres, Sci Affairs & pres, Res Div, 73-80, SR VPRES SCI, SCHERING-PLOUGH CORP, 80- *Concurrent Pos:* James Hudson Brown res fel, Yale Univ, 48-49; mem hemat study sect, NIH, 51-53; comt blood & related probs, Nat Acad Sci, 53-57; inst grant comt, Am Cancer Soc, 55-60; training grant comt, Nat Res Coun, 59-64; mem bd dirs, Morristown Mem Hosp, 80- & NJ State Sci Adv Comt, 80- *Mem:* AAAS; Am Fedn Clin Res; Am Col Cardiologists; NY Acad Sci; Am Soc Internal Med. *Res:* Cancer and leukemia in inbred strains of mice; hematology; medical education and administration; research management. *Mailing Add:* Science Schering-Plough Corp Kenilworth NJ 07033

LAWRASON, GEORGE C, US citizen. AUTOMOTIVE ENGINEERING. *Educ:* La State Univ, BS, 49. *Prof Exp:* Engr, Friedrich Refrig Corp, 50-52; res engr, Dept Engines, Fuels & Lubricants, 53-56 & Dept Aviation, Engines, Fuels & Lubricants, 56-57, sr res engr, Dept Engines, Fuels & Lubricants, 57-59, mgr radioisotope appl sect, Dept Automotive Prod & Equip Res, 59-61, mgr spec projs, Dept Automotive Res, 61-67, asst dir, 67-74, dir, Dept Spec Projs, Automotive Res Div, 74-78, dir, Dept Vehicle & Traffic Safety, Automotive Res Div, 78-81, DIR, DEPT VEHICLE & TRAFFIC SAFETY, ENERGY SYSTS RES DIV, SOUTHWEST RES INST, 81- *Mem:* Sigma Xi; Soc Automotive Engrs. *Res:* Vehicle safety, including the parameters pertinent to the occupant, the vehicle and the vehicular environment. *Mailing Add:* Dept of Vehicle & Traffic Safety Southwest Res Inst PO Drawer 28510 San Antonio TX 78284

LAWRENCE, ADDISON LEE, cell physiology, comparative physiology, see previous edition

LAWRENCE, ALONZO WILLIAM, b Rahway, NJ, Apr 11, 37; m 60; c 3. ENVIRONMENTAL ENGINEERING. *Educ:* Rutgers Univ, BS, 59; Mass Inst Technol, MS, 60; Stanford Univ, PhD(civil eng), 67. *Prof Exp:* Asst prof civil eng, Drexel Inst Technol, 65-67; from asst prof to assoc prof environ eng, Cornell Univ, 67-76; vpres environ resources & occup health, 76-81, VPRES, SCI & TECHNOL, KOPPERS CO, PITTSBURGH, 81- *Honors & Awards:* Eng Sci Award, Am Asn Environ Eng Prof, 77. *Mem:* Am Soc Civil Engrs; Water Pollution Control Fedn. *Res:* Wastewater treatment technology; wastewater reclamation and reuse; biokinetics; solid wastes disposal; occupational safety and health; technological innovation; strategic management of technology. *Mailing Add:* Rm 1201 Koppers Bldg Pittsburgh PA 15219

LAWRENCE, B(ENJAMIN), b Boston, Mass, May 1, 29; m 52; c 2. CHEMICAL ENGINEERING, PRODUCT & PROCESS DEVELOPMENT. *Educ:* Princeton Univ, BSE, 50. *Prof Exp:* Engr, 50-55, group leader, 57-62, sect head, 62-70, ASSOC DIR PROD DEVELOP, PROCTER & GAMBLE CO, 70- *Mem:* Am Inst Chem Engrs. *Res:* Process development in foods; mixing and metering equipment; fats and oils technology; emulsion systems and surfactants. *Mailing Add:* 8677 Hollyhock Dr Cincinnati OH 45231

LAWRENCE, CHRISTOPHER WILLIAM, b London, Eng, Oct 2, 34; m 61; c 3. GENETICS, RADIOBIOLOGY. *Educ:* Univ Wales, BSc, 56; Univ Birmingham, PhD(genetics), 59. *Prof Exp:* Sci officer radiation biol, Wantage Labs, UK Atomic Energy Authority, 59-61, sr sci officer, 61-70; ASSOC PROF RADIATION BIOL, UNIV ROCHESTER, 70- *Concurrent Pos:* Vis asst prof radiation biol, Univ Rochester, 69. *Mem:* AAAS; Genetics Soc Am; Brit Genetical Soc; Brit Asn Radiation Res. *Res:* Radiation molecular genetics of Saccharomyces cerevisiae. *Mailing Add:* Dept of Radiation Biol & Biophys Univ of Rochester Med Ctr Rochester NY 14642

LAWRENCE, DAVID A, b Paterson, NJ, Jan 9, 45; m 67. IMMUNOLOGY. *Educ:* Rutgers Univ, BA, 66; Boston Col, MS, 68, PhD(biol), 71. *Prof Exp:* USPHS fel, Scripps Clin & Res Found, 71-74; asst prof, 74-78, ASSOC PROF MICROBIOL & IMMUNOL, ALBANY MED COL, 78- *Mem:* NY Acad Sci; Am Soc Microbiol; Am Asn Immunologists. *Res:* Cellular and subcellular events resulting from antigen activation and regulation of immune response; tumor immunology; immunotoxicology. *Mailing Add:* Dept of Microbiol & Immunol Albany Med Col Albany NY 12208

LAWRENCE, DAVID JOSEPH, b Johnson City, NY, June 15, 51. ELECTRONICS, SEMICONDUCTORS. *Educ:* Syracuse Univ, BS, 73; Cornell Univ, MS, 75, PhD(electrophys), 77. *Prof Exp:* Develop engr, Western Elec Co, 77-78; RES PHYSICIST SEMICONDUCTOR MAT, EASTMAN KODAK RES LABS, 78- *Mem:* Electrochem Soc; Inst Elec & Electronics Engrs. *Res:* III-V compounds; epitaxial growth; solid state light emitters and detectors. *Mailing Add:* Eastman Kodak Res Labs Kodak Park Bldg 81 Rochester NY 14650

LAWRENCE, DAVID REED, b Woodbury, NJ, Oct 11, 39; m 66. GEOLOGY, INVERTEBRATE PALEONTOLOGY. *Educ:* Johns Hopkins Univ, AB, 61; Princeton Univ, PhD(geol), 66. *Prof Exp:* Asst geol, Princeton Univ, 63-64, prof assoc, 66; asst prof, 66-69, ASSOC PROF GEOL & MARINE SCI, UNIV SC, 69- *Concurrent Pos:* NSF sci fac fel, Univ Tübingen, Ger, 71-72. *Mem:* Int Paleont Union; Geol Soc Am; Paleont Soc. *Res:* Evolutionary, ecologic and biogeographic aspects of fossil invertebrates; taphonomy; historiography of the earth sciences. *Mailing Add:* Dept of Geol Univ of SC Columbia SC 29208

LAWRENCE, DONALD BUERMANN, b Portland, Ore, Mar 8, 11; m 35. PLANT ECOLOGY, ETHNOBOTANY. *Educ:* Johns Hopkins Univ, PhD(plant physiol), 36. *Prof Exp:* Researcher Sigma Xi grant, 36-37; from instr to prof, 37-76, EMER PROF BOT, UNIV MINN, MINNEAPOLIS, 76- *Concurrent Pos:* Mem, Johns Hopkins Univ exped, Jamaica, 32, Am Geog Soc exped, Alaska, 41, 49, 50, 52, 55 & SChile, 59; spec consult, US Air Force, 48; dir terrestrial ecosyst proj, Hill Found, 57-61; Fulbright res fel, NZ, 64-65; US del Int Sea Ice Conf, Reykjavik, Nat Acad Sci Nat Res Coun, 71. *Mem:* AAAS; Am Geog Soc. *Res:* Vegetation development; physiographic ecology; ecological life histories of plants; causes of climatic change; glaciology; Asian plant names and place names in the New World; history of plant dispersal by man. *Mailing Add:* 108 Zool 318 Church St SE Minneapolis MN 55455

LAWRENCE, DONALD GILBERT, b Kingston, Ont, Jan 18, 32; m 56; c 3. NEUROLOGY, NEUROANATOMY. *Educ:* Bishop's Univ, BSc, 53; McGill Univ, MDCM, 57; Royal Col Physicians & Surgeons, FRCP(C), 74. *Prof Exp:* Res fel neuroanat, Western Reserve Univ, 65-66; Nat Multiple Sclerosis Soc fel neurophysiol, Univ Lab Physiol, Oxford Univ, 66-68; from asst prof to assoc prof neuroanat, Erasmus Univ, 68-72; assoc prof neurol & neurosurg, 72-80, ASSOC PROF ANAT, MCGILL UNIV, 72-, PROF NEUROL & NEUROSURG, 80-; HEAD, LAB NEUROANAT, MONTREAL NEURO INST, 72- *Concurrent Pos:* Asst physician, Montreal Gen Hosp, 72-77, assoc physician, 77- *Honors & Awards:* Osler Medal, Am Asn Hist Med, 58. *Mem:* AAAS; Am Asn Hist Med; Am Asn Anat; Soc Neurosci; Am Acad Neurol. *Res:* Anatomical, behavioral and clinical investigations of motor pathways in the central nervous system. *Mailing Add:* Lab Neuroanat Montreal Neuro Inst 3801 University St Montreal PQ H3A 2B4 Can

LAWRENCE, FRANCIS JOSEPH, b Glen Arm, Md, May 12, 25; m 51; c 4. PLANT BREEDING. *Educ:* Univ Md, BS, 51, MS, 58, PhD(hort, breed), 65. *Prof Exp:* Asst hort, Univ Md, 53-62, from instr to asst prof, 62-65; RES HORTICULTURIST, CORVALLIS RES STA, USDA, 65- *Mem:* Am Soc Hort Sci; Am Pomol Soc. *Res:* Breeding of Fragaria and Rubus. *Mailing Add:* Dept of Hort USDA Ore State Univ Corvallis OR 97331

LAWRENCE, FRANKLIN ISAAC LATIMER, b Brooklyn, NY, July 14, 05; m 34; c 1. ORGANIC CHEMISTRY. *Educ:* NY Univ, BS, 28, MS, 30. *Prof Exp:* Jr engr, Atlantic Ref Co, Pa, 30-34, tech sales supvr, 34-42; develop engr, Permutit Co, NY, 42-44; res dir, Kendall Ref Div, Witco Chem Corp, 44-68, vpres res & develop, 68-70, CONSULT, 70- *Honors & Awards:* Cert Appreciation, Am Petrol Indust. *Mem:* Am Chem Soc; Soc Automotive Eng; fel Am Inst Chem. *Res:* Petroleum chemistry; ion exchange. *Mailing Add:* 600 McClellan Circle Elizabethton TN 37643

LAWRENCE, FREDERICK VAN BUREN, JR, b Hyannis, Mass, May 16, 38; m 62; c 3. METALLURGY, CIVIL ENGINEERING. *Educ:* Swarthmore Col, BS, 60; Mass Inst Technol, SM, 62, CE, 65, ScD(mat sci), 68. *Prof Exp:* PROF METALL & CIVIL ENG, UNIV ILL, URBANA, 68- *Mem:* Am Welding Soc; Am Soc Metals; Am Inst Mining, Metall & Petrol Engrs. *Res:* Fatigue strength of welded joints; microstructure of cementitious materials. *Mailing Add:* Dept of Civil Eng 2129 CEB Univ of Ill Urbana IL 61801

LAWRENCE, GENE ARTHUR, b Lewiston, Idaho, Aug 5, 39. ELECTRICAL ENGINEERING. *Educ:* Univ Idaho, BSEE, 61; Univ Southern Calif, MSEE, 63; Northwestern Univ, PhD(elec eng), 69. *Prof Exp:* Mem tech staff aerospace systs, Hughes Aircraft Co, 61-63; from instr to asst prof elec eng, Wash State Univ, 63-77, assoc prof, 77-80; WITH GEN DYNAMICS, 80- *Mem:* Inst Elec & Electronics Engrs. *Res:* Control theory; optimization; modeling and simulation; estimation. *Mailing Add:* PO Box 748 Gen Dynamics Fort Worth TX 76101

LAWRENCE, GEORGE EDWIN, b Berkeley, Calif, Mar 25, 20; m 43; c 4. ZOOLOGY. *Educ:* Univ Calif, AB, 46, MA, 49, PhD, 60. *Prof Exp:* Asst zool, Univ Calif, 46-47; from instr to assoc prof, 47-67, PROF LIFE SCI, BAKERSFIELD STATE COL, 67-, HEAD DEPT, 70- *Mem:* Wilderness Soc; Cooper Ornith Soc; Ecol Soc Am; Nat Biol Teachers Asn. *Res:* Natural history of mammals and birds; ecology of chaparral association; temperature tolerance of small mammals. *Mailing Add:* 1208 Telegraph Ave Bakersfield CA 93305

LAWRENCE, GEORGE MELVIN, b Salt Lake City, Utah, Mar 26, 37; m 59; c 3. PHYSICS. *Educ:* Univ Utah, BS, 59; Calif Inst Technol, PhD(physics), 63. *Prof Exp:* Res assoc astrophys sci, Princeton Univ, 63-65, staff physicist, 65-67; res scientist, McDonnell Douglas Advan Res Lab, Calif, 67-70; vis fel, Joint Inst Lab Astrophys-Lab Atmospheric & Space Physics, 70-71, res assoc, 71-74, FEL, LAB ATMOSPHERIC & SPACE PHYSICS, UNIV COLO, BOULDER, 74- *Concurrent Pos:* Vis assoc, Calif Inst Technol, 68-70. *Mem:* Fel Am Phys Soc; Am Geophys Union. *Res:* Transition probabilities; cross sections; physical chemistry; detectors; space science. *Mailing Add:* Lab Atmospheric & Space Phys Univ of Colo Boulder CO 80302

LAWRENCE, HENRY SHERWOOD, b New York, NY, Sept 22, 16; m 43; c 3. IMMUNOLOGY, MEDICINE. *Educ:* NY Univ, AB, 38, MD, 43; Am Bd Internal Med, dipl. *Prof Exp:* Intern, 3rd Med Div, Bellevue Hosp, New York, 43-44, from asst resident to chief resident, 46-48; asst, 47-49, from instr to assoc prof, 49-61, dir, NY Univ Cancer Inst, 74-78, prof med, 61-79, JEFFREY BERGSTEIN PROF MED, MED SCH, NY UNIV, 79-, HEAD INFECTIOUS DIS & IMMUNOL UNIT, 59-, CO-DIR, NY UNIV-BELLEVUE MED SERV, 64- *Concurrent Pos:* Wyckoff fel, NY Univ, 48-49; dir student health serv, NY Univ-Bellevue Med Serv, 49-57; Commonwealth Fund fel, Univ Col, Univ London, 59; USPHS career develop award, 60-65; assoc mem streptococcal comt, Armed Forces Epidemiol Bd; consult, Allergy & Immunol Study Sect, USPHS, 60-65, chmn, 63-65; mem comt cutaneous syst & comt tissue transplantation, Div Med Sci, Nat Res Coun-Nat Acad Sci, chmn comt tissue transplantation, 63-65, mem, Nat Res Coun, 70; lectr, Harvey Soc, 73; consult & chmn allergy & infectious dis panel, Health Res Coun City of New York, infectious dis prog comt res serv, Vet Admin & res comts, Arthritis Found, Am Cancer Soc & Am Thoracic Soc. *Honors & Awards:* Von Pirquet Gold Medal Award, Annual Forum Allergy, 72; Am Col Physicians Award, 73; NY Acad Med Sci Medal, 74; Bristol Award, Infectious Dis Soc Am, 74; Hon Fel Royal Col Phys & Surg, Glasgow, 77; Chapin Medal, 75; Lila Gruber Award Cancer Res, 75. *Mem:* Nat Acad Sci; Am Soc Clin Invest; Am Asn Immunol; Harvey Soc (secy, 57-60); Asn Am Physicians. *Res:* Infection and immunity; transfer factor in delayed bacterial hypersensitivity; homograft reactions; tissue transplantation. *Mailing Add:* Infectious Dis & Immunol Div NY Univ Med Ctr New York NY 10016

LAWRENCE, IRVIN E, JR, b Raleigh, NC, Apr 18, 26. EMBRYOLOGY, HISTOLOGY. *Educ:* Univ NC, AB, 50; Univ Wyo, MS, 55; Univ Kans, PhD(anat), 63. *Prof Exp:* Teacher high sch, NC, 51-54; instr biol, Louisburg Col, 55-57; asst prof zool, Univ Wyo, 60-64; assoc prof biol, 64-70, assoc prof, 70-78, PROF ANAT, EAST CAROLINA UNIV, 78- *Concurrent Pos:* Univ Res fel, Univ Wyo, 63-64; USPHS res grant, 64-65; NIH res grant, 75- *Mem:* Am Soc Zool; Soc Develop Biol; AAAS; Pan-Am Asn Anat; Soc Study Reproduction. *Res:* Biogenic amines in development; experimental analysis of morphogenetic patterns and histochemical and hormonal correlations in the chicken comb; ovarian nerves and reproductive function. *Mailing Add:* Dept of Anat ECarolina Univ Sch of Med Greenville NC 27834

LAWRENCE, JAMES FRANKLIN, b Okemah, Okla, Aug 20, 50. MATHEMATICS. *Educ:* Okla State Univ, BS, 72; Univ Wash, PhD(math), 75. *Prof Exp:* Instr math, Univ Tex, Austin, 75-77; res assoc, Nat Bur Standards, 77-79; ASST PROF, UNIV KY, 79- *Concurrent Pos:* vis asst prof, Univ Mass, Boston, 80-81. *Mem:* Math Asn Am; Am Math Soc. *Res:* Field of combinatorics; study of oriented matroids. *Mailing Add:* Math Dept Univ Ky Lexington KY 40506

LAWRENCE, JAMES HAROLD, JR, b Beatrice, Nebr, Feb 9, 32; m 55; c 2. MECHANICAL ENGINEERING. *Educ:* Tex Tech Col, BS, 56, MS, 60; Tex A&M Univ, PhD(mech eng), 65. *Prof Exp:* From instr to asst prof, 56-62, assoc prof, 64-71, PROF MECH ENG, TEX TECH UNIV, 71-, CHMN DEPT, 72- *Mem:* Am Soc Eng Educ; Am Soc Mech Engrs; Am Soc Heat, Refrig & Air-Conditioning Engrs. *Res:* Conduction; convection; radiation heat transfer; systems engineering. *Mailing Add:* Dept of Mech Eng Tex Tech Univ PO Box 4289 Lubbock TX 79409

LAWRENCE, JAMES NEVILLE PEED, b Norfolk, Va, May 29, 29; m 48; c 1. HEALTH PHYSICS, PHYSICS. *Educ:* Johns Hopkins Univ, BA, 50; Vanderbilt Univ, MA, 58, PhD(physics), 68. *Prof Exp:* Res asst health physics, 51-54, mem staff, 54-68, ASSOC GROUP LEADER, LOS ALAMOS NAT LAB, UNIV CALIF, 68- *Mem:* Health Physics Soc. *Res:* Theoretical treatment of nuclear fission, especially liquid drop applications; health physics, especially dosimetry, internal exposure calculations and radionuclide identification. *Mailing Add:* 206 El Conejo Los Alamos NM 87544

LAWRENCE, JAMES VANTINE, b Middletown, Ohio, July 2, 18; m 42; c 3. BACTERIOLOGY. *Educ:* Univ Ill, BS, 43; Ohio State Univ, MS, 48, PhD(bact), 50. *Prof Exp:* From asst prof to assoc prof, 50-70, prof bact, 70-80, PROF ZOOL MICROBIOL, OHIO UNIV, 80- *Concurrent Pos:* Vis prof, WVa Univ, 51 & 52; clin lab dir, Athens State Hosp, 53, 54 & 56. *Mem:* Am Soc Microbiol; Am Pub Health Asn. *Res:* General and pathogenic bacteriology and parasitology. *Mailing Add:* Dept of Zool & Microbiol Ohio Univ Athens OH 45701

LAWRENCE, JOHN, b UK, Mar 23, 43; Can citizen; m 65; c 2. ENVIRONMENTAL CHEMISTRY, ANALYTICAL CHEMISTRY. *Educ:* Bristol Univ, BSc, 64, PhD(chem), 67. *Prof Exp:* Res assoc electrochem, Univ Ottawa, 67-69 & Colo State Univ, 69-71; res chemist semiconductos, Bell-Northern Res, 71-73; res scientist environ toxic contaminants, 73-80, RES MGR, ENVIRON ANAL METHODOLOGY, NAT WATER RES INST CAN, 80- *Res:* Water chemistry; water treatment; toxic contaminants; analytical methods. *Mailing Add:* Nat Water Res Inst PO Box 5050 Burlington ON L7R 4A6 Can

LAWRENCE, JOHN FRANCIS, entomology, see previous edition

LAWRENCE, JOHN HUNDALE, b Canton, SDak, Jan 7, 1904. MEDICINE. *Educ:* Univ SDak, AB, 26; Harvard Univ, MD, 30. *Hon Degrees:* DSc, Univ SDak, 42 & Cath Univ Am, 59; Dr, Univ Bordeaux, France, 58. *Prof Exp:* Intern, Peter Bent Brigham Hosp, Boston, 30-31; trainee, Strong Mem Hosp, Univ Rochester, 31-32; trainee, New Haven Hosp, Yale Univ, 32-34, assoc physician hosp & instr med univ, 34-37; res assoc, 37, prof & dir Donner Lab, 50-70, EMER PROF MED PHYSICS, UNIV CALIF, BERKELEY, 70-, EMER DIR, DONNER LAB, 70- *Concurrent Pos:* Regent, Univ Calif, Berkeley; William H Welch lectr; Ludwig Kast Mem lectr, 49; Stephen Walter Ranson Mem lectr; Von Hevesy Mem lectr, Athens, 74; Richardson lectr, Harvard Univ, 63; Pasteur Inst lectr, 63; AEC cons & vis prof AEE of India, Univ Bombay, 61; vis prof med, Am Univ, Beirut, Lebanon, 63 & Ohio State Univ, 65; mem sci & tech adv comt, NASA, 65-67, led 3-man med mission to USSR, 74; lectr, Univ Damascus & Univ Aleppo, 76; partic, John H Lawrence Interdisciplinary Biannual Sem, Sch Med, Univ SDak, Sioux Falls, 81. *Honors & Awards:* Decorated Silver Cross, Royal Order Phoenix, Greece; Caldwell Medal, US; Davidson Medal, Eng; Cert Appreciation, War & Navy Depts, 47; Medal, Univ Bordeaux, 58; Pasteur Medal, Pasteur Inst, Paris, 63; Nuclear Pioneer Award, Soc Nuclear Med, 70; First Marshall Brucer Medal & Katharine Berkan Judd Award, Sloan-Kettering Mem Hosp, New York, 75. *Mem:* Fel Am Nuclear Soc; Am Soc Clin Invest; hon mem Soc Nuclear Med (pres, 66); Am Asn Neurol Surgeons; Endocrine Soc. *Res:* Aerospace medicine; hematology; metabolism; physiology; medical physics; radioisotopes and nuclear radiations in research, diagnosis and therapy. *Mailing Add:* Donner Lab Univ of Calif Berkeley CA 94720

LAWRENCE, JOHN KEELER, b New York, NY, Oct 11, 40; m 67; c 1. GENERAL RELATIVITY, ASTROPHYSICS. *Educ:* Harvard Univ, AB, 62; Northeastern Univ, MS, 64, PhD(physics), 68. *Prof Exp:* Vis asst prof physics & astron, Univ Ga, 67-68; Univ asst physics, Univ Vienna, 68-71; vis res assoc, Northeastern Univ, 71-72; fel, Univ Windsor, 72-73; asst prof, 73-76, assoc prof physics & astron, 76-80, PROF PHYSICS & ASTRON, CALIF STATE UNIV, 80-, DEPT CHMN PHYSICS & ASTRON, 76- *Mem:* Am Phys Soc; AAAS; Austrian Phys Soc. *Res:* Deflection of null radiation by gravitational fields; cosmological models; cosmological coincidences; galactic structure; active galaxies and quasars. *Mailing Add:* Dept of Physics & Astron Calif State Univ Northridge CA 91330

LAWRENCE, JOHN M, b Cape Girardeau, Mo, Oct 11, 37. PHYSIOLOGY. *Educ:* Southeast Mo State Col, BS, 58; Univ Mo, AM, 60; Stanford Univ, PhD(biol), 66. *Prof Exp:* Instr physiol, Stanford Univ, 64-65; from asst prof to assoc prof, 65-75, PROF DEPT BIOL, UNIV SOUTH FLA, 75- *Concurrent Pos:* Fel, Marine Biol Lab, Hebrew Univ Israel, 69-70. *Mem:* Am Soc Zool; Marine Biol Asn UK. *Res:* Nutritional and reproductive physiology of marine invertebrates. *Mailing Add:* Dept of Biol Univ of SFla Tampa FL 33620

LAWRENCE, JOHN MCCUNE, b Carmichaels, Pa, Feb 17, 16; m 38; c 3. BIOCHEMISTRY. *Educ:* Carnegie Inst Technol, BS, 37, MS, 39; Univ Pittsburgh, PhD(biochem), 43. *Prof Exp:* Res asst, Mellon Inst, 39-41; Nutrit Found fel, Dept Dairy Indust, Cornell Univ, 43-45, from instr to asst prof biochem, 45-48; assoc chemist, Wash State Univ, 48-58, agr chemist, 58-81; RETIRED. *Mem:* AAAS; Am Soc Plant Physiol. *Res:* Enzymes; proteins; amino acids; biochemistry of seed germination and nutritional quality of seeds. *Mailing Add:* Dept of Agr Chem Wash State Univ Pullman WA 99163

LAWRENCE, JOHN MEDLOCK, b Cedar Bluff, Ala, Sept 25, 19; m 47; c 3. FISHERIES. *Educ:* Ala Polytech Inst, BS, 41, MS, 43; Iowa State Univ, PhD, 56. *Prof Exp:* Asst fish culturist, 46-57, assoc fish culturist, 57-63, PROF FISHERIES, AUBURN UNIV, 63- *Mem:* Am Fisheries Soc; Weed Sci Soc Am. *Res:* Methods for control of aquatic weeds and their effects upon fish production. *Mailing Add:* Dept Fisheries & Allied Aquacult Auburn Univ Auburn AL 36830

LAWRENCE, KENNETH BRIDGE, b Susquehanna, Pa, June 18, 18; m 45; c 2. MECHANICAL ENGINEERING. *Educ:* Pa State Univ, BS, 39, MS, 48. *Prof Exp:* Asst engr, SKF Industs, Inc, 40-41 & 44-45; instr math, Pa State Univ, 46-47, from instr to assoc prof mech eng, 47-56; sr res engr, Res Div, Curtiss-Wright Corp, 56-59, proj engr, Curtiss Div, 59-63; head dept, 63-68, PROF MECH ENG, MANHATTAN COL, 63- *Mem:* Soc Automotive Engrs; Am Soc Eng Educ. *Res:* Lubrication, friction and wear; lightweight reinforced materials and construction; industrial products. *Mailing Add:* Dept of Mech Eng Manhattan Col Bronx NY 10471

LAWRENCE, KENNETH OLIVER, b Cambridge, Md, Oct 5, 24; m 64. ENTOMOLOGY, HORTICULTURE. *Educ:* Mich State Univ, BS, 48. *Prof Exp:* ENTOMOLOGIST JAPANESE BEETLE, RES LAB, SCI & EDUC ADMIN, USDA, 69- *Mem:* Entom Soc Am; Am Registry Prof Entomologists; Coun Agr Sci & Technol. *Res:* Development of pesticides for control of adult and larvae of the Japanese beetle. *Mailing Add:* 2325 Southway SW Massillon OH 44691

LAWRENCE, KENT L(EE), b Beatrice, Nebr, Jan 23, 37; m 61; c 3. MECHANICAL ENGINEERING, ENGINEERING MECHANICS. *Educ:* Tex Tech Col, BS, 59, MS, 60; Ariz State Univ, PhD(eng mech), 65. *Prof Exp:* Instr mech, Univ Ill, 60-61; assoc prof mech eng, 61-62 & 64-77, PROF MECH ENG, UNIV TEX, ARLINGTON, 77- *Concurrent Pos:* Consult, Aerotechnol Dept, Bell Helicopter Co, 65- *Mem:* Am Inst Aeronaut & Astronaut; Am Soc Mech Engrs; Soc Exp Stress Anal; Am Helicopter Soc. *Res:* Vibrations; dynamics; structural mechanics; finite element methods. *Mailing Add:* Dept Mech Eng Box 19023 Univ Tex Arlington TX 76019

LAWRENCE, LLOYD ROBERT, JR, energy conversion, see previous edition

LAWRENCE, LOUISE DE KIRILINE, b Sweden, Jan 30, 94; Can citizen; m 18, 39. ORNITHOLOGY. *Hon Degrees:* LittD, Laurentian Univ, 71. *Prof Exp:* Ornithologist; RESEARCHER & WRITER. *Mem:* Am Ornith Union; Wilson Ornith Soc; Ornith Soc Sweden. *Res:* Breeding history of the Canada Jay, Warblers, the Red-eyed Vireo and Woodpeckers; body weight of the Black-capped Chickadee. *Mailing Add:* Pimisi Bay R R 1 Rutherglen ON P0H 2E0 Can

LAWRENCE, MERLE, b Remsen, NY, Dec 26, 15; m 42; c 3. PHYSIOLOGY. *Educ:* Princeton Univ, AB, 38, MA, 40, PhD(psychol), 41. *Prof Exp:* Nat Res Coun fel, Johns Hopkins Univ, 41; from asst prof to assoc prof psychol, Princeton Univ, 46-52; assoc prof physiol acoust, 52-57, PROF OTOLARYNGOL & PSYCHOL, MED SCH, UNIV MICH, ANN ARBOR, 57-, PROF PHYSIOL, 59-, RES ASSOC, INST INDUST HEALTH, 52-, DIR KRESGE HEARING RES INST, 61- *Concurrent Pos:* Consult, Surgeon Gen Off, 53- & Secy Defense, 55-58; mem commun disorders res training comt, Nat Inst Neurol Dis & Stroke, 61-65 & commun sci study sect, NIH, 65-70, mem communicative disorders rev comt, Nat Inst Neurol & Communicative Disorders & Stroke, 72-76, Nat Adv Neurol & Commun Dis & Stroke Coun, 76-80. *Mem:* Fel Acoust Soc Am; Am Laryngol, Rhinol & Otol Soc; Am Otol Soc; Col Oto-Rhino-Laryngol Amicitiae Sacrum; Asn Res Otolaryngol. *Res:* Physiology of hearing. *Mailing Add:* Kresge Hearing Res Inst Univ of Mich Med Sch Ann Arbor MI 48104

LAWRENCE, MONTAGUE SCHIELE, medicine, surgery, see previous edition

LAWRENCE, PAUL J, b Hazleton, Pa, Dec 18, 40; m 63; c 1. BIOCHEMISTRY. *Educ:* King's Col, Pa, BS, 62; Univ Wis, Madison, MS, 64, PhD(biochem), 67. *Prof Exp:* From asst prof to assoc prof biochem, Col Med, Univ Utah, 68-77; dir immunol res & develop, 77-81, DIR, SMITHKLINE DIAGNOSTICS RES & DEVELOP, 79- *Concurrent Pos:* Fel biochem, Univ Wis, 67-68; NIH fel, 67-69. *Mem:* AAAS; Am Chem Soc; Fedn Am Socs Exp Biol; Am Soc Microbiol; NY Acad Sci. *Res:* Mechanisms of drug action; development of diagnostic tests. *Mailing Add:* Smith Kline Instruments 880 Maude Ave Sunnyvale CA 94086

LAWRENCE, PAULINE OLIVE, b Buff Bay, Jamaica, WI, Nov 10, 45; m 76. INSECT PARASITE ECOLOGY, INSECT ENDOCRINOLOGY. *Educ:* Univ WI, Jamica, BSc Hons, 68; Univ Fla, Gainesville, MS, 72, PhD(entomol), 75. *Prof Exp:* Asst entomologist res, Ministry Agr, Jamaica, WI, 68-69; grad res fel, Dept Entomol, 69-72, res asst, 72-75, asst prof, 76-81, ASSOC PROF RES & TECHING, DEPT ZOOL, UNIV FLA, GAINESVILLE, 81- *Mem:* AAAS; Am Soc Zoologists; Entom Soc Am; Sigma Xi; Animal Behav Soc. *Res:* Parasite biology and the influence of host hormones on parasite development; development of resistance by hosts to parasites and resulting feed-back on host and parasite populations; parasite ecology and behavior. *Mailing Add:* Dept Zool 223 Bartram Hall Univ Fla Gainesville FL 32611

LAWRENCE, PHILIP LINWOOD, b New Bedford, Mass, Mar 27, 23; m 48; c 2. GEOPHYSICS. *Educ:* Colo Sch Mines, GeolE, 49, Southern Methodist Univ, MS, 60. *Prof Exp:* Res geophysicist, Magnolia Petrol Co, Tex, 49-62; staff adv, Mobil Petrol Co, NY, 63-65; unit supvr, Geophys Serv Ctr, Mobil Oil Co, Tex, 66-68, corp geophysicist, 69-81, CONSULT, MOBIL OIL CORP, 81- *Concurrent Pos:* Lectr elec eng, Southern Methodist Univ, 60-62. *Mem:* Sigma Xi. *Res:* Seismic, magnetic, gravity data gathering, processing and interpretation techniques and development for mineral exploration. *Mailing Add:* 467 Harvest Glen Richardson TX 75081

LAWRENCE, PHILIP SIGNOR, b Oak Park, Ill, Nov 6, 14; m 41; c 4. APPLIED STATISTICS, PUBLIC HEALTH. *Educ:* Denison Univ, BA, 37; Johns Hopkins Univ, DSc(biol, statist), 40. *Prof Exp:* Res asst, Johns Hopkins Univ, 40; res statistician, Harvard Univ, 41; biostatistician, Div Pub Health Methods, USPHS, 46-52; chief Hagerstown familial studies, 53-57, chief health interview surv br, 57-60, chief div health interview statist, Nat Ctr Health Statist, 60-66, assoc dir nat ctr health statist, USPHS, 67-70, dep dir, 70-73; HEALTH STATIST CONSULT, 73- *Concurrent Pos:* Exp adv, WHO, 70; tech consult, Ministry Health, Columbia, 65, Indian Coun Med Res, 72-78 & Polish Nat Inst Hyg, 73-79. *Honors & Awards:* Super Serv Award, HEW, 73. *Mem:* Fel Am Statist Asn; Int Asn Surv Statist; Inter-Am Statist Inst. *Res:* Health statistics survey methodology; applied research in vital statistics and population dynamics; promotion of domestic and international research on these subjects. *Mailing Add:* 9848 Singleton Dr Bethesda MD 20817

LAWRENCE, RAYMOND JEFFERY, b Cornwall, NY, Feb 25, 39; m 63; c 2. SHOCK WAVE PHYSICS. *Educ:* Lawrence Col, BA, 61; Univ NMex, MS, 70. *Prof Exp:* Res physicist shock wave physics, Air Force Weapons Lab, Kirtland AFB, NMex, 63-67; MEM TECH STAFF SHOCK WAVE PHYSICS, SANDIA LABS, 67- *Mem:* Am Phys Soc; Int Soc Rock Mech. *Res:* Shock wave physics; numerical wave propagation computer code development and application; constitutive model development; application of these fields to weapons development and energy research. *Mailing Add:* Sandia Labs PO Box 5800 Albuquerque NM 87185

LAWRENCE, RICHARD AUBREY, b Logan, Utah, Feb 17, 47; m 70; c 5. BIOCHEMISTRY, NUTRITION. *Educ:* Brigham Young Univ, BS, 71; UniV Wis-Madison, PhD(biochem), 75. *Prof Exp:* Fel med, Univ Tex Health Sci Ctr, Dallas, 75-77, instr med, 77-78; instr, 78-79, ASST PROF MED & BIOCHEM, SCH MED, LA STATE UNIV, SHREVEPORT, 79- *Mem:* Am Inst Nutrit; Sigma Xi. *Res:* Selenium nutrition and metabolism; role of lipid peroxidation in tissue injury and disease and physiological mechanisms for protection against it; mechanism of lipid peroxidation; mechanisms of oxygen toxicity. *Mailing Add:* School of Med La State Univ Shreveport LA 71130

LAWRENCE, ROBERT D, b Ithaca, NY, May 24, 43; m 66. GEOLOGY. *Educ:* Earlham Col, BA, 65; Stanford Univ, PhD(geol), 68. *Prof Exp:* Asst prof geol, Earlham Col, 68-70; assoc prof, 70-77, ASSOC PROF GEOL, ORE STATE UNIV, 77- *Mem:* AAAS; Geol Soc Am; Geologischen Vereinigung; Am Geophys Union. *Res:* Major faults of western North America; deformation features of minerals; structural petrology; tectonics of Pakistan; tectonic history of Pacific Northwest. *Mailing Add:* Dept of Geol Ore State Univ Corvallis OR 97331

LAWRENCE, ROBERT G, b Wilmington, NY, Feb 14, 21; m 46; c 2. ZOOLOGY. *Educ:* Eastern Nazarene Col, AB, 44; Boston Univ, MA, 46; Okla State Univ, PhD, 64. *Prof Exp:* Teacher, Henry Ford's Boys Sch, Mass, 45-46; prof biol & head dept, Bethany Nazarene Col, 47-68; assoc dean, Mid-Am Nazarene Col, 68-71; prof biol sci, 68-75, dir instnl res, 71-74, acad dean, 74-75; PROF BIOL, MT VERNON NAZARENE COL, OHIO, 75-, ACAD DEAN, 75-, V PRES ACAD AFFAIRS, 76- *Concurrent Pos:* Chmn div natural sci, Bethany Nazarene Col, 49-68. *Mem:* AAAS; Am Ornith Union; Nat Audubon Soc; Wilson Soc. *Res:* Ornithology; relation of weather factors to migration of water fowl. *Mailing Add:* Mt Vernon Nazarene Col Martinsburg Rd Mt Vernon OH 43050

LAWRENCE, ROBERT HOWARD, JR, plant physiology, biochemistry, see previous edition

LAWRENCE, ROBERT MARSHALL, b Kennecott, Alaska, June 28, 23; m 50; c 9. ANESTHESIOLOGY. *Educ:* Univ Rochester, MD, 49. *Prof Exp:* Resident surg, Strong Mem Hosp, 49-54, resident anesthesiol, 54-56; from instr to assoc prof surg & med, 56-68, PROF ANESTHESIOL, SCH MED, UNIV ROCHESTER, 68- *Concurrent Pos:* Consult, Vet Admin Hosps, Batavia & Canandaigua, 56- *Mem:* Am Soc Anesthesiol; Am Asn Respiratory Ther. *Res:* Oxygen toxicity; respiratory therapy. *Mailing Add:* Dept of Anesthesiol Univ of Rochester Sch of Med Rochester NY 14642

LAWRENCE, ROBERT SWAN, b Philadelphia, Pa, Feb 6, 38; m 60; c 3. INTERNAL MEDICINE, PREVENTIVE MEDICINE. *Educ:* Harvard Univ, AB, 60; Harvard Med Sch, MD, 64. *Prof Exp:* Intern & jr resident, Mass Gen Hosp, 64-66; asst surgeon epidemiol, Epidemic Intel Serv, Ctr Dis Control, USPHS, Atlanta, 66-69; sr resident, Mass Gen Hosp, 69-70; from asst prof med to assoc prof, Sch Med, Univ NC, 70-74; asst prof, 74-80, ASSOC PROF MED, HARVARD MED SCH, 80-, DIR, DIV PRIMARY CARE, 74- *Concurrent Pos:* Chief, Dept Med, Cambridge Hosp, 80- *Mem:* Inst Med-Nat Acad Sci; Am Col Physicians; Soc for Res & Educ Primary Care Med (pres, 78-79); Am Fedn for Clin Res; Soc Teachers Prev Med. *Res:* Health beliefs of patients; medical sociology; primary care education; manpower issues. *Mailing Add:* Div Primary Care 25 Shattuck St Boston MA 02115

LAWRENCE, SIGMUND J(OSEPH), b Chicago, Ill, May 20, 18; m; c 6. CHEMICAL ENGINEERING. *Educ:* Ill Inst Technol, BS, 39; Univ Iowa, MS, 42, PhD(chem eng), 43. *Prof Exp:* Apprentice engr, Caterpillar Tractor Co, Ill, 39-40; res chem engr, Armour Res Found, Ill Inst Technol, 40-41; chem engr, Shell Develop Co, Calif, 43-46; chem engr, Gen Elec Co, Wash, 46-48, res assoc, Knolls Atomic Power Lab, 48-51, Res Lab, 51-52, process engr, Chem Div, Silicone Prods Dept, 52-57, chem engr, Gen Eng Lab, 57-59, appln engr, Process Comput Control, Syst Sales & Eng, 60-67, appln engr spec sensors, Instrument Dept, 67, mgr sensor progs, 67-69, consult engr indust process systs, Reentry & Environ Systs Div, 69-73; SUPVRY ENGR DESIGN CHEM PLANTS, CATALYTIC INC, PHILADELPHIA, 74- *Mem:* Am Chem Soc; Am Inst Chem Eng. *Res:* Process instrumentation, automation and control; computer monitoring and control; air, water and waste monitoring; pollution control; instrument development and design; process analysis and design. *Mailing Add:* 100 Linda Lane Media PA 19063

LAWRENCE, THOMAS, b Colonsay, Sask, July 19, 27; m 51; c 2. PLANT BREEDING. *Educ:* Univ Sask, BSc, 50, MSc, 52; Univ Alta, PhD(plant breeding, genetics), 55. *Prof Exp:* Asst, Univ Sask, 50-52 & Univ Alta, 52-54; res scientist, 54-76, HEAD FORAGE PROD & UTILIZATION SECT, RES STA, CAN DEPT AGR, 76- *Mem:* Can Soc Agron; Agr Inst Can. *Res:* Grass breeding, genetics and seed production; forage crop use on dry and irrigated land in the great plains of western Canada. *Mailing Add:* Res Sta PO Box 1030 Swift Current SK S9H 3X2 Can

LAWRENCE, VINNEDGE MOORE, b Bangor, Maine, Feb 19, 40; m 66; c 1. ENTOMOLOGY, ECOLOGY. *Educ:* Miami Univ Ohio, BS, 62, MA, 64; Purdue Univ, PhD(entom), 68. *Prof Exp:* Instr biol, Xavier Univ Ohio, 64-65; asst prof, 68-72, ASSOC PROF BIOL, WASHINGTON & JEFFERSON COL, 72- *Concurrent Pos:* Mem citizen's adv coun, Pa Dept Environ Resources, 71-81. *Mem:* AAAS; Am Inst Biol Sci; Sigma Xi; NAm Benthological Soc. *Res:* Population dynamics of Odonata naiads in farm-pond ecosystems; distribution of Odonata in Pennsylvania; microdistribution of capniid plecoptera. *Mailing Add:* Dept of Biol Washington & Jefferson Col Washington PA 15301

LAWRENCE, WALTER, JR, b Chicago, Ill, May 31, 25; m 47; c 4. SURGERY. *Educ:* Univ Chicago, PhB, 45, SB, 46, MD, 48. *Prof Exp:* Intern surg, Johns Hopkins Hosp, 48-49, asst resident & asst, Sch Med, Johns Hopkins Univ, 49-50, Halsted fel, Johns Hopkins Hosp, 50; resident, Mem Ctr Cancer & Allied Dis, 51-52 & 54-56; res fel exp surg, Mem Ctr Cancer

& Allied Sci, 56; instr surg, Med Col, Cornell Univ, 57-58, asst prof, 58-63, clin assoc prof, 63-66; chmn div surg oncol, 66-75, Am Cancer Soc prof clin oncol, 72-75, PROF SURG, MED COL VA, 66-, DIR CANCER CTR, 74- *Concurrent Pos:* Asst mem, Sloan-Kettering Inst Cancer Res, 57-60, assoc mem & assoc chief div exp surg, 60-66; clin asst attend surgeon, Mem Hosp, 57-59, asst attend surgeon, 59-62, assoc vis surgeon, 62-; asst vis surgeon, James Ewing Hosp, 57-62, assoc vis surgeon, 62-; mem surg staff, NY Hosp, 57- *Honors & Awards:* Sloan Award Cancer Res, 64; Horsley Award, 73. *Mem:* Halsted Soc (pres, 75); fel Am Col Surg; fel NY Acad Sci; fel NY Acad Med; fel Royal Soc Med. *Res:* Surgery, particularly cancer and cancer research. *Mailing Add:* Box 11 Dept of Surg Med Col of Va Richmond VA 23298

LAWRENCE, WALTER EDWARD, b Albany, NY, May 22, 42; m 69. THEORETICAL SOLID STATE PHYSICS. *Educ:* Carnegie Inst Technol, BS, 64; Cornell Univ, PhD(physics), 70. *Prof Exp:* Res assoc physics, Stanford Univ, 69-71; asst prof, 71-77, ASSOC PROF PHYSICS, DARTMOUTH COL, 77- *Mem:* Am Phys Soc. *Res:* Solid state theory, principally superconductivity; transport theory of metals. *Mailing Add:* Dept of Physics Dartmouth Col Hanover NH 03755

LAWRENCE, WILLARD EARL, b Chassell, Mich, Apr 8, 17; m 43; c 5. STATISTICS. *Educ:* Marquette Univ, BS, 51, MS, 53; Univ Wis, MS, 62, PhD(statist), 64. *Prof Exp:* From instr to assoc prof, 53-69, asst chmn dept, 58-63, PROF MATH, MARQUETTE UNIV, 69-, CHMN DEPT MATH & STATIST, 73- *Concurrent Pos:* Consult, NSF, 66-69; statistician, Oak Ridge Nat Lab, 79-80. *Mem:* Math Asn Am; Am Statist Asn; Inst Math Statist; Soc Indust & Appl Math. *Res:* Experimental design; response surface designs which minimize variance and bias errors; designs for mixtures; probability. *Mailing Add:* Dept of Math & Statist Marquette Univ 540 N 15th St Milwaukee WI 53233

LAWRENCE, WILLIAM CHASE, b Cambridge, Mass, July 10, 34; m 55; c 3. VIROLOGY, MOLECULAR BIOLOGY. *Educ:* Univ Mass, BS, 55; Univ Pa, VMD, 59, PhD(microbiol), 66. *Prof Exp:* Asst prof, 65-72, ASSOC PROF MIBROBIOL, UNIV PA, 72- *Concurrent Pos:* USPHS res grant, 67-74; USDA Res Grant, 75- *Mem:* AAAS; Am Vet Med Asn; Am Soc Microbiol; NY Acad Sci; Sigma Xi. *Res:* Biochemistry of viral infection. *Mailing Add:* Dept of Pathobiol Sch Vet Med Univ of Pa 3800 Spruce St Philadelphia PA 19104

LAWRENCE, WILLIAM HOBART, forestry, wildlife management, see previous edition

LAWRENCE, WILLIAM HOMER, b Magnet Cove, Ark, Mar 20, 28; m 54; c 4. TOXICOLOGY, PHARMACOLOGY. *Educ:* Col of Ozarks, BS, 50; Univ Md, MS, 52, PhD(pharmacol), 55. *Prof Exp:* Instr materia medica, Sch Nursing, Univ Md, 51, asst pharmacol, Sch Pharm, 51-54; from asst prof to assoc prof pharmacol & physiol, Col Pharm, Univ Houston, 56-66; assoc prof, 66-73, asst dir mat sci toxicol labs, 67-75, PROF TOXICOL, UNIV TENN CTR FOR HEALTH SCI, 73-, ASSOC DIR MAT SCI TOXICOL LABS, 75-, HEAD ANIMAL TOXICOL SECT, 67- *Concurrent Pos:* Consult, Drug-Plastic Res & Toxicol Labs, Univ Tex, 63-68, lectr, Med Br, 64-67; consult, Vet Admin Hosp, Houston, 64-66 & Memphis, 66- *Mem:* AAAS; Soc Toxicol; Am Pharmaceut Asn; Sigma Xi. *Res:* Toxicity of biomaterials and medical devices, especially dental materials, blood bags, intravenous administration tubings, extracorporeal devices, implantable devices and carcinogenic studies of plastics. *Mailing Add:* Mat Sci Toxicol Lab Univ Tenn Ctr Health Sci Memphis TN 38163

LAWRENCE, WILLIAM MASON, b Brooktondale, NY, Oct 2, 18; m 42; c 2. FISHERIES, NATURAL RESOURCES. *Educ:* Cornell Univ, BS, 38, PhD(fishery biol), 41. *Prof Exp:* Biometrician bur game, NY State Conserv Dept, 41-42, sr aquatic biologist, 46-52, chief bur fish, 52-55, dir fish & game, 55-58, asst comnr, 58-64, dep comnr, NY State Dept Environ Conserv, 64-74; CONSULT, 74- *Concurrent Pos:* US comnr, Great Lakes Fishery Comn; chmn, Atlantic States Marine Fisheries Comn, 71-73. *Mem:* Am Fisheries Soc (pres, 59); Wildlife Soc; NY Acad Sci; Int Asn Game, Fish & Conserv Comnrs (pres, 69). *Res:* Fish and wildlife conservation; water resources. *Mailing Add:* 991 White Church Rd Brooktondale NY 14817

LAWREY, JAMES DONALD, b Arlington, Va, Dec 15, 49. LICHENOLOGY. *Educ:* Wake Forest Univ, BS, 71; Univ SDak, MA, 73; Ohio State Univ, PhD(bot), 77. *Prof Exp:* ASST PROF ECOL, GEORGE MASON UNIV, 77- *Mem:* Am Bryol & Lichenological Soc; Ecol Soc Am; Brit Lichen Soc; Mycol Soc Am; Bot Soc Am. *Res:* Population and community ecology of lichens; ecological significance of lichen secondary compounds; use of lichens as biological indicators of atomospheric pollution. *Mailing Add:* Biol Dept George Mason Univ Fairfax VA 22030

LAWRIE, DUNCAN H, b Chicago, Ill, Apr 26, 43. COMPUTER SCIENCE, ELECTRICAL ENGINEERING. *Educ:* DePauw Univ, BA, 66; Purdue Univ, BSEE, 66; Univ Ill, MS, 69, PhD(comput sci), 73. *Prof Exp:* Sr res programmer, 70-73, vis res asst prof, 73-74, asst prof, 74-79, ASSOC PROF COMPUT SCI, UNIV ILL, URBANA-CHAMPAIGN, 79- *Concurrent Pos:* Consult, ATI, Inc, 71, Burroughs Corp, 72-77, NASA, 72; John Wiley & Sons, Inc, 77-78 & US Air Force Weapons Lab, 79- *Mem:* Inst Elec & Electronics Engrs; Asn Comput Mach; Am Asn Univ Professors. *Res:* Computer system organization; especially very large systems; memory hierarchies; data base management. *Mailing Add:* 222 Digital Comput Lab Univ of Ill Urbana IL 61801

LAWROSKI, HARRY, b Dalton, Pa, Oct 10, 28; m 62. CHEMICAL & NUCLEAR ENGINEERING. *Educ:* Pa State Univ, BS, 50, MS, 56, PhD(chem eng), 59. *Prof Exp:* Asst, Pa State Univ, 50-56, instr petrol refining, 56-58; assoc chem engr, Idaho Div, Argonne Nat Lab, 58-63, tech mgr, Zero Power Plutonium Reactor, 63-68; supt EBR II Opers, 68-73; gen mgr environ, Nuclear Serv Corp, 73-76; asst gen mgr, Idaho Chem Progs,

Allied Chem Corp, 76-80; CONSULT, 80- *Concurrent Pos:* Instr, Nat Reactor Testing Sta, Univ Idaho, 59- *Mem:* Fel Am Nuclear Soc (treas, 71-77, vpres, 79-80, pres, 80-81); Am Inst Chem Engrs. *Res:* Reactor engineering; petroleum refining. *Mailing Add:* 2375 Belmont Ave Idaho Falls ID 83401

LAWROSKI, STEPHEN, b Scranton, Pa, Jan 17, 14; m 47; c 2. CHEMICAL ENGINEERING. *Educ:* Pa State Col, BS, 34, MS, 39, PhD(chem eng), 43. *Prof Exp:* From asst to supvr res & develop, Petrol Refining Lab, Pa, 34-43; res chem engr, Standard Oil Develop Co, NJ, 43-44, asst sect chief, 46; group leader Manhattan Dist, Metall Lab, Univ Chicago, 44-46; adv prof trainee, Clinton Lab, Univ Tenn, 46-47; dir, Chem Eng Div, 47-63, assoc lab dir, 63-70, SR ENGR, ARGONNE NAT LAB, 70- *Concurrent Pos:* Consult, US Army Chem Corps, 60-66; mem gen adv comt, US AEC, 64-70; mem adv comt reactor safeguards, US Nuclear Regulatory Comn, 74- *Honors & Awards:* Robert E Wilson Award, 71. *Mem:* Nat Acad Eng; AAAS; Am Chem Soc; fel Am Nuclear Soc; Sigma Xi; Am Inst Chem Engrs. *Res:* Petroleum technology; separations processes in atomic energy field; composition and utilization of several typical hydrocarbon naphthas; nuclear technology. *Mailing Add:* 144 S Sleight St Naperville IL 60540

LAWS, EDWARD ALLEN, b Columbus, Ohio, Feb 4, 45. OCEANOGRAPHY. *Educ:* Harvard Univ, BA, 67, PhD(chem physics), 71. *Prof Exp:* Instr oceanog, Fla State Univ, 71-74; asst prof oceanog, 74-80, ASSOC PROF OCEANOG, UNIV HAWAII, 80- *Mem:* AAAS; Am Soc Limnol & Oceanog; Ecol Soc Am; Phycol Soc Am. *Res:* Metabolism of carbon and nitrogen by marine phytoplankton; importance of conditioning in regulating growth characteristics and metabolism; response of phytoplankton communities to nutrient enrichments. *Mailing Add:* Dept of Oceanog Univ of Hawaii Honolulu HI 96822

LAWS, EDWARD RAYMOND, JR, b New York, NY, Apr 29, 38; m 62; c 4. NEUROSURGERY. *Educ:* Princeton Univ, AB, 59; Johns Hopkins Univ, MD, 63. *Prof Exp:* Intern, Johns Hopkins Hosp, 63-64; asst chief toxicol, Commun Dis Ctr, USPHS, Ga, 64-66; asst prof neurol surg & neurol surgeon, Johns Hopkins Hosp, 66-72; assoc prof, 72-80, PROF NEUROL SURG, MAYO MED SCH, 80-, NEUROL SURGEON, MAYO CLIN, 72- *Concurrent Pos:* USPHS res grants, 60-62; Henry Strong Denison fel, 62-63; fel surg, Johns Hopkins Univ, 63-64. *Mailing Add:* Dept of Neurosurg Mayo Clin Rochester MN 55901

LAWS, KENNETH LEE, b Pasadena, Calif, May 30, 35; m 65; c 2. SOLID STATE PHYSICS, METEOROLOGY. *Educ:* Calif Inst Technol, BS, 56; Univ Pa, MS, 59; Bryn Mawr Col, PhD(physics), 62. *Prof Exp:* Instr physics, Hobart & William Smith Cols, 58-59; asst prof, 62-66, assoc prof, 66-78, asst dean, 71-72, assoc dean, 72-77, PROF PHYSICS, DICKINSON COL, 78- *Mem:* Am Asn Physics Teachers; Am Meteorol Soc; Sigma Xi. *Res:* Meteorology; physics of dance. *Mailing Add:* Dickinson Col Carlisle PA 17013

LAWS, LEONARD STEWART, b Pocasset, Okla, Dec 29, 17; m 43; c 4. MATHEMATICS. *Educ:* Willamette Univ, AB, 39; Stanford Univ, MA, 41; Mich State Univ, EdD, 53. *Prof Exp:* Asst math, Stanford Univ, 39-41; asst math & mech, Univ Minn, 41-42, from instr to asst prof, 42-52; dean-registr, 53-55, chmn natural sci div, 55-74, PROF MATH, SOUTHWESTERN COL, KANS, 55- *Concurrent Pos:* Asst, Mich State Univ, 47 & 53; NSF fel, Stanford Univ, 61-62; mgt consult, 64- *Mem:* Am Soc Qual Control; Am Statist Asn. *Res:* Industrial reliability; design of experiments. *Mailing Add:* Dept of Math Southwestern Col 100 Col St Winfield KS 67156

LAWS, PRISCILLA WATSON, b New York, NY, Jan 18, 40; m 65. NUCLEAR PHYSICS. *Educ:* Reed Col, BA, 61; Bryn Mawr Col, MA, 63, PhD(physics), 66. *Prof Exp:* Asst physics, Bryn Mawr Col, 61-63; sr tech aide, Bell Labs, 62; asst prof, 65-70, assoc prof, 70-79, PROF PHYSICS, DICKSON COL, 79- *Concurrent Pos:* Mem med radiation adv comt, Bur Radiation Health, Food & Drug Admin, Dept Health, Educ & Welfare, 74-78. *Mem:* Am Asn Physics Teachers; Health Physics Soc. *Res:* Nuclear beta decay; environmental radiation; effects of medical x-rays, energy and environment. *Mailing Add:* Dept Physics & Astron Dickinson Col Carlisle PA 17013

LAWS, WILFORD DERBY, JR, b Colonia Diaz, Mex, Nov 19, 11; US citizen; m 47; c 2. SOIL FERTILITY. *Educ:* Brigham Young Univ, BS, 39; Utah State Agr Col, MS, 41; Ohio State Univ, PhD(soil chem), 44. *Prof Exp:* Asst, Utah State Agr Col, 39-41; res assoc, Res Found, Ohio State Univ, 43-47; sr soil scientist, Tex Res Found, 47-56, prin soil scientist, 56-58, chmn dept soil sci, 47-58, chmn dept soil sci & chem, 58-60; chmn dept agron, 65-66, prof, 60-77, EMER PROF AGRON, BRIGHAM YOUNG UNIV, 77- *Concurrent Pos:* Dir agr res, Tex Res Found, 67-68. *Mem:* Am Soc Agron; Soil Sci Soc Am; Int Soc Soil Sci. *Res:* Farming systems for Texas Blacklands; slow release nitrogen fertilizers for stony soils; corn planting density and silage quality; fall versus spring phosphate on irrigated alfalfa; soil chemistry. *Mailing Add:* 519 East 600 S Orem UT 84057

LAWSON, ALLEN C, JR, b Battle Creek, Mich, Jan 30, 28; m 50; c 3. ELECTRICAL & SYSTEMS ENGINEERING. *Educ:* Milwaukee Sch Eng, BS, 56. *Prof Exp:* Res engr, Inst Sci & Technol, Univ Mich, 57-60, res assoc electronic countermeasures, 60-61, assoc res engr, 61-65, RES ENGR, COUNTERMEASURES GROUP, RADAR & OPTICS LAB, ENVIRON RES INST MICH, ANN ARBOR, 65- *Mem:* Inst Elec & Electronics Engrs; Sigma Xi. *Res:* Techniques for navigating manned interplanetary vehicles; reconnaissance techniques for limited-war environment; antenna sidelobe reduction techniques; synthetic aperture radar techniques; climatological constraints on remote sensing. *Mailing Add:* 1560 Gattegno Ypsilanti MI 48197

LAWSON, ANDREW COWPER, II, b Chicago, Ill, Oct 21, 46. PHYSICS. *Educ:* Pomona Col, BA, 67; Univ Calif, San Diego, MS, 69, PhD(physics), 72. *Prof Exp:* Asst res physicist, Inst Pure & Appl Physics, Univ Calif, San Diego, 72-77; ASST PROF PHYSICS, POMONA COL, 77- *Mem:* AAAS; Am Phys Soc; Am Asn Physics Teachers; NY Acad Sci. *Res:* Superconductivity in relation to crystal structure; behavior of the electrical resistance of metals; occurance of crystallographic transformations at low temperatures. *Mailing Add:* 241 E Green St Claremont CA 91711

LAWSON, ANTON ERIC, b Lansing, Mich, Oct 24, 45; m 68; c 3. SCIENCE EDUCATION. *Educ:* Univ Ariz, BS, 67; Univ Ore, MS, 69; Univ Okla, PhD(sci educ), 73. *Prof Exp:* Teacher math & sci, Ralston Intermediate Sch, Belmont, Calif, 69-71; instr sci educ, Univ Okla, 72-73; res assoc biol educ, Purdue Univ, 73-74; res educr, Univ Calif, Berkeley, 74-77; asst prof, 77-80, ASSOC PROF SCI EDUC, ARIZ STATE UNIV, 80- *Honors & Awards:* Res in Sci Teaching Award, Nat Asn for Res in Sci Teaching, 76. *Mem:* Nat Asn Res Sci Teaching; Asn Educ Teachers Sci; Sch Sci & Math Asn; Nat Asn Biol Teaching; AAAS. *Res:* Development of formal reasoning; psychology of teaching science and mathematics. *Mailing Add:* Dept of Physics Ariz State Univ Tempe AZ 85281

LAWSON, BENJAMIN F, b Montgomery, Ala, May 29, 31; m 56; c 3. ORAL MEDICINE, PERIODONTOLOGY. *Educ:* Auburn Univ, BS, 53; Emory Univ, DDS, 61; Ind Univ, MSD, 63; Univ Ala, cert periodont, 68. *Prof Exp:* Asst prof oral diag & chmn dept, Sch Dent, Emory Univ, 63-66; asst prof, Sch Dent, Univ Ala, 66-68; from assoc prof to prof oral med & periodont, Sch Dent, 68-72, chmn dept, 68-70, chmn dept, Col Dent Med, 70-72, DEAN COL ALLIED HEALTH SCI, MED UNIV SC, 72- *Concurrent Pos:* NIH teacher training grant, 61-63; Eli Lilly & Co grant, 62-66; gen pract, 65-66; consult, Ft Jackson & Ft Benning Vet Admin Hosp Coastal Ctr, 68-; Warner-Lambert grant, 70- *Mem:* Am Dent Asn; Am Soc Allied Health Professions. *Res:* Histology-histopathology of dental pulp, ceramic and titanium implants; vital pulpal therapy. *Mailing Add:* Col of Allied Health Sci Med Univ of SC Charleston SC 29403

LAWSON, CHERYL ANN, b Shawnee, Okla, June 5, 47; m 65. PLANT TAXONOMY, ECOLOGY. *Educ:* Univ Okla, BS, 69, MS, 71, PhD(bot), 76. *Prof Exp:* Res assoc, Univ Okla, 76-77; CONSULT, ESPEY, HUSTON & ASSOCS, 78- & WESTON CO, 78- *Mem:* Am Soc Plant Taxonomists; Int Asn Plant Taxon; Bot Soc Am; Southwestern Asn Naturalists. *Res:* Taxonomy of the genus Galium in the southeastern United States and Oklahoma; spring flora of Oklahoma; botanical history of Oklahoma. *Mailing Add:* 960 Oakridge Duncan OK 73533

LAWSON, CHESTER ALVIN, b Salamanca, NY, Apr 22, 08; m 34; c 2. BIOLOGY, PSYCHOLOGY. *Educ:* Thiel Col, BS, 30; Univ Mich, MS, 31, PhD(zool), 34. *Hon Degrees:* LLD, Thiel Col, 59. *Prof Exp:* Asst, Univ Mich, 31-33; instr zool, Mich State Col, 34-35; from asst prof to assoc prof biol, Wittenberg Col, 35-42; from instr to asst prof zool, Mich State Univ, 42-44; prof biol sci & head dept, 44-52, prof natural sci, 52-63, res prof, 63-65; dir biol, Sci Curric Improv Study, Univ Calif, Berkeley, 65-80; RETIRED. *Concurrent Pos:* Vis res biologist, Sci Curric Improv Study, Univ Calif, Berkeley, 65-67; consult, Sci Teaching Ctr, Philippines, 65-66. *Mem:* AAAS; Am Soc Zoologists; Am Genetics Soc; hon mem Asn Teachers Biol. *Res:* Chromosomes of aphids; microscopic and experimental embryology of aphids; differential development in regeneration of chicory roots; evolution of ideas; learning. *Mailing Add:* 1624 Golden Rain Rd 4 Walnut Creek CA 94595

LAWSON, DANIEL DAVID, b Tucson, Ariz, Jan 13, 29; m 57; c 2. ORGANIC CHEMISTRY, POLYMER CHEMISTRY. *Educ:* Univ Southern Calif, BS, 57, MS, 59. *Prof Exp:* Biomed res fel, Charles Cook Hastings Found, 59-61; res polymer scientist, 61-71, MEM TECH STAFF, POLYMER RES SECT, JET PROPULSION LAB, CALIF INST TECHNOL, 71- *Mem:* AAAS; Am Chem Soc; The Chem Soc; fel Am Acad Forensic Sci; Brit Soc Chem Indust. *Res:* Physical organic chemistry of polymers; synthesis of new biomaterials; use of thermoluminescence as applied to criminalistics. *Mailing Add:* 5542 Halifax Rd Arcadia CA 91006

LAWSON, DAVID EDWARD, b Moncton, NB, Sept 17, 39; m 67. SEDIMENTOLOGY. *Educ:* Univ NB, BSc, 60, MSc, 62; Univ Reading, PhD(geol), 71. *Prof Exp:* Res geologist, Sedimentology Res Lab, Univ Reading, 62-66; lectr, 66-68, asst prof, 68-76, ASSOC PROF SEDIMENTOLOGY, UNIV WATERLOO, 76- *Mem:* Int Asn Sedimentol; Soc Econ Paleontologists & Mineralogists; fel Geol Asn Can. *Res:* Environmental fluvial sedimentology; nearshore sedimentation; primary sedimentary structures; volcanic sediments; continental shelf sedimentation; Torridonian sediments of northwest Scotland. *Mailing Add:* Dept Earth Sci Univ Waterloo Waterloo ON N2L 3G1 Can

LAWSON, DAVID FRANCIS, b Chicago, Ill, June 24, 45; div; c 2. POLYMER ORGANIC CHEMISTRY. *Educ:* Lewis Univ, BA, 67; Iowa State Univ, PhD(org chem), 71. *Prof Exp:* Instr chem, Iowa State Univ, 68-69; res scientist, 70-75; sr res scientist, 75-81, ASSOC SCIENTIST, CENT RES LABS, FIRESTONE TIRE & RUBBER CO, 82- *Mem:* Am Chem Soc; Combustion Inst; Sigma Xi. *Res:* Organic polymer chemistry; polymer synthesis; polymer stabilization; combustion and flammability; additives for flame and smoke retardation; synthetic and physical organic chemistry; elastomer chemistry; engineering thermoplastics. *Mailing Add:* Cent Res Labs Firestone Tire & Rubber Co Akron OH 44317

LAWSON, DAVID MICHAEL, b Denver, Colo, Nov 13, 43; m 66; c 3. REPRODUCTIVE ENDOCRINOLOGY, LACTATION. *Educ:* Va Polytech Inst, BS, 65, MS, 67; Cornell Univ, PhD(physiol), 70. *Prof Exp:* NIH trainee physiol, Cornell Univ, 71; res assoc, 71-73, asst prof, 73-79, ASSOC PROF PHYSIOL, SCH MED, WAYNE STATE UNIV, 79- *Mem:* Endocrine Soc; Soc Exp Biol & Med. *Res:* Control of prolactin secretion; molecular nature of prolactin form synthesis through release; endocrine control of mammary gland function. *Mailing Add:* Dept Physiol Sch Med Wayne State Univ 540 E Canfield Ave Detroit MI 48201

LAWSON, DEWEY TULL, b Kinston, NC, Feb 6, 44; m 66; c 2. ACOUSTICS. *Educ:* Harvard Univ, AB, 66; Duke Univ, PhD(physics), 72. *Prof Exp:* Res assoc physics, Lab Atomic & Solid State Physics, Cornell Univ, 72-74; asst prof physics, Duke Univ, 74-79; SR PHYSICIST, RES TRIANGLE INST, 79- *Concurrent Pos:* Consult archit & environ acoust & adj prof physics, Duke Univ, 80- *Mem:* Am Phys Soc; Am Asn Physics Teachers. *Res:* Low temperature physics, especially liquid and solid helium. *Mailing Add:* PO Box 12194 Res Triangle Inst Research Triangle Park NC 27709

LAWSON, DOUGLAS ALLAN, b San Antonio, Tex, Nov 27, 47; m 76. INVERTEBRATE PALEOECOLOGY, SEDIMENTOLOGY. *Educ:* Tex A&M Univ, BS, 69; Univ Tex, Austin, MA, 72; Univ Calif, Berkeley, PhD(paleont), 77. *Prof Exp:* asst prof paleont, Dept Earth Sci, Univ New Orleans, 77-80. *Mem:* AAAS; Soc Vertebrate Paleont. *Res:* Paleosynecology; invertebrate biostratigraphy; early tetrapod phylogeny; lower paleozoic invertebrate chordates. *Mailing Add:* 6668 Ave B New Orleans LA 70124

LAWSON, EDWARD CHARLES, b Brooklyn, NY, Nov 27, 15; m 44; c 5. MECHANICAL ENGINEERING. *Educ:* Polytech Inst Brooklyn, BME, 39; Rensselaer Polytech Inst, MME, 41. *Prof Exp:* Instr mech eng, Carnegie Inst Technol, 41-42 & Rice Inst, 42-44; assoc prof, Univ Del, 47-51; prof & head dept, NDak Univ, 52-62; dean eng, Wis State Univ, 62-63; Mich State Univ eng adv to Univ Nigeria, 63-68; dean sch eng, Univ Zambia, 68-77; HEAD, BUNDA AGR COL, MALAWI, 77- *Concurrent Pos:* Draftsman, Hughes Tool Co, 42-43; engr, Gen Elec Co, 48, Westinghouse Elec Corp, 51, E I du Pont de Nemours & Co, 51, 52, 53 & Babcock & Wilcox Co, 54, 55, 56 & 57; consult dept head, Middle East Tech Univ Ankara, Turkey, 60-61; consult, Atomic Energy Div, Babcock & Wilcox Co. *Mem:* Am Soc Eng Educ; Am Soc Mech Engrs; Nat Soc Prof Engrs. *Res:* Heat power and transfer; nuclear energy. *Mailing Add:* Bunda Agr Col Box 219 Lilongwe Malawi

LAWSON, EDWARD EARLE, b Winston-Salem, NC, Aug 6, 46; m 69; c 2. PEDIATRICS, NEONATOLOGY. *Educ:* Harvard Univ, BA, 68; Sch Med, Northwestern Univ, MD, 72. *Prof Exp:* Residency pediat, Children's Hosp, Boston, 72-75; fel neonatology, Harvard Med Sch, 75-78, instr pediat, 77-78; asst prof, 78-82, ASSOC PROF PEDIAT, UNIV NC, CHAPEL HILL, 82- *Concurrent Pos:* E L Trudeau fel, Am Lung Asn, 78-81; prin investr, NIH res grant, 79-82; assoc pediatrician, NC Mem Hosp, 82- *Mem:* Am Thoracic Soc; Soc Pediat Res; Am Physiol Soc; Am Acad Pediat. *Res:* Neural mechanisms of central respiratory control, particularly in newborns. *Mailing Add:* Dept Pediat Univ NC Chapel Hill NC 27514

LAWSON, FRED AVERY, b Washington Co, Ark, Oct 25, 19. ENTOMOLOGY. *Educ:* Univ Ark, BSc, 43; Ohio State Univ, MS, 47, PhD(entom), 49. *Prof Exp:* Asst prof entom, Univ Tenn, 49-52; from asst prof to assoc prof, Kans State Univ, 52-60; assoc prof, Colo State Univ, 61-63; assoc prof, 63-70, PROF ENTOM, UNIV WYO, 70- *Mem:* Entom Soc Am; Electron Micros Soc Am; Coleopterists Soc. *Res:* Insects; electron microscopy; morphology, physiology, biology and taxonomy of Coleoptera. *Mailing Add:* Dept of Entom Univ of Wyo Box 3354 Univ Sta Laramie WY 82071

LAWSON, HERBERT BLAINE, JR, b Norristown, Pa, Jan 4, 42; m 64; c 2. MATHEMATICS. *Educ:* Brown Univ, ScB & AB, 64; Stanford Univ, PhD(math), 69. *Prof Exp:* Lectr math, Univ Calif, Berkeley, 68-70; vis prof, Inst Pure & Appl Math, Rio de Janeiro, Brazil, 70-71; vis asst prof, State Univ NY Stony Brook, 71; assoc prof, 71-75, PROF MATH, UNIV CALIF, BERKELEY, 75- *Concurrent Pos:* Sloan Found fel, Univ Calif, Berkeley, 70-; mem, Inst Advan Study, Princeton, 72-73. *Honors & Awards:* Steele Prize, Am Math Soc, 75. *Mem:* Am Math Soc. *Res:* Minimal surfaces; minimal varieties in Riemannian manifolds; Riemannian geometry; foliations; several complex variables. *Mailing Add:* Dept of Math Univ of Calif Berkeley CA 94720

LAWSON, JAMES EVERETT, b Derby, Va, Jan 8, 33; m 60; c 2. ZOOLOGY. *Educ:* ETenn State Univ, BS, 58, MA, 59; Va Polytech Inst, PhD(zool), 67. *Prof Exp:* Instr biol, ETenn State Univ, 59-61; instr, Va Polytech Inst, 61-62; assoc prof, 64-76, PROF BIOL, E TENN STATE UNIV, 76- *Concurrent Pos:* Dir, Off Preprofessional Advert. *Res:* Ecology and systematics of pseudoscorpions. *Mailing Add:* Dept of Biol ETenn State Univ Johnson City TN 37601

LAWSON, JAMES LLEWELLYN, b Pasumalai, SIndia, Dec 17, 15; US citizen; m 76; c 4. PHYSICS. *Educ:* Univ Kans, AB, 35, AM, 36; Univ Mich, PhD(physics), 39. *Prof Exp:* Res physicist, Univ Mich, 39-40; mem staff, Radiation Lab, Mass Inst Technol, 40-45; physicist, Res & Develop Lab, Gen Elec Co, 45-65, mgr electron physics res, 52-65, mgr, Info Lab, Res & Develop Ctr, 65-70, res & develop mgr, Info Sci & Eng, 70-74, mgr res & develop planning, 74-76, consult, Gen Elec Corp Res & Develop, 76-80; RETIRED. *Concurrent Pos:* Consult, Sci Adv Bd, 53-59. *Mem:* AAAS; Am Phys Soc; Inst Elec & Electronics Engrs. *Res:* Nuclear physics and electronics, especially electronic components and systems, high energy radiation, particle acceleration, thermonuclear physics and information systems. *Mailing Add:* 2532 Troy Rd Schenectady NY 12309

LAWSON, JIMMIE BROWN, b Checotah, Okla, June 29, 34; m 54; c 2. PETROLEUM CHEMISTRY. *Educ:* Southeastern State Col, BS, 56; Tex Christian Univ, MA, 60; Rice Univ, PhD(chem), 64. *Prof Exp:* Chemist, Gen Dynamics Corp, 56-60; res chemist, Shell Develop Co, 64-72, sr chem engr, Shell Oil Co, 72-74, SR PETROL ENGR, SHELL DEVELOP CO, 74- *Mem:* Am Chem Soc; Soc Petrol Eng. *Res:* Properties of semiconductors; x-ray crystallography; corrosion and metal coatings; petroleum production; development of chemical systems for the tertiary recovery of petroleum; surface chemistry. *Mailing Add:* 4626 Briarbend Houston TX 77035

LAWSON, JIMMIE DON, b Waukegan, Ill, Dec 6, 42; m 64; c 2. MATHEMATICS. *Educ:* Harding Col, BS, 64; Univ Tenn, PhD(math), 67. *Prof Exp:* Asst prof math, Univ Tenn, 67-68; from asst prof to assoc prof math, La State Univ, 68-75; vis assoc prof, Univ Houston, 76; PROF MATH, LA STATE UNIV, BATON ROUGE, 76- *Concurrent Pos:* NSF grants prin investr, 68-81; Alexander von Humboldt fel & hon Fullbright fel, Tech Univ, Damstadt, WGer, 80-81. *Mem:* Am Math Soc. *Res:* Topological algebra; algebraic topology and semigroups; topology; continuous lattices. *Mailing Add:* Dept Math La State Univ Baton Rouge LA 70803

LAWSON, JOEL S(MITH), b New York, NY, July 3, 24; m 46; c 4. PHYSICS, ELECTRONICS. *Educ:* Williams Col, BA, 47; Univ Ill, MS, 49, PhD(physics), 53. *Prof Exp:* Res assoc, Control Systs Lab, Univ Ill, 53-55, from res asst prof to res assoc prof, 55-57; sr staff mem, Sci Eng Inst, 58-65; spec asst electronics, Off Asst Secy Navy, 65-67; res & eng consult, Comdr-in-Chief Pac, 67-68; dir, Naval Labs, Washington, DC, 68-74; tech dir, 74-81, CHIEF SCIENTIST, NAVAL ELECTRONICS SYSTS COMMAND, 81- *Mem:* AAAS; Am Phys Soc; Inst Elec & Electronics Engrs. *Res:* Applications of digital data processing techniques to information handling; communications systems; radar techniques; development of advanced electronic devices for military applications; theory of military command control. *Mailing Add:* 8921 Durham Dr Potomac MD 20854

LAWSON, JOHN DOUGLAS, b Meaford, Ont, Sept 2, 37; m 60; c 3. COMPUTER SCIENCE. *Educ:* Univ Toronto, BASc, 59; Univ Waterloo, MSc, 60, PhD(appl math), 65. *Prof Exp:* Teaching fel math, 59-60, lectr, 60-64, from asst prof to assoc prof, 64-73, assoc dean math, 68-71, chmn dept comput sci, 74-78, PROF MATH, UNIV WATERLOO, 73- *Concurrent Pos:* Asst scientist, Med Div, Oak Ridge Inst Nuclear Studies, 64-65; vis lectr, Univ Dundee, 71-72. *Mem:* Can Appl Math Soc. *Res:* Numerical solution of ordinary differential equations. *Mailing Add:* Dept Comput Sci Univ Waterloo Waterloo ON N2L 3G1 Can

LAWSON, JOHN EDWARD, b Detroit, Mich, Feb 25, 31; m 57; c 2. MEDICINAL CHEMISTRY. *Educ:* Wayne State Univ, BS, 53; Vanderbilt Univ, MA, 56, PhD(org chem), 57. *Prof Exp:* Fel, Mass Inst Technol, 57-58; GROUP LEADER, MEAD JOHNSON & CO, 58- *Mem:* Am Chem Soc. *Res:* Pharmaceutical Chemistry; organic synthesis; heterocyclic chemistry; natural products. *Mailing Add:* 6711 Hogue Rd Evansville IN 47712

LAWSON, JOHN EDWIN, b Shoal Lake, Man, Nov 28, 33; m 58; c 1. ANIMAL BREEDING. *Educ:* Univ Man, BSAgr, 56, MSA, 63. *Prof Exp:* RES SCIENTIST BEEF CATTLE BREEDING, RES BR, AGR CAN RES STA, 57- *Mem:* Can Soc Animal Sci. *Res:* Evaluation of cattle breeds and crosses for reproductive performance and efficiency of production in specific environments; investigation of genotype-environment interactions; direct and correlated response to single trait selection. *Mailing Add:* Res Br Agr Can Res Sta Lethbridge AB T1J 4B1 Can

LAWSON, JUAN (OTTO), b Bluefield, WVa, Apr 18, 39; m 63; c 2. PHYSICS. *Educ:* Va State Col, BS, 60; Howard Univ, MS, 62, PhD(physics), 66. *Prof Exp:* From asst prof to assoc prof, 67-74, asst dean, Grad Sch, 70-71, dean, Col Sci, 75-80, PROF PHYSICS, UNIV TEX, EL PASO, 74- *Mem:* Am Phys Soc; Am Asn Physics Teachers; Sigma Xi. *Res:* Mathematical physics; solid state theory. *Mailing Add:* Dept of Physics Univ of Tex El Paso TX 79968

LAWSON, KENNETH DARE, b Clinchport, Va, May 12, 34; m 56; c 1. ELECTRON MICROSCOPY. *Educ:* East Tenn State Univ, BA, 59; Univ Fla, MS, 61, PhD(chem), 63. *Prof Exp:* SECT HEAD, MIAMI VALLEY LABS, PROCTER & GAMBLE CO, 63- *Mem:* AAAS; Am Chem Soc. *Res:* Nuclear magnetic resonance spectroscopy; structure of mesomorphic phases; biophysics. *Mailing Add:* Miami Valley Labs Procter & Gamble Co Cincinnati OH 45239

LAWSON, KENT DELANCE, b Binghamton, NY, Feb 17, 21; m 42; c 3. THEORETICAL PHYSICS. *Educ:* Cornell Univ, BA, 43; Rensselaer Polytech Inst, MS, 51, PhD(physics), 56. *Prof Exp:* Instr physics, Rensselaer Polytech Inst, 46-52; mem fac, Bennington Col, 53-66; prof physics, 65-75, DISTINGUISHED TEACHING PROF, STATE UNIV NY COL ONEONTA, 75- *Concurrent Pos:* Res & educ prof consult, 56-70; dir EDUX prog, 70- *Mem:* Am Phys Soc; Am Asn Physics Teachers. *Res:* Eduction theory: unified theory of physical reality, man and awareness; particle theory. *Mailing Add:* Dept of Physics State Univ of NY Col Oneonta NY 13820

LAWSON, LARRY DALE, b Elkhart, Ind, Dec 23, 46; m 73; c 4. LIPID BIOCHEMISTRY. *Educ:* Purdue Univ, BS, 68; Brigham Young Univ, MS, 73; Univ Ill, PhD(nutrit sci), 79. *Prof Exp:* FEL, HORMEL INST, UNIV MINN, 78- *Mem:* Am Oil Chemists Soc; Sigma Xi. *Res:* Lipid biochemistry, particularly trans fatty acid metabolism and their effects on polyunsaturated fatty acids. *Mailing Add:* Hormel Inst Univ Minn Austin MN 55912

LAWSON, MERLIN PAUL, b Jamestown, NY, Jan 12, 41; m 64; c 3. CLIMATOLOGY. *Educ:* State Univ NY Buffalo, BA, 63; Clark Univ, MA, 66, PhD(geog climat), 73. *Prof Exp:* Instr climat, Northeastern Univ, 67-68; asst prof, 68-74, ASSOC PROF CLIMAT, UNIV NEBR-LINCOLN, 74-, CHMN, DEPT GEOG, 80- *Mem:* Sigma Xi; Am Meteorol Soc; Asn Am Geogrs. *Res:* Historical climate of the Great American Desert; severe droughts since 1700 in the western United States; descriptive climatic change; dendroclimatology. *Mailing Add:* 350 Avery Hall Univ of Nebr Lincoln NE 68588

LAWSON, MILDRED WIKER, b New London, Conn, Nov 10, 22; m 63. MATHEMATICS, COMPUTER SCIENCES. *Educ:* Univ Md, BS, 47, MA, 49. *Prof Exp:* Asst math, Univ Md, 47-49, instr, 49-50; cartog compilation aide, Corps Engrs, Army Map Serv, 50-51, mathematician, 51-55, proj leader math & comput prog, 55-57, asst chief prog, 57-58; assoc mathematician, 58-65, SR MATHEMATICIAN, APPL PHYSICS LAB, JOHNS HOPKINS UNIV, LAUREL, 65- *Res:* Analysis and programming of computer solutions of problems arising in scientific projects; computer language training. *Mailing Add:* 5113 Durham Rd E Columbia MD 21044

LAWSON, NEAL D(EVERE), b; m 41; c 2. CHEMICAL ENGINEERING. *Educ:* Pa State Col, BS, 38, MS, 42, PhD(chem eng), 46. *Prof Exp:* Asst petrol ref lab, Pa State Col, 38-42, instr, 42-47; group leader petrol chem lab, E I Du Pont de Nemours & Co, Inc, 47-50, head chem div, 50-56, additives mgr, Cent Region, 56-58, tech mgr, Ill, 58-56, develop specialist, 65-66, supvr new prod develop, 66-77, spec asst tech info res & develop, 77-80; RETIRED. *Mem:* Am Chem Soc; Soc Automotive Engrs; Am Soc Lubrication Engrs; Am Soc Testing & Mat. *Res:* Stability of petroleum products; additives for lubricating oils and gasoline; fuel oil stabilizers; additives and thickeners for greases. *Mailing Add:* 1005 Chickadee Lane Penn Wood S W Chester PA 19380

LAWSON, NORMAN C, b Glasgow, Scotland, Nov 3, 29; Can citizen; m 60; c 3. PLANT BREEDING. *Educ:* Glasgow Univ, BSc, 53; Univ Reading, dipl agr, 54; McGill Univ, MSc, 58, PhD, 61. *Prof Exp:* Res off, Exp Farm, Can Dept Agr, BC, 61-65, res scientist, Res Sta, Sask, 65-67; ASSOC PROF AGRON, McGILL UNIV, 67-, DIR, DIPL PROG, 73- *Mem:* Am Soc Agron; Crop Sci Soc Am; Genetics Soc Can; Agr Inst Can; Can Soc Agron. *Res:* Genetics and breeding of forage and oil crop species. *Mailing Add:* Dept of Plant Sci McGill Univ Ste Anne de Bellevue PQ H9X 1C0 Can

LAWSON, ROBERT BARRETT, b Oakland, Calif, Aug 24, 11; m 39; c 2. PEDIATRICS. *Educ:* Harvard Univ, BA, 32, MD, 36; Am Bd Pediat, dipl, 41. *Prof Exp:* From asst prof to prof pediat & dir dept, Bowman Gray Sch Med, 40-54; prof & chmn dept, Sch Med, Univ Miami, 54-62, actg dean, Sch Med, 61-62; prof pediat, Sch Med, Northwestern Univ, 62-71, chmn dept, 62-70, vpres health sci, 70-71; CHIEF STAFF, VARIETY CHILDREN'S HOSP, 71- *Concurrent Pos:* Pro Sch Pub Health, Univ NC & assoc, Sch Med, Duke Univ, 40-42; pediat consult, State Bd Health, NC, 40-42; Nat Res Coun fel, Univ Calif & Yale Univ, 45; chief staff, Children's Mem Hosp, Chicago, Ill, 62-71; clin prof pediat, Sch Med, Univ Miami, 71- *Mem:* Am Soc Pediat Res; Am Pediat Soc; AMA; Am Acad Pediat. *Res:* Infectious disease. *Mailing Add:* Variety Children's Hosp 6125 S W 31st St Miami FL 33155

LAWSON, ROBERT DAVIS, b Sydney, Australia, July 14, 26; nat US; m 50; c 3. THEORETICAL PHYSICS. *Educ:* Univ BC, BASc, 48, MASc, 49; Stanford Univ, PhD, 53. *Prof Exp:* Asst, Univ BC, 47-48; asst, Stanford Univ, 49-53; jr res physicist, Univ Calif, 53-57; res physicist, Enrico Fermi Inst Nuclear Studies, Ill, 57-59; assoc physicist, 59-66, SR PHYSICIST, ARGONNE NAT LAB, 66- *Concurrent Pos:* Vis physicist, UK Atomic Energy Authority, Harwell, Eng, 62-63; Weizmann sr fel, Weizmann Inst Sci, Israel, 67-68; vis prof, State Univ NY, Stoneybrook, 72-73; Nordita fel, Niels Bohr Inst, Copenhagen, 76-77. *Mem:* Am Phys Soc. *Res:* Nuclear physics. *Mailing Add:* Physics Div Argonne Nat Lab Bldg 203 Argonne IL 60439

LAWSON, RONALD PETER WALFORD, materials science, electrical engineering, see previous edition

LAWSON, VERNA REBECCA, b Crossville, Tenn, Apr 7, 43. PLANT PHYSIOLOGY, CYTOCHEMISTRY. *Educ:* Tenn Technol Univ, BS, 66, MS, 69; George Washington Univ, PhD(cytochem), 73. *Prof Exp:* Assoc prof biol, Alcorn State Univ, 73-77; assoc prof biol, 77-78, CHMN, SCI & MATH DIV, BETHUNE-COOKMAN COL, 78- *Mem:* Am Soc Plant Physiol; Am Soc Hort Sci; AAAS; Sigma Xi. *Res:* Developmental physiology; ultrastructure of coleoptile segments of wheat. *Mailing Add:* Div of Sci & Math 640 2nd Ave Daytona Beach FL 32015

LAWSON, WILLIAM BURROWS, b Detroit, Mich, June 8, 29; m 63; c 1. BIOCHEMISTRY. *Educ:* Wayne State Univ, BS, 51; Univ Md, PhD(chem), 56. *Prof Exp:* Res assoc, Mass Inst Technol, 55-56 & 57-58, Nat Cancer Inst fel, 56-57; sr asst scientist, Nat Insts Health, Md, 58-60; Nat Cancer Inst fel, Max Planck Inst Biochem, 60-61; sr res scientist, 61-66, ASSOC RES SCIENTIST, DIV LABS & RES, NY STATE DEPT HEALTH, 66- *Mem:* AAAS; Am Chem Soc; Am Soc Biol Chem; Int Soc Thrombosis & Hemostasis. *Res:* Amino acids; synthesis and degradation of peptides; chemical modification and inhibition of enzymes; blood coagulation. *Mailing Add:* Div of Labs & Res NY State Health Dept Albany NY 12201

LAWTON, ALEXANDER R, III, b Nov 8, 38. MEDICINE. *Educ:* Yale Univ, BA, 60; Vanderbilt Univ, MD, 64. *Prof Exp:* Intern, Vanderbilt Univ Hosp, 64-65, asst resident, 65-66; clin assoc, Lab Clin Invest, Nat Inst Allergy & Infectious Dis, 66-68, clin investr, 68-69; from asst prof to assoc prof, 71-76, PROF PEDIAT & MICROBIOL, SCH MED, UNIV ALA, BIRMINGHAM, 76- *Concurrent Pos:* NIH spec fel immunol, Sch Med, Univ Ala, Birmingham, 69-71. *Res:* Pediatrics; microbiology; immunology. *Mailing Add:* Dept of Pediat Univ of Ala Sch of Med Birmingham AL 35294

LAWTON, ALFRED HENRY, b Carson, Iowa, July 26, 16; m 40, 74; c 3. GERIATRICS. *Educ:* Simpson Col, AB, 37; Northwestern Univ, MS, 39, BM, 40, MD, 41, PhD(physiol), 43. *Hon Degrees:* ScD, Simpson Col, 58. *Prof Exp:* Intern, Passavant Mem Hosp, Chicago, 40-41; resident, Henry Ford Hosp, Detroit, 41-42; asst prof med, physiol & pharm, Sch Med, Univ Ark, 46-47; dean & prof physiol & pharm, Univ NDak, 47-48; chief res div, US Vet Admin, Washington, DC, 48-51; med res adv, US Dept Air Force, 51-55; asst dir prof serv res & educ & chief intermediate serv, US Vet Admin Ctr, Bay Pines, 55-62; dir study ctr, Nat Inst Child Health & Human Develop, 62-66; from asst to assoc dean acad affairs, Univ SFla, 66-70, actg vpres acad affairs, 70-73; exec dir tech adv comn aging res, US Dept Health, Educ & Welfare, 73-74; dir geriat res, Educ & Clin Ctr & assoc chief staff res & develop, Vet Admin Ctr, 75-78; CLIN PROF COMMUNITY HEALTH & FAMILY PRAC, UNIV FLA SCH MED & DIR GERONTOL ADVENT CHRISTIAN VILLAGE, 78- *Concurrent Pos:* Asst clin prof, Sch Med, George Washington Univ, 48-55; liaison mem coun arthritis & metab dis, USPHS, 50-55; mem exec coun, Nat Res Coun, US Armed Forces Vision Comt & Nat Coun Aging; actg dean, Col Med, Univ SFla, 68-70. *Mem:* Am Physiol Soc; Am Soc Pharmacol & Exp Therapeut; Am Geriat Soc; Geront Soc; Am Chem Soc. *Res:* Aging; chronic diseases. *Mailing Add:* Community Health Family Practice Med Sch Univ Fla Dowling Park FL 32060

LAWTON, EMIL ABRAHAM, b Detroit, Mich, Oct 12, 22; c 3. SYNTHETIC CHEMISTRY, WATER CHEMISTRY. *Educ:* Wayne State Univ, AB, 46; Purdue Univ, PhD(inorg chem), 52. *Prof Exp:* res chemist, Nat Bur Standards, 52-53; proj leader, Battelle Mem Inst, 53-57; prog mgr, Rocketdyne Div, Rockwell Int, 57-72; sect head, Wesatch Div, Thiokol Corp, 72-75; proj mgr, Neus, Inc, 75-76; vpres res & develop, Tech & Mgt Consults, 76-77; MGR ADVAN PROG, SHOCK HYDRODYNAMICS DIV, WHITTAKER CORP, 77- *Mem:* Am Chem Soc; Am Sect Int Solar Energy Soc. *Res:* Combustion; fuels and propellants. *Mailing Add:* 13025 Hesby St Sherman Oaks CA 91423

LAWTON, ERNEST LINWOOD, II, organic & polymer chemistry, see previous edition

LAWTON, JOHN G, b Vienna, Austria, June 3, 23; m; c 7. ELECTRICAL ENGINEERING. *Educ:* City Col New York, BEE, 49; Mass Inst Technol, SM, 51; Cornell Univ, PhD, 60. *Prof Exp:* Jr engr electronics, Stanford Res Inst, 51; from asst engr to prin staff engr, Cornell Aeronaut Lab, Inc, 54-70, staff scientist, 70-78; PRES, J & J TECHNOLOGIES, INC, 78- *Mem:* Inst Elec & Electronics Engrs. *Res:* Communications; modulation; information and communications theory; fire control; guidance equipment; computers; statistics. *Mailing Add:* 326 Walton Dr Buffalo NY 14226

LAWTON, RICHARD G, b Berkeley, Calif, Aug 29, 34; m 58; c 5. SYNTHETIC ORGANIC CHEMISTRY, BIO-ORGANIC CHEMISTRY. *Educ:* Univ Calif, Berkeley, BS, 56; Univ Wis, PhD(chem), 62. *Prof Exp:* Asst isolation & identification, Merck Sharp & Dohme Res Labs, 56-57; asst org chem, Univ Wis, 59-62; from instr to assoc prof, 62-70, PROF ORG CHEM, UNIV MICH, ANN ARBOR, 70- *Concurrent Pos:* Vis prof, Univ Wis, 70-71; consult, Colgate-Palmolive Res Labs, 70- & Deutsches Wollforschungsinstitut, Aachen, WGer, 79-80; John S Guggenheim Found award, 79-80. *Mem:* AAAS; Am Chem Soc. *Res:* Synthetic organic chemistry including peptide chemistry, alkaloids, terpenes and polycyclic aromatic hydrocarbons. *Mailing Add:* Dept of Chem Univ of Mich Ann Arbor MI 48104

LAWTON, RICHARD L, b Council Bluffs, Iowa, June 18, 18; m 43; c 7. SURGERY. *Educ:* Univ Omaha, AB, 39; Univ Nebr, BS & MD, 43. *Prof Exp:* Intern, St Mary's & St Louis Hosps, Mo, 43-44; resident, US Vet Hosp, Omaha, Nebr, 46-50, asst chief surg, 50-51; pvt pract, 52-53; staff physician, Vet Admin Hosp, 53-58, chief cancer chemother, 58-76, asst chief surg, 63-76, dir renal dialysis, 64-76; chief, Div Transplantation, & actg chief oncol, Sch Med, Tex Tech Univ, 76-78, prof & vchmn, Dept Surg, 76-80, surg, 63-80, dir renal dialysis, 64-80; MEM STAFF, GEN SURG & SURG ONCOL, FRANKLIN GEN HOSP, 80- *Concurrent Pos:* Instr, Creighton Univ, 50-51; from clin asst prof to clin assoc prof, Univ Iowa, 54-64, assoc prof, 64-68, prof surg, 68-; res grant angiol, Univ Iowa, 64-65. *Mem:* Am Asn Cancer Res; Am Soc Artificial Internal Organs; fel Am Col Surg; Soc Exp Biol & Med; Am Soc Clin Oncol. *Res:* Renal dialysis; cancer chemotherapy; transplant and preservation. *Mailing Add:* Dept of Surg Franklin Med Ctr Hampton IA 50441

LAWTON, RICHARD WOODRUFF, b New York, NY, June 22, 20; m 46; c 2. PHYSIOLOGY, BIOPHYSICS. *Educ:* Dartmouth Col, AB, 42; Cornell Univ, MD, 44. *Prof Exp:* Fel physiol sci, Med Sch, Dartmouth Col, 46-48; from instr to asst prof physiol, Med Col, Cornell Univ, 48-54; assoc prof, Sch Med, Univ Pa, 54-58; mgr bioastronaut sect, Missile & Space Div, Pa, 58-67, mgr bioastronaut sect, Res & Eng Space Systs Orgn, 67-69, Life Systs, 69-70, med res dir, Med Develop Oper, Chem & Med Div, 70-71, mgr ventures develop, Med Ventures Oper, Med Syst Bus Div, 72-74, CONSULT MED SYSTS, CORP RES & DEVELOP, GEN ELEC CO, 74- *Concurrent Pos:* Head physiol sect, Aviation Med Lab, Naval Air Develop Ctr, Pa, 54-58; adj assoc prof, Sch Med, Univ Pa, 58-70. *Mem:* Am Physiol Soc. *Res:* Elasticity of body tissues; aerospace physiology; cardiovascular physiology. *Mailing Add:* 1340 Stanley Lane Schenectady NY 12309

LAWTON, ROBERT ARTHUR, b Sanford, Colo, July 2, 32; m 57; c 6. ELECTRONICS, ELECTROOPTICS. *Educ:* Brigham Young Univ, BS, 60; Univ Colo, MS, 68, PhD(elec eng), 72. *Prof Exp:* Physicist radio frequency standards, 60-70, pulse measurement, 70-74, PHYSICIST PULSED ELECTRO-OPTICS, NAT BUR STANDARDS, 74-, GROUP LEADER, ELECTROMAGNETIC WAVEFORM METROLOGY, 80- *Concurrent Pos:* Sci & Technol Fel energy & power, US House Rep, Dept Com, 78-79. *Honors & Awards:* Super Accomplishment, Nat Bur Standards, 66 & 75, Outstanding Performance, 77 & Spec Achievement, 78. *Mem:* Inst Elec & Electronics Engrs; Optical Soc Am; Sigma Xi. *Res:* Electrical and optical pulse generation and measurement including time domain autocorrelation and power spectral analysis; laser pulse demodulation; signal detection in noise; electromagnetic field effects in materials. *Mailing Add:* Sect 724-04 Rm 1-3550 Nat Bur Standards 325 Broadway Boulder CO 80302

LAWTON, STEPHEN LATHAM, b Milwaukee, Wis, Nov 12, 39; m 67; c 2. STRUCTURAL CHEMISTRY. *Educ:* Univ Wis, BS, 63; Iowa State Univ Sci & Technol, MS, 66. *Prof Exp:* Res chemist, Socony Mobil Oil Co, Inc, 66-69, sr res chemist, 69-75, assoc chemist, 75-78, RES ASSOC, MOBIL RES & DEVELOP CORP, 78- *Mem:* Am Chem Soc; Am Crystallog Asn. *Res:* X-ray crystallography; crystal and molecular structures of inorganic and organometallic compounds and zeolites; computer applications in chemistry. *Mailing Add:* Mobil Res & Develop Corp Res Dept Paulsboro NJ 08066

LAWTON, WALLACE CLAYTON, b Can, July 20, 23; m 43; c 1. DAIRY BACTERIOLOGY. *Educ:* Univ Sask, BSA, 50, MSc, 51; Iowa State Univ, PhD(dairy bact), 54. *Prof Exp:* Dir lab, Qual Control Comt, 54-60; tech serv, Twin City Milk Producers Asn, 60-70, mgr opers, Northern Div, Mid-Am Dairymen, Inc, 70-75; GEN MGR, A&L LABS, INC, 75- *Concurrent Pos:* Lectr, Univ Minn, 58-60. *Mem:* Int Asn Milk, Food & Environ Sanit (past pres). *Res:* Laboratory control of dairy products; laboratory methods and procedures. *Mailing Add:* 1001 Glenwood Minneapolis MN 55405

LAWTON, WILLIAM HARVEY, b Indianapolis, Ind, Nov 1, 37. APPLIED STATISTICS. *Educ:* Univ Calif, Berkeley, AB, 59, MA, 62, PhD(statist), 65. *Prof Exp:* Teaching asst statist, Univ Calif, Berkeley, 60-62, teaching assoc, 63-65; math analyst, 62-63, consult math & statist, 65-75, supvr appl math sect, 75-77, supvr corp com serv, 77-79, DIR MKT RES, ASIA, AFRICA, AUSTRALIA-ASIA REGION, EASTMAN KODAK CO, 79- *Concurrent Pos:* Lectr, Univ Rochester, 65-70; ed, Technometrics, 74-77. *Honors & Awards:* Shewell Award, Am Soc Qual Control, 71; Wixcuxon Award, Am Statist Asn, 71 & 75. *Mem:* Fel Am Statist Asn; fel Am Soc Qual Control; Sigma Xi. *Res:* Probability; new tools for mathematical model building for problems in the physical sciences and management sciences. *Mailing Add:* Eastman Kodak Co Int Div 343 State St Rochester NY 14650

LAWVER, DONALD ALLEN, mathematics, see previous edition

LAWVERE, FRANCIS WILLIAM, b Muncie, Ind, Feb 9, 37; m 66; c 5. ALGEBRA. *Educ:* Ind Univ, BA, 60; Columbia Univ, MA & PhD(math), 63. *Prof Exp:* Syst analyst, Litton Industs, Inc, 62-63; asst prof math, Reed Col, 63-64; NATO fel, Swiss Fed Inst Technol, 64-65, res assoc, 65-66; asst prof, Univ Chicago, 66-67; assoc prof, Grad Ctr, City Univ New York, 67-68; Sloan fel, Swiss Fed Inst Technol, 68-70; res prof, Dalhousie Univ, 70-71; vis prof, Aarhus Univ, 71-72 & Nat Res Inst Italy, 72-74; PROF MATH, STATE UNIV NY BUFFALO, 74- *Mem:* Am Math Soc. *Res:* Foundations of category theory; categorical foundations of mathematics; algebraic theories and equational doctrines; axiomatic theory of topoi; closed categories and metric spaces; synthetic differential geometry; functorial thermodynamics and continuum mechanics. *Mailing Add:* Dept of Math State Univ NY 4246 Ridge Lea Rd Buffalo NY 14226

LAWWILL, STANLEY JOSEPH, b London, Ohio, May 23, 16; m 40; c 5. MATHEMATICS. *Educ:* Univ Cincinnati, AB, 37, MA, 39, PhD(math), 41. *Prof Exp:* Instr math, Northwestern Univ, 41-44; mathematician appl math group, Columbia Univ, 44; gunnery analyst, 2nd & 20th air forces, US Air Force, 44-46, opers analyst, HQ Strategic Air Command, 46-48, dep chief opers anal off, 48-50, chief atomic capabilities div, 50-54, dep chief scientist, 54-58; tech dir sci anal off, Melpar, Inc Div, Westinghouse Air Brake Co, 58; pres, Anal Servs, Inc, 58-81; RETIRED. *Mem:* Opers Res Soc Am. *Res:* Orthogonal functions; overconvergence of approximations in terms of rational harmonic functions; operations analysis; weapon systems evaluation. *Mailing Add:* 6532 Copa Ct Falls Church VA 22044

LAWYER, TIFFANY, JR, b Albany, NY, Jan 3, 15; m 42; c 4. NEUROLOGY. *Educ:* Albany Med Col, MD, 42. *Prof Exp:* Instr neurol & psychiat, Albany Med Col, 48-49; assoc neurol, Columbia Univ, 49-52; assoc prof, Georgetown Univ, 52-54; from assoc prof to prof clin neurol, Columbia Univ, 54-64; prof, 64-80, EMER PROF NEUROL, ALBERT EINSTEIN COL MED, 80- *Concurrent Pos:* Chief sect neurol, Vet Admin Cent Off, DC, 52-53; chief div neurol, Montefiore Hosp & Med Ctr, 54-69, consult neurol & dep dir, 69- *Mem:* AMA; Am Neurol Asn; Asn Res Nerv & Ment Dis; Am Psychiat Asn; Am Acad Neurol. *Res:* Convulsive disorders; multiple and amyotrophic lateral sclerosis. *Mailing Add:* Montefiore Hosp & Med Ctr Bronx NY 10467

LAX, ANNELI, b Kattowitz, Ger, Feb 23, 22; nat US; m 48; c 2. MATHEMATICS. *Educ:* Adelphi Col, BS, 42; NY Univ, MA, 45, PhD, 55. *Prof Exp:* Asst aeronaut, 43-44, asst math, Inst Mech Sci, 45-55, asst res scientist, 55-65, assoc prof, 65-71, PROF MATH, WASH SQ COL, NY UNIV, 72- *Concurrent Pos:* Instr, Wash Sq Col, 45-55; ed, New Math Library, 60- *Mem:* AAAS; Am Math Soc; Math Asn Am. *Res:* Mathematical analysis and exposition; partial differential equations. *Mailing Add:* Dept of Math Wash Sq Col NY Univ New York NY 10003

LAX, BENJAMIN, b Miskolz, Hungary, Dec 29, 15; m 42; c 2. SOLID STATE PHYSICS, PLASMA PHYSICS. *Educ:* Cooper Union, BME, 41; Mass Inst Technol, PhD(physics), 49. *Hon Degrees:* DSc, Yeshiva Univ, 75. *Prof Exp:* Mech engr, US Eng Off, 41-42; consult, Sylvania Elec Prod, Inc, 46 & Air Force Cambridge Res Ctr, 46-51; mem staff solid state group, Lincoln Lab, 51-53, head ferrites group, 53-55, mem staff solid state group, 55-57, assoc head, Commun Div, 57-58, head, Solid State Div, 58-63, assoc dir, Lincoln Lab, 64-65, dir, Francis Bitter Magnet Lab, 60-81, PROF PHYSICS, MASS INST TECHNOL, 65-, EMER DIR, FRANCIS BITTER MAGNET LAB, 81- *Concurrent Pos:* Chmn, Comn Quantum Electronics, Int Union Pure & Appl Physics, 75-81; Guggenheim fel, 81-82. *Honors & Awards:* Cooper Union Distinguished Professional Achievement Award, 64; Outstanding Achievement Award, US Air Force Off Aerospace Res, 70; Buckley Prize, Am Phys Soc, 60. *Mem:* Nat Acad Sci; NY Acad Sci; Sigma Xi; fel Am Phys Soc; fel Am Acad Arts & Sci. *Res:* Radar; microwave ferrites; semiconductors; cyclotron resonance; magnetospectroscopy; high magnetic fields; fusion; x-rays. *Mailing Add:* Francis Bitter Nat Mag Lab MIT Bldg NW14-4104 Cambridge MA 02139

LAX, EDWARD, b Toronto, Ont, Aug 29, 31; US citizen; m 60; c 1. CRYOGENICS. *Educ:* Univ Calif, Los Angeles, AB, 52, MA, 59, PhD(physics), 60. *Prof Exp:* Sr physicist, Ultrasonic Systs, Inc, 60-61; mem tech staff, Aerospace Corp, 61-67; MEM TECH STAFF, AUTONETICS DIV, ROCKWELL INT CORP, 67- *Mem:* Am Phys Soc; Inst Elec & Electronics Engrs. *Res:* Electron-phonon effects in metals at low temperatures; acoustical-optical effects; cryogenic heat transfer and thermodynamics; hypersonics and delay lines; infra-red systems. *Mailing Add:* 5637 Wilhelmina Ave Woodland Hills CA 91367

LAX, LOUIS CARL, b Toronto, Ont, Apr 25, 30; m 58. PHYSIOLOGY, MEDICINE. *Educ:* Univ Toronto, BA, 52, MA, 53, MD, 57, PhD(physiol), 66. *Prof Exp:* Asst, Banting & Best Dept Med Res, Univ Toronto, 52-57; med assoc, Dept Med, Brookhaven Nat Lab, 61-62, asst scientist, 62-64; asst prof surg & physiol, Sch Med, Univ Calif, Los Angeles, 64-69; assoc prof surg, Abraham Lincoln Sch Med, Univ Ill Med Ctr, 70-75; vpres & med dir, Telemed Cardio-Pulmonary Systs Div, Becton, Dickinson & Co, 73-81; PRES

& MED DIR, AMBULATORY MONITORING LAB INC, 81- *Concurrent Pos:* Fel, Sunnybrook Vet Hosp, Toronto, 57-61; res collabr dept med, Brookhaven Nat Lab, 64-71; consult, Rand Corp, Calif, 65-66 & Epoxylite Corp, 68-69; sr clin investr med dept, Hosp Prod Div, Abbott Labs, Ill, 69-71; med dir, Telemed Corp, 71-73. *Mem:* AAAS; Biophys Soc; NY Acad Sci; Can Physiol Soc; Inst Elec & Electronics Eng. *Res:* ambulatory monitoring and analysis of physiological parameters; study of compartmental kinetics in living systems; influence of hormones and postsurgical trauma on fluid and electrolyte distribution in the body; mathematical simulation of living systems; computer processed electrocardiography; biomedical applications of computers. *Mailing Add:* Ambulatory Monitoring Lab Inc 1375 Remington Rd Schaumburg IL 60195

LAX, MELVIN, b New York, NY, Mar 8, 22; m 49; c 4. THEORETICAL SOLID STATE PHYSICS, QUANTUM OPTICS. *Educ:* NY Univ, BA, 42; Mass Inst Technol, SM, 43, PhD(physics), 47. *Prof Exp:* Res physicist, Underwater Sound Lab, Mass Inst Technol, 42-45, res assoc physics, 47; from asst prof to prof, Syracuse Univ, 47-55; mem tech staff, Bell Tel Labs, 55-71, head theoret physics dept, 62-64; DISTINGUISHED PROF PHYSICS, CITY COL NEW YORK, 71- *Concurrent Pos:* Consult, Crystal Br, US Naval Res Lab, 51-55, US Army Res Off & Bell Labs, 71- & Los Alamos Nat Lab, 76-; lectr, Oxford Univ, 61-62; mem basic res adv comt, Nat Acad Sci, 66-69. *Mem:* AAAS; fel Am Phys Soc. *Res:* Meson creation and absorption; multiple scattering; phase transitions; optical and electrical properties of solids; impurity bands; classical and quantum relaxation and noise; group theory in solids; quantum communication theory; nonlinear optical properties in deforming solids; optics, lasers, continuum mechanics. *Mailing Add:* Dept of Physics City Col of New York New York NY 10031

LAX, MELVIN DAVID, b Boston, Mass, Mar 20, 47. RANDOM DIFFERENTIAL EQUATIONS. *Educ:* Rensselaer Polytech Inst, BS, 69, MS, 71, PhD(math), 74. *Prof Exp:* Lectr math, Southern Ill Univ, Carbondale, 74-76; vis asst prof, Okla State Univ, 76-77; asst prof, 77-81, ASSOC PROF MATH, CALIF STATE UNIV, LONG BEACH, 81- *Concurrent Pos:* Mem, Panel Reviewers, Zentralblatt für Mathematik und ihre Grenzgebiete, 77- *Mem:* Am Math Soc; Soc Indust & Appl Math. *Res:* Approximate solution of random differential equations and random integral equations. *Mailing Add:* Dept Math Calif State Univ Long Beach CA 90840

LAX, PETER DAVID, b Hungary, May 1, 26; nat US; m 48; c 2. MATHEMATICS. *Educ:* NY Univ, AB, 47, PhD, 49. *Prof Exp:* From asst prof to assoc prof math, 49-58, asst to dir math ctr, 59-63, PROF MATH, NY UNIV, 58-, DIR AEC COMPUT & APPL MATH CTR, COURANT INST MATH SCI, 63-, HEAD DEPT MATH & COMPUT SCI, 72- *Concurrent Pos:* Consult, Los Alamos Sci Lab, 50. *Mem:* Nat Acad Sci; Am Acad Sci; NY Acad Sci; Math Asn Am; Am Math Soc (pres, 79-80). *Res:* Theory of partial differential equations; numerical analysis; scattering theory; functional analysis; fluid dynamics. *Mailing Add:* Courant Inst Math Sci NY Univ 251 Mercer St New York NY 10012

LAXAR, F(RANCIS) H(AROLD), b Corona, NY, June 3, 22; m 46; c 4. PHYSICAL METALLURGY. *Educ:* Columbia Univ, BS, 43; Lehigh Univ, MS, 54, PhD(metall eng), 56. *Prof Exp:* Contract employee, Div Phys Metall, US Naval Res Lab, 43-44; sales engr, White Metal Rolling & Stamping Corp, 45-46; instr eng, WVa Inst Technol, 46-49; from instr to asst prof metall, Lehigh Univ, 49-57; res engr, 57-61, supvr, 61-65, appln engr, 65-67, asst sect mgr, 67-71, ASST TO MGR, HOMER RES LABS, BETHLEHEM STEEL CORP, 71- *Mem:* Am Soc Metals. *Res:* Development of high strength and corrosion-resistant sheet steels. *Mailing Add:* Homer Res Labs Bethlehem Steel Corp Bethlehem PA 18016

LAXER, CARY, b Brooklyn, NY, July 16, 55. COMPUTER AIDED INSTRUCTION. *Educ:* New York Univ, BA, 76; Duke Univ, PhD(biomed eng), 80. *Prof Exp:* Res asst prof comput sci, Duke Univ, 80-81; ASST PROF COMPUT SCI, ROSE-HULMAN INST TECHNOL, 81- *Mem:* Inst Elec & Electronics Engrs; Asn Comput Mach; Biomed Eng Soc; Am Soc Eng Educ. *Res:* Computer analysis of cardiac electrical signals with relation to myocardial infarct geometry. *Mailing Add:* Rose-Hulman Inst Technol 5500 Wabash Ave Terre Haute IN 47803

LAXPATI, SHARAD R, b Bombay, India, July 16, 38; div. ANTENNAS, ELECTROMAGNETIC THEORY. *Educ:* Gujarat Univ, India, BE, 57; Univ Ill, MS, 61, PhD(elec eng), 65. *Prof Exp:* Jr scientific officer, Reactor Control Div, Atomic Energy Estab, India, 58-60; asst prof elec eng, Pa State Univ, 65-69; asst prof info eng, 69-73, ASSOC PROF INFO ENG, UNIV ILL, CHICAGO CIRCLE, 73- *Concurrent Pos:* Vis sr assoc, Syst Res Ltd, Richmond, UK, 76-77; dir, Matrix Publishers Priv LTD, India, 78-; consult, Naval Res Lab, Washington, DC, 79- *Mem:* Inst Elec Engrs, Eng; Inst Elec & Electronics Engrs; Int Union Radio Sci. *Res:* Radiation and propagation of electromagnetic waves; applied mathematics; educational technology systems; optical communication. *Mailing Add:* Dept of Info Eng PO Box 4348 Chicago IL 60680

LAY, DAVID CLARK, b Los Angeles, Calif, Mar 1, 41; m 70. MATHEMATICS. *Educ:* Aurora Col, BA, 62; Univ Calif, Los Angeles, MA, 65, PhD(math), 66. *Prof Exp:* Teaching asst math, Univ Calif, Los Angeles, 63-64, asst prof, 66; from asst prof to assoc prof, 66-77, PROF MATH, UNIV MD, COLLEGE PARK, 77- *Concurrent Pos:* NSF res grants, Univ Md, College Park, 68-73 & 76-77; res grant, Neth Orgn Advan Pure Res, 73; vis prof, Univ Amsterdam, 80. *Mem:* Am Math Soc; Math Asn Am. *Res:* Functional analysis; spectral theory of linear operators; operator-valued analytic functions. *Mailing Add:* Dept of Math Univ of Md College Park MD 20742

LAY, DOUGLAS M, b Jackson, Miss, July 3, 36; m 61; c 2. ANATOMY, ZOOLOGY. *Educ:* Millsaps Col, BS, 58; La State Univ, MS, 61; Univ Chicago, PhD(anat), 68. *Prof Exp:* Instr anat, Univ Chicago, 68-69; asst prof zool & cur mammals, Univ Mich, 69-73; ASSOC PROF ANAT, UNIV NC,

CHAPEL HILL, 73- *Mem:* Am Soc Mammal; Am Soc Zool; Soc Study Evol; Soc Syst Zool; Soc Vert Palaeont. *Res:* The adaptive significance of specializations of mammals for life in deserts, particularly the structure and function of the ear in desert rodents; origin, evolution, functional anatomy, biology and systematics of rodents. *Mailing Add:* Div of Health Sci Univ of NC Dept of Anat Chapel Hill NC 27514

LAY, JOACHIM E(LLERY), b Peking, China, Sept 25, 19; nat US. MECHANICAL ENGINEERING. *Educ:* Univ Liege, Cand, 40; Univ Mich, BS, 44, MS, 47, PhD(mech eng), 57. *Prof Exp:* Stress & weight engr, Willow Run Bomber Plant, 43-45; res engr, Ford Motor Co, 45-48; from instr to asst prof mech eng, Univ Detroit, 48-57; assoc prof, 57-59, PROF MECH ENG, MICH STATE UNIV, 59- *Concurrent Pos:* Consult, US Army, 58- *Mem:* Am Soc Mech Engrs; Am Soc Eng Educ. *Res:* Thermodynamics; gas dynamics; heat transfer. *Mailing Add:* Dept of Mech Eng Mich State Univ East Lansing MI 48823

LAY, JOHN CHARLES, b Ponca City, Okla, Mar 6, 48; m 68; c 3. VETERINARY PATHOLOGY. *Educ:* Univ Mo, Columbia, BS, 71, DVM, 75. *Prof Exp:* Assoc scientist vet med, Inhalation Toxicol Res Inst, Lovelace Found for Med Educ & Res, 75-77; gen vet practr, Lakin, Kans, 77-78; FEL TRAINEE EXP PATH, NY STATE COL VET MED, CORNELL UNIV, 78- *Mem:* Am Vet Med Asn. *Res:* Bovine Respiratory Disease; pulmonary inflammatory response and mechanisms of deep lung clearance and lung defense. *Mailing Add:* Dept Path Cornell Univ Ithaca NY 14853

LAY, KENNETH W(ILBUR), b Ringgold Co, Iowa, Feb 4, 39; m 64; c 3. CERAMICS. *Educ:* Iowa State Univ, BS, 61; Northwestern Univ, PhD(mat sci), 66. *Prof Exp:* Res scientist, 65-73, commun mgr mat sci & engr, 73-75, MGR CERAMICS PROCESSING, GEN ELEC RES & DEVELOP CTR, 75- *Mem:* Fel Am Ceramic Soc. *Res:* Ceramics processing and properties; diffusion; nuclear fuels; non-stoichiometric compounds. *Mailing Add:* Gen Elec Res & Develop Ctr PO Box 8 Schenectady NY 12301

LAY, STEVEN R, b Los Angeles, Calif, Nov 28, 44; m 71; c 2. MATHEMATICS. *Educ:* Aurora Col, BA, 66; Univ Calif, Los Angeles, MA, 68, PhD(math), 71. *Prof Exp:* assoc prof, 71-80, PROF MATH, AURORA COL, 80- *Mem:* Am Math Soc; London Math Soc. *Res:* Combinatorial geometry and convexity; the separation of convex sets. *Mailing Add:* Dept of Math Aurora Col Aurora IL 60507

LAYBOURNE, PAUL C, b Akron, Ohio, Dec 21, 19; m 45; c 3. PSYCHIATRY. *Educ:* NY Med Col, MD, 44; Ind Univ, MS, 49. *Prof Exp:* Assoc, 49-51, from asst prof to assoc prof, PROF PSYCHIAT, MED CTR, UNIV KANS, 65-, ASSOC PROF PEDIAT, 54-, PROF PSYCHIATRY & FAMILY PRACT, 80- *Concurrent Pos:* Consult, Spofford Home, Kansas City, Mo, 50-; dir, Atchison County Guid Clin, 51-59; supvr extern prog, State Hosps, 53-55; dir child guid clin, Mercy Hosp, 57-66. *Mem:* AMA; fel Am Psychiat Asn. *Res:* Child psychiatry. *Mailing Add:* Dept of Psychiat Univ of Kans Med Ctr Kansas City KS 66103

LAYBURN, ROBERT L(OUIS), b West New York, NJ, Sept 20, 20; m 44; c 3. ELECTRICAL ENGINEERING. *Educ:* Cornell Univ, BS, 44; Stevens Inst Technol, MS, 50. *Prof Exp:* Proj engr crystal units develop, Western Elec Co, 46-55; sr engr carrier systs develop, 55-57, mgr transmission-components sect, 57-60, dist rep, Corp Field Off, 60-70, TECH STAFF ENGR SWITCHING DESIGN, STROMBERG-CARLSON CORP, DIV GEN DYNAMICS CORP, 70- *Concurrent Pos:* Chmn eng comt microwave-multiplex terminating equip, Electronic Industs Asn, 60-64. *Mem:* Inst Elec & Electronics Engrs. *Mailing Add:* PO Box 7000 Stromberg Carlson Corp Longwood FL 32750

LAYCOCK, DAVID GERALD, b Aurora, Ill, Apr 14, 43; m 66; c 2. MOLECULAR GENETICS. *Educ:* St Procopius Col, BS, 65; Univ Hawaii, MS, 67; University, PhD, 69. *Prof Exp:* Res assoc molecular biol, Northwestern Univ, 69-70; staff fel molecular hemat, Nat Heart & Lung Inst, 70-72; ASST PROF BIOCHEM, COL MED, UNIV SOUTH ALA, 72- *Concurrent Pos:* Ala Heart Asn res grant in aid, 73; NIH res grants, 74 & 76. *Mem:* Am Chem Soc. *Res:* Control of globin gene expression assessed by in vitro transcription and translation. *Mailing Add:* 134 Yester Oaks Dr Mobile AL 36608

LAYCOCK, MAURICE VIVIAN, b Liverpool, Eng, Sept 3, 38; Can citizen; m 66; c 2. PROTEIN CHEMISTRY, MARINE ALGAE. *Educ:* Liverpool Univ, BSc, 62, PhD(plant physiol), 65. *Prof Exp:* RES OFFICER BIOCHEM, NAT RES COUN CAN, 68- *Res:* Protein chemistry; biochemistry of nitrogen compounds in algae. *Mailing Add:* Nat Res Coun 1411 Oxford St Halifax NS B3H 3Z1 Can

LAYCOCK, WILLIAM ANTHONY, b Ft Collins, Colo, Mar 17, 30; m 55; c 2. PLANT ECOLOGY. *Educ:* Univ Wyo, BS, 52, MS, 53; Rutgers Univ, PhD(bot), 58. *Prof Exp:* Range technician, State Game & Fish Comn, Wyo, 55; asst, Rutgers Univ, 55-58; range scientist, Intermountain Forest & Range Exp Sta, 58-74, asst dir, Rocky Mt Forest Range Exp Sta, US Forest Serv & Fac Affil, 74-76, RANGE SCIENTIST, AGR RES SERV, COLO STATE UNIV, USDA, 76- *Concurrent Pos:* Collabr range sci, Utah State Univ, 64-74; NZ Nat Res Adv Coun-NZ Forest Serv sr res fel, 69-70; coordr site dir western coniferous biome, US Int Biol Prog, 71-72; affil fac, Colo State Univ, 74- *Mem:* Ecol Soc Am; Am Range Mgt; NZ Ecol Soc. *Res:* Ecology and management of shortgrass plains rangelands; autecology of range species; natural areas. *Mailing Add:* Agr Res Serv USDA Colo State Univ Ft Collins CO 80523

LAYDE, DURWARD CHARLES, b La Crosse, Wis, Dec 29, 12; m 43; c 5. INORGANIC CHEMISTRY. *Educ:* St Norbert Col, AB, 33; Univ Wis, PhD(gen chem), 40. *Prof Exp:* Instr math, St Norbert Col, 33-34; asst chem, Univ Wis, 36-39, instr exten, 39-43 & army specialized training prog, 43-44, asst prof exten, 44-51, from assoc prof to prof chem, 51-81, EMER PROF CHEM, UNIV WIS-MILWAUKEE, 81- *Mem:* AAAS; Am Chem Soc. *Mailing Add:* 4968 N Idlewild Ave Milwaukee WI 53217

LAYDEN, GEORGE KAVANAUGH, b Greenport, NY, Apr 13, 29; m 60; c 3. MATERIALS SCIENCE. *Educ:* Lafayette Col, BS, 53; Pa State Univ, MS, 59, PhD(ceramic technol), 61. *Prof Exp:* MAT SCIENTIST, UNITET TECHNOL RES CTR, 61- *Mem:* Am Ceramic Soc; AAAS. *Res:* Fabrication and characterization of aerospace materials, including fibrilar carbon and graphite, structrual ceramics, nickel based superalloys and fiber and whisker feinforced glass/ceramic matrix composites. *Mailing Add:* 5 Avalon Pl Wethersfield CT 06109

LAYER, ROBERT WESLEY, b Brooklyn, NY, Aug 11, 28; m 55; c 3. ORGANIC CHEMISTRY. *Educ:* NY Univ, AB, 50; Univ Cincinnati, PhD, 55. *Prof Exp:* Control chemist, Naugatuck Chem Co, 50-52; sr tech man, 55-57, sr res chemist, 57-71, res assoc, 71-79, SR RES ASSOC, B F GOODRICH CO, 79- *Mem:* Am Chem Soc. *Res:* Rubber chemicals; reactions of ozone; chemistry of p-phenylenediamines and of anils; antioxidants. *Mailing Add:* B F Goodrich Co 9921 Brecksville Rd Brecksville OH 44141

LAYLOFF, THOMAS, b Granite City, Ill, Jan 29, 37; c 2. ANALYTICAL CHEMISTRY. *Educ:* Wash Univ, AB, 58, MA, 61; Univ Kans, PhD(anal chem), 64. *Prof Exp:* From asst prof to prof, 64-76, ADJ PROF CHEM, ST LOUIS UNIV, 76- *Concurrent Pos:* Sci adv nat ctr drug anal, Food & Drug Admin, 67-76, dir, 76- *Mem:* AAAS; Sigma Xi; Am Chem Soc. *Res:* Solution behavior of reactive organic intermediates; biopotentiometry; electron transport; data acquisition and processing. *Mailing Add:* FDA Nat Ctr Drug Anal 1114 Market/Rm 1002 St Louis MO 63101

LAYMAN, WILBUR A, b Blair, Nebr, Jan 9, 29; m 53; c 5. ANALYTICAL CHEMISTRY, PHYSICAL CHEMISTRY. *Educ:* Dana Col, BS, 53; Univ Nebr, MS, 58; Mont State Univ, PhD(anal chem), 63. *Prof Exp:* Chemist, Harris Labs, 54-58; instr chem, Hastings Col, 58-60 & Dana Col, 62-63; asst prof, S Dak State Univ, 63-66; assoc prof, Adams State Col, 66-67; PROF CHEM & CHMN PHYS SCI DEPT, EASTERN MONT COL, 67- *Mem:* Am Chem Soc. *Res:* Stability constants of metal complexes; polarized infrared spectroscopy of thin crystal films. *Mailing Add:* Dept of Phys Sci Eastern Mont Col Billings MT 59101

LAYMAN, WILLIAM ARTHUR, b West New York, NJ, Feb 8, 29; c 1. PSYCHIATRY. *Educ:* St Peter's Col, NJ, BS, 51; Georgetown Univ, MD, 55; Am Bd Psychiat & Neurol, dipl, 62. *Prof Exp:* Intern, Hackensack Hosp, NJ, 55-56; jr resident psychiat, Vet Admin Hosp, Lyons, 56-57; sr resident, Fairfield Hills Hosp, Newtown, Conn, 57-59; from instr to assoc prof, 59-74, clin prof, 74-77, PROF PSYCHIAT, COL MED & DENT NJ, 77- *Concurrent Pos:* Clin fel psychiat, Sch Med, Yale Univ, 58-59. *Mem:* AAAS; Am Asn Univ Prof; Am Psychiat Asn. *Res:* Nonverbal communication; psycotherapeutic technique. *Mailing Add:* Dept of Psychiat Col of Med & Dent of NJ Newark NJ 07103

LAYNE, CLYDE BROWNING, b El Paso, Tex, Feb 19, 47; m 69; c 1. APPLIED PHYSICS. *Educ:* Princeton Univ, AB, 69; Univ Calif, Davis, MS, 73, PhD(appl sci), 75. *Prof Exp:* Physicist, Div Laser Physics, Lawrence Livermore Lab, Univ Calif, 69-80; TECH STAFF, COMBUSTION PHYSICS DIV, SANDIA NAT LAB, LIVERMORE, CALIF, 80- *Mem:* Am Phys Soc; Optical Soc Am. *Res:* Relaxation and energy transfer in ions in solids; atomic vapor-laser isotope separation of uranium; lasers applied to combustion diagnostics. *Mailing Add:* Div 8511 Sandia Nat Labs Livermore CA 94550

LAYNE, DONALD SAINTEVAL, b Lime Ridge, Que, Apr 5, 31; m 59; c 3. BIOCHEMISTRY. *Educ:* McGill Univ, BSc, 53, MSc, 55, PhD, 57. *Prof Exp:* Fel biochem, Univ Edinburgh, 57-58; res assoc psychiat, Queen's Univ Ont, 58-59; from scientist to sr scientist, Worcester Found Exp Biol, 59-66; head physiol & endocrinol sect, Food & Drug Directorate, Can, 66-68; prof biochem, Univ Ottawa, 68-79; VPRES, CONNAUGHT LAB, LTD, 79- *Mem:* AAAS; Am Physiol Soc; Endocrine Soc; Am Soc Biol Chemists; Royal Soc Can. *Res:* Biochemistry of estrogenic hormones. *Mailing Add:* Connaught Lab Ltd 1755 Steeles Ave W Willowdale ON M2R 3T4 Can

LAYNE, ENNIS C, biochemistry, physcial chemistry, see previous edition

LAYNE, JAMES NATHANIEL, b Chicago, Ill, May 16, 26; m 50; c 5. VERTEBRATE BIOLOGY. *Educ:* Cornell Univ, BA, 50, PhD(zool), 54. *Prof Exp:* Asst vert zool, Cornell Univ, 50-54; asst prof zool, Southern Ill Univ, 54-55; from asst prof to assoc prof biol, Univ Fla, 55-63; assoc prof zool, Cornell Univ, 63-67; DIR ARCHBOLD BIOL STA & ARCHBOLD CUR DEPT MAMMAL & MEM ADV BD, ARCHBOLD EXPEDS, AM MUS NATURAL HIST, 67- *Concurrent Pos:* From asst cur to assoc cur biol sci, Fla State Mus, 55-63, res assoc, 63-65; adj prof, Univ S Fla, 68- *Honors & Awards:* C Hart Merriam Award, Am Soc Mammalogists, 76. *Mem:* AAAS; Am Soc Zoologists; Am Soc Mammal (vpres, 65-70, pres, 70-72); Wildlife Soc; Ecol Soc Am. *Res:* Mammalian ecology, systematics, behavior and morphology; general vertebrate biology. *Mailing Add:* Archbold Biol Sta Rte 2 Box 180 Lake Placid FL 33852

LAYNE, PORTER PRESTON, b Martin, Ky, Sept 20, 45; m 72; c 1. BIOCHEMISTRY. *Educ:* Univ Ky, BS, 66, PhD(biochem), 71; Boston Univ, MBA, 78. *Prof Exp:* Fel protein chem, Sch Med, Tufts Univ, 71-73, asst prof, 74-80; assoc investr, 80-81, SR INVESTR DEVELOP, SMITH KLINE CORP, 82- *Concurrent Pos:* Actg Chmn, Div Chem, Sch Med, Tufts Univ, 75-76. *Mem:* Sigma Xi. *Res:* Extra chromosomal inheritance; bacterial physiology; enzyme mechanism (phosphoglucomutase); adenylate cyclase and tuftsin research. *Mailing Add:* 1016 Windy Hill Rd Norristown PA 19403

LAYNE, RICHARD C, b St Vincent, WI, Dec 14, 36; Can citizen; m 63; c 2. PLANT BREEDING. *Educ:* McGill Univ, BSc, 59; Univ Wis, MS, 60, PhD(agron, plant path), 63. *Prof Exp:* RES SCIENTIST, RES STA, AGR CAN, 63- *Concurrent Pos:* Chmn, NAm working group on winterhardiness woody perennials, Int Soc Hort Sci. *Honors & Awards:* Shepard Award, Am Pomol Soc, 67; Carrol R Miller Award, Am Soc Hort Sci, 77 & 78. *Mem:* Can Soc Hort Sci (pres, 77); Am Soc Hort Sci; Am Pomol Soc; Sigma Xi; Int Soc Hort Sci. *Res:* Fruit breeding of cultivars and rootstocks of peach, nectarine and apricot; breeding for cold hardiness and disease resistance; environmental and genetic factors affecting cold hardiness; rootstock-scion physiology. *Mailing Add:* Can Agr Res Sta Harrow ON N0R 1G0 Can

LAYNG, EDWIN TOWER, b Greenville, Pa, Jan 20, 09; m 46; c 2. CHEMISTRY. *Educ:* Allegheny Col, ScB, 30; NY Univ, PhD(chem), 33. *Prof Exp:* Asst, NY Univ, 30-33; res chemist, M W Kellogg Co, NJ, 34-42, assoc dir res, 43; dir res, Hydrocarbon Res, Inc, 43-44, asst to the pres, 44-46, vpres, 47-63, exec vpres, 64-72, pres, 72-74; vpres, Dynalectron Corp, 64-74; consult, 74-77. *Mem:* Am Chem Soc; Am Inst Chem Eng; Am Petrol Inst. *Res:* Reaction kinetics; catalysis in petroleum processes; synthetic fuels; coal gasification; coal liquefaction. *Mailing Add:* 8 Surrey Rd Summit NJ 07901

LAYSON, WILLIAM M(CINTYRE), b Lexington, Ky, Sept 24, 34; m 67; c 2. PHYSICS, MECHANICAL ENGINEERING. *Educ:* Mass Inst Technol, BS, 56, PhD(physics), 63. *Prof Exp:* Res physicist, Univ Calif, 62-63, lectr physics, 63-64; sr systs engr tech staff, Pan Am World Airways, 64-67; mem tech staff, Gen Res Corp, 67-69, mgr dept, 69-70; vpres & mgr, Wash Div, 70-76, V PRES CONTINUIUM MECH DIV, SCI APPLN INC, 76- *Mem:* Am Phys Soc; Am Inst Aeronaut & Astronaut; Inst Elec & Electronics Engrs. *Res:* Nuclear weapons effects; dust and debris clouds; radiation transport; ground coupling; fireball effects; radar systems; fluid mechanics; electromagnetic propagation; atmospheric physics; systems analysis. *Mailing Add:* Sci Appln Inc 8400 Westpart Dr McClean VA 22101

LAYTON, DAVID WARREN, b Woburn, Mass, Sept 19, 48; m 77. WATER RESOURCES. *Educ:* Bridgewater State Col, BA, 70; Univ Ariz, PhD(water resources admin), 75. *Prof Exp:* ENVIRON SCIENTIST RISK ANALYSIS WATER RESOURCES & ENERGY, LAWRENCE LIVERMORE NAT LAB, UNIV CALIF, 75- *Mem:* Am Water Resources Asn. *Res:* Geothermal energy; environmental studies; pollution control technologies; risk analysis. *Mailing Add:* Environ Sci Div PO Box 5507 Livermore CA 94550

LAYTON, E MILLER, JR, b Monticello, NY, Feb 28, 31; m 59; c 3. PHYSICAL CHEMISTRY, CHEMICAL PHYSICS. *Educ:* Union Col, BSChem, 54; Iowa State Univ, MS, 59, PhD(phys chem), 62. *Prof Exp:* Asst prof, Mont State Univ, 62-68; assoc prof, Colo Col, 68-71; res assoc, Ames Lab, Iowa State Univ, 73-78; ASSOC PROF CHEM, STERLING COL, 78- *Mem:* Am Chem Soc. *Res:* Molecular structure and spectroscopy; liquid state structure; coal and inorganic analysis. *Mailing Add:* Dept of Chem Sterling Col Sterling KS 67579

LAYTON, EDWIN THOMAS, JR, b Sept 13, 28; wid; c 1. HISTORY OF TECHNOLOGY. *Educ:* Univ Calif, Los Angeles, BA, 50, MA, 53, PhD(hist), 57. *Prof Exp:* Instr hist, Univ Wis, 56-57; instr hist, Ohio State Univ, 57-60; asst prof, Purdue Univ, 60-65; assoc prof hist sci & technol, Case Western Reserve Univ, 65-75; PROF HIST SCI & TECHNOL, UNIV MINN, 75- *Concurrent Pos:* Comt mem partic, Fourteenth Int Cong His Sci, Tokyo, 74. *Mem:* Soc Hist Technol; Hist Sci Soc; fel AAAS; Am Soc Mech Engrs. *Res:* Interaction of science and technology in nineteenth century America. *Mailing Add:* Dept of Mech Eng Univ of Minn Minneapolis MN 55455

LAYTON, HERBERT WALLACE, bacteriology, see previous edition

LAYTON, JACK MALCOLM, b Ossian, Iowa, Sept 27, 17; m 43; c 2. PATHOLOGY. *Educ:* Luther Col, AB, 39, DSc, 74; Univ Iowa, MD, 43; Am Bd Path, dipl, 50. *Prof Exp:* Intern, Univ Iowa Hosps, 43, asst path, 46-47, instr, 47-49, assoc, 49-50, from asst prof to prof, 50-67; PROF PATH & HEAD DEPT, COL MED, UNIV ARIZ, 67- *Concurrent Pos:* Actg dean col med & actg dir med ctr, Univ Ariz, 71-73; trustee, Am Bd Path, 74-; dir clin path, Ariz Health Servs, 77- *Mem:* Am Soc Clin Path (pres, 73); Col Am Path; Am Asn Path & Bact; Am Soc Exp Path; Int Acad Path (pres, 75-76). *Res:* Virology; host-parasite relationships in viral and rickettsial diseases; comparative pathology of inflammation; ultramicroscopic pathologic anatomy of infectious diseases; biological activities of teratomas; influenza and psittacosis-lymphogranuloma groups of viruses. *Mailing Add:* Dept of Path Univ of Ariz Col of Med Tucson AZ 85724

LAYTON, LIONEL H, b Layton, Utah, Mar 3, 24; m 54; c 2. MATERIALS SCIENCE. *Educ:* Brigham Young Univ, BS, 49; Rutgers Univ, PhD(chem), 53. *Prof Exp:* Chemist, Standard Oil Co Ind, 52-54; instr chem, Colo Sch Mines, 54-56; prof, Ricks Col, 56-58; SUPVR, THIOKOL CORP, 58- *Concurrent Pos:* Adj prof, Univ Utah. *Mem:* AAAS. *Res:* Mechanical properties of elastomeric materials; solution properties of high polymeric soaps; solvent extraction; combustion; chemistry of material aging. *Mailing Add:* 448 S Seventh W Brigham City UT 84302

LAYTON, RICHARD GARY, b Salt Lake City, Utah, Dec 24, 35; m 63; c 3. PHYSICS, CLOUD PHYSICS. *Educ:* Univ Utah, BA, 60, MA, 62; Utah State Univ, PhD(physics), 65. *Prof Exp:* Asst physics, Univ Utah, 60-62; asst res physicist electro-dynamics Labs, Utah State Univ, 63-64; from asst prof to assoc prof physics, State Univ NY Col Fredonia, 65-69; ASSOC PROF PHYSICS, NORTHERN ARIZ UNIV, 69- *Concurrent Pos:* Res Assoc, Lowell Observ, 71 & 72; sci callabr, Grand Canyon Nat Park, 72-75. *Mem:* Am Asn Physics Teachers; Am Phys Soc; Am Vacuum Soc; Am Asn Physics Teachers. *Res:* Ice nucleation surfaces, ellipsometry; atmospheric optics; frost damage prevention for plants. *Mailing Add:* Dept of Physics Box 5763 Northern Ariz Univ Flagstaff AZ 86011

LAYTON, ROGER, b Idaho Falls, Idaho, May 7, 42; m 61; c 5. ORGANIC CHEMISTRY. *Educ:* Idaho State Univ, BS, 64; Ohio State Univ, PhD(org mechanisms), 67. *Prof Exp:* NIH fel, Univ Utah, 67-68; res chemist, Res & Develop Div, Kraftco Corp, 68-71 & Searle Biochemics, Div G D Searle & Co, 71-74, LECTR, HARPER COL, 74- *Mem:* Am Chem Soc. *Res:* Synthetic aspects of vitamin E; formaldehyde reactions; hydrogenation; fatty chemicals; food additives; photochemistry. *Mailing Add:* 400 Castle Wood Lane Buffalo Grove IL 60090

LAYTON, THOMAS WILLIAM, b Kaysville, Utah, Feb 24, 27; m 47; c 1. PHYSICS. *Educ:* Calif Inst Technol, BS, 51, PhD(physics, math), 57. *Prof Exp:* Res engr, Jet Propulsion Lab, Calif Inst Technol, 53-55; mem tech staff, Inertial Guid Dept, Thompson-Ramo-Wooldridge, Inc, 55-59, mgr, 59-64, SR STAFF ENGR, DEFENSE & SPACE SYSTS GROUP, TRW, INC, 64- *Mem:* Am Phys Soc; Am Inst Aeronaut & Astronaut. *Res:* Cosmic rays; navigation and guidance systems for ballistic missiles and space flight vehicles. *Mailing Add:* 4836 W Elmdale Dr Rolling Hills CA 90274

LAYZER, ARTHUR JAMES, b Cleveland, Ohio, Aug 21, 27; m 64; c 1. THEORETICAL PHYSICS. *Educ:* Case Western Reservd Univ, BS, 50; Columbia Univ, PhD(physics), 60. *Prof Exp:* Res scientist, Courant Inst, NY Univ, 60-63; asst prof, 64-67, ASSOC PROF PHYSICS, STEVENS INST TECHNOL, 68-, ASSOC PROF ENG PHYSICS, 77- *Concurrent Pos:* Vis res scientist, Brookhaven Nat Lab, 66; resident visitor comput music, Acoust Div, Bell Labs, 67-; US Dept Educ grant deafness res & reading, 78-80. *Mem:* AAAS; Am Educ Res Asn. *Res:* Quantum mechanical theory of critical phenomena, especially superconductivity; sound-analogic text representations in deafness and language; score-mediated generation of music and text;test measures and analysis in reading and writing; language and art media applications of computer science. *Mailing Add:* Stevens Inst of Technol Castle Point Sta Hoboken NJ 07030

LAYZER, DAVID, b Ohio, Dec 31, 25; m 49, 59; c 6. ASTRONOMY. *Educ:* Harvard Univ, AB, 47, PhD(theoret astrophys), 50. *Prof Exp:* Nat Res Coun res fel, 50-51; lectr astron, Univ Calif, Berkeley, 51-52; res assoc physics, Princeton Univ, 52-53; res assoc, 53-55, res fel & lectr, 55-60, prof astron, 60-80, DONALD H MENZEL PROF ASTROPHYS, HARVARD UNIV, 80- *Concurrent Pos:* Consult, Geophys Corp Am, 59-65. *Honors & Awards:* Bok Prize, 60. *Mem:* Am Acad Arts & Sci; Am Astron Soc; Int Astron Union; Royal Astron Soc. *Res:* Cosmology and cosmogony; theoretical astrophysics and atomic physics; ionospheric physics. *Mailing Add:* Harvard Col Observ 60 Garden St Cambridge MA 02138

LAZAR, BENJAMIN EDWARD, b Vatra-Dornei, Romania, Feb 27, 30; US citizen; m 54; c 1. CIVIL ENGINEERING. *Educ:* Bucharest Polytech Inst, Dipl eng, 54; McGill Univ, grad dipl, 68; Sir George Williams Univ, DE, 70. *Prof Exp:* Engr, Precast Concrete Co, 54-61, Found Can Eng Corp, 61-64, Swan Wooster Eng Corp Ltd, 64-67 & Rust Eng, 67-68; res engr, Sir George Williams Univ, 68-70, asst prof civil eng, 70-71; asst prof, 71-80, ASSOC PROF CIVIL TECHNOL, UNIV HOUSTON, 80- *Concurrent Pos:* Can Steel Industs Construct Coun grant, Sir George Williams Univ, 70-71. *Mem:* Am Soc Civil Engrs. *Res:* Structural behavior and technology of civil engineering systems. *Mailing Add:* Col of Technol Univ of Houston Houston TX 77004

LAZAR, JAMES TARLTON, JR, b Whiteville, NC, Oct 24, 22; m 47. DAIRY SCIENCE. *Educ:* Clemson Univ, BS, 43; Cornell Univ, MS, 49; NC State Univ, PhD(dairy sci), 55. *Prof Exp:* Supt off prod testing, Clemson Univ, 46-48, asst prof dairy sci, 49-51; teaching asst, Cornell Univ, 48-49; res asst, NC State Univ, 51-53; assoc prof, 53-65, PROF DAIRY SCI, CLEMSON UNIV, 65- *Mem:* Am Dairy Sci Asn. *Res:* Dairy management; labor efficiencies and economies of dairy plant operation; pricing plans for purchasing milk, processing for flavor control; influence of vacuum pasteurization upon the freezing point value, total solids and concentration of milk; use of vacuum pasteurizer to increase solids-not-fat in low fat milk. *Mailing Add:* Dept of Dairy Sci Clemson Univ Clemson SC 29631

LAZAR, NORMAN HENRY, b Brooklyn, NY, June 21, 29. PHYSICS. *Educ:* City Col New York, BS, 49; Ind Univ, MS, 51, PhD(physics), 53. *Prof Exp:* Physicist, Oak Ridge Nat Lab, Union Carbide Nuclear Co, 53-80; WITH TRW DEFENSE & SPACE SYST, 80- *Mem:* Fel Am Phys Soc. *Res:* Controlled thermonuclear reactions; beta and gamma ray spectroscopy; plasma physics. *Mailing Add:* One Space Park TRW Defense & Space Syst Redondo Beach CA 90278

LAZARETH, OTTO WILLIAM, JR, b Brooklyn, NY, Sept 16, 38. SOLID STATE PHYSICS, REACTOR PHYSICS. *Educ:* Wagner Col, BS, 61; Queens Col, MA, 68; City Univ NY, PhD(physics), 73. *Prof Exp:* Res asst physics, Queens Col, 65-67; physics assoc, 67-73, ASSOC PHYSICIST, BROOKHAVEN NAT LAB, 74- *Mem:* Am Phys Soc; Am Nuclear Soc. *Res:* Nucleonics; radiation damage and effects in solids; point defects in solids; crystallites and crystal surfaces; modelling physical systems with computers. *Mailing Add:* Bldg 820M Brookhaven Nat Lab Upton NY 11973

LAZARIDIS, ANASTAS, b Istanbul, Turkey, Dec 8, 40; US citizen; m 66; c 2. MECHANICAL ENGINEERING, SOLAR ENERGY. *Educ:* Bosphorus Univ, Turkey, BS, 63; Columbia Univ, MS, 64, EngScD, 69. *Prof Exp:* Res engr, Heat & Mass Transfer Lab, Columbia Univ, 65-68, res engr, Textile Fibers Dept, E I du Pont de Nemours & Co Inc, 69-72; heat transfer specialist-process eng, Day & Zimmermann Inc, Philadelphia, 72-75; regional mkt mgr process control, Control Automation Technol Co, 75-76; PRES CONSTRUCT & SOLAR ENERGY, HELIOS INC, WILMINGTON, DEL, 76- *Concurrent Pos:* Fulbright Scholar Award, Columbia Univ, 63-64, Boese Scholar Award, 64-65; lectr mech eng, Manhattan Col, 65-67 & Richmond Col, City Univ New York, 67-68; adj prof mech eng, Drexel Univ, 72-75; referee, Heat Transfer Sect, Am Soc Mech Engrs, Int J Heat & Mass Transfer, NSF. *Mem:* Am Soc Mech Engrs. *Res:* Energy conservation; heat transfer; solidification; textile engineering; technical management; various papers and technical reports. *Mailing Add:* PO Box 9076 Helios Inc Wilmington DE 19809

LAZARIDIS, ATHANASIUS NASSOS, b Athens, Greece, Oct 6, 43; m 73; c 1. MECHANICAL METALLURGY, PHYSICAL METALLURGY. *Educ:* Nat Tech Univ, Athens, BS & MS, 67; Univ Wis-Madison, MS, 70, PhD(metall eng), 71. *Prof Exp:* Prod engr metal working, Nat Can Corp, Greece, 73-74; lectr & proj assoc, Univ Wis-Madison, 74-75; sr res engr, 75-79, spec consult, Sec Steel Refining & Continuous Casting, 79-80, SUPVR RES ENGR, RES LAB, INLAND STEEL CO, 80- *Concurrent Pos:* Proj assoc, Am Motors Corp, 74-75; adj prof, Purdue Univ, Calumet Campus, 78- *Mem:* Am Soc Metals; Am Soc Testing & Mat; Am Inst Mining, Metall & Petrol Engrs; Greek Tech Chamber Prof Engrs; Sigma Xi. *Res:* Fracture toughness; fatigue; product development; formability, effect of metallurgy on machinability; hot deformation of steel and other alloys. *Mailing Add:* Inland Steel Res Labs 3001 E Columbus Dr East Chicago IN 46312

LAZARIDIS, CHRISTINA NICHOLSON, b New York, NY, Jan 12, 42; m 66; c 2. ORGANIC CHEMISTRY, PHOTOGRAPHIC CHEMISTRY. *Educ:* Mt Holyoke Col, BA, 62; Columbia Univ, MA, 63, PhD(chem), 66. *Prof Exp:* Res chemist, Colgate-Palmolive Co, 66-68; SR RES CHEMIST E I DU PONT DE NEMOURS & CO INC, 68- *Mem:* Am Chem Soc; Int Soc Hybrid Microelectronics. *Res:* Photosensitive systems, including conventional silver halide as well as novel photopolymeric materials. *Mailing Add:* Photo Prod Dept Du Pont Co Exp Sta Wilmington DE 19898

LAZARO, ERIC JOSEPH, b Muttra, India, Dec 28, 21; m 49; c 3. SURGERY. *Educ:* Univ Madras, MBBS, 46; Georgetown Univ, MS, 55; Am Bd Surg, dipl, 55; FRCS(C), 56. *Prof Exp:* Instr surg, Georgetown Univ, 54-57; assoc prof, All India Inst Med Sci, 58-60, prof thoracic surg, 60-61, prof surg, 61-62; assoc prof, 62, PROF SURG, COL MED & DENT NJ, 62- *Concurrent Pos:* Rockefeller Found fels, 57 & 62; Colombo Plan fel, 61. *Mem:* AAAS; fel Am Col Surg; Soc Surg Alimentary Tract; AMA. *Res:* Pathogenesis of pancreatitis; biologic effects of splenic extracts. *Mailing Add:* Dept of Surg Col of Med & Dent NJ Newark NJ 07103

LAZAROFF, NORMAN, b Brooklyn, NY, Nov 24, 27; m 58; c 2. MICROBIOLOGY. *Educ:* Syracuse Univ, AB, 50, MS, 52; Yale Univ, PhD(microbiol), 60. *Prof Exp:* Asst enzymol, Res Found, State Univ NY, 55; bacteriologist, Schwarz Labs, Inc, 55-56; proj leader, Evans Res & Develop Corp, 56-57, consult, 57-59; fel microbiol, Brandeis Univ, 60-61; microbiologist, BC Res Coun, 61-62; asst prof biol sci, Univ Southern Calif, 62-64; sr res scientist, Res Corp, Syracuse, 64-66; ASSOC PROF BIOL, STATE UNIV NY BINGHAMTON, 66- *Mem:* Am Soc Microbiol; Am Soc Photobiol; Phycol Soc Am; Brit Soc Gen Microbiol. *Res:* Chemolithotrophy; cyanobacterial photophysiology; environmental microbiology. *Mailing Add:* Dept of Biol Sci State Univ NY Binghamton NY 13901

LAZARTE, JAIME ESTEBAN, b Lima, Peru, July 26, 43. HORTICULTURE, DEVELOPMENTAL PHYSIOLOGY. *Educ:* Agrarian Univ, BS & Ing Agr, 66; Rutgers Univ, MS, 70, PhD(hort), 76. *Prof Exp:* Lab supvr tissue cult, Rutgers Univ, 73-76; res assoc veg crops, Univ Fla, 76-78; ASST PROF HORT, TEX A&M UNIV, 78- *Mem:* Am Soc Hort Sci; AAAS; Bot Soc Am; Sigma Xi. *Res:* Tissue culture of horticultural crops; flower initiation and sex expression; sex modification; morphology and embryology of horticultural crops; asparagus officinalis L. *Mailing Add:* Dept of Hort Sci Tex A&M Univ College Station TX 77801

LAZARUK, WILLIAM, b Willingdon, Alta, Jan 15, 12; m 54. HORTICULTURE, BIOLOGY. *Educ:* Univ Alta, BSc, 47, BEd, 48; SDak State Univ, MS, 50; Rutgers Univ, PhD, 61. *Prof Exp:* Asst hort, SDak State Univ, 48-50; instr adult educ, Univ NDak, 50-52 & Exten Serv, Univ Ill, 52-53; instr animal sci, Berea Col, 53-56; res asst plant nutrit, Rutgers Univ, 56-60, asst exp biol, Douglass Col, 59-60; assoc prof biol, Trenton State Col, 60-61; from assoc prof to prof, High Point Col, 61-68; assoc prof biol, Fairfield Univ, 68-77; RETIRED. *Concurrent Pos:* Partic, NSF Genetics Conf, Duke Univ, 63, Colo State Univ, 65 & Yale Univ, 69; NSF grant, 64; Piedmont Univ Ctr res grants, 64-67; Fairfield Univ grants, 69- *Mem:* Am Soc Plant Physiol. *Res:* Plant growth functions as influenced by environment; plant nutrition; microstudy of lower plants and their relationship and usefulness to man in regards to food supply and water contamination; anther culture of monocotyledonous plants to produce perennial grains. *Mailing Add:* 288 Birch Rd Fairfield CT 06430

LAZARUS, ALLAN KENNETH, b Bangor, Maine, May 20, 31; m 57; c 3. CHEMISTRY. *Educ:* NY Univ, BA, 52, MS, 55, PhD(org chem), 57. *Prof Exp:* Chemist, Cities Serv Res & Develop Co, 57-59, Inorg Chem Div, FMC Corp, 59-65 & Esso Res & Eng Co, 65-66; group leader synthetic lubricants, Intermediates Div, Tenneco Chem, Inc, 66-71; ASST PROF CHEM, TRENTON STATE COL, 72- *Mem:* Am Chem Soc; Sigma Xi; Sci Res Soc Am. *Res:* Stereochemistry; organic synthesis; product and process development; fuels; automatic transmission fluids; synthetic lubricants. *Mailing Add:* Dept of Chem Trenton State Col CN 550 Trenton NJ 08625

LAZARUS, DAVID, b Buffalo, NY, Sept 8, 21; m 43; c 4. SOLID STATE PHYSICS. *Educ:* Univ Chicago, PhD(physics), 49. *Prof Exp:* Instr electronics, Univ Chicago, 42-43; res assoc, Radio Res Lab, Harvard Univ, 43-45; asst physics, Univ Chicago, 46-49, instr, 49; from instr to assoc prof, 49-59, PROF PHYSICS, UNIV ILL, URBANA, 59- *Concurrent Pos:* Guggenheim fel, 68-69; vis prof, Harvard Univ & Mass Inst Technol, 78-79; chmn, Coun Mat Sci, US Dept Energy, 81- *Mem:* Fel Am Phys Soc; Am Asn Physics Teachers; AAAS. *Res:* Defect and electronic properties of solids; high pressure physics. *Mailing Add:* Dept of Physics Univ of Ill Urbana IL 61801

LAZARUS, GERALD SYLVAN, b New York, NY, Feb 16, 39; m 61; c 4. DERMATOLOGY. *Educ:* Colby Col, BS, 59; George Washington Univ, MD, 63. *Prof Exp:* Med intern, Univ Mich Med Ctr, 63-64, med resident, 64-65; clin assoc, Med Neurol Br, Nat Inst Neurol Dis & Blindness, 65-67; prin investr, Lab Histol & Path, Nat Inst Dent Res, 67-68; clin & res assoc, Dept Dermat, Harvard Med Sch, 68-70; chief resident dermat, 69-70; vis scientist, Strangeways Labs, Univ Cambridge, Eng, 70-72; assoc prof med & co-dir dermat training prog, Albert Einstein Col Med, 72-75; chmn, Div Dermat, 75-78, PROF MED, DUKE UNIV MED CTR, 75-, J LAMAR CALLOWAY CHAIR PROF DERMAT, 78- *Concurrent Pos:* Carl Herzog fel, 70-72; res fel, Arthritis Found, 70-72, sr investr, 72-77; consult dermat, Addenbrookes Hosp, Cambridge, Eng, 70-72; vis fel, Clare Hall, Cambridge; head sect dermat, Dept Med, Montefiore Hosp, 72-75. *Mem:* Am

Rheumatism Asn; Soc Invest Dermat; Am Fedn Clin Res; fel Am Col Physicians; Royal Soc Med. *Res:* Study of the role of proteinases in catabolic processes in skin and evaluation of the mechanisms by which these proteinases can instigate an inflammatory response. *Mailing Add:* Dept of Med Div of Dermat Duke Univ Med Ctr Box 2987 Durham NC 27710

LAZARUS, MARC SAMUEL, b Brooklyn, NY, Sept 9, 46. PHYSICAL INORGANIC CHEMISTRY. *Educ:* City Univ New York, BS, 68; Princeton Univ, MA, 71, PhD(chem), 74. *Prof Exp:* Res assoc chem, Lawrence Berkeley Lab, Univ Calif, 73-74; asst prof, 74-79, ASSOC PROF CHEM, HERBERT H LEHMAN COL, CITY UNIV NEW YORK, 79- *Concurrent Pos:* Res collabr, Brookhaven Nat Lab, 74- *Mem:* Am Chem Soc; Am Phys Soc; AAAS. *Res:* Applications of x-ray photoelectron spectroscopy to the study of transition metal compounds and alloys. *Mailing Add:* Dept of Chem Herber H Lehman Col Bronx NY 10468

LAZARUS, ROGER BEN, b New York, NY, June 3, 25; m 46; c 5. THEORETICAL PHYSICS. *Educ:* Harvard Univ, AB, 47, MA, 48, PhD(physics), 51. *Prof Exp:* Mem staff, 51-58, group leader, 58-68, div leader, 68-73, MEM STAFF, LOS ALAMOS SCI LAB, 73- *Mem:* NY Acad Sci; Am Phys Soc; Asn Comput Mach. *Res:* Simultaneous partial differential equations; computing machines. *Mailing Add:* Los Alamos Sci Lab PO Box 1663 Los Alamos NM 87545

LAZARUS, SYDNEY SIMON, b Glasgow, Scotland, Apr 28, 19; nat US; m 45; c 1. PATHOLOGY. *Educ:* City Col NY, 38; Chicago Med Sch, MD, 43; Queen's Univ, Ont, MSc, 56; Am Bd Path, dipl, 57. *Prof Exp:* Asst resident path, Coney Island Hosp, Brooklyn, NY, 51-52; asst to dir labs, 53-54, asst dir dept labs, 57-68, ASSOC DIR DEPT LABS, KINGSBROOK JEWISH MED CTR, 68-, CHIEF ANAT PATH & ASST DIR ISAAC ALBERT RES INST, 57- *Concurrent Pos:* Fel clin path, Kingsbrook Jewish Med Ctr, 56-57; vis asst prof path, Albert Einstein Col Med, 57-60; clin assoc prof, State Univ NY Downstate Med Ctr, 69-73, clin prof, 73- *Mem:* Am Soc Exp Path; Am Asn Path & Bact; Am Diabetes Asn; Col Am Path; Histochem Soc. *Res:* Human and experimental diabetes mellitus; pancreatic morphology; histochemistry; experimental morphology; pancreatic islets; tissue culture cells; electron microscopy. *Mailing Add:* Isaac Albert Res Inst Kingsbrook Jewish Med Ctr Brooklyn NY 11203

LAZAY, PAUL DUANE, b Philadelphia, Pa, June 2, 39; m 61. SOLID STATE PHYSICS. *Educ:* Trinity Col, Conn, BS, 61; Mass Inst Technol, PhD(physics), 68. *Prof Exp:* SUPVR, OPTICAL MEASUREMENT & PROCESS AUTOMATION GROUP, NAT RES LAB, BELL LABS, 69- *Mem:* Am Phys Soc; Optical Soc Am; Sigma Xi. *Res:* Optical fiber research and optical communications. *Mailing Add:* Bell Labs 1D-150 Murray Hill NJ 07974

LAZDA, VELTA ABULS, b Riga, Latvia, Dec 16, 39; US citizen; m 62. IMMUNOLOGY, MOLECULAR BIOLOGY. *Educ:* Purdue Univ, BS, 62; Northwestern Univ, PhD(microbiol), 67. *Prof Exp:* Res assoc, Immunol Div, Res Inst, Am Dent Asn Health Found, 69-77; ASST PROF, DEPT SURG, UNIV ILL MED CTR, 77- *Concurrent Pos:* Am Cancer Soc fel ribosome struct, Northwestern Univ, 67-69; USPHS career develop award. *Mem:* AAAS; Am Asn Immunologists; Am Soc Microbiol. *Mailing Add:* Dept Surg PO Box 6998 Chicago IL 60680

LAZELL, JAMES DRAPER, JR, zoology, ecology, see previous edition

LAZEN, ALVIN GORDON, b Baltimore, Md, May 28, 35; m 60; c 3. BIOCHEMISTRY, RESEARCH ADMINISTRATION. *Educ:* Univ Md, BS, 57; Ohio State Univ, PhD(microbiol), 63. *Prof Exp:* Opers res analyst, Opers Res Group, US Dept Defense, 58-60; microbiologist, Ft Detrick, 63; NIH fel, Weizmann Inst, 63-64; Arthritis Found fel, NIH, Sch Med, Johns Hopkins Univ, 64-67; asst prof & asst adminr, Johns Hopkins Univ, 67-70, from asst dean to dean res progs, Sch Med, 70-75; assoc exec dir, 75-81, EXEC DIR ASSEMBLY LIFE SCI, NAT RES COUN-NAT ACAD SCI, 81- *Mem:* AAAS; Am Soc Microbiol; Fedn Am Scientists. *Res:* Science policy-planning and decision making. *Mailing Add:* Nat Acad Sci 2101 Constitution Ave Washington DC 20418

LAZERSON, EARL EDWIN, b Detroit, Mich, Dec 10, 30; m 66; c 2. ALGEBRA, NUMBER THEORY. *Educ:* Wayne State Univ, BS, 53; Univ Mich, MA, 54. *Prof Exp:* Actg chmn, Dept Math, 71-72, chmn, 72-73, dean, Sch Sci & Technol, 73, actg vpres & provost, 76-77, vpres & provost, 77-79, actg pres, 79-80, PROF MATH, SOUTHERN ILL UNIV, 73-, PRES, 80- *Concurrent Pos:* NSF res grant, 62-67. *Mem:* Am Math Soc; Math Asn Am; London Math Soc; Soc Math de France. *Mailing Add:* Off Pres Southern Ill Univ Edwardsville IL 62026

LAZIER, CATHERINE BEATRICE, biochemistry, see previous edition

LAZO-WASEM, EDGAR ARTHUR, b Guatemala City, Guatemala, Jan 18, 26; nat US; m 50; c 3. PHARMACEUTICS. *Educ:* Carroll Col, Mont, BA, 49; Mont State Univ, MA, 51; Purdue Univ, PhD(endocrinol, pharmacol), 54. *Prof Exp:* Chief physiologist, Wilson Labs, 54-58, dir control, 58-63; dir sci serv, Strong Cobb Arner Inc, 63-64; vpres & sci dir, 65-67; vpres & tech dir, Wampole Labs Div, 67-74, vpres & tech dir, Wallace Labs, 74-77; V PRES TECH, BARNES-HIND PHARMACEUT INC, 77- *Mem:* AAAS; Endocrine Soc; Soc Exp Biol & Med; Am Physiol Soc. *Res:* Enzyme analysis; pharmaceutical development; clinical diagnostic reagents; ophthalmics. *Mailing Add:* Barnes-Hind Inc 895 Kifer Rd Sunnyvale CA 94086

LAZZARA, RALPH, b Tampa, Fla, Aug 14, 34; m 59; c 3. MEDICINE. *Educ:* Univ Chicago, BA, 55; Tulane Univ, MD, 59. *Prof Exp:* Instr med, Tulane Univ, 60-67; asst prof med, Sch Med, Univ Miami, 71-72, assoc prof, 72-77; chief sect cardiol, Vet Admin Hosp, 74-78; PROF MED, SCH MED, UNIV OKLA, 78- *Concurrent Pos:* Asst, Charity Hosp, New Orleans, 60-64; resident, Med Sch, Tulane Univ & Charity Hosp, 63-64; fel, Col Physicians

& Surgeons, Columbia Univ, 64-65; staff mem & dir cardiovasc res lab, Ochsner Clin & Ochsner Found Hosp, New Orleans, 65-67; staff cardiologist & chief sect electrophysiol, Mt Sinai Hosp, Miami Beach, 70-72; dir coronary care unit, Vet Admin Hosp, Miami, 72-75; chief sect cardiol, Univ Okla Health Sci Ctr & Vet Admin Hosp, Okla City, 78- *Mem:* Am Physiol Soc; Soc Chem Invest. *Res:* Cardiac electrophysiology. *Mailing Add:* Univ Okla Helath Sci Ctr PO Box 26901 Oklahoma City OK 73190

LAZZARI, EUGENE PAUL, b Archbald, Pa, Mar 12, 31. BIOCHEMISTRY. *Educ:* Scranton Univ, BS, 53; Williams Col, MA, 55; Iowa State Univ, PhD(biochem), 61. *Prof Exp:* Res assoc biol, Brookhaven Nat Lab, 61-62; res assoc biochem, City of Hope Med Ctr, 62-63; from asst prof to assoc prof, 63-75, PROF BIOL CHEM, UNIV TEX DENT BR, HOUSTON, 75- *Mem:* AAAS; Am Chem Soc; Int Asn Dent Res; Sigma Xi. *Res:* Isolation and sequence determination of human pancreatic enzymes, human dentin and enamel proteins; amino acid chemistry and chemical modification of enzymes. *Mailing Add:* Dept of Physiol-Biochem Univ of Tex Dent Br PO Box 20068 Houston TX 77025

LAZZARINI, ALBERT JOHN, b Lucca, Italy, Oct 11, 52; US citizen. NUCLEAR PHYSICS. *Educ:* Mass Inst Technol, SB, 74, PhD(nuclear physics), 78. *Prof Exp:* RES ASSOC NUCLEAR PHYSICS, UNIV WASH, 78- *Mem:* Am Phys Soc. *Res:* Heavy ion experimental nuclear physics: reaction mechanisms for processes such as fusion, deep inelastic scattering and resonance phenomena. *Mailing Add:* 2014 E Miller Seattle WA 98112

LE, CHAP THAN, b Vietnam, Aug 1, 48; m 75. STATISTICS, BIOMETRICS. *Educ:* Calif State Univ, BA, BS & MA, 71; Univ NMex, PhD(statist), 78. *Prof Exp:* ASST PROF BIOMET, UNIV MINN, 78- *Mem:* Biomet Soc. *Res:* Reliability and life testing; nonparametric statistics; survey sampling; theory of survivorship; epidemiology. *Mailing Add:* Dept Biomet Univ Minn Minneapolis MN 55455

LEA, ARDEN OTTERBEIN, b Cleveland, Ohio, Oct 19, 26; m 52; c 3. ENTOMOLOGY. *Educ:* Univ Rochester, BA, 48; Ohio State Univ, MSc, 50, PhD(entom), 57. *Prof Exp:* Res assoc insecticide testing, Ohio State Univ, 50-51, insect nutrit, 56-58; USPHS med entomologist, Onchocerciasis Proj, Pan Am Sanit Bur, Guatemala, 51-53; chief physiol sect, Entom Res Ctr, State Bd Health, Fla, 58-69; assoc prof entom, 69-74, PROF ENTOM, UNIV GA, 74- *Concurrent Pos:* USPHS spec res fel, Denmark, 60-61; mem trop med & parasitol study sect, NIH, 74-78; mem sci adv panel onchocerciasis, WHO. *Mem:* AAAS; Entom Soc Am; Am Mosquito Control Asn. *Res:* Endocrine physiology of Diptera; physiology and behavior of mosquitoes. *Mailing Add:* Dept of Entom Univ of Ga Athens GA 30602

LEA, JAMES DIGHTON, b Monticello, Ill, Apr 9, 33; m 53; c 2. SYSTEMS SCIENCE. *Educ:* Tex Western Col, BA, 57; Univ Tex, MA, 60, PhD(physics), 63. *Prof Exp:* Sr res scientist physics, Esso Prod Res Co, Stand Oil NJ, 63-69, sr prof systs analyst, Humble Oil & Refining Co, 69-73, explor systs adv, Exxon Co USA, 73-75, RES ASSOC SYSTS, EXXON PROD RES CO, EXXON CORP, 75- *Mem:* Am Math Soc; Am Phys Soc; Soc Explor Geophysicists; Am Asn Petrol Geologists. *Res:* Application of computer science to geological problems. *Mailing Add:* PO Box 2180 Exxon Co USA Houston TX 77001

LEA, JAMES WESLEY, JR, b Lebanon, Tenn, Mar 17, 41; m 66; c 2. TOPOLOGY, ALGEBRA. *Educ:* Tenn Polytech Inst, BS, 63, MS, 65; La State Univ, PhD(math), 71. *Prof Exp:* Instr math, Univ Tenn, Martin, 65-66; instr, Tenn Technol Univ, 66-67; from asst prof to assoc prof, 71-81, PROF MATH, MIDDLE TENN STATE UNIV, 81- *Concurrent Pos:* Vis assoc prof math, Univ Tenn, Knoxville, 76-77. *Mem:* Am Math Soc; Math Asn Am; Sigma Xi. *Res:* Lattice theory. *Mailing Add:* Middle Tenn State Univ Murfreesboro TN 37132

LEA, MICHAEL ANTHONY, b Leeds, Eng, Dec 26, 39; m 61; c 2. BIOCHEMISTRY. *Educ:* Univ Birmingham, BSc, 61, PhD(biochem), 64. *Prof Exp:* Res assoc pharmacol, Sch Med, Ind Univ, 64-66, instr, 66-67; asst prof, 67-71, assoc prof, 71-78, PROF BIOCHEM, COL MED & DENT NJ, 78- *Mem:* AAAS; Am Chem Soc; Am Soc Cell Biol; Am Asn Cancer Res; Am Soc Biol Chemists. *Res:* Metabolism of the nuclear proteins and the control of tissue growth rate. *Mailing Add:* Dept of Biochem Col of Med & Dent of NJ Newark NJ 07103

LEA, ROBERT MARTIN, b New York, NY, Nov 4, 31; m 53; c 1. PHYSICS. *Educ:* Union Col, NY, BS, 53; Yale Univ, PhD(physics), 57. *Prof Exp:* Chmn dept, 70-74, PROF PHYSICS, CITY COL NEW YORK, 57- *Concurrent Pos:* Vis physicist, Brookhaven Nat Lab, 59-70; prin investr, NSF res grants, City Col New York, 59-70, dir, NSF dept develop grant, 70-74. *Mem:* Am Phys Soc; Am Asn Physics Teachers. *Res:* High energy experimental physics. *Mailing Add:* Dept of Physics City Col of New York New York NY 10031

LEA, SUSAN MAUREEN, b Cardiff, Wales, UK, July 10, 48; m 74; c 1. ASTROPHYSICS. *Educ:* Cambridge Univ, BA, 69, MA, 73; Univ Calif, Berkeley, PhD(astron), 74. *Prof Exp:* Res assoc astrophys, Ames Res Ctr, NASA, 74-76; res fel, Univ Md, College Park, 76-77; asst res astronomer, Univ Calif, Berkeley, 77-80; ASSOC PROF, DEPT PHYSICS & ASTRON, SAN FRANCISCO STATE UNIV, 80- *Mem:* Am Astron Soc; Royal Astron Soc; Int Astron Union. *Res:* High energy astrophysics, especially x-ray and radio astronomy; numerical hydrodynamics; compact galactic x-ray sources, clusters of galaxies, intergalactic matter and cosmology. *Mailing Add:* Dept of Astron Univ of Calif Berkeley CA 94720

LEA, WAYNE ADAIR, b Helena, Mont, Jan 16, 40; c 7. COMPUTER RECOGNITION OF SPEECH. *Educ:* Mont State Col, BS, 62, MS, 64; Mass Inst Technol, SM & EE, 66, Purdue Univ, PhD, 72. *Prof Exp:* Res assoc, Electronics Res Lab, Mont State Col, 62-64; NSF fel, Electronics Res Lab, Mass Inst Technol, 64-66; proj leader, Electronics Res Ctr, NASA, 66-70; instr elec eng, Res Found, Purdue Univ, 70-72; prin investr, Defense Systs

Div, Sperry Univac, 72-77; res scientist, Speech Commun Res Lab, 77-81; DIR, SPEECH SCI PUBL, 80- *Concurrent Pos:* Adj assoc prof, Dept Linguistics, Univ Southern Calif, 78- & Dept Elec & Comput Eng, Univ Calif, Santa Barbara, 81-; consult speech recognition, various co, 79-; chmn, Acad Forensic Appl Commun Sci, 78- *Mem:* Sr mem Inst Elec & Electronics Engrs; Acoust Soc Am; Am Acad Forensic Sci; Am Asn Phonetic Sci; Sigma Xi. *Res:* Computer recognition of speech; intonation, linguistic stress and rhythm; acoustic phonetics, forensic phonetics. *Mailing Add:* 889 Sanford Court Santa Barbara CA 93111

LEABO, DICK ALBERT, b Walcott, Iowa, Oct 30, 21; m 55; c 1. APPLIED STATISTICS, ECONOMIC STATISTICS. *Educ:* Univ Iowa, BS, 49, MA, 50, PhD(statist, econ), 53. *Prof Exp:* Res asst econ, Bur Bus & Econ Res, Univ Iowa, 48-49, res assoc, 49-53, asst prof econ & asst dir, 53-56; asst prof econ & asst dir, Bur Econ & Bus Res, Mich State Univ, 56-57; from asst prof statist to assoc prof, 57-63, assoc dean, Grad Sch Bus, 62-65, dir PhD prog, 65-81, prof, 63-79, FRED M TAYLOR DISTINGUISHED PROF STATIST, UNIV MICH, ANN ARBOR, 79- *Concurrent Pos:* Consult, Brookings Inst, 57-59 & NCent Accrediting Asn, 74-; exchange prof, Rotterdam Sch Econ, 65. *Mem:* Am Statist Asn; Am Econ Asn; Asn Bus Economists. *Res:* Regional economic research and the application of regression and correlation techniques. *Mailing Add:* Grad Sch of Bus Admin Univ of Mich Ann Arbor MI 48109

LEACH, BARRIE WILLIAM, b Winnipeg, Man, Nov 25, 45; m 66; c 2. APPLIED MATHEMATICS, ELECTRICAL ENGINEERING. *Educ:* Univ Man, BSc, 67, MSc, 68, PhD(elec eng), 72. *Prof Exp:* asst res officer, 72-80, ASSOC RES OFFICER, FLIGHT RES, NAT RES COUN CAN, 80- *Mem:* Inst Elec & Electronics Engrs. *Res:* Optimal parameter and state estimation; aeromagnetics; geophysical and anti-submarine warfare applications; digital filtering techniques multi-sensor navigation techniques. *Mailing Add:* Nat Aeronaut Estab Montreal Rd Ottawa ON K1A 0R6 Can

LEACH, BERTON JOE, b Tuscola, Ill, Mar 30, 32; m 55; c 2. BIOLOGY, SCIENCE ADMINISTRATION. *Educ:* Washington Univ, AB, 57; Univ Mo, MA, 60, PhD(zool), 63. *Prof Exp:* Asst zool, Univ Mo, 58-60, instr, 60-62, USPHS res fel, 62-63; asst prof, George Washington Univ, 63-66; asst prog dir, Undergrad Student Prog, NSF, 66-67, asst prog dir col sci improv prog, 67-68; prof biol, Cent Methodist Col, 68-70, F H Dearing prof, 70-74, chmn dept biol & geol, 68-74; exec secy, Cardiovasc & Pulmonary Study Sect, Div Res Grants, NIH, 74-; CHIEF CONSULT, BERTON J LEACH ASSOC, ROCKVILLE, MD, 76- *Concurrent Pos:* NSF res grant, 63-65; assoc prof, George Washington Univ, 66; USPHS res evaluator, 66-67; vis scholar, Harvard Univ, 69; med technol educ adv, Jewish Hosp, St Louis, 72; comput data bases, US Govt Contracts Pvt Indust, 76- *Mem:* AAAS; NY Acad Sci; Nat Asn Biol Teachers; Am Statist Asn; Sigma Xi. *Res:* Cancer construction data base. *Mailing Add:* 12707 Weiss St Rockville MD 20853

LEACH, CAROLYN S, b Leesville, La, Aug 25, 40; m 69; c 1. ENDOCRINOLOGY, PHYSIOLOGY. *Educ:* Northwestern State Col, La, BS, 62; Baylor Univ, MS, 66, PhD(physiol), 68. *Prof Exp:* Med technologist, Univ Tex M D Anderson Hosp & Tumor Inst, Houston, 62-64, spec med technologist, 64-68; head endocrine & biochem labs, 68-74, chief space metab & biochem br, 74-76, CHIEF BIOMED LABS BR, L B JOHNSON SPACE CTR, NASA, 76- *Concurrent Pos:* Consult, Proj Sea Lab, US Navy, 68-69, Proj Tektite I, US Navy-NASA-Gen Elec-Dept of Interior, 69 & Proj Tektite II, NASA-Dept of Interior, 70; Nat Res Coun-Nat Acad Sci res assoc, Manned Spacecraft Ctr, NASA, 68-70; adj instr physiol, Baylor Col Med, 68-70, adj asst prof, 70-; assoc investr, Inst Environ Med, Sch Med, Univ Pa, 70; mem res staff, Univ Tex Marine Biomed Inst. *Mem:* Aerospace Med Asn; Int Aviation Fedn; Endocrine Soc; Am Physiol Soc; Am Soc Med Technol; Am Soc Clin Path. *Res:* The study of the physiological adaptation of man to changing environments, particularly the endocrine mechanisms involved in adaptation; aerospace medicine. *Mailing Add:* Biomed Labs Br SD4 Med Sci Div NASA L B Johnson Space Ctr Houston TX 77058

LEACH, CHARLES MORLEY, b Sacramento, Calif, Oct 28, 24; m 49; c 3. PLANT PATHOLOGY. *Educ:* Queen's Univ, Ireland, BS, 49, BAgr, 50; Ore State Univ, PhD(plant path), 56. *Prof Exp:* Instr bot, 51-57, from asst plant pathologist to assoc plant pathologist, 57-66, PROF PLANT PATH, ORE STATE UNIV, 66- *Concurrent Pos:* NSF fel, Univ Bristol, 62-63; NZ sr sci fel, 73-74. *Mem:* Am Phytopath Soc; Mycol Soc Am; Brit Mycol Soc; Int Soc Plant Path; Can Plant Path Soc. *Res:* Biology of plant pathogenic fungi, especially reproduction and spore discharge; seed-borne diseases of agricultural crops. *Mailing Add:* Dept of Bot & Plant Path Ore State Univ Corvallis OR 97331

LEACH, EDDIE DILLON, b Clovis, NMex, Aug 12, 36; m 59; c 4. MICROBIOLOGY, TOXICOLOGY. *Educ:* Baylor Univ, BA, 60, MA, 62; Tex A&M Univ, PhD(zool), 65. *Prof Exp:* Asst prof biol, Am Univ, 65-70; assoc prof, 70-77, PROF BIOL, MILLIGAN COL, 77-, CHMN AREA SCI LEARNING, 70- *Concurrent Pos:* Res assoc, R Schattner Found Med Res, Washington, DC; sabbatical leave, vis investr, Georgetown Univ, 79-80. *Mem:* AAAS. *Res:* Effects of x-irradiation on mice testes and the possibility of repairing the damage by administering grafts of unirradiated testicular tissue into the irradiated testes; pursuit of cold sterilizing solution; pine oil disinfectants and toxicity of same; cold sterilizing solution, Sporicidin. *Mailing Add:* Milligan College TN 37682

LEACH, ERNEST BRONSON, b Huchow, China, Dec 21, 24; US citizen; div. MATHEMATICS. *Educ:* Case Inst Technol, BS, 49; Mass Inst Technol, PhD(math), 53. *Prof Exp:* From instr to asst prof, 53-59, ASSOC PROF MATH, CASE WESTERN RESERVE UNIV, 59- *Concurrent Pos:* Partic, Indo-Am Prog, Indian Inst Technol, Kanpur, 63-64; mem staff, Northwestern Univ Proj, Univ Khartoum, 66-67; partic inelec proj, Inst Nat Elec & Electronics, Boumerdes, Algeria, 76-78. *Res:* Algebraic topology; functional analysis. *Mailing Add:* Dept of Math Case Western Reserve Univ Cleveland OH 44106

LEACH, FRANKLIN ROLLIN, b Gorman, Tex, Apr 2, 33; m 56, 70; c 6. BIOCHEMISTRY. *Educ:* Hardin-Simmons Col, BA, 53; Univ Tex, PhD(chem), 57. *Prof Exp:* Res scientist I, Biochem Inst, 53-56; Nat Acad Sci fel med sci, Univ Calif, 57-59; res assoc, 59-60, from asst prof to assoc prof biochem, 60-68, chmn grad fac genetics, 76-78, PROF BIOCHEM, OKLA STATE UNIV, 68- *Concurrent Pos:* Soc Am Bacteriologists pres fel, Univ Ill, 60; NIH res career develop award, 62-72; res fel, Calif Inst Technol, 65-66. *Mem:* AAAS; Am Chem Soc; Am Soc Microbiol; Am Soc Biol Chemists. *Res:* Biochemical genetics of microbial and cell culture cells; transport mechanisms; enzymology; environmental biochemistry. *Mailing Add:* Dept of Biochem Okla State Univ Stillwater OK 74078

LEACH, GLENN JAMES, b Washington, DC, Dec 14, 46; m 68; c 2. TOXICOLOGY, ENDOCRINOLOGY. *Educ:* Univ Md, BS, 68; Univ Del, PhD(biol sci), 78; Am Bd Toxicol, cert, 81. *Prof Exp:* Instr, Dept Physiol, La State Univ Med Ctr, 78-80; physiologist, 80-82, TOXICOLOGIST, US ARMY CHEM SYSTS LAB, 82- *Res:* Elucidating the effects of environmental factors as well as chemicals on endocrine systems regulating intermediary metabolism. *Mailing Add:* 2034 Greylock Ct Bel Air MD 21014

LEACH, JAMES L(INDSAY), b Lawrenceville, Ill, Apr 9, 18; m; c 3. MECHANICAL ENGINEERING. *Educ:* Univ NMex, BS, 42; Univ Ill, MS, 50; Ill State Univ, PhD, 76. *Prof Exp:* Engr, Texas Co, Ill, 40-41, US Ord Res & Gage Dept, Washington, DC, 42, Pac Bridge Co, US Navy Cont Dock & Yards Comb & Control Eng, Southwest Pac, 43; from asst prof to assoc prof, 48-59, PROF MECH ENG, UNIV ILL, URBANA, 59- *Concurrent Pos:* Consult, US Air Force, 50-51, Aluminum Co Am, 52-53, Cater- pillar Tractor Co, 55-56 & Universal Bleacher Co, 56- *Mem:* Foundrymen's Soc; Sigma Xi; Am Soc Mech Engrs; Am Soc Mil Engrs; Am Soc Petrol Engrs. *Res:* Carbon dioxide process for hardening molds and cores for casting metal; shell molding. *Mailing Add:* Foundry Lab Univ of Ill Urbana IL 61801

LEACH, JAMES MOORE, b Littleton, NC, Nov 29, 24; m 53; c 3. ORGANIC CHEMISTRY. *Educ:* High Point Col, BS, 45. *Prof Exp:* Res asst, Morton Chem Co, 45-46, res chemist, 46-49, chief chemist, Morton-Withers Chem Co, 49-58; res chemist, Greensboro Plant, Pfizer Inc, 58-60, mgr appln res, 60-62, mgr prod develop, 62-71; RES DIR, PIEDMONT CHEM INDUSTS, INC, 71- *Concurrent Pos:* Consult, George C. Brown Co, 53-55. *Mem:* Am Chem Soc; Am Asn Textile Chemists & Colorists; Am Asn Qual Control; Am Oil Chemists Soc. *Res:* Antistatic agents for plastics and textiles; vinyl plasticizers and plastics; organic sulphonates; organic esters; textile chemistry; synthetic lubricants. *Mailing Add:* 603 Florham Dr High Point NC 27260

LEACH, JAMES WOODROW, b Bonham, Tex, May 3, 39; m 68; c 1. THERMODYNAMICS, HEAT TRANSFER. *Educ:* Univ Tex, Arlington, BS, 61; Ariz State Univ, MS, 62; Rice Univ, PhD(thermodyn), 67. *Prof Exp:* Eng specialist, Ling-Temco-Vought Aerospace Corp, 67-68; asst prof mech & aerospace eng, Va Polytech Inst & State Univ, 68-77; eng specialist, Vought Systs Div, LTV Aerospace Corp, 77-80. *Mem:* Am Soc Eng Educ; Am Soc Mech Engrs. *Res:* Statistical thermodynamics; numerical analysis; boundary layer stability analysis. *Mailing Add:* 1112 Greencove Richardson TX 75081

LEACH, JOHN KLINE, b Buffalo, NY, July 11, 22; m 45; c 5. CARDIOLOGY, PHYSIOLOGY. *Educ:* Baldwin-Wallace Col, BS, 43; Albany Med Col, MD, 47; Am Bd Internal Med, dipl, 68; Am Bd Cardiovasc Dis, dipl, 69. *Prof Exp:* Instr med, Albany Med Col, 55-62, asst prof physiol, 62-63; assoc chief staff res, Vet Admin Ctr, Wadsworth, Kans, 63-64; from asst prof to assoc prof med, 66-76, asst prof physiol, 72-76, PROF MED & PHYSIOL, MED SCH, UNIV NMEX, 76- *Concurrent Pos:* Clin asst & asst attend, Albany Hosp, 55-62; NIH res fel physiol, Albany Med Col, 61-63, res grant cardiol, Univ NMex, 69-72; lectr, Med Ctr, Univ Kans, 63-64; chief cardiol sect, Vet Admin Hosp, Albuquerque, 66-72 & 77-, assoc chief staff res, 69-73; attend med, Bernalillo County Med Ctr, Albuquerque, NMex, 66-; consult med, Bataan Hosp, Albuquerque, 69-; consult med & cardiol, St Joseph Hosp, Albuquerque, 69-; consult cardiol, Presby Hosp, Albuquerque, 69-; vis assoc prof, Med Ctr, Univ Calif, Los Angeles, 71-72. *Mem:* Fel Am Col Cardiol; Am Fedn Clin Res; Am Heart Asn; fel Am Col Physicians; Am Physiol Soc. *Res:* Cardiovascular research; cardiac muscle mechanics and hemodynamics. *Mailing Add:* Cardiol Sect Vet Admin Hosp Albuquerque NM 87108

LEACH, LEONARD JOSEPH, b Rochester, NY, Aug 3, 24; m 53; c 3. TOXICOLOGY, ENVIRONMENTAL HEALTH. *Educ:* Brigham Young Univ, BS, 49. *Prof Exp:* Phys chemist, Army Chem Ctr, Md, 51-52; assoc indust hyg, Atomic Energy Proj, 52-55, unit chief toxicol, 55-57, instr indust hyg, 57-65, ASST PROF RADIATION BIOL & BIOPHYS, SCH MED & DENT, UNIV ROCHESTER, 65- *Concurrent Pos:* Speaker, Gordon Res Conf Toxicol & Safety Eval, NH, 60. *Mem:* Am Soc Toxicol; Am Acad Indust Hyg; Pan-Am Med Asn; Am Indust Hyg Asn; NY Acad Sci. *Res:* Inhalation toxicity of airborne agents related to air pollution and all aspects of environmental health. *Mailing Add:* Dept Radiation Biol & Biophys Sch Med Dent Univ of Rochester Rochester NY 14642

LEACH, ROBERT ELLIS, b Sanford, Maine, Nov 25, 31; m 55; c 6. MEDICINE, ORTHOPEDIC SURGERY. *Educ:* Princeton Univ, BA, 53; Columbia Univ, MD, 57. *Prof Exp:* Chmn orthop, Lahey Clin Found, 67-70; PROF ORTHOP SURG, MED SCH, BOSTON UNIV, 70- *Concurrent Pos:* Dir orthop serv, Boston City Hosp, 70-72; lectr, Tufts Univ, 70-; Am, Brit & Can traveling fel, 71. *Mem:* Am Orthop Asn; Am Orthop Soc Sports Med; Am Acad Orthop Surgeons. *Res:* Joint transplantation. *Mailing Add:* Dept of Orthop Surg Boston Univ Hosp Boston MA 02118

LEACH, ROLAND MELVILLE, JR, b Framingham, Mass, Aug 27, 32; m 54; c 3. ANIMAL NUTRITION. *Educ:* Univ Maine, BS, 54; Purdue Univ, MS, 56; Cornell Univ, PhD(nutrit), 60. *Prof Exp:* Asst prof animal nutrit, Cornell Univ, 60-68, chemist, Plant Soil & Nutrit Lab, USDA, 59-68; assoc prof poultry sci, 68-73, PROF POULTRY SCI, PA STATE UNIV,

UNIVERSITY PARK, 73- *Mem:* Poultry Sci Asn; Am Inst Nutrit. *Res:* Mineral nutrition of animals; role of trace elements in bone formation. *Mailing Add:* 205 Animal Industs Bldg Pa State Univ University Park PA 16802

LEACH, WILLIAM MATTHEW, b Pine Mountain, Ky, June 26, 33; m 60; c 3. CELL BIOLOGY, RADIOBIOLOGY. *Educ:* Berea Col, BA, 56; Univ Tenn, MS, 62, PhD(zool), 65. *Prof Exp:* USAEC res assoc zool & entom, Inst Radiation Biol, Univ Tenn, 64-66; res biologist, Radiation Bio-effects Prog, Nat Ctr Radiol Health, 66-67, chief radiation cytol lab, Div Biol Effects, Bur Radiol Health, 67-71, CHIEF EXP STUDIES BR, BUR RADIOL HEALTH, FOOD & DRUG ADMIN, USPHS, 71- *Concurrent Pos:* Adj prof genetics, George Washington Univ, 72- *Mem:* AAAS; Am Inst Biol Sci; Am Soc Cell Biol; Am Genetic Asn. *Res:* Cell responses to radiation in relation to the cell cycle; cell synthetic activities during the cell cycle; behavior of particulates and molecules in cells; developmental biology; microwave radiation research. *Mailing Add:* USPHS Bur of Radiol Health 5600 Fishers Lane Rockville MD 20857

LEACHMAN, ROBERT BRIGGS, b Lakewood, Ohio, June 11, 21; m 45; c 3. NUCLEAR PHYSICS. *Educ:* Case Inst Technol, BS, 42; Iowa State Univ, PhD(physics), 50. *Prof Exp:* Staff mem, Radiation Lab, Mass Inst Technol, 43-46; staff mem, Los Alamos Sci Lab, Univ Calif, 50-67, leader cyclotron group, 57-67; dir nuclear sci labs, Kans State Univ, 67-72, head dept physics, 67-71; asst dep dir, Defense Nuclear Agency, US Dept Defense, 72-74; spec asst, Nuclear Regulatory Comn, 74-78; mem staff waste mgt study, Off Technol Assessment, US Congress, 78-79; mem staff sci & technol comt, US House Rep, 79-81; NUCLEAR ENGR, NUCLEAR & CHEM DIRECTORATE, US ARMY HQ, 82- *Concurrent Pos:* Guggenheim fel, Nobel Inst, Sweden, 55-56; Fulbright fel, Inst Theoret Physics, Denmark, 62-63. *Mem:* Fel Am Phys Soc; fel AAAS. *Res:* Nuclear fission; nuclear materials safeguards. *Mailing Add:* Nuclear & Chem Dir HQ US Army Washington DC 20310

LEACOCK, ROBERT A, b Detroit, Mich, Oct 3, 35; m 61; c 3. THEORETICAL PHYSICS, HIGH ENERGY PHYSICS. *Educ:* Univ Mich, BS, 57, MS, 60, PhD(physics), 63. *Prof Exp:* Instr physics, Univ Mich, 63-64; Am-Swiss Found Sci Exchange fel theoret physics, Europ Orgn Nuclear Res, 64-65; assoc physics, 65-67, asst prof, 67-71, ASSOC PROF PHYSICS, IOWA STATE UNIV & PHYSICIST, AMES LAB, 71- *Concurrent Pos:* Corning Glass Works Found fel, 62-63. *Mem:* Am Phys Soc. *Res:* Theoretical high energy physics. *Mailing Add:* Dept of Physics Iowa State Univ Ames IA 50011

LEACOCK, ROBERT JAY, b New York, NY, Mar 1, 39; m 64; c 2. ASTRONOMY. *Educ:* Univ Fla, BS, 60, MS, 62, PhD(astron), 71. *Prof Exp:* Instr physics, Pensacola Jr Col, 62-63; res asst astron, 63-71, asst prof, 71-76, ASSOC PROF PHYS SCI & ASTRON, UNIV FLA, 76-, ASSOC CHMN, 80- *Mem:* AAAS; Am Astron Soc. *Res:* Nonthermal radio observations of the major planets; optical variations of extragalactic radio sources. *Mailing Add:* 458 Winston W Little Hall Univ of Fla Dept of Phys Sci Gainesville FL 32611

LEADABRAND, RAY LAURENCE, b Pasadena, Calif, Oct 12, 27; m 55; c 1. ELECTRONIC ENGINEERING. *Educ:* San Jose State Col, BS, 50; Stanford Univ, MS, 53. *Prof Exp:* Field engr, Philco Corp, 50-52; asst, Stanford Univ, 52-55, res engr, 55-58, head propagation group, 59-60, mgr radio physics lab, 60-68, EXEC DIR, ELECTRONICS & RADIO SCI DIV, SRI INT, 68-, SR VPRES, 80- *Mem:* AAAS; Inst Elec & Electronics Engrs; Am Geophys Union; Int Union Radio Sci; Sigma Xi. *Res:* Ionospheric radio propagation; auroral radar; moon and satellite reflection and transmission; propagation studies related to nuclear explosions and missile flight; radio and radar astronomy research of solar systems. *Mailing Add:* Electronics & Radio Sci Div 333 Ravenswood Ave Menlo Park CA 94025

LEADBETTER, EDWARD RENTON, b Barnesboro, Pa, Jan 26, 34; m 56; c 4. MICROBIOLOGY. *Educ:* Franklin & Marshall Col, BS, 55; Univ Tex, PhD(bact), 59. *Hon Degrees:* MA, Amherst Col, 70. *Prof Exp:* Instr, Amherst Col, 59-61, from asst prof to assoc prof, 61-70, chmn dept, 67-71, prof biol, 70-78; exec officer, 78-80, PROF BIOL SCI GROUP, UNIV CONN, 78-, HEAD DEPT, 80- *Concurrent Pos:* NSF fel, Hopkins Marine Sta, Pacific Grove, Calif, 62-63; NIH spec fel, Univ Mass, 66-67; vis prof, Hampshire Col, 71; instr, Marine Biol Lab, Woods Hole, 71-78, mem corp, 71-; NATO sr fel, Univ Seville, 72. *Mem:* AAAS; Am Soc Microbiol; Soc Develop Biol; Brit Soc Gen Microbiol. *Res:* Microbial ecology, physiology, and biochemistry; amine metabolism; photosynthesis; myxobacteria; oral microbiology; hydrocarbon oxidation; ultrastructure. *Mailing Add:* Biol Sci Group Univ of Conn Storrs CT 06250

LEADER, GORDON ROBERT, b Milwaukee, Wis, Jan 27, 16; m 46; c 4. PHYSICAL CHEMISTRY. *Educ:* Univ Wis, BS, 37; Univ Minn, PhD(phys chem), 40. *Prof Exp:* Res chemist, Monsanto Chem Co, Mo, 40-42, Nat Defense Res Comt, Northwestern Univ, 42-43 & Manhattan Dist Proj, Univ Chicago, 43-47; asst prof chem, Univ Ky, 47-51; res chemist, Mallinckrodt Chem Works, Mo, 51-53 & Olin Mathieson Chem Corp, 53-58; sr res chemist, Thiokol Chem Corp, 58-64; SR RES CHEMIST, PENNWALT CORP, 64- *Mem:* Am Chem Soc. *Res:* Chemical process development; Raman and nuclear magnetic resonance spectroscopy; radiochemistry; conductance and dielectric constants of organic solutions. *Mailing Add:* 1661 Weedon Rd Wayne PA 19087

LEADER, JOHN CARL, b St Louis, Mo, Oct 25, 38. STATISTICAL OPTICS, COHERENCE THEORY. *Educ:* Rensselaer Polytech Inst, BS, 60, PhD(nuclear physics), 69. *Prof Exp:* Sr engr, McDonnel Aircraft Reconnaissance Lab, 69-74, sr scientist, 74-81, CHIEF SCIENTIST RADIATION SCI, MCDONNELL DOUGLAS RES LABS, MCDONNELL DOUGLAS CORP, 81- *Mem:* Optical Soc Am; Soc Photo-Optical Instrumentation Engrs; Union Radio Sci Int. *Res:* Theoretical research on radiation scattering from rough surfaces; optical propagation through atmospheric turbulence; partial coherence theory; laser radar; charged particle beam propagation. *Mailing Add:* McDonnell Douglas Res Labs Box 516 St Louis MO 63166

LEADER, ROBERT WARDELL, b Tacoma, Wash, Jan 16, 19; m 40, 69; c 3. COMPARATIVE PATHOLOGY. *Educ:* Wash State Univ, BS & DVM, 52, MS, 55. *Hon Degrees:* DMedSci, Univ Toledo, 76. *Prof Exp:* Instr vet path, Wash State Univ, 52-55; USPHS fel, Univ Calif, 55-56; asst prof vet path, Wash State Univ, 56-60; assoc prof, Rockefeller Univ, 65-71; prof animal path, Univ Conn, 71-75; PROF PATH & CHMN DEPT, MICH STATE UNIV, 75- *Concurrent Pos:* Mem path training comt, NIH, 66-71, mem virol study sect, 71-; mem bd div, Mark Morris Found, 71- *Mem:* Am Vet Med Asn; Am Soc Exp Path; Am Col Vet Path; NY Acad Sci; Int Acad Path. *Res:* Studies of model diseases in animals with objective of elucidating pathogenetic mechanisms of similar diseases in man; chronic degenerative and connective tissue diseases. *Mailing Add:* Dept of Path Mich State Univ East Lansing MI 48824

LEADER, SOLOMON, b Spring Lake, NJ, Nov 14, 25. MATHEMATICS. *Educ:* Rutgers Univ, BS, 49; Princeton Univ, MA, 51, PhD(math), 52. *Prof Exp:* From instr to assoc prof, 52-61, PROF MATH, RUTGERS UNIV, NEW BRUNSWICK, 61- *Mem:* Am Math Soc; Math Asn Am. *Res:* Functional analysis; general topology. *Mailing Add:* Dept of Math Rutgers Univ New Brunswick NJ 08903

LEADERS, FLOYD EDWIN, JR, b Denison, Iowa, Dec 11, 31; m 75; c 1. PHARMACOLOGY, RESEARCH ADMINISTRATION. *Educ:* Drake Univ, BS, 55; Univ Iowa, MS, 60, PhD(pharmacol), 62. *Prof Exp:* From instr to asst prof pharmacol, Med Ctr, Univ Kans, 62-67; head pharmacol res, Alcon Labs, Tex, 67-72; dir res serv, Plough, Inc, Tenn, 72-73; dir res & develop labs, Pharmaceut Div, Pennwalt Corp, NY, 73-78; PRES, TECH EVAL & MGT SYSTS INC, 78- *Concurrent Pos:* NIH res grant, 62-67; consult, Midwest Res Inst, 65-67; adj asst prof, Univ Tex Southwestern Med Sch; adj prof, Purdue Univ. *Mem:* AAAS; Am Soc Pharmacol & Exp Therapeut; Soc Exp Biol & Med; Asn Res Vision & Opthal; NY Acad Sci. *Res:* Managing all aspects of pharmaceutical drug research and development, both ethical and proprietary, including data management, regulatory compliance and regulatory submissions; drug-vehicle systems; physiology and pharmacology of the eye, cardiovascular system and autonomic nervous systems; use of computers in biomedical data management. *Mailing Add:* Tech Eval & Mgt Systs Inc 13601 Preston Rd 820 CTW Dallas TX 75240

LEADLEY, JOHN DAVID, mathematics, see previous edition

LEADON, BERNARD M(ATHEW), b Farmington, Minn, Nov 29, 17; m 46; c 10. FLUID MECHANICS. *Educ:* Col St Thomas, BS, 38; Univ Minn, MS, 42, PhD(fluid mech), 55. *Prof Exp:* Engr, Pac Gas & Elec Co, Calif, 41; asst aerodyn, Univ Minn, 42, instr, 42-43; aerodynamicist, Curtiss-Wright Corp, NY, 43-44, sr aerodynamicist, 44-45; head propulsion exp sect, Cornell Aeronaut Lab, 45-46; chief aerodynamicist, Rosemount Aeronaut Lab, 46-48, scientist, 48-57; sr staff scientist, Gen Off, Gen Dynamics|Convair, 57-64; PROF ENG SCI, UNIV FLA, 64- *Concurrent Pos:* Instr, Univ Buffalo, 44-45; lectr, Univ Minn, 46-57; consult, Minneapolis-Honeywell Regulator Corp, 56-57, Gen Dynamics/Convair, 64-65, US Air Force, 66, AMF Beaird, 69, Martinez & Costa & Assocs, 71 & 78 & Pratt & Whitney Aircraft Corp, 74 & 76-; vis prof, San Diego State Col, 62-64; NATO fel, 72; chmn, Third US Nat Conf Wind Eng, 78. *Mem:* Am Phys Soc; Am Inst Aeronaut & Astronaut; Sigma Xi. *Res:* Heat transfer; gas dynamics; wind engineering. *Mailing Add:* 412 NE 13th Ave Gainesville FL 32601

LEAF, ALBERT LAZARUS, b Seattle, Wash, May 16, 28; m 52; c 3. FOREST SOILS. *Educ:* Univ Wash, BSF, 50, MF, 52; Univ Wis, PhD(soils), 57. *Prof Exp:* Jr res forester, Univ Wash, 51-52; asst soils, Univ Wis, 52-57; from instr to assoc prof silvicult, 57-65, chmn forest resources coun, Sch Environ & Resources Mgt, 72-73, PROF FOREST SOIL SCI, STATE UNIV NY COL ENVIRON SCI & FORESTRY, 65-, PROJ LEADER, 68-, FAC EXCHANGE SCHOLAR, 74- *Concurrent Pos:* Forestry vchmn, Nat Joint Comt on Fertilizer Appln, 58-60; forestry chmn, Am Coun Fertilizer Appln, 60-62; Japan Soc Prom Sci vis prof, Tokyo Univ Agr & Technol, 72-73; co-chmn work group folair anal, Int Union Forestry Res Orgn. *Mem:* Fel AAAS; Soc Am Foresters; Soil Sci Soc Am; Am Soc Agron; NY Acad Sci. *Res:* Tree nutrition; soil and foliar diagnosis of nutrient deficiencies and response to cultural treatments; forest fertilization and soil chemistry; nursery soil management. *Mailing Add:* Col Environ Sci & Forestry State Univ NY 124 Haddonfield Dr Syracuse NY 13214

LEAF, ALEXANDER, b Yokohama, Japan, Apr 10, 20; nat US; m 43; c 3. INTERNAL MEDICINE. *Educ:* Univ Wash, BS, 40; Univ Mich, MD, 43. *Hon Degrees:* AM, Harvard Univ, 61. *Prof Exp:* Instr med, Univ Mich, 47-49; assoc, 53-56, from asst prof to assoc prof, 56-65, JACKSON PROF CLIN MED, HARVARD MED SCH, 66-, PROF MED, RIDLEY WATTS PROF PREV MED & CHMN, DEPT PREV MED & CLIN EPIDEMIOL, 80- *Concurrent Pos:* From asst physician to assoc physician, Mass Gen Hosp, 53-62, physician, 62-, chief med serv, 66-81; John Simon Guggenheim Mem Found fel, Balliol Col, Oxford Univ, 71-72. *Mem:* Inst Med-Nat Acad Sci; Am Soc Clin Invest; Am Physiol Soc; Asn Am Physicians; Am Acad Arts & Sci. *Res:* Ion transport and membrane physiology; kidney physiology. *Mailing Add:* Mass Gen Hosp Boston MA 02114

LEAF, BORIS, b Yokohama, Japan, Mar 4, 19; nat US; m 47; c 3. STATISTICAL MECHANICS. *Educ:* Univ Wash, BS, 39; Univ Ill, PhD(phys chem), 42. *Prof Exp:* Spec asst chem, Univ Ill, 42-43, instr phys chem, 43-44; assoc chemist, Metall Lab, Univ Chicago, 44-45; Jewett fel, Yale Univ, 45-46; assoc prof physics, Kans State Univ, 46-54, prof, 54-65; PROF PHYSICS & CHMN DEPT, STATE UNIV NY COL CORTLAND, 65- *Concurrent Pos:* Spec asst, Nat Defense Res Comt, Univ Ill, 45; res fel, Brussels, 58-60; prof, State Univ NY Binghamton, 67-71; fac fel & grants-in-aid, Res Found, State Univ NY, 70-72, scholar exchange prof, 74-; vis prof, Cornell Univ, 73-74; assoc ed, Am J Physics, 76-79; partic, State Univ NY-Moscow State Univ fac exchange, USSR, 81. *Mem:* Fel AAAS; fel Am Phys Soc; Am Asn Physics Teachers; NY Acad Sci. *Res:* Thermodynamic theory; transport processes; quantum theory. *Mailing Add:* Dept of Physics State Univ of NY Col Cortland NY 13045

LEAHY, RICHARD GORDON, b Buffalo, NY, Mar 6, 29; m 53; c 3. GEOCHEMISTRY. *Educ:* Yale Univ, BS, 52; Harvard Univ, AM, 54, PhD(geol), 57. *Prof Exp:* Asst geochem, Yale Univ, 52-53; asst to dir & res assoc geol, Woods Hole Oceanog Inst, 56-60; dir labs, Div Eng & Appl Physics, 60-68, asst to pres civic & govt rels, 70-71, ASSOC DEAN FAC ARTS & SCI, HARVARD UNIV, 68- *Concurrent Pos:* Mem US tech panel geochem, Int Geophys Year, 57-58. *Mem:* AAAS; Am Geophys Union; NY Acad Sci. *Res:* Geochemistry of heavy isotopes in sea water and marine sediments; chemical processes of submarine weathering; variation of carbon dioxide in the atmosphere and its relation to air mass properties. *Mailing Add:* Univ Hall 20 Harvard Univ Cambridge MA 02138

LEAHY, SISTER MARY GERALD, b San Francisco, Calif, Oct 11, 17. INSECT PHYSIOLOGY, ACAROLOGY. *Educ:* Univ Southern Calif, BA, 45; Cath Univ Am, MA, 47; Univ Notre Dame, PhD(biol), 62. *Prof Exp:* From asst prof to assoc prof, 47-70, chmn dept, 62-65, PROF BIOL, MT ST MARY'S COL, CALIF, 70- *Concurrent Pos:* NSF res grants, 62-64, 65-67 & 70-71; fel trop pub health, Harvard Univ, 66; WHO grant, Israel Inst Biol Res, Ness Ziona & Hebrew Univ Jerusalem, 68-69; sr res scientist, Nairobi, Kenya, 73-74; collab scientist, EAfrican Vet Res Orgn, Kenya, 73-74; prin investr, NIH grant, 74-77; vis scientist, Ga Southern Col, 74-75; exchange scientist tick pheromones & hormones, Poland, Czech & Russia, Nat Acad Sci. *Mem:* AAAS; Entom Soc Am; Am Inst Biol Sci. *Res:* Mosquitoes and ticks; pheromones and reproductive physiology. *Mailing Add:* Dept of Biol Mt St Mary's Col Los Angeles CA 90049

LEAK, JOHN CLAY, JR, b Washington, DC, Aug 31, 28; m 54; c 3. ORGANIC CHEMISTRY, RADIO PHARMACEUTICALS. *Educ:* Univ Vt, BS, 49; Univ Ill, PhD(chem), 54. *Prof Exp:* Asst, Univ Ill, 51-54, res assoc animal nutrit, 55-56; Fulbright scholar, Ger, 54-55; chemist, Isotopes Specialties Co, 56-59, dir carbon-14 dept, 59-60; res dir, Cyclo Chem Corp, 60-61; tech dir, ChemTrac Corp, 61-62, vpres, 62-65, oper mgr, Baird-Atomic, Inc, Mass, 62-65; mgr chem dept, Tracerlab, 65-67, sr staff chemist, 67-69; sr staff chemist, ICN Pharmaceut, Inc, 69-75, mgr prod opers, Life Group, 75-76; res chemist, 76-79, RES CHEMIST, FOOD & DRUG ADMIN, 79- *Res:* Mechanism of organic reactions; metabolic fate of labeled hydroxy-proline in rats; synthesis of labeled compounds; applications for stable and radioactive isotopes; manufacture and control of radiopharmaceuticals. *Mailing Add:* 1439 Chesapeake Ave Rte 7 Annapolis MD 21403

LEAK, LEE VIRN, b Chesterfield, SC, July 22, 32; m 64; c 2. CELL BIOLOGY, ELECTRON MICROSCOPY. *Educ:* SC State Col, BS, 54; Mich State Univ, MS, 59, PhD(cell biol), 62. *Prof Exp:* Asst prof biol sci, Mich State Univ, 62; res fel electron micros, Mass Gen Hosp & Harvard Med Sch, 62-64; asst surg, Mass Gen Hosp, 64-65; asst biol, Harvard Med Sch, 65-68, from instr to asst prof anat, 67-71; chmn dept, 71-81, PROF ANAT, COL MED, HOWARD UNIV, 71-, PROF, GRAD SCH ART & SCI, 76- *Concurrent Pos:* USPHS res grant, 66-; consult, Shriners Burns Res Inst, 67-71; mem, Anat Sci Training Comt, 72-73; Am Heart Asn res grant, 67-70; mem, Div Biol & Agr, Nat Res Coun, 72-75; ed staff, Anat Rec; mem, Nat Bd Med Examr, 73-76; mem, Marine Biol Lab Corp, 73-; mem, Div Cancer Biol, Diag Bd, Nat Cancer Inst, 79; mem panel basic biomed sci, Nat Res Coun, 80. *Mem:* Am Asn Anat; Am Soc Cell Biol; Am Soc Zool; Genetics Soc Am; Sigma Xi. *Res:* Biology of the lymphatic vascular system and its role during the inflammatory response; pulmonary lymphatic drainage; ontogeny of the lymphatic system. *Mailing Add:* Dept of Anat Howard Univ Col of Med Washington DC 20001

LEAKE, LEWIS A(LBERT), b Denver, Colo, May 20, 25; m 45; c 7. OPERATIONS RESEARCH. *Educ:* Purdue Univ, BS, 47, MS, 47; Mass Inst Technol, SM, 58. *Prof Exp:* Jr engr propulsion develop unit, Boeing Airplane Co, Wash, 47-48; instr mech eng, Univ Utah, 48-49; from aeronaut engr to dir opers res group, Pac Missile Range, 49-64; mem tech staff, Res Anal Corp, 64-72; Scientist, McLean, 72-78, SCIENTIST, SCI APPLICATIONS, ENGLEWOOD, 78- *Mem:* Opers Res Soc Am; Sigma Xi. *Res:* Analysis of tactical communications systems; computer assisted simulations of combat; safety, scheduling analyses for missile range; test and evaluation of missile-weapon systems; military systems analysis. *Mailing Add:* 12588 Pine Cone Rd Parker CO 80134

LEAKE, LOWELL, JR, b Denver, Colo, May 25, 28; m 59; c 2. MATHEMATICS. *Educ:* Tufts Col, AB, 50; Univ Wis, MS, 56, PhD(math, educ), 62. *Prof Exp:* Traffic chief, Northwestern Bell Tel Co, 50-54; high sch teacher, Ill, 56-58; from instr to assoc prof math, 60-74, PROF MATH, UNIV CINCINNATI, 74- *Mem:* Math Asn Am; Nat Coun Teachers Math; Asn Teachers Math (Eng). *Res:* Training of secondary and elementary mathematics teachers at undergraduate and graduate levels; learning of mathematics; piaget and probability; microcomputers in education. *Mailing Add:* Dept of Math Univ of Cincinnati Cincinnati OH 45221

LEAKE, PRESTON HILDEBRAND, b Proffit, Va, Aug 8, 29; m 54; c 2. ORGANIC CHEMISTRY. *Educ:* Univ Va, BS, 50; Duke Univ, MA, 53, PhD(chem), 54. *Prof Exp:* Res supvr org chem, Nitrogen Div, Allied Chem Corp, 54-60; asst res dir, Albemarle Paper Mfg Co, 60-65; asst to managing dir, Res & Develop Dept, 65-68, asst managing dir, 68-70, ASST DIR RES & DEVELOP DEPT, AM TOBACCO CO, 70- *Concurrent Pos:* Adj prof, Richmond Prof Inst, 63-64. *Mem:* Am Chem Soc; Am Inst Chemists; Tech Asn Pulp & Paper Indust. *Res:* Polycyclic aromatic chemistry: Psychorr synthesis; amino acids and cyanuric acid derivatives; polyethylene; sizing; silica fume; specialty and filter papers; tobacco. *Mailing Add:* Am Tobacco Co R&D Dept PO Box 899 Hopewell VA 23860

LEAKE, WILLIAM WALTER, b Johnstown, Pa, Apr 24, 26; m 57; c 2. ORGANIC CHEMISTRY. *Educ:* Duquesne Univ, BS, 51; Duke Univ, MA, 53; Univ Pittsburgh, PhD(chem), 58. *Prof Exp:* Res chemist, Monsanto Chem Co, 57-60; from asst prof to assoc prof chem, 61-77, assoc dean, 68-80, DEAN ACAD ADMIN, MIL ADV & VET REP & DIR PROGS, WASHINGTON & JEFFERSON COL, 80- *Mem:* Am Chem Soc. *Res:* Instrumental methods of analysis. *Mailing Add:* Dept of Chem Washington & Jefferson Col Washington PA 15301

LEAL, JOSEPH ROGERS, b New Bedford, Mass, Sept 14, 18; m 44; c 4. ORGANIC CHEMISTRY. *Educ:* Univ Mass, BS, 49; Ind Univ, PhD(chem), 53. *Prof Exp:* Res asst, Corn Prod Refining Co, 40-42; asst chemist, Revere Copper & Brass Co, 42-43 & 45-46; res chemist, Am Cyanamid Co, 52-57, tech rep govt res liaison, Washington, DC, 57-63, mgr contract rels, 63-67; SR STAFF ASSOC, CELANESE RES CO, 67- *Mem:* AAAS; Am Chem Soc; NY Acad Sci; Am Inst Chemists. *Res:* High temperature resistant aromatic and heterocyclic polymers; nonflammable fibers; high strength, high modulus reinforcement materials. *Mailing Add:* 10 S Crescent Maplewood NJ 07040

LEAL, LESLIE GARY, b Bellingham, Wash, Mar 18, 43; m 65; c 3. CHEMICAL ENGINEERING. *Educ:* Univ Wash, BS, 65; Stanford Univ, MS, 67, PhD(chem eng), 69. *Prof Exp:* Nat Sci Found fel, Cambridge Univ, 69-70; from asst prof to assoc prof, 70-77, PROF CHEM ENG, CALIF INST TECHNOL, 77- *Concurrent Pos:* Petrol Res Fund grant, Calif Inst Technol, 70-; Guggenheim fel & vis scholar, Trinity Col, Univ Cambridge, Eng, 76-77. *Honors & Awards:* Camille & Henry Dreyfus Found Teacher-Scholar Award, 75; Tech Achievement Award, Am Inst Chem Engrs, 78 & Allan Colburn Award, 78. *Mem:* Am Inst Chem Engrs; Soc Rheol; Am Inst Physics; Brit Soc Rheol. *Res:* Fluid mechanics; suspension mechanics; rheology and polymaric liquids; transport phenomena. *Mailing Add:* Dept Chem Eng Calif Inst Technol Pasadena CA 91125

LEAMAN, WILBUR KAUFFMAN, b Neffsville, Pa, Feb 17, 21; m 42; c 1. PETROLEUM CHEMISTRY. *Educ:* Franklin & Marshall Col, BS, 47. *Prof Exp:* Res chemist, Res Labs, Mobil Oil Corp, 47-51, sr res chemist, 51-67, staff asst to mgr process res & develop sect, 67-75, adv budgets & admin, 75-79, res & develop, 80, ADMIN MGR, PROCESS RES & TECH SERV DIV, MOBIL RES & DEVELOP CORP, 81- *Mem:* Am Chem Soc; Int Cong Catalysis. *Res:* Catalysis. *Mailing Add:* Process Res & Tech Serv Div Mobil Res & Develop Corp Paulsboro NJ 08066

LEAMER, ROSS WILSON, b Ellendale, NDak, Apr 23, 15; m 44; c 1. SOIL SCIENCE. *Educ:* NDak Agr Col, BS, 37; NC State Col, MS, 39; Ohio State Univ, PhD(soils), 42. *Prof Exp:* Tech agr rep, US Rubber Co, NY, 44-45; soil physicist, Irrig Exp Sta, Bur Plant Indust, Soils & Agr Eng, USDA, 45-53, soil scientist, Western Soil & Water Mgt Res Br, Soil & Water Conserv Res Div, Agr Res Serv, 53-65, soil scientist, Southern Plains Br, 65-73, soil scientist, Souther Region Subtrop Tex Area, Agr Res Serv, 73-80; RETIRED. *Mem:* Soil Sci Soc Am; Am Soc Agron; Am Soc Photogram; AAAS. *Res:* Remote sensing; automated identification of soil and surface cover from aircraft and satellite signals. *Mailing Add:* 1110 D Valley View Dr Weslaco TX 78596

LEAMY, HARRY JOHN, b Alton, Ill, Nov 15, 40. PHYSICAL METALLURGY, PHYSICS. *Educ:* Univ Mo-Rolla, BS, 63; Iowa State Univ, PhD(metall), 67. *Prof Exp:* Res fel metall, Max Planck Inst Metall Res, 67-69; mem tech staff, Mat Physics Res Group, 69-77, MEM TECH STAFF, ELECTRONIC MAT RES DEPT, BELL LABS, 77- *Concurrent Pos:* Vis scientist, Philips Res Labs, Eindhoven, The Neth, 76-77. *Mem:* Am Soc Metals; Am Inst Mining, Metall & Petrol Eng; Am Asn Crystal Growth; Am Phys Soc; Electron Micros Soc Am. *Res:* Alloy properties and crystal growth; electron microscopy of crystal lattice defects; magnetic materials; metallic glasses; semiconductor defects; laser beam processing of semiconductor materials. *Mailing Add:* Bell Labs Murray Hill NJ 07974

LEAMY, LARRY JACKSON, b Alton, Ill, Nov 15, 40; m 65; c 2. QUANTITATIVE GENETICS. *Educ:* Eastern Ill Univ, BS, 62; Univ Ill, Urbana, MS, 65, PhD(zool), 67. *Prof Exp:* Asst prof, 67-71, assoc prof, 71-76, PROF BIOL, CALIF STATE UNIV, LONG BEACH, 76-, CHMN DEPT, 78- *Concurrent Pos:* Calif State Univ Found new fac grant, Calif State Univ, Long Beach, 67-68, fac grant-in-aid, 69-70, 73, 78, 79-80, 80-81; NSF grant, 81-82; vis prof entomol/genetics, Univ Wis-Madison. *Mem:* Genetics Soc Am; Am Genetic Asn; Soc Study Evolution; Behavior Genetics Soc; Soc Syst Zool. *Res:* Quantitative genetics of mice. *Mailing Add:* Dept Biol Calif State Univ Long Beach CA 90840

LEAN, DAVID ROBERT SAMUEL, b Peterborough, Ont, Oct 18, 37; div; c 3. BIOLOGY, CHEMISTRY. *Educ:* Univ Toronto, BASc, 62, PhD(zool), 73. *Prof Exp:* Engr chem, Union Carbide Corp, 63-67; lectr ecol, Univ Toronto, 71-73; RES SCIENTIST BIOL & LIMNOL, CAN DEPT ENVIRON, 72- *Mem:* Am Soc Limnol & Oceanog; Int Asn Theoret & Appl Limnol; Soc Prof Engrs. *Res:* Interrelationships of carbon, nitrogen, phosphorous and iron on algae growth and decomposition in lakes. *Mailing Add:* Nat Water Res Inst Box 5050 Burlington ON L7R 4A6 Can

LEAN, ERIC GUNG-HWA, b Fukien, China, Jan 1, 38; m 65; c 1. ACOUSTICS, OPTICS. *Educ:* Cheng Kung Univ, Taiwan, BS, 59; Univ Wash, MS, 63; Stanford Univ, PhD(elec eng), 67. *Prof Exp:* Res asst elec eng, Univ Wash, 61-63; res asst microwave acoust, Hanson Lab Physics, Stanford Univ, 63-67, res assoc microwave acoust & laser, 67; mem res staff nonlinear optics, T J Watson Res Ctr, 67-69, mgr acoust & optical physics, 69-71, mgr, Optical Solid State Technol, 71-79, mgr, Printer Technol, 79-81, MGR, OUTPUT DEVICE TECHNOL, T J WATSON RES CTR, IBM CORP, 81- *Mem:* Inst Elec & Electronic Engrs; Sigma Xi; Optical Soc Am. *Res:* Microwave acoustic waves in solids; nonlinear optics; optical signal processing devices; surface wave devices; laser applications; integrated optics; fiber optics; printers. *Mailing Add:* IBM Corp Watson Res Ctr PO Box 218 Yorktown Heights NY 10598

LEANDER, JOHN DAVID, b Mt Vernon, Wash, Apr 8, 44; m 65; c 3. PSYCHOPHARMACOLOGY. *Educ:* Pac Lutheran Univ, BA, 66; Western Wash State Col, MA, 67; Univ Fla, PhD(psychol), 71. *Prof Exp:* Fel neurobiol prog, Univ NC Chapel Hill 71-73, instr pharmacol, 73-74, asst prof, 74-78, assoc prof pharmacol, 78-81; RES SCIENTIST, LILLY RES LAB, ELI LILLY & CO, 81- *Mem:* AAAS; Am Psychol Asn; Behavioral Pharmacol Soc; Am Soc Pharmacol & Exp Therapeut. *Res:* Behavioral pharmacology; effects of drugs on behavior and the interaction of drugs with ongoing behavior. *Mailing Add:* Cent Nerv Syst Pharmacol Lilly Res Lab Eli Lilly & Co Indianapolis IN 46285

LEANING, WILLIAM HENRY DICKENS, b Whakatane, NZ, Feb 24, 34; m 56; c 4. TECHNICAL MANAGEMENT, PARASITOLOGY. *Educ:* Univ Sydney, BVSc, 56. *Prof Exp:* Vet gen pract, Nth Canterbury Vet Club, NZ & Putaruru Vet Club, NZ, 57-62; vet tech dir appl res parasitol, Merck Sharp & Dohme NZ Ltd, 62-69; from dir mkt develop large animal prod, 69-72, sr dir clin res animal sci res, 72-74, exec dir animal sci res develop res & admin, 75-81, EXEC DIR TECH SERV, MERCK SHARP & DOHME CO, INC, AGVET, 81- *Mem:* NZ Vet Asn; Am Asn Vet Parasitologist; World Asn Adv Vet Parasitol; Am Vet Med Asn; Am Asn Indust Vet. *Res:* Concepts of applied preventive medicine on whole herd/flock basis throughout productive life of animal/bird; primary areas helminthology, entomology; innovation in formulation and treatment application; applied parasitology and agri-economic benefits of year-round parasite control programs. *Mailing Add:* MSD-AGVET Div Merck & Co PO Box 2000 Rahway NJ 07065

LEAP, DARRELL IVAN, b Huntington, WVa, Oct 19, 37. WATER RESOURCES, AQUIFER ANALYSIS. *Educ:* Marshall Univ, BS, 60; Ind Univ, MA, 66; Pa State Univ, PhD(geol), 74. *Prof Exp:* Geologist, SDak State Geol Surv, 66-71; instr geol, Univ SDak, 66-69; hydrologist, US Geol Surv, 74-80; ASSOC PROF HYDROGEOL, PURDUE UNIV, 80- *Concurrent Pos:* Prin investr, Hydrol Nev Test Site, Nev Nuclear Waste-Storage Invest, US Dept Energy, 78-80. *Mem:* Am Geophys Union; AAAS; Sigma Xi; Am Water Resources Asn; Int Water Resources Asn. *Res:* Regional aquifer systems for recharge-discharge relationships and water resources; ground-water modeling; ground-water tracers; radioactive-waste disposal; flow in fractured rocks; flow in glaciated terranes; glacial geology. *Mailing Add:* Dept Geosci Purdue Univ West Lafayette IN 47907

LEAPHART, CHARLES DONALD, forest pathology, deceased

LEAR, BERT, b Logan, Utah, June 10, 17; m 50; c 1. PLANT PATHOLOGY. *Educ:* Utah State Univ, BS, 41; Cornell Univ, PhD(plant path), 47. *Prof Exp:* Agt, Exp Sta, USDA, 41-43; Dow Chem Co fel & res assoc, Cornell Univ, 47-48, asst prof plant path, 48-52; nematologist, NMex Col, 52-53; from asst nematologist to nematologist, 53-74, PROF NEMATOL, UNIV CALIF, DAVIS, 63- *Mem:* Am Phytopath Soc; Soc Nematol; Orgn Trop Am Nematologists. *Res:* Soil treatment for control of nematodes; fate of chemicals in soils and plants when applied for control of nematodes; role of plant parasitic nematodes in diseases of plants. *Mailing Add:* Dept of Plant Path Univ of Calif Davis CA 95616

LEAR, CLEMENT S C, b Christchurch, NZ, Oct 24, 29; m 67. ORTHODONTICS. *Educ:* Univ NZ, BDS, 53; Harvard Univ, DMD, 63. *Prof Exp:* Pvt pract, 54-58; res assoc orthod, Harvard Univ, 62-64, assoc, 64-67; PROF ORTHOD & HEAD DEPT, FAC DENT, UNIV BC, 67- *Concurrent Pos:* Clin fel dent med, Forsyth Dent Ctr, Sch Dent Med, Harvard Univ, 58-59, res fel orthod, 59-62; mem univ comt, Med Res Coun Can. *Mem:* AAAS; Am Dent Asn; Int Asn Dent Res; Int Soc Cranio-Facial Biol; Can Asn Orthod. *Res:* Oro-facial muscle physiology and mechanisms of tooth support, particularly as they relate to dental arch form. *Mailing Add:* Dept of Orthod Univ of BC Vancouver BC V6T 1W5 Can

LEAR, W(ILLIAM) E(DWARD), b Lexington, Ky, Aug 29, 18; m 47; c 4. ELECTRICAL ENGINEERING. *Educ:* Univ Ala, BS, 42; Stanford Univ, MS, 49; Univ Fla, PhD(elec eng), 53. *Hon Degrees:* DEng, Pusan Nat Univ, Korea, 76; DEng Tech, Wentworth Inst, 81. *Prof Exp:* Electronics engr, Radio Corp Am, NJ, 42-44; instr elec eng, Univ Ala, 46-48; asst prof, Univ Fla, 49-53; assoc prof, Univ Tenn, 53-54; from assoc prof to prof, Univ Fla, 54-66; assoc dean, Col Eng, Univ Ala, Tuscaloosa, 66-67, dean col, 67-81; EXEC DIR, AM SOC ENG EDUC, 81- *Concurrent Pos:* Res partic, Oak Ridge Nat Lab, 50-51; consult, US Air Force Armament Ctr, 52-56, Fairchild Engine & Aircraft Co, 55-56, Sperry Corp, 55-63, Nat Sci Found, 64- & Comt on Sci & Technol, US House Rep, 78; prog dir eng systs & actg head eng sect, Nat Sci Found, 63-64. *Mem:* Am Soc Eng Educ; sr mem Inst Elec & Electronics Engrs; AAAS; Cosmos Club. *Res:* Microwave devices; plasma. *Mailing Add:* Am Soc Eng Educ 11 Dupont Circle Suite 200 Washington DC 20036

LEARN, ARTHUR JAY, b Lewistown, Mont, Mar 25, 33; m 59; c 2. SOLID STATE PHYSICS. *Educ:* Reed Col, BA, 54; Mass Inst Technol, PhD(physics), 58. *Prof Exp:* Mem tech staff, TRW Systs, Calif, 58-67; mem staff, Electronics Res Ctr, NASA, 67-70; sr mem res staff, Fairchild Camera & Instrument Corp, 70-76; prog mgr, Intel Corp, 76-81; ENG MGR, SUPERTEX, INC, 81- *Mem:* Am Phys Soc; Electrochem Soc; Am Vacuum Soc. *Res:* X-ray diffraction; electron microscopy; properties of thin films; thin film superconductor and semiconductor devices; metallization. *Mailing Add:* 10822 Wilkinson Ave Cupertino CA 95014

LEARNED, ROBERT EUGENE, b Glendale, Calif, July 3, 28; m 56; c 2. ECONOMIC GEOLOGY, GEOCHEMISTRY. *Educ:* Occidental Col, AB, 55; Univ Calif, Los Angeles, MA, 62; Univ Calif, Riverside, PhD(geol), 66. *Prof Exp:* Geologist, Aerogeophys Co, Calif, 55-56; asst prof geol, Chapman Col, 65-67; GEOLOGIST, US GEOL SURV, 67- *Mem:* Geol Soc Am; Geochem Soc; Asn Explor Geochemists; Soc Econ Geologists; Asn Geoscientists Int Develop. *Res:* Geology and geochemistry of ore deposits; geochemical exploration methods. *Mailing Add:* 614 Wyoming St Golden CO 80401

LEARNED, VINCENT (ROY), electrical engineering, see previous edition

LEARY, FRANCIS CHRISTIAN, b West Hartford, Conn, April 23, 49; m 76; c 2. ALGEBRA. *Educ:* Univ Conn, BA, 71; State Univ NY, Albany, MA, 74, PhD(math), 79. *Prof Exp:* Instr & asst prof, Skidmore Col, 79-80; ASST PROF MATH, TRANSYLVANIA UNIV, 80- *Concurrent Pos:* Adj asst prof, Union Col, Schenectady, 75-76; lectr math, Waterbury State Tech Col & Post Jr Col, 73. *Mem:* Am Math Soc; assoc mem Sigma Xi. *Res:* Extension of several classical results to a generalized summability setting; study of matrix transformations from one Banach valued sequence space to another which sum no bounded divergent sequence. *Mailing Add:* Div Natural Sci & Math Transylvania Univ Lexington KY 40508

LEARY, JAMES FRANCIS, b Portsmouth, NH, Apr 12, 48. BIOPHYSICS. *Educ:* Mass Inst Technol, BS(aeronaut & astronaut) & BS(phil & hist), 70; Univ NH, MS, 74; Pa State Univ, PhD(biophys), 77. *Prof Exp:* Res fel biophys & instrumentation, Los Alamos Scientific Lab, 77-78; ASST PROF PATH, MED SCH, UNIV ROCHESTER, 78-, ASST PROF PEDIAT, 81- *Concurrent Pos:* Vis staff mem, Los Alamos Scientific Lab, 78-80. *Mem:* Soc Anal Cytol; Histochem Soc; AAAS; NY Acad Sci. *Res:* Development of new automated laser flow cytometric instrumentation and clinically useful diagnostic tests; biomedical applications in human genetics, virology, immunology, cell kinetics, somatic cell genetics, and developmental biology. *Mailing Add:* Dept of Path Box 626 Univ of Rochester Med Ctr Rochester NY 14642

LEARY, JOHN DENNIS, b New Bedford, Mass, Dec 6, 34; m 57; c 4. BIOCHEMISTRY. *Educ:* Mass Col Pharm, BS, 56, MS, 58; Univ Conn, PhD(pharmacog), 64. *Prof Exp:* Asst pharmacog, Univ Conn, 58-59; asst prof, Ore State Univ, 59-61; from asst prof to assoc prof phytochem, St John's Univ, NY, 63-68; assoc prof pharmacog & bot, 68-74, ASSOC PROF BIOCHEM, MASS COL PHARM, 74- *Mem:* Sigma Xi; Am Soc Pharmacog. *Res:* Phytochemical studies, primarily Solanaceae; chemotaxonomy and biogenesis; microbial transformation of organic compounds. *Mailing Add:* 179 Longwood Ave Boston MA 02115

LEARY, JOHN VINCENT, b Buffalo, NY, Dec 27, 37; m 60; c 3. GENETICS. *Educ:* State Univ NY Buffalo, BS, 59, MA, 64; Mich State Univ, PhD(bot, plant path), 69. *Prof Exp:* NIH fel genetics, Cornell Univ, 69-70; asst prof plant path, 70-77, ASSOC PROF PLANT PATH, UNIV CALIF, RIVERSIDE, 77- *Mem:* AAAS; Am Phytopath Soc; Genetics Soc Am. *Res:* Molecular basis of fungal morphogenesis; molecular basis of incompatibility; genetics of fungi. *Mailing Add:* Dept of Plant Path Univ of Calif Riverside CA 92502

LEARY, JOSEPH ALOYSIUS, b New York, NY, Nov 22, 19; m 43; c 2. PHYSICAL CHEMISTRY, CHEMICAL ENGINEERING. *Educ:* Newark Col Eng, BS, 43; Univ NMex, PhD(phys chem), 56. *Prof Exp:* Prod supvr, Am Cyanamid Co, 43-44; res sect leader, Los Alamos Sci Lab, Univ Calif, 46-47, alt res group leader, 47-74; DIR, INT NUCLEAR AFFAIRS, OFF NUCLEAR ENERGY PROGS, DEPT ENERGY, WASHINGTON DC, 74- *Mem:* NY Acad Sci; fel Am Inst Chemists; Am Nuclear Soc. *Res:* Materials of interest to the nuclear field, particularly transuranium elements and special isotopes. *Mailing Add:* US Dept Energy Washington DC 20545

LEARY, RALPH JOHN, b Elizabeth, NJ, Nov 3, 29; m 52; c 6. ORGANIC CHEMISTRY. *Educ:* Seton Hall Univ, BS, 51; Univ Ill, PhD(chem), 57. *Prof Exp:* Jr chemist, Merck & Co, Inc, 51-54; group leader, Esso Res & Eng Co, 57-67, group leader & res assoc, 67-75, lab head, Exxon Chem Co USA, 75-77, res assoc, 78-80, SECT HEAD, EXXON RES & ENG CO, 78-, SR RES ASSOC, 80- *Mem:* Am Chem Soc. *Res:* Gas chromatography and automation of laboratory instruments; Am Soc Testing & Mat. *Mailing Add:* Exxon Res & Eng Co PO Box 121 Linden NJ 07036

LEARY, ROLFE ALBERT, b Waterloo, Iowa, Mar 5, 38; m 67; c 2. FOREST MENSURATION. *Educ:* Iowa State Col, BS, 59; Purdue Univ, MS, 61, PhD(forest mgt), 68. *Prof Exp:* Vol forester, US Peace Corps, St Lucia, WIndies, 61-63; instr forest mensuration, Southern Ill Univ, 64-65; mensurationist, 68-72, PRIN MENSURATIONIST FORESTRY, US FOREST SERV, NCENT FOREST EXP STA, 72- *Mem:* AAAS; Ecol Soc Am; Sigma Xi; Coun Unified Res & Educ. *Res:* Boundary value problem method of calibrating forest growth models; generalized forest growth projection system; philosophy and methods of forest research; multiple-use decision-making. *Mailing Add:* 1382 Iowa Ave W St Paul MN 55108

LEAS, J(OHN) W(ESLEY), b Delaware, Ohio, June 14, 16; m 43. ELECTRICAL ENGINEERING. *Educ:* Ohio State Univ, BS, 38. *Prof Exp:* Sales engr, Armstrong Cork Co, Pa, 38-41; electronic engr airborne radar, Airborne Instrument Lab, NY, 46-47; consult engr air navig, Air Transport Asn, DC, 47-49; electronic res scientist, Air Navig Develop Bd, Dept Commerce, DC, 49-51; chief engr, Electronic Data Processing Div, Radio Corp Am, 51-60, mgr data commun & custom proj dept, Electronic Data Processing Div, 60-63; gen mgr Valley Forge Div, Control Data Corp, 64-72; PRES, J W LEAS & ASSOCS, TRANSP CONSULT, 72- *Concurrent Pos:* Mem tech staff telecommun res estab, Ministry Aviation, Eng, 42-43; asst head eng, US Naval Res Lab, 43-46; tech adv, US State Dept, 46; consult, Civil Aeronaut Admin, 48-49 & Dept Defense, 58-63; mem adv group comput, Dept Defense, 55. *Mem:* Fel Inst Elec & Electronics Engrs. *Res:* Development, design and management of engineering digital computers; general management of data communications and custom projects in data processing field. *Mailing Add:* 910 Potts Lane J W Leas & Assoc Bryn Mawr PA 19010

LEASE, ALFRED A(RNOLD), b St Cloud, Minn, Sept 20, 22; m 44; c 4. INDUSTRIAL ENGINEERING. *Educ:* Univ Minn, PhD(indust eng), 64. *Prof Exp:* PROF ENG & TECHNOL & CHMN DEPT, ST CLOUD STATE UNIV, 59-, VPRES ADMIN AFFAIRS, 67-, DEAN COL INDUST, 80- *Concurrent Pos:* Consult, Dansen Mfg Co, 62-66. *Mem:* Am Soc Eng Educ. *Res:* Electronics and electronics teaching devices. *Mailing Add:* Dept of Indust Eng & Technol St Cloud State Univ St Cloud MN 56301

LEASK, R(AYMOND) A(LEXANDER), b Edmonton, Alta, Jan 15, 19; m 42; c 4. PULP AND PAPER. *Educ:* Univ Alberta, BSc, 41, MSc, 47. *Prof Exp:* Chemist, Brit-Am Oil Co, 41; res chemist, Can Int Paper Co, 42-44; res asst, Res Coun Alberta, 45-47; chem engr, Powell River Co, 48-50; supvr pulping sect, Cent Res Div, Abitibi Power & Paper Co, 50-64; dir res, Bauer Bros Co, 64-71; process engr, Sandwell & Co, 71-73; ASST RES DIR, ONT PAPER CO, 73- *Mem:* Fel Tech Asn Pulp & Paper Indust; Can Pulp & Paper Asn; Asn Prof Engrs. *Res:* Pulping methods on a pilot-plant scale and on a commercial scale; improving paper machine performance and improving newsprint quality. *Mailing Add:* Ont Paper Co Thorold ON L2V 3Z5 Can

LEATH, KENNETH T, b Providence, RI, Apr 29, 31; m 55; c 4. PLANT PATHOLOGY. *Educ:* Univ RI, BS, 59; Univ Minn, MS & PhD(phytopath), 66. *Prof Exp:* Res technician cereal rusts, Coop Rust Lab, Minn, 59-66, PLANT PATHOLOGIST, REGIONAL PASTURE RES LAB, USDA, 66- *Concurrent Pos:* Adj prof, Dept Plant Path, Pa State Univ, 66- *Mem:* Am Phytopath Soc; Am Soc Agron; Am Forage & Grassland Coun; Int Soc Plant Path. *Res:* Clover and alfalfa diseases; host-parasite interaction. *Mailing Add:* Regional Pasture Res Lab Northeastern Region USDA University Park PA 16802

LEATH, PAUL LARRY, b Moberly, Mo, Jan 9, 41; m 62; c 2. SOLID STATE PHYSICS. *Educ:* Univ Mo-Columbia, BS, 61, MS, 63, PhD(physics), 66. *Prof Exp:* Res assoc theoret physics, Oxford Univ, 66-67; asst prof, 67-71, assoc chmn dept, 73-75, assoc prof, 71-78, PROF PHYSICS, RUTGERS UNIV, NEW BRUNSWICK, 71-, ASSOC PROVOST SCI, 78- *Mem:* AAAS; Am Phys Soc; Sigma Xi; Brit Inst Physics; NY Acad Sci. *Res:* Theoretical solid state physics; inelastic neutron scattering; vibrational and electronic properties of alloys; anharmonic crystals; disordered and dilute magnets; percolation processes. *Mailing Add:* Serin Physics Lab Rutgers Univ Piscataway NJ 08854

LEATHEM, WILLIAM DOLARS, b Chicago, Ill, Jan 6, 31; m 52; c 3. MEDICAL NUTRITION, MEDICAL PARASITOLOGY. *Educ:* Univ Wis, BS, 61, MS, 63, PhD(zool), 65. *Prof Exp:* Asst zool, Univ Wis, 62; asst prof biol, Wis State Univ, Whitewater, 65-66; asst prof, Univ Wis, Waukesha Ctr, 66-69, NSF grants, 67-69; res assoc, Norwich Pharmacal Co, 69-74, asst dir clin nutrit, Eaton Labs, 74-76; med monitor nutrit, 76-78, MGR NUTRIT RES, ABBOTT LABS, 78- *Mem:* AAAS; Am Soc Parasitol; Soc Protozool; Am Soc Trop Med & Hyg; Am Soc Parenteral & Enteral Nutrit. *Res:* General parasitology and protozoology. *Mailing Add:* Abbott Labs Hosp Prod Div North Chicago IL 60064

LEATHEN, WILLIAM WARRICK, b Pittsburgh, Pa, July 7, 12; m; c 3. MICROBIOLOGY. *Educ:* Univ Pittsburgh, BS, 36, MS, 37. *Prof Exp:* Bacteriologist, Morris Knowles, Inc, Pa, 36-42; chief bacteriologist, Hektoen Inst, Cook County Hosp, Chicago, 46; fel bact, Mellon Inst, 46-52, head microbiol & micros sect, 52-63, sr fel, 63-69; supvr microbiol res, Gulf Res & Develop Co, 69-73; microbiologist, Gulf Oil Corp, 73-76; MICROBIOL CONSULT, 76- *Concurrent Pos:* Bacteriologist, West Penn Hosp, Pittsburgh, 37-42. *Honors & Awards:* Charles Porter Award, Soc Indust Microbiol, 80. *Mem:* Fel AAAS; Am Chem Soc; Soc Indust Microbiol; Am Soc Microbiol; Inst Food Technologists. *Res:* Variation of hemolytic streptococci; bacteriological oxidation of ferrous iron; effect of industrial wastes on bacteriological flora of streams; microbiological deterioration of materials; petroleum microbiology; single cell protein research; microbial pesticides; geomicrobiology. *Mailing Add:* 165 Weller Dr Wexford PA 15090

LEATHER, GERALD ROGER, b Smithsburg, Md, Oct 16, 37; m 63; c 3. PLANT PHYSIOLOGY. *Educ:* Shepherd Col, BS, 68; Hood Col, MA, 73; Va Polytech Inst & State Univ, PhD(plant physiol), 76. *Prof Exp:* Biologist, US Army, 70-74; biologist, 74-76, PLANT PHYSIOLOGIST, US DEPT AGR, 76- *Concurrent Pos:* Lectr, Hood Col, 76-; adj prof, Va Polytech Inst & State Univ, 80- *Mem:* Weed Sci Soc Am; Am Soc Plant Physiologists. *Res:* Secondary plant chemicals in the allelopathic interaction of weeds and crops; dormancy and germination mechanisms in weed seeds; maternal influence on the physiology and biochemistry of seed dormancy. *Mailing Add:* 8653 Chestnut Grove Rd Frederick MD 21701

LEATHERMAN, ANNA D, b Centre Square, Pa, Jan 17, 09. PLANT ECOLOGY. *Educ:* Goshen Col, BS, 38, AB, 39; Cornell Univ, MA, 47; Univ Tenn, PhD, 55. *Prof Exp:* Teacher, Rural Sch, Va, 39-44 & Pub Sch, 44-47; from instr to prof biol, Upland Col, 47-64; asst, Univ Tenn, 52-53; prof, Bethel Col, 64-66; prof biol, 66-77, EMER PROF BOT, SPRING ARBOR COL, 77- *Mem:* Ecol Soc Am. *Res:* Ecological life history of Lonicera japonica Thunb. *Mailing Add:* 6650 W Butler Dr Apt 2 Glendale AZ 85302

LEATHERMAN, NELSON E(ARLE), b Grand Rapids, Mich, Mar 22, 39; m 68. BIOENGINEERING. *Educ:* Univ Mich, BSE, 62, MSE, 63, PhD(bioeng), 67. *Prof Exp:* Res asst physiol, Univ Mich, 67-68; asst prof, Ind Univ, Bloomington, 68-77; RES ASSOC, VT LUNG CTR, UNIV VT, 77- *Mem:* Biomed Eng Soc. *Res:* Modeling of biological control systems; particularly identification of nonlinear systems. *Mailing Add:* 102 Nodding Oak Chapel Hill NC 27514

LEATHERS, CHESTER RAY, b Claremont, Ill, May 15, 29; m 53; c 4. MYCOLOGY. *Educ:* Eastern Ill Univ, BS, 50; Univ Mich, MS, 51, PhD(bot), 55. *Prof Exp:* Res mycologist, Biol Warfare Labs, US Army, Md, 55-57; asst prof, 57-61, ASSOC PROF BOT, ARIZ STATE UNIV, 61- *Mem:* Fel AAAS; Mycol Soc Am; Am Phytopath Soc; Am Inst Biol Sci. *Res:* Mycology and plant pathology, particularly fleshy fungi, cereal and vegetable diseases; allergenic fungi; medical mycology. *Mailing Add:* Dept of Bot & Microbiol Ariz State Univ Tempe AZ 85281

LEATHERS, JOEL MONROE, b Guy's Store, Tex, Jan 10, 20; m 45; c 3. CHEMISTRY. *Educ:* Sam Houston State Teachers Col, BS, 41. *Hon Degrees:* DEng, Mich Technol Univ, 72. *Prof Exp:* Chemist, 42-45, proj leader, Org Lab, 45-48, asst supt vinyl & vinylidene prod, 48-50, asst dir org lab, 50-53, dir org pilot plant lab, 54-61, dir res & develop, 61-66, gen mgr, Tex Div, 66-68, DIR US AREA OPERS, DOW CHEM CO, 68-, VPRES, 70-, DIR, 71-, EXEC VPRES, DOW CHEM USA, 71- *Mem:* Am Chem Soc; Am Inst Chem Engrs. *Res:* Chlorination of saturated hydrocarbons. *Mailing Add:* PO Box 1302 Midland MI 48640

LEATHERWOOD, JAMES M, b Waynesville, NC, Mar 22, 30; m 56; c 1. ANIMAL NUTRITION. *Educ:* Berea Col, BS, 52; NC State Univ, MS, 57, PhD(animal sci), 61. *Prof Exp:* From instr to assoc prof, 57-69, PROF ANIMAL SCI, NC STATE UNIV, 69- *Concurrent Pos:* Fel biochem, Duke Univ, 60-61. *Mem:* Am Soc Microbiol; Am Soc Animal Sci; Am Inst Nutrit. *Res:* Carbohydrate metabolism; enzymatic cellulose degradation; bacterial cell walls and microbiology of the rumen; animal efficiency and energetics. *Mailing Add:* Dept of Animal Sci NC State Univ Raleigh NC 27650

LEATHRUM, JAMES FREDERICK, b Dover, Del, Dec 24, 37; m 60; c 3. COMPUTER SCIENCE, COMPUTER ENGINEERING. *Educ:* Univ Del, BChE, 59; Princeton Univ, MA, 61, PhD(chem eng), 63. *Prof Exp:* Proj scientist, Union Carbide Corp, 65-67; from asst prof to assoc prof comput sci, Univ Del, 67-80; PROF ELEC & COMPUT ENG, CLEMSON UNIV, 80- *Concurrent Pos:* Consult, US Army, 68- & Burroughs Corp, 69-73. *Mem:* Asn Comput Mach; Am Inst Chem Engrs; Sigma Xi. *Res:* Programming systems for real time and interactive computers; software engineering. *Mailing Add:* Dept Elec & Comput Eng Clemson Univ Clemson SC 29631

LEATON, JOHN ROGER, analytical chemistry, pharmaceutical chemistry, see previous edition

LEAV, IRWIN, b Brooklyn, NY, July 4, 37; m 61; c 2. PATHOLOGY. *Educ:* Ohio State Univ, BA, 59, DVM, 65; Am Col Vet Pathologists, Dipl, 70. *Prof Exp:* Res fel path, 65-68, NIH spec fel, 68-70, ASST PATH, HARVARD MED SCH, 68-, ASSOC PROF PATH, SCH OF MED, TUFTS UNIV, 70- *Concurrent Pos:* Res assoc, Steroid Biochem Lab, 69-; assoc dir path, Angell Mem Hosp, 74-76; consult, US Armed Forces Inst Environ Med, 74- & Angell Mem Hosp, 76-; grant, Nat Cancer Inst, 78-81; assoc dean basic sci, Sch Vet Med, Tufts Univ, 78- *Mem:* Int Acad Path; Am Col Vet Pathologists; Am Vet Med Asn. *Res:* Mechanisms of action of sex hormones on normal, hyperplastic and neoplastic male accessory sex organs. *Mailing Add:* Dept of Path Dent & Vet Med Boston MA 02111

LEAVENS, PETER BACKUS, b Summit, NJ, June 20, 39; m 58; c 1. MINERALOGY. *Educ:* Yale Univ, BA, 61; Harvard Univ, MA, 64, PhD, 66. *Prof Exp:* Res assoc, Dept Mineral Sci, Smithsonian Inst, 65-67; asst prof, 67-70, ASSOC PROF GEOL, UNIV DEL, 70- *Concurrent Pos:* Res assoc, Smithsonian Inst, 67- *Mem:* AAAS; Mineral Soc Am. *Res:* Descriptive mineralogy; description of new mineral species; conditions of mineral occurrence and stability; mineralogy and geochemistry of pegmatites; phosphate mineralogy; carbonate metamorphism. *Mailing Add:* Dept of Geol Univ of Del Newark DE 19711

LEAVENWORTH, HOWARD W, JR, b Waterbury, Conn, June 3, 28; m 55; c 3. METALLURGY. *Educ:* Stevens Inst Technol, ME, 51; Yale Univ, MS, 53. *Prof Exp:* Metallurgist, Franklin Inst, 53-55; sr scientist, Pratt & Whitney Aircraft Co, 55-61 & Oak Ridge Nat Lab, 55-57; prog mgr solid state physics, Air Force Off Sci Res, 61-62; asst mgr, Am Mach & Foundry Co, 62-67; METALLURGIST, BUR MINES, 67-, RES SUPVR, ALBANY METALL RES CTR, 78- *Honors & Awards:* NASA Award, 67. *Mem:* Fel AAAS; Sigma Xi; Am Inst Mining, Metall & Petrol Engrs. *Res:* Alloy development; corrosion; surface science; extractive metallurgy. *Mailing Add:* 2905 Park Terr Albany OR 97321

LEAVENWORTH, RICHARD S, b Oak Park, Ill, Sept 30, 30; m 55. INDUSTRIAL ENGINEERING, OPERATIONS RESEARCH. *Educ:* Stanford Univ, BSIE & MSIE, 62, PhD(indust eng), 64. *Prof Exp:* Eng asst, Light Div, Dept Pub Utilities, Tacoma, Wash, 56-59; asst prof indust eng, Va Polytech Inst, 64-66; PROF INDUST & SYSTS ENG & ACTG CHMN DEPT, UNIV FLA, 66- *Concurrent Pos:* Consult, Off Transp Res, US Dept Commerce, 65-66, mfg educ serv, Gen Elec Co, NY, 65-67 & Manhattan Industs, 70-73; ed, The Eng Economist, 76- *Mem:* Am Inst Indust Engrs (vpres, 77-79); Am Soc Qual Control; Am Soc Eng Educ; Inst Mgt Sci. *Res:* Engineering economics as applied to public expenditure decision making; quality control. *Mailing Add:* Dept of Indust & Systs Eng 303 Weil Hall Univ of Fla Gainesville FL 32611

LEAVITT, CHRISTOPHER PRATT, b Boston, Mass, Nov 20, 27; m 59; c 5. PHYSICS. *Educ:* Mass Inst Technol, BS, 48, PhD(physics), 52. *Prof Exp:* Res assoc physics, Brookhaven Nat Lab, NY, 52-54, assoc physicist, 54-56; from asst prof to assoc prof physics, 56-65, actg chmn dept physics & astron, 58-60, PROF PHYSICS, UNIV NMEX, 65- *Concurrent Pos:* Consult, Res Directorate, Phyisc Div, Kirtland AFB, 56-60; directorate res & develop, Air Force Missile Develop Ctr, Holloman AFB, 56-60; mem particles & fields subcomt, NASA, 65-67; mem tech adv panel, Los Alamos Meson Physics Facility, 69-71; mem, Nuclear Physics Steering Comt, 70-71. *Mem:* Am Phys Soc. *Res:* Nuclear and high energy physics; cosmic rays; space physics. *Mailing Add:* Dept of Physics & Astron Univ of NMex Albuquerque NM 87106

LEAVITT, FRED W, b Elizabeth, NJ, Oct 16, 28. CHEMICAL ENGINEERING, APPLIED MATHEMATICS. *Educ:* Newark Col Eng, BS, 50; Rensselaer Polytech Inst, MS, 55, PhD(chem eng), 57. *Prof Exp:* Chem engr, Biol Labs, US Army, Camp Detrick, 52-54; chem engr, 57-61, group leader, 61-63, SR ENGR, LINDE DIV, UNION CARBIDE CORP, 63- *Mem:* AAAS; Am Chem Soc. *Res:* Development of adsorptive separation processes; automatic data logging; development of computer systems for reducing, analyzing and correlating data and making design calculations; chemical kinetics and equilibria. *Mailing Add:* Scarborough Manor Ossining NY 10562

LEAVITT, FREDERICK CARLTON, polymer chemistry, see previous edition

LEAVITT, J ROBERT CARLTON, weed science, pesticide chemistry, see previous edition

LEAVITT, JOHN ADAMS, b Lewis, Colo, Dec 8, 32; m 55; c 5. PHYSICS. *Educ:* Univ Colo, BA, 54; Harvard Univ, MA, 56, PhD, 60. *Prof Exp:* From asst prof to assoc prof, 60-71, PROF PHYSICS, UNIV ARIZ, 71- *Res:* Atomic physics. *Mailing Add:* Dept of Physics Univ of Ariz Tucson AZ 85721

LEAVITT, JULIAN JACOB, b Boston, Mass, Sept 4, 18; m 43; c 3. LICENSING, TECHNOLOGY ACQUISITION. *Educ:* Harvard Univ, AB, 39, AM, 40, PhD(org chem), 42. *Prof Exp:* Res chemist, Nat Defense Res Comt, Harvard Univ, 42 & Univ Pa, 42-44; res chemist, Calco Chem Div, 44-54, Res Div, 54-58, Org Chem Div, 58-64, mgr explor res, 64-69, tech dir, Decision Making Systs Dept, 69-70, asst to mgr com develop, 70-74, mgr licensing & technol, 74-77, dir licensing & technol acquisition chem, 77-81, DIR LICENSING, AM CYANAMID CO, 81- *Concurrent Pos:* Ed, Sect 40, Chem Abstr Serv, 61-; mem, Adv Bd Mil Personnel Supplies & Comt Textile Dyeing & Finishing, Nat Acad Sci-Nat Res Coun, 63-68. *Mem:* AAAS; Com Develop Asn; Am Chem Soc; Soc Info Display; Licensing Exec Soc. *Res:* Dyes; applied photochemistry. *Mailing Add:* Technol Assessment & Licensing Dept Am Cyanamid Co Stamford CT 06904

LEAVITT, MILO DAVID, JR, b Beloit, Wis, June 24, 15. MEDICINE, SCIENCE ADMINISTRATION. *Educ:* Univ Wis, BA, 38; Univ Pa, MD, 40; Univ Minn, MSc, 48; Harvard Univ, MPH, 59. *Prof Exp:* Mayo Clin fel, Univ Minn, 45-49; asst chief perinatal res br, Nat Inst Neurol Dis & Blindness, 59-62, head spec int progs sect, Off Int Res, 62-66, dep asst secy sci & pop, off secy, Dept Health, Educ & Welfare, 66-67, dir off prog planning, 67-68, DIR FOGARTY INT CTR ADVAN STUDIES HEALTH SCI, 68- *Concurrent Pos:* Del, World Health Assembly, Geneva, 72, 73 & 74. *Mem:* Am Diabetes Asn; Asn Am Med Cols; Indust Med Asn; Am Pub Health Asn. *Res:* Government administration; internal medicine; cardiology. *Mailing Add:* 8017 Eastern Ave Silver Spring MD 20910

LEAVITT, RICHARD IRWIN, microbiology, see previous edition

LEAVITT, RICHARD PAUL, theoretical physics, applied mathematics, see previous edition

LEAVITT, WENDELL W, b North Conway, NH, Jan 15, 38; m 59; c 4. ENDOCRINOLOGY, REPRODUCTIVE PHYSIOLOGY. *Educ:* Dartmouth Col, AB, 59; Univ NH, MS, 61, PhD(zool), 63. *Prof Exp:* Res analyst zool, Agr Exp Sta, Univ NH, 60-63, res assoc endocrinologist & instr zool, 63-64; asst prof, 64-67, from asst prof to assoc prof physiol & dir grad studies, Col Med, 67-75, prof physiol, Col Med, Univ Cincinnati, 75-77; SR SCIENTIST, WORCESTER FOUND EXP BIOL, 77- *Concurrent Pos:* Spec fel endocrinol & reprod physiol, Univ Wis, 67-68; grants, NSF, Pop Coun & NIH; vis scientist, Ctr Pop Res & Studies in Reprod Biol, Vanderbilt Univ, 72-73; consult, Merrell Nat Labs, Cincinnati, Oh; res prof, Med Sch, Univ Mass, 78- *Mem:* Sigma Xi; Am Soc Zool; Endocrine Soc; Soc Study Reprod; Am Physiol Soc. *Res:* Mechanism of pituitary function in relation to gonadotrophin secretion; control of female reproductive cycle; estrogens and pituitary function; aging and the reproductive system; steroid hormone receptor systems. *Mailing Add:* Worcester Found Exp Biol Shrewsbury MA 01545

LEAVITT, WILLIAM GRENFELL, b Omaha, Nebr, Mar 19, 16; m 41; c 3. ALGEBRA. *Educ:* Univ Nebr, AB, 37, MA, 38; Univ Wis, PhD(math), 47. *Prof Exp:* Actg instr math, Univ Wis, 46; from instr to assoc prof, 47-56, chmn dept, 54-64, PROF MATH, UNIV NEBR-LINCOLN, 56- *Concurrent Pos:* NSF fel, 59-60; Univ Nebr Res Coun vis fel, Leeds, Eng, 73. *Mem:* Am Math Soc; Math Asn Am. *Res:* Ring theory; theory of modules; theory of radicals. *Mailing Add:* Dept of Math Univ of Nebr Lincoln NE 68508

LEAVY, THOMAS A, earth science, see previous edition

LEBARON, FRANCIS NEWTON, b Framingham, Mass, July 26, 22; m 53; c 1. NEUROCHEMISTRY, LIPID CHEMISTRY. *Educ:* Mass Inst Technol, BS, 44; Boston Univ, MA, 48; Harvard Univ, PhD(biochem), 51. *Prof Exp:* Asst biochemist, McLean Hosp, Mass, 52-53 & 54-57, assoc biochemist, 57-64; assoc prof, 64-69, chmn dept, 71-78, PROF BIOCHEM, SCH MED, UNIV NMEX, 69- *Concurrent Pos:* USPHS fel, McLean Hosp, Waverley, Mass, 51-52 & Maudsley Hosp, 53-54; res assoc, Harvard Med Sch, 56-59, assoc, 59-64, tutor, Harvard Univ, 57-64; vis scholar, Mass Inst Technol, 74-75. *Mem:* AAAS; Am Soc Neurochem; Am Soc Biol Chem; Am Inst Nutrit. *Res:* Biochemistry of the nervous system, especially the chemistry of proteins and lipids and their nervous complexes as they occur in mammalian nervous tissues; role of polyunsaturated fatty acids in nervous tissues. *Mailing Add:* 1713 Morningside Dr NE Albuquerque NM 87110

LEBARON, HOMER MCKAY, b Barnwell, Alta, May 13, 26; US citizen; m 52; c 7. PESTICIDE CHEMISTRY, PESTICIDE EFFECTS. *Educ:* Utah State Univ, BS, 56, MS, 58; Cornell Univ, PhD(chem), 60. *Prof Exp:* Plant physiologist, Va Truck Exp Sta, 60-63; mem field res & develop, Geigy Chem Corp, 64; group leader herbicide res, 64-75, SR STAFF SCIENTIST, CIBA-GEIGY CORP, 75- *Mem:* Fel Weed Sci Soc Am; Am Soc Agron; Entom Soc Am; Am Soc Plant Physiologists; Am Chem Soc. *Res:* Direct and coordinate all basic greenhouse and laboratory studies on herbicides, insecticides, fungicides, and other agricultural chemicals in areas of mode of action, environmental studies, soil interactions, metabolism and residues outside Ciba-Geigy; pesticide fate. *Mailing Add:* Agr Div Biochem Dept Ciba-Geigy Corp PO Box 18300 Greensboro NC 27419

LE BARON, I(RA) MILTON, b Taunton, Mass, July 20, 11. METALLURGY, ELECTROCHEMISTRY. *Educ:* Syracuse Univ, BS, 33; RI State Col, MSc, 34; Colo Sch Mines, DrMetE, 41. *Prof Exp:* Res metallurgist, Aluminum Co Am, 42-43; res supvr, Int Minerals & Chem Corp, 43-50, dir res, 50-57, vpres res, 57-58, vpres eng & develop, 58-62; mgr, Electro-Optics Dept, Tex Instruments Inc, Tex, 62-64, mgr, Power Dept, 64-65, gen dir, Tex Instruments Deutschland, WGer, 65-74, dir planning, Tex Instruments Inc, 69-74; CONSULT ENGR, 74- *Mem:* Electrochem Soc; Am Soc Metals; Am Inst Mining, Metall & Petrol Engrs; Am Inst Chem Engrs. *Res:* Development of high strength aluminum alloys; co-deposition of metals; metallurgy of brass; development of concentration processes and of heavy chemical process methods. *Mailing Add:* Box 9615 St Thomas VI 00801

LEBARON, MARSHALL JOHN, b Spokane, Wash, Sept 22, 20; m 48; c 2. FIELD CROPS. *Educ:* Univ Idaho, BS, 47, MS, 50. *Prof Exp:* Asst agronomist, 47-50, Supt, Twin Falls Br Exp Sta, Univ Idaho, 50-77, assoc & exten agronomist, 65-77, res prof agron, 70-77, RES PROF PLANT SCI, 77-, SUPT KIMBERLY RES & EXTEN CTR & EXTEN PROF, 74- *Mem:* Sigma Xi. *Res:* Bean production, including variety, fertility, population and damage assessment studies; breeding for disease and plant improvement in dry edible beans. *Mailing Add:* Twin Falls Br Exp Sta Rte 1 Kimberly ID 83341

LEBARON, ROBERT (FRANCIS), b Binghamton, NY, Oct 31, 91; m 26. CHEMISTRY. *Educ:* Union Col, NY, BS, 15; Princeton Univ, MS, 17; Nat Sch Mines, Paris, grad, 19. *Hon Degrees:* DSc, Union Col, NY & Thiel Col, 54. *Prof Exp:* Asst chem, Princeton Univ, 14-16; res chemist, Arthur D Little, Inc, Mass, 19-21, res sales, 21-23, coordr sci & tech activities, 23-25, asst to pres, 24-25; tech vpres, Petrol Chem Corp & vpres, Nat Distillers Prod Corp, NY, 26-32; sales dir, Va Smelting Co, 37-41, dir res & develop, 45-48, dir, 48-49; dep to Secy Defense in atomic energy, 49-54; mem vis comt, Brookhaven Nat Lab, 55-57; managing dir, LeBaron Assocs, 56-72, PRES, LeBARON FOUND, 65- *Concurrent Pos:* Mem planning comt, Va Smelting Co, 38-41, exec comt, 48-49; consult, War Dept, 42-44; tech consult, Oronite Chem Co, 45-49; mem chem res comt, Calif Res Corp, 45-49; mem adv bd dirs, Southern Res Inst, Ala, 47-49; chmn mil liaison comt, AEC, 49-54, consult to chmn comn, 54-58; chmn comt atomic energy, Res & Develop Bd, 49-54; indust consult, 54. *Res:* Chemicals from petroleum; atomic energy. *Mailing Add:* Suite I-842 Sheraton Park Hotel Washington DC 20008

LE BEAU, LEON JOSEPH, b Kankakee, Ill, Dec 30, 19; m 48; c 5. MICROBIOLOGY, IMMUNOLOGY. *Educ:* Univ Ill, PhD(bact), 52. *Prof Exp:* From instr bact to assoc prof microbiol, Univ Ill, Col Med, 52-63; vis prof, Fac Med, Univ Chiengmai, 63-66; ASSOC DIR LABS, UNIV HOSP & PROF PATH & MICROBIOL, UNIV ILL COL MED, 66- *Mem:* AAAS; Biol Photog Asn (vpres & pres elect, 75). *Res:* Anaerobic bacteriology; visual communication in medical education. *Mailing Add:* Dept of Path Univ of Ill Col of Med Chicago IL 60612

LEBEL, JACK LUCIEN, b Montreal, Que, Sept 16, 33; US citizen; m 60; c 2. RADIOLOGY, RADIATION BIOLOGY. *Educ:* Univ Montreal, DVM, 58; Colo State Univ, MS, 66, PhD(radiation biol), 67; Am Col Vet Radiol, dipl, 68. *Prof Exp:* Asst prof vet med, Univ Montreal, 61-64, assoc prof radiol, 67-68; assoc prof radiol & radiation biol, 68-73, asst dean curric col, 70-72, PROF RADIOL & RADIATION BIOL, COL VET MED & BIOMED SCI, COLO STATE UNIV, 73- *Concurrent Pos:* Consult, Orthop Found for Animals, 69- *Mem:* Am Vet Med Asn; Am Vet Radiol Soc. *Res:* Bone pathology; biological effects of plutonium contamination; nuclear medicine. *Mailing Add:* Vet Hosp Colo State Univ Ft Collins CO 80521

LEBEL, JEAN EUGENE, b Can, Mar 21, 22. MATHEMATICS. *Educ:* McGill Univ, BSc, 44; Univ Toronto, MA, 50, PhD(appl math), 58. *Prof Exp:* Theoret physicist, Newmont Explor, Ltd, Ariz, 52-54; lectr, McGill Univ, 55-57; from asst prof to assoc prof math, Georgetown Univ, 58-65; ASSOC PROF MATH, UNIV TORONTO, 65- *Mem:* Am Math Soc; Can Math Cong. *Res:* Analysis; applied mathematics. *Mailing Add:* Dept of Math Univ of Toronto Toronto ON M5S 1A1 Can

LEBEL, NORMAN ALBERT, b Augusta, Maine, Mar 22, 31; m 52; c 3. ORGANIC CHEMISTRY. *Educ:* Bowdoin Col, AB, 52; Mass Inst Technol, PhD, 57. *Prof Exp:* Chemist, Merck & Co, Inc, 52-54; from asst prof to assoc prof, 57-64, chmn dept, 71-78, PROF CHEM, WAYNE STATE UNIV, 64- *Concurrent Pos:* Sloan Found fel, 61-65; Welch Found lectr, 74. *Mem:* AAAS; Am Chem Soc; Sigma Xi; Royal Soc Chem. *Res:* Stereochemistry and mechanism of elimination reactions; chemistry of nitrones and isoxazolidines; additions to olefins; bridged polycyclic molecules. *Mailing Add:* 277 Chem Bldg Wayne State Univ Detroit MI 48202

LEBEL, RONALD GUY, b Edmundston, NB, Feb 10, 32; m 64; c 1. PHYSICAL CHEMISTRY, CHEMICAL ENGINEERING. *Educ:* NS Tech Col, BEng, 55; Mass Inst Technol, SM, 56; McGill Univ, PhD(phys chem), 62. *Prof Exp:* Res engr, Fraser Pulp & Paper Co Ltd, 58-59; demonstr, McGill Univ, 59-62; sr develop engr, Anglo Paper Prod Ltd, 63-65; res & develop proj coordr pulp & paper, 65-69, tech dir, Papeterie Reed Ltd, 69-80, DIR RES & DEVELOP, REED INC, 80- *Mem:* Sr mem Can Pulp & Paper Asn. *Res:* Planning, organization and coordination of research and development of projects related to the manufacture of newsprint and other paper products. *Mailing Add:* PO Box 1487 Reed Inc Quebec PQ G1K 7H9 Can

LEBEN, CURT (CHARLES), b Chicago, Ill, July 7, 17; m 44; c 2. PLANT PATHOLOGY. *Educ:* Ohio Univ, BS, 40; Univ Wis, PhD(plant path), 46. *Prof Exp:* Asst bot, Ohio Univ, 39-40; asst, Univ Wis, 42, asst plant path, 42-46, res assoc, 46-49, asst prof, 49-55; plant pathologist, Eli Lilly & Co, Ind, 55-57, head agr res labs, 57-59; prof bot & plant path & assoc chmn dept, 59-67, actg chmn, 67-68, PROF PLANT PATH, AGR RES & DEVELOP CTR, OHIO STATE UNIV, 67- *Mem:* AAAS; fel Am Phytopath Soc. *Res:* Antibiotics and antibiosis in relation to plant diseases; microbiology; epiphytic microorganisms; bacterial and decay diseases; forest tree diseases; biological control. *Mailing Add:* Dept of Plant Path Ohio Agr Res & Develop Ctr Wooster OH 44691

LEBENBAUM, MATTHEW T(OBRINER), b Portland, Ore, Nov 29, 17; m 42; c 2. ELECTRONIC ENGINEERING. *Educ:* Stanford Univ, BA, 38; Mass Inst Technol, MS, 45. *Prof Exp:* Asst elec eng, Stanford Univ, 38-39 & Mass Inst Technol, 39-41; asst syst planning engr, Am Gas & Elec Corp, 41-42; res assoc, Radio Res Lab, Harvard Univ, 42-45; DIR, APPL ELECTRONICS DIV, AIRBORNE INSTRUMENTS LAB, CUTLER-HAMMER, INC, 45- *Mem:* Fel Inst Elec & Electronics Engrs; Int Union Radio Sci. *Res:* Radio receivers, especially microwave; methods and techniques of noise measurement; intermediate frequency amplifiers; application of electronic methods to power systems; radio astronomy instrumentation; low noise devices. *Mailing Add:* 80 Whitehall Blvd Garden City NY 11530

LEBENSOHN, ZIGMOND MEYER, b Kenosha, Wis, Sept 8, 10; m 40; c 4. PSYCHIATRY. *Educ:* Northwestern Univ, BS, 30, MB, 33, MD, 34; Am Bd Psychiat & Neurol, dipl, 41. *Prof Exp:* Instr neurol, Med Sch, George Washington Univ, 36-41; PROF CLIN PSYCHIAT, MED SCH, UNIV HOSP, GEORGETOWN UNIV, 41-; CHIEF EMER, DEPT PSYCHIAT, SIBLEY MEM HOSP, 76- *Concurrent Pos:* Med officer, St Elizabeth's Hosp, 35-39; mem staff, Doctors Hosp, 41-74; consult, Vet Admin, 46-49, US Naval Hosp, Bethesda, Md, 52-, US Info Agency, 58-61, Walter Reed Army Hosp, Washington, DC, 58-66, 77- & NIMH, 68-; consult med adv panel, Fed Aviation Agency, 61-66. *Mem:* Fel Am Psychiat Asn; fel AMA; Am Psychopath Asn; Asn Res Nerv & Ment Dis. *Res:* Legal aspects of psychiatry; psychiatric hospital design; trans-cultural psychiatry. *Mailing Add:* 2015 R St NW Washington DC 20009

LEBER, PHYLLIS ANN, b Scranton, Pa. REACTION MECHANISMS. *Educ:* Albright Col, Pa, BS, 76; Univ NMex, PhD(chem), 81. *Prof Exp:* Jr chemist, Am Color & Chem Co, Reading, Pa, 71-76; asst prof org chem, Pomona Col, Claremont, Calif, 81-82; ASST PROF ORG CHEM, FRANKLIN & MARSHALL COL, PA, 82- *Mem:* Am Chem Soc; Sigma Xi. *Res:* Physical organic chemistry as it relates to the elucidation of reaction mechanisms of thermal unimolecular isomerizations, both uncatalyzed and catalyzed. *Mailing Add:* Franklin & Marshall Col Lancaster PA 17603

LEBER, SAM, b Rockford, Ill, Nov 15, 25; m 52; c 2. METALLURGY. *Educ:* Univ Ill, BS, 48, MS, 49. *Prof Exp:* X-ray crystallographer, Horizons Inc, 50-55; metallurgist, Lamp Metals & Components Dept, 55-66, supvr struct eval unit, 66-71, MGR METALS EVAL SUBSECT, REFRACTORY METALS DEPT, GEN ELEC CO, 71- *Mem:* Am Soc Metals; Am Inst Mining, Metall & Petrol Engrs. *Res:* Physical metallurgy; x-ray, optical and electron metallurgy. *Mailing Add:* Refractory Metals Dept 21800 Tungsten Rd Cleveland OH 44117

LEBERMAN, PAUL R, b NY, Mar 1, 04; m 32. UROLOGY. *Educ:* NY Univ, BS, 25; Univ Pa, MS, 27, MD, 31; Am Bd Urol, dipl, 42. *Prof Exp:* Assoc prof clin urol & asst prof urol, Grad Sch Med, 51-66, PROF CLIN UROL, UNIV PA, 66-, CHIEF UROL SURG, OUTPATIENT DEPT, HOSP, 51- *Concurrent Pos:* Chief urol, Philadelphia Gen Hosp, 59-; consult, US Naval Hosp, Philadelphia, 60- *Mem:* Fel Am Col Surg; fel Royal Soc Med; fel Int Soc Urol; fel Am Acad Pediat; fel Pan-Pac Surg Asn. *Res:* Urological surgery. *Mailing Add:* 802 Church Rd PO Box 8826 Elkins Park PA 19117

LEBERMANN, KENNETH WAYNE, b Davenport, Iowa; m 62; c 2. FOOD SCIENCES. *Educ:* Univ Ill, Urbana, BS, 59, PhD(food sci), 64; Univ Calif, Davis, MS, 61. *Prof Exp:* Scientist, CPC Int, 64-66; group leader cereals, 66-67, sr group leader bakery prod, 67-69, sect mgr bakery prod, 69-70, sect mgr pet foods, 70-75, mgr pet food res, 75-78, asst dir, 78, dir, 78-79, VPRES RES, QUAKER OATS CO, 79- *Mem:* Inst Food Technologists; Sigma Xi. *Res:* Industrial research related to new product development, pet food research. *Mailing Add:* Quaker Oats Co 617 W Main St Barrington IL 60010

LEBHERZ, HERBERT G, b San Francisco, Calif, July 27, 41; div. BIOCHEMISTRY. *Educ:* San Francisco State Univ, BA, 64, MA, 66; Univ Wash, PhD(biochem), 70. *Prof Exp:* From res assoc to sr res assoc cell biol, Swiss Fed Inst Technol, 71-75; cancer res sci biochem, Roswell Park Mem Inst, 75-76; assoc prof, 76-80, PROF BIOCHEM, SAN DIEGO STATE UNIV, 80- *Mem:* Am Heart Asn; Am Soc Biol Chemists; AAAS. *Res:* Elucidation of the mechanisms involved in the regulation of protein synthesis and protein degradation in developing adult and diseased organisms. *Mailing Add:* Dept of Chem San Diego State Univ San Diego CA 92115

LEBIEDZIK, JOZEF, b Feb 13, 40; US citizen; m 69; c 1. QUANTITATIVE MICROSCOPY, MATERIALS SCIENCE. *Educ:* Pa State Univ, BS, 70, MS, 72, PhD(solid state sci), 75. *Prof Exp:* Res asst quant micros, Mat Res Lab, Pa State Univ, 70-75; res assoc, 75-76; V PRES RES & DEVELOP QUANT MICROS, LEMONT SCI INC, 76- *Mem:* Microbeam Anal Soc. on automated scanning electron microscopes or electron probe systems; laboratory automation. *Mailing Add:* 2638 Acacia Dr State College PA 16801

LEBLANC, ADRIAN DAVID, b Salem, Mass, May 21, 40; m 66; c 2. RADIOLOGICAL PHYSICS, NUCLEAR MEDICINE. *Educ:* Univ Mass, BA, 62; Iowa State Univ, MS, 66; Univ Kans, PhD(radiation biophys), 72; Am Bd Health Physics, cert; Am Bd Radiol, cert in nuclear med physics. *Prof Exp:* HEALTH PHYSICIST, HOSP & RADIOL PHYSICIST, DEPT NUCLEAR MED, METHODIST HOSP, 66-; ASST PROF MED, BAYLOR COL MED, 72- *Concurrent Pos:* Radiation physicist, Vet Admin Hosp, 67- *Mem:* Health Physics Soc; Soc Nuclear Med; Am Asn Physicists in Med; Am Col Radiol; Sigma Xi. *Res:* Coronary blood flow; neutron activation analysis; x-ray fluorescence; health physics. *Mailing Add:* 7810 Braeburn Valley Dr Houston TX 77036

LEBLANC, ARTHUR EDGAR, b Moncton, NB, Sept 29, 23; US citizen; m 52; c 2. GEOLOGY, PALYNOLOGY. *Educ:* Univ Mass, Amherst, BS, 52, MS, 54. *Prof Exp:* Paleontologist, Shell Oil Co, Tex, 54-62 & Calif, 62-65; sr res scientist, Res Ctr, Pan Am Petrol Corp, Okla, 65-69; proj palynologist, 69-77, SR PROJ GEOLOGIST, GULF OIL RES & DEVELOP CO, 77- *Mem:* AAAS; Am Asn Petrol Geologists; Soc Econ Paleontologists & Mineralogists; Am Asn Stratig Palynologists. *Res:* Stratigraphic Paleozoic palynology; Mesozoic and Cenozoic stratigraphic palynology. *Mailing Add:* Gulf Oil Res & Develop Co HTSC PO Box 36506 Houston TX 77036

LEBLANC, FABIUS, bryology, ecology, see previous edition

LEBLANC, FRANCIS ERNEST, b North Sydney, NS, June 10, 35; m 61; c 3. NEUROPHYSIOLOGY, NEUROSURGERY. *Educ:* St Francis Xavier Univ, BSc, 55; Univ Ottawa, MD, 59; Univ Montreal, MSc, 62, PhD(neurophysiol), 64; FRCS(C), 68. *Prof Exp:* Intern, Montreal Gen Hosp, Que, 59-60, jr asst resident surg, Queen Mary Vet Hosp, Montreal, 60-61; res asst, Neurol Sci Lab, Univ Montreal, 61-62, lectr physiol, Univ, 61-64;

demonstr neurol, McGill Univ, 64-67, lectr neurosurg, 67-68, asst prof, 68-70; asst prof, 71-74, ASSOC PROF SURG, UNIV CALGARY, 74-; CHIEF, DIV NEUROSURG, FOOTHILLS HOSP, CALGARY, 74- *Concurrent Pos:* Med Res Coun fel, Univ Montreal, 61-64, res fel, 62-64; clin fel & chief resident, Montreal Neurol Inst, 66-67, res scholar, 67-70, asst neurosurgeon, 68; consult, Queen Mary Vet Hosp, Montreal, 67; vis neurosurgeon, Royal Victoria Hosp, Montreal, 68; consult neurosurgeon, Foothills Hosp, 71-74. *Mem:* Can Neurosurg Soc; Cong Neurol Surg; Asn Acad Surg; fel Am Col Surg. *Res:* Cerebrovascular physiology; epilepsy; movement disorders. *Mailing Add:* Sch of Med Univ of Calgary Calgary AB T2N 1N4 Can

LEBLANC, GABRIEL, b Montreal, Que, June 24, 27; m 68. GEOPHYSICS, SEISMOLOGY. *Educ:* Univ Montreal, BA, 52; L'Immaculee-Conception, Montreal, LPh, 53; Boston Col, MSc, 58, SThL, 60; Pa State Univ, PhD(geophys), 66. *Prof Exp:* Res asst seismol, Pa State Univ, 63-66; assoc prof geophys, Laval Univ, 66-71; sr res scientist, Seismol Div, Dept Energy, Mines & Resources, 71-76; SR STAFF CONSULT & CHIEF SEISMOLOGIST, WESTON GEOPHYS CORP, 77- *Mem:* Am Geophys Union; Can Geophys Union; Can Asn Physicists; Seismol Soc Am; Soc Explor Geophys. *Res:* Regional tectonics and local seismicity; seismic risk analysis; strong motion; induced seismicity; local arrays. *Mailing Add:* Weston Geophys Corp PO Box 550 Westboro MA 01581

LEBLANC, JACQUES ARTHUR, b Quebec, Que, Aug 23, 21; nat US; m 51; c 3. PHYSIOLOGY. *Educ:* Laval Univ, BA, 43, BSc, 47, PhD(physiol), 51. *Prof Exp:* Physiologist human physiol, Defence Res Bd, Can Dept Nat Defence, 49-56; PROF HUMAN PHYSIOL, FAC MED, LAVAL UNIV, 58- *Mem:* AAAS; Am Physiol Soc; Fedn Am Socs Exp Biol; Soc Exp Biol & Med; Fr-Can Asn Advan Sci. *Res:* Amines in stress conditions; tranquilizers; mast cells; basic and applied work in environmental physiology. *Mailing Add:* Dept of Physiol Fac of Med Laval Univ Quebec PQ C1K 7P4 Can

LEBLANC, JERALD THOMAS, b Baton Rouge, La, Mar 10, 43; m 68. PHOTOGRAPHIC SCIENCE, ORGANIC CHEMISTRY. *Educ:* Birmingham-Southern Col, BS, 65; Fla State Univ, PhD(org chem), 70. *Prof Exp:* SR CHEMIST, RES LABS, EASTMAN KODAK CO, 70- *Mem:* Soc Photog Scientists & Engr. *Res:* Silver halide chemistry and physics; organic dye synthesis. *Mailing Add:* Eastman Kodak Res Lab Rochester NY 14650

LE BLANC, JOHN ROGER, b Montreal, Can, Feb 7, 27; US citizen; m 48; c 7. ORGANIC POLYMER CHEMISTRY. *Educ:* Boston Col, BS, 50; Ohio State Univ, MS, 60. *Prof Exp:* Supvr anal chem, 51-52, supvr prod, 52-53, res chemist cent res, 53-59 & plastics res, 61-63, GROUP LEADER PLASTICS RES, MONSANTO CO, INDIAN ORCHARD, 63- *Mem:* Am Chem Soc. *Res:* Exploratory research in organic-aromatic chemistry; kinetics; photochemistry; free radical polymerization; condensation polymers; phenolic chemistry. *Mailing Add:* Springfield Lab Monsanto Co 730 Worchester St Indian Orchard MA 01151

LEBLANC, LARRY JOSEPH, b New Orleans, La, July 21, 47; m 69; c 2. OPERATIONS RESEARCH, TRANSPORTATIONS SYSTEMS. *Educ:* Loyola Univ La, New Orleans, BS, 69; Northwestern Univ, Evanston, MS, 71, PhD(opers res), 73. *Prof Exp:* Asst prof, 73-77, assoc prof opers res, Southern Methodist Univ, 77-80; ASSOC PROF MGT, VANDERBILT UNIV, 80- *Concurrent Pos:* Consult, Mississippi Chem Corp, Dr Pepper Co, Trailways, McDermott, WFAA Radio, Pan Technol, Urban Systs, US Army Inventory Res Off, US Dept Transp, US Dept Justice & John Hamburg & Assoc, Inc, 77- *Mem:* Opers Res Soc Am; Inst Mgt Sci. *Res:* Computer implementation techniques for traffic management, production and inventory control; applied optimization techniques; applied optimization techniques. *Mailing Add:* Owen Grad Sch Math Vanderbilt Univ Nashville TN 37203

LEBLANC, LEONARD JOSEPH, b Moncton, NB, Nov 6, 37; m 59; c 3. SOLID STATE PHYSICS. *Educ:* St Joseph's Univ, NB, BSc, 59; Univ Notre Dame, PhD(physics), 64. *Prof Exp:* From asst prof to assoc prof physics, 64-71, vdean fac sci, 69-74, dean fac sci & eng, 75-80, PROF PHYSICS, UNIV MONCTON, 71-, VPRES ACAD, 80- *Mem:* Am Asn Physics Teachers; Can Asn Physicists. *Res:* Optical and photoelectric properties of metals in the vacuum ultraviolet. *Mailing Add:* Dept of Physics & Math Univ de Moncton Moncton NB E1A 3E9 Can

LE BLANC, MARCEL A R, b Gravelbourg, Sask, Mar 25, 29; m 62; c 3. PHYSICS. *Educ:* Univ Ottawa, BA, 49; Univ Sask, BA, 52, MA, 54; Univ BC, PhD(physics), 58. *Prof Exp:* Res assoc physics, Stanford Univ, 59-63; asst prof elec eng, Univ Southern Calif, 63-68; PROF PHYSICS, UNIV OTTAWA, 68- *Concurrent Pos:* Asst prof, San Jose State Col, 61-62; consult, Varian Assocs, 61-62 & Spectromagnetic Industs, 62-63; mem tech staff & consult, Aerospace Corp, 63-68. *Mem:* Am Phys Soc; Can Asn Physicists. *Res:* Photonuclear cross-sections; nuclear polarization; low temperature physics; superconductivity. *Mailing Add:* Dept of Physics Univ of Ottawa Ottawa ON K1N 6N5 Can

LEBLANC, NORMAN FRANCIS, b Boston, Mass, June 28, 26; m 52; c 4. ANALYTICAL CHEMISTRY, RESEARCH ADMINISTRATION. *Educ:* Tufts Univ, BS, 47; Mass Inst Technol, PhD(anal chem), 50. *Prof Exp:* Res chemist, 50-56, res chemist solid rocket res & develop, 56-68, dir develop, Polymers Dept, 68-73, dir, Home Furnishings Div, 73-81, DIR PLASTICS BUS GROUP, HERCULES, INC, 81- *Mem:* Am Chem Soc. *Mailing Add:* Hercules Inc 910 Market St Wilmington DE 19899

LEBLANC, OLIVER HARRIS, JR, b Beaumont, Tex, Nov 14, 31; m 56; c 1. PHYSICAL CHEMISTRY. *Educ:* Rice Univ, BA, 53; Univ Calif, PhD, 57. *Prof Exp:* PHYS CHEMIST, RES & DEVELOP CTR, GEN ELEC CO, 57- *Mem:* AAAS; Am Chem Soc. *Res:* Electrochemical sensors; high temperature chemistry; membrane biophysics. *Mailing Add:* 1173 Phoenix Ave Schenectady NY 12308

LEBLANC, ROBERT BRUCE, b Alexandria, La, Jan 28, 25; m 68; c 7. INORGANIC CHEMISTRY. *Educ:* Loyola Univ, BS, 47; Tulane Univ, MS, 49, PhD(chem), 50. *Prof Exp:* Asst prof chem, Tex A&M Univ, 50-52; res specialist, Org Res Dept, Dow Chem Co, 52-63, sr textile specialist, 63-67; textile chem develop mgr, ADM Chem Div, Ashland Oil Co, 67-68; res mgr, Nat Cotton Coun, 68-70; PRES, LEBLANC RES CORP, 70- *Concurrent Pos:* Mem, Info Coun Fabric Flammability. *Mem:* Am Chem Soc; Am Asn Textile Chemists & Colorists; Am Soc Testing & Mat; Nat Fire Protection Asn. *Res:* Textile chemistry and phosphorus chemistry; flammability and fire retardance of textiles and plastics. *Mailing Add:* LeBlanc Res Corp 6172 Post Rd North Kingstown RI 02852

LEBLANC, RUFUS JOSEPH, b Erath, La, Oct 12, 17; m 40; c 4. GEOLOGY. *Educ:* La State Univ, BS, 39, MS, 41. *Prof Exp:* Asst geologist, La State Univ, 41-43; geologist, Miss River Comn, US War Dept, 44-46, chief geol sect, 47-48; sr res geologist, 48-52, mgr dept geol res, 53-56, sr geologist, Tech Servs, 57-60, sr staff geologist, Explor Dept, Offshore Div, 61-65, MEM STAFF EXPLOR TRAINING DEPT, CLASTIC SEDIMENTS, SHELL OIL CO, 65- *Concurrent Pos:* Mem comt fundamental res occurrence and recovery petrol, Am Petrol Inst, 52-57; assoc ed, J Am Asn Petrol Geologists. *Mem:* Fel Geol Soc Am; hon mem Soc Econ Paleont & Mineral; hon mem Am Asn Petrol Geologists. *Res:* Fundamental research in stratigraphy and sedimentology; exploration for oil and gas; quaternary geology; exploration training. *Mailing Add:* Shell Oil Co 3737 Bellaire Blvd Box 481 Houston TX 77001

LEBLEU, RONALD EUGENE, b Lexington, Ky, Feb 26, 37; m 60; c 1. ORGANIC CHEMISTRY. *Educ:* Transylvania Col, BA, 57; Duke Univ, PhD(org chem), 61. *Prof Exp:* Res chemist, Org Chem Dept, 60-63, col rels rep, Employee Rels Dept, 63-67, res asst, 67-68, proj leader, 68-70, prod mgr, Indust Finishes Dept, 70-71, mgr consult serv group cent res & develop dept, E I du Pont de Nemours & Co, Inc, 71-78; corp mgr orgn planning & employee develop, 78-81, CORP MGR PERSONNEL PLANNING, DIGITAL EQUIP CORP, 81- *Mem:* Am Chem Soc. *Res:* Nitrogen-containing heterocycles arising from aromatic cyclodehydration, synthesis and characterization of fluoropolymers; doctoral recruitment and college relations. *Mailing Add:* Digital Equip Corp Maynard MA 01754

LEBLOND, CHARLES PHILIPPE, b Lille, France, Feb 5, 10; m 36; c 4. ANATOMY. *Educ:* Univ Nancy, Lic es S, 32; Univ Paris, MD, 34; Univ Montreal, PhD(iodine metab), 42; Univ Sorbonne, DSc, 45. *Prof Exp:* Asst histol, Med Sch Paris, 34-35; Rockefeller fel, Sch Med, Yale Univ, 36-37; asst, Lab de Synthese Atomique, Paris, 38-40; lectr histol & embryol, 41-43, from asst prof to assoc prof, 43-48, chmn dept, 57-75, PROF ANAT, McGILL UNIV, 48- *Mem:* Am Asn Anat; Am Asn Cancer Res; fel Royal Soc; fel Royal Soc Can. *Res:* Histological localization of vitamin C; uptake of iodine by thyroid; tracing of radio elements and labelled precursors of nucleic acids, proteins and glycoproteins by means of radioautography. *Mailing Add:* Dept Anat 3640 University St Montreal PQ H3A 2B2 Can

LEBLOND, PAUL HENRI, b Quebec, Que, Dec 30, 38; m 63; c 3. PHYSICAL OCEANOGRAPHY. *Educ:* Laval Univ, BA, 57; McGill Univ, BSc, 61; Univ BC, PhD(physics), 64. *Prof Exp:* Nat Res Coun Can fel, Inst Meereskunde, Kiel, Ger, 64-65; from asst prof to assoc prof physics, Dept Physics & Inst Oceanog, 65-75, PROF PHYSICS & OCEANOG, INST OCEANOG, UNIV BC, 75- *Concurrent Pos:* Vis assoc prof, Simon Fraser Univ, 70; vis scientist, Inst Oceanology, USSR Acad Sci, Moscow, 73-74; vis prof, Laval Univ, 79-80; dir, Seaconsult Marine Res Ltd. *Honors & Awards:* President's Prize, Can Meteorol Oceanog Soc, 81. *Mem:* Can Meteorol Oceanog Soc; Am Geophys Union; Am Meteor Soc; Int Soc Cryptozool. *Res:* Surface, internal, planetary waves; ocean currents; tides; estuarine circulation. *Mailing Add:* Inst of Oceanog Univ of BC Vancouver BC V6T 1W5 Can

LEBO, GEORGE ROBERT, b Chadron, Nebr, Sept 27, 37; m 58; c 2. PHYSICS, RADIO ASTRONOMY. *Educ:* Wheaton Col, BS, 59; Univ Ill, MS, 60; Univ Fla, PhD(physics), 64. *Prof Exp:* Res assoc radio astron, 64-65, asst prof, 65-77, ASSOC PROF PHYSICS & ASTRON, UNIV FLA, 77- *Mem:* Am Astron Soc; Am Geophys Union; Am Phys Soc. *Res:* Study of decametric radiation from the planets, particularly Jupiter. *Mailing Add:* Dept of Physics & Astron Univ of Fla Gainesville FL 32601

LEBO, JERRY ALLEN, b Winamac, Ind, Feb 19, 39; m; c 2. ELECTRONICS ENGINEERING. *Educ:* Purdue Univ, BSEE, 61, MSEE, 62, PhD(elec eng), 65; George Washington Univ, MS, 77. *Prof Exp:* Tech staff syst anal, Autonetics Div, Rockwell Int Corp, 64-65, supvr avionics syst design, 65-71; tech staff commun syst eng, Defense Commun Agency, 71-72, chief anal studies div command control syst design, 72-74, chief syst eng div commun syst eng, Defense Commun Eng Ctr, 74-76, chief plans & anal div command control sys eng, Command Control Tech Ctr, 76-78; CHIEF COMMUN DIV COMMUN SYST ENG, SHAPE TECH CTR, 78- *Mem:* Oper Res Soc Am; Am Inst Aeronaut & Astronaut. *Res:* Communications; system engineering; operations research; command and control; computer systems; systems analysis. *Mailing Add:* Shape Tech Ctr Oude Waalsdorperweg 61 The Hague Neth

LEBOFSKY, LARRY ALLEN, b Brooklyn, NY, Aug 31, 47; m 80. PLANETARY SCIENCES. *Educ:* Calif Inst Technol, BS, 69; Mass Inst Technol, PhD(earth & planetary sci), 74. *Prof Exp:* Res assoc planetary sci, Jet Propulsion Lab, 75-77; SR RES ASSOC, UNIV ARIZ, 77- *Mem:* Am Astron Soc. *Res:* Remote sensing of the visual, near infrared and thermal infrared spectra of asteroids and satellites for the study of composition; related studies of laboratory frost reflection spectra. *Mailing Add:* Lunar & Planetary Lab Univ of Ariz Tucson AZ 85721

LEBOFSKY, MARCIA JEAN, b Hillsdale, Mich, June 13, 51; div. ASTRONOMY. *Educ:* Mass Inst Technol, SB, 72, PhD(physics), 76. *Prof Exp:* Res assoc, Lunar & Planetary Lab, 76-78, res assoc infrared astron, 78-79, ASST ASTRON, STEWARD OBSERV, UNIV ARIZ, 79- *Honors & Awards:* Van Biesbroeck Prize, 80. *Mem:* Sigma Xi; Am Astron Soc. *Res:* Infrared observations of extragalactic objects; development of infrared detectors for astronomical use. *Mailing Add:* Lunar & Planetary Lab Univ of Ariz Tucson AZ 85721

LEBOUTON, ALBERT V, b La Salle, Ill, July 10, 37; m 59; c 3. MICROSCOPIC ANATOMY, CELL BIOLOGY. *Educ:* San Diego State Col, BS, 60; Univ Calif, Los Angeles, PhD(anat), 66. *Prof Exp:* Asst prof anat, Univ Calif, Los Angeles, 66-72, actg head dept, 72-74, ASSOC PROF ANAT, UNIV ARIZ, 72- *Mem:* AAAS; Am Inst Biol Sci; Fedn Am Sci; Am Soc Cell Biol; Am Asn Anat. *Res:* Radioautography, radiobiochemistry, and immunocytochemistry of protein metabolism and growth in the liver. *Mailing Add:* Dept of Anat Univ of Ariz Col of Med Tucson AZ 85724

LEBOVITZ, NORMAN RONALD, b New York, NY, Sept 27, 35; m 71. APPLIED MATHEMATICS, ASTROPHYSICS. *Educ:* Univ Calif, Los Angeles, AB, 56; Univ Chicago, MS, 57, PhD(physics), 61. *Prof Exp:* Moore instr math, Mass Inst Technol, 61-63; from asst prof to assoc prof, 63-69, PROF MATH, UNIV CHICAGO, 69- *Concurrent Pos:* Sloan Found fel, 67; Guggenheim Found fel, 77. *Mem:* Am Astron Soc; Am Math Soc; Soc Indust & Appl Math. *Res:* Stability theory; bifurcation theory; rotating fluid masses; singular perturbation theory. *Mailing Add:* Dept of Math Univ of Chicago Chicago IL 60637

LEBOVITZ, ROBERT MARK, b Scranton, Pa, May 6, 37. NEUROPHYSIOLOGY, BIOENGINEERING. *Educ:* Calif Inst Technol, BS, 59, MS, 60; Univ Calif, Los Angeles, PhD(neurophysiol), 67. *Prof Exp:* Mem tech staff, Hughes Aircraft Co, 59-62; resident consult, Dept Math, Rand Corp, 67; NSF fel, Sch Med, NY Univ, 67-69; res assoc neural models, Ctr Theoret Biol, State Univ NY Buffalo, 69; staff scientist auditory & visual info processing, Recognition Equip, Inc, 69-70; assoc prof, 70-80, PROF NEUROPHYSIOL, UNIV TEX HEALTH SCI CTR, DALLAS, 80- *Concurrent Pos:* Consult, Dept Path & Eng Sci, Rand Corp, 69, Recognition Equip, Inc, 69, Neurosyst, Inc, 71, Dallas Epilepsy Asn, 71, Energy Conversion Devices, 71 & Equitable Environ Health, 71-; chief technical officer, Centra-Guard Inc & Neighborhood Coop Patrol, 69-71; NSF fel, Univ Tex Regents, 70-72; adj prof, Inst Technol, Southern Methodist Univ, 71-74; prof bd, Home Health Serv, Dallas, 74-; NIH grants, 71-, Food & Drug Admin grant, 74-, Nat Inst Environ Health Sci grant, 77- & Off Naval Res Contracts, 78-; Sloan Consortium scholar, 74-75. *Mem:* Am Physiol Soc; NY Acad Sci; Biophys Soc; Inst Elec & Electronics Eng; Soc Neurosci. *Res:* Neurophysiology of epilepsy and behavior; modification and control of behavior via drugs and implanted or extraneous brain stimulating arrays; microwave interactions with the nervous system and behavior; electronic medicine. *Mailing Add:* Dept Physiol Univ Tex Health Sci Ctr Dallas TX 75235

LEBOW, ARNOLD, mathematics, see previous edition

LEBOW, IRWIN L(EON), b Boston, Mass, Apr 27, 26; m 51; c 3. ELECTRONICS. *Educ:* Mass Inst Technol, SB, 48, PhD(physics), 51. *Prof Exp:* Mem staff, Lincoln Lab, Mass Inst Technol, 51-60, assoc group leader, 60-65, group leader, 65-70, assoc div head, 70-75; chief scientist & assoc dir technol, Defense Commun Agency, 75-81; VPRES ENG, AM SATELLITE CO, 81- *Mem:* Fel Am Phys Soc; fel Inst Elec & Electronics Engrs; AAAS. *Res:* Communication systems, including, satellite communications, command and control systems and information processing systems. *Mailing Add:* 1801 Research Blvd Rockville MD 20850

LEBOWITZ, ELLIOT, b Monticello, NY, June 19, 41; m 63; c 4. NUCLEAR MEDICINE, NUCLEAR CHEMISTRY. *Educ:* Columbia Univ, BA, 61, PhD(nuclear chem), 67. *Prof Exp:* Res assoc chem kinetics & asst chemist, Dept Chem, Brookhaven Nat Lab, NY, 67-69, assoc chemist, Dept Appl Sci, 69-75; asst to vpres & actg dir drug regulatory affairs, 75-76, div mgr radiopharmaceut div, 76-78, DIV MGR, MED DIAG DIV, 78- NEW ENG NUCLEAR CORP, 75- *Res:* Nuclear technology. *Mailing Add:* New England Nuclear Corp North Billerica MA 01862

LEBOWITZ, JACOB, b Brooklyn, NY, Oct 20, 35; m 78. MOLECULAR BIOLOGY, BIOCHEMISTRY. *Educ:* Brooklyn Col, BS, 57; Purdue Univ, PhD(phys chem), 62. *Prof Exp:* Res fel biophys chem, Calif Inst Technol, 62-66; from asst prof to assoc prof biochem, Syracuse Univ, 66-74; assoc prof, 74-77, PROF MICROBIOL, MED CTR, UNIV ALA, BIRMINGHAM, 77- *Mem:* AAAS; Am Chem Soc; Am Soc Microbiol; Biophys Soc; Am Soc Biol Chemists. *Res:* Physical chemistry and molecular biology of nucleic acids and proteins in relation to their biological structure-function relationships, with particular emphasis on super helical DNA. *Mailing Add:* Dept of Microbiol Univ of Ala Med Ctr Birmingham AL 35294

LEBOWITZ, JACOB MORDECAI, b New York, NY, Mar 21, 36; m 65; c 2. NUCLEAR PHYSICS. *Educ:* Yeshiva Univ, BA, 57; Columbia Univ, MA, 60, PhD(physics), 65. *Prof Exp:* From instr to asst prof, 59-70, ASSOC PROF PHYSICS, BROOKLYN COL, 70- *Mem:* Am Phys Soc. *Res:* Nuclear forces; fission. *Mailing Add:* Dept of Physics Brooklyn Col Brooklyn NY 11210

LEBOWITZ, JOEL LOUIS, b Taceva, Czech, May 10, 30; nat US; m 53. PHYSICS. *Educ:* Brooklyn Col, BS, 52; Syracuse Univ, MS, 55, PhD(physics), 56. *Prof Exp:* NSF res fel, Yale Univ, 56-57; asst prof physics, Stevens Inst Technol, 57-59; from asst prof to assoc prof, 57-65, prof physics, Grad Sch Sci, Yeshiva Univ, 65-77; PROF MATH & PHYSICS & DIR CTR MATH SCI RES, RUTGERS UNIV, 77- *Concurrent Pos:* Vis prof, Sch Med, Cornell Univ; Guggenheim fel, 76-77. *Mem:* Nat Acad Sci; NY Acad Sci (pres-elect, 77-79, pres, 79); Am Phys Soc; Am Math Soc; AAAS. *Res:* Statistical mechanics of equilibrium and nonequilibrium processes; theory of liquids; biomathematics and mathematical economics. *Mailing Add:* Dept of Math Hill Ctr Rutgers Univ New Brunswick NJ 08903

LEBOWITZ, MICHAEL DAVID, b New York, NY, Dec 21, 39; m 60; c 3. EPIDEMIOLOGY, PULMONARY DISEASES. *Educ:* Univ Calif, Berkeley, AB, 61, MA, 65; Univ Wash, PhC, 69, PhD(epidemiol), 71. *Prof Exp:* Pub health statistician, Alameda County Health Dept, 62-63; biostatistician, Calif Dept Pub Health, 67; res assoc environ health, Univ Wash, 67-71; asst prof internal med, 71-75, assoc prof, 75-80, PROF INTERNAL MED, COL MED, UNIV ARIZ, 80-, ASST DIR SPECIALIZED CTR RES, 71-, ASST DIR DIV RESPIRATORY SCI, 74- *Concurrent Pos:* Partic, NSF-Japan Soc Promotion Sci Coop Sci Group in Air Pollution, 69-70; consult, NIH & Nat Heart & Lung Inst, 72-; mem, toxicol prog comt, Univ Ariz, 74-, environ coun,75-; mem, environ health effects comt, Ariz State Dept Health, 75-; mem, epidemiol study sect, NIH, 75-78, behav study sect, 77; assoc prog dir, NIH Inst Training Prog, 77-; Fogarty sr int fel, 78-79; sr fel, Univ London, Postgrad Cardiothoracic Inst, Brompton, 78-79; co-chmn, comt indoor pollutants, Nat Res Coun, Nat Acad Sci, 79-81; WHO adv, 79- *Mem:* Int Epidemiol Asn; Asn Teachers Prev Med; Am Thoracic Soc; Biomet Soc; Soc Epidemiol Res. *Res:* Pulmonary and chronic disease epidemiology; etiology and natural history of pulmonary diseases and other chronic diseases; air pollution health effects research. *Mailing Add:* Ariz Med Ctr Sect Pulmonary Dis Univ Ariz Col of Med Tucson AZ 85724

LEBOY, PHOEBE STARFIELD, b Brooklyn, NY, July 29, 36. BIOCHEMISTRY. *Educ:* Swarthmore Col, AB, 57; Bryn Mawr Col, PhD(biochem), 62. *Hon Degrees:* MA, Univ Pa, 71. *Prof Exp:* Res assoc biochem, Bryn Mawr Col, 61-63; res assoc, Sch Med, 63-66, from instr to assoc prof, 65-76, PROF BIOCHEM, SCH DENT MED, UNIV PA, 76- *Concurrent Pos:* NATO fel, Weizmann Inst Sci, 66-67; USPHS res grant, Univ Pa, 68-, NIH res career develop award, 71-76; vis prof, Univ Calif, San Francisco, 79-80. *Mem:* Am Soc Biol Chem; Am Soc Microbiol; Am Soc Cell Biol; Am Asn Cancer Res. *Res:* Control of protein and nucleic acid metabolism; RNA methylation. *Mailing Add:* Dept of Biochem Sch Dent Med Univ of Pa Philadelphia PA 19104

LEBRETON, PIERRE ROBERT, b Chicago, Ill, Sept 17, 42; m 69; c 2. CHEMICAL PHYSICS, BIOPHYSICS. *Educ:* Univ Chicago, BS, 64; Harvard Univ, MA, 66, PhD(chem Physics), 70. *Prof Exp:* Fel physics, Phys Inst, Univ Freiburg, Ger, 70-71; fel chem, Jet Propulsion Lab, Calif Inst Technol, 71-73; asst prof, 73-78, ASSOC PROF CHEM, UNIV ILL, CHICAGO, 78- *Concurrent Pos:* NIH grant, 80-83. *Mem:* Am Chem Soc; Am Phys Soc. *Rcs:* Photoclcctron and fluorescence studies of electronic structure and its influence upon the activity of nuclotide bases and carcinogenic hydrocarbons. *Mailing Add:* Dept of Chem Univ of Ill Chicago IL 60680

LEBRIE, STEPHEN JOSEPH, b Long Island City, NY, Jan 23, 31; m 56; c 2. MEDICAL PHYSIOLOGY. *Educ:* Long Island Univ, BS, 53; Princeton Univ, MA, 55, PhD(biol), 56. *Prof Exp:* Assoc surg res, Sch Med, Univ Pa, 56-57; from instr to assoc prof, Sch Med, Tulane Univ, 57-66; assoc prof, 66-70, PROF PHYSIOL, OHIO STATE UNIV, 70- *Honors & Awards:* Lederle Med Fac Award, 59-62. *Mem:* Am Physiol Soc; Am Soc Nephrology; Int Soc Nephrology; Soc Exp Biol & Med. *Res:* Renal lymphatics; comparative renal; renal endocrines. *Mailing Add:* Dept Physiol Ohio State Univ Columbus OH 43210

LEBRUN, ROGER ARTHUR, b Providence, RI, May 26, 46. ENTOMOLOGY, INVERTEBRATE PATHOLOGY. *Educ:* Providence Col, AB, 68; Cornell Univ, MSc, 73, PhD(invert path), 77. *Prof Exp:* ASST PROF INVERT PATH, UNIV RI, 77- *Mem:* Soc Invert Path; Entom Soc Am; Sigma Xi. *Res:* Protozoan and fungal pathogens of insects; ciliate parasites of medically important insects; fungal pathogens of coleoptera; host-parasite relationships; microbial ecology of pathogens. *Mailing Add:* Dept of Plant Path & Entom Univ of RI Kingston RI 02881

LEBSOCK, KENNETH L, b Brush, Colo, Oct 19, 21; m 43; c 2. AGRONOMY. *Educ:* Mont State Col, BS, 49; NDak State Univ, MS, 51; Iowa State Col, PhD(plant breeding), 53. *Prof Exp:* Wheat breeding & genetics, 53-72, AGR ADMINR, AGR RES SERV, USDA, 72- *Mem:* Fel Am Soc Agron. *Mailing Add:* 3045 Shorewood Lane St Paul MN 55113

LE CAM, LUCIEN MARIE, b Croze, France, Nov 18, 24; m 52; c 3. MATHEMATICAL STATISTICS. *Educ:* Univ Paris, Lic, 45; Univ Calif, PhD, 52. *Prof Exp:* Statistician, Elec of France, 45-50; instr math & asst, Statist Lab, 50-52, instr & jr res statistician, 52-53, from asst prof to prof statist, 53-73, chmn dept, 61-65, PROF STATIST & MATH, UNIV CALIF, BERKELEY, 73- *Concurrent Pos:* Dir, Ctr Math Res, Univ Montreal, 72, mem adv comt, 74- *Mem:* Am Math Soc; Inst Math Statist (pres, 72-73); Int Statist Inst; fel Am Acad Arts & Sci; fel AAAS. *Res:* General statistics. *Mailing Add:* Dept Statist Univ Calif Berkeley CA 94720

LECAR, HAROLD, b Brooklyn, NY, Oct 18, 35; m 58; c 2. BIOPHYSICS. *Educ:* Columbia Univ, AB, 57, PhD(physics), 63. *Prof Exp:* BIOPHYSICIST, LAB BIOPHYS, NAT INST NEUROL & COMMUNICATIVE DISORDERS & STROKE, 63- *Concurrent Pos:* Fel commoner, Churchill Col, Cambridge Univ, 75-76; regents lectr, Univ Calif, San Diego, 82. *Mem:* AAAS; Am Phys Soc; Biophys Soc; Sigma Xi. *Res:* Masers; biophysics of excitable membranes. *Mailing Add:* Rm 2A29 Bldg 36 Nat Inst Neurol Communicative Disorders & Stroke Bethesda MD 20014

LECAR, MYRON, b Brooklyn, NY, Apr 10, 30. ASTROPHYSICS. *Educ:* Mass Inst Technol, BS, 51; Case Inst Technol, MS, 53; Yale Univ, PhD(astron), 63. *Prof Exp:* Lectr astrophys, Yale Univ Observ, 62-65; LECTR ASTROPHYS, COL OBSERV, HARVARD UNIV, 65-; ASTRONR, SMITHSONIAN ASTROPHYS OBSERV, 65- *Concurrent Pos:* Astronr, Inst Space Studies, NASA, 62-65. *Mem:* Am Astron Soc; Fedn Am Scientists; Royal Astron Soc; Int Astron Union. *Res:* Dynamics of the solar system; stellar dynamics and galactic structure; cosmology. *Mailing Add:* Ctr Astrophys Harvard Col Observ & Smithsonian Astrophys Observ Cambridge MA 02138

LECAT, ROBERT J(OSEPH), aerodynamics, see previous edition

LECATO, GEORGE LEONARD, III, entomology, see previous edition

LECCE, JAMES GIACOMO, b Williamsport, Pa, Jan 11, 26; m 50. MICROBIOLOGY. *Educ:* Dartmouth Col, BA, 49; Pa State Univ, MS, 51; Univ Pa, PhD(microbiol), 53. *Prof Exp:* Instr prev med, Sch Vet Med, Univ Pa, 53-55; from asst prof to assoc prof microbiol, 55-63, PROF MICROBIOL, NC STATE UNIV, 63-, PROF ANIMAL SCI, 76- *Mem:* Am Soc Microbiol. *Res:* Pleuropneumonia-like organisms; large viruses; plasma proteins. *Mailing Add:* Dept of Animal Sci NC State Univ Raleigh NC 27607

LECH, JOHN JAMES, b Passaic, NJ, June 21, 40. PHARMACOLOGY. *Educ:* Rutgers Univ, Newark, BS, 62; Marquette Univ, PhD(pharmacol), 67. *Prof Exp:* From instr to asst prof, 67-74, assoc prof pharmacol, 74-80, PROF PHARMACOL & TOXICOL, MED COL WIS, 80- *Concurrent Pos:* Am Heart Asn grant, Med Col Wis, 72-75, Sea grant, 71-75. *Mem:* AAAS; Soc Toxicol; Am Fisheries Soc; Am Soc Pharmacol & Exp Therapeut. *Res:* Cardiac triglyceride metabolism; metabolism of foreign compounds by fish. *Mailing Add:* Med Col Wis PO Box 26509 Milwaukee WI 53226

LECHEVALIER, HUBERT ARTHUR, b Tours, France, May 12, 26; nat US; m 50; c 2. MICROBIOLOGY. *Educ:* Laval Univ, MS, 48; Rutgers Univ, PhD(microbiol), 51. *Prof Exp:* Asst prof, 51-56, assoc prof, Inst Microbiol, 56-66, PROF MICROBIOL, WAKSMAN INST MICROBIOL, RUTGERS UNIV, NEW BRUNSWICK, 66- *Concurrent Pos:* Exchange scientist, Acad Sci USSR, 58-59; USPHS spec fel, Pasteur Inst, Paris, 61-62. *Mem:* Mycol Soc Am; Am Soc Microbiol; Soc for Indust Microbiol; assoc foreign mem Fr Soc Microbiol; Can Soc Microbiol. *Res:* Morphology, classification and products of actinomycetes, including antibiotics; history of microbiology. *Mailing Add:* 28 Juniper Lane Piscataway NJ 08854

LECHEVALIER, MARY P, b Cleveland, Ohio, Jan 27, 28; m 50; c 2. MICROBIOLOGY. *Educ:* Mt Holyoke Col, BA, 49; Rutgers Univ, MS, 51. *Prof Exp:* Res microbiologist, E R Squibb & Sons, 60-61; res assoc, 62-75, asst res prof, 75-81, ASSOC RES PROF MICROBIOL, RUTGERS UNIV, PISCATAWAY, 81- *Mem:* AAAS; Brit Soc Gen Microbiol; Am Soc Microbiol; Soc Indust Microbiol. *Res:* Classification, ecology, physiology and natural products of actinomycetes; microbial transformations. *Mailing Add:* Waksman Inst Microbiol Rutgers Univ PO Box 759 Piscatway NJ 08854

LECHLEIDER, J W, b Brooklyn, NY, Feb 22, 33; m 55; c 2. MATHEMATICS, COMPUTER SOFTWARE. *Educ:* Cooper Union, BME, 54; Polytech Inst Brooklyn, MEE, 57, PhD(elec eng), 65. *Prof Exp:* Engr, Gen Elec Co, 54-55; mem tech staff, Bell Tel Labs, 55-65, supvr transmission studies, Outside Plant & Underwater Systs Div, 65-67, head outside plant eng dept, 67-70, head loop transmission maintenance eng dept, 70-76, HEAD, MDF SOFTWARE DESIGN DEPT, BELL LABS, 76- *Mem:* Sr mem Inst Elec & Electronics Engrs; Am Math Soc. *Res:* Electromagnetic theory; communication theory; transmission theory. *Mailing Add:* Bell Labs Whippany Rd Whippany NJ 07981

LECHNER, BERNARD J, b New York, NY, Jan 25, 32; m 53. RESEARCH MANAGEMENT, TELEVISION SYSTEMS. *Educ:* Columbia Univ, BSEE, 57. *Prof Exp:* Mem tech staff, 57-62, group head, 62-77, LAB DIR, RCA LABS, 77- *Honors & Awards:* David Sarnoff Award, RCA Corp, 62, RCA Labs Achievement Awards, 62 & 67; Paper Prize, Int Solid State Circuits Conf, 65; Frances Rice Darne Award, Soc Info Display, 71. *Mem:* Fel Inst Elec & Electronics Engrs; fel Soc Info Display (vpres, 76-78, pres, 78-80). *Res:* Video-tape recording; high speed digital computer circuits; tunnel diodes; display devices and systems; ferroelectrics; electroluminescence; magnetic thin films; instrumentation; liquid crystals; digital television systems; TV receivers; TV tuning systems; TV broadcast equipment. *Mailing Add:* RCA Labs Princeton NJ 08540

LECHNER, JAMES ALBERT, b Danville, Pa, Aug 6, 33; m 56; c 3. APPLIED STATISTICS, RELIABILITY. *Educ:* Carnegie Inst Technol, BS, 54; Princeton Univ, PhD(math statist), 59. *Prof Exp:* Instr math, Princeton Univ, 57-58; sr mathematician, Res Labs, Westinghouse Elec Corp, Pa, 60-63, adv mathematician, Aerospace Div, Md, 63-67; mem tech staff, Res Anal Corp, Va, 67-71; MATH STATISTICIAN, STATIST ENG LAB, NAT BUR STANDARDS, 71- *Mem:* Am Soc Testing & Mat; Am Statist Asn. *Res:* Probability; theory of reliability; systems analysis; stochastic processes. *Mailing Add:* Statist Eng Lab Nat Bur of Standards Washington DC 20234

LECHNER, ROBERT JOSEPH, b Danville, Pa, Oct 16, 31; m 55; c 6. APPLIED MATHEMATICS, INFORMATION SCIENCE. *Educ:* Carnegie Inst Technol, BS, 52, MS, 53; Harvard Univ, PhD(appl math), 63. *Prof Exp:* Sr engr, Sylvania Electronics Corp, 55-57, res engr, 57-59, adv res engr, 59-61, eng specialist, 61-63, sr eng specialist, 63-70; sr engr, Honeywell Info Systs, 70-75; sr engr, C S Draper Lab, 75-76; ASSOC PROF ELEC ENG, NORTHEASTERN UNIV, 76- *Mem:* Inst Elec & Electronics Engrs; Asn Comput Mach. *Res:* Applications of modern algebra to the information sciences; information processing and communications systems; programming languages; software engineering; computer architecture. *Mailing Add:* Dept of Elec Eng 300 Huntington Ave Boston MA 02115

LECHOWICH, RICHARD V, b Chicago, Ill, June 23, 33; m 57; c 5. FOOD SCIENCE, FOOD MICROBIOLOGY. *Educ:* Univ Chicago, AB, 52, MS, 55; Univ Ill, PhD(food sci), 58. *Prof Exp:* Microbiologist, Am Meat Inst Found, Ill, 52-55; res asst food sci, Univ Ill, Urbana, 55-58; res microbiologist, Continental Can Co, Inc, Ill, 58-63; asst prof food sci, Mich State Univ, 63-66, from assoc prof to prof, 66-71; PROF FOOD SCI & TECHNOL & HEAD DEPT, VA POLYTECH INST & STATE UNIV, 71- *Mem:* AAAS; Int Asn Milk, Food & Environ Sanitarians; Inst Food Technologists; Am Soc Microbiologists; Brit Soc Appl Bact. *Res:* Mechanisms of bacterial spore formation and germination; chemical composition and thermal resistance phenomena of bacterial spores; food poisoning microorganisms, especially Clostridium botulinum; thermal and radiation resistances of microorganisms. *Mailing Add:* Dept of Food Sci & Technol Va Polytech Inst & State Univ Blacksburg VA 24061

LECHOWICZ, MARTIN JOHN, b Chicago, Ill, Feb 23, 47; m 77. PLANT ECOLOGY, EVOLUTIONARY BIOLOGY. *Educ:* Mich State Univ, BA, 69; Univ Wis-Madison, MSc, 73, PhD(plant ecol), 76. *Prof Exp:* Lectr ecol, Dept Bot, Univ Wis-Madison, 75; asst prof, 76-80, ASSOC PROF PLANT ECOL, MCGILL UNIV, 81- *Concurrent Pos:* Operating grant, Nat Res Coun Can, 77-83, strategic grant, 80-83; Dept Indian & Northern Affairs grant, 77-78; Environ Can contracts, 79-82; Atmospheric Environ Serv grant, 81- *Mem:* Ecol Soc Am; Can Bot Asn; Soc Study Evolution; Am Soc Naturalists. *Res:* Physiological ecology and population biology of plants in diverse environments, and particularly on the uptake and allocation of carbon. *Mailing Add:* Dept of Biol McGill Univ 1205 McGregor St Montreal PQ H3A 1B1 Can

LECHTENBERG, VICTOR L, b Butte, Nebr, Apr 14, 45; m 67; c 4. AGRONOMY. *Educ:* Univ Nebr, BS, 67; Purdue Univ, PhD(agron), 71. *Prof Exp:* From instr to asst prof agron, 69-75, assoc prof, 75-79, prof, 79-82, ASSOC DIR, AGR EXP STA, PURDUE UNIV, WEST LAFAYETTE, 82- *Honors & Awards:* Ciba-Geigy Award, Am Soc Agron, 77. *Mem:* Am Soc Agron; Crop Sci Soc Am; Am Soc Animal Sci; Am Forage & Grassland Coun; Am Asn Advan Sci. *Res:* Factors that affect forage crop quality and utilization; environmental physiology of forage crops; genetic improvement of crop quality. *Mailing Add:* Dept of Agron Purdue Univ West Lafayette IN 47906

LECHTMAN, MAX DRESSLER, b Providence, RI, Apr 24, 35; m 62; c 3. MICROBIOLOGY. *Educ:* Univ RI, AB, 57; Univ Mass, MS, 59; Univ Southern Calif, PhD(microbiol), 68. *Prof Exp:* Microbiologist, Douglas Aircraft Co, Calif, 61-62 & Res & Develop Div, Magna Chem Co, 62-64; instr microbiol, Univ Southern Calif, 64; microbiol consult, Garrett Corp, 64-65, microbiologist, AiRes Mfg Co Div, 65-67; mem tech staff aerospace microbiol, Autonetics Div, NAm, Rockwell Corp, Anaheim, 67-71; INDUST CONSULT, 71- *Concurrent Pos:* Instr, Calif Community Col Syst, 71- *Mem:* Am Soc Microbiol; Soc Indust Microbiol. *Res:* Microbial cytology, cytochemistry and physiology; bioluminescent bacteria for detection of toxic chemicals. *Mailing Add:* 8641 Delray Circle Westminster CA 92683

LECK, CHARLES FREDERICK, b Princeton, NJ, June 20, 44. ORNITHOLOGY, ECOLOGY. *Educ:* Muhlenberg Col, BS, 66; Cornell Univ, PhD(vert zool), 70. *Prof Exp:* Vis res assoc, Smithsonian Trop Res Inst, 68-69; ASSOC PROF ECOL, RUTGERS UNIV, NEW BRUNSWICK, 70-, DIR ECOL PROG, 74- *Concurrent Pos:* Vis fac mem, West Indies Lab, Smithsonian Trop Res Inst, 70-73. *Mem:* Wilson Ornith Soc; Cooper Ornith Soc; Am Ornith Union; Ecol Soc Am; Asn Trop Biologists. *Res:* Avian behavior and feeding ecology; tropical biology. *Mailing Add:* Dept of Zool Rutgers Univ New Brunswick NJ 08903

LECKIE, DONALD STEWART, b Chicago, Ill, June 3, 20; m 52; c 1. OPERATIONS RESEARCH, STATISTICS. *Educ:* Purdue Univ, BS, 48; Case Inst Technol, MS, 55, PhD(opers res), 60. *Prof Exp:* Qual control engr, 48-57, planning engr, Res & Planning Div, 57-65, head div math, Res Ctr, 65-77, MGR OPERS RES, CORP PLANNING DEPT, REPUB STEEL CORP, 77- *Concurrent Pos:* Lectr, Case Western Reserve Univ, 62- *Mem:* Sr mem Am Soc Qual Control; Am Iron & Steel Inst; Inst Math Statist; assoc Opers Res Soc Am; Inst Mgt Sci. *Res:* Application of mathematical and statistical methods to the solution of management problems; application of computers to process control and to problems in research and development; systems engineering. *Mailing Add:* Corp Planning Dept 307 Rep Bldg Cleveland OH 44101

LECKIE, FREDERICK ALEXANDER, b Dundee, Scotland, Mar 26, 29; m 57; c 3. ENGINEERING MECHANICS, MATERIALS ENGINEERING. *Educ:* Univ St Andrew, BSc, 49; Stanford Univ, MS, 55, PhD(eng mech), 58. *Prof Exp:* Civil engr, Mott, Hay & Anderson, Westminister, London, 49-51; res asst mech, Tech Hochsch, Hannover, Ger, 57-58; lectr, Univ Cambridge, 58-68; prof eng, Univ Leicester, 68-78; PROF THEORET & APPL MECH & MECH ENG, UNIV ILL, URBANA-CHAMPAIGN, 78- *Mem:* Am Soc Mech Engrs; Am Acad Mech. *Res:* Properties of load bearing mechanical components operating at elevated temperatures; creep rupture and fractures of materials at elevated temperatures. *Mailing Add:* Dept of Mat Eng Univ of Ill Urbana IL 61801

LECKIE, HENRY PAUL, b Ayrshire, Scotland, Sept 20, 39; m 63; c 3. METALLURGY. *Educ:* Univ London, BSc, 61, PhD(metall), 64. *Prof Exp:* Asst lectr phys chem, Univ London, 62-64; res staff corrosion, Mass Inst Technol, 64-65; sr res engr electrochem, Appl Res Lab, US Steel Corp, 65-68; assoc mgr res, Inland Steel Res Labs, 68-77, DIR RES, INLAND STEEL CO, 77- *Honors & Awards:* Eng Mat Achievement Award, Am Soc Metals, 76; John Chipman Award, Am Inst Metall Engrs, 77. *Mem:* Am Soc Metals; Am Inst Metall Engrs; Nat Asn Corrosion Engrs; Soc Automotive Engrs. *Res:* Raw materials beneficiation; iron and steel production and processing; steel product development. *Mailing Add:* Inland Steel Co 3001 E Columbus Dr East Chicago IN 46312

LECKONBY, ROY ALAN, b Bethlehem, Pa, Aug 1, 49; m 71; c 2. PHYSICAL ORGANIC CHEMISTRY, SYNTHETIC ORGANIC CHEMISTRY. *Educ:* Hamilton Col, AB, 71; Univ Rochester, MS, 74, PhD(chem), 76. *Prof Exp:* Fel res, Robert A Welch Found, Rice Univ, 76-77; sr res chemist, Akron, Ohio, 77-82, PLANT CHEMIST, GOODYEAR TIRE & RUBBER CO, LA PORTE, TEX, 82- *Mem:* Soc Eval Thermochem Hazards. *Res:* Organic synthesis; age resistors for rubbers and plastics; monomers; oxidation of organic chemicals. *Mailing Add:* Goodyear Tire & Rubber Co PO Box 669 LaPorte TX 77571

LECKRONE, DAVID STANLEY, b Salem, Ill, Nov 30, 42; m 64; c 2. ASTROPHYSICS. *Educ:* Purdue Univ, BS, 64; Univ Calif, Los Angeles, MA, 66, PhD(astron), 69. *Prof Exp:* ASTROPHYSICIST, LAB ASTRON & SOLAR PHYSICS, GODDARD SPACE FLIGHT CTR, 69- *Mem:* Am Astron Soc; Int Astron Union. *Res:* Ultraviolet stellar spectroscopy and photometry from space vehicles; magnetic and chemically peculiar stars; stellar atomsheres; abundances of the elements in astronomical objects; instrumentation for space astronomy. *Mailing Add:* Code 681 NASA-Goddard Space Flight Ctr Greenbelt MD 20771

LECLAIRE, CLAIRE DEAN, b Huron, SDak, Aug 26, 10; m 41. ORGANIC CHEMISTRY. *Educ:* SDak State Sch Mines, BS, 33; Univ Minn, PhD(org chem), 39. *Prof Exp:* Chemist, Coal Res Lab, Carnegie Inst Technol, 38-41 & Rohm and Haas Co, Pa, 41-42; rubber fel, Mellon Inst, 42-47; res chemist, Firestone Tire & Rubber Co, 47-49; asst dir rubber res proj, Univ Minn, 49-51; sect leader appl res, Adhesives & Coatings Div, Minn Mining & Mfg Co, 51-58; sr res chemist, Int Latex Corp, 58-69 & Standards Brands Chem Industs, Inc, 69-76; res chemist, Reichhold Polymers Inc, 76-81; CONSULT, INT PLAYTEX INC, 81- *Mem:* AAAS. *Res:* Organic synthesis; structure; polymerization; properties and utilization of high polymers; bituminous coals; elastomers; resins; adhesives. *Mailing Add:* 134 Lakeview Ave Dover DE 19901

LECOURS, MICHEL, b Montreal, Que, Aug 1, 40; m 66; c 3. COMMUNICATIONS SYSTEMS, SIGNAL PROCESSING. *Educ:* Univ Montreal, BScA, 63; Univ London, DIC & PhD(electronics), 67. *Prof Exp:* Engr commun, Bell Can, 63; head, Elec Eng Dept, 75-77, PROF ELEC ENG, UNIV LAVAL, 67-, VDEAN, FAC SCI & ENG, 77- *Concurrent Pos:* Mem sci staff, Bell Northern Res, 71-72; consult, UN Develop Prog, 73 & 81, Lab-Volt, Inc, 82- *Mem:* Can Soc Elec Eng; Inst Elec & Electronics Engrs. *Res:* Performance of digital communications systems (including mobile) in non-gaussian noise, interference and fading; signal processing in the radio and audio frequency bands. *Mailing Add:* Fac Sci & Eng Laval Univ Quebec PQ G1K 7P4 Can

L'ECUYER, JACQUES, b St-Jean, Que, Mar 6, 37; m 59; c 3. APPLIED & NUCLEAR PHYSICS. *Educ:* Col St Jean, BA, 56; Univ Montreal, BSc, 59, MSc, 61, PhD(physics), 66. *Prof Exp:* Lectr, Univ Montreal, 61-63 & Univ Sherbrooke, 63-64; asst prof physics, Laval Univ, 64-67; Nat Res Coun Can fel, Oxford Univ, 67-69; from asst prof to assoc prof, 69-73, PROF PHYSICS, UNIV MONTREAL, 73- *Concurrent Pos:* Mem bd gov, Univ Montreal, 76-79; mem, Queens Univ Coun, 77-81, pres, 81- *Mem:* Am Phys Soc; Can Asn Physicists; Fr-Can Asn Advan Sci. *Res:* Experimental nuclear physics. *Mailing Add:* Nuclear Physics Lab Univ of Montreal CP 6128 Montreal PQ H3C 3T8 Can

L'ECUYER, MEL R, b Concordia, Kans, June 4, 36; m 62. MECHANICAL ENGINEERING, HEAT TRANSFER. *Educ:* Purdue Univ, BS, 59, MS, 60, PhD(mech eng), 64. *Prof Exp:* Res prof eng, Jet Propulsion Ctr, 60-64, from asst prof to assoc prof, 64-76, PROF MECH ENG, PURDUE UNIV, 76- *Concurrent Pos:* Sr eng specialist, LTV Aerospace Div, Ling-Temco-Vought, Inc, Tex, 68- *Mem:* Am Inst Aeronaut & Astronaut; Am Soc Mech Engrs; Am Soc Eng Educ. *Res:* Mass transfer cooling; two-phase flow; propulsion gas dynamics. *Mailing Add:* Dept of Mech Eng Purdue Univ West Lafayette IN 47907

LEDBETTER, HARVEY DON, b Pierson, Ill, June 26, 26; m 47; c 3. ORGANIC CHEMISTRY. *Educ:* Univ Ariz, BS, 49, MS, 50; Univ Tenn, PhD(chem), 54. *Prof Exp:* Asst gen chem, Univ Tenn, 50-52; res group leader, Dow Chem USA, 53-67, res supvr, 67-71, tech mgr, Designed Prod Dept, 71-76, lab dir, Cent Res plastics Lab, 76-81; DIR TECHNOL RES & DEVELOP, ACQUISITION CORP, 81- *Mem:* AAAS; Am Chem Soc; Soc Plastics Engrs. *Res:* Polymer nucleation and stabilization; vacuum processes; preparation and physics of composite structures. *Mailing Add:* 1006 Sterling Dr Midland MI 48640

LEDBETTER, JOE O(VERTON), b New Hope, Ala, Feb 1, 27; m 47. ENVIRONMENTAL HEALTH, CIVIL ENGINEERING. *Educ:* Univ Ala, BS, 50; Univ Tex, MS, 58, PhD(civil eng), 63. *Prof Exp:* Proj engr, Ala Hwy Dept, 50-51; resident engr, Tex Hwy Dept, 51-56. from instr to assoc prof, 56-71, PROF CIVIL ENG, UNIV TEX, AUSTIN, 71- *Mem:* Air Pollution Control Asn; Am Indust Hyg Asn; assoc Am Conf Govt Indust Hygienists; Health Physics Soc. *Res:* Air pollution control--sampling, evaluation, and abatement; disposal of solid radioactive and hazardous wastes; radiological and industrial health engineering; air pollution from wastewater treatment. *Mailing Add:* Univ of Tex 8-6 Cockrell Hall Austin TX 78712

LEDBETTER, MARY LEE STEWART, b Monterrey, Mex, Aug 30, 44; US citizen; m 66; c 2. CELL BIOLOGY, BIOCHEMICAL GENETICS. *Educ:* Pomona Col, BA, 66; Rockefeller Univ, PhD(genetics), 72. *Prof Exp:* Res assoc microbiol, Dartmouth Med Sch, 72-75, instr, 75-78, res assoc prof biochem, 77-79, res assoc prof biochem, 79-80; ASST PROF BIOL, COL HOLY CROSS, 80- *Concurrent Pos:* USPHS res trainee, Sch Med, NY Univ, 72; Damon Runyon-Walter Winchell fel, 72-73; Leukemia Soc Am Fel, Dartmouth Med Sch, 73-75 & 77-78; USPHS, NCI fel, Dartmouth Med Sch, 75-77. *Mem:* Genetics Soc Am; Am Soc Cell Biol; AAAS; Sigma Xi. *Res:* Somatic cell genetics; study of metabolic regulation in cultured mammalian cells. *Mailing Add:* Dept Biol Col Holy Cross Worcester MA 01610

LEDBETTER, MYRON C, b Ardmore, Okla, June 25, 23. CELL BIOLOGY, BOTANY. *Educ:* Okla State Univ, BS, 48; Univ Calif, MA, 51; Columbia Univ, PhD, 58. *Prof Exp:* Fel plant physiol, Boyce Thompson Inst, 53-57, asst plant anatomist, 57-60; guest investr & fel, Rockefeller Inst, 60, res assoc, 61; res assoc, Harvard Univ, 61-65; cell biologist, 65-74, SR CELL BIOLOGIST, BROOKHAVEN NAT LAB, 74- *Concurrent Pos:* Guest assoc, Brookhaven Nat Lab, 58-60. *Mem:* AAAS; Am Soc Cell Biol; Bot Soc Am; Electron Micros Soc Am (pres, 78); Am Inst Biol Sci. *Res:* Morphology of physiologically dwarfed tree seedlings; feeding damage to plant tissues by lygus bugs; histopathology of ozone on plants; distribution of fluorine in plants; plant fine structure, microtubules in plants; plant cell walls. *Mailing Add:* Biol Dept Brookhaven Nat Lab Upton NY 11973

LEDBETTER, W(ILLIAM) B(URL), b El Paso, Tex, Sept 15, 34; m; c 4. CIVIL ENGINEERING. *Educ:* Tex A&M Univ, BS, 56; Univ Tex, Austin, PhD(civil eng), 64. *Prof Exp:* From asst prof to assoc prof, 64-71, from asst res engr to assoc res engr, 64-71, PROF CIVIL ENG & RES ENGR, TEX A&M UNIV, 71- *Concurrent Pos:* Chmn Transp Res Bd Comt, Nat Res Coun-Nat Acad Sci, 70-79. *Honors & Awards:* K B Woods Award, Transp Res Bd, Nat Acad Sci, 76. *Mem:* Nat Soc Prof Engrs; Am Soc Civil Engrs; Am Soc Eng Educ; Am Soc Testing & Mat; Am Concrete Inst. *Res:* Construction materials; concrete materials engineering; synthetic aggregates; composite materials. *Mailing Add:* Dept of Civil Eng Tex A&M Univ College Station TX 77843

LEDDY, JAMES JEROME, b Detroit, Mich, July 28, 29; m 51; c 6. INDUSTRIAL CHEMISTRY. *Educ:* Univ Detroit, BS, 51; Univ Wis, PhD(chem), 55. *Prof Exp:* Chemist inorg res, Dow Chem USA, 55-59, proj leader, 59-60, proj leader, Electrochem & Inorg Res Lab, 60-63, sr res chemist, 63-67, assoc res scientist, 67-71, res scientist, Electrochem & Inorg Res Lab, 71-73, res scientist, Mich Div Inorg Res, 73-80. *Concurrent Pos:* Asst prof, Assumption Univ, 59-60. *Mem:* AAAS; Am Chem Soc; Electrochem Soc. *Res:* Chemistry of less familiar elements, especially titanium, zirconium and hafnium; coordination compounds; unfamiliar oxidation states; amalgam chemistry; electrochemistry; inorganic polymers; industrial inorganic and electrochemistry; chlor-alkali. *Mailing Add:* 5742 Brazos River Rd Rte 1 Freeport TX 77541

LEDDY, JOHN PLUNKETT, b New York, NY, Sept 10, 31; m 56; c 3. IMMUNOLOGY. *Educ:* Fordham Univ, BA, 52; Columbia Univ, MD, 56. *Prof Exp:* From intern to resident internal med, Boston City Hosp, Harvard Med Serv, 56-59; USPHS trainee hemat, Med Ctr, Univ Rochester, 59-60; sr instr, 62-64, from asst prof to assoc prof med, 64-73, PROF MED & MICROBIOL, MED CTR, UNIV ROCHESTER, 73-, DIR CLIN IMMUNOL UNIT, 70- *Concurrent Pos:* Res med officer immunochem, Walter Reed Army Inst Res, 60-62; Nat Found fel, 62-64; NIH res grant, 65-; sr investr, Arthritis Found, 65-70; dir, USPHS Training Grant, 70-; prog dir, NIH Specialized Res Ctr grant immunol, 78- *Mem:* Am Soc Clin Invest; Am Asn Immunologists. *Res:* Biology of complement system in man; erythrocyte autoantibodies in human diseases. *Mailing Add:* Dept of Med Univ of Rochester Med Ctr Rochester NY 14642

LEDDY, SUSAN, b Jersey City, NJ, Feb 23, 39; m 72; c 2. NURSING. *Educ:* Skidmore Col, BS, 60; Boston Univ, MS, 65; NY Univ, PhD(nursing), 73. *Prof Exp:* Instr nursing, Mt Auburn Hosp, 62-65 & New Rochelle Hosp, 65-66; asst prof, Columbia Univ, 66-70 & Pace Univ, 73-75; consult nursing educ, Nat League Nursing, 75; chairperson & prof nursing, Mercy Col, 76-81; DEAN & PROF NURSING, UNIV WYO, 81- *Concurrent Pos:* Independent consult, 75- *Mem:* Nat League Nursing. *Res:* Biological rhythms; nursing education and curriculum. *Mailing Add:* Dean Sch Nursing Univ Wyo Univ Sta Box 3065 Laramie WY 82071

LEDEEN, ROBERT, b Denver, Colo, Aug 19, 28. BIOCHEMISTRY, NEUROBIOLOGY. *Educ:* Univ Calif, Berkeley, BS, 49; Ore State Univ, PhD(org chem), 53. *Prof Exp:* Fel, Univ Chicago, 53-54; res chemist, Mt Sinai Hosp, New York, 56-59; res chemist, 59-61, from asst prof to assoc prof biochem in neurol, 62-75, PROF BIOCHEM IN NEUROL, ALBERT EINSTEIN COL MED, 75- *Mem:* AAAS; Am Chem Soc; Am Soc Biol Chem; Am Soc Neurochem; Int Soc Neurochem. *Res:* Chemistry of the nervous systems; gangliosides and other lipids; myelin lipids; methods in structure determination and stereochemistry. *Mailing Add:* Dept of Neurol Albert Einstein Col of Med Bronx NY 10461

LEDER, FREDERIC, b New York, NY, Nov 1, 39; m 71; c 2. CHEMICAL ENGINEERING. *Educ:* Queens Col, BS, 61; Columbia Univ, BS, 61; Yale Univ, MS, 63, PhD(chem eng), 65. *Prof Exp:* Res engr, Esso Res & Eng Co, Exxon Corp, Linden, 65-68, sr res engr, 68-73, gas separations res assoc, 73; DIR EXPLOR RES, OCCIDENTAL RES CORP, IRVINE, 76- *Mem:* Am Inst Chem Eng; Sigma Xi. *Res:* Phase equilibria at high pressure; gas separations. *Mailing Add:* 1635 Reef View Circle Corona Del Mar CA 92625

LEDER, IRWIN GORDON, b New York, NY, June 16, 20; m 45; c 3. BIOCHEMISTRY. *Educ:* Brooklyn Col, AB, 42; NY Univ, MS, 47; Duke Univ, PhD(biochem), 51. *Prof Exp:* Res assoc, Duke Univ, 51; USPHS fel, NY Univ, 51-52 & Yale Univ, 52-53; asst, Pub Health Res Inst, Inc, NY, 53-54; BIOCHEMIST, NAT INST ARTHRITIS, METAB & DIGESTIVE DIS, BETHESDA, 54- *Mem:* Fedn Am Socs Exp Biol. *Res:* Niacin metabolism; pyridine nucleotide synthesis; intermediary carbohydrate metabolism; enzymology. *Mailing Add:* 4004 Wexford Dr Kensington MD 20795

LEDER, LEWIS BEEBE, b Brooklyn, NY, Oct 28, 20; m 48; c 1. EXPERIMENTAL PHYSICS. *Educ:* Univ Idaho, BS, 43. *Prof Exp:* Instr physics, Williams Col, 43-44; physicist gas flow, Inst Gas Technol, 44-45; physicist, Dielectric Studies, Indust Condenser Corp, 45-46; physicist electron heat controls, Wheelco Instruments Co, 46-48; physicist nuclear physics, Inst Nuclear Studies, 48-51; physicist electron physics, Nat Bur Standards, 51-62; physicist, Appl Res Lab, Philco Corp, 62-65; physicist electron scattering & superconductivity, Ford Sci Lab, 65-69; RES SCIENTIST, XEROX CORP, 69- *Mem:* Am Vacuum Soc; Am Phys Soc. *Res:* Electron scattering; superconductivity; thin films preparation and properties; photoreceptors. *Mailing Add:* Xerox Corp Bldg 103 Xerox Square Rochester NY 14644

LEDER, PHILIP, b Washington, DC, Nov 19, 34; m 59; c 3. MOLECULAR GENETICS. *Educ:* Harvard Col, AB, 56, Med Sch, MD, 60. *Prof Exp:* Lab chief molecular genetics, Nat Inst Child Health & Human Develop, NIH, 72-80; PROF & CHMN GENETICS, HARVARD MED SCH, 80- *Honors & Awards:* Richard Lounsberry Award, Nat Acad Sci. *Mem:* Nat Acad Sci; Am Soc Biol Chemists; Genetics Soc Am; Am Acad Arts & Sci. *Res:* Molecular biology and genetics. *Mailing Add:* Dept Genetics Harvard Med Sch 25 Shattuck St Boston MA 02115

LEDERBERG, ESTHER MIRIAM, b New York, NY, Dec 18, 22; m 46, 68. GENETICS, MICROBIOLOGY. *Educ:* Hunter Col, AB, 42; Stanford Univ, MA, 46; Univ Wis, PhD(genetics), 50. *Prof Exp:* Proj assoc genetics, Univ Wis, 50-59; res geneticist, Med Sch, 59-68, res assoc, 68-71, sr scientist, 71-74, ADJ PROF MED MICROBIOL, STANFORD UNIV, 74- *Concurrent Pos:* Fulbright fel, Australia, 57; Am Cancer Soc Sr Dernham fel, 68-70. *Honors & Awards:* Co-recipient, Pasteur Award, Soc Ill Bact, 56. *Mem:* Fel AAAS; Genetics Soc Am; Brit Soc Gen Microbiol; Am Soc Microbiol. *Res:* Genetics of microorganisms; lysogenicity; bacterial recombination and transformation; DNA repair; phase variation of Flagellar antigens in Salmonella; R plasmids. *Mailing Add:* Dept of Med Microbiol Stanford Univ Stanford CA 94305

LEDERBERG, JOSHUA, b NJ, May 23, 25; m 68; c 2. GENETICS. *Educ:* Columbia Univ, BA, 44; Yale Univ, PhD(microbiol), 47. *Hon Degrees:* ScD, Yale Univ, 60 & Columbia Univ, 67; MD, Univ Turin, 69; ScD, Univ Wis, 67 & Albert Einstein Col Med, 70; ScD, Mt Sinai, 79, DLitt, Jewish Theol Seminary, 79; LLD, Univ Pima, 79, ScD, Rutgers, 81. *Prof Exp:* From asst prof to prof genetics, Univ Wis, 47-58, prof med & genetics & chmn dept, 58-59; prof genetics & chmn dept, Med Sch, Stanford Univ, 59-78; PRES, ROCKEFELLER UNIV, NEW YORK, 78- *Concurrent Pos:* Consult, Ctr Advan Study Behav Sci; mem, Annual Reviews, Inc & bd of trustees, Natural Resources Def Coun, 72-; sci consult, Cetus Corp, Berkeley, Calif; coun mem, Inst Med-Nat Acad Sci, 78-81; bd dir, Charles Babbage Inst, Palo Alto, Calif, 78-, chem Indust Inst Toxicol, NC, 80-, Bulletin Atomic Scientists, 81- & Inst for Sci Info, Philadelphia. *Honors & Awards:* Nobel Prize, 58. *Mem:* Nat Acad Sci; Inst Med-Nat Acad Sci; foreign mem The Royal Soc. *Res:* Molecular genetics and evolution; science policy; computer science. *Mailing Add:* Rockefeller Univ New York NY 10021

LEDERBERG, SEYMOUR, b New York, NY, Oct 30, 28; m 59; c 2. MOLECULAR BIOLOGY, GENETICS. *Educ:* Cornell Univ, BA, 51; Univ Ill, PhD(bact), 55. *Prof Exp:* Am Cancer Soc fel, Univ Calif, 55-57, vis asst prof bact, 57-58; from asst prof to assoc prof, 58-66, chmn microbiol sect, 70-78, PROF BIOL, BROWN UNIV, 66-, COORDR GRAD PROGS BIOL MED, 78-; LECTR, PROG IN PUB HEALTH, BOSTON UNIV, 77- *Concurrent Pos:* USPHS fel, Inst Biol Phys Chem, Paris, 65-66; consult, Nat Inst Gen Med Sci, 70-74, Gen Med & Sci Adv Coun, Cystic Fibrosis Found, 72-76, Comt Genetic Screening Cystic Fibrosis, Nat Acad Sci-Nat Res Coun, 74-75 & Nat Inst Arthritis, Metab & Digestive Diseases, 75-78; vis scholar, Harvard Law Sch; lectr, Law Sch Ctr for Law & Health Sci, Boston Univ, 73-77, adj prof public health law, 77- *Mem:* Am Soc Microbiol; Genetics Soc Am; Am Soc Human Genetics; Environ Mutagen Soc. *Res:* Human, microbial and viral genetics; cystic fibrosis; yeast and bacterial biochemistry; chromosomal, mocrotubule and lysosomal functions in cell cycles; environmental mutagens; microbial biopolymer and mineral metabolism. *Mailing Add:* Biol & Med Box G Brown Univ Providence RI 02912

LEDERER, JEROME, b New York, NY, Sept 26, 02; m; c 2. AEROSPACE SAFETY. *Educ:* NY Univ, BS, 24, ME, 25. *Prof Exp:* Aeronaut engr, US Air Mail Serv, 26-27, dir aeronaut tech, 27-29; chief engr, Aero Ins Underwriters, 29-40 & 44-48; dir safety bur, Civil Aeronaut Bd, 40-42, airlines war training inst, 42-44; tech dir, Flight Safety Found, 48-67; dir manned space flight safety, NASA, 67-70, dir safety, 70-72. *Concurrent Pos:* James Jackson Cabot prof lectr, Norwich Univ, 39; dir, Cornell-Guggenheim Aviation Safety Ctr, 50-68; adj prof, Inst Safety & Systs Mgt, Univ Southern Calif, 74-; emer pres, Flight Safety Found. *Honors & Awards:* Arthur Williams Award, 53, Von Baumhauer Medal, 54, Monsanto Award, 57, Guggenheim Medal, 61, Laura Tabor Barbour Medal, 64, Wright Bros Award, 65 & Amelia Earhart Medal. *Mem:* Nat Acad Eng; fel Am Inst Aeronaut & Astronaut; Soc Automotive Engrs; Am Soc Mech Engrs; fel Royal Aeronaut Soc. *Res:* Aviation and space safety. *Mailing Add:* 468-D Calle Cadiz Laguna Hills CA 92653

LEDERER, WILLIAM JONATHAN, US citizen. CARDIAC MUSCLE ELECTROPHYSIOLOGY. *Educ:* Harvard Univ, BA, 70; Yale Univ, PhD(physiol), 75, MD, 76. *Prof Exp:* Intern internal med, Univ Wash, 76-77; fel physiol, Oxford Univ, 77-79; ASST PROF PHYSIOL, UNIV MD, 79- *Concurrent Pos:* Vis researcher, Univ Col London, 81; estab investr, Am Heart Asn, 81-, mem, Basic Sci Coun. *Mem:* Soc Gen Physiologists; Biophys Soc; NY Acad Sci; AAAS. *Res:* Mammalian heart muscle to determine how it functions at the cellular level; links between the electrical activity and the ion transport function of cardiac cells and how these properties relate to the force generated by the heart. *Mailing Add:* Dept Physiol Sch Med Univ Md 660 W Redwood St Baltimore MD 21201

LEDERIS, KARL, b Lithuania, Aug 1, 20; m 52; c 2. PHARMACOLOGY, ENDOCRINOLOGY. *Educ:* Bristol Univ, BSc, 58, PhD(pharmacol), 61, DSc(endocrinol), 68. *Prof Exp:* Jr fel pharmacol, Bristol Univ, 61-63, lectr, 63-66, sr lectr, 66-68, reader, 68-69; PROF PHARMACOL & THERAPEUT, MED SCH, UNIV CALGARY, 69- *Concurrent Pos:* Wellcome Trust & Ger Res Asn fel, Univ Kiel, 61-62; NSF fel, Univ Calif, Berkeley, 67-68; mem grants comt endocrinol & univs consult comt, Med Res Coun Can, 70, assoc, Coun, 70-, chmn, 81; ed, Pharmacol, Int J Exp & Clin Pharmacol; vis prof, Univ Bristol, Eng, 79 & Kyoto Univ, Japan, 80. *Mem:* Int Brain Res Orgn; Endocrine Soc; Brit Soc Endocrinol; Brit Pharmacol Soc; Can Physiol Soc. *Res:* Hypothalamo-neurohypophysial system, mechanisms of hormone storage and secretion; caudal neurosecretory system of teleosts, chemistry and pharmacology of urotensin peptides. *Mailing Add:* Div of Pharmacol Univ of Calgary Med Sch Calgary AB T2N 1N4 Can

LEDERMAN, DAVID MORDECHAI, b Bogota, Colombia, May 26, 44; m 67; c 2. BIOMEDICAL ENGINEERING. *Educ:* Univ Los Andes, BEng, 66; Cornell Univ, BSc, 66, MEng, 67, PhD(aerospace eng), 73. *Prof Exp:* From prof appl math, Fac Arts & Sci, to dir div biomed eng, Fac Eng, Univ Los Andes, 72-73; sr staff mem, Avco-Everett Res Lab Inc, Avco Corp, 73-76, prin res scientist, 76-79, chmn, Med Res Comt, 79-81, consult, 81-82; PRES & BD CHMN, APPLIED BIOMED CORP, 81- *Concurrent Pos:* Prin investr, NIH, 80-84. *Mem:* AAAS; NY Acad Sci; Sigma Xi; Am Phys Soc;

Am Soc Artificial Internal Organs. *Res:* Development of clinical cardiovascular devices; prosthetic heart valves; blood-compatible biomaterials; hemodynamics and thrombosis; laser physics and applications to medicine; plastics technology; artificial hearts. *Mailing Add:* PO Box 462 Marblehead MA 01945

LEDERMAN, FRANK L, b Buffalo, NY, Aug 19, 49; m 71. PHYSICS, MATHEMATICS. *Educ:* Carnegie-Mellon Univ, BS & MS, 71; Univ Ill, Urbana, PhD(physics), 75. *Prof Exp:* Physicist solid state physics & ultrasonics, 75-78, ACTING MGR ULTRASOUND IMAGER PROG, GEN ELEC CORP RES & DEVELOP CTR, 78- *Mem:* Am Phys Soc; Sigma Xi. *Res:* Solid state physics; signal processing; medical imaging. *Mailing Add:* Gen Elec Corp Res & Develop Ctr PO Box 8 Schenectady NY 12301

LEDERMAN, LEON MAX, b NY, July 15, 22; m 45; c 3. NUCLEAR PHYSICS. *Educ:* City Col New York, BS, 43; Columbia Univ, AM, 50, PhD(physics), 51. *Prof Exp:* Assoc, 51-52, from asst prof to assoc prof, 52-58, PROF PHYSICS, COLUMBIA UNIV, 58-, DIR, NEVIS LABS, 68- *Concurrent Pos:* Guggenheim fel, 58-59; mem bd trustees, Univs Res Asn, 66-69; NSF sr fel, 67; mem high energy physics adv panel, Atomic Energy Comn, 67-70. *Honors & Awards:* Nat Medal of Sci, 65. *Mem:* Nat Acad Sci; Am Phys Soc. *Res:* Properties and interactions of elementary particles. *Mailing Add:* Fermi Nat Accelerator Lab PO Box 500 Batavia IL 60510

LEDERMAN, PETER B, b Weimar, Ger, Nov 16, 31; US citizen; m 57; c 2. CHEMICAL & ENVIRONMENTAL ENGINEERING. *Educ:* Univ Mich, BSE, 53, MS, 57, PhD(chem eng), 61. *Prof Exp:* Jr technologist chem eng, Shell Oil Co, 53; technologist, Cent Res Div, Gen Foods Corp, 56; instr, Univ Mich, 59-61; engr, Esso Res Labs, 61-63, engr chem develop, Esso Res & Eng Co, 63-65, sr chem engr, 66; assoc prof chem eng, Polytech Inst Brooklyn, 66-72; dir indust waste treatment, Res & Develop, US Environ Protection Agency, 72-76; mgr tech develop & res, Cottrell Environ Sci, 76-78, vpres & gen mgr, 78-80; VPRES HAZARDOUS/TOXIC MATS MGT, ROY F WESTON, 80- *Concurrent Pos:* Teaching fel, Univ Mich, 55-59; lectr, Columbia Univ, 65-67. *Honors & Awards:* Silver Medal, US Environ Protection Agency, 76. *Mem:* Fel Am Inst Chem Engrs; Am Chem Soc; Am Soc Eng Educ; Nat Soc Prof Engrs; Air Pollution Control Asn. *Res:* Environmental studies; solid waste management; computer application; process optimization; polymers; mass transfer. *Mailing Add:* 17 Pittsford Way New Providence NJ 07974

LEDFORD, RICHARD ALLISON, b Charlotte, NC, June 30, 31; m 57; c 5. FOOD MICROBIOLOGY. *Educ:* NC State Univ, BS, 54, MS, 56; Cornell Univ, PhD(food sci), 62. *Prof Exp:* Dir, NY State Food Lab, NY State Dept Agr & Mkts, 61-64; asst prof, 64-70, chmn dept, 72-77, assoc head, Inst Food Sci, 75-77, ASSOC PROF FOOD SCI, CORNELL UNIV, 71- *Mem:* Am Soc Microbiol; Inst Food Technologist; Am Dairy Sci Asn. *Res:* Microbiological aspects of food science, especially food fermentations and analytical methods. *Mailing Add:* Dept of Food Sci Cornell Univ Ithaca NY 14853

LEDFORD, THOMAS HOWARD, b Macon, Ga, Aug 24, 42; m 65; c 2. ORGANIC CHEMISTRY. *Educ:* Univ Ga, BS, 64; Univ Fla, PhD(chem), 73. *Prof Exp:* Res chemist polymer intermediates, Tenn Eastman Res Labs, Kingsport, Tenn, 64-68; res chemist fuels processing, 73-80, SR RES CHEMIST, EXXON RES & DEVELOP, 80- *Concurrent Pos:* Adj assoc prof chem, La State Univ, 81- *Mem:* Am Chem Soc. *Res:* Polymers; reactions in strong acids; fuel processing chemistry; sulfur chemistry. *Mailing Add:* Exxon Res & Develop Labs PO Box 2226 Baton Rouge LA 70821

LEDIAEV, JOHN P, b Goorgan, Iran, Sept 8, 40; US citizen; div; c 1. MATHEMATICS. *Educ:* Occidental Col, BA, 63; Univ Calif, Riverside, MA, 65, PhD(noether lattices), 67. *Prof Exp:* Asst prof, 67-71, ASSOC PROF MATH, UNIV IOWA, 71- *Mem:* Am Math Soc. *Res:* Structure; representation and embedding of Noether lattices; primary decomposition in multiplicative lattices; semi-prime operations in Noether lattices. *Mailing Add:* Dept of Math Univ of Iowa Iowa City IA 52240

LEDIG, F THOMAS, b Dover, NJ, Aug 13, 38; div; c 3. GENETICS. *Educ:* Rutgers Univ, BS, 62; NC State Univ, MS, 65, PhD(genetics), 67. *Prof Exp:* Lectr, 66-67, asst prof, 67-72, assoc prof, 72-80, PROF FOREST GENETICS, YALE UNIV, 80- *Mem:* Scand Soc Plant Physiologists; Soc Am Foresters; Bot Soc Am. *Res:* Genecology, including population genetics, hybridization, and evolution; physiological mechanisms of adaptation in wild populations; physiological analysis of genetic variation in productivity; photosynthetic physiology; quantitative genetics and breeding. *Mailing Add:* Greeley Mem Lab Yale Univ New Haven CT 06511

LEDIN, GEORGE, JR, b Seekirchen, Austria, Jan 28, 46; US citizen; m 68; c 2. COMPUTER SCIENCE, STATISTICS. *Educ:* Univ Calif, Berkeley, BS, 67. *Hon Degrees:* JD, Univ San Francisco, 82. *Prof Exp:* Statistician & mathematician, 65-70, lectr math & comput sci, 68-74, sr res assoc statist & math biosci, 70-75, asst prof comput sci, 75-79, ASSOC PROF COMPUT SCI, UNIV SAN FRANCISCO, 80-, CHMN DEPT, 76- *Concurrent Pos:* Consult comput sci & statist, 66-; US rep, Int Fedn Info Processing, 72-74. *Mem:* AAAS; Am Statist Asn; Asn Comput Mach; Math Asn Am; NY Acad Sci. *Res:* Algorithmic languages; programming methodology; heuristic programming; pattern recognition; robotics; mathematical models for biosciences; number theory; combinatorics; graph theory; game theory; information theory; algebra. *Mailing Add:* Dept of Comput Sci Univ of San Francisco San Francisco CA 94117

LEDINKO, NADA, b Girard, Ohio, Dec 16, 25. VIROLOGY. *Educ:* Ohio State Univ, BS, 46; Pa State Col, MS, 49; Yale Univ, PhD(microbiol), 52. *Prof Exp:* Res asst virol, Yale Univ, 52-53; Nat Found Infantile Paralysis fel, Walter & Eliza Hall Inst, Australia, 53-55; virologist, Pub Health Res Inst, 56-62; USPHS fel, Carnegie Inst Genetics Res Unit & Salk Inst Biol Studies, 63-65; assoc investr & NIH res career develop awardee, Putnam Mem Hosp Inst Med Res, Bennington, Vt, 65-71; PROF BIOL, UNIV AKRON, 71- *Mem:* AAAS; Am Asn Path & Bact; Tissue Cult Asn; Am Soc Microbiol; Am Asn Cancer Res. *Res:* Genetical and biochemical aspects of viral growth. *Mailing Add:* Dept of Biol Univ of Akron Akron OH 44304

LEDLEY, BRIAN G, b Brisbane, Australia, Sept 29, 28; m 58; c 1. MAGNETOSPHERIC PHYSICS. *Educ:* Univ Queensland, BSc, 50; Univ Birmingham, PhD(physics), 55. *Prof Exp:* Asst lectr physics, Univ Birmingham, 55-57; res assoc nuclear physics, Fermi Inst, Univ Chicago, 57-60; res fel cosmic rays, Univ Sydney, 60-62; Nat Acad Sci-NASA res fel space sci, 62-63; sect head, 63-70, PHYSICIST, NASA, 70- *Mem:* Am Geophys Union. *Res:* Geomagnetic field measurements using satellites; magnetometer instrumentation; remote optical sensing instrumentation. *Mailing Add:* Code 696 Goddard Space Flight Ctr Greenbelt MD 20771

LEDLEY, ROBERT STEVEN, b New York, NY, June 28, 26; m 49; c 2. BIOPHYSICS, COMPUTER SCIENCE. *Educ:* NY Univ, DDS, 48; Columbia Univ, MA, 49. *Prof Exp:* Res physicist, Radiation Lab, Columbia Univ, 48-50, instr physics, 49-50; vis scientist, Nat Bur Standards, 51-52, physicist, External Control Group, Electronic Comput Lab, 53-54; opers res analyst, Opers Res Off, Strategic Div, Johns Hopkins Univ, 54-56; assoc prof elec eng, Sch Eng, George Washington Univ, 57-60; instr pediat, Sch Med, Johns Hopkins Univ, 60-63; prof elec eng, Sch Eng & Appl Sci, George Washington Univ, 68-70; PROF PHYSIOL & BIOPHYS, MED CTR, GEORGETOWN UNIV, 70-; PRES & RES DIR, NAT BIOMED RES FOUND, 60- *Concurrent Pos:* Consult mathematician, Data Processing Systs Div, Nat Bur Standards, 57-60; mem staff, Nat Acad Sci-Nat Res Coun, 57-61; pres, Digital Info Sci Corp, 70-75. *Mem:* Soc Math Biophys; Inst Elec & Electronics Engrs; Biophys Soc; NY Acad Sci; Pattern Recognition Soc. *Res:* Mathematical methods for application of symbolic logic; data processing techniques for computers; digital computer engineering; mathematical biophysics applied to physiology and other fields; use of computers in biomedical research and medical data processing; development of whole body computerized tomography; computer medicine. *Mailing Add:* 1002 La Grande Rd Silver Spring MD 20903

LEDNEY, GEORGE DAVID, b Sharon, Pa, June 25, 37. BIOLOGY. *Educ:* Youngstown Univ, BS, 60; Univ Notre Dame, PhD(biol), 65. *Prof Exp:* Asst prof radiation biol, Med Units, Univ Tenn, Memphis, 65-67, assoc prof, 70-73; HEAD DIV IMMUNOL, ARMED FORCES RADIOBIOL RES INST, 73- *Concurrent Pos:* Nat Cancer Inst fel, 65-67; Am Cancer Soc grants, 68 & 70. *Mem:* Radiation Res Soc; Transplantation Soc; Asn Gnotobiotics; Int Soc Exp Hemat; Soc Exp Biol Med. *Res:* Radiation biology; bone marrow transplantation; wound trauma. *Mailing Add:* Div of Immunol Armed Forces Radiobiol Res Inst Bethesda MD 20814

LEDNICER, DANIEL, b Antwerp, Belg, Oct 15, 29; nat US; m 56; c 2. ORGANIC CHEMISTRY. *Educ:* Antioch Col, BS, 52; Ohio State Univ, PhD(chem), 55. *Prof Exp:* Sr chemist, G D Searle & Co, 55-56; res assoc, Duke Univ, 56-58; Esso Res & Develop Co fel, Univ Ill, 58-59; chemist, Upjohn Co, 59-73, sr scientist, 73-76; dir chem res, Mead Johnson & Co, 76-80; DIR MED CHEM & PHARM, ADRIA LABS, 80- *Mem:* Am Chem Soc. *Res:* Stereochemistry; medicinal chemistry; hypotensives; analgesics. *Mailing Add:* PO Box 16529 Adria Labs Columbus OH 43216

LEDOUX, ROBERT LOUIS, b Marieville, Que, Apr 19, 33; m 61; c 2. MINERALOGY. *Educ:* Univ Montreal, BSc, 56; Laval Univ, MScA, 60; Purdue Univ, PhD(mineral), 64. *Prof Exp:* From assoc prof to prof mineral, 64-74, PROF PETROL & MINERAL, LAVAL UNIV, 74- *Res:* Infrared studies of layered silicates. *Mailing Add:* Dept of Geol Laval Univ Quebec PQ G1K 7P4 Can

LEDSOME, JOHN R, b Bebington, Eng, June 18, 32; m 57; c 3. PHYSIOLOGY, MEDICINE. *Educ:* Univ Edinburgh, MB, ChB, 55, MD, 62. *Prof Exp:* Lectr physiol, Univ Leeds, 59-68; PROF PHYSIOL, UNIV BC, 68- *Concurrent Pos:* USPHS int fel, 64-65, res grant, 66-68; Med Res Coun Eng res grant, 65-68; Med Red Coun Can res grant, 68-80; BC Heart Found res grant, 72-79. *Mem:* Can Physiol Soc; Brit Physiol Soc. *Res:* Control of the cardiovascular system; function of left atrial receptors. *Mailing Add:* Dept of Physiol Univ of BC Vancouver BC V6T 1W5 Can

LEDUC, ELIZABETH, b Rockland, Maine, Nov 19, 21. CELL BIOLOGY. *Educ:* Univ Vt, BS, 43; Wellesley Col, MA, 45; Brown Univ, PhD(biol), 48. *Prof Exp:* Res assoc biol, Brown Univ, 48-49; instr & assoc anat, Harvard Med Sch, 49-53; from asst prof to assoc prof, 53-64, PROF BIOL, BROWN UNIV, 64-, DEAN DIV BIOL & MED, 73- *Concurrent Pos:* Mem adv coun, Nat Inst Gen Med Sci, 72-76. *Mem:* AAAS; Am Soc Cell Biol; Soc Francaise de Microscopie Electronique; Histochem Soc; Am Soc Exp Path. *Res:* Histophysiology and pathology of the liver; cellular mechanism in antibody production; ultrastructural and cytochemical effects of cancer chemotherapeutic compounds on normal and neoplastic cells. *Mailing Add:* Div of Biol & Med Sci Brown Univ Providence RI 02912

LEDUC, GERARD, b Verdun, Que, Sept 7, 34; m 59; c 3. FISHERIES, BIOCHEMISTRY. *Educ:* Univ Montreal, BSc, 58, MSc, 60; Ore State Univ, PhD(fisheries), 66. *Prof Exp:* Biologist, Que Wildlife Serv, 63-66; asst prof biol sci, 66-72, chmn dept, 69-72, ASSOC PROF BIOL SCI, SIR GEORGE WILLIAMS UNIV, 72- *Res:* Fisheries problems in water pollution, mainly the long-term effects of sublethal concentrations of toxicant; artificial streams. *Mailing Add:* Dept Biol Sci Concordia Univ Montreal PQ H4G 1M8 Can

LE DUC, J-ADRIEN MAHER, b Can, July 2, 24; nat US; m 49; c 2. ELECTROCHEMISTRY, INORGANIC CHEMISTRY. *Educ:* Sir George William Univ, BSc, 47; Polytech Inst Brooklyn, MS, 51; Univ Dijon, DSc(phys inorg chem), 53. *Prof Exp:* Anal paper chemist, Howard Smith Paper Co, 43-44; anal paper chemist dyes & colors, L B Holliday & Co, 45; res chemist zirconium alloys, St Lawrence Alloys & Metals Co, 46; consult chemist, Milton Hersey Co, 47; res consult chemist, Wyssmont Co, 47-49; sr inorg chemist, J T Baker Chem Co, 49-50; sr electroplating chemist, MacDermid, Inc, 53-54; head electrolytic sect, Diamond Alkali Co, 54-56, group leader res, Electrochem Div, 56-59; supvr explor & process res, M W Kellogg Co, 59-62, dir electrochem res, 62-70, mgr electrochem res & develop, 63-70; CONSULT CHEM & ELECTROCHEM TECHNOL,

LICENSING & PROCESS TECHNOL EXCHANGE, 70- Concurrent Pos: Ed, Int Electrochem Progress & Chemicals Today; Dir, Int Electrochem Inst, Millburn, NJ & Industrialists Int Inc, Summit, NJ. Honors & Awards: Order of Merit of Res & Invention Award, Paris, 68, Gold Medal Award Res & Invention, 75. Mem: Sr mem Am Chem Soc; Electrochem Soc; NY Acad Sci; Soc Indust Chem; Sigma Xi. Res: Inorganic and organic chemicals; electrochemistry; non-ferrous electrometallurgy; metal finishing molten salts; licensing negotiations and technical exchange; research and invention management; aquisitions and ventures. Mailing Add: 189 Parsonage Hill Rd Short Hills NJ 07078

LE DUC, JAMES WAYNE, b Long Beach, Calif, Nov 23, 45; m 70; c 3. EPIDEMIOLOGY, MEDICAL ENTOMOLOGY. Educ: Calif State Univ, Long Beach, BS, 67; Univ Calif, Los Angeles, MS, 72, PhD(pub health), 77. Prof Exp: Med entomologist, Smithsonian Inst, Washington, DC, 67-68, team leader entom & mammal, 68-69; entomologist, Walter Reed Army Inst Res, 69-71, chief virol & entom, Arbovirus Prog, 73-75; COMDR ARBOVIROL, US ARMY MED RES UNIT, BELEM, BRAZIL, 77- Honors & Awards: Paul A Siple Award, US Army Sci Conf, 74. Mem: Am Soc Trop Med & Hyg; Am Mosquito Control Asn; Soc Vector Ecologists. Res: Arbovirology; medical entomology; infectious disease epidemiology; ecological aspects of disease maintenance. Mailing Add: US Army Med Res Unit-Belem Brazil APO Miami FL 34030

LEDUC, SHARON KAY, b Hattiesburg, Miss, Apr 28, 43. STATISTICS. Educ: Eastern Ill Univ, BS, 65; Univ Mo-Columbia, MA, 67, PhD(statist), 71. Prof Exp: Teaching asst statist, Univ Mo-Columbia, 67-68, res asst atmospheric sci, 69-70, res specialist, 71-72, instr, 73-74; STATISTICIAN, CTR ENVIRON ASSESSMENT SERV, ENVIRON DATA INFO SERV, NAT OCEANIC & ATMOSPHERIC ADMIN, MO, 74- Mem: Asn Women Math; Am Statist Asn; Am Meteorol Soc; Sigma Xi; Biometeorol Soc. Res: Statistical analysis of meteorology and climatology for the purpose of assessing impact on food production, fisheries and economy. Mailing Add: 1112 W Rollins Rd Columbia MO 65201

LEDUY, ANH, b Vietnam, Feb 6, 46; Can citizen; m 77; c 2. BIOCHEMICAL ENGINEERING, APPLIED MICROBIOLOGY. Educ: Univ Sherbrooke, BScA, 69, MScA, 72; Univ Western Ont, PhD(biochem eng), 75. Prof Exp: Res assoc chem eng, Univ Sherbrooke, 75-77; asst prof, 77-81, ASSOC PROF CHEM ENG, LAVAL UNIV, 81- Concurrent Pos: Consult, 81- Mem: Can Soc Chem Eng; Chem Inst Can; Am Inst Chem Engrs; Am Soc Microbiol; Can Soc Mech Eng. Res: Utilization of microorganisms; enzymes systems in the production of biomass and precious metabolites from abundant raw materials, waste materials and industrial agricultural by-products. Mailing Add: Dept of Chem Eng Laval Univ Ste Foy PQ G1K 7P4 Can

LEDVINA, STEPHEN JAMES, b Chicago, Ill, June 9, 40; m 67; c 4. COMMUNICATIONS, ELECTRICAL ENGINEERING. Educ: Ill Inst Technol, BS, 67; Northern Ill Univ, MS, 74. Prof Exp: Lead engr relay appln design, C P Clare Co, 63-67; proj engr radio equip mfg eng, Motorola, 67-71; planning engr tel off testing equip, Western Elec Co, 71-75; sr engr electronic test equip design, Northrop Co, 75-76; PROG MGR & COMMUN CONSULT, IIT RES INST, 76- Res: Communications research, especially satellite, mass transit and navigational. Mailing Add: IIT Res Inst 10 W 35th St Chicago IL 60616

LEDWELL, THOMAS AUSTIN, b PEI, June 13, 38; m 64; c 4. MECHANICAL ENGINEERING. Educ: NS Tech Col, BE, 60, ME, 65; Univ Waterloo, PhD(mech eng), 68. Prof Exp: Res coordr, Nat Res Coun, 75-77; tech adv, Renewable Energy Policy, 77-78, head res coord, 78-80, SR TECH ADV, CONSERV & RENEWABLE ENERGY, ENERGY, MINES & RESOURCES, 80- Concurrent Pos: Coordr renewable energy res & develop, Fed Govt Can, 76-77, coordr conserv res & develop, 78-80. Mem: Combustion Inst. Res: Thermodynamics; engine design and development; applied mathematics; energy research and development. Mailing Add: Conserv & Renewable Energy 580 Booth St Ottawa ON K1A 0E4 Can

LEDWITZ-RIGBY, FLORENCE INA, b New York, NY, Feb 14, 46; m 68; c 2. REPRODUCTIVE ENDOCRINOLOGY. Educ: City Col NY, BS, 66; Case-Western Reserve Univ, MS, 68; Univ Wis-Madison, PhD(endocrinol & reprod physiol), 72. Prof Exp: Res fel reprod physiol, Sch Med, Dept Physiol, Univ Pittsburgh, 72-74, vis asst prof physiol, Dept Biol, 74-75; asst prof, 75-80, ASSOC PROF PHYSIOL, DEPT BIOL SCI, NORTHERN ILL UNIV, 80- Mem: Am Physiol Soc; Soc Study Reprod; Endocrine Soc. Res: Endocrine and physiological control mechanisms of ovarian cell function and differentiation. Mailing Add: Dept of Biol Sci Northern Ill Univ DeKalb IL 60115

LEE (LI), HON CHI, b Canton, China, Aug 25, 30; US citizen; m 60; c 3. MINERAL & CHEMICAL ENGINEERING. Educ: Tufts Univ, BS, 53; Mass Inst Technol, SM, 55, ScD(mineral eng, chem), 58. Prof Exp: Res assoc mineral eng, Mass Inst Technol, 58; res engr, Duval Corp, 59-62 & Int Minerals & Chem Corp, 62-63; mineral proj analyst, Kern County Land Co, Tenneco, Inc, 63-68; metall engr, 68-74, MGR MINERAL PROCESSING, KAISER STEEL CORP, 74- Mem: Am Chem Soc; Am Inst Mining, Metall & Petrol Engrs; Soc Mining Engrs; Am Soc Testing & Mat. Res: Surface chemistry as related to mineral processing; chemical processing of minerals concerning phase chemistry; crystallization; hydrometallurgy; coal processing and utilization. Mailing Add: Kaiser Steel Corp PO Box 58 Oakland CA 94604

LEE, ADDISON EARL, b Maydelle, Tex, June 18, 14; m 37; c 2. BOTANY, SCIENCE EDUCATION. Educ: Stephen F Austin State Teachers Col, BS, 34; Agr & Mech Col Tex, MS, 37; Univ Tex, PhD(bot), 49. Prof Exp: Lab instr, Stephen F Austin State Teachers Col, 33-36 & Agr & Mech Col Tex, 36-37; from instr to assoc prof bot, 46-59, morphologist & asst dir plant res inst, 49-53, prof, 59-80, EMER PROF SCI EDUC & BIOL & DIR SCI EDUC CTR, UNIV TEX, AUSTIN, 80- Concurrent Pos: High sch teacher,

Tex, 34-36; vis prof, Univ Va, 57-58. Honors & Awards: Robert H Carleton Award, Nat Sci Teachers Asn, 75. Mem: Nat Sci Teachers Asn (pres, 67); hon mem Nat Asn Biol Teachers (pres, 73); Nat Asn Res Sci Teaching. Res: Experimental plant morphology. Mailing Add: Sci Educ Ctr Univ of Tex Austin TX 78712

LEE, AGNES C, biochemistry, see previous edition

LEE, ALFRED M, b Bloomington, Ind, Aug, 23, 51. TELECOMMUNICATIONS POLICY, TECHNOLOGY ASSESSMENT. Educ: Univ Ill, BSEE, 73; Cornell Univ, MS, 75, PhD(civil eng & pub policy), 81. Prof Exp: Res specialist mobile commun, 75-78, res asst electronic message transfer, 78-80, FEL, PROG SCI, TECHNOL & SCI, CORNELL UNIV, 80- Concurrent Pos: Mem, Transp Res Bd, Subcomt Telecommun & Transp, Trade-offs, 80; assoc ed, Inst Elec & Electronics Engrs Technol & Soc Mag, 81. Mem: Inst Elec & Electronics Engrs; Sigma Xi. Res: Transportation-communications trade-offs and the social impact of developments in telecommunications; mobile communications; electronic message transfer. Mailing Add: 632 Clark Hall Cornell Univ Ithaca NY 14853

LEE, ALFRED TZE-HAU, b Hong Kong, July 22, 39; US citizen; m 70; c 2. ANALYTICAL CHEMISTRY, ORGANIC CHEMISTRY. Educ: Univ Calif, Berkeley, BS, 63; Univ Calif, Los Angeles, PhD(chem), 68. Prof Exp: Instr chem, East Los Angeles Col, 67-68; PROF CHEM, CITY COL OF SAN FRANCISCO, 68- Mem: Am Chem Soc. Res: Oxidation-state diagrams; pulse polarography; analytical methods in general, vacuum-ultraviolet spectra of olefins. Mailing Add: Dept of Chem City Col of San Francisco San Francisco CA 94112

LEE, AMY SHIU, b Canton, China, Aug 5, 47; US citizen; m 72; c 2. MOLECULAR BIOLOGY, BIOCHEMISTRY. Educ: Univ Calif, Berkeley, BA, 70; Calif Inst Technol, MSc, 72, PhD(biophysics, molecular biol), 75. Prof Exp: Res asst bact, Univ Calif, Los Angeles, 70-71; teaching asst biol, Calif Inst Technol, 71-74, res fel, 74-77, sr res fel, 78-79; ASST PROF BIOCHEM, SCH MED, UNIV SOUTHERN CALIF, 79- Concurrent Pos: Am Cancer Soc fel, Calif Inst Technol, 75-76, sr res fel, 78-69, NIH Pub Health Serv fel, 77-78. Mem: AAAS. Res: DNA sequence organization and gene expression in eukaryotes; recombinant DNA technology. Mailing Add: Dept Biochem Univ Southern Calif Los Angeles CA 90033

LEE, ANTHONY, b Canton, China, Dec 8, 41; US citizen; m 69; c 2. PLASMA PHYSICS. Educ: Drexel Univ, BS, 66; Stevens Inst Technol, MS, 69, PhD(physics), 71. Prof Exp: Fel plasma physics, Univ Sask, 71-73; adj asst prof, Univ S Fla, 73-75, vis asst prof physics, 75-76; SR ENGR, WESTINGHOUSE ELEC CORP, RES & DEVELOP CTR, 76- Mem: Am Phys Soc; Inst Elec & Electronic Engrs. Res: Nonlinear plasma wave theory; linear and nonlinear low frequency waves in plasmas with density, potential and temperature gradients; catalytic turbulent heating of plasmas as supplementary tokamac heating. Mailing Add: Westinghouse Elec Corp 1310 Beulah Rd Pittsburgh PA 15235

LEE, ANTHONY L, b Tsing Tao, China, Nov 16, 34; US citizen; m 62; c 2. CATALYSIS, THERMODYNAMICS. Educ: Univ Calif, Berkeley, BS, 58; Mo Sch Mines, MS, 61. Prof Exp: Res asst, Calif Inst Technol, 58-59; chemist, Stepan Chem Co, 60; chem engr, 61-66, supvr fundamental properties res, 66-69, supvr catalytic processing, 69-78, SR CHEM ENGR, INST GAS TECHNOL, 78- Mem: Am Inst Chem Engrs. Res: Transport and thermodynamic peoperties of hydrocarbons; coal gasification research; methanation, water-gas shift, hydrotreating, hydrocracking, and steam reforming catalysis. Mailing Add: Inst of Gas Technol 3424 S State St Chicago IL 60616

LEE, ARNOLD (YING-HO), b China, Feb 7, 42; m 69; c 1. ELECTRICAL ENGINEERING. Educ: Kans State Univ, BS, 65; Univ Wis-Madison, MS, 67, PhD(elec eng), 69. Prof Exp: Lectr elec eng, Univ Wis, 69-70; asst prof, 70-80, ASSOC PROF ELEC ENG, MICH TECHNOL UNIV, 80- Mem: Inst Elec & Electronics Engrs. Res: Network and system theory; application of computers to network and system design. Mailing Add: Dept of Elec Eng Mich Technol Univ Houghton MI 49931

LEE, ARTHUR CLAIR, b Abilene, Kans, Aug 3, 23; m 51; c 5. OPTHALMOLOGY, RADIATION RESEARCH. Educ: Colo State Univ, DVM, 52, MS, 63, PhD(radiation biol), 70. Prof Exp: Practitioner vet med, 52-60; Morris Found fel, 60-62; vet radiologist, AEC Proj, 63-66, VET SECT LEADER, COLLAB RADIOL HEALTH LAB, USPHS, COLO STATE UNIV, FOOTHILLS CAMPUS, 64- Mem: AAAS; Am Vet Med Asn; Radiation Res Soc Am. Res: Late effects of ovarian irradiation; radiation effects on canine growth and development; ocular lesions as a result of age at exposure. Mailing Add: Collab Radiol Health Lab Colo State Univ Foothills Campus Ft Collins CO 80523

LEE, BENEDICT HUK KUN, b Hong Kong, Oct 17, 40; Can citizen; m 66; c 2. MECHANICAL ENGINEERING, AERONAUTICS. Educ: McGill Univ, BEng, 63, MEng, 64, PhD(mech eng), 66. Prof Exp: Res assoc, McGill Univ, 66-67; RES SCIENTIST, NAT RES COUN, 67- Mem: Am Inst Aeronaut & Astronaut; Acoust Soc Am. Res: Combustion; gas dynamics; acoustics and aerodynamics; aeroelasticity. Mailing Add: Nat Res Coun Bldg U66 Montreal Rd Ottawa ON K1A 0R6 Can

LEE, BERNARD S, b China, Dec 14, 34; US citizen; m 63; c 3. CHEMICAL ENGINEERING, PHYSICAL CHEMISTRY. Educ: Polytech Inst Brooklyn, BChE, 56, PhD(chem eng), 60. Prof Exp: Mem staff, Arthur D Little, Inc, 60-65; supvr, mgr & dir coal gasification, 65-75, asst vpres process res, 75-76, vpres, 76-77, exec vpres, 77-78, PRES, INST GAS TECHNOL, 78- Concurrent Pos: lectr, Am Inst Chem Engrs, 81. Mem: Fel Am Inst Chem Engrs; Am Chem Soc; Am Inst Mining, Metall & Petrol Engrs; AAAS; Am Gas Asn. Res: Energy conversion processes for its production of synthetic fuels from coal, lignite, peat, oil shale, biomass, urban and industrial wastes and efficient energy utilization systems involving solar energy and fuel cells. Mailing Add: 6900 N Kilpatrick Ave Chicago IL 60646

LEE, BYUNGKOOK, b Korea, Feb 7, 41; m 64. X-RAY CRYSTALLOGRAPHY, BIOLOGICAL STRUCTURE. *Educ:* Seoul Nat Univ, BS, 61; Cornell Univ, PhD(phys chem), 67. *Prof Exp:* USPHS res fel, Yale Univ, 69-70; asst prof, 70-74, ASSOC PROF CHEM, UNIV KANS, 74-*Mem:* Am Chem Soc; Am Crystallog Asn. *Res:* Structural studies of large and small molecules through x-ray crystallographic techniques. *Mailing Add:* Dept of Chem Univ of Kans Lawrence KS 66045

LEE, C(HIA) H(UAN), b China, Oct 1, 19; m 53; c 4. ELECTRICAL ENGINEERING. *Educ:* Chiao Tung Univ, China, BS, 42; Cornell Univ, MS, 49, PhD(elec eng), 51. *Prof Exp:* Design engr, Cent Elec Mfg Works, China, 42-47; distribution engr, Canton Power Co, 47-48; develop engr, Reliance Elec & Eng Co, Ohio, 51-55; asst prof elec eng, Polytech Inst Brooklyn, 55-58; fel engr, Westinghouse Elec Corp, 58-64. SR ENG SPECIALIST, AIRESEARCH MFG CO, 64- *Mem:* Inst Elec & Electronics Engrs; Am Soc Naval Engrs; China Elec Eng Soc. *Res:* Electric machinery; electric power systems; electromagnetic devices; electronic components; circuit theory; land, sea and air transportation; electronic power converter; control systems. *Mailing Add:* 30584 Ganado Dr Rancho Palos Verdes CA 90274

LEE, CHANG LING, b Chiang King, China, Nov 4, 16; nat US; m 45; c 3. IMMUNOLOGY, PATHOLOGY. *Educ:* West China Union Univ, MD, 43; Univ Liverpool, DTM&H, 50; Am Bd Path, dipl, 62, cert blood banking, 73. *Prof Exp:* Instr internal med, West China Union Univ, 49; res assoc & instr microbiol, Univ Chicago, 53-57; head div immunohemat, Mt Sinai Hosp Med Ctr, 57-69; DIR BLOOD CTR, MT SINAI HOSP MED CTR, 69-; PROF MED & PATH, RUSH MED COL, 75- *Concurrent Pos:* Res asst prof, Chicago Med Sch, 58-68, prof path, 68-74; sci dir, Mid-Am Regional Red Cross Blood Prog, 75- *Honors & Awards:* Morris H Parker Award, 65 & 68. *Mem:* Am Asn Immunol; Am Soc Clin Path; AMA. *Res:* Immunochematology; immunopathology. *Mailing Add:* Mt Sinai Blood Ctr 2746 W 15th St Chicago IL 60608

LEE, CHARLES ALEXANDER, b New York, NY, Aug 28, 22; m 53; c 1. PHYSICS. *Educ:* Rensselaer Polytech Inst, BEE, 44; Columbia Univ, PhD(physics), 54. *Prof Exp:* Res assoc molecular beam spectros, Columbia Univ, 52-53; mem tech staff semiconductors, Bell Tel Labs, 53-67; PROF ELEC ENG, CORNELL UNIV, 67- *Mem:* Am Phys Soc; Inst Elec & Electronics Engr. *Res:* Solid state device physics; molecular beam spectroscopy. *Mailing Add:* Sch of Elec Eng Cornell Univ Phillips Hall Ithaca NY 14853

LEE, CHARLES NORTHAM, b Syracuse, NY, Jan 13, 25; m 52; c 4. ENGINEERING, FORESTRY. *Educ:* Syracuse Univ, BS, 49, BCE, 57, MCE, 59. *Prof Exp:* Instr civil eng, Syracuse Univ, 57-59; asst prof forest mgt, 59-63, assoc prof forest eng, 64-68, PROF FOREST ENG, STATE UNIV NY COL ENVIRON SCI & FORESTRY, 68-, DIR COMPUT CTR, 64-*Mem:* Am Soc Civil Engrs; Soc Am Foresters; Nat Soc Prof Engrs; Asn Comput Mach. *Res:* Land locomotion under off-highway conditions; modulation techniques applied to roadway design; information coding content and transformations for analysis and design of engineering systems. *Mailing Add:* Comput Ctr State Univ of NY Col of Environ Sci & Forestry Syracuse NY 13210

LEE, CHARLES RICHARD, b Tarrytown, NY, Dec 3, 42; m 65; c 3. SOIL CHEMISTRY, PLANT NUTRITION. *Educ:* Univ Tampa, BS, 64; Clemson Univ, MS, 65, PhD(agron), 68. *Prof Exp:* Res scientist, Can Dept Agr, 68-73; RES SOIL SCIENTIST, US ARMY CORPS OF ENGRS, ENVIRON LAB, WATERWAYS EXP STA, 73- *Mem:* Am Chem Soc; Am Soc Agron; Can Soc Soil Sci. *Res:* Land treatment of wastewater; heavy metal uptake by marsh plants; soil fertility; minor elements; influence of soil acidity on potato production; plant growth in high zinc, aluminum or manganese media. *Mailing Add:* Envrion Lab US Army Engr Waterways Exp Sta PO Box 631 Vicksburg MS 39180

LEE, CHEN HUI, b Taipei, Taiwan, Dec 2, 29; m 62; c 2. FORESTRY. *Educ:* Nat Taiwan Univ, BS, 53; Mich State Univ, MS, 60, PhD(forestry), 66. *Prof Exp:* Asst forestry, Nat Taiwan Univ, 54-59, instr, 59-62; res asst, Mich State Univ, 62-66; from asst prof to assoc prof, 66-77, PROF FORESTRY, UNIV WIS-STEVENS POINT, 77- *Concurrent Pos:* US Forest Serv res grants, 77 & 79. *Mem:* Soc Am Foresters; Chinese Soc Forestry; Japanese Forestry Soc. *Res:* Forest genetics and tree improvement, especially tree physiology, pine leaf anatomy and wood quality. *Mailing Add:* Col of Natural Resources Univ of Wis Stevens Point WI 54481

LEE, CHENG-CHUN, b Youngchow, China, May 24, 22; nat US; m 59; c 2. PHARMACOLOGY, TOXICOLOGY. *Educ:* Nat Cent Univ, China, BS, 45, MS, 48; Mich State Univ, MS, 50, PhD(physiol), 52. *Prof Exp:* Asst vet med, Nat Cent Univ, 45-48; asst physiol, Mich State Univ, 49-51; from pharmacologist to sr pharmacologist, Eli Lilly & Co, 52-62; from sr pharmacologist to prin pharmacologist, Midwest Res Inst, 62-67, head pharmacol & toxicol, 67-78, asst dir, 76-77, assoc dir, 77-78, dep dir, biol sci div, 78-79; SR SCIENTIST, HEALTH REV DIV, OFF TOXIC SUBSTANCES, ENVIRON PROTECTION AGENCY, 79- *Concurrent Pos:* Lectr, Univ Mo-Kansas City, 65-66 & Med Ctr, Univ Kans, 66-79; lectr, Med Ctr, George Washington Univ, 81-; spec consult antimalarils & drug develop, WHO, 80, 81. *Mem:* Am Physiol Soc; Am Soc Pharmacol & Exp Therapeut; Soc Toxicol; Am Col Toxicol; NY Acad Sci. *Res:* Teratology; carcinogenesis; drug metabolism and disposition; antimalarials; antineoplastics; pharmaceuticals; chemicals; drug development; mechanism of drug action and toxicity; liver and renal functions; author or coauthor of over 90 publications. *Mailing Add:* 401 M St SW Environ Protection Agency Washington DC 20460

LEE, CHEUK MAN, b China, Feb 22, 29. ORGANIC CHEMISTRY, PHARMACEUTICAL CHEMISTRY. *Educ:* Univ Hong Kong, BSc, 54, MSc, 57; Univ Mich, PhD(pharmaceut chem), 60. *Prof Exp:* SR RES CHEMIST, ABBOTT LABS, 60- *Mem:* Am Chem Soc. *Res:* Synthesis of organic compounds of neuropharmacological activities; heterocyclic chemistry; neurotropic drugs. *Mailing Add:* Abbott Labs 1400 Sheridan Rd North Chicago IL 60064

LEE, CHI C, engineering, mathematics, see previous edition

LEE, CHI-HANG, b Vinh Long, SVietnam, Jan 1, 39; nat US; m 64; c 2. NATURAL PRODUCTS CHEMISTRY. *Educ:* Southern Ill Univ, Carbondale, BA, 60; Rutgers Univ, New Brunswick, PhD(natural prod chem), 66. *Prof Exp:* Res asst, Rutgers Univ, 61-65, res assoc, 66; sr chemist, Gen Foods Corp, 67-71, res specialist, Corp Res Dept, 72-77, sr res specialist, 76-78; sr res scientist, RJR Foods, 78-80; BIOCHEM MGR, DEL MONTE CORP, 80- *Concurrent Pos:* Vis prof, King's Col, 73-77. *Mem:* Am Chem Soc; Am Sci Affil (pres, 82). *Res:* Carbohydrates; flavors; sweeteners; food chemistry. *Mailing Add:* Del Monte Corp Res Ctr 205 N Wiget Lane Walnut Creek CA 94598

LEE, CHI-HO, b Taitung, Taiwan, July 2, 41; US citizen; m 72; c 1. PHARMACOLOGY. *Educ:* Kaohsiung Med Col, Taiwan, BS, 67; Univ Tokyo, MS, 72; Sch Med Sci, Cornell Univ, PhD(pharmacol), 76. *Prof Exp:* Fel pharmacol, Roche Inst Molecular Biol, 75-76 & Med Col, Cornell Univ, 76-78; fel, 78-79, staff researcher I, 79-81, STAFF RESEARCHER II, CARDIOVASC PHARMACOL, SYNTEX RES, 81- *Mem:* AAAS; Western Pharmacol Soc. *Res:* Cardiovascular pharmacology; antihypertensive drugs; evaluation of drug mechanisms; cerebral and peripheral blood vessels; heart. *Mailing Add:* Dept Pharmacol Syntex Res 3401 Hillview Ave Palo Alto CA 94304

LEE, CHIN OK, b Choong-buk, Korea, June 8, 39; US citizen; m 69; c 2. CARDIAC ELECTROPHYSIOLOGY. *Educ:* Seoul Nat Univ, BS, 65, MS, 67; Ind Univ, PhD(physiol), 73. *Prof Exp:* Res fel biochem, Atomic Energy Res Inst, 67-68; fel cardiac electrophysiol, Univ Chicago, 72-76; asst prof, 76-81, ASSOC PROF CARDIAC ELECTROPHYSIOL, MED COL, CORNELL UNIV, 78- *Concurrent Pos:* Louis N Katz young investr, Am Heart Asn, 74, estab investr, 76; Adv consult, Site Visit, NIH, 80. *Mem:* Am Physiol Soc; Biophys Soc; NY Acad Sci; AAAS. *Res:* Ionic mechanism of the heart beat; relationship between ion activity and contractile force in heart muscle; intracellular application of ion-selective microelectrodes for study of ion transport. *Mailing Add:* Dept Physiol Med Col Cornell Univ 1300 York Ave New York NY 10021

LEE, CHIN-CHIU, b Hunan, China, Aug 10, 34; m 64; c 1. MICROBIOLOGY, ELECTRON MICROSCOPY. *Educ:* Taiwan Norm Univ, BSc, 55; Loyola Univ, MS, 64; La State Univ, PhD(parasitol), 68. *Prof Exp:* Biol teacher, Taiwan Prov Agr Sch, 55-56 & High Sch, Taiwan, 56-58; asst instr biol, Taiwan Norm Univ, 58-59 & Nanyang Univ, 59-61; res technologist biochem, La State Univ, 63, res assoc parasitol, 64; ASSOC PROF BIOL, KING'S COL, PA, 68-, CHMN DEPT, 77- *Mem:* Am Soc Parasitol; Electron Micros Soc Am; AAAS. *Res:* Medical parasitology; studies on the physiological and ultrastructural aspects of parasites, particularly of parasitic nematodes. *Mailing Add:* Dept of Biol King's Col Wilkes-Barre PA 18702

LEE, CHING TSUNG, b Taiwan, July 1, 37; m 67; c 2. QUANTUM OPTICS, MATHEMATICAL PHYSICS. *Educ:* Nat Taiwan Univ, BS, 62; Rice Univ, MA, 65, PhD(physics), 67. *Prof Exp:* Welch Found fel, Tex A&M Univ, 67-68; NASA fel, Rice Univ, 68-69; assoc prof, 69-73, PROF PHYSICS & MATH, ALA A&M UNIV, 73- *Mem:* Am Phys Soc; Optical Soc Am. *Res:* Superradiance. *Mailing Add:* Dept of Physics Ala A&M Univ Normal AL 35762

LEE, CHING-LI, b Taiwan, Repub China, Mar 30, 42; US citizen; m 71; c 2. IMMUNOLOGY. *Educ:* Chung-Hsing Univ, Taiwan, BS, 69; Wayne State Univ, MS, 72, PhD(biochem), 75. *Prof Exp:* Res assoc, Dept Immunol, Mayo Clinic, 75-77; res scientist, 77-79, SR CANCER RES SCIENTIST, ROSWELL PARK MEM INST, 79-, RES ASST PROF, 81- *Mem:* Am Chem Soc. *Res:* Antigenic structure of globular proteins with various biochemical, chemical and physical approaches; isolation and characterization of human tumor associated antigens (enzymes) or tumor specific antigens and development immunoassays for clinical immunodiagnosis. *Mailing Add:* Diag Immunol Res & Biochem Roswell Park Mem Inst 666 Elm St Buffalo NY 14263

LEE, CHING-TSE, b Sinchu, Taiwan, China, May 21, 40; m 69; c 2. ANIMAL BEHAVIOR. *Educ:* Nat Taiwan Univ, BS, 63; Bowling Green State Univ, MA, 67, PhD(psychol), 69. *Prof Exp:* Fac assoc psychol, Univ Tex-Austin, 69-71; asst prof, 71-76, ASSOC PROF PSYCHOL, BROOKLYN COL, CITY UNIV NEW YORK, 76- *Concurrent Pos:* Fac res award, City Univ New York, 71, 73, 74; fel, Dept Health Educ & Welfare, 74. *Honors & Awards:* Nat Sci Coun Award, 79 & 80. *Mem:* Animal Behav Soc; Am Psychol Asn; AAAS; Behav Genetics Asn. *Res:* Investigation of animal communication processes through olfaction and hormonal determinants of the production of olfactory signals; effects of neonatal hormones on behavioral differentation; mathematical models applied to animal behavior; biofeedback; Chinese medicine theories; states of consciousness. *Mailing Add:* Dept of Psychol Brooklyn Col City Univ of New York Brooklyn NY 11210

LEE, CHING-WEN, b Yunnan, China, Nov 19, 21; US citizen; m 51; c 1. ENGINEERING MECHANICS, SOLID MECHANICS. *Educ:* Nat Inst Technol, Chungking, China, BS, 44; Ill Inst Technol, MS, 56, PhD(mech), 58. *Prof Exp:* Staff mem, Res & Develop Lab, Int Bus Mach Corp, NY, 59-60; asst prof eng mech, Case Inst Technol, 60-62; assoc prof, 62-66, PROF ENG SCI & MECH, UNIV TENN, KNOXVILLE, 66- *Mem:* Am Soc Mech Engrs; Am Soc Eng Educ; Am Acdd Mech. *Res:* Mechanics of deformable solids; elasticity; plates and shells; thermal stresses. *Mailing Add:* Dept Eng Sci & Mech Univ of Tenn Knoxville TN 37916

LEE, CHIUNG PUH, b China; US citizen. PHYSIOLOGY. *Educ:* Univ Minn, PhD(physiol), 53. *Prof Exp:* Res mem physiol, Nat Acad Sci, 41-43; res assoc, Med Sch, Univ Minn, 57-70; res assoc biochem, Med Sch, Univ Pittsburgh, 56-57; ASSOC PROF PHYSIOL, MED SCH, UNIV MINN, 72-

Mem: Am Physiol Soc; Sigma Xi; AAAS; Soc Exp Biol Med. *Res:* Mechanism of blood cell destruction, controlling antibody formation, aging and nutrition; cardiac muscle physiology; energy metabolism, ion fluxes and excitation-contraction coupling. *Mailing Add:* Dept of Physiol Univ Minn 424 Millard Hall Minneapolis MN 55455

LEE, CHOI CHUCK, b Vancouver, BC, Apr 27, 24; m 53; c 4. ORGANIC CHEMISTRY. *Educ:* Univ Sask, BE, 47, MSc, 49; Mass Inst Technol, ScD(chem), 52. *Prof Exp:* Res off chem, Prairie Regional Lab, Nat Res Coun, 52-53; spec lectr chem, Univ Sask, 53-54; asst prof, Univ BC, 54-55; from asst prof to prof, 55-78, THORVALDSON PROF CHEM, UNIV SASK, 78- *Mem:* Am Chem Soc; Chem Inst Can. *Res:* Mechanisms of organic reactions; applications of radioactive isotopes as tracers; cereal and agricultural chemistry. *Mailing Add:* Dept of Chem Univ of Sask Saskatoon SK S7N 0W0 Can

LEE, CHONG SUNG, b Seoul, Korea, Sept 4, 39; nat US; m 72; c 2. MOLECULAR BIOLOGY. *Educ:* Seoul Nat Univ, BS, 64; Calif Inst Technol, PhD(chem), 70. *Prof Exp:* Grad res asst biophys, Calif Inst Technol, 65-69; fel biochem, Harvard Med Sch, 69-72; asst prof, 72-78, ASSOC PROF MOLECULAR GENETICS, UNIV TEX, AUSTIN, 78- *Concurrent Pos:* Jane Coffin Childs Mem Fund for Med Res fel, 70-72; *Mem:* Genetics Soc Am; Am Soc Cell Biol; Am Soc Biol Chemists; Korean Chem Soc. *Res:* Structure and function of DNA and chromosomes in Drosophila. *Mailing Add:* Dept of Zool Univ of Tex Austin TX 78712

LEE, CHONG-JIN, mechanical engineering, see previous edition

LEE, CHUAN-PU, b Tsing-Tao, China, Sept 24, 31. BIOCHEMISTRY, PHYSICAL CHEMISTRY. *Educ:* Nat Taiwan Univ, BS, 54; Ore State Univ, PhD(biochem), 61. *Hon Degrees:* DPhil, Univ Stockholm, 78. *Prof Exp:* Instr chem, Nat Taiwan Univ, 54-56; res assoc biochem, Ore State Univ, 60-61; Johnson Found res fel, Univ Pa, 61-63; Jane Coffin Childs Mem Fund Med Res fel physiol chem, Wenner-Gren Inst, Stockholm, 63-65, docent, 65-66; mem staff, Johnson Found, Univ Pa, 66-75, from assoc prof to prof biochem, 70-75; PROF BIOCHEM, SCH MED, WAYNE STATE UNIV, 75- *Concurrent Pos:* USPHS career develop award, 68-73; ed, Biochimica et Biophysica Acta & Biochimica et Biophysica Acta Review on Bioenergetics, 73-; ed, Topics of Bioenergetics, 81- *Honors & Awards:* Silver Medal, Chinese Chem Soc, 55; Merck Index Award, 60. *Mem:* AAAS; Chinese Chem Soc; Am Soc Biol Chem; Biophys Soc; NY Acad Sci. *Res:* Reaction mechanisms of electron and energy transfer in oxidative phosphorylation. *Mailing Add:* Dept of Biochem Sch of Med Wayne State Univ Detroit MI 48201

LEE, CHUNG, b Shanghai, China, Sept 18, 36; US citizen; m 65; c 2. REPRODUCTIVE ENDOCRINOLOGY, NUTRITION. *Educ:* Nat Taiwan Univ, BS, 59; WVa Univ, MS, 66, PhD(nutrit & endocrinol), 69. *Prof Exp:* USPHS fel, Albany Med Col, 69-71; assoc obstet & gynec, 71-74, asst prof, 74-79, ASSOC PROF UROL, MED SCH, NORTHWESTERN UNIV, CHICAGO, 79-; ASSOC STAFF MEM RES, EVANSTON HOSP, 74- *Concurrent Pos:* Am Cancer Soc grant, Med Sch, Northwestern Univ, Chicago, 73-74; USPHS grants, 74-86. *Mem:* Endocrine Soc; Soc Study Reproduction; Am Asn Cancer Res. *Res:* Hormonal regulation of breast and prostate cancer; mechanism of sex steroid action; cancer and hormones. *Mailing Add:* Dept of Urol Northwestern Univ Med Sch Chicago IL 60611

LEE, CHUNG N, b Sinuiju, Korea, Nov 7, 31. MATHEMATICS. *Educ:* Seoul Nat Univ, BA, 54; Univ Va, MA, 57, PhD, 59. *Prof Exp:* From instr to asst prof, 60-68, ASSOC PROF MATH, UNIV MICH, ANN ARBOR, 68- *Mem:* Am Math Soc. *Res:* Algebraic topology; transformation groups; topology of manifolds. *Mailing Add:* Dept of Math Univ of Mich Ann Arbor MI 48109

LEE, CLARENCE EDGAR, b San Jose, Calif, Aug 18, 31; c 3. MATHEMATICAL PHYSICS. *Educ:* Univ Calif, Berkeley, BA, 53; Cornell Univ, MA, 62; Univ Colo, Boulder, PhD(physics), 73. *Prof Exp:* Staff mem, Los Alamos Sci Lab, 53-77, team leader, 71-77; PROF NUCLEAR SCI & RES ASSOC, DEPT NUCLEAR ENG, TEX A&M UNIV, 77- *Mem:* Am Physics Soc; Am Nuclear Soc. *Res:* Theoretical, nuclear, plasma, solid state, chemical reactor, radiation and applied physics; hydrodynamics, chemical metallurgy and kinetics, heat transfer; computer sciences and numerical analysis; fuel technology. *Mailing Add:* Dept of Nuclear Eng Tex A&M Univ College Station TX 77840

LEE, D(ON) WILLIAM, b Everett, Pa, Oct 30, 27; m 55; c 6. CERAMICS, METALS. *Educ:* Bethany Col, BS, 51; Mass Inst Technol, ScD(ceramics), 58. *Prof Exp:* Asst ceramics, Mass Inst Technol, 54-58; mem res staff, Cent Res Dept, E I du Pont de Nemours & Co, 58-63; sr staff mem, Res & Develop Div, 63-67; fel biochem, Harvard Med Sch, ARTHUR D LITTLE, INC, 67-, VPRES, 75- *Mem:* Am Ceramic Soc. *Res:* Physical properties of solids; thermal, mechanical and electrical properties of materials; research and development organizational studies; product and process development; high performance material technology; strategic assessment and utilization of material technology. *Mailing Add:* Arthur D Little Inc 15 Acorn Park Cambridge MA 02140

LEE, DAEYONG, b Ham Nam, Korea, June 16, 33; US citizen; m 62; c 3. MATERIALS SCIENCE, MATERIALS MECHANICS. *Educ:* Ripon Col, BA, 58; Mass Inst Technol, BS, 58, MS, 62, ScD(metall), 65. *Prof Exp:* Res asst metall, Mass Inst Technol, 61-65, staff mem, 65-66; METALLURGIST, GEN ELEC RES & DEVELOP CTR, SCHENECTADY, 66- *Concurrent Pos:* Adj prof, Rensselaer Polytech Inst, Troy, 81. *Mem:* Am Inst Mining, Metall & Petrol Engrs; Am Soc Metals. *Res:* Mechanical metallurgy; plasticity theory, mechanics, constitutive equations, nuclear materials, fracture, friction and lubrication, materials processing. *Mailing Add:* 111 Governor Dr Scotia NY 12302

LEE, DAH-YINN, b Tsingtao, China, June 4, 34; m 62; c 1. CIVIL ENGINEERING, HIGHWAY MATERIALS. *Educ:* Cheng Kung Univ, Taiwan, BSc, 58; Iowa State Univ, PhD(civil eng), 64. *Prof Exp:* Res assoc, Eng Res Inst, 64-65; from asst prof to assoc prof, 65-78, PROF CIVIL ENG, IOWA STATE UNIV, 78- *Concurrent Pos:* Comt mem, Hwy Res Bd, Nat Acad Sci-Nat Res Coun. *Mem:* Am Soc Testing & Mat; Am Soc Civil Engrs; Am Concrete Inst. *Res:* Asphalt durability; aggregates used for asphalt mixtures; waste materials in construction; pavement recycling; foamed asphalt; sulfur in construction. *Mailing Add:* Dept of Civil Eng Iowa State Univ Ames IA 50011

LEE, DAISY SI, b Peiping, China, July 21, 34; US citizen; m 66; c 2. PEDIATRICS, ALLERGY. *Educ:* Okla Baptist Univ, BA, 56; Bowman Gray Sch Med, MD, 61; Am Bd Pediat, dipl. *Prof Exp:* Intern med, Georgetown Div, Washington Gen Hosp, 61-62; resident pediat, St Luke's Hosp Ctr, New York, 62-64, NY Heart Asn fel med, 64-65; fel, Inst Nutrit Sci, Columbia Univ & Dept Med, St Lukes Hosp Ctr, 65-66; fel pediat, Sch Med, Stanford Univ, 66-69; pediatrician, Ctr Develop & Learning Disorders, 69-72, asst prof, 69-76, dir pediat allergy prog, 72-76, ASST CLIN PROF PEDIAT, MED CTR, UNIV ALA, BIRMINGHAM, 76- *Mem:* NY Acad Sci; Sigma Xi. *Res:* Quantitation of milk antibodies in atopic children. *Mailing Add:* 1025 S 18th St Suite 303 Birmingham AL 35205

LEE, DANIEL DIXON, JR, b Dillon, SC, Sept 27, 35; m 58; c 4. ANIMAL NUTRITION. *Educ:* Clemson Univ, BS, 57, MS, 64; NC State Univ, Raleigh, PhD(biochem & nutrit), 70. *Prof Exp:* Res supvr biochem, NC State Univ, 67-70; asst prof, 70-73, ASSOC PROF MINERAL METAB, DEPT ANIMAL INDUST, SOUTHERN ILL UNIV, 73-, ASST DEAN RES, SCH AGR, 76- *Mem:* Am Soc Animal Sci. *Res:* Trace mineral metabolism; nonprotein nitrogen utilization; wintering of cattle on crop residues and feeding of recycled animal wastes to ruminants. *Mailing Add:* Dept of Animal Indust Southern Ill Univ Carbondale IL 62901

LEE, DAVID LOUIS, b Oakland, Calif, Oct 19, 48; m 75; c 1. CHEMISTRY. *Educ:* Univ Calif, Berkeley, BS, 70, PhD(chem), 76; Univ Ill, Urbana, MS, 72. *Prof Exp:* Res assoc chem, Univ Calif, San Francisco, 76-77; sr chemist, Cordova Chem Co, 77-80; RES CHEMIST, STAUFFER CHEM CO, 80- *Res:* Defining the structure-activity space of new classes of herbicides. *Mailing Add:* Stauffer Chem Co 1200 South 47th St Richmond CA 94804

LEE, DAVID MALLIN, b Brooklyn, NY, Jan 18, 44; m 66; c 5. EXPERIMENTAL NUCLEAR PHYSICS, NUCLEAR SAFEGUARDS. *Educ:* Manhattan Col, BS, 66; Univ Va, PhD(physics), 71. *Prof Exp:* Res assoc physics, Univ Va, 71-74; MEM STAFF, LOS ALAMOS NAT LAB, 74- *Concurrent Pos:* US expert, Int Atomic Energy Agency, 80-81. *Mem:* Am Phys Soc; Sigma Xi. *Res:* Medium energy nuclear physics; position sensitive detectors; beam line instrumentation. *Mailing Add:* MS 540 Q1 Los Alamos Nat Lab Los Alamos NM 87545

LEE, DAVID MORRIS, b Rye, NY, Jan 20, 31; m 60; c 2. PHYSICS. *Educ:* Harvard Univ, AB, 52; Univ Conn, MS, 55; Yale Univ, PhD(physics), 59. *Prof Exp:* From instr to assoc prof, 59-68, PROF PHYSICS, CORNELL UNIV, 68- *Concurrent Pos:* Guggenheim fel, 66-67 & 74-75; guest assoc physicist, Brookhaven Nat Lab, 66-67; Japan Soc Prom Sci fel, 77. *Honors & Awards:* Sir Francis Simon Mem Prize, British Inst Physics, 76; Oliver Buckley Prize, Am Phys Soc, 81. *Mem:* Am Phys Soc; NY Acad Sci; AAAS. *Res:* Low temperature physics with emphasis on quantum fluids and solids, and superconductivity; solid helium three and solid helium four; superfluid phases of liquid helium three. *Mailing Add:* Lab Atomic & Solid State Physics Cornell Univ Dept of Physics Ithaca NY 14853

LEE, DAVID ROBERT, b Grand Forks, NDak, May 9, 45; m 75; c 4. HYDROLOGY, RADIOECOLOGY. *Educ:* Univ NDak, BS, 68, MS, 72; Va Polytech Inst & State Univ, PhD(zool), 76. *Prof Exp:* Res asst prof earth sci & biol, Univ Waterloo, 76-79; RES OFFICER HYDROL & RADIOECOL, ATOMIC ENERGY CAN, CHALK RIVER, ONT, 79- *Concurrent Pos:* Adj asst prof, Dept Earth Sci, Univ Waterloo, Ont, 79- *Mem:* Am Geophys Union; Am Soc Limnol & Oceanog; NAm Benthological Soc. *Res:* Groundwater contaminant flux to surface waters. *Mailing Add:* Environ Res Br Chalk River Nuclear Labs Chalk River ON K0J 1J0 Can

LEE, DAVID WEBSTER, b Wenatchee, Wash, Dec 10, 42; m 72; c 2. PLANT EVOLUTION STRUCTURE, PLANT FUNCTION. *Educ:* Pac Lutheran Univ, BS, 66; Rutgers Univ, MS, 68, PhD(bot), 70. *Prof Exp:* Res assoc bot & microbiol, Ohio State Univ, 70-72; lectr, Univ Malaya, Kuala Lumpur, 73-76; maite de conf assoc, Univ Montpellier II, 77-78; ASST PROF BIOL, FLA INT UNIV, 80- *Mem:* Am Bot Soc; Soc Trop Biol; Int Soc Trop Ecol. *Res:* Evolution and adaptation of plants in humid tropical forests. *Mailing Add:* Dept Biol Sci Fla Int Univ Miami FL 33199

LEE, DER-TSAI, b Taipei, China, Apr 5, 49; m 74; c 2. COMPUTER SCIENCE. *Educ:* Nat Taiwan Univ, BS, 71; Univ Ill, MS, 76, PhD(comput sci), 78. *Prof Exp:* Res asst comput sci, Univ Ill, 74-78; asst prof, 78-81, ASSOC PROF ELEC ENG & COMPUT SCI, NORTHWESTERN UNIV, 81- *Mem:* Inst Elec & Electronics Engrs; Asn Comput Mach. *Res:* Design and analysis of algorithms; computational geometry and data structures; very large scale integration systems; computer graphics. *Mailing Add:* Dept of Elec Eng & Comput Sci Northwestern Univ Evanston IL 60201

LEE, DIANA MANG, b Mukden, China; US citizen; m 60; c 1. LIPOPROTEINS. *Educ:* Nat Taiwan Univ, BS, 55; Utah State Univ, MS, 60; Univ Okla, PhD(biochem), 67. *Prof Exp:* Chemist, anal chem, Yung-Kang Cement Corp, 55-57; univ asst, chem eng, Nat Taiwan Univ, 57-59; clin chem, Presby-St Luke's Hosp, 61-64, trainee, lipoproteins, 64-67; sr investr, 67-71, asst mem, 71-75, ASSOC MEM, LIPOPROTEINS, OKLA MED RES FOUND, 75-; ASSOC PROF BIOCHEM, UNIV OKLA SCH MED, 76- *Concurrent Pos:* Res assoc, dept biochem, Univ Okla Sch Med, 68-71; asst prof, 72-76; mem, Credential Comt, Coun Arteriosclerosis, Am Heart Asn,

73-75; assoc ed, Artery, 75-; reviewer, Biochimica et Biophysica Acta, 77-; consult, NIH, 79- *Mem:* Am Chem Soc; Sigma Xi; AAAS; Am Oil Chemists Soc. *Res:* Structural aspects of human plasma lipoproteins and apolipoproteins, particularly in low density lipoproteins and apolipoprotein B, their properties, the oxidative effets and the proteolytic effects, and their relationship with atherosclerosis. *Mailing Add:* Lab Lipid & Lipoprotein Studies Okla Med Res Found 825 NE 13th St Oklahoma City OK 73104

LEE, DO IK, b Chinnampo, Korea, Mar 6, 37; nat US; m 70; c 1. CHEMICAL ENGINEERING, POLYMER SCIENCE. *Educ:* Seoul Nat Univ, BS, 59; Columbia Univ, MS, 64, EngScD(chem eng), 67. *Prof Exp:* Res chem engr, 67-72, res specialist, 72-75, sr res specialist, 75-79, ASSOC SCIENTIST, DOW CHEM USA, 79- *Mem:* Am Inst Chem Engrs; Am Chem Soc; Tech Asn Pulp & Paper Indust; Sigma Xi. *Res:* Rheology of disperse systems; coating rheology; colloid science; paper coating; emulsion polymerization; inverse emulsion polymerization; suspension polymerization; latex technology; polymer morphology; polymerization kinetics; structured latex technology. *Mailing Add:* Dow Chem USA 1604 Bldg Midland MI 48640

LEE, DO-JAE, b Namwon, Korea, Jan 24, 28; US citizen; m 57; c 2. PHYSICAL ORGANIC CHEMISTRY. *Educ:* Long Beach State Col, BS, 60; San Diego State Col, MS, 64; Univ Calif, San Diego, PhD(chem), 67. *Prof Exp:* RES CHEMIST, TOMS RIVER CHEM CORP, 68- *Mem:* Am Chem Soc. *Res:* Development of new dyestuff and economic process for plant production. *Mailing Add:* 34 Oakside Dr Toms River NJ 08753

LEE, DONALD D(OUGLAS), b Chicago, Ill, Jan 5, 14; m 35; c 3. PHYSICAL CHEMISTRY, CHEMICAL ENGINEERING. *Educ:* Univ Calif, BS, 35, PhD(chem), 38. *Prof Exp:* Asst chem, Univ Calif, 35-37; from res chemist to mgr new prod, Plastics Dept, E I du Pont de Nemours & Co, 38-65, mkt res mgr, 65-71, bus & mkt res mgr, 71-73; assoc prof, 73-76, PROF MGT, WIDENER COL, 76- *Concurrent Pos:* Chemist, Standard Oil Calif, 36-37; dir, Widener Bus Res Ctr, 77-81; consult marketing res & corp planning, 77- *Mem:* Am Chem Soc; Chem Mkt Res Asn. *Res:* Processes for synthesis of organic compounds, especially those involving oxidation, hydrogenation and high pressures; industrial marketing research. *Mailing Add:* 367 Devon Way West Chester PA 19380

LEE, DONALD EDWARD, b Detroit, Mich, Jan 31, 21; m 71. MINERALOGY. *Educ:* Carleton Col, AB, 43; Univ Minn, MS, 47; Stanford Univ, PhD(mineral, ore deposits), 54. *Prof Exp:* Sci consult, Nat Resources Sect, Supreme Comdr Allied Powers, Japan, 47-51; instr phys sci, Stanford Univ, 53-56, asst prof, 56-57; prof geol, Univ Bahia, 57-58; GEOLOGIST, REG GEOCHEM BR, US GEOL SURV, 59- *Mem:* Geol Soc Am; Mineral Soc Am. *Res:* Manganese minerals of Japan; glaucophane schists of California; intrusive rocks of eastern great basin; applied mineralogy and geochemistry; granitoid rocks of the basin-range area. *Mailing Add:* 12979 W Ohio Ave Lakewood CO 80228

LEE, DONALD GARRY, b Midale, Sask, June 21, 35; m 59; c 3. PHYSICAL CHEMISTRY, ORGANIC CHEMISTRY. *Educ:* Univ Sask, BA, 58, MA, 60; Univ BC, PhD(chem), 63. *Prof Exp:* Instr chem, Camrose Lutheran Col, 62-65; res assoc, Harvard Univ, 65-66; assoc prof, Pac Lutheran Univ, 66-67; PROF CHEM, UNIV REGINA, 67- *Concurrent Pos:* Vis scholar, Stanford Univ, 80-81. *Mem:* Chem Inst Can; Am Chem Soc. *Res:* Oxidation mechanisms; protonation studies. *Mailing Add:* Dept of Chem Univ of Regina Regina SK S4S 0A2 Can

LEE, DONALD JACK, b Goldendale, Wash, Jan 28, 32; m 58; c 3. NUTRITIONAL BIOCHEMISTRY. *Educ:* Wash State Univ, BS, 58, MS, 60; Univ Ill, PhD(nutrit, biochem), 65. *Prof Exp:* Assoc prof food sci & technol, Food Protection Sect, Ore State Univ, 65-75; ASST DIR, AGR RES CTR, WASH STATE UNIV, 75- *Concurrent Pos:* USPHS res grant, 66-75. *Mem:* AAAS; Am Inst Nutrit. *Res:* Nutritional biochemistry, especially lipid metabolism; toxicity and carcinogenicity of natural compounds. *Mailing Add:* Agr Res Ctr Wash State Univ Pullman WA 99163

LEE, DONALD WILLIAM, b Buffalo, NY, Nov 4, 47; m 78; c 1. FLUID MECHANICS, APPLIED MECHANICS. *Educ:* Clarkson Col, BS, 69, MS, 73; Univ Mich, PhD(appl mech), 77. *Prof Exp:* Engr, Ford Motor Co, 69-70; teaching fel mech eng, Clarkson Col Technol, 70-71; res asst appl mech, Univ Mich, 71-76; res assoc fluid mech, 77-81, RES MEM STAFF, OAK RIDGE NAT LAB, 81- *Concurrent Pos:* Instr gen sci, Wayne State Univ, 75-76. *Mem:* Am Phys Soc; Am Soc Civil Engrs; Am Soc Mech Engrs; Sigma Xi. *Res:* Environmental fluid dynamics of surface water and groundwater; environmental impact assessment of energy technologies. *Mailing Add:* Oak Ridge Nat Lab PO Box X Oak Ridge TN 37830

LEE, DOUGLAS HARRY KEDGWIN, b Bristol, Eng, Feb 22, 05; nat US; m 52. ENVIRONMENTAL SCIENCES. *Educ:* Univ Queensland, MSc, 27; Univ Sydney, MB & BS, 29, dipl trop med, 33, MD, 40; FRACP, 40; Am Bd Indust Hyg, dipl. *Prof Exp:* Med officer, Commonwealth Dept Health, Australia, 30-33; prof physiol, King Edward VII Col Med, Singapore, 35-36; prof physiol, Univ Queensland, 36-48, dean fac med, 38-42; prof physiol climat & lectr environ med, Johns Hopkins Univ, 48-55; chief res br, Off Qm Gen, 55-58; assoc sci dir res, Qm Res & Eng Command, 58-60; chief occup health res & training facility, USPHS, 60-66, assoc dir, Nat Inst Environ Health Sci, 66-73; CONSULT, 74- *Concurrent Pos:* Consult, US Qm Corps, 47-55 & Food & Agr Orgn, UN, 47-60; Cutter lectr, Sch Pub Health, Harvard Univ, 50; adj prof, NC State Univ, 68-74. *Mem:* AAAS; Am Physiol Soc; fel NY Acad Sci. *Res:* Climatic physiology, effects of climate on man and animals and application to clothing, housing and tropical development; occupational and environmental health. *Mailing Add:* Nazareth S-1 Deer Hill Rd St Thomas VI 00801

LEE, E(RNEST) BRUCE, b Brainerd, Minn, Feb 1, 32; m 54; c 6. CONTROL ENGINEERING. *Educ:* Univ NDak, BS, 55, MS, 56; Univ Minn, PhD(appl math), 60. *Prof Exp:* Sr res scientist, Honeywell Inc, 56-60, vis scientist, Res Inst Advan Studies, 60-61; sr res scientist, Honeywell Inc, 61-63; assoc prof, 63-66, PROF ELEC ENG, UNIV MINN, MINNEAPOLIS, 66-, HEAD DEPT, 76- *Mem:* Soc Indust & Appl Math; Inst Elec & Electronics Engrs. *Res:* Learning systems; differential equations; optimal control theory. *Mailing Add:* Dept of Elec Eng Univ of Minn 123 Church St 139 EE Minneapolis MN 55455

LEE, E(UGENE) STANLEY, b Hopei, China, Sept 7, 30; US citizen; m 57; c 2. CHEMICAL ENGINEERING, COMPUTER SCIENCE. *Educ:* Ord Eng Col Taiwan, BChE, 53; Univ NC, MS, 57, Princeton Univ, PhD(chem eng), 62. *Prof Exp:* Res engr, Phillips Petrol Co, Okla, 60-66; asst prof chem eng, 66-67, assoc prof, 67-71, PROF INDUST ENG, KANS STATE UNIV, 71- *Concurrent Pos:* NSF grant, 71-; vis prof, Univ Southern Calif, Los Angeles, 72-76; ed, Energy Sci & Technol, 77-; assoc ed, J Math Anal & Appln & Math With Appln. *Mem:* Soc Indust & Appl Math; Am Inst Chem Engrs; Opers Res Soc Am. *Res:* Process dynamics and control; optimization theory; numerical solution of non-linear differential equations; applied mathematics; quasilinearization and invariant imbedding. *Mailing Add:* Dept of Indust Eng Kans Univ Manhattan KS 66502

LEE, EDWARD HSIEN-CHI, b Taiwan, Aug 31, 35; m 67; c 2. PLANT PHYSIOLOGY, CELL BIOLOGY. *Educ:* Nat Taiwan Univ, BS, 59; Univ Kans, MA, 66; Univ Okla, PhD(bot), 69. *Prof Exp:* Lab instr gen bot & taxon, Nat Taiwan Univ, 61-64; teaching asst gen bot & physiol, Univ Okla, 66-69; assoc prof cellular physiol, genetics & microbiol, Cent Methodist Col, Mo, 69-78; PLANT PHYSIOLOGIST, FED RES SERV, USDA, 78- *Mem:* AAAS; Am Soc Plant Physiol. *Res:* Environmental stress, air pollution, photosynthesis and tissue culture. *Mailing Add:* USDA/SEA-FR-NER Bldg 001 Rm 206 Beltsville MD 20705

LEE, EDWARD KYUNG CHAI, b Seoul, Korea, Jan 24, 35; m 65; c 2. PHYSICAL CHEMISTRY. *Educ:* Kans Wesleyan Univ, BA, 59; Univ Kans, PhD(chem), 63. *Prof Exp:* Res assoc chem, Univ Kans, 63-65; from asst prof to assoc prof, 65-71, PROF CHEM, UNIV CALIF, IRVINE, 71- *Concurrent Pos:* NSF sr post doc fel, Cambridge Univ, England, 72; Alexander von Humboldt US sr scientist award, Tech Univ Munich, Ger, 77 & 79. *Mem:* AAAS; Am Chem Soc; Am Phys Soc. *Res:* Photochemistry; atomic and molecular energy transfer; reaction kinetics; spectroscopy; lasers. *Mailing Add:* Dept of Chem Univ of Calif Irvine CA 92717

LEE, EDWARD PRENTISS, b Tulsa, Okla, Oct 3, 42. PHYSICS. *Educ:* Calif Inst Technol, BS, 64; Univ Chicago, MS, 66, PhD(physics), 68. *Prof Exp:* Mem staff plasma physics, Inst Advan Study, Princeton, NJ, 68-70; STAFF PHYSICIST PLASMA PHYSICS, LAWRENCE LIVERMORE LAB, 70- *Mem:* Fel Am Phys Soc. *Res:* High current charged particle beams; controlled thermonuclear fusion; astrophysics; particle accelerators. *Mailing Add:* Lawrence Livermore Nat Lab PO Box 808 L-321 Livermore CA 94550

LEE, EMERSON HOWARD, b Okmulgee, Okla, Feb 23, 21; m 48; c 4. PHYSICAL CHEMISTRY. *Educ:* Univ Tex, BS, 52, PhD(chem), 55. *Prof Exp:* Chemist, Darco Div, Atlas Powder Co, 46-50; res engr, Develop & Res Dept, Continental Oil Co, 54-56; res chemist, 56-59, res specialist, 59-60, group leader, 60-65, SCIENTIST, MONSANTO CO, 65- *Mem:* Am Chem Soc; Sigma Xi. *Res:* Surface chemistry and catalysis. *Mailing Add:* Monsanto Co 800 N Lindbergh Blvd St Louis MO 63166

LEE, ERIC KIN-LAM, b Hong Kong, June 25, 48; m 72; c 1. CONTROLLED RELEASE ENGINEERING. *Educ:* NC State Univ, BS, 70, MS, 72, PhD(chem eng), 76. *Prof Exp:* PROJ MGR, BEND RES, INC, 77- *Concurrent Pos:* Res fel, Max Planck Inst Biophysics, 76-77. *Mem:* Am Inst Chem Engrs; Am Chem Soc. *Res:* Development of synthetic membranes for desalination and other industrial separation applications; design of machinery for membrane fabrication; development of membrane processes for resource management and power generation; membrane transport theory; membrane science and separations technology. *Mailing Add:* Bend Res Inc 64550 Research Rd Bend OR 97701

LEE, EUN SUL, b Gongju, Korea, Sept 19, 34; US citizen; m 64; c 2. ETHNIC DEMOGRAPHY, DEMOGRAPHIC METHODS. *Educ:* Seoul Nat Univ, BA, 57; Univ Ky, MA, 64; NC State Univ, PhD(exp statist & sociol), 70. *Prof Exp:* Res assoc statist anal, NC Bd Higher Educ, 66-69; res biometrician, 69-72, asst prof, 72-76, ASSOC PROF BIOMET & DEMOG, SCH PUBLIC HEALTH, UNIV TEX HEALTH SCI CTR, HOUSTON, 76- *Concurrent Pos:* Vis prof, Dept Sociol, Utah State Univ, 75; UN Fund Pop Activities, Pop & Develop Inst, Seoul Nat Univ, 76; fel hist med, Univ Cincinnati, Nat Endowment Humanities, 80. *Mem:* Am Sociol Asn; Am Statist Asn; Pop Asn Am; Am Public Health Asn; Int Union Sci Study Pop. *Res:* Ethnic differentials in mortality, fertility and health behavior; analysis of community nutritional status; changing cardiovascular mortality and morbidity trends. *Mailing Add:* Sch Pub Health Univ Tex Health Sci Ctr PO Box 20186 Houston TX 77025

LEE, FLOYD DENMAN, b Hays, Kans, Apr 27, 38. NUCLEAR PHYSICS. *Educ:* Univ Kans, BS, 60, PhD(physics), 66. *Prof Exp:* Instr physics, Univ Kans, 65-66; Nat Acad Sci-Nat Res Coun assoc, 66-68; ASSOC PROF PHYSICS, MONT STATE UNIV, 68- *Mem:* Am Asn Physics Teachers; Am Phys Soc. *Res:* Low-energy nuclear research with Van-de-Graaf accelerators; nuclear structure. *Mailing Add:* Dept of Physics Mont State Univ Bozeman MT 59715

LEE, FRANKLIN FONG-MING, materials science, see previous edition

LEE, FREDERICK STRUBE, b Baltimore, Md, Dec 26, 27; m 52; c 3. PHYSICAL CHEMISTRY. *Educ:* Johns Hopkins Univ, AB, 50; Brown Univ, PhD(chem), 58. *Prof Exp:* Res chemist, Agr Div, W R Grace & Co, 58-60 & Anal & Phys Div, 60-61; prof chem, Baltimore Jr Col, 61-71,; dir gen studies, 71-76, dir sci, bus & technol studies, 76-79, PROF MATH, COMMUNITY COL BALTIMORE, 79- *Mem:* Am Chem Soc; Sigma Xi. *Res:* X-ray crystallography; inorganic synthesis; physical inorganic chemistry. *Mailing Add:* 9126 Winands Rd Owings Mills MD 21117

LEE, GARTH LORAINE, b Hinkley, Utah, Sept 25, 20; m 43; c 9. PHYSICAL CHEMISTRY. *Educ:* Univ Utah, BA, 44, MA, 47; Univ Toronto, PhD(phys chem), 49. *Prof Exp:* Asst chem, Univ Utah, 45-46; asst, Univ Toronto, 46-48, spec lectr, 48-49; instr, Univ Colo, 49-51, asst prof, 52-54; assoc prof, 54-60, head dept chem, 69-73, head dept chem & biochem, 73-77, PROF CHEM & BIOCHEM, UTAH STATE UNIV, 61- *Mem:* Am Chem Soc. *Mailing Add:* Dept of Chem & Biochem Utah State Univ Logan UT 84321

LEE, GARY ALBERT, b Scottsbluff, Nebr, May 18, 41; m 62; c 3. WEED SCIENCE. *Educ:* Univ Wyo, BS, 64, MS, 65, PhD(agron), 71. *Prof Exp:* Instr weed sci, Univ Wyo, 65-71, from asst prof to assoc prof, 71-75; asst dir agr res, 79-80, PROF WEED SCI, UNIV IDAHO, 75-, HEAD, DEPT PLANT & SOIL SCI, 80- *Concurrent Pos:* Consult, US Borax Res Corp, 75-; Idaho Gov's Adv Comt on Noxious Weed Control. *Mem:* Weed Sci Soc Am (bd dirs); Am Soc Sugarbeet Technologists; Soc Range Mgt. *Res:* Mechanisms of herbicide selectivity in agronomic crops and perennial weed control; population dynamics of weeds in agronomic crops and rangeland; influence of herbicides on the metabolism of weed species. *Mailing Add:* Dept of Plant & Soil Sci Univ of Idaho Col of Agr Moscow ID 83843

LEE, GEORGE C, b Peiping, China, July 17, 32; m 61; c 2. STRUCTURAL & BIOMEDICAL ENGINEERING. *Educ:* Nat Taiwan Univ, BSE, 55; Lehigh Univ, MS, 58, PhD(civil eng), 60. *Prof Exp:* Res fel civil eng, Lehigh Univ, 56-57, from res asst to res assoc, Fritz Eng Lab, 57-61; asst prof civil eng, 61-63, assoc prof, 63-67, actg chmn, Dept Civil Eng, 70-71, chmn, 72-77, dir grad studies, 71-78, dir socio-eng prog, 71-78, PROF ENG & APPL SCI, STATE UNIV NY BUFFALO, 67-, DEAN ENG & APPL SCI, 78- *Concurrent Pos:* Spec eng consult, Struct Dynamics Dept, Bell Aerosysts Co, 65-; Nat Insts Health grant & sr res fel, Dept Physiol, Harvard Univ, Sch Pub Health, 69-70; head eng mech sect, NSF, 77-78. *Honors & Awards:* Adams Mem Award, Am Welding Soc, 74; Superior Accomplishment Award, NSF, 77. *Mem:* Am Soc Civil Engrs; Am Soc Eng Educ; Am Welding Soc; Sigma Xi; AAAS. *Res:* Buckling and stability analysis of structural members, frames, plates and shells; ultimate strength design; respiratory mechanics and lung elasticity; earthquake engineering. *Mailing Add:* 288 Countryside Lane Williamsville NY 14221

LEE, GEORGE FRED, b Delano, Calif, July 27, 33; m 53; c 1. WATER CHEMISTRY, ENVIRONMENTAL ENGINEERING. *Educ:* San Jose State Col, BA, 55; Univ NC, MSPH, 57; Harvard Univ, PhD(water chem-environ qual-environ eng), 60; Am Acad Environ Engrs, dipl. *Prof Exp:* From asst prof to prof civil & environ eng, Univ Wis-Madison, 61-73; prof eng-environ sci, Univ Tex, Dallas, 73-78; PROF CIVIL ENG, COLO STATE UNIV, 78- *Concurrent Pos:* Consult, gov agencies & indust. *Mem:* AAAS; Am Chem Soc; Am Fisheries Soc; Am Water Works Asn. *Res:* Chemistry of natural waters; water treatment and pollution control. *Mailing Add:* Eng Res Ctr Colo State Univ Fort Collins CO 80523

LEE, GEORGE H(AMOR), b Oakmont, Pa, June 3, 08; m 29, 63; c 1. MECHANICS. *Educ:* Univ Pittsburgh, BS, 36; Cornell Univ, MS, 37, PhD(mech), 40. *Prof Exp:* Asst, Res Labs, Aluminum Co Am, 28-33; Westinghouse res assoc, Cornell Univ, 36, instr mech, 37-40, asst prof mech & coordr & supvr, eng sci & mgt war training, 41-45, assoc prof mech, 45; instr, Carnegie Inst Technol, 40-41; assoc prof mech eng, US Naval Post-Grad Sch, 45-50, prof, 50-51; prof mech, Rensselaer Polytech Inst, 51, assoc head dept, 52-53, head dept, 53-55, dir res, 54-60; chief scientist & tech dir res & develop, Off Chief Ord, Dept Army, 60-62; chief ground warfare technol, Minneapolis-Honeywell Regulator Co, 62-63; prof aerospace eng, 63-74, adminr, Univ Res, Res Found, 63-67, asst vpres res, 67-74, EMER PROF AEROSPACE ENG, UNIV CINCINNATI, 74-, CONSULT TO EXEC VPRES FOR ACAD AFFAIRS, 71- *Concurrent Pos:* Researcher, Babcock & Wilcox Co, Ohio, 42 & Naval Ord Labs, 50-51; mem exec comt, Nat Coun Admin Res, 58-59; coun mem, Assoc Midwest Univ & Nat Conf Univ Res Admin. *Mem:* AAAS; Am Soc Mech Engrs; Am Soc Eng Educ; Am Ord Asn. *Res:* Experimental stress analysis; theory of elasticity; pressure responsive elements. *Mailing Add:* 2856 Almester Dr Cincinnati OH 45211

LEE, GEORGE H, II, b Ithaca, NY, Feb 26, 39; m 64; c 2. ANALYTICAL CHEMISTRY. *Educ:* Rensselaer Polytech Inst, 61, PhD(phys chem), 65. *Prof Exp:* Res assoc, Cornell Univ, 65-67; res chemist, Res Ctr, Hercules Inc, Del, 67-71; Sr Res Chemist, Dept Phys & Biol Sci, Southwest Res Inst, 71-73; assoc found scientist, Southwest Found Res & Educ, 73-77; sr res scientist fire technol, 77-81, SR RES SCIENTIST, US ARMY FUELS & LUBRICANTS RES LAB, SOUTHWEST RES INST, 81- *Mem:* Sigma Xi; Am Soc for Testing & Mat. *Res:* Determination of the mechanisms for fuel (diesel) decomposition; effect of additives on these mechanisms and study of the causes for fuel filter clogging on certain diesel powered engines. *Mailing Add:* 11107 Whispering Wind San Antonio TX 78230

LEE, GLENN RICHARD, b Ogden, Utah, May 18, 32; m 69; c 2. INTERNAL MEDICINE, HEMATOLOGY. *Educ:* Univ Utah, BS, 53, MD, 56. *Prof Exp:* Intern med, Boston City Hosp, 56-57, asst resident, 57-58; clin fel hemat, 60-61, res fel, 61-63, from instr to assoc prof, 63-73, assoc dean acad affairs, 73-76, PROF MED, 73- & DEAN COL MED, UNIV UTAH, 78- *Mem:* Am Fedn Clin Res; Am Soc Hemat; Am Col Physicians; Am Soc Clin Invest. *Res:* Clinical and experimentally induced abnormalities in heme biosynthesis; physiologic consequences of copper deficiency; iron metabolism. *Mailing Add:* Off Dean Col Med Univ Utah Salt Lake City UT 84132

LEE, GORDON M(ELVIN), b Minneapolis, Minn, Jan 3, 17; m 41; c 4. ELECTRICAL ENGINEERING. *Educ:* Univ Minn, BEE, 38; Univ Mo, MS, 39; Mass Inst Technol, DSc(elec eng), 44. *Prof Exp:* Asst elec eng, Univ Mo, 38-39; asst elec engr, Mass Inst Technol, 39-44, mem staff, Div Indust Coop, 44-45; tech dir elec eng & secy-treas, Cent Res Labs, Inc, Sargent Industs, 45-73, pres, 73-79; CONSULT, 79- *Concurrent Pos:* Mem, Nat Defence Res Comt, 44; lectr, Univ Minn, 48. *Honors & Awards:* Thompson Mem Prize, Inst Elec & Electronics Engrs, 46. *Mem:* AAAS; Am Nuclear Soc; Inst Elec & Electronics Engrs. *Res:* Remote handling equipment; properties of dielectrics; high-speed oscillography; development of high-speed micro-oscillograph and remote handling equipment. *Mailing Add:* Cent Res Labs Inc Red Wing MN 55066

LEE, GRIFF C, b Jackson, Miss, Aug 17, 26; m 50; c 3. OFFSHORE DESIGN, OFFSHORE CONSTRUCTION. *Educ:* Tulane Univ, BE, 48; Rice Univ, MS, 51. *Prof Exp:* Civil engr, Humble Oil & Refining Co, 48-54; prin engr & design engr, 54-66, chief engr, 66-75, group vpres, 75-78, VPRES RES & DEVELOP, MCDERMOTT INC, 78- *Concurrent Pos:* Mem, Marine Bd Nat Res Coun, Offshore Comt Am Petrol Inst, Adv Comt-Offshore Technol Detnorske Veritas, Welding Res Coun, Tech Panel Offshore Installations for Lloyd's Register Shipping, Comt Offshore Platforms & Bd Adv, Tulane Univ, 80- *Mem:* Nat Acad Eng; Am Soc Civil Engrs; Am Concrete Inst; Am Welding Soc; Soc Petrol Eng. *Res:* Advanced engineering technology; offshore construction for the petroleum industry. *Mailing Add:* McDermott Inc PO Box 60035 New Orleans LA 70160

LEE, H(O) C(HONG), b Seoul, Korea, Aug 2, 33; m 65; c 2. MECHANICAL ENGINEERING. *Educ:* Univ Bridgeport, BS, 57; Rensselaer Polytech Inst, MME, 59, PhD(mech eng), 62. *Prof Exp:* Asst prof mech eng, Rensselaer Polytech Inst, 62-68; staff engr, 68-70, adv engr, 70-77, SR ENGR, IBM CORP, 77- *Concurrent Pos:* Consult, Mech Tech, Inc, 62-65 & Gen Elec Co, 65-68; adj assoc prof, Rensselaer Polytech Inst, 68-70. *Mem:* Am Soc Mech Engrs. *Res:* Dynamics of structural elements; rotor dynamics. *Mailing Add:* 8 Tudor Dr Endicott NY 13760

LEE, HARLEY CLYDE, b Bellville, Ohio, Nov 7, 01; m 32. MINERALOGY, CHEMISTRY. *Educ:* Ohio State Univ, BEM, 27. *Prof Exp:* Chief chemist, Dolomite Inc, 26-30; res asst mineral, US Steel Corp, 30-31; dir res ceramics, Basic Dolomite Inc, 31-41; supt metall, Tech Dept, Basic Magnesium Inc, 41-45; vpres mineral technol, Basic Inc, 45-74, dir, 53-79, consult mineral technol, 74-79. *Concurrent Pos:* Dir, Elgin Electronics Inc, 60-79. *Mem:* Fel Am Ceramic Soc; Am Chem Soc; fel Mineral Soc Am; Geol Soc Am; Am Inst Mining, Metall & Petrol Engrs. *Res:* Res: Refractories, slags, calcium and magnesium compounds; steel and magnesium production; mineral processing; silicate chemistry and high temperature chemistry of refractory oxides. *Mailing Add:* 1111 N Gulfstream Ave Apt 15-B Sarasota FL 33577

LEE, HAROLD HON-KWONG, b China, Jan 31, 34; m 66; c 1. DEVELOPMENTAL BIOLOGY. *Educ:* Okla Baptist, AB, 56; Univ Tenn, MS, 58, PhD(embryol), 65. *Prof Exp:* USPHS fel, Carnegie Inst, 65-67; DIR, NSF INSTR SCI EQUIP GRANT, UNIV TOLEDO, 67-, PROF BIOL, 75- *Concurrent Pos:* Am Cancer Soc, NIH grants. *Honors & Awards:* Labor Found Res Award. *Mem:* Soc Develop Biologists; Tissue Culture Asn; Soc Reprod Biol. *Res:* Cell interactions and fertilization development of reproduction. *Mailing Add:* Dept of Biol Univ of Toledo Toledo OH 43606

LEE, HARVIE HO, b Chiang-si, China, Aug 17, 37; US citizen; m 65; c 3. METALLURGY, CORROSION. *Educ:* Nat Taiwan Univ, BS, 59; Va Polytech Inst, MS, 63; Mass Inst Technol, PhD(metall), 71. *Prof Exp:* Res metallurgist coating & corrosion, Inland Steel Res Labs, 63-67; res asst corrosion & metall, Corrosion Lab, Mass Inst Technol, 67-71; SR RES ENGR CORROSION & METALLIC COATINGS, INLAND STEEL RES LABS, 67- *Mem:* Nat Asn Corrosion Engrs; Am Soc Metals; Am Soc Testing & Mat. *Res:* Stress corrosion cracking of high strength low alloy steels; development of new hot dip metallic coatings with improved corrosion resistance. *Mailing Add:* Inland Steel Res Labs 3001 E Columbus Dr East Chicago IN 46312

LEE, HAYNES A, b Johnson City, Tenn, Oct 14, 32; m 59; c 3. LASERS, GLASS TECHNOLOGY. *Educ:* Emory & Henry Col, BS, 54; State Univ NY Col Ceramics, Alfred Univ, MS, 61. *Prof Exp:* Glass technologist, Thatcher Glass Mfg Co, NY, 61-63; glass technologist, 63-66, glass scientist, 66-68, CHIEF LASER SCIENTIST, OWENS-ILL, INC, TOLEDO, 68- *Mem:* Am Ceramic Soc; Sigma Xi. *Res:* Electronic pheonmena in glasses, particularly laser phenomena. *Mailing Add:* 31 Lansdowne Rd Sylvania OH 43623

LEE, HENRY C, b China, Nov 22, 38; US citizen; m 63; c 2. FORENSIC SCIENCE, BIOCHEMISTRY. *Educ:* John Jay Col NY, BS, 72; NY Univ, MS, 74, PhD(biochem), 75. *Prof Exp:* Asst prof, 75-76, assoc prof & dir forensic sci, 76-78, PROF FORENSIC SCI, UNIV NEW HAVEN, 78-, DIR, CTR FOR APPLIED RES, 76-; DIR, NEW JERSEY BRILINGTON COUNTY FORENSIC SCI LAB, 77-; CHIEF, CONN STATE FORENSIC SCI LAB, 79- *Concurrent Pos:* Consult, Conn State Police Forensic Lab, 75; vis prof, Seton Hall Univ, 76, Northeastern Univ, 77-79; dir, New Jersey Brilington County Forensic Sci Lab, 77-; vis fac, Yale Univ, 78; res grant, Univ New Haven, 78 & 79; chief, Conn State Forensic Sci Lab, 79-; ed, Forensic Sci, 81- *Mem:* NY Acad Sci; fel Am Acad Forensic Sci; AAAS; Am Soc Testing & Mat; Am Soc Crime Lab Dirs. *Res:* Protein biosynthesis; blood individualization and forensic science. *Mailing Add:* Univ of New Haven 300 Orange Ave West Haven CT 06516

LEE, HOONG-CHIEN, b Hong Kong, Aug 12, 41; m 65; c 3. PHYSICS. *Educ:* Nat Taiwan Univ, BSc, 63; McGill Univ, MSc, 67, PhD(physics), 69. *Prof Exp:* Tech collabr physics, Brookhaven Nat Lab, 67-68; ASSOC RES OFFICER THEORET PHYSICS, CHALK RIVER NUCLEAR LABS, ATOMIC ENERGY CAN, LTD, 68- *Mem:* Am Phys Soc; Can Asn Physicists. *Res:* Theoretical nuclear physics; structure of nuclei; electromagnetic and weak interaction; structure and decay of elementary particles and nuclei. *Mailing Add:* Physics Div Chalk River Nuclear Labs Chalk River ON K0J 1J0 Can

LEE, HSI-NAN, b Taiwan, July 15, 46; m 74; c 2. ATMOSPHERIC SCIENCE, MATHEMATIC NUMERICAL TECHNIQUES. *Educ:* Col Chinese Cult, BS, 70; Univ Utah, MS, 73, PhD(meteorol), 77. *Prof Exp:* Res asst meteorol, Univ Utah, 71-77; asst meteorologist atmospheric sci, Brookhaven Nat Lab, 77-79, assoc meteorologist, 79-80; RES ASST PROF, DEPT METEOROL, UNIV UTAH, 80- *Mem:* Sigma Xi; Am Meteorol Soc. *Res:* Advanced numerical modeling study in environmental air pollution; large scale atmospheric wave structure and nonlinear interaction in wave number frequency space; mathematic numberical techniques; numerical techniques for solving partial and ordinary differential equation. *Mailing Add:* Dept Meteorol Univ Utah Salt Lake City UT 84112

LEE, HSIN-YI, b Hsin-chu, Taiwan. DEVELOPMENTAL BIOLOGY. *Educ:* Nat Taiwan Univ, BS, 59; Oberlin Col, MA, 64; Univ Minn, Minneapolis, PhD(zool), 67. *Prof Exp:* Res assoc tissue cult, Cardiovasc Inst, Michael Reese Hosp & Med Ctr, 68; asst prof biol, 68-73, res coun grant, 69-81, assoc prof, 73-78, PROF ZOOL, RUTGERS UNIV, CAMDEN, 78- *Mem:* AAAS; Am Soc Zoologists. *Res:* Cell differentiation and biochemistry of chick development. *Mailing Add:* Dept of Biol Rutgers Univ Camden NJ 08102

LEE, HUA-TSUN, b Nanking, China, May 11, 37; m 63; c 4. MATHEMATICS. *Educ:* Tunghai Univ, Taiwan, BS, 59; Univ Pittsburgh, PhD(math), 71. *Prof Exp:* Asst physics, Tunghai Univ, Taiwan, 61; asst physics, Univ Pittsburgh, 61-64, asst math, 65-67 & 68-69, instr biostatist, Grad Sch Pub Health, 67-68; asst prof, 69-74, ASSOC PROF MATH, POINT PARK COL, 74- *Mem:* Math Asn Am. *Res:* Summability methods of infinite series. *Mailing Add:* Dept of Math Point Park Col Pittsburgh PA 15222

LEE, HULBERT AUSTIN, b Chelsea, Que, June 17, 23; m 47; c 5. GEOLOGY. *Educ:* Queen's Univ, Ont, BSc, 49; Univ Chicago, PhD(geol), 53. *Prof Exp:* Geologist, Geol Surv Can, 50-69; CONSULT GEOLOGIST & PRES, LEE GEO-INDICATORS LTD, 69- *Concurrent Pos:* Vis lectr, Univ NB, 64-65. *Mem:* Fel Geol Soc Am. *Res:* Correlation of quaternary events around Hudson Bay, the Tyrrell Sea and Keewatin ice divide; quaternary studies in New Brunswick; esker and till methods of mineral exploration; kimberlite petrology, engineering terrain analysis of Ontario. *Mailing Add:* Lee Geo-Indicators Ltd 94 Alexander St Box 68 Stittsville ON K0A 3G0 Can

LEE, HYUNG MO, b Tanchon, Korea, Sept 27, 26; US citizen; m 59; c 2. MEDICINE, SURGERY. *Educ:* Keijo Imp Univ, BS, 45; Seoul Nat Univ, MD, 49. *Prof Exp:* Res fel surg, Med Col Va, 59-61; from instr to assoc prof, 63-70, PROF SURG, MED COL VA, 70-, CHMN DIV VASCULAR GEN SURG, 76- *Concurrent Pos:* Dir, Clin Transplant Prog. *Mem:* Am Col Surg; Am Soc Nephrology; Transplantation Soc; NY Acad Sci. *Res:* Renal homotransplantation. *Mailing Add:* Dept of Surg Med Col of Va Richmond VA 23298

LEE, I-YANG, b Nanking, China, Dec 21, 46; m 72; c 2. NUCLEAR PHYSICS. *Educ:* Nat Taiwan Univ, BSc, 68; Univ Pittsburgh, PhD(physics), 74. *Prof Exp:* Physicist nuclear physics, Lawrence Berkeley Lab, 75-77; PHYSICIST NUCLEAR PHYSICS, OAK RIDGE NAT LAB, 77- *Mailing Add:* Oak Ridge Nat Lab Bldg 6000 PO Box X Oak Ridge TN 37830

LEE, J(OHN) C(HIA-CHIN), mechanical engineering, thermodynamics, see previous edition

LEE, JA H, b Hamyang, SKorea, Apr 25, 25; US citizen; m; c 4. PLASMA PHYSICS. *Educ:* Kyungpook Nat Univ, Korea, BS, 48; George Peabody Col, Nashville, MS, 61; Vanderbilt Univ, Nashville, MS, 62, PhD(physics), 64. *Prof Exp:* Prof physics, Kyungpook Nat Univ, Daegu, Korea, 65-67; res assoc physics, NASA/Nat Acad Sci, 67-69; sr res assoc, 69-73, res assoc prof, 73-78, RES PROF PHYSICS, VANDERBILT UNIV, NASHVILLE, 78- *Concurrent Pos:* Prin investr grants, Langley Res Ctr, NASA, 69- *Mem:* Am Phys Soc; Inst Elec & Electronics Engrs. *Res:* Pulsed high beta plasma; solar pumped laser and laser pumping source development. *Mailing Add:* 37 East Governor Dr Newport News VA 23602

LEE, JAMES A, b Troy, NY, July 11, 25; m 46; c 1. HUMAN ECOLOGY, PUBLIC HEALTH. *Educ:* Union Col, BS, 49; Cornell Univ, MS, 51; George Washington Univ, MPh, 69, PhD, 70; Univ Sarajevu, Dr(med), 78. NH, 51-53, sr res biologist, 53-56; tech asst dir, State Conserv Dept, Minn, 56-61, from dep comnr to comnr, State Dept Resources Develop, 61-63; scientist adminr, USPHS, Washington, DC, 63-66, asst environ health to asst secy health & sci affairs, Dept Health, Educ & Welfare, 67-69, dir human ecol, 69-70; DIR ENVIRON & HEALTH, THE WORLD BANK, 70- *Concurrent Pos:* Adj assoc prof, Sch Med, George Washington Univ, 70-; vis prof, Sch Med, Cornell Univ, 76-; co-chmn, Int Trop Dis Res Prog & Int Diarrheal Dis Control Prog; Woodrow Wilson vis fel, 81- *Mem:* Am Pub Health Asn; Ecol Soc Am; Am Soc Trop Med & Hyg; Royal Soc Trop Med & Hyg; Am Acad Health Admin. *Res:* Environmental, public health, and socio-cultural aspects of international economic development; human ecology with emphasis on multi-environmental causation of diseases; social anthropology and medical sociology; natural resources planning and management. *Mailing Add:* 11919 Stonewood Lane Rockville MD 20852

LEE, JAMES B, b Ware, Mass, June 30, 30; m 64; c 2. ENDOCRINOLOGY, METABOLISM. *Educ:* Col Holy Cross, AB, 51; Jefferson Med Col, MD, 56. *Prof Exp:* Intern med, St Vincent Hosp, Worcester, Mass, 56-57; resident, Pa Hosp, Philadelphia, 57-58; resident, Georgetown Univ Hosp, 58-59; USPH res fel renal metab, Peter Bent Brigham Hosp, Boston, 59-62; dir res metab & endocrinol, St Vincent Hosp, Worcester, 62-68; assoc prof med & chief sect exp med, Sch Med, St Louis Univ, 68-71; PROF MED, STATE UNIV NY BUFFALO, 71- *Concurrent Pos:* Mass Heart Asn res grant, 62-; USPHS res grant, 62-, develop training grant, 64-; asst prof, Georgetown Univ Hosp, 63-68. *Mem:* Am Physiol Soc; Am Soc Clin Invest; Am Fedn Clin Res; Endocrine Soc; Am Heart Asn. *Res:* Hypertension; in vitro metabolism of kidney cortex and medulla related to sodium excretion; isolation and identification of medullin, a peripheral visodilator, from renal medulla. *Mailing Add:* Sch of Med State Univ of NY Buffalo NY 14214

LEE, JAMES KELLY, b Covington, Ky, Mar 4, 43; m 66. MECHANICAL ENGINEERING, CONTROL SYSTEMS. *Educ:* Univ Cincinnati, BS, 66; Univ Wis-Madison, MS, 67, PhD(mech eng), 71. *Prof Exp:* SR RES PHYSICIST, EASTMAN KODAK CO, 71- *Mem:* Am Soc Mech Engrs. *Res:* Mechanical design. *Mailing Add:* Eastman Kodak Co Kodak Park B81 Rochester NY 14650

LEE, JAMES WILLIAM, b North Vancouver, BC, Jan 16, 24; m 52; c 3. GEOLOGY. *Educ:* Univ BC, BASc, 47, MASc, 49; Stanford Univ, PhD(geol), 51. *Prof Exp:* Jr engr, Pac Lime Co, BC, 47; jr geologist, Kelowna Explor Co, 48-50; geologist, Kaiser Aluminum & Chem Corp, 51-58, Kaiser Bauxite Co, 58-63, mine engr, Jamaica, WI, 63-66; property mgt supt, Alumina Partners, 66-68; gen mgr, Farms Jamaica, Ltd, 68-73; LANDS MGR, ALPART FARMS, JAMAICA, LTD, 73- *Concurrent Pos:* Mem, Jamaica Sci Res Coun, 60-72 & 81- *Mem:* Fel Geol Soc Am; Soc Am Archaeol; Soc Econ Geol; Archaeol Soc Jamaica (pres, 70-). *Res:* Petrography; petrology; Caribbean archaeology. *Mailing Add:* Alpart Farms Jamaica Ltd PO Box 206 Mandeville Jamaica

LEE, JEAN CHOR-YIN WONG, b Canton, China, Aug 26, 41; m 67; c 2. BIOCHEMISTRY. *Educ:* Chung Chi Col, Hong Kong, dipl, 62; Univ Nebr, Lincoln, PhD(chem), 67. *Prof Exp:* Res instr biochem, Col Med, Univ Nebr, Omaha, 67-70; FEL CHEM & RES ASSOC, UNIV NEBR, LINCOLN, 70- *Mem:* Am Chem Soc. *Res:* Biomembranes, structure and transport. *Mailing Add:* Dept of Chem Univ of Nebr Lincoln NE 68588

LEE, JEFFREY STEPHEN, b Salt Lake City, Utah, Aug 25, 44; m 69; c 1. INDUSTRIAL HYGIENE, OCCUPATIONAL HEALTH. *Educ:* Univ Utah, BS, 67; Univ Calif, Berkeley, MPH, 71, PhD(environ health), 80. *Prof Exp:* Indust hygienist, Nat Inst Occup Safety & Health, 69-76; dep dir, Health Response Team, Occup Safety & Health Admin, US Dept Labor, 76-79; DIR INDUST HYG, ROCKY MT CTR ENVIRON HEALTH, UNIV UTAH, 79-, ASST PROF, DEPT FAMILY & COMMUNITY MED, MED SCH, 80- *Mem:* Am Acad Indust Hyg; Am Indust Hyg Asn; Am Conf Gov Indust Hyg. *Res:* Industrial hygiene and occupational health, principally quantification and toxicology of particulates specifically cadmium; industrial hygiene problems related to mining and new energy development. *Mailing Add:* Rocky Mt Ctr Environ Health Bldg 512 Univ Utah Salt Lake City UT 84112

LEE, JEN-SHIH, b Kwangtung, China, Aug 22, 40; nat US; m 66; c 3. BIOMEDICAL ENGINEERING. *Educ:* Nat Taiwan Univ, BS, 61; Calif Inst Technol, MS, 63, PhD(aeronaut, math), 66. *Prof Exp:* Asst res engr, Univ Calif, San Diego, 66-69; asst prof, 69-74, ASSOC PROF BIOMED ENG, UNIV VA, 74- *Concurrent Pos:* San Diego County Heart Asn advan res fel, 66-69; USPHS res grant, Univ Va, 71; Nat Heart & Lung Inst res career develop award, 75-80. *Mem:* Am Physiol Soc; Biomed Eng Soc; Am Soc Mech Eng; Microcirc Soc. *Res:* Hemodynamics; pulmonary mechanics and edema; indicator dilution technique as applied to microcirculation and transcapillary exchange in microvessels. *Mailing Add:* Div of Biomed Eng PO Box 377 Univ Va Med Ctr Charlottesville VA 22901

LEE, JOHN ALEXANDER HUGH, b Isle of Wight, Eng, Oct 10, 25; m 49; c 3. EPIDEMIOLOGY. *Educ:* Univ Edinburgh, BSc, 47, MB, ChB, 49, MD, 55; Univ London, DPH, 52. *Prof Exp:* Fel epidemiol, London Sch Hyg & Trop Med, 52-55; mem sci staff, Social Med Res Unit, Med Res Coun, London Hosp, 55-66; PROF EPIDEMIOL, UNIV WASH, 66- *Mem:* Am Epidemiol Soc; Brit Soc Social Med; Brit Med Asn; Int Epidemiol Asn. *Res:* Epidemiology of neoplastic diesease. *Mailing Add:* Dept Epidemiol & Int Health Univ Wash Seattle WA 98195

LEE, JOHN CHAESEUNG, b Seoul, Korea, July 29, 41; US citizen; m 71; c 1. NUCLEAR ENGINEERING. *Educ:* Seoul Nat Univ, BS, 63; Univ Calif, Berkeley, PhD(nuclear eng), 69. *Prof Exp:* Sr engr nuclear eng, Westinghouse Elec Corp, 69-73; sr engr, Gen Elec Co, 73-74; asst prof, 74-78, ASSOC PROF NUCLEAR ENG, UNIV MICH, ANN ARBOR, 78- *Concurrent Pos:* Consult, Adv Comt Reactor Safeguards, US Nuclear Regulatory Comn, 75-, Brooks & Perkins, Inc, Livonia, Mich, 76-77, Los Alamos Sci Lab, 77- & Argonne Nat Lab, 78- *Mem:* Am Nuclear Soc; AAAS. *Res:* Nuclear reactor theory; reactor core physics and design analysis; reactor kinetics; nuclear-thermal-hydraulic interface calculations; fuel cycle analysis; reactor safety analysis; power plant simulation and control. *Mailing Add:* Dept of Nuclear Eng Univ of Mich Ann Arbor MI 48109

LEE, JOHN CHEUNG HAN, b China, Dec 1, 45; m 77; c 1. INDUSTRIAL MICROBIOLOGY, INFECTIOUS DISEASES-ANTIBOTICS. *Educ:* Rutgers Univ, BA, 67; Long Island Univ, MS, 72; St John's Univ, PhD(microbiol), 79. *Prof Exp:* Sect head, Julius Schmid, Inc, 67-73; SUPVR, MILES PHARMACEUT, 79- *Mem:* Am Soc Microbiol; NY Acad Sci; Soc Indust Microbiol. *Res:* In vitro activity of new antibiotics; effect of antibiotics on functions of macrophages. *Mailing Add:* 80-59 Surrey Place Jamaica Estates NY 11432

LEE, JOHN CHUNG, b Shanghai, China, Mar 2, 37; US citizen; m 63; c 2. BIOCHEMISTRY. *Educ:* Taylor Univ, AB, 61; Purdue Univ, West Lafayette, MSc, 64, PhD(molecular biol), 67. *Prof Exp:* Res assoc biochem, Mass Inst Technol, 67-69; asst prof, 69-72, ASSOC PROF BIOCHEM, UNIV TEX MED SCH SAN ANTONIO, 72- *Concurrent Pos:* USPHS res grant, Univ Tex Med Sch San Antonio, 71- *Mem:* Am Soc Cell Biol; Am Chem Soc; Am Soc Biol Chem. *Res:* Structure and function of nucleic acids; differentiation. *Mailing Add:* Dept of Biochem Univ of Tex Med Sch San Antonio TX 78284

LEE, JOHN D(AVID), b Barrie, Ont, Aug 24, 24; nat US; m 49; c 3. AERODYNAMICS. *Educ:* Univ Toronto, BSc & MSc, 50, PhD(aerophys), 52. *Prof Exp:* Asst prof & res assoc, 53-55, assoc prof aeronaut eng, 55-59, dir aerodyn lab, 55-68, PROF AERONAUT & ASTRONAUT ENG, OHIO STATE UNIV, 59-, DIR AERONAUT & ASTRONAUT RES LAB, 68- *Concurrent Pos:* Consult, Naval Ord Lab, Wright Air Develop Ctr, Fluidyne Eng Corp, Sandia Corp & US Army. *Mem:* Am Inst Aeronaut & Astronaut. *Res:* Hypersonic fluid mechanics; boundary layer phenomena; low density flows; transonic high Reynolds number flows. *Mailing Add:* Dept of Aeronaut & Astronaut Eng Ohio State Univ Columbus OH 43210

LEE, JOHN DENIS, b Trinidad, WI, Apr 22, 29; m 58; c 3. METEOROLOGY. *Educ:* Fla State Univ, BS, 70, MS, 71, PhD(meteorol), 73. *Prof Exp:* Fel, Nat Ctr Atmospheric Res, 73-74; ASST PROF METEOROL, PA STATE UNIV, 74- *Concurrent Pos:* Lectr meteorol, UN Develop Prog for Advan Training in Meteorol in Eng-speaking Caribbean Territories, 78-79. *Mem:* Am Meteorol Soc. *Res:* Numerical modeling of cooling tower plumes and urban pollution; time series analysis. *Mailing Add:* Dept of Meteorol Pa State Univ University Park PA 16802

LEE, JOHN HAK SHAN, b Hong Kong, Sept 7, 38; Can citizen; m 62; c 2. COMBUSTION, EXPLOSIONS. *Educ:* McGill Univ, BSc, 60, PhD(physics), 65; Mass Inst Technol, MSc, 62. *Prof Exp:* Res asst mech eng, Mass Inst Technol, 60-62; jr res officer, Nat Res Coun, 62-63; lectr, 62-64, from asst prof to assoc prof, 64-66, PROF MECH ENG, MCGILL UNIV, 73- *Concurrent Pos:* Adv, assoc comt on aerodyn, Nat Res Coun, 68-71. *Honors & Awards:* Silver Medal, Combustion Inst, 80. *Mem:* Order Engrs Quebec; Am Phys Soc; Combustion Inst. *Res:* Cause, effects, prevention and mitigation of accidental explosions in the production, transport, storage of flammable gases, liquids, organic, metallic and coal dusts; hydrogen combustion problems pertaining to nuclear reactor accident. *Mailing Add:* Dept of Mech Eng Rm 459 McGill Univ Montreal PQ H2A 2T5 Can

LEE, JOHN JOSEPH, b Philadelphia, Pa, Feb 23, 33; m 56; c 2. MARINE MICROBIOLOGY, PROTOZOOLOGY. *Educ:* Queens Col, NY, BS, 55; Univ Mass, MA, 57; NY Univ, PhD(biol), 60. *Prof Exp:* Asst prof, NY Univ, 61-66; from asst prof to assoc prof, 66-72, PROF BIOL, CITY COL NEW YORK, 72- *Concurrent Pos:* Res fel & dir, Living Foraminifera Lab, Am Mus Natural Hist, 60-68, res assoc, 70-; dir, Marine Microbiol Ecol Lab, Inst Oceanog, City Univ New York, 68-; res assoc, Lamont-Doherty Geol Observ, 70- *Mem:* Fel AAAS; Soc Protozool; Phycological Soc Am; Am Soc Microbiol; Am Micros Soc. *Res:* Cytology, fine structure, life history, ecology, cultivation and nutrition of foraminifera; algal endosymbiosis in foraminifera, meiofauna, benthic marine food webs and diatom assembleges. *Mailing Add:* Dept of Biol City Col of New York New York NY 10031

LEE, JOHN NORMAN, b Schenectady, NY, Dec 2, 44; m 68; c 2. PHYSICS. *Educ:* Union Col, Schenectady, BS, 66; Johns Hopkins Univ, MA, 68, PhD(physics), 71. *Prof Exp:* Res asst physics, Johns Hopkins Univ, 69-71; physicist, Electronics Res & Develop Command, Harry Diamond Labs, 71-80; SUPVR RES PHYSICIST, NAVAL RES LAB, 80- *Mem:* Am Phys Soc. *Res:* Signal processing using acousto-optics and surface acoustic wave devices; radiation damage in optical materials and components; spectroscopy of optical and magnetic materials. *Mailing Add:* Naval Res Lab Code 6530 Washington DC 20375

LEE, JOHN WILLIAM, b Sydney, Australia, Apr 7, 35; m 60; c 2. CHEMICAL PHYSICS, BIOPHYSICS. *Educ:* Univ New South Wales, BSc, 56, PhD(phys chem), 60. *Prof Exp:* Res assoc biochem, McCollum-Pratt Inst, Johns Hopkins Univ, 61-63; staff scientist, New Eng Inst Med Res, 63-69; assoc prof, 69-75; PROF BIOCHEM, UNIV GA, 75- *Mem:* Am Chem Soc; Am Phys Soc. *Res:* Positron annihilation in matter; radiation chemistry; energy exchange processes in chemical and biological systems; bioluminescence; chemiluminescence; radiation physics. *Mailing Add:* Dept of Biochem Univ of Ga Athens GA 30602

LEE, JON H(YUNKOO), b Seoul, Korea, Mar 5, 34; US citizen. APPLIED MATHEMATICS, MATHEMATICAL PHYSICS. *Educ:* Seoul Nat Univ, BS, 56; Ohio State Univ, MS, 58, PhD(chem eng), 62. *Prof Exp:* Chem engr, US Dept Air Force Mat Lab, 62-64, res engr, Aerospace Res Labs, 64-75, APPL MATHEMATICIAN, AIR FORCE FLIGHT DYNAMICS LAB, WRIGHT-PATTERSON AFB, 75- *Mem:* Am Phys Soc; Am Inst Chem Engrs; Sigma Xi. *Res:* Fluid dynamics; structural dynamics; turbulence; random processes; mechanical vibration. *Mailing Add:* 10661 Putnam Rd Englewood OH 45322

LEE, JONATHAN K P, b Kiangsu, China, July 13, 37; m 67; c 2. NUCLEAR PHYSICS. *Educ:* McGill Univ, BEng, 60, MSc, 62, PhD(nuclear physics), 65. *Prof Exp:* Nat Res Coun Can overseas fel, 65-66; res asst, Univ Toronto, 66-68; asst prof, 68-77, ASSOC PROF NUCLEAR PHYSICS, McGILL UNIV, 77- *Mem:* Can Asn Physicists. *Res:* Nuclear structure studies. *Mailing Add:* Dept of Physics McGill Univ Montreal PQ H3A 2T6 Can

LEE, JONG SUN, b Suwon, Korea, July 10, 32; m 58; c 3. MICROBIOLOGY. *Educ:* Univ Calif, Berkeley, BA, 58; Ore State Univ, MS, 62, PhD(microbiol), 63. *Prof Exp:* Asst prof, 63-69, assoc prof, 69-76, prof food microbiol, 76-80, PROF FOOD SCI & TECH, ORE STATE UNIV, 80- *Mem:* AAAS; Am Soc Microbiol; Inst Food Technol; Brit Soc Appl Bact. *Res:* Microbiology of seafoods. *Mailing Add:* Dept of Food Sci & Technol Ore State Univ Corvallis OR 97331

LEE, JOSEPH CHING-YUEN, b Hutow, Anchi, China, Feb 25, 22; m 54; c 1. ANATOMY. *Educ:* Lingnan Univ, BSc, 47; Univ Sask, MSc, 58, PhD(exp neuropath), 61, MD, 62. *Prof Exp:* Asst anat, Med Col, Lingnan Univ, 47-51, lectr, 51-54; demonstr, Med Fac, Univ Hong Kong, 55-57; res asst exp neuropath, Univ Sask, 57-58, spec lectr anat, 58-62, asst prof, 62-63; from asst prof neurosurg to prof anat & assoc res prof neurosurg, State UniY NY, Buffalo, 63-76; PROF & HEAD DEPT ANAT SCI & ADJ PROF DERMAT, HEALTH SCI CTR, UNIV OKLA, 76- *Concurrent Pos:* Lederle med fac award, Univ Sask & Buffalo Gen Hosp, NY, 62-65; Am Cancer Soc & Nat Inst Neurol Dis & Stroke res grant, State Univ NY Buffalo, 65-73. *Mem:* AAAS; Am Asn Anat; Am Soc Cell Biol; Electron Micros Soc Am; Am Asn Neurol Surg. *Res:* Experimental neuropathology; various types of cerebral edema, including those associated with intracranial tumors studied by combination of electron microscopy, autoradiography and cytochemistry; permeability of the cerebral blood vessels under normal and pathological conditions; pathogenesis of experimental brain tumors. *Mailing Add:* Dept of Anat Sci Univ Okla PO Box 26901 Oklahoma City OK 73190

LEE, JOSEPH CHUEN KWUN, b Chungking, China, Oct 6, 38; m . PATHOLOGY, CELL BIOLOGY. *Educ:* Univ Hong Kong, MB, BS, 64; Univ Rochester, PhD(path), 70; FRCP(C), 71. *Prof Exp:* Intern, Hong Kong, 64; rotating intern, St Francis Hosp, New York, 66; resident path, New York Hosp-Cornell Med Ctr, 66-67, Toronto Gen Hosp, Univ Toronto, 70-71 & Princess Margaret Hosp, Ont Cancer Inst Can, 71-72; asst prof to assoc prof path & oncol, Univ Rochester Med Ctr, 72-80; vis prof, NIH, 80; res fel, Armed Forces Inst Pathol, 81; PROF PATHOL, CHINESE UNIV, HONG KONG, 82- *Mem:* AAAS; Am Soc Cell Biol; Am Soc Exp Path; Am Asn Path & Bact. *Res:* Experimental pathology of iron metabolism; control of cell replication in normal cells and in neoplastic cells. *Mailing Add:* Fac Med Chinese Univ Hong Kong Shatin New Territories Hong Kong

LEE, JOSHUA ALEXANDER, b Rocky Ford, Ga, Oct 30, 24; m 56; c 2. GENETICS. *Educ:* San Diego State Col, AB, 50; Univ Calif, PhD(genetics), 58. *Prof Exp:* Technician, Univ Calif, 51-53, asst, 54-56; GENETICIST, AGR EXP STA, NC STATE UNIV, 58-, PROF CROP SCI, UNIV, 71- *Mem:* Crop Sci Soc Am; Soc Study Evolution. *Res:* Genetical problems pertaining to the improvement of domesticated cotton species. *Mailing Add:* 5104 New Castle Rd Raleigh NC 27606

LEE, JU PEI, b Nanking, China, Jan 10, 19; US citizen; m 51; c 2. ENGINEERING MECHANICS. *Educ:* Wuhan Univ, BSc, 41; Mass Inst Technol, SM, 47; Univ Mich, PhD(eng mech), 50. *Prof Exp:* Asst prof eng mech, Iowa State Univ, 52-55; sr res engr, Sci Lab, Ford Motor Co, 55-59; assoc prof eng mech, 59-66, prof, 66-69, prof mech eng sci, 69-74, asst chmn dept, 71-74, assoc chmn, Dept Mech Eng, 74-78, PROF MECH ENG, WAYNE STATE UNIV, 78- *Mem:* Am Soc Eng Educ. *Res:* Theory of plates and shells; dynamics and vibrations. *Mailing Add:* Dept of Mech Eng 667 Merrick Wayne State Univ Detroit MI 48202

LEE, JUI SHUAN, b Hopei, China, Aug 14, 13; US citizen. PHYSIOLOGY. *Educ:* Tsinghua Univ, Peking, BS, 36; Univ Minn, Minneapolis, PhD(physiol), 53. *Prof Exp:* Res fel, Biol lab, Sci Soc China, 36-38; res fel physiol, 39-41, from lectr physiol to assoc prof, Col Med, Nat Cent Univ, Chengtu, 42-47; res fel physiol, Univ Minn, Minneapolis, 53-56; res assoc biochem nutrit, Grad Sch Pub Health, Univ Pittsburgh, 56-57; from res assoc to asst prof physiol, 57-68, ASSOC PROF PHYSIOL, UNIV MINN, MINNEAPOLIS, 69- *Mem:* Am Physiol Soc; Microcirculatory Soc. *Res:* Mechanism of water absorption and secretion by the mammalian small intestine; lymph flow and capillary pressure; tissue fluid pressure of the small intestine during water transport. *Mailing Add:* Dept of Physiol Univ of Minn Minneapolis MN 55455

LEE, JUNE KEY, b Seoul, Korea, Aug 9, 43; US citizen; m 70; c 3. ENGINEERING MECHANICS. *Educ:* Han-Yang Univ, BS, 65; Tenn Technol Univ, MS, 70; Univ Tex, Austin, PhD(eng mech), 76. *Prof Exp:* Res asst comput mech, Res Inst, Univ Ala, Huntsville, 70-73; asst instr, Univ Tex, 75-76; asst prof eng, Drexel Univ, 76-77; asst prof, 77-81, ASSOC PROF MECH, OHIO STATE UNIV, 81- *Concurrent Pos:* Prin investr, NSF & Ohio State Univ, 78-80; co-prin investr various grants, Dept Energy, 80-82, Ohio State Univ, 80-83 & NASA, 81-83. *Mem:* Am Acad Mech; Soc Eng Sci; Sigma Xi. *Res:* Theory and application of the finite element method in applied mechanics; numerical methods; continuum mechanics. *Mailing Add:* Dept of Eng Mech 155 W Woodruff Columbus OH 43210

LEE, KAH-HOCK, b Jan 28, 41; US citizen; m 67; c 3. INORGANIC CHEMISTRY. *Educ:* Nanyang Univ, BS, 64; Georgetown Univ, PhD(inorg chem), 70. *Prof Exp:* Environ chemist, DC Dept Environ Serv, 69-80; PRES, ADVAN INVESTMENT MGT CO, 77- *Concurrent Pos:* Res fel, Dept Chem, Grad Sch, Georgetown Univ, 71-73. *Mem:* Am Chem Soc. *Res:* Environmental toxic trace metals; effect of x-ray film developer on radiation protection; heteropoly inorganic anions exchange mechanisms. *Mailing Add:* 6201 S Crain Hwy Mitchellville MD 20716

LEE, KAI NIEN, b New York, NY, Oct 19, 45; m 71. ENVIRONMENTAL MANAGEMENT, SCIENCE POLICY. *Educ:* Columbia Univ, AB, 66; Princeton Univ, PhD(physics), 71. *Prof Exp:* Soc Sci Res Coun res training fel, 71-72; asst res social scientist, Inst Governmental Studies, Univ Calif, Berkeley, 72-73; res asst prof, Prog Social Mgt of Technol & Dept Polit Sci, 73-75, asst prof, 75-80, ASSOC PROF INST ENVIRON STUDIES & DEPT POLIT SCI, UNIV WASH, 80- *Concurrent Pos:* Mem selection comts, Danforth grad fel, 72-; mem int adv bd, Policy Sci, 74-; White House fel, US Dept Defense, 76-77; mem Naval Res adv comt, 78-; mem adv panel radioactive waste disposal, Off Tech Assessment, 78-81; mem, Environ Studies Bd, Nat Acad Sci, 80-82; Kellogg Nat fel, 80-83. *Mem:* Fel Soc Religion in Higher Educ; AAAS; Fedn Am Scientists. *Res:* Energy and environmental policy and politics: regional power development, nuclear waste management, environmental conflict and dispute settlement; influence of technological change on American political life. *Mailing Add:* Inst for Environ Studies FM-12 Univ of Wash Seattle WA 98195

LEE, KAI-LIN, b Nanking, China, Sept 16, 35; m 64. BIOCHEMISTRY, ENDOCRINOLOGY. *Educ:* Nat Taiwan Univ, BS, 60; Tulane Univ, PhD(biochem), 66. *Prof Exp:* Teaching asst bot, Nat Taiwan Univ, 61-62; res asst biochem, Tulane Univ, 62-66, fel biochem endocrinol, 66-67, instr, 67-68; Hoffmann-La Roche fel, Biochem, Biol Div, 68-69, res assoc, 69-70, BIOCHEMIST, BIOL DIV, OAK RIDGE NAT LAB, 70- *Mem:* AAAS; Endocrine Soc; Am Chem Soc; Am Soc Biol Chemists. *Res:* Hormonal regulation of metabolic processes. *Mailing Add:* Biol Div Oak Ridge Nat Lab PO Box Y Oak Ridge TN 37830

LEE, KANG IN, b Korea, Nov 2, 46; US citizen; m 75; c 2. POLYMER CHEMISTRY, ORGANIC CHEMISTRY. *Educ:* Murray State Univ, BA, 70; State Univ NY Buffalo, MA, 72; Polytech Inst New York, PhD(chem), 76. *Prof Exp:* res scientist polymer chem, Cent Res Labs, Firestone Tire & Rubber Co, 77-80; MEM TECH STAFF, GEN TEL & ELECTRONICS LAB, 80- *Concurrent Pos:* Res assoc, Inst Polymer Sci, Univ Akron, 76-77.

Mem: Am Chem Soc; Sigma Xi. *Res:* Cationic and ziegler natta polymerizations; new plastic and rubber developments; high pressure organic chemistry; ring opening polymerization. *Mailing Add:* 5 Rolling Dr Framingham MA 01701

LEE, KEENAN, b Huntington, NY, Nov 20, 36; m 66; c 2. GEOLOGY. *Educ:* La State Univ, Baton Rouge, BS, 60, MS, 63; Stanford Univ, PhD(geol), 69. *Prof Exp:* Geophys trainee, Cuban Stanalind Oil Co, Pan Am Petrol Corp, 57-58; geologist, Mobil Oil Libya, Ltd, 63-66; asst prof, 69-74, ASSOC PROF GEOL, COLO SCH MINES, 74- *Mem:* AAAS; Geol Soc Am; Am Soc Photogram. *Res:* Hydrogeology; remote sensing. *Mailing Add:* Dept of Geol Colo Sch of Mines Golden CO 80401

LEE, KENNETH, b San Francisco, Calif, July 3, 37; m 59; c 2. SOLID STATE PHYSICS. *Educ:* Univ Calif, Berkeley, AB, 59, PhD(physics), 63. *Prof Exp:* Res physicist, Varian Assocs, 63-68; RES STAFF MEM & MGR, RES LAB, IBM CORP, 68- *Concurrent Pos:* Consult, Lawrence Radiation Lab, Univ Calif, 63-68; comt mem, Magnetism & Magnetic Mat Conf, 64-65, prog comt 71 & adv comt, 71-74, 74-77 & 80-83, prog co-chmn, 75, steering comt, 77, 78 & 81, prog comt, 79. *Mem:* Fel Am Phys Soc; Inst Elec & Electronics Engrs; Sigma Xi. *Res:* Antiferromagnetism; crystal defects and motion of nuclei in solids; electron and nuclear magnetic resonance; magnetism in thin films; amorphous magnetism; thin film technology; magnetic recording. *Mailing Add:* IBM Res Lab K64 281 5600 Cottle Rd San Jose CA 95193

LEE, KEUN MYUNG, b Korea, Oct 17, 45; m 74; c 1. ACOUSTIC EMISSION, SOFTWARE ENGINEERING. *Educ:* Seoul Nat Univ, BS, 67; State Univ NY Stony Brook, PhD(astrophysics), 79. *Prof Exp:* Systs analyst x-ray spectromet, Princeton Gamma Tech, Inc, 79-81; SR SCIENTIST ACOUSTIC EMISSION, PHYS ACOUSTICS CORP, 81- *Mem:* Inst Elec & Electronics Engrs. *Res:* Industrial applications and theory of x-ray spectrometry; signal processing; acoustic emission; computer applications of acoustic signal processing. *Mailing Add:* Phys Acoustic Corp 743 Alexander Rd Princeton NJ 08540

LEE, KIUCK, b Hamhung, Korea, Jan 15, 22; m; c 5. NUCLEAR PHYSICS. *Educ:* Seoul Nat Univ, BS, 47, MS, 49; Fla State Univ, PhD(physics), 55. *Prof Exp:* Res assoc physics, Fla State Univ, 55-56 & Argonne Nat Lab, 56-57; from asst prof to assoc prof, 57-68, PROF PHYSICS, MARQUETTE UNIV, 68- *Concurrent Pos:* Res assoc, Argonne Nat Lab, 60. *Mem:* Am Phys Soc. *Res:* Nuclear structure studies on deformed nucleus, fission and the superheavy nucleus. *Mailing Add:* Marquette Univ Dept of Physics 1131 Wisconsin Ave Milwaukee WI 53233

LEE, KOTIK KAI, b Chungking, China, May 30, 41; US citizen; m 67; c 2. MATHEMATICAL PHYSICS. *Educ:* Chung-Yuan Col, BSc, 64; Univ Ottawa, MSc, 67; Syracuse Univ, PhD(physics), 72. *Prof Exp:* Res asst physics, Syracuse Univ, 68-72, instr, 72-73; asst prof, Rio Grande Col, 73-74; asst physics, 65-67, vis prof math, Univ Ottawa, 74-76; scientist, Lab Laser Energetics, Univ Rochester, 77-78; physicist, Santa Barbara Res Ctr, 78-79; SCIENTIST, LAB LASER ENERGETICS, UNIV ROCHESTER, 79- *Mem:* Am Math Soc; Am Phys Soc; Can Asn Physicists; Soc Indust & Appl Math; Int Soc Gen Relativity & Gravitation. *Res:* Global structures of spacetimes, singularities in general relativity, gravitational collapse, quantization of the gravitational field, cosmology, mathematical foundations of quantum field theory and statistical mechanics, plasma physics, laser physics and astrophysics. *Mailing Add:* 18 Winding Brook Dr Fairport NY 14450

LEE, KUO-HSIUNG, b Taiwan, Jan 4, 40; m 68; c 2. MEDICINAL CHEMISTRY, NATURAL PRODUCTS CHEMISTRY. *Educ:* Kaohsiung Med Col, Taiwan, BS, 61; Kyoto Univ, MS, 65; Univ Minn, Minneapolis, PhD(med chem), 68. *Prof Exp:* Postdoc scholar chem, Univ Calif, Los Angeles, 68-70; from asst prof to assoc prof, 70-77, PROF MED CHEM, SCH PHARM, UNIV NC, CHAPEL HILL, 77- *Concurrent Pos:* USPHS res grants, Univ NC, 71- Am Cancer Soc grant, Univ NC, 75- *Mem:* Am Chem Soc; Am Soc Pharmacog; fel Am Pharmaceut Asn; fel Acad Pharmaceut Sci; The Chem Soc. *Res:* Isolation, structure determination, synthesis, structure-activity relationships and mechanisms of action of plant antitumor agents; antibiotics-isolation and structural determination; antiinflammatory agents. *Mailing Add:* Sch Pharm Univ NC Chapel Hill NC 27514

LEE, KWANG, b Seoul, Korea, Jan 18, 42; m 70; c 2. POULTRY NUTRITION. *Educ:* Seoul Nat Univ, BS, 64; Southern Ill Univ, MS, 69; Mich State Univ, PhD(poultry sci & nutrit), 73. *Prof Exp:* ASSOC PROF POULTRY SCI & NUTRIT, UNIV ARK, PINE BLUFF, 73- *Mem:* Poultry Sci Asn; Korean Soc Animal Sci; Arkansas Acad Sci Asn; World Poultry Sci Asn. *Res:* Nutritional and environmental factors affecting liver fat accumulation and liver hemorrhages associated with fatty liver problems in laying hens; production efficiency and economics of egg production as influenced by nutrition and management practice. *Mailing Add:* Dept of Agr Univ of Ark Pine Bluff AR 71601

LEE, KWANG SOO, b Seoul, Korea, Feb 1, 18; m 40; c 1. PHARMACOLOGY. *Educ:* Keijo Imp Univ, Korea, MD, 42, PhD, 45; Johns Hopkins Univ, 56. *Prof Exp:* Asst prof pharmacol, Seoul Nat Univ, 48-49; instr, Jefferson Med Col, 49-50, assoc, 50-51, from asst prof to assoc prof, 51-56; PROF PHARMACOL, STATE UNIV NY DOWNSTATE MED CTR, 62- *Mem:* Am Soc Pharmacol & Exp Therapeut. *Res:* Cardiac metabolism; mechanisms of drug actions. *Mailing Add:* Dept of Pharmacol State Univ NY Downstate Med Ctr Brooklyn NY 11203

LEE, KWANG-YUAN, b Shantung, China, Oct 8, 19; nat US; m 52; c 2. PETROLOGY, SEDIMENTOLOGY. *Educ:* Nat Southwest Assoc Univs, Nat Peking Univ, China, BSc, 42; Ohio State Univ, MSc, 50, PhD, 53. *Prof Exp:* Geologist, Nat Geol Surv China, 43-48; instr geol, Univ Ark, 53-54; geologist, Ohio State Geol Surv, 54-55 & SDak State Geol Surv, 55-59; geologist, 59-73, proj chief, Culpeper Basin Va & Md, Br Eastern Environ

Geol, 73-77, mem staff, Valley & Ridge Va, 77-81, RESEARCHER COAL, GAS & OIL, BR COAL RESOURCES, US GEOL SURV, 81- *Mem:* AAAS; Geol Soc Am; Am Asn Petrol Geol. *Res:* Stratigraphy, petrology, and economic geology. *Mailing Add:* Nat Ctr US Geol Surv Mail Stop 928 Reston VA 22092

LEE, KWOK-CHOY, b Hong Kong, China, Aug 24, 45; Can & UK citizen. IMMUNOLOGY. *Educ:* Univ Cambridge, BA, 68, MA, 72, PhD(biochem), 73. *Prof Exp:* Fel immunol, 72-76, ASST PROF IMMUNOL, UNIV ALTA, 76- Concurrent Pos: Res scholar, Nat Cancer Inst Can, 76- *Mem:* Am Asn Immunologist; NY Acad Sci. *Res:* The development and mode of action of macrophage subpopulations in immune and nonimmune mechanisms. *Mailing Add:* Dept of Immunol 845 Med Sci Bldg Edmonton AB T6G 2H7 Can

LEE, KYU TAIK, b Taegu, Korea, Sept 17, 21; m 44; c 2. MEDICINE, PATHOLOGY. *Educ:* Severence Union Med Col, MD, 43; Wash Univ, PhD(path), 56. *Prof Exp:* Physician in chief, Presby Gen Hosp, Taegu, Korea, 50-53; prof med & chmn dept, Kyung-Pook Nat Univ, 56-60; assoc prof, 60-66, PROF PATH, 66- & ASSOC DEAN FOR GRAD STUDIES AND RES, ALBANY MED COL, 76-, DIR, GEOG PATH DIV, 60-, DIR SECT MOLECULAR BIOL & PATH, 68- *Concurrent Pos:* NIH res grants, 56-; dir, Saratoga Conf Molecular Biol & Path, 68; managing ed, Exp & Molecular Path, 69; mem comt comp path, Nat Res Coun, 69-71, mem comt path, 70-71; mem nutrit study sect, NIH, 69-73. *Mem:* Am Heart Asn; Am Soc Exp Path; Int Acad Path; Am Soc Cell Biol; Int Soc Cardiol. *Res:* Ulstructural and biochemical aspects of atherosclerosis and thrombosis; geographic aspects of atherosclerosis. *Mailing Add:* Dept of Path Albany Med Col Albany NY 12208

LEE, L(AWRENCE) H(WA) N(I), b Shanghai, China, Jan 5, 23; nat US; m 48; c 1. ENGINEERING MECHANICS, STRUCTURAL ENGINEERING. *Educ:* La Univ Utopia, China, BS, 45; Univ Minn, MS, 47, PhD(struct eng & mech), 50. *Prof Exp:* Engr, Lin-Hu Reconstruct Asn, 45-46; instr math & mech, Univ Minn, 49; from asst prof to assoc prof eng mech, 50-60, prof eng sci, 60-69, PROF AEROSPACE & MECH ENG, UNIV NOTRE DAME, 69- *Concurrent Pos:* Consult, Bendix Corp, 53-75, Gen Motors Corp, 60-63 & 73, Rock Island Arsenal, US Army, 76 & Dodge Div, Reliance Elec Corp, 80. *Honors & Awards:* Struct Mech Res Award, Off Naval Res & Am Inst Aeronaut & Astronaut, 71. *Mem:* Am Soc Mech Engrs; Am Soc Civil Engrs; Soc Exp Stress Anal; Soc Eng Sci; Am Soc Eng Educ. *Res:* Inelastic stability; dynamic plasticity; elasticity; experimental stress analysis and dynamic stability. *Mailing Add:* Dept of Aerospace & Mech Eng Univ of Notre Dame Notre Dame IN 46556

LEE, LARRY DUANE, b Casey, Ill, Sept 12, 41; m 41; c 2. RELIABILITY THEORY, INFERENCE. *Educ:* Ill State Univ, BS, 65, MS, 68; Univ Mo, Columbia, PhD(statist), 75. *Prof Exp:* ASST PROF STATIST, VA POLYTECH INST & STATE UNIV, 75- *Concurrent Pos:* Prin investr, Off Naval Res grant, 76-77. *Mem:* Am Statist Asn; Inst Math Statist. *Res:* Reliability theory and applications; survival analysis; statistical inference; stochastic point processes. *Mailing Add:* Statist Dept Polytech Inst & State Univ Blacksburg VA 24061

LEE, LEAVIE EDGAR, JR, b Norfolk, Va, June 23, 30; m 64; c 2. PATHOLOGY, MEDICAL ADMINISTRATION. *Educ:* Univ Va, BA, 52, MD, 56. *Prof Exp:* Intern med, Columbia-Presby Med Ctr, 56-57; res assoc, Nat Inst Arthritis & Metab Dis, 57-58, exec secy res training br, Div Gen Med Sci, NIH, 58-60; from instr to asst prof path, Yale Univ, 63-66; asst chief clin progs, Res Grants Br, Nat Inst Gen Med Sci, 66-68, assoc chief, 68-70, actg dean admis & hosp prog, 77-78, ASST PROF PATH & ASSOC DEAN ADMIN, CASE WESTERN RESERVE UNIV SCH MED, 70-, ASST PROF COMMUNITY HEALTH, 74-, DEAN ADMIS & HOSP PROG, 78- *Concurrent Pos:* NIH trainee, Sch Med, Yale Univ, 60-63; consult & collabr, Dept Animal Dis, Univ Conn, 63-65; asst dir, Jane Coffin Childs Mem Fund Med Res, 63-66. *Res:* Support of biomedical research and the development of medical scientists; comparative pathology; oncology; fish tumors; ultrastructural aspects of disease; analysis and planning of health education, research and care delivery programs. *Mailing Add:* Sch of Med Case Western Reserve Univ Cleveland OH 44106

LEE, LEONARD A, b Rochester, NY, June 11, 26; m 78; c 2. ENVIRONMENTAL SCIENCES, POLYMER CHEMISTRY. *Educ:* Univ Rochester, BS, 48, PhD(biochem), 52. *Prof Exp:* Res chemist, Philip Morris & Co, 52-54; sr res fel, Am Spice Trade Asn, 54-56; sr res chemist, Celanese Fibers Co, 63-64; group leader spec projs, 64-77; mgr chem & biosci, 77-80, GEN MGR, FRANKLIN INST RES LAB, 80- *Mem:* AAAS; Am Chem Soc; NY Acad Sci. *Res:* Research and development planning and evaluation; long range research; environmental science and technology; reverse osmosis process and products, including hollow fiber research; advanced waste treatment methods and anti-pollution studies. *Mailing Add:* Franklin Inst Res Lab Inc 20th Race St Philadelphia PA 19103

LEE, LESTER TSUNG-CHENG, b Tsing-tao, China, Dec 16, 34; US citizen; m 59; c 2. POLYMER CHEMISTRY, ORGANIC CHEMISTRY. *Educ:* Nat Taiwan Univ, BS, 56; State Univ NY Syracuse, MS, 60; State Univ NY Buffalo, PhD(org chem), 68. *Prof Exp:* Chemist monogram indust, Spaulding Fiber Co, 60-68; res chemist, Dept Polymer Sci, Cent Res Lab, Chem Res Ctr, 68-72, sr res chemist, 72-75, COORDR, ALLIED CHEM CORP, 75- *Mem:* Am Chem Soc. *Res:* Synthesis and characterization of new polymers, polymer structure-property relationship, polymer applications; fiber, industrial laminates, flame-retardant, high temperature performance, membrane preparation and technology. *Mailing Add:* Allied Chem Corp Box 1087R Morristown NJ 07960

LEE, LIENG-HUANG, b Fukien, China, Nov 6, 24; m 49; c 4. ORGANIC CHEMISTRY. *Educ:* Amoy Univ, BSc, 47; Case Inst Technol, MSc, 54, PhD(chem), 55. *Prof Exp:* Jr chemist, Nantou Sugar Factory, China, 47-48; asst res chemist, Chia-yee Solvent Works, 48-51 & Rain Stimulation Res Inst, 51-52; res assoc, Case Inst Technol, 55-56; lectr, Tunghai Univ, 56-57; vis prof, Taiwan Prov Norm Univ, 57-58; res org chemist, Dow Chem Co, 58-63, sr res chemist, 63-68; SR SCIENTIST, XEROX CORP, 68- *Concurrent Pos:* Consult, Union Res Inst, Taiwan, China, 57-58. *Mem:* Am Chem Soc; Sigma Xi; Am Phys Soc; Fel Am Inst Chemists. *Res:* Polymer friction and wear; adhesion and surface chemistry; electrophotography. *Mailing Add:* Wilson Ctr for Technol Xerox Corp Xerox Sq Rochester NY 14580

LEE, LIH-SYNG, b China, Oct 28, 45; m 74; c 1. BIOCHEMISTRY, BIOPHYSICS. *Educ:* Nat Taiwan Univ, BS, 68; Yale Univ, MPh, 71, MS, 72, PhD(chem), 74. *Prof Exp:* Res scientist biochem & fel, Roswell Park Mem Inst, 74-76; STAFF ASSOC CARCINOGENESIS, COLUMBIA UNIV, 76- *Mem:* NY Acad Sci; AAAS; Am Chem Soc. *Res:* Chemical carcinogenesis; tumor promotion; growth factors; hormone receptors; cell culture; transport; enzymology; DNA metabolism; cell cycle; gene transfer; membrane biophysics; drug design. *Mailing Add:* Res & Develop Ctr Gen Elec Co PO Box 8 Schenectady NY 12301

LEE, LINWOOD LAWRENCE, JR, b Trenton, NJ, Aug 5, 28; m 57; c 1. NUCLEAR PHYSICS. *Educ:* Princeton Univ, AB, 50; Yale Univ, MS, 51, PhD(physics), 55. *Prof Exp:* Asst physicist, Argonne Nat Lab, 54-59, assoc physicist, 60-65; vis asst prof physics, Univ Minn, 59-60; PROF PHYSICS, STATE UNIV NY STONY BROOK, 65-, DIR NUCLEAR STRUCTURE LAB, 65- *Mem:* Am Phys Soc. *Res:* Experimental studies of nuclear structure and spectroscopy; nucleon transfer reactions; gamma ray transitions in nuclei. *Mailing Add:* Dept of Physics State Univ of NY Stony Brook NY 11790

LEE, LLOYD LIEH-SHEN, b China, Jan 25, 42; US citizen. STATISTICAL MECHANICS, POLYMER TECHNOLOGY. *Educ:* Nat Taiwan Univ, BS, 63; Northwestern Univ, PhD(chem eng), 71. *Prof Exp:* Res engr polymer, Du Pont Chem Co, 71-72; researcher liquids, Univ Paris, 72; mgr textiles, Tashing Chem Co, 73-75; asst prof, 76-80, ASSOC PROF CHEM ENG & MAT SCI, UNIV OKLA, 80- *Res:* Natural gas properties; electrolyte solutions; perturbation theory for liquid structure and liquid thermodynamics; Monte Carlo and molecular dynamics simulations; turbulence; high-speed spinning of polymeric filaments. *Mailing Add:* Dept of Chem Eng Univ of Okla Norman OK 73019

LEE, LONG CHI, b Kaohsiung, Taiwan, Oct 19, 40; m 67; c 2. EXPERIMENTAL PHYSICS. *Educ:* Taiwan Normal Univ, BS, 64; Univ Southern Calif, MA, 67, PhD(physics), 71. *Prof Exp:* From res asst to res assoc, 67-72, res staff physicist, 72-77, adj asst prof physics, Univ Southern Calif, 77; sr physicist, Stanford Res Inst Int, 77-81; PROF ELEC & COMPUT ENG, SAN DIEGO STATE UNIV, 82- *Concurrent Pos:* Vis Scientist, Universitat Kaiserslautern, Ger, 75. *Mem:* Am Phys Soc; Inter-Am Photochemical Soc. *Res:* Study on the photoionization and photodissociation processes of small molecules and radicals using vacuum ultraviolet radiation; photodestruction processes of atmospheric positive and negative ions; developing carbon dioxide laser modulator; molecular processes in electrical discharges; optical characteristics of small aerosol particles. *Mailing Add:* Dept Elec & Comput Eng San Diego State Univ San Diego CA 92182

LEE, LOU-CHUANG, b Taiwan, China, Apr 20, 47; m; c 2. PLASMA PHYSICS, SPACE PHYSICS. *Educ:* Nat Taiwan Univ, BS, 69; Calif Inst Technol, MS, 72, PhD(physics), 75. *Prof Exp:* Res assoc physics, Goddard Space Flight Ctr, NASA, 75-77; vis asst prof, Inst Phys Sci & Technol, Univ Md, 77-78; ASST PROF, GEOPHYSICS INST, UNIV ALASKA, 78- *Mem:* Am Phys Soc; Am Geophys Union. *Res:* Magnetospheric physics. *Mailing Add:* Geophys Inst Univ of Alaska Fairbanks AK 99701

LEE, LYNDON EDMUND, JR, b Islip, NY, Aug 11, 12; m 43; c 3. SURGERY, PHARMACOLOGY. *Educ:* Duke Univ, BS, 37, MD, 38. *Prof Exp:* Asst cardiol, Univ Va, 38; resident obstet & gynec, Duke Univ Hosp, 40; intern surg, Med Col Va, 41; instr, Med Sch, Univ Mich, 42-43, instr pharmacol & surg, 42-47; instr post-grad educ comt, State Med Asn, Tenn, 47-49; dir cancer control, PR Dept Health, 49-54; instr pharmacol & surg, Med Sch, Univ Mich, 54-57; coordr res, 57-69, dir surg servs, 65-69, asst chief med dir res & educ, 69-71, asst chief med dir prof serv, 71-76, special asst chief med dir, US Vet Admin, 76-77, chief staff, Vet Admin Hosp, Richmond, Va & assoc dean & prof surg, Med Col Va, 76-78; SURG, US VET ADMIN, WASHINGTON, DC, 78- *Concurrent Pos:* Nat Res Coun fel, 38-40 & 41-42; assoc physician, Blue Ridge Sanatorium, Charlottesville, Va, 38; physician, Am Hosp in Brit, Oxford, Eng, 41 & Pondville State Hosp Cancer, Walpole, Mass; assoc surg, Mass Gen Hosp, Boston; prof, Sch Med, Univ PR, 52-54; dir surg, Wayne County Gen Hosp, 54-57; mem, Med Sci Div, Nat Acad Sci, 69-76 & White House Fed Coun Sci & Technol, 69-76 Consult, Smithsonian Inst, 58-76, Nat Adv Cancer Coun, NIH, 58-76 & training grants rev bd & Cancer Chemother Nat Serv Ctr, Nat Cancer Inst, 58-76; mem nat adv coun child health & human develop, NIH. *Mem:* AAAS; Am Pub Health Asn; Pub Health Cancer Asn Am; fel Am Col Surgeons; fel Int Soc Surg. *Res:* Analgesics and sedatives; neoplasms. *Mailing Add:* 4111 Saul Rd Chevy Chase View Kensington MD 20895

LEE, MARTIN ALAN, b Bromley, Eng, Oct 9, 45; US citizen. ASTROPHYSICS. *Educ:* Stanford Univ, BSc, 66; Univ Chicago, PhD(physics), 71. *Prof Exp:* NATO fel astrophysics, Max Planck Inst Extraterrestrial Physics, WGer, 71-72; res assoc, 72-73; res assoc, Lab Astrophysics & Space Res, Univ Chicago, 73-74; asst prof physics, Washington Univ, 74-79; RES SCIENTIST ASTROPHYSICS, UNIV NH, 79- *Mem:* Am Astron Soc; Am Geophys Union. *Res:* Energetic particle transport and plasma processes in the solar-terrestrial environment including ion shock acceleration, solar modulation of galactic cosmic rays, plasma instabilities and wave propagation. *Mailing Add:* Space Sci Ctr De Meritt Hall Univ NH Durham NH 03824

LEE, MARTIN J G, b Kings Lynn, Eng, Mar 16, 42. SOLID STATE PHYSICS. *Educ:* Cambridge Univ, BA, 63, MA & PhD(physics), 67. *Prof Exp:* Instr, 67-69, asst prof physics, James Franck Inst & Dept Physics, Univ Chicago, 69-74; assoc prof, 74-79, PROF PHYSICS, UNIV TORONTO, 79- *Mem:* Am Asn Physics Teachers; Can Asn Physicists; Brit Inst Physics. *Res:* Experimental and theoretical study of Fermi surfaces and electronic structure of metals; photo-induced field emission phenomena. *Mailing Add:* McLennan Phys Lab 60 St George St Toronto ON M5S 1A7 Can

LEE, MARTIN JEROME, b Bayonne, NJ, May 24, 43; m 67; c 1. BIOCHEMISTRY. *Educ:* Rutgers Univ, New Brunswick, BA, 65, MS, 68, PhD(biochem), 69. *Prof Exp:* Nat Inst Gen Med Sci fel, Univ Wis-Madison, 69-70, res assoc biochem, Enzyme Inst, 70-71; sr res assoc, Pharmacia Fine Chem, Inc, 71-73; staff scientist, Technicon Instruments Corp, 73-80; DIR APPL RES, COULTER DIAG, 80- *Mem:* Biophys Soc; Am Chem Soc; Sigma Xi; NY Acad Sci. *Res:* Bioenergetics; chromatography; separational techniques and instrumentation; automated cytochemistry, immunology, clinical chemistry and enzymology. *Mailing Add:* 740 W 83rd St Coulter Diag Hialeah FL 33014

LEE, MARTIN JOE, US citizen. ACCELERATOR PHYSICS, MICROWAVES. *Educ:* Univ Calif, BS, 60; NY Univ, MS, 62; Stanford Univ, PhD(elec eng), 67. *Prof Exp:* Microwave engr commun, Bell Tel Lab, 60-62; microwave engr accelerator eng, Stanford Linear Accelerator Ctr, 62-67; accelerator physicist, Brookhaven Nat Lab, 67-69; accelerator theorist, 69-78, DEP CHIEF, PEP THEORY GROUP, ACCELERATOR PHYSICS, STANFORD LINEAR ACCELERATOR CTR, 78- *Concurrent Pos:* Spec consult, Electron Storage Ring Corp, 78- *Mem:* Inst Elec & Electronics Engrs. *Mailing Add:* Stanford Linear Accelerator Ctr PO Box 4349 Stanford CA 94305

LEE, MATHEW HUNG MUN, b Hawaii, July 28, 31; m 58; c 3. PHYSICAL MEDICINE & REHABILITATION. *Educ:* Johns Hopkins Univ, AB, 53; Univ Md, MD, 56; Univ Calif, MPH, 62; Am Bd Phys Med & Rehab, dipl, 66. *Prof Exp:* Resident, Inst Phys Med & Rehab, Med Ctr, NY Univ, 62-64, NY State Health Dept assignee, Rehab Serv, 64-65, from asst prof to assoc prof rehab med, 65-73, dir educ & training, Dept Rehab Med, 66-68, assoc dir, 68, DIR DEPT REHAB MED, GOLDWATER MEM HOSP, 68-, PROF REHAB MED, SCH MED, NY UNIV, 73- *Concurrent Pos:* Assoc vis physician, Goldwater Mem Hosp, 65-68, vis physician, 68-, chief electrodiag unit, 66-, vpres med bd, 69-70, pres, 71-; asst clin prof, Col Dent, NY Univ, 66-69, clin asst prof, 69-70, clin assoc prof, 70-; consult, Daughters of Israel Hosp, New York, 65-72, Bur Adult Hyg, 65- & Human Resources Ctr, 66-; asst attending physician, Hosp, NY Univ, 68-; World Rehab Fund consult, Gordon Seagrave & Maryknoll Hosps, Korea, 69; attend physician, Bellevue Hosp Ctr, 71-; consult, US Dept Interior. *Mem:* AAAS; fel Am Acad Phys Med & Rehab; fel Am Col Physicians; Pan-Am Med Asn; fel Am Pub Health Asn. *Mailing Add:* 86-71 Marengo St Holliswood NY 11423

LEE, MELVIN, b New York, NY, Jan 5, 26; m 49; c 4. NUTRITION, BIOCHEMISTRY. *Educ:* Univ Calif, Los Angeles, BA, 47; Univ Calif, Berkeley, MA, 52, PhD(nutrit), 58. *Prof Exp:* From instr to asst prof prev med, Sch Med, Univ Calif, San Francisco, 58-67, asst prof biochem, 63-67, lectr dent, 61-67; prof nutrit & dir, Sch Home Econ, 67-74, PROF HOME ECON, SCH HOME ECON, UNIV BC, 74- *Concurrent Pos:* USPHS res fel, 66; sci exchange fel, Japan Soc Promotion, 81. *Mem:* AAAS; Am Inst Nutrit; Soc Environ Geochem & Health; Soc Nutrit Latin Am; Can Soc Nutrit Sci. *Res:* Relation of diet to metabolic patterns; factors influencing growth. *Mailing Add:* Sch Home Econ Univ BC Vancouver BC V6T 1W5 Can

LEE, MERLIN RAYMOND, b Hoytsville, Utah, Mar 21, 28; m 49; c 2. EVOLUTIONARY BIOLOGY. *Educ:* Univ Utah, BS, 52, MS, 54, PhD, 60. *Prof Exp:* Asst zool, biol & genetics, Univ Utah, 52-56, instr biol, 58-59; field collector, Mus Natural Hist, Univ Kans, 60-61; res assoc, Mus Natural Hist, 61-63, asst prof zool, 63-67, ASSOC PROF ZOOL, UNIV ILL, URBANA, 67- *Concurrent Pos:* Ed, J Mammal, 64-66. *Mem:* Am Soc Mammal. *Res:* Mammalogy, karyology, chromosome evolution and mammalian systematics. *Mailing Add:* Dept of Ecol Ethol & Evolution Univ of Ill Urbana IL 61801

LEE, MING T, b Taipei, Taiwan, Aug 15, 40; US citizen; m 70; c 2. HYDRAULICS, WATER RESOURCES. *Educ:* Nat Taiwan Univ, BS, 63, MS, 66; Univ Cincinnati, MS, 68; Purdue Univ, PhD(civil eng), 72. *Prof Exp:* Res engr, Hydraul Lab, Water Resources Planning Comn, 66-67; hydraul engr, Vogt, Iver & Assoc, Ohio, 68; res engr hydraul, Agr Econ Dept, Univ Ill, 72-75; ASSOC PROF SCIENTIST HYDRAUL, ILL STATE WATER SURV, 75- *Mem:* Am Geophys Union; Soil Conserv Soc Am; Am Soc Civil Engrs; Sigma Xi. *Res:* Soil erosion; sediment transport; lake hydrology; watershed erosion control; hydrologic computer modeling. *Mailing Add:* PO Box 5050 Sta A Champaign IL 61820

LEE, MING-LIANG, b Tainan, Taiwan, June 26, 36; m 65; c 3. MEDICAL GENETICS, BIOCHEMISTRY. *Educ:* Nat Taiwan Univ, MD, 62; Univ Miami, PhD(biochem), 69. *Prof Exp:* Asst prof, Sch Med, Univ Miami, 72-76; chief fel med genetics, Sch Med, Johns Hopkins Univ, 76-77; ASSOC PROF MED GENETICS & CHIEF DIV, RUTGERS MED SCH, 77- *Mem:* Am Soc Biol Scientist; Am Soc Med Genetics. *Mailing Add:* Div of Med Genetics Dept of Pediat Rutgers Med Sch Piscataway NJ 08902

LEE, MIN-SHIU, b Taipei, Taiwan, June 30, 40; US citizen; m 66; c 2. PHYSICAL CHEMISTRY, POLYMER SCIENCE & TECHNOLOGY. *Educ:* Nat Taiwan Univ, BS, 62; NMex Highlands Univ, MS, 66; Case Western Reserve Univ, PhD(macromolecular sci), 69. *Prof Exp:* Res fel chem, Chinese Ord Res Inst, 62-64; teaching asst, NMex Highlands Univ, 64-65, res fel hot atom chem, Inst Sci Res, 65-66; res asst polymer res, Case Western Reserve Univ, 66-69; res chemist, FMC Corp, 69-73, sr res chemist, 73-76; sr res scientist, Jelco Labs, Johnson & Johnson, 76-80. *Mem:* Sigma Xi; Am Chem Soc; NY Acad Sci; AAAS; Am Asn Univ Prof. *Res:* Medical products improvement and development; collagen research and development; chemical process improvement; new polymer products development; textile and non-woven applications; polymer characterization; polymer modification and application; process/quality control; biomaterial development; colloidal macromolecular phenomena. *Mailing Add:* 4319 Southpark Dr Tampa FL 33624

LEE, MINYOUNG, b Seoul, Korea, Aug 11, 38; US citizen; m 66; c 2. MATERIALS SCIENCE. *Educ:* Seoul Nat Univ, BS, 61; Providence Col, MS, 67; Brown Univ, PhD(mat sci), 71. *Prof Exp:* MEM TECH STAFF MAT, CORP RES & DEVELOP CTR, GEN ELEC CO, 71- *Concurrent Pos:* Vis scientist, Cavendish Lab, Cambridge Univ, 76. *Mem:* Am Inst Mining, Metall & Petrol Engrs; AAAS. *Res:* Development of very hard materials primarily for cutting tools and wear parts; advanced materials processing technology; tribology. *Mailing Add:* Corp Res & Develop Ctr Gen Elec Co PO Box 8 Schenectady NY 12309

LEE, MONHE HOWARD, b Pusan, Korea, May 21, 37; US citizen; m 67; c 1. THEORETICAL PHYSICS. *Educ:* Univ Pa, BS, 59, PhD(physics), 67. *Prof Exp:* Fel physics, Theoret Physics Inst, Univ Alta, 67-69; res assoc, Dept Physics & Mat Sci Ctr, Mass Inst Technol, 69-71; NIH res grant & investr biomat, Health Sci & Technol, Mass Inst Technol & Harvard Univ, 71-73; asst prof, 73-77, ASSOC PROF PHYSICS, UNIV GA, 77- *Concurrent Pos:* Guest lectr, Inst Theoret Physics, Univ Leuven, Belgium, 76; grants, NATO, 76-78, Air Force Off Sci Res, 77-78, Dept Energy, 77-; Fulbright-Hays Sr Res Scholar Award, Belgium, 78-79; vis prof, Dept Physics, Seoul Nat Univ, Korea, 80. *Mem:* Am Phys Soc; Biophys Soc. *Res:* Many-body theory; statistical mechanics of phase transitions; biophysics of membrane transport. *Mailing Add:* Dept of Physics Univ of Ga Athens GA 30602

LEE, MYAU-YIN PHYLLIS, cosmic ray physics, see previous edition

LEE, NANCY ZEE-NEE MA, b Shanghai, China, Oct 28, 40; US citizen; m 65; c 2. BIOCHEMISTRY. *Educ:* Southwestern Univ, BS, 63; Univ Tex, PhD(chem), 67. *Prof Exp:* Fel biochem, Northwestern Univ, 68; RES BIOCHEM PHARMACOL, UNIV CALIF, SAN FRANCISCO, 69- *Concurrent Pos:* Res biochem, Bay Area Heart Res, 70-72. *Mem:* Sigma Xi; Soc Neurosci. *Res:* Biochemical mechanism for narcotic addiction. *Mailing Add:* Dept of Pharmacol Third St & Parnassus San Francisco CA 94143

LEE, NEVILLE KA-SHEK, b Hong Kong, Jan 2, 47. PHYSICS, HARDWARE SYSTEMS. *Educ:* Univ Calif, Los Angeles, BS, 67; Mass Inst Technol, PhD(physics), 73. *Prof Exp:* Res staff physics, Francis Bitter Nat Magnet Lab, Mass Inst Technol, 73-78; sr engr, Polaroid, 78-81; MGR OPTICAL MEMORY MEDIA, BURROUGHS CORP, 81- *Mem:* Sigma Xi; Optical Soc Am. *Res:* Quantum optics; working on noncollinear nonlinear light mixing to generate infrared coherent sources; development of optical memory; laser material processing; nonlinear optics; solid state theory. *Mailing Add:* 5411 N Lindero Canyon Rd Westlake Village CA 91360

LEE, NORMAN DAVID, b Bridgeport, Conn, May 25, 20; m 41; c 3. BIOCHEMISTRY. *Educ:* Univ Calif, Los Angeles, AB, 46; Univ Calif, Berkeley, PhD(biochem), 50. *Prof Exp:* Instr med, Med Sch, Univ Wash, 49-53; asst chief radioisotope serv, Vet Admin Hosp, Memphis, 53-59; chief radioisotope div, Biosci Labs, 59-65, asst to dir, 65-67, dir dept endocrinol, 67-68, asst dir br labs, 68-70, ASST DIR AFFIL LABS, BIO-SCI ENTERPRISES, 70-, MGR TECH OPERS, 77- *Mem:* Am Soc Biol Chem; Soc Nuclear Med; Am Asn Clin Chem; Am Thyroid Asn. *Res:* Thyroid methodology; laboratory management. *Mailing Add:* Bio-Sci Enterprises 7600 Tyrone Ave Van Nuys CA 91405

LEE, NORMAN K, b Frankfort, Ind, Feb 3, 34; m 56; c 2. APPLIED MATHEMATICS. *Educ:* Hanover Col, BA, 56; Vanderbilt Univ, MA, 58; Purdue Univ, PhD(bionucleonics), 69. *Prof Exp:* Asst prof, 58-66, ASSOC PROF MATH, BALL STATE UNIV, 69-, ADMIN ASST, DEPT MATH SCI, 79- *Concurrent Pos:* NSF fel, 63-64, partic, Acad Year Inst, 62-63; sr instr, Somerset Community Col, 68-69. *Mem:* AAAS; Sigma Xi. *Res:* Mathematical models. *Mailing Add:* Dept of Math Sci Ball State Univ Muncie IN 47306

LEE, NORMAN KUNHAN, b China, July 11, 17; m 50; c 2. PATHOLOGY. *Educ:* Nat Chung Cheng Med Col, China, MD, 47. *Prof Exp:* From instr to asst prof path, Sch Med, Univ Okla, 59-62, dir blood bank & sch med technol, 60-61; asst prof path, Univ Kans, 62-63; CHIEF LAB SERV, VET ADMIN MED CTR, 63- *Mailing Add:* Vet Admin Med Ctr Lab Serv Perry Hill Rd Montgomery AL 36109

LEE, PANG-KAI, b Kiangsu, China, Nov 3, 22; m 49; c 3. PHYSICAL CHEMISTRY. *Educ:* Nat Kwangsi Univ, BS, 45; Oberlin Col, MA, 62; Pa State Univ, PhD(chem), 67. *Prof Exp:* Teaching asst chem, Nat Kwangsi Univ, 45-48; chemist, Taiwan Indust & Mining Corp, 48-53; factory supt, Soong-San Chem Works, 53-58; lectr chem, Nanyang Univ, Singapore, 58-60; SR RES SCIENTIST, WESTINGHOUSE RES LABS, 61- *Mem:* Am Chem Soc. *Res:* High temperature and surface chemistry; arc chemistry; thermionic oxide-cathode technology; tribochemistry of solid lubricants; steam turbine chemistry. *Mailing Add:* Westinghouse Res & Develop Ctr Churchill Boro Pittsburgh PA 15235

LEE, PATRICK A, b Hong Kong, Sept 8, 46; m 69; c 2. CONDENSED MATTER THEORY. *Educ:* Mass Inst Technol, BS, 66, PhD(physics), 70. *Prof Exp:* J W Gibbs instr physics, Yale Univ, 70-72; mem tech staff, Bell Labs, 72-73; asst prof physics, Univ Wash, Seattle, 73-74; MEM TECH STAFF, BELL LABS, 74- *Mem:* Am Phys Soc. *Mailing Add:* Bell Labs 600 Mountain Ave Murray Hill NJ 07974

LEE, PAUL D, b Ina, Ill, Feb 15, 40; m 61. ASTRONOMY, ASTROPHYSICS. *Educ:* Univ Ill, BS, 63, MS, 65, PhD, 68. *Prof Exp:* Asst prof, 68-73, ASSOC PROF PHYSICS & ASTRON, LA STATE UNIV, BATON ROUGE, 73- *Mem:* Royal Astron Soc; Am Astron Soc. *Res:* Spectrophotometry of stellar and nonstellar objects; stellar atmospheres and chemical abundances in stars. *Mailing Add:* Dept of Physics & Astron La State Univ Baton Rouge LA 70803

LEE, PAUL POO-KAM, b Macau, China, Aug 13, 50. ELECTRICAL ENGINEERING, APPLIED PHYSICS. *Educ:* Cornell Univ, BS, 72, MS, 74; Univ Rochester, PhD(elec eng), 78. *Prof Exp:* asst prof radiol, Univ Rochester, 78-81; PRIN RES SCIENTIST, HONEYWELL INC, 81- *Mem:* Inst Elec & Electronics Engrs; Acoust Soc Am; Am Inst Ultrasound Med; Asn Comput Mach. *Res:* Diagnostic ultrasound; communications; digital signal and image processing; biomedical engineering; wave propagation and scattering; computers. *Mailing Add:* 4800 E Dry Creek Rd PO Box 5227 Honewell Inc Denver CO 80217

LEE, PETER CHUNG-YI, b Hankow, Hupei, China, Sept 29, 34; m 61; c 1. ENGINEERING MECHANICS. *Educ:* Cheng Kung Univ, Taiwan, BS, 57; Rutgers Univ, MS, 61; Columbia Univ, MS, 65, DEngSc(eng mech), 65. *Prof Exp:* Sloan fel, 65-66, from asst prof to assoc prof, 66-76, PROF CIVIL ENG, PRINCETON UNIV, 76- *Honors & Awards:* C B Sawyer Memorial Award, 80. *Mem:* Am Soc Mech Engrs; assoc mem Am Soc Civil Engrs; Acoust Soc Am. *Res:* Theory of elasticity; vibrations and wave propagation in elastic solids and piecoelectric crystals; effects of initial stresses and accelerations; temperature changes on the vibrations of elastic and crystal plates. *Mailing Add:* Dept of Civil Eng Princeton Univ Princeton NJ 08544

LEE, PETER E, b Trinidad, WI, Oct 18, 30; m 60; c 2. PLANT VIROLOGY. *Educ:* Univ Man, BSc, 58; Univ Wis, MSc, 59, PhD(entom), 61. *Prof Exp:* Jr res entomologist, Univ Calif, Berkeley, 61; res officer virus-vector studies, Can Dept Agr, 61-65; from asst prof to assoc prof, 65-77, PROF BIOL, CARLETON UNIV, 77- *Mem:* Electron Micros Soc Am. *Res:* Characterization of leafhopper-transmitted viruses and insect viruses; virus purification and electron microscopy. *Mailing Add:* Dept of Biol Carleton Univ Ottawa ON K1S 5B6 Can

LEE, PETER FRANK WILLIAM, b Colchester, Eng, Mar 25, 50; m 75; c 1. FLUID MECHANICS, HEAT TRANSFER. *Educ:* Univ Auckland, BS, 72, PhD(eng), 75. *Prof Exp:* Lectr chem eng, Univ Auckland, 75-76 & Inst Paper Chem, 76-77; scientist chem eng, 77-81, MGR, NEWSPRINT RES & DEVELOP, WEYERHAEUSER TECHNOL CTR, 81- *Mem:* Am Inst Chem Engrs; Tech Asn Pulp & Paper Indust; Can Pulp & Paper Asn. *Res:* Rheology of heterogeneous flow; heat and mass transfer in porous media; mechanical communication. *Mailing Add:* Weyerhaeuser Co Weyerhaeuser Technol Ctr Tacoma WA 98401

LEE, PETER VAN ARSDALE, b San Francisco, Calif, Mar 31, 23; m 51; c 4. PHARMACOLOGY, MEDICINE. *Educ:* Stanford Univ, AB, 44, MD, 47. *Prof Exp:* Intern, San Francisco Hosp, 46-47; asst resident path, Stanford Univ Hosps, 49-50; resident med, 50-51; clin asst, Col Med, State Univ NY, 51-52; instr pharmacol, Sch Med, Stanford Univ, 52-54, asst prof, 54-55; asst prof & asst dean, 55-58, assoc prof pharmacol, 58-67, assoc prof med, 60-67, assoc dean, 58-60, admis chmn, 60-65, prof pharmacol, 67-80, PROF MED, SCH MED, UNIV SOUTHERN CALIF, 67-, PROF FAMILY & PREV MED, 80- *Concurrent Pos:* Resident, King's County Hosp, NY, 51-52; consult, Commonwealth Fund, 58-59; vis fel, Brit Asn Study Med Educ, 71-72. *Mem:* AAAS; Am Fedn Clin Res; Asn Am Med Cols; Brit Asn Study Med Educ; fel Royal Soc Med. *Res:* Medical education; clinical pharmacology. *Mailing Add:* Univ of Southern Calif Sch of Med Los Angeles CA 90033

LEE, PHILIP CALVIN, JR, mycology, see previous edition

LEE, PHILIP RANDOLPH, b San Francisco, Calif, Apr 17, 24; m 53; c 4. INTERNAL MEDICINE. *Educ:* Stanford Univ, AB, 45, MD, 48; Univ Minn, MS, 56. *Prof Exp:* Asst prof clin phys med & rehab, Sch Med, NY Univ, 55-56; clin instr med, Sch Med, Stanford Univ, 56-59, asst clin prof, 59-67; chancellor, 69-72, PROF SOCIAL MED, MED CTR, UNIV CALIF, SAN FRANCISCO, 69-, PROF AMBULATORY & COMMUNITY MED, 77- *Concurrent Pos:* Mem dept internal med, Palo Alto Med Clin, Calif, 56-65; consult, Bur Pub Health Serv, USPHS, 58-63; dir health serv, Off Tech Coop & Res, AID, 63-65; dep asst secy health & sci affairs, Dept Health, Educ & Welfare, 65, asst secy, 65-69. *Mem:* Inst of Med of Nat Acad Sci; AAAS; AMA; Am Pub Health Asn; Am Fedn Clin Res. *Res:* Arthritis and rheumatism, especially Rubella arthritis; cardiovascular rehabilitation; academic medical administration; health policy. *Mailing Add:* Dept of Social Med Univ Calif Med Ctr San Francisco CA 94143

LEE, PING, b Taiwan, Apr 6, 50; US citizen; m 78. PLASMA PHYSICS. *Educ:* Univ Calif, Berkeley, 73; Mass Inst Technol, PhD(physics), 76. *Prof Exp:* STAFF MEM X-RAY PHYSICS, LOS ALAMOS NAT LAB, 77- *Mem:* Am Phys Soc. *Res:* Plasmas generlate by laser-matter interaction; measurement and analysis of x-rays produced in high temperature and high density plasmas. *Mailing Add:* Los Alamos Nat Lab L-4 Mail Stop 554 Los Alamos NM 87544

LEE, PUI KUM, b Peking, China, June 22, 16; US citizen; m 41; c 4. OPTICS. *Educ:* Lingnam Univ, BS, 40; Columbia Univ, MS, 49. *Prof Exp:* Asst chem, Nat Kwangsi Univ, China, 40-41; res chemist, Inst Indust Res, 41-42; mgr, China Chem Corp, 42-46; res assoc chem, Columbia Univ, 49-56; sr chemist reprography, 56-63, res specialist imaging, 63-67, SR RES SPECIALIST, CENT RES LABS, 3M CO, 67- *Honors & Awards:* IR.100 Award, Indust Res Mag, 78. *Mem:* Am Chem Soc; Soc Photog Sci & Eng; Optical Soc Am. *Res:* Imaging optics. *Mailing Add:* Graphic Technol Lab 3M Co PO Box 33221 St Paul MN 55144

LEE, R(OBERT) E(DWARD), b Quincy, Mass, Mar 16, 31; m 54; c 3. CHEMICAL ENGINEERING. *Educ:* Northeastern Univ, BSChE, 53; Univ Mich, MBA, 61. *Prof Exp:* Chem engr, 53-55, proj leader, 55-59, asst lab dir, 59-63, lab dir, 63-68, mgr tech serv, Films Tech Serv & Develop, 68, tech mgr packaging res & develop, 68-77, tech dir, 77-81, MGR ROCKY MOUNTAIN RES & DEVELOP, DOW CHEM USA, 81- *Mem:* Am Inst Chem Eng; Sigma Xi. *Res:* High polymers, particularly olefin and styrene polymers and copolymers; product and process development in plastics; fabricated plastic products; natural resources and energy research and development. *Mailing Add:* 8056 S Kramena Way Eaglewood CO 80112

LEE, RALPH EDWARD, b Gilliam, Mo, July 1, 21; m 42; c 5. COMPUTER SCIENCE. *Educ:* Mo Valley Col, BS, 42; Univ Mo, MS, 49; Ind Univ, MA, 53. *Prof Exp:* From instr to assoc prof, Sch Mines, 46-59, PROF MATH, UNIV MO-ROLLA, 59-, DIR COMPUT CTR, 60- *Concurrent Pos:* NSF fel, Nat Bur Standards, 59. *Mem:* Data Processing Mgt Asn; Asn Comput Mach; Soc Indust & Appl Math; Asn Educ Data Systs. *Res:* Numerical analysis; matrix computations. *Mailing Add:* Comput Ctr Univ of Mo-Rolla Rolla MO 65401

LEE, RALPH HEWITT, b Lexington, Ky, Apr 10, 38; m 59; c 4. INORGANIC CHEMISTRY, ACADEMIC ADMINISTRATION. *Educ:* Morehouse Col, BS, 57; Univ Kans, PhD(inorg chem), 64. *Prof Exp:* From assoc prof to prof chem, Ala Agr & Mech Col, 64-69, head dept, 65-69; acad dean, Morehouse Col, 69; dir SEEK prog, Queens Col, City Univ New York, 69-71; pres, Forest Park Community Col, 71-77; PRES, CENTRAL YMCA COMMUNITY COL, 78- *Concurrent Pos:* NSF India Prog, 67-68. *Mem:* AAAS; Am Chem Soc; Sigma Xi. *Res:* Structure of nitrogen-donor transition metal complex compounds; education of secondary school science teachers. *Mailing Add:* 211 W Wacker Dr Chicago IL 60606

LEE, RAY H(UI-CHOUNG), b Canton, China, Mar 28, 18; nat US; m; c 4. ELECTRICAL ENGINEERING, MATHEMATICS. *Educ:* Nat Cent Univ, China, BS, 41; Stanford Univ, MA, 45, EE, 46, MS, 47. *Prof Exp:* Design engr, Cent Radio Works China, 41-44; founder & prin, Honolulu Trade Sch, 47-51; engr-specialist, Boeing Airplane Co, 51-55; res specialist & chief mathematician, Chromatic TV Labs & Auktometric Corp, 55-63; staff mem, David Sarnoff Res Ctr, Radio Corp Am, NJ, 64-66; staff mem & mgr, Tex Instruments, 66-69; chief engr, Liquid Crystal Display, Backman Instruments, 69-73; CONSULT PROD DEVELOP & STRATEGIC PLANNING, 73- *Mem:* Inst Elec & Electronics Engrs; Soc Info Display. *Res:* Processings; energy; communication. *Mailing Add:* 23203 Park Esperanza Calabasas Park CA 91302

LEE, RAYMOND CURTIS, b Dallas, Tex, Oct 22, 29; m 53; c 2. PHYSICAL CHEMISTRY. *Educ:* Rice Univ, BA, 50, MA, 53; Univ Tenn, PhD(chem), 61. *Prof Exp:* Tech engr, Gen Elec Co, 56-61; asst prof chem, San Jose State Col, 61-63; res specialist, Lockheed Missiles & Space Co, 63-66; mem tech staff, Aerospace Corp, 66-70; SCIENTIST, SCI APPLNS, INC, 70- *Mem:* Am Chem Soc; Am Nuclear Soc; Am Inst Aeronaut & Astronaut; Am Sci Affil. *Res:* Reactor engineering, in-pile experiment design; testing and evaluation for aircraft nuclear propulsion reactor; nuclear safety evaluation for nuclear rocket project; systems analysis; computer systems modeling and simulation; advanced development engineering. *Mailing Add:* 5275 Soledad Rancho Ct San Diego CA 92109

LEE, RICHARD, hydrology, microclimatology, see previous edition

LEE, RICHARD FAYAO, b Shanghai, China, July 13, 41; US citizen; m 70; c 2. ENVIRONMENTAL CHEMISTRY, BIOLOGICAL OCEANOGRAPHY. *Educ:* San Diego State Col, BA, 64, MA, 66; Univ Calif, San Diego, PhD(marine biol), 70. *Prof Exp:* Res assoc biochem, Pa State Univ, 71-72 & Scripps Inst Oceanog, 72-73; RES PROF OCEANOG, SKIDAWAY INST OCEANOG, 74- *Concurrent Pos:* Lectr oceanog, San Diego State Univ, 71-73; mem adv comt, Marine Resources Res Group Biol Accumulators, UN Food & Agr Orgn, 74-; consult, Exxon Corp, 75. *Mem:* AAAS; Am Chem Soc; Am Soc Limnol & Oceanog; Am Oil Chemists Soc; Sigma Xi. *Res:* Fate of petroleum hydrocarbons in the marine food web; role of lipids in the ecology of marine zooplankton. *Mailing Add:* Skidaway Inst of Oceanog PO Box 13687 Savannah GA 31406

LEE, RICHARD J, b Minot, NDak, July 23, 44; m 60. SOLID STATE PHYSICS. *Educ:* Univ NDak, BSEd, 66; Colo State Univ, PhD(physics), 70. *Prof Exp:* Instr physics, Lake Regional Jr Col, 66; res asst, Colo State Univ, 68-70; asst prof, Purdue Univ, Ft Wayne, 70-74; MEM STAFF, US STEEL CORP, 74- *Mem:* Am Phys Soc; Am Asn Physics Teachers. *Res:* Theory of quantum solids; phase transition; light scattering. *Mailing Add:* US Steel Corp 125 Jamison Lane Monroeville PA 15146

LEE, RICHARD JUI-FU, b China, May 26, 19; nat US; m 40; c 3. ORGANIC CHEMISTRY. *Educ:* Loyola Univ, Ill, BS, 42; Ohio State Univ, PhD(chem), 54. *Prof Exp:* Sr res chemist, Sherwin-Williams Co, 46-49; fel, Ohio State Univ, 54-55; res chemist, Armour & Co, 55-59; mgr polymer sect, Am Marietta Co, 59-61; SR RES CHEMIST, AMOCO CHEM CORP, STANDARD OIL CO, IND, 61- *Mem:* Am Chem Soc; Sigma Xi. *Res:* Free radical chemistry in organic mechanisms and synthesis; transition metal chemistry; catalysis. *Mailing Add:* Amoco Chem Corp 200 E Randolph Dr Chicago IL 60601

LEE, RICHARD K C, b Honolulu, Hawaii, Oct 2, 09; m 52; c 3. PUBLIC HEALTH. *Educ:* Tulane Univ, MD, 33; Yale Univ, DrPH, 38. *Hon Degrees:* DSc, Tulane Univ, 73. *Prof Exp:* Instr anat, Sch Med, Tulane Univ, 33-35; intern, Hotel Dieu Hosp, New Orleans, 35-36; dep comnr health, Territory Hawaii, 36-43, dir pub health, 43-53; pres, Hawaii Bd Health, 53-60; dir health, Hawaii Dept Health, 60-62; dir pub health & med activities, 62-65, dean, Sch Pub Health, 65-69, prof, 62-69, exec dir, Res Corp, 70-80, EMER PROF PUB HEALTH & EMER DEAN, SCH PUB HEALTH, UNIV HAWAII, 69- *Concurrent Pos:* Lectr, Univ Hawaii, 37-55; WHO fel, 52; mem US deleg, Western Pac Regional Comt Meetings, WHO, 52-65, chief US rep, Manila, 66 & Taiwan, 67, mem US deleg, Assembly Meetings, 57-61; Dept State specialist, Int Educ Exchange Prog, Far East, 55; mem, Western Interstate Comn Higher Educ, Western Ment Health Coun, 60-; coordr-consult health & med prog, East-West Ctr Inst Tech Interchange, 62-; mem task force pub health & med educ, World Affairs of New York & Food Found, 65-; consult, WHO, Manila, 67, Alexandria, UAR, 69 & Am Pub Health Asn, Korea, 69; chief div environ health & occup med & med coord dept commun med, Straub Clin, 69-71; consult, Water Qual Mgt Prog, City & County of Honolulu, 69-71 & Southern Calif Coastal Water Res Proj, 69-; actg dir, Cancer Ctr Hawaii, 71-73; mem, Nat Adv Coun, Nat Inst Aging, NIH, 75-77; chmn adv bd, Health Manpower Planning Proj, Hawaii, 75-77; prof dir gerontol develop prog, Hawaii, 78-; res fel, E W Pop Inst, 80- *Honors & Awards:* Pfizer Award of Merit, US Civil Defense Coun, 60; Samuel J Crumbine Award, Kans State Univ Interfraternity Coun, 63. *Mem:* AAAS; AMA; Am Pub Health Asn (vpres, 62-63). *Res:* Public health administration; international health activities in the Pacific and Asian areas of the world. *Mailing Add:* E W Pop Inst 1777 E W Cent Rd Honolulu HI 96822

LEE, RICHARD NORMAN, b Waukegan, Ill, Nov 3, 39; m 64; c 2. ATMOSPHERIC CHEMISTRY. *Educ:* Park Col, BA, 61; Univ Kans, PhD(chem), 68. *Prof Exp:* Asst prof chem, St Norbert Col, 66-72; RES SCIENTIST, ATMOSPHERIC SCI DEPT, BATTELLE PAC NORTHWEST LABS, 72- *Mem:* Am Chem Soc. *Res:* Reaction kinetics; environmental chemistry; chemical analysis; atmospheric pollutants and tracers. *Mailing Add:* Atmospheric Sci Dept Battelle Pac Northwest Labs Richland WA 99352

LEE, RICHARD SHAO-LIN, b Looshan, Taiwan, July 19, 29; US citizen. FLUID MECHANICS. *Educ:* Nat Taiwan Univ, BS, 52; NC State Univ, MS, 55; Harvard Univ, PhD(eng & appl sci), 60. *Prof Exp:* Asst prof mech eng, NC State Univ, 60-62, assoc prof, 62-64; assoc prof, 64-68, Chmn Dept, 69-75, PROF ENG, STATE UNIV NY, STONY BROOK, 68- *Concurrent Pos:* Vis prof, Univ Queensland, Australia, 70-71; guest prof, Univ Karlsruhe, WGer, 77-78; vis res scientist, Nuclear Res Ctr Karlsruhe, WGer, 81-82; Alexander von Humboldt award, 80. *Mem:* Am Soc Mech Engrs; Am Inst Aeronaut & Astronaut; Combustion Inst. *Res:* Fire research; combustion gasdynamics; flow instability; vartex flows; biomedical fluid mechanics; synovial lubrication; artificial heart valves; two-phase suspension flows; laser-Doppler anemometry for dispersed flows; particle migration in laminar and turbulent flows. *Mailing Add:* Dept Mech Eng State Univ NY Stony Brook NY 11794

LEE, ROBERT BUMJUNG, b Seoul, Korea, Jan 24, 37; US citizen; m 65; c 2. TRANSPORTATION ENGINEERING, CIVIL ENGINEERING. *Educ:* Seoul Nat Univ, BSCE, 61; Polytech Inst Brooklyn, MSTP, 69, PhD(transp eng), 73. *Prof Exp:* Hwy engr civil, Madigan-Hyland Eng Co, 64-67; traffic engr, Port of NY Authority, 67-69; res assoc traffic & transp, Polytech Inst Brooklyn, 69-73, asst prof, 73-75; sr traffic engr, Louis Berger Int Inc, 75-80; vpres consult engr, 80-81, PRES, URBITRAN ASSOCS INC, 81- *Mem:* Am Soc Civil Engrs; Sigma Xi. *Res:* Transportation; transit; environmental impacts. *Mailing Add:* Urbitran Assocs Inc 15 Park Row New York NY 10038

LEE, ROBERT E, b Rochester, NY, May 22, 32; m 57; c 4. ELECTRICAL & BIOMEDICAL ENGINEERING. *Educ:* Univ Rochester, BS, 54, MS, 62, PhD(elec eng), 66. *Prof Exp:* Instr thermodyn, Univ Buffalo, 56-57; proj engr, Gen Rwy Signal Co, 57-58; asst prof thermodyn, fluids, calculus & eng, Rochester Inst Technol, 58-62; tech specialist, Bausch & Lomb, Inc, 65-66; asst prof elec eng, Univ WVa, 66-68; ASSOC PROF ELEC ENG, ROCHESTER INST TECHNOL, 68- *Concurrent Pos:* Consult, Eastman Kodak, 81. *Mem:* Am Soc Eng Educ; Inst Elec & Electronics Engrs; Optical Soc Am; Sigma Xi. *Res:* Visual systems, specifically latency to response of human pupil for contraction and dilation; effects of intensity, adaptation and size of change on latency. *Mailing Add:* Dept Elec Eng Rochester Inst Technol Rochester NY 14623

LEE, ROBERT E, JR, b Albany, NY, Sept 21, 36; m 60; c 2. PHYSICAL CHEMISTRY, AIR POLLUTION. *Educ:* Siena Col, BS, 58; George Washington Univ, MEA, 64; Univ Cincinnati, MS, 67, PhD(phys chem), 69. *Prof Exp:* Chemist, US Army Biol Labs, Md, 58-62; scientist, Melpar, Inc, Va, 62-64; RES CHEMIST, US ENVIRON PROTECTION AGENCY, 64- *Mem:* AAAS; Air Pollution Control Asn; Am Chem Soc. *Res:* Aerosol and biological chemistry; diffusion and ion interactions; surface and colloid chemistry; technical administration; fuels and source sample analysis; air pollution chemistry; pesticides and toxic substances. *Mailing Add:* US EPA Nat Environ Res Ctr Research Triangle Park NC 27711

LEE, ROBERT JEROME, b New York, NY, Nov 2, 14; m 41; c 2. VETERINARY MEDICINE. *Educ:* NY Univ, BS, 35; Kans State Univ, DVM, 39. *Prof Exp:* Vet med off, Fed Meat Grading Br, USDA, 49-58, head, Regulatory Sect, Fed Poultry Inspection, 58-61, Poultry Prod Sect, 61-64, training off, 64-68; chief, Meat & Poultry Inspection Sect, Md Dept Agr, 68-80; STAFF VETERINARIAN, FLOW LABS, 80- *Concurrent Pos:* Mem, Expert Comt Food Hyg Comt, Codex Alimentarius, WHO-UN Food & Agr Org, 65-68, alt deleg, Poultry Comt, 66-68; mem, Food Hyg Comt, US Animal Health Asn, 70-80, chmn, 78-80 & mem animal welfare comt, 81- *Mem:* Nat Asn State Meat & Food Inspection Dirs (pres, 70-73); Am Asn Food Hyg Vets (secy, 73-78, exec vpres, 78-); Nat Asn Fed Vets (secy-treas, 60-61); Am Vet Med Asn. *Mailing Add:* 1125 Laurelwood Dr McLean VA 22102

LEE, ROBERT JOHN, b Worcester, Mass, July 2, 29; m 60; c 3. MEDICAL PHYSIOLOGY. *Educ:* Adelphi Univ, AB, 58; Yeshiva Univ, MS, 59; State Univ NY, PhD(physiol), 67. *Prof Exp:* Teacher, NY Schs, 58-59; teaching asst surg, State Univ NY, 59-63; sr scientist, Geigy Res Labs, 66-70; res group leader, Squibb Inst Med Res, 70-77; dir dept pharmacol, 77-78, DIR PHARMACEUT RES, ARNAR-STONE LABS, 78- *Mem:* AAAS; Am Soc Pharmacol & Exp Therapeut; Sigma Xi; Am Col Cardiol; Am Heart Asn. *Res:* Mechanical aspects of cardiovascular physiology; ventricular function. *Mailing Add:* Pharmaceut Res Dept 1600 Waukegan Rd McGaw Park IL 60085

LEE, ROBERT RUE, b Ashton, Idaho, Feb 28, 32; m 60; c 4. ENGINEERING ECONOMICS, WATER PLANNING. *Educ:* Univ Idaho, BS, 54; Stanford Univ, MS, 61, PhD(eng), 65. *Prof Exp:* Engr trainee, Chicago Bridge & Iron Co, 54-55; engr hwy bridge design, Utah Eng Consult, 60; asst prof eng econ, Stanford Univ, 63-67; dir, Idaho Water Resource Bd, 67-72. *Concurrent Pos:* Carnegie Found White House fel, 65-66; vpres, Gem State Irrigation Inc, 72-81. *Res:* Engineering-economic planning of public enterprises, particularly in the water resources field. *Mailing Add:* PO Box 488 Rexburg ID 83440

LEE, ROBERT W, b Cedar Rapids, Iowa, Feb 28, 31; m 51; c 2. EXPERIMENTAL PHYSICS. *Educ:* Mich State Univ, BS, 53, MS, 55. *Prof Exp:* SR RES PHYSICIST, RES LABS, GEN MOTORS CORP, 55- *Res:* Permanent magnets; electro-optics; gas diffusion in solids. *Mailing Add:* Physics Dept Tech Ctr Gen Motors Res Warren MI 48090

LEE, ROBERTO, b Shanghai, China, Jan 10, 37; m 63; c 2. CHEMICAL ENGINEERING. *Educ:* Univ Ill, BS, 58; Purdue Univ, MS, 60, PhD(chem eng), 64. *Prof Exp:* Engr, Corning Glass Works, 60; res engr, E I du Pont de Nemours & Co, 61; sr res chem engr & prin engr specialist, 63-76, engr supt, 77-79, ENGR MGR, MONSANTO CO, 80- *Mem:* Am Inst Chem Engrs; Am Chem Soc. *Res:* Reaction engineering; separation and purification methods; chemical process research and development; chemical process design. *Mailing Add:* Monsanto Co 800 N Lindbergh Blvd St Louis MO 63166

LEE, RONALD NORMAN, b Springfield, Mo, Oct 21, 35; m 59. SURFACE PHYSICS. *Educ:* Univ Ill, BS, 58, MS, 60; Brown Univ, PhD(physics), 65. *Prof Exp:* Res assoc physics, Coord Sci Lab, Univ Ill, 60 & Brown Univ, 64-65; fel phys chem, Battelle Mem Inst, Ohio, 65-68; physicist, US Naval Ord Lab, 68-74, PHYSICIST, SOLID STATE DIV, NAVAL SURFACE WEAPONS CTR, 74- *Mem:* Am Phys Soc; Am Vacuum Soc. *Res:* Surface science; semiconductor thin film phenomena. *Mailing Add:* Solid State Br Naval Surf Weapons Ctr White Oak Silver Spring MD 20910

LEE, RONALD S, b Ames, Iowa, Dec 29, 38; m 60; c 2. SOLID STATE PHYSICS. *Educ:* Luther Col, Iowa, BA, 61; Iowa State Univ, PhD(physics), 67. *Prof Exp:* Asst prof, 67-74, ASSOC PROF PHYSICS, KANS STATE UNIV, 74- *Mem:* Am Phys Soc; Am Asn Univ Prof. *Res:* Shock waves in chemically reacting media; radiation effects in solids. *Mailing Add:* Dept of Physics Kans State Univ Manhattan KS 66502

LEE, RONNIE, b China, Nov 6, 42. TOPOLOGY. *Educ:* Chinese Univ Hong Kong, BS, 65; Univ Mich, PhD(math), 68. *Prof Exp:* Mem, Inst Advan Studies, 68-70; asst prof, 70-73, ASSOC PROF MATH, YALE UNIV, 73-, DIR UNDERGRAD STUDIES, 77- *Concurrent Pos:* Sloan Found fel, 73. *Res:* Differential topology. *Mailing Add:* Dept of Math Yale Univ New Haven CT 06520

LEE, RU-LIN, engineering science & mechanics, see previous edition

LEE, RUPERT ARCHIBALD, b Guyana, Jan 21, 32; m 56; c 8. RADIATION CHEMISTRY. *Educ:* Univ West Indies, BSc, 54; Univ London, MSc, 59, PhD(chem), 67. *Prof Exp:* Asst prof chem, Univ PR, Mayaguez, 65-67; res assoc, PR Nuclear Ctr, 65-67, scientist, 67-70, head radiation chem prog, 70-76; assoc prof chem, Univ PR, Mayaguez, 67-76; SR SCIENTIST, KMS FUSION, INC, 76- *Concurrent Pos:* AEC res grant, PR Nuclear Ctr, 70-76. *Mem:* Am Chem Soc. *Mailing Add:* 3640 Charter Place Ann Arbor MI 48105

LEE, S(ENG) L(IP), civil engineering, see previous edition

LEE, SAMUEL C, b Hong-Chow, China, May 4, 37; US citizen. ELECTRICAL ENGINEERING, COMPUTER SCIENCE. *Educ:* Nat Taiwan Univ, BS, 60; Univ Calif, Berkeley, MS, 63; Univ Ill, Urbana, PhD(elec eng), 65. *Prof Exp:* Mem tech staff elec eng, Bell Labs, Murray Hill, 65-67; assoc prof, NY Univ, 67-70 & Univ Houston, 70-75; PROF ELEC ENG & COMPUTER SCI, UNIV OKLA, 75- *Concurrent Pos:* Consult, Bell Labs, 67-70 & NAm Aircraft Co, Conn, 68-69; vis assoc prof, Baylor Col Med & asst neurophysiologist, Methodist Hosp, Houston, 72-75. *Mem:* Inst Elec & Electronics Engrs; Asn Comput Mach; Am Soc Eng Educ. *Res:* Digital systems; logical design; pattern recognition; artificial intelligence. *Mailing Add:* Sch of Elec Eng & Comput Sci Univ of Okla Norman OK 73019

LEE, SHAW-GUANG LIN, b Miao-Li, Taiwan, Oct 9, 44; US citizen; m 68; c 3. BIOCHEMISTRY. *Educ:* Nat Taiwan Univ, BS, 67; Northwestern Univ, PhD(biochem), 72. *Prof Exp:* Fel biochem, Northwestern Univ, 73-75; RES BIOCHEMIST MOLECULAR VIROL, ABBOTT LABS, 75- *Mem:* Am Chem Soc. *Res:* Cyclic AMP and protein kinase; RNA tumor virus replication; drug metabolism and disposition. *Mailing Add:* Molecular Virol Lab D474 Abbott Labs North Chicago IL 60064

LEE, SHIH-SHUN, b Taiwan, May 25, 36; US citizen; m 69; c 2. MOLECULAR GENETICS, CANCER CHEMOTHERAPY. *Educ:* Nat Taiwan Univ, BS, 59, MS, 64; Mont State Univ, PhD(genetics), 69. *Prof Exp:* Instr agron, Prov Taiwan Agr Col, 64-66; res asst genetics, Mont State Univ, 66-69; res assoc cancer res, 73-74, ASSOC DIR CANCER RES, STEHLIN FOUND CANCER RES, 75- *Concurrent Pos:* Fels, Indiana Univ, 69-70 & M D Anderson Hosp & Tumor Inst, 70-73. *Mem:* Sigma Xi. *Res:* Mechanism of DNA replication; tumor tissue culture; tumor chemotherapy. *Mailing Add:* Stehlin Found 777 St Joseph Prof Bldg Houston TX 77002

LEE, SHUI LUNG, b Canton, China, Sept 15, 38; m 69; c 2. ORGANIC CHEMISTRY. *Educ:* Univ Western Australia, BS, 65, PhD(org chem), 69. *Prof Exp:* Fel org chem, McMaster Univ, 69-71; Queens Univ, Can, 71-74; sr chemist, Aldrich Chem Co, 74-75; sr res chemist, pigments div, Chemetron Corp, 75-78; chemist, 78-80, SR CHEMIST, GANES CHEMICALS, 80- *Mem:* Am Chem Soc. *Res:* Medicinal and fine organic chemicals. *Mailing Add:* 16 Harbor Dr Lake Hopatcong NJ 07849

LEE, SHUISHIH SAGE, b Soo-chow, China, Jan 5, 48; m 73; c 2. EXPERIMENTAL PATHOLOGY, ANATOMIC PATHOLOGY. *Educ:* Nat Taiwan Univ, MD, 72; Univ Rochester, PhD(path), 76. *Prof Exp:* Intern path, Med Ctr, Univ Rochester, 76-78, resident, 78-79; RESIDENT PATH, NORTHWESTERN MEM HOSP, 79-; PATHOLOGIST, PARKVIEW MEM HOSP, 81- *Mem:* Int Acad Pathol; Am Asn Pathologists; Am Soc Clin Pathologists; Can Asn Pathologists. *Res:* Synthesis of ferritin in rat liver and hepatoma cells. *Mailing Add:* Dept Path Parkview Mem Hosp Ft Wayne IN 46805

LEE, SHUNG-YAN LUKE, b China, Sept 10, 38; US citizen; m 62; c 2. ORGANIC CHEMISTRY. *Educ:* Univ Wis, BS, 59; Ohio State Univ, MS, 62, PhD(phys org chem), 66. *Prof Exp:* RES CHEMIST PHOTOG SYST, E I DU PONT DE NEMOURS & CO, INC, 66- *Mem:* Am Chem Soc. *Res:* Investigations of photopolymerization systems. *Mailing Add:* Exp Sta Bldg 352 E I du Pont de Nemours & Co Inc Wilmington DE 19898

LEE, SI DUK, b Ham Hung, Korea, Jan 2, 32; US citizen; m 57; c 3. ENVIRONMENTAL SCIENCES, BIOLOGICAL CHEMISTRY. *Educ:* Seoul Nat Univ, BS, 55; Univ Md, MS, 59, PhD(biochem), 62. *Prof Exp:* Res assoc biochem, Med Ctr, Duke Univ, 61-62, NIH fel, 62-63, Am Heart Asn adv res fel, 63-64; res chemist, USPHS, 64-65, supvry res chemist, 65-67, chief biochem unit, 67-69, chief biochem sect, Nat Air Pollution Control Admin, 69-71; DEP BR CHIEF, BIOL EFFECTS BR, NAT ENVIRON RES CTR, ENVIRON PROTECTION AGENCY, 71- *Concurrent Pos:* Adj res prof, Dept Biol, Col Med, Univ Cincinnati, 67- & Dept Environ Health, 75- *Mem:* AAAS; Am Chem Soc; Am Oil Chemists Soc; Am Col Toxicol; Air Pollution Control Asn. *Res:* Effects of air pollutants on metabolism; lipid metabolism; effects of pollutants on aging; effects of sulfur dioxide on subcellular metabolism. *Mailing Add:* ECAO MD-52 Environ Protection Agency Research Triangle Park NC 27711

LEE, SIDNEY, b Philadelphia, Pa, Apr 20, 21; div; c 2. CHEMICAL ENGINEERING, PHYSICAL CHEMISTRY. *Educ:* Univ Pa, BS, 39; Cornell Univ, MChE, 40. *Prof Exp:* Chem engr, Atlantic Refining Co, Pa, 38-42, sr chem engr, Tex, 42-45; dir, 45-70, PRES, DALLAS LABS & ASSOC LABS, INC, 70- *Concurrent Pos:* Dir, Am Shipbldg Co; pres, W I Investment Co & St Croix Real Estate Develop Corp; chmn, Sidney Lee Assocs; mem exec comt, W I Bank & Trust Co. *Mem:* Am Chem Soc; Am Pub Health Asn; fel Am Inst Chemists; Am Inst Chem Engrs; Am Inst Mining, Metall & Petrol Engrs. *Res:* Design and cost economics; process and product evaluation. *Mailing Add:* Dallas Labs PO Box 15705 1323 Wall St Dallas TX 75215

LEE, SIU-LAM, b Macao, China, Oct 3, 41; m 68. INSECT ECOLOGY, EVOLUTION. *Educ:* Chung Chi Col, Chinese Univ, Hong Kong, BSc, 62; Oberlin Col, AM, 63; Cornell Univ, PhD(entom), 67. *Prof Exp:* ASST PROF BIOL, UNIV LOWELL, NORTH CAMPUS, 67- *Concurrent Pos:* NSF res award, 69-72. *Mem:* Am Entom Soc; Animal Behav Soc; Bee Res Asn. *Res:* Learning ability of fruit fly; behavioral ecology of the leaf-cutter bee. *Mailing Add:* Dept Biol Univ Lowell North Campus Lowell MA 01854

LEE, SOOK, b Pukchong, Korea, July 13, 29; m 60; c 2. SOLID STATE PHYSICS. *Educ:* Korea Univ, BSc, 57; Brown Univ, PhD(physics), 63. *Prof Exp:* Res assoc physics, Brown Univ, 63-64; from asst prof to assoc prof, 64-70, PROF PHYSICS, ST LOUIS UNIV, 70- *Concurrent Pos:* Consult, McDonnell Douglas Res Labs, McDonnell Douglas Corp, 66-; NATO sr fel, Clarendon Lab, Oxford Univ, 76. *Mem:* Am Phys Soc. *Res:* Electron spin and nuclear magnetic resonances and dynamic nuclear polarization in various types of solids. *Mailing Add:* Dept of Physics St Louis Univ St Louis MO 63103

LEE, STANLEY L, b Newburgh, NY, Aug 27, 19; m 47; c 3. INTERNAL MEDICINE, HEMATOLOGY. *Educ:* Columbia Univ, AB, 39; Harvard Univ, MD, 43. *Prof Exp:* Intern, Mt Sinai Hosp, New York, 43-44, resident med, 46-48, Georg Escherich fel path, 48-49, asst, 49-53, asst attend hematologist, 53-59; assoc prof, 59-68, dean fac, 78-79, actg pres, 79-81, PROF MED, STATE UNIV NY DOWNSTATE MED CTR, 68-, DEAN COL MED & VPRES ACAD AFFAIRS, 81- *Concurrent Pos:* Dir hemat, Maimonides Med Ctr, Brooklyn, 59-71; treas, Int Cong Hemat, NY, 65-68; dir med, Jewish Hosp & Med Ctr, Brooklyn, 71-77. *Mem:* Am Soc Hemat; Am Rheumatism Asn; Soc Human Genetics; Am Fedn Clin Res; fel Am Col Physicians. *Res:* Systematic lupus erythematosus; leukemia. *Mailing Add:* Downstate Med Ctr Box 12A Brooklyn NY 11203

LEE, STUART M(ILTON), b New York, NY, Apr 14, 20; m 48; c 3. MATERIALS SCIENCE, PHYSICAL ORGANIC CHEMISTRY. *Educ:* Long Island Univ, BS, 41; Univ Nev, MS, 47; Fla State Univ, PhD(chem), 53. *Prof Exp:* Chemist anal & testing, NY Testing Labs, 41-42; chemist anal develop, Gen Dyestuffs Corp, 42-43; chief chemist org synthesis, Trinity Res Found, 49-50; sr res chemist & proj leader org res, Allied Chem Corp, 52-59; res chemist, Aerojet-Gen Corp, 59-61; mgr chem res & develop, Electro-Optical Systs, Inc, Xerox Corp, 61-64; sr tech specialist, Autonetics Div, NAm Rockwell, Calif, 64-71; SR STAFF SCIENTIST, FORD AEROSPACE & COMMUN CORP, 71- *Concurrent Pos:* Ed, Soc Advan Mat & Process Engrs J, 79- *Mem:* Am Chem Soc; Soc Advan Mat & Process Engrs. *Res:* Electronic materials; instrumental failure analysis; thin films; space materials research; electronic and laser organics; high temperature and organic polymers; bioelectrochemistry; chelates; acetylenic and petrochemical derivatives. *Mailing Add:* G-97 Ford Aerospace & Commun Corp 3939 Fabian Way Palo Alto CA 94303

LEE, SUE YING, b Schenectady, NY, Jan 11, 40. VERTEBRATE MORPHOLOGY. *Educ:* State Univ NY Albany, BS, 61, MS, 63; Univ Ill, Urbana, PhD(zool), 68. *Prof Exp:* Instr vert morphol & human anat, Univ Ill, Chicago, 67-69; asst prof, 69-72, assoc prof, 73-77, PROF VERT MORPHOL & HUMAN ANAT, HUMBOLDT STATE UNIV, 78- *Mem:* AAAS; Am Soc Zool; Am Inst Biol Sci; Western Soc Naturalists; Soc Vert Paleont. *Res:* Reproductive biology; ultrastructure of fetal membranes. *Mailing Add:* Dept of Biol Sci Humboldt State Univ Arcata CA 95521

LEE, SUK YOUNG, b Seoul, Korea, June 18, 40; US citizen; m 66; c 2. SOIL SCIENCE, ENVIRONMENTAL CHEMISTRY. *Educ:* Univ Sask, MS, 68; Univ Wis, PhD(soil sci), 73. *Prof Exp:* Fel, Univ Wis, 74-75, Univ S Fla, 75-76 & Tex A&M Univ, 76-77; RES SCIENTIST ENVIRON SCI, OAK RIDGE NAT LAB, 77- *Mem:* Am Soc Agron; Soil Sci Soc Am; Clay Minerals Soc. *Res:* Transport of trace elements and radio nuclides, such as plutonium and uranium, in environment. *Mailing Add:* Environ Sci Div Oak Ridge Nat Lab Oak Ridge TN 37830

LEE, SUN, b Seoul, Korea, June 2, 20; US citizen; m 45; c 6. SURGERY. *Educ:* Seoul Nat Univ, MD, 45. *Prof Exp:* From instr to asst prof, Univ Pittsburgh, 57-64; assoc prof surg, 68-74, PROF EXP SURG, UNIV CALIF, SAN DIEGO, 74-; ASSOC, SCRIPPS CLIN & RES FOUND, 64- *Concurrent Pos:* Surg fel, Univ Pittsburgh, 55-57. *Honors & Awards:* Gold Medal, Pioneer Exp Microsurgery, Ger; Gold Medal, Lombardo Surgical, Italy. *Mem:* Int Microsurgical Soc; Int Proctol Soc. *Res:* Development of organ transplant in the rat to study transplantation immunology and associated physiology; techniques of heart-lung, liver, spleen, pancreas, testicle, kidney and stomach transplantation and allied microsurgical techniques in rats. *Mailing Add:* Dept Surg Univ Calif San Diego La Jolla CA 92093

LEE, SUNG KI, b Seoul, Korea, Feb 17, 33; US citizen; m 60; c 4. ORGANIC CHEMISTRY, POLYMER CHEMISTRY. *Educ:* Baylor Univ, BS, 58, MS, 60; Carnegie Inst Technol, PhD(org chem), 64. *Prof Exp:* Jr fel polymer chem, Mellon Inst, 61-63; proj chemist, Carnegie Inst Technol, 63-64; res chemist, Cent Res, Hooker Chem Corp, 64-65, sr res chemist, 65-66, res supvr, 66-68, res sect mgr, 68-71; dir res & develop, 3 B Develop Inc, 71-72; vpres, Andco Res & Develop, 72-74; pres, Frontier Chem Corp, 74-77; DIR TECH DEVELOP, SCA CHEMICAL SERV, 77-, VPRES & DIR RES, 80- *Mem:* Am Chem Soc; Am Mgt Asn; Electrochem Soc; Asn Consult Chemists & Chem Engrs; AAAS. *Res:* Nitrogen heterocyclics; Fischer indole synthesis; reactions of polymer electroplating; electrosynthesis; electro-organic synthesis; environmental control and pollution control systems; energy and resource recovery systems; detoxification of hazardous materials. *Mailing Add:* 39 Fox Hunt Lane East Amherst NY 14051

LEE, SUNG MOOK, b Seoul, Korea, Mar 2, 33; m 58; c 3. THEORETICAL MECHANICS, SOLID STATE PHYSICS. *Educ:* Chosun Christian Univ, BSc, 55; Ohio State Univ, MSc, 59, PhD(crystal dynamics), 65. *Prof Exp:* Teacher, Hansung Boy's High Sch, Korea, 54-55; asst prof physics, Denison Univ, 61-65; from asst prof to assoc prof, 65-72, PROF PHYSICS, MICH TECHNOL UNIV, 72-, DIR, KEWEENAW RES CTR, 76- *Concurrent Pos:* NATO sr fel sci, 74; vis sr res fel, Inst Sound & Vibration Res, Univ Southampton, Eng, 80 & 81. *Mem:* Am Phys Soc; Am Asn Physics Teachers. *Res:* Vibrational analysis of periodic systems, crystal lattices, and molecules; wave propagation in solids; mechanical properties of solids; mechanics; acoustics; optics. *Mailing Add:* Dept of Physics Mich Technol Univ Houghton MI 49931

LEE, T(IEN) P(EI), b Nanking, China, Sept 8, 33; m 63; c 2. ELECTRICAL ENGINEERING. *Educ:* Taiwan Norm Univ, BS, 57; Ohio State Univ, MS, 59; Stanford Univ, PhD(elec eng), 63. *Prof Exp:* MEM TECH STAFF, BELL TEL LABS, 63- *Mem:* Inst Elec & Electronics Engrs; Sigma Xi. *Res:* Microwave electronics; microwave solid state devices; varactor diodes; parametric amplifiers; semiconductor lasers and related optical communication. *Mailing Add:* 5 Marion Dr Holmdel NJ 07733

LEE, T(HOMAS) S(HAO-CHUNG), b Soochow, China, Nov 18, 31; m 60; c 2. ELECTRICAL ENGINEERING. *Educ:* Nat Taiwan Univ, BS, 54; Univ Minn, Minneapolis, MS, 56, PhD(elec eng), 61. *Prof Exp:* From instr to asst prof, 57-66, ASSOC PROF ELEC ENG, UNIV MINN, MINNEAPOLIS, 66- *Concurrent Pos:* Consult, mil prod group, Honeywell Regulator Co, 61-62, aero div, 63-64 & US Naval Res Lab, 65- *Mem:* Am Phys Soc; Am Geophys Union. *Res:* Acoustics; explosive phenomena; gas-dynamics; systems; electromagnetism; interplanetary phenomena. *Mailing Add:* Dept of Elec Eng Univ of Minn Minneapolis MN 55455

LEE, TALMAGE HOYLE, b Belwood, NC, July 22, 12; m 39; c 1. MATHEMATICS. *Educ:* Wake Forest Col, BA, 33; Univ NC, MA, 36, PhD(math), 53. *Prof Exp:* Teacher, High Sch, NC, 33-35; asst math, Univ NC, 36; instr, Brown Univ, 36-37; asst, Univ Wis, 37-40; assoc prof, Univ SC, 40-41; asst, Univ Wis, 41-44, instr, 44-45; instr, La State Univ, 45-46; asst prof, 46-53, from assoc prof to prof, 53-78, distinguished prof, 78-80, EMER DISTINGUISHED PROF MATH, UNIV SC, 80- *Concurrent Pos:* Dir math, US Armed Forces Inst, Univ Wis, 44-45. *Mem:* Am Math Soc; Math Asn Am; Sigma Xi. *Res:* Matrix theory. *Mailing Add:* 739 Kipling Dr Columbia SC 29205

LEE, TEH HSUN, b Shaoshin, China, Mar 25, 17; m 45; c 1. BIOCHEMISTRY. *Educ:* Chekiang Univ, BS, 38; Univ Mich, PhD, 54. *Prof Exp:* Res assoc, Sch Med, Univ Ore, 54-55; res assoc, Sch Med, Yale Univ, 55-60, asst prof exp med, 60-62; sr biochemist, Merck, Sharp & Dohme, 62-64; asst dir, Vet Admin Human Protein Hormone Bank, 64-66, CHIEF PROTEIN HORMONE RES LAB, VET ADMIN HOSP, 66-; VIS ASSOC PROF BIOCHEM, ALBERT EINSTEIN COL MED, 67- *Concurrent Pos:* Assoc prof, Sch Med, Univ Colo, Denver, 64-66. *Mem:* Am Chem Soc; Am Soc Biol Chem; Endocrine Soc. *Res:* Pituitary hormones. *Mailing Add:* Vet Admin Hosp Bldg 7 130 W Kingsbridge Rd Bronx NY 10468

LEE, TEH-HSUANG, b Shanghai, China, Aug 15, 36; m 61; c 2. SOLID STATE PHYSICS. *Educ:* Nat Taiwan Univ, BS, 58; Purdue Univ, West Lafayette, PhD(physics), 67. *Prof Exp:* SR PHYSICIST, RES LABS, EASTMAN KODAK CO, 67- *Mem:* Am Phys Soc. *Res:* Optical properties of solids; semiconductors; magnetic semiconductors. *Mailing Add:* Eastman Kodak Co Res Labs Bldg 81 1669 Lake Ave Rochester NY 14650

LEE, THOMAS HENRY, b China, May 11, 23; nat US; m 48; c 3. PHYSICS. *Educ:* Nat Chiao-Tung Univ, China, BS; Union Col, MS, 50; Rensselaer Polytech Inst, PhD(elec eng, physics), 54. *Prof Exp:* Eng analyst, Gen Elec Co, Pa, 54-55, sr res physicist, 55-59, mgr eng res, 59-67, mgr lab opers, 67-71, mgr group tech resources oper, 71-74, mgr strategic planning opers, 74-78, staff exec power systs technol oper, 78-80; PROF & ASSOC DIR, ENERGY LAB, MASS INST TECHNOL, 80- *Concurrent Pos:* Adj prof, Rensselaer Polytech Inst, 54-55; lectr, Univ Pa. *Mem:* Nat Acad Eng; Am Phys Soc; Inst Elec & Electronics Engrs; Power Eng Soc (pres). *Res:* Electron physics; gaseous discharges; magnetohydrodynamics; ultra high vacuum technology; electrical systems; plasma physics. *Mailing Add:* Beacon Hill 44 Chestnut St Boston MA 02108

LEE, THOMAS N, physical oceanography, see previous edition

LEE, THOMAS W, b New Britain, Conn, Sept 12, 37; div; c 2. COMPARATIVE PHYSIOLOGY. *Educ:* Bates Col, BS, 59; Duke Univ, MA, 61; Rice Univ, PhD(biol), 64. *Prof Exp:* Lectr biol, Rice Univ, 64-65; from asst prof to assoc prof, 65-72, asst to chmn, 74-79, actg chmn dept, 69-74, PROF BIOL, CENT CONN STATE COL, 72- *Concurrent Pos:* Vis prof biol, Wesleyan Univ, 74- *Mem:* AAAS; Am Soc Zool; Sigma Xi; Ecol Soc Am. *Res:* Embryonic development of amphibians; nitrogen metabolism in invertebrate animals. *Mailing Add:* Dept of Biol Cent Conn State Col New Britain CT 06050

LEE, TIEN-CHANG, b Nantou, Taiwan, July 1, 43; m 69; c 2. GEOPHYSICS. *Educ:* Nat Taiwan Univ, BS, 65; Univ Southern Calif, PhD(geophys), 74. *Prof Exp:* Fel marine geophys, Woods Hole Oceanog Inst, 73-74; asst prof, 74-79, ASSOC PROF GEOPHYS, UNIV CALIF, RIVERSIDE, 79- *Mem:* Am Geophys Union; Soc Explor Geophysicists; Geol Soc Am. *Res:* Terrestrial heat flow, electrical exploration and micro-earthquake. *Mailing Add:* Dept of Earth Sci Univ of Calif Riverside CA 92521

LEE, TONG-NYONG, b July 22, 27; US citizen; m 59; c 3. PLASMA PHYSICS, ATOMIC PHYSICS. *Educ:* Seoul Nat Univ, BS, 50; Univ London, PhD(physics), 59. *Prof Exp:* Asst prof physics, Seoul Nat Univ, 60-63; assoc prof appl physics, Cath Univ Am, 64-70; RES PHYSICIST PLASMA PHYSICS & OPTICAL SCI, NAVAL RES LAB, 70- *Mem:* Am Phys Soc. *Res:* Short wavelength laser generation; plasma physics and spectroscopy of high temperature; high density plasma and solar flare study. *Mailing Add:* Naval Res Lab Washington DC 20375

LEE, TONY JER-FU, b Hualien, Taiwan, Nov 10, 42; US citizen. PHARMACOLOGY. *Educ:* Taipei Med Col, Taiwan, BS, 67; WVa Univ, PhD(pharmacol), 73. *Prof Exp:* Asst prof, 75-80, ASSOC PROF PHARMACOL, SCH MED, SOUTHERN ILL UNIV, SPRINGFIELD, 80- *Concurrent Pos:* Fel, Univ Calif, Los Angeles, 73-75. *Res:* Innervation of cerebral blood vessels; supersensitivity in denervated smooth muscle. *Mailing Add:* Dept of Pharmacol PO Box 3926 Springfield IL 62708

LEE, TSUNG DAO, b China, Nov 25, 26; m 50; c 2. THEORETICAL PHYSICS. *Educ:* Univ Chicago, PhD(physics), 50. *Hon Degrees:* DSc, Princeton Univ, 58. *Prof Exp:* Res assoc astrophys, Univ Chicago, 50; res assoc physics, Univ Calif, 50-51; mem, Inst Advan Study, 51-53; from asst prof to prof, Columbia Univ, 53-60; prof, Inst Advan Study, 60-63; ENRICO FERMI PROF PHYSICS, COLUMBIA UNIV, 63- *Honors & Awards:* Nobel Prize in Physics, 57; Einstein Award Sci, 57. *Mem:* Nat Acad Sci. *Res:* Field theory; statistical mechanics; hydrodynamics; astrophysics. *Mailing Add:* Dept of Physics Columbia Univ New York NY 10027

LEE, TSUNG TING, b Anhwei, China, Mar 21, 23; m 50; c 3. PLANT PHYSIOLOGY. *Educ:* Nat Cent Univ, China, BS, 47; Univ Wis, MS, 59, PhD(plant physiol), 62. *Prof Exp:* Res asst plant physiol, Taiwan Sugar Res Inst, 47-52, asst plant physiologist, 52-57; plant physiologist, Res Sta, Ont, 62-68, PLANT PHYSIOLOGIST, LONDON RES CTR, CAN DEPT AGR, 68- *Concurrent Pos:* Hon lectr, Univ Western Ont, 76- *Mem:* Am Soc Plant Physiol; Plant Growth Regulator Soc Am; Sigma Xi; Int Asn Plant Tissue Culture; Can Soc Plant Physiol. *Res:* Plant growth regulators; auxin metabolism; tissue and cell culture; pesticide-plant interaction. *Mailing Add:* London Res Ctr Can Dept Agr Univ Western Ont London ON N6A 5B7 Can

LEE, TSUNG-SHUNG HARRY, b Taipei, Taiwan, June 7, 43; m 68; c 1. NUCLEAR PHYSICS. *Educ:* Taiwan Norm Univ, BS, 65; Nat Tsing-Hua Univ, MS, 67; Univ Pittsburgh, PhD(physics), 73. *Prof Exp:* Res assoc physics, Bartol Res Found, 73-75; res assoc physics, 75-77, asst physicist, 77-81, PHYSICIST, ARGONNE NAT LAB, 81- *Mem:* Am Phys Soc. *Res:* Intermediate-energy nuclear physics and low-energy nucleon-nucleon interaction. *Mailing Add:* Physics Div Argonne Nat Lab Argonne IL 60439

LEE, TYRONE YIU-HUEN, b China, Sept 6, 44; Can citizen; m 76. NEUROPHARMACOLOGY, PSYCHOPHARMACOLOGY. *Educ:* Univ Calif, Los Angeles, BSc, 68; Univ Toronto, MSc, 72, PhD(pharmacol), 75. *Prof Exp:* Res fel pharmacol, Ont Ment Health Found, 75-78; res assoc, 77-78, lectr pharmacol, 78-79, ASST PROF PHARMACOL & PSYCHIAT, UNIV TORONTO, 79-, GRAD FAC, SCH GRAD STUDIES, 80-; RES SCIENTIST & ASST DIR, PSYCHOPHARMACOL SECT, CLARK INST PSYCHIAT, 80- *Honors & Awards:* Paul Christie Mem Award, Ont Ment Health Found, 78. *Mem:* Soc Neurosci. *Res:* Study of the mechanism of action of anti-psychotic drugs in the central nervous system; radio-receptor binding analysis of post-mortem human brains in the study of schizophrenia, Parkinson's disease and Huntington's chorea; effect of chronic neuroleptic treatment in animals and tardive dyskinesia; interaction of neuronal systems in affective disorders; animal models of schizophrenia. *Mailing Add:* Dept Pharmacol Fac Med Med Sci Bldg Univ Toronto Toronto ON M5S 1A1 Can

LEE, TZOONG-CHYH, b Taiwan, Jan 2, 36; m 62; c 3. ORGANIC CHEMISTRY, BIO-ORGANIC CHEMISTRY. *Educ:* Yamagata Univ, Japan, BSc, 63; Tohoku Univ, Japan, MSc, 65; Australian Nat Univ, PhD(med chem), 68. *Prof Exp:* USPHS fel, 68-71, Damon Runyon res fel, 69-70, res assoc, 71-75, ASSOC ORG CHEM, SLOAN-KETTERING INST CANCER RES, 75- *Mem:* Am Chem Soc. *Res:* Nitrogen heterocyclic chemistry; organic synthesis; structure-activity relationship; imaging chemicals. *Mailing Add:* 272 Buffalo Ave Lea Ronal Inc Freeport NY 11520

LEE, TZUO-YAN, b China, Jan 13, 42; US citizen; m 70; c 2. STATISTICS, HEALTH SCIENCES. *Educ:* Univ Pittsburgh, ScD, 73; Univ Pa, assoc MBA, 76. *Prof Exp:* Biometrician, Merck Sharp & Dohme, 73-75; asst dir, Am Hoechst Coop, 75-78; DIR BIOSTATIST, AYERST LABS, AM HOME PROD, 78- *Mem:* Am Statist Asn; Biomet Soc. *Res:* Pharmaceutical research; experimental design. *Mailing Add:* Ayerst Labs 685 Third Ave New York NY 10017

LEE, VERNON HAROLD, b Flandreau, SDak, Oct 27, 31; m 62. MEDICAL ENTOMOLOGY. *Educ:* SDak State Col, BS, 53, MS, 57; Univ Wis, PhD(med entom), 62. *Prof Exp:* Res fel med entom, Univ Wis, 61-62; med entomologist, Rockefeller Found, 62; hon vis asst prof, Univ del Valle, Colombia, 62-66; hon vis asst prof, Univ Ibadan, 67-73; with US Naval Med Res Unit, Addis Ababa, Ethiopia, 73-77, WITH US NAVAL MED RES UNIT, JAKARTA, INDONESIA, 77- *Mem:* Entom Soc Am; Mosquito Control Asn; Am Soc Trop Med & Hyg; AAAS; Sigma Xi. *Res:* Biological and ecological study of haematophagous diptera, in relationship to their role as vectors of Arboviruses; filaria and malaria. *Mailing Add:* US Naval Med Res Unit 2 Jakarta Det APO San Francisco CA 96356 Indonesia

LEE, VING JICK, b Columbus, Ohio, July 28, 51; m 74; c 1. CHEMISTRY, NATURAL PRODUCTS CHEMISTRY. *Educ:* Ohio State Univ, BA, 71; Univ Ill, Urbana, MS, 73, PhD(chem), 75. *Prof Exp:* Res assoc chem, Univ Ill, Urbana, 71-75; teaching assoc, 71-73; NIH res assoc, Harvard Univ, 75-77; RES CHEMIST, LEDERLE LABS, AM CYANAMID CO, 77- *Mem:* Am Chem Soc. *Mailing Add:* Infectious Dis Res Sect Lederle Labs Bldg 65-239 Pearl River NY 10965

LEE, VIN-JANG, b Honan, China, Feb 14, 31; m 62. HETEROGENEOUS CATALYSIS, QUANTUM THEORY. *Educ:* Ord Eng Col, Taiwan, Dipl eng, 52; Notre Dame Univ, MS, 58; Univ Mich, PhD(chem eng), 63. *Prof Exp:* Chem engr, 26th Arsenal, Repub China, 52-57; res specialist, Monsanto Chem Co, 64-65; ees specialist, Univ Mo-Columbia, 65-68, assoc prof chem eng, 68-74; vis prof, Dept Chem, Univ Calif, Los Angeles, 72-73; consult catalysis, Libby Corp, 74-77; pres, Lee Securities & Investment Co, 75-80 & Econo Trading Corp, 80-81; PRES, CYBERDYNE INVESTMENT, INC, 81- *Mem:* Am Phys Soc; Am Chem Soc; Am Inst Chem Eng. *Res:* Surface physics; catalysis and kinetics; tunneling in catalysis; physical foundations of quantum theory. *Mailing Add:* Cyberdyne Investment Inc 1045 Ocean Ave suite 2 Santa Monica CA 90403

LEE, VIRGINIA ANN, b Grand Rapids, Mich, Oct 30, 22. BIOCHEMISTRY. *Educ:* Univ Ill, BS, 44; Univ Colo, MS, 46, PhD(biochem), 52. *Prof Exp:* Instr biochem, Sch Med, Univ Colo, Denver, 55-59, asst prof, 59-67; asst prof, 67-78, ASSOC PROF FOOD SCI & NUTRIT, COLO STATE UNIV, 78- *Mem:* Am Dietetics Asn; Soc Nutrit Educ; Sigma Xi. *Res:* Nutrition. *Mailing Add:* Dept of Food Sci & Nutrit Colo State Univ Ft Collins CO 80523

LEE, WAI-HON, b Haiphong, Vietnam, Apr 29, 42; US citizen; m 68; c 2. OPTICAL PHYSICS, COMMUNICATIONS SCIENCE. *Educ:* Mass Inst Technol, BSc, 65, MSc, 67, DSc, 69. *Prof Exp:* Assoc prin eng coherent optics, Electronic Syst Div, Harris Corp, 69-73; staff mem res optical sci, Palo Alto Res Ctr, Xerox Corp, 73-81; MGR LASER IMAGING SYSTS, XIDEX CORP, 81- *Mem:* Inst Elec & Electronics Engrs; Optical Soc Am; Soc Photo-Optical Instrumentation Engrs; Soc Photog Scientist & Engrs. *Res:* Applications of grating structures for testing optical surfaces and scanning laser beam; optical methods for storing digital information at high density. *Mailing Add:* 305 Soquel Way Xidex Sunnyvale CA 94086

LEE, WARREN FORD, b Harriston, Ont, Aug 25, 41; m 66; c 3. AGRICULTURAL ECONOMICS. *Educ:* Univ Toronto, BSA, 63; Univ Ill, MS, 67; Mich State Univ, PhD(agr econ), 70. *Prof Exp:* Credit adv, Farm Credit Corp, 63-65; assoc prof agr finance, 70-80, PROF AGR ECON & RURAL SOCIOL, OHIO STATE UNIV, 80- *Concurrent Pos:* Economist, Econ Br, Agr Can, 75-76. *Mem:* Am Agr Econ Asn. *Res:* Agricultural credit and finance; farm firm growth; rural capital markets; bank structure and performance; financial institutions. *Mailing Add:* Dept of Agr Econ Ohio State Univ 2120 Fyffe Rd Columbus OH 43210

LEE, WARREN G, b Abington, Pa, June 10, 24; m 51; c 3. PHYSICAL ORGANIC CHEMISTRY. *Educ:* Roosevelt Univ, BS, 50; Ill Inst Technol, PhD(chem), 61. *Prof Exp:* Sr res scientist, Res & Develop Lab, Gen Am Transportation Co, 51-63; mgr chem res & instrumentation, Liquid Carbonic Div, Gen Dynamic Corp, 63-67; asst to dir res & com develop, 67-68 & planning & facilities eng, 68-70, adminr corp pollution control & tech adv, 70-73, MKT & TECH SPECIALIST, LIQUID CARBONIC CORP, 73-, NAT ACCTS COORDR, 77- *Mem:* AAAS; Am Chem Soc; Am Inst Chemists. *Res:* Radiochemistry; electroless methods of metal plating; corrosion protection; catalytic processes; chemical kinetics and isotope studies; organic synthesis; marketing sales of semiconductor materials; environmental medicine, health and safety; specialty gases and chemical products. *Mailing Add:* Indust & Med Div Liquid Carb Corp 135 S LaSalle St Chicago IL 60603

LEE, WEI HWA, b Shanghai, China, July 7, 32; US citizen; m 59; c 2. MICROBIOLOGY, FOOD TECHNOLOGY. *Educ:* Cornell Univ, BS, 54; Univ Ill, MS & PhD(food technol), 61. *Prof Exp:* RES MICROBIOLOGIST, FOOD SAFETY & QUAL SERV, USDA, 71- *Mem:* Am Soc Microbiol. *Res:* Basic and applied research in microbiology. *Mailing Add:* 4 Surrey Ct Rockville MD 20850

LEE, WEI-LI S, b Kiangsi, China, Feb 14, 45; m 70. BIOCHEMISTRY. *Educ:* Tunghai Univ, BS, 66; State Univ NY Buffalo, MA, 69, PhD(biol), 72. *Prof Exp:* Asst biol sci, State Univ NY Buffalo, 66-72; res assoc immunochem, Col Physicians & Surgeons, Columbia Univ, 72-75; INSTR DERMAT BIOCHEM, STATE UNIV NY DOWNSTATE MED CTR, BROOKLYN, 75- *Mem:* Sigma Xi; NY Acad Sci; Soc Investigative Dermat; Am Fedn Clin Res. *Res:* Identification of specific extracellular and cell surface factors (enzymes) derived from major skin microflora, propionibacterium acnes and studies of their role in leukocytes chemotaxis and chemiluminescence in order to elucidate the mechanisms of inflammation in acne. *Mailing Add:* Dept of Med Dermat Div PO Box 46 State Univ of NY Brooklyn NY 11203

LEE, WEI-MING, b Kiangsu, China, June 11, 36; m 62. PHYSICAL CHEMISTRY, POLYMER CHEMISTRY. *Educ:* Nat Taiwan Univ, BS, 57; Southern Ill Univ, MA, 61; Univ Ill, PhD(phys chem), 64. *Prof Exp:* Teacher chem & math, Univ High Sch, Taiwan Norm Univ, 59; res assoc theoret chem kinetics, Univ Calif, Santa Barbara, 64-65; sr res engr styrene molding polymers res & develop, Dow Chem USA, 65-74, staff mem olefin plastics res & develop, 74-76, SR RES SPECIALIST, PLASTICS DEPT, DOW CHEM CO, 76-, STAFF MEM PLASTICS RES & DEVELOP, 78- *Mem:* Am Chem Soc; Soc Rheol. *Res:* Mechanical properties of polymeric materials and plastic foams; computer simulation of chemical and physical processes. *Mailing Add:* Plastics Res & Develop Dow Chem Co Bldg 433A Midland MI 48640

LEE, WELTON LINCOLN, marine ecology, physiological ecology, see previous edition

LEE, WILLIAM CHIEN-YEH, b London, Eng, July 20, 32; m 64; c 2. ELECTRICAL ENGINEERING. *Educ:* Chinese Naval Acad, Taiwan, BSc, 54; Ohio State Univ, MS, 60, PhD(elec eng), 63. *Prof Exp:* Mem tech staff commun, Bell Labs, 64-79; SR SCIENTIST & MGR, DEFENSE COMMUN DIV, ITT, 79- *Concurrent Pos:* Assoc ed, Int Elec & Electronics Engrs Transactions on Vehicular Technol, 79- *Mem:* Brit Inst Elec Engrs; fel Inst Elec & Electronics Engrs; Sigma Xi. *Res:* Wave propagation in anisotropic medium; antennas; signal fading; communication systems, particularly those relating to the ultrahigh frequency and X-band regions. *Mailing Add:* ITT Defense Commun Div 492 River Rd Nutley NJ 07110

LEE, WILLIAM GLEN, food science, see previous edition

LEE, WILLIAM HUNG KAN, b Kwangsi, China, Oct 6, 40; m 66; c 2. GEOPHYSICS. *Educ:* Univ Alta, BSc, 62; Univ Calif, Los Angeles, PhD(planetary & space physics), 67. *Prof Exp:* Asst res geophysicist, Univ Calif, Los Angeles, 67; RES GEOPHYSICIST, US GEOL SURV, 67- *Concurrent Pos:* Secy, Heat-Flow Comt, Int Union Geod & Geophys, 63-65; ed, Geophys Monogr 8, Am Geophys Union, 65; guest lectr, Stanford Univ, 69; translation bd mem, Am Geophys Union, 75-78; co-ed, Chinese Geophys J, 78. *Mem:* AAAS; Am Geophys Union; Seismol Soc Am; Soc Explor Geophys. *Res:* Terrestrial heat-flow; thermal evolution of the planets; computer modeling of geologic processes; earthquake seismology. *Mailing Add:* Off Earthquake Studies US Geol Surv Menlo Park CA 94025

LEE, WILLIAM JOHN, b Lubbock, Tex, Jan 16, 36; m 61; c 2. PETROLEUM ENGINEERING. *Educ:* Ga Inst Technol, PhD(chem eng), 63. *Prof Exp:* Sr res specialist, Esso Prod Res Co, 62-68; assoc prof petrol eng, Miss State Univ, 68-71; tech adv, Exxon Co, USA, 71-77; PROF PETROL ENG, TEX A&M UNIV, 77- *Concurrent Pos:* Sr consult, S A Holdutch & Assocs, 80-; lectr, Am Inst Mining, Metall & Petrol Engrs, 70- & Am Asn Petrol Geologists, 77- *Mem:* Am Inst Mining, Metall & Petrol Engrs. *Res:* Pressure transient testing; low permeability gas well analysis. *Mailing Add:* Dept of Petrol Eng Tex A&M Univ College Station TX 77843

LEE, WILLIAM ORVID, b Brigham City, Utah, July 2, 27; m 51; c 4. FIELD CROPS. *Educ:* Utah State Univ, BS, 50, MS, 54; Ore State Univ, PhD(farm crops), 65. *Prof Exp:* Soil scientist, Bur Reclamation, US Dept Interior, 50-51; agronomist, Utah, 51-54 & Wyo, 54-56, RES AGRONOMIST, SCI & EDUC ADMIN-AGR RES, USDA, 56- *Mem:* Weed Sci Soc Am. *Res:* Crop science; control of weeds in forage and turf seed crops; legumes and grasses. *Mailing Add:* Crop Sci Dept USDA-SEA CR Ore State Univ Corvallis OR 97331

LEE, WILLIAM ROSCOE, b Little Rock, Ark, Feb 14, 30; m 53; c 3. GENETICS. *Educ:* Univ Ark, BSA, 53; Univ Wis, MS, 53, PhD(genetics, entom), 56. *Prof Exp:* Asst, Univ Wis, 52-56; from asst prof to assoc prof entom, Univ NH, 56-63; asst prof zool, Univ Tex, Austin, 63-67; assoc prof, 67-73, PROF ZOOL & PHYSIOL, LA STATE UNIV, BATON ROUGE, 73- *Concurrent Pos:* Res exec for H J Muller, Ind Univ, 62-63. *Mem:* Genetics Soc Am; Radiation Res Soc; Environ Mutagen Soc. *Res:* Radiation genetics; mutagenesis. *Mailing Add:* Dept of Zool & Physiol La State Univ Baton Rouge LA 70803

LEE, WILLIAM STATES, b Charlotte, NC, June 23, 29; m 51; c 3. ENGINEERING. *Educ:* Princeton Univ, BS, 51. *Prof Exp:* Mem staff, 55-62, eng mgr, 62-65, vpres eng, 65-71, sr vpres, 71-75, EXEC V PRES ENG, DUKE POWER CO, 76- *Concurrent Pos:* Mem, US Comt Large Dams, 80-; trustee, Queens Col; mem bd visitors, Sch Eng, Duke Univ; mem exec adv comt nuclear policy, Edison Elec Inst. *Honors & Awards:* George Westinghouse Gold Medal, Am Soc Mech Engrs, 72. *Mem:* Nat Acad Eng; fel Am Soc Mech Engrs; Nat Soc Prof Engrs; Am Nuclear Soc. *Mailing Add:* Duke Power Co Box 33189 Charlotte NC 28242

LEE, WILLIAM WAI-LIM, b Shanghai, China, Aug 6, 48; US citizen. RESOURCE MANAGEMENT, ENVIRONMENTAL ENGINEERING. *Educ:* Tulane Univ, BSE, 69; Univ Mich, MSE, 70; Mass Inst Technol, SMCE, 76, ScD(resources systs mgt), 77. *Prof Exp:* Proj engr water reuse, Los Angeles County Sanit Dists, 70-72; proj engr decision anal, Woodward-Clyde Consults, 77-79; ASST PROF, CIVIL & URBAN ENG, UNIV PA, 79- *Mem:* Am Soc Civil Engrs; AAAS; Inst Mgt Sci; Opers Res Soc Am; Soc Risk Anal. *Res:* Applicability of quantitative analytical techniques in resources and environmental problems. *Mailing Add:* Dept Civil-Urbn Engr Univ Pa Philadelphia PA 19104

LEE, WILLIAM WEI, b San Francisco, Calif, May 17, 23; m 47; c 3. ORGANIC CHEMISTRY. *Educ:* Univ Calif, BS, 47; Univ Minn, PhD(org chem), 52. *Prof Exp:* Jr chemist org anal chem, Shell Develop Co, 47-48; asst org chem, Univ Minn, 48-51; org res chemist, Cent Res Dept, Monsanto Chem Co, 52-54; assoc chemist org chem, 54-56, SR ORG CHEMIST, STANFORD RES INST, 56- *Mem:* Am Chem Soc; Sigma Xi; Radiation Res Soc. *Res:* Allylic and acetylenic compounds; nucleosides, amino acids and alkylating agents; enzyme chemistry; active halogen compounds; folic acid antagonists; heterocyclic chemistry; chemotherapy, particularly cancer chemotherapy; radiosensitizing agents. *Mailing Add:* Bioorg Dept Stanford Res Inst 333 Ravenswood Ave Menlo Park CA 94025

LEE, WONYONG, b Korea, Dec 29, 30; m 61; c 1. HIGH ENERGY PHYSICS. *Educ:* Calif Inst Technol, BS, 57; Univ Calif, Berkeley, PhD(physics), 61. *Prof Exp:* Res assoc physics, Lawrence Radiation Lab, Univ Calif, 61-62; res assoc, 62-64, from asst prof to assoc prof, 64-72, PROF PHYSICS, COLUMBIA UNIV, 72- *Concurrent Pos:* Sloan Found fel, 65-67. *Mem:* Am Phys Soc. *Res:* High energy experimental physics. *Mailing Add:* Dept of Physics Columbia Univ New York NY 10027

LEE, WOOK BAE, b Korea, Nov 12, 43; m 71; c 2. GEOPHYSICS, PHYSICS. *Educ:* Seoul Nat Univ, BS, 66; Ind Univ, MS, 72; Mass Inst Technol, PhD(geophysics), 77. *Prof Exp:* Assoc instr physics, Ind Univ, 69-72; res asst geophysics, Mass Inst Technol, 72-77, staff scientist, Lincoln Lab, 74; RES ASSOC GEOPHYSICS, UNIV CALIF, LOS ANGELES, 77- *Mem:* Am Geophys Union. *Res:* Seismology; geophysical fluid dynamics; physics of condensed matters; geophysical inverse problem; planetology. *Mailing Add:* 6345 Green Valley Circle (212) Culver City CA 90230

LEE, WOOYOUNG, b Pusan, Korea, Jan 2, 38; m 66; c 1. CHEMICAL ENGINEERING. *Educ:* Seoul Nat Univ, BS, 61; Univ Wis-Madison, MS, 64, PhD(chem eng), 66. *Prof Exp:* Fel chem eng, Univ Wis, 66; res engr, 66-69, sr res engr, 69-74, res assoc, 74-77, mgr reforming & spec process develop, 77-80, MGR SYNTHETIC FUELS DEVELOP, MOBIL RES & DEVELOP CORP, 80- *Mem:* Am Inst Chem Engrs; Am Chem Soc. *Res:* Conversion of oxygenates to hydrocarbons; aromatics and olefin upgrading process development; fluid bed catalytic cracking; kinetics and reaction engineering; computer control. *Mailing Add:* Mobil Res & Develop Corp Paulsboro NJ 08066

LEE, WYLIE IN-WEI, b Taiwan, Aug 18, 41; c 3. BIOPHYSICS, BIOENGINEERING. *Educ:* Taiwan Normal Univ, BS, 63; Univ Mass, MS, 67, PhD(physics), 71. *Prof Exp:* Res assoc physics, Manchester Univ, 70-72; res & teaching assoc physics, 72-75, NIH fel & res assoc, 75-76, asst prof bioeng, 76-81, RES ASSOC PROF BIOENG & BIOL STRUCT, UNIV WASH, 81- *Mem:* Am Phys Soc; Biophys Soc; Am Asn Physicists in Med. *Res:* The dynamics of macromolecules in solution or network state by laser light scattering; applications of the intensity fluctuation spectroscopy in biomedical studies such as the structures of mucus and control of activity of cilia or flagella; biomedical application of lasers. *Mailing Add:* Ctr for Bioeng Univ of Wash FL-20 Seattle WA 98195

LEE, YAT-SHIR, b Kwangtung, China. INORGANIC CHEMISTRY. *Educ:* Nat Taiwan Univ, BS, 58; Kent State Univ, MS, 67, PhD(chem), 71. *Prof Exp:* MEM TECH STAFF LIQUID CRYSTAL RES, HUGHES AIRCRAFT CO, 72- *Concurrent Pos:* Fel, Harvard Univ, 72. *Mem:* Am Chem Soc. *Res:* Structure, hydrodynamics and electro-optical effects of liquid crystals. *Mailing Add:* 2601 Campus Irvine CA 92715

LEE, YEAN, b China, Aug 15, 30; US citizen; m 66; c 2. ATMOSPHERIC SCIENCES. *Educ:* Univ Alta, MSc, 69; Univ Mich, PhD(atmospheric sci), 74. *Prof Exp:* Res assoc precipitation scavenging, Univ Mich, 72-74; meteorologist meteorol & air qual, Sargent & Lundy Engrs, 74-76; METEOROLOGIST METEOROL & AIR QUAL, STONE & WEBSTER ENG CORP, 77- *Mem:* Am Meteorol Soc; Sigma Xi. *Res:* Precipitation scavenging; air pollution; cloud physics. *Mailing Add:* Stone & Webster Eng Corp 245 Summer St Boston MA 02107

LEE, YIEN-HWEI, b Taiwan, China, Oct 20, 37; m 68; c 3. MEDICINE, PHARMACOLOGY. *Educ:* Nat Taiwan Univ, MD, 63; Univ Calif, Los Angeles, PhD(pharmacol), 68. *Prof Exp:* Res asst pharmacol, Univ Calif, Los Angeles, 64-66, res pharmacologist, 66-68, res assoc, Neuropsychiat Inst, 66-68; sr investr pharmacol, Searle Res Lab, G D Searle & Co, 68-72; sect head, Abbott Labs, 72-76; staff, Chicago Med Sch Hosp, 76-77; staff physician, St Joseph Hosp, Chicago, 77-78; fel sect hemat, Rush-Presbyterian & St Luke's Hosp, Chicago, 78-; Am Cancer Soc fel clin onocol, Sect Hemat & Oncol, Cook County Hosp, Chicago, 80-81; CONSULT SPECIALIST, BETHESDA RES LAB, GAITHERSBURG, 81- *Mem:* AAAS; Am Soc Pharmacol & Exp Therapeut; Am Col Physicians; Sigma Xi; Am Chem Soc. *Res:* Gastrointestinal pharmacology and physiology; biochemical pharmacology; cancer chemotherapy; experimental leukemia; hematology; oncology. *Mailing Add:* 14960 Carry Back Dr Gaithersburg MD 20878

LEE, YING KAO, b Shanghai, China, Dec 14, 32; US citizen; m 61; c 3. POLYMER CHEMISTRY. *Educ:* Tai Tung Univ, BSc, 52; Univ Cincinnati, PhD(chem), 61. *Prof Exp:* Res chemist, Tex-US Chem Co, 60-63, proj leader, 65; res chemist, 65-68, staff chemist, 68-70, res assoc, 70-76, RES FEL, MARSHALL RES & DEVELOP LAB, E I DU PONT DE NEMOURS & CO, INC, 76- *Mem:* Am Chem Soc. *Res:* Polymers or polymeric systems used in coating field; high temperature polymer for electronics applications. *Mailing Add:* Marshall Res & Develop Lab E I du Pont de Nemours & Co Inc Philadelphia PA 19146

LEE, YONG YUNG, b Kyungpook, Korea, Feb 12, 36; US citizen; m 63; c 2. HIGH ENERGY PHYSICS. *Educ:* Kyung-Pook Nat Univ, BS, 58, MS, 60; Univ Mich, PhD(physics), 64. *Prof Exp:* Res assoc physics, Univ Wis, 64-67; asst prof, State Univ NY, Stony Brook, 67-71; PHYSICIST ACCELERATOR PHYSICS, BROOKHAVEN NAT LAB, 71- *Mem:* Fel Am Phys Soc. *Res:* Accelerator physics. *Mailing Add:* Bldg 911B Brookhaven Nat Lab Upton NY 11973

LEE, YOON CHAI, chemistry, see previous edition

LEE, YOUNG HIE, b Seoul, Korea, Jan 12, 46; m 72; c 2. CHEMICAL ENGINEERING, BIOCHEMICAL ENGINEERING. *Educ:* Seoul Nat Univ, BS, 71; Purdue Univ, MS, 74, PhD(chem eng), 77. *Prof Exp:* ASST PROF CHEM ENG, DREXEL UNIV, 78- *Concurrent Pos:* Prin investr, NSF proj, 78-80. *Mem:* Am Inst Chem Engrs; Am Chem Soc. *Res:* Transport phenomena; gas liquid reaction; waste water treatment; biomass utilization. *Mailing Add:* Dept of Chem Eng Drexel Univ Philadelphia PA 19104

LEE, YOUNG JACK, b Seoul, Korea, Feb 25, 42; m 67; c 3. STATISTICS. *Educ:* Seoul Nat Univ, BSE, 64; Ohio State Univ, MS, 72, PhD(statist), 74. *Prof Exp:* Instr electronics eng, Korean Air Force Acad, 67-69; asst prof statist, Univ Md, College Park, 74-79; MATH STATISTICIAN, NIH, 79- *Mem:* Am Statist Asn; Biomet Soc. *Res:* Nonparametric/robust design of experiment and statistical analysis in hypothesis testing, ranking and selection and estimation; applications of statistics to social science and life science; method in clinical trial, statistical design and analysis for carcinogenesis and mutagenesis bioassays. *Mailing Add:* NIH Fed Bldg Rm 7C10B Bethesda MD 20205

LEE, YOUNG-HOON, b Korea, Sept 18, 35; m 65; c 1. SOLID STATE PHYSICS. *Educ:* Dong-Guk Univ, BS, 61, MS, 63; State Univ NY Albany, PhD(physics), 72. *Prof Exp:* Sr asst physics, Dong-Guk Univ, 63-66; fel physics, State Univ NY, Albany, 73-78; MEM RES STAFF, IBM THOMAS J WATSON RES CTR, 78- *Mem:* Am Phys Soc; Korean Phys Soc. *Res:* Defects in solids and electron spin resonance. *Mailing Add:* IBM T J Watson Res Ctr PO Box 218 Yorktown Heights NY 10598

LEE, YOUNG-JIN, b Seoul, Korea, Nov 22, 46; m 72. CHEMISTRY, ORGANIC CHEMISTRY. *Educ:* Millikin Univ, BA, 68; Univ Rochester, MS, 70; State Univ NY Albany, PhD(chem), 74. *Prof Exp:* Fel chem, Cornell Univ, 74-75; CHEMIST, UNION CARBIDE CORP, 75- *Mem:* Am Chem Soc. *Res:* Syntheses and process development of agricultural chemicals; new pesticides. *Mailing Add:* Union Carbide Corp Tech Ctr South Charleston WV 25303

LEE, YUAN CHUAN, b Taiwan, China, Mar 30, 32; m 58; c 1. BIOCHEMISTRY. *Educ:* Nat Taiwan Univ, BS, 55, MS, 57; Univ Iowa, PhD(biochem), 62. *Prof Exp:* Res assoc biochem, Univ Iowa, 62 & Univ Calif, Berkeley, 62-65; from asst prof to assoc prof, 65-74, PROF BIOL, JOHNS HOPKINS UNIV, 74- *Mem:* Am Chem Soc; Am Soc Biol Chem; Brit Biochem Soc. *Res:* Complex carbohydrates. *Mailing Add:* Dept Biol Johns Hopkins Univ Baltimore MD 21218

LEE, YUAN TSEH, b Hsinchu, Taiwan, Nov 29, 36; m 63; c 3. CHEMISTRY. *Educ:* Nat Taiwan Univ, BS, 59; Nat Tsing Hua Univ, Taiwan, MS, 61; Univ Calif, Berkeley, PhD(chem), 65. *Prof Exp:* From asst prof to prof chem, Univ Chicago, 68-74; PROF CHEM, UNIV CALIF, BERKELEY, 74- *Concurrent Pos:* Alfred P Sloan res fel, Univ Chicago, 69-71; assoc ed, J Chem Phys, 75-78. *Mem:* Nat Acad Sci; Am Phys Soc; fel Am Acad Arts Sci; Am Chem Soc. *Res:* Chemical kinetics and molecular interaction. *Mailing Add:* Dept Chem Lawrence Berkeley Lab Univ of Calif Berkeley CA 94720

LEE, YUEN SAN, b Taipei, Taiwan, Oct 13, 39; m 67; c 2. FOODS, BIOCHEMISTRY. *Educ:* Nat Taiwan Univ, BS, 62; Utah State Univ, MS, 65; Univ Md, College Park, PhD(food sci, biochem), 68. *Prof Exp:* CHEMIST, HEALTH SERV ADMIN, DC GOVT, 68- *Concurrent Pos:* Assoc prof, Univ District of Columbia, 75- *Mem:* Inst Food Technol; Am Chem Soc; Am Dietetic Asn. *Res:* Method development in the determination of pesticides in meat, milk and water; quality control of detecting adulteration in meat and meat products for consumer protection; heavy metals in foods. *Mailing Add:* 5 Maplewood Ct Greenbelt MD 20770

LEE, YUE-WEI, b San-Tung, China, Mar 9, 46; m 72; c 2. ORGANIC CHEMISTRY, MEDICINAL CHEMISTRY. *Educ:* Calif State Univ, Sacramento, MS, 73; Columbia Univ, MS, 75, PhD(chem), 78. *Prof Exp:* Res grad asst, Columbia Univ, 74-78; RES STAFF SYNTHESIS & RES CHEMIST, RES TRIANGLE INST, 78- *Mem:* Am Chem Soc. *Res:* Synthesis of steroidal hormone for contraceptive purpose; isolation and structure determination of medicinal component from natural resources. *Mailing Add:* Res Triangle Inst PO Box 12194 Research Triangle Park NC 27709

LEE, YUNG, b Inchon, Korea, May 11, 32; Can citizen; m 60; c 1. MECHANICAL ENGINEERING. *Educ:* Seoul Nat Univ, BEng, 59, MEng, 61; Univ Liverpool, PhD(mech eng), 64. *Prof Exp:* Lectr mech eng, Liverpool Polytech Inst, 64-65; res officer, Chalk River Nuclear Lab, Atomic Energy Can, Ltd, 65-67; from asst prof to assoc prof mech eng, 67-73, PROF MECH ENG, UNIV OTTAWA, 73- *Mem:* Can Soc Mech Engrs; Eng Inst Can. *Res:* Fluid flow; heat transfer. *Mailing Add:* Dept of Mech Eng Univ of Ottawa Ottawa ON K1H 5T1 Can

LEE, YUNG-CHANG, b Canton, China, Nov 7, 35; US citizen. PHYSICS. *Educ:* Nat Taiwan Univ, BSc, 55; Univ Md, PhD(physics), 63. *Prof Exp:* Mem tech staff, Bell Tel Lab, 61-67; ASSOC PROF PHYSICS, STATE UNIV NY, BUFFALO, 67- *Concurrent Pos:* Vis prof, Nat Tsing Hua Univ & Nat Taiwan Univ, 73-74; physicist, Lawrence Livermore Lab, 78-79. *Mem:* Am Phys Soc. *Res:* Solid state physics and quantum optics, including superradiance in thin crystal films; excitons in thin films; Anderson localization and Thouless' maximum resistance; interaction of electromagnetic radiation with plasmas; parametric coupling in plasmas; two dimensional crystalline order. *Mailing Add:* Physics Dept State Univ NY Buffalo Amherst NY 14260

LEE, YUNG-KEUN, b Seoul, Korea, Sept 26, 29; m 58; c 4. NUCLEAR PHYSICS. *Educ:* Johns Hopkins Univ, BA, 56; Univ Chicago, MS, 57; Columbia Univ, PhD(physics), 61. *Prof Exp:* Res scientist, Columbia Univ, 61-64; from asst prof to assoc prof, 64-71, PROF PHYSICS, JOHNS HOPKINS UNIV, 71- *Mem:* Am Phys Soc. *Res:* Nuclear beta decay; nuclear reactions; Mossbauer effects; intermediate energy physics. *Mailing Add:* Dept of Physics Johns Hopkins Univ Baltimore MD 21218

LEECH, GEOFFREY BOSDIN, b Montreal, Que, Aug 28, 18; m 46; c 1. GEOLOGY. *Educ:* Univ BC, BASc, 42; Queen's Univ, Ont, MSc, 43; Princeton Univ, PhD(petrol, econ geol), 49. *Prof Exp:* Field asst, Geol Surv Can, 40-41 & 42; geologist, Int Nickel Co Can, Ltd, Ont, 43-46; chief party, BC Dept Mines, 47-48; geologist, 49-72, head, Econ Geol Subdiv, 73-78, DIR, ECON GEOL DIV, GEOL SURV CAN, DEPT ENERGY, MINES

& RESOURCES, 79- *Mem:* Fel Geol Soc Am; Soc Econ Geol; fel Royal Soc Can; Can Inst Mining & Metall; fel Geol Asn Can. *Res:* Regional metallogeny; mineral resource evaluation; problems of resource adequacy. *Mailing Add:* 1113 Greenland Crescent Ottawa ON K2C 1Z4 Can

LEECH, HARRY WILLIAM, b Triadelphia, WVa, Apr 28, 40; m 66; c 1. PHYSICS, COMPUTER SCIENCE. *Educ:* WVa Univ, BS, 62, MS, 64; Univ Md, PhD(physics), 75. *Prof Exp:* From instr to asst prof physics & math, W Liberty State Col, 64-68; mem tech staff computer sci, Comput Sci Corp, 73-77; asst prof physics, Southern Conn State Col, 77-78; asst prof physics, Bethany Col, 78-80; ASSOC PROF ENG TECHNOLOGIES, JEFFERSON TECH COL, 80- *Mem:* Am Asn Physics Teachers. *Res:* Cosmic ray astrophysics; celestial mechanics; orbit determination; scientific applications of computer science. *Mailing Add:* 324 Thomas St Wintersville OH 43952

LEECH, JOHN G, b Norwood, Pa, May 28, 23; m 44; c 3. PULP CHEMISTRY, PAPER CHEMISTRY. *Educ:* Pa State Univ, BS, 47; Inst Paper Chem, Lawrence Col, MS, 49, PhD(chem), 52. *Prof Exp:* Proj leader, WVa Pulp & Paper Co, 51-55, res lab dir, 55-62; asst dir res, 62-64, dir proj planning, 64-70, DIR RES DEVELOP ADMIN, UNION CAMP CORP, 70- *Mem:* Am Inst Chem Eng; Tech Asn Pulp & Paper Indust. *Res:* Pulp and paper; packaging; silvichemicals. *Mailing Add:* Union Camp Corp PO Box 412 Princeton NJ 08540

LEECH, JOHN WARNER, aerospace engineering, see previous edition

LEECH, ROBERT LELAND, b Chicago, Ill, Oct 21, 38; m 61; c 4. ELECTRICAL ENGINEERING, COMPUTER SCIENCE. *Educ:* US Mil Acad, BS, 60; Purdue Univ, West Lafayette, MSE, 66; Duke Univ, AM, 76, PhD(elec eng), 77. *Prof Exp:* Proj officer & comdr automatic commun syst off, US Army Electronics Command, Ft Monmouth, NJ, 63-64; instr & opers officer, Acad Comput Ctr, US Mil Acad, 66-67, instr dept elec, 67-68, asst prof off of Dean, Educ Syst, 68-69; chief automatic data processing sect, opers group, US Army War Col, Carlisle Barracks, Pa, 70-72; chief comput opers info systs div, Supreme Hqs Allied Powers Europe, 72-75; ASSOC PROF COMPUT SCI, DEPT ELEC ENG, US MIL ACAD, 75- *Concurrent Pos:* Res officer, US Army Res Off, 76-77. *Mem:* Inst Elec & Electronics Engr; Asn Comput Mach. *Res:* Computer systems architecture; computer performance evaluation; military computer command and control system. *Mailing Add:* Dept Elec Eng US Mil Acad West Point NY 10996

LEED, RUSSELL ERNEST, b Denver, Pa, Dec 24, 15. PHYSICAL CHEMISTRY, CHEMICAL PLANT ENGINEERING. *Educ:* Franklin & Marshall Col, BS, 37; Univ Md, MS, 40, PhD(phys chem), 41. *Prof Exp:* From instr to asst prof chem, Va Mil Inst, 41-48; assoc prof, Va Polytech Inst, 48-51; chemist, Prod Div, AEC, Oak Ridge Opers, 51-73, dep dir, 58-73, asst & asst mgr uranium enrichment prog, Dept Energy, 73-80; RETIRED. *Mem:* Am Chem Soc. *Res:* Solutions-electrochemistry; war gases; physical properties of alloys; solubility of mercurous iodate; thermal conductivity; phase diagrams; process development; nuclear weapons and separation of uranium isotopes; gas centrifuge and gaseous diffusion processes. *Mailing Add:* Rte 1 Box 310 Jones Rd Lenoir City TN 37771

LEEDER, JOSEPH GORDEN, b Oil City, Pa, July 4, 16; m 39; c 2. DAIRY CHEMISTRY. *Educ:* Ohio State Univ, BS, 38; Univ Vt, MS, 40; Pa State Univ, PhD, 44. *Prof Exp:* Dir labs & Supvr zone qual control, Nat Dairy Prod Co, Ohio, 44-46, chief res chemist, Ramsey Labs, 46-48; from assoc prof to prof dairy indust, Dept Animal Sci, 48-65, RES PROF FOOD SCI, DEPT FOOD SCI, RUTGERS UNIV, 65- *Mem:* Am Dairy Sci Asn; Inst Food Technologists. *Res:* Immobilized enzymes for whey utilization; food emulsions; chemistry of butter oil used in deep-fat frying. *Mailing Add:* Dept of Food Sci Rutgers Univ New Brunswick NJ 08903

LEEDHAM, CLIVE D(OUGLAS), b London, Eng, Nov 1, 28; m 55; c 2. ELECTRICAL ENGINEERING. *Educ:* Univ London, BSc, 49; Mass Inst Technol, SM, 55; Purdue Univ, PhD(elec eng), 63. *Prof Exp:* Asst lectr elec eng, Univ London, 48-49; apprentice, Metrop Vickers Elec Co Ltd, 49-51, jr engr, 51-52; teaching asst, Mass Inst Technol, 53-55; instr, Purdue Univ, 58-62; asst prof, Univ Calif, 62-65; consult, 63-65, staff engr, 65-76, BUS DEVELOP MGR DIGITAL SYSTS, DELCO ELECTRONICS DIV, GEN MOTORS CORP, 76- *Concurrent Pos:* Consult, US Air Force, 61-62. *Res:* Automatic control; signal processing; acoustics; digital computers. *Mailing Add:* 6767 Hollister Ave Delco Elec Div Gen Motors Goleta CA 93117

LEEDOM, JOHN MILTON, b Peoria, Ill, Oct 18, 33; m 56; c 2. INTERNAL MEDICINE. *Educ:* Univ Ill, BA, 55, BS, 56, MD, 58; Am Bd Internal Med, dipl, 67. *Prof Exp:* Resident med, Univ Ill Res & Educ Hosps, 59-60 & 61-62; from asst prof to assoc prof, 62-76, PROF MED, SCH MED, UNIV SOUTHERN CALIF, 76- *Concurrent Pos:* Res fel, Univ Ill Res & Educ Hosps, 60-61; officer res proj, Epidemic Intel Serv, USPHS, Infectious Dis Lab, Univ Southern Calif, 62-64, consult health facil construction div, Health Serv & Ment Health Admin. *Mem:* Am Fedn Clin Res; Am Soc Microbiol; Infectious Dis Soc Am. *Res:* Infectious disease, particularly viral and bacterial diseases of the central nervous system. *Mailing Add:* Dept of Med Univ of Southern Calif Los Angeles CA 90033

LEEDS, J VENN, JR, b Wharton, Tex, Oct 26, 32; m 56; c 2. ELECTRICAL ENGINEERING, ENVIRONMENTAL ENGINEERING. *Educ:* Rice Univ, BA, 55, BSEE, 56; Univ Pittsburgh, MSEE, 60, PhD(elec eng), 63; JD, Univ Houston, 72. *Prof Exp:* Sr engr, Bettis Atomic Lab, Westinghouse Elec Corp, 56-63; asst prof elec eng, 63-65, elec & environ eng, 65-67, assoc prof, 67-72, master, Sid W Richardson Col, 70-76, PROF ELEC & ENVIRON ENG, RICE UNIV, 72- *Concurrent Pos:* Consult, Esso Prod Res Co Div, Humble Oil & Refining Co, 63-68 & Geospace Corp, 68-72; mem safety & licensing panel, US Nat Res Coun, 71-; consult, var ins co, 74- *Mem:* Inst Elec & Electronics Engrs. *Res:* Design and analysis of large, complex systems; applied mathematics; design of large, complex systems; interactions of law and engineering; applied mathematics. *Mailing Add:* 10807 Atwell Houston TX 77096

LEEDS, MORTON W, b Brooklyn, NY, Dec 18, 16; m 45; c 1. ORGANIC CHEMISTRY. *Educ:* Polytech Inst Brooklyn, BS, 38, MS, 39, PhD(org chem), 44. *Prof Exp:* Chemist, Bio-Med Res Lab, NY, 35-39; sr chemist, Res Lab, Interchem Corp, 39-45, head develop dept amino acids, Biochem Div, NJ, 45-48; sr chemist, E I du Pont de Nemours & Co, Inc, 48-50; asst chief chemist, Schwarz Labs, NY, 50-52; head appln & develop, Res Labs, Air Reduction Co, 52-56, supvr org chem develop & res, 56-60, from asst dir to assoc dir chem res, 60-71; mgr clin develop, 71-77, ASST DIR MED PRODS MGT, MED RES DIV, CIBA PHARMACEUT CO, 77- *Concurrent Pos:* Permanent adj prof, Kean Col, 71-80. *Mem:* Am Chem Soc; fel Am Inst Chem; NY Acad Sci. *Res:* Organic synthesis and development; acetylene and pharmaceutical chemistry; petrochemicals. *Mailing Add:* 100 Chestnut Hill Dr Murray Hill NJ 07974

LEEDY, CLARK D, b Chicago, Ill, June 3, 33; m 56; c 5. SOILS SCIENCE. *Educ:* Purdue Univ, BS, 55; NMex State Univ, MS, 64, MA, 66; Tex A&M Univ, PhD(educ), 74. *Prof Exp:* Exten Soils Specialist, NMex State Univ, 57-71; div leader, WVa Univ, 73-76; ASSOC SOIL SCIENTIST, UNIV NEV, RENO, 76- *Mem:* Sigma Xi. *Res:* Forms, rates, methods and timing of phosphorous fertilizer application on alfalfa yield and quality. *Mailing Add:* Col Agr Univ Nev Reno NV 89507

LEEDY, DANIEL LONEY, b North Liberty, Ohio, Feb 17, 12; m 45; c 2. ZOOLOGY, ECOLOGY. *Educ:* Miami Univ, AB, 34, BSc, 35; Ohio State Univ, MSc, 38, PhD(wildlife mgt), 40. *Prof Exp:* Lab asst geol & zool, Miami Univ, 34-35; asst leader, Ohio Wildlife Res Unit, Ohio State Univ, 40-42; leader, Ohio Unit, US Fish & Wildlife Serv, 45-48, coordr, Coop Wildlife Res Unit Prog, 49-57, chief br wildlife res, 57-63; chief div res & educ, Bur Outdoor Recreation, 63-65, water resources res scientist, Off Water Resources Res, US Dept Interior, 65-74; RES DIR & SR SCIENTIST, URBAN WILDLIFE RES CTR, 75- *Mem:* Fel AAAS; assoc Am Soc Mammalogists; Wildlife Soc (pres, 53, exec secy, 54-57); Am Fisheries Soc; Ecol Soc Am. *Res:* Wildlife ecology; socioeconomics of fish and wildlife and recreation; natural resources training and employment; wildlife-land use relationships; water resources; urban wildlife and ecology; ecologic impacts of water development, surface mining, highways, and electric utilities. *Mailing Add:* 10707 Lockridge Dr Silver Spring MD 20901

LEEF, JAMES LEWIS, b San Francisco, Calif, Mar 6, 37; m 64; c 4. CRYOBIOLOGY, IMMUNOLOGY. *Educ:* Univ Calif, San Francisco, BA, 67; Univ Tenn, PhD(biol), 74. *Prof Exp:* SR INVESTR CRYOBIOL & HEAD, MALARIA RES DEPT, BIOMED RES INST, AM FOUND BIOL RES, 76- *Concurrent Pos:* Consult, Sci & Indust Res & Develop Co, 67-69; fel, Univ Ill, 73-76; guest scientist, Navy Med Res Inst, 76- *Mem:* Soc Cryobiol; Tissue Cult Asn; Am Asn Tissue Banks; NY Acad Sci. *Res:* Malariology; mechanisms of freezing injury; study of various developmental stages of malaria and schistosomiasis parasites as antigens in developing a malaria and schistosomiasis vaccine and preservation of these forms at low temperatures. *Mailing Add:* Biomed Res Inst 12111 Parklawn Dr Rockville MD 20852

LEE-FRANZINI, JULIET, b Paris, France, May 18, 33; US citizen; m 64; c 1. EXPERIMENTAL PHYSICS. *Educ:* Hunter Col, BA, 53; Columbia Univ, MA, 57, PhD(physics), 60. *Prof Exp:* Res assoc physics, Columbia Univ, 60-62; res fel astrophys, Nat Acad Sci-Nat Res Coun, 62-63; from asst prof to assoc prof elem particle physics, 63-74, PROF PHYSICS, STATE UNIV NY STONY BROOK, 74- *Concurrent Pos:* State Univ NY Res Found grant, 63-66; vis assoc physicist, Brookhaven Nat Lab, 64-; Atomic Energy Comn grant, 66-72; NSF grant, 72-; vis prof, Cornell Univ, 80-81. *Res:* Elementary particle physics; weak interactions. *Mailing Add:* Dept of Physics State Univ of NY Stony Brook NY 11790

LEEG, KENTON J(AMES), b Spokane, Wash, Aug 31, 11. PLASTICS CHEMISTRY, ENGINEERING. *Educ:* Univ Calif, AB, 35; Univ Southern Calif, PhD(chem), 40. *Prof Exp:* Dir res, Baker Oil Tools, Inc, 40-51; pres, Lebec Chem Corp, 51-55; pres, Rez-Coat of Calif, 55-64; CONSULT PLASTICS, 64- *Concurrent Pos:* Lectr, Univ Southern Calif, 40-50. *Mem:* Am Chem Soc. *Res:* Plastics; plastics finishes; high and ultra high temperature plastics; solar heating. *Mailing Add:* PO Box 1423 Rancho Santa Fe CA 92067

LEE-HAM, DOO YOUNG, b Seoul, Korea, Mar 31, 32; US citizen; m 66; c 2. PHARMACOLOGY, TOXICOLOGY. *Educ:* Mercer Univ, BA, 57; Catholic Univ Am, MS, 61, PhD(physiol), 66. *Prof Exp:* Res scientist, Microbiol Assoc, Inc, 62-66; spec lectr physiol & biochem, Sungshin Womans Univ & Ewha Womans Univ, 66-67; sr scientist, Melpar, Inc, 67-69; PHYSIOLOGIST, DIV ONCOL & RADIOPHARM DRUG PROD, FOOD & DRUG ADMIN, 69- *Mem:* NY Acad Sci. *Res:* Basic and applied cell physiology; in vitro and in vivo testing of drugs and chemicals for their carcinogenic potential, mutagenicity and cell transformation. *Mailing Add:* Food & Drug Admin HFD-150 Parklawn Bldg 5600 Fishers Lane Rockville MD 20857

LEEHEY, PATRICK, b Waterloo, Iowa, Oct 27, 21; m 44; c 6. APPLIED MECHANICS. *Educ:* US Naval Acad, BSc, 42; Brown Univ, PhD(appl math), 50. *Prof Exp:* Proj officer, US Off Naval Res, DC, 51-53, prog officer, David Taylor Model Basin, 53-56, design supt, Puget Sound Naval Shipyard, Wash, 56-58, head ship silencing br, Bur Ships, DC, 58-63, head acoustics & vibration lab, David Taylor Model Basin, 63-64; assoc prof mech eng & naval archit, 64-67, prof naval archit, 67-71, PROF APPL MECH, MASS INST TECHNOL, 71- *Honors & Awards:* Gold Medal, Am Soc Naval Eng, 62. *Mem:* Am Math Soc; fel Acoust Soc Am; Am Soc Naval Eng. *Res:* Hydrodynamics; hydrofoil craft development, unsteady airfoil theory; supercavitating flow theory; acoustics; ship silencing, underwater acoustics, boundary layer noise; mathematics; hyperbolic partial differential equations; singular integral equations; boundary layer stability. *Mailing Add:* Dept Ocean Eng Rm 1-207 Mass Inst Technol Cambridge MA 02139

LEE-HUANG, SYLVIA, b Shanghai, China, July 14, 30; US citizen; m 57; c 3. BIOCHEMISTRY, MOLECULAR BIOLOGY. *Educ:* Nat Taiwan Univ, BS, 52; Univ Idaho, MS, 57; Univ Pittsburgh, PhD(biophys), 61. *Prof Exp:* NIH fel microbiol, Sch Med, Univ Pittsburgh, 61-62; res assoc chem physics, Sloan-Kettering Inst, 62-64; instr biochem, Med Col, Cornell Univ, 64-66; res scientist, 66-67, from instr to asst prof, 67-70, res assoc prof, 70-71, ASSOC PROF BIOCHEM, SCH MED, NY UNIV, 71- *Mem:* AAAS; Am Soc Biol Chemists; Biophys Soc; Harvey Soc; NY Acad Sci. *Res:* Molecular mechanism of transmission and expression of genetic information; control and mechanism of differentiation and development; erythropoietin and the regulation of red cell production. *Mailing Add:* Dept of Biochem NY Univ Sch of Med New York NY 10016

LEEKLEY, ROBERT MITCHELL, b Montrose, SDak, July 18, 11; m 41; c 3. ORGANIC CHEMISTRY. *Educ:* Dakota Wesleyan Univ, BS, 33; Univ SDak, MA, 34; Univ Minn, PhD(chem), 38. *Prof Exp:* Asst, State Chem Lab, SDak, 33-34 & Univ Minn, 34-37; res chemist, E I du Pont de Nemours & Co, 38-45; chem consult, Springdale Labs, Time Inc, 45-50, assoc res dir, 51-62; res assoc, 63-68, sr res assoc, Inst Paper Chem, 68-76; CONSULT, 76- *Mem:* Am Chem Soc; Tech Asn Pulp & Paper Indust; Tech Asn Graphic Arts. *Res:* Light sensitive plastics and coatings; papers for graphic reproduction processes; paper coatings. *Mailing Add:* 75 Fox Point Dr Appleton WI 54911

LEELA, SRINIVASA (G), b Mysore, India. MATHEMATICS. *Educ:* Osmania Univ, India, BSc, 55, MSc, 57; Marathwada Univ, India, PhD(math), 65. *Prof Exp:* Lectr math, Women's Col, Kurnool, India, 59-65; instr, Calgary Univ, 65-66; asst prof, Univ RI, 66-68; assoc prof, 68-73, PROF MATH, STATE UNIV NY COL GENESEO, 73- *Mem:* Am Math Soc; Math Asn Am. *Res:* Qualitative analysis in differential equations; stability theory. *Mailing Add:* Dept of Math State Univ of NY Col Geneseo NY 14454

LEELAVATHI, DODDA E, b Mysore, India, Feb 8, 38; US citizen; m 71; c 1. DRUG KINETICS, DRUG METABOLISM. *Educ:* Univ Mysore, India, BSc Hons, 61, MSc, 62; Indian Inst Sci, PhD(biochem), 70. *Prof Exp:* Res fel biochem path, Univ Pittsburgh, 68-74 & neurochem, Univ Tex, Houston, 76; chief neurochemist, Tex Res Inst Mental Sci, 76-80; SR CHEMIST DRUG KINETICS, WYETH LABS, INC, 80- *Mem:* AAAS; Soc Neurosci; Am Chem Soc. *Res:* Instrumental methods of analyses of drugs in biological fluids and pharmacokinetic evaluation. *Mailing Add:* 333 Lancaster Ave 1014 Frazer PA 19355

LEELING, JERRY L, b Ottumwa, Iowa, July 11, 36; m 57; c 3. PHARMACOLOGY. *Educ:* Parsons Col, BS, 59; Univ Iowa, MS, 62, PhD(biochem), 64. *Prof Exp:* Res biochemist, 64-70, SR RES SCIENTIST, TOXICOL DEPT, MILES LABS, INC, 70-, SECT HEAD, 73- *Mem:* Am Chem Soc; AAAS; NY Acad Sci; Soc Toxicol; Am Soc Pharmacol Exp Ther. *Res:* Disposition and metabolism of drugs; analytical toxicology. *Mailing Add:* Toxicol Dept Miles Labs Inc Elkhart IN 46515

LEEMAN, SUSAN EPSTEIN, b Chicago, Ill, May 9, 30; m 57; c 1. PHYSIOLOGY. *Educ:* Goucher Col, BA, 51; Radcliffe Col, MA, 54, PhD, 58. *Prof Exp:* Instr physiol, Harvard Med Sch, 58-59; fel neurochem, Brandeis Univ, 59-62, sr res assoc biochem, 62-68, adj asst prof, 66-68, asst res prof, 68-71; asst prof physiol, Lab Human Reprod & Reprod Biol, Harvard Med Sch, 72-73, assoc prof, 73-80; PROF PHYSIOL, MED SCH, UNIV MASS, 80- *Concurrent Pos:* USPHS career develop award, 62-; mem, Endocrinol Study Sect, Div Res Grants, NIH, 81; Albert Heritage med res vis prof, 81. *Honors & Awards:* Astwood Award, 81. *Mem:* Am Physiol Soc; Endocrine Soc. *Res:* Neuroendocrinology. *Mailing Add:* Univ Mass Med Ctr 55 Lake Ave N Worcester MA 01605

LEEMANN, CHRISTOPH WILLY, b Basel, Switz, Jan 12, 39; m 69; c 2. EXPERIMENTAL & ACCELERATOR PHYSICS. *Educ:* Univ Basel, PhD(nuclear physics), 69. *Prof Exp:* Res asst nuclear physics, Univ Basel, 63-69, res assoc, 69-70; fel, 70-72, fel accelerator physics, 72-73, STAFF SCIENTIST ACCELERATOR PHYSICS, LAWRENCE BERKELEY LAB, UNIV CALIF, 73- *Concurrent Pos:* Sabbatical leave, Europ Orgn Nuclear Res, Geneva, Seitz, 80-81. *Mem:* AAAS. *Res:* Design and development of particle accelerators and related devices; beam cooling techniques; colliding beam devices; relativistic heavy ion accelerators. *Mailing Add:* Lawrence Berkeley Lab One Cyclotron Rd Berkeley CA 94720

LEEMING, DAVID JOHN, b Victoria, BC, June 8, 39; m 66; c 3. MATHEMATICS. *Educ:* Univ BC, BSc, 61; Univ Ore, MA, 63; Univ Alta, PhD(math), 69. *Prof Exp:* Instr, 63-66, asst prof, 69-75, ASSOC PROF MATH, UNIV VICTORIA, BC, 75- *Concurrent Pos:* Course writer, Open Learning Inst, 79. *Mem:* Math Asn Am; Can Math Cong. *Res:* Approximation theory; error bounds for interpolation schemes; rational approximation. *Mailing Add:* Dept of Math Univ of Victoria Victoria BC V8W 2Y2 Can

LEENHEER, MARY JANETH, b Zeeland, Mich, Mar 4, 54; m 81. ORGANIC GEOCHEMISTRY. *Educ:* Calvin Col, BS, 76; Univ Mich, MS, 78, PhD(oceanic sci), 81. *Prof Exp:* RES GEOCHEMIST, CITIES SERV CO, 81- *Mem:* Geochem Soc; Sigma Xi; Int Asn Great Lakes Res. *Res:* Chromatographic techniques to characterize organic constituents present in petroleum and recent and ancient sediments in order to better understand depositional environments and post-depositional alteration processes. *Mailing Add:* Cities Serv Technol Ctr 4500 129th E Ave Box 3908 Tulsa OK 74102

LEEPER, CHARLES K(ENDAL), b DeQueen, Ark, June 20, 23; c 3. MECHANICAL ENGINEERING. *Educ:* Univ Tex, BS, 44; Mass Inst Technol, SM, 48, ScD(mech eng), 54. *Prof Exp:* Tool designer, Am Mfg Co Tex, 44-45; fuel control engr, Appl Physics Lab, Johns Hopkins Univ, 45-46; from asst to chief designer, Fuels Res Lab, Mass Inst Technol, 46-54; mgr, Develop Div, Nuclear Develop Corp Am, 54-59; dir, Mech Eng Div, Atlantic Res Corp, 60-63; tech specialist, Aerojet-Gen Corp, 63-65, mgr, Liquid Rocket Eng Div, 65-69, vpres & tech dir, Aerojet Nuclear Systs Co, 69-71, asst gen mgr res & eng, Aerojet Nuclear Co, 71-72, pres & gen mgr, 72-77; vpres eng, C-E Air Preheater Co, 77-78, CORP V PRES CORP TECHNOL, COMBUSTION ENG, INC, 79- *Concurrent Pos:* Consult, Atlantic Res Corp, 49-54 & United Aircraft Corp, 50-52. *Mem:* Am Nuclear Soc; Am Soc Mech Eng; Am Inst Aeronaut & Astronaut; fel NY Acad Sci. *Res:* Dynamics; fluid mechanics; combustion; remote handling; systems reliability and safety. *Mailing Add:* Combustion Eng Inc 900 Long Ridge Rd PO Box 9308 Stamford CT 06904

LEEPER, DENNIS BURTON, b Glendale, Calif, May 3, 41; div; c 5. RADIATION BIOLOGY, CANCER. *Educ:* Univ Iowa, BS, 64, PhD(radiation biol), 69. *Prof Exp:* Asst prof, 70-75, assoc prof, 75-80, PROF RADIATION THERAPY, THOMAS JEFFERSON UNIV HOSP, 80- *Concurrent Pos:* Atomic Energy Comn fel, Colo State Univ, 69-70, affil grad fac, 70-72; consult radiation biol, Franklin Inst, Pa, 76-; adj assoc prof biomed eng, Univ Pa, 76- *Mem:* Radiation Res Soc; Am Asn Cancer Res; Cell Kinetics Soc; AAAS; Am Soc Thermal Radiol. *Res:* Interaction of radiation, hyperthermia, and anti-cancer drugs in mammalian cells in culture and in normal and tumor tissues in vivo; cell cycle kinetics; experimental radiation oncology. *Mailing Add:* Dept of Radiation Therapy & Nuclear Med Thomas Jefferson Univ Hosp Philadelphia PA 19107

LEEPER, GEORGE FREDERICK, b Detroit, Mich, Sept 27, 43; m 66; c 3. ECONOMIC BOTANY, PROCESS ENGINEERING. *Educ:* Univ Iowa, BA, 65, MS, 66; Wash Univ, St Louis, PhD(bot), 69. *Prof Exp:* Botanist fruit & veg lab, Richard B Russell Agr Res Ctr, Agr Res Serv, USDA, 69-76; mgr agr technol sect, RJR Foods, 76-78, Proj Coordr, Mech Develop Dept, 78-81, MGR, LONG RANGE PROCESS DEVELOP DIV, R J REYNOLDS TOBACCO CO, WINSTON-SALEM, NC, 81- *Concurrent Pos:* Fel, Wash Univ, St Louis, 69. *Res:* Process development; post-harvest crop handling; minor crops utilization. *Mailing Add:* Mech Develop Dept R J Reynolds Tobacco Co Winston-Salem NC 27102

LEEPER, HAROLD MURRAY, b Akron, Ohio, July 14, 20; m 42; c 3. POLYMER CHEMISTRY. *Educ:* Univ Akron, BS, 42, MS, 47. *Prof Exp:* Rubber technologist, US Eng Bd, 42-44; polymer chemist rubber, Govt Rubber Labs, 44-47; res chemist polymers, Wm Wrigley Jr Co, 47-54; group leader, Monsanto Co, 54-70; res scientist, 79-80, PRIN SCIENTIST POLYMERS, ALZA CORP, 80- *Mem:* Am Chem Soc; Soc Plastics Engrs; AAAS. *Res:* Chemistry, physics, and technology of rubbers and plastics. *Mailing Add:* Alza Corp 950 Page Mill Rd Palo Alto CA 94304

LEEPER, JOHN ROBERT, b Hackensack, NJ, July 12, 47; m 73; c 2. ENTOMOLOGY. *Educ:* Carthage Col, BA, 69; Univ Hawaii, MS, 71, PhD(entom), 75. *Prof Exp:* Res assoc entom, Tree Fruit Res Ctr, Wash State Univ, 75-77; asst prof entom, NY State Agr Exp Sta, Cornell Univ, 77-80; SR RES BIOLOGIST, DU PONT EXP STA, DU PONT INC, 80- *Mem:* Entom Soc Am. *Res:* Tree fruit entomology and insect resistance. *Mailing Add:* Biochem Dept Du Pont Exp Sta Wilmington DE 19898

LEEPER, RAMON JOE, b Princeton, Mo, Apr 1, 48; m 76; c 1. PLASMA PHYSICS, HIGH ENERGY NUCLEAR PHYSICS. *Educ:* Mass Inst Technol, SB, 70; Iowa State Univ, PhD(high energy nuclear physics), 75. *Prof Exp:* Res assoc high energy nuclear physics, Ames Lab, US Dept of Energy, 75-76; MEM TECH STAFF PLASMA PHYSICS, SANDIA NAT LABS, 76- *Concurrent Pos:* Guest scientist, Argonne Nat Lab, 71-76. *Mem:* Am Phys Soc; Sigma Xi. *Res:* Particle beam induced controlled thermonuclear fusion; neutron physics; fusion plasma diagnostic techniques; neutron production of inertially confined high temperature fusion plasmas; high intensity pulsed neutron sources; high current ion beams; meson spectroscopy. *Mailing Add:* Fusion Res Dept Sandia Nat Labs Albuquerque NM 87185

LEEPER, ROBERT DWIGHT, b Lewiston, Idaho, Nov 9, 24; m 52; c 4. NUCLEAR MEDICINE, ENDOCRINOLOGY. *Educ:* Univ Idaho, BS, 49; Columbia Univ, MD, 53. *Prof Exp:* Intern, Brooklyn Hosp, 53-54, from resident to sr resident, 54-57; fel clin invest, 57-60, assoc, 60-66, ASSOC MEM, SLOAN-KETTERING INST CANCER RES, 66- *Concurrent Pos:* NY Heart Asn fel, 58-60; asst attend physician, Mem Hosp & James Ewing Hosp, 58-66, assoc attend physician, 66-; Am Cancer Soc scholar, 61-66; chief endocrine clin, Mem Hosp, 65-; asst attend physician, New York Hosp, 66-; asst prof, Med Col, Cornell Univ, 63-74, clin assoc prof med, 74-; attend physician endocrinol & nuclear med, Mem Hosp, 77- *Mem:* AAAS; Endocrine Soc; Am Thyroid Asn; NY Acad Sci. *Res:* Thyroid physiology; effects of exogenous enzymes in man; use of radionuclides in diagnosis and therapy in cancer. *Mailing Add:* Sloan-Kettering Inst for Cancer Res 444 E 68th St New York NY 10021

LEEPER, ROBERT WALZ, b Waterloo, Iowa, Apr 28, 15; m 42; c 3. ORGANIC CHEMISTRY. *Educ:* Univ Iowa, BA, 36, MS, 38; Iowa State Univ, PhD(org chem), 42. *Prof Exp:* Nat Defense Res Coun fel, Iowa State Univ, 42-43; org chemist, Gelatin Prod Corp, Mich, 43-45; dir res, Boyle-Midway Div, Am Home Prod Co, NJ, 45-48; org chemist, Pineapple Res Inst, Hawaii, 48-66, head chem dept, 61-66; chem consult & group leader, 69-77, sr scientist & leader, Agr Div, Amchem Prod, Inc, 77-78; RETIRED. *Concurrent Pos:* Vis prof, Mich State Univ, 55; vis scientist, NZ, 62. *Mem:* AAAS; Am Chem Soc. *Res:* Organometallics; synthesis of potential herbicides and plant growth regulators. *Mailing Add:* 83 Woodside Ave Chalfont PA 18914

LEER, JOHN ADDISON, JR, b Carlisle, Pa, Dec 8, 22; m 46; c 2. MEDICINE, PEDIATRICS. *Educ:* Temple Univ, MD, 46, MSc, 52; Am Bd Pediat, dipl, 52. *Prof Exp:* Pvt pract, Pa, 52-63; physician monitor, 63-65, assoc dir, 65-68, dir clin invest, 68-73, sr fel med res, 73-76, SR DIR DERMATOL, MED RES DIV, SCHERING CORP, 76- *Concurrent Pos:* Clin asst prof pediat, Col Med & Dent NJ, 67-72. *Mem:* Fel Am Acad Pediat; Am Acad Dermat; Am Soc Clin Pharmacol & Therapeut; Soc Pediat Dermat; Am Soc Photobiol. *Res:* Clinical investigation of new drugs. *Mailing Add:* Schering Corp 60 Orange St Bloomfield NJ 07003

LEERBURGER, BENEDICT ALAN, JR, b New York, NY, Jan 2, 32; m 58; c 2. SCIENCE WRITING, JOURNALISM. *Educ:* Colby Col, BA, 54. *Prof Exp:* Asst ed, Prod Eng Mag, 54-59; sci ed, Grolier, Inc, 59-61; ed, Cowles Ed Corp, 61-68; proj dir, CCM Info Sci, Inc, 68-70; vpres & ed dir, Nat Micro-Publ Corp, 70-72; dir publ, NY Times, 72-74; publ, Kraus-Thomson Org, Ltd, 74-76; CONSULT COMPUT SCI, PHYSICAL SCI & GEN SCI COMMUN, 76- *Concurrent Pos:* Consult, Sci Digest, 59-61, Cross, Hinshaw & Lindberg, Inc, 65-67, Storrington Printing & Pub Co, Inc, 67-70 & NSF Deep Freeze Prog, Antarctica, 67; ed-in-chief, McGraw-Hill Book Co, 71-80, freelance sci ed, 80- *Mem:* Nat Asn Sci Writers; Am Hist Asn; Nat Sci Teachers Asn. *Res:* Physical science; Antarctica; American scientific history. *Mailing Add:* 338 Heathcote Rd Scarsdale NY 10583

LEERS, WOLF-DIETRICH, b Halle, Ger, Aug 9, 27; Can citizen; c 4. MEDICAL MICROBIOLOGY. *Educ:* Univ Würzburg, MD, 55; Univ Toronto, dipl bact, 63, PhD(microbiol), 67; Am Bd Med Microbiol, cert pub health, 71; FRCP(C). *Prof Exp:* Intern, Univ Clin, Hamburg-Eppendorf, Ger, 55-56; resident otolaryngol, City Hosp, Verden, Ger, 56-58; intern, Victoria Hosp, London, Ont, 58-59; asst resident med, pediat & surg, St Jospeh's Hosp, 59-60; resident clin microbiol, Victoria Hosp, 60-61; resident path & microbiol, Lab Serv Br, Ont Dept Pub Health, 61-62; Fitzgerald Mem fel, 63-65, ASSOC PROF MED MICROBIOL, FAC MED & ASST PROF MICROBIOL, SCH HYG, UNIV TORONTO, 66-; CHIEF MICROBIOLOGIST, WELLESLEY HOSP, 67- *Concurrent Pos:* Consult, Ontario Cancer Inst & Princess Margaret Hosp, 67; civil aviation examr, dept transport, Ministry Ont. *Mem:* Can Asn Med Microbiol; Can Soc Assoc Clin Microbiol & Infectious Dis; Am Soc Microbiol; Can Pub Health Asn; Can Soc Microbiol. *Res:* Reoviruses; hepatitis B; urinary tract infections; opportunistic fungal and bacterial infections; respiratory tract infections. *Mailing Add:* Dept of Microbiol Wellesley Hosp Toronto ON M4Y 1J3 Can

LEE-RUFF, EDWARD, b Shanghai, China, Jan 4, 44; Can citizen; m 69. CHEMISTRY. *Educ:* McGill Univ, BSc, 64, PhD(org chem), 67. *Prof Exp:* Nat Res Coun fel, Columbia Univ, 67-69; asst prof, 69-74, ASSOC PROF CHEM, YORK UNIV, 74- *Mem:* Am Chem Soc; Chem Inst Can. *Res:* Organic photochemistry; reactions of strained molecules; gas-phase organic ion-molecule reactions. *Mailing Add:* Dept of Chem York Univ Downsview ON M3J 1P3 Can

LEES, DAVID ERIC BERMAN, b Boston, Mass, July 22, 50; m 77. IMAGE PROCESSING. *Educ:* Oakland Univ, BS, 72; Univ Rochester, MS, 74, PhD(optics), 79. *Prof Exp:* PRIN DEVELOP ENGR, HONEYWELL, 79- *Mem:* Optical Soc Am. *Res:* Thin film polarizers; digital image processing. *Mailing Add:* 3 Rolling Lane Lexington MA 02173

LEES, HELEN, b Detroit, Mich, June 1, 25. BIOCHEMISTRY. *Educ:* Wayne State Univ, BS, 47, PhD(physiol chem), 56. *Prof Exp:* Fel biochem, Edsel B Ford Inst Med Res, 56-58; biochemist, Lafayette Clin, State Dept Health, Mich, 58-62; asst prof biochem, Med Sch, Northwestern Univ, 62-68; ASSOC PROF MED TECHNOL, STATE UNIV NY BUFFALO, 68- *Mem:* AAAS; Am Chem Soc; Am Soc Med Technol; Am Soc Clin Chem. *Res:* Intermediary metabolism; clinical chemistry. *Mailing Add:* Dept Med Technol State Univ NY Buffalo NY 14214

LEES, LESTER, b New York, NY, Nov 8, 20; m 41; c 1. AERONAUTICAL ENGINEERING. *Educ:* Mass Inst Technol, SB, 40, ScM, 41. *Prof Exp:* Asst aeronaut eng, Mass Inst Technol, 40-41; aeronaut engr, Air Materiel Command, US Army, Wright Field, 41-42; instr aeronaut eng, Calif Inst Technol, 42-44; aeronaut engr, Nat Adv Comt Aeronaut, Langley Field, Va, 44-46; assoc prof aeronaut eng, Princeton Univ, 46-53; aeronaut & appl mech, 53-55, PROF AERONAUT, CALIF INST TECHNOL, 55- *Mem:* Nat Acad Eng; Am Phys Soc; fel Am Inst Aeronaut & Astronaut; fel Am Acad Arts & Sci. *Res:* Problems of subsonic and supersonic gas flows, including boundary layers, shock waves and gas dynamic aspects of combustion; plasma dynamics; environmental engineering; large-scale environmental problems, including air pollution control, energy supply and electric power plant siting and transportation. *Mailing Add:* 1911 N Pepper Dr Altadena CA 91001

LEES, MARJORIE BERMAN, b New York, NY, Mar 17, 23; m 46; c 3. NEUROCHEMISTRY. *Educ:* Hunter Col, BA, 43; Univ Chicago, MS, 45; Harvard Univ, PhD(med sci), 51. *Prof Exp:* Asst, Univ Chicago, 43-45; asst, Col Physicians & Surgeons, Columbia Univ, 45-46; Am Cancer Soc res fel, 51-53; asst res lab, McLean Hosp, 53-55, asst biochemist, 55-58, assoc biochemist, 58-62; sr res assoc pharmacol, Dartmouth Med Sch, 62-66; assoc biochemist, McLean Hosp, 66-76; 66-; SR RES ASSOC, HARVARD MED 75-; BIOCHEMIST, EUNICE KENNEDY SHRIVER CTR, 76- *Concurrent Pos:* Instr neuropath, Harvard Med Sch, 55-59, res assoc, 59-62 & 66-71, prin res assoc, 71-75. *Mem:* Am Soc Biol Chem; Am Soc Neurochem (treas, 75-81); Soc Neurosci; Am Soc Neuropath; Int Soc Neurochem. *Res:* Chemistry of the nervous system; lipid chemistry; brain proteins; myelin and demyelinating diseases. *Mailing Add:* E K Shriver Ctr 200 Trapelo Rd Waltham MA 02254

LEES, MARTIN H, b London, Eng, May 11, 29; m 59; c 3. PEDIATRICS, CARDIOLOGY. *Educ:* Univ London, MB, BS, 55. *Prof Exp:* Assoc prof, 62-71, PROF PEDIAT, MED SCH, UNIV ORE, 71- *Res:* Pediatric cardiology; newborn and infant cardiopulmonary physiology and pathophysiology. *Mailing Add:* Dept of Pediat Univ of Ore Med Sch Portland OR 97201

LEES, NORMAN DOUGLAS, b Providence, RI, Sept 16, 45; m 81; c 1. MICROBIOLOGY, MOLECULAR BIOLOGY. *Educ:* Providence Col, AB, 67; Northwestern Univ, PhD(microbiol), 73. *Prof Exp:* Teaching asst biol sci, Northwestern Univ, 67-73; ASST PROF BIOL, IND UNIV-PURDUE UNIV, INDIANAPOLIS, 73- *Concurrent Pos:* Grants, Ind Univ-Purdue Univ, Indianapolis, 74 & Biomed Sci Res, 75 & 77. *Mem:* Am Soc Microbiol; Sigma Xi. *Res:* Role of sterols in biological membranes. *Mailing Add:* Dept of Biol 1201 E 38th St Indianapolis IN 46205

LEES, ROBERT S, b New York, NY, July 16, 34; m 60; c 4. MEDICINE, BIOCHEMISTRY. *Educ:* Harvard Univ, AB, 55, MD, 59; Am Bd Internal Med, dipl. *Prof Exp:* Intern surg, Mass Gen Hosp, Boston, 59-60, asst resident, 61-62; hon asst registr cardiol, Nat Heart Hosp, Eng. 62-63; staff assoc & attend physician med, Nat Heart Inst, 63-66; asst prof med & attend physician, Rockefeller Univ, 66-69; dir clin res ctr, 69-74, assoc prof, 69-71, PROF CARDIOVASC DIS & DIR ARTERIOSCLEROSIS CTR, MASS INST TECHNOL, 71-; CHIEF, DIV PERIPHERAL VASCULAR DIS & DIR MED RES, NEW ENG DEACONESS HOSP, 82- *Concurrent Pos:* USPHS res fel med, 60-61; Dalton scholar, Harvard Med Sch, 60; USPHS fel, 62-63; fel coun arteriosclerosis, Am Heart Asn, 65-; lectr, Harvard Med Sch; assoc in med, Peter Bent Brigham Hosp; asst in med, Mass Gen Hosp. *Mem:* Am Heart Asn; Am Fedn Clin Res; Am Soc Clin Invest; Am Soc Pharmacol & Exp Therapeut. *Res:* Cardiology, especially ischemic heart disease; lipid and lipoprotein metabolism. *Mailing Add:* New Eng Deaconess Hosp 185 Pilgram Rd Boston MA 02215

LEES, RONALD MILNE, b Sutton, Eng, Oct 28, 39; Can citizen; m 62; c 2. MOLECULAR SPECTROSCOPY. *Educ:* Univ BC, BSc, 61, MSc, 65; Bristol Univ, PhD(physics), 67. *Prof Exp:* Nat Res Coun Can fel, Nat Res Coun, Ottawa, 66-68; assoc prof, 68-77, PROF PHYSICS, UNIV NB, FREDERICTON, 77- *Concurrent Pos:* Nat Res Coun Can grant, Univ NB, Fredericton, 68- vis assoc prof, Physics Dept, Univ BC, Vancouver, 74-75. *Mem:* Can Asn Physicists; Am Asn Physics Teachers. *Mailing Add:* Dept of Physics Univ of NB Fredericton NB E3B 5A3 Can

LEES, SIDNEY, b Philadelphia, Pa, Apr 17, 17; m 46; c 3. ENGINEERING. *Educ:* City Col New York, BS, 38; Mass Inst Technol, SM, 48, ScD(eng), 50. *Prof Exp:* Observer, US Weather Bur, 38-40; engr, US Signal Corps, 40-43; res assoc aeronaut, Mass Inst Technol, 47-50, asst prof, 50-57; consult instrumentation, 57-59; vpres, United Res, Inc, 59; pres, Lees Instrument Res, Inc, 59-63; prof eng, Dartmouth Col, 62-66; SR STAFF MEM & HEAD BIOENG DEPT, FORSYTH DENT CTR, BOSTON, 66- *Concurrent Pos:* Chmn, Joint Automatic Control Conf, 65 & Res Conf Instrumentation Sci, 71; vis scientist, Univ Amsterdam Dent Sch, 75; chmn, Conf Ultrasonics, 78; joint chmn, NE Doppler Conf, 81; adj prof, Northeastern Univ. *Mem:* Am Phys Soc; Am Soc Mech Engrs; Inst Elec & Electronics Engrs; Am Acoust Soc. *Res:* Ultrasonics; bioinstrumentation; measurement systems and components; control systems; geophysical instrumentation. *Mailing Add:* 50 Eliot Memorial Rd Newton MA 02158

LEES, THOMAS MASSON, b New York, NY, June 16, 17; m 43; c 2. BIOCHEMISTRY. *Educ:* Long Island Univ, BS, 39; Iowa State Univ, MS, 42, PhD(biophys chem), 44. *Prof Exp:* Res chemist, Am Distilling Co, 44-46; anal res chemist, Pfizer, Inc, 46-80; RETIRED. *Mem:* Am Chem Soc. *Res:* Fermentative production of glycerol; antibiotics development, production and identification; analysis of medicinal compounds. *Mailing Add:* 35 Woodridge Circle Gales Ferry CT 06335

LEES, WAYNE LOWRY, b Washington, DC, July 18, 14; m 39; c 2. EXPERIMENTAL PHYSICS, ENGINEERING PHYSICS. *Educ:* Swarthmore Col, BA, 37; Harvard Univ, MA, 40, PhD(physics), 49. *Prof Exp:* Asst, Bartol Res Found, Pa, 39-40; physicist, Geophys Lab, Wash, DC, 42-44, Nat Bur Standards, 44-46, Tracerlab, Inc, 49-50, Metall Proj, Mass Inst Technol, 50-54, Nuclear Metals, Inc, 54-58, Instrumentation Lab, Mass Inst Technol, 58-65 & Electronics Res Ctr, NASA, Cambridge, 65-70; assoc prof math, Wash Tech Inst, 71-72; proj engr, Design Automation, Inc, Lexington, Mass, 72-73; STAFF MEM, LAB PHYS SCI, P R MALLORY & CO, INC, BURLINGTON, MASS, 74-; MEM STAFF, DURACELL INT, INC, 80- *Mem:* AAAS; Am Phys Soc; Fedn Am Sci; Inst Elec & Electronics Engrs. *Res:* Quasistatic electrical systems and dielectric properties; physics of high pressures and metals; electrode phenomena; electron and ion transport; engineering physics. *Mailing Add:* 29 Tower Rd Lexington MA 02173

LEESE, BERNARD M, b Keyser, WVa, Jan 17, 25; m 50; c 3. PLANT PHYSIOLOGY. *Educ:* George Washington Univ, BS, 51. *Prof Exp:* Res botanist, 51-55, plant explorer, 56-59, plant variety specialist, 59-62, head fed seed lab, 62-70, chief plant exam, 70-78, COMNR PLANT VARIETY PROTECTION OFF, USDA, 78- *Concurrent Pos:* Mem plant nomenclature comt, USDA, 61-; consult, Am Soc Hort Sci, 65-; plant explorer for world sorghum germ plasm collection in Ethiopia, 67; observer, Int Union Protection New Varieties Plants, 72-; exec secy, Plant Variety Protection Bd, USDA, 78- *Mem:* Asn Off Seed Analysts; Int Seed Testing Asn; NY Acad Sci. *Res:* Identification of plant and seed material by morphological characteristics; identification of plant germ plasm; plant variety nomenclature and plant variety identification. *Mailing Add:* Plant Var Protect Off Grain Div Agr & Mkt Serv Nat Agr Libr USDA Beltsville MD 20705

LEESER, DAVID O(SCAR), b El Paso, Tex, Aug 3, 17; m 45; c 2. METALLURGY, MATERIALS ENGINEERING. *Educ:* Univ Tex, BS, 43; Ohio State Univ, MS, 50. *Prof Exp:* Metallurgist, Bradley Mining Co, Idaho, 43-44; res engr, Battelle Mem Inst, 44-50; assoc metallurgist, Argonne Nat Lab, 50-54; staff metallurgist & chief mat sect, Atomic Power Develop Assocs, Inc, 54-61; chief scientist, Missile Div, Chrysler Corp, 61-68, chief metallurgist, Amplex Div, 68-75; MGR, ENG MAT LAB, BURROUGHS CORP, 75- *Concurrent Pos:* Reactor mat engr, Nuclear Power Dept, Detroit Edison Co, 54-61; mem, Atomic Indust Forum; mem welding forum, US Atomic Energy Comn, 54-64, high temperature nuclear fuel comt, 57-61; US del, World Metall Cong, 57, Int Conf Peaceful Uses of Atomic Energy, Geneva, 58 & Int Atomic Energy Agency Conf, Vienna, 61. *Honors & Awards:* Award, Off Sci Res & Develop; Award, Nat Adv Comt Aeronaut, 44. *Mem:* Am Soc Testing & Mat; Sigma Xi; Am Soc Mech Engrs; Am Mgt Asn; Am Soc Metals. *Res:* Evaluation of aerospace designs with regard to conventional and nonconventional materials applications and advanced aerospace requirements; ground and launch support equipment; materials for high-speed computer and electromechanical business machine systems under development; failure analysis in each category. *Mailing Add:* 13144 Winchester Huntington Woods MI 48070

LEESON, BRUCE FRANK, b Florence, Ont, Aug 20, 43; m 66; c 1. ECOLOGY, ENVIRONMENTAL MANAGEMENT. *Educ:* Univ Guelph, BSc, 67, MSc, 69; Mont State Univ, PhD(natural resources), 72. *Prof Exp:* Researcher soil sci, Ont Dept Agr & Food, 66-69; RES ECOLOGIST, PARKS CAN, CAN GOVT NAT & HIST PARKS BR, 72- *Mem:* Can Nature Fedn; Soil Conserv Soc Am. *Res:* Scientific management of wilderness environments in Canada's Rocky Mountain National Parks where the objective is to facilitate recreation without disturbing wildland ecosystems. *Mailing Add:* 10011 5th St SE Calgary AB T2J 1L4 Can

LEESON, CHARLES ROLAND, b Halifax, Eng, Jan 26, 26; m 54; c 5. ANATOMY. *Educ:* Cambridge Univ, BA, 47, MB, BChir, 50, MA, 50, MD, 59, PhD(anat), 71. *Prof Exp:* Lectr anat, Univ Col SWales, 55-58; assoc prof, Dalhousie Univ, 58-61; assoc prof anat & histol, Queen's Univ, Ont, 61-63; prof anat, Univ Iowa, 63-66; prof anat & chmn dept, Univ Mo-Columbia, 66-78; PROF ANAT & DIR PROG ANAT, SCH BASIC MED SCI, UNIV ILL, 78- *Concurrent Pos:* Vis prof anat, London Hosp Med Col, Eng, 73-74. *Mem:* Anat Soc Gt Brit & Ireland; Am Asn Anat; Electron Micros Soc Am. *Res:* Post natal development, particularly in marsupials and rodents and with reference to certain organ systems. *Mailing Add:* Sch of Basic Med Sci Univ of Ill Urbana IL 61801

LEESON, LEWIS JOSEPH, b Paterson, NJ, Apr 26, 27; m 53; c 3. PHARMACY. *Educ:* Rutgers Univ, BS, 50, MS, 54; Univ Mich, PhD(pharmaceut chem), 57. *Prof Exp:* Intern pharm, Mack Drug Co, 50-51; pharmacist, Silver Rod Drugs, 51-52; asst, Rutgers Univ, 52-54 & Univ Mich, 55-56; res chemist, Lederle Labs, Am Cyanamid Co, 57-67; proj leader pharmaceut, Union Carbide Res Inst, 67-69; asst dir pharmaceut develop, Geigy Chem Corp, 69-71, asst dir, 71-73, dir, 73-78, sr dir pharm res & develop, 78-80, SR RES FEL BIOPHARM, CIBA-GEIGY PHARMACEUT CO, 80- *Concurrent Pos:* Relief pharmacist, Frieds Pharm, 52-54. *Mem:* Am Chem Soc; Am Pharmaceut Asn; fel Acad Pharmaceut Sci; Sigma Xi; fel Acad Pharmaceut Sci. *Res:* Pharmaceutical product development; application of physical chemical techniques for developing various pharmaceutical dosage forms; biopharmaceutics; pharmacokinetics. *Mailing Add:* Pharm Res Ciba-Geigy Pharm Co Morris Ave Summit NJ 07901

LEESON, THOMAS SYDNEY, b Halifax, UK, Jan 26, 26; m 52; c 3. ANATOMY. *Educ:* Cambridge Univ, BA, 46, MA, 49, MD & BCh, 50, MD, 59, PhD, 71. *Prof Exp:* Asst lectr anat, Univ Wales, 55-57; from asst prof to assoc prof, Univ Toronto, 57-63; PROF ANAT & HEAD DEPT, UNIV ALTA, 63- *Mem:* Am Asn Anat; Can Fedn Biol Soc; Anat Soc Gt Brit & Ireland. *Res:* Electron microscopy, histology and embryology. *Mailing Add:* Dept Anat Univ Alta Edmonton AB T6G 2E8 Can

LEESTMA, JAN E, b Flint, Mich, Nov 30, 38; m 61; c 2. PATHOLOGY, NEUROPATHOLOGY. *Educ:* Hope Col, BA, 60; Univ Mich, MD, 64. *Prof Exp:* Resident & intern path, Univ Colo Med Sch, Denver, 64-67; fel neuropath, Einstein Med Col & instr path, Univ Colo Med Sch, Denver, 67-68; asst prof, 71-76, ASSOC PROF PATH, SCH MED, NORTHWESTERN UNIV, 76- *Concurrent Pos:* Consult, DC Gen Hosp, Washington, DC, 69-71, Nat Naval Med Ctr, Bethesda, Md, 69-70, Vet Admin Lakeside Hosp & Vet Admin North Chicago Hosp, Ill, 71-, Baxter-Travenol Labs, Morton Grove, Ill, 73-76, Great Lakes Naval Hosp, Ill, 74- & W Suburban Hosp, Oak Park, Ill, 76-; attend physician, Northwestern Mem Hosp, Chicago, 71-; asst med examr, Cook County Off Med Examr, Chicago, 77- *Mem:* Am Asn Neuropathologists; Sigma Xi; AAAS; Am Asn Univ Profs. *Res:* Experimental neurology; axoplasmic transport; neurological degenerative disease; central nervous system tissue culture; motor neuron disease; computerized data analysis; electron microscopy. *Mailing Add:* Dept of Path 303 E Chicago Ave Chicago IL 60611

LEET, DUANE GARY, b Duncan, Okla, May 29, 44; m 66; c 2. DESIGN AUTOMATION, INFORMATION SCIENCE. *Educ:* Mich State Univ, BS, 66, MS, 68, PhD(systs sci), 71. *Prof Exp:* Res assoc environ mgt, Mich State Univ, 71-72; asst prof comput sci, Univ Evansville, 72-74; assoc res analyst bionics, Univ Dayton Res Inst, 74-78; sr assoc programmer, 78-79, STAFF ENGR, IBM CORP, 79- *Res:* Very large scale integration architecture and design for testability; very large scale integration design automation systems, especially relating to testing; speech recognition; information processing in mammalian auditory system; simulation of whole body and body segment dynamics. *Mailing Add:* Dept G44 IBM Corp Essex Junction VT 05452

LEET, HENRY PETER, b El Dorado, Kans, Dec 4, 32; m 63; c 2. OPTICS. *Educ:* Univ Kans, BS, 55. *Prof Exp:* Physicist, 55-61, head, Detection Br, 61-70 & Optics Technol Br, 70-74, HEAD, OPTICS & SENSORS BR, MICHAELSON LABS, NAVAL WEAPONS CTR, 74- *Concurrent Pos:* Consult, targeting syst. *Mem:* AAAS; Sigma Xi; Optical Soc Am; NY Acad Sci. *Res:* Infrared detection; spectro-radiometric analysis of all types of thermal emitters; visual and infrared image converters and trackers; infrared and electro-optical active and passive sensors; signal processing. *Mailing Add:* 627 Kevin Ct Ridgecrest CA 93555

LEETCH, JAMES FREDERICK, b Butler, Pa, Sept 27, 29; m 58; c 2. MATHEMATICS. *Educ:* Grove City Col, BS, 51; Ohio State Univ, MA, 57, PhD(math), 61. *Prof Exp:* From asst prof to assoc prof, 61-71, PROF MATH, BOWLING GREEN STATE UNIV, 71- *Mem:* Math Asn Am. *Res:* Mathematical analysis. *Mailing Add:* 19 Darlyn Dr Bowling Green OH 43402

LEETE, EDWARD, b Leeds, Eng, Apr 18, 28; nat US; m 54, 76; c 5. ORGANIC CHEMISTRY. *Educ:* Univ Leeds, BSc, 48, PhD(chem), 50, DSc, 65. *Prof Exp:* Goldsmith fel, Nat Res Coun Can, 50-52, res fel, 52-54; from instr to asst prof org chem, Univ Calif, Los Angeles, 54-58; from asst prof to assoc prof, 58-63, PROF ORG CHEM, UNIV MINN, MINNEAPOLIS, 63- *Concurrent Pos:* Mem med chem study sect, NIH, 61-65; Alfred P Sloan fel, 61, 63 & 64; Guggenheim mem fel, 65-66; consult, Philip Morris Res Ctr, Richmond, Va, 74- *Mem:* Am Chem Soc; Am Soc Pharmacog; Royal Soc Chem. *Res:* Biosynthesis of natural substances, especially alkaloids; synthesis of heterocyclic compounds; isolation of enzymes from plants; use of radioactive and stable isotopes. *Mailing Add:* Dept of Chem Univ of Minn Minneapolis MN 55455

LEEVY, CARROLL M, b Columbia, SC, Oct 13, 20; m 56; c 2. MEDICINE, NUTRITION. *Educ:* Fisk Univ, AB, 41; Univ Mich, MD, 44. *Prof Exp:* Intern med, Jersey City Med Ctr, 44-45, resident, 45-48, dir clin invest & outpatient dept, 48-58; res assoc, Harvard Univ, 58-59; assoc prof, 59-62, actg chmn dept med, 66-68, PROF MED, COL MED NJ, 62-, DIR DIV HEPATIC METAB & NUTRIT, 59- *Concurrent Pos:* USPHS spec res fel, 58-59; consult, US Naval Hosp, St Albans, 48; consult & mem med adv comt, Vet Admin Hosp, East Orange, NJ, 64; physician-in-chief, Martland Hosp, 66-68; mem dean's comt, East Orange Vet Admin Hosp, 66-68, chief med, 66-71; mem clin cancer training comt, NIH, 69-73; consult, Food & Drug Admin, 70- *Honors & Awards:* Mod Med Award, 72. *Mem:* AAAS; Soc Exp Biol & Med; Nat Med Asn; fel AMA; fel Am Col Physicians. *Res:* Pathogenesis of cirrhosis of alcoholics; factors which control hepatic desoxyribonucleic acid synthesis and regeneration; mechanism of portal hypertension and malutilization of vitamins and proteins. *Mailing Add:* Col of Med 100 Bergen St Newark NJ 07103

LEFAR, MORTON SAUL, b New York, NY, Apr 11, 37; m 61; c 2. ORGANIC CHEMISTRY. *Educ:* Brooklyn Col, BS, 58, MA, 62; Rutgers Univ, PhD(chem), 65. *Prof Exp:* Res chemist, Inst Environ Med, Med Sch, NY Univ, 58-60; sect head org chem div nutrit, Food & Drug Admin, Washington, DC, 66-68; sr scientist, Warner-Lambert Res Inst, 68-69; mgr anal chem, Rhodia, Inc, 69-74; dir qual control, Hoechst-Roussel Pharmaceut, Inc, 75-78; LECTR CHEM, RUTGERS UNIV, 79-; CONSULT PHARMACEUT, 79- *Mem:* Am Pharmaceut Asn; Am Chem Soc. *Res:* Natural products chemistry; analytical chemistry; photochemistry; environmental health; analytical methods development on new pharmaceuticals, identification and proof of structure. *Mailing Add:* Cherry Tree Lane Chester NJ 07930

LEFAVE, GENE M(ARION), b Green Bay, Wis, May 18, 24; m 48; c 7. CHEMISTRY, ENGINEERING. *Educ:* Univ Notre Dame, BS, 48, MS, 50. *Prof Exp:* Staff engr, P R Mallory & Co, Ind, 53-54; sr staff engr, Lear, Inc, 54-56; chief engr, M Giannini & Co, 56; tech dir, Coast Pro-Seal & Mfg Co, 56-64; consult chemist, 65-75; PRES, FLUID POLYMER SYST INC, 75- *Concurrent Pos:* Consult, US Corps Engrs, 65-71, Joslyn Mfg & Supply Co, 65-, Diamond Shamrock Corp, 66-71 & Arco Chem Co, 70- *Mem:* Am Chem Soc; Soc Plastics Engrs; Am Concrete Inst; fel Am Inst Chem; Am Inst Chem Eng. *Res:* Polymer development and engineering. *Mailing Add:* PO Box 235 El Cajon CA 92022

LEFCOE, NEVILLE, b Montreal, Que, July 19, 25; m 54; c 4. PHYSIOLOGY. *Educ:* McGill Univ, BSc, 46; Vanderbilt Univ, MD, 50; FRCP(C), 56. *Prof Exp:* From instr to assoc prof, 57-72, PROF MED, UNIV WESTERN ONT, 72- *Mem:* Am Fedn Clin Res; Can Soc Clin Invest. *Res:* Pulmonary physiology, chiefly exercise physiology, cellular mechanisms in bronchial mouth muscle and the domestic microenvironment. *Mailing Add:* Dept of Med Victoria Hosp London ON N6A 5B8 Can

LEFEBRE, VERNON GLEN, b Hammond, Ind, July 2, 36; m; c 4. THERMODYNAMICS. *Educ:* Purdue Univ, BS, 58; Univ Utah, PhD(phys chem), 63. *Prof Exp:* Asst prof, 64-68, ASSOC PROF PHYSICS, NMEX INST MINING & TECHNOL, 68- *Mem:* Am Geophys Union. *Res:* Mixing theory in aquifers. *Mailing Add:* Dept of Physics NMex Inst of Mining & Technol Socorro NM 87801

LE FEBVRE, EDWARD ELLSWORTH, b Great Falls, Mont, Mar 9, 33; m 53; c 4. ENVIRONMENTAL CHEMISTRY, ANALYTICAL CHEMISTRY. *Educ:* Univ Wash, BA, 54; Univ Tex, San Antonio, MS, 75. *Prof Exp:* Chemist, State Health Dept, Helena, Mont, 58-62; US Air Force, 62-, chief anal div, Environ Health Lab, McClellan AFB, Calif, 62-66, res chemist, Sch Aerospace Med, Brooks AFB, Tex, 66-68, chief environ studies br, Environ Health Lab, Kelly AFB, Tex, 68-74, dep chief anal div, 74-76, CHIEF ANAL SERV DIV, OCCUP & ENVIRON HEALTH LAB, US AIR FORCE, 76- *Concurrent Pos:* Comnr, Nat Cert Comn in Chem & Chem Eng, 77-81. *Mem:* Am Chem Soc; Am Indust Hyg Asn; Am Inst Chemists; Am Conf Govt Indust Hygenists. *Mailing Add:* US Air Force Occup & Environ Health Lab Brooks AFB TX 78235

LE FEBVRE, EUGENE ALLEN, b St Paul, Minn, Oct 18, 29; m 54. ZOOLOGY. *Educ:* Univ Minn, BS, 52, AP, 53, MS, 58, PhD(zool), 62. *Prof Exp:* Teaching asst ornith & zool, Univ Minn, Minneapolis, 53-59, res fel ornith, Mus Natural Hist, 60-61, res assoc, 61-66; asst prof, 66-72, ASSOC PROF ZOOL, SOUTHERN ILL UNIV, 72- *Concurrent Pos:* Res assoc, NIH grant, 60-65, coprin investr, 63-65; NSF res grant, Midway Island, 69-73. *Mem:* AAAS; Am Ornith Union; Cooper Ornith Soc; Ecol Soc Am; Am Inst Biol Sci. *Res:* Physiological ecology of birds and mammals, especially bioenergetics of flight and migratory behavior. *Mailing Add:* Dept of Zool Southern Ill Univ Carbondale IL 62901

LEFEBVRE, PAUL ALVIN, b Washington, DC, Mar 12, 50; m 81. DEVELOPMENTAL BIOLOGY. *Educ:* Univ Va, BA, 72; Yale Univ, MPhil, 78, PhD(biol), 80. *Prof Exp:* Fel, Mass Inst Technol, 80-81; ASST PROF GENETICS & CELL BIOL, UNIV MINN, 82- *Res:* Regulation of expression of genes for flagellar proteins in chlamydomonas. *Mailing Add:* Dept Genetics & Cell Biol 250 Biosci Ctr 1445 Gortner Ave St Paul MN 55108

LEFEBVRE, RENE, b Verdun, Que, Apr 5, 23; m 51; c 2. MEDICINE. *Educ:* Col Montreal, BA, 44; Univ Montreal, MD, 50; Univ Pa, DSc(med), 54. *Prof Exp:* From asst prof to assoc prof, 60-70, PROF PATH, FAC MED, UNIV MONTREAL, 70-; PATHOLOGIST, HOTEL DIEU HOSP, 50- *Mem:* Can Asn Path (pres-elect, 65-66, pres, 66-). *Res:* Pathology of kidney. *Mailing Add:* Dept of Path Hotel Dieu Hosp Montreal PQ H2W 1T6 Can

LEFEBVRE, RICHARD HAROLD, b Detroit, Mich, Dec 11, 33; m 59; c 3. GEOLOGY. *Educ:* Univ Mich, BS, 57; Univ Kans, MS, 61; Northwestern Univ, PhD(geol), 66. *Prof Exp:* Asst prof geol, Univ Ga, 65-67; from asst prof to assoc prof, 67-73, chmn dept, 70-75, PROF GEOL, GRAND VALLEY STATE COLS, 75-; GEOLOGIST, US GEOL SURV, 75- *Mem:* Geol Soc Am; Nat Asn Geol Teachers; Int Asn Volcanology. *Res:* Flood basalts of the northwestern United States; remote sensing of Holocene basaltic lava flows, especially Craters of the Moon National Monument, Idaho. *Mailing Add:* Dept of Geol Grand Valley State Cols Allendale MI 49401

LEFEBVRE, YVON, b Montreal, Que, June 20, 31; m 62; c 2. ORGANIC CHEMISTRY, INFORMATION SCIENCE. *Educ:* Col Stanislas, BA, 50; Univ Mont, BSc, 53, MSc, 55, PhD(chem), 57. *Prof Exp:* Res chemist, Ayerst Labs, 58-75, group leader, 68-75, DIR INFO DEPT, AYERST RES LABS, 75- *Res:* Steroids chemistry; progestational agents; estrogens; oxidation of furan derivatives in steroid and non-steroid series. *Mailing Add:* Ayerst Res Labs PO Box 6115 Montreal PQ H4T 1J7 Can

LEFER, ALLAN MARK, b New York, NY, Feb 1, 36; m 59; c 4. CARDIOVASCULAR PHYSIOLOGY. *Educ:* Adelphi Univ, BA, 57; Western Reserve Univ, MA, 59; Univ Ill, PhD(physiol), 62. *Prof Exp:* Instr physiol, Case Western Reserve Univ, 62-64; from asst prof to prof, Sch Med, Univ Va, 64-72; PROF PHYSIOL & CHMN DEPT, JEFFERSON MED COL, THOMAS JEFFERSON UNIV, 74- *Concurrent Pos:* USPHS fel, 62-64; estab investr, Am Heart Asn, 67-72; vis prof & USPHS sr fel, Hadassah Med Sch, Hebrew Univ, Israel, 71-72; mem comt pub affairs, Fedn Am Socs Exp Biol; ed, Circulatory Shock; consult, Task Group on Shock, NIH; mem, Int Study Group Res Cardiac Metab & Pancreatic Study Group; mem, coun basic sci, Am Heart Asn, circulation coun; mem, Study Sect Pharmacol, NIH. *Mem:* Am Physiol Soc; Cardiac Muscle Soc; Soc Exp Biol & Med; Am Soc Pharmacol & Exp Therapeut; Reticuloendothelial Soc. *Res:* Cardiovascular effects of adrenal hormones; humoral regulation of myocardial contractility; corticosteroid pharmacology; experimental myocardial infarction; metabolic alterations in shock; pathogenesis of circulatory shock; prostaglandins and thromboranes; pharmacology of coronary circulation. *Mailing Add:* Jefferson Med Col Dept of Physiol Thomas Jefferson Univ Philadelphia PA 19107

LEFEUVRE, ALBERT RICHARD, civil engineering, see previous edition

LE FEVER, HERMON MICHAEL, b Pomona, Calif, Dec 22, 37; m 57; c 2. GENETICS, ELECTRON MICROSCOPY. *Educ:* Okla State Univ, BS, 60, MS, 62; Univ Tex, PhD(zool), 66. *Prof Exp:* Res scientist asst genetics, Univ Tex, 63-65; asst prof biol, 65-70, ASSOC PROF BIOL, EMPORIA KANS STATE COL, 70- *Mem:* Genetics Soc Am. *Res:* Genetics of Drosophilia; pseudoallelism; chromosome ultrastructure; electron microscopy of chromosomes. *Mailing Add:* Dept of Biol Emporia Kans State Col Emporia KS 66801

LEFEVER, ROBERT ALLEN, b York, Pa, May 29, 27; m 46; c 3. SOLID STATE CHEMISTRY, MATERIALS SCIENCE. *Educ:* Juniata Col, BS, 50; Mass Inst Technol, PhD(inorg chem), 53. *Prof Exp:* Res chemist, Linde Co, 53-56; sr scientist, Va Inst Sci Res, 56-58; mem tech staff, Hughes Res Labs, 58-59; head chem physics group, 59-61; staff mem, Gen Tel & Electronics Labs, Inc, 61-63; supvr, Mat Res Div, Sandia Labs, 63-74; dir mat preparation, Sch Eng, Univ Southern Calif, 74-77; mgr, Process Eng Dept, 77-80, PLANT MGR, FERRITE MEMORY CORE PLANT, AMPEX CORP, 80- *Concurrent Pos:* Consult, Spectrotherm Corp, 74-77 & Luxtron Corp, 77- *Mem:* Am Phys Soc; Am Chem Soc; Am Ceramic Soc; fel Am Inst Chemists; Sigma Xi; Am Asn Crystal Growth. *Res:* Single crystal growth; growth mechanisms and characterization; sintering processes and mechanisms; ferrites; garnets; metal and rare earth oxides; semiconductors; phosphors; thermoelectrics. *Mailing Add:* 17609 Trosa St Granada Hills CA 91344

LEFEVRE, GEORGE, JR, b Columbia, Mo, Sept 13, 17; m 43, 72; c 3. GENETICS. *Educ:* Univ Mo, AB, 37, AM, 39, PhD(genetics), 49. *Prof Exp:* Asst zool, Columbia Univ, 41-42; res biologist, Oak Ridge Nat Lab, 46-47; instr zool, Univ Mo, 47-48; from asst prof to assoc prof biol, Univ Utah, 49-56; prog dir genetic biol, NSF, 56-59; dir biol labs, Harvard Univ, 59-65; chmn 65-79, PROF BIOL, CALIF STATE UNIV, NORTHRIDGE, 65- *Concurrent Pos:* Consult, NSF, 59-62 & NIH, 62-66, 79-; ed, Genetics, 76- *Mem:* Genetics Soc Am (treas, 72-75); Sigma Xi. *Res:* Radiation genetics of Drosophila melanogaster; mutation of individual loci; cytogenetics. *Mailing Add:* Dept of Biol Calif State Univ Northridge CA 91330

LEFEVRE, HARLAN W, b Great Falls, Mont, May 19, 29; m 51; c 8. NUCLEAR PHYSICS. *Educ:* Reed Col, BA, 51; Univ Idaho, MS, 57; Univ Wis, PhD(physics), 61. *Prof Exp:* Physicist, Hanford Atomic Prod Oper, Gen Elec Co, Wash, 51-58; assoc prof, 61-71, PROF PHYSICS, UNIV ORE, 71- *Concurrent Pos:* Consult, Lawrence Livermore Lab, Univ Calif, 62- *Mem:* Am Phys Soc. *Res:* Experimental nuclear physics; nuclear reactions; fast neutron spectrometry. *Mailing Add:* Dept of Physics Univ of Ore Eugene OR 97403

LEFEVRE, MARIAN E WILLIS, b Washington, DC, Jan 21, 23; m 48; c 3. PHYSIOLOGY. *Educ:* Iowa State Univ, BS, 44; Univ Pa, MS, 47; Univ Louisville, PhD(physiol), 69. *Prof Exp:* Assoc, 68-73, ASST PROF PHYSIOL, MT SIANI SCH MED, 73-; SCIENTIST, SCI, BROOKHAVEN NAT LAB, 78- *Concurrent Pos:* Res collabr, Brookhaven Nat Lab, 68-75. *Mem:* Am Physiol Soc; Am Gastroenterol Asn; Reticuloendothelial Soc; Am Soc Cell Biol; Soc Exp Biol & Med. *Res:* Structure and function of multicellular membranes; ion transport and metabolism; intestinal barrier function. *Mailing Add:* Med Dept Brookhaven Nat Lab Upton NY 11973

LEFEVRE, PAUL GREEN, b Baltimore, Md, Dec 27, 19; m 48; c 4. CELL PHYSIOLOGY. *Educ:* Johns Hopkins Univ, AB, 40; Univ Pa, PhD(physiol, zool), 45. *Prof Exp:* Asst zool, Univ Pa, 43-45; from instr to asst prof physiol, Col Med, Univ Vt, 45-49, assoc prof physiol & biophys, 49-52; asst to chief

med br, AEC, 52-55; scientist, Med Res Ctr, Brookhaven Nat Lab, 55-60; prof pharmacol, Sch Med, Univ Louisville, 60-68; PROF PHYSIOL & BIOPHYSICS, HEALTH SCI CTR, STATE UNIV NY STONY BROOK, 68- *Concurrent Pos:* mem corp, Marine Biol Lab, Woods Hole, Mass. *Mem:* AAAS; Soc Gen Physiol; Am Physiol Soc; Biophys Soc; Am Soc Cell Biologists. *Res:* Mechanisms, kinetics and model systems for cell membrane mediated transport; phospholipid-carbohydrate complexing. *Mailing Add:* Dept of Physiol & Biophys State Univ NY Health Sci Ctr Stony Brook NY 11794

LEFF, HARVEY SHERWIN, b Chicago, Ill, July 24, 37; m 58; c 6. THERMAL PHYSICS. *Educ:* Ill Inst Technol, BS, 59; Northwestern Univ, MS, 60; Univ Iowa, PhD(physics), 63. *Prof Exp:* Res assoc physics, Case Inst Technol, 63-64; from asst prof to assoc prof, 64-71; assoc prof & chmn dept phys sci, Chicago State Univ, 71-75, prof physics, 75-79; SCIENTIST, OAK RIDGE ASSOC UNIV, 79- *Concurrent Pos:* Vis prof physics, Col Sci & Eng, Harvey Mudd Col, 77-78. *Mem:* Am Asn Physics Teachers; Am Phys Soc; Sigma Xi. *Res:* Analysis of energy-related topics relevant to energy policymaking, including industrial energy conservation, energy emergency conservation potential and strategies, US natural gas information system, heat pump development; connections between entropy, forces and disorder; entropy production and efficiency for cyclic processes. *Mailing Add:* Inst Energy Anal Oak Ridge Assoc Univ Oak Ridge TN 37830

LEFF, JUDITH, b Vienna, Austria, July 6, 35; US citizen; m 61; c 3. MICROBIOLOGY, ANALYTICAL CHEMSITRY. *Educ:* Sorbonne, Lic natural sci, 58, PhD(photobiol), 61. *Prof Exp:* Jr researcher photobiol seed germination, Nat Ctr Sci Res, Paris, 60-61; res assoc photobiol, 61; fel biol, Brandeis Univ, 62-63; fel pharmacol, Sch Med, Tufts Univ, 65; res assoc, 66-67; res assoc plant morphogenesis, Manhattan Col, 67-71; NY Univ, 71-72 & Hebrew Univ, Jerusalem, 72-73; NIH spec res fel, Albert Einstein Col Med, 74-79; APPLN CHEMIST, FARRAND OPTICAL, 79- *Concurrent Pos:* Nat Res Serv award, Albert Einstein Col Med, 76-77. *Mem:* Sigma Xi; Am Soc Microbiol. *Res:* Photobiology; chloroplast development; molecular biology; microbiology; nucleic acids as tools for solving physiological or developmental questions; microbiology of crown gall; replication of mitochondrial DNA in yeast; fluorescence spectroscopy. *Mailing Add:* 5829 Liebig Ave Bronx NY 10471

LEFFAK, IRA MICHAEL, b New York, NY, Oct 13, 47; m 69; c 1. BIOCHEMISTRY. *Educ:* City Col New York, BS, 69; City Univ New York, PhD(biochem), 76. *Prof Exp:* Res fel biochem, Princeton Univ, 76-78; ASST PROF BIOCHEM, WRIGHT STATE UNIV, 70- *Concurrent Pos:* NIH fel, 76-78. *Mem:* AAAS. *Res:* Molecular biology of development; cell differentiation. *Mailing Add:* Dept of Biol Chem Wright State Univ Dayton OH 45435

LEFFALL, LASALLE DOHENY, JR, b Tallahassee, Fla, May 22, 30; m 56; c 1. SURGERY. *Educ:* Fla A&M Univ, BS, 48; Howard Univ, MD, 52; Am Bd Surg, dipl. *Prof Exp:* Intern, Homer G Phillips Hosp, St Louis, 52-53; resident, Freedmen's Gen Hosp, Washington, DC, 53-57 & Mem Sloan Kettering Cancer Ctr, New York, 57-59; from asst prof to assoc prof surg, 62-69, PROF SURG & CHMN DEPT, COL MED, HOWARD UNIV, 70- *Concurrent Pos:* Pvt pract med, Washington, DC, 62-; mem staff, Howard Univ Hosp. *Mem:* Inst of Med of Nat Acad Sci; Soc Surg Oncol (pres elect, 77-); Am Cancer Soc (pres elect, 77-); Am Surg Asn; Am Chem Soc. *Res:* Cancer diseases. *Mailing Add:* Howard Univ Hosp Washington DC 20060

LEFFEK, KENNETH THOMAS, b Nottingham, Eng, Oct 15, 34; m 58; c 2. PHYSICAL ORGANIC CHEMISTRY. *Educ:* Univ London, BSc, 56, PhD(chem), 59. *Prof Exp:* Nat Res Coun Can fel, 59-61; from asst prof to assoc prof, 61-72, PROF CHEM & DEAN GRAD STUDIES, DALHOUSIE UNIV, 72- *Concurrent Pos:* Leverhulme vis fel, Univ Kent, Canterbury, 67-68. *Mem:* Fel Chem Inst Can; Royal Soc Chem. *Res:* Kinetics and mechanisms of organic reactions; primary and secondary kinetic deuterium isotope effects. *Mailing Add:* Dept Chem Dalhousie Univ Halifax NS B3H 3J5 Can

LEFFEL, CLAUDE SPENCER, JR, b Pearisburg, Va, Dec 21, 21; m 80; c 2. PHYSICS. *Educ:* St John's Col, Md, BA, 43; Johns Hopkins Univ, PhD(physics), 60. *Prof Exp:* Tutor math & physics, St John's Col, Md, 46-50; SR PHYSICIST, APPL PHYSICS LAB, JOHNS HOPKINS UNIV, 60- *Mem:* AAAS; Am Phys Soc. *Res:* Plasma physics; nuclear physics; applied physics; atmospheric physics; cryogenics. *Mailing Add:* Appl Physics Lab Johns Hopkins Univ Laurel MD 20707

LEFFEL, EMORY CHILDRESS, b Pearisburg, Va, July 31, 23; m 56; c 2. ANIMAL SCIENCE. *Educ:* Univ Md, BS, 43, MS, 47, PhD(animal nutrit), 53. *Prof Exp:* Asst animal & dairy husb, Univ Md, 46-50; dairy husbandman, USDA, 50-51; instr dairy husb, 51-52; from asst prof to assoc prof animal husb, 53-68, PROF ANIMAL SCI, COL AGR, UNIV MD, COLLEGE PARK, 68- *Mem:* AAAS; Am Soc Animal Sci; Am Dairy Sci Asn. *Res:* Ruminant nutrition and physiology; protein and energy intake and effect of diet on rumen function in cattle and sheep; etiology of bloat in ruminants; bioenergetics. *Mailing Add:* Dept of Animal Sci Univ of Md College Park MD 20740

LEFFEL, ROBERT CECIL, b Woodbine, Md, Apr 26, 25; m 59; c 2. AGRONOMY, PLANT BREEDING. *Educ:* Univ Md, BS, 48; Iowa State Univ, MS, 50, PhD, 52. *Prof Exp:* Res agronomist, Agr Res Serv, 52-57; assoc prof agron, Univ Md, 57-62; investigative leader, 62-72, chief plant nutrit lab, Agr Res Serv, 72-75, chief, Cell Cult & Nitrogen Fixation Lab, 75-76; STAFF SCIENTIST OILSEED CROP PROD, NAT PROG STAFF, USDA, 76- *Mem:* AAAS; Am Soc Agron. *Res:* Soybean, forage crop and clover genetics; breeding and production. *Mailing Add:* Bldg 005-BARC-W Agr Res Serv USDA Beltsville MD 20705

LEFFELL, W(ILL) O(TIS), b Tazewell Co, Va, Dec 11, 12; m 41; c 2. ELECTRICAL ENGINEERING. *Educ:* Washington & Lee Univ, BS, 34; Univ Tenn MS, 39. *Prof Exp:* Asst, 36-39, from instr to prof, 40-77, EMER PROF ELEC ENG, UNIV TENN, KNOXVILLE, 77- *Mem:* Inst Elec & Electronics Engrs. *Res:* Physics; mathematics; magnetism; power generation; transmission and distribution; electrical apparatus and machinery. *Mailing Add:* Rte 1 Box 72 Louisville TN 37777

LEFFERT, CHARLES BENJAMIN, b Logansport, Ind, May 22, 22; m 45. ENERGY CONVERSION, CHEMICAL PHYSICS. *Educ:* Purdue Univ, BS, 43; Univ Pittsburgh, MS, 57; Wayne State Univ, PhD(chem eng), 74. *Prof Exp:* Chem engr, Res Dept, Union Oil Co Calif, 43-49; chem engr, Pittsburgh Consol Coal Co, 49-52; asst physics, Univ Pittsburgh, 52-56; sr res physicist, Res Labs, Gen Motors Corp, 57-70; res asst, Res Inst Eng Sci, 70-74, ASSOC PROF CHEM ENG, WAYNE STATE UNIV, 74-, DIR COL ENG ENERGY CTR, 74- *Mem:* Am Phys Soc; Am Inst Chem Engrs; Sigma Xi. *Res:* Chemical engineering. *Mailing Add:* Wayne State Col Eng Energy Ctr 5050 Anthony Wayne Dr Detroit MI 48202

LEFFERT, HYAM LERNER, b New York, NY, May 11, 44. CELL BIOLOGY. *Educ:* Univ Rochester, BA, 65; Brandeis Univ, MA, 67; Albert Einstein Col Med, MD, 71. *Prof Exp:* Fel, Salk Inst Biol Studies, 71-72, res assoc, 72-73, asst res prof cell biol, 73-80; ASSOC PROF MED, SCH MED, UNIV CALIF, SAN DIEGO, 80- *Concurrent Pos:* Res grant, Nat Cancer Inst, NSF & Diabetes Asn Southern Calif, 74; consult cell biol, Dept Nutrit Path, Mass Inst Technol, 76, Nat Heart & Lung Inst, 73- & Dept Med, Vet Admin Hosp, Dallas, 74-; res grant, Nat Cancer Inst, 76-80, Nat Inst Arthritis, Metab & Digestive Dis, 80- & Nat Inst Alcohol Abuse & Alcoholism, 80- *Mem:* Int Study Group Carcinoembryonic Proteins. *Res:* Mechanism of liver regeneration and differentiation in mammals. *Mailing Add:* Dept Med M-013-H Univ Calif San Diego La Jolla CA 92038

LEFFINGWELL, JOHN C, b Evanston, Ill, Feb 16, 38; m 60; c 3. ORGANIC CHEMISTRY. *Educ:* Rollins Col, BS, 60; Emory Univ, MS, 62, PhD(org chem), 63. *Prof Exp:* Res assoc org chem, Columbia Univ, 63-64; res chemist, Org Chem Div, Glidden Co, Fla, 64-65 & R J Reynolds Tobacco Co, 65-70; sect head res dept, R J Reynolds Industs Inc, 70-73, head flavor develop, R J Reynolds Tobacco Co, 73-75; vpres, Aromatics Int, 75-77; VPRES RES & DEVELOP, SUNKIST SOFT DRINKS, 78- *Concurrent Pos:* NIH fel, 63-64. *Honors & Awards:* Philip Morris Award for Distinguished Achievement in Tobacco Sci, Philip Morris Inc & Tobacco Sci, 74. *Mem:* Am Chem Soc; Royal Soc Chem; NY Acad Sci; Inst Food Technologists; AAAS. *Res:* Natural products; flavor chemistry; olfaction; consumer products. *Mailing Add:* 3945 Johnsons Ferry Ct Marietta GA 30062

LEFFINGWELL, THOMAS PEGG, JR, b San Marcos, Tex, June 27, 26; m 60; c 1. CELL BIOLOGY. *Educ:* Southwest Tex State Col, BS, 48, MA, 49; Univ Tex, Austin, PhD(biol sci), 70. *Prof Exp:* Asst dept head & instr aerospace physiol & radiobiol, US Air Force Sch Aerospace Med, Gunter AFB, 51-53; res assoc physiol, Univ Tex, 53-55; radiobiologist, Nat Hq, Fed Civil Defense Admin, 55-56; res physiologist & group leader, Radiobiol Lab, Univ Tex, Austin & US Air Force Sch Aerospace Med, 56-65; RES SCIENTIST, CELL RES INST, UNIV TEX, AUSTIN, 65- *Mem:* AAAS; Electron Micros Soc Am; Am Soc Cell Biologists. *Res:* Biosynthesis and physicochemical characteristics of extracellular protein-polysaccharides; matrix materials, antigenic and other recognition factors on the cell surface; specific receptor sites for biological molecules. *Mailing Add:* 8102 Hillrise Dr Austin TX 78759

LEFFLER, AMOS J, b New York, NY, Sept 9, 24; m 49; c 3. INORGANIC CHEMISTRY, PHYSICAL CHEMISTRY. *Educ:* Brooklyn Col, BS, 49; Univ Chicago, PhD(inorg chem), 53. *Prof Exp:* Chemist, Callery Chem Co, 52-55; res chemist, Stauffer Chem Co, 55-60; res assoc chem, Arthur D Little, Inc, 60-65; assoc prof, 65-75, PROF CHEM, VILLANOVA UNIV, 75- *Concurrent Pos:* Am Inst Chemists Award, Brooklyn Col, 49; sr res assoc, Nat Acad Sci-Nat Res Coun, 73. *Mem:* Am Chem Soc; Royal Soc Chem. *Res:* Inorganic and physical chemistry, especially boron and metallorganic chemistry, catalysis and metal oxides and fluorine chemistry. *Mailing Add:* Dept of Chem Villanova Univ Villanova PA 19085

LEFFLER, CHARLES WILLIAM, b Cleveland, Ohio, May 21, 47; m 68; c 1. CARDIOVASCULAR-PULMONARY PHYSIOLOGY, PERINATAL PHYSIOLOGY. *Educ:* Univ Miami, BS, 69; Univ Fla, MS, 71, PhD(zool), 74. *Prof Exp:* Teaching asst zool, Univ Fla, 69-73, coun fel, 73-74, fel, 74-76; asst prof physiol & biophys, Univ Louisville, 76-77; asst prof, 77-81, ASSOC PROF PHYSIOL & BIOPHYS, UNIV TENN CTR HEALTH SCI, 81- *Mem:* Am Physiol Soc; Soc Exp Biol & Med; AAAS; Sigma Xi; Am Soc Zoologists. *Res:* Pulmonary hemodynamics and the role of prostaglandins in the pulmonary vasculature; pharmacology; autacoids in control of perinatal circulation; prostaglandins and hormones in preeclampsia. *Mailing Add:* Dept Physiol & Biophys 894 Union Ave NA427 Memphis TN 38163

LEFFLER, ESTHER BARBARA, b Clearfield, Pa, Feb 1, 25. PHYSICAL CHEMISTRY. *Educ:* Pa State Univ, BS, 45; Univ Va, PhD(chem), 50. *Prof Exp:* Asst chemother, Stanford Res Labs, Am Cyanamid Co, 45-46; instr chem, Randolph-Macon Woman's Col, 49-53; from asst prof to prof chem, Sweet Briar Col, 53-66, chem dept, 56-59 & 60-66; from asst prof to assoc prof, 67-75, actg chmn dept, 73-74, PROF CHEM, CALIF STATE POLYTECH UNIV, 75-, ASSOC DEAN, SCH SCI, 78- *Concurrent Pos:* Res assoc & vis lectr, Stanford Univ, 66-67; res assoc, Oxford Univ, 74-75; resident dir, Calif State Univ Int Prog in UK, 74-75. *Mem:* Am Chem Soc; Sigma Xi. *Res:* Dissociation constants and reaction rates of bio-inorganic compounds; biochemical kinetics. *Mailing Add:* Sch of Sci Calif State Polytech Univ Pomona CA 91768

LEFFLER, HARRY REX, b Rensselaer, Ind, Sept 20, 42; m 71; c 3. PLANT PHYSIOLOGY, PLANT GENETICS. *Educ:* Iowa State Univ, BS, 64; Purdue Univ, MS, 67, PhD(plant physiol), 70. *Prof Exp:* Res assoc agron, Univ Ill, 70-71; res assoc hort, Purdue Univ, 71-72; PLANT PHYSIOLOGIST, COTTON PHYSIOL & GENETICS UNIT, AGR RES SERV, USDA, 72- *Concurrent Pos:* Assoc ed, Agron J, 82- *Mem:* Am Soc Agron; Am Soc Plant Physiologists; Crop Sci Soc Am. *Res:* Physiological genetics of seed development. *Mailing Add:* Cotton Physiol & Genetics Unit Agr Res Serv USDA Stoneville MS 38776

LEFFLER, JOHN EDWARD, b Brookline, Mass, Dec 27, 20; m 52. CHEMISTRY. *Educ:* Harvard Univ, BS, 42, PhD(org chem), 48. *Prof Exp:* Res assoc chem, Harvard Univ, 42-44 & Univ Chicago, 44-45; res assoc rocket fuels, US Navy Proj, Mass Inst Technol, 45-46; du Pont fel, Cornell Univ, 48-49; mem fac, Brown Univ, 49-50; from asst prof to assoc prof, 50-59, PROF CHEM, FLA STATE UNIV, 59- *Mem:* Am Chem Soc; The Chem Soc. *Res:* Reaction rate theory; polar and radical reactions; reactive intermediates of organic chemistry; peroxides; reactions of adsorbed organic compounds. *Mailing Add:* Dept of Chem Fla State Univ Tallahassee FL 32306

LEFFLER, MARLIN TEMPLETON, b College Corner, Ind, Feb 28, 11; m 33; c 3. ORGANIC CHEMISTRY. *Educ:* Miami Univ, AB, 32; Univ Ill, MA, 33, PhD(org chem), 36. *Prof Exp:* Asst chemist, Univ Ill, 33-35; res chemist, Abbott Labs, Ill, 36-46, head org dept, 46-49, asst dir res, 49-50, assoc dir, 50-57, dir chem & agr res, 57-59, dir sci liaison, 59-71; CONSULT, 71- *Mem:* Am Chem Soc. *Res:* Local anesthetics; antiseptics; chemotherapy; optical activity of organic deuterium compounds; organic medicinal chemistry; biochemistry; overseas technological advances. *Mailing Add:* 102 Whispering Sands Dr Sarasota-Siesta Key FL 33581

LEFKOWITZ, IRVING, b New York, NY, July 8, 21; m 55; c 2. SYSTEMS & CONTROL ENGINEERING. *Educ:* Cooper Union Sch Eng, BChE, 43; Case Inst Technol, MS, 55, PhD(control eng), 58. *Prof Exp:* Instrument engr, Calvert Distilling Co, 44-47; instrument engr, J E Seagram & Sons, Inc, 47-51, head instrumentation res, 51-53; res assoc instrumentation eng, 53-58, from asst prof to prof eng, 58-65, PROF SYSTS ENG & CHEM ENG, CASE WESTERN RESERVE UNIV, 65- *Concurrent Pos:* NATO fel, 62-63; res fel, Int Inst Appl Systs Anal, 74-75; mem systs eng comt, Int Fedn Automatic Control, 78-; fel, NATO. *Mem:* AAAS; fel Inst Elec & Electronics Engrs; Int Fedn Automatic Control; Sigma Xi. *Res:* Hierarchical computer control; control of industrial processes; energy conservation through integrated systems control. *Mailing Add:* Dept of Systs Eng, Comput Sci Case Western Reserve Univ Cleveland OH 44106

LEFKOWITZ, ISSAI, b New York, NY, Mar 13, 26; m 52; c 2. SOLID STATE PHYSICS. *Educ:* Brooklyn Col, BA, 59; Cambridge Univ, PhD(physics), 64. *Prof Exp:* Chief engr, Haines Industs, Inc, NJ, 53-54; physicist, Gulton Industs, Inc, 54-60; physicist res physics, Cavendish Lab, Cambridge Univ, 60-64; physicist, Pitman-Dunn Lab, Frankford Arsenal, Philadelphia, 64-72; pres, Princeton Mat Sci Inc, 72-75; prog mgr, Army Res Off, 75-76; gen mgr, Princeton Mat Sci Inc, 76-82; PROF UNIV NC, CHAPEL HILL, 82- *Concurrent Pos:* Guest scientist, Brookhaven Nat Lab, 54-60; fel neutron physics, Europ Atomic Energy Comn, Italy, 62-63; adj prof, Hunter Col; co-ed, Int J Ferroelec. *Mem:* Am Phys Soc; assoc Brit Inst Physics & Phys Soc. *Res:* Ferroelectricity; solid state; lattice dynamics; biophysics; administration with computer assistance. *Mailing Add:* PO Box 12211 US Army Res Off Reseach Triangle Park NC 27709

LEFKOWITZ, LEWIS BENJAMIN, JR, b Dallas, Tex, Dec 18, 30; m 61; c 3. MEDICINE. *Educ:* Denison Univ, BA, 51; Univ Tex Southwest Med Sch Dallas, MD, 56. *Prof Exp:* USPHS res fel med, Univ Tex Southwest Med Sch Dallas, 59-60, instr, 60-61; USPHS res fel, Univ Ill, 61-62, USPHS trainee infectious dis, 62-63; asst prof, 65-70, assoc prof, 70-78, PROF PREV MED, SCH MED, VANDERBILT UNIV, 78-, ASST PROF MED, 71- *Concurrent Pos:* Asst clin prof internal med, Meharry Med Col, 66-78, clin prof family & community med, 78-81, assoc clin prof internal med, 78-; consult, US Army Hosp, Ft Campbell, Ky, 69- *Mem:* AAAS; Am Col Prev Med; Am Pub Health Asn. *Res:* Epidemiology and pathogenesis of infectious diseases; health care delivery. *Mailing Add:* Dept of Prev Med Vanderbilt Univ Sch of Med Nashville TN 37232

LEFKOWITZ, ROBERT JOSEPH, b New York, NY, Apr 15, 43; m 63; c 5. MOLECULAR PHARMACOLOGY, MEDICAL SCIENCE. *Educ:* Columbia Univ, BA, 62, MD, 66. *Prof Exp:* From intern to jr asst resident, Columbia Presbyterian Med Ctr, NY, 66-68; clin & res assoc, Nat Inst Arthritis & Metab Dis, 68-70; sr asst resident, Mass Gen Hosp, Harvard Univ, 70-71, fel cardiol, 71-73; ASSOC assoc prof med & asst prof biochem, 73-77, PROF MED, MED CTR, DUKE UNIV, 77- *Concurrent Pos:* Estab investr, Am Heart Asn, 73-76; investr, Howard Hughes Med Inst, 76- *Honors & Awards:* George Thorn Award, Howard Hughes Med Inst, 79. *Mem:* Am Soc Clin Invest; Am Soc Biol Chem; Asn Am Physicians; Am Heart Asn; Am Soc Pharmacol & Exp Therapeut. *Res:* Molecular pharmacology of drug and hormone receptors. *Mailing Add:* Med Ctr Duke Univ PO Box 3325 Durham NC 27710

LEFKOWITZ, RUTH SAMSON, b Cincinnati, Ohio, Oct 7, 10; m 40; c 2. MATHEMATICS. *Educ:* Hunter Col, BA, 30; Columbia Univ, MA, 60, EdD(math educ), 66. *Prof Exp:* Sec Sch teacher math, New York City Bd Educ, 38-59; from asst prof to assoc prof, Bronx Community Col, 60-67; assoc prof, 67-75, chmn dept, 73-75, prof math, 70-76, PROF EMER, JOHN JAY COL CRIMINAL JUSTICE, CITY UNIV NEW YORK, 76- *Mem:* AAAS; Math Asn Am; NY Acad Sci. *Res:* Mathematics for open admissions students. *Mailing Add:* 900 W 190 St New York NY 10040

LEFKOWITZ, STANLEY A, b Philadelphia, Pa, Aug 5, 43; m 82. PHYSICAL INORGANIC CHEMISTRY. *Educ:* Temple Univ, AB, 65; Princeton Univ, PhD(chem), 70. *Prof Exp:* Asst to vchancellor Urban Affairs, City Univ New York, 70-73; asst dir instruct develop, Queens Col, 73-75; EXEC ASST TO CHMN BD, MOCATTA METALS CORP, 75- *Concurrent Pos:* Environ consult, NY State Temp Comn Powers Local Govt, 72-73; consult, Prof Exam Serv, 74-75 & Guana Island Hotel Corp, 76-; dir, Iron Mountain Depository Corp, 79- *Mem:* Am Phys Soc; Fedn Am Scientists. *Res:* Alternative techniques for the extraction, refining and analysis of precious metals; the development and design of a solar-wind energy installation on Guana Island in the British Virgin Islands. *Mailing Add:* 60 East 8th St Apt 10D New York NY 10003

LEFKOWITZ, STANLEY S, b New York, NY, Nov 26, 33; m 78; c 3. MICROBIOLOGY, VIROLOGY. *Educ:* Univ Miami, BS, 55, MS, 57; Univ Md, PhD(plant path), 61; Am Bd Med Microbiol, dipl, 74. *Prof Exp:* Fel viral oncol, Variety Childrens Res Found, 61-64, res assoc, 64-65; from asst prof to assoc prof virol, Med Col Ga, 65-69; assoc prof, 72-78, actg chairperson, Microbiol Dept, 78-81, PROF VIROL, SCH MED, TEX TECH UNIV, 78-, ASSOC DEAN, 75-, RES COORDR, 78- *Concurrent Pos:* Assoc scientist, Sloan Kettering Inst Cancer Res, 77-; mem, Clin Cancer Educ Comt, NIH, 78-81. *Mem:* AAAS; fel Am Acad Microbiol; Am Soc Microbiol; Tissue Cult Asn; Soc Exp Biol & Med; Reticuloendothelial Soc (treas); NY Acad Sci; Am Asn Immunol. *Res:* Viral oncogenesis including its physical and biological implications; properties of interferon; cancer immunology; effects of highly abused drugs on immunity. *Mailing Add:* 3801 67th St Lubbock TX 79413

LEFLORE, WILLIAM B, b Mobile, Ala, Feb 22, 32; m 65. PARASITOLOGY. *Educ:* St Augustine's Col, BS, 50; Univ Atlanta, MSc, 52; Univ Southern Calif, MS, 61, PhD(biol), 65. *Prof Exp:* Instr biol, Bennett Col, NC, 52-57; assoc prof, 64-68, PROF BIOL, SPELMAN COL, 68- *Concurrent Pos:* Consult, Off Educ, USPHS, 68, 71-72; ad hoc consult, Minority Biomed Support Prog, NIH, 75; vis prof, Col St Teresa, 68-69; MARC fac res fel, Univ Leeds, England, 78. *Mem:* Am Micros Soc; Am Soc Zoologists; Am Soc Parasitologists; Helminthological Soc Washington; Am Physiol Soc. *Res:* Serology of marine trematodes; life cycle of Cloacitrema michiganensis; histochemical demonstration of cercarial morphology; serology of Cysticercus fasciolaris; histochemistry of whole mounts of Cysticercus fasciolaris; histochemistry of hydrocytic and oxidative enzymes of cloacitrema michiganesis; histochemical localization of hydrolytic and oxidative enzymes in plagiorchis elegams cercariae. *Mailing Add:* Dept of Biol Spelman Col Atlanta GA 30314

LEFORT, HENRY G(ERARD), b Mineola, NY, Apr 4, 28; m 55; c 3. CEARMICS ENGINEERING. *Educ:* Clemson Col, BCerE, 52; Univ Ill, MS, 57, PhD(ceramic eng), 60. *Prof Exp:* Ceramic engr, Nat Bur Standards, 52-55; res assoc ceramic eng, Univ Ill, 55-60; chemist, Lawrence Radiation Lab, Univ Calif, 60-62; ASSOC PROF CERAMIC ENG, CLEMSON UNIV, 62- *Mem:* Am Ceramic Soc; Nat Inst Ceramic Engrs. *Res:* Ceramic structural adhesives for high temperature use; ceramic coatings; procelain enamels; nuclear ceramics. *Mailing Add:* Box 65 Clemson SC 29631

LEFTIN, HARRY PAUL, b Beverly, Mass, Oct 23, 26; m 54; c 3. PHYSICAL ORGANIC CHEMISTRY, INDUSTRIAL CHEMISTRY. *Educ:* Boston Univ, AB, 50, PhD(chem), 55. *Prof Exp:* Res fel, Mellon Inst, 54-59; res chemist, 59-60, supvr chem res, 60-67, sr res assoc, Res & Develop Lab, 67-73, MGR RES, PULLMAN KELLOGG 73- *Concurrent Pos:* Instr, Fairleigh Dickinson Univ, 60-75; ed, Catalysis Rev. *Mem:* Am Chem Soc; Catalysis Soc NAm; Sigma Xi; fel Am Inst Chemists. *Res:* Heterogeneous catalysis; chemisorption; electronic infrared and nuclear magnetic resonance spectra of molecules in the adsorbed state; petroleum and petrochemical process development; gas phase kinetics. *Mailing Add:* 2314 Lexford Lane Houston TX 77080

LEFTON, PHYLLIS, b Neptune, NJ, Feb 10, 49. MATHEMATICS, NUMBER THEORY. *Educ:* Columbia Univ, BA, 71, MA, 72, MPhil & PhD(math), 75; Jewish Theol Sem, BHL, 75. *Prof Exp:* Teaching asst calculus, Columbia Univ, 70-73; instr math, Belfer Grad Sch & Stern Col, Yeshiva Univ, 75-77; ASST PROF MATH, MANHATTANVILLE COL, 77- *Mem:* Am Math Soc; Math Asn Am; Asn Women in Math. *Res:* Algebraic number theory; analytic number theory; group representation theory; theory of polynomials and field theory. *Mailing Add:* Dept of Math Manhattanville Col Purchase NY 10577

LEGAL, CASIMER CLAUDIUS, JR, b Farrell, Pa, Feb 3, 15; m 38; c 4. INORGANIC CHEMISTRY. *Educ:* Thiel Col, BS, 37. *Prof Exp:* Anal chemist soap & raw mat, Lever Bros Co, 37-42; res chemist & supvr res lab & chem eng dept, Davison Chem Corp, 42-47, supvr res eng, 47-56; supvr agr chem res, 56-65, mgr fertilizer res, 65-74, MGR INDUST RES, W R GRACE & CO, 74- *Mem:* Am Chem Soc; Am Inst Chem Engrs. *Res:* Fertilizer; superphosphate; wet process phosphoric acid; silica gel; land reclamation. *Mailing Add:* 3340 S Cathay St Aurora CO 80013

LEGAN, SANDRA JEAN, b Cleveland, Ohio, Sept 10, 46. REPRODUCTIVE PHYSIOLOGY, NEUROENDOCRINOLOGY. *Educ:* Univ Mich, BS, 67, MS, 70, PhD(physiol), 74. *Prof Exp:* Lab asst, Geigy Co, Basel, Switz, 67-68; instr physiol, Univ Mich, 71-72, teaching fel, 72-73; NIH fel physiol, Emory Univ, 74-75; NIH fel, Reproductive Endocrinol Prog, Univ Mich, Ann Arbor, 75-77, res assoc, 77-79; ASST PROF PHYSIOL, UNIV KY, LEXINGTON, 79- *Mem:* Am Physiol Soc; Endocrine Soc; Soc Study Reproduction; AAAS; Soc Study Fertil. *Res:* Neuroendocrine control of gonadotrophin secretion, specifically how modulations in steroid concentrations, environmental stimuli and neural input are transduced into endocrine events in the hypothalamo-hypophyseal axis. *Mailing Add:* Dept of Physiol Univ of Ky Lexington KY 40506

LEGARE, RICHARD J, b Central Falls, RI, Dec 27, 34; m 57; c 2. POLYMER CHEMISTRY, CHEMICAL KINETICS. *Educ:* Providence Col, BS, 56; Univ Minn, MS, 60, PhD(phys chem), 62. *Prof Exp:* Sr res chemist, Allegany Ballistics Lab, Md, 62-71, staff scientist, Bacchus Works, 71-76 & Fibers Technol Ctr, Research Triangle Park, NC, 76-78, STAFF SCIENTIST, FIBERS TECHNOL CTR, HERCULES INC, 78- *Mem:* Am Chem Soc. *Res:* High speed kinetics; biophysical and polymer chemistry; rocket propellants; high temperature resins; composite materials. *Mailing Add:* 2619 Country Club Dr Conyers GA 30208

LEGATES, JAMES EDWARD, b Milford, Del, Aug 1, 22; m 44; c 4. ANIMAL GENETICS. *Educ:* Univ Del, BS, 43; Iowa State Col, MS, 47, PhD, 49. *Prof Exp:* Asst, Iowa State Col, 48-49; from asst prof to prof animal indust, 49-56, actg head dairy husb sect, 55-58, head animal breeding sect, 58-70, WILLIAM NEAL REYNOLDS PROF ANIMAL SCI & GENETICS, NC STATE UNIV, 56-, DEAN SCH AGR & LIFE SCI, 71- *Concurrent Pos:* Consult agr prog, Rockefeller Found, Colombia, 59; consult, Exp Sta Div, USDA, 59-65; vis prof, Nat Inst Animal Sci, Copenhagen, 63 & State Agr Univ, Wageningen, 71. *Honors & Awards:* Borden Award, Am Dairy Sci Asn, 67; J Rockeffeller Prentice Animal Breeding & Genetics Award, Am Soc Animal Sci, 77. *Mem:* AAAS; Biomet Soc; Am Soc Animal Sci; Am Dairy Sci Asn. *Res:* Selection in dairy cattle; genetics of mastitis resistance; quantitative inheritance in mice. *Mailing Add:* Sch Agr & Life Sci NC State Univ PO Box 5847 Raleigh NC 27650

LEGAULT, ALBERT, b Hull, Que, June 7, 19; m 57. SYSTEMATIC BOTANY, PHYTOGEOGRAPHY. *Educ:* Univ Montreal, BA, 48, BPed, 53, BSc, 55, MSc, 58; Yale Univ, MSc, 59. *Prof Exp:* Teacher biol, Montreal-St Louis Col, Montreal, 50-57; researcher palynol, Serv Biogeog, Prov of Que, 61-62; from asst prof to assoc prof, 62-76, PROF BOT, UNIV SHERBROOKE, 76- *Mem:* Can Bot Asn; Int Asn Plant Taxon; Fr-Can Asn Advan Sci. *Res:* Floristics of southeastern, arctic and subarctic Quebec. *Mailing Add:* Dept of Biol Univ of Sherbrooke Sherbrooke PQ J1K 2R1 Can

LEGECKIS, RICHARD VYTAUTAS, b Panevezys, Lithuania, Jan 28, 41; US citizen; m 67; c 2. PHYSICAL OCEANOGRAPHY, REMOTE SENSING. *Educ:* City Univ New York, BS, 65; Fla Inst Technol, MS, 68; Fla State Univ, PhD(phys oceanog), 74. *Prof Exp:* Space engr, Grumman Corp, 65-70; res assoc sci, Fla State Univ, 74; assoc oceanog, Nat Res Coun, 74-75; SCIENTIST OCEANOG, NAT ENVIRON SATELLITE SERV, NAT OCEANIC & ATMOSPHERIC ADMIN, 75- *Concurrent Pos:* Nat Res Coun grant, 74. *Mem:* Am Geophys Union. *Res:* Ocean currents and temperature fronts; application of satellite remote sensing to ocean studies. *Mailing Add:* 6512 White Oak Ave Temple Hills MD 20748

LEGENDRE, LOUIS, b Montreal, Que, Feb 16, 45; m 67. BIOLOGICAL OCEANOGRAPHY, NUMERICAL ECOLOGY. *Educ:* Univ Montreal, BSc, 67; Dalhousie Univ, PhD(oceanog), 71. *Prof Exp:* NATO fel oceanog, Marine Sta Villefranche-sur-Mer, Univ Paris, 71-73; res assoc, 73-74, asst prof, 74-77, assoc prof, 77-81, PROF OCEANOG, LAVAL UNIV, 81- *Concurrent Pos:* Secy gen interuniv group res oceanog, Que, Laval, McGill & Montreal Univs, 77-79; mem Can nat comt for sci, comt oceanog res, Nat Res Coun Can, 78-; mem Pop Biol Comt, Nat Sci Eng Res Coun Can, 80-; mem Comt Perfect, Inst Ocean Paris Monaco, 81- *Mem:* Am Soc Limnol & Oceanog; Union Oceanog France. *Res:* Marine primary production; physiological ecology of photosynthesis in marine phytoplankton; numerical analysis of ecological data sets. *Mailing Add:* Dept of Biol Laval Univ Quebec PQ G1K 7P4 Can

LEGENDY, CHARLES RUDOLF, b Budapest, Hungary, Nov 2, 36; US citizen. BRAIN RESEARCH. *Educ:* Princeton Univ, BSE, 59; Cornell Univ, PhD(theoret physics), 64. *Prof Exp:* Theoret physicist, Res Labs, United Aircraft Corp, 64-67; sr physicist, Westinghouse Cambridge Lab, 67-68, fel physicist, Westinghouse Aerospace Div, 68-71; vis fel, Cybernet Lab, Nat Res Coun, Italy, 71-73; vis lectr, Univ Tubingen, 73-75; res assoc, Max Planck Inst Biophys Chem, Gottingen, 75-76; staff assoc, Columbia Univ Col Physicians & Surgeons, 76-77; res fel, 78-80, ASST PROF, ALBERT EINSTEIN COL MED, ROSE KENNEDY CTR, BRONX, NY, 80- *Res:* Solid state plasmas; boundary value problems; organization of the brain; electrophysiology of cat and monkey visual cortex. *Mailing Add:* 579 W 215th ST New York NY 10034

LEGER, ROBERT M(ARSH), b Foochow, China, June 3, 21; US citizen; m 44; c 3. ELECTRICAL ENGINEERING. *Educ:* Antioch Col, BS, 44; Ill Inst Technol, MS, 50, PhD(elec eng), 55. *Prof Exp:* Final test foreman, Collins Radio Co, 43-44, qual control engr, 44-46; asst elec eng, Ill Inst Technol, 47-48, instr, 48-52, asst prof, 52-53; from electronics engr to mgr info systs, Convair Astronaut Div, Gen Dynamics/Convair, 53-70, ENG SPECIALIST, GEN DYNAMICS/ELECTRONICS, 71- *Mem:* Sr mem Inst Elec & Electronics Engrs. *Res:* Information handling systems. *Mailing Add:* 6517 Altair Ct San Diego CA 92120

LEGERTON, CLARENCE W, JR, b Charleston, SC, July 8, 22; m 58; c 3. GASTROENTEROLOGY. *Educ:* Davidson Col, BS, 43; Med Col SC, MD, 46. *Prof Exp:* Instr med, Duke Univ Hosp, 51-53; instr, 56-58, asst, 58-60, from asst prof to assoc prof, 61-70, chief div gastroenterol, 70-77, PROF MED, MED UNIV SC, 70- *Concurrent Pos:* Consult, Vet Admin Hosp, Charleston, 66-; hon consult, Addenbrookes Hosp, Sch Med, Cambridge Univ, Eng, 78; nat liaison comt, Am Gastroenterol Asn, 79-; med adv bd, US Ther Chang Index, 80- *Mem:* Am Gastroenterol Asn; Am Fedn Clin Res; Am Col Physicians; Am Col Gastroenterol. *Res:* Mechanism of pain in peptic ulcer; effects of anticholinergic drugs on gastric motility and secretion. *Mailing Add:* Dept Med Med Univ SC Charleston SC 29425

LEGG, DAVID ALAN, b Elwood, Ind, Sept 7, 47. MATHEMATICAL ANALYSIS. *Educ:* Purdue Univ, BS, 69, MS, 70, PhD(math), 73. *Prof Exp:* Asst prof, 74-80, ASSOC PROF MATH, IND UNIV-PURDUE UNIV, FT WAYNE, 80- *Mem:* Am Math Soc; Math Asn Am. *Res:* Approximation theory in the space of operators on Hilbert space. *Mailing Add:* Dept of Math Ind Univ-Purdue Univ Ft Wayne IN 46805

LEGG, FRANK E(VARISTE), JR, b Ann Arbor, Mich, May 1, 09; m 35. ENGINEERING. *Educ:* Univ Mich, AB, 33, MS, 34. *Prof Exp:* Sr lab asst, State Hwy Lab, 35-36, off engr, 36-42, lab engr, 46-49, asst supvr lab & asst prof eng, 49-57, assoc prof, 57-75, EMER PROF CONSTRUCT MAT, UNIV MICH, ANN ARBOR, 75- *Concurrent Pos:* Mat consult, Mich State Hwy Dept, 57-70; mem mineral aggregates comt, Hwy Res Bd, Nat Acad Sci, 57-, chmn, 64-70, chmn gen mat sect. *Mem:* Am Soc Testing & Mat; Am Concrete Inst. *Res:* Highway construction materials, particularly portland cement concrete. *Mailing Add:* 4040 Huron River Dr Ann Arbor MI 48104

LEGG, JAMES C, b Kokomo, Ind, Sept 17, 36; m 73; c 3. NUCLEAR PHYSICS. *Educ:* Ind Univ, BS, 58; Princeton Univ, MA, 60, PhD(physics), 62. *Prof Exp:* Instr physics, Princeton Univ, 61-62; res assoc, Rice Univ, 62-63, asst prof, 63-67; assoc prof, 67-73, PROF PHYSICS, KANS STATE UNIV, 73-, DIR NUCLEAR SCI LAB, 72- *Mem:* Am Phys Soc. *Res:* Nuclear spectroscopy as studied by nuclear reactions. *Mailing Add:* Dept of Physics Kans State Univ Manhattan KS 66502

LEGG, JOHN IVAN, b New York, NY, Oct 15, 37; m 62; c 2. BIOINORGANIC CHEMISTRY. *Educ:* Oberlin Col, BA, 60; Univ Mich, MS, 63, PhD(inorg chem), 65. *Prof Exp:* Res assoc inorg chem, Univ Pittsburgh, 65-66; from asst prof to assoc prof, 66-75, PROF CHEM & ASSOC IN BIOCHEM, WASH STATE UNIV, 75-, CHMN DEPT CHEM, 78- *Concurrent Pos:* NIH spec fel, Harvard Med Sch, 72-73. *Mem:* Am Chem Soc. *Res:* Use of metal ions to probe structure-function relationships in metalloenzymes; development of models for metal ions binding sites in proteins. *Mailing Add:* Dept of Chem Wash State Univ Pullman WA 99163

LEGG, JOHN WALLIS, b Minter City, Miss, Sept 20, 36; m 56; c 3. PHYSICAL CHEMISTRY. *Educ:* Miss Col, BS, 58; Univ Fla, MS, 60, PhD, 64. *Prof Exp:* Chemist, Shell Oil Co, Tex, 58; asst, Univ Fla, 58-60; asst prof, Miss Col, 60-62; asst, Univ Fla, 62-64, instr, 63; assoc prof, 64-71, PROF CHEM, MISS COL, 71- *Mem:* Am Chem Soc; Am Sci Affil. *Res:* Adsorption at solid surfaces and heterogeneous catalysis, specifically reactions over thorium oxide catalysts, primarily of the alcohols; dielectric properties of freon hydrates; coal powders and slurries. *Mailing Add:* Dept Chem Miss Col Clinton MS 39058

LEGG, JOSEPH OGDEN, b Tex, Oct 16, 20; m 44. SOIL SCIENCE. *Educ:* Univ Ark, BS, 50, MS, 51; Univ Md, PhD(soil fertil), 57. *Prof Exp:* Soil scientist, USDA, 51-79. *Concurrent Pos:* USDA exchange scientist to USSR, 63-64; adj prof, Agron Dept, Univ Ark, 80- *Mem:* Fel AAAS; Soil Sci Soc Am; Am Soc Agron; Int Soc Soil Sci; Coun Agr Sci & Technol. *Res:* Nitrogen transformations in soils; biological nitrogen fixation; soil organic matter. *Mailing Add:* Agron Dept Univ Ark Fayetteville AR 72701

LEGG, KENNETH DEARDORFF, b Ogdensburg, NY, Feb 19, 43; m 67. ANALYTICAL CHEMISTRY. *Educ:* Union Col, BS, 64; Mass Inst Technol, PhD(chem), 69. *Prof Exp:* Vis prof chem, Univ Southern Calif, 74-75; asst prof chem, Calif State Univ, Long Beach, 69-74, assoc prof, 75-78; prin scientist, 78-81, MGR, ANAL RES, INSTRUMENTATION LAB INC, 81- *Mem:* Am Asn Clin Chem; Am Chem Soc; Electrochem Soc. *Res:* Study of fast photophysical processes using laser excitation; biomedical instrumentation; electrogenerated chemiluminescence; ion selective electrodes, amperometric sensors and biomedical instrumentation. *Mailing Add:* Instrumentation Lab 113 Hartwell Ave Lexington MA 02173

LEGG, THOMAS HARRY, b Kamloops, BC, May 4, 29; m 57; c 2. PHYSICS, RADIO ASTRONOMY. *Educ:* Univ BC, BASc, 53; McGill Univ, MSc, 56, PhD(physics), 60. *Prof Exp:* Radar engr, Can Aviation Electronics Ltd, 53-54; sci officer radio physics, Defense Res Bd Can, 56-57; SR RES OFFICER, HERZBERG INST ASTROPHYS, NAT RES COUN CAN, 60- *Mem:* AAAS; Am Astron Soc; Can Asn Physicists; Royal Astron Soc Can; Inst Elec & Electronics Eng. *Res:* Microwave diffraction; electronic circuitry; radio interferometry. *Mailing Add:* Nat Res Coun 100 Sussex Dr Ottawa ON K1M 2C9 Can

LEGGE, THOMAS NELSON, b Erie, Pa, Sept 23, 36; m 60; c 2. ZOOLOGY, LIMNOLOGY. *Educ:* Edinboro State Col, BS, 59; Miami Univ, MAT, 62; Univ Vt, PhD(zool), 69. *Prof Exp:* Instr biol, Northwestern Mich Col, 62-64; from asst prof to assoc prof, 67-70, PROF BIOL, EDINBORO STATE COL, 70- *Mem:* Am Soc Limnol & Oceanog; Int Asn Gt Lakes Res; Int Asn Theoret & Appl Limnol. *Res:* Physical and biological limnology, especially the distribution and ecology of calanoid copepods. *Mailing Add:* Dept of Biol Edinboro State Col Edinboro PA 16412

LEGGETT, ANNE MARIE, b Columbus, Ohio, May 28, 47. RECURSION THEORY. *Educ:* Ohio State Univ, BA, 69; Yale Univ, PhD(math), 73. *Prof Exp:* Instr math, Mass Inst Technol, 73-75; asst prof math, Univ Tex, Austin, 75-79; ASSOC PROF MATH, WESTERN ILL UNIV, 79- *Mem:* Asn Symbolic Logic; Asn Women Math; Math Asn Am; Am Math Soc. *Res:* Recursion theory on admissible ordinals, especially the lattice of recursively enumerable sets and its relationships with the upper semi-lattice of degrees. *Mailing Add:* Dept Math Western Ill Univ Macomb IL 61455

LEGGETT, GLEN EUGENE, b Brigham City, Utah, Mar 13, 22; m 43; c 2. SOIL SCIENCE. *Educ:* Utah State Univ, BS, 50, MS, 51; Wash State Univ, PhD(agron), 58. *Prof Exp:* Jr soil scientist, Wash State Univ, 52-57; SOIL SCIENTIST, SNAKE RIVER CONSERV RES CTR, AGR RES SERV, USDA, 57- *Mem:* Am Soc Agron; Soil Sci Soc Am; Soil Conserv Soc Am. *Res:* Chemistry of soil. *Mailing Add:* Agr Res Serv USDA Rte 1 Box 186 Kimberly ID 83341

LEGGETT, JAMES EVERETT, b West Union, WVa, Oct 20, 26; m 48; c 3. PLANT PHYSIOLOGY. *Educ:* Glenville State Col, AB, 49; Univ Md, College Park, MS, 54, PhD(bot), 65. *Prof Exp:* Plant physiologist, USDA, 53-70; From assoc prof to prof agron, Univ KY, 70-80; PLANT PHYSIOLOGIST, USDA, 80- *Mem:* AAAS; Am Soc Plant Physiologists; Soil Sci Soc Am; Am Soc Agron; Crop Sci Soc Am. *Res:* Ion transport; application of ion transport mechanism to growth of plants and relationships to other environmental factors. *Mailing Add:* Dept of Agron Agr Sci Ctr Univ of Ky Lexington KY 40546

LEGGETT, JOSEPH EDWIN, b Warren, Ark, Sept 9, 37; m 60; c 2. ENTOMOLOGY. *Educ:* Univ Ark, BS, 60; Univ Ariz, MS, 68; Miss State Univ, PhD(entom), 75. *Prof Exp:* RES ENTOMOLOGIST, USDA AGR RES SERV, 68- *Honors & Awards:* Cert Merit, Agr Res Serv, 73. *Mem:* Entom Soc Am. *Res:* The physiological and behavioral aspects of boll weevil migration, and the relative importance of color and pheromone on boll weevil traps. *Mailing Add:* 1817 Mars Hill Circle Florence SC 29501

LEGGETT, ROBERT DEAN, b Midvale, Ohio, Aug 2, 29; m 51; c 6. METALLURGICAL ENGINEERING. *Educ:* Ohio State Univ, BMetE & MSc, 52; Carnegie Inst Technol, PhD(metall eng), 59. *Prof Exp:* Engr, Bettis Lab, Westinghouse Elec Corp, 52-55; res asst, Metals Res Lab, Carnegie Inst Technol, 58-59; sr engr, Hanford Labs, Gen Elec Co, 59-64, tech specialist, 64-65; res assoc irradiation effects in metals, Pac Northwest Labs, Battelle Mem Inst, 65-70 & WADCO Corp, 70-71; RES ASSOC, WESTINGHOUSE-HANFORD CO, 72- *Mem:* Am Soc Metals; Am Nuclear Soc. *Res:* Basic mechanisms of irradiation behavior of materials, especially fissionable metals; corrosion of single crystals and bi crystals of stainless steel; hot water corrosion of uranium base alloys and stainless steel; irradiation behavior of mixed oxide; stainless steel clad fuel elements. *Mailing Add:* 2113 Harris Ave Richland WA 99352

LEGGETT, WILLIAM C, b Orangeville, Ont, June 25, 39; m 64; c 2. FISH ECOLOGY, POPULATION DYNAMICS. *Educ:* Waterloo Univ Col, BA, 62; Univ Waterloo, MSc, 65; McGill Univ, PhD(zool), 69. *Prof Exp:* Res scientist fisheries, Essex Marine Lab, 65-70, res assoc, 70-78; asst prof, 70-72, assoc prof, 72-79, PROF BIOL, MCGILL UNIV, 79-, CHMN DEPT, 81- *Concurrent Pos:* Mem, Group Interuniv Oceanog Res Que, 73-; assoc ed, J Am Fisheries Soc, 76-78 & Am J Fisheries Aquatic Sci, 80-; mem comt prof cert, Am Fisheries Soc, 76-78; mem bd dirs, Memphremagog Conserv Inc, 76-80; mem grants adv comt, Can Nat Sportsmans Fund, 77-81; mem grant selection comt pop biol, Natural Sci & Eng Res Coun Can, 78-81, chmn, 81-82; pres & chmn bd, Huntsman Marine Lab, 80-83. *Mem:* Can Soc Zoologists; Am Fisheries Soc. *Res:* Life history strategies in fishes; reproductive ecology of fish; environmental regulation of migration in fish; larval fish ecology; regulation of mortality in fish; lake ecosystem ecology. *Mailing Add:* Dept Biol 1205 Ave Dr Penfield Montreal PQ H3A 1B1 Can

LEGLER, DONALD WAYNE, b Minneapolis, Minn, Oct 2, 31; m 57; c 3. IMMUNOLOGY, PHYSIOLOGY. *Educ:* Univ Minn, BS, 54, DDS, 56; Univ Ala, PhD(physiol), 66. *Prof Exp:* From instr pedodont to assoc prof oral biol, 63-71, asst dean sch dent, 71-74, prof oral biol & chmn dept, 71-80, asst dean admin affairs, 74-80, VIS PROF DENT, SCH DENT, UNIV ALA, BIRMINGHAM, 80- *Concurrent Pos:* NIH trainee, 62-66; Swedish Med Res Coun fel, 67-68. *Mem:* Am Dent Asn; fel Am Col Dent; Am Soc Microbiol. *Res:* Comparative immunology; germ free research; preventive dentistry. *Mailing Add:* Dept of Oral Biol Univ of Ala Sch of Dent Birmingham AL 35294

LEGLER, JOHN MARSHALL, b Minneapolis, Minn, Sept 9, 30; m 52; c 4. ZOOLOGY. *Educ:* Gustavus Adolphus Col, BA, 53; Univ Kans, PhD(zool), 59. *Prof Exp:* Asst human anat, Gustavus Adolphus Col, 52-53; asst zool, Univ Kans, 53-57, asst cur herpet, Mus Natural Hist, 55-59, asst instr zool, 58; res asst physiol execise lab, Univ Kans, 58-59, asst instr herpet, 59; vis prof zool, Univ New England, Armidale, NSW, Australia, 72-74, 76-77 & 80; from asst prof to assoc prof, 59-69, PROF ZOOL, UNIV UTAH, 69-, CUR HERPET, 59-; CUR REPTILES & AMPHIBIANS, UTAH MUS NATURAL HIST, 69- *Concurrent Pos:* Var individual res grants, 59-; res assoc, Gorgas Mem Lab, Panama, 64- & Los Angeles County Mus Natural Hist, 75- *Mem:* Soc Study Evolution; Am Soc Ichthyologists & Herpetologists; fel Herpetologists League (pres, 68-70); SigM Xi; Brit Herpet Soc. *Res:* Herpetology; the biology of chelonians, the turtles of Middle America and Australia; biosystematics; evolution; ecology and morphology. *Mailing Add:* Dept of Biol Univ of Utah Salt Lake City UT 84112

LEGLER, WARREN KARL, b Hiawatha, Kans, Apr 28, 30; m 52; c 3. COMPUTER SCIENCE, ELECTRICAL ENGINEERING. *Educ:* Univ Kans, BS, 52, PhD(elec eng), 69; Mass Inst Technol, MS, 60. *Prof Exp:* Physicist, US Naval Ord Test Sta, 52-63; instr elec eng, Med Ctr, Univ Kans, 63-68, instr comput sci, 68-70, asst prof physiol, 70-80; SYSTS ANALYST, DIT-MCO INT, 80- *Mem:* Inst Elec & Electronics Engrs; Asn Comput Mach. *Res:* Application of computers to medical research, practice and teaching. *Mailing Add:* DIT-MCO Int 5612 Brighton Terrace Kansas City KS 64130

LEGNER, E FRED, b Chicago, Ill, Oct 17, 32; m 60; c 1. ENTOMOLOGY, ECOLOGY. *Educ:* Univ Ill, Urbana, BS, 54; Utah State Univ, MS, 58; Univ Wis, PhD(entom), 61. *Prof Exp:* Asst entom, Univ Wis, 61-62; from asst entomologist to assoc entomologist, 62-75, ENTOMOLOGIST, UNIV CALIF, RIVERSIDE, 75-, ASSOC PROF ENTOM, 70-, PROF BIOL CONTROL, 73- *Concurrent Pos:* Consult, Africa, Australasia, SAm, Mid-E, Micronesia, WI & Europe, 62, 63 & 65-75; USPHS grants, 64-70 & NSF, 72-74. *Mem:* Entom Soc Am; Int Orgn Biol Control; Entom Soc Can; Am Mosquito Control Asn. *Res:* Population dynamics of arthropods and their biological control; behavior of parasitic hymenoptera. *Mailing Add:* Div of Biol Control Univ of Calif Riverside CA 92502

LEGOFF, EUGENE, b Passaic, NJ, Aug 18, 34; m 60; c 2. ORGANIC CHEMISTRY. *Educ:* Rutgers Univ, BS, 56; Cornell Univ, PhD(org chem), 59. *Prof Exp:* Fel, Harvard Univ, 59-60; fel org chem, Mellon Inst, 60-65; assoc prof, 65-78, PROF ORG CHEM, MICH STATE UNIV, 78- *Mem:* Am Chem Soc. *Res:* Synthesis of pseudoaromatics, non-benzenoid aromatics, heterroannulenes organic conductors, porphyrins new synthetic methods. *Mailing Add:* Dept of Chem Mich State Univ East Lansing MI 48824

LEGORE, RICHARD STEPHEN, pollution biology, invertebrate pathology, see previous edition

LEGRAND, DONALD GEORGE, b Springfield, Mass, Apr 3, 30; m 51; c 4. PHYSICAL CHEMISTRY. *Educ:* Boston Univ, BA, 52; Univ Mass, PhD(chem), 59. *Prof Exp:* Res chemist, Mallinckrodt Chem Works, 52; asst prof chem, Univ Mass, 58-59; RES CHEMIST, RES LABS, GEN ELEC CO, 59- *Mem:* Am Chem Soc; Am Phys Soc; Soc Rheol. *Res:* Polymer physics; surface physics; rheo-optics. *Mailing Add:* Gen Elec Res Lab PO Box 1088 Schenectady NY 12301

LEGRAND, FRANK EDWARD, b Mayfield, Okla, Dec 18, 26; m 49; c 5. GENETICS, ECOLOGY. *Educ:* Okla State Univ, BS, 59; NDak State Univ, PhD(plant breeding), 63. *Prof Exp:* Exten agronomist, 63-79, PROF AGRON, OKLA STATE UNIV, 74-, DIR, OKLA PEDIGREED SEED SERV, 79- *Mem:* Am Soc Agron. *Res:* Genetic studies of wheat in relation to the inheritance of several quantitative and qualitative characters. *Mailing Add:* Dept of Agron Okla State Univ Stillwater OK 74074

LEGRAND, HARRY E, b Concord, NC, May 19, 17; m 45; c 2. HYDROGEOLOGY. *Educ:* Univ NC, BS, 38. *Prof Exp:* Geol aide, US Geol Surv, 38-40, geologist, Ground Water Br, 46-49, dist geologist, 49-56, consult geologist, 56-59, res geologist, 59-60, chief radiohydrol sect, 60-62, res geologist, 62-74; CONSULT HYDROLOGIST, 74- *Mem:* AAAS; Geol Soc Am; Soc Econ Geologists; Am Geophys Union; Am Water Works Asn. *Res:* Contamination and geochemistry of ground water; ground water geology; ground water in igneous and metamorphic rocks; pollution and ground waste disposal. *Mailing Add:* 331 Yadkin Dr Raleigh NC 27609

LEGROW, GARY EDWARD, b Toronto, Ont, Mar 9, 38; m 63; c 3. CHEMISTRY. *Educ:* Univ Toronto, BA, 60, MA, 62, PhD(organosilicon chem), 64. *Prof Exp:* Res assoc metalloorganosiloxanes, Dept Chem, Univ Sussex, 64-65; res chemist, 65-68, group leader organo-functional silicon chem, 68-70, group leader resins & chem res, 70-73, sr group leader resins res, 73-77, assoc res scientist resins res, 77-80, ASSOC RES SCIENTIST, BASIC MAT RES, DOW CORNING CORP, 80- *Concurrent Pos:* Lectr, Mich State Univ, 66-68. *Mem:* Am Chem Soc; Sigma Xi. *Res:* Synthesis, kinetics and molecular rearrangements of organo-functional silanes; influence of the proximity of silicon on the reactivity of organic functions; silicon resin process; computer modelling of organosilicon reactions. *Mailing Add:* 2038 Ridgewood Lane Madison IN 47250

LEGTERS, LLEWELLYN J, b Clymer, NY, May 23, 32; m 56; c 2. PREVENTIVE MEDICINE, TROPICAL PUBLIC HEALTH. *Educ:* Univ Buffalo, BA & MD, 56; Harvard Univ, MPH, 61. *Prof Exp:* Rotating intern, Akron Gen Hosp, Ohio, 56-57; surgeon, 82nd Airborne Div, US Army, 57-58, 504th Infantry, Ger, 58-59, prev med officer, 8th Infantry Div, Ger, 59-60 & John F Kennedy Ctr Mil Assistance, 63-66, chief, Walter Reed Amy Inst Res Field Epidemiol Surv Team, Vietnam, 66-68, prev med officer, 68-70, command & gen staff col, Ft Leavenworth, Kans, 70-71, chief volar eval group, Training Ctr, Infantry & Ft Ord, 71-72, chief ambulatory health serv, Silas B Hays Army Hosp, Ft Ord, 72-74, US Army War Col, Carlisle Barracks, Pa, 74-75, chief health & environ div, Off Surg Gen, 75-77, comdr surg & US Army Med Dept Activity, XVIII Airborne Corps, Ft Bragg, NC, 77-78; sr med consult, Enviro Control Inc, 79-80; PROF & CHMN DEPT PREV MED & BIOMED, UNIFORMED SERV UNIV HEALTH SCI, BETHESDA, MD, 80- *Concurrent Pos:* La State Univ fel trop med & parasitol, Cent Am, 63. *Mem:* AAAS; fel Am Col Prev Med; Am Soc Trop Med & Hyg; Am Pub Health Asn; NY Acad Sci. *Res:* Epidemiology of infectious diseases, especially malaria, schistosomiasis and plague. *Mailing Add:* 4341 Ashrod Lane Fairfax VA 22032

LEGVOLD, SAM, b Huxley, Iowa, Jan 8, 14; m 41; c 3. PHYSICS. *Educ:* Luther Col, AB, 35; Iowa State Univ, MS, 36, PhD(physics), 46. *Hon Degrees:* DSc, Luther Col, 75. *Prof Exp:* Asst prof physics, Luther Col, 37-39; assoc prof, 46-56, prof, 56-80, EMER PROF PHYSICS, AMES LAB, IOWA STATE UNIV, 80- *Honors & Awards:* Meritorious Civilian Serv Award, US Navy, 46; Distinguished Prof Sci & Humanities, 77. *Mem:* AAAS; fel Am Phys Soc; Sigma Xi. *Res:* Cryogenics; magnetism; electricity; solid state physics. *Mailing Add:* Ames Lab Iowa State Univ Ames IA 50011

LEHAN, FRANK W(ELBORN), b Los Angeles, Calif, Jan 26, 23; m 44; c 1. ELECTRICAL ENGINEERING. *Educ:* Calif Inst Technol, BSEE, 44. *Prof Exp:* Chief telemetry sect, Jet Propulsion Lab, Calif Inst Technol, 44-49, telecommun sect, 49-52 & electronics res, 53-54; sr staff mem, Ramo-Wooldridge Corp, 54-56, assoc dir electronics res & develop staff, Guided Missile Res Div, 56-58; exec vpres & pres, Space Gen Corp, Calif, 58-66; consult, 66-67; asst secy res & technol, Dept Transp, Washington, DC, 67-69; CONSULT, 69-; DIR SYST DEVELOP CORP, 71- *Concurrent Pos:* Mem res & develop bd, Dept Defense, 48-52, Gov Coun Ocean Resources, 65-66, President's Health Manpower Comt, 65-67 & naval warfare panel, President's Sci Adv Group, 65-; chmn elec intel panel, Defense Sci Bd, 70-71. *Mem:* Nat Acad Eng; fel Inst Elec & Electronics Engrs. *Res:* Technical management. *Mailing Add:* 1696 E Valley Rd Santa Barbara CA 93108

LEHENY, ROBERT FRANCIS, b New York, Ny, Dec 8, 38; m 62; c 2. APPLIED PHYSICS. *Educ:* Univ Conn, BS, 60; Columbia Univ, MS, 63, DrEngrSc, 66. *Prof Exp:* Engr electronic systs, Sperry Gyroscope Co, 60-61; res asst, Columbia Univ, 62-66, asst prof, 66-67; MEM TECH STAFF SEMICONDUCTOR RES & OPTICAL PROPERTIES SEMICONDUCTORS, BELL LABS INC, 67- *Mem:* AAAS; Am Phys Soc; Inst Elec & Electronics Engrs; Sigma Xi. *Res:* Optical properties of semiconductors; plasma physics; electromagnetic radiation. *Mailing Add:* 176 Fox Hill Dr Little Silver NJ 07739

LEHMAN, ALFRED BAKER, b Cleveland, Ohio, Mar 21, 31. MATHEMATICS. *Educ:* Ohio Univ, BS, 50; Univ Fla, PhD(math), 54. *Prof Exp:* Instr math, Tulane Univ, 54; mem staff, Acoust Lab & Res Lab Electronics, Mass Inst Technol, 55-57; asst prof math, Case Inst Technol, 57-61; vis mem, Math Res Ctr, Univ Wis, 61-63; res assoc, Rensselaer Polytech Inst, 63; res mathematician, Walter Reed Army Inst Res, 64-67; PROF MATH & COMP SCI, UNIV TORONTO, 67- *Concurrent Pos:* Vis prof, Univ Toronto, 65-67. *Mem:* Math Asn Am; Soc Indust & Appl Math. *Res:* Combinatorics. *Mailing Add:* Dept of Math Univ of Toronto Toronto ON M5S 1A1 Can

LEHMAN, AUGUST F(ERDINAND), b Waukesha, Wis, July 10, 24; c 3. HYDRODYNAMICS, FLUID MECHANICS. *Educ:* Agr & Mech Col, Tex, BS, 50; Pa State Univ, MS, 54. *Prof Exp:* Engr, Ord Res Lab, Pa State Univ, 51-53, group leader, 53-54, proj leader, 54-62, asst prof, 55-59, assoc prof, 59-62; head water tunnel div, Oceanics, Inc, 62-77; PRES, A F LEHMAN ASSOCS INC, 77- *Mem:* Am Soc Mech Engrs; Sigma Xi. *Res:* Hydrodynamics and low speed aerodynamics; marine propulsion; flow visualization; cavitation; tip vortices; drag reduction; design and construction of water and wind tunnels and special instrumentation and equipment. *Mailing Add:* A F Lehman Assocs Inc PO Box 27 Centerport NY 11721

LEHMAN, DAVID HERSHEY, b Lancaster, Pa. GEOLOGY. *Educ:* Franklin & Marshall Col, AB, 68; Univ Tex, Austin, PhD(geol), 74. *Prof Exp:* Res geologist, Exxon Co, 74-77, exploration geologist, 77-78, prod geologist, 79; PROJ SURVRY GEOLOGIST, NORTH ALASKA, 80- *Mem:* Am Asn Petrol Geol; Geol Soc Am. *Res:* Structural geology; tectonics; radiometric age determinations; petroleum geochemistry; petroleum geology; regional geology. *Mailing Add:* 15210 Benfer Rd Houston TX 77069

LEHMAN, DENNIS DALE, b Youngstown, Ohio, July 14, 45; div; c 2. CHEMICAL INSTRUMENTATION, PHYSIOLOGICAL CHEMISTRY. *Educ:* Ohio State Univ, BSc, 67; Northwestern Univ, MS, 68, PhD(chem), 73. *Prof Exp:* Asst prof, 68-77, assoc prof, 77-81, PROF CHEM, LOOP COL, 81- *Concurrent Pos:* Vis scholar, Dept Chem, Northwestern Univ, 73-, vis assoc prof, 77-81, vis prof, 81- & lectr, Med Sch, 81- *Mem:* Am Chem Soc; Chem Soc London; AAAS. *Res:* The use of organometallic complexes as catalyst for a variety of inorganic reactions; the reaction of transition metal complexes with small molecules and structural studies on the resulting products. *Mailing Add:* Loop Col 64 East Lake St Chicago IL 60601

LEHMAN, DONALD RICHARD, b York, Pa, Dec 13, 40; m 62. THEORETICAL NUCLEAR PHYSICS. *Educ:* Rutgers Univ, BA, 62; Air Force Inst Technol, MS, 64; George Washington Univ, PhD(physics), 70. *Prof Exp:* Proj scientist nuclear physics, Air Force Off Sci Res, 64-68; instr physics, George Washington Univ, 69-70; Nat Acad Sci-Nat Res Coun res assoc nuclear physics, Nat Bur Standards, 70-72; asst prof, 72-76, ASSOC PROF PHYSICS, GEORGE WASHINGTON UNIV, 76- *Concurrent Pos:* Guest worker, Nat Bur Standards, 72-; vis staff mem, Los Alamos Nat Lab, 74- *Mem:* Am Phys Soc. *Res:* Nuclear few-body problem; photonuclear physics; intermediate energy physics; hypernuclei; scattering theory. *Mailing Add:* Dept of Physics George Washington Univ Washington DC 20052

LEHMAN, DUANE STANLEY, b Berne, Ind, Jan 18, 32; m 55; c 3. INORGANIC CHEMISTRY. *Educ:* Wheaton Col, Ill, BS, 54; Ind Univ, PhD(chem), 59. *Prof Exp:* Res chemist, 58-65, proj leader, Chem Dept Res Lab, 65-67, group leader, Chem Eng Lab, lab dir, chem eng lab, Dow Chem Co, 71-76; res mgr high impact polystyrene, 76-78, MGR, RES & DEVELOP RECRUITING & PLACEMENT, STYRENE MOLDING RES LAB, 78- *Mem:* Am Chem Soc; Sigma Xi. *Res:* Coordination chemistry; brine chemistry; inorganic process research; basic refractories; new product development. *Mailing Add:* 704 Linwood Dr Midland MI 48640

LEHMAN, ERNEST DALE, b Woodward, Okla, Mar 2, 42; m 65; c 3. BIOCHEMISTRY. *Educ:* Northwestern State Col, Okla, BS, 65; Okla State Univ, PhD(biochem), 71. *Prof Exp:* Res assoc biochem, Okla State Univ, 71-72; NIH fel, Case Western Reserve Univ, 72-74; sr res biochem, 74-78, RES FEL, DEPT VIRUS & CELL BIOL RES, MERCK, SHARP & DOHME RES LABS, 78- *Mem:* AAAS; Am Chem Soc; Am Soc Microbiol; Soc Complex Carbohydrates. *Res:* Biochemistry and function of glycoproteins; isolation and identification of bacterial and viral antigens. *Mailing Add:* Dept of Virus & Cel Biol Res Merck Sharp & Dohme Res Labs West Point PA 19486

LEHMAN, EUGENE H, b New York, NY, Jan 26, 13; m 61; c 4. MATHEMATICAL STATISTICS. *Educ:* Yale Univ, BA, 33; Columbia Univ, MA, 37; NC State Univ, PhD(math statist), 61. *Prof Exp:* Res assoc math, Univ Alaska, 49-51; asst prof, Univ Fla, 55-57 & Univ San Diego, 57-58; consult statistician, Los Angeles, 61-64; consult biostatistician, Cedars of Lebanon Hosp, 64-66; assoc prof math, Northern Mich Univ, 66-69; prof math, Mo Southern Col, 69-70; prof statist, Univ Que, Trois-Rivieres, 70-76; prof math, Univ Nat du Rwanda, 76-78; PROF STATIST, CONCORDIA UNIV, MONTREAL, 78-, PROF MATH, 82- *Concurrent Pos:* Corresp abstractor, Math Rev, 60-; referee, La Rev Can de Statist. *Mem:* Am Math Soc; Am Statist Asn; Asn Can-Fr Advan Sci; Soc Statist Can. *Res:* Children in mathematics. *Mailing Add:* 3435 rue Bordeaux Trois-Rivieres PQ G8Y 3P5 Can

LEHMAN, FREDERICK G(OODWIN), b Brooklyn, NY, Feb 26, 18; m 44; c 3. CIVIL ENGINEERING. *Educ:* City Col New York, BCE, 38; Mass Inst Technol, SM, 39, ScD(civil eng), 60. *Prof Exp:* Asst civil eng, Mass Inst Technol, 39-42; struct engr, Curtiss-Wright Corp, 42-47; from asst prof to prof civil eng, 47-67, chmn dept, 68-75, DISTINGUISHED PROF CIVIL ENG, NJ INST TECHNOL, 67- *Concurrent Pos:* Consult, Curtiss-Wright Corp, 47-60; mem, Transp Res Bd, Nat Acad Sci-Nat Res Coun. *Mem:* Am Soc Civil Engrs; Am Soc Eng Educ. *Res:* Educational development in engineering; urban systems analysis. *Mailing Add:* NJ Inst of Technol 323 High St Newark NJ 07102

LEHMAN, GRACE CHURCH, b Mt Holly, NJ, June 10, 41. ZOOLOGY, ENDOCRINOLOGY. *Educ:* Drew Univ, AB, 63; Ind Univ, Bloomington, PhD(zool), 67. *Prof Exp:* USPHS fel, 67 & 68-70, univ fel, 70-71, res assoc, 71-74, RES INVESTR ZOOL, UNIV MICH, ANN ARBOR, 74-, ASST PROF BIOL SCI, 80- *Mem:* Am Soc Zool. *Res:* Endocrine interactions; influence of thyroid activity on reproduction; comparative and developmental endocrinology; reproductive biology of the amphibia. *Mailing Add:* Dept of Biol Sci Univ of Mich Ann Arbor MI 48109

LEHMAN, GUY WALTER, b Walkerton, Ind, Sept 21, 23. THEORETICAL PHYSICS. *Educ:* Purdue Univ, BSEE, 48, MS, 50, PhD(physics), 54. *Prof Exp:* Jr engr electronics, Eastman Kodak Co, 48; asst physicist, Cornell Aeronaut Lab, 51; asst physics, Purdue Univ, 51-54; res specialist, Res Dept, Atomics Int Div, NAm Aviation, Inc, 54-62, group leader theoret physics, Sci Ctr, 63-67, mem tech staff, 67-70; PROF PHYSICS, UNIV KY, 70- *Mem:* Fel Am Phys Soc. *Res:* Solid state; mathematical physics; electronic structure; statistical mechanics; electromagnetic theory; lattice dynamics. *Mailing Add:* Dept of Physics Univ of Ky Lexington KY 40506

LEHMAN, HARVEY EUGENE, b Yuhsien, China; US citizen; m 58. DEVELOPMENTAL BIOLOGY, EMBRYOLOGY. *Educ:* Maryville Col, Tenn, BA, 41; Univ NC, MA, 44; Stanford Univ, PhD(embryol), 48. *Prof Exp:* From asst prof to assoc prof, 48-59, chmn dept, 62-67, PROF ZOOL, UNIV NC, 59-, CHMN DEPT, 76- *Concurrent Pos:* Fel, Univ Berne, 52-53; chg exp embryol course, Bermuda Biol Sta, 60-75; vis prof zool, Univ Vienna, 76. *Mem:* AAAS; Soc Develop Biol; Am Soc Zoologists; Am Micros Soc; Am Soc Cell Biol. *Res:* Rhabdocoele parasitology; amphibian pigmentation; nuclear transplantation in Triton; hybridization in Echinoderms; tissue culture; cell migration and differentiation of the neural crest; invertebrate larvae and metamorphosis; cytochemistry of embryonic differentiation. *Mailing Add:* Dept of Zool Univ of NC Chapel Hill NC 27514

LEHMAN, HUGH ROBERTS, b Ft Leavenworth, Kans, Jan 25, 21; m 45; c 3. CHEMICAL ENGINEERING, PHYSICS. *Educ:* The Citadel, BS, 41; Ohio State Univ, MSc, 47; Univ Calif, Berkeley, PhD(chem eng), 51. *Prof Exp:* Proj officer, Power Plant Lab, Wright Field, US Air Force, 45-46, Air Proving Ground, Fla, 47-48 & Armed Forces Spec Weapons Proj, 51-52; staff mem nuclear weapons, Los Alamos Sci Lab, 52-55; dep chief anal div, Air Force Spec Weapons Ctr, 55-58; br chief, Air Force Intel Ctr, 58-62; staff asst nuclear disarmament, US Atomic Energy Comn, 62-64; STAFF MEM NUCLEAR WEAPONS, LOS ALAMOS NAT LAB, 64- *Concurrent Pos:* Mem consult panel, Ballistics Missile Re-entry Systs, 66-68 & defense technol steering group, Atomic Energy Comn. *Mem:* Am Nuclear Soc; Am Inst Aeronaut & Astronaut. *Res:* Employment and effects of nuclear weapons; vulnerability of targets, nuclear and conventional. *Mailing Add:* Los Alamos Nat Lab PO Box 1663 Los Alamos NM 87545

LEHMAN, ISRAEL ROBERT, b Tauroggen, Lithuania, Oct 5, 24; US citizen; m 59; c 3. BIOCHEMISTRY. *Educ:* Johns Hopkins Univ, AB, 50, PhD(biochem), 54. *Prof Exp:* Am Cancer Soc fel, 55-57; instr microbiol, Wash Univ, 57-59; from asst prof to assoc prof, 59-66, chmn dept, 74-79, PROF BIOCHEM, SCH MED, STANFORD UNIV, 66- *Mem:* Nat Acad Sci; Am Acad Arts & Sci; Am Soc Biol Chem. *Res:* Nucleic acid metabolism; biochemistry of virus infection. *Mailing Add:* Dept of Biochem Stanford Univ Sch of Med Stanford CA 94305

LEHMAN, JOE JUNIOR, b Versailles, Mo, July 1, 21; m 43; c 4. ORGANIC CHEMISTRY. *Educ:* Bethel Col, Kans, AB, 43; Wash State Univ, MS, 47, PhD, 49. *Prof Exp:* From instr to assoc prof, 49-64, PROF CHEM, COLO STATE UNIV, 63- *Concurrent Pos:* Res fel, Midwest Res Inst, 58-59; vis prof, US Naval Acad, 61-62. *Mem:* AAAS; Am Chem Soc; Am Soc Microbiol. *Res:* Organic synthesis; modification of compounds by microorganisms; steric acceleration of hydrolytic reactions. *Mailing Add:* Dept of Chem Colo State Univ Ft Collins CO 80521

LEHMAN, JOHN MICHAEL, b Abington, Pa, June 19, 42. EXPERIMENTAL PATHOLOGY, VIROLOGY. *Educ:* Philadelphia Col Pharm & Sci, BS, 64; Univ Pa, PhD(path), 70. *Prof Exp:* NIH fel, Wistar Inst Anat & Biol, 70; NIH fel, 70-71, from instr to assoc prof, 71-80, PROF PATH, MED SCH, UNIV COLO MED CTR, DENVER, 80- *Concurrent Pos:* Vis staff mem, Los Alamos Nat Lab, 72- *Mem:* Am Soc Microbiol; Tissue Cult Asn; Am Asn Cancer Res; Am Asn Exp Path; Am Soc Cell Biol. *Res:* Tumor biology and virus transformation with oncogenic DNA viruses. *Mailing Add:* Dept of Path Univ of Colo Med Ctr Denver CO 80262

LEHMAN, JOHN THEODORE, b Taylor, Pa, Oct 13, 52; m 74; c 2. LIMNOLOGY, ECOLOGY. *Educ:* Yale Univ, BS & MS, 74; Univ Wash, PhD(zool), 78. *Prof Exp:* Asst prof limnol, 78-80, ASST PROF BIOL, UNIV MICH, 80-, MEM, GREAT LAKES RES DIV, 80- *Mem:* Am Soc Limnol & Oceanog; Int Asn Theoret & Appl Limnol; Phycol Soc Am; Sigma Xi. *Res:* Aquatic ecology; population dynamics of phytoplankton and zooplankton; mathematical models and numerical simulations of biological and chemical processes. *Mailing Add:* Div of Biol Sci Natural Sci Bldg Univ of Mich Ann Arbor MI 48109

LEHMAN, LILLIAN MARGOT YOUNGS, b Charleston, WVa, Jan 3, 28; m 58. EMBRYOLOGY. *Educ:* Catawba Univ, BA, 49; Univ NC, MA, 52, PhD, 54. *Prof Exp:* USPHS fel, Stanford Univ, 54-55; res asst embryol, Univ NC, 55-57; instr zool, Univ Vt, 57-58; from vis asst prof to vis assoc prof, 58-74, REGISTR & DIR INSTNL RES, UNIV NC, CHAPEL HILL, 75- *Mem:* AAAS. *Res:* Differentiation of pigment cells in amphibians. *Mailing Add:* Off of the Registrar Univ of NC Chapel Hill NC 27514

LEHMAN, RICHARD LAWRENCE, b Portland, Ore, Nov 7, 29; m 63; c 4. BIOPHYSICS. *Educ:* Univ Ore, BS, 51, MA, 53; Univ Calif, Berkeley, PhD(biophys), 63. *Prof Exp:* High sch instr math & sci, Calif, 53-56; physicist, Lawrence Radiation Lab, Univ Calif, 57-64, asst prof biophys & nuclear med, med ctr, Univ Calif, Los Angeles, 64-68; res physicist, lab nuclear sci, Mass Inst Technol, 68-71; dept dir Off Ecol, 71-81, PHYS SCIENTIST, CLIMATE ANAL CTR, NAT WEATHER SERV, NAT OCEANIC & ATMOSPHERIC ADMIN, 81- *Concurrent Pos:* Vis scientist, Am Inst Biol Sci, 61-; vis scientist, Swiss Fed Inst Technol, 63 & Cambridge Univ, 66. *Mem:* AAAS; Radiation Res Soc; Biophys Soc; Am Geophys Union; Am Soc Photobiol; Environ Mutagen Soc; Health Physics Soc. *Res:* Forecast applications; definition of forecast; contigent probability distributions. *Mailing Add:* Climate Anal Ctr Nat Oceanic & Atmospheric Admin Washington DC 20233

LEHMAN, ROBERT HAROLD, b Duncannon, Pa, Nov 15, 29; m 52; c 1. PHYSIOLOGY, ECOLOGY. *Educ:* Bloomsburg State Col, BS, 60; Univ Okla, MNS, 65, PhD(physiol, ecol), 70. *Prof Exp:* Asst prof biol, 66-70, assoc prof bot, 70-74, asst dean, 74-79, ASSOC PROF BIOL, LONGWOOD COL, 74-, DEAN, CONTINUING STUDIES, 79- *Res:* Allelopathic effects of caffeoylquinic acids and scopolin on vegetational patterning. *Mailing Add:* 1101 Sixth Ave Farmville VA 23901

LEHMAN, ROGER H, b Neosho, Wis, Apr 24, 21; m 57; c 3. MEDICINE, OTOLARYNGOLOGY. *Educ:* Univ Wis, BA, 42, MD, 44. *Prof Exp:* Resident otolaryngol, Vet Admin Ctr, Wood, Wis, 48-51; resident ophthal, Milwaukee County Gen Hosp, 51-52; chief otolaryngol, Vet Admin Ctr, Wood, 54-78; PROF OTOLARYNGOL & CHMN DEPT, MED COL WIS, 66- *Concurrent Pos:* Chief otolaryngol, Vet Admin Med Ctr, Milwaukee County Hosp, Wis, 60-, Milwaukee Children's Hosp, 71-74 & Froedtept Mem Lutheran Hosp, 80-82. *Mem:* AMA; Am Col Surg; Am Laryngol, Rhinol & Otol Soc; Soc Univ Otolaryngol; Am Acad Otolaryngol. *Mailing Add:* Vet Admin Ctr Wood WI 53193

LEHMAN, RUSSELL SHERMAN, b Ames, Iowa, Jan 25, 30; div; c 6. MATHEMATICS. *Educ:* Stanford Univ, BS, 51, MS, 52, PhD, 54. *Prof Exp:* Prob analyst, Comput Lab, Ballistic Res Labs, Aberdeen Proving Ground, 55-56; Fulbright res grant, Univ Gottingen, 56-57; from asst prof to assoc prof, 58-66, PROF MATH, UNIV CALIF, BERKELEY, 66- *Concurrent Pos:* Consult, Rand Corp, 54-65. *Mem:* Am Math Soc; Math Asn Am; Asn Symbolic Logic. *Res:* Numerical analysis and computing; number theory. *Mailing Add:* Dept of Math Univ of Calif Berkeley CA 94720

LEHMAN, WILLIAM FRANCIS, b Montgomery, Minn, Apr 25, 26; m 50; c 2. PLANT GENETICS, AGRONOMY. *Educ:* Wartburg Col, BS, 50; Univ Minn, Minneapolis, MS & PhD(plant genetics), 56. *Prof Exp:* Grade sch teacher, Iowa, 50-51; asst plant genetics, Univ Minn, 53-56; from jr agronomist to assoc agronomist, 56-74, AGRONOMIST, UNIV CALIF, DAVIS, 74- *Mem:* Am Soc Agron; Am Genetic Asn; Crop Sci Soc Am. *Res:* Genetics, breeding, agronomy, and disease and insect resistance primarily on alfalfa but also on rice, wheat, and sunflower. *Mailing Add:* Dept of Agron & Range Sci Univ of Calif 1004 E Holton Rd El Centro CA 92243

LEHMANN, A(LDO) SPENCER, b Los Angeles, Calif, Sept 23, 16; m 43; c 2. CHEMISTRY, CHEMICAL ENGINEERING. *Educ:* Stanford Univ, AB, 38; Brown Univ, PhD(chem), 41. *Prof Exp:* Res chemist, Brown Univ, 40-42, 43-45 & Naval Res Lab, 42-43; sr engr, Tenn Eastman Corp, Oak Ridge, Tenn, 45-46; chemist, Shell Develop Co, 46-50, supvr develop, 50-52, tech rep, 52-53, asst to pres, 53-54, mgr, Tech Dept, Wood River Refinery, Shell Oil Co, 54-58, asst mgr, NY Tech Dept, 58-62, process supt, 62-63, chief technologist, 63-64, refinery supt, Houston Refinery, 64-66, refinery mgr, Wilmington Refinery, Calif, 66-68, gen mg, Tech Depts, 68-73, gen mgr, Res Orgn & Facil, 73-76; RETIRED. *Mem:* Am Petrol Inst; Am Chem Soc; Sigma Xi; Am Inst Chem Engrs. *Res:* Infrared spectroscopy; development of reaction for producing metallic potassium; chemistry of uranium; design of special equipment for uranium recovery and processing; development of processes for production of petrochemicals; petroleum process design; research laboratory design and construction. *Mailing Add:* 1917 Santa Margarita Dr Fallbrook CA 92028

LEHMANN, ELROY PAUL, b Tigerton, Wis, June 22, 28; m 51; c 2. RESOURCE MANAGEMENT, PETROLEUM GEOLOGY. *Educ:* Univ Wis, BS, 50, MS, 51, PhD(geol), 55. *Prof Exp:* Asst prof geol, Wesleyan Univ, 52-59, actg chmn, 55-57; paleontologist, Mobil Oil Can, Libya, 59-60, sr paleontologist, 60-61, geol lab supvr, 61-63, staff geologist, Mobil Oil Libya Ltd, 63-65, sr staff geologist, Mobil Latin Am Inc, 65-67, sr res geologist, Mobil Res & Develop Corp, 67-69, chief geoscientist, Int Div, Mobil Oil Corp, 69-72, sr staff explorationist, 72-74, explor mgr, Mobil Oil Libya Ltd, 74-78; explor mgr new areas, Mobil Explor & Producing Serv, Inc, 78-79; PRES & GEN MGR, MOBIL EXPLOR EGYPT, INC, 79- *Concurrent Pos:* Mem educ comt, Am Geol Inst, 55-57; Fulbright lectr, Karachi, 58-59. *Mem:* AAAS; fel Geol Soc Am; Am Asn Petrol Geologists; Soc Econ Paleontologists & Mineralogists; Libya Petrol Explor Soc (treas, 64, pres, 65). *Res:* Geoscience aspects of energy resource identification and evaluation. *Mailing Add:* Mobil Explor Egypt Inc 54 Rd 105 Maadi Cairo 75221 United Arab Republic

LEHMANN, ERICH LEO, b Strasbourg, France, Nov 20, 17; nat US; m 39; c 3. MATHEMATICAL STATISTICS. *Educ:* Univ Calif, MA, 42, PhD(math statist), 46. *Prof Exp:* From asst to assoc prof math, 42-54, chmn dept statist, 73-76, PROF STATIST, UNIV CALIF, BERKELEY, 54- *Concurrent Pos:* Vis assoc prof, Columbia Univ, 50 & Stanford Univ, 51; vis lectr, Princeton Univ, 51. *Mem:* Nat Acad Sci; Am Statist Asn; Inst Math Statist; Int Statist Inst; Am Acad Arts & Sci. *Res:* Theories of testing hypotheses and of estimation; nonparametric statistics. *Mailing Add:* Dept of Statist Univ of Calif Berkeley CA 94720

LEHMANN, GILBERT MARK, b Libertyville, Ill, Aug 4, 33; m 58; c 1. GAS DYNAMICS, HEAT TRANSFER. *Educ:* Valparaiso Univ, BS, 55; Ill Inst Technol, MS, 57; Purdue Univ, PhD(jet propulsion), 66. *Prof Exp:* dean, Col Eng, 72-79, PROF MECH ENG, VALPARAISO UNIV, 56- *Mem:* Am Soc Mech Engrs; Am Soc Eng Educ. *Res:* Internal ballistics of solid propellant rockets. *Mailing Add:* Dept of Mech Eng Valparaiso Univ Valparaiso IN 46383

LEHMANN, HEINZ EDGAR, b Berlin, Ger, July 17, 11; nat Can; m 40; c 1. PSYCHIATRY. *Educ:* Univ Berlin, MD. *Hon Degrees:* LLD, Univ Calgary. *Prof Exp:* From asst prof to assoc prof, 52-65, prof, 65-81, chmn dept, 70-74, EMER PROF PSYCHIAT, McGILL UNIV, 81- *Concurrent Pos:* Dir med educ & res, Douglas Hosp, 48-; vis prof, Univ Cincinnati, 58-; dep commr res, Off Mental Health, State NY, 81- *Honors & Awards:* Lasker Award, Am Pub Health Asn, 57; McNeill Award, Can Psychiat Asn, 69, 70 & 74. *Mem:* Life fel Am Psychiat Asn; Can Psychiat Asn; Can Ment Health Asn; fel Am Col

Neuropharmacol; fel Int Col Neuropsychopharmacol. *Res:* Diagnosis and therapy of psychotic conditions; effects of drugs on mental processes. *Mailing Add:* Div Psychopharmacol Dept Psychiat McGill Univ 1033 Pine Ave W Montreal PQ H3A 1A1 Can

LEHMANN, HERMANN PETER, b London, Eng, June 24, 37. CLINICAL BIOCHEMISTRY. *Educ:* Univ Durham, BSc, 59, PhD(phys chem), 64. *Prof Exp:* Weizmann fel, Weizmann Inst Sci, 65-66; Volkswagen Found fel, Max Planck Inst, Mulheim Ruhr, WGer, 66-67; res assoc, Radiation Lab, Univ Notre Dame, 67-69; NIH sr fel biochem, Univ Wash, 69-71; asst prof, 71-77, ASSOC PROF PATH, LA STATE UNIV MED CTR, NEW ORLEANS, 77- *Concurrent Pos:* Vis scientist, Charity Hosp La, New Orleans, 71-; consult, Vet Admin Hosp, New Orleans, 72- *Mem:* Am Chem Soc; The Chem Soc; Am Asn Clin Chem; Brit Asn Clin Biochem. *Res:* Clinical chemistry; physical biochemistry. *Mailing Add:* Dept of Path La State Univ Med Ctr New Orleans LA 70112

LEHMANN, JOHN R(ICHARD), b Oak Park, Ill, Mar 24, 34; m 56; c 2. COMPUTER SYSTEMS DESIGN, RESEARCH ADMINISTRATION. *Educ:* Univ Ill, BS, 56, MS, 58, PhD(elec eng), 64. *Prof Exp:* Actg asst prog dir, Eng Systs Prog, Eng Div, 63-65, asst prog dir, 65-66, assoc prog dir, 66-67, staff assoc, Off Comput Activities, 67-70, PROG DIR COMPUT SYSTS DESIGN, COMPUT SCI SECT, DIV MATH & COMPUT SCI, NSF, 70- *Concurrent Pos:* Mem, Simulation Coun, 65- *Mem:* Inst Elec & Electronics Engrs; Am Soc Eng Educ. *Res:* Computer systems design; linear and nonlinear network; analog, digital and hybrid computer systems and utilization techniques; electronics; engineering education; methodology. *Mailing Add:* Comput Systs Design Prog Nat Sci Found Washington DC 20550

LEHMANN, JUSTUS FRANZ, b Koenigsberg, Ger, Feb 27, 21; nat US; m 43; c 3. PHYSICAL MEDICINE. *Educ:* Univ Frankfurt, MD, 45. *Prof Exp:* Asst physician internal med, Univ Frankfurt, 45-46; res asst, Max Planck Inst Biophys, 46-48; asst physician internal med, Univ Frankfurt, 48-51; assoc prof med, Mayo Clinic, 51-55; asst prof & assoc dir dept, Ohio State Univ, 55-57; PROF PHYS MED & CHMN DEPT PHYS MED & REHAB, UNIV WASH, 57- *Concurrent Pos:* Fel phys med, Mayo Clin, 51-55. *Mem:* Biophys Soc; AMA; Am Asn Electromyog & Electrodiag; Am Acad Phys Med & Rehab; Am Cong Rehab Med. *Res:* Biophysics of physical agents used in medicine; rehabilitation. *Mailing Add:* Dept of Rehab Med Univ of Wash Seattle WA 98195

LEHMANN, WILMA HELEN, b Chicago, Ill, Nov 14, 29. VERTEBRATE MORPHOLOGY. *Educ:* Mundelein Col, BA, 51; Northwestern Univ, MS, 54; Univ Ill, PhD(zool), 61. *Prof Exp:* Res asst allergy, Med Sch, Northwestern Univ, 54-56; asst prof zool, Pa State Univ, 61-64; asst prof natural sci, Mich State Univ, 64-67; from asst prof to assoc prof, 67-73, PROF BIOL, NORTHEASTERN ILL UNIV, 73- *Concurrent Pos:* Indexer, Evolution, 60-66; NSF instnl res grant, 63-64; vis res assoc, Argonne Nat Lab, 69-70. *Mem:* Fel AAAS; Soc Study Evolution; Am Soc Zool. *Res:* Comparative vertebrate anatomy; adaptive radiation of primates and rodents; functional mammalian anatomy; functional morphology, gross and microscopic, of bone. *Mailing Add:* Dept of Biol Northeastern Ill Univ Chicago IL 60625

LEHMER, DERRICK HENRY, b Berkeley, Calif, Feb 23, 05; m 28; c 2. MATHEMATICS. *Educ:* Univ Calif, AB, 27; Brown Univ, ScM, 29, PhD(math), 30. *Prof Exp:* Asst, Brown Univ, 28; Nat Res Coun fel, Calif Inst Technol, 30-32; res worker, Inst Advan Study, 33-34; from instr to asst prof math, Lehigh Univ, 34-38 & 39-40; Guggenheim fel, Cambridge Univ, 38-39; from asst prof to prof, 40-72, EMER PROF MATH, UNIV CALIF, BERKELEY, 72- *Concurrent Pos:* Nat Res Coun fel, Stanford Univ, 30-32; mathematician, Aberdeen Proving Ground, Md, 45-46; dir, Inst Numerical Analysis, 51-53; adv panel, NSF, 52- *Mem:* AAAS; Soc Indust & Appl Math; Am Math Soc (vpres, 53); Math Asn Am; Asn Comput Mach (vpres, 54-57). *Res:* Theory of numbers; computing devices; mathematical tables and other aids to computation. *Mailing Add:* 1180 Miller Ave Berkeley CA 94708

LEHMKUHL, DENNIS MERLE, b Pierre, SDak, Aug 22, 42; m 65. ENTOMOLOGY, ECOLOGY. *Educ:* Univ Mont, BA, 64, MS, 66; Ore State Univ, PhD(entom), 69. *Prof Exp:* asst prof, 69-74, ASSOC PROF BIOL, UNIV SASK, 74- *Mem:* AAAS; Entom Soc Can; Entom Soc Am; Ecol Soc Am; Can Soc Zool. *Res:* Taxonomy and biology of Ephemeroptera; ecology of rivers; arctic and northern aquatic insects, especially ecological adaptations and limiting factors and the resulting zoogeographical implications. *Mailing Add:* Dept of Biol Univ of Sask Saskatoon SK S7N 0W0 Can

LEHMKUHLE, STEPHEN W, b Dayton, Ohio, Apr 22, 51; m 72; c 2. VISUAL ELECTROPHYSIOLOGY, VISUAL PSYCHOPHYSICS. *Educ:* Wright State Univ, BS, 73; Vanderbilt Univ, PhD(psychol), 77. *Prof Exp:* Res fel, Univ Va, 77-79; ASST PROF PSYCHOL, BROWN UNIV, 79- *Mem:* AAAS. *Res:* Psychophysical, electrophysiological, and animal behavioral techniques are utilized to investigate the nature of usual processing of information. *Mailing Add:* Dept Psychol Brown Univ Providence RI 02912

LEHN, WILLIAM LEE, b Spring Valley, Ill, Mar 17, 32; m 54; c 4. MATERIALS ENGINEERING, CHEMISTRY. *Educ:* Univ Ill, BS, 54; Univ Rochester, PhD(chem), 58. *Prof Exp:* Chemist polymers, E I du Pont de Nemours, 58-60; res chemist, 60-61, group leader, 61-67, tech area mgr, 67-81, MATERIALS ENGR COATINGS, AIR FORCE MAT LAB, 81- *Honors & Awards:* Sky Lab Achievement Award, NASA, 74. *Mem:* Am Chem Soc; Res Soc Am; Am Inst Aeronaut & Astronaut. *Res:* Materials; coatings; protective and functional coatings and materials for aircraft and spacecraft. *Mailing Add:* Air Force Mat Lab MBE Wright-Patterson AFB OH 45433

LEHNE, RICHARD KARL, b Newark, NJ, Nov 18, 20; m 45; c 4. ORGANIC CHEMISTRY. *Educ:* Muhlenberg Col, BS, 41; Yale Univ, PhD(org chem), 49. *Prof Exp:* Process develop chemist, Gen Aniline & Film Co, 49-52; from assoc dir to dir res & develop, Wildroot Co, 52-59; mgr hair prod, Colgate-Palmolive Co, 59-63; dir res & develop, Mennen Co, 63-66; dir consumer prod res & develop, Cyanamid Int, 66-71; DIR REGULATORY AFFAIRS, CHURCH & DWIGHT CO, INC, 71- *Mem:* AAAS; Am Chem Soc; Soc Cosmetic Chemists (secy, 60-63). *Res:* Emulsion technology and viscosity versus stability; effects of phenolic additives. *Mailing Add:* Church & Dwight Co Inc 20 Kingsbridge Rd Piscataway NJ 08854

LEHNER, FLORIAN KONRAD, b Berlin, Ger, Feb 14, 37; Austrian citizen; m 63; c 3. CONTINUUM MECHANICS. *Educ:* Montan Univ, Austria, Dipl Ing, 63; Princeton Univ, PhD(geol), 79. *Prof Exp:* Res engr petrol reservoir eng, Shell Res, Neth, 63-75; res assoc geol & hydrol, Dept Geol & Geophys Sci, Princeton Univ, 75-78; res assoc, 78-79, ASST PROF SOLID MECH ENG, DIV ENG, BROWN UNIV, 79- *Mem:* Am Geophys Union; Soc Petrol Engrs; Int Soc Eng Sci. *Res:* Theoretical description of transport processes in porous media; mechanical behavior of geological materials; mechanics of geological structures; mechanisms of earthquake faulting. *Mailing Add:* Div Eng Box D Brown Univ Providence RI 02912

LEHNER, GUYDO R, b Chicago, Ill, Apr 14, 28. TOPOLOGY. *Educ:* Loyola Univ, Ill, BS, 51; Univ Wis, MS, 53, PhD, 58. *Prof Exp:* Instr math, Univ Wis-Milwaukee, 57-58; from instr to assoc prof, 58-68, PROF MATH, UNIV MD, COLLEGE PARK, 68- *Mem:* Am Math Soc; Math Asn Am. *Res:* Abstract spaces; continua; point set topology. *Mailing Add:* Dept of Math Univ of Md College Park MD 20742

LEHNER, PHILIP NELSON, b NH, July 5, 40; m 67; c 1. ANIMAL BEHAVIOR, ECOLOGY. *Educ:* Syracuse Univ, BS, 62; Cornell Univ, MS, 64; Utah State Univ, PhD(wildlife), 69. *Prof Exp:* Biologist, Bur Sport Fisheries & Wildlife, 62; res asst, Cornell Univ, 62-64 & Smithsonian Inst, 64-65; biologist, USPHS, 65; asst prof, 69-74, ASSOC PROF ANIMAL BEHAV, COLO STATE UNIV, 74- *Concurrent Pos:* NIH grant, Colo State Univ, 69-; consult, Stearns-Roger Corp, 70- *Mem:* AAAS; Animal Behav Soc; Soc Exp Anal Behav; Wildlife Soc; Soc Vet Ethology. *Res:* Animal behavior, its description, analysis and the effects of environmental variables; wild and domestic species; fish and wildlife; zoology. *Mailing Add:* Dept of Zool Colo State Univ Ft Collins CO 80521

LEHNERT, JAMES PATRICK, b Mecosta, Mich, Mar 29, 36. ZOOLOGY. *Educ:* Univ Mich, BS, 58, MA, 61; Univ Ill, PhD(parasitol), 67. *Prof Exp:* Asst prof, 67-72, assoc prof, 72-77, PROF BIOL, FERRIS STATE COL, 77- *Mailing Add:* 221 Sci Ferris State Col Big Rapids MI 49307

LEHNERT, SHIRLEY MARGARET, b London, Eng, June 2, 34; m 61; c 2. RADIOBIOLOGY. *Educ:* Univ Nottingham, BSc, 55; Univ London, MSc, 58, PhD(biophys), 61. *Prof Exp:* Fel, Univ Rochester, 61-63; res biophysicist, Montreal Gen Hosp, 63-65; sci serv officer, Defence Bd Can, 65-67; res assoc phys biol, Sloan-Kettering Inst Cancer Res, 68-71; asst prof radiol, Radiol Res Lab, Col Physicians & Surgeons, Columbia Univ, 71-74; ASST PROF THERAPEUT RADIOL, McGILL UNIV, 74- *Mem:* AAAS; Radiation Res Soc. *Res:* Biological and biochemical effects of ionizing radiation. *Mailing Add:* Dept of Therapeut Radiol Montreal Gen Hosp 1650 Cedar Ave Montreal PQ H3Q 1A4 Can

LEHNHOFF, HENRY JOHN, JR, b Lincoln, Nebr, Sept 13, 11; m 39; c 2. INTERNAL MEDICINE. *Educ:* Univ Nebr, AB, 33; Northwestern Univ, MD, 38; Am Bd Internal Med, dipl, 44. *Prof Exp:* PROF INTERNAL MED, COL MED, UNIV NEBR, OMAHA, 53- *Concurrent Pos:* Med dir, Northwestern Bell Tel Co & Woodman of the World Life Ins Co, 58. *Mem:* Am Soc Internal Med; Indust Med Asn; AMA; fel Am Col Physicians; Am Fedn Clin Res. *Res:* Nephrosis; infectious hepatitis; liver disease; arthritis; cardiac decompensation. *Mailing Add:* 650 Doctors Bldg Omaha NE 68131

LEHNHOFF, TERRY FRANKLIN, b St Louis, Mo, July 7, 39; m 60; c 3. MECHANICAL ENGINEERING, ENGINEERING MECHANICS. *Educ:* Univ Mo-Rolla, BS, 61, MS, 62; Univ Ill, Urbana, PhD(theoret & appl mech), 68. *Prof Exp:* Res engr, Caterpillar Tractor Co, 62-65; asst prof mech eng, 68-71, assoc prof, 71-77, PROF MECH & AEROSPACE ENG, UNIV MO-ROLLA, 77-, RES ASSOC, ROCK MECH RES CTR, 70- *Concurrent Pos:* Consult, Rockwell Int, 81-82. *Mem:* Sigma Xi; Am Soc Mech Engrs. *Res:* Thermal stresses; aerospace structures; solid mechanics; rock mechanics; finite elements; experimental stress analysis. *Mailing Add:* Dept of Mech & Aerospace Eng Univ of Mo Rolla MO 65401

LEHNINGER, ALBERT LESTER, b Bridgeport, Conn, Feb 17, 17; m 42; c 2. BIOCHEMISTRY. *Educ:* Wesleyan Univ, BA, 39; Univ Wis, MS, 40, PhD(biochem), 42. *Hon Degrees:* DSc, Wesleyan Univ, 54, Univ Notre Dame, 68, Acadia Univ, 72 & Mem Univ Nfld, 73; MD, Univ Padua, 66 & Univ Louvain, 78. *Prof Exp:* From instr to asst prof physiol chem, Univ Wis, 42-45; from asst prof to assoc prof biochem, Univ Chicago, 45-52; Delamar prof physiol chem, 52-78, dir dept physiol chem, 52-78, UNIV PROF MED SCI, DEPT PHYSIOL CHEM, SCH MED, JOHNS HOPKINS UNIV, 78- *Concurrent Pos:* Exchange prof, Univ Frankfurt, 51; Guggenheim fel & Fulbright scholar, Cambridge Univ, 51-52; Fulbright fel, Weizmann Inst & Univs Rome, Padua & Gottingen, 64; assoc mem, Neurosci Res Prog. *Honors & Awards:* Paul-Lewis Award, Am Chem Soc, 48; Remsen Award, 69; Distinguished Serv Award, Univ Chicago, 65; La Madonnina Award Sci, City Milan, 76. *Mem:* Inst of Med of Nat Acad Sci; Am Acad Arts & Sci; Am Philos Soc (vpres, 75-); Am Chem Soc; Am Soc Biol Chem (pres, 72-73). *Res:* Biological oxidations and phosphorylations; biochemistry of mitochondria; bioenergetics. *Mailing Add:* Dept of Physiol Chem Johns Hopkins Univ Sch Med Baltimore MD 21205

LEHOCZKY, JOHN PAUL, b Columbus, Ohio, June 29, 43; m 66; c 2. STATISTICS. *Educ:* Oberlin Col, BA, 65; Stanford Univ, MS, 67, PhD(statist), 69. *Prof Exp:* Asst prof, 69-73, assoc prof, 73-81, PROF STATIST, CARNEGIE-MELLON UNIV, 81- *Concurrent Pos:* Area ed, Mgt Sci. *Mem:* Opers Res Soc Am; Inst Math Statist; Am Statist Asn; Inst Mgt Sci. *Res:* Applied probability theory; stochastic processes and their application to computer, communication, and repair systems; diffusion approximations. *Mailing Add:* Dept of Statist Carnegie-Mellon Univ Schenley Park Pittsburgh PA 15213

LEHOTAY, DENIS CSABA, biochemistry, endocrinology, see previous edition

LEHOTAY, JUDITH MONA, forensic medicine, pathology, deceased

LEHOUX, JEAN-GUY, b St Severin, Que, Jan 9, 39; m 63; c 3. BIOCHEMISTRY, ENDOCRINOLOGY. *Educ:* Univ Montreal, BSc, 63, MSc, 67, PhD(biochem), 69. *Prof Exp:* Chief chemist, Cyanamid Can Ltd, 63-65; res asst biochem, Univ Montreal, 65-69, lectr med, 69-71; asst prof obstet & gynec, 71-75, assoc prof, 75-81, PROF, DEPT BIOCHEM, OBSTET & GYNEC, UNIV SHERBROOKE, 81-, HEAD, CLIN ENDOCRINOL LAB, 74-, CHMN, DEPT BIOCHEM, 80- *Concurrent Pos:* Biochemist, Hosp Maisonneuve, 69-70; Med Res Coun Can fels, Fac Med, Univ Montreal, 69-70 & Dept Zool, Univ Sheffield, 70-71; Med Res Coun Que & Med Res Coun Can grant, Univ Sherbrooke, 71-74; Med Res Coun Can scholar, 74. *Mem:* Brit Soc Endocrinol. *Res:* Studies on steroid hydroxylation with a special interest to aldosterone regulation. *Mailing Add:* Fac of Med Univ of Sherbrooke Sherbrooke PQ J1K 2R1 Can

LEHR, CARLTON G(ORNEY), b Boston, Mass, Sept 11, 21; m 47; c 3. ELECTRICAL ENGINEERING. *Educ:* Mass Inst Technol, BS, 43, MS, 48. *Prof Exp:* Mem staff, Div Indust Coop, Mass Inst Technol, 46-47, asst elec eng, 47-48; sr engr, Microwave & Power Tube Div, Raytheon Co, 48-54, mem staff, Microwave Group, Res Div, 54-58, mgr, 58-64; staff engr, Smithsonian Astrophys Observ, 64-76; consult, 76-79; SR RADAR & OPTICAL ENGR, FORD AEROSPACE & COMMUN CORP, 79- *Concurrent Pos:* Lectr, Northeastern Univ, 63-70. *Mem:* Inst Elec & Electronics Engrs; Math Asn Am; Am Phys Soc. *Res:* Satellite tracking; lasers; mathematics. *Mailing Add:* 5 Childs Rd Lexington MA 02173

LEHR, DAVID, b Sadagura, Austria, Mar 22, 10; US citizen; div; c 2. PHARMACOLOGY, MEDICINE. *Educ:* Univ Vienna, BA, 29, MD, 35. *Prof Exp:* Asst pharm. ol, Univ Vienna, 34-48; instr, Univ Lund, 38-39; pharmacologist & res assoc, Path Dept, Newark Beth Israel Hosp, NJ, 39-42; from instr to asst prof pharmacol & med, 41-49, assoc prof pharmacol, 49-54, chmn dept, 54-56, prof physiol & pharmacol & chmn dept, 56-64, chmn res comt, Metrop Med Ctr, 54-72, ASSOC PROF MED, NEW YORK MED COL, 49-, PROF PHARMACOL & CHMN DEPT, 64- *Concurrent Pos:* Asst vis physician, Metrop Hosp, Welfare Island, NY, 42-54, vis physician, 54-; asst attend physician, Flower & Fifth Ave Hosps, 44-49, assoc attend physician, 49-; vis physician, Bird S Coler Hosp, 54-; Claud Bernard prof, Inst Exp Med & Surg, Univ Montreal, 61; mem rev comt, Health Res Coun New York, 61-65; vchmn panel neurol & psychiat dis, 61-; chmn ad hoc comt use of new therapeut agents & procedures in human beings, Assoc Med Schs, NY, 67-; mem coun arteriosclerosis, Am Heart Asn. *Honors & Awards:* Cert Merit, Asn Mil Surg US. *Mem:* Fel AAAS; fel Am Col Physicians; fel Am Col Cardiol; fel AMA; fel Am Soc Clin Pharmacol & Therapeut. *Res:* Cardiology; hypertension; experimental arteriosclerosis; toxicity of sulfonamides; sulfonamide mixtures; chemotherapy; experimental cardiovascular necrosis; parathyroid hormone interrelations; tissue electrolytes. *Mailing Add:* Dept of Pharmacol One E 105th St New York NY 10029

LEHR, GARY FULTON, b Rockville Centre, NY, July 16, 52; m 81. CHEMICAL DYNAMICS. *Educ:* Manhattanville Col, AB, 75; Brown Univ, PhD(chem), 81. *Prof Exp:* Res assoc res, Dept Chem, Columbia Univ, 79-81; STAFF SCIENTIST RES, CENT RES & DEVELOP DEPT, E I DU PONT DE NEMOURS & CO, INC, 81- *Mem:* Am Chem Soc; AAAS. *Res:* Study of reaction mechanisms involving free radical and carbene intermediates, including radical-radical, radical-molecule photochemical, organometallic and autoxidation reactions. *Mailing Add:* Exp Sta E I Du Pont de Nemours & Co Inc Wilmington DE 19898

LEHR, HANNS H, b Sadagora, Austria, Jan 1, 08; nat US; m 34; c 3. PHARMACEUTICAL CHEMISTRY. *Educ:* Univ Vienna, PhD(chem), 31, MPharm, 32. *Prof Exp:* Asst org chem, Univ Vienna, 30-32; managing dir pharmaceut lab, Salvatorapotheke, Vienna, 33-38; asst pharmacol, Paris, 38-40 & French Pub Health Serv, 40; asst biochem, Univ Aix Marseille, 40-42; asst org chem, Univ Basle, Switz, 43-46; sr res chemist, Hoffmann-La Roche, Inc, 46-66, asst to vpres chem res, 66-68, asst dir, 68-73, consult, 73-76; RETIRED. *Mem:* AAAS; Am Chem Soc; fel Am Inst Chemists. *Res:* Organic chemistry; biochemistry; chemotherapy; antibiotics; synthetic drugs; research administration. *Mailing Add:* 10 Tuers Pl Upper Montclair NJ 07043

LEHR, JAY H, b Teaneck, NJ, Sept 11, 36; m 57; c 2. HYDROLOGY, GROUNDWATER GEOLOGY. *Educ:* Princeton Univ, BSE, 57; Univ Ariz, PhD(hydrol), 62. *Prof Exp:* Hydrol field asst, Groundwater Br, US Geol Surv, NY, 55-56; res assoc hydrol, Univ Ariz, 59-62, from instr to asst prof, 62-64; asst prof, Ohio State Univ, 64-67; EXEC DIR, NAT WATER WELL ASN, 67- *Concurrent Pos:* Ed, Ground Water, 66-; ed-in-chief, Water Well J, 72- *Res:* Groundwater model studies utilizing consolidated porous medias; groundwater pollution; groundwater and surfacewater law; water well construction techniques. *Mailing Add:* Suite 135 Nat Water Well Asn 500 W Wilson Bridge Rd Worthington OH 43085

LEHR, MARVIN HAROLD, b Brooklyn, NY, Mar 17, 33; m 56; c 4. POLYMER PHYSICS, POLYMER CHEMISTRY. *Educ:* Reed Col, BA, 54; Yale Univ, MS, 55, PhD(kinetics), 59. *Prof Exp:* Res chemist, B F Goodrich Res Ctr, 59-61, sr res chemist, 61-66, res assoc, 66-73, sr res assoc, 73-78, RES

FEL CORP RES, B F GOODRICH RES & DEVELOP CTR, 78- *Res:* Viscoelastic-fracture behavior; polymer morphology; relation of polymer structure to properties. *Mailing Add:* B F Goodrich Res & Develop Ctr Brecksville OH 44141

LEHR, ROLAND E, b Quincy, Ill, Nov 7, 42. ORGANIC CHEMISTRY. *Educ:* Princeton Univ, AB, 64; Harvard Univ, AM, 66, PhD(chem), 69. *Prof Exp:* From asst prof to assoc prof, 68-80, PROF CHEM, UNIV OKLA, 80- *Concurrent Pos:* Res grants, NASA, 68-69; Am Chem Soc, 68-70 & NIH, 77- *Mem:* Am Chem Soc; Am Asn Cancer Res; Sigma Xi. *Res:* Chemical carcinogenesis of polycyclis aronatic hydrocarbons; synthesis of more complete and selective neurotoxins. *Mailing Add:* Dept of Chem Univ of Okla Norman OK 73019

LEHRER, GERARD MICHAEL, b Vienna, Austria, May 29, 27; US citizen; m 60; c 2. NEUROLOGY. *Educ:* City Col New York, BS, 50; NY Univ, MD, 54. *Prof Exp:* Res asst neurol, Col Physicians & Surgeons, Columbia Univ, 53-54; intern, Mt Sinai Hosp, NY, 54-55, asst resident neurologist, 55-57, resident, 58; asst neurol, Sch Med, Wash Univ, 58-60; from asst attend neurologist to assoc attend neurologist, Mt Sinai Hosp, NY, 60-68; assoc prof, 66-67, PROF NEUROL, MT SINAI SCH MED, 67-, DIR DIV NEUROCHEM, 66-; ATTEND NEUROLOGIST, MT SINAI HOSP, NY, 68- *Concurrent Pos:* NIH trainee, Mt Sinai Hosp, NY, 56-58; NIH spec trainee neurochem & res fel pharmacol, Sch Med, Wash Univ, 58-61; consult, Preclin Psychopharmacol Res Rev Comt, NIMH, 65-69; res collabr, Brookhaven Nat Lab, NY, 67-69; consult neurologist, Vet Admin Hosp, Bronx, NY, 67-75; staff neurologist, 76-; attend neurologist, St Vincent's Hosp, NY, 76- *Mem:* Fel Am Acad Neurol; Am Asn Neuropath; Int Soc Neurochem; Soc Neurosci; Am Neurol Asn. *Res:* Brain maturation and metabolism; molecular mechanisms of central nervous system differentiation and disease, especially demyelination. *Mailing Add:* Dept Neurol Mt Sinai Sch Med New York NY 10029

LEHRER, HAROLD Z, b New York, NY, Aug 22, 27. RADIOLOGY. *Educ:* Columbia Univ, AB, 47; NY Univ, MD, 53; Am Bd Radiol, dipl, 60. *Prof Exp:* Am Cancer Soc fel, 58; asst adj radiologist, Beth Israel Hosp & Med Ctr, New York, 59-63; instr neuroradiol, NY Univ-Bellevue Med Ctr, 63-65; from asst to assoc prof, Sch Med, Tulane Univ, 65-67; ASSOC PROF NEURORADIOL, NY MED COL, 68-; DIR DEPT RADIOL, BIRD S COLER HOSP, NEW YORK, 73- *Concurrent Pos:* NIH spec fel neuroradiol, NY Univ-Bellevue Med Ctr, 63-65. *Mem:* AAAS; Radiol Soc NAm; Am Roentgen Ray Soc; Am Soc Neuroradiol. *Res:* Neuroradiology, especially analysis of clinical data mathematically. *Mailing Add:* Dept of Radiol NY Med Col New York NY 10029

LEHRER, HARRIS IRVING, b Boston, Mass, May 28, 39. BIOCHEMISTRY, IMMUNOCHEMISTRY. *Educ:* Brandeis Univ, BA, 60, PhD(biochem), 65. *Prof Exp:* Sr biochemist, Monsanto Corp, 68-69; sr scientist immunochem, Ortho Diag, 69-76, group leader, 76-77; supvr, Sherman-Abrams Lab, 77-78; SR IMMUNOCHEMIST, ICL SCI, 78- *Concurrent Pos:* NIH fels, Marine Biol Lab, Woods Hole, 65, Univ Palermo, 65-67 & Brandeis Univ, 67-68. *Mem:* AAAS; Am Asn Clin Chem; NY Acad Sci; Am Chem Soc. *Res:* Development of new immunochemical techniques and their application to diagnostic testing. *Mailing Add:* ICL Scientific 18249 Euclid St Fountain Valley CA 92708

LEHRER, PAUL LINDNER, b Chicago, Ill, Feb 9, 28; m 53; c 4. PHYSICAL GEOGRAPHY. *Educ:* Univ Cincinnati, BS, 49; Ohio State Univ, MA, 51; Univ Nebr, PhD(geog), 62. *Prof Exp:* Instr geog, Ohio Univ, 56-59; from instr to asst prof, Univ Wis-Milwaukee, 60-66; assoc prof, 66-69, PROF GEOG, UNIV NORTHERN COLO, 69- *Concurrent Pos:* NSF sci fac fel, Univ Witwatersrand, 64-65. *Mem:* Asn Am Geogr; Sigma Xi. *Res:* Soils and regional geography of Subsaharan Africa. *Mailing Add:* Dept of Geog Univ of Northern Colo Greeley CO 80639

LEHRER, ROBERT N(ATHANIEL), b Sandusky, Ohio, Jan 17, 22; m 45; c 2. INDUSTRIAL & SYSTEMS ENGINEERING. *Educ:* Purdue Univ, BS, 45, MS, 47, PhD(indust eng), 49. *Prof Exp:* Asst & instr indust eng, Purdue Univ, 46-49; asst prof, Ore State Col, 49-50; assoc prof, Ga Inst Technol, 50-54, prof, 54-58, res assoc, 50-58; prof & chmn dept, Technol Inst, Northwestern Univ, Ill, 58-62; UNESCO expert, Guadalajara & Guanajuato, 62-63; assoc dir, Sch Indust Eng, 63-66, PROF INDUST ENG, GA INST TECHNOL, 63-, DIR SCH INDUST ENG, 66- *Concurrent Pos:* Consult opers res, 50-; ed-in-chief, J Indust Eng, 53-62; adv indust & systs eng sem, Japan, 59 & 62; adv indust eng, Eindhoven & Dutch Ministry Educ, 62-; Nat Acad Sci workshop panel indust & technol res, Indonesia, 71; consult ed indust eng & mgt sci ser, Reinhold Publ Corp; mem adv bd mil personnel supplies, Nat Acad Sci-Nat Res Coun. *Honors & Awards:* Outstanding Indust Eng Award, Am Inst Indust Engrs. *Mem:* Opers Res Soc Am; Am Soc Eng Educ; fel Am Inst Indust Engrs (vpres, 60); Inst Mgt Sci. *Res:* Work simplification; operations research and management science; management of improvement. *Mailing Add:* Sch of Indust & Systs Eng Ga Inst of Technol Atlanta GA 30332

LEHRER, SAMUEL BRUCE, b New Britain, Conn, Apr 1, 43; m 71; c 1. ALLERGY, IMMUNOLOGY. *Educ:* Upsala Col, BS, 66; Temple Univ, PhD, 71. *Prof Exp:* Lab technician, Microbiol Dept, State Lab Hartford, 65-69; researcher, Univ Lausanne, Switz, 69; fel, Scripps Clin & Res Found, La Jolla, 71-75; asst prof, 75-79, ASSOC PROF MED, SCH MED, TULANE UNIV, 79- *Concurrent Pos:* NIH fel, 74; Nat Inst Allergy & Infectious Dis young investr award, 78-81; Am Lung Asn grant, 78-80; consult, Food & Drug Admin, 78-80; assoc adj prof microbiol & immunol, 80- *Mem:* Am Soc Microbiol; Am Acad Allergy; Am Asn Immunologists; Am Thoracic Soc; Col Int Allergologicum. *Res:* Allergic disease in man; environmental and host factors regulating IgE response; molecular aspects of allergenicity. *Mailing Add:* Tulane Univ Sch of Med 1700 Perdido St New Orleans LA 70112

LEHRER, SHERWIN SAMUEL, b New York, NY, Apr 2, 34; m 60; c 2. BIOCHEMISTRY. *Educ:* Univ Pittsburgh, BS, 56; Univ Calif, Berkeley, PhD(chem), 61. *Prof Exp:* Staff scientist thin magnetic films, Lincoln Lab, Mass Inst Technol, 61-62; fel biochem, Brandeis Univ, 63-66; res assoc, Retina Found, Mass, 66-70; SR STAFF SCIENTIST BIOCHEM, BOSTON BIOMED RES INST, 70- *Concurrent Pos:* USPHS res grant, Retina Found, Mass & Boston Biomed Res Inst, 67-; assoc, Harvard Med Sch, 68- *Mem:* AAAS; NY Acad Sci; Am Soc Biol Chem; Am Chem Soc; Biophys Soc. *Res:* Application of fluorescence techniques to protein conformation and interactions; muscle protein interactions. *Mailing Add:* Dept Muscle Res Boston Biomed Res Inst Boston MA 02114

LEHRER, WILLIAM PETER, JR, b Brooklyn, NY, Feb 6, 16; m 45; c 1. ANIMAL SCIENCE, ANIMAL NUTRITION. *Educ:* Pa State Univ, BS, 41; Univ Idaho, MS, 46 & 54; Wash State Univ, PhD(animal nutrit, chem), 51; Blackstone Sch of Law, LLB, 72, JD, 74; Pepperdine Univ, MBA, 75. *Prof Exp:* Salesman, Swift & Co, WVa, 41-42; mgr livestock farm, NY, 44-45; from asst prof & asst animal husbandman to assoc prof animal husb & assoc animal husbandman, Univ Idaho, 46-60, prof, 60; dir nutrit, Albers Milling Co, 60-62, dir nutrit & res, 62-74, dir nutrit & res, Albers Milling Co & John W Eshelman & Sons, 74-76; dir nutrit & res, Milling Div, Carnation Co, 76-81; CONSULT. *Concurrent Pos:* Mem, Comt Animal Nutrit & Comt Dog Nutrit, Nat Acad Sci-Nat Res Coun & Tech Comt, Western Livestock Range Livestock Nutrit, USDA; mem nutrit coun, Am Feed Mfrs, 62-, chmn, 69-70; mem, Res Adv Coun, US Brewers Asn, 69- & Adv Coun Calif State Polytech Univ, Pomona, 69- *Honors & Awards:* WAP Award, Agr-Bus Award, 64. *Mem:* Fel AAAS; Am Inst Nutrit; Animal Nutrit Res Coun; Sigma Xi; fel Am Soc Animal Sci. *Res:* Animal production and nutrition; reproduction and growth of beef cattle and dairy cattle, dogs, horses, sheep and swine. *Mailing Add:* 12518 Hortense St Studio City CA 91604

LEHRMAN, GEORGE PHILIP, b New York, NY, Nov 28, 26; m 48; c 3. PHARMACY ADMINISTRATION. *Educ:* Univ Conn, BS, 50, PhD, 55; Purdue Univ, MS, 52. *Prof Exp:* Asst pharm, Purdue Univ, 50-52, instr chem, 52-53; mkt analyst, Mead Johnson & Co, 55-57; res chemist, Am Cyanamid Co, 57-59; head develop, Cent Pharmacal Co, Ind, 59-61; pharmaceut develop mgr, Baxter Labs, 61-62; dir labs, Conal Pharmaceut, 62-64; vpres, Owen Labs, 64-67; assoc prof pharm, Univ Okla, 67-75; ASST DEAN COL PHARM, UNIV NMEX, 75- *Mem:* Am Chem Soc; Am Pharmaceut Asn; Soc Cosmetic Chemists. *Res:* Product development; drug law. *Mailing Add:* 8431 Palo Duro NE Albuquerque NM 87111

LEI, KAI YUI, b Macau, July 30, 44; m 66; c 1. NUTRITION. *Educ:* Univ London, BS, 68; Univ Guelph, MS, 70; Mich State Univ, PhD(human nutrit), 73. *Prof Exp:* Res asst nutrit, Mich State Univ, 70-73; res assoc hemat, Wayne State Univ, 74-75; from asst prof to assoc prof nutrit, Miss State Univ, 75-80; ASSOC PROF NUTRIT, UNIV ARIZ, 80- *Mem:* Am Inst Nutrit; Am Dietetic Asn; Sigma Xi. *Res:* Oral contraceptives and nutrient interactions; trace mineral metabolism; carbohydrate and lipid metabolism. *Mailing Add:* Dept Nutrit & Food Sci Univ Ariz Tucson AZ 85721

LEIB, JOHN COADY, b Hazelton, Pa, Dec 13, 35; m 59; c 2. PHYSICS. *Educ:* Georgetown Univ, BS, 57; Fla State Univ, MS, 63. *Prof Exp:* Scientist/engr, Boeing Co, 63-70; mgr, BDM Corp, 70-73; scientist/engr, Boeing Aerospace Co, 74-76; scientist, EG&G, Inc, 76-79; MGR, BDM CORP, 79- *Res:* Nuclear weapons effects; survivability of strategic system subject to nuclear weapons effects; pioneer in developing methodology to assess and improve survivability. *Mailing Add:* 1801 Randolph Rd SE Albuquerque NM 87106

LEIBACH, FREDRICK HARTMUT, b Kitzingen, Ger, Sept 21, 30; US citizen; m 61; c 3. BIOCHEMISTRY, ENDOCRINOLOGY. *Educ:* Southwest Mo State Col, BS, 59; Emory Univ, PhD(biochem), 64. *Prof Exp:* Nat Acad Sci-Nat Res Coun res assoc, Ames Res Ctr, NASA, 64-67; assoc prof endocrinol, 76-79, ASSOC PROF BIOCHEM, MED COL GA, 67-, PROF CELL & MOLECULAR BIOL, 79- *Mem:* AAAS; Am Chem Soc; Am Soc Biol Chemists; Am Physiol Soc. *Res:* Enzymes in protein and amino acid metabolism; peptidases, transpeptidases and esterases; protein turnover; membrane transport of organic solutes. *Mailing Add:* Dept Cell & Molecular Biol Med Col Ga Augusta GA 30912

LEIBACHER, JOHN WILLIAM, astrophysics, solar physics, see previous edition

LEIBBRANDT, VERNON DEAN, b McCook, Nebr, Oct 31, 44; m 67; c 2. ANIMAL NUTRITION. *Educ:* Univ Nebr, BS, 66; Iowa State Univ, PhD(animal nutrit), 72. *Prof Exp:* Asst prof animal nutrit, Univ Fla, 75-78; asst prof, 78-80, ASSOC PROF ANIMAL NUTRIT, UNIV WIS-MADISON, 80- *Concurrent Pos:* Fel, Res Div, Cleveland Clin Found, 72-75. *Mem:* Am Soc Animal Sci. *Res:* Husbandry and nutritional aspects of swine production. *Mailing Add:* Dept Animal Sci 1675 Observatory Dr Madison WI 53706

LEIBERMAN, KENNETH W, b Brooklyn, NY, Feb 7, 38; m 62; c 2. NERUOCHEMISTRY, BIOLOGICAL PSYCHIATRY. *Educ:* Brooklyn Col, BA, 60; Tex Tech Univ, MS, 63; Univ Ky, PhD(phys chem), 66. *Prof Exp:* Res fel, Dept Path, Harvard Univ, 66-67; res fel, Dept Neurol, Columbia Univ, 69-71; instr, 73-75, asst prof, 75-82, ASSOC PROF PSYCHIAT & BIOCHEM, CORNELL UNIV, 82- *Concurrent Pos:* Jr fel, New England Deaconess Hosp, 66-67; asst dir, Psychiat & Psychobiol Study Unit, Cornell Univ, 77- *Mem:* AAAS; Am Chem Soc; Soc Neurosci; Am Soc Biol Chemists. *Res:* Biochemical bases of mental illness and alcoholism; neurochemical aspects of behavior. *Mailing Add:* Dept Psychiat Cornell Univ 1300 York Ave New York NY 10021

LEIBHARDT, EDWARD, b New Rome, Wis, Oct 13, 19; m 61; c 2. ASTRONOMY, SPECTROSCOPY. *Educ:* Northwestern Univ, BA, 54, PhD(astron), 59. *Prof Exp:* PRES, DIFFRACTION PROD, INC, 51- *Mem:* Optical Soc Am; Soc Appl Spectros. *Res:* Spectroscopy and photometry in astronomy; diffraction grating manufacture. *Mailing Add:* PO Box 645 Woodstock IL 60098

LEIBHOLZ, STEPHEN W, b Berlin, Ger, Jan 28, 32; US citizen; m 58; c 3. INFORMATION & COMMUNICATION SCIENCES. *Educ:* NY Univ, AB, 52. *Prof Exp:* Res asst & teaching fel physics, NY Univ, 52-53; tutor, Queens Col, 53-54; res assoc electronics, Adv Group Electron Devices, US Dept Defense, 54-56; prin engr, Repub Aviation Corp, 57-60; sr mem tech staff, Auerbach Corp, 60-64, prog mgr opers res & anal, 64-66, mgr syst design & anal, 66-67; PRES, ANALYTICS, 67- *Concurrent Pos:* Mem var adv panels, Dept of Defense, 70-; mem, Simulation Coun; ed, Mil Oper Res Monogra. *Mem:* Inst Elec & Electronics Engrs; Soc Indust & Appl Math; Opers Res Soc Am; Mil Oper Res Soc. *Res:* Applied mathematics and operations research in areas of information systems and military systems, especially statistical problems; systems architecture and engineering in areas of information, communications, automation control and surveillance systems for industry and government. *Mailing Add:* Analytics 2500 Maryland Rd Willow Grove PA 19090

LEIBMAN, KENNETH CHARLES, b New York, NY, Aug 7, 23; m 46; c 2. BIOCHEMICAL PHARMACOLOGY. *Educ:* Polytech Inst Brooklyn, BS, 43; Ohio State Univ, MSc, 48; NY Univ, PhD(biochem), 53. *Prof Exp:* Org res chemist, Nat Lead Co, 43-44; asst chem, Ohio State Univ, 46-48; instr, Univ Louisville, 48-49; fel oncol, Univ Wis, 53-54, proj assoc, 54-55; specialist tracer techniques, US Tech Coop Mission, India, 55-56; from instr to assoc prof, 56-68, PROF PHARMACOL, COL MED, UNIV FLA, 68- *Concurrent Pos:* Ed, Drug Metab & Disposition, 72- *Mem:* AAAS; Am Soc Pharmacol & Exp Therapeut. *Res:* Drug metabolism; enzymology; toxicology. *Mailing Add:* Dept of Pharmacol & Therapeut Univ of Fla Col of Med Gainesville FL 32610

LEIBMAN, LAWRENCE FRED, b Bronx, NY, Sept 10, 47. ORGANIC CHEMISTRY. *Educ:* City Univ New York, PhD(chem), 76. *Prof Exp:* Fel org biochem, Columbia Univ, 75-76; chemist, Am Cyanamid Co, 76-80; MEM STAFF, BASF WYANDOTTE CORP, 80- *Mem:* Am Chem Soc; Sigma Xi. *Res:* Organic reaction mechanisms. *Mailing Add:* BASF Wyandotte Corp 33 Riverside Ave Rensselaer NY 12144

LEIBO, STANLEY PAUL, b Pawtucket, RI, Apr 8, 37; m 61; c 2. CRYOBIOLOGY, EMBRYOLOGY. *Educ:* Brown Univ, AB, 59; Univ Vt, MS, 61; Princeton Univ, MA, 62, PhD(biol), 63. *Prof Exp:* Res assoc, Oak Ridge Nat Lab, 63-64, USPHS res fel, 64-65, staff biologist, Biol Div, 65-80; VPRES, RES & DEVELOP DIV, RIO VISTA INT, 81- *Concurrent Pos:* Lectr, Oak Ridge Grad Sch Biomed Sci, Univ Tenn, 69-80; mem adv bd, Am Type Culture Collection, 71-74; vis scientist health sci & technol, Mass Inst Technol, 74; mem sci staff, Inst Immunol, Basel, Switz, 77-78; mem fac, UNESCO-ICLA-ICRO Training Course & Roving Seminars on Deep Freeze Preservation of Mouse Strains, Neth, 75, Denmark, Hungary & Poland, 76 & Czech, Italy & Yugoslavia, 77. *Mem:* AAAS; Soc Cryobiol; Soc Study Reproduction; Soc Cryobiol (vpres, 78-80); Int Cell Res Orgn. *Res:* Biology of bacteriophage; cryobiology of bacteriophage, proteins and algae; cryobiology and physiology of mammalian embryos, erythrocytes, lymphocytes and tissue-culture cells. *Mailing Add:* Rt 9 Box 242 San Antonio TX 78227

LEIBOVIC, K NICHOLAS, b Plunge, Lithuania, June 14, 21; m 43; c 3. NEUROSCIENCES, BIOPHYSICS. *Prof Exp:* Mathematician, Dulwich Col, Eng, 46-53 & Courtaulds, 53-56; proj leader indust math, Brit Oxygen Res & Develop Co, 56-60; sr mathematician, Westinghouse Res Labs, 60-63; prin mathematician, Cornell Aeronaut Lab, 63-64; assoc prof biophys, 64-74, asst dir ctr theoret biol, 67-68, PROF BIOPHYS, STATE UNIV NY BUFFALO, 74- *Concurrent Pos:* Lectr, Norwood Col, Eng, 52-53; mem math adv coun, Battersea Col Technol, 59-60; vis prof, Univ Calif, Berkeley, 69, Hadassah Med Sch, Hebrew Univ, 71 & Inst Ophthalmol, London, 78; prog dir, Neurosci Res Prog, 78-79; vis scholar, Harvard Univ, 79-80. *Mem:* AAAS; Soc Neurosci; Biophys Soc; Asn Res Vision & Ophthalmol. *Res:* Information processing in the nervous system; electrophysiology and psychopyhsics of vision; nervous system theory; mathematical models in biology; industrial mathematics; applications to chemical, mechanical and electrical engineering; computers and operations research. *Mailing Add:* Dept of Biophys State Univ of NY Buffalo NY 14214

LEIBOVICH, SIDNEY, b Memphis, Tenn, Apr 2, 39; m 62; c 2. FLUID DYNAMICS, APPLIED MATHEMATICS. *Educ:* Calif Inst Technol, BS, 61; Cornell Univ, PhD(theoret mech), 65. *Prof Exp:* NATO fel, London, 65-66; from asst prof to assoc prof thermal eng, 66-78, PROF MECH & AEROSPACE ENG, CORNELL UNIV, 78- *Concurrent Pos:* Sr vis fel, Math Inst, Univ St Andrews, 77. *Mem:* Am Phys Soc; Soc Indust & Appl Math; Am Soc Mech Engrs; Am Geophys Union; AAAS. *Res:* Fluid mechanics, particularly dynamics of vortex flows, geophysical fluid dynamics and wave propagation phenomena in fluids. *Mailing Add:* Sibley Sch of Mech & Aerospace Eng Upson Hall Cornell Univ Ithaca NY 14853

LEIBOVITZ, LOUIS, b Philadelphia, Pa, May 29, 21; m 52; c 3. VETERINARY MEDICINE. *Educ:* Pa State Col, BS, 46; Univ Pa, VMD, 50. *Prof Exp:* Pvt vet pract, 50-56; prof avian dis & dir regional poultry diag lab, Del Valley Col, 56-63; AVIAN PATHOLOGIST, NY STATE VET COL, CORNELL UNIV, 63-, PROF AQUATIC ANIMAL DIS, 81-; DIR, LAB MARINE ANIMAL HEALTH, MARINE BIOL LAB, WOODS HOLE, MASS, 73-, SEA GRANT PRIN INVESTR, 81- *Mem:* Am Vet Med Asn; Am Asn Avian Path; Am Soc Parasitol; Soc Protozool; Am Soc Microbiol. *Res:* Diseases of birds and marine animals, their history, etiology, pathogenesis, immunology prevention, treatment and cure. *Mailing Add:* Lab Marine Animal Health Marine Biol Lab Woods Hole MA 02543

LEIBOWITZ, GERALD MARTIN, b New York, NY, Feb 17, 36; m 63; c 4. MATHEMATICAL ANALYSIS. *Educ:* City Col New York, BS, 57; Mass Inst Technol, SM, 59, PhD(math), 63. *Prof Exp:* Instr math, Mass Inst Technol, 63; from instr to asst prof, Northwestern Univ, 63-68; assoc dir, CUPM, Calif, 68-69; ASSOC PROF MATH, UNIV CONN, 69- *Mem:* Am Math Soc; Math Asn Am. *Res:* Functional analysis; Banach algebras. *Mailing Add:* Dept of Math Univ of Conn Storrs CT 06268

LEIBOWITZ, JACK RICHARD, b Bridgeport, Conn, July 21, 29; m 54; c 2. LOW TEMPERATURE PHYSICS, SUPERCONDUCTIVITY. *Educ:* NY Univ, BA, 51, MS, 55; Brown Univ, PhD(physics), 62. *Prof Exp:* Physicist, Signal Corps Eng Labs, 51-54 & Electronics Corp Am, 55-56; res physicist, Lincoln Labs, Mass Inst Technol, 56-61 & Westinghouse Res Lab, 61-64; asst prof physics, Univ Md, College Park, 64-69; PROF PHYSICS, CATH UNIV AM, 69- *Concurrent Pos:* consult, Nat Res Lab, 78-80 & Nat Broadcasting Co, 79- *Mem:* Fel Am Phys Soc; Sigma Xi. *Res:* Superconductivity; ultrasonic interactions in solids; intermediate and mixed states; Fermi surfaces; electron-phonon interaction; excitation spectra of inhomogeneous superconductors; physical acoustics of solids. *Mailing Add:* Dept of Physics Cath Univ of Am Washington DC 20064

LEIBOWITZ, JULIAN LAZAR, b New York, NY, Dec 14, 47. VIROLOGY, PATHOLOGY. *Educ:* Alfred Univ, BA, 68; Albert Einstein Col Med, PhD(cell biol, biol), 74, MD, 75. *Prof Exp:* Med scientist trainee virol, Albert Einstein Col Med, 70-74, med scientist trainee med, 74-75; path resident, 75-77, USPHS FEL NEUROPATH & VIROL, UNIV CALIF, SAN DIEGO, 77- *Mem:* AAAS; Am Soc Microbiol. 12. *Res:* Animal virology; virus induced demyelinating disease. *Mailing Add:* Dept of Path M-012 Univ of San Diego La Jolla CA 92093

LEIBOWITZ, LEONARD, b New York, NY, Feb 5, 31. THERMOPHYSICAL PROPERTIES. *Educ:* NY Univ, AB, 51, MS, 54, PhD(chem), 56. *Prof Exp:* Chemist, Pigments Dept, E I du Pont de Nemours & Co, 56-58; asst chemist, 58-61, assoc chemist, 61-72, CHEMIST, CHEM ENG DIV, ARGONNE NAT LAB, 72- *Mem:* Am Chem Soc; Sigma Xi; AAAS. *Res:* Experimental and theoretical determination of thermodynamic and transport properties of materials, particularly at high temperature. *Mailing Add:* Chem Eng Div Argonne Nat Lab Argonne IL 60439

LEIBOWITZ, LEWIS PHILLIP, b Chicago, Ill, June 22, 42; m 67; c 3. ENERGY SYSTEMS, SOLAR & THERMAL TECHNOLOGY. *Educ:* Northwestern Univ, BS, 64; Univ Calif, San Diego, MS, PhD(eng sci), 69. *Prof Exp:* Mem tech staff atmospheric entry technol, Calif Inst Technol, 69-75, team leader geothermal energy, 75-77, mgr advan solar planning, 77-78; supvr advan solar technol, 78-80, SUPVR ENERGY TECHNOL DEVELOP, JET PROPULSION LAB, 80- *Concurrent Pos:* Team leader, oil explor assessment, Jet Propulsion Lab, Calif Inst Technol, 77. *Honors & Awards:* New Technol Award, NASA, 76. *Mem:* Am Phys Soc; Sigma Xi. *Res:* Energy systems projects in desalination, synthetic fuels, solar power production, and waste treatment; development and testing of ceramic heat exchangers, catalytic reactors, advanced heat engines, and high temperature collectors which can lead to commercial solar products. *Mailing Add:* 65 E Grandview Arcadia CA 91006

LEIBOWITZ, MARTIN ALBERT, b New York, NY, Oct 15, 35. APPLIED MATHEMATICS, OPERATIONS RESEARCH. *Educ:* Columbia Univ, BA, 56; Harvard Univ, MA, 57, PhD(appl math), 61. *Prof Exp:* Staff scientist, Int Bus Mach Res Ctr, 60-63; mem tech staff, Bellcomm, Inc, Washington, DC, 63-66; assoc prof eng, 66-73, ASSOC PROF APPL MATH & STATISTICS, STATE UNIV NY STONY BROOK, 73- *Mem:* Opers Res Soc Am; Asn Comput Mach. *Res:* Random processes with application to control theory; guidance and communications; scientific programming. *Mailing Add:* Col of Eng State Univ of NY Stony Brook NY 11790

LEIBOWITZ, SARAH FRYER, b White Plains, NY, May 23, 41; m 66; c 3. PSYCHOPHARMACOLOGY. *Educ:* NY Univ, BA, 64, PhD(physiol psychol), 68. *Prof Exp:* USPHS fel & guest investr, 68-70, asst prof, 70-78, ASSOC PROF PHYSIOL PSYCHOL, ROCKEFELLER UNIV, 78- *Honors & Awards:* First Prize, Div Psychopharmacol, Am Psychol Asn, 69. *Mem:* AAAS; Am Psychol Asn; NY Acad Sci; Am Soc Pharmacol & Exp Therapeut; Soc Neurosci. *Res:* Study of neurochemical mechanisms in the brain which regulate behavioral and physiological responses. *Mailing Add:* Rockefeller Univ New York NY 10021

LEIBSON, IRVING, b Wilkes Barre, Pa, Sept 28, 26; m 50. CHEMICAL ENGINEERING. *Educ:* Univ Fla, BChE, 45, MS, 47; Carnegie Inst Technol, 49, DSc(chem eng), 52. *Prof Exp:* Chem engr, Humble Oil & Refining Co, 52, staff engr, 57-59, supv engr, 59-61; mgr process engr, Rexall Chem Co, 61-63, develop mgr, 63-65, dir res & develop, 65-67, dir commercial develop, 67, gen mgr acrylonitrile-butadiene-styrene plastic div, 67-69; vpres, Dart Indust Chem Group, 69-74, mgr com ventures & investment dept, 74-75; mgr process & environ sci develop, 75-78, VPRES & MGR RES & ENG, BECHTEL GROUP INC, 78- *Concurrent Pos:* Lectr, Univ Md; prof Rice Univ, 58; mem, Eng Manpower Comn; assoc, Coal Indust Adv Bd, Int Energy Agency, 80- & World Coal Study, 79-80. *Mem:* Am Chem Soc; Am Inst Chem Eng; fel Am Inst Chem. *Res:* Unit operations. *Mailing Add:* Bechtel Group Inc PO Box 3965 San Francisco CA 94119

LEIBU, HENRY J, b Schlesiengrube, Ger, Apr 22, 17; m; c 2. CHEMISTRY. *Educ:* Swiss Fed Inst Technol, ChemE, 42, ScD(chem), 45. *Prof Exp:* Instr & res assoc indust chem, Swiss Fed Inst Technol, 45-49; chemist res plant develop, Polychem Dept, 49-59, sales develop, Europe, SAm & Australia, 59-66, sr res chemist res & develop elastomers, 66-73, TECH SALES & DEVELOP, E I DU PONT DE NEMOURS & CO, INC, 73- *Mem:* Am Chem Soc. *Res:* Elastomers; urethanes. *Mailing Add:* Elastomer Dept E I du Pont de Nemours & Co Inc Wilmington DE 19898

LEIBY, CLARE C, JR, b Ashland, Ohio, May 4, 24; m 52; c 5. PHYSICS. *Educ:* Mass Inst Technol, SB, 54; Univ Ill, MS, 58. *Prof Exp:* Physicist, Air Force Cambridge Res Labs, 54-56; res assoc, Univ Ill, 60-61 & Sperry Rand Res Ctr, 61-64; res physicist, Air Force Cambridge Res Labs, 64-76; RES PHYSICIST, ROME AIR DEVELOP CTR, 76- *Concurrent Pos:* Consult, Leghorn Labs. *Mem:* Sigma Xi. *Res:* Experimental and theoretical research in area of laser interactions with molecules; molecular beams; atomic clocks; gravitational theory. *Mailing Add:* Electro-Optical Device Technol Br Rome Air Develop Ctr Hanscom AFB MA 01731

LEIBY, ROBERT WILLIAM, b Allentown, Pa, Apr 2, 49; m 74. ORGANIC CHEMISTRY. *Educ:* Albright Col, BS, 71; Lehigh Univ, MS, 73, PhD(org chem), 75. *Prof Exp:* Res assoc org chem, Dartmouth Col, 75-76; med chemist, Purdue Frederick Co, 76-77; vis asst prof chem, Hampden-Sydney Col, 77-78; vis asst prof chem, Duke Univ, 78-80; MEM FAC, DEPT CHEM, UNIV WIS-WHITEWATER, 80- *Mem:* Am Chem Soc; Sigma Xi. *Res:* Organic mass spectroscopy; heterocyclic synthesis; synthesis of pharmaceutical agents particularly central nervous system agents and antineoplastic agents: organic rearrangements and mechanisms; development of new synthetic techniques and reagents. *Mailing Add:* Dept Chem Univ Wis Whitewater WI 53190

LEICH, DOUGLAS ALBERT, b Paterson, NJ, Jan 26, 47; m 72; c 1. NUCLEAR COSMOCHEMISTRY, MASS SPECTROMETRY. *Educ:* Colgate Univ, BA, 68; Calif Inst Technol, PhD(physics), 74. *Prof Exp:* Asst res physicist, Univ Calif, Berkeley, 73; CHEMIST NUCLEAR CHEM, LAWRENCE LIVERMORE LAB, UNIV CALIF, 76- *Concurrent Pos:* Mem, Lunar & Planetary Sample Team, Lunar & Planetary Inst, 81- *Mem:* Meteoritical Soc. *Res:* Isotopic anomalies in extraterrestrial materials and their uses in interpreting galactic and solar system chronology and stellar nucleosynthetic processes. *Mailing Add:* Nuclear Chem Div Mail Code L-232 PO Box 808 Livermore CA 94550

LEICHENSTEIN, MICHAEL J, applied mathematics, electrical engineering, see previous edition

LEICHNER, GENE H(OWARD), b Richmond, Ind, Nov 14, 29; m 59; c 1. ELECTRICAL ENGINEERING. *Educ:* Univ Ill, BS, 51, MS, 55, PhD(elec eng), 58. *Prof Exp:* Elec engr electronics, Ballistic Res Lab, Aberdeen Proving Ground, Md, 51-52; elec engr, Control Systs Lab, Univ Ill, 55-56, asst, Digital Comput Lab, 56-58, assoc prof elec eng, 58-67, dir eng, Intersci Res Inst, 65-67; leader systs eval, RCA Instructional Systs, Palo Alto, 67-69, mgr eng, 69-72, PROG MGR, SYSTS CONTROL, INC, 72- *Mem:* Inst Elec & Electronics Engrs; Asn Comput Mach. *Res:* Applications of computers to business and scientific problems; computer system performance analysis and prediction; on line computer applications. *Mailing Add:* 20200 Ljepava Dr Saratoga CA 95070

LEICHNETZ, GEORGE ROBERT, b Buffalo, NY, Oct 15, 42; m 67; c 3. NEUROANATOMY. *Educ:* Wheaton Col, Ill, BS, 64; Ohio State Univ, MS, 66, PhD(anat), 70. *Prof Exp:* Instr anat, Ohio State Univ, 69-70; asst prof, 70-78, ASSOC PROF ANAT, MED COL VA, VA COMMONWEALTH UNIV, 78- *Concurrent Pos:* A D Williams res grant, Med Col Va, Va Commonwealth Univ, 71-72. *Mem:* Am Asn Anatomists; Soc Neurosci. *Res:* Comparative neuroanatomy of primates; connections from cerebral cortex to brainstem pre-oculomotor nuclei; central nervous system connections related to pain mechanisms. *Mailing Add:* Dept Anat Med Col Va Box 709 Va Commonwealth Univ Richmond VA 23298

LEICHTER, JOSEPH, b Feb 4, 32; US citizen. NUTRITION, FOOD SCIENCE. *Educ:* Cracow Col, Poland, BS, 56; Univ Calif, Berkeley, MS, 66, PhD(nutrit), 69. *Prof Exp:* Chemist, Pharmaceut Plant, Cracow, Poland, 56-57; chemist, Ministry Com & Indust, Haifa, Israel, 57-60; chemist, Anresco Lab, Calif, 60-65; asst prof, 69-76, ASSOC PROF NUTRIT, UNIV BC, 76- *Mem:* Nutrit Soc Can; Am Inst Nutrit; Can Soc Nutrit Sci. *Res:* Folic acid metabolism; effect of protein-calorie malnutrition on carbohydrate digestion and absorption; effect of dietary lactose on intestinal lactase activity; effect of maternal alcohol consumption on growth and development of offspring. *Mailing Add:* Human Nutrit Div Univ of BC Sch Home Econ Vancouver BC V6T 1W5 Can

LEIDECKER, HENNING WILLIAM, JR, b Birmingham, Ala, Sept 9, 41; m 66; c 1. PHYSICS. *Educ:* Cath Univ Am, BA, 63, PhD(theoret physics), 69. *Prof Exp:* Asst prof, 68-74, ASSOC PROF PHYSICS, AM UNIV, 74- *Concurrent Pos:* Consult, Cath Univ Am, 68-69. *Res:* Statistical mechanics of fluids and polymers. *Mailing Add:* Dept of Physics Am Univ Washington DC 20016

LEIDER, HERMAN R, b Detroit, Mich, Jan 14, 29; m 60; c 2. SOLID STATE CHEMISTRY. *Educ:* Wayne State Univ, BS, 51, PhD(chem), 54. *Prof Exp:* Asst, Wayne State Univ, 51-52; res assoc, 52-54; aeronaut res scientist, Solid State Physics Br, Chem Mat Sec, Nat Adv Comt Aeronaut, 54-56; CHEMIST, LAWRENCE LIVERMORE LAB, UNIV CALIF, 56- *Mem:* Am Phys Soc. *Res:* Alkali halides; compatibility of materials; color center; luminescence; radiation effects; hydrides. *Mailing Add:* Dept of Chem Lawrence Livermore Lab Livermore CA 94550

LEIDERMAN, P HERBERT, b Chicago, Ill, Jan 30, 24; m 47; c 4. PSYCHIATRY. *Educ:* Calif Inst Technol, MS, 49; Univ Chicago, MA, 49; Harvard Med Sch, MD, 53. *Prof Exp:* Asst psychol, Univ Chicago, 48-49; intern med, Beth Israel Hosp, 53-54; resident neurol, Boston City Hosp, 54-56; resident psychiat, Mass Gen Hosp, 56-57; res fel, Mass Ment Health Ctr, 57-58; assoc, Harvard Med Sch, 58-63; assoc prof, 63-68, PROF PSYCHIAT, MED SCH, STANFORD UNIV, 68- *Concurrent Pos:* Consult, USPHS & Nat Res Coun. *Mem:* AAAS; Am Psychosom Soc; Soc Res Child Develop; Am Acad Child Psychiat. *Res:* Child development; psychology; transcultural psychiatry; psychophysiology. *Mailing Add:* Dept of Psychiat Stanford Univ Med Sch Palo Alto CA 94306

LEIDHEISER, HENRY, JR, b Union City, NJ, Apr 18, 20; m 44; c 2. PHYSICAL CHEMISTRY. *Educ:* Univ Va, BS, 41, MS, 43, PhD(phys chem), 44. *Prof Exp:* Res worker, Nat Adv Comt Aeronaut Proj, Univ Va, 43-45, res assoc, Cobb Chem Lab, 46-49; proj dir, Va Inst Sci Res, 49-52, gen lab, 52-58, dir res, Lab, 58-60, dir res, Inst, 60-68; PROF CHEM & DIR CTR SURFACE & COATINGS RES, LEHIGH UNIV, 68- *Concurrent Pos:* Mem adv comt, Oak Ridge Nat Lab; chmn, Gordon Conf Corrosion, 64; NATO sr scientist fel, Cambridge Univ, 69; consult, Marshall Space Flight Ctr, NASA, 71- *Honors & Awards:* Award, Oak Ridge Inst Nuclear Studies, 48;

J Shelton Horsley Res Prize, Va Acad Sci, 49; Young Auth Prize, Electrochem Soc; Silver Medal, Am Electroplaters' Soc, 78; Arch T Colwell Award, Soc Automotive Engrs, 78. *Mem:* Am Chem Soc; Electrochem Soc; Nat Asn Corrosion Engrs. *Res:* Corrosion; surface science; electrodeposition; Mossbauer spectroscopy; polymer coatings; long-term food storage; paint adherence. *Mailing Add:* Ctr for Surface & Coatings Res Lehigh Univ Bethlehem PA 18015

LEIDY, BLAINE I(RVIN), b Conemaugh, Pa, Aug 15, 23; m 57; c 1. MECHANICAL ENGINEERING. *Educ:* Univ Pittsburgh, BS, 51, MS, 57, PhD(mech eng), 62. *Prof Exp:* From instr to asst prof, 51-62, ASSOC PROF MECH ENG, UNIV PITTSBURGH, 62- *Concurrent Pos:* Consult, Westinghouse Elec Corp, 54-57 & 69- *Mem:* Am Soc Eng Educ; Am Soc Mech Engrs. *Res:* Heat transfer; fluid mechanics; thermodynamics; energy conservation in small industries under federally supported grant. *Mailing Add:* Dept of Mech Eng Sch of Eng Univ of Pittsburgh Pittsburgh PA 15261

LEIDY, ROSS BENNETT, b Newark, Ohio, June 1, 39; m 71; c 2. PESTICIDE CHEMISTRY. *Educ:* Tex A&M Univ, BS, 63, MS, 66; Auburn Univ, PhD(biochem), 72. *Prof Exp:* Res asst radiation biol, Radiation Biol Lab, Tex A&M Univ, 65-66; instr & lab supvr, Biol Br, Microbiol Lab, US Army Chem Ctr & Sch, Ft McClellan, Ala, 66-68; supvr pesticide chem, Lab Div, NC Dept Human Resources, 73-74; CHEMIST PESTICIDE CHEM, PESTICIDE RESIDUE RES LAB, NC STATE UNIV, 74- *Concurrent Pos:* NIH res assoc, Dept Animal Sci, NC State Univ, 72-73. *Mem:* Sigma Xi; NY Acad Sci. *Res:* Methodology and analyses of pesticide residues on plant and animal products and in air relating to the laboratory's research projects. *Mailing Add:* Pesticide Residue Res Lab PO Box 5215 NC State Univ Raleigh NC 27650

LEIES, GERARD M, b Chicago, Ill, Aug 19, 18. NUCLEAR PHYSICS. *Educ:* Loyola Univ, Ill, BS, 40; Univ Calif, MA, 53; Georgetown Univ, PhD(physics), 62. *Prof Exp:* TECH DIR, AIR FORCE TECH APPLNS CTR, 57- *Mem:* Am Phys Soc. *Res:* Nuclear weapon test detection. *Mailing Add:* Air Force Tech Applns Ctr/TD Patrick AFB FL 32925

LEIF, ROBERT CARY, b New York, NY, Feb 27, 38; m 63; c 2. IMMUNOHEMATOLOGY, BIOMEDICAL ENGINEERING. *Educ:* Univ Chicago, BS, 59; Calif Inst Technol, PhD(chem), 64. *Prof Exp:* Fel, Univ Calif, Los Angeles, 64-66; res assoc microbiol, Sch Med, Univ Southern Calif, 66-67; asst prof chem & biochem, Fla State Univ, 67-71; assoc scientist, Papanicolaou Cancer Res Inst, 71-72, sr scientist, 72-81; PRIN SCIENTIST, COULTER ELECTRONICS, 81- *Concurrent Pos:* Consult, Int Equip Corp, 65-73, Xerox Corp, 66-67, Damon Eng, 69-73, Solid State Radiation, Calif, 67-73, Coulter Electronics, 75- & Photometrics, 75-; res scientist, Dept Microbiol, Univ Miami, 71-72, adj asst prof microbiol, 73-76 & adj asst prof biomed eng, 74-76, assoc prof microbiol & biomed eng, 76-, assoc prof oncol, 80- *Mem:* AAAS; Sigma Xi; Biomed Eng Soc; Am Chem Soc; Am Soc Cytol. *Res:* Cellular differentiation; cytology automation; clinical chemistry instrumentation; cytology specimen preparation; computer based instrumentation; cytophysical and histochemical techniques to separate, purify and analyze heterogeneous cell populations; identification of biological activities with cell morphology. *Mailing Add:* Coulter Electronics 590 W 20th St Hialeah FL 33010

LEIFER, CALVIN, b New York, NY, Mar 4, 29; m 63; c 2. EXPERIMENTAL PATHOLOGY, ELECTRON MICROSCOPY. *Educ:* NY Univ, BA, 50, DDS, 54; State Univ NY Buffalo, PhD(exp path), 71. *Prof Exp:* Pvt pract, 58-65; USPHS fels, State Univ NY Buffalo, 65-70; assoc prof, 70-78, PROF PATH, SCH DENT, TEMPLE UNIV, 78- *Mem:* Am Dent Asn; Am Acad Periodontol; AAAS; Int Asn Dent Res; Am Acad Oral Path. *Res:* Ultrastructural and biochemical alterations of the rat parotid gland following single and multiple doses of x-irradiation; ultrastructural and histochemical features of tumors of the salivary glands in humans. *Mailing Add:* Dept of Path Temple Univ Sch of Dent Philadelphia PA 19140

LEIFER, HERBERT NORMAN, b New York, NY, Jan 30, 25; m 48; c 3. SOLID STATE PHYSICS. *Educ:* Univ Calif, Los Angeles, BA, 48, PhD(physics), 52. *Prof Exp:* Asst physics, Univ Calif, Los Angeles, 48-51, res engr, 51-52; res assoc, Res Lab, Gen Elec Corp, 52-55; staff scientist, Lockheed Missiles & Space Co, 55-59, mgr solid state electronics dept, 61-62; mgr basic physics, Fairchild Semiconductor Corp, 62-65; staff scientist, Electro optical Lab, Autonetics Div, NAm Aviation, Inc, Calif, 65-67 & High Energy Laser Lab, TRW Systs Group, 68-72; SR STAFF SCIENTIST, RAND CORP, 72- *Concurrent Pos:* Mem staff, Physics Lab, Ecole Normale Superieure, Paris, 60. *Mem:* Am Phys Soc. *Res:* Semiconductors; thermoelectric effects; electron-acoustic interactions; electrooptic effects; lasers. *Mailing Add:* 16557 Park Lane Circle Los Angeles CA 90040

LEIFER, LESLIE, b New York, NY, Apr 13, 29; m 57; c 1. PHYSICAL CHEMISTRY. *Educ:* City Col New York, BS, 50; Univ Kans, PhD(phys chem), 59. *Prof Exp:* Res assoc nuclear & inorg chem, Mass Inst Technol, 56-59; asst prof chem, Clark Univ, 59-60; res assoc & staff mem, Lab Nuclear Sci, Mass Inst Technol, 61-63; assoc prof, Boston Col, 63-66; PROF CHEM, MICH TECHNOL UNIV, 66- *Mem:* AAAS; Am Chem Soc; Sigma Xi. *Res:* Solution physical chemistry; Mossbauer spectroscopy; quantum chemistry; energy storage materials. *Mailing Add:* Dept of Chem & Chem Eng Mich Technol Univ Houghton MI 49931

LEIFER, ZER, b Brooklyn, NY, May 24, 41; m 72; c 5. GENETIC TOXICOLOGY, POLYAMINE BIOSYNTHESIS. *Educ:* Yeshiva Univ, BA, 63; Harvard Univ, MA, 65; NY Univ, PhD(microbiol), 72. *Prof Exp:* Fel microbiol, NY Univ, 72-74, Queens Col, City Univ New York, 74-76; res asst prof, 76-81, RES ASSOC PROF MICROBIOL, NY MED COL, 81- *Concurrent Pos:* Mem, DNA Repair Deficient Bacterial Assay Work Group, Genetic Toxicol Prog, Environ Protection Agency, 78-81. *Mem:* Am Soc Microbiol; Am Chem Soc; AAAS; Environ Mutagen Soc; Sigma Xi. *Res:* Development and utilization of microbiol assay systems for the detection of environment mutagens and carcinogens; biosynthesis and biological role of polyamines. *Mailing Add:* Dept Microbiol NY Med Col Valhalla NY 10595

LEIFIELD, ROBERT FRANCIS, b St Louis, Mo, Jan 29, 28; m 52; c 7. INORGANIC CHEMISTRY. *Educ:* St Louis Univ, BS, 52, MS, 59. *Prof Exp:* Chemist, Great Lakes Carbon Co, 52-56; chemist, Mallinckrodt Chem Works, 56-58, supvr metall & ceramics, 58-61, group leader process develop, 61-62, res chemist, 62-66, assoc mgr res, 66-69, res & develop mgr, Calsicat Div, 69-70, tech mgr, 70-77, DIR RES & DEVELOP, CHEM DIV, MALLINCKRODT INC, 77- *Mem:* Catalysis Soc; Am Chem Soc. *Res:* Column and thin layer chromatography; analytical reagents; product and process research and development; uranium metallurgical chemistry; heterogeneous catalysis. *Mailing Add:* Mallinckrodt Inc PO Box 5439 St Louis MO 63147

LEIGA, ALGIRD GEORGE, b New York, NY, Mar 25, 33; m 55; c 4. PHYSICAL CHEMISTRY. *Educ:* NY Univ, BA, 55, MS, 60, PhD(phys chem), 63. *Prof Exp:* Res scientist, Dept Chem, NY Univ, 62-64; sr scientist, Mat Sci Lab, NY, 64-73, mgr mat develop, Xeroradiography, Pasadena, 73-77; corp res & develop staff, Xerox Corp, Palo Alto, 77-81; MGR MAT DEVELOP, XEROX MED SYSTS, PASADENA, 81- *Mem:* Am Chem Soc; Optical Soc Am; Soc Photog Scientists & Engrs. *Res:* Vacuum ultraviolet photochemistry and spectroscopy; decomposition reactions of solids; materials development for electrophotography. *Mailing Add:* 19743 Yuba Ct Saratoga CA 95070

LEIGH, DONALD C, b Toronto, Ont, Feb 25, 29; nat US; m 52; c 3. CONTINUUM MECHANICS. *Educ:* Univ Toronto, BASc, 51; Cambridge Univ, PhD(math), 54. *Prof Exp:* Sr aerophys engr, Gen Dynamics/Ft Worth, 54-56; supvr tech comput, Curtiss-Wright Corp, 56-57; lectr mech eng, Princeton Univ, 57-58, asst prof aerospace & mech sci, 58-65; assoc prof eng mech & math, 65-68, chmn dept eng mech, 72-80, PROF ENG MECH & MATH, UNIV KY, 68- *Mem:* Soc Natural Philos; Soc Rheol; Am Acad Mech; Am Soc Mech Engrs. *Res:* Continuum mechanics; systems engineering; pressure vessels. *Mailing Add:* Dept of Eng Mech Univ of Ky Lexington KY 40506

LEIGH, EGBERT G, JR, b Richmond, Va, July 27, 40; m 68. ECOLOGY, POPULATION GENETICS. *Educ:* Princeton Univ, AB, 62; Yale Univ, PhD(biol), 66. *Prof Exp:* Actg instr biol, Stanford Univ, 66; asst prof, Princeton Univ, 66-72; BIOLOGIST, SMITHSONIAN TROP RES INST, 69- *Res:* Ecological aspects of population genetics; patterns of evolution in communities and in individual species; evolutionary biology; physiognomy and trophic organization of tropical rain forests. *Mailing Add:* Smithsonian Trop Res Inst Box 2072 Balboa Panama

LEIGH, G(ILBERT) M(ERLIN), b Asbury Park, NJ, Mar 29, 17; m 39; c 4. CHEMICAL ENGINEERING. *Educ:* Columbia Univ, AB, 39, BS, 40, MS, 44. *Prof Exp:* Asst, Columbia Univ, 38-40; asst, Metal & Thermit Corp, 40-41, asst prod engr, 41-42, prod engr, 42-44, res engr, 44-49; res engr, Colgate Palmolive-Peet Co, 49-54, asst dir res & develop, Colgate Palmolive Co, 54-58, mgr tech serv, 58-59, mgr pioneering res, 59-63, mgr opers res, 63-81; RETIRED. *Mem:* Am Soc Metals; Soc Cosmetic Chem; Am Soc Qual Control; Soc Chem Indust; NY Acad Sci. *Res:* Detergents and toilet articles. *Mailing Add:* Res & Develop Dept Colgate-Palmolive Co 909 River Rd Piscataway NJ 08854

LEIGH, RICHARD WOODWARD, b New York, NY, Apr 26, 42. ENERGY SYSTEMS ANALYSIS, LASER SPECTROSCOPY. *Educ:* Oberlin Col, AB, 65; Columbia Univ, PhD(physics), 73. *Prof Exp:* Res assoc physics, City Col New York, 72-73, adj asst prof, 73-75; res fel, Lab Spectrosc Hertzienne, Ecole Normale Superieure, Paris, 75-77; asst scientist, 77-80, ASSOC SCIENTIST ENERGY SYST, BROOKHAVEN NAT LAB, 80- *Concurrent Pos:* Consult energy conserv & utility anal. *Mem:* Int Solar Energy Soc; AAAS. *Res:* Coherent optics; energy technologies; conservation, storage and solar; technical, economic and infrastructural requirements, and the benefits attendant on their integration into the current energy system. *Mailing Add:* Dept of Energy & Environ Brookhaven Nat Lab Upton NY 11973

LEIGH, THOMAS FRANCIS, b Loma Linda, Calif, Mar 6, 23; m 54; c 2. ENTOMOLOGY. *Educ:* Univ Calif, BS, 49, PhD(entom), 56. *Prof Exp:* Res asst entom, Univ Calif, 52-54; asst prof, Univ Ark, 54-58; from asst entomologist to assoc entomologist, 58-68, ENTOMOLOGIST, UNIV CALIF, 68- *Concurrent Pos:* NIH, USDA & NSF-Int Biol Prog & Rockefeller Found grants; consult, Commonwealth Sci & Indust Res Orgn, Australia, Int Atomic Energy Agency UN & Food & Agr Orgn UN. *Mem:* AAAS; Entom Soc Am; Ecol Soc Am; Mex Soc Entom; Am Registry Prof Entomologists. *Res:* Biology, ecology and control of cotton insects; insect resistance in crop plants; plant nutrition and insect abundance. *Mailing Add:* Univ Calif 17053 Shafter Ave Shafter CA 93263

LEIGHLY, HOLLIS PHILIP, JR, b St Joseph, Ill, May 28, 23; m 51; c 2. PHYSICAL METALLURGY. *Educ:* Univ Ill, BS, 48, MS, 50, PhD(metall eng), 52. *Prof Exp:* Res metallurgist, Bendix Aviation Corp, 52-54; res metallurgist, Denver Res Inst, 54-60, asst prof metall & chmn dept, Univ Denver, 58-60; assoc prof, 60-70, PROF METALL ENG, UNIV MO-ROLLA, 70- *Concurrent Pos:* Sabbatical, Dept Phys Metall, Birmingham Univ, 67-68 & Oak Ridge Nat Lab, 74-75; NATO fel, Univ Guelph, 74; res fel, Univ East Anglia, Norwich, Eng, 79-80. *Mem:* AAAS; Am Soc Metals; Am Inst Mining, Metall & Petrol Engrs; fel Am Inst Chem; fel Inst Metallurgists. *Res:* Recrystallization; nuclear reactor materials; radiation damage; electron microscopy; positron annihilation. *Mailing Add:* Dept of Metall & Nuclear Eng Univ of Mo Rolla MO 65401

LEIGHT, WALTER GILBERT, b New York, NY, Nov 19, 22; m 48; c 2. OPERATIONS RESEARCH, STANDARDS ENGINEERING. *Educ:* City Col New York, BS, 42. *Prof Exp:* High sch instr, NY, 42; res meteorologist, US Weather Bur, 46-53; from sci analyst to dir opers anal div, Opers Eval Group & sr sci analyst, Systs Eval Group, Ctr Naval Anal, 53-70; prog mgr decision systs, Tech Anal Div, 71-74, chief, Off Consumer Prod Safety, 74-78, chief, Prod Safety Technol Div, 78-81, CHIEF, OFF STANDARDS INFO

ANALYSIS & DEVELOP, NAT BUR STANDARDS, 81- *Mem:* Fel AAAS; Opers Res Soc Am; Am Meteorol Soc; Standards Eng Soc. *Res:* Decision systems; criminal justice; search and rescue; nuclear safeguards; military systems; extended forecasting; consumer product safety. *Mailing Add:* 9416 Bulls Run Pkwy Bethesda MD 20817

LEIGHTON, ALEXANDER HAMILTON, b Philadelphia, Pa, July 17, 08. PSYCHIATRIC EPIDEMIOLOGY, CULTURAL ANTHROPOLOGY. *Educ:* Princeton Univ, BA, 32; Cambridge Univ, MA, 34; Johns Hopkins Univ, MD, 36. *Hon Degrees:* AM, Harvard Univ, 66; SD, Acadia Univ, 74. *Prof Exp:* Social Sci Res Coun fel field work among Navajos & Eskimos, Columbia Univ, 39-40; Guggenheim fel, 46-47; dir, Southwest Proj, Cornell Univ, 48-53, dir, Prog Social Psychiat, 55-66, prof sociol & anthrop, Col Arts & Sci, 47-66; prof social psychiat, Med Col, 56-66; prof social psychiat & Head dept behav sci, 66-75, EMER PROF SOCIAL PSYCHIAT, HARVARD SCH PUB HEALTH, 75-; PROF PSYCHIAT & PREVENTIVE MED, DALHOUSIE UNIV, 75- *Concurrent Pos:* Prof, Sch Indust & Labor Rels, 47-52; consult Bur Indian Affairs, US Dept Interior, 48-50; mem bd dirs, Social Sci Res Coun, 48-58, chmn comt psychiat & social sci, 50-58; dir, Stirling County Proj, 48-; consult, Surgeon Gen Adv Comt Indian Affairs, 56-59; tech adv, Milbank Mem Fund, 56-63; fel, Ctr Advan Study Behav Sci, 57-58; mem expert adv panel ment health, WHO, 57-75; Thomas W Salmon Mem Lectr, NY Acad Med, 58; mem sub-panel behav sci, President's Sci Adv Comt, 61-62; consult, Peace Corps, 61-63; reflective fel, Carnegie Corp NY, 62-63; vis lectr, Cath Univ Louvain, 71; mem comt effects of herbicides in Vietnam, Nat Acad Sci, 71-73. *Honors & Awards:* Human Rels Award, Am Soc Advan Mgt, 46; La Pouse Award, Am Pub Health Asn, 75; Mental Health Asn Res Achievement Award, 75; Nat Health Scientist Award, Can, 75. *Mem:* Fel AAAS; fel Am Psychiat Asn; Asn Am Indian Affairs; fel Am Anthrop Asn; Am Psychopath Asn. *Res:* Social and cultural change; social psychiatry; psychiatric epidemiology. *Mailing Add:* Dept Psychiat Dalhousie Univ Halifax NS B3H 3J5 Can

LEIGHTON, ALVAH THEODORE, JR, b Portland, Maine, Apr 17, 29; m 53; c 4. GENETICS, PHYSIOLOGY. *Educ:* Univ Maine, BS, 51; Univ Mass, MS, 53; Univ Minn, PhD(poultry genetics, physiol), 60. *Prof Exp:* Asst poultry genetics, Univ Mass, 51-52 & Univ Minn, 55-59; assoc prof, 59-71, PROF POULTRY SCI, VA POLYTECH INST & STATE UNIV, 71- *Mem:* AAAS; Am Inst Biol Sci; World Poultry Sci Asn; Am Genetic Asn; Poultry Sci Asn. *Res:* Reproductive physiology and management of turkey populations. *Mailing Add:* Dept of Poultry Sci Va Polytech Inst & State Univ Blacksburg VA 24061

LEIGHTON, DOROTHEA CROSS, b Lunenburg, Mass, Sept 2, 08; m 37; c 2. MEDICINE, PSYCHIATRY. *Educ:* Bryn Mawr Col, AB, 30; Johns Hopkins Univ, MD, 36. *Prof Exp:* Chem technician, Univ Hosp, Johns Hopkins Univ, 30-32, house officer psychiat, 37-39; intern med, Baltimore City Hosps, 36-37; Social Sci Res Coun res fel, 39-40; spec physician, US Indian Serv, 41-45; soc sci analyst, US Off of War Info, 45; Guggenheim fel, 46-47; prof home econ, Cornell Univ, 49-52, res assoc sociol & anthrop, 52-65; from assoc prof to prof, 65-74, chmn dept, 72-74, EMER PROF MENT HEALTH, SCH PUB HEALTH, UNIV NC, CHAPEL HILL, 74- *Concurrent Pos:* From asst prof to assoc prof psychiat, Med Col, Cornell Univ, 54-65; vis prof anthrop, Univ Calif, Berkeley, 81-82. *Mem:* Am Pub Health Asn; fel Am Psychiat Asn; Am Anthrop Asn; Am Social Psychiat (vpres, 71-72). *Res:* Relationship between socio-cultural environment and psychiatric symptoms; child development. *Mailing Add:* 2614 Warring St Berkeley CA 94704

LEIGHTON, FREEMAN BEACH, b Champaign, Ill, Dec 19, 24; c 4. GEOLOGY. *Educ:* Univ Va, BS, 46; Calif Inst Technol, MS, 49, PhD(geol), 51. *Prof Exp:* From asst prof to prof geol, Whittier Col, 50-78; PRES, LEIGHTON & ASSOCS, INC, 60- *Concurrent Pos:* Dir undergrad res prog, NSF, 59-65; mem eng qual bd, City Los Angeles, 62-70; state-of-the-art reviewer, US Geol Surv/HUD/Asn Bay Area Govts, 72-74; adj res prof, Whittier Col, 78- *Honors & Awards:* Claire P Holdredge Award, Nat Asn Eng Geologists, 67. *Mem:* AAAS; Geol Soc Am; Am Asn Petrol Geologists; Am Asn Prof Geologists; Nat Asn Geol Teachers. *Res:* Active faulting; environmental planning; landslides; hillside development; geomorphology; engineering geology. *Mailing Add:* Leighton & Assocs Inc Suite H Irvine CA 92714

LEIGHTON, HENRY GEORGE, b London, Eng, May 2, 40; Can citizen; m 62; c 3. METEOROLOGY. *Educ:* McGill Univ, BS, 61, MS, 64; Univ Alta, PhD(nuclear physics), 68. *Prof Exp:* Res assoc nuclear physics, R J van de Graaff Lab, Holland, 68-70; vis asst prof, Univ Ky, 70-71; res assoc, 71-72, ASST PROF METEOROL, McGILL UNIV, 72- *Mem:* Can Meteorol Soc; Am Meteorol Soc. *Res:* Development of precipitation; weather modification, particularly hail suppression; interaction of solar radiation with atmospheric aerosols. *Mailing Add:* Dept of Meteorol McGill Univ Montreal PQ H3A 2T6 Can

LEIGHTON, JOSEPH, b New York, NY, Dec 13, 21; m 46; c 2. PATHOLOGY, ONCOLOGY. *Educ:* Columbia Univ, AB, 42; Long Island Univ, MD, 46. *Prof Exp:* From assoc prof to prof path, Sch Med, Univ Pittsburgh, 46-71; PROF PATH & CHMN DEPT, MED COL PA, 71- *Concurrent Pos:* Intern, Mt Sinai Hosp, New York, 46-47; resident path anat, Mass Gen Hosp, Boston, 48-49; resident clin path, USPHS Hosp, Baltimore, 50, exp pathologist, Path Lab, Nat Cancer Inst, 51-56, consult, Nat Serv Ctr, USPHS, 59-; mem coun, Gordon Res Confs, 63-66, chmn, Gordon Res Conf Cancer, 63. *Mem:* Am Soc Exp Path; Soc Develop Biol; Am Asn Path & Bact; Tissue Cult Asn; Am Asn Cancer Res. *Res:* Experimental surgical pathology; development of matrix methods and histophysiologic gradient methods for tissue culture; pathogenesis of tumor invasion and metastasis. *Mailing Add:* Dept of Path Med Col of Pa Philadelphia PA 19129

LEIGHTON, MORRIS WELLMAN, b Champaign, Ill, June 17, 26; m 47; c 3. EXPLORATION GEOLOGY. *Educ:* Univ Ill, BS, 47; Univ Chicago, MS, 48, PhD(geol), 51. *Prof Exp:* Res geologist, Jersey Prod Res Co, 51-58, geol sect head, 58-61, geologist-in-chg Europ study group, Esso Prod Res Co, 61-63, sr res geologist, Jersey Prod Res Co, 63-64, geol adv, Esso Explor Inc, 64-68, asst explor mgr, Esso Standard Oil Ltd, Australia, 69-70, explor mgr, Esso Australia Ltd, 70-72, div mgr, Esso Prod Res Co, 72-74, CHIEF GEOLOGIST, ESSO INTERAMERICA, 74- *Mem:* Am Asn Petrol Geologists; fel Geol Soc Am. *Res:* Petroleum geology; basin studies; sedimentary and igneous petrology; basin and play assessment; estimating hydrocarbon potential. *Mailing Add:* Esso InterAmerica 396 Alhambra Circle Miami FL 33134

LEIGHTON, ROBERT BENJAMIN, b Detroit, Mich, Sept 10, 19; m 43; c 2. ASTROPHYSICS. *Educ:* Calif Inst Technol, BS, 41, MS, 44, PhD(physics), 47. *Prof Exp:* Mem res staff, 43-45, res fel, 47-49, from asst prof to assoc prof, 49-59, PROF PHYSICS, CALIF INST TECHNOL, 59- *Mem:* Nat Acad Sci; AAAS; Am Phys Soc; Am Astron Soc; Am Acad Arts & Sci. *Res:* Millimeter-wave; submillimeter; infrared-astronomy. *Mailing Add:* Calif Inst of Technol Dept of Physics Pasadena CA 91109

LEIGHTON, WALTER (WOODS), b Toledo, Ohio, Sept 6, 07; m 37; c 2. MATHEMATICS. *Educ:* Northwestern Univ, BA, 31, MA, 32; Harvard Univ, AM, 33, PhD(math), 35. *Prof Exp:* Instr & tutor math, Harvard Univ, 33-36; instr, Univ Rochester, 36-37; lectr, Rice Inst, 37-43; sr res mathematician, Appl Math Group, Off Sci Res & Develop, Columbia Univ, 43-44; dir appl math group, Northwestern Univ, 44-45; prof & chmn dept, Washington Univ, 46-54 & Carnegie Inst Technol, 54-59; Elias Loomis prof & chmn dept, Western Reserve Univ, 59-67; chmn math sci, 68-72, Defoe prof math, 72-78, EMER DISTINGUISHED PROF MATH, UNIV MO-COLUMBIA, 78- *Concurrent Pos:* Secy bd trustees, Rice Inst, 43; res assoc, Brown Univ, 45-46; chief math div, Off Sci Res, US Air Force, 53-54; consult, 54-62. *Mem:* Am Math Soc; Math Asn Am. *Res:* Stability theory for ordinary nonlinear differential equations; calculus of variations and associated problems of oscillation of solutions of self-adjoint differential equations. *Mailing Add:* Math Sci Bldg Univ of Mo Columbia MO 65211

LEIGHTY, EDITH GARDNER, b Zanesville, Ohio, Nov 4, 28; div; c 1. XENOBIOTIC METABOLISM, MEDICINAL CHEMISTRY. *Educ:* Marshall Univ, BS, 62; Ohio State Univ, MS, 65, PhD(physiol chem), 67. *Prof Exp:* Technician, Cabell Huntington Hosp, 56-63; res chemist, Holland-Suco Color Co, 62-63; asst physiol chem, Ohio State Univ, 63-65; PRIN BIOCHEMIST, BATTELLE-COLUMBUS LABS, 67- *Mem:* Am Chem Soc; Am Soc Pharmacol & Exp Therapeut; AAAS; NY Acad Sci; Sigma Xi. *Res:* Metabolism and distribution of marihuana, drugs and other xenobiotics; identification of metabolites; toxicology; new drug development. *Mailing Add:* Pharmacol & Toxicol Sect Battelle-Columbus Columbus OH 43201

LEIMANIS, EUGENE, b Koceni, Latvia, Apr 10, 05; m 42; c 6. APPLIED MATHEMATICS. *Educ:* Univ Latvia, Mag Math, 29; Univ Hamburg, Dr rer nat(math), 47. *Prof Exp:* Asst math, Univ Latvia, 29-35, privat-docent, 35-37, docent, 37-44; docent, Univ Greifswald, 44-45; assoc prof, Baltic Univ, Ger, 46-48; from asst prof to prof, 49-74, EMER PROF MATH, UNIV BC, 74- *Concurrent Pos:* Mem nat comt, Int Union Theoret & Appl Mech. *Mem:* Am Math Soc; Math Asn Am; London Math Soc; Asn Advan Baltic Studies; Am Astron Soc. *Res:* Dynamical systems; differential equations; non-linear and celestial mechanics. *Mailing Add:* Dept of Math Univ of BC Vancouver BC V6T 1W5 Can

LEIMKUHLER, FERDINAND F, b Baltimore, Md, Dec 31, 28; m 56; c 6. INDUSTRIAL ENGINEERING, OPERATIONS RESEARCH. *Educ:* Loyola Col, Md, BS, 50, Johns Hopkins Univ, BEng, 52, Dr Eng, 62. *Prof Exp:* Engr, E I du Pont de Nemours & Co, 52-57; res assoc & instr indust eng, Johns Hopkins Univ, 57-61; head, Sch Indust Eng, 69-74 & 81-82, assoc prof, 61-66, PROF INDUST ENG, PURDUE UNIV, 66- *Concurrent Pos:* Vis prof, Univ Calif, Berkeley, 68-69; Fulbright prof, Univ Ljubljana, Yugoslavia, 74-75. *Mem:* Opers Res Soc Am; Inst Mgt Sci; Am Inst Indust Engrs; Am Soc Eng Educ. *Res:* Library operations research and systems analysis; engineering economic analysis; transportation of highly radioactive materials; stochastic service and storage system theory. *Mailing Add:* Purdue Univ Sch of Indust Eng Lafayette IN 47907

LEINBACH, HAROLD, b Ft Collins, Colo, Jan 7, 29; m 53; c 2. PHYSICS. *Educ:* SDak State Univ, BS, 49; Calif Inst Technol, MS, 50; Univ Alaska, PhD(geophys), 62. *Prof Exp:* Geophysicist, Geophys Inst, Alaska, 50-53 & 56-62; asst prof physics, Univ Iowa, 62-66; INSTR, UNIV COLO, 78-PHYSICIST, SPACE ENVIRON LAB, NAT OCEANOG & ATMOSPHERIC ADMIN, 66- *Mem:* Am Astron Soc; Am Geophys Union; Am Asn Physics Teachers. *Res:* High latitude ionospheric absorption of cosmic radio noise; solar cosmic rays and their interaction with the ionosphere; solar physics; space physics; laboratory plasma physics. *Mailing Add:* Space Environ Lab Nat Oceanic & Atmospheric Admin Boulder CO 80302

LEINEWEBER, JAMES PETER, b Cicero, Ill, Nov 30, 22; m 48. PHYSICAL CHEMISTRY, CHEMICAL TOXICOLOGY. *Educ:* Ohio Univ, BS, 43; NY Univ, MS, 47; Polytech Inst Brooklyn, PhD, 55. *Prof Exp:* Res chemist, Am Cyanamid Co, 45-56; sr res chemist, 56-57, chief basic chem res, 67-69, mgr corp res & develop, Res & Eng Ctr, 69-72, mgr appl res, 72-73, mgr appl res, Res & Develop Ctr, 73-78, TECH DIR HEALTH, SAFETY & ENVIRON DEPT & V PRES, MANVILLE SERV CORP, 78- *Mem:* Am Chem Soc; Am Ceramic Soc; Am Col Toxicol; Thermal Insulation Mfrs Asn. *Res:* Crystal growth; chemical kinetics; silicate chemistry; environmental health. *Mailing Add:* Manville Serv Corp Ken-Caryl Ranch Denver CO 80217

LEINHARDT, THEODORE EDWARD, b Gretna, La, Sept 5, 21; m 52; c 3. SOLID STATE PHYSICS. *Educ:* La Polytech Inst, BS, 50; La State Univ, MS, 52, PhD(physics), 56. *Prof Exp:* Assoc prof physics, La Polytech Inst, 55-56; res engr, Sperry Rand Res & Develop Lab, NY, 56-57; PROF PHYSICS, VA POLYTECH INST & STATE UNIV, 58- *Mem:* Am Phys Soc. *Res:* Low temperature experiments; behavior of superconducting compounds and alloys near critical temperatures and critical magnetic fields. *Mailing Add:* Dept of Physics Va Polytech Inst & State Univ Blacksburg VA 24061

LEININGER, CHARLES W, b Los Angeles, Calif, Aug 14, 13; wid; c 5. MATHEMATICS. *Educ:* Univ Ariz, BS, 36, MS, 37; Univ Tex, PhD(math), 63. *Prof Exp:* Var eng & acct pos, 37-42; pvt pract cert pub acct, 45-55; from asst prof to assoc prof math, Univ Tex, Arlington, 56-66; assoc prof, Univ Dallas, 66-68; PROF MATH, STATE UNIV NY COL CORTLAND, 68- *Mem:* Am Math Soc; NY Acad Sci. *Res:* Summability; ordered systems; foundations of mathematics. *Mailing Add:* Dept of Math State Univ of NY Cortland NY 13045

LEININGER, HAROLD VERNON, b Baton Rouge, La, June 18, 25; m 50; c 1. MICROBIOLOGY. *Educ:* La State Univ, BS, 48, MS, 51. *Prof Exp:* Lab technician, Dairy Improv Ctr, La State Univ, 51; food & drug inspector, Food &Drug Admin, 51, from bacteriologist to dir biol warfare proj, 52-63, res microbiologist, 63-71, dir, Minneapolis Ctr Microbiol Invest, 71-80; CONULT MICROBIOL, FOOD, DRUGS & COSMETICS, 80- *Concurrent Pos:* Proj officer, Test Site, AEC, Nev, 57. *Mem:* Asn Off Anal Chemists; Am Soc Microbiologists; Inst Food Technologists; Int Asn Milk, Food & Environ Sanit. *Res:* Microbiological research in food toxicity, decomposition, natural flora, and sanitation. *Mailing Add:* 3200 Voss Dr El Paso TX 79936

LEININGER, PAUL MILLER, b Pa, Oct 29, 11; m 37; c 3. PHYSICAL CHEMISTRY. *Educ:* Univ Pa, BS, 32 & 34, MS, 36, PhD(phys chem), 39. *Prof Exp:* Asst instr chem, Univ Pa, 34-38; chemist, E I du Pont de Nemours & Co, 39-49; asst prof chem, Lafayette Col, 49-54; from assoc prof to prof, 54-77, chmn dept, 69-77, EMER PROF CHEM, ALBRIGHT COL, 78- *Concurrent Pos:* Lectr, Sch Nurses, Reading Hosp, Pa, 54-61; mem teaching staff exp prog teacher educ, Temple Univ, 55-60; consult, George W Bollman Co. *Mem:* AAAS; Am Chem Soc; Am Soc Metals; Am Leather Chemists Asn; NY Acad Sci. *Res:* Case hardening and heat treatment of metals in molten salts; new uses and processes for sodium cyanide and related cyanogen compounds; reaction kinetics in solutions; chemical education; electrolytic dissociation and technology of felting. *Mailing Add:* 1726 Hampden Blvd Reading PA 19604

LEININGER, ROBERT IRVIN, b Cleveland, Ohio, May 11, 19; m 42; c 4. BIOMEDICAL ENGINEERING, POLYMER CHEMISTRY. *Educ:* Fenn Col, BChE, 40; Western Reserve, MS, 41, PhD, 43. *Prof Exp:* Instr chem eng, Fenn Col, 40-43; res chemist, Monsanto Chem Co, 43-48; prin chemist, Battelle Mem Inst, 48-51, asst chief rubber & plastics div, 51-60, chief polymer res sect, 60-65, mgr, 65-69; tech adv, Korean Inst Sci & Technol, Seoul, 69-70; prof dir biomat, Dept Biol, Environ & Chem, 70-73, mem res coun, 74-80, DIR RES COUN, COLUMBUS LABS, BATTELLE MEM INST, 80- *Concurrent Pos:* Mem adv comt, Div Technol Devices, Nat Heart & Lung Inst, 72-73; mem adv comt, Nuclear Powered Artificial Heart Prog, Energy Res & Develop Admin, 75-76; mem, Surg & Bioengineering Study Sect, 76-79, chmn, Biomat Adv Panel, NIH, 80- *Honors & Awards:* IR-100 Indust Res Award, 72; Clemson Award, Soc Biomat, 81. *Mem:* AAAS; Am Soc Artificial Internal Organs; Am Heart Asn; Am Chem Soc; NY Acad Sci. *Res:* Biomaterials; biomedical engineering; polymer chemistry. *Mailing Add:* Battelle-Columbus Labs 505 King Ave Columbus OH 43201

LEINONEN, ELLEN A, b Oct 15, 12; US citizen. ANATOMY, PHYSIOLOGY. *Educ:* Univ Mich, BS, 56, MS, 62; Ohio State Univ, PhD(anat), 67. *Prof Exp:* ASST PROF DENT, SCH DENT, UNIV MICH, ANN ARBOR, 65-, ASST PROF ANAT, MED SCH, 71- *Mem:* Am Asn Anat; NY Acad Sci; fel Am Inst Chemists; AAAS. *Res:* DNA and RNA metabolism in the primitive cells of acute lymphocytic leukemia; L-asparaginase activity in the cells of acute lymphocytic leukemia. *Mailing Add:* 3093 Lexington Dr Ann Arbor MI 48105

LEINROTH, JEAN PAUL, JR, b Utica, NY, July 4, 20; m 46; c 3. CHEMICAL ENGINEERING. *Educ:* Cornell Univ, BMechEng, 41; Mass Inst Technol, SM, 48, ScD(chem eng), 63. *Prof Exp:* Trainee, Standard Oil Co, Ohio, 41-42; asst job engr, M W Kellogg Co, NY, 42-43; proj engr, Union Carbide Chem Co, 48-56, proj leader, 56-59; instr thermodyn, Mass Inst Technol, 60-61, vis assoc prof & res, 63-64; assoc prof chem eng, Cornell Univ, 64-71; vis prof, Mass Inst Technol, 71-72; process dir, 72-80, MGR SPEC PROJS, CRAWFORD & RUSSELL, INC, 80- *Concurrent Pos:* Consult, Union Carbide Chem Co, 64-68 & Develop Sci, 71- *Mem:* Am Chem Soc; Am Inst Chem Engrs. *Res:* Chemical kinetics; thermodynamics; staged operations; computer applications; desalination. *Mailing Add:* 33 Millstone Rd Wilton CT 06897

LEINWEBER, FRANZ JOSEF, b Berlin, Ger, Jan 18, 31; US citizen; m 60; c 2. DRUG METABOLISM. *Educ:* Univ Tübingen, Dr rer nat(biol), 56. *Prof Exp:* Fel biochem, Tex A&M Univ, 57-60 & Johns Hopkins Univ, 60-63; res assoc, Univ Tenn, 63-65; res scientist, McNeil Labs, Inc, 65-69; sr scientist, Warner-Lambert Res Inst, 69-77; ASST RES GROUP CHIEF, HOFFMANN-LA ROCHE INC, 77- *Mem:* Am Soc Pharmacol & Exp Therapeut. *Res:* Photoperiodism and biological clocks; enzymology, intermediary metabolism and metabolic regulation of sulfur amino acid biosynthesis in bacteria and molds; drug metabolism and separation methods. *Mailing Add:* Dept of Biochem & Drug Metab Hoffmann-La Roche Inc Nutley NJ 07110

LEIPHOLZ, HORST HERMANN EDUARD, b Plonhofen, Ger, Sept 26, 19; m 42; c 2. MECHANICS, APPLIED MATHEMATICS. *Educ:* Holzminden Inst Technol, Eng grad, 51; Univ Stuttgart, dipl math, 58, Dr Ing, 59. *Prof Exp:* Engr, K Ellsasser, Stuttgart, Ger, 51-58; asst mech, Univ Stuttgart, 58-62, docent, 62-63; from assoc prof to prof, Univ Karlsruhe, 63-69; PROF CIVIL ENG, UNIV WATERLOO, 69- *Concurrent Pos:* Mem, Nat Res Coun Nat Comt, Int Union Theoret & Appl Mech, 71; ed, Transactions, Can Soc Mech Engrs. *Honors & Awards:* Can Nat Conf Appl Mech Award, 75. *Mem:* Am Soc Mech Engrs; fel Am Acad Mech; Ger Soc Appl Math & Mech; Can Soc Mech Engrs; fel Eng Inst Can. *Res:* Gyrodynamics; stability theory; variational methods; space mechanics. *Mailing Add:* Dept of Civil Eng Univ of Waterloo Waterloo ON N2L 3G1 Can

LEIPNIK, ROY BERGH, b Los Angeles, Calif, May 6, 24; m 44; c 3. MATHEMATICAL ANALYSIS, MATHEMATICAL PHYSICS. *Educ:* Univ Chicago, SB, 45, SM, 48; Univ Calif, PhD(math), 50. *Prof Exp:* Asst math statist & econ, Univ Chicago, 45-46; from asst to assoc math, Univ Calif, 46-48; fel, Sch Math, Inst Advan Study, 48-50; asst prof, Univ Wash, 50-57; sr res scientist, Naval Weapons Ctr, Calif, 57-75; PROF APPL MATH & MEM ALGEBRA INST, UNIV CALIF, SANTA BARBARA, 75- *Concurrent Pos:* Fulbright res prof, Univ Adelaide, 55, 63 & 68; lectr, Univ Calif, Los Angeles, 59-; prof, Univ Fla, 61-62, 64-65 & 70; consult, Decisional Controls Assocs & Commun Res Labs. *Mem:* Am Math Soc; Math Asn Am; Inst Math Statist; Inst Elec & Electronics Engrs; Soc Indust & Appl Math. *Res:* Operator analysis; mathematical physics; control systems; stochastic processes; information theory; plasma physics; solid state physics; microprocessor design; transportation theory; allocation and assignment algorithms; recursive algorithms; differential equations. *Mailing Add:* Univ of Calif at Santa Barbara Math Dept Goleta CA 93017

LEIPOLD, MARTIN H(ENRY), b Englewood, NJ, July 4, 32; m 58; c 1. CERAMICS. *Educ:* Rutgers Univ, BS, 54; Ohio State Univ, MS, 55, PhD(ceramics), 58. *Prof Exp:* Res assoc ceramics, Ohio State Univ Res Found, 55-58; sr scientist, Jet Propulsion Lab, Calif Inst Technol, 58-62, res specialist, 62-67; assoc prof mat sci, Col Eng, Univ Ky, 67-74; MEM TECH STAFF, JET PROPULSION LAB, 74- *Concurrent Pos:* Adj prof, Univ Calif, Los Angeles, 76- *Mem:* Am Ceramic Soc; Am Inst Ceramic Engrs; Am Soc Metals. *Res:* Properties, fabrication and structure of ceramics; photovoltaic power systems. *Mailing Add:* 1118 Sheraton Dr La Canada CA 91011

LEIPPER, DALE F, b Salem, Ohio, Sept 8, 14; m 42; c 4. OCEANOGRAPHY. *Educ:* Wittenberg Col, BS, 37; Ohio State Univ, MA, 39; Univ Calif, PhD(oceanog), 50. *Hon Degrees:* DSc, Wittenberg Univ, 68. *Prof Exp:* Weight & balance engr, Consol Aircraft, Calif, 40; sch teacher, Calif, 40-41; oceanogr, Scripps Inst, Univ Calif, 46-49; from assoc prof to prof oceanog & head dept, Tex A&M Univ, 49-68; chmn, Dept Oceanog, Naval Postgrad Sch, Monterey, 68-80. *Concurrent Pos:* Head dept, Tex A&M Univ, 50-64, assoc exec dir, Res Found, 53-54, trustee, Univ Corp Atmospheric Res, 59-65; dir, World Data Ctr Oceanog, 57-60; consult, Comt Sci & Astronaut, US House Rep, 60; mem joint panel sea-air interaction, Nat Acad Sci, 60-62; adj prof oceanog, Naval Postgrad Sch, 80- *Mem:* Am Meteorol Soc; Am Soc Limnol & Oceanog (pres, 58); Am Soc Oceanog (pres, 67); Am Geophys Union. *Res:* Coastal fog forecasting; analysis of sea temperature variations; use of the bathythermograph; interaction between ocean and atmosphere; physical oceanography; marine meteorology. *Mailing Add:* Dept of Oceanog Naval Postgrad Sch Code 68 Monterey CA 93940

LEIPUNER, LAWRENCE BERNARD, b Long Beach, NY, May 27, 28; m 48; c 3. HIGH ENERGY PHYSICS, ELEMENTARY PARTICLE PHYSICS. *Educ:* Univ Pittsburgh, BS, 50; Carnegie Inst Technol, MS, 54, PhD(physics), 62. *Prof Exp:* SR RES PHYSICIST, BROOKHAVEN NAT LAB, 55- *Concurrent Pos:* Vis prof, Yale Univ, 67-68. *Mem:* Fel Am Phys Soc. *Res:* Lepton and quark experiments. *Mailing Add:* Brookhaven Nat Lab Upton NY 11973

LEIPZIGER, FREDRIC DOUGLAS, b New York, NY, Aug 26, 29; m 51; c 2. ANALYTICAL CHEMISTRY. *Educ:* Univ Conn, BA, 51; Univ Mass, MS, 53, PhD(chem), 56. *Prof Exp:* Res assoc chem, Gen Elec Co, 55-62; head anal chem dept, Sperry Rand Res Ctr, 62-66; mgr anal serv, Ledgemont Lab, Kennecott Copper Corp, 66-81; PRES, NORTHERN ANAL LAB, INC, 82- *Mem:* Am chem Soc; Soc Appl Spectros; Am Soc Mass Spectrometry; Asn Off Anal Chemists; Am Asn Crystal Growth. *Res:* Electron microscopy; mass spectrometry; atomic absorption; automated analyses; process control. *Mailing Add:* Northern Anal Lab Inc 3 Northern Blvd Amherst NH 03031

LEIPZIGER, STUART, b Chicago, Ill, Apr 17, 38. CHEMICAL ENGINEERING. *Educ:* Ill Inst Technol, BS, 59, PhD(chem eng), 64. *Prof Exp:* Lectr chem eng, 64-66, asst prof 65-77, ASSOC PROF GAS TECHNOL, INST GAS TECHNOL, 77- *Mem:* Am Gas Asn; Am Inst Chem Eng. *Res:* Heat transfer; thermodynamics. *Mailing Add:* 2801 S King Dr Apt 1212 Chicago IL 60616

LEIS, DONALD GEORGE, b Jeannette, Pa, Aug 26, 19; m 45; c 3. ORGANIC CHEMISTRY. *Educ:* St Vincent Col, BS, 41; Univ Notre Dame, MS, 42, PhD(org chem), 45. *Prof Exp:* Chemist, Carbide & Carbon Chem Co, 46-55; group leader, 55-63, mgr mkt develop-cellular prod, 63-71, com mkt mgr, 71-75, SR MKT CONSULT, SILICONES & URETHANES DIV, UNION CARBIDE CORP, 75- *Mem:* AAAS; Nat Fire Protection Asn; Soc Plastics Engrs; Am Chem Soc; Soc Plastics Indust. *Res:* Urethane products; polyethers; polyglycols; alkylene oxides; alkylene oxide derivatives; ethylene oxide; propylene oxide; urethanes; surfactants; lubricants and coatings. *Mailing Add:* Union Carbide Corp Old Ridgebury Rd Danbury CT 06817

LEIS, JONATHAN PETER, b Brooklyn, NY, Aug 17, 44; m 70; c 3. NUCLEIC ACID ENZYMOLOGY, VIROLOGY. *Educ:* Hofstra Univ, BA, 65; Cornell Univ, PhD(biochem), 70. *Prof Exp:* Fel develop biol & cancer, Albert Einstein Col Med, 70-73; asst prof surg, microbiol & immunol, Med

Ctr, Duke Univ, 74-79; ASSOC PROF BIOCHEM, MED SCH, CASE WESTERN RESERVE UNIV, 79- *Concurrent Pos:* Damon Runyon res fel, 71; res career develop awards, NIH, 74. *Mem:* Am Soc Biol Chemists. *Res:* Control of expression of eukaryotic genes; biochemical mechanism of replication of RNA viruses; author of over 30 publications. *Mailing Add:* Dept Biochem Med Sch Case Western Reserve Univ 2119 Abington Rd Cleveland OH 44106

LEISE, JOSHUA MELVIN, b Baltimore, Md, Mar 12, 19; m 48; c 2. MEDICAL MICROBIOLOGY. *Educ:* Univ Md, BS, 40, MS, 43; Yale Univ, PhD(bact), 47. *Prof Exp:* Bacteriologist, Flavorex, Inc, 40-41; res bacteriologist, Univ Md, 42-45; lab asst, Yale Univ, 45-47; med bacteriologist, Walter Reed Army Med Ctr, 51-52; chief, Bio-Detection Br, Ft Detrick, Md, 52-59; chief, Biophys-Biochem Br, Army Res Off, 59-60; prog dir, Life Sci Facil, NSF, Washington, DC, 60-62, head sect, 62-70, dep dir, Sci Develop Div, 70-71, sr staff assoc, Off Dept Asst Dir Math, Phys Sci & Eng, 71-76, sr staff assoc, US-USSR Joint Comn Support Staff, Div Int Prog, 76-79; RETIRED. *Mem:* AAAS; fel Am Acad Microbiol; Am Soc Microbiol. *Res:* Microbial virulence; methodology; research administration. *Mailing Add:* 7813 Winterberry Pl Bethesda MD 20817

LEISENRING, KENNETH BAYLIS, mathematics, deceased

LEISERSON, LEE, b Toledo, Ohio, Mar 30, 16; m 43, 71; c 6. ORGANIC CHEMISTRY, PHYSICAL CHEMISTRY. *Educ:* Antioch Col, BS, 37; Univ NC, MA, 40, PhD(org chem), 41. *Prof Exp:* Res chemist, Eastman Kodak Co, NY, 41-45; fel, Va Smelting Co, NC, 45-47; chemist, Am Cyanamid Co, NJ, 47-51; chief org chemist, Liggett & Myers Tobacco Co, 51-55; chemist & res adminr, Air Force Off Sci Res, Washington, DC, 55-62; chief chem div, Off Saline consult, 74-76; field serv coordr, Environ Protection Agency, 76-80; CONSULT, 80- *Mem:* AAAS; Am Chem Soc. *Res:* Surface active agents; organic synthesis; development of natural products; turpentine and tall oil separation processes; reactions in liquid sulfur dioxide; tobacco; water and aqueous solutions; human effects monitoring; pesticides. *Mailing Add:* 431 N Harper Drive Hendersonville NC 28739

LEISMAN, GILBERT ARTHUR, b Washington, DC, May 12, 24; m 52. BOTANY. *Educ:* Univ Wis, BS, 49; Univ Minn, MS, 52, PhD, 55. *Prof Exp:* Asst plant physiol, Univ Wis, 49-50; asst bot, Univ Minn, 50-55; from asst prof to assoc prof, 55-64; PROF BIOL, EMPORIA STATE UNIV, 64- *Concurrent Pos:* Mem world orgn paleobot, Int Union Biol Sci. *Mem:* AAAS; Bot Soc Am; Nat Asn Biol Teachers; Int Asn Plant Taxon. *Res:* Coal ball plants; morphology of pteridosperm leaves and fructifications; plant succession and soil development of mine dumps. *Mailing Add:* Dept of Biol Emporia State Univ Emporia KS 66801

LEISS, ABRAHAM, b Pittsburgh, Pa, July 18, 23; m 46; c 4. AEROSPACE ENGINEERING, MECHANICAL ENGINEERING. *Educ:* Univ Pittsburgh, BSME, 47. *Prof Exp:* Dep head, Scout Proj Off, Nat Adv Comt Aeronaut, NASA, 47-80; VPRES, WILLIAMSBURG WEST RES CONSULT, 80- *Res:* Space research. *Mailing Add:* 20 Lakeshore Dr Newport News VA 23602

LEISS, JAMES ELROY, b Youngstown, Ohio, June 2, 24; m 45; c 4. PHYSICS. *Educ:* Case Inst Technol, BS, 49; Univ Ill, MS, 51, PhD(physics), 54. *Prof Exp:* Lab asst, Gen Elec Co, 48-49; asst physics, Univ Ill, 49-54; DIR, CTR RADIATION RES, NAT BUR STANDARDS, 54- *Mem:* Am Phys Soc. *Res:* Nuclear physics, especially photonuclear reactions and photomeson reactions; design of particle accelerators. *Mailing Add:* High Energy & Nuclear Physics Off Energy Res US Dept Energy Washington DC 20545

LEISSA, A(RTHUR) W(ILLIAM), b Wilmington, Del, Nov 16, 31; m 53; c 2. VIBRATIONS, BUCKLING. *Educ:* Ohio State Univ, BME & MSc, 54, PhD(eng mech), 58. *Prof Exp:* Assoc engr, Sperry Gyroscope Co, 54-55; res assoc, Res Found, 55-56, from instr to assoc prof, 56-64, PROF ENG MECH, OHIO STATE UNIV, 64-, RES FOUND SUPVR, 62- *Concurrent Pos:* Mech engr, Ralph & Curl Engrs, 54-58; fac assoc, Boeing Airplane Co, 57; consult, NAm Aviation, Inc, 58-64, Battelle Mem Inst, 64- & Kaman Nuclear, 68-; vis prof, Swiss Fed Inst Technol, 72-73. *Mem:* Assoc fel Am Inst Aeronaut & Astronaut; Am Soc Eng Educ; Int Asn Shell Struct; Am Soc Mech Engrs; fel Am Acad Mech. *Res:* Elasticity; plates and shells; vibration of continuous systems; buckling; numerical methods for solving boundary value and eigenvalue problems; composite structures. *Mailing Add:* Dept Eng Mech Ohio State Univ 155 W Woodruff Columbus OH 43210

LEISTER, HARRY M, b Quakertown, Pa, Mar 3, 41; m 62; c 4. PHYSICAL CHEMISTRY. *Educ:* Pa State Univ, BS, 63; Drexel Univ, MS, 65; Temple Univ, PhD(phys chem), 70. *Prof Exp:* Res chemist, E I du Pont de Nemours & Co, 69-70; chemist, Amchem Div, Union Carbide Corp, 71-73, group leader, 73-81, SCIENTIST, AMCHEM PROD, INC, 81- *Res:* Organic coatings; inorganic coatings. *Mailing Add:* Amchem Prod Inc Ambler PA 19002

LEISURE, ROBERT GLENN, b Cromwell, Ky, Jan 29, 38; m 62. METAL PHYSICS. *Educ:* Western Ky Univ, BS, 60; Wash Univ, PhD(physics), 67. *Prof Exp:* Res scientist, Boeing Sci Res Lab, 67-70; from asst prof to assoc prof, 70-78, PROF PHYSICS, COLO STATE UNIV, 78- *Concurrent Pos:* Vis scientist, Univ Paris VI, 78-79. *Mem:* Am Phys Soc. *Res:* Ultrasonics; propagation of ultrasound in metals; acoustic excitation of nuclear magnetic resonance; metal hydrides. *Mailing Add:* Dept of Physics Colo State Univ Ft Collins CO 80523

LEITCH, LEONARD CHRISTIE, b Ottawa, Ont, Aug 22, 14; m 42; c 2. ORGANIC CHEMISTRY. *Educ:* Univ Ottawa, BSc, 35; Laval Univ, DSc, 49. *Prof Exp:* Res chemist, Mallinckrodt Chem Works, 37-46; res chemist, Div Chem, Nat Res Coun Can, 46-70, prin res chemist, 70-80; RETIRED. *Mem:* Chem Inst Can; Royal Soc Chem; Chem Soc France. *Res:* Synthetic drugs and plant hormones; synthesis of organic compounds with stable isotopes; reaction mechanisms. *Mailing Add:* Div Chem Nat Res Coun 100 Sussex Dr Ottawa ON K1A 0R6 Can

LEITCH, ROBERT EDGAR, JR, analytical chemistry, see previous edition

LEITER, EDWARD HENRY, b Columbus, Ga, Apr 17, 42; m 64. CELL BIOLOGY. *Educ:* Princeton Univ, BS, 64; Emory Univ, MS, 66, PhD(biol), 68. *Prof Exp:* NIH trainee, Univ Tex, Austin, 68-71; asst prof biol, Brooklyn Col, 71-74; assoc staff scientist, 74-75, STAFF SCIENTIST, JACKSON LAB, 75- *Concurrent Pos:* Nat Inst Arthritis & Metab Dis res grant, 74-; Juvenile Diabetes Found grant, 76- *Mem:* Tissue Cult Asn; Am Soc Cell Biol; Endocrine Soc. *Res:* Function of normal and diabetic pancreatic endocrine cells in vitro; genetic, viral, and environmental parameters producing pancreatic pathologies in the mouse. *Mailing Add:* Jackson Lab Bar Harbor ME 04609

LEITER, ELLIOT, b Brooklyn, NY, May 24, 33; m 63; c 3. MEDICINE, UROLOGY. *Educ:* Columbia Univ, AB, 54; NY Univ, MD, 57. *Prof Exp:* Asst urol, Johns Hopkins Hosp, 58-59; asst urol, NY Univ, 60-63; instr, Columbia Univ, 66-67; from asst prof to assoc prof, 66-78, PROF UROL, MT SINAI SCH MED, 78-; ATTEND UROL, MT SINAI HOSP, 78-; DIR UROL, BETH ISRAEL HOSP & MED CTR, 78- *Concurrent Pos:* Fel, NY Univ, 60-61, USPHS trainee, 61-62, fel hypertensive renal group, 63; asst vis surgeon, Bellevue Hosp, New York, 63 & Greenpoint Hosp, Brooklyn, 64; asst attend urologist, Mt Sinai Hosp, New York, 63-69, assoc attend urologist, 69- *Mem:* Asn Acad Surg; Am Urol Asn; Am Col Surg; Soc Univ Urol; Soc Pediat Urol. *Res:* Renal disease; pediatric urology; kidney transplantation; hypertension. *Mailing Add:* Beth Israel Med Ctr 10 Nathan D Perlman Pl New York NY 10003

LEITER, HOWARD ALLEN, b Mt Gilead, Ohio, Feb 16, 18; m 52; c 3. PHYSICS. *Educ:* Miami Univ, AB, 40; Univ Ill, AM, 42, PhD(physics), 49. *Prof Exp:* Asst physics, Univ Ill, 40-42; mem staff, Radiation Lab, Mass Inst Technol, 42-45; asst physics, Univ Ill, 45-48, res assoc, 48-49; physicist, Res Labs, Westinghouse Elec Corp, 49-58; sr engr, Labs, Int Tel & Tel Corp, 58-69; assoc prof physics, Tri-State Col, 70-75; instr, Inventive Indust, 75-77; INSTR, INT TEL & TEL CORP, 78- *Concurrent Pos:* Guest lectr, Off-campus Grad Prog, Purdue Univ, 59-60. *Mem:* Am Phys Soc. *Res:* Charged particle scattering; microwave components; interaction of electromagnetic radiations with matter; infrared detectors and systems; image tubes; cryogenic equipment; field emission microscopy; satellite instrumentation. *Mailing Add:* 2703 Capitol Ave Ft Wayne IN 46806

LEITER, JOSEPH, b New York, NY, May 14, 15; m 39; c 2. BIOCHEMISTRY. *Educ:* Brooklyn Col, BS, 34; Georgetown Univ, PhD(biochem), 49. *Prof Exp:* Jr chemist org & fibrous mat, Nat Bur Standards, 35-38; carcinogenesis, Nat Cancer Inst, 38-40, asst chemist, 40-42, assoc chemist chemotherapy, 46-47, chemist, 47-49, from sr chemist to sr scientist & chief biochem sect, Lab Chem Pharmacol, 49-55, scientist dir & asst chief lab activities, Cancer Chemother Nat Serv Ctr, 55-63, chief, Ctr, 63-65, ASSOC DIR LIBR OPERS, NAT LIBR MED, 65- *Mem:* AAAS; Soc Pharmacol & Exp Therapeut; Am Chem Soc; Am Asn Cancer Res. *Res:* Carcinogenesis, production of tumors with chemical agents, air dust; chemotherapy of cancer; drug metabolism, effect of chemical agents on enzymes in normal and malignant tissues. *Mailing Add:* Nat Libr of Med NIH Bethesda MD 20014

LEITH, CARLTON JAMES, b Madison, Wis, Sept 24, 19; m 41; c 2. GEOLOGY. *Educ:* Univ Wis, BA, 40, MA, 41; Univ Calif, PhD(geol), 47. *Prof Exp:* Asst geol, Univ Calif, 41-42; from jr mineral economist to asst mineral economist, Mineral Prod & Econ Div, US Bur Mines, 42-43; geologist, Standard Oil Co, Tex, 46; asst geol, Univ Calif, 46-47; from instr to asst prof geol, Univ Ind, 47-49; chief petrog unit, US Engrs Testing Lab, 49-51; geologist, Standard Oil Co, Calif, 51-60 & Holmes & Narver, Inc, 60-61; assoc prof, 61-65, prof geol eng, 65-80, EMER PROF GEOSCI, NC STATE UNIV, 80-, HEAD DEPT, 67- *Mem:* AAAS; Geol Soc Am; Soc Econ Paleont & Mineral; Am Asn Petrol Geol; Am Geophys Union. *Res:* Engineering geology; sedimentary petrology; areal geology; gravity and magnetics. *Mailing Add:* Dept of Geosci NC State Univ Box 5966 Raleigh NC 27650

LEITH, CECIL ELDON, JR, b Boston, Mass, Jan 31, 23; m 42; c 3. ATMOSPHERIC SCIENCES. *Educ:* Univ Calif, AB, 43, PhD(math), 57. *Prof Exp:* Physicist, Lawrence Radiation Lab, Univ Calif, 46-68; sr scientist, 68-78, dir, Atmospheric Anal & Prediction Div, 78-81, SR SCIENTIST, NAT CTR ATMOSPHERIC RES, NSF, 81- *Concurrent Pos:* Mem Int Comn Dynamic Meteorol, Int Asn Meteorol & Atmospheric Physics, 72- & Int Comn Climate, 78-; mem joint organizing comt, Global Atmospheric Res Prog, World Meteorol Orgn & Int Counc Sci Unions, 76-80, officer, Joint Sci Comt, World Climate Res Prog, 81-; chmn, Comt Atmospheric Sci, Nat Res Coun, 78-80. *Honors & Awards:* Meisinger Award, Am Meteorol Soc, 67, Carl-Gustaf Rossby Res Medal, 81. *Mem:* Fel AAAS; fel Am Phys Soc; fel Am Meteorol Soc; Am Math Soc. *Res:* Numerical simulation of the atmosphere; geophysical fluid dynamics; statistical hydrodynamics; turbulence. *Mailing Add:* Nat Ctr for Atmospheric Res PO Box 3000 Boulder CO 80307

LEITH, DAVID W G S, b Glasgow, Scotland, Sept 5, 37; m 62; c 3. HIGH ENERGY PHYSICS. *Educ:* Univ Glasgow, BSc, 59, PhD(natural philos), 62. *Prof Exp:* Glasgow Univ res fel physics, Europ Orgn Nuclear Res, Geneva, Switz, 62-63, staff physicist, 63-66; assoc prof, 66-70, PROF PHYSICS, LINEAR ACCELERATOR CTR, STANFORD UNIV, 70- *Mem:* Am Phys Soc; Brit Inst Physics & Phys Soc. *Res:* Strong interaction physics with emphasis on scattering experiments and investigations of resonance properties, their classification and the associated phenomenological analysis. *Mailing Add:* 754 Mayfield Ave Stanford Univ Stanford CA 94305

LEITH, EMMETT NORMAN, b Detroit, Mich, Mar 12, 27; m 56; c 1. OPTICS. *Educ:* Wayne State Univ, BS, 49, MS, 52. *Prof Exp:* Lab instr physics, Wayne State Univ, 51; asst eng res inst, 52-56, res assoc, 56-59, assoc res engr, 59-65, assoc prof, 65-68, PROF ELEC ENG, INST SCI & TECH, UNIV MICH, ANN ARBOR, 68- *Honors & Awards:* Gordon Memorial Award, Soc Photo-Optical Instrumentation Eng, 65, Liebmann Award, Inst

Elec & Electronics Eng, 67; Daedalion Award, 68; Stuart Ballantine Medal, Franklin Inst, 69; R W Wood Prize, Optical Soc Am, 75; Holly Medal, Am Soc Chem Engrs, 76; Inventor Year Award, Asn Adv Invention & Innovation, 76; Nat Medal Sci, 79. *Mem:* Fel Optical Soc Am; fel Inst Elec & Electronics Eng. *Res:* Wavefront reconstruction; electronic physics; electromagnetics; radar; resonant cavity design; data processing; optical system design; coherent optics; interferometry; holography. *Mailing Add:* Dept Elec & Comput Eng Univ of Mich Ann Arbor MI 48109

LEITH, JOHN DOUGLAS, JR, b Grand Forks, NDak, Apr 20, 31; m 57; c 2. PATHOLOGY, CELL BIOLOGY. *Educ:* Lehigh Univ, BA, 52; Univ Pa, MD, 56; Univ Wis, PhD(cytol), 64; Am Bd Path, cer anat & clin path, 74, cert radioisotopic path, 75. *Prof Exp:* Intern, Med Ctr, Univ Calif, San Francisco, 56-57; asst zool, Univ Wis, 59-60, NSF fel, 60-63; Nat Cancer Inst spec fel, 63-64; asst prof anat & cell biol, Med Sch, Univ Pittsburgh, 64-67; from asst prof to assoc prof biol, Univ Wis-Oshkosh, 67-71; resident path, Peter Bent Brigham Hosp, Boston, 71-74; ASSOC PATHOLOGIST, BROCKTON HOSP, 75- *Concurrent Pos:* Am Cancer Soc Inst res grant, 65-66; Health Res Serv Found res grant, 66-67; NSF grant, 68-70; Univ Wis res grants, 68-71. *Mem:* Col Am Path; Am Soc Clin Path; Am Soc Cell Biol; Sigma Xi. *Res:* Structure and function of chromosomes. *Mailing Add:* Dept of Path Brockton Hosp Brockton MA 02402

LEITH, THOMAS HENRY, b Toronto, Ont, Sept 11, 27; m 53; c 3. PHILOSOPHY OF SCIENCE, GEOPHYSICS. *Educ:* Univ Toronto, BA, 49, MA, 50; Boston Univ, PhD(philos sci), 62. *Prof Exp:* Instr geol & physics, Gordon Col, 52-55, asst prof, 55-58, assoc prof, 58-61, chmn, Div Natural Sci, 55-61; consult, R Woike Assocs, 61-62; asst prof philos, Univ RI, 62-64, coordr honors prog, 63-64; assoc dean & actg dir, Div Natural Sci, 66-69, dir, 69-71, ASSOC PROF GEN EDUC & NATURAL SCI, ATKINSON COL, YORK UNIV, 64-, CHMN, DEPT NATURAL SCI, 81- *Mem:* AAAS; Am Sci Affil; Philos Sci Asn; Hist Sci Soc; Sigma Xi. *Res:* Tectonic theories and theory formation in geology and other physical sciences; techniques and principles of science education for the nonscientist in college; relationships of theorizing in science and in religion. *Mailing Add:* Atkinson Col York Univ Downsview ON M3J 1P3 Can

LEITH, WILLIAM CUMMING, b Kimberley, BC, Apr 15, 25; m 50; c 3. MECHANICAL ENGINEERING, POLLUTION CONTROL. *Educ:* Univ BC, BAppSc, 48, MAppSc, 49; McGill Univ, PhD(mech eng), 60. *Prof Exp:* Jr engr, Dominion Eng Works, Que, 49-50 & Cominco-Trail, BC, 51-52; mech res engr, Dominion Eng Works, Que, 53-61; sr res scientist, Hydronautic Inc, Md, 61-62; design engr, Cominco-Trail, BC, 62-64 & H G Acres Co, Ont, 64-67; res assoc prof nuclear eng, Univ Wash, 67-73; MECH ENGR, COMINCO LTD, 73- *Honors & Awards:* Duggan Prize & Medal, Eng Inst Can, 59. *Mem:* Am Soc Mech Engrs; Am Nuclear Soc; Am Soc Artificial Internal Organs. *Res:* Design of devices for access to blood circulatory systems such as cannulas, fistulas and catheters; pollution control; scrubbing of gases; uranium enrichment by gas centrifuge. *Mailing Add:* Cominco Ltd Eng Dept Trail BC V1R 4L4 Can

LEITMAN, MARSHALL J, b Yonkers, NY, Jan 16, 41. APPLIED MATHEMATICS, CONTINUUM PHYSICS. *Educ:* Rensselaer Polytech Inst, BS, 62; Brown Univ, PhD(appl math), 65. *Prof Exp:* Res assoc appl math, Brown Univ, 65-66; asst prof, 66-71, assoc prof, 71-81, PROF MATH, CASE WESTERN RESERVE UNIV, 81- *Concurrent Pos:* Vis asst prof, Cath Univ Louvain, 70-71. *Mem:* Soc Natural Philos; Soc Indust & Appl Math. *Res:* Mechanics; viscoelasticity. *Mailing Add:* Dept of Math Case Western Reserve Univ Cleveland OH 44106

LEITMANN, G(EORGE), b Vienna, Austria, May 24, 25; nat US; m 55; c 2. MECHANICS. *Educ:* Columbia Univ, BS, 49, MA, 50; Univ Calif, PhD(eng sci), 56. *Prof Exp:* Physicist, Naval Ord Test Sta, 50-55, head aeroballistics anal sect, 55-57; from asst prof to assoc prof eng sci, 57-63, chmn, Div Appl Mech, 71-72, Univ Ombudsman, 68-70, PROF ENG SCI, UNIV CALIF, BERKELEY, 63-, ASSOC DEAN, COL ENG, 81- *Concurrent Pos:* Consult, Martin Co, 57-58 & Lockheed Missiles & Space Co, 58-66; Alexander von Humboldt sr scientist award, 81. *Honors & Awards:* Pendray Aerospace Lit Award, Am Inst Aeronaut & Astronat, 77; Levy Medal, Franklin Inst, 81. *Mem:* Corresp mem Int Acad Astronaut; Acad Sci Bologna. *Res:* Exterior ballistics of rockets and astrodynamics; variational problems in mechanics and astronautics; optimal control of dynamic systems; game theory; control of uncertain systems; applications to economics, engineering. *Mailing Add:* Dept Mech Eng Univ Calif Berkeley CA 94720

LEITNER, ALFRED, b Vienna, Austria, Nov 3, 21; nat US; m 48; c 3. MATHEMATICAL PHYSICS, SCIENCE EDUCATION. *Educ:* Univ Buffalo, BA, 44; Yale Univ, MS, 45, PhD(physics), 48. *Prof Exp:* Asst, Yale Univ, 43-47; res scientist, Courant Inst Math Sci, NY Univ, 47-51; from asst prof to prof physics, Mich State Univ, 51-67; PROF PHYSICS, RENSSELAER POLYTECH INST, 67- *Concurrent Pos:* Guggenheim fel & vis prof, Aachen Tech Univ, 58-59; res assoc, Harvard Univ, 65-66, consult proj physics, 66-69; Ger Acad Exchange fel, 77. *Mem:* Fel Am Phys Soc; Am Asn Physics Teachers; Am Asn Univ Prof; Am Sci Film Asn. *Res:* Special functions; boundary value problems; waves; history of science; educational films. *Mailing Add:* Dept of Physics Rensselaer Polytechnic Inst Troy NY 12181

LEITNER, FELIX, b Oradea, Rumania, Oct 8, 21; nat US; m 62; c 2. MICROBIOLOGY, CHEMOTHERAPY. *Educ:* Univ Geneva, MA, 46, MS, 50, PhD(chem), 54. *Prof Exp:* Res fel pharmacol, Col Med, NY Univ, 54-56, from res asst to res assoc, 56-58; res assoc microbiol, Michael Reese Hosp, 58-65, asst dir biochem, 65-68; asst dir, 68-77, DIR MICROBIOL RES, BRISTOL LABS, 77- *Mem:* AAAS; Am Soc Microbiol; NY Acad Sci. *Res:* Cellular regulatory mechanisms; antibiotics; beta-lactamase: biosynthesis and properties. *Mailing Add:* Microbiol Res Dept Bristol Labs Thompson Rd Syracuse NY 13201

LEITNER, PHILIP, b Peking, China, June 16, 36; US citizen; m 60; c 2. VERTEBRATE ZOOLOGY. *Educ:* St Mary's Col, Calif, BS, 58; Univ Calif, Los Angeles, MA, 60, PhD(zool), 61. *Prof Exp:* Jr res zoologist, Univ Calif, Los Angeles, 61-62; from instr to assoc prof, 62-76, chmn dept, 70-76, PROF BIOL, ST MARY'S COL, CALIF, 76- *Concurrent Pos:* NIH res grant, 63-65, NSF res grants, 65-70. *Mem:* AAAS; Am Soc Zoologists; Soc Study Evolution; Am Soc Mammalogists. *Res:* Environmental physiology of mammals, especially physiological responses to temperature and photoperiod. *Mailing Add:* Dept of Biol St Mary's Col Moraga CA 94575

LEITZ, FRED JOHN, JR, b Portland, Ore, Feb 2, 21; m 45; c 3. PHYSICAL CHEMISTRY. *Educ:* Reed Col, BA, 40; Univ Calif, PhD(phys chem), 43. *Prof Exp:* Instr chem, Univ Calif, 43-44; sr res chemist, Monsanto Chem Co, Ohio, 44-46; sr chemist, Oak Ridge Nat Lab, Tenn, 46-48; chemist, Radiochem & Reactor Metall Res, Hanford Works, Gen Elec Co, Wash, 48-56; nuclear engr, Atomic Power Develop Assocs, Mich, 56-58; develop proj engr, Atomic Power Equip Dept, Gen Elec Co, 58-64, mgr fast reactor core eng & test, Adv Prod Oper, 64-66, mgr steam reactor technol, 66-68; consult to dir, Battelle Northwest Lab, 69-7O; sr staff scientist, 70-76, mgr planning & anal, 76-79, STAFF MGR TECHNOL, WESTINGHOUSE HANFORD CO, 79- *Mem:* Am Chem Soc; Am Nuclear Soc. *Res:* Heavy element and fission product chemistry; nuclear fuel cycle development; fast and steam cooled reactor design and technology. *Mailing Add:* Westinghouse Hanford Co PO Box 1970 Richland WA 99352

LEITZ, FREDERICK HENRY, b Hastings, Mich, Nov 20, 28; m 70. PHARMACOLOGY. *Educ:* Kalamazoo Col, BA, 52; Univ Calif, Los Angeles, PhD(chem), 62. *Prof Exp:* Res grant, Inst Org Chem, Royal Inst Technol, Sweden, 62-63; res scientist, Lamont Geol Observ, 63-65; staff fel, Lab Chem Pharmacol, Nat Heart Inst, 65-70; PRIN SCIENTIST, SCHERING CORP, 70- *Mem:* Am Chem Soc. *Res:* Role of biogenic amines in function of sympathetic nervous systems, including synthesis and metabolism; nature of drug action on nerve endings. *Mailing Add:* Schering Corp 86 Orange St Bloomfield NJ 07003

LEITZ, VICTORIA MARY, b Yorkshire, Eng. BIOCHEMISTRY, LABORATORY MEDICINE. *Educ:* Oxford Univ, BA, 64, DPhil(clin chem), 68. *Prof Exp:* Res scientist human genetics, Med Res Coun, Oxford, Eng, 67-68; chemist neurochem, Sect Child Neurol, Nat Inst Neurol Dis & Stroke, NIH, 68-70; mgr develop chem & clin chem, Becton-Dickinson, NJ, 71-72; mgr diag chem & clin chem, 74-79, DIR TECH SERV, ELECTRO-NUCLEONICS, INC, 79- *Mem:* Am Asn Clin Chem; Nat Comt Clin Lab Standards. *Mailing Add:* 219 Fernwood Ave Upper Montclair NJ 07043

LEITZEL, JAMES ROBERT C, b Shenandoah, Pa, May 27, 36; m 65; c 2. MATHEMATICS. *Educ:* Pa State Univ, BA, 58, MA, 60; Ind Univ, PhD(math), 65. *Prof Exp:* Asst prof math, Bloomsburg State Col, 59-63; asst prof, 65-69, ASSOC PROF MATH, OHIO STATE UNIV, 69- *Mem:* Am Math Soc; Math Asn Am; AAAS. *Res:* Algebra, especially class field theory and algebraic function fields. *Mailing Add:* Dept of Math Ohio State Univ Columbus OH 43210

LEITZEL, JOAN PHILLIPS, b Valparaiso, Ind, July 2, 36; m 65; c 2. MATHEMATICS. *Educ:* Hanover Col, AB, 58; Brown Univ, AM, 61; Univ Ind, PhD(algebra), 65. *Prof Exp:* Instr math, Oberlin Col, 61-62; asst prof, 65-70, ASSOC PROF MATH, OHIO STATE UNIV, 70- *Concurrent Pos:* Vchmn math dept, Ohio State Univ, 73- *Mem:* Am Math Soc; Math Asn Am. *Res:* Field theoretical proofs for cohomological results in class field theory. *Mailing Add:* Dept of Math Ohio State Univ Columbus OH 43210

LEITZMANN, CLAUS, b Dahlenburg, Ger, Feb 6, 33; US citizen; m 57; c 4. BIOCHEMISTRY, NUTRITION. *Educ:* Capital Univ, BS, 62; Univ Minn, MS, 64, PhD(biochem), 67. *Prof Exp:* Nat Inst Gen Med Sci res asst molecular biol inst, Univ Calif, Los Angeles, 67-69; vis prof biochem, Mahidol Univ, Thailand, 69-71; chief labs, Anemia & Malnutrit Res Ctr, Thailand, 71-74; assoc, 74-78, PROF INST NUTRIT, UNIV GIESSEN, 78- *Concurrent Pos:* Mem, Trop Inst, Univ Giessen, 74- *Mem:* AAAS; Sigma Xi; Am Soc Clin Nutrit; Am Inst Nutrit. *Res:* Nutrition in developing countries; interaction of nutrition and infection; adaptations to changes in food intake; hunger and satiety; obesity; dietary fibers. *Mailing Add:* Inst of Nutrit Univ Giessen 6300 Giessen Germany

LEIVE, LORETTA, b New York, NY, Apr 12, 36; c 1. BIOCHEMISTRY, MICROBIOLOGY. *Educ:* Barnard Col, Columbia Univ, AB, 56; Harvard Univ, AM, 61, PhD, 63. *Prof Exp:* RES BIOLOGIST, LAB BIOCHEM PHARMACOL, NAT INST ARTHRITIS & METAB DIS, NIH, 63- *Mem:* Am Soc Biol Chemists; Am Soc Microbiol. *Res:* Membrane structure and function in bacteria and macrophages. *Mailing Add:* Lab of Biochem Pharmacol Nat Inst Arthritis & Metab Dis Bethesda MD 20014

LEIVO, WILLIAM JOHN, b New Castle, Pa, Sept 11, 15; m 39; c 2. PHYSICS. *Educ:* Carnegie Inst Technol, BS, 39, MS, 45, DSc(physics), 48. *Prof Exp:* Supt bldg construct, Matthew Leivo & Sons, Inc, Pa, 33-35 & 39-42; from instr to asst prof physics, Carnegie Inst Technol, 42-55; PROF PHYSICS, OKLA STATE UNIV, 55- *Mem:* Fel Am Phys Soc; Am Asn Physics Teachers. *Res:* Color centers in crystals; radiation effects in solids; optics; solid state physics; semiconducting diamond; ESR studies of blood cell membranes. *Mailing Add:* Dept of Physics Okla State Univ Stillwater OK 74074

LEJA, J(AN), b Grodzisko, Poland, May 27, 18; m 47; c 6. CHEMISTRY, METALLURGY. *Educ:* Univ London, BSc, 45; Univ Krakow, dipl, 47; Cambridge Univ, PhD(surface chem), 54. *Hon Degrees:* Dr, Marie Curie-Sklodowska Univ, Poland, 76. *Prof Exp:* Res metallurgist, Southwest Africa Co, Eng, 47-49, reduction officer, SAfrica, 49-52; res fel colloid sci, Cambridge Univ, 54-57; from asst prof to prof metall, Univ Alta, 57-65; PROF METALL, UNIV BC, 65- *Mem:* Am Inst Mining, Metall & Petrol Engrs; Am Chem Soc; Brit Inst Mining & Metall; fel Can Inst Chem; Can Inst Mining & Metall. *Res:* Surface chemistry; infrared spectroscopy of adsorption; effluent control; dissolution of metals; corrosion. *Mailing Add:* Dept of Mineral Eng Univ of BC Vancouver BC V6T 1W5 Can

LEJA, STANISLAW, b Grodzisko, Poland, Jan 3, 12; nat US; m 39, 64; c 5. MATHEMATICS. *Educ:* Jan Kazimierz Univ, Poland, MA, 38; Cornell Univ, PhD(math), 58. *Prof Exp:* Instr math, Jan Kazimierz Univ, 38-40; teacher high schs, Palestine & Eng, 45-51; from asst to instr, Cornell Univ, 53-57; asst prof, 57-67, PROF MATH, WESTERN MICH UNIV, 67- *Mem:* Am Math Soc; Math Asn Am. *Res:* Real variable; Fourier analysis. *Mailing Add:* 931 Oakland Dr Kalamazoo MI 49008

LEJEUNE, ANDRE JOSEPH, agronomy, genetics, deceased

LEKLEM, JAMES ERLING, b Rhinelander, Wis, Aug 1, 41; m 67; c 2. NUTRITION. *Educ:* Univ Wis, BS, 64, MS, 66, PhD(nutrit), 73. *Prof Exp:* Proj assoc clin oncol, Univ Wis, 66-71, res assoc, 73-75; asst prof, 75-80, ASSOC PROF NUTRIT, ORE STATE UNIV, 81- *Mem:* Sigma Xi; Am Inst Nutrit. *Res:* Vitamin B6; metabolism of tryptophan; nutrient relationship to cancer etiology. *Mailing Add:* Dept of Foods & Nutrit Ore State Univ Corvallis OR 97331

LELACHEUR, ROBERT MURRAY, b Ottawa, Ont, Oct 12, 20; US citizen; m 46; c 4. PHYSICS. *Educ:* Mt Allison Univ, BSc, 42; Dalhousie Univ, MSc, 47; Univ Va, PhD(physics), 49. *Prof Exp:* Physicist, Nat Res Coun Can, 49-53; mem tech staff, Bell Labs, NJ, 53-58; asst supt eng, 58-62, dir mat & chem processes res & develop, NY, 62-66, MGR DEVELOP & MFG ENG, WESTERN ELEC CO, INC, READING, 66- *Mem:* Am Phys Soc; Inst Elec & Electronics Engrs. *Res:* Materials properties and processing; semiconductor device engineering. *Mailing Add:* Western Elec Co Inc PO Box 241 Reading PA 19603

LELAND, FRANCES E(LBRIDGE), b Chicago, Ill, Apr 22, 32. PHYSICAL CHEMISTRY. *Educ:* Swarthmore Col, BA, 54; Northwestern Univ, PhD(phys chem), 59. *Prof Exp:* Instr chem, Brooklyn Col, 59-61; from asst prof to assoc prof, 62-73, PROF CHEM, MacMURRAY COL, 73- *Mem:* Am Chem Soc. *Res:* Molecular quantum mechanics. *Mailing Add:* Dept of Chem MacMurray Col Jacksonville IL 62650

LELAND, HAROLD R(OBERT), b Eau Claire, Wis, Apr 18, 31; m 58; c 2. ELECTRICAL ENGINEERING, SYSTEMS ANALYSIS. *Educ:* Univ Wis, BS & MS, 54, PhD(elec eng), 58. *Prof Exp:* Various res & supvry positions, Cornell Aeronaut Lab, Inc, 58-63, staff scientist, 63-66, asst head, Syst Res Dept, 66-70, head, 70-71, vpres & dir elec syst group, 71-73, vpres commercial develop group, 73-76, pres, 74-76, vpres electronics & systs group, 76-78, VPRES & GEN MGR, ADVAN TECHNOL CTR, CALSPAN CORP, 78- *Mem:* Am Inst Aeronaut & Astronaut; Inst Elec & Electronics Engrs. *Res:* Automatic controls and pattern recognition; electronic warfare; military systems analysis; mathematical modeling of large systems. *Mailing Add:* Calspan Corp Advan Technol Ctr 4455 Genesee St Buffalo NY 14225

LELAND, STANLEY EDWARD, JR, b Chicago, Ill, Aug 1, 26; m 50; c 3. PARASITOLOGY. *Educ:* Univ Ill, BS, 49, MS, 50; Mich State Univ, PhD(parasitol), 53. *Prof Exp:* Asst parasitol, Mich State Univ, 50-53; from assoc parasitologist to parasitologist, Univ Ky, 53-60, prof animal path, 60-63; assoc parasitologist, Univ Fla, 63-67; actg head dept infectious dis, 70-72, PROF PARASITOL, KANS STATE UNIV, 67-, ASSOC DIR AGR EXP STA, 75- *Concurrent Pos:* Coop agent animal dis & parasite res div, USDA, 53-59; consult, Eli Lilly Co, 62-66. *Honors & Awards:* Col Vet Med Res Award, Kans State Univ, 71 & Distinguished Grad Fac Award, 75. *Mem:* Am Soc Parasitol. *Res:* Electrophoresis; drug testing; pathology; physiology; biochemistry; in vitro cultivation; immunology as related to parasitology. *Mailing Add:* Agr Exp Sta Kans State Univ Manhattan KS 66506

LELAND, THOMAS W, JR, b Chicago, Ill, May 21, 24; m 49; c 2. CHEMICAL ENGINEERING. *Educ:* Tex A&M Univ, BS, 47; Univ Mich, MSE, 49; Univ Tex, PhD(chem eng), 54. *Prof Exp:* Chmn dept, 66-69, PROF CHEM ENG, RICE UNIV, 54-, ASSOC, JONES COL, 77- *Mem:* Am Inst Chem Engrs; Am Chem Soc. *Res:* Thermodynamic properties of pure fluids and mixtures; applications of the corresponding states principle; virial coefficients and compressibility of gases; phase equilibria; physical absorption; radiation effects on catalysis; nuclear engineering. *Mailing Add:* Dept of Chem Eng Rice Univ PO Box 1892 Houston TX 77001

LELAND, WALLACE THOMPSON, b Minn, Jan 21, 22; m 43; c 4. LASERS. *Educ:* Univ Minn, BEE, 43, PhD(physics), 50. *Prof Exp:* Head, Instrument Develop Dept, Carbide & Carbon Chem Corp, 46-47; MEM STAFF NUCLEAR RES, LOS ALAMOS NAT LAB, 50- *Mem:* Am Phys Soc. *Res:* Mass spectroscopy and nuclear reactions; high energy lasers. *Mailing Add:* Los Alamos Nat Lab Los Alamos NM 87545

LELE, SHREEDHAR G, b Varanasi, India, Apr 19, 31; m 66; c 2. ELECTRICAL ENGINEERING, PHYSICS. *Educ:* Banaras Hindu Univ, India, MSc, 52; Univ Mich, MSE, 62, PhD(elec eng), 66. *Prof Exp:* Lectr physics, Banaras Hindu Univ, India, 52-60; res asst elec eng, Univ Mich, 61-66; assoc prof elec eng, Tenn Technol Univ, 66-80. *Mem:* Inst Elec & Electronics Engrs. *Res:* Ionospheric physics; microwave tubes; design of electron guns and solid-state devices. *Mailing Add:* 18 Sarah St Burlington MA 01803

LELEK, ANDREW STANISLAUS, topology, see previous edition

LE LEVIER, ROBERT ERNEST, b Los Angeles, Calif, Nov 7, 23; m 45; c 3. THEORETICAL PHYSICS. *Educ:* Univ Calif, Los Angeles, PhD(physics), 51. *Prof Exp:* Mem staff, Lawrence Radiation Lab, Univ Calif, 51-57 & Rand Corp, 57-71; mem staff, 71-80, CHIEF SCIENTIST, R&D ASSOCS, 80- *Res:* Ionospheric physics; nuclear physics; geophysics. *Mailing Add:* R&D Assocs 4640 Admiralty Way Marina Del Rey CA 90291

LELLINGER, DAVID BRUCE, b Chicago, Ill, Jan 24, 37; m 63; c 2. TAXONOMIC BOTANY. *Educ:* Univ Ill, AB, 58; Univ Mich, MS, 60, PhD(bot), 65. *Prof Exp:* ASSOC CUR FERNS, US NAT HERBARIUM, SMITHSONIAN INST, 63- *Concurrent Pos:* Ed-in-chief, Am Fern Soc, 66-; Nat Geog Soc & Smithsonian Res Found explor & res grants, 71, 74. *Mem:* Int Asn Plant Taxon; Brit Pterid Soc. *Res:* Taxonomy of ferns and fern allies, especially those of the New World tropics. *Mailing Add:* US Nat Herbarium NHB 166 Smithsonian Inst Washington DC 20560

LELLOUCHE, GERALD S, b New York, NY, June 21, 30; m 58; c 1. THEORETICAL PHYSICS, NUCLEAR ENGINEERING. *Educ:* Purdue Univ, BS, 52; NC State Col, PhD(nuclear eng), 60. *Prof Exp:* Jr engr, Brookhaven Nat Lab, 52-55, asst nuclear eng, 60-64, assoc physicist, 64-68, physicist, 68-74; prog mgr, Probabilistics & Statist, 74-80, SR PROG MGR CODE DEVELOP & VALIDATION, ELEC POWER RES INST, 80- *Mem:* Am Chem Soc; Am Inst Chem Eng; Am Nuclear Soc; NY Acad Sci. *Res:* Reactor kinetics, nonlinear dynamics; thermal hydraulics, twophase flow; probabilistics, risk analysis. *Mailing Add:* Elec Power Res Inst 3412 Hillview Ave Palo Alto CA 94304

LELONG, MICHEL GEORGES, b Casablanca, Morocco, Mar 20, 32; US citizen; m 59; c 3. PLANT TAXONOMY. *Educ:* Univ Algiers, baccalaureat, 50; Northwestern State Col, La, BS, 59, MS, 60; Iowa State Univ, PhD(syst bot), 65. *Prof Exp:* assoc prof, 65-77, PROF BIOL, UNIV S ALA, 77- *Mem:* Am Soc Plant Taxon; Int Asn Plant Taxon; Asn Southeastern Biologists. *Res:* Systematics of Panicum subgenus Dichanthelium; floristics of the Mobile Bay region. *Mailing Add:* Dept of Biol Sci Univ of SAla Mobile AL 36688

LEMAISTRE, CHARLES AUBREY, b Lockhart, Ala, Feb 10, 24; m 52; c 4. INTERNAL MEDICINE, EPIDEMIOLOGY. *Educ:* Univ Ala, BA, 43; Cornell Univ, MD, 47. *Prof Exp:* From instr to asst prof internal med, Med Col, Cornell Univ, 51-54; assoc prof, Sch Med, Emory Univ, 54-59, prof prev med & chmn dept, 57-59; prof, Univ Tex Southwestern Med Sch, Dallas, 59-66, assoc dean, 65-66; vchancellor health affairs, Univ Tex, Austin, 66-68; from exec vchancellor to chancellor-elect, 68-70, chancellor, Univ Tex Syst, 71-78; PRES, UNIV TEX SYST CANCER CTR, 78- *Concurrent Pos:* Mem human ecol study sect, NIH, 62-65; mem, Surgeon Gen Adv Comt Smoking & Health, 63-64; mem, Gov Comt Eradication Tuberc, 63-64; mem comt res tobacco & health, AMA Educ & Res Found, 64-66; mem, Nat Citizens Comn Int Coop, 65-; mem Surgeon Gen emergency health preparedness adv comt, Dept Health, Educ & Welfare, 67, consult, Div Physician Manpower, 67-70; mem, President's Comn White House Fel, 71; mem, Comn Non-Traditional Study, 71-73; mem joint task force continuing competence pharm, Am Pharmaceut Asn-Am Asn Col Pharm, 73-74; mem bd comnr, Nat Comn Accrediting, 73-76; trustee, Biol Humanics Found, Dallas, 73-; mem, Nat Coun Educ Res, 73-75, consult, 75; chmn subcomt diversity & pluralism, Nat Coun Educ Res, 73-75; mem, United Negro Col Fund Develop Coun, 74-78; mem, Nat Adv Coun, Inst Serv Educ, 74-77. *Mem:* Am Thoracic Soc (vpres, 64-65). *Res:* Chest diseases. *Mailing Add:* Univ of Tex Syst Cancer Ctr 723 Bertner Houston TX 77030

LE MAISTRE, JOHN WESLEY, b Lockhart, Ala, Sept 27, 09; m 47; c 4. CHEMISTRY. *Educ:* Univ Mich, BSE, 30, MS, 31; Duke Univ, PhD(chem), 34. *Prof Exp:* Res chemist, Dow Chem Co, Mich, 31-32; group leader, Oxford Paper Co, Maine, 34-36; res dir, Swann & Co, Ala, 36-42; chief org chemist, Indust Res Inst, Chattanooga, 46-48; res dir, Chattanooga Med Co, 47-50; chem res dept, Atlas Chem Industs, 53-70, dir biomed res labs, ICI Am, Wilmington, Del, 70-75; RETIRED. *Concurrent Pos:* Lectr, Univ Chattanooga, 47-50; adj prof, Lehigh Univ, 77- *Mem:* AAAS; Am Chem Soc. *Res:* Sugar derivatives; industrial chemicals; drug synthesis and metabolism. *Mailing Add:* 6 Glenrock Dr Claymont DE 19703

LEMAL, DAVID M, b Plainfield, NJ, Feb 20, 34; m 63; c 4. ORGANIC CHEMISTRY. *Educ:* Amherst Col, AB, 55; Harvard Univ, PhD, 59. *Prof Exp:* From instr to asst prof chem, Univ Wis, 58-65; assoc prof, 65-69, PROF CHEM, DARTMOUTH COL, 69- *Concurrent Pos:* A P Sloan Found res fel, 68-70; trustee, Gordon Res Conf, 73- *Mem:* AAAS; Am Chem Soc. *Res:* Unusual species, stable and short-lived, in organic chemistry; organic reaction mechanisms; organic photochemistry; organofluorine chemistry. *Mailing Add:* Dept of Chem Dartmouth Col Hanover NH 03755

LEMAN, ALLEN DUANE, b Peoria, Ill, Jan 15, 44. VETERINARY MEDICINE. *Educ:* Univ Ill, BS, 66, DVM, 68, PhD(physiol), 74. *Prof Exp:* Instr, Univ Ill, 69-75; ASSOC PROF VET MED, UNIV MINN, 75- *Concurrent Pos:* Dir, Nat Pork Producers Coun Res Comt, 72-; prog chmn, Int Pig Vet Cong, 73-; ed, Dis Swine, Iowa State Press, 74-; dir, Soc Study of Breeding Soundness & Nat Swine Improv Fedn, 75- *Mem:* Am Asn Swine Practitions (pres, 75); Am Vet Med Asn; Soc Study Reproduction; Am Soc Animal Sci; Soc Study Breeding Soundness. *Res:* Causes of swine infertility; causes of lameness in boars; maximum economic returns from pork production. *Mailing Add:* Col of Vet Med Univ of Minn St Paul MN 55101

LEMANSKI, MICHAEL FRANCIS, b Cleveland, Ohio, Nov 16, 46. HETEROGENEOUS CATALYSIS. *Educ:* Univ Dayton, BS, 69; Ohio State Univ, MS, 72, PhD(inorg chem), 75. *Prof Exp:* Sr res chemist, Diamond Shamrock Corp, 75-78; RES PROJ LEADER, STANDARD OIL CO, OHIO, 78- *Concurrent Pos:* Vis researcher, Ctr Catalytic Sci & Technol, Univ Del, 80. *Mem:* Am Inst Chem Engrs; Am Chem Soc. *Res:* Heterogeneous catalysis, including selective oxidation and selective reduction of small molecules. *Mailing Add:* Sohio Res Ctr 4440 Warrensville Ctr Rd Cleveland OH 44128

LEMAR, WILLIAM B(ERNHARDT), b Rapid City, SDak, Sept 24, 22; div; c 1. CIVIL ENGINEERING. *Educ:* Stanford Univ, BA, 43; Yale Univ, MEng, 47. *Prof Exp:* Struct designer, Anaconda Copper Mining Corp, 48 & NY, New Haven & Hartford RR, 48-50; dir eng, P F Petersen Baking Co, Nebr, 50-56, vpres, 56-60; asst prof civil eng, 61-64, ASSOC PROF CIVIL ENG, UNIV NEBR, OMAHA, 64- *Concurrent Pos:* Consult, Sewage

Treatment Plant Oper Sch, Omaha, Nebr, 63- & Strategic Air Command Hq, Offutt AFB, 66-67. *Mem:* AAAS; Am Soc Civil Engrs; Nat Soc Prof Engrs; Am Soc Eng Educ. *Res:* Sanitary and transportation engineering; history of engineering. *Mailing Add:* Dept of Civil Eng 63rd & Dodge Sts Omaha NE 68132

LEMASTER, EDWIN WILLIAM, b Perryton, Tex, Apr 27, 40; m 64; c 1. SOLID STATE PHYSICS. *Educ:* West Tex State Univ, BS, 62; Tech Tech Univ, MS, 66; Univ Tex, PhD(physics), 70. *Prof Exp:* Asst prof physics, Gen Motors Inst, 64-66; ASST PROF PHYSICS, PAN AM UNIV, 70-, CHMN PHYS SCI DEPT, 73- *Mem:* Am Phys Soc; Am Asn Physics Teachers. *Res:* Metalammonia solution properties; amorphous semiconductors; remote sensing of vegetative canopies; mathematical modeling. *Mailing Add:* Dept of Phys Sci Pan Am Univ Edinburg TX 78539

LEMASURIER, WESLEY ERNEST, b Wash, DC, May 3, 34; m 63; c 3. GEOLOGY. *Educ:* Union Col, BS, 56; Univ Colo, MS, 62; Stanford Univ, PhD(geol), 65. *Prof Exp:* Geologist, US Geol Surv, 61-64; asst prof geol, Cornell Univ, 64-68; assoc prof, 68-76, PROF GEOL, DIV NAT & PHYS SCI, UNIV COLO, DENVER, 76- *Mem:* AAAS; Geol Soc Am; Am Geophys Union; Int Asn Volcanol & Chem Earth's Interior. *Res:* Subglacial volcanism; petrology and tectonic relationships of volcanism in Antarctica. *Mailing Add:* Div Nat & Phys Sci Univ of Colo Denver CO 80202

LEMAY, CHARLOTTE ZIHLMAN, b Ft Worth, Tex, June 30, 19; m 44; c 3. SOLID STATE PHYSICS. *Educ:* Tex Christian Univ, AB, 40; Mt Holyoke Col, MA, 41; La State Univ, PhD(physics), 50. *Prof Exp:* Res physicist, Monsanto Chem Co, 43-44; instr physics, Mt Holyoke Col, 45-46; instr physics, La State Univ, 46-48, asst, 48-50; engr, Tex Instruments, Inc, 52-53, 55-57; res physicist, Stanford Res Inst, 53-54; engr, Westinghouse Elec Corp, 58-60 & Int Bus Mach Corp, 60-63; from asst prof sci to assoc prof, 63-69, PROF PHYSICS & CHMN DEPT, WESTERN CONN STATE COL, 69- *Mem:* Am Phys Soc; Am Asn Physics Teachers; Inst Elec & Electronics Eng; Sigma Xi; Am Soc Eng Educ. *Res:* Dielectric liquids; transistors. *Mailing Add:* 60 Chestnut Ridge Rd Mt Kisco NY 10549

LEMAY, HAROLD E, JR, b Tacoma, Wash, May 28, 40; m 64; c 2. INORGANIC CHEMISTRY. *Educ:* Pac Lutheran, BS, 62; Univ Ill, MS, 64, PhD(inorg chem), 66. *Prof Exp:* Asst prof, 66-70, assoc prof, 70-78, vchmn dept, 74-76, PROF CHEM, UNIV NEV, RENO, 78- *Concurrent Pos:* Vis prof, Univ NC, Chapel Hill, 77-78 & Univ Col Wales, 78. *Mem:* Am Chem Soc; NAm Thermal Anal Soc; Sigma Xi. *Res:* Preparation and characterization of coordination compounds; reactions of coordination compounds in the solid phase; kinetic studies of ligand exchange reactions. *Mailing Add:* Dept of Chem Univ of Nev Reno NV 89557

LE MAY, I(AIN), b Helensburgh, Scotland, Oct 30, 36; Brit citizen; m 63; c 3. METALLURGY, MECHANICAL ENGINEERING. *Educ:* Univ Glasgow, BSc, 57, PhD(eng mat), 63; Univ Strathclyde, ARCST, 57. *Prof Exp:* Tech asst mech eng, N Brit Locomotive Co Ltd, 57; res asst, Univ Glasgow, 57-63; from asst prof to assoc prof, 63-71, PROF MECH ENG, UNIV SASK, 71-; PRES, METALLURGICAL CONSULT SERV LTD, 78- *Concurrent Pos:* Tech ed, J Eng Mat & Technol, 72-75; tech adv, NUCLEBRAS, Empresas Nucleares Brasileiras, 75-76. *Mem:* Int Metallograph Soc; Am Soc Mech Engrs; fel Am Soc Metals; Can Inst Mining & Metall; Am Soc Testing & Mat. *Res:* Creep and fatigue of metals; fractography; metallography; biomaterials including orthopedic implants; precipitation hardening; high-strength low-alloy steels; mechanics of fracture. *Mailing Add:* Metall Lab Col of Eng Univ of Sask Saskatoon SK S7N 0W0 Can

LEMAY, JEAN-PAUL, b St Hyacinthe, Que, Apr 7, 23; m 52; c 2. ANIMAL PHYSIOLOGY, ANIMAL BREEDING. *Educ:* Classical Col St Hyacinthe, BA, 45; Univ Montreal, BSA, 49; Univ Mass, MSc, 51. *Prof Exp:* Mem artificial insemination unit, Classical Col St Hyacinthe, 48-49; from instr to prof animal sci, Res Sta La Pocatiere, Que, 51-62; PROF ANIMAL SCI, LAVAL UNIV, 62- *Mem:* Am Soc Animal Sci; Can Soc Animal Prod. *Res:* Early weaning of sheep; histophysiology of sperm atogenesis and ovogenesis in sheep; sterility in dairy cattle. *Mailing Add:* Dept of Animal Sci Laval Univ Fac of Agr Ste Foy PQ C1K 7P4 Can

LEMAY, YVAN, b Montreal, Que, Mar 24, 31; m 55; c 2. BOTANY, ZOOLOGY. *Educ:* Univ Montreal, BA, 52, BSc, 55, MSc, 56. *Prof Exp:* Botanist, 56-67, electron microscopist, 67-74, SR MICROSCOPIST, CIP RES LTD, 74- *Mem:* Assoc Tech Asn Pulp & Paper Indust; assoc Can Pulp & Paper Asn. *Res:* Tree physiology; wood anatomy; microscopy; pulp and paper products fiber analysis; wood identification. *Mailing Add:* CIP Res Ltd 179 Main St W Hawkesbury ON K6A 2H4 Can

LEMBACH, KENNETH JAMES, b Rochester, NY, June 16, 39; m 65; c 2. BIOCHEMISTRY. *Educ:* Mass Inst Technol, BS, 61; Univ Pa, PhD(biochem), 66. *Prof Exp:* USPHS fel, Mass Inst Technol, 66-68, res assoc biochem, 68-69; asst prof, Sch Med, Vanderbilt Univ, 69-76, assoc prof, 76-80; PLASMA PROD RES SECT HEAD, CUTTER LABS INC, 80- *Concurrent Pos:* US Nat Cancer Inst res grants, 71-74 & 75-79. *Mem:* AAAS; NY Acad Sci; Am Soc Cell Biol; Sigma Xi; Am Soc Biol Chem. *Res:* Growth regulation in normal and malignant cells; metabolic control mechanisms. *Mailing Add:* Dept Biochem Cutter Labs Inc Berkeley CA 94710

LEMBECK, WILLIAM JACOBS, b Kansas City, Mo, Aug 29, 28; m 60; c 1. MICROBIOLOGY, ACADEMIC ADMINISTRATION. *Educ:* La State Univ, BS, 50, MS, 56, PhD(bact), 62. *Prof Exp:* Supvry bacteriologist, US Army Chem Corps, Pine Bluff Arsenal, Ark, 57-59; from asst prof to assoc prof biol, Ark Agr & Mech Col, 61-62; asst prof bact, McNeese State Col, 62-65, assoc prof microbiol, 65-66; asst prof bot, Baton Rouge, 66-68, assoc prof biol & head div sci, 68-75, PROF BIOL, LA STATE UNIV, EUNICE, 75- *Mem:* AAAS; Am Inst Biol Sci; Sigma Xi. *Res:* Effects of herbicides on normal soil microflora; biological catalysis of herbicides in soil; effects of herbicides on cellulose decomposition by Sporocytophaga myxococcoides. *Mailing Add:* Div of Sci La State Univ PO Box 1129 Eunice LA 70535

LEMBERG, HOWARD LEE, b Queens, NY, July 29, 49; m 70. CHEMICAL PHYSICS, COMPUTER SCIENCES. *Educ:* Columbia Univ, BA, 69; Univ Chicago, PhD(chem physics), 73. *Prof Exp:* Res chem physics, Bell Labs, 73-75; asst prof chem, Univ NC, 75-78; MEM TECH STAFF, BELL LABS, 78- *Mem:* Inst Elec & Electronics Engrs; Am Phys Soc; AAAS. *Res:* Statistical mechanics of liquids; electronic structure of surfaces; fluctuations and instabilities in chemical systems; computer protocols; communications networks. *Mailing Add:* Bell Labs Crawfords Corner Rd Holmdel NJ 07733

LEMBERG, LOUIS, b Chicago, Ill, Dec 27, 16; m 39. PHYSIOLOGY. *Educ:* Univ Ill, BS, 38, MD, 40; Am Bd Internal Med, dipl, 50; Am Bd Cardiovasc Dis, dipl, 55. *Prof Exp:* Intern, Mt Sinai Hosp, Chicago, Ill, 40-41, res, 45-48; PROF CLIN CARDIOL, SCH MED, UNIV MIAMI, 69- *Concurrent Pos:* Dir cardiol, Dade County Hosp, 55-57; attend specialist, Vet Admin Hosp, 55-64; chief staff, Nat Children's Cardiac Hosp, Miami, 55-66; attend cardiologist, Mercy & Cedars of Lebanon Hosp; chief div electrophysiol, 56-74, dir coronary care unit, Jackson Mem Hosp, 68-74; chief div cardiol, Mercy Hosp, 76- mem coun clin cardiol, Am Heart Asn. *Honors & Awards:* Savage Award, 60; Luis Guerrero Mem Award, Philippines. *Mem:* Hon mem Philippine Med Asn; fel Am Col Physicians; Am Col Chest Physicians; Am Col Cardiol; NY Acad Sci. *Res:* Cardiology. *Mailing Add:* Div of Cardiol (D39) PO Box 016960 Miami FL 33101

LEMBERGER, AUGUST PAUL, b Milwaukee, Wis, Jan 25, 26; m 47; c 7. PHARMACEUTICS. *Educ:* Univ Wis, BS, 48, PhD(pharm), 52. *Prof Exp:* Sr chemist pharmaceut res, Merck & Co, Inc, 52-53; from instr to prof pharm, Univ Wis-Madison, 53-69, coordr exten serv, 65-69; prof pharm & dean, Col, Univ Ill Med Ctr, 69-80; PROF PHARM & DEAN, SCH PHARM, UNIV WIS-MADISON, 80- *Concurrent Pos:* Mem & secy, Wis Pharm Internship Comn, 65-69; consult, Dept Health, Educ & Welfare, 72-74; mem, Am Coun Pharmaceut Educ; mem, Tech Adv Coun Ill Dept Pub Health Drug Substitution law, 78-80. *Honors & Awards:* Kiekhofer Award, Univ Wis, 57; Distinguished Serv Award, Wis Pharm Asn, 69. *Mem:* Am Pharmaceut Asn; fel Acad Pharm Sci; fel AAAS. *Mailing Add:* Sch Pharm Univ Wis 425 N Charter St Madison WI 53706

LEMBERGER, LOUIS, b Monticello, NY, May 8, 37; m 59; c 2. CLINICAL PHARMACOLOGY. *Educ:* Long Island Univ, BS, 60; Albert Einstein Col Med, PhD(pharmacol), 64, MD, 68. *Prof Exp:* Fel pharmacol, Albert Einstein Col Med, 64-68; med intern, Metropolitan Hosp Ctr-NY Med Col, 68-69; pharmacol & toxicol res assoc clin pharmacol, Lab Clin Sci, NIMH, 69-71; clin pharmacologist, 71-75, chief, 75-78; DIR CLIN PHARMACOL, LILLY LAB CLIN RES, LILLY RES LABS, 78- *Concurrent Pos:* Dir, Clin Pharmacol Training Prog, Sch Med, Ind Univ, 72-75, asst prof pharmacol & med, 72-73, assoc prof, 73-77, prof pharmacol, med & psychiat, 77-; assoc prof, Grad Fac, 75-77, prof, 77-; adj prof clin pharmacol, Ohio State Univ, 75-; chmn, 2nd World Conf Clin Pharmacol, Int Union Clin Pharmacol. *Mem:* Am Soc Pharmacol Exp Ther; Am Soc Clin Pharmacol Ther; Am Col Neuro Psychopharm; NY Acad Sci; Am Col Physicians. *Res:* Drug metabolism and drug-drug interactions; synthesis and metabolism of biogenic amines; biochemical mechanisms of drug action; psychopharmacology; marihuana & cannabinoids. *Mailing Add:* Lilly Lab for Clin Res Lilly Res Labs Indianapolis IN 46206

LEMBKE, ROGER ROY, b Clayton Co, Iowa, Apr 24, 40; m 69; c 2. PHYSICAL CHEMISTRY, RADIATION CHEMISTRY. *Educ:* Luther Col, AB, 62; Univ Nebr-Lincoln, MS, 66; Wayne State Univ, PhD(phys chem), 73. *Prof Exp:* Instr chem, Hastings Col, 65-69; guest scientist, Hahn-Meitner Inst, Berlin, 73-74; res assoc, Univ Fla, 75; asst prof, Cornell Col, 75-76; assoc prof, 76-78, PROF CHEM & CHMN DEPT, CENT METHODIST COL, 78- *Mem:* Am Chem Soc. *Res:* Radiolysis and photolysis; rate constants and mechanisms. *Mailing Add:* Dept of Chem Cent Methodist Col Fayette MO 65248

LEMBO, NICHOLAS J, b Boston, Mass, Aug 18, 29; m 56; c 4. ANALYTICAL CHEMISTRY. *Educ:* Boston Col, BS, 51; Teachers Col City Boston, EdM, 52; Northeastern Univ, MS, 62. *Prof Exp:* Instr pub schs, Mass, 52-56; instr phys sci, 56-59, asst prof chem, 59-65, ASSOC PROF CHEM, BOSTON STATE COL, 65- *Concurrent Pos:* Lectr, Lincoln Col, Northeastern Univ, 53-65. *Res:* Improvement of science teaching in the elementary schools. *Mailing Add:* Dept of Chem Boston State Col Boston MA 02115

LEMCOE, M M(ARSHALL), b St Louis, Mo; m 51; c 2. CIVIL ENGINEERING. *Educ:* Wash Univ, BS, 43, MS, 49; Univ Ill, PhD(civil eng), 57. *Prof Exp:* Struct engr, Curtiss-Wright Corp, 43-46; mem staff, Res Found & Dept Civil Eng, Wash Univ, 47-51; supvr aeroelasticity & spec consult, Southwest Res Inst, 51-52, mgr strength anal sect, Dept Struct Res, 52-61; supvr exp mech & sr tech specialist, Atomics Int Div, NAm Rockwell Corp, Calif, 61-71; TECH ADV, COLUMBUS DIV, BATTELLE MEM INST, 71- *Honors & Awards:* Award, Curtiss-Wright Corp, 45; IR-100 Award, 76. *Mem:* Soc Exp Stress Anal; Sigma Xi. *Res:* Experimental stress analysis; structures; pressure vessels; high temperature materials technology and strain gage technology; high temperature behavior of structures. *Mailing Add:* Columbus Div Battelle Mem Inst Columbus OH 43201

LE MEE, JEAN M, b June 4, 31; US citizen; m 64. ENGINEERING. *Educ:* Carnegie-Mellon Univ, MS, 59, PhD(mech eng), 63. *Prof Exp:* Design engr, James Gordon & Co Ltd, Eng, 55-58; teaching asst eng, Carnegie-Mellon Univ, 59-61; res engr, Lawrence Radiation Lab, Univ Calif, Berkeley, 60 & Westinghouse Res Labs, 62-64; assoc prof, 64-80, PROF MECH ENG, COOPER UNION SCH OF ENG & SCI, 80- *Mem:* Inst Elec & Electronics Engrs. *Res:* Control systems; semiconductor devices. *Mailing Add:* Cooper Union Sch of Eng & Sci Cooper Sq New York NY 10003

LE MEHAUTE, BERNARD J, b Brieuc, France, Mar 29, 27; m 53; c 2. HYDRODYNAMICS. *Educ:* Univ Rennes, Baccalaureat, 47; Univ Toulouse, lic es sc, 51; Univ Grenoble, Dr es Sc(hydrodyn), 57. *Prof Exp:* Res engr, Neyrpic-Sogreah, France, 53-57; assoc prof hydrodyn, Polytech Sch, Montreal, 57-59; res prof, Queen's Univ, Ont, 59-61; mem tech staff, Nat Eng Sci Co, 61-62; mem sr staff, 62-64, assoc dir hydrodyn, 64-66; vpres, 66-70, sr vpres, 66-78, MEM BD TETRA TECH, INC, 78-; PROF & CHMN OCEAN ENG, UNIV MIAMI, ROSENSTIEL SCH MARINE & ATMOSPHERIC SCI, 78- *Honors & Awards:* Int Gasfal Eng Award, Am Soc Chem Engrs, 79. *Mem:* Am Geophys Union; Am Soc Civil Eng; Marine Technol Soc; Int Asn Hydraul Res. *Res:* Hydrodynamics and hydraulic and coastal engineering, ranging from theoretical fluid mechanics to physical oceanography applied to the design of engineering structures for water power, coastal harbors and offshore drilling. *Mailing Add:* Univ Miami Rosenstiel Sch of 4600 Rickenbacker Causeway Miami FL 33149

LEMENT, BERNARD S, b Boston, Mass, Feb 11, 17; m 42; c 3. FAILURE ANALYSIS, ACCIDENT RECONSTRUCTION. *Educ:* Mass Inst Technol, BS, 38, ScD(metall), 49. *Prof Exp:* Metallurgist testing, NY Testing Labs, 38-39; res asst tool steels, Mass Inst Technol, 40; assoc metallurgist army ord, Watertown Arsenal, 40-46; instr physics, Univ Mass, 46-47; res staff mem dimensional stability, Mass Inst Technol, 47-49; asst prof metall, Univ Notre Dame, 49-51; mem res staff electron microscopy, Mass Inst Technol, 51-57; proj dir res & develop, ManLabs, Inc, 57-67; MAT ENG CONSULT, LEMENT & ASSOCS, 67- *Mem:* Fel Am Soc Metals; Am Inst Metall Engrs; Am Welding Soc; Am Soc Testing & Mat; Am Soc Safety Engrs. *Mailing Add:* 24 Graymore Rd Waltham MA 02154

LEMESHOW, STANLEY ALAN, b Brooklyn, NY, Jan 29, 48; m 72; c 2. SAMPLING, EXPERIMENTAL DESIGN. *Educ:* City Col New York, BBA, 69; Univ NC, Chapel Hill, MSPH, 70; Univ Calif, Los Angeles, PhD(biostatist), 76. *Prof Exp:* Res asst, Dept Prev Med, NY Med Col, 68-69; statist supvr, Health Res Training Prog, New York City Dept Health, 69; anal statistician, Comn Off, Nat Ctr Health Statist, US Pub Health Servs, 70-72; sr statisticin, Sch Pub Health, Univ Calif, Los Angeles, 74-75; asst prof, 76-80, ASSOC PROF BIOSTATISTS, UNIV MASS, 80- *Concurrent Pos:* Dir, Coord Ctr for Multicenter Clin Trial of Hyperbaric Oxygen in Treatment of Burn Injuries, Univ Mass, 77-78; prog dir, Biopharmceut Res Unit, Div Pub Health, Univ Mass, Amherst, 78- *Mem:* Am Statist Asn; Soc Epidemiol Res; Am Pub Health Asn. *Res:* Sampling; variance estimation in complex sampling designs; sample size determination and logistic regression analysis; medical and other applied health sciences. *Mailing Add:* Div Pub Health Sch Health Sci Univ Mass Amherst MA 01003

LEMESSURIER, WILLIAM JAMES, b Pontiac, Mich, June 12, 26; m 53; c 3. STRUCTURAL ENGINEERING. *Educ:* Harvard Univ, AB, 47; Mass Inst Technol, SM, 53. *Prof Exp:* Founder, Goldberg-LeMessurier, 52-61, founder & partner, LeMessurier Assoc, Inc, 61-73, CHMN & CHIEF EXEC OFFICER, SIPPICAN CONSULT INT, INC, 73- *Concurrent Pos:* Asst prof, Mass Inst Technol, 52-56, assoc prof, 64-67, sr lectr, 76-77; assoc prof, Harvard Grad Sch Design, 56-61, lectr, 73- *Honors & Awards:* Allied Prof Medal, Am Inst Architects, 68; Special Award, Am Inst Steel Construction, 72. *Mem:* Nat Acad Eng; Am Soc Civil Engrs; fel Am Concrete Inst. *Res:* Structural engineering design; precast concrete high rise housing system; staggered truss system for high rise steel structures; tuned mass damper system used to reduce tall building motion; structural stability. *Mailing Add:* Sippican Consult Int Inc 1033 Massachusetts Ave Cambridge MA 02238

LEMIEUX, GUY, internal medicine, see previous edition

LEMIEUX, RAYMOND URGEL, b Lac la Biche, Alta, June 16, 20; m 48; c 6. ORGANIC CHEMISTRY. *Educ:* Univ Alta, BSc, 43; McGill Univ, PhD(org chem), 46. *Hon Degrees:* DSc, Univ NB, 67, Laval Univ, 70, Univ Ottawa, 75, Waterloo Univ, 80 & Mem Univ, 81; Doctorate, Univ de Provence, France, 72; LLD, Univ Calgary, 79. *Prof Exp:* Res assoc carbohydrate chem, Ohio State Univ, 46-47; asst prof org chem, Univ Sask, 47-49; res officer chem natural prod, Prairie Regional Lab, Nat Res Coun, 49-54; prof chem, chmn dept & vdean fac pure & appl sci, Ottawa Univ, Can, 54-61; PROF ORG CHEM, UNIV ALTA, 61- *Concurrent Pos:* Merck lectr, 56; Folkers lectr, 58; Karl Pfister lectr, 68; Purves lectr, 70; pres & dir res, Raylo Chem Ltd, Alta, 66-76. *Honors & Awards:* Medal, Chem Inst Can, 64; C S Hudson Award, Am Chem Soc, 66; Medal of Serv, Order of Can, 68; Haworth Medal Chem Soc, Eng, 78; Killam Prize, Can Coun, 81. *Mem:* AAAS; The Chem Soc; Am Chem Soc; fel Chem Inst Can; fel Royal Soc Can. *Res:* Stereochemistry; conformational analysis; carbohydrate chemistry; synthesis and conformation; especially antibiotics and blood group determinants. *Mailing Add:* Dept of Chem Univ of Alta Edmonton AB T6G 2G2 Can

LEMING, CHARLES WILLIAM, b Cutler, Ill, Nov 5, 43; m 65; c 1. PHYSICS. *Educ:* Eastern Ill Univ, BS, 65; Mich State Univ, MS, 67, PhD(physics), 70. *Prof Exp:* PROF PHYSICS, HENDERSON STATE UNIV, 70- *Concurrent Pos:* Res assoc, Fac Develop Prog, NSF, 77 & Student Sci Training Prog, 78, proj dir, 79; res assoc, Carbondale Mining Technol Ctr, 81. *Mem:* AAAS; Am Asn Physics Teachers. *Res:* Optical devices; thermal physics; thermomagnetic flow; radom detection; applications in mineral exploration. *Mailing Add:* Box HSU-1970 Henderson State Univ Arkadelphia AR 71923

LEMIRE, ROBERT JAMES, b Toronto, Ont, Mar 12, 45; m 68. SOLUTION CHEMISTRY. *Educ:* Univ Toronto, BSc, 68, MSc, 71, PhD(chem), 75. *Prof Exp:* Researcher fel chem, Univ Ky, 75-77; ASST RES OFFICER CHEM, WHITESHELL NUCLEAR RES ESTAB, ATOMIC ENERGY CAN LTD, 77- *Mem:* Chem Inst Can; Am Chem Soc. *Res:* Properties of aqueous and non-aqueous solutions; complexation; solvent extraction. *Mailing Add:* Whiteshell Nuclear Res Estab Atomic Energy Can Ltd Pinawa MB R0E 1L0 Can

LEMIRE, RONALD JOHN, b Portland, Ore, Apr 20, 33; m 55; c 5. TERATOLOGY, PEDIATRICS. *Educ:* Univ Wash, MD, 62. *Prof Exp:* Intern, King County Hosp, Seattle, Wash, 62-63; NIH fel teratology & embryol, Univ Wash, 63-65, asst resident pediat, 65-67; chief resident, Children's Orthop Hosp & Med Ctr, 67-68; asst prof, 68-72, assoc prof, 72-77, PROF PEDIAT, UNIV WASH, 77- & DIR INPATIENT SERV, CHILDREN'S ORTHOP HOSP & MED CTR, SEATTLE. *Mem:* Soc Pediat Res; Teratology Soc. *Res:* Neuroembryology; neuroteratology. *Mailing Add:* Dir Inpatient Serv 4800 Sand Point Way NE PO Box 5371 Seattle WA 98105

LEMISH, JOHN, b Rome, NY, July 4, 21; m 46; c 5. ECONOMIC GEOLOGY, GEOCHEMISTRY. *Educ:* Univ Mich, BS, 47, MS(geol), 48, PhD, 55. *Prof Exp:* Geologist, US Geol Surv, 48, 49-51; instr geol, Univ Mich, 53-55, from asst prof to assoc prof, 55-62, PROF GEOL, IOWA STATE UNIV, 62- *Concurrent Pos:* Mem comts, Hwy Res Bd, Nat Acad Sci-Nat Res Coun, 58-70; chmn, State Mining Bd, 64-73, chmn publ comt, Am Geol Inst; mem adv comt, Iowa Coal Proj, 74-; mem tech adv comt, Nat Gas Surv, Fed Power Comn, 75- *Mem:* AAAS; fel Geol Soc Am; Geochem Soc; Am Asn Petrol Geol; Am Inst Mining, Metall & Petrol Eng. *Res:* Weathering studies of concrete; behavior of carbonate aggregates in Portland cement concrete; aggregate-cement reactions; physical and chemical phenomena related to ore deposition; structural geology; trace elements in Pennsylvania shales; occurrence of coal deposits in Iowa; coal exploration; occurrence of deep coal in Iowa; geology of Forest City Basin. *Mailing Add:* Dept of Earth Sci Iowa State Univ Ames IA 50011

LEMKE, CALVIN A(UBREY), b Waco, Tex, Aug 25, 21; m 48; c 1. CIVIL ENGINEERING. *Educ:* Agr & Mech Col, Tex, BS, 43, MS, 61. *Prof Exp:* Instr math, Baylor Univ, 52-56; asst prof, 56-65, ASSOC PROF CIVIL ENG, LA TECH UNIV, 65- *Res:* Structures and highways; highway culverts; soils. *Mailing Add:* Dept of Civil Eng La Tech Univ Ruston LA 71272

LEMKE, CARLTON EDWARD, b Buffalo, NY, Oct 11, 20; m 55; c 2. MATHEMATICS. *Educ:* Univ Buffalo, BA, 49; Carnegie Inst Technol, MA, 51, PhD(math), 53. *Prof Exp:* Instr math, Carnegie Inst Technol, 52-54; res assoc anal, Knolls Atomic Power Lab, Gen Elec Co, NY, 54-55; engr Radio Corp Am, NJ, 55-56; from asst prof to prof math, 56-67, FORD FOUND PROF MATH, RENSSELAER POLYTECH INST, 67- *Mem:* Am Math Soc; Soc Indust & Appl Math; Opers Res Soc Am; Economet Soc; Math Asn Am. *Res:* Algebra; mathematical programming; probability and statistics; operations research. *Mailing Add:* Dept of Math Rensselaer Polytech Inst Troy NY 12181

LEMKE, DONALD G(EORGE), b Chicago, Ill, Mar 25, 32; m 55; c 4. MECHANICAL ENGINEERING. *Educ:* Ill Inst Technol, BS, 55; Univ Pa, MS, 60, PhD(mech eng), 70. *Prof Exp:* Jr engr, Int Harvester Co, 54-55; engr, Teletype Corp, 55-58 & Westinghouse Elec Corp, 58-59; appl mech specialist, Dyna/Struct, Inc, 60-61; res engr, Advan Space Proj Dept, Gen Elec Co, 62-63; assoc scientist, Missile Div, Chrysler Corp, 63-64, res mgr aero ballistics & mech, 64-65; asst prof eng mech, Mich Technol Univ, 65-68, asst prof mech eng, 68-77, ASSOC PROF MECH ENG, UNIV ILL, CHICAGO CIRCLE, 77- *Mem:* Am Soc Mech Engrs; Am Inst Aeronaut & Astronaut. *Res:* Machine mechanics; dynamics; structural mechanics. *Mailing Add:* Dept of Mat Eng PO Box 4348 Chicago IL 60680

LEMKE, PAUL ARENZ, b New Orleans, La, July 14, 37; m; c 2. GENETICS, MICROBIOLOGY. *Educ:* Tulane Univ, BS, 60; Univ Toronto, MA, 62; Harvard Univ, PhD(biol), 66. *Prof Exp:* Instr biol, Tulane Univ, 62-63; sr microbiologist, Eli Lilly & Co, Ind, 66-72; assoc prof biol sci, Carnegie-Mellon Univ, 72-79; PROF BOT, PLANT PATH, MICROBIOL & HEAD DEPT, AUBURN UNIV, 79- *Concurrent Pos:* Instr, Franklin Col, 67; sr fel, Carnegie-Mellon Inst Res, 72-79; Alexander von Humboldt award, 77-78; vis prof, Ruhr Univ, W Ger, 77-78. *Mem:* Am Soc Microbiol; Genetics Soc Am; Mycol Soc Am; Bot Soc Am; Soc Indust Microbiol (treas, 76-78, pres-elect, 78-79, pres, 79-80). *Res:* Genetics and viruses of fungi; plasmid DNA in fungi; immunochemistry of fungal viruses and double-stranded RNA; biosynthesis of antibiotics; cytoplasmic inheritance in fungi; fluorescent staining of fungal nuclei and chromosomes. *Mailing Add:* Dept Bot Plant Path & Microbiol Auburn Univ Auburn AL 36849

LEMKE, THOMAS FRANKLIN, b Tremont, Pa, July 28, 42; m 65. ORGANIC CHEMISTRY, CORROSION. *Educ:* Wake Forest Univ, BS, 64; Marshall Univ, MS, 66; Lehigh Univ, PhD(chem), 68. *Prof Exp:* Biochemist, Med Res Labs, Edgewood Arsenal, 68-70; asst prof chem, Marshall Univ, 70-72; tech serv specialist, 72-80, MEM STAFF SALES DEVELOP, HUNTINGTON ALLOYS, INC, 80- *Mem:* Am Chem Soc; Nat Asn Corrosion Engrs; Sigma Xi. *Res:* Synthesis of heterocyclic compounds of medicinal interest; corrosion of nickel base alloys. *Mailing Add:* Huntington Alloys Inc Huntington WV 25720

LEMKE, THOMAS LEE, b Waukesha, Wis, June 1, 40; m 63; c 3. MEDICINAL CHEMISTRY. *Educ:* Univ Wis, BS, 62; Univ Kans, PhD(med chem), 66. *Prof Exp:* Res assoc org chem & patent liaison, Upjohn Co, Mich, 66-70; asst prof, 70-75, ASSOC PROF PHARM, UNIV HOUSTON, 75- *Mem:* Am Chem Soc; Am Pharmaceut Asn; Am Asn Col Pharm; AAAS. *Res:* Heterocyclic chemistry; anticancer agents; Favorskii rearrangement; drugs for mental disease; cardiovascular agents. *Mailing Add:* Col of Pharm Univ of Houston Houston TX 77004

LEMLICH, ROBERT, b Brooklyn, NY, Aug 22, 26. CHEMICAL ENGINEERING. *Educ:* NY Univ, BChE, 48; Polytech Inst Brooklyn, MChE, 51; Univ Cincinnati, PhD(chem eng), 54. *Prof Exp:* Chem res engr, Gen Chem Div, Allied Chem & Dye Corp, 48-49; from asst prof to assoc prof, 52-62, PROF CHEM ENG, UNIV CINCINNATI, 62- *Concurrent Pos:* Res grants, Res Corp, Procter & Gamble, USPHS, HEW & NSF, 54-81; Fulbright lectr, Israel Inst Technol, 58-59 & Univ Arg, 66; fel, Grad Sch, Univ Cincinnati, 71-, chmn fels, 76-78. *Honors & Awards:* Sigma Xi award, 69. *Mem:* Fel AAAS; Am Chem Soc; Am Soc Eng Educ; Am Inst Chem Engrs. *Res:* Foam fractionation and properties. *Mailing Add:* Dept of Chem & Nuclear Eng Univ of Cincinnati Cincinnati OH 45221

LEMMERMAN, KARL EDWARD, b Willoughby, Ohio, May 30, 23; m 46; c 3. PHYSICAL CHEMISTRY. *Educ:* Oberlin Col, AB, 47; Cornell Univ, PhD(chem), 51. *Prof Exp:* Asst gen chem, Cornell Univ, 47-50; RES CHEMIST, PROCTER & GAMBLE CO, 51- *Mem:* Am Chem Soc. *Res:* Kinetics of gas-phase photochemical reactions; complex inorganic electrolytes; surfactant solutions; colloids. *Mailing Add:* 1952 Compton Rd Cincinnati OH 45231

LEMMING, JOHN FREDERICK, b Dayton, Ohio, Oct 31, 43. NUCLEAR PHYSICS. *Educ:* Univ Dayton, BS, 66; Ohio Univ, MS, 68, PhD(physics), 72. *Prof Exp:* Fel physics, Ohio Univ, 72-74; SR PHYSICIST NUCLEAR SPECTROS, MONSANTO RES CORP, MOUND LAB, 74- *Concurrent Pos:* Nuclear infor res assoc, Nat Acad Sci, Nat Res Coun Comt Nuclear Sci, 72-74. *Mem:* Am Inst Physics. *Res:* Nuclear safeguards. *Mailing Add:* 4137 Woodedge Dr Bellbrook OH 45305

LEMMON, ALEXIS WILLIAM, JR, chemical engineering, see previous edition

LEMMON, DONALD H, b Sugar Grove, Pa, Oct 19, 35; m 56; c 1. SPECTROSCOPY. *Educ:* Univ Pittsburgh, PhD(chem), 66. *Prof Exp:* Fel, State Univ NY, Stony Brook, 66-67; SR ENGR, WESTINGHOUSE RES CTR, 67- *Mem:* Am Chem Soc. *Res:* Infrared, Raman and nuclear magnetic resonance spectroscopy; mass spectrometry. *Mailing Add:* 304 Sixth St Oakmont PA 15139

LEMMON, RICHARD MILLINGTON, b Sacramento, Calif, Nov 24, 19; m 49; c 3. RADIATION CHEMISTRY. *Educ:* Stanford Univ, AB, 41; Calif Inst Technol, MS, 43; Univ Calif, PhD(chem), 49. *Prof Exp:* Res chemist, Calif Inst Technol, 43-45; fel, Med Sch, Univ Calif, 49-50; USPHS fel, Fed Inst Tech, Switz, 50-51; RES CHEMIST, LAWRENCE BERKELEY LAB, UNIV CALIF, 51- *Concurrent Pos:* Guggenheim fel, Helsinki, 65; assoc dir, Lab Chem Biodynamics, Univ Calif, 57- *Mem:* AAAS; Am Chem Soc; Am Inst Chemists. *Res:* Radiochemistry; hot-atom chemistry; radiation decomposition of organic compounds; chemical evolution. *Mailing Add:* Lawrence Berkeley Lab Bldg 3 Univ of Calif Berkeley CA 94720

LEMNIOS, A(NDREW) Z, b Newburyport, Mass, Nov 23, 31; m 54; c 2. AERONAUTICAL ENGINEERING, APPLIED MECHANICS. *Educ:* Mass Inst Technol, BS, 53, MS, 54; Univ Conn, PhD(appl mech), 67. *Prof Exp:* Asst, Aeroelastic Struct & Res Labs, Mass Inst Technol, 53-54; res engr, Res Labs, United Aircraft Corp, 54-61; sr anal engr, Kaman Corp, 61-63, res proj mgr, 63-65, chief fluid mech res, 65-69, chief res engr, 69-76, DIR RES & TECHNOL, KAMAN AEROSPACE CORP, BLOOMFIELD, CONN, 76- *Concurrent Pos:* Instr, Western New Eng Col, 57-; adj fac, Univ Mass, 77-; mem aeronaut adv comt, NASA, 78- *Mem:* Am Inst Aeronaut & Astronaut; Am Helicopter Soc. *Res:* Aeroelastic behavior of rotating structures; structural dynamics and vibrations; structures and structural mechanics; computer modeling. *Mailing Add:* 144 Primrose Dr Longmeadow MA 01106

LEMNIOS, WILLIAM ZACHARY, b Athens, Greece, Sept 13, 25; US citizen; m 54; c 4. PHYSICS, ELECTRICAL ENGINEERING. *Educ:* Mass Inst Technol, BS, 49; Univ Ill, MS, 51. *Prof Exp:* Staff mem systs anal, 52-65, asst group leader, 64-65, group leader, 65-69, ASSOC DIV HEAD RADAR MEASUREMENTS DIV, LINCOLN LAB, MASS INST TECHNOL, 69- *Mem:* AAAS; Am Phys Soc; sr mem Inst Elec & Electronics Engrs. *Res:* Computer systems and simulation; radar systems. *Mailing Add:* Lincoln Lab Mass Inst Technol Lexington MA 02173

LEMOINE, ALBERT N, JR, b Nelson, Nebr, Apr 13, 18; m 40; c 3. OPHTHALMOLOGY. *Educ:* Univ Kans, AB, 39; Wash Univ, MD, 43; Am Bd Ophthal, dipl. *Prof Exp:* Teaching & res fel ophthal, Harvard Med Sch, 45-46; chmn dept, 50-80, PROF OPHTHAL, SCH MED, UNIV KANS MED CTR, KANSAS CITY, 50- *Mem:* AAAS; Asn Res Vision & Ophthal; fel Am Col Surg; Sigma Xi; Am Acad Ophthal & Otolaryngol. *Res:* Surgical and applied anatomy of the eye and orbit. *Mailing Add:* Dept of Ophthal Univ of Kans Med Ctr Kansas City KS 66103

LEMON, EDGAR ROTHWELL, b Buffalo, NY, Aug 22, 21; m 44; c 3. SOIL SCIENCE. *Educ:* Cornell Univ, BS, 43, MS, 49; Mich State Univ, PhD(soil physics), 54. *Prof Exp:* Prof agron, Tex A&M Univ, 51-56; prof agron, Cornell Univ, 56-80; soil scientist, Agr Res Serv, USDA, 51-80; RETIRED. *Concurrent Pos:* Guggenheim & Fulbright fel, Australia, 62-63; USSR-US exchange scientist, 69; Dept Sci & Indust Res fel, NZ, 70-71. *Mem:* Fel AAAS; fel Am Soc Agron; Soil Sci Soc Am; Am Meteorol Soc. *Res:* Applied physics, particularly physical processes in the micrometeorological field associated with agricultural crops. *Mailing Add:* PO Box 612 West End Tortola British Virgin Islands

LEMON, LESLIE ROY, b Greenville, SC, Jan 19, 47; m 68; c 3. RADAR SYSTEMS DESIGN, METEOROLOGY. *Educ:* Univ Okla, BS, 70. *Prof Exp:* Meteorologist, Severe Storms Res, Nat Severe Storms Lab, Nat Oceanic & Atmospheric Admin Comn Corps, 69-70; mem staff oceanog data collection, 70-73, res meteorologist, 73-76, meteorologist, Nat Severe Storms Forecast Ctr, 76, res meteorologist, Tech Develop Unit, 76-81; PROG CONTROL MGR, NEXRAD RADAR DEVELOP, SPERRY GYROSCOPE/DIV SPERRY CORP, 81- *Mem:* Am meteorol Soc. *Res:* Understanding and documenting severe storm structure and evolution and tornado genesis, as well as operational application of conventional and meteorological Doppler radar to the warning services. *Mailing Add:* 16416 Cogan Dr Independence MO 64055

LEMON, ROY RICHARD HENRY, b Birmingham, Eng, July 13, 27; Can citizen; m 59. GEOLOGY. *Educ:* Univ Wales, BSc, 51; Univ Toronto, MA, 53, PhD, 55. *Prof Exp:* Geologist, Ghana Geol Surv, 56-57; asst cur invert paleont, Royal Ont Mus, 57-58, 59-61, assoc cur, 61-67; staff geologist, Texaco Oil Co, Trinidad, WI, 67-68; PROF GEOL, FLA ATLANTIC UNIV,

68-, CHMN DEPT, 77- *Concurrent Pos:* Nat Res Coun res grant, 63-66; asst prof, Queen's Univ, Ont, 58-59; assoc prof, Univ Toronto, 62-67. *Mem:* Geol Soc Am; Am Asn Petrol Geol. *Res:* Pliocene and Pleistocene geology and faunas of the west coast of South America and the Caribbean; world wide Pleistocene sea level changes; origin of sedimentary phosphates. *Mailing Add:* Dept of Geol Fla Atlantic Univ Boca Raton FL 33432

LEMONDE, ANDRE, b Saint-Liboire, Que, May 30, 21; m 53; c 2. BIOCHEMISTRY, PHYSIOLOGY. *Educ:* Univ Montreal, BA, 42; Laval Univ, BS, 47, ScD(biol), 51. *Prof Exp:* Demonstr physiol, Laval Univ, 47-51; hon fel biochem & entom, Cornell Univ, 51-52; from asst prof to assoc prof, 52-66, head dept, 76-81, PROF BIOCHEM, SCH MED, LAVAL UNIV, 66- *Mem:* AAAS; Am Physiol Soc; Can Biochem Soc; Nutrit Soc Can. *Res:* Comparative biochemistry and physiology. *Mailing Add:* Dept of Biochem Laval Univ Sch of Med Quebec PQ G1K 7P4 Can

LEMONDE, PAUL, b St Libiore, Que, Nov 4, 13; m 47; c 5. CANCER. *Educ:* St Hyacinthe Col, BA, 33; Univ Montreal, lic, 38, PhD(exp med), 54. *Prof Exp:* From asst to assoc prof biol, Univ Montreal, 38-54; res prof, 54-78, EMER PROF MED, INST MICROBIOL & HYG MONTREAL, 78- *Concurrent Pos:* Prof, Que Sch Vet Med, 47-49. *Honors & Awards:* Award, Prov Que, 57. *Mem:* AAAS; Am Asn Cancer Res. *Res:* Endocrine factors in infections; experimental tuberculosis; viruses, immunological and environmental factors in cancer. *Mailing Add:* Inst A-Frappier Laval-des-Rapides PQ H7N 4Z3 Can

LEMONE, DAVID V, b Columbia, Mo, Apr 16, 32; m 55; c 2. INVERTEBRATE PALEONTOLOGY, PALEOBOTANY. *Educ:* NMex Inst Mining & Technol, BS, 55; Univ Ariz, MS, 59; Mich State Univ, PhD(geol), 64. *Prof Exp:* Geologist, Stanolind Oil & Gas Co, 55-56 & Tex Co, 58-59; assoc prof geol, Southern Miss Univ, 61-64; assoc prof, 64-77, PROF GEOL, UNIV TEX, EL PASO, 77- *Mem:* Fel AAAS; Am Paleont Soc; Soc Econ Paleontologists & Mineralogists; Paleont Soc Japan; Geol Soc Am. *Res:* Paleophycology; stratigraphic paleontology; systematic invertebrate paleontology and paleobotany; palynology; paleoecology; numerical taxonomy. *Mailing Add:* Dept of Geol Univ of Tex El Paso TX 79968

LEMONE, MARGARET ANNE, b Columbia, Mo, Feb 21, 46; m 76; c 2. CONVECTIVE STORMS. *Educ:* Univ Mo, AB, 67; Univ Wash, PhD(atmospheric sci), 72. *Prof Exp:* Fel, Advan Study Prog, 72-73, SCIENTIST, NAT CTR ATMOSPHERIC RES, 73- *Mem:* Am Meteorol Soc; AAAS; Am Geophys Union. *Res:* Structure and dynamics of atmospheric boundry layer and its interaction with cumulus clouds; structure and dynamics of cumulonimbus clouds and their interaction with the environment and larger-scale flow. *Mailing Add:* Nat Ctr Atmospheric Res PO Box 3000 Boulder CO 80307

LEMONICK, AARON, b Philadelphia, Pa, Feb 2, 23; m 50; c 2. HIGH ENERGY PHYSICS. *Educ:* Univ Pa, BA, 50; Princeton Univ, MA, 52, PhD, 54. *Prof Exp:* Instr physics, Princeton Univ, 53-54; asst prof, Haverford Col, 54-57, assoc prof & chmn dept, 57-61; assoc prof, 61-64, assoc dir, Princeton-Penn Accelerator, 61-67, assoc chmn dept, 67-69, dean grad sch, 69-73, PROF PHYSICS, PRINCETON UNIV, 64-, DEAN FAC, 73- *Concurrent Pos:* NSF sci fac fel, Univ Calif, Berkeley, 60-61. *Mem:* Fel Am Phys Soc; Am Asn Physics Teachers. *Mailing Add:* Rm 9 Nassau Hall Princeton Univ Princeton NJ 08540

LEMONS, JACK EUGENE, b St Petersburg, Fla, Jan 20, 37; m 62; c 1. BIOMATERIALS, MATERIALS ENGINEERING. *Educ:* Univ Fla, BS, 63, MS, 64, PhD(metall, chem, physics), 68. *Prof Exp:* Owner & operator, J E Lemons Gen Repair & Mach Shop, 55-60; res assoc metall & mat, Univ Fla, 63-64, asst, 64-68; res metall & head, Phys Metall, Eng Div, Southern Res Inst, Ala, 68-70; asst prof interdisciplinary studies, Clemson Univ, 70-71; from instr to assoc prof, 71-77, PROF ENG & CHMN DEPT, UNIV ALA, BIRMINGHAM, 77- *Concurrent Pos:* NIH spec fel, Med Sch, Univ Ala, 71-73. *Mem:* Am Soc Metals; Am Inst Mining, Metall & Petrol Engrs; Soc Biomat; Int Asn Dent Res. *Res:* Properties of materials for applications in physiological environments; interfacial interactions between synthetic biomaterials and tissues. *Mailing Add:* Dept of Biomat SDB49 Univ of Ala Birmingham AL 35294

LEMONTT, JEFFREY FIELDING, b New York, NY, July 1, 44; m 70; c 1. MOLECULAR GENETICS. *Educ:* Rensselaer Polytech Inst, BS, 65; Univ Calif, Berkeley, MBiorad, 67, PhD(biophysics), 70. *Prof Exp:* Res fel genetics, Nat Res Coun Can, 70-72 & Nat Inst Med Res, 73-74; res staff mem yeast genetics, Oak Ridge Nat Lab, 74-81; SR SCIENTIST, INTEGRATED GENETICS, INC, 82- *Concurrent Pos:* Lectr, Oak Ridge Grad Sch Biomed Sci, Univ Tenn, 74-81. *Mem:* Genetics Soc Am; Environ Mutagen Soc; AAAS. *Res:* Yeast genetics and molecular biology; mechanisms of mutagenesis and DNA repair in yeast; expression of cloned genes for DNA repair; yeast transformation; recombinant DNA technology. *Mailing Add:* Integrated Genetics Inc 51 New York Ave Framingham MA 01701

LEMOS, ANTHONY M, b Arlington, Mass, Aug 31, 30; m 53; c 3. THEORETICAL PHYSICS, SOLID STATE PHYSICS. *Educ:* Boston Col, AB, 52; Univ Chicago, MS, 54; Ill Inst Technol, PhD(physics), 64. *Prof Exp:* Instr physics, Lake Forest Col, 58-63; assoc prof, 64-71, PROF PHYSICS, ADELPHI UNIV, 71- & CHMN DEPT, 77- *Concurrent Pos:* Res collabr, Brookhaven Nat Lab, 65- *Mem:* Am Phys Soc. *Res:* Theoretical understanding of the phenomena surrounding the F-center; color centers in the alkali halides. *Mailing Add:* Dept of Physics Adelphi Univ Grad Sch Arts & Sci Garden City NY 11530

LEMP, JOHN FREDERICK, JR, b Alton, Ill, May 25, 28; m 53; c 3. MICROBIOLOGY, BIOENGINEERING. *Educ:* Univ Ill, BS, 50; Nat Registry Microbiologists, Regist. *Prof Exp:* Bacteriologist, Commercial Solvents Corp, Ind, 51, fermentation supt & microbiologist, Ill, 53-57; microbiologist, Pilot Plants Div, US Army Biol Labs, Ft Detrick, Md, 57-61, prin investr, Process Develop Div, 61-63; sr microbiologist & asst br chief, Biol Ctr, 63-71; proj mgr RNA tumor virus, Electro-Nucleonics Labs, Inc, Md, 71-72; DIR, VIRAL SCI LAB, 72- *Mem:* Am Soc Microbiol; NY Acad Sci; Sigma Xi. *Res:* Fermentation, purification microbial products, B-12, riboflavin and penicillin; bacitracin, alcohols, fungal amylase, continuous sterilization and culture, pH control, polarographic dissolved oxygen; mammalian tissue culture; virus propagation and purification; electrophoresis; polymer phase; human interferons. *Mailing Add:* Box 1 RR 1 Lovettsville VA 22080

LEMPER, ANTHONY LOUIS, b Buffalo, NY, June 3, 39; m 62; c 4. ORGANIC CHEMISTRY. *Educ:* Univ Buffalo, BA, 60; State Univ NY Buffalo, PhD(org chem), 66. *Prof Exp:* Res chemist, Res Div, Goodyear Tire & Rubber Co, 65-66, sr res chemist, 66; res chemist, Corp Res Ctr, Hooker Chem Corp, 66-68, sr res chemist, 68-71, res group leader, 71-75, res mgr, 75-78; DIR PROD RES APPL & SALES SERV, FMC CORP, 78- *Mem:* Soc Plastics Engrs; Am Chem Soc. *Res:* Inorganic industrial chemicals and flame retardant chemicals; engineering thermoplastics research and development; polyvinyl chloride chemistry and technology; organophosphorus chemistry; organofluorine chemistry; inorganic industrial and flame retardant chemicals. *Mailing Add:* FMC Corp Box 8 Princeton NJ 08540

LEMPERT, JOSEPH, b North Adams, Mass, July 3, 13; m 41; c 3. MAGNETOHYDRODYNAMICS. *Educ:* Mass Inst Technol, BS, 35; Stevens Inst Technol, MS, 42. *Prof Exp:* Engr, Lamp Div, 36-44, sect engr, 44-53, mgr eng sect, Electronic Tube Div, 53-56, adv develop, 56-58, sect mgr camera tubes, 58, res engr, 58-66, adv engr, Westinghouse Res & Develop Ctr, 66-78; CONSULT ENG, 78- *Mem:* Am Phys Soc; fel Inst Elec & Electronics Engrs. *Res:* Photoemission; photoconductivity; secondary emission; thin films; vacuum tube electronics; electronic imaging; x-ray image intensification; x-rays; storage techniques; electron beams; electron beam welding; thermionic emission; magnetohydrodynamics. *Mailing Add:* 140 Spring Grove Rd Pittsburgh PA 15235

LEMPERT, NEIL, b New York, NY, Nov 25, 33; m 62; c 5. BIOLOGY, CHEMISTRY. *Educ:* Hamilton Col, BS, 54. *Prof Exp:* Asst instr, 60-65, instr, 67-68, asst prof, 68-72, assoc prof, 72-78, PROF SURG, ALBANY MED COL, 78- *Concurrent Pos:* Resident exp surg, Albany Med Ctr, 60-61; res fel surg, Mary Imogene Bassett Hosp & Clin, Cooperstown, NY, 63-64; consult surg, Vet Admin Med Ctr, 67-; dir, Histocompatibility Lab, Albany Med Col, 72- *Mem:* Cryobiol Soc; Asn Acad Surg; Transplantation Soc; Am Soc Transplant Surgeons; Cent Surg Asn. *Res:* Transplantation and preservation of tissues and organs; basic immunology of organ transplantation. *Mailing Add:* Dept Surg Albany Med Col Albany NY 12208

LEMPICKI, ALEXANDER, b Warsaw, Poland, Jan 26, 22; nat US; m 52; c 2. PHYSICS. *Educ:* Imp Col, Univ London, MSc, 52, PhD, 60. *Prof Exp:* Res physicist, Electronic Tube Co, Ltd, Eng, 49-54; head quantum physics group, 65-72, MGR ELECTROOPTICS LAB, GOVT TECHNOL CTR, GEN TEL & ELECTRONICS LABS, INC, 73- *Concurrent Pos:* Mem adv subcomt electrophys, NASA, 69-71. *Mem:* Fel Am Phys Soc; fel Optical Soc Am. *Res:* electro luminescence; optical properties of solids; spectroscopy and molecular structure of organo metallic complexes; optical maser materials, particularly liquid luminescence; luminescence and structure of glasses; luminescent solar collectors; semiconductors; spectroscopy of transition metal ions. *Mailing Add:* GTE Labs Inc 40 Sylvan Rd Waltham MA 02154

LEMPKE, ROBERT EVERETT, b Dover, NH, Nov 27, 24; m 49; c 4. SURGERY. *Educ:* Yale Univ, MD, 48. *Prof Exp:* Intern surg, Johns Hopkins Hosp, Baltimore, 48-49; resident, Med Ctr, Ind Univ, Indianapolis, 49-51; med officer, Army Med Res Lab, Ft Knox, Ky, 51-53; resident, Med Ctr, Ind Univ, Indianapolis, 53-55; assoc chief of staff med res, Vet Admin Hosp, Indianapolis, 56-71; from instr to assoc prof, 56-65, PROF SURG, SCH MED, IND UNIV, INDIANAPOLIS, 65-; CHIEF OF SURG, VET ADMIN HOSP, INDIANAPOLIS, 59- *Concurrent Pos:* Vis prof surg, Jinnah Postgrad Med Ctr, Karachi, Pakistan, 64-65. *Mem:* Soc Surg Alimentary Tract; Cent Surg Asn; Am Col Surg; Asn Vet Admin Surgeons. *Res:* Diseases of the alimentary tract. *Mailing Add:* 1481 W Tenth St Indianapolis IN 46202

LEMYRE, C(LEMENT), b Shawinigan, Que, Apr 2, 34; m 62; c 4. ELECTRICAL ENGINEERING. *Educ:* Laval Univ, BScEng, 57; Univ London, PhD(transistors), 62. *Prof Exp:* From asst prof to assoc prof, Laval Univ, 62-69; secy fac sci & eng, 70-73, chmn dept, 71-78, ASSOC PROF ELEC ENG, UNIV OTTAWA, 69-, DIR, COOP EDUC PROGS, 80- *Concurrent Pos:* Asn Orgn Stages France fel, 65-66. *Mem:* Inst Elec & Electronics Engrs; fel Eng Inst Can; Can Soc Elec Eng. *Res:* Characterization of transistors. *Mailing Add:* Dept of Elec Eng Univ of Ottawa Ottawa ON K1N 9B4 Can

LENARD, ANDREW, b Balmazujvaros, Hungary, July 18, 27; US citizen; m 53; c 2. MATHEMATICAL PHYSICS. *Educ:* State Univ Iowa, BA, 49, PhD(physics), 53. *Prof Exp:* Res assoc physics, Columbia Univ, 55-57; res staff mem, Plasma Physics Lab, Princeton Univ, 57-65; PROF MATH PHYSICS, IND UNIV, BLOOMINGTON, 66- *Concurrent Pos:* Mem, Inst Haute Etudes Sci, 79-80. *Mem:* Am Phys Soc; Am Math Soc. *Res:* Kinetic theory; statistical mechanics; fundamental problems of quantum physics; mathematical problems related to physics. *Mailing Add:* Dept of Physics & Math Ind Univ Bloomington IN 47401

LENARD, JOHN, b Vienna, Austria, May 17, 37; US citizen; m 59; c 4. BIOCHEMISTRY. *Educ:* Cornell Univ, BA, 58, PhD(biochem), 64. *Prof Exp:* Res assoc biochem, Cornell Univ, 63-64; fel biol, Univ Calif, San Diego, 64-65, Am Heart Asn advan res fel, 65-67; asst prof biochem, Albert Einstein Col Med, 67-68; assoc, Sloan-Kettering Inst Cancer Res, 68-72; assoc prof, 73-76, PROF PHYSIOL & BIOPHYS, RUTGERS MED SCH, COL MED & DENT NJ, 76- *Concurrent Pos:* Am Heart Asn estab investr, 70-72; adj asst prof biol, Hunter Col, 70-73. *Mem:* Am Soc Biol Chemists; Am Soc Cell Biol; Am Soc Microbiophys Soc. *Res:* Structures of biological membranes and enveloped viruses; entry and assembly of enveloped viruses; function of viral glycoproteins. *Mailing Add:* Dept of Physiol & Biophys Rutgers Med Sch Piscataway NJ 08854

LENARZ, WILLIAM HENRY, b Sacramento, Calif, Sept 18, 40. FISH BIOLOGY, BIOSTATISTICS. *Educ:* Humboldt State Univ, BS, 63; Univ Wash, MS, 66, PhD(fisheries), 69. *Prof Exp:* Fishery biologist, La Jolla, 68-76, FISHERY BIOLOGIST, SOUTHWEST FISHERIES CTR, MARINE FISHERIES SERV, 76- *Concurrent Pos:* Sci adv, US Deleg Int Comn Conserv of Atlantic Tunas, 70-74 & Pac Fisheries Mgt Coun, 77- *Mem:* Am Statist Asn; Biometric Soc; Sigma Xi; AAAS; Ecol Soc Am. *Res:* Dynamics of exploited populations of fish. *Mailing Add:* Southwest Fisheries Ctr 3150 Paradise Dr Tiburon CA 94920

LENDARIS, GEORGE G(REGORY), b Helper, Utah, Apr 2, 35; m 58; c 2. SYSTEMS SCIENCE, SYSTEMS DESIGN FACILITATOR. *Educ:* Univ Calif, Berkeley, BS, 57, MS, 58, PhD(elec eng), 61. *Prof Exp:* Sr staff scientist adaptive flight control systs, Gen Motors Defense Res Labs, 61-63, sr res engr, 63-69; assoc prof systs sci & chmn fac, Ore Grad Ctr Study & Res, 69-71; PROF SYSTS SCI, SYSTS SCI PHD PROG, PORTLAND STATE UNIV, 71- *Concurrent Pos:* Mem, Gov Tech Adv Comt, Ore, 70-72; consult to pres, Ore State Senate, 71; mem, Ore State Senate Task Force Econ Develop, 72-73; vis scientist, Johnson Space Ctr, NASA, 73-74; vis scholar, Eng & Econ Systs Dept, Stanford Univ, 78. *Mem:* Inst Elec & Electronics Engrs; Soc Gen Systs Res; Pattern Recognition Soc; Asn Transpersonal Psychol. *Res:* Developing methodologies for assisting teams of people to carry out systems design, engineering; analysis of social and human systems; models for complex systems; structural modeling; artificial intelligence. *Mailing Add:* Systs Sci Inst PO Box 751 Portland OR 97207

LENEL, FRITZ (VICTOR), b Kiel, Ger, July 7, 07; nat US; m 43; c 5. METALLURGY. *Educ:* Univ Heidelberg, PhD, 31. *Prof Exp:* Fel, Univ Goettingen, 31-33; metallurgist, Charles Hardy, Inc, NY, 33-37 & Delco-Moraine Div, Gen Motors Corp, Ohio, 37-47; from asst prof to prof, 47-73, chmn dept, 65-69, EMER PROF METALL ENG, RENSSELAER POLYTECH INST, 73- *Honors & Awards:* Am Soc Testing & Mat Award, 58. *Mem:* Fel Am Soc Metals; Am Inst Mining, Metall & Petrol Engrs; Brit Inst Metals. *Res:* Powder metallurgy. *Mailing Add:* Dept of Mat Eng Rensselaer Polytech Inst Troy NY 12181

LENER, WALTER, b New York, NY, Mar 20, 25. ENTOMOLOGY. *Educ:* NY Univ, BA, 48, MA, 50, PhD(biol), 57; Rutgers Univ, MS, 60. *Prof Exp:* Instr biol, State Univ NY Col Oneonta, 50-51, sci consult, New Paltz, 51-52, from instr to prof biol, Geneseo, 52-64, coordr biol sci, 62-64; PROF BIOL, NASSAU COMMUNITY COL, 64- *Concurrent Pos:* Res grant, Res Found, State Univ NY, 63-64, 65-67; fel trop med, Sch Med, La State Univ, 64; NSF res grant, 66-68; consult, Choice. *Mem:* AAAS; Ecol Soc Am; Animal Behav Soc; NY Acad Sci; Sigma Xi. *Res:* Investigating the physiology, genetics and ethology of large milkweed bug, Oncopeltus fasciatus. *Mailing Add:* Dept of Biol Nassau Community Col Garden City NY 11530

LENES, BRUCE ALLAN, b White Planes, NY, April 4, 49; m 74; c 2. HEMATOLOGY. *Educ:* Union Col, Union Univ, BS, 71; Albany Med Col, Union Univ, MD, 75. *Prof Exp:* Resident int med, Shands Teaching Hosp & Clin, Univ Fla, 75-78; fel hematol, Georgetown Univ Hosp, Washington, DC, 78-80; fel blood banking, NIH, Bethesda Md, 80-81; ASSOC MED DIR, SOUTH FLA BLOOD SERV, MIAMI, 81-; ASST PROF MED & PATH, SCH MED, UNIV MIAMI, 81- *Concurrent Pos:* Clin asst prof med, Sch Med, Georgetown Univ, 80- *Mem:* Sigma Xi; Am Med Asn; Am Asn Blood Banks. *Res:* Clinical research in hematology and blood banking; special emphasis on pheresis and hemolytic anemia. *Mailing Add:* South Fla Blood Serv PO Box 420100 Miami FL 33142

LENEY, LAWRENCE, b New York, NY, Dec 14, 17; m 45; c 5. WOOD SCIENCE, MICROSCOPY. *Educ:* State Univ NY Col Forestry, Syracuse, BS, 42, MS, 48, PhD, 60. *Prof Exp:* Instr wood tech, State Univ NY Col Forestry, Syracuse, 46-52; asst prof, Univ Mo, 52-60; assoc prof, 60-80, PROF WOOD & FIBER SCI, COL FOREST RESOURCES, UNIV WASH, 80- *Mem:* AAAS; Forest Prod Res Soc; Tech Asn Pulp & Paper Indust; Int Asn Wood Anat; Soc Wood Sci & Technol. *Res:* Wood anatomy; microtechnique; machining wood; photomicrography of woody tissue; seasoning and preservation of wood; pulp and paper fiber analysis. *Mailing Add:* Col of Forest Resources AR-10 Univ of Wash Seattle WA 98195

LENFANT, CLAUDE J M, b Paris, France, Oct 12, 28; US citizen; m 49; c 5. PHYSIOLOGY. *Educ:* Univ Rennes, BS, 48; Univ Paris, MD, 56. *Prof Exp:* Intern clin med, Univ Paris, 51-52; resident, Hosp Rothschild, Paris, 53; from res asst to dir res, Ctr Marie Lannelongue, France, 54-57; res fel, Univ Buffalo, 57-58; res fel, Columbia Univ, 58; asst prof physiol, Univ Lille, 59-60; from clin instr to clin asst prof, Univ Wash, 61-67, assoc prof, 68-71; assoc dir lung progs & actg assoc dir collab res & develop prog, Nat Heart & Lung Inst, 70-72, actg chief, Pulmonary Res Br, 72-74, dir, Div Lung Dis, 72-80, DIR, FOGARTY INT CTR & ASSOC DIR INT RES, NIH, 81- *Concurrent Pos:* Scholar, Univ Paris, 56; Fulbright fel, 56-58; assoc dir, Inst Respiratory Physiol & staff physician, Firland Sanitorium, Seattle, 61-68; mem physiol study sect, NIH, 69-70; consult, Univ Hosp, Seattle, 69-; prof med, physiol & biophys, Univ Wash, 71-72. *Mem:* Am Physiol Soc; Am Soc Clin Res; Fr Physiol Soc; Asn Am Physicians. *Res:* Respiratory physiology, especially in gas exchange; comparative physiology related to the development and environmental adaptation of the respiratory system. *Mailing Add:* Bldg 38A Rm 605 Fogarty Int Ctr Nat Inst Health Bethesda MD 20205

LENG, DOUGLAS E, b Kitchener, Ont, May 28, 28; m 55; c 3. CHEMICAL ENGINEERING. *Educ:* Queen's Univ, Ont, BSc, 51, MSc, 53; Purdue Univ, PhD(chem eng), 56. *Prof Exp:* Chem engr, Benzene Prod Lab, 56-61, res engr, Process Fundamentals Lab, 62-63, sr res engr, 63-70, assoc scientist, Dow Interdisciplinary Groups Eng, 70-74, RES SCIENTIST, CENT RES LABS,

DOW CHEM CO, 75- *Mem:* Am Chem Soc; Am Inst Chem Engrs. *Res:* Multiphase behavior; coalescence and dispersion; mixing; chemicals from renewable resources. *Mailing Add:* Cent Res Eng Dow Chem Co 1776 Bldg Midland MI 48640

LENG, EARL REECE, b Williamsfield, Ill, June 12, 21; m 44; c 3. GENETICS, RESEARCH ADMINISTRATION. *Educ:* Univ Ill, BS, 41, MS, 46, PhD(agron), 48. *Prof Exp:* Spec asst agron, 41-42, asst plant genetics, 46-48, from asst prof to assoc prof, 48-58, from asst dir to assoc dir int prog, 69-73, crop specialist, USAID, 75-77; prof, 58-77, EMER PROF AGRON, UNIV ILL, URBANA, 77- *Concurrent Pos:* Fulbright sr res fel, Max Planck Inst, Ger, 61; consult, Fed Govt Yugoslavia & USAID, 60-61; res adv, USAID & Uttar Pradesh Agr Univ, India, 64-66; adv, USAID & Midwest Univs Consortium for Int Activities, Indonesia, 71; consult, Food & Agr Orgn, Thailand, 71; consult, Int Coffee Orgn, 72; consult, UNDP|FAO, Yugoslavia, 73, 75; consult, World Bank, Malaysia, 74, USAID & Pac Consults, Sudan, Jamaica & Mauretania, 77-78; prof dir, INTSORMIL, Univ Nebr-Lincoln, 79- *Mem:* Crop Sci Soc Am; Am Soc Agron. *Res:* Comparative international agriculture; genetics and breeding of maize; breeding systems; evolution of maize and relatives; international soybean improvement; international agricultural development, emphasis on major cereal crops. *Mailing Add:* 406 F Plant Sci Univ Nebr Lincoln NE 68583

LENG, MARGUERITE LAMBERT, b Edmonton, Alta, Can, Sept 25, 26; m 55; c 3. AGRICULTURAL BIOCHEMISTRY, ANALYTICAL BIOCHEMISTRY. *Educ:* Univ Alta, BSc, 47; Univ Sask, MSc, 50; Purdue Univ, PhD(biochem), 56. *Prof Exp:* Ed asst chem & physics, Nat Res Coun Can, 47-48, anal chemist, 48-49; sr chemist, Allergy Res Lab, Univ Mich Hosp, Ann Arbor, 50-53; anal chemist, Agr Dept, 56-59, registr specialist, Ag-Org Dept, 66-73, sr regist specialist, 73-80, RES ASSOC INT REGULATORY AFFAIRS, HEALTH & ENVIRON SCI, DOW CHEM CO, MIDLAND, MICH, 80- *Mem:* Am Chem Soc; fel Am Chem Soc; AAAS; NY Acad Sci; Sigma Xi. *Res:* Pesticides, their toxicology, metabolism, residues, analytical methods and realistic evaluation of hazard to the environment; meaningful communication of scientific information; international regulation of hazardous chemicals. *Mailing Add:* Health & Environ Sci Dow Chem Co 1803 Bldg Midland MI 48640

LENGEMANN, FREDERICK WILLIAM, b New York, NY, Apr 8, 25; m 50; c 2. PHYSICAL BIOLOGY. *Educ:* Cornell Univ, BS, 50, MNS, 51; Univ Wis, PhD(dairy husb), 54. *Prof Exp:* Res assoc radiation biol, Univ Tenn, 54-55, asst prof chem, 55-59; assoc prof, 59-67, PROF PHYS BIOL, NY STATE VET COL, CORNELL UNIV, 67- *Mem:* Fel AAAS; Am Dairy Sci Asn; Am Inst Nutrit; Coun Agr Sci & Technol. *Res:* Environmental contamination; fission product and mineral metabolism; milk secretion; mineral absorption; bone calcification. *Mailing Add:* Dept Phys Biol Cornell Univ Ithaca NY 14853

LENGYEL, G(ABRIEL), b Budapest, Hungary, Apr 30, 27; Can citizen. ELECTRICAL ENGINEERING, SOLID STATE PHYSICS. *Educ:* Budapest Tech Univ, BASc, 49; Univ Toronto, PhD(elec eng), 63. *Prof Exp:* Demonstr math, Budapest Tech Univ, 49-50; res engr, Elec Power Res Inst, Budapest, 50-56; proj engr, E B Eddy Co, Que, 56-58; develop engr, Sangamo Co, Ont, 58-59; sr res fel appl & solid state physics, Ont Res Found, 59-66; assoc prof solid state physics, 66-76, PROF ELEC ENG, UNIV RI, 76- *Concurrent Pos:* Res asst, Univ Toronto, 60-63; mem assoc comt elec insulation, Nat Res Coun Can, 60-64. *Mem:* Inst Elec & Electronics Engrs; Am Phys Soc. *Res:* Power systems analysis; instrumentation; properties of dielectrics. *Mailing Add:* Dept of Elec Eng Kelley Hall Univ of RI Kingston RI 02881

LENGYEL, ISTVAN, b Kaposvar, Hungary, July 12, 31; US citizen; m 62; c 2. ORGANIC CHEMISTRY. *Educ:* Eotvos Lorand, dipl, 55; Mass Inst Technol, PhD(org chem), 64. *Prof Exp:* Res chemist, G Richter Pharmaceut Co, 54-55; sci coworker geochem, Geophys Res Inst of Hungary, 55-56; lab chemist, Kundl Tirol Austria Pharmaceut Co, 57-58; res asst biochem, Sch Med, Johns Hopkins Univ, 58-59; res assoc org synthesis, Mass Inst Technol, 59-64; fel, Munich Tech Univ, 64-65; res assoc mass spectrometry, Mass Inst Technol, 65-67; from asst prof to assoc prof, 67-73, PROF CHEM, ST JOHN'S UNIV, NY, 73- *Honors & Awards:* Sr Awardee, Alexander Von Humboldt Found, Germany, 73-74. *Mem:* Fel Royal Soc Chem; Ger Chem Soc. *Res:* Organic mass spectrometry; amino acids; peptides; synthesis, reactions and spectroscopic characteristics of small heterocycles; skeletal rearrangements upon electron impact. *Mailing Add:* Dept Chem St John's Univ Jamaica NY 11439

LENGYEL, JUDITH ANN, b Rochester, NY, May 15, 45. MOLECULAR BIOLOGY, DEVELOPMENTAL BIOLOGY. *Educ:* Univ Calif, Los Angeles, BA, 67, MA, 68; Univ Calif, Berkeley, PhD(molecular biol), 72. *Prof Exp:* Fel molecular biol, Univ Calif, Berkeley, 72-73; fel cell biol, Mass Inst Technol, 73-75; ASST PROF MOLECULAR & DEVELOP BIOL, UNIV CALIF, LOS ANGELES, 76- *Concurrent Pos:* Prin investr,NIH,79-82 & NSF, 81-84. *Mem:* Sigma Xi; Soc Develop Biol; Am Soc Cell Biol. *Res:* Analysis of genes involved in early embryogenesis in Drosophila using recombinant DNA. *Mailing Add:* Dept Biol Univ of Calif Los Angeles CA 90024

LENGYEL, PETER, b Budapest, Hungary, May 24, 29; US citizen; m 56; c 2. BIOCHEMISTRY. *Educ:* Budapest Tech Univ, Dipl, 51; NY Univ, PhD(biochem), 62. *Prof Exp:* Instr biochem, Sch Med, NY Univ, 62-63, asst prof, 63-65; assoc prof molecular biophys, 65-69, PROF MOLECULAR BIOPHYS & BIOCHEM, YALE UNIV, 69- *Concurrent Pos:* NIH spec fel, Pasteur Inst, Paris, 63-64. *Mem:* Am Soc Biol Chem. *Res:* Protein biosynthesis; nucleic acid and protein metabolism of animal cells and viruses; interferon defense mechanism. *Mailing Add:* Dept of Biophys & Biochem Box 6666 Yale Univ New Haven CT 06511

LENHARD, JOSEPH ANDREW, b Detroit, Mich, June 18, 29; div; c 2. HEALTH PHYSICS, NUCLEAR PHYSICS. *Educ:* Vanderbilt Univ, BA, 53, MS, 57; Am Bd Health Physics, dipl, 60. *Prof Exp:* Health physicist radiation protection, 57-61, sr health physicist broad nuclear safety, US AEC, 61-67, dir safety & environ control div, 67-72, dir res, Oak Ridge Opers Off, Energy Res & Develop Admin, 72-77, DIR RES OAK RIDGE OPERS OFF, DEPT ENERGY, 77- *Mem:* Health Physics Soc. *Res:* Research administration; physical, life and engineering sciences. *Mailing Add:* 125 Newell Lane Oak Ridge TN 37830

LENHARDT, MARTIN LOUIS, b Elizabeth, NJ, Dec 14, 44; m 66; c 8. AUDIOLOGY, SPEECH & HEARING SCIENCES. *Educ:* Seton Hall Univ, BS, 66, MS, 68; Fla State Univ, PhD(audiol, speech sci), 70. *Prof Exp:* Nat Inst Neurol Dis & Stroke fel, Johns Hopkins Univ, 70-71; asst prof, 71-75, ASSOC PROF OTORHINOLARYNGOL, MED COL VA, VA COMMONWEALTH UNIV, 71-, ASSOC PROF PEDIAT DENT, 76- *Concurrent Pos:* Mem staff adj fac, Va Inst Marine Sci, Col William & Mary, 80- *Mem:* Acoust Soc Am; Am Audiol Soc; Animal Behav Soc. *Res:* Psychological and physiological acoustics; speech communication; bioacoustics and linguistics. *Mailing Add:* Med Col of Va Box 168 MCV Sta Richmond VA 23298

LENHART, JACK G, b Bremen, Ohio, May 6, 29; m 51; c 3. FLUID CONTROLS, THERMODYNAMIC SYSTEMS. *Educ:* Case Inst Technol, BSME, 51. *Prof Exp:* Mat res engr, NAm Aviation, 51-54; proj eng, TRW Equip Lab, 56-67; prog mgr, mgr contracts admin, mgr & chmn, Dept Eng & sr proj engr, Accessories Div, Parker-Hannifin, 67-75; engr, Scott & Fetzer-Meriam Instrument, 75-78; DIR ENG, TELEDYNE REPUB MFG, 78- *Mem:* Nat Fluid Power Asn; Instrument Soc Am. *Mailing Add:* 2000 Winchester Rd Lyndhurst OH 44124

LENHERT, ANNE GERHARDT, b Lynchburg, Va, Apr 1, 36; m 67; c 2. ORGANIC CHEMISTRY. *Educ:* Hollins Col, BA, 58; Univ NMex, MS, 63, PhD(chem), 65. *Prof Exp:* Res fel, Univ NMex, 64-65; asst prof chem, Cent Mo State Col, 65-67; ASST PROF CHEM, KANS STATE UNIV, 67- *Mem:* Am Chem Soc; Sigma Xi; Int Heterocyclic Chem. *Res:* Synthesis of heterocyclic ring systems as potential purine and pteridine antagonists; anti-cancer agents and anti-radiation drugs. *Mailing Add:* Dept of Chem Kans State Univ Manhattan KS 66506

LENHERT, DONALD H, b Winfield, Kans, Nov 25, 34; m 67; c 1. ELECTRICAL ENGINEERING. *Educ:* Kans State Univ, BS, 56; Syracuse Univ, MS, 58; Univ NMex, PhD(elec eng), 66. *Prof Exp:* Syst engr, Gen Elec Co, NY, 56-58; res engr, Dikewood Corp, NMex, 60-62; res & teaching assoc elec eng, Univ NMex, 62-66; asst prof, 66-69, ASSOC PROF ELEC ENG, KANS STATE UNIV, 69- *Concurrent Pos:* Consult Air Force Spec Weapons Ctr, NMex, 60-62 & Am Inst Prof Educ, 77- *Mem:* Inst Elec & Electronics Engrs; Nat Soc Prof Engrs. *Res:* Radar scattering from rough surfaces; statistical communication theory; signal processing; microprocessor systems; microprocessor applications. *Mailing Add:* Dept of Elec Eng Kans State Univ Manhattan KS 66506

LENHERT, P GALEN, b Dayton, Ohio, July 31, 33; m 56; c 2. CRYSTALLOGRAPHY, COMPUTER SCIENCE. *Educ:* Wittenburg Univ, AB, 55; Johns Hopkins Univ, PhD(biophys), 60. *Prof Exp:* USPHS res fel chem crystallog, Oxford Univ, 60-61; asst prof physics, Wittenburg Univ, 61-64; asst prof, 64-68, ASSOC PROF PHYSICS, VANDERBILT UNIV, 68- *Concurrent Pos:* USPHS grants, 62-63, 64-75, NSF grants, 72-76, 78-81. *Mem:* AAAS; Am Crystallog Asn. *Res:* Determination of molecular structures by x-ray crystallographic methods; phase changes and modulated structures. *Mailing Add:* Dept of Physics Vanderbilt Univ Box 1807 Sta B Nashville TN 37235

LENHOFF, HOWARD MAER, b North Adams, Mass, Jan 27, 29; m 54; c 2. BIOCHEMISTRY, INVERTEBRATE ZOOLOGY. *Educ:* Coe Col, BA, 50; Johns Hopkins Univ, PhD(biol), 55. *Hon Degrees:* DSc, Coe Col, 76. *Prof Exp:* USPHS fel, Loomis Lab, Nat Cancer Inst, 54-56; actg chief, Biochem Sect, Armed Forces Insts Path, 56-57; assoc consult res, George Washington Univ, 57-58; fel, Dept Terrestrial Magnetism, Carnegie Inst Technol, 58; assoc prof biol, Univ Miami, Fla, 59-65, prof, 66-69, dir lab quant biol, 63-69; assoc dean sch biol sci, 69-71, dean grad div, 71-73, PROF DEVELOP & CELL BIOL, FAC RES FACIL, UNIV CALIF, IRVINE, 69- *Concurrent Pos:* Vis lectr, Howard Univ, 57-58; investr, Biochem Labs, Howard Hughes Med Inst, 58-63; USPHS career develop award, 65-69; vis scientist, Polymer Lab, Weizmann Inst Sci, Israel, 68-69; vis prof, Hebrew Univ Jerusalem, 70, 71, 77-78; vis prof chem eng, Israel Inst Technol, 73-74, social ecol, Ben Gurion Univ, Beersheka, Israel, 74. *Mem:* Am Soc Biol Chem; Am Soc Cell Biol; Am Chem Soc; Biophys Soc; Soc Develop Biol. *Res:* Invertebrate biology; chemoreception; symbiosis; cellular differentiation; immobilized enzymes; enzyme immunoassays. *Mailing Add:* Fac Res Facil Univ of Calif Irvine CA 92717

LENIART, DANIEL STANLEY, b Norwich, Conn, Jan 5, 43; m 71. PHYSICAL CHEMISTRY. *Educ:* The Citadel, BS, 64; Cornell Univ, PhD(phys chem), 69. *Prof Exp:* Fel, Varian Assocs, 69-70, appln engr, 70-75, mgr EPR res & develop, 75-80. *Mem:* Am Phys Soc. *Res:* Study of relaxation phenomena using the techniques of electron spin resonance, electron nuclear double resonance and electron electron double resonance. *Mailing Add:* 13211 W Sunset Dr Los Altos Hills CA 94022

LENKFR, SUSAN STAMM, b Bridgeport, Conn, Nov 13, 45; m 68; c 1. MATHEMATICAL LOGIC, STATISTICS. *Educ:* Western Conn State Col, BS, 69; Univ Colo, MA, 70; Univ Mont, PhD(math), 75. *Prof Exp:* Asst prof math, Univ Louisville, 75-76; ASST PROF OPER RES, CENT MICH UNIV, 76- *Mem:* Am Statist Asn; Opers Res Soc Am; Am Inst Decision Sci; Am Math Soc; Sigma Xi. *Res:* Category theory; decision theory including fuzzy sets; negative binomial estimation and applications. *Mailing Add:* Dept of Info Systs & Anal Cent Mich Univ Mt Pleasant MI 48859

LENKOSKI, L DOUGLAS, b Northampton, Mass, May 13, 25; m 52; c 4. MEDICINE, PSYCHIATRY. *Educ:* Harvard Univ, AB, 48; Western Reserve Univ, MD, 53. *Prof Exp:* Fel psychiat, Yale Univ, 55-56; teaching fel, 57-60, from instr to assoc prof, 60-69, dir dept, Cleveland Metrop Gen Hosp, 69-76; PROF PSYCHIAT, SCH MED, CASE WESTERN RESERVE UNIV, 69-, CHMN DEPT, 70- & DIR DEPT, UNIV HOSPS CLEVELAND, 69- *Concurrent Pos:* Consult, DePaul Maternity & Infant Home, 58-67, & Cleveland Ctr on Alcoholism, 58-61; actg dir dept psychiat, Univ Hosps Cleveland, 62-66, assoc dir dept, 66-69; dir dept, 69-; consult, St Ann's Hosp & Cleveland Vet Admin Hosp, 65-; indust personnel, US Dept Defense, 66- & White Cliff Nursing Home, 66- *Mem:* AAAS; Am Col Psychiat; fel Am Psychiat Asn. *Res:* Psychiatric education; community mental health planning. *Mailing Add:* Dept of Psychiat Sch of Med Case Western Reserve Univ Cleveland OH 44106

LENN, NICHOLAS JOSEPH, b Chicago, Ill, Nov 26, 38; m 64; c 3. NEUROLOGY, ANATOMY. *Educ:* Univ Chicago, SB, 59, MS & MD, 64, PhD(anat), 67. *Prof Exp:* Res assoc neuroanat, NIH, 64-66; asst prof pediat & med, Univ Chicago, 70-74; asst prof neurol, Univ Calif, Davis, 74-80, asst prof pediat, 76-80; MEM FAC NEUROL, SCH MED, UNIV VA, CHARLOTTESVILLE, 80- *Mem:* AAAS; Am Asn Anat; Am Acad Neurol. *Res:* Synaptic organization of mammalian brain; cerebral lipidoses. *Mailing Add:* Dept Neurol Univ Va Sch Med Charlottesville VA 22908

LENNARD, WILLIAM NORMAN, b Toronto, Ont, Apr 14, 46; m 75; c 1. ATOMIC PHYSICS. *Educ:* Univ Toronto, BASc, 69; Calif Inst Technol, PhD(physics), 74. *Prof Exp:* RES OFFICER, CHALK RIVER NUCLEAR LABS, ATOMIC ENERGY CAN LTD, 78- *Concurrent Pos:* Fel, Nat Res Coun Can, 74-76. *Mem:* Am Phys Soc; Can Asn Physicists; Chem Inst Can. *Res:* Atomic collision studies; beam foil spectroscopy; materials analyses using ion beams. *Mailing Add:* Chalk River Nuclear Labs Atomic Energy of Can Ltd Chalk River ON K0J 1J0 Can

LENNARZ, WILLIAM JOSEPH, b New York, NY, Sept 28, 34; m 56; c 3. BIOCHEMISTRY. *Educ:* Pa State Univ, BS, 56; Univ Ill, PhD(chem), 59. *Prof Exp:* Teaching asst, Univ Ill, 56-57; from asst prof to assoc prof, 62-71, PROF PHYSIOL CHEM, SCH MED, JOHNS HOPKINS UNIV, 71- *Concurrent Pos:* Res fel, Harvard Univ, 59-62; NSF fel, 59-60, grant, 69-71; NIH fel, 60-62, grants, 62-75; Clayton scholar, 62-65; consult, NIH, 71-75. *Honors & Awards:* Lederle Med Fac Award, 66. *Mem:* Am Chem Soc; Am Soc Microbiol; Am Soc Biol Chemists; Am Soc Cellular Biol. *Res:* Structure and function of cell membranes and glycoproteins; biochemistry of fertilization and embryonic development. *Mailing Add:* Dept of Physiol Chem Johns Hopkins Univ Sch of Med Baltimore MD 21205

LENNERT, ANDREW E, b Jugoslavia, Jan 28, 21; US citizen; m 58; c 2. PHYSICS. *Educ:* Drury Col, BS, 48. *Prof Exp:* Engr nuclear propulsion, Sverdrup & Parcel, Consult Engrs, 50-53; physicist, Olin Mathieson Chem Co, 53-55; engr, Aircraft Nuclear Propulsion Dept, Gen Elec Co, 55-56; design specialist & physicist, Nuclear Div, Martin Co, 56-60; MGR, ARO, INC, 60- *Mem:* Am Nuclear Soc; Am Phys Soc; Am Inst Aeronaut & Astronaut; NY Acad Sci; Nat Safety Coun. *Res:* Research and development of electrooptical instrumentation for fluid flow and other diagnostic applications; conceptual and detailed design of nuclear and nuclear-electric propulsion systems for aircraft and space applications. *Mailing Add:* ARO Inc Arnold Air Force Sta TN 37389

LENNETTE, DAVID ALAN, b San Francisco, Calif, May 24, 45; m 68. VIROLOGY. *Educ:* Univ Calif, Berkeley, AB, 66; Wash Univ, PhD(molecular biol), 71. *Prof Exp:* Trainee microbiol, Biomed Labs, Calif Dept Health, 71-73; asst prof microbiol, 74-81, VIS ASST PROF, HAHNEMANN MED COL, 81- *Concurrent Pos:* Head virol sect, Univ Lab Med, Inc, 74-; mem Yirol sect, Exam & Standards Comt, Am Bd Med Microbiol, 77-80. *Mem:* AAAS; Am Soc Microbiol; Am Soc Trop Med & Hyg; Soc Gen Microbiol. *Res:* Development of laboratory diagnosis of human Yiral and chlamydial infections. *Mailing Add:* Dept of Microbiol & Immunol 235 N 15th St Philadelphia PA 19102

LENNETTE, EDWIN HERMAN, b Pittsburgh, Pa, Sept 11, 08; m 30; c 2. EPIDEMIOLOGY, EXPERIMENTAL PATHOLOGY. *Educ:* Univ Chicago, BS, 31, PhD(bact), 35; Rush Med Col, MD, 36. *Prof Exp:* Instr bact, Univ Chicago, 36-37, res assoc, 37-38; instr path, Wash Univ, 38-39; mem staff, Int Health Div, Rockefeller Found, 39-46; chief med-vet div, Chem Corps, US Dept Army, 46-47; chief biomed lab, 73-78, chief, 47-78, EMER CHIEF VIRAL & RICKETTSIAL DIS LAB, CALIF STATE DEPT HEALTH SERV, 78-, INTERIM DIR, WALTON JONES CELL SCI CTR, 81- *Concurrent Pos:* Consult physician, Highland-Gen Hosp, 48-; mem adv panel, Naval Biol Lab, 48-56; dir regional lab, Influenza Study Prog, WHO, 49-75, mem expert adv panel virus dis, 51-, mem expert adv panel zoonoses, 52-62, mem WHO sci group on virus dis, 66 & 75-, mem sci adv comt to WHO team, EAfrican Virus Res Inst, 71-; mem viral & rickettsial registry, Am Type Cul Collection, 49-, mem coun, 60-63; coordr sect XII, sect res prog, NIH, 51-56; mem virus & rickettsial study sect, NIH Commun Dis Ctr, 50-62, chmn, 52-53, consult, 52-62, mem med lab serv adv comt, 68-72; mem adv comt poliomyelitis vaccine eval ctr, Nat Found Infantile Paralysis, 53-54; chmn bd sci counsr, Nat Inst Allergy & Infectious Dis, 57-61, mem panel respiratory & related viruses, 60-63, mem comt vaccine develop, 63-68, chmn, 67-68, mem & chmn subcomt rubella virus, 65-66, mem nat adv allergy & infectious dis coun, 63-66; chmn ad hoc comt rubella vaccine, Nat Inst Neurol Dis & Blindness, 63-64; mem microbiol panel, Wooldridge Comt, White House, 64; mem sci adv comt, Hastings Found, 66-76; consult, Univ Tex, MD Anderson Hosp & Tumor Inst, 66-; mem solid tumor-virus segment, Spec Virus-Cancer Prog, Nat Cancer Inst, 66-72; mem, Am Biol Coun, 68-70, chmn, 69-70; mem bd dir, Rush Med Col, 71-74; consult, Bur of Biologics, Fed Drug Admin. *Mem:* Fel Am Pub Health Asn; fel Am Soc Clin Path; Soc Gen Microbiol; Tissue Cult Asn (pres, 76-78); fel Royal Soc Trop Med & Hyg. *Res:* Virology; clinical, epidemiologic and immunologic research on viral and rickettsial diseases, including poliomyelitis, enteroviruses, respiratory disease, Q fever and virus-cancer relationships. *Mailing Add:* Viral & Rickettsial Dis Lab Calif State Dept of Health Serv Berkeley CA 94704

LENNETTE, EVELYNE TAM, b Kunming, China, Feb 12, 44; US citizen; m 68. MEDICAL VIROLOGY. *Educ:* Univ Calif, Berkeley, BA, 66; Wash Univ, PhD(molecular biol), 71. *Prof Exp:* Fel virol, Calif Dept of Health, 71-74; res staff, Children's Hosp Philadelphia, 75-78; RES ASST PROF VIROL, DEPT PEDIAT, UNIV PA, 78- *Mem:* Am Soc Microbiol. *Res:* Purification and characterization of Epstein-Barr virus associated antigens; study of unusual viral infections; development of diagnostic procedures for viral infections. *Mailing Add:* Joseph Stoke's Jr Res Inst 34th & Civic Ctr Blvd Philadelphia PA 19104

LENNEY, JAMES FRANCIS, b St Louis, Mo, Oct 11, 18; m 42, 73; c 2. PHARMACOLOGY. *Educ:* Wash Univ, BA, 39; Mass Inst Technol, PhD(gen physiol), 46. *Prof Exp:* Asst zool, Wash Univ, 41; asst, Mass Inst Technol, 42-43; res chemist, 44-45; res biochemist, Fleischmann Labs, 46-49, head, Enzyme Dept, 49-56; sect head, Union Starch & Ref Co, 56-63; assoc prof, 64-74, PROF PHARMACOL, UNIV HAWAII, 74- *Mem:* Am Soc Pharmacol & Exp Therapeut; AAAS; Am Chem Soc. *Res:* Biochemical pharmacology; enzyme and protein chemistry. *Mailing Add:* Dept of Pharmacol Univ of Hawaii Sch of Med Honolulu HI 96822

LENNON, DORIS LYNN FILES, b New York, NY, Dec 2, 52; m 73. EXERCISE & CARDIAC REHABILITATION. *Educ:* Hunter Col, BS, 73; Lehman Col, MS, 75; Univ Wis, Madison, PhD(exercise physiol), 81. *Prof Exp:* Instr phys educ & dance, New York City High Schs, 73-75; coordr phys educ, Bilingual/Bilcult Mini Sch, 76-77; teaching asst gymnastics, Dept Phys Educ & Dance, Univ Wis, Madison, 77-79, exercise physiol, 80, res assoc, 81-82; DIR EXERCISE, EXERCISE PHYSIOL, PHYSIOL & RES CARDIAC REHAB, C P REHAB CORP, 82- *Concurrent Pos:* Mobility instr, Jewish Guild Blind, New York, NY, 72; womens varsity gymnastics coach, Columbus High Sch, 74-75; modern dance club supvr, Bronx High Sch Sci, NY, 74-75, womens varsity tennis coach, 74-76; fitness & conditioning instr, J F Kennedy Youth & Adult Ctr, NY, 76-77; exercise leader & stress test tech, Biodynamics Lab, Univ Wis, Madison, 78. *Mem:* Am Col Sports Med; Am Alliance Health, Phys Educ & Recreation; Am Asn Fitness Dirs Bus & Indust. *Res:* Carnitine's role in substrate utilization and clinical exercise physiology; degenerative diseases. *Mailing Add:* Suite 300 C P Rehab Corp 3700 Washington St Hollywood FL 33021

LENNON, EDWARD JOSEPH, b Chicago, Ill, Aug 2, 27; m 73; c 3. INTERNAL MEDICINE. *Educ:* Univ Ill, BA, 47, MA, 48; Northwestern Univ, MD, 52. *Prof Exp:* Intern med, Milwaukee County Hosp, Wis, 52-53, resident internal med, 55-58; from instr to assoc prof, 58-68, prof med & assoc dean, 68-78, PROF MED & DEAN, MED COL WIS, 78- *Concurrent Pos:* Fel Mass Mem Hosp, Boston, 60-61; dir clin res ctr, Milwaukee County Hosp, 61-68, chief renal serv, 63-70. *Mem:* AAAS; Am Soc Clin Invest; Am Physiol Soc; Am Fedn Clin Res; Am Diabetes Asn. *Res:* Endocrine disorders; renal disease; acid-base metabolism. *Mailing Add:* Med Col Wis 8701 Watertown Plank Rd Milwaukee WI 53226

LENNON, JOHN W(ILLIAM), b Columbus, Ohio, Oct 21, 17; m 44; c 7. CERAMIC ENGINEERING. *Educ:* Ohio State Univ, BCerE, 40, MSc, 43. *Prof Exp:* Ceramic engr, Stupakoff Ceramic & Mfg Co, Pa, 40-42; asst ceramic eng, Ohio State Univ, 42-43; ceramic engr, Isolantite Inc, NJ, 43-44; fel, Mellon Inst, 45-46; ceramic engr, Orefraction, Inc, 46-49; eng exp sta, Ohio State Univ, 49-51; res engr, Battelle Mem Inst, 51-82; RETIRED. *Mem:* Am Ceramic Soc; Mineral Soc Am. *Res:* High frequency electrical insulation; special oxide compositions; high dielectrics; heat shock compositions; enamels; refractory coatings; glass; ceramic microstructure; electrodeposition of ceramic coatings; ferroelectric and ferromagnetic ceramics. *Mailing Add:* Batelle Mem Inst 505 King Ave Columbus OH 43201

LENNON, PATRICK JAMES, b Amsterdam, NY, July 24, 50. HOMOGENEOUS CATALYSIS. *Educ:* State Univ NY at Binghamton, BA, 72; Brandeis Univ, PhD(org chem), 77. *Prof Exp:* Res fellowship, Oxford Univ, 77-79; SR RES CHEMIST, MONSANTO CO, 80- *Mem:* Am Chem Soc; Royal Soc Chem. *Res:* Homogeneous catalysis of organic reactions by transition metal complexes. *Mailing Add:* Monsanto Co 800 N Lindbergh Blvd St Louis MO 63167

LENNON, VANDA ALICE, b Sydney, Australia, Aug 1, 43; m 75. NEUROIMMUNOLOGY. *Educ:* Univ Sydney, MB, BS, 66; Univ Melbourne, PhD(immunol), 73. *Prof Exp:* Res asst nuclear med, Univ Sydney, 66; from jr intern to asst med resident, Montreal Gen Hosp, 66-68; fel immunol, Walter & Eliza Hall Inst Med Res, 68-72; res assoc, Salk Inst Biol Studies, 72-73, asst res prof, 73-77; CONSULT NEUROL & IMMUNOL, MAYO CLINIC, 78-, ASSOC PROF NEUROL & IMMUNOL, MAYO GRAD SCH MED, 78- *Concurrent Pos:* Assoc adj prof, Dept Neurosci, Univ Calif, San Diego, 77-78. *Mem:* Am Acad Neurol; Sigma Xi; Am Asn Immunol; Soc Neurosci; Tissue Culture Asn. *Res:* Autoimmunity to antigens of central and peripheral nervous systems and muscle; identification of neural cells using immunologic markers; immunologic studies of patients with neurological diseases of presumed autoimmune basis. *Mailing Add:* Neuroimmunol Lab Dept Neurol & Immunol Mayo Clinic Rochester MN 55901

LENNOX, ARLENE JUDITH, b Cleveland, Ohio, Dec 3, 42. ELEMENTARY PARTICLE PHYSICS. *Educ:* Notre Dame Col, Ohio, BS, 63; Univ Notre Dame, MS, 73, PhD(physics), 74. *Prof Exp:* Teacher, Marymount High Sch, 63-64, Regina High Sch, 64-65 & Shrine High Sch, 65-69; res assoc physics, Fermilab, 74-77; prof physics, NCent Col, 77-80; STAFF PHYSICIST, FERMI NAT ACCELERATOR LAB, 90- *Concurrent Pos:* Vis physicist, Fermilab, 78-80. *Mem:* Am Phys Soc; AAAS; Am Asn Physics Teachers. *Res:* Experiments to study backward peak in pi-p elastic scattering; experiments to measure pion form factor; p-p colliding beams. *Mailing Add:* Fermilab PO Box 500 Batavia IL 60510

LENNOX, DONALD HAUGHTON, b Toronto, Ont, June 7, 24; m 47; c 2. HYDROLOGY. *Educ:* Univ Toronto, BA, 49; Univ Alta, MSc, 60. *Prof Exp:* Tech off, Occup Health Lab, Dept Nat Health & Welfare Can, 50-57; asst res off, Res Coun Alta, 57-61, head groundwater div, 61-68; maritime res sect, 68-70, head groundwater subdiv, 70-72; chief, Hydrol Res Div, 72-79, DIR, NAT HYDROL RES INST, INLAND WATERS DIRECTORATE, ENVIRON CAN, 79- *Mem:* Soc Explor Geophys; Geol Soc Am; Geol Asn Can; Nat Water Well Asn. *Res:* Application of geophysical techniques to shallow groundwater exploration; investigation of analytical methods for the determination of aquifer and well characteristics. *Mailing Add:* Inland Waters Directorate Environ Can Ottawa ON K1A 0H3 Can

LENNOX, EDWIN SAMUEL, biochemistry, see previous edition

LENNOX, WILLIAM C(RAIG), b Mount Forest, Ont, May 22, 37; m 61. MECHANICS. *Educ:* Univ Waterloo, BASc, 62, MSc, 63; Lehigh Univ, PhD(mech), 66. *Prof Exp:* From asst prof to assoc prof, 66-71, chmn dept, 76-77 & 79-82, PROF CIVIL ENG, UNIV WATERLOO, 71-, DEAN ENG, 82- *Concurrent Pos:* Vis prof, Col Petrol & Minerals, Saudi Arabia, 70-71 & Harvey Mudd Col, 77-79. *Mem:* Am Inst Aeronaut & Astronaut; Am Soc Eng Educ; Am Acad Mech. *Res:* Stochastic processes; nonlinear mechanisms. *Mailing Add:* Dept of Civil Eng Univ of Waterloo Waterloo ON N2L 3G1 Can

LE NOBLE, WILLIAM JACOBUS, b Rotterdam, Netherlands, July 19, 28; nat US; m 71. ORGANIC CHEMISTRY. *Educ:* Advan Tech Sch, Netherlands, BS, 49; Univ Chicago, PhD, 57. *Prof Exp:* Res chemist, Indust Lab, Rohm & Haas Co, 57; instr chem, Rosary Col, 58; NSF fel & res asst, Purdue Univ, 58-59; from asst prof to assoc prof, 59-69, PROF ORG CHEM, STATE UNIV NY STONY BROOK, 69- *Mem:* Am Chem Soc. *Res:* Chemical kinetics, mechanisms and equilibria in liquid systems under high pressure. *Mailing Add:* Dept of Chem State Univ of NY Stony Brook NY 11794

LENOE, EDWARD M, b Brooklyn, NY, Jan 13, 36; m 60; c 4. APPLIED MATHEMATICS, MATERIALS SCIENCE. *Educ:* Columbia Univ, AB, 57, BS, 58, MS, 59, DEngSc(eng mech), 64. *Prof Exp:* Engr, Grumman Aircraft Eng Corp, 59-60; asst, Columbia Univ, 60-64; sr staff scientist, Res & Advan Develop Div, Avco Corp, Mass, 64-67, group leader, 67-69, asst sect chief struct, Appl Tech Div, 69-71; CHIEF MECH MAT DIV, ARMY MAT & MECH RES CTR, 71- *Mem:* Am Soc Testing & Mat; Am Soc Civil Engrs; Am Soc Mech Engrs; Am Ceramics Soc; Soc Advan Mat & Process Eng. *Res:* Constitutive equations; fatigue and fracture of materials; gas turbine applications of ceramics; reliability analysis; probabilistic approaches to design. *Mailing Add:* US Army Mat & Mech Res Arsenal St Watertown MA 02172

LENOIR, J(OHN) M, b Oak Park, Ill, May 20, 18; m; c 2. CHEMICAL ENGINEERING. *Educ:* Univ Ill, BS, 42, PhD(chem eng), 49; Univ Iowa, MS, 47. *Prof Exp:* Res engr, Pan-Am Refining Corp, 47 & C F Braun & Co, 48; assoc prof chem eng, Univ Ark, 49-53; prof & chmn dept, Univ Denver, 53-55; prof, Univ Southern Calif, 55-76; PROF CHEM ENG, CALIF STATE UNIV, LONG BEACH, 76- *Mem:* Am Soc Eng Educ; fel Am Inst Chem Engrs. *Res:* Measurement of thermal conductivities of gases at high pressure; prediction methods for vapor-liquid equilibria; prediction methods for physical properties of mixtures; extensive measurments on erthalpy of mixtures. *Mailing Add:* Dept of Eng Calif State Univ Long Beach CA 90840

LENOIR, WILLIAM BENJAMIN, b Miami, Fla, Mar 14, 39; m 64; c 1. GEOPHYSICS, ELECTRICAL ENGINEERING. *Educ:* Mass Inst Technol, SB, 61, SM, 62, PhD(elec eng), 65. *Prof Exp:* Asst elec eng, Mass Inst Technol, 62-64, instr, 64-65, asst prof, 65-67, Ford fel eng, 65-66; SCIENTIST-ASTRONAUT, JOHNSON SPACE CTR, NASA, 67- *Mem:* AAAS; Am Geophys Union. *Res:* Microwave studies of planetary atmospheres; propagation of partially polarized waves. *Mailing Add:* NASA Code TE Johnson Space Ctr Houston TX 77058

LENOIR, WILLIAM CANNON, JR, b Loudon, Tenn, Sept 22, 29; m 56; c 3. BOTANY. *Educ:* Maryville Col, BS, 51; Univ Ga, MS, 62, PhD(bot), 65. *Prof Exp:* Instr high sch, Tenn, 57-59; asst prof biol, 60-62, from asst prof to assoc prof bot, 62-73, PROF BOT, COLUMBUS COL, 73-, CHMN DIV SCI & MATH, 73- *Mem:* Am Inst Biol Sci; Bot Soc Am. *Res:* Role of light in morphogenesis; organogenesis in pine; morphogenesis of the leaf of Lygodium japonicum. *Mailing Add:* Dept of Biol Columbus Col Columbus GA 31907

LENON, HERBERT LEE, b Battle Creek, Mich, June 8, 39; m 62; c 3. FISH BIOLOGY. *Educ:* Albion Col, AB, 61; Wayne State Univ, MS, 64, PhD(fisheries), 68. *Prof Exp:* Asst prof, 67-74, ASSOC PROF FISHERIES BIOL & ICHTHYOL, CENT MICH UNIV, 74- *Concurrent Pos:* Mem Great Lakes Found. *Mem:* Am Fisheries Soc; Nat Audubon Soc; Nat Wildlife Fedn. *Res:* Freshwater fish population dynamics; management evaluation. *Mailing Add:* Dept of Biol Cent Mich Univ Mt Pleasant MI 48858

LENOX, RONALD SHEAFFER, b Lancaster, Pa, Jan 25, 48; m 71; c 1. ORGANIC CHEMISTRY. *Educ:* Juniata Col, BS, 69; Univ Ill, PhD(org chem), 73. *Prof Exp:* asst prof chem, Wabash Col, Crawfordsville, Ind, 73-79; RES SCIENTIST, ARMSTRONG WORLD INDUSTS, 79- *Mem:* Am Chem Soc; Sigma Xi. *Res:* Synthesis of natural products; particularly insect pheremones, insect repellents; new synthetic reactions. *Mailing Add:* Res & Develop Ctr Armstrong World Indust Lancaster PA 17604

LENSCHOW, DONALD HENRY, b LaCrosse, Wis, July 17, 38; m 64; c 2. METEOROLOGY. *Educ:* Univ Wis, BS, 60, MS, 62, PhD(meteorol), 66. *Prof Exp:* SCIENTIST, NAT CTR ATMOSPHERIC RES, 66-; AFFIL PROF, COLO STATE UNIV, 74- *Mem:* Am Meteorol Soc. *Res:* Atmospheric boundary layer; airborne turbulence measurements and airplane research instrumentation. *Mailing Add:* 95 Pawnee Dr Boulder CO 80303

LENTINI, EUGENE ANTHONY, b Boston, Mass, July 6, 29; m 51; c 4. PHYSIOLOGY. *Educ:* Boston Univ, AB, 51, MA, 55, PhD(myocardial metab), 58. *Prof Exp:* Instr physiol, Med Sch, Univ Ore, 58-64; asst prof, Med Col Va, 64-68; assoc prof physiol, Albany Col Pharm, 68-75; assoc prof, Dept Physiol & Pharmacol, Philadelphia Col Obsteopath Med, 77-; SCIENTIST, VET ADMIN HOSP, PHILADELPHIA, 81- *Concurrent Pos:* Nat Heart & Lung Inst fel, 56-58; Heart & Lung res awards, 60-65 & 69-72; vis prof, Mass State Col & Univ Lowell, 75-77; adj prof physiol, Sch Vet Med, Univ Penn, 81- *Mem:* Sigma Xi; NY Acad Sci; AAAS; Am Physiol Soc. *Res:* Bioelectronics, electronic micrometer, chart viewer; biophysics determination of oxygen diffusion coefficient through heart muscle; biochemical interrelation between ventricular dynamics and oxidative metabolism; effects of metabolic inhibitors on endogenous substrate; analysis of endogenous lipids and glycogen; physiological myocardial contract; substrate utilization. *Mailing Add:* Dept of Physiol & Pharmacol 4150 City Ave Philadelphia PA 19131

LENTON, PHILIP A(LFRED), b Detroit, Mich, Aug 13, 19; m 42; c 2. CHEMICAL ENGINEERING. *Educ:* Wayne State Univ, BSChE, 41; Mich State Col, MSChE, 43. *Prof Exp:* Chem engr res, Girdler Corp, 43-44; prod supvr gas mfr, Houdaille Hershey Corp, 44-45; mem staff chem eng res, Wyandotte Chem Corp, 45-49, head sect, BASF Wyandotte Corp, 49-56, develop engr, 56-63, acquisition specialist, 63-69, corp planning coordr, 69-77, sr indust engr, 77-80; RETIRED. *Mem:* Am Chem Soc; Am Inst Chem Engrs. *Res:* Process for manufacturing of lubricating grease; development of various organic and inorganic processes, including sodium carboxymethylcellulose and sodium alkyl aryl sulfonate; evaluation of business opportunities, including possible corporate acquisitions; long-range corporate planning. *Mailing Add:* 1920 Dacosta St Dearborn MI 48128

LENTZ, CHARLES WESLEY, b Mt Pleasant, Mich, May 6, 24; m 47; c 6. CHEMISTRY. *Educ:* Mich State Univ, BS, 46. *Prof Exp:* Chemist, Mich Chem Corp, 46-52 & Columbia-Southern Div, Pittsburgh Plate Glass Co, 52-55; chemist, 55-61, supvr develop, 61-68, mgr develop, 68-70, mgr res, 70-75, mgr life sci res & develop, 75-77, DIR HEALTH & ENVIRON SCI, DOW CORNING CORP, 77- *Concurrent Pos:* Mem comt MC-B5, Hwy Res Bd, Nat Acad Sci-Nat Res Coun, 67- *Honors & Awards:* Sigma Xi Award, 65. *Mem:* AAAS; Am Chem Soc; Sigma Xi; NY Acad Sci; Chem Specialties Mfrs Asn. *Res:* Study of silica as a reinforcing agent for silicone rubber, silicate minerals and the silicate structure changes that occur in portland cement during hydration. *Mailing Add:* Dow Corning Corp Mail CO3101 Midland MI 48640

LENTZ, CLAUDE PETER, b Westerham, Sask, Nov 27, 19; m 45; c 4. FOOD REFRIGERATION. *Educ:* Univ Sask, BSc, 49; Univ Toronto, MASc, 51. *Prof Exp:* Prin res officer, Nat Res Coun Can, 49-53, head, Food Technol Sect, Div Biol Sci, 53-79; RETIRED. *Concurrent Pos:* Consult, 80-81. *Honors & Awards:* W J Eva Award, Can Inst Food Technol, 67; John Labatt Award, Chem Inst Can, 78. *Mem:* Can Inst Food Technol; Am Soc Heating, Refrig & Air-Conditioning Engrs. *Res:* Food preservation by refrigeration and related heat and mass transfer problems; waste treatment. *Mailing Add:* 19 David Dr Nepean ON K2G 2M8 Can

LENTZ, GARY LYNN, b North Hollywood, Calif, July 15, 43; m 65; c 4. ECONOMIC ENTOMOLOGY. *Educ:* Univ Mo-Columbia, AB, 65; Iowa State Univ, PhD(entom), 73. *Prof Exp:* Res assoc entom, Iowa State Univ, 68-72; asst prof, Univ Ariz, 72-74; asst prof, 74-80, ASSOC PROF ENTOM, AGR EXP STA, UNIV TENN, 80- *Mem:* Entom Soc Am; Sigma Xi. *Res:* Pest management of cotton and soybean insects. *Mailing Add:* WTenn Exp Sta 605 Airways Blvd Jackson TN 38301

LENTZ, KENNETH EUGENE, b Chicago, Ill, Dec 9, 23; m 47; c 3. BIOCHEMISTRY. *Educ:* Iowa State Col, BS, 47, MS, 49; Western Reserve Univ, PhD(biochem), 56. *Prof Exp:* Asst chem, Iowa State Col, 48-49; from asst to asst prof, 49-70, ASSOC PROF BIOCHEM, SCH MED, CASE WESTERN RESERVE UNIV, 70-; RES BIOCHEMIST, HYPERTENSION UNIT, VET ADMIN HOSP, 55- *Mem:* Am Chem Soc; NY Acad Sci. *Res:* Enzymes, proteins and peptides of the renin-angiotensin system; mechanism of action of biological active principles. *Mailing Add:* Hypertension Unit Vet Admin Hosp 10701 East Blvd Cleveland OH 44106

LENTZ, PAUL JACKSON, JR, b Niagara Falls, NY, Oct 10, 44; m 68; c 2. BIOCHEMISTRY, X-RAY CRYSTALLOGRAPHY. *Educ:* Univ Alaska, BS(chem) & BS(zool), 66; Purdue Univ, PhD(molecular biol), 71. *Prof Exp:* Fel biol, Wallenberg Lab, Uppsala Univ, Sweden, 71-75; scholar chem, Univ Mich, 75-78; ASST PROF BIOL, KING'S COL, 78- *Concurrent Pos:* NIH grant, 71-73; lectr chem, Univ Mich, 76-78. *Mem:* Am Crystallog Asn; AAAS. *Res:* X-ray crystallographic structure determination of proteins, nucleic acids and viruses. *Mailing Add:* Dept Biol King's Col Wilkes-Barre PA 18711

LENTZ, PAUL LEWIS, b Indianapolis, Ind, May 26, 18; m 43; c 2. MYCOLOGY. *Educ:* Butler Univ, AB, 40; Univ Iowa, MS, 42, PhD(mycol), 53. *Prof Exp:* Asst bot lab, Butler Univ, 38-40, bact lab, 40; asst mycol, Univ Iowa, 40-42, 46-47; assoc mycologist, Plant Indust Sta, 47-56, mycologist, Plant Sci Res Div, 56-72, instr advan educ sci, Grad Sch-Found, 58-71, CHIEF, MYCOL LAB, SCI & EDUC ADMIN-AGR RES, USDA, 72- *Mem:* Bot Soc Am; Mycol Soc Am; Int Soc Plant Taxon. *Res:* Basidiomycete taxonomy, anatomy, morphology and biology; Aphyllophorales; National Fungus Collections. *Mailing Add:* Mycol Lab Agr Res Ctr-West US Dept of Agr Beltsville MD 20705

LENZ, ALFRED C, b Olds, Alta, Jan 6, 29; m 54; c 2. GEOLOGY. *Educ:* Univ Alta, BSc, 54, MSc, 56; Princeton Univ, PhD(paleont), 59. *Prof Exp:* Paleontologist, Calif Standard Co, 59-64; from asst rpof to assoc prof, 64-75, prof paleont & stratig, 75-80, PROF GEOL, UNIV WESTERN ONT, 80- *Concurrent Pos:* Lectr, Univ Alta, 60-61. *Mem:* Int Palaeont Asn; Paleont Soc; Can Palaeont Asn. *Res:* Lower Paleozoic biostratigraphy; Devonian stratigraphy and paleontology; graptolite biostratigraphy; Upper Silurian and Lower Devonian brachiopods. *Mailing Add:* Dept of Geol Univ of Western Ont London ON N6A 5B8 Can

LENZ, ARNO T(HOMAS), b Fond du Lac, Wis, Sept 22, 06; m 32; c 3. ENGINEERING. *Educ:* Univ Wis, BS, 28, MS, 30, CE, 37, PhD(hydraul eng), 40. *Prof Exp:* From instr to assoc prof hydraul & sanit eng, 28-48, prof hydraul eng, 48-77, chmn dept civil eng, 58-72, dir hydraul model tests, 45-58, EMER PROF HYDRAUL ENG, UNIV WIS-MADISON, 77- *Concurrent Pos:* Consult, 51- *Mem:* Am Soc Civil Engrs; Am Meteorol Soc; Nat Soc Prof Engrs; Am Water Works Asn; Am Geophys Union. *Res:* Hydrology of rain fall-runoff relations; model tests of hydraulic structures; oil tests on v-notch weirs. *Mailing Add:* 930 Cornell Ct Madison WI 53705

LENZ, CHARLES ELDON, b Omaha, Nebr, Apr 13, 26. ENGINEERING, MATHEMATICS. *Educ:* Mass Inst Technol, SB, 51, SM, 53; Cornell Univ, PhD, 57; Univ Calif, MS, 71. *Prof Exp:* Engr, Gen Elec Co, 49-56; consult, Assoc Univs, 56; sr staff engr, Avco Corp, 58-60; mem tech staff, Armour Res Found, 60-62; sr scientist, Autonetics Div, NAm Aviation, Inc, 62-69; consult, 69-72; chief engr, Valmont Inc, 72-80; STAFF DEVELOP ENGR, US AIR FORCE, OFFUTT AFB, 80- *Concurrent Pos:* Prof, Univ Hawaii, 66-68; guest lectr, Univs Hawaii & Minn, Cornell Univ & Col Aeronaut, Cranfield, Eng; lectr, Univ Calif. *Mem:* Sigma Xi; Inst Elec & Electronics Engrs; Instrument Soc Am. *Res:* Operations research; network analysis; environmental systems; public health; digital and analog sampled-data control systems; system-engineering automation; electro-optical devices. *Mailing Add:* US Air Force 3925 ICMFES/DEBNE Offutt AFB NE 68113

LENZ, GEORGE H, b Irvington, NJ, Oct 9, 39; m 61; c 2. NUCLEAR PHYSICS. *Educ:* Rutgers Univ, AB, 61, MS, 63, PhD(physics), 67. *Prof Exp:* Asst prof physics, Univ Va, 67-71; assoc prof, 71-76, WHITNEY-GUION PROF PHYSICS, SWEET BRIAR COL, 76-, CHMN DEPT, 71- *Mem:* Am Phys Soc; Am Asn Physics Teachers. *Res:* Analogue states; compound nucleus and direct reactions; Coulomb energy systematics. *Mailing Add:* Dept of Physics Sweet Briar Col Sweet Briar VA 24595

LENZ, GEORGE RICHARD, b Chicago, Ill, Nov 22, 41; m 70; c 3. ORGANIC CHEMISTRY. *Educ:* Ill Inst Technol, BS, 63; Univ Chicago, MS, 65, PhD(chem), 67. *Prof Exp:* Nat Cancer Inst fel, Yale Univ, 67-69; res investr, 69-71, SECT HEAD, G D SEARLE & CO, 71- *Mem:* AAAS; Am Chem Soc; Royal Soc Chem. *Res:* Photochemistry; medicinal chemistry. *Mailing Add:* Div of Chem Res G D Searle & Co PO Box 5110 Chicago IL 60680

LENZ, LEE WAYNE, b Bozeman, Mont, Oct 12, 15. BOTANY. *Educ:* Mont State Col, BS, 37; Univ La, MS, 39; Wash Univ, PhD(bot), 48. *Prof Exp:* Assoc prof, 51-58, cytologist & plant breeder, 48-59, actg dir, 59-60, PROF BOT, CLAREMONT GRAD SCH, 58-, DIR, RANCHO SANTA ANA BOT GARDEN, 60- *Concurrent Pos:* Rockefeller Found fel, Mexico. *Res:* Taxonomy; cytology; evolution of the tribe Allieae (Liliaceae); taxonomy of the genus Iris. *Mailing Add:* Rancho Santa Ana Bot Garden 1500 N College Ave Claremont CA 91711

LENZ, PAUL HEINS, b Newark, NJ, Mar 29, 38; m 60; c 4. PHYSIOLOGY, ENDOCRINOLOGY. *Educ:* Franklin & Marshall Col, BS, 60; Rutgers Univ, MS, 64, PhD(endocrinol), 66. *Prof Exp:* Asst prof, 66-70, assoc prof physiol, 70-80, PROF BIOL SCI, FAIRLEIGH DICKINSON UNIV, 80- *Concurrent Pos:* Univ res grants, 68-71, Eli Lilly grant, 70; Ciba grants, 70-71. *Mem:* Endocrine Soc; Am Oil Chemists' Soc; Am Asn Clin Chemists; Am Heart Asn. *Res:* Development of micro-chemical techniques; hormonal and biochemical control of lipid metabolism; platelet aggregation and its control. *Mailing Add:* Dept of Biol Sci Fairleigh Dickinson Univ Madison NJ 07940

LENZ, ROBERT WILLIAM, b New York, NY, Apr 28, 26; m 53; c 4. POLYMER CHEMISTRY. *Educ:* Lehigh Univ, BS, 49; Inst Textile Technol, MS, 51; State Univ NY, PhD(polymer chem), 56. *Prof Exp:* Res chemist, Chicopee Mfg Corp, 51-53; res chemist, Polymer Res Lab, Dow Chem Co, 55-61, Eastern Res Lab, 61-63; asst dir, Fabric Res Labs, Inc, 63-66; assoc prof, 66-69, PROF CHEM ENG, UNIV MASS, AMHERST, 69- *Concurrent Pos:* Vis prof, Univ Mainz, Germany, 72-73, Royal Inst Technol, Stockholm, Sweden, 75, Univ Freiburg, Germany, 79-80 & Japan Soc Prom Sci, 79. *Honors & Awards:* Humboldt Prize, 79. *Mem:* Am Chem Soc; Fiber Soc; Am Inst Chem Eng. *Res:* Monomer and polymer synthesis; kinetics and mechanism of polymerization; structure-property relations of polymers; reactions of polymers; new polymeric materials and applications. *Mailing Add:* Dept of Chem Eng Univ of Mass Amherst MA 01002

LENZEN, K(ENNETH) H(ARVEY), b Evanston, Ill, Sept 18, 21; m 44; c 1. CIVIL ENGINEERING, ENGINEERING MECHANICS. *Educ:* Northwestern Univ, BS, 43, MS, 47; Purdue Univ, PhD(eng sci), 57. *Prof Exp:* Res engr, Portland Cement Asn, 45-46; res assoc, Northwestern Univ, 46-49; instr & res assoc, Purdue Univ, 49-55; assoc prof, 55-60, dir eng mech, 67-76, assoc dean res & grad studies, Sch Eng, 75-80, PROF ENG MECH, UNIV KANS, 60- *Concurrent Pos:* Chmn subcomts, Res Coun Riveted & Bolted Struct Joints, 50; Fulbright grant, Al-Hikma Univ, Baghdad, 62-63; Am Iron & Steel Inst res grant, Univ Kans, 63-65, Steel Joist Inst res grant, 64-67; Polish Acad Sci lectr tour, 67; consult, Monsanto Co, 68-70 & Steel Joist Inst, 68-71; chmn vibrations, Hwy Res Bd, Nat Acad Sci-Nat Res Coun, 68-72; advisor univ affairs, NASA, 80-81. *Honors & Awards:* Croes Medal, Am Soc Civil Engrs, 56. *Mem:* Am Soc Civil Engrs; Am Rwy Eng Asn; Am Soc Eng Educ; Nat Asn Prof Engrs. *Res:* Structural mechanics, especially vibrations, dynamic loads, fatigue and buckling. *Mailing Add:* 4010 Learned Hall Sch Eng Univ of Kans Lawrence KS 66045

LEO, ALBERT JOSEPH, b Winfield, Ill, Sept 29, 25; m 47; c 3. MEDICAL CHEMISTRY. *Educ:* Pomona Col, BA, 48; Univ Chicago, MS, 49, PhD(chem), 52. *Prof Exp:* Res assoc med chem, 68-71, DIR, MED CHEM PROJ, POMONA COL, 71-, ADJ ASST PROF, 81- *Mem:* Sigma Xi; Am Chem Soc. *Res:* Database of parameters useful in drug design, toxicological and environmental fate studies. *Mailing Add:* Chem Dept Pomona Col Claremont CA 91711

LEO, MICAH WEI-MING, b Hangchow, China, Apr 18, 26; m 59; c 2. CHEMISTRY. *Educ:* Nat Taiwan Univ, BS, 50; Univ RI, MS, 57; Rutgers Univ New Brunswick, PhD(soils, agr biochem), 60. *Prof Exp:* Chemist, Taiwan Fertilizer Co, 50-55; res officer soil physics, Can Dept Agr, 60-62; sr res scientist, Atomic Energy Comn fel radioactive fallout in precipitation & Dept Defense Stardust Proj fel, Isotopes Inc, NJ, 62-64; assoc prof chem, Fla Mem Col, 64-65 & Biola Col, 65-67; plant nutritionist & NSF fel exudation, Univ Calif, Los Angeles, 67-68; assoc prof, 68-69, PROF CHEM, BARRINGTON COL, 69- *Concurrent Pos:* Ed-in-chief, Chinese Christians Today, 61-; abstractor, Chem Abstr Serv, 67-; provost, Chung Yuan Col Sci & Eng, 74-75; pastor, Chinese Christian Church RI, 78- *Mem:* Am Chem Soc; Am Nuclear Soc; Am Asn Physics Teachers; Am Inst Chemists; Am Asn Univ Professors. *Res:* Chemistry curriculum research in self-paced studies; environmental and food chemistry and related subjects; relationship between science and Bible. *Mailing Add:* Sci Div Barrington Col Barrington RI 02806

LEON, ARTHUR SOL, b Brooklyn, NY, Apr 26, 31; m 56; c 3. MEDICAL RESEARCH, NUTRITION. *Educ:* Univ Fla, BS, 52; Univ Wis-Madison, MS, 54, MD, 57. *Prof Exp:* Intern, Henry Ford Hosp, Detroit, 57-58; fel internal med, Lahey Clin, Boston, 58-60; fel cardiol, Sch Med, Univ Miami & Jackson Mem Hosp, 60-61; chief gen med & cardiol, 34th Gen Hosp, US Army, France, 61-64, cardiol consult, US Armed Forces, France, 61-64, res cardiologist, Dept Cardiorespiratory Dis, Walter Reed Army Inst Res, 64-67, mem med eval team, Gemini & Apollo Projs, 66-67; dir clin pharmacol, Roche Spec Treatment Unit, Newark Beth Israel Med Ctr, 67-73; assoc prof, 73-80, PROF CLIN PHARMACOL & CARDIOL, LAB PHYSIOL HYG, SCH PUB HEALTH, UNIV MINN, MINNEAPOLIS, 80-, DIR APPL RES, 73- *Concurrent Pos:* Res assoc, Dept Clin Pharmacol, Hoffmann-La Roche Inc, 67-73; from instr to assoc prof, Col Med & Dent NJ, 67-73; chief med serv, 322nd Gen Hosp, US Army Reserve, Newark, 67-73; sr investr multiple coronary risk factor intervention and lipid research clinic trials, Univ Minn, Minneapolis, 73-; chief cardiol, 5501st Army Hosp, Ft Snelling, Minn, 73-; attd physicisn, Univ Hosp, Minneapolis & St Paul Ramsay Hosp, 73- *Honors & Awards:* William G Anderson Award, Am Alliance & Health Phys Educ, 81. *Mem:* Am Col Cardiol; Am Col Chest Physicians; Am Physiol Asn; Am Soc Pharmacol & Exp Therapeut; Am Col Sports Med (vpres, 77-79). *Res:* Prevention of coronary heart disease by risk factor modification; metabolic and cardiovascular effects of exercise; exercise testing; effects of exercise conditioning; evaluation of new cardiovascular and lipid-lowering drugs. *Mailing Add:* Lab Phys Hyg Stadium Gate 27 611 Beacon St SE Minneapolis MN 55455

LEON, B(ENJAMIN) J(OSEPH), b Austin, Tex, Mar 20, 32; m 54; c 4. ELECTRICAL ENGINEERING. *Educ:* Univ Tex, BS, 54; Mass Inst Technol, SM, 57, ScD, 59. *Prof Exp:* Mem staff, Lincoln Lab, Mass Inst Technol, 54-59; tech staff, Hughes Aircraft Co, 59-62; assoc prof, 62-65, PROF ELEC ENG, PURDUE UNIV, WEST LAFAYETTE, 65-; PROF & CHMN ELEC ENG, UNIV KY, LEXINGTON, 80- *Concurrent Pos:* Ed, Trans Circuit Theory, Inst Elec & Electronics Engrs, 67-69; consult ed, Holt, Rinehart & Winston series elec eng, electronics & systs, 67-73; Rome Air Develop Ctr fel & vis prof, Cornell Univ, 68-69; elec engr, Defense Commun Agency, 75-76; Consult, Westinghouse Telecommunications, 80. *Mem:* Am Asn Univ Prof; AAAS; Inst Elec & Electronics Engrs; Am Soc Eng Educ. *Res:* Communications systems, circuit and system theory. *Mailing Add:* Sch of Elec Eng Purdue Univ West Lafayette IN 47907

LEON, H(ERMAN) I, b Chicago, Ill, Mar 27, 24; m 46; c 2. ENGINEERING. *Educ:* Univ Calif, BS, 47, MS, 48, PhD(eng), 55. *Prof Exp:* Systs analyst, Commun Div, Ramo-Wooldridge Corp, 55-56, assoc mgr reentry systs dept, Space Tech Labs, Inc, Div, Thompson Ramo Wooldridge, Inc, 56-62; dir systs res & technol, ITT Fed Labs, 62-63; asst dir systs anal, Apollo Spacecraft Systs Anal Prog, TRW Systs Group, 63-68, asst mgr plans, Houston Opers, 68-70, mgr electronic systs lab, Washington Opers, McLean, 70-75, asst mgr eng, 72-75, sr staff planning div, 75-78, PROJ MGR, OIL SHALE DEVELOP, TRW ENERGY SYSTS GROUP, 78- *Concurrent Pos:* Lectr, Univ Calif, Los Angeles, 50-60. *Mem:* Am Inst Aeronaut & Astronaut. *Res:* Reentry and space dynamics; nose cone vulnerability; fuzing; instrumentation techniques; military space systems; manned spacecraft systems; energy systems and policy analysis; shale oil development. *Mailing Add:* TRW Energy Eng Div 8301 Greensboro Dr McLean VA 22102

LEON, HENRY A, b San Francisco, Calif, Sept 25, 28; m 58; c 3. ENVIRONMENTAL PHYSIOLOGY, AEROSPACE BIOLOGY. *Educ:* Univ Calif, Berkeley, BS, 52, PhD(physiol), 60. *Prof Exp:* Nat Cancer Inst fel, Wenner-Gren Inst, Stockholm, Sweden, 60-61; Milton res fel path, Harvard Med Sch, 61-62; RES SCIENTIST AEROSPACE BIOL, AMES RES CTR, NASA, 62- *Concurrent Pos:* Mem staff, Mass Gen Hosp, Boston, 61-62. *Mem:* AAAS; Am Physiol Soc; Undersea Med Soc; Aerospace Med Asn. *Res:* Effect of space cabin environments on blood elements; stress and the control of liver protein synthesis; nutrition and stress. *Mailing Add:* Ames Res Ctr NASA Moffett Field Mountain View CA 94035

LEON, KENNETH ALLEN, b New York, NY, Nov 19, 37; m 63; c 2. FISH BIOLOGY. *Educ:* Ohio State Univ, BS, 60; Col William & Mary, MS, 63; Univ Wash, PhD(fisheries mgt), 70. *Prof Exp:* Biol consult, Ichthyol Assocs, 70-71; res biologist, Tunison Lab Fish Nutrit, US Bur Sport Fisheries & Wildlife, 71-74; PRIN BIOLOGIST, FISH REHAB, ENHANCEMENT & DEVELOP DIV, ALASKA DEPT FISH & GAME, JUNEAU, 75- *Mem:* Am Fisheries Soc. *Res:* Enhancement and rehabilitation of salmonid species, specialty salmon incubation and hatchery design. *Mailing Add:* Alaska Dept Fish & Game PO Box 3 2000 Juneau AK 99801

LEON, MELVIN, b Brooklyn, NY, Sept 2, 36; m 63; c 2. THEORETICAL PHYSICS. *Educ:* Univ Md, BS, 57; Cornell Univ, PhD(physics), 61. *Prof Exp:* Imp Chem Industs res fel & NSF fel theoret physics, Univ Birmingham, 61-63; res physicist, Carnegie Inst Technol, 63-66; asst prof physics, Rensselaer Polytech Inst, 66-72; MEM STAFF, LOS ALAMOS NAT LAB, 72- *Mem:* Fel Am Phys Soc. *Res:* Exotic atoms; muon spin rotation. *Mailing Add:* Los Alamos Nat Lab Mp 3 MS 844 Los Alamos NM 87545

LEON, MYRON A, b Troy, NY, July 13, 26. IMMUNOLOGY. *Educ:* Columbia Univ, BS, 50, PhD(biochem), 54. *Prof Exp:* Assoc surg res, 53-64, ASSOC HEAD PATH RES, ST LUKE'S HOSP, 64-74; PROF IMMUNOL, SCH MED, WAYNE STATE UNIV, 74- *Concurrent Pos:* Fel, Univ Lund, Sweden, 58. *Mem:* Am Asn Immunol; AAAS; Am Soc Microbiol. *Res:* Immunochemistry; mechanisms of natural resistance to infection; complement; myeloma proteins; lymphocyte stimulation. *Mailing Add:* Dept of Immunol Wayne State Univ Sch of Med Detroit MI 48201

LEON, RAMON V, b Holguin, Oriente, Cuba, Sept 29, 48; m 79. RELIABILITY THEORY, STOCHASTIC INEQUALITIES. *Educ:* Fla State Univ, BS, 72, MS, 76, PhD(statist), 79; Tulane Univ, MS, 75. *Prof Exp:* Vis instr statist, Fla State Univ, 78-79; asst prof statist, Rutgers Univ, 79-81; MEM TECH STAFF STATIST, BELL LABS, 81- *Honors & Awards:* Ralph A Bradley Award, Fla State Univ, 79. *Mem:* Inst Math Statist; Am Statist Asn; Am Soc Quality Control; Inst Environ Sci. *Res:* Reliability theory and the mathematics and statistics associated with it; characterizations of distributions; stochastic inequalities; probability modeling of systems. *Mailing Add:* Bell Labs Rm HP-1A-239 Holmdel NJ 07733

LEON, ROBERT LEONARD, b Denver, Colo, Jan 18, 25; m 47; c 4. MEDICINE, PSYCHIATRY. *Educ:* Univ Colo, MD, 48. *Prof Exp:* Intern, Univ Hosp, Ann Arbor, Mich, 48-49; resident psychiat, Med Ctr, Univ Colo, 49-52; resident child psychiat, State Dept Health, Conn, 52-53; asst dir child psychiat, Greater Kansas City Ment Health Found, 53-54; prof psychiat, Southwest Med Sch, Univ Tex, 57-67; PROF PSYCHIAT & CHMN DEPT, UNIV TEX HEALTH SCI CTR SAN ANTONIO, 67- *Concurrent Pos:* Chief ment health serv, USPHS, Mo, 54-57; consult, Bur Indian Affairs, 62-67; consult regional off VI, NIMH, 57-, mem psychiat training rev comt, 70-74; consult, Audie Murphy Mem Vet Hosp, 73- *Mem:* Fel Am Psychiat Asn; fel Am Col Psychiatrists; Am Orthopsychiat Asn; Am Acad Child Psychiat; AMA. *Res:* Social psychiatry. *Mailing Add:* 7703 Floyd Curl Dr San Antonio TX 78284

LEON, SHALOM A, b Sofia, Bulgaria, Apr 7, 35; m 62; c 3. BIOCHEMISTRY, RADIOBIOLOGY. *Educ:* Hebrew Univ, Jerusalem, MSc, 60, PhD(pharmacol), 64. *Prof Exp:* Jr res asst pharmacol, Med Sch, Hebrew Univ, Jerusalem, 60-64; res assoc biochem, Ind Univ, 65-67; MEM BIOSCI STAFF, ALBERT EINSTEIN MED CTR, 68- *Mem:* Am Asn Cancer Res; AAAS; Radiation Res Soc; Am Chem Soc; NY Acad Sci. *Res:* Mechanism of antibiotic action; biosynthesis of nucleic acids and proteins; use of radioactive isotopes in clinical research and diagnosis; relationship between structure and biological activity of toxins from microorganisms; effect of radioprotective agents against ionizing radiation. *Mailing Add:* Radiation Res Lab Albert Einstein Med Ctr Philadelphia PA 19141

LEONARD, A(NTHONY), b June 2, 38; US citizen; m 60; c 2. ENGINEERING. *Educ:* Calif Inst Technol, BS, 59; Stanford Univ, MS, 60, PhD(nuclear eng), 63. *Prof Exp:* Mem tech staff, Rand Corp, 63-66; from asst prof to assoc prof mech eng, Stanford Univ, 66-73; RES SCIENTIST, NASA AMES RES CTR, 75- *Concurrent Pos:* Lectr, Calif Inst Technol, 65-66; consult, Gen Elec Co; NASA Ames Res Ctr sr fel, 73-75. *Honors & Awards:* Edward Teller Award, 63. *Mem:* Am Phys Soc; Soc Indust & Appl Math; Am Inst Aeronaut & Astronaut. *Res:* Nuclear reactor theory; particle transport theory; turbulence theory; numerical fluid mechanics. *Mailing Add:* Mailstop 202-1 NASA Ames Res Ctr Moffett Field CA 94035

LEONARD, ALVIN ROBERT, b New York, NY, Jan 9, 18; m 42; c 2. MEDICINE, EPIDEMIOLOGY. *Educ:* Univ Southern Calif, MD, 42; Harvard Univ, MPH, 47. *Prof Exp:* Health officer, Solano County, Calif, 47-48; pub health physician, State Dept Pub Health, Calif, 48-50, asst dir pub health, San Diego County, 50-57, dir pub health, Berkeley, 57-70; prof community med, Col Med, Univ Ariz, 70-75; ASSOC CHIEF ADULT HEALTH, CALIF DEPT HEALTH SERV, 75- *Concurrent Pos:* Clin prof, Sch Pub Health, Univ Calif, Berkeley, 57-70; clin prof community health, Univ Calif, Davis, 75- *Mem:* Fel Am Pub Health Asn; fel Am Col Prev Med. *Res:* Application of public health and administration principles in operating programs; community and social forces in health and disease; cardio-vasc dis epidemiology. *Mailing Add:* Dept of Health Serv 714 P St Sacramento CA 95814

LEONARD, ARNOLD S, b Minneapolis, Minn, Oct 26, 30; m 50; c 4. SURGERY. *Educ:* Univ Minn, Minneapolis, BA, 52, BS, 53, MD, 55, PhD(surg path), 63. *Prof Exp:* Univ fel, 56-63, from asst prof to assoc prof, 63-73, PROF SURG, UNIV MINN, MINNEAPOLIS, 73- *Mem:* Am Soc Artificial Internal Organs; Am Soc Exp Path; Int Soc Hist Med; Soc Univ Surg; Am Pediat Surg Asn. *Res:* Gastrointestinal physiology; hypothalamic stimulation and study of gastric secretion; transplantation; extracorporeal organ perfusion; pediatric surgery; computer technology. *Mailing Add:* Dept of Surg Univ of Minn Minneapolis MN 55455

LEONARD, B(ENJAMIN) F(RANKLIN), b Dobbs Ferry, NY, May 12, 21; m 50; c 2. GEOLOGY. *Educ:* Hamilton Col, BS, 42; Princeton Univ, MA, 47, PhD(geol), 51. *Prof Exp:* Geol field asst, Geol Surv Nfld, 42; from jr geologist to geologist, 43-62, GEOLOGIST-IN-CHARGE, ORE MICROS LAB, US GEOL SURV, 62- *Concurrent Pos:* Vis prof, Colo Sch Mines, 67-68; mem, Int Comn Ore Micros, 68-70; mem Paragenetic Comn, Int Asn Genesis of Ore Deposits, 74- *Mem:* Fel Mineral Soc Am; fel Geol Soc Am; Soc Econ Geol; Soc Geol Appl Mineral Deposits; Mineral Asn Can. *Res:* Ore deposits, especially gold, iron and tungsten; geology of central Idaho and northwest Adirondacks; ore minerals; rock-forming minerals, especially amphiboles and iron borates. *Mailing Add:* Cent Mineral Resources Br US Geol Survey Box 25046 Stop 905 Denver CO 80225

LEONARD, BOWEN RAYDO, JR, b Houston, Tex, Mar 7, 26; div; c 2. PHYSICS. *Educ:* Tex Western Col, BS, 47; Univ Wis, MS, 49, PhD(physics), 52. *Prof Exp:* Asst, Univ Wis, 47-51; physicist, Hanford Labs, Gen Elec Co, 52-53, sr scientist, 53-57, mgr exp physics res, 57-64; mgr exp physics res, Pac Northwest Lab, Battelle Mem Inst, 65-67, sr staff scientist, 67-82; RETIRED. *Concurrent Pos:* Mem, nuclear cross sect adv group, Atomic Energy Comn, 57-63, ad-hoc mem, 69-, mem cross sect eval working group, 66- *Mem:* Fel Am Phys Soc; Am Nuclear Soc; Sigma Xi. *Res:* Neutron cross section measurements; nuclear physics; x-ray scattering; slow neutron in-elastic scattering studies of solids and liquids. *Mailing Add:* 212 S Morain St Kennewick WA 99336

LEONARD, BRIAN PHILLIP, b Melbourne, Australia, June 4, 36; m 64; c 2. PLASMA PHYSICS, FLUID MECHANICS. *Educ:* Univ Melbourne, BMechE, 58; Cornell Univ, MAeroE, 61, PhD(aerospace eng), 65. *Prof Exp:* Asst aerospace eng, Cornell Univ, 61-64, asst elec eng, 64-65, vis asst prof, 65-66; sr lectr aeronaut eng, Royal Melbourne Inst Technol, 67; lectr appl math, Monash Univ, Australia, 67-68; Air Force Off Sci Res assoc plasma physics, Columbia Univ, 69-70; asst prof eng sci, Richmond Col NY, 70-76; ASSOC PROF, CITY UNIV NEW YORK, 76- *Mem:* Am Phys Soc; Am Inst Aeronaut & Astronaut; Am Nuclear Soc. *Res:* High temperature gas dynamics; shock wave structure; magnetically driven shock waves; applied mathematics; control systems; hydrodynamics and ship stability and control; thermonuclear fusion. *Mailing Add:* City Univ of New York 130 Stuyvesant Pl Staten Island NY 10301

LEONARD, BYRON PETER, b Morgan City, La, Feb 26, 25; m 46. PHYSICS. *Educ:* Southwestern La Univ, BS, 43; Univ Tex, MA, 52, PhD, 53. *Prof Exp:* Proj engr, US Naval Ord Test Sta, 46-47; instr physics, Southwestern La Univ, 48-50 & Univ Tex, 50-53; chief nuclear res & develop, Gen Dynamics Corp, 53-59; sr staff engr, Space Technol Labs, 59-60; dir satellite-missile observation syst prog, 60-65, vpres & gen mgr, Man Orbiting Lab, Systs Eng Off, 65-68, VPRES & GEN MGR EL SEGUNDO TECH OPERS & GROUP VPRES, PROGS GROUP, AEROSPACE CORP, 68- *Mem:* Am Nuclear Soc; Am Inst Aeronaut & Astronaut. *Res:* Nuclear shielding; radiation effects to materials and operating components; radiation hazards of fission products released to the atmosphere; design of research reactors; design and use of satellite systems, particularly for surveillance applications. *Mailing Add:* Aerospace Corp 2350 E El Segundo Blvd El Segundo CA 90045

LEONARD, CHARLES ARTHUR, b Penns Grove, NJ, June 23, 21; m 55. PHARMACOLOGY. *Educ:* Philadelphia Col Pharm, BSc, 50, MSc, 51, DSc(pharmacol), 54. *Prof Exp:* Asst tech lab, E I du Pont de Nemours & Co, NJ, 39-42, 46-48; res asst, Philadelphia Col Pharm, 54-55; sr pharmacologist, Smith Kline & French Labs, Pa, 55-66; GROUP MGR GEN PHARMACOL, A H ROBINS RES LABS, 66- *Mem:* AAAS; Am Pharmaceut Asn; NY Acad Sci. *Res:* Pharmacology of antiemetic agents; appetite depressants; nasal decongestants, thrombolytics, antihistamines and local anesthetics. *Mailing Add:* A H Robins Res Labs 1211 Sherwood Ave PO Box 26609 Richmond VA 23261

LEONARD, CHARLES BROWN, JR, b Woodbury, NJ, May 28, 34; m 55; c 2. BIOCHEMISTRY. *Educ:* Rutgers Univ, AB, 55; Univ Md, MS, 57, PhD(biochem), 63. *Prof Exp:* Asst, 55-58, from instr to assoc prof, 58-76, dir off admis, 75-77, PROF BIOCHEM, DENT SCH, UNIV MD, BALTIMORE, 76-, ASST DEAN RECRUITMENT & ADMIS, 77- *Concurrent Pos:* Consult, Dr H L Wollenweber, clin pathologist, 59-61. *Mem:* AAAS; Am Chem Soc; NY Acad Sci; Am Inst Chem; Am Asn Col Registr & Admis Officers. *Res:* Amino acid incorporation into rat liver ribosomes; effect of divalent ions on structure of rat liver RNA; effect of o,p'-DDD on cellular metabolism; metabolic products of o,p'-DDD. *Mailing Add:* Dept of Biochem Univ of Md Dent Sch Baltimore MD 21201

LEONARD, CHARLES GRANT, b Detroit, Mich, Apr 7, 39; m 64; c 2. ASTRONOMY. *Educ:* Eastern Mich Univ, BS, 63; Wayne State Univ, MA, 66. *Prof Exp:* Instr physics, Wis State Univ-Whitewater, 66-68; ASST PROF ASTRON & PHYSICS, JACKSON COMMUNITY COL, 68- *Mem:* Am Asn Physics Teachers. *Mailing Add:* Dept of Physics Jackson Community Col Jackson MI 49201

LEONARD, CHESTER D, b New Sharon, Iowa, Aug 27, 07. SOILS. *Educ:* Colo Agr & Mech Col, BS, 31; Rutgers Univ, PhD(soils), 50. *Prof Exp:* From asst county agt to county agt, Colo Agr Mech Col, 34-35, asst exten agronomist, 35-37; state compliance supvr, Agr Adj Admin & Prod & Mkt Admin, USDA, 37-40 & 46-47, assoc horticulturist, Agr Res & Educ Ctr, 50-66, horticulturist, 66-80. *Mem:* Am Soc Hort Sci. *Res:* Mineral nutrition of plants. *Mailing Add:* 800 Lake Jessie Dr Winter Haven FL 33880

LEONARD, CHRISTIANA MORISON, b Boston, Mass, Jan 22, 38; div; c 2. NEUROANATOMY, PSYCHOLOGY. *Educ:* Radcliffe Col, BA, 59; Mass Inst Technol, PhD(psychol), 67. *Prof Exp:* USPHS trainee, Rockefeller Univ, 67-70, res assoc, 70-71, asst prof neuropsychol, 71-74; asst prof anat, Mt Sinai Sch Med, 74-76; ASSOC PROF NEUROSCI, COL MED, UNIV FLA, 76- *Mem:* AAAS; Soc Neurosci; NY Acad Sci. *Res:* Neurological basis of behavior. *Mailing Add:* JHM Health Ctr Col of Med Univ of Fla Gainesville FL 32610

LEONARD, DAVID E, b Greenwich, Conn, Dec 28, 34; m 57; c 2. ENTOMOLOGY. *Educ:* Univ Conn, BS, 56, MS, 60, PhD(entom), 64. *Prof Exp:* Asst entomologist, Conn Agr Exp Sta, 64-69, assoc entomologist, 69-70; assoc prof, 70-76, PROF ENTOM, UNIV MAINE, ORONO, 76- *Concurrent Pos:* Co-ed, Annals Entom Soc Am. *Mem:* Entom Soc Am; Entom Soc Can; Ecol Soc Am; AAAS. *Res:* Biosystematics, biology and ecology of insects; host-parasite relationships. *Mailing Add:* 306 Deering Hall Dept of Entom Univ of Maine Orono ME 04469

LEONARD, E(DMUND) A(LBERT), b New York, NY, Apr 5, 19; m 44; c 3. CHEMICAL ENGINEERING. *Educ:* Columbia Univ, BA, 42, MA, 48. *Prof Exp:* Asst res engr, Alexander Smith, 41-44, develop engr, 46-47, asst dept chief, 47-50, mgr tech labs, 50-51, div supt fiber preparation, 51-53; asst mgr, Yonkers Mfg & Qual Control, 53, mgr process develop & tech serv sects,

53-56; sect head packaging technol, 56-59, packaging coordr, Maxwell House Div, 59-62, packaging develop mgr, 62-73, corp packaging mgr, 74-80, PRIN SCIENTIST, GEN FOODS CORP, 80- *Concurrent Pos:* Vpres, Packaging Educ Found, 73-74; lectr, NY Univ; vpres packaging div, Am Mgt Asn, 75-76; treas, World Packaging Orgn, 76-78. *Honors & Awards:* Packaging Inst USA Prof Award, 74. *Mem:* Hon mem Australian Inst Packaging; Am Chem Soc; Am Mgt Asn. *Res:* Packaging technology; climatic barrier science. *Mailing Add:* Tech Ctr Gen Foods Corp 555 S Broadway Tarrytown NY 10591

LEONARD, EDWARD (FRANCIS), b Paterson, NJ, July 6, 32; m 55; c 5. CHEMICAL ENGINEERING. *Educ:* Mass Inst Technol, BS, 53; Univ Pa, MS, 55, PhD(chem eng), 60. *Prof Exp:* Res engr, Barrett Div, Allied Chem Corp, 53-55; instr chem eng, Univ Pa, 55 & 57-58; from asst prof to assoc prof, 58-67, chmn bioeng comn, 65-68, PROF CHEM ENG, COLUMBIA UNIV, 67- *Concurrent Pos:* Resident eng pract, Ford Found, 64-65; consult, Mt Sinai & St Luke's Hosp, NY, Procter & Gamble Co & Baxter Labs; mem bd, Assoc Univs Inc, 71-78. *Honors & Awards:* Allan P Colburn Award, Am Inst Chem Engrs, 69. *Mem:* Am Inst Chem Engrs; Am Soc Artificial Internal Organs (pres elect, 72); Biomed Eng Soc. *Res:* Heat, mass, momentum transport in fluid systems; distributed parameter chemical systems; transient behavior of chemical process systems; design of transport devices in medicine, particularly the artificial kidney. *Mailing Add:* Dept of Chem Eng Columbia Univ New York NY 10027

LEONARD, EDWARD CHARLES, JR, b Burlington, NC, Aug 21, 27; m 52; c 1. POLYMER CHEMISTRY. *Educ:* Univ NC, BS, 47, PhD(chem), 51; Univ Chicago, MBA, 74. *Prof Exp:* Asst, Univ NC, 47-50; sr res chemist, Res Dept, Bakelite Co, 51-56, group leader, Union Carbide Plastic Co, 56-64; res mgr, Borden Chem Co, 64-67; mgr indust chem prod lab, Res & Develop Div, Kraft, Inc, 67-73; tech dir, Humko Sheffield Chem Co Div, Kraft, Inc, 73-77, vpres res & develop, Humko Sheffield Chem Co Div, 77-80, VPRES RES & DEVELOP, HUMKO CHEM DIV, WITCO CHEM CORP, 80-; V PRES & MEM BD DIRS, ENENCO, INC, 74- *Mem:* Am Chem Soc. *Res:* Synthetic surface active agents; ionic polymerizations; graft polymers; fatty acids; homogeneous catalysis; chemical economics. *Mailing Add:* Hunko Chem Div Witco Chem Corp PO Box 125 Memphis TN 38101

LEONARD, EDWARD H, b Berwick, Maine, Feb 21, 19; m 51; c 1. ANALYTICAL CHEMISTRY. *Educ:* Dartmouth Col, AB, 42; Univ NH, MA, 54; Univ NH, MS, 61. *Prof Exp:* Res & develop engr, Elec Res Lab, Simplex Wire & Cable Co, 42-46, Eng Dept, 46-51; head sci dept high sch, NJ, 51-60, sci coord, 60-64; ASSOC PROF PHYSICS & NAT SCI, WORCESTER STATE COL, 64- *Mem:* AAAS; Am Chem Soc; Am Asn Physics Teachers; Nat Sci Teachers Asn. *Res:* Design and development of apparatus and aids for the teaching of physical science. *Mailing Add:* Dept of Physics Worcester State Col Worcester MA 01602

LEONARD, EDWARD JOSEPH, b Boston, Mass, Mar 20, 26; m 56; c 3. MEDICINE. *Educ:* Harvard Med Sch, MD, 49. *Prof Exp:* Investr, Nat Heart Inst, 53-69; investr, 69-73, head tumor antigen sect, Biol Br, 73-76, HEAD IMMUNOPATH SECT, LAB IMMUNOBIOL, NAT CANCER INST, 76- *Concurrent Pos:* From instr to assoc clin prof, George Washington Univ, 57-74. *Mem:* Am Fedn Clin Res; Soc Gen Physiologists; Am Asn Immunol. *Res:* Tumor immunology. *Mailing Add:* Immunopath Sect Nat Cancer Inst Bethesda MD 20014

LEONARD, FREDERIC ADAMS, b Bangor, Maine, Mar 14, 21; m 52. PHYSIOLOGY. *Educ:* Univ Maine, BS, 43, MS, 48; George Washington Univ, PhD, 55. *Prof Exp:* Res bacteriologist, US Army Biol Labs, Ft Detrick, 48-55, asst dir biol res, 56-61, chief, Med Bact Div, 61-64; staff assoc, Sci Facil Eval Group, NSF, 64-72, assoc prog dir neurobiol, 72-77; DEP SCI DIR, AM LEPROSY FOUND, 77- *Mem:* Am Soc Microbiol; Am Acad Microbiol. *Res:* Infectious diseases; combined infections; immunology. *Mailing Add:* Am Leprosy Found 5400 Pooks Hill Rd Bethesda MD 20014

LEONARD, HENRY SIGGINS, JR, b Needham, Mass, Oct 12, 30; m 54; c 1. MATHEMATICS. *Educ:* Mich State Univ, BS, 52; Harvard Univ, AM, 53, PhD(math), 58. *Prof Exp:* From asst prof to assoc prof math, Carnegie Inst Technol, 58-68; asst chmn dept math sci, 75-78, PROF MATH, NORTHERN ILL UNIV, 68- *Concurrent Pos:* Prin investr, NSF grants, 59-70; vis assoc prof, Univ Ill, Urbana, 67-68; vis fel, Yale Univ, 73-74; vis scholar, Univ Chicago, 80-81. *Mem:* Am Math Soc; Math Asn Am. *Res:* Theory of groups of finite order. *Mailing Add:* Dept of Math Northern Ill Univ DeKalb IL 60115

LEONARD, JACK E, b Chickasha, Okla, Feb 6, 43; m 65; c 3. CHEMISTRY. *Educ:* Harvard Univ, AB, 65; Southern Methodist Univ, BD, 67; Calif Inst Technol, PhD(chem & biol), 71. *Prof Exp:* Asst prof chem, State Univ NY, 61-75 & Tex A&M Univ, 75-81; VIS ASSOC PROF CHEM, UNIV TEX, EL PASO, 81- *Concurrent Pos:* Sr res chemist, Allied Corp, 80. *Mem:* Am Chem Soc; AAAS; Royal Soc Chem. *Res:* Physical organic chemistry from mechanisms of photochemical and electrochemical reactions to laser synthesis of catalysts to mathematical group and graph theory. *Mailing Add:* Dept Chem Univ Tex El Paso TX 79968

LEONARD, JACQUES WALTER, b Montreal, Que, Aug 7, 36; m 63; c 2. POLYMER CHEMISTRY, PHYSICAL CHEMISTRY. *Educ:* Univ Montreal, BSc, 60, MSc, 61, PhD(chem), 64. *Prof Exp:* Can Nat Res Coun fel, Univ Leeds, 64-66; from asst prof to assoc prof chem, 66-75, dept dir, 78-81, PROF CHEM, LAVAL UNIV, 75- *Concurrent Pos:* Vis prof, Univ Sussex, Eng, 77-78. *Mem:* Chem Inst Can. *Res:* Kinetics and thermodynamics of polymerizations in solution; effect of the medium on the equilibrium of reversible of homo- and copolymerizations; thermodynamics of polymer solutions and binary liquid mixtures. *Mailing Add:* Dept of Chem Laval Univ Quebec PQ C1K 7P4 Can

LEONARD, JAMES HOWARD, b Cincinnati, Ohio, Oct 15, 32; m 54; c 4. CHEMICAL ENGINEERING, NUCLEAR ENGINEERING. *Educ:* Univ Cincinnati, BS, 55; Univ Pittsburgh, MS, 58, PhD(chem eng), 60. *Prof Exp:* Mgr nuclear reactor design, Westinghouse Elec Corp, 55-65; assoc prof nuclear eng, Univ Cincinnati, 65-70, prof chem & nuclear eng & chmn dept, 70-74; exec vpres, Nuclear Eng Co, 74-75; pres, Leonard Engrs, 75-76; DIR ADVAN TECHNOL CTR, ALLIS-CHALMERS CORP, 76- *Concurrent Pos:* Consult, US Atomic Energy Comn, 66-74, Nuclear Eng Ctr, US Air Force, 67-72, Monsanto Res Corp, 69-76 & NL Industs, Inc, 75-76; mem grant rev comt, US Environ Protection Admin, 70-73. *Honors & Awards:* Meritorious Achievement Award, Am Nuclear Soc, 60. *Mem:* Am Nuclear Soc; Indust Res Inst. *Res:* Processing and disposal of hazardous wastes; coal processing and gasification; biomass utilization; administration of research and development. *Mailing Add:* 16240 Wildwood Ct Brookfield WI 53005

LEONARD, JAMES JOSEPH, b Schenectady, NY, June 17, 24; m 54; c 4. INTERNAL MEDICINE. *Educ:* Georgetown Univ, MD, 50. *Prof Exp:* From intern to jr asst resident med, Georgetown Univ Hosp, 50-52; asst resident med serv, Boston City Hosp, Mass, 52-53; resident, Pulmonary Dis Div, DC Gen Hosp, 54-55; instr, Sch Med, Georgetown Univ, 55-56; instr, Med Sch, Duke Univ, 56-57; asst prof & dir, Div Cardiol, Georgetown Univ Serv, DC Gen Hosp, 57-59; from asst prof to assoc prof med, Univ Tex Med Br, 59-62; dir cardiopulmonary lab, 61-62; assoc prof med & dir cardiac diag lab, Ohio State Univ, 62-63; assoc prof med & dir div cardiol, Sch Med, Univ Pittsburgh, 63-67, actg chmn dept med, 70-71, prof med, 67-77, chmn dept, 71-77; PROF MED & CHMN DEPT, UNIV HEALTH SCI, 77- *Concurrent Pos:* Washington Heart Asn fel cardiol, Georgetown Univ Hosp, 53-54; Am Trudeau Soc fel, Pulmonary Dis Div, DC Gen Hosp, 54-55; NIH cardiac trainee, Duke Univ Hosp, 56-57; med officer, DC Gen Hosp, 55-56, chief cent heart sta, 57-59; attend cardiol, Mt Alto's Vet Hosp, DC, 57-59. *Mem:* Asn Am Physicians; Asn Prof Med; Asn Univ Cardiologists; Am Clin & Climat Asn; Am Col Physicians. *Res:* Cardiopulmonary physiology. *Mailing Add:* Dept Med Uniformed Serv Univ 4301 Jones Bridge Rd Bethesda MD 20814

LEONARD, JANET LOUISE, b Ames, Iowa, Feb 24, 53. NEUROETHOLOGY, INVERTEBRATE ZOOLOGY. *Educ:* Univ Wis, Madison, BS, 73, PhD(zool), 80. *Prof Exp:* asst prof, Univ Maine-Orono, 80-81; FEL ZOOL, UNIV CALGARY, CAN, 81- *Mem:* Animal Behav Soc; Am Soc Zoologists; Midwest Neurobiologists; Western Soc Naturalists. *Res:* Ethology and neuroethology of invertebrates; temporal organization of jellyfish behavior; mating systems; neuroethology of opisthcbranchs. *Mailing Add:* Div Med Physiol Univ Calgary Calgary AB T2N 1N7 Can

LEONARD, JOHN ALEX, b Swindon, Eng, Dec 13, 37; m 61; c 2. INDUSTRIAL CHEMISTRY. *Educ:* Univ London, BSc, 59, PhD(chem), 62. *Prof Exp:* Res chemist polymers, Shell Develop Co, Calif, 63-66; from sr scientist catalysis to bus planning, Imperial Chem Indust, UK, 66-74; res adv, 74-77, TECHNOL & AGREEMENTS MGR, CAN INDUST LTD, 77- *Concurrent Pos:* Fel, Harvard Univ, 62-63. *Mem:* Am Chem Soc; Chem Can; The Chem Soc. *Res:* Catalytic, electrochemical and biological processes and research management. *Mailing Add:* Can Indust Ltd 630 Dorchester Blvd Montreal PQ H3B 2H6 Can

LEONARD, JOHN EDWARD, b Great Falls, Mont, Apr 18, 18; div; c 2. ORGANIC CHEMISTRY, PHYSICAL CHEMISTRY. *Educ:* Antioch Col, BS, 42; Ohio State Univ, PhD(chem), 49. *Prof Exp:* Res engr, Battelle Mem Inst, 42-46; res fel, Calif Inst Technol, 49-52; res scientist, Beckman Instruments, Inc, 52-56, chief proj engr, 56-62, sr scientist, 62-66, mgr appl res, Med Develop Activity, 66-69; chief scientist, Int Biophysics Corp, 69-71; consult electrochem sensors & instrumentation, 71-78; RES DIR, BROADLEY-JAMES CORP, SANTA ANA, 78- *Mem:* Am Chem Soc; AAAS; NY Acad Sci. *Res:* Analytical instruments, particularly electrochemical, for chemical research and industrial use; biomedical engineering; medical instrumentation research. *Mailing Add:* PO Box #19124 Irvine CA 92714

LEONARD, JOHN JOSEPH, b Philadelphia, Pa, Feb 12, 49; m 72; c 2. PHYSICAL ORGANIC CHEMISTRY. *Educ:* Drexel Univ, BS, 72, PhD(phys org chem), 72. *Prof Exp:* Res assoc chem, Univ Pa, 72-73; asst res chemist, 73-78, supvr catalyst res, 78-79, MGR CATALYST RES, ARCO CHEM CO, DIV ATLANTIC RICHFIELD CO, 79- *Concurrent Pos:* Adj prof math, Drexel Univ Evening Div, 73- *Mem:* Am Chem Soc; Int Catalysis Soc; AAAS. *Res:* Kinetics and mechanisms of organic reactions especially catalysis of organic oxidation reactions(heterogeneous and homogeneous catalysis); spectroscopy of organic molecules. *Mailing Add:* Arco Chem Co 3801 W Chester Pike Newtown Square PA 19073

LEONARD, JOHN LANDER, b Jamaica, NY, Oct 20, 35; m 65; c 1. MATHEMATICS. *Educ:* Carnegie Inst Technol, BS, 57; Univ Calif, Santa Barbara, MA, 63, PhD(math), 66. *Prof Exp:* Opers analyst, Comput Dept, Gen Elec Co, 59-60, mem tech staff, Tech Mil Planning Oper, 60-61; asst math, Univ Calif, Santa Barbara, 61-63, asst prof math, 66-76, LECTR MATH, UNIV ARIZ, 76- *Mem:* Math Asn Am; Sigma Xi. *Res:* Graph theory, extremal problems, connectivity; real function theory; mathematical analysis. *Mailing Add:* Dept of Math Univ of Arizona Tucson AZ 85721

LEONARD, JOHN WILLIAM, civil engineering, structural mechanics, see previous edition

LEONARD, JOSEPH THOMAS, b Scranton, Pa, Aug 8, 32; m 58; c 4. FUEL SCIENCE. *Educ:* Univ Scranton, BS, 54; Pa State Univ, University Park, PhD(fuel technol), 59. *Prof Exp:* Res asst chem, Pa State Univ, University Park, 54-59; RES CHEMIST FUELS, NAVAL RES LAB, WASHINGTON, DC, 59- *Mem:* Am Chem Soc. *Res:* Electrostatic charging of hydrocarbon liquids and fuels; suppression of evaporation of hydrocarbons and smoke abatement techniques. *Mailing Add:* Naval Res Lab Washington DC 20375

LEONARD, JOSEPH WILLIAM, b Pottsville, Pa, Dec 24, 30; m 52; c 4. MINING ENGINEERING. *Educ:* Pa State Univ, BS, 52, MS, 58. *Prof Exp:* Asst to div supt coal mining, Philadelphia & Reading Coal & Iron, Pottsville, Pa, 52-54; asst pre engr, United Elec Coal Co, Chicago, Ill, 54-56; res asst coal prep, Pa State Univ, 56-58; res engr coal mining, US Steel Corp, Monroeville, Pa, 58-61; dir bur, 61-81, dean, 78-81, PROF MINING, WVA UNIV, 74-, WILLIAM N POUNDSTONE RES PROF, 81- *Concurrent Pos:* Consult, Pa Elec Co, Johnstown, 71-, Cortix, Bochum, WGer, 78- *Honors & Awards:* Howard N Eavenson Award, Am Inst Mining Engrs, 69. *Mem:* Fel Am Inst Chemists; Am Inst Mining Engrs; Am Mining Cong. *Res:* Mining; coal reserve analysis; coal preparation including design; coal utilization. *Mailing Add:* Dept Mining Eng WVa Univ Morgantown WV 26505

LEONARD, JUDSON SLATER, b New York, NY, Aug 28, 45. COMPUTER SCIENCE. *Educ:* Oberlin Col, BA, 69. *Prof Exp:* prin engr, 70-80, CONSULT ENGR, DIGITAL EQUIP CORP, 80- *Res:* High performance computer arithmetic; multiprocessor computer systems. *Mailing Add:* Digital Equip Corp 200 Forest St Marlboro MA 01752

LEONARD, LAURENCE, b New York, NY, Jan 9, 32; m 58; c 4. PHYSICAL METALLURGY, MATERIALS SCIENCE. *Educ:* Mass Inst Technol, SB, 54, SM, 56, ScD(metall), 62. *Prof Exp:* Asst prof metall, Case Western Reserve Univ, 62-69; group supvr, SKF Industs, Inc, 69-71; SR STAFF METALLURGIST, RES LABS, FRANKLIN INST, 71- *Concurrent Pos:* Lectr, King of Prussia Grad Ctr, Pa State Univ; adj assoc prof, Drexel Univ Eve Col, 78- *Mem:* Am Soc Metals. *Res:* Materials failure analysis; physical metallurgy of rolling contact bearings; scanning electron microscopy; metal embrittlement; x-ray diffraction; residual stresses; phase transformations; heat treatment; nondestructive testing; wear monitoring by oil analysis. *Mailing Add:* Franklin Inst 20th & Race Sts Philadelphia PA 19103

LEONARD, MARTHA FRANCES, b New Brunswick, NJ, May 10, 16. PEDIATRICS. *Educ:* NJ Col Women, BSc, 36; Johns Hopkins Univ, MD, 40. *Prof Exp:* Intern, Baltimore City Hosp, 40-41; asst resident med, Vanderbilt Univ Hosp, 42-43; asst resident pediat, New York Hosp, 43-46; pvt pract, 46-60; from instr to assoc prof pediat, 62-69, assoc prof, 69-79, PROF PEDIAT, CHILD STUDY CTR, YALE UNIV, 79- *Concurrent Pos:* Fel, Child Study Ctr, Yale Univ, 60-62. *Mem:* Am Acad Pediat; Soc Res Child Develop; Asn Ambulatory Pediat. *Res:* Normal and deviant child development; effects of deprivation; failure to thrive; child abuse; developmental impact of conditions such as genetic, metabolic and endocrine disorders. *Mailing Add:* Child Study Ctr Yale Univ New Haven CT 06510

LEONARD, NELSON JORDAN, b Newark, NJ, Sept 1, 16; m 47; c 4. ORGANIC BIOCHEMISTRY. *Educ:* Lehigh Univ, BS, 37; Oxford Univ, BSc, 40; Columbia Univ, PhD(org chem), 42. *Hon Degrees:* DSc, Lehigh Univ, 63; Dr, Adam Mickiewicz Univ, Poznan, Poland, 80. *Prof Exp:* Fel & asst chem, Univ Ill, 42-43, instr, 43-44, assoc, 44-45; sci consult & spec investr, Field Intel Agency Tech, US Army Dept & US Dept Commerce, 45-46; assoc, 46-47, from asst prof to prof chem, 47-73, head, Div Org Chem, 54-63, PROF CHEM & BIOCHEM, UNIV ILL, URBANA, 73-, MEM STAFF, CTR ADVAN STUDY, 68- *Concurrent Pos:* Mem, Comt Med Res, 44-46; ed, Org Syntheses, 51-58, ed-in-chief, 56, pres, bd dirs, 80; Am-Swiss Found lectr, 53, 70; Guggenheim Mem Found fel, 59, 67; mem prog comt basic phys sci, Alfred P Sloan Found, 61-66; Stieglitz lectr, 62; mem educ adv bd, John Simon Guggenheim Mem Found, 69-; Edgar Fahs Smith Mem lectr, Univ Pa, 75; Arapahoe lectr, Univ Colo, 79; Calbiochem-Boehring lectr, US Dept Agr, 81. *Honors & Awards:* Award, Am Chem Soc, 63, Edgar Fahs Smith Award, 75, Roger Adams Award, 81; Synthetic Org Chem Mfrs Award, 70. *Mem:* Nat Acad Sci; Am Acad Arts & Sci; Am Chem Soc; Royal Soc Chem; Swiss Chem Soc. *Res:* Structure, synthesis and biological activity of cytokinins; modification of nucleic acid bases; fluorescent probes of coenzyme and nucleic acid structures; intramolecular interactions. *Mailing Add:* Dept of Chem & Biochem Univ of Ill Urbana IL 61801

LEONARD, RALPH AVERY, b Louisburg, NC, Mar 2, 37; m 58; c 3. SOIL CHEMISTRY. *Educ:* NC State Univ, BS, 59, PhD(soil chem), 66; Purdue Univ, MS, 62. *Prof Exp:* Instr soil sci, NC State Univ, 62-66; RES SOIL SCIENTIST, USDA, 66- *Mem:* Am Chem Soc; Soil Sci Soc Am; Am Soc Agron. *Res:* Physical chemistry of soils; fate of pesticides in soil and water; soil chemical aspects of waste disposal and utilization on the land. *Mailing Add:* Southeast Watershed Res Prog PO Box 5677 Athens GA 30604

LEONARD, RAYMOND EDWIN, b Proctor, Vt, Dec 2, 28; m 57; c 2. FOREST ECOLOGY, FOREST INFLUENCES. *Educ:* Univ Vt, BS, 55; Univ Helsinki, MMT, 57; Yale Univ, MS, 64; State Univ NY Col Environ Sci & Forestry, Syracuse, PhD(forestry), 67. *Prof Exp:* Forester, State of Vt Forest Serv, 51-53; RES FORESTER, USDA FOREST SERV, 57- *Mem:* Fel AAAS; Ecol Soc Am; Am Soc Agron. *Res:* Ecology of wildlands, including coastal areas; biological and physical impacts of recreationists. *Mailing Add:* USDA Forest Serv PO Box 640 Concord Mast Rds Durham NH 03824

LEONARD, REID HAYWARD, b Littleton, NH, Aug 28, 18; m 46; c 3. CHEMISTRY. *Educ:* Univ Vt, BS, 40; Univ WVa, MS, 42; Univ Wis, PhD(biochem), 47. *Prof Exp:* Asst, Exp Sta, Univ WVa, 40-42; asst, Univ Wis & Forest Prod Lab, US Forest Serv, 43-45; res chemist, Salvo Chem Corp, Wis, 46-47; res chemist, Newport Industs, 47-56; CONSULT BIOCHEMIST, 56- *Mem:* AAAS; Am Chem Soc. *Res:* Chemistry of wood; sugars from wood; lignin; levulinic acid; kidney stones; blood lipids; gas chromatography. *Mailing Add:* 537 Brent Lane Pensacola FL 32503

LEONARD, ROBERT GRESHAM, b Roanoke, Va, Jan 27, 37; m 60; c 2. MECHANICAL ENGINEERING, CONTROL ENGINEERING. *Educ:* Va Polytech Inst, BS, 60, MS, 65; Pa State Univ, PhD(mech eng), 70. *Prof Exp:* Eng trainee, Gen Elec Co, Va, 56-59; instr mech eng, Va Polytech Inst, 60-65 & Pa State Univ, 65-70; from asst prof to assoc prof mech eng, Purdue Univ, 70-78; PROF MECH ENG & ASST DEPT HEAD, VA POLYTECH INST & STATE UNIV, 78- *Concurrent Pos:* Lectr, Purdue Univ, 67, asst dir,

Ray W Herrick Labs, 76-78. *Honors & Awards:* Homer Addams Award, Am Soc Heating Refrig & Air-Conditioning Engrs, 75. *Mem:* Am Soc Mech Engrs. *Res:* Automatic controls; dynamic systems modeling; simulation; fluid power systems; parameter identification. *Mailing Add:* 207 Smithfield Dr Blacksburg VA 24060

LEONARD, ROBERT MEYER, b Pocatello, Idaho, Oct 2, 22; m 46; c 3. PHARMACOGNOSY, PHARMACOLOGY. *Educ:* Idaho State Univ, BS, 44; Univ Minn, PhD(pharmacog), 53. *Prof Exp:* Pharmacist, retail pharms, 45; asst pharm, Univ Minn, 45-46, asst pharmacog, 46-47; pharmacist, retail pharms, 47-48; from asst prof to prof pharmacol & pharmacog, George Washington Univ, 51-64, asst dean Sch Pharm, 56-61, actg dean, 61-62, dean, 62-64; grants assoc, 64-65, HEALTH SCI ADMINR, DIV RES GRANTS, NIH, 65- *Mem:* AAAS; NY Acad Sci. *Res:* General pharmacology; biological origin of drugs; general metabolism. *Mailing Add:* 1009 Laredo Rd Silver Spring MD 20901

LEONARD, ROBERT STUART, b Berkeley, Calif, Jan 20, 30; m 56; c 2. GEOPHYSICS, AERONOMY. *Educ:* Univ Nev, BS, 52, MS, 53; Univ Alaska, PhD(geophys), 61. *Prof Exp:* Res asst auroral studies, Geophys Inst, Univ Alaska, 53-58, instr, 58-60; radio physicist, 61-62, sr ionospheric physicist, 62-69, prog mgr, 69-72, asst dir, 72-77, DIR, RADIO PHYSICS LAB, SRI INT, 77- *Mem:* Int Union Radio Sci; Am Geophys Union; Am Phys Soc. *Res:* Chemical seeding in the ionosphere; transionospheric propagation; ionospheric disturbances. *Mailing Add:* SRI Int 333 Ravenswood Ave Menlo Park CA 94025

LEONARD, ROBERT THOMAS, b Providence, RI, Dec 18, 43; m 66; c 1. PLANT PHYSIOLOGY. *Educ:* Univ RI, BS, 65, MS, 67; Univ Ill, Urbana, PhD(biol), 71. *Prof Exp:* Fel plant physiol, Univ Ill & Purdue Univ, 71-73; asst prof, 73-78, ASSOC PROF PLANT PHYSIOL & VCHMN DEPT, UNIV CALIF, RIVERSIDE, 78- *Mem:* Am Soc Plant Physiologists; Am Inst Biol Sci; AAAS. *Res:* Physiology and biochemistry of ion transport in plants. *Mailing Add:* Dept of Bot & Plant Sci Univ of Calif Riverside CA 92521

LEONARD, ROY J, b Central Square, NY, Aug 17, 29; c 2. GEOTECHNICAL ENGINEERING. *Educ:* Clarkson Col Technol, BSCE, 52; Univ Conn, MS, 54; Iowa State Univ, PhD(civil eng), 58. *Prof Exp:* Asst prof civil eng, Univ Del, 57-59; from asst prof to assoc prof, Lehigh Univ, 59-66; PROF CIVIL ENG, UNIV KANS, 66- *Concurrent Pos:* NSF res grants, 59 & 62, sci fac fel, 63-65. *Mem:* Asn Eng Geologists; Soc Mining Engrs; Am Soc Eng Educ; Int Soc Found Eng & Soil Mechanics; fel Am Soc Civil Engrs. *Mailing Add:* Dept Civil Eng Univ of Kans 2006 Engineering Lawrence KS 66045

LEONARD, SAMUEL LEESON, b Elizabeth, NJ, Nov 26, 05; m 34; c 2. ZOOLOGY. *Educ:* Rutgers Univ, BSc, 27; Univ Wis, MSc, 29, PhD(zool), 31. *Prof Exp:* Asst zool, Univ Wis, 27-31; fel, Nat Res Coun, Col Physicians & Surg, Columbia Univ, 31-33; asst prof biol, Union Univ, NY, 33-37; asst prof zool, Rutgers Univ, 37-41; from assoc prof to prof, 41-71, EMER PROF ZOOL, CORNELL UNIV, 71- *Mem:* AAAS; Am Soc Zool; Soc Exp Biol & Med; Endocrine Soc; Am Physiol Soc; Am Asn Anat. *Res:* Endocrinology; physiology of reproduction; mechanisms of hormone action. *Mailing Add:* Div of Biol Sci Emerson Hall Cornell Univ Ithaca NY 14850

LEONARD, STANLEY LEE, b Oakland, Calif, Aug 27, 26; wid; c 4. PLASMA PHYSICS. *Educ:* Principia Col, BS, 47; Univ Calif, PhD(physics), 53. *Prof Exp:* Physicist, Radiation Lab, Univ Calif, 52-53; instr physics, Principia Col, 53-55, asst prof, 55-56; mem tech staff, Ramo-Wooldridge Corp, 56-59 & Space Technol Labs, Inc, 59-60; mem tech staff, 60-64, head, plasma radiation dept, Plasma Res Lab, 64-73, head, chem physics dept, Chem & Physics Lab, 73-74, DIR PHOTOVOLTAIC SYSTS, ENERGY SYSTS DIRECTORATE, AEROSPACE CORP, 74- *Mem:* Am Phys Soc; Int Solar Energy Soc. *Res:* Analysis of terrestrial photovoltaic applications. *Mailing Add:* 5019 Rockvalley Rd Palos Verdes Peninsula CA 90274

LEONARD, THOMAS JOSEPH, b Watertown, Mass, July 27, 37; m 65; c 1. DEVELOPMENTAL GENETICS. *Educ:* Clark Univ, AB, 62; Ind Univ, PhD(microbiol), 67. *Prof Exp:* NIH fel, Harvard Univ, 67-68; assoc prof mycol, Univ Ky, 68-74; PROF BOT & GENETICS, UNIV WIS-MADISON, 74- *Mem:* AAAS; Genetics Soc Am; Mycol Soc Am; Brit Mycol Soc. *Res:* Physiology and genetics of fungi as applied to development; genetics and physiological aspects of cell differentiation. *Mailing Add:* Dept of Bot Univ of Wis Madison WI 53705

LEONARD, WALTER RAYMOND, b Scott Co, Va, July 5, 23; m 51; c 2. ZOOLOGY, PHYSIOLOGY. *Educ:* Tusculum Col, BA, 46; Vanderbilt Univ, MS, 47, PhD(zool), 49. *Prof Exp:* Asst prof biol, 49-50, assoc prof & acting chmn dept, 50-53, REEVES PROF BIOL & CHMN DEPT, WOFFORD COL, 54- *Res:* Respiratory metabolism of Allomyces arbuscula; effects of activity on growth in hydra. *Mailing Add:* Dept of Biol Wofford Col Spartanburg SC 29301

LEONARD, WILLIAM F, b Hampton, Va, Jan 18, 38; m 58, 75; c 5. ELECTRICAL ENGINEERING. *Educ:* Univ Va, BSEE, 60, MSEE, 63, ScD(elec eng), 66. *Prof Exp:* Aerospace technologist, NASA-Langley Res Ctr, Va, 60-66; asst prof elec eng, Inst Technol, 66-69, assoc prof, 74, assoc dean & dir, Grad Div, 79-81 PROF ELEC ENG, SOUTHERN METHODIST UNIV, 74-, DEAN AD INTERIM, 81- *Concurrent Pos:* Consult, WTex Eng, 69-74, Nuclear Systs Inc, 70-71, Marlow Indust, 77- & Varo Semiconductor, 77-78. *Mem:* Sigma Xi; Inst Elec & Electronics Engrs; Am Soc Eng Educ; Am Vacuum Soc. *Res:* Physical electronics; bulk and surface electronic transport studies in solids; fabrication of III-V compound and alloy semiconductors; infrared photodetectors. *Mailing Add:* Sch Eng & Appl Sci Southern Methodist Univ Dallas TX 75275

LEONARD, WILLIAM J, JR, b Ravenna, Ohio, Apr 28, 36. PHYSICAL CHEMISTRY. *Educ:* Kent State Univ, BS, 58; Purdue Univ, PhD(chem), 63. *Prof Exp:* Fel phys polymer chem, Stanford Univ, 63-65; chemist, Shell Develop Co, 65-72; dir polymer sci, 72-78, DIR TECH EVAL, DYNAPOL, INC, 78- *Mem:* AAAS; Am Chem Soc; NY Acad Sci; Inst Food Technologists. *Res:* Protein conformation; polymer chain statistics; solution thermodynamics; optical rotatory dispersion; liquid crystals. *Mailing Add:* 1454 Page Mill Rd Palo Alto CA 94304

LEONARD, WILLIAM WILSON, b Portland, Maine, May 1, 34; m 61; c 2. MATHEMATICS. *Educ:* Univ Tampa, BS, 60; Univ SC, MS, 63, PhD(math), 65. *Prof Exp:* Asst prof math, Susquehanna Univ, 64-65; from asst prof to assoc prof, 65-74, PROF MATH, GA STATE UNIV, 74-, MEM, URBAN LIFE FAC, 77- *Mem:* Am Math Soc; Math Asn Am; Math Soc France. *Res:* Module theory; homological algebra. *Mailing Add:* Dept of Math Ga State Univ Atlanta GA 30303

LEONARDS, G(ERALD) A(LLEN), b Montreal, Que, Apr 29, 21; m 45; c 2. CIVIL ENGINEERING. *Educ:* McGill Univ, BSCE, 43; Purdue Univ, MSCE, 48, PhD(soil mech), 52. *Prof Exp:* Lectr mech, McGill Univ, 43-46; from instr to prof soil mech, 46-72, head sch civil eng, 65-70, PROF CIVIL ENG, PURDUE UNIV, 72- *Concurrent Pos:* Mem adv bd, joint hwy res proj, Int State Hwy Dept, 58-72, dir, 65-70; res award, Hwy Res Bd, Nat Acad Sci-Nat Res Coun, 65. *Honors & Awards:* Norman Medal, Am Soc Civil Engrs, 65. *Mem:* Am Soc Civil Engrs; Int Soc Soil Mech & Found Engrs. *Res:* Physicochemical and engineering properties of soils; foundation engineering. *Mailing Add:* Sch of Civil Eng Purdue Univ West Lafayette IN 47907

LEONE, CHARLES ABNER, b Camden, NJ, July 13, 18; m 41; c 3. IMMUNOLOGY, RADIATION BIOLOGY. *Educ:* Rutgers Univ, BS, 40, MS, 42, PhD, 49. *Prof Exp:* Asst zool, Rutgers Univ, 40-42, instr, 46-49; from asst prof to prof, Univ Kans, 49-68; prof biol & dean grad sch, Bowling Green State Univ, 68-71, vprovost res & grad studies, 71-75; vpres & vprovost, 75-79, vpres res & grad studies, 79-81, PROF ZOOL, UNIV ARK, FAYETTEVILLE, 81- *Concurrent Pos:* Resident res assoc, Argonne Nat Lab, 55, consult, 55-60; adj prof, Med Col Ohio, Toledo, 69-75. *Mem:* Fel AAAS; Am Asn Immunologists. *Res:* Immunochemistry; radiation biophysics; comparative serology among arthropods, mollusks and mammals. *Mailing Add:* Zool Dept Univ Ark Fayetteville AR 72701

LEONE, FRED CHARLES, b New York, NY, Aug 3, 22; m 45; c 7. STATISTICS. *Educ:* Manhattan Col, BA, 41; Georgetown Univ, MS, 43; Purdue Univ, PhD(math statist, educ), 49. *Prof Exp:* Instr, Georgetown Univ, 42-43; instr, Purdue Univ, 43-44 & 46-49; from instr to prof math, Case Western Reserve Univ, 49-66, dir statist lab, 51-65, actg chmn dept, 63-65; prof statist & indust eng, Univ Iowa, 66-75; EXEC DIR & SECY-TREAS, AM STATIST ASN, 73- *Concurrent Pos:* Fulbright prof, Univ Sao Paulo, Brazil, 68-69; ed, Technometrics, 63-68; NAm ed, Statist Theory & Methods Abstracts, 69-73. *Mem:* Fel AAAS; fel Am Soc Qual Control; fel Am Statist Asn; Sigma Xi; Math Asn Am. *Res:* Experimental design and statistics applied to engineering; order statistics, especially in analysis of variance. *Mailing Add:* Am Statist Asn 806 15th St NW Washington DC 20005

LEONE, IDA ALBA, b Elizabeth, NJ, Apr 28, 22. POLLUTION BIOLOGY. *Educ:* Rutgers Univ, BS, 44, MS, 46. *Prof Exp:* Asst plant path, Col Agr, Rutgers Univ, New Brunswick, 46-50, res assoc, 50-58, asst res specialist, 58-70, assoc res prof, 70-76, PROF PLANT BIOL, COOK COL, RUTGERS UNIV, NEW BRUNSWICK, 76- *Concurrent Pos:* Consult, NY State Environ Protection Bur, 75-76. *Mem:* Sigma Xi; Am Phytopath Soc; Am Soc Plant Physiologists; Air Pollution Control Asn. *Res:* Effect of air pollution; nutritional, physiological and environmental factors on plant growth; plants as sources of air pollution; undergraduate and graduate courses in air pollution effects; effect of cooling-tower salt spray on crops; phytotoxicity of anaerobic landfill gases. *Mailing Add:* 876 Rayhon Terr Rahway NJ 07065

LEONE, JAMES A, b Braddock, Pa, Dec 11, 37; m 61; c 1. PHYSICAL CHEMISTRY, INSTRUMENTATION. *Educ:* Univ Cincinnati, BS, 61; Johns Hopkins Univ, MA, 63, PhD(phys chem), 65. *Prof Exp:* Res assoc, Univ Notre Dame, 65-67; from asst prof to assoc prof phys chem, 67-74, dir med technol, 74-77, ASSOC PROF CHEM & COMPUT SCI, CANISIUS COL, 77- *Concurrent Pos:* Vis assoc prof, Va Polytech Inst & State Univ, 75-76. *Mem:* Am Chem Soc; Sigma Xi; Soc Appl Spectros. *Res:* Radiation chemistry; ESR; on-line minicomputers; minicomputer and microprocessor interfacing; minicomputers and microprocessors in instrumentation automation. *Mailing Add:* Dept of Chem Canisius Col Buffalo NY 14208

LEONE, RONALD EDMUND, b New York, NY, Aug 11, 42. ORGANIC CHEMISTRY. *Educ:* Northwestern Univ, BA, 64; Princeton Univ, MA, 67, PhD(org chem), 70. *Prof Exp:* Fel org chem, Yale Univ, 69-71; SR RES CHEMIST, EASTMAN KODAK CO, 71- *Mem:* Am Chem Soc; Sigma Xi. *Res:* Aspects of physical organic chemistry including organic reaction mechanisms and nuclear magnetic resonance spectroscopy; synthesis of sensitizing dyes and silver halide fogging agents; photographic chemistry. *Mailing Add:* Eastman Kodak Co Res Labs 1669 Lake Ave Rochester NY 14650

LEONE, STEPHEN ROBERT, b New York, NY, May 19, 48. CHEMICAL PHYSICS. *Educ:* Northwestern Univ, BA, 70; Univ Calif, Berkeley, PhD(phys chem), 74. *Prof Exp:* Asst prof chem, Univ Southern Calif, 74-76; physicist, Nat Bur Standards, 76-78. *Concurrent Pos:* Adj asst prof chem, Univ Colo, 76-80, adj prof, 80-; Alfred P Sloan Found fel, 77. *Mem:* Am Phys Soc; Am Chem Soc; Am Inst Physics; Sigma Xi; fel Optical Soc Am. *Res:* Laser-excited chemical reactions and isotope separation; kinetics and spectroscopic investigations of excited states using specific laser excitation; energy transfer and dynamical processes of small gas phase molecules; photodissociation; new laser development; ion molecule reaction dynamics. *Mailing Add:* Joint Inst for Lab Astrophysics Univ of Colo Boulder CO 80309

LEONG, BASIL K J, pharmacology, toxicology, see previous edition

LEONG, JO-ANN CHING, b Honolulu, Hawaii, May 15, 42; c 1. VIROLOGY. *Educ:* Univ Calif, Berkeley, BA, 64; Univ Calif, PhD(microbiol), 71. *Prof Exp:* Sr res asst virol, Dept Surg, Stanford Univ Sch Med, 65-67; from teaching assoc microbiol to res biochemist, Univ Calif, San Francisco, 71-73, res fel biochem, 73-75; asst prof, 75-80, ASSOC PROF MICROBIOL, ORE STATE UNIV, 80- *Concurrent Pos:* Dernham fel, Am Cancer Soc, Calif Div, 73-75. *Honors & Awards:* Giannini Found fel for med res, 73. *Mem:* Am Soc Microbiologists; AAAS; Soc Gen Microbiol; NY Acad Sci; Am Asn Cancer Res. *Res:* Virus-cell interactions; tumor virology. *Mailing Add:* Dept of Microbiol Ore State Univ Nash Hall Corvallis OR 97331

LEONG, JOHN YICK-CHUNG, solid state electronics, material science, see previous edition

LEONG, KAM CHOY, b Honolulu, Hawaii, Dec 17, 20; m 50; c 3. BIOCHEMISTRY, POULTRY NUTRITION. *Educ:* Wash State Univ, BS, 49, MS, 50; Univ Wis, PhD(biochem, poultry), 58. *Prof Exp:* Asst, Wash State Univ, 48-50; jr animal husbandman, Univ Hawaii, 51-54; asst, Univ Wis, 54-57; fel, Wash State Univ, 57-58; jr poultry scientist, 58-61; res chemist, Bur Commercial Fisheries, 61-65; NUTRITIONIST, ALBERS MILLING CO DIV, CARNATION CO, 65- *Mem:* Am Poultry Sci Asn; Am Inst Nutrit. *Res:* Amino acids; enzymes; vitamins; protein; metabolizable energy. *Mailing Add:* Albers Milling Co Div Carnation Co 5045 Wilshire Blvd Los Angeles CA 90036

LEONHARD, FREDERICK WILHELM, b Rheinhausen, Ger, Oct 25, 14; US citizen; m 50; c 4. PHYSICS. *Educ:* Univ Tübingen, dipl, 49, Dr rer nat, 54. *Prof Exp:* Asst exp physics & electron micros, Univ Tübingen, 48-50; scientist, Deutsche Gold und Silber Scheideanstalt, 50-56; res team leader, US Army Signal Res & Develop Lab, NJ, 56-60; scientist lab head, McDonnell Aircraft Corp, Mo, 60-69; PROF ELEC ENG, UNIV MO-COLUMBIA, 69- *Mem:* Am Vacuum Soc. *Res:* Crystallography; metallography; physical electronics of semiconductors; dielectrics; metals; thin films and surfaces; growth of single crystal thin films; electronic devices; thin film and semiconductor microelectronic materials, techniques and circuitry. *Mailing Add:* 218 Parkway Columbia MO 65201

LEONHARDT, EARL A, b Council Bluffs, Iowa, Apr 18, 19; m 41; c 3. MATHEMATICS. *Educ:* Union Col, Nebr, BA, 50; Univ Nebr, ME, 52, PhD(sec educ, math), 62. *Prof Exp:* High sch instr, Nebr, 51-52; from instr to assoc prof, 52-62, PROF MATH, UNION COL, NEBR, 62- *Concurrent Pos:* Mem, Nat Coun Teachers Math. *Mem:* Math Asn Am. *Mailing Add:* Dept of Math Union Col Lincoln NE 68506

LEONORA, JOHN, b Milwaukee, Wis, Jan 30, 28; m 52; c 2. ENDOCRINOLOGY. *Educ:* Univ Wis, BS, 49, MS, 54, PhD(zool), 57. *Prof Exp:* Asst endocrinol, Univ Wis, 52-57; from instr to assoc prof, 59-69, PROF MED, SCH MED, LOMA LINDA UNIV, 69-, CO-CHMN DEPT PHYSIOL & PHARMACOL, 74- *Concurrent Pos:* NIH fel, Univ Wis, 57-59. *Mem:* AAAS; NY Acad Sci; Endocrine Soc; Sigma Xi. *Res:* Hypothalamic-parotid endocrine axis; relationship of dentinal fluid movement to dental caries. *Mailing Add:* Dept of Physiol Loma Linda Univ Sch of Med Loma Linda CA 92354

LEONTIS, T(HOMAS) E(RNEST), b Plainfield, NJ, Mar 13, 17; m 54; c 2. PHYSICAL METALLURGY. *Educ:* Stevens Inst Technol, ME, 38; Carnegie Inst Technol, MS, 42, DSc(phys metall), 46. *Prof Exp:* Instr chem, Stevens Inst Technol, 38-39; res metallurgist, Vanadium Corp Am, 39-41; grad fel, Carnegie Inst Technol, 41-44; metallurgist, Dow Chem Co, 44-51, sect chief metall lab, 51-57, asst to dir metall labs, 57-62, proj planning mgr, Dow Metal Prod Co Div, 62-65, mgr govt bus, 65-68, mgr tech & govt laison, 68-71; sr tech adv & assoc mgr, 71-75, MGR, MAGNESIUM RES CTR, BATTELLE-COLUMBUS, 75- *Mem:* AAAS; Am Soc Metals (secy, 66-68, vpres, 70, pres, 71); Am Inst Mining, Metall & Petrol Engrs; Am Soc Metals Found Educ & Res (pres, 72). *Res:* Oxidation of metals; age hardening; powder metallurgy extrusion; extrusion of metals; high temperature magnesium alloys; magnesium alloy development; melting, casting and solidification; die casting; metal protection; surface finishing. *Mailing Add:* Magnesium Res Ctr 505 King Ave Battelle-Columbus Labs Columbus OH 43201

LEOPOLD, ALDO CARL, b Albuquerque, NMex, Dec 18, 19; c 3. PLANT PHYSIOLOGY. *Educ:* Univ Wis, BA, 41; Harvard Univ, MA, 47, PhD(biol), 48. *Prof Exp:* Plant physiologist, Hawaiian Pineapple Co, Hawaii, 48-49; from asst prof to prof hort, Purdue Univ, 49-75; grad dean & asst vpres res, Univ Nebr, 75-77; distinguished scientist, 77-78, WILLIAM C CROCKER SCIENTIST, BOYCE THOMPSON INST, ITHACA, NY, 78- *Concurrent Pos:* Carnegie vis prof, Univ Hawaii, 62; mem panel regulatory biol, NSF, 65; bd govs, Am Inst Biol Sci; sr policy analyst NSF, 74-75; mem bd agr & renewable resources, Nat Res Coun, 75-78. *Mem:* AAAS; Bot Soc Am; Am Soc Plant Physiol (vpres, 59, pres, 65); Crop Sci Soc Am. *Res:* Plant hormones; plant growth and development; seed viability. *Mailing Add:* Boyce Thompson Inst Ithaca NY 14853

LEOPOLD, ALDO STARKER, b Burlington, Iowa, Oct 22, 13; m 38; c 2. ZOOLOGY, FORESTRY. *Educ:* Univ Wis, BS, 36; Univ Calif, PhD(zool), 44. *Prof Exp:* Jr biologist, Soil Erosion Serv, USDA, Wis, 34-35; field biologist, State Conserv Comn, Mo, 39-44; dir field res, Conserv Sect, Pan Am Union, Mex, 44-46; from instr to prof zool, 46-68, assoc dir, Mus Vert Zool, 59-69, prof, 68-78, EMER PROF ZOOL & FORESTRY, UNIV CALIF, BERKELEY, 78-, DIR, SAGEHEN CREEK FIELD STA & CONSERVATIONIST, 69- *Concurrent Pos:* Guggenheim fel, 48. *Mem:* Nat Acad Sci; Wildlife Soc (pres, 57-58); Cooper Ornith Soc (pres, 58-60); Wilson Ornith Soc; assoc Am Soc Mammalogists. *Res:* Wildlife ecology and management; field ornithology and mammalogy; comparative anatomy and behavior of wild and domestic turkeys; nature of heritable wildness in turkeys; ecology and management of deer, moose and caribou; California quail; wildlife of Mexico. *Mailing Add:* Sch of Forestry & Conserv Univ of Calif 145 Mulford Hall Berkeley CA 94720

LEOPOLD, BENGT, b Valbo, Sweden, Dec 23, 22; m 45; c 3. PAPER CHEMISTRY, PULP & PAPER TECHNOLOGY. *Educ:* Royal Inst Tech, Sweden, BChem Eng, 47, MS, 49, PhD(org chem), 52. *Prof Exp:* Sr res chemist, Columbia-Southern Chem Corp, Ohio, 52-53; mgr pioneering res div, Indust Cellulose Res Ltd, Can Inst Paper Co, 53-58; mgr basic res div, Mead Corp, Ohio, 58-60, assoc dir res, 60-61; PROF PULP & PAPER RES & DIR, EMPIRE STATE PAPER RES INST, STATE UNIV NY COL ENVIRON SCI & FORESTRY, SYRACUSE UNIV, 61-, CHMN DEPT PAPER SCI & ENG, 74- *Concurrent Pos:* Ed, J Tech Asn Pulp & Paper Indust, 66- *Mem:* AAAS; Am Chem Soc; fel Tech Asn Pulp & Paper Indust; Paper Indust Mgt Asn; Can Pulp & Paper Asn. *Res:* Fiber physics; structure of lignin; mechanical properties of wood fibers; cellulose-water interactions. *Mailing Add:* Dept Paper Sci & Eng State Univ NY Col Forestry Syracuse NY 13210

LEOPOLD, ESTELLA (BERGERE), b Madison, Wis, Jan 8, 27. BOTANY. *Educ:* Univ Wis, PhB, 48; Univ Calif, MS, 50; Yale Univ, PhD(bot), 55. *Prof Exp:* Asst physiol & embryol, Genetics Exp Sta, Smith Col, 51-52; asst biol, Yale Univ, 52-53, asst animal ecol, 54; botanist, paleont & stratig br, US Geol Surv, 55-76; dir, 76-82, PROF BOT & FOREST RESOURCES, QUATERNARY RES CTR, 76- *Concurrent Pos:* Asst, Lab Tree Ring Res, Univ Ariz, 51 & US Forest Prod Lab, 52; NSF travel grants, Int Asn Quaternary Res, Spain, 57, Poland, 61 & England, 77; adj prof, Univ Colo, Boulder, 67-; vis prof, Inst Environ Studies, Univ Wis-Madison, 71-72. *Honors & Awards:* Co-recipient, Conservationist of Year Award, Nat Wildlife Fedn, 69. *Mem:* Nat Acad Sci; Ecol Soc Am; Bot Soc Am; fel AAAS. *Res:* Paleobotany, palynology and paleoecology; pollen and spore floras of late Cenozoic age in Wyoming, Colorado and Alaska; palynology research in late quaternary deposits of Connecticut, Washington & California; Upper Cretaceous pollen and spore floras of Alabama and Wyoming. *Mailing Add:* Quaternary Res Ctr Univ of Wash Seattle WA 98195

LEOPOLD, LUNA BERGERE, b Albuquerque, NMex, Oct 8, 15; m 40; c 2. GEOMORPHOLOGY. *Educ:* Univ Wis, BS, 36; Harvard Univ, PhD(geol), 50; Univ Calif, Los Angeles, MA, 45. *Hon Degrees:* DrGeog, Univ Ottawa, 70; DSc, Iowa Wesleyan Univ, 72, Univ Wis, 80, St Andrews Univ, Scotland, 81. *Prof Exp:* From jr engr to assoc engr, Soil Conserv Serv, USDA, NMex, 36-40; assoc engr, US Eng Off, Los Angeles, 41-42; assoc engr, bur reclamation, US Dept Interior, Washington, DC, 46-47; head meteorologist, Pineapple Res Inst, 47-50; hydraul engr, US Geol Surv, 50-56, chief hydrologist, 56-66, sr res hydrologist, 66-72; PROF GEOL, UNIV CALIF BERKELEY, 72- *Honors & Awards:* Dept Interior Distinguished Serv Award, 58; Bryan Award, Geol Soc Am, 58; Royal Netherlands Geog Soc Veth Medal, 63; Liege Univ Medal, 66; Cullum Medal, Am Geog Soc, 68; Rockefeller Pub Serv Award, 71. *Mem:* Nat Acad Sci; Am Soc Civil Eng; Geol Soc Am (pres, 71); Am Philos Soc; Am Acad Arts & Sci. *Res:* Hydrology of arid regions; rainfall characteristics; river morphology, erosion and sedimentation. *Mailing Add:* Dept Geol Univ Calif Berkeley CA 94720

LEOPOLD, REUVEN, b Arad, Rumania, May 5, 38; US citizen; m 62; c 2. OCEAN ENGINEERING, HYDRODYNAMICS. *Educ:* Mass Inst Technol, BS, 61, MS, 63, Marine Mech Engr, 65, PhD(eng), 77; George Washington Univ, MBA, 77. *Prof Exp:* Res scientist hydrodyn, Hydronautics Inc, 61-62; res engr, Mass Inst Technol, 62-66; dir ship eng & design, Shipbldg Div, Litton Indusrs, 66-71; tech dir surface ship & submarine design, Naval Ship Eng Ctr, 72-78; vpres advan systs aerospace, Govt Prod Div, Pratt & Whitney Aircraft Group, 78-; MGR BUS DEVELOP & STRATEGIC PLAN, MILITARY ENGINES OPER, GEN ELEC CO, 81- *Concurrent Pos:* Mem vis comt, Mass Inst Technol, 73-76; assoc mem, Defense Sci Bd, 74-75; task force mem, Atlantic Coun US, 76-78. *Mem:* Fel Soc Naval Architects & Marine Engrs; Am Soc Naval Engrs; Sigma Xi; Am Inst Aeronaut & Astronaut. *Res:* Computers; materials; ship design. *Mailing Add:* 36 Columbia St Brookline MA 02146

LEOPOLD, ROBERT L, b Philadelphia, Pa, Oct 5, 22; m 44; c 3. PSYCHIATRY. *Educ:* Harvard Univ, AB, 43; Univ Pa, MD, 46. *Prof Exp:* Intern neurol, Grad Hosp, 47-50, from instr to assoc prof psychiat, 50-68, clin psychiat, 68-69, PROF COMMUNITY PSYCHIAT & COMMUNITY MED, DIV GRAD MED, SCH MED, UNIV PA, 68-, CHMN DEPT COMMUNITY MED, 71-, DIR DIV COMMUNITY PSYCHIAT, 65- *Concurrent Pos:* Resident, Philadelphia Psychoanal Inst, 49-55; fel, Psychiat Inst Pa, 50-51; resident, Univ Hosp, Univ Pa, 51-52; psychiat consult, Am Friends Serv Comt, 56-; sr psychiat consult, Peace Corps, 61-67; dir, WPhiladelphia Community Ment Health Consortium, 67-72; psychiatrist-in-chief, Philadelphia Psychiat Ctr, 80- *Mem:* Am Sci Affil; Am Psychoanal Asn; fel Am Psychiat Asn; AMA. *Res:* Community psychiatry; psychoanalysis. *Mailing Add:* 2 Piersol Box 498 3400 Spruce St Philadelphia PA 19104

LEOPOLD, ROBERT SUMMERS, b Dayton, Ohio, June 21, 15; m 43; c 3. ORGANIC CHEMISTRY. *Educ:* Miss State Univ, BS, 37; Univ NC, MA, 40; Univ Fla, PhD(chem), 42. *Prof Exp:* Instr, Va Mil Inst, 42-43; asst prof chem, Ga Inst Tech, 46; assoc prof chem, Fla State Univ, 46-49; mem staff, US Naval Dent Sch, 49-52; head chemist, Naval Med Field Res Lab, 52-57, head personnel protection div, 59-62; assoc prof chem, The Citadel, 63-80. *Mem:* Am Chem Soc. *Res:* Biochemistry. *Mailing Add:* 225 Sea Myrtle Ct Johns Island SC 29455

LEOPOLD, ROGER ALLEN, b Redwood Falls, Minn, Mar 23, 37; m 58; c 2. ENTOMOLOGY, CYTOCHEMISTRY. *Educ:* Concordia Col, Minn, BA, 62; Mont State Univ, PhD(entom), 67. *Prof Exp:* Res asst stress physiol, Mont State Univ, 62-67; PROF ZOOL, N DAK STATE UNIV, 71-; RES ENTOMOLOGIST, METAB & RADIATION RES LAB, AGR RES SERV, USDA, 67- *Mem:* AAAS; Entom Soc Am; Am Soc Zoologists. *Res:* Insect cytochemistry and genetics; reproductive physiology. *Mailing Add:* Metabolism & Radiation Res Lab USDA Fargo ND 58102

LEOPOLD, WILBUR RICHARD, III, b Paterson, NJ, July 26, 49; m 73; c 1. EXPERIMENTAL CHEMOTHERAPY, TUMOR BIOLOGY. *Educ:* Univ Ill, BS, 71, MS, 73; Univ Wis, PhD(oncol), 81. *Prof Exp:* Chem engr, Exxon Co, 71-72 & 73-75; RES ONCOLOGIST, SOUTHERN RES INST, 81- *Mem:* Am Chem Soc; AAAS. *Res:* Model development for cancer therapy; evaluation of anticancer drugs; chemical carcinogenesis and toxicological evaluations. *Mailing Add:* Southern Res Inst PO Box 3307-A Birmingham AL 35255

LEOSCHKE, WILLIAM LEROY, b Lockport, NY, May 2, 27; m 56; c 2. BIOCHEMISTRY. *Educ:* Valparaiso Univ, BA, 50; Univ Wis, MS, 52, PhD(biochem), 54. *Prof Exp:* Proj assoc biochem, Univ Wis, 54-59; from asst prof to assoc prof, 59-69, PROF CHEM, VALPARAISO UNIV, 69- *Concurrent Pos:* Consult, Milk Specialties Co, Ill, 55-; mem, Nat Res Coun Sub-comt Fur Animal Nutrit. *Mem:* Am Chem Soc. *Res:* Biochemistry and nutrition of mink; fundamental nutritional requirements of mink; mink diseases of nutritional origin; composition of blood and urine of mink. *Mailing Add:* Dept of Chem Valparaiso Univ Valparaiso IN 46383

LEOVY, CONWAY B, b Hermosa Beach, Calif, July 16, 33; m 58; c 4. METEOROLOGY. *Educ:* Univ Southern Calif, BA, 54; Mass Inst Technol, PhD(meteorol), 63. *Prof Exp:* Res asst meteorol, Mass Inst Technol, 58-63; meteorologist, Rand Corp, Calif, 63-69; assoc prof atmospheric sci, 69-74, PROF ATMOSPHERIC SCI & GEOPHYS & ADJ PROF ASTRON, UNIV WASH, 74- *Concurrent Pos:* Mem, Comt on Atmospheric Sci, Nat Acad Sci, 72-75 & comt on Lunar & Planetary Exploration, 74-76; assoc ed, J Atmos Sci; consult, NASA. *Honors & Awards:* NASA Outstanding Sci Achievement Award, 1972. *Mem:* Am Meteorol Soc; Am Geophys Union; AAAS. *Res:* Dynamics, radiation and photochemistry of earth and planetary atmospheres. *Mailing Add:* Dept of Atmospheric Sci & Geophys Col of Arts & Sci Univ of Wash Seattle WA 98195

LEPAGE, MARIUS, b Rimouski, Que, July 26, 30; m 57; c 2. BIOCHEMISTRY. *Educ:* Laval Univ, BA, 53, BScA, 57; Pa State Univ, MSc, 59, PhD(agr & biol chem), 61. *Prof Exp:* Res chemist, Food Res Inst, Cent Exp Farm, Dept Agr Can, 61-68; assoc prof food sci, Fac Agr, 68-69, ASSOC PROF BIOCHEM, MED SCH, LAVAL UNIV, 69- *Mailing Add:* 1279 Rouville Ste-Foy PQ G1W 3T8 Can

LEPAGE, RAOUL, b Detroit, Mich, Mar 5, 38; m 61; c 2. RANDOM PROCESSES, SEQUENTIAL ANALYSIS. *Educ:* Mich State Univ, BS, 61, MS, 62; Univ Minn, PhD(math statist), 67. *Prof Exp:* Asst prof statist & probability, Columbia Univ, NY, 65-70; vis assoc prof statist & probability, Univ Colo, 71; ASSOC PROF STATIST & PROBABILITY, MICH STATE UNIV, 72- *Mem:* Inst Math Statist. *Res:* Isolating and proving significant properties of random processes; nonstandard statistical questions of an applied character and the interface between probability, statistics and computing. *Mailing Add:* Dept Statist & Probability Wells Hall Mich State Univ East Lansing MI 48824

LEPAGE, ROBERT A(RCH), b Akron, Ohio, Mar 25, 24; m 51; c 5. CHEMICAL ENGINEERING. *Educ:* Fenn Col, BChE, 48; Univ Wis, MS, 49. *Prof Exp:* Instr physics, Fenn Col, 47-48; chem engr, Abrasive Lab, 49-53, supvr basic res, 53-54, process eng, 54-55, mgr develop, 55-59, mgr new prod, 59-65, mgr abrasive div adm admin, 65, mfg mgr, Bldg Serv Cleaning & Prod Div, 65-78, VPRES FILM & ALLIED PROD, MINN MINING & MFG CO, ST PAUL, 78- *Res:* Heat transfer; abrasive technology. *Mailing Add:* 3M Ctr Minn Mining & Mfg Co Minneapolis MN 55401

LE PAGE, WILBUR R(EED), b Kearney, NJ, Nov 16, 11; m; c 1. ELECTRICAL ENGINEERING. *Educ:* Cornell Univ, EE, 33, PhD(elec eng), 41; Univ Rochester, MS, 39. *Prof Exp:* Instr elec eng, Univ Rochester, 33-38; res engr advan develop sect, Photophone Div, Radio Corp Am Mfg Co, 41-42; res physicist radiation lab, Johns Hopkins Univ, 42-46; sr res engr, Stromberg-Carlson Co, 46-47; assoc prof, 47-50, chmn dept, 56-74, PROF ELEC & COMPUTER ENG, SYRACUSE UNIV, 50- *Mem:* Fel Inst Elec & Electronics Engrs; Asn Comput Mach. *Res:* Network theory; applied mathematics; education; computer applications. *Mailing Add:* Dept of Elec Eng Link Hall Syracuse Univ Syracuse NY 13210

LEPARD, DAVID WILLIAM, b Newmarket, Ont, Nov 1, 37; m 61; c 2. MOLECULAR PHYSICS. *Educ:* Univ Toronto, BA, 59, MA, 60, PhD(physics), 64. *Prof Exp:* Asst prof physics, Mem Univ, 64-65; fel spectros sect, Div Pure Physics, Nat Res Coun Can, 65-67; asst prof, 67-72, ASSOC PROF PHYSICS, BROCK UNIV, 72- *Concurrent Pos:* Nat Res Coun Can res grants, 64-65, 67-; Ont Dept Univ Affairs res grants, 68-69. *Mem:* Can Asn Physicists; Am Phys Soc. *Res:* Theory; infrared and Raman spectra of polyatomics; electronic spectra of diatomics. *Mailing Add:* Dept of Physics Brock Univ St Catherines ON L2S 3A1 Can

LEPESCHKIN, EUGENE, b Kazan, Russia, Apr 15, 14; nat US; m 49; c 3. CARDIOLOGY. *Educ:* Univ Vienna, MD, 39. *Prof Exp:* Asst physiol, Univ Vienna, 39-40; asst, Balneolog Inst, Bad Nauheim, Ger, 40-42; asst, I Med Clin, Vienna, 42-44; cardiologist, Hosp Team 1064, UNRRA, Munich, Ger, 45-47; from asst prof to prof exp med, 47-65, prof, 65-79, EMER PROF MED, COL MED, UNIV VT, 79- *Concurrent Pos:* Nat Heart Inst res career award, 62-; res cardiologist, Life Ins Hosp, Bad Nauheim, Ger, 40-42; chief cardiographer, Goesbriand Hosp, Burlington, 52-62, consult, 62-79; consult, Middlebury Hosp, 52-68; estab investr, Am Heart Asn, 53-58, mem basic sci clin cardiol coun, Comt Standard Electrocardiograph Vectorcardiograph Leads, 53-67. *Honors & Awards:* Einthoren Medal, 19th Cong Electrocardiol, Budapest, 78. *Mem:* Am Physiol Soc; Am Col Cardiol; NY Acad Sci. *Res:* Physiology and pathology of the heart and circulation, especially electrophysiology of the heart, arrhythmias, electrocardiography, magnetocardiography and phonocardiography. *Mailing Add:* Dept of Med Univ of Vt Col of Med Burlington VT 05401

LEPIE, ALBERT HELMUT, b Malapane, Ger, Aug 6, 23; US citizen; m 56; c 1. PHYSICAL CHEMISTRY. *Educ:* Aachen Tech Univ, MS, 58; Munich Tech Univ, PhD(chem), 61. *Prof Exp:* Res chemist, Ger Inst Res Aeronaut, 61-63 & US Naval Propellant Plant, Md, 63-64; RES CHEMIST, NAVAL WEAPONS CTR, 64- *Concurrent Pos:* Mem, Interagency Chem Rocket Propulsion Group. *Mem:* AAAS; Sigma Xi; Am Chem Soc; fel Am Inst Chem. *Res:* Performance calculations of propellants; hypergolic ignitions; mechanical behavior of polymers; dynamic testing methods. *Mailing Add:* 121 Desert Candles Ridgecrest CA 93555

LEPLAE, LUC A, b Hammemille, Belgium, Nov 27, 30; m 59; c 4. THEORETICAL SOLID STATE PHYSICS. *Educ:* Cath Univ Louvain, Lic en Theoret Physics, 55; Univ Md, PhD(physics), 62. *Prof Exp:* Res assoc physics, Inst Theoret Physics, Naples, Italy, 62-66; res assoc, 66-67, vis asst prof, 67-68, asst prof, 68-77, ASSOC PROF PHYSICS, UNIV WIS-MILWAUKEE, 77- *Res:* Application of the Boson method to superconductivity, superfluidity, magnetism and phase transitions; many body problem; solid state physics. *Mailing Add:* Dept of Physics Univ of Wis Milwaukee WI 53201

LEPLEY, ARTHUR RAY, b Peoria, Ill, Nov 1, 33; m 57; c 4. PHYSICAL ORGANIC CHEMISTRY. *Educ:* Bradley Univ, AB, 54; Univ Chicago, SM, 56, PhD(chem), 58. *Prof Exp:* Res assoc org chem, Univ Munich, 58-59 & Univ Chicago, 59-60; asst prof chem, State Univ NY Stony Brook, 60-65; assoc prof, 65-68, PROF CHEM, MARSHALL UNIV, 68- *Concurrent Pos:* NSF fel, 58-59; USPHS gen med fel, 60; vis prof, Univ Utah, 69-71; guest worker, Lab Chem Phys, Nat Inst Arthritis, Metabolism & Digestive Dis, Md, 75-76. *Mem:* AAAS; Am Chem Soc; Royal Soc Chem; Am Inst Chem; Sigma Xi. *Res:* Flow nmr; microprocessor application in chemical education; hydroxy radical oxidations; direct alpha alkylation of tertiary amines; free radical intermediates; nuclear magnetic resonance emission spectroscopy; chemically induced dynamic nuclear polarization; word processing. *Mailing Add:* Dept Of Chem Marshall Univ Huntington WV 25701

LEPLEY, DERWARD, JR, surgery, see previous edition

LEPLEY, LARRY KENT, b Alma, Mich, Apr 17, 34; m 68; c 2. GEOPHYSICS, OCEANOGRAPHY. *Educ:* Colo Sch Mines, BS, 59; Tex A&M Univ, MS, 64; Univ Hawaii, PhD(geophys), 70. *Prof Exp:* Geologist, US Naval Oceanog Off, 59-60, civil engr, 60-67; res asst oceanogr, Univ Hawaii, 66-70; res assoc remote sensing mgt, Univ Ariz, 71-74; CONSULT GEOLOGIST, 74- *Mem:* AAAS; Inst Elec & Electronics Engrs; Am Geophys Union; Optical Soc Am; Am Soc Photogram. *Res:* Remote sensing as a geophysical tool applied to hydrology, oceanography and exploration geology; optical and radio properties of natural water; remote sensing interpretation and instrumentation from audio to ultraviolet frequencies; optical Fourier image processing. *Mailing Add:* 8841 N Calle Loma Linda Tucson AZ 85704

LEPOCK, JAMES RONALD, b Fairmont, WVa, Oct 20, 48; m 70; c 1. BIOPHYSICS, MEMBRANES. *Educ:* WVa Univ, BS, 70, MS, 72; Pa State Univ, PhD(biophys), 76. *Prof Exp:* Fel radiobiol, New Eng Med Ctr, Tufts Univ, 76-77; asst prof, 77-81, ASSOC PROF PHYSICS, UNIV WATERLOO, 81- *Concurrent Pos:* Med Res Coun Can grants, 70 & 80-; Nat Sci & Eng Res Coun Can grant, 78- *Mem:* AAAS; Biophys Soc; Radiation Res Soc. *Res:* Membrane biology; spin labeling and electron spin resonance; mammalian cell tissue culture; hypothermia and hyperthermia, radiation biology; fluorescence spectroscopy. *Mailing Add:* Dept of Physics Univ of Waterloo Waterloo ON N2L 3G1 Can

LEPOFF, JACK H, b Portland, Maine, July 22, 23; m 47; c 2. PHYSICS. *Educ:* Univ NH, BS, 43; Columbia Univ, MA, 48. *Prof Exp:* Electronic scientist, Nat Bur Standards, 49-50, Naval Res Lab, 50-51, Nat Bur Standards, 51-53 & Naval Ord Lab, 53-54; sr staff mem, Motorola, Inc, 54-59; eng specialist, Sylvania Electronic Defense Lab, Gen Tel & Electronics Corp, 59-65; diode appln mgr, HPA Div, 65-73, DIODE APPLNS ENGR, HEWLETT PACKARD CO, 73- *Mem:* Sigma Xi; Inst Elec & Electronics Engrs. *Res:* Microwaves; semiconductors. *Mailing Add:* 595 Templeton Dr Sunnyvale CA 94087

LEPORE, JOHN A(NTHONY), b Philadelphia, Pa, Feb 19, 35; m 59; c 4. CIVIL ENGINEERING, APPLIED MECHANICS. *Educ:* Drexel Inst, BSCE, 57; Univ Pa, MS, 61, PhD(appl mech), 67. *Prof Exp:* Nuclear engr, NY Ship Bldg Corp, 57-61; supv engr missile & space div, Gen Elec Co, 61-68; asst prof civil eng, 68-71, Winterstein asst prof, 71-78, assoc prof, 78-80, PROF & CHMN DEPT, CIVIL & URBAN ENG, UNIV PA, 80- *Concurrent Pos:* Danforth assoc. *Mem:* Am Soc Civil Engrs; Am Soc Mech Engrs; Am Soc Eng Educ; Am Acad Mech; Earthquake Eng Res Inst. *Res:* Stability of dynamic systems; applied mathematics; random processes; earthquake, wind and ocean engineering; disaster mitigation; solar energy applications. *Mailing Add:* 113 Towne Bldg Univ of Pa Philadelphia PA 19104

LEPORE, JOSEPH VERNON, b Detroit, Mich, Oct 9, 22. PHYSICS. *Educ:* Allegheny Col, BS, 43; Harvard Univ, PhD(physics), 48. *Prof Exp:* Instr physics, Princeton Univ, 43-44; physicist, Tenn Eastman Corp, 44-46; AEC fel, Inst Advan Study, 48-50; asst prof physics, Ind Univ, 50-51; lectr, Univ Calif, Berkeley, 54-65, physicist, Lawrence Berkeley Lab, Univ Calif, 51-81; RETIRED. *Concurrent Pos:* Adv to test dir, Nev Test Site, 57. *Mem:* Am Phys Soc. *Res:* Nuclear physics; quantum field theory; scattering theory. *Mailing Add:* 712 Moraga Rd Moraga CA 94556

LEPOUTRE, PIERRE, b Roubaix, France, July 28, 33; Can citizen; m 62; c 3. POLYMER CHEMISTRY, PAPER SCIENCE. *Educ:* Sch Advan Indust Studies, Lille, BSc, 57; NC State Univ, MSc, 60, PhD(chem eng), 68. *Prof Exp:* Chem engr, Olegum, France, 57-58, Rohm & Haas France, 60-63; res engr, Int Cellulose Res, 63-66; res engr, Consol Bathurst, 68-71; res engr, 71-78, HEAD POLYMER SECT, PULP & PAPER RES INST, 78- *Mem:* Tech Asn Pulp & Paper Indust; Can Tech Asn Pulp & Paper Indust. *Res:* Chemical modification of cellulose; adhesion; polymer latexes. *Mailing Add:* Pulp & Paper Res Inst Can 570 St John Blvd Pointe Claire PQ H9R 3J9 Can

LEPOVETSKY, BARNEY CHARLES, b Ridgway, Pa, Jan 17, 26; m 50; c 2. SCIENCE ADMINISTRATION. *Educ:* Ohio State Univ, BSc, 49, MSc, 51, PhD(microbiol), 54; Ohio Northern Univ, JD, 63. *Prof Exp:* Prof microbiol, Ohio Northern Univ, 54-64; scientist adminstr, NIH, 64-69, dep assoc dir extramural progs, Nat Inst Dent Res, 69-71, chief, Off Collab Res, 71-75, CHIEF RES MANPOWER BR, NAT CANCER INST, 75- *Mem:* Int Acad Law & Sci Res. *Res:* Law. *Mailing Add:* 3326 Lowell Lane Ijamsville MD 21754

LEPOW, IRWIN HOWARD, b New York, NY, Sept 2, 23; m 58; c 3. IMMUNOLOGY, EXPERIMENTAL MEDICINE. *Educ:* Pa State Univ, BS, 42; Case Western Reserve Univ, PhD(immunochem), 51, MD, 58. *Prof Exp:* Biol res & develop, Lederle Labs, 43, 46 & 48; sr instr biochem, Case Western Reserve Univ, 51-52, asst prof biochem & exp path, 52-59, assoc prof exp path, 59-65, from assoc prof to prof med, 65-67; prof path & head dept, Health Ctr, Univ Conn, 67-73, prof med & head dept, 73-78; PRES, STERLING-WINTHROP RES INST, 78- *Concurrent Pos:* USPHS res career award, 63-67; mem allergy & immunol study sect, NIH, 62-65 & 69-73, chmn, 70-73; dir comn immunization, Armed Forces Epidemiol Bd, 63-67, adv mem, 67-74; mem, Conn Comn Medico-legal Invests, 69-73; mem bd trustees, Trudeau Inst, NY, 72-78, Albany Col Pharm, 81-; assoc ed, J Immunol, 71-73; elect mem coun, Am Asn Immunol. *Mem:* AAAS; Asn Am Physicians; Am Asn Immunol (vpres, 78-79, pres 79-80); NY Acad Sci; fel Am Col Physicians. *Res:* Complement; mechanisms of immunological injury. *Mailing Add:* Sterling-Winthrop Res Inst Rensselaer NY 12144

LEPOWSKY, JAMES IVAN, b New York, NY, July 5, 44. LIE ALGEBRAS, COMBINATORICS. *Educ:* Harvard Univ, AB, 65; Mass Inst Technol, PhD(math), 70. *Prof Exp:* Lectr & res assoc math, Brandeis Univ, 70-72; asst prof math, Yale Univ, 72-77; assoc prof, 77-80, PROF MATH, RUTGERS UNIV, 80- *Concurrent Pos:* Mem, Sch Math, Inst Advan Study, 75-76 & 80; Alfred P Sloan fel, 77-78; vis assoc prof math, Univ Paris, 78; assoc ed, Am Math Soc, 80- *Mem:* Am Math Soc; Math Asn Am. *Res:* Representations of lie algebras and interactions with other branches of mathematics such as combinatorics. *Mailing Add:* Dept of Math Rutgers Univ New Brunswick NJ 08903

LEPP, ALBERT, b Chicago, Ill, Feb 11, 14; m 51; c 4. BIOCHEMISTRY. *Educ:* Univ Ill, BS, 38; Univ Calif, Los Angeles, PhD(biochem), 46; Univ Wis, MS, 47. *Prof Exp:* Asst biochem, Univ Wis, 46-48; asst hort, Iowa State Col, 49-50; asst physiol chem, Med Ctr, Univ Calif, Los Angeles, 52-53, asst biochem, 53-55; biochemist, Med Sch, Univ Southern Calif, 56-57, vis instr biochem & nutrit, 57-60; biochemist, Radioisotope Serv, Vet Admin Hosp, Indianapolis, Ind, 60-69, asst chief thyroid res, DC, 69-71, CHIEF RADIOIMMUNO ASSAY RES LAB, 71- *Concurrent Pos:* Biochemist, Los Angeles County Hosp, 58-60; from instr to asst prof, Sch Med, Univ Ind, Indianapolis, 60-63. *Mem:* Am Thyroid Asn; Endocrine Soc; NY Acad Sci. *Res:* Immunoassays of hormones in biological fluids. *Mailing Add:* Radioimmuno Assay Res Lab Vet Admin Hosp Washington DC 20422

LEPP, CYRUS ANDREW, b Brooklyn, NY, Aug 11, 46; m 72; c 2. CLINICAL BIOCHEMISTRY, CLINICAL CHEMISTRY. *Educ:* Syracuse Univ, BS, 68, PhD(biochem), 74. *Prof Exp:* Lab technician clin chem, Nassau Hosp, 68-69; sr biochemist clin chem & biochem, 74-80, MGR, DEVELOP, CORNING MED & SCI, CORNING GLASS WORKS, 80- *Mem:* AAAS; Am Asn Clin Chem; Am Chem Soc; NY Acad Sci; Tissue Culture Asn. *Res:* Electrophoretic separations of isoenzymes and hemoglobins; development of specific isoenzyme assay procedures; development of immunologic assays. *Mailing Add:* Corning Med & Sci 333 Coney St East Walpole MA 02032

LEPP, HENRY, b Russia, Mar 4, 22; m 52; c 4. GEOLOGY. *Educ:* Univ Sask, BSc, 44; Univ Minn, PhD(geol), 54. *Prof Exp:* Geologist & mining engr, Consol Mining & Smelting Co, Ltd, 44-46; mining engr, N W Byrne, Consult Mining Engr, 46-48; geologist, Aluminum Labs, Ltd, 48-50 & Freeport Sulphur Co, 54; from asst prof to prof, Univ Minn, Duluth, 54-64; PROF GEOL & CHMN DEPT, MACALESTER COL, 64- *Mem:* AAAS; Geol Soc Am; Soc Econ Geol. *Res:* Mining geology; sedimentary iron formations, particularly the geochemistry of these formations and its possible relation to the evolutionary pattern of the atmosphere. *Mailing Add:* Dept of Geol Macalester Col St Paul MN 55105

LEPPARD, GARY GRANT, b Medicine Hat, Can, Aug 6, 40; m 70; c 2. CELL BIOLOGY. *Educ:* Univ Sask, BA, 62, BA hons, 63, MA, 64; Yale Univ, MS, 66, MPhil, 67, PhD(biol), 68. *Prof Exp:* RES SCIENTIST BIOL, CAN DEPT ENVIRON, 71- *Concurrent Pos:* NATO Sci fel, Fac Med, Univ Paris, 68, Inst Pharmacol, Univ Milan, 69; Nat Res Coun Sci fel, Fac Sci, Univ Laval, 69-70, Biochem Lab, Nat Res Coun Can, 70-71; sci res exec mem, Prof Inst Pub Serv Can, 71-73; adj prof, Dept Biol, Univ Ottawa, 74-75. *Mem:* Sigma Xi; Can Fedn Biol Soc; Can Soc Cell Biol. *Res:* Physical relationships between living cells and materials in their external milieu. *Mailing Add:* Aquatic Ecol Div Nat Water Res Inst Burlington ON L7R 4A6 Can

LEPPELMEIER, GILBERT WILLISTON, b Cleveland, Ohio, Aug 19, 36; m 59; c 2. PHYSICS. *Educ:* Yale Univ, BS, 57; Univ Calif, Berkeley, PhD(physics), 65. *Prof Exp:* Jr physicist neutron physics, Lawrence Livermore Lab, 57-59; NATO fel physics, Free Univ Brussels, 65-66; lectr physics, Univ Sussex, 66-67; physicist laser physics, Lawrence Livermore Lab, 67-75; sr scientist laser-fusion, Lab for Laser Energetics, Univ Rochester, 75-77; PHYSICIST MAGNETIC-FUSION, LAWRENCE LIVERMORE LAB, 77- *Mem:* Am Phys Soc; Inst Elec & Electronics Engrs. *Res:* Plasma diagnostics; application of small computers to instrument development and control. *Mailing Add:* Lawrence Livermore Lab PO Box 5511 L637 Livermore CA 94550

LEPPERT, G(EORGE), b Kansas City, Mo, July 17, 24; m. MECHANICAL ENGINEERING. *Educ:* Univ Wis, BS, 47; Ill Inst Technol, MS, 52, PhD(mech eng), 54. *Prof Exp:* Mech engr, Monsanto Chem Co, 47-49, mgr, Eng Res Sect, 53-54; instr mech eng, Washington Univ, St Louis, 49-50; assoc mech engr, Argonne Nat Lab, 50-53; from asst prof to prof mech eng, Stanford Univ, 54-69; prof & chmn dept, Clarkson Col Technol, 69-74; SR MECH ENGR & DIR, OFF ENVIRON POLICY ANAL, ARGONNE NAT LAB, 75- Mem: Am Soc Mech Engrs; AAAS. Res: Heat transfer; energy and environmental policy analysis. Mailing Add: Argonne Nat Lab 9700 S Cass Ave Argonne IL 60439

LEPPI, THEODORE JOHN, b Mountain Iron, Minn, May 30, 33; m 59; c 3. ANATOMY. Educ: Albion Col, BA, 59; Yale Univ, PhD(anat), 63. Prof Exp: From asst prof to assoc prof anat, Sch Med, Univ NMex, 66-71; assoc dean & dir admissions, 71-77, PROF BIOMED ANAT & CHMN DEPT, SCH MED, UNIV MINN, DULUTH, 71- Concurrent Pos: Staff fel, Lab Exp Path, Nat Inst Arthritis & Metab Dis, 64-66; Lederle Med Fac Award, 68-71; guest lectr, Sch Med, Georgetown Univ, 63-64; asst prof lectr, Sch Med, George Washington Univ, 65-66; vis scientist, Pac Biomed Res Ctr, Univ Hawaii, 78-79. Mem: Am Asn Anat; Am Soc Cell Biol; Histochem Soc. Res: Effects of hormones on connective tissues; histochemistry and cytochemistry of glycosaminoglycans. Mailing Add: Dept of Biomed Anat Univ of Minn Sch of Med Duluth MN 55812

LEPPIK, ELMAR EMIL, plant pathology, see previous edition

LEPPLE, FREDERICK KARL, b Newark, NJ, July 1, 44; m 75; c 2. CHEMICAL OCEANOGRAPHY, GEOCHEMISTRY. Educ: Univ Miami, BS, 67, MS, 71; Univ Del, PhD(marine studies), 75. Prof Exp: Res chemist org polymers, Air Reduction Corp, 67-68; RES CHEMIST MARINE AEROSOLS, NAVAL RES LAB, 74- Concurrent Pos: Res assoc, Nat Acad Sci-Nat Res Coun, Naval Res Lab, 74-76. Mem: AAAS; Am Chem Soc; Am Geophys Union. Res: Chemistry, transport and effects of aerosols in the marine environment; marine geochemistry and oceanography. Mailing Add: Code 4332 Environ Sci Div Naval Res Lab Washington DC 20375

LEPS, THOMAS MACMASTER, b Keyser, WVa, Dec 3, 14; m 40; c 1. CIVIL ENGINEERING, GEOTECHNICAL ENGINEERING. Educ: Stanford Univ, AB, 36; Mass Inst Technol, MS, 39. Prof Exp: Asst engr dams, US Bur Reclamation, 41-42; chief civil engr power plants, Southern Calif Edison Co, 46-61; chief engr dams & foundations, Shannon & Wilson, 61-63; CONSULT CIVIL ENGR DAMS & POWER PLANTS, THOMAS M LEPS, INC, 63- Concurrent Pos: Mem peer group mem comt, Nat Acad Eng, 75-77; mem exec comt, US Comt Large Dams, 76-, vchmn, 78-80. Honors & Awards: Cert of Appreciation, Am Soc Civil Engrs, 61. Mem: Nat Acad Eng; Am Soc Civil Engrs. Res: Soil mechanics and seismologic engineering. Mailing Add: PO Box 2228 Menlo Park CA 94025

LEPSE, PAUL ARNOLD, b Seattle, Wash, Mar 18, 37; m 61; c 2. ORGANIC CHEMISTRY. Educ: Seattle Pac Col, BS, 58; Univ Wash, PhD(org chem), 62. Prof Exp: NSF fel, Univ Munich, 62; from asst prof to assoc prof, 63-72, PROF CHEM, SEATTLE PAC UNIV, 72- Mem: AAAS; Am Chem Soc. Res: Organic reaction mechanisms; carbene chemistry. Mailing Add: Dept of Chem Seattle Pac Univ Seattle WA 98119

LEPSON, BENJAMIN, b New York, NY, Mar 4, 24; m 48; c 1. MATHEMATICAL ANALYSIS, COMPUTATIONAL MATHEMATICS. Educ: Yale Univ, BS, 43, MS, 44; Columbia Univ, PhD(math), 50. Prof Exp: Lab asst physics, Yale Univ, 43-44; math physicist, Naval Ord Lab, 44-46; lectr math, Columbia Univ, 46-48; mem, Inst Advan Study, 50-52; mathematician, Off Naval Res, 52-53; asst prof math, Cath Univ Am, 53-54; head, Res Comput Ctr, 54-61, Numerical Anal Br, 61-65, math consult, Nucleonics Div, 65-66, Nuclear Physics Div, 66-67, Math & Info Sci Div, 67-69, Space Sci Div, 69-74, res mathematician, Math Res Ctr, 74-75, res mathematician & actg head, appl math staff, 75-76, consult, Res Comput Ctr, 76-79, MATHEMATICIAN & COMPUT SCI CONSULT, MGT INFO DIV, US NAVAL RES LAB, 79- Concurrent Pos: Instr, Univ Ill, 48; lectr, Univ Md, 52-53 & Am Univ, 52-53, 56-57; lectr & res assoc, Cath Univ Am, 54-64, adj prof, 64-74; vis prof math & statist, Univ Md, 74-75. Mem: Am Math Soc; Math Asn Am; Inst Math Statist; Inst Elec & Electronics Engrs; Comput Soc. Res: Complex function theory, especially entire and meromorphic functions; Dirichlet type series; real function theory; potential theory; computer science; numerical analysis; applied mathematics; probability; mathematical statistics; application of mathematics, computers and statistics to physical sciences. Mailing Add: US Naval Res Lab Code 1439 Washington DC 20375

LE QUESNE, PHILIP WILLIAM, b Auckland, NZ, Jan 6, 39; m 65; c 2. ORGANIC CHEMISTRY. Educ: Univ Auckland, MSc, 61, PhD(chem), 64. Hon Degrees: DSc, Univ Auckland, 79. Prof Exp: Res assoc org chem, Oxford Univ, 64-65; res assoc, Univ BC, 65-66, teaching fel, 66-67; asst prof, Univ Mich, Ann Arbor, 67-73; assoc prof org chem, 73-78, PROF CHEM & MED CHEM, NORTHEASTERN UNIV, 78-, CHMN DEPT, 79- Mem: Am Chem Soc; Phytochem Soc NAm; The Chem Soc; assoc NZ Inst Chem; Am Soc Pharmacog. Res: Natural product chemistry, especially steroids, alkaloids, terpenoids, fungal metabolites; comparative phytochemistry; physiologically active compounds. Mailing Add: Dept of Chem Northeastern Univ Boston MA 02115

LEQUIRE, VIRGIL SHIELDS, b Maryville, Tenn, June 15, 21; m 46; c 4. PATHOLOGY. Educ: Maryville Col, BA, 42; Vanderbilt Univ, MD, 46. Prof Exp: NIH res asst, 49-50, from asst prof to assoc prof anat, 50-66, actg chmn dept path, 71-73; PROF ANAT & EXP PATH, SCH MED, VANDERBILT UNIV, 66- Concurrent Pos: USPHS sr fel. Mem: AAAS; Am Asn Anat; Am Fedn Clin Res; Am Soc Exp Path; fel Royal Micros Soc. Res: Lipoprotein transport; fat embolization; membrane structure. Mailing Add: Dept of Path Vanderbilt Univ Sch of Med Nashville TN 37232

LERBEKMO, JOHN FRANKLIN, b Alta, Can, Dec 8, 24; m 49; c 4. GEOLOGY. Educ: Univ BC, BASc, 49; Univ Calif, Berkeley, PhD(geol), 56. Prof Exp: Asst prof geol, 56-59, assoc prof sedimentary geol, 59-68, PROF SEDIMENTARY GEOL, UNIV ALTA, 68- Mem: Soc Econ Paleontologists & Mineralogists; Int Asn Sedimentol; Geol Asn Can; Can Soc Petrol Geologists. Res: Sedimentary petrology; detrital sediments; magnetostratigraphy. Mailing Add: Dept of Geol Univ of Alta Edmonton AB T6G 2E3 Can

LERCH, IRVING A, b Chicago, Ill, June 29, 38; m 63. MEDICAL PHYSICS. Educ: US Mil Acad, BS, 60; Univ Chicago, SM, 66, PhD(med physics), 69. Prof Exp: Res assoc med physics, Univ Chicago, 69-72; first officer, Int Atomic Energy Agency, Vienna, 73-75; PROF & SR PHYSICIST, NY UNIV MED CTR, 76- Concurrent Pos: Consult med radiation physics, Int Atomic Energy Agency & WHO, 76- Mem: Am Phys Soc; Am Asn Physicists in Med; Radiation Res Soc. Res: Diagnostic radiological physics as applied to problems in image quality; cell kinetic and modelling studies as applied to problems in radiation therapy; dosimetry in radiation oncology physics; radiofrequency induced tissue hyperthermia; computers in medicine. Mailing Add: Dept of Radiation Oncol NY Univ Med Ctr New York NY 10016

LERCHE, IAN, b Corbridge, Eng, Aug 24, 41; m 62; c 4. ASTROPHYSICS, PLASMA PHYSICS. Educ: Univ Manchester, BSc, 62, PhD(astron), 65. Prof Exp: Res assoc, Univ Chicago, 65-66, from asst prof physics to assoc prof, 66-81; SR RES GEOPHYSICIST, GULF RES & DEV CO, 81- Concurrent Pos: Alexander von Humboldt sr scientist award, 74. Mem: Am Astron Soc; fel Royal Astron Soc. Res: Geomagnetic field and plasma effects; instabilities and power spectra of relativistic plasmas; dynamical state of interstellar gas; radiation from cosmic ray air showers. Mailing Add: Gulf Bldg 439 7th Ave Pittsburgh PA 15219

LERCHER, BRUCE L, b Milwaukee, Wis, June 7, 30; m 60; c 2. MATHEMATICAL LOGIC. Educ: Univ Wis, BS, 51, MS, 52; Pa State Univ, PhD(math), 63. Prof Exp: Instr math, Univ Rochester, 59-62; asst prof, 62-67, ASSOC PROF MATH, STATE UNIV NY BINGHAMTON, 67- Mem: Am Math Soc; Math Asn Am; Asn Symbolic Logic. Res: Combinatory logic. Mailing Add: Dept of Math State Univ of NY Binghamton NY 13901

LE RICHE, WILLIAM HARDING, b Dewetsdorp, SAfrica, Mar 21, 16; Can citizen; m 43; c 5. MEDICINE. Educ: Univ Witwatersrand, BSc, 37, MB, BCh, 43, MD, 49; Harvard Univ, MPH, 50; FRCP(C), 72. Prof Exp: Med officer, Union Health Dept, 44-49, epidemiologist, 50-52; consult epidemiol, Dept Nat Health & Welfare, Ottawa, Can, 52-54; res med officer, Physicians Serv, Inc, 54-57; res assoc pub health, 57-59, prof, 59-62, prof epidemiol & biomet & Head Dept, Sch Hyg, 62-75, PROF EPIDEMIOL, DEPT PREV MED, FAC MED, UNIV TORONTO, 75- Concurrent Pos: Carnegie fel, Bur Educ & Social Res, SAfrica, 37-39; consult, Physicians Serv Inc, 57-66, Ont Med Serv Ins Plan, 66-, Res Inst, Hosp Sick Children, Toronto & Can Forces Med Coun, 69- Honors & Awards: Defries Medal, Can Pub Helth Asn, 81. Mem: Can Med Asn; fel Am Col Physicians. Res: Child growth, nutrition and infectious diseases; medical care studies; epidemiology; cardiovascular disease; education in public health and preventive medicine; hospital infections. Mailing Add: Fac of Med McMurrich Bldg 12 Queen's Park Crescent W Toronto ON M5S 1A8 Can

LERKE, PETER A, b Paris, France, June 6, 28; US citizen; m 53; c 3. BACTERIOLOGY. Educ: Univ Calif, Berkeley, AB, 51, MA, 53, PhD(bact), 58. Prof Exp: Asst res microbiologist, 55-68, assoc res microbiologist, 68-75, DIR LAB RES IN CANNING INDUST, GEORGE WILLIAMS HOOPER FOUND, UNIV CALIF, SAN FRANCISCO, 75- Mem: AAAS; Am Soc Microbiol; Inst Food Technol; Royal Soc Health. Res: Food microbiology; bacterial spoilage of protein foods; antibiotics and food preservation; food-borne intoxications; nutrition; public health aspects of canned foods. Mailing Add: George Williams Hooper Found Univ of Calif 1950 Sixth St Berkeley CA 94710

LERMAN, ABRAHAM, b Harbin, China, Nov 14, 35; c 1. MARINE GEOCHEMISTRY, LIMNOLOGY. Educ: Hebrew Univ, Israel, MSc, 60; Harvard Univ, PhD(geol), 64. Prof Exp: Lectr geol, Johns Hopkins Univ, 64, asst prof, 64-65; asst prof, Univ Ill, Chicago, 65-68; sr scientist, Weizmann Inst, Israel, 66-69; res scientist chem limnol, Can Centre Inland Waters, Can Dept Environ, 69-71; assoc prof, 71-75, PROF GEOL SCI, NORTHWESTERN UNIV, 75- Concurrent Pos: Guggenheim fel, 76; vis prof, Inst Aquatic Sci, Swiss Fed Inst Technol, Duebendorf, 76-77, Univ Karlsruhe, 79 & 81. Mem: AAAS; Geochem Soc; Am Chem Soc; Geol Soc Am; Am Geophys Union. Res: Chemical and physical dynamics of sediments; fresh and ocean waters and saline brines; mathematical models of transport processes, material balance and water quality in natural water systems. Mailing Add: Dept of Geol Sci Northwestern Univ Evanston IL 60201

LERMAN, CHARLES LEW, b Elizabeth, NJ, Apr 23, 48. BIO-ORGANIC CHEMISTRY. Educ: Yale Univ, BS, 69; Harvard Univ, AM, 70, PhD(org chem), 74. Prof Exp: Asst prof chem, Juniata Col, 74-76; asst prof chem, Haverford Col, 76-81; SR SCIENTIST, ICI AMERICAS, 81- Mem: Am Chem Soc; AAAS. Res: Enzyme mechanisms and model systems; specificity of molecular interactions; mechanism of 5-aminolevulinic acid dehydratase; model for the active site of ribonuclease; NMR studies of biochemical systems. Mailing Add: Stuart Pharmaceut Div ICI Americas Wilmington DE 19897

LERMAN, LEONARD SOLOMON, b Pittsburgh, Pa, June 27, 25; m 74; c 3. MOLECULAR BIOLOGY. Educ: Carnegie Inst Technol, BS, 45; Calif Inst Technol, PhD(chem), 50. Prof Exp: Asst org chem & explosives, Explosives Res Lab, Carnegie Inst Technol, 45; asst chem, Calif Inst Technol, 45-49; Schenley fel, Univ Chicago, 49-51; instr pediat, Univ Colo, 51-52, asst prof, 52-53, asst prof biophys, 53-59, from assoc prof to prof, 59-65; prof molecular biol, Vanderbilt Univ, 65-77; PROF & CHMN DEPT BIOL SCI, STATE UNIV NY, ALBANY, 77- Concurrent Pos: USPHS Res Career Award, 63-65, mem, Nat Sci Found Adv Panel, 65-68; NIH study sect, 69-73; Guggenheim fel, 71-72. Mem: NY Acad Sci; Biophys Soc; Am Chem Soc. Res: DNA microbial genetics; DNA structure, mutagenesis; DNA complexes, genetics. Mailing Add: Dept of Biol Sci 1400 Washington Ave Albany NY 12222

LERMAN, MANUEL, b New York, NY, Feb 5, 43; m 75; c 2. MATHEMATICAL LOGIC. *Educ:* City Col New York, BS, 64; Cornell Univ, PhD(math logic), 68. *Prof Exp:* Instr math, Mass Inst Technol, 68-70; asst prof, Yale Univ, 70-73; assoc prof, 73-76, PROF MATH, UNIV CONN, 76- *Concurrent Pos:* Vis prof, Univ Ill, Chicago Circle, 75-76 & Univ Chicago, 80. *Mem:* Am Math Soc; Math Asn Am; Asn Symbolic Logic. *Res:* Recursive function theory; recursive model theory. *Mailing Add:* Dept of Math Univ of Conn Storrs CT 06268

LERMAN, SIDNEY, b Montreal, Can, Oct 6, 27; m 57; c 2. OPHTHALMOLOGY, CHEMISTRY. *Educ:* McGill Univ, BSc, 48, MD, CM, 52; Univ Rochester, MS, 61. *Prof Exp:* Dir ophthalmic res, Univ Rochester, 57-68, asst prof biochem, 61-68, assoc prof ophthal, 62-68; prof ophthal & biochem & dir exp ophthal, McGill Univ, 68-73; PROF OPHTHAL, SCH MED, EMORY UNIV, 75- *Concurrent Pos:* Nat Eye Inst grants, 58-; chmn, Int Conf Ophthalmic Biochem, Woods Hole, Mass, 64-72; consult, Bausch & Lomb, 66-69, Nat Patent Develop Corp, 68-73 & Alza Corp, 69-72; adj prof chem, Ga Inst Technol, 75- *Honors & Awards:* Award in Ophthal & J B Cramer Mem Award, Rochester Acad Med, 58. *Mem:* Am Asn Res Vision & Ophthal; Am Chem Soc; Am Soc Biol Chem; Am Soc Photobiol. *Res:* Ophthalmic biochemistry. *Mailing Add:* Dept of Ophthal Emory Univ Sch of Med Atlanta GA 30322

LERMAN, STEPHEN PAUL, b Philadelphia, Pa, Oct 3, 44. IMMUNOLOGY. *Educ:* Philadelphia Col Pharm & Sci, BS, 66; Hahnemann Med Col, MS, 70, PhD(microbiol), 73. *Prof Exp:* Fel, 72-74, asst res scientist, 74-75, res asst prof path, Sch Med, NY Univ, 75-78; ASSOC PROF IMMUNOL & MICROBIOL, WAYNE STATE UNIV SCH MED, 78- *Concurrent Pos:* Spec fel, Leukemia Soc Am, 76-78. *Mem:* Am Asn Immunologists; Am Soc Microbiol. *Res:* Tumor immunology; immunological tolerance; immunological deficiencies; suppressor cells; cell cooperation in the immune response. *Mailing Add:* Wayne State Univ Sch Med Dept Immunol & Microbiol 540 E Canfield Ave Detroit MI 48201

LERNER, AARON BUNSEN, b Minneapolis, Minn, Sept 21, 20; m 45; c 4. DERMATOLOGY, BIOCHEMISTRY. *Educ:* Univ Minn, BA, 41, MS, 42, MB & PhD(physiol chem), 45, MD, 46. *Prof Exp:* Asst physiol chem, Univ Minn, 41-45; Am Cancer Soc fel, Sch Med, Western Reserve Univ, 48-49; asst prof dermat, Med Sch, Univ Mich, 49-52; assoc prof, Univ Ore, 52-55; assoc prof, 55-57, PROF, SCH MED, YALE UNIV, 57- *Mem:* Nat Acad Sci; Soc Invest Dermat; Am Acad Dermat; Am Soc Biol Chemists. *Res:* Plasma proteins associated with disease; metabolism of phenylalanine and tyrosine; biochemistry of melanin pigmentation; mechanism of endocrine control of pigmentation; malignant melanomas; cryoglobulins; biochemistry of skin. *Mailing Add:* Dept of Dermat Yale Univ Sch of Med New Haven CT 06510

LERNER, ALBERT MARTIN, b St Louis, Mo, Sept 3, 29; m 57; c 4. INTERNAL MEDICINE. *Educ:* Wash Univ, BA, 50, MD, 54; Am Bd Internal Med, dipl, 61. *Prof Exp:* Intern, Barnes Hosp, St Louis, Mo, 54-55; lab investr, Nat Inst Allergy & Infectious Dis, 55-57; asst resident, Harvard Med Serv, Boston City Hosp, Mass, 57-58; sr asst resident, Barnes Hosp, Mo, 58-59; res assoc biol, Mass Inst Technol, 62-63; assoc prof med & assoc microbiol & path, Col Med, Wayne State Univ, 63-67; assoc med & path & dir bact lab, 64-69, CLIN CONSULT BACT LAB, DETROIT GEN HOSP, 69-; PROF MED, COL MED, WAYNE STATE UNIV, 67-, CHIEF, HUTZEL HOSP MED UNIT, 70- *Concurrent Pos:* Res fel med, Thorndike Mem Lab, Boston City Hosp & Harvard Med Sch, 59-62; fel, Med Found Greater Boston, Inc, 60-63; consult, Vet Admin Hosp, Allen Park, Mich, 63- *Mem:* Fel Am Col Physicians Am Fedn Clin Res; Am Soc Clin Invest; NY Acad Sci; dipl mem Pan-Am Med Asn. *Res:* Infectious diseases. *Mailing Add:* Dept Med Hutzel Hosp 4707 St Antoine Detroit MI 48201

LERNER, B(ERNARD) J, b Brooklyn, NY, Apr 28, 21; m 51; c 3. CHEMICAL ENGINEERING. *Educ:* Cooper Union, BChE, 43; Univ Iowa, MS, 47; Syracuse Univ, PhD(chem eng), 49. *Prof Exp:* Instr chem eng, Univ Iowa, 46-47; res engr, Inst Indust Res, Syracuse Univ, 47-48; asst prof, Univ Tex, 49-54; group leader, Gulf Res & Develop Co, 54-59; consult, Dominion Gulf Co, 59-63; pres, Patent Develop Assocs, Inc, Pa, 63-68; vpres res & dir chem eng res, MK Res & Develop Co, Pa, 68-70; PRES, BECO ENG CO, 70-; PRIVATE CONSULT CHEM ENGR, 59- *Concurrent Pos:* Consult, Mansanto Chem Co, 52-53 & Maurice A Knight Co, 63- *Mem:* Am Chem Soc; Am Inst Chem Engrs. *Res:* Mass transfer; heterogeneous catalysis; two-phase fluid flow; extractive metallurgy; air pollution control. *Mailing Add:* Beco Eng Co PO Box 39 Glenshaw PA 15116

LERNER, DAVID EVAN, b Kansas City, Mo, Mar 21, 44. MATHEMATICAL PHYSICS. *Educ:* Haverford Col, BA, 64; Univ Pittsburgh, PhD(math), 72. *Prof Exp:* Instr math, Univ Pittsburgh, 72-73; res assoc physics, Syracuse Univ, Relativity Group, 73-75; asst prof, 75-81, ASSOC PROF MATH, UNIV KANS, 81- *Concurrent Pos:* Math Inst, Univ Oxford, 76-77. *Mem:* Am Phys Soc; Am Math Soc. *Res:* Application of Lie groups and differential geometry to general relativity. *Mailing Add:* Dept of Math Univ of Kans Lawrence KS 66045

LERNER, EDWARD CLARENCE, b Brooklyn, NY, Sept 10, 24. THEORETICAL PHYSICS. *Educ:* Mass Inst Technol, BS, 45, PhD(physics), 52. *Prof Exp:* Mem staff, Lincoln Lab, Mass Inst Technol, 52-58; assoc prof, 57-62, PROF PHYSICS, UNIV SC, 62- *Mem:* AAAS; Am Phys Soc. *Res:* Electrodynamics; field theory; classical and quantum dynamics. *Mailing Add:* Dept of Physics & Astron Univ of SC Columbia SC 29208

LERNER, HARRY, b New York, NY, Apr 24, 30; m 57; c 4. ELECTROCHEMISTRY. *Educ:* City Univ New York, BS, 51; Polytech Inst Brooklyn, MS, 53; Pa State Univ, PhD(chem), 64. *Prof Exp:* Phys chemist, Air Reduction Labs, 56-57; chemist, US Testing Co, 57-58 & Nopco Chem Co, 58-60; res assoc electrochem, Pa State Univ, 64-65; mem sci staff, Itek Corp, 65-76; tech mgr, 76-80, DIR BIOMED APPLN RES, GINER INC, 80- *Concurrent Pos:* Consult, US Marine Labs, 64-65. *Mem:* Am Chem Soc; Electrochem Soc. *Res:* Thermodynamics and kinetics of electrode reactions; kinetics and mechanisms of photographic development reactions; research and development on electrochemical and solar energy systems; biomedical devices. *Mailing Add:* 10 Angier Rd Lexington MA 02173

LERNER, JOSEPH, b Wilkes-Barre, Pa, Jan 16, 42; m 63; c 2. BIOCHEMISTRY. *Educ:* Rutgers Univ, BS, 63, PhD(biochem), 67. *Prof Exp:* Sr res investr biochem, Eastern Utilization Res & Develop Div, USDA, 67-68; asst prof, 68-71, assoc prof, 71-77, PROF BIOCHEM, UNIV MAINE, ORONO, 77-, CHMN DEPT, 78- *Concurrent Pos:* Coe Res Fund grant, 68-69; Hatch Fund grant, 69-; NIH res grant, 73-; res assoc, Dept Avian Sci, Univ Calif, Davis, 74. *Mem:* Am Chem Soc; Am Inst Nutrition; NY Acad Sci. *Res:* Intestinal absorption of amino acids in chicken; metabolism of small intestine; genetic aspects of transport processes; separation of nucleotide derivatives by column chromatography. *Mailing Add:* 236 Hitchner Hall Univ of Maine Orono ME 04473

LERNER, JULES, b Englewood, NJ, Oct 24, 41; m 69. GENETICS, CYTOLOGY. *Educ:* Bowdoin Col, BA, 63; Johns Hopkins Univ, PhD(biol), 67. *Prof Exp:* Asst prof, 67-71, assoc prof, 71-77, PROF BIOL, NORTHEASTERN ILL UNIV, 77- *Mem:* AAAS. *Res:* Developmental biology and genetics. *Mailing Add:* Dept of Biol Northeastern Ill Univ Chicago IL 60625

LERNER, LAWRENCE ROBERT, b New York, NY, Mar 17, 43; m 64; c 2. ORGANIC CHEMISTRY. *Educ:* City Col New York, BS, 64; Mich State Univ, PhD(org chem), 68. *Prof Exp:* Res chemist org pigments, E I du Pont de Nemours & Co, 68-72; group leader, Harmon Colors Corp, 72-73, supvr org pigments, 73-81, MGR PROCESS CONTROL & DEVELOP, MOBAY CHEM CORP, 81- *Concurrent Pos:* Adj asst prof, County Col Morris, NJ, 73-74. *Mem:* Sigma Xi; Am Chem Soc; AAAS; Inter-Soc Color Coun. *Res:* Synthesis of colored organic pigments; study of the effects of structure on the photostability, color and physical properties of organic pigments. *Mailing Add:* Mobay Chem Corp PO Box 419 Hawthorne NJ 07507

LERNER, LAWRENCE S, b New York, NY, Mar 10, 34; m 59. SOLID STATE PHYSICS, HISTORY OF SCIENCE. *Educ:* Univ Chicago, AB, 53, MS, 55, PhD(physics), 62. *Prof Exp:* Staff mem, Labs Appl Sci, Univ Chicago, 58-60; physicist, Hughes Res Labs, 62-65 & Hewlett-Packard Labs, Calif, 65-67; res scientist, Lockheed Palo Alto Res Lab, 67-69; assoc prof, 69-73, dir, Gen Honors Prog, 76-80, PROF PHYSICS & ASTRON, CALIF STATE UNIV, LONG BEACH, 73- *Concurrent Pos:* Danforth assoc, 75-; mem, Nat Humanities Fac, 78-; foreign mem, Centre d'Histoire des Idees dens le Monde Anglo-American (Sorbonne). *Mem:* AAAS; Am Phys Soc; Am Asn Physics Teachers; Hist Sci Soc. *Res:* Fermi surfaces of metals and semimetals; preparation and properties of ternary compound semiconductors; semiconductor physics; influence of non-scientific philosophical movements on early scientific revolution. *Mailing Add:* Dept of Physics & Astron Calif State Univ Long Beach CA 90840

LERNER, LEON MAURICE, b Chicago, Ill, Feb 2, 38; m 59; c 3. BIOCHEMISTRY. *Educ:* Ill Inst Technol, BS, 59, MS, 61; Univ Ill, PhD(biochem), 64. *Prof Exp:* Res assoc biochem, Col Med, Univ Ill, 64-65; from instr to asst prof, 65-73, assoc prof, 73-80, PROF, STATE UNIV NY DOWNSTATE MED CTR, 80- *Mem:* AAAS; Am Chem Soc. *Res:* Potential nucleic acid antimetabolites; nucleoside analogs; chemistry and biochemistry of carbohydrates. *Mailing Add:* 450 Clarkson Ave Brooklyn NY 11203

LERNER, LEONARD JOSEPH, b Roselle, NJ, Sept 26, 22. ENDOCRINOLOGY, REPRODUCTION & FERTILITY. *Educ:* Rutgers Univ, BS, 43, AB, 51, MS, 53, PhD(zool), 54. *Prof Exp:* Pharmacist, 46-51; asst, Bur Biol Res, Rutgers Univ, 53-54; endocrinologist, Wm S Merrell Co, 54-58; head endocrine res, Squibb Inst Med Res, 58-71; dir endocrinol, Gruppo Lepetit Spa, 71-77; RES PROF DEPTS OBSTET & GYNEC & PHARMACOL, THOMAS JEFFERSON MED COL, 77- *Concurrent Pos:* Assoc mem, Bur Biol Res, Rutgers Univ; vis prof obstet & gynec, Hahnemann Med Sch; mem, Steering Comt Int Study Group, Steroid Hormones; mem, Nat Cancer Inst, Breast Cancer Task Force Comt. *Mem:* Endocrine Soc; Am Physiol Soc; fel NY Acad Sci; Am Fertil Soc; Soc Study Reprod. *Res:* Hormone antagonists; fertility control; reproduction; placenta; prostaglandins; ovulation; steroids; endocrine-tumor relationships; hormone treatment of newborn; endocrine biochemistry; central nervous system-endocrine system relationship; adrenal physiology; pregnancy physiology and biochemistry. *Mailing Add:* Thomas Jefferson Univ Med Col Dept Obstet & Gynec 1025 Walnut St Philadelphia PA 19107

LERNER, LOUIS LEONARD, b Chicago, Ill, Feb 25, 15; m 49; c 1. COSMETIC CHEMISTRY. *Educ:* Cent YMCA Col, BS, 42. *Prof Exp:* Chem asst, Universal Merchandise Co, 34, assoc chemist, 35-37; chief chemist, Russian Duchess Labs, 37; pres & dir res, LaLerne Labs, 37-40; dir res & prod, Consol Royal Chem Corp, 40-46; exec vpres & dir res & prod, Allied Home Prods Corp, 46-49; vpres & dir res, Kalech Res Labs, 49-50; vpres & dir res & new prod develop, Bymart, Inc, 50-52; sr scientist, Personal Care Div, Gillette Co, 52-74; consumer prod specialist, 74, PHYSICAL SCIENTIST, FED TRADE COMN, US GOVT, 75- *Concurrent Pos:* Dir, Brokers, Inc, 37-40; instr, Cent YMCA Col, 42-44; dir, Allied Home Prods Corp, Ill, 47-49; vpres, Phil Kalech Co, 49-50; dir, AD Prods Corp, 64-66; consult, Seaquist Valve Co, 74-; sect ed, Chem Bull, Am Chem Soc, 71-77, consult ed, 78-80. *Mem:* Fel AAAS; Am Chem Soc; Soc Cosmetic Chem; NY Acad Sci; Nat Asn Sci Writers. *Res:* Product development, exploratory research; pharmaceuticals, proprietaries, cosmetics, detergents, emulsions, waving compositions, dyes and pigments; chemistry of polymers, proteins and enzymes; mechanical devices; surface chemistry; consumer products. *Mailing Add:* 900 N Lake Shore Dr Chicago IL 60611

LERNER, MARGUERITE RUSH, b Minneapolis, Minn, May 17, 24; m 45; c 4. DERMATOLOGY. *Educ:* Univ Minn, Minneapolis, BA, 45; Case Western Reserve Univ, Md, 50. *Prof Exp:* From intern to resident dermat, Univ Mich Hosp, Ann Arbor, 50-52; resident, Multnomah County Hosp, Univ Ore, 52-54; from clin instr to assoc clin prof dermat, 47-73, PROF CLIN DERMAT, SCH MED, YALE UNIV, 73- *Mem:* Am Acad Dermat; Soc Invest Dermat. *Res:* Psoriasis. *Mailing Add:* Dept of Dermat Yale Univ Sch of Med New Haven CT 06510

LERNER, MELVIN, b Milwaukee, Wis, June 8, 17; m 68; c 2. ANALYTICAL CHEMISTRY. *Educ:* City Col NY, BS, 37. *Prof Exp:* Res chemist, Univ Patents, Inc, 38-39; chemist, Hoover & Strong, Inc, 39-41; chemist, US Customs Lab, 41-50, from asst chief chemist to chief chemist, 50-67; DIR TECH SERV, BUR CUSTOMS, 67- *Mem:* AAAS; Am Chem Soc; Am Soc Test & Mat. *Res:* Analytical chemistry of marijuana; narcotics and dangerous drugs; sampling of bulk materials; instrumental analytical chemistry. *Mailing Add:* US Customs Serv Washington DC 20229

LERNER, MICHAEL PAUL, b Los Angeles, Calif, May 2, 41; m 65; c 2. VIROLOGY, CELL BIOLOGY. *Educ:* Univ Calif, Los Angeles, BA, 63; Kans State Univ, MS, 67; Northwestern Univ, PhD(microbiol), 70. *Prof Exp:* Nat Inst Neurol Dis & Stroke fel, Univ Calif, Los Angeles, 70-71, asst res biologist neurochem, Ctr Health Sci, 72-73; ASSOC PROF MICROBIOL, HEALTH SCI CTR, UNIV OKLA, 73- *Concurrent Pos:* Fel, NATO Advan Study Inst, Italy, 72. *Mem:* Am Soc Microbiol. *Res:* Mammalian cell biochemistry and development. *Mailing Add:* Dept of Microbiol & Immunol Univ Okla Health Sci Ctr Oklahoma City OK 73190

LERNER, MOISEY, b Kiev, USSR, May 15, 31; US citizen; wid; c 2. ELECTRICAL ENGINEERING. *Educ:* Polytech Inst, USSR, MS, 53; Pedagogical Inst, BA, 54; Power Eng Inst, USSR, MS, 57, PhD(elec eng), 61. *Hon Degrees:* Docent, Supreme Cert Comn, Moscow, USSR, 64. *Prof Exp:* Asst prof physics, Inst Elec Commun, USSR, 62-68; asst prof elec eng, Air Force Mil Eng Acad, USSR, 68-73; DIR RES & DEVELOP, SANFORD PROCESS CORP, 75- *Concurrent Pos:* Patent agent, Duralectra Inc, Mass, 80-; consult, BBF Inc, Mass, 80- *Mem:* Am Electroplaters Soc; Inst Elec & Electronics Engrs; Am Soc Testing & Mat. *Res:* Low voltage hardcoating of aluminum; alternating current and direct current anodizing and electroplating; design and development of alternating current and direct current power supplier; heat dissipation at non-sinusoidal voltages; fourier series and tamara lerner indexes. *Mailing Add:* 75 Rolling Lane Needham MA 02192

LERNER, NARCINDA REYNOLDS, b Brooklyn, NY, Oct 10, 33; m 59. POLYMER CHEMISTRY. *Educ:* Hofstra Univ, BA, 56; Univ Chicago, MS, 59, PhD(chem), 62. *Prof Exp:* Mem tech staff, Hughes Res Labs Labs, Calif, 62-63; res scientist, Lockheed Palo Alto Res Lab, 66-70; RES SCIENTIST, AMES RES CTR, NASA, 70- *Mem:* AAAS; Am Phys Soc. *Res:* Paramagnetic resonance; electron nuclear double resonance; crystalline field theory; crystal preparation; electrical properties of polymers; polymer degradation. *Mailing Add:* Ames Res Ctr NASA MS 223-6 Moffett Field CA 94035

LERNER, RICHARD ALAN, b Chicago, Ill, Aug 26, 38; m 66; c 3. IMMUNOLOGY. *Educ:* Stanford Univ, MD, 64. *Prof Exp:* Intern med, Stanford Univ, 64-65; assoc cell biol, Wistar Inst, 68-70; assoc immunol, 70-71, assoc mem, 71-73, MEM IMMUNOL, SCRIPPS CLIN & RES FOUND, 74- *Concurrent Pos:* USPHS grant, Scripps Clin & Res Found, 65-68; consult, Nat Cancer Inst, 72- *Mem:* Am Soc Immunol; Am Soc Path; Biophys Soc; Am Soc Microbiol. *Res:* Molecular medicine; differentiation. *Mailing Add:* Scripps Clin 10666 W Torrey Pines Rd La Jolla CA 92037

LERNER, RITA GUGGENHEIM, b New York, NY, May 7, 29; m 54; c 2. INFORMATION SCIENCE. *Educ:* Radcliffe Col, AB, 49; Columbia Univ, MA, 51, PhD(chem phys), 56. *Prof Exp:* Res assoc chem phys, Columbia Univ, 56-64; staff physicist info sci, Am Inst Physics, 65, dep dir, Info Anal & Retrieval Div, 66-67; dir labs, Dept Biol Sci, Columbia Univ, 68; mgr planning & develop, 69-73, MGR MKT, AM INST PHYSICS, 79- *Concurrent Pos:* Info sci series ed, Hutchinson Ross Publ Co, 73-; ed, Encycl Physics, Addison- Wesley Publ Co, 81. *Mem:* Am Phys Soc; Am Chem Soc; AAAS; Am Soc Info Sci; NY Acad Sci. *Res:* Information systems and information retrieval; applications of new technology to publishing and distribution of information. *Mailing Add:* Am Inst of Physics 335 E 45th St New York NY 10017

LERNER, SAMUEL, b Providence, RI, Jan 21, 08; m 39; c 1. ENGINEERING. *Educ:* Brown Univ, BSc, 30; Syracuse Univ, MS, 33; Turin Polytech, DrEng, 57. *Prof Exp:* Instr hydraul, Syracuse Univ, 31-33; instr civil eng, from asst prof to prof, 41-76, dir construct planning, 63-76, EMER PROF CIVIL ENG, BROWN UNIV, 76- *Concurrent Pos:* Owner, Lerner Assocs, 76- *Mem:* Am Soc Civil Engrs; Am Concrete Inst; Int Asn Bridge & Struct Eng. *Res:* Building construction. *Mailing Add:* 14 Cooke St Pawtucket RI 02860

LERNER, SIDNEY ISAAC, b Baltimore, Md, May 2, 32; m 56; c 4. OCCUPATIONAL MEDICINE. *Educ:* Univ Md, BS, 53, MD, 57; Ohio State Univ, MS, 60. *Prof Exp:* Staff occup med, Army Environ Hyg Agency, 60-62 & Corp Med Dept, Ethyl Corp, 62-74; MEM FAC ENVIRON HEALTH, COL OF MED, UNIV CINCINNATI, 62- *Concurrent Pos:* Dir personal health, Cincinnati Gen Hosp, 64-78; consult occup med, 62- *Mem:* AMA; Am Acad Occup Med; Am Occup Med Asn; Am Indust Hyg Asn; Am Conf Govt Indust Hygienists. *Res:* Clinical effects of inorganic lead and other heavy metals, clinical industrial toxicology; medical surveillance; clinical practice of occupational medicine. *Mailing Add:* Dept Environ Health Col of Med Univ of Cincinnati Cincinnati OH 45267

LEROI, GEORGE EDGAR, b London, Eng, June 23, 36; US citizen; m; c 4. CHEMICAL PHYSICS. *Educ:* Univ Wis, BA, 56; Harvard Univ, AM, 58, PhD(chem), 60. *Prof Exp:* Res assoc chem, Univ Calif, Berkeley, 60-62; lectr, Princeton Univ, 62-64, asst prof, 64-67; assoc prof, 67-72, PROF CHEM, MICH STATE UNIV, 72- *Concurrent Pos:* Guest Prof, Lab Phys Chem, Swiss Fed Inst Technol, 74-75; Japan Soc Promotion Sci vis prof, 77; Syncrotron Ultraviolet Radiation Facility fel, US Nat Bur Standards, 81-82. *Honors & Awards:* Coblentz Award, 72. *Mem:* Am Phys Soc. *Res:* Molecular spectroscopy and structure; vacuum ultraviolet, visible, infrared, far infrared, Raman; photoionization mass spectrometry; laser spectroscopy and photochemistry. *Mailing Add:* Dept of Chem Mich State Univ East Lansing MI 48824

LEROITH, DEREK, b Cape Town, SAfrica, Jan 3, 45; m 79; c 3. MEDICINE, DIABETES. *Educ:* Univ Cape Town, MB, ChB, 67, PhD(med), 73. *Prof Exp:* Registr med, Univ Cape Town, SAfrica, 72-75; sr registr med, Middlesex Med Sch, London, England, 75; sr lectr med, Univ Ben Gurion, Israel, 76-79; VIS SCIENTIST DIABETES, NIH, 79- *Mem:* Fel Col Physicians SAfrica; Am Endocrine Soc. *Res:* Evolutionary origins of the vertebrate endocrine systems; hormonal substances in invertebrates. *Mailing Add:* Bldg 10 Rm 85243 Diabetes Branch NIH Bethesda MD 20205

LEROUX, EDGAR JOSEPH, b Ottawa, Ont, Jan 24, 22; m 44; c 3. INSECT ECOLOGY. *Educ:* Carleton Univ, Can, BA, 50; McGill Univ, MSc, 52, PhD(entom), 54. *Hon Degrees:* DSc, McGill Univ, 73. *Prof Exp:* Asst entomologist, Fruit Insect Invests, Sci Serv, 49-53, assoc entomologist, Orchard Insect Ecol, 53-60, entomologist, Res Lab, 60-62, sr entomologist, 62-66, res coordr entom, 66-67, asst dir gen, Insts, Res Br, 68-72, assoc dir gen, Planning & Coord, Res Br, 72-75, dir gen, Opers Directorate, Res Br, 75-78, ASST DEP MINISTER, RES BR, AGR CAN, 75- *Concurrent Pos:* Demonstr, Macdonald Col, McGill Univ, 50-51, asst, 53-54, lectr, 58-62, assoc prof, 62-65, hon prof, 70-71; Grace Griswold lectr, Cornell Univ, 71. Mem orchard protection comt, Info & Res Serv, Que Dept Agr, 59-63; mem adv comt entom probs, Defence Res Bd, Dept Nat Defence, 64-67; sci ed, Can J Plant Sci, 65-68; mem panel experts integrated pest control, Food & Agr Orgn, 66-71; dir, Biol Coun Can, 66-70, pres, 70-71; off cor entom, Commonwealth Inst Biol Control, 67-73; Can rep, Int Soc Hort Sci, 67-73; mem, World Hort Coun, 68-70; chmn panel insect ecol, Study of Basic Biol in Can, Biol Coun Can, Sci Coun Can, 69-70; mem, Can Govt Tech Apple Mission, Japan, Australia, NZ & SAfrica, 71; mem, Asn Sci, Eng & Technol Community Can Mgt Comt, Sci Coun Can Spec Study on Sci Soc, 72; mem negotiated grants comt & adv comt on biol, Nat Res Coun Can, 73-78; Can rep, Comt Int Plant Protection Cong, 74-; mem, Agr Can Dept Publ Comt, 74-; Serv Coord Comt, 75-; mem, Agr Stabilization Bd & Agr Prod Bd, 75-, vchmn 77; vchmn, Can Agr Res Coun, 77-; co-chmn, Can/Russia Agrobus Working Group, 78; chmn, OECD Comt Agr, 78- *Honors & Awards:* Jubilee Medal, Governor Gen Can, 77. *Mem:* Entom Soc Can (pres, 69-70); Fr-Can Asn Advan Sci; Agr Inst Can; Can Soc Zoologists; Asn Sci Eng & Technol Community Can (hon treas, 70-72). *Res:* Insect ecology; integrated pest control; morphology; toxicology. *Mailing Add:* Res Br Cent Exp Farm Ottawa ON K1A 0C5 Can

LEROUX, EDMUND FRANK, b Muskegon Heights, Mich, Mar 8, 25; m 49; c 3. HYDROLOGY. *Educ:* Mich State Univ, BS, 48. *Prof Exp:* Geologist, 49-60, chief manpower sect, 61-64, ASST DIST CHIEF HYDROL, US GEOL SURV, 64- *Mem:* Am Geophys Union; Int Asn Hydrogeologists; AAAS. *Res:* Ground water temperature; hydrology of glacial terrain in a semiarid climate. *Mailing Add:* Water Resources Div US Geol Surv 317 Fed Bldg Huron SD 57350

LEROY, ANDRE FRANCOIS, b Philadelphia, Pa, Sept 30, 33. ANALYTICAL CHEMISTRY, PHYSICAL CHEMISTRY. *Educ:* Yale Univ, BE, 56; Calif Inst Technol, MS, 57; Harvard Univ, AM, 65, PhD(eng), 67. *Prof Exp:* Engr, Radiol Health Res Activities, USPHS, 58-60, res chemist, Northeastern Radiol Health Lab, Mass, 63-68; engr, NIH, Md, 69-78; mem staff, Sci Off, Am Embassy, Paris, France, 78-80; CHIEF, ANAL METHODS, BIOMED ENG & INSTRUMENTATION BR, DIV RES SERV, NIH, 80- *Concurrent Pos:* Dir, Tech Equip Seminars, US Dept Com, France, 80, Spain, Italy & Greece, 81. *Honors & Awards:* Clemens Herschel Prize. *Mem:* Am Chem Soc; Am Inst Chem Engrs. *Res:* Physical chemistry of transition metal complexes; analytical chemical and ultra-trace level quantitations of metal complex species and kinetics of their transformations in biological systems and natural waters; high spatial resolution analysis of elements by instrumental micro analysis (electron-probe). *Mailing Add:* Biomed Eng & Instrumentation Br Bldg 13 Rm 3W13 Nat Inst Health Bethesda MD 20205

LEROY, DONALD JAMES, b Detroit, Mich, Mar 5, 13; m 40; c 4. CHEMICAL KINETICS, SCIENCE POLICY. *Educ:* Univ Toronto, BA, 35, MA, 36, PhD, 39. *Hon Degrees:* LLD, Trent Univ, 71; DSc, Laurentian Univ, 73; McMaster Univ, 74; Dr es Sc, Univ Laval, 76; DSc, Waterloo Univ & Toronto Univ, 78. *Prof Exp:* Ont Res Found, 39; chem div, Nat Res Labs, 40-44; from asst prof to prof chem, Univ Toronto, 44-74, chmn dept, 60-71; sci vpres, Nat Res Coun Can, 69-74, prin res officer, 75-78; sci adv, 79-81, SPEC ADV, SCI COUN CAN, 81- *Honors & Awards:* Palladium Medal, Chem Inst Can; Centennial Medal, Govt of Can, 67; Queen's Jubilee Medal, 77. *Mem:* Am Chem Soc; fel Chem Inst Can; Royal Soc Chem; Am Phys Soc; fel Royal Soc Can. *Res:* Reactions of atoms and free radicals; photosensitization; energy transfer processes; science policy; university research policy; university/industry interaction. *Mailing Add:* 1008-111 Wurtemburg Ottawa ON K1N 8M1 Can

LEROY, ROBERT FREDERICK, b Passaic, NJ, July 24, 50; m 74; c 2. NEUROLOGY, ELECTROENCEPHALOGRAPHY. *Educ:* Brown Univ, AB, 72; Pa State Univ, MD, 77. *Prof Exp:* Intern, Dept Med, Baltimore City Hosp, 77-78; resident neurol, Dept Neurol, Sch Med, Yale Univ, 78-81, fel, Merritt Pulnam Epilepsy Found Am, 81-82; ASST PROF & DIR CLIN NEUROPHYSIOL, DEPT NEUROL, HEALTH SCI CTR,

SOUTHWESTERN MED SCH, UNIV TEX, 82- *Concurrent Pos:* Consult, Dallas Tex Vet Admin, Med Ctr, 82. *Mem:* Am Acad Neurol. *Res:* Electroencephalography and general clinical neurophysiology as it pertains to epilepsy and its treatments. *Mailing Add:* Dept Neurol Univ Tex 5323 Harry Hinos Blvd Dallas TX 75235

LEROY, RODNEY LASH, b Ottawa, Ont, Nov 15, 41; m 65; c 4. PHYSICAL CHEMISTRY, ELECTROCHEMISTRY. *Educ:* Univ Toronto, BSc, 64, MA, 65, PhD(phys chem), 68; McGill Univ, dipl mgt, 78. *Prof Exp:* Fel phys chem, Univ Colo & Yale Univ, 68-70; assoc scientist chem, 70-72, group leader electrochem, 72-78, prin scientist electrochem, 78-79, prog mgr res, Normanda Res Centre, 78-79, ; TECH DIR, ELECTROLYSER, INC, 80- *Mem:* Chem Inst Can; Electrochem Soc; Nat Asn Corrosion Engrs; Int Asn Hydrogen Energy; Ordre des Chemistes de Quebec. *Res:* Corrosion research; electrometallurgy of non-ferrous metals, especially copper and zinc; hydrogen production by electrolysis of water. *Mailing Add:* 240 Hymus Blvd Pointe Claire PQ H9R 1G5 Can

LERSTEN, NELS R, b Chicago, Ill, Aug 6, 32; m 58; c 3. BOTANY. *Educ:* Univ Chicago, BS, 58, MS, 60; Univ Calif, Berkeley, PhD(bot), 63. *Prof Exp:* From asst prof to assoc prof, 63-70, PROF BOT, IOWA STATE UNIV, 70- *Mem:* Bot Soc Am; Sigma Xi. *Res:* Systematic and developmental anatomy of angiosperms; embryology of flowering plants. *Mailing Add:* Dept Bot Iowa State Univ Ames IA 50011

LES, EDWIN PAUL, b Adams, Mass, Dec 28, 23; m 67; c 2. GENETICS. *Educ:* Northeastern Univ, BS, 52; Ohio State Univ, MS, PhD(genetics), 59. *Prof Exp:* Assoc staff scientist, Jackson Lab, 59-60; biologist, Biol Div, Oak Ridge Nat Lab, 60-62; staff scientist, 62-75, SR STAFF SCIENTIST, JACKSON LAB, 75- *Mem:* AAAS; Am Genetic Asn; Am Asn Lab Animal Sci. *Res:* Effect of environment on reproduction, growth and survival of laboratory mice; mouse husbandry techniques and practices; laboratory animal health. *Mailing Add:* Jackson Lab Bar Harbor ME 04609

LESAGE, LEO G, b Concordia, Kans, Apr 15, 35; m 58; c 2. NUCLEAR ENGINEERING, PHYSICS. *Educ:* Univ Kans, BS, 57; Stanford Univ, MS, 62, PhD(nuclear eng), 66; Univ Chicago, MBA, 81. *Prof Exp:* Nuclear engr, Fast Breeder Reactor Develop, 66-75, DIR, APPL PHYSICS DIV, ARGONNE NAT LAB, 75- *Mem:* Am Nuclear Soc. *Res:* Fast reactor physics; fast reactor critical experiments. *Mailing Add:* Appl Physics Div Argonne Nat Lab Argonne IL 60439

LESCARBOURA, JAIME AQUILES, b Barcelona, Spain, Aug 29, 37; US citizen; m 57; c 2. CHEMICAL ENGINEERING. *Educ:* Univ Kans, BS, 59, PhD(chem eng), 67; Univ Wis-Madison, MS, 61. *Prof Exp:* Engr, Cardon Refinery, Shell Oil Co Venezeula, 61-63; res scientist, 67-76, SR RES SCIENTIST, CONTINENTAL OIL CO, 76- *Concurrent Pos:* Am Oil Found fel, 67-68. *Mem:* Am Inst Chem Engrs; Soc Petrol Engrs. *Res:* Flow of Newtonian and non-Newtonian fluids; falling cylinder viscometer for non-Newtonian fluids; turbulent flow drag reduction by addition of polymers; well testing; formation evaluation. *Mailing Add:* 1613 Monument Rd Ponca City OK 74601

LESENSKY, LEONARD, b New York, NY, Sept 22, 22; m 48; c 1. PHYSICS. *Educ:* Brooklyn Col, BA, 42; Columbia Univ, MA, 49, PhD(physics), 56. *Prof Exp:* Asst, Radiation Lab, Columbia Univ, 42-44; physics dept, 50-53; physicist, Microwave Tubes, Raytheon Co, 53-57, mgr mat res, Spencer Lab, 57-61; prin scientist mat, Avco Corp, 61-64; PRIN ENGR MAT, MICROWAVE & POWER TUBE DIV, RAYTHEON CO, 64- *Mem:* Am Phys Soc. *Res:* Physical, chemical and electronic properties of microwave tube materials; microwave tubes; low temperature physics. *Mailing Add:* Raytheon Co-Microwave & Power Tube Div New Prod Ctr Willow St Waltham MA 02154

LESER, ERNST GEORGE, b Mineola, NY, May 3, 43; m 69. ORGANIC CHEMISTRY. *Educ:* Bucknell Univ, BS, 65; Fordham Univ, PhD(org chem), 70. *Prof Exp:* Res chemist, Jackson Lab, 69-74, PROD SUPVR, CHAMBERS WORKS, E I DU PONT DE NEMOURS & CO, INC, 74- *Mem:* Am Chem Soc. *Res:* Supervision of dyes and intermediates production. *Mailing Add:* Chambers Works E I du Pont de Nemours & Co Inc Wilmington DE 19898

LESER, RALPH ULRICH, b Bloomington, Ind, Dec 31, 05; m 66; c 2. INTERNAL MEDICINE. *Educ:* Ind Univ, AB, 27, MD, 30; Am Bd Internal Med, dipl, 44. *Prof Exp:* Intern, Philadelphia Gen Hosp, Pa, 30-32; fel internal med, Mayo Clin, 34-37; from instr to assoc med, 38-50, asst prof, 50-67, ASSOC PROF MED, SCH MED, IND UNIV, INDIANAPOLIS, 67- *Concurrent Pos:* Vis physician, Marion County Gen Hosp, 38-, chief, Diag Clin, 46-58; vis physician, Methodist, St Vincent's & Community Hosps. *Mem:* AMA; fel Am Col Physicians. *Res:* Cardiology; diseases of metabolism; gastroenterology. *Mailing Add:* 5434 Ashurst St Indianapolis IN 46220

LESH, JANET ROUNTREE, b Chicago, Ill, Aug 14, 37. ASTROPHYSICS. *Educ:* Cornell Univ, AB, 58; Univ Chicago, PhD(astron, astrophys), 67. *Prof Exp:* Res assoc astron, Yerkes Observ, Univ Chicago, 67-68; sci officer astron, Leiden Observ, Univ Leiden, Netherlands, 68-70; astronr adjoint, Meudon Observ, Observ Paris, France, 70-71; vis fel astrophys, Joint Inst Lab Astrophys, Univ Colo, 71-72; lectr astron & res astronr, Univ Denver, 72-77, dir observ opers, 74-77; sr res assoc, NASA Goddard Space Flight Ctr, 77-79; PHYS SCIENTIST, US DEPT AIR FORCE, 79- *Concurrent Pos:* Eng lang ed & translr, Astron & Astrophys, 69-72; translr, D Reidel Co, Dordrecht, Netherlands, 69-72 & Joint Publ Res Serv, 73-79. *Mem:* Int Astron Union; Am Astron Soc; Royal Astron Soc; Netherlands Astron Soc. *Res:* Spectral classification of early type stars; short-period variable stars; local galactic structure; stellar associations and clusters; infrared astronomy. *Mailing Add:* 6001 Wynnwood Rd Bethesda MD 20816

LESH, THOMAS ALLAN, b Chicago, Ill, Aug 6, 29; m 79. PHYSIOLOGY. *Educ:* Mich State Univ, BS, 51; Ind Univ, PhD(physiol), 68. *Prof Exp:* Assoc ed, Howard W Sams & Co, Inc, Ind, 55-63; USPHS cardiovasc trainee, Bowman Gray Sch Med, 68-70; asst prof physiol, Med Ctr, Univ Ark, Little Rock, 70-72; asst prof, 72-77, ASSOC PROF PHYSIOL & HEALTH SCI, BALL STATE UNIV & MUNCIE CTR MED EDUC, 77- *Mem:* Assoc Am Physiol Soc; AAAS; Sigma Xi; Microcirculation Soc. *Res:* Respiratory insufficiency. *Mailing Add:* Dept Physiol & Health Sci Ball State Univ Muncie IN 47306

LESHER, DEAN ALLEN, b Endicott, NY, Feb 18, 27; m 49; c 3. CLINICAL PHARMACOLOGY, NEPHROLOGY. *Educ:* Colgate Univ, AB, 48; Univ Wis, PhD(pharmacol), 56; Univ Buffalo, MD, 62. *Prof Exp:* Asst pharmacol, Univ Mich, 51-52; asst, Univ Wis, 52-55; instr, Univ Buffalo, 55-58, assoc, 58-62; from intern to resident, Henry Ford Hosp, Detroit, 62-63, assoc med, 64-71; assoc dir med res, Lederle Labs, 71-73; assoc dir, 74-77, dir clin pharmacol, 77-78, sr dir clin res, 78-80, SR RES FEL, CIBA GEIGY CORP, 80- *Mem:* Am Soc Clin Invest; Int Soc Nephrol; Am Soc Nephrol; Am Soc Clin Pharmacol & Therapeut; fel Am Col Clin Pharm. *Res:* Renal transport of acids and bases; renal potassium transport; diuretics; renal disease; hemodialysis; peritoneal dialysis; renal transplantation; drug evaluation: anti inflammatory, central nervous system, antibiotic, ophthalmic; drug intoxication. *Mailing Add:* CIBA-Geigy Corp 556 Morris Ave Summit NJ 07901

LESHER, GARY ALLEN, b Chicago, Ill, June 29, 50; m 73; c 1. PHARMACOLOGY, DRUG METABOLISM. *Educ:* Carroll Col, Wis, BS, 72; Purdue UniY, West Lafayette, MS, 75, PhD(pharmacol), 77. *Prof Exp:* ASST PROF PHARMACOL, SCH PHARM, UNIV MD, 77- *Mem:* Am Asn Col Pharm. *Res:* Narcotic drug dependence and drug interactions in narcotic dependent animals, effects of narcotics on drug metabolism; effects of environmental contaminants on drug metabolism; toxicology. *Mailing Add:* Dept of Pharmacol 636 W Lombard St Baltimore MD 21201

LESHER, GEORGE YOHE, b Mt Erie, Ill, Feb 22, 26; m 57; c 2. PHARMACEUTICAL CHEMISTRY, SYNTHETIC ORGANIC CHEMISTRY. *Educ:* Univ Ill, BA, 50; Dartmouth Col, MS, 52; Rensselaer Polytech Inst, PhD(chem), 56. *Prof Exp:* Sr res assoc & sect head, 52-67, ASST DIR CHEM DIV, STERLING-WINTHROP RES INST, 67- *Mem:* Am Chem Soc. *Res:* Heterocyclic chemistry. *Mailing Add:* Sterling-Winthrop Res Inst Rensselaer NY 12144

LESHER, SAMUEL WALTER, b Spokane, Wash, June 9, 16; m 70; c 2. CELL BIOLOGY, RADIOBIOLOGY. *Educ:* Univ Ill, BS, 42; Wash Univ, PhD(zool), 50. *Prof Exp:* Biologist, Div Biol & Med Res, Argonne Nat Lab, Ill, 54-68; dir, Cell & Radiobiol Labs & Cancer Res Unit, 68-79, ASSOC DIR, CLIN RADIATION THER RES CTR, ALLEGHENY GEN HOSP, PITTSBURGH, 73-; adj prof, Dept Life Sci, Univ Pittsburgh. *Concurrent Pos:* Adj prof, Dept Life Sci, Univ Pittsburgh; dir, Geriat/Geront Ctr for the Aging, 79. *Honors & Awards:* Litchfield lect, Oxford Univ, Eng, 75. *Mem:* Radiation Res Soc; Am Asn Cancer Res; Cell Kinetics Soc; Am Soc Cell Biol. *Res:* Cell kinetics; effects of radiation and drugs on normal and malignant cells; combined modality research; cancer biology; effects of age on organ function in man in the organ systems: cardiovascular, pulmonary, endocrines, renal, neurological, hematological. *Mailing Add:* Allegheny Gen Hosp Cancer Res Unit 320 E North Ave Pittsburgh PA 15213

LESHIN, RICHARD, b New York, NY, June 16, 24; m 50; c 3. ORGANIC CHEMISTRY. *Educ:* City Col New York, BS, 44; NY Univ, MS, 47, PhD(chem), 52. *Prof Exp:* Sr res chemist, 52-65, SECT HEAD, GOODYEAR TIRE & RUBBER CO, 65- *Concurrent Pos:* Instr, eve sch, Univ Akron, 54-56. *Mem:* Am Chem Soc. *Res:* Organic synthesis; rubber additives; vulcanization of rubber; protection of rubber against aging. *Mailing Add:* 1527 Shanabrook Dr Akron OH 44313

LESH-LAURIE, GEORGIA ELIZABETH, b Cleveland, Ohio, July 28, 38; m 69. DEVELOPMENTAL BIOLOGY. *Educ:* Marietta Col, BS, 60; Univ Wis, MS, 61; Case Western Reserve Univ, PhD(biol), 66. *Prof Exp:* Instr biol, Case Western Reserve Univ, 65-66; asst prof biol sci, State Univ NY Albany, 66-69; from asst prof to assoc prof biol, Western Reserve Col, Case Western Reserve Univ, 69-77, asst dean, 73-76; chmn, Dept Biol, 77-81, PROF BIOL, CLEVELAND STATE UNIV, 77-, DEAN COL GRAD STUDIES, 81- *Concurrent Pos:* NY State Res Found res fel, 66-67; USPHS instnl grant, 70-71; Am Cancer Soc grants, 68-71 & 77-80; Res Corp grant, 71; Am Cancer Soc instnl grant, 73. *Mem:* AAAS; Am Soc Zool; Soc Develop Biol; NY Acad Sci; Am Soc Cell Biol. *Res:* Study of the neurosecretory control of cellular differentiation in cnidarian systems and the role of these differentiations in the establishment and maintenance of polarized form. *Mailing Add:* Dept of Biol Cleveland State Univ Cleveland OH 44115

LESHNER, ALAN IRVIN, b Lewisburg, Pa, Feb 11, 44; m 69. PHYSIOLOGICAL PSYCHOLOGY. *Educ:* Franklin & Marshall Col, AB, 65; Rutgers Univ, MS, 67, PhD(psychol), 69. *Prof Exp:* From asst prof to prof psychol, Bucknell Univ, 69-81; PROJ MGR, NSF, 80- *Concurrent Pos:* NIMH res grant, 70-71, 78-80; NSF res grant, 70-72, 75-77. *Mem:* AAAS; Am Psychol Asn; Soc Neurosci; NY Acad Sci. *Res:* Biological basis of behavior; current and emerging science and technology problems and opportunities; and major science and technology policy issues. *Mailing Add:* Off Special Proj Nat Sci Found Washington DC 20550

LESIEWICZ, JEANNE LEE, molecular biology, see previous edition

LESIKAR, ARNOLD VINCENT, b Galveston, Tex, Nov 3, 37; m 76. CHEMICAL PHYSICS, PHYSICS. *Educ:* Rice Univ, BS, 58; Calif Inst Technol, PhD(physics), 65. *Prof Exp:* Res asst physics, Calif Inst Technol, 60-65; asst physics, Tech Univ, Munich, Ger, 65-66; PROF PHYSICS, ST CLOUD STATE UNIV, 66- *Concurrent Pos:* Vis prof chem physics, Cath Univ Am, 78- *Mem:* Sigma Xi; Am Chem Soc; Am Asn Physics Teachers; Am Phys Soc. *Mailing Add:* Dept of Physics St Cloud State Univ St Cloud MN 56301

LESINS, KARLIS A, b Latvia, July 30, 06; m 39. CYTOGENETICS, PLANT BREEDING. *Educ:* Royal Agr Col, Sweden, Lic Agr, 50; Univ Alta, DSc, 59. *Prof Exp:* Headmaster, Sch Agr Bebrene, Latvia, 31-41; supt, Agr Res Sta, Osupe, Latvia, 41-44; agronomist, Swedish Seed Asn, 44-51; res fel, 51-54, res assoc forage crops, 54-60, assoc res prof, 60-65, prof, 66-71, EMER PROF GENETICS, UNIV ALTA, 71- *Mem:* Am Soc Agron; Am Genetic Asn; Can Agr Inst. *Res:* Specialty Medicago; taxonomy. *Mailing Add:* 9727-65 Ave Edmonton AB T6E 0K5 Can

LESINSKI, JOHN SILVESTER, b Philadelphia, Pa, Mar 29, 13; m 40; c 4. OBSTETRICS & GYNECOLOGY. *Educ:* Jagellonian Univ, Poland, MD, 39; Johns Hopkins Univ, MPH, 67. *Prof Exp:* Dep dir, Nat Res Inst Mother & Child Health, Warsaw, 52-65; chmn obstet & gynec, Med Acad, Warsaw & Inst Postgrad Training Physicians, Warsaw, 58-65; ASSOC PROF MOTHER & CHILD HEALTH, OBSTET & GYNEC, JOHNS HOPKINS UNIV, 67- *Concurrent Pos:* Expert, Mother & Child Health, WHO, 60- *Honors & Awards:* Medal Exemplary Serv Health, Govt Poland, 62, Order Polonia Restituta, 50 & 63. *Mem:* Fel Am Acad Reproductive Med; fel Am Pub Health Asn; fel Am Col Obstetricians & Gynecologists; fel Royal Soc Health; fel Am Col Prev Med. *Res:* High risk factors in reproductive failure; sequelae of induced abortion; study of reproductive performance of individuals born prematurely or with low birth weight. *Mailing Add:* 615 N Wolfe St Baltimore MD 21205

LESK, MICHAEL E, b Brooklyn, NY, May 21, 45; m 68. COMPUTER & INFORMATION SCIENCE. *Educ:* Harvard Univ, BA, 64, MA, 66, PhD(chem phys), 69. *Prof Exp:* MEM TECH STAFF, BELL TEL LABS, 69- *Mem:* Asn Comput Mach; Am Soc Info Sci. *Res:* Word processing; programming languages; computer systems; information retrieval. *Mailing Add:* Bell Tel Labs Mountain Ave Murray Hill NJ 07974

LESKO, PATRICIA MARIE, b Oakland, Calif, Jan 19, 47. POLYMER CHEMISTRY. *Educ:* Rice Univ, BA, 68, MS, 72, PhD(org chem), 73. *Prof Exp:* Fel org chem, Syntex Corp, 73-75; CHEMIST POLYMER CHEM, RES LABS, ROHM & HAAS CO, 75- *Mem:* AAAS; Am Chem Soc. *Res:* Emulsion polymers; coatings; polymeric controlled release formulations; corrosion. *Mailing Add:* Res Labs Rohm & Haas Co Spring House PA 19477

LESKO, STEPHEN ALBERT, b Cassandra, Pa, Dec 30, 31; m 81. BIOCHEMISTRY. *Educ:* Ind Univ, Pa, BS, 59; Univ Md, PhD(biochem), 65. *Prof Exp:* Instr, 65-68, res assoc, 68-73, ASST PROF BIOPHYS SCI, JOHNS HOPKINS UNIV, 73- *Mem:* AAAS; Am Chem Soc; Am Asn Cancer Res; Biophys Soc. *Res:* Chemical carcinogenesis; nucleic acid chemistry and biology; oxygen toxicity. *Mailing Add:* Div Biophys Sci Johns Hopkins Univ Baltimore MD 21205

LESKOWITZ, SIDNEY, b New York, NY, Nov 15, 22; m 48; c 3. IMMUNOLOGY. *Educ:* City Col New York, BS, 43; Columbia Univ, MA, 48, PhD(chem), 50. *Prof Exp:* Res asst microbiol, Col Physicians & Surgeons, Columbia Univ, 50-54; from res assoc to asst prof bact & immunol, Harvard Med Sch, 54-70; PROF PATH, MED SCH, TUFTS UNIV, 70- *Concurrent Pos:* Asst immunol, Mass Gen Hosp, 54-57, assoc, 57-70. *Mem:* AAAS; Am Asn Immunol; Soc Exp Biol & Med. *Res:* Delayed hypersensitivity; induction of immunologic tolerance; structure of antigens. *Mailing Add:* Dept Path Tufts Med Sch Boston MA 02155

LESLEY, FRANK DAVID, b El Paso, Tex, Dec 20, 44; m 67; c 1. MATHEMATICS. *Educ:* Stanford Univ, BS, 66; Univ Calif, San Diego, MA, 68, PhD(math), 70. *Prof Exp:* From asst prof to assoc prof, 70-77, PROF MATH, SAN DIEGO STATE UNIV, 77- *Mem:* Am Math Soc. *Res:* Boundary behavior of conformal mappings, including minimal surfaces and approximation theory. *Mailing Add:* Dept of Math San Diego State Univ San Diego CA 92182

LESLIE, CHARLES MILLER, b Lake Village, Ark, Nov 8, 23; m 46; c 3. MEDICAL ANTHROPOLOGY. *Educ:* Univ Chicago, PhB, 49, MA, 50, PhD(anthrop), 59. *Prof Exp:* Instr anthrop, Southern Methodist Univ, 50-51; instr, Univ Minn, 54-56; from instr to assoc prof, Pomona Col, 56-65; vis prof, Univ Wash, 65; assoc prof, Case Western Reserve Univ, 66-67; chmn dept, Univ Col, NY Univ, 67-71, prof anthrop, 67-76; PROF, SCH LIFE & HEALTH SCI, CTR SCI & CULT, UNIV DEL, 76- *Concurrent Pos:* NSF fel, Sch Oriental & African Studies, Univ London, 62-63; res assoc, Dept Anthrop, Univ Chicago, 74-75; NSF res grant, 74, grant, 76; chmn ed bd, Comparative Studies of Health Systems & Med Care, 72-; assoc ed, Cult, Med & Psychiat, 76-; med Anthrop ed, Social Sci & Med, 77- *Mem:* Fel AAAS; fel Am Anthrop Asn; fel Royal Anthrop Inst Gt Brit & Ireland; fel Asn Asian Studies; Fel Soc Med Anthrop. *Res:* World view and social change in India and Latin America; comparative study of medical systems. *Mailing Add:* 32 W 4th New Castle DE 19720

LESLIE, GERRIE ALLEN, b Red Deer, Alta, Nov 19, 41; m 65; c 2. IMMUNOLOGY, IMMUNOCHEMISTRY. *Educ:* Univ Alta, BSc, 62, MSc, 65; Univ Hawaii, PhD(microbiol), 68. *Prof Exp:* From asst prof to assoc prof microbiol, Sch Med, Tulane Univ, 70-74; assoc prof, 74-81, PROF MICROBIOL & IMMUNOL, ORE HEALTH SCI UNIV, 81- *Concurrent Pos:* USPHS fel, Col Med, Univ Fla, 68-70; adj assoc prof microbiol, Sch Med, Tulane Univ, 74-; res affil, Delta Regional Primate Res Ctr, Covington, La. *Mem:* Am Asn Immunol; Am Soc Microbiol; Am Soc Zoologists. *Res:* Phylogeny of immunoglobulin structure and function; regulation of the immune response; secretory immunologic system. *Mailing Add:* Dept of Microbiol & Immunol Ore Health Sci Univ Portland OR 97201

LESLIE, JAMES, b Belfast, Ireland, Apr 25, 34; m 64; c 3. PHARMACEUTICAL CHEMISTRY. *Educ:* Queen's Univ, Belfast, BSc, 56, PhD(chem), 59. *Prof Exp:* Fel, Okla State Univ, 59-61, asst prof & res assoc, 61-62; asst prof chem, Wash Col, 62-63; asst prof, 63-66, assoc prof med chem, 66-79, ASSOC PROF PHARM, SCH PHARM, UNIV MD, BALTIMORE, 79- *Concurrent Pos:* NIH res grant, 64, vis, Dept Clin Physics & Bioeng, Western Regional Hosp Bd, Glasgow, Scotland, 71-72. *Mem:* Am Chem Soc; Am Asn Cols Pharm. *Res:* Kinetics of processes of biological interest; drug analysis. *Mailing Add:* Univ Md Sch Pharm 636 W Lombard St Baltimore MD 21201

LESLIE, JAMES C, b Berlin, Pa, July 14, 33; div; c 4. MATERIALS SCIENCE, CHEMICAL ENGINEERING. *Educ:* Pa State Univ, BS, 56; Ohio State Univ, MS, 58, PhD(chem eng), 64. *Prof Exp:* Asst chem anal, Pa State Univ, 55-56; eng exp sta, Ohio State Univ, 56-57, Chem Eng Dept, 57-58, fel, 58-59, res asst chem eng, Res Found, 59-62; sr res engr, Allegany Ballistics Lab, Hercules Inc, 62-66, group supvr mat res, 66-67, composite mat group suvpr, 67, group supvr, Adv Fiber Struct Group, 67-69, dept head mat res, 69-71, dept head advan composite mat struct, Prod & Process Develop, 71-72, western regional mgr, Advan Composites, 72-75, mgr advan compos, Reliable Mfg, 75-76; OWNER, JIMLESLIE CONSULTS & SALES REPS, 76-; OWNER & GEN MGR, ADVAN COMPOSITE PROD & TECH, 81- *Concurrent Pos:* Instr, Frostburg State Col, 62-63 & WVa Univ Exten Serv, Allegany Ballistics Lab, 64-65; mgr mkt & eng, Advan Composite Pipe & Tube, 77-81. *Mem:* Assoc fel Am Inst Aeronaut & Astronaut; Am Inst Chem Eng; Soc Aerospace Mat & Process Eng; Soc Advan Mat & Process Eng (first vpres, 73, pres, 74). *Res:* Rocket propulsion; internal dynamics of rocket motors and nozzles; two phase kinetics; tracer techniques; development of graphite fibers; graphite polymer materials and structures. *Mailing Add:* 2601 Huntington St No 6 Huntington Beach CA 92648

LESLIE, JAMES D, b Toronto, Ont, July 6, 35; m 64; c 3. SOLID STATE PHYSICS. *Educ:* Univ Toronto, BASc, 57; Univ Ill, MS, 60, PhD(physics), 63. *Prof Exp:* Asst prof, 63-68, ASSOC PROF PHYSICS, UNIV WATERLOO, 68- *Mem:* Am Phys Soc; Can Asn Physicists. *Res:* Low temperature physics; far infrared spectroscopy; superconductivity; electron tunneling. *Mailing Add:* 200 University W Waterloo ON N2L 3G1 Can

LESLIE, JOHN FRANKLIN, b Dallas, Tex, July 2, 53; m 76; c 1. FUNGAL GENETICS. *Educ:* Univ Dallas, BA, 75; Univ Wis, Madison, MS, 77, PhD(genetics), 79. *Prof Exp:* Fel trainee, NIH, Lab Genetics, Univ Wis, Madison, 76-79; fel res affil, Dept Biol Sci, Stanford Univ, Calif, 79-81; RES MICROBIOLOGIST GENETICS, INT MINERAL & CHEM CORP, 81- *Concurrent Pos:* Tech adv, Inst Christian Resources, San Jose, Calif, 81- *Mem:* Genetics Soc Am; Mycol Soc Am; Am Soc Microbiol; Brit Mycol Soc; Soc Gen Microbiol. *Res:* Basic and applied fungal genetics including synthesis and application of chromosomal rearrangements, population genetics and developmental genetics; theoretical studies of molecular recombination models and breeding systems and their effects in natural and laboratory populations. *Mailing Add:* Res & Develop Int Mineral Chem Corp PO Box 207 Terre Haute IN 47808

LESLIE, PAUL WILLARD, b Peekskill, NY, Apr 23, 48. POPULATION GENETICS, DEMOGRAPHY. *Educ:* Bucknell Univ, BA, 70; Pa State Univ, MA, 72, PhD(anthrop), 77. *Prof Exp:* Asst prof anthrop, Univ Tex, Austin, 76-78; ASST PROF ANTHROP, STATE UNIV NY, BINGHAMTON, 78- *Mem:* AAAS; Am Asn Phys Anthropologists; Human Biol Coun; Pop Asn Am; Soc Study Social Biol. *Res:* Population genetics, demography of small populations, mathematical modeling and computer simulation; interactions among the social, demographic, and genetic structures of human populations. *Mailing Add:* Dept Anthrop State Univ NY Binghamton NY 13901

LESLIE, RONALD ALLAN, b Welland, Ont, Oct 11, 48; m 74. CEREBROVASCULAR ANATOMY, NEUROANATOMY. *Educ:* Brock Univ, Ont, BSc, 70; Cambridge Univ, PhD(neurobiol), 75. *Prof Exp:* Fel neurosci, McMaster Univ, 75-76; asst prof, 76-82, ASSOC PROF ANAT, DALHOUSIE UNIV, 82- *Mem:* Am Asn Anatomists; Soc Neurosci; AAAS; Can Asn Anatomists; Can Asn Neurosci. *Res:* Morphological basis for regulation of the fluid environment of the brain; central organization of visceral afferent fibres in the central nervous system. *Mailing Add:* Dept Anat Dalhousie Univ Halifax NS B3H 4H7 Can

LESLIE, STEPHEN HOWARD, b New York, NY, Nov 6, 18; m 43; c 2. MEDICINE. *Educ:* NY Univ, BS, 38, MD, 42. *Prof Exp:* Clin asst, 46-49, clin instr med, 49-54, asst prof, 54-69, ASSOC PROF CLIN MED, SCH MED, NY UNIV, 69- *Concurrent Pos:* Fel, Sch Med, NY Univ, 44-46. *Mem:* Endocrine Soc; Am Diabetes Asn; Am Fedn Clin Res. *Res:* Metabolic diseases; endocrinology. *Mailing Add:* 120 E 34th St New York NY 10016

LESLIE, STEVEN WAYNE, b Franklin, Ind, Jan 23, 46; m 70; c 1. PHARMACOLOGY. *Educ:* Purdue Univ, BS, 69, MS, 72, PhD(pharmacol), 74. *Prof Exp:* asst prof, 74-81, ASSOC PROF PHARMACOL, UNIV TEX, AUSTIN, 81- *Mem:* Sigma Xi; AAAS. *Res:* Investigations concerning the role of cellular organelles in calcium-mediated termination mechanisms in secretory tissues and the effects of various drugs on these termination mechanisms. *Mailing Add:* Col of Pharm Univ of Tex Austin TX 78712

LESLIE, THOMAS M, b Philadelphia, Pa, Nov 11, 54; m 82. PHOTOCHEMISTRY, SYNTHETIC ORGANIC CHEMISTRY. *Educ:* Rider Col, BS, 76; Univ Notre Dame, PhD(chem), 80. *Prof Exp:* MEM TECH STAFF, BELL TELEPHONE LABS, 80- *Res:* Mechanism of photochemical reactions via reaction intermediates produced in laser flash photolysis; study of the effect of subtle changes in chemical constitution on materials exhibiting liquid crystal phases. *Mailing Add:* Bell Telephone Labs 600 Mountain Ave M/S 2D-338 Murray Hill NJ 07974

LESLIE, WALLACE DEAN, b Dacoma, Okla, Nov 9, 22; m 48; c 3. ANALYTICAL CHEMISTRY. *Educ:* Northwestern State Col, Okla, BS, 47; Okla State Univ, MS, 50. *Prof Exp:* Asst chem, Okla State Univ, 47-49; instr, Northwestern State Col, Okla, 49-51; anal chemist, Mfg Dept, 51-52, from assoc res chemist to sr res chemist, 52-62, res group leader, res & develop dept, 62-77, DIR ANAL RES SECT, CONTINENTAL OIL CO, 77- *Mem:* Am Chem Soc. *Res:* Analytical research and development; petroleum and petroleum products; petrochemicals. *Mailing Add:* Res & Develop Dept Continental Oil Co Ponca City OK 74601

LESLIE, WILLIAM C(AIRNS), b Dundee, Scotland, Jan 6, 20; nat US; m 48; c 1. METALLURGY. *Educ:* Ohio State Univ, BMetE, 47, MSc, 48, PhD(metall), 49. *Prof Exp:* Res assoc, Res Found, Ohio State Univ, 47-49; metallurgist, US Steel Corp, 49-53; assoc dir res, Thompson Prod Inc, 53-54; metallurgist, US Steel Corp, 54-57, sr scientist, Fundamental Res Lab, 57-63, asst dir phys metall, 63-69, mgr phys metall, E C Bain Lab Fundamental Res, 69-73; PROF MAT ENG, UNIV MICH, 73- *Concurrent Pos:* Battelle vis prof, Ohio State Univ, 64-65; chmn, Int Conf Strength Metals & Alloys, Calif, 70; Garofalo lectr, Northwestern Univ, 77. *Honors & Awards:* Krumb lectr, Am Inst Mining, Metal & Petrol Engrs, 67, Howe lectr, 82; Andrew Carnegie lectr, Am Soc Metals, 70, Campbell lectr, 71, Sauveur lectr & Jeffries lectr, 75. *Mem:* Fel Am Soc Metals; Am Inst Mining, Metall & Petrol Engrs (vpres, 75); Metals Soc Gt Brit; Am Soc Eng Educ; Iron Steel Inst Japan. *Res:* Physical metallurgy, especially of steels. *Mailing Add:* Dept of Mat & Metall Eng Univ of Mich Ann Arbor MI 48109

LESNAW, JUDITH ALICE, b Chicago, Ill, July 30, 40. VIROLOGY. *Educ:* Univ Ill, BS, 62, MS, 64, PhD(cell biol), 69. *Prof Exp:* Res assoc virol, Univ Ill, 69-74; ASST PROF VIROL, UNIV KY, 74- *Mem:* Am Soc Microbiol; AAAS. *Res:* Structure and function of viral proteins and RNA; replication of RNA viruses; defective interfering particles. *Mailing Add:* Sch of Biol Sci Univ of Ky Lexington KY 40506

LESNER, SHARON A, b Lorain, Ohio, April 1, 51. REHABILITATIVE AUDIOLOGY. *Educ:* Hiram Col, BA, 73; Kent State Univ, MA, 75; Wayne State Univ, MA, 76; Ohio State Univ, PhD(audiol), 79. *Prof Exp:* ASST PROF AUDIOL, UNIV AKRON, 79- *Mem:* Am Speech, Lang & Hearing Asn; Acad Rehab Audiol; Acoust Soc Am; Alexander Graham Bell Asn Deaf. *Res:* Visual, auditory and audio-visual recption of speech. *Mailing Add:* Speech & Hearing Ctr Univ Akron Akron OH 44325

LESNEWICH, A(LEXANDER), b Ridgefield Park, NJ, Apr 16, 23; m 49; c 3. PHYSICAL METALLURGY. *Educ:* Rensselaer Polytech Inst, BS, 48, PhD(metall), 52. *Prof Exp:* Instr metall, Rensselaer Polytech Inst, 48-50; sr engr res lab, Air Reduction, Inc, 52-57, supvr welding & joining res, 57-62, mgr welding res & develop, Airco Welding Prod Div, 62-64, dir metall res, Cent Res Lab, 64-69, DIR RES & DEVELOP, AIRCO WELDING PROD DIV, AIRCO INC, 69- *Concurrent Pos:* Adams Mem lectr, Am Welding Soc, 69; mem mat adv bd, Nat Acad Sci, 72; mem spec comt welding, Am Bur Shipping, 81-, welding task force, Nat Res Coun, 79- & gov sci adv comt, State NJ, 81- *Honors & Awards:* Lincoln Gold Medal, 58 & Meritorious Award, 68, Am Welding Soc. *Mem:* Am Soc Metals; Am Welding Soc (pres, 78-79); Sigma Xi. *Res:* Inert gas arc welding; welding; welding metallurgy. *Mailing Add:* Airco Welding Prod PO Box 6686 Sparrows Point MD 21219

LESNIAK-FOSTER, LINDA, b Gary, Ind, Aug 14, 48. MATHEMATICS. *Educ:* Western Mich Univ, BA, 70, MA, 71, PhD(math), 74. *Prof Exp:* Asst prof, La State Univ, Baton Rouge, 74-78; asst prof, 78-81, ASSOC PROF MATH, WESTERN MICH UNIV, 81- *Mem:* Am Math Soc; Sigma Xi; Math Asn Am; Soc Indus & Appl Math; Asn Women in Math. *Res:* Extremal problems in graph theory; generalized Ramsey numbers; degree sets for graphs and digraphs; graph connectivity. *Mailing Add:* Dept of Math Western Mich Univ Kalamazoo MI 49008

LESNIK, ABRAHAM, b Linz, Austria, Feb 6, 46; US citizen; m 68; c 2. HIGH ENERGY PHYSICS. *Educ:* Columbia Col, AB, 68; Univ Chicago, MS, 69, PhD(physics), 73. *Prof Exp:* Res asst high energy physics, Univ Chicago, 68-69; asst comput scientist physics, Argonne Nat Lab, 69-70; res student assoc, Argonne Nat Lab & Univ Cicago, 70-73; res assoc, Ohio State Univ, 73-77; ASST PHYSICIST, BROOKHAVEN NAT LAB, 77- *Mem:* Am Phys Soc. *Res:* Production, polarization and decay properties of strange particles; spectroscopy of mesons. *Mailing Add:* Dept of Physics Brookhaven Nat Lab Upton NY 11973

LESPERANCE, PIERRE J, b Montreal, Que, Aug 16, 34; m 60; c 3. INVERTEBRATE PALEONTOLOGY. *Educ:* Univ Montreal, BSc, 56; Univ Mich, MS, 57; McGill Univ, PhD(geol), 61. *Prof Exp:* Geologist, Dept Natural Resources, Que, 60-61; from asst prof to assoc prof, 61-71, chmn dept, 75-79, PROF GEOL, UNIV MONTREAL, 71- *Mem:* Geol Soc Can; Am Asn Petrol Geol; Soc Econ Paleont & Mineral; Paleont Soc; Brit Palaeont Asn. *Res:* Low and middle Paleozoic field mapping in Quebec; paleontology and biostratigraphy of Upper Ordovician to Lower Devonian trilobites and brachiopods. *Mailing Add:* Dept of Geol Univ of Montreal Montreal PQ H3C 3J7 Can

L'ESPERANCE, ROBERT LOUIS, b Montreal, Que, June 19, 22; m 51. MINING ENGINEERING, GEOLOGY. *Educ:* McGill Univ, BEng, 44, MSc, 48, PhD(geol), 51. *Prof Exp:* Consult geologist, 51-53; local dir, Cie Miniere de l'Ogooue, Gabon, 53-54; dir tech liaison raw mat, 59-61, pres, Cia Meridional de Mineracao, Rio de Janeiro, 61-66, dir corp explor & invests, 66-82, DIR RESOURCE PLANNING, MINING RES, US STEEL CORP, 82- *Concurrent Pos:* mem panel, Manganese & Indust Implications, Nat Acad Sci, 79-81. *Mem:* Soc Econ Geologists; Am Inst Mining, Metall & Petrol Engrs; Can Inst Mining & Metall; Geol Soc France. *Res:* Economic geology; mineral deposits. *Mailing Add:* Rd #2 Box 108 Red Gate Rd Sweickley PA 15143

LESSARD, JAMES LOUIS, b Eau Claire, Wis, Mar 9, 43; m 65; c 2. BIOCHEMISTRY. *Educ:* Marquette Univ, BS, 65, PhD(biochem), 70. *Prof Exp:* Fel, Roche Inst Molecular Biol, Nutley, NJ, 69-71; res scholar biochem, Children's Hosp Res Found, 71-72; assoc prof, 72-79, ASSOC PROF RES PEDIAT, MED SCH, UNIV CINCINNATI, 79-, ASST PROF BIOL CHEM, 74- *Concurrent Pos:* Fel pharmacol-morphol, Pharmaceut Mfrs Asn Found, Cincinnati, Ohio, 72-74. *Mem:* Am Chem Soc; AAAS; Sigma Xi. *Res:* Regulatory processes in development; cell motility; immunochemistry. *Mailing Add:* Fetal Pharm Div Children's Hosp Res Found Elland Ave & Bethesda Cincinnati OH 45229

LESSARD, JEAN, b East-Broughton, Que, Apr 29, 36; div; c 2. ORGANIC CHEMISTRY. *Educ:* Laval Univ, BA, 56, BSc, 60, PhD(org chem), 65. *Prof Exp:* Nat Res Coun Can fel, Imp Col, Univ London, 65-67; asst res officer org chem, Nat Res Coun Can, 67-69; asst prof, 69-71, assoc prof, 71-76, PROF ORG CHEM, UNIV SHERBROOKE, 76- *Mem:* Chem Inst Can; The Chem Soc; Am Chem Soc. *Res:* Transition metals; electrochemistry and photochemistry used to study new methods of effecting organic reactions or new organic reactions, investigation of the mechanism, scope and synthetic utility of these reactions. *Mailing Add:* Dept Chem Univ Sherbrooke Sherbrooke PQ J1K 2R1 Can

LESSARD, RICHARD R, b Lowell, Mass, Mar 15, 43; m 66; c 2. SYNTHETIC FUELS. *Educ:* Lowell Technol Inst, BS, 66; Univ Maine, MS, 68, PhD(chem eng), 70. *Prof Exp:* Proj staff engr, 70-76, sect head, 76-79, LAB DIR RES & DEVELOP, EXXON RES & ENG CO, 80- *Concurrent Pos:* Mem, Fossil Energy Res Working Group III, Dept Energy, 80. *Mem:* Am Inst Chem Engrs; Sigma Xi. *Res:* currently responsible for experimental development of Exxon's catalytic coal gasification process for converting coal to substitute natural gas; operation of a one-ton-day process development unit and supporting bench research. *Mailing Add:* Exxon Res & Eng Co PO Box 4255 Baytown TX 77520

LESSARD, ROGER ALAIN, b East Broughton, Que, Sept 11, 44; m 67; c 2. OPTICS. *Educ:* Laval Univ, BS, 69, DSc(optics), 73. *Prof Exp:* Res officer lasers, Gentec Co, 71-72; lectr optics, 72-73, asst prof, 73-78, ASSOC PROF OPTICS, LAVAL UNIV, 78- *Mem:* Can Asn Advan Sci; Can Asn Physicists; Optical Soc Am; Am Phys Soc. *Res:* Holography and optical information processing. *Mailing Add:* Dept Physics Laval Univ Quebec PQ B1K 7P4 Can

LESSE, HENRY, b Philadelphia, Pa, Feb 7, 26; m 50; c 1. PSYCHIATRY, NEUROPHYSIOLOGY. *Educ:* Jefferson Med Col, MD, 50; Am Bd Psychiat & Neurol, dipl, 57. *Prof Exp:* Asst physiol, Jefferson Med Col, 46-50; asst neurophysiol, Col Physicians & Surgeons, Columbia Univ, 48-49; staff psychiatrist, US Med Ctr for Fed Prisoners, 51-53; vis scientist, 58-59, asst prof, 59-62, ASSOC PROF PSYCHIAT, UNIV CALIF, LOS ANGELES, 62-, CHIEF OF RES, NEUROPSYCHIAT INST, 59- *Concurrent Pos:* USPHS fel psychiat, Tulane Univ, 53-54, NIMH career investr award, 54-59; vis psychiatrist, Charity Hosp, New Orleans, 53-58; vis scientist, Vet Admin Hosps, Long Beach, Calif, 58-59; consult, Vet Admin Ctr, Brentwood Hosp, 65-; res adv comt mem, State Dept Ment Hyg, 66-69; mem adv comt brain res inst, Univ Calif, Los Angeles; consult, Vet Admin Hosp, Sepulveda. *Mem:* AAAS; Am Psychiat Asn; NY Acad Sci; Soc Neurosci. *Res:* Electrophysiology and behavior. *Mailing Add:* Neuropsychiat Inst Univ of Calif Los Angeles CA 90024

LESSELL, SIMMONS, b Brooklyn, NY, May 25, 33; m 55; c 4. NEUROLOGY, OPHTHALMOLOGY. *Educ:* Amherst Col, BA, 54; Cornell Univ, MD, 58. *Prof Exp:* Intern med, Cornell Univ, 58-59; resident neurol, Univ Vt, 59-60; resident ophthal, Mass Eye & Ear Hosp, 63-66; assoc prof neurol, 67-70, PROF ANAT, NEUROL & OPHTHAL, SCH MED, BOSTON UNIV, 70- *Concurrent Pos:* Physician, NIH, 59-60; lectr, Sch Med, Tufts Univ, 66-; vis surgeon & dir dept ophthal, Boston City Hosp; vis surgeon, Univ Hosp; consult ophthal, Vet Admin Hosp & Tufts-New England Med Ctr. *Mem:* Asn Res Vision & Ophthal. *Res:* Optic neuropathies, clinical and experimental; histochemistry and experimental pathology of the optic nerve. *Mailing Add:* Dept of Ophthal Boston Univ Sch of Med Boston MA 02118

LESSEN, MARTIN, b New York, NY, Sept 6, 20; m 48; c 3. MECHANICAL ENGINEERING. *Educ:* City Col New York, BME, 40; NY Univ, MME, 42; Mass Inst Technol, ScD(mech eng), 48. *Prof Exp:* Mech engr, Navy Dept, 41-46; asst fluid mech, Mass Inst Technol, 48; aeronaut res scientist, Nat Adv Comt Aeronaut, 48-49; prof aero eng, Pa State Col, 49-53; prof appl mech, Univ Pa, 53-60; prof mech & aerospace sci & chmn dept, 60-70, YATES MEM PROF ENG, UNIV ROCHESTER, 68- *Concurrent Pos:* Nat Sci Found sr fel shock waves & instabilities, Cambridge Univ, 66-67; Nat Acad Sci exchange visitor, USSR, 67; IBM Corp pure sci div grant; consult, RCA Corp, NJ & Rochester Appl Sci Assocs; liaison scientist, US Off Naval Res, London, 76- *Mem:* Fel Am Phys Soc; fel Am Soc Mech Engrs; Am Soc Eng Educ; Ger Soc Appl Math & Mech; Am Inst Aeronaut & Astronaut. *Res:* Fluid mechanics; thermodynamics and heat transfer; vibrations; hydrodynamic stability and transition to turbulence; continuum mechanics; thermoelasticity; biomechanics; biophysics; plasma dynamics; field theory. *Mailing Add:* Dept of Mech & Aerospace Sci Univ of Rochester Rochester NY 14627

LESSEPS, ROLAND JOSEPH, b New Orleans, La, Aug 13, 33. DEVELOPMENTAL BIOLOGY. *Educ:* Spring Hill Col, BS, 58; Johns Hopkins Univ, PhD(biol), 62. *Prof Exp:* Asst prof, 67-71, assoc prof, 71-81, CHMN DEPT, 78-, PROF BIOL, LOYOLA UNIV, LA, 81- *Concurrent Pos:* Vis prof, Roman Cath Univ, Nijmegen. *Mem:* AAAS; Am Soc Zool; Electron Micros Soc Am; Soc Develop Biol; Nat Asn Biol Teachers. *Res:* Morphogenetic movements of embryonic cells; electron microscopy of the cell surface; time-lapse filming of cell movements in living embryos. *Mailing Add:* Dept Biol Loyola Univ New Orleans LA 70118

LESSHAFFT, CHARLES THOMAS, JR, b Louisville, Ky, Oct 6, 18; m 39; c 2. PHARMACY. *Educ:* Univ Ky, BS, 41; Purdue Univ, MS, 53, PhD(pharm), 55. *Prof Exp:* From instr to assoc prof pharm, Univ Ky, 47-70, prof, 70-80. *Res:* Formulation and properties of ointment bases; pharmaceutical applications of suspending agents. *Mailing Add:* 3236 Carriage Lane Lexington KY 40502

LESSIE, THOMAS GUY, b New York, NY, Dec 14, 36; m 62; c 3. MICROBIAL PHYSIOLOGY. *Educ:* Queens Col, NY, BS, 58; Harvard Univ, AM, 61, PhD(biol sci), 63. *Prof Exp:* Res asst microbiol, Haskins Labs, NY, 58-59; NIH fels biochem, Oxford Univ, 63-65 & biol sci, Purdue Univ, 65-67; res assoc microbiol, Univ Wash, 67-68; asst prof, 68-74, assoc prof, 74-

81, PROF MICROBIOL, UNIV MASS, AMHERST, 81- Concurrent Pos: Grants, Nat Sci Found, 68-70; NIH grants, Inst Arthritis & Metab Dis, 68-74, Inst Gen Med Sci, 74-81. Mem: AAAS; Am Soc Microbiol; Am Chem Soc; Brit Soc Gen Microbiol. Res: Regulation of photopigment synthesis in photosynthetic bacteria; enzyme regulatory mechanisms in Pseudomonas species; characterization of Pseudomonas bacteriophage. Mailing Add: Dept of Microbiol Univ of Mass Amherst MA 01002

LESSIN, LAWRENCE STEPHEN, b Washington, DC, Oct 14, 37; m 62; c 3. HEMATOLOGY, ONCOLOGY. Educ: Univ Chicago, MD, 62. Prof Exp: Instr med, Univ Pa, 65-67; Nat Heart Inst spec fel hematol med, Inst Cell Path, France, 67-68; asst prof med, Sch Med, Duke Univ, 68-70; assoc prof, 70-74, PROF MED PATH & DIR HEMATOL & ONCOL, SCH MED, GEORGE WASHINGTON UNIV, 74- Concurrent Pos: Consult, Nat Heart, Lung & Blood Inst & US Naval Med Ctr, 74- & Walter Reed Army Med Ctr, 75- Mem: Am Col Physicians; Am Soc Hematol; Am Fedn Clin Res; Int Soc Hematol; Am Soc Clin Oncol. Res: Red cell membrane structure in hemocytic anemias; red cell rhelogy; pathophysiology of sickle cell disease. Mailing Add: 2150 Pennsylvania Ave NW Washington DC 20037

LESSING, PETER, b Englewood, NJ, June 15, 38; m 65; c 2. ENVIRONMENTAL GEOLOGY. Educ: St Lawrence Univ, BS, 61; Dartmouth Col, MA, 63; Syracuse Univ, PhD(geol), 67. Prof Exp: Asst prof geol, St Lawrence Univ, 66-71; environ geologist, 71-73, HEAD ENVIRON GEOL SECT, W VA GEOL SURV, 73-, CHIEF, GEOL DIV, 80- Concurrent Pos: Adj prof, WVa Univ, 73- Mem: Geol Soc Am; Am Inst Prof Geologists. Res: Geologic field mapping; environmental geology investigations; land use planning; landslide evaluation; geologic hazard studies; hydrology and water use. Mailing Add: WVa Geol Surv PO Box 879 Morgantown WV 26507

LESSIOS, HARILAOS ANGELOU, marine zoology, marine ecology, see previous edition

LESSLER, JUDITH THOMASSON, b Charlotte, NC, Oct, 10, 43; m 70; c 2. SURVEY RESEARCH METHODS. Educ: Univ NC, Chapel Hill, AB, 66, PhD(biostatist), 74; Emory Univ, Ga, MAT, 67. Prof Exp: Statistician, 74-78, SR STATISTICIAN, RES TRIANGLE INST, 78-, DEPT MGR, 80- Concurrent Pos: Prin investr, NSF grant, 79-81; adj asst prof, Biostatist Dept, Univ NC, 81- Mem: Am Statist Asn; Am Pub Health Asn; AAAS; Pop Asn Am. Res: Survey research methods; statistical treatment of nonsampling errors and multiframe-multiplicity estimators. Mailing Add: Res Triangle Inst PO Box 12194 Research Triangle Park NC 27709

LESSLER, MILTON A, b New York, NY, May 18, 15; m 43; c 3. PHYSIOLOGY. Educ: Cornell Univ, BS, 37, MS, 38; NY Univ, PhD(biochem cell physiol), 50. Prof Exp: Technician cardiac res, NY State Health Dept, 40-42; from asst prof to assoc prof, 51-63, PROF PHYSIOL, COL MED, OHIO STATE UNIV, 63- Concurrent Pos: Nat Cancer Inst fel, NY Univ-Washington Square Col, 49-50; NSF fac fel, Univ Mich, Ann Arbor, 58-59; vis lectr, Am Physiol Soc, 62-66; consult, Yellow Springs Instrument Co, 65-; ed-in-chief, Ohio J Sci, 74-81. Mem: Fel AAAS; fel NY Acad Sci; Am Physiol Soc; Am Asn Cancer Res; Am Soc Cell Biol. Res: Cell physiology; effects of environmental pollutants on the hemopoietic system; cellular radiobiology; erythropoiesis and lead poisoning. Mailing Add: Dept of Physiol Ohio State Univ Col of Med Columbus OH 43210

LESSMAN, GARY M, b Hillsboro, Ill, July 15, 38. SOIL FERTILITY. Educ: Southern Ill Univ, BS, 60, MS, 62; Mich State Univ, PhD(soil sci), 67. Prof Exp: Exten agronomist, Purdue Univ, 67-68; asst prof, 69-77, ASSOC PROF AGRON, UNIV TENN, KNOXVILLE, 77- Mem: Sigma Xi; Am Soc Agron. Res: Micronutrient nutrition . Mailing Add: Dept of Plant & Soil Sci Univ of Tenn Knoxville TN 37916

LESSMANN, RICHARD CARL, b New York, NY, Oct 14, 42; m 65; c 3. MECHANICAL ENGINEERING, FLUID MECHANICS. Educ: Syracuse Univ, BSME, 64; Brown Univ, ScM, 66, PhD(eng), 69. Prof Exp: Asst prof, 69-75, ASSOC PROF MECH ENG & APPL MECH, UNIV RI, 75- Mem: Am Inst Aeronaut & Astronaut; Am Phys Soc. Res: Turbulent flows; boundary layer theory; heat transfer. Mailing Add: Dept of Mech Eng Univ of RI Kingston RI 02881

LESSNER, HOWARD E, b Philadelphia, Pa, Feb 28, 27; m 57; c 3. INTERNAL MEDICINE, ONCOLOGY. Educ: Univ Pa, MD, 53. Prof Exp: Jr asst resident, Jackson Mem Hosp, 54-55; sr asst resident, 55-56, clin fel, 56-57; res fel, Nat Heart Inst, Barnes Hosp, 57-58, clin fel, Nat Cancer Inst, 58-59; from instr to prof med, 59-75, PROF ONCOL, UNIV MIAMI, 74- Concurrent Pos: Dir, Comprehensive Cancer Ctr, 72-74, clin dir, 74- Mem: Am Col Physicians; AMA; Am Soc Clin Oncol; Am Asn Cancer Res; AAAS. Mailing Add: Dept Oncol D-8-4 PO Box 016960 Miami FL 33101

LESSO, WILLIAM GEORGE, b Cleveland, Ohio, Mar 23, 31; m 52; c 5. OPERATIONS RESEARCH. Educ: Univ Notre Dame, BSME, 53; Xavier Univ, Ohio, MBA, 63; Case Inst Technol, MS, 66, PhD(opers res), 67. Prof Exp: Design engr, Clevite Corp, 53-58; proj engr, Flight Propulsion Div, Gen Elec Co, 58-64; assoc prof mech eng, 67-72, PROF MECH ENG, UNIV TEX, AUSTIN, 72- Mem: Am Inst Indust Engrs; Opers Res Soc Am; Inst Mgt Sci. Res: Application of operations research to industrial and economic problems. Mailing Add: Dept of Mech Eng Univ of Tex Austin TX 78712

LESSOFF, HOWARD, b Boston, Mass, Sept 23, 30; m 59; c 2. SOLID STATE SCIENCE. Educ: Northeastern Univ, BS, 53, MS, 57. Prof Exp: Staff engr, Radio Corp Am, Mass, 57-60, sr staff mem, 61-64; staff mem, Bell Tel Labs, 60-61; aerospace technologist, Electronic Res Ctr, NASA, 64-70; supvry physicist, 70-75, BR HEAD ELECTRONIC MAT TECHNOL, NAVAL RES LAB, 75- Concurrent Pos: Lectr, Lincoln Col, Northeastern Univ, 57-70; consult, Datacove Corp, NJ, 69- Mem: AAAS; Inst Elec & Electronics Engrs; Sigma Xi. Res: Crystal growth; semiconductor materials; microwave and optic properties; solid state physics; magnetic materials. Mailing Add: Code 5220 Electronic Technol Div Naval Res Lab Washington DC 20375

LESSOR, ARTHUR EUGENE, JR, b Schenectady, NY, Apr 2, 25; m 55; c 2. ANALYTICAL CHEMISTRY, CRYSTALLOGRAPHY. Educ: Union Univ, NY, BS, 49; Indiana Univ, PhD(chem), 55. Prof Exp: Fel crystallog, Indiana Univ, 55; asst prof chem, Univ Cincinnati, 55-56; anal chemist, Gen Elec Co, 56-59; mgr crystallog lab, Fed Systs Div, Int Bus Mach Corp, 59-61; film electronics develop, Components Div, 61-65, interconnection & packaging develop systs develop div, Oswego, 65-66, mgr tech serv, Components Div, 66-70, mgr mfg, 71-73, mgr semiconductor mat prod, 73-75, mgr chem energy resources, East Fishkill Facil, 75-76, RES STAFF MEM, IBM RES LAB, YORKTOWN HEIGHTS, IBM CORP, 76- Mem: AAAS; Am Chem Soc; Am Crystallog Asn; Sigma Xi. Res: Thin film electronic and solid state devices; solid state electronic materials; conservation of energy and process materials; superconducting electronics and materials. Mailing Add: 7 Rock Garden Way Poughkeepsie NY 12603

LESSOR, DELBERT LEROY, US citizen. PHYSICS, APPLIED MATHEMATICS. Educ: Ft Hays State Univ, BS, 62; Kans State Univ, PhD(physics), 67. Prof Exp: Temp asst prof physics, Kans State Univ, 66-67; sr res scientist phys sci, 67-80, SR RES SCIENTIST ENG PHYSICS, PAC NORTHWEST LABS, BATTELLE MEM INST, 80- Mem: Am Phys Soc; Sci Res Soc NAm. Res: Electromagnetic field computation in industrial and instrument configurations; air filtration theory; nuclear particle transport; nuclear reaction theory; nuclear reactor instrumentation; geothermal chemistry; fluid flow calculation; optics theory. Mailing Add: Battelle Pac Northwest Battelle Blvd Richland WA 99352

LESSOR, EDITH DORA, b Chicago, Ill, Aug 5, 30; m 55; c 2. ANALYTICAL CHEMISTRY. Educ: Valparaiso Univ, BS, 52; Indiana Univ, Bloomington, PhD(anal chem), 55. Prof Exp: Instr chem, Ulster Community Col, 64-65; lectr, Harpur Col, State Univ New York, Binghamton, 65-67; asst prof, 67-71, assoc prof, 71-76, PROF CHEM, MT ST MARY COL, NY, 76-, CHMN DEPT, 68-, CHMN DIV NATURAL SCI & MATH, 73- Mem: AAAS; Am Chem Soc; Sigma Xi. Res: Spectrophotometry of organic analytical reagents and analytical chemistry of water pollution control. Mailing Add: Dept of Chem Mt St Mary Col Newburgh NY 12550

LESTER, CHARLES TURNER, b Covington, Ga, Nov 10, 11; m 36; c 2. ORGANIC CHEMISTRY. Educ: Emory Univ, AB, 32, MA, 34; Pa State Univ, PhD(org chem), 41. Prof Exp: Teacher high sch, Ga, 34-35; instr chem, Emory Jr Col, 35-39; res chemist, Calco Div, Am Cyanamid Corp, NJ, 41-42; from asst prof to assoc prof, 42-50, chmn, Dept Chem, 54-57, vpres grad studies, 70-74, vpres arts & sci, 74-78, PROF CHEM, EMORY UNIV, 50-, DEAN GRAD SCH, 57-, EXEC VPRES & DEAN FAC, 78- Concurrent Pos: Mem bd dirs, Oak Ridge Assoc Univs, 62-65; mem, Ga Sci & Technol Comn, 63-72; mem bd dirs, Atlanta Speech Sch, 65-71; mem exec comt, Coun Grad Schs US, 65-68; mem bd dirs, Southeastern Educ Lab, 66-68; bd trustees, Reinhardt Col, 66-72; vchmn, Ocean Sci Ctr, Atlantic Comn, 67-72; mem bd trustees, Huntingdon Col, 68; chief acad progs br, Bur Higher Educ, 69-70; chmn elect, Coun Grad Sch, 73, chmn, 74; coun mem, Oak Ridge Assoc Univs, 58-62, 70-79. Honors & Awards: Herty Medal, 65. Mem: Am Chem Soc; Sigma Xi; Am Inst Chem. Res: Sterically hindered ketones; indigosol dyes; biphenyl mercaptan; oxetanones; alkyl aryl ketones; antimicrobial compounds. Mailing Add: 281 Chelsea Circle Decatur GA 30030

LESTER, DAVID, b New Haven, Conn, Jan 22, 16; m 38; c 2. BIOCHEMISTRY, PHARMACOLOGY. Educ: Yale Univ, BS, 36, PhD(org chem), 40; Am Bd Clin Chem, dipl. Prof Exp: Res asst drug metab & toxicol, Lab Appl Physiol, Yale Univ, 40-45, res assoc, 45-58, res assoc, Lab Appl Biodyn, 58-62; PROF BIOCHEM, CTR ALCOHOL STUDIES, RUTGERS UNIV, NEW BRUNSWICK, 62-, SCI DIR, NAT ALCOHOL RES CTR, 78-, DIR GRAD PROG PHARMACOL, 80- Concurrent Pos: Consult, Allied Chem Corp; assoc ed, Quart J Studies Alcohol. Mem: Fel AAAS; Am Chem Soc; Am Soc Pharmacol & Exp Therapeut; Am Indust Hyg Asn; NY Acad Sci. Res: Analytical biochemistry; metabolism of drugs; toxicology of plastics, resins and industrial materials; behavioral pharmacology; alcoholism. Mailing Add: Ctr of Alcohol Studies Rutgers Univ New Brunswick NJ 08903

LESTER, DONALD THOMAS, b New London, Conn, Aug 26, 34; m 62; c 2. FORESTRY. Educ: Univ Maine, BS, 55; Yale Univ, MF, 57, PhD(forest genetics), 62. Prof Exp: From asst prof to prof forestry, Univ Wis-Madison, 62-77; SUPVR, FOREST BIOL, FORESTRY RES DIV, CROWN ZELLERBACH CORP, 77- Res: Tree breeding; genecology. Mailing Add: CZ-FRD PO Box 368 Wilsonville OR 97070

LESTER, GEORGE RONALD, b War Eagle, WVa, Sept 6, 34; m 56; c 4. PHYSICAL CHEMISTRY, PETROLEUM CHEMISTRY. Educ: Berea Col, BA, 54; Univ Ky, MS, 56, PhD(chem), 58. Prof Exp: Chemist, Universal Oil Prod Co, 58-63, assoc res coordr, 63-74, mgr appl catalysis, 74-76, DIR MAT SCI RES, UOP, INC, 76- Mem: AAAS; Am Chem Soc; The Faraday Soc; Sigma Xi; Catalysis Soc. Res: Conductivity of nonaqueous solutions; adsorption of gases on solids; heterogeneous catalysis; petrochemical processes; material science; automotive exhaust catalysis; solar systems; energy conservation; heat exchanger technology; catalytic combustion; automotive gas turbine engines; electric power plant catalytic combustion; electrocatalysts for fuel cells for power plants. Mailing Add: 1030 N Greenwood Ave Park Ridge IL 60068

LESTER, HENRY ALLEN, b New York, NY, July 4, 45. NEUROBIOLOGY, BIOPHYSICS. Educ: Harvard Col, AB, 66; Rockefeller Univ, PhD(biophys), 71. Prof Exp: Res fel molecular neurobiol, Inst Pasteur, 71-73; ASST PROF BIOL, CALIF INST TECHNOL, 73- Mem: Soc Neurosci; Biophys Soc; Soc Gen Physiologists. Res: Mechanisms and development of synaptic transmission. Mailing Add: Div of Biol Calif Inst of Technol Pasadena CA 91125

LESTER, JOHN BERNARD, b San Diego, Calif, Mar 11, 45; m 72; c 2. ASTRONOMY, ASTROPOHYSICS. *Educ:* Northwestern Univ, BA, 67; Univ Chicago, MS, 69, PhD(astron), 72. *Prof Exp:* Lectr physics, Univ Wis-Milwaukee, 69-71; presidential intern astron, Smithsonian Astrophys Observ, 72-73, physicist, 73-76; asst prof, 76-81, ASSOC PROF ASTRON, UNIV TORONTO, 81- *Mem:* Am Astron Soc; Astron Soc Pac; Int Astron Union. *Res:* High dispersion stellar spectroscopy; stellar abundances; ultraviolet astronomy. *Mailing Add:* Erindale Col Univ of Toronto Mississauga ON L5L 1C6 Can

LESTER, JOSEPH EUGENE, b Bay City, Tex, July 2, 42; m 59; c 2. PHYSICAL CHEMISTRY. *Educ:* Rice Univ, BA, 64; Univ Calif, Berkeley, PhD(chem), 68. *Prof Exp:* Asst prof chem, Northwestern Univ, Evanston, 67-74; mem staff, GTE Labs, 73-77; sr res chemist, 78-81, RES ASSOC, GULF SCI & TECHNOL, 81- *Mem:* Am Chem Soc; Am Phys Soc; Catalysis Soc. *Res:* Kinetics and mechanisms of surface reactions; catalysis; extended x-ray absorption spectroscopy. *Mailing Add:* Gulf Res & Develop PO Drawer 2038 Pittsburgh PA 15044

LESTER, JOSEPH THOMAS, JR, b Jacksonville, Fla, Jan 31, 23; m 51; c 4. MECHANICAL ENGINEERING. *Educ:* Mass Inst Technol, BS, 44, MS, 49. *Prof Exp:* Res engr aerodyn, Naval Supersonic Lab, Mass Inst Technol, 50-53; res engr mech eng, Mech Res Lab, 53-56, res supvr, 56-62, develop assoc, 62-65, consult, Eng Serv Div, 65-69, sr consult, 69-77, PRIN CONSULT, ENG SERV DIV, E I DU PONT DE NEMOURS & CO, INC, 77- *Mem:* Am Soc Mech Engrs; Asn Comput Mach; Numerical Control Soc. *Res:* Dynamics, fluid mechanics and stress analysis; applied mathematics and computation. *Mailing Add:* 2520 Blackwood Rd Foulk Woods Wilmington DE 19810

LESTER, LARRY JAMES, b Bay City, Tex, July 15, 47; m 69, 75; c 1. POPULATION GENETICS. *Educ:* Univ Tex, Austin, BA, 69, PhD(pop genetics), 75. *Prof Exp:* ASST PROF BIOL, UNIV HOUSTON, 75- *Concurrent Pos:* Adj res scientist, Nat Marine Fisheries Serv, Nat Oceanic & Atmospheric Admin, 75- *Mem:* Soc Study Evolution; Genetic Soc Am. *Res:* Genetics of gametic selection; genetic population structure of marine invertebrates. *Mailing Add:* Dept of Biol Univ of Houston Houston TX 77004

LESTER, RICHARD GARRISON, b New York, NY, Oct 24, 25; m 53; c 2. RADIOLOGY. *Educ:* Princeton Univ, AB, 46; Columbia Univ, MD, 48. *Prof Exp:* From instr to assoc prof radiol, Univ Minn, 54-61; prof & chmn dept, Med Col Va, 61-65; prof radiol & chmn dept, Duke Univ, 65-76; PROF RADIOL, UNIV TEX MED SCH-HOUSTON, 76-, CHMN RADIOL, 77- *Concurrent Pos:* Mem comt acad radiol, Nat Acad Sci, 66; mem steering comt, Soc Chmn Acad Radiol Dept, 67; mem bd trustees, Am Bd Radiol; mem bd trustees, Meharry Med Col, 75- *Mem:* AMA; Am Roentgen Ray Soc; Am Col Radiol; Soc Pediat Radiol (secy-treas, 58-62); regent Am Col Chest Physicians. *Res:* Cardiovascular and pediatric radiology. *Mailing Add:* Dept of Radiol 6431 Fannin Houston TX 77030

LESTER, ROBERT LEONARD, b New Haven, Conn, Aug 21, 29; m 54; c 2. BIOCHEMISTRY. *Educ:* Yale Univ, BS, 51; Calif Inst Technol, PhD(biochem), 56. *Prof Exp:* Asst prof biochem, Univ Wis, 58-60; from asst prof to assoc prof, 60-68, PROF BIOCHEM, MED SCH, UNIV KY, 68-, CHMN DEPT, 74- *Concurrent Pos:* Res fel, Inst Enzyme Res, Univ Wis, 55-58; NIH res grants, 60-; vis res biologist, Univ Calif, San Diego, 69-70. *Mem:* AAAS; Am Soc Biol Chemists; Am Chem Soc; Am Soc Microbiol; Fedn Am Sci. *Res:* Electron transport; mitochondrial functions; lipid metabolism. *Mailing Add:* Univ of Ky Med Sch Lexington KY 40506

LESTER, ROGER, b Brooklyn, NY, Dec 26, 29; m 54; c 2. MEDICINE. *Educ:* Princeton Univ, AB, 50; Yale Univ, MD, 55. *Prof Exp:* From intern to resident med, Col Med, Univ Utah, 55-57, resident, 59-60; NIH fel, 56-59; fel Thorndike Mem Lab, Harvard Univ, 60-62; asst prof, Sch Med, Univ Chicago, 62-65; from assoc prof to prof med, Sch Med, Boston Univ, 65-73; PROF GASTROENTEROL & CHIEF DIV, SCH MED, UNIV PITTSBURGH, 73- *Concurrent Pos:* NIH career develop award, 63-73, res grant, 65- *Mem:* Am Fedn Clin Res; Am Asn Study Liver Dis; Am Soc Clin Invest; Am Gastroenterol Asn; Int Asn Study Liver. *Res:* Fetal hepatic and intestinal function; effect of alcohol and liver disease on sexual function. *Mailing Add:* Dept of Gastroenterol Univ of Pittsburgh Sch of Med Pittsburgh PA 15261

LESTER, THOMAS WILLIAM, JR, b Chicago, Ill, Oct 12, 15; m 41; c 2. MEDICINE. *Educ:* Univ Chicago, BS, 38, MD, 41. *Prof Exp:* Intern, US Marine Hosp, 41-42; from instr to assoc prof med, Sch Med, Univ Chicago, 46-55, clin assoc prof, 55-62; from clin assoc prof to prof med, Sch Med, Univ Colo, Denver, 62-72; prof, 73-81, EMER PROF MED, SCH MED, UNIV CHICAGO, 73- *Concurrent Pos:* Consult, Naval Med Res Unit 4, 49-54 & Commun Dis Ctr, USPHS, Ga, 50-55; dir student health serv, Sch Med, Univ Chicago, 50-55; assoc mem comn acute respiratory dis, Armed Forces Epidemiol Bd, 52-55; chief of staff, Suburban Cook County Tuberc Hosp Sanitarium, 55-62; chief chest med, Nat Jewish Hosp, Denver, 62-72; consult, Fitzsimons Army Hosp, 63-72. *Mem:* Am Thoracic Soc; Am Pub Health Asn; Am Acad Microbiol; fel Am Col Chest Physicians. *Res:* Aerial disinfection; survival of pathogenic agents in environment; air hygiene; airborne infections; preventive medicine; pulmonary diseases; tuberculosis; atypical mycobacterial infections. *Mailing Add:* Dept Med Sch Med Univ Chicago Chicago IL 60637

LESTER, WILLIAM ALEXANDER, JR, b Chicago, Ill, Apr 24, 37; m 59; c 2. COLLISION DYNAMICS, POTENTIAL ENERGY SURFACES. *Educ:* Univ Chicago, BS, 58, MS, 59; Catholic Univ, PhD(chem), 64. *Prof Exp:* Proj asst physics, lab molecular struct & spectra, Univ Chicago, 57-59; asst chem, Wash Univ, 59-60 & Catholic Univ, 60-62; phys chemist, Phys Chem Div, Nat Bur Standards, 61-64; proj assoc, Theoret Chem Inst, Univ Wis-Madison, 64-65; asst dir theoret chem, 65-68; mem permanent prof staff theoret chem, IBM Res Lab, 68-75; mem tech planning staff, T J Watson Res Ctr, IBM Corp,

Yorktown Heights, NY, 75-76, mgr molecular interactions group, IBM Res Lab, San Jose, Calif, 76-78; dir nat resource comput chem, Lawrence Berkeley Lab, 78-81, PROF CHEM, UNIV CALIF, BERKELEY, 81- *Concurrent Pos:* Lectr, Univ Wis-Madison, 66-68; consult, NSF, 76-77; mem, US Nat Comt, Int Union Pure & Appl Chem, 76-79. *Honors & Awards:* Percy L Julian Award, Nat Orgn Black Chemists & Chem Engrs. *Mem:* Am Chem Soc; Am Phys Soc; Sigma Xi; NY Acad Sci. *Res:* Molecular quantum mechanics and molecular collision theory. *Mailing Add:* Dept Chem Univ of Calif Berkeley CA 94720

LESTER, WILLIAM LEWIS, b Webster City, Iowa, July 21, 32; m 64; c 3. MICROBIOLOGY. *Educ:* San Jose State Col, BA, 58; Univ Calif, Davis, PhD(microbiol), 68. *Prof Exp:* Lab technician pharmacol, Univ Calif, Davis, 62-66; supvr res & develop, Cutter Labs, 68-70; asst prof, 70-74, ASSOC PROF MICROBIOL, HUMBOLDT STATE UNIV, 74- *Concurrent Pos:* Nat Oceanic & Atmospheric Admin sea grant, Samoa & Calif, 70-73; bd dirs, Redwood Health Consortium, 73-75; univ rep, Conf Assist Undergrad Sci Educ, 75- *Mem:* AAAS; Am Soc Microbiol; Wildlife Soc; Am Soc Allied Health Prof. *Res:* Biodegradation of kraft pulp mill effluent; microbial ecology; marine bioassays utilizing echino embryo. *Mailing Add:* Dept of Biol Humboldt State Col Arcata CA 95521

LESTER, WILLIAM WRIGHT, b Lansing, Mich, May 14, 34; m 65; c 2. APPLIED PHYSICS. *Educ:* Mich State Univ, BS, 56, MS, 58, PhD(physics), 63. *Prof Exp:* Res fel, Acoustics Lab, Harvard Univ, 64-65; physicist, Fundamental Physics Dept, Corning Glass Works, 65-68; sr scientist, Tracor, Inc, 68-72; chief res & develop scientist, Gillette Co, 72-78; HEAD ADVAN RES, GEN SCANNING CORP, 78- *Mem:* Acoust Soc Am; Inst Elec & Electronics Eng. *Res:* Ultrasonics; physical and engineering acoustics; propagation phenomena, transducers and applications for industrial uses; mechanical radiation; optics; shaving processes; instrumentation for applied physics; magnetic materials. *Mailing Add:* 249 Weston Rd Wellesley MA 02181

LESTINGI, JOSEPH FRANCIS, b Long Island, NY, Apr 24, 35; m 57; c 4. ENGINEERING MECHANICS, STRUCTURAL ENGINEERING. *Educ:* Manhattan Col, BCE, 57; Va Polytech Inst, MS, 59; Yale Univ, DEng(solid mech), 66. *Prof Exp:* Instr eng mech, Va Polytech Inst, 57-59 & Pa State Univ, 59-60; struct res engr, Elec Boat Div, Gen Dynamics Corp, Conn, 60-65; sr mech engr, Battelle Mem Inst, Ohio, 65-67; from asst prof to prof civil eng, Univ Akron, 67-78; prof eng mech & chmn, Dept Math & Eng Mech, 78-79, PROF MECH ENG & HEAD DEPT, GEN MOTORS INST, 79- *Concurrent Pos:* Res fel, Am Soc Civil Engrs. *Mem:* Am Soc Civil Engrs; Am Soc Mech Engrs; Am Soc Eng Educ; Am Acad Mech; Sigma Xi. *Res:* Computer assisted design; computer assisted manufacturing; finite element methods; shock and vibration analysis; computer methods. *Mailing Add:* 1179 Tumbleweed Ct Flint MI 48504

LESTON, GERD, b Germany, Sept 19, 24; nat US; m 50; c 2. ORGANIC CHEMISTRY. *Educ:* City Col New York, BS, 48; Purdue Univ, MS, 49, PhD(chem), 52; Univ Pittsburgh, BS, 81. *Prof Exp:* Chemist, 52-54, sr chemist, 54-58, group mgr, 58-66, sr group mgr, 67-72, SR PROJ SCIENTIST, KOPPERS CO, INC, 72- *Mem:* Am Chem Soc; Sigma Xi. *Res:* Synthetic organic chemistry, particularly phenol chemistry, aromatic substitution; aromatic alkylation and dealkylation; hydrogenation; aromatic acylation; ultraviolet stabilizers; antioxidant synthesis and testing; homogenous and heterogenous catalysis; pesticides; drugs; separation techniques; organics-salt complexes. *Mailing Add:* 440 College Park Dr Monroeville PA 15146

LESTOURGEON, WALLACE MEADE, b Alexandria, La, Jan 16, 43; div. MOLECULAR BIOLOGY. *Educ:* Univ Tex, Austin, BS, 66, PhD(cell biol), 70. *Prof Exp:* NIH fel oncol, McArdle Lab Cancer Res, 70-74, asst scientist, 74-75; asst prof molecular biol, 75-78, ASSOC PROF MOLECULAR BIOL, VANDERBILT UNIV, 78- *Concurrent Pos:* Prin investr, NSF grants, 75, 78 & 81. *Mem:* AAAS; Am Soc Cell Biol; Sigma Xi; Mycological Soc Am. *Res:* Molecular biological, biochemical and physical chemical studies on the structure of 40's nuclear ribonucleoprotein particles and their role in RNA splicing and in the modulation of information flow in eucaryotes; gene regulation. *Mailing Add:* Dept of Molecular Biol Vanderbilt Univ Nashville TN 37235

LESTRADE, JOHN PATRICK, b New Orleans, La, Mar 25, 49; m 74; c 2. ATMOSPHERIC PHYSICS, SPACE PHYSICS. *Educ:* La State Univ, New Orleans, BS, 71; Purdue Univ, MS, 72; Rice Univ, MS, 76, PhD(space physics), 78. *Prof Exp:* Design scientist nuclear reactors, Westinghouse-Bettis Labs, 73-74; res assoc planetary atmospheres, Rice Univ, 78-80; ASST PROF PHYSICS, TEXAS A&M UNIV, 80- *Res:* Radiative transfer in various media; clouds, soil, oceans; determination of cloud parameters such as aerosol content, optical thickness; soil moisture content; application of light scattering formulae to sound transport. *Mailing Add:* Dept Physics Tex A&M Univ College Station TX 77843

LESTZ, SIDNEY J, US citizen. FUEL ENGINEERING. *Educ:* Pa State Univ, BS, 57, MS, 59. *Prof Exp:* Asst, Dept Petrol & Natural Gas Eng, Pa State Univ, 58-61; asst proj engr, Wright Aeronaut Div, Curtiss Wright Corp, 61-64; sr res engr, Exxon Res & Eng Co, 64-70; sr res engr, 70-71, mgr fuels & lubricants eng, 71-78, DIR, US ARMY FUELS & LUBRICANTS RES LAB, SOUTHWEST RES INST, 78-, DIR MERADCOM FUELS & LUBRICANTS PROG, 76- *Mem:* Combustion Inst; Soc Automotive Engrs; Coord Res Coun; Sigma Xi. *Res:* Wider boiling range fuels; synthetic fuels; alternate fuels; synthetic lubricants; universal hydraulic/power transmission fluid development; safety fuels and fluids technology. *Mailing Add:* Southwest Res Inst PO Drawer 28510 San Antonio TX 78284

LESUER, WILLIAM MONROE, b Ingram, Pa, Oct 13, 20; m 44; c 4. PETROLEUM CHEMISTRY. *Educ:* Monmouth Col, BS, 42; Indiana Univ, PhD(org chem), 48. *Prof Exp:* Res chemist, 48-52, dir, Org Res Labs, 52-60, asst div head res & develop, 60-68, div head, 68-69, vpres res & develop, 69-79, SR VPRES RES & DEVELOP, LUBRIZOL CORP, 79- *Mem:* Am Chem Soc; Indust Res Inst. *Res:* Oil additive chemistry; phosphorus chemistry; sulfonation methods; mineral resources of eastern wilderness areas; geochemistry. *Mailing Add:* Lubrizol Corp 29400 Lakeland Blvd Wickliffe OH 44092

LESURE, FRANK GARDNER, b Camden, SC, Jan 28, 27; m 63; c 2. GEOLOGY. *Educ:* Va Polytech Inst, BS, 51; Yale Univ, MS, 52, PhD(geol), 55. *Prof Exp:* GEOLOGIST, US GEOL SURV, 55- *Mem:* AAAS; Soc Econ Geol; Mineral Soc Am; Geol Soc Am; Geochem Soc. *Res:* Geology of Oriskany iron deposits in Virginia, uranium deposits in southeastern Utah, gold deposits in North Carolina and Georgia, mica pegmatites of southeastern United States; mineral resources of eastern wilderness areas; geochemistry. *Mailing Add:* US Geol Surv 954 Nat Ctr Reston VA 22092

LE SURF, JOSEPH ERIC, b London, Eng, July 21, 29; Can citizen; m 52; c 3. PHYSICAL CHEMISTRY. *Educ:* Univ London, BSc, 50 & 51. *Prof Exp:* Sci officer corrosion, Royal Naval Sci Serv, 51-57; sr sci officer, UK Atomic Energy Authority, 57-64; head, Syst Mat Br, Atomic Energy Can LTD, 64-78; TECH DIR, LONDON NUCLEAR LTD, 78- *Mem:* Nat Asn Corrosion Engrs. *Res:* Marine corrosion; corrosion, material selection, for nuclear decontamination processing plants and nuclear power plants. *Mailing Add:* London Nuclear Ltd Niagara Falls ON L2E 6V9 Can

LETARTE, JACQUES, b Montreal, Que, Aug 19, 34; m 60; c 2. PEDIATRICS, ENDOCRINOLOGY. *Educ:* Univ Montreal, BA, 57, MD, 62. *Prof Exp:* Resident med, Notre Dame Hosp, Montreal, 62; resident pediat, St Justine Hosp, 63-64; resident, Royal Postgrad Med Sch, London, 68; assoc prof, 69-80, PROF PEDIAT, UNIV MONTREAL, 80- *Concurrent Pos:* Mead-Johnson fel pediat, Univ Montreal, 63-64; res fel biochem, Children's Hosp, Zurich, 64-65; Queen Elizabeth II res fel, Can 64-68; res fel, Clin Biochem Inst, Geneva, 65-67; res fel metab, Royal Postgrad Med Sch, London, 68-69; Med Res Coun Can fel, 68-69, scholar, 69-74. *Mem:* AAAS; Can Soc Clin Invest; Soc Pediat Res; Endocrine Soc. *Res:* Hormonal regulation of carbohydrate metabolism; hyperammonemia in children; lipid and carbohydrate metabolism in children. *Mailing Add:* Dept Endocrinol St Justine Hosp 3175 Chemin St Catherine Montreal PQ H3T 1C5 Can

LETARTE-MUIRHEAD, MICHELLE, biochemistry, see previous edition

LETBETTER, WILLIAM DEAN, b Manhattan, Kans, Sept 21, 40; m 62; c 4. NEUROPHYSIOLOGY, NEUROANATOMY. *Educ:* Tex A&M Univ, BS, 63, MS, 64; Univ Tex, PhD(biophys), 69. *Prof Exp:* asst prof, 69-81, SR ASSOC PROF ANAT & PHYS MED, SCH MED, EMORY UNIV, 81- *Concurrent Pos:* USPHS fel, Univ Tex Southwestern Med Sch Dallas, 69; Nat Inst Neurol Dis & Stroke res grants, 71- *Mem:* AAAS; Am Asn Lab Animal Sci; Soc Neurosci. *Res:* Mammalian spinal cord neurophysiology and neuroanatomy; sensory-motor organization; muscle innervation. *Mailing Add:* Dept of Anat Emory Univ Sch of Med Atlanta GA 30322

LETCHER, DAVID WAYNE, b Dover, NJ, May 5, 41; m 63; c 4. METEOROLOGY, GENERAL COMPUTER SCIENCE. *Educ:* Rutgers Univ, BS, 63; Univ Nebr, MS, 65; Cornell Univ, PhD(meteorol), 71. *Prof Exp:* Grad asst agr climat, Univ Nebr, 63-65; grad asst meteorol, Cornell Univ, 65-68; asst prof, 68-72, assoc prof meteorol, Physics Dept, 72-81, COORDR ACADEMIC COMPUTING, TRENTON STATE COL, 81- *Mem:* Air Pollution Control Asn; Am Meteorol Soc; Sigma Xi. *Res:* Atmospheric dispersion modeling of power plant stacks used in district heating. *Mailing Add:* Comput Ctr Trenton State Col Trenton NJ 08625

LETCHER, JOHN HENRY, III, b Wilkes-Barre, Pa, July 18, 36; m 60; c 2. PHYSICS, COMPUTER SCIENCE. *Educ:* Univ Tulsa, BS, 57; Univ Mo, MS, 59, PhD(physics), 63. *Prof Exp:* Mem staff, Advan Electronics Techniques Div, McDonnell Corp, 63-64; mem staff, Cent Res Dept, Monsanto Co, 64-68; vpres systs & res, Data Res Corp, 68-70; PRES, SYNERGISTIC CONSULTS, INC, 70- *Concurrent Pos:* Mem staff, Dept Comput Sci, Southern Methodist Univ, Dallas, 75-79. *Mem:* Sigma Xi. *Res:* Computer software; hardware systems development; quantum physics and chemistry. *Mailing Add:* 7421 S Marion Ave Tulsa OK 74136

LETCHER, STEPHEN VAUGHAN, b Chicago, Ill, Dec 13, 35; m 59; c 2. PHYSICS. *Educ:* Trinity Col, BS, 57; Brown Univ, PhD(physics), 64. *Prof Exp:* From asst prof to assoc prof, 63-75, PROF PHYSICS, UNIV RI, 75- *Mem:* Am Phys Soc; Am Asn Physics Teachers; Acoust Soc Am. *Res:* Physical acoustics; physics of fluids. *Mailing Add:* Dept of Physics Univ of R I Kingston RI 02881

LETEY, JOHN, JR, b Carbondale, Colo, June 13, 33; m 55; c 3. BIOPHYSICS. *Educ:* Colo State Univ, BS, 55; Univ Ill, PhD, 59. *Prof Exp:* Asst agron, Univ Ill, 55-59; asst prof, Univ Calif, Los Angeles, 59-64; assoc prof, 64-68, chmn div environ sci, 68-75, PROF SOIL PHYSICS, UNIV CALIF, RIVERSIDE, 68-, CHMN DEPT SOIL SCI & & ENVIRON SCI, 75- *Honors & Awards:* Soil Sci Award, Soil Sci Soc Am, 70. *Mem:* Fel Am Soc Agron; Soil Sci Soc Am. *Res:* Soil aeration; soil-water-plant relationships; soil wettability, infiltration; environmental pollutants. *Mailing Add:* Dept of Soil & Environ Sci Univ of Calif Riverside CA 92521

LETKEMAN, PETER, b Winkler, Man, Feb 12, 38; m 64; c 3. CHEMISTRY. *Educ:* Univ Man, BSc, 60, MSc, 61, PhD(chem), 69. *Prof Exp:* Teacher high sch, Man, Can, 61-63; lectr, 63-66, from asst prof to assoc prof chem, 66-75, PROF CHEM, BRANDON UNIV, 76-, DEPT HEAD, 72- *Concurrent Pos:* Mem sci curric coun, Dept Educ, Man, 68-; grant, Univ Calif, Riverside, 70; consult, Christie Sch Supplies, Man, 70-; mem bd gov & senate, Brandon Univ, 73-77; pres, Western Man Sci Fair, 76; judge-in-chief, Can Wide Sci Fair, 75; mem staff, Tex A&M Univ, 77-78. *Mem:* Chem Inst Can. *Res:* The polarography and nuclear magnetic resonance of metal complexes in aqueous media; environmental research with regard to water and soil analysis; determination of stability constants of metal complexes. *Mailing Add:* Dept of Chem Brandon Univ Brandon MB R7B 2E5 Can

LETOURNEAU, BUDD W(EBSTER), b Portland, Ore, Apr 8, 32. MECHANICAL & NUCLEAR ENGINEERING. *Educ:* Calif Inst Technol, BS, 53. *Prof Exp:* From assoc engr to sr engr, 54-62, fel engr, 62-74, ADV ENGR, BETTIS ATOMIC POWER LAB, WESTINGHOUSE ELEC CORP, 74- *Mem:* Am Soc Mech Engrs. *Res:* Boiling heat transfer; two phase fluid flow; thermal and hydraulic design of nuclear reactors. *Mailing Add:* 1680 Skyline Dr Pittsburgh PA 15227

LETOURNEAU, DUANE JOHN, b Stillwater, Minn, July 12, 26; m 47; c 3. PLANT BIOCHEMISTRY. *Educ:* Univ Minn, BS, 48, MS, 51, PhD(agr bot), 54. *Prof Exp:* Asst, Univ Minn, 48-53; asst prof agr chem & asst agr chemist, 53-58, assoc prof & assoc agr chemist, 58-63, prof agr biochem & agr biochemist, 63-73, actg head dept agr biochem & soils, 61-62, PROF BIOCHEM & BIOCHEMIST, UNIV IDAHO, 73- *Concurrent Pos:* Resident res assoc, USDA, 64-65; vis scientist, Nat Res Coun, Saskatoon, Can, 81. *Mem:* Fel AAAS; Am Soc Plant Physiol; Am Chem Soc; Am Phytopath Soc; Mycol Soc Am. *Res:* Plant biochemistry; plant cell culture techniques. *Mailing Add:* Dept of Bacteriol & Biochem Univ of Idaho Moscow ID 83843

LETOURNEUX, JEAN, b Quebec, Que, Mar 23, 35; m 70. THEORETICAL NUCLEAR PHYSICS. *Educ:* Laval Univ, BSc, 59; Oxford Univ, DPhil(physics), 62. *Prof Exp:* Ciba fel, Inst Theoret Physics, Copenhagen, 62-64; res assoc physics, Univ Va, 64-65; asst prof, 65-66; from asst prof to assoc prof, 66-74, PROF PHYSICS, UNIV MONTREAL, 74- *Mem:* Am Phys Soc; Can Asn Physicists. *Res:* Nuclear theory. *Mailing Add:* Dept of Physics Univ of Montreal PO Box 6128 Montreal PQ H3C 3J7 Can

LETSINGER, ROBERT LEWIS, b Bloomfield, Ind, July 31, 21; m 43; c 3. ORGANIC CHEMISTRY. *Educ:* Mass Inst Technol, BS, 43, PhD(org chem), 45. *Prof Exp:* Asst, Mass Inst Technol, 43-45, res assoc, 45-46; res chemist, Tenn Eastman Corp, 46; from instr to assoc prof, 46-59, chmn dept, 72-75, PROF CHEM, NORTHWESTERN UNIV, 59- *Concurrent Pos:* Guggenheim fel, 56; mem, NIH Fel Rev Panel, 65-69; med chem study sect, NIH, 71-75. *Mem:* Am Chem Soc; Am Soc Biol Chemists; AAAS; fel Japan Soc Prom Sci. *Res:* Bioorganic chemistry; synthesis of polynucleotides and nucleotide analogs; photochemistry; organoboron and organoalkali metal compounds. *Mailing Add:* Dept of Chem Molecular Biol & Biochem Northwestern Univ Evanston IL 60201

LETT, JOHN TERENCE, b London, Eng, Dec 23, 33; m 56; c 1. BIOPHYSICS, RADIATION BIOLOGY. *Educ:* Univ London, BSc, 56, PhD(phys org chem), 60. *Prof Exp:* Sr lectr, Inst Cancer Res, Univ London, 56-67; PROF RADIOL & RADIATION BIOL, GRAD SCH, COLO STATE UNIV, 68- *Concurrent Pos:* Res assoc, Univ Calif, 61; vis scientist, Oak Ridge Nat Lab, 64. *Mem:* Radiation Res Soc; Brit Biophys Soc; Biophys Soc; Brit Asn Radiation Res. *Res:* DNA structure of the chromosome; repair of radiation damage to cellular DNA; radiation and aging. *Mailing Add:* Dept of Radiol & Radiation Biol Colo State Univ Ft Collins CO 80521

LETT, PHILIP W(OOD), JR, b Newton, Ala, May 4, 22; m 48; c 3. MECHANICAL ENGINEERING. *Educ:* Auburn Univ, BME, 43; Univ Ala, MS, 47; Univ Mich, PhD(mech eng), 50; Mass Inst Technol, ScM, 61. *Prof Exp:* Instr eng, Univ Mich, 48-50; proj engr, Eng Div, Chrysler Corp, 50-54, asst chief engr, 54-58, chief engr, 58-61, operating mgr, Chrysler Defense Eng, 61-74, gen mgr, Defense Div, 74-76, gen mgr, Sterling Defense Div, 76-79, dir, Defense Eng Div, 79-80, VPRES ENG, CHRYSLER DEFENSE INC, 80- *Mem:* Int Soc Terrain-Vehicle Systs; Soc Automotive Engrs; Soc Logistics Engrs; Asn US Army; Am Defense Preparedness Asn. *Res:* Analytical and experimental studies of dynamic stability of surface vehicles employing models in wind tunnels and full scale instrumented vehicles on roads; computer simulation of business systems using industrial dynamics techniques; vehicular systems and surface mobility. *Mailing Add:* Chrysler Defense Inc 25999 Lawrence Ave Center Line MI 48015

LETTAU, KATHARINA, b Plauen, Ger, July 20, 10; US citizen; m 37; c 3. CLIMATOLOGY. *Educ:* Univ Leipzig, PhD(meteorol, math physics), 35. *Prof Exp:* Meteorologist, Ger Weather Serv, 35-37, 39-44; meteorologist, Ctr Climate Res, Univ Wis-Madison, 44-76; RETIRED. *Res:* Bioclimatology; phenology. *Mailing Add:* 122 Bascom Pl Madison WI 53705

LETTERMAN, GORDON SPARKS, b St Louis, Mo, Aug 17, 14; m 47; c 1. SURGERY. *Educ:* Wash Univ, AB, 37, BS, 40, MD, 41; Am Bd Surg, dipl; Am Bd Plastic Surg, dipl. *Prof Exp:* Asst surg, Wash Univ, 43-48; instr, 49-53, from assoc to asst prof, 53-60, from assoc clin prof to clin prof, 60-64, PROF SURG, GEORGE WASHINGTON UNIV, 64- *Concurrent Pos:* Mem, Int Cong Plastic Surgeons, 55. *Mem:* Am Soc Plastic & Reconstruct Surg; Am Asn Plastic Surg; Int Soc Aesthetic Plastic Surg; Am Soc Aesthetic Plastic Surg; fel Am Col Surgeons. *Res:* Plastic surgery. *Mailing Add:* 5272 River Rd #310 Washington DC 20816

LETTERMAN, HERBERT, b Brooklyn, NY, Oct 8, 36; m 57; c 4. ANALYTICAL CHEMISTRY, LABORATORY MANAGEMENT. *Educ:* City Col New York, BS, 58; Brooklyn Col, MA, 62; Seton Hall Univ, MS, 67, PhD(anal chem), 73. *Prof Exp:* Anal chemist, Brooklyn Jewish Hosp, NY, 58-59; anal chemist, Ciba Pharmaceut Co, NJ, 59-63; group leader phys chem res & develop, 63-66, head qual control, 66-78, MGR QUAL SERV, BRISTOL-MYERS PROD DIV, 78- *Mem:* Sigma Xi; Am Chem Soc; Acad Pharmaceut Sci; sr mem Am Soc Qual Control. *Res:* Quality control; analytical method development. *Mailing Add:* 44 Delaware Ave New Providence NJ 07974

LETTIERI, THOMAS ROBERT, b Scranton, Pa, Sept 9, 14, 52. OPTICS, MICROMETROLOGY. *Educ:* Univ Miami, BS, 73; Univ Rochester, MS, 76, PhD(optics), 78. *Prof Exp:* Physicist liquids, 78-79, PHYSICIST OPTICS, NAT BUR STANDARDS, 79- *Mem:* Sigma Xi; Am Phys Soc; AAAS; Optical Soc Am. *Res:* Light scattering studies of liquids and solids; ultrasonic properties of materials; phase transitions; metastability in liquids; high pressure research; microparticle measurements; holography. *Mailing Add:* Mech Prod Metrol Div Nat Bur Standards Washington DC 20234

LETTON, JAMES CAREY, b Paris, Ky, June 9, 33; m 56; c 3. PHARMACEUTICAL CHEMISTRY. *Educ:* Ky State Col, BS, 55; Univ Ill, Chicago Circle, PhD(chem), 71. *Prof Exp:* Prod foreman, Julian Labs, 57-62, supt prod, Smith Kline & French Labs, 62-64, res & develop chemist, Julian Res Inst, 64-69; instr org chem, Triton Col, 68-70; assoc prof org chem, Ky State Univ, 70-73, chmn, Dept Chem, 71-75, prof org chem, 73-75; ORG CHEMIST, PROCTER & GAMBLE CO, 76- *Mem:* Fel Am Inst Chemists; Am Chem Soc. *Res:* Medicinal chemistry, especially beta amino ketones and analgesic properties; morphine-like compounds; steroid synthesis. *Mailing Add:* Proctor & Gamble Co 11530 Reed Hartman Hwy Cincinnati OH 45241

LETTVIN, JEROME Y, b Chicago, Ill, Feb 23, 20; m 47; c 3. NEUROPHYSIOLOGY. *Educ:* Univ Ill, BS, 42, MD, 43. *Prof Exp:* Intern neurol, Boston City Hosp, 43-44; physiologist, Dept of Psychol, Univ Rochester, 47-48; neuropsychiatrist & physiologist, Manteno State Hosp, 48-51; PROF COMMUN PHYSIOL, DEPTS BIOL, ELEC ENG & COMPUT SCI, MASS INST TECHNOL, 66-, NEUROPHYSIOLOGIST, LAB ELECTRONICS, 51- *Concurrent Pos:* Lectr neurol, Harvard Med Sch, 75- *Mem:* Am Physiol Soc. *Res:* Experimental epistemology. *Mailing Add:* Dept of Biol Mass Inst of Technol Cambridge MA 02139

LEU, RICHARD WILLIAM, b Argonia, Kans, Jan 5, 35; m 60; c 2. MICROBIOLOGY, IMMUNOLOGY. *Educ:* Northwestern State Col, Okla, BS, 60; Univ Okla, MS, 63, PhD(microbiol, immunol), 70. *Prof Exp:* USPHS res training fel pediat & path, Med Sch, Univ Minn, Minneapolis, 70-74; MEM STAFF, NOBLE FOUND, 74-, HEAD IMMUNOL SECT, 76- *Res:* Cellular immunity; effector molecules associated with macrophage inhibition, proliferation and activation; role of cytophilic antibody in cellular immunity; localized immunity in the lung. *Mailing Add:* 2101 Oak Glenn Dr Ardmore OK 73401

LEUBNER, GERHARD WALTER, b Walton, NY, Aug 31, 21; m 44; c 3. ORGANIC CHEMISTRY. *Educ:* Union Col, BS, 43; Univ Ill, PhD(chem), 49. *Prof Exp:* Chemist, Winthrop Chem Co, 43-45; asst, Univ Ill, 45-46; RES ASSOC, EASTMAN KODAK CO, 48- *Mem:* Am Chem Soc. *Res:* Patent information storage and retrieval systems. *Mailing Add:* Eastman Kodak Co Res Labs B 85 1669 Lake Ave Kodak Park Rochester NY 14650

LEUBNER, INGO HERWIG, b Prittlbach, Ger, Apr 9, 38; m 69. PHYSICAL CHEMISTRY. *Educ:* Munich Tech Univ, Dipl, 63, PhD(phys chem), 66. *Prof Exp:* Ger Res Asn res fel phys chem, Munich Tech Univ, 66-68; Welch Found fel & lectr photochem, Tex Christian Univ, 68-69; SR RES CHEMIST, RES LABS, EASTMAN KODAK CO, 69- *Mem:* Soc Photog Scientists & Engrs; Am Chem Soc. *Res:* Photochemistry of organic and inorganic compounds. *Mailing Add:* Res Labs Eastman Kodak Co 343 State St Rochester NY 14650

LEUCHTAG, H RICHARD, b Breslau, Ger, June 2, 27; US citizen; m 55; c 1. MEMBRANE BIOPHYSICS, ELECTRODIFFUSION. *Educ:* Univ Calif, Los Angeles, BA, 50, MA, 55; Ind Univ, PhD(physics), 74. *Prof Exp:* Instr, Don Bosco Tech High Sch, 61-62, Univ San Diego Col Men, 62-63, San Diego State Col, 63-65 & Ind Univ-Purdue Univ, Indianapolis, 65-70; res assoc, Biophys Lab, Phys Dept, NY Univ, 72-74; assoc ed, Physics Today, Am Inst Physics, 74-78; RES SCIENTIST, DEPT PHYSIOL & BIOPHYS, UNIV TEX MED BR, 78- *Concurrent Pos:* Physicist, Western Elec Co, 66; consult, dept physiol & biophys, NY Univ Med Ctr, 78; secy, Int Conf Structure & Function Excitable Cells, 81. *Mem:* Am Phys Soc; Biophys Soc; Soc Neurosci; Soc Indust & Appl Math; Soc Gen Physiologists. *Res:* Physical basis of excitability in nerve, including membrane electrodiffusion; measurement of noise, admittance and impedance in axons; Schwann-cell-layer effects and nonlinear dielectric effects; monitored retrievable disposal of high-level radioactive waste. *Mailing Add:* Dept Physiol & Biophysics Univ Tex Med Br Galveston TX 77550

LEUCHTENBERGER, CECILE, b Leipzig, Ger, Mar 17, 06; nat US; m 33. CYTOLOGY. *Educ:* Columbia Univ, MA, 46, PhD(biol), 49. *Prof Exp:* Biologist, Cancer Res Lab, Mt Sinai Hosp, NY, 36-47; res assoc, Columbia Univ, 47-50; head, Cytochem Lab, Inst Path, Western Reserve Univ, 50-59; sr biologist & cytochemist, Children's Cancer Res Found, Inc, Boston, Mass, 59-63; prof cytochem, Swiss Inst Exp Cancer Res, Univ Lausanne, 63-80, head dept, 63-76; RETIRED. *Mem:* Am Chem Soc; Am Soc Zool; Am Soc Exp Path; Am Asn Cancer Res. *Res:* Cancer research; cytochemistry; microspectrophotometry; biology. *Mailing Add:* Hirzbodenpark 18 Basel 4052 Switzerland

LEUNG, ALBERT YUK-SING, b Hong Kong, May 24, 38; nat US; m 68; c 2. PHARMACOGNOSY, BIOMEDICAL INFORMATION SERVICES. *Educ:* Nat Taiwan Univ, BS, 61; Univ Mich, Ann Arbor, MS, 65, PhD(pharmacog), 67. *Prof Exp:* NIH res chemist, Med Ctr, Univ Calif, 67-69; res supvr microbial protein prod, Bohna Eng & Res, Inc, 69-71; tech dir chem & microbiol consult, Sci Res Info Serv, Inc, 71-74; dir res & develop, Dr Madis Labs, Inc, 74-77; CONSULT NATURAL PRODS, 77- *Concurrent Pos:* Lily Found fel, 63-67. *Mem:* AAAS; Am Chem Soc; Am Soc Pharmacog; NY Acad Sci; Sigma Xi. *Res:* Production of food products from wastes by fermentation; isolation of active principles from plants and microorganisms; biosynthesis of plant products; retrieval and dissemination of biomedical information, especially from Chinese sources. *Mailing Add:* 381 Ackerman Ave Glen Rock NJ 07452

LEUNG, BENJAMIN SHUET-KIN, b Hong Kong, June 30, 38; US citizen; m 64; c 3. ENDOCRINOLOGY, ONCOLOGY. *Educ:* Seattle Pac Col, BS, 63; Colo State Univ, PhD(biochem), 69. *Prof Exp:* Res asst steroid hormones, Pac Northwest Res Found, 63-66; from asst prof to assoc prof surg, Med Sch, Univ Ore, dir lab, Cancer Res, Clin Res Ctr, 71-76; sr res scientist, Dept Surg, Cedars-Sinai Med Ctr, Los Angeles, 76-78; ASSOC PROF & DIR, HORMONE RES LAB, DEPT OBSTET & GYNEC, UNIV MINN, 78- *Concurrent Pos:* NIH & Ford Found res fel reprod endocrinol, Med Sch, Vanderbilt Univ, 69-71; Med Res Found Ore grant, Med Sch, Univ Ore, 71-72, Am Cancer Soc Ore Div res grants, 72-74; Cammack Trust Fund grant, 74-75; NIH grants, 75-79; assoc oncologist, Div Surg Oncol, Univ Calif, Los Angeles, 76-78; Med Res Found Ore res grant, 76-77; Nat Cancer Inst res grant, 77-82; Minn Med Found res grant, 78-79. *Mem:* Am Soc Biol Chemists; AAAS; Endocrine Soc; NY Acad Sci. *Res:* Mechanism of steroid hormones action related to male and female reproductive physiology in normal and neoplastic state. *Mailing Add:* Dept of Obstet & Gynec Box 395 Mayo Mem Bldg Minneapolis MN 55455

LEUNG, CHARLES CHEUNG-WAN, b Hong Kong, June 27, 46; US citizen; m 73; c 1. SEMICONDUCTOR PROCESSING, DEVICE PHYSICS. *Educ:* Univ Hong Kong, BSc, 69; Univ Chicago, MS, 71, PhD(physics), 76. *Prof Exp:* sr scientist, Corning Glass Works, 76-80; sr staff engr, Motorola, 80-81; SR MEM TECH STAFF, AVANTEK, 81- *Mem:* Am Phys Soc; Am Chem Soc; Am Vacuum Soc; Soc Info Display. *Res:* Electro-optic materials; glassification; carbon; vacuum deposition; thin film; surface science. *Mailing Add:* Corning Glass Works Sullivan Park FR3 Corning NY 14830

LEUNG, CHRISTOPHER CHUNG-KIT, b Hong Kong, Jan 3, 39; m 70; c 2. EMBRYOLOGY, IMMUNOLOGY. *Educ:* Howard Univ, BSc, 64; Jefferson Med Col, PhD(anat, embryol), 69. *Prof Exp:* Res asst, Sch Med, Univ Rochester, 64-65; from instr to asst prof pediat, Jefferson Med Col, 69-74, instr anat, 69-75, instr, Col Allied Health Sci, Thomas Jefferson Univ, 70-75, res assoc prof pediat, 74-75; asst prof anat, Univ Kans Med Ctr, 75-79; ASSOC PROF ANAT, SCH MED, LA STATE UNIV, 79- *Concurrent Pos:* NIH fel, Stein Res Ctr, Thomas Jefferson Univ, 69-75; NIH res grant, 79. *Mem:* Teratol Soc; Am Asn Anatomists; Am Asn Immunologists. *Res:* Teratology; immunopathology; cell biology. *Mailing Add:* Dept of Anat La State Univ Shreveport LA 71105

LEUNG, CHUN MING, b Hong Kong, June 5, 46; m 73; c 1. ASTROPHYSICS, ASTRONOMY. *Educ:* Western Mich Univ, BS, 69; Univ Calif, Berkeley, PhD(astron), 75. *Prof Exp:* Res assoc radio astron, Nat Radio Astron ObserY, 74-76, asst scientist, 76-78; ASST PROF PHYSICS, RENSSELAER POLYTECH INST, 78- *Mem:* Am Astron Soc; Int Astron Union; Sigma Xi. *Res:* Theoretical astrophysics; interstellar matter; star formation; radiative transfer. *Mailing Add:* Dept of Physics Rensselaer Polytech Inst Troy NY 12181

LEUNG, IRENE SHEUNG-YING, b Hong Kong, July 10, 34. MINERALOGY. *Educ:* Univ Hong Kong, BA, 57; Ohio State Univ, MA, 63; Univ Calif, Berkeley, PhD(geol), 69. *Prof Exp:* Res staff geologist, Yale Univ, 69-71; asst prof, 71-77, ASSOC PROF GEOL, LEHMAN COL, 77- *Mem:* Sigma Xi; Mineral Soc Am; Am Geophys Union; Geochem Soc; Asian Environ Soc. *Res:* X-ray investigation of mineral inclusions in natural diamonds; magmatic crystallization and sector-zoning in crystals; deformation structures and glide mechanisms in deformed minerals. *Mailing Add:* Dept of Geol & Geog Herbert H Lehman Col Bronx NY 10468

LEUNG, JOSEPH YUK-TONG, b Hong Kong, June 25, 50; m 73. COMPUTER SCIENCE. *Educ:* Southern Ill Univ, Carbondale, BA, 72; Pa State Univ, PhD(comput sci), 77. *Prof Exp:* Asst prof comput sci, Va Polytech Inst & State Univ, 76-77; asst prof comput sci, 77-81, ASSOC PROF ENG & COMPUT SCI, NORTHWESTERN UNIV, EVANSTON, 81- *Mem:* Asn Comput Mach; Inst Elec & Electronics Engrs. *Res:* Operating systems; scheduling theory; analysis of algorithms; data structure; computational complexity. *Mailing Add:* Dept of Elec Eng & Comput Sci Northwestern Univ Evanston IL 60201

LEUNG, KAM-CHING, b Hong Kong, June 16, 35; m 63; c 2. ASTRONOMY, ASTROPHYSICS. *Educ:* Queen's Univ, Ont, BSc, 61; Univ Western Ont, MA, 63; Univ Pa, PhD(astron), 67. *Prof Exp:* Nat Acad Sci-Nat Res Coun res fel astron, Inst Space Studies, NASA, 68-70; asst prof physics, 70-72, assoc prof, 72-78, PROF PHYSICS & ASTRON, UNIV NEBR, LINCOLN, 78- *Concurrent Pos:* NSF res grant, Univ Nebr, Lincoln, 70-71 & 75, dir observ, 72-75; staff assoc astron sect, NSF, 75; mgt specialist, Off Nuclear Energy, ERDA, 77; sr assoc, Off Energy Res, Dept of Energy. *Mem:* Fel AAAS; Int Astron Union; Am Astron Soc. *Res:* Stellar photometry and spectroscopy; intrinsic variable stars; binary stars. *Mailing Add:* Behlen Lab of Physics Univ of Nebr Lincoln NE 68508

LEUNG, KA-NGO, Canton, China. ELECTRICAL ENGINEERING, SYSTEMS DESIGN. *Educ:* Chinese Univ Hong Kong, BS, 68; Univ Akron, MS, 71; Univ Calif, Los Angeles, PhD(physics), 75. *Prof Exp:* Asst prof physics, James Madison Univ, Va, 75-78; STAFF PHYSICIST, LAWRENCE BERKELEY LAB, 78- *Mem:* Am Phys Soc. *Res:* Development of positive and negative ion sources for neutral beam heating in fusion reactors. *Mailing Add:* Lawrence Berkeley Lab Bldg 4 Berkeley CA 94720

LEUNG, LAI-WO STAN, b Macau, July 7, 52; stateless. NEUROPHYSIOLOGY, BEHAVIOR & NEURAL ACTIVITY. *Educ:* Calif State Univ, Northridge, BSc, 73; Univ Calif, Berkeley, PhD(biophysics), 78. *Prof Exp:* Teaching assoc physiol & biophysics, Univ Calif, Berkeley, 77-78; fel physiol psychol, Univ Western Ont, London, Can, 78-79, fel brain res, Int Brain Res Orgn & UNESCO fel, Inst Med Physics, Utrecht, Holland, 79-80; ASST PROF PHYSIOL PSYCHOL, UNIV WESTERN ONT, LONDON, CAN, 80- *Concurrent Pos:* Univ res fel, Natural Sci & Eng Res Coun, 80- *Mem:* Soc Neurosci; Europe Neurosci Asn. *Res:* Analyses of brain waves, evoked by potentials and single neuronal activities in the cerebral cortex during various behavioral states. *Mailing Add:* Dept Psychol Univ Western Ont London ON N6A 5C2 Can

LEUNG, PAK SANG, b Shanghai, China, June 8, 35; US citizen; m 65; c 2. COLLOID CHEMISTRY. *Educ:* Nat Taiwan Univ, BSc, 57; Columbia Univ, MA, 62, PhD(phys chem), 67. *Prof Exp:* Dyes lab asst, Imp Chem Industs, 57-59; demonstr chem, Hong Kong Baptist Col, 59-61; res scientist, Brookhaven Nat Lab-Columbia Univ, 66-67; RES SCIENTIST, UNION CARBIDE CORP, TARRYTOWN, 67- *Concurrent Pos:* Mem chem adv bd, Harriman Col, 74- *Mem:* Sigma Xi. *Res:* Surface and collidal chemistry; polymer composite; clinical chemistry; ultrafiltration; membrane technology. *Mailing Add:* 15 Woodland Rd Highland Mills NY 10930

LEUNG, PHILIP MAN KIT, b Hong Kong, June 22, 33; Can citizen; m 59; c 2. MEDICAL PHYSICS, BIOPHYSICS. *Educ:* Univ Toronto, BASc, 60; McMaster Univ, MSc, 61; Univ Toronto, PhD(biophys), 67. *Prof Exp:* Lectr, Ryerson Inst Technol, Can, 61-62; physicist, British Columbia Cancer Inst, Can, 67-68; SR PHYSICIST, ONT CANCER INST, 68- *Concurrent Pos:* Fel, Univ BC, 67-68; consult physicist, Orillia Soldier Mem Hosp, Can, 69-70 & Can Soc Radiol Technicians, 69-78; ed, Physics in Med & Biol, 72-75; investr, Children's Cancer Study Group, Nat Cancer Inst, USPHS, 76-77 & 77-78; lectr, Dept Med Biophys, Univ Toronto, 79- *Mem:* Can Asn Physicists. *Res:* Radiation dosimetry; radiotherapy treatment techniques and new equipment associated with radiation oncology. *Mailing Add:* Ont Cancer Inst 500 Sherbourne St Toronto ON M4X 1K9 Can

LEUNG, PHILIP MIN BUN, b Canton, China, July 31, 34; m; c 3. NUTRITION, BIOCHEMISTRY. *Educ:* Chung Hsing Univ, Taiwan, BSc, 56; McGill Univ, MSc, 59; Mass Inst Technol, PhD(nutrit biochem), 65. *Prof Exp:* Res asst, McGill Univ, 56-59; res asst, Mass Inst Technol, 59-65; group leader biochem res, Med Sci Res Lab, Miles Labs Inc, Ind, 65-67; asst res nutritionist, 67-77, ASSOC RES NUTRITIONIST, SCH VET MED, UNIV CALIF, DAVIS, 77- *Mem:* AAAS; Am Inst Nutrit; Inst Food Technol; NY Acad Sci. *Res:* Nutrition and biochemistry of amino acid imbalance; nutritional regulation of protein intake and metabolism; influence of nutrition, especially amino acid balance on food intake regulation. *Mailing Add:* Dept of Physiol Sci Sch of Vet Med Univ of Calif Davis CA 95616

LEUNG, SHAU PARK P, b Canton, China, June 7, 51. HIGH ENERGY PHYSICS. *Educ:* NY State Col Geneseo, BA, 72; Columbia Univ, MA, 74, PhD(physics), 77. *Prof Exp:* Res assoc, Columbia Univ, 77; RES ASSOC HIGH ENERGY PHYSICS, STANFORD LINEAR ACCELERATOR CTR, STANFORD UNIV, 77- *Res:* High energy experimental physics. *Mailing Add:* Bin 94 Stanford Univ Stanford CA 94305

LEUNG, SO WAH, b China, Nov 2, 18; nat US; m 57; c 1. DENTISTRY, PHYSIOLOGY. *Educ:* McGill Univ, DDS, 43, BSc, 45; Univ Rochester, PhD(physiol), 50; FRCDent(C). *Prof Exp:* Intern dent, Royal Victoria Hosp, Montreal, 43-44; from assoc prof to prof physiol, Sch Dent, Univ Pittsburgh, 50-61, head dept, 52-61, prof dent res & dir grad educ, 57-61; prof oral biol, Sch Dent & lectr physiol, Sch Med, Univ Calif, Los Angeles, 61-62; dean sch dent, 62-77, PROF ORAL BIOL, UNIV BC, 62- *Concurrent Pos:* Mem comt dent, Nat Acad Sci-Nat Res Coun, 57-61; consult, Colgate-Palmolive Co, 58-62; mem dent study sect, NIH, 59-63; consult, Nat Bd Dent Exam, 60-66 & Lever Bros, 63-65; mem assoc comt dent res, Nat Res Coun Can, 63-68, exec comt, 65-68; mem, Nat Dent Exam Bd Can, 65-67, chmn exam comt, 67-71; chmn res comt, Asn Can Fac Dent, 68-70, pres, 70-72. *Mem:* Am Dent Asn; fel Am Col Dent; fel Int Col Dent; NY Acad Sci; Sigma Xi. *Res:* Salivary chemistry; oral calculus formation; physiology of salivary glands. *Mailing Add:* Fac of Dent Univ of BC Vancouver BC V6T 1W5 Can

LEUNG, WAI-CHOI, b Hong Kong, May 23, 48; Can citizen; m 73; c 1. VIROLOGY. *Educ:* Chinese Univ Hong Kong, BS, 70; Baylor Col Med, PhD(virol), 74. *Prof Exp:* Res assoc virol, Div Biochem Virol, Baylor Col Med, 74-75; trainee, 75-77, ASST PROF VIROL, DEPT PATH, McMASTER UNIV, 77- *Mem:* Am Soc Microbiol. *Res:* Molecular cloning of viral neutralization antigens and human tumor specific antigens; mechanism for viral persistence. *Mailing Add:* Dept of Path McMaster Univ Hamilton ON L8S 4L8 Can

LEUPOLD, HERBERT AUGUST, b Brooklyn, NY, Jan 6, 31. PHYSICS, MATERIALS SCIENCE. *Educ:* Queens Col, NY, BS, 53; Columbia Univ, AM, 58, PhD(physics), 64. *Prof Exp:* Fel physics, Lawrence Radiation Lab, Livermore, Calif, 64-67; RES PHYSICIST, ELECTRONICS RES DEVELOP COMMAND, US ARMY, 67- *Concurrent Pos:* Lectr physics, Queens Col, NY, 57 & Monmouth Col, 67-70. *Honors & Awards:* Commendation, Inst for Explor Res, US Army, 69 & Electronics Technol & Devices Lab, US Army, 72. *Mem:* Am Phys Soc; Sigma Xi; Inst Elec & Electronics Engrs. *Res:* Magnetism; semiconductors; superconductivity; thermodynamics; cryogenics; magnetic circuit design; magnetic materials. *Mailing Add:* US Army ERADCOM Delet-E ETDL Ft Monmouth NJ 07703

LEUSSING, DANIEL, JR, b Cincinnati, Ohio, Oct 8, 24; m 57; c 3. ANALYTICAL CHEMISTRY. *Educ:* Univ Cincinnati, BA, 45; Univ Ill, MS, 47; Univ Minn, PhD(chem), 53. *Prof Exp:* Instr anal chem, Univ Minn, 51-52; chemist, Am Cyanamid Co, 53; instr anal chem, Mass Inst Technol, 53-55; from instr to asst prof, Univ Wis, 55-60; chemist, Nat Bur Standards, 60-62; from asst prof to assoc prof, 62-70, PROF CHEM, OHIO STATE UNIV, 70- *Mem:* Am Chem Soc. *Res:* Physical chemistry of aqueous solutions; coordination chemistry; metal mercaptide complexes; Schiff base complexes; kinetics. *Mailing Add:* Dept of Chem Ohio State Univ Columbus OH 43210

LEUTENEGGER, WALTER, b Winterthur, Switz, Oct 18, 41; US citizen. BIOLOGICAL ANTHROPOLOGY, PRIMATOLOGY. *Educ:* Univ Zurich, PhD(biol anthrop), 69. *Prof Exp:* Anthropologist, Bern Natural Mus Hist, Switz, 67-69; sci res asst biol anthrop, Univ Zurich, 69-71; asst prof, 71-77, ASSOC PROF BIOL ANTHROP, UNIV WIS-MADISON, 77- *Concurrent Pos:* Affil scientist, Wis Regional Primate Res Ctr, 72- *Mem:* Am Asn Phys Anthropologists; Am Soc Naturalists; Am Soc Primatologists; Soc Vert Paleont. *Res:* Functional anatomy of the primate locomotor apparatus; determinants of behavioral and morphological sexual dimorphism; reconstruction of early hominid social organization and behavior. *Mailing Add:* Dept of Anthrop Univ of Wis Madison WI 53706

LEUTERT, WERNER WALTER, b Ottenback, Switz, Nov 9, 22; nat US; m 48; c 5. APPLIED MATHEMATICS. *Educ:* Swiss Fed Inst Technol, DSc, 48. *Prof Exp:* Asst prof math, Univ Md, 48-51; mathematician, Comput Lab, Ballistic Res Labs, Aberdeen Proving Ground, Md, 51-53, chief, 53-55; mgr math & comput serv dept, Lockheed Missile Systs Div, 55-57; sr mathematician, Tidewater Oil Co, 57-59; mgr adv prog & appl math, Remington Rand Univac Div, Sperry Rand Corp, NY, 59-61, dir systs prog, 61-62; CONSULT, 62- *Mem:* Asn Comput Mach; Inst Mgt Sci. *Res:* Large real time systems; applications of electronic computers; optimization of operations; automatic programming of computers. *Mailing Add:* Laurel Ledge Park Stamford CT 06903

LEUTGOEB, ROSALIA ALOISIA, b Vienna, Austria, Apr 2, 01; nat US; m 20; c 1. CHEMISTRY. *Educ:* Marquette Univ, BS, 35, MS, 36, PhD(electroeng chem), 38. *Prof Exp:* Instr chem & math, St Ambrose Col, 40-42; res chemist dried yeast, Red Star Yeast Co, 42-44; res chemist synthetic rubber, US Govt Labs, 44-45; asst prof chem, Mundelein Col, 45-49; res chemist, Froedtert Grain & Malting Co, Inc, 50-52; prof chem & chmn dept, 53-70, EMER PROF CHEM, NORTHLAND COL, 70- *Mem:* AAAS; Am Chem Soc. *Res:* Synthesis of glucuronic acid; oxidation mechanism. *Mailing Add:* Rte 1 Box 164 Ashland WI 54806

LEUTHEUSSER, H(ANS) J(OACHIM), b Eisenach, Ger, Feb 1, 27; Can citizen; m 55; c 3. FLUID MECHANICS, HYDRAULIC ENGINEERING. *Educ:* Karlsruhe Univ, Dipl Ing, 52; Univ Toronto, MASc, 57, PhD(mech eng), 61. *Prof Exp:* Asst hydraul eng, Theodor-Rehbock Lab, Karlsruhe Univ, 51-52; field engr, Oulujoki Oy, Helsinki, Finland, 52-53; sr engr, Friedrich Buchner, Wuerzburg, Ger, 53-54; instr fluid mech, Dept Mech Eng, 55-57, lectr, 57-62, from asst prof to assoc prof, 63-70, assoc chmn dept, 77-79, PROF FLUID MECH, DEPT MECH ENG, UNIV TORONTO, 70- *Concurrent Pos:* Consult engr, 57-; sabbatical leaves, Inst Mech Statist of Turbulence, Univ Aix Marseille, 66-67 & Inst Hydromech, Karlsruhe Univ, 75-76. *Mem:* Am Soc Civil Engrs; Inst Asn Hydraul Res. *Res:* Fundamental fluid mechanics and applications; turbulence; fluid elasticity and transients; biomechanics; air pollution control; building aerodynamics. *Mailing Add:* Dept of Mech Eng Univ of Toronto Toronto ON M6S 1A1 Can

LEUTRITZ, JOHN, JR, b Saginaw, Mich, June 22, 03; m 28, 61. CHEMISTRY. *Educ:* Bowdoin Col, BS, 29; Columbia Univ, MA, 34, PhD(bot), 46. *Prof Exp:* Res engr, Bell Tel Labs, Inc, 29-66; chem engr, Rural Electrification Admin, USDA, 65-72, timber prod specialist, 72-76; RETIRED. *Concurrent Pos:* Consult wood preserv res. *Mem:* AAAS; Am Chem Soc; Soc Indust Microbiol; Am Wood Preservers Asn; NY Acad Sci. *Res:* Microbiological deterioration; wood preservation; climatic effects on materials; miscellaneous materials preservation; quality control. *Mailing Add:* 303 Fair Cross Circle Sun City Center FL 33570

LEUTZE, WILLARD PARKER, b Burlington, Vt, Mar 2, 27; m 51; c 2. GEOLOGY. *Educ:* Syracuse Univ, BS, 51, MS, 55; Ohio State Univ, PhD(geol), 59. *Prof Exp:* Geologist, US Geol Surv, 54-55; asst geol, Ohio State Univ, 55-58; instr geol & soil sci, Earlham Col, 58-60; geologist, Texaco, Inc, 60-66; biostratigrapher, Atlantic Richfield Co, 66-71, sr geologist, 71-75; sr geologist, Stone Oil, 75-77; INDEPENDENT CONSULT, 77- *Mem:* Geol Soc Am; assoc Soc Econ Paleont & Mineral; Soc Prof Well Log Analysts. *Res:* Paleontology, particularly foraminifera, arthropods and echinoderms; stratigraphy of Upper Silurian and of Gulf Coast; subsurface stratigraphy of south Louisiana. *Mailing Add:* Box 52641 OCS Lafayette LA 70501

LEUTZINGER, RUDOLPH L(ESLIE), b Dallas Center, Iowa, June 17, 22; m 50; c 6. MECHANICAL ENGINEERING, AEROSPACE ENGINEERING. *Educ:* Iowa State Univ, BS, 43; Univ Mich, MS, 52; Univ Iowa, PhD(mech eng), 76. *Prof Exp:* Stress analyst, Douglas Airplane Co, 44-46 & McDonnell Airplane Co, 46 & 47; instr aeronaut eng, Iowa State Univ, 47-50; res assoc dynamics, Aeronaut Res Ctr, Univ Mich, 51; res engr, Midwest Res Inst, Mo, 51-53; asst prof aeronaut eng & appl mech, Univ Kans, 54-56; assoc prof aerodyn, Agr & Mech Col Tex, 56-58; assoc prof thermodyn, Univ Mo-Rolla, 58-60; assoc prof eng & chmn dept, Univ Mo-Kansas City, 62-76; assoc prof mech eng, 76-79, EMER PROF MECH ENG, UNIV MO-COLUMBIA, 79-; DIR, AERO TURB MFG, 79-; CONSULT ENGR, LEUTZINGER CONSULT ASSOCS, 79- *Concurrent Pos:* Consult, Boeing Airplane Co, 57, Gas Turbine Div, Westinghouse Elec Corp, 56 & McDonnell Aircraft Corp, 58, 59 & 62; assoc mem grad fac & eng admin coun, Agr & Mech Col Tex, 58; mem grad fac, Univ Mo, 59; NSF inst res grants, 61, 62 & 64; Kans City Regional Coun Higher Educ grant, 64-65; vis lectr, Col Eng, Univ Iowa, 69-; NASA fel propulsion, 73 & 77. *Mem:* AAAS; Soc Eng Sci; Am Inst Aeronaut & Astronaut (secy-treas, 42 & 75-78); Am Soc Eng Educ; Nat Soc Prof Engrs. *Res:* Structural mechanics and dynamics; gas dynamics; flow fields in turbomachinery, especially three-dimensional and boundary layers; vehicle design and analysis; internal and external aerodynamics of ducts and bodies. *Mailing Add:* Leutzinger Consult Assocs 1521 N Holder Independence MO 64050

LEUZE, REX ERNEST, b Sabetha, Kans, Mar 7, 22; m 48; c 3. CHEMICAL ENGINEERING, PROCESS CHEMISTRY. *Educ:* Kans State Univ, BS, 44; Univ Tenn, Knoxville, MS, 56. *Prof Exp:* Anal chemist, Monsanto Chem Co, Ill, 44-45; anal chemist, Clinton Labs, 45-47, chem engr tech div, 47-49, develop group leader inorg fluorides, Chem Tech Div, 49-54, develop group leader transuranium element chem, 54-63, asst chief chem develop sect, 63-72, asst chief pilot plant sect, 72-76, sect head exp eng sect, 76-81, HEAD PILOT PLANT, OAK RIDGE NAT LAB, 76- *Mem:* Am Nuclear Soc; Am Chem Soc; fel Am Inst Chem; Sigma Xi. *Res:* Ion exchange and solvent extraction, especially of the transuranium elements, neptunium through fermium; preparation and properties of concentrated colloids of metal oxides and hydroxides; nuclear fuel reprocessing and waste treatment. *Mailing Add:* 517 W Fifth Ave Lenoir City TN 37771

LEV, MAURICE, b St Joseph, Mo, Nov 13, 08; m 47; c 2. PATHOLOGY. *Educ:* NY Univ, BS, 30; Creighton Univ, MD, 34; Northwestern Univ, MA, 66; Am Bd Path, dipl path anat, 41, dipt clin path, 43. *Hon Degrees:* LHD, De Paul Univ, 81. *Prof Exp:* From instr to assoc prof path, Col Med, Univ Ill, 39-41; asst prof, Sch Med, Creighton Univ, 46-47; from assoc prof to prof, Sch Med, Univ Miami, 51-57; prof, 57-77, EMER PROF PATH, MED SCH, NORTHWESTERN UNIV, CHICAGO, 77-; DIR CONGENITAL HEART DIS RES & TRAINING CTR, HEKTOEN INST MED RES, 57- *Concurrent Pos:* Pathologist, Chicago State Hosp, 40-42; pathologist & dir res labs, Mt Sinai Hosp, Miami Beach, 51-57; career investr & educr, Chicago Heart Asn, 66-; consult, Children's Mem Hosp, Chicago, 57-; prof lectr, Univ Chicago, 59-; lectr, Col Med, Univ Ill, 63-, Chicago Med Sch, Univ Health Sci, 70- & Stritch Sch Med, Loyola Univ, 71-; distinguished prof pediat, Rush Med Col, 74-, distinguished prof int med, 75-, distinguished prof path, 77-; lectr, Cook County Grad Sch Med, 77. *Mem:* Am Soc Clin Path; Am Asn Path & Bact; AMA; fel NY Acad Sci. *Res:* Cardiac pathology; pathology of congenital heart disease and of conduction system. *Mailing Add:* Congenital Heart Dis Res & Training Ctr Hektoen Inst Med Res Chicago IL 60612

LEV, OVADIA EZRA, b Baghdad, Iraq, Mar 28, 38; US citizen; m 62; c 3. CIVIL ENGINEERING, SYSTEM ENGINEERING. *Educ:* Israel Inst Technol, BS, 62; Columbia Univ, MS, 67, EngScDr(civil eng & eng mech), 71. *Prof Exp:* Proj engr design, A N Weidenfeld, Consult Engrs, Tel Aviv, 62-64; proj engr construct, Mekoroth, Water Co, Tel-Aviv, 64-66; field supvr Dead Sea earth dams, Von Hassel en de Konig, Nijmegen, Holland, 65-66; asst civil engr struct design, Bd Water Supply, City of New York, 70-71; proj engr, Weidlinger Assoc, New York, 71-73; asst prof civil eng, Univ Ill, Urbana-Champaign, 73-77; adv engr & scientist, Merritt Cases Inc, 77-81; STAFF ENGR, TRW INC, SAN BERNARDINO, CALIF, 81- *Concurrent Pos:* Mem fac, Calif State Univ, Fullerton, 78-80, Calif State Polytech Univ, Pomona, 80-; prin investr, NSF res grant, 78-80. *Mem:* Am Soc Civil Engrs; Sigma Xi. *Res:* Structural optimization; automated analysis; seismic design; system engineering. *Mailing Add:* 1624 Benita Marie Crest Redlands CA 92373

LEVAN, MARIJO O'CONNOR, b Detroit, Mich, Oct 27, 36; m 59; c 3. MATHEMATICS. *Educ:* Spring Hill Col, BS, 59; Univ Ala, MA, 61; Univ Fla, PhD(math), 64. *Prof Exp:* From instr to asst prof math, Univ Fla, 62-67; asst prof, Southeast Mo State Col, 67-69; assoc prof, 69-74, PROF MATH, EASTERN KY UNIV, 74-, ACTG CHMN, 78- *Mem:* Am Math Soc. *Res:* Number theory; partition functions and translated geometric progressions. *Mailing Add:* Dept of Math Eastern Ky Univ Richmond KY 40475

LEVAN, MARTIN DOUGLAS, JR, b Chattanooga, Tenn, Aug 30, 49; m 77; c 2. ADSORPTION, FLUID MECHANICS. *Educ:* Univ Va, BS, 71; Univ Calif, Berkeley, PhD(chem eng), 76. *Prof Exp:* Sr res engr, Amoco Prod Co, Standard Oil Co, 76-78; ASST PROF CHEM ENG, UNIV VA, 78- *Mem:* Am Inst Chem Engrs; Am Chem Soc. *Res:* Adsorption and fluid mechanics; fixed-bed adsorption; adsorption equilibria; low Reynolds number hydrodynamics; free surface flows. *Mailing Add:* Dept Chem Eng Univ Va Charlottesville VA 22901

LEVAN, NHAN, b Quang Yen, Vietnam, Nov 6, 36; m 60; c 2. SYSTEMS SCIENCE. *Educ:* Univ New Eng, Australia, BSc, 60; Univ New South Wales, MSc, 62; Monash Univ, Australia, PhD(elec eng), 66. *Prof Exp:* Lectr elec eng, Monash Univ, Australia, 65-66; asst prof syst sci, 67-73, assoc prof, 73-81, PROF SYST SCI, SCH ENG & APPL SCI, UNIV CALIF, LOS ANGELES, 81- *Mem:* AAAS; Inst Elec & Electronics Engrs; Sigma Xi. *Res:* System theory; circuit theory; distributed parameter systems; applied functional analysis and scattering systems; control theory and applications. *Mailing Add:* 4532 Boelter Hall Univ of Calif Los Angeles CA 90024

LEVAN, NORMAN E, b Cleveland, Ohio, Mar 17, 16; m 50. MEDICINE. *Educ:* Univ Southern Calif, AB, 36, MD, 40. *Hon Degrees:* MA, St John's Col, NMex, 74. *Prof Exp:* PROF DERMAT & CHMN DEPT, SCH MED, UNIV SOUTHERN CALIF, 61- *Mailing Add:* Dept of Dermat Sch of Med Univ of Southern Calif Los Angeles CA 90033

LEVAND, OSCAR, b Parnu, Estonia, Nov 3, 27; US citizen. ORGANIC CHEMISTRY. *Educ:* Miss State Col, BS, 54; Purdue Univ, MS, 58; Univ Hawaii, PhD(org chem), 63; Univ Minn, Mineapolis, MPH, 70. *Prof Exp:* Jr res chemist, Mead Johnson Co, Ind, 54-56; res chemist, Knoll Pharmaceut Co, NJ, 58-59; fel NIH, 62-63; res chemist, Dole Co, Hawaii, 63-68; consult, Air Pollution Control Prog, Govt of Guam, 70-74; asst prof, 74-80, ASSOC PROF CHEM, UNIV GUAM, 80- *Mem:* Am Chem Soc; Sigma Xi; Sci Res Soc NAm. *Res:* Air and water chemistry. *Mailing Add:* Dept of Chem Univ Guam Sta Mangilao 96913 Guam

LEVANDER, ORVILLE ARVID, b Waukegan, Ill, Apr 6, 40. NUTRITION. *Educ:* Cornell Univ, BA, 61; Univ Wis-Madison, MS, 63, PhD(biochem), 65. *Prof Exp:* Res fel biochem, Col Physicians & Surgeons, Columbia Univ, 65-66; res assoc, Sch Public Health, Harvard Univ, 66-67; res chemist, Food & Drug Admin, 67-69, RES CHEMIST, USDA HUMAN NUTRIT RES CTR, 69- *Concurrent Pos:* Mem, Nat Res Coun Comt Biol Effects Environ Pollutants, 74-77, mem subcomt nutrit, Safe Drinking Water Comt, 77-79; temp adv, Environ Health Criteria Doc on Selenium, WHO, 77- *Mem:* AAAS; Am Inst Nutrit; Am Chem Soc. *Res:* Toxicology and nutrition of selenium; pharmacology of heavy metals; trace mineral nutrition; vitamin E; drug metabolism; lead poisoning. *Mailing Add:* USDA Human Nutrit Res Ctr Beltsville MD 20705

LEVANDOWSKI, DONALD WILLIAM, b Stockett, Mont, Dec 20, 27; m 55; c 2. GEOLOGY. *Educ:* Mont Col Mineral Sci & Technol, BS, 50; Univ Mich, MS, 52, PhD(mineral), 56. *Hon Degrees:* Geol Engr, Mont Col Mineral Sci & Technol, 68. *Prof Exp:* Res geologist, Calif Res Corp, Standard Oil Co, Calif, 55-64, staff asst to mgr explor res, Chevron Res Co, 64-65, geophysicist, Western Opers, Inc, 65-67; assoc prof, 67-75, assoc head dept, 70-76, actg head dept, 76-78, PROF GEOSCI, PURDUE UNIV, 75-, HEAD DEPT, 78- *Mem:* Fel Geol Soc Am; AAAS; Am Asn Petrol Geologists; fel Geol Asn Can; Am Soc Photogrammetry. *Res:* Mineral deposits; remote sensing; igneous and metamorphic petrology; geophysics. *Mailing Add:* Dept Geosci Purdue Univ Lafayette IN 47907

LEVANDOWSKY, MICHAEL, b Knoxville, Tenn, Aug 15, 35. MARINE ECOLOGY, MATHEMATICAL BIOLOGY. *Educ:* Antioch Col, AB, 61; Columbia Univ, Ma, 65, PhD(biol), 70; NY Univ, MS, 73. *Prof Exp:* Instr biol, Bard Col, 67-69; instr, Bronx Community Col, 69-70; asst prof biol, Col, 70-71, RES ASSOC, HASKINS LABS, PACE UNIV, 70- *Concurrent Pos:* Nat Sci Found sci fac fel, Courant Inst Math Sci, NY Univ, 71-72; asst prof biol, York Col, NY, 73-74; mem citizens' adv comt on resource recovery for borough of Brooklyn, 81- *Mem:* Soc Protozool; Phycol Soc Am; Water Pollution Control Fedn; Am Soc Limnol & Oceanog; Am Soc Microbiol. *Res:* Mathematical models in ecology and evolution; microbial ecology; marine biology; gnotobiotic systems; sensory physiology and behavior of Protista; human evolution; resource recovery. *Mailing Add:* Haskins Labs Pace Univ 41 Park Row New York NY 10038

LEVANONI, MENACHEM, acoustics, fluid physics, see previous edition

LEVEAU, BARNEY FRANCIS, b Denver, Colo, Oct 2, 39; m 61; c 3. PHYSICAL MEDICINE. *Educ:* Univ Colo, BS, 61, MS, 66; Mayo Clin, RPT, 65; Pa State Univ, PhD(phys educ), 73. *Prof Exp:* Teacher math & sci, Colo Springs Sch Dist, 61-63; from asst prof to assoc prof phys educ, WChester State Col, 66-70; asst prof, 72-76, ASSOC PROF PHYS THER, SCH MED, UNIV NC, CHAPEL HILL, 76- *Mem:* Am Phys Ther Asn; Am Col Sports Med; Int Soc Biomech; Am Asn Health, Phys Educ & Recreation. *Res:* Biomechanics as it applies to physical therapy and physical education; sports medicine. *Mailing Add:* Div of Phys Ther Univ of NC Sch of Med Chapel Hill NC 27514

LEVEEN, HARRY HENRY, b Woodhaven, NY, Aug 10, 16; m; c 2. SURGERY. *Educ:* Princeton Univ, BA, 36; NY Univ, MD, 40; Univ Chicago, MS, 47; Am Bd Surg, dipl. *Prof Exp:* Instr & res assoc, Univ Chicago, 45-47; instr surg, Col Med, NY Univ, 47-50; assoc prof physiol, Sch Med, Loyola Univ, Ill, 50-55; assoc prof surg, Chicago Med Sch, 55-56; assoc prof surg, Col Med, State Univ NY, Downstate Med Ctr, 57-59, prof, 60-79; PROF SURG, MED UNIV SC, 79- *Concurrent Pos:* Assoc prof, NMex Mil Inst, 52-55; chief surgeon, Vet Admin Hosp, 57- *Mem:* Soc Exp Biol & Med; Am Physiol Soc; Int Soc Surg; fel Am Col Surg; NY Acad Med. *Res:* Surgical physiology; radiofrequency thermotherapy; cirrhosis. *Mailing Add:* Surg Dept Med Univ SC Charleston SC 29425

LEVEILLE, GILBERT ANTONIO, b Fall River, Mass, June 3, 34; m 81; c 3. NUTRITION, BIOCHEMISTRY. *Educ:* Univ Mass, BVA, 56; Rutgers Univ, MS, 58, PhD(nutrit), 60. *Prof Exp:* Biochemist, US Army Med Res & Nutrit Lab Colo, 60-66; assoc prof nutrit biochem, Univ Ill, Urbana, 66-69, prof, 69-71; prof food sci & human nutrit & chmn dept, Mich State Univ, 71-80; DIR NUTRIT & HEALTH SCI, GEN FOODS CORP, 80- *Honors & Awards:* Res Award, Poultry Sci Asn, 65; Mead Johnson Res Award, Am Inst Nutrit, 71. *Mem:* AAAS; Am Inst Nutrit; Am Soc Clin Nutrit; Am Chem Soc; Poultry Sci Asn. *Res:* Lipid metabolism; protein and amino acid nutrition and metabolism; atherosclerosis; obesity. *Mailing Add:* Dir Nutrit & Health Sci Gen Foods Corp 250 North St White Plains NY 10625

LEVELTON, B(RUCE) HARDING, b Bella Coola, BC, June 18, 25; m 50; c 3. CHEMICAL ENGINEERING. *Educ:* Univ BC, BASc, 47, MASc, 48; Tex A&M Univ, PhD(chem eng), 51. *Prof Exp:* Asst res engr, BC Res Coun, 51-54, assoc res engr, 54-58, res engr, 58-64, assoc head div appl chem, 64-66; PRIN, B H LEVELTON & ASSOCS LTD, 66- *Concurrent Pos:* Spec lectr, Univ BC, 57-65. *Mem:* Am Inst Chem Engrs; Nat Asn Corrosion Engrs; Air Pollution Control Asn; Chem Inst Can; Forest Prod Res Soc. *Res:* Treatment and beneficiation of industrial minerals; utilization of wood wastes by carbonization; corrosion of metals in chemical industry and in marine service; corrosion of copper in potable waters; environmental technology; solid waste disposal; toxic and hazardous waste disposal. *Mailing Add:* 6130 St Clair Pl Vancouver BC V6N 2A5 Can

LEVENBERG, MILTON IRWIN, b Chicago, Ill, Nov 5, 37; div; c 2. MASS SPECTROMETRY, COMPUTER SCIENCE. *Educ:* Ill Inst Technol, BS, 58; Calif Inst Technol, PhD(chem), 65. *Prof Exp:* SR CHEM PHYSICIST, ABBOTT LABS, 65- *Mem:* Am Chem Soc; Sigma Xi; Am Soc Mass Spectrometry. *Res:* Computer applications to instrumentation; instrumentation; electronics; mass spectrometry; nuclear magnetic resonance spectroscopy. *Mailing Add:* D-417 Abbott Labs North Chicago IL 60064

LEVENBOOK, LEO, b Kobe, Japan, Dec 29, 19; nat US; m 50; c 1. BIOCHEMISTRY. *Educ:* Univ London, BSc, 41; Cambridge Univ, PhD(biochem), 49. *Prof Exp:* Asst insect biochem, Cambridge Univ, 46-50; fel, Harvard Univ, 50-51; res assoc biochem genetics, Inst Cancer Res, Philadelphia, 51-54; asst prof biochem, Jefferson Med Col, 54-58; BIOCHEMIST, NAT INST ARTHRITIS, METAB & DIGESTIVE DIS, NIH, 58- *Concurrent Pos:* Lectr, Haverford Col, 53-54. *Mem:* Am Soc Biol Chemists. *Res:* Insect physiology and biochemistry. *Mailing Add:* Nat Inst Arthritis Diabetes & Digestive & Kidney Dis NIH Bethesda MD 20205

LEVENE, CYRIL, b Gateshead, Eng, May 27, 26; m 52; c 3. ANATOMY. *Educ:* Queen's Univ Belfast, MB, BCh & BAO, 48, MD, 60. *Prof Exp:* Demonstr anat, Queen's Univ Belfast, 51-52, asst lectr, 52-54; lectr human anat, Univ Col WIndies, 54-65, sr lectr anat, 65-67; assoc prof, Univ Western Ont, 67-69; assoc prof, 69-74, PROF ANAT, DIV MORPHOL SCI, FAC MED, UNIV CALGARY, 74- *Concurrent Pos:* WHO fel human genetics, 66. *Mem:* Am Asn Anat; Can Asn Anat; Anat Soc Gt Brit & Ireland. *Res:* Medical education. *Mailing Add:* Dept Anat Univ of Calgary Calgary AB T2N 1W4 Can

LEVENE, HOWARD, b New York, NY, Jan 17, 14. MATHEMATICAL STATISTICS. *Educ:* NY Univ, BA, 41; Columbia Univ, PhD(math statist), 47. *Prof Exp:* Exten lectr zool & math statist, 47-48, from instr to assoc prof math statist & biomet, 48-70, PROF MATH STATIST & GENETICS, COLUMBIA UNIV, 70-, CHMN, DEPT MATH STATIST, 76- *Mem:* AAAS; Am Math Soc; Soc Study Evolution; Biomet Soc; Soc Human Genetics. *Res:* Mathematical genetics; nonparametric tests; biometrics; population genetics and evolution. *Mailing Add:* Dept of Math Statist Columbia Univ New York NY 10027

LEVENE, JOHN REUBEN, b Hull, Eng, Dec 7, 29; m 59; c 2. OPTOMETRY, PHYSIOLOGICAL OPTICS. *Educ:* City Univ, London, dipl ophthalmic optics, 54; Ind Univ, MS, 62; Oxford Univ, PhD(biol sci), 66; Pa Col Optom, OD, 81. *Prof Exp:* Asst prof optom & physiol optics, Univ Houston, 62-63; lectr optom, City Univ, London, 65-67; from assoc prof to prof optom, Ind Univ, Bloomington, 67-75, chmn physiol optics prog & dir low vision clin, 70-75; DEAN FAC & PROF OPTOM, SOUTHERN COL OPTOM, MEMPHIS, TENN, 75- *Honors & Awards:* Obrig Labs Mem Award, 69. *Mem:* Am Acad Optom (vpres, Brit chap, 66); Brit Soc Hist Sci; Royal Micros Soc; Optom Hist Soc (vpres, 69); Am Asn Hist Med. *Res:* Pathological processes concerning vision; history of visual science. *Mailing Add:* Southern Col Optom 1245 Madison Ave Memphis TN 38104

LEVENE, MARTIN BARRACK, radiotherapy, deceased

LEVENE, RALPH ZALMAN, b Winnipeg, Man, May 17, 27; nat US; m 54; c 1. OPHTHALMOLOGY. *Educ:* Univ Man, MD, 49; NY Univ, DSc(ophthal), 57; Am Bd Ophthal, dipl, 55. *Prof Exp:* Intern, Winnipeg Gen Hosp, Can, 49-50, resident ophthal, 51-55; from instr to assoc prof, Med Sch, NY Univ, 55-73; PROF OPHTHAL, UNIV ALA, BIRMINGHAM, 73- *Mem:* AMA; Asn Res Vision & Ophthal; Am Acad Ophthal & Otolaryngol; NY Acad Med. *Res:* Clinical and basic science aspects of glaucoma. *Mailing Add:* 2018 Brookwood Med Ctr Dr Birmingham AL 35209

LEVENGOOD, WILLIAM CAMBURN, biophysics, see previous edition

LEVENSON, ALAN IRA, b Boston, Mass, July 25, 35; m 60; c 2. PSYCHIATRY. *Educ:* Harvard Univ, AB, 57, MD, 61, MPH, 65; Am Bd Psychiat & Neurol, Dipl, 67. *Prof Exp:* Intern, Univ Hosp, Ann Arbor, 61-62; resident in psychiat, Mass Ment Health Ctr, Boston, 62-65; staff psychiatrist, NIMH, 65-66, dir servs div, 67-69; PROF PSYCHIAT & HEAD DEPT, COL MED, UNIV ARIZ, 69- *Concurrent Pos:* Consult, Vet Admin, 69-; pres, Palo Verde Ment Health Serv, 71- *Mem:* Fel Am Pub Health Asn; fel Am Psychiat Asn; fel Am Col Psychiat; Group Advan Psychiat. *Res:* Organization and delivery of mental health services. *Mailing Add:* Dept of Psychiatry Ariz Health Sci Ctr Univ of Ariz Tucson AZ 85724

LEVENSON, HAROLD SAMUEL, b Allentown, Pa, July 12, 16; m 38; c 3. FOOD SCIENCE. *Educ:* Lehigh Univ, BSChE, 37, MS, 39, PhD(chem physics), 41. *Prof Exp:* Asst chem, Lehigh Univ, 37-41; res chemist, Gen Foods Corp, NJ, 41-46, chief chemist, Maxwell House Div, Calif, 46-51, res mgr, NJ, 51-64, dir coffee res, Tech Ctr, NY, 65-78; RETIRED. *Mem:* AAAS; Am Chem Soc; Inst Food Technol. *Res:* Antioxidants; food spoilage; kinetics of saponification; hydrocaffeic acid and esters as antioxidant for edible materials; coffee technology. *Mailing Add:* 5577 Inverness Ave Santa Rosa CA 95404

LEVENSON, JAMES BRUCE, b San Francisco, Calif, Aug 22, 44; m 68; c 2. PLANT ECOLOGY. *Educ:* Ind State Univ, Terre Haute, BS, 71, MA, 73; Univ Wis-Milwaukee, PhD(bot), 76. *Prof Exp:* Res assoc, Univ Wis-Milwaukee, 76-77; asst prof ecol, Saginaw Valley State Col, 77-79; ASST ENVIRON SCI, ARGONNE NAT LAB, 79- *Concurrent Pos:* Co-investr, NSF grant, 78-80. *Mem:* AAAS; Am Inst Biol Sci; Ecol Soc Am; Sigma Xi. *Res:* Interactions and resultant impacts of man-dominated systems on remnant ecosystem patches; identification, description and quantification of natural areas; application of ecological concepts to regional assessments of projected energy scenarios for federal agencies; development of natural resource data bases and spatial display systems for assessment of energy-related impacts to natural and man-dominated ecosystems. *Mailing Add:* Energy & Environ Systs Argonne Nat Lab Argonne IL 60439

LEVENSON, LEONARD L, b San Francisco, Calif, Sept 18, 28; m 57; c 3. PHYSICS. *Educ:* Univ Calif, Berkeley, AB, 52, MS, 55; Univ Paris, PhD(physics), 68. *Prof Exp:* Physicist, US Naval Ord Test Sta, 52; res engr, Univ Calif, Berkeley, 52-58, physicist, Lawrence Radiation Lab, 58-62; physicist, Nuclear Res Ctr, Saclay, France, 62-68; from asst prof to assoc prof physics, Univ Mo-Rolla, 68-76, prof, 76-81, dir grad ctr mat res, 75-81; CHMN, DEPT PHYSICS & ENERGY SCI, UNIV COLO, COLORADO SPRINGS, 81- *Concurrent Pos:* vis surgeon, Bronx Munic Hosp Ctr, 61- *Mem:* AAAS; Am Phys Soc. *Res:* Gas-surface interactions; thin films; surface physics. *Mailing Add:* Dept Physics & Energy Sci Univ Colo Colorado Springs CO 80907

LEVENSON, MARC DAVID, b Philadelphia, Pa, May 28, 45; m 71. LASERS, QUANTUM ELECTRONICS. *Educ:* Mass Inst Technol, BS, 67; Stanford Univ, MS, 68, PhD(physics), 72. *Prof Exp:* Res fel non-linear optics, Gordon McKay Lab, Harvard Univ, 71-74; asst prof physics, Univ Southern Calif, 74-77, assoc prof physics & elec eng, 77-79; MEM TECH STAFF, IBM RES LAB, 79- *Concurrent Pos:* Alfred P Sloan fel, 75-77; Joint Inst Lab Astrophys vis fel, Univ Colo, 78-79. *Honors & Awards:* Adolph Lomb Award, Optical Soc Am, 76. *Mem:* Am Phys Soc; Inst Elec & Electronics Engrs; Optical Soc Am. *Res:* Development and application of new techniques of laser spectroscopy to problems in atomic, molecular and condensed matter physics; application of optical and laser techniques to electronics manufacturing. *Mailing Add:* IBM Res Lab Cottle Rd San Jose CA 95123

LEVENSON, MILTON, b St Paul, Minn, Jan 4, 23; m 50; c 5. NUCLEAR REACTORS. *Educ:* Univ Minn, BChE, 43. *Prof Exp:* Jr engr, Houdaille-Hershey Corp, 44; asst engr, Oak Ridge Nat Labs, 44-48; from assoc engr to assoc dir energy & environ, Argonne Nat Lab, 48-73; DIR NUCLEAR POWER, ELEC POWER RES INST, 73- *Honors & Awards:* Robert E Wilson Award, Am Inst Chem Engrs, 75. *Mem:* Nat Acad Eng; Am Inst Chem Engrs; fel Am Nuclear Soc. *Res:* Water reactor technology; fuel cycle technology; breeder reactor development. *Mailing Add:* 3412 Hillview Palo Alto CA 94304

LEVENSON, MORRIS E, b New York, NY, Nov 13, 14; m 43. MATHEMATICS. *Educ:* NY Univ, PhD(math), 48. *Prof Exp:* Asst, Duke Univ, 37-38; instr math, NY Univ, 43-44; mathematician, David Taylor Model Basin, 44-46; instr math, Cooper Union, 46-49; from instr to assoc prof, 49-71, PROF MATH, BROOKLYN COL, 71- *Mem:* Am Math Soc; Math Asn Am. *Res:* Nonlinear vibrations. *Mailing Add:* Dept of Math Brooklyn Col Brooklyn NY 11210

LEVENSON, STANLEY MELVIN, b Dorchester, Mass, May 25, 16; m 42; c 2. SURGERY. *Educ:* Harvard Univ, AB, 37, MD, 41; Am Bd Nutrit, dipl, 52; Am Bd Surg, dipl, 57. *Prof Exp:* Surg house officer, Beth Israel Hosp, Boston, Mass, 41-42; resident burn serv & res assoc surg, Boston City Hosp, 42-43; surg scientist, Med Nutrit Lab, Univ Chicago, 47-49; from asst resident to sr asst resident surg, Med Col Va, 50-52; chief dept surg metab & physiol, Walter Reed Army Inst Res, 56-61, from assoc dir to dir dept germfree res, 56-61, dir div basic surg res, 61; PROF SURG, ALBERT EINSTEIN COL MED, 61-, DEP DIR RES SURG, COL MED, 67- *Concurrent Pos:* Res fel med, Thorndike Mem Lab, Harvard Univ, 44-47; NIH res career award, 62-; chmn subcomt burns & radiation injury, Food & Nutrit Bd, Nat Res Coun, 49-50, comt on trauma, 56-; dir surg metab lab & clin assoc prof, Georgetown Univ, 59-61; res assoc physiol, Sch Pub Health, Harvard Univ, 41-; consult, Walter Reed Army Inst Res, 61-63; Am Surg Asn rep, Nat Res Coun-Nat Acad Sci, 71-75. *Honors & Awards:* Harvey Allen Distinguished Serv Medal, Am Burn Asn, 76. *Mem:* AAAS; AMA; Am Inst Nutrit; Am Soc Clin Nutrit; Am Col Surgeons. *Res:* Metabolic and clinical response to trauma; wound healing; germfree life; infection; burns. *Mailing Add:* Dept of Surg Albert Einstein Col of Med Bronx NY 10461

LEVENSPIEL, OCTAVE, b Shanghai, China, July 6, 26; nat US; m 52; c 3. CHEMICAL ENGINEERING. *Educ:* Univ Calif, BS, 47; Ore State Col, MS, 49, PhD(chem eng), 52. *Prof Exp:* Jr res engr, Inst Eng Res, Univ Calif, 51-52; asst prof chem eng, Ore State Col, 52-54; asst & assoc prof, Bucknell Univ, 54-58; assoc & prof, Ill Inst Technol, 58-68; PROF CHEM ENG, ORE STATE UNIV, 68- *Concurrent Pos:* NSF sr fel, Cambridge Univ, 63-64, Fulbright fel, 68-69. *Honors & Awards:* Lectureship Award, Chem Eng Div, Am Soc Eng Educ, 66; Wilhelm Award, Am Inst Chem Engrs, 79. *Mem:* Am Chem Soc; Am Inst Chem Engrs. *Res:* Chemical reactor design; fluidization. *Mailing Add:* Dept of Chem Eng Ore State Univ Corvallis OR 97331

LEVENSTEIN, IRVING, b Fair Lawn, NJ, Aug 14, 12; m 37; c 2. ENDOCRINOLOGY, TOXICOLOGY. *Educ:* NY Univ, BA, 34, MSc, 36, PhD, 38. *Prof Exp:* Instr biol sci, NY Univ, 36-40; PRES & DIR, LEBERCO LABS, 42- *Concurrent Pos:* Res fel, Nat Comt Maternal Health, 38-42. *Mem:* Am Soc Zoologists; Am Asn Anatomists; Am Pharmaceut Asn; Soc Toxicol; Am Chem Soc. *Res:* Hormones; histology; anatomy. *Mailing Add:* Leberco Labs 123 Hawthorne St Roselle Park NJ 07204

LEVENTHAL, BRIGID GRAY, b London, Eng, Aug 31, 35; US citizen; m 62; c 4. PEDIATRICS, ONCOLOGY. *Educ:* Univ Calif, Los Angeles, BA, 55; Harvard Univ, MD, 60. *Prof Exp:* Sr investr leukemia serv, Med Br, Nat Cancer Inst, 65-73, head chemoimmunother sect, Pediat Oncol Br, 73-76; CHIEF PEDIAT ONCOL DIV, JOHNS HOPKINS HOSP, 76- *Concurrent Pos:* Fel pediat, Harvard Univ, 60-62; fel, Boston Univ, 62-63; fel med, Tufts Univ, 63-64; fel hemat, Nat Cancer Inst, 64; assoc prof oncol & pediat, Johns Hopkins Univ, 76- *Mem:* Soc Pediat Res; Am Soc Hemat; Am Asn Cancer Res; Am Soc Clin Oncol; Am Soc Clin Invest. *Res:* Pediatric hematology and oncology. *Mailing Add:* Oncol Ctr Rm 3-121 Nat Cancer Inst Baltimore MD 20014

LEVENTHAL, CARL M, b New York, NY, July 28, 33; m 62; c 4. NEUROLOGY, NEUROPATHOLOGY. *Educ:* Harvard Univ, AB, 54; Univ Rochester, MD, 59. *Prof Exp:* Intern med, Johns Hopkins Hosp, 59-60, asst res physician, 60-61; asst resident neurol, Mass Gen Hosp, 61-62, resident, 63-64; assoc neuropathologist, Nat Neurol Dis & Blindness, 64-66, neurologist, Nat Cancer Inst, 66-68, asst to dep dir sci, NIH, 68-74, actg dep dir sci, 73-74; dep dir, Bur Drugs, Food & Drug Admin, 74-77; dep dir, Nat Inst Arthritis, Metab & Digest Dis, 77-81. *Concurrent Pos:* Fel, Johns Hopkins Univ, 59-61; fel, Harvard Univ, 61-64, clin & res fel neuropath, 62-63; instr, Georgetown Univ, 64-66, asst prof, 67-74. *Mem:* Am Acad Neurol; Am Asn Neuropath. *Res:* Government research administration; clinical neuropathology. *Mailing Add:* Nat Inst Arthritis Metab & Diag Dis Bethesda MD 20205

LEVENTHAL, EDWIN ALFRED, b Brooklyn, NY, Jan 26, 34; m 56; c 2. SOLID STATE PHYSICS. *Educ:* Cornell Univ, BEng Phys, 56; Polytech Inst Brooklyn, MS, 59; NY Univ, PhD(physics), 63. *Prof Exp:* Sr physicist, Philips Labs Div, NAm Philips Co, 61-70; ed & publ, Med Instrument Reports, 70-74; DIR SYSTS PLANNING, FRIESEN INT, 74- *Mem:* Am Phys Soc; Asn Advan Med Instrumentation; NY Acad Sci. *Res:* Materials handling and information processing in hospital management and design; medical equipment planning. *Mailing Add:* 12710 Saddlebrook Dr Silver Spring MO 20906

LEVENTHAL, HOWARD L(EONARD), b New York, NY, 1917; m 42; c 3. CHEMICAL ENGINEERING. *Educ:* Univ Ill, BS, 40, MS, 42. *Prof Exp:* Res chem engr, Visking Corp, 44, tech dir, Little Rock Fabrics Div, 49-52, gen mgr, 52-56, admin asst to mgr, Tech Div, Visking Co Div, Union Carbide Corp, 56-59, asst dir res & develop planning, 59-62, mgr qual eval, 62-64; tech dir, VisQueen Div, Ethyl Corp, La, 65-67, tech mgr polyethylene resin, 67-69, gen mgr converted film prod, 67-71; gen mgr, Plastics Div, Hudson Pulp & Paper Corp, 71-72, vpres technol, 73-79; pres, Alpha Plastics Corp, 72-79; pres, Adams Indust, 79-81; SR VPRES, BANCROFT BAG, INC, 81- *Mem:* Am Chem Soc; Am Soc Qual Control; Am Asn Textile Chem & Colorists; Am Inst Chem Engrs. *Res:* Continuous structures, particularly nonwoven fabrics and natural and synthetic films; operational control and methods; general management and planning. *Mailing Add:* 3811 Scenic Dr Monroe LA 71201

LEVENTHAL, JACOB J, b Brooklyn, NY, Dec 18, 37; m 62. ATOMIC PHYSICS, MOLECULAR PHYSICS. *Educ:* Wash Univ, BS, 60; Univ Fla, PhD(physics), 65. *Prof Exp:* Res assoc physics & chem, Brookhaven Nat Lab, 65-67, assoc chemist, 67-68; from asst prof to assoc prof, 68-77, PROF PHYSICS, UNIV MO-ST LOUIS, 77- *Mem:* Am Phys Soc. *Res:* Interactions of positive ions with neutral molecules; spectroscopic observations of excited state production in low energy atomic and molecular collision processes. *Mailing Add:* Dept of Physics Univ of Mo St Louis MO 63121

LEVENTHAL, LEON, b New York, NY, Jan 25, 22; m 52; c 4. RADIOCHEMISTRY, CHEMICAL ENGINEERING. *Educ:* Univ Calif, BS, 42; Va Polytech Inst, BS, 44; Univ Calif, Los Angeles, MS, 48. *Prof Exp:* Control chemist, Richfield Oil Corp, Calif, 42-43; res chemist, Metall Lab, Chicago, 44-45; jr chem engr, Oak Ridge Nat Lab, 45; chem engr, Atomic Bomb Lab, Los Alamos Sci Lab, 45-46; res chemist, Radiol Defense Lab, San Francisco Naval Shipyard, 47-49; res radiochemist, Tracerlab, Inc, 49-50, sr chemist, 50-57, dept head, 57-59, div mgr tech serv, 59-67, vpres, 75-81, gen mgr, LFE Environ Anal Labs, Div LFE Corp, 67-, TECH DIR, EAL CORP, 81- *Mem:* Am Chem Soc; Am Health Phys Soc; fel Am Nuclear Soc; fel Am Inst Chem. *Res:* Nuclear, plutonium and semimicro chemistry; plutonium metallurgy; complex compounds of zinc with zinc 65; general radiochemistry of radiological defense and radioactive waste problems; fission products; environmental and fallout studies; particle analysis; mass spectrometry of plutonium and uranium; applications of radioisotopes to science and industry; transuranium nuclides in the environment; decontomination and decommissioning. *Mailing Add:* EAL Corp 2030 Wright Ave Richmond CA 94804

LEVENTHAL, MARVIN, b New York, NY, Dec 4, 37; m 61. ASTROPHYSICS, ATOMIC PHYSICS. *Educ:* City Col New York, BS, 58; Brown Univ, PhD(physics), 64. *Prof Exp:* Res assoc physics, Yale Univ, 63-67, asst prof, 67-68; MEM TECH STAFF, BELL LABS, 68- *Mem:* Am Phys Soc; Am Astronom Soc. *Res:* Precision measurements of atomic physics quantities which have bearing on quantum electrodynamics; experimental and theoretical gamma ray astronomy. *Mailing Add:* Bell Labs Rm 1E-349 Murray Hill NJ 07974

LEVEQUE, THEODORE FRANCOIS, b Lewiston, Maine, June 30, 21; m 47; c 2. ANATOMY. *Educ:* Univ Denver, BA, 49, MS, 50; Univ Colo, PhD(anat), 54. *Prof Exp:* Instr histol, Dept Anat, McGill Univ, 54-55; from asst prof to prof anat, Sch Med, Univ Md, 55-68; chmn dept, 68-76, PROF ANAT, FAC MED, UNIV SHERBROOKE, 68- *Concurrent Pos:* Secy fac med, Univ Sherbrooke, 71- *Mem:* AAAS; Can Asn Anatomists (pres, 77-79); Am Asn Anat. *Res:* Endocrinology; neuroendocrinology; neurosecretion and connective tissue; wound healing. *Mailing Add:* Dept of Anat Fac of Med Univ of Sherbrooke Sherbrooke PQ J1K 2R1 Can

LEVEQUE, WILLIAM JUDSON, b Boulder, Colo, Aug 9, 23; m 49, 70; c 1. MATHEMATICS. *Educ:* Univ Colo, BA, 44; Cornell Univ, MA, 45, PhD(math), 47. *Prof Exp:* Benjamin Peirce instr math, Harvard Univ, 47-49; from instr to prof, Univ Mich, Ann Arbor, 49-70, chmn dept, 67-70; prof math, Claremont Grad Sch, 70-77; EXEC DIR, AM MATH SOC, 77- *Concurrent Pos:* Fulbright res scholar, 51-52; Sloan res fel, 57-60; exec ed, Math Rev, 65-66; chmn, Conf Bd Math Sci, 73-74. *Mem:* Am Math Soc; Math Asn Am; fel AAAS. *Res:* Theory of numbers. *Mailing Add:* Am Math Soc Box 6248 Providence RI 02940

LEVER, ALFRED B P, b London, Eng, Feb 21, 36; m 63; c 3. INORGANIC CHEMISTRY. *Educ:* Univ London, BSc & ARCS, 57, dipl, Imp Col & PhD(chem), 60. *Prof Exp:* Hon res asst, Univ Col, London, 60-61, hon res assoc, 61-62; lectr chem, Inst Sci & Tech, Univ Manchester, 62-66; vis lectr, Ohio State Univ, 67; assoc prof, 67-72, PROF CHEM, YORK UNIV, 72- *Concurrent Pos:* Ed, Coord Chem Rev, 66-; prog chmn, XIVth Int Conf Coord Chem, Toronto, 72; vis prof, Calif Inst Technol, 76-77 & Sydney Univ, 78. *Mem:* Am Chem Soc; Chem Inst Can; Royal Soc Chem. *Res:* Inorganic electronic spectroscopy; solar energy conversion. *Mailing Add:* Dept Chem York Univ Downsview ON M3J 1P3 Can

LEVER, CYRIL, JR, b Abington, Pa, June 5, 29; m 61; c 2. ORGANIC CHEMISTRY. *Educ:* Pa Mil Col, BS, 53. *Prof Exp:* Asst treas & asst dir res, 53-57, PRES & DIR RES, C LEVER CO, INC, 57- *Mem:* Soc Am Mil Eng. *Res:* Dyes and colors for paper. *Mailing Add:* C Lever Co Inc The Lever Bldg 736 Dunks Ferry Rd Cornwells Heights PA 19020

LEVER, REGINALD FRANK, b Birmingham, Eng, July 5, 30; wid; c 1. MATERIALS SCIENCE. *Educ:* Oxford Univ, BA, 51, MA, 54. *Prof Exp:* Sci officer, Serv Electronics Res Lab, Baldock, Eng, 51-57; sr sci officer, UK Atomic Energy Agency Indust Group, Lancashire, 57-58; staff mem, Res Div, Philco Corp, 58-60; staff mem, Thomas J Watson Res Ctr, 60-70, STAFF MEM COMPONENTS DIV, IBM CORP, 70- *Mem:* Am Phys Soc. *Res:* Growth of crystals from vapor by chemical deposition; gaseous diffusion; semiconductors; surfaces; silicon device processing; material analysis by MeV ion backscattering; plasma etching; process modeling. *Mailing Add:* IBM 9TD D62G Bldg 300-45A Route 52 Hopewell Junction NY 12533

LEVER, WILLIAM EDWIN, b Skewen, Wales, Dec 21, 35; US citizen; m 64; c 2. STATISTICS. *Educ:* Col Steubenville, BA, 58; Fla State Univ, MS, 63, PhD(statist), 68. *Prof Exp:* STATISTICIAN, NUCLEAR DIV, UNION CARBIDE CORP, 66- *Mem:* Am Statist Asn; Biometric Soc. *Res:* Risk analysis associated with the fuel cycle of nuclear and coal-fired power plants. *Mailing Add:* Math & Statist Res Dept Union Carbide Corp PO Box Y Oak Ridge TN 37830

LEVERANT, GERALD ROBERT, b Hartford, Conn, June 18, 40; m 62; c 2. METALLURGY. *Educ:* Rensselaer Polytech Inst, BMetE, 62, PhD(metall), 66. *Prof Exp:* Sr res scientist, Res Lab, United Aircraft Corp, 66, res assoc, Mat Eng & Res Lab, Pratt & Whitney Aircraft Div, 66-68, sr res assoc, 68-74, group leader, 74-77; mgr metall, 77-81, ASST DIR MAT SCI, SOUTHWEST RES INST, 81- *Honors & Awards:* Henry Marion Howe Gold Medal, Am Soc Metals, 70. *Mem:* Am Soc Metals; Am Inst Mining, Metall & Petrol Engrs. *Res:* Relation of metallurgical structure to mechanical properties. *Mailing Add:* Southwest Res Inst PO Drawer 28510 San Antonio TX 78284

LEVERE, RICHARD DAVID, b Brooklyn, NY, Dec 13, 31; m 78; c 3. INTERNAL MEDICINE, HEMATOLOGY. *Educ:* State Univ NY, MD, 56. *Prof Exp:* From intern to asst resident med, Bellevue Hosp, 56-58; resident, Kings County Hosp, 60-61; instr med, State Univ NY, 62-63; res assoc biochem, Rockefeller Inst, 62-63, asst prof, 64-65; from asst prof to prof med, State Univ NY Downstate Med Ctr, 65-77, chief hemat sect, 70-77; PROF MED & CHMN DEPT, NEW YORK MED COL, 77- *Concurrent Pos:* Fel hemat, State Univ NY, 61-62; NIH grant, 65-82; adj prof, Rockefeller Univ, 73-; dir med serv, Westchester County Med Ctr, 78- *Mem:* AAAS; Am Soc Clin Invest; Am Fedn Clin Res; Am Soc Hemat; Am Col Physicians. *Res:* Control mechanisms in heme and porphyrin synthesis; metabolism of normal and abnormal hemoglobins; diseases of porphyrin metabolism. *Mailing Add:* Dept of Med New York Med Col Valhalla NY 10595

LEVERENZ, HUMBOLDT WALTER, b Chicago, Ill, July 11, 09; m 40; c 4. SOLID STATE SCIENCE. *Educ:* Stanford Univ, AB, 30. *Prof Exp:* Res chemico-physicist, Radio Corp Am, 31-54, dir phys & chem lab, 54-57, asst dir res, 57-59, dir, 59-61, assoc dir, RCA Labs, 61-66, staff vpres, Res & Bus Eval, 66-68, staff vpres & chmn educ aid comt, RCA Corp, 68-74; RETIRED. *Concurrent Pos:* With advan mgt prog, Bus Sch, Harvard Univ, 58; mem, Mat Adv Bd, Nat Acad Sci, 64-68; mem conf comt, Nat Conf Admin Res, 64-68. *Honors & Awards:* Brown Medal, Franklin Inst, 54. *Mem:* Nat Acad Eng; fel AAAS; Am Chem Soc; fel Am Phys Soc; fel Inst Elec & Electronics Eng. *Res:* Syntheses and applications of solids used in electronics; phosphors; secondary-emitters; photoconductors; semiconductors; nonmetallic magnetic materials; scotophors; crystals used in electronics. *Mailing Add:* 22 Gulf Shore Blvd N Apt K4 Naples FL 33940

LEVERETT, DENNIS HUGH, b Cleveland, Ohio, June 22, 31; m; c 7. DENTISTRY, CLINICAL RESEARCH. *Educ:* Ohio State Univ, DDS, 56; Harvard Univ, MPH, 68; Am Bd Dent Pub Health, dipl. *Prof Exp:* Intern dent, USPHS, 56-57, dent officer, 57-60; pvt pract gen dent, 60-66; pub health dentist, NMex Dept Pub Health, 66-67; res fel ecol dent, Sch Dent Med, Harvard Univ, 67-69; resident dent pub health, Mass Dept Pub Health & Sch Dent Med, Harvard Univ, 68-69; exec dir, Ctr Community Dent Health, Portland, Maine, 69-73; CHMN DEPT COMMUNITY DENT, EASTMAN DENT CTR, 73- *Concurrent Pos:* Consult, Bio-Dynamics, Inc, Mass, 68, Maine Dept Health & Welfare, 69-70, Mass Dept Pub Health, 69, Southern Maine Comp Health Asn, Inc, 70-73, Genesee Valley Group Health Asn, 73, Rochester Regional Med Prog, 76-77 & Health Econ Group, Inc, 78-; lectr dent ecol, Sch Dent Med, Harvard Univ, 69-73; clin instr social dent, Sch Dent Med, Tufts Univ, 70-73; clin assoc prof prev med & community health & clin dent, Sch Med & Dent, Univ Rochester, 73-; adj prof dent hyg, Monroe Community Col, 73-; dir dent care progs, Portland, Maine Model Cities, 69-73, chmn health task force, 70-72; mem prof adv comt, Portland City Health Dir, 69-73; mem med adv comt, Southern Maine Comprehensive Health Asn, 69-73; mem attend staff, Maine Med Ctr, Portland; mem courtesy staff, Mercy Hosp, Portland, Maine, 70-73; mem bd dirs, Smilemobile, Monroe County, NY, 73-77; mem dent hyg adv comt, Monroe Community Col, 73-; dent dir, Monroe County Health Dept, 73-; mem bd dir, Westside Health Serv, Rochester, NY, 75-, chmn prog comt, 76-; co-prin investr, USPHS res grants, 74-77 & 78-81; prin investr, Nat Inst Dent Res grants, 75-79 & 77-81; lectr dent, var hosps & orgn, 73-81. *Mem:* Am Asn Pub Health Dentists; Int Asn Dental Res; Am Asn Dental Res; Am Pub Health Asn; AAAS. *Res:* Clinical trials of therapeutic and preventive agents, including adhesive sealants and fluorides; evaluation of third party payment mechanisms, dental care delivery systems and post-doctoral dental education. *Mailing Add:* Dept of Community Dent 625 Elmwood Ave Rochester NY 14620

LEVERETT, GLENN FRED, chemical engineering, see previous edition

LEVERETT, M(ILES) C(ORRINGTON), b Danville, Ill, Dec 18, 10; m 38. NUCLEAR ENGINEERING. *Educ:* Kans State Col, BS, 31; Univ Okla, MSE, 32; Mass Inst Technol, ScD(chem eng), 38. *Prof Exp:* Asst chemist, Marathon Paper Mills Co, Wis, 32-33 & Phillips Petrol Co, Okla, 33-35; sr res engr, Humble Oil & Ref Co, Tex, 38-42; assoc div dir, Metall Lab, Univ Chicago, 42-43, div dir, 43-48; res assoc, Humble Oil & Ref Co, 48-49; tech dir nuclear engine propulsion aircraft proj, Fairchild Eng & Airplane Corp, 49-51; mgr eng, Aircraft Nuclear Propulsion Dept, Gen Elec Co, 51-56 & Develop Labs, 56-61, mgr res & eng, Nuclear Reactor Dept, 61-67, safety & qual mgr, Nuclear Energy Div, 67-71 & Nuclear Safety & Boiling Water Reactor Qual Assurance, 71-76; NUCLEAR CONSULT ENGR, 76- *Concurrent Pos:* Div dir, Monsanto Chem Co, 43-48 & Carbide & Chem Co, Tenn, 43-48; leader US deleg, Int Standardization Orgn Meeting Reactor Safety Stand, 58, 60; mem res adv comt nuclear energy processes, NASA, 59-60. *Mem:* Am Phys Soc; fel Am Nuclear Soc (vpres, 59-60, pres, 60-61); Am Inst Mining, Metall & Petrol Engrs; Am Inst Chem Engrs; assoc fel Am Inst Aeronaut & Astronaut. *Res:* Petroleum emulsions; flow of fluids in porous solids; nuclear reactors; reactor materials; reactor safety; nuclear physics. *Mailing Add:* 15233 Via Pinto Monte Sereno CA 95030

LEVERETT, SIDNEY DUNCAN, JR, b Houston, Tex, Nov 27, 25; m 48; c 2. PHYSIOLOGY. *Educ:* Agr & Mech Col Tex, BS, 49; Ohio State Univ, MS, 55, PhD, 60. *Prof Exp:* Chief acceleration sect, Aeromed Lab, Wright Air Develop Ctr, 55-58; aviation physiologist, 60-63, CHIEF BIODYN BR, US AIR FORCE SCH AEROSPACE MED, 63- *Concurrent Pos:* Consult, Manned Space Ctr, NASA, Houston, Tex, 65- *Honors & Awards:* Achievement Award, US Air Force Sch Aerospace Med, 62; Eric Liljencrantz

Award, 70; Meritorious Civilian Serv Award, Dept of the Air Force, 72; Award for Excellence, Life Sci & Biomed Eng Br, 75. *Mem:* Fel Acrospace Med Asn; Int Acad Aviation & Space Med. *Res:* Cardiovascular physiology, particularly hemodynamics; aviation medicine, particularly acceleration stress. *Mailing Add:* 103 Encino Blanco San Antonio TX 78232

LEVERING, DALE FRANKLIN, JR, botany, plant ecology, see previous edition

LEVERTON, WALTER FREDERICK, b Imperial, Sask, Dec 24, 22; m 48; c 2. SOLID STATE PHYSICS, MATERIALS SCIENCE. *Educ:* Univ Sask, BS, 46, MS, 48; Univ BC, PhD(physics), 50. *Prof Exp:* Asst prof elec eng, Univ Minn, 50-51; asst div mgr semiconductors, Res Div, Raytheon Co, 51-60; group vpres develop, Aerospace Corp, 60-79; CONSULT, 79- *Concurrent Pos:* Mem, Defence Commun Agency Sci Adv Group, 74-79. *Mem:* Am Phys Soc; fel Inst Elec & Electronics Engrs. *Res:* Cathode materials; semiconductors; space science. *Mailing Add:* 2350 E El Segundo Blvd El Segundo CA 90245

LEVESQUE, ALLEN HENRY, b Jewett City, Conn, Nov 1, 36; m 60; c 3. COMMUNICATION THEORY, ELECTRONICS ENGINEERING. *Educ:* Worcester Polytech Inst, BSEE, 59; Yale Univ, MEng, 60, DEng, 65. *Prof Exp:* Sr engr commun, Sylvania Appl Res Lab, 60-62; res asst elec eng, Sch Eng, Yale Univ, 63-65; eng spcialist commun res & develop, Sylvania Appl Res Lab, 65-66, eng specialist, Sylvania Commun Systs Labs, 66-69, sr mem tech staff, GTE Labs, Inc, 69-74, sr eng specialist, Eastern Div, 74-81, SR ENG SPECIALIST COMMUN RES & DEVELOP, COMMUN SYSTS DIV, GTE SYLVANIA INC, 81- *Concurrent Pos:* Adj prof elec eng, Northeastern Univ, 78- *Mem:* Sr mem Inst Elec & Electronics Engrs; assoc mem Sigma Xi. *Res:* Information theory; algebraic coding theory; communication systems development; computer communications; digital signal processing. *Mailing Add:* Commun Systs Div GTE Sylvania Inc 77 A St Needham Heights MA 02194

LEVESQUE, CHARLES LOUIS, b Manchester, NH, Feb 16, 13; m 38; c 3. ORGANIC CHEMISTRY. *Educ:* Dartmouth Col, AB, 34, AM, 36; Univ Ill, PhD(org chem), 39. *Prof Exp:* Instr anal chem, Dartmouth Col, 34-36; sr chemist, Resinous Prod & Chem Co, 39-41, group leader, 41-45, lab head, 45-48; res supvr, Rohm & Haas Co, 48-69, asst dir res, 69-71; prof appl sci & dir, Eve Sch, Ursinus Col, 71-79, dean continuing educ, 79-81; RETIRED. *Mem:* Am Chem Soc. *Res:* Structures of vinyl polymers; polyester resins and raw materials; new organic synthesis; surface active agents; pharmaceuticals. *Mailing Add:* 965 Dale Rd Meadowbrook PA 19046

LEVESQUE, RENE J A, b St-Alexis, Que, Oct 30, 26; m 56; c 3. NUCLEAR PHYSICS. *Educ:* Sir George Williams Col, BSc, 52; Northwestern Univ, PhD(physics), 57. *Prof Exp:* Res assoc physics, Univ Md, 57-59; from asst prof to assoc prof, 59-67, dir, Lab Nuclear Physics, 65-69, dir, Dept Physics, 68-73, vdean res fac arts & sci, 73-75, dean fac arts & sci, 75-78, PROF PHYSICS, UNIV MONTREAL, 67-, VPRES RES, 78- *Concurrent Pos:* Asst ed, Can J Physics, 73-75; vpres, Can-France-Hawaii Telescope Corp, 79, pres, 80; pres, Asn Sci, Eng & Techol Community Can, 80. *Honors & Awards:* Queen Elizabeth Jubilee Medal. *Mem:* Can Asn Physicists (pres, 76-77); Natural Sci & Eng Res Coun Can (vpres, 81). *Res:* Nuclear spectroscopy; nuclear reactions at low energy. *Mailing Add:* Off of the VPres Univ of Montreal PO Box 6128 Montreal PQ H3C 3J7 Can

LEVETIN-AVERY, ESTELLE, b Boston, Mass, Mar 24, 45; m 74; c 2. MYCOLOGY, BOTANY. *Educ:* State Col Boston, BS, 66; Univ RI, PhD(bot & mycol), 71. *Prof Exp:* Lab instr & teaching asst bot, Univ RI, 69-71, asst prof, Exten Div, 71-72, fel res assoc, Dept Plant Path, 71-72; asst prof physiol, Mt St Joseph Col, 72; asst prof, 72-78, ASSOC PROF BOT, UNIV TULSA, 78- *Concurrent Pos:* Res grant, Univ Tulsa, 74, 80 & 81; consult, Joint Res Prog, Allergy Clin Tulsa, Inc, 75-76. *Mem:* Mycol Soc Am; Bot Soc Am; Am Inst Biol Sci; AAAS; Brit Mycol Soc. *Res:* Physiology and development of fungi; the distribution of fleshy. fungi in Oklahoma; distribution of air-borne fungi and pollen in Tulsa County. *Mailing Add:* Fac of Nat Sci Univ of Tulsa 600 S College Tulsa OK 74104

LEVEY, GERALD SAUL, b Jersey City, NJ, Jan 9, 37; m 61; c 2. INTERNAL MEDICINE, ENDOCRINOLOGY. *Educ:* Cornell Univ, AB, 57; NJ Col Med, MD, 61. *Prof Exp:* Intern med, Jersey City Med Ctr, 61-62, resident, 62-63; resident, Mass Gen Hosp, Boston, 65-66; clin assoc endocrinol, Nat Inst Arthritis & Metab Dis, 66-68; sr investr endocrinol, Nat Heart & Lung Inst, 69-70; assoc prof, 70-73, PROF MED, SCH MED, UNIV MIAMI, 73- *Concurrent Pos:* NIH fel biochem, Med Sch, Harvard Univ, 63-65; consult med, Vet Admin Hosp, Miami, Fla, 70-; investr, Howard Hughes Med Inst, 71- *Mem:* Am Soc Clin Invest; Am Col Physicians; Am Thyroid Asn; Am Fedn Clin Res; Soc Exp Biol & Med. *Res:* Mechanism of hormone action; cyclic adenosine monophosphate. *Mailing Add:* Dept of Med Sch of Med Univ of Miami PO Box 016960 Miami FL 33101

LEVEY, GERRIT, b Friesland, Wis, Jan 9, 24; m 52; c 3. PHYSICAL CHEMISTRY. *Educ:* Hope Col, BA, 46; Univ Wis, PhD(chem), 49. *Prof Exp:* Assoc prof, 49-58, PROF CHEM, BEREA COL, 58-, DEPT CHMN, 58- *Concurrent Pos:* NSF sci fac fel, Mass Inst Technol, 57-58 & Univ Leeds, 65-66; fac res partic, Argonne Nat Lab, 73-74; res assoc, Radiation Lab, Univ Notre Dame, 81-82. *Mem:* Am Chem Soc; The Chem Soc. *Res:* Chemical reactions resulting from nuclear energy activation; use of radiotracers in reaction kinetics studies; radiation chemistry of inorganic peroxides. *Mailing Add:* Dept of Chem Berea Col Berea KY 40403

LEVEY, HAROLD ABRAM, b Boston, Mass, Aug 14, 24; m 59; c 2. ENDOCRINE PHYSIOLOGY. *Educ:* Harvard Univ, AB, 47; Univ Calif, Los Angeles, PhD(zool), 53. *Prof Exp:* Jr & asst res physiol chemist, Univ Calif, Los Angeles, 53-56; from instr to asst prof, 56-64, ASSOC PROF PHYSIOL, COL MED, STATE UNIV NY DOWNSTATE MED CTR, 64- *Concurrent Pos:* USPHS fel, 53-; China Med Bd vis prof physiol, Fac Med, Univ Singapore, 66-67. *Mem:* AAAS; Am Physiol Soc; Endocrine Soc; NY Acad Sci; Harvey Soc. *Res:* Pituitary chemistry and physiology; pituitary-thyroid interrelationships; factors influencing metabolism of endocrine organs; electrophysiology of thyroid. *Mailing Add:* Dept of Physiol State Univ NY Downstate Med Ctr Brooklyn NY 11203

LEVI, BARBARA GOSS, b Washington, DC, May 5, 43; m 66; c 2. ENERGY RESEARCH. *Educ:* Carleton Col, BA, 65; Stanford Univ, MS, 67, PhD(physics), 71. *Prof Exp:* Asst ed, Physics Today Mag, Am Inst Physics, 69-70; lectr physics, Fairleigh Dickinson Univ, 70-76; lectr physics, Ga Inst Technol, 77-80; MEM STAFF RES, CTR ENERGY & ENVIRON STUDIES, PRINCETON UNIV, 81- *Concurrent Pos:* Contrib ed, Physics Today Mag, Am Inst Physics, 71-; mem task force energy, Am Asn Univ Women, 75-77; consult, Off Technol Assessment, US Cong, 76- *Mem:* Am Asn Physics Teachers; Am Phys Soc. *Res:* Energy problems and policy; writing news of current physics research. *Mailing Add:* 20 N Point Dr Colts Neck NJ 07722

LEVI, DAVID WINTERTON, b Berryville, Va, Sept 2, 21; m 47; c 2. POLYMER CHEMISTRY. *Educ:* Randolph-Macon Col, BS, 43; Va Polytech Inst, MS, 51, PhD(chem), 54. *Prof Exp:* From instr to assoc prof chem, Va Polytech Inst, 46-59; SUPVRY CHEMIST, PICATINNY ARSENAL, DOVER, 59- *Mem:* Am Chem Soc. *Res:* Solution properties of high polymers; polymer-energetic compatibility; adhesives; thermal degradation of polymers. *Mailing Add:* 2 Oak Hill Dr Succasunna NJ 07876

LEVI, ELLIOTT J, b Brooklyn, NY, June 12, 40; m 64; c 2. ORGANIC CHEMISTRY, PHYSICAL CHEMISTRY. *Educ:* City Col New York, BS, 61; Univ Cincinnati, PhD(chem), 66. *Prof Exp:* Chief chemist, Apollo Chem Corp, 66-68; group leader, Chem Systs Inc, 68-70; res mgr chem, 70-80, DIR RES & DEVELOP, DREW CHEM CORP, 81- *Concurrent Pos:* Adj asst prof, Upsala Col, 67-71. *Mailing Add:* One Drew Chem Plaza Boonton NJ 07005

LEVI, ENRICO, b Milano, Italy, May 20, 18; US citizen; m 41. ENERGY CONVERSION, PLASMA PHYSICS. *Educ:* Israel Inst Technol, BSc, 41, Ing, 42; Polytech Inst Brooklyn, MEE, 56, DEE, 58. *Prof Exp:* Foreman elec shop, Shipwrights & Engrs Ltd, Israel, 42-44; mech engr, Palestine Elec Co, 44-45; sect head elec eng, Mouchly Eng Co, 45-48; lectr, Israel Inst Technol, 48-55; fel, Microwave Res Inst, Polytech Inst Brooklyn, 56-57; sr scientist, Elec & Electronic Res Found, Westbury, 57-58; assoc prof, PROF ELECTROPHYS, POLYTECH INST NY, 58-; DIR POWER ENG INST, 78- *Concurrent Pos:* Consult, Lever Bros, Israel, 48-55, Hudson Paper Mill Co, 54-55, Am Mach & Foundry Co, 60-62, Westinghouse Elec Astronuclear Labs, Pa, 62-64, Gen Appl Sci Labs, 65, Van Karman Inst Fluid Dynamics, 66, Consol Edison Co, New York, 72, Long Island Lighting Co, 73-74, US Dept Energy, 76-78, Lawrence Livermore Lab, 78, Argonne Nat Lab, 78 & Nasa Lewis Res Ctr, 80; mem, Israel Govt Comt, 50-51 & Elec Wire Standard Comt, Israel, 50-55; Technion vis prof, 80-81. *Honors & Awards:* Charles J Hirsch Award, Inst Elec & Electronics Engrs, 80. *Mem:* Inst Elec & Electronics Engrs; Sigma Xi. *Res:* Electromechanical power conversions; magnetic amplifiers; automatic control; linear electric propulsion; variable speed drives, electric power. *Mailing Add:* Apt 620 110-20 71st Rd Forest Hill NY 11375

LEVI, HERBERT WALTER, b Frankfurt am Main, Ger, Jan 3, 21; nat US; m 49; c 1. ARACHNOLOGY, SYSTEMATICS. *Educ:* Univ Conn, BS, 46; Univ Wis, MS, 47, PhD(zool), 49. *Hon Degrees:* AM, Harvard Univ, 70. *Prof Exp:* From instr to assoc prof bot & zool, Exten Div, Univ Wis, 49-56; from asst cur to assoc cur, Mus, 55-66, mem fac educ, Univ, 64-66, lectr biol, 64-70, PROF BIOL, HARVARD UNIV, 70-, AGASSIZ PROF ZOOL, 72-, CUR ARACHNOL, MUS COMP ZOOL, 66- *Concurrent Pos:* Secy, Rocky Mountain Biol Lab, 59-65; vpres, Ctr Int Document Arachnol, 65-68, pres, 80-83; vis prof, Hebrew Univ Jerusalem, 75. *Mem:* Fel AAAS; Am Arachnol Soc (pres, 79-81); Soc Syst Zool; Am Ecol Soc; Am Inst Biol Sci. *Res:* Evolution; systematic zoology; spiders and other arachnids; animal transplantation; systematic studies of orb-weaving spiders in the family Araneidae. *Mailing Add:* Mus of Comp Zool Harvard Univ Cambridge MA 02138

LEVI, HOWARD, b New York, NY, Nov 9, 16; m 35, 63; c 3. MATHEMATICS. *Educ:* Columbia Univ, AB, 37, PhD(math), 42. *Prof Exp:* Lectr math, Columbia Univ, 39-41; instr math & physics, US Navy Pre-Flight Sch, Iowa, 41-42; res scientist, Sam Labs, Columbia Univ, 43-46, from instr to prof math, 42-61; consult, Orgn Econ Coop & Develop, Paris, 61-62; prof math, Hunter Col, 62-69; PROF MATH, LEHMAN COL, 69- *Concurrent Pos:* NSF sr sci fac fel, 60-61; vis prof, Univ Turin, 68-69. *Mem:* Am Math Soc; Math Asn Am. *Res:* Geometry; mathematics education. *Mailing Add:* Dept of Math Herbert H Lehman Col Bronx NY 10468

LEVI, IRVING, b Winnipeg, Man, Dec 15, 14; m 44; c 4. MEDICINAL CHEMISTRY. *Educ:* Univ Man, BSc, 38, MSc, 39; McGill Univ, PhD(chem), 42. *Prof Exp:* Carnegie Corp res fel, McGill Univ, 42-43, res assoc, 44-46, lectr, 46-47; sr res chemist, Charles E Frosst & Co, 48-68; PRES, ALMEDIC DIV, RHOING LTD, 68- *Concurrent Pos:* Civilian with Can Govt, 40-44. *Mem:* Am Chem Soc; fel Chem Inst Can. *Res:* Organic synthesis; carbohydrates; synthetic analgesics and sedatives; antibiotic and cancer chemotherapy; amino acids and derivatives; steroids and hormones; medicinal applications of natural products and derivatives. *Mailing Add:* Almedic Div Rhoing Ltd 4900 Cote Vertu Rd St Laurent PQ H4S 1J9 Can

LEVI, MICHAEL PHILLIP, b Leeds, Eng, Feb 5, 41; m 66; c 2. FOREST PRODUCTS. *Educ:* Univ Leeds, BS, 61, PhD(biophys), 64. *Prof Exp:* Fulbright travel scholar & res fel wood prod path, Sch Forestry, Yale Univ, 65; res fel, NC State Univ, 65-66; Sci Res Coun-NATO res fel, Univ Leeds, 66-67; sr biologist, Timber Res & Develop Lab, Hickson & Welch, Eng, 67-68, head res wood preservation, 68-71; assoc prof forestry, 71-77, PROF WOOD PAPER SCI, NC STATE UNIV, 77- *Mem:* Forest Prod Res Soc; Royal Soc Chem; Am Phytopath Soc. *Res:* Wood preservation; mode of action of fungicides; wood deterioration by fungi; wood as fuel. *Mailing Add:* Sch of Forest Resources NC State Univ Raleigh NC 27607

LEVI, RALPH SIGMUND, b Chicago, Ill, June 15, 30; m 75; c 5. PHARMACEUTICAL CHEMISTRY, PHYSICAL PHARMACY. *Educ:* Univ Ill, BS, 51; Univ Fla, MS, 52, PhD(pharm), 55. *Prof Exp:* Res pharmacist, Div Indian Health, USPHS, 55-56 & NIH, 56-58; group supvr parenteral prod, 58-60, proj coordr res & develop div, 60-63, mgr pharm develop sect, 63-76, ASSOC DIR PHARM RES & DEVELOP, WYETH LABS, AM HOME PROD CORP, 76- *Mem:* AAAS; Am Pharmaceut Asn; Acad Pharmaceut Sci. *Res:* Pharmaceutical dosage form design and grealetz castrol including chemical and physical properties related to biological availability, stability and preservation, specifically lyophilization, parenteral products, powder flow and compaction. *Mailing Add:* Pharm Res & Develop Div Wyeth Labs PO Box 8299 Philadelphia PA 19101

LEVI, ROBERTO, b Milano, Italy, Mar 2, 34; m 62; c 2. PHARMACOLOGY. *Educ:* Univ Florence, MD, 60. *Prof Exp:* Asst pharmacol, Univ Florence, 60-61; from asst prof to assoc prof, 66-77, PROF PHARMACOL, MED COL, CORNELL UNIV, 77- *Concurrent Pos:* Fulbright travel fel pharmacol & exp therapeut, Sch Med, Johns Hopkins Univ, 61-63; sr res fel electrophysiol, Univ Florence, 63-66; prin investr, USPHS grant, 67-68; co-investr, NIH grant, 67-69; prin investr, NY Heart Asn grant, 68-71, 71-73 & 74-76; Nat Inst Gen Med Sci grant, 74-81; fel, Polachek Found Med Res, 73-76; vis prof pharmacol, Col Physicians & Surgeons, Columbia Univ, 77-78. *Honors & Awards:* Alberico Benedicenti Prize, 64; J Murray Steele Prize, 70. *Mem:* Am Soc Pharmacol & Exp Therapeut; Harvey Soc. *Res:* Cardiovascular pharmacology; heart electrophysiology; neuropharmacology; immunopharmacology. *Mailing Add:* Dept of Pharmacol Cornell Univ Med Col New York NY 10021

LEVICH, CALMAN, b Iowa City, Iowa, May 26, 21; m 46; c 4. BIOPHYSICS. *Educ:* Morningside Col, BS, 49; Cath Univ Am, PhD(physics), 66. *Prof Exp:* Biophysicist, Naval Med Res Inst, 50-61; proj dir, Armed Forces Radiobiol Res Inst, 61-67; assoc prof physics, Cent Mich Univ, 67-68; chmn dept, Seton Hall Univ, 68-70; PROF PHYSICS, CENT MICH UNIV, 70-, CHMN DEPT, 75- *Mem:* AAAS; Biophys Soc; Radiation Res Soc; Am Asn Physics Teachers. *Res:* Mechanical properties of muscle; radiation biophysics; reactor operator education. *Mailing Add:* Box 546 Pentwater MI 49449

LEVIE, HAROLD WALTER, b Augusta, Ga, Jan 17, 49. SURFACE PHYSICS. *Educ:* William Marsh Rice Univ, BA, 71, MS, 73, PhD(mat sci), 76. *Prof Exp:* Physicist, Phys Sci Lab, US Army Missile Command, 71; MAT SCIENTIST SURFACE TECHNOL, INORG MAT DIV, LAWRENCE LIVERMORE LAB, 75- *Concurrent Pos:* Instr corrosion eng, Nat Asn Corrosion Engrs, 75. *Mem:* Nat Asn Corrosion Engrs. *Res:* Analysis and characterization of solid surfaces; kinetics of surface reactions and interface formation. *Mailing Add:* 3500 Deer Creek Rd Palo Alto CA 94304

LEVIEN, LOUISE, b New York, NY, Mar 23, 52. CRYSTALLOGRAPHY. *Educ:* Brown Univ, ScB, 74; State Univ NY, Stony Brook, MS, 75, PhD(earth & space sci), 79. *Prof Exp:* Weizmann fel, Calif Inst Technol, 79-81; RES GEOLOGIST, EXXON PROD RES CO, 81- *Concurrent Pos:* mem, Am Geol Inst Women Geoscientists Comt, 78-80, chmn, 80; mem educ & human resources comt, Am Geophys Union, 80-82. *Mem:* Am Asn Petrol Geologists; Am Geophys Union; Am Crystallo Soc; Mineral Soc Am; Asn Women Geoscientists. *Res:* Geochemistry and geophysics of hydrocarbon reservoirs; relationship of elastic properties and crystal chemistry of minerals. *Mailing Add:* Exxon Prod Res Co PO Box 2189 Houston TX 77001

LEVIEN, ROGER ELI, b Brooklyn, NY, Apr 16, 35; m 60; c 2. SYSTEMS ANALYSIS, INFORMATION SCIENCE. *Educ:* Swarthmore Col, BS, 56; Harvard Univ, MS, 58, PhD(appl math), 62. *Prof Exp:* Engr, Rand Corp, 60-67, head syst sci dept, 67-71, mgr, Washington Domestic Progs, 71-74; proj leader, Int Inst Appl Systs Anal, Austria, 74-75, dir, 75-81; DIR STRATEGIC SYSTS ANAL, XEROX CORP, 82- *Concurrent Pos:* Adj prof, Univ Calif, Los Angeles, 70- *Honors & Awards:* Austrian Ehrenkreutz First Class, Sci & Art. *Mem:* Asn Comput Mach; Inst Elec & Electronics Engrs; Opers Res Soc Am; Asn Pub Policy Anal & Mgt. *Res:* Systems analysis; operations research; research and development management; information sciences; strategic planning. *Mailing Add:* 28 Fresh Meadow Rd Weston CT 06883

LEVIER, ROBERT RAMSEY, b Algona, Iowa, May 8, 40; m 61; c 2. PHARMACOLOGY, ENDOCRINOLOGY. *Educ:* Univ Iowa, BS, 62, MS, 64, PhD(zool), 68. *Prof Exp:* Res toxicol, Dow Chem Co, 67-68; res pharmacol, 68-75, MGR BIOMED, DOW CORNING CORP, 75- *Concurrent Pos:* Adj assoc prof biol, Cent Mich Univ, 77- *Res:* Pharmacology and the bioactivity of organosilicon compounds. *Mailing Add:* Dow Corning Corp Midland MI 48640

LEVI-MONTALCINI, RITA, b Torino, Italy, Apr 22, 09; nat US. NEUROLOGY. *Educ:* Univ Turin, MD, 40. *Prof Exp:* Res assoc zool, Washington Univ, 47-51, assoc prof, 51-58, prof, 58-81; WITH LAB DI BIOLOGIA, ROME, 81- *Mem:* Nat Acad Sci; AAAS; Soc Develop Biol; Am Asn Anatomists; Tissue Cult Asn. *Res:* Experimental neurology; effect of a nerve growth factor isolated from the mouse salivary gland on the sympathetic nervous system and of an antiserum to the nerve growth factor; study of other specific growth factors. *Mailing Add:* Lab Di Biologia Cellulare Via G Romagnosa Rome 00196 Italy

LEVIN, AARON R, b Johannesburg, SAfrica, Mar 19, 29; m 55; c 3. PEDIATRICS, CARDIOLOGY. *Educ:* Univ Witwatersrand, BSc, 48, MBBCh, 53, MD, 68; Royal Col Physicians & Surgeons, dipl child health, 60. *Prof Exp:* Intern, Edenvale Hosp, SAfrica, 54-55; sr intern, Johannesburg Fever Hosp, 55; pediat intern, Coronation Hosp, 55-56; pediat registr, 56-60; pediat registr, Charing Cross Hosp, Eng, 61; gen pract, 62-63; instr pediat, Med Ctr, Duke Univ, 64-66; from asst prof to assoc prof, 66-74, PROF PEDIAT, MED CTR, CORNELL UNIV, 74- *Concurrent Pos:* NIH fel cardiol, Med Ctr, Duke Univ, 64-66; attend physician, Pediat Intensive Care Unit, New York Hosp-Cornell Med Ctr. *Mem:* Fel Am Acad Pediat; Soc Pediat Res. *Res:* Pediatric cardiology, specifically related to studies of pressure-flow dynamics in various forms of congenital heart disease; extra cardiac factors in congenital heart disease; right ventricular hypertrophy at cellular level. *Mailing Add:* Pediat Cardiopulmonary Lab New York Hosp-Cornell Med Ctr New York NY 10021

LEVIN, BARRY EDWARD, b Brooklyn, NY, May 1, 42. NEUROBIOLOGY, NEUROLOGY. *Educ:* Emory Univ, MD, 67; Am Bd Psychiat & Neurol, dipl. *Prof Exp:* Instr & chief resident neurol, Cornell Med Sch, 71-72; clin assoc, Nat Inst Neurol Dis & Blindness, 72-74; asst prof neurol & psychiat, Dartmouth Med Sch, 74-77; ASSOC PROF NEUROSCI, COL MED NJ, 77- *Concurrent Pos:* Grantee, Vet Admin Res & Educ grant, 74-; dir lab of neuropharmacol & dept neurosci, Col Med NJ, 77-; staff neurologist, Vet Admin Hosp, East Orange, NJ, 77-; attend neurologist, Martland Hosp, Col Med NJ, 78- *Mem:* Soc Neurosci; Am Acad Neurol. *Res:* Metabolism, axonal transport and rhythms of catecholamines in health and disease. *Mailing Add:* Dept of Neurol (127) Vet Admin Hosp East Orange NJ 07019

LEVIN, BERTRAM, radiology, see previous edition

LEVIN, BRUCE, b New York, NY, Mar 14, 48; m 70; c 1. MATHEMATICAL STATISTICS. *Educ:* Columbia Univ, AB, 68; Harvard Univ, MA, 72, PhD(appl math), 74. *Prof Exp:* Data analyst & comput programmer, Albert Einstein Col Med, 66-72; ASST PROF MATH STATIST & BIOSTATIST, COLUMBIA UNIV, 74- *Concurrent Pos:* Consult, Statistica, Inc, 78- *Mem:* Am Statist Asn; Inst Math Statist; Sigma Xi. *Res:* Statistical inference and data analysis. *Mailing Add:* Div Biostatist Sch Pub Health Columbia Univ New York NY 10032

LEVIN, EDWIN ROY, b Philadelphia, Pa, Nov 4, 27; m 51; c 3. SOLID STATE SCIENCE. *Educ:* Temple Univ, AB, 49, MA, 51, PhD(physics), 59. *Prof Exp:* Asst physics, Temple Univ, 49-51; physicist, Frankford Arsenal, US Army, 51-63; MEM TECH STAFF, RCA LABS, 63- *Concurrent Pos:* Secy Army res & study fel, Cavendish Lab, Cambridge Univ, 61-62; guide prof, World Univ, 73- *Mem:* AAAS; Am Phys Soc; Electron Micros Soc Am. *Res:* Solid state physics; theory of dielectrics; photoconductivity; quantum electronics; analysis of solid materials for electronics, including electron microscopy and related methodologies. *Mailing Add:* RCA Labs Princeton NJ 08540

LEVIN, EUGENE (MANUEL), b New York, NY, Aug 14, 34; m 60; c 3. PHYSICS. *Educ:* Univ Vt, BA, 56; Columbia Univ, MA, 59; NY Univ, PhD(physics), 67. *Prof Exp:* ASSOC PROF PHYSICS, YORK COL, NY, 67- *Mem:* Am Phys Soc; Am Asn Physics Teachers; Sigma Xi. *Res:* Excited states and fluorescence properties of organic molecules; applications of fluorescence techniques to charged particle dosimetry. *Mailing Add:* Dept of Physics York Univ Jamaica NY 11432

LEVIN, FRANK S, b Bronx, NY, Apr 14, 33; m 55; c 2. NUCLEAR PHYSICS. *Educ:* Johns Hopkins Univ, AB, 55; Univ Md, PhD(physics), 61. *Prof Exp:* Res assoc physics, Rice Univ, 61-63 & Brookhaven Nat Lab, 63-65; temporary res assoc, Atomic Energy Res Estab, Eng, 65-67; assoc prof, 67-77, PROF PHYSICS, BROWN UNIV, 77- *Res:* Nuclear reaction theory; scattering theory; atomic collision theory. *Mailing Add:* Dept of Physics Brown Univ Providence RI 02912

LEVIN, FRANKLYN KUSSEL, b Terre Haute, Ind, June 28, 22; m 46; c 3. EXPLORATION GEOPHYSICS. *Educ:* Purdue Univ, BS, 43; Univ Wis, PhD(physics), 49. *Prof Exp:* Physicist, Sam Labs, Columbia Univ, 43-44, Carbide & Carbon Chem Corp, 44-46; asst physics, Univ Wis, 46-47; physicist, Carter Oil Co, 49-53; asst dir, Hudson Labs, Columbia Univ, 53-54; physicist, Carter Oil Co, 54-58; physicist, Jersey Prod Res Co, Standard Oil Co (NJ), 58-59, res assoc, 59-63, sr res assoc, 63-64, sr res assoc, Esso Prod Res Co, 65-67, res scientist, 67-73, SR RES SCIENTIST, EXXON PROD RES CO, 73- *Concurrent Pos:* Lectr, Univ Tulsa, 58-63; ed, Geophys, 69-71. *Honors & Awards:* Robert Earll McConnell Award, 81. *Mem:* AAAS; Am Phys Soc; Seismol Soc Am; Am Geophys Union; Acoust Soc Am. *Mailing Add:* Exxon Prod Res Co PO Box 2189 Houston TX 77001

LEVIN, GERSON, b Philadelphia, Pa, Oct 27, 39; m 69. MATHEMATICS. *Educ:* Univ Pa, AB, 61; Univ Chicago, MS, 62, PhD(math), 65. *Prof Exp:* NSF fel, Univ Ore, 66, vis asst prof math, 66-67; asst prof, NY Univ, 67-74; asst prof, 74-76, ASSOC PROF MATH, BROOKLYN COL, 76- *Res:* Commutative rings and homological algebra. *Mailing Add:* Dept of Math Brooklyn Col Brooklyn NY 11210

LEVIN, GIDEON, b Mazkeret Ratia, Israel, Apr 6, 36; US citizen; m 63; c 2. PHYSICAL ORGANIC CHEMISTRY, PHOTOCHEMISTRY. *Educ:* Israel Inst Technol, BSc, 60; Purdue Univ, West Lafayette, MS, 65; State Univ NY Col Environ Sci & Forestry, PhD(chem), 71. *Prof Exp:* Chemist polymers, Dow Corning Corp, 65-67; res assoc photochem, Upsala Univ, 72; res assoc, 72-75, SR RES ASSOC PHOTOCHEM, COL ENVIRON SCI & FORESTRY, STATE UNIV NY, 75- *Concurrent Pos:* Vis scientist, Weizmann Inst Sci, 78- *Mem:* Am Chem Soc. *Res:* Mechanism of photochemical reaction initiated by flash of light which includes conversion of light energy to chemical energy and photo-oxidation and photoreduction of organic and organo metallic molecules which have biological significance. *Mailing Add:* Dept of Chem State Univ of NY Syracuse NY 13210

LEVIN, GILBERT VICTOR, b Baltimore, Md, Apr 23, 24; m 53; c 3. ENVIRONMENTAL HEALTH, ENGINEERING. *Educ:* Johns Hopkins Univ, BE, 47, MS, 48, PhD(sanit eng), 63. *Prof Exp:* Jr asst sanit engr, State Dept Health, Md, 48-50; asst sanit engr, Dept Pub Health, Calif, 50-51; pub health engr, DC, 51-56; vpres, Resources Res, Inc, 56-63; dir spec res, Hazleton Labs, Inc, 63-65, dir life systs div, 65-67; PRES, BIOSPHERICS INC, 67- *Concurrent Pos:* Res asst biochem, Schs Med & Dent, Georgetown Univ, 52-61, clin asst prof, 53-60; biochemist, Dept Sanit Eng, DC, 62-63;

consult, Dept Interior, 63-71; NASA planetary quarantine adv, 65-74; NASA experimenter, Mariner 9, 71 & Viking Mission to Mars, 76. *Honors & Awards:* IR100 Indust Res Mag, 75; Pub Serv Medal, NASA, 77; Necomb Cleveland Prize, AAAS, 77. *Mem:* Am Soc Civil Eng; Am Water Works Asn; fel Am Pub Health Asn; Water Pollution Control Fedn; NY Acad Sci; Am Inst Biol Sci. *Res:* Inventor PhoStrip process for wastewater phosphorus removal; Lev-O-Cal noncaloric sweetener; life sciences; applied biology; water supply; waste disposal; sanitary biology; environmental sanitation; life detection techniques; public health and medical microbiology; instrumentation; space biology. *Mailing Add:* Biospherics Inc 4928 Wyaconda Rd Rockville MD 20852

LEVIN, HAROLD LEONARD, b St Louis, Mo, Mar 11, 29; m 54; c 3. GEOLOGY, PALEONTOLOGY. *Educ:* Univ Mo, AB, 51, MA, 52; Wash Univ, PhD(paleont), 56. *Prof Exp:* Geologist, Standard Oil Co Calif, 56-61; from asst prof to assoc prof, 61-71, chmn dept earth & planetary sci, 73-76, PROF PALEONT, WASH UNIV, 71-, ASSOC DEAN COL ARTS & SCI, 76- *Concurrent Pos:* Res grants, Wash Univ, 61-72; consult, Ecol Serv, Mo Bot Garden, 73- *Mem:* AAAS; Soc Econ Paleont & Mineral; Paleont Soc. *Res:* Foraminifera, Coccolithophoridae and related microfossils; biostratigraphy of microorganisms; geological education. *Mailing Add:* Dept Earth & Planetary Sci Wash Univ St Louis MO 63130

LEVIN, HARVEY STEVEN, b New York, NY, Dec 12, 46; m 68; c 1. NEUROPSYCHOLOGY. *Educ:* City Col, Univ NY, BA, 67; Univ Iowa, MA, 71, PhD(clin psychol), 72. *Prof Exp:* Fel, Dept Neurol, Univ Iowa, 72-73; intern clin psychol, Ill Masonic Med Ctr, 73-74; asst prof, 74-79, ASSOC PROF NEUROPSYCHOL, UNIV TEX MED BR, 79- *Concurrent Pos:* Consult, Dept Neurol, Univ Hosps, Iowa, 73-74; vis lectr, Dept Psychol, Univ Mo, Columbia, 81; vis prof, Dept Neurosurg, Univ Pa,81; prin investr, Neuropsychol Sect, Nat Inst Neurol & Commun Disorders & Stroke Prog Proj, 75-; investr, Int Study Group Pharmacol Memory, 78-; ed, Cortex, 81- *Mem:* AAAS; fel Am Psychol Asn; Soc Neurosci; Acad Aphasia. *Res:* Recovery from brain injury in children and adults; cholinergic augmentation in dementia of the Alzheimer type; visual perception in patients with focal brain lesions. *Mailing Add:* Div Neurosurg E17 Univ Tex Med Br Galveston TX 77550

LEVIN, HERMAN WESTLEY, biochemistry, enzymology, see previous edition

LEVIN, IRA WILLIAM, b Washington, DC, Sept 20, 35; m 61; c 1. CHEMICAL PHYSICS. *Educ:* Univ Va, BS, 57; Brown Univ, PhD(chem), 61. *Prof Exp:* Res instr chem, Univ Wash, 61-62; guest worker, 63-65, staff fel, 65-66, res chem, Phys Biol Lab, 66-72, RES CHEMIST, LAB CHEM PHYSICS, NIH, 72-, CHIEF, SECT MOLECULAR BIOPHYS, 79- *Concurrent Pos:* Lectr, Georgetown Univ, 64-65; assoc mem grad fac chem, 74- *Mem:* Coblentz Soc (pres, 77-78); Am Phys Soc; Biophys Soc. *Res:* Vibrational spectroscopy; absolute intensities; molecular dynamics and structure; spectra; spectroscopy of biomembranes. *Mailing Add:* Lab Chem Physics Nat Inst Health Bethesda MD 20014

LEVIN, IRVIN, b Baltimore, Md, Dec 18, 12; m 49; c 3. PHYSICAL CHEMISTRY. *Educ:* Johns Hopkins Univ, BS, 35; Univ Md, MS, 40, PhD(chem), 48. *Prof Exp:* Res chemist, Nat Dairy Prod Corp, Md, 35-42; phys chemist, Signal Corps, US Army, Camp Evans, NJ, 42-45; instr chem, Univ Md, 45-46, res assoc, 48-50; chief dept biophys instrumentation, Army Med Serv Grad Sch, Walter Reed Army Med Ctr, 50-55, dir instrumentation div, Walter Reed Army Inst Res, 55-76; res assoc, Am Univ, 78-79. *Concurrent Pos:* Consult, Power Condenser & Electronics Corp, Washington, DC, 49-50; consult, US Army Inst Dent Res, Washington, 76-77, Lab Tech Develop, Nat Heart & Lung Inst, Bethesda, 77-78 & Nuclear Support Serv, Inc, 79-80. *Mem:* Am Chem Soc; Am Phys Soc; Sigma Xi. *Res:* Electrochemistry; photochemistry; design of laboratory apparatus; photovoltaic behavior of chemical substances. *Mailing Add:* 1404 Billman Ln Wheaton MD 20902

LEVIN, JACK, b Newark, NJ, Oct 11, 32. INTERNAL MEDICINE, HEMATOLOGY. *Educ:* Yale Univ, BA, 53, MD, 57; Am Bd Internal Med, dipl, 65, recert, 74. *Prof Exp:* Chief resident & instr, Yale Univ, 64-65; from instr to assoc prof, 65-78, PROF MED, DIV HEMAT, JOHNS HOPKINS UNIV, 78- *Concurrent Pos:* Fel med, Sch Med, Johns Hopkins Univ, 62-64; Markle scholar acad med, 68-73; mem corp, Marine Biol Lab, 65-; physician chg hemat out-patient clin, Johns Hopkins Hosp, 67-71, 76-; consult, Vet Admin Hosp, Baltimore, Md, 68- *Mem:* Int Soc Hemat; Int Soc Exp Hemat; fel Am Col Physicians; Am Soc Hemat; Am Soc Clin Invest. *Res:* Blood coagulation, platelets; thrombopoiesis; endotoxin and endotoxemia; Shwartzman phenomenon; thrombocytosis; invertebrate coagulation; von Willebrand's disease. *Mailing Add:* Div of Hemat Johns Hopkins Hosp Baltimore MD 21205

LEVIN, JACOB JOSEPH, b New York, NY, Dec 21, 26; m 52; c 3. MATHEMATICAL ANALYSIS. *Educ:* City Col New York, BEE, 49; Mass Inst Technol, PhD, 53. *Prof Exp:* Instr math, Mass Inst Technol, 52-53; instr, Purdue Univ, 53-55; vis lectr, Mass Inst Technol, 55-56, staff mem, Lincoln Lab, 56-63; assoc prof, 63-66, PROF MATH, UNIV WIS-MADISON, 66- *Concurrent Pos:* NSF sr fel, Univ Calif, Los Angeles, 70-71; vis prof, Univ BC, 77-78. *Mem:* Am Math Soc; Soc Indust & Appl Math. *Res:* Differential equations; integral equations. *Mailing Add:* 1110 Frisch Rd Madison WI 53711

LEVIN, JEROME ALLEN, b Washington, DC, Aug 25, 39; m; c 2. BIOCHEMICAL PHARMACOLOGY. *Educ:* Philadelphia Col Pharm & Sci, BSc, 61; Univ Mich, PhD(pharmacol), 66. *Prof Exp:* Res assoc pharmacol, State Univ NY Downstate Med Ctr, 66-68; asst prof, 68-74, interim chmn, 73-75, ASSOC PROF PHARMACOL, MED COL OHIO, 74- *Concurrent Pos:* USPHS fel, State Univ NY Downstate Med Ctr, 66-68; Am Heart Asn res grant, Med Col Ohio, 69-75, USPHS res grant, 70-76. *Mem:*

AAAS; Am Heart Asn; Am Soc Pharmacol & Exp Therapeut. *Res:* Inactivation of norepinephrine in vascular tissue; drug-receptor interactions. *Mailing Add:* Dept Pharmacol & Exp Therapeut Med Col of Ohio PO Box 6190 Toledo OH 43614

LEVIN, JOSEPH DAVID, b New York, NY, Feb 7, 18; m 47; c 2. INDUSTRIAL MICROBIOLOGY. *Educ:* Queens Col, NY, BS, 41. *Prof Exp:* Tech aide, E R Squibb & Sons, 47-50, res asst, 50-53, res asst supvr, Squibb Div, Olin Mathieson Chem Corp, 53-59, res scientist, 59-64, sr res scientist, 64-69, lab supvr, Inst Med Res, Squibb Corp, New Brunswick, 68-82; RETIRED. *Mem:* NY Acad Sci; Am Soc Microbiol. *Res:* Analytical microbiology; test and develop microbiological assays of antibiotics including traces in mammalian tissues; test and development methods for pharmaceutical preservative efficacy; co-patentee, diagnostic aid for fungal infection. *Mailing Add:* 244 Benner St Highland Park NJ 08904

LEVIN, JUDITH GOLDSTEIN, b Brooklyn, NY, Nov 8, 34; m 57; c 2. BIOCHEMISTRY, VIROLOGY. *Educ:* Barnard Col, Columbia Univ, BA, 55; Harvard Univ, MA, 57; Columbia Univ, PhD(biochem), 62. *Prof Exp:* Sr scientist molecular biol viruses, Nat Cancer Inst, 69-73, SR SCIENTIST, LAB MOLECULAR GENETICS, NAT INST CHILD HEALTH & HUMAN DEVELOP, 73- *Concurrent Pos:* Nat Heart Inst res fel biochem genetics, 62-69; USPHS fel, 63-65; Am Heart Asn advan res fel, 66-68; consult lab path, Nat Cancer Inst, 69; estab investr, Am Heart Asn, 69-74. *Mem:* AAAS; Am Soc Biol Chem; Am Chem Soc; Am Soc Microbiol. *Res:* Biochemistry of RNA tumor viruses; mechanisms of protein biosynthesis, in particular, studies on the codon recognition step; regulation of transcription and translation in mammalian cells. *Mailing Add:* Nat Inst Health & Nat Inst Children Health & Human Develop Bethesda MD 20205

LEVIN, KATHRYN J, b Lawrence, Kans, Feb 25, 44; m 69. SOLID STATE PHYSICS. *Educ:* Univ Calif, Berkeley, BA, 66; Harvard Univ, PhD(physics), 70. *Prof Exp:* Res assoc physics, Univ Rochester, 70-72; asst res physicist, Univ Calif, Irvine, 72-75; ASST PROF PHYSICS, UNIV CHICAGO, 75- *Mem:* Am Phys Soc. *Res:* Phase transitions in disordered systems; superconductivity. *Mailing Add:* James Franck Inst Univ of Chicago Chicago IL 60637

LEVIN, LEONID A, b USSR, Nov 2, 48. ALGORITHMIC COMPLEXITY. *Educ:* Moscow Univ, 72; Mass Inst Technol, PhD(math), 79. *Prof Exp:* ASSOC PROF MATH & COMPUT SCI, BOSTON UNIV, 80- *Concurrent Pos:* Vis scientist comput sci, Mass Inst Technol, 78-; prin investr, NSF, 81- *Res:* Foundations of mathematics, statistics and computer science; algorithmic complexity with applications to randomness and information theories, inductive inference, functional analysis, combinatorics and graph theory, mathematical logic, theory of computations; randomness and information. *Mailing Add:* 150-3 Kendrick St Brighton MA 02135

LEVIN, LOUIS, biochemistry, deceased

LEVIN, MARSHALL DAVID, b Brownwood, Tex, May 18, 22; m 45; c 3. ENTOMOLOGY, APICULTURE. *Educ:* Univ Conn, AB, 47; Univ Minn, MS, 49, PhD(entom, agr biochem), 56. *Prof Exp:* Asst entom, Conn Agr Exp Sta, 47; asst apicult, Univ Minn, 46-50; entomologist, 50-64, honey bee pollination invests leader, Honey Bee Res Lab, Ariz, 64-69, chief apicult res br, Plant Indust Sta, 69-72, scientist, 72-78, CHIEF CROP SCI STAFF, NAT PROG STAFF, AGR RES SERV, USDA, 78- *Mem:* AAAS; Entom Soc Am; Bee Res Asn. *Res:* Biology and behavior of Bombus, Osmia, Nomia; biology, foraging behavior, management, pollinating activities of honey bees; honey bee nutrition; effects of insecticides on honey bees and wild bees. *Mailing Add:* Nat Prog Staff Agr Res Serv USDA Agr Res Ctr-West Beltsville MD 20705

LEVIN, MARTIN ALLEN, b Philadelphia, Pa, Aug, 14, 49; m 77; c 2. MICROANATOMY. *Educ:* Rutgers Univ, BA, 71, MS, 73; Ohio Univ, PhD(zool), 77. *Prof Exp:* Teaching asst biol, Rutgers Univ, 71-73; teaching assoc biol, Ohio Univ, 74-77; ASST PROF BIOL, EASTERN CONN STATE COL, 78- *Concurrent Pos:* Consult, Amity Indust, 79-80. *Mem:* Am Inst Biol Sci; Electron Micros Soc; Am Soc Zoologists. *Res:* Utilizing histochemistry and electron microscopy; study of the effects of activity on various fast-and-slow-twitch muscles in genetically spastic mice and the interosseus dorsalis muscle in humans with hallux-abductovalgus deformity. *Mailing Add:* Dept Biol Eastern Conn State Col Willimantic CT 06226

LEVIN, MICHAEL HOWARD, b New York, NY, Sept 25, 36; div; c 1. ENVIRONMENTAL SCIENCES, ECOLOGY. *Educ:* Univ Vt, BS, 58; Rutgers Univ, MS, 60, PhD(bot), 64. *Prof Exp:* Res assoc taxon, NY Bot Garden, 63-64; cur, Greene-Nieuwland Herbarium & asst prof biol, Univ Notre Dame, 64-66; asst prof bot & cur herbarium, Univ Man, 66-68; asst prof landscape archit & regional planning, Univ Pa, 68-73; PRES, ENVIRON RES ASSOCS, INC, 73-, DIR RES & CHMN BD, 74-; DIR RES & PRIN CORP ENVIRON SCIENTIST, AMBRIC ENVIRON SCIENCES, INC, 79- *Concurrent Pos:* Coop investr, Delta Waterfowl Res Sta, Man, 65-66; adj prof agr & natural resources, Del State Col, 79- *Mem:* Fel AAAS; Ecol Soc Am; Am Soc Plant Taxon; Int Asn Plant Taxon; Brit Ecol Soc. *Res:* Forensic environmental sciences and geotechnical investigations; ecology of altered communities and ecosystems; ecological management; application of gradient analysis to terrestrial communities; wetlands ecology; hydrobiology, hydrology and water resources. *Mailing Add:* Environ Res Assocs Inc Carriage House 490 Darby-Paoli Rd Villanova PA 19085

LEVIN, MORRIS A, b New York, NY, May 15, 34; m 57; c 2. MICROBIOLOGY. *Educ:* Univ Chicago, BS, 59; Univ RI, PhD(microbiol), 70. *Prof Exp:* Microbiologist aerobiol, Dept Defense, 57-66; microbiologist marine microbiol, Dept Health Educ & Welfare, 66-70; MICROBIOLOGIST HEALTH EFFECTS, ENVIRON PROTECTION AGENCY, 70- *Concurrent Pos:* Adj prof civil eng & microbiol, Univ RI, 75. *Prof Exp:. Res:* Quantitating of microorganisms in the environment, dose-response relationships and epidemiological considerations correlating the public health effects of exposure to microbial populations under natural conditions; forecasting, trend analysis of environmental problems, genetic engineering. *Mailing Add:* 401 M St SW Washington DC 20460

LEVIN, MORTON LOEB, b Russia, Aug 25, 03; div; c 2. PREVENTIVE MEDICINE, PUBLIC HEALTH. *Educ:* Univ Md, MD, 30; Johns Hopkins Univ, DrPH, 34. *Prof Exp:* Intern & asst resident, Mt Sinai Hosp, Baltimore, Md, 30-32; asst dispensary physician, Johns Hopkins Hosp, 32-33; comnr health, Ottawa County, Mich, 34-35; instr epidemiol, Sch Hyg & Pub Health, Johns Hopkins Univ, 35-36; assoc physician, Roswell Park Mem Inst, NY, 36-39; asst dir div cancer control, State Dept Health, NY, 39-46, dir, 46 46-47, asst comnr med serv, 47-60; chief dept epidemiol, Roswell Park Mem Inst, 60-67; VIS PROF EPIDEMIOL, SCH HYG & PUB HEALTH, JOHNS HOPKINS UNIV, 67- *Concurrent Pos:* Dir Comn Chronic Illness, 50-51. *Honors & Awards:* Biggs Medal, 60; Haven Emerson Award, 62; John Snow Award 78. *Mem:* Am Epidemiol Soc; Am Pub Health Asn; AAAS. *Res:* Epidemiology of malignant tumors. *Mailing Add:* 615 N Wolfe St Baltimore MD 21205

LEVIN, MURRAY LAURENCE, b Boston, Mass, Nov 14, 35; m 61; c 2. INTERNAL MEDICINE, NEPHROLOGY. *Educ:* Harvard Col, AB, 57; Tufts Univ, MD, 61. *Prof Exp:* Intern med, Beth Israel Hosp, Boston, Mass, 61-62, resident, 62-64; assoc, 66-69, asst prof, 69-72, assoc prof, 72-80, PROF MED, MED SCH, NORTHWESTERN UNIV CHICAGO, 80- *Concurrent Pos:* Res fel renal dis, Univ Tex Southwestern Med Sch Dallas, 64-66; NIH res fel, 65-66; Chicago Heart Asn res grants, 66-70 & 73-75; Nat Inst Arthritis & Metab Dis res grant, 67-70; attend physician, Vet Admin Lakeside Hosp, Chicago, Ill, 66-, chief renal sect, 72-76, chief med serv, 76-; adj staff, Passavant Mem Hosp, 68-, assoc attend physician, 75- *Mem:* AAAS; Am Fedn Clin Res; Int Soc Nephrol; Am Soc Nephrol. *Res:* Salt and water metabolism; uremia; membrane transport; calcium and phosphorus metabolism. *Mailing Add:* Vet Admin Res Hosp Med Serv 333 E Huron St Chicago IL 60611

LEVIN, NATHAN, b Baltimore, Md, July 30, 15; m; c 1. PHARMACEUTICAL CHEMISTRY. *Educ:* Univ Md, BS, 36, MS, 38, PhD(org pharmaceut chem), 41. *Prof Exp:* Asst instr bact, Sch Pharm, Univ Md, Baltimore City, 36-37, asst org chem, 37-41; fel synthetic org chem, Upjohn Co, Mich, 41-42, res chemist, 42-44; res chemist, Schering Corp, NJ, 44-45; res develop chemist, Burroughs Wellcome & Co, Inc, NY, 45-48; assoc prof pharmaceut chem, Col Pharm, Howard Univ, 48-59; pharmacist, Washington, DC, 59-68; HEAD PHARM CHEM LAB, MD STATE BUR LABS, 68- *Concurrent Pos:* Abstractor, Pharmaceut Abstr, Am Pharmaceut Asn, 39-48 & Chem Abstr, Am Chem Soc, 53-55. *Mem:* Am Pharmaceut Asn; Am Chem Soc. *Res:* Analysis of drugs and pharmaceutical preparations; identification of narcotics and/or dangerous drugs; quality control and methods of analysis of pharmaceutical products. *Mailing Add:* Md State Bur Labs PO Box 2355 Baltimore MD 21203

LEVIN, NORMAN LEWIS, b Hartford, Conn, Mar 31, 24; m 50; c 2. ZOOLOGY, PARASITOLOGY. *Educ:* Univ Conn, BS, 48, MS, 49; Univ Ill, PhD(zool, parasitol), 56. *Prof Exp:* Asst zool, Univ Ill, 53-56, instr, 56-57; asst prof biol, Westminster Col, Mo, 57-60; from instr to assoc prof, 60-76, PROF BIOL, BROOKLYN COL, 76- *Mem:* Fel AAAS; Am Soc Zool; Am Soc Parasitol; Am Soc Trop Med & Hyg; Am Micros Soc. *Res:* General taxonomy; morphology; life cycles; interrelationship of larval trematodes and marine snails. *Mailing Add:* Dept of Biol Brooklyn Col Brooklyn NY 11210

LEVIN, ROBERT AARON, b New York, NY, July 25, 29; m 55; c 4. CLINICAL CHEMISTRY. *Educ:* St John's Univ, NY, BS, 51, MS, 55. *Prof Exp:* Res toxicologist, Norwich Pharmacal Co, 55-58, sr researcher clin path & toxicol, 58-62, unit leader clin path, 62-80, UNIT LEADER CLIN PATH, NORWICH-EATON PHARMACEUT, 80-; UNIT LEADER CLIN PATH, NORWICH-EATON PHARMACEUT, 80- *Concurrent Pos:* Sci adv, Med Technol Dept, State Univ NY Agr & Tech Col Morrisville. *Mem:* Am Chem Soc; Am Asn Clin Chem; Am Soc Vet Clin Pathologists. *Res:* Automation and computerization of chemical technics; drug toxicity testing; establishing effects on clinical pathology parameters; veterinary hematology. *Mailing Add:* Clin Path Unit Norwich-Eaton Pharmaceut Norwich NY 13815

LEVIN, ROBERT E, b Boston, Mass, Dec 1, 30; m; c 2. MICROBIOLOGY, FOOD SCIENCE. *Educ:* Los Angeles State Col, BS, 52; Univ Southern Calif, MS, 54; Univ Calif, Davis, PhD(microbiol), 63. *Prof Exp:* Asst prof microbiol, Ore State Univ, 63-64; from asst prof to assoc prof, 64-77, PROF FOOD SCI, UNIV MASS, AMHERST, 77- *Concurrent Pos:* NIH res grant, 65-68. *Mem:* Am Soc Microbiol; Inst Food Technologists; Soc Cryobiol. *Res:* Microbiological sulfate reduction; yeast cytology; psychophilic bacteria; enzymology; molecular taxonomy. *Mailing Add:* Dept of Food Sci Univ of Mass Amherst MA 01002

LEVIN, ROBERT EDMOND, b Orange, Calif, Oct 11, 31; m 58; c 2. OPTICS, OPTICAL ENGINEERING. *Educ:* Stanford Univ, BS, 53, MS, 54, Engr, 56, PhD(elec eng), 60. *Prof Exp:* Assoc prof elec eng, Calif State Univ, San Jose, 58-63; SR SCIENTIST LIGHT & RADIATION, GTE SYLVANIA INC, 63- *Concurrent Pos:* Consult engr, 58-63; instr continuing educ, Northeastern Univ, 68-; contrib ed, McGraw-Hill, 71-75. *Mem:* Optical Soc Am; sr mem Inst Elec & Electronics Engrs; fel Illum Eng Soc; Am Soc Photobiol. *Res:* Control and application of non-ionizing radiation in photobiological, photochemical and visual systems; radiometric optics. *Mailing Add:* GTE Sylvania Inc 60 Boston St Salem MA 01970

LEVIN, ROBERT HAROLD, b Chicago, Ill, Nov 1, 15; m 41; c 4. ORGANIC CHEMISTRY. *Educ:* Univ Ill, AB, 37; Univ Wis, PhD(org chem), 41. *Prof Exp:* Chem libr asst, Univ Ill, 34-36; asst chem, Univ Wis, 37-41; res chemist, Upjohn Co, Mich, 41-46, group leader chem res, 46-52, head dept chem, 52-58, asst dir res, 58-68; vpres res, Richardson-Merrell, Inc, 68-78; RES/MGT CONSULT, 78- *Concurrent Pos:* Mem subcomt steroid nomenclature, Nat Res Coun, 50-55; mem coun, Gordon Res Conf. *Mem:* AAAS; Am Chem Soc; NY Acad Sci. *Res:* Chemistry of steroids, especially the cortical hormones; biomedical research and new drug development long range planning for pharmaceutical research; international pharmaceutical product licensing. *Mailing Add:* 906 Oregon Trail Cincinnati OH 45215

LEVIN, ROBERT MARTIN, pharmacology, see previous edition

LEVIN, ROGER L(EE), b Clearfield, Pa, Mar 21, 36; m 60; c 3. MATERIALS SCIENCE. *Educ:* Pa State Univ, BS, 58; Yale Univ, MEng, 61; Northwestern Univ, PhD(mat sci), 63. *Prof Exp:* US Navy, 58-70, anal officer, sonar opers anal, Naval Test & Eval Detachment, Fla, 63-65, sonar proj officer, Acoust Warfare Proj Off, Naval Ship Systs Command, DC, 56-70; mgr undersea warfare progs, Hydrospace Res Corp, 70-72; PRES, MAR INC, 72-, TECH DIR, 77- *Mem:* Am Soc Metals; Am Chem Soc. *Res:* Underwater acoustics. *Mailing Add:* MAR Inc 1335 Rockville Pike Rockville MD 20852

LEVIN, RONALD HAROLD, b San Francisco, Calif, Sept 26, 45; m 69; c 2. ORGANIC CHEMISTRY. *Educ:* Case Western Reserve Univ, BS, 67; Princeton Univ, PhD(chem), 70. *Prof Exp:* Fel chem, Univ Freiburg, 70-71 & Calif Inst Technol, 71-72; asst prof chem, Harvard Univ, 72-77; MEM STAFF, IBM CORP, 78- *Mem:* Am Chem Soc; Chem Soc London. *Res:* Reactive intermediates; thermal and photochemical transformations; applications of magnetic resonance; electrophotography. *Mailing Add:* IBM 57R/023 Boulder CO 80302

LEVIN, SAMUEL JOSEPH, b Detroit, Mich, Sept 19, 35; m 63; c 2. BIOCHEMISTRY. *Educ:* Wayne State Univ, BA, 58, PhD(chem), 61; Am Bd Clin Chem, dipl. *Prof Exp:* Res assoc chem, Col Med, Wayne State Univ, 55-61; scientist, Warner Lambert Pharmaceut Co, 61-62; from instr to asst prof biochem, Div Grad Studies, Med Col, Cornell Univ, 63-66; from asst prof to assoc prof biochem, Sch Dent, Univ Mo-Kansas City, 67-74, from asst prof to assoc prof, Sch Med, 68-74; asst dir clin path, Michael Reese Hosp, 74-76, mem, Michael Reese Inst, 74-76, DIR, DIV BIOCHEM, MICHAEL REESE HOSP, 77- *Concurrent Pos:* Asst attend biochemist, Mem Hosp Cancer & Allied Dis, 62-66; assoc, Sloan-Kettering Inst, 63-66; chief biochemist, Dept Path, Kansas City Gen Hosp, 66-74. *Mem:* AAAS; Am Asn Clin Chem; Nat Acad Clin Biochem. *Res:* Clinical biochemistry. *Mailing Add:* Div Biochem 2 Blum Michael Reese Hosp Chicago IL 60616

LEVIN, SEYMOUR A(RTHUR), b Newark, NJ, Sept 16, 22; m 48; c 4. CHEMICAL ENGINEERING. *Educ:* Johns Hopkins Univ, BE, 43. *Prof Exp:* Res asst, Columbia Univ, 43-45; dept head, Union Carbide Nuclear Co Div, 45-68, HEAD LONG RANGE PLANNING, NUCLEAR DIV, UNION CARBIDE CORP, 68- *Mem:* Am Chem Soc; AAAS; Nat Soc Prof Engrs. *Res:* Design and analysis of isotope separation process. *Mailing Add:* 956 W Outer Dr Oak Ridge TN 37830

LEVIN, SEYMOUR R, b Chicago, Ill, Apr 27, 34; m 57; c 3. INTERNAL MEDICINE. *Educ:* Univ Ill, BS, 56, MD, 61; Am Bd Internal Med, dipl internal med, 70 & endocrinol, 73. *Prof Exp:* Intern, Cook Co Hosp, Chicago, 61-62; resident, Wadsworth Vet Admin Hosp, Los Angeles, 62-65; physician, US Army Hosp, Ft Carson, 65-67; res fel endocrinol, Univ Calif, San Francisco, 67-69, asst res physician, 69-73; DIR DIABETES CLIN & CHIEF METAB UNIT, WADSWORTH VET ADMIN HOSP, 73-; PROF MED, UNIV CALIF, LOS ANGELES, 81- *Concurrent Pos:* Consult, Fresno Valley Med Ctr & Endocrine Div, Univ Calif, Los Angeles, 73- *Honors & Awards:* Grant, Am Diabetes Asn Southern Calif, 74 & 75. *Mem:* Fel Am Col Physicians; Am Fedn Clin Res; Am Diabetes Asn; Endocrine Soc. *Res:* Studies of insulin secretion and mechanisms of secretion by the endocrine pancreas. *Mailing Add:* Wadsworth Vet Admin Hosp 691/111K Los Angeles CA 90073

LEVIN, SIDNEY SEAMORE, b Philadelphia, Pa, Mar 29, 29; m 62; c 2. PHYSIOLOGY, PHARMACOLOGY. *Educ:* Univ Pittsburgh, BS, 51, MS, 53, PhD(biol sci), 55. *Hon Degrees:* MA, Univ Pa, 71. *Prof Exp:* RES ASSOC, HARRISON DEPT SURG RES, SCH MED, UNIV PA, 58- *Mem:* AAAS; NY Acad Sci. *Res:* Adrenal output in shock; effect of hypertension on adrenal cortical steroids; cytochrome P-450. *Mailing Add:* 565 Dulles Bldg Hosp of the Univ of Pa Philadelphia PA 19104

LEVIN, SIMON ASHER, b Baltimore, Md, Apr 22, 41; m 64; c 2. MATHEMATICS, BIOLOGY. *Educ:* Johns Hopkins Univ, BA, 61; Univ Md, PhD(math), 64. *Prof Exp:* Asst math, Univ Md, 61-62; NSF fel biomath, Univ Calif, Berkeley, 64-65; asst prof math, 65-70, assoc prof appl math, 71-77, assoc prof ecol & systs & theoret & appl math, 72-77, chmn sect ecol & systs, 74-79, PROF APPL MATH & ECOL, CORNELL UNIV, 77-, DIR, ECOSYSTS RES CTR, 80- *Concurrent Pos:* Res assoc, Univ Md, College Park, 64; co-chmn biomath, Gordon Res Conf, 70, chmn theoret biol & biomath, 71; vis scholar, Univ Wash, 73-74; assoc ed, Ecol & Ecol Monographs, Ecol Soc Am, 73-75, ed, 75-77; assoc ed, Theoret Pop Biol, 76-; managing ed, Lecture Notes Biomath, 73-79 J Appl Math, Soc Indust & Appl Math, 75-79 & Biomathematics, 76-; adv ed, J Math Biol, 73-76, ed, 76-; ed, Lect on Math in Life Sci, 74-79; mem US comt, Israel Environ, 75-; adv ed, J Theoret Biol, 76-; consult ed, Evolutionary Theory, 76-, Math Intelligence, 77- & Int J Math Modeling, 79-; mem adv comt, Environ Sci Div, Oak Ridge Nat Lab, 78-81; vis scientist, Weizmann Inst, 77-80 & Univ BC, 79-80; Guggenheim fel, 79-80; co-dir, Math Col, Inter-Am Educ Asn, UNESCO, 82; Vchmn math, Comt Concerned Scientists, 79- *Mem:* AAAS; Am Math Soc; Am Soc Naturalists; Ecol Soc Am; Soc Indust & Appl Math. *Res:* Applied mathematics; ecology; population biology; mathematical physics and biology; partial differential equations. *Mailing Add:* Sect of Ecol & Syst Cornell Univ Ithaca NY 14853

LEVIN, SIMON EUGENE, b Philadelphia, Pa, Nov 29, 20; m 48; c 2. TOXICOLOGY, INDUSTRIAL HYGIENE. *Educ:* Philadelphia Col Pharm, BS, 41; Pa State Col, MS, 42, PhD, 49. *Prof Exp:* Bacteriologist, La Wall & Harrison Res Labs, 38-41; lab asst bact, Pa State Col, 41-42;

bioassayist, La Wall & Harrison Res Labs, 42-43 & 46; asst bact, Pa State Col, 46-49; res assoc chemother, E R Squibb & Sons, 49-50; head div biol, La Wall & Harrison Res Labs, 50-56; pres, Huntingdon Farms, Inc, West Conshohocken, 57-74; dir life sci div, Am Standards Testing Bur, 74-77; OCCUP HEALTH CONSULT, NJ STATE DEPT LABOR & INDUST, 77- *Concurrent Pos:* Dir, Syndot Labs, 57-74; consult, Decker Corp, 59-70. *Mem:* AAAS; Am Indust Hyg Asn; Toxicol Soc; Am Chem Soc; NY Acad Sci. *Res:* Medical and industrial pharmacology and toxicology. *Mailing Add:* 222 Glendalough Rd Erdenheim PA 19118

LEVIN, VICTOR ALAN, b Milwaukee, Wis, Nov 22, 41; m 63; c 2. CANCER, NEUROLOGY. *Educ:* Univ Wis-Madison, BS, 63, MD, 66. *Prof Exp:* Intern med, St Louis City Hosp, Washington Univ, 66-67; staff assoc chem pharm, Nat Cancer Inst, 67-69; resident neurol, Mass Gen Hosp, 69-71, Nat Inst Neurol Dis & Stroke fel, 71-72; instr, 72-73, asst prof, 73-77, assoc prof neurol, 77-81, PROF NEUROSURG, PHARM CHEM & PHARMACOLOGY, SCH MED & PHARM, UNIV CALIF, SAN FRANCISCO, 81- *Mem:* Am Acad Neurol; Am Asn Cancer Res. *Res:* Pharmacology and pharmacokinetics of brain tumor chemotherapeutic agents and experimental brain tumor chemotherapy. *Mailing Add:* Brain Tumor Res Ctr HSW-783 Univ of Calif Sch of Med San Francisco CA 94143

LEVIN, WILLIAM COHN, b Waco, Tex, Mar 2, 17; m 41; c 2. INTERNAL MEDICINE. *Educ:* Univ Tex, BA, 38, MD, 41. *Hon Degrees:* Dr, Univ Montpellier, 80. *Prof Exp:* From instr to assoc prof internal med, 44-65, dir hemat res lab & blood bank, 46-74, PROF INTERNAL MED, UNIV TEX MED BR GALVESTON, 65-, PRES, 74- *Concurrent Pos:* Consult, USPHS Hosp, Nassau Bay, 52; dir clin res ctr, John Sealy Hosp, 62-75. *Honors & Awards:* Ordre des Palmes Academiques, 81. *Mem:* Am Fedn Clin Res; Am Soc Hemat; AMA; fel Am Col Physicians; fel Int Soc Hemat. *Res:* Hematology; immunology; oncology. *Mailing Add:* Off of Pres Univ of Tex Med Br Galveston TX 77550

LEVIN, ZEV, b Haifa, Israel, Dec 17, 40; US citizen; m 65; c 2. ATMOSPHERIC SCIENCES, CLOUD PHYSICS. *Educ:* Calif State Univ, Los Angeles, BS, 66; Univ Wash, PhD(atmospheric sci), 70. *Prof Exp:* Res meteorologist, Univ Calif, Los Angeles, 70-71; PROF ATMOSPHERIC SCI, TEL AVIV UNIV, ISRAEL, 71- *Concurrent Pos:* Vis sr scientist atmospheric sci, Nat Ctr Atmospheric Res, 76-77; sr res assoc, Nat Res Coun, Ames Res Ctr, NASA, 81. *Mem:* Am Meteorol Soc; Am Geophys Union; Sigma Xi. *Res:* Formation of clouds and precipitation; cloud electrifications; atmospheric aerosols; ice nucleation. *Mailing Add:* Dept of Geophys & Planetary Sci Tel Aviv Univ Ramat Aviv 69978 Israel

LEVINE, AARON WILLIAM, b New York, NY, July 14, 43; m 64; c 3. PHYSICAL CHEMISTRY, POLYMER CHEMISTRY. *Educ:* Yeshiva Univ, BA, 63; City Col New York, MA, 66; Seton Hall Univ, PhD(org chem), 70. *Prof Exp:* Teacher, High Schs, NY, 63-66; res chemist, M&T Chem, Inc, 66-69; teaching asst chem, Seton Hall Univ, 69; MEM TECH STAFF, DAVID SARNOFF RES CTR, RCA LABS, 69- *Mem:* Am Chem Soc; fel Am Inst Chemists; Soc Plastics Engrs. *Res:* Liquid crystals; kinetics of organic reactions in solution; polymer syntheses and reaction; organic electrochemistry. *Mailing Add:* RCA Labs David Sarnoff Res Ctr Princeton NJ 08540

LEVINE, ALAN STEWART, b New York, NY, Aug 11, 44; m 67; c 2. HEMATOLOGY, BIOCHEMISTRY. *Educ:* Monmouth Col, NJ, BS, 55; Univ Del, PhD(chem), 71. *Prof Exp:* Teaching asst chem, Univ Del, 66-71; res assoc, Sch Pharm, Univ Kans, 71-72; staff fel, 72-74, sr staff fel, 74-77, HEALTH SCIENTIST ADMINR, NIH, 77- *Mem:* Am Soc Hematol; Am Chem Soc; Biophys Soc; AAAS. *Res:* Molecular mechanism of human red blood cell sickling; diseases of the red blood cell. *Mailing Add:* Fed Bldg Rm 5A12 Nat Heart Lung & Blood Inst NIH Bethesda MD 20205

LEVINE, ALFRED MARTIN, b Brooklyn, NY, Apr 5, 41; m 65; c 2. PLASMA PHYSICS, ENVIRONMENTAL SCIENCES. *Educ:* Cooper Union, BEE, 61; Princeton Univ, MA, 64, PhD(elec eng), 66. *Prof Exp:* Mem res staff, Plasma Physics Lab, Princeton Univ, 66; scientist, Laboratoria Gas, Ionizatti, Frascati, Italy, 66-68; mem tech staff, Bell Labs, 68-70; ASSOC PROF ENG SCI, COL STATEN ISLAND, CITY UNIV NEW YORK, 70-, MEM DOCTORAL FAC PHYSICS, UNIV, 71- *Mem:* Am Phys Soc. *Res:* Modeling of environmental systems; damped quantum mechanical oscillators. *Mailing Add:* Appl Sci Dept 130 Stuyvesant Pl Staten Island NY 10301

LEVINE, ALVIN SAUL, b Hamlet, NC, Aug 29, 25; m 51; c 4. VIROLOGY. *Educ:* Wake Forest Col, BS, 48; Univ NC, MSPH, 50; Rutgers Univ, PhD(microbiol), 54. *Prof Exp:* Res asst biochem, Duke Univ, 50-51; instr bact & immunol, Harvard Med Sch, 56-58; from asst prof to assoc prof microbiol, 58-64, PROF MICROBIOL & IMMUNOL, SCH MED, IND UNIV, INDIANAPOLIS, 64-, ASST DEAN, 81-; PROF LIFE SCI & DIR TERRE HAUTE CTR MED EDUC, IND STATE UNIV, TERRE HAUTE, 71- *Concurrent Pos:* Res fel microbiol, Rutgers Univ, 51-54; teaching fel bact & immunol, Harvard Med Sch, 54-56; Fulbright vis prof, Univ West Indies, 67-68. *Mem:* Fel Am Soc Microbiol; Am Asn Path; Am Asn Immunol; Am Asn Cancer Res. *Res:* Infectious diseases; viral oncology; RNA viruses; biochemical, biophysical and immunological studies. *Mailing Add:* Terre Haute Ctr for Med Educ Ind State Univ Sch Med HH 135 Terre Haute IN 47809

LEVINE, ARNOLD DAVID, b Brooklyn, NY, Oct 24, 25; m 62. THEORETICAL PHYSICS. *Educ:* Columbia Univ, PhD(physics), 58. *Prof Exp:* Asst prof physics, WVa Univ, 57-60; asst prof, Wayne State Univ, 60-62; from asst prof to assoc prof, 62-71, PROF PHYSICS, WVA UNIV, 71- *Concurrent Pos:* Consult, Columbia Liquified Natural Gas Corp, 71-73; consult, Am Gas Asn, currently. *Mem:* Combustion Inst; Am Phys Soc; Am Asn Physics Teachers. *Res:* Meson physics; quantum field theory; non-equilibrium thermodynamics; fluid dynamics; combustion. *Mailing Add:* Dept of Physics WVa Univ Morgantown WV 26505

LEVINE, ARNOLD JAY, virology, see previous edition

LEVINE, ARNOLD MILTON, b Preston, Conn, Aug 15, 16; m 41; c 3. COMMUNICATION ENGINEERING. *Educ:* Tri-State Col, BS, 39; Univ Iowa, MS, 40. *Hon Degrees:* DSc, Tri-State Col, 60. *Prof Exp:* Head, Sound Dept, Columbia Broadcasting Co, 40-42; from asst engr to vpres & dir missile & space systs, 42-71, vpres & gen mgr, ITT Aerospace, 71, vpres & tech dir, ITT Gilvillan Inc, 71-74, SR SCIENTIST, ITT GILFILLAN, INT TEL & TEL CORP, 74- *Mem:* Fel Inst Elec & Electronics Engrs; Am Inst Navig. *Res:* Research and development in communication and missile guidance navigation; time division systems; pulse code modulation; psuedo noise modulation; pulse and continuous wave missile guidance; radar research and development; fiber optics. *Mailing Add:* 10828 Fullbright Ave Chatsworth CA 91311

LEVINE, BARRY FRANKLIN, b Brooklyn, NY, Sept 5, 42; m 68. LASERS. *Educ:* Polytech Inst Brooklyn, BS, 63; Harvard Univ, PhD(physics), 69. *Prof Exp:* PHYSICIST, BELL LABS, 68-, DEPT HEAD, 77- *Mem:* Am Phys Soc. *Res:* Experimental and theoretical nonlinear optics of crystals and liquids; coherent Raman scattering; optical picosecond spectroscopy of surfaces; novel high speed semiconductor devices (phototransistors, functional element tests, lasers, photodetectors). *Mailing Add:* Bell Labs Murray Hill NJ 07974

LEVINE, BERNARD BENJAMIN, b New York, NY, Nov 8, 28. IMMUNOLOGY, MEDICINE. *Educ:* City Col New York, BS, 50; NY Univ, MD, 54. *Prof Exp:* From asst prof to assoc prof, 62-70, PROF MED, MED CTR, NY UNIV, 70-, DIR ALLERGY, 62- *Concurrent Pos:* Res fel path, Med Ctr, NY Univ, 60-62. *Mem:* Am Asn Immunol; Soc Exp Biol & Med; Am Soc Clin Invest; Am Acad Allergy. *Res:* Immunopathology; hypersensitivity; antigenicity; immune response; allergy. *Mailing Add:* Dept of Med NY Univ Med Ctr New York NY 10016

LEVINE, CHARLES (ARTHUR), b Des Moines, Iowa, Dec 25, 22; m 48; c 2. PHYSICAL CHEMISTRY, ELECTROCHEMISTRY. *Educ:* Iowa State Col, BS, 47; Univ Calif, PhD(chem), 51. *Prof Exp:* Asst, Univ Calif, 48-49, asst, Radiation Lab, 49-51; res chemist, 51-65, ASSOC SCIENTIST, DOW CHEM CO, 65- *Mem:* AAAS; Electrochem Soc; Am Chem Soc; Am Phys Soc; Am Inst Chem Eng. *Res:* Nuclear chemistry; radiation chemistry; electrochemistry. *Mailing Add:* 5869 Pine Hollow Rd Clayton CA 94517

LEVINE, D(ONALD) J(AY), b Brooklyn, NY, Oct 10, 21; m 46; c 2. ELECTRICAL ENGINEERING. *Educ:* City Col New York, BEE, 43; Polytech Inst Brooklyn, MEE, 52. *Prof Exp:* Sr asst, Microwave Res Inst, Polytech Inst Brooklyn, 46-48; dir, Radio Transmission & Anti-Submarine Warfare Lab, Int Tel & Tel Corp, 48-65; vpres & mgr, Transmission Systs Div, Commun Systs Inc, Comput Sci Corp, 65-67; dept head, Network Eng & Anal Dept, Commun Div, Mitre Corp, 67-73; dir systs eng, Page Commun Eng, Vienna, Va, 73-74; dir commun systs, Litton-Amecom, College Park, 74-75; dir commun eng, Aerospace Corp, Washington, DC, 75-76; V PRES ENG, KINGS ELECTRONICS CO, INC, TUCKAHOE, NY, 76- *Mem:* Nat Soc Prof Engrs; sr mem Inst Elec & Electronics Engrs. *Res:* Microwave components, systems, antennas and antenna systems; radio communications; line of sight and troposcatter systems; switched telecommunications systems; network management planning and analysis; economic engineering for fixed, mobile, surface, air, space and submarine environments; operations analysis. *Mailing Add:* 463 Martling Ave Tarrytown NY 10591

LEVINE, DANIEL, b New York, NY, July 21, 20; m 57; c 5. ELECTRICAL ENGINEERING. *Educ:* Univ Mich, BS, 41, MS, 42; Ohio State Univ, MSc, 48, PhD(elec eng), 55. *Prof Exp:* Electronics engr, Aircraft Radiation Lab, Wright-Patterson AFB, Ohio, 46-51, br tech consult, Aerial Reconnaissance Lab, 53-54; sr engr, Goodyear Aircraft Corp, Ariz, 54-56; consult engr, 56-61; CONSULT SCIENTIST, LOCKHEED MISSILES & SPACE CO, 61- *Mem:* Optical Soc Am; Am Soc Photogram; Inst Elec & Electronics Engrs. *Res:* System design of aerospace reconnaissance and mapping equipments; instrumentation for photographic and radar stereoanalysis; analogue simulators for radar trainers and guidance equipments; digital simulators for radar detection and tracking systems. *Mailing Add:* 1043 Enderby Way Sunnyvale CA 94087

LEVINE, DAVID ALAN, b Boston, Mass, Apr 12, 29; m 53; c 2. COMPUTER SCIENCE, MATHEMATICS. *Educ:* Univ Chicago, BA, 48; NY Univ, MS, 57, PhD(math), 63. *Prof Exp:* Res asst appl math, Nat Adv Comt Aeronaut, 51 & Courant Inst Math Sci, NY, 53-59; analyst comput sci, Brookhaven Nat Lab, 59-62; sr analyst, Repub Aviation Corp, 62-65; asst mgr comput ctr, State Univ NY, Stony Brook, 65-70; asst prof comput sci, Queens Col, 70-75; pres, Info Systs, Westburg, 75-77; engr, PRD Electronics, 77-78; ENG SYSTS ANALYST, AIL DIV, CUTLER-HAMMER, INC, EATON CORP, 80- *Concurrent Pos:* Consult, Fairchild-Hiller Corp, 65-66 & Nassau Heart Asn, 66-; res collabr, Brookhaven Nat Lab, 66-68. *Mem:* Asn Comput Mach; Simulation Coun; Inst Elec & Electronics Engrs. *Res:* Computer simulations; mathematical modelling; computer graphics. *Mailing Add:* AIL Div Cutler-Hammer Inc Comac Rd Deer Park NY 11729

LEVINE, DAVID MORRIS, b Boston, Mass, Dec 15, 39; m 65; c 2. BEHAVIORAL SCIENCES, HEALTH EDUCATION. *Educ:* Brandeis Univ, AB, 59; Univ Vt, MD, 64; Johns Hopkins Univ, MPH, 69, SCD, 72; Nat Bd Med Examr, dipl, 65; Am Col Prev Med, dipl, 71; Pan Am Med Assoc, dipl. *Prof Exp:* Intern, Montefiore Hosp, Pittsburgh, 64-65; resident, Waltham Hosp, Mass, 65-66; US Army Med Corp, 66-68; resident prev med, 68-70, assoc prof pub health, med educ & internal med, 72-81, PROF BEHAV SCI, HEALTH EDUC, JOHNS HOPKINS UNIV, 81-, DIR MANPOWER STUDIES, CTR HEALTH SERV RES & DEVELOP, 72- *Concurrent Pos:* Fel pub health serv, Sch Hyg & Pub Health, Johns Hopkins Univ, 68-71; consult, Nat Ctr Health Serv Res, 72- & Am Asn Med Col, 73-; mem study sect, Nat Heart-Lung Inst, NIH, 75-, Vet Admin Mert Rev, 80- *Mem:* AAAS; Am Pub Health Asn; Am Fedn Clin Res; Am Col Prev Med; Pan Am Med Asn. *Res:* Health behavior, health education and health promotion; health care manpower-services, health education strategies in managing chronic disease process and outcome of medical education. *Mailing Add:* Dept Behav Sci Johns Hopkins Sch Hygiene & Pub Health Baltimore MD 21205

LEVINE, DONALD MARTIN, b Boston, Mass, Oct 17, 29. ZOOLOGY, PARASITOLOGY. *Educ:* Univ Vt, BA, 51; Univ RI, MS, 53; Univ Pa, PhD(zool), 58. *Prof Exp:* USPHS fel, 58-60; helminthologist, Liberian Inst, Am Found Trop Med, 60-62; assoc prof, 62-74, PROF BIOL SCI, WILLIAM PATERSON COL NJ, 74- *Mem:* Am Soc Trop Med & Hyg; Am Inst Biol Sci; Royal Soc Trop Med & Hyg. *Res:* Immunology and ecology of parasitic infections. *Mailing Add:* Dept of Biol Sci William Paterson Col of NJ Wayne NJ 07470

LEVINE, DUANE GILBERT, b Baltimore, Md, July 5, 33; m 57; c 6. CHEMISTRY, PHYSICS. *Educ:* Johns Hopkins Univ, BES, 56, MS, 58. *Prof Exp:* Combustion, electrochem & petrol researcher, Exxon Res & Eng Co, 59-68, head air pollution control res & develop, Automotive Emission Res Sect, 68-70, adv logistics, Exxon Corp, 70-71, mgr petrol fuels res & develop, Fuels Prod Qual Res Lab, Exxon Res & Eng Co, 71-74, mgr petrol process eng, Gasoline & Lubes Process Eng Div, 74-76, gen mgr synthetic fuels res & develop, Baytown Res & Develop Div, 76-78, DIR, CORP RES-SCI LABS, EXXON RES & ENG CO, 78- *Concurrent Pos:* Mem, Eng & Tech Res Comt, Am Petrol Inst, 71-74; mem, Air Pollution Res Adv Comt, joint comt US Govt, Petrol Indust & Automotive Indust, 71-74. *Mem:* AAAS; fel Am Inst Chemists; Am Inst Chem Engrs; Am Petrol Inst; Int Combustion Inst. *Res:* solid state sciences; surface sciences; optics; catalysis; materials; theoretical and mathematical sciences; biosciences; engineering sciences; laser chemistry; polymer sciences; emulsion chemistry; chemical physics. *Mailing Add:* Corp Res-Sci Labs Exxon Res & Eng Co Linden NJ 07036

LEVINE, ELLIOT MYRON, b Brooklyn, NY, June 16, 37; m 59; c 3. CELL BIOLOGY, CELL CULTURE. *Educ:* Queens Col, NY, BS, 57; Yale Univ, PhD(biochem), 61. *Prof Exp:* Sr asst scientist biochem, Nat Inst Arthritis, Metab & Digestive Dis, 61-63; from assoc to asst prof cell biol, Albert Einstein Col Med, 63-72; coordr res training, 74-80, asst prof, 73-80, ASSOC PROF, WISTAR INST, 80-; ASSOC PROF MICROBIOL, UNIV PA, 75- *Concurrent Pos:* NIH fel, Albert Einstein Col Med, 63-64, NIH spec res fel, 64-65, NIH career develop award, 68-72; NSF res grants, Albert Einstein Col Med & Wistar Inst, 70-; NIH res grants, Wistar Inst, 72-; Lung Cell Comt, Am Type Cult Col, 76-; staff mycoplasma detection course, W Alton Jones Cell Sci Ctr, 77-; mem, Cell Biol Study Sect, NIH, 78-82. *Mem:* AAAS; Tissue Cult Asn. *Res:* Growth regulation, cellular senesence, differentiation, and mycoplasma detection in cultured cells, especially endothelial cells. *Mailing Add:* Wistar Inst 36th St at Spruce Philadelphia PA 19104

LEVINE, ERNEST NORMAN, metallurgy, see previous edition

LEVINE, EUGENE, b Brooklyn, NY, Jan 11, 25; m 48; c 3. ANALYTICAL STATISTICS, OPERATIONS RESEARCH. *Educ:* City Col New York, BBA, 48; NY Univ, MPA, 50; Am Univ, PhD(pub admin), 60. *Prof Exp:* Statistician, New York City Dept Health, 47-50; chief, Manpower Anal & Resources Br, Div Nursing, USPHS, 50-78, dep dir, Div Health Prof Anal, 78-80; PRES, EUGENE LEVINE ASSOC, 80- *Honors & Awards:* Super Serv Award, Dept Health, Educ & Welfare, 62. *Mem:* Am Pub Health Asn; Nat League Nursing; Am Statist Asn. *Res:* Health manpower analysis; problems of health services organization and delivery; psychometric analysis into problems of job satisfaction; career choice and motivation; evaluation of health care programs. *Mailing Add:* 8135 Inverness Ridge Rd Potomac MD 20854

LEVINE, GEOFFREY, b Washington, DC, Sept 2, 42; m 70; c 3. NUCLEAR PHARMACY, HEALTH PHYSICS. *Educ:* Temple Univ, BS, 65, MS, 67; Northwestern Univ, PhD(civil eng & environ health), 78. *Prof Exp:* Clin asst prof, Dept Pharmaceut, Sch Pharm, 72-80, ASST PROF RADIOL, SCH MED, UNIV PITTSBURGH, 72- *Concurrent Pos:* Grants, Am Cancer Soc, Union Carbide Corp, Soc Nuclear Med & others, 74-; dir radiopharmaceut serv, Univ Pittsburgh Health Ctr, 72-; nuclear pharmacist, Presbyterian-Univ Hosp, 72- *Mem:* Health Physics Soc; Soc Nuclear Med (secy-treas, 74); Sigma Xi; Am Pharmaceut Asn; AAAS. *Res:* Drug interactions; radioactive pharmaceuticals and radioactive antibodies for tumor detection; pathogenesis of radiation induced lung cancer; cost-benefit risk analysis; inventory control modeling of radiopharmaceuticals; radiopharmacology. *Mailing Add:* Dept Nuclear Med Presby Univ Hosp Pittsburgh PA 15213

LEVINE, GILBERT, b Teaneck, NJ, Apr 12, 27; m 50; c 3. AGRICULTURAL ENGINEERING. *Educ:* Cornell Univ, BS, 49, PhD(agr eng), 52. *Prof Exp:* From asst prof to assoc prof, 52-65, PROF AGR ENG, CORNELL UNIV, 65-, DIR, CTR ENVIRON RES, 74- *Concurrent Pos:* Vis assoc prof, Univ Calif, 58-59; vis assoc prof, Univ Philippines, 63-65, vis prof, 68-69; consult, Ford Found, 72- & Int Food Policy Res Inst, 78-; sr consult, Ministry Pub Works, Venezuela, 76-77. *Mem:* Am Soc Agr Engrs; Am Soc Eng Educ; Soil Conserv Soc Am. *Res:* Engineering and management aspects of tropical irrigation. *Mailing Add:* Dept of Agr Eng Cornell Univ Ithaca NY 14853

LEVINE, HAROLD, b New York, NY, Mar 24, 22; m 47. APPLIED MATHEMATICS. *Educ:* City Col New York, BS, 41; Cornell Univ, PhD(physics), 44. *Prof Exp:* Res fel physics, Harvard Univ, 45-54; assoc prof, 55-70, PROF MATH, STANFORD UNIV, 70- *Concurrent Pos:* Lectr, Harvard Univ, 52-54; consult, Lawrence Radiation Lab, Univ Calif. *Mem:* Am Phys Soc. *Res:* Boundary value problems of classical field theories, particularly acoustics, electrodynamics and hydrodynamics. *Mailing Add:* Dept of Math Stanford Univ Stanford CA 94305

LEVINE, HAROLD IRVING, b Lynn, Mass, Dec 14, 28; m 61. MATHEMATICS. *Educ:* Univ Chicago, PhD(math), 57. *Prof Exp:* Fulbright fel & Ger Res Asn grant, Univ Bonn, 57-59; instr math, Yale Univ, 59-60; from asst prof to assoc prof, 60-70, PROF MATH, BRANDEIS UNIV, 70- *Mem:* Am Math Soc. *Res:* Differential topology. *Mailing Add:* Dept of Math Brandeis Univ Waltham MA 02154

LEVINE, HARVEY ROBERT, b New York, NY, Sept 15, 31; m 56; c 2. PARASITOLOGY, ENTOMOLOGY. *Educ:* City Col New York, BS, 53; Univ Mass, MS, 55, PhD(entom), 58. *Prof Exp:* Instr entom, Univ Mass, 55; from asst prof to prof biol, Bemidji State Col, 58-68; chmn dept biol, 68-76, asst dean acad affairs, Sch Sci, 71-72, PROF BIOL, QUINNIPIAC COL, 68- *Concurrent Pos:* Consult, Trout Unlimited; mem, Mus Natural Hist. *Mem:* Am Inst Biol Sci; Am Asn Lab Animal Sci; Nat Environ Health Asn; Entom Soc Am. *Res:* Zoonoses; freshwater insects; medical entomology. *Mailing Add:* Dept of Biol Sci Quinnipiac Col Hamden CT 06518

LEVINE, HERBERT JEROME, b Boston, Mass, July 22, 28; m 58; c 1. CARDIOLOGY. *Educ:* Harvard Univ, AB, 50; Johns Hopkins Univ, MD, 54; Am Bd Internal Med, dipl, 63. *Prof Exp:* Intern med, Peter Bent Brigham Hosp, 54-55, sr resident, 58-59; resident, Mass Gen Hosp, 57-58; res fel, Harvard Med Sch, 59-61; sr instr, 61-63, from asst prof to assoc prof, 63-70, PROF MED, SCH MED, TUFTS UNIV, 70-; CHIEF CARDIOL SERV, NEW ENG MED CTR HOSPS, 66- *Concurrent Pos:* Res fel cardiol, Peter Bent Brigham Hosp, 56-61; consult, Vet Admin Hosp, Mass, 66-; lectr, US Naval Hosp, Mass, 67- *Mem:* Fel Am Fedn Clin Res; fel Asn Univ Cardiol; fel Am Col Cardiol; fel Am Soc Clin Invest; Asn Am Physicians. *Res:* Clinical cardiology; physiology of congestive heart failure; muscle mechanics and energetics in the intact heart. *Mailing Add:* New Eng Med Ctr Hosp 171 Harrison Ave Boston MA 02111

LEVINE, HERMAN SAUL, b Jeannette, Pa, Feb 11, 22; m 47; c 3. PHYSICAL CHEMISTRY, HIGH TEMPERATURE CHEMISTRY. *Educ:* Univ Pittsburgh, BS, 43; Univ Ill, PhD(phys chem), 48. *Prof Exp:* Res asst, Ill State Geol Surv, 44-46; staff mem, NY State Col Ceramics, Alfred Univ, 48-51 & USPHS, R A Taft Sanit Eng Ctr, 51-57; STAFF MEM, SANDIA LABS, 57- *Mem:* Am Chem Soc. *Res:* Radioactive waste management. *Mailing Add:* Sandia Labs Div 5812 Albuquerque NM 87185

LEVINE, HILLEL BENJAMIN, b Montreal, Que, July 9, 23; nat US; m 49; c 2. BACTERIOLOGY. *Educ:* McGill Univ, BSc, 45; Univ Wis, MS, 46, PhD(bact, biochem), 49. *Prof Exp:* Chief biochem div, 53-58, chief mycol div, 58-70, RES BACTERIOLOGIST, NAVAL BIOMED RES LAB, UNIV CALIF, 50-, CHMN MED MICROBIOL DEPT, 70- *Concurrent Pos:* Consult, Sir Herbert Reddy Mem Hosp, Montreal, 49; secy comt on mycoses, Pan Am Health Orgn, 71. *Honors & Awards:* Lab Award, Am Pub Health Asn, 63. *Mem:* Med Mycol Soc Am; NY Acad Sci; Int Soc Human & Animal Mycol. *Res:* Bacterial and fungal physiology and virulence; fungal vaccines; respiratory metabolism; antifungal drugs. *Mailing Add:* Univ Calif Naval Biosci Lab Naval Supply Ctr Oakland CA 94625

LEVINE, HOWARD ALLEN, b St Paul, Minn, Jan 15, 42. MATHEMATICS. *Educ:* Univ Minn, Duluth, BA, 64; Cornell Univ, MA, 67, PhD(math), 69. *Prof Exp:* Asst prof math, Univ Minn, Minneapolis, 69-73; asst prof, 73-75, ASSOC PROF MATH, UNIV RI, 75- *Concurrent Pos:* Vis scientist, Battelle Advan Studies Ctr, Switz, 71 & 72; Sci Res Coun Gt Brit grant, Univ Dundee, 72; NSF res grant, 74-77 & 78-79; part-time res consult, Naval Underwater Systs Ctr, 77-78; assoc prof, Iowa State Univ, 78-79. *Mem:* Am Math Soc. *Res:* Partial differential equations; numerical analysis. *Mailing Add:* Dept of Math Univ of RI Kingston RI 02881

LEVINE, HOWARD BERNARD, b Brooklyn, NY, Apr 15, 28; m 67; c 2. PHYSICAL CHEMISTRY. *Educ:* Univ Ill, BS, 50; Univ Chicago, MS, 52, PhD(chem), 55. *Prof Exp:* Res fel chem, Inst Atomic Res, Iowa State Univ, 55-56; chemist, Lawrence Radiation Lab, Univ Calif, 56-62; mem tech staff, NAm Aviation Sci Ctr, 62-70; proj assoc, Theoret Chem Inst & Space Sci & Eng Ctr, Univ Wis, 70-71; prof chem eng, Va Polytech Inst & State Univ, 71-73; prog mgr chem systs, Systs, Sci & Software, 73-76; PRIN SCIENTIST, JAYCOR, 76- *Concurrent Pos:* Consult, Tech Adv Bd Supersonic Transport, Dept Com; mem ad hoc comt ozone & environ studies bd, Nat Acad Sci. *Mem:* Am Chem Soc; fel Am Phys Soc; Am Inst Chem Eng. *Res:* Thermodynamics; statistical mechanics; quantum mechanics; spectroscopy; atmospheric chemistry; molecular physics; applied mathematics; chemical kinetics. *Mailing Add:* Jaycor PO Box 85154 San Deigo CA 92138

LEVINE, IRA NOEL, b Brooklyn, NY, Sept 8, 37. PHYSICAL CHEMISTRY. *Educ:* Carnegie Inst Technol, BS, 58; Harvard Univ, AM, 59, PhD(chem), 63. *Prof Exp:* Res assoc chem, Univ Pa, 63-64; from instr to assoc prof, 64-77, PROF CHEM, BROOKLYN COL, 78- *Concurrent Pos:* Am Chem Soc Petrol Res Fund starter grant, 65-66. *Mem:* Am Chem Soc; Am Phys Soc. *Res:* Quantum chemistry. *Mailing Add:* Dept of Chem Brooklyn Col Brooklyn NY 11210

LEVINE, ISIDORE, b New York, NY, Dec 1, 22; m 51; c 4. INTERNAL MEDICINE. *Educ:* City Col New York, BS, 48; Univ Rochester, MD, 52. *Prof Exp:* Instr med & psychiat, Sch Med & Dent, Univ Rochester, 56-58, asst prof prev med & community health, 58-62, assoc prof med, health serv, prev med & community health, 62-67; ASSOC PROF PREV MED, ALBERT EINSTEIN COL MED, 67-; DEP DIR, MONTEFIORE HOSP & MED CTR, 67- *Concurrent Pos:* Commonwealth Fund fel med & psychiat, Sch Med & Dent, Univ Rochester, 56-58, asst prof med & assoc physician, 58-64; sr assoc physician, 64-67; consult, Genesee Hosp, Rochester, 58-; assoc med dir, Strong Mem Hosp, 65- *Res:* Educational programs in comprehensive patient care. *Mailing Add:* Dept of Community Health Albert Einstein Col Med Bronx NY 10461

LEVINE, J(OSEPH) S(AMUEL), b San Antonio, Tex, Sept 14, 15; m 55; c 2. PETROLEUM ENGINEERING. *Educ:* Univ Tex, BS, 36; Pa State Col, MS, 38, PhD(petrol eng), 41. *Prof Exp:* Asst & instr petrol eng, Pa State Col, 36-42; sr chemist fluid flow res, Shell Develop Co Div, 46-60, sr exploitation engr, 60-64, STAFF ENGR, SHELL OIL CO, 64- *Mem:* Am Inst Mining, Metall & Petrol Engrs; Soc Petrol Engrs. *Res:* Fluid flow; hydrodynamics; fluid flow through porous media; mechanism of displacement of oil by water; secondary recovery of oil. *Mailing Add:* Shell Develop Co PO Box 481 Houston TX 77001

LEVINE, JACK, b Philadelphia, Pa, Dec 15, 07; m 38. MATHEMATICS. *Educ:* Univ Calif, Los Angeles, AB, 29; Princeton Univ, PhD(math), 34. *Prof Exp:* Asst math, Univ Calif, Los Angeles, 29-30; instr, Princeton Univ, 30-35; from instr to assoc prof, 35-47, PROF MATH, NC STATE UNIV, 47- *Concurrent Pos:* Res analyst, US Dept War, 42-43. *Mem:* Am Math Soc; Am Soc Eng Educ; Math Asn Am. *Res:* Differential geometry; tensor analysis; combinatorial analysis. *Mailing Add:* Dept of Math NC State Univ Raleigh NC 27650

LEVINE, JEFFREY, b Brooklyn, NY, Feb 7, 45; m 66. MATHEMATICS. *Educ:* State Univ NY Stony Brook, BS, 66; Rutgers Univ, New Brunswick, PhD(math), 70. *Prof Exp:* Asst prof math, Monmouth Col, NJ, 69-71; asst prof math, State Univ NY Col Geneseo, 71-80; MEM STAFF, MC DONNELL DOUGLAS CORP, 80- *Mem:* Am Math Soc; Math Asn Am. *Res:* Ring theory. *Mailing Add:* 761 LaFeil Dr Manchester MO 63011

LEVINE, JEROME PAUL, b New York, NY, May 4, 37; m 58; c 3. TOPOLOGY. *Educ:* Mass Inst Technol, BS, 58; Princeton Univ, PhD(math), 62. *Prof Exp:* Instr math, Mass Inst Technol, 61-63; NSF fels, 63-64; from asst prof to assoc prof math, Univ Calif, Berkeley, 64-66; assoc prof, 66-69, chmn dept, 74-76, PROF MATH, BRANDEIS UNIV, 69- *Concurrent Pos:* Sloan Found fel, 66-68. *Mem:* Am Math Soc. *Res:* Differential topology; knot theory. *Mailing Add:* Dept of Math Brandeis Univ Waltham MA 02154

LEVINE, JOEL S, b Brooklyn, NY, May 14, 42; m 68; c 1. GEOCHEMISTRY, GEOPHYSICS. *Educ:* Brooklyn Col, BS, 64; NY Univ, MS, 67; Univ Mich, MS, 73, PhD, 77. *Prof Exp:* Res scientist atmospheric sci, Goddard Inst Space Studies, 64-70; SR RES SCIENTIST, ATMOSPHERIC SCI, LANGLEY RES CTR, NASA, 70- *Concurrent Pos:* Instr physics & dir astron observ, Brooklyn Col, 64-70; res scientist atmospheric sci, Geophys Res Lab, NY Univ, 64-70; consult, Mars Aeronomy, Viking Proj NASA, 72-76; prin guest investr, Orbiting Astron Observ-Copernicus, 74-76; res adv, Sch Eng, Old Dominion Univ, 77-; lectr atmospheric & space sci, Col William & Mary, 78-; co-ed, Man's Impact on the Troposphere, 78; prin investr, Global Tropospheric Chem Photochem Processes, 77-, Atmospheric Chem Exp & NASA Storm Hazards Proj, 79-; consult, Comt Planetary Biol Chem Evolution, Space Sci Bd, Nat Res Coun-Nat Acad Sci, 79- *Honors & Awards:* H J E Reid Award, NASA Langley Res Ctr, 74. *Mem:* Am Geophys Union; Sigma Xi; AAAS; Am Inst Aeronaut & Astronaut. *Res:* Origin, evolution, physics and chemistry of planetary atmospheres; ozone photochemistry; tropospheric and stratospheric chemistry; lightning as a source of gases in planetary atmospheres. *Mailing Add:* Atmospheric Sci Br Atmospheric Environ Sci Div NASA Langley Res Ctr Hampton VA 23665

LEVINE, JON DAVID, b New York, NY, Mar 20, 45. MEDICAL SCIENCES. *Educ:* Univ Mich, BS, 66; Yale Univ, PhD(neurobiol), 72; Univ Calif, San Francisco, MD, 78. *Prof Exp:* FEL RHEUMATOL & CLIN IMMUNOL, UNIV CALIF, SAN FRANCISCO, 81-, FEL CLIN PHARMACOL & THERAPEUT, 82-, CLIN RES NEUROPHYSIOLOGIST, 79-, LECTR PHYSIOL, 81- *Res:* Mechanisms of pain and anlygesia and application of research in this area to the diagnosis and mangement of clinical pain; pathophyisology of inflammatory joint. *Mailing Add:* Sch Med Univ Calif San Francisco CA 94143

LEVINE, JON HOWARD, b Toronto, Ont, July 13, 41; m 64; c 3. ENDOCRINOLOGY. *Educ:* Univ Toronto, MD, 65, MSc, 69; Royal Col Physicians & Surgeons Can, FRCP(C), 71; Am Bd Internal Med, cert endocrinol, 77. *Prof Exp:* Instr, Vanderbilt Univ, 71-73; asst prof, 73-78, ASSOC PROF ENDOCRINOL, MED UNIV SC, 78- *Concurrent Pos:* Fel, Med Res Coun Can, 71-73. *Mem:* Am Fedn Clin Res; Endocrine Soc; Can Soc Endocrin & Metab. *Res:* Hormonal regulation of polyamine biosynthesis; pituitary regulation of adrenal steroidogenesis. *Mailing Add:* Dept of Med Med Univ of SC Charleston SC 29403

LEVINE, JULES DAVID, b New York, NY, June 24, 37; m 66; c 2. SYSTEMS DESIGN, SOLAR ENERGY ENGINEERING. *Educ:* Columbia Univ, BS, 59; Mass Inst Technol, PhD(physics, nuclear eng), 63. *Prof Exp:* Mem tech staff surface & mat res, David Sarnoff Res Ctr, RCA Labs, 63-73, proj mgr flat panel TV, 73-76, proj mgr cathode red & develop, 76-79; BR MGR SOLAR ENERGY SYSTS, TEXAS INSTRUMENTS, 79- *Concurrent Pos:* Vis lectr elec eng, Princeton Univ, 71-72 & 74-75. *Honors & Awards:* Outstanding Achievement Awards, RCA Corp, 68, 72 & 75. *Mem:* Fel Inst Elec & Electronics Engrs; sr mem Am Vacuum Soc. *Res:* Physical processes and engineering of surfaces; thin films; semiconductors; electron emitters; display and power tubes; thermionic energy conversion; high voltage phenomena; electron beams; varistors; vacuum science and technology. *Mailing Add:* Texas Instruments MS 158 PO Box 225303 Dallas TX 75265

LEVINE, JULES IVAN, b Brooklyn, NY, Apr 17, 38; m 62; c 2. HEALTH SCIENCES, MEDICAL ADMINISTRATION. *Educ:* Univ Va, BEE, 60, PhD(biomed eng), 72; Johns Hopkins Univ, MS, 68. *Prof Exp:* Sr engr aerospace electronics, Westinghouse Elec Corp, 63-68; asst prof pediat, 72-77, asst dean allied health, 74-78, ASSOC PROF PEDIAT, UNIV VA, 77-, ASST VPRES HEALTH AFFAIRS, 78- *Concurrent Pos:* Consult, Health Resources Admin, Hyattsville, Md, Dept Health, Educ & Welfare, 74- *Mem:* Am Pub Health Asn. *Res:* Planning and evaluation of health resources and the health care delivery system. *Mailing Add:* Div of Health Serv Res Univ of Va Med Ctr Charlottesville VA 22908

LEVINE, LAURENCE, b New York, NY, July 10, 26; m 51; c 3. CELL BIOLOGY. *Educ:* NY Univ, BA, 49; Univ Wis, MA, 52, PhD(zool, biochem), 55. *Prof Exp:* Asst parasitol, Univ Wis, 50-55; from instr to assoc prof biol, 55-66, PROF BIOL, WAYNE STATE UNIV, 66-, COORDR FRESHMAN BIOL, 68- *Mem:* AAAS; Am Soc Cell Biol. *Res:* Cell contractility; chromosome motion; chromosome structure and function; mechanism of meiosis. *Mailing Add:* Dept of Biol Wayne State Univ Detroit MI 48202

LEVINE, LAWRENCE, b Hartford, Conn, July 18, 24. IMMUNOCHEMISTRY. *Educ:* Univ Conn, BA, 48; Univ Mich, MS, 50; Johns Hopkins Univ, DSc(microbiol), 53. *Prof Exp:* Instr microbiol, Johns Hopkins Univ, 53-54; res scientist, Div Labs & Res, State Dept Health, NY, 54-57; from asst prof to assoc prof, 57-70, PROF BIOCHEM, BRANDEIS UNIV, 70- *Res:* Blood proteins and their immunological properties. *Mailing Add:* Grad Dept of Biochem Brandeis Univ Waltham MA 02154

LEVINE, LAWRENCE ELLIOTT, b Chelsea, Mass, June 23, 41; m 65; c 7. APPLIED MATHEMATICS. *Educ:* Rensselaer Polytech Inst, BS, 63; Univ Md, PhD(appl math), 68. *Prof Exp:* Asst prof, 68-72, assoc prof, 68-77, PROF MATH, STEVENS INST TECHNOL, 77- *Mem:* Am Math Soc; Soc Indust & Appl Math. *Res:* Fluid dynamics; partial differential equations; perturbation methods. *Mailing Add:* Dept Math Stevens Inst of Technol Hoboken NJ 07030

LEVINE, LEO MEYER, b Brooklyn, NY, May 26, 22; m 49; c 3. MATHEMATICS. *Educ:* City Col New York, BS, 42; NY Univ, PhD(math), 60. *Prof Exp:* Asst physicist, Signal Corps Labs, Eatontown, NJ, 42-43; sr physicist, Mat Lab, NY Naval Shipyard, 47-59; from asst res scientist to assoc res scientist, Courant Inst Math Sci, NY Univ, 59-63, from asst prof to assoc prof, 63-70; assoc prof, 70-81, PROF MATH, QUEENSBOROUGH COMMUNITY COL, 81- *Concurrent Pos:* Consult, Radio Corp Am, 61-62. *Mem:* Am Math Soc; Math Asn Am. *Res:* Applied mathematics; ordinary and partial differential equations; acoustics; electromagnetic theory. *Mailing Add:* Queensborough Community Col Bayside NY 11364

LEVINE, LEON, b Brooklyn, NY, Jan 6, 34; m 66; c 2. POLYMER CHEMISTRY. *Educ:* Brooklyn Col, BS, 56; Polytech Inst New York, PhD(org chem), 63. *Prof Exp:* Res & develop chemist polymers, Foster Grant Co, 63-66; Gaylord assoc, 66-67; res & develop chemist polymers, Sun Chem Co, 67-68; res & develop chemist dent mat, Warner Lambert Co, 68-72; res & develop chemist polymers, Nat Patent Develop Corp, 72-76; res & develop chemist polymers, Loctite Corp, 76-80; SR CHEMIST, COATS & LEVINE, INC, 81- *Concurrent Pos:* Consult, L & E Assocs, 82- *Mem:* Am Chem Soc. *Res:* Adhesives; photopolymerizations; do it yourself products; dental materials; hydrophilic polymers. *Mailing Add:* L & E Assocs 94 Brewster Rd W Hartford CT 06117

LEVINE, LEONARD, b Atlantic City, NJ, Jan 28, 29; m 52; c 2. NEUROPHYSIOLOGY. *Educ:* Rutgers Univ, BS, 50; Columbia Univ, PhD(physiol), 59. *Prof Exp:* Instr physiol, Columbia Univ, 57-60; from asst prof to assoc prof, Univ Va, 61-66; PROF PHYSIOL, PAC UNIV, 66-, PROF PHARMACOL, 76- *Concurrent Pos:* USPHS fel physiol, Columbia Univ, 59-60; fel biophys, Univ Col, Univ London, 60-61; USPHS res grants, 62-65, 67-68 & 70-72; res grant proposal evaluator, Regulatory Biol Prog, NSF, 78- *Mem:* AAAS; Am Physiol Soc; Biophys Soc; Am Soc Zool; Am Soc Pharmacol & Exp Therapeut. *Res:* Electrophysiology and pharmacology of ocular tissues; trophic interrelations between nerve and muscle tissues. *Mailing Add:* Col of Optom Pac Univ Forest Grove OR 97116

LEVINE, LEONARD P, b Newark, NJ, July 24, 32; m 54; c 1. HUMAN-COMPUTER INTERFACING. *Educ:* Queens Col, NY, BS, 54; Syracuse Univ, MS, 56, PhD(physics), 60. *Prof Exp:* Engr, Sperry-Gyroscope Co, 59-60; sr scientist, Honeywell Res Ctr, 60-64, prin res scientist, 64-66; PROF ELEC ENG & COMPUT SCI, UNIV WIS-MILWAUKEE, 66- *Mem:* Asn Comput Mach. *Res:* Human and machine interfacing; system to system interfacing; small machine system design; computer teaching techniques. *Mailing Add:* Dept Elec Eng & Comput Sci Univ of Wis Milwaukee WI 53201

LEVINE, LOUIS, b New York, NY, May 14, 21. GENETICS, ANIMAL BEHAVIOR. *Educ:* City Col New York, BS, 42, MS, 47; Columbia Univ, MA, 49, PhD(zool), 55. *Prof Exp:* From instr to assoc prof, 55-67, PROF BIOL, CITY COL NEW YORK, 68- *Concurrent Pos:* NSF grants, 60-; AEC grant, 63- *Mem:* Fel AAAS; Animal Behav Soc; Am Genetic Asn; Genetics Soc Am; Am Soc Naturalists. *Res:* Genetics of animal behavior and population genetics. *Mailing Add:* Dept of Biol City Col of New York New York NY 10031

LEVINE, MAITA FAYE, b Cincinnati, Ohio, Oct 17, 30. MATHEMATICS. *Educ:* Univ Cincinnati, BA, 52, BE, 53, MAT, 66; Ohio State Univ, PhD(math educ), 70. *Prof Exp:* Teacher, High Sch, Ohio, 53-63; instr, 63-70, asst prof, 70-76, ASSOC PROF MATH, UNIV CINCINNATI, 76- *Concurrent Pos:* NSF res grant, 74. *Mem:* Math Asn Am; Am Educ Res Asn; Nat Coun Teachers Math; Asn Women Math. *Res:* Relationship between mathematical competence and mathematical confidence; mathematical modeling; reasons why qualified women do not pursue mathematical careers; applications of programmable calculators in the undergraduate curriculum. *Mailing Add:* 1106 Louis Dr Cincinnati OH 45237

LEVINE, MARK DAVID, b Cleveland, Ohio, May 26, 44. ENERGY ANALYSIS, CHEMISTRY. *Educ:* Princeton Univ, BA, 66; Univ Calif, Berkeley, PhD(chem), 75. *Prof Exp:* Staff scientist, Ford Found Energy Policy Proj, 72-73; sr policy analyst, Stanford Res Inst, 74-78; PROG LEADER, LAWRENCE BERKELEY LAB, 78- *Res:* Lead activity analyzing the energy performance of buildings; analysis of energy conservation and electric utility peak loads; international energy analysis and environmental studies. *Mailing Add:* Lawrence Berkeley Lab Bldg 90 Rm 3124 Berkeley CA 94720

LEVINE, MARTIN, b Brooklyn, NY, Oct 27, 25; m 60; c 2. ENGINEERING, EDUCATION. *Educ:* City Col New York, BSEE, 50; Univ Pittsburgh, MLitt, 50, MEd, 60; Univ Mich, PhD(higher educ), 69. *Prof Exp:* Proj engr, Air Res & Develop, 50-53; mem fac, Pa State Univ, 53-63 & Harrisburg Area Community Col, 65-68; PROF ELEC TECHNOL, VA WEST COMMUNITY COL, 68- *Mem:* Inst Elec & Electronics Engrs; Am Soc Eng Educ. *Res:* Student-work interface. *Mailing Add:* Va West Community Col PO Box 4195 Roanoke VA 24015

LEVINE, MARTIN DAVID, b Montreal, Que, Mar 30, 38; m 61; c 2. COMPUTER VISION. *Educ:* McGill Univ, BEng, 60, MEng, 63; Univ London, DIC & PhD(control theory), 65. *Prof Exp:* From asst prof to assoc prof, 65-77, PROF ELEC ENG, McGILL UNIV, 77- *Concurrent Pos:* Vis prof comput sci, Hebrew Univ, Jerusalem, Israel, 79-80; Am Soc Eng Educ-Ford Found fel, 72. *Mem:* Sr mem Inst Elec & Electronics Engrs; Pattern Recognition Soc; Asn Comput Mach. *Res:* Computer vision; biomedical image processing; picture languages; artificial intelligence; intelligent robotics. *Mailing Add:* Dept of Elec Eng McGill Univ 3480 University St Montreal PQ H3A 2A7 Can

LEVINE, MARTIN GOLD, b Chattanoga, Tenn, July 19, 36. ANATOMY. *Educ:* Vanderbilt Univ, BA, 58; Med Col Ga, MS, 62; George Washington Univ, MPhil, 71, PhD(anat), 76. *Prof Exp:* Cur, Am Psychiat Mus Asn, 68-69; dir, Wood Libr, Mus Anesthesiol, 69-72; DIR, NJ MED SCH, UNIV MED & DENT NJ, 74-, ASST PROF ANAT, 77- *Concurrent Pos:* Assoc, Univ Sch Med, 69-72. *Mailing Add:* Dept Anat NJ Med Sch Univ Med & Dent NJ 100 Gergen St Newark NJ 07103

LEVINE, MELVIN MORDECAI, b Richmond, Va, Nov 20, 25; m 50; c 3. NUCLEAR ENGINEERING, NUCLEAR REACTOR PHYSICS. *Educ:* Mass Inst Technol, SB, 46; Univ Va, PhD(physics), 55. *Prof Exp:* Instr physics, Pa State Univ, 46-48; physicist, Babcock & Wilcox Co, 55-59; PHYSICIST, BROOKHAVEN NAT LAB, 59- *Mem:* Am Nuclear Soc. *Res:* Nuclear reactor safety research and applications, including neutronics and thermal-hydraulic phenomena; computational methods for reactor physics and engineering problems. *Mailing Add:* Brookhaven Nat Lab Upton NY 11973

LEVINE, MICHAEL S, b Brooklyn, NY, Sept 22, 44; m 66; c 1. NEUROSCIENCES. *Educ:* Queens Col, BA, 66; Univ Rochester, PhD(physiol psychol), 70. *Prof Exp:* Fel neurophysiol, Brain Res Inst, 70-72, asst res neurophysiologist, 72-76, lectr psychol, 75-76, asst prof, 76-79, ASSOC PROF PSYCHIAT, UNIV CALIF, LOS ANGELES, 79- *Concurrent Pos:* Consult neurophysiologist, Hereditary dis Found, 75. *Mem:* Soc Neurosci; Am Psychol Asn; Am Asn Anatomists; Sigma Xi. *Res:* Neurophysiology and neuroanatomy of basal ganglia in mature and developing animals; role of basal ganglia in regulation of behavior; development and prediction of learning ability in developing animals. *Mailing Add:* Ment Retardation Res Ctr Dept of Psychiat Univ of Calif Los Angeles CA 90024

LEVINE, MICHEAL JOSEPH, b Oak Park, Ill, Dec 1, 40; m 68; c 1. NUCLEAR PHYSICS, HYPERNUCLEAR PHYSICS. *Educ:* Yale Univ, BS, 62, MS, 64, PhD(physics), 68. *Prof Exp:* PHYSICIST NUCLEAR PHYSICS, BROOKHAVEN NAT LAB, 68- *Concurrent Pos:* Consult, High Voltage Eng Corp, 72-75; guest physicist, Max Planck Inst Nuclear Physics, Heidelberg, Ger, 75, Ctr d'Etudes Nucleaires, Saclay, France, 80-81. *Mem:* Am Phys Soc. *Res:* Study of nuclear reactions induced by charged particles, principally heavy ions; development of magnetic spectrometers and associated focal plane detectors; hypernuclear spectroscopy studied with kauns. *Mailing Add:* Brookhaven Nat Lab Bldg 510A Upton NY 11973

LEVINE, MYRON, b Brooklyn, NY, July 28, 26; m 50; c 2. GENETICS, VIROLOGY. *Educ:* Brooklyn Col, BA, 47; Ind Univ, PhD(zool), 52. *Prof Exp:* Res assoc microbiol, Univ Ill, 54-56; asst to assoc biologist, Brookhaven Nat Lab, 56-61; assoc prof, 61-66, PROF HUMAN GENETICS, SCH MED, UNIV MICH, ANN ARBOR, 66- *Concurrent Pos:* Am Cancer Soc fel, Johns Hopkins Univ, 53-54; Commonwealth Fund fel, Univ Geneva, 66-67; ed, J Virol, 72-76; vis scientist, Imp Cancer Res Fund, London, 73-74; chmn grad prog cell & molecular biol in health sci, Univ Mich, 74-; mem & chmn genetic basis of dis rev comt, Nat Inst Gen Med Sci, NIH, 75- *Mem:* Genetics Soc Am; Am Soc Microbiol; Am Inst Biol Sci. *Res:* Genetics and biochemistry of animal viruses; herpesvirus genetics, latency and immunology; tumor virology. *Mailing Add:* Dept of Human Genetics Univ of Mich Sch of Med Ann Arbor MI 48109

LEVINE, NATHAN, b Brooklyn, NY, Aug 7, 30; m 53; c 2. COMMUNICATIONS ENGINEERING. *Educ:* Mass Inst Technol, BS, 52; Univ Ill, MS, 54, PhD(physics), 57. *Prof Exp:* Mem tech staff, 57-61, supvr re-entry physics, 61-64, dept head, 64-68, dir anti-missile systs res, 68-71, DIR TOLL TRANSMISSION ENG CTR, BELL TEL LABS, 71- *Mem:* Inst Elec & Electronics Engrs. *Res:* System and planning studies for future transmission facilities to be employed in the national toll network. *Mailing Add:* 105 Townsend Dr Middletown NJ 07748

LEVINE, NORMAN DION, b Boston, Mass, Nov 30, 12; m 35. PARASITOLOGY, PROTOZOOLOGY. *Educ:* Iowa State Col, BS, 33; Univ Calif, PhD(zool), 37; Am Bd Med Microbiol, cert pub health & med lab parasitol. *Prof Exp:* Asst zool, Univ Calif, 33-37; asst animal parasitologist, 37-41, assoc animal pathologist, 41-42, from asst prof to assoc prof vet parasitol, 46-53, asst to dean col vet med, 47-57, sr mem, Ctr Zoonoses Res, 60-74, prof zool, 65-77, dir, Ctr Human Ecol, 68-74, PROF VET PARASITOL & VET RES, COL VET MED, UNIV ILL, URBANA, 53- *Concurrent Pos:* Mem, Nat Res Coun, 56-62; mem bd gov, Am Bd Microbiol, 59-64; vis prof, Univ Hawaii, 62, Santa Catalina Marine Biol Lab, 72 & J Hopkins Marine Sta, 80; mem comt health sci achievement award prog, NIH, 65-66, mem trop med & parasitol study sect, 65-69, chmn, 66-69, mem animal resources adv comt, 71-75; ed, J Protozool, 65-71. *Mem:* AAAS; Am Soc Parasitol; hon mem Soc Protozool (secy, 52-58, vpres, 58-59, pres, 59-60, actg secy, 60-62); hon mem Micros Soc Am (pres, 69-70); fel Am Acad Microbiol. *Res:* Protozoan and roundworm parasites of domestic and wild animals; malaria and other insect-borne diseases. *Mailing Add:* Col of Vet Med Univ of Ill Urbana IL 61801

LEVINE, OSCAR, b Brooklyn, NY, Feb 6, 23; m 48; c 2. PHYSICAL CHEMISTRY. *Educ:* City Col New York, BS, 43; Columbia Univ, AM, 48; Georgetown Univ, PhD(chem), 57. *Prof Exp:* With Nat Adv Comt Aeronaut, Ohio, 48-52; chemist, US Naval Res Lab, 52-58; CHEMIST, CHEM & MAT RES, GILLETTE SAFETY RAZOR CO, BOSTON, 58- *Mem:* AAAS; Am Chem Soc. *Res:* Chemistry and physics of solid and liquid surfaces and interfaces; lubrication; adhesion. *Mailing Add:* 43 Connolly St Randolph MA 02368

LEVINE, PAUL HERSH, b New York, NY, Sept 27, 35; m 63. THEORETICAL PHYSICS, APPLIED PHYSICS. *Educ:* Mass Inst Technol, BS, 56; Calif Inst Technol, MS, 57, PhD(theoret physics), 63. *Prof Exp:* Sr scientist, Jet Propulsion Lab, Calif Inst Technol, 63-64; chief scientist, Astrophys Res Corp, 64-72; chief scientist, Megatek Corp, 72-82. *Mem:* Am Phys Soc. *Res:* Ionospheric physics; over-the-horizon radar; quantum many-body problem; exploding wire phenomena; electron field emission; radiative transport; electromagnetic propagation; navigation and communication systems analysis; minicomputer applications; electroencephalography; psychobiology of consciousness. *Mailing Add:* PO Box 8827 Incline Village NV 89450

LEVINE, PAUL HOWARD, b New York, NY, Sept 11, 37; m 60; c 3. VIRAL ONCOLOGY, INTERNAL MEDICINE. *Educ:* Cornell Univ, BA, 59; Univ Rochester, MD, 63. *Prof Exp:* Intern internal med, Strong Mem Hosp, 63-64; resident fel oncol, Roswell Park Mem Inst, 64-66; resident internal med, Univ Colo, 66-68; RES INVESTR VIRAL ONCOL, NAT CANCER INST, 68- *Concurrent Pos:* Co-chmn immunol group, Nat Cancer Inst, 71-72, chmn immunol-epidemiol segment, Virus Cancer Prog, 72-75, head clin studies sect, Viral Leukemia & Lymphoma Br, 74-75, chmn clin adv group, Div Cancer Cause & Prev, 76-81, head clin studies sect, Lab Viral Carcinogenesis, 78- *Mem:* Am Asn Cancer Res; Am Col Physicians; Am Fedn Clin Res. *Res:* Epstein-Barr virus and related herpes viruses; viral immunology, application of assays to cancer etiology, diagnosis, treatment; etiology and control of breast cancer. *Mailing Add:* Nat Cancer Inst Bethesda MD 20205

LEVINE, PHILIP, b Kletsk, Russia, Aug 10, 00; nat US; m 38; c 4. IMMUNOLOGY, CANCER. *Educ:* City Col New York, BS, 19; Cornell Univ, MD, 23, MA, 25; FRCP, 73. *Hon Degrees:* DS, Mich State Univ, 67. *Prof Exp:* Asst, Rockefeller Inst, 25-28, assoc, 28-32; instr path & bact, Univ Wis, 32-35; bacteriologist & serologist, Newark Beth Israel Hosp, 35-44; dir, 44-66, emer dir immunohemat div, 66-75, CONSULT, ORTHO RES FOUND, 76- *Concurrent Pos:* Seminar assoc, Columbia Univ, 53-; vis investr, Sloan-Kettering Inst Cancer Res, 76. *Honors & Awards:* Johnson Award; Lasker Award, Am Pub Health Asn; Award, Passano Found; Landsteiner Award; Townsend Harris Award; Kennedy Award; Ward Burdick Award, Am Soc Clin Path; Gold Medal, Norwegian Soc Immunohemat, 75; Allan Award, Am Soc Human Genetics, 75. *Mem:* Nat Acad Sci; Am Soc Clin Path; fel Am Col Physicians; Am Soc Human Genetics (pres, 69); fel NY Acad Sci. *Res:* Blood groups, individual blood differences and their heredity; the Rh-Hr system and role in erythroblastosis; differences in Rh and ABO disease of newborn; blood group antigens in malignancy and use of their antibodies as cytotoxic agents in malignancies. *Mailing Add:* Ortho Res Found Rte 202 Raritan NJ 08869

LEVINE, PHILLIP J, b Providence, RI, Jan 7, 34; m 55; c 2. PHARMACY. *Educ:* Univ RI, BS, 55; Univ Md, MS, 57, PhD(pharm), 63. *Prof Exp:* Instr pharm, Sch Pharm, Univ Md, 57-63; from asst prof to assoc prof, 63-70, PROF PHARM, COL PHARM, DRAKE UNIV, 70-, COORDR CONTINUING EDUC PROG PHARM, 77- *Concurrent Pos:* Consult, Dr Salsbury's Labs, Charles City, Iowa, 65-70; dir, Coop IV Additive Proj, 67-69; chmn, Mayor's Task Force on Drugs, Des Moines, Iowa, 69-70; consult, Gov, State of Iowa, 70-72. *Mem:* Am Pharmaceut Asn. *Res:* Development of topical anesthetic suspensions to test their applicability to long duration of anesthesia in dental patients; product development in area of suspension and formulations. *Mailing Add:* Col of Pharm Drake Univ Des Moines IA 50311

LEVINE, RACHMIEL, b Poland, Aug 26, 10; nat US; m 43; c 2. ENDOCRINOLOGY. *Educ:* McGill Univ, BA, 32, MD, 36. *Hon Degrees:* MD, Univ Ulm, 69. *Prof Exp:* Asst dir dept metab & endocrine res, Michael Reese Hosp, 39-42, dir, 42-58, chmn dept med & dir med educ, 52-60; prof & chmn dept, NY Med Col, 60-70; dir, 70-78, DEP DIR RES, CITY OF HOPE MED CTR, 78- *Concurrent Pos:* Williams fel, Michael Reese Hosp, 36-37, res fel, 37-39; Endocrine Soc Upjohn scholar, 57; Guggenheim Found fel, 71-72; consult, NSF, 56-59 & 70-; pres, Int Fedn Diabetes, 67-70; mem bd dirs, Found Fund Psychiat Res. *Honors & Awards:* Thompson Award, Am Geriat Soc, 71; Gairdner Found Award, 71. *Mem:* Am Physiol Soc; Soc Exp Biol & Med; Endocrine Soc; Am Diabetes Asn (pres, 64-65); fel Am Acad Arts & Sci. *Res:* Hormonal control of metabolism; mode of action of insulin; diabetes. *Mailing Add:* City of Hope Med Ctr Duarte CA 91010

LEVINE, RANDOLPH HERBERT, b Denver, Colo, Nov 20, 46; m 70; c 2. ASTROPHYSICS, SOLAR PHYSICS. *Educ:* Univ Calif, Berkeley, AB, 68; Harvard Univ, AM, 69, PhD(physics), 72. *Prof Exp:* Vis scientist solar physics, High Altitude Observ, Nat Ctr Atmospheric Res, Boulder, Colo, 72-74; res fel solar physics, 74-75, RES ASSOC SOLAR PHYSICS, CTR ASTROPHYS, HARVARD COL OBSERV, 75-, LECTR ASTRON, 77- *Mem:* Am Astron Soc; Am Geophys Union; Int Astron Union; Am Phys Soc. *Res:* Physics and astrophysics of plasmas and magnetic fields, especially pertaining to the sun; image processing. *Mailing Add:* Ctr for Astrophys 60 Garden St Harvard Col Observ Cambridge MA 02138

LEVINE, RHEA JOY COTTLER, b Brooklyn, NY, Nov 26, 39; m 60; c 3. CELL BIOLOGY, CYTOCHEMISTRY. *Educ:* Smith Col, AB, 60; NY Univ, MS, 63, PhD(biol), 66. *Prof Exp:* Lab instr biol, Sch Com, Acct & Finance, Wash Sq Col, NY Univ, 63-64; res assoc neuropath, Sch Med, Univ Pa, 68-69; from asst prof to assoc prof, 69-80, PROF ANAT, MED COL PA, 80- *Concurrent Pos:* A H Robins Co fel biochem res, Manhattan State Hosp, Ward's Island, New York, 66; USPHS fel, Sch Med, Yale Univ, 66-68; Nat

Heart & Lung Inst grant, Pa Muscle Inst, 73-; Nat Inst Neurol Commun Dis & Stroke career develop award, 74-79; Nat Inst Gen Med Sci res grant, 75-; NSF grants, 79-80 & 79-82; mem, Cardiovasc & Pulmonary Study Sect, Div Res Grants, NIH, 80-84; co-ed, Basic Biol Muscle. *Mem:* AAAS; Histochem Soc; Am Asn Anat; NY Acad Sci; Soc Gen Physiol. *Res:* Ultrastructure; muscle structure and function; comparative aspects of immunohistochemistry and cytochemistry. *Mailing Add:* Med Col of Pa Dept of Anat 3300 Henry Ave Philadelphia PA 19129

LEVINE, RICHARD JOSEPH, b New York, NY, Nov 12, 39; m 69; c 2. OCCUPATIONAL MEDICINE. *Educ:* Princeton Univ, AB, 60; Calif Inst Technol, MS, 64, St Louis Univ, MD, 76; Harvard Univ MPH, 76. *Prof Exp:* Intern med, Grady Mem Hosp, 71-72; epidemiologist, Ctr Dis Control, Epidemic Intell serv, 72-75; sr med scientist, Ctr Occup & Environ Health, Stanford Res Inst, 76-77; CHIEF EPIDEMIOL, CHEM INDUST INST TOXICOL, 77- *Concurrent Pos:* Asst state epidemiologist, Ala State Health Dept, 72-73; epidemiologist, Cholera Res Lab, Dacca, Bangladesh, 73-75; partic, Working Group Asbestos, Int Agency Cancer Res, 77; adj asst prof, Dept Family Commun Med, Div Occup Med, Duke Univ, 78- *Mem:* Soc Epidemiol Res; Am Occup Med Asn. *Res:* Epidemiology of cholera and mass hysteria; effects of occupation on male reproduction. *Mailing Add:* Chem Indust Inst Toxicol PO Box 12137 Research Triangle Park NC 27709

LEVINE, ROBERT, b Boston, Mass, July 30, 19; m 50; c 3. ORGANIC CHEMISTRY. *Educ:* Dartmouth Col, BA, 40, MA, 42; Duke Univ, PhD(org chem), 45. *Prof Exp:* Asst, Dartmouth Col, 40-42; asst, Duke Univ, 42-45; chemist, Mathieson Chem Corp, NY, 45-46; from instr to assoc prof, 46-59, PROF CHEM, UNIV PITTSBURGH, 59- *Concurrent Pos:* Consult, Monsanto Co, 52-62, Schering Corp, 59-63, Reilly Tar & Chem Corp, 64-66, FMC Corp, 65-67, Columbia Org Chem Co, 70-73, Pressure Chem Co, 70-75, Fike Chem Inc, 71-74 & Mallinckrodt Chem Works, 74-75. *Mem:* Am Chem Soc; Int Asn Heterocyclic Chem; NY Acad Sci; Israel Chem Soc. *Res:* Heterocyclic nitrogen chemistry, including pyridine, pyrazine, pyrimidine and triazine; synthesis of organic fluorine compounds; chemistry of organometallic compounds; synthesis of potential medicinals. *Mailing Add:* Dept of Chem Univ of Pittsburgh Pittsburgh PA 15260

LEVINE, ROBERT, b New York, NY, Nov 10, 26; m 54; c 2. PEDIATRIC CARDIOLOGY. *Educ:* City Col New York, BS, 48; Western Reserve Univ, MD, 54. *Prof Exp:* From intern to resident pediat, State Univ NY Upstate Med Ctr, 54-57; from instr to assoc prof, Col Physicians & Surgeons, Columbia Univ, 62-72; PROF PEDIAT & DIR PEDIAT CARDIOL, NJ MED SCH, COL MED & DENT NJ, 72- *Concurrent Pos:* NIH trainee pediat cardiol, Col physicians & Surgeons, Columbia Univ, 59-61 & NIH fel cardiorespiratory physiol, 61-62; NY City Health Res Coun career scientist award, 62-72; John Polachek Found fel, 68-69; prin investr, NIH Grad Training Prog Pediat Cardiol, Columbia Univ, 70-72, responsible investr, Nat Heart & Lung Inst-SCOR, Col Physicians & Surgeons, 71-72. *Honors & Awards:* Borden Award, Western Reserve Univ, 54. *Mem:* Am Acad Pediat; Am Pediat Soc; Am Physiol Soc. *Res:* Cardiorespiratory physiology. *Mailing Add:* 533 Upper Blvd Ridgewood NJ 07450

LEVINE, ROBERT ALAN, b New York, NY, June 12, 32; m 56; c 3. MEDICINE, PHARMACOLOGY. *Educ:* Cornell Univ, AB, 54, MD, 58; Am Bd Gastroenterol, cert. *Prof Exp:* Intern med, NY Hosp-Cornell Med Ctr, 58-59, asst resident, 59-60; clin fel med, Liver Study Unit, Sch Med, Yale Univ, 61-62, res fel, 62-63; from asst chief to chief metab div, Army Med Res & Nutrit Lab, Fitzsimons Gen Hosp, 63-65; chief div gastroenterol, Brooklyn-Cumberland Med Ctr, 65-71, assoc prof med, 69-71; PROF MED, STATE UNIV NY UPSTATE MED CTR, 71-, CHIEF DIV GASTROENTEROL, STATE UNIV HOSP, 71- *Concurrent Pos:* Clin fel gastroenterol, NY Hosp-Cornell Med Ctr, 60-61. *Mem:* Am Soc Pharmacol & Exp Therapeut; Am Fedn Clin Res; Am Gastroenterol Asn. *Res:* Basic and clinical research in gastroenterology, metabolism and pharmacology; cyclic adenosine 3', 5'-monophosphate in vivo and in vitro; isolated perfused rat liver; chronic hepatitis; hormone regulation of gastrointestinal function. *Mailing Add:* State Univ Hosp 750 E Adams St Syracuse NY 13210

LEVINE, ROBERT JOHN, b New York, NY, Dec 29, 34; c 2. INTERNAL MEDICINE, PHARMACOLOGY. *Educ:* George Washington Univ, MD, 58; Am Bd Internal Med, dipl, 65. *Prof Exp:* Intern internal med, Peter Bent Brigham Hosp, Boston, Mass, 58-59, asst resident, 59-60; clin assoc clin pharmacol, Nat Heart Inst, 60-62; resident internal med, Vet Admin Hosp, West Haven, Conn, 62-63; investr clin pharmacol, Nat Heart Inst, 63-64; from instr to assoc prof internal med & pharmacol, 64-73, chief sect clin pharmacol, 66-74, dir physician's assoc prog, 73-75, PROF INTERNAL MED & LECTR PHARMACOL, SCH MED, YALE UNIV, 73- *Concurrent Pos:* Clin asst, Yale-New Haven Hosp, 64-65, asst attend physician, 65-68, attend physician, 68-; clin investr, Vet Admin Hosp, West Haven, Conn, 64-66, attend physician, 66-; mem myocardial infarction comt, Nat Heart & Lung Inst, 69-72; mem div med sci, Nat Res Coun, 71-75; ed, Clin Res, Am Fedn Clin Res, 71-; consult, Nat Comn Protection Human Subj Biomed & Behav Res, 74-78; mem lipid metab adv comt, Nat Heart, Lung & Blood Inst, 77-79; ed, IRB: Review Human Subjects Res, 79-; vchmn, Comn Fed Drug Approval Process, 81- *Mem:* Am Soc Pharmacol; Am Soc Clin Pharmacol & Therapeut; Am Soc Clin Invest; fel Am Col Physicians; fel Am Col Cardiol. *Res:* Clinical pharmacology; metabolism of biologically active aromatic amines in man; ethics of human experimentation. *Mailing Add:* Dept of Internal Med Yale Univ Sch of Med New Haven CT 06510

LEVINE, ROBERT PAUL, b Brooklyn, NY, Dec 18, 26; m 69. GENETICS. *Educ:* Univ Calif, Los Angeles, AB, 49, PhD(genetics), 51. *Hon Degrees:* AM, Harvard Univ, 57. *Prof Exp:* Instr biol, Amherst Col, 51-53; from asst prof to prof, Harvard Univ, 53-78, chmn dept, 67-70; PROF GENETICS, MED SCH, WASHINGTON UNIV, 78- *Concurrent Pos:* NSF sr fel, 63-64. *Mem:* AAAS; Genetics Soc Am; Sigma Xi; Soc Gen Physiologists; Am Soc Cell Biol. *Res:* Genetic specification of membrane structure. *Mailing Add:* Dept of Genetics Washington Univ Sch of Med St Louis MO 63110

LEVINE, ROBERT S(IDNEY), b Des Moines, Iowa, June 4, 21; m 47; c 2. CHEMICAL ENGINEERING. *Educ:* Iowa State Col, BS, 43; Mass Inst Technol, SM, 46, ScD(chem eng), 49. *Prof Exp:* Res engr, Rocketdyne Div, N Am Aviation, Inc, 48-50, supvr combustion & thermodyn, 50-56, group leader physics & phys processes, 56-59, chief phys sci res, 59-66; chief liquid rocket res & technol, Off Advan Res & Technol, NASA, 66-71, staff scientist, Langley Res Ctr, 71-74; CHIEF, FIRE RES RESOURCES DIV, NAT BUR STANDARDS, 74- *Concurrent Pos:* Mem subcomt combustion, Nat Adv Comt Aeronaut, 58; lectr, Univ Calif, Los Angeles, 58-59. *Mem:* Am Chem Soc; Am Inst Aeronaut & Astronaut; Am Inst Chem Engrs; Combustion Inst (vpres, 70, pres, 74-78). *Res:* Combustion and combustion stability; heat transfer; engineering processes as applied to rockets; fire science. *Mailing Add:* Nat Bur of Standards Washington DC 20234

LEVINE, RUTH R, b New York, NY; m 53. PHARMACOLOGY. *Educ:* Hunter Col, BA, 38; Columbia Univ, MA, 39; Tufts Univ, PhD(pharmacol), 55. *Prof Exp:* From instr to asst prof pharmacol, Sch Med, Tufts Univ, 55-58; from asst prof to prof, 58-65, UNIV PROF PHARMACOL, SCH MED, BOSTON UNIV, 72-, CHMN DIV MED & DENT SCI, GRAD SCH, 64-, ASSOC DEAN, SCH MED, 81- *Mem:* Am Soc Pharmacol & Exp Therapeut (secy-treas elect, 74, secy-treas, 75); Biophys Soc; Acad Pharmaceut Sci; Am Chem Soc. *Res:* Mechanisms of transport of drugs across biological barriers, particularly the intestinal epithelium; biochemical, histological and physiological factors influencing intestinal absorption. *Mailing Add:* Div of Med & Dent Sci Boston Univ Sch of Med Boston MA 02118

LEVINE, SAMUEL, b Brooklyn, NY, Jan 21, 21; m 53; c 3. PHYSICAL CHEMISTRY. *Educ:* Brooklyn Col, BA, 46; Columbia Univ, MA, 52, PhD(chem), 55. *Prof Exp:* Electrochemist, Arc Anodying & Plating Co, 46-47; phys chemist thermodyn, Nat Bur Standards, 47-51, proj leader, Macromolecular Properties Unit, Northern Regional Res & Develop Div, 55-58; assoc prof chem, Western Ill Univ, 58-59; chemist, Dow Chem Co, 59-61; prof chem & dir sci, Delta Col, 61-64; PROF CHEM & DEAN, SAGINAW VALLEY STATE COL, 64- *Mem:* AAAS; Am Chem Soc. *Res:* Physical chemistry of polymers; thermodynamics; kinetics. *Mailing Add:* Saginaw Valley State Col 2250 Pierce Rd University Center MI 48710

LEVINE, SAMUEL GALE, b Malden, Mass, Nov 1, 28; m 53; c 4. ORGANIC CHEMISTRY. *Educ:* Tufts Univ, BS, 50; Harvard Univ, MA, 52, PhD(org chem), 54. *Prof Exp:* Res assoc, Forrestal Res Ctr, Princeton Univ, 53-54; res chemist, Walter Reed Army Inst Res, 54-56; res chemist, Eastern Regional Res Br, USDA, 56-60; sr chemist, Natural Prod Lab, Res Triangle Inst, 60-64; assoc prof, 64-68, PROF CHEM, NC STATE UNIV, 68- *Concurrent Pos:* Consult, Res Triangle Inst, 64-; Weizmann fel, Weizmann Inst Sci, 71-72. *Mem:* AAAS; Am Chem Soc. *Res:* New methods in organic synthesis; stereochemistry and conformational analysis; structure determination and synthesis of natural products; chromiumtricarbonyl complexes in organic synthesis. *Mailing Add:* Dept of Chem NC State Univ Raleigh NC 27650

LEVINE, SAMUEL HAROLD, b Hazlehurst, Ga, Nov 30, 25; m 55; c 3. NUCLEAR ENGINEERING, REACTOR PHYSICS. *Educ:* Va Polytech Inst, BS, 47; Univ Ill, MS, 48; Univ Pittsburgh, PhD(physics), 54. *Prof Exp:* Instr physics, Va Polytech Inst, 49-50; sr scientist, Bettis Atomic Power Lab, Westinghouse Elec Corp, 54-55, supv scientist, 55-57, mgr, 57-59; physicist in charge, Gen Atomic Div, Gen Dynamics Corp, 59-61; group physicist, Rocketdyne Div, NAm Aviation, Inc, 61-62; lab head nuclear sci, Northrop Space Labs, 62-68; PROF NUCLEAR ENG & DIR NUCLEAR REACTOR FACILITY, PA STATE UNIV, UNIVERSITY PARK, 68- *Concurrent Pos:* Lectr, Univ Calif, Los Angeles, 64-68; consult, Int Atomic Energy Agency, 77- *Honors & Awards:* Invention Award, NASA, 73. *Mem:* Am Phys Soc; Am Nuclear Soc. *Res:* In-core fuel management; neutron detection; experimental reactor physics; design of space superconducting magnets; nuclear reactor fuel management. *Mailing Add:* Breazeale Nuclear Reactor PA State Univ University Park PA 16802

LEVINE, SAMUEL W, b Dallas, Tex, May 15, 16; m 44; c 1. PHYSICAL CHEMISTRY. *Educ:* Agr & Mech Col Tex, BS, 38, MS, 41; Mass Inst Technol, PhD(phys chem), 48. *Prof Exp:* Combustion engr, Lone Star Gas Co, Tex, 38-39; instr thermodyn, Agr & Mech Col Tex, 41-42; assoc chemist, Atlantic Refining Co, 48-51; dir develop labs, Fisher Sci Co, 51-53; assoc dir res & develop, Fairchild Camera & Instrument Corp, 53-55, dir res & eng, Graphic Equip Div, 55-59, dir res & eng, Defense Prod Div, 59-61, tech dir, Corp, NY, 61-70; vpres technol, Varadyne, Inc, Calif, 70-72; vpres corp develop, Mass, 72-76, V PRES SEMI-ALLOYS, DATEL SYSTS, 76- *Mem:* Am Chem Soc; Optical Soc Am; Inst Elec & Electronics Engrs; NY Acad Sci; fel Am Inst Chemists. *Res:* X-ray spectroscopy; emission spectroscopy; petroleum reservoir characteristics; thermodynamic properties of hydrocarbons; radar systems research and development; instrumentation physics; radioactive tracers; photogrammetry instrumentation; corporate technical management; semiconductors; integrated circuits. *Mailing Add:* 11 Melby Lane East Hills NY 11576

LEVINE, SAUL, b Montreal, Que, May 31, 38; m 62; c 3. PSYCHIATRY. *Educ:* McGill Univ, BSc, 59, MD & CM, 63; Stanford Univ, dipl psychiat, 68; FRCP(C), 69. *Prof Exp:* SR PSYCHIATRIST, HOSP FOR SICK CHILDREN, 71-; PROF PSYCHIAT & ASSOC DIR, CHILD IN THE CITY PROG, UNIV TORONTO, 77- *Mem:* Fel Am Orthopsychiat Asn; fel Am Psychiat Asn; Can Psychiat Asn; Am Soc Adolescent Psychiat; Int Cong Social Psychiat. *Mailing Add:* Hosp for Sick Children 555 University Ave Toronto ON M5G 1X8 Can

LEVINE, SEYMOUR, b New York, NY, Mar 13, 25; m 45; c 2. PATHOLOGY, NEUROPATHOLOGY. *Educ:* NY Univ, BA, 46; Chicago Med Sch, MB, 47, MD, 48. *Prof Exp:* Pathologist, St Francis Hosp, Jersey City, NJ, 56-64; pathologist & chief labs, Bird S Coler Hosp, Ctr Chronic Dis, 64-77, PROF PATH, NY MED COL, 64-, CHIEF NEUROPATH, WESTCHESTER COUNTY MED CTR, 77- *Concurrent Pos:* Consult, Vet

Admin Hosp, Montrose, NY, 77- *Mem:* Am Asn Path; Soc Exp Biol & Med; Am Soc Exp Path; Am Asn Neuropath (pres, 68-69). *Res:* Demyelinating diseases; autoimmune disease. *Mailing Add:* Dept Path Westchester County Med Ctr Valhalla NY 10595

LEVINE, SEYMOUR, b New York, NY, Jan 25, 25; m 49; c 3. PSYCHOPHYSIOLOGY. *Educ:* NY Univ, PhD(psychol), 52. *Prof Exp:* Res assoc, Queens Col, NY, 51-52; asst prof, Boston Univ, 52-53; lectr, Northwestern Univ, 54-56; asst prof psychiat, Med Sch, Ohio State Univ, 56-60; assoc prof, 62-69, PROF PSYCHOL, SCH MED, STANFORD UNIV, 69- *Concurrent Pos:* USPHS fel, 53-55; res assoc, Inst Psychosom & Psychiat, Michael Reese Hosp, 55-56; consult, Nat Cancer Inst, 57-; Found Fund Res Psychiat fel, Dept Neuroendocrinol, Inst Psychiat, Maudsley Hosp, London, 60; consult, Nat Inst Child Health & Human Develop, 66-67, mem neuropsychol res, 67-70, consult, Nat Comt Causes & Prev Violence, 68. *Honors & Awards:* Hoffheimer Res Award, 61. *Mem:* Am Psychol Asn; Endocrine Soc; Int Soc Develop Psychobiol. *Res:* Infantile experience development physiology and endocrinology. *Mailing Add:* Dept of Psychiat Stanford Univ Sch of Med Stanford CA 94305

LEVINE, SEYMOUR, b Chicago, Ill, Apr 30, 22; m 43, 66; c 2. VIROLOGY. *Educ:* Univ Chicago, BS, 43; Univ Ill, MS, 45, PhD(bact), 49; Am Bd Med Microbiol, cert pub health & med lab virol. *Prof Exp:* Asst bact, Med Sch, Univ Ill, 45-49; from instr to asst prof biophys, Univ Colo, 51-56; res biologist, Lederle Labs, Am Cyanamid Co, 56-65; sr res scientist, Upjohn Co, Mich, 65-71; assoc prof, 71-81, PROF MICROBIOL, SCH MED, WAYNE STATE UNIV, 81- *Concurrent Pos:* Nat Res Coun AEC fel, Univ Colo, 49-50; Case Western Reserve Univ, 50-51. *Mem:* Am Soc Microbiol; Tissue Cult Asn; Am Acad Microbiol; Soc Exp Biol & Med. *Res:* Viral-host cell interactions; tissue culture; viral replication; viral interference and interferon. *Mailing Add:* Dept of Immunol & Microbiol Wayne State Univ Sch of Med Detroit MI 48201

LEVINE, SOLOMON LEON, b Schenectady, NY, Jan 7, 40; m 60; c 3. ANALYTICAL CHEMISTRY. *Educ:* Rensselaer Polytech Inst, BS, 61; Univ RI, PhD(anal chem), 66. *Prof Exp:* Sr assoc engr, Components Div, 65-66, sr assoc chemist, Systs Develop Div, 66-68, staff chemist, 68-69, proj chemist, 69-72, develop chemist, 72-74, adv chemist, 74-77, SR CHEMIST, IBM CORP, 77- *Mem:* Am Chem Soc; Sigma Xi; Electrochem Soc. *Res:* Spectroscopy, absorption and emission; electroanalytical chemistry; environmental chemistry; technical management. *Mailing Add:* 417 Robin Lane Vestal NY 13850

LEVINE, STEPHEN ALAN, b Brooklyn, NY, Dec 24, 38; m 61; c 4. ORGANIC CHEMISTRY, PRODUCT DEVELOPMENT. *Educ:* City Col New York, BS, 61; Purdue Univ, PhD(org chem), 66. *Prof Exp:* Res chemist, Acme Shellac Prod Co, 61; chemist, 66-67, sr chemist, 67-73, res chemist, 73-79, SR RES CHEMIST, TEXACO RES CTR, 79- *Mem:* Fel Am Inst Chem; Am Chem Soc; NY Acad Sci. *Res:* Polymer chemistry; catalytic oxidation; organic synthesis through catalytic conversion; process research; lubricant additive synthesis. *Mailing Add:* Texaco Res Ctr PO Box 509 Beacon NY 12508

LEVINE, STUART ZANE, b New York, NY. PHOTOCHEMISTRY. *Educ:* Hunter Col, AB, 64; Univ Pittsburgh, PhD(phys chem), 73. *Prof Exp:* Instr & res fel phys chem, Univ Sask, 73-74; res assoc, Ohio State Univ, 74-77; ASSOC CHEMIST, BROOKHAVEN NAT LAB, 77- *Mem:* Am Chem Soc. *Res:* Kinetic, mechanistic, photochemical, and computer modeling studies of reaction rates and product formations occurring in complex reaction systems such as air-pollution chemistry. *Mailing Add:* Dept Energy & Environ Brookhaven Nat Lab Upton NY 11973

LEVINE, SUMNER NORTON, b Boston, Sept 5, 23; m 52; c 1. PHYSICAL CHEMISTRY. *Educ:* Brown Univ, BS, 46; Univ Wis, PhD(phys chem), 49. *Prof Exp:* Instr phys chem, Univ Chicago, 49-50; sr res fel, Columbia Univ, 50-54; dir res labs, US Vet Admin Hosp, East Orange, NJ, 54-56; mgr chem & physics lab, Gen Eng Labs, Am Mach & Foundry Co, 56-58; sr staff scientist, Surface Commun Div, Radio Corp Am, 58-60, head solid state devices & electronics, 60-61; chmn dept, 61-67, PROF MAT SCI, STATE UNIV NY STONY BROOK, 61- *Concurrent Pos:* Childs fel, Univ Chicago, 49; Runyan fel, Columbia Univ, 52; lectr, Atomic Indust Forum, 56, Albert Einstein Med Col, 57 & Grad Div, Univ Conn, 57-58; instr, Grad Div, Brooklyn Col, 60 & City Col New York, 60; vis prof & dir urban res, Grad Ctr, City Univ New York, 67-68; ed-in-chief, Advan in Biomed Eng & Med Physics, J Socio-Econ Planning Sci & J Biomed Mat Res; NSF guest lectr, Berlin Acad Sci. *Mem:* Am Chem Soc; Electrochem Soc; Sigma Xi; sr mem Inst Elec & Electronics Engrs; Inst Mgt Sci. *Res:* Biophysical investigation of reaction mechanisms and isotopes; semiconductor physics; solid state high frequency devices; thermoelectric materials and devices; energy conversion techniques. *Mailing Add:* Dept of Mat Sci State Univ of NY Stony Brook NY 11790

LEVINE, WALTER (GERALD), b Detroit, Mich, Dec 18, 30; m 55; c 3. PHARMACOLOGY. *Educ:* Wayne State Univ, BS, 52, MS, 54, PhD(physiol, pharmacol), 58. *Prof Exp:* Res assoc physiol & pharmacol, Wayne State Univ, 54-56 & 57-58, asst, 56-57; from asst prof to assoc prof pharmacol, 61-76, PROF PHARMACOL, ALBERT EINSTEIN COL MED, 76- *Concurrent Pos:* Fel pharmacol, Albert Einstein Col Med, 58-61; USPHS career develop award. *Mem:* Am Soc Pharmacol & Exp Therapeut; NY Acad Sci; Int Soc Biochem Pharmacol; AAAS. *Res:* Biochemical pharmacology; drug metabolism and disposition. *Mailing Add:* Dept of Molecular Pharmacol Col of Med Yeshiva Univ Bronx NY 10461

LEVINE, WILLIAM SILVER, b Brooklyn, NY, Nov 19, 41; m 63; c 2. ELECTRICAL ENGINEERING. *Educ:* Mass Inst Technol, SB, 62, SM, 65, PhD(elec eng), 69. *Prof Exp:* Asst, Mass Inst Technol, 65-69; asst prof, 69-73, assoc prof, 73-81, PROF ELEC ENG, UNIV MD, COLLEGE PARK, 81- *Concurrent Pos:* Res engr, Data Technol Inc, Mass, 62-64; NSF res initiation grant, Univ Md, College Park, 70-71. *Mem:* Inst Elec & Electronics Engrs; Soc Neurosci. *Res:* Optimal controls and systems with special emphasis on the theories of optimal feedback control and system identification and the application of this theory to biological and transportation systems. *Mailing Add:* Dept of Elec Eng Univ of Md College Park MD 20742

LEVINGER, BERNARD WERNER, b Berlin, Ger, Sept 3, 28; nat US; m 54; c 3. MATHEMATICS. *Educ:* Lehigh Univ, BS, 48; Mass Inst Technol, MS, 50; NY Univ, PhD(math), 60. *Prof Exp:* Asst metallurgist, Armour Res Found, Ill Inst Technol, 51-52; res metallurgist, Tung-Sol Elec, Inc, 52-57; res engr, Labs, Gen Tel & Electronics Corp, 57-62; asst prof math, Case Western Reserve Univ, 62-68; ASSOC PROF MATH, COLO STATE UNIV, 68- *Mem:* Am Math Soc; Math Asn Am; Soc Indust & Appl Math. *Res:* Matrix theory; numerical analysis; group theory. *Mailing Add:* Dept of Math Colo State Univ Ft Collins CO 80521

LEVINGER, JOSEPH S, b New York, NY, Nov 14, 21; m 43; c 4. PHYSICS. *Educ:* Univ Chicago, BS, 41, MS, 44; Cornell Univ, PhD(physics), 48. *Prof Exp:* Jr physicist, Metall Lab, Univ Chicago, 42-44; physicist, Franklin Inst, 45-46; asst, Cornell Univ, 46-48, instr physics, 48-51; from asst prof to prof, La State Univ, 51-61; Avco vis prof, Cornell Univ, 61-64; PROF PHYSICS, RENSSELAER POLYTECH INST, 64- *Concurrent Pos:* Guggenheim fel, 57-58; Fulbright travel grant, 72-73; assoc prof, Univ Paris, 72-73. *Mem:* Am Phys Soc. *Res:* Theoretical physics: specialities, the few-nucleon problem and nuclear photoeffect. *Mailing Add:* Dept of Physics Rensselaer Polytech Inst Troy NY 12181

LEVINGS, CHARLES SANDFORD, III, b Madison, Wis, Dec 1, 30; m; c 4. GENETICS. *Educ:* Univ Ill, BS, 53, MS, 56, PhD(agron), 63. *Prof Exp:* Res instr, 62-64, from asst prof to assoc prof, 64-72, PROF GENETICS, NC STATE UNIV, 72- *Mem:* Am Soc Agron; Am Genetic Asn; Genetics Soc Am; Am Soc Plant Physiologists. *Res:* Autotetraploid genetics; maize biochemical genetics. *Mailing Add:* Dept of Genetics NC State Univ Raleigh NC 27607

LEVINGS, COLIN DAVID, b Victoria, BC, May 23, 42; m 68; c 2. BIOLOGICAL OCEANOGRAPHY, FISHERIES ECOLOGY. *Educ:* Univ BC, BSc Hons, 65, MSc, 67; Dalhousie Univ, PhD(oceanog), 73. *Prof Exp:* Field biologist technician marine fish ecol, Int Pac Halibut Comn, Seattle, Wash, 62-63; scientist, Fisheries Res Bd Can, Pac Biol Sta, Nanaimo, BC, 67-68; RES SCIENTIST ESTUARINE BIOL OCEANOG, FISHERIES RES BD, CAN PAC ENVIRON INST, 72- *Concurrent Pos:* Hon lectr benthic biol oceanog, Inst Oceanog, Univ BC, 74-79. *Mem:* Can Soc Zoologists; Can Soc Environ Biologists; Pac Estuarine Res Soc; Marine Technol Soc. *Res:* Ecology of marine and estuarine benthos; community structure at disrupted habitats; ocean dumping and dredging; coastal fish habitats and food webs; ecology of fjords; juvenile salmonid ecology. *Mailing Add:* Dept of Fisheries & Oceans W Vancouver Lab 4160 Marine Dr West Vancouver BC V7V 1N6 Can

LEVINGS, WILLIAM STEPHEN, b Denver, Colo, Dec 28, 96; m 32; c 2. GEOLOGY. *Educ:* Colo Sch Mines, EM, 20, MSc, 30, DSc(geol), 51. *Prof Exp:* Asst geologist, Mex Eagle Oil Co, 20-22; field engr & asst, Shell Oil Co, 22-23; draftsman, Standard Oil Col, 23-24, asst geologist, Standard Oil Co Calif, 24-25; geologist, Gulf Oil Corp, 25-27; instr geol, Colo Sch Mines, 27-28; torsion balance party chief, Gulf Oil Corp, 28-29; geologist, Sinclair Explor Co, 30-31; asst geol, Harvard Univ, 32-33; tech adv grade 13, Petrol Admin Bd, Washington, DC, 33-36; from instr to assoc prof geol, Colo Sch Mines, 36-55; assoc prof math, 55-57, prof geol, 57-75, EMER PROF GEOL, REGIS COL, 75- *Honors & Awards:* Bartlett Medal, Am Soc Photogram, 52. *Mem:* Am Soc Photogram; fel Geol Soc Am. *Res:* Geomorphology of the Raton Mesa region, New Mexico and Colorado; photogeology. *Mailing Add:* Dept Geol Regis Col W 50th & Lowell Blvd Denver CO 80221

LEVINS, RICHARD, b New York, NY, June 1, 30; m 50; c 3. POPULATION BIOLOGY, MATHEMATICAL BIOLOGY. *Educ:* Cornell Univ, AB, 51; Columbia Univ, PhD(zool), 65. *Prof Exp:* Res assoc pop genetics, Univ Rochester, 60-61; assoc prof biol, Univ PR, 61-66; from assoc prof to prof math biol, Univ Chicago, 67-75; JOHN ROCK PROF POP SCI, SCH PUB HEALTH, HARVARD UNIV, 75- *Concurrent Pos:* NIH res grant, 63-66; consult genetics prog, Cuban Acad Sci, 64-65; NSF res grant, 64-66. *Mem:* Soc Study Evolution; Genetics Soc Am; Soc Gen Syst Res; Am Soc Naturalists. *Res:* Ecology and genetics; complex systems; agriculture. *Mailing Add:* Dept Pop Sci Harvard Sch Pub Health Boston MA 02115

LEVINSKAS, GEORGE JOSEPH, b Tariffville, Conn, July 8, 24; m 46; c 3. TOXICOLOGY, PHARMACOLOGY. *Educ:* Wesleyan Univ, AB, 49; Univ Rochester, PhD(pharmacol), 53. *Prof Exp:* Res assoc biol sci, USAEC, Univ Rochester, 52-53; dept occup health, Grad Sch Pub Health, Univ Pittsburgh, 53-54, res assoc & lectr, 54-56, asst prof appl toxicol, 56-58; res pharmacologist, Cent Med Dept, Am Cyanamid Co, 58, chief indust toxicologist & dir environ health lab, 59-71; mgr prod eval, 71, mgr environ assessment & toxicol, 72-77, DIR ENVIRON ASSESSMENT & TOXICOL, DEPT MED & ENVIRON HEALTH, MONSANTO CO, 77- *Mem:* Soc Toxicol; Am Chem Soc; Am Indust Hyg Asn; Environ Mutagen Soc; Am Soc Pharmacol & Exp Therapeut. *Res:* Pharmacology and toxicology of boron compounds; organic phosphates; industrial chemicals; food additives; insecticides; chemistry of bone mineral. *Mailing Add:* Dept of Med & Environ Health 800 N Lindbergh Blvd St Louis MO 63166

LEVINSKY, NORMAN GEORGE, b Boston, Mass, Apr 27, 29; m 56; c 3. MEDICINE. *Educ:* Harvard Univ, AB, 50, MD, 54. *Prof Exp:* Intern & resident med, Beth Israel Hosp, Boston, Mass, 54-56; clin assoc, Nat Heart Inst, 56-58; NIH spec fel med, Boston Univ Hosp, 58-60; from instr to assoc prof, 60-68, Wesselhoeft prof, 68-72, WADE PROF MED & CHMN DIV, SCH MED, BOSTON UNIV, 72-, DIR EVANS MEM DEPT CLIN RES & PREV MED & PHYSICIAN-IN-CHIEF, UNIV HOSP, 72- *Concurrent Pos:* Asst dir, Univ Med Serv, Boston City Hosp, 61-68, dir, 68- *Mem:* Am Fedn Clin Res; Am Soc Clin Invest; Asn Am Physicians. *Res:* Renal physiology and medical research. *Mailing Add:* Boston Univ Med Ctr 80 E Concord St Boston MA 02118

LEVINSKY, WALTER JOHN, b Meadville, Pa, Sept 16, 20; m 48; c 4. MEDICINE. *Educ:* Allegheny Col, BS, 42; Temple Univ, MD, 45, MS, 52; Am Bd Internal Med, dipl, 54 & 74. *Prof Exp:* Intern med, Hamot Hosp, Erie, Pa, 45-46; resident path, Univ Hosp, 48-49, resident internal med, 49-52, instr, Sch Med, 52-54, assoc, 54-58, from asst prof to assoc prof internal med, 58-74, CLIN PROF MED, SCH MED, TEMPLE UNIV, 74- *Concurrent Pos:* Chief dept med, Northeastern Hosp, Philadelphia, Pa, 54-58. *Honors & Awards:* Christian Lindback Found Award, Temple Univ, 65. *Mem:* Sr mem am Fedn Clin Res; fel Am Col Physicians; fel Royal Soc Med. *Res:* Internal medicine; clinical research. *Mailing Add:* Dept of Internal Med Temple Univ Sch of Med Philadelphia PA 19140

LEVINSON, ALFRED ABRAHAM, b Staten Island, NY, Mar 31, 27. EXPLORATION GEOCHEMISTRY. *Educ:* Univ Mich, BS & MS, 49, PhD(mineral), 52. *Prof Exp:* Asst, Univ Mich, 50-52, res assoc, 52-53; asst prof mineral, Ohio State Univ, 53-56; mineralogist, Dow Chem Co, 56-62; sr res geologist, Gulf Res & Develop Co, 62-67; PROF GEOL, UNIV CALGARY, 67- *Concurrent Pos:* Lectr, Univ Houston, 57-59; exec ed, Geochimica et Cosmochimica Acta, 67-70; ed, Proc Apollo 11 & Second Lunar Sci Conf. *Mem:* Fel Mineral Soc Am; Geochem Soc; fel Geol Soc Am; Mineral Asn Can. *Res:* General mineralogy and geochemistry with industrial application; environmental geochemistry; relation of geochemistry to health. *Mailing Add:* Dept of Geol Univ of Calgary Calgary AB T2N 1N4 Can

LEVINSON, ALFRED STANLEY, b Portland, Ore, Aug 27, 32; m 58; c 3. ORGANIC CHEMISTRY. *Educ:* Reed Col, BA, 54; Wesleyan Univ, MA, 57; Ind Univ, PhD(org chem), 63. *Prof Exp:* Res assoc chem, Ind Univ, 62-63; from asst prof to assoc prof, 63-73, PROF CHEM, PORTLAND STATE UNIV, 73- *Mem:* AAAS; Sigma Xi; Am Chem Soc; The Chem Soc. *Res:* Isolation and characterization of natural products; organic synthesis. *Mailing Add:* Dept of Chem Portland State Univ Box 751 Portland OR 97207

LEVINSON, CHARLES, b San Antonio, Tex, Dec 31, 36; m 67; c 2. CELL PHYSIOLOGY. *Educ:* Univ Tex, BA, 58; Trinity Univ, MA, 60; Rutgers Univ, PhD(physiol), 64. *Prof Exp:* Nat Cancer Inst fel, Med Col, Cornell Univ, 65-66; sr cancer res scientist, Roswell Park Mem Inst, 66-68; assoc prof, 68-72, PROF PHYSIOL, MED SCH, UNIV TEX, SAN ANTONIO, 72- *Mem:* Biophys Soc; Soc Gen Physiol; Am Physiol Soc. *Res:* Membrane phenomena; ion transport in tumor cells. *Mailing Add:* 942 Serenade San Antonio TX 78213

LEVINSON, DAVID W, b Chicago, Ill, Feb 24, 25; m 49; c 3. PHYSICAL METALLURGY. *Educ:* Ill Inst Technol, BS, 48, MS, 49, PhD(metall eng), 53. *Prof Exp:* Res metallurgist, Armour Res Found, 53-57, supvr non-ferrous metall res, 57-59, asst dir metals res, 59-62, sci adv, Metals & Ceramics Div, IIT Res Inst, 62-64; assoc head dept mat eng, 64-67, actg dean col eng, 67-69, PROF METALL, UNIV ILL, CHICAGO CIRCLE, 64- *Concurrent Pos:* Consult, IIT Res Inst, 64-, Mat Tech Lab, Wright-Patterson AFB, 65- & Fotofabrication Corp. *Mem:* Am Soc Metals; Am Inst Mining, Metall & Petrol Engrs; Am Soc Eng Educ. *Res:* High temperature alloy development; coatings for thermal control of surfaces; metallurgical transformations in alloys in thin film form; binary and ternary phase equilibria in metallic systems. *Mailing Add:* Dept of Mat Eng Box 4348 Chicago IL 60680

LEVINSON, GILBERT E, b New York, NY, Jan 25, 28; m 50; c 2. MEDICINE, CARDIOLOGY. *Educ:* Yale Univ, AB, 48; Harvard Med Sch, MD, 53. *Prof Exp:* Intern med, Harvard Med Serv, Boston City Hosp, 53-54, asst resident, 54-55, chief resident, Thorndike Mem Ward, 58-59; from asst prof to prof med, Col Med & Dent NJ, NJ Med Sch, 68-76, assoc dean admin affairs, 70-73; PROF MED, MED SCH, UNIV MASS, 76-; CHIEF MED, ST VINCENT HOSP, WORCESTER, MASS, 76- *Concurrent Pos:* Teaching fel, Harvard Med Sch, 54-55; Nat Heart Inst res fel, Thorndike Mem Lab, Boston City Hosp, 57-59; Nat Heart & Lung Inst res career develop award, 67-70; assoc dir, T J White Cardiopulmonary Inst, B S Pollak Hosp, Jersey City, NJ, 61-71; consult, USPHS Hosp, Staten Island, NY, 63-; estab investr, Union County Heart Asn, NJ, 61-66 & 70-75. *Mem:* Am Fedn Clin Res; fel Am Col Cardiol; Am Physiol Soc; Am Soc Clin Invest; fel Am Col Physicians. *Res:* Hemodynamics in valvular heart disease; indicator-dilution theory and methodology; cardiopulmonary blood volumes; relations between myocardial performance and metabolism. *Mailing Add:* Dept of Med St Vincent Hosp Worcester MA 01604

LEVINSON, HILLEL SALMON, b New York, NY, Feb 16, 18; m 43; c 1. MICROBIOLOGY. *Educ:* City Col New York, BS, 37, MS, 39; Univ Pa, PhD(med microbiol), 54. *Prof Exp:* With Nat Bur Standards, 42-43; bacteriologist, Biol Labs, Qm Res & Eng Ctr, 46-60, head bact group, Pioneering Res Lab, US Army Natick Lab, 60-74, res microbiologist, Food Sci Lab, US Army Natick Develop Ctr, 74-80, RES MICROBIOLOGIST, SCI & ADVAN TECHNOL, US ARMY NATICK RES & DEVELOP LABS, 80- *Concurrent Pos:* Lectr microbiol, Sch Med, NY Univ, 66-; adj prof biol, Northeastern Univ, 75-; vis prof biol, Univ Miami, 80- *Mem:* Am Soc Microbiol; Am Acad Microbiol; NY Acad Sci. *Res:* Physiology and biochemistry of aerobic and anaerobic bacterial spore formers; physiology and biochemistry of bacterial sporulation, spore germination and growth. *Mailing Add:* Food Sci Lab US Army Natick Res & Develop Command Natick MA 01760

LEVINSON, JOHN Z, b Odessa, Ukraine, Apr 21, 16; US citizen; m 41; c 3. PSYCHOLOGY, COMMMUNICATIONS ENGINEERING. *Educ:* Univ Toronto, BA, 39, MA, 40, PhD(physics), 48. *Prof Exp:* Demonstr physics, Univ Toronto, 46-48; res assoc, Mass Inst Technol, 48-50; asst prof physics, Alfred Univ, 50-54; sr physicist, Transistor Products, 54-56; mem tech staff, Bell Tel Lab, 56-71; PROF PSYCHOL, UNIV MD, 71- *Concurrent Pos:* Prin investr, Nat Eye Inst grant, Univ Md, 76-; consult, NIH Study Section, Vision B, 76-80; vis res scholar, Cambridge Univ, England, 67-68 & Syracuse Univ, 77-78. *Mem:* Fel Optical Soc Am; Asn Res Vision & Opthalmol; fel AAAS. *Res:* Temporal and spatial aspects of human vision studied by psychophysical methods; processes that underlie vision, emphasising how they limit speed and acuity. *Mailing Add:* Psychol Dept Univ Md College Park MD 20742

LEVINSON, LIONEL MONTY, b Johannesburg, SAfrica, Mar 12, 43. SOLID STATE PHYSICS. *Educ:* Univ Witwatersrand, BSc, 65, MSc, 66; Weizmann Inst Sci, PhD(solid state physics), 70. *Prof Exp:* PHYSICIST, GEN ELEC CORP RES & DEVELOP, 70- *Mem:* Am Phys Soc. *Res:* Electronic ceramics; varistors; Mossbauer effect. *Mailing Add:* Gen Elec Corp Res & Develop PO Box 8 Schenectady NY 12301

LEVINSON, LORNE JOEL, b Winnipeg, Man. STRANGE QUARK SPECTROSCOPY. *Educ:* Univ Man, BSc, 70; Brown Univ, PhD(physics), 78. *Prof Exp:* ASSOC PHYSICIST, STANDARD LINEAR ACCELERATOR CTR, STANFORD UNIV, 78- *Mem:* Am Phys Soc; Can Asn Physicists. *Res:* Experimental high energy physics, specifically strange quark spectroscopy; data acquisition and analysis. *Mailing Add:* Standard Linear Accelerator Ctr Bin 62 Stanford Univ Stanford CA 94305

LEVINSON, MARK, b Brooklyn, NY, June 12, 29; m 53; c 2. MECHANICS. *Educ:* Polytech Inst Brooklyn, BAeroE, 51, MS, 59; Calif Inst Technol, PhD, 64. *Prof Exp:* Asst appl mech, Polytech Inst Brooklyn, 51-52, instr math, 56, sr asst appl mech, 59; stress analyst, Foster-Wheeler Corp, 57-58; asst prof mech eng, Ore State Col, 60-61; assoc prof, Clarkson Col Technol, 64-66; assoc prof theoret & appl mech, WVa Univ, 66-67; prof eng mech, McMaster Univ, 67-80; A O WILLEY PROF MECH ENG, UNIV MAINE, ORONO, 80- *Mem:* AAAS; Am Soc Mech Engrs; Am Inst Aeronaut & Astronaut; Soc Indust & Appl Math; Soc Hist Technol. *Res:* Theory of elasticity; continuum mechanics; elastic stability; structural dynamics. *Mailing Add:* Dept Mech Eng Univ Maine Orono ME 04469

LEVINSON, SIDNEY BERNARD, b Russia, July 4, 11; nat US; wid; c 2. CHEMISTRY, CHEMICAL ENGINEERING. *Educ:* City Col New York, BS(chem) & BS(eng), 32, Chem Engr, 33. *Prof Exp:* Consult, Protective Coating Lab, Joachim Res Labs, 33-36; pres, Indust Consult Labs, 36-42; vpres & tech dir, Adco Chem Co, 42-48; supt & tech dir, Garland Co, 48-52; vpres & tech dir, D H Litter Co, 52-73, pres, David Litter Labs, 74-77, PRES, DAVID LITTER LABS, INC, DBA D/L Labs, 77- *Concurrent Pos:* Dir, Artists Tech Res Inst, 65- *Honors & Awards:* PaVac Award & lectr; Roy H Kienle Award, NY Soc Coating Technol. *Mem:* Am Chem Soc; Am Soc Testing & Mat; Nat Asn Corrosion Engrs; Fedn Socs Coating Technol; Com Develop Asn. *Res:* Protective coatings; thermosetting and reinforced plastics, sealants and allied products; evaluation of raw materials; formulation; testing of finished products; certification; preparation of specifications and manuals, personnel training, investigation of failures and legal assistance. *Mailing Add:* D/L Labs 116 E 16th St New York NY 10003

LEVINSON, SIMON ROCK, b Buffalo, NY, Dec 2, 46; m 69; c 2. MEMBRANE TRANSPORT PHENOMENA, BIOELECTRIC PHENOMENA. *Educ:* Calif Inst Technol, BS, 68; Univ Cambridge, PhD(physiol), 75. *Prof Exp:* Fel chem, Calif Inst Technol, 76-79; ASST PROF PHYSIOL, UNIV COLO HEALTH SCI CTR, 79- *Mem:* Biophys Soc. *Res:* Molecular mechanisms which underlie electrical excitation phenomena in nerve and muscle cells; mechanisms of the voltage-sensitive sodium channel and the molecular structures which mediate its complex function. *Mailing Add:* Dept Physiol C240 Med Sch Univ Colo Denver CO 80262

LEVINSON, STEVEN R, b Brooklyn, NY, Oct 13, 47. ANALYTICAL CHEMISTRY, PHOTOGRAPHY. *Educ:* Rensselaer Polytech Inst, BS, 68, PhD(anal chem), 73. *Prof Exp:* SR RES CHEMIST, PHOTOG RES DIV, KODAK RES LABS, EASTMAN KODAK CO, 73- *Concurrent Pos:* Instr, Rochester Inst Technol, 76- *Mem:* Am Chem Soc; Sigma Xi; Soc Photog Scientists & Engrs. *Res:* Research and development of photographic materials. *Mailing Add:* 102 Mountain Rd Rochester NY 14625

LEVINSON, STUART ALAN, b Detroit, Mich, Oct 29, 20; m 47; c 3. PALEONTOLOGY, GEOLOGY. *Educ:* Wayne State Univ, BS, 47; Washington Univ, AM, 49, PhD(geol), 51. *Prof Exp:* Asst geol, Washington Univ, 47-51; sr geologist, Humble Oil & Refining Co, 51-64; res supvr, 64-66, RES ASSOC, ESSO PROD RES CO, 66- *Concurrent Pos:* Instr, Washington Univ, 50-51. *Mem:* AAAS; Paleont Soc; Soc Econ Paleontologists & Mineralogists (vpres, 57); Geol Soc Am; Am Asn Petrol Geologists. *Res:* Invertebrate paleontology, micropaleontology, palynology, and zoology. *Mailing Add:* 6334 Coachwood Houston TX 77035

LEVINSON, WARREN E, b Brooklyn, NY, Sept 28, 33; m 65. MICROBIOLOGY, CELL BIOLOGY. *Educ:* Cornell Univ, BS, 53; Univ Buffalo, MD, 57; Univ Calif, Berkeley, PhD(virol), 65. *Prof Exp:* Assoc prof, 65-70, PROF MICROBIOL, MED CTR, UNIV CALIF, SAN FRANCISCO, 70- *Concurrent Pos:* Am Cancer Soc fel tumor viruses, Univ Col, Univ London, 65-67; R W Johnson Health Policy fel, 80-81. *Res:* Tumor viruses. *Mailing Add:* Dept of Microbiol Univ of Calif Med Ctr San Francisco CA 94143

LEVINSTEIN, H J, b Ironwood, Mich, May 3, 31; m 54; c 3. METALLURGY. *Educ:* Univ Mich, BS(metal eng) & BS(chem eng), 53; Carnegie Inst Technol, MS, 61, PhD(metal), 62. *Prof Exp:* Engr, Westinghouse Atomic Power Lab, 57-61; MEM TECH STAFF PHYS METALL, BELL LABS, 62- *Mem:* AAAS; Am Soc Metals; Am Inst Mining, Metall & Petrol Engrs; Metall Soc. *Res:* Superconductivity; laser materials; ferrites and ferromagnetic materials. *Mailing Add:* Bell Labs Mountain Ave Murray Hill NJ 07971

LEVINSTEIN, HENRY, b Themar, Ger, Dec 4, 19; nat US; m 62; c 3. PHYSICS. *Educ:* Univ Mich, BS, 42, MS, 43, PhD(physics), 47. *Prof Exp:* Lectr physics, Univ Mich, 46; from asst prof to assoc prof, 47-55, PROF PHYSICS, SYRACUSE UNIV, 55- *Concurrent Pos:* Consult, Westinghouse Elec Corp, 55-60; mem tech adv bd, Aerojet-Gen Corp, 61-66; univ adv, Tex Instruments, Inc, 61-; consult, Jet Propulsion Lab, Calif Inst Technol, 62-66, Int Bus Mach Corp & Gen Elec Co, 65-68. *Mem:* Am Phys Soc; Am Asn Physics Teachers; Optical Soc Am. *Res:* Photoconductivity; formation and structure of thin metallic films; infrared detectors. *Mailing Add:* Dept of Physics Syracuse Univ Syracuse NY 13210

LEVINTHAL, CYRUS, b Philadelphia, Pa, May 2, 22; m 44, 63; c 4. BIOPHYSICS. *Educ:* Swarthmore Col, BA, 43; Univ Calif, PhD(physics), 50. *Prof Exp:* From instr to assoc prof physics, Univ Mich, 50-57; prof biophys, Mass Inst Technol, 57-68; prof, 68-77, WILLIAM R KENAN, JR PROF BIOL, COLUMBIA UNIV, 77-, CHMN DEPT BIOL SCI, 68- *Mem:* Inst of Med of Nat Acad Sci; fel Am Acad Arts & Sci; Am Phys Soc; Am Soc Cell Biol; Genetics Soc Am; Biophys Soc. *Res:* Molecular biophysics and genetics. *Mailing Add:* Dept of Biol Sci Columbia Univ New York NY 10027

LEVINTHAL, ELLIOTT CHARLES, b Brooklyn, NY, Apr 13, 22; m 44; c 4. PHYSICS. *Educ:* Columbia Univ, BA, 42; Mass Inst Technol, MS, 43; Stanford Univ, PhD(physics), 49. *Prof Exp:* Proj engr, Sperry Gyroscope Co, NY, 43-46; res assoc nuclear physics, Stanford Univ, 46-48; res physicist, Varian Assocs, 49-50, res dir, 50-52; chief engr, Century Electronics & Instruments, Inc, 52-53; pres, Levinthal Electronic Prod, Inc, 53-61; assoc dean res affairs, Sch Med, Stanford Univ, 71-74, dir Instrumentation Res Lab, 61-81; DIR, DEFENSE SCI OFF, DEFENSE ADVAN RES AGENCY, DEPT ENERGY, 81- *Concurrent Pos:* Adj prof genetics, Sch Med, Stanford Univ, 61-81. *Mem:* AAAS; fel Am Phys Soc; sr mem Inst Elec & Electronics Eng; Optical Soc Am; Biomed Eng Soc. *Res:* Measurements of nuclear moments; applications of computers to image processing and medical instrumentation; exobiology and planetary sciences. *Mailing Add:* 59 Sutherland Dr Atherton CA 94025

LEVINTHAL, MARK, b Brooklyn, NY, Mar 3, 41; m 62; c 2. MICROBIAL GENETICS, MOLECULAR EVOLUTION. *Educ:* Brooklyn Col, BS, 62; Brandeis Univ, PhD(biol), 66. *Prof Exp:* Fel genetics, Johns Hopkins Univ, 66-68; staff fel genetics lab molecular biol, Nat Inst Arthritis & Metab Dis, 68-72; ASSOC PROF BIOL, PURDUE UNIV, WEST LAFAYETTE, 72- *Mem:* Am Soc Microbiol; Sigma Xi; Genetics Soc Am; AAAS; Italian Molecular Biol Soc. *Res:* Regulation of enzyme synthesis of biosynthetic pathways and its relationship to general metabolic controls in bacteria; regulatory mechanisms-their evolution and contribution to general evolutionary theory. *Mailing Add:* Dept of Biol Sci Purdue Univ West Lafayette IN 47906

LEVINTON, JEFFREY SHELDON, b New York, NY, Mar 20, 46; m 67, 79. ECOLOGY, PALEONTOLOGY. *Educ:* City Col New York, BS, 66; Yale Univ, MPhil, 69, PhD(paleoecol), 71. *Prof Exp:* From instr to asst prof, 70-74, ASSOC PROF PALEOECOL, STATE UNIV NY STONY BROOK, 74- *Concurrent Pos:* State Univ NY Stony Brook Res Found fel & grant-in-aid, 71; managing ed, Am Naturalist, 74-75; vis prof, Uppsala Univ, Sweden, 81. *Mem:* AAAS; Paleont Soc; Genetics Soc Am; Am Soc Naturalists; Soc Study Evolution. *Res:* Marine benthic ecology; paleoecology; isoenzymes of marine benthos; fossil population dynamics; benthic deposit feeder-detritus-microbial interactions. *Mailing Add:* Dept of Ecol & Evolution State Univ NY Stony Brook NY 11794

LEVINTOW, LEON, b Philadelphia, Pa, Nov 10, 21; m 46; c 4. BIOCHEMISTRY, VIROLOGY. *Educ:* Haverford Col, AB, 43; Jefferson Med Col, MD, 46. *Prof Exp:* Intern, Jefferson Hosp, Philadelphia, Pa, 46-47; chief of lab, US Army Hepatitis Res Ctr, Ger, 47-49; biochemist, Nat Cancer Inst, 49-56, asst chief lab cell biol, Nat Inst Allergy & Infectious Dis, 56-61, asst chief lab biol viruses, 61-65; PROF MICROBIOL, SCH MED, UNIV CALIF, SAN FRANCISCO, 65-, CHMN, DEPT MICROBIOL & IMMUNOL, 80- *Concurrent Pos:* Res fel, Biochem Res Lab, Mass Gen Hosp, Boston, 51-52. *Mem:* Am Soc Microbiol; Am Chem Soc; Am Soc Biol Chemists. *Res:* Biochemistry of viruses. *Mailing Add:* Dept of Microbiol & Immunol Univ of Calif Sch of Med San Francisco CA 94143

LEVIS, ALEXANDER HENRY, b Yannina, Greece, Oct 3, 40; m 70. SYSTEMS THEORY. *Educ:* Ripon Col, BA, 63; Mass Inst Technol, BS & MS, 65, ME, 67, ScD(mech eng), 68. *Prof Exp:* Res asst control systs, Eng Projs Lab, Mass Inst Technol, 63-65; engr, Christina Lab, E I du Pont de Nemours & Co, Inc, 65; res asst transp systs, Electronic Systs Lab, Mass Inst Technol, 65-68; from asst prof to assoc prof elec eng, Polytech Inst New York, 68-74; sr engr, 73-76, DEPT MGR, SYSTS CONTROL, INC, 76-; SR RES SCIENTIST, MASS INST TECHNOL, 79- *Mem:* Inst Elec & Electronics Engrs; AAAS; Int Asn Energy Economists. *Res:* Policy analysis; socio-economic systems modeling; large scale system theory, energy and agricultural systems; power systems. *Mailing Add:* Systs Control Inc 1801 Page Mill Rd Palo Alto CA 94304

LEVIS, C(URT) A(LBERT), b Ger, Apr 16, 26; nat US; m 58; c 3. ELECTRICAL ENGINEERING. *Educ:* Case Inst Technol, BS, 49; Harvard Univ, AM, 50; Ohio State Univ, PhD(elec eng), 56. *Prof Exp:* Studio engr, Radio Sta WSRS, Inc, 48-49; res assoc, Antenna Lab, 50-56, assoc supvr, 56-61, from asst prof to assoc prof elec eng, 56-63, dir, Antenna Lab, 61-69, PROF ELEC ENG, OHIO STATE UNIV, 63- *Mem:* Sr mem Inst Elec & Electronics Engrs. *Res:* Electromagnetic theory; antennas; microwaves. *Mailing Add:* Dept of Elec Eng Col of Eng Ohio State Univ Columbus OH 43210

LEVIS, WILLIAM WALTER, JR, b Chicago, Ill, May 14, 18; m 41; c 2. ORGANIC CHEMISTRY. *Educ:* Univ Fla, BS, 41. *Prof Exp:* Res chemist, Fla Chem Indust, 41-42; sr res chemist, Sharples Chem, Inc, 42-52; sr res chemist, 52-55, sect head, 55-56, RES SUPVR, BASF WYANDOTTE CORP, 56- *Mem:* Am Chem Soc. *Res:* Organic synthesis; catalysis; hydrogenation; amination; oxyalkyation. *Mailing Add:* 2233 17th St Wyandotte MI 48192

LEVI SETTI, RICCARDO, b Milan, Italy, July 11, 27; m 59; c 2. PHYSICS. *Educ:* Univ Pavia, Dr, 49. *Prof Exp:* Asst physics, Univ Pavia, 49-51 & Univ Milan, 52-56; res assoc, Inst, 56-57, from asst prof to assoc prof, Univ, 57-64, PROF PHYSICS, ENRICO FERMI INST, UNIV CHICAGO, 65- *Concurrent Pos:* Guggenheim fel, 63-64. *Mem:* Fel Am Phys Soc; Ital Phys Soc. *Res:* Elementary particles; high energy nuclear physics. *Mailing Add:* Enrico Fermi Inst Univ of Chicago 5630 Ellis Ave Chicago IL 60637

LEVISON, MATTHEW EDMUND, b New York, NY, May 18, 37; m 66; c 1. MEDICAL SCIENCE, HEALTH SCIENCES. *Educ:* Columbia Univ, BA, 58; State Univ NY, MD, 62. *Prof Exp:* Asst instr med, Downstate Med Ctr, State Univ NY, 65-67; asst physician, NY Hosp, 67-69; instr, Med Col, Cornell Univ, 68-69; clin instr, Downstate Med Ctr, State Univ, NY, 69-70; from asst prof to assoc prof med & chief, 70-77, PROF MED & CHIEF INFECTIOUS DIS DIV, MED COL PA, 77- *Concurrent Pos:* Attend physician & chief infectious dis unit, Queens Hosp Ctr, Long Island Jewish Med Ctr affil, 69-70; attend staff, Philadelphia Vet Admin Hosp, 70- *Mem:* Am Soc Microbiol; Am Fedn Clin Res; Infectious Dis Soc Am; fel Am Col Clin Pharmacol; fel Am Col Physicians. *Res:* Anaerobic bacteria, the pathogenesis of the renal concentrating defect in experimental pylonephritis and the pathogenesis of experimental endocarditis. *Mailing Add:* Med Col Pa 3300 Henry Ave Philadelphia PA 19129

LEVISON, SANDRA PELTZ, b New York, NY, Apr 20, 41; m 66; c 2. NEPHROLOGY. *Educ:* Hunter Col, NY, BA, 61; New York Univ, MD, 65. *Prof Exp:* Asst instr med, State Univ NY, Downstate, 66-67 & 68-70; asst instr med, New York Univ Med Ctr, 67-68; from instr to assoc prof med, 70-81, dir, Hypertension Ctr, 74, Nephrology Fel Training Prog, 76 & Hemodialysis Serv, 78, chief hypertension, renal & dialysis, 78, PROF MED, MED COL PA, 81- *Mem:* Am Soc Nephrology; Int Soc Nephrology. *Res:* Elucidation of the renal concentrating defect in experimental infective Pyelonephritis; effects of exercise on blood pressure of adolescents; comparing blood pressures in infants and children of toxemic, hypertensive and normal mothers. *Mailing Add:* Med Col Pa 300 Henry Ave Philadelphia PA 19129

LEVISON, WILLIAM H(ENRY), b Cincinnati, Ohio, Mar 21, 36; m 66; c 2. HUMAN OPERATOR TECHNOLOGY, ENGINEERING PSYCHOLOGY. *Educ:* Mass Inst Technol, BS, 58, MS, 60, ScD, 64. *Prof Exp:* SR SCIENTIST, BOLT BERANEK & NEWMAN INC, CAMBRIDGE, 64- *Mem:* Inst Elec & Electronics Engrs; Am Inst Aeronaut & Astronaut. *Res:* Manual control systems and human operator modelling. *Mailing Add:* 19 Phinney Rd Lexington MA 02173

LEVIT, EDITHE J, b Wilkes-Barre, Pa, Nov 29, 26; m 52; c 2. MEDICINE. *Educ:* Bucknell Univ, BS, 46; Woman's Med Col Pa, MD, 51. *Hon Degrees:* DMS, Med Col Pa, 78. *Prof Exp:* Intern med, Philadelphia Gen Hosp, 51-52, fel endocrinol, 52-53, clin instr, 53-57, dir med educ, 57-61; asst dir, 61-67, secy & assoc dir, 67-75, vpres & secy, 75-77, PRES & DIR, NAT BD MED EXAMR, 77- *Concurrent Pos:* Consult, 61-; mem steering comt foreign med grads, Inst Med-Nat Acad Sci, 74-76; mem steering comt human aging med educ, 77-78; chmn prof adv comt, Philadelphia Coun Int Visitors, 58-61, bd dirs, 66-72; bd dirs, Philadelphia Gen Hosp Charitable Found, 64-70 & Philadelphia Elec Co, 80-; bd mgrs, Germantown Savings Bank, Philadelphia, 79-; mem sci coun, Nat Lib Med Bd, 81- *Honors & Awards:* Commonwealth Comt of Woman's Med Col Award, 70. *Mem:* Inst Med-Nat Acad Sci; AMA; master Am Col Physicians; Asn Am Med Cols. *Res:* Evaluation of professional competence in medicine. *Mailing Add:* Nat Bd of Med Examr 3930 Chestnut St Philadelphia PA 19104

LEVIT, LAWRENCE BRUCE, b Cleveland, Ohio, Sept 24, 42; m 67; c 1. PHYSICS. *Educ:* Case Western Reserve Univ, BS, 64, PhD(physics), 71. *Prof Exp:* Res assoc physics, Case Western Reserve Univ, 66-69; asst prof, La State Univ, Baton Rouge, 69-74; MKT MGR, DIV HIGH ENERGY PHYSICS, LECROY RES SYST CORP, 74- *Mem:* Am Phys Soc; Am Inst Physics. *Res:* Ultrahigh energy physics research using cosmic rays as a particle source. *Mailing Add:* Lecroy Res Syst Corp 700 S Main St Spring Valley NY 10977

LEVIT, ROBERT JULES, b San Francisco, Calif, Aug 17, 16; m 43; c 3. NUMBER THEORY. *Educ:* Calif Inst Technol, BS, 38, MS, 39; Univ Calif, PhD(math), 41. *Prof Exp:* Asst math, Univ Calif, 40-41; from asst prof to assoc prof, Univ Ga, 46-53; vis asst prof, Mass Inst Technol, 54-55; mem staff, Appl Sci Div, Int Bus Mach Corp, 55-57; from asst prof to prof math, 57-72, EMER PROF MATH, SAN FRANCISCO STATE UNIV, 72- *Mem:* Am Math Soc; Math Asn Am; Asn Symbolic Logic. *Res:* Foundations of mathematics; algebra; computer science. *Mailing Add:* 148 Miraloma Dr San Francisco CA 94127

LEVITAN, HERBERT, b Brooklyn, NY, Apr 25, 39; m 64; c 2. NEUROBIOLOGY, MEMBRANE BIOPHYSICS. *Educ:* Cornell Univ, BEE, 62, PhD(phys biol), 65. *Prof Exp:* NIH fel, neurophysiol, Brain Res Inst, Univ Calif, Los Angeles, 65-67, anatomist, Anat Dept, 67; NIH fel, Lab Neurophysiol Cellulaire Ctr Etude Physiol Nerveuse, Paris, France, 68-70, Lab Neurophysiol, NIMH, 70, Lab Neurobiol, Nat Inst Child Health & Human Develop, 70-72; ASSOC PROF, DEPT ZOOL, UNIV MD, COL PARK, 72- *Concurrent Pos:* Instr neurobiol, Marine Biol Lab, Woods Hole, 74-; neurophysiologist, Lab Neurosci Gerontol Res Ctr, Nat Inst Aging, 79- *Mem:* Soc Neurosci; Am Physiol Soc; Soc Gen Physiologists; Am Soc Cell Biol. *Res:* Physics, chemical and biophysical mechanisms underlying the efffects of drugs on the physiology of nerves and muscles and on fertilization and early development. *Mailing Add:* Dept Zool Univ Md College Park MD 20742

LEVITAN, MAX, b Tverai, Lithuania, Mar 1, 21; nat US; m 47; c 3. GENETICS, ANATOMY. *Educ:* Univ Chicago, AB, 44; Univ Mich, MA, 46; Columbia Univ, PhD(zool), 51. *Prof Exp:* Statistician, USPHS, 44-45; asst zool, Columbia Univ, 46-49; assoc prof genetics, Va Polytech Inst, 49-55; from asst prof to assoc prof anat, Woman's Med Col Pa, 55-62, prof anat & med genetics, 62-66; prof biol & chmn dept, George Mason Col, Univ Va, 66-68; assoc prof anat, 68-70, PROF ANAT, MT SINAI SCH MED, 70- *Concurrent Pos:* Seminar assoc, Columbia Univ, 58-; spec lectr, Univ Pa, 62-63; actg chmn dept anat, Woman's Med Col Pa, 64-66; adj prof anat & genetics, George Washington Univ & Sch Med, Univ Va, 66-68, assoc ed, Evolution, 77-79. *Mem:* Am Asn Anatomists; Am Soc Naturalists; A.. Soc Human Genetics; Genetics Soc Am; Soc Study Social Biol. *Res:* Cytogenetics; population genetics of linked loci; chromosome breakage; cytoplasmic inheritance; medical genetics. *Mailing Add:* 1212 Fifth Ave New York NY 10029

LEVITAN, MICHAEL LEONARD, b Brooklyn, NY, Sept 12, 41; m 64; c 2. MATHEMATICS. *Educ:* Rensselaer Polytech Inst, BS, 62; Univ Minn, MS, 66, PhD(math), 67. *Prof Exp:* Asst prof math, Drexel Univ, 67-70; asst prof, 70-74, ASSOC PROF MATH, VILLANOVA UNIV, 74- *Mem:* Am Math Soc; Math Asn Am. *Res:* Probability theory; Markov processes; operations research; statistics; math anxiety. *Mailing Add:* Dept of Math Villanova Univ Villanova PA 19085

LEVITAN, RUVEN, b Kaunas, Lithuania, Mar 12, 27; US citizen; m 49; c 3. INTERNAL MEDICINE, GASTROENTEROLOGY. *Educ:* Hebrew Univ, Israel, MD, 53; Am Bd Internal Med, dipl & cert gastroenterol. *Prof Exp:* Resident, Mt Sinai Hosp, NY, 56-57; resident, Beth Israel Hosp, Boston, 58-59; dir gastroenterol res, New Eng Med Ctr Hosps, 64-68; assoc prof, 68-70, PROF MED, ABRAHAM LINCOLN SCH MED, UNIV ILL MED CTR, 70- *Concurrent Pos:* Spec fel med neoplasia, Mem Ctr Cancer & Allied Dis, NY, 57-58; fel gastroenterol & res fel med, Mass Mem Hosps & Sch Med, Boston Univ, 59-61, sr res fel, Mass Mem Hosps, 61-62; from asst prof to assoc prof, Sch Med, Tufts Univ, 64-69; lectr, Sch Med, Boston Univ, 65-68; pres, Chicago Soc Gastroenterol; chief gastroenterol sect, Vet Admin West Side Hosp, 68-77. *Mem:* Fel Am Col Physicians; Am Physiol Soc; Am Gastroenterol Asn; Am Asn Study Liver Dis; Am Soc Clin Invest. *Res:* Water electrolyte absorption from the intestine; hormonal influences on absorption; lymphomas, including involvement of liver and gastrointestinal tract. *Mailing Add:* 64 Old Orchard Rd Skokie IL 60076

LEVITAS, ALFRED DAVE, b New York, NY, Mar 27, 20; m 43; c 1. PHYSICS. *Educ:* Syracuse Univ, BA, 47, MS, 50, PhD(physics), 58. *Prof Exp:* Res engr solid state physics, Sylvania Elec Corp, 53-55 & Sprague Elec Corp, 55-56; physicist, Honeywell Res Ctr, 56-58; PROF PHYSICS, STATE UNIV NY ALBANY, 58- *Concurrent Pos:* Consult, Naval Res Lab, 60-63. *Mem:* Am Phys Soc. *Res:* Solid state and statistical physics; thermodynamics. *Mailing Add:* Dept of Physics State Univ of NY Albany NY 12222

LEVITON, ALAN EDWARD, b Brooklyn, NY, Jan 11, 30; m 52; c 2. SYSTEMATIC ZOOLOGY, ZOOGEOGRAPHY. *Educ:* Stanford Univ, AB, 49, AM, 53, PhD, 60. *Prof Exp:* From asst cur to assoc cur, 57-62, CUR HERPET & CHMN DEPT, CALIF ACAD SCI, 62- *Concurrent Pos:* Assoc cur div syst biol, Stanford Univ, 62-63, lectr, 62-70; adj prof biol sci, San Francisco State Univ, 67- *Mem:* Fel AAAS (secy-treas, Pac Div, 75-79, exec dir, 80); Soc Syst Zool; Soc Study Amphibians & Reptiles; Am Soc Ichthyol & Herpet; Soc Vert Paleontol. *Res:* Herpetology of Asia; Tertiary paleogeography; phylogeny and taxonomy of reptiles. *Mailing Add:* Dept of Herpet Calif Acad of Sci San Francisco CA 94118

LEVITSKY, LYNNE LIPTON, b Columbia, SC, May 14, 42; m 67; c 3. ENDOCRINOLOGY, PEDIATRICS. *Educ:* Bryn Mawr Col, BA, 62; Yale Univ, MD, 66. *Prof Exp:* Intern pediat, Bronx Munic Hosp Ctr, 66-67; resident, Childrens Hosp Philadelphia, 67-68; fel endocrinol & metab, Sch Med, Univ Md, 68-70; asst prof pediat, Sch Med, Univ Ill, 70-73; DIR DIV PEDIAT ENDOCRINOL, MICHAEL REESE HOSP MED CTR, 73- *Concurrent Pos:* Asst prof pediat, Pritzker Sch Med, Univ Chicago, 73-78, assoc prof, 78- *Mem:* Soc Pediat Res; Endocrine Soc; Lawson Wilkins Pediat Endocrine Soc. *Res:* Carbohydrate metabolism; diabetes; fetal and neonatal metabolism and endocrinology. *Mailing Add:* Dept Pediat Michael Reese Med Ctr 29th & Ellis Chicago IL 60616

LEVITSKY, MYRON, b New York, NY, June 22, 30. MECHANICAL ENGINEERING. *Educ:* Cooper Union, BME, 51; NY Univ, MS, 64, PhD(mech eng), 69. *Prof Exp:* Res engr, Heat & Mass Flow Analyzer Lab, Columbia Univ, 51-53; instr mech eng, NY Univ, 53-54; proj engr, Consumer's Union, 62-63; LECTR & ASSOC PROF MECH ENG, CITY COL NEW YORK, 65- *Concurrent Pos:* Assoc res scientist, NY Univ, 65-70, vis mem, Courant Inst, 77-78; NSF res grant, City Col New York, 71-72. *Mem:* AAAS; Am Soc Mech Engrs; Am Phys Soc; Am Soc Eng Educ; Am Acad Mech. *Res:* Elasticity theory; heat transfer; thermal stresses in chemically hardening media; applications to concrete and plastic molding. *Mailing Add:* Dept of Mech Eng Convent Ave at 138th St New York NY 10031

LEVITSKY, SIDNEY, b New York, NY, Mar 3, 36; m 67; c 3. CARDIOVASCULAR SURGERY, SURGERY. *Educ:* Albert Einstein Col Med, MD, 60; Bd Surg & Bd Thoracic Surg, dipl, 68. *Prof Exp:* Instr surg, Sch Med, Yale Univ, 64-66; chief surg, Third Surg Hosp, Vietnam, 66-67; thoracic surgeon, Valley Forge Army Hosp, 67-68; sr investr cardiac surg, Nat Heart Inst, NIH, 68-70; assoc prof surg, 70-75, PROF SURG & PHARMACOL, COL MED, UNIV ILL, 75-, CHIEF, DIV CARDIOTHORACIC SURG, MED CTR, 74-, LECTR SURG, COOK COUNTY, GRAD SCH, 70- *Concurrent Pos:* Estab investr, Am Heart Asn, 71; attend surgeon, Cook County Hosp, 73-; sr consult, West Side Vet Hosp, 75- *Mem:* Soc Univ Surgeons; Am Physiol Soc; Soc Thoracic Surgeons; Am Asn Thoracic Surg; Asn Acad Surg. *Res:* Thoracic surgery; non-invasive methods of monitoring myocardial contractility; intra-operative protection of myocardium; myocardial ischemia and metabolism. *Mailing Add:* Dept of Surg PO Box 6998 Col Med Univ of Ill Chicago IL 60680

LEVITT, ABEL, internal medicine, deceased

LEVITT, ALBERT P, b Lynn, Mass, Jan 17, 24; m 51; c 3. MATERIALS SCIENCE, MECHANICAL ENGINEERING. *Educ:* Harvard Univ, AB, 44, MS, 47. *Prof Exp:* Mech engr, Pratt & Whitney Aircraft Proj, Harvard Univ, 44-46, engr jet engine compressor res, 47-51; mech engr, US Naval Ord Lab, Md, 51-52; guided missile design engr, Rocket Br, Res & Develop Div, Off Chief Ord, Pentagon, 52-54; consult high temperature missile mat probs, 54-55, chief high temperature mat br, Metals Lab, 54-66, chief, Interdisciplinary Res Lab, 66-68, staff adv composites, 68-70, CHIEF, METAL MATRIX COMPOSITES GROUP, ARMY MAT & MECH RES CTR, 70- *Concurrent Pos:* Army rep panels, Mat for Guided Missiles, Mat Adv Bd, Nat Acad Sci, 55-56, Ceramics, 57, Alloys for Use Elevated temperatures, 56-57, Aircraft Appln, 58-59 & Plasma Phenomena, 59-60; mem bd, US Civil Serv Exam for Engrs New Eng Area, 58-; mem, Inorg Non-Metallic Mat Panel, Tripartite Tech Coop Prog, 60-63; consult, Army Mat Prob, Bell Tel Labs, NJ, 62; chmn achievement awards comt, Army Mat & Mech Res Ctr, 62-; alt mem composites for turbines res panel, US Air Force, 65; co-developer magnesium alloy-graphite fiber composites, 71; guest lectr, Ohio State Univ & Univ NH. *Mem:* Am Soc Mech Engrs; Am Soc Testing & Mat. *Res:* Developing new and improved materials for high temperature service in army weapons; metals, ceramics, whisker and reinforced composites; research and development of advanced metal matrix composites for army aircraft, bridging, vehicles and weapon systems; production of graphite fiber reinforced metals. *Mailing Add:* 75 Lovett Rd Newton Centre MA 02159

LEVITT, BARRIE, b Brooklyn, NY, Aug 19, 35; m 68; c 1. PHARMACOLOGY, INTERNAL MEDICINE. *Educ:* State Univ NY Downstate Med Ctr, MD, 59. *Prof Exp:* Rotating intern, Mt Sinai Hosp, New York, 59-60, resident med, 60-63; fel pharmacol, State Univ NY Downstate Med Ctr, 63-64; fel, Med Col, Cornell Univ, 64-65, from instr to asst prof pharmacol, 65-69; asst prof med, New York Med Col, 69-70, assoc prof med & pharmacol & dir, Div Clin Pharmacol, 70-80; PROF MED & CARDIOL, ALBERT EINSTEIN COL MED, 80- *Concurrent Pos:* NY Heart Asn sr investr, Med Col, Cornell Univ, 66-69; consult, Bur Drugs, US Food & Drug Admin, 71-; clin prof med, Albert Einstein Col Med. *Mem:* Am Soc Pharmacol & Exp Therapeut; Am Heart Asn. *Res:* Clinical and cardiovascular pharmacology; cardiology. *Mailing Add:* Albert Einstein Col Med 1300 Morris Park Ave Bronx NY 10461

LEVITT, DAVID GEORGE, b Minneapolis, Minn, May 9, 42; m 64; c 2. PHYSIOLOGY. *Educ:* Univ Minn, BS, 66, MD & PhD(physiol), 68. *Prof Exp:* assoc prof, 68-77, PROF PHYSIOL, UNIV MINN, MINNEAPOLIS, 77- *Res:* Theoretical transport processes across membranes and in capillary beds; intestinal absorption; microcirculation in skeletal muscle. *Mailing Add:* Dept of Physiol Univ of Minn Minneapolis MN 55455

LEVITT, GEORGE, b Newburg, NY, Feb 19, 25; m 50; c 4. ORGANIC CHEMISTRY. *Educ:* Duquesne Univ, BS, 50, MS, 52; Mich State Univ, PhD, 57. *Prof Exp:* Res chemist, Exp Sta, 56-63, res chemist, Stine Lab, 63-66, res chemist, Exp Sta, 66-68, sr res chemist, 68-80, RES ASSOC, EXP STA, E I DU PONT DE NEMOURS & CO, INC, 81- *Mem:* Am Chem Soc. *Res:* Organic syntheses; herbicides, fungicides, medicinals; pesticides; heterocyclic compounds. *Mailing Add:* 3218 Romilly Rd Wilmington DE 19810

LEVITT, ISRAEL MONROE, b Philadelphia, Pa, Dec 19, 08; m 37; c 2. ASTRONOMY. *Educ:* Drexel Inst Technol, BS, 32; Univ Pa, AM, 37, PhD(astron), 48. *Hon Degrees:* DSc, Temple Univ, 58, Drexel Inst Technol, 58, Philadelphia Col Pharm, 63. *Prof Exp:* Engr, Abrasive Co, 29-30; astronr, Franklin Inst, 33-39, asst dir, Fels Planetarium, 39-48, dir, 48-70, vpres, Inst, 70-72; EXEC DIR, SCI & TECHNOL COUN, MAYOR PHILADELPHIA, PA, 72- *Concurrent Pos:* Engr, Eclipse Exped, Franklin Inst, 32, asst assoc dir astron, photog & seismol, 38-48 & assoc dir astron & seismol, 49-70; astronr, Cook Observ, Univ Pa, 35-46; mem, Air Pollution Control Bd, Philadelphia, 64-, chmn, 66- *Honors & Awards:* Bryant Gold Medal, Geog Soc Philadelphia, 62; Joseph Priestly Award, Spring Garden Inst, 63; Samuel S Fels Medal, 70. *Mem:* AAAS; fel Am Astronaut Soc; Am Inst Aeronaut & Astronaut; Am Astron Soc; Brit Astron Soc. *Res:* Lunar studies; scientific museum and planetarium operation; technology transfer. *Mailing Add:* 3900 Ford Rd Philadelphia PA 19131

LEVITT, JACOB, b Montreal, Que, Sept 22, 11; nat US; m 42; c 2. PLANT PHYSIOLOGY. *Educ:* McGill Univ, BSc, 32, MSc, 33, PhD(bot), 35. *Prof Exp:* Asst plant physiol, Macdonald Col, McGill Univ, 34, Nat Res Coun Can bursary, 35-36; Royal Soc Can res fel, Univ Minn, 36-37; lectr bot, Macdonald Col, McGill Univ, 38-40; instr plant physiol, Univ Minn, 40-42, asst prof bot, 42-47; from assoc prof to prof, Univ Mo-Columbia, 47-73, chmn dept, 65-68; sr scientist, Volcani Ctr, Israel, 73-74; vis prof hort sci, Univ Minn, St Paul, 74-78; VIS FEL, CARNEGIE INST WASHINGTON, 78- *Concurrent Pos:* Guggenheim fel, 54-55; NSF sr fel, 61-62. *Mem:* AAAS; Am Soc Plant Physiol; Soc Cryobiol (pres, 71-72); Scand Soc Plant Physiol. *Res:* Frost hardiness and drought resistance of plants; cell physiology; water relations of plants; ion absorption. *Mailing Add:* Dept of Plant Biol 290 Panama St Stanford CA 94305

LEVITT, JOSEPH R(OBERT), engineering, medical physics, see previous edition

LEVITT, KARL NORMAN, computer science, see previous edition

LEVITT, LEONARD SIDNEY, b Philadelphia, Pa, Feb 1, 26; m 52; c 2. INORGANIC CHEMISTRY, PHYSICAL ORGANIC CHEMISTRY. *Educ:* Univ Pa, BA, 46; Pa State Univ, BS, 47; Haverford Col, MS, 48; Temple Univ, PhD(phys org chem), 53. *Prof Exp:* Asst chem, Haverford Col, 47-48, instr, 52; assoc prof & head dept, Union Col, Ky, 53; instr, Stevens Inst Technol, 53-54, from asst prof to assoc prof, 54-61; prof, Seton Hall Univ, 61-65; PROF CHEM, UNIV TEX, EL PASO, 65- *Concurrent Pos:* Asst, Temple Univ, 53; vis lectr, Farleigh Dickinson Univ, 59-60; vis lectr, St John's Univ, NY, 60; vis prof, Univ Va, 78. *Mem:* Am Phys Soc; Am Chem Soc. *Res:* Kinetics and mechanism of persulfate oxidation; mechanism of organic oxidations; photoionization theory of photosynthesis; equation of state of gases, liquids, and solids at extreme pressures; ionization potentials of organic molecules and coordination compounds; base strengths of weak organic bases; linear free energy relations; alkyl inductive effect; theory of expansion of the universe; helical theory of photons; theory of aqueous electrons; compressoelectric effect in metals; Hall effect in ionic solutions; mass spectrum of elementary particles. *Mailing Add:* Dept of Chem Univ of Tex El Paso TX 79968

LEVITT, LEROY P, b Plymouth, Pa, Jan 8, 18; m 71; c 4. PSYCHIATRY. *Educ:* Pa State Univ, BS, 39; Chicago Med Sch, MD, 43; Inst Psychoanal, cert, 59. *Prof Exp:* Pvt pract, 49-66; prof psychiat & dean, Chicago Med Sch, 66-73; dir dept ment health, State of Ill, 73-76; PROF PSYCHIAT, RUSH MED COL, 76-; VPRES MED AFFAIRS, MT SINAI HOSP MED CTR, 76- *Concurrent Pos:* Consult, Chicago Am Red Cross, 50-54, Asn Family Living, 50-54 & Nat Coun Aging, 52-; mem, Mayor's Comn Aging, 60- & Gov Comn Ment Health Planning Bd, 66-; pres, Chicago Bd Health, 78- *Honors & Awards:* Chicagoan of Year Award in Med, 71; Gold Medal Sci Award, Phi Lambda Kappa, 74. *Mem:* Fel Am Psychiat Asn; fel Am Psychoanal Asn; fel Acad Psychoanal; Am Col Psychiat; Am Col Psychoanal (1st vpres, 81-). *Res:* Process of aging; medical education and administration and study of personality of medical students; psychoanalysis; geriatric psychiatry; mental health. *Mailing Add:* 1500 S Fairfield Ave Chicago IL 60612

LEVITT, MARVIN FREDERICK, b New York, NY, Dec 9, 20; c 2. NEPHROLOGY. *Educ:* Cornell Univ, BA, 41; NY Univ, MD, 44. *Prof Exp:* Res asst med, Mt Sinai Sch Med, 50-53; asst attend physician, Mt Sinai Hosp, 53-60; CHIEF DIV NEPHROLOGY, DEPT MED, MT SINAI SCH MED, 60-, PROF MED, 68- *Concurrent Pos:* Mem cardio-vascular renal panel, Mayor's Res Coun, 69-72; mem sci adv bd, NY State Kidney Dis Inst, 69-72; emer mem, Nat Heart Inst Training Comt; chmn med adv bd, NY Kidney Dis Found. *Mem:* NY Acad Sci; Am Soc Clin Invest; Am Fedn Clin Res; fel Am Col Physicians; Asn Am Physicians. *Mailing Add:* 1176 Fifth Ave New York NY 10029

LEVITT, MELVIN, b Chicago, Ill, Mar 13, 25. NEUROBIOLOGY. *Educ:* Roosevelt Univ, BS, 49, MA, 53; Mich State Univ, PhD(psychol), 58. *Prof Exp:* Res asst neurol & psychiat, Med Sch, Northwestern Univ, 52-54; res assoc neurophysiol, Rockefeller Inst, 61; assoc anat, Sch Med, Univ Pa, 61-65, asst prof anat & mem, Inst Neurol Sci, 65-70; ASSOC PROF PHYSIOL, BOWMAN GRAY SCH MED, 70- *Concurrent Pos:* USPHS fel, Inst Neurol Sci, Sch Med, Univ Pa, 57-61. *Mem:* Am Physiol Soc; Am Asn Anat; Soc Neurosci; Int Asn Study Pain. *Res:* Sensory organization in central nervous system of vertebrates. *Mailing Add:* 724 Chester Rd Winston-Salem NC 27104

LEVITT, MICHAEL D, b Chicago, Ill, May 10, 35; m 56; c 3. GASTROENTEROLOGY. *Educ:* Univ Minn, BS, 58, MD, 50. *Prof Exp:* Intern, Univ Minn Hosp, 60-61; resident, Boston Univ Hosp, 61-64; resident, Beth Israel Hosp, Boston, 64-65; fel gastroenterol, Boston City Hosp, 65-68; from asst to assoc prof, 68-74, PROF MED, MED SCH, UNIV MINN, 74- *Concurrent Pos:* Guest lectr, Gastroenterol Res Group, 72; counr, Am Fedn Clin Res, 74-76; consult med, Minneapolis Vet Admin Hosp, 74- *Mem:* Am Fedn Clin Res; Am Soc Clin Invest; Am Gastroenterol Soc. *Res:* Studies employing gas to investigate gastrointestinal physiology and studies of serum and urinary isoamylases. *Mailing Add:* Gastroenterol Sect Dept of Med Box 36 Univ of Minn Hosp Minneapolis MN 55455

LEVITT, MORRIS REUBEN, b Newark, NJ, Apr 29, 40; m 72; c 3. PHYSICS, FUSION ENERGY. *Educ:* Case Inst Technol, BS, 61; Columbia Univ, MA, 63, PhD(physics), 68. *Prof Exp:* Res assoc physics, Columbia Univ Radiation Lab, 68-70; adj assoc prof nat sci, Queens Col, 72-74; EXEC DIR FUSION, FUSION ENERGY FOUND, 74- *Concurrent Pos:* Fel NSF, 70-71; ed fusion, Int J Fusion Energy, Fusion Energy Found, 77-, ed in chief, Fusion Mag, 77- *Mem:* Sigma Xi. *Res:* Scientific, technical and economic aspects of fusion energy; epistemological significance of critical phenomena, such as superfluidity and superconductivity. *Mailing Add:* Fusion Energy Found 888 Seventh Ave New York NY 10019

LEVITT, NEIL HILLIARD, virology, immunology, see previous edition

LEVITT, SEYMOUR H, b Chicago, Ill, July 18, 28; div; c 3. RADIOTHERAPY. *Educ:* Univ Colo, BA, 50, MD, 54. *Prof Exp:* Instr radiation ther & radiol, Med Sch, Univ Mich, 61-62; asst radiotherapist, Sch Med & Dent, Univ Rochester, 62-63; assoc prof radiation ther & chief div, Sch Med, Univ Okla, 63-66; prof radiol & chmn div radiation ther, Med Col Va, 66-70; PROF THERAPEUT RADIOL & HEAD DEPT, UNIV MINN, MINNEAPOLIS, 70- *Concurrent Pos:* Consult radiother, Vet Admin Hosp, Minneapolis; trustee, Am Bd Radiol; mem, Am Joint Comt; pres, Soc Chmn Acad Radiol Oncol Prog, 74-76, mem bd dirs, 76-78. *Mem:* Fel Am Col Radiol; Am Radium Soc; Soc Nuclear Med; Radiol Soc NAm; Am Soc Therapeut Radiol (pres, 78-79). *Res:* Experimental and clinical radiation therapy; radiation biology. *Mailing Add:* Dept of Therapeut Radiol Univ of Minn Hosps Minneapolis MN 55455

LEVITZ, HILBERT, b Lebanon, Pa, Nov 13, 31; m 66. MATHEMATICS. *Educ:* Univ NC, BA, 53; Pa State Univ, PhD(math), 65. *Prof Exp:* Instr math, Williams Col, 65; asst prof, NY Univ, 65-69; ASSOC PROF MATH, FLA STATE UNIV, 69- *Mem:* Am Math Soc; Asn Symbolic Logic. *Res:* Mathematical logic; concrete systems of ordinal notations. *Mailing Add:* Dept of Math Fla State Univ Tallahassee FL 32306

LEVITZ, MORTIMER, b New York, NY, May 11, 21; m 47; c 2. BIOCHEMISTRY, ENDOCRINOLOGY. *Educ:* City Col New York, BS, 41; Columbia Univ, MA, 47, PhD(org chem), 51. *Prof Exp:* Res assoc steroid biochem, Col Physicians & Surgeons, Columbia Univ, 51-52; res assoc, 52-56, from asst prof to assoc prof, 56-67, PROF STEROID BIOCHEM, MED CTR, NY UNIV, 67- *Concurrent Pos:* NIH res career award, 62-72; consult, Endocrine Study Sect, NIH, 66-70 & 73-75. *Mem:* Am Chem Soc; Am Soc Biol Chemists; Endocrine Soc; Soc Gynec Invest. *Res:* Estrogen metabolism and mechanisms of action in pregnancy and cancer. *Mailing Add:* NY Univ Med Ctr 550 First Ave New York NY 10016

LEVITZKY, MICHAEL GORDON, b Elizabeth, NJ, Jan 3, 47; m 69. PULMONARY PHYSIOLOGY, CARDIOVASCULAR PHYSIOLOGY. *Educ:* Univ Pa, BA, 69; Albany Med Col, Union Univ, PhD(physiol), 75. *Prof Exp:* Instr physiol, Albany Med Col, Union Univ, 74-75; asst prof, 75-80, ASSOC PROF PHYSIOL, MED CTR, LA STATE UNIV, 80- *Concurrent Pos:* Consult, NIH grants, 74-76 & 79-80, prin investr, 76-81; chmn, Acad Studies Comt, La State Univ, 81-82, Curric Comt, 82-; mem, Basic Sci Coun, Am Heart Asn. *Mem:* Am Physiol Soc; Sigma Xi; Soc Exp Biol & Med; NY Acad Sci. *Res:* Cardiopulmonary physiology, particularly in those factors which control pulmonary blood flow. *Mailing Add:* Dept Physiol Med Col La State Univ 1901 Perdido St New Orleans LA 70112

LEVKOV, JEROME STEPHEN, b New York, NY, June 12, 39; m 70. PHYSICAL CHEMISTRY, FORENSIC SCIENCES. *Educ:* City Col New York, BS, 61; Univ Pa, PhD(phys chem), 67. *Prof Exp:* Swiss Copper Inst fel, Swiss Fed Inst Technol, 67-68; asst prof gen & phys chem, Drexel Univ, 68-69; asst prof, 70-80, PROF GEN & PHYS CHEM, IONA COL, 80- *Mem:* N Am Thermal Anal Soc; Am Chem Soc. *Res:* Transport properties in electrolyte solutions; structure of solutions of electrolytes in solvents of low dielectric constatn; polymorphic transitions; forensic chemistry; computers in chemistry education. *Mailing Add:* Dept of Chem Iona Col New Rochelle NY 10801

LE VON, ERNEST FRANKLIN, b Chicago, Ill, Dec 17, 31; m 55, 77; c 3. ORGANIC CHEMISTRY. *Educ:* Univ Ill, BS, 54; Univ Mich, MS, 56, PhD(chem), 59. *Prof Exp:* RES SCIENTIST, G D SEARLE & CO, 58- *Mem:* AAAS; Am Chem Soc. *Res:* Synthesis and chemistry of organic compounds having therapeutic activity; synthesis and use of Nutrasweet. *Mailing Add:* Searle Labs PO Box 5110 Chicago IL 60680

LEVOW, ROY BRUCE, b Richmond, Va, June 3, 43; m 62; c 2. COMPUTER SCIENCE, MATHEMATICS. *Educ:* Univ Pa, AB, 64, PhD(math), 69. *Prof Exp:* Sci programmer, Atlantic-Richfield Co, 64-65; asst prof math, Univ Hawaii, 69-70; from asst prof to assoc prof math, 70-80, chmn dept, 74-78, ASSOC PROF COMPUT & INFO SYST, FLA ATLANTIC UNIV, 80- *Concurrent Pos:* Consult comput aids, classification & retrieval, 75- & prof develop & comput personnel, 79- *Mem:* Asn Comput Mach; Inst Elec & Electronics Engrs Comput Soc; AAAS. *Res:* Programming languages and programming environments; software engineering; information retrieval; database systems; operating systems; computer science education; combinatorial optimization; computability theory. *Mailing Add:* Comput & Info Syst Fla Atlantic Univ Boca Raton FL 33431

LEVY, ALAN, b New York, July 25, 37; m 62; c 2. POLYMER CHEMISTRY. *Educ:* City Col New York, BS, 58; Purdue Univ, PhD(chem), 62. *Prof Exp:* Sr res chemist, Cent Res Lab, Allied Chem Corp, NJ, 62-66; sr res scientist org polymer chem, 66-70, prin scientist & group leader, 70-75, mgr, Polymer Dept, 75-77, assoc dir res, 77-78, dir develop, 78-81, VPRES RES & DEVELOP, ETHICON INC, 81- *Honors & Awards:* Johnson Medal, 81. *Mem:* AAAS; Am Chem Soc; NY Acad Sci. *Res:* Biomedical materials; polymer and synthetic organic chemistry. *Mailing Add:* Ethicon Inc Rte 22 Somerville NJ 08876

LEVY, ALAN B, b San Francisco, Calif, Apr 12, 45; m 69; c 1. ORGANOMETALLIC CHEMISTRY. *Educ:* Univ Calif, Berkeley, BS, 67; Univ Colo, Boulder, PhD(chem), 71. *Prof Exp:* Fel chem, Purdue Univ, 71-74; asst prof chem, State Univ NY Stony Brook, 74-80; SR RES CHEMIST, ALLIED CORP, 80- *Mem:* Am Chem Soc; Sigma Xi; AAAS. *Res:* The use of organoboranes and organocopper reagents for the development of new synthetic methods; the total synthesis of natural products; homogenous and heterogenous catalysis in organic synthesis. *Mailing Add:* Allied corp PO Box 1021 R Morristown NJ 07869

LEVY, ALAN C, b Baltimore, Md, Feb 24, 30; m 56; c 2. PHYSIOLOGY, TOXICOLOGY. *Educ:* Univ Md, BS, 52; George Washington Univ, MS, 56; Georgetown Univ, PhD(physiol), 58. *Prof Exp:* Instr physiol, Sch Med, Howard Univ, 58-60; sect head, Dept Endocrinol, Wm S Merrell Co, 60-67; dir labs, Woodard Res Corp, 67-69; group chief, 69-74, SECT HEAD, DEPT TOXICOL & PATH, HOFFMANN-LA ROCHE INC, 74- *Mem:* Am Physiol Soc; Reticuloendothelial Soc; Endocrine Soc; NY Acad Sci; Soc Toxicol. *Res:* Inflammation; anti-inflammation; adrenal cortex; neuroendocrinology; lipid metabolism; acute and chronic toxicology; teratology. *Mailing Add:* Dept Toxicol & Path Hoffmann-La Roche Inc Nutley NJ 07110

LEVY, ALLAN HENRY, b New York, NY, Nov 2, 29; m 61; c 1. COMPUTER SCIENCES, VIROLOGY. *Educ:* Columbia Univ, AB, 49; Harvard Med Sch, MD, 53. *Prof Exp:* From intern to asst resident, Harvard Med Serv, Boston City Hosp, 53-55; clin assoc, Nat Cancer Inst, 55-57; from instr to asst prof microbiol, Johns Hopkins Univ, 59-65; assoc prof virol & comput sci, Baylor Col Med, 65-71, prof comput sci, 71-73, prof virol & Epidemiol, 73-75; PROF CLIN SCI & PROF COMPUT SCI, COL MED, UNIV ILL, URBANA, 75- *Concurrent Pos:* Res fel, Sch Med, Johns Hopkins Univ, 57-59; USPHS res career develop award, 60-65; consult div hosp & med facil, Bur State Serv, USPHS, 65- *Mem:* Am Fedn Clin Res. *Res:* Artifical intellegence in medicine hospital resistance to virus diseases; viral interference; medical models of virus cell interaction; general applications of digital computers to medicine and biology. *Mailing Add:* 190 Med Sci Bldg Univ of Ill Urbana IL 61801

LEVY, ALVIN, b Brooklyn, NY, June 26, 40; m 62. STRUCTURAL MECHANICS. *Educ:* Cooper Union, BME, 62; Columbia Univ, MS, 64, PhD(appl mech wave propagation), 66. *Prof Exp:* Res scientist, 66-80, SR RES SCIENTIST, GRUMMAN AEROSPACE CORP, 80-, NASA-GRUMMAN RES ASSOC, LANGLEY AFB, HAMPTON, VA, 71- *Mem:* Am Inst Aeronaut & Astronaut. *Res:* Mechanics of composite materials; finite element methods and applications; stability of shells. *Mailing Add:* Grumman Res Assoc NASA Langley AFB VA 23665

LEVY, ARTHUR, b New York, NY, Sept 29, 21; m 49; c 4. COMBUSTION KINETICS, ATOMOSPHERIC CHEMISTRY. *Educ:* Queen's Col, BS, 43; Univ Minn, MS, 48. *Prof Exp:* Chemist, Los Alamos Nat Lab, 44-46; aeronaut res scientist, Nat Adv Comt Aeronaut, 48-50; phys chemist, Brookhaven Nat Lab, 50-51; prin phys chemist, 51-59, asst chief, 56-69, fel, 69-71, sr fel, 71-73, sr res leader, 73-76, mgr combustion, 76-79, RES LEADER, COLUMBUS LABS, BATTELLE MEM INST, 79- *Mem:* Am Chem Soc; Combustion Inst; Air Pollution Control Asn. *Res:* Kinetics of hydrogen and hydrocarbon oxidation; combustion chemistry; kinetics of radiation and ionic reactions; boron hydride chemistry; induced reactions; flame structure; air pollution kinetics; coal-oil combustion and environmental assessments; synthetic fuel combustion. *Mailing Add:* Columbus Labs Battelle Mem Inst 505 King Ave Columbus OH 43201

LEVY, ARTHUR LOUIS, b Bridgeport, Conn, Aug 2, 17; m 43; c 1. ANALYTICAL CHEMISTRY, CLINICAL CHEMISTRY. *Educ:* Univ Mo, AB, 38; Yale Univ, PhD(phys chem), 48. *Prof Exp:* From instr to asst prof phys chem, Rensselaer Polytech Inst, 48-54; chemist, Hodgkins Dis Res Lab, 54-58, CHIEF CHEMIST, ST VINCENT'S HOSP, 58- *Concurrent Pos:* Ford Found fel, 53-54; dir labs, New York Dept Health, 64- *Mem:* Fel AAAS; Am Asn Clin Chem; Am Chem Soc; NY Acad Sci; Asn Clin Sci. *Res:* Electrolyte solutions; immunochemistry of Hodgkins disease; enzymes; standards and methodologies in clinical chemistry including automation and data processing. *Mailing Add:* St Vincent's Hosp Chem Lab 153 W 11th St New York NY 10011

LEVY, ARTHUR MAURICE, b New York, NY, Nov 20, 30; c 3. CARDIOLOGY. *Educ:* Harvard Univ, BA, 52; Cornell Univ, MD, 56; Am Bd Internal Med, dipl, 66. *Prof Exp:* Intern, Cornell Med Div, Bellevue Hosp, 56-57, resident med, 57-58; resident, 58-59, from instr to asst prof, 63-68, assoc prof med, Col Med, 68-76, assoc prof pediat, 69-77, PROF MED, COL MED, UNIV MT, 76-, PROF PEDIAT, 77- *Concurrent Pos:* NIH fel cardiol, Col Med, Univ Vt, 59-60; Nat Heart Inst res fel, 59-60; trainee cardiol, Harvard Med Sch, Boston Children's Hosp, 62-63; teaching scholar, Am Heart Asn, 66-71; fel coun clin cardiol, Am Heart Asn, 69- *Mem:* Am Fedn Clin Res; fel Am Col Physicians; fel Am Col Cardiol. *Res:* Clinical electrophysiology. *Mailing Add:* Cardiopulmonary Lab Med Ctr Hosp of Vt Burlington VT 05401

LEVY, BARNET M, b Scranton, Pa, Jan 13, 17; m 40. HISTOPATHOLOGY. *Educ:* Univ Pa, AB, 38, DDS, 42; Med Col Va, MS, 44; Am Bd Oral Path, dipl. *Prof Exp:* Instr bact, path & clin dent, Med Col Va, 42-44; asst prof bact & path, Wash Univ, 44-47, assoc prof path. 47-49; prof dent & dir res & postgrad studies, Sch Dent & Oral Surg, Columbia Univ, 49-57; PROF PATH, UNIV TEX DENT BR HOUSTON, 57-, DIR, DENT SCI INST, 64- *Concurrent Pos:* Assoc attend dent surgeon, Presby Hosp, New York, 49-57; consult-instr, US Naval Hosp, St Albans, NY, 52-57; USPHS Hosp, Staten Island, 51-57; consult, Vet Admin Hosp, Bronx, 54-57, Houston, 57-, Univ Tex M D Anderson Hosp & Tumor Inst, 57-; mem Nat Res Coun, 52; chmn dent study sect, NIH, 57-62, training grants comt, 62-67; mem adv comt dent, Comt Int Exchange Persons; pres, Am Bd Oral Path, 65-66, ed, J Dent Res, 76-; adj prof anat, Sch Vet Med, Tex A&M Univ; vis prof, Facultad De Ontologia, Univ Nat Autonoma De Mexico, Mexico City, 78- *Honors & Awards:* Isaac Schour Mem Award, Int Asn Dent Res, 75. *Mem:* Am Soc Exp Path; Soc Exp Biol & Med; Am Asn Cancer Res; fel Am Acad Oral Path (pres, 69-70); Int Asn Dent Res (pres, 65-66). *Res:* Experimental pathology; inflammation; immunopathology and oncology. *Mailing Add:* 1018 Blodgett Houston TX 77004

LEVY, BERNARD, JR, b New Orleans, La, Oct 27, 24; m 51; c 3. MECHANICAL ENGINEERING. *Educ:* Univ Nebr, BS, 45, MS, 48. *Prof Exp:* Engr, 48-57, mgr var activ, 57-82, MGR, STEAM GENERATOR PROG, ADVAN REACTORS DIV, WESTINGHOUSE ELEC CORP, 80- *Mem:* Am Soc Mech Engrs; Sigma Xi. *Res:* Design and development of nuclear reactor plants for naval application. *Mailing Add:* Westinghouse Advan Reactors Div PO Box 158 Madison PA 15663

LEVY, BORIS, b New York, NY, Nov 24, 27; m 56; c 3. PHOTOGRAPHIC CHEMISTRY. *Educ:* NY Univ, BA, 48, MS, 50, PhD(phys chem), 55. *Prof Exp:* Res chemist, Sylvania Elec Co, 50-51; sr res chemist, Radio Corp Am, 55-56; sr scientist, Westinghouse Elec Corp, 56-60; sr res chemist, Socony Mobil Oil Co, 60-65; RES CHEMIST, POLAROID CORP, 65- *Concurrent Pos:* Assoc prof, Trenton Jr Col, 62-65; assoc ed, Photog Sci & Eng, 75. *Honors & Awards:* Honorable Mention, Soc Photog Scientists & Engr, 74. *Mem:* Am Chem Soc; fel Soc Photog Scientists & Engrs. *Res:* Radiotracers; surface chemistry; electrokinetics; photoconductivity; photoelectron emission from semiconductors; spectral sensitization; energy and electron transfer reactions across phase boundaries; photographic emulsion preparation and characterization; preparation of novel image rector layers in diffusion transfer photography; kinetics of photo-induced processes. *Mailing Add:* Polaroid Corp Res Div 750 Main St Cambridge MA 02139

LEVY, CHARLES KINGSLEY, b Boston, Mass, Dec 25, 24; div; c 3. RADIATION ECOLOGY. *Educ:* George Washington Univ, BSc, 48, MSc, 51; Univ NC, Chapel Hill, PhD(physiol), 56. *Prof Exp:* Instr physiol, Vassar Col, 56-58; staff scientist, Worcester Found Exp Biol, 58-62; assoc prof radiol & biol, 62-70, PROF BIOL, BOSTON UNIV, 70- *Concurrent Pos:* Res collabr, Brookhaven Nat Lab, 57-61; Am Physiol Soc fel, Boston Univ, 58; staff scientist, Worcester Found Exp Biol, 58-62; consult, Mass Gen Hosp, 62-; consult bioinstrumentation, NASA, 67-; Fulbright prof zool, Univ Nairobi, 69-70; proj dir avian radioecol nuclear reactor site, AEC, Dept Energy, 73-78. *Mem:* Am Physiol Soc; Radiation Res Soc; Soc Gen Physiol. *Res:* Effect of high energy particulate radiation mammalian systems; dose-rate phenomena and responses of sensory and neural tissues to ionizing radiation; biological impact of reactor effluents on free ranging populations of wild birds; kinship in voles by radionuclide tagging and whole-body gamma spectroscopy. *Mailing Add:* Dept of Biol Boston Univ Boston MA 02215

LEVY, DANIEL, b New York, NY, Nov 27, 40; m 68. BIOCHEMISTRY, MEMBRANES. *Educ:* City Col New York, BS, 61; Brandeis Univ, MS, 63, PhD(chem), 65. *Prof Exp:* Res biochemist, Univ Calif, Berkeley, 67-68; assoc prof, 74-80, PROF BIOCHEM, SCH MED, UNIV SOUTHERN CALIF, 80- *Concurrent Pos:* NIH fel biochem, Univ Calif, Berkeley, 65-67; NIH res grant, 73-; vis prof biochem, Univ Basel, Switzerland, 77-78. *Mem:* AAAS; Am Soc Biol Chem; Am Chem Soc. *Res:* Membrane structure and function; mechanism of hormone action. *Mailing Add:* Dept of Biochem Sch of Med Univ of Southern Calif Los Angeles CA 90033

LEVY, DAVID ALFRED, b Washington, DC, Aug 27, 30; m 51; c 3. IMMUNOLOGY, ALLERGY. *Educ:* Univ Md, BS, 52, MD, 54; Am Bd Internal Med, cert, 62; Am Bd Allergy & Immunol, cert, 74. *Prof Exp:* From intern to chief resident med, Univ Hosp, Baltimore, Md, 54-59; physician, Pulmonary Dis Serv, Fitzsimons Gen Hosp, Denver, 59-61; staff physician, Chest Serv, Vet Admin Hosp, Baltimore, 61-62; USPHS fel, Sch Med, 62-66, asst prof radiol sci, 66-68, from assoc prof to prof radiol sci & epidemiol, 68-73, PROF BIOCHEM & EPIDEMIOL, SCH HYG & PUB HEALTH, JOHNS HOPKINS UNIV, 73-, PROF PATHOBIOL, 80- *Concurrent Pos:* Fogarty Sr Int fel, Col de France, Paris, 76. *Mem:* AAAS; Am Asn Immunol; fel Am Acad Allergy; Am Soc Trop Med & Hyg; Soc Exp Biol & Med. *Res:* Mechanisms of allergic reactions; mechanisms of immunotherapy for allergic diseases; alpha-antitrypsin and pulmonary disease; parasite immunology. *Mailing Add:* Dept Biochem Sch Hyg & Pub Health Johns Hopkins Univ Baltimore MD 21205

LEVY, DAVID EDWARD, b Washington, DC, May 10, 41; m 67. NEUROLOGY. *Educ:* Harvard Univ, AB, 63; Harvard Med Sch, MD, 68; Am Bd Internal Med, dipl, 72; Am Bd Psychiat & Neurol, dipl, 75. *Prof Exp:* From intern to resident, New York Hosp, 68-72; fel & instr, 72-75, asst prof, 75-80, ASSOC PROF NEUROL, MED COL, CORNELL UNIV, 80- *Concurrent Pos:* Asst attend neurologist, New York Hosp, 75-80, assoc attend neurologist, 80- *Honors & Awards:* Teacher-Scientist Award, Andrew W Mellon Found, 75; Estab Investigatorship, Am Heart Asn, 78. *Mem:* Soc Neurosci; Fel Am Col Physicians; Am Acad Neurol; Am Neurol Asn; Fel Am Heart Asn. *Res:* Brain carbohydrate and energy metabolism in cerebral ischemia; prediction of outcome from stroke and coma. *Mailing Add:* Dept of Neurol New York Hosp Cornell Med Ctr New York NY 10021

LEVY, DONALD HARRIS, b Youngstown, Ohio, June 30, 39; m 61; c 3. CHEMICAL PHYSICS, SPECTROSCOPY. *Educ:* Harvard Univ, BA, 61; Univ Calif, Berkeley, PhD(chem), 65. *Prof Exp:* From asst prof to assoc prof, 67-78, PROF CHEM, UNIV CHICAGO, 78- *Concurrent Pos:* NIH fel, Cambridge Univ, 65-66, NATO fel, 66-67, Alfred P Sloan fel; Guggenheim fel, Univ Leiden, 75-76. *Mem:* Am Phys Soc. *Res:* Optical spectroscopy in supersonic molecular beams; spectroscopy and photochemistry of vander waals molecules; laser induced fluorescence spectroscopy; energy transfer; spectroncopy of porphyrim and related molecules. *Mailing Add:* Dept of Chem Univ of Chicago Chicago IL 60637

LEVY, DONALD M(ARC), b Lynbrook, NY, Mar 27, 35; m 57; c 2. DIGITAL SIGNAL PROCESSING, COMMUNICATION SYSTEMS. *Educ:* Univ Wis, BS, 56, PhD(elec eng), 65; Mass Inst Technol, MS, 58. *Prof Exp:* Mem tech staff, Hycon Eastern, Inc, 56-57; res asst & staff mem, Instrumentation Lab, Mass Inst Technol, 57-58; instr elec eng, Univ Wis, 59-61; staff engr, Commun Systs Dept, Int Bus Mach Corp, 61-63; instr elec eng, Univ Wis, 63-65; from asst prof to assoc prof info eng, Univ Iowa, 65-79; SUPVR SIGNAL PROCESSING SYSTS, WESTERN DEVELOP LABS, FORD AEROSPACE & COMMUN CORP, 79- *Mem:* Inst Elec & Electronics Engrs. *Res:* Statistical communication theory; topological network theory; bioengineering; digital signal processing. *Mailing Add:* 4245 Ponce Dr Palo Alto CA 94306

LEVY, EDWARD ROBERT, b New York, NY, Oct 3, 27; m 51; c 4. ORGANIC CHEMISTRY. *Educ:* City Col New York, BS, 49; Univ Kans, PhD(org chem), 63. *Prof Exp:* Asst instr chem, Univ Kans, 49-50 & 51-53; res chemist, Glyco Prod, Inc, 53-57; process chemist, Chemagro Corp, 57-65, asst supvr, Process Develop Lab, 65-66, supvr, 66-68, asst mgr, 68-70, mgr, 70-73, PRIN CHEMIST, AGR DIV, MOBAY CHEM CORP, 73- *Mem:* AAAS; Am Chem Soc; Sigma Xi. *Res:* Organophosphorus insecticides; carbamates; chelating agents; synthesis and process development. *Mailing Add:* Mobay Chem Corp PO Box 4913 Kansas City MO 64120

LEVY, EUGENE HOWARD, b New York, NY, May 6, 44; m 67; c 3. ASTROPHYSICS, PLANETARY GEOPHYSICS. *Educ:* Rutgers Univ, AB, 66; Univ Chicago, PhD(physics), 71. *Prof Exp:* Fel physics & astron, Univ Md, 71-73; asst prof, Bartol Res Found, Franklin Inst, 73-75; asst prof, 75-78, ASSOC PROF PLANETARY SCI, LUNAR & PLANETARY LAB, UNIV ARIZ, 78-, ASSOC DEPT HEAD, 81-, MEM FAC APPL MATH, 81- *Concurrent Pos:* Ctr Theoret Physics fel, Univ Md, 71-73; mem comt planetary & lunar explor, Nat Acad Sci, 76-77, chmn, 78-82; partic, Comet Halley Sci Working Group, NASA, 77-78; mem space sci bd, Nat Acad Sci, 78-82; mem Ad Hoc Panels, Space Sci Steering Comt, NASA, 79-80, Solar System Exp Comt, 80-82; sci consult, Rockwell Corp, 80; mem, Comt Space Res, Int Tech Panel Comets, 80-82. *Mem:* Am Phys Soc; Am Astron Soc; Am Geophys Union; Int Astron Union. *Res:* Theoretical astrophysics and solar system studies; magnetohydrodynamics; space physics; planetary and geophysics. *Mailing Add:* Dept of Planetary Sci Univ of Ariz Tucson AZ 85721

LEVY, GABOR BELA, b Budapest, Hungary, July 16, 13; nat US; m 38; c 2. CHEMISTRY. *Educ:* Karlsruhe Tech Univ, Dipl Ing, 38; Inst Divi Thomae, PhD(chem), 53. *Prof Exp:* Asst physics, NY Univ, 38-41; sr res chemist & sect head, Schenley Labs, Inc, 42-50, head anal & phys chem res, 50-55; head chem div, Consumers Union US, 55-57; asst to pres, 57-64, SR VPRES, PHOTOVOLT CORP, 64- *Concurrent Pos:* Adj prof, Polytech Inst NY. *Mem:* AAAS; Am Chem Soc; Sigma Xi. *Res:* Applied colloid chemistry; spectrophotometry; polarography; electron microscopy; swelling of casein; determination of antibiotics; physical methods in organic chemistry; enzymes; optical rotation. *Mailing Add:* 48 Roseville Rd Westport CT 06880

LEVY, GEORGE CHARLES, b Brooklyn, NY, June 4, 44; m 79; c 1. NUCLEAR MAGNETIC RESONANCE, COMPUTER METHODS. *Educ:* Syracuse Univ, AB, 65; Univ Calif, Los Angeles, PhD(chem), 68. *Prof Exp:* Res staff, Gen Elec Corp, 68-73; assoc prof chem, Fla State Univ, 73-77, prof, 77-81; PROF CHEM, SYRACUSE UNIV, 81- *Concurrent Pos:* Dir, NIH Res Resource for Multi-Nuclear Nuclear Magnetic Resonance & Data Processing, 71-; ed, Comput Enhanced Spectros J, 82-; Alfred P Sloan res fel, 75-77. *Mem:* Am Chem Soc; Royal Soc Chem; Sigma Xi. *Res:* Nuclear magnetic resonance spectroscopy and computer methods in chemistry; chemical and biophysical applications of carbon-13, nitrogen-15, and other nuclei nuclear magnetic resonance; optimization of spectroscopic studies. *Mailing Add:* Chem Dept Bowne Hall Syracuse Univ Syracuse NY 13210

LEVY, GERALD FRANK, b Paterson, NJ, June 20, 38; m 60; c 4. ECOLOGY. *Educ:* Bowling Green State Univ, BS, 60, MA, 61; Univ Wis, PhD(bot), 66. *Prof Exp:* Teach asst, Univ Wis, 63-65; asst prof bot & zool, Univ Wis, Marinette Campus, 65-67; asst prof biol & ecol, 67-71, assoc prof biol & ecol, 71-77, PROF BIOL SCI, OLD DOMINION UNIV, 78- *Concurrent Pos:* Bot consult, Animal Ecol Proj, 68-69; vpres, Environ Consult Inc, 73-81, chmn bd, 81- *Mem:* Ecol Soc Am. *Res:* Phytosociology; tick ecology research; small mammals; transpiration; terpine emission; ecology of red heart disease. *Mailing Add:* Dept of Biol Sci Old Dominion Univ Norfolk VA 23508

LEVY, GERHARD, b Wollin, Ger, Feb 12, 28; nat US; m 58; c 3. PHARMACOLOGY. *Educ:* Univ Calif, BS, 55, PharmD, 57. *Hon Degrees:* Dr, Univ Uppsala, 75, Phila Col Pharm & Sci, 79, Long Island Univ, 81. *Prof Exp:* Res pharmacist, Med Ctr, Univ Calif, 57-58; from asst prof to assoc prof pharm, 58-64, prof biopharmaceut, 64-72, actg chemn dept, 59-60, chmn, 66-70; DISTINGUISHED PROF PHARMACEUT, SCH PHARM, STATE UNIV NY BUFFALO, 72- *Concurrent Pos:* Vis prof, Hebrew Univ Jerusalem, 66-; consult, Bur Drugs, Food & Drug Admin, 71-73; mem comt probs drug safety, Nat Acad Sci-Nat Res Coun, 71-75; vis prof, Univ Rochester, 72-73; grad prof, Victorian Col Pharm, Melbourne, Australia, 73- *Honors & Awards:* Richardson Pharm Award, 57; Found Achievement Award, Am Pharmaceut Asn, 69, Ebert Prize, 69; McKeen Cattell Distinguished Achievement Award Clin Pharmacol, Am Col Clin Pharmacol, 78; Host-Madsen Medal, Int Pharmaceut Fedn, 78. *Mem:* Inst Med-Nat Acad Sci; Am Chem Soc; fel Am Pharmaceut Asn; Am Soc Pharmacol & Exp Therapeut; fel AAAS. *Res:* Biopharmaceutics; clinical pharmacology; pharmacokinetics. *Mailing Add:* Dept of Pharmaceut State Univ NY Sch Pharm Amherst NY 14260

LEVY, HANS RICHARD, b Leipzig, Ger, Oct 22, 29; nat US; m 60; c 1. BIOCHEMISTRY. *Educ:* Rutgers Univ, BSc, 50; Univ Chicago, PhD(biochem), 56. *Prof Exp:* USPHS fel, Ben May Lab, Univ Chicago, 56-58 & Hammersmith Hosp, London, Eng, 58-59; from instr to asst prof biochem, Ben May Lab, Univ Chicago, 59-63; from asst prof to assoc prof, 63-71, PROF BIOCHEM, SYRACUSE UNIV, 71- *Mem:* AAAS; Am Soc Biol Chem; Am Chem Soc; Brit Biochem Soc. *Res:* Mechanism of action of enzymes; mechanisms of control of enzymes. *Mailing Add:* Biol Res Labs Dept Biol Syracuse Univ Syracuse NY 13210

LEVY, HARRIS BENJAMIN, b Philadelphia, Pa, Nov 29, 28; m 62; c 1. DATA ANALYSIS. *Educ:* Univ Pa, BS, 50; Univ Calif, PhD(chem), 53. *Prof Exp:* Asst chem, Univ Calif, Berkeley, 51-53; chemist, 53-80, SR CHEMIST, LAWRENCE LIVERMORE NAT LAB, 80- *Mem:* Am Chem Soc. *Res:* General radiochemical research; plowshare applications of nuclear explosives; statistical data analysis; migration of radionuclides in groundwater; nuclear waste management; radiochemical analysis of nuclear explosion debris. *Mailing Add:* Nuclear Chem Div Lawrence Livermore Lab PO Box 808 Livermore CA 94550

LEVY, HARVEY LOUIS, b Augusta, Ga, Oct 3, 35; m 61; c 2. MEDICINE, PEDIATRICS. *Educ:* Med Col Ga, MD, 60. *Prof Exp:* Intern pediat, Boston City Hosp, 60-61; asst resident path, Columbia-Presby Med Ctr, 61-62; asst resident pediat, Johns Hopkins Hosp, 64-65; chief resident, Boston City Hosp, 65-66; instr, 68-70, asst prof, 70-77, ASSOC PROF NEUROL, HARVARD MED SCH, 77- *Concurrent Pos:* NIH fel neurol, Harvard Med Sch, 66-68; consult, Walter E Fernald Sch Ment Retardation, 67-; lectr, Grad Sch Dent, Boston Univ, 68-; prin investr, Mass Dept Pub Health, 69-75; dir, Mass Metab Dis Prog, 75-; assoc, Ctr Human Genetics, Harvard Med Sch, 71-; assoc neurologist & pediatrician, Mass Gen Hosp, 77-; dir, Inborn Errors of Metabolism-Phenylketonuria Prog, Children's Hosp Med Ctr, 78- *Mem:* Fel Am Acad Pediat; Soc Pediat Res. *Res:* Inborn errors of metabolism; biochemical and genetic disorders. *Mailing Add:* Dept of Neurol Mass Gen Hosp Boston MA 02114

LEVY, HARVEY MERRILL, b Pittsburgh, Pa, May 12, 28; m 57; c 1. BIOCHEMISTRY, PHYSIOLOGY. *Educ:* Univ Calif, Los Angeles, BA, 50, PhD(biochem), 55. *Prof Exp:* Asst res biochemist, Army Med Res Lab, Ky, 54-56; assoc res biochemist, Brookhaven Nat Lab, 56-58; asst prof pharmacol, Sch Med, NY Univ, 58-60, from asst prof to prof physiol & biophys, 60-71; PROF PHYSIOL & BIOPHYS, STATE UNIV NY STONY BROOK, 71- *Mem:* Am Chem Soc; Am Soc Biol Chemists; Harvey Soc; Biophys Soc; Soc Gen Physiol. *Res:* Muscle biochemistry; enzymology; kinetics. *Mailing Add:* Dept of Physiol State Univ of NY Stony Brook NY 11790

LEVY, HILTON BERTRAM, b New York, NY, Sept 21, 16; m 42; c 2. VIROLOGY. *Educ:* City Col New York, BS, 35; Columbia Univ, MA, 36; Polytech Inst Brooklyn, PhD(biochem), 46. *Prof Exp:* Chief chemist, Gen Sci Labs, NY, 37-41; res biochemist, Mem Hosp Cancer & Allied Dis, 41-46; res biochemist, Overly Biochem Res Found, 46-52; HEAD SECT MOLECULAR VIROL, NAT INST ALLERGY & INFECTIOUS DIS, 52- *Concurrent Pos:* Prof, Med Sch, Howard Univ. *Mem:* AAAS; Soc Exp Biol & Med; Am Asn Immunol; Soc Gen Physiol; Am Soc Biol Chem. *Res:* Enzymes; cancer; nucleic acid metabolism; infectious diseases; virus reproduction; interferon action and induction. *Mailing Add:* Sect of Molecular Virol Nat Inst of Allergy & Infect Dis Bethesda MD 20014

LEVY, HIRAM, II, atmospheric chemistry, atomic physics, see previous edition

LEVY, JACK BENJAMIN, b Savannah, Ga, Jan 17, 41; m 63. ORGANIC CHEMISTRY. *Educ:* Duke Univ, AB, 62, NC State Univ, MS, 64, PhD(chem), 67. *Prof Exp:* From asst prof to assoc prof, 68-73, PROF CHEM, UNIV NC, WILMINGTON, 73-, CHMN DEPT, 75- *Mem:* AAAS; Am Chem Soc; Am Inst Chemists. *Res:* Synthesis of heterocyclic organophosphorus compounds; synthesis, spectral properties and biological testing of new phenoxaphosphine derivatives. *Mailing Add:* Dept of Chem Univ of NC Wilmington NC 28401

LEVY, JERRE MARIE, b Birmingham, Ala, Apr 7, 38; m 69; c 2. PSYCHOBIOLOGY. *Educ:* Univ Miami, BA, 62, MS, 66; Calif Inst Technol, PhD(psychobiol), 69. *Prof Exp:* Res tech neuropsychol, Vet Admin Hosp, Denver, 69-70; fel psychol, Univ Colo, 70-71; fel biochem, Ore State Univ, 71-72; from asst prof to assoc prof psychol, Univ Pa, 72-77; ASSOC PROF BIOPSYCHOL, UNIV CHICAGO, 77- *Concurrent Pos:* Prin investr, NSF grant, 75-77 & NIH grant, 77-79; consult ed, J Exp Psychol: Human Perception & Performance, 78- *Res:* Cerebral asymmetry and cognitive function; evolution and genetics of human brain, especially hemispheric lateralization and correlated behaviors; variations in human lateralization patterns. *Mailing Add:* Dept of Behav Sci Univ of Chicago Chicago IL 60637

LEVY, JOSEPH, b New Haven, Conn, June 30, 13; m 41; c 3. ORGANIC CHEMISTRY. *Educ:* Yale Univ, BS, 35, PhD(org chem), 38. *Prof Exp:* Asst chem, Yale Univ, 35-38; res chemist, Polyxor Chem Co, 39-40; dir org res, Ernst Bischoff Co, 40-46; res chemist, Nopco Chem Co, 46-50; sr res assoc, Chem Div, Universal Oil Prod Co, 50-72, sr res assoc, Res Ctr, UOP Inc, Des Plaines, 72-78. *Concurrent Pos:* Adj prof chem, Fla Atlantic Univ, 80- *Mem:* Am Chem Soc. *Res:* Organic synthesis; fine organics; aromatics; process development; pharmaceuticals. *Mailing Add:* 123 Grantham-B Century Village E Deerfield Beach FL 33441

LEVY, JOSEPH BENJAMIN, b Manchester, Eng, Feb 23, 23; nat US; m 48; c 3. PHYSICAL CHEMISTRY, ORGANIC CHEMISTRY. *Educ:* Univ NH, BS, 43; Harvard Univ, MA, 45, PhD(chem), 48. *Prof Exp:* Mem sci staff, Columbia Univ, 47-49; res chemist, US Naval Ord Lab, 49-56 & Atlantic Res Corp, 56-65; PROF CHEM, GEORGE WASHINGTON UNIV, 65- *Mem:* Am Chem Soc. *Res:* Thermal decomposition of nitrate esters; reactions of free radicals; chemistry of rocket propellants; fluorine chemistry. *Mailing Add:* Dept of Chem George Washington Univ Washington DC 20052

LEVY, JOSEPH VICTOR, b Los Angeles, Calif, Apr 7, 28; m 54; c 2. PHYSIOLOGY, PHARMACOLOGY. *Educ:* Stanford Univ, BA, 50; Univ Calif, Los Angeles, MS, 56; Univ Wash, PhD(pharmacol), 59. *Prof Exp:* Asst physiol, Stanford Univ, 51-53, asst pharmacol, 54-56; asst Univ Wash, 56-57; pharmacologist, Western Labs Resources Res, 60; sr res pharmacologist, Res Labs, Presby Med Ctr, 60-65; assoc prof, Sch Med Sci, 69-77, ASSOC PROF PHYSIOL & PHARMACOL, SCH DENT, UNIV OF THE PACIFIC, 72-, DIR LAB PHARMACOL & EXP THERAPEUT, INST MED SCI, PAC MED CTR, 61- *Concurrent Pos:* NIH res trainee, 58-59; Am Heart Asn res fel, 59-60; Nat Heart Inst, res career prog scientist, 65-70; mem drug interaction panel, Am Pharmaceut Asn, 73-; mem, Coun Basic Res, Am Heart Asn; mem res comt, Calif Heart Asn, 75-77; mem, Hypertenison Task Force, Nat Heart Inst, NIH, 76-77; consult, WHO & UN Develop Prog, 81. *Mem:* Int Soc Hypertension; Soc Exp Biol & Med; Am Fedn Clin Res; Cardiac Muscle Soc; Am Soc Clin Pharmacol & Therapeut. *Res:* Physiology and pharmacology; hypertension; diabetes; prostaglandins; inflammation; arthritis; immunopharmacology. *Mailing Add:* Pac Med Ctr Inst Med Sci PO Box 7999 San Francisco CA 94120

LEVY, JULIA GERWING, b Singapore, May 15, 34; nat Can; m 55, 69; c 3. MICROBIOLOGY. *Educ:* Univ BC, BA, 55; Univ London, PhD(bact), 58. *Prof Exp:* From instr to assoc prof, 58-74, PROF MICROBIOL, UNIV BC, 74-, MEM CANCER RES UNIT, 77- *Mem:* Am Asn Immunologists; fel Royal Soc Can. *Res:* Characterization of antigenic determinants on natural antigens and the effect of these determinants on the cellular immune response. *Mailing Add:* Dept Bact & Immunol Univ BC Vancouver BC V6T 1W5 Can

LEVY, LAWRENCE S, b Cleveland, Ohio, Oct 2, 33; m 61; c 2. ALGEBRA. *Educ:* Juilliard Sch Music, BS, 54, MS, 56; Univ Ill, MA, 58, PhD(math), 61. *Prof Exp:* Instr math, Univ Ill, 61; from asst prof to assoc prof, 61-71, PROF MATH, UNIV WIS-MADISON, 71- *Mem:* Am Math Soc. *Res:* Structure of associative rings and their modules. *Mailing Add:* 2528 Van Hiss Ave Madison WI 53705

LEVY, LEO, b New York, NY, July 11, 28; m 57; c 2. PSYCHOLOGY, PREVENTIVE MEDICINE. *Educ:* City Col New York, BS, 50, MA, 51; Univ Wash, PhD(psychol), 58; Harvard Univ, SMHyg, 64. *Prof Exp:* Instr psychol, Univ Mich, 58-60; adminr & chief psychologist, Pueblo Guid Ctr, Pueblo, Colo, 60-63; dir planning & eval, Ill Dept Ment Health, 64-69; asst prof psychiat, 65-69, assoc prof prev med, 69-75, PROF PREV MED & PUB HEALTH, UNIV ILL MED CTR, 75- *Concurrent Pos:* NIMH fels, Univ Mich, 58-60 & Harvard Univ, 63-64; Fulbright Hays res grant, State Univ Leiden, 72-73; vis assoc prof psychiat, McMaster Univ, 69-71; Fogerty Sr Int fel, Inst Psychiat, London, 79-80; vis prof, St George's Hosp Med Sch, London, 79-80. *Mem:* Am Asn Univ Prof; AAAS; Am Psychol Asn; Am Pub Health Asn. *Res:* Promotion and maintenance of mental health; social planning; drug abuse; social ecology; psychosocial epidemiology; problems of urban mental health. *Mailing Add:* Dept Prev Med & Community Health Univ of Ill Med Ctr PO Box 6998 Chicago IL 60680

LEVY, LEON BRUCE, b New York, NY, July 20, 37. INDUSTRIAL ORGANIC CHEMISTRY. *Educ:* NY Univ, BA, 58; Harvard Univ, AM, 59, PhD(chem), 62. *Prof Exp:* Res chemist, Clarkwood Res Lab, 62-65, sr res chemist, Tech Ctr, 65-71, RES ASSOC, TECH CTR, CELANESE CHEM CO, 72- *Mem:* Catalysis Soc. *Res:* Kinetics and mechanisms of homolytic organic reactions; vapor phase oxidations of hydrocarbons; heterogeneous catalysis. *Mailing Add:* Celanese Chem Co Box 9077 Corpus Christi TX 78408

LEVY, LEON SHOLOM, b Perth Amboy, NJ, June 28, 30; m 54; c 3. COMPUTER SCIENCE. *Educ:* Yeshiva Univ, BA, 52; Harvard Univ, SM, 55, ME, 57; Univ Pa, PhD(comput sci), 70. *Prof Exp:* Engr, RCA Corp, 55-58; sr staff engr, Hughes Aircraft Co, 58-63; mgr comput & displays sect, Aerospace Corp, 63-66; systs architect, IBM Corp, 66-67; asst prof statist & comput sci, Univ Del, 70-74, assoc prof, 74-80. *Concurrent Pos:* Consult, Linguistics Proj, Univ Pa, 70- *Mem:* Asn Comput Mach; Inst Elec & Electronics Eng. *Res:* Relationship of machines and their languages; relationship of functional and structural aspects of computers. *Mailing Add:* 4717 Lafayette Ave Pennsauken NJ 08110

LEVY, LOUIS, pharmacology, see previous edition

LEVY, LOUIS, b Brooklyn, NY, Feb 1, 23; m 54; c 5. PHARMACOLOGY. *Educ:* Univ Iowa, BS, 49, MS, 51, PhD(pharmacol), 54. *Prof Exp:* Asst chem, Syracuse Univ, 49-50; asst pediat, Univ Iowa, 50-52, instr pharmacol, 53-54; asst prof, Med Sch, Georgetown Univ, 54-55; asst prof, Col Med, Univ Cincinnati, 55-59; sr pharmacologist, Riker Labs, Calif, 59-71; assoc prof, 71-76, PROF PHARMACOL, SCH MED, UNIV CALIF, LOS ANGELES, 76- *Concurrent Pos:* Res collabr, Brookhaven Nat Lab, 53-55. *Mem:* AAAS; Am Soc Pharmacol & Exp Therapeut; NY Acad Sci. *Res:* Biochemical pharmacology. *Mailing Add:* Dept of Med Univ of Calif Sch of Med Los Angeles CA 90024

LEVY, LOUIS A, b New York, NY, Mar 6, 41; m 67; c 1. ORGANIC CHEMISTRY. *Educ:* City Col New York, BS, 61; Univ Colo, PhD(chem), 66. *Prof Exp:* Proj leader synthesis, Int Flavors & Fragrances, Inc, 65-66; scientist, Nat Air Pollution Control Admin, USPHS, 66-67, SCIENTIST, LAB ENVIRON CHEM, NAT INST ENVIRON HEALTH SCI, 67- *Mem:* Am Chem Soc; The Chem Soc. *Res:* Chemistry and synthesis of chemicals of environmental concern; heterocyclic chemistry. *Mailing Add:* Nat Inst Environ Health Sci PO Box 12233 Research Triangle Park NC 27709

LEVY, MARILYN, b New York, NY, Apr 3, 22. PHOTOGRAPHIC ENGINEERING, CHEMISTRY. *Educ:* Hunter Col, AB, 42. *Prof Exp:* Chemist anal-drugs, NY Quinine & Chem Co, 42-43; chemist lacquer formulation, Roxalin Flexible Finishes, 43-46, chemist lacquer mfg, Valspar Corp, 46-48; inspector chem, NY Quartermaster Proc Agency, 51-52; res chemist photog process, US Army Electronics Command, 53-74; chief photog optics div, Photog Eng, US Army Combat & Surveillance Lab, 75-80; CONSULT, 80- *Concurrent Pos:* Mem & US Army rep, Am Nat Standards Inst, 62-; US Army adv, NATO Photog Standards Comt & Air Standardization Coord Comt, 78- *Honors & Awards:* US Army Spec Act Awards, US Army Res & DeVelop Achievement Award; US Army Meritorious Civilian Serv Award. *Mem:* Soc Photog Scientists & Engrs; Am Chem Soc. *Res:* Photographic processing; non-conventional photographic systems; aerial photography; photographic sensitometry; color photography; rapid processing. *Mailing Add:* 56 Cheshire Sq Little Silver NJ 07739

LEVY, MARTIN J LINDEN, b Philadelphia, Pa, June 19, 25; m 58; c 3. MEDICAL SCIENCES, RESEARCH ADMINISTRATION. *Educ:* Pa State Univ, BS, 47; NJ Inst Technol, MS, 56; Stevens Inst Technol, DrSci, 63. *Prof Exp:* Specialist engr, Jet Engine Div, Gen Elec, 56-58; PROF ENG, NJ INST TECHNOL, 58- *Concurrent Pos:* Adj prof, NJ Med Sch, Univ Med & Dent, 80-82; med staff affil, St Barnabas Med Ctr, NJ & bd dir, Southern Inst Biomed Sci, 80-82. *Mem:* Am Col Cryosurg; NY Acad Sci; Int Soc Cryosurg. *Res:* Biomedical sciences; application of engineering and technical methods to instrumentation for diagnosis and therapy. *Mailing Add:* NJ Inst Technol 323 High St Newark NJ 07102

LEVY, MATTHEW NATHAN, b New York, NY, Dec 2, 22; m 46; c 3. PHYSIOLOGY, BIOMEDICAL ENGINEERING. *Educ:* Western Reserve Univ, BS, 43, MD, 45. *Prof Exp:* From instr to asst prof physiol, Western Reserve Univ, 49-53; from asst prof to assoc prof, Albany Med Col, 53-57; dir res, St Vincent Charity Hosp, Cleveland, Ohio, 57-67; assoc prof, 61-68, PROF MED, PHYSIOL & BIOMED ENG, CASE WESTERN RESERVE UNIV, 68-; CHIEF DEPT INVESTIGATIVE MED, MT SINAI HOSP, 67- *Concurrent Pos:* Res fel, Western Reserve Univ, 48-49; assoc prof, Case Inst Technol, 63-67; assoc ed, Circulation Res, 70-74; sect ed, Am J Physiol, 75- *Honors & Awards:* Lederle Med Fac Award, 55-57. *Mem:* Am Physiol Soc; Am Heart Asn. *Res:* Cardiovascular physiology. *Mailing Add:* Dept of Investigative Med Mt Sinai Hosp Cleveland OH 44106

LEVY, MICHAEL GREEN, b Brooklyn, NY, May 8, 50; m 72; c 1. PARASITOLOGY. *Educ:* State Univ NY Col Buffalo, BA, 72; Rice Univ, PhD(biol), 75. *Prof Exp:* NIH trainee, Rice Univ, 75; RES FEL TROP PUB HEALTH, HARVARD SCH PUB HEALTH, 75- *Mem:* Am Soc Parasitologists. *Res:* Dynamics of host-parasite interface; membrane transport; vector ecology and control; biochemical basis of parasitism; schistosomiasis and Chagas' disease. *Mailing Add:* Dept of Trop Pub Health Harvard Sch Pub Health Boston MA 02115

LEVY, MICHAEL R, b Los Angeles, Calif, Aug 8, 35; m 62; c 2. CELLULAR BIOLOGY. *Educ:* Univ Calif, Los Angeles, BS, 57, MA, 59, PhD(zool), 63. *Prof Exp:* USPHS fel, 63-65, trainee, 65-66; teaching fel, Univ Mich, 66-67; from asst prof to assoc prof, 67-74, PROF BIOL, SOUTHERN ILL UNIV, EDWARDSVILLE, 74- *Concurrent Pos:* USPHS res grants, 69-80. *Mem:* AAAS; Am Soc Cell Biol. *Res:* Regulation of protein degradation; proteolytic enzymes; lysosomes. *Mailing Add:* Dept of Biol Southern Ill Univ Edwardsville IL 62026

LEVY, MOISES, b Panama, Apr 8, 30; US citizen; m 59. SOLID STATE PHYSICS. *Educ:* Calif Inst Technol, BS, 52, MS, 55; Univ Calif, Los Angeles, PhD(physics), 63. *Prof Exp:* Res chemist, Speciality Resins, Inc, 53-54; mem tech staff, Semiconductor Div, Hughes Aircraft Co, 56-58; asst prof solid state physics, Univ Pa, 64-65; asst prof ultrasonic invest solid state, Univ Calif, Los Angeles, 65-70; assoc prof, 71-73, chmn dept, 75-78, PROF PHYSICS, UNIV WIS-MILWAUKEE, 73- *Res:* Experimental investigation of electron phonon interaction in superconductors and normal metals; spin phonon interaction in the rare earth metals; surface wave investigation of superconducting films and magnetic films. *Mailing Add:* Dept of Physics Univ of Wis Milwaukee WI 53201

LEVY, MORRIS, b Chicago, Ill, May 22, 44; m 74; c 1. EVOLUTIONARY BIOLOGY, BIOSYSTEMATICS. *Educ:* Univ Ill, Chicago Circle, 67; Yale Univ, MPh, 72, PhD(ecol, evolution), 73. *Prof Exp:* asst prof, 73-79, ASSOC PROF BIOL SCI, PURDUE UNIV, 79- *Concurrent Pos:* Dir, Kriebel Herbarium, Purdue Univ, 73-; NSF grant, Res Prog Biomed Sci, 75; NSF grant, 78 & 79. *Mem:* Bot Soc Am; Soc Study Evolution; Soc Am Naturalists; AAAS. *Res:* Systematics and biochemical ecology of plants; evolution of hybrid and polyploid species; population biology of weeds; host plant-fungal pathogen co-evolution; pollinetion ecology. *Mailing Add:* Dept of Biol Sci Purdue Univ Lafayette IN 47907

LEVY, MORTIMER, b Rochester, NY, July 7, 24; m 50; c 2. RESEARCH ADMINISTRATION. *Educ:* Cornell Univ, BSEE, 49; Columbia Univ, MA, 51. *Prof Exp:* Physicist, Xerox Corp, 54-57, sect leader, 58-61; dir appl res, Mat Res Corp, 61-63; res scientist, 63-64, sr scientist, 64-67, mgr explor res, 67-73, mgr process sect, 73-75, mgr, Process Element Sect, 75-78, MGR MAT, PROCESSES & CORP STAFF, XEROX CORP, 78- *Mem:* Soc Photog Sci & Eng. *Res:* Electrostatic photography. *Mailing Add:* Wilson Ctr Res & Technol Xerox Corp Webster NY 14580

LEVY, MORTON FRANK, b New York, NY, May 31, 25; m 55; c 3. ORGANIC CHEMISTRY. *Educ:* Queens Col, NY, BS, 50; Columbia Univ, MA, 51; Yale Univ, PhD(chem), 56. *Prof Exp:* Group leader org synthesis & anal develop, Argus Chem Co, 55-60; group leader org synthesis, Harchem Div, Wallace & Tiernan, NJ, 60-64; SR CHEMIST, MAT SCI COMPLEX, IBM CORP, SAN JOSE, 64- *Concurrent Pos:* Res assoc, Univ Calif, Berkeley, 75-76. *Mem:* AAAS; Am Chem Soc. *Res:* Utilization of new raw materials in organic synthesis; photosensitive materials; dibasic acids; dye chemistry; preparation of radiolabeled compounds; new polymers; application of computers to chemistry. *Mailing Add:* 105 Stacia St Los Gatos CA 95030

LEVY, NELSON LOUIS, b Somerville, NJ, June 19, 41; m 74; c 3. IMMUNOLOGY, NEUROSCIENCES. *Educ:* Yale Univ, BA & BS, 63; Columbia Univ, MD, 67; Duke Univ, PhD(immunol), 73. *Prof Exp:* Intern surg, Univ Colo Med Ctr, 67-68; res assoc virol & immunol, NIH, 68-70; resident neurol, Duke Univ Med Ctr, 71-72, from asst prof to assoc prof immunol, 76-80; VPRES, PHARMACEUT DISCOVERY, ABBOTT LABS, 81- *Concurrent Pos:* Mem gastrointestinal cancer study group, Nat Cancer Inst, 74- *Mem:* Am Asn Cancer Res; Am Asn Immunologists; Sigma Xi. *Res:* Immunologic and non-immunologic defenses against human cancer; pathogenesis and etiology of multiple sclerosis; neurologic control of the immune system. *Mailing Add:* Pharmareut Prod Div Abbott Lab North Chicago IL 60064

LEVY, NEWTON, JR, b Tampa, Fla, Oct 10, 35; m 61; c 2. INORGANIC CHEMISTRY, TECHNICAL MANAGEMENT. *Educ:* Univ Fla, BSCh, 61, PhD(kinetics), 64. *Prof Exp:* Res chemist, Wash Res Ctr Div, W R Grace & Co, 64-67, sr chemist, 67-69, res supvr, 69-72; sect head refractories, Martin Marietta Labs, 72-74, mgr fuel additives, Refractories Div, 74-76, mgr prod develop, Refractories Div, 77-81, VPRES SALES-CHEM, MARTIN MARIETTA CHEM, 81- *Res:* Preparation, fabrication, characterization and applications of reactive, fine sized ceramic oxide powders; properties and uses of magnesium oxide; chemical treatment of oils for combustion; chemical market studies; marketing specialty chemicals. *Mailing Add:* Martin Marietta Chem Exec Plaza II Hunt Valley MD 21030

LEVY, NORMAN B, b New York, NY, May 28, 31; m 58, 70; c 4. PSYCHIATRY, PSYCHOSOMATIC MEDICINE. *Educ:* NY Univ, BA, 52; State Univ NY Downstate Med Ctr, MD, 56. *Prof Exp:* Res physician & teaching fel med, Sch Med, Univ Pittsburgh, 57-58; dir med serv, US Air Force Hosp, Ashiya, Japan, 58-60; resident physician psychiat, Kings County Hosp Ctr, Brooklyn, NY, 60-63; from instr to asst prof med & psychiat, 63-73, dir continuing educ psychiat, 74-76, presiding officer fac, Col Med, 75-76, assoc prof, 73-79, prof psychiat, 79-80, assoc dir, Med Psychiat Liaison Serv, State Univ NY Downstate Med Ctr, 72-80; PROF PSYCHIAT, MED & SURG, NY MED COL & DIR, LIAISON PSYCHIAT DIV, WESTCHESTER COUNTY MED CTR, 80- *Concurrent Pos:* NIMH career teacher award, 66; vis prof psychiat & med, Univ Hawaii, 81; consult psychiat educ, NIMH, 74-; examr psychiat, Am Bd Psychiat & Neurol, 74-; assoc ed, The Int J Psychiat Med, 77-78; assoc ed, General Hosp Pschiat & ed of sect, Liaison Rounds, 79- *Mem:* Fel Am Col Physicians; fel Am Psychiat Asn; fel Int Col Psychosom Med; fel Am Asn Psychoanal Physicians; Asn Appl Psychoanal. *Res:* Effects of psychological stresses on kidney transplant rejections; psychological adaptation to hemodialysis; psychiatry and the changing role of males in society; attitudes of students and physicians on informing patients of their fatal diagnosis; problems of spouses of psychoanalytical candidates. *Mailing Add:* State Univ NY Downstate Med Ctr Box 127 450 Clarkson Ave Brooklyn NY 11203

LEVY, NORMAN STUART, b Detroit, Mich, July 17, 40; m 64; c 4. OPHTHALMOLOGY, GLAUCOMA. *Educ:* Case Western Reserve, MD, 65; Univ Chicago, PhD(ophthal), 75. *Prof Exp:* Asst prof ophthal & pediat, 72-75, ASST PROF FAMILY MED, UNIV FLA, 81- *Concurrent Pos:* Chief ophthal, Vet Admin Hosp, Gainesville, 73-75 & Vet Admin Med Ctr, Lake City, 76-81. *Mem:* Am Acad Ophthal; Asn Res Vision & Ophthal; Am Col Surgeons; Kerato Refractive Soc. *Res:* Mechanism of damage in the disease, glaucoma, and method of diagnosis and early treatment. *Mailing Add:* 7106 NW 11th Pl Gainesville FL 32605

LEVY, PAUL, b New York, NY, May 25, 41; m 65; c 1. APPLIED MATHEMATICS. *Educ:* Rensselaer Polytech Inst, BS, 63, MS, 65, PhD(math), 68. *Prof Exp:* Asst prof math, NY Univ, 67-74; asst prof math, NY Inst Technol, 74-77; ASST PROF MATH, STATE UNIV NY MARITIME COL, 77- *Mem:* Am Math Soc; Soc Indust & Appl Math. *Res:* Investigation of problems in wave propagation and elasticity. *Mailing Add:* Dept of Math Ft Schuyler Bronx NY 10465

LEVY, PAUL F, b New York, NY, Dec 9, 34; m 59; c 4. ANALYTICAL CHEMISTRY, INSTRUMENTATION. *Educ:* City Col New York, BS, 59; Columbia Univ, MA, 61, PhD(anal chem), 65. *Prof Exp:* Lectr chem, City Col New York, 59-65; proj engr, 65-68, sr proj engr, 68-69, supvr appln lab, 69-73, prod mgr thermal anal, 73-75, PROD MGR LIQUID CHROMATOG, INSTRUMENT PROD DIV, E I DU PONT DE NEMOURS & CO, 75- *Mem:* Am Chem Soc; Am Soc Testing & Mat. *Res:* Theory, applications, design and development of thermal analysis and other material characterization instrumentation; coulostatic impulse-chain and other forms of polarography; electrochemical instrumentation. *Mailing Add:* Instrument Prod Div E I du Pont de Nemours & Co Wilmington DE 19898

LEVY, PAUL SAMUEL, b New Haven, Conn, May 30, 36; m 75; c 2. BIOSTATISTICS, EPIDEMIOLOGY. *Educ:* Yale Univ, BS, 58; Columbia Univ, MA, 62; Johns Hopkins Univ, ScD(biostatist), 64. *Prof Exp:* Statistician, Ctr for Dis Control, Dept Health, Educ & Welfare, 60-62; res fel biomath, Med Sch, Harvard Univ, 64-65, from instr to asst prof biostatist, 66-70; math statistician, Nat Ctr Health Statist, Dept Health, Educ & Welfare, 70-72; from assoc prof to prof biometry, Sch Pub Health, Univ Ill Med Ctr, 72-78; prof pub health, Univ Mass, 78-80. *Concurrent Pos:* Consult, Nat Ctr Health Statist, Dept Health, Educ & Welfare, 72- & Ill Col Podiatric Med, 75-; statist expert, US Food & Drug Admin, 75- *Mem:* AAAS; Am Statist Asn; Biometric Soc. *Res:* Epidemiology of accidents and trauma; analysis of data from the National Health Surveys; epidemiology of foot conditions; methods of obtaining estimates for local populations. *Mailing Add:* 6401 Windermere Circle Rockville MD 20852

LEVY, PAUL WARREN, b Chicago, Ill, Mar 17, 21; m 44; c 4. SOLID STATE PHYSICS. *Educ:* Univ Chicago, BS, 43; Carnegie Inst Technol, PhD, 54. *Prof Exp:* Jr physicist, Metall Lab, Univ Chicago, 43-44; physicist beta-ray spectros, Oak Ridge Nat Lab, 44-48; assoc physicist, 52-58, PHYSICIST RADIATION DAMAGE INSULATORS, BROOKHAVEN NAT LAB, 58- *Concurrent Pos:* Indust consult to civilian & mil agencies, 55-; adj prof, Adelphi Univ, 66-; adj prof geol, Univ Pa, 76- *Mem:* Fel Am Phys Soc; Optical Soc Am. *Res:* Nuclear physics; luminescence of solids; optical and defect properties of solids; optical spectrophotometry; radiation effects in insulators, metals, explosives and propellants; crystal growth; geoscience applications of solid state physics; thermoluminescence of solids and applications to dosimetry, mineralogy and mineral exploration. *Mailing Add:* Dept of Physics Brookhaven Nat Lab Upton NY 11973

LEVY, PETER MICHAEL, b Frankfurt, Ger, Jan 10, 36; US citizen; m 65; c 2. SOLID STATE PHYSICS. *Educ:* City Col New York, BME, 58; Harvard Univ, MA, 60, PhD(appl physics), 63. *Prof Exp:* Res assoc physics, Lab Electrostatics & Physics of Metals, Grenoble, France, 63-64; res assoc, Univ Pa, 64-66; asst prof, Yale Univ, 66-70; assoc prof, 70-75, PROF PHYSICS, NY UNIV, 75-, CHMN DEPT, 76- *Concurrent Pos:* Fel, CNRS, France, 63-64; Air Force Off Sci Res grant, Yale Univ & NY Univ, 67-72; NSF grant, NY Univ, 72-; Fulbright-Hays res scholar, France, 75-76; res exchange scientist, CNRS/NSF, 75-76. *Mem:* Am Phys Soc; fel NY Acad Sci. *Res:* Theory of the magnetic behavior of insulators; magneto-elastic and thermodynamic behavior of the rare-earth pnictides; magnetoresistivity of rare earth metallic compound; orbital effects in rare earth compounds; anisotropy in disordered magnetic systems; orbital and spin polarization of conduction electrons in rare-earth compounds. *Mailing Add:* Dept Physics NY Univ New York NY 10003

LEVY, RALPH, b London, Eng, Apr 12, 32; US citizen; m 59; c 2. MICROWAVE THEORY, CIRCUIT THEORY. *Educ:* Cambridge Univ, MA, 53; Univ London, PhD(appl sci), 66. *Prof Exp:* Mem sci staff microwave eng, Gen Elec Co, Stanmore, Eng, 53-59, Mullard Res Labs, Redhill, 59-64; lectr elec eng, Univ Leeds, 64-67; VPRES RES MICROWAVE ENG, MICROWAVE DEVELOP LABS, 67- *Concurrent Pos:* Consult, Decca Radar Ltd & Gen Elec Co, 64-67, Weinschel Eng, 65-66. *Mem:* Fel Inst Elec & Electronics Engrs. *Res:* Microwave passive components; distributed circuit theory; military microwave systems. *Mailing Add:* Microwave Develop Labs Inc 11 Michigan Dr Natick MA 01760

LEVY, RAM LEON, b Samokov, Bulgaria, Oct 7, 33; US citizen; m 58; c 3. SEPARATION SCIENCE, CHEMICAL INTRUMENTATION. *Educ:* Israel Inst Technol, BSc, 61, MSc, 63; Univ Man, PhD(anal chem), 67. *Prof Exp:* Res assoc, Dept Plant Sci, Univ Man, 63-67; assoc chemist, Midwest Res Labs, Kansas City, 67-68; SCIENTIST, POLYMER CHEMISTRY, MCDONNELL DOUGLAS RES LABS, MCDONNELL DOUGLAS CORP, 68- *Concurrent Pos:* Affil dir, Sch Continuing Prof Educ, Washington Univ, 70-72; vis lectr, Chem Dept, St Louis Univ, 75. *Mem:* Am Chem Soc; Am Soc Mass Spectrometry. *Res:* Chemical mechanisms of polymer aging; detection of stress and fatigue induced molecular phenomena in polymers by infra red spectroscopy; chemluminescence of polymers; chromatographic characterization of oligimers; incorporation of molecular probes in polymer networks; thermal degradation of polymers. *Mailing Add:* McDonnell Douglas Res Labs McDonnell Douglas Corp St Louis MO 63166

LEVY, RENE HANANIA, b Casa Blanca, Morocco, Sept 30, 42; US citizen; m 64; c 3. PHARMACODYNAMICS. *Educ:* Univ Bordeaux, Baccalaureat, 60; Univ Paris, Pharm, 65; Univ Calif, San Francisco, PhD(pharm, pharmaceut chem), 70. *Prof Exp:* Intern, Hosps of Paris, Hopital Corentin Celton, 64-66; asst prof pharm, Col Pharm, 70-74, assoc prof, 74-77, PROF PHARMACEUT, SCH PHARM & PROF NEUROL SURG, SCH MED, UNIV WASH, 77- *Mem:* Am Epilepsy Soc; Fedn Int Pharmaceutique; Am Pharmaceut Asn; Acad Pharmaceut Sci. *Res:* Pharmacokinetic evaluation of anticonvulsants prior to efficacy testing in primates; clinical pharmacology of new antiepileptic drugs; kinetics of drug metabolites. *Mailing Add:* Sch of Pharm BG-20 Univ of Wash Seattle WA 98195

LEVY, RICARDO BENJAMIN, b Quito, Ecuador, Jan 11, 45; US citizen; m 67; c 2. SURFACE CHEMISTRY, CHEMICAL ENGINEERING. *Educ:* Stanford Univ, BSc, 66, PhD(chem eng), 72; Princeton Univ, MA, 67. *Prof Exp:* Gen mgr mfg, Sudam Cia Ltda, 67-69; res eng chem physics, Exxon Res & Eng Co, 72-74; vpres, 74-77, EXEC VPRES CONSULT RES & DEVELOP, CATALYTICA ASSOCS, INC, 77- *Concurrent Pos:* Prof chem eng, Inst Politecnico Nac, Quito, Ecuador, 67-69. *Mem:* Am Inst Chem Engrs; Am Chem Soc; Faraday Soc; Catalysis Soc. *Res:* Reactivity of solid surfaces in catalytic reactions; new materials for catalysis; chemical vapor transport. *Mailing Add:* Catalytica Assocs Inc 3255 Scott Blvd Suite 7-E Santa Clara CA 95051

LEVY, RICHARD, b Brooklyn, NY, June 29, 44; m 69; c 1. MEDICAL ENTOMOLOGY, INVERTEBRATE ZOOLOGY. *Educ:* Univ Fla, BS, 67 & BS, 68, MS, 69, PhD(entom), 71. *Prof Exp:* Res asst med entom, Dept Entom & Nematol, UniY Fla, 71-74; tech & training consult pest control, Orkin Exterminating Co, 74; res entomologist med entom, WFla Arthropod Res Lab, 74-76; RES ENTOMOLOGIST MED ENTOM, LEE COUNTY MOSQUITO CONTROL DIST, 76- *Mem:* Am Registry Prof Entomologists; Entom Soc Am; Am Mosquito Control Asn; Int Orgn Biol Control Noxious Animals & Plants; Soc Invert Path. *Res:* Biological and chemical control of insects of medical and veterinary importance. *Mailing Add:* Lee County Mosquito Control Dist PO Box 06005 Ft Myers FL 33906

LEVY, ROBERT, b Montreal, Que, Apr 12, 38; m 64; c 1. BIOCHEMISTRY, CLINICAL CHEMISTRY. *Educ:* McGill Univ, BS, 59, PhD(biochem), 65, Am Bd Clin Chem, dipl, 80. *Prof Exp:* NIH fel, Vet Admin Hosp/Univ Mo-Kansas City, 64-66; chief chemist, Vet Admin Hosp, Washington, DC, 66-67; asst prof neurobiol, Psychiat Inst, Univ Md, Baltimore City, 67-71; DIR LAB SERV, PATH DEPT, CHURCH HOSP CORP, 71- *Concurrent Pos:* Asst prof, George Washington Univ, 66-67; guest lectr, Towson State Col, 69. *Mem:* AAAS; Am Asn Clin Chem. *Res:* Neurochemistry of membranes; neurotransmitters; neuroenzymology; clinical enzymology. *Mailing Add:* Dept of Path Church Hosp Corp Baltimore MD 21231

LEVY, ROBERT I, b New York, NY, May 3, 37; m 58; c 4. MEDICINE, BIOCHEMISTRY. *Educ:* Cornell Univ, BA, 57; Yale Univ, MD, 61. *Prof Exp:* Intern med, Yale-New Haven Med Ctr, 61-62, resident, 62-63; clin asst med res, 63-65, chief resident med, 65-66, dep clin dir, 68-69, chief clin serv, Molecular Dis Br, 69-73, chief lipid metab br, 70-74, dir, Div Heart & Vascular Dis, 73-75, HEAD SECT LIPOPROTEINS, NAT HEART LUNG & BLOOD INST, 66-, DIR, 75- *Concurrent Pos:* Mem coun arteriosclerosis, Am Heart Asn. *Mem:* Am Fedn Clin Res; Am Soc Clin Invest; fel Am Col Cardiol. *Res:* Lipid metabolism; lipid transport; atherosclerosis; hyperlipoproteinemia. *Mailing Add:* Lipid Metab Br Bldg 10-7N220 Nat Heart Lung & Blood Inst Bethesda MD 20014

LEVY, ROBERT S(AMUEL), b New York, NY, May 28, 20; m 54; c 2. ENGINEERING. *Educ:* City Col New York, BME, 40; Polytech Inst Brooklyn, MME, 43, DrAeroEng, 46. *Prof Exp:* Mech Engr, NY Naval Shipyard, 41-46; struct engr, Repub Aviation Div, Fairchild-Hiller Corp, 46-59, develop engr, 59-65, proj engr manned space vehicles, 65-66, eng prog mgr supersonic transp, 66-71, mgr design eng, 71-75, dir eng, 75, mgr tech eng, 76, mgr new systs res, 77-78, TECH SPECIALIST, FAIRCHILD REPUB CO, FAIRCHILD INDUSTS, 79- *Concurrent Pos:* Civilian with Nat Adv Comt Aeronaut, 44. *Mem:* Assoc fel Am Inst Aeronaut & Astronaut; Sigma Xi. *Res:* Aircraft structures. *Mailing Add:* Fairchild Repub Co Fairchild Industs Inc Farmingdale NY 11735

LEVY, ROBERT SIGMUND, b Fresno, Calif, Nov 3, 21; m 52; c 1. BIOCHEMISTRY, BIOLOGICAL PSYCHIATRY. *Educ:* Univ Calif, Berkeley, AB, 48, AM, 52; Univ Southern Calif, PhD(biochem, nutrit), 57. *Prof Exp:* Asst zool, Univ Calif, Berkeley, 49-52; asst biochem & nutrit, Sch Med, Univ Southern Calif, 55-57; from asst prof to assoc prof biochem, 57-72, PROF BIOCHEM, SCH MED, UNIV LOUISVILLE, 72-, DIR, LAB BIOL PSYCHIAT, 78- *Concurrent Pos:* Assoc psychiat & emergency med, Sch Med, Univ Louisville; fel coun arteriosclerosis, Am Heart Asn. *Mem:* Asn Multidiscipline Educ Health Sci; Sigma Xi; Am Chem Soc; Am Soc Biol Chem; Soc Neurosci. *Res:* Isolation of unusual peptides from blood and hemodialysates of schizophrenic patients; detection of enkephalins and endorphins in biological fluids by radioimmunoassay and radioreceptor assay; biochemistry of brain function and role of neuropeptides; reversal of atherosclerosis by lipoproteins in cell culture. *Mailing Add:* Dept of Biochem Sch of Med Univ Louisville Health Sci Ctr Box 35260 Louisville KY 40232

LEVY, ROLAND ALBERT, solid state physics, see previous edition

LEVY, RONALD FRED, b St Louis, Mo, Dec 11, 44; m 66; c 1. TOPOLOGY. *Educ:* Wash Univ, AB, 66, AM, 70, PhD(math), 74. *Prof Exp:* Asst prof math, Goucher Col, 74-75; instr math, Wash Univ, 75-76; asst prof, 76-81, ASSOC PROF MATH, GEORGE MASON UNIV, 81- *Mem:* Am Math Soc; Math Asn Am. *Res:* Compact Hausdorff spaces; almost-P-spaces; linearly ordered topological spaces. *Mailing Add:* Dept of Math George Mason Univ Fairfax VA 22030

LEVY, SALOMON, b Jerusalem, Apr 4, 26; US citizen; m 51; c 2. MECHANICAL ENGINEERING. *Educ:* Univ Calif, Berkeley, BS, 49, MS, 51, PhD(mech eng), 53. *Prof Exp:* Mgr systs eng, Gen Elec Co, 66-68, mgr design eng dept, 68-71, gen mgr nuclear fuel dept, 71-73, gen mgr boiling water reactor systs dept, 73-75, gen mgr boiling water reactor opers, 75-77; PRES, S LEVY INC, ENG CONSULT, 77-; PROF, UNIV CALIF, LOS ANGELES, 81- *Concurrent Pos:* Consult, Assoc Midwestern Univ, 76-81; Brookhaven Nat Lab, 77- & Elec Power Res Inst, 77- *Honors & Awards:* Heat Transfer Mem Award, Am Soc Mech Engrs, 66. *Mem:* Nat Acad Eng; fel Am Soc Mech Engrs. *Res:* Heat transfer and fluid flow, particularly two-phase flow and boiling heat transfer; nuclear reactor power plant design and analysis. *Mailing Add:* 1999 S Bascom Ave Campbell CA 95008

LEVY, SAMUEL C, b Far Rockaway, NY, Jan 5, 37; m 58; c 2. ELECTROCHEMISTRY, ELECTROANALYTICAL CHEMISTRY. *Educ:* Hofstra Col, BA, 58; Iowa State Univ, PhD(inorg chem), 62. *Prof Exp:* STAFF MEM, SANDIA CORP, 62- *Mem:* Am Chem Soc; Electrochem Soc. *Res:* Chemical to electrical energy conversion; mechanism of electrochemical reactions. *Mailing Add:* Sandia Labs Div 2523 PO Box 5800 Albuquerque NM 87115

LEVY, SAMUEL WOLFE, b Montreal, Que, Feb 26, 22; m 67; c 2. CLINICAL CHEMISTRY. *Educ:* McGill Univ, BSc, 49, PhD(physiol), 54; Univ Sask, MSc, 51. *Prof Exp:* Multiple Sclerosis Soc Can res fel biochem, McGill-Montreal Gen Hosp Res Inst, 54-56; res assoc, Hotel-Dieu Hosp, Montreal, 56-61; dir, Dept Biochem, Queen Mary Vet Hosp, Montreal, 61-79; DIR, DEPT BIOCHEM, QUEEN ELIZABETH HOSP, MONTREAL, 79- *Concurrent Pos:* Dom-Prov Health grant, 56-61; Dept Vet Affairs grant, 64-71. *Honors & Awards:* Ames Award, Can Soc Clin Chem, 75. *Mem:* Chem Inst Can; Can Soc Clin Chem (pres, 70-71); Am Asn Clin Chem. *Res:* Lysosomal enzymes in blood in inflammation disease; effects of heparin in vivo on enzymes and lipid in blood. *Mailing Add:* Dept Biochem Queen Elizabeth Hosp Montreal PQ H4A 2L6 Can

LEW, CHEL WING, b San Antonio, Tex, Dec 9, 35; m 59; c 4. CHEMISTRY. *Educ:* Tex A&M Univ, BS, 60. *Prof Exp:* Technician chem, 60-61, asst res chemist, 61-65, res chemist 65-73, SR RES CHEMIST, SOUTHWEST RES INST, 73- *Mem:* Sigma Xi. *Res:* Microencapsulation. *Mailing Add:* Southwest Res Inst 6220 Culebra San Antonio TX 78238

LEW, GLORIA MARIA, b Kingston, Jamaica, March 7, 34; US citizen. BIOCHEMISTRY, PHARMACOLOGY. *Educ:* Mt St Vincent Col, BA, 56; Boston Col, MS, 58; Univ Calif, Berkeley, PhD(zool), 72. *Prof Exp:* Chmn, Sci Dept, Alpha Jr Col, 64-66; instr biol, Cardinal Cushing Col, 66-68, asst prof, 68-69; asst prof, 72-76, ASSOC PROF ANAT & EMBRYOL, MICH STATE UNIV, 76- *Mem:* Am Soc Zoologists; Am Soc Neurosci; Am Physiol Soc; Int Soc Chronobiol; Am Asn Anatomists. *Res:* Circadian rhythms in catecholamine metabolism; effects of estrogen on catecholamine metabolism in genetic hypertension; circadian rhythms in biochemistry; ultrastructure of pineal gland and autonomic ganglia. *Mailing Add:* Dept Anat Mich State Univ East Lansing MI 48824

LEW, HIN, b Vancouver, BC, Apr 18, 21; m 59; c 3. PHYSICS. *Educ:* Univ BC, BA, 40; Univ Toronto, MA, 42; Mass Inst Technol, PhD(physics), 48. *Prof Exp:* Jr res physicist acoust, Mass Inst Technol, 42-45; res assoc atomic beams, Mass Inst Technol, 48-49; ASSOC & SR RES OFFICER ATOMIC BEAMS & MOLECULAR SPECTROS, NAT RES COUN CAN, 49- *Mem:* Am Phys Soc; Can Asn Physicists. *Res:* Hyperfine structure of atoms and molecules by the atomic beam magnetic resonance method; spectra and structure of molecular ions. *Mailing Add:* Herzberg Inst of Astrophys Nat Res Coun of Can Ottawa ON K1A 0R6 Can

LEW, JOHN S, b New York, NY, Sept 9, 34; m 63, 75; c 2. APPLIED MATHEMATICS. *Educ:* Yale Univ, BS, 55; Princeton Univ, PhD(physics), 60. *Prof Exp:* C L E Moore instr math, Mass Inst Technol, 62-64; asst prof appl math, Brown Univ, 64-70; RES STAFF MEM MATH SCI, T J WATSON RES CTR, IBM CORP, 70- *Mem:* Math Asn Am; Soc Indust & Appl Math. *Res:* Applied analysis, especially asymptotic expansions. *Mailing Add:* T J Watson Res Ctr IBM Corp Yorktown Heights NY 10598

LEWANDOS, GLENN S, b Dallas, Tex. ORGANIC CHEMISTRY, ORGANOMETALLIC CHEMISTRY. *Educ:* Southern Methodist Univ, BS, 67; Univ Tex, Austin, PhD(chem), 72. *Prof Exp:* Asst prof chem, Sul Ross State Univ, 72-76; vis asst prof, Univ Tex, Austin, 76-77; asst prof, 77-79, ASSOC PROF CHEM, CENT MICH UNIV, 79- *Concurrent Pos:* Res Corp grant, 78-80, Am Chem Soc grant, 81. *Mem:* Am Chem Soc; Royal Soc Chem; Sigma Xi. *Res:* Synthesis and reactivity of organometallic pi complexes; catalysis by transition metals; crown ethers. *Mailing Add:* Dept of Chem Cent Mich Univ Mt Pleasant MI 48859

LEWANDOWSKI, MELVIN A, b Chicago, Ill, Dec 8, 30; m 54; c 1. CHEMICAL ENGINEERING. *Educ:* Northwestern Univ, BS, 54; Univ Chicago, MBA, 74. *Prof Exp:* Res engr, Int Minerals & Chem Corp, 57-61, purchasing agt, 61-65, mgr eng & distrib, 65-74; exec vpres, Chinhae Chem Co, Seoul, Korea, 75-78; corp staff vpres res & develop, 78-80, vpres chem group, 80-81, VPRES VENTURE DEVELOP FERTILIZER GROUP, INT MINERALS & CHEM CORP, 81- *Mem:* Am Inst Chem Engrs; Am Chem Soc. *Res:* Administration. *Mailing Add:* Int Minerals & Chem Corp 2315 Sanders Rd Northbrook IL 60062

LEWARS, ERROL GEORGE, Can citizen. ORGANIC CHEMISTRY. *Educ:* LondonUniv, BSc, 64; Univ Toronto, PhD(chem), 68. *Prof Exp:* Fel chem, Harvard Univ, 68-70, Univ Western Ont, 70-72; fel, 72-73, asst prof, 73-78, ASSOC PROF CHEM, TRENT UNIV, 78- *Mem:* Am Chem Soc. *Res:* Synthetic organic chemistry; compounds of theoretical interest. *Mailing Add:* Dept Chem Trent Univ Petersborough ON K9J 7B8 Can

LEWBART, MARVIN LOUIS, b Philadelphia, Pa, May 28, 29; m 57; c 4. BIOCHEMISTRY. *Educ:* Philadelphia Col Pharm & Sci, BSc, 51, MSc, 53; Jefferson Med Col, MD, 57; Univ Minn, PhD(biochem), 61. *Prof Exp:* Intern pharm, Jefferson Med Col, 51-52, res assoc biochem, 53-57; intern med, Lankenau Hosp, 57-58; fel biochem, Mayo Found, Univ Minn, 58-61; USPHS spec res fel, Univ Basel, 61-62; res assoc, Jefferson Med Col, 62-67, from asst prof to assoc prof med, 67-75; ASSOC MED DIR, FRANKLIN MINT CORP, 74-; DIR, STEROID LAB, CROZER-CHESTER MED CTR, 75-; CLIN ASSOC PROF MED, HAHNEMANN MED COL, 75- *Concurrent Pos:* USPHS res fel, 59-61. *Mem:* Am Occup Med Asn; Am Chem Soc. *Res:* Steroid chemistry and metabolism. *Mailing Add:* Dept of Med Crozer-Chester Med Ctr Chester PA 19013

LEWELLEN, ROBERT THOMAS, b Nyssa, Ore, Apr 27, 40; m 62. GENETICS, PLANT BREEDING. *Educ:* Ore State Univ, BS, 62; Mont State Univ, PhD(genetics), 66. *Prof Exp:* Asst agronomist, Mont State Univ, 65-66; RES GENETICIST, AGR RES SERV, USDA, 66- *Mem:* AAAS; Am Soc Agron; Crop Sci Soc Am; Am Phytopath Soc; Am Soc Sugar Beet Technol. *Res:* Genetics of virus resistance in sugar beet, Beta vulgaris, and development of resistant lines. *Mailing Add:* USDA Agr Res Sta PO Box 5098 Salinas CA 93915

LEWELLEN, WILLIAM STEPHEN, b Reedy, WVa, Aug 7, 33; m 58; c 2. FLUID DYNAMICS. *Educ:* WVa Univ, BS, 57; Cornell Univ, MAeroE, 59; Univ Calif, Los Angeles, PhD(eng), 64. *Prof Exp:* Mem tech staff, Space Tech Labs, Inc, 59-60; mem tech staff, Aerospace Corp, 60-64, mgr fluid dynamics sect, 64-66; vis assoc prof aeronaut & astronaut, Mass Inst Technol, 66-67, assoc prof, 67-72; sr consult, 72-79, VPRES FLUID MECH, AERONAUT RES ASSOCS PRINCETON, INC, 79- *Concurrent Pos:* Consult, Aerojet Gen Corp, 68-70; assoc ed, Am Inst Aeronaut & Astronaut Jour, 78-79. *Mem:* AAAS; Am Inst Aeronaut & Astronaut; Am Meteorol Soc. *Res:* Energy conversion; fluid dynamics of vortex flows; micrometeorology; computer modeling of turbulent transport; pollutant dispersal. *Mailing Add:* Aeronaut Res Assocs Princeton Inc 50 Washington Rd Princeton NJ 08540

LEWENZ, GEORGE F, b Berlin, Ger, Aug 29, 20; US citizen; m 55; c 4. ORGANIC CHEMISTRY. *Educ:* Western Reserve Univ, BS, 47, MS, 52. *Prof Exp:* Aeronaut res scientist, NASA, 48-53; chemist, Texaco, Inc, 53-58 & Esso Res & Eng Co, NJ, 59-68; res logician, 68-71, sr info chemist, 71-73, RES SPECIALIST, DOW CHEM CO, 73- *Mem:* Am Soc Info Sci; Am Chem Soc; fel Am Inst Chemists. *Res:* Organic synthesis; abstracting, indexing and information science. *Mailing Add:* Dow Chem Co 2020 Bldg Midland MI 48640

LEWERT, ROBERT MURDOCH, b Scranton, Pa, Sept 30, 19; m 48; c 2. MEDICAL PARASITOLOGY, IMMUNOLOGY. *Educ:* Univ Mich, BS, 41; Lehigh Univ, MS, 43; Johns Hopkins Univ, ScD(parasitol), 49. *Prof Exp:* Asst instr biol, Lehigh Univ, 42-43; instr zool, Cols of Seneca, 43-44; instr parasitol, Dept Bact & Parasitol, 48-52, asst prof, 52-54, microbiol, 54-56, assoc prof, 57-61, PROF MICROBIOL, UNIV CHICAGO, 61- *Concurrent Pos:* Fulbright res fel, Philippines, 61; Guggenheim fel, 61; vis prof, Inst Hyg, Univ Philippines, 61 & 63-65; consult, Surg Gen, US Army, 59-75 & clin parasitol, Hines Vet Admin Hosp, 75-; mem, Comn parasitic diseases, Armed Forces Edpidemiol Bd, 59-66, parasitol study sect, NIH Trop Med, 65-69, Am Bd Microbiol, 65 & Training Grant Study Sect, Nat Inst Allergy & Infectious Dis, 69-73. *Mem:* AAAS; fel Am Acad Microbiol; Am Soc Parasitol; Am Soc Trop Med & Hyg; Royal Soc Trop Med & Hyg. *Res:* Host parasite relationships with emphasis on immunity, tolerance and immunopathology of schistosomiasis; histochemical and cytochemical studies of parasite effects on host; immunity and invasiveness of helminths; schistosomiasis. *Mailing Add:* Dept of Microbiol Univ of Chicago Chicago IL 60637

LEWIN, ANITA HANA, b Bucarest, Rumania, Oct 27, 35; m 56; c 2. PHYSICAL ORGANIC CHEMISTRY. *Educ:* Univ Calif, Los Angeles, BS, 59, PhD(phys org chem), 63. *Prof Exp:* Res asst prof chem, Univ Pittsburgh, 64-66; from asst prof to assoc prof chem, Polytech Inst Brooklyn, 66-74; fel, 74-75, SR CHEMIST, RES TRIANGLE INST, 75- *Mem:* AAAS; Am Chem Soc; The Chem Soc. *Res:* Reaction mechanisms; catalysis by transition metals and their salts; organometallic reaction intermediates; conformational analysis; hindered rotation; diazonium ion decompositions; retinoids-synthesis and properties; organic synthesis; synthesis of radiolabeled compounds. *Mailing Add:* Chem & Life Sci Group PO Box 12194 Research Triangle Park NC 27709

LEWIN, JOYCE CHISMORE, b Ilion, NY, Nov 13, 26; m 50. MICROBIOLOGY. *Educ:* Cornell Univ, BS, 48; Yale Univ, MS, 50, PhD(bot, microbiol), 53. *Prof Exp:* Guest res worker biol, Lab, Nat Res Coun Can, 52-55; res assoc marine biol, Woods Hole Oceanog Inst, 56-60; asst res biologist, Scripps Inst, Univ Calif, San Diego, 60-65; from asst prof to prof, 65-74, RES PROF OCEANOG, UNIV WASH, 74- *Mem:* Am Soc Limnol & Oceanog; Phycol Soc Am; Am Inst Biol Sci; Marine Biol Asn UK; Int Phycol Soc. *Res:* Culture of marine microalgae, especially diatoms; physiology and nutrition of marine diatoms; physiology and ecology of surf diatom blooms. *Mailing Add:* Dept of Oceanog Univ of Wash Seattle WA 98195

LEWIN, LAWRENCE M, b New York, NY, Mar 3, 32; m 58; c 3. BIOCHEMISTRY, CHEMICAL PATHOLOGY. *Educ:* Mass Inst Technol, BS, 53; Cornell Univ, PhD(biochem), 59. *Prof Exp:* Res asst biochem, Cornell Univ, 53-54; res asst biochem, NY State Agr Exp Sta, 56-59; res assoc, Mass Inst Technol, 59-61; NIH fel, Weizmann Inst, 61-62; from asst prof to assoc prof biochem, Schs Med & Dent, Georgetown Univ, 63-71; assoc prof, 72-79, PROF BIOCHEM, DEPT CHEM PATH, SACKLER MED SCH, TEL AVIV UNIV, 79- *Mem:* Israel Biochem Soc; Am Chem Soc; Israel Soc Chem Path. *Res:* Biosynthesis and metabolic functions of vitamins, particularly carnitine and inositol; structure and function of inositol lipids. *Mailing Add:* Dept of Chem Path Tel Aviv Univ Tel Hashomer Israel

LEWIN, LEONARD, b Southend, Eng, July 27, 19; US citizen; m 43; c 2. ELECTRICAL ENGINEERING, MATHEMATICS. *Hon Degrees:* DSc, Univ Colo, 67. *Prof Exp:* Sci officer radar, Brit Admiralty, 41-45; sr engr microwaves, Standard Telecommun Labs, 46-50, dept head, 50-60, asst mgr transmissions, 60-66, sr prin res electromagnetic theory, 67-68; PROF ELEC ENG, UNIV COLO, BOULDER, 68-, COORDR TELECOMMUN PROG, 74- *Concurrent Pos:* Consult, Standard Telecommun Labs, 68-, Medion Ltd, 70-, Westinghouse Corp, 71 & Nat Bur Standards, 78-; Sci Res Coun grants, UK, 73 & 75. *Honors & Awards:* Premium Awards, Brit Inst Elec Engrs, 52 & 60; Microwave Prize & W G Baker Award, Inst Elec & Electronics Engrs, 62. *Mem:* Fel Brit Interplanetary Soc; Brit Inst Elec Engrs; fel Inst Elec & Electronics Engrs. *Res:* Electromagnetic theory; wave propagation; waveguides and antennas; mathematics; mathematical applications to engineering. *Mailing Add:* Dept of Elec Eng Univ of Colo Boulder CO 80309

LEWIN, RALPH ARNOLD, b London, Eng, Apr 30, 21; m 69. PHYCOLOGY. *Educ:* Cambridge Univ, BA, 42, MA, 46, ScD, 72; Yale Univ, MSc, 49, PhD, 50. *Prof Exp:* Spec lectr phycol, Yale Univ, 50-51, instr bot, 51-52; asst res off biol, Maritime Regional Lab, Nat Res Coun Can, 52-55; investr phycol, NIH grant, Marine Biol Lab, Woods Hole, 55-60; assoc prof marine biol, 59-67, PROF EXP PHYCOL, SCRIPPS INST OCEANOG, UNIV CALIF, 67- *Concurrent Pos:* Mem, Corp Marine Biol Lab, Woods Hole. *Honors & Awards:* Darbaker Prize, Bot Soc Am, 58. *Mem:* Soc Exp Biol; Marine Biol Asn UK; Brit Phycol Soc; Phycol Soc Am (pres, 70); Indian Phycol Soc. *Res:* Experimental phycology; microbiology; microbial genetics; marine biology. *Mailing Add:* Scripps Inst of Oceanog Univ of Calif La Jolla CA 92093

LEWIN, SEYMOUR Z, b New York, NY, Aug 16, 21; m 43; c 2. PHYSICAL CHEMISTRY, ANALYTICAL CHEMISTRY. *Educ:* City Col New York, BS, 41; Univ Mich, MS, 42, PhD(chem), 50. *Prof Exp:* Lectr chem, Univ Mich, 47; from instr to assoc prof, 51-60, PROF CHEM, NY UNIV, 60- *Concurrent Pos:* Belg-Am Educ Found fel, 62; hon prof, Inst Quimico Sarria, Barcelona, Spain, 62; ed, Art & Archeol Tech Abstr, 66-69; consult, US Army Chem Corp, Smithsonian Inst, Food & Drug Admin & Warner-Lambert Co. *Honors & Awards:* A Cressy Morrison Prize, NY Acad Sci, 56; Kasimir Fajans Prize, 58; Medal Hon, Govt Ethiopia, 74. *Mem:* AAAS; Am Chem Soc; Soc Appl Spectros; Am Inst Chemists; fel NY Acad Sci. *Res:* Crystal growth; spectroscopy; instrumentation; materials of art and archaeology; polymorphism; solid state chemistry; stone decay and preservation. *Mailing Add:* Dept Chem NY Univ 4 Wash Place New York NY 10003

LEWIN, VICTOR, b San Francisco, Calif, Sept 8, 30; m 50; c 3. ECOLOGY. *Educ:* Univ Calif, AB, 53, PhD(zool), 58. *Prof Exp:* Asst zool, Univ Calif, 54-58; from asst prof to assoc prof, 58-70, dir, 58-80, CUR HERPET, MUS ZOOL, UNIV ALBERTA, 80-, PROF ZOOL, 70- *Concurrent Pos:* Asst cur, Mus Vert Zool, Univ Calif, 55-56. *Honors & Awards:* Painton Award, Cooper Ornith Soc, 65. *Mem:* Wildlife Soc; Am Soc Mammalogists; Cooper Ornith Soc; Am Ornithologists Union; Can Soc Wildlife & Fishery Biol. *Res:* Wildlife ecology; ecology of game birds and mammals, particularly reproductive anatomy and physiology of gallinaceous birds; effects of chlorinated hydrocarbon residues on birds; ecology of exotic game bird species. *Mailing Add:* Dept Zool Univ Alta Edmonton AB T6G 2E9 Can

LEWIN, WALTER H G, b The Hague, Netherlands, Jan 29, 36; m 59, 81; c 4. HIGH ENERGY ASTROPHYSICS. *Educ:* Univ Delft, Ir, 60, Dr(physics), 65. *Prof Exp:* Res assoc physics, Univ Delft, 59-66; fel space res & asst prof, 66, assoc prof x-ray astron, 68-74, PROF PHYSICS, MASS INST TECHNOL, 74- *Honors & Awards:* Outstanding Sci Achievement Award, NASA, 78. *Mem:* Int Astron Union; Am Astron Soc; Am Phys Soc. *Res:* Radioactive isotope applications; nuclear and atomic physics; x-ray astronomy; high-altitude ballooning; satellite observations, orbital solar observatory-7, small astronomy satellite-3, high energy astronomy observatory-1; astrophysics. *Mailing Add:* Ctr for Space Res Mass Inst of Technol Cambridge MA 02139

LEWINSON, VICTOR A, b New York, NY; m 57; c 2. OPERATIONS RESEARCH. *Educ:* Harvard Col, AB, 39; Columbia Univ, MA, 45, PhD(chem), 50. *Prof Exp:* Asst chem, Columbia Univ, 39-42; res scientist & sect leader, Manhattan Proj, 42-45; res fel chem, Calif Inst Technol, 50-51; fel, Mellon Inst, 51-54; analyst opers res, Nat Acad Sci, 54-61; MEM PROF STAFF, ARTHUR D LITTLE, INC, 61- *Mem:* Transp Res Forum; Int Cargo Handling Coord Asn. *Res:* Freight transportation, especially maritime and railroad. *Mailing Add:* Arthur D Little Inc Acorn Park Cambridge MA 02140

LEWIS, A(LBERT) D(ALE) M(ILTON), b Paoli, Ind, May 20, 20; m 46; c 1. CIVIL ENGINEERING, STRUCTURAL ENGINEERING. *Educ:* Purdue Univ, BS, 41, MS, 51. *Prof Exp:* Field engr oil refinery construct, M W Kellogg Co, 41-44, 46-47 & Gulf Oil Corp, 47-49; instr struct eng, Purdue Univ, 51-52; design engr, Standard Oil Co, Calif, 52-54; ASSOC PROF STRUCT ENG, PURDUE UNIV, WEST LAFAYETTE, 54- *Concurrent Pos:* Consult, Truss Bridge Res Proj, Northwestern Univ; vis assoc prof struct eng, Univ Calif, Los Angeles, 71. *Mem:* Am Soc Civil Engrs; Am Soc Eng Educ; Am Concrete Inst; Am Rwy Eng Asn; Asn Comput Mach. *Res:* Structural analysis; structural design; design optimization; digital computers; experimental mechanics. *Mailing Add:* Civil Eng Bldg Purdue Univ West Lafayette IN 47907

LEWIS, AARON, b Calcutta, India, Oct 14, 45; US citizen; m. BIOPHYSICS. *Educ:* Univ Mo, BS, 66; Case Western Reserve Univ, PhD(phys chem), 70. *Prof Exp:* Instr phys chem, Case Western Reserve Univ, 70; NIH fel, 70-72, instr, 71-72, asst prof, 72-76, ASSOC PROF BIOPHYS, CORNELL UNIV, 76- *Concurrent Pos:* Sloan fel, 74-76; vis prof, Calif Inst Technol, 77 & Hebrew Univ, 79-80; Guggenheim fel, 79-80. *Mem:* AAAS; Am Chem Soc; Biophys Soc; Asn Res Vision & Ophthal; Am Photobiol Soc. *Res:* Molecular mechanism of ion gates and pumps, specifically bacteriorhodopsin and rhodopsin. *Mailing Add:* Dept of Appl Physics Cornell Univ Ithaca NY 14850

LEWIS, ALAN ERVIN, b Milwaukee, Wis, Feb 1, 36; m 61; c 2. MEDICINE. *Educ:* Univ Wis-Madison, BS, 57; Marquette Univ, MD, 60. *Prof Exp:* Intern, Hosp Univ Pa, 60-61; resident, Med Ctr, Univ Mich, 61 & 63-65; from instr to sr instr internal med, 67-71, asst prof, 71-75, ASSOC PROF MED, HAHNEMANN MED COL & HOSP, 75- *Concurrent Pos:* Fel endocrinol, Sch Med, Tufts Univ, 65-67. *Mem:* Am Diabetes Asn; Am Fedn Clin Res; Am Col Physicians; Endocrine Soc. *Mailing Add:* 191 Presidential Blvd Bala Cynwyd PA 19004

LEWIS, ALAN GRAHAM, b Pasadena, Calif, Mar 14, 34; m 57; c 2. BIOLOGICAL OCEANOGRAPHY, ZOOLOGY. *Educ:* Univ Miami, BSc, 56, MSc, 58; Univ Hawaii, PhD(zool), 61. *Prof Exp:* Asst prof zool, Univ NH, 61-64; from asst prof to assoc prof, 64-76, PROF OCEANOG & ZOOL, UNIV BC, 76- *Mem:* Am Geophys Union; Sigma Xi. *Res:* Ecology of marine zooplankton. *Mailing Add:* Inst of Oceanog Univ of BC Vancouver BC V6T 1W5 Can

LEWIS, ALAN JAMES, b Green Bay, Wis, June 43; m; c 1. BOTANY. *Educ:* Wis State Univ-Eau Claire, BS, 68; Rutgers Univ, PhD(plant ecol), 71. *Prof Exp:* Teaching asst gen biol, Rutgers Univ, New Brunswick, 68-69, NSF fel, 69-70, teaching asst gen biol & plant ecol, 70-71; asst prof biol, Kean Col NJ, 71-74; landscape contractor, Green Bay, 74-75; vis asst prof, Swarthmore Col, 75-76; asst prof life & earth sci & chmn dept, Mercyhurst Col, 76-78; assoc prof bot & chmn sci & math div, Univ Maine, Machias, 78-80; MGR, WYETH LABS INC, 80- *Concurrent Pos:* Caretaker, William L Hutcheson Mem Forest, Rutgers Univ, New Brunswick, 70-71; adj asst prof, Richmond Col Staten Island, 73-74. *Mem:* AAAS; Am Inst Biol Sci; Ecol Soc Am; Sigma Xi. *Res:* Effects of chemical and mechanical manipulation of old-field plant populations; ragweed control techniques. *Mailing Add:* Wyeth Labs Inc PO Box 8299 Philadelphia PA 19101

LEWIS, ALAN LAIRD, b Holyoke, Mass. OPTOMETRY. *Educ:* Mass Col Optom, BSc, 65, OD, 70; Ohio State Univ, PhD(physiol optics), 71. *Prof Exp:* Optometrist, US Navy, 65-68; asst prof, 72-73, ASSOC PROF PHYSIOL OPTICS, COL OPTOM, STATE UNIV NY, 73- *Concurrent Pos:* Mem, US Nat Comt, Comn Int de L'Eclairage, 73-; vis researcher, Nat Bur Standards, 79-80; mem, Int Res Group Colour Vision Deficiencies. *Mem:* Am Acad Optom; Illum Eng Soc; Asn Res Vision & Opthal; Optic Soc Am. *Res:* Clinical aspects of color vision; biological effects of optical radiation; accommodation; visibility of objects as a funciton of illuminance. *Mailing Add:* Col Optom State Univ NY 100 E 24th St New York NY 10010

LEWIS, ALEXANDER D(ODGE), b Minneapolis, NC, Mar 6, 12; m 41; c 2. MECHANICAL ENGINEERING. *Educ:* Univ Tenn, BS, 39; Yale Univ, MS, 46. *Prof Exp:* Designer, Aluminum Co Am, 39-41; asst prof mech eng, Clemson Univ, 41-44; asst prof, Yale Univ, 44-46; from assoc prof to prof & head mech eng labs, 46-77, EMER PROF MECH ENG, CLEMSON UNIV, 77- *Concurrent Pos:* Asst proj engr, Arnold Eng Develop Ctr, Tenn. *Mem:* Nat Soc Prof Engrs; Am Soc Mech Engrs; Am Soc Eng Educ; Soc Automotive Engrs. *Res:* Thermochemistry and kinetics of combustion; gas power dynamics; infinity dynamics. *Mailing Add:* PO Box 1252 Clemson SC 29631

LEWIS, ALVIN EDWARD, b New York, NY, Nov 21, 16; m 43; c 2. BIOSTATISTICS, PHYSIOLOGY. *Educ:* Univ Calif, Los Angeles, AB, 38; Stanford Univ, AM, 39, MD, 44. *Prof Exp:* Asst path, Stanford Univ, 47-48; clin instr & chief path sect, AEC Proj, Univ Calif, Los Angeles, 49-53; dir labs, Mt Zion Hosp, 53-66; prof path, Mich State Univ, 66-72; prof path & chmn dept, Med Sch, Univ SAla, 72-74; PROF PATH, UNIV CALIF, DAVIS, 74- *Concurrent Pos:* Am Cancer Soc fel, Stanford Univ, 48-49; vis physician, Los Angeles County Harbor Hosp, 49-53; attend physician, Wadsworth Gen Hosp, 50-53; asst clin prof, Med Ctr, Univ Calif, San Francisco, 59-66. *Mem:* AAAS; Am Physiol Soc; AMA; fel Col Am Path. *Res:* Hepatic function tests; plasma volume and distribution. *Mailing Add:* Dept of Path Univ of Calif Davis CA 95616

LEWIS, ANTHONY JAMES, physical geography, see previous edition

LEWIS, ANTHONY WETZEL, b Welch, WVa, Nov 4, 42; m 63; c 2. VERTEBRATE ECOLOGY, PUBLIC HEALTH. *Educ:* Loma Linda Univ, BA, 66, MPH, 74; Ariz State Univ, MS, 69, PhD(zool), 73. *Prof Exp:* Chmn dept biol & health, Mountain View Col, Philippines, 72-77; ASST PROF BIOL, LOMA LINDA UNIV, 77- *Concurrent Pos:* Traineeship, USPHS, 71-72. *Mem:* Am Soc Mammalogists; Soc Study Amphibians & Reptiles. *Res:* Vertebrate population ecology. *Mailing Add:* Dept of Biol Loma Linda Univ Riverside CA 92515

LEWIS, ARMAND FRANCIS, b Fairhaven, Mass, May 22, 32; m 58; c 2. PHYSICAL CHEMISTRY, MATERIALS SCIENCE. *Educ:* Southeastern Mass Univ, BS, 53; Okla State Univ, MS, 55; Lehigh Univ, PhD(chem), 58. *Prof Exp:* Res asst rheol, Lehigh Univ, 58-59; res chemist, Cent Res Div, Am Cyanamid Co, 59-63, sr res chemist, Plastics & Resins Div, 63-64, group leader polymer physics & adhesion, 64-69, proj leader noise control mat, 70-71; sr res assoc, 71-73, SR MAT SCIENTIST, LORD CORP, 73- *Honors & Awards:* Union Carbide Award, Am Chem Soc, 63. *Mem:* Am Chem Soc; Soc Rheol (treas, 66-). *Res:* Polymer physics; rheology; surface chemistry and adhesion; dynamic mechnical properties of polymers; glass transition phenomena in polymeric systems; polymer to metal adhesion and fracture of adhesive joints; vibration and noise control materials; rubber chemicals; engineering composites; marine materials. *Mailing Add:* Lord Corp 1635 W 12th St Erie PA 16512

LEWIS, ARNOLD D, b Philadelphia, Pa, May 6, 20; m 45; c 2. ANALYTICAL CHEMISTRY. *Educ:* Philadelphia Col Pharm, BS, 40; Polytech Inst Brooklyn, MS, 47. *Prof Exp:* Control chemist, Hance Bros & White, 40-41; pilot plant chemist, United Gas Improv Corp, 41-43; asst scientist to Dr E A H Friedheim, 43-44; jr scientist, G D Res Inst, 44-47; scientist, Dept Org Chem, Warner-Lambert Co, 47-54, sr scientist, 54-63, sr res assoc, Chem Res Div, 63-64, dir anal & phys chem, Prof Prod Group, 64-77; CONSULT, 78- *Mem:* AAAS; Am Chem Soc; NY Acad Sci. *Res:* Organic synthesis of heterocycles; infrared and ultraviolet absorption spectrophotometry; microanalysis; gas, paper, thin-layer and column chromatography; chemical safety; proton magnetic resonance spectroscopy. *Mailing Add:* 42 Intervale Rd Livingston NJ 07039

LEWIS, ARNOLD LEROY, II, b Portland, Ore, Sept 24, 52. INSTRUMENTATION, SPECTROSCOPY. *Educ:* Pac Lutheran Univ, BA, 75; Ore State Univ, PhD(anal chem), 81. *Prof Exp:* Teaching asst chem, Ore State Univ, 75-78, res asst, 78-81; SR CHEMIST, EXXON NUCLEAR IDAHO CO, INC, 81- *Mem:* Am Chem Soc. *Res:* Laser atomic fluorescence studies of laser microprobe plumes; microcomputer interfacing to analytical instrumentation; methods development of analytical techniques in the nuclear industry. *Mailing Add:* Exxon Nuclear Idaho Co Inc CPP602 B PO Box 2800 Idaho Falls ID 83401

LEWIS, ARTHUR EDWARD, b Jamestown, NY, Jan 11, 29; m 53; c 3. EARTH SCIENCE. *Educ:* St Lawrence Univ, BS, 50; Calif Inst Technol, MS, 55, PhD(geol), 58. *Prof Exp:* Sr engr, Curtiss Wright Corp, 58-60; scientist, Hoffman Sci Ctr, 60-62; mem tech staff, Fairchild Semiconductor, Calif, 62-67; geologist, 67-69, group leader, Plowshare Prog, Peaceful Appln Nuclear Explosives, 69-73, PROJ LEADER, OIL SHALE, LAWRENCE LIVERMORE LAB, UNIV CALIF, 73- *Concurrent Pos:* Consult, Fed Energy Agency, 74. *Honors & Awards:* Peele Award, Am Inst Mining & Metall Engrs, 74. *Mem:* Geol Soc Am. *Res:* Processes for recovery of oil from oil shale; energy resource development. *Mailing Add:* 884 Santa Rita Ave Los Altos CA 94022

LEWIS, AUSTIN JAMES, b Poole, Eng, Nov 29, 45; m 73; c 1. ANIMAL NUTRITION. *Educ:* Univ Reading, BSc, 67; Univ Nottingham, PhD(nutrit), 71. *Prof Exp:* Assoc animal nutrit, Iowa State Univ, 71-74; res assoc, Univ Nebr, 74-75; asst prof, Univ Alta, 75-77; asst prof, 77-80, ASSOC PROF ANIMAL NUTRITION, UNIV NEBR, 80- *Mem:* Am Soc Animal Sci; Am Inst Nutrit. *Res:* Nutritional requirements of swine, especially proteins and amino acids. *Mailing Add:* Dept of Animal Sci Univ of Nebr Lincoln NE 68583

LEWIS, BARBARA-ANN GAMBOA, environmental sciences, soil science, see previous edition

LEWIS, BENJAMIN MARZLUFF, b Scranton, Pa, Oct 7, 25; m 56, 69; c 3. PHYSIOLOGY. *Educ:* Univ Pa, MD, 49. *Prof Exp:* Res fel med, Harvard Univ, 50-52; actg chmn dept, 70-71, from asst prof to assoc prof, 56-62, PROF INTERNAL MED, WAYNE STATE UNIV, 62- *Concurrent Pos:* Teaching fel med, Harvard Univ, 52-53; fel, Grad Sch Med, Univ Pa, 53-55; consult, Vet Admin Hosp, 56. *Mem:* Fel Am Col Physicians; Am Physiol Soc; Am Soc Clin Invest. *Res:* Pulmonary physiology, particularly gas diffusion and pulmonary circulation. *Mailing Add:* Dept of Med Wayne State Univ Sch of Med Detroit MI 48201

LEWIS, BERNARD, b London, Eng, Nov 1, 99; nat US; m 34; c 2. PHYSICAL CHEMISTRY. *Educ:* Mass Inst Technol, BS, 23; Harvard Univ, MA, 24; Cambridge Univ, PhD(phys chem), 26. *Hon Degrees:* ScD, Cambridge Univ, 53. *Prof Exp:* Demonstr phys chem, Cambridge Univ, 25-26; Nat Res Coun fel, Univ Berlin & Univ Minn, 26-29; phys chemist, US Bur Mines, 29-42, chief, Explosives & Phys Sci Div, 46-53; PRES, COMBUSTION & EXPLOSIVES RES, INC, 53- *Concurrent Pos:* Dir res powder & explosives, Ord Dept, US Army, 51-52; consult, US Army, US Navy, US Air Force & Nat Bur Standards; mem, Sci Adv Comt, Ord Corps, Aberdeen Proving Ground, Md, Combustion Comt, Nat Adv Comt Aeronaut, Fire Res Conf, Nat Acad Sci; pres, Comt High Temperature, Int Union Pure & Appl Chem; US ed, J Combustion & Flame; co-ed, Phys Measurements in Gas Dynamics & Combustion, 54 & Combustion Processes, 56; consult, Tech Adv Comt, US Dept Interior, numerous industs & res insts. *Honors & Awards:* Lewis Gold Medal, Combustion Inst, 58; Gold Medal, Ital Thermotech Asn, 61; Pittsburgh Award, Am Chem Soc, 74; Orleans Medal, City Orleans, France, 75; Bordeaux Medal, City Bordeaux, France, 81. *Mem:* Emer mem, Am Chem Soc; Am Phys Soc; fel Am Inst Aeronaut & Astronaut; Combustion Inst (pres, 54-66, hon pres, 66-); fel NY Acad Sci. *Res:* Chemical kinetics of gas reactions; thermodynamics of explosives; flame propagation; ignition; combustion in jet propulsion; propellants; detonation; internal combustion engines; oxidation of hydrocarbons; fuels, interior ballistics; combustion and flame phenomena; explosion hazard prevention in industry; nuclear power plant safety. *Mailing Add:* Combust & Explos Res Inc 1016 Oliver Bldg Pittsburgh PA 15222

LEWIS, BERTHA ANN, b Lewisville, Minn, Oct 21, 27. BIOCHEMISTRY, FOOD SCIENCE. *Educ:* Univ Minn, BChem, 49, MS, 54, PhD(biochem), 57. *Prof Exp:* Res fel biochem, Univ Minn, St Paul, 57-65, res assoc, 65-67; assoc prof design & environ anal, 67-70, assoc dean, Col Human Ecol, 74-80, ASSOC PROF, DIV NUTRIT SCI, CORNELL UNIV, 70-, ASSOC DEAN, COL HUMAN ECOL, 74- *Mem:* Am Chem Soc; Inst Food Technologists; Soc Complex Carbohydrates; Fiber Soc; Am Asn Cereal Chemists. *Res:* Carbohydrate chemistry and biochemistry; chemistry of glycoproteins; protein structure and functionality; dietary fiber. *Mailing Add:* Col of Human Ecol Cornell Univ Ithaca NY 14853

LEWIS, BILLY M, meteorology, deceased

LEWIS, BRIAN KREGLOW, b SAfrica, Sept 2, 32; US citizen; m 53; c 6. HUMAN PHYSIOLOGY, ENDOCRINOLOGY. *Educ:* Ohio State Univ, BS, 54; Tufts Univ, PhD(physiol), 71. *Prof Exp:* Res assoc physiol, Sch Med, Tufts Univ, 71, May Inst Med Res, Jewish Hosp Cincinnati, 71-74 & Col Med, Univ Cincinnati, 74-75; from asst prof to assoc prof health sci, Grand Valley State Col, 75-81; ASSOC PROF PHYSIOL, PONCE SCH MED, 81- *Concurrent Pos:* Adj asst prof physiol, Col Med, Univ Cincinnati, 72-75. *Mem:* AAAS; Endocrine Soc; Soc; Study Reprod; Study Fertil; Sigma Xi. *Res:* Changes in endocrine function related to the pathogenesis of cardiovascular disease; function of prolactin in the male. *Mailing Add:* Dept Physiol Ponce Sch Med PO Box 7004 Ponce PR 00732

LEWIS, BURNADINE LANGSTON, b Texarkana, Tex, Nov 23, 21; m 42; c 1. FOOD SCIENCE, NUTRITION. *Educ:* Prairie View Agr & Mech Col, BS, 41; Colo State Univ, MS, 52; Kans State Univ, PhD(foods, nutrit), 55. *Prof Exp:* Teacher, High Sch, NC, 45 & Tex, 46-52; asst instr, Kans State Univ, 52-55; prof foods & nutrit & chmn div home econ, Tex Southern Univ, 57-68; prof food & nutrit, Dept Home Econ, Southwest Tex State Univ, 68-73; NUTRIT CONSULT, 73- *Mem:* AAAS; Am Dietetic Asn; Inst Food Technologists. *Res:* Chemistry, zoology; food research including organoleptic and chemical testing; histological study of animal tissues. *Mailing Add:* 318 Brookwood Dr Texarkana TX 75501

LEWIS, CAMERON DAVID, b Staunton, Va, June 1, 20; m 45; c 2. ORGANIC CHEMISTRY. *Educ:* Univ Buffalo, AB, 42; Univ Ill, AM, 45, PhD(org chem), 47. *Prof Exp:* Asst chemist, Ill Geol Surv, 42-46; asst chem, War Prod Bd Prog, Univ Ill, 46-47; chemist, 47-74, SR RES CHEMIST, E I DU PONT DE NEMOURS & CO, W VA, 74- *Mem:* Am Chem Soc. *Res:* Analytical test methods; polymer intermediates. *Mailing Add:* Potomac River Develop Lab E I du Pont de Nemours & Co Martinsburg WV 25401

LEWIS, CARMIE PERROTTA, b New Castle, Pa, June 9, 29; m 65. HISTOLOGY. *Educ:* Thiel Col, BS, 51; Univ NH, MS, 53; Univ Wis, PhD(anat, zool), 56. *Prof Exp:* Res asst, Univ Wis, 53-56; Am Asn Univ Women res fel, Cambridge Univ, 56-57; lectr embryol & histol, Fac Med, Queen's Univ, Ont, 57-58; instr anat, Sch Med, Yale Univ, 58-61; asst radiobiologist, Brookhaven Nat Lab, 61-64, res collabr, 64-67; assoc prof, 67-74, PROF BIOL, SUFFOLK COUNTY COMMUNITY COL, 74- *Concurrent Pos:* USPHS res fel, 61-64; asst prof, Queens Univ, NY, 64-67. *Mem:* Am Asn Anat. *Res:* Radiobiology; endocrines of reproduction. *Mailing Add:* Dept of Biol Suffolk County Community Col 533 College Rd Selden NY 11784

LEWIS, CHARLES E, medicine, preventive medicine, see previous edition

LEWIS, CHARLES J, b Park River, NDak, May 20, 27; m 50; c 2. ANIMAL SCIENCE. *Educ:* Utah State Univ, BS, 52; Iowa State Univ, MS, 54, PhD(animal sci), 56. *Prof Exp:* Dir nutrit, Kent Feeds, Inc, 56-58; vpres & nutritionist, 58-67, mem, Bd Dirs, 60-67; prof animal sci & head dept, SDak State Univ, 67-68; EXEC VPRES RES & DEVELOP, GRAIN PROCESSING CORP & KENT FEEDS, INC, 68- *Mem:* AAAS; Am Inst Biol Sci; Am Soc Animal Sci; Inst Food Technologists; Poultry Sci Asn Am. *Res:* Animal nutrition and research. *Mailing Add:* 7 Colony Dr Muscatine IA 52761

LEWIS, CHARLES JOSEPH, b New York, NY, Sept 18, 17; m 67; c 2. MATHEMATICS. *Educ:* Georgetown Univ, AB, 41, MS, 45; Brown Univ, PhD(math), 57. *Prof Exp:* Instr math, Georgetown Univ, 43-44 & St Peters Col, 45; instr, Fordham Univ, 54-56, asst prof, 56-65, chmn dept, 58-65; assoc prof, 65-66, PROF MATH, MONMOUTH COL, NJ, 66- *Concurrent Pos:* NSF fac fel math, Harvard Univ, 59-60; chmn dept math, Monmouth Col, NJ, 68-74. *Mem:* Am Math Soc; Math Asn Am. *Res:* Complex function theory; extremal problems; growth of entire functions; generalized potential theory; special functions and differential equations of mathematical physics. *Mailing Add:* 8 Timothy Lane Tinton Falls NJ 07724

LEWIS, CHARLES WILLIAM, b New York, NY, Oct 29, 20; m 42; c 1. PHYSICAL CHEMISTRY. *Educ:* City Col, New York, BS, 41; Polytech Inst Brooklyn, PhD(chem), 50. *Prof Exp:* Res chemist, Res Labs, Westinghouse Elec Corp, 49-58; assoc dir basic res, Int Resistance Co, 58-65; STAFF SCIENTIST, PPG INDUSTS, INC, 65- *Mem:* Am Chem Soc. *Res:* Polymer chemistry; solid and liquid dielectrics; kinetics and mechanism of organic reactions; physics of thin films; mechanical behavior of polymers. *Mailing Add:* 2137 Beechwood Blvd Pittsburgh PA 15217

LEWIS, CLARK HOUSTON, b McMinnville, Tenn, Nov 6, 29; m 58; c 2. FLUID MECHANICS, GAS DYNAMICS. *Educ:* Univ Tenn, BSME, 51, MS, 59, PhD(viscous flow), 68. *Prof Exp:* Supvr theoret gas dynamics, Aerophys Div, Aro Inc, Arnold Eng Develop Ctr, Tenn, 51-68; PROF AEROSPACE ENG, VA POLYTECH INST & STATE UNIV, 68- *Mem:* Assoc fel Am Inst Aeronaut & Astronaut; Am Phys Soc; Am Soc Mech Engrs. *Res:* Physical gas dynamics; high-speed viscous flows; chemically reacting flows; thermophysical gas properties; numerical methods in engineering. *Mailing Add:* Dept of Aerospace Eng Va Polytech Inst & State Univ Blacksburg VA 24061

LEWIS, CLAUDE IRENIUS, b Stanley, NC, Apr 21, 35; m 56; c 2. ANALYTICAL CHEMISTRY. *Educ:* Duke Univ, BS, 57; Va Poltech Inst, MS, 59, PhD(chem), 62. *Prof Exp:* Res chemist, Texaco, Inc, 61-62 & E I du Pont de Nemours & Co, 62-65; res chemist, 65-66, sr res chemist, 66-70, supvr anal develop, 70-76, DIR QUALITY ASSURANCE, LORILLARD CORP, 70- *Concurrent Pos:* Instr, Guilford Col, 67-70. *Mem:* AAAS; Am Chem Soc; Am Inst Chem Eng; Am Soc Quality Control. *Res:* Cigarette tobacco technology; tobacco smoke chemistry; polyester fiber technology; alkyl benzene synthesis; synthesis of polycyclic aromatic compounds. *Mailing Add:* Lorillard Corp 2525 E Market St Greensboro NC 27401

LEWIS, CLIFFORD JACKSON, b Altoona, Pa, Aug 18, 12. INORGANIC CHEMISTRY, METALLURGICAL ENGINEERING. *Educ:* Franklin & Marshall Col, BS, 33; Univ Pittsburgh, BS, 44; Pa State Univ, MA, 37. *Prof Exp:* Tech dir, Warner Co, 45-51; sr res fel, Mellon Inst, 51-54; res dir, Res Inst, Colo Sch Mines, 55-70; environ consult indust wastes & sulfur oxides control, 70-73; environ consult, 73-80, DIR ENVIRON SERV, NAT LIME ASN, 80- *Mem:* Am Chem Soc; Am Inst Chem Engrs; Am Pub Works Asn. *Res:* Municipal waste treatment; control of sulfur oxides emission by wet scrubbing and metals recovery by hydrometallurgical processes. *Mailing Add:* 2446 Otis Ct Edgewater CO 80214

LEWIS, CORNELIUS CRAWFORD, b Appomattox, Va, May 24, 21; m 49. AGRONOMY, SOIL SCIENCE. *Educ:* Va State Col, BS, 42; Mich State Univ, MS, 45; Univ Mass, PhD(agron), 48. *Prof Exp:* Prof agron, Ft Valley State Col, 47-48; head dept agr, WVa State Col, 48-49; prof agron, Univ Md, 49-50; anal chemist, New York Testing Lab, 50-51; soil specialist, USDA For Serv, Liberia, WAfrica, 51-53; head dept plant industs, Agr & Tech Col, NC, 54-56; head dept agr, Grambling Col, 56-63; PROF AGRON & NUCLEAR SCI, VA STATE COL, 63- *Mem:* AAAS; Am Chem Soc; Am Soc Agron; Soil Sci Soc Am; Sigma Xi. *Res:* Field crops; soil fertility; plant nutrient relationship, particularly fertility levels and nutrient requirements for economic crops. *Mailing Add:* 20412 Woodpecker Rd Petersburg VA 23803

LEWIS, CYNTHIA LUCILLE, b Los Angeles, Calif, Nov 26, 48; m 72; c 1. INVERTEBRATE BIOLOGY, DEVELOPMENTAL BIOLOGY. *Educ:* Calif Polytech State Univ, BS, 70; Univ Alta, PhD(zool), 75. *Prof Exp:* Lab instr physiol & invert embryol, Ore State Univ, 70-71; lab instr invert zool, marine biol & gen biol, Univ Alta, 71-75; fel develop biol & anomalies, Dent Inst, NIH, 75-77; asst prof zool & biol, San Diego State Univ, 77-78; asst prof biol & chem, Point Loma Col, 78-79; res assoc, Scripps Inst Oceanog, 79-81; ASST PROF, BIOL DEPT, POINT LOMA COL, 82- *Concurrent Pos:* Fel, Smithsonian Inst, Washington, DC, 73-75. *Mem:* Sigma Xi; Am Soc Zoologists; Grad Women Sci. *Res:* Physiological mechanisms, morphological changes and morphogenetic movements involved in invertebrate development; larval development, physiological ecology and settlement of invertebrate larvae. *Mailing Add:* Dept of Biol 3900 Lomaland Dr San Diego CA 92106

LEWIS, DANIEL RALPH, b Camden, Ark, Oct 31, 44. MATHEMATICS. *Educ:* La State Univ, Baton Rouge, 66, MS, 68, PhD(math), 70. *Prof Exp:* Asst prof math, Va Polytech Inst & State Univ, 70-72; asst prof math, Univ Fla, 72-77; ASSOC PROF MATH, OHIO STATE UNIV, 77- *Mem:* Am Math Soc. *Res:* Functional analysis. *Mailing Add:* Dept of Math Ohio State Univ Columbus OH 43210

LEWIS, DANNY HARVE, b Decatur, Ala, Apr 9, 48; m 68; c 2. POLYMER CHEMISTRY. *Educ:* Univ NAla, BS, 69; Univ Ala, PhD(chem), 73. *Prof Exp:* Res chemist textile fibers, E I du Pont de Nemours Co Inc, 73-75; sr chemist polymer chem, 75-77, head, Biomat Sect, 77-80, HEAD, BIOSYSTS DIV, SOUTHERN RES INST, 80- *Concurrent Pos:* Consult, NIH. *Mem:* Sigma Xi; Controlled Release Soc (pres elect). *Res:* Controlled-release delivery systems; biomaterials for dental and orthopedic use; synthesis and characterization of new polymers; physical properties of polymers; polymers for fiber spinning, polymers as adhesives and membranes. *Mailing Add:* Southern Res Inst PO Box 3307-A Birmingham AL 35255

LEWIS, DAVID EDWIN, b Tailem Bend, SAustralia, Nov 21, 51; m 78. NATURAL PRODUCT SYNTHESIS. *Educ:* Univ Adelaide, BSc, 72, PhD(org chem), 80. *Prof Exp:* Res assoc chem, Univ Ark, 77-78, lectr, 79-80; vis asst prof, Univ Ill, Urbana-Champaign, 80-81; ASST PROF CHEM, BAYLOR UNIV, 81- *Mem:* Royal Australian Chem Inst; Am Chem Soc. *Res:* Total synthesis of natural products; development of new synthetic strategy; applications of cycloaddition reactions to the total synthesis of terpenoid compounds. *Mailing Add:* Dept Chem Baylor Univ Waco TX 76798

LEWIS, DAVID HAROLD, b New York, NY, Dec 22, 25; m 47, 63; c 2. CARDIOLOGY. *Educ:* Columbia Univ, AB, 44, MD, 47. *Prof Exp:* Intern med, Bellevue Hosp, New York, 47-48; intern, Kings County Hosp, 48-49, resident, 49-50; from instr to asst prof physiol, Sch Med, Univ Pa, 50-57, assoc cardiol, Grad Sch Med, 55-63; guest investr, First Surg Dept, Univ Goteborg, 63-78; guest investr, 78-80, CHIEF CLIN RES, CLIN RES CTR, UNIV HOSP, LINKOPING UNIV, 80- *Concurrent Pos:* Chief hemodynamics sect, Div Cardiol, Philadelphia Gen Hosp, 55-63; estab investr, Am Heart Asn, 57-62. *Mem:* Am Physiol Soc; Am Fedn Clin Res; Am Heart Asn. *Res:* Cardiovascular physiology. *Mailing Add:* Clin Res Ctr Univ Hosp Linkoping Univ S-581 85 Linkoping Sweden

LEWIS, DAVID JAMES, b Montreal, Que, May 28, 20; c 5. PSYCHIATRY, MEDICAL EDUCATION. *Educ:* McGill Univ, BA, 41; Univ Toronto, MD, 50; FRCP(C), 57. *Prof Exp:* Jr intern med, Toronto Gen Hosp, 50-51; sr intern, Sunnybrook Hosp, 51-52; resident psychiat, Johns Hopkins Hosp, 52-54; sr house officer, Bethlem, Royal & Maudsley Hosps, 54-56; asst psychiatrist, St Michael's Hosp, 56-65; asst prof psychiat, Univ Toronto, 64-65; assoc prof, McGill Univ, 65-71; PROF PSYCHIAT, UNIV CALGARY, 71-, ACTG DIV HEAD, 80- *Concurrent Pos:* R S McLaughlin Found res fel, Bethlem, Royal & Maudsley Hosps, 54-56; coordr postgrad educ psychiat, McGill Univ, 65-71, dir behav growth & develop course, 67-71; clin dir psychiat, Allan Mem Inst, 66-71; consult, Rehab Inst Montreal, 67, St Lawrence State Hosp, NY, 67, St Anne's Dept Vet Asmin Hosp, 68 & Banff Mineral Springs Hosp, 72; clin dir psychiat, Foothills Hosp, Calgary, 71-78. *Mem:* Fel Am Psychiat Asn; Royal Col Psychiat; Can Psychiat Asn; Royal Soc Med; sci assoc Acad Psychoanal. *Res:* Psychiatric and interdisciplinary teaching and research; rural psychiatric services. *Mailing Add:* Serendip RR 1 Calgary AB T2N 1N4 Can

LEWIS, DAVID KENNETH, b Poughkeepsie, NY, Feb 11, 43; m 64; c 3. PHYSICAL CHEMISTRY. *Educ:* Amherst Col, AB, 64; Cornell Univ, PhD(phys chem), 70. *Prof Exp:* Asst prof, 69-76, ASSOC PROF CHEM, COLGATE UNIV, 76- *Mem:* Am Chem Soc; Sigma Xi. *Res:* Chemical kinetcis and energy transfer in gases at high temperatures; atmospheric chemistry and physics; innovative teaching methods. *Mailing Add:* Dept of Chem Colgate Univ Hamilton NY 13346

LEWIS, DAVID KENT, b Madison, Wis, June 11, 38; m 62; c 3. FOREST MANAGEMENT, FOREST ECONOMICS. *Educ:* Univ Minn, BS, 60; Yale Univ, MF, 66; Univ Oxford, D Phil, 76. *Prof Exp:* Forester, Ore, 63-65, silviculturist, Forestry Res Ctr, 67-76, FOREST ECONOMIST, RES & DEVELOP, WEYERHAEUSER CO, WASH, 76- *Mem:* Soc Am Foresters; Am Econ Asn. *Res:* Economics of producing timber crops. *Mailing Add:* 3124 Cooks Hill Rd Centralia WA 98531

LEWIS, DAVID S(LOAN), JR, b North Augusta, SC, July 6, 17; m 41; c 4. AERONAUTICAL ENGINEERING. *Educ:* Ga Tech Univ, BS, 39. *Hon Degrees:* DSc, Clarkson Col Technol, 71; LLD, St Louis Univ. *Prof Exp:* Aerodynamicist, Martin Co, 39-46; chief aerodyn, McDonnell Aircraft Corp, 46-52, chief preliminary design, 52-55, mgr sales, 55-56, mgr all projs, 56-57, vpres, 57-59, sr vpres, 59-61, sr vpres opers, 60-61, exec vpres, 61-62, pres, 62-67, pres, McDonnell Douglas Corp, 67-70; CHMN BD & CHIEF EXEC OFFICER, GEN DYNAMICS CORP, 70- *Concurrent Pos:* Mem subcomt highspeed aerodyn & subcomt stability & control, Nat Adv Comt Aeronaut, 51-57. *Mem:* Nat Acad Eng; Am Inst Aeronaut & Astronaut. *Res:* Aerodynamics; high speed flight characteristics; space mechanics. *Mailing Add:* Gen Dynamics Corp Pierre Laclede Ctr St Louis MO 63105

LEWIS, DAVID THOMAS, b Downing, Mo, Sept 27, 35; m 68; c 1. AGRONOMY, SOIL MORPHOLOGY. *Educ:* Univ Maine, BS, 60, MS, 62; Univ Nebr, PhD(agron), 71. *Prof Exp:* Instr soil sci, Dept Agron, Univ Maine, 60-62; soil scientist, Soil Conserv Serv, USDA, 62-67; instr agron, 67-71, asst prof soil classification, 71-75, assoc prof, 75-80, PROF SOIL CLASSIFICATION, DEPT AGRON, UNIV NEBR, 80- *Mem:* Soil Sci Soc Am; Soil Conserv Soc Am; Sigma Xi. *Res:* Studies relating to the genesis and classification of soils and to the solution of problems that relate to proper correlation of survey mapping units. *Mailing Add:* Dept Agron Rm 228 Keim Hall Univ of Nebr Lincoln NE 68588

LEWIS, DAVID W(ARREN), b Salem, Ohio, June 16, 30; m 53; c 4. MECHANICS. *Educ:* Rice Univ, BA, 52, BS, 53, MS, 55; Northwestern Univ, PhD(mech), 58. *Prof Exp:* Instr mech eng, Northwestern Univ, 55-57; asst prof, US Naval Postgrad Sch, 58-60; staff engr, IBM Corp, 60-63; assoc prof mech eng, 63-71, PROF MECH ENG & BIOMED ENG, UNIV VA, 71- *Mem:* Am Soc Eng Educ; Am Soc Mech Engrs. *Res:* Mechanics, especially elasticity and kinematics. *Mailing Add:* Dept of Mech & Aerospace Eng Univ of Va Charlottesville VA 22901

LEWIS, DENNIS ALLEN, b Morristown, NJ, Dec 25, 42; m 70; c 2. ORGANIC CHEMISTRY. *Educ:* St Peters Col, BS, 64; Univ Conn, PhD(org chem), 72. *Prof Exp:* Instr & sr instr, Nuclear Weapons Employ Div, Ft Sill, Okla, 70-71; asst prof, 72-76, ASSOC PROF CHEM, ROSE-HULMAN INST TECHNOL, 76- *Concurrent Pos:* Instr, US Army Reserve Sch, Ft Benjamin Harrison, Ind, 73- *Mem:* Am Chem Soc. *Res:* Synthesis of small-ring compounds via photochemical reactions involving carbene and nitrene intermediates; investigation of chemiluminescent systems. *Mailing Add:* Dept of Chem Rose-Hulman Inst of Technol Terre Haute IN 47803

LEWIS, DENNIS OSBORNE, b Wales, UK, July 7, 39; m 69; c 1. ORGANIC CHEMISTRY. *Educ:* Univ Wales, BS, 60, PhD(chem), 64. *Prof Exp:* Chemist, Brit Drug Houses, Ltd, London, 63-65; staff scientist, Worcester Found Exp Biol, 65-66, Nat Heart Inst fel plant biochem, 66-67; res chemist, Toms River Chem Corp, 67-75; SUPT PROD, PHARMACEUT DIV, CIBA-GEIGY CORP, RI, 75- *Mem:* Am Chem Soc. *Res:* Medium membered ring chemistry; steroids; phytochemistry; anthraquinone synthesis. *Mailing Add:* 69 Brookside Dr East Greenwich RI 02818

LEWIS, DONALD EDWARD, b Ironton, Ohio, May 14, 31; m 57; c 1. ELECTRICAL ENGINEERING. *Educ:* Univ Cincinnati, Ohio, EE, 54; Ohio State Univ, Columbus, MSc, 57, PhD(elec engr), 64. *Prof Exp:* Instr elec engr, Ohio State Univ, 57-59; engr, US Air Force, 59-65; PROF ELEC ENG, UNIV DAYTON, OHIO, 65- *Concurrent Pos:* Consult, Mead Corp, 79-80, Systs Res Labs, Inc, 77-, Raytheon Serv Co & Systs & Appl Sci Corp, 80- *Mem:* Inst Elec & Electronics Engrs; Am Soc Eng Educ. *Res:* Automatic control; convolution and transform theory; signal processing; image processing; special television-video techniques and apparatus. *Mailing Add:* Dept Elec Eng Univ Dayton Dayton OH 45469

LEWIS, DONALD EVERETT, b Paducah, Tex, July 3, 31; m 68; c 2. BIOCHEMISTRY. *Educ:* Abilene Christian Col, BS, 52; Fla State Univ, MS, 54, PhD(biochem), 57. *Prof Exp:* From assoc prof to prof chem, Queen's Col, NC, 57-66; assoc prof, 66-68, PROF CHEM, ABILENE CHRISTIAN COL, 68- *Concurrent Pos:* Vis assoc prof, Abilene Christian Col, 63-64; vis prof chem, Univ Tex, Austin, 80-81. *Mem:* AAAS; Am Chem Soc. *Res:* Synthesis and biological assay of amino acid analogues. *Mailing Add:* 2541 Campus Courts Abilene TX 79601

LEWIS, DONALD HOWARD, b Stamford, Tex, May 31, 36; m 60; c 3. FISH PATHOLOGY, MICROBIOLOGY. *Educ:* Univ Tex, Austin, BA, 59; Southwest Tes State Univ, MA, 64; Tex A&M Univ, PhD(vet microbiol), 67. *Prof Exp:* Res assoc, 66-68, asst prof, 69-75, assoc prof, 75-79, PROF MICROBIOL, TEX A&M UNIV, 79-, ACTG HEAD VET MICROBIOL & PARASITOL, 81- *Concurrent Pos:* Consult, TerEco Corp, 75. *Mem:* AAAS; Am Soc Microbiol; Am Fisheries Soc; Soc Invert Path; World Maricult Soc. *Res:* Microbial diseases and immune mechanisms of aquatic animals; role of microflora upon host welfare; antibiotic resistance; molecular biology. *Mailing Add:* Dept of Vet Microbiol Col of Vet Med Tex A&M Univ College Station TX 77843

LEWIS, DONALD JOHN, b Adrian, Minn, Jan 25, 26; m 53. MATHEMATICS. *Educ:* Col St Thomas, BS, 46; Univ Mich, MS, 49, PhD(math), 50. *Prof Exp:* Instr math, Ohio State Univ, 50-52; NSF fel, Inst Adv Study, 52-53; from asst prof to assoc prof, Univ Notre Dame, 53-61; assoc prof, 61-63, PROF MATH, UNIV MICH, ANN ARBOR, 63- *Concurrent Pos:* NSF sr fel, Manchester & Cambridge Univs, 59-61; sr vis fel, Cambridge Univ, 65-69; vis fel, Brasenose Col, Oxford, 69; guest prof, Heidelberg Univ, 79-80. *Honors & Awards:* Humboldt Stiftung Sr Award, 80 & 82. *Mem:* Am Math Soc; London Math Soc; Math Asn Am. *Res:* Diophantine equations; finite fields; algebraic number theory. *Mailing Add:* Dept of Math Univ of Mich Ann Arbor MI 48109

LEWIS, DONALD RICHARD, b New Leipzig, NDak, May 18, 20; m 43; c 2. PHYSICAL CHEMISTRY. *Educ:* Univ Wis, BS, 42, MS, 47, PhD(chem), 48. *Prof Exp:* Ballistics supvr, Hercules Powder Co, 42-46; asst, Univ Wis, 46; chemist, 48-50, sr chemist, 50-63, res assoc, 63-67, group leader instrumentation, Explor & Prod Res Ctr, Shell Develop Co Div, 67-72; STAFF RES CHEMIST, WESTHOLLOW RES CTR, 72- *Concurrent Pos:* Shell exchange scientist, Amsterdam, 56-57; res assoc, Ctr Archaeol Res, Univ Tex, San Antonio, 77-, lectr archaeol, 78-79. *Mem:* AAAS; Am Chem Soc; Am Phys Soc; Mineral Soc Am; Geochem Soc; Instrument Soc Am. *Res:* Process control; defect dominated properties of insulating solids; computer control of experiments and data acquisition; archaeometry; applications of chemistry and physics to archaeology. *Mailing Add:* Westhollow Res Ctr Shell Develop Co PO Box 1380 Houston TX 77001

LEWIS, EDWARD B, b Wilkes-Barre, Pa, May 20, 18; m 46; c 3. BIOLOGY. *Educ:* Univ Minn, BA, 39; Calif Inst Technol, PhD(genetics), 42. *Hon Degrees:* Dr, Univ Umea, Sweden, 81. *Prof Exp:* From instr genetics to assoc prof genetics, 46-56, prof biol, 56-66, THOMAS HUNT MORGAN PROF BIOL, CALIF INST TECHNOL, 66- *Concurrent Pos:* Rockefeller Found fel, Sch Bot, Cambridge Univ, 48-49; mem, Nat Adv Comt Radiation, 58-61; guest prof, Univ Copenhagen, 75-76. *Mem:* Nat Acad Sci; AAAS; Am Acad Arts & Sci; Genetics Soc Am. *Res:* Genetics; somatic effects of radiation. *Mailing Add:* Dept of Biol Calif Inst of Technol Pasadena CA 91125

LEWIS, EDWARD LYN, b Aberystwyth, UK, Oct 9, 30; m 59; c 3. OCEANOGRAPHY. *Educ:* Univ London, BSc, 51, MSc, 58, PhD(physics), 62. *Prof Exp:* Physicist, Mullard Res Labs, 52-56; Hatwell res fel, Univ London, 56-59; res assoc microwave electronics, Univ BC, 59-62; RES SCIENTIST, MARINE SCI BR, DEPT FISHERIES & OCEANOG, CAN, 62- *Mem:* Am Geophys Union; Glaciol Soc. *Res:* Arctic oceanography; ice physics; energy exchange ocean-atmosphere; arctic instrument development. *Mailing Add:* Frozen Sea Res Group 9860 W Saanich Rd Sidney BC V8L 4B2 Can

LEWIS, EDWARD R(OBERT), b July 21, 19; US citizen; m 46; c 2. STRUCTURAL MECHANICS, EXPERIMENTAL MECHANICS. *Educ:* City Col New York, BChE, 42; NY Univ, MME, 44, MIE, 55. *Prof Exp:* Naval architect, NY Naval Shipyard, 42-45; mech engr, Naval Appl Sci Lab, 46-60; assoc prof eng sci, 60-73, PROF ENG, HOFSTRA UNIV, 73- *Concurrent Pos:* Consult, Cross-Austin & Ireland Co, 62-63, Biomed Eng Measurements, 65-, Alcorn Combustion Co, 66-73, Consult Serv Inst, Inc, & Intercity Testing & Consult Corp, 79- *Mem:* Soc Exp Stress Anal; Am Soc Eng Educ. *Res:* Naval architecture; structural mechanics; material science and engineering; experimental mechanics; biomedical engineering; fracture mechanics. *Mailing Add:* Dept of Eng & Comput Sci Hofstra Univ Hempstead NY 11550

LEWIS, EDWARD SHELDON, b Berkeley, Calif, May 7, 20; m 55; c 2. CHEMISTRY. *Educ:* Univ Calif, BS, 40; Harvard Univ, MA, 47, PhD(chem), 47. *Prof Exp:* Nat Res Coun fel, Univ Calif, Los Angeles, 47-48; from asst prof to assoc prof, 48-58, PROF CHEM, RICE UNIV, 58-, CHMN DEPT, 80- *Concurrent Pos:* Vis prof, Univ Southampton, 57; chmn dept chem, Rice Univ, 65-67; Guggenheim fel, 67; vis prof, Phys Chem Lab, Oxford Univ, 67-68. *Mem:* Am Chem Soc; The Chem Soc. *Res:* Mechanism of reactions of organic compounds, especially diazonium salts, hydrogen isotope effects, methyl transfers and phosphonium salts. *Mailing Add:* Dept of Chem Rice Univ PO Box 1892 Houston TX 77001

LEWIS, EDWIN REYNOLDS, b Los Angeles, Calif, July 14, 34; m 60; c 2. BIOENGINEERING. *Educ:* Stanford Univ, AB, 56, MS, 57, PhD(elec eng), 62. *Prof Exp:* Mem res staff neural modeling, Lab Automata Res, Gen Precision, 61-67; PROF BIOENG & ASSOC DEAN GRAD DIV, UNIV CALIF, BERKELEY, 67- *Mem:* Fel Inst Elec & Electronics Engrs; Biomed Eng Soc; Soc Neurosci; AAAS; Electron Micros Soc Am. *Res:* Applications of engineering analytical tools to problems in neurobiology, ecology; network models of dynamical biological systems; morphology and physiology of vestibular and auditory apparatus. *Mailing Add:* Dept of Elec Eng & Comput Sci Univ of Calif Berkeley CA 94720

LEWIS, FLORENCE SCOTT, biochemistry, see previous edition

LEWIS, FORBES DOWNER, b New Haven, Conn, Apr 15, 42. COMPUTER SCIENCE. *Educ:* Cornell Univ, BS, 67, MS, 69, PhD(comput sci), 70. *Prof Exp:* Asst prof, Harvard Univ, 70-75; assoc prof, State Univ NY, Albany, 75-78; ASSOC PROF COMPUT SCI & CHMN DEPT, UNIV KY, 78- *Mem:* Asn Comput Mach; Asn Symbolic Logic; Inst Elec & Electronics Engrs; Am Math Soc. *Res:* Theory of computation; computational complexity. *Mailing Add:* Dept of Comput Sci 917 Patterson Off Tower Lexington KY 40506

LEWIS, FRANCIS HOTCHKISS, JR, b Milwaukee, Wis, Aug, 14, 37; m 75; c 3. PHYSICS, MECHANICAL ENGINEERING. *Educ:* Stevens Inst Technol, ME, 59; Stanford Univ, PhD(physics), 64; Univ San Francisco, JD, 74. *Prof Exp:* Res asst prof physics, Univ Wash, 64-66; physicist, Lawerence Livermore Lab, Univ Calif, 66-81. *Concurrent Pos:* Patent atty, Lewis & Lewis, 76- *Mem:* Am Phys Soc; Sigma Xi. *Res:* Theoretical nuclear and particle physics; solid state physics. *Mailing Add:* Lewis & Lewis 2329 Santa Clara Ave #206 Alameda CA 94501

LEWIS, FRANK HARLAN, b Redlands, Calif, Jan 8, 19; m 45, 68; c 2. BOTANY. *Educ:* Univ Calif, Los Angeles, BA, 41, MA, 42, PhD(bot), 46. *Prof Exp:* Asst instr bot, Univ Calif, Los Angeles, 42-44, instr, 46-47; Nat Res Coun fel, John Innes Hort Inst, London, 47-48; from asst prof to assoc prof, 48-56, PROF BOT, UNIV CALIF, LOS ANGELES, 56- *Concurrent Pos:* Teaching fel, Calif Inst Technol, 43-44; Guggenheim fel, 54-55; consult, NSF, 58-69; chmn, Dept Bot, Univ Calif, Los Angeles, 59-62, dean, Div Life Sci, 62-81; vpres, Int Orgn Biosyst, 64-69, pres, 69-75; ed, Evolution, 72-74. *Mem:* AAAS; Am Inst Biol Sci; Am Soc Naturalists (pres, 71); Am Soc Plant Taxonomists (pres, 69); Soc Study Evolution (secy, 53-58, vpres, 59, pres, 61). *Res:* Mechanisms of evolution; systematics of flowering plants. *Mailing Add:* Dept Biol Univ Calif Los Angeles CA 90024

LEWIS, FRANKLIN BEACH, b Derby, Conn, Nov 10, 23; m 54; c 5. INSECT PATHOLOGY, MEDICAL ENTOMOLOGY. *Educ:* Union Univ, NY, BS, 48; Univ Conn, MS, 50, PhD(zool), 55. *Prof Exp:* Asst zool & entom, Univ Conn, 49-53, parasitol, 54-55; entomologist plant pest, Forest Insect Lab, US Forest Serv, 55-69, PRIN INSECT PATHOLOGIST, NORTHEASTERN FOREST EXP STA, US FOREST SERV, 69-, PROJ LEADER, 74- *Mem:* AAAS; Entom Soc Am; Sigma Xi; Soc Invert Path. *Res:* Insect pathology; epidemiology of insect disease; forest insect parasites; biological control of forest insects. *Mailing Add:* Hallsey Lane Woodbridge CT 06525

LEWIS, FREDERICK D, b Boston, Mass, Aug 12, 43; m 68. PHOTOCHEMISTRY. *Educ:* Amherst Col, BA, 65; Rochester Univ, PhD(chem), 68. *Prof Exp:* USPHS res fel chem, Columbia Univ, 68-69; asst prof, 69-74, assoc prof, 74-79, PROF, NORTHWESTERN UNIV, 79- *Concurrent Pos:* Fel, Dreyfus Found, 73-78 & Sloan Found, 75-77. *Mem:* Am Chem Soc. *Res:* Organic photochemistry; energy transfer mechanisms; free radicals; cycloaddition reactions; exciplexes. *Mailing Add:* Dept of Chem Northwestern Univ Evanston IL 60201

LEWIS, GEORGE CAMPBELL, JR, b Williamsburg, Ky, Mar 25, 19; m 45; c 6. OBSTETRICS & GYNECOLOGY, ONCOLOGY. *Educ:* Haverford Col, BS, 42; Univ Pa, MD, 44; Am Bd Obstet & Gynec, dipl, 53. *Prof Exp:* Intern med, Hosp Univ Pa, 44-45, resident obstet & gynec, 47-50, instr, Sch Med, Univ Pa, 50-53, instr radium ther, 51-63, res asst, 53-56, asst prof obstet & gynec, 56-63; prof obstet & gynec & chmn dept, Hahnemann Med Col & Hosp, 62-73, dir div gynec oncol, 71-73; PROF GYNEC ONCOL & DIR DIV, JEFFERSON MED COL, 73- *Concurrent Pos:* Am Cancer Soc fel gynec oncol, Hosp Univ Pa, 50-52; consult lectr, US Naval Hosp Philadelphia, 56-77; consult, Lankenau Hosp & Philadelphia Gen Hosp, 62-, Am Oncol Hosp, 63- & Magee Mem Hosp Rehab Ctr, 68-; mem div gynec oncol, Am Bd Obstet & Gynec; chmn, Gynec Oncol Group, 75- *Mem:* Am Cancer Soc; Soc Gynec Oncol (pres, 69); Am Gynec Soc; Am Asn Obstet & Gynec; Am Col Obstet & Gynec. *Res:* Etiology, early diagnosis and evaluation of modes of therapy of gynecologic oncology. *Mailing Add:* 1025 Walnut St Philadelphia PA 19107

LEWIS, GEORGE D(EVENPORT), mechanical engineering, see previous edition

LEWIS, GEORGE EDWARD, b Lorain, Ohio, Oct 27, 08; m m 37, 61; c 3. STRATIGRAPHY, VERTEBRATE PALEONTOLOGY. *Educ:* Yale Univ, PhB, 30, PhD, 37. *Prof Exp:* Instr geol, Yale Univ, 38-43, asst prof, 43-45; GEOLOGIST, US GEOL SURV, 44- *Concurrent Pos:* Cur, Peabody Mus, Yale Univ, 39-45. *Mem:* Fel Geol Soc Am; Soc Vert Paleont. *Res:* Continental stratigraphy; Cenozoic mammals, primates; strategic and terrain intelligence. *Mailing Add:* MS 919 US Geol Surv Box 25046 Fed Ctr Denver CO 80225

LEWIS, GEORGE EDWIN, b Decatur, Ga, Jan 6, 33; m 56. ORGANIC CHEMISTRY. *Educ:* Emory Univ, AB, 52, MS, 53; Fla State Univ, PhD(chem), 58. *Prof Exp:* Res asst, Ga Inst Technol, 58-59; asst prof chem, La State Univ, 59-66; assoc prof, 66-80, PROF CHEM, JACKSONVILLE UNIV, 80- *Mem:* Am Chem Soc; The Chem Soc. *Res:* Mechanisms of organic reactions. *Mailing Add:* Div of Sci & Math Jacksonville Univ Jacksonville FL 32211

LEWIS, GEORGE KENNETH, chemical physics, see previous edition

LEWIS, GEORGE MCCORMICK, b Los Angeles, Calif, Sept 14, 40; m 64; c 3. GEOMETRY. *Educ:* Stanford Univ, BA, 61; Univ Southern Calif, MA, 64, PhD(math), 70. *Prof Exp:* Asst prof, 67-72, assoc prof, 72-79, PROF MATH, CALIF POLYTECH STATE UNIV, SAN LUIS OBISPO, 79- *Mem:* Am Math Soc; Math Asn Am; Soc Indust & Appl Math. *Res:* Synthetic differential geometry; computer chess. *Mailing Add:* Dept of Math Calif State Polytech Univ San Luis Obispo CA 93407

LEWIS, GEORGE R(OBERT), b Kansas City, Mo, June 26, 24; m 54; c 3. CHEMICAL ENGINEERING. *Educ:* Ohio State Univ, BChE, 48, MSc, 49, PhD(chem eng), 51. *Prof Exp:* Res engr cellophane process, E I du Pont de Nemours & Co, 51-53, chem develop supvr, Film Dept, 53-55; res engr paperboard, Res Labs, 55-60, staff consult, 60-64, prod mgr, 64-69, TECH DIR, PAPERBOARD PROD DIV, MEAD CORP, DAYTON, 69- *Mem:* Tech Asn Pulp & Paper Indust; Am Inst Chem Engrs. *Res:* Industrial wastes; cellophane process; pulp and paper. *Mailing Add:* Paperboard Prod Div Courthouse Plaza NE Dayton OH 45463

LEWIS, GLENN C, b Oakley, Idaho, July 13, 20; m 56; c 3. SOIL CHEMISTRY. *Educ:* Univ Idaho, BS, 46, MS, 49; Purdue Univ, PhD(soils), 62. *Prof Exp:* Anal agr chem, 47-52, from asst prof agr chem to assoc prof soils, 52-67, PROF SOILS, UNIV IDAHO, 67- *Mem:* Soil Sci Soc Am; Int Soc Soil Sci; AAAS. *Res:* Chemical and mineralogical studies on slick spot soils; water quality, including effects of irrigation water quality on soil characteristics; phosphorus reactions in calcareous soils; mineralogical studies on loess. *Mailing Add:* Dept of Plant & Soil Sci Univ of Idaho Moscow ID 83843

LEWIS, GORDON, b Cincinnati, Ohio, Apr 7, 33; m 58; c 3. CERAMIC ENGINEERING. *Educ:* Alfred Univ, BS, 56, PhD(ceramics), 63. *Prof Exp:* Ceramic engr, Carborundum Co, NY, 57-58; res assoc chem, Univ Kans, 62-64; assoc prof ceramic eng, 64-73, PROF CERAMIC ENG, UNIV MO-ROLLA, 73- *Mem:* Am Ceramic Soc; Nat Inst Ceramic Engrs; Am Soc Eng Educ. *Res:* High temperature chemistry; phase equilibria and vaporization behavior in oxide systems; thermogravimetric behavior and phase identification of high alumina refractory cements. *Mailing Add:* Dept of Ceramic Eng Univ of Mo Rolla MO 65401

LEWIS, GORDON DEPEW, b Charlottesville, Va, July 22, 29; m 54. FOREST ECONOMICS, MARKETING. *Educ:* Va Polytech Inst, BS, 51; Duke Univ, MFor, 57; Mich State Univ, PhD(forest econ), 61. *Prof Exp:* Asst prof forest econ, Univ Mont, 59-62; proj leader, Southeastern Forest Exp Sta, US Forest Serv, 62-66, economist, Washington, DC, 66-67, br chief, 68-71, proj leader, Rocky Mountain Forest Exp Sta, 71-77, prof mgr, western environ forestry res, Rocky Mountain Forest Exp Sta, 77-81, ASST DIR, SOUTHEASTERN FOREST STA, US FOREST SERV, 81- *Mem:* Soc Am Foresters; Am Econ Asn. *Res:* Economic evaluations of alternative methods of exploiting natural resources for regional development consistent with the maintenance of the quality of rural and wildlife environments. *Mailing Add:* Southeastern Forest Exp Sta Forest Serv USDA Asheville NC 28801

LEWIS, GWYNNE DAVID, b Hackensack, NJ, June 12, 28; m 60; c 1. PLANT PATHOLOGY. *Educ:* Rutgers Univ, BS, 51; Purdue Univ, MS, 53; Cornell Univ, PhD, 58. *Prof Exp:* Asst plant path, Purdue Univ, 51-53 & Cornell Univ, 53-58; from asst prof to assoc prof, 58-70, PROF PLANT PATH, RUTGERS UNIV, NEW BRUNSWICK, 70- *Mem:* Am Phytopath Soc; Soc Nematol. *Res:* Diseases of vegetable crops; plant nematology; control of plant and vegetable diseases. *Mailing Add:* Dept of Plant Path Rutgers Univ New Brunswick NJ 08903

LEWIS, H(ERBERT) CLAY, b Newton, Mass, Aug 7, 13; m 49. CHEMICAL ENGINEERING. *Educ:* Bowdoin Col, AB, 34; Mass Inst Technol, MS, 37; Carnegie Inst Technol, ScD(chem eng), 42. *Prof Exp:* Chem engr, Humble Oil & Ref Co, Tex, 37-40; res assoc, Nat Defense Res Comt, 41-42; from instr to asst prof chem eng, Univ Ill, 42-45; res assoc, Mass Inst Technol, 45-46; from asst prof to assoc prof chem eng, Ga Inst Technol, 46-53, prof, 53-80; RETIRED. *Concurrent Pos:* Vis prof, Imp Col, Univ London, 60-61; fel, Ctr Advan Eng Study, Mass Inst Technol, 71-72. *Mem:* Am Chem Soc; Am Inst Chem Engrs. *Res:* Chemical technology. *Mailing Add:* 212 Winnona Dr Decatur GA 30030

LEWIS, H(ARRELL) J(ULIAN), b Kinston, NC, Nov 12, 27; m 52; c 2. CHEMICAL ENGINEERING, PHYSICAL CHEMISTRY. *Educ:* NC State Col, BChE, 48, MS, 50. *Prof Exp:* Sr res chem engr, 50-67, res assoc, 67-70, DEPT HEAD, TENN EASTMAN CO, 70-, DEVELOP ASSOC, 79- *Mem:* Am Inst Chem Engrs; Am Chem Soc. *Res:* Chemical research and process development. *Mailing Add:* Tenn Eastman Co PO Box 511 Kingsport TN 37662

LEWIS, HAROLD RALPH, b Chicago, Ill, June 7, 31; m 61; c 2. PHYSICS. *Educ:* Univ Chicago, AB, 51, SB, 53; Univ Ill, MS, 55, PhD(physics), 58. *Prof Exp:* Res assoc physics, Univ Heidelberg, 58-60; instr, Princeton Univ, 60-63; mem staff, 63-75, assoc group leader, 75-81, DEP GROUP LEADER, LOS ALAMOS NAT LAB, 81- *Concurrent Pos:* Ger Acad Exchange Serv fel, Univ Heidelberg, 58-59. *Mem:* Am Phys Soc. *Res:* Plasma physics; nulcear spectroscopy; superconductivity. *Mailing Add:* Los Alamos Nat Lab PO Box 1663 Los Alamos NM 87544

LEWIS, HAROLD WALTER, b Keene, NH, May 7, 17; m 46; c 2. NUCLEAR PHYSICS. *Educ:* Middlebury Col, BS, 38; Univ Buffalo, AM, 40; Duke Univ, PhD(physics), 50. *Prof Exp:* Vis instr & res assoc, 46-49, from asst prof to assoc prof, 49-59, vprovost, 63-80, dean fac, 69-80, PROF PHYSICS, DUKE UNIV, 59-, CHMN DEPT PHYSICS, 81- *Concurrent Pos:* Dean arts & sci, Duke Univ, 63-69. *Mem:* fel Am Phys Soc; Am Asn Physics Teachers. *Mailing Add:* 1708 Woodburn Rd Durham NC 27705

LEWIS, HAROLD WARREN, b New York, NY, Oct 1, 23; m 47. PHYSICS. *Educ:* NY Univ, AB, 43; Univ Calif, AM, 44, PhD(physics), 48. *Prof Exp:* Asst prof physics, Univ Calif, 48-53; mem tech staff, Bell Tel Labs, NJ, 51-56; from assoc prof to prof physics, Univ Wis, 56-64; PROF PHYSICS, UNIV CALIF, SANTA BARBARA, 64- *Concurrent Pos:* Mem staff, Inst Advan Study, 47-48 & 50-51; dir, Quantum Inst, Univ Calif, Santa Barbara, 69-73. *Mem:* Am Phys Soc. *Res:* Theoretical physics. *Mailing Add:* Dept of Physics Univ of Calif Santa Barbara CA 93106

LEWIS, HARVYE FLEMING, b Hodge, La, Dec 24, 17. NUTRITION. *Educ:* La Polytech Inst, BS, 38; Univ Tenn, MS, 42; Iowa State Col, PhD(nutrit), 50. *Prof Exp:* Teacher high sch, La, 38-40; nutritionist, State Dept Pub Health, Tenn, 42; res assoc, Agr Exp Sta, La State Univ, 43-47, asst nutritionist, 50-52; assoc prof food & nutrit, Fla State Univ, 52-65; PROF FOOD & NUTRIT, SCH HOME ECON, LA STATE UNIV, 65- *Mem:* AAAS; Am Dietetic Asn; Am Home Econ Asn; Inst Food Technologists; Am Inst Nutrit. *Res:* Vitamin content of foods; nutritional requirements; food patterns and nutritional health of children. *Mailing Add:* Sch of Home Econ La State Univ Baton Rouge LA 70803

LEWIS, HENRY RAFALSKY, b Yonkers, NY, Nov 19, 25; m 57; c 3. PHYSICS. *Educ:* Harvard Univ, AB, 48, MA, 49, PhD(physics), 56. *Prof Exp:* Mem staff opers res, Opers Eval Group, Mass Inst Technol, 51-53, 56; group head quantum electronics, David Sarnoff Res Ctr, RCA Corp, 57-66, dir, electronic res lab, 66-70; vpres res & develop, Itek Corp, 70-73; pres, Optel Corp, 73-74; GROUP VPRES & DIR, DENNISON MFG CORP, 74- *Mem:* Am Phys Soc; Opers Res Soc Am; Inst Elec & Electronics Eng. *Res:* Paramagnetic resonance; quantum electronics; operations research; molecular beams. *Mailing Add:* 35 Clover St Belmont MA 02178

LEWIS, HERMAN WILLIAM, b Chicago, Ill, July 10, 23; c 2. GENETICS, ZOOLOGY. *Educ:* Univ Ill, BS, 47, MS, 49; Univ Calif, PhD(genetics), 53. *Prof Exp:* USPHS res fel, Univ Calif, 52-54; asst prof biol, Mass Inst Technol, 54-61; prof life sci & chmn dept, Mich State Univ, 61-62; prog dir genetic biol, 62-66, head, Cellular Biol Sect, 66-77, SR SCIENTIST, NSF, 77- *Honors & Awards:* Mendel Medal. *Mem:* AAAS; Biophys Soc; Genetics Soc Am; Am Soc Cell Biol. *Res:* Biochemical, physiological and molecular genetics; biophysics and cytology of genetic material; human cell biology. *Mailing Add:* Cellular Biol Sect Nat Sci Found Washington DC 20550

LEWIS, HOMER DICK, b Covington, Ky, Oct 4, 26; m 48; c 4. METALLURGY, NUCLEAR ENGINEERING. *Educ:* Univ Cincinnati, MetE, 52; Univ NMex, MS, 64, MSc, 71. *Prof Exp:* Staff mem uranium casting, Los Alamos Sci Lab, Univ Calif, 52-57; res engr, Boeing Airplane Co, 57-58; STAFF MEM, LOS ALAMOS SCI LAB, UNIV CALIF, 58- *Concurrent Pos:* Co-prin investr, Liquid Metal Fast Breeder Reactor Fuels Properties, 75-78, mem, Nat Task Group, Los Alamos Lab Rep, 77-81. *Mem:* Am Soc Metals; fel Am Inst Chem. *Res:* Packing behavior of particulate solids; small particle statistics; physics of particulate systems; powder metallurgy; carbon and graphite research and development; electrical and thermal transport properties of plutonium and plutomium alloys and compounds. *Mailing Add:* 77 Mesa Verde Dr Los Alamos NM 87544

LEWIS, HOWARD PHELPS, b San Francisco, Calif, Feb 18, 02; m 27; c 2. INTERNAL MEDICINE. *Educ:* Ore State Col, BS, 24; Univ Ore, MD, 30; Am Bd Internal Med, dipl, 38. *Prof Exp:* Asst anat, 26-30, instr med, 29-30, instr clin med, 32-36, assoc, 36-38, asst prof, 38-46, assoc prof med, 46-47, prof & head dept, 47-71, EMER PROF MED, MED SCH, UNIV ORE, 72- *Concurrent Pos:* Mem, Nat Adv Heart Coun, Nat Heart Inst, 56-60 & Bd Dirs, Am Bd Family Pract, 70-78; mem, Am Bd Internal Med, 52, chmn, 59-61. *Honors & Awards:* Merit Award, Am Heart Asn, 60; Alfred Stengel Award, Am Col Physicians, 66. *Mem:* Asn Am Physicians; Am Heart Asn (ed, Modern Concepts of Cardiovasc Dis, 56-); Am Clin & Climat Asn (pres, 68); Am Col Physicians (3rd vpres, 51, pres, 59-60). *Mailing Add:* 2151 SW Laurel St Portland OR 97201

LEWIS, IRVING JAMES, b Boston, Mass, July 9, 18; m 41; c 3. COMMUNITY HEALTH. *Educ:* Harvard Univ, AB, 39; Univ Chicago, AM, 41. *Prof Exp:* With US Govt, 42 & 46-55, dep chief, Int Div, Bur Budget, 55-57, dept head, Intergovt Comn Europ Migration, Geneva, Switz, 57-59, dep chief, Int Div, Bur Budget, 59-65, chief, Health & Welfare Div, 65-67, dep asst dir, 67-68, dep adminr health serv & ment health admin, Dept Health, Educ & Welfare, 68-70; PROF COMMUNITY HEALTH, ALBERT EINSTEIN COL MED, 70- *Concurrent Pos:* WHO fel. *Honors & Awards:* Except Serv Award, Bur Budget, 64; Career Serv Award, Nat Civil Serv League, 69. *Mem:* Inst of Med of Nat Acad Sci; Am Polit Sci Asn; Am Soc Pub Adminr; Am Pub Health Asn; Asn Am Med Cols. *Mailing Add:* Dept of Community Health Albert Einstein Col of Med New York NY 10641

LEWIS, J(OHN) E(UGENE), b St John, NB, Apr 11, 41; m 64; c 2. ELECTRICAL ENGINEERING. *Educ:* Univ NB, Fredericton, BScE, 64; Univ BC, PhD(elec eng), 68. *Prof Exp:* Nat Res Coun Can fel, Univ Southampton, 68-69; asst prof elec eng, 69-74, assoc prof elec eng, 74-80, PROF & CHMN, UNIV NB, FREDERICTON, 80- *Mem:* Inst Elec & Electronics Engrs; Brit Inst Elec Engrs; Int Microwave Power Inst. *Res:* Industrial applications of microwaves to materials processing and process control; microwave measurement of nonelectrical quantities; low-loss waveguides. *Mailing Add:* Elec Eng Dept Univ NB PO Box 4400 Fredericton NB E3B 5A3 Can

LEWIS, J(ACK) R(OCKLEY), b Eureka, Kans, July 30, 20; m 52; c 1. METALLURGY. *Educ:* Stanford Univ, BS, 47, PhD(metall), 51. *Prof Exp:* Res assoc metall, Stanford Univ, 47-50; metallurgist, Fairchild Engine & Airplane Corp, 50-51; engr, Gen Elec Co, 51-57, supvr fuel element develop, 57-60, consult engr, 60-61; group leader mat develop, Atomics Int Div, NAm Aviation, Inc, 61-67, MGR ADVAN MAT, ROCKETDYNE DIV, ROCKWELL INT, 67- *Mem:* Am Inst Mining, Metall & Petrol Engrs; Am Nuclear Soc; fel Am Soc Metals; Am Inst Chem Engrs. *Res:* Nuclear reactor and radioisotope materials; liquid metals; high-temperature materials; intermetallic compounds and cermets; rocket engine materials and processes; composite materials. *Mailing Add:* 11300 Yarmouth Ave Granada Hills CA 91344

LEWIS, JACK A, b Brooklyn, NY, Apr 8, 39; m 68; c 2. PLANT PATHOLOGY, SOIL MICROBIOLOGY. *Educ:* Brooklyn Col, BS, 60; Rutgers Univ, PhD(microbiol), 65. *Prof Exp:* MICROBIOLOGIST, USDA, 65- *Mem:* Am Soc Microbiol; Am Phytopath Soc. *Res:* Biological control of soil-borne plant pathogenic fungi; microbial decomposition of natural materials in soil. *Mailing Add:* Soilborne Dis Lab Plant Prot Inst Agr Res Serv USDA Beltsville MD 20705

LEWIS, JACK SMITH, b Whitesburg, Ky, June 10, 26; m 75; c 3. GAS CHROMATOGRAPHY. *Educ:* Univ Ky, BS, 50. *Prof Exp:* Jr res physicist, Tenn Eastman Co, 51-52, sales corresp, Eastman Chem Prod, Inc, 52-53, res physicist, Tenn Eastman Co, 53-63, sr res physicist, 63-73, res assoc, Tenn Eastman Co, 73-81, RES ASSOC, EASTMAN CHEM DIV, 81- *Mem:* Am Chem Soc; Am Soc Testing & Mat; Am Soc Mass Spectrometry. *Res:* Computer collection and reporting of gas chromatographic data; determination of structure of organic compounds; gas chromatography-mass spectrometry; high resolution mass spectrometry; storage and retrieval of gas chromatographic data; computer interpretation of mass spectral data; high resolution gas chromatography; laboratory automation systems for gas chromatography. *Mailing Add:* Eastman Chem Div Res Labs Kingsport TN 37662

LEWIS, JAMES BRYAN, b York, Pa, Dec 14, 45; m 67; c 2. MOLECULAR BIOLOGY. *Educ:* Univ Pa, BA, 67; Harvard Univ, MA, 68, PhD(chem), 71. *Prof Exp:* Damon Runyan-Walter Winchell Cancer Fund fel, Swiss Inst Exp Cancer Res, 71-73; fel, 73-74, staff investr, 74-75, SR STAFF INVESTR, COLD SPRING HARBOR LAB, 75- *Res:* Mapping the adenovirus genes for specific polypeptides by cell-free translation of messenger RNA fractionated by hybridization to fragments of adenovirus DNA. *Mailing Add:* Cold Spring Harbor Lab Box 100 Cold Spring Harbor NY 11724

LEWIS, JAMES CHESTER, b Kalamazoo, Mich, Jan 31, 36; m 57; c 3. WILDLIFE ECOLOGY. *Educ:* Univ Mich, BS, 57; Mich State Univ, MS, 63; Okla State Univ, PhD(wildlife ecol), 74. *Prof Exp:* Biologist aide, Mich Game Div, 57-59; dist biologist, Tenn Game Div, 59-60, res proj leader game mgt,

60-64, res supvr, 64-67; asst unit leader, Okla Coop Wildlife Res Unit, 67-77, from asst prof to assoc prof life sci, Sch Biophys Sci, Okla State Univ, 67-77; TECH ED, US FISH & WILDLIFE SERV, COLO STATE UNIV, 77- *Concurrent Pos:* Consult, Nat Audubon Soc, 80. *Mem:* Wildlife Soc. *Res:* Endangered species research; deer and turkey management; ecology of wildlife rabies; mourning dove and sandhill crane behavior and ecology. *Mailing Add:* US Fish & Wildlife Serv 270 Aylesworth Hall Ft Collins CO 80521

LEWIS, JAMES CLEMENT, b Lewisville, Minn, Aug 10, 15; m 39; c 3. BIOCHEMISTRY. *Educ:* Univ Minn, BCh, 36; Ore State Col, MS, 39, PhD(soils, agr chem), 40. *Prof Exp:* Analyst, Univ Minn, 36-37; asst chemist animal nutrit, Exp Sta, Ore State Col, 40-41; biochemist, Western Regional Res Lab, Bur Agr & Indust Chem, USDA, 41-53, BIOCHEMIST, WESTERN REGIONAL RES LAB, AGR RES SERV, USDA, 53- *Mem:* AAAS; Am Chem Soc; Am Soc Microbiol; Am Soc Biol Chem. *Res:* Microbial biochemistry; trace elements in plant and microbiology; bacterial spores. *Mailing Add:* 1 Harvard Circle Berkeley CA 94708

LEWIS, JAMES EDWARD, b Ashland, Ky, July 11, 27; m 52; c 3. PHYSICAL CHEMISTRY. *Educ:* Centre Col, AB, 50; Purdue Univ, MS, 54, PhD(chem), 56. *Prof Exp:* Sr chemist, E I du Pont de Nemours & Co, 55-56; gen mgr, Radiochem Inc, Ky, 56-57, pres, 57-65; sr res assoc, United Carbon Co Div, Ashland Oil & Refining Co, 65-66, exec asst to pres res & develop, 66-67, dir res & develop, 67-70, Ashland Oil Inc, 70-74, vpres, 74-79, VPRES EXEC STAFF, ASHLAND CHEM CO, 79- *Concurrent Pos:* Mem, Adv Comt Nuclear Sci, Ky Atomic Energy Authority, 59-65. *Mem:* AAAS; Am Chem Soc; Am Phys Soc; Am Nuclear Soc. *Res:* Radiochemistry; thermodynamics and transport properties of liquids; instrumentation; high vacuum phenomena; carbon black and rubber chemistry; missile fuels; technology transfer. *Mailing Add:* Ashland Chem Co PO Box 2458 Columbus OH 43216

LEWIS, JAMES KELLEY, b Waco, Tex, Oct 24, 24; m 49; c 4. RANGE SCIENCE. *Educ:* Colo State Univ, BS, 48; Mont State Univ, MS, 51. *Prof Exp:* Asst prof, 50-58, ASSOC PROF ANIMAL SCI, SDAK STATE UNIV, 58- *Mem:* Soc Range Mgt; Am Soc Animal Sci; Ecol Soc Am; Wildlife Soc; Brit Grassland Soc. *Res:* Structure, function, measurement, manipulation, uses and systems analysis of range ecosystems; range animal nutrition and management; coupling of range and agronomic ecosystems. *Mailing Add:* 504 Medary Ave Brookings SD 57006

LEWIS, JAMES LABAN, III, b Nashville, Tenn, Sept 17, 42; m 69; c 3. ELECTRICAL ENGINEERING. *Educ:* Vanderbilt Univ, BE, 63; Princeton Univ, MSE, 65; Purdue Univ, PhD(elec eng), 69. *Prof Exp:* Instr elec eng, Purdue Univ, 66-67; mem tech staff, TRW Systs Group, 69-75, head signal design sect, TRW Defense & Space Systs Group, 75-77, SR STAFF ENGR, TRW DEFENSE & SPACE SYSTS GROUP, 78- *Concurrent Pos:* Japan Soc Prom Sci fel, Kyoto Univ, 71-72; lectr, Loyola Marymount Univ, 77- *Mem:* Inst Elec & Electronics Engrs; Inst Math Statist. *Res:* Systems engineering; communication theory; stochastic processes; digital systems. *Mailing Add:* Systs Eng Lab TRW Defense & Space Systs Group One Space Park Redondo Beach CA 90278

LEWIS, JAMES VERNON, b Neligh, Nebr, May 2, 15; div; c 3. MATHEMATICS. *Educ:* Univ Calif, AB, 37, MA, 39, PhD(math), 42. *Prof Exp:* Asst, Univ Calif, 39-42; jr physicist, US Navy, Calif, 42-43; mathematician, Radiation Lab, Univ Calif, 43-45; mathematician, Aberdeen Proving Ground, 45-53; ASSOC PROF MATH, UNIV N MEX, 53- *Concurrent Pos:* Asst prof, Univ Nev, 46-47. *Mem:* Am Planning Asn; Math Asn Am; Sigma Xi; Fedn Am Scientists. *Res:* Urban planning; iterative methods for decision making in urban planning; calculuc of variations. *Mailing Add:* Dept of Math & Statist Univ of NMex Albuquerque NM 87131

LEWIS, JAMES W L, b Natchez, Miss, May 3, 38; m 61; c 3. MOLECULAR PHYSICS, FLUID PHYSICS. *Educ:* Univ Miss, BS, 60, MS, 64, PhD(physics), 66. *Prof Exp:* Physicist, US Naval Weapons Lab, 61-62 & ARO, Inc, 66-68; UK Sci Res Coun fel physics, Queen's Univ, Belfast, 68-69; assoc prof physics, Space Inst, Univ, Tenn, 66-77; physicist, Aro, Inc, 69-80; PROF PHYSICS, SPACE INST, UNIV TENN, 77-; PHYSICIST, CALSPAN, INC, 81- *Mem:* Am Inst Aeronaut & Astronaut; Am Phys Soc. *Res:* Vibrational relaxation processes in gases; molecular processes in hypersonic flow phenomena; molecular and atomic beam collision processes using high temperature shock tube source; raman-rayleigh scattering in gases; condensation processes in gases; nonlinear optics. *Mailing Add:* ARO Inc Arnold AFB TN 37389

LEWIS, JANE SANFORD, b Pasdena, Calif, Dec 26, 18; m 42; c 4. NUTRITION. *Educ:* Pomona Col, BA, 40; Cornell Univ, MS, 42; Univ Calif, Los Angeles, MPH, 66, DrPH(nutrit), 69. *Prof Exp:* Home economist, Wilson & Co, Ill, 42-43; anal chemist, Nat Defense Res Coun, Northwestern Univ, 43-45; anal chemist, Nat Defense Res Coun Proj, Calif Inst Technol, 45-46; technician, Nutrit Lab, Sch Pub Health, Univ Calif, Los Angeles, 65; nutritionist, Head Start Prog, Fedn Settlements & Recreation Ctr, Calif, 66; technician, Nutrit Lab, Sch Pub Health, Univ Calif, Los Angeles, 67; assoc prof, 68-73, PROF HOME ECON, CALIF STATE COL, LOS ANGELES, 73- *Concurrent Pos:* Chmn, Task Force, Calif Nutrit Coun, 70- *Mem:* Am Pub Health Asn; Am Dietetic Asn; Soc Nutrit Educ; Am Inst Nutrit; Am Home Econ Asn. *Res:* Nutritional status of children of varying backgrounds; effect of oral contraceptives and anticonvulsant drugs on nutritional status; food habits of various ethnic groups, anthropometric measurements of Oriental children. *Mailing Add:* Dept of Home Econ Calif State Univ Los Angeles CA 90032

LEWIS, JASPER PHELPS, b Danville, Va, Nov 8, 17; m 50. CHEMISTRY, BIOCHEMISTRY. *Educ:* Univ Va, BSChem, 46; Univ Louisville, MS, 58; Med Col Ga, PhD(biochem), 66. *Prof Exp:* Res chemist biochem, Sch Med, Univ Va, 46-50; clin chemist, Vet Admin Hosp, Bay Pines, Fla, 50-52, clin chemist, Louisville, Ky, 52-60 & res chemist, St Louis, Mo, 60-62; BASIC SCIENTIST ERYTHROPOIESIS RES, VET ADMIN HOSP, AUGUSTA, 62- *Concurrent Pos:* Res prof, Med Col Ga, 67- *Mem:* AAAS; Am Soc Hemat; Am Soc Biol Chemists; Am Chem Soc; Am Asn Clin Chemists. *Res:* Erythropoiesis regulatory factors. *Mailing Add:* Vet Admin Hosp Med Res Forest Hills Div Augusta GA 30904

LEWIS, JERRY PARKER, b Terre Haute, Ind, Sept 20, 31; m 56; c 4. MEDICINE. *Educ:* James Millikin Univ, 52; Univ Ill, BS, 53, MD, 56. *Prof Exp:* Asst prof med, Univ Ill, 64-67; assoc prof, 67-69, chief sect hemat & oncol, 67-80, lectr clin path & vet med, 68-74, chief staff, Med Ctr, 79-80, PROF MED, UNIV CALIF, DAVIS, 69-, PROF PATH, 78-, ACTG CHMN, DEPT INT MED, 80- *Concurrent Pos:* NIH fel hemat, Presby-St Luke's Hosp, Chicago, 61-63, res fel, 63-65; actg chief clin hemat & chief spec hemat, Presby-St Luke's Hosp, Chicago, 65-67; consult, David Grant Hosp, Travis, AFB, Calif, 68- *Mem:* Am Soc Hemat; Am Soc Clin Oncol; fel Am Col Physicians; Soc Exp Hemat; Am Soc Human Genetics. *Res:* Bone marrow transplantation; preservation of marrow using cryobiologic techniques; erythropoietin; leukemia; cytogenetics; toxicity of laetrile. *Mailing Add:* Sch of Med Univ of Calif Davis CA 95616

LEWIS, JESSE C, b Vaughan, Miss, June 26, 29; m 59; c 1. MATHEMATICS, COMPUTER SCIENCES. *Educ:* Univ Ill, MS, 55, MA, 59; Syracuse Univ, PhD(math), 66. *Prof Exp:* Instr math, Southern Univ, 55-57 & Prairies View Agr & Mech Col, 57-58; asst prof, Jackson State Col, 59-61; res asst, Comput Ctr, Syracuse Univ, 63-66; dir, Comput Ctr & chmn, Dept Comput Sci, 66-80, prof math & chmn Div Natural Sci, 67-80, ASSOC DEAN COMPUT SERV & PROF COMPUT SCI, JACKSON STATE UNIV, 80- *Concurrent Pos:* Consult, Comt Undergrad Prog Math, Jackson State Col; mem eval panel sci comput, Nat Bur Standards, 80-83. *Mem:* Math Asn Am; Am Math Soc; Asn Comput Mach; Asn Educ Data Systs. *Res:* Computer study of permanents of n-square (0,1)-matrices with k l's in each row and column. *Mailing Add:* Dept Comput Sci Jackson State Univ Jackson MS 39217

LEWIS, JESSICA HELEN, b Harpswell, Maine, Oct 26, 17; m 46; c 5. MEDICINE. *Educ:* Goucher Col, AB, 38; Johns Hopkins Univ, MD, 42. *Prof Exp:* Intern, Hosp Women, Baltimore, Md, 42-43; asst resident, Univ Calif Hosp, 43-44; res fel, Thorndike Mem Lab & Harvard Univ, 44-46; res assoc physiol, Univ NC, 48-55; res assoc med, 55-58, res assoc prof, 58-70, res prof med, 70-77, PROF MED, UNIV PITTSBURGH, 77- *Concurrent Pos:* USPHS res fel, Univ NC, 47-48; asst med, Boston City Hosp, 44-46; res assoc, Med Sch, Emory Univ, 46-47; assoc med, Med Sch, Duke Univ, 51-55; staff mem, Presby-Univ Hosp, 55-; dir res, Cent Blood Bank Pittsburgh, 69-75, vpres, 75- *Mem:* Am Soc Hemat; World Fedn Hemophilia; Am Physiol Soc; Am Soc Clin Invest; Am Fedn Clin Res. *Res:* Blood coagulation; enzyme and protein chemistry; comparative hematology. *Mailing Add:* Dept Med Sch Med Univ Pittsburgh Pittsburgh PA 15261

LEWIS, JOHN ALLEN, b Detroit, Mich, Jan 21, 23; m 48; c 3. APPLIED MATHEMATICS. *Educ:* Worcester Polytech Inst, BS, 44; Brown Univ, ScM, 48, PhD(appl math), 50. *Prof Exp:* Asst appl math, Brown Univ, 46-50; res physicist, Corning Glass Works, 50-51; MEM TECH STAFF MATH, BELL TEL LABS, 51- *Mem:* Am Math Soc; Soc Indust & Appl Math. *Res:* Applied mechanics; viscous flow, elasticity; heat transfer; piezoelectricity. *Mailing Add:* Bell Tel Labs Rm 2-C456 Murray Hill NJ 07971

LEWIS, JOHN BRADLEY, b Ottawa, Ont, Jan 12, 25; m 80; c 3. MARINE BIOLOGY. *Educ:* McGill Univ, BSc, 40, MSc, 50, PhD(zool), 54. *Prof Exp:* Asst marine biol, Inst Marine Sci, Univ Miami, 51-54; dir Bellairs Res Inst, McGill Univ, 54-71, assoc prof, 61-69, PROF MARINE SCI, INST OCEANOG, MCGILL UNIV, 69-, DIR, REDPATH MUS, 71- *Mem:* Can Soc Zool; Int Soc Reef Studies. *Res:* Tropical marine ecology and physiology; tropical marine organisms and coral reef ecology. *Mailing Add:* Redpath Mus McGill Univ 859 Sherbrooke St W Montreal PQ H3A 2K6 Can

LEWIS, JOHN G(ALEN), b Panora, Iowa, Oct 26, 20; m 52; c 3. CHEMICAL ENGINEERING. *Educ:* Iowa State Univ, BS, 43; Univ Mich, MS, 51, PhD(chem eng), 54. *Prof Exp:* Staff engr, Pennwalt Corp, 43-46; chem engr, BASF Wyandotte Corp, 47-50; assoc res engr, Univ Mich, 54-58; asst dir, Res Div, Lear Siegler, Inc/Fabricated Prod Group, 58-62; CONSULT ENGR, 62- *Mem:* Am Chem Soc; Am Inst Chem Engrs; Nat Soc Prof Engrs. *Res:* Promotion of chemical reactions with gamma radiation; nuclear fuel reprocessing; design, construction of vacuum and atmospheric furnaces and their application to refractories and graphite; heat exchange and thermal stress analysis; design and construction of organic and inorganic chemical processes and related facilities. *Mailing Add:* 1340 Burgundy Rd Ann Arbor MI 48105

LEWIS, JOHN HUBBARD, b Jamestown, NY, Apr 13, 29; m 56; c 4. GEOLOGY. *Educ:* Allegheny Col, BS, 56; Univ Colo, PhD(geol), 65. *Prof Exp:* From instr to assoc prof geol, Colo Col, 58-74, chmn dept, 70-78, prof, 74-80. *Concurrent Pos:* Lectr, Exten Div, Univ Colo, 58-66; dir, NSF Sec Sci Training Prog, Colo Col, 65-67; US Antarctic res partic, Tex Tech Col, 67-68. *Res:* Sedimentary petrology; petrology and diagenesis of upper Cambrian rocks of Colorado; structural geology. *Mailing Add:* 913 N Royer Colorado Springs CO 80903

LEWIS, JOHN L, JR, b San Antonio, Tex, June 5, 29; m 55; c 3. OBSTETRICS & GYNECOLOGY. *Educ:* Harvard Univ, BA, 52, MD, 57; Am Bd Obstet & Gynec, dipl, 67. *Prof Exp:* Clin assoc endocrinol br, Nat Cancer Inst, 59-61, sr investr surg br, 65-67; assoc prof, 68-71, PROF OBSTET & GYNEC, MED COL, CORNELL UNIV, 71-; CHIEF GYNEC SERV, MEM HOSP CANCER & ALLIED DIS & JAMES EWING HOSP, 68- *Concurrent Pos:* Sr investr clin ctr, NIH, 65-67; assoc attend gynecologist, Francis Delafield Hosp, 67; assoc attend obstetrician & gynecologist, Presby Hosp, NY, 67; assoc attend obstetrician & gynecologist, New York Lying-in Hosp, 68-71, attend obstetrician & gynecologist, 71-; attend surgeon, Mem

Hosp Cancer & Allied Dis, 68-; assoc, Sloan-Kettering Inst Cancer Res, 68-73, mem, 73-; assoc prof, Col Physicians & Surgeons, Columbia Univ, 67, lectr, 68-; dir, Am Bd Obstet & Gynec, 70-76 & Div Gynec Oncol, 70-76; consult Am joint comt cancer staging & end result reporting. *Mem:* Soc Gynec Invest; AMA; Soc Surg Oncol; Am Radium Soc; Am Asn Cancer Educ. *Res:* Gynecologic cancer; hormonal, immunologic and therapeutic aspects of gestational trophoblastic neoplasms. *Mailing Add:* Mem Hosp for Cancer & Allied Dis 1275 York Ave New York NY 10021

LEWIS, JOHN MORGAN, b Joliet, Ill, June 5, 20; m 44; c 3. ANIMAL HUSBANDRY. *Educ:* Univ Ill, BS, 43. *Prof Exp:* Asst supt, 43-59, actg supt, 59-62, ASSOC PROF ANIMAL SCI, DIXON SPRINGS EXP STA, UNIV ILL, URBANA, 62- *Mem:* Am Soc Animal Sci. *Res:* Sheep breeding, feeding and management. *Mailing Add:* 6-121 Coord Sci Lab Univ of Ill Simpson IL 62985

LEWIS, JOHN RAYMOND, b Philadelphia, Pa, July 25, 18; m 42; c 1. POLYMER CHEMISTRY. *Educ:* Franklin & Marshall Col, BS, 42. *Prof Exp:* Chemist, Naval Stores Div, Res Ctr, Hercules Inc, 42-44, shift supvr explosives dept, Sunflower Ord Works, Kans, 44-45, chemist, Naval Stores Div, 45-49, res chemist, 49-55, res supvr, 55-59, res mgr, Plastics & Elastomers Div, 59-64, res assoc, Cent Res Div, 64, mgr develop, Res Dept, 64-69, venture projs, New Enterprise Dept, 69-75, mgr planning & acquisitions, New Enterprise Dept, 75-77, MGR CORP ACQUISITIONS, HERCULES, INC, 77- *Mem:* Am Chem Soc; Financial Analysts Asn; Sigma Xi; Com Develop Asn. *Res:* Commercial development; polymers, energy and raw materials; acquisitions. *Mailing Add:* Hercules Inc 910 Market St Wilmington DE 19899

LEWIS, JOHN REED, b Ottawa, Kans, Dec 27, 15; m 38; c 3. PHARMACOLOGY. *Educ:* Ottawa Univ, AB, 37; Mich State Col, MS, 40; Univ Mich, PhD, 49. *Prof Exp:* Asst chem exp sta, Mich State Col, 39-41; supvr biol control, Frederick Stearns & Co, 41-45; sr biologist, Sterling-Winthrop Res Inst, 47-53, assoc dir sect coord & integration, 53-60; asst secy coun drugs, 60-64, assoc dir, 64-72, sr scientist, Dept Drugs, 72-81, CONSULT, DIV DRUGS, AMA, 81- *Mem:* Am Soc Pharmacol & Exp Therapeut; Soc Toxicol; Am Soc Clin Pharmacol Therapeut; NY Acad Sci; Drug Info Asn. *Res:* Vitamin assays; pharmacology of sympathomimetics and analgesics; diuretics; anticholinesterases; coordination of research projects in development of new drugs; medical writing. *Mailing Add:* Am Med Asn 535 N Dearborn St Chicago IL 60610

LEWIS, JOHN SIMPSON, b Trenton, NJ, June 27, 41; m 64; c 5. GEOCHEMISTRY, METEORITICS. *Educ:* Princeton Univ, AB, 62; Dartmouth Col, MA, 64; Univ Calif, San Diego, PhD, 68. *Prof Exp:* From asst prof to assoc prof chem, earth & planetary sci, 68-80, PROF PLANETARY SCI, MASS INST TECHNOL, 80- *Concurrent Pos:* Mem, Working Group Outer Planet Probe Sci, NASA-Ames Res Ctr, 74-, NASA Phys Sci Comt, 75-78 & Space Sci Bd spec panels outer solar syst & explor Venus, Nat Acad Sci-Nat Res Coun; chmn, Uranus Sci Adv Comt, NASA-Jet Propulsion Lab, 74-75, mem, Sci Adv Group Outer Solar Syst; consult, Aerospace Div, Martin-Marietta Corp, 72 & Avco Systs Div, Avco Corp; Guggenheim lectr, Nat Air & Space Mus, Smithsonian Inst, 73; sci lectr, Div Planetary Sci, Am Astron Soc, 74; Space Sci Bd, Nat Acad Sci, 80-82. *Honors & Awards:* J B Macelwayne Award, Am Geophys Union, 76. *Mem:* AAAS; Am Chem Soc; NY Acad Sci; Am Astron Soc. *Res:* Composition, structure and origin of planetary atmospheres; atmosphere-lithosphere interactions; application of thermodynamics to problems of composition and origin of meteorites. *Mailing Add:* Rm 54-1220 Mass Inst of Technol Cambridge MA 02139

LEWIS, KENNETH PAUL, terrestrial ecology, environmental science, see previous edition

LEWIS, L GAUNCE, JR, b Boston, Mass, Sept 14, 49. MATHEMATICS, ALGEBRAIC TOPOLOGY. *Educ:* Harvard Col, AB, 71; Univ Chicago, MS, 76, PhD(math), 78. *Prof Exp:* asst prof math, Univ Mich, Ann Arbor, 78-81; ASST PROF MATH, SYRACUSE UNIV, NY, 81- *Mem:* Am Math Soc; Math Asn Am. *Res:* Infinite loop space theory; generalized cohomology theories; stable category. *Mailing Add:* Dept of Math Syracuse Univ Syracuse NY 13210

LEWIS, LAWRENCE GUY, b Logan, Utah, July 28, 41; m 64; c 4. MATHEMATICS, INFORMATION SCIENCE. *Educ:* Univ Utah, BA, 65; Ind Univ, PhD(math), 69. *Prof Exp:* Fel math, Grad Ctr, City Univ New York, 69-70; asst prof math, Univ Utah, 70-73; mgr licensees, 73-78, DIR MGT INFO SERV, IRECO CHEMICALS, 78- *Concurrent Pos:* Pres-elect, Nat Prime Comput Users Group. *Mem:* AAAS; Data Processing Mgt Asn; Planning Exec Group. *Res:* Ideal boundaries and information systems. *Mailing Add:* IRECO Chemicals Seventh Floor Kennecott Bldg Salt Lake City UT 84133

LEWIS, LENA ARMSTRONG, b Lancaster, Pa, July 12, 10. PHYSIOLOGY. *Educ:* Lindenwood Col, AB, 31; Ohio State Univ, MA, 38, PhD(physiol), 40. *Hon Degrees:* LLD, Lindenwood Col, 52. *Prof Exp:* Asst biochem, Sch Med, Johns Hopkins Univ, 31-32; bacteriologist & technologist, Gen Hosp, Lancaster, Pa, 32-36; asst physiol, Ohio State Univ, 36-41; mem res staff & supvr electrophoresis lab, 43-45, MEM STAFF & SUPVR ELECTROPHORESIS LAB, CLEVELAND CLIN FOUND, 45- *Concurrent Pos:* Spec fel endocrinol, Cleveland Clin Found, 41-43; adj prof, Cleveland State Univ, 71-74, clin prof chem, 74-; fel arteriosclerosis coun, Am Heart Asn. *Honors & Awards:* Award Outstanding Contrib Clin Chem in Field Lipids & Lipoproteins, Am Asn Clin Chem, 74. *Mem:* AAAS; Am Physiol Soc; Soc Exp Biol & Med. *Res:* Relation of adrenal to electrolyte metabolism; changes in plasma proteins in endocrine disease hypertension; factors regulating lipid and protein metabolism, especially their relation to atherosclerosis; electrophoresis in physiology; electrophoresis of lipoproteins. *Mailing Add:* Cleveland Clin Found 9500 Euclid Ave Cleveland OH 44106

LEWIS, LEROY CRAWFORD, b Pocatello, Idaho, Mar 18, 40; m 62; c 2. PHYSICAL CHEMISTRY, INORGANIC CHEMISTRY. *Educ:* Col Idaho, BS, 62; Ore State Univ, PhD(phys chem), 68. *Prof Exp:* Sr res chemist, Idaho Nuclear Corp, 68-71; sr res chemist, Allied Chem Corp, 71-72, group supvr, 72-74, sect leader, 74-76, br mgr, 76-79; BR MGR, EXXON NUCLEAR IDAHO CO, 79- *Mem:* Am Chem Soc; Sigma Xi. *Res:* Nuclear fuel reprocessing chemistry; chemical waste handling chemistry; actinide chemistry; electrochemistry; analytical chemistry. *Mailing Add:* Exxon Nuclear Idaho Co PO Box 2800 Idaho Falls ID 83401

LEWIS, LESLIE ARTHUR, b Castries, WI, May 17, 40; m 68; c 1. GENETICS, MICROBIOLOGY. *Educ:* Univ Toronto, BSA, 63, MSA, 64; Columbia Univ, PhD(genetics), 68. *Prof Exp:* NIH fel, Mich State Univ, 68-69; lectr, 69-70; asst prof, 70-74, ASSOC PROF BIOL, YORK COL, NY, 74- *Mem:* Genetics Soc Am. *Res:* Non-reciprocal recombination in the fungus Sordaria. *Mailing Add:* Sci 233 Sci Bldg York Col 150-14 Jamaica Ave Jamaica NY 11451

LEWIS, LEWIS JAMES, b Washington, Pa, Sept 6, 16; m 52; c 4. VIROLOGY, BACTERIOLOGY. *Educ:* Waynesburg Col, BS, 39; Univ Pittsburgh, PhD(med bact), 43. *Prof Exp:* Res assoc, Sharpe & Dohme Div, Merck & Co, Inc, 43-44; asst dir biol res, Nat Drug Co, 44-46; res assoc, E R Squibb & Sons, 47-49; res assoc, Sch Med, Univ Pittsburgh, 49-57; dir virus res, Nat Drug Co, 57-59; asst dir biol div & res fel virol, Sterling-Winthrop Res Inst, 59-67; dir virus res, Abbott Labs, 67-72; DIR CELL CULT LAB, COL MED, UNIV IOWA, 72-; MEM STAFF, RES DIV, CLEVELAND CLIN, 77- *Mem:* AAAS; Am Soc Microbiol; Brit Biochem Soc. *Res:* Inactivated poliomyelitis vaccine; rubella viruses; physiological products from tissue culture; fibrinolytic agents; endothelial cells, platelets and lipids. *Mailing Add:* Res Div Cleveland Clin Cleveland OH 44106

LEWIS, LLOYD GEORGE, b Brocton, Ill, Dec 22, 17; m 41; c 5. NUCLEAR PHYSICS. *Educ:* Univ Chicago, BS, 39, PhD(physics), 46. *Prof Exp:* Assoc physicist, Armour Res Found, 40-42 & Univ Chicago, 43-45; instr physics, Princeton Univ, 46-50; sect head, Eng Res Dept, Standard Oil Co, Ind, 50-60; physicist, Electronic Assocs, Inc, 60-61; SR PHYSICIST, ARGONNE NAT LAB, 61- *Mem:* Am Phys Soc; Instrument Soc Am. *Res:* Cosmic ray air showers using the method of coincident bursts in two unshielded ionization chambers. *Mailing Add:* Argonne Nat Lab 9700 S Cass Ave Argonne IL 60439

LEWIS, LOWELL N, b Kingston, Pa, July 9, 31; m 53; c 3. PLANT PHYSIOLOGY. *Educ:* Pa State Univ, BS, 53; Mich State Univ, MS, 58, PhD(hort, biochem), 60. *Prof Exp:* Asst horticulturist, 60-65, assoc prof hort, 66-70, PROF PLANT PHYSIOL, UNIV CALIF, RIVERSIDE, 70-, ASSOC DEAN RES, COL NATURAL & AGR SCI, 71- *Concurrent Pos:* Guggenheim res fel, Mich State Univ-AEC Plant Res Lab, 67-68. *Mem:* Am Soc Hort Sci; Am Soc Plant Physiol; Japanese Soc Plant Physiol. *Res:* Hormonal regulation of plant cell development, especially senescence and abscission. *Mailing Add:* Dept of Bot & Plant Sci Univ of Calif Riverside CA 92521

LEWIS, LYNN LORAINE, b Terra Alta, WVa, Mar 2, 29; m 54; c 4. ANALYTICAL CHEMISTRY. *Educ:* WVa Wesleyan Col, BS, 50; Marshall Univ, MS, 52; Univ Tenn, PhD(chem), 55. *Prof Exp:* Engr semiconductors, Westinghouse Elec Corp, 55-56; sr res chemist, Res Lab, US Steel Corp, Pa, 56-66; asst head, 66-75, HEAD ANAL CHEM DEPT, GEN MOTORS RES LAB, 76- *Mem:* Am Chem Soc (chmn, Div Anal Chem, 78); Am Soc Testing & Mat; Soc Appl Spectros. *Res:* Behavior and determination of gases in metals; analysis of metals; instrumentation for chemical analysis. *Mailing Add:* Res Lab Gen Motors Corp Warren MI 48090

LEWIS, MARC SIMON, b Cleveland, Ohio, Oct 30, 26; m 48; c 3. BIOCHEMISTRY, BIOPHYSICS. *Educ:* Western Reserve Univ, BS, 46, MS, 47; Georgetown Univ, PhD(biochem), 55. *Prof Exp:* Guest scientist, Nat Inst Arthritis & Metab Dis, 52-55; USPHS fel, 55-57; biochemist, Nat Inst Arthritis & Metab Dis, 57-58, biochemist, Nat Inst Dent Res, 58-62, head sect opthal chem, Nat Inst Neurol Dis & Blindness, 62-70, sr res investr, lab vision res, Nat Eye Inst, 70-78; BIOPHYSICIST, BIOMED ENG & INSTRUMENTATION, DIV RES SERV, NIH, 78- *Concurrent Pos:* Lectr, Found Advan Educ in Sci Grad Prog, NIH. *Mem:* Am Chem Soc; NY Acad Sci; Biophys Soc; Am Soc Biol Chem. *Res:* Physical biochemistry; physical chemistry of proteins; biophysical techniques, especially ultracentrifugation. *Mailing Add:* Biomed Eng & Instrumentation Br NIH Bethesda MD 20205

LEWIS, MARGARET NAST, b Baltimore, Md, Aug 20, 11. PHYSICS. *Educ:* Goucher Col, AB, 31; Johns Hopkins Univ, PhD(physics), 37. *Prof Exp:* Asst physics, Vassar Col, 37-38; Am Asn Univ Women Berliner fel, Univ Calif, 38-39, fel, Crocker Radiation Lab, 39-40, Howell fel, 40-42; instr, Vassar Col, 42-43; instr physics, Univ Pa, 43-48, assoc physics res, 53-54; lectr, Boston Univ, 48-50; physicist, Nat Bur Stand, 50-52; asst prof res, Brown Univ, 54-58; assoc prof, Univ Mass, 58-61; res fel, 61-70, ASSOC, HARVARD COL OBSERV, 70- *Concurrent Pos:* Radioisotopes res, Mass Mem Hosp, 48-49 & Haverford Col, 52-54; consult, Cushing Vet Hosp, 49-50. *Mem:* Am Phys Soc. *Res:* Spectroscopy; atomic structure. *Mailing Add:* Harvard Col Observ 60 Garden St Cambridge MA 02138

LEWIS, MARK HENRY, b Boston, Mass, Feb 5, 50; m 77; c 1. PSYCHOPHARMACOLOGY. *Educ:* Bowdoin Col, BA, 72; Western Mich Univ, MA, 75; Vanderbilt Univ, PhD(psychol), 80. *Prof Exp:* FEL, BIOL SCI RES CTR, MED SCH, UNIV NC, 80- *Mem:* Sigma Xi; Soc Neurosci. *Res:* Neuropharmacology of oxidative metabolitics of pherothiazine anti-psychotic drugs both in vivo and in vitro; dopamine receptor supersensitivity; function ascorbic acid in brain. *Mailing Add:* 230 Biol Sci Res Ctr 220-H Sch Med Univ NC Chapel Hill NC 27514

LEWIS, MARVIN BURTON, b Chicago, Ill, Aug 28, 27; m 53; c 3. THEORETICAL PHYSICS. *Educ:* Northwestern Univ, PhD, 56. *Prof Exp:* Asst prof physics, Yale Univ, 55-60; assoc prof mech eng, 60-65, PROF MECH ENG, NORTHWESTERN UNIV, 65-, PROF ASTROPHYS, 68- *Mem:* Am Phys Soc. *Res:* Statistical mechanics. *Mailing Add:* Dept of Mech Eng Northwestern Univ Evanston IL 60201

LEWIS, MICHAEL ANTHONY, b South Bend, Ind, Oct 20, 48; m 74; c 1. AQUATIC ECOLOGY, FISH BIOLOGY. *Educ:* Gannon Col, BS, 70; Pa State Univ, MS, 72; Ariz State Univ, PhD(zool), 77. *Prof Exp:* Instr environ biol, Scottsdale Community Col, 77-78; AQUATIC BIOLOGIST, PROCTER & GAMBLE CO, 78- *Mem:* Sigma Xi; Am Fisheries Soc; Am Inst Fishery Res Biologists. *Res:* Effects of pollutants on stream primary productivity, biotic survival and community structure and diversity; fish life history studies; fish ecology. *Mailing Add:* Dept of Environ Safety Procter & Gamble Co Cincinnati OH 45217

LEWIS, MICHAEL EDWARD, b Chicago, Ill, Nov 9, 51; m 81. NEUROPHARMACOLOGY, HISTOCHEMISTRY. *Educ:* George Washington Univ, BA, 73; Clark Univ, MA, 75, PhD(psychol), 77. *Prof Exp:* Guest worker neurochem, Sect Intermediary Metab, Lab Develop Neurobiol, Nat Inst Child Health & Human Develop, NIH, 77; fel behav neurochem, Psychol Lab, Cambridge Univ, 77-79; instr, Europ Div, Univ Col, Univ Md, 79; res psychologist, Sect Biochem & Pharmacol, Biol Psychiat Br, NIMH & Nat Inst Drug Abuse, 80-81; RES INVESTR, MENTAL HEALTH RES INST, UNIV MICH, 81- *Concurrent Pos:* Felix & Elizabeth Brunner fel, Ment Health Found, London, 77-79; Twinning grant, Europ Training Prog in Brain & Behav Res, Europ Sci Found, Strasbourg, 79-; Wellcome res fel, The Wellcome Trust, London, 79; John G Searle clin pharmacol fel, 81. *Res:* Histochemical and biochemical analysis of receptors and endogenous ligands; pharmacology of neuropeptides and psychoactive drugs; recovery of function after brain damage; neuropsychology. *Mailing Add:* 811 South Seventh St Ann Arbor MI 48103

LEWIS, MILTON, b New York, NY, Dec 30, 21; m 43; c 3. NUCLEAR ENGINEERING. *Educ:* Univ Wash, BS; Univ Calif, PhD(chem), 50. *Prof Exp:* Field serv consult, Off Sci Res Develop, 43-46; asst, Univ Calif, 46-48; chemist, Gen Elec Co, 48-51, chg pile coolant studies, 51-54, supvr, Nonmetallic Mat Develop, 54-56, sr engr prog, 56-62, mgr chem & metall, 62-67; mgr chem & metall, Douglas United Nuclear, Inc, 67-68, fuel & target technol, 68, asst chief, Mat Br, Donald W Douglas Labs, 68-70, mgr, Betacel Prog, 70-74; pres, Columbia Engrs Serv, Inc, Wash, 74-80; CONSULT, 80- *Concurrent Pos:* Vis lectr, Univ Calif, Los Angeles, 60-61. *Mem:* Am Nuclear Soc. *Res:* Mechanism of irreversible reactions; analytical chemistry of fission products; corrosion in aqueous media; radiation effects on materials; safety of nuclear processes. *Mailing Add:* 2600 Harris Ave Richland WA 99352

LEWIS, MORTON, b Oak Park, Ill, June 28, 36; m 63; c 3. ORGANIC CHEMISTRY. *Educ:* Purdue Univ, BS, 58; Univ Chicago, PhD(org chem), 62. *Prof Exp:* Res chemist, Swift & Co, 62-74, head, Specialty Chem Res Div, Swift & Co Div, 74-76, head, Tech Prod Div, Unitech Chem, Inc Div, Esmark Inc, 76-81; SR CHEMIST, WILSON SPORTING GOODS CO, 81- *Mem:* Am Chem Soc; Sigma Xi; Royal Soc Chem; NY Acad Sci. *Res:* Synthesis and reactions of steroid derivatives; products of fats and oils; surface active agents; quaternary ammonium salts and organophosphorous compounds; flame retardants; plastics and coatings; specialty chemicals; ultraviolet cured monomers; epoxidized oils and epoxy resins. *Mailing Add:* Wilson Sporting Goods Co 2233 West St River Grove IL 60171

LEWIS, NEIL JEFFREY, b New York, NY, Feb 10, 45. MEDICINAL CHEMISTRY, ORGANIC CHEMISTRY. *Educ:* City Col New York, BS, 66; Univ Kans, PhD(med chem), 72. *Prof Exp:* NIH res assoc, Ohio State Univ, 72, from asst prof to assoc prof med chem, Div Chem, Col Pharm, 72-82, dir, Environ Chem Anal Lab, 77-82; ASST DIR RES PROG, MUSCULAR DYSTROPHY ASN, 82- *Concurrent Pos:* Lady Davis vis prof, 79-80. *Mem:* Am Asn Cols Pharm; Am Chem Soc; Am Pharmaceut Asn; Sigma Xi. *Res:* Chemotherapeutics; environmental carcinogenesis and toxicology; pesticides; immunochemotheraphy; antiviral agents. *Mailing Add:* Muscular Dystrophy Asn 810 Seventh Ave NY NY 10019

LEWIS, OTIS GRIFFIN, polymer chemistry, see previous edition

LEWIS, PAUL EDWARD, reproductive physiology, see previous edition

LEWIS, PAUL HERBERT, b New York, NY, Jan 19, 24; m 55; c 3. PHYSICAL CHEMISTRY. *Educ:* Columbia Univ, AB, 47, MA, 48; Iowa State Col, PhD(chem), 52. *Prof Exp:* Chemist paints, E I du Pont de Nemours & Co, Inc, 48; PETROL CHEMIST, TEXACO INC, 52- *Mem:* Am Chem Soc. *Res:* X-ray analysis; catalysts. *Mailing Add:* PO Box 1608 Texaco Inc Port Arthur TX 77640

LEWIS, PAUL KERMITH, JR, b Monticello, Ark, Jan 24, 31; m 55; c 3. MEAT SCIENCE. *Educ:* Okla State Univ, BS, 53; Univ Wis, MS, 55, PhD, 58. *Prof Exp:* Res asst animal husb & biochem, Univ Wis, 53-57; from asst prof to assoc prof animal indust, 57-68, PROF ANIMAL SCI, UNIV ARK, FAYETTEVILLE, 68- *Mem:* AAAS; Am Soc Animal Sci; Am Meat Sci Asn; Inst Food Technologists; Inst Briquetting & Agglomeration. *Res:* Pre-slaughter stress and storage life of beef and pork; sensory characteristics of beef and pork. *Mailing Add:* Dept of Animal Sci Univ of Ark Fayetteville AR 72701

LEWIS, PAUL WELDON, b Dallas, Tex, Jan 31, 43; m 65; c 2. MATHEMATICS. *Educ:* NTex State Univ, BA, 65, MS, 66; Univ Utah, PhD(math), 70. *Prof Exp:* Asst prof, 70-74, ASSOC PROF MATH, NTEX STATE UNIV, 74- *Mem:* Am Math Soc. *Res:* Vector measures; functional analysis; operators on function spaces. *Mailing Add:* Dept of Math N Tex State Univ Denton TX 76203

LEWIS, PETER ADRIAN WALTER, b Johannesburg, SAfrica, Oct 3, 32; US citizen; m 60; c 2. STATISTICS. *Educ:* Columbia Univ, BA, 54, BS, 55, MS, 57; Univ London, PhD(statist), 64. *Prof Exp:* Res staff mem statist, Int Bus Mach Res Labs, 55-71; PROF STATIST & OPERS RES, NAVAL POSTGRAD SCH, 71- *Concurrent Pos:* NIH spec fel, Imp Col, Univ London, 69-70. *Mem:* Inst Math Statist; Royal Statist Soc; Am Statist Asn. *Res:* Stochastic process; applications of statistics in computer applications. *Mailing Add:* Dept of Oper Res Naval Postgrad Sch Monterey CA 93940

LEWIS, PHILIP M, b New York, NY, May 30, 31; m 53; c 2. ELECTRICAL ENGINEERING. *Educ:* Rensselaer Polytech Inst, BEE, 52; Mass Inst Technol, SM, 54, ScD, 56. *Prof Exp:* From instr to asst prof elec eng, Mass Inst Technol, 54-59; mem tech staff, 59-69, consult automata theory & software design, 59, mgr, 69-78, MGR COMPUT SCI BR, GEN ELEC RES & DEVELOP CTR, 78- *Concurrent Pos:* Consult, Epsco, Inc, 55, Lincoln Labs, Mass Inst Technol, 55-56, Hycon Eastern Inc, 56-57 & Sanders Assocs, Inc, 58; adj prof, Rensselaer Polytech Inst, 60-; managing ed, Jour Comput, Soc Indust & Appl Math, 71-; Coolidge fel, Gen Elec Res & Develop Corp, 77- *Mem:* Asn Comput Mach; fel Soc Indust & Appl Math; Inst Elec & Electronics Engrs. *Res:* Theory of information processing, including compiler design, retrieval and self organization; automata theory; abstract languages. *Mailing Add:* Gen Elec Res & Develop Ctr PO Box 8 Schenectady NY 12309

LEWIS, PHILLIP ALBERT, b Indianapolis, Ind, Feb 11, 21; m 44; c 5. ANALYTICAL CHEMISTRY. *Educ:* Aurora Col, BS, 42; Okla State Univ, MS, 54, PhD(chem), 56. *Prof Exp:* Instr chem & math, Duluth Jr Col, 46; asst prof chem & head dept, Aurora Col, 46-47 & 49-51; asst, Ill Inst Technol, 47-49 & Okla State Univ, 51-54; asst prof, Univ Kansas City, 54-56; sr chemist, Midwest Res Inst, 56-59; prof chem & head dept, Iowa Wesleyan Col, 59-64; vis Fulbright lectr, Meerut Col, Agra, 64-65; prof chem, Hastings Col, 65-68; PROF CHEM & DEAN, WESTMINSTER COL, PA, 68- *Concurrent Pos:* Lectr, Univ Kansas City, 56-57, William Jewell Col, 57-58 & Nat Col Mo, 58-59; prog dir, Off Prog Integration, Sci Educ Directorate, NSF, 77. *Mem:* AAAS; Am Chem Soc; Sigma Xi. *Res:* Nonaqeous polarography; spectrophotometric analytical methods; electrochemical phenomena; spectrophotometry. *Mailing Add:* Dept of Chem Westminster Col New Wilmington PA 16142

LEWIS, RALPH WILLIAM, b Marion, Mich, May 21, 11; m 37; c 2. PLANT PATHOLOGY, MOLECULAR ECOLOGY. *Educ:* Mich State Col, BS, 34, MS, 37, PhD(plant path), 45. *Prof Exp:* From instr to asst prof bot, 37-44, from asst prof to prof biol, 44-80, EMER PROF BIOL, MICH STATE UNIV, 80- *Concurrent Pos:* Fel, Calif Inst Technol, 47; NIH spec res fel, Instituto Superiore Sanita, Rome, 58-59. *Mem:* Fel AAAS; Bot Soc Am; Am Soc Naturalists; Nat Sci Teachers Asn; Nat Asn Biol Teachers. *Res:* Study of patterns in the molecular environment of differentiational events in fungi; study of the structure of biological knowledge. *Mailing Add:* Dept of Natural Sci Mich State Univ East Lansing MI 48824

LEWIS, RICHARD JOHN, b Chicago, Ill, Jan 20, 35; m 61; c 3. HEMATOLOGY, CLINICAL PHARMACOLOGY. *Educ:* Univ Notre Dame, BS, 56; Northwestern Univ, Chicago, MD, 60. *Prof Exp:* Rotating intern, Cook County Hosp, Chicago, 60-61; med intern & resident, Columbia Div, Bellevue Hosp, 61-63; med resident, Presby Hosp, New York, 63-64; chief nuclear med lab, USPHS Hosp, San Francisco, 66-68; clin instr, Med Ctr, Univ Calif, San Francisco, 68-70, asst prof med, 70-75; ASST CLIN PROF MED, MED SCH, UNIV CALIF, LOS ANGELES, 75- *Concurrent Pos:* Fel hemat, Montefiore Hosp, 64-65; NIH res fel, Med Sch, Univ Wash, 65; clin investr hemat, Vet Admin Hosp, San Francisco, 70-74. *Mem:* Int Soc Hemat; Soc Nuclear Med; Am Fedn Clin Res; NY Acad Sci; Am Soc Hemat. *Res:* Metabolism of coumarin anticoagulant drugs. *Mailing Add:* 2200 Santa Monica Blvd Santa Monica CA 90404

LEWIS, RICHARD NEWTON, b Berkeley, Calif, May 3, 16; m 43; c 4. SILICONES, FILM TECHNOLOGY. *Educ:* Univ Calif, Berkeley, AB, 37; Calif Inst Technol, PhD(org chem), 43. *Prof Exp:* Res chemist, Gen Elec Co, 42-48; asst prof chem, Univ Del, 48-51; res assoc, Olin Mathieson Chem Corp, 52-65; sr res assoc, SWS Silicones Corp, Adrian, Mich, 65-80. *Mem:* Am Chem Soc. *Res:* Organometallics; silicone oligomers, polymers, grafting and crosslinking; polyamides; polyesters; cellulose; science writer. *Mailing Add:* PO Box 233 Inverness CA 94937

LEWIS, RICHARD THOMAS, b East Cleveland, Ohio, Jan 9, 43. PHYSICAL CHEMISTRY. *Educ:* Case Western Reserve Univ, BS, 64; Univ Chicago, PhD(phys chem), 70. *Prof Exp:* Staff scientist chem, 70-74, group leader, 74-78, res scientist, 78-80, SR RES SCIENTIST, CARBON PROD DIV, UNION CARBIDE CORP, 80- *Mem:* Am Chem Soc. *Res:* Surface chemistry; chemistry of hydrocarbon pyrolysis and carbonization. *Mailing Add:* Union Carbide Corp 12900 Snow Rd Parma OH 44130

LEWIS, RICHARD WHEATLEY, JR, b Montclair, NJ, Apr 15, 25; m 53; c 4. EXPLORATION GEOLOGY. *Educ:* Bowdoin Col, AB, 49; Stanford Univ, MS, 51, PhD, 64. *Prof Exp:* Geologist, US Geol Surv, 51-72, geochemist & tech adv, 72-73; PRES, GEOQUIMICA, SERVICOS GEOLOGICOS E ANALITICOS, LTD, 73- *Mem:* AAAS; Soc Geol Peru; Soc Brasil Geol; Geochem Soc; Acad Brasil Ciencas. *Res:* Geochemical exploration of tropical terrain; statistical interpretation of geochemical data. *Mailing Add:* Rua Aguaraiba 86 Bonsucesso Rio de Janeiro Brazil

LEWIS, ROBERT DONALD, b Wyalusing, Pa, Nov 4, 97; m 22; c 2. AGRONOMY. *Educ:* Pa State Col, BS, 19; Cornell Univ, PhD(plant breeding), 26. *Prof Exp:* Instr exp agron, Pa State Col, 19-24; asst plant breeding, Cornell Univ, 23-24, instr, 24-26, exten asst prof, 26-30; exten prof agron, Ohio State Univ, 30-39, from assoc prof to prof, 33-46; dir, 46-62, EMER DIR, TEX AGR EXP STA, TEX A&M UNIV, 62-, CONSULT, 62- *Concurrent Pos:* Agent, Div Cereal Crops & Dis, Bur Plant Indust, USDA, Md, 36-46; assoc, Ohio Exp Sta, 39-46; vchmn dept agron, Ohio State Univ, 39-40, chmn, 40-46; mem, Nat Rice Res & Mkt Adv Comn, 53-62 & Comt of Nine, 53-55; chmn, Southern Regional Exp Sta Dirs, USDA, 55-57; adv, Venezuela Ministry Agr, 56; Ford Found sr consult, Univ Aleppo, 62-65; consult agr res & educ, 65-67 & agr res, USAID, Korea, 67-70. *Mem:* AAAS; fel Am Soc Agron; Genetics Soc Am; hon mem Int Crop Improv Asn. *Res:* Genetics of oats; corn breeding; seeding methods; forage crops; seed production and distribution; administration of agricultural research. *Mailing Add:* 102 Greenway Bryan TX 77801

LEWIS, ROBERT EARL, b Richmond, Ind, Dec 1, 29; m 52. ENTOMOLOGY, VERTEBRATE ZOOLOGY. *Educ:* Earlham Col, AB, 52; Univ Ill, MS, 56, PhD(entom), 59. *Prof Exp:* From asst prof to assoc prof zool, Am Univ, Beirut, 59-67; assoc prof entom, 67-71, PROF ENTOM, IOWA STATE UNIV, 71- *Concurrent Pos:* Consult, US Naval Med Res Unit, Egypt, 63-; grants, Off Naval Res, 66-71 & NIH, 64-67. *Mem:* Entom Soc Am; Am Entom Soc; Am Soc Mammal; Soc Syst Zool; Am Soc Parasitol. *Res:* Siphonaptera of the world, their host relationships and zoogeography. *Mailing Add:* 306 21st St Ames IA 50010

LEWIS, ROBERT FRANK, b Wis, Dec 13, 20; m 45; c 2. PUBLIC HEALTH. *Educ:* Univ Calif, BS, 50, MPH, 53; Univ Mich, PhD(public health statist), 58. *Prof Exp:* Asst sanitarian epidemiol res, Commun Dis Ctr, USPHS, Ga, 49-52; health analyst, San Joaquin Local Health Dist, Calif, 53-54; state health analyst, Calif, 54-56; res assoc cerebral palsy, Univ Mich, 58; from asst prof to prof biomet, Sch Med, Tulane Univ, 58-67, head div, 60-67; prof human med, Col Human Med, Mich State Univ, 67-75; PROF, DEPT EPIDEMIOL & BIOSTATIST, SCH PUB HEALTH, UNIV SC, 78- *Concurrent Pos:* Consult, Div Radiol Health, NIH, 66-70, div manpower intel, 71; chief, Mich Ctr Health Statist, 67-69; consult, Nat Ctr Health Servs Res, 75- & US Cong Off Technol & Assessment, 77-78. *Mem:* Fel AAAS; fel Am Pub Health Asn; Am Statist Asn; Biomet Soc; Soc Epidemiol Res. *Res:* Public health and medicine, especially development of methodology in community health research. *Mailing Add:* 4836 Landrum Dr Columbia SC 29206

LEWIS, ROBERT GLENN, b Morehead City, NC, Nov 11, 37; m 60; c 3. ORGANIC CHEMISTRY. *Educ:* Univ NC, BS, 60; Univ Wis, PhD(org chem), 64. *Prof Exp:* Res chemist, Chemstrand Res Ctr, Inc, 64-69, group leader and res specialist, 69-71; sect chief, 71-79, CHIEF, ADVAN ANAL TECH BR, ENVIRON MONITORING SYSTS LAB, ENVIRON PROTECTION AGENCY, 79- *Concurrent Pos:* NSF fel, 61; NIH fel, 61-64. *Mem:* Am Chem Soc; Sigma Xi; AAAS. *Res:* Environmental chemistry; environmental toxicology; air pollution analysis; reaction mechanisms; organic photochemistry; ultra violet-visible absorption and luminescence spectroscopy; organic analyses; pesticide chemistry and analysis; mass spectrometry. *Mailing Add:* Environ Monitoring Systs Lab MD-44 US Environ Protection Agency Research Triangle Park NC 27711

LEWIS, ROBERT L(LOYD), b Kit Carson, Colo, May 27, 13; m 40; c 2. CIVIL ENGINEERING. *Educ:* Colo Agr & Mech Col, BSCE, 34; Cornell Univ, MCE, 43. *Prof Exp:* Instrument man, State Hwy Dept, Colo, 35-36; from instr to prof civil eng, Colo Agr & Mech Col, 36-49, head dept & chief civil eng sect, Exp Sta, 46-49; prof & chmn dept, NY Univ, 49-51; pres, Imp Col Technol, Ethiopia, 51-57; prof civil eng & chmn dept, 57-77, EMER PROF CIVIL & ENVIRON ENG, CLARKSON COL TECHNOL, 77- *Mem:* Am Soc Civil Engrs; Am Concrete Inst. *Res:* Structural mechanics of thin gauge cold rolled structural shapes of steel; model studies of hydraulic structures. *Mailing Add:* 107 Van Dyke Pl Apt 3 Guilderland NY 12084

LEWIS, ROBERT MILLER, b Flushing, NY, May 20, 37; m 58; c 2. IMMUNOLOGY. *Educ:* Wash State Univ, DVM, 61. *Prof Exp:* Intern, Angell Mem Animal Hosp, 61-62; res fel, Harvard Med Sch, 62-65; from instr to sr instr surg, Sch Med, Tufts Univ, 65-67, from asst prof to assoc prof, 67-75, dir lab animal sci, 69-75; PROF PATH & CHMN DEPT, NY STATE COL VET MED, CORNELL UNIV, 75- *Concurrent Pos:* Res assoc path, Angell Mem Animal Hosp, 62-63, assoc pathologist, 65-67, affil in med, 68-75; consult surg res, New Eng Med Ctr Hosp, 62-65, mem spec sci staff, 66-75, chief vet serv, 70-75; asst path, Harvard Med Sch, 65-68, clin asst, 68-76. *Honors & Awards:* Mary Mitchell Award Outstanding Res, 61. *Mem:* Am Vet Med Asn; Am Col Vet Pathologists; Int Acad Path; Am Asn Lab Animal Sci; Am Soc Vet Clin Pathologists. *Res:* Investigations on the etiology and pathogenesis of spontaneous immunologic diseases of animals which mimic human diseases. *Mailing Add:* Dept of Path Schurman Hall NY State Col Vet Med Cornell Univ Ithaca NY 14853

LEWIS, ROBERT MINTURN, b Hempstead, NY, Aug 23, 24; m 53; c 3. FISH BIOLOGY. *Educ:* Cornell Univ, BS, 54, MS, 56. *Prof Exp:* Res fishery biologist, Striped Bass Prog, Mid-Atlantic Coastal Fisheries Res Ctr, 56-63, Menhaden Prog, 63-78, RES FISHERY BIOLOGIST, ATLANTIC ESTUARINE FISHERIES CTR, NAT MARINE FISHERIES SERV, 63- *Mem:* Am Fisheries Soc; Am Inst Fisheries Res Biol. *Res:* Effects of environmental conditions on larval and juvenile marine fishes; population dynamics of marine fishes; electrophoretic studies of fish protein; analysis of large scale tagging; analysis and identification of off-shore and estuarine larval fish populations; fecundity of Atlantic and Gulf menhaden. *Mailing Add:* Beaufort Lab Nat Marine Fisheries Serv Beaufort NC 28516

LEWIS, ROBERT RICHARDS, JR, b New Haven, Conn, Mar 7, 27; m 50; c 4. THEORETICAL PHYSICS. *Educ:* Univ Mich, BS, 50, MS, 53, PhD(physics), 54. *Prof Exp:* Asst prof physics, Univ Notre Dame, 54-58; from asst prof to assoc prof, 58-65, PROF PHYSICS, UNIV MICH, ANN ARBOR, 65- *Concurrent Pos:* Mem, Inst Advan Study, 56-58. *Res:* Quantum theory; angular correlation theory; parity nonconservation in atoms; partial coherence theory. *Mailing Add:* Dept of Physics Univ of Mich Ann Arbor MI 48104

LEWIS, ROBERT TABER, b New York, NY, May 12, 32; m 58; c 1. PHYSICS. *Educ:* Alfred Univ, BS, 54; Univ Calif, Berkeley, PhD(solid state physics), 64. *Prof Exp:* Res physicist, 63-72, SR RES PHYSICIST, CHEVRON RES CO, 72- *Mem:* Am Phys Soc. *Res:* Magnetism; heterogenous catalysts; x-ray photoelectron spectroscopy. *Mailing Add:* Chevron Res Co 576 Standard Ave Richmond CA 94802

LEWIS, ROBERT WARREN, b Mansfield, Ohio, Feb 4, 43; m 78; c 2. ELECTRICAL ENGINEERING, OPTICS. *Educ:* Univ Cincinnati, BSEE, 66; Univ Mich, MSE, 68, MA, 69, PhD(elec eng), 73. *Prof Exp:* Res asst coherent optics, Willow Run Labs, Univ Mich, 69-72; res assoc radar, Environ Res Inst Mich, 72-73; ASSOC SR RES SCIENTIST OPTICS & COMPUTERIZED TOMOGRAPHY, GEN MOTORS RES LABS, 78- *Mem:* Optical Soc Am; Inst Elec & Electronics Engrs; Sigma Xi. *Res:* Optics and electrical engineering; computerized tomographic mapping of temperature induced refractive index fields in combusting mixtures. *Mailing Add:* Gen Motors Res Labs Gen Motors Tech Ctr Warren MI 48090

LEWIS, ROGER ABBOTT, b Far Rockaway, NY, Jan 29, 12; m; c 3. PHARMACOLOGY. *Educ:* Johns Hopkins Univ, AB, 34, MD, 38. *Prof Exp:* Asst prof pediat, Sch Med, Johns Hopkins Univ, 48-51; WHO vis prof pharmacol, Med Col, Airlangga Univ, Indonesia, 52-63; prof pharmacol & head dept, Ghana Med Sch, 63-77; PROF PHARM, SCH MED SCI, UNIV SCI & TECHNOL, GHANA, 77-, PROF CLIN PHARM, ZIMABWE, 81- *Concurrent Pos:* Fel, Harvard Med Sch; Archbold, Ciba, Commonwealth & Am Cancer Soc fels, Sch Med, Johns Hopkins Univ. *Mem:* Royal Soc Med. *Res:* Chemotherapy; endocrinology; application of chemical principles to medical problems; clinical investigation. *Mailing Add:* Sch Med Sci Univ Sci & Technol Kumasi Ghana

LEWIS, ROGER ALLEN, b Wellington, Kans, June 1, 41; m 62; c 3. BIOCHEMISTRY. *Educ:* Phillips Univ, BA, 63; Ore State Univ, PhD(biochem), 68. *Prof Exp:* Res assoc pyrimidine nucleotide metab, Stanford Univ, 68-69; asst prof, 69-75, ASSOC PROF BIOCHEM, UNIV NEV, RENO, 75- *Mem:* Am Chem Soc; Sigma Xi; AAAS; Am Soc Pharmacol & Exp Therapeut. *Res:* Purine deoxynucleotide biosynthesis and its control; toxicology of pesticides with respect to nucleotide metabolism and DNA and/or RNA synthesis. *Mailing Add:* Dept of Biochem Univ of Nev Reno NV 89557

LEWIS, ROSCOE WARFIELD, b Beaumont, Tex, Dec 27, 20; m 42; c 1. ANIMAL NUTRITION, BIOCHEMISTRY. *Educ:* Prairie View State Col, BS, 39; Kans State Univ, MS, 52, PhD, 55. *Prof Exp:* Teacher high sch, 42-44 & Bowie County Training Sch, 46-51; asst, Kans State Univ, 52-55; prof nutrit & biochem, Tex Agr Exp Sta & Prairie View Exp Sta, Tex A&M Univ, 55-69 & Southwest Tex State Univ, 69-70; PROF NUTRIT & BIOCHEM, TEX A&M UNIV, 70- *Honors & Awards:* Fribourg Award, 55. *Mem:* AAAS; Poultry Sci Asn; Inst Food Technologists; Am Chem Soc; NY Acad Sci. *Res:* Chicken flavor; skin homografts in the chicken; tolerance of anticarcinogenic purine derivatives in the chick; nutrition of pre-adolescent females. *Mailing Add:* Dept of Biochem & Biophys Tex A&M Univ College Station TX 77843

LEWIS, ROY STEPHEN, b Oakland, Calif, Aug 10, 44; m 66; c 3. METEORITICS. *Educ:* Univ Calif, Berkeley, AB, 67, PhD(atmospheric & space sci), 73. *Prof Exp:* SR RES ASSOC METEORITICS, DEPT CHEM, UNIV CHICAGO, 73- *Res:* Isotopic composition and elemental abundances of noble gases in meteorites and other samples. *Mailing Add:* Enrico Fermi Inst Univ of Chicago 5630 Ellis Ave Chicago IL 60637

LEWIS, RUSSELL J, b Liberty Road, Ky, Jan 23, 29; m 54; c 2. SOIL CHEMISTRY. *Educ:* Univ Ky, BS, 56, MS, 57; NC State Col, PhD(soils), 61. *Prof Exp:* Int Atomic Energy Agency fel chem, Univ NC, 61-62; asst prof soil chem, Univ Tenn, Knoxville, 62-66, assoc prof, 66-80. *Mem:* Am Soc Agron; Soil Sci Soc Am; Clay Minerals Soc. *Res:* Surface chemistry of colloids; ion exchange, fixation and nutrient availability. *Mailing Add:* 1124 Burton Rd Knoxville TN 37919

LEWIS, RUSSELL M(ACLEAN), b New York, NY, June 20, 30; m 57; c 4. TRAFFIC ENGINEERING, TRANSPORTATION PLANNING. *Educ:* Trinity Col, Conn, BS, 52; Rensselaer Polytech Inst, BCE, 53, MCE, 59; Purdue Univ, PhD, 62. *Prof Exp:* From instr to assoc prof civil eng, Rensselaer Polytech Inst, 57-68; assoc, Byrd, Tallamy, MacDonald & Lewis, Div Wilbur Smith & Assocs, 68-70, partner, 71-72, sr assoc, 72-80; CONSULT ENGR, 80- *Concurrent Pos:* Ford Found fel, Purdue Univ, 60-62; affil, Transp Res Bd, Nat Res Coun-Nat Acad Sci; mem construct & maintenance subcomt, Nat Comt Uniform Traffic Control Devices, 79- *Mem:* Am Soc Civil Engrs; Inst Traffic Engrs; Nat Soc Prof Engrs; Am Soc Eng Educ; Am Soc Training & Develop. *Res:* Highway accident analysis; highway safety research; traffic and parking studies; expert witness testimony in accident cases; training programs for transportation agencies. *Mailing Add:* 8302 Epinard Ct Annandale VA 22003

LEWIS, SALLY, b Calcutta, India, July 21, 14; m 44; c 1. BOTANY, HORTICULTURE. *Educ:* Univ Calcutta, BSc, 35, MSc, 37; Univ Mo, PhD(plant path), 64. *Prof Exp:* Head dept bot & vprin col, Bethune Col, Univ Calcutta, 39-59; instr bot & res asst, Univ Mo, 59-60, asst hort, 60-63, asst prof, 64-66; ASSOC PROF BIOL, CLEVELAND STATE UNIV, 66- *Concurrent Pos:* Govt India overseas scholar bot, Eng, 44-47; mem Pub Serv Comn, Bengal, India, 57-59; NSF grant, 65-67. *Mem:* Int Fedn Univ Women; fel Royal Hort Soc. *Res:* Electromicroscopy; plant phytopathology, especially diseases related to horticultural plants; gross morphology; anatomy; taxonomy; tropical and medicinal plants. *Mailing Add:* Dept of Biol Cleveland State Univ Cleveland OH 44115

LEWIS, SEYMOUR, b New York, NY, Mar 14, 19; m 57; c 2. MICROBIOLOGY, BOTANY. *Educ:* Univ Wis, BA, 49, MS, 50; Columbia Univ, MA, 55, PhD(biol sci), 68. *Prof Exp:* Bacteriologist, Med Sch, Cornell Univ, 52; res asst, Nat Agr Col, 52-53; bacteriologist, Columbia Univ, 53-55; sci teacher, Bd Educ, City of New York, 55-59; microbiologist, Dept Urol, Columbia Univ, 59-60, bacteriologist, Lamont Geol Observ, 60-64, res asst marine biol, 66-69; PROF BIOL, BERGEN COMMUNITY COL, 69- *Mem:* Am Soc Microbiol. *Mailing Add:* Dept of Biol Bergen Community Col Paramus NJ 07652

LEWIS, SHELDON NOAH, b Chicago, Ill, July 1, 34; m 57; c 3. PHYSICAL CHEMISTRY, ORGANIC CHEMISTRY. *Educ:* Northwestern Univ, BA & MS, 56; Univ Calif, Los Angeles, PhD(phys & org chem), 59. *Prof Exp:* NSF fel, Univ Basel, 59-60; sr chemist, Rohm and Haas Co, 60-61, group leader org chem, 61-63, lab head, 63-68, res supvr, 68-73, dir specialty chem res, 73-74, gen mgr, DCL Lab AG, Switz, 74-75, dir, European Labs, France, 75, corp dir res polymers, resins & monomers worldwide, 75-78; vpres res & develop, 78, GROUP VPRES & DIR, CLOROX CO, 78- *Mem:* Am Chem Soc; Indust Res Inst; Soc Chem Indust. *Res:* Reaction mechanisms; organic synthesis; process development; agricultural chemicals; polymers and surface coatings; leather, paper, textile, cosmetic and petroleum chemicals; plastics and modifiers; ion exchange resins; adhesives; building products. *Mailing Add:* Clorox Co PO Box 24305 Oakland CA 94623

LEWIS, SILAS DAVIS, b Gastonia, NC, June 26, 30; m 62; c 1. ORGANIC CHEMISTRY. *Educ:* Wake Forest Col, BS, 52; Ga Inst Technol, PhD(org chem), 59. *Prof Exp:* Sr chemist, Atlast Chem Industs, Inc, 59-63; assoc prof chem, Del Valley Col, 63-66; ASSOC PROF CHEM, AUGUSTA COL, 66- *Mem:* Am Chem soc. *Res:* Polyphenyls; Ullmann reaction; nitro and nitrato compounds and explosives. *Mailing Add:* Dept of Chem Augusta Col Augusta GA 30904

LEWIS, SIMON ANDREW, b Welling Kent, Eng, Apr 18, 48; Can citizen; m 76. EPITHELIAL TRANSPORT, ELECTROPHYIOLOGY. *Educ:* Univ BC, BSc, 70, MSc, 71; Univ Calif, Los Angeles, PhD(physiol), 75. *Prof Exp:* Res assoc physiol, Univ Calif, Los Angeles, 75-76; res assoc physiol, Med Br, Univ Tex, 76-77; ASST PROF PHYSIOL, YALE MED SCH, 77- *Mem:* Biophys Soc. *Res:* Mechanisms of salt and water transport across epithelial cells membranes using electrophysiological methods. *Mailing Add:* Dept Physiol Yale Med Sch 333 Cedar St New Haven CT 06510

LEWIS, STANDLEY EUGENE, b Twin Falls, Idaho, Nov 15, 40; m 65; c 3. ENTOMOLOGY, PALEONTOLOGY. *Educ:* Univ Nebr, Omaha, BA, 62, MA, 64; Wash State Univ, PhD(entom), 68. *Prof Exp:* Teaching asst biol, Univ Nebr, Omaha, 63-64; teaching asst zool-entom, Wash State Univ, 64-68; from asst prof to assoc prof biol, 68-78, Sigma Xi, Geol Soc Am & St Cloud instnl grants, 69-70, PROF BIOL, ST CLOUD STATE COL, 78- *Concurrent Pos:* Res asst mosquito control, Adams County Abate Dist, 65- *Mem:* Sigma Xi; Paleontol Soc Am; Entom Soc Am. *Res:* Paleobiology, specifically paleoentomology. *Mailing Add:* Dept of Biol St Cloud State Col St Cloud MN 56301

LEWIS, STEPHEN ALBERT, b Sodus, NY, Sept 9, 42; m 68; c 1. PLANT NEMATOLOGY. *Educ:* Pa State Univ, BS, 64; Rutgers Univ, MS, 69; Univ Ariz, PhD(plant path), 73. *Prof Exp:* Sales rep, Stand Oil Calif, 65-66; asst prof, 73-77, ASSOC PROF NEMATOL, DEPT PLANT PATH & PHYSIOL, CLEMSON UNIV, 77- *Mem:* Soc Nematologists; Sigma Xi. *Res:* Host-parasite relations of the phytoparasitic nematodes, Hoplolaimus columbus and Criconemoides xenoplax on field crops and peach trees, respectively; nematode-mycorrhizae-rhizobium relationships; gnotobiotic culture of nematodes. *Mailing Add:* Dept of Plant Path & Physiol Clemson Univ Clemson SC 29631

LEWIS, STEPHEN ROBERT, b Mt Horeb, Wis, Aug 26, 20; m 48; c 2. PLASTIC SURGERY. *Educ:* Carroll Col, Wis, BA, 41; Marquette Univ, MD, 44. *Prof Exp:* Instr surg, 50-53, from asst prof to assoc prof plastic & maxillofacial surg, 53-61, asst dean med, 58-62, chief staff, 69-73, dir postgrad educ, 56-80, PROF SURG, UNIV TEX MED BR GALVESTON, 61-, CHIEF PLASTIC SURG, 61- *Concurrent Pos:* Consult, St Mary's Infirmary, Galveston, 54-, Galveston County Mem Hosp, 54-, US Air Force, 57- & USPHS Hosp, 58-; mem, Am Bd Plastic Surg, 66-72, chmn, 71-72. *Honors & Awards:* First Sci Exhibit Award, Tex Med Asn, 63. *Mem:* Am Soc Plastic & Reconstruct Surg (past-pres, 56-); fel Am Col Surg; AMA; Am Asn Plastic Surg. *Res:* Tissue culture studies on human skin; burns; multiple studies in systemic and local problems; lymphatics in Lymphedema; congenital deformities of face, neck and hands. *Mailing Add:* Div Plastic & Maxillofacial Surg Univ of Tex Med Br Galveston TX 77550

LEWIS, STEVEN CRAIG, b Anderson, Ind, Dec 30, 43; m 69. CHEMICAL CARCINOGENESIS, BIOSTATISTICS. *Educ:* Ind Univ, BA, 70, PhD(toxicol), 75; Am Bd Toxicol, Dipl, 80. *Prof Exp:* Res asst biochem, Ind Univ Med Sch, 65-71, res fel toxicol, 71-75, supvr, Statist Cancer Res Unit, 72-75; toxicologist, 75-79, SR TOXICOLOGIST & UNIT HEAD, EXXON CORP, 79- *Concurrent Pos:* Feature ed, Neurotoxicol, 79- *Mem:* Environ Mutagen Soc; European Soc Toxicol. *Res:* Chemical carcinogenesis; biostatistics; risk analysis; neurotoxicology. *Mailing Add:* PO Box 235 East Millstone NJ 08873

LEWIS, T(HOMAS) SKIPWITH, b Bluefield, WVa, Nov 21, 36; m 62; c 2. ELECTRICAL ENGINEERING. *Educ:* Va Polytech Inst, BS, 59; Univ Va, MS, 64, ScD(elec eng), 67. *Prof Exp:* Engr, Air Arm Div, Westinghouse Elec Corp, 59-62; instr elec eng, Univ Va, 64-67; sr res engr, United Aircraft Res Labs, 67-70; adj asst prof elec eng, Univ Hartford, 67-70, assoc prof, 70-81, dean, Col Eng, 71-81; ASST VPRES, HARTFORD STEAM BOILER, 81- *Res:* Microwave engineering and antennas; microwave properties of materials. *Mailing Add:* Hartford Steam Boiler 56 Prospect St Hartford CT 06102

LEWIS, THEODORE, b New York, NY, Apr 9, 24. CHEMICAL ENGINEERING, POLYMER CHEMISTRY. *Educ:* Rensselaer Polytech Inst, BChE, 46, MChE, 48; Princeton Univ, PhD(chem eng), 55; NY Univ, MBA, 71. *Prof Exp:* Res engr chem & chem eng, Esso Res Eng Co, Standard Oil Co, NJ, 54-59, sr mkt develop engr, Enjay Chem Co, 59-65, assoc synthetic elastomers dept, 65-71; assoc prof, Col Bus, dir pharmaceut/chem prog & admin asst to dean, Col Bus, Fairleigh Dickinson Univ, Rutherford, 71-74; INDUST, GOVT & UNIV CONSULT, 74- *Concurrent Pos:* Adj fac, Fairleigh Dickinson Univ & Adelphi Univ, 74- *Mem:* Am Chem Soc; Am Inst Chem Engrs. *Res:* Textile fibers; synthetic elastomers; petrochemicals; products and process research; market development of thermosets, synthetic elastomers and special industries. *Mailing Add:* PO Box 177 Roselle NJ 07203

LEWIS, THOMAS BRINLEY, b Cleveland, Ohio, Nov 3, 38; m 65; c 3. POLYMER SCIENCE. *Educ:* John Carrol Univ, BS, 60, MS, 62; Mass Inst Technol, PhD(physics), 65. *Prof Exp:* Res assoc phys chem, Cornell Univ, 65-66; group leader, Cent Res Dept, 66-72, proj mgr, Rubber Chem Div, 72-77, mgr com develop, 77-78, dir results mgt, Corp Res & Develop Staff, 78-80, DIR, CORP RES LABS, MONSANTO CO, 80- *Mem:* Am Phys Soc; Soc Plastic Engrs; Sigma Xi; Am Chem Soc; Soc Rheol. *Res:* Rates for characteristic processes in polymer systems using using fast reaction chemical kinetic techniques; methods, including ultrasonic absorption relaxation and temperature jump; mechanical and physical properties of composite materials; dynamic mechanical properties of composite materials, polymers and rubber. *Mailing Add:* Monsanto Co 800 N Lindbergh Blvd St Louis MO 63166

LEWIS, TRENT R, b Baltimore, Md, Feb 3, 32; m 65; c 3. OCCUPATIONAL HEALTH. *Educ:* Univ Md, BS, 54, MS, 57; Mich State Univ, PhD(nutrit), 61. *Prof Exp:* Res asst dairy sci, Univ Md, 55-57; res instr, Mich State Univ, 57-61; asst prof animal sci, Univ Maine, 61-63; res chemist, R A Taft Sanit Eng Ctr, USPHS, 63-68; chief chronic & explor toxicol, Nat Air Pollution Control Admin, 68-71; chief explor toxicol sect, 71-77, CHIEF EXPLOR TOXICOL BR, NAT INST OCCUP SAFETY & HEALTH, 78- *Mem:* Am Dairy Sci Asn; Am Soc Microbiol; Soc Toxicol; Sigma Xi; NY Acad Sci. *Res:* Occupational toxicology; environmental toxicology; mammalian cardiopulmonary physiology; biochemical mechanisms; development or modification of standard toxicity testing regimens; mutagenic chemical agents via reproductive and teratogenic methodology; development of dose-response criteria. *Mailing Add:* Exp Toxicol Br Nat Inst Occup Safe & Health 4676 Columbia Pkwy Cincinnati OH 45226

LEWIS, TREVOR JOHN, b Vancouver, BC, Jan 19, 40; m 64; c 2. GEOPHYSICS. *Educ:* Univ BC, BASc, 63, MSc, 64; Univ Western Ont, PhD(geophys), 75. *Prof Exp:* RES SCIENTIST GEOTHERMAL STUDIES, DEPT ENERGY MINES & RESOURCES, EARTH PHYSICS BR, 64- *Mem:* Geol Asn Can; Can Geophys Union; Am Geophys Soc. *Mailing Add:* Pac Geosci Ctr PO Box 6000 Sidney BC V8L 4B2 Can

LEWIS, URBAN JAMES, b Flagstaff, Ariz, Apr 28, 23; m 50; c 2. ENDOCRINOLOGY. *Educ:* San Diego State Col, BA, 48; Univ Wis, MS, 50, PhD(biochem), 52. *Prof Exp:* NIH fel, Med Nobel Inst, Stockholm, 52-53; instr biochem & biochemist, Am Meat Found, Univ Chicago, 53-54; sr biochemist, Merck & Co, Inc, 54-61; MEM, SCRIPPS CLIN & RES FOUND, 61- *Mem:* Am Soc Biol Chem; Am Chem Soc; Endocrine Soc. *Res:* Proteolytic enzymes; pituitary hormones. *Mailing Add:* Whittier Inst Diabetes & Endocrinol 9894 Genesee Ave La Jolla CA 92037

LEWIS, VANCE DE SPAIN, b Los Angeles, Calif, June 26, 09; m 36; c 2. PHYSICS. *Educ:* Univ Calif, Berkeley, BA, 33, MA, 40; Univ Southern Calif, PhD(educ), 54. *Prof Exp:* From asst prof to prof, 46-72, EMER PROF PHYSICS, CALIF POLYTECH STATE UNIV, SAN LUIS OBISPO, 72- *Concurrent Pos:* Assoc dean, Sch Sci & Math, Calif Polytech State Univ, San Luis Obispo, 68-72. *Mem:* Am Phys Soc; NY Acad Sci. *Res:* Optics; statistical analysis. *Mailing Add:* 1386 Oceanaire Dr San Luis Obispo CA 93401

LEWIS, W DAVID, b Towanda, Pa, June 24, 31; div; c 3. HISTORY OF TECHNOLOGY. *Educ:* Pa State Univ, BA, 52, MA, 54; Cornell Univ, PhD(hist), 61. *Prof Exp:* Instr pub speaking, Hamilton Col, 54-57; fel coordr, Eleutherian Mills-Hagley Found, Inc, Wilmington, 59-65; from assoc prof to prof, State Univ NY, Buffalo, 65-71; HUDSON PROF HIST & ENG, AUBURN UNIV, 71- *Concurrent Pos:* Dir, Nat Endowment Humanities Proj Technol, Human Values & Southern Future, Auburn Univ, 74-; fel, Nat Humanities Inst, Univ Chicago, 78-; grants, State Univ NY, Auburn Univ, Eleutherian Mills Hist Libr & Delta Air Lines Found. *Mem:* Soc Hist Technol. *Res:* History of technology, particularly history of iron and steel industry and history of aviation; interface between science, technology and religion. *Mailing Add:* 7008 Haley Ctr Auburn Univ Auburn AL 36830

LEWIS, WALLACE JOE, b Smithdale, Miss, Oct 30, 42; m 65; c 2. ENTOMOLOGY. *Educ:* Miss State Univ, BS, 64, MS, 65, PhD(entom), 68. *Prof Exp:* ENTOMOLOGIST, SOUTHERN GRAIN INSECTS RES LAB, ENTOM RES DIV, AGR RES SERV, USDA, 67- *Concurrent Pos:* Asst prof, Univ Fla, 70- *Mem:* Entom Soc Am. *Res:* Ecological and physiological relationships between parasitic insects and their hosts; development of methods for the use of parasitic insects for control of insect pests. *Mailing Add:* 3400 Bleckley Dr Lithonia GA 30058

LEWIS, WALTER HEPWORTH, b Carleton Place, Ont, June 26, 30; m 57; c 2. BOTANY. *Educ:* Univ BC, BA, 51, MA, 54; Univ Va, PhD(bot), 57. *Prof Exp:* Asst prof biol & dir herbarium, Stephen F Austin State Col, 57-61, assoc prof biol, 61-64; assoc prof, 64-69, PROF BOT, WASH UNIV, 69- *Concurrent Pos:* Guggenheim fel, 63-64; mem, Int Orgn Biosyst; dir herbarium, Mo Bot Garden, 64-72, sr botanist, 72- *Honors & Awards:* Horsley Res Award, Va Acad Sci, 57. *Mem:* Bot Soc Am; Am Soc Plant Taxon; Asn Trop Biol; Int Asn Plant Taxon. *Res:* Cytotaxonomy of Rosa, the Rubiaceae, palynotaxonomy of angiosperms and southern flora; medical plants; allergy. *Mailing Add:* 7915 Park Dr St Louis MO 63117

LEWIS, WARREN BURTON, physical inorganic chemistry, molecular spectroscopy, see previous edition

LEWIS, WILFRID BENNETT, b Cumberland, Eng, June 24, 08; Can citizen. PHYSICS. *Educ:* Univ Cambridge, BA, 30, MA & PhD(physics), 34. *Hon Degrees:* DSc, Queen's Univ, Ont, 60, Univ Sask, 64, McMaster Univ, 65, Dartmouth Col, 69, Univ Toronto, 72, Royal Mil Col, Kingston, Ont, 74, Univ Victoria, BC, 75, Laurentian Univ, Sudbury, Ont, 77 & Univ Birmingham, UK, 77; McGill Univ, 69; LLD, Dalhousie Univ, 60, Carleton Univ, 62 & Trent Univ, 68. *Prof Exp:* Demonstr, Univ Cambridge, 35-37, lectr, 37-39; chief supt, Telecommun Res Estab, Ministry Aircraft Prod, UK, 45-46; dir atomic energy div, Nat Res Coun Can, 46-52; vpres res & develop, Atomic Energy Can Ltd, 52-63, sr vpres sci, 63-73; DISTINGUISHED

PROF SCI, QUEEN'S UNIV, 73- *Concurrent Pos:* Res fel, Gonville & Caius Cols, Univ Cambridge, 34-40, hon fel, 71; Can rep, Sci Adv Comt, Secy Gen, UN, 55-; mem sci adv comt to dir gen, Int Atomic Energy Agency, 57-78. *Honors & Awards:* Comdr, Order of Brit Empire, 46; Am Medal of Freedom with Silver Palms, 46; Outstanding Achievement Award, Pub Serv Can, 66; Companion of Order of Can, 67; Atoms for Peace Award, 67; Spec Gold Medal, Can Asn Physicists, 70; Royal Medal, Univ Manchester, 72. *Mem:* Foreign Assoc Nat Acad Eng; fel Am Phys Soc; fel Am Nuclear Soc (vpres, 60, pres, 61-62); fel Royal Soc; fel Royal Soc Can. *Res:* Radioactivity; radio; electronics; radar; radiation; nuclear reactor physics; nuclear physics; fluctuations; reactor economics and materials; fission gas behavior; economics of nuclear power; high power accelerators. *Mailing Add:* Dept of Physics Queen's Univ Kingston ON K7L 3N6 Can

LEWIS, WILLARD DEMING, b Augusta, Ga, Jan 6, 15; m 41; c 5. PHYSICS, ACADEMIC ADMINISTRATION. *Educ:* Harvard Univ, AB, 35, AM, 39, PhD(math physics), 41; Oxford Univ, BA, 38, MA, 45. *Hon Degrees:* LLD, Lafayette Col, 65, Rutgers Univ, 66 & Hahnemann Med Col, 66; LHD, Moravian Col, 66; DEng, Lehigh Univ, 74. *Prof Exp:* Mem tech staff, Bell Tel Labs, 41-51, dir switching res, 51-58, dir res, Commun Systs, 58-60, exec dir, 60-62; managing dir systs studies, Bellcomm, Inc, 62-64; PRES, LEHIGH UNIV, 64- *Concurrent Pos:* Mem, Vis Comt, Div Appl Sci, Harvard Univ, 56-66 & Coun, Harvard Found Advan Study & Res, 59-64, chmn, 61-62, mem, Harvard Grad Soc Advan Study & Res, 66-69, Defense Indust Adv Comt, 62-63 & Naval Res Adv Comt, 64-70, from vchmn to chmn, 65-69; dir, Pa Power & Light Co, 67-; mem, Defense Sci Bd, 67-69; chmn, State Bd Educ Commonwealth Pa, 68-73 & Comt Power Plant Siting, Nat Acad Eng, 67; mem coun, 72-78; dir, Fairchild Industs, 73-, Bethlehem Steel, 75-, Fischer Porter Co, 77- & Zenith Radio Corp, 80. *Mem:* Nat Acad Eng; Am Phys Soc; fel Inst Elec & Electronics Eng. *Res:* Magnetism; phonograph distortion; radar antennas; microwave filters and radio repeaters; telephone switching. *Mailing Add:* Off Pres Lehigh Univ Bethlehem PA 18015

LEWIS, WILLIAM E(RVIN), b Hagerstown, Md, Sept 10, 40; m 58; c 5. COMPUTER SCIENCE, OPERATIONS RESEARCH. *Educ:* Johns Hopkins Univ, BES, 62; Northwestern Univ, Evanston, MS, 64, PhD(indust eng), 66. *Prof Exp:* assoc prof, 65-80, PROF COMPUT SSCI, ARIZ STATE UNIV, 80- *Concurrent Pos:* Consult, Good Samaritan Hosp, 66-68, Gen Elec Info Systs, 69-71 & Honeywell Info Systs, 71-79; eval analyst, Phoenix Alcohol Safety Action Proj, 71-73. *Mem:* Am Inst Indust Engrs; Asn Comput Mach. *Res:* Application of operations research and computer techniques to industrial problems. *Mailing Add:* Dept of Indust Eng Eng Ctr Ariz State Univ Tempe AZ 85281

LEWIS, WILLIAM JAMES, b Talahassee, Fla, Feb 11, 45; m 66; c 1. MATHEMATICS. *Educ:* La State Univ, Baton Rouge, BS, 66, PhD(math), 71. *Prof Exp:* Instr math, La State Univ, 71; asst prof, 71-77, ASSOC PROF MATH, UNIV NEBR-LINCOLN, 77-, VCHMN DEPT, 80- *Mem:* Am Math Soc. *Res:* Commutative algebra; valuation theory; ring theory. *Mailing Add:* Dept of Math Univ of Nebr Lincoln NE 68508

LEWIS, WILLIAM MADISON, b Faison, NC, Nov 26, 22; m 43; c 4. FISHERIES. *Educ:* NC State Col, BS, 43; Iowa State Col, MS, 48, PhD(zool), 49. *Prof Exp:* Sci bact aide, USDA, 42; asst prof, 49-60, PROF ZOOL, SOUTHERN ILL UNIV, 60-, DIR, COOP FISHERIES LAB, 49-, CHMN DEPT ZOOL, 72- *Mem:* Am Fisheries Soc. *Res:* Aquaculture and fish management. *Mailing Add:* Dept of Zool Southern Ill Univ Carbondale IL 62901

LEWIS, WILLIAM MASON, b Ithaca, NY, Aug 13, 29; m 57; c 5. WEED SCIENCE. *Educ:* Tex A&M Univ, BS, 52; Univ Minn, MS, 56, PhD(plant genetics), 57. *Prof Exp:* Asst agron & plant genetics, Univ Minn, 52-56; from instr to assoc prof, 56-69, PROF CROP SCI, NC STATE UNIV, 69- *Mem:* Am Soc Agron; Crop Sci Soc Am; Weed Sci Soc Am. *Res:* Agronomy; turf weed control. *Mailing Add:* Dept of Crop Sci NC State Univ Raleigh NC 27650

LEWIS, WILLIAM PERRY, b Swatow, China, Aug 12, 29; US citizen; m 51; c 2. MEDICAL MICROBIOLOGY. *Educ:* Univ Redlands, BS, 51; Univ Calif, Los Angeles, PhD(infectious dis), 62. *Prof Exp:* Asst res parasitologist & instr parasitol, Sch Pub Health, Univ Calif, Los Angeles, 62-69; ASST PROF PATH, SCH MED, UNIV SOUTHERN CALIF & SUPV MED MICROBIOLOGIST, MICROBIOL II, LOS ANGELES COUNTY-UNIV SOUTHERN CALIF MED CTR, 69- *Mem:* AAAS; Am Soc Trop Med & Hyg; Am Soc Microbiol; Am Soc Parasitol. *Res:* Immunology of parasitic diseases, especially toxoplasmosis, amebiasis and filariases; diagnostic bacteriology, parasitology and immunology. *Mailing Add:* Mycobact Lab Los Angeles County- Univ Southern Calif Med Ctr 1200 N State St Los Angeles CA 90033

LEWIS, WILLIAM WESTON, b Marblehead, Mass, Feb 2, 32; m 68. LABORATORY MEDICINE. *Educ:* Bates Col, BA, 59. *Prof Exp:* Res asst, Protein Found, 61-63, Tufts Med Sch, 63-66; Harvard Med Sch, 66-69; PRIN SCIENTIST, INSTRUMENTATION LAB, INC, 69- *Mem:* Am Asn Clin Chemists. *Res:* Development and implementation of state of the art methods for the measurement of clinically important materials in human blood and body fluids. *Mailing Add:* Instrumentation Lab Inc 113 Hartwell Ave Lexington MA 02173

LEWISTON, NORMAN JAMES, b Perry, Iowa, Oct 8, 38. PEDIATRICS, CELL BIOLOGY. *Educ:* Iowa State Univ, BS, 60; Univ Iowa, MD, 65. *Prof Exp:* Fel allergy, 72-73, fel respiratory med, 73-74, ASST PROF PEDIAT, SCH MED, STANFORD UNIV, 74-, CHIEF PEDIAT ALLERGY & PULMONARY DIS, CHILDREN'S HOSP, 75- *Concurrent Pos:* Consult, US Air Force Hosp, Travis AFB, Fairfield, Calif & Calif Med Asn, 76-; instr exten serv, Univ Calif, Santa Cruz & vchmn, Consumer Serv Comt, Cystic Fibrosis Found, 77- *Mem:* Am Fedn Clin Res; Am Thoracic Soc; Am Acad Allergy; Am Acad Pediat. *Res:* Oxygen utilization by cells and organelles; humoral response to chronic respiratory infection. *Mailing Add:* Children's Hosp 520 Willow Rd Palo Alto CA 94304

LEWKE, ROBERT EDWARD, avian & reptilian ecology, see previous edition

LEWONTIN, RICHARD CHARLES, b New York, NY, Mar 29, 29; m 47; c 4. GENETICS, POPULATION BIOLOGY. *Educ:* Harvard Univ, AB, 51; Columbia Univ, MA, 52, PhD(zool), 54. *Prof Exp:* Reader biomet, Columbia Univ, 53-54; asst prof genetics, NC State Col, 54-58; from asst prof to prof biol, Univ Rochester, 58-64; prof biol, Univ Chicago, 64-73; PROF BIOL, HARVARD UNIV, 73- *Concurrent Pos:* NSF fel, 54-55, sr fel, 61-62 & 71-72; lectr, Columbia Univ, 59, seminar assoc, 59-61; Fulbright fel, 61-62; co-ed, Am Naturalist, Am Soc Nat, 65. *Mem:* AAAS; fel Am Acad Arts & Sci; Genetics Soc Am; Soc Study Evolution (pres, 70). *Res:* Population genetics, ecology and evolution. *Mailing Add:* Mus of Comp Zool Harvard Univ Cambridge MA 02138

LEX, R(OWLAND) G(ARBER), JR, b Philadelphia, Pa, Dec 29, 24; m 52; c 2. ELECTRICAL ENGINEERING. *Educ:* Univ Pa, BS, 49, MS, 50. *Prof Exp:* Elec engr, 49-55, group chief, 55-58, sect head, 58-62, mgr develop div, 62-68, gen mgr digital equip div, 68-69, mgr eng coord & serv dept, 69-72, gen mgr recorder & test instrument div, 72-76, DIR DEVELOP & ENG DEPT, INSTRUMENT GROUP, LEEDS & NORTHRUP CO, 76- *Mem:* Inst Elec & Electronics Engrs; fel Instrument Soc Am. *Res:* Application of digital techniques including computers to measurement and control of processes. *Mailing Add:* Leeds & Northrup Co North Wales PA 19454

LEY, ALLYN BRYSON, b Springfield, Mass, Dec 5, 18; m 43, 67; c 2. MEDICINE. *Educ:* Dartmouth Col, AB, 39; Columbia Univ, MD, 42; Am Bd Internal Med, dipl. *Prof Exp:* Asst med, Med Col, Cornell Univ, 47-49; instr, 51-52, asst dir, Sloan-Kettering Div, 54-55, cancer coord, 54-63, from asst prof to assoc prof, 54-63, PROF MED, MED COL, CORNELL UNIV, 63-, CLIN DIR UNIV HEALTH SERV, 71- *Concurrent Pos:* Asst, Boston City Hosp, 49-51; dir blood bank, Mem Hosp, 51-63, dir hemat labs, 55-63; asst attend physician, New York Hosp, 54-63, attend physician & dir ambulatory serv, 63-69; consult, Manhattan Vet Admin Hosp, 58-60, Hosp Spec Surg, 58-71 & Mem Sloan Kettering Cancer Ctr, 71-; assoc vis physician, Bellevue Hosp, 60-67; chief staff, SS Hope, 69-70; attend physician, Tompkins Community Hosp, 71- *Mem:* AAAS; Harvey Soc; Am Soc Hemat; Am Fedn Clin Res; Int Soc Blood Transfusion. *Res:* Immunohematology; erythrocyte biochemistry; medical education and care. *Mailing Add:* Gannett Health Ctr Cornell Univ Ithaca NY 14853

LEY, B JAMES, b New York, NY, May 26, 21; m 42; c 2. ELECTRICAL ENGINEERING. *Educ:* NY Univ, BEE, 42, MEE, 48. *Prof Exp:* Elec engr, Gen Elec Co, 42-44; from instr to prof elec eng, NY Univ, 46-73; PROF ELEC ENG, MANHATTAN COL, 73- *Concurrent Pos:* Grant, Ford Found, 61; indust consult. *Mem:* Inst Elec & Electronics Engrs; Am Soc Eng Educ. *Res:* Active networks and analog and digital computers; computer aided design; alternate energy sources. *Mailing Add:* Dept of Elec Eng Manhattan Col Pkwy Bronx NY 10471

LEYBOURNE, A(LLEN) E(DWARD), III, b Jacksonville, Fla, Aug 26, 34; m 54; c 2. CHEMICAL ENGINEERING. *Educ:* Univ Fla, BS, 56, PhD(chem eng), 61; Pa State Univ, MS, 58. *Prof Exp:* Res Assoc petrol res, Pa State Univ, 56-58, instr chem, Univ Fla, 58-59; res chemist, Atlantic Refining Co, 60; sr engr, Am Oil Co, 61-62; supvr textile develop, Textile Div, Monsanto Co, 63-71; plant mgr, Texfi Industs, Inc, 71-77, dir prod eng, 77-80; DIR ENG, INTERPINE LUMBER CO, 80- *Mem:* Am Chem Soc; Am Inst Chem Eng; Am Asn Textile Technol; Am Soc Heating & Airconditioning Engrs. *Res:* Polymer textiles. *Mailing Add:* Box 841-F Lake Serene Hattiesburg MS 39401

LEYDA, JAMES PERKINS, b Youngstown, Ohio, Oct 2, 35; m 67; c 3. PHARMACY, PHARMACEUTICAL CHEMISTRY. *Educ:* Ohio Northern Univ, BS, 57; Ohio State Univ, MS, 59, PhD(pharm), 62. *Prof Exp:* Develop chemist, Lederle Labs Div, Am Cyanamid Co, 62-66, mgr prod develop, Int Med Res & Develop, 66-69; mgr new prod develop, Merrell Int Div, Richardson-Merrell, 69-76, dir, 76-81, HEAD, DEPT PHARM RES & DEVELOP, MERRELL DOW PHARMACEUT, INC, 81- *Mem:* AAAS; Am Pharmaceut Asn; NY Acad Sci; Acad Pharmaceut Sci; Sigma Xi. *Res:* Drug delivery systems; antibiotics; cardiovascular agents; complexation; stability and analysis of pharmaceutical products. *Mailing Add:* 10597 Tanager Hills Dr Cincinnati OH 45242

LEYDEN, DONALD E, b Gadsden, Ala, June 26, 38; m 61; c 2. ANALYTICAL CHEMISTRY. *Educ:* Kent State Univ, BS, 60; Emory Univ, MS, 61, PhD, 64. *Prof Exp:* Res assoc, Univ NC, 64-65; from asst prof to assoc prof chem, Univ Denver, 65-76, Phillipson prof, 76-81; PROF CHEM, COLO STATE UNIV, 82- *Honors & Awards:* Chemist of the Year, Am Chem Soc, 81. *Mem:* Am Chem Soc; Soc Appl Spectros; Spectros Soc Can. *Res:* Chemically modified surfaces; ion-exchange; applications of nuclear magnetic resonance to the study of chemical systems of analytical importance. *Mailing Add:* Dept Chem Colo State Univ Fort Collins CO 80523

LEYDEN, RICHARD NOEL, b Santa Monica, Calif, Nov 14, 48. ORGANOMETALLIC CHEMISTRY, POLYMER CHEMISTRY. *Educ:* Univ Calif, Los Angeles, BS, 71, PhD(chem), 75. *Prof Exp:* Res asst polymer res, Univ Witwatersrand, 75-76; res asst inorg chem, Calif Inst Technol, 76-77; TECH STAFF. POLYMER RES, HUGHES AIRCRAFT CO, 77- *Mem:* Am Chem Soc. *Res:* Polymers, especially with semiconducting or electrical properties; organometallic polymers; organic metals; ultra high pressure chemistry. *Mailing Add:* Hughes Aircraft Co Culver City CA 90230

LEYDEN, ROBERT FULLERTON, b Glasgow, Scotland, Apr 26, 21; nat US; m; c 3. AGRONOMY, SOILS. *Educ:* NMed State Univ, BSc, 51; Kans State Univ, MSc, 53; Rutgers Univ, PhD(soil chem), 56. *Prof Exp:* From asst prof to assoc prof, 56-70, PROF AGR, CITRUS CTR, TEX A&I UNIV, 56- *Res:* Soil fertility and plant nutrition. *Mailing Add:* Citrus Ctr Tex A&I Univ Weslaco TX 78596

LEYDORF, GLENN E(DWIN), b Perrysburg, Ohio, June 7, 14; m 43; c 2. ELECTRONICS. *Educ:* Univ Toledo, BE, 42; Univ Md, MS, 54. *Prof Exp:* Instr elec & eng & physics, Univ Toledo, 42-44; from instr to assoc prof elec eng, 46-57, PROF ELEC ENG, US NAVAL ACAD, 57- *Mem:* Inst Elec & Electronics Engrs; Am Soc Eng Educ. *Res:* Electronic circuit applications to metastable atom studies. *Mailing Add:* Dept of Elec Eng US Naval Acad Annapolis MD 21402

LEYENDECKER, PHILIP JORDON, b Albuquerque, NMex, July 8, 14; m 37; c 4. PHYTOPATHOLOGY. *Educ:* Univ NMex, BS, 38; Iowa State Univ, MS, 40, PhD(phytopath), 48. *Prof Exp:* Assoc prof biol, 41-42, assoc biologist, 45-50, assoc plant pathologist & head dept agr serv, 50-59, asst dean agr, 59-60, dean & dir, Col Agr & Home Econ, 60-77, EMER PROF BOT, EMER DEAN, COL AGR & HOME ECON, EMER DIR, AGR EXP STA & COOP EXTEN SERV, NMEX STATE UNIV, 77- *Res:* Soil borne pathogens. *Mailing Add:* 509 El Prado Las Cruces NM 88001

LEYLAND, HARRY MOURS, b Newark, Ohio, July 8, 25; m 48. ORGANIC CHEMISTRY. *Educ:* Williams Col, AB, 46; Univ Cincinnati, MS, 48, PhD(chem), 53. *Prof Exp:* Assoc prof biol sci, Col Pharm, Univ Cincinnati, 48-50, instr chem, 51-52; asst dir res, Lloyd Bros, Inc, 53-55, dir prof serv & clin invest, 55-59; assoc dir res, Lakeside Labs, Inc, 59-61; actg dir clin pharmacol & dir toxicol lab, Miles Labs, Inc, 61-63; assoc dir clin res, 63-66, dir prod develop, 66-71, dir clin therapeut, 71-78, ASSOC SCI DIR, INT CLIN RES, WM S MERRELL CO DIV, RICHARDSON-MERRELL, INC, 78- *Mem:* AAAS; Am Chem Soc; Am Soc Clin Pharmacol & Therapeut; NY Acad Sci. *Mailing Add:* Merrell Dow Pharmsceut Inc 2110 E Galbraith Rd Cincinnati OH 45237

LEYMASTER, GLEN RONALD, b Aurora, Nebr, Aug 7, 15; m 42; c 3. MEDICINE. *Educ:* Univ Nebr, AB, 38; Harvard Univ, MD, 42; Johns Hopkins Univ, MPH, 50; Am Bd Prev Med, dipl. *Prof Exp:* Intern, Boston City Hosp, 42-43, asst resident, 43, resident, 44; clin instr, Sch Med, Johns Hopkins Univ, 44-46; from instr to asst prof bact, Sch Hyg & Pub Health, 46-48; assoc prof pub health & prev med, Sch Med, Univ Utah, 48-50, prof prev med & head dept, 50-60; assoc secy, Coun Med Educ & Hosps, AMA, 60-63; pres, dean, prof prev med & assoc prof med, Med Col, Pa, 64-70; dir dept undergrad med Educ, AMA, 70-75; exec dir, 75-81, EXEC VPRES, AM BD MED SPECS, 81- *Concurrent Pos:* Clin asst, Harvard Med Sch, 42-44; asst prof & dir univ health serv, Univ Utah, 50-60; med educ adv, US Dept State, Int Coop Admin, Thailand, 57-58. *Mem:* AMA. *Res:* Clinical and epidemiological character of influenza and of data regarding encephalitis; experimental immunity and epidemiology of mumps; industrial toxicology; epidemiology of gastroenteritis; medical education. *Mailing Add:* Am Bd of Med Specs 1603 Orrington Ave Evanston IL 60201

LEYON, ROBERT EDWARD, b Newton, Mass, July 28, 36; m 62; c 2. ANALYTICAL CHEMISTRY. *Educ:* Williams Col, BA, 58; Princeton Univ, MA, 60, PhD(chem), 62. *Prof Exp:* Instr chem, Princeton Univ, 61-62; from instr to asst prof, Swarthmore Col, 62-69; asst prof, 69-72, ASSOC PROF CHEM, DICKINSON COL, 72-, CHMN DEPT, 80- *Concurrent Pos:* Res assoc, Univ NC, 67-68 & Colo State Univ, 75-76. *Mem:* AAAS; Am Chem Soc. *Res:* Environmental chemistry; trace metal analysis by atomic absorption. *Mailing Add:* Dept of Chem Dickinson Col Carlisle PA 17013

LEYSE, CARL F(ERDINAND), b Kewaunee, Wis, Feb 11, 17; m 46; c 2. MECHANICAL ENGINEERING, PHYSICS. *Educ:* Univ Wis, BS, 48. *Prof Exp:* Phys sci aide rocket res, Naval Res Lab, 48; mech eng, Argonne Nat Lab, 48-51; chief eng res sect, Atomic Energy Div, Phillips Petrol Co, 51-56; tech dir, Internuclear Co, 56-59; asst mgr, Nuclear Dept, Res Div, Curtiss-Wright Corp, 59-60; mem staff, Gen Atomics Div, Gen Dynamics Corp, 60-61; pres, Internuclear Co, 61-63; mgr, Nuclear & Radiation Safety Dept, Reon Div, Aerojet Nuclear Systs Co, Sacramento, 63-67, mgr, Nuclear Safety, 67-72, staff scientist, Aerojet Nuclear Co, Idaho Falls, 72-76; MGR TECH DEVELOP, EG&G IDAHO INC, 76- *Mem:* Am Nuclear Soc. *Res:* Nuclear reactor development and design. *Mailing Add:* 2245 Calkins Idaho Falls ID 83401

LEYSIEFFER, FREDERICK WALTER, b Milwaukee, Wis, Jan 30, 33; m 64; c 3. MATHEMATICS. *Educ:* Univ Wis-Madison, BA, 55, MA, 56; Univ Mich, PhD(math), 64. *Prof Exp:* Asst prof, 64-70, assoc head dept, 69-76, ASSOC PROF STATIST, FLA STATE UNIV, 70-, CHMN, DEPT STATIST, 81- *Concurrent Pos:* Vis lectr, Sheffield Univ, Sheffield, Eng, 73-74, Leverhulme Commonwealth-Am fel, 73. *Mem:* Am Math Soc; Am Statist Asn; Math Asn Am; Inst Math Statist; AAAS. *Res:* Probability theory; stochastic processes; sampling theory; environmental statistics. *Mailing Add:* Dept of Statist Fla State Univ Tallahassee FL 32306

LEYSON, JOSE FLORANTE JUSTININANE, b Philippines, Aug 17, 46. HUMAN SEXUALITY, URODYNAMICS. *Educ:* Cebu Inst Technol, BS, 65, MD, 70; Am Bd Urol, dipl, 79. *Prof Exp:* Fel entom, US Agency Int Develop, 70-71; fel sexuality, Johns Hopkins Hosp, 76; fel urodynamics, Yale Univ Hosp, 78; fel spinal cord, 76-77, CLIN CHIEF, SPINAL CORD INJURY UNIT, VET ADMIN HOSP, ORANGE, NJ, 77-; ASST PROF UROL, NJ MED SCH, 80-; ASSOC PROF SEXUALITY, FAIRLEIGH DICKINSON UNIV, NJ, 80- *Concurrent Pos:* Vis prof urodynamics, Yale Univ Hosp, 79; fel sex educ & parenthood, Am Univ, Washington, DC, 81; consult, Urodynamics, Bronx Vet Admin Hosp, NY, 79 & Forum & MS Quarterly Mag, 78-; dir, Urodynamics & Sex Clin, Vet Admin Hosp, NJ, 79- & Sexual Dysfunction Ctr, Newark, NJ, 80- *Mem:* Philippines Am Sexologists Am (pres, 80-82); Philippine Med Asn Am; Am Urol Asn Inc. *Res:* Sexuality for both abled-bodied and disabled persons; drugs or electrical stimulations to produce erection in impotent patients; ways to produce urination in patients with paralysis and spinal defects due to injury or birth defects. *Mailing Add:* Spinal Cord Injury Unit Vet Admin Hosp Med Ctr East Orange NJ 07019

LEZBERG, ERWIN A, b Boston, Mass, Sept 20, 29; m 56; c 6. COMBUSTION KINETICS, FUELS CHEMISTRY. *Educ:* Tufts Univ, BS, 52. *Prof Exp:* AERONAUT RES SCIENTIST, LEWIS RES CTR, NASA, 52-, HEAD KENETICS & THERMODYN SECT, AEROTHERMODYN & FUELS DIV, 80- *Res:* Combustion research; physical properties; hypersonic airbreathing propulsion; aerothermodynamics; spectroscopic measurements in high temperature gas streams; atmospheric sampling; fuels research. *Mailing Add:* NASA/Lewis Res Ctr 21000 Brookpark Rd Cleveland OH 44135

LEZNOFF, ARTHUR, b Montreal, Que, Apr 7, 30; m 54; c 4. MEDICINE, IMMUNOLOGY. *Educ:* McGill Univ, BSc, 51, MD, CM, 55, MSc, 60; FRCPS(C), 60. *Prof Exp:* ASSOC PROF MED, UNIV TORONTO, 71- *Concurrent Pos:* Physician, Dept Med, St Michael's Hosp, Toronto, 71- *Mem:* Am Acad Allergy; Can Med Asn; Can Soc Immunol. *Res:* Immunology; clinical allergy; histoplasmosis. *Mailing Add:* 38 Shuter St 217 Toronto ON M5B 1A6 Can

LEZNOFF, CLIFFORD CLARK, b Montreal, Que, May 30, 40; m 63; c 3. ORGANIC CHEMISTRY. *Educ:* McGill Univ, BSc, 61, PhD(org chem), 65. *Prof Exp:* Fel org chem, Northwestern Univ, 64-65; Nat Res Coun Can overseas fel, Cambridge Univ, 65-67; from asst prof to assoc prof, 67-79, PROF ORG CHEM, YORK UNIV, 80- *Mem:* Am Chem Soc; Chem Inst Can. *Res:* Polymer supports in organic synthesis; synthesis of chiral compounds, pheromones, phthalocyanines and flourinated heterocyclic compounds. *Mailing Add:* Dept of Chem York Univ Downsview ON M3J 1P3 Can

LHERMITTE, ROGER M, b Pontchartrain, France, May 28, 20; US citizen; m 45; c 2. PHYSICAL METEOROLOGY. *Educ:* Univ Paris, MS, 51, DrSci(meteorol), 55. *Prof Exp:* Physicist meteorol res, Meteorol Nat, France, 46-60, Air Force Cambridge Res Lab, 60-63; head res br, Nat Oceanic & Atmospheric Admin, 63-70; PROF PHYS METEOROL, UNIV MIAMI, 70- *Concurrent Pos:* Mem, Active Microwave Workshop, NASA, 74-75; chmn, Nat Ctr Atmospheric Res Adv Panel, 74-; secretariat, Thunderstorm Res Int Prog; mem, Coun Atmospheric Elec, Am Meteorol Soc. *Honors & Awards:* Authorship Award, Nat Oceanic & Atmospheric Admin, 69, Spec Achievement Award, 70; Second Half Century Award, Am Meteorol Soc, 76. *Mem:* Fel Am Meteorol Soc; Int Union Geodesy & Geophys; Int Union Radio Sci. *Res:* Use of Doppler radars for the observation and study of atmospheric motion; the observation of three dimensional motion fields inside these systems by use of three Doppler radars operated simultaneously. *Mailing Add:* Univ of Miami Coral Gables FL 33134

L'HEUREUX, JACQUES (JEAN), b Trois-Rivieres, Que, Dec 20, 39; div; c 3. COSMIC RAY PHYSICS, ASTROPHYSICS. *Educ:* Univ Montreal, BSc, 61; Univ Chicago, MSc, 62, PhD(physics), 66. *Prof Exp:* Res assoc physics, Univ Chicago, 66-69; asst prof physics, Univ Ariz, 69-77; SR RES ASSOC, UNIV CHICAGO, 78- *Mem:* Fel Am Phys Soc; Am Geophys Union. *Res:* Primary cosmic ray electrons; solar modulation of cosmic rays; primary heavy nuclei at high energies. *Mailing Add:* Enrico Fermi Inst LASR 933 E 56th St Chicago IL 60637

L'HEUREUX, LEON-J J, b Gravelbourg, Sask, Mar 2, 19; m 46; c 8. ENGINEERING PHYSICS, ELECTRICAL ENGINEERING. *Educ:* Univ Ottawa, Ont, BA, 40; Univ Sask, BSc, 44; Johns Hopkins Univ, MEng & DEng(elec eng), 49. *Prof Exp:* Asst proj engr, Defence Res Bd, Can, 49-52, dir guided missile, 53-55, dept dir gen, Can Armament Res & Develop Estab, 55-60, mem, Nat Defence Col, 60-61, sci adv to chief gen staff, Can Forces Hq, 61-63, dir gen, Can Armament Res & Develop Estab, 63-67, vchmn, 67-69, CHMN, DEFENCE RES BD CAN, 69- *Concurrent Pos:* Consult, Comt for Athlone fels, 64-; chmn adv comt bilingualism & biculturalism, Defence Res Bd Can, 68-69. *Mem:* AAAS; Inst Elec Eng; Eng Inst Can; French-Can Asn Advan Sci (pres, 67-68). *Res:* Accuracy in basic primary measurements; automatic control; system design and engineering; planning techniques and modern administration methods. *Mailing Add:* 717 Portage Ave Ottawa ON K1G 1T2 Can

L'HEUREUX, MAURICE VICTOR, b Lewiston, Maine, May 23, 14; m 46; c 5. BIOCHEMISTRY. *Educ:* Col of the Holy Cross, BS, 36, MS, 37; Yale Univ, PhD(biochem), 44. *Prof Exp:* Control chemist, Stokely Bros-Van Camp, Inc, Ind, 40-41; assoc, 46-49, from asst prof to assoc prof, 49-59, PROF BIOCHEM, STRITCH SCH MED, LOYOLA UNIV CHICAGO, 59- *Mem:* Am Chem Soc; Am Soc Biol Chem. *Res:* Lipid metabolism; modifying and regulatory effects of parathyroid hormone, calcitonin and vitamin D upon calcium metabolism. *Mailing Add:* Dept of Biochem & Biophys Loyola Univ Stritch Sch of Med Maywood IL 60153

LHOTKA, JOHN FRANCIS, b Butte, Mont, Dec 13, 21; m 51. HISTOCHEMISTRY, MICROANATOMY. *Educ:* Univ Mont, BA, 42; Northwestern Univ, MS, 47, MB, 49, MD, 51, PhD(anat), 53. *Prof Exp:* Asst anat, Northwestern Univ, 46-49; mem clin staff, Minneapolis Gen Hosp, 50-51; asst prof microanat, 51-54, assoc prof, 54-69, PROF ANAT, MED SCH, UNIV OKLA, 69- *Concurrent Pos:* VPres, Introgene Found, 75- *Mem:* Am Asn Anatomists; Histochem Soc; Int Acad Path; Am Chem Soc. *Res:* Polysaccharide histochemistry (theoretical and applied) in aging, in human embryo and fetus; argyrophilia (neurofibrillar and reticular); heavy metal histochemistry in toxicology; applied histochemistry in selected lower animals; aging in the mouse. *Mailing Add:* Anat Sci Univ Okla Health Sci Ctr PO Box 26901 Oklahoma City OK 73190

LI, C(HING) C(HUNG), b Changshu, China, Mar 30, 32; m 61; c 2. ELECTRICAL ENGINEERING, COMPUTER SCIENCE. *Educ:* Nat Taiwan Univ, BS, 54; Northwestern Univ, MS, 56, PhD(elec eng), 61. *Prof Exp:* Asst prof , 59-60, 61-62, assoc prof, 62-67, PROF ELEC ENG, UNIV PITTSBURGH, 67-, PROF COMPUT SCI, 77- *Concurrent Pos:* Vis assoc prof, Univ Calif, Berkeley, 64, vis prin scientist, Alaza Corp, Palo Alto, Calif, 70; prin investr NSF res grants, 75-; consult, Westinghouse Res Develop Ctr,

81. *Mem:* AAAS; fel Inst Elec & Electronics Engrs; Soc Pattern Recognition; Biomed Eng Soc; Soc Indust & Appl Math. *Res:* Systems and control theory; integral pulse frequency modulated control systems; stability of nonlinear systems; adaptive and learning systems; differential games; modelling of physiological control systems; biomedical pattern recognition; image processing. *Mailing Add:* Dept of Elec Eng Univ of Pittsburgh Pittsburgh PA 15261

LI, CHE-YU, b Honan, China, Nov 15, 34; m 61; c 3. METALLURGY. *Educ:* Nat Taiwan Univ, BSE, 54; Cornell Univ, PhD(chem eng), 60. *Prof Exp:* Res assoc, 60-62, asst prof, 62-66, ASSOC PROF METALL, CORNELL UNIV, 66- *Concurrent Pos:* Mem staff, US Steel Res Ctr, 65-66; mem staff, Argonne Nat Lab, 69-71, consult, 71- *Mem:* Am Phys Soc; Am Inst Mining, Metall & Petrol Engrs. *Res:* Mechanical behavior; radiation damage; surface and interface. *Mailing Add:* Bard Hall Dept Mat Sci & Eng Cornell Univ Ithaca NY 14850

LI, CHIA-YU, b Shanghai, China, May 5, 41; m 69; c 2. ELECTROANALYTICAL CHEMISTRY. *Educ:* Taiwan Normal Univ, BS, 63; Univ Louisville, MS, 67; Wayne State Univ, PhD(anal chem), 72. *Prof Exp:* Res fel electrochem, Univ Ariz, 72-73; asst prof, 73-78, ASSOC PROF CHEM, ECAROLINA UNIV, 78- *Mem:* Am Chem Soc; Sigma Xi. *Res:* Electrochemistry of organic and biological model compounds-phthalocyanines, diquinones and quinoneimines; computer-controlled electrochemical instrumentation; electrochemical detecting techniques for high performance liquid chromatography. *Mailing Add:* Dept of Chem ECarolina Univ Greenville NC 27834

LI, CHING CHUN, b Tientsin, China, Oct 27, 12; nat US; m 41; c 2. POPULATION GENETICS, BIOMETRICS. *Educ:* Nanking Univ, BS, 36; Cornell Univ, PhD(plant breeding), 40. *Prof Exp:* Plant breeder, Agr Exp Sta, Yenching Univ, 36-37; asst prof, Agr Col, Nat Kwangsi Univ, 42-43; prof genetics & biomet, Agr Col, Nanking Univ, 43-46; prof agron & head dept, Peking Univ, 46-50; from res fel to asst prof, 51-58, from assoc prof to prof, 58-75, head dept, 69-75, UNIV PROF BIOSTATIST, GRAD SCH PUB HEALTH, UNIV PITTSBURGH, 75- *Mem:* Am Soc Human Genetics (pres, 60); AAAS; Int Statist Inst; Biomet Soc; fel Am Statist Asn. *Res:* Biometry; design of experiments; population genetics. *Mailing Add:* Dept of Biostatist Univ of Pittsburgh Grad Sch Pub Health Pittsburgh PA 15261

LI, CHIN-HSIU, b Taiwan, China, Jan 3, 38; m 69; c 2. ENGINEERING MECHANICS. *Educ:* Nat Cheng Kung Univ, BS, 61; Nat Cent Univ, MS, 64; Brigham Young Univ, MS, 66; Univ Mich, PhD(eng mech), 68. *Prof Exp:* Res assoc fluid mech, Case Western Reserve Univ, 69-71; vis assoc prof, Nat Cheng Kung Univ, 71-72; res assoc, Univ Mich, 72; assoc sr res engr, 72-76, sr res engr, eng mech, 76-81, STAFF RES ENGR, MECH RES DEPT, GEN MOTORS RES LABS, 81- *Mem:* Am Phys Soc; Am Soc Mech Engrs. *Res:* Hydrodynamic stability; fluid flow and heat transfer; lubrication theory; rotor dynamics; mechanics of automotive components. *Mailing Add:* Eng Mech Dept Gen Motors Res Labs Warren MI 48090

LI, CHI-TANG, b Ningtu, Kiangsi, China, Oct 16, 34; m 62; c 4. PHYSICAL CHEMISTRY, CRYSTALLOGRAPHY. *Educ:* Nat Taiwan Univ, BS, 55; Univ Louisville, MS, 59; Mont State Univ, PhD(chem), 64. *Prof Exp:* Scientist, 64-67, sr scientist, Adv Mat Res Sect, Owens-Ill Tech Ctr, 67-78; supvr fuel-cell mat res, 78-80, PRIN ENGR, INST GAS TECHNOL, 80- *Mem:* Am Chem Soc; Am Crystallog Asn. *Res:* Crystal structure and chemistry; studies of glass ceramic materials, research on high temperature materials; fuel cell research. *Mailing Add:* Mat Res 3424 S State St Chicago IL 60616

LI, CHOH HAO, b Canton, China, Apr 21, 13; nat US; m. BIOCHEMISTRY. *Educ:* Nanking Univ, BS, 33; Univ Calif, Berkeley, PhD(chem), 38. *Hon Degrees:* Dr, Cath Univ Chile, 62; LLD, Chinese Univ Hong Kong, 70; DSc, Univ Pac, Marquette Univ, St Peter's Col, 71, Uppsala Univ, 77, Univ San Francisco, 78, Long Island Univ, 79 & Univ Colo, 81. *Prof Exp:* Instr chem, Nanking Univ, 33-35; res asst, Univ Calif, Berkeley, 35-38, res assoc, 38-42, lectr chem morphol, 42-44, from asst prof to assoc prof exp biol, 44-49, dir, Hormone Res Lab, 50-67, PROF BIOCHEM & EXP ENDOCRINOL, UNIV CALIF, BERKELEY, 50- *Concurrent Pos:* Claude Bernard vis prof, Univ Mont, 47; John Simon Guggenheim Mem Found fel, 48; mem sci adv bd, Sloan Kettering Inst Cancer Res, 52-55; vis scientist, Children's Cancer Res Found, Boston, 55, sci adv, 63-; China Found vis prof, Nat Taiwan Univ, 58, mem adv bd, Chem Res Ctr, 64-; sect ed, Chem Abstracts, 60-63; mem acad adv bd, Chinese Univ Hong Kong, 63-; co-chmn, Conf Glycoproteins with Hormonal Activity, NIH, 71; chmn adv bd, Inst Biochem, Acad Sinica, 71-75. *Honors & Awards:* Ciba Award, 47; Francis Amory Prize, Am Acad Arts & Sci, 55; Repub China Minister Educ Gold Medal, 58; Chinese-Am Citizen Alliance Award, 61; Lasker Award, 62; Albert Lasker Award lectr, Salk Inst, 69; Pfizer lectr, Clin Res Inst Montreal, 71; Nord lectr, Fordham Univ, 72; Mendel lectr, St Peter's Col, 72; Andry Award, Asn Bone Joint Surgeons, 72; Fitch lectr, Marquette Univ, 73; Evans lectr, Univ Calif, 76, Gerschwind Mem lectr, 80; Lewis Prize, Am Philos Soc, 77; Nichols Medal, Am Chem Soc, 79; Koch Award, Endocrine Asn, 81; Grattanola Mem lectr, Univ Milan, 81. *Mem:* Nat Acad Sci; fel AAAS; fel NY Acad Sci; fel Am Acad Arts & Sci; fel Am Inst Chem. *Res:* Protein chemistry; chemistry and biology of pituitary hormones; biochemistry of protein hormones. *Mailing Add:* Hormone Res Lab Univ of Calif San Francisco CA 94143

LI, CHOH-LUH, b Canton, China, Sept 19, 19; nat US; m 48; c 3. NEUROPHYSIOLOGY, NEUROSURGERY. *Educ:* Nat Med Col Shanghai, China, MD, 42; McGill Univ, MSc, 51, PhD, 54. *Prof Exp:* Asst resident surg, Nat Med Col Shanghai Hosp, China, 42 & 44-45, resident, 45-46; sr asst resident neurosurg, Montreal Inst, 47-51, resident, 48, res EEG, 51-52; assoc neurosurgeon, 55-78, MED OFFICER NEUROSURG, NAT INST NEUROL, COMMUNICATIVE DISORDERS & STROKE, 78-; CLIN PROF, DEPT NEUROSURG, SCH MED, GEORGE WASHINGTON UNIV, 74- *Concurrent Pos:* Clin prof neurol surg, George Washington Univ. *Mem:* Int Brain Res Orgn; Am Physiol Soc; Res Soc Am Neurosurg; AAAS; Int Asn Pain Res. *Res:* Neurology. *Mailing Add:* Nat Inst of Neurol Dis & Stroke Bethesda MD 20014

LI, CHOU H(SIUNG), b Haining, China, June 8, 23; US citizen; m 53; c 2. PHYSICAL METALLURGY, STATISTICS. *Educ:* Chiao Tung Univ, BS, 44; Purdue Univ, MS, 49, PhD(phys metall), 51. *Prof Exp:* Metallurgist, Radio Corp Am, 51-59; sr scientist, Shockley Transistor Corp, 59-60; mgr semiconductors, Gen Instrument Corp, 60-62; sr res scientist, Grumman Aerospace Corp, 62-77; staff technologist, Singer Co, 78-79; PRES, LINTEL TECHNOL, INC, 79- *Concurrent Pos:* Ed, Chinese Inst Engrs J, 65-68; NASA Skylab consult specialist, 72-75; adj prof mat sci, State Univ NY, Stony Brook, 77- *Honors & Awards:* David Gessner Prize, Am Soc Eng Educ, 55 & 56; NASA New Technol Innovation Award, 77. *Mem:* Sr mem Inst Elec & Electronics Engrs; sr mem Am Soc Qual Control; Am Inst Mining, Metall & Petrol Engrs; Am Phys Soc; Chinese Inst Engrs. *Res:* Space manufacturing; semiconductors and thin films; solidification and related phenomena; powder packing, pressing and sintering; particle-surface interactions; friction; physics of failures; reliability, factorial and screening experiments; computer programming. *Mailing Add:* 379 Elm Dr Roslyn NY 11576

LI, FREDERICK P, b China, May 7, 40; US citizen; m 72; c 1. CANCER ETHOLOGY. *Educ:* Univ NY, Rochester, BA, 60, MD, 65; Georgetown Univ, MA, 69. *Prof Exp:* EPIDEMIOLOGIST, NAT CANCER INST, 67-; ASSOC PROF MED, HARVARD MED SCH, 80- *Mem:* Am Soc Clin Oncol; Am Asn Cancer Res. *Res:* Identification of persons at high risk of cancer; genetic and environmental causes of cancer susceptability. *Mailing Add:* 44 Binngey St Boston MA 02146

LI, GEORGE SU-HSIANG, b Chunking, China, Oct 24, 43; m 71; c 1. POLYMER CHEMISTRY, ORGANIC CHEMISTRY. *Educ:* Cheng Kung Univ, BS, 65; Purdue Univ, PhD(org chem), 71. *Prof Exp:* Res assoc, Med Chem Dept, Purdue Univ, 71-73; sr res chemist, 74-77, RES ASSOC POLYMER RES, STANDARD OIL CO, OHIO, 77- *Mem:* Am Chem Soc. *Res:* Synthesis of novel organosilicon compounds; exploration of novel polymers with high heat resistance and barrier characteristics; energy efficient separation means and processes. *Mailing Add:* 4440 Warrensville Ctr Rd Cleveland OH 44128

LI, HSIN LANG, b Shangtung, China, Sept 25, 30; US citizen; m 58. POLYMER SCIENCE. *Educ:* Univ Mich, Ann Arbor, BS, 54; Univ Ill, Urbana, MS, 55, PhD(mech eng), 59. *Prof Exp:* Res asst prof, Univ Ill, 59-60; sr res engr, E I Du Pont de Nemours & Co Inc, 60-64; RES ASSOC, ALLIED CORP, 64- *Mem:* Sigma Xi; Am Phys Soc. *Res:* Heat transfer; fluid dynamics; viscoelastic properties of polymers; polymer processing; fundamentals of polymer deformation; rheology of polymers; amorphous alloys; textile fibers; texturing of fibers. *Mailing Add:* Bldg CRL Allied Corp Morristown NJ 07960

LI, HSUEH MING, b Taiwan, Rep China, Oct 25, 39; US citizen; m 63; c 2. POLYMER CHEMISTRY. *Educ:* Tunghai Univ, Taiwan, BS, 62; Southern Methodist Univ, MS, 66; Polytech Inst Brooklyn, PhD(polymer chem), 71. *Prof Exp:* Fel x-ray diffraction, Polytech Inst Brooklyn, 70-72; res assoc polymer chem, Midland Macromolecular Inst, 72-73; RES CHEMIST POLYMER RES, ETHYL CORP, 73- *Mem:* Am Chem Soc. *Res:* Opacifying plastic pigment; polymeric flame retardants based on phosphazene-synthesis and evaluation; synthesis, characterization and mechanism of linear and cyclic phosphonitrillic chloride oligomers. *Mailing Add:* Ethyl Corp PO Box 341 Baton Rouge LA 70821

LI, HUI HUBERT, b Shanghai City, China, July 5, 32; US citizen; m 67; c 2. ATOMIC SPECTROSCOPY, NUCLEAR PHYSICS. *Educ:* Nat Cheng-Kung Univ, BS, 61; Nat Tsing-Hua Univ, MS, 63; Purdue Univ, PhD(physics, atomic spectros), 69. *Prof Exp:* Res assoc spectros, Dept Physics, 69-74, asst sr researcher, 74-75, ASSOC SR RESEARCHER OPTICAL CONSTANTS, CTR INFO & NUMERICAL DATA ANAL & SYNTHESIS, PURDUE UNIV, 75- *Res:* Atomic energy level determination and configuration interaction calculation; optical constants of optical materials. *Mailing Add:* CINDAS Purdue Univ West Lafayette IN 47906

LI, HUI-LIN, b Soochow, China, July 15, 11; US citizen; m 46; c 2. BOTANY. *Educ:* Soochow Univ, BS, 30; Yenching Univ, MS, 32; Harvard Univ, PhD(biol), 42. *Prof Exp:* Instr biol, Soochow Univ, 32-40, prof, 46-47; Harrison res fel, Univ Pa, 42-46; prof bot & chmn dept, Nat Taiwan Univ, 47-50; Blandy Farm res fel, Univ Va, 50-51; US State Dept res fel, 51-52; res assoc bot, Morris Arboretum, 52-55, taxonomist, 55-74, dir, 72-75, from assoc prof to prof bot, 58-74, JOHN BARTRAM PROF BOT, UNIV PA, 74- *Concurrent Pos:* John Simon Guggenheim Found fel, 61-62; academician, Acad Sinica, Taiwan, 64. *Mem:* AAAS; Bot Soc Am; Soc Econ Bot; Am Soc Plant Taxon. *Res:* Plant taxonomy and geography; biosystematics; economic botany. *Mailing Add:* Dept of Biol Univ of Pa Philadelphia PA 19174

LI, HUNG CHIANG, b Kinhwa, China, Dec 10, 21; US citizen; m 57; c 2. STATISTICS, ANALYTICAL MATHEMATICS. *Educ:* Univ Chekiang, BS, 46; Mich State Univ, MS, 64; Purdue Univ, PhD(statist), 69. *Prof Exp:* Asst math, Taiwan Normal Univ, 47-50; instr, Nat Taiwan Univ, 50-52; asst prof, Taiwan Inst Technol, 52-55; assoc prof, Tunghai Univ, 55-62; PROF STATIST, UNIV SOUTHERN COLO, 69- *Concurrent Pos:* Consult, Univ Southern Colo, 69- *Mem:* Inst Math Statist; Am Math Soc; Math Asn Am; Sigma Xi. *Res:* Multivariate analysis, particularly interested in normal distributions and the asymptotic expansions for distributions of characteristic roots of normal populations. *Mailing Add:* Dept of Math Univ of Southern Colo Pueblo CO 81001

LI, J(AMES) C(HEN) M(IN), b Nanking, China, Apr 12, 25; m 50; c 3. MATERIALS SCIENCE, MECHANICAL ENGINEERING. *Educ:* Nat Cent Univ, China, BS, 47; Univ Wash, MS, 51, PhD, 53. *Prof Exp:* Res chemist, Sch Med, Univ Wash, 51-53; res chemist & fel, Univ Calif, 53-55; supvr res proj, Mfg Chemists Asn, Carnegie Inst Technol, 55-56; phys chemist, Res Labs, Westinghouse Elec Corp, 56-57; scientist, Fundamental Res Lab, US Steel Corp, 57-60, sr scientist, 60-64, staff scientist, 65-69; mgr strength physics dept, Mat Res Ctr, Allied Chem Corp, 69-71; ALBERT

ARENDT HOPEMAN PROF ENG, UNIV ROCHESTER, 71- Concurrent Pos: Vis prof, Columbia Univ, 64-65; adj prof, 65-71; consult, Mat Res Ctr, Allied Chem Corp, 71-, NSF, 75-77 & US Steel Corp, 76; vis prof, Ruhr Universität Bochum, Ger & Humboldt award, Fed Repub Ger, 78-79; Alexander von Humbolt Award, 78. Honors & Awards: Mathewson Gold Medal, Metall Soc, 72; Robert Mehl Gold Medal, Am Inst Mining, Metall & Petrol Engrs & Inst Metals lectr, 78. Mem: fel Am Phys Soc; Am Inst Mining, Metall & Petrol Engrs; fel Am Soc Metals. Res: Dislocations and defects; plastic deformation; amorphous and polymeric materials; microstructural interactions; equilibrium and non-equilibrium phenomena. Mailing Add: Dept of Mech & Aerospace Sci Univ of Rochester Rochester NY 14627

LI, JANE CHIAO, b Shanghai, China, May 1, 39; US citizen; m 63; c 2. APPLIED STATISTICS. Educ: Hunter Col, BS, 63; Rutgers Univ, MS, 65, PhD(statist), 71. Prof Exp: Res chemist org chem, Endo Labs, Long Island, NY, 61-63; statist consult comput sci & statist, Rutgers Univ, 74-78; sr analyst, Paramins Div, Exxon Chem Co, 78-79; sect head world-wide testing, 79-81; MGR DATA ANAL & PROCESSING, PROCESS DIV, UOP, INC, 81- Mem: Sigma Xi; Am Statist Asn; Inst Math Statist. Res: Design and analysis of mixture experiments with process variables; evaluation of computer programs for efficient statistical analysis, data analysis in physical, medical and behavior sciences; data management in chemical research; data processing in petroleum and petrochemical industries. Mailing Add: Process Div UOP Inc Des Plaines IL 60016

LI, JEANNE B, b New York, NY, Apr 15, 44. BIOCHEMISTRY, PHYSIOLOGY. Educ: Vassar Col, AB, 66; Harvard Univ, PhD(biochem), 71. Prof Exp: Res fel physiol, Harvard Med Sch, 71-73; asst prof physiol, 73-79, RES ASSOC PEDIAT, HERSHEY MED CTR, PA STATE UNIV, 79- Concurrent Pos: Nat Cancer Inst & Muscular Dystrophy Asn fels, Harvard Med Sch, 71-73; Am Diabetes Asn grant, Hershey Med Ctr, Pa State Univ, 74-76. Mem: Am Physiol Soc; AAAS. Res: Regulation of protein synthesis and degradation in mammalian tissues. Mailing Add: Dept of Physiol Hershey Med Ctr Pa State Univ 500 Univ Dr Hershey PA 17033

LI, JOHN KONG-JIANN, b Taiwan, China, Aug 28, 50; US citizen; m 74; c 2. CARDIOVASCULAR SYSTEM, BIOMEDICAL INSTRUMENTATION. Educ: Univ Manchester, BSc, 72; Univ Pa, MSEng, 74, PhD(bioeng), 78. Prof Exp: Instr physics, Cent Found High Sch, London, 72; res fel bioeng, Univ Pa, 73-77, thesis supvr, 78-79; ASST PROF ELEC ENG, RUTGERS UNIV, 79-, ADJ ASST PROF SURG & BIOENG, UNIV MED & DENT NJ, RUTGERS MED SCH, 81- Concurrent Pos: Biomed engr cardiol, Presby Univ Pa Med Ctr, 77-79; prin investr, Rutgers Univ, NSF, 80-; vchmn, Eng Med & Biol, Princeton Sect, Inst Elec & Electronics Engrs, 80-; vis scientist, Fedn Am Soc Exp Biol, 81- Mem: Inst Elec & Electronics Engrs; Am Physiol Soc; NY Acad Sci; AAAS; Sigma Xi. Res: Cardiovascular dynamics; biomedical instrumentation; diagnostic cardiology; comparative physiology; physiological controls. Mailing Add: Dept Elec Eng Rutgers Univ Piscataway NY 08854

LI, KAM W(U), b China, Feb 16, 34; m 56; c 2. MECHANICAL ENGINEERING. Educ: Chu Hai Col, Hong Kong, BSME, 57; Colo State Univ, MSME, 61; Okla State Univ, PhD, 65. Prof Exp: Asst prof, Tex A&I Univ, 65-67; from asst prof to assoc prof mech eng, 67-73, PROF MECH ENG, N DAK STATE UNIV, 73- Concurrent Pos: Consult engr, Scott Eng Sci Corp, 67-68; NSF Instnl Fund grants, NDak State Univ, 67-68 & 71; Dept Defense grant, 69; Am Soc Eng Educ-Ford Found resident fel, Northern States Power Co, Minneapolis, Minn, 71-72; eng consult, Chas T Main Inc, Boston, 73-; USDA res grants, 74-78 & 76-78. Mem: Am Soc Mech Engrs; NY Acad Sci. Res: Heat transfer; fluid dynamics; thermodynamics; power generation; thermal system design; applied mathematics; energy models; new power generation systems. Mailing Add: Dept of Mech Eng NDak State Univ Fargo ND 58102

LI, KE WEN, b Taiwan, Sept 28, 33; m 63; c 2. CHEMICAL ENGINEERING. Educ: Cheng Kung Univ, Taiwan, BS, 57; Purdue Univ, MS, 63, PhD(chem eng), 69. Prof Exp: Asst chem eng, Cheng Kung Univ, Taiwan, 59-63, instr, 63-66; instr, Purdue Univ, 62-63; res chem engr, Continental Oil Co, 68-74; sr chem engr, 75-76, group leader, 77-80, PROCESS DESIGN MGR, LUMMUS TECH CTR, C-E LUMMUS CO, 80- Res: Reaction engineering, kinetics, process development and design. Mailing Add: Reaction Eng Chem Eng Dept 1515 Broad St Bloomfield NJ 07003

LI, KELVIN K, b Kwantung, China, Mar 25, 34; US citizen; m 65; c 4. PHYSICS. Educ: McGill Univ, BEng, 58; Mass Inst Technol, PhD(physics), 64. Prof Exp: PHYSICIST, BROOKHAVEN NAT LAB, 65- Mem: Am Phys Soc. Res: Elementary particle interactions. Mailing Add: Dept of Physics Brookhaven Nat Lab Upton NY 11973

LI, KOIBONG, b Pingtung, Taiwan, Jan 12, 14; US citizen; m 46; c 2. MICROBIOLOGY. Educ: Seoul Nat Univ, MD, 40; Tokyo Univ, PhD(microbiol), 47. Prof Exp: Res mem microbiol, Inst Infectious Dis, Univ Tokyo, 40-46; sr microbiologist, 406th Med Gen Lab, US Army, 46-58; res assoc microbiol, Sch Med, NY Univ, 58-61; res assoc, 61-64; chief bact lab, Fordham Hosp, New York, 64-66; asst prof & dir bact lab, Bird S Coler Hosp, Ctr Chronic Dis, NY Med Col, 67-69; ASST PROF, STATE UNIV NY DOWNSTATE MED CTR, 69- Concurrent Pos: Adj assoc prof & res adv, York Col, City Univ New York, 75- Mem: AAAS; Harvey Soc; Am Soc Microbiol. Res: Leptospirosis; streptococci; interaction of bacteriophage and Shigella dysenteriae; toxin production of Shigella dysenteriae; a novel type of resistant bacteria induced by gentamicin; anti-evolutionary effect of gentamicin on bacteria; embryos and development of bacterial cells. Mailing Add: 74-11 44th Ave Elmhurst NY 11373

LI, KUANG-PANG, b Kwang-tung, China, Oct 11, 38; m; c 2. ANALYTICAL CHEMISTRY. Educ: Nat Taiwan Univ, BS, 61; Univ Ill, MS, 68, PhD(anal chem), 70. Prof Exp: Lectr chem, Kaohsiung Prov Inst Technol, Taiwan, 64-65; res assoc, Ariz State Univ, 70-72; res assoc, Univ Ill, 72-73; asst prof chem, Univ Fla, 73-80; MEM FAC, DEPT CHEM, UNIV LOWELL, 80- Mem: Am Chem Soc. Res: Metallic ion transport in biomembranes; membrane interactions of chemical carcinogens; theoretical and practical developments of chromatographic methods; analysis of polynuclear aromatics in auto exhaust particulates. Mailing Add: Dept Chem Univ Lowell Lowell MA 01854

LI, KUN, b Kunming, China, Nov 20, 23; m 51; c 2. CHEMICAL ENGINEERING. Educ: Nat Southwest Assoc Univ, China, BEng, 45; Carnegie Inst Technol, MS, 49, DSc, 52. Prof Exp: Res chemist, Petrol Res Lab, Carnegie Inst Technol, 52-55, supvr & sr res chemist, 55-56; sr res engr, Jones & Laughlin Steel Corp, 56-58, res assoc, 58-62; assoc prof chem eng, 62-64, PROF CHEM ENG, CARNEGIE-MELLON UNIV, 64- Concurrent Pos: Consult, Jones & Laughlin Steel Corp. Mem: Am Chem Soc; Am Inst Chem Engrs; Am Inst Mining, Metall & Petrol Engrs. Res: Fluid flow; kinetics of high-temperature processes. Mailing Add: Dept of Chem Eng Carnegie-Mellon Univ Pittsburgh PA 15213

LI, LI-HSIENG, b Peking, China, Dec 31, 33; m 60; c 2. BIOCHEMISTRY. Educ: Nat Taiwan Univ, BS, 55; Va Polytech Inst, MS, 62, PhD(biochem), 64. Prof Exp: Res assoc, Ind Univ, 64-65; SR RES SCIENTIST, UPJOHN CO, 65-, RES ASSOC, 80- Mem: Am Chem Soc; Am Asn Cancer Res; Am Asn Biol Chemists. Res: Enzymology; mechanism of action of anticancer agent; virus and cancer; cell biology. Mailing Add: Upjohn Co Cancer Res 301 Henrietta St Kalamazoo MI 49001

LI, LING-FONG, b Fukien, China, Apr 17, 44. THEORETICAL HIGH ENERGY PHYSICS. Educ: Nat Taiwan Univ, BS, 65; Univ Pa, MS, 67, PhD(physics), 70. Prof Exp: Res assoc physics, Rockefeller Univ, 70-72; res assoc, Stanford Linear Accelerator Ctr, Stanford Univ, 72-74; asst prof, 74-79, ASSOC PROF PHYSICS, CARNEGIE-MELLON UNIV, 79- Mem: Am Phys Soc. Res: Unified theories of weak and electromagnetic interactions in relation to the fundamental structure of the elementary particles. Mailing Add: Dept of Physics Carnegie-Mellon Univ Pittsburgh PA 15213

LI, LU KU, b Honan, China, Apr 26, 36; m 61; c 1. BIOCHEMISTRY, PROTEIN CHEMISTRY. Educ: Nat Taiwan Univ, BS, 58; Princeton Univ, PhD(biol), 64. Prof Exp: Res asst biol, Princeton Univ, 63-64; res assoc chem, Cornell Univ, 64-66; instr ophthal, 66-68, assoc, 68-69, asst prof, 69-74, RESEARCHER OPHTHAL, COLUMBIA UNIV, 74- Mem: Sigma Xi; Am Chem Soc; Am Soc Biol Chemists. Res: Maturation of lens fiber cells and its relation to cataractogenesis; the subunits interactions of lens proteins; vision and opthalmology. Mailing Add: Dept of Ophthal Columbia Univ New York NY 10032

LI, MIN CHIU, internal medicine, oncology, deceased

LI, MING CHIANG, b Ningpo, China, June 18, 35; US citizen; m 65; c 2. PHYSICS, MATHEMATICS. Educ: Peking Univ, BS, 58; Univ Md, PhD(physics, math), 65. Prof Exp: Lectr physics, Norm Col Inner Mongolia, China, 58-61; res asst, Univ Md, 64-65; fel & mem sci, Inst Advan Study, 65-67; asst prof, 68-72, ASSOC PROF PHYSICS, VA POLYTECH INST & STATE UNIV, 72- Mem: Am Phys Soc. Res: Atomic and molecular physics; interferometry; laser optics. Mailing Add: Dept of Physics Va Polytech Inst & State Univ Blacksburg VA 24061

LI, MING FANG, b Chickiang, China, Oct 28, 22; m 56; c 3. ANIMAL NUTRITION, MICROBIOLOGY. Educ: St John's Univ, Shanghai, BS, 47; Univ Man, MSc, 57; Univ Alta, PhD(animal nutrit), 63. Prof Exp: Dairy specialist, Taiwan Animal Prod Co, Formosa, 49-54; assoc scientist, 63-71, RES SCIENTIST, HALIFAX LAB, FISHERIES & MARINE SCI SERV CAN, 71- Mem: Can Soc Microbiol; Tissue Cult Asn; Can Inst Food Sci & Technol. Res: Tissue culture; fish diseases; fatty acid metabolism in rumen microorganisms; keeping quality of pasteurized milk. Mailing Add: Fisheries & Marine Sci Serv PO Box 550 Halifax NS B3J 2S7 Can

LI, MING KUNG, chemical engineering, see previous edition

LI, NORMAN CHUNG, b Foochow, China, Jan 13, 13; nat US; m 37; c 5. PHYSICAL CHEMISTRY. Educ: Kenyon Col, BS, 33; Univ Mich, MS, 34; Univ Wis, PhD(chem), 36. Prof Exp: Prof chem, Anhwei Univ, China, 36-38; lectr, Yenching Univ, 38-40; lectr, Cath Univ, China, 40-43; from assoc prof to prof, 43-46; from asst prof to assoc prof, St Louis Univ, 46-52; prof chem, 52-78, DISTINGUISHED SERV PROF CHEM, DUQUESNE UNIV, 78- Concurrent Pos: Consult, Argonne Nat Lab, 56-58; vis scientist, NIH, 62; tech asst expert, Int Atomic Energy Agency, 64; vis prof, Tsing Hua Univ, China, 64; adv chem res ctr, Nat Taiwan Univ, 66-; consult, Nat Res Coun of Repub China, 74-75; adv, Inst Chem, Nat Tsing Hua Univ, Repub China, 74-; sabbatical leave, res chemist, Naval Res Lab, 81-82. Mem: Fel AAAS; Am Chem Soc; Sigma Xi. Res: Nuclear magnetic resonance studies of hydrogen and metal binding; hydrogen bonding in coal and asphaltenes; research on metalloproteins. Mailing Add: Dept of Chem Duquesne Univ Pittsburgh PA 15219

LI, NORMAN NIAN-TZE, b Shanghai, China, Jan 14, 33; US citizen; m 63; c 2. CHEMICAL ENGINEERING. Educ: Taiwan Nat Univ, BS, 54; Wayne State Univ, MS, 57; Stevens Inst Technol, ScD(chem eng), 63. Prof Exp: Chem engr, Shinlin Paper & Pulp Co, 53 & Parke-Davis & Co, 56; instr chem, Newark Col Eng, 61-63; res engr, Exxon Res & Eng Co, 63-66, sr res engr, 66-70, res assoc, 70-77, sr res assoc, 77-81, head, Separation Sci Group, 76-81; DIR SEPARATIONS RES, UOP INC, 81- Concurrent Pos: Vis lectr, Newark Col Eng, 63-67; consult, Bell Aerosysts Co, 67; chmn, Gordon Res Conf Separations & Purification, 73; chmn, Gordon Res Conf Transport Phenomena in Membranes, 75. Mem: Am Inst Chem Engrs; Am Chem Soc; NY Acad Sci; Am Inst Chem. Res: Mass transfer; surface chemistry; interfacial phenomena; transport through membranes; separation techniques. Mailing Add: UOP Inc 10 UOP Plaza Des Plaines IL 60016

LI, PAUL H, b China, May 4, 33; US citizen; m 63; c 2. HORTICULTURE, PLANT PHYSIOLOGY. *Educ:* Ore State Univ, PhD(hort & plant physiol), 63. *Prof Exp:* PROF HORT & PLANT PHYSIOL, UNIV MINN, 63- *Concurrent Pos:* Vis prof, Int Potato Ctr, 73, Inst Low Temperature Sci, Hookkaido Univ, 76 & Peking Agr Univ, 80. *Honors & Awards:* Dow Chem Co Award, Am Soc Hort Sci, 65, Alex Laurie Award, 66. *Mem:* Am Soc Hort Sci; Am Soc Plant Physiologists; Potato Asn Am; Soc Cryobiol; Am Soc Agron. *Res:* Plant hardiness, potato frost resistance and crop heat stress physiology. *Mailing Add:* Dept of Hort Sci Univ of Minn St Paul MN 55108

LI, PEI-CHING, b Kiangsu, China, Nov 2, 19; m 45; c 3. CHEMICAL ENGINEERING. *Educ:* Nat Southwest Assoc Univ, China, BE, 45; Univ Rochester, MS, 55, PhD(chem eng), 59. *Prof Exp:* Asst chem eng, Nat Southwest Assoc Univ, China, 44-46; teacher sci, Chungking Women's Norm Sch, 46-47; chemist & engr, Taiwan Sugar Corp, 47-53; asst chem eng, Univ Rochester, 54-57, res assoc glass, 58-59; mem res staff, Raytheon Co, 59-64; res scientist, Am Standard Corp, 64-65; res scientist ceramics div, IIT Res Inst, 65-68; ADV ENGR, IBM CORP, 68- *Mem:* Am Ceramic Soc; Am Chem Soc. *Res:* Physical properties of molten glass, particularly enamel glass and binary system of borates; solid state reactions of ferrites; pyrolytic high temperature materials; chemical vapor deposition and plasma enhanced chemical vapor deposition dielectric films. *Mailing Add:* Bykenhulle Rd Hopewell Junction NY 12533

LI, SEUNG P(ING), b Hong Kong, Jan 15, 32; m 57; c 3. PHYSICS, ENGINEERING. *Educ:* Univ Hong Kong, BSc, 54; Princeton Univ, MSE, 60; Univ Colo, PhD(physics), 66. *Prof Exp:* Demonstr gen eng, Univ Hong Kong, 54-57; engr, Scott & Wilson Consult Engrs, 57-59; asst lectr physics, Chung Chi Col, Hong Kong, 60-63, lectr & chmn dept, 65-68; from asst prof to assoc prof, 68-75, PROF ELEC & ELECTRONICS ENG, CALIF STATE POLYTECH UNIV, POMONA, 75- *Mem:* Inst Elec & Electronics Engrs. *Res:* Semiconductor physics and devices; electromagnetic theory. *Mailing Add:* Dept of Elec & Electronics Eng 3801 W Temple Ave Pomona CA 91766

LI, SHENG-SAN, b Hsin-Chu, Taiwan, Dec 10, 38; m 64; c 3. ELECTRICAL ENGINEERING. *Educ:* Cheng Kung Univ, Taiwan, BS, 62; Rice Univ, MS, 66, PhD(elec eng), 68. *Prof Exp:* Engr, China Elec Mfg Co, Taiwan, 63-64; teaching asst elec eng, Rice Univ, 64-67; from asst prof to assoc prof, 68-73, PROF ELEC ENG, UNIV FLA, 73- *Concurrent Pos:* Electronic engr, Nat Bur Standards, 75-76; consult, Battelle Columbus Labs, Ohio, 75-77 & Harris Semiconductors Inc, Fla, 78- *Mem:* sr mem Am Phys Soc; Inst Elec & Electronics Engrs; Am Soc Testing & Measurements; Electrochem Soc. *Res:* Semiconductor device physics; transport phenomena in semiconductors; photoelectric effects in semiconductors and devices; defect and recombination properties in semiconductor materials and devices; solar cells and photodetectors. *Mailing Add:* 227 Benton Hall Univ of Fla Gainesville FL 32611

LI, SHU-TIEN, b Hopei, China, Feb 10, 00; m 19; c 5. CIVIL ENGINEERING. *Educ:* Nat Peiyang Univ, China, BSCE, 23; Cornell Univ, PhD(civil eng), 26. *Prof Exp:* Design engr, J A L Waddel, Consult Engr, NY, 26-27; prof civil eng, Nat Peiyang Univ, 27-28; chmn bd & chief engr, Great Northern Port Develop Bd, 29-34; pres & dir eng, Res Inst, Nat Pieyang Univ, 32-39; first pres, Nat Sikang Inst Technol, 39-41 & Nat Kweichow Col Agr & Eng, 41-42; vpres, Yellow River Comn, 43-47; dean univ fac, dean eng & dean of sci to reestablish Nat Peiyang Univ after WWII, 46-50; vis prof civil eng, Rutgers Univ, 53-54; chief tech writer, Palmer & Baker Engrs, 55-61; prof civil eng, Grad Div, 62-70, dir struct mech & concrete technol res, 66-70, chmn grad div struct & concrete technol, 67-70, exec dir interdisciplinary coun geotechnol, 69-70, EMER PROF CIVIL ENG, S DAK SCH MINES & TECHNOL, 70-; FOUNDER, CHMN BD & PRES, LONG ISLAND INST SCI & TECHNOL, 70- & WORLD OPEN UNIV, 73- *Concurrent Pos:* Exec mem, NChina River Comn, 28-37; chancellor & dir eng, Res Inst, Nat Tangshan Eng Col, 30-32; mem exec comt & dean eng, Nat Northwest United Univ, 37-38, chmn admin comt, 38-39; pres, Peiyang Siking Inst, 44-46; mem acad coun, Nat Acad Peiping, 48-; consult engr, 49-; academician, China Acad, 65- *Honors & Awards:* Chinese Govt First Class Hydraul Medal, 36, Victory Decoration, 46; Distinguished Serv Award, Am Chem Soc, 70. *Mem:* Sigma Xi; fel Am Soc Civil Engrs; fel AAAS; Am Chem Inst; Nat Soc Petrol Engrs. *Mailing Add:* PO Drawer 5505 Orange CA 92667

LI, SHU-TUNG, b China, Aug 29, 39; US citizen; c 2. BIOPHYSICAL CHEMISTRY. *Educ:* Nat Taiwan Normal Univ, BS, 63; Univ Conn, PhD(phys chem), 71. *Prof Exp:* Res Assoc, 71-77, ASST PROF ORAL BIOL, UNIV CONN, 77- *Mem:* AAAS. *Res:* Physical chemistry of proteins and mineralized tissues; structure and function of biopolymers; collagen, cell interactions. *Mailing Add:* 76 St James West Hartford CT 06119

LI, STEVEN SHOEI-LUNG, b Taiwan, China, Oct 20, 38; m 67; c 2. GENETICS, BIOCHEMISTRY. *Educ:* Nat Taiwan Univ, BS, 61, MS, 63; Univ Mo, PhD(genetics), 68. *Prof Exp:* Res assoc, Univ Tex, Austin, 68-70; res assoc biol sci, Stanford Univ, 70-74; assoc prof, Mt Sinai Sch Med, 74-77; RES GENETICIST, NAT INST ENVIRON HEALTH SCI, NIH, 77- *Mem:* AAAS; Am Soc Biol Chemist; Genetics Soc Am. *Res:* Biochemical genetics; structure and evolution of eukayotic genes and proteins. *Mailing Add:* Nat Inst Environ Health Sci NIH Research Triangle Park NC 27709

LI, SU-CHEN, b Taipei, Taiwan, June 8, 35; US citizen; m 62; c 2. BIOCHEMISTRY. *Educ:* Nat Taiwan Univ, BS, 58; Univ Okla, PhD(biochem), 65. *Prof Exp:* from asst prof to assoc prof, 72-80, PROF BIOCHEM, SCH MED, TULANE UNIV, 80- *Concurrent Pos:* Career Develop Award, NIH, 75-80. *Mem:* Am Soc Biol Chemists; AAAS; Soc Complex Carbohydrates. *Res:* Biochemical studies of glycoconjugates and glycosidases. *Mailing Add:* Delta Primate Res Ctr Tulane Univ Three Rivers Rd Covington LA 70433

LI, TAO PING, b Szechwan, China, Nov 16, 20; m 48; c 3. ORGANIC CHEMISTRY. *Educ:* Nat Szechwan Univ, China, BS, 41; Univ Tex, MA, 59, PhD(org chem), 60. *Prof Exp:* Fel, Univ Tex, 60-61; sr proj chemist, Am Oil Co, Ind, 61-64; res specialist, 64-66, group leader, 66-69, SR GROUP LEADER, MONSANTO CO, 69- *Mem:* AAAS; Am Chem Soc; Catalysis Soc; NY Acad Sci. *Res:* Chemical kinetics, heterogeneous catalysis and chemistry of metal organic compounds. *Mailing Add:* Monsanto Co 800 N Lindbergh Blvd St Louis MO 63166

LI, TA-YUNG, meteorology, see previous edition

LI, TIEN-YIEN, b Hunan, China, June 28, 45; m 71; c 1. MATHEMATICS. *Educ:* Nat Tsing-Hua Univ, BS, 68; Univ Md, PhD(math), 74. *Prof Exp:* Instr math, Univ Utah, 74; asst prof, 74-78, ASSOC PROF MATH, MICH STATE UNIV, 79- *Concurrent Pos:* Vis asst prof math, Res Ctr, Univ Wis, 78-79. *Res:* Differential equations, dynamical systems and numerical analysis. *Mailing Add:* Dept of Math Mich State Univ East Lansing MI 48824

LI, TING KAI, b Nanking, China, Nov 13, 34; m 60; c 2. MEDICINE, BIOCHEMISTRY. *Educ:* Northwestern Univ, AB, 55; Harvard Med Sch, MD, 59; Mass Inst Technol, 60-61. *Prof Exp:* House officer, Peter Bent Brigham Hosp, 59-60, asst med, 60-63, jr assoc, 63-65; instr med, Harvard Med Sch, 65-67, assoc, 67-69; dep dir div biochem, Walter Reed Army Inst Res, 69-71; PROF MED & BIOCHEM, SCH MED, IND UNIV, INDIANAPOLIS, 71- *Concurrent Pos:* Helen Hay Whitney Found fel, 60-64; Med Found Boston fel, 64-68; Markle scholar acad med, 67-73; asst med, Harvard Med Ach, 60-63, res assoc biochem, 63-65; chief resident, Peter Bent Brigham Hosp, 65-66; guest scientist, Nobel Med Inst, Sweden, 68. *Mem:* Am Chem Soc; Am Soc Clin Invest; Endocrine Soc; Am Soc Biol Chem; Am Fedn Clin Res. *Res:* Enzymology; metabolism; chemical basis of biological specificity; alcohol metabolism. *Mailing Add:* Dept of Med Ind Univ Med Ctr Indianapolis IN 46202

LI, TINGYE, b Nanking, China, July 7, 31; m 56; c 2. ELECTRICAL ENGINEERING, PHYSICS. *Educ:* Univ Witwatersrand, BSc, 53; Northwestern Univ, MS, 55, PhD(elec eng), 58. *Prof Exp:* Mem tech staff, 57-67, head, Repeater Tech Res Dept, 67-76, HEAD, TRANSMISSION & CIRCUITS RES DEPT, BELL TEL LABS, INC, 76- *Honors & Awards:* Co-recipient, W R G Baker Prize, Inst Elec & Electronics Engrs, 75, David Sarnoff Award, 79. *Mem:* Nat Acad Eng; fel Optical Soc Am; AAAS; Chinese Inst Engrs-USA; fel Inst Elec & Electronics Engrs. *Res:* Optical communications; lasers and coherent-wave optics; electromagnetic field theory; antennas and propagation; microwave theory and techniques. *Mailing Add:* Crawford Hill Lab Bell Tel Labs Inc Holmdel NJ 07733

LI, WEN-CH'ING WINNIE, b China, Dec 25, 48. NUMBER THEORY. *Educ:* Nat Taiwan Univ, BS, 70; Univ Calif, Berkeley, PhD(math), 74. *Prof Exp:* Asst prof math, Harvard Univ, 74-78; asst prof math, Univ Ill, Chicago Circle, 78-79; ASSOC PROF MATH, PA STATE UNIV, 79- *Concurrent Pos:* Alfred Sloan fel, 81-83. *Mem:* Am Math Soc. *Res:* Automorphic forms, representation theory and number theory. *Mailing Add:* Dept Math Pa State Univ University Park PA 16802

LI, WEN-HSIUNG, b Guongdong, China, Nov 5, 18; m 50; c 1. MECHANICS, CIVIL ENGINEERING. *Educ:* Chiao-Tung Univ, BS, 41; Univ Manchester, PhD(eng), 47. *Prof Exp:* Fel civil eng, Johns Hopkins Univ, 48-50, from asst prof to assoc prof, 50-59; PROF CIVIL ENG, SYRACUSE UNIV, 59- *Honors & Awards:* Eddy Award, Fedn Sewage & Indust Wastes Asn, 54. *Mem:* Am Soc Civil Engrs; Int Asn Hydraul Res. *Res:* Fluid and solid mechanics. *Mailing Add:* Dept of Civil Eng Syracuse Univ Syracuse NY 13210

LI, WEN-HSIUNG, b Ping-Tung, Taiwan, Sept 22, 42; m 75; c 2. POPULATION GENETICS, APPLIED MATHEMATICS. *Educ:* Chung-Yuang Col Sci & Eng, Taiwan, BE, 65; Nat Cent Univ, Taiwan, MS, 68; Brown Univ, PhD(appl math), 72. *Prof Exp:* Proj assoc, Univ Wis-Madison, 72-73; asst prof, 73-78, ASSOC PROF POP GENETICS, UNIV TEX, HOUSTON, 78- *Concurrent Pos:* Assoc ed, Theoret Pop Biol. *Mem:* Genetics Soc Am; AAAS; Am Soc Human Genetics. *Res:* Molecular evolution; biomathematics; human genetics. *Mailing Add:* Ctr Demog & Pop Genetics Univ Tex Houston TX 77030

LI, WU-SHYONG, b Taipei, Taiwan, Aug 20, 43; m 75. PHYSICAL ORGANIC CHEMISTRY. *Educ:* Nat Taiwan Univ, BS, 66; Kent State Univ, MS, 69; Univ Minn, PhD(org chem), 73. *Prof Exp:* Fel, Ohio State Univ, 73-75; sr chemist plastic, Rohm & Haas Co, 75-78; sr chemist, 78-80, RES SPECIALIST, 3M CO, 80- *Mem:* Am Chem Soc. *Res:* Reaction mechanism, kinetics, polymers and UV curing. *Mailing Add:* 3M Co 3M Ctr Bldg 209 St Paul MN 55101

LI, YUAN, b Ningpo, China, Sept 15, 36. SOLID STATE PHYSICS, HIGH ENERGY PHYSICS. *Educ:* Nat Taiwan Univ, BS, 58; Ind Univ, PhD(physics), 66. *Prof Exp:* Res assoc physics, Rutgers Univ, 65-68, asst prof, 65-77; assoc prof, Tuskegee Inst, 75-77; ASSOC PROF PHYSICS, RUTGERS UNIV, 77- *Concurrent Pos:* NSF res grant, 76-77. *Mem:* Am Phys Soc; Am Asn Physics Teachers. *Res:* Crystallography and lattice dynamics. *Mailing Add:* Dept of Physics NCAS Rutgers Univ Newark NJ 07102

LI, YU-TEH, b Hsin-Chu City, Formosa, Apr 1, 34; m 62; c 2. BIOCHEMISTRY. *Educ:* Nat Taiwan Univ, BS, 57, MS, 60; Univ Okla, PhD(biochem), 63. *Prof Exp:* From instr to asst prof biochem, Sch Med, Univ Okla, 63-66; CHIEF, DELTA REGIONAL PRIMATE RES CTR, 66-, PROF BIOCHEM, SCH MED, TULANE UNIV, 74- *Concurrent Pos:* Fel biochem, Sch Med, Univ Okla, 63-64; Nat Cancer Inst grant, 64-66; NSF grant, 68-; NIH grant, 71-; USPHS res career develop award, 71-76. *Mem:* Am Chem Soc; Am Soc Biol Chem. *Res:* Biochemical studies on glycoproteins and various glycosidases. *Mailing Add:* Dept of Biochem Sch of Med Tulane Univ New Orleans LA 70112

LIAN, ERIC CHUN-YET, b Tainan Hsien, Taiwan, Nov 11, 38; m 73; c 2. HEMATOLOGY. *Educ:* Nat Taiwan Univ, MD, 64. *Prof Exp:* Res fel hemat, Univ Miami, 69-71; res assoc hemostasis, Harvard Med Sch, 71-73; asst prof med, Sch Med, 73-76, DIR, COMPREHENSIVE HEMOPHILIA CTR, UNIV MIAMI, 76-, DIR HEMOSTASIS LAB, 76-, ASSOC PROF MED, SCH MED, 78- *Concurrent Pos:* Prin investr biochem, immunol & physiol of antihemophilic factor, 76- & pathogenesis of thrombotic thrombocytopenic purpura, 78- *Mem:* Fel Am Col Physicians; AAAS; Am Fedn Clin Res; Am Soc Hemat; Am Heart Asn. *Res:* Thrombosis and hemostasis. *Mailing Add:* Vet Admin Hosp 1201 NW 16th St Miami FL 33125

LIAN, HAROLD MAYNARD, b Fairdale, NDak, Dec 25, 22; m 53; c 4. GEOLOGY. *Educ:* Univ Calif, Los Angeles, PhD(geol), 53. *Prof Exp:* VPRES EXPLOR, INT DIV, UNION OIL CO, CALIF, 52- *Concurrent Pos:* Fulbright res scholar, Austria, 54-55. *Mem:* Geol Soc Am; Am Asn Petrol Geol. *Res:* Stratigraphy; petroleum geology. *Mailing Add:* Union Oil Co of Calif Box 7600 Los Angeles CA 90054

LIANG, CHARLES CHI, b Nanking, China, June 9, 34; m 61; c 3. PHYSICAL CHEMISTRY, ANALYTICAL CHEMISTRY. *Educ:* Nat Taiwan Univ, BS, 56; Baylor Univ, PhD(phys chem), 62. *Prof Exp:* Res chemist, Houdry Process & Chem Co, 62-63; from asst prof to assoc prof phys chem, WVa Inst Technol, 63-65; sr staff mem electrochem, P R Mallory Co, Inc, 65-73, asst tech dir batteries, Lab Phys Sci, 73-77; dir, VP Technol, Wilson Greatbatch, LTD, 77-79; PRES, ELECTROCHEM INDUSTS, INC, 79- *Honors & Awards:* IR 100 Award, Indust Res Mag, 71. *Mem:* Am Chem Soc; Electrochem Soc. *Res:* Mechanisms and kinetics of electrode processes; chemical thermodynamics; analytical techniques; solid state chemistry. *Mailing Add:* Electrochem Industs Inc 9990 Wehrle Dr Clarence NY 14031

LIANG, CHARLES SHIH-TUNG, b Peking, China, Dec 10, 40; US citizen; m 65; c 2. ELECTRICAL ENGINEERING, APPLIED PHYSICS. *Educ:* Univ Ill, BS, 62, PhD(elec eng), 68; Harvard Univ, SM, 63. *Prof Exp:* Asst elec eng, Univ Ill, 63-68; PROJ AEROSYSTS ENGR, CONVAIR AEROSPACE DIV, FT WORTH OPER, GEN DYNAMICS CORP, 69- *Mem:* AAAS; Inst Elec & Electronics Engrs. *Res:* Electromagnetism; scattering research as related to radar signature analysis and target identification; microwave antenna design and development; plasma physics; applied mathematics and advanced data processing techniques. *Mailing Add:* 6816 Dwight Ft Worth TX 76116

LIANG, CHING YU, b Hupeh, China, Dec 16, 16; US citizen; m 49; c 1. PHYSICS. *Educ:* Nat Cent Univ, China, BS, 43; Univ Okla, MS, 50, PhD(physics), 52. *Prof Exp:* Instr physics, Nat Cent Univ, China, 43-48; fel, Univ Mich, 52-55; res assoc physics, Am Viscose Corp, Pa, 55-63; sr res scientist, Lear Siegler, Inc, Calif, 63-64; assoc prof, 64-68, PROF PHYSICS & ANAT, CALIF STATE UNIV, 68- *Concurrent Pos:* Consult & intermittent physicist, Navy Electronic Lab, San Diego, Calif, 65- *Mem:* Am Phys Soc. *Res:* Infrared spectra and structures of polymers; semiconductivity of organic crystals and biological molecules; solid state physics. *Mailing Add:* Dept of Physics & Astron Calif State Univ Northridge CA 91330

LIANG, EDISON PARK-TAK, b Canton, China, July 22, 47; nat US; m 71. ASTROPHYSICS, COSMOLOGY. *Educ:* Univ Calif, Berkeley, BA, 67, PhD(physics), 71. *Prof Exp:* Res assoc, Univ Tex, Austin, 71-73; res assoc & assoc instr astrophys & relativity, Univ Utah, 73-75; asst prof astrophys, Mich State Univ, 75-76; asst prof physics, Stanford Univ, 76-79; PHYSICIST, LAWRENCE LIVERMORE NAT LAB, 80- *Concurrent Pos:* Lectr appl physics, Stanford Univ, 80- *Res:* Origin and dynamics of cosmic fluctuations; astrophysics of compact objects (x-ray sources); gravitational collapse; galaxy formation problems; space-time singularities; nonlinear fluid mechanics; relativity. *Mailing Add:* Lawrence Livermore Nat Lab Livermore CA 94550

LIANG, GEORGE H L, b Peiping, China, Oct 1, 34; m 63; c 1. PLANT GENETICS, PLANT BREEDING. *Educ:* Taiwan Prov Col Agr, BS, 56; Univ Wyo, MS, 61; Univ Wis, PhD(agron), 65. *Prof Exp:* Agronomist, Taiwan Prov Res Inst Agr, 58-59; asst prof, 64-69, ASSOC PROF PLANT GENETICS & CYTOGENETICIST, KANS STATE UNIV, 69- *Mem:* Am Soc Agron; Crop Sci Soc Am; Am Genetic Asn; Genetics Soc Am; Genetics Soc Can. *Res:* Quantitative genetics in plant species; cytogenetics and breeding aspects in cultivated crops; taxonomy of plant in relation to cytology and biochemistry. *Mailing Add:* Dept of Agron Kans State Univ Manhattan KS 66506

LIANG, JOHNNIE C, b Peking, China, Apr 26, 47; m 73; c 1. COMPUTER SYSTEMS, CONTROL ENGINEERING. *Educ:* Chiao-Tung Univ, BSEE, 69; Univ Pittsburgh, MS, 72, PhD(elec eng), 76. *Prof Exp:* Syst energy mgt, Westinghouse Elec Corp, 75-76; control engr, 77-80, PRIN CONTROL ENGR UTILITY BUS, HONEYWELL INC, 80- *Concurrent Pos:* Mem fac, Ariz State Univ, 78- *Mem:* Inst Elec & Electronics Engrs; Instrument Soc Am. *Res:* Industrial process control systems; energy and environmental protection management; power system control theory. *Mailing Add:* 2222 W Peoria Ave Phoenix AZ 85029

LIANG, JOSEPH JEN-YIN, b China; US citizen; m 65; c 2. MATHEMATICS. *Educ:* Nat Taiwan Univ, BA, 58; Univ Detroit, MA, 62; Ohio State Univ, PhD(math), 69. *Prof Exp:* Res fel math, Calif Inst Technol, 69-70; from asst prof to assoc prof, 70-77, PROF MATH, UNIV S FLA, 78- *Concurrent Pos:* Vis asst prof, Ohio State Univ, 72; vis assoc, Calif Inst Technol, 75 & 77. *Res:* Number theory; coding theory; algorithms. *Mailing Add:* Dept of Math Univ of SFla Tampa FL 33620

LIANG, KAI, b Hunan, China, Mar 23, 34; m 64. PHYSICAL CHEMISTRY. *Educ:* Nat Taiwan Univ, BS, 56; Univ Utah, PhD(phys chem), 64. *Prof Exp:* Res asst phys chem, Univ Utah, 60-64; sr res chemist, 64-70, MEM SR STAFF, COLOR PHOTOG DIV, RES LABS, EASTMAN KODAK CO, 70- *Mem:* Am Chem Soc. *Res:* Diffusion and transport processes; mathematical modelling of diffusion kinetics; color photography. *Mailing Add:* Res Labs Color Photog Div Eastman Kodak Co Kodak Park Rochester NY 14650

LIANG, KENG-SAN, b Tainan, Taiwan, Dec 17, 43; m 69; c 2. MATERIALS SCIENCE, SOLID STATE PHYSICS. *Educ:* Nat Taiwan Univ, BS, 66; Stanford Univ, MS, 70, PhD(appl physics), 73. *Prof Exp:* From assoc scientist to scientist mat sci, Xerox Corp, 73-78; STAFF PHYSICIST MAT SCI, CORP RES LABS, EXXON RES & ENG CO, 78- *Mem:* Am Phys Soc; Am Vacuum Soc. *Res:* Amorphous solids, x-ray diffraction, x-ray photoelectron spectroscopy, electronic structure, thin films. *Mailing Add:* Corp Res Lab PO Box 45 Linden NJ 07036

LIANG, TA, b Canton, China, June 11, 16; US citizen; m 42; c 1. CIVIL ENGINEERING. *Educ:* Tsinghua Univ, Peking, BEng, 37; Cornell Univ, MCE, 48, PhD(civil eng), 52. *Prof Exp:* Civil engr, Chinese Nat Govt, 37-42; sr engr, US Army, 42-46; res assoc, Cornell Univ, 50-55; sr engr, Tippetts-Abbett-McCarthy-Stratton, NY, 55-57; assoc prof civil eng, 57-63, PROF CIVIL ENG, CORNELL UNIV, 63- *Concurrent Pos:* Eng consult, xAm consult. *Mem:* Am Soc Photogram. *Res:* Engineering interpretation of airphotos; engineering problems in the tropics; remote sensing of physical environment. *Mailing Add:* Hollister Hall Cornell Univ Ithaca NY 14853

LIANG, TEHMING, biochemistry, see previous edition

LIANG, TUNG, b Peking, China, June 7, 32; m 58; c 2. OPERATIONS RESEARCH, AGRICULTURAL ENGINEERING. *Educ:* Nat Taiwan Univ, BS, 56; Mich State Univ, MS, 63; NC State Univ, PhD(biol eng), 67. *Prof Exp:* Assoc prof, 68-76, PROF AGR ENG, UNIV HAWAII, 76- *Mem:* Am Soc Agr Engrs. *Res:* Agricultural system modeling and optimization; development of natural resource database. *Mailing Add:* Dept Agr Eng Univ Hawaii 3050 Maile Way Honolulu HI 96822

LIANG, WEI CHUAN, b Shanghai, China, Nov 23, 36; m 70; c 2. ORGANIC CHEMISTRY. *Educ:* Kalamazoo Col, BA, 61; Case Western Reserve Univ, MS, 66; Ohio State Univ, PhD(org chem), 72. *Prof Exp:* Res chemist, Lubrizol Corp, 61-67; fel org chem res, Ga Inst Technol, 72-74; res chemist, 74-77, GROUP LEADER PROCESS DEVELOP, UNION CARBIDE CORP, 77- *Mem:* Am Chem Soc. *Res:* Exploratory syntheses; pesticide process research. *Mailing Add:* Union Carbide Corp Agr Prod Co Inc PO Box 12014 Res Triangle Park NC 27709

LIANG, WINSTON WEE-PAW, b Rangoon, Burma, Nov 13, 46; Chinese citizen; m 73; c 1. MATERIALS ENGINEERING. *Educ:* Nat Taiwan Univ, BS, 70; Univ Wis-Milwaukee, MS, 72; Mass Inst Technol, ScD, 76. *Prof Exp:* Asst prof, Univ Ill, Chicago, 76-78; asst prof mat eng, Univ Wis-Milwaukee, 78-80; RES ENGR, CORP RES DEPT, AMOCO RES CTR, STANDARD OIL CO IND, 80- *Concurrent Pos:* Consult, Amoco Res Ctr, 78-80; prin investr, NSF res grant, 77-79. *Mem:* Am Soc Metals; Am Inst Mining, Metall & Petrol Engrs; Electrochem Soc; Nat Asn Corrosion Engrs; Sigma Xi. *Res:* Chemical and extractive metallurgy; hot corrosion; plasma technology for materials processing; thermodynamics and phase equilibria; physical chemistry of molten salts and slags. *Mailing Add:* Amoco Res Ctr Standard Oil Co Ind PO Box 400 Naperville IL 60565

LIANG, YOLA YUEH-O, b Taiwan, Feb 12, 47; m 75; c 2. ANALYTICAL CHEMISTRY. *Educ:* Nat Taiwan Normal Univ, BS, 70; Univ Kans, PhD(chem), 78. *Prof Exp:* Fel chem, Ill Inst Technol, 77-78; SR RES CHEMIST ANAL CHEM, DOW CHEM CO, 81- *Mem:* Am Chem Soc; AAAS; Asn Women Sci. *Res:* Analytical chemistry; organic electrochemistry; neurochemistry; enzyme kinetics; analytical separations using gas chromatography and liquid chromatography. *Mailing Add:* 709 Sylvan Lane Midland MI 48640

LIANIDES, SYLVIA PANAGOS, b Lynn, Mass, Sept 2, 31; m 56; c 3. PHYSIOLOGY, BIOCHEMISTRY. *Educ:* Tufts Univ, BS, 53, PhD(physiol), 59. *Prof Exp:* Res biologist, US Naval Radiol Defense Lab, 59-60; lectr biol, Col Notre Dame, Calif, 62-71; instr biol sci, De Anza Col, 71-73; instr biol, 73-80, INSTR ANAT & PHYSIOL, WEST VALLEY COL, 80-, CHMN, DEPT BIOL, 81- *Mem:* AAAS; Sigma Xi; Coun Technol Advan. *Res:* Hormonal and environmental influences upon mitochondrial oxidative phosphorylation; effects of environmental cold on lipid and carbohydrate metabolism; radiation physiology; anatomy. *Mailing Add:* 19643 Montauk Dr Saratoga CA 95070

LIAO, HSIANG PENG, organic chemistry, see previous edition

LIAO, HSUEH-LIANG, b Silo, Taiwan, Jan 24, 41; US citizen; m 52; c 2. ANALYTICAL CHEMISTRY. *Educ:* Cheng Kong Univ, BS, 65; Drexel Univ, MS, 69; Georgetown Univ, PhD(chem), 72. *Prof Exp:* Sr res assoc chem, Northeastern Univ, 72-74; sr res chemist, Norwich Pharmacal Co, Morton-Norwich Prod Inc, 74-76; sr res scientist, Bristol Myers Co, 76-77; GROUP LEADER & SCIENTIST, LEDERLE LABS, AM CYANAMID CO, 77- *Mem:* Am Chem Soc; Am Inst Chem Eng. *Res:* Analytical methods development; chromatographic methods of separation (HPLC, GC & TLC) and quantitation; analytical and physical chemistry of drug compounds; solution thermodynamics. *Mailing Add:* 10 Amundsen Lane Suffern NY 10901

LIAO, JI-CHIA, anesthesiology, pharmacology, see previous edition

LIAO, PAUL FOO-HUNG, b Philadelphia, Pa, Nov 10, 44; m 68; c 2. PHYSICS. *Educ:* Mass Inst Technol, BS, 66; Columbia Univ, PhD(physics), 73. *Prof Exp:* Res assoc, Radiation Lab, Columbia Univ, 72-73; mem tech staff physics, 73-80, HEAD, QUANTUM ELECTRONICS RES DEPT, BELL LABS, 80- *Mem:* Am Phys Soc; Optical Soc Am; Inst Elec & Electronics Engrs. *Res:* Laser spectroscopy; nonlinear optics. *Mailing Add:* Bell Labs Holmdel NJ 07733

LIAO, SHU-CHUNG, b Tainan, Taiwan, Oct 18, 39; m 71. PHYSICAL-ANALYTICAL CHEMISTRY. *Educ:* Nat Taiwan Univ, BSc, 63; Univ Western Ont, PhD(phys chem), 70. *Prof Exp:* Res assoc polymer chem, Univ Mich, Ann Arbor, 70-71, human nutrit prog, Sch Pub Health, 72-73; SR RES ASSOC, CLIMAX MOLYBDENUM CO, MICH, 73- *Mem:* Am Chem Soc; Am Asn Textile Chemists & Colorists (secy, 80-). *Res:* Physical chemistry of molecular complexes and macromolecules; food chemistry and nutrition; instrumental analysis; analytical chemistry. *Mailing Add:* 1600 Huron Pkwy Ann Arbor MI 48106

LIAO, SHUEN-KUEI, b Morioka, Japan, June 27, 40; Can citizen; m 72; c 2. CANCER, IMMUNOLOGY. *Educ:* Tunghai Univ, Taiwan, BSc, 64; McMaster Univ, PhD(immunol), 71. *Prof Exp:* Demonstr, fel histol, Univ Toronto, 70-73; prof asst cancer, Hamilton Clin, Ont Cancer Found, 73-74; lectr, Dept Pediat, 74-76, asst prof, 76-80, ASSOC PROF PATH & PEDIAT, SCH MED, MCMASTER UNIV, 80- *Concurrent Pos:* Mem staff lab med, Henderson Gen Hosp, Hamilton, 74-; res grants, Med Res Coun Can, Ont Cancer Treatment & Res Found, 74 & Nat Cancer Inst Can, 81- *Mem:* AAAS; Can Soc Cell Biol; Am Asn Cancer Res; Can Soc Immunol; NY Acad Sci. *Res:* Cancer immunology; cell biology. *Mailing Add:* Dept Path McMaster Univ Hamilton ON L8N 3Z5 Can

LIAO, SHUTSUNG, b Taiwan, Formosa, Jan 1, 31; m 60; c 4. BIOCHEMISTRY, ENDOCRINOLOGY. *Educ:* Nat Taiwan Univ, BSc, 54, MSc, 56; Univ Chicago, PhD(biochem), 61. *Prof Exp:* From asst prof to assoc prof, 64-71, PROF BIOCHEM, BEN MAY LAB CANCER RES, UNIV CHICAGO, 72- *Concurrent Pos:* NIH res grant, 63-; Am Cancer Soc res grant, 74-; mem study sect, NIH; assoc ed, Cancer Res. *Mem:* Am Soc Biol Chem; Endocrine Soc; Int Soc Biochem Endocrinol. *Res:* Mechanism of hormone action; control of intermediate reactions involved in the biosynthesis of proteins and nucleic acids; enzymology. *Mailing Add:* Ben May Lab Cancer Res Univ Chicago 950 E 59 St Chicago IL 60637

LIAO, SUNG JUI, b Changsha, China, Nov 15, 17; nat US; m 53; c 4. PHYSICAL MEDICINE. *Educ:* Hsiang Ya Med Col, China, MD, 42; Nat Cent Univ, China, MPH, 44; London Sch Hyg & Trop Med, Univ London, DPH, 46, dipl bact, 47; Am Bd Phys Med & Rehab, dipl, 58. *Prof Exp:* Asst prof prev med, Sch Med, Yale Univ, 50-54; assoc res prof bact, Col Med, Univ Utah, 49-50; dir phys med & rehab, Waterbury Hosp, 57-73; CLIN ASSOC PROF REHAB MED, NY UNIV, 71-, CLIN PROF ORAL & MAXILLO FACIAL SURG, 78- *Concurrent Pos:* Milbank Mem fel prev med, Sch Med, Yale Univ, 47-49; clin fel phys med, Mass Gen Hosp, Boston, 55-57; consult physiatrist, Middlesex Mem Hosp, Middletown, Conn, 57-60 & St Raphael Hosp, New Haven, Conn, 72-; med dir, Waterbury Area Rehab Ctr, 57-62; dir phys med & rehab, St Mary's Hosp, 57-67 & Danbury Hosp, 57-69; attend physiatrist, Waterbury Hosp, 57-, med consult, Waterbury, Conn State Div Voc Rehab, 63-72, chief admin med consult, State Div, 69-73; assoc clin prof, Sch Med, Boston Univ, 67-73; lectr rehab med, 73-; hon consult biomech, NY Univ Inst Rehab Med, 69-76; chmn ad hoc comt acupuncture, Conn State Med Soc; secy, Am Acad Acupuncture, Inc; pres, Res Inst Acupuncture & Chinese Med. *Mem:* Fel Am Col Physicians; fel Am Pub Health Asn; Am Asn Immunol; fel Royal Soc Med; fel Am Acad Phys Med & Rehab. *Res:* Excitability and conduction nerve and muscle; biomedical engineering; acupuncture. *Mailing Add:* Rte 188 & N Benson Rd Middlebury CT 06762

LIAO, TSUNG-KAI, b Chiayi, Taiwan, Aug 1, 23; m 63; c 3. ORGANIC CHEMISTRY, PHARMACEUTICAL CHEMISTRY. *Educ:* Nat Taiwan Univ, BS, 52; Wesleyan Univ, MA, 57; Univ Kans, PhD(chem), 60. *Prof Exp:* Asst chem, Nat Taiwan Univ, 53-55; fel, Wesleyan Univ, 55-57; asst, Univ Kans, 57-60; res assoc, Univ Mich, 60-61; assoc chemist, Midwest Res Inst, 61, sr chemist, 61-77; DIR, MOLECULAR ELECTRONICS, CARNEGIE-MELLON INST RES, CARNEGIE-MELLON UNIV, 78-; SR CHEMIST, MIDWEST RES INST, 79- *Concurrent Pos:* Fel, Res Inst, Univ Mich, 60-61; vis prof, Nat Taiwan Univ, vis specialist of Nat Sci Coun, Repub China & Lectr of Sixth Tamkang Chair, Tamkang Col, 76. *Mem:* Am Chem Soc; Sigma Xi. *Res:* Synthesis of biologically active organic compounds; organic semiconductors; chemistry of nitrogen heterocyclic compounds; polymer chemistry, reverse osmosis composite membranes. *Mailing Add:* 1317 E 101 St Terrace Kansas City MO 64131

LIAUW, KOEI-LIANG, b Indonesia, May 4, 35; US citizen; m 61; c 1. ORGANIC CHEMISTRY. *Educ:* Nanyang Univ, Singapore, BSc, 60; Univ Calif, Berkeley, MS, 62, PhD(chem), 64. *Prof Exp:* Res chemist, Gen Chem Div, Allied Chem Corp, 64-66; sr res chemist, Mobil Chem Co, Div Mobil Oil Corp, 66-68; PROJ LEADER CENT RES, TECH CTR, WITCO CHEM CORP, 69- *Mem:* Sigma Xi; Am Chem Soc. *Res:* Textile treating agents; paper sizings; process development; synthetic organic chemistry; organotin chemistry; stabilizers for polyvinyl chloride and polyolefins; flame retardants; vapor phase catalysis. *Mailing Add:* Tech Ctr Witco Chem Corp 100 Bauer Dr Oakland NJ 07436

LIAW, JYE REN, b Hsin-Chu, Taiwan, May 12, 46; m 72; c 2. NUCLEAR ENGINEERING, RADIATION PHYSICS. *Educ:* Nat Tsing Hua Univ, Taiwan, BS, 68; Univ Ore, Eugene, MS, 71; Ore State Univ, PhD(nuclear eng), 75. *Prof Exp:* Res asst physics, Univ Ore, Eugene, 71-73; res asst nuclear eng, Ore State Univ, 73-75; asst prof nuclear eng, Univ Okla, 75-80; consult, Los Alamos Sci Lab, 77-80; MEM STAFF, APPL PHYSICS DIV, ARGONNE NAT LAB, 80- *Mem:* Am Phys Soc; Am Nuclear Soc; Sigma Xi; Am Asn Univ Prof; Nat Soc Prof Engrs. *Res:* Nuclear reactor design and analysis; radiation transport and dosimetry; nuclear fission product data evaluation; Van de Graff accelerator and nuclear reactor experiments; high vacuum technology. *Mailing Add:* Appl Physics Div Argonne Nat Lab Argonne IL 60439

LIBAN, ERIC, b Vienna, Austria, June 20, 21; nat US; m 54; c 3. APPLIED MATHEMATICS. *Educ:* NY Univ, BA, 48, MS, 49, PhD(math), 57. *Prof Exp:* Instr math, Long Island Univ, 49 & NY Univ, 49-50; asst, Ind Univ, 50-51; mathematician, Naval Res Lab, 51-52; assoc mathematician, Proj

Cyclone, Reeves Instrument Corp, NY, 52; sr dynamics engr, Repub Aviation Corp, 52-55; staff mem analog comput & consult ctr, Dian Labs, Inc, 55-58; assoc prof eng sci, Pratt Inst, 58-61; res scientist, Grumman Aircraft Eng Corp, 61-67; assoc prof, 67-71, PROF MATH, YORK COL, 71-, CHMN DEPT, 75- *Concurrent Pos:* Lectr, Univ Md, 50; consult, Avco Res & Develop Corp, Mass, 59-60 & Comput Systs, Inc, NJ, 59-61; adj lectr, Polytech Inst Brooklyn, 62-65; adj prof, Adelphi Univ, 66-67; adj assoc prof, Queens Col, 67-68. *Mem:* Am Math Soc; Asn Comput Mach. *Res:* Applications and methods of simulation on analog computers; logical design of computing systems; automata studies; theory of servo and feedback systems; information and communication theory; operations research. *Mailing Add:* 251-37 43rd Ave Little Neck NY 11363

LIBBER, LEONARD MITCHELL, b Boston, Mass, Jan 29, 19; m 46; c 3. PHYSIOLOGY. *Educ:* Cath Univ, BS, 47; Univ Pa, PhD(gen physiol), 52. *Prof Exp:* Physiologist, Air Crew Equip Lab, Philadelphia Naval Base, 51-59; head physiol br, 59-67, sci liaison officer, London, 67-69, DIR PHYSIOL PROG, US OFF NAVAL RES, VA, 69- *Mem:* Am Inst Biol Sci; Sigma Xi; Undersea Med Soc. *Res:* Stress physiology. *Mailing Add:* Off of Naval Res 800 N Quincy St Arlington VA 22217

LIBBEY, LEONARD MORTON, b Boston, Mass, Apr 17, 30; m 71. FOOD SCIENCE. *Educ:* Univ Mass, BVA, 53; Univ Wis, MS, 54; Wash State Univ, PhD(food technol), 61. *Prof Exp:* Asst prof, 61-69, assoc prof, 69-81, PROF FOOD SCI & TECHNOL, ORE STATE UNIV, 81- *Mem:* AAAS; Inst Food Technologists; Am Dairy Sci Asn; Am Chem Soc; Am Oil Chemists Soc. *Res:* Food chemistry; chromatographic and spectrometric analysis, especially gas chromatography and mass spectrometry. *Mailing Add:* Dept of Food Sci & Technol Ore State Univ Corvallis OR 97331

LIBBEY, WILLIAM JERRY, b Grand Rapids, Minn, Mar 18, 42; m 64; c 2. POLYOLEFINS. *Educ:* Carleton Col, BA, 64; Univ Wis, PhD(org chem), 69. *Prof Exp:* Res chemist, 68-72, sr res chemist, Continental Oil Co, 72-76, RES GROUP LEADER, CONOCO, INC, 77- *Mem:* Am Chem Soc. *Res:* Carbonium ion chemistry; thermal rearrangements; alkyl halide chemistry; Fischer-Tropsch chemistry; polyolefins; Ziegler-Natta catalysis; hydrocarbon pyrolysis; high density polyethylene. *Mailing Add:* Conoco Inc Ponca City OK 74601

LIBBY, CAROL BAKER, b South Kingstown, RI, Apr 20, 49; m 69; c 1. ENZYMOLOGY. *Educ:* Pa State Univ, BS, 71, PhD(org chem), 75. *Prof Exp:* Asst prof chem, Oberlin Col, 74-75; vis asst prof chem, Kenyon Col, 75-77; asst prof chem & physics, Skidmore Col, 77-79; MEM STAFF, A E STALEY MFG CO, 79- *Concurrent Pos:* Res assoc, State Univ NY, 78. *Mem:* Am Chem Soc; AAAS; Asn Women Sci. *Res:* Enzyme catalyzed reactions, especially mechanism and isolation of enzymes with emphasis on application of enzymes in industrial processes; carbohydrate hydrolases. *Mailing Add:* A E Staley Mfg Co 2200 E Eldorado Decatur IL 62525

LIBBY, JOHN LESTER, entomology, see previous edition

LIBBY, LEONA MARSHALL, b LaGrange, Ill, Aug 9, 19; m 43, 66; c 2. PHYSICS, CHEMISTRY. *Educ:* Univ Chicago, BS, 38, PhD(chem), 43. *Prof Exp:* Res assoc, Metall Lab, Manhattan Dist, 42-44; consult physicist, E I du Pont de Nemours & Co, Wash, 44-46; fel, Inst Nuclear Studies, Chicago, 46-47, res assoc, 47-54, asst prof, 54-57; fel, Inst Advan Studies, NJ, 57-58; vis scientist, Brookhaven Nat Lab, NY, 58-60; from assoc prof to prof physics, NY Univ, 60-63; assoc prof, Univ Colo, Boulder, 63-72; ADJ PROF ENG, UNIV CALIF, LOS ANGELES, 72- *Concurrent Pos:* Consult, Los Alamos Sci Lab, 51-; consult, Rand Corp, 57-; staff mem, 66-70; consult, TRW Space Systs Group, 60-; vis prof eng, Univ Calif, Los Angeles, 70-72; staff mem, R&D Assocs, 70- *Mem:* Fel Am Phys Soc; fel Royal Geog Soc. *Res:* High energy nuclear physics; nuclear reactions; fundamental particles; astrophysics; stable isotopes in tree thermometers; neutron physics. *Mailing Add:* Dept of Environ Sci & Eng Univ of Calif Los Angeles CA 90024

LIBBY, PAUL A(NDREWS), b Mineola, NY, Sept 4, 21; m 55; c 2. AERONAUTICAL ENGINEERING. *Educ:* Polytech Inst Brooklyn, BAE, 42, MS, 47, PhD, 49. *Prof Exp:* Design engr, Chance Vought Aircraft Co, Conn, 42-43; instr aeronaut eng, Polytech Inst Brooklyn, 43-44, 46-49, from asst prof to prof, 49-64, asst dir aerodyn lab, 59-64; assoc dean grad studies, 67-72, PROF FLUID MECH, UNIV CALIF, SAN DIEGO, 64- *Concurrent Pos:* Consult, Gen Bronze Corp, 48, NAm Aviation, Inc, 55, Gen Elec Co, 56, Gen Appl Sci Labs, Inc, 56-72, Avco, 76 & Systs Sci & Software, 76-; mem, Fluid Dynamics Panel, Adv Group Aerospace Res & Develop, NATO, 60-72, Fluid Mech Adv Comn, NASA, 63-69, Air Force Systs Command Scramjet Panel, 64-65 & Nat Acad Sci Adv Comn on Scramjet, 65-; corresp mem, Eng Sci Sect, Int Acad Astronaut, Int Astronaut Fedn, 66-; Guggenheim fel, 72-73. *Mem:* Fel Am Inst Aeronaut & Astronaut; Am Phys Soc. *Res:* Boundary layer theory; turbulent flow. *Mailing Add:* Dept of Appl Mech & Eng Sci Univ of Calif San Diego CA 92037

LIBBY, PAUL ROBERT, b Torrington, Conn, Sept 2, 34; m 59; c 3. BIOCHEMISTRY. *Educ:* Yale Univ, BS, 56; Univ Chicago, PhD(biochem), 62. *Prof Exp:* Fel biochem, Univ Calif, Davis, 62-63; sr cancer res scientist, Roswell Park Mem Inst, 63-72, from asst to assoc res prof, Dept Physiol, State Univ NY, 71-80, ASSOC RES PROF, DEPT PHARMACOL, STATE UNIV NY, 80-; ASSOC CANCER RES SCIENTIST, ROSWELL PARK MEM INST, 72- *Concurrent Pos:* Res prof, Niagara Univ, NY, 78- *Mem:* AAAS; Am Asn Cancer Res; Endocrine Soc; Am Chem Soc; Am Soc Cell Biol. *Res:* Biochemical mechanisms of chemical carcinogenesis. *Mailing Add:* Roswell Park Mem Inst 666 Elm St Buffalo NY 14263

LIBBY, PETER, b Berkeley, Calif, Feb 13, 47; m 75. CELL BIOLOGY, INTERNAL MEDICINE. *Educ:* Univ Calif, Berkeley, BA, 69; Univ Calif, San Diego, MD, 73. *Prof Exp:* Res physician, Peter Bent Brigham Hosp, 73-76; res fel physiol, Med Sch, Harvard Univ, 76-79; cardiol fel, Brigham & Women's Hosp, 79-80; ASST PROF MED, SCH MED, TUFTS UNIV, 80-

Concurrent Pos: S A Levine fel, Am Heart Asn, 76-77; Nat Heart, Lung & Blood Inst nat res serv award, 76-77. *Mem:* Am Heart Asn; Am Soc Cell Biol; AAAS; Am Fedn Clin Res. *Res:* Cellular and biochemical aspects of cardiovascular and neuromuscular diseases; mechanism and control of growth, atrophy and protein breakdown in cardiac, skeletal and smooth muscle. *Mailing Add:* Sch Med Tufts Univ 136 Harrison Ave M&V Box 79 Boston MA 02111

LIBBY, WILLARD FRANK, chemistry, deceased

LIBBY, WILLARD GURNEA, b Eugene, Ore, July 18, 29; m 65; c 3. GEOLOGY. *Educ:* Ore State Col, BS, 51; Northwestern Univ, MS, 59; Univ Wash, PhD(geol), 64. *Prof Exp:* Explor geologist, Stand Oil Co Calif, 56-59; asst prof geol, Univ SC, 63-65; lectr, Univ BC, 65-68; from asst prof to assoc prof, San Diego State Col, 69-71; PETROLOGIST, GEOL SURV WESTERN AUSTRALIA, 71- *Mem:* Geol Soc Australia. *Res:* Igneous and metamorphic petrology; geochronology. *Mailing Add:* Geol Surv of Western Australia Mineral House 66 Adelaide Terr Perth Australia

LIBBY, WILLIAM HARRIS, b Winona, Minn, Jan 25, 22; m 44; c 2. ORGANIC CHEMISTRY. *Educ:* Carleton Col, AB, 46; Univ Ill, PhD(chem), 49. *Prof Exp:* Res chemist, Gen Aniline & Film Corp, 49-53; res chemist, Minn Mining & Mfg Co, 53-66, lab mgr, 65-73, prod mkt mgr, Microfilm Prod Div, 73-81, MKT MGR COM & ENGR, PROD DEPT, 3M CO, 81- *Mem:* Nat Micrographics Asn; Am Chem Soc. *Res:* Hindered ketones; fluorescent dyes; cyclic monomers; photochemistry; imaging systems. *Mailing Add:* 3M Co 3M Ctr Bldg 220-9E St Paul MN 55101

LIBBY, WILLIAM JOHN, (JR), b Oak Park, Ill, Sept 10, 32; m 56; c 3. FORESTRY, GENETICS. *Educ:* Univ Mich, BS, 54; Univ Calif, Berkeley, MS, 59, PhD(genetics), 61. *Prof Exp:* NSF fel genetics, NC State Col, 61-62; asst prof forestry, 62-67, assoc prof forestry & genetics, 67-72, PROF FORESTRY & GENETICS, UNIV CALIF, BERKELEY, 72- *Concurrent Pos:* Pack lectr, Yale Univ, 67; L T Murray distinguished vis lectr forest resources, Univ Wash, 68; Fulbright res scholar, NZ Forest Res Inst, Univ Canterbury, Australian Forest Res Inst, 71. *Mem:* Soc Am Foresters; Genetics Soc Am. *Res:* Quantitative genetics of forest trees; gene conservation; vegetation propagation of conifers; maturation of woody plant meristens. *Mailing Add:* Mulford Hall Univ of Calif Dept of Forestry & Resource Mgt Berkeley CA 94720

LIBELO, LOUIS FRANCIS, b Brooklyn, NY, Oct 12, 30; m 54; c 4. THEORETICAL PHYSICS. *Educ:* Brooklyn Col, BS, 53; Univ Md, MS, 56; Rensselaer Polytech Inst, PhD(physics), 64. *Prof Exp:* Engr physics, Md Electronics Co, 54; proj engr, Ahrendt Instrument Co, 55; physicist, Opers Res Off, Johns Hopkins Univ, 57-58; asst prof, 65-68, ADJ PROF PHYSICS, AM UNIV, 68- & STATE UNIV NY, ALBANY, 73- *Concurrent Pos:* Res Physicist, US Naval Surface Weapons Ctr, 64-80, Harry Diamond Lab, 80-82; consult physicist, Entron Inc & LuTech Inc, 78- *Mem:* Inst Elec & Electronics Engrs; Am Phys Soc; Electromagnetic Soc; Sigma Xi; NY Acad Sci. *Res:* Scattering theory for non-spherical targets and by apertures; theory of cooperative phenomena in solids; theory of nonlinear phenomena in insulators; microvaves and electromagnetic theory; interaction and coupling. *Mailing Add:* L&L Assocs 9413 Bulls Run Pkwy Bethesda MD 20817

LIBERA, RICHARD JOSEPH, b Thorndike, Mass, Aug 26, 29; m 54; c 2. MATHEMATICS. *Educ:* Am Int Col, BA, 56; Univ Mass, MA, 58; Rutgers Univ, PhD(math), 62. *Prof Exp:* Instr math, Rutgers Univ, 60-62; from asst prof to assoc prof, 62-73, PROF MATH, UNIV DEL, 73- *Mem:* Am Math Soc; Math Asn Am. *Res:* Geometric function theory. *Mailing Add:* Dept of Math Univ of Del Newark DE 19711

LIBERATORE, FREDERICK ANTHONY, b Framingham, Mass, Dec 11, 44; m 68. BIOCHEMISTRY. *Educ:* Mass State Col Framingham, BA, 70; Univ NH, PhD(biochem), 74. *Prof Exp:* Fel, Ohio State Univ, 74-76; mem staff, Sigma Chem Co, 76-78; MEM STAFF NEW ENG NUCLEAR CORP, 78- *Mem:* AAAS; Sigma Xi. *Res:* Labeling proteins with radioactive isotopes. *Mailing Add:* 601 Treble Cove Rd North Billerica MA 01862

LIBERLES, ARNO, b Aschaffenburg, Ger, July 7, 34; US citizen; m 66; c 2. ORGANIC CHEMISTRY. *Educ:* Univ Mass, BS, 56; Yale Univ, MS, 59, PhD(chem), 60. *Prof Exp:* Fel chem, Col of France, 60-61; res chemist, W R Grace & Co, 61-62; from asst prof to prof chem, Fairleigh Dickinson Univ, 62-81. *Mem:* Am Chem Soc; Sigma Xi. *Res:* Theoretical organic chemistry. *Mailing Add:* Dept of Chem Fairleigh Dickinson Univ Teaneck NJ 07666

LIBERMAN, ALLEN HARVEY, b Memphis, Tenn, Sept 15, 43. ELECTRICAL ENGINEERING. *Educ:* Rensselaer Polytech Inst, BEE, 65; Carnegie Inst Technol, MSEE, 66; Univ Detroit, DEng(elec eng), 68. *Prof Exp:* Asst prof comput design, Univ Detroit, 67-69, assoc dir comput eng, 69; vpres comput res & develop, Mgt Sci Inc, 69-70; vpres & dir comput res & develop, Nat Info Serv, Inc, 69-74; vpres finance, DBX Inc, Newton, 74-81; PARTNER, TRADE QUOTES INC, 81- *Concurrent Pos:* Technician, Digital Electronics Inc, 62-63; engr, Fairchild Camera & Instrument Corp, 64-67 & Hell Corp, 65; consult, Burroughs Corp, 68-69; adj prof & grant, Univ Detroit, 69-70. *Mem:* Am Soc Eng Educ; Inst Elec & Electronics Engrs. *Res:* Digital computer applications in personal identification and high density photographic memories; multi-user/multi-task minicomputer operating systems. *Mailing Add:* 26 Park Lane Newton Centre MA 02159

LIBERMAN, ARTHUR DAVID, b Newark, NJ, Oct 13, 40; m 68; c 2. HIGH ENERGY PHYSICS. *Educ:* Dartmouth Col, AB, 62; Harvard Univ, MA, 63, PhD(physics), 69. *Prof Exp:* Res assoc high energy physics, Linear Accelerator Lab, Univ Paris, 69-70; adj asst prof particle physics, Univ Calif, Los Angeles, 70-74; res physicist, High Energy Physics Lab, Stanford Univ, 74-80; WITH SCHLUMBERGER-DOLL RES CTR, 80- *Mem:* Am Phys Soc. *Res:* The study of gamma rays and entirely neutral final states in the annihilation interactions at electron-positron storage rings by utilizing the Crystal Ball, a large solid angle, good energy resolution, highly modularized NaI(Tl) detector. *Mailing Add:* Schlumberger-Doll Res Ctr Ridgefield CT 06877

LIBERMAN, DANIEL FRANKLIN, clinical microbiology, industrial microbiology, see previous edition

LIBERMAN, DAVID ARTHUR, b Los Angeles, Calif, Nov 8, 26; m 61. ELECTRONIC STRUCTURE OF ATOMS AND SOLIDS. *Educ:* Calif Inst Technol, BS, 49, PhD(physics), 55. *Prof Exp:* STAFF MEM, LOS ALAMOS NAT LAB, 55- *Mem:* Am Phys Soc; AAAS. *Res:* Atomic and solid state physics. *Mailing Add:* Los Alamos NatLab Los Alamos NM 87545

LIBERMAN, IRVING, lasers, optical physics, see previous edition

LIBERMAN, ROBERT PAUL, b Newark, NJ, Aug 16, 37; m 61, 73; c 4. PSYCHIATRY, CLINICAL PSYCHOLOGY. *Educ:* Dartmouth Col, AB, 59; Dartmouth Med Sch, dipl med, 60; Univ Calif, MS, 61; Johns Hopkins Univ, MD, 63. *Prof Exp:* Intern internal med, Bronx Munic Hosp Ctr, Albert Einstein Col Med, 63-64; res scientist, NIMH, 68-70; asst prof to assoc prof, 70-79, PROF PSYCHIAT, SCH MED, UNIV CALIF, LOS ANGELES, 79-; DIR, PROG CLIN RES, CAMARILLO-NEUROPSYCHIAT INST RES PROG, 70-; CHIEF, REHAB MED SERV, BRENTWOOD VA MED CTR, 80- *Concurrent Pos:* NIMH res grants, 67-; consult various insts & govt, 70-; consult, Los Angeles County Ment Health Dept & Calif State Dept Ment Health, 72-; Fogarty sr res int fel, NIH, 75-76; assoc ed, J Appl Behav Anal, 76-77; mem med staff, var hosps, 70-; prin investr, Mental Health Clin Res Ctr, 77- & proj dir, Rehab Res & Training Ctr, 80-; mem, Res Rev Comt, NIMH, 79-81. *Mem:* Am Psychiat Asn; Asn Advan Behav Ther. *Res:* Experimental analysis of behavior in clinical psychiatry and psychology; interactions between drug effects and behavior modification; community mental health; behavior therapy; schizophrenia; narcotic addiction; suicide. *Mailing Add:* Camarillo-Neuropsy Inst Res Ctr Univ of Calif Los Angeles Box A Camarillo CA 93010

LIBERTA, ANTHONY E, b La Salle, Ill, May 17, 33; m 60; c 2. MYCOLOGY. *Educ:* Knox Col, Ill, AB, 55; Univ Ill, Urbana, MS, 59, PhD(bot), 61. *Prof Exp:* Res mycologist, Ill State Natural Hist Surv, 61; assoc prof, 61-67, PROF MYCOL, ILL STATE UNIV, 67- *Concurrent Pos:* NSF grants, 63-71. *Mem:* Mycol Soc Am. *Res:* Effects of soil disturbance and surface-mining on endomycorrhizae. *Mailing Add:* Dept of Biol Ill State Univ Normal IL 61761

LIBERTI, FRANK NUNZIO, b Warsaw, NY, Nov 2, 39; m 66; c 2. POLYMER CHEMISTRY, PHYSICAL CHEMISTRY. *Educ:* Rensselaer Polytech Inst, BChE, 61, PhD(phys chem), 67. *Prof Exp:* Develop chemist, 67-69, specialist prod develop, 69-73, mgr qual assurance, 73-75, specialist advan develop, 75-76, specialist prod develop, 76-79, MGR PROCESS TECHNOL, PLASTICS OPER, GEN ELEC CO, 79- *Mem:* Soc Plastics Engrs. *Res:* Stabilization of polymers; flame retardant polymers; solid state of polymers; polymer crystallinity; thermal analysis of polymers. *Mailing Add:* Plastics Oper Gen Elec Co Lexan Lane Mt Vernon IN 47620

LIBERTI, PAUL A, b Lyndhurst, NJ, Mar 18, 36; m 61; c 4. IMMUNOLOGY, PHYSICAL BIOCHEMISTRY. *Educ:* Columbia Col, AB, 59; Loyola Univ, Ill, MS, 61; Stevens Inst Technol, PhD(phys chem), 66. *Prof Exp:* From instr to assoc prof, 67-76, PROF BIOCHEM, JEFFERSON MED COL, 76- *Concurrent Pos:* Res fel phys chem, Stevens Inst TEchnol, 66; res fel biochem, NJ Col Med & Dent, 66-67; Nat Inst Allergy & Infectious Dis res career develop award, 73; lectr, Fairleigh Dickinson Univ, 64-67 & Temple Univ, 67-; adv ed, Immunochemistry, 76-81. *Honors & Awards:* Co-recipient Ottens Res Award, 69. *Mem:* Am Asn Immunol; Am Asn Biol Chem. *Res:* Physical chemistry of antigen-antibody interactions and complement proteins; proteins and polyelectrolytes; design of biophysical instruments; viral immunity. *Mailing Add:* Jefferson Med Col 1020 Locust St Philadelphia PA 19107

LIBERTINY, GEORGE ZOLTAN, b Szolnok, Hungary, June 14, 34; m 56; c 2. MECHANICAL ENGINEERING, MATERIALS SCIENCE. *Educ:* Bristol Univ, PhD(mech eng), 64. *Prof Exp:* Res & develop engr, English Elec Co Ltd, Eng, 59-60; from asst prof to assoc prof mech eng, Univ Miami, 63-68; assoc prof, Ill Inst Technol, 68-71; sr res engr, 71-73, prin res eng assoc, Advan Testing Methods Dept, 73-78, PRIN RES ENG ASSOC, AUTOMOTIVE SAFETY OFF, FORD MOTOR CO, 78- *Honors & Awards:* R R Teetor Award, Soc Automotive Engrs, 67. *Mem:* Am Soc Mech Engrs; Brit Inst Mech Engrs; Soc Automotive Engrs; Soc Exp Stress Anal. *Res:* Fatigue of metals; static and dynamic fractures due to multiaxial stress-strain systems; nondestructive testing; experimental stress analysis; high pressure engineering; design; safety risk analysis; expert witness; special transducer. *Mailing Add:* Ford Motor Co One Parklane Blvd Dearborn MI 48121

LIBERTY, BRUCE ARTHUR, b Toronto, Ont, Sept 29, 19; m 45; c 3. STRATIGRAPHY. *Educ:* Univ Toronto, BA, 47, MA, 49, PhD(geol), 53. *Prof Exp:* Instr geol, Univ Toronto, 47-51; sr res geologist, Int Petrol, Ltd, Peru, 51-52; tech officer, Geol Surv Can, 52-53, geologist, 53-66; assoc prof geol, Univ Guelph, 66-68; prof geol, 69-75, chmn dept geol sci, 73-75, PROF GEOL SCI, BROCK UNIV, 75- *Concurrent Pos:* Asst, Royal Ont Mus, 47-51. *Mem:* Geol Soc Am; Paleont Soc; Am Asn Petrol Geol; fel Geol Asn Can; Soc Econ Paleontologists & Mineralogists. *Res:* Stratigraphy; stratigraphic paleontology; paleozoic stratigraphy and biostratigraphy in the Great Lakes Area, Canada and the United States. *Mailing Add:* Dept of Geol Sci Brock Univ St Catharines ON L2S 3A1 Can

LIBET, BENJAMIN, b Chicago, Ill, Apr 12, 16; m 39; c 3. PHYSIOLOGY. *Educ:* Univ Chicago, BS, 36, PhD(physiol), 39. *Prof Exp:* Asst physiol, Univ Chicago, 37-39; instr, Albany Med Col, 39-40; res assoc physiol & biochem, Inst Pa Hosp, 40-43; instr physiol, Sch Med, Univ Pa, 43-44; mat engr, Personal Equip Lab, US Air Force, Ohio, 44-45; from instr to asst prof physiol, Univ Chicago, 45-48; staff physiologist, Kabat-Kaiser Inst, 48-49; from asst prof to assoc prof, 49-62, PROF PHYSIOL, MED SCH, UNIV CALIF, SAN FRANCISCO, 62- *Concurrent Pos:* Consult, Mt Zion Neurol

Inst, 56-; vis scientist, Japan Soc for Promotion of Sci, 79. *Mem:* fel AAAS; Am Physiol Soc; Soc Neurosci; Int Brain Res Orgn. *Res:* Neurophysiology; electrical and metabolic aspects of neural function; synaptic mechanisms; cerebral mechanisms in conscious experience. *Mailing Add:* Dept of Physiol S-762 Univ of Calif Med Ctr San Francisco CA 94143

LIBOFF, ABRAHAM R, b Paterson, NJ, Aug 27, 27; m 52; c 1. MEDICAL PHYSICS, BIOPHYSICS. *Educ:* Brooklyn Col, BS, 48; NY Univ, MS, 52, PhD(physics), 64. *Prof Exp:* Jr physicist, Naval Ord Lab, Md, 48-50; sr physicist, Metall Res Lab, Sylvania Elec Prod, Inc, 51-58; res asst cosmic ray lab, NY Univ, 59-64, assoc res scientist, 64-68, assoc dir environ radiation lab, 68-69, sr res scientist & proj coordr, Biophys Res Lab, 69-72; PROF PHYSICS & CHMN DEPT, OAKLAND UNIV, 72-; DIR MED PHYSICS PROG, 73- *Concurrent Pos:* Adj assoc prof physics, Hunter Col, NY, 68-72. *Mem:* Am Phys Soc; Biophys Soc; Am Geophys Union; Am Asn Physicists in Med; Bioelec Repair & Growth Soc (secy, 81). *Res:* Physics of collagenous tissues; biophysics of growth and development; electrically induced osteogenesis; sea-level cosmic ray ionization; environmental radiation; acoustic detection of nucleonic cascades; pyroelectric properties of bone. *Mailing Add:* 345 Berwyn Rd Birmingham MI 48009

LIBOFF, RICHARD L, b New York, NY, Dec 30, 31; m 54; c 2. THEORETICAL PHYSICS. *Educ:* Brooklyn Col, AB, 53; NY Univ, PhD(physics), 61. *Prof Exp:* Res asst appl math, Courant Inst Math Sci, NY Univ, 56-61, asst prof physics, NY Univ, 62-64; assoc prof, 64-69, PROF ELEC ENG & APPL PHYSICS, CORNELL UNIV, 69-, PRIN INVESTR, AIR FORCE OFF SCI RES, 77- *Concurrent Pos:* Chief consult, NRA, Inc, 63-65; Solvay fel, Univ Brussels, 71; prin investr, Off Naval Res Contract, 66-76. *Mem:* AAAS; fel Am Phys Soc. *Res:* Kinetic theory; quantum mechanics; short wavelength lasing; fusion physics; astrophysics; dense recombining plasma; strongly coupled plasmas and fluids. *Mailing Add:* Dept of Appl Physics Clark Hall Cornell Univ Ithaca NY 14850

LIBONATI, JOSEPH PETER, b Philadelphia, Pa, Nov 16, 41; m 69; c 3. CLINICAL MICROBIOLOGY. *Educ:* St Joseph's Col, Pa, BS, 63; Duquesne Univ, MS, 65; Univ Md, Baltimore, PhD(microbiol), 68. *Prof Exp:* From instr to asst prof med in clin microbiol, Sch Med, 68-77, SPEC LECTR MICROBIOL, SCH DENT, UNIV MD, BALTIMORE, 69-; CHIEF, DIV MICROBIOL, LABS ADMIN, MD STATE DEPT HEALTH & MENTAL HYG, 77- *Mem:* AAAS; Am Soc Microbiol. *Res:* Enteric bacterial diseases; pathophysiology; immunologic response and vaccine development. *Mailing Add:* 3801 Juniper Rd Baltimore MD 21218

LIBOVE, CHARLES, b New York, NY, Nov 7, 23; m 51; c 2. STRUCTURES, FAILURE ANALYSIS. *Educ:* City Col New York, BCE, 44; Univ Va, MS, 52; Syracuse Univ, PhD(mech eng), 62. *Prof Exp:* Aeronaut res scientist, Nat Adv Comt Aeronaut, 44-53; appl mathematician, Brush Labs, 53-55; assoc prof aeronaut eng, Tri-State Col, 55-58; from instr to assoc prof, 58-67, PROF MECH & AEROSPACE ENG, SYRACUSE UNIV, 67- *Concurrent Pos:* NSF fel, Nottingham Univ, 67-68. *Mem:* Am Soc Civil Engrs; Am Inst Aeronaut & Astronaut; Am Soc Mech Engrs. *Res:* Stress analysis of swept wings, sandwich plates, corrugated plates and microelectronic packaging; elastic stability. *Mailing Add:* Dept of Mech & Aerospace Eng Syracuse Univ Syracuse NY 13210

LIBOW, LESLIE S, b New York, NY, US citizen. GERIATRICS, INTERNAL MEDICINE. *Educ:* Brooklyn Col, BA, 54; Univ Chicago, MD, 58. *Prof Exp:* Intern, Mt Sinai Hosp New York, 58-59, resident, 63-64; resident, Bronx Vet Admin Hosp, 59-60; clin assoc bio-med psychiat, NIH, 60-62, res assoc, 62-63; chief geriat med, Mt Sinai City Hosp Ctr, Elmhurst, NY, 64-75; from asst prof to assoc prof med, Mt Sinai Sch Med, NY, 67-75; assoc prof, 75-78, PROF MED, STATE UNIV NY STONY BROOK, 78-; MED DIR, JEWISH INST GERIAT CARE, NEW HYDE PARK, NY & CHIEF GERIAT MED, LONG ISLAND JEWISH HILLSIDE MED CTR, NY, 75- *Concurrent Pos:* Consult to dir, Nat Inst Aging, Bethesda, 76-; consult, NIH, 75- *Mem:* Geront Soc; Am Geriat Soc; Am Col Physicians; AAAS. *Res:* Diseases of late life; brain and behavioral changes; human aging; thyroid disease; health care delivery. *Mailing Add:* 88 Clover Dr Great Neck NY 11021

LIBOWITZ, GEORGE GOTTHART, b Brooklyn, NY, June 18, 23; m 49; c 2. SOLID STATE CHEMISTRY. *Educ:* Brooklyn Col, BA, 45, MA, 50; Cornell Univ, PhD(phys chem), 54. *Prof Exp:* Chemist, Chromium Corp Am, 45-46, R Kann Chem Lab, 47-48 & Picatinny Arsenal, US Dept Army, 49; asst physics, Cornell Univ, 49-53; sr engr chem, Sylvania Elec Prod, Inc, 54; res assoc, Tufts Univ, 54-57; res supvr, Atomics Int Div, NAm Aviation, Inc, 57-61; sect head, Mat Sci Lab, Aerospace Corp, 61-63; staff scientist, Ledgemont Lab, Kennecott Copper Corp, 63-73; mgr, Solid State Chem Dept, Mat Res Ctr, 73-78, mgr, Inorg & Solid State Chem Dept, Corp Res Ctr, 78-80, SR SCIENTIST, ALLIED CORP, 80- *Concurrent Pos:* Assoc ed, Solid State Ionics, 80- & Mat Letters, 81-; co ed, Mat Sci & Technol Series, 80-; consult, Dept Energy & Environ, Brookhaven Nat Lab, 81-82. *Mem:* AAAS; Am Chem Soc; fel Am Phys Soc; Sigma Xi; NY Acad Sci. *Res:* Solid state chemistry; metal hydrides; nonstoichiometric compounds; thermodynamic properties of solids; materials for energy conversion and storage. *Mailing Add:* Corp Res Div Allied Corp PO Box 1021R Morristown NJ 07960

LIBSCH, JOSEPH F(RANCIS), b Rockville, Conn, May 7, 18; m 41; c 3. METALLURGY. *Educ:* Mass Inst Technol, SB & SM, 40, ScD(metall), 41. *Prof Exp:* From assoc prof to prof metall, 46-54, dir magnetic mat lab, 46-55, head dept metall, 55-69, dir Mat Res Ctr, 62-69, ALCOA FOUND PROF METALL ENG, LEHIGH UNIV, 66-, VPRES RES, 69- *Concurrent Pos:* Consult, Bullard Co, Conn, 46-47, Lepel High Frequency Labs, Inc, NY, 46-, Quaker State Metals Co, 56-58 & Smith Kline & French Labs, 56-73; consult ed metall ser, Chilton Publ Co, 58-60; bd mem, Pa Sci & Eng Found; mem, Gov Sci Adv Coun, Pa; bd mem, Eng Joint Coun; Alco-Richards prof, Lehigh Univ, 67-; vpres & pres, Am Soc Metals, 72-74, mem bd educ & res, 74-79; chmn, Alt Energy Res, US Nat World Energy Conf, 77- *Mem:* Fel Am Soc Metals; Am Inst Mining, Metall & Petrol Engrs; Am Inst Mining, Metall & Petrol Engrs; Am Soc Eng Educ; Sigma Xi. *Res:* Metallurgy of induction heating; materials selection. *Mailing Add:* Whitaker Lab Lehigh Univ Bethlehem PA 18015

LICARI, JAMES JOHN, b Norwalk, Conn, July 22, 30; m 48. ORGANIC CHEMISTRY. *Educ:* Fordham Univ, BS, 52; Princeton Univ, PhD, 55. *Prof Exp:* Res chemist, Am Cyanamid Co, 55-57; res proj chemist, Am Potash & Chem Corp, 57-59; sr res engr, NAm Aviation, Inc, 59-61, supvr org chem, 61-67, group scientist, Res & Eng Div, NAm Rockwell Corp, 67-70, supvr chem lab, 70-72, MGR MICROCIRCUIT ENG LABS, ROCKWELL INT CORP, ANAHEIM, 72- *Concurrent Pos:* Asst prof, Fordham Univ, 55-56; lectr, Cal State Univ, Fullerton. *Mem:* Am Chem Soc; Int Soc Hybrid Microelec. *Res:* Materials and processes for microelectronics. *Mailing Add:* 15711 Arbela Dr Whittier CA 90603

LICHSTEIN, HERMAN CARLTON, b New York, NY, Jan 14, 18; m 42; c 2. MICROBIOLOGY, MEDICAL EDUCATION. *Educ:* NY Univ, AB, 39; Univ Mich, MSPH, 40, ScD(bact), 43; Am Bd Microbiol, dipl. *Prof Exp:* Asst bact, Univ Mich, 40-43; instr, Univ Wis, 43-46; Nat Res Coun fel, Cornell Univ, 46-47; from assoc prof to prof, Univ Tenn, 47-50; from assoc prof to prof, Univ Minn, 50-61; dir dept, 61-78, dir grad studies, 62-78, fel, Grad Sch, 80-82, PROF MICROBIOL, COL MED, UNIV CINCINNATI, 61-, DIR GRAD STUDIES, 81- *Concurrent Pos:* Lewis lectr; Novy lectr; consult, Carbide & Carbon Chem Corp, Oak Ridge Nat Lab, 48-54 & Vet Admin Hosp, 57-65; consult ed, Life Sci Series, Burgess Pub Co, 60-67; mem sci fac fel panel, NSF, 60-63, Microbiol Training Comt, Nat Inst Gen Med Sci & Adv Bd Methods Biochem Anal; mem microbiol fels rev comt, NIH; trustee, Asn Med Sch Microbiol chmn, 74-77; mem staff, Linacre Col, Oxford Univ. *Mem:* Fel AAAS; Am Soc Biol Chem; Am Soc Microbiol; Soc Exp Biol & Med; fel Am Acad Microbiol. *Res:* Microbial physiology and metabolism. *Mailing Add:* 2253 Med Sci Bldg Univ of Cincinnati Col of Med Cincinnati OH 45267

LICHT, ARTHUR LEWIS, b Hartford, Conn, Dec 18, 34; m 58. PHYSICS. *Educ:* Brown Univ, BSc, 57; Univ Md, PhD(physics), 63. *Prof Exp:* Physicist, Nat Bur Standards, 57-59; res physicist, NASA, 59-61 & US Naval Ord Lab, 61-70; ASSOC PROF, DEPT PHYSICS, UNIV ILL CHICAGO CIRCLE, 70- *Concurrent Pos:* Asst prof, Univ Md, 63-65; mem sch math, Inst Adv Study, 65-66. *Mem:* Am Phys Soc. *Res:* Space physics; quantum field theory. *Mailing Add:* Dept of Physics Univ of Ill Box 4348 Chicago IL 60680

LICHT, LAZAR, b Drohobycz, Poland, July 31, 19; US citizen; m 58. ENGINEERING MECHANICS, FLUID DYNAMICS. *Educ:* Columbia Univ, BS, 52, MS, 54, DrEngSci, 61. *Prof Exp:* Mgr mech inspection, Sci & Projs Ltd, London, 41-42; instr eng design, City Col New York, 53-54; instr fluid dynamics, NY Univ, 54-55; sr res engr, Franklin Inst, Pa, 57-62; sr res staff mem pneumatics & fluid dynamics, Int Bus Mach Thomas J Watson Res Ctr, NY, 62-64; sr res engr foil bearings, Columbia Univ, 64-66; sr res staff mem dynamics of high-speed rotors, Ampex Corp, 66-68; CONSULT, 68- *Concurrent Pos:* Mem adv group gas lubrication, Off Naval Res, 57-68; consult to numerous indust & univs, 64-; Alexander von Humboldt sr US scientist award, Ger, 77-79; resident consult, Motoren u Turbinen Union, Munich, Ger, 77-79. *Mem:* Am Soc Mech Engrs; Sigma Xi. *Res:* Gas lubricated bearings for high speed machinery; dynamics and stability of rotors supported in externally pressurized and self-acting fluid-film bearings; compliant-surface bearings; dynamics of rotating machinery; pneumatic devices. *Mailing Add:* 123 N El Camino Real No 18 San Mateo CA 94401

LICHT, PAUL, b St Louis, Mo, Mar 12, 38; m 63. ZOOLOGY. *Educ:* Washington Univ (Mo), AB, 59; Univ Mich, MS, 61, PhD(zool), 64. *Prof Exp:* From asst prof to assoc prof, 64-73, PROF ZOOL & CHMN DEPT, UNIV CALIF, BERKELEY, 73- *Concurrent Pos:* Lalor Found grant, 67-68; NSF grants, 64-72; consult ed, Col Div, McGraw-Hill Book Co, 68- *Mem:* Fel AAAS; Soc Study Reproduction; Am Soc Zoologists; Am Soc Ichthyologists & Herpetologists. *Res:* Comparative physiology and evolution of pituitary hormones with special reference to reproduction. *Mailing Add:* 940 Contra Costa Dr El Cerrito CA 94530

LICHT, W(ILLIAM), JR, b Cincinnati, Ohio, Sept 29, 15; m 42. CHEMICAL ENGINEERING. *Educ:* Univ Cincinnati, ChE, 37, MS, 39, PhD(chem eng), 50. *Prof Exp:* Asst, 37-39, from instr to assoc prof, 39-52, head dept, 54-68, PROF CHEM ENG, UNIV CINCINNATI, 52- *Concurrent Pos:* Consult govt & var indust concerns, 42-; vis prof, Univ Minn, 68 & 72. *Honors & Awards:* Award, Am Inst Chem Engrs, 72. *Mem:* Am Soc Eng Educ; fel Am Inst Chem Engrs; Air Pollution Control Asn. *Res:* Properties of azeotropic mixtures; drying of gases and refrigerants; adsorption in dessicant beds; dewpoint indicators; mechanics of drops; air pollution control; dust collection; design of systems; mathematical modelling particulate collection. *Mailing Add:* Dept of Chem & Nuclear Eng Univ Cincinnati (ML 171) Cincinnati OH 45221

LICHTBLAU, IRWIN MILTON, b Woodmere, NY, May 11, 36; m 65. CHEMICAL ENGINEERING. *Educ:* Princeton Univ, BSE, 58; Yale Univ, MEng, 60, DEng, 63. *Prof Exp:* Sr res engr, Chevron Res Corp, 63-69, asst mgr systs develop & appln, Western Opers Inc, 69-71, mgr comput opers, Comput Serv Dept, 71-74, sr eng assoc, Chevron Res Corp, sr staff econ analyst, Anal Div, 76-80, CONSULT, CORP DEVELOP, STANDARD OIL CALIF, 80- *Mem:* Am Inst Chem Engrs; Sigma Xi. *Res:* Petroleum process design; high pressure technology; compressibility of gas mixtures at high pressures and temperatures. *Mailing Add:* 1096 Upper Happy Valley Rd Lafayette CA 94549

LICHTEN, WILLIAM LEWIS, b Philadelphia, Pa, Mar 5, 28; m 50; c 3. PHYSICS. *Educ:* Swarthmore Col, BA, 49; Univ Chicago, MS, 53, PhD(physics), 56. *Prof Exp:* NSF fel, 56-57; res physicist, Radiation Lab, Columbia Univ, 57-58; from asst prof to assoc prof physics, Univ Chicago, 58-64; dir undergrad studies, 69-71, PROF PHYSICS, YALE UNIV, 64-,

PROF ENG & APPL SCI, 75- *Concurrent Pos:* Mem bd dirs, Nat Asn Metric Educ. *Mem:* Fel Am Phys Soc. *Res:* Psychology of perception; biophysics; chemical physics; optics; laser spectroscopy; atomic physics. *Mailing Add:* Dept of Physics Yale Univ New Haven CT 06520

LICHTENBAUM, STEPHEN, b Brooklyn, NY, Aug 24, 39; m 61; c 5. NUMBER THEORY. *Educ:* Harvard Univ, AB, 60, AM, 61, PhD(math), 64. *Prof Exp:* Lectr math, Princeton Univ, 64-67; from asst prof to assoc prof, 67-73, PROF MATH, CORNELL UNIV, 73-, CHMN DEPT, 79- *Concurrent Pos:* Guggenheim fel, John Simon Guggenheim Mem Found, 73-74. *Mem:* Am Math Soc. *Res:* Algebraic number theory and algebraic geometry, particularly the study of the values of zeta and L-functions. *Mailing Add:* Dept of Math Cornell Univ Ithaca NY 14853

LICHTENBERG, BYRON KURT, b Stroudsburg, Pa, Feb 19, 48; m 70; c 2. BIOENGINEERING, BIOMEDICAL ENGINEERING. *Educ:* Brown Univ, ScB, 69; Mass Inst Technol, MS, 75, ScD, 79. *Prof Exp:* RES SCIENTIST, MASS INST TECHNOL, 78- *Mem:* Sigma Xi. *Mailing Add:* 37-219 Mass Inst Technol Cambridge MA 02139

LICHTENBERG, DON BERNETT, b Passaic, NJ, July 2, 28; m 54; c 2. THEORETICAL PHYSICS. *Educ:* NY Univ, BA, 50; Univ Ill, MS, 51, PhD(physics), 55. *Prof Exp:* Res assoc physics, Ind Univ, 55-57; guest prof, Univ Hamburg, 57-58; from asst prof to assoc prof, Mich State Univ, 58-63; physicist, Linear Accelerator Ctr, Stanford Univ, 62-63; assoc prof, 63-66, PROF PHYSICS, IND UNIV, BLOOMINGTON, 66- *Concurrent Pos:* Vis prof, Tel-Aviv Univ, 67-68, Imp Col, Univ London, 71 & Oxford Univ, 79-80. *Mem:* Fel Am Phys Soc. *Res:* Physics of the elementary particles. *Mailing Add:* Dept of Physics Ind Univ Bloomington IN 47401

LICHTENBERGER, GERALD BURTON, b St Louis, Mo, Jan 14, 45; m 73; c 2. COMPUTER SCIENCE, COMMUNICATIONS ENGINEERING. *Educ:* Mass Inst Technol, BS, 66, MS, 67; Yale Univ, PhD(elec eng), 72. *Prof Exp:* Consult appln statist, IBM Res, 70-72; mem tech staff ocean systs res, Bell Labs, 72-75; prin scientist, dir & co-founder comput systs, Xybion Corp, 75-79; PRES & FOUNDER, SYSTS OF THE FUTURE, INC, 79- *Mem:* Inst Elec & Electronics Engrs. *Res:* Application of state of the art computer technology to diverse disciplines such as interactive data management and analysis in medical research; signal and information processing; array processing; random process modeling. *Mailing Add:* Heather Hill Way Mendham NJ 07945

LICHTENBERGER, HAROLD V, b Decatur, Ill, Apr 22, 20; m 43; c 5. PHYSICS. *Educ:* Millikin Univ, AB, 42. *Prof Exp:* From mem staff to dir, Idaho Div, Metall Lab & Argonne Nat Lab, 42-56; yres, Gen Nuclear Eng Corp, 56-61; asst div dir & mgr mfg, Nuclear Div, 61-69, dir nuclear prod mfg div, 69-74, VPRES NUCLEAR FUEL NUCLEAR POWER SYSTS, COMBUSTION ENG, INC, 74- *Mem:* Fel Am Nuclear Soc. *Res:* Design and use of nuclear reactors for production of heat and electrical power. *Mailing Add:* 34 Fox Den Rd West Simsbury CT 06092

LICHTENFELS, JAMES RALPH, b Robinson, Pa, Feb 14, 39; m 61; c 2. PARASITOLOGY, TAXONOMY. *Educ:* Ind Univ Pa, BS, 62; Univ Md, MS, 66, PhD(zool), 68. *Prof Exp:* ZOOLOGIST, ANIMAL PARASITOL INST, SCI & EDUC ADMIN-AGR RES, USDA, 67-, CUR NAT PARASITE COLLECTION, AGR RES CTR, 71- *Concurrent Pos:* Instr, USDA Grad Sch, 71-77; res assoc, Div Worms, Mus Natural Hist, Smithsonian Inst, Wash, DC, 72-; res affiliate, Div Parasitol, State Mus, Univ Nebr, Lincoln, 72-; mem coun resources, Asn Syst Collections, 75-77. *Mem:* Am Soc Parasitol; Wildlife Dis Asn; Am Micros Soc; Sigma Xi. *Res:* Intra and interspecific variation in parasitic nematodes; effects of host on morphology of parasitic nematodes; identification, classification and description of parasitic nematodes of vertebrates. *Mailing Add:* 12311 Whitehall Dr Bowie MD 20715

LICHTENSTEIN, E PAUL, b Selters, WGer, Feb 24, 15; nat US; m 51; c 2. ENTOMOLOGY. *Educ:* Hebrew Univ, Israel, MSc, 41, PhD(entom, biochem), 48. *Prof Exp:* Lectr biol, Sch Educ, Israel, 41-53; asst prof physiol & anat, Ill Wesleyan Univ, 53-54; proj assoc, 54-56, asst prof, 56-65, PROF ENTOM, UNIV WIS-MADISON, 65-, ASSOC DIR, CTR ENVIRON TOXICOL, 72- *Mem:* Entom Soc Am; Am Chem Soc; Soc Toxicol. *Res:* Pesticidal residues and their effect on the biological complex on our environment; factors affecting persistence and breakdown of pesticides in soils, crops and water; naturally occurring toxicants. *Mailing Add:* Dept of Entom Univ of Wis Madison WI 53706

LICHTENSTEIN, HARRIS ARNOLD, b Houston, Tex, May 7, 41; m 69; c 2. ANALYTICAL CHEMISTRY. *Educ:* Tulane Univ, BA, 63; Univ Houston, BS, 66, MS, 67, PhD(biol), 70. *Prof Exp:* PRES, SPECTRIX CORP, 69- *Mem:* AAAS; Am Chem Soc; Am Soc Testing & Mat; Sigma Xi. *Res:* Development of analytical methods for potentially hazardous organic chemicals in air, water and body fluids. *Mailing Add:* 7408 Fannin Houston TX 77054

LICHTENSTEIN, IVAN EDGAR, b Brooklyn, NY, Dec 17, 33; m 63; c 2. ORGANIC ANALYSIS, INROGANIC ANALYSIS. *Educ:* Columbia Univ, AB, 55; Univ Calif, Davis, PhD(chem), 60. *Prof Exp:* Res assoc chem, Univ Kans, 60-61; asst prof, Villanova Univ, 61-66; res chemist, Corning Glass Works, 66-75; mgr catalyst develop, 75-80, MGR RES SERV, JOHNSON MATTHEY INC, 80- *Mem:* Am Chem Soc; Soc Automobile Eng. *Res:* Provide technical services for research staff; develop new or improved methods for characterizing research materials; recommend new research projects. *Mailing Add:* Johnson Matthey Inc Malvern PA 19355

LICHTENSTEIN, LAWRENCE M, b Washington, DC, May 31, 34; m 56; c 3. MEDICINE, IMMUNOLOGY. *Educ:* Univ Chicago, BA, 54, MD, 60; Johns Hopkins Univ, PhD(immunol), 65. *Prof Exp:* Intern med, 60-61, fel microbiol, 61-65, resident, 65-66, from asst prof to assoc prof, 66-75, PROF

MED, SCH MED, JOHNS HOPKINS UNIV, 75- *Mem:* Am Acad Allergy; Am Asn Immunol; Am Fedn Clin Res; Am Soc Clin Invest; Am Asn Physicians. *Res:* Mechanisms of reactions of immediate hypersensitivity and relationship to clinical problems. *Mailing Add:* Dept of Med Johns Hopkins Univ Sch of Med Baltimore MD 21239

LICHTENWALNER, HART K, b Easton, Pa, Oct 1, 23; m 45; c 3. CHEMICAL ENGINEERING. *Educ:* Lafayette Col, BS, 43; Lehigh Univ, MS, 49, PhD(chem eng), 50. *Prof Exp:* Org chemist, Res Labs, Gen Motors Corp, 43-48; chem engr, Silicone Prod Dept, 50-61, eng leader, 61-62, mgr process develop, 62-66, mgr room-temp vulcanising rubber develop, 66-68, mgr res & develop, 68-70, mgr var prod sect, 70-77, managing dir, Gen Elec Silicones-Europe, 77-80, MGR STRATEGIC PLANNING & VENTURE DEVELOP, GEN ELEC CO, 80- *Mem:* Am Chem Soc; fel Am Inst Chem Engrs; NY Acad Sci. *Res:* Chemical process technology of organosilanes and siloxanes. *Mailing Add:* c/o Silicone Prod Dept Gen Elec Co Waterford NY 12188

LICHTENWALTER, GLEN, organic chemistry, see previous edition

LICHTER, BARRY D(AVID), b Boston, Mass, Nov 29, 31; m 58, 71; c 1. MATERIALS SCIENCE, SCIENCE. *Educ:* Mass Inst Technol, SB, 53, SM, 55, ScD(metall), 58. *Prof Exp:* Asst, Mass Inst Technol, 52-58; metallurgist, Air Force Cambridge Res Ctr, 58-61 & Oak Ridge Nat Lab, 61-62; fel, Lawrence Radiation Lab, Univ Calif, Berkeley, 62-64; assoc prof metall eng, Univ Wash, 64-68; assoc prof mat sci, 68-72, PROF MAT SCI & TECHNOL PUB POLICY, VANDERBILT UNIV, 72- *Concurrent Pos:* Tech consult, Boeing Co, 66; centennial fel, Vanderbilt Univ, 74-75; NSF fac fel, 75-76; consult, Off Technol Assessment, 76- & Oak Ridge Nat Lab, 78- *Mem:* Am Inst Mining, Metall & Petrol Engrs; NY Acad Sci; Nat Asn Corrosion Engrs; AAAS; Am Soc Metals. *Res:* Corrosion; oxidation thermodynamics; technology and human values; materials policy studies; philosophy and engineering ethics. *Mailing Add:* Sch of Eng Vanderbilt Univ Nashville TN 37235

LICHTER, EDWARD A, b Chicago, Ill, June 5, 28; m 52; c 2. PREVENTIVE MEDICINE, COMMUNITY HEALTH. *Educ:* Univ Chicago, PhB, 47; Roosevelt Univ, BS, 49; Univ Ill, MS, 51, MD, 55. *Prof Exp:* Asst physiol, Col Med, Univ Ill, 50-51, resident internal med, 58-61, instr med, 60-61; USPHS fel immunochem, Nat Inst Allergy & Infectious Dis, 61-63, mem staff, 63-66; assoc prof, 66-68, prof health care serv & head dept, Sch Pub Health, 72-79, PROF PREV MED & HEAD DEPT, COL MED, UNIV ILL MED CTR, 68-, PROF, COMMUNITY HEALTH SCI, SCH PUB HEALTH, 80- *Mem:* Am Pub Health Asn; Soc Clin Res; fel Am Col Prev Med; fel Am Col Physicians. *Res:* Radiation effects on peripheral circulation; chronic pulmonary infections; clinical pharmacology and therapeutic evaluation of antibiotics; immunochemistry; immunogenetics of immunoglobulins and other serum proteins; structure and function of health care services. *Mailing Add:* Dept of Prev Med Col of Med Univ of Ill at the Med Ctr Chicago IL 60680

LICHTER, JAMES JOSEPH, b Algona, Iowa, Apr 29, 39. COMPUTER SCIENCE, MOLECULAR PHYSICS. *Educ:* Loras Col, BS, 61; Fordham Univ, MS, 63; Duke Univ, PhD(physics), 69. *Prof Exp:* Physicist, US Naval Ord Lab, 60-65; res physicist, 65; res asst, Duke Univ, 65-69; assoc scientist, 69-77, SOFTWARE SPECIALIST, ITT FED ELEC CORP, 77- *Mem:* Am Phys Soc; Am Chem Soc. *Res:* Radiation damage to bases of DNA; molecular biophysics; electron paramagnetic resonance; nuclear magnetic resonance; quantum biochemistry; missile range instrumentation; radar; computer simulation models; computer data base systems; atmospheric processes. *Mailing Add:* ITT Fed Elec Corp PO Box 1886 Vandenberg AFB CA 93437

LICHTER, ROBERT (LOUIS), b Cambridge, Mass, Oct 26, 41; m 66; c 2. ORGANIC CHEMISTRY. *Educ:* Harvard Univ, AB, 62; Univ Wis-Madison, PhD(chem), 67. *Prof Exp:* USPHS fel, Brunswick Tech Univ, 67-68; res fel chem, Calif Inst Technol, 68-70; asst prof, 70-74, assoc prof, 75-79, PROF CHEM, HUNTER COL, 80-, CHMN DEPT, 77- *Mem:* Am Chem Soc; The Chem Soc; Soc Appl spectros. *Res:* Organonitrogen chemistry; nuclear magnetic resonance spectroscopy; application of carbon and nitrogen nuclear magnetic resonance to organic chemistry. *Mailing Add:* Dept of Chem Hunter Col 695 Park Ave New York NY 10021

LICHTI, ROGER L, b Milford, Nebr, Aug 27, 45; m 70; c 2. EXPERIMENTAL SOLID STATE PHYSICS. *Educ:* Ottawa Univ, BSc, 67; Univ Ill, MS, 69, PhD(physics), 72. *Prof Exp:* Vis asst prof, Univ Kans, 72-73, res assoc, 73-74; res assoc, Univ Mass, 74-77, vis asst prof, 78-79; ASST PROF PHYSICS, TEX TECH UNIV, 79- *Mem:* Am Phys Soc. *Res:* Magnetic resonance of dilute paramagnetic systems; spin-phonon and spin-spin interactions; structural transitions; impurity centers in semiconductors. *Mailing Add:* Physics Dept Tex Tech Univ Lubbock TX 79409

LICHTIG, LEO KENNETH, b Brooklyn, NY, Oct 20, 53; m 77; c 1. PUBLIC POLICY RESEARCH, HEALTH CARE. *Educ:* Rensselaer Polytech Inst, BS & MS, 74, PhD(commun res), 76. *Prof Exp:* Res asst commun res, Rensselaer Polytech Inst, 74-76; asst prof commun, State Univ NY Albany, 76-77; asst proj mgr, NY State Dept Health, 77-82, assoc proj mgr, 82; POLICY RES SPECIALIST, BLUE CROSS NORTHEASTERN NY, 82- *Concurrent Pos:* Mem, Ad-hoc Comt, US Dept Health, Educ & Welfare, 79-81. *Mem:* NY Acad Sci; AAAS; Am Statist Asn; Int Commun Asn. *Res:* Application of advanced statistical, data gathering, and data processing techniques to public policy issues, especially in health care. *Mailing Add:* 104 River Rd Mechanicville NY 12118

LICHTIN, J LEON, b Philadelphia, Pa, Mar 5, 24; m 50; c 2. PHARMACEUTICAL CHEMISTRY, COSMETIC CHEMISTRY. *Educ:* Philadelphia Col Pharm, BS, 44, MS, 47; Ohio State Univ, PhD(pharmaceut chem), 50. *Prof Exp:* Asst prof, Cincinnati Col Pharm, 50-51, assoc prof pharm, 51-55; from assoc prof to prof, 55-71, ANDREW JERGENS PROF PHARM, UNIV CINCINNATI, 72- *Mem:* AAAS; fel Soc Cosmetic Chem; Am Pharmaceut Asn. *Res:* Dermatologicals; formulation of pharmaceutical products; cosmetics. *Mailing Add:* Dept of Pharm Univ of Cincinnati Cincinnati OH 45221

LICHTIN, NORMAN NAHUM, b Newark, NJ, Aug 10, 22; m 47; c 3. PHOTO CHEMISTRY, RADIATION CHEMISTRY. *Educ:* Antioch Col, BS, 44; Purdue Univ, MS, 45; Harvard Univ, PhD(phys org chem), 48. *Prof Exp:* Teaching fel, Harvard Univ, 45-47; lectr, 47, from instr to prof, 48-73, UNIV PROF CHEM & CHMN DEPT, Boston Univ, 73- *Concurrent Pos:* Vis chemist, Brookhaven Nat Lab, 57-58, res collab, 58-70; NSF sr fel, 62-63; guest scientist, Weizmann Inst, 62-63; vis prof, Hebrew Univ Jerusalem, 62-63, 70-71, 72, 73, 76 & 80; assoc ed, Solar Energy, 76-; vis prof, Inst Physics & Chem Res, Wako, Saitama, Japan, 80; sabbatical vis, Solar Energy Res Inst, Golden, Colo, 80. *Honors & Awards:* Coochbehar lectr, Soc Cult Sci, Calcutta, India, 80. *Mem:* Fel AAAS; Am Chem Soc; fel Am Inst Chem; Radiation Res Soc; Int Solar Energy Soc. *Res:* Radiation chemistry; atomic nitrogen chemistry; photochemical conversion of solar energy; physical photochemistry; electrolyte chemistry in liquid S0 2. *Mailing Add:* 195 Morton St Newton Centre MA 02159

LICHTMAN, DAVID, b New York, NY, Feb 7, 27; m 48; c 3. SURFACE PHYSICS. *Educ:* City Col New York, BS, 49; Columbia Univ, MS, 50. *Prof Exp:* Physicist, Airborne Instruments Lab, 50-56; res engr, Sperry Gyroscope Co, 56-62; sr prin res scientist, Honeywell Res Ctr, 62-67; assoc prof, 67-70, PROF PHYSICS, UNIV WIS-MILWAUKEE, 70- *Concurrent Pos:* NATO sr sci fel, 71. *Mem:* AAAS; Am Phys Soc; Am Vacuum Soc. *Res:* Mass spectrometry; beam-surface interactions; thin films; metal-ceramic seals; dark trace tubes; gaseous discharge phenomena; high and ultra-high vacuum; surface physics; electron spectroscopy; photodesorption. *Mailing Add:* Dept of Physics Univ of Wis Milwaukee WI 53201

LICHTMAN, HERBERT CHARLES, b New York, NY, Sept 6, 21; m 46; c 3. INTERNAL MEDICINE, CLINICAL PATHOLOGY. *Educ:* Brooklyn Col, BA, 42; Long Island Col Med, MD, 45; Am Bd Internal Med, dipl, 53. *Prof Exp:* Intern, Long Island Col Serv, Kings County Hosp Ctr, 45-46; asst resident path, Montefiore Hosp, Bronx, NY, 48-49; asst resident med, Long Island Col Div, Kings County Hosp Ctr, 49-50; from instr to prof med, Col Med, State Univ NY Downstate Med Ctr, 51-70; PROF MED, BROWN UNIV, 70- *Concurrent Pos:* Res fel clin med, Long Island Col Med, 50; clin fel hemat, Col Med, Univ Utah, 50-51; clin asst vis physician, Kings County Hosp, 51-53, assoc attend physician, 53-59, attend physician, 59-; chief hemat & blood bank, State Univ NY Hosp, 66-70; dir div clin path, Dept Lab Med & chief div lab med, Miriam Hosp, 70-74, physician-in-chief, 74- *Mem:* AAAS; Am Soc Hemat; Soc Exp Biol & Med; Am Fedn Clin Res; Harvey Soc. *Res:* Hematology; leukemia and malignant lymphona; heme synthesis. *Mailing Add:* Miriam Hosp Dept of Lab Med 164 Summit Ave Providence RI 02906

LICHTMAN, IRWIN A, b New York, NY, Nov 3, 20; m 48; c 1. PHYSICAL CHEMISTRY. *Educ:* City Col New York, BS, 43; NY Univ, MS, 48, PhD(phys chem), 51. *Prof Exp:* Instr chem, Seton Hall Col, 47-48; asst prof, Community Col, NY, 48-52; sr res chemist, Lever Bros Res Ctr, 52-55; group leader phosphates & detergents, Food Mach & Chem Co, 55-60; sr res chemist, Shell Chem Co, 60-64; mgr phys chem lab, 64-77, GROUP MGR RES & DEVELOP, PROCESS CHEM DIV, DIAMOND SHAMROCK CHEM CO, MORRISTOWN, 77- *Mem:* Am Chem Soc; Am Inst Chem. *Res:* Surface and colloid chemistry; defoamers; insecticide decomposition mechanisms; reaction kinetics; mechanism of defoamer action, particularly role of hydrophobic particles. *Mailing Add:* 350 Mt Kemble Ave Morristownship NJ 07960

LICHTMAN, MARSHALL A, b New York, NY, June 23, 34; m 57; c 3. HEMATOLOGY, BIOPHYSICS. *Educ:* Cornell Univ, AB, 55; Univ Buffalo, MD, 60; Am Bd Internal Med, dipl, 67. *Prof Exp:* Resident internal med, Med Ctr, Univ Rochester, 60-63; res assoc epidemiol, Sch Pub Health, Univ NC, 63-65; instr med, Sch Med & chief resident, Med Ctr, 65-66, sr instr med, Sch Med, 66-67, asst prof, 68-71, assoc prof med, Radiation Biol & Biophys, 71-74, PROF MED, RADIATION BIOL & BIOPHYS, SCH MED, UNIV ROCHESTER, 74-, CHIEF HEMATOL UNIT, 75- SR ASSOC DEAN, ACAD AFFAIRS & RES, 79- *Concurrent Pos:* USPHS res fel, Univ Rochester, 67-69; Leukemia Soc scholar, 69-74; from asst physician to sr assoc physician, Strong Mem Hosp, 65-71, sr physician, 74- *Mem:* Fel Am Col Physicians; Am Soc Hemat; Am Soc Clin Invest; Asn AmPhysicians; Am Physiol Soc. *Res:* Biochemical and biophysical studies of human erythrocytes and leukocytes. *Mailing Add:* Dept of Med Sch of Med Univ of Rochester Rochester NY 14642

LICHTNER, FRANCIS THOMAS, JR, b Philadelphia, Pa, Mar 21, 53; m 76. AGRICULTURAL CHEMICALS, TRANSPORT PHYSIOLOGIST. *Educ:* Lebanon Valley Col, BS, 75; Cornell Univ, PhD(plant physiol), 79. *Prof Exp:* Asst prof bot, Univ Calif, Davis, 79-82; RES SCIENTIST, BIOCHEM DEPT, EXP STA, E I DU PONT DE NEMOURS & CO, INC, 82- *Mem:* Am Soc Plant Physiologists; Weed Sci Soc Am. *Res:* Mechanisms of absorption and translocation of agricultural chemicals, ions and organic nutrients (sugars and amino acids), by plants. *Mailing Add:* Biochem Dept E I Du Pont De Nemours & Co Inc Wilmington DE 19898

LICHTON, IRA JAY, b Chicago, Ill, Sept 18, 28; m 49; c 1. NUTRITION. *Educ:* Univ Chicago, PhB, 47; Univ Ill, BS, 50, MS, 51, PhD(physiol), 54. *Prof Exp:* Res assoc obstet & gynec, Univ Chicago, 54-56; Am Heart Asn res fel cardiovasc physiol, Med Res Inst, Michael Reese Hosp, Chicago, Ill, 56-58; instr physiol, Stanford Univ, 58-62; assoc prof, 62-68, PROF NUTRIT, UNIV HAWAII, 68- *Mem:* Nutrit Today Soc; AAAS; Am Physiol Soc; Soc Study Reprod; NY Acad Sci. *Res:* Reproduction, water and electrolyte metabolism in pregnancy; growth; appetite control. *Mailing Add:* Dept Human Nutrit & Food Sci Hawaii 1800 East-West Rd Honolulu HI 96822

LICHTWARDT, ROBERT WILLIAM, b Rio de Janeiro, Brazil, Nov 27, 24; US citizen; m 51; c 2. MYCOLOGY. *Educ:* Oberlin Col, AB, 49; Univ Ill, MS, 51, PhD(bot), 54. *Prof Exp:* Fel, NSF, 54-55; res assoc bot, Iowa State Univ, 55-57, asst prof, 57; from asst prof to assoc prof, 57-65, chmn dept, 71-74, PROF BOT, UNIV KANS, 65-, CHMN DEPT, 81- *Concurrent Pos:* NSF sr fel, 63-64; ed-in-chief, Mycologia, 65-70. *Mem:* AAAS; Bot Soc Am; Mycol Soc Am (pres, 71-72); Mycol Soc Japan. *Res:* Fungi association with arthropods, particularly those inhabiting their guts; human pathogens. *Mailing Add:* Dept of Bot Univ of Kans Lawrence KS 66045

LICHY, CHARLES THORNE, agricultural chemistry, see previous edition

LICK, DALE W, b Marlette, Mich, Jan 7, 38; m 56; c 4. PURE MATHEMATICS, APPLIED MATHEMATICS. *Educ:* Mich State Univ, BS, 58, MS, 59; Univ Calif, Riverside, PhD(math, partial differential equations), 65. *Prof Exp:* Instr math & chmn dept, Port Huron Jr Col, 59-60; asst to comptroller, Mich Bell Tel Co, 60-61; from instr to asst prof math, Univ Redlands, 61-63; asst prof, Univ Tenn, 65-67; asst res mathematician, Dept Appl Math, Brookhaven Nat Lab, 67-68; assoc prof math, Univ Tenn, 68-69; assoc prof & head dept, Drexel Univ, 69-72; vpres acad affairs, Russell Sage Col, 72-74; prof math & dean, Sch Sci & Health Professions, Old Dominion Univ, 74-78; PROF MATH & COMPUT SCI & PRES, GA SOUTHERN COL, 78- *Concurrent Pos:* Consult, Union Carbide Corp, AEC, Oak Ridge Nat Lab, 66-67; adj assoc prof, Med Sch, Temple Univ. *Mem:* AAAS; Am Math Soc; Asn Comput Mach; Math Asn Am; Soc Indust & Appl Math. *Res:* Singular non-linear hyperbolic second order partial differential equations; non-linear Dirichlet problems; systems of non-linear boundary and initial value problems; partial differential equations and their numerical solution. *Mailing Add:* Ga Southern Col Statesboro GA 30458

LICK, DON R, b Marlette, Mich, Sept 3, 34; m 61; c 2. MATHEMATICS. *Educ:* Mich State Univ, BS, 56, MS, 57, PhD(math), 61. *Prof Exp:* Asst prof math, Purdue Univ, 61-63 & NMex State Univ, 63-66; vis assoc prof, 65-66, assoc prof, 66-72, PROF MATH, WESTERN MICH UNIV, 72- *Concurrent Pos:* NSF res grant, 69-70; US Army Res Off Conf grant, 71-72; vis prof, Univ Calif, Irvine, 72-73 & Calif State Univ, Los Angeles, 72-73. *Mem:* Math Asn Am; Am Math Soc; London Math Soc; Am Asn Univ Prof. *Res:* Complex analysis; sets of convergence of series; representation of measurable functions by series; graph theory; connectivity; structural problems. *Mailing Add:* Dept of Math Western Mich Univ Kalamazoo MI 49008

LICK, WILBERT JAMES, b Cleveland, Ohio, June 12, 33; m 65; c 2. ENVIRONMENTAL SCIENCES, APPLIED MATHEMATICS. *Educ:* Rensselaer Polytech Inst, BA, 55, MA, 57, PhD(aeronaut eng), 58. *Prof Exp:* Res fel & lectr mech eng, Harvard Univ, 59-61, asst prof, 61-66; sr res fel aeronaut, Calif Inst Technol, 66; assoc prof eng, Case Western Reserve Univ, 66-70, chmn dept earth sci, 73-76, prof geophys & eng, 70-79; PROF MECH & ENVIRON ENG, UNIV CALIF, SANTA BARBARA, 79-, CHMN DEPT, 82- *Concurrent Pos:* Guggenheim fel, 65; Fulbright fel, 78. *Mem:* Am Geophys Union; Am Soc Mech Eng; Int Asn Great Lakes Res. *Res:* Applied mathematics. *Mailing Add:* Dept Mech Eng Univ Calif Santa Barbara CA 93106

LICKLIDER, JOSEPH CARL ROBNETT, b St Louis, Mo, Mar 11, 15; m 45; c 2. COMPUTER SCIENCE. *Educ:* Washington Univ, AB, 37, AM, 38; Univ Rochester, PhD(psychol), 42. *Prof Exp:* Res assoc psychol, Swarthmore Col, 40-41; res assoc & res fel, Psycho-Acoust Lab, Harvard Univ, 41-46, lectr, Psychol Labs, 46-49; assoc prof psychol, Mass Inst Technol, 49-57; head eng psychol dept, Bolt Beranek & Newman, Inc, 57-61, vpres, 61-62; dir behav sci & info processing res, Advan Res Proj Agency, US Dept Defense, 62-64; consult to dir res, IBM Corp, NY, 64-66; PROF ELEC ENG & COMPUT SCI, MASS INST TECHNOL, 66- *Concurrent Pos:* Nat Res Coun fel, 42; mem coun, Armed Forces-Nat Res Coun Comt Hearing & Bio-Acoust, 57-; dir info processing, Advan Res Proj Agency, US Dept Defense, 74-75. *Honors & Awards:* Franklin V Taylor Award, Soc Eng Psychologists, 54. *Mem:* Nat Acad Sci; fel Acoust Soc Am (pres, 58); fel Am Acad Arts & Sci; Asn Comput Mach. *Res:* Man-computer interaction; computer networks. *Mailing Add:* Mass Inst Technol 244 Wood Lexington MA 02173

LICKO, VOJTECH, b Banska Stiavnica, Czech, Aug 30, 32; US citizen; m 59; c 1. MATHEMATICAL BIOLOGY. *Educ:* Czech Acad Sci, CSc(biophys), 63; Univ Chicago, PhD(math biol), 66. *Prof Exp:* Chief radioisotope lab, Inst Endocrinol, Slovak Acad Sci, Bratislava, 54-63; fel math biol, Univ Chicago, 63-66; scientist & assoc prof biophys, Inst Physics, Comenius Univ, Bratislava, 66-68; res fel biomath, Dept Biochem & Biophys, 68-71, res asst, 73-74, RES ASST BIOMATH, CARDIOVASC INST, UNIV CALIF, SAN FRANCISCO, 74- *Concurrent Pos:* Assoc adj prof biomath, Cardiovasc Res Inst, Univ Calif, San Francisco, 78-; assoc ed, Bull Math Biol. *Mem:* Biophys Soc; AAAS; Fedn Am Scientists; Soc Math Biol. *Res:* Pharmacokinetics and pharmacodynamics; mathematical modeling of biochemical and physiological processes; theory of secretory mechanisms; dynamics of glucose-insulin control in man; kinetics of transport of substances through epithelia. *Mailing Add:* 1259 16th Ave San Francisco CA 94122

LIDDELL, ROBERT WILLIAM, JR, b Pittsburgh, Pa, Sept 11, 13; m 40; c 3. ORGANIC CHEMISTRY, BIOCHEMISTRY. *Educ:* Univ Pittsburgh, BS, 34, PhD(chem), 40. *Prof Exp:* Chem engr, Swindell-Dressler Corp, 34-35; chemist, Hall Labs, 35-36; res chemist, Hagan Chem & Controls, Inc, 40-55, asst res mgr, 55-63; mgr prod eng, Calgon Corp, 63-70, mgr pilot res & develop, 70-78; CONSULT, 78- *Mem:* Am Chem Soc. *Res:* Water treatment; phosphate chemicals. *Mailing Add:* PO Box 132 Amado AZ 85640

LIDDELL, WILLIAM DAVID, b Dayton, Ohio, Sept 17, 51; m 77. PALEOECOLOGY. *Educ:* Miami Univ, BA, 73; Univ Mich, MS, 75, PhD(geol), 80. *Prof Exp:* Asst prof geol & paleont, Earth Sci Dept, Univ New Orleans, 79-81; ASST PROF GEOL & PALEONT, GEOL DEPT, UTAH STATE UNIV, 81- *Mem:* AAAS; Ecol Soc Am; Int Palaeont Asn. *Res:* Paleoecology of ancient, primarily Paleozoic, communities; geology and ecology of modern coral reefs. *Mailing Add:* Dept Geol UMC 07 Utah State Univ Logan UT 84322

LIDDICOAT, RICHARD THOMAS, JR, b Kearsage, Mich, Mar 2, 18; m 39; c 2. GEMOLOGY, MINERALOGY. *Educ:* Univ Mich, BS, 39, MS, 40; dipl, Gemol Inst Am, 41; Calif Inst Technol, MS, 44. *Prof Exp:* Asst mineral, Univ Mich, 37-40; instr, 40-41, dir ed, 41-42, 46-49, asst dir, 49-52, EXEC DIR, GEMOL INST AM, 52-, PRES, 70- *Concurrent Pos:* Ed, Gems & Gemology, 52-; US deleg, Int Gem Conf, 60-81. *Mem:* Sigma Xi; AAAS; fel Geol Soc Am; fel Mineral Soc Am. *Res:* Gem identification and grading. *Mailing Add:* 1484 Allenford Ave Los Angeles CA 90049

LIDDICOET, THOMAS HERBERT, b Placerville, Calif, Nov 1, 27; m 80; c 7. PESTICIDE CHEMISTRY. *Educ:* Col of Pac, AB, 49; Univ Wash, PhD(chem), 53. *Prof Exp:* Instr chem, Univ Calif, 53-54 & San Francisco State Col, 54-55; from res chemist to sr res chemist, Chevron Res Co Div, 55-69, supvr pesticide formulations, 69-76, REGIST SPECIALIST, ORTHO DIV, CHEVRON CHEM CO, STAND OIL CO CALIF, 76- *Mem:* Am Chem Soc. *Res:* Pesticide formulations; surface active agents. *Mailing Add:* Chevron Chem Co 940 Hensley St Richmond CA 94804

LIDDLE, CHARLES GEORGE, b Detroit, Mich, Mar 22, 36; m 60; c 4. VETERINARY MEDICINE, RADIATION BIOLOGY. *Educ:* Mich State Univ, BS, 58, DVM, 60; Univ Rochester, MS, 63. *Prof Exp:* Vet, Pvt Pract, Mich, 60-61; chief radioisotopes div, Fourth Army Med Lab, Vet Corps, US Army, Ft Sam Houston, 61-62, res vet, Walter Reed Army Inst Res, 63-65, chief small animal test, Dept Med Chem, 65, chief radioisotope sect, Army Med Res & Nutrit Lab, Denver, 65-69, lab vet, Navy Prev Med Unit, Viet Nam, 69; chief biophys unit, Twinbrook Res Lab, 70-73, RES VET, EXP BIOL DIV, HEALTH EFFECTS RES LAB, ENVIRON RES CTR, ENVIRON PROTECTION AGENCY, 73- *Mem:* Am Vet Med Asn. *Res:* The effects of microwaves on the immunologic competence of laboratory animals. *Mailing Add:* 4004 Oak Park Rd Raleigh NC 27612

LIDDLE, GRANT WINDER, b American Fork, Utah, June 27, 21; m 42, 71; c 5. ENDOCRINOLOGY. *Educ:* Univ Utah, BS, 43; Univ Calif, MD, 48. *Prof Exp:* Asst med & asst resident, Sch Med, Univ Calif, 49-51, instr, 53; from sr asst surgeon to surgeon sect clin endocrinol, Nat Heart Inst, 53-56; assoc prof med & chief endocrine serv, 56-61, PROF MED & DIR ENDOCRINOL, SCH MED, VANDERBILT UNIV, 61-, CHMN DEPT MED, 68- *Concurrent Pos:* USPHS res fel, Metab Unit, Univ Calif, 51-53; USPHS res career award, 62; mem endocrinol study sect, USPHS, 58-62, consult to Surg Gen, 58-66, mem diabetes & metab training grants comt, 62-66, chmn, 63-66, mem nat adv arthritis & metab dis coun, 67-71; mem coun, Asn Prof Med, 73-77. *Honors & Awards:* Upjohn Award, Endocrine Soc, 62, Distinguished Leadership Award Endocrinol, 71; Sir Henry Hallet Dale Medal, Brit Soc Endocrinol, 73. *Mem:* Am Soc Clin Invest (secy-treas, 63-66, pres, 66-67); Endocrine Soc (pres, 73-74); Asn Am Physicians; Asn Profs Med (pres, 77-78); Int Soc Endocrinol (pres, 76-80). *Res:* Adrenal physiology; methods of assaying steroids; pituitary physiology; renal function as influenced by steroids; steroid hypertension; endocrinology of tumors. *Mailing Add:* 770 Norwood Dr Nashville TN 37204

LIDDLE, LARRY BROOK, marine phycology, see previous edition

LIDDLE, SIDNEY G(EORGE), propulsion systems, fluid mechanics, see previous edition

LIDE, DAVID REYNOLDS, JR, b Gainesville, Ga, May 25, 28; m 55; c 4. CHEMICAL PHYSICS. *Educ:* Carnegie Inst Technol, BS, 49; Harvard Univ, AM, 51, PhD(chem physics), 52. *Prof Exp:* Fulbright scholar & Ramsay mem fel, Oxford Univ, 52-53; res fel, Harvard Univ, 53-54; physicist, 54-63, chief infrared & microwave spectros sect, 63-68, CHIEF OFF STAND REF DATA, NAT BUR STANDARDS, 68- *Concurrent Pos:* Lectr, Univ Md, 56-66; NSF sr fel, Univ London, 59-60 & Univ Bologna, 67-68; US nat deleg, Comt Data Sci & Technol, Int Coun Sci Unions 73-81, assoc ed, CODATA Bulletin, 74-, mem, Exec Comt, 79-; ed, J Phys & Chem Ref Data; chmn, Comn Symbols, Terminology & Units, Int Union Pure & Appl Chem, 77-81, vpres, Phys Chem Div, 79- & Am Inst Physics Publ Bd, 78-; mem, Nat Res Coun, Nat Acad Sci. *Honors & Awards:* Silver Medal, US Dept Com, 65, Gold Medal, 68; Stratton Award, Nat Bur Standards, 68. *Mem:* AAAS; Am Chem Soc; fel Am Phys Soc. *Res:* Free radicals, high temperature, microwave and infrared spectroscopy; molecular structure; critical data evaluation; molecular lasers. *Mailing Add:* Off of Stand Ref Data Nat Bur of Standards Washington DC 20234

LIDE, ROBERT WILSON, b Hwanghsien, Shantung, China, June 27, 22; US citizen; m 55; c 3. NUCLEAR PHYSICS. *Educ:* Wake Forest Col, BS, 43; Univ Mich, MS, 50, PhD, 59. *Prof Exp:* Asst prof, 57-65, ASSOC PROF PHYSICS, UNIV TENN, KNOXVILLE, 65- *Mem:* Am Phys Soc. *Res:* Low-energy nuclear physics; gamma-gamma angular correlation; gamma-ray spectroscopy. *Mailing Add:* Dept of Physics Univ of Tenn Knoxville TN 37916

LIDER, LLOYD A, genetics, see previous edition

LIDIAK, EDWARD GEORGE, b La Grange, Tex, Mar 14, 34. GEOLOGY. *Educ:* Rice Univ, BA, 56, MA, 60, PhD(geol), 63. *Prof Exp:* Res scientist, Univ Tex, 62-64; from asst prof to assoc prof geol, 64-80, PROF GEOL & PLANETARY SCI, UNIV PITTSBURG, 76-, CHMN, DEPT GEOL, 71- *Concurrent Pos:* Geologist, US Geol Surv, Pa, 65- *Mem:* AAAS; Geochem Soc; Geol Soc Am. *Res:* Petrology of island arc volcanic rocks; geology of buried Precambrian rocks of United States; phase equilibria in mineral systems. *Mailing Add:* Dept Geol & Planetary Sci Univ Pittsburgh Pittsburgh PA 15260

LIDICKER, WILLIAM ZANDER, JR, b Evanston, Ill, Aug 19, 32; m 56; c 2. POPULATION BIOLOGY, MAMMALOGY. *Educ:* Cornell Univ, BS, 53; Univ Ill, MS, 54, PhD(zool), 57. *Prof Exp:* From instr to assoc prof, Univ, 57-69, vchmn dept zool, 66-67, from asst cur to assoc cur, Mus, 57-69, actg dir, 74-75, PROF ZOOL, UNIV CALIF, BERKELEY, 69-, ASSOC DIR, MUS VERTEBRATE ZOOL, 68-, CUR MAMMALS, 69- *Concurrent Pos:* NSF sr fel, 63-64; assoc res prof, Miller Inst Basic Res Sci, 67-68; hon res fel, Dept Animal Genetics, Univ Col London, 71-72; hon lectr, Dept Biol, Royal Free Hosp Sch Med, London, 71-72. *Mem:* Am Soc Mammal (2nd vpres, 74-76, pres, 76-78); Soc Study Evolution; Am Soc Naturalists; Am Soc Zoologists. *Res:* Ecology and evolution of mammals. *Mailing Add:* Mus of Vertebrate Zool Univ of Calif Berkeley CA 94720

LIDIN-LAMON, BODIL INGER MARIA, b Malmo, Sweden, May 31, 39; m 73; c 1. MICROBIOLOGY. *Educ:* Univ Stockholm, MS, 74; Univ Ala, Birmingham, PhD(microbiol), 79. *Prof Exp:* Sr technologist, Inst Gustove-Rossy, Paris, 67-68; res asst, Karolinska Inst, Stockholm, 70-73; fel, Dept Pediat & Infectious Dis, Univ Ala, Birmingham, 79-80 & Wallenberg Lab, Uppsala Univ, 80-81; RES ASSOC DEPT MICROBIOL, UNIV ALA, BIRMINGHAM, 81- *Mem:* Am Soc Microbiol. *Res:* Immunological studies on non-structural proteins of influenza virus and isolation and characterization of glycoproteins of parainfluenza virus with the intent to produce a vaccine. *Mailing Add:* Dept Microbiol Rm 618 Univ Ala Birmingham AL 35294

LIDMAN, WILLIAM G, b Rochester, NY, Nov 22, 21; m 43; c 3. METALLURGY, CERAMICS. *Educ:* Univ Mich, BS, 43. *Prof Exp:* Res scientist, NASA, Ohio, 43-52; eng sect head, Sylcor Div, Gen Tel & Electronics Corp, 52-57, eng dept head, 57-60, proj mgr nuclear fuel elements, 60-61; tech dir beryllium mfg, Gen Astrometals Corp, 61-71; mgr Hazleton, Pa Plant & Yonkers NY Div, 71-74, group mgr metall res & develop, Kawecki Berylco Industs, 74-80, TECH SALES MGR DEVELOP PRODS, KAWECKI BERYLCO INDUSTS DIV, CABOT CORP, 80- *Mem:* Sigma Xi; Am Soc Metals (treas, 55-57); Am Inst Aeronaut & Astronaut. *Res:* Sintering mechanism of powder metallurgy products; production methods for manufacturing fuel elements for nuclear reactors and beryllium products; chemical specialty metals and beryllium; non-ferrous materials; refractory metals and ceramics. *Mailing Add:* KBI Div Cabot Corp PO Box 1462 Reading PA 19603

LIDOFSKY, LEON JULIAN, b Norwich, Conn, Nov 8, 24; m 48; c 2. NUCLEAR ENGINEERING, COMPUTER SCIENCE. *Educ:* Tufts Univ, BS, 45; Columbia Univ, MA, 47, PhD(physics), 52. *Prof Exp:* Instr physics, NY State Maritime Col, 48-49; res asst, 49-52, res assoc, 52-59, from asst prof to assoc prof nuclear sci & eng, 59-64, PROF APPL PHYSICS & NUCLEAR ENG, COLUMBIA UNIV, 64- *Concurrent Pos:* Res scholar, Inst Nuclear Physics, Amsterdam, 68-69; consult, Mt Sinai Sch Med, 70-77 & Am Phys Soc Study Group, 76-77. *Mem:* Am Nuclear Soc; Am Phys Soc. *Res:* Radiation transport; nuclear physics. *Mailing Add:* Dept of Appl Physics & Nuclear Eng Columbia Univ New York NY 10027

LIDOW, ERIC, b Vilnius, Lithuania, Dec 9, 12; US citizen; m 52; c 4. ELECTRICAL ENGINEERING, SOLID STATE PHYSICS. *Educ:* Tech Univ, Berlin, MS, 37. *Prof Exp:* Chief engr, Selenium Corp Am, 41-44, vpres in charge res & eng, 44-46; PRES & CHMN BD, INT RECTIFIER CORP, 47- *Mem:* Sr mem Inst Elec & Electronics Engrs. *Res:* Photoelectric phenomena; selenium photocells; selenium rectifiers; silicone power devices. *Mailing Add:* 9220 Sunset Blvd Los Angeles CA 90069

LIDTKE, DORIS KEEFE, b Bottineau County, NDak, Dec 6, 29; m 51. COMPUTER SCIENCE. *Educ:* Univ Ore, BS, 52, PhD(comput sci), 79; Johns Hopkins Univ, MEd, 74. *Prof Exp:* Jr mathematician, Shell Develop Co, 55-59; programmer, Univ Calif, Berkeley, 60-62; asst prof comput, Lansing Community Col, 63-67; educ specialist, Johns Hopkins Univ, 68; asst prof comput sci & math, 68-81, ASSOC PROF COMPUT SCI, TOWSON STATE UNIV, 81- *Concurrent Pos:* Vis assoc prof, Univ Ore, 81. *Mem:* Asn Comput Mach; Inst Elec & Electronics Engrs; Nat Educ Comput Conf. *Res:* Impact of computer on society; computer literacy and computer awareness. *Mailing Add:* Dept Math & Comput Sci Towson State Univ Baltimore MD 21204

LIDZ, THEODORE, b New York, NY, Apr 1, 10; m 39; c 3. PSYCHIATRY. *Educ:* Columbia Univ, AB, 31, MD, 36; Am Bd Psychiat & Neurol, dipl. *Hon Degrees:* MA, Yale Univ, 51. *Prof Exp:* From instr to assoc prof psychiat, Johns Hopkins Univ, 40-51; prof, 51-77, sterling prof, 77-78, EMER STERLING PROF PSYCHIAT, YALE UNIV, 78- *Concurrent Pos:* Examr, Am Bd Psychiat & Neurol, 46-51; psychiatrist-in-chief, Grace-New Haven Hosp, 51-61 & Yale Psychiat Inst, 51-61; chmn comt educ, Am Psychiat Asn, 52-55; mem study sect res grants, NIMH, 52-56, mem training grants comt, 59-63, career investr, 61-, mem ment health prog-proj comt, 63-67; consult, Off Surgeon Gen, 58-72; fel, Ctr Advan Study Behav Sci, 65-66; chmn dept psychiat, Sch Med, Yale Univ, 67-69. *Honors & Awards:* Frieda Fromm-Reichmann Award, Acad Psychoanal, 61; William C Menninger Award, Am Col Physicians, 72; Stanley R Dean Award, Am Col Psychiat, 73; Van Gieson Award, NY State Psychiat Inst, 73. *Mem:* Am Psychosom Soc (secy-treas, 52-56, pres, 57-58); fel Am Psychiat Asn; fel Am Col Psychoanal; fel Am Col Psychiat; Am Psychoanal Asn. *Res:* Schizophrenia; family. *Mailing Add:* Dept of Psychiat Sch of Med Yale Univ New Haven CT 06510

LIEB, CARL SEARS, b San Antonio, Tex, May 27, 49. EVOLUTIONARY BIOLOGY, HERPETOLOGY. *Educ:* Tex A&M Univ, BS, 71, MS, 73; Univ Calif, Los Angeles, PhD(biol), 81. *Prof Exp:* ASST CURATOR, LAB ENVIRON BIOL, UNIV TEX, EL PASO, 81- *Concurrent Pos:* Mus assoc, Natural Hist Mus Los Angeles County, 72-80. *Mem:* Am Soc Ichthyologists & Herpetologists; Herpetologists' League; Soc Study Amphibians & Reptiles; Southwestern Asn Naturalists. *Res:* Evolution, biosystematics and biogeography of vertebrate animals, particularly amphibians and reptiles. *Mailing Add:* Dept Biol Univ Tex El Paso TX 79968

LIEB, ELLIOTT HERSHEL, b Boston, Mass, July 31, 32; c 2. MATHEMATICAL PHYSICS. *Educ:* Mass Inst Technol, BSc, 53; Univ Birmingham, PhD(physics), 56. *Hon Degrees:* DSc, Univ Copenhagen, 79. *Prof Exp:* Fulbright fel physics, Kyoto Univ, 56-57; res assoc, Univ Ill, 57-58;

lab nuclear studies, Cornell Univ, 58-60; staff physicist, Res Lab, IBM Corp, 60-63; assoc prof physics, Belfer Grad Sch Sci, Yeshiva Univ, 63-66; prof, Northeastern Univ, 66-68; prof math, Mass Inst Technol, 68-75; PROF MATH & PHYSICS, PRINCETON UNIV, 75- Concurrent Pos: Sr lectr, Univ Col Sierra Leone, 61-62; consult, IBM Corp, 63-65; vis mem staff, Los Alamos Nat Lab, 66-, Theoret Div Adv Comt, 78-; guest prof, Inst Advan Sci Studies, France, 72-73; fel, Guggenheim Found, 72 & 78; vis prof, Inst Advan Study, NJ, 82; ed, Commun Math Phys, Adv Appl Math, Studies Appl Math, Lett Math Phys & Rev Mod Phys. Honors & Awards: Boris Pregel Award, NY Acad Sci, 70; Heineman Prize, Am Phys Soc & Am Inst Physics, 78. Mem: Fel Am Phys Soc; Austrian Acad Sci. Res: Statistical mechanics; field theory; solid state physics; atomic physics. Mailing Add: Dept of Physics-Jadwin Hall Princeton Univ PO Box 708 Princeton NJ 08540

LIEB, MARGARET, b Bronxville, NY, Nov 28, 23. GENETICS. Educ: Smith Col, BA, 45; Ind Univ, MA, 46; Columbia Univ, PhD, 50. Prof Exp: Asst prof biol, Brandeis Univ, 55-60; vis assoc prof, 60-62, assoc prof, 62-67, PROF MICROBIOL, SCH MED, UNIV SOUTHERN CALIF, 67- Concurrent Pos: USPHS fel, Calif Inst Technol, 50-52, Nat Found Infantile Paralysis fel, 52-53; fel, Inst Pasteur, 53-54; French Govt fel, Inst Radium, 54-55; NIH res career award, 62-72; prog dir genetic biol, NSF, 72-73. Mem: Fel AAAS; Genetics Soc Am; Am Soc Microbiol. Res: Bacteriophage genetics; lysogeny. Mailing Add: Dept of Microbiol Sch Med Univ of Southern Calif Los Angeles CA 90033

LIEB, WILLIAM ROBERT, b Chicago, Ill, Aug 31, 40; div. BIOPHYSICS. Educ: Univ Ill, BS, 62, MS, 63, PhD(biophys), 67. Prof Exp: Air Force Off Sci Res-Nat Res Coun fel biochem, Univ Manchester, 67-68; res fel, Dept Polymer Sci, Weizmann Inst Sci, 69; inst life sci, Hebrew Univ, Jerusalem, 69-70; staff scientist, Med Res Coun Biophys Unit, 70-76, RES FEL, DEPT BIOPHYS, KING'S COL, LONDON, 76- Concurrent Pos: Prin investr, Med Res Coun grants, 78- Res: Molecular mechanisms of anesthesia; transport across biological membranes; x-ray and neutron diffraction analysis of membrane structure. Mailing Add: Dept Biophys King's Col 26-29 Drury Lane London England

LIEBE, DONALD CHARLES, b Cleveland, Ohio, Nov 16, 42; m 64; c 4. PHYSICAL CHEMISTRY. Educ: Case Western Reserve Univ, BA, 66, MA, 68, PhD(phys chem), 70. Prof Exp: Res assoc chem, Yale Univ, 70-71, NIH res fel, 71-73, asst instr, 74; res investr, 74-79, SECT HEAD, RES & DEVELOP DIV, G D SEARLE & CO, 79- Mem: Am Chem Soc; Royal Soc Chem; NY Acad Sci. Res: Physical chemistry of nucleic acids, protein-nucleic acid interactions; binding to nucleic acids; mechanism of animal virus replication; growth factors; physical pharmacy in pharmaceutical development; emulsion science; novel drug delivery systems; polyene macrolide antibiotic physical chemistry; polymer physical chemistry; packaging science. Mailing Add: G D Searle & Co Res & Develop Div Chicago IL 60680

LIEBE, RICHARD MILTON, b Norwalk, Conn, May 26, 32; m 55; c 3. GEOLOGY. Educ: Bates Col, BS, 54; Univ Houston, MS, 59; Univ Iowa, PhD(geol), 62. Prof Exp: Assoc prof geol, Col Wooster, 61-67; PROF GEOL, STATE UNIV NY COL BROCKPORT, 67- Mem: Paleont Soc; Soc Econ Paleont & Mineral; Nat Asn Geol Teachers. Res: Stratigraphic paleontology of the Paleozoic era using conodonts; shallow water sedimentology and coral reef ecology. Mailing Add: Dept of the Earth Sci State Univ NY Col at Brockport Brockport NY 14420

LIEBELT, ANNABEL GLOCKLER, b Washington, DC, June 27, 26; m 54; c 4. MICROSCOPIC ANATOMY, CANCER. Educ: Western Md Col, BA, 48; Univ Ill, MS, 55; Baylor Col Med, PhD(anat), 60. Prof Exp: Biologist, Path Sect, Nat Cancer Inst, 49-52; asst anat, Col Med, Univ Ill, 52-54; asst, Col Med, Baylor Univ, 54-58, from instr to assoc prof, 58-71; assoc prof cell & molecular biol, Med Col Ga, 71-74; PROF ANAT, NORTHEASTERN OHIO UNIVS COL MED, 74- Concurrent Pos: Dir, Kirschbaum Mem Lab, Col Med, Baylor Univ, 62-71 & coordr, Micros Anat Teaching Prog, 77, dir, 78-79, chmn, 79-81; consult, Breast Cancer Task Force, Nat Cancer Inst, 76-80. Mem: Am Asn Cancer Res; Am Asn Anat; NY Acad Sci; Am Soc Exp Path; Am Asn Lab Animal Sci. Res: Carcinogenesis and aging in inbred mice of several organ systems, especially the endocrine and reproductive (emphasis on mammary gland); biology histopathology; etiology; behavioral relationships; animal models. Mailing Add: Basic Med Sci Northeastern Ohio Univs Col Med Rootstown OH 44272

LIEBELT, ROBERT ARTHUR, b Chicago, Ill, Feb 3, 27; m 80; c 4. ANATOMY, EXPERIMENTAL PATHOLOGY. Educ: Loyola Univ, Ill, BS, 50; Wash State Univ, MS, 52; Baylor Univ, PhD(anat), 57, MD, 58. Prof Exp: Asst, Wash State Univ, 50-52; asst, Col Med, Baylor Univ, 54-57, from instr to prof anat & chmn dept, 57-71; prof cell & molecular biol & exp med & assoc dean curriculum, Med Col Ga, 71-72, provost, 72-74; charter dean, 74-79, PROF ANAT, NORTHEASTERN OHIO UNIVS COL MED, 74-, PROVOST/DEAN, 79- Concurrent Pos: Vis prof, Okayama Univ, 61. Mem: AAAS; Soc Exp Biol & Med; Am Asn Anat; Am Asn Cancer Res; NY Acad Sci. Res: Adipose tissue in obesity; relationship between nutrition and neoplasia; hypothalamus and appetite control; hypothalmic-pituitary relationships in experimental neoplasia; effects of pressure on food intake and body composition; biostereometric analysis for breast cancer; medical education. Mailing Add: Northeastern Ohio Univs Col Med Rootstown OH 44272

LIEBEN, JAN, b Trnovany, Czech, Mar 13, 15; US citizen; div; c 2. OCCUPATIONAL MEDICINE, PREVENTIVE MEDICINE. Educ: Univ Liverpool, MB, ChP, 43; Harvard Univ, MPH, 49; Am Bd Indust Hyg, dipl; Am Bd Prev Med, Pub Health & Occup Med, cert. Prof Exp: Asst health officer, New York City Dept Health, 49-50; epidemiologist, State Dept Health, Conn, 50-51; indust physician, 51-54; plant physician, Am Cyanamid Co, Pa, 54-55; dir occup health, State Dept Health, Pa, 55-69; med dir, Chem Group, FMC Corp, 69-75; prof occup med, Community Health & Prev Med,

Jefferson Med Col, Thomas Jefferson Univ, 75-76, clin prof, 76-80; CLIN PROF OCCUP HEALTH, RUTGERS MED SCH, COL MED & DENT, PISCATAWAY, NJ, 80- Concurrent Pos: Vis prof, Jefferson Med Col, 61-; consult, Radioactivity Ctr, Mass Inst Technol, 62-; consult div radiobiol, Argonne Nat Lab; former chmn manganese panel comt biol effects air pollution, Nat Acad Sci. Mem: Fel Indust Med Asn. Res: Epidemiology of beryllium, pneumoconiosis, pesticides and other chemical exposures, including radium. Mailing Add: Dept Occup Health Rutgers Med Sch Col Med & Dent Piscataway NJ 08854

LIEBENAUER, PAUL (HENRY), b Cleveland, Ohio, Sept 21, 35; m 62; c 2. EXPERIMENTAL NUCLEAR PHYSICS. Educ: Case Western Reserve Univ, BS, 57, MS, 60, PhD(physics), 71. Prof Exp: Instr physics, Clarkson Col Technol, 60-62; asst prof, 68-70, ASSOC PROF PHYSICS, STATE UNIV NY COL OSWEGO, 70- Concurrent Pos: Consult, NASA, 71-; NSF grant, 72. Mem: Am Phys Soc; Am Asn Physics Teachers; Sigma Xi. Res: Low energy nuclear physics. Mailing Add: Dept of Physics State Univ of NY Col at Oswego Oswego NY 13126

LIEBENBERG, DONALD HENRY, b Madison, Wis, July 10, 32; m 57; c 2. LOW TEMPERATURE PHYSICS, HIGH PRESSURES. Educ: Univ Wis, BS, 54, MS, 56, PhD, 71. Prof Exp: Asst, Univ Wis, 54-61; STAFF MEM PHYSICS, LOS ALAMOS NAT LAB, 61- Concurrent Pos: Solar-terrestrial res prog dir, NSF, 67-68; app liaison to Geophys Res Bd, Nat Acad Sci & US Comt Solar Terrestrial Res; US coord, 1970 Solar Eclipse; sabbatical leave, prog dir low temp physics, NSF, 80- Mem: AAAS; Am Astron Soc; Am Phys Soc; Am Geophys Union. Res: Low temperature physics, especially superfluidity and helium films; solar physics; magneto optics; high pressure physical measurements; high pressure physics. Mailing Add: 5100 Pheasant Ridge Rd Fairfax VA 22030

LIEBER, ALBERT JOHN, electrooptics, nuclear physics, see previous edition

LIEBER, CHARLES SAUL, b Antwerp, Belg, Feb 13, 31; US citizen; m 74; c 3. INTERNAL MEDICINE, NUTRITION. Educ: Univ Brussels, MD, 55. Prof Exp: Asst resident med, Univ Hosp Brugmann Brussels, Belg, 55-56; instr med, Harvard Med Sch, 61-62, assoc, 62-63; assoc prof, Med Col, Cornell Univ, 63-68; assoc prof, 68-69, PROF MED, MT SINAI SCH MED, 69-; CHIEF SECT LIVER DIS & NUTRIT, VET ADMIN HOSP, 68-; DIR, ALCOHOLISM RES & TREAT CTR, 77- Concurrent Pos: Belg Coun Sci Res fel internal med, Med Found Queen Elizabeth, 56-58; Belg-Am Found res fel med, Harvard Med Sch, 58-60; mem fat comt, Food & Nutrit Bd, Nat Acad Sci-Nat Res Coun, 61-67; dir liver dis & nutrit unit, Bellevue Hosp, 63-68; NIH res career develop award, 64-68. Honors & Awards: Laureate, Belg Govt, 56; McCollum Award, Am Soc Clin Nutrition, 73; E M Jellinek Mem Award, 77; W S Middleton Award, US Vet Admin, 77. Mem: Am Soc Clin Invest; Am Med Soc Alcoholism (pres, 75); Am Soc Clin Nutrit (pres, 75); Asn Am Physicians; Res Soc Alcoholism (pres, 79). Res: Diseases of the liver; nutrition and intermediary metabolism, especially alcoholic cirrhosis, fatty liver, hyperlipemia, hyperuricemia, pathogenesis and treatment of hepatic coma and ascites, and pathophysiology of liver regeneration and drug abuse. Mailing Add: Vet Admin Hosp Sect of Liver Dis 130 W Kingsbridge Rd Bronx NY 10468

LIEBER, MICHAEL, b Brooklyn, NY, Dec 28, 36; m 64; c 3. THEORETICAL PHYSICS. Educ: Cornell Univ, AB, 57; Harvard Univ, AM, 58, PhD(physics), 67. Prof Exp: Sr scientist, Res & Advan Develop Div, Avco Corp, 63-66, chief sci probs, 66-67; assoc res scientist & adj asst prof physics, NY Univ, 67-70; asst prof, 70-75, dir, Reach Kit Proj, 74-78, ASSOC PROF PHYSICS, UNIV ARK, FAYETTEVILLE, 75-, PLANETARIUM LECTR, 72- Concurrent Pos: Prin investr, Dept Energy grant, 80- Mem: Am Phys Soc; Am Asn Physics Teachers; Sigma Xi. Res: Quantum scattering theory; few body problems; quantum electrodynamics and field theory; mathematical methods; atomic collisions; cosmic rays; elementary particles; general relativity and cosmology. Mailing Add: Dept of Physics Univ of Ark Fayetteville AR 72701

LIEBERMAN, ALVIN, b Chicago, Ill, June 14, 21; m 47; c 2. CHEMICAL ENGINEERING. Educ: Cent YMCA Col, BS, 42; Ill Inst Technol, MS, 49. Prof Exp: Res assoc metal-ceramics, Alfred Univ, 49-51; res chem engr, IIT Res Inst, 51-63, sect mgr fine particles res, 63-68; dir res, 68-74, vpres, Royco Instruments, Inc, 74-80, VPRES, ADV DEVELOP, HIAC/ROYCO INSTRUMENT DIV, PAC SCI CO, 80- Concurrent Pos: Regional ed, Powder Technol, 69- Mem: AAAS; Am Chem Soc; Am Inst Chem Engrs; Am Asn Contamination Control (vpres, 62-63); Fine Particle Soc (pres, 77-78). Res: Aerosol studies and application of electronic techniques; cloud physics; dust-free assembly area control and procedures; particle technology for gas/liquid suspensions. Mailing Add: 141 Jefferson Dr Menlo Park CA 94025

LIEBERMAN, ARTHUR STUART, b Brooklyn, NY, Feb 24, 31; m 56; c 3. REGIONAL LANDSCAPE PLANNING, ENVIRONMENTAL HORTICULTURE. Educ: Cornell Univ, BS, 52, MS & LD 58. Prof Exp: Teacher high sch, NY, 52-53; from instr to assoc prof ornamental hort, 56-76, PROF PHYS ENVIRON QUAL, CORNELL UNIV, 77- Concurrent Pos: Adv, Nature Reserves Authority & Ministry Agr, Israel, 71-72; res fel, Technion Israel Inst Technol, Haifa, 75-76, Lady Davis vis prof award, 80-81, prof, Technion, 80-81; chmn & coordr Cornell Tree Crops Res Proj, coordr Multidisciplinary Int Land-Use Planning training prog, Cornell Univ. Mem: Int Soc Hort Sci; Int Asn Ecol; Soc Int Develop. Res: Physical environmental quality; ecology-based regional land-use planning; regional landscape inventories and information systems for physical planning; analysis and use of vegetation in comprehensive land planning; tree crops for food and forage on rough marginal lands. Mailing Add: Dept Floricult & Ornamental Hort Landscape Archit Prog Cornell Univ Ithaca NY 14853

LIEBERMAN, BURTON BARNET, b Boston, Mass, Sept 28, 38; m 63; c 2. MATHEMATICS. *Educ:* Harvard Univ, BA, 60; NY Univ, MS, 62, PhD(math), 67. *Prof Exp:* Asst prof, 65-69, ASSOC PROF MATH, POLYTECH INST NY, 69- *Mem:* Am Math Soc; Sigma Xi. *Res:* Ordinary differential equations; random differential equations. *Mailing Add:* Dept of Math Polytech Inst NY 333 Jay St Brooklyn NY 11201

LIEBERMAN, DANIEL, b Gunnison, Utah, Feb 21, 19; c 1. PSYCHIATRY. *Educ:* Univ Calif, AB, 42, MD, 46. *Prof Exp:* Chief hosp serv, Sonoma State Hosp, Calif, 49-54; supt & med dir, Mendocino State Hosp, 54-60; from chief dep dir to dir, State Dept Ment Health, 60-63; pvt pract, 63-64; comnr ment health, Del Dept Ment Health, 64-67; dir, Jefferson Community Ment Health-Ment Retardation Ctr, 67-76, prof psychiat & actg chmn, Dept Psychiat & Human Behav, 74-76, PROF & DIR, PSYCHOSOM SERV, JEFFERSON MED COL, THOMAS JEFFERSON UNIV, 76- *Concurrent Pos:* Consult forensic psychiat, Calif Superior Courts, 54-63; consult ment hosp serv, Am Psychiat Asn, 60-62; consult forensic psychiat, US Fed Court, 61-; consult, Ment Health Res Inst, Palo Alto, Calif, 63-64; consult state ment progs, NIMH, 65-68, consult alcohol rev comt, 67-70, consult, Nat Coun Community Health Ctrs, 72-73; consult, Vet Admin Hosp, Coatesville, Pa, 67- *Mem:* Fel AAAS; charter fel Am Col Psychiat; life fel Am Asn Ment Deficiency; fel Acad Psychosom Med; fel Am Psychiat Asn. *Mailing Add:* Jefferson Med Col 11th & Walnut St Philadelphia PA 19107

LIEBERMAN, DAVID S(AMUEL), physical metallurgy, see previous edition

LIEBERMAN, DIANA DALE, b Los Angeles, Calif, Jan 19, 49; m 68; c 1. POPULATION BIOLOGY, TROPICAL ECOLOGY. *Educ:* Univ Ghana, Legon, BSc, 76, PhD(bot), 79. *Prof Exp:* Demonstr plant ecol, Dept Bot, Univ Ghana, 76-79; vis scholar forest ecol & trop biol, Dept Environ Sci, Univ Va, 80-81; ASST PROF POP BIOL, DEPT BIOL, UNIV NDAK, 81- *Concurrent Pos:* NSF res grant, 81-84. *Mem:* Ecol Soc Am. *Res:* Tree growth rates, age-size relationships and tropical forest dynamics; plant population biology, phenology and seed dispersal. *Mailing Add:* Dept Biol Univ NDak Grand Forks ND 58202

LIEBERMAN, EDWARD MARVIN, b Lowell, Mass, Feb 10, 38; m 60; c 3. PHYSIOLOGY. *Educ:* Tufts Univ, BS, 59; Univ Mass, MA, 61; Univ Fla, PhD(physiol), 65. *Prof Exp:* Res assoc physiol, Col Med, Univ Fla, 66; asst prof, 68-72, assoc prof, Bowman Gray Sch Med, 72-76; assoc prof, 76-78; PROF PHYSIOL, SCH MED, E CAROLINA UNIV, 78- *Concurrent Pos:* Swed Med Res Coun fel, Col Med, Univ Uppsala, 66-68. *Mem:* Soc Neurosci; Biophys Soc; Am Heart Asn; Am Physiol Soc; NY Acad Sci. *Res:* Cellular nerve physiology; membrane ion and water transport and metabolism; ultraviolet radiation effects on membranes; Schwann cell axon interactions. *Mailing Add:* Dept of Physiol E Carolina Univ Sch of Med Greenville NC 27834

LIEBERMAN, EDWIN JAMES, b Milwaukee, Wis, Nov 21, 34; m 59; c 2. PSYCHIATRY, SOCIAL PSYCHOLOGY. *Educ:* Univ Calif, Berkeley, AB, 55; Univ Calif, San Francisco, MD, 58; Harvard Univ, MPH, 63; Am Bd Psychiat & Neurol, dipl, 66. *Prof Exp:* Psychiat fel, Mass Ment Health Ctr, Boston, 59-61; child psychiat fel, Putnam's Children Ctr, Boston, 61-62; psychiatrist & chief, Ctr Child & Family Ment Health, NIMH, 63-70; dir family ther, Hillcrest Children's Ctr, DC, 71-74, dir ment health proj, 72-75, dir family planning proj, Am Pub Health Asn, 75-77; CLIN ASSOC PROF PSYCHIAT, SCH MED, GEORGE WASHINGTON UNIV, 77- *Concurrent Pos:* Child psychiat fel, Hillcrest Children's Ctr, DC, 65-66; mem bd dirs, Sex Info & Educ Coun US, 66-69 & 73-76; clin asst prof psychiat, Sch Med, Howard Univ, 67-76; mem bd dirs, Nat Coun Family Rels, 69-73; vis lectr maternal & child health, Harvard Sch Pub Health, 69-73. *Mem:* AAAS; fel Am Psychiat Asn; fel Am Pub Health Asn; fel Am Asn Marriage & Family Therapists; Esperanto League NAm (pres, 72-75). *Res:* Mental health; preventive psychiatry; family planning; nonviolence; Esperantic studies; international language planning. *Mailing Add:* 6451 Barnaby St N W Washington DC 20015

LIEBERMAN, GERALD J, b New York, NY, Dec 31, 25; m 50; c 4. OPERATIONS RESEARCH, STATISTICS. *Educ:* Cooper Union, BME, 48; Columbia Univ, AM, 49; Stanford Univ, PhD(statist), 53. *Prof Exp:* Math statistician, Nat Bur Standards, 49-50; from asst prof to prof statist & indust eng, 53-67, chmn dept opers res, 67-75, assoc dean, Sch Humanities & Sci, 75-77, PROF STATIST & OPERS RES, STANFORD UNIV, 67-, VICE PROVOST & DEAN RES, 77- *Concurrent Pos:* Mem adv panel math sci, NSF, 68-73. *Honors & Awards:* Shewhart Medal, Am Soc Qual Control, 72. *Mem:* Opers Res Soc Am; fel Am Soc Qual Control; fel Am Statist Asn; fel Inst Math Statist; Int Statist Inst. *Res:* Industrial statistics; quality control; reliability. *Mailing Add:* Dept of Statist & Opers Res Stanford Univ Stanford CA 94305

LIEBERMAN, HERBERT A, b New York, NY, Aug 6, 21; m 60; c 2. PHARMACEUTICAL CHEMISTRY. *Educ:* Univ Ark, BS, 40; Columbia Univ, AM, 48, BS, 51, MS, 52; Purdue Univ, PhD(pharmaceut chem), 55. *Prof Exp:* Res fel biochem, Beth Israel Hosp, New York, 40-41; chemist, Pine Bluff Arsenal, Ark, 41-43; instr & assoc anal chem, Col Pharm, Columbia Univ, 46-52, res pharmacist, Res Inst, Wyeth Labs, 54-57; mgr pharmaceut prod develop, Isodine Pharmacal Co, 57-61; sr res assoc, 61-63, dir pharmaceut res & develop, 63-72, vpres, Personal Prods Div, 72-77, DIR RES & DEVELOP ADMIN, WARNER LAMBERT CO INC, 77- *Mem:* Am Chem Soc; Am Pharmaceut Asn; fel Acad Pharmaceut Sci; Sigma Xi. *Res:* Industrial pharmacy; pharmaceutical technology, particularly process and product development; analytical methods development for pharmaceutical products; biochemical research, particularly metabolic pathways. *Mailing Add:* Consumer Prods Group Warner Lambert Co 170 Tabor Rd Morris Plains NJ 07950

LIEBERMAN, HILLEL, b Philadelphia, Pa, Jan 24, 42; m 66; c 2. ORGANIC CHEMISTRY, MICROBIAL BIOCHEMISTRY. *Educ:* Temple Univ, BS, 63, MS, 65, PhD(med org chem), 70. *Prof Exp:* Var admin & sci asst dir res, 73-76, asst vpres res, 76-79, VPRES RES, BETZ LABS, TREVOSE, 79- *Mem:* Am Soc Microbiol; Am Chem Soc; Sigma Xi; Tech Asn Pulp & Paper Indust. *Res:* Development of chemical agents of an antimicrobial and/or antipollution nature to be employed in industrial water systems; development of conceptual information to aid in application of the aforementioned. *Mailing Add:* 3782 Midvale Lane Huntingdon Valley PA 19006

LIEBERMAN, IRVING, b Brooklyn, NY, Oct 25, 21; m 47; c 2. CELL BIOLOGY. *Educ:* Brooklyn Col, BA, 44; Univ Ky, MS, 48; Univ Calif, PhD(bact), 52. *Prof Exp:* Asst prof bact, Miami Univ, 48-49; from instr to asst prof microbiol, Sch Med, Washington Univ, 53-56; from asst prof to prof microbiol, 56-66, PROF ANAT & CELL BIOL, SCH MED, UNIV PITTSBURGH, 66- *Concurrent Pos:* Mem cell biol study sect, USPHS, 60-64, chmn, 71-73; fel engr, Westinghouse Res Ctr, 69- *Mem:* Am Soc Biol Chemists. *Res:* Chemistry. *Mailing Add:* 6717 Reynolds Pittsburgh PA 15206

LIEBERMAN, JACK, b Chicago, Ill, Jan 4, 26; m 55; c 4. PULMONARY DISEASES, ENZYMOLOGY. *Educ:* Univ Calif, Los Angeles, AB, 49; Univ Southern Calif, MD, 54; Am Bd Internal Med, dipl, 62. *Prof Exp:* Intern, Harbor Gen Hosp, 54-55, resident internal med, 55-58; clin investr, Vet Admin Hosp, Long Beach, Calif, 60-63, sect chief internal med, 63-68; assoc clin prof med, Sch Med, Univ Calif, Los Angeles, 68-71; assoc clin prof med, Sch Med, Univ Calif, Irvine, 71-76; assoc dir, Dept Respiratory Dis, City of Hope Med Ctr, 71-76; CHIEF, RESPIRATORY DIS DIV, SEPULVEDA VET ADMIN HOSP, 76-; PROF MED, UNIV CALIF, LOS ANGELES, 77- *Concurrent Pos:* Long Beach Heart Asn res fel, Harbor Gen Hosp, 58-60. *Mem:* AAAS; fel Am Col Physicians; fel Am Col Chest Physicians; Am Fedn Clin Res. *Res:* Cystic fibrosis; emphysema; antitrypsin deficiency; blood test for sarcoidosis. *Mailing Add:* Vet Admin Hosp 16111 Plummer St Sepulveda CA 91343

LIEBERMAN, JAMES, b New York, NY, June 2, 21; m 43; c 1. PUBLIC HEALTH. *Educ:* Middlesex Univ, DVM, 44; Univ Minn, MPH, 47. *Prof Exp:* Sr consult vet, UNRRA, 46; regional milk & food consult, USPHS, Kansas City, 48-50, asst to the chief, Milk & Food Br, DC, 50-51, from asst chief to chief spec proj br, Bur State Serv, 51-52, liaison officer to US Navy, 52, consult, spec regulatory prog, 52-54, detailed epidemiologist, Div Epidemiol & Commun Dis Control, NY State Health Dept, 54-55, training consult, Training Br, Commun Dis Ctr, asst chief training br & chief audio visual sect, 59-62, chief med audio visual br dir, Pub Health Serv Audio Visual Fac, Commun Dis Ctr, 62-67, dir, Nat Med audio visual Ctr & assoc dir audio visual & telecommun, Nat Libr Med, 67-70, asst surgeon gen, USPHS, 68-70; vpres, med div, Videorecord Corp Am, 70-73; consult health sci educ & commun, 73-76; DIR, DEPT HEALTH, GREENWICH, CONN, 76- *Concurrent Pos:* Secy, Conf Pub Health Vets, 53-57; consult, WHO, Geneva, 55; chmn, Fed Adv Coun Med Training Aids, 60; mem task force sci commun, Surgeon Gen Conf Health Commun, 62; secy AV Conf Med & Allied Sci, 62-70; pres, Metrop Atlanta Commun Coun, 65; chmn conf biomed commun, NY Acad Sci, 67; mem comt bio-technol, Ga Sci & Technol Comn, 69-70; mem prof adv coun, Nat Easter Seal Soc Crippled Children & Adults, 69-; vis prof, Hahnemann Med Col, 73-; mem bd gov & pres-elect, Conn Inst Health Manpower Resources, 74-78. *Honors & Awards:* Cert Commendation, UNRRA, 46; Letter of Commendation, Surgeon Gen, US Navy, 52; Citation, Nat League Nursing, 62; Meritorious Serv Medal, USPHS, 65; Citation, Fulton County Med Soc, Ga, 66 & Nat AV Asn, 67; Brenda Award, Theta Sigma Phi, 68; Myrtle Wreath Award, Hadassah, 69; Except Serv Award, Ga Easter Seal Soc, 70. *Mem:* Fel Am Pub Health Asn; Asn Mil Surg US; Am Vet Med Asn; NY Acad Sci; Sigma Xi. *Res:* Biomedical communication and education; public health practice and epidemiology; training and administration; relationship of animal health to human welfare. *Mailing Add:* 12 Silver Brook Rd Westport CT 06880

LIEBERMAN, LESLIE SUE, b Rockville Ctr, NY, June 23, 44; c 1. BIOLOGICAL ANTHROPOLOGY. *Educ:* Univ Colo, BA, 65; Univ Ariz, MA, 71; Univ Conn, PhD(biobehav sci), 75. *Prof Exp:* Proj assoc body composition, Human Performance Res Lab, Pa State Univ, University Park, 75-76; asst prof anthrop, 76-81, ASSOC PROF ANTHROP & PEDIAT, UNIV FLA, 81-, GRAD COORDR, CTR GERONT STUDIES, 79-, RES EPIDEMIOLOGIST, DIABETES RES, EDUC & TREAT CTR, 79- *Concurrent Pos:* Fel, Nat Inst Gen Med Sci Human Performance Res Lab & Dept Anthrop, Pa State Univ, 74-75; prin investr, NSF grant, 81-83; vis lectr, Am Anthrop Asn, 81- *Mem:* AAAS; Am Anthrop Asn; Am Asn Phys Anthropologists; Human Biol Coun; Comt Nutrit Anthrop (vpres, 80-82). *Res:* Study of body composition and the effects of nutritional behavior and diet on adaptation and microevolution in human populations; epidemiology of diabetes mellitus. *Mailing Add:* Dept of Anthrop Gen Purpose Bldg A Univ of Fla Gainesville FL 32611

LIEBERMAN, MELVYN, b Brooklyn, NY, Feb 4, 38; m 61; c 2. PHYSIOLOGY. *Educ:* Cornell Univ, BA, 59; State Univ NY, PhD(physiol), 65. *Prof Exp:* Instr biol, Queen's Col, NY, 60; asst physiol, State Univ NY Downstate Med Ctr, 60-64; res assoc, Div Biomed Eng, Sch Eng & Dept Physiol & Pharmacol, 67-68, asst prof, 68-73, assoc prof, 73-78, PROF PHYSIOL, MED CTR, DUKE UNIV, 78- *Concurrent Pos:* Nat Heart Inst fel, 64-65; Carnegie Inst fel, 65; Nat Heart Inst fel, Biophys Inst, Brazil, 65-67; Nat Heart Inst spec fel, Med Ctr, Duke Univ, 67-68; lectr, Queen's Col, NY, 63-64; vis investr, Jan Swammerdam Inst, Netherlands, 75; Soc Gen Physiol rep, Nat Res Coun, 71-75; chmn res rev comt, NC Heart Asn, 75-76; co-coordinator, US Japan Coop Sci Prog, 74 & US Brazil Coop Sci Prog, 80; Porter Develop Prog, Am Physiol Soc, 74-77, educ mat rev bd, 75-; assoc ed, Am J Physiol, 81-84; consult, Macy Found, Nat Heart Lung & Blood Inst, NSF, Vet Admin & Am Heart Asn; mem, Physiol Study Sect, Am Heart Asn, 80-84. *Mem:* Am Heart Asn; Am Physiol Soc; Biophys Soc; Cardiac Muscle Soc; Soc Gen Physiol (secy, 69-71, pres, 81-82). *Res:* Electrophysiology and ion transport of cardiac muscle; developmental and comparative physiology of heart; structure-function relationships of heart cells in tissue culture; excitable cells in tissue culture. *Mailing Add:* Dept of Physiol Duke Univ Med Ctr Durham NC 27710

LIEBERMAN, MICHAEL MERRIL, microbiology, see previous edition

LIEBERMAN, MICHAEL WILLIAMS, b Pittsburgh, Pa, Apr 20, 41; m 68; c 2. EXPERIMENTAL PATHOLOGY, MOLECULAR BIOLOGY. *Educ:* Yale Univ, BA, 63; Univ Pittsburgh, MD, 67, PhD(biochem), 72. *Prof Exp:* Res assoc, Fels Inst, Temple Health Sci Ctr, 70-72 & Exp Path Br, Nat Cancer Inst, 72-74; head somatic cell genetics sect, Nat Inst Environ Health Sci, 74-76; assoc prof, 76-80, PROF, DEPT PATH, SCH MED, WASHINGTON UNIV, 80-, DIR GRAD STUDIES, DIV BIOL & BIOMED SCI, 80- *Concurrent Pos:* Adj asst & assoc prof, Dept Path, Med Sch, Univ NC, 74-76; assoc pathologist, Barnes Hosp, St Louis, 76-; mem, Chem Path Study Sect, NIH, 78-; mem, Bd Toxicol, & Environ Health Hazards, Nat Res Coun, 80- *Honors & Awards:* Warner-Lambert/Parke-Davis Award, Am Asn Pathologists, 81. *Mem:* Am Asn Cancer Res; AAAS; Am Asn Pathologists; Environ Mutagen Soc; Am Soc Biol Chemists. *Res:* Chemical carcinogenesis; DNA repair in eukaryotes; chromatin structure. *Mailing Add:* Dept of Path Box 8118 660 S Euclid Ave St Louis MO 63110

LIEBERMAN, MILTON EUGENE, b Chicago, Ill, Aug 30, 34; m 68; c 1. EVOLUTIONARY BIOLOGY, TROPICAL ECOLOGY. *Educ:* Univ Calif, Berkeley, AB, 62; Ariz State Univ, MS, 66; Univ Calif, Irvine, PhD(biol sci), 69. *Prof Exp:* Sr lectr ecol, Dept Zool, Univ Ghana, 74-79; vis prof, Dept Environ Sci, Univ Va, 80-81; RES PROF ECOL, DEPT BIOL, UNIV NDAK, 81- *Concurrent Pos:* NSF res grant, 81-84; res assoc, Mo Bot Garden, St Louis, 80- *Mem:* Ecol Soc Am; Am Soc Naturalists; Sigma Xi. *Res:* Ecology of new world tropical forests, tropical marine benthic algal assemblages; reproductive phenology of temperate and tropical fleshy-fruited plants; plant-animal interactions. *Mailing Add:* Dept Biol Univ NDak Grand Forks ND 58202

LIEBERMAN, MORRIS, b Brooklyn, NY, Sept 4, 19; m 47; c 1. PLANT PHYSIOLOGY. *Educ:* City Col New York, BS, 41; Rutgers Univ, MS, 47; Univ Md, PhD(plant physiol), 52. *Prof Exp:* Chemist, E R Squibb Co, 47-48; from asst plant physiologist to prin plant physiologist, 48-72, chief, Post-Harvest Plant Physiol Lab, Plant Indust Sta, 72-81, CHIEF, PLANT HORMONE LAB, BELTSVILLE AGR RES CTR, USDA, 81- *Concurrent Pos:* Res assoc, Univ Calif, 53-55 & low temperature res sta, Cambridge Univ, 61-62. *Mem:* AAAS; Am Soc Plant Physiol; Am Chem Soc; Am Soc Biol Chem; Brit Biochem Soc. *Res:* Post harvest physiology of fruits and vegetables; respiratory metabolism of plants; oxidation and phosphorylation by mitochondrial systems isolated from fruits and vegetables; oxidative enzymes; ethylene biosynthesis and physiology of ethylene action in plants; plant hormones; metabolic regulation. *Mailing Add:* Beltsville Agr Res Ctr West USDA Beltsville MD 20705

LIEBERMAN, MORTON LEONARD, b Chicago, Ill, Nov 22, 37; m 62; c 2. PHYSICAL CHEMISTRY. *Educ:* Ill Inst Technol, BS, 59, MS, 63, PhD(phys chem), 65. *Prof Exp:* Sr chemist, Res & Develop Labs, Corning Glass Works, 65-68; STAFF MEM TECH RES, SANDIA LABS, 68- *Mem:* Am Chem Soc; Inst Elec & Electronics Eng. *Res:* High-temperature chemistry, thermodynamics; phase transitions; thin films; optical properties; fossil fuels; pyrotechnics and explosives; carbon research. *Mailing Add:* 1316 Paisano Northeast Albuquerque NM 87112

LIEBERMAN, ROBERT, b Columbus, Ohio, Apr 9, 24; m 62; c 3. RADIOCHEMISTRY. *Educ:* Ohio State Univ, BA, 48, MSc, 52. *Prof Exp:* Chemist, Plastics Div, Battelle Mem Inst, 55-58, res scientist, Chem Physics Div, 58-64, sr chemist, 64-67, chief bioassay sect, Southeastern Radiol Health Lab, USPHS, 67-69, chief chem & biol, 69-71; chief phys sci br, Eastern Environ Radiation Lab, 71-74, chief qual assurance sect, 74-79, RES & DEVELOP CHEMIST, EASTERN ENVIRON RADIATION FACIL, ENVIRON PROTECTION AGENCY, 74- . *Res:* Polyurethane foams; fission gas release; neutron dosimetry; radiation effects on plastics; use of radiotracers on wear studies; measurement of radionuclides in environmental samples. *Mailing Add:* 3707 Laconia Lane Montgomery AL 36111

LIEBERMAN, SAMUEL VICTOR, b Philadelphia, Pa, Nov 3, 14; m 38; c 2. CHEMISTRY. *Educ:* Univ Pa, BS, 36, MS, 37, PhD(chem), 48. *Prof Exp:* Asst, Sharp & Dohme, Inc, 41-42; res chemist, Wyeth Inst Med Res, 45-47, sr res chemist, 48-55; scientist in charge, Phys Anal Dept, Prod Div, Bristol-Myers Co, 55-57, dir develop & phys sci, 57-60; CONSULT PHARMACEUT PROD, 61- *Mem:* AAAS; Sigma Xi. *Res:* Research, development and testing of pharmaceutical products. *Mailing Add:* 3400 N Ocean Dr #508 Singer Island FL 33404

LIEBERMAN, SEYMOUR, b New York, NY, Dec 1, 16; m 44; c 1. BIOCHEMISTRY. *Educ:* Brooklyn Col, AB, 36; Univ Ill, MS, 37; Stanford Univ, PhD(chem), 41. *Prof Exp:* Chemist, Schering Corp, 38-39; Rockefeller Found asst, Stanford Univ, 39-41; spec res assoc, Harvard Univ, 41-45; assoc, Sloan-Kettering Inst, 45-50; from asst prof to assoc prof, 50-62, PROF BIOCHEM, COL PHYSICIANS & SURGEONS, COLUMBIA UNIV, 62- *Concurrent Pos:* Mem panel steroids, Comt on Growth, Nat Res Coun, 46-50 & panel endocrinol, 55-56; traveling fel from Mem Hosp, New York to Basel, Switz, 46-47; mem endocrinol study sect, NIH, 58-63, mem, Insts, 59-65, chmn, 63-65, chmn gen clin res ctrs comn, 67-70; mem med adv comt, Pop Coun, 61-; assoc ed, J Clin Endocrinol & Metab, 63-67; prog officer, Ford Found, 74; pres, St Luke's-Roosevelt Inst Health Sci, 81- *Honors & Awards:* Ciba Award, Endocrine Soc, 52 & Koch Award, 70. *Mem:* Nat Acad Sci; Am Chem Soc; Am Soc Biol Chem; fel NY Acad Sci; Endocrine Soc (vpres, 67, pres, 74). *Res:* Steroid chemistry and biochemistry; biogenesis and metabolism of steroid hormones; steroid hormone-protein conjugates; steroid sulfates and lipoidal derivatives of steroids. *Mailing Add:* Col of Physicians & Surgeons Columbia Univ 630 W 168 St New York NY 10032

LIEBERMANN, HOWARD HORST, b Ger, Nov 27, 49; m 79. METALLURGY, MATERIALS SCIENCE. *Educ:* Polytech Inst New York, BS, 72; Univ Pa, MS, 75, PhD(metall & mat sci), 77. *Prof Exp:* staff metallurgist amorphous alloys, Corp Res & Develop, Gen Elec Co, 77-81; SR

METALLURGIST AMORPHOUS ALLOYS, METGLAS PROD DIV, ALLIED CORP, 82- *Mem:* Sigma Xi; Magnetics Soc; Am Soc Metals; Am Inst Mining, Metall & Petrol Engrs. *Res:* Materials processing; amorphous alloys; magnetic materials. *Mailing Add:* Allied Corp Technol Metglas Bldg 6 Eastmans Rd Parsippany NJ 07054

LIEBERMANN, LEONARD NORMAN, b Ironwood, Mich, May 14, 15; m 41; c 3. PHYSICS. *Educ:* Univ Chicago, BS, 37, MS, 38, PhD(physics), 40. *Prof Exp:* Instr physics, Wash Univ, 40-41; instr, Univ Kans, 41-43, asst prof, 43-44; prin physicist bur ships, Woods Hole Oceanog Inst, Mass, 44-46; res assoc, marine phys lab, 46-48, assoc prof geophys, 48-54, PROF PHYSICS, UNIV CALIF, SAN DIEGO, 54- *Concurrent Pos:* Guggenheim Found fel, 52-53; dir, Proj Sorrento, 59. *Mem:* Fel Am Phys Soc; fel Acoust Soc Am. *Res:* Ultrasonics; underwater sound; hydrodynamics; properties of liquids; electromagnetic propagation; solid state. *Mailing Add:* Dept of Physics Univ of Calif La Jolla CA 92037

LIEBERMANN, ROBERT C, b Ellwood City, Pa, Feb 6, 42; m 64; c 3. GEOPHYSICS. *Educ:* Calif Inst Technol, BS, 64; Columbia Univ, PhD(geophys), 69. *Prof Exp:* Res scientist, Lamont-Doherty Geol Observ, 69-70; res fel geophys, Calif Inst Technol, 70; mem fac, Australian Nat Univ, 70-76; ASSOC PROF, STATE UNIV NY, STONY BROOK, 76- *Concurrent Pos:* Assoc ed, J Geophys Res, 73-76. *Mem:* Fel Royal Astron Soc; Am Geophys Union; Seismol Soc Am. *Res:* Relative excitation of seismic waves by earthquakes and underground explosions; elastic properties of minerals and rocks as a function of pressure and temperature; composition and mineralogy of earth's mantle. *Mailing Add:* Dept of Earth Space Sci State Univ of NY Long Island NY 11794

LIEBERT, JAMES WILLIAM, b Coffeyville, Kans, June 19, 46. ASTRONOMY, ASTROPHYSICS. *Educ:* Univ Kans, BA, 68; Univ Calif, Berkeley, MA, 70, PhD(astron), 77. *Prof Exp:* RES ASSOC ASTRON, STEWARD OBSERV, UNIV ARIZ, 76- *Concurrent Pos:* Prin investr, NSF grant, Univ Ariz, 78-80. *Mem:* Am Astron Soc. *Res:* Observational stellar astronomy and astrophysics; white dwarf stars. *Mailing Add:* Steward Observ Univ of Ariz Tucson AZ 85721

LIEBES, SIDNEY, JR, b San Francisco, Calif, Dec 13, 29; m 58; c 2. PHYSICS. *Educ:* Princeton Univ, BSE, 52; Stanford Univ, PhD(physics), 58. *Prof Exp:* Instr physics, Princeton Univ, 57-61, asst prof, 61-64; res assoc-physicist, Dept Genetics, Med Ctr, 64-80, MEM STAFF, DEPT COMPUT SCI, STANFORD UNIV, 80- *Mem:* Am Phys Soc; Am Asn Physics Teachers. *Res:* Experimental atomic and electron physics; gravitation experiments; mass spectrometry; physical microanalysis; techniques applied to bio-medical research; computer imagery processing; Martian Lander imagery. *Mailing Add:* Dept Comput Sci Stanford Univ Stanford CA 94305

LIEBESKIND, HERBERT, b New York, NY, Nov 24, 21; m 43; c 2. PHYSICAL CHEMISTRY. *Educ:* NY Univ, BS, 41. *Prof Exp:* Asst instr chem, NY Univ, 43-45; from instr to assoc prof, 45-66, asst dean, 68-72, PROF CHEM, COOPER UNION, 66-, DIR ADMISSIONS & REGISTR, 70-, DEAN ADMISSIONS & RECORDS, 72- *Concurrent Pos:* Vis lectr, Stevens Inst Technol, 52-54; vis assoc prof, Yeshiva Univ, 61-62. *Mem:* AAAS; Am Chem Soc; Am Soc Eng Educ; NY Acad Sci. *Mailing Add:* Off of Admissions & Registr Cooper Union New York NY 10003

LIEBESKIND, LANNY STEVEN, b Buffalo, NY, Sept 5, 50. ORGANIC CHEMISTRY, ORGANOMETALLIC CHEMISTRY. *Educ:* State Univ NY, Buffalo, BS, 72; Univ Rochester, MS, 74, PhD(chem), 76. *Prof Exp:* NSF fel chem, Mass Inst Technol, 76-77; NIH fel, Stanford Univ, 77-78; ASST PROF CHEM, FLA STATE UNIV, 78- *Mem:* Am Chem Soc. *Res:* Application of organotransition metal chemistry to the solution of problems in synthetic organic chemistry. *Mailing Add:* Dept of Chem Fla State Univ Tallahassee FL 32306

LIEBHAFSKY, HERMAN ALFRED, b Zwittau, Austria-Hungary, Nov 18, 05; US citizen; m 35; c 2. CHEMISTRY. *Educ:* Agr & Mech Col, Tex, BS, 26; Univ Nebr, MS, 27; Univ Calif, PhD(chem), 29. *Prof Exp:* Instr phys & inorg chem, Univ Calif, 29-34; inorg & anal chemist, Consult & Res Assoc, Gen Elec Co, 34-51, mgr phys chem res, 51-65, electrochem br, 65-67; prof, 67-72, EMER PROF CHEM, TEX A&M UNIV, 72- *Honors & Awards:* Fisher award, Am Chem Soc, 61. *Mem:* Am Chem Soc; Soc Appl Spectros. *Res:* Photoelectric spectrophotometry and x-ray methods in chemical analysis; kinetics of reactions in solution; chemistry of the mercury boiler and of amalgams; rocket propellants; catalyses in homogeneous system; hydrolysis and hydration equilibria of halogens; statistics in analytical chemistry; analytical methods of silicones; corrosion; constitution of hydroxyanthraquinone lakes; fuel cells and batteries. *Mailing Add:* 2610 Melba Circle Bryan TX 77801

LIEBHARDT, WILLIAM C, b Duluth, Minn, Feb 16, 36; m 61; c 4. SOILS, PLANT PHYSIOLOGY. *Educ:* Univ Wis-Madison, BS, 58, MS, 64, PhD(soils), 66. *Prof Exp:* Agronomist, Stand Fruit Co, 66-68; sr agronomist, Allied Chem Corp, 68-69; asst prof, 70-76, ASSOC PROF PLANT SCI, UNIV DEL, 76- *Res:* Soil fertility; plant nutrition; waste disposal; water use. *Mailing Add:* Dept of Plant Sci Univ of Del Newark DE 19711

LIEBLEIN, JULIUS, b New York, NY, Aug 5, 14; m 43; c 2. MATHEMATICAL STATISTICS. *Educ:* City Col, BS, 35; Brooklyn Col, MA, 40; American Univ, PhD(math), 53. *Prof Exp:* Teacher high sch, NY, 36-37; actuarial clerk, State Ins Fund, 37-39; statistician, New York Bd Ed, 42-43; econ analyst, Div Tax Res, US Dept Treas, DC, 43-47; mathematician & math statistician, Statist Eng Lab, Nat Bur Standards, 47-56; mathematician, Appl Math Lab, David Taylor Model Basin, US Navy Dept, 56-64; math statistician, Off Statist Prog, Bur Finance & Admin, US Post Off Dept, 64-68; opers res analyst, Tech Anal Div, Nat Bur Standards, 68-75; consult extreme values & statist, 75-78; RETIRED. *Honors & Awards:* Belden Math Medal, 33. *Mem:* Am Statist Asn. *Res:* Income tax proposals; environmental problems; submarine defense problems; application of operations research to health fields. *Mailing Add:* 1621 E Jefferson St Rockville MD 20852

LIEBLEIN, SEYMOUR, b New York, NY, June 17, 23. AEROSPACE ENGINEERING. *Educ:* City Col New York, BS, 44; Case Inst Technol, MS, 52. *Prof Exp:* Researcher, Nat Adv Comt Aeronauts, Lewis Res Ctr, NASA, 44-57, chief, Flow Anal Br, 57-65, chief, Vertical Takeoff & Landing Propulsion Br, 65-70, div tech asst, Short Takeoff, Landing & Noise Div, 70-74; MGR & OWNER, TECH REPORT SERV, 77- *Honors & Awards:* Except serv medal, Nat Adv Comt Aeronaut, 57; Gas Turbine Award, Am Soc Mech Engrs, 61; Goddard Award, Am Inst Aeronaut & Astronaut, 67. *Mem:* Am Soc Mech Engrs; assoc fel Am Inst Aeronaut & Astronaut. *Res:* Fluid flow and design in axial flow compressors; aerodynamic performance and design of vertical takeoff and landing propulsion systems; waste-heat systems, space power; technical report writing; wind turbine blades and flow. *Mailing Add:* PO Box 16163 Cleveland OH 44116

LIEBLING, RICHARD STEPHEN, b Brooklyn, NY, Aug 31, 38; m 70. MINERALOGY. *Educ:* Columbia Univ, BA, 60, MA, 61, PhD(mineral), 63. *Prof Exp:* Sr ceramist, Carborundum Co, 63-68; asst prof, 68-73, ASSOC PROF GEOL, HUNTER COL, 73- *Mem:* Mineral Soc Am. *Res:* Clay mineralogy of sediments. *Mailing Add:* Dept of Geol & Geog Hunter Col 695 Park Ave New York NY 10021

LIEBMAN, ALAN JOEL, b New York, NY, US citizen. PHYSICS, ELECTROPHOTOGRAPHY. *Educ:* Columbia Univ, BA, 64; Yale Univ, MS, 66, PhM, 68, PhD(appl sci), 70. *Prof Exp:* SCIENTIST, XEROX CORP, 69- *Concurrent Pos:* Adj prof, Rochester Inst Technol, 73- *Mem:* Am Asn Physics Teachers; Soc Photog Sci & Eng. *Res:* Development of electrostatic latent images; physics of fine particles; theory of phase transitions. *Mailing Add:* 266 Willowcrest Dr Rochester NY 14618

LIEBMAN, ARNOLD ALVIN, b St Paul, Minn, Mar 5, 31; m 55, 77; c 4. ORGANIC CHEMISTRY, RADIOCHEMISTRY. *Educ:* Univ Minn, BS, 56, PhD(pharmaceut chem), 61. *Prof Exp:* Asst prof biochem, Loyola Univ, La, 61-63; Nat Inst Gen Med Sci res fel chem, Univ Calif, Berkeley, 63-66; asst prof chem, Sch Pharm, Univ Md, 66-68; sr chemist, 68-72, res group chief, 72-80, sr res group chief, 80-81, RES SECT CHIEF, HOFFMANN-LA ROCHE, INC, 82- *Mem:* AAAS; fel Am Inst Chem; Am Chem Soc. *Res:* Heterocyclic chemistry of natural products; isotopic synthesis, heterocyclic chemistry. *Mailing Add:* Chem Res Dept Hoffmann-La Roche Inc Nutley NJ 07110

LIEBMAN, FREDERICK MELVIN, b New York, NY, July 26. 22; m 48; c 3. PHYSIOLOGY. *Educ:* NY Univ, BA, 42, PhD, 56; Univ Pa, DDS, 47. *Prof Exp:* Asst, 53-56, from instr to assoc prof, 56-65, PROF PHYSIOL & BIOPHYS, COL DENT, NY UNIV, 65-, CHMN DEPT, 69- *Concurrent Pos:* Int Asn Dent Res rep, Int Cong Physiol, Buenos Aires, Arg, 59. *Mem:* AAAS; Am Physiol Soc; Harvey Soc; NY Acad Sci; fel Am Col Dent. *Res:* Peripheral circulation; control of circulation in the dental pulp and oral cavity; functional activity of the muscles of mastication; control of posture and movement; pain; analgesics; narcotic-antagonists; opioid agonists. *Mailing Add:* Dept of Physiol NY Univ Col of Dent New York NY 10010

LIEBMAN, JEFFREY MARK, b Milwaukee, Wis, Nov 7, 46; m 74; c 2. PSYCHOPHARMACOLOGY, PHYSIOLOGICAL PSYCHOLOGY. *Educ:* Oberlin Col, BA, 68; Univ Calif, Los Angeles, PhD(psychol), 73. *Prof Exp:* Res assoc fel psychopharmacol, Sch Med, Univ Calif, San Diego, 73-76; SR STAFF SCIENTIST PSYCHOPHARMACOL, CIBA-GEIGY PHARMACEUT, 76- *Concurrent Pos:* Res fels, Sloan Found, 73-74 & Alcoholism, Drug Abuse & Ment Health Admin, 74-76. *Mem:* Soc Neurosci. *Res:* Neurotransmitter mechanisms of behavior; psychopharmacological models of mental disorders. *Mailing Add:* · Ciba-Geigy Pharmaceut 556 Morris Ave Summit NJ 07901

LIEBMAN, JOEL FREDRIC, b Brooklyn, NY, May 6, 47; m 70. THEORETICAL CHEMISTRY. *Educ:* Brooklyn Col, BS, 67; Princeton Univ, MA, 68, PhD(chem), 70. *Prof Exp:* NATO fel, Depts Phys & Theoret Chem, Cambridge Univ, 70-71; Nat Res Coun & Nat Bur Standards fel, Inorg Chem Sect, Nat Bur Standards, 71-72; asst prof chem, 72-77, ASSOC PROF, DEPT CHEM, UNIV MD, BALTIMORE COUNTY, 77- *Concurrent Pos:* Ramsay hon fel, Ramsay Mem Fel Trust, 70; consult & contractor, Nat Bur Standards, 72-; unofficial consult, Argonne Nat Lab, 72-75; guest scientist, 75- *Mem:* Am Chem Soc; Am Phys Soc; Sigma Xi. *Res:* Chemical bonding theory, rules and regularities of molecular geometry and energetics; strain and resonance energy of alicyclic and aromatic hydrocarbons; noble gas and fluorine compounds; thermochemistry of molecular ions; mathematical chemistry. *Mailing Add:* Dept of Chem Univ of Md Baltimore County Catonsville MD 21228

LIEBMAN, JON C(HARLES), b Cincinnati, Ohio, Sept 10, 34; m 58; c 3. ENGINEERING, OPERATIONS RESEARCH. *Educ:* Univ Colo, BS, 56; Cornell Univ, MS, 63, PhD(sanit eng), 65. *Prof Exp:* From asst prof to assoc prof environ eng, Johns Hopkins Univ, 65-72; assoc head dept civil eng, 76-78, PROF ENVIRON ENG, UNIV ILL, URBANA-CHAMPAIGN, 72-, HEAD DEPT CIVIL ENG, 78- *Mem:* Fel AAAS; Inst Mgt Sci; Am Soc Civil Engrs. *Res:* Applications of operations research to the field of environmental engineering. *Mailing Add:* Dept of Civil Eng Univ of Ill Urbana-Champaign Urbana IL 61801

LIEBMAN, JUDITH STENZEL, b Denver, Colo, July 2, 36; m 58; c 3. OPERATIONS RESEARCH. *Educ:* Univ Colo, BA, 58; Johns Hopkins Univ, PhD(opers res), 71. *Prof Exp:* Engr data anal, Convair Astronaut, Gen Dynamics, 58-59; programmer eng systs, Gen Elec Co, 63-64; programmer chem, Cornell Univ, 64-65; res asst opers res, Johns Hopkins Univ, 65-71, asst prof & health serv res scholar, 71-72; asst prof opers res, 72-77, ASSOC PROF OPERS RES, UNIV ILL, URBANA, 77- *Mem:* Opers Res Soc Am; Am Inst Indust Engrs; Am Pub Health Asn. *Res:* Mathematical optimization; model building; applications of operations research in health and engineering. *Mailing Add:* 234 Mech & Indust Eng Univ of Ill Urbana IL 61801

LIEBMAN, PAUL ARNO, b Pittsburgh, Pa, Aug 1, 33. BIOPHYSICS, PHYSIOLOGY. *Educ:* Univ Pittsburgh, BS, 54; Johns Hopkins Univ, MD, 58. *Prof Exp:* Intern internal med, Barnes Hosp, St Louis, Mo, 58-59; res assoc physiol, 63-65, asst prof, 65-69, assoc prof, 69-76, PROF ANAT, UNIV PA, 76-, PROF OPHTHALMOL, 77- *Concurrent Pos:* Fel biophys, Univ Pa, 59-63. *Mem:* Biophys Soc; Asn Res Vision & Ophthal; Am Soc Neurosci. *Res:* Vision; microspectrophotometry of single visual receptors; transducer mechanism of photoreceptors in vision. *Mailing Add:* Dept of Anat Univ of Pa Philadelphia PA 19104

LIEBMAN, SUSAN WEISS, b New York, NY, Dec 2, 47; m 69; c 2. MOLECULAR GENETICS. *Educ:* Mass Inst Technol, BS, 68; Harvard Univ, MA, 69; Univ Rochester, PhD(biophys), 74. *Prof Exp:* Am Cancer Soc fel, Sch Med & Dent, Univ Rochester, 74-76; asst prof, 77-81, ASSOC PROF BIOL, UNIV ILL, CHICAGO CIRCLE, 81- *Concurrent Pos:* USPHS career develop award. *Mem:* AAAS; Genetics Soc Am; Am Soc Microbiol. *Res:* Molecular genetics of yeast, including nonsense suppression, mutators, transposable elements. *Mailing Add:* Dept of Biol Sci Box 4348 Chicago IL 60680

LIEBNER, EDWIN J, b Chicago, Ill, July 12, 21; m 63; c 2. RADIOLOGY. *Educ:* Univ Ill, BS, 44, MD, 46. *Prof Exp:* Resident radiol, Ill Res Hosps, 53-56; from asst prof to assoc prof, 56-66, PROF RADIOL, UNIV ILL HOSP, 66-, ACTG HEAD DEPT RADIOL, UNIV ILL COL MED, 71-; DIR RADIOTHER DIV, ILL RES & EDUC HOSPS, 61- *Concurrent Pos:* Consult radiol, Vet Admin Hosp, Hines, 64- *Mem:* Am Radium Soc; Roentgen Ray Soc; Am Soc Therapeut Radiol; Radiol Soc NAm. *Res:* Therapeutic lymphography; refrigeration and irradiation; therapeutic pediatric radiology. *Mailing Add:* Dept of Radiol Univ of Ill Col of Med Chicago IL 60612

LIEBNITZ, PAUL W, b Kansas City, Mo, Jan 18, 35; m 61; c 4. MATHEMATICS. *Educ:* Rockhurst Col, BS, 55; Univ Kans, MA, 57, PhD(math), 64. *Prof Exp:* Asst prof, 61-67, ASSOC PROF MATH, UNIV MO-KANSAS CITY, 67- *Mem:* Am Math Soc; Math Asn Am. *Res:* Topology, theory of retracts. *Mailing Add:* Dept of Math Univ of Mo Kansas City MO 64110

LIEBOWITZ, HAROLD, b Brooklyn, NY, June 25, 24; m 51; c 3. MECHANICS, AERONAUTICAL ENGINEERING. *Educ:* Polytech Inst Brooklyn, BAeroE, 44, MAeroE, 46, DAeroE, 48. *Prof Exp:* Res asst, Polytech Inst Brooklyn, 45-46, res assoc, 46-47, sr res assoc, 47-48; aeronaut engr, Off Naval Res, 48-50, eng mech scientist, 50-51, physicist, 51-54, aeronaut res engr & tech consult, 54-56, chief tech eng consult & coordr struct mech, 56-59, head struct mech br, 59-60, eng consult, 60-61, head struct mech br, 61-69, eng adv & coordr Polaris prog & dir prog solid propellant mech, 62-68; PROF ENG & APPL SCI & DEAN SCH ENG & APPL SCI, GEORGE WASHINGTON UNIV, 68- *Concurrent Pos:* Vis prof aeronaut eng, actg asst dean grad sch & exec dir exp sta, Univ Colo, 60-61, dir eng curricula study, NSF grant, 60-61; res prof, Cath Univ Am, 62-68; tech adv, US House of Rep, founder & ed-in-chief, J Eng Fracture Mech, & prin investr, NASA res grants, 68-; founder & ed-in-chief, J Comput & Struct, 70-; mem, Adv Comt Space Vehicles, NASA, Inter-Agency Eng Sci Group, Adv Comt Mat, Submarine Struct Res, Submarine Acoustics Comt & Deep Submergence Steering Task Group, US Navy, Ad Hoc Working Group Micromech & Design for Brittle Mat Group, Mat Adv Bd, Nat Acad Sci-Nat Res Coun & Tech Adv Group Cent Activity for Shock, Vibration & Assoc Environ, Dept Defense. *Mem:* Nat Acad Eng; fel AAAS; fel Am Inst Aeronaut & Astronaut; Soc Eng Sci (pres, 72-80); Am Soc Mech Engrs. *Res:* Applied mechanics; engineering curricula; astronautics and aeronautics; materials engineering; solid mechanics; solid propellant propulsion; rheology; dynamics; aeronautical missile, space and ship structures; weapons and weapons systems; fundamental engineering research. *Mailing Add:* Sch of Eng & Appl Sci George Washington Univ Washington DC 20006

LIEBOWITZ, STEPHEN MARC, PHARMACEUTICAL CHEMISTRY. *Educ:* State Univ NY, Buffalo, BS, 74; Va Commonwealth Univ, PhD(med chem), 80. *Prof Exp:* Fel, Ohio State Univ, 80 & Adria Labs, 80-81; fel, Adria Labs, 80-81; ASST PROF ANAL PHARMACEUT CHEM, UNIV TEX, AUSTIN, 81- *Concurrent Pos:* Prin investr, Robert A Welch Found, 82- *Mem:* Am Chem Soc; NY Acad Sci; AAAS. *Res:* Synthesis of organic molecules to aid in a basic understanding of biochemical processes on a molecular level; new synthetic methodology. *Mailing Add:* Col Pharm Univ Tex Austin TX 78712

LIEBSON, SIDNEY HAROLD, b New York, NY, July 9, 20; m 47; c 2. PHYSICS. *Educ:* City Col New York, BS, 39; Univ Mich, MS, 40; Univ Md, PhD(physics), 47. *Prof Exp:* Physicist, Naval Res Lab, 40-49, head electromagnetics br, 49-55; mgr res & develop, Nuclear Develop Corp Am, 55-59; asst dir physics, Armour Res Found, Ill Inst Technol, 59-60; mgr phys res, Nat Cash Register Co, 60-66; mgr xerographic technol, 66-69; sr corp planner, 69-74, MGR MFG RES & DEVELOP, XEROX CORP, 74- *Mem:* Fel Am Phys Soc; Inst Elec & Electronics Eng. *Res:* Solid state phenomena; Geiger counters; electronic circuit analysis and design; discharge mechanism of self-quenching Geiger-Müller counters; scintillation and fluorescence of organics; photoconductivity; manufacturing technologies; research administration. *Mailing Add:* Xerox Corp PO Box 1600 Stamford CT 06904

LIEDL, GERALD L(EROY), b Fergus Falls, Minn, Mar 2, 33; m 57; c 2. MATERIALS SCIENCE, METALLURGICAL ENGINEERING. *Educ:* Purdue Univ, BS, 55, PhD(metall eng), 60. *Prof Exp:* From instr to asst prof metall eng, 58-65, assoc prof, 65-73, asst head dept, 66-78, PROF, METALL ENG, PURDUE UNIV, WEST LAFAYETTE, 73-, HEAD DEPT, 78- *Mem:* Am Soc Eng Educ; Am Soc Metals; Am Inst Mining, Metall & Petrol Engrs. *Res:* Diffraction; electron microscopy; correlations among structure, texture, and properties of crystalline solids and thin films. *Mailing Add:* Sch of Mat Sci & Metall Eng Purdue Univ West Lafayette IN 47907

LIEF, FLORENCE SUSKIND, b New York, NY, July 30, 11; m 33; c 3. MEDICAL MICROBIOLOGY, VETERINARY VIROLOGY. *Educ:* Barnard Col, BA, 31; NY Univ, MSc, 33; Univ Pa, PhD(med microbiol), 55; Am Bd Microbiol, dipl. *Prof Exp:* Asst bact, Col Med, NY Univ, 31-34; bacteriologist dept med, NY Hosp-Cornell Med Ctr, 34-40; mem res staff, Children's Hosp, Philadelphia, 54-55; asst prof microbiol, NY Med Col, 55-56; assoc virol, Dept Prev Med, Pub Health & Pediat, Sch Med, 56-59, asst prof, 59-65, assoc prof pediat, Sch Med & Microbiol, Sch Vet Med, 65-71, prof microbiol, Sch Vet Med, 71-76, PROF VIROL, SCH VET MED, UNIV PA, 76- *Concurrent Pos:* Mem res staff, Children's Hosp, Philadelphia, 56-66; consult animal influenza, WHO, 61- *Mem:* Fel Am Acad Microbiol; Am Soc Microbiol; Am Asn Immunol; NY Acad Sci. *Res:* Influenza and parainfluenza viruses of man and lower animals; human papilloma virus; viral etiology of multiple sclerosis. *Mailing Add:* Lippincott Bldg Univ of Pa Philadelphia PA 19103

LIEF, HAROLD ISAIAH, b New York, NY, Dec 29, 17; m 61; c 5. PSYCHIATRY. *Educ:* Univ Mich, AB, 38; NY Univ, MD, 42; Columbia Univ, cert psychoanal, 50. *Hon Degrees:* MA, Univ Pa, 71. *Prof Exp:* Intern, Queens Gen Hosp, Jamaica, NY, 42-43; resident psychiat, Long Island Med Col, 46-48; res asst, Col Physicians & Surgeons, Columbia Univ, 49-51; from asst prof to prof psychiat, Sch Med, Tulane Univ, 51-67; dir, Div Family Study, 67-81, dir, Marriage Coun Philadelphia & Ctr Study Sex Educ in Med, 68-81, PROF PSYCHIAT, SCH MED, UNIV PA, 67- *Concurrent Pos:* Vis prof, Sch Med, Univ Va, 58; pres, Sex Info & Educ Coun of US, 68-70; consult, HEW, 69-76, WHO, 71 & 74, AMA, 70-78 & Psychiat Educ Br, NIMH, 74-75; assoc psychiatrist, Pa Hosp, 81- *Mem:* Fel Am Acad Psychoanal (pres, 67-68); fel Am Psychiat Asn; fel Am Col Psychiat; fel Am Col Psychoanal; Am Psychosomatic Soc. *Res:* Marital and sexual relations; sex education in medicine; adult development; psycho-endocrinological-pharmacologic aspects human sexuality. *Mailing Add:* 700 Spruce St Suite 503 Philadelphia PA 19106

LIEFF, MORRIS, b Ottawa, Ont, Feb 25, 15; nat US; m 38; c 3. ORGANIC CHEMISTRY. *Educ:* Queen's Univ, Ont, BA, 34, MA, 35; McGill Univ, PhD(wood & cellulose chem), 38. *Prof Exp:* Res chemist, Elmendorf Corp, Ill, 38-40, dir res, 40-47; tech dir, Smith & Kanzler Corp, 47-50; vpres & tech dir, S K Insulrock Corp, 50-56, tech dir, Insulrock Div, Flintkote Co, 56-59; vpres & tech dir, Smith & Kanzler Corp, 59-65; assoc prof sci, Jersey City State Col, 65-66; prof chem & chmn dept sci, Middlesex Co Col, 66-68; PROF CHEM & PHYSICS & CHMN DIV MATH, PHYS SCI & INDUST TECHNOL, COUNTY COL OF MORRIS, 68- *Concurrent Pos:* Lectr, Ill Inst Technol, 43-45, Sch Art Inst, Ill, 45-47 & Sch Design, 46-47. *Mem:* AAAS; Am Chem Soc; Am Soc Testing & Mat. *Res:* Wood chemistry; development of building materials, especially those related to wood; sprayed mineral fiber fireproofing. *Mailing Add:* 100 Stonehill Rd Apt A-12 Springfield NJ 07081

LIEGEY, FRANCIS WILLIAM, b Frenchville, Pa, Jan 4, 23; m 47; c 6. MICROBIOLOGY. *Educ:* St Bonaventure Univ, BS, 47, MS, 50, PhD(microbiol), 59. *Prof Exp:* From instr to assoc prof biol, St Bonaventure Univ, 48-64; PROF BIOL, IND UNIV PA, 64-, CHMN DEPT, 72- *Mem:* Am Soc Microbiol. *Res:* Microbial ecology of acid mine streams. *Mailing Add:* Dept of Biol Weyandt Hall Ind Univ of Pa Indiana PA 15701

LIELMEZS, JANIS, b Riga, Latvia, June 1, 26; US citizen; m 70. CHEMICAL ENGINEERING. *Educ:* Univ Denver, BS, 54; Northwestern Univ, MS, 56. *Prof Exp:* Engr, Snow, Ice & Permafrost Res Estab, US Army Corps Eng, 56; engr, Shell Develop Co, 57-58, 59, consult chem eng, 58-59; res engr, Inst Mineral Res, Mich Col Mining & Technol, 60-63, asst prof chem eng, 62-63; from asst prof to assoc prof, 63-78, PROF CHEM ENG, UNIV BC, 78- *Concurrent Pos:* Ed chem, Tech Rev, Latvian Engrs Asn, 74-; ed sci & technol, Latvian Encycl, 76- *Mem:* Fel NY Acad Sci; Am Chem Soc; Am Inst Chem Engrs; fel Chem Inst Can; AAUP. *Res:* Applied and theoretical thermodynamics; applied mathematics; fluid flow; magnetism and phase transformations; magnetocatalytic effect in chemical reactions; transport properties of fluids. *Mailing Add:* Dept of Chem Eng Univ of BC Vancouver BC V6T 1W5 Can

LIEM, KAREL F, b Java, Indonesia, Nov 24, 35; m 65. VERTEBRATE MORPHOLOGY. *Educ:* Indonesia Univ, BSc, 57, MSc, 58; Univ Ill, PhD(zool), 61. *Prof Exp:* Asst prof zool, Leiden Univ, 62-64; from asst prof to assoc prof anat, Univ Ill Col Med, 64-72; HENRY BRYANT BIGELOW PROF, CUR ICHTHYOL & PROF BIOL, HARVARD UNIV, 72- *Concurrent Pos:* Head, Div Vert Anat, Chicago Natural Hist Mus, Ill, 65-72; mem comt Latimeria, Nat Acad Sci, 67; Guggenheim fel, 70-71; mem vis comt, New Eng Aquarium, 74-; trustee, Cohosset Marine Biol Sta, 74-; ed, Copeia & assoc ed, J Morphol, 74- *Mem:* Am Soc Zool; Am Soc Ichthyol & Herpet; Am Soc Syst Zool; fel Zool Soc London; Neth Royal Zool Soc. *Res:* Evolution of chordate structure; functional anatomy of teleosts; morphology and hydrodynamics of air-breathing teleost blood circulations; sex reversal in teleosts; functional anatomy and evolution of African cichlid fishes. *Mailing Add:* Mus of Comp Zool Harvard Univ Cambridge MA 02138

LIEM, RONALD KIAN HONG, b Lombok, Indonesia, Feb 8, 46; US citizen. NEUROBIOLOGY. *Educ:* Amherst Col, AB, 67; Cornell Univ, MSc, 69, PhD(chem). *Prof Exp:* ASST PROF PHARMACOL, NEW YORK UNIV SCH MED, 78- *Mem:* Am Soc Cell Biol. *Res:* Biochemical studies on the neuronal cytoskeleton, especially with regard to the assembly of neurofilaments and their interactions with other cytoskeletal elements, both in vivo and in vitro. *Mailing Add:* Dept Pharmacol New York Univ Sch Med 550 First Ave New York NY 10016

LIEMOHN, HAROLD BENJAMIN, b Minneapolis, Minn, Feb 2, 35; m 57; c 5. SPACECRAFT-ENVIRONMENT INTERACTIONS. *Educ:* Univ Minn, BA, 56, MS, 59; Univ Wash, PhD(physics), 62. *Prof Exp:* Teaching asst physics, Univ Minn, 56-59; staff mem geo-astrophys, Sci Res Labs, Boeing Co, 59-63; asst prof atmospheric & space sci, Southwest Ctr Advan Studies,

63-66; staff mem Environ Sci Res Labs, Boeing Co, 66-72; res staff math-physics, Pac Northwest, Battelle Mem Inst, 72-77; MGR SPACE PHYSICS, ENG TECHNOL, BOEING AEROSPACE CO, 77- *Concurrent Pos:* Adj asst prof, Southern Methodist Univ, 64-65; vis assoc prof, Univ Wash, 68-; chmn & secy local arrangements, Ann Meeting, Comt Space Res, Seattle, 71; reporter particle-wave interactions, Comn V, Int Asn Geomag & Aeronomy, 71-73. *Mem:* AAAS; Am Phys Soc; Am Geophys Union; Am Asn Physics Teachers; Am Inst Aeronaut & Astronaut. *Res:* Theoretical research in radiation belt physics, electromagnetic waves in magnetoplasma, hydromagnetic waves in magnetosphere, and spacecraft charging and contamination. *Mailing Add:* PO Box 3999 MS 8C-23 Boeing Aerospace Co Seattle WA 98124

LIEN, ERIC JUNG-CHI, b Kaohsiung, Taiwan, Nov 30, 37; m 65; c 2. PHARMACEUTICAL CHEMISTRY. *Educ:* Taiwan Univ, BS, 60; Univ Calif, San Francisco, PhD(pharmaceut chem), 66. *Prof Exp:* Res assoc bio-org chem, Pomona Col, 67-68; from asst prof to assoc prof, 68-76, PROF PHARMACEUT & BIOMED CHEM & COORDR, SCH PHARM, UNIV SOUTHERN CALIF, 76- *Mem:* AAAS; Am Pharmaceut Asn; Am Chem Soc; Am Asn Cols Pharm. *Res:* Structure-activity relationship and bio-organic chemistry; physical organic chemistry; natural products. *Mailing Add:* Sect Biomed Chem Sch of Pharm 1985 Zonal Ave Los Angeles CA 90033

LIEN, ERIC LOUIS, b Hammond, Ind, Apr 9, 46; m 69; c 4. BIOCHEMISTRY. *Educ:* Col Wooster, BA, 68; Univ Ill, Urbana-Champaign, MS, 71, PhD(biochem), 72. *Prof Exp:* Fel biochem, Sch Med, Univ Pa, 72-75; SR BIOCHEMIST, WYETH LABS, 75- *Mem:* AAAS; Am Chem Soc. *Res:* Diabetes; hypothalmic releasing factors; vitamin B12 absorption. *Mailing Add:* Wyeth Labs Box 8299 Philadelphia PA 19101

LIEN, YEONG-CHUNG EDMUND, b Fu-Kian, China, May 20, 47; US citizen; m 71; c 2. COMPUTER SCIENCES. *Educ:* Nat Taiwan Univ, BS, 68; Univ Calif, Berkeley, MS, 70, PhD(comput sci), 72. *Prof Exp:* From asst prof to assoc prof comput sci, Univ Kans, 72-77; mem tech staff, 77-81, HEAD, COMPUT SYSTS TECHNOL RES DEPT, BELL LABS, 81- *Mem:* Asn Comput Mach; Soc Indust & Appl Math. *Res:* Database management; theory of computation; machine organization. *Mailing Add:* Bell Labs Murray Hill NJ 07974

LIENER, IRVIN ERNEST, b Pittsburgh, Pa, June 27, 19; m 46; c 2. BIOCHEMISTRY, NUTRITION. *Educ:* Mass Inst Technol, BS, 41; Univ Southern Calif, PhD(biochem, nutrit), 49. *Prof Exp:* From instr asst prof to assoc prof, 49-59, PROF BIOCHEM, UNIV MINN, ST PAUL, 59- *Concurrent Pos:* Guggenheim fel, Carlsberg Lab, Copenhagen, Denmark, 57. *Honors & Awards:* Spencer Award for Outstanding Achievement Agr & Food Chem, Am Chem Soc, 77. *Mem:* Hon fel Venezuelan Asn Advan Sci; Am Chem Soc; Am Soc Biol Chem; Am Inst Nutrit. *Res:* Isolation and characterization of antinutritional factors in legumes; structure and mechanism of action of proteolytic enzymes and their naturally-occurring inhibitors. *Mailing Add:* Dept of Biochem Col of Biol Sci Univ of Minn St Paul MN 55108

LIENGME, BERNARD V F, physical chemistry, see previous edition

LIENHARD, GUSTAV E, b Plainfield, NJ, June 21, 38; m 60; c 2. BIOCHEMISTRY. *Educ:* Amherst Col, BA, 59; Yale Univ, PhD(biochem), 64. *Prof Exp:* From asst prof to assoc prof biochem & molecular biol, Harvard Univ, 65-72; assoc prof, 72-75, PROF BIOCHEM, DARTMOUTH MED SCH, 75- *Concurrent Pos:* Res fel biochem, Brandeis Univ, 63-65; NSF res grant, 66- *Mem:* Am Chem Soc; Am Soc Biol Chem. *Res:* Structure and function of membranes; mechanisms of transport across biological membranes; regulation of transport by hormones. *Mailing Add:* Dept Biochem Dartmouth Med Sch Hanover NH 03755

LIENHARD, JOHN H(ENRY), b St Paul, Minn, Aug 17, 30; m 59; c 2. MECHANICAL ENGINEERING. *Educ:* Ore State Col, BS, 51; Univ Wash, Seattle, MS, 53; Univ Calif, Berkeley, PhD(mech eng), 61. *Prof Exp:* Design engr, Boeing Airplane Co, 51-52; instr mech eng, Univ Wash, Seattle, 55-56; assoc, Univ Calif, Berkeley, 56-61; assoc prof, Wash State Univ, 61-67; prof mech eng, Univ KY, 67-80; PROF MECH ENG, UNIV HOUSTON, 80- *Mem:* Fel Am Soc Mech Engrs; Am Soc Eng Educ; AAAS; Soc Hist Technol. *Res:* Statistical mechanical modeling of macroscopic systems; thermal systems with emphasis on boiling and other two-phase problems; nuclear thermohydraulics; history of technology; equatims of state. *Mailing Add:* Dept of Mech Eng Univ Houston Houston TX 77004

LIENK, SIEGFRIED ERIC, b Gary, Ind, Oct 16, 16; m 51; c 1. ENTOMOLOGY. *Educ:* Univ Idaho, BS, 42; Univ Ill, MS, 47, PhD, 51. *Prof Exp:* Entomologist pear psylla control, USDA, 42, Alaska Insect Control Proj, 49; assoc prof fruit invests, 50-70, PROF ENTOM, STATE AGR EXP STA, STATE UNIV NY COL AGR, CORNELL UNIV, 70-, ENTOMOLOGIST, 50- *Mem:* Entom Soc Am. *Res:* Biology, ecology and control of phytophagous mites; biology and control of stone fruit insects. *Mailing Add:* Dept of Entom NY State Agr Exp Sta Geneva NY 14456

LIENTZ, BENNET PRICE, b Hollywood, Calif, Oct 24, 42; m 64; c 3. OPERATIONS ANALYSIS, INFORMATION SYSTEMS. *Educ:* Claremont Men's Col, BA, 64; Univ Wash, MS, 66, PhD(math), 68. *Prof Exp:* Instr math, Univ Wash, 65-68; sr res scientist, Syst Develop Corp, 68-70; assoc prof indust eng & Air Force Off Sci Res grant, Univ Southern Calif, 70-77; PROF GRAD SCH MGT, UNIV CALIF, LOS ANGELES, 77- *Mem:* Opers Res Soc Am (secy-treas, 71); Inst Math Statist; Am Statist Asn; Am Math Soc. *Res:* Communication and network analysis; computers and systems analysis; computer security. *Mailing Add:* Grad Sch of Mgt 405 Hilgard Los Angeles CA 90024

LIEPINS, ATIS AIVARS, b Aloja, Latvia, Apr 17, 35; m 60; c 2. STRUCTURAL ENGINEERING, APPLIED MECHANICS. *Educ:* Mass Inst Technol, SB, 57, SM, 60, Engr, 60. *Prof Exp:* Res engr appl mech, Res Labs, United Aircraft Corp, 60-61; prin engr, Dynatech Corp, 61-68; sr staff engr, Littleton Res & Eng Corp, 68-77; STAFF CONSULT, SIMPSON GUMPERTZ & HEGER INC, 77- *Mem:* Am Inst Aeronaut & Astronaut; Am Soc Mech Engrs. *Res:* Static and dynamic response of thin shell structures; propeller induced ship vibration. *Mailing Add:* 1696 Massachusetts Ave Cambridge MA 02138

LIEPINS, RAIMOND, b Plavinas, Latvia, May 19, 30; US citizen; m 61; c 4. POLYMER CHEMISTRY, ORGANIC CHEMISTRY. *Educ:* Southern Ill Univ, BA, 54; Univ Minn, MS, 56; Kans State Univ, PhD(org chem), 60. *Prof Exp:* Res chemist, B F Goodrich Co, 60-64; res assoc polymer res, Univ Ariz, 64-66; sr chemist, Res Triangle Inst, 66-77; STAFF MEM, LOS ALAMOS NAT LAB, 77- *Concurrent Pos:* Lectr, NC State Univ, 76, Clemson Univ, 76 & State Univ NY, New Paltz, 77; prin investr, Indust Org Chem Indust, Res Triangle Inst, Environ Protection Agency, 76-77. *Mem:* Am Vacuum Soc; Am Chem Soc; fel Am Inst Chem. *Res:* Coatings for laser fusion targets; gas phase coating techniques; flame retardance; low pressure plasma applications; high temperature polymers; piezoelectric polylmers; organometallic polymers; sorption/diffusion. *Mailing Add:* Los Alamos Nat Lab PO Box 1663 Los Alamos NM 87544

LIEPMAN, H(ANS) P(ETER), b Kiel, Ger, Oct 24, 13; nat US; m 46; c 4. AEROSPACE ENGINEERING. *Educ:* Swiss Fed Inst Technol, Dipl, 37; Harvard Univ, MS, 39; Univ Mich, PhD(aeronaut), 53. *Prof Exp:* From instr to asst prof aeronaut eng, Univ Cincinnati, 39-44; sr aerodynamicist, Goodyear Aircraft Corp, 44-46; chief aerodynamicist, 46-49; lectr aeronaut eng, Univ Mich, 49-55, assoc prof, 56-59, dir supersonic wind tunnel, 49-59; asst mgr, Systs Develop Dept & asst prog mgr, Aerosci Lab, TRW Systs Group, Calif, 59-71; educ & technol admin & develop consult, 71-73; mem res staff, Inst for Defense Anal, 73-78; AEROSPACE ENGR, DEPT DEFENSE, 81- *Concurrent Pos:* Consult, Space Technol Labs, 57-59 & Appl Physics Lab, Johns Hopkins Univ, 78-80; vis prof aerospace eng, Iowa State Univ, 80-81. *Mem:* Assoc fel Am Inst Aeronaut & Astronaut. *Res:* Reentry system performance and penetration aids system studies; multiple nozzle plume interactions; rocket exhaust interactions; base heating; supersonic nozzle design; system engineering of space and missile systems; comparative analysis and evaluation of tactical and strategic weapons systems. *Mailing Add:* 2000 S Eads St No 1103 Arlington VA 22202

LIEPMANN, H(ANS) WOLFGANG, b Berlin, Ger, July 3, 14; nat US; m 39, 54; c 2. AERONAUTICS. *Educ:* Univ Zurich, PhD(physics), 38. *Prof Exp:* Fel physics, Univ Zurich, 38-39; fel aeronaut, 39-45, from asst prof to prof, 45-76, CHARLES LEE POWELL PROF FLUID MECH & THERMODYN, CALIF INST TECHNOL, 76-, DIR, GRAD AERONAUT LABS, 72- *Honors & Awards:* Prize, Univ Zurich, 39; Ludwig-Prandtl-Ring, Ger Soc Aeronaut & Astronaut, 68; Worcester Reed Warner Medal, Am Soc Mech Engrs, 69; Monie A Ferst Award, Sigma Xi, 78; Fluid Dynamics Prize, Am Phys Soc, 80. *Mem:* Nat Acad Sci; Nat Acad Eng; AAAS; hon fel Am Inst Aeronaut & Astronaut; fel Am Acad Arts & Sci. *Res:* Laminar instability, transition and turbulence; shock wave boundary layer interaction; transonic flow; aerodynamic noise; fluid mechanics of Helium II. *Mailing Add:* Mail Stop 105-50 Calif Inst of Technol Pasadena CA 91125

LIER, FRANK GEORGE, b New York, NY, Feb 19, 13; m 37. BOTANY, ECOLOGY. *Educ:* Columbia Univ, PhD, 50. *Prof Exp:* Asst bot, 46-47, lectr, Sch Gen Studies, 47-50, from asst prof to prof bot, 50-77, prof biol sci, 77-80, EMER PROF BIOL SCI, SCH GEN STUDIES, COLUMBIA UNIV, 80- *Mem:* Bot Soc Am; Torrey Bot Club (pres, 64); Am Inst Biol Sci; NY Acad Sci; Am Bryol & Lichenological Soc. *Res:* Plant morphology; developmental anatomy. *Mailing Add:* 2 Cambridge Court East Old Saybrook CT 06475

LIES, THOMAS ANDREW, b Oak Park, Ill, Jan 16, 29; m 59; c 2. ORGANIC CHEMISTRY. *Educ:* John Carroll Univ, BS, 49; Univ Chicago, SM, 51; Univ Wis-Madison, PhD(org chem), 58. *Prof Exp:* Res chemist, Wyandotte Chem Corp, 58-59; RES CHEMIST, AM CYANAMID CO, 59- *Mem:* Am Chem Soc. *Res:* Synthesis of pesticides. *Mailing Add:* Cherry Hill Rd RD 5 Princeton NJ 08540

LIESCH, JERROLD MICHAEL, b Chicago, Ill, Dec 12, 49. NATURAL PRODUCTS CHEMISTRY, ORGANIC CHEMISTRY. *Educ:* Ill Inst Technol, BS, 71; Univ Ill, MS, 73, PhD(org chem), 75. *Prof Exp:* NIH fel org chem, Mass Inst Technol, 76-77; SR RES CHEMIST, MERCK INST THERAPEUT RES, 77- *Mem:* Am Chem Soc; Am Soc Mass Spectrometry. *Res:* Structure elucidation; mass spectrometry; proton and carbon magnetic resonance spectrometry. *Mailing Add:* Merck Inst PO Box 2000 R80M203 Rahway NJ 07065

LIESE, HOMER C, b New York, NY, Oct 25, 31; m 55. MINERALOGY, PETROLOGY. *Educ:* Syracuse Univ, BS, 53; Univ Utah, MS, 57, PhD(mineral), 62. *Prof Exp:* X-ray technician, Kennecott Copper Inc, 60-61; ASSOC PROF GEOL, UNIV CONN, 62- *Mem:* Geol Soc Am; Mineral Soc Am; Soc Appl Spectros. *Res:* Spectroscopy of minerals. *Mailing Add:* Dept of Geol Univ of Conn Storrs CT 06268

LIETMAN, PAUL STANLEY, b Chicago, Ill, Mar 24, 34; m 56; c 3. CLINICAL PHARMACOLOGY. *Educ:* Western Reserve Univ, AB, 55; Columbia Univ, MD, 59; Johns Hopkins Univ, PhD(physiol chem), 68. *Prof Exp:* Asst prof pediat, 68-72, asst prof pharmacol, 69-72, assoc prof med, pediat & pharmacol, 72-80, WELLCOME PROF CLIN PHARMACOL & PROF MED, PEDIAT & PHARMACOL, JOHNS HOPKINS UNIV, 80- *Concurrent Pos:* Investr, Howard Med Inst, 68-72. *Mem:* Am Soc Pharmacol & Exp Therapeut; Soc Microbiol; Soc Pediat Am Pediat Soc; Res; Am Acad Pediat. *Res:* Developmental pharmacology; antibiotics; antiviral agents. *Mailing Add:* Johns Hopkins Hosp Dept of Pediat Baltimore MD 21205

LIETZ, GERARD PAUL, b Chicago, Ill, Dec 10, 37; m 64; c 4. NUCLEAR PHYSICS. *Educ:* DePaul Univ, BS, 59; Univ Notre Dame, PhD(nuclear physics), 64. *Prof Exp:* Exchange asst nuclear physics, Univ Basel, 66-67; asst prof, 67-77, ASSOC PROF PHYSICS, DePAUL UNIV, 77- *Mem:* Am Phys Soc; Am Asn Physics Teachers. *Res:* Energy levels in nuclei. *Mailing Add:* Dept of Physics DePaul Univ Chicago IL 60604

LIETZE, ARTHUR, immunochemistry, allergy, see previous edition

LIETZKE, DAVID ALBERT, b Pontiac, Mich, Apr 20, 40. PEDOLOGY, CLAY MINERALOGY. *Educ:* Mich State Univ, BS, 62, MS, 68, PhD(clay mineral geomorphol), 72. *Prof Exp:* Soil scientist, Soil Conserv Serv, Mich, 62-68 & 71-73, Mich Agr Exp Sta, 68-71; asst prof & urban soils specialist, Va Polytech Inst & State Univ, 73-79; ASSOC PROF SOILS, UNIV TENN, KNOXVILLE, 79- *Mem:* Am Soc Agron; Soil Sci Soc Am. *Res:* Processes of soil formation, soil-geomorphic relationships, soil-climatic relationships and fundamental weathering processes of earth materials to form soil parent materials. *Mailing Add:* Dept Plant Soil Sci Univ Tenn Knoxville TN 37996

LIETZKE, MILTON HENRY, b Syracuse, NY, Nov 23, 20; m 43, 65; c 3. PHYSICAL CHEMISTRY. *Educ:* Colgate Univ, BA, 42; Univ Wis, MS, 44, PhD(chem), 49. *Prof Exp:* Asst, Univ Wis, 42-43, instr chem, 43-44; lab foreman, Tenn Eastman Corp, 44-47; asst, Univ Wis, 47-49; RES CHEMIST, OAK RIDGE NAT LAB, 49- *Concurrent Pos:* Prof, Univ Tenn, 63- *Mem:* Am Chem Soc; fel NY Acad Sci; fel Am Inst Chemists. *Res:* Electrochemistry, electrodeposition; potential measurements; high temperature solution thermodynamics; corrosion research; phase studies; application of high speed computing techniques to chemical problems. *Mailing Add:* 4165 Towanda Trail Knoxville TN 37919

LIEU, BING HOU-YI, b Shanghai, China, Oct 18, 35; US citizen; m 64; c 3. AEROSPACE ENGINEERING, COMPUTING SCIENCE. *Educ:* Polytech Inst New York, BME, 57; George Washington Univ, MS, 73. *Prof Exp:* Engr aerophys, Gen Elec Co, 58-61; res aerospace engr, US Naval Ord Lab, 61-65; sr res engr, Gen Motors Defense Res Labs, 65-69; mem tech staff systs res, Gen Res Corp, 69-74 & Sci Appl, Inc, 74-77; SR SPEC ENGR, BOEING AEROSPACE CO, SEATTLE, 77- *Concurrent Pos:* Lieu eng anal & software, Renton, Wash. *Mem:* Am Inst Aeronaut & Astronaut; Nat Soc Prof Engrs. *Res:* Computer solution of scientific and engineering problems in gas dynamics for aerospace applications. *Mailing Add:* 13022 SE 189th Ct Renton WA 98055

LIEUX, MEREDITH HOAG, b Morgan City, La, Nov 9, 39; m 68. PALYNOLOGY, BOTANY. *Educ:* La State Univ, Baton Rouge, BS, 60, PhD(bot), 69; Univ Miss, MS, 64. *Prof Exp:* Teacher pub schs, Lake Charles & Monroe, La, 60-71; fel geol, 71-72, instr bot, 72-74, asst prof, 74-80, ASSOC PROF BOT, LA STATE UNIV, BATON ROUGE, 80- *Mem:* Am Asn Stratig Palynologists; Int Bee Res Asn; Bot Soc Am; Sigma Xi; Asn Women Sci. *Res:* Holocene spore and pollen studies in the Gulf of Mexico Region; pollen morphology involving light, scanning electron and transmission electron microscopy; applied insect-pollen related studies, or melissopalynology. *Mailing Add:* Dept of Bot La State Univ Baton Rouge LA 70803

LIEVENSE, STANLEY JAMES, b Holland, Mich, Nov 20, 18; m 45; c 4. FISHERIES. *Educ:* Univ Mich, BS, 43. *Prof Exp:* Dist fisheries biologist, Inst Fisheries Res, Dept Natural Resources, Mich, 45-48, dist fisheries supvr, 48-65, tech asst to chief fisheries div, 65-74; MGR NATURAL RESOURCES, MICH TRAVEL BUR, 74- *Mem:* Outdoor Writers Asn Am. *Res:* Trout lakes; lake management; fisheries gear development. *Mailing Add:* Mich Travel Bur PO Box 30226 Lansing MI 48909

LIEW, CHOONG-CHIN, b Malaysia, Sept 2, 37; Can citizen; m 64; c 3. BIOCHEMISTRY, PROTEIN CHEMISTRY. *Educ:* Nanyang Univ, Singapore, BSc, 60; Univ Toronto, MA, 64, PhD(path chem), 67. *Prof Exp:* Guest investr, Rockefeller Univ, 69-70; asst prof, 70-73, assoc prof biochem, 73-78, assoc prof med, 78-79; PROF CLIN BIOCHEM & MED, UNIV TORONTO, 79- *Mem:* Can Biochem Soc; Biochem Soc; Am Soc Cell Biol. *Res:* Gene regulation in eukaryotes; chromosomal proteins; structure and function of chromatin subunits; correlation of chromatin process and genetically determined heart diseases. *Mailing Add:* Dept of Clin Biochem 100 College St Toronto ON M5G 1L5 Can

LIFKA, BERNARD WILLIAM, b Chicago, Ill, Apr 8, 31; m 56; c 4. METALLURGICAL ENGINEERING. *Educ:* Purdue Univ, BS, 58. *Prof Exp:* Engr corrosion, 58-62, sr engr, 63-77, sr engr alloy develop, 77-79, staff engr, 80-81, TECH SUPVR, ALCOA LABS, 81- *Mem:* Am Soc Metals; Nat Asn Corrosion Engrs; Sigma Xi. *Res:* Alloy development; increased plant production and resistance to corrosion of high-strength, heat-treatable aluminum alloys for aerospace and automotive applications. *Mailing Add:* Alcoa Tech Ctr Alcoa Center PA 15069

LIFSON, NATHAN, b Minneapolis, Minn, Jan 30, 11; m 39; c 2. PHYSIOLOGY. *Educ:* Univ Minn, BA, 31, PhD(physiol), 43; Columbia Univ, MD, 37. *Prof Exp:* Intern, San Diego County Gen Hosp, 37-38; asst, 39-42, from instr to assoc prof, 42-49, prof, 49-81, EMER PROF PHYSIOL, UNIV MINN, MINNEAPOLIS, 81- *Mem:* Am Physiol Soc; Soc Exp Biol & Med. *Res:* Secretion of gastric juice; glycogen deposition in liver; metabolism of perfused organs; transcapillary exchange; energy and material balance; intestinal absorption and secretion; pancreatic blood flow. *Mailing Add:* 405 Millard Hall Univ of Minn Minneapolis MN 55455

LIFSON, WILLIAM E(UGENE), b Newark, NJ, Apr 17, 21; m 46; c 2. CHEMICAL ENGINEERING. *Educ:* Mass Inst Technol, BS, 41, MS, 42. *Prof Exp:* Res engr petrol prod res, Esso Res & Eng Co, 46-51, group head, 51-54, sect head, 54-56, asst dir, 56-62, dir, Prod Res Div, 62-64, dir, Chem Res Div, 64-65, dir, Enjay Chem Labs, 65-66, mgr chem planning & coord, 66-69, asst gen mgr, Exxon Eng Technol Dept, 69-80, relocation mgr, 80-81,

NEW FACIL PROJ EXEC, EXXON RES & ENG CO, 81- *Mem:* Am Chem Soc; Soc Automotive Engrs. *Res:* Petroleum products and petrochemicals; engineering research and development process industries. *Mailing Add:* Exxon Eng Technol Dept Exxon Res & Eng Co PO Box 101 Florham Park NJ 07932

LIFTON, ROBERT JAY, b New York, NY, May 16, 26; m 52; c 2. PSYCHIATRY. *Educ:* NY Med Col, MD, 48. *Hon Degrees:* ScD, Lawrence Univ, 71 & Merrimac Col, 73; DHL, Wilmington Col, Ohio, 75 & New York Med Col, 77. *Prof Exp:* Intern gen med, Jewish Hosp, Brooklyn, NY, 48-49; psychiat resident, State Univ NY Downstate Med Ctr, 49-51; res assoc, Asia Found, 54; mem fac, Wash Sch Psychiat, 54-55; res psychiatrist, Walter Reed Army Inst Res, 56; res assoc psychiat & assoc EAsian studies, Harvard Univ, 56-61; Found Fund Res Psychiat assoc prof, Yale Univ, 61-67, PROF PSYCHIAT & FEL, BRANFORD COL, YALE UNIV, 67- *Concurrent Pos:* Asia Found fel, Hong Kong & Washington, DC, 54-55; Ford Found fel, 56-57 & Found Fund Res Psychiat fel, 58-61; res assoc, Univ Tokyo, 60-61; consult, var organizations, 62-; Comt Fac Res Int Studies res fel Japanese Youth, Japan, 64-67; coordr, Group Study Psychohist Process, 66-; fel, Branford Col, Yale Univ, 67-; Edward W Hazen Found fel, 70. *Honors & Awards:* Gay lectr, Harvard Med Sch, 76; Messenger lectr, Cornell Univ, 80. *Mem:* AAAS; Am Psychiat Asn; Asn Asian Studies; Am Anthrop Asn; Am Acad Psychoanal. *Res:* Relationship between individual psychology and historical change; individual patterns in extreme historical situations; long-term reactions to the atomic bomb in Hiroshima; death symbolism. *Mailing Add:* Dept Psychiat Sch Med Yale Univ 25 Park St New Haven CT 06519

LIGENZA, JOSEPH RAYMOND, b Chicago, Ill, June 18, 24; m 48; c 3. SOLID STATE CHEMISTRY. *Educ:* Ill Inst Technol, BS, 51; Columbia Univ, MA, 52, PhD(phys chem), 54. *Prof Exp:* Res asst chem, Cyclotron Labs, Columbia Univ, 51-54; MEM TECH STAFF PHYS CHEM, BELL TEL LABS, 54- *Mem:* AAAS. *Res:* Silicon semiconductor surface physics and chemistry; chemical reactions in plasmas; plasma oxidation of metals and semiconductors; glass physics and chemistry. *Mailing Add:* Bell Tel Labs 600 Mountain Ave Murray Hill NJ 07974

LIGETT, WALDO BUFORD, b Middletown, Ohio, Nov 2, 16; m 40; c 5. CHEMICAL ENGINEERING, MECHANICAL ENGINEERING. *Educ:* Antioch Col, BS, 39; Purdue Univ, MS, 41, PhD(org chem), 44, DSc, 65. *Prof Exp:* Res supvr, Ethyl Corp, 44-51, asst dir chem res, 51-52, assoc dir, 52-62, dir res & develop, 62-63; vpres & tech dir, Celanese Chem Co, 63-64, vpres tech & mfg, 64-66; corp tech dir, Celanese Corp, 66-67, vpres & tech dir, 67-72; V PRES, FRANKLIN INST & PRES, FRANKLIN RES CTR, 73- *Mem:* AAAS; Am Chem Soc; Am Nuclear Soc; Sigma Xi. *Res:* Petroleum additives; organometallic chemistry; organic synthesis; agricultural chemicals; fluorine compounds; hydrocarbon oxidation; materials; energy; environment; health; safety. *Mailing Add:* 2 Blackwell Pl Philadelphia PA 19147

LIGGERO, SAMUEL HENRY, b Amsterdam, NY, Apr 17, 42; m 66; c 1. PHYSICAL ORGANIC CHEMISTRY. *Educ:* Fordham Univ, BS, 64; Georgetown Univ, PhD(chem), 69. *Prof Exp:* NIH fel, Princeton Univ, 69-70; sr lab supvr film develop, 70-71, res group leader film develop, 72-76, mgr polavision cassette process eng, 77-78, SR TECH MGR, POLAROID CORP, 79- *Mem:* The Chem Soc; AAAS; Soc Photog Scientists & Engrs; Am Chem Soc. *Res:* Application of physical organic chemistry principles to the development of instant color photographic transparencies employing diffusion transfer processes; application of chemistry, physics and engineering to the manufacture and development of the polaroid polavision cassette. *Mailing Add:* 69 Sheridan Rd Wellesley Hills MA 02181

LIGGETT, JAMES ALEXANDER, b Los Angeles, Calif, June 29, 34; m 60. CIVIL ENGINEERING. *Educ:* Tex Tech Col, BS, 56; Stanford Univ, MS, 57, PhD(civil eng), 59. *Prof Exp:* Engr, Chance Vought Aircraft Corp, 59-60; asst prof hydraul, Univ Wis, 60-61; PROF HYDRAUL, CORNELL UNIV, 61- *Mem:* Am Soc Civil Engrs; Int Asn Hydraul Res. *Res:* Hydraulics; fluid mechanics; free surface flow; circulation and temperature distribution in lakes; groundwater flow. *Mailing Add:* Holister Hall Cornell Univ Ithaca NY 14853

LIGGETT, LAWRENCE MELVIN, b Denver, Colo, June 22, 17; m 43; c 2. ANALYTICAL CHEMISTRY, ORGANIC CHEMISTRY. *Educ:* Cent Col, Iowa, AB, 38; Iowa State Col, PhD(chem), 43. *Prof Exp:* Res chemist, Nat Defense Res Comt, Iowa State Col, 41-43; plant supt, Alkali Chlorates & Perchlorates Cardox Corp, 43-48; supvr inorg res, Wyandotte Chems Corp, 48-55; dir res, Speer Carbon Co, 55-64, vpres & tech dir, 65-67, vpres & gen mgr, Airco Speer Electronics, 67-70, pres, Airco Speer Electronics Div, 70-75, PRES, VACUUM EQUIPMENT & SYSTS, AIRCO TEMESCAL DIV, AIRCO INC, 75- *Mem:* Am Chem Soc; Electrochem Soc. *Res:* Alkali perchlorate production; nonblack pigments for rubber and paper; carbon and graphite technology; resistors; capacitors and electronic components; technical management. *Mailing Add:* 1856 Piedras Circle Danville CA 94526

LIGGETT, THOMAS MILTON, b Danville, Ky, Mar 29, 44. MATHEMATICS. *Educ:* Oberlin Col, AB, 65; Stanford Univ, MS, 66, PhD(math), 69. *Prof Exp:* From asst prof to assoc prof, 69-76, PROF MATH, UNIV CALIF, LOS ANGELES, 76- *Concurrent Pos:* Sloan fel, 73. *Mem:* Am Math Soc; Math Asn Am; Inst Math Statist. *Res:* Probability theory. *Mailing Add:* Dept of Math Univ of Calif 405 Hilgard Ave Los Angeles CA 90024

LIGGETT, WALTER STEWART, JR, b Abington, Pa, Aug 27, 40; m 62; c 3. STATISTICS. *Educ:* Rensselaer Polytech Inst, BS, 61, MS, 64, PhD(math), 67. *Prof Exp:* Prin engr, Submarine Signal Div, Raytheon Co, Portsmouth, 65-73; mathematician, Rand Inst, New York, 73-75; statistician, Div Environ Planning, Tenn Valley Authority, 75-80. *Mem:* Inst Math Statist; Soc Indust & Appl Math; Am Statist Asn. *Res:* Water and air quality; aquatic biology; radiological hygiene; sampling; data analysis; experimental design. *Mailing Add:* 20418 Shadow Oak Ct Gaithersburg MA 20879

LIGH, STEVE, b Canton, China, Nov 12, 37; US citizen. MATHEMATICS. *Educ:* Univ Houston, BS, 61; Univ Mo-Columbia, MA, 62; Tex A&M Univ, PhD(math), 69. *Prof Exp:* Instr math, Ohio Univ, 62-64, Houston Baptist Col, 65-66 & Tex A&M Univ, 68-69; asst prof, Univ Fla, 69-70; assoc prof, 70-72, PROF MATH, UNIV SOUTHWESTERN LA, 72- *Mem:* Math Asn Am; Am Math Soc. *Res:* Algebra; generalizations of rings; near rings. *Mailing Add:* Dept Math Univ Southwestern La Lafayette LA 70504

LIGHT, ALBERT, b Brooklyn, NY, June 19, 27; m 52; c 2. BIOCHEMISTRY. *Educ:* City Col New York, BS, 48; Yale Univ, PhD(biochem), 55. *Prof Exp:* Fel biochem, Cornell Univ, 55-57; asst res prof, Univ Utah, 57-63; assoc prof, Univ Calif, Los Angeles, 63-65; assoc prof, 65-77, PROF BIOCHEM, PURDUE UNIV, 77-, HEAD, DIV BIOCHEM, 78- *Mem:* AAAS; Am Chem Soc; Am Soc Biol Chem; Am Asn Univ Prof. *Res:* Protein chemistry and enzymology; protein folding; relationship of structure to function of biologically active proteins; biological membranes. *Mailing Add:* Dept of Chem Purdue Univ West Lafayette IN 47907

LIGHT, AMOS ELLIS, b Greencastle, Ind, Oct 22, 10; m 43; c 2. PHARMACOLOGY, NUTRITION. *Educ:* DePauw Univ, AB, 30; Syracuse Univ, MA, 32; Army Med Col, cert, 43; Am Bd Nutrit, dipl, 51; Am Bd Clin Chem, dipl, 52. *Prof Exp:* Asst chem, DePauw Univ, 29-30; asst, Syracuse Univ, 30-32; asst, Yale Univ, 33-34; asst, Columbia Univ, 34-36; asst, Welcome Res Labs, 36-42, biochemist, 46-63; pharmacologist, Bur Med, US Food & Drug Admin, 63-77; RETIRED. *Concurrent Pos:* Nutritionist, Spanish Nutrit Surv Team, Int Comt Nutrit Nat Defense, 58. *Honors & Awards:* Cosmetic Indust Buyers & Suppliers Award, Toilet Goods Asn, 54. *Mem:* AAAS; Am Chem Soc; fel Am Asn Clin Chem; Am Inst Nutrit; fel NY Acad Sci. *Res:* Biological effects of x-rays; nucleic acids and anti-metabolites; pituitary growth hormones; vitamin B complex in rats and bacteria; chronic toxicity tests; hair growth; sex hormones; radiopaques; polymyxins; diuretics; antispasmodics; busulfan cataracts. *Mailing Add:* 3565 John Anderson Dr Ormond Beach FL 32074

LIGHT, IRWIN JOSEPH, b Montreal, Que, July 21, 34; m 59; c 2. PEDIATRICS. *Educ:* McGill Univ, BS, 55, MD, 59. *Prof Exp:* Intern med, Royal Victoria Hosp, 59-60, resident, 60-61; resident pediat, Montreal Children's Hosp, 61-63; from asst prof to assoc prof pediat, 65-73, from asst prof to assoc prof obstet & gynec, 68-73, PROF PEDIAT, OBSTET & GYNEC, UNIV CINCINNATI, 73-, DIR NEWBORN CLIN SERV, 73-; RES ASSOC PEDIAT, CHILDREN'S HOSP RES FOUND, 63- *Concurrent Pos:* Clin fel pediat, Cincinnati Gen Hosp & res fel, Univ Cincinnati, 63-65. *Mem:* AAAS; Am Acad Pediat; Soc Pediat Res; Am Pediat Soc; Am Fedn Clin Res. *Res:* Neonatal infectious diseases; newborn metabolism. *Mailing Add:* Children's Hosp Res Found Elland & Bethesda Ave Cincinnati OH 45229

LIGHT, JOHN CALDWELL, b Mt Vernon, NY, Nov 24, 34; c 3. CHEMICAL PHYSICS. *Educ:* Oberlin Col, BA, 56; Harvard Univ, PhD(chem), 60. *Prof Exp:* NSF fel, Brussels, 59-61; from instr to assoc prof chem, 61-70, dir, Mat Res Lab, 70-73, PROF CHEM, UNIV CHICAGO, 70-, CHMN, DEPT CHEM, 80- *Concurrent Pos:* Sloan fel, 66; vis fel, Joint Inst Lab Astrophys, Univ Colo, 76-77. *Mem:* AAAS; Am Inst Phys. *Res:* Theoretical studies of elementary gas phase reactions; quantum mechanics and chemical kinetics; scattering theory. *Mailing Add:* Dept of Chem Univ of Chicago Chicago IL 60637

LIGHT, JOHN HENRY, b Annville, Pa, Dec 15, 24; m 50; c 3. MATHEMATICS. *Educ:* Lebanon Valley Col, BS, 48; Pa State Univ, MS, 50 & 57. *Prof Exp:* Res assoc, Ord Res Lab, Pa State Univ, 51-58, eng mech, 58-59; assoc prof, 59-74, PROF MATH, DICKINSON COL, 74- *Concurrent Pos:* Consult, Naval Supply Depot, Mechanicsburg, Pa, 59-62. *Mem:* Am Math Soc. *Res:* Spectroscopy; environmental testing. *Mailing Add:* Dept of Math Dickinson Col Carlisle PA 17013

LIGHT, KENNETH FREEMAN, b Detroit, Mich, Jan 22, 22; m 43; c 3. MECHANICAL ENGINEERING. *Educ:* Univ Ill, Urbana, BS, 49; Mich State Univ, MA, 52, PhD(higher educ), 67. *Prof Exp:* Instr mech & eng, Mich Technol Univ, 56-60, assoc prof technol, 60-65; prof mech eng & acad vpres, Lake Superior State Col, 65-77; PRES, ORE INST TECHNOL, 77- *Mem:* Am Soc Eng Educ. *Res:* Mechanical engineering technology; programmed learning; computer assisted instruction. *Mailing Add:* 1895 Park Klamath Falls OR 97601

LIGHT, KENNETH KARL, b Palmyra, Pa, Nov 6, 40; m 64; c 2. ORGANIC CHEMISTRY. *Educ:* Lebanon Valley Col, BS, 62; Univ Del, PhD(org chem), 66. *Prof Exp:* Res chemist, Mobil Oil Corp, 66-68; proj leader, Int Flavors & Fragrances, Inc, 68-79; ASSOC SCIENTIST, WASATCH DIV, THIOKOL CORP, 79- *Mem:* Am Chem Soc. *Res:* Synthesis of natural products; isolation and identification of natural products; synthesis of fragrance chemicals. *Mailing Add:* PO Box 524 MS 240 Wasatch Div Thiokol Corp Brigham City UT 84302

LIGHT, KIM EDWARD, Indianapolis, Ind, Sept 21, 51; m 75; c 1. BIOGENIC AMINES, RECEPTORS. *Educ:* Ind State Univ, Terre Haute, BS, 73; Ind Univ, Bloomington, MS, 75, PhD(pharmacol), 77. *Prof Exp:* Fel physiol, Sch Med, Tex Tech Univ, 79; ASST PROF PHARMACOL, UNIV ARK MED SCI, 79-, ASST PROF INTERDISCIPLINARY TOXICOL, 80- *Concurrent Pos:* Collabr, Col Med, Tex Tech Univ Health Sci, 79- *Mem:* Soc Neurosci; Am Physiol Soc; Sigma Xi. *Res:* Investigations into the functions and interactions of membrane receptors for biogenic amines; functional aspects and regulation of H1 and H2 histamine receptors in various tissues. *Mailing Add:* Col Pharm Univ Ark Med Sci 4301 W Markham Slot 522 Little Rock AR 72205

LIGHT, MITCHELL A, b Philadelphia, Pa, Nov 8, 21; m 49; c 3. GEOLOGY, ECONOMICS. *Educ:* Univ Mo, AB, 46, MA, 48; Rutgers Univ, PhD(geol), 50; Calif State Univ, Dominguez Hills, MA, 77. *Prof Exp:* Geologist, Tex Co, 47-48; from instr to asst prof geol, Univ Mass, 50-54; res geologist, Calif Res Corp, Div Standard Oil Calif, 54-57; div geologist, Richmond Petrol Co, Columbia, 57-59; investment analyst, Citizen's Nat Bank, 59-62; sr partner geol & econ consult, Light & Farrington Assoc, 62-70; DIR & MEM EXEC COMT, STONEBRIDGE CAPITAL MGT, 70- *Concurrent Pos:* Field geologist, Bur Mineral Res, 48; res consult, Idarado Mining Co, 52-53; lectr, Calif State Univ, Long Beach, 62-67, Whittier Col, 68-70 & Univ Calif, Los Angeles, 71-73. *Mem:* Am Asn Petrol Geologists; AAAS; Am Prof Geologists; Nat Asn Petrol Investment Analysts; Financial Analyst Fedn. *Res:* Geology of petroleum; alternative forms of energy; geothermal potentials; environmental impact of geological exploitation. *Mailing Add:* 1880 Century Park E Suite 717 Los Angeles CA 90067

LIGHT, ROBERT G(ORDON), agricultural engineering, see previous edition

LIGHT, ROBLEY JASPER, b Roanoke, Va, Nov 8, 35; m 60; c 1. BIOCHEMISTRY, ORGANIC CHEMISTRY. *Educ:* Va Polytech Inst, BS, 57; Duke Univ, PhD(org chem), 61. *Prof Exp:* NSF fel biochem, Harvard Univ, 60-62; from instr to assoc prof, 63-67, 62-72, BIOCHEM, FLA STATE UNIV, UNIV, 72- *Concurrent Pos:* USPHS res career develop award, 67-72; Alexander von Humboldt US sr scientist award, 77. *Mem:* Am Chem Soc; Am Soc Biol Chemists. *Res:* Lipid metabolism, structure, and function; polyketides and other secondary metabolites of microorganisms. *Mailing Add:* Dept of Chem Fla State Univ Tallahassee FL 32306

LIGHT, THOMAS BURWELL, b Dayton, Ohio, July 9, 28; m 51; c 4. SOLID STATE PHYSICS, MATERIALS SCIENCE. *Educ:* Antioch Col, BS, 51; Ill Inst Technol, MS, 54; Yale Univ, PhD(mat sci), 66. *Prof Exp:* Mem tech staff, Bell Tel Labs, 53-62; MEM RES STAFF, THOMAS J WATSON RES CTR, IBM CORP, 65- *Mem:* AAAS; Am Phys Soc; Am Vacuum Soc; Electrochem Soc; Inst Elec & Electronics Engrs. *Res:* Deposition, structure and properties of thin films; structure of and crystallization in amorphous materials; structure of oxide layers and interface reactions. *Mailing Add:* 2 Briarcliff Rd Chappaqua NY 10514

LIGHT, TRUMAN S, b Hartford, Conn, Dec 16, 22; m 46, 80; c 3. ANALYTICAL CHEMISTRY. *Educ:* Harvard Univ, SB, 43; Univ Minn, MS, 49; Univ Rome, DrChem, 61. *Prof Exp:* Asst prof chem, Boston Col, 49-59; staff scientist, Res & Adv Develop Div, Avco Corp, 59-64; sr res chemist, 64-72, mgr, Chem Anal & Mat Lab, 72-80, PRIN RES SCIENTIST, FOXBORO CO, 80- *Concurrent Pos:* NSF fel, Chem Inst, Univ Rome, Italy, 60-61; consult, Children's Med Ctr, Boston, Mass, 56-60 & Watertown Arsenal, 51-55. *Mem:* Am Chem Soc; Electrochem Soc; Soc Appl Spectros; Instrument Soc Am; Sigma Xi. *Res:* Instrumental methods of analysis; electrochemistry; physical chemistry; materials sciences, water quality and pollution controls. *Mailing Add:* 4 Webster Rd Lexington MA 02173

LIGHTBODY, JAMES JAMES, b Detroit, Mich, Mar 1, 39; m 64; c 2. IMMUNOLOGY, BIOCHEMISTRY. *Educ:* Wayne State Univ, BA, 61, BS, 64, PhD(biochem), 66. *Prof Exp:* Res assoc biochem & NIH trainee, Brandeis Univ, 67-69; instr pediat & Swiss Nat Sci Found grant, Univ Bern, 69-70; sr res assoc immunol, Basel Inst Immunol, 70-71; res assoc, Univ Wis, 71-72; asst prof, 72-76, ASSOC PROF BIOCHEM, SCH MED, WAYNE STATE UNIV, 76-, ASSOC IMMUNOL, 73-, CLIN ASSOC PROF INTERNAL MED, 76- *Concurrent Pos:* Vis prof, Mem Sloan-Kettering Cancer Res, 73; lectr, Cancer Inst, Cairo Univ, 74. *Mem:* AAAS; Am Asn Immunol; Transplantation Soc. *Mailing Add:* Dept of Biochem Wayne State Univ Sch of Med Detroit MI 48202

LIGHTFOOT, DONALD RICHARD, b Los Angeles, Calif, Aug 8, 40. BIOCHEMICAL GENETICS. *Educ:* Univ Redlands, BA, 62; Univ Ariz, MS, 67, PhD(biochem), 72. *Prof Exp:* Teacher, Philippine High Sch, Peace Corps, 62-64; res trainee biochem, Med Sch, Univ Ore, 69-71; fel, Univ Calif, Riverside, 71-74; ASST PROF BIOCHEM & NUTRIT, VA POLYTECH INST & STATE UNIV, 74- *Mem:* AAAS; Am Chem Soc. *Res:* Plant virology; tobacco mosaic virus infection process; biochemical genetics; gene titration in tobacco species; minor nucleosides; transfer RNA, messenger RNA and viral RNA structure and function. *Mailing Add:* Dept of Biochem & Nutrit Va Polytech Inst & State Univ Blacksburg VA 24061

LIGHTFOOT, E(DWIN) N(IBLOCK), JR, b Milwaukee, Wis, Sept 25, 25; m 49; c 5. CHEMICAL ENGINEERING. *Educ:* Cornell Univ, BS, 47, PhD(chem eng), 51. *Prof Exp:* Chem engr, Chas Pfizer & Co, 50-53; asst prof biochem eng, 53-58, assoc prof chem eng, 58-61, PROF CHEM ENG, UNIV WIS-MADISON, 61- *Res:* Physical separation techniques; mass transfer; biomedical engineering. *Mailing Add:* Dept of Chem Eng Univ of Wis 1415 Johnson Dr Madison WI 53706

LIGHTFOOT, RALPH B(UTTERWORTH), b Fall River, Mass, June 19, 13; m 37; c 2. AERONAUTICAL ENGINEERING. *Educ:* Univ RI, BS & ME, 35. *Prof Exp:* Wind tunnel engr, Sikorsky Aircraft Div, United Technologies Corp, 35-37, chief wind tunnel engr, 38-40, chief flight test engr, 40-43, chief flight res, 44-57, chief engr, 57-66, engr mgr, 66-67, sr staff engr, 68-74; CONSULT ENGR, 74- *Concurrent Pos:* Instr, Univ Bridgeport, 39, 77, lectr, 63-65; instr, Bullard Havens Tech Inst, 41-43; lectr, NY Univ, 43; designated eng rep, Fed Aviation Agency, 55-60, mem airworthiness stand eval comt, 66; mem, NASA, 56-68; mem adv coun, Bridgeport Eng Inst, Univ Bridgeport, Housatonic Community Col & Adv Group Aerospace Res & Develop, NATO, 59, 62; navigator, US Power Squadron; lectr, Univ Conn, 62; mem adv coun, Univ RI, 81- *Honors & Awards:* Merit Award, Am Helicopter Soc, 48; Gold Medal, NY Acad Sci & Cierva Prize, Royal Aeronaut Soc, 65. *Mem:* Nat Soc Prof Engrs; hon fel Am Helicopter Soc (vpres, 50, pres, 51); fel Am Inst Aeronaut & Astronaut; fel NY Acad Sci; fel Royal Aeronaut Soc. *Res:* Aerodynamics; wind tunnel; analytical flight test; flying boats; helicopters; management; airplanes. *Mailing Add:* 55 Eliphamets Lane Chatham MA 02633

LIGHTHOLDER, RICHARD K, b Canonsburgh, Pa, Jan 4, 12; m 40; c 2. CIVIL ENGINEERING. *Educ:* Univ Pittsburgh, BS, 39, MS, 42. *Prof Exp:* Asst engr drawing, 39-40, instr surv, 40-51, prof civil eng, 51-77, EMER PROF CIVIL ENG, UNIV PITTSBURGH, 77-; PRES, RICHARD CONSTRUCT CO, INC, 52- *Concurrent Pos:* Partner, L & L Construct Co, 46-51; pres, Sherwood Builders, Inc, 58-81; secy, Wilshire Village, Inc, 70-81. *Mem:* Am Soc Civil Engrs; Am Rd Builders Asn; Am Soc Eng Educ. *Res:* Highways. *Mailing Add:* 121 Willhaven Rd McMurray PA 15317

LIGHTMAN, ALAN PAIGE, b Memphis, Tenn, Nov 28, 48; m 76; c 1. THEORETICAL ASTROPHYSICS, THEORETICAL PHYSICS. *Educ:* Princeton Univ, AB, 70; Calif Inst Technol, MA, 73, PhD(physics), 74. *Prof Exp:* Res assoc physics, Calif Inst Technol, 74; res assoc astrophys, Cornell Univ, 74-75; res assoc theoret astrophys, 75-76; asst prof astron, 76-79, LECTR PHYSICS & ASTRON, HARVARD UNIV, 79-; MEM STAFF, SMITHSONIAN ASTROPHYS OBSERV, 79- *Mem:* Int Soc Gen Relativity & Gravitation. *Res:* Theoretical frameworks for analyzing modern gravitation theories; relativistic astrophysics, x-ray astronomy; stellar dynamics. *Mailing Add:* Dept of Astron Harvard Univ Cambridge MA 02138

LIGHTNER, DAVID A, b Los Angeles, Calif, Mar 25, 39. ORGANIC CHEMISTRY. *Educ:* Univ Calif, Berkeley, AB, 60; Stanford Univ, PhD, 63. *Prof Exp:* NSF fels, Stanford Univ, 63-64 & Univ Minn, 64-65; asst prof chem, Univ Calif, Los Angeles, 65-72; assoc prof, Tex Tech Univ, 72-74; assoc prof, 74-76, PROF CHEM, UNIV NEV, RENO, 76- *Mem:* AAAS; Am Chem Soc; Royal Soc Chem; Ger Chem Soc; NY Acad Sci. *Res:* Photooxidation of biological materials; mass spectrometry; synthesis and stereochemistry; circular dichroism and optical rotatory dispersion; phototherapy and jaundice. *Mailing Add:* Dept of Chem Univ of Nev Reno NV 89557

LIGHTNER, JAMES EDWARD, b Frederick, Md, Aug 29, 37. MATHEMATICS, EDUCATION. *Educ:* Western Md Col, AB, 58; Northwestern Univ, AM, 62; Ohio State Univ, PhD(math, educ), 68. *Prof Exp:* Teacher, Frederick County Bd Educ, Md, 58-62; from instr to assoc prof math, 62-77, chmn dept, 68-73, PROF MATH & EDUC, WESTERN MD COL, 77-, DIR JANUARY TERM, 69- *Concurrent Pos:* Fed Liaison Rep, Western Md Col, 73-78, coordr int studies, 80-; consult sch systs. *Mem:* Sch Sci & Math Asn; Nat Coun Teachers Math. *Res:* Undergraduate mathematics curricula; secondary mathematics curricula and methodology; secondary school geometry. *Mailing Add:* Dept of Math Western Md Col Westminster MD 21157

LIGHTSTONE, ALBERT HAROLD, mathematics, deceased

LIGHTY, RICHARD WILLIAM, b Freeport, Ill, Nov 8, 33; m 55; c 2. PLANT GENETICS, HORTICULTURE. *Educ:* Pa State Univ, BS, 55; Cornell Univ, MS, 58, PhD(genetics), 60. *Prof Exp:* Geneticist, Longwood Gardens, Pa, 60-67; ASSOC PROF PLANT SCI & COORDR LONGWOOD PROG ORNAMENTAL HORT, UNIV DEL, 67- *Mem:* AAAS; Am Asn Bot Gardens & Arboretums. *Res:* Plant breeding; cytotaxonomy; horticultural taxonomy; floriculture. *Mailing Add:* Agr Hall Univ of Del Newark DE 19711

LIGLER, FRANCES SMITH, b Louisville, Ky, June 11, 51; m 72; c 1. CANCER RESEARCH, CYTOFLUORIMETRY. *Educ:* Furnam Univ, BS, 72; Oxford Univ, Eng, DPhil. *Prof Exp:* Fel biochem, Univ Tex Health Sci Ctr, San Antonio, 75-76; asst instr immunol, Southwestern Med Sch, 76-78, instr, 78-80; PRIMARY SCIENTIST IMMUNOL, E I DUPONT DE NEMOURS & CO, INC, 80- *Mem:* Am Asn Immunologists; AAAS. *Res:* Cytofluorimetry and tissue culture to study differentiation of human lymphoid tumor cells for cancer research. *Mailing Add:* 606 Kilburn Rd Wilmington DE 19803

LIGON, JAMES DAVID, b Wewoka, Okla, Feb 2, 39; m 67; c 1. ZOOLOGY. *Educ:* Univ Okla, BS, 61; Univ Fla, MS, 63; Univ Mich, PhD(zool), 67. *Prof Exp:* Asst prof biol, Idaho State Univ, 67-68; from asst prof to assoc prof, 68-77, PROF BIOL, UNIV NMEX, 77- *Mem:* Am Ornith Union; Cooper Ornith Soc. *Res:* Avian ecology and behavior. *Mailing Add:* Dept of Biol Univ of NMex Albuquerque NM 87131

LIGON, JAMES T(EDDIE), b Easley, SC, Feb 20, 36; m 58; c 3. AGRICULTURAL ENGINEERING. *Educ:* Clemson Univ, BS, 57; Iowa State Univ, MS, 59, PhD(agr eng, soil physics), 61. *Prof Exp:* Asst prof agr eng, Univ Ky, 61-66; assoc prof, 66-71, chmn directorate, Water Resources Res Inst, 75-77, PROF AGR ENG, CLEMSON UNIV, 71- *Mem:* Am Soc Agr Engrs; Am Geophys Union; Sigma Xi. *Res:* Soil drainage and physics; soil, water and plant relationships; hydrologic modeling. *Mailing Add:* Dept of Agr Eng Clemson Univ Clemson SC 29631

LIGON, WOODFIN VAUGHAN, JR, b Farmville, Va, Apr 24, 44. ORGANIC MASS SPECTROMETRY, ORGANIC CHEMISTRY. *Educ:* Longwood Col, BS, 66; Univ Va, PhD(org chem), 70. *Prof Exp:* Vis asst prof org chem, Univ Ill, 72-73; STAFF SCIENTIST ORG MASS SPECTROMETRY, GEN ELEC CORP RES & DEVELOP, 73- *Concurrent Pos:* NIH fel, Univ Ill, Urbana, 71-72. *Mem:* Sigma Xi; Am Soc Mass Spectrometry. *Res:* New modes of ionization for mass spectrometry; mass spectrometry above mass 1000. *Mailing Add:* PO Box 8 K1-2A40 Schenectady NY 12301

LIGUORI, VINCENT ROBERT, b Brooklyn, NY, Dec 15, 28; m 49, 52; c 5. MARINE MICROBIOLOGY. *Educ:* St Francis Col, NY, BS, 51; Long Island Univ, MS, 58; NY Univ, PhD(microbiol), 67. *Prof Exp:* Res asst cancer chemother, Sloan-Kettering Inst Cancer Res, 55-56; supvr oncol lab, Vet Admin Hosp, NY, 56-62; staff scientist microbiol, New York Aquarium, 62-65; asst prof biol & marine sci, Long Island Univ, 65-66; res assoc microbiol, Osborn Labs Marine Sci, New York Aquarium, 66-71; lectr, 66-68, ASSOC PROF BIOL & DEP CHMN DEPT BIOL SCI, KINGSBOROUGH COMMUNITY COL, 71- *Concurrent Pos:* Lectr, Nassau County Mus

Natural Hist, 65-68, Richmond Col, 67- & Queens Col, 68-; mem bd dir, Mid Atlantic Natural Sci Coun, Inc, 75-; mem, Bermuda Biol Sta Res, 75-78. *Mem:* AAAS; Am Soc Microbiol; Am Soc Zool. *Res:* Biological effects of natural products and the mechanism of adhesion in marine invertebrates; role of marine microorganisms in the disease processes of marine animals; aquaculture; invertebrates. *Mailing Add:* Dept Biol Sci 2001 Oriental Blvd Brooklyn NY 11235

LIH, MARSHALL MIN-SHING, chemical engineering, see previous edition

LIIMATAINEN, T(OIVO) M(ATTHEW), b Gloucester, Mass, Nov 14, 10; m 50. ENGINEERING PHYSICS, MATHEMATICS. *Prof Exp:* Engr, Gen Elec Co, 41-46 & Sylvania Elec Prod Co, 46-48; proj engr, Nat Bur Standards, 48-53; asst br chief electron devices, Diamond Ord Fuze Labs, US Dept Army, 53-59, br chief microelectronics, 59-63; aerospace engr, Goddard Space Flight Ctr, NASA, Md, 63-66 & Electronics Res Ctr, Cambridge, 66-70; gen engr, Transp Systs Ctr, Dept Transp, Mass, 70-71; consult, 71-80; RETIRED. *Mem:* AAAS; sr mem Inst Elec & Electronics Engrs; NY Acad Sci. *Res:* Semiconductor devices; integrated circuits; microelectronics; high vacuum and gas discharge devices. *Mailing Add:* 1004 Union St Schenectady NY 12308

LIITTSCHWAGER, JOHN M(ILTON), b Alden, Iowa, Oct 24, 34; m 55; c 4. OPERATIONS RESEARCH, INDUSTRIAL ENGINEERING. *Educ:* Iowa State Univ, BS, 55; Northwestern Univ, MS, 61. *Prof Exp:* Engr, foods div, Anderson Clayton & Co, 55-56; consult pub utility, Mid West Serv Co, 56-60; chmn dept, 74-81, PROF INDUST & MGT ENG, UNIV IOWA, 61- *Mem:* Opers Res Soc Am; Inst Mgt Sci; Am Inst Indust Eng; Asn Comput Mach; Am Soc Eng Educ. *Res:* Legislative districting by computer; mathematical programming; reliability theory. *Mailing Add:* 4104 Eng Bldg Univ of Iowa Iowa City IA 52242

LIJEWSKI, LAWRENCE EDWARD, b Milwaukee, Wis, Mar 12, 48; m 75. MISSILE AERODYNAMICS, INTERFERENCE AERODYNAMICS. *Educ:* Univ Notre Dame, BSAE, 70, MSAE, 72, PhD(aerospace), 74. *Prof Exp:* Mech engr, Army Aviation Systs Command, 74-77; AEROSPACE ENGR, AIR FORCE ARMAMENT LAB, 77- *Mem:* Am Inst Aeronaut & Astronaut. *Res:* Aerodynamics of aircraft and missiles; theoretical and experimental methods to obtain aerodynamic characteristics and fundamental understanding of basic aerodynamic phenomena. *Mailing Add:* US Air Force Armament Lab AFATL/DLJCA Eglin AFB FL 32542

LIKENS, GENE ELDEN, b Pierceton, Ind, Jan 6, 35; div; c 3. AQUATIC ECOLOGY, LIMNOLOGY. *Educ:* Manchester Col, BS, 57; Univ Wis, MS, 59, PhD(zool), 62. *Hon Degrees:* DSc, Manchester Col, 79. *Prof Exp:* Asst zool, Univ Wis, 57-61; instr, Dartmouth Col, 61; from proj asst to res assoc, Univ Wis, 62, res assoc meteorol, 62-63; from instr to assoc prof biol sci, Dartmouth Col, 63-69; assoc prof, 69-72, actg chmn sect, 73-74, PROF ECOL & SYSTS, CORNELL UNIV, 72- *Concurrent Pos:* Vis lectr, Univ Wis, 63; vis assoc ecologist, Brookhaven Nat Lab, 68; NATO sr fel, Eng & Sweden, 69; Guggenheim fel, 72-73; mem, US Nat Comt Int Hydrol Decade, 66-70; mem adv panel, US Senate Comt Pub Works, 70-73; US Nat Rep, Int Asn Theoret & Appl Limnol, 70-; mem ecol adv comt & sci adv bd, Environ Protection Agency, 74-78; mem comt water qual policy, Nat Acad Sci, 73-76, mem assembly life sci, 77-; mem biol res comt, Edmund Niles Huyck Preserves & resource adv, NY State Dept Environ Conserv, 74-; vis prof, Ctr Advan Sci, Dept Environ Sci, Univ Va, 78-79. *Honors & Awards:* Am Motors Conserv Award, 69. *Mem:* Fel AAAS; Am Polar Soc; Am Soc Limnol & Oceanog (vpres, 75-76, pres, 76-77); Ecol Soc Am (vpres, 78-79, pres, 81-82); Int Asn Theoret & Appl Limnol. *Res:* Circulation in lakes using radioactive tracers; meromictic lakes; biogeochemistry and analysis of ecosystems; antarctic and arctic limnology; precipitation chemistry. *Mailing Add:* Sect of Ecol & Systs Div of Biol Sci Cornell Univ Ithaca NY 14853

LIKES, CARL JAMES, b Charleston, SC, Sept 11, 16; m 43. PHYSICAL CHEMISTRY. *Educ:* Col Charleston, BS, 37; Univ Va, PhD(phys chem), 41. *Prof Exp:* Instr chem, Univ Va, 41-43; asst prof, Tulane Univ, 43, asst prof, 44-46; prof & head dept, Hampden-Sydney Col, 47-52; proj supvr, Va Inst for Sci Res, 52-58; PROF CHEM, COL CHARLESTON, 58- *Mem:* Am Chem Soc. *Res:* Electrophoretic and ultracentrifugal analysis of proteins. *Mailing Add:* Dept of Chem Col of Charleston Charleston SC 29401

LIKINS, PETER WILLIAM, b Tracy, Calif, July 4, 36; m 55; c 6. DYNAMICS, CONTROL SYSTEMS. *Educ:* Stanford Univ, BS, 57, PhD(eng mech), 65; Mass Inst Technol, SM, 58. *Prof Exp:* Develop engr, Jet Propulsion Lab, Calif Inst Technol, 58-60; from asst prof to prof eng, Univ Calif, Los Angeles, 64-76, from asst dean to assoc dean, 74-76; FROM PROF & DEAN TO PROVOST, COLUMBIA UNIV, 76- *Concurrent Pos:* Consult to various industs & govt res agencies, 66- *Mem:* Assoc fel Am Inst Aeronaut & Astronaut; Am Soc Eng Educ; Am Soc Mech Engrs. *Res:* Problems of space vehicle dynamics, stability and control. *Mailing Add:* 205 Low Libr Columbia Univ New York NY 10027

LIKINS, ROBERT CAMPBELL, b Springfield, Mo, July 1, 21; m 43; c 2. BIOCHEMISTRY. *Educ:* Univ Kansas City, DDS, 45, BA, 46. *Prof Exp:* Carnegie fel, Univ Rochester, 45-46; dent officer, Nat Inst Dent Res, 46-62, chief extramural prog br, 62-68; PROF DENT SURG, UNIV CHICAGO & DIR, WALTER G ZOLLER MEM DENT CLIN, 68- *Concurrent Pos:* Mem dent study sect, USPHS, 60-64. *Mem:* Fel AAAS; Am Col Dent; Biophys Soc; Soc Exp Biol & Med; Int Asn Dent Res. *Res:* Biochemistry and biophysics of calcification; calcium metabolism; research administration. *Mailing Add:* 1842 Honover Lane Flossmore IL 60422

LIKOFF, WILLIAM, b Philadelphia, Pa, Feb 5, 12; m 32; c 2. MEDICINE. *Educ:* Dartmouth Col, BA, 33; Hahnemann Med Col, MD, 38. *Prof Exp:* Assoc prof med, 45-58, prof med, head cardiovasc div & dir cardiovasc inst, 59-68, DIR CATEGORIC PROGS, HAHNEMANN MED COL, 68- *Mem:* fel AMA; fel Am Heart Asn; fel Am Col Physicians; distinguished fel Am Col Cardiol (pres, 67-68); fel Am Col Chest Physicians. *Res:* Cardiovascular diseases. *Mailing Add:* 1320 Race St Philadelphia PA 19107

LIKUSKI, HENRY JOHN, b Hillcrest, Alta, Sept 27, 35; m 58; c 4. ANIMAL NUTRITION, POULTRY NUTRITION. *Educ:* Univ Alta, BSc, 58, MSc, 59; Univ Ill, PhD(nutrit), 64. *Prof Exp:* Res assoc, Vet Admin Hosp & State Univ NY Downstate Med Ctr, 63-65; researcher, 65-68, sr scientist, 68-72, group leader, 72-80, RES MGR, RES CTR, CAN PACKERS INC, 80- *Res:* Hypothalmic regulation of food intake; nutrient requirements of livestock and poultry; nutrient composition of feeds. *Mailing Add:* Can Packers Ltd Res Ctr 2211 St Clair Ave W Toronto ON M6N 1K4 Can

LIKUSKI, ROBERT KEITH, b Hillcrest, Alta, Oct 16, 37; m 71; c 1. BIOMEDICAL ENGINEERING. *Educ:* Univ Alta, BS, 59; Univ Ill, MS, 61, PhD(elec eng), 64. *Prof Exp:* Asst prof elec eng, Univ Tex, Austin, 65-70; proj engr comput memories, Micro-Bit Corp, 70-76; chief engr biomed eng, 76-80, DIR RES & DEVELOP, BERKELEY BIO-ENG, INC, 80- *Mem:* Inst Elec & Electronics Engrs. *Res:* Development of instrumentation for medical use. *Mailing Add:* Berkeley Bio-Eng Inc 600 McCormick St San Leandro CA 94577

LILENFELD, HARVEY VICTOR, b Brooklyn, NY, Aug 25, 45. PHYSICAL CHEMISTRY. *Educ:* Polytech Inst Brooklyn, BS, 66; Mass Inst Technol, PhD(phys chem), 71. *Prof Exp:* Res assoc, Brookhaven Nat Lab, 71-72; scientist chem, McDonnell Douglas Corp, 72-80. *Mem:* Am Chem Soc; Sigma Xi. *Res:* Laser chemistry; kinetics of gas phase reactions. *Mailing Add:* 2340 Driftwood Pl Creve Coeur MD 63141

LILES, JAMES NEIL, b Akron, Ohio, Apr 25, 30; m 55; c 3. COMPARATIVE PHYSIOLOGY, HUMAN PHYSIOLOGY. *Educ:* Miami Univ, BA, 51; Ohio State Univ, MSc, 53, PhD(insect physiol), 56. *Prof Exp:* Asst prof biol, Univ SC, 56-58; res assoc entom, Ohio State Univ, 58-60; from asst prof to assoc prof, 60-71, PROF ENTOM, UNIV TENN, 71- *Mem:* Am Inst Biol Sci; Am Soc Zool; Geront Soc; Entom Soc Am; Am Col Sports Med. *Res:* Aging in insects; insect nutrient utilization. *Mailing Add:* Dept of Zool Univ of Tenn Knoxville TN 37916

LILES, SAMUEL LEE, b Texas City, Tex, June 24, 42; m 63; c 1. PHYSIOLOGY. *Educ:* McNeese State Col, BS, 64; La State Univ Med Ctr, New Orleans, PhD(physiol), 68. *Prof Exp:* Instr, 68-70, asst prof, 70-75, ASSOC PROF PHYSIOL, LA STATE UNIV MED CTR, NEW ORLEANS, 75- *Concurrent Pos:* Nat Inst Neurol Dis & Stroke grant, La State Univ Med Ctr, New Orleans, 70- *Mem:* AAAS; Am Physiol Soc; NY Acad Sci; Soc Neurosci. *Res:* Regional neurophysiology; electrophysiological correlates between brain neuronal activity and voluntary motor and sensory function. *Mailing Add:* Dept Physiol La State Univ Med Ctr 1100 Florida Ave New Orleans LA 70119

LILEY, NICHOLAS ROBIN, b Halifax, Eng, Dec 17, 36; m 61. ZOOLOGY. *Educ:* Oxford Univ, BA, 59, DPhil(zool), 64. *Prof Exp:* Nat Res Coun Can fel zool, 63-65, from asst prof to assoc prof, 65-78, PROF ZOOL, UNIV BC, 78- *Mem:* Animal Behav Soc; Can Soc Zool. *Res:* Comparative ethology and the evolution of behavior; endocrine mechanisms in control of behavior. *Mailing Add:* Dept Zool Univ BC Vancouver BC V6T 1W5 Can

LILEY, PETER EDWARD, b Barnstaple, Eng, Apr 22, 27; m 63; c 2. PHYSICS, CHEMICAL ENGINEERING. *Educ:* Univ London, BSc, 51, PhD(physics), 57; Imp Col, Univ London, dipl, 57. *Prof Exp:* Chem engr, Brit Oxygen Eng, Ltd, 55-57; from asst prof to assoc prof, 57-72, PROF MECH ENG, PURDUE UNIV, WEST LAFAYETTE, 72- *Mem:* Brit Inst Physics. *Res:* Thermodynamic and transport properties of fluids; cryogenic engineering; high pressure. *Mailing Add:* Sch of Mech Eng Purdue Univ West Lafayette IN 47907

LILIEN, OTTO MICHAEL, b New York, NY, Apr 26, 24; m; c 6. GENITOURINARY SURGERY. *Educ:* Jefferson Med Col, MD, 49; Columbia Univ, MA, 60. *Prof Exp:* Lectr zool, Columbia Univ, 56-58; from asst prof urol surg to assoc prof urol, 61-67, PROF UROL, STATE UNIV NY UPSTATE MED CTR, 67-, CHMN DEPT, 63- *Concurrent Pos:* Nat Cancer Inst trainee, 56-58. *Mem:* AMA; Am Urol Asn; fel Am Col Surg. *Res:* Renal and cell physiology. *Mailing Add:* Dept of Urol State Univ of NY Upstate Med Ctr Syracuse NY 13210

LILIENFELD, ABRAHAM MORRIS, b New York, NY, Nov 13, 20; m 43; c 3. EPIDEMIOLOGY, BIOSTATISTICS. *Educ:* Johns Hopkins Univ, AB, 41, MPH, 49; Univ Md, MD, 44. *Hon Degrees:* DSc, Univ Md, 75. *Prof Exp:* Assoc pub health physician, State Dept Health, NY, 49-50; dir southern health dist, City Dept Health, Baltimore, 50-52; lectr public health, Sch Hyg & Pub Health, Johns Hopkins Univ, 50-52, asst prof epidemiol, 52-54; assoc prof med statist, Med Sch, Univ Buffalo, 54-58; prof pub health admin & dir, Div Chronic Dis, Sch Hyg & Pub Health, 58-70, prof epidemiol & chmn dept, Sch Hyg & Pub Health, 70-75, UNIV DISTINGUISHED SERV PROF EPIDEMIOL, SCH MED, JOHNS HOPKINS UNIV, 75-, ASSOC PROF MED & MEM ONCOL COUN, 76-, DIR, MPH PROG, 80- *Concurrent Pos:* Dir, Nat Gamma Globulin Eval Ctr, 53-54, consult, NIH, 57-; cheif, Dept Statist & Epidemiol, Roswell Park Mem Inst, 54-58; mem, Nat Adv Heart Coun, 62-66; staff dir, President's Comn Heart Dis, Cancer & Stroke, 64-65. *Honors & Awards:* Bronfman Award, Am Pub Health Asn, John Snow Award, Epidemiol Sect. *Mem:* AAAS; Am Epidemiol Soc; Am Pub Health Asn; Am Statist Asn; Soc Epidemiol Res. *Res:* Epidemiology of cirrhosis and inflammatory bowel diseases; cancer; cardiovascular diseases; history of epidemiology. *Mailing Add:* Sch of Med Johns Hopkins Univ Baltimore MD 21205

LILIENFIELD, LAWRENCE SPENCER, b New York, NY, May 5, 27; m 50; c 3. MEDICINE, PHYSIOLOGY. *Educ:* Villanova Col, BS, 45; Georgetown Univ, MD, 49, MS, 54, PhD, 56; Am Bd Internal Med, dipl, 57, 74. *Prof Exp:* Intern med, Georgetown Univ Hosp, 49-50, from jr asst resident to sr asst resident, 50-53, asst chief cardiovasc res lab & attend physician, 56; instr med, Med Sch, 55-57, instr physiol, 56-57, from asst prof to assoc prof med, physiol & biophys, 57-64, PROF PHYSIOL & BIOPHYS, SCHS MED

&DENT, GEORGETOWN UNIV, 64-, CHMN DEPT PHYSIOL & BIOPHYS, SCH MED, 63- *Concurrent Pos:* Am Heart Asn res fel, 57; USPHS sr res fel, 59 & res career award, 63; attend physician, DC Gen Hosp, 56 & Vet Admin Hosp, 57; estab investr, Am Heart Asn, 58; consult, USPHS, 65-72; vis prof, Univ Saigon; vis prof, Univ Tel-Aviv, 67-68; assoc, Comt Int Exchange Persons, 71-76. *Mem:* AAAS; Biophys Soc; Am Physiol Soc; Soc Exp Biol & Med; AMA. *Res:* Transcapillary exchange; hemodynamics; blood distribution in organs; renal concentrating mechanisms; method of blood flow measurement. *Mailing Add:* Dept Physiol Sch Med Georgetown Univ Washington DC 20007

LILL, GORDON GRIGSBY, b Mt Hope, Kans, Feb 23, 18; m 43; c 2. MARINE GEOLOGY. *Educ:* Kans State Col, BS, 40, MS, 46. *Hon Degrees:* DSc, Univ Miami, 66. *Prof Exp:* Asst chief party, State Hwy Comn, Kans, 41; asst geol, Univ Calif, 46-47; head geophys br, US Off Naval Res, 47-59, earth sci adv, 59-60; corp res adv, Lockheed Aircraft Corp, 60-64; dir proj Mohole, NSF, 64-66; sr sci adv, Lockheed Aircraft Corp, 66-70; dep dir, Nat Ocean Surv, Nat Oceanic & Atmospheric Admin, US Dept Com, 70-79; RETIRED. *Concurrent Pos:* Pvt res, US Nat Mus; geologist, Bikini Sci Resurv, 47; mem mineral surv, Cent & Western Prov, Liberia, 49-50; consult comt geophys & geol res & develop bd, Nat Mil Estab, 47-53; chmn panel oceanog, Int Geophys Year; mem comt, Am Miscellaneous Soc, Proj Mohole, Nat Acad Sci-Nat Res Coun; vchmn, Calif Adv Comn Marine & Coastal Resources, 68-70; mem adv coun, Inst Marine Resources, Univ Calif, 69-71. *Mem:* Fel AAAS; Geol Soc Am; Am Geophys Union; Marine Technol Soc. *Res:* Sedimentary petrology; submarine geology. *Mailing Add:* 9606 Hillridge Dr Kensington MD 20795

LILL, PATSY HENRY, b Mesa, Ariz, July 6, 43. IMMUNOLOGY, PATHOLOGY. *Educ:* Northwestern Univ, BS, 66; Univ Wis, MST, 72; Chicago Med Sch-Univ Health Sci, PhD(path), 75. *Prof Exp:* Teacher biol, Highland Park High Sch, Ill, 66-70; lab supvr cancer res, Dept Exp Path, Mt Sinai Hosp Med Ctr, 70-75; fel tumor immunology & cancer biol, Frederick Cancer Res Ctr, 75-77; ASST PROF PATH, SCH MED, UNIV SC, 77- *Concurrent Pos:* Prin investr, Univ SC Res & Prod Scholarship grant, 79 & Nat Cancer Inst grant, 79-82; mem, Charles Louis Davis Doctor Vet Med Found. *Mem:* AAAS; Am Asn Pathologists; Am Asn Cancer Res. *Res:* Tumor immunology; effect of physical and chemical carcinogens on syngeneic tumor growth. *Mailing Add:* Dept of Path Univ SC Sch of Med Columbia SC 29208

LILLARD, DORRIS ALTON, b Thompson Station, Tenn, July 17, 36. FOOD CHEMISTRY, BIOCHEMISTRY. *Educ:* Middle Tenn State Univ, BS, 58; Ore State Univ, MS, 61, PhD(food sci), 64. *Prof Exp:* Res fel lipid autoxidation, Ore State Univ, 58-64; asst prof food flavor chem, Iowa State Univ, 64-68; assoc prof, 68-80, PROF FOOD SCI, UNIV GA, 80- *Mem:* AAAS; Am Chem Soc; Am Oil Chem Soc; Inst Food Technol; Am Meat Sci Asn. *Res:* Flavor chemistry of foods; autoxidation of lipids; mycotoxins in foods; food microbiology. *Mailing Add:* Dept of Food Sci Univ of Ga Athens GA 30602

LILLEGRAVEN, JASON ARTHUR, b Mankato, Minn, Oct 11, 38; m 64; c 2. PALEONTOLOGY. *Educ:* Calif State Col Long Beach, BA, 62; SDak Sch Mines & Technol, MS, 64; Univ Kans, PhD(zool), 68. *Prof Exp:* Instr zool, Calif State Col Long Beach, summer, 64; NSF fel paleont, Univ Calif, Berkeley, 68-69; asst prof zool, San Diego State Univ, 69-71, assoc prof, 71-74, prof, 74-75; assoc prof, 76-78, PROF GEOL, UNIV WYO, 78-, CUR, GEOL MUS, 76- *Concurrent Pos:* Prog dir, syst biol prog, NSF, 77-78; co-ed, Contrib to Geol, 76- *Mem:* Geol Soc Am; Paleont Soc; Soc Vert Paleont; Am Soc Mammal; Am Soc Zoologists. *Res:* Paleogeography; Mesozoic and early Cenozoic mammalian paleontology, comparative anatomy and evolution of mammalian reproduction. *Mailing Add:* Dept Geol & Geophys Univ Wyo Laramie WY 82071

LILLEHEI, RICHARD CARLTON, surgery, deceased

LILLEHOJ, EIVIND B, plant physiology, biochemistry, see previous edition

LILLELAND, OMUND, b Stavanger, Norway, Mar 12, 99; US citizen; m 34; c 2. POMOLOGY. *Educ:* Univ Calif, BS, 21, PhD, 34. *Prof Exp:* Jr pomologist, 26-30, from asst to assoc pomologist, 31-46, pomologist, 46-66, EMER POMOLOGIST, UNIV CALIF, DAVIS, 67-; CONSULT, 67- *Res:* Growth of fruits; thinning of deciduous tree fruits; phosphate and potash nutrition of fruit trees. *Mailing Add:* 40 College Park Davis CA 95616

LILLELEHT, L(EMBIT) U(NO), b Parnu, Estonia, Mar 9, 30; US citizen; m 60; c 2. FLUIDS, THERMAL PHYSICS. *Educ:* Univ Del, BChE, 53; Princeton Univ, MSE, 55; Univ Ill, PhD(chem eng), 62. *Prof Exp:* Engr process develop & res, E I du Pont de Nemours & Co, Inc, 54-57; from asst prof to assoc prof chem eng, Univ Alta, 60-66; ASSOC PROF CHEM ENG, UNIV VA, 66- *Concurrent Pos:* Partner, Assoc Environ Consults, 72-; vis assoc prof, Solar Energy Res Inst, 78-79; lectr solar energy, US Int Comn Agency, 78-79. *Mem:* Am Inst Chem Engrs; Am Chem Soc; Int Solar Energy Soc; Sigma Xi. *Res:* Multiphase flows; air pollution control; polymer rheology; heat transfer; utilization of solar energy. *Mailing Add:* Dept of Chem Eng Thornton Hall Univ of Va Charlottesville VA 22901

LILLER, MARTHA HAZEN, b Cambridge, Mass, July 15, 31; m 59; c 2. ASTRONOMY. *Educ:* Mt Holyoke Col, AB, 53; Univ Mich, MA, 55, PhD(astron), 58. *Prof Exp:* Instr astron, Mt Holyoke Col, 57-59; lectr & res assoc, Univ Mich, 59-60; res fel, 57-59, res fel, 60-69, CUR ASTRON PHOTOGS, COL OBSERV, HARVARD UNIV, 69- *Concurrent Pos:* Lectr, Wellesley Col, 61-63 & 67-68; adj assoc prof, Boston Univ, 79. *Mem:* Am Astron Soc; Int Astron Union. *Res:* Photometry; globular clusters; variable stars. *Mailing Add:* Harvard Col Observ 60 Garden St Harvard Univ Cambridge MA 02138

LILLER, WILLIAM, b Philadelphia, Pa, Apr 1, 27; m 59; c 3. ASTRONOMY. *Educ:* Harvard Univ, AB, 49; Univ Mich, AM, 50, PhD(astron), 53. *Prof Exp:* Mem meteor exped, Harvard Univ, 47-48, supt, 52-53; asst, McMath-Hulbert Observ, Univ Mich, 52, from instr astron to assoc prof astron, 53-60; chmn dept astron, 60-66, prof, 60-70, ROBERT WHEELER WILLSON PROF APPL ASTRON, HARVARD UNIV, 70- *Concurrent Pos:* Guggenheim fel, 64-65; master, Adams House, Harvard Univ, 68-73, head tutor, Astron Dept, 77-80; vis comnr, Bartol Found, 68-, chmn, 76-79; sr res fel, Isaac Newton Inst, Santiago, Chile, 81- *Mem:* Am Astron Soc; fel Royal Astron Soc; fel AAAS; Am Acad Arts & Sci. *Res:* Photoelectric photometry of planetary nebulae and hot stars; investigation of x-ray sources; spectrophotometry; globular clusters. *Mailing Add:* Harvard Col Observ 60 Garden St Cambridge MA 02138

LILLEVIK, HANS ANDREAS, b Sherman, SDak, Feb 4, 16; m 46; c 4. BIOCHEMISTRY. *Educ:* St Olaf Col, BA, 38; Univ Minn, MS, 40, PhD(biochem), 46. *Prof Exp:* Instr biochem, Univ Minn, 42-44; res chemist, Minn Mining & Mfg Co, 44-45; from instr to assoc prof chem & biochem, 46-70, PROF BIOCHEM, MICH STATE UNIV, 70- *Concurrent Pos:* Am Scand Found fel, Carlsberg Lab, Denmark, 47-48. *Mem:* AAAS; Am Chem Soc; Am Soc Biol Chemists; Am Dairy Sci Asn. *Res:* Chemical properties and biological function of proteins and enzymes. *Mailing Add:* Dept of Biochem Mich State Univ East Lansing MI 48824

LILLEY, ARTHUR EDWARD, b Mobile, Ala, May 29, 28. ASTRONOMY. *Educ:* Univ Ala, BS, 50, MS, 51; Harvard Univ, PhD(radio astron), 54. *Prof Exp:* Physicist, Naval Res Lab, 54-57; asst prof radio astron, Yale Univ, 57-59; assoc prof, 59-63, PROF RADIO ASTRON, HARVARD UNIV, 63-; ASTRONOMER-IN-CHARGE, SMITHSONIAN ASTROPHYS OBSERV, 65-, ASSOC DIR, HARVARD-SMITHSONIAN CTR ASTROPHYS, 77- *Concurrent Pos:* Res Corp grant, 57-59; Sloan res fel, 58-60. *Honors & Awards:* Bok Prize, Harvard Univ, 58. *Mem:* AAAS; Int Union Radio Sci; Int Astron Union; Am Astron Soc; Am Phys Soc. *Res:* Spectral line and satellite radio astronomy; radio astronomical navigation techniques. *Mailing Add:* Harvard Univ Ctr for Astrophys 60 Garden St Cambridge MA 02138

LILLEY, DAVID GRANTHAM, b Shipley, Eng. COMBUSTION, AERODYNAMICS. *Educ:* Sheffield Univ, Eng, BSc, 66, MSc, 67, PhD(chem eng), 70. *Prof Exp:* Lectr math, Sheffield Polytech, Eng, 70-73; sr res assoc, Cranfield Inst Technol, Eng, 73-75; vis assoc prof combustion, Univ Ariz, 75-76; assoc prof mech eng, Concordia Univ, Montreal, 76-78; ASSOC PROF MECH ENG, OKLA STATE UNIV, 78- *Mem:* Assoc fel Am Inst Aeronaut & Astronaut; Am Soc Mech Engrs; Inst Fuel; assoc fel Inst Math & Applns. *Res:* Theoretical combustion aerodynamics; computational fluid dynamics; swirling flows; combustor design; numerical methods; finite difference methods; turbulent reacting flows; heat transfer. *Mailing Add:* Sch Mech & Aerospace Eng Okla State Univ Stillwater OK 74074

LILLEY, JOHN RICHARD, b Fall River, Mass, Apr 2, 34; m 66; c 4. RADIATION FLOW, SHOCK PHYSICS. *Educ:* Univ Calif, Berkeley, AB, 56; Univ Idaho, MSc, 62. *Prof Exp:* Physicist, Gen Elec Co, Wash, 56-62; sr scientist, Western Div, McDonnell Douglas Astronaut Co, 62-72; STAFF MEM, LOS ALAMOS NAT LAB, 72- *Concurrent Pos:* Lectr, Radiol Physics Fel Prog, AEC, 61; collabr, Comm Atomic Energy, Bruyeres-le-Chatel, France, 79-80. *Res:* Radiation shielding; reactor physics; statistics; nonlinear optimization; experimental data analysis; thermal analysis; nuclear weapons effects; nuclear weapons design theory. *Mailing Add:* Los Alamos Nat Lab Univ of Calif PO Box 1663 Los Alamos NM 87545

LILLICH, THOMAS TYLER, b Cincinnati, Ohio, Sept 8, 43; m 65; c 2. MICROBIOLOGY, CELL BIOLOGY. *Educ:* Miami Univ, AB, 65; NC State Univ, MS, 68, PhD(microbiol), 70. *Prof Exp:* Asst prof, 72-75, mem microbiol grad fac, Sch Biol Sci, 74-77, ASSOC PROF ORAL BIOL, COL DENT, UNIV KY, 75-, ASST PROF CELL BIOL, COL MED, 73-, ASSOC MEM MICROBIOL GRAD FAC, SCH BIOL SCI, 77- *Concurrent Pos:* NIH res fel, Univ Ky, 70-72, & Agr Res Serv contractee, 73-76. *Mem:* Am Soc Microbiol; Am Asn Dent Schs (secy microbiol sect, 74-75, chmn-elect, 75-76); Int Asn Dent Res. *Res:* Effects of tobacco smoke components on microbial electron transport structure and function. *Mailing Add:* Dept of Oral Biol Col of Dent Univ of Ky Lexington KY 40506

LILLIE, CHARLES FREDERICK, b Indianola, Iowa, Feb 20, 36; wid; c 3. AERONAUTICAL ENGINEERING, ASTRONAUTICAL ENGINEERING. *Educ:* Iowa State Univ, BS, 57; Univ Wis, Madison, PhD(astrophys), 68. *Prof Exp:* Instr eng, NASA Flight Res Ctr, Edwards, Calif, 60-62; teaching asst, Dept Astron, Univ Wis, 62-64, res asst, Washburn Observ, 64-68, proj assoc, Space Astrophys Lab, 68-70; from asst prof to assoc prof physics & astrophys, Univ Colo, 70-77, assoc prof astrogeophys, Attendant Rank & Lab Atmospheric & Space Physics, 77-79; SYSTS ENGR, SPACE SYSTS DIV, TRW DEFENSE & SPACE SYSTS GROUP, REDONDO BEACH, CALIF, 79- *Concurrent Pos:* Prin investr, Voyager Photopolarimeter Exp, 72-79; co-investr, Apollo 17 Ultraviolet Spectrometer Exp, 72-74; team mem, Large Space Telescope Inst Definition Team High Resol Spectrograph, 73-75. *Mem:* Am Astron Soc; AAAS; Soc Photo-Optical Instrumentation Engrs; Int Astron Union; Am Inst Aeronaut & Astronaut. *Res:* Surface brightness of the night sky, zodiacal light, diffuse galactic light, interstellar radiation density, extragalactic light; cometary physics, ultraviolet spectroscopy of stars and nebulae; spacecraft design, RF environment, contamination. *Mailing Add:* TRW Defense & Space Systs Group One Space Park Redondo Beach CA 90278

LILLIE, JOHN HOWARD, b Oak Park, Ill, Dec 16, 40; m 63; c 2. ANATOMY, DENTISTRY. *Educ:* Univ Mich, DDS, 66, PhD(anat), 72. *Prof Exp:* ASST PROF ANAT, SCH MED & ASSOC PROF, SCH DENT, UNIV MICH, ANN ARBOR, 72-, STAFF MEM, DENT RES INST, 72- *Mem:* Am Soc Cell Biol; Am Asn Anat. *Res:* Cellular control mechanisms in endocrine secretion and epithelia-connective tissue interactions; features of synthesis and control in the production of basal lamina constituents. *Mailing Add:* Dept of Anat Med Sci II Bldg Univ of Mich Ann Arbor MI 48109

LILLIE, RALPH DOUGALL, pathology, histochemistry, deceased

LILLIE, ROBERT JONES, b Rochester, Minn, Apr 15, 21; m 46; c 2. POULTRY NUTRITION. *Educ:* Pa State Col, BS, 44, MS, 46; Univ Md, PhD(poultry nutrit), 49. *Prof Exp:* Asst poultry dept, Univ Md, 45-47; poultry husbandman, Animal & Poultry Husb Res Br, USDA, 47-72, res animal scientist, Nonruminant Animal Nutrit Lab, Nutrit Inst, Sci & Educ Admin Agr Res, 72-78; RETIRED. *Concurrent Pos:* Mem standard diet subcomt, Nat Res Coun, 54. *Honors & Awards:* Award, Am Poultry Sci Asn, 50. *Mem:* Am Poultry Sci Asn; Am Inst Nutrit; Worlds Poultry Cong. *Res:* Vitamins, antibiotics, surfactants, arsenicals, unidentified factors, proteins and amino acids; pesticides; reproductive efficiency; air pollutants affecting poultry; trace minerals in swine. *Mailing Add:* 11212 Emack Rd Beltsville MD 20705

LILLIEFORS, HUBERT W, b Reading, Pa, June 14, 28; m 53, 80; c 2. STATISTICS. *Educ:* George Washington Univ, BA, 52, PhD(statist), 64; Mich State Univ, MA, 53. *Prof Exp:* Mathematician, Diamond Ord Fuze Labs, 53-55; sr scientist opers res, Lockheed Missile Systs Div, 55-56, opers analyst, Opers Eval Group, 56-57; mathematician opers res, Appl Physics Lab, Johns Hopkins Univ, 57-64; instr, 62-64, assoc prof, 64-67, PROF STATIST, GEORGE WASHINGTON UNIV, 67- *Mem:* Am Statist Asn; Inst Math Statist. *Res:* Nonparametric statistics; statistical inference. *Mailing Add:* Dept of Statist George Washington Univ Washington DC 20052

LILLIEN, IRVING, b New York, NY, Feb 2, 29. ORGANIC CHEMISTRY, COMPUTER SCIENCES. *Educ:* Univ Denver, BS, 50; Purdue Univ, MS, 52; Polytech Inst Brooklyn, PhD(org chem), 59. *Prof Exp:* Fel org chem, Wayne State Univ, 59-61; asst prof, Georgetown Univ, 61-62; asst prof, Univ Miami, 62-65, Sch Med, 65-67; assoc prof, Marshall Univ, 67-69; assoc prof org chem, 69-80, PROF CHEM, MIAMI-DADE COMMUNITY COL, 80- *Concurrent Pos:* Air Force Off Sci & Res grant, 63-65. *Mem:* AAAS; Am Chem Soc; Royal Soc Chem. *Res:* Physical-organic chemistry; mechanisms of organic reactions; chemistry and conformation of small and medium size rings; science education and administration. *Mailing Add:* Dept Chem Miami-Dade Community Col 11011 SW 104 St Miami FL 33176

LILLINGTON, GLEN ALAN, b Winnipeg, Can, Oct 20, 26; m 57; c 3. PULMONARY MEDICINE, CONTINUING MEDICAL EDUCATION. *Educ:* Univ Manitoba, BSc, 46, MD, 51; Univ Minn, MS, 57; FRCP, 59. *Prof Exp:* Asst staff med, Mayo Clin & Found, 57-58; lectr, Univ Manitoba Fac Med, 58-60; asst clin prof, Sch Med, Stanford Univ, 60-73; PROF MED, SCH MED, UNIV CALIF, DAVIS, 73- *Concurrent Pos:* Res assoc, Palo Alto Med Res Found, 65-73; consult, Rand Corp, Santa Monica, 69-70; med dir respiratory therapy, Sch Respiratory Therapy, Foothill Col, 72-73; travelling fel, Webb-Waring Inst, Denver, 73-74; actg chmn, Dept Med, Med Sch, Univ Calif, Davis, 79-80, chief staff, 79-80, dir residency med, Med Ctr, 79-80, prof med, 75-81. *Res:* Experimental emphysema; pulmonary mechanics; differential diagnosis of pulmonary diseases based on voentgenographic patterns. *Mailing Add:* Med Ctr Univ Calif 4301 X St Sacramento CA 95817

LILLWITZ, LAWRENCE DALE, b Hinsdale, Ill, June 1, 44; m 68; c 5. INDUSTRIAL ORGANIC CHEMISTRY, INDUSTRIAL PROCESS CHEMISTRY. *Educ:* Ill Benedictine Col, BS, 66; Univ Notre Dame, PhD(org chem), 70. *Prof Exp:* group leader, Chem Div, Quaker Oats Co, 70-77; res chemist, 77-79, staff res chemist, 79-81, SR RES CHEMIST, AMOCO CHEM CO, 81- *Mem:* Am Chem Soc. *Res:* Monomer synthesis; organic reaction mechanisms; homogeneous and heterogeneous catalysis. *Mailing Add:* Amoco Res Ctr PO Box 400 Naperville IL 60540

LILLY, ARNYS CLIFTON, JR, b Beckley, WVa, June 3, 34; m 56; c 3. PHYSICS. *Educ:* Va Polytech Inst, BS, 57; Carnegie Inst Technol, MS, 63. *Prof Exp:* Res physicist, Gulf Res & Develop Co, Pa, 57-65; res physicist, 65-71, sr scientist, Physics Div, 71-74, ASSOC PRIN SCIENTIST, PHILIP MORRIS RES CTR, 74- *Mem:* Am Phys Soc. *Res:* Ion & electron optics; dielectric theory and experiment; electrostatics and organic conduction; space charge in insulators; thermal physics; combustion; laser processing; fluid mechanics. *Mailing Add:* Physics Div Philip Morris Res Ctr PO Box 26583 Richmond VA 23261

LILLY, DAVID J, b Washington, DC, Sept 21, 31; m 56; c 4. AUDIOLOGY. *Educ:* Univ Redlands, BA, 54, MA, 57; Univ Pittsburgh, PhD(audiol), 61. *Prof Exp:* Res assoc, Cent Inst Deaf, St Louis, Mo, 61-64; prof audiol, Univ Iowa, 64-80; PROF OTOLARYNGOL & MAXILLOFACIAL SURG, SPEECH PATH & AUDIOL, UNIV MICH, 80- *Concurrent Pos:* NIH res fel, 61, Nat Inst Neurol Dis & Blindness trainee, 62-63; consult hearing aid res & procurement prog, Vet Admin, 66- *Mem:* Acoust Soc Am; Am Speech & Hearing Asn; Audio Eng Soc. *Res:* Experimental audiology, especially on measurements of acoustic impedance at the tympanic membrane of normal and pathologic ears; speech audiometry; masking; auditory adaptation; bone conduction; audiometric standards and calibration. *Mailing Add:* Dept Otolaryngology Univ Mich Hosp Ann Arbor MI 48109

LILLY, DOUGLAS KEITH, b San Francisco, Calif, June 16, 29; m 54; c 3. MESOSCALE DYNAMICS. *Educ:* Stanford Univ, BS, 50; Fla State Univ, MS, 54, PhD(meteorol), 59. *Prof Exp:* res meteorologist, US Weather Bur, 58-65; prog scientist, 65-73, SR SCIENTIST, NAT CTR ATMOSPHERIC RES, 73- *Honors & Awards:* 2nd Half Century Award, Am Meteorol Soc, 72. *Mem:* Fel Am Meteorol Soc. *Res:* Atmospheric convection, turbulence and gravity waves; numerical simulation of meteorological flows. *Mailing Add:* Nat Ctr for Atmospheric Res PO Box 3000 Boulder CO 80307

LILLY, FRANK, b Charleston, WVa, Aug 28, 30. GENETICS, ONCOLOGY. *Educ:* WVa Univ, BS, 51; Univ Paris, PhD(org chem), 59; Cornell UNIV, PhD(biol, genetics), 65. *Prof Exp:* Res fel, 65-67, from asst prof to assoc prof, 67-74, PROF IMMUNOGENETICS & ONCOGENETICS, ALBERT EINSTEIN COL MED, 74- *Concurrent Pos:* New York City Health Res Coun career scientist award, Albert Einstein Col Med, 67-72, chmn, Dept of Genetics, 76-; mem, Breast Cancer-Virus Working Group, Nat Cancer Inst, 72-79; mem bd dirs, Leukemia Soc Am, 73- 78; mem, Sci Adv Coun, Cancer Res Inst, Inc, 75- *Mem:* AAAS; NY Acad Sci; Genetics Soc Am; Am Asn Immunologists; Am Asn Cancer Res. *Res:* Oncogenetics, study of genes which influence susceptibility or resistance to oncogenic agents in mice; immunogenetics. *Mailing Add:* Dept of Genetics Albert Einstein Col of Med Bronx NY 10461

LILLY, PERCY LANE, b Spanishburg, WVa, July 14, 27; m 51; c 4. PLANT TAXONOMY. *Educ:* Concord Col, BS, 50; Univ WVa, MS, 51; Pa State Univ, PhD, 57. *Prof Exp:* Instr biol, Salem Col, WVa, 51-53; from asst to assoc prof, 56-64, PROF BIOL, HEIDELBERG COL, 64-, CHMN DEPT, 65- *Concurrent Pos:* Spec field staff mem, Rockefeller Found, Colombia, 68-69. *Mem:* AAAS; Bot Soc Am. *Res:* Plant genetics and microbiology; nitrogen fixation in Azotobacter. *Mailing Add:* Dept Biol Heidelberg Col Tiffin OH 44883

LILLYA, CLIFFORD PETER, b Chicago, Ill, May 23, 37; m 62; c 2. ORGANIC CHEMISTRY. *Educ:* Kalamazoo Col, AB, 59; Harvard Univ, PhD(chem), 64. *Prof Exp:* Staff assoc, 63-64, from asst prof to assoc prof, 64-73, PROF CHEM, UNIV MASS, AMHERST, 73- *Concurrent Pos:* Alfred P Sloan Found fel, 69-71. *Mem:* Am Chem Soc. *Res:* Photochemistry and chemistry of organotransition metal compounds. *Mailing Add:* Dept of Chem Univ of Mass Amherst MA 01003

LILOIA, G(ERALD) J(OSEPH), chemical engineering, see previous edition

LILYQUIST, MARVIN RUSSELL, b Barnum, Minn, Oct 2, 25; m 47; c 3. ORGANIC CHEMISTRY. *Educ:* Manchester Col, BA, 48; Univ Fla, MS, 50, PhD(org chem), 55. *Prof Exp:* Chemist, Fla State Rd Dept, 50-51; res assoc org fluorine chem, Univ Fla, 51-55; res chemist, Chemstrand Corp, 55-61, group leader, Chemstrand Res Ctr, 61-74, SR RES SPECIALIST MKT, MONSANTO TEXTILES CO, 74- *Mem:* Am Chem Soc; Fiber Soc. *Res:* Synthetic polymers; elastomers; fibers; characterization methods; fiber technology; organic synthesis; fluorine compounds; monomers; heterocyclics; non-woven fabric technology. *Mailing Add:* Monsanto Triangle Pk Develop Ctr PO Box 12274 Research Triangle Park NC 27709

LIM, DAVID J, b Seoul, Korea, Nov 27, 35; US citizen; m 66; c 2. OTOLARYNGOLOGY, ELECTRON MICROSCOPY. *Educ:* Yonsei Univ, Korea, AB, 55, MD, 60. *Prof Exp:* Intern, Nat Med Ctr, Seoul, Korea, 60-61, resident otolaryngol, 61-64; res assoc, 66-67, from asst prof to assoc prof, 67-76, PROF OTOLARYNGOL, COL MED, OHIO STATE UNIV, 76- & PROF ANAT, 77- *Concurrent Pos:* Spec fel otol res, Mass Eye & Ear Infirmary & Harvard Med Sch, 65-66; dir, Otol Res Labs, Ohio State Univ, 67-; mem task force, Am Acad Ophthal & Otolaryngol & Am Bd Otolaryngol, 69-72; consult comt res otolaryngol, Am Acad Ophthal & Otolaryngol, 77-; mem ad hoc adv comt, Commun Disorders Prog, Nat Inst Neurol & Commun Disorders & Stroke, 76-79; mem sci rev comt, Deafness Res Found, 77-80; mem commun sci study sect, NIH, 79; mem, Nat Adv Neurol & Commun Disorders & Stroke Coun, NIH, 79-83; adv-at-large, Comt Hearing, Bioacoust & Biomech, Nat Res Coun, 80-; mem bd dir, Deafness Res Found, 80-; prin investr, various grants & contracts, 69- *Mem:* AAAS; Electron Micros Soc Am; Am Otol Soc; Asn Res Otolaryngol (secy-treas, 73-75, pres, 76-77); Barany Soc. *Res:* Investigation of the ear as to the normal function and disorders of hearing and balance with the use of light and electron microscopy; immunocytochemistry; immunochemistry and microbiology. *Mailing Add:* Otol Res Labs Dept Otolaryngol Ohio State Univ Col of Med Columbus OH 43210

LIM, EDWARD C, b Seoul, Korea, Nov 17, 32; nat US; m 58; c 2. PHYSICAL CHEMISTRY. *Educ:* St Procopius Col, BS, 54; Okla State Univ, MS, 57, PhD(chem), 59. *Prof Exp:* Instr phys chem, Loyola Univ, Ill, 58-60, from asst prof to prof, 60-68; PROF CHEM, WAYNE STATE UNIV, 68- *Mem:* Am Phys Soc; Am Chem Soc. *Res:* Molecular electronic spectrosocpy; solid state photochemistry. *Mailing Add:* Dept of Chem Wayne State Univ Detroit MI 48202

LIM, H(ENRY) C(HOL), b Seoul, Korea, Oct 24, 35; US citizen; m 59; c 3. CHEMICAL & BIOCHEMICAL ENGINEERING. *Educ:* Okla State Univ, BS, 57; Univ Mich, MSE, 59; Northwestern Univ, PhD(chem eng), 67. *Prof Exp:* Process develop engr, Pfizer, Inc, 59-63; from asst prof to assoc prof chem eng, 66-74, PROF CHEM ENG, PURDUE UNIV, 74- *Concurrent Pos:* Vis scholar, Calif Inst Technol, 77. *Mem:* Am Inst Chem Engrs; Am Soc Microbiol; Am Chem Soc; Inst Food Technologists. *Res:* Modelling, optimization and control of chemical and biochemical processes; microbial and enzyme reactor engineering; microbial growth kinetics. *Mailing Add:* Sch of Chem Eng Purdue Univ West Lafayette IN 47907

LIM, HENRY S, b Pung Chun, Korea, Sept 28, 29; US citizen; m 56; c 2. ANESTHESIOLOGY. *Educ:* Yonsei Univ, Korea, MD, 53; Am Bd Anesthesiol, dipl, 65. *Prof Exp:* From instr to asst prof anesthesiol, Med Sch, Johns Hopkins Univ, 63-69, asst prof gynec & obstet, 65-74, assoc prof anesthesiol, gynec & obstet, 69-76; ASSOC PROF ANESTHESIOL, GYNEC & OBSTET, PRITZKER SCH MED, UNIV CHICAGO, 77- *Mem:* Fel Am Col Anesthesiol; Am Soc Anesthesiol; Int Anesthesia Res Soc; Soc Obstet Anesthesiol & Perinatol; Am Soc Regional Anethesiol. *Res:* Obstetric anesthesia. *Mailing Add:* Box 443 Univ of Chicago Hosp Chicago IL 60637

LIM, JAMES KHAI-JIN, b Batavia, Java, March 11, 33; US citizen; m 62; c 3. PHARMACEUTICS. *Educ:* Univ Malaya, Singapore, BPharm, 58; Univ NC, MS, 62, PhD(pharmaceut), 65. *Prof Exp:* asst prof, 66-70, assoc prof, 70-76, PROF PHARMACEUT, SCH PHARM, WVA UNIV, 76- *Concurrent Pos:* Res fel, Biochem Dept, Univ NC, 65-66; vis scientist, Lipid Dept, Med Div, Oak Ridge, 65-66; dent res, Inst Advan Educ Dent Res, 71. *Mem:* Am Pharmaceut Asn; Acad Pharmaceut Sci; Am Asn Col Pharm; Am Asn Dent Res; Malayan Pharmaceut Asn. *Res:* Pharmaceutical formulations for solubilization and stability of drugs, including aspirin, phenobarbital and nitroglycerin; caries research involving in vitro pellicle and streptococci plaque; blood cholesterol and triglyceride levels with fiber diets. *Mailing Add:* Sch Pharm Med Ctr WVa Univ Morgantown WV 26506

LIM, JOHNG KI, b Seoul, Korea, Feb 12, 30. GENETICS. *Educ:* Univ Minn, BS, 58, MS, 60, PhD(genetics), 64. *Prof Exp:* From asst prof to assoc prof, 63-69, PROF BIOL, UNIV WIS-EAU CLAIRE, 69- *Concurrent Pos:* Vis prof, Dept of Med Genetics, Univ Wis-Madison, 77-78. *Mem:* AAAS; Genetics Soc Am; Environ Mutagen Soc. *Res:* Chemical mutagenesis; cytogenetics. *Mailing Add:* Dept of Biol Univ of Wis Eau Claire WI 54701

LIM, KIOK-PUAN, b Rengam, Malaysia, Oct 6, 47; Can citizen; m 74; c 1. BIOLOGICAL CONTROL, INSECT PATHOGENS. *Educ:* Nat Taiwan Univ, BSc, 71; McGill Univ, MSc, 74, PhD(entom), 79. *Prof Exp:* Vector control officer, Vector Control & Res Dept, Ministry Environ, Singapore, 74-75; lab demonstr, Dept Entom, McGill Univ, MacDonald Campus, 75-79; vis fel, Res Inst, Agr Can, London, Ont, 80; RES SCIENTIST, NFLD FOREST RES CTR, CAN FORESTRY SERV, 80- *Concurrent Pos:* Res asst, Dept Entom, McGill Univ, MacDonald Campus, 75-79. *Mem:* Entom Soc Can; Entom Soc Am; Int Orgn Biol Control; Soc Invert Path; Soc Nematologists. *Res:* Biological control of insect pests; biology of parasitic hymenoptera; insect diseases; entomogenous nematodes. *Mailing Add:* Nfld Forest Res Ctr Can Forestry Serv PO Box 6028 St John's NF A1C 5X8 Can

LIM, LOUISE CHIN, b Honolulu, Hawaii, Apr 9, 22; m 53. MATHEMATICS. *Educ:* Univ Calif, AB, 43, MA, 44, PhD(math), 48. *Prof Exp:* Asst math, Univ Calif, 43-48; asst prof, 48-70, ASSOC PROF MATH, UNIV ARIZ, 70- *Concurrent Pos:* Res assoc, Univ Calif, 53, Ford Found fel, 53-54; res assoc, Radcliffe Col, 53-54. *Mem:* Am Math Soc; Math Asn Am; Asn Symbolic Logic. *Res:* Relation, projective and cylindric algebras. *Mailing Add:* Dept of Math Univ of Ariz Tucson AZ 85721

LIM, RAMON (KHE SIONG), b Cebu, Philippines, Feb 5, 33; m 61; c 3. NEUROCHEMISTRY. *Educ:* Univ Santo Tomas, Manila, MD, 58; Univ Pa, PhD(biochem), 66. *Prof Exp:* Intern, Long Island Col Hosp, NY, 59-60; USPHS trainee & fel, Univ Pa, 62-66; asst res biochemist, Ment Health Res Inst, Univ Mich, 66-69; asst prof neurosurg & biochem, Brain Res Inst & Sect Of Neurosurg, Univ Chicago, 69-76, assoc prof neurochem, 76-81; ASSOC PROF NEUROLOGY & NEUROCHEM, DEPT NEUROLOGY, UNIV IOWA, 81- *Concurrent Pos:* NIMH spec res fel, 68-69. *Mem:* AAAS; Am Soc Neurochem; Int Soc Neurochem; Am Soc Biol Chem; Soc Neurosci. *Res:* Brain proteins and peptides; tissue culture; growth and maturation of brain cells. *Mailing Add:* Dept Neurology Univ Iowa Iowa City IA 52242

LIM, SUNG MAN, US citizen; m 68; c 2. PLANT PATHOLOGY. *Educ:* Seoul Univ, Korea, MS, 59; Miss State Univ, MS, 63; Mich State Univ, PhD(crop sci & plant path), 66. *Prof Exp:* Agronomist, Crop Exp Sta, Suwon, Korea, 60-61; res asst, Miss State Univ, 61-63 & Mich State Univ, 63-66; res assoc, 67-71, asst prof, 71-77, ASSOC PROF PLANT PATH, UNIV ILL, URBANA, 77-, PLANT PATHOLOGIST, USDA, 77- *Concurrent Pos:* Assoc ed, Plant Dis; mem, Soybean Germplasm Adv Comt, USDA. *Mem:* Am Phytopath Soc; Am Genetic Asn; Am Soc Agron; Crop Sci Soc Am. *Res:* Epidemics of plant diseases; genetics of host-pathogen interactions. *Mailing Add:* Dept of Plant Path Univ of Ill Urbana IL 61801

LIM, TECK-KAH, b Malacca, Malaysia, Dec 1, 42; m 66; c 2. THEORETICAL NUCLEAR PHYSICS. *Educ:* Univ Adelaide, BS, 64, PhD(nuclear physics), 68. *Prof Exp:* Lectr math, Univ Malaya, 68; res assoc nuclear physics, Fla State Univ, 68-70; asst prof physics, 70-75, ASSOC PROF PHYSICS & ATMOSPHERIC SCI, DREXEL UNIV, 75- *Mem:* Am Phys Soc; Sigma Xi. *Res:* Few-nucleon problem; direct reaction theory; chemical physics; molecular physics. *Mailing Add:* Dept of Physics Drexel Univ Philadelphia PA 19104

LIM, TEONG CHENG, b Penang, Malaysia, Oct 4, 39; m 66. APPLIED PHYSICS, ELECTRICAL ENGINEERING. *Educ:* Nat Taiwan Univ, BSc, 63; Ottawa Univ, MSc, 64; McGill Univ, PhD(elec eng), 68. *Prof Exp:* Elec engr, Malayan Racing Asn, 62-63; res asst elec eng, Ottawa Univ, 63-64; electronic engr, Can Marconi Co, Montreal, 65; res asst elec eng, McGill Univ, 65-68; Nat Res Coun Can fel, Imp Col, Univ London, 68-70; mem tech staff, Sci Ctr, NAm Rockwell Corp, 70-74, group leader, 75-80, MGR, SCI CTR, ROCKWELL INT, 80- *Mem:* Sr mem Inst Elec & Electronics Engrs; Brit Inst Elec Engrs. *Res:* Physics of ferroelectric and display materials and devices. *Mailing Add:* Rockwell Int PO Box 1085 Thousand Oaks CA 91360

LIM, THOMAS PYUNG KEE, b Seoul, Korea, June 1, 24; nat US; m 55; c 3. THORACIC DISEASES. *Educ:* Severance Union Med Col, MD, 48; Northwestern Univ, Ill, MS, 51, PhD(physiol), 53. *Prof Exp:* Res assoc physiol, Sch Med, Stanford Univ, 53-54 & Northwestern Univ, Ill, 54-56; mem staff, Lovelace Found, 56-61; dir cardiopulmonary lab, Tucson Med Ctr, Ariz, 61-67; mem staff, Dept Med, Syracuse Univ Hosp, 67-68; assoc prof med & physiol, Med Ctr, Univ Nebr, Omaha, 68-69; DIR CARDIOPULMONARY LAB, IMMANUEL MED CTR, 70- *Mem:* AAAS; Am Physiol Soc; Am Heart Asn; Am Thoracic Soc; Am Col Chest Physicians. *Res:* Pulmonary diseases; clinical cardiopulmonary physiology. *Mailing Add:* Immanuel Med Ctr 6901 N 72nd St Omaha NE 68122

LIM, YONG WOON (PETER), b Seoul, Korea, Oct 25, 35; m 68; c 3. SURFACE CHEMISTRY, COLLOID CHEMISTRY. *Educ:* Ohio Wesleyan Univ, AB, 57; Univ Dayton, MS, 63; State Univ NY Col Forestry, Syracuse, PhD(polymer chem), 69. *Prof Exp:* Res chemist, Paper Res Dept, NCR Corp, 69-71, group leader anal chem, Appleton Papers Div, 71-74; res assoc chem, Tissue & Towel Res & Develop, Am Consumer Prod, Am Can Co, Neenah, Wis, 74-77; PROJ LEADER, CROWN ZELLERBACH CENT RES, CAMAS, WASH, 77- *Mem:* Am Chem Soc; Tech Asn Pulp & Paper Indust. *Res:* Application of surface and colloid chemistry to pulp and paper research and development; morphology of cellulose and synthetic fibers; functional coatings; microencapsulation. *Mailing Add:* 5220 NE 51st St Vancouver WA 98661

LIMARZI, LOUIS ROBERT, b Chicago, Ill, Nov 27, 03; m; c 2. MEDICINE. *Educ:* Univ Ill, BS, 28, MD, 30, MS, 35. *Prof Exp:* Intern, Ill Res & Educ Hosp, Chicago, 30-31; clin asst med, 32-35, clin assoc, 35-40, from asst prof to assoc prof, 40-55, PROF MED & DIR HEMAT SECT, UNIV ILL COL MED, 55- *Concurrent Pos:* Resident, Ill Res & Educ Hosp, Chicago, 32-35, attend physician, 35-; investr, Midwest Coop Chemother Group, USPHS; civilian med consult, Hines Vet Admin Hosp, Ill & Surgeon Gen Off, 40-45, USPHS, 40- & Fed Civil Defense Admin, 50-; mem adv bd, Hemat Res Found, 40-; mem comt civil defense blood & blood derivatives, Ill Civil Defense Orgn, 50-; attend physician, West Side Vet Admin Hosp, 54-; hemat ed, Abstr Bioanal Tech, 61; consult hematologist, Augusta Hosp, Am Orthop Asn, Chicago. *Mem:* AAAS; fel Am Soc Clin Path; fel AMA; fel Col Am Path; fel Am Col Physicians. *Res:* Leukemia; intermediate metabolism of leukemic leukocytes and effects of anti-leukemic agents; idiopathic throbocytopenic purpura; polycythemia vera. *Mailing Add:* 910 N East Ave Oak Park IL 60302

LIMB, JOHN ORMOND, b Pinjarra, Western Australia. COMMUNICATIONS, ELECTRICAL ENGINEERING. *Educ:* Univ Western Australia, BEE, 63, PhD(elec eng), 67. *Prof Exp:* Engr, res labs, Australian Post Off, 66-67; mem tech staff, 67-71, DEPT HEAD, COMMUN, BELL TEL LABS, 71- *Concurrent Pos:* Ed on commun, Inst Elec & Electronics Engrs. *Honors & Awards:* Leonard G Abraham Award, Inst Elec & Electronics Engrs, 73. *Mem:* Optical Soc Am; fel Inst Elec & Electronics Engrs; Asn Res Vision & Ophthalmol. *Res:* Visual communications; efficient coding of picture signals; human visual perception; local area networks. *Mailing Add:* Telecommun Serv Res Dept Bell Labs Murray Hill NJ 07974

LIMBERT, DAVID EDWIN, b Omaha, Nebr, Oct 21, 42. DYNAMIC SYSTEMS, CONTROL ENGINEERING. *Educ:* Iowa State Univ, BS, 64; Case Inst Technol, MS, 65; Case Western Reserve Univ, PhD(control eng), 69. *Prof Exp:* ASSOC PROF MECH ENG, UNIV NH, 69- *Mem:* Am Soc Mech Engrs; Inst Elec & Electronics Engrs; Forest Prod Res Soc. *Res:* Track-train dynamics and simulation; dynamics of injection mold filling; estimation of states and parameters for nonuniformly sampled data systems; stress development during the drying of wood; finite element analysis. *Mailing Add:* Dept of Mech Eng Kingsbury Hall Univ of NH Durham NH 03824

LIMBERT, DOUGLAS ALAN, b Council Bluffs, Iowa, Feb 6, 48. MECHANICAL ENGINEERING, CONTROL ENGINEERING. *Educ:* Mass Inst Technol, SB & SM, 70, ScD, 77. *Prof Exp:* Instr mech eng, Mass Inst Technol, 74-76; ASST PROF MECH ENG, ARIZ STATE UNIV, 77- *Mem:* Sigma Xi; Am Soc Mech Engrs; Inst Elec & Electronics Engrs. *Res:* Modeling, dynamics and control of physical systems; advanced ground transportation suspensions; magnetic bearings; vibration control; robotics. *Mailing Add:* Dept of Mech Eng Ariz State Univ Tempe AZ 85281

LIMBURG, WILLIAM W, b Buffalo, NY, Nov 9, 35; m 66. ORGANIC POLYMER CHEMISTRY. *Educ:* Univ Buffalo, BA, 59, MA, 62; Univ Toronto, PhD(organosilicon chem), 65. *Prof Exp:* From sr chemist to assoc scientist, 65-66, scientist, 67-73, sr scientist, 73-80, TECH SPECIALIST & PROJ MGR, XEROX CORP, 80- *Mem:* Am Chem Soc; Royal Soc Chem; Soc Photog Scientists & Engrs. *Res:* Synthesis of organometallic compounds; mechanistic and stereochemical studies of molecular rearrangements of carbon-functional silicon-containing compounds; non-silver halide imaging methods; synthesis of organic photoconductive materials; synthesis of novel polysiloxanes. *Mailing Add:* Xerox Corp 800 Phillips Rd Webster NY 14580

LIME, BRUCE JAMES, b Kansas City, Mo, July 31, 21; m 52; c 6. FOOD CHEMISTRY. *Educ:* Kans State Teachers Col Pittsburg, BS, 50; NC State Univ, MS, 68. *Prof Exp:* Sales rep, A J Griner Co, Mo, 50; res fel chem, Tex Citrus Comn, 50-52; chemist, Food Crops Utilization Lab, USDA, 52-62, res leader, 72-80; RETIRED. *Mem:* Am Chem Soc; Inst Food Technol. *Res:* Chemistry of southern grown fruits and vegetables; utilization research of citrus, avocados and all vegetables; sugar crops. *Mailing Add:* 650 Bougainvillea Weslaco TX 78596

LIMERICK, JACK MCKENZIE, SR, b Fredericton, NB, July 16, 10; m 37. CHEMISTRY. *Educ:* Univ NB, BSc, 31, MSc, 34. *Prof Exp:* Res chemist, Fraser Co, 34-37; chief chemist, Bathurst Power & Paper Co, 37-41, supt control dept, 41-44, tech & res dir, Bathurst Paper Co, Ltd, 44-67, assoc dir res & develop, Consol-Bathurst Ltd, 67-71; CONSULT, 72- *Concurrent Pos:* Lectr, Royal Tech Inst, Sweden, 52; fel, Chem Inst Can, 53; fel, Tech Asn, Pulp & Paper Indust, 68; consult, Iran, 72-78, pulp, paper & container indust, Brazil, 73- & US & Can, 80- *Honors & Awards:* Award, Tech Asn Pulp & Paper Indust, 59. *Mem:* Can Soc Chem Eng; Tech Asn Pulp & Paper Indust; Can Pulp & Paper Asn; fel Chem Inst Can; Pulp & Paper Res Inst Can. *Res:* Pulp; paper; containers; author of over 100 publications. *Mailing Add:* 36 E St PH4 Oakville ON L6L 5K2 Can

LIMPEL, LAWRENCE EUGENE, entomology, see previous edition

LIMPERIS, THOMAS, b Detroit, Mich, Feb 19, 31; m; c 5. PHYSICS. *Educ:* Univ Mich, BS, 58, MSEE, 60. *Prof Exp:* Mem res staff, Univ Mich, 58-66, dir info & optical sci group, 66-68; pres, Sensors, Inc, 68-77; dir infrared & optics, Environ Res Inst Mich, 77-80; PRES, AVIATION SYST INC, 80- *Res:* Infrared detectors; infrared spectroscopy; optical properties of materials; author of over 60 technical publications. *Mailing Add:* 1955 Pauline Blvd Ann Arbor MI 48103

LIMPERT, FREDERICK ARTHUR, b Frankfort, NY, Feb 4, 21; m 44. HYDROLOGY. *Educ:* Wash State Univ, BSCE, 43. *Prof Exp:* Civil engr, Columbia Basin Proj, Wash Bur Reclamation, 46-61; HEAD HYDROL SECT & CHIEF HYDROLOGIST, BONNEVILLE POWER ADMIN, 61- *Concurrent Pos:* Mem, Interagency Adv Comt Water Data, 72- & Coord Coun Water Data Acquisition Methods, 74- *Mem:* Fel Am Soc Civil Engrs; Nat Soc Prof Engrs. *Res:* Use of satellite data for determining areal snow cover and cloud classification for areal precipitation. *Mailing Add:* 5590 SW Chestnut Beaverton OR 97005

LIMPERT, RUDOLF, b Neuhaldensleben, Ger, Mar 19, 36; US citizen; m 62; c 6. MECHANICAL ENGINEERING. *Educ:* Wolfenbuettel Univ, Ger, Ing, 58; Brigham Young Univ, BES & MS, 68; Univ Mich, Ann Arbor, PhD(mech eng), 72. *Prof Exp:* Proj engr, Alfred Teves Corp, Ger, 63-65; res asst, Hwy Safety Res Inst, Univ Mich, Ann Arbor, 69-72; safety standards engr, Nat Hwy Traffic Safety Admin, Dept Transp, 72-73; RES PROF, UNIV UTAH, 73- *Mem:* Soc Automotive Engrs. *Res:* Motor vehicle accident reconstruction and cause analysis; product liability research; automotive systems design. *Mailing Add:* 700 Aspen Dr Summit Park UT 84060

LIN, BENJAMIN MING-REN, US citizen. COMPUTER SCIENCES. *Educ:* Taipei Inst Technol, dipl, 61; Univ Wyo, MS, 67; Univ Iowa, PhD(elec eng), 73. *Prof Exp:* Engr, Radio Wave Res Labs, 62-65; design & develop engr, Collins Radio Co, 67-68; engr, Addressograph Multigraph Corp, 68-69; PROF COMPUT SCI, MOORHEAD STATE UNIV, 73- *Concurrent Pos:* Dir, Grad Sch Info Eng, Tamkang Univ, Taiwan, 80-81. *Mem:* Sigma Xi; Asn Comput Mach; Inst Elec & Electronics Engrs; Comput Soc. *Res:* Application of microprocessors in consumer products and data communications; fault-tolerant computing systems design; computer architecture in distributed computing systems. *Mailing Add:* Dept of Comput Sci Moorhead State Univ Moorhead MN 56560

LIN, BOR-LUH, b Fukien, China, Mar 4, 35; m 63. MATHEMATICS. *Educ:* Nat Taiwan Univ, BS, 56; Univ Notre Dame, MS, 60; Northwestern Univ, PhD(math), 63. *Prof Exp:* Asst prof math, 63-67, assoc prof, 67-72, PROF MATH, UNIV IOWA, 72- *Concurrent Pos:* Vis assoc prof, Ohio State Univ, 70-71; vis prof, Univ Calif, Santa Barbara. *Mem:* Am Math Soc. *Res:* Functional analysis, general topology. *Mailing Add:* Dept of Math Univ of Iowa Iowa City IA 52240

LIN, CHANG KWEI, b Taiwan, Sept 11, 41; m 67; c 2. PHYCOLOGY. *Educ:* Chung Shim Univ, BSc, 64; Univ Alta, MSc, 68; Univ Wis-Milwaukee, PhD(bot), 73. *Prof Exp:* Asst cur, Acad Natural Sci, Philadelphia, 72-74; assoc res limnol, Univ Mich, Ann Arbor, 80- *Concurrent Pos:* Scientist, WHO, 77-78. *Mem:* AAAS; Phycol Soc Am; Am Soc Limnol & Oceanog; Soc Int Limnol. *Res:* Physio-ecology of algae in general, with particular interest in nutrient limitation to phytoplankton growth in the Great Lakes. *Mailing Add:* Great Lakes Res Div Univ of Mich Ann Arbor MI 48109

LIN, CHENG-SHAN, b Pingtan, China, Mar 2, 12; m 52. ENTOMOLOGY. *Educ:* Fukien Christian Univ, BS, 37; Ft Hays Kans State Col, MS, 50; Cornell Univ, PhD, 55. *Prof Exp:* Instr biol, Fukien Sci Inst, China, 34-36; prin high sch, 37-45; dir, Fukien Christian Univ, China, 45-46; instr biol, Foochow Col, 46-47; asst, Cornell Univ, 52-55; chmn natural sci div, 56-66, prof, 56-78, EMER PROF BIOL, HUSTON-TILLOTSON COL, 78- *Res:* Insect biology and ecology; immature insects; biology and behavior of solitary digger wasps. *Mailing Add:* 704 Baylor Austin TX 78703

LIN, CHE-SHUNG, b Taipei, Formosa, Oct 20, 33; Can citizen; m 64; c 1. QUANTUM CHEMISTRY. *Educ:* Nat Taiwan Univ, BSc, 56, MSc, 60; Univ Sask, PhD(chem), 65. *Prof Exp:* Fel chem, Univ Alta, 64-66 & Ind Univ, 66-67; asst prof, 67-71, ASSOC PROF CHEM, UNIV WINDSOR, 71- *Concurrent Pos:* Vis prof, Univ Ill, Urbana-Champaign, 76. *Mem:* Am Phys Soc. *Res:* Low energy collisions; mathematical analysis and formalism. *Mailing Add:* Dept of Chem Fac of Arts & Sci Univ of Windsor Windsor ON N9B 3P4 Can

LIN, CHIA CHIAO, b Foochow, China, July 7, 16; m. APPLIED MATHEMATICS. *Educ:* Nat Tsing Hua Univ, China, BSc; Univ Toronto, MA, 41; Calif Inst Technol, PhD(aeronaut), 44. *Prof Exp:* Asst, Tsing Hua Univ, China, 37-39; from asst to res engr, Calif Inst Technol, 43-45; from asst prof appl math to assoc prof appl math, Brown Univ, 45-47; assoc prof math, 47-53, prof, 53-66, INST PROF MATH, MASS INST TECHNOL, 66- *Concurrent Pos:* Guggenheim fels, 54-55, 60. *Mem:* Nat Acad Sci; Am Astron Soc; Soc Indust & Appl Math; Am Math Soc; Am Inst Aeronaut & Astronaut. *Res:* Hydrodynamics; stellar dynamics; astrophysical problems; spiral structure of galaxies; density wave theory developed in great mathematical detail with predictions checked against various astronomical observations. *Mailing Add:* Dept of Math Mass Inst Technol Cambridge MA 02139

LIN, CHII-DONG, b Taiwan. ATOMIC PHYSICS. *Educ:* Nat Taiwan Univ, BS, 69; Univ Chicago, MS, 73, PhD(physics), 74. *Prof Exp:* Fel astrophys, Ctr Astrophys, Harvard Col Observ, 74-76; asst prof, 76-80, ASSOC PROF, KANS STATE UNIV, 80- *Mailing Add:* Dept of Physics Kans State Univ Manhattan KS 66506

LIN, CHIN-CHUNG, b Taipei, Taiwan, Oct 8, 37. BIOCHEMICAL PHARMACOLOGY. *Educ:* Chung Hsing Univ, Taiwan, BS, 60; Tuskegee Inst, MS, 65; Northwestern Univ, PhD(biochem), 69. *Prof Exp:* Sr scientist, 69-75, prin scientist, 75-79, RES FEL, SCHERING CORP, 79- *Concurrent Pos:* Res fel biochem, Med Sch, Northwestern Univ, 69. *Mem:* AAAS; Am Chem Soc; Am Soc Pharmacol & Exp Therapeut; NY Acad Sci. *Res:* Drug metabolism and the mechanism of enzymatic hydroxylation. *Mailing Add:* Schering Corp Dept of Biochem 60 Orange St Bloomfield NJ 07003

LIN, CHING Y, b Taiwan, May 22, 40; Can citizen; m 65; c 2. ANIMAL BREEDING, QUANTITATIVE GENETICS. *Educ:* Nat Chung-Hsing Univ, Taiwan, BS, 63; Iowa State Univ, MS, 71; Ohio State Univ, PhD(dairy sci), 76. *Prof Exp:* Jr specialist agr extension, Taiwan Prov Dept Agr & Forestry, 64-68; res assoc poultry breeding, Dept Animal Sci, Univ Guelph, Can, 76-80; RES SCIENTIST DAIRY CATTLE BREEDING, ANIMAL RES CTR, AGR CAN, 80- *Mem:* Am Soc Animal Sci; Am Dairy Sci Asn; Genetics Soc Can. *Res:* Dairy cattle breeding; quantitative genetics; statistical analysis as applied to animal breeding. *Mailing Add:* Animal Res Ctr Agr Can Ottawa ON K1A 0C6 Can

LIN, CHINLON, b Taiwan, Rep of China, Jan 19, 45; m 69; c 2. QUANTUM ELECTRONICS, OPTICAL COMMUNICATION. *Educ:* Nat Taiwan Univ, BS, 67; Univ Ill, MS, 70; Univ Calif, Berkeley, PhD(elec eng), 74. *Prof Exp:* MEM TECH STAFF, BELL LABS, HOLMDEL, 74- *Mem:* Inst Elec & Electronics Engrs; Optical Soc Am. *Res:* Lasers and quantum electronics; optical fibers and lightwave communications. *Mailing Add:* Bell Labs 4C416 Holmdel NJ 07733

LIN, CHI-WEI, b Hong Kong, May 16, 37; m 65; c 1. CANCER, BIOCHEMISTRY. *Educ:* Nat Taiwan Univ, BS, 61; Univ Wis-Madison, MS, 65, PhD(biochem), 69. *Prof Exp:* Fel cancer res, Sch Med, Tufts Univ, 69-71, res assoc, 71-72, asst prof path, 72-80; MEM STAFF, UROL RES LAB, MASS GEN HOSP, 80- *Mem:* Biochem Soc; AAAS; Histochem Soc; Am Asn Cancer Res; Sigma Xi. *Res:* Biochemical characteristics of cancer, specifically, the studies of tumor-associated enzymes and isozymes, including histaminase, acid phosphatase and alkaline phosphatase; processes of synthesis and distribution of acid hydrolases and the biogenesis of lysosomes. *Mailing Add:* Urol Res Lab Mass Gen Hosp Boston MA 02114

LIN, CHYI-CHYANG, b China, May 21, 33; m; c 1. GENETICS. *Educ:* Nat Taiwan Univ, BS, 60; Univ Man, MSc, 64, PhD(genetics), 68. *Prof Exp:* Cytogeneticist, Winnipeg Children's Hosp, 68-69; from instr to asst prof pediat & path, McMaster Univ, 69-73; assoc prof, 73-80, PROF PEDIAT & MED BIOCHEM, UNIV CALGARY, 80- *Concurrent Pos:* Dir cytogenetics lab, Med Ctr, McMaster Univ, 71-73. *Mem:* Am Genetic Asn; Can Asn Genetics & Cytol; Am Human Genetics Soc. *Res:* Cytogenetic studies on plants and animals; biochemical genetics; somatic cell genetics. *Mailing Add:* Div of Pediat & Med Biochem Univ of Calgary Fac of Med Calgary AB T2N 1N4 Can

LIN, DENIS CHUNG KAM, b Hong Kong, July 7, 44; Can citizen; m 69; c 1. ANALYTICAL CHEMISTRY, MASS SPECTROMETRY. *Educ:* Univ Man, BSc, 68, MSc, 70, PhD(chem), 72. *Prof Exp:* Fel, Univ Montreal, 72-74; staff chemist, Battelle Mem Inst, 74-80; WITH ETC CORP, 80- *Mem:* Am Chem Soc; Am Soc Mass Spectrometry; Int Asn Forensic Toxicologists. *Res:* Identification and quantification of low levels of drugs and their metabolites in biological samples by mass spectrometry and other techniques; nucleic acid and protein sequencing; pyrolytic reactions. *Mailing Add:* ETC Corp 284 Raritan Ctr Pkwy Edison NJ 08817

LIN, DIANE CHANG, b China, Aug 6, 44; US citizen; m 69; c 2. CELL BIOLOGY, CELL MOTILITY. *Educ:* Nat Taiwan Univ, BS, 66; Univ Calif, Los Angeles, PhD(biol), 71. *Prof Exp:* Asst res scientist pharmacol, Univ Calif, San Francisco, 71-74; RES SCIENTIST BIOPHYS, JOHNS HOPKINS UNIV, 74- *Concurrent Pos:* Prin investr, Johns Hopkins Univ, 78- *Mem:* Biophys Soc; Am Soc Cell Biol; Sigma Xi. *Res:* Contractile and structural proteins of the human red blood cell membrane, in relation to their role in cell shape maintenance and aging. *Mailing Add:* Dept Biophys Johns Hopkins Univ Baltimore MD 21218

LIN, DONG LIANG, b Taiwan, China, Mar 5, 47; m 71; c 3. PHYSICS, ELECTRICAL ENGINEERING. *Educ:* Nat Taiwan Univ, BS, 69; Columbia Univ, MS, 72, PhD(physics), 75. *Prof Exp:* Res fel physics, Johns Hopkins Univ, 75-77; staff scientist physics, Sci Appln Inc, 77-80; MEM STAFF, BELL LABS, HOLMDEL, NJ, 80- *Mem:* Am Phys Soc; Nat Soc Prof Engrs. *Res:* Atomic physics; plasma physics; solid state physics. *Mailing Add:* Bell Labs WB 1J 306 Crawford Corner Rd Holmdel NJ 07733

LIN, DUO-LIANG, b Juian, China, May 16, 30; m 63; c 1. PHYSICS. *Educ:* Taiwan Prov Norm Univ, BSc, 56; Tsing Hua Univ, China, MSc, 58; Ohio State Univ, PhD(physics), 61. *Prof Exp:* Res assoc physics, Yale Univ, 61-64; asst prof, 64-67, ASSOC PROF PHYSICS, STATE UNIV NY BUFFALO, 67- *Concurrent Pos:* Sr vis, Oxford Univ, 70-71; vis prof, Nat Taiwan Univ, 71, Tsing Hua Univ, Peking, 78 & Liao Ning Univ, Shen Yang, 81. *Mem:* Am Phys Soc. *Res:* Problems in nuclear physics such as nuclear forces and structure; electronic properties near surfaces in solids; coherent radiation from a system of atoms. *Mailing Add:* Dept Physics State Univ NY Buffalo NY 14260

LIN, EDMUND CHI CHIEN, b Peking, China, Oct 28, 28; nat US. BIOCHEMISTRY. *Educ:* Univ Rochester, AB, 52; Harvard Univ, PhD, 57. *Prof Exp:* Instr biochem, 57-60, assoc, 60-63, from asst prof to assoc prof, 63-69, PROF MICROBIOL & MOLECULAR GENETICS, HARVARD MED SCH, 69- *Concurrent Pos:* Vis prof, Univ Calif, Berkeley, 72; Guggenheim fel, Pasteur Inst Paris, 69; prof chmn dept, Harvard Med Sch, 73-75; Fogarty Sr Int fel, Univ Paris, VI, 77-78; vis prof biol, Univ Konstanz, Ger, 81; hon res prof, Inst Plant Physiol, Academia Sinica, Shanghai, 80- *Mem:* Am Soc Microbiol; Am Soc Biol Chem. *Res:* Bacterial physiology and genetics and biochemical evolution. *Mailing Add:* Microbiol & Molecular Genetics Harvard Med Sch Boston MA 02115

LIN, FU HAI, b Fukien, China, Feb 15, 28; US citizen; m 56; c 5. BACTERIOLOGY, BIOCHEMISTRY. *Educ:* Nat Taiwan Univ, BS, 55; Univ WVa, MS, 59; Rutgers Univ, PhD(bact), 65. *Prof Exp:* Asst, Univ WVa, 58-59; tech asst biochem, Boyce Thompson Inst, 59-61; res asst, Rutgers Univ, 61-65; asst mem biochem, Albert Einstein Med Ctr, 65-69; sr res scientist, 69-70, assoc res scientist, 70-76, RES SCIENTIST, INST BASIC RES MENT RETARDATION, 76-, HEAD LAB VIRAL BIOCHEM, 80- *Mem:* AAAS; Am Soc Microbiol; Sigma Xi. *Res:* Biochemistry and replication of animal ribonucleic acid virus; metabolism of ribonucleic acid and the control mechanisms of its biosynthesis; gene expression of animal RNA viruses of slow infection; biochemistry and function of proteins of slow viruses. *Mailing Add:* Inst Basic Res Ment Retardation 1050 Forest Hill Rd Staten Island NY 10314

LIN, GEORGE HUNG-YIN, b Shantung, China, Mar 9, 38; m 69; c 1. PHYSICAL CHEMISTRY, TOXICOLOGY. *Educ:* Tunghai Univ, Taiwan, BS, 60; Univ Nev, MS, 65; Univ Calif, Davis, PhD(chem), 69. *Prof Exp:* NSF fel biochem, Univ Wis-Madison, 69-71; Rockefeller fel chem, Univ Calif, Riverside, 71-74; prog specialist, 74-76, tech specialist, 76-78, STAFF TOXICOLOGIST, XEROX CORP, 78- *Concurrent Pos:* Adj fac toxicol, Univ Rochester, 80- *Mem:* Am Chem Soc; AAAS; NY Acad Sci; Am Col Toxicol; Environ Mutagen Soc. *Res:* Industrial toxicology; gaseous emissions; trace metal sampling and analysis; trace organic compounds sampling and analysis; inhalation toxicology; biometrics; chemical carcinogenesis; x-ray crystallography; general toxicology. *Mailing Add:* Xerox Corp Webster NY 14580

LIN, GRACE WOAN, b Taipei, Taiwan; US citizen. NUTRITIONAL BIOCHEMISTRY. *Educ:* Nat Taiwan Univ, BS, 59; Tex Woman's Univ, MS, 64; Univ Calif, Berkeley, PhD(nutrit), 71. *Prof Exp:* Res asst, US Naval Med Res Unit #2, 59-62, Thorndike Mem Lab, Med Sch, Harvard Univ, 64; res fel, Columbia Univ, 69-70; ASST RES SPECIALITST NUTRIT, RUTGERS UNIV, 74- *Mem:* Res Soc Alcoholism. *Res:* Effects of ethanol on absorption and metabolism of nutrients (amino acids and water soluble vitamins) and on fetal development. *Mailing Add:* Ctr Alcohol Studies Rutgers Univ New Brunswick NJ 08903

LIN, GREGORY S B, b New York, NY, June 3, 49. RADIOLOGY. *Educ:* Univ Calif, Santa Cruz, BA(physics) & BA(info & comput sci), 71; Univ Calif, Berkeley, PhD(biophysics & med physics), 79. *Prof Exp:* Programmer Analyst, Univ Calif, Santa Cruz & Berkeley, 69-71; MGR, DEPT THERAPY PLANNING, MED PHYSICS, ATC MED TECHNOL, INC, CA, 80- *Concurrent Pos:* Consult, All-India Inst Med Sci, New Delhi, India, 79-80 & Dept Physiol & Anat, Univ Calif, Berkeley, 80- *Res:* Computer applications in diagnostic and therapeutic radiology; biological membrane structure and function; electrochemistry; science and public health policy. *Mailing Add:* 919 Almarida Dr Campbell CA 95008

LIN, H(UA), b Peiping, China, Nov 25, 19; nat US; m 47; c 2. AERONAUTICAL ENGINEERING. *Educ:* Nat Tsing Hua Univ, China, BS, 40; Univ Mich, MS, 44; Mass Inst Technol, ScD(aeronaut eng), 55. *Prof Exp:* Engr, aeronaut dept, Cent Aircraft Mfg Co, China, 40-42; instr, Nat Tsing Hua Univ, 42-43; stress analyst, Stinson Div, Consol Vultee Aircraft Corp, Mich, 44-45; engr, Cincinnati Milling Mach Co, Ohio, 45-47; asst mgr, Far East Develop Corp, NY, 47-49; res aeronaut engr, aeroelastic & struct res lab, Mass Inst Technol, 49-56; res specialist, struct dynamics staff, Boeing Airplane Co, 56-58, chief dynamics, systs mgt off, 58-59, chief struct tech unit, aerospace div, 59-64, mgr, struct & mat tech dept, Aerospace Group Div, Boeing Co, 65-66, chief missile tech, missile & info systs div, 66-68, chief engr, minuteman prog, missile div, 68-70, dep prog mgr, minuteman prog, Aerospace Group, 70-71, prog mgr hardsite defense, 71-73, prod develop mgr, 73-75; dir offensive systs, US Directorate Res & Eng, Dept Defense, 75-78; CHIEF SCIENTIST, BOEING AEROSPACE CO, 78- *Concurrent Pos:* Partic, sr exec prog, Sloan Sch Indust Mgt, Mass Inst Technol, 69. *Mem:* Sr mem Am Astron Soc; fel Am Inst Aeronaut & Astronaut; fel Brit Interplanetary Soc; Am Soc Mech Engrs. *Res:* Aeroelasticity; structural dynamics; structural analysis; steady-state and unsteady aerodynamics; aerodynamic heating and thermal analysis; stability and control; structural flexility and servo-control interaction. *Mailing Add:* Boeing Aerospace Co PO Box 3999 Seattle WA 98124

LIN, HUNG CHANG, b Shanghai, China, Aug 8, 19; US citizen; m 59; c 2. ELECTRONICS. *Educ:* Chiao Tung Univ, BSEE, 41; Univ Mich, MS, 48; Polytech Inst Brooklyn, DEE(elec eng), 56. *Prof Exp:* Engr, Cent Radio Works of China, 41-44 & Cent Broadcasting Admin of China, 44-47; res engr, RCA, 48-56; mgr appln, CBS Semiconductor Opers, 56-59; lectr, 66-69, vis prof elec eng, 69-71, PROF ELEC ENG, UNIV MD, COLLEGE PARK, 71-; MGR ADVAN DEVELOP, MOLECULAR ELECTRONICS DIV, WESTINGHOUSE CORP, LINTHICUM HEIGHTS, 63-, SR ADV ENGR, AEROSPACE DIV, BALTIMORE, 69- *Concurrent Pos:* Adv engr, Res Lab, Westinghouse Corp, Baltimore, 59-63; adj prof, Univ Pittsburgh, 59-63; vis lectr, Univ Calif, Berkeley, 65-66. *Mem:* Fel Inst Elec & Electronics Engrs; Sigma Xi; Electrochem Soc. *Res:* Semiconductor and integrated circuits. *Mailing Add:* Dept of Elec Eng Univ of Md College Park MD 20742

LIN, JAMES C H, b Macao, Aug 12, 32; m 67; c 3. GENETICS, CELL PHYSIOLOGY. *Educ:* Taiwan Prov Norm Univ, BS, 54; Rice Univ, MA, 60, NC State Univ, PhD(genetics), 65. *Prof Exp:* Lab instr zool, Nat Taiwan Univ, 55-57; res asst nuclear med, Methodist Hosp, Houston, Tex, 59-60 & Hermann Hosp, 60; from asst prof to assoc prof, 65-75, PROF BIOL, NORTHWESTERN STATE UNIV, 75- *Concurrent Pos:* Vis prof, Univ Tex, M D Anderson Hosp & Tumor Inst, 80-81. *Mem:* Genetics Soc Am; Sigma Xi. *Res:* Chemical mutagenesis; cholinesterase in fire ants; crossing over in Drosophila; nuclear organizing regions of Chinese hamster ovary cells. *Mailing Add:* Dept of Biol Sci Northwestern State Univ Natchitoches LA 71457

LIN, JAMES CHIH-I, b Seoul, Korea, Dec 29, 43; m 70; c 3. BIOENGINEERING, BIOMEDICAL ENGINEERING. *Educ:* Univ Wash, Seattle, BS, 66, MS, 68, PhD(elec eng), 71. *Prof Exp:* Elec engr, Crown Zellerbach Corp, 66-67; teaching & res asst elec eng, Univ Wash, Seattle, 67-71, asst prof rehab med, 71-74, asst dir, Bioelectromagnetic Res Lab, 74; prof elec eng, Wayne State Univ, Detroit, 74-80; PROF ELEC ENG & BIOENG, UNIV ILL, CHICAGO, 80- *Concurrent Pos:* Consult, Walter Reed Army Inst Res, 73-75, Battelle Mem Inst, 76-80, SRI Int, 78-79 & Arthur D Little, Inc, 80-82; appointee, Diag Radiol Study Sect, NIH, 81-84, Nat Acad Sci, 80-82. *Mem:* Inst Elec & Electronics Engrs; Bioelectromagnetic Soc; Biomed Eng Soc; AAAS. *Res:* Biomedical imaging using nonionizing electromagnetic radiation; biological effects of electromagnetic fields; hyperthermia for cancer therapy; modern applications of radio science and electromagnetics. *Mailing Add:* Dept Bioeng Univ Ill Box 4348 Chicago IL 60680

LIN, JEONG-LONG, b Taichung, Formosa, Dec 17, 35; m 59; c 3. PHYSICAL CHEMISTRY. *Educ:* Queen's Univ, Ont, PhD(chem), 64. *Prof Exp:* Res assoc chem, Univ Chicago, 64-66; asst prof, 66-68, assoc prof, 68-74, PROF CHEM, BOSTON COL, 74- & CHMN, 77- *Mem:* Am Chem Soc; Am Phys Soc. *Res:* Irreversible thermodynamics and electrochemistry; theory of elementary reactions. *Mailing Add:* Dept of Chem Boston Col Chestnut Hill MA 02167

LIN, JIA DING, b Fuzhou, China, Dec 24, 31; US citizen; m 58; c 3. FLUID MECHANICS, HYDROLOGY AND WATER RESOURCES. *Educ:* Nat Univ Taiwan, BS, 53, Univ Ill, MS, 56; Mass Inst Technol, ScD(hydromech), 61. *Prof Exp:* Res scientist, Hydronautics, Inc, 60-62; asst prof, 62-64, assoc prof, 64-81, PROF CIVIL ENG, UNIV CONN, 81- *Concurrent Pos:* Vis prof, Taiwan Univ, 79-80. *Mem:* Asn Hydrol Res; Am Geophys Union. *Res:* hydrodynamics; hydrology. *Mailing Add:* Dept Civil Eng Univ Conn Storrs CT 06268

LIN, JIM YUNG-HUAN, forestry, biometry, see previous edition

LIN, JUI-TENG, b Puli, Taiwan, May 5, 48; m 76; c 1. SOLID STATE PHYSICS. *Educ:* Nat Taiwan Normal Univ, BS, 71; Nat Tsing-Hua Univ, MS, 74; Univ Rochester, PhD(chem), 80. *Prof Exp:* Instr physics, Puli High Sch, Taiwan, 71-72, Chinese Army Commun & Electronics Sch, 74-76; RES ASSOC, UNIV ROCHESTER, 80- *Mem:* Am Phys Soc; Am Chem Soc; Sigma Xi. *Res:* Theoretical laser-matter interactions with applications to surface physics; atomic-molecular physics; materials processing; microelectronics and laser development; experimental laser-induced transient effects. *Mailing Add:* 407 University Pk Rochester NY 14620

LIN, KANG, b Chen-Tu, China, Dec 17, 40; m 64; c 4. ORGANIC CHEMISTRY. *Educ:* Tunghai Univ, BS, 61; Univ Chicago, PhD(org chem), 66. *Prof Exp:* Res fel org chem, Harvard Univ, 66-68; res chemist, 68-75, sr res chemist, 75-80, RES ASSOC, E I DU PONT DE NEMOURS & CO, INC, 80- *Mem:* Am Chem Soc. *Res:* Process development of biochemicals. *Mailing Add:* 108 Jupiter Rd Newark DE 19711

LIN, KUANG-FARN, b Taiwan, China, Feb 25, 36; m 58; c 2. POLYMER SCIENCE. *Educ:* Cheng Kung Univ, Taiwan, BSc, 57; NDak State Univ, MS, 63, PhD(polymers, coatings), 69. *Prof Exp:* Asst instr chem, Chinese Naval Acad, 57-59; supt synthetic resins, Yung Koo Paint & Varnish Mfg Co, 59-61; chemist, 63-67, res chemist, 69-73, proj leader, 73-75, sr res chemist, 74-78, RES CHEMIST, HERCULES RES CTR, 78-, TECH MGR, 79- *Concurrent Pos:* Asst, NDak State Univ, 63 & 67. *Mem:* Am Chem Soc; Sigma Xi; Tech Asn Pulp & Paper Indust; fel Am Inst Chemists; Am Inst Mining, Metall & Petrol Engrs. *Res:* Structure-property relationship; mineral processing; adhesion, coatings and polymer synthesis. *Mailing Add:* Metals Sci Div Hercules Res Ctr Wilmington DE 19899

LIN, KUANG-MING, b Tapei, Taiwan, Mar 10, 32; m 62; c 4. FLUID MECHANICS, DYNAMICS. *Educ:* Nat Taiwan Univ, BS, 56; Auburn Univ, MS, 58; Mich State Univ, PhD(appl mech), 64; Bowling Green State Univ, MBA, 79. *Prof Exp:* Asst res instr fluid mech, Mich State Univ, 58-60; asst prof eng mech, Tri-State Col, 61-63; from asst prof to assoc prof eng sci, Tenn Technol Univ, 64-66; sr res engr, Brown Eng Co, 66-68; specialist reliability eng, ITT Fed Elec Corp, 68; sr staff engr, Corp Res & Develop, 68-73, dep dir planning & develop, Asia-Pac, Dana Int, Div, 73-75, MGR INT PLANNING, DANA CORP, 75- *Concurrent Pos:* NSF res initiation grant, 65-66. *Mem:* Am Soc Mech Engrs; Soc Automotive Engrs. *Res:* Two-phase flow through porous medias; boundary layer theory; hydrology; aerodynamics; lubrication of porous bearings; control systems for power transmission devices. *Mailing Add:* Dana Corp PO Box 1000 Toledo OH 43697

LIN, KUANG-TZU DAVIS, b Nantou, Taiwan, Aug 12, 40; m 68; c 2. BIOCHEMISTRY. *Educ:* Nat Taiwan Univ, BM, 66; Univ Wis-Madison, PhD(physiol chem), 71. *Prof Exp:* Rotating intern, Nat Taiwan Univ Hosp, 65-66; surg officer, Tainan Air Force Hosp, 66-67; res asst physiol chem, Univ Wis-Madison, 67-71, proj assoc, 71-74; ASST PROF MED BIOL, MEM RES CTR, UNIV TENN, 74- *Mem:* Soc Exp Biol Med; Am Soc Biol Chemists. *Res:* Structure and function, especially carbonic anhydrase, hemoglobin, protease inhibitors and erythropoietin. *Mailing Add:* Univ Tenn Mem Res Ctr 1924 Alcoa Hwy Knoxville TN 37920

LIN, LARRY Y H, b China. CIVIL ENGINEERING. *Educ:* Nat Taiwan Univ, BS, 57; WVa Univ, MS, 63, PhD(civil eng), 66; Am Acad Environ Engrs, dipl. *Prof Exp:* Teaching asst, Nat Taiwan Univ, 59-61; res asst assoc, WVa Univ, 61-64; MEM STAFF, ROY WESTON INC, 66- *Mem:* Water Pollution Control Fedn. *Res:* Process design of industrial and municipal wastewater treatment facilities; physical, chemical and biological aspects of water pollution; air and solid waste problems; data analysis and computer programming; energy conservation. *Mailing Add:* Roy Weston Inc Weston Way West Chester PA 19380

LIN, LAWRENCE I-KUEI, b Fuchou, China, May 21, 48; m 71; c 1. STATISTICS, DATA MANAGEMENT. *Educ:* Nat Chengchi Univ, Taiwan, BS, 70; Univ Iowa, MS, 73, PhD(statist), 79. *Prof Exp:* Res asst, Dept Preventive Med, Univ Iowa, 73, statistician, Iowa Epidemiol Study Pesticides, 73-79; SR STATISTICIAN, TRAVENOL LABS, MORTON GROVE, ILL, 79- *Mem:* Am Statist Asn; Biomet Soc. *Res:* Robustness of multiple discriminant analysis; evaluate and design models for risk assessment when the distribution is heavy tailed with data clumping at zero. *Mailing Add:* 125 Carriage Way Dr Burr Ridge IL 60521

LIN, LEU-FEN HOU, b Kwangtung, China; US citizen; m 72; c 2. BIOCHEMISTRY, ORGANIC CHEMISTRY. *Educ:* Nat Taiwan Univ, BS, 67; Univ Minn, PhD(biochem), 72. *Prof Exp:* Instr biochem, Mt Sinai Sch Med, 72-76; res fel, Harvard Univ, 76-79; RES ASSOC BIOCHEM, E K SHRIVER CTR MENTAL RETARDATION, & HARVARD MED SCH, 79- *Concurrent Pos:* Asst neurol, Mass Gen Hosp, 81- *Res:* Membrane structure, function and biosynthesis. *Mailing Add:* Dept Biochem E K Shriver Ctr Mental Retardation 200 Trapelo Rd Waltham MA 02254

LIN, MAO-SHIU, b Tainan, Taiwan, June 20, 31. ELECTRICAL ENGINEERING. *Educ:* Nat Taiwan Univ, BSE, 55; Univ Mich, MSE, 58, PhD(elec eng), 64. *Prof Exp:* Asst engr elec mach, Ta-Tung Elec Mfg Co, Taiwan, 55-56; assoc res engr, Electron Physics Lab, Univ Mich, 64-66; from asst prof to assoc prof elec eng, 66-72, PROF ELEC ENG, SAN DIEGO STATE UNIV, 72-, CHMN, ELEC & COMPUT ENG DEPT, 76- *Mem:* Inst Elec & Electronics Engrs. *Res:* Material science; solid state electronics; quantum electronics. *Mailing Add:* Dept of Elec Eng 5402 College Ave San Diego CA 92182

LIN, MICHAEL C J, b Taiwan; m 71; c 2. SYNTHETIC FUEL TECHNOLOGY. *Educ:* Nat Taiwan Univ, BS, 68; Univ Conn, MS, 71; Univ Okla, PhD(chem eng), 7. *Prof Exp:* Res assoc chem eng, Dept Chem Eng, Auburn Univ, 75-78; SR ENGR RES & DEVELOP, EXXON RES & ENG CO, 78- *Mem:* Am Inst Chem Engrs; Combustion Inst. *Res:* Polymer science; reaction engineering; catalysis and coal combustion and conversion technology; synfuel energy. *Mailing Add:* PO Box 4255 Baytown TX 77520

LIN, MING CHANG, b Hsinpu, Hsinchu, Taiwan, Oct 24, 36; US citizen; m 65; c 3. CHEMICAL KINETICS, LASERS. *Educ:* Taiwan Normal Univ, BSc, 59; Univ Ottawa, Can, PhD(phys chem), 66. *Prof Exp:* Fel res, Univ Ottawa, 65-67; res assoc, Cornell Univ, 67-69; res chemist, 70-74, SUPVRY RES CHEMIST, NAVAL RES LAB, 74- *Concurrent Pos:* Adj prof, Dept Chem, Catholic Univ, Washington, DC, 81-; Guggenheim fel, 82. *Honors & Awards:* Pure Science Award, Sigma Xi, 78. *Mem:* Am Chem Soc; Combustion Inst; Sigma Xi. *Res:* Kinetics of chemical reactions are studies with modern diagnostic tools such as lasers witn special emphasis on the elucidation of mechanisms of combustion and planetary reactions, heterogeneous catalytic processes and chemical laser systems. *Mailing Add:* Code 6110 Chem Div Naval Res Lab Washington DC 20375

LIN, MOW SHIAH, b Kwangtung, China, June 18, 41; US citizen; m 68; c 3. BIOCHEMISTRY, ORGANIC CHEMISTRY. *Educ:* Tamkang Col, BS, 65; Univ Wyo, PhD(chem), 73. *Prof Exp:* Fel vision, NIH, 73-75; res assoc enzyme, 75-77, ASSOC CHEMIST, BROOKHAVEN NAT LAB, 77- *Mem:* AAAS; Am Chem Soc; Sigma Xi. *Res:* Chemistry of vision; isomerase and bacteriorhodopsin; nuclear engineering; nuclear wastes. *Mailing Add:* Dept Nuclear Eng 830 Brookhaven Nat Lab Upton NY 11973

LIN, OTTO CHUI CHAU, b Kwongtang, China, Aug 8, 38; m 63; c 2. POLYMER CHEMISTRY, RHEOLOGY. *Educ:* Nat Taiwan Univ, BS, 60; Columbia Univ, MA, 63, PhD(phys chem), 67. *Prof Exp:* Res chemist, 67-69, staff chemist, 69-71, RES ASSOC, MARSHALL RES LAB, FABRICS & FINISHES DEPT, E I DU PONT DE NEMOURS & CO, INC, 71- *Concurrent Pos:* Vis prof, Inst Polymer Sci & actg dean, Col of Eng, Nat Tsing Hua Univ, 78- *Mem:* AAAS; Am Chem Soc; Am Inst Chem Engrs; NY Acad Sci; Soc Rheol. *Res:* Physical chemical characterization of polymers; rheological properties of polymers; sedimentation; viscometry; organic coatings; ecological impacts of polymer applications; polymers for electronics applications. *Mailing Add:* Res Lab 3500 Grays Ferry Ave E I du Pont de Nemours & Co Inc Philadelphia PA 19146

LIN, P(EN) M(IN), b China, Oct 17, 28; nat US; m 62; c 3. ELECTRICAL ENGINEERING. *Educ:* Taiwan Univ, BS, 50; NC State Col, MS, 56; Purdue Univ, PhD(elec eng), 60. *Prof Exp:* From instr to asst prof elec eng, Purdue Univ, 56-60; mem tech staff, Bell Tel Labs, NJ, 60-61; from asst prof to assoc prof elec eng, 61-74, PROF ELEC ENG, PURDUE UNIV, 74- *Concurrent Pos:* Assoc ed, Trans Circuit Theory, Inst Elec & Electronics Engrs, 71-73. *Mem:* Fel Inst Elec & Electronics Engrs. *Res:* Circuit theory; passive and active network synthesis; linear graphs; computer-aided circuit analysis. *Mailing Add:* Sch Elec Eng Purdue Univ Lafayette IN 47907

LIN, PAUL KUANG-HSIEN, b Tung-Shih, Taiwan, Nov 12, 46; m 78. EXPERIMENTAL DESIGN, ROBUST ESTIMATION. *Educ:* Fu-Jen Univ, Taiwan, BS, 70; Brigham Young Univ, 75; Wayne State Univ, PhD(statist), 80. *Prof Exp:* ASST PROF STATIST, OAKLAND UNIV, 80- *Mem:* Am Statist Asn; Am Math Soc; Inst Math Statist; Math Asn Am; Sigma Xi. *Res:* Experimental design; interval estimation and hypothesis testing. *Mailing Add:* Dept Math Sci Oakland Univ Ann Arbor MI 48105

LIN, PAUL PO-CHAO, b Kaohsiung, Taiwan, Oct 2, 42; c 3. PLANT BIOCHEMISTRY, DEVELOPMENTAL BIOLOGY. *Educ:* Nat Taiwan Univ, BSc, 65; Mich State Univ, PhD(biochem), 71. *Prof Exp:* Vis assoc prof, Nat Taiwan Univ, 73-74; sr res assoc, Univ Ga, 75-77; res biochemist, US Borax Chem & Res Co, 77-78; asst prof plant biochem, Univ Ky, 78-80. *Concurrent Pos:* Fels, Calif Inst Technol, 71-72, Nat Res Coun Can, 72-73 & Montreal Cancer Inst, 74-75. *Mem:* Am Chem Soc; Am Soc Plant Physiol; AAAS. *Res:* Mechanisms of hormone action and metabolic regulation in the control of plant growth and development. *Mailing Add:* 2055 Manor Dr Lexington KY 40502

LIN, PI-ERH, b Taiwan, China, Jan 8, 38; m 63; c 3. MATHEMATICAL STATISTICS. *Educ:* Taiwan Norm Univ, BSc, 61; Columbia Univ, PhD(math statist), 68. *Prof Exp:* Consult med ctr, Columbia Univ, 67-68; asst prof, 68-74, assoc prof, 74-80, PROF STATIST, FLA STATE UNIV, 80- *Concurrent Pos:* Fla State Univ fac res grant, 71-72. *Mem:* Inst Math Statist; Am Statist Asn; Bernoulii Soc. *Res:* Multivariate analysis; statistical inference. *Mailing Add:* Dept of Statist Fla State Univ Tallahassee FL 32306

LIN, PING-WHA, b Canton, China, July 11, 25; m 60; c 2. ENVIRONMENTAL ENGINEERING. *Educ:* Chiao Tung Univ, BS, 47; Purdue Univ, MS, 49, PhD(sanit eng), 51. *Prof Exp:* Engr, Amman & Whitney, NY, 51-54, Ebesco, 54-55, Parsons, Brinkerhoff, Hall & MacDonald, 55-57 & Lockwood Greene Engrs, 57-59; engr, World Health Orgn, 59-60, consult, 62-66; engr, John Graham & Co, NY, 60-61; prof environ eng, Tri-State Univ, 66-79; PROJ MGR, WHO, 79- *Concurrent Pos:* Fel, NSF workshop, Mass Inst Technol, 69. *Honors & Awards:* Achievement Award, United Inventors & Scientists of Am, 74. *Mem:* Fel Am Soc Civil Engrs; Am Water Works Asn; AAAS; Sigma Xi; Water Pollution Control Fedn. *Res:* A new sulfur dioxide removal and waste products reclamation process; acid neutralization; metal waste treatment; fly ash utilization; soil stabilization. *Mailing Add:* 506 S Darling St Angola IN 46703

LIN, RENG-LANG, b Hsin-Chu, Taiwan, Feb 28, 37; m 65; c 2. TOXICOLOGY, PSYCHOPHARMACOLOGY. *Educ:* Nat Taiwan Univ, BS, 59, MS, 63; Okla State Univ, PhD(biochem), 69. *Prof Exp:* Fel, Univ Wis-Madison, 69-71; res scientist, Galesburg State Hosp, Ill, 71-75; res scientist, Ill State Psychiat Inst, 75-78; ASST CHIEF TOXICOLOGIST, OFF MED EXAMINER, COOK COUNTY, 78- *Mem:* Am Chem Soc; AAAS. *Res:* Forensic toxicology; biochemistry of mental illness; biosynthesis and metabolism of biogenic amines; biochemistry and pharmacology of psychoactive drugs. *Mailing Add:* Toxicol Dept Off Med Examr 1828 W Polk St Chicago IL 60612

LIN, ROBERT I-SAN, b Fukien, China. SCIENCE ADMINISTRATION, RESOURCE MANAGEMENT. *Educ:* Nat Taiwan Univ, BS, 61; Univ Calif, Los Angeles, MS, 65, PhD(biophysics & nuclear med), 68. *Prof Exp:* Res fel chem, Calif Inst Technol, 68-70; clin trainee metab dis, Univ Calif Med Ctr, 70-71; life sci mgr, Gen Tel & Electronic Corp, 71-73; dir enzyme prod, Worthington Biochem Corp, 73-74; vpres technol diag prod, RIA Inc, 74-75; CHIEF SCIENTIST, FRITO-LAY INC, 75- *Concurrent Pos:* Vis prof biochem & molecular biol, Pepperdine Univ, 69-70; trainee biotechnol & mat sci, Mass Inst Technol, 71-72; vis distinguished prof nutrit & food sci, Tex Woman's Univ, 81- *Mem:* NY Acad Sci; Sigma Xi; Am Photobiol Soc; Soc Appl Nutrit; Am Agr Econ Asn. *Res:* Biotechnology and genetic engineering: recombiant DNA--hybridoma and subcellular organelle transfer; chemistry and rheology of natural and synthetic polymers; physical chemistry of surfactants and viscosity modifiers; nutrition, aging and degenerative diseases; management of technological development and industrialization; operation research and econometrics. *Mailing Add:* 1319 Brookhurst Dr Irving TX 75061

LIN, ROBERT PEICHUNG, b China, Jan 24, 42; US citizen. SOLAR PHYSICS, HIGH ENERGY ASTROPHYSICS. *Educ:* Calif Inst Technol, BS, 62; Univ Calif, Berkeley, PhD(physics), 67. *Prof Exp:* Asst res physicist, 67-74, assoc res physicist, 74-79, RES PHYSICIST, SPACE SCI LAB, UNIV CALIF, BERKELEY, 79-, SR FEL, 80- *Concurrent Pos:* Prin investr, NASA & NSF, high resolution x-ray and gamma ray spectroscopy, 79-, NASA-US participation in Europ Space Agency GIOTTO Mission, 81- *Mem:* Am Geophys Union; Am Astron Soc. *Res:* Solar flares, radio bursts and cosmic rays; interplanetary particles; magnetospheric processes; lunar magnetism; astrophysical x-ray and gamma ray spectroscopy; comets. *Mailing Add:* Space Sci Lab Univ of Calif Berkeley CA 94720

LIN, SHAO-CHI, b Canton, China, Jan 5, 25; nat US; m 55. AEROSPACE ENGINEERING. *Educ:* Nat Cent Univ, China, BSc, 46; Cornell Univ, PhD(aeronaut eng), 52. *Prof Exp:* Engr, Bur Aircraft Indust, China, 47-48; asst, Cornell Univ, 48-51, actg instr, 52, res assoc, 52-54, actg asst prof, 54; prin res scientist, Avco-Everett Res Lab, Mass, 55-64; PROF ENG PHYSICS, UNIV CALIF, SAN DIEGO, 64- *Concurrent Pos:* Consult, Aerospace Corp, Avco-Everett Res Lab, Inst Defense Anal & Rand Corp; panel mem re-entry physics, Nat Acad Sci-Nat Res Coun. *Honors & Awards:* Res Award, Am Inst Aeronaut & Astronaut, 66. *Mem:* Am Inst Aeronaut & Astronaut; Am Phys Soc; Am Astronaut Soc; Am Geophys Union. *Res:* Physical gas dynamics; hypersonic flight; re-entry physics; laser physics and interaction. *Mailing Add:* Dept of Appl Mech & Eng Sci Univ of Calif San Diego La Jolla CA 92093

LIN, SHEN, b Amoy, China, Feb 4, 31; m 56, 71; c 3. COMPUTER SCIENCE, MATHEMATICS. *Educ:* Univ Philippines, BS, 51; Ohio State Univ, MA, 53, PhD(math), 63. *Prof Exp:* Asst prof math, Univ Ohio, 59-62; lectr & res assoc, Ohio State Univ, 62-63; MEM TECH STAFF, MATH & STATIST RES CTR, BELL LABS, INC, 63- *Concurrent Pos:* Vis lectr, Princeton Univ, 72. *Mem:* AAAS; Am Math Soc; Math Asn Am; Soc Indust & Appl Math. *Res:* Application of computers to mathematical science. *Mailing Add:* Math & Statist Res Ctr Bell Labs Inc Murray Hill NJ 07974

LIN, SHENG HSIEN, b Sept 17, 37; US citizen; m 70. CHEMICAL KINETICS, CHEMICAL PHYSICS. *Educ:* Nat Taiwan Univ, BS, 59, MS, 61; Univ Utah, PhD(chem), 64. *Prof Exp:* Fel chem, Columbia Univ, 64-65; from asst to assoc prof, 65-72, PROF CHEM, ARIZ STATE UNIV, 72- *Concurrent Pos:* A P Sloan fel, 67-69; Guggenheim fel, 71-73; Humboldt Sr US scientist awardee, 78-80. *Mem:* Am Chem Soc. *Res:* Energy transfer; atomic collisions; optical rotations and the Faraday effect; reaction kinetics; high order phase transactions; magnetic properties of molecules; multi-photon processes; molecular relaxation processes; theory of time-resolved x-ray diffraction. *Mailing Add:* Dept of Chem Ariz State Univ Tempe AZ 85281

LIN, SHERMAN S, b Changhua, Taiwan, Jan 10, 41; US citizen; c 2. FOOD SCIENCE, FLAVOR CHEMISTRY. *Educ:* Nat Taiwan Univ, BS, 64; Rutgers Univ, MS, 68, PhD(food sci), 71. *Prof Exp:* Proj leader, Standard Brands Inc, 72-73; group leader flavor chem, 73-81, RES ASSOC, ANDERSON CLAYTON FOODS, 81- *Mem:* Am Chem Soc; Am Oil Chemists Soc; Inst Food Technologists. *Res:* Flavor research on cheeses, casein, soy isolates, fats and oils; development of cheese substitute. *Mailing Add:* W L Clayton Res Ctr 3333 N Central Expressway Richardson TX 75080

LIN, SHIN, b Hong Kong, Feb 14, 45; US citizen; m 69; c 2. BIOCHEMISTRY, BIOPHYSICS. *Educ:* Univ Calif, Davis, BS, 65; San Diego State Univ, MS, 67; Univ Calif, Los Angeles, PhD(biol chem), 71. *Prof Exp:* Fel, Univ Calif, San Francisco, 71-74; asst prof, 74-79, ASSOC PROF BIOPHYSICS, JOHNS HOPKINS UNIV, 79- *Concurrent Pos:* NIH res career develop award, 76-81. *Honors & Awards:* Robert C Kirkwood Mem Award, San Francisco Heart Asn, 74. *Mem:* AAAS; Am Soc Biol Chemists; Am Soc Cell Biol; Biophys Soc. *Res:* Biochemical and biophysical studies on cytoskeletal and motile functions of eukaryotic cells, with emphasis on drugs and cellular proteins affecting the assembly and interactions of actin filaments in vivo and in vitro. *Mailing Add:* Dept of Biophys Johns Hopkins Univ Baltimore MD 21218

LIN, SHU, b Nanking, China, May 20, 36; m 63; c 2. ELECTRICAL ENGINEERING, INFORMATION SCIENCES. *Educ:* Nat Taiwan Univ, BS, 59; Rice Univ, MS, 64; PhD(elec eng), 65. *Prof Exp:* Res assoc, Univ Hawaii, 65-66, from asst prof to assoc prof elec eng, 66-73, prof, 73-81; PROF ELEC ENG, TEX A&M UNIV, 82- *Concurrent Pos:* NSF grants, 67-80; Air Force Cambridge Res Lab grant, 70-71; vis scholar, Univ Utah, 71-72; vis scientist, IBM Watson Res Ctr, 78-79. *Mem:* Sr mem Inst Elec & Electronics Engrs; Sigma Xi. *Res:* Coding theory and error control in data transmission systems; coding theory and multi-access communications. *Mailing Add:* Dept of Elec Eng Tex A&M Univ College Station TX 77843

LIN, SHU-REN, radiology, deceased

LIN, SHWU-YENG TZEN, b Tainan, Formosa, May 11, 34; m 60; c 3. TOPOLOGY. *Educ:* Nat Taiwan Univ, BSc, 58; Tulane Univ, MS, 62; Univ Fla, PhD(math), 65. *Prof Exp:* Asst math, Inst Math, Academia Sinica, 58-60; instr, Tulane Univ, 61-63; lectr, 64-65, asst prof, 65-71, ASSOC PROF MATH, UNIV SOUTH FLA, 71- *Concurrent Pos:* Reviewer, Math Rev, Am Math Soc, 68-; Zentralblatt fur Mathmatik, 70- *Mailing Add:* Dept of Math Univ of SFla Tampa FL 33620

LIN, SIN-SHONG, b Taiwan, Oct 24, 33; m 64; c 3. HIGH TEMPERATURE CHEMISTRY. *Educ:* Nat Taiwan Univ, BS, 56; Nat Tsing-Hua Univ, Taiwan, MS, 58; Univ Kans, PhD(chem), 66. *Prof Exp:* Fel, Northwestern Univ, Evanston, 66-67; RES CHEMIST, MAT RES LAB, ARMY MAT & MECH RES CTR, 67- *Mem:* Am Chem Soc; Am Vacuum Soc; Electrochem Soc. *Res:* Thermodynamics of vaporization processes; material research and development; atmospheric sampling of gases; nucleation and condensation studies by mass spectrometry; electron spectroscopy for chemical analysis & auger electron spectroscopy & section mass spectrometry. *Mailing Add:* 40 Lyons Rd Westwood MA 02090

LIN, SPING, b Canton, China, Sept 8, 18; nat US; m 46; c 2. NEUROCHEMISTRY, PHYSIOLOGY. *Educ:* Sun Yat-Sen Univ, BA, 40; Univ Minn, MS, 50, PhD(biochem), 52. *Prof Exp:* Asst entom, Sun Yat-Sen Univ, 40-44, instr, 44-47; res fellow, 54-61, res assoc, 61-63, asst prof, 63-69, ASSOC PROF NEUROL, MED SCH, UNIV MINN, MINNEAPOLIS, 69- *Mem:* Int Soc Neurochem; AAAS; Am Soc Neurochem. *Res:* Neurobiology. *Mailing Add:* Dept of Neurol Univ of Minn Med Sch Minneapolis MN 55455

LIN, STEPHEN FANG-MAW, b Nantou, Taiwan, Aug 21, 37; m 66; c 1. PHYSICAL CHEMISTRY. *Educ:* Nat Taiwan Univ, BS, 60; Univ Ill, Urbana, MS, 68, PhD(phys chem), 70. *Prof Exp:* ASSOC PROF CHEM, NC CENT UNIV, 70- *Mem:* AAAS; Sigma Xi; Am Chem Soc. *Res:* Conformation and stability of sulfur ring compounds; molecular spectroscopy. *Mailing Add:* Dept of Chem NC Cent Univ Durham NC 27707

LIN, SUE CHIN, b Taipei, China, Nov 8, 36; m 62; c 2. MATHEMATICS. *Educ:* Univ Calif, Berkeley, MA, 64, PhD(math), 67. *Prof Exp:* Asst prof math, Univ Miami, 67-69; mem, Inst Advan Study, 69-71; ASSOC PROF MATH, UNIV ILL, CHICAGO CIRCLE, 71- *Mem:* Am Math Soc. *Res:* Functional analysis. *Mailing Add:* Dept of Math Univ of Ill Chicago IL 60680

LIN, SUI, b Wenlin, Chekiang, China; Can citizen. ENERGY CONVERSION. *Educ:* Ord Eng Col, Taiwan, BS, 53; Univ Karlsruhe, WGer, Dipl-Ing 62, Dr-Ing(mech eng), 64. *Prof Exp:* Res assoc refrig, Inst Refrig Eng, Univ Karlsruhe, WGer, 62-65, gasdynamics, Inst Fluid Mech & Fluid Mach, 65-69; fel sonic boom, Inst Aerospace studies, Univ Toronto, Ont, 69-70; asst prof thermodynamics & fluid mech, 70-75, assoc prof, 75-81, PROF HEAT TRANSFER & SOLAR ENERGY, DEPT MECH ENG, CONCORDIA UNIV, MONTREAL, 81- *Mem:* Eng Inst Can; Can Soc Mech Eng; Am Soc Heating, Refrig & Air Conditioning Engrs; Int Solar Energy Soc. *Res:* Heat and mass transfer with phase changes; fluid mechanics and energy transfer in vortex chambers; solar energy systems for cold climates. *Mailing Add:* Dept Mech Eng Concordia Univ 1455 de Maisonneuve Blvd W Montreal PQ H3G 1M8 Can

LIN, SUNG P, b Taipei, Taiwan, Apr 18, 37; US citizen; m 66; c 2. FLUID MECHANICS, MATHEMATICS. *Educ:* Taiwan Univ, BS, 58; Univ Utah, MS, 61; Univ Mich, PhD(eng mech), 65. *Prof Exp:* Engr, Ministry Econ, China, 58-60; lectr eng mech, Univ Mich, 65-66; from asst prof to assoc prof mech eng, 66-74, chmn fluid & thermal sci group, 78-80, PROF MECH ENG, CLARKSON COL TECHNOL, 74-, CHMN APPL MECH PROG, 81- *Concurrent Pos:* NSF initiation grant, 67-69, res grants, 70-72 & 74-76; sr vis, Cambridge Univ, 73-74; Kodak grant, 74-76, consult, Eastman Kodak Co, 77-; vis prof, Rochester Univ & Stanford Univ, 80-81; Bausch & Lomb grant, 80-81. *Mem:* Am Phys Soc. *Res:* Theory and application of mechanics; fluid mechanics. *Mailing Add:* Dept of Mech & Indust Eng Clarkson Col of Technol Potsdam NY 13676

LIN, TAI-SHUN, b Fukien, China, Oct 10, 38; m 65; c 1. MEDICINAL CHEMISTRY, ORGANIC CHEMISTRY. *Educ:* Nat Taiwan Norm Univ, BSc, 59; Univ Wash, MS, 65; Western Mich Univ, PhD(org & med chem), 70. *Prof Exp:* Fel org chem, NC State Univ, 70-71; res assoc med chem, Western Mich Univ, 71-74; res assoc, 74-76, ASST PROF PHARMACOL, SCH MED, YALE UNIV, 76- *Concurrent Pos:* Assoc ed, J Carbohydrates, Nucleosides, Nucleotides, 74- *Mem:* Am Chem Soc. *Res:* Design, synthesis, mechanism of action and development of anticancer and antiviral agents; pharmacology. *Mailing Add:* Dept of Pharmacol Yale Univ Sch of Med New Haven CT 06510

LIN, TIEN-SUNG TOM, b Taiwan, China, Jan 9, 38; m 66; c 3. PHYSICAL CHEMISTRY. *Educ:* Tunghai Univ, BS, 60; Syracuse Univ, MS, 66; Univ Pa, PhD(phys chem), 69. *Prof Exp:* Res fel, Harvard Univ, 70; asst prof, 70-76, ASSOC PROF CHEM, WASHINGTON UNIV, 76- *Mem:* Am Chem Soc. *Res:* Molecular spectroscopy; photophysical and photochemical processes; structural aspects of organic free radicals. *Mailing Add:* Dept of Chem Washington Univ St Louis MO 63130

LIN, TSAU-YEN, b Taiwan, China, July 18, 32; m 67. BIOCHEMISTRY. *Educ:* Nat Taiwan Univ, BS, 55, MS, 57; Univ Calif, Berkeley, PhD(biochem), 65. *Prof Exp:* Instr clin chem, Kaohsiung Med Col, Taiwan, 57-58; res chemist, China Chem & Pharmaceut Co, 58-59; res asst biochem, US Naval Med Res Unit Number 2, Taiwan, 59-61; res assoc, Univ Calif, Berkeley, 65-67, asst res biochem, 67-68; SR RES BIOCHEMIST, MERCK INST THERAPEUT RES, MERCK SHARP & DOHME RES LABS, MERCK & CO, 69- *Mem:* AAAS; Am Chem Soc; Am Soc Biol Chemists. *Res:* Biosynthesis and function of complex carbohydrates; mechanism and active site structure of enzymes; biochemical characterization of complement. *Mailing Add:* Merck Sharp & Dohme Res Labs Rahway NJ 07065

LIN, TSU H, toxicology, computer science, see previous edition

LIN, TSUE-MING, b Ping-tung, Taiwan, June 10, 35; US citizen; m 64; c 3. IMMUNOLOGY, MICROBIOLOGY. *Educ:* Nat Taiwan Univ, DVM, 58, dipl pub health, 60; Tulane Univ, MS, 64; Univ Tex Med Br, PhD(microbiol), 68. *Prof Exp:* Teaching asst med parasitol, Col Med, Nat Taiwan Univ, 60-62; res assoc, 68-69, from instr to asst prof, 69-77, assoc prof pediat, 77-80, RES ASSOC PROF PEDIAT, MED SCH, UNIV MIAMI, 80- *Concurrent Pos:* Teaching asst, Taipei Med Col, 61-62; consult, Cordis Labs, 72-74 & sr staff immunologist, 77- *Mem:* AAAS; Am Soc Parasitol; Am Soc Microbiol; Am Asn Immunol. *Res:* Host-parasite relationship; pathophysiology; immunology; human heart autoimmune system; trichinosis; amebiasis; toxoplasmasis; human pregnancy-associated plasma proteins. *Mailing Add:* Dept Pediat Univ Miami Med Sch Miami FL 33152

LIN, TSUNG-I, b Taipei, Taiwan, May 10, 46. BIOPHYSICS, CHEMISTRY. *Educ:* Nat Taiwan Univ, BS, 68; Univ Chicago, MS, 71; Ohio State Univ, PhD(biophys), 75. *Prof Exp:* Fel biophys, Cardiovasc Res Inst, Univ Calif, San Francisco, 75-77; ASST PROF PHYSIOL & BIOPHYS, UNIV TEX HEALTH SCI CTR, DALLAS, 77- *Mem:* Am Biophys Soc. *Res:* Muscle biophysics; protein chemistry; optical spectroscopy. *Mailing Add:* Dept of Physiol 5323 Harry Hines Blvd Dallas TX 75235

LIN, TSUNG-MIN, b Chefoo, China, Oct 8, 16; nat US; m 43; c 2. PHYSIOLOGY. *Educ:* Nat Tsing Hua Univ, China, BS, 38; Univ Ill, MS, 52, PhD, 54. *Prof Exp:* Asst physiol, Nat Tsing Hua Univ, China, 39-40; asst, Nat Chung Cheng Med Col, 40-41, instr physiol, 41-43; lectr, Nat Kweiyang Med Col, 43-46, asst prof, 46-48; sr instr, Peking Union Med Col, 48-51; asst prof clin sci, Col Med, Univ Ill, 54-58; sr pharmacologist, 56-63, RES ASSOC, RES LABS, ELI LILLY & CO, 64- *Mem:* Am Physiol Soc; Am Soc Pharmacol & Exp Therapeut; Am Gastroenterol Asn. *Res:* Gastrointestinal physiology and pharmacology. *Mailing Add:* Res Labs Eli Lilly & Co Indianapolis IN 46285

LIN, TUNG HUA, b Chungking, China, May 26, 11; nat US; m 39; c 3. MECHANICS. *Educ:* Tangshan Col Eng, BS, 33; Mass Inst Technol, SM, 36; Univ Mich, DSc(eng mech), 53. *Prof Exp:* From assoc prof to prof aeronaut eng, Tsing Hua Univ, China, 37-39; from designer to chief engr & prod mgr, Chinese Aircraft Mfg Plant, 39-45; mem, Chinese Tech Mission in Eng, 45-49; from assoc prof to prof aeronaut eng, Univ Detroit, 49-56; PROF ENG, UNIV CALIF, LOS ANGELES, 56- *Concurrent Pos:* Consult, Continental Motor Corp, Mich, 54-55, Off Ord Res, 58, NAm Aviation Inc, 62-68 & ARA Inc, 66-; prin investr, res projs, Off Sci Res, US Air Force, 55-59 & NSF, 61- *Mem:* Fel Am Soc Mech Engrs; Soc Eng Sci; fel Am Acad Mech; Am Soc Civil Engrs. *Res:* Micromechanics; multiaxial stress-strain relations based on microstress fields in polycrystals; fatigue crack initiation mechanism based microstresses; inelastic structures; el asto-plastic analysis of beams, columns and plates; creep analysis of columns and plates. *Mailing Add:* 906 Las Palgas Rd Pacific Palisades CA 90272

LIN, TUNG YEN, b Foochow, China, Nov 14, 11; m; c 2. CIVIL ENGINEERING. *Educ:* Tangshan Col, China, BS, 31; Univ Calif, MS, 33. *Hon Degrees:* LLD, Chinese Univ Hong Kong, 72. *Prof Exp:* From engr to chief designer, Ministry of Rwy, China, 33-41; prof bridge eng, Tungchi Univ, 39-41; chief engr, Kung Sing Eng Corp, 41-45; comnr, Taiwan Sugar Rwy, 45-46; assoc prof, 46-60, chmn div struct eng & mech & dir lab, 60-63, PROF CIVIL ENG, UNIV CALIF, BERKELEY, 60-; CHMN BD, T Y LIN INT, 77- *Mem:* Nat Acad Eng; fel Am Soc Civil Engrs; Int Asn Bridge & Struct Engrs; Am Concrete Inst. *Res:* Bridge and structural engineering; design of prestressed concrete and steel structures. *Mailing Add:* T Y Lin Int 315 Bay St San Francisco CA 94133

LIN, TUNG-PO, b Fukien, China, Dec 31, 26; nat US; m 56; c 4. MATHEMATICS. *Educ:* Nat Cent Univ, China, BSc, 49; Mass Inst Technol, PhD(phys chem), 58. *Prof Exp:* Res chemist, E I du Pont de Nemours & Co, Del, 58-61; from asst prof to assoc prof math, 61-69, PROF MATH, CALIF STATE UNIV, NORTHRIDGE, 69- *Concurrent Pos:* Consult, IBM Corp, 61-68. *Mem:* Am Math Soc; Math Asn Am. *Res:* Functional analysis; applied mathematics. *Mailing Add:* 9674 Vanalden Ave Northridge CA 91324

LIN, TZ-HONG, b Taiwan, Jan 30, 34; m 69; c 2. ORGANIC CHEMISTRY, RADIOPHARMACEUTICAL RESEARCH. *Educ:* Nat Taiwan Univ, BS, 56; NMex Highlands Univ, MS, 64; Univ Calif, Berkeley, PhD(org chem), 69. *Prof Exp:* Teaching & res asst, Dept Chem, NMex Highlands Univ, 61-63; teaching asst, Dept Chem, Univ Calif, Berkeley, 63-64, res asst, Biodynamics Lab, Lawrence Radiation Lab, 64-69; vis asst prof, Dept Chem, La State Univ, 69-71; dir res chem, 71-74, res group leader, 74-78, PROJ MGR, MEDI-PHYSICS, INC, 78- *Mem:* Soc Nuclear Med; Am Chem Soc. *Res:* Research and development of new radiopharmaceuticals; hot atom chemistry; free radical chemistry; antibody research. *Mailing Add:* Medi-Physics Inc 5801 Christie Ave Emeryville CA 94608

LIN, WEI-CHING, b Taipei, China, Dec 31, 30; m 59. SPACE PHYSICS. *Educ:* Nat Taiwan Univ, BSc, 54; Univ Iowa, MSc, 61, PhD(physics), 65. *Prof Exp:* Res assoc space physics, Univ Iowa, 63-64; asst prof, Dalhousie Univ, 64-68; ASSOC PROF SPACE PHYSICS, UNIV PRINCE EDWARD ISLAND, 68- *Mem:* Am Geophys Union; Am Asn Physics Teachers. *Res:* Galactic and solar cosmic rays. *Mailing Add:* Dept of Physics Univ of Prince Edward Island Charlottetown PE C1A 4P3 Can

LIN, WEN-C(HUN), b Kutien, China, Feb 22, 26; US citizen; m 56; c 3. ELECTRICAL & COMPUTER ENGINEERING. *Educ:* Taiwan Univ, BS, 50; Purdue Univ, MS, 56, PhD(elec eng), 65. *Prof Exp:* Engr, elec lab, Taiwan Power Co, 50-54; engr high voltage lab, Gen Elec Co, 56-59; sr engr, electronic data processing div, Honeywell, Inc, 59-61; instr, Purdue Univ, 61-65; from asst prof to prof syst eng, Case Western Reserve Univ, 65-78; PROF ELEC & COMPUT, UNIV CALIF, DAVIS, 78- *Mem:* Inst Elec & Electronics Engrs. *Res:* Special electronic instrumentation; signal processing; pattern recognition; microcomputers. *Mailing Add:* Dept Elec & Comput Eng Univ Calif Davis CA 95616

LIN, WEN-HWANG, b Taiwan, Jan 3, 48; m 72; c 2. APPLIED MECHANICS, HYDRODYNAMICS. *Educ:* Nat Taiwan Univ, BSc, 71; Princeton Univ, MSc, 74, MA, 75, PhD(mech), 77. *Prof Exp:* res asst aerospace, Princeton Univ, 72-74, teaching asst mech, 74-76, res assoc civil eng, 77; asst mech engr, 77-81, MECH ENGR, ARGONNE NAT LAB, 81- *Mem:* Acoust Soc Am. *Res:* Hydrodynamics; acoustics; hydro-aeroelasticity; vibration; structural dynamics; hydro-aerodynamics and fluid/structure interaction; author or coauthor of 24 publications. *Mailing Add:* Componoents Technol Div Bldg 308-D148 Argonne Nat Lab Argonne IL 60439

LIN, WILLY, b Taiwan, China, July 2, 44; m 71; c 2. PLANT PHYSIOLOGY. *Educ:* Nat Taiwan Norm Univ, BS, 67; Ill State Univ, MS, 72; Univ Ill, Urbana, PhD(biol), 76. *Prof Exp:* Res assoc, Dept Biol, Brookhaven Nat Lab, 76-77; STAFF SCIENTIST, CENT RES & DEVELOP EXP STA, E I DU PONT DE NEMOURS & CO, INC, 77- *Mem:* Am Soc Plant Physiologists; Am Inst Biol Sci; Sigma Xi; NY Acad Sci. *Res:* Ion transport mechanism in plant tissues. *Mailing Add:* Cent Res & Develop Exp Sta E I du Pont de Nemours & Co Wilmington DE 19801

LIN, WUNAN, b Tainan, Taiwan, Aug 1, 42; US citizen; m 71. GEOPHYSICS, ROCK MECHANICS. *Educ:* Cheng-Kung Univ, BSE, 64; Univ Calif, Berkeley, MS, 69, PhD(geophys), 77. *Prof Exp:* Prof asst mining eng, Cheng-Kung Univ, 65-67; GEOPHYSICIST, LAWRENCE LIVERMORE LAB, UNIV CALIF, 77- *Concurrent Pos:* Res asst, Univ Calif, Berkeley, 67-68 & 71-77. *Mem:* Am Geophys Union; Int Soc Rock Mech. *Res:* Solid earth geophysics; physical properties of rocks at high pressure and high temperature. *Mailing Add:* Lawrence Livermore Lab L-201 PO Box 808 Livermore CA 94550

LIN, Y(U) K(WENG), b Foochow, China, Oct 30, 23; US citizen; m 52; c 4. STRUCTURAL ENGINEERING, APPLIED PROBABILITY. *Educ:* Amoy Univ, BS, 46; Stanford Univ, MS, 55, PhD(struct eng), 57. *Prof Exp:* Stress engr, Vertol Aircraft Corp, Pa, 56-57; prof eng, Imp Col Eng, Ethiopia, 57-58; res engr, Boeing Co, 58-60; asst prof aeronaut eng, 60-62, assoc prof aeronaut & astronaut eng, 62-65, PROF AERONAUT & ASTRONAUT ENG, UNIV ILL, URBANA, 65- *Concurrent Pos:* Consult, transport div, Boeing Co, 61, Wichita Div, 62, Gen Dynamics/Convair, 67, US Army Weapons Command, Ill, 72-77, Res Labs, Gen Motors Corp, 75- & TRW Defense & Space Systs, 78-; vis prof, Mass Inst Technol, 67-68; NSF sr fel, 67-68. *Mem:* Am Inst Aeronaut & Astronaut; Acoust Soc Am; Am Acad Mech. *Res:* Structural dynamics; random vibrations; systems reliability. *Mailing Add:* Dept Aeronaut & Astronaut Eng Univ Ill Urbana IL 61801

LIN, YEONG-JER, b Taiwan, China, Nov 11, 36; m 66; c 2. METEOROLOGY, ATMOSPHERIC SCIENCES. *Educ:* Nat Taiwan Univ, BS, 59; Univ Wis-Madison, MS, 64; NY Univ, PhD(meteorol), 69. *Prof Exp:* Res asst meteorol, Univ Wis-Madison, 62-64; asst res scientist, NY Univ, 65-69, assoc res scientist, 69; from asst prof to assoc prof, 69-76, PROF METEOROL, ST LOUIS UNIV, 76- *Concurrent Pos:* NSF res grants, St Louis Univ, 70-83. *Mem:* Am Meteorol Soc; Am Geophys Union. *Res:* Dynamical and observational studies of severe local storms; numerical modelling of meso-scale circulation. *Mailing Add:* Dept Earth & Atmospheric Sci St Louis Univ St Louis MO 63103

LIN, YONG YENG, b Feb 2, 33; Taiwan citizen; m 61; c 2. BIO-ORGANIC CHEMISTRY. *Educ:* Nat Taiwan Univ, BSc, 56; Tokyo Kyoiku Univ, MSc, 63; Tohoku Univ, Japan, PhD(org chem), 66. *Prof Exp:* Res assoc chem, Fla State Univ, 66-68; res assoc biochem, Univ Tex Med Br, Galveston, 68-70; res assoc chem, Univ Toronto, 70-72; RES SCIENTIST CHEM, UNIV TEX MED BR, 72- *Mem:* AAAS; Am Chem Soc; Sigma Xi. *Res:* Mechanisms of biological oxidation; enzyme models; application of enzymes and enzyme models to preparative organic chemistry; organic synthesis. *Mailing Add:* Div of Biochem Univ of Tex Med Br Galveston TX 77550

LIN, YOU-FENG, b Feng-Shan, Taiwan, July 31, 32; m 60; c 3. TOPOLOGY. *Educ:* Nat Taiwan Univ, BS, 57; Univ Fla, PhD(math), 64. *Prof Exp:* Asst math, Inst Math, Chinese Acad Sci, 56-59; from asst to assoc prof, 64-69, res asst prof, 65-66, PROF MATH, UNIV S FLA, 69- *Mem:* Am Math Soc; Math Asn Am. *Res:* Topological algebra; structure of topological semigroups; semigroup of measures; topology and relation-theory. *Mailing Add:* Dept of Math Univ of S Fla Tampa FL 33620

LIN, YU-CHONG, b Taiwan, Repub China, Apr 24, 35; m 60; c 2. PHYSIOLOGY. *Educ:* Taiwan Norm Univ, BS, 59; Univ NMex, MS, 64; Rutgers Univ, PhD(physiol), 68. *Prof Exp:* Teaching asst biol, Taiwan Norm Univ, 60-62; from asst prof to assoc prof, 69-76, PROF PHYSIOL, SCH MED, UNIV HAWAII, MANOA, 76- *Concurrent Pos:* Fel, Inst Environ Stress, Univ Calif, Santa Barbara, 68-69; physiologist consult, Cardiopulmonary Div, St Francis Hosp, 69- *Mem:* AAAS; Am Physiol Soc; Fedn Am Socs Exp Biol. *Res:* Cardiovascular research in the area of diving, exercise, and effect of environmental factors. *Mailing Add:* Dept of Physiol Sch of Med Univ of Hawaii Honolulu HI 96822

LIN, YUE JEE, b Canton, China, Oct 8, 45; US citizen; m 72; c 2. CYTOGENETICS. *Educ:* Nat Taiwan Univ, BS, 67; Ohio State Univ, MS, 72, PhD(genetics), 76. *Prof Exp:* Res asst, Nat Taiwan Univ, 68-69, Taiwan Agr Res Inst, 69-70; teaching assoc genetics & biol, Ohio State Univ, 70-76; asst prof, 76-82, ASSOC PROF GENETICS & CYTOGENETICS, ST JOHN'S UNIV, 82- *Mem:* Am Soc Cell Biol; Genetics Soc Am; Am Genetic Asn; Sigma Xi; AAAS. *Res:* Cytogenetics of complex heterozygotes, Rhoeo spathacea; cytogenetics of polyploids; cytogenetic effects of mutagens and environmental chemicals. *Mailing Add:* Dept Biol St John's Univ Jamaica NY 11439

LINAM, JAY H, b Carey, Idaho, Mar 9, 31; m 65; c 2. ENTOMOLOGY. *Educ:* Univ Idaho, BS, 53; Univ Utah, MS, 57, PhD(entom, zool), 65. *Prof Exp:* Asst entomologist, Ecol Res Lab, Univ Utah, 58-59; mgr, Magna Mosquito Abatement Dist, Utah, 60-62; from instr to assoc prof, 65-75, PROF BIOL, UNIV SOUTHERN COLO, 75- *Mem:* Entom Soc Am; Am Mosquito Control Asn. *Res:* Taxonomy and biology of mosquitoes of Western United States. *Mailing Add:* Dept of Biol Univ of Southern Colo Pueblo CO 81001

LINAWEAVER, FRANK PIERCE, b Woodstock, Va, Aug 22, 34; m 68; c 2. ENVIRONMENTAL ENGINEERING, CIVIL ENGINEERING. *Educ:* Johns Hopkins Univ, BES, 55, PhD(water resources, sanit eng), 65; Am Acad Environ Engrs, dipl. *Prof Exp:* From jr civil engr to sr civil engr, Bur Water Supply, Baltimore, 55 & 58-61; res staff asst, dept sanit eng & water resources, Johns Hopkins Univ, 61-65, res assoc, dept environ eng sci, 65-66; res staff mem, water resources group, Resources for Future, Inc, DC, 66; White House fel, US Govt, 66-67; assoc prof environ sci, dept environ eng & geog, Johns Hopkins Univ, 67-68; dep dir, Dept Pub Works, City of Baltimore, 68-69, dir, 69-74; consult environ & civil eng, 74-78; PARTNER, RUMMEL, KLEPPER & KAHL, CONSULT ENGRS, 78- *Concurrent Pos:* Mem, President's Air Qual Adv Bd, 68-71; consult rev panel, URS, Inc, 70-72; vis comt, Sch Archit, Univ Md, 75-78; prof geog & environ eng, Johns Hopkins Univ, 77-80, trustee, 80-86. *Mem:* Fel Am Soc Civil Engrs; Am Acad Environ Eng; fel AAAS; Nat Soc Prof Engrs; Am Water Works Asn. *Res:* Residential and commerical water use and their impact on urban water systems; urban water management and water resources; street cleaning relation to water pollution control; public works; sanitary environmental engineering; hydrology. *Mailing Add:* 224 Wendover Rd Baltimore MD 21218

LINCICOME, DAVID RICHARD, b Champaign, Ill, Jan 17, 14; m 41, 53; c 2. PARASITOLOGY, PHYSIOLOGY. *Educ:* Univ Ill, BS & MS, 37; Tulane Univ, PhD(parasitol), 41; Am Bd Med Microbiol, dipl, 65. *Prof Exp:* Asst zool, Univ Ill, 37; asst trop med, Sch Med, Tulane Univ, 34-41; from instr to asst prof zool, Univ Ky, 41-47; asst prof parasitol, Univ Wis, 47-49; sr res parasitologist, E I du Pont de Nemours & Co, 49-54; from asst prof to prof zool, Howard Univ, 55-70. *Concurrent Pos:* USPHS res grants, 58-68; ed, Exp Parasitol, 49- & chmn ed bd, 50-76; guest scientist, Naval Med Res Inst, 55-61; ed, Int Rev Trop Med, 60-; vis scientist, Lab Phys Biol, Nat Inst Arthritis & Metab Dis, 64-65; chmn comt exam & cert, Am Bd Med Microbiol, 72-; dir res, Am Dairy Goat Asn, mem bd dirs, 73-; ed, Trans, Am Micros Soc, 70-71; founder & ed, Int Goat & Sheep Res; guest scientist, Animal Parasitol Inst, USDA Exp Sta, Beltsville, Md, 78- *Mem:* Fel AAAS; Am Soc Parasitol; Helminth Soc (secy, 60, vpres, 61, pres, 68); fel NY Acad Sci; Am Dairy Goat Asn. *Res:* Diagnosis of protozoan and helminthic diseases; amebiasis; taxonomy and systematics of Acanthocephala, Nematoda and Cestoda; epidemiology of tropical diseases; molecular biology of parasitism; nutritional exchange between parasite and host. *Mailing Add:* Frogmoor Farm Box 634 Ft Valley Rte Seven Fountains VA 22653

LINCK, ALBERT JOHN, b Portsmouth, Ohio, Aug 18, 26; m 57; c 2. PLANT PHYSIOLOGY. *Educ:* Ohio State Univ, BSc, 50, MSc, 51, PhD(plant physiol), 55. *Prof Exp:* Instr plant physiol, 55-56, from asst prof to assoc prof, 56-61, asst dir, Minn Agr Exp Sta, 66-71, dean, Col Agr, 71-73, PROF PLANT PHYSIOL, UNIV MINN, ST PAUL, 61-, ASSOC V PRES ACAD ADMIN, 73- *Mem:* AAAS; Am Soc Plant Physiol; Bot Soc Am; Scand Soc Plant Physiol; Am Inst Biol Sci. *Res:* Translocation of inorganic and organic compounds; mechanism of action of growth regulators. *Mailing Add:* 213 Morrill Hall Univ of Minn Minneapolis MN 55455

LINCK, RICHARD WAYNE, b Los Angeles, Calif, Apr 9, 45; m 72; c 1. CELL BIOLOGY. *Educ:* Stanford Univ, BA, 67; Brandeis Univ, PhD(biol), 72. *Prof Exp:* Fel res microtubules, Med Res Coun, Eng, 71-73; instr, 74-75, ASST PROF, DEPT ANAT, HARVARD MED SCH, 75- *Concurrent Pos:* Fel, Europ Molecular Biol Org, 73; res grant, NIH, 74. *Mem:* Am Soc Cell Biol; Biophys Soc. *Res:* Relation of structure to motility; biochemistry and ultrastructure of microtubule proteins in cilia and flagella; reassembly of such proteins and enzymatic interaction with accessory components; optical diffraction of electron micrographs. *Mailing Add:* Dept of Anat Harvard Med Sch 25 Shattuck St Boston MA 02115

LINCK, ROBERT GEORGE, b St Louis, Mo, Nov 18, 38; m 62. INORGANIC CHEMISTRY. *Educ:* Case Western Reserve Univ, BS, 60; Univ Chicago, PhD(chem), 63. *Prof Exp:* Asst prof chem, Univ Calif, 66-72, assoc prof, 72-81; ASST PROF CHEM, SMITH COL, 81- *Mem:* AAAS; Am Chem Soc. *Res:* Rates of inorganic reactions, especially electron-transfer reactions; electronic structure and photochemistry of complex ions. *Mailing Add:* Dept of Chem Smith Col Northampton MA 01063

LINCOLN, CHARLES ALBERT, b Rudyard, Mont, May 13, 39; m 63; c 2. THEORETICAL PHYSICS. *Educ:* Mont State Univ, BS, 62, MS, 64; Univ Va, DSc(eng physics), 69. *Prof Exp:* From instr to asst prof physics, State Univ NY Col Fredonia, 64-76, prof, 76-80. *Concurrent Pos:* Fulbright exchange prof, Newcastle upon Tyne Polytech, Newcastle/Tyne, Eng, 73-74. *Mem:* Am Phys Soc; Am Asn Physics Teachers; Math Asn Am; Inst Elec & Electronics Eng. *Res:* Field theoretic methods in statistical mechanics and fluids; a generalized dynamical formalism of statistical mechanics; information theory and electroacoustics. *Mailing Add:* 2163 Granite Dr Walla Walla WA 99362

LINCOLN, CHARLES GATEWOOD, b Bentonville, Ark, Feb 23, 14; m 38. ENTOMOLOGY. *Educ:* Univ Ark, BSA, 34; Cornell Univ, PhD(entom), 38. *Prof Exp:* Asst entom, Cornell Univ, 34-35, instr, 35-41, asst prof, 41-42; exten entomologist, Exten Serv, 42-50, head dept, 51-69, prof, 50-81, EMER PROF ENTOM, DIV AGR, UNIV ARK, 81- *Concurrent Pos:* Mem, Ark State Plant Bd, 51- *Mem:* Entom Soc Am. *Res:* Cotton insects. *Mailing Add:* Dept Entom A-317 Univ Ark Fayetteville AR 72701

LINCOLN, DAVID ERWIN, b Detroit, Mich, Oct 8, 44; m 70. CHEMICAL ECOLOGY. *Educ:* Kalamazoo Col, BA, 71; Univ Calif, Santa Cruz, PhD(biol), 78. *Prof Exp:* Fel, Stanford Univ, 78-80; ASST PROF BIOL, UNIV SC, 80- *Mem:* Ecol Soc Am; Bot Soc Am; AAAS. *Res:* Environmental and genetic control of secondary chemical production by plants and the roles of these chemicals in plant-herbivore coevalution. *Mailing Add:* Dept Biol Univ SC Columbia SC 29208

LINCOLN, JEANNETTE VIRGINIA, b Ames, Iowa, Sept 7, 15. GEOPHYSICS, SOLAR PHYSICS. *Educ:* Wellesley Col, BA, 36; Iowa State Univ, MS, 38. *Prof Exp:* Asst household equip, Iowa State Univ, 37-38, instr, 38-42; physicist, Nat Bur Standards, DC, 42-54, sect chief, Radio Warning Serv, Colo, 59-65, dep chief data serv, Inst Telecommun Sci & Aeronomy, Environ Sci Serv Admin, 65-66, dep chief data serv & chief, Upper Atmosphere Geophys, 66-70, chief data serv & dir, World Data Ctr A, Solar-Terrestrial Physics, Nat Geophys & Solar Terrestrial Data Ctr, Environ Data & Info Serv, Nat Oceanic & Atmospheric Admin, 70-81. *Concurrent Pos:* Mem US preparatory comt study group ionospheric propagation, Int Radio Consult Comt, 59-80; secy, Int Ursigram & World Days Serv, 61-81, mem, US Comn G, Int Sci Radio Union, 63-, secy, Ionospheric Network Adv Group, 69-81; forecasting reporter, Int Asn Geomagnetism & Aeronomy, 63-67, mem comns IV & V, 67-73; mem working groups 3 & 5, Inter-Union Comn on Solar-Terrestrial Physics, 69-72; Am Geophys Union mem, Am Geophys Union-Int Sci Radio Union Bd of Radio Sci, 69-74; chmn working group V6, Geophys Indices, 73-81; mem comn 40, Int Astron Union, 76- *Honors & Awards:* Gold Medal, Dept of Com, 73. *Mem:* Fel AAAS; Sigma Xi; fel Am Geophys Union; Am Astron Soc; Int Asn Geomagnetism & Aeronomy. *Res:* Radio propagation disturbances and forecasts; solar-terrestrial relationships; publication of solar and geophysical data; prediction of solar indices; data center management. *Mailing Add:* 2005 Alpine Dr Boulder CO 80302

LINCOLN, KENNETH ARNOLD, b Oakland, Calif, Oct 1, 22; m 56; c 4. HIGH TEMPERATURE CHEMISTRY. *Educ:* Stanford Univ, AB, 44, MS, 48, PhD(phys chem), 57. *Prof Exp:* Phys chemist, US Naval Radio Defense Lab, 58-69; RES SCIENTIST, NASA-AMES RES CTR, 70- *Mem:* Am Chem Soc; Am Soc Mass Spectrometry; Am Sci Affil; Combustion Inst; Am Vacuum Soc. *Res:* Thermochemistry of the vaporization of refractory materials; thermokinetics of pulsed energy deposition; development of instrumentation combining lasers and high-speed mass spectrometry for in-situ analyses of short-lived chemical species; space flight spectrometric instrumentation. *Mailing Add:* 2016 Stockbridge Ave Redwood City CA 94061

LINCOLN, LEWIS LAUREN, b Canandaigua, NY, Oct 9, 26; m 49; c 6. PHOTOGRAPHIC CHEMISTRY. *Prof Exp:* Lab technician, 46-60, res chemist, 60-65, sr res chemist, 65-70, RES ASSOC CHEM, RES LABS, EASTMAN KODAK, 70- *Res:* The study and synthesis of photographic sensitizing dyes and addenda. *Mailing Add:* 426 Mount Airy Dr Rochester NY 14617

LINCOLN, RICHARD CRIDDLE, b Boston, Mass, Nov 25, 42; c 2. APPLIED PHYSICS. *Educ:* Cornell Univ, BEP, 66, MS, 68, PhD(mat sci), 71. *Prof Exp:* Instr & res assoc mat sci, Cornell Univ, 70-71; TECH STAFF MEM APPL PHYSICS, SANDIA LABS, 71- *Res:* High pressure and high temperature experimental techniques; analysis of nuclear waste management systems. *Mailing Add:* Sandia Labs Albuquerque NM 87115

LINCOLN, RICHARD G, b Portland, Ore, Nov 1, 23; m 46; c 2. PLANT PHYSIOLOGY. *Educ:* Ore State Univ, BS, 49; Univ Calif, Los Angeles, PhD, 55. *Prof Exp:* Plant physiologist, Sugarcane Field Sta, USDA, La, 55-56; PROF BOT, CALIF STATE UNIV, LONG BEACH, 56- *Mem:* AAAS; Am Soc Plant Physiol. *Res:* Plant photoperiodism; inhibition of flowering and extraction of the flowering stimulus; rhythmic phenomena in fungi. *Mailing Add:* Dept of Biol Calif State Univ Long Beach CA 90804

LIND, ARTHUR CHARLES, b Chicago, Ill, May 28, 32; m 57; c 3. APPLIED PHYSICS, SPACE PHYSICS. *Educ:* Univ Ill, Urbana, BS, 55; Rensselaer Polytech Inst, PhD(physics), 66. *Prof Exp:* Physicist, Knolls Atomic Power Lab, 58-61 & Watervliet Arsenal, US Army, 63-66; assoc scientist, 66-76, scientist, 76-79, SR SCIENTIST, MCDONNELL DOUGLAS RES LABS, 79- *Mem:* Am Phys Soc; Am Chem Soc; Int Soc Magnetic Resonance. *Res:* Nuclear magnetic resonance studies of polymers; theoretical and experimental studies of electromagnetic scattering; propagation of electromagnetic waves in turbulent media; measurement of dielectric properties at high temperatures. *Mailing Add:* 15450 Country Mill Ct Chesterfield MO 63017

LIND, CHARLES DOUGLAS, b Pittsburgh, Pa, May 12, 30; m 55; c 2. PHYSICAL CHEMISTRY. *Educ:* Pa State Univ, BS, 52; Univ Ore, MS, 54, PhD(chem), 56. *Prof Exp:* Fel chem, Univ Ore, 56-57; CHEMIST, NAVAL WEAPONS CTR, 57- *Mem:* Am Chem Soc. *Res:* Chemistry of explosives; detonation theory; combustion theory. *Mailing Add:* Naval Weapons Ctr Code 3262 China Lake CA 93555

LIND, DAVID ARTHUR, b Seattle, Wash, Sept 12, 18; m 45; c 4. NUCLEAR PHYSICS. *Educ:* Univ Wash, Seattle, BS, 40; Calif Inst Technol, MS, 43, PhD(physics), 48. *Prof Exp:* Jr aerodynamicist, Boeing Airplane Co, Wash, 42-43; physicist, Appl Physics Lab, Univ Wash, Seattle, 43-45; res fel physics, Calif Inst Technol, 48-50; Guggenheim fel, Nobel Inst Physics, Stockholm, 50-51; asst prof, Univ Wis, 51-56; assoc prof, 56-59, chmn dept physics & astrophys, 74-78, PROF PHYSICS, UNIV COLO, BOULDER, 59- *Concurrent Pos:* Consult off instnl prog, NSF, 63-66; physicist div res, US AEC, 69-70; mem prog adv comn, Los Alamos Meson Facil, 71-74, chmn users group, 75-76. *Mem:* Fel Am Phys Soc; Sigma Xi; Am Asn Physics Teachers. *Res:* X-rays; crystal diffraction; nuclear spectroscopy; sector focused cyclotron design; charged particle scattering; reaction studies; fast neutron spectroscopy. *Mailing Add:* Dept of Physics & Astrophys Univ of Colo Boulder CO 80302

LIND, HOWARD ERIC, b Providence, RI, Feb 22, 13; m 37; c 4. BACTERIOLOGY. *Educ:* RI State Col, BS, 34, MS, 35; Mass Inst Technol, MPH, 37; Northwestern Univ, PhD(bact), 43; Am Bd Microbiol, dipl. *Prof Exp:* Asst bact, RI State Col, 34-35; lectr, RI Sch Educ, 35; asst bacteriologist, State Health Dept, RI, 35-36, sanitarian & bacteriologist, 36-37; bacteriologist, St Louis County Hosp & dir labs, County Health Dept, 37-40; sr bacteriologist, Chicago Br Lab, State Dept Health, Ill, 40-43; bacteriologist, Dow Chem Co, Mich, 45-46; res dir, Sias Lab, Brooks Hosp, Brookline, Mass, 46-71; mem staff, Maine Dept Health & Welfare, 70-71, asst dir, 71-76, DIR, PUB HEALTH LABS, MAINE DEPT HUMAN SERV, 76- *Concurrent Pos:* Consult, RI Health Labs, 62; lectr sch med, Wash Univ, 38; supvr lab, Booth Mem Hosp, 48-50; pres & dir res, Lind Labs, Inc, 56-70. *Mem:* Am Soc Microbiol; Am Pub Health Asn; Inst Food Technol; NY Acad Sci. *Res:* Evaluation of antibiotics in urinary tract infections; electronic counting of bacteria; hospital infections and phage typing; state laboratory evaluation; quality control. *Mailing Add:* Pub Health Labs Dept of Human Serv Augusta ME 04330

LIND, JAMES FOREST, surgery, see previous edition

LIND, MAURICE DAVID, b Jamestown, NY, July 25, 34; m 62; c 1. PHYSICAL CHEMISTRY, X-RAY CRYSTALLOGRAPHY. *Educ:* Otterbein Col, BS, 57; Cornell Univ, PhD(phys chem), 62. *Prof Exp:* NSF fel, 62-63; res chemist phys chem, Union Oil Co, Calif, 63-66; MEM TECH STAFF, MICROELECTRONICS RES & DEVELOP CTR, ROCKWELL INT, 66- *Mem:* AAAS; Am Chem Soc; Am Phys Soc; Am Crystallog Asn; Sigma Xi. *Res:* Crystal chemistry; crystal growth. *Mailing Add:* 1690 Stoddard Ave Thousand Oaks CA 91360

LIND, NIELS CHRISTIAN, b Copenhagen, Denmark, Mar 10, 30; Can citizen; m 57; c 3. APPLIED MECHANICS. *Educ:* Royal Tech Univ Denmark, MSc, 53; Univ Ill, PhD(theoret & appl mech), 59. *Prof Exp:* Design engr, Dominia Ltd, Denmark, 53-54; engr, Bell Tel Co, Can, 54-55; field engr, Drake & Merritt Co, Labrador, 55-56; design engr, Fenco, Que, 56; asst stress anal, Univ Ill, 56-57, instr, 57-58, res assoc, 58-59, asst prof theoret & appl mech, 59-60; assoc prof civil eng, 60-62, PROF CIVIL ENG, UNIV WATERLOO, 62- *Concurrent Pos:* Mem, Can Nat Study Group Math Higher Educ, Orgn for Econ Coop & Develop, 63-65, adv comt nuclear safety, Atomic Energy Control Bd, 81-; vis prof, Univ Laval, 69, Inst Eng, Nat Univ Mex, 75 & 81 & Tech Univ Denmark, 77-78. *Mem:* Fel Am Acad Mech (pres, 71-72); fel Royal Soc Can. *Res:* Structural mechanics; theory of design; structural reliability and optimization. *Mailing Add:* Dept of Civil Eng Univ of Waterloo Waterloo ON N2L 3G1 Can

LIND, OWEN THOMAS, b Emporia, Kans, June 2, 34; m 54; c 2. LIMNOLOGY, BIOLOGY. *Educ:* William Jewell Col, AB, 56; Univ Mich, MS, 60; Univ Mo, PhD(zool), 66. *Prof Exp:* Biologist, Parke, Davis & Co, Mich, 56-60; asst prof biol, William Jewell Col, 60-62; res assoc limnol, Univ Mo, 66; asst prof biol, 66-69, assoc prof, 69-79, PROF BIOL, BAYLOR UNIV, 79- *Concurrent Pos:* Investr, Off Water Resources Res grants, 66, prin investr thermal pollution, 71-73 & prin investr eutrophication, 76; consult, US Nat Park Serv, Guadalupe Mt Nat Park, 69- & Big Bend Nat Park, 74-76; dir, Inst Environ Studies, 71-76; mem selection comt, Tyler Ecol Award, 74- *Mem:* Am Soc Limnol & Oceanog; Sigma Xi; Int Asn Theoret & Appl Limnol; Brit Freshwater Biol Asn. *Res:* Limnology of polluted waters; primary production and community metabolism in relation to water quality and eutrophication. *Mailing Add:* Dept of Biol Baylor Univ Waco TX 76703

LIND, ROBERT WAYNE, b Ishpeming, Mich, Aug 25, 39; m 64; c 2. THEORETICAL PHYSICS. *Educ:* Mich Technol Univ, BS, 61; Univ Pittsburgh, PhD(physics), 70. *Prof Exp:* Engr, Ford Motor Co, 61-63; res assoc physics, Syracuse Univ, 70-72; sr res assoc, Temple Univ, 72-73; res assoc, Fla State Univ, 73-74; asst prof physics, WVa Inst Technol, 74-78, chmn dept, 76-78; ASSOC PROF PHYSICS, UNIV WIS-PLATTEVILLE, 78- *Mem:* Am Asn Physics Teachers; Int Soc Gen Relativity & Gravitation; AAAS. *Res:* Investigation of the long range forces, gravitational and electromagnetic, and their relationship to the nature of space and time; some cosmology and mathematical physics. *Mailing Add:* Dept of Physics Univ Wis Platteville WI 53818

LIND, VANCE GORDON, b Brigham City, Utah, Feb 12, 35; m 64; c 9. PHYSICS, ASTROPHYSICS. *Educ:* Utah State Univ, BS, 59; Univ Wis, MS, 61, PhD(elem particles), 64. *Prof Exp:* Eng asst, Edgerton, Germeshausen & Grier, Inc, summer, 59, res asst, 60; res assoc, Univ Mich, summer, 64; asst prof physics, 64-68, assoc prof, 68-75, PROF PHYSICS, UTAH STATE UNIV, 75-, DEPT HEAD, PHYSICS, 81- *Concurrent Pos:* Utah State Univ Res Found grant, 64-66, 72-76 & 78-79; investr, NSF res grant, Utah State Univ, 66-68, 68-71, 78-80 & 80-83. *Mem:* Am Phys Soc; Sigma Xi. *Res:* Basic interactions; elementary particle interactions, meson and nucleon interactions with nuclei, astronomy and astrophysics. *Mailing Add:* Dept of Physics Utah State Univ Logan UT 84321

LIND, WILTON H(OWARD), b Oakland, Calif, Feb 14, 27; m 51; c 2. CHEMICAL ENGINEERING. *Educ:* Univ Calif, Berkeley, BS, 50, MS, 52; Empire Col, Santa Rosa, JD, 77. *Prof Exp:* From asst res engr to sr res engr, Chevron Res Co, 51-78, analyst, 78-80, ASST SECY, FINANCE DEPT, CHEVRON CHEM CO, 80- *Mem:* Am Chem Soc; Am Inst Chem Engrs. *Res:* Petrochemical research and development; aromatics chemistry; pilot plant design and operation. *Mailing Add:* 575 Market St San Francisco CA 94105

LINDAHL, CHARLES BLIGHE, b N Platte, Nebr, Feb 4, 39; m 59; c 2. SYNTHETIC INORGANIC CHEMISTRY, INORGANIC CHEMISTRY. *Educ:* Iowa State Univ, BS, 60; Univ Calif, Berkeley, PhD(chem), 64. *Prof Exp:* Sr chemist, Eastman Kodak, 64-65; mem tech staff, Rocketdyne Div, Rockwell Int, 65-70; sr chemist, Reheis Chem, 70-71; head new prod develop, 71-72, TECH DIR, OZARK MAHONING CO, 73- *Concurrent Pos:* Sr chemist, Reheis Chem, 70-71. *Mem:* Am Chem Soc; Am Asn Dent Res; Int Asn Dent Res; Sigma Xi. *Res:* Inorganic synthesis; fluorides for dental applications; oxidizer chemistry; unusual oxidation states. *Mailing Add:* 1870 S Boulder Tulsa OK 74119

LINDAHL, LASSE ALLAN, b Copenhagen, Denmark, Sept 9, 44; m 78; c 1. MOLECULAR GENETICS, BACTERIAL PHYSIOLOGY. *Educ:* Univ Copenhagen, MSc, 69, PhD(microbiol), 73. *Prof Exp:* Fel molecular biol, Univ Wis-Madison, 73-76; asst prof, Univ Aarhus, Denmark, 76-78; ASST PROF MOLECULAR GENETICS, DEPT BIOL, UNIV ROCHESTER, 78- *Mem:* Am Soc Microbiol. *Res:* Molecular basis for the regulation of ribosome synthesis in E coli; in vitro DNA recombination and biochemical measurements of the synthesis of specific RNA and protein molecules. *Mailing Add:* Dept Biol Univ Rochester Rochester NY 14627

LINDAHL, RONALD GUNNAR, b Detroit, Mich, Aug 11, 48; m 70; c 2. BIOCHEMISTRY. *Educ:* Wayne State Univ, BA, 70, PhD(biol), 73. *Prof Exp:* Fel biochem, Argonne Nat Lab, 74-75; asst prof, 75-78, ASSOC PROF BIOL, UNIV ALA, 78- *Mem:* Am Asn Cancer Res; AAAS; Genetics Soc Am; Asn Southeastern Biologists; Int Soc Biomed Res Alcoholism. *Res:* Biochemical changes during neoplasia; developmental biochemistry; transplacental and perinatal carcinogenesis; genetic regulation of enzyme activity. *Mailing Add:* Dept Biol Univ of Ala University AL 35486

LINDAHL, ROY LAWRENCE, b Los Angeles, Calif, Aug 22, 25; m 48, 76; c 4. DENTISTRY. *Educ:* Univ Southern Calif, BS & DDS, 50; Univ Mich, MS, 52; Am Bd Pedodontics, dipl, 56. *Prof Exp:* Asst prof, 52-56, PROF PEDODONTICS, UNIV DENT, UNIV NC, CHAPEL HILL, 56-, DIR CONTINUING EDUC & DENT DEMONSTR PRACT, 70- *Concurrent Pos:* Mem bd trustees, NC Cerebral Palsy Hosp, 57-63; consult, Womack Army Hosp, Ft Bragg, NC, 60-78; examr, Am Bd Pedodontics, 60-67, chmn, 67. *Mem:* AAAS; Am Soc Dent for Children (from secy to pres, 69-73); Am Dent Asn; Am Acad Pedodontics (vpres, 62-63, pres-elect, 63-64, pres, 64-65); Int Asn Dent Res. *Res:* Pedodontics; effective utilization of dental auxiliary personnel; problems of the handicapped patient; pre-payment dental care programs; health services research-quality assurance. *Mailing Add:* Off of Continuing Educ Univ of NC Sch of Dent 209H Chapel Hill NC 27514

LINDAL, GUNNAR F(JELDBO), b Oslo, Norway, Mar 24, 36; US citizen; m 62; c 1. ELECTRICAL ENGINEERING. *Educ:* Stanford Univ, PhD(elec eng), 64. *Prof Exp:* Res assoc, Stanford Electronics Lab, 64-69; MEM TECH STAFF, JET PROPULSION LAB, 69- *Mem:* Am Astron Soc; Am Geophys Union; Union Radio Sci Int. *Res:* Applied mathematics and computer science; radio propagation and communication; planetary atmospheres and surfaces; participated in the radio occultation measurements of the atmospheres of Mercury, Venus, Mars, Jupiter, Saturn and Titan during the Mariner, Pioneer, Viking and Voyager spaceflight missions to these planets and satellites. *Mailing Add:* Jet Propulsion Lab 4800 Oak Grove Dr Pasadena CA 91109

LINDAMOOD, JOHN BENFORD, b Galax, Va, Aug 6, 29; m 53; c 1. DAIRY TECHNOLOGY. *Educ:* Va Polytech Inst & State Univ, BS, 53, MS, 55; Ohio State Univ, PhD(educ), 74. *Prof Exp:* Prod mgr, Evaporated Milk Div, Carnation Co, 56-61; asst prof, 74-78, ASSOC PROF FOOD SCI, DEPT FOOD SCI & NUTRIT, OHIO STATE UNIV, 78- *Mem:* Inst Food Technologists; Am Dairy Sci Asn; Coun Agr Sci & Technol. *Res:* Milk and milk products. *Mailing Add:* Dept Food Sci & Nutrit Ohio State Univ 2121 Fyffe Rd Columbus OH 43210

LINDAU, EVERT INGOLF, b Vaxjo, Sweden, Oct 4, 42. SOLID STATE PHYSICS. *Educ:* Chalmers Univ Technol, Sweden, Civilingenjor, 68, Technol Licentiat, 70, PhD(physics), 71, DrTechnol, 72. *Prof Exp:* Res asst physics, Chalmers Univ Technol, Sweden, 68-71; res scientist, Varian Assocs, 71-72; res assoc physics, 72-74, PROF PHYSICS, STANFORD UNIV, 74- *Mem:* Am Phys Soc; Am Vacuum Soc; Swed Soc Technol. *Res:* Optical and photoemission studies of the electronic structure of materials using synchrotron radiation with emphasis on surface properties; surface states, surface photoemission, physisorbtion, chemisorbtion, surface composition and catalytic activities. *Mailing Add:* Stanford Electronics Lab Stanford Univ Stanford CA 94305

LINDAUER, GEORGE CONRAD, b Queens, NY, Nov 5, 35; m 59; c 3. NUCLEAR ENGINEERING, INFORMATION SCIENCE. *Educ:* Cooper Union, BS, 56; Mass Inst Technol, ScM, 57; Univ Pittsburgh, PhD(mech eng), 62; Long Island Univ, MS, 71. *Prof Exp:* From jr engr to sr engr, Bettis Atomic Power Lab, Westinghouse Elec Corp, 57-64; from asst chem engr to chem engr, Brookhaven Nat Lab, 64-71; assoc prof, PROF NUCLEAR ENG & LIBRN, SPEED SCI SCH, UNIV LOUISVILLE, 71- *Mem:* Am Soc Mech Engrs; Am Soc Eng Educ; Am Nuclear Soc. *Res:* Information retrieval; heat transfer; fluidized beds; fluid dynamics. *Mailing Add:* Speed Sci Sch Univ of Louisville Louisville KY 40208

LINDAUER, IVO EUGENE, b Grand Valley, Colo, Apr 7, 31; m 57; c 2. PLANT ECOLOGY. *Educ:* Colo State Univ, BS, 53, PhD(bot), 70; Univ Northern Colo, MA, 60. *Prof Exp:* Instr biol, Univ Northern Colo, 60-64, asst prof sci, 64-65; res assoc & teaching asst bot, Colo State Univ, 65-67; from asst prof to assoc prof, 67-75, asst dean, Col Arts & Sci, 76-81, PROF BOT, UNIV NORTHERN COLO, 75- *Concurrent Pos:* Tri-Univ Proj grant, NY Univ, 70; US Bur Reclamation grant, proposed Narrows Dam site, 70-72 & 72-75; mem, vpres & pres bd trustees, Colo Nature Conserv; Northwest Colo Wildlife Consortium grant, 81-82. *Mem:* Ecol Soc Am; Nat Asn Biol Teacher (secy-treas, 69-70); Am Inst Biol Sci. *Res:* Analysis of vegetational communities found along flood plains; ecological studies of river bottom ecosystems. *Mailing Add:* Dept of Biol Sci Univ of Northern Colo Greeley CO 80639

LINDAUER, MAURICE WILLIAM, b Millstadt, Ill, Sept 25, 24; m 46; c 3. ANALYTICAL CHEMISTRY, PHYSICAL CHEMISTRY. *Educ:* Wash Univ, AB, 49, AM, 53; Harvard Univ, MEd, 62; Fla State Univ, PhD, 70. *Prof Exp:* Res chemist, Mallinckrodt Chem Works, 52-55 & Am Zinc, Ill, 55-56; res chemist, Nitrogen Div, Allied Chem & Dye Corp, 56-57; assoc prof anal & phys chem, 57-71, PROF CHEM, VALDOSTA STATE COL, 71-, ACTG HEAD DEPT, 81- *Concurrent Pos:* NSF sci fac fel, 64-65. *Mem:* Am Chem Soc; Sigma Xi. *Res:* Mossbauer spectroscopy; history of chemistry; thermodynamics and chemical equilibrium. *Mailing Add:* Dept of Chem Valdosta State Col Valdosta GA 31601

LINDBECK, WENDELL ARTHUR, b Rockford, Ill, Sept 28, 12; m 38; c 3. ORGANIC CHEMISTRY. *Educ:* Beloit Col, BS, 36; Univ Wis, PhM, 37, PhD(chem), 40. *Prof Exp:* Teacher, Tenn Jr Col, 40-44; tech coord, Goodyear Synthetic Rubber Corp, Ohio, 44-47; assoc prof & chmn, Natural Sci Div, Univ Ill, 47-49; from assoc prof to prof phys sci & chem, 49-78, EMER PROF CHEM, NORTHERN ILL UNIV, 78- *Concurrent Pos:* NSF sci fac fel, Univ Calif, Berkeley, 60-61; US AEC grant, Argonne Nat Lab, 69-70. *Mem:* Am Chem Soc. *Res:* Synthesis of organic compounds. *Mailing Add:* 204 Windsor Dr De Kalb IL 60115

LINDBERG, DAVID SEAMAN, SR, b Merrill, Wis, July 17, 29; m 51; c 3. ACADEMIC ADMINISTRATION, HEALTH SCIENCES. *Educ:* Univ Wis-Stevens Point, BS, 58; Univ Fla, MEd, 69, EdD, 70. *Prof Exp:* Lab supvr, Marshfield Clin, Wis, 58-66; res asst clin path, Col Med, Univ Fla, 66; supvry med technologist, Lab Serv, Vet Admin Hosp, Gainesville, Fla, 67-68; asst prof health related professions, Ctr Allied Health Instrnl Personnel, Univ Fla, 71-72, asst prof med technol, Col Health Related Professions, 72-74; assoc prof, 74-80, PROF MED TECHNOL, LA STATE UNIV MED CTR, NEW ORLEANS, 80-, ASSOC DEAN SCH ALLIED HEALTH PROFESSIONS 74- *Concurrent Pos:* Dep dir, Reserve Forces Med Contingency Planning, Off Asst Sec Defense for Health Affairs, 81- *Honors & Awards:* Prof Achievement Award Educ, Am Soc Med Technologists, 74, Outstanding Performance Recognition Certs, 74 & 75. *Mem:* Am Soc Allied Health Professions; Asn Mil Surgeons US; Am Soc Clin Pathologists; Am Soc Med Technologists. *Res:* Continuing education in the health professions. *Mailing Add:* Rte 4 Box 203XL Covington LA 70433

LINDBERG, DONALD ALLAN BROR, b Brooklyn, NY, Sept 21, 33; m 57; c 3. PATHOLOGY, COMPUTER SCIENCE. *Educ:* Amherst Col, AB, 54; Columbia Univ, MD, 58; Am Bd Path, dipl, 63. *Hon Degrees:* ScD, Amherst Col, 79. *Prof Exp:* From instr to assoc prof path, Sch Med, 62-69, chmn dept info sci, Med Ctr, 68-71, PROF PATH, SCH MED, UNIV MO-COLUMBIA, 69-, DIR INFO SCI GROUP, MED CTR, 71-, DIR HEALTH CARE TECHNOL CTR, 76- *Concurrent Pos:* Markle scholar, 64-69; mem, Comput Res & Biomath Study Sect, NIH, 67-71 & Comput Sci & Eng Bd, Nat Acad Sci, 71-73; chmn, CBX Adv Comt, Nat Bd Med Examrs, 71-74, mem, Joint CBX Comt, Nat Bd Med Examrs & Am Bd Internal Med, 74-; US rep, Comt Comput Med, Int Fedn Info Processing; mem, Biomed Review Libr Comt, Nat Libr Med, 79-80; consult & mem, Peer Review Group, TRIMIS, Dept Defense, 77- *Mem:* Am Soc Exp Path; Soc Exp Biol & Med; Am Soc Clin Path; Col Am Path. *Res:* Information processing; computers in medicine; infectious diseases. *Mailing Add:* 605 Lewis Hall Univ of Mo Columbia MO 65211

LINDBERG, EDWARD E, b Boston, Mass, Aug 16, 38; m 58; c 2. MECHANICAL ENGINEERING. *Educ:* Worcester Polytech Inst, BSME, 60, MSME, 63. *Prof Exp:* Test engr, Scintilla Div, Bendix Corp, 60-61; engr, Alden Res Labs, Worcester Polytech Inst, 61-63; asst prof mech eng, 63-67, ASSOC PROF MECH ENG, WESTERN NEW ENG COL, 67-, DIR COMPUT CTR, 68- *Mem:* Am Soc Mech Engrs; Am Soc Eng Educ; Instrument Soc Am. *Res:* Automatic controls; fluid mechanics; thermodynamics; computer sciences. *Mailing Add:* Dept of Mech Eng Western New Eng Col Springfield MA 01119

LINDBERG, GEORGE DONALD, b Salt Lake City, Utah, Feb 9, 25; m 55; c 3. PLANT PATHOLOGY. *Educ:* Ariz State Univ, BS, 50; Okla State Univ, MS, 52; Univ Wis, PhD(plant path), 55. *Prof Exp:* Asst prof, 55-59, assoc prof, 59-70, PROF PLANT PATH, LA STATE UNIV, BATON ROUGE, 70- *Mem:* Am Phytopath Soc. *Res:* Plant virology; diseases of forage crops; abnormalities in the fungi. *Mailing Add:* Dept of Bot & Plant Path La State Univ Baton Rouge LA 70803

LINDBERG, JAMES DAVID, b Lewiston, Idaho, Mar 22, 36. ATMOSPHERIC AEROSOLS, SPECTROSCOPY. *Educ:* Wash State Univ, BS, 59; Univ Tex, MS, 70. *Prof Exp:* Design engr electronics, Boeing Airplane Co, 59-61; sr engr Titan Missile, Fed Elec Corp, Int Tel & Tel, 61-62; physicist atmosphere, US Army Electronics Command, 63-69; RES PHYSICIST ATMOSPHERIC AEROSOLS, US ARMY ATMOSPHERIC SCI LAB, 69- *Mem:* AAAS; Optical Soc Am; Mineral Soc Am; Ger Gemmol Soc; Brit Mineral Soc. *Res:* Visible and infrared propagation through fog, haze, dust and smoke; determination of optical constants of particulate matter by transmission and diffuse reflectance spectroscopic methods; optical properties of minerals and gemstones. *Mailing Add:* PO Box 88 White Sands Missile Range NM 88002

LINDBERG, JAMES GEORGE, b Grand Rapids, Mich, Sept 19, 40; m 62, 78; c 3. ORGANIC CHEMISTRY. *Educ:* Kalamazoo Col, BA, 62; Baylor Univ, PhD, 69. *Prof Exp:* From asst prof to assoc prof, 67-78, PROF CHEM, DRAKE UNIV, 78- *Concurrent Pos:* Drake Univ Res Coun grant, 68-70; Res Corp grant, 73- *Mem:* Am Chem Soc; Royal Soc Chem. *Res:* Nuclear magnetic resonance spectroscopic studies of steric effects. *Mailing Add:* Dept of Chem Drake Univ Des Moines IA 50311

LINDBERG, JOHN ALBERT, JR, b New York, NY, Apr 19, 34; m 64; c 2. MATHEMATICAL ANALYSIS. *Educ:* Wagner Col, BA, 54; Univ Minn, MA, 57, PhD(math), 60. *Prof Exp:* Instr math, Univ Minn, 58-59 & Yale Univ, 60-62; from asst to assoc prof, 62-72, PROF MATH, SYRACUSE UNIV, 72- *Concurrent Pos:* Res fel math, Yale Univ, 68-69. *Mem:* AAAS; Am Math Soc; Math Asn Am; Sigma Xi. *Res:* Theory of algebraic extensions of Banach algebras and factorization of polynomials over such algebras; inverse producing normed extensions. *Mailing Add:* Dept of Math Room 200 Carnegie Syracuse Univ Syracuse NY 13210

LINDBERG, LOIS HELEN, b Scott Air Force Base, Ill, Sept 1, 32. MEDICAL MICROBIOLOGY. *Educ:* San Jose State Col, AB, 52; Univ Calif, MPH, 58; Stanford Univ, PhD, 67. *Prof Exp:* Jr microbiologist, State Dept Pub Health, Calif, 53-54; instr bact, San Jose State Col, 54-55; assoc pub health, Pub Health Lab, Univ Calif, 55-58; asst prof bact, 58-65, assoc prof biol, 65-70, prof biol, 70-80, assoc dean fac, 78-79, PROF MICROBIOLOGY, SAN JOSE STATE UNIV, 80- *Concurrent Pos:* NSF sci teachers fel, 62, fel, 66 & 67; res assoc, Stanford Univ Med Sch. *Mem:* AAAS; Am Pub Health Asn; Am Soc Microbiol. *Res:* Medical microbiology as related with the pathology and immunology of streptococcal infections. *Mailing Add:* Dept of Biol Sci San Jose State Col San Jose CA 95114

LINDBERG, R(OBERT) G(ENE), b Los Angeles, Calif, June 9, 24; m 47; c 4. ZOOLOGY. *Educ:* Univ Calif, Los Angeles, BA, 48, PhD(zool), 52. *Prof Exp:* Asst zool, Univ Calif, Los Angeles, 50, jr res biologist radiation ecol, Atomic Energy Proj, 52-55, asst res biologist, 55-59; head bioastronaut lab, Northrop Corp, 59-67, mem sr tech staff, Labs, 67-74; LECTR ENVIRON SCI ENG, UNIV CALIF, LOS ANGELES, 74-, RES BIOLOGIST, LAB NUCLEAR MED & RADIATION BIOL, 75- *Concurrent Pos:* Instr, Art Ctr Col Design, 51-; Pauley fel, Univ Hawaii, 52; consult, Sch Med, Univ Calif, Los Angeles, 59-65 & Am Inst Biol Sci, 67-70; secy, Bd Trustees, BIOSIS, 74-79; mem, Space Biol Adv Panel, Am Inst Biol Sci/NASA, 75- *Mem:* AAAS; Ecol Soc Am; Am Soc Zoologists. *Res:* Radiobiology; circadian rhythms; chronobiology; environmental radiobiology. *Mailing Add:* Environ Sci & Eng Univ of Calif Los Angeles CA 90024

LINDBERG, ROBERT BENJAMIN, b Grand Rapids, Mich, Dec 26, 14; m 42; c 2. MEDICAL MICROBIOLOGY. *Educ:* Univ Mich, BS, 35, MS, 36, PhD(bact), 50. *Prof Exp:* Instr bact, Univ Mich, 37-41; US Army, 42-, chief dept bact, 18th Med Gen Lab, 44-47, 406th Med Gen Lab, Japan, 50-53, Walter Reed Army Inst Res, 54-57 & Med Lab, Ger, 57-61, CHIEF DEPT MICROBIOL, INST SURG RES, US ARMY, 61- *Concurrent Pos:* Consult, Int Soc Burn Injuries, 80- *Honors & Awards:* Army Res & Develop Achievement Award, US Army Res & Develop Command, 72. *Mem:* AAAS; Am Soc Microbiol; Am Asn Immunol; Am Pub Health Asn; Am Acad Microbiol. *Res:* Pathogenesis and epidemiology of salmonellosis and shigellosis; antigenic structure shigella and pathogenic fungi; pathogenic coliform bacteria; bacteriology gas gangrene; chemotherapy of burns; phage typing Pseudomonas; diagnostic methods; bacteriology of Mima group. *Mailing Add:* Dept of Microbiol US Army Inst of Surg Res Ft Sam Houston TX 78234

LINDBERG, STEVEN EDWARD, b St Paul, Minn, Oct 17, 42; m 65; c 2. ORGANIC CHEMISTRY, POLYMER CHEMISTRY. *Educ:* Gustavus Adolphus Col, BS, 64; Univ Minn, Minneapolis, PhD(org chem), 69. *Prof Exp:* Res chemist, 69-75, RES SUPVR, RES & DEVELOP DEPT, AMOCO CHEM CORP, 75- *Mem:* Am Chem Soc; Soc Petrol Engrs. *Res:* Petroleum additives, lubricant formulation; polyelectrolytes; tertiary oil recovery; cold flow improvers. *Mailing Add:* Res & Develop Dept Box 400 Amoco Chem Corp Warrenville Rd Naperville IL 60540

LINDBERG, STEVEN ERIC, b Waukegan, Ill, May 9, 47; m 69. GEOCHEMISTRY, ENVIRONMENTAL SCIENCES. *Educ:* Duke Univ, BS, 69; Fla State Univ, MS, 73, PhD(oceanog), 79. *Prof Exp:* Teacher & adv, Antioch Upper Grade Ctr, 69-71; fel chem oceanog, Fla State Univ, 71-74; MEM STAFF GEOCHEM, ENVIRON SCI DIV, OAK RIDGE NAT LAB, 74- *Concurrent Pos:* Co-chmn, Nat Atmosphere Depostion Prog Comt on Data Mgt & Interpretation. *Mem:* Int Asn Aerobiology. *Res:* Influence of fossil fuel utilization on geochemical cycles. *Mailing Add:* Environ Sci Div Bldg 1505 Oak Ridge Nat Lab Oak Ridge TN 37830

LINDBERG, VERN WILTON, b Rimbey, Alta, May 5, 49; m 73. SOLID STATE PHYSICS. *Educ:* Univ Alta, BSc, 69; Case Western Reserve Univ, MS, 72, PhD(physics), 76. *Prof Exp:* asst prof physics, Hartwick Col, 76-79; ASST PROF PHYSICS, ROCHESTER INST TECHNOL, 79- *Concurrent Pos:* Vis researcher, Case Western Reserve Univ, 76 & 78. *Mem:* Am Phys Soc; Am Asn Physics Teachers; Am Vacuum Soc. *Res:* Study of defects in solids using positron lifetime and positron angular correlation techniques; neutron irradiated aluminum; quenched aluminum; deposition of thin films by evaporation, sputtering and other methods, characterizing those films; application of computers to undergraduate education. *Mailing Add:* Dept Physics Rochester Inst Technol Rochester NY 14623

LINDBURG, DONALD GILSON, b Wagner, SDak, Nov 6, 32; m 54; c 3. ANIMAL BEHAVIOR. *Educ:* Houghton Col, BA, 56; Univ Chicago, MA, 62; Univ Calif, Berkeley, PhD(anthrop), 67. *Prof Exp:* Res asst primatol, Nat Ctr Primate Biol, 64-66; res anthropologist, Sch Med, Univ Calif, Davis, 69-72, asst prof anthrop, Univ Calif, Davis, 67-73; chmn & assoc prof, Ga State Univ, 73-75; assoc prof anthrop, Univ Calif, Los Angeles, 75-79; RES BEHAVIORIST, SAN DIEGO ZOO, 79- *Concurrent Pos:* Res

anthropologist, Nat Ctr Primate Biol, 66-69; NSF fel, Univ Calif, Davis, 72-75. *Mem:* Am Soc Primatology; Animal Behav Soc; Am Anthrop Asn; Am Asn Phys Anthrop Int Primatol Soc. *Res:* Captive reproduction of exotic mammals; behavioral correlates of steroid hormone secretions during different phases of the reproductive cycle in primates and carnivores. *Mailing Add:* Zool Soc San Diego PO Box 551 San Diego CA 92112

LINDE, ALAN TREVOR, b Lowood, Australia, Feb 13, 38; m 60; c 3. GEOPHYSICS. *Educ:* Univ Queensland, BSc, 59, PhD(physics), 72. *Prof Exp:* Lectr physics, Univ Queensland, 62-72; STAFF MEM GEOPHYS, DEPT TERRESTRIAL MAGNETISM, CARNEGIE INST WASHINGTON, 72- *Mem:* Am Geophys Union; Seismol Soc Am. *Res:* Theoretical and observational studies of earthquake source mechanisms to determine properties of the earth's interior and hence to understand the earth's tectonic engine. *Mailing Add:* Carnegie Inst 5241 Branch Rd NW Washington DC 20015

LINDE, HARRY WIGHT, b Woodridge, NJ, Jan 1, 26; m 56; c 2. PHARMACOLOGY, ANESTHESIOLOGY. *Educ:* Tufts Col, BS, 50; Mass Inst Technol, PhD(chem), 53. *Prof Exp:* Sr chemist, Res Labs, Air Reduction Co, Inc, 53-56; res assoc anesthesia, Med Sch, Univ Pa, 56-64; group leader, Air Prod & Chem, Inc, 63-65; asst prof anesthesia, 65-70, asst dir, Anesthesia Res Ctr, 67-71, coordr res & sponsored progs, 71-76, assoc prof anesthesia, 70-76, PROF ANESTHESIA, VCHMN RES & ASSOC DEAN HONS PROG MED EDUC, MED SCH, NORTHWESTERN UNIV, CHICAGO, 76- *Concurrent Pos:* Res assoc, Col Med, Univ Ill, 55-56; mem, Comt Admis, Northwestern Univ, 67-72, human subjects rev, 70-76 & res comt, 71-76; consult res anesthesia, Vet Admin Lakeside Hosp, Chicago, 68-; assoc staff mem, Chicago Wesley Mem Hosp, 69-72 & Northwestern Mem Hosp, 72-; consult, US Naval Hosp, Great Lakes, 69-; assoc ed, Yearbk Anesthesia, 70-81. *Mem:* Fel AAAS; Am Chem Soc; Int Anesthesia Res Soc; Am Soc Anesthesiol; Sigma Xi. *Res:* Pharmacology of anesthesia; cardiovascular and respiratory physiology; gas analysis; bioanalytical chemistry. *Mailing Add:* Dept of Anesthesia Northwestern Univ Med Sch Chicago IL 60611

LINDE, LEONARD M, b New York, NY, June 1, 28; m 51; c 2. CARDIOLOGY, PHYSIOLOGY. *Educ:* Univ Calif, BS, 47, MD, 51; Am Bd Pediat, dipl & cert cardiol, 57. *Prof Exp:* Intern, Morrisania City Hosp, New York, 51-52; sr resident pediat, Children's Hosp, Los Angeles, 52-53 & 55-56; prof pediat & cardiol, Sch Med, Univ Calif, Los Angeles, 57-76, physiol, 59-76; CLIN PROF PEDIAT CARDIOL, SCH MED, UNIV SOUTHERN CALIF, 76- *Concurrent Pos:* Fel pediat cardiol, Med Ctr, Univ Calif, Los Angeles, 56-57; consult, Child Cardiac Clin, Los Angeles City Health Dept, 57- & Surg Gen, US Air Force; vis prof, Univ Tokyo, 65-; chief pediat cardiol, St Vincent's Hosp, Los Angeles, 73-76. *Mem:* Soc Pediat Res; Am Pediat Soc; Fel Am Acad Pediat. *Res:* Pediatric cardiology; cardiopulmonary physiology; clinical cardiology; cardiac catheterization. *Mailing Add:* Los Angeles Pediat Cardiol Med Group 10921 Wilshire Blvd Los Angeles CA 90024

LINDE, PETER FRANZ, b Berlin, Ger, June 9, 26; nat US; m 53; c 4. PHYSICAL CHEMISTRY. *Educ:* Reed Col, BA, 46; Univ Ore, MA, 49; Wash State Univ, PhD(chem), 54. *Prof Exp:* Phys chemist, Sandia Corp, 53-57; from asst prof to assoc prof, 57-66, PROF CHEM, SAN FRANCISCO STATE UNIV, 66- *Concurrent Pos:* Ed, Gmelin, Frankfurt, Ger, 81- *Mem:* Am Chem Soc. *Res:* Electrochemistry of quaternary ammonium compounds; supporting electrolytes in polarography; shock tube measurements; chemometrics. *Mailing Add:* Dept of Chem San Francisco State Univ San Francisco CA 94132

LINDE, RONALD K(EITH), b Los Angeles, Calif, Jan 31, 40; m 60. PHYSICS OF SOLIDS, ENVIRONMENTAL SCIENCES. *Educ:* Univ Calif, Los Angeles, BS, 61; Calif Inst Technol, MS, 62, PhD(mat sci), 64. *Prof Exp:* Engr, Litton Systs, Inc, 61; res asst, Calif Inst Technol, 61-64; mat scientist, SRI Int, 64-67, head solid state res, Poulter Labs, 65-67, chmn shock & high pressure physics dept & mgr tech serv, 67-68, chief exec, 68-69, dir phys sci, SRI Int, 68-69; CHMN BD & CHIEF EXEC OFFICER, ENVIRODYNE INDUSTS, INC, 69- *Res:* Environmental engineering; pollution control; solid state physics; properties of materials; physical chemistry; crystallographic phase transformations; shock wave propagation in solids. *Mailing Add:* Envir Ind Inc 222 W Adams Chicago IL 60606

LINDEBERG, GEORGE KLINE, b Spencer, Iowa, June 6, 30; m 54; c 2. SOLID STATE PHYSICS. *Educ:* St Olaf Col, BA, 52; Princeton Univ, PhD(exp physics), 57. *Prof Exp:* Asst physics, Princeton Univ, 56-57; PHYSICIST, MINN MINING & MFG CO, 57- *Mem:* Am Phys Soc. *Res:* Non-equilibrium electronic processes in solids; thermodynamics; physics operations research. *Mailing Add:* Rte 3 Hudson WI 54016

LINDELL, THOMAS JAY, b Red Wing, Minn, July 22, 41; m 65; c 2. MOLECULAR PHARMACOLOGY. *Educ:* Gustavus Adolphus Col, BS, 63; Univ Iowa, PhD(biochem), 69. *Prof Exp:* ASSOC PROF PHARMACOL, HEALTH SCI CTR, UNIV ARIZ, 70- *Concurrent Pos:* USPHS fel biochem, Univ Wash, 68-69 & biochem, biophys & develop biol, Univ Calif, San Francisco, 69-70; assoc ed, J Life Sci. *Mem:* AAAS; Am Chem Soc; Sigma Xi; Am Soc Biol Chemists; Am Soc Pharmacol & Exp Therapeut. *Res:* Control of eukaryotic transcription. *Mailing Add:* Dept of Pharmacol Univ of Ariz Health Sci Ctr Tucson AZ 85724

LINDEMAN, ROBERT D, b Ft Dodge, Iowa, July 19, 30; m 54; c 5. INTERNAL MEDICINE, NEPHROLOGY. *Educ:* State Univ NY Col Forestry, Syracuse Univ, BS, 52; State Univ NY, MD, 56. *Prof Exp:* From asst resident to asst instr internal med, State Univ NY Upstate Med Ctr, 57-60; med officer, Okla State Dept Health, 60-62; med officer geront, Baltimore City Hosps, Md, 62-66; asst prof med & prev med, Med Ctr, Univ Okla, 66-68, assoc prof med & physiol, 68-71, assoc prof biostatist & epidemiol, 69-77, prof med & physiol, 71-77, chief renal sect, 67-77; ASSOC DEAN VET ADMIN AFFAIRS & PROF MED, UNIV LOUISVILLE SCH MED, 77-; CHIEF STAFF, LOUISVILLE VET ADMIN MED CTR, 77- *Concurrent*

Pos: Clin asst med, Univ Okla, 60-62; instr, Sch Med, Johns Hopkins Univ, 62-66; asst chief res staff, Oklahoma City Vet Admin Hosp, 67-77; assoc ed, The Kidney, 74-77; mem, US Pharmacopeia Comt Rev & chmn, Subcomt Electrolytes, Large Volume Parenterals & Renal Drugs, 75- *Mem:* Am Fedn Clin Res; Cent Soc Clin Res; Int Soc Nephrology; Southern Soc Clin Invest; fel Am Col Physicians. *Res:* Renal and electrolyte problems; hypertension; renal and cardiovascular physiology; aging; trace metal metabolism and nutrition. *Mailing Add:* Oklahoma City Vet Admin Hosp 921 NE 13th St Oklahoma City OK 73104

LINDEMANN, CHARLES BENARD, b Staten Island, NY, Dec 17, 46. CELL PHYSIOLOGY, BIOPHYSICS. *Educ:* State Univ NY Albany, BS, 68, PhD(biol), 72. *Prof Exp:* Res assoc cell physiol, Pac Biomed Res Ctr, Univ Hawaii, 72-73; res assoc biophys, State Univ NY Albany, 73-74; ASST PROF PHYSIOL, OAKLAND UNIV, 74- *Mem:* Biophys Soc; Am Soc Cell Biol. *Res:* Flagellar motility: the mechanisms of force production and the factors which control motility onset are under investigation in mammalian sperm. *Mailing Add:* Dept of Biol Sci Oakland Univ Rochester MI 48063

LINDEMANN, WALLACE W(ALDO), b Bigelow, Minn, Aug 7, 25; m 50; c 6. ELECTRICAL ENGINEERING. *Educ:* Univ Minn, BEE, 50, MS & PhD(elec eng), 55. *Prof Exp:* Asst, Univ Minn, 50-51; prin scientist, Gen Mills, Inc, 55-60; dir solid state res, 60-69, gen mgr, 69-79, VPRES, COMPUT COMPONENTS DIV, CONTROL DATA CORP, 79- *Mem:* Inst Elec & Electronics Engrs. *Res:* Solid state device development; microelectronics including thin film and semiconductor technologies. *Mailing Add:* 7979 Martindale Dr Prior Lake MN 55372

LINDEMANN, WILLIAM CONRAD, b East St Louis, Ill, Aug 31, 48; m 78. SOIL MICROBIOLOGY. *Educ:* Southern Ill Univ, BS, 70; Univ Minn, MS, 74, PhD(soil sci), 78. *Prof Exp:* Res asst, Univ Minn, 72-74, 75-77; tech asst, Res Seeds Inc, 74-75; ASST PROF SOIL MICROBIOL, N MEX STATE UNIV, 78- *Mem:* AAAS; Am Soc Microbiol; Am Soc Agron; Soil Sci Soc Am; Sigma Xi. *Res:* Soil nitrogen fixation; rhizobiology; legume innoculation; legume nutrition. *Mailing Add:* 2500 Jordan Rd Las Cruces NM 88001

LINDEMER, TERRENCE BRADFORD, b Gary, Ind, Feb 17, 36; m 62; c 2. HIGH TEMPERATURE CHEMISTRY, NUCLEAR CHEMISTRY. *Educ:* Purdue Univ, BS, 58; Univ Fla, PhD(metall eng), 66. *Prof Exp:* Mem res staff, Inland Steel Co, 58-61 & Solar Aircraft Co, 61-63; MEM RES STAFF, CHEM TECHNOL DIV, OAK RIDGE NAT LAB, 66- *Mem:* Fel Am Ceramic Soc. *Res:* Thermodynamic and kinetic factors affecting reactor performance of nuclear fuels and fission products. *Mailing Add:* Oak Ridge Nat Lab PO Box X Oak Ridge TN 37830

LINDEMEYER, ROCHELLE G, b Philadelphia, Pa, June 14, 52. PEDIATRIC DENTISTRY. *Educ:* West Chester State Col, BA, 72; Univ Pittsburgh, DMD, 77. *Prof Exp:* Residency pedodontics, Children's Hosp Philadelphia, 77-79; asst prof oper dent, 79-81, ASST PROF ORAL PEDIAT, SCH DENT, TEMPLE UNIV, 81- *Concurrent Pos:* Pvt pract pedodontics, 77-; clin affil, Children's Hosp Philadelphia, 79-; St Christopher's Hosp Children, 82- *Honors & Awards:* Am Acad Gen Dent award, 77. *Mem:* Int Asn Dent Res; Sigma Xi; Am Acad Pedodontics; Am Dent Asn; Am Soc Dent Children. *Res:* Relationship of tobacco to dental caries; adherence of cariogenic streptococci on various dental composite materials; bacterial contamination of currently used dental materials, particularly cavity varnishes. *Mailing Add:* Dept Oral Pediat Sch Dent Temple Univ 3223 N Broad St Philadelphia PA 19140

LINDEN, DENNIS ROBERT, b Greeley, Colo, June 22, 42; m 66; c 2. SOIL SCIENCE, HYDROLOGY. *Educ:* Colo State Univ, BS, 68, MS, 70; Univ Minn, PhD(soil), 79. *Prof Exp:* SOIL SCIENTIST, SCI & EDUC ADMIN-AGR RES, USDA, 70- *Mem:* Am Soc Agron; Soil Sci Soc Am. *Res:* Soil physics and hydrology; water and energy transport within soil and exchange with the atmosphere at the soil-atmosphere interface. *Mailing Add:* Soil Sci Bldg 1529 Gortner Ave St Paul MN 55108

LINDEN, DUANE B, b Toledo, Ohio, June 1, 30; m 67; c 3. PLANT GENETICS, CELL BIOLOGY. *Educ:* Hiram Col, AB, 52; Univ Minn, PhD(plant genetics), 56. *Prof Exp:* Res assoc plant genetics, Univ Minn, 56-57; asst prof genetics, Univ Fla, 57-61; assoc scientist, PR Nuclear Ctr, 61-65; assoc prof biol, 65-69, PROF BIOL, KEAN COL NJ, 69-, CHMN DEPT, 73- *Mem:* AAAS; Am Inst Biol Sci; Genetics Soc Am; Nat Asn Biol Teachers; Inst Soc Ethics & Life Sci. *Res:* Effects of radiation on biological systems; study of paramutagenic systems in maize. *Mailing Add:* Dept of Biol Kean Col of NJ Union NJ 07083

LINDEN, HENRY R(OBERT), b Vienna, Austria, Feb 21, 22; nat US; m 67; c 2. CHEMICAL ENGINEERING. *Educ:* Ga Inst Technol, BS, 44; Polytech Inst Brooklyn, MChE, 47; Ill Inst Technol, PhD(chem eng), 52. *Prof Exp:* Chem engr, petrol fuel res, Socony-Vacuum Labs, 44-47; supvr oil gasification, Inst Gas Technol, 47-52, asst res dir, 52-53, assoc res dir, 53-55, res dir, 56-61, dir, 61-69, exec vpres, 69-74, pres & trustee, 74-78; PRES & MEM BD DIRS, GAS RES INST, 76- *Concurrent Pos:* Adj assoc prof, Ill Inst Technol, 54-62, adj prof, 62-78, res prof chem eng & prof gas eng, 78-; chmn, Gordon Res Conf Coal Sci, 65. *Honors & Awards:* Coal res awards, Am Chem Soc, 59 & 65, H M Storch Award, 67; Oper Sect Award, Am Gas Asn, 56, Distinguished Serv Award, 74; Walton Clark Medal, Franklin Inst, 72; Bunsen Pettenkofer Ehrentafel Award, Deut Ver des Gas und Wasserfaches, 78. *Mem:* Am Chem Soc; Am Gas Asn; fel Am Inst Chem Engrs; Am Petrol Inst; fel Brit Inst Fuel. *Res:* Petroleum properties; petrochemicals; fossil fuel combustion and gasification; synthetic fuels; coal and petroleum pyrolysis and hydrogenolysis; energy economics. *Mailing Add:* Gas Res Inst 10 West 35th St Chicago IL 60616

LINDEN, JAMES CARL, b Greeley, Colo, Sept 12, 42; m 68; c 1. PLANT BIOCHEMISTRY. *Educ:* Colo State Univ, BS, 64; Iowa State Univ, PhD(biochem), 69. *Prof Exp:* Alexander von Humboldt stipend, Bot Inst, Univ Munich, 69; fel plant biochem, 71; fel cancer res, Med Sch, St Louis Univ, 71-72; biochemist, Great Western Sugar Co, 72-76; sr chemist, Adolph Coors Co, 77-78; RES ASSOC, DEPT AGR & CHEM ENG, COLO STATE UNIV, 78- *Mem:* Am Chem Soc; Sigma Xi. *Res:* Fuels from biomass, lignocellulose pretreatment, cellulase enzymology; lignin biochemistry, solvent effects on bacterial membrane, microbial fermentations. *Mailing Add:* Dept of Agr & Chem Eng ERC Foothills Campus Ft Collins CO 80523

LINDEN, JOEL MORRIS, b Boston, Mass, May 30, 52. PHARMACOLOGY, CARDIOLOGY. *Educ:* Brown Univ, BS, 74; Univ Va, PhD(pharmacol), 78. *Prof Exp:* res assoc, Dept Pharmacol, 78-80, RES ASST PROF PHYSIOL & PHARMACOL, UNIV VA, 80- *Res:* Mechanism of action of cardioactive drugs and the involvement of cyclic nucleotides in the control of cardiac contractility. *Mailing Add:* Dept of Pharmacol Sch of Med Charlottesville VA 22908

LINDEN, KURT JOSEPH, b Berlin Ger, Dec 27, 36; US citizen; m 62; c 3. SOLID STATE PHYSICS, ELECTRICAL ENGINEERING. *Educ:* Univ Utah, BS, 59; Mass Inst Technol, MS, 61; Purdue Univ, PhD(elec eng), 66. *Prof Exp:* Engr physics, Air Force Cambridge Res Lab, 63; sr engr infrared, Raytheon Co, 66-76; MGR SOLID STATE DEVICE ACTIV, LASER ANAL, DIV SPECTRA PHYSICS, 76- *Concurrent Pos:* Res asst elec eng, Mass Inst Technol, 59-61, teaching asst, 61-63; instr, Purdue Univ, 63-66, NSF fel, 65; instr, Northeastern Univ, Ctr Continuing Educ, 77-; guest lectr, Mass Inst Technol, 79- *Mem:* Sr mem Inst Elec & Electronics Engrs; Am Phys Soc. *Res:* Optoelectronic semiconductor materials and devices; infrared detectors and emitters; low energy detectors and diode lasers of gallium arsenide, gallium aluminum arsenide and lead salts; management of research and development and manufacturing activities. *Mailing Add:* 17 Keith Rd Wayland MA 01778

LINDENA, SIEGFRIED JOHANNES, b Uthwerdum, WGer, July 7, 24; US citizen; m 67; c 1. ENERGY CONVERSION, MAGNETISM. *Educ:* Tech Univ Hannover, Dipl Ing, 52, Dr Ing(elec & electronics eng), 55. *Prof Exp:* Sci asst high voltage direct current transmission & energy conversion & distribution, Tech Univ Hannover, 52-55; dir res magnetics & control & supvr MS degree studies, Calor Emag EAG, Ratingen, WGer, 55-57; chief engr power conversion, Magnetic Res Corp, El Segundo, Calif, 57-59; sr scientist inverter technol, Electro Solids Corp, San Fernando, 59-63; dir res energy conversion & mil applns & mgr mil prod, Int Tel & Tel Co, Sylmar, 63-68, instr energy conversion technol, 64-68; SR STAFF SCIENTIST MIL & SPACE APPLNS & SOLAR ENERGY CONVERSION, XEROX ELECTRO OPTICAL SYSTS, PASADENA, 68- *Concurrent Pos:* Lectr magnetism & magnetic design, Jet Propulsion Lab, 70, on loan, res & design leader solar energy conversion & utilization demonstr, 76- *Mem:* Sr mem Inst Elec & Electronics Engrs. *Res:* Solar energy collection, conversion and utilization; energy conversion in space applications; high voltage, direct current power transmission and distribution; magnetism and continued studies to simplify design approaches. *Mailing Add:* 11002 Densmore Ave Granada Hills CA 91344

LINDENAUER, S MARTIN, b New York, NY, Dec 10, 32; m 56; c 4. SURGERY. *Educ:* Tufts Univ, MD, 57. *Prof Exp:* From instr to assoc prof, 64-72, asst dean, Med Sch, 74-81, PROF SURG, UNIV MICH, ANN ARBOR, 72- *Concurrent Pos:* Chief surg serv, Vet Admin Hosp, 68-74, chief staff, 74-81. *Mem:* Am Col Surg; Asn Acad Surg; Soc Vascular Surg; Int Cardiovasc Soc; Soc Surg Alimentary Tract. *Res:* Vascular surgery; biliary tract surgery. *Mailing Add:* Dept of Surg Univ of Mich Ann Arbor MI 48109

LINDENBAUM, S(EYMOUR) J(OSEPH), b New York, NY, Feb 3, 25; m 58. EXPERIMENTAL HIGH ENERGY PHYSICS. *Educ:* Princeton Univ, AB, 45; Columbia Univ, MA, 48, PhD(physics), 51. *Prof Exp:* Res assoc, Nevis Cyclotron Lab, Columbia Univ, 47-51; assoc physicist, 51-54, physicist, 54-63, SR PHYSICIST, BROOKHAVEN NAT LAB, 63-; MARK W ZEMANSKY CHAIR PHYSICS, CITY COL NEW YORK, 70- *Concurrent Pos:* Group leader high energy counter res group, Brookhaven Nat Lab, 54-; vis prof, Univ Rochester, 58-59; dep sci affairs, High Energy Prog, Div Phys Res, Energy Res & Develop Agency, 76-77; vis, Europ Orgn Nuclear Res; consult, Saclay Nuclear Res Ctr. *Mem:* AAAS; fel Am Phys Soc; NY Acad Sci. *Res:* High energy elementary particle interactions; high energy experimental techniques. *Mailing Add:* Physics Dept Brookhaven Nat Lab Upton NY 11973

LINDENBAUM, SIEGFRIED, b Unna, Ger, July 24, 30; nat US; m 56; c 3. PHYSICAL CHEMISTRY. *Educ:* Rutgers Univ, BS, 52, PhD(chem), 55. *Prof Exp:* Chemist, Oak Ridge Nat Lab, 55-71; assoc prof pharmaceut chem, 71-76, PROF PHARMACEUT CHEM, UNIV KANS, 76- *Res:* Physical chemistry of ion exchange; solvent extraction; separations; thermodynamics of electrolyte solutions; physical chemistry of bile; solution calorimetry. *Mailing Add:* Sch Pharm Univ Kans Lawrence KS 66045

LINDENBERG, KATJA LAKATOS, b Quito, Ecuador, Nov 2, 41; US citizen; m 70. PHYSICAL CHEMISTRY, CHEMICAL PHYSICS. *Educ:* Alfred Univ, BA, 62; Cornell Univ, PhD(theoret physics), 67. *Prof Exp:* Res assoc & asst prof physics, Univ Rochester, 67-69; lectr chem & res chemist, 69-72, asst prof chem residence, 72-73, asst prof chem, 73-75, ASSOC PROF CHEM, UNIV CALIF, SAN DIEGO, 75- *Concurrent Pos:* Res physicist, Univ Calif, San Diego, 69-71; researcher, Oak Ridge Summer Inst Theoret Biophys, 69-75; consult, Chem Div, Oak Ridge Nat Lab, 75. *Mem:* Am Phys Soc; Am Chem Soc. *Res:* Theory of stochastic processes with applications to physical and chemical systems. *Mailing Add:* Dept of Chem Univ of Calif at San Diego La Jolla CA 92093

LINDENBERG, RICHARD, b Bocholt, Ger, Feb 18, 11; US citizen; m 37; c 1. NEUROPATHOLOGY. *Educ:* Univ Berlin, MD, 44. *Prof Exp:* Chief resident neuropath, Kaiser-Wilhelm Inst Brain Res, 36-39; resident & dir anat lab, Neuropsychiat Hosp, Univ Frankfurt, 45-47; res neuropathologist, Sch Aviation Med, Randolph Field, Tex & Army Chem Ctr, Md, 47-51; dir neuropath & legal med, Md State Dept Health & Ment Hyg, 51-78; RETIRED. *Concurrent Pos:* Clin prof path, Sch Med, Univ Md, 51-, lectr neuroanat, Dent Sch, 55-; lectr neuro-ophthal, Sch Med, Johns Hopkins Univ, 59-, lectr forensic path, Sch Hyg, 64-; consult, Greater Baltimore Med Ctr, 59- *Mem:* Am Asn Neuropath; Am Soc Clin Path; fel Col Am Path; AMA; World Fedn Neurol. *Res:* Neuropathology of head injury and circulatory disorders; neuro-ophthalmologic pathology; forensic neuropathology. *Mailing Add:* 20 Florida Rd Towson MD 21204

LINDENBLAD, GORDON ERIC, b Port Jefferson, NY, May 7, 28; m 54; c 3. BIOCHEMISTRY. *Educ:* Bates Col, BS, 48; Georgetown Univ, MS, 55, PhD(chem), 58. *Prof Exp:* Asst biol, Brookhaven Nat Lab, 49-50; res biochemist, Cancer Res Lab, Garfield Mem Hosp, 57-58; sr chemist, Radioisotope Lab, E R Squibb & Sons Div, Olin Mathieson Chem Corp, 57-58, supvr, 59-65; mgr radioisotopes & labeled compounds div, Isotopes, Inc, 65-66; asst dir radiopharmaceut dept, Neisler Labs, Inc, Union Carbide Corp, 66-69; dir radiopharmaceut res & develop, 69-80, DIR INT TECH LIAISON, MED PRODS GROUP, MALLINCKRODT, INC, 80- *Concurrent Pos:* Consult, Children's Hosp, DC, 57-58. *Mem:* Soc Nuclear Med; NY Acad Sci. *Res:* Medical applications of radioisotopes; clinical chemistry. *Mailing Add:* Mallinckrodt Inc 675 Brown Rd St Louis MO 63134

LINDENBLAD, IRVING WERNER, b Port Jefferson, NY, July 31, 29; m 58; c 2. ASTRONOMY. *Educ:* Wesleyan Univ, BA, 50; Colgate Rochester Divinity Sch, MDiv, 56; George Washington Univ, MA, 63. *Prof Exp:* Astronr, 53 & 58-60, ASTRONR, US NAVAL OBSERV, 63- *Mem:* Fel The Royal Astron Soc; Am Astron Soc; Am Geophys Union; NY Acad Sci. *Res:* Photographic study of visual binary stars; motion and magnitude difference of the components of sirius; improvement of astronomical time determination; rotation and polar motion of the earth; sunspots. *Mailing Add:* US Naval Observ Mass Ave & 34th St NW Washington DC 20390

LINDENFELD, PETER, b Vienna, Austria, Mar 10, 25; nat US; m 53; c 2. LOW TEMPERATURE PHYSICS, SUPERCONDUCTIVITY. *Educ:* Univ BC, BASc, 46, MASc, 48; Columbia Univ, PhD(physics), 54. *Prof Exp:* Asst physics, Univ BC, 46-47; asst, Columbia Univ, 48-52, res scientist, 53; vis lectr, Drew Univ, 52-53; from instr to assoc prof, 53-66, PROF PHYSICS, RUTGERS UNIV, 66- *Concurrent Pos:* Dir NSF in-serv insts for high sch teachers, 64-66; regional counr NJ, Am Inst Physics, 63-71; Rutgers Res Coun fel & guest scientist fac sci, Univ Paris-South, 70-71. *Mem:* Fel Am Phys Soc; Am Asn Physics Teachers. *Mailing Add:* Dept Physics Rutgers Univ New Brunswick NJ 08903

LINDENLAUB, JOHN CHARLES, b Milwaukee, Wis, Sept 10, 33; m 57; c 4. ELECTRICAL ENGINEERING. *Educ:* Mass Inst Technol, BS, 55, MS, 57; Purdue Univ, PhD(elec eng), 61. *Prof Exp:* From asst prof to assoc prof, 61-72, dir, Ctr Instrnl Develop Eng, 77-81, PROF ELEC ENG, PURDUE UNIV, 72- *Concurrent Pos:* Mem tech staff, Bell Tel Labs, Inc, 68-69. *Mem:* Inst Elec & Electronics Engrs; Am Soc Eng Educ. *Res:* Statistical communication theory; remote sensing of earth resources; engineering education. *Mailing Add:* Sch of Elec Eng Purdue Univ West Lafayette IN 47907

LINDENMAYER, ARISTID, b Budapest, Hungary, Nov 17, 25; nat US; m 58; c 1. THEORETICAL BIOLOGY. *Educ:* Pazmany Peter Univ, Hungary, Dipl, 48; Univ Mich, MS, 53, PhD(bot), 56. *Prof Exp:* Fel, Johnson Res Found, Univ Pa, 55-56, instr bot, 56-58; NSF fel, Univ London, 58-59; asst prof bot, Univ Pa, 59-62; USPHS fel, Inst Statist, NC State Col, 62-63; from asst prof to assoc prof biol, Queens Col NY, 63-68; PROF PHILOS BIOL, UNIV UTRECHT, 68- *Concurrent Pos:* Vis prof, Univ Mich & Univ Waterloo, Can, 74, Univ Fla, 78 & Univ Calif, Davis, 80. *Mem:* Neth Soc Theory Biol (pres, 76-79); Am Soc Plant Physiol; Bot Soc Am; Neth Soc Logic & Philos Sci (treas, 70-74); Neth Systs Res Soc (pres, 70-71). *Res:* Mathematical models of plant development; logical foundations of developmental biology. *Mailing Add:* Theoret Biol Group Univ of Utrecht 8 Padualaan Utrecht Netherlands

LINDENMAYER, GEORGE EARL, b Port Arthur, Tex, Aug 22, 40; m 63; c 2. BIOCHEMICAL PHARMACOLOGY. *Educ:* Baylor Univ, BS, 62; Baylor Col Med, MD & MS, 67, PhD(pharmacol), 70. *Prof Exp:* Instr pharmacol, Baylor Col Med, 69-70; staff assoc cardiol, Nat Heart & Lung Inst, 70-72; asst prof pharmacol & med, Baylor Col Med, 72-74, assoc prof cell biophys & med, 74-75; assoc prof pharmacol & med, 75-77, PROF PHARMACOL & ASSOC PROF MED, MED UNIV SC, 77- *Concurrent Pos:* Estab investr, Am Heart Asn, 73-78. *Mem:* Am Soc Pharmacol & Exp Therapeut; Int Study Group Res Cardiac Metab; Am Chem Soc; Biophys Soc; Am Heart Asn. *Res:* Information transfer between extracellular and intracellular environments of myocardial cells. *Mailing Add:* Dept of Pharmacol Med Univ of SC Charleston SC 29401

LINDENMEIER, CHARLES WILLIAM, b Ft Collins, Colo, Dec 2, 30; m 58; c 2. THEORETICAL PHYSICS, NUCLEAR PHYSICS. *Educ:* Colo State Univ, BS, 52; Cornell Univ, PhD(theoret physics), 60. *Prof Exp:* Sr physicist, Hanford Labs, Gen Elec Co, 60-63, mgr theoret physics, 63-64; mgr, Pac Northwest Labs, Battelle Mem Inst, 65-70, mgr math & physics res, 70-73; mgr design anal, Laser Enrichment Dept, 74-81, MGR NEUTRON DEVELOP, NEUTRON & FUEL MGT, EXXON NUCLEAR CO, 81- *Mem:* Am Phys Soc; Am Nuclear Soc. *Res:* Reactor physics; neutron thermalization; nuclear reactions; computer applications; laser isotope separation. *Mailing Add:* Exxon Nuclear Co 2101 Horn Rapids Rd Richland WA 99352

LINDENMEYER, PAUL HENRY, b Bucyrus, Ohio, May 4, 21; m 44; c 3. PHYSICAL CHEMISTRY, MATERIALS SCIENCE. *Educ:* Bowling Green State Univ, BS, 44; Ohio State Univ, PhD(chem), 51. *Prof Exp:* Asst, Ohio State Univ, 46-49, res assoc, Res Found, 49-51; res chemist, Visking Co Div, Union Carbide Corp, 51-53, res supvr, 53-57, mgr, Pioneering Res Dept, 57-59; mgr fiber sci, Chemstrand Res Ctr, Inc, 59-69; head mat sci lab, Boeing Sci Res Labs, 69-72, sci adv, Boeing Aerospace Co, 72-73; prog dir, Div Mat Res, NSF, 73-75; MAT RES CONSULT, 75-; SR PRIN SCIENTIST, BOEING AEROSPACE CO, 77- *Honors & Awards:* US Sr Scientist Award, Humboldt Found, 75. *Mem:* AAAS; Fiber Soc; Am Chem Soc; Am Phys Soc; Am Crystallog Asn. *Res:* X-ray crystallography; spectroscopy; microscopy; crystal growth and structure of high polymers; materials processing; irreversible thermodynamics and materials properties. *Mailing Add:* 165 Lee St Seattle WA 98109

LINDER, ALLAN DAVID, b Grand Island, Nebr, Sept 27, 25; m 49; c 1. VERTEBRATE ZOOLOGY. *Educ:* Univ Nebr, BSc, 51; Okla State Univ, MSc, 52, PhD(zool), 56. *Prof Exp:* Asst prof zool, Univ Wichita, 56-59 & Southern Ill Univ, 59-60; chmn dept, 60-75, assoc dean, Col Lib Arts, 66-69 & 76-78, PROF ZOOL, IDAHO STATE UNIV, 60- *Mem:* Am Soc Ichthyologists & Herpetologists; Soc Study Amphibians & Reptiles; Sigma Xi; Soc Vert Paleont; Wilderness Soc. *Res:* Ichthyology, paleo-ichthyology and herpetology. *Mailing Add:* Idaho State Univ Box 8007 Pocatello ID 83209

LINDER, BRUNO, b Sniatyn, Poland, Sept 3, 24; nat US; m 53; c 5. THEORETICAL CHEMISTRY, CHEMICAL PHYSICS. *Educ:* Upsala Col, BS, 48; Univ Ohio, MS, 50; Univ Calif, Los Angeles, PhD(chem), 55. *Prof Exp:* Asst chem, Univ Ohio, 48-49; asst chem, Univ Calif, Los Angeles, 50-55, asst res chemist, 55; proj assoc theoret chem, Naval Res Lab, Wis, 55-57; from asst prof to assoc prof, 57-65, PROF PHYS CHEM, FLA STATE UNIV, 65-, ASSOC CHMN DEPT, 80- *Concurrent Pos:* Guggenheim fel, Inst Theoret Physics, Univ Amsterdam, 64-65; chmn chem physics prog, Fla State Univ, 71-73 & 75-; vis prof, Hebrew Univ, Jerusalem, 73. *Mem:* Am Chem Soc; Am Phys Soc. *Res:* Intermolecular forces; nuclear reactions; spectral shifts and intensities; dielectric theory; theory of adsorption. *Mailing Add:* Dept of Chem Fla State Univ Tallahassee FL 32306

LINDER, CLARENCE H, b Jan 18, 03; US citizen. ELECTRICAL ENGINEERING. *Educ:* Univ Tex, BS, 23, MS, 25. *Hon Degrees:* DEng, Worchester Polytech Inst, 55 & Clarkson Col, 56; LLD, Union Col, 65 & Lehigh Univ, 72. *Prof Exp:* Mem staff, Gen Elec Co, 24-51, gen mgr large appliance div, 51-53, vpres eng serv, 53-60, vpres exec elec utilities group, 60-61, mem staff, 61-63; RETIRED. *Concurrent Pos:* Dir, Western Union Tel & Western Union Corp; res prof elec eng, Union Col. *Mem:* Nat Acad Eng (vpres, 66-70, pres, 70-73); fel Am Inst Elec Engrs (pres, 60-61); Inst Elec & Electronics Engrs (pres, 64); Am Soc Mech Engrs; Am Soc Eng Educ. *Mailing Add:* 875 E Camino Real Boca Raton FL 33432

LINDER, DONALD ERNST, b Yoakum, Tex, Oct 4, 38; m 61; c 3. ANALYTICAL CHEMISTRY. *Educ:* Sul Ross State Univ, BS, 61; Tex A&M Univ, MS, 64, PhD(chem), 67. *Prof Exp:* RES GROUP LEADER, CONOCO, INC, 66- *Mem:* Am Chem Soc. *Res:* Liquid chromatography, adsorption, liquid-liquid, ion exchange and gel permeation; large scale preparative gas-liquid chromatography; analytical distillations. *Mailing Add:* CONOCO Inc PO Drawer 1267 RDE 228 Ponca City OK 74601

LINDER, FORREST EDWARD, b Waltham, Mass, Nov 21, 06; m 31; c 2. STATISTICS. *Educ:* State Univ Iowa, BA, 30, MA, 31, PhD(psychol, math), 32. *Prof Exp:* Tech expert, Div Vital Statist, Bur of Census, 35-42, asst chief, 42-45; asst chief, Med Statist Div, US Navy, 44-46; dep chief, Nat Off Vital Statist, USPHS, 46-47; chief, Demog & Social Statist Br, UN, 47-56; dir nat health surv, USPHS, 56-60, dir, Nat Ctr Health Statist, 66-67; prof biostatist & dir int prog labs pop statist, Univ NC, Chapel Hill, 67-77; EXEC DIR, INT INST VITAL REGIST & STATIST, 77- *Concurrent Pos:* Consult, Ford Found, India, 62 & 64 & WHO, 66 & 68-71, mem expert adv panel health statist, 67; mem policy res adv comt, Nat Inst Child Health & Human Develop, 67-71; mem res adv comt, AID, 68; consult, Pan Am Health Orgn, 68 & 69; chmn, Nat Comt Health & Vital Statist, Nat Ctr Health Statist, 69-72; mem adv comt statist policy, Off Budget & Mgt, US Exec Off, 72; mem world fertility surv steering comt, Int Statist Inst, 72; mem, Inter-Am Statist Inst; pres, Int Inst Vital Regist & Statist, 74-77. *Honors & Awards:* Bronfman Prize, Am Pub Health Asn, 67. *Mem:* Fel AAAS; Int Union Sci Study Pop; fel Am Statist Asn; fel Am Pub Health Asn; Pop Asn Am. *Res:* Development of statistical methods for measurement of population change; public health statistics; census and vital statistics methods. *Mailing Add:* 15115 Vantage Hill Rd Silver Spring MD 20906

LINDER, HARRIS JOSEPH, b Brooklyn, NY, Jan 3, 28; m 52; c 4. ZOOLOGY. *Educ:* Long Island Univ, BS, 51; Cornell Univ, MS, 55, PhD(zool), 58. *Prof Exp:* Asst zool, Cornell Univ, 52-57; resident res assoc, Div Biol & Med, Argonne Nat Lab, 57-58; asst prof, 58-63, ASSOC PROF ZOOL, UNIV MD, COLLEGE PARK, 63- *Concurrent Pos:* Contrib ed, Instrnl Media, J Col Sci Teaching, 76-79. *Mem:* AAAS; Am Soc Zool; Am Micros Soc; Am Inst Biol Sci; Soc Study Reproduction. *Res:* Comparative invertebrate endocrinology; neurosecretion; experimental studies on earthworm reproduction. *Mailing Add:* Dept of Zool Univ of Md College Park MD 20742

LINDER, JACQUES FRANCOIS, applied physics, see previous edition

LINDER, JOHN SCOTT, b Baton Rouge, La, May 3, 35. MICROELECTRONICS, SOLID STATE PHYSICS. *Educ:* La State Univ, BS, 56, MS, 60; Univ Ariz, PhD(elec eng), 67. *Prof Exp:* Tech investr chem processing, E I du Pont de Nemours & Co, 56-58; assoc elec eng, La State Univ, 58-60, instr, 62-63; sr engr, comput div, Bendix Corp & Control Data Corp, 60-62; instr elec eng, Univ Ariz, 63-67; asst prof elec eng, Tex A&M Univ, 67-68, assoc prof, 68-79; ASSOC PROF ELEC ENG, TEX A&I UNIV, 79- *Concurrent Pos:* Mem tech staff, Sandia Corp, 66; consult, Burr Brown

Corp, 67-68, missiles & space div, LTV Aerospace Corp & Consoltec Inc, 69- *Mem:* Inst Elec & Electronics Engrs; Am Soc Eng Educ; Am Phys Soc. *Res:* Solid state devices; semiconductor technology; solid state materials; active and distributed synthesis. *Mailing Add:* Col Eng Tex A&I Univ Kingsville TX 78363

LINDER, LOUIS JACOB, b East St Louis, Ill, May 10, 16; m 48; c 3. ANALYTICAL CHEMISTRY. *Educ:* Wash Univ, AB, 41. *Prof Exp:* Chemist, Eagle-Picher Lead Co, 41-44; anal chemist, Alumina & Chem Div, Res Labs, Aluminum Co Am, 46-50, res chemist, 50-72; LAB MGR, SCH SCI & TECHNOL, SOUTHERN ILL UNIV, EDWARDSVILLE, 72- *Mem:* Soc Appl Spectros. *Res:* Analytical procedures on aluminous materials; application of optical emission spectroscopy to analysis of alumina, aluminous ores and sodium aluminate liquors; spectrographic analysis of gallium oxide and metal. *Mailing Add:* 7907 W Washington St Belleville IL 62223

LINDER, RAYMOND, b Grand Island, Nebr, Sept 9, 22; m 49; c 4. WILDLIFE ECOLOGY. *Educ:* Univ Nebr, BS, 53, PhD(zool, physiol), 64; Iowa State Univ, MS, 55. *Prof Exp:* Biologist, Nebr Game Comn, 55-60; instr zool, 60-62, from asst prof to assoc prof wildlife, 64-77, PROF WILDLIFE, S DAK STATE UNIV, 77-, LEADER S DAK COOP WILDLIFE RES UNIT, 67- *Mem:* Wildlife Soc. *Res:* Ecology of black-footed ferret and prairie dogs; prairie wetlands. *Mailing Add:* Dept Wildlife & Fisheries Sci SDak State Univ Brookings SD 57006

LINDER, REGINA, b New York, NY, June 21, 45. MICROBIOLOGY, BIOCHEMISTRY. *Educ:* City Col New York, BS, 67; Univ Mass, MS, 69; NY Univ, PhD(microbiol), 75. *Prof Exp:* Asst res scientist microbiol, 75-78, ASST PROF MICROBIOL, SCH MED, NY UNIV, 78- *Mem:* Am Soc Microbiol. *Res:* Investigation of the mechanism of action of bacterial and animal toxins which specifically interact with membrane lipids; studies on the enzyme target of penicillin in bacterial cells. *Mailing Add:* Dept of Microbiol Sch of Med NY Univ New York NY 10016

LINDER, SEYMOUR MARTIN, b New York, NY, Dec 17, 25; m 55; c 2. ORGANIC ANALYTICAL CHEMISTRY, INDUSTRIAL ORGANICAL CHEMISTRY. *Educ:* City Col New York, BS, 46; Polytech Inst Brooklyn, MS, 49, PhD(chem), 53. *Prof Exp:* Jr chemist, Hoffmann-La Roche, Inc, 46-51; proj leader, Becco Chem Div, FMC Corp, 53-58 & Org Chem Div, 58-72; dir synthesis res, Alcolac, Inc, 72-80; PRIN CHEMIST, BACK RIVER WASTEWATER TREATMENT PLANT, BALTO CITY, 81- *Mem:* AAAS; Am Chem Soc; Am Inst Chemists. *Res:* Chemistry of hydrogen peroxide and peroxy acids; epoxidations; hydroxylations; epoxyresins; process development; terpene and medicinal chemistry; insecticides; gas chromatography; specialty organic chemicals; functional monomers; (meth) acrylate esters; organometallic compounds; quaternary salts; copolymerizable surfactants; analysis of wastewater; determination of primary pollutants. *Mailing Add:* 1902 Tadcaster Rd Baltimore MD 21228

LINDER, SOLOMON LEON, b Brooklyn, NY, Mar 13, 29; m 53; c 3. INFRARED SYSTEMS, LASER SYSTEMS. *Educ:* Rutgers Univ, BS, 50; Wash Univ, PhD(physics), 55. *Prof Exp:* Mem tech staff, Bell Tel Labs, Inc, 55-62; sr group engr, McDonnell Aircraft Corp, 62-67, SR GROUP ENGR & TECH SPECIALIST, McDONNELL DOUGLAS ASTRONAUT CO, 67- *Concurrent Pos:* Eve instr, Fairleigh Dickinson Univ, 59-62, univ col, Wash Univ, 63-67, Fla Technol Univ, 70-71, Southern Ill Univ, Edwardsville, 74-75 & univ col, Wash Univ, 75- *Mem:* Optical Soc Am; sr mem Inst Elec & Electronics Eng. *Res:* Nuclear magnetic resonance; military systems; electrooptics. *Mailing Add:* 14571 Coeur D'Alene Ct Chesterfield MO 63017

LINDER, WILLIAM HINES, b Florence, SC, Jan 17, 34; m 67; c 2. COMPUTER SCIENCE. *Educ:* US Mil Acad, BS, 56; Mass Inst Technol, MS, 65, PhD(systs eng), 68. *Prof Exp:* Instr systs eng, Mass Inst Technol, 65-67; asst prof comput sci, 67-70, ASSOC PROF COMPUT SCI, UNIV SC, 70- *Mem:* Asn Comput Mach. *Res:* System modeling and simulation; information structures. *Mailing Add:* Dept of Comput Sci Univ of SC Columbia SC 29208

LINDERMAN, ROBERT G, b Crescent City, Calif, Feb 2, 39; m 61; c 3. PLANT PATHOLOGY. *Educ:* Fresno State Col, BA, 60; Univ Calif, Berkeley, PhD(plant path), 67. *Prof Exp:* Lab technician plant path, Univ Calif, Berkeley, 64-67, asst res plant pathologist, 67; res plant pathologist, Agr Res Serv, USDA, 67-73; SUPVRY RES PLANT PATHOLOGIST, RES LEADER & COURTESY PROF BOT & PLANT PATH, ORE STATE UNIV, 73- *Mem:* Am Phytopath Soc. *Res:* Ecology of soil-borne fungus plant pathogens; biological control; biological effects of plant residue decomposition in soil; ornamental plant diseases; mycorrhigal fungi. *Mailing Add:* Dept of Bot Ore State Univ Corvallis OR 97331

LINDEROTH, C(LIFFORD) E(DWARD), b Milwaukee, Wis, July 24, 24; m 81; c 2. CHEMICAL ENGINEERING. *Educ:* Univ Wis, BS, 50. *Prof Exp:* Engr chem develop, Gen Elec Co, 50-54, engr plant process, 54-57, supvr res & develop, 57-64; unit mgr, Pac Northwest Labs Div, Battelle Mem Inst, 65-67; mgr test facil oper, Wadco Div, 70-80, MGR FIELD ENG, WESTINGHOUSE ELEC CORP, 80- *Mem:* Am Inst Chem Engrs. *Res:* Reprocessing of nuclear fuels; safe and permanent disposal of radioactive wastes; safety and integrity of nuclear power reactor containment systems; liquid metals systems maintenance engineering. *Mailing Add:* 2383 Hood Ave Richl nd WA 99352

LINDER JAMES GUS, b St Catharines, Ont, June 27, 36; m 65; c 2. COMP TER SCIENCE, MATHEMATICS. *Educ:* Univ Toronto, BASc, 60, M Sc, 61; Univ London, DIC & PhD(comput sci), 69. *Prof Exp:* Teach g fel math, St Michael's Col, Univ Toronto, 61-63; lectr comput sci, Ryer n Polytech Inst, 62-65; lectr, Imp Col, Univ London, 65-69; asst prof, Univ Waterloo, 69-77; CHMN DEPT COMPUT & INFO SCI, UNIV GUI LPH, 77-, PROF, 80- *Concurrent Pos:* Consult, Dept Energy, Mines & Res urces, Can, 67- & Ministry Natural Resources, Ont, 77- *Mem:* Fel Brit

Comput Soc; fel Royal Geog Soc; Asn Comput Mach; Inst Elec & Electronics Engrs. *Res:* Computer-aided design; data base design; communication network design; development of automated cartography; geo referenced data system. *Mailing Add:* Dept of Comput & Info Sci Univ of Guelph Guelph ON N1G 2W1 Can

LINDFORS, KARL RUSSELL, b Saginaw, Mich, July 10, 37; m 58; c 2. PHYSICAL CHEMISTRY. *Educ:* Univ Mich, BS, 59; Univ Wis, PhD(phys chem), 64. *Prof Exp:* Spectroscopist, Tracerlab, 63-64; PROF CHEM, CENT MICH UNIV, 64-, CHMN DEPT, 78- *Mem:* Am Chem Soc; Sigma Xi. *Res:* Molecular spectroscopy; species in solution. *Mailing Add:* Dept of Chem Cent Mich Univ Mt Pleasant MI 48858

LINDGREN, ALICE MARILYN LINDELL, b Minneapolis, Minn, Jan 31, 37; m 59; c 3. RADIATION BIOLOGY, IMMUNOLOGY. *Educ:* Augsburg Col, BA, 58; Univ Minn, Minneapolis, MS, 61; Univ Iowa, PhD(radiation biol), 70. *Prof Exp:* From instr to assoc prof, 63-81, PROF BIOL, BEMIDJI STATE UNIV, 81- *Concurrent Pos:* Consult, Agassiz Nursing Educ Consortium, 72- & Itasca Nursing Educ Consortium, 81-; vis asst prof radiation biol, Univ Iowa, 75. *Mem:* Sigma Xi; Radiation Res Soc; Cell Kinetics Soc. *Res:* Cell cycle kinetics; effect of radiation on the cell cycle; control of the cell cycle by cyclic nucleotides; response of rat lens epithelial cells to a wound stimulus; lymphocyte blast cell formation. *Mailing Add:* Sci Div Dept Biol Bemidji State Univ Bemidji MN 56601

LINDGREN, BERNARD WILLIAM, b Minneapolis, Minn, May 13, 24; m 45; c 3. MATHEMATICS. *Educ:* Univ Minn, PhD(math), 49. *Prof Exp:* Instr math, Univ Minn, 43-44, 46-49 & Mass Inst Technol, 49-51; res mathematician, Minn-Honeywell Regulator Co, 51-53; from instr to assoc prof, 53-69, chmn dept, 63-73, PROF STATIST, UNIV MINN, MINNEAPOLIS, 69- *Mem:* Fel Am Statist Asn; Int Statist Inst. *Res:* Analysis; probability; statistics. *Mailing Add:* 1860 Noble Dr Golden Valley MN 55422

LINDGREN, DAVID LEONARD, b St Paul, Minn, Sept 17, 06; m 33; c 3. ENTOMOLOGY. *Educ:* Univ Minn, BS, 30, MS, 31, PhD(entom), 35. *Prof Exp:* Jr entomologist, 35-41, from asst entomologist to entomologist, 41-74, EMER ENTOMOLOGIST & LECTR, CITRUS EXP STA, UNIV CALIF, RIVERSIDE, 74- *Mem:* Fel AAAS; Entom Soc Am; Am Asn Cereal Chemists. *Res:* Insecticides; citrus insects; stored product insects. *Mailing Add:* Dept of Entom Univ of Calif Riverside CA 92502

LINDGREN, E(RIK) RUNE, b Sodertlje, Sweden, Aug 15, 19; m 63; c 4. THEORETICAL & EXPERIMENTAL FLUID MECHANICS. *Educ:* Tech Col Stockholm, BS, 43; Royal Inst Technol, Sweden, MS, 47, Tekn lic, 56, Dr Sc(fluid mech), 57. *Prof Exp:* Resident assoc, Lumalampan Inc, Sweden, 45-47 & Aeronaut Lab, Royal Inst Technol, Sweden, 47-49; lectr physics & mech, Tech Col Stockholm, 49-51; res fel fluid mech, Royal Inst Technol, Sweden, 51-59, lectr, 59-61; vis asst prof mech, Johns Hopkins Univ, 61-63; assoc prof mech & fluid mech, Okla State Univ, 63-65; PROF ENG SCI, UNIV FLA, 65- *Concurrent Pos:* Consult, Kockums Shipyard & Royal Swedish Naval Bd, 51-59 & Res Lab, Presby Hosp, 62-63; res grants, Swedish State Coun Tech Res, 53-56, Air Res & Develop Command, US Air Force, 56-59, Docent Fluid Dynamics, Royal Inst Technol, Sweden, 59-, David Taylor Model Basin, US Bur Ships, 62-65, NSF, 66-80 & Off Naval Res, 75-80; vis prof mech, Roy Inst Technol, Sweden, 72- *Mem:* Am Phys Soc; Soc Natural Philos; Swedish Math Soc. *Res:* Experimental mechanics; cavitation; turbulent transition; structure of shear in flows of Newtonian and non-Newtonian systems, specifically liquid crystals; dynamics of immersed bodies; theory of inviscid, incompressible fluid dynamics; non-linear and relativistic mechanics. *Mailing Add:* Dept Eng Sci Univ Fla Aero Bldg Gainesville FL 32611

LINDGREN, FRANK TYCKO, b San Francisco, Calif, Apr 14, 24; m 53. BIOPHYSICS. *Educ:* Univ Calif, Berkeley, BA, 47, PhD(biophys), 55. *Prof Exp:* Res asst biophysicist, 55-56, res assoc biophysicist, 56-67, RES BIOPHYSICIST, DONNER LAB, UNIV CALIF, BERKELEY, 67- *Concurrent Pos:* Assoc ed, Lipids, Am Oil Chemists Soc, 66-76. *Mem:* Am Oil Chemists Soc. *Res:* Physical chemistry and biochemistry of blood lipids and lipo-proteins as they occur in states of health and diseases; instrumentation and engineering necessary to facilitate such investigations. *Mailing Add:* 108 Donner Lab Univ of Calif Berkeley CA 94720

LINDGREN, GORDON EDWARD, b Minneapolis, Minn, Apr 29, 36; m 59; c 3. PHYSICS, MATH. *Educ:* Augsburg Col, BA, 59; Univ SDak, MA, 63; Univ Iowa, PhD(sci educ), 70. *Prof Exp:* Teacher physics/math, Minnetonk High Sch, Excelsior, Minn, 59-61; from instr to assoc prof, 63-77, dean sci & math, 72-80, PROF PHYSICS, BEMIDJI STATE UNIV, 77- *Mem:* Am Asn Physics Teachers; Am Asn Univ Prof; Radiation Res Soc. *Res:* Electron spin resonance; radiation physics. *Mailing Add:* Dept of Physics Bemidji State Univ Bemidji MN 56601

LINDGREN, RICHARD ARTHUR, b Providence, RI, June 2, 40; m 63; c 4. NUCLEAR PHYSICS. *Educ:* Univ RI, BA, 62; Wesleyan Univ, MA, 64; Yale Univ, PhD(nuclear physics), 69. *Prof Exp:* Res assoc nuclear physics, Univ Md, College Park, 69-70; res assoc, Nat Res Coun, Nat Acad Sci, 70-71 & Univ Rochester, 71-73; res physicist nuclear physics, Naval Res Lab, Washington, DC, 73-77; ASSOC PROF, NUCLEAR PHYSICS GROUP, UNIV MASS, AMHERST, 77- *Concurrent Pos:* Instr, George Mason Univ, 73-75; assoc prof, Cath Univ Am, 75-76; consult, Naval Res Lab, 77- & Lawrence Livermore Nat Lab, 81- *Mem:* Sigma Xi. *Res:* Nuclear structure studies using inelastic electron scattering, particularly those nuclear states excited strongly via nuclear magnetization currents; comparison of inelastic proton and electron scattering for high spin stretched states. *Mailing Add:* Nuclear Physics Group Univ of Mass Amherst MA 01003

LINDGREN, ROBERT M, b Concord, NH, June 16, 32; m 57; c 5. PHYSICAL CHEMISTRY. *Educ:* Univ Maine, BS, 59, MS, 62, PhD(phys chem), 67. *Prof Exp:* Instr, Univ Maine, 62-64; scientist, Oxford Paper Co, Maine, 64-69; sr res prof, Plastic Coating Corp, Mass, 69-71; assoc prof chem, Husson Col, 71-79; RES PROF, JAMES RIVER GRAPHICS, 79- *Mem:* Tech Asn Pulp & Paper Indust. *Res:* Molten salt chemistry; environmental science; electrophotography. *Mailing Add:* 11 Chileab Rd South Hadley MA 01075

LINDGREN, WILLIAM FREDERICK, b San Mateo, Calif, Dec 23, 42; c 1. MATHEMATICS. *Educ:* SDak Sch Mines & Technol, BS, 64, MS, 66; Southern Ill Univ, PhD(math), 71. *Prof Exp:* Mathematician & analyst, Atomic Energy Div, Phillips Petrol Co, 66-67; assoc prof, 71-80, PROF MATH, SLIPPERY ROCK STATE COL, 80- *Concurrent Pos:* Vis prof math, Va Polytech Inst, 78-79. *Mem:* Am Math Soc; Sigma Xi. *Res:* General topology. *Mailing Add:* Dept of Math Slippery Rock State Col Slippery Rock PA 16057

LINDHEIM, ROSLYN ITTELSON, b New York, NY, 1921; m 42; c 2. ARCHITECTURAL ENGINEERING. *Educ:* Columbia Univ, BArch, 44. *Prof Exp:* Asst dean, Col Environ Design, 67-70, assoc prof archit, 68-71, PROF ARCHIT, UNIV CALIF, BERKELEY, 71- *Concurrent Pos:* USPHS & NIMH grants. *Mem:* Inst of Med of Nat Acad Sci; Am Inst Architects. *Res:* Developing methods of analysis for making design decision in hospitals; exploring relationships between physical design and health. *Mailing Add:* 390 Wurster Hall Univ of Calif Berkeley CA 94720

LINDHEIMER, MARSHALL D, b Brooklyn, NY, June 28, 32; m 58; c 5. INTERNAL MEDICINE, NEPHROLOGY. *Educ:* Cornell Univ, AB, 52; Univ Geneva, BSM, 57, MD, 61. *Prof Exp:* Intern, Rochester Gen Hosp, 61-62; resident, Brooklyn Vet Admin Hosp, 62-63; resident & chief resident, Brookdale Hosp, Brooklyn, 63-64; US Pub Health Serv fel, Boston Univ, 64-66; sr instr med, Case Western Reserve Univ, 66-69; asst prof, Northwestern Univ, 69-70; from asst to assoc prof, 70-76, PROF MED, OBSTET & GYNEC, UNIV CHICAGO, 76- *Concurrent Pos:* Prin investr grants, NIH, 72-; fel, High Blood Pressure Res Coun, Am Heart Asn, 80. *Mem:* Am Phsiol Soc; Soc Gynec Invest; fel Am Col Physicians; Int Soc Study Hypertension Pregnancy (secy-treas, 81-). *Res:* Salt and water physiology and renal disease; hypertension in pregnancy; volume homeostasis and vasopressin in gravid animal models. *Mailing Add:* 950 E 59th St Univ Chicago Hosp & Clins Chicago IL 60637

LINDHOLM, FREDRIK ARTHUR, b Tacoma, Wash, Feb 26, 36; m 59, 69. ELECTRICAL ENGINEERING. *Educ:* Stanford Univ, BS, 58, MS, 60; Univ Ariz, PhD(elec eng), 63. *Prof Exp:* From instr to assoc prof elec eng, Univ Ariz, 60-66; PROF ELEC ENG, UNIV FLA, 66- *Concurrent Pos:* Mem res adv comt electronics, NASA, 68-70; vis prof, Univ Leuven, Belg, 73; consult, Jet Propulsion Lab, 78- *Honors & Awards:* Awards, Inst Elec & Electronics Engrs, 63 & 65. *Mem:* Fel Inst Elec & Electronics Engrs. *Res:* Modeling of solid state devices; solar cells. *Mailing Add:* Dept Elec Eng Univ Fla Gainesville FL 32601

LINDHOLM, JOHN C, b Wichita, Kans, Nov 3, 23; m 47; c 4. MACHINE DESIGN, DYNAMICS. *Educ:* Kans State Univ, BS(mech eng) & BS(bus admin), 49; Univ Kans, MS, 56; Purdue Univ, PhD(mach design), 61. *Prof Exp:* Design engr, Gen Elec Co, 49-52; sr engr, Midwest Res Inst, 52-54; instr mech eng, Univ Kans, 54-57 & Purdue Univ, 57-59; assoc prof, 60-74, prof mech eng, 74-80, PROF TECH ENG & HEAD DEPT, KANS STATE UNIV, 80- *Concurrent Pos:* Vis prof, Univ Assiut, 64-66; year-in-indust prof, E I du Pont de Nemours & Co, Inc, 71-72. *Mem:* Am Soc Mech Engrs; Soc Exp Stress Anal; Am Soc Eng Educ. *Res:* Three-dimensional photoelastic stress analysis; mechanical properties materials at intermediate strain rates; kinematic synthesis of mechanisms. *Mailing Add:* Dept Tech Eng Kans State Univ Manhattan KS 66506

LINDHOLM, ROBERT D, b Rockford, Ill, June 17, 40; m 62; c 2. PHYSICAL CHEMISTRY. *Educ:* Northern Ill Univ, BS, 63, MS, 64; Univ Southern Calif, PhD(phys chem), 69. *Prof Exp:* Sr res chemist, 68-73, RES ASSOC, EASTMAN KODAK CO, 73- *Mem:* Am Chem Soc. *Res:* Photochemistry of transition-metal complexes; silver halide photochemistry. *Mailing Add:* Res Lab Eastman Kodak Co Rochester NY 14650

LINDHOLM, ROY CHARLES, b Washington, DC, Mar 8, 37; m 65; c 2. GEOLOGY. *Educ:* Univ Mich, BS, 59; Univ Tex, MA, 63; Johns Hopkins Univ, PhD(geol), 67. *Prof Exp:* Instr, Johns Hopkins Univ, 65-66; from asst prof to assoc prof, 67-77, PROF GEOL, GEORGE WASHINGTON UNIV, 77- *Mem:* Am Asn Petrol Geol; Soc Econ Paleont & Mineral. *Res:* Paleozoic carbonate rocks of eastern United States; Precambrian sandstones of New Mexico; sequences of carbonate cements; geology of Triassic-Jurassic rocks in Virginia; lacustrine deposits. *Mailing Add:* Dept of Geol George Washington Univ Washington DC 20052

LINDHOLM, ULRIC S, b Washington, DC, Sept 11, 31; m 62; c 2. MATERIALS SCIENCE, APPLIED MECHANICS. *Educ:* Mich State Univ, BS, 53, MS, 55, PhD(appl mech), 60. *Prof Exp:* Sr res engr, 60-64, mgr eng mech, 64-71, asst dir dept mech sci, 71-73, DIR DEPT MAT SCI, SOUTHWEST RES INST, 73- *Mem:* Fel Am Soc Mech Engrs; Soc Exp Stress Anal; Sigma Xi; Am Soc Metals; fel AAAS. *Res:* Applied mechanics, structural dynamics and vibrations; wave propagation; material properties. *Mailing Add:* Southwest Res Inst 8500 Culebra Rd San Antonio TX 78206

LINDHORST, TAYLOR ERWIN, b St Louis, Mo, Aug 11, 28; m 51; c 2. MYCOLOGY. *Educ:* St Louis Col Pharm, BS, 51; Wash Univ, MA, 54, PhD(mycol), 67. *Prof Exp:* Instr pharm, 51-52, resident biol, 52-55, assoc instr, 56-59, assoc prof, 59-67, assoc prof, 67-74, PROF BIOL & DEAN STUDENTS, ST LOUIS COL PHARM, 74- *Mem:* Am soc Pharmacog; Bot Soc Am. *Res:* Mycological studies concerning response and growth variation to antibiotic substances. *Mailing Add:* Dept of Biol St Louis Col of Pharm St Louis MO 63110

LINDLEY, BARRY DREW, b Orleans, Ind, Jan 25, 39; div; c 3. PHYSIOLOGY, BIOPHYSICS. *Educ:* DePauw Univ, BA, 60; Western Reserve Univ, PhD(physiol), 64. *Prof Exp:* Asst prof, 65-68, ASSOC PROF PHYSIOL, SCH MED, CASE WESTERN RESERVE UNIV, 68- *Concurrent Pos:* NSF fel neurophysiol, Nobel Inst Neurophysiol, Karolinska Inst, Sweden, 64-65; Lederle med fac award, 6770; USPHS res career develop award, 71-76; mem, Physiol Study Sect, NIH, 75-79. *Mem:* Am Physiol Soc; Soc Gen Physiologists; Biophys Soc. *Res:* Muscle biophysics; ion and water transport; membrane permeability; irreversible thermodynamics; electrophysiology of nerve, muscle and glandular tissue. *Mailing Add:* Dept of Physiol Case Western Reserve Univ Sch Med Cleveland OH 44106

LINDLEY, CHARLES A(LEXANDER), b Union City, Ind, May 12, 24; m 46; c 2. AEROSPACE SYSTEMS ENGINEERING, ALTERNATIVE ENERGY SYSTEMS. *Educ:* Ohio State Univ, BAeroEng & MS, 49; Calif Inst Technol, PhD(aeronaut), 56. *Prof Exp:* Instr, Ohio State Univ, 47-48; eng aid, Nat Adv Comt Aeronaut, 48; compressor design engr, Thompson Aircraft Prod, Inc, 49-52, consult, 52-55; eng specialist, Marquardt Corp, 55-57; mgr engine res, 57-59, res consult, 59-61, chief res consult, 61-63; sr staff engr, Appl Mech Div, Aerospace Corp, 63-65; dir vehicle design, Satellite Systs Div, 65-73; res assoc, Environ Qual Lab, Calif Inst Technol, 73-74; assoc dir advan systs off, Energy Systs Group, 74-78, SR STAFF ENGR, THREAT ANAL OFF, AEROSPACE CORP, 78- *Concurrent Pos:* Lectr & consult wind power & wind resources, Univ Calif, Santa Barbara. *Mem:* AAAS; assoc fel Am Inst Aeronaut & Astronaut; Sigma Xi. *Res:* Aeronautical and space propulsion; air breathing and recoverable boosters; physics and chemistry of the upper atmosphere; satellite systems engineering; wind and solar energy; manned and unmanned space vehicle systems engineering; energy conversion devices; meteorology. *Mailing Add:* Aerospace Corp PO Box 92957 Los Angeles CA 90009

LINDLEY, CHARLES EDWARD, b Macon, Miss, Dec 21, 21; m 45. ANIMAL HUSBANDRY. *Educ:* Miss State Univ, BS, 46; Wash State Univ, MS, 48; Okla State Univ, PhD, 57. *Prof Exp:* Asst, Wash State Univ, 46-48, asst prof animal husb, 48-51; asst, Okla State Univ, 51-52; chmn dept animal sci, 52-69, PROF ANIMAL SCI, MISS STATE UNIV, 52-, DEAN COL AGR, 69- *Mem:* Am Soc Animal Sci. *Res:* Livestock production and animal breeding. *Mailing Add:* Off of Dean Col of Agr Miss State Univ Drawer AG Mississippi State MS 39762

LINDLEY, KENNETH EUGENE, b Stratton, Colo, Mar 16, 24; m 48; c 4. ELECTRICAL ENGINEERING, MATHEMATICS. *Educ:* Univ Wis, BS, 48, MS, 49; State Univ Iowa, PhD(elec eng), 53. *Prof Exp:* From instr to prof elec eng, SDak State Col, 49-63; PROF PHYSICS & MATH & CHMN SCI & MATH DIV, HOUGHTON COL, 63- *Concurrent Pos:* Develop consult, Acme Elec Corp, 66- *Mem:* Am Sci Affil; Am Inst Elec & Electronics Engrs; Am Soc Eng Educ. *Res:* Electrical power supplies. *Mailing Add:* Rte 1 Box 43A Houghton NY 14744

LINDMAN, ERICK LEROY, JR, b Seattle, Wash, Mar 20, 38; m 63; c 4. PLASMA PHYSICS. *Educ:* Calif Inst Technol, BS, 60; Univ Calif, Los Angeles, MS, 63, PhD(physics), 64. *Prof Exp:* Res scientist, Univ Tex, Austin, 64-65, asst prof physics, 65-68; physicist, Austin Res Assocs, 68-71; staff mem, 71-78, assoc group leader laser fusion target design, 78-80, ASSOC GROUP LEADER INERTIAL FUSION SUPPORTING PHYSICS, LOS ALAMOS NAT LAB, 80- *Mem:* Am Phys Soc. *Res:* Collisionless shocks; plasma instabilities; numerical simulation of plasma effects; laser interaction with matter; laser fusion target design. *Mailing Add:* MS-531 Los Alamos Nat Lab Los Alamos NM 87545

LINDMARK, RONALD DORANCE, forest economics, see previous edition

LINDMAYER, JOSEPH, b Budapest, Hungary, May 8, 29; US citizen; m 55; c 2. SOLID STATE PHYSICS. *Educ:* Williams Col, MS, 63; Aachen Tech Univ, PhD, 68. *Prof Exp:* Scientist, Inst Measurements Tech, Hungarian Acad Sci, 55-56; scientist res ctr, Sprague Elec Co, 57-63, dept head semiconductor physics, 63-68; br mgr, Comsat Labs, Commun Satellite Corp, Clarksburg, 68-74; dir physics lab, Defense Language Inst, 74-76; PRES, SOLAREX CORP, 76- *Concurrent Pos:* Vis lectr, Yale Univ, 68-69. *Mem:* Inst Elec & Electronics Eng. *Res:* Semiconductor physics, electronics and devices. *Mailing Add:* 1335 Piccard Dr Rockville MD 20850

LINDNER, ELEK, b Budapest, Hungary, June 3, 24; US citizen; m 60; c 1. ANALYTICAL BIOCHEMISTRY, MARINE BIOLOGY. *Educ:* Budapest Tech Univ, Dipl Chem Eng, 46, PhD(biochem), 74. *Prof Exp:* Prof asst agr chem, Budapest Tech Univ, 47-48 & food chem, 48-50; chief chemist, Anal & Res Lab, Elida Cosmetic Factory, 50-51; res chemist, Res Inst, Fatty Oil Chem Indust, 51-56, Res & Develop Div, Lever Bros Co, NJ, 57-61 & Chevron Res Corp, Calif, 61-64; prod mgr, Sawyer Tanning Co, Calif, 64-65; res chemist, Paint Lab, Mare Island Naval Shipyard, 65-73; SUPVRY RES CHEMIST, NAVAL OCEAN SYSTS CTR, 73- *Concurrent Pos:* Res chemist, Naval Ship Res & Develop Ctr, Annapolis, Md, 73. *Mem:* Am Chem Soc. *Res:* Chemistry and biochemistry of food and agricultural products; analytical methods; chemistry of fatty oils; detergents and surfactants; biochemistry of marine organisms. *Mailing Add:* Naval Ocean Systs Ctr San Diego CA 92152

LINDNER, LUTHER EDWARD, b Toledo, Ohio, Aug 6, 42; m 69; c 3. PATHOLOGY. *Educ:* Univ Toledo, BS, 64; Western Reserve Univ, MD, 67, Case Western Reserve Univ, PhD(exp path), 74. *Prof Exp:* From intern to resident, Univ Hosp, Cleveland, 67-72; fel path, Case Western Reserve Univ, 69-72; staff pathologist, William Beaumont Army Med Ctr, 72-74, chief, Anatomic Path, 74-75; ASST PROF LAB MED, UNIV NEV, 75- *Concurrent Pos:* Consult path, Reno Vet Admin Hosp. *Mem:* Am Soc Cytol; Am Soc Clin Path; Col Am Pathologists. *Res:* Studies of anatomic changes in disease with histochemical correlations and application to diagnosis. *Mailing Add:* Manville Bldg Univ of Nev Reno NV 89557

LINDNER, MANFRED, b Chicago, Ill, Oct 21, 19; m 46; c 2. NUCLEAR CHEMISTRY. *Educ:* Northwestern Univ, Ill, BS, 40; Univ Calif, Berkeley, PhD(nuclear chem), 48. *Prof Exp:* Chemist, Hanford Eng Works, Wash, 44-46; res asst, Univ Calif, Berkeley, 46-48; asst prof chem, Wash State Col, 48-51; chemist, Calif Res & Develop Co, 51-53; SR CHEMIST, RADIOCHEM DIV, LAWRENCE LIVERMORE LAB, 53- *Concurrent Pos:* Rothschild fel, Weizmann Inst Sci, 62-63. *Mem:* AAAS; Am Phys Soc. *Res:* Neutron capture cross-sections; nuclear structure. *Mailing Add:* Lawrence Livermore Nat Lab Livermore CA 94550

LINDORFF, DAVID EVERETT, b Moline, Ill, Aug 25, 45; m 72; c 2. HYDROGEOLOGY. *Educ:* Augustana Col, BA, 67; Univ Wis-Madison, MA, 69, MS, 71. *Prof Exp:* Geologist, Pa Dept Environ Resources, 71-75; asst geologist, Ill State Geol Surv, 75-80; HYDROGEOLOGIST, WIS DEPT NAT RESOURCES, 81- *Mem:* Nat Water Well Asn. *Res:* Ground-water contamination; hydrogeology of strip mines; siting of sanitary landfills. *Mailing Add:* Dept Natural Resources PO Box 7921 Madison WI 53707

LINDOWER, JOHN OLIVER, b Ashland, Ohio, March 15, 29; m 51; c 3. SCIENCE EDUCATION. *Educ:* Ashland Col, AB, 50; Ohio State Univ, MD, 55, PhD(pharmacol), 68. *Prof Exp:* Instr pharmacol, Col Med, Ohio State Univ, 68-69, asst prof, 69-73, assoc prof, 73-75; PROF & CHMN PHARMACOL, SCH MED, WRIGHT STATE UNIV, 75-, ASSOC DEAN CURRIC AFFAIRS, 77- *Concurrent Pos:* Coordr curric affairs, Sch Med, Wright State Univ, 75-76, asst dean, 76-77; mem, Comn Accrediting, Asn Theol Schs US & Can, 78-80; mem, NCent Res Rev & Adv Comn, Am Heart Asn, 79- *Mem:* AMA; Asn Med Sch Pharmacol. *Res:* Clinical pharmacology; cardiovascular research; subcellular and ultrastructural pharmacology. *Mailing Add:* Sch Med PO Box 927 Wright State Univ Dayton OH 45401

LINDQUIST, ANDERS GUNNAR, b Lund, Sweden, Nov 21, 42; m 66; c 2. APPLIED MATHEMATICS. *Educ:* Royal Inst Technol, Sweden, MS, 67, TeknL, 68, TeknD(optimization), 72. *Prof Exp:* Res assoc optimization, Royal Inst Technol, Sweden, 69-72, docent, 72; vis asst prof math, Univ Fla, 72-73; assoc prof, 74-80, PROF MATH, UNIV KY, 80- *Mem:* Soc Indust & Appl Math; Inst Elec & Electronics Engrs. *Res:* Stochastic systems theory, control theory and estimation. *Mailing Add:* Dept of Math Univ of Ky Lexington KY 40506

LINDQUIST, CARL GUSTAV, b Middletown, Conn, Dec 11, 13; m 39; c 2. CHEMICAL ENGINEERING. *Educ:* Purdue Univ, BS, 36. *Prof Exp:* Chem engr, Tenn Eastman Corp, 36-37 & Eastman Kodak Co, 37-42; from actg asst prof to assoc prof chem eng, Stanford Univ, 43-53; chem engr, Cent Res Dept, Food Mach & Chem Corp, 53-55; mgr coolant chem, Knolls Atomic Power Lab, Gen Elec Co, 55-60; asst mgr, Waltham Lab, Polaroid Corp, Mass, 60-61; mgr, Ledgemont Lab, Kennecott Copper Corp, 61-71; CONSULT, 71- *Concurrent Pos:* Consult, 47-53. *Mem:* AAAS; Am Chem Soc. *Res:* Cracking of light hydrocarbons; application wetting agents photo emulsion; hydrodynamics of coating processes; rheology; chemical process development; research and development administration. *Mailing Add:* 230 Foster St Littleton MA 01460

LINDQUIST, DAVID GREGORY, b Chicago, Ill, Feb 14, 46; m 73; c 2. ICHTHYOLOGY. *Educ:* Univ Calif, Los Angeles, BA, 68; Calif State Univ, Hayward, MA, 72; Univ Ariz, PhD(zool), 75. *Prof Exp:* Asst prof, 75-81, ASSOC PROF BIOL, UNIV NC, WILMINGTON, 81- *Mem:* Am Soc Ichthyologists & Herpetologists. *Res:* Ethology and behavioral ecology of reef fishes; natural history of Southeastern freshwater fishes. *Mailing Add:* Dept of Biol Univ of NC Wilmington NC 28403

LINDQUIST, DONALD ARTHUR, entomology, see previous edition

LINDQUIST, EVERT E, b Susanville, Calif, June 26, 35; m 57; c 4. ACAROLOGY, SYSTEMATIC ENTOMOLOGY. *Educ:* Univ Calif, Berkeley, BS, 57, MS, 59, PhD(entom), 63. *Prof Exp:* res scientist, 62-75, SR RES SCIENTIST, BIOSYST RES INST, AGR CAN, 75- *Concurrent Pos:* Adj prof, Carleton Univ, 71-; vis lectr, Ohio State Univ Summer Acarology Prog, 72-; vis lectr, Univ Nat Auton Mexico, 82. *Mem:* Entom Soc Can; Acarological Soc Am; Soc Entom Quebec. *Res:* Systematics and cladistics of Acari; symbiotic relationships between mites and insects; geographic distribution of arctic mites. *Mailing Add:* Biosyst Res Inst Can Agr Ottawa ON K1A 0C6 Can

LINDQUIST, RICHARD KENNETH, b Minneapolis, Minn, Oct 2, 42; m 69. ENTOMOLOGY. *Educ:* Gustavus Adolphus Col, BA, 64; Kans State Univ, MS, 67, PhD(entom), 69. *Prof Exp:* Instr entom, Kans State Univ, 68-69; asst prof, 69-74, ASSOC PROF ENTOM, OHIO AGR RES & DEVELOP CTR, 74- *Mem:* Entom Soc Am. *Res:* Biology, ecology and control of insect and mite pests of floral and greenhouse vegetable crops. *Mailing Add:* 1594 Sunset Ln Wooster OH 44691

LINDQUIST, RICHARD WALLACE, b Worcester, Mass, May 6, 33; m 57; c 2. PHYSICS. *Educ:* Worcester Polytech Inst, BS, 54; Princeton Univ, AM, 57, PhD(physics), 62. *Prof Exp:* Instr physics, Princeton Univ, 58-60; asst prof, Adelphia Univ, 60-64; res assoc, Univ Tex, 64-65; assoc prof, 65-77, PROF PHYSICS, WESLEYAN UNIV, 77- *Mem:* Am Phys Soc; Am Asn Physics Teachers. *Res:* General relativity; geometrodynamics; gravitational collapse; relativistic transport theory. *Mailing Add:* Dept of Physics Wesleyan Univ Middletown CT 06457

LINDQUIST, ROBERT HENRY, b Minneapolis, Minn, Feb 27, 28; m 50; c 2. PHYSICAL CHEMISTRY. *Educ:* Univ Minn, BChem, 49, MS, 50; Univ Calif, PhD(chem), 55. *Prof Exp:* Res chemist, Chevron Res Co, 55-60, sr res chemist, 60-64, sr res assoc, 64-75, asst to pres, 75-78, mgr solar, 78-80; CONSULT CORP DEVELOP, STANDARD OIL CO CALIF, 80- *Mem:* Am Chem Soc; Am Phys Soc. *Res:* Solid state physics; magnetic resonance; physics of ultra-fine particles; heterogeneous catalysis; reaction kinetics; synthetic fuels; alternate energy sources. *Mailing Add:* Standard Oil Co Calif 225 Bush St San Francisco CA 94104

LINDQUIST, ROBERT MARION, b Cumberland, Wis, Dec 4, 23; m; c 3. ORGANIC CHEMISTRY, PHOTOGRAPHIC CHEMISTRY. *Educ:* Univ Wis, BS, 44; Univ Minn, PhD, 50. *Prof Exp:* Res chemist photog res, Gen Aniline & Film Corp, 50-56; assoc chemist photog processes, 56-57, staff chemist, 57-62, adv chemist, 62-63, develop chemist, 63-65, SR CHEMIST, IBM CORP, 65- *Honors & Awards:* First Level Invention Award, IBM Corp, 62, Outstanding Contrib Award, 74. *Mem:* Sr mem Am Chem Soc; Sigma Xi; fel Am Inst Chemists; sr mem Soc Photog Scientists & Engrs. *Res:* Electrophotographic processes. *Mailing Add:* 4788 Briar Ridge Trail Boulder CO 80301

LINDQUIST, ROBERT NELS, b Bakersfield, Calif, Sept 29, 42; m 68. BIOCHEMISTRY, ORGANIC CHEMISTRY. *Educ:* Occidental Col, BA, 65; Ind Univ, PhD(chem), 68. *Prof Exp:* Chemist, Shankman Labs, 65; res chemist, Shell Develop Co, 68-71; asst prof, 71-75, assoc prof, 75-80, PROF CHEM, SAN FRANCISCO STATE UNIV, 80- *Mem:* AAAS; Am Chem Soc. *Res:* Enzyme and enzyme model reaction kinetics and mechanisms. *Mailing Add:* Dept of Chem San Francisco State Univ San Francisco CA 94132

LINDROOS, ARTHUR E(DWARD), b Worcester, Mass, Aug 14, 22; m 44; c 4. CHEMICAL ENGINEERING. *Educ:* Worcester Polytech Inst, BS, 43, MS, 44; Yale Univ, DEng(chem eng), 49. *Prof Exp:* Chem engr res & develop, Kellex Corp, 49-53; chem engr process develop, Air Reduction Chem Co, NJ, 53-59, mgr develop, 59-61; tech mgr, Cumberland Chem Corp, 61-62; mgr process eng, Air Reduction Chem & Carbide Co, 62-67; mgr process eng, Airco Chem & Plastics Co, 67-69, eng mgr, 69-71; vpres, Techni-Chem Co, 71-76; div supvr, Unit CPC Int, 76-79, ASSOC MGR ENG, PENICK CORP, 79- *Mem:* Am Chem Soc; Am Inst Chem Engrs; Sigma Xi. *Res:* Mass transfer; phase equilibria at elevated pressures; nuclear reactor fuel reprocessing; acetylenic chemistry; vinyl monomers; resins and emulsions; polyvinyl alcohol; calcium carbide; lime recovery; chlorinated hydrocarbons; narcotics; pharmaceuticals. *Mailing Add:* 20 N Briarcliff Rd Mountain Lakes NJ 07046

LINDSAY, CHARLES MCCOWN, b Fayetteville, Tenn, July 5, 32; m 55; c 4. MATHEMATICS. *Educ:* Univ of the South, BS, 54; Univ Iowa, MS, 57; George Peabody Col, PhD(math), 65. *Prof Exp:* From instr to assoc prof, 57-71, interim dean, 75-76, PROF MATH, COE COL, 71-, CHMN DEPT, 63- *Mem:* Am Math Soc; Math Asn Am. *Res:* Mathematics education. *Mailing Add:* Dept of Math Coe Col Cedar Rapids IA 52402

LINDSAY, DAVID TAYLOR, b Philadelphia, Pa, Mar 22, 35; m 59; c 1. DEVELOPMENTAL BIOLOGY. *Educ:* Amherst Col, BA, 57; Johns Hopkins Univ, PhD(biol), 62. *Prof Exp:* From asst prof to assoc prof zool, 62-77, MEM FAC, UNIV GA, 77- *Concurrent Pos:* Nat Sci Found res grant develop biol, 63-66. *Mem:* AAAS; Soc Develop Biol; Am Soc Zoologists; NY Acad Sci. *Res:* Mechanisms of cellular differentiation; regulation of protein synthesis in differentiation; biological role of histone proteins; bilateral symmetry. *Mailing Add:* Dept of Zool Univ of Ga Athens GA 30602

LINDSAY, DELBERT W, b Blackfoot, Idaho, May 9, 24; m 49; c 3. SYSTEMATIC BOTANY. *Educ:* Univ Utah, BS, 46, MS, 49, PhD(biol), 61. *Prof Exp:* PROF BIOL, RICKS COL, 60- *Mem:* Bot Soc Am. *Res:* Ecology and climatology; the flora of Eastern Idaho. *Mailing Add:* Dept of Biol Ricks Col Rexburg ID 83440

LINDSAY, DEREK MICHAEL, b Belfast, Northern Ireland, Oct 3, 44; m 70. PHYSICAL CHEMISTRY, CHEMICAL PHYSICS. *Educ:* Trinity Col, Dublin, BA, 67; Harvard Univ, PhD(chem), 75. *Prof Exp:* Res asst, Mass Inst Technol, 75-76; res asst chem, Coop Inst Res Environ Sci & Univ Colo, Boulder, 76-78; ASST PROF CHEM, CITY COL NEW YORK, 78- *Mem:* Am Chem Soc; Am Phys Soc. *Res:* Laser fluorescence and electron spin resonance studies of small metal clusters; application of this research to catalysis, surface science and solid state physics; intramolecular perturbations and gas-phase energy transfer processes. *Mailing Add:* Dept Chem City Col Convent Ave & 138th St New York NY 10031

LINDSAY, DOUGLAS ROME, b Port Arthur, Ont, Apr 10, 21; m 51; c 1. PLANT ECOLOGY, TAXONOMY. *Educ:* Queen's Univ, Ont, BA, 49; Univ Wis, MS, 51. *Prof Exp:* Res off, Plant Res Inst, Can Dept Agr, 49-56; chmn dept biol, 73-77, PROF BIOL, LAKEHEAD UNIV, 57- *Mem:* AAAS; Am Inst Biol Sci; Can Bot Asn. *Res:* Ecology of weedy plants; phytogeography of Northwestern Ontario; biology of boreal forest plants. *Mailing Add:* Dept of Biol Lakehead Univ Thunder Bay ON P7B 5E1 Can

LINDSAY, DWIGHT MARSEE, b Versailles, Ind, June 19, 21; m 43; c 2. MAMMALOGY. *Educ:* Hanover Col, AB, 47; Univ Ky, MS, 49; Univ Cincinnati, PhD, 58. *Prof Exp:* Asst zool, Univ Ky, 47-48, instr, 51-52; from instr to assoc prof, 49-63, PROF BIOL, GEORGETOWN COL, 63-, CHMN DEPT BIOL SCI, 74- *Mem:* Am Soc Mammalogists. *Res:* Endocrinology; physiology; histology; embryology. *Mailing Add:* Dept of Biol Georgetown Col Georgetown KY 40324

LINDSAY, EVERETT HAROLD, JR, b La Junta, Colo, July 2, 31; m 53; c 3. VERTEBRATE PALEONTOLOGY. *Educ:* Chico State Col, AB, 53, MA, 57; Cornell Univ, MST, 62; Univ Calif, Berkeley, PhD(paleont), 67. *Prof Exp:* Asst prof, 67-71, assoc prof, 71-80, PROF GEOL, UNIV ARIZ, 80- *Mem:* AAAS; Soc Vert Paleont; Am Soc Mammalogists; Paleont Soc. *Res:* Biostratigraphy; magnetostratigraphy; taxonomy and evolution of small mammal fossils. *Mailing Add:* Dept of Geosci Univ of Ariz Tucson AZ 85721

LINDSAY, GEORGE EDMUND, b Pomona, Calif, Aug 17, 16. PLANT TAXONOMY. *Educ:* Stanford Univ, BA, 51, PhD, 56. *Prof Exp:* Dir, Desert Bot Garden, Ariz, 39-40; admin asst, Arctic Res Lab, Off Naval Res, 52-53; exec dir, San Diego Mus Natural Hist, 56-63; exec dir, Calif Acad Sci, 63-82. *Mem:* AAAS; Cactus & Succulent Soc Am; Int Orgn Succulent Plant Studies; Am Asn Mus; Asn Dirs Sci Mus. *Res:* Taxonomic botany; taxonomy and ecology of Cactaceae and xerophytic plants of Baja California and other parts of Mexico. *Mailing Add:* Calif Acad of Sci Golden Gate Park San Francisco CA 94118

LINDSAY, GLENN FRANK, b Portland, Ore, June 13, 35; m 65. INDUSTRIAL ENGINEERING, OPERATIONS RESEARCH. *Educ:* Ore State Univ, BSc, 60; Ohio State Univ, MSc, 62, PhD(indust eng), 68. *Prof Exp:* Res assoc, Systs Res Group, Ohio State Univ, 61-65; asst prof opers res, 65-69, ASSOC PROF OPERS RES, NAVAL POSTGRAD SCH, 69- *Mem:* Opers Res Soc Am; Inst Mgt Sci; Am Soc Eng Educ. *Res:* Counter-insurgency small-unit military operations; industrial inspection systems. *Mailing Add:* Dept of Opers Anal Naval Postgrad Sch Monterey CA 93940

LINDSAY, HAGUE LELAND, JR, b Ft Worth, Tex, Jan 24, 29; m 56; c 4. VERTEBRATE ZOOLOGY. *Educ:* Tex Christian Univ, BA, 49; Univ Tex, MA, 51, PhD(zool), 58. *Prof Exp:* Res scientist, Univ Tex, 54; PROF ZOOL, UNIV TULSA, 56- *Mem:* AAAS; Am Fisheries Soc; Am Soc Ichthyol & Herpet. *Res:* Vertebrate speciation, especially with Amphibians; fish distribution and ecology, especially with darters. *Mailing Add:* Fac of Natural Sci Univ of Tulsa Tulsa OK 74104

LINDSAY, HARRY LEE, b Cotesfield, Nebr, Sept 3, 25; m 49; c 4. VIROLOGY. *Educ:* Univ Nebr, BS, 50, MS, 52; Univ Wis, PhD(bact), 63. *Prof Exp:* Microbiologist, Gateway Chemurgic Co, 51-52 & Hiram Walker & Sons, Inc, 53-59; MICROBIOLOGIST, LEDERLE LABS, AM CYANAMID CO, 63- *Mem:* Am Soc Microbiol; Am Chem Soc. *Res:* Respiratory viruses, including rhinoviruses and influenza; herpesviruses, antiviral agents; organ cultures; tissue culture and mycoplasma; antibiotic fermentations and culture improvement. *Mailing Add:* Lederle Labs Am Cyanamid Co Pearl River NY 10965

LINDSAY, HUGH ALEXANDER, physiology, see previous edition

LINDSAY, JACQUE K, b Rochester, NY, Dec 6, 25; m 53; c 1. ORGANIC CHEMISTRY. *Educ:* Hobart Col, BS, 49; Duke Univ, PhD(org chem), 57. *Prof Exp:* Lab asst, 45-46, chemist, Distillation Prod Industs Div, 49-53, res chemist, 57-63, RES ASSOC, EASTMAN KODAK CO, 64- *Mem:* Am Chem Soc. *Res:* Organometallic and photographic chemistry. *Mailing Add:* Res Labs Eastman Kodak Co Rochester NY 14604

LINDSAY, JAMES EDWARD, JR, b Denver, Colo, Feb 26, 28; m 49; c 5. ELECTRICAL ENGINEERING. *Educ:* Univ Denver, BS, 53; Univ Colo, Boulder, MS, 58, PhD(elec eng), 60. *Prof Exp:* Res engr, RCA Labs, 53-55; instr elec eng, Univ Denver, 55-56, res engr, Denver Res Inst, 57-58; from instr to assoc prof appl math & elec eng, Univ Colo, 58-62; from asst prof to assoc prof elec eng, Univ Denver, 62-65; res engr, Martin Marietta Co, 66-67; assoc prof geophys & basic eng, Colo Sch Mines, 67-70; res engr, Denver Res Inst, Univ Denver, 70-76; assoc prof, 76-80, PROF ELEC ENG, UNIV WYO, 80- *Mem:* Soc Indust & Appl Math; Inst Elec & Electronics Engrs. *Res:* Electromagnetic field theory; antennas and propagation; teaching of graduate and undergraduate courses in electrical engineering, geophysics and applied mathematics. *Mailing Add:* Dept of Elec Eng Univ of Wyo Laramie WY 80270

LINDSAY, JAMES GORDON, physical chemistry, ceramics, see previous edition

LINDSAY, JAMES GORDON, JR, b Norfolk, Va, Jan 23, 41; m 62; c 1. NUCLEAR PHYSICS. *Educ:* Va Polytech Inst & State Univ, BS, 64, MS, 66, PhD(physics), 71. *Prof Exp:* From asst prof to assoc prof, 69-77, PROF PHYSICS, APPALACHIAN STATE UNIV, 77- *Mem:* Am Asn Physics Teachers; Am Nuclear Soc; Am Soc Mech Engrs. *Res:* Neutron activation analysis; thermal neutron cross sections. *Mailing Add:* Dept of Physics Appalachian State Univ Boone NC 28608

LINDSAY, JOHN FRANCIS, b Gosford, Australia, Jan 22, 41; m 64. GEOSTATISTICS, COMPUTER APPLICATIONS. *Educ:* Univ New England, Australia, BSc Hons, 63, MSc, 65; Ohio State Univ, PhD(geol), 68. *Prof Exp:* Res assoc, Ohio State Univ, 68-69; fel, Johnson Space Ctr, NASA, 69-71; res scientist, Lunar Sci Inst, 71-72; prof geol, Latrobe Univ, 72-74; res assoc, Univ Tex, 74-77; RES SPECIALIST, EXXON PROD RES, 78- *Res:* Antarctic geology; evolution of the lunarsoil; mass movement phenomena. *Mailing Add:* Exxon Prod Res PO Box 2189 Houston TX 77001

LINDSAY, KENNETH LAWSON, b Springfield, Ill, Aug 26, 25; m 49; c 1. ORGANIC CHEMISTRY. *Educ:* Univ Ill, BS, 48; Univ Minn, PhD(chem), 52. *Prof Exp:* Res chemist, 52-55, develop chemist, 55-61, develop assoc, 61-63, process res supvr, 63-78, SR RES ASSOC, ETHYL CORP, 78- *Mem:* Am Chem Soc; Am Inst Chem. *Res:* Applied kinetics; organometallic chemistry; chlorine chemistry. *Mailing Add:* Ethyl Corp PO Box 341 Baton Rouge LA 70821

LINDSAY, RAYMOND H, b Perry, Ga, Dec 9, 28; m 54; c 5. BIOCHEMISTRY, PHARMACOLOGY. *Educ:* Jacksonville State Col, BS, 48; Univ Ala, MS, 57, PhD(pharmacol), 61. *Prof Exp:* From asst prof to assoc prof pharmacol, 63-71, from asst prof to assoc prof med, 63-72, PROF MED, MED CTR, UNIV ALA, BIRMINGHAM, 72-, PROF PHARMACOL, 71-; DIR PHARMACOL RES UNIT, VET ADMIN HOSP, 71- *Concurrent Pos:* NIH fel physiol chem, Univ Wis, 60-62, univ fel, 62-63; dir metab res, Vet Admin Hosp, Birmingham, 65-67; asst chief radioisotope serv, 64-72. *Mem:* AAAS; Endocrine Soc; Am Thyroid Asn; Am Chem Soc; Am Fedn Clin Res; Am Soc Pharmacol & Exp Therapeut. *Res:* Biochemistry, pharmacology and physiology of thyroid function; intermediary metabolism of amino acids; pyrimidine biosynthesis. *Mailing Add:* Vet Admin Hosp Birmingham AL 35233

LINDSAY, RICHARD H, b Portland, Ore, Sept 24, 34; m 58; c 6. NUCLEAR PHYSICS. *Educ:* Univ Portland, BS, 56; Stanford Univ, MS, 58; Wash State Univ, PhD(nuclear physics), 61. *Prof Exp:* Teaching assoc physics, Wash State Univ, 60-61; instr, asst prof, 61-66, PROF PHYSICS, WESTERN WASH UNIV 66- *Mem:* Am Phys Soc; Am Asn Physics Teachers. *Res:* Nuclear reactions with 30 to 65 million electron volts alpha particles; reactions with 14 million electron volts neutrons; theoretical nuclear physics; instrument design. *Mailing Add:* Dept of Physics Western Wash Univ Bellingham WA 98225

LINDSAY, ROBERT, b New Haven, Conn, Mar 3, 24; m 52; c 3. MAGNETISM. *Educ:* Brown Univ, ScB, 47; Rice Inst, MA, 49, PhD(physics), 51. *Prof Exp:* Physicist thermodynamics sect, Nat Bur Standards, 51-53; asst prof physics, Southern Methodist Univ, 53-56; from asst prof to assoc prof, 56-65, prof physics, 65-78, BROWNELL-JARVIS PROF NATURAL PHILOS & PHYSICS, TRINITY COL CONN, 78- *Mem:* Am Phys Soc; Am Asn Physics Teachers; Sigma Xi. *Mailing Add:* Dept of Physics Trinity Col Hartford CT 06106

LINDSAY, ROBERT CLARENCE, b Montrose, Colo, Nov 30, 36; m 57; c 2. FOOD SCIENCE, FOOD CHEMISTRY. *Educ:* Colo State Univ, BS, 58, MS, 60; Ore State Univ, PhD(food sci), 65. *Prof Exp:* Asst prof food sci, Ore State Univ, 64-69; assoc prof, 69-74, PROF FOOD SCI, UNIV WIS-MADISON, 74- *Mem:* Am Chem Soc; Inst Food Technologists; Am Dairy Sci Asn; Am Soc Microbiol. *Res:* Flavor chemistry; sensory evaluation of food. *Mailing Add:* Dept of Food Sci Univ of Wis-Madison Madison WI 53706

LINDSAY, ROBERT ERNEST, electrical engineering, see previous edition

LINDSAY, W(ESLEY) N(EWTON), b Ontario, Calif, Dec 29, 13; m 38. CHEMICAL ENGINEERING. *Educ:* Univ Calif, AB, 35. *Prof Exp:* Chemist, Arabol Mfg Co, NY, 35-43; chief, Spec Prob Sect, Food Mach & Chem Corp, 43-52, chief, Chem Sect, 52-55; assoc prof eng, San Jose State Col, 55-59; eng specialist, Jennings Radio & Mfg Corp, 59-60, mgr, Eng Design Dept, 60-64 & Res Dept, 64-72; INDUST CONSULT, 72- *Concurrent Pos:* Consult, 55-59. *Mem:* Am Chem Soc; Inst Elec & Electronics Engrs. *Res:* Starch, protein and resin adhesives; drying of gases and foodstuffs; high pressure water sprays; recovery of nitrous gases; fluidization and high vacuum techniques; ultrahigh temperature furnaces. *Mailing Add:* 10710 Ridgeview Ave San Jose CA 95127

LINDSAY, WILLARD LYMAN, b Dingle, Idaho, Apr 7, 26; m 51; c 4. SOIL SCIENCE. *Educ:* Utah State Univ, BS, 52, MS, 53; Cornell Univ, PhD(soil sci), 56. *Prof Exp:* Res asst Utah State Univ, 52-53 & Cornell Univ, 53-56; soil chemist, Soils & Fertilizer Res Br, Tenn Valley Authority, 56-60; asst prof agron, 60-62, from assoc prof to prof, 62-70, centennial prof, 70-78, PROF AGRON, COLO STATE UNIV, 74- *Concurrent Pos:* Vis prof, State Agr Univ, Wageningen, Netherlands, 72. *Mem:* Soil Sci Soc Am; fel Am Soc Agron; Int Soc Soil Sci. *Res:* Chemical reactions of phosphate in soils; physicochemical equilibria of plant nutrients in soils; chemistry and availability of micronutrients to plants; equilibrium of metal chelates in soils; solubility of heavy metals in soils. *Mailing Add:* Dept of Agron Colo State Univ Ft Collins CO 80521

LINDSAY, WILLIAM GERMER, JR, b Cleveland, Ohio, Nov 22, 28; m 56; c 3. PHYSIOLOGY. *Educ:* Oberlin Col, AB, 51; Univ Pa, MS, 57, PhD(zool), 62. *Prof Exp:* Instr physiol, Albany Med Col, 62-66; asst prof biol, 66-69, assoc prof, 69-75, PROF BIOL, ELMIRA COL, 75- *Mem:* AAAS; Soc Study Reproduction. *Res:* Spermatozoa metabolism; biological limnology. *Mailing Add:* Dept of Biol Elmira Col Elmira NY 14901

LINDSAY, WILLIAM TENNEY, JR, b Scranton, Pa, Apr 4, 24; m 51; c 2. PHYSICAL CHEMISTRY. *Educ:* Rensselaer Polytech Inst, BChE, 48; Mass Inst Technol, PhD(phys chem), 52. *Prof Exp:* Engr, Procter & Gamble Co, 48; asst, Mass Inst Technol, 49-51, res assoc, 52-53; sr scientist, Atomic Power Div, Westinghouse Elec Corp, 53-54, supv engr, 55-59, fel engr, Res Labs, 59-64, mgr phys chem dept, 64-73, mgr phys & inorg chem dept, Res Labs, 73-77, CONSULT SCIENTIST, RES & DEVELOP CTR, WESTINGHOUSE ELEC CORP, 77- *Mem:* Fel AAAS; Am Chem Soc; Am Phys Soc; Electrochem Soc; NY Acad Sci. *Res:* Electrolytic solutions; nuclear reactor coolant technology. *Mailing Add:* Westinghouse Res Beulah Rd Pittsburgh PA 15235

LINDSEY, ALTON ANTHONY, b Monaca, Pa, May 7, 07; m 39; c 2. PLANT ECOLOGY. *Educ:* Allegheny Col, BS, 29; Cornell Univ, PhD(bot), 37. *Prof Exp:* Asst bot, Cornell Univ, 29-33; biologist, Byrd Antarctic Exped, 33-35; asst bot, Cornell Univ, 35-37; instr bot, Am Univ, 37-40; asst prof, Univ Redlands, 40-42 & Univ NMex, 42-47; from asst prof to prof, 47-74, EMER PROF BOT, PURDUE UNIV, 74- *Concurrent Pos:* Botanist, Purdue Can-Arctic Permafrost Exped, 51, ecologist, Purdue Res Team, Sonoran Desert, 53-54; bot ed, Ecol, Ecol Soc Am, 57-61, managing ed, Ecol & Ecol Monogr, 72-74; dir, Ind Natural Areas Surv, 67-68. *Mem:* Fel AAAS; Ecol Soc Am; Sigma Xi. *Res:* Indiana vegetation; flood plain ecology; biographer of ecologists. *Mailing Add:* Dept of Biol Sci Purdue Univ West Lafayette IN 47907

LINDSEY, BRUCE GILBERT, b Rockland, Maine, June 22, 49. NEUROPHYSIOLOGY, NEUROANATOMY. *Educ:* Williams Col, BA, 71; Univ Pa, PhD(neuroanat), 74. *Prof Exp:* Fel neurophysiol, Univ Pa, 74-77; ASST PROF PHYSIOL, UNIV S FLA MED CTR, 77- *Mem:* Soc Neurosci; AAAS; Am Physiol Soc. *Res:* Information processing in simple nervous systems; cellular mechanisms controlling behavior; mammalian rspiratory rhythm generation. *Mailing Add:* Dept Physiol Univ SFla Tampa FL 33612

LINDSEY, CASIMIR CHARLES, b Toronto, Ont, Mar 22, 23; m 48. ICHTHYOLOGY. *Educ:* Univ Toronto, BA, 48; Univ BC, MA, 50; Cambridge Univ, PhD(zool), 52. *Prof Exp:* Res biologist, BC Dept Game, 52-57; from asst prof to assoc prof zool, Univ BC, 57-66; cur fishes, Inst Fisheries, 52-66; PROF ZOOL, UNIV MAN, 66- *Concurrent Pos:* Vis prof, Univ Singapore, 62-63, Wallace mem lectr, 63; fisheries consult, Pakistan, 64 & Fiji, 71-72. *Mem:* Am Soc Ichthyologists & Herpetologists; Am Fisheries Soc; fel Royal Soc Can; Can Soc Zoologists (pres, 77-78); Can Soc Environ Biologists (vpres, 74-). *Res:* Meristic variation; taxonomy; zoogeography of northern freshwater fishes; comparison of tropical and temperate fisheries. *Mailing Add:* Dept of Zool Univ of Man Winnipeg MB R3T 2N2 Can

LINDSEY, DAVID ALLEN, b Nebraska City, Nebr, May 26, 42; m 66; c 2. GEOLOGY. *Educ:* Univ Nebr, BS, 63; Johns Hopkins Univ, PhD(geol), 67. *Prof Exp:* Geologist, US Geol Surv, Colo, 67-74, staff geologist mineral resources, Va, 74-75, GEOLOGIST, US GEOL SURV, COLO, 76- *Concurrent Pos:* Geol Soc Am res grant, 65-66. *Mem:* Geol Soc Am; Am Asn Petrol Geol; Soc Econ Geol; Soc Econ Paleontologists & Mineralogists. *Res:* Precambrian glacial deposits, Tertiary alluvial conglomerates and sandstones; beryllium deposits and volcanic rocks in Utah; intrusive complexes in central Montana; copper in sedimentary rocks. *Mailing Add:* US Geol Surv MS 905 Fed Ctr Lakewood CO 80225

LINDSEY, DONALD L, b Stockton, Kans, May 25, 37; m 61; c 3. PLANT PATHOLOGY. *Educ:* Ft Hays Kans State Col, BS, 59; Colo State Univ, MS, 62, PhD(plant path), 65. *Prof Exp:* Jr plant pathologist, Colo State Univ, 61-65, asst plant pathologist, 66-69; instr bot, Colo State Col, 66; asst prof, 69-74, assoc prof, 74-81, PROF PLANT PATH, NMEX STATE UNIV, 81- *Mem:* Am Phytopath Soc; Sigma Xi; Soc Nematologist. *Res:* Biological control of plant pathogens; ecology of soil fungi; mine spoil revegetation. *Mailing Add:* Dept of Bot & Entom NMex State Univ Las Cruces NM 88003

LINDSEY, DORTHA RUTH, b Kingfisher, Okla, Oct 26, 26. HEALTH SCIENCE. *Educ:* Okla State Univ, BS, 48; Univ Wis, MS, 56; Ind Univ, PED, 63. *Prof Exp:* Instr health, phys educ & recreation, Okla Stae Univ, 48-50; instr, Monticello Col, 51-54; instr, DePauw Univ, 54-56; prof health, phys educ & recreation, Okla State Univ, 56-75. *Concurrent Pos:* Consult, Payne County Guid Ctr, 66-71; ed, Fencing Guide, Am Asn Health, Phys Educ & Recreation, 61-62; vis prof, Utah State Univ & Calif State Univ Long Beach, 76- *Mem:* Am Asn Health, Phys Educ & Recreation; Am Corrective Ther Asn; Am Col Sports Med. *Res:* Physical education; corrective therapy; electromyographical and kinesiological analyses of muscle action; quackery in physical fitness and reducing; therapeutic exercise; gerokinesiatrics. *Mailing Add:* Dept of Phys Educ Calif State Univ Long Beach CA 92683

LINDSEY, EDWARD STORMONT, b West Palm Beach, Fla, June 3, 30; m 53; c 2. MEDICINE. *Educ:* Tulane Univ, BS, 51, MD, 58, MMedSci, 68. *Prof Exp:* Intern, Charity Hosp, La, 58-59, resident surg, 59-61 & thoracic surg, 63-64; from instr to assoc prof, 63-76, CLIN ASSOC PROF SURG, TULANE UNIV, 76-, DIR TRANSPLANTATION RES UNIT, 66- *Concurrent Pos:* Resident surg, Southern Baptist Hosp, 61-62; Nat Heart Inst spec fel, Univ Edinburgh, 64-65; consult surg, Charity Hosp La & Keesler Air Force Hosp, 65-; mem adv comt, Nat Transplant Registry, 66-67. *Mem:* Transplantation Soc; Am Col Surg; NY Acad Sci; Asn Advan Med Instrumentation; Am Soc Artificial Internal Organs. *Res:* Thoracic and vascular surgery; transplantation biology. *Mailing Add:* Dept of Surg Tulane Univ New Orleans LA 70112

LINDSEY, GEORGE ROY, b Toronto, Ont, June 2, 20; m 51; c 2. SYSTEMS ANALYSIS. *Educ:* Univ Toronto, BA, 42; Queen's Univ Ont, MA, 46; Cambridge Univ, PhD(physics), 50. *Prof Exp:* Defence sci officer oper res, Can Defence Res Bd, 50-53; sr oper res officer, Air Defence Command, Royal Can Air Force, 54-59; dir defence systs anal group, Can Dept Nat Defence, 59-61; oper res group leader, Antisubmarine Warfare Res Ctr, Supreme Allied Comdr, Atlantic, Italy, 61-64; sr oper res scientist, 64-67, CHIEF OPER RES ANAL ESTAB, DEPT NAT DEFENCE, 68- *Concurrent Pos:* Mem, Can Govt Bicult Develop Prog, 70-71 & Can Comt Int Inst Appl Systs Anal, 73-79; consult, Inst Res Pub Policy, 75-78. *Mem:* Opers Res Soc Am; Can Inst Strategic Studies; Int Inst Strategic Studies; Can Oper Res Soc (pres, 61); Can Inst Int Affairs. *Res:* Military operational research; forecasting and analysis of trends for research on public policy. *Mailing Add:* Oper Res & Anal Estab Dept of Nat Defence Ottawa ON K1L 5A8 Can

LINDSEY, GERALD HERBERT, b Marshall, Mo, Aug 3, 34; m 58; c 6. MECHANICAL & AERONAUTICAL ENGINEERING. *Educ:* Brigham Young Univ, BES, 60, MS, 62; Calif Inst Technol, PhD(aeronaut eng), 66. *Prof Exp:* PROF AERONAUT ENG, NAVAL POSTGRAD SCH, 65- *Concurrent Pos:* Consult, Chem Systs Div, United Technol, 66- *Mem:* Am Inst Aeronaut & Astronaut. *Res:* Fracture, aircraft fatigue and design; viscoelastic stress and fracture. *Mailing Add:* Dept of Aeronaut Naval Postgrad Sch Monterey CA 93940

LINDSEY, JAMES RUSSELL, b Tifton, Ga, Dec 6, 33; m 58; c 4. PATHOLOGY. *Educ:* Univ Ga, BS, 56, DVM, 57; Auburn Univ, MS, 60. *Prof Exp:* From instr to asst prof parasitol, Sch Vet Med, Auburn Univ, 57-61; from instr to asst prof path & lab animal med, Johns Hopkins Univ, 63-68; PROF COMP MED & ASSOC PROF PATH, SCH MED, UNIV ALA, BIRMINGHAM, 68- *Concurrent Pos:* Fel path, Johns Hopkins Univ, 61-63; chief, RILAMSAT, Birmingham Vet Admin Hosp, 68-; adj prof, Sch Vet Med, Auburn Univ, 80- *Mem:* Am Vet Med Asn. *Res:* Comparative pathology. *Mailing Add:* Dept of Comp Med Univ of Ala Sch of Med Birmingham AL 35294

LINDSEY, JULIA PAGE, b Pine Bluff, Ark, Dec 9, 48. MYCOLOGY, PLANT PATHOLOGY. *Educ:* Hendrix Col, BA, 70; Univ Ariz, MS, 72, PhD(plant path), 75. *Prof Exp:* Teaching asst biol, Univ Ariz, 70-72, teaching asst plant path, 72-75; seed analyst seed cert, Ark State Plant Bd, 75-78; ASST PROF BIOL, FT LEWIS COL, 78- *Mem:* Mycol Soc Am. *Res:* A compilation of descriptive, cultural and taxonomic data concerning woodrotting basidiomycetes that decay aspen in North America; identification and taxonomy of plant pathogenic fungi. *Mailing Add:* Dept of Biol Ft Lewis Col Durango CO 81301

LINDSEY, MARVIN FREDERICK, b Stockville, Nebr. PLANT BREEDING. *Educ:* Univ Nebr, BSc, 53, MSc, 55; NC State Univ, PhD(genetics), 60. *Prof Exp:* Asst prof agron, Univ Nebr, 60-63; geneticist, Rockefeller Found, 64-66; asst prof agron, Univ Wis, 66-69; RES AGRONOMIST, DEKALB AGRES, INC, 70- *Mem:* Am Soc Agron; Crop Sci Soc Am. *Res:* Maize breeding and genetics. *Mailing Add:* DeKalb AgRes Inc Dayton IA 50530

LINDSEY, NORMA JACK, b Canton, Tex, June 16, 29. CLINICAL MICROBIOLOGY. *Educ:* Tex Woman's Univ, BA & BS, 51; Univ Calif, MPH, 64; Colo State Univ, PhD(microbiol), 69. *Prof Exp:* Bacteriologist, Dallas Health Dept Lab, Tex, 51-54; microbiologist, Ariz Health Dept Labs, Phoenix, 56-65; teaching asst microbiol, Colo State Univ, 66-67; chief of microbiol, NMex Health Labs, 69-70; res microbiologist, Dept Health, Educ & Welfare, 70-73; ASST PROF PATH & ACTG HEAD, MICROBIOL SECT, CLIN LABS, UNIV KANS MED CTR, 73- *Mem:* AAAS; Am Soc Microbiol; Am Pub Health Asn; NY Acad Sci; Sigma Xi. *Res:* Clinical and applied microbiology. *Mailing Add:* Univ of Kans Med Ctr 39th & Rainbow St Kansas City KS 66103

LINDSEY, ROLAND GRAY, b Sylvatus, Va, June 26, 27; m 48; c 3. CHEMICAL ENGINEERING. *Educ:* Univ Del, BChE, 51, MSc, 54, PhD(chem eng), 59. *Prof Exp:* Chem engr, Polychem Div, Dow Chem Corp, 56-59, proj leader polymer res, 59-60; res engr, Fabrics & Finishes Dept, 60-66, staff engr, 66-70, RES ASSOC, E I DU PONT DE NEMOURS & CO, INC, 70- *Mem:* Am Chem Soc; Am Inst Chem Engrs. *Res:* Computerized kinetic model description of free radical and condensation polymer processes. *Mailing Add:* 613 Sherman Rd Springfield PA 19064

LINDSEY, WILLIAM B, b Iowa Park, Tex, July 26, 22; m 48; c 2. ORGANIC CHEMISTRY. *Educ:* Univ Tex, BS, 48; Ind Univ, MA, 49, PhD(chem), 54. *Prof Exp:* Res chemist, E I du Pont de Nemours & Co, Inc, Buffalo, 52-70, staff scientist, Film Dept, Richmond, 70-75, SR RES CHEMIST, PLASTIC PROD & RESINS DEPT, E I DU PONT DE NEMOURS & CO INC, 77- *Res:* Organic coatings; polymerization; surface phenomena; polymer stabilization; coating techniques; surface treatment for adhesion; adhesion; film extrusion and orientation; film evaluation; monomer and general organic synthesis; cellulose chemistry. *Mailing Add:* 1019 Eighth Ave N Clinton IA 52732

LINDSKOG, GUSTAF ELMER, b Boston, Mass, Feb 7, 03; m 34; c 2. SURGERY. *Educ:* Mass Agr Col, BS, 23; Harvard Univ, MD, 28; Am Bd Surg, dipl, 52 & Am Bd Thoracic Surg, cert. *Prof Exp:* Intern surg, Lakeside Hosp, 28-29; asst surg & path, Sch Med, Yale Univ, 29-30; asst res surgeon, obstetrician & gynecologist, New Haven Hosp, 30-32; Nat Res Coun fel, Mass Gen Hosp, 32-33; from instr to prof, 33-71, EMER PROF SURG, SCH MED, YALE UNIV, 71- *Concurrent Pos:* Res surgeon, New Haven Hosp, 33-34; chmn, Am Bd Surg, 57-58. *Mem:* Soc Univ Surg; Soc Clin Surg; Am Asn Thoracic Surg; Am Surg Asn; fel Am Col Surg. *Res:* Thoracic surgery and physiology. *Mailing Add:* Dept of Surg Yale Univ Sch Med 333 Cedar St New Haven CT 06511

LINDSLEY, DAN LESLIE, JR, b Evanston, Ill, Oct 13, 25; m 47; c 4. GENETICS. *Educ:* Univ Mo, AB, 47, MA, 49; Calif Inst Technol, PhD(genetics), 52. *Prof Exp:* Nat Res Coun fel biol, Princeton Univ, 52-53; NSF fel, Univ Mo, 53-54; from assoc biologist to biologist, Oak Ridge Nat Lab, 54-67; chmn dept, 77-79, PROF BIOL, UNIV CALIF, SAN DIEGO, 67- *Concurrent Pos:* NSF sr fels, Univ Sao Paulo, 60-61 & Inst Genetics, Univ Rome, 65-66; USPHS spec fel, Dept Genetics, Div Plant Indust, Commonwealth Sci & Indust Res Orgn, Canberra, Australia, 72-73, Fogarty Int Fel, Dept Develop Genetics, Ctr Molecular Biol, Autonomous Univ Madrid, Spain, 80-81. *Mem:* Nat Acad Sci; Genetics Soc Am (treas, 75-78); Am Acad Arts & Sci. *Res:* Cytogenetics of Drosophila. *Mailing Add:* Dept of Biol Univ of Calif San Diego La Jolla CA 92093

LINDSLEY, DAVID FORD, b Cleveland, Ohio, May 18, 36; m 60; c 3. NEUROPHYSIOLOGY. *Educ:* Stanford Univ, BA, 57; Univ Calif, Los Angeles, PhD(anat, neurophysiol), 61. *Prof Exp:* Asst prof physiol, Med Sch, Stanford Univ, 63-67; ASSOC PROF PHYSIOL, MED SCH, UNIV SOUTHERN CALIF, 67- *Concurrent Pos:* USPHS fels, Moscow State Univ, 61-62 & Cambridge Univ, 62-63; Lederle med fac award, 64-67; visitor, Max Planck Inst Psychiat, Munich, 71 & 74-75; Guggenheim fel, 74-75. *Mem:* AAAS; Am Physiol Soc; Am Asn Anatomists; Soc Neurosci; Int Brain Res Orgn. *Res:* Central nervous system neurophysiology; behavioral neurophysiology. *Mailing Add:* Dept of Physiol 2025 Zonal Ave Los Angeles CA 90033

LINDSLEY, DONALD B, b Brownhelm, Ohio, Dec 23, 07; m 33; c 4. PSYCHOPHYSIOLOGY, NEUROPSYCHOLOGY. *Educ:* Wittenberg Univ, AB, 29; Univ Iowa, MA, 30, PhD, 32. *Hon Degrees:* DSc, Brown Univ, 58, Wittenberg Univ, 59, Trinity Col, Conn, 65 & Loyola Univ Chicago, 68; PhD, Johannes Gutenberg Univ, Mainz, WGer. *Prof Exp:* Instr psychol, Univ Ill, 32-33; Nat Res Coun fel physiol & neuropsychiat, Harvard Med Sch & Mass Gen Hosp, Boston, 33-35; res assoc anat, Sch Med, Western Reserve Univ, 35-38; asst prof psychol, Brown Univ, 38-46; prof, Northwestern Univ, 46-51; chmn dept psychol, 59-62, prof psychol & physiol, 51-77, EMER PROF PSYCHOL & PHYSIOL, UNIV CALIF, LOS ANGELES, 77- *Concurrent Pos:* Dir, Psychol & Neurophysiol Labs, Bradley Hosp, East Providence, RI, 38-46 & Nat Defense Res Comt Proj, Yale Univ Contract, Camp Murphy & Boca Raton AFB, Fla, 43-46; mem sci adv bd, US Air Force, 47-49, chmn human resources comt, 48-49; mem aviation psychol comt, Nat Res Coun, 47-49 & undersea warfare comt, 50-66; consult, USPHS, 51-54, 58-61, 65-69 & NSF, 52-54; Am Inst Biol Sci, NASA Panel, 65-70; mem space sci bd, Nat Acad Sci, 67-70, chmn long-duration missions in space comt, 67-71, mem space med comt, 67-; treas, Int Brain Res Orgn, 67-71; mem sci & technol adv coun, Calif Assembly, 69-71. *Honors & Awards:* President's Cert Merit, 48. *Mem:* Nat Acad Sci; AAAS (vchmn, 53); Soc Exp Psychol; Am Physiol Soc; Am Electroencephalog Soc (pres, 65). *Res:* Brain function; emotion; behavior disorders; electroencephalography; neurophysiology; vision and visual perception. *Mailing Add:* Dept of Psychol Univ of Calif Los Angeles CA 90024

LINDSLEY, DONALD HALE, b Princeton, NJ, May 22, 34. PHASE EQUILIBRIA, GEOTHERMOMETRY. *Educ:* Princeton Univ, AB, 56; Johns Hopkins Univ, PhD(geol), 61. *Prof Exp:* Fel, Geophys Lab, Carnegie Inst, Washington, 60-62, petrologist, 62-70; PROF PETROL, DEPT EARTH

& SPACE SCI, STATE UNIV NY STONY BROOK, 70- *Concurrent Pos:* Vis assoc prof, Calif Inst Technol, 69; vis scientist, Univ BC, 76-77. *Mem:* Mineral Soc Am (vpres, 81, pres, 82); Geol Soc Am; Geochem Soc; Am Geophys Union; AAAS. *Res:* High-pressure and high-temperature phase relations and thermodynamic solution models of mineral systems; redox reactions in earth; origin of anorthosites and related rocks; origin of lunar magmas. *Mailing Add:* Dept Earth & Space Sci State Univ NY Stony Brook NY 11794

LINDSTEDT, P(AUL) M, b Stromsburg, Nebr, Feb 28, 17; m 42; c 2. CHEMICAL ENGINEERING. *Educ:* Univ Nebr, BS, 39. *Prof Exp:* Trainee eng, Goodyear Tire & Rubber Co, 39-40, jr chem engr, 40-44, sect head, 44-49, asst mgr chem eng & pilot plants, 49-51, mgr, 51-80; RETIRED. *Mem:* Am Inst Chem Engrs. *Res:* Synthetic rubber drying process; process development of elastomers and resins. *Mailing Add:* 2830 Hastings Rd Akron OH 44309

LINDSTEDT-SIVA, K JUNE, b Minneapolis, Minn, Sept 24, 41; m 69. BIOLOGY. *Educ:* Univ Southern Calif, AB, 63, MS, 67, PhD(biol), 71. *Prof Exp:* Asst coordr sea grant progs, Univ Southern Calif, 71; environ specialist, Southern Calif Edison Co, 71-72; asst prof biol, Calif Lutheran Col, 72-73; sci adv, 73-77, sr sci adv, 77-81, MGR, ENVIRON SCI, ATLANTIC RICHFIELD CO, 81- *Concurrent Pos:* Consult, Jacques Cousteau, Metromedia Producers Co, 70 & Southern Calif Edison Co, 72; mem task force, Fate & Effects of Oil, Am Petrol Inst, 73-, chmn biol res subcomt; mem opers subcomt, Marine Water Qual Comn, Water Pollution Control Fedn, 75-76; chmn environ subcomt, Marine Indust Group, 81-; mem bd trustees, Bermuda Biol Sta Res, 79- *Honors & Awards:* Trident Award Marine Sci, Int Rev Underwater Activities, Ustica, Italy, 70. *Mem:* Soc Petrol Indust Biologists (pres); Marine Technol Soc; AAAS; Sigma Xi; Am Soc Zoologists. *Res:* Chemoreception in aquatic animals, especially chemical control of feeding behavior in sea anemones; effects of oil on marine organisms; oil spill response planning; oil spill cleanup and control; environmental planning in industry, implementing planning during the early stages of project development. *Mailing Add:* Environ Affairs 515 S Flower St Los Angeles CA 90071

LINDSTROM, DAVID JOHN, b Ashland, Wis, Mar 1, 45; m 71. GEOCHEMISTRY. *Educ:* Univ Wis-Madison, BS, 66; Univ Chicago, SM, 68; Univ Ore, PhD(chem), 76. *Prof Exp:* Res assoc lunar sci, Goddard Space Flight Ctr, NASA, 75-77; RES SCIENTIST GEOCHEM, DEPT EARTH & PLANETARY SCI, WASH UNIV, 77- *Res:* Experimental trace element geochemistry; experimental petrology; properties of silicate liquids; extraterrestrial materials processing. *Mailing Add:* Dept of Earth & Planetary Sci Wash Univ St Louis MO 63130

LINDSTROM, DUAINE GERALD, b Raymond, Wash, Jan 18, 37; m 67. NUCLEAR ENGINEERING. *Educ:* Univ Wash, BS, 59, PhD(nuclear eng), 68; Univ Mich, MS, 60. *Prof Exp:* Physics specialist, Aerojet Nuclear Systs Co, Sacramento, 68-71; lectr nuclear technol, Imperial Col, London, 71-75; ASSOC PROF NUCLEAR ENG, UNIV OKLA, 75- *Concurrent Pos:* Lectr, Calif State Univ, Sacramento, 69-70. *Mem:* Am Nuclear Soc; Brit Nuclear Energy Soc; Health Physics Soc. *Res:* Radiation transport, radiation shielding and protection; nuclear fuel cycle; reactor operations. *Mailing Add:* Dept Nuclear Eng Univ Okla Norman OK 73019

LINDSTROM, EUGENE SHIPMAN, b Ames, Iowa, Jan 12, 23; m 49; c 4. BACTERIOLOGY. *Educ:* Univ Wis, BA, 47, MS, 48, PhD(bact), 51. *Prof Exp:* Asst bact, Univ Wis, 46-51, AEC fel enzyme chem, 51-52; from asst prof to assoc prof, 52-64, from asst dean to assoc dean col sci, 66-77, PROF BACT, PA STATE UNIV, 64-, HEAD DEPT BIOL, 77- *Concurrent Pos:* NSF fel, Univ Minn, 61. *Mem:* AAAS; Am Soc Microbiol; Am Acad Microbiol; Am Soc Biol Chem; Brit Soc Gen Microbiol. *Res:* Bacterial physiology; physiology of Athiorhodaceae; physiology and ecology of photosynthetic bacteria. *Mailing Add:* 208 Mueller Lab Pa State Univ University Park PA 16802

LINDSTROM, FREDERICK JOHN, b La Crosse, Wis, Dec 22, 29. ANALYTICAL CHEMISTRY. *Educ:* Univ Wis, BS, 51, MS, 53; Iowa State Univ, PhD(chem), 59. *Prof Exp:* Asst, Univ Wis, 51-53; asst, Iowa State Univ, 55-58; from asst prof to assoc prof chem, 58-69, PROF CHEM, CLEMSON UNIV, 69- *Mem:* Am Chem Soc. *Res:* Organic analytical reagents; complexometric titrations; spectrochemistry. *Mailing Add:* Dept of Chem Clemson Univ Clemson SC 29631

LINDSTROM, FREDRICK THOMAS, b Astoria, Ore, July 30, 40; m 64; c 2. APPLIED MATHEMATICS. *Educ:* Ore State Univ, BS, 63, MS, 65, PhD(appl math), 69. *Prof Exp:* Res asst, 64-69, asst prof, 69-74, ASSOC PROF STATISTICS & MATH, ORE STATE UNIV, 74- *Mem:* Soc Indust & Appl Math; Am Math Soc; Am Statist Asn. *Res:* Mass transport phenomenon, especially in porous and permeable mediums; compartmental analysis and the mathematical modeling of drug distributions in mammalian tissue systems. *Mailing Add:* Statist Dept Ore State Univ Corvallis OR 97331

LINDSTROM, IVAR E, JR, b Milligan, nebr, Oct 15, 29; m 52; c 2. PHYSICS. *Educ:* Nebr Wesleyan Univ, AB, 50; Univ Ore, MA, 52, PhD(physics), 59. *Prof Exp:* MEM STAFF PHYSICS, LOS ALAMOS NAT LAB, UNIV CALIF, 58- *Mem:* Am Phys Soc. *Res:* Explosives, particularly initiation by shock waves; nuclear spectroscopy; solid state physics. *Mailing Add:* Los Alamos Nat Lab Box 1663 Los Alamos NM 87545

LINDSTROM, JON MARTIN, b Moline, Ill, Oct 9, 45; m 77; c 2. NEUROBIOLOGY, AUTOIMMUNITY. *Educ:* Univ Ill, BA, 67; Univ Calif, San Diego, PhD(biol), 71. *Prof Exp:* Muscular Dystrophy Asn fel, 71-73, asst res prof, 73-77, ASSOC RES PROF, SALK INST, 78- *Concurrent Pos:* mem sci adv coun, Muscular Dystrophy Asn & Myasthenia Gravis Found. *Mem:* Soc Neurosci. *Res:* Acetylcholine receptor structure and function; pathological mechanisms in myasthenia gravis. *Mailing Add:* Salk Inst for Biol Studies PO Box 1809 San Diego CA 92112

LINDSTROM, MARILYN MARTIN, b Jacksonville, Fla, Nov 28, 46; m 71; c 1. GEOCHEMISTRY, IGNEOUS PETROLOGY. *Educ:* Univ Calif, San Diego, BA, 69; Univ Ore, PhD(geochem), 76. *Prof Exp:* Technician geochem, Geol Dept, Univ Ore, 68-69; res assoc, Univ Md, 75-77; res scientist, 77-80, SR RES SCIENTIST GEOCHEM, DEPT EARTH & PLANETARY SCI, WASH UNIV, 80- *Concurrent Pos:* Prin investr, NSF grant; assoc ed, 12th Proc Lunar & Planetary Sci Conf. *Mem:* Geol Soc Am; Geochem Soc; Am Geophys Union. *Res:* Geochemistry and petrology of igneous rocks and extraterrestrial materials; oceanic and continental volcanic rocks, lunar basalts, anorthosites and breccias; trace element geochemistry; instrumental neutron activation analysis. *Mailing Add:* Dept of Earth & Planetary Sci Wash Univ St Louis MO 63130

LINDSTROM, MERLIN RAY, b New Rockford, NDak, Oct 28, 51; m 72; c 3. COATINGS CHEMISTRY, POLYMER CHEMISTRY. *Educ:* NDak State Univ, BS, 73, PhD(chem), 78. *Prof Exp:* CHEMIST, PHILLIPS PETROL CO, 78- *Mem:* Fedn Coatings Technol; Soc Mfg Engrs. *Res:* Coatings; sulfur chemicals; metal cleaners; adhesives; water soluble resins; electroplating; sealants. *Mailing Add:* Phillips Petrol Co 117-CL-PRC Bartlesville OK 74004

LINDSTROM, RICHARD EDWARD, b Bristol, Conn, June 15, 32; m 52; c 3. PHYSICAL PHARMACY. *Educ:* Univ Conn, BS, 55; Syracuse Univ, MS, 62, PhD(phys chem), 67. *Prof Exp:* Asst prof chem, US Air Force Acad, 62-66 & Salem State Col, 66-68; assoc prof, 68-80, PROF PHARMACEUT, UNIV CONN, 80- *Concurrent Pos:* Consult, Vick Chem Co, 74-; US Air Force, 80- & US Army, 81- *Mem:* Am Chem Soc; Am Pharmaceut Asn; Acad Pharmaceut Sci. *Res:* Thermodynamics of solution phenomena via molar volume and solubility data. *Mailing Add:* Sch of Pharm Univ of Conn Storrs CT 06268

LINDSTROM, RICHARD S, b Cleveland, Ohio, Mar 5, 27; m 53; c 3. HORTICULTURE. *Educ:* Ohio State Univ, BS, 50, MS, 51, PhD(hort), 56. *Prof Exp:* Instr hort, Mich State Univ, 53-56, from asst prof to assoc prof, 56-68; PROF HORT, VA POLYTECH INST & STATE UNIV, 68- *Mem:* Am Soc Hort Sci. *Res:* Physiology of floricultural plants including work with growth regulators, nutrition and photoperiodic control. *Mailing Add:* Dept of Hort Va Polytech Inst & State Univ Blacksburg VA 24061

LINDSTROM, WENDELL DON, b Kiron, Iowa, Feb 7, 27; m 50; c 2. MATHEMATICS. *Educ:* Univ Iowa, AB, 49, MS, 51, PhD(math), 53. *Prof Exp:* Instr math, Iowa State Univ, 53-54, asst prof, 54-58; assoc prof, 58-66, PROF MATH, KENYON COL, 66- *Concurrent Pos:* NSF sci fac fel, Univ Calif, Berkeley, 62-63; vis prof, Robert Col, Istanbul, 68-69. *Mem:* Am Math Soc; Math Asn Am. *Res:* Fields, rings, algebras, differential algebra; algebraic geometry. *Mailing Add:* Dept of Math Kenyon Col Gambier OH 43022

LINDT, JAN THOMAS, b Amsterdam, Holland, July 8, 42; m 77; c 3. POLYMER ENGINEERING, CHEMICAL ENGINEERING. *Educ:* Delft Univ Technol, MSc, 64, PhD(chem eng), 71. *Prof Exp:* Asst prof chem eng, Delft Univ Technol, 69-71; scientist polymer eng, Shell Res Ltd, 72-77; ASSOC PROF POLYMER ENG, UNIV PITTSBURGH, 78- *Mem:* Soc Rheology; Soc Plastics Engrs. *Res:* Plasticating extrusion; reaction injection molding; reactive extrusion of polymers; mass transfer with bubbles; polyurethane foaming processes; polymer composites. *Mailing Add:* Dept of Mat Eng Univ of Pittsburgh Pittsburgh PA 15261

LINDUSKA, JOSEPH PAUL, b Butte, Mont, July 25, 13; m 36; c 2. BIOLOGY. *Educ:* Univ Mont, BA, 36, MA, 38; Mich State Univ, PhD, 49. *Prof Exp:* Asst zool, Mich State Univ, 39-40; leader, Pittman-Robertson res proj, Game Div, Mich State Conserv Dept, 41-42, game biologist, 42-43, 46-47; foreign plant quarantine inspector, Bur Entom & Plant Quarantine, USDA, La, 43-44, entomologist, Fla, 44-46; biologist, Patuxent Res Refuge, US Fish & Wildlife Serv, 47-49, asst chief br wildlife res, 49-51, chief br game mgt, 51-56, actg chief br wildlife res, 54-55; dir wildlife mgt, Remington Arms Co, Md, 56-59, pub rels & wildlife mgt, 59-66; assoc dir, US Bur Sport Fisheries & Wildlife, 66-73, sr scientist, 73-75; vpres for sci, Nat Audubon Soc, 75-79. *Honors & Awards:* Conserv educ award, Wildlife Soc, 63; conserv serv award, US Dept Interior, 65. *Mem:* Wildlife Soc (pres, 65-66); Soc Exp Biol & Med; Wildlife Mgt Inst; Soil Conserv Soc Am. *Res:* Vertebrate ecology; insect control; biology of insects; game animal research; pheasants; ecological study of small mammals on Michigan farmland. *Mailing Add:* 220 Richards Dr Chestertown MD 20240

LINDVALL, F(REDERICK) C(HARLES), b Moline, Ill, May 29, 03; m 28; c 3. ENGINEERING. *Educ:* Univ Ill, BS, 24; Calif Inst Technol, PhD(elec eng), 28. *Hon Degrees:* DSc, Nat Univ Ireland, 63; DrEng, Purdue Univ, 66. *Prof Exp:* With elec eng dept, Los Angeles Rwy Corp, 24-25; engr, gen dept, Gen Elec Co, 28-30; from instr elec eng to prof elec & mech eng, Calif Inst Technol, 30-69, chmn div eng & appl sci, 45-69; vpres eng, Deere & Co, Ill, 69-72; consult, 72-80; RETIRED. *Mem:* Nat Acad Eng; AAAS; Am Soc Mech Engrs; Am Soc Eng Educ (pres, 57-58); fel Inst Elec & Electronics Engrs. *Res:* Electrical switching phenomena; electrical welding; electrodynamic systems; railroad engineering development; thyratron control system; steel fabrication. *Mailing Add:* 1224 Arden Rd Pasadena CA 91106

LINDZEN, RICHARD SIEGMUND, b Webster, Mass, Feb 8, 40; m 65; c 2. DYNAMIC METEOROLOGY, APPLIED MATHEMATICS. *Educ:* Harvard Univ, AB, 60, SM, 61, PhD(appl math), 64. *Prof Exp:* Res fel meteorol, Univ Wash, 64 & Univ Oslo, 64-65; res scientist, Nat Ctr Atmospheric Res, 65-68; prof, Univ Chicago, 68-72; PROF METEOROL, HARVARD UNIV, 72-, DIR, CTR EARTH & PLANETARY PHYSICS, 80- *Concurrent Pos:* Exec mem, Nat Acad Comt Global Atmospheric Res Prog, 68-; consult, Naval Res Lab, 72-; Control Data Corp, 77 & NASA, 77-; mem, Nat Acad Assembly Math & Phys Sci, 78- *Honors & Awards:* Meisinger Award, Am Meteorol Asn, 68; Macelwane Award, Am Geophys Union, 69. *Mem:* Nat Acad Sci; fel Am Acad Arts & Sci; fel Am Meteorol Soc. *Res:* Hydrodynamic stability; climatology; upper atmosphere dynamics; general atmospheric circulation; tides. *Mailing Add:* Pierce Hall 107c Harvard Univ Cambridge MA 02138

LINE, JOHN PAUL, b Pontiac, Mich, Mar 2, 29; m 57; c 4. MATHEMATICS. *Educ:* Univ Mich, BS, 50, MS, 51. *Prof Exp:* Instr math, Oberlin Col, 55 & Univ Rochester, 55-56; asst prof, 56-62, ASSOC PROF MATH, GA INST TECHNOL, 62- *Mem:* Am Math Soc; Math Asn Am. *Res:* Integral transformations as applied to solution of boundary value problems in partial differential equations. *Mailing Add:* Sch of Math Ga Inst of Technol Atlanta GA 30332

LINEBACK, DAVID R, b Russellville, Ind, June 7, 34; m 56; c 3. CARBOHYDRATE CHEMISTRY. *Educ:* Purdue Univ, BS, 56; Ohio State Univ, PhD(org chem), 62. *Prof Exp:* Res chemist, Monsanto Chem Co, 56-57; fel, Univ Alta, 62-64; from instr to asst prof biochem, Univ Nebr, Lincoln, 64-69; from assoc prof to prof grain sci & indust, Kans State Univ, 69-76; prof food sci & head dept, Pa State Univ, 76-80; PROF FOOD SCI & HEAD DEPT, NC STATE UNIV, 80- *Mem:* Am Asn Cereal Chem; Inst Food Technol; Am Chem Soc. *Res:* Reaction and structure of carbohydrates; characterization of enzymes of starch hydrolysis and synthesis; cereal chemistry. *Mailing Add:* Dept Food Sci 111 Borland Lab Pa State Univ University Park PA 16802

LINEBACK, JERRY ALVIN, b Ottawa, Kans, Oct 25, 38; m 69; c 3. REGIONAL GEOLOGY. *Educ:* Univ Kans, BS, 60, MS, 61; Ind Univ, PhD(geol), 64. *Prof Exp:* Asst geologist, stratig & areal geol sect, Ill State Geol Surv, 64-67, assoc geologist, 67-76, geologist, 76-81; SR GEOLOGIST, ROBERTSON RES, 81- *Mem:* Geol Soc Am; Soc Econ Paleontologists & Mineralogists. *Res:* Stratigraphy of Illinois Basin; geologic mapping; paleoecology and paleontology of Paleozoic and Pleistocene sediments; Pleistocene stratigraphy; geology and geochemistry of lake sediments; regional geological studies; sedimentology of carbonates. *Mailing Add:* Robertson Res 16730 Hedgecraft 306 Houston TX 77060

LINEBERGER, ROBERT DANIEL, b Dallas, NC, Nov 9, 48; m 71; c 2. HORTICULTURE, PLANT PHYSIOLOGY. *Educ:* NC State Univ, BS, 71; Cornell Univ, MS, 74, PhD(hort), 78. *Prof Exp:* L H Bailey res asst, Dept Floricult, Cornell Univ, 71-77; ASST PROF HORT, OHIO STATE UNIV, 77- *Res:* Plant cell and tissue culture; freeze preservation of germ plasm; freezing injury to plant cells; plant cell ultrastructure. *Mailing Add:* 1104 Caniff Columbus OH 43221

LINEBERGER, WILLIAM CARL, b Hamlet, NC, Dec 5, 39. CHEMICAL PHYSICS. *Educ:* Ga Inst Technol, BEE, 61, MSEE, 63, PhD, 65. *Prof Exp:* Asst prof elec eng, Ga Inst Technol, 65; res physicist atmospheric physics, Aberdeen Res & Develop Ctr, Md, 67-68; res assoc physics, Inst, 68-70, asst prof chem, Univ, 70-74, PROF CHEM, UNIV COLO, BOULDER, 74-, FEL PHYSICS, JOINT INST LAB ASTROPHYS, 71- *Concurrent Pos:* J S Guggenheim fel. *Honors & Awards:* Broida Prize, Am Phys Soc, 81. *Mem:* Fel AAAS; Am Chem Soc; fel Am Phys Soc. *Res:* Negative ion structure; molecular fluorescence; ion molecule reactions; tunable lasers. *Mailing Add:* Dept of Chem Univ of Colo Boulder CO 80309

LINEHAN, JOHN HENRY, b Chicago, Ill, July 8, 38; m 60; c 5. MECHANICAL & BIOMEDICAL ENGINEERING. *Educ:* Marquette Univ, BSME, 60; Rensselaer Polytech Inst, MSME, 62; Univ Wis-Madison, PhD(mech eng), 68. *Prof Exp:* Engr, Knolls Atomic Power Lab, NY, 60-62; instr mech eng, 62-64, asst prof mech & biomed eng, 68-76, assoc prof, 76-78, PROF MECH & BIOMED ENG, MARQUETTE UNIV, 78-; PROF PHYSIOL, MED COL WIS, 79- *Mem:* Am Soc Mech Engrs; Am Physiol Soc; NY Acad Sci. *Res:* Multiphase flow; heat and mass transfer; hemodynamics; thermodynamics; lung physiology. *Mailing Add:* Col Eng Marquette Univ 1131 W Wisconsin Ave Milwaukee WI 53233

LINEHAN, URBAN JOSEPH, b Brockton, Mass, Oct 13, 11; m 50; c 3. PHYSICAL GEOGRAPHY. *Educ:* Bridgewater State Col, BS, 33; Clark Univ, MA, 46, PhD(geog), 55. *Prof Exp:* Instr geog, Univ Cincinnati, 40-45; from instr to asst prof, Univ Pittsburgh, 45-48; asst prof, Cath Univ Am, 48-56; analyst, US Govt, 56-73; RETIRED. *Res:* Synoptic climatology of Pittsburgh, Pennsylvania; areal and temporal distribution of tornado deaths in the United States; landscapes and off-road recreation of Southwestern United States. *Mailing Add:* PO Box 113 Moab UT 84532

LINES, ELLWOOD LEROY, b Macon, Ga, Jan 31, 49; m 78; c 2. CONSUMER PRODUCTS, GENERAL CHEMISTRY. *Educ:* DEmory Univ, BS, 70, PhD(chem), 73. *Prof Exp:* Technician, Southern Sizing Co, Atlanta, 72-73; sr res chemist, 73-75, proj leader, 75-77, group leader, 77-81, SECT MGR, OLIN CORP, 81- *Mem:* Sigma Xi; Soc Cosmetic Chemists. *Res:* Consumer products research and commercial development; product and process research and development from chemical specialties to commodities. *Mailing Add:* Olin Res Ctr 275 Winchester Ave PO Box 30-275 New Haven CT 06511

LINES, MALCOLM ELLIS, b Banbury, Eng, Apr 26, 36; m 62; c 2. THEORETICAL SOLID STATE PHYSICS. *Educ:* Oxford Univ, BA, 59, MA & DPhil(physics), 62. *Prof Exp:* Fel physics, Magdalen Col, Oxford Univ, 61-63, 65-66; MEM TECH STAFF, BELL LABS, 63-65, 66- *Concurrent Pos:* Consult, Atomic Energy Res Estab, Harwell, Eng, 73. *Mem:* Fel Brit Inst Physics; Am Ceramic Soc; fel Phys Soc Gt Brit. *Res:* Statistical mechanics; magnetism; ferroelectricity; structure of glasses. *Mailing Add:* Bell Labs Murray Hill NJ 07974

LINFIELD, WARNER MAX, b Hannover, Ger, Jan 8, 18; nat US; m 45; c 1. SURFACE & SURFACTANT CHEMISTRY, LIPID CHEMISTRY. *Educ:* George Washington Univ, BS, 40; Univ Mich, MS, 41, PhD(pharmaceut chem), 43. *Prof Exp:* Anna Fuller Fund res fel, Northwestern Univ, 43-44; res chemist, Emulsol Corp, Ill, 44-46; group leader, E F Houghton & Co, Pa, 46-52 & Quaker Chem Prod Co, 52-55; dir res, Soap Div, Armour & Co Ill, 55-58; tech dir grocery prod div, 58-63; vpres, Culver Chem Co, 63-65; mgr org chem res, IIT Res Inst, 65-71; RES LEADER, EASTERN REGIONAL RES CTR DIV, USDA, 71- *Concurrent Pos:* Assoc ed, J Am Oil Chemists Soc, 74-

Mem: AAAS; Am Chem Soc; Am Oil Chemists Soc; Am Inst Chem. *Res:* Surface-active agents; soaps and detergents; synthesis of germicides; antimalarial drugs; textile finishing agents; food technology; enzymatic fat splitting. *Mailing Add:* 600 E Mermaid Lane Philadelphia PA 19118

LINFOOT, JOHN ARDIS, b Grand Forks, NDak, May 16, 31; m 55; c 2. MEDICINE, ENDOCRINOLOGY. *Educ:* Univ NDak, BA, 53, BS & MS, 55; Harvard Univ, MD, 57; Am Bd Internal Med & Am Bd Endocrinol, dipl; Am Bd Nuclear Med, sr staff scientist, LBL, 61-76, dipl. *Prof Exp:* Fel metab & endocrinol, Univ Utah Hosps, 59-60; dir endocrine & metab serv, Alta Bates Hosp, 70; consult, Martinez Vet Admin, Hosp & Children's Hosp East Bay. *Mem:* AAAS; Am Fedn Clin Res; fel Am Col Physicians; Endocrine Soc; Am Diabetes Asn. *Res:* Growth hormone; acromegaly; Cushing's syndrome; diabetic retinopathy; heavy particle pituitary irradiation. *Mailing Add:* Donner Lab Univ Calif Berkeley CA 94720

LINFORD, GARY JOE, b Laramie, Wyo, June 13, 40; m 63; c 3. LASER PHYSICS, NON-LINEAR OPTICS. *Educ:* Mass Inst Technol, BS, 62; Univ Utah, PhD(physics), 71. *Prof Exp:* Res asst physics, Electronics Res Lab, Mass Inst Technol, 61-62; mem tech staff laser physics, Laser Technol Dept, Aerospace Group, Hughes Aircraft Co, 63-68, group head, Laser Div, 68-69; teaching asst physics & astron, Univ Utah, 69-71; sect head, Laser Div, Hughes Aircraft Co, 71-74; group head laser res, Laser Fusion Prog, Lawrence Livermore Nat Lab, Univ Calif, 74-82; PHYSICIST LASER RES, MAX PLANCK INST QUANTUM OPTICS, WGER, 82- *Concurrent Pos:* Guest lectr, Dept Physics, Calif State Univ, 81-82. *Res:* Inertial confinement laser fusion experiments; harmonic conversion of infrared light to ultraviolet at intensities of up to 8 gigawatt/cubic centimeter; design of laser amplifiers and high power propagation optics; target irradiation experiments and diagnostics. *Mailing Add:* Max Planck Inst für Quantenoptik D-8046 Garching bei Munchen West Germany

LINFORD, HENRY B(LOOD), electrochemistry, deceased

LING, ALAN CAMPBELL, b London, Eng, July 28, 40. RADIOCHEMISTRY, PHYSICAL CHEMISTRY. *Educ:* London Univ, BSc, 63, PhD(chem), 66. *Prof Exp:* Fel chem, Univ Wis-Madison, 66-68; prof, WVa Univ, 68-75; PROF CHEM & ASSOC DEAN, SAN JOSE STATE UNIV, 75- *Concurrent Pos:* Proj dir, NASA-Ames Res Ctr, Mountain View, Calif, 75- *Mem:* Royal Inst Chem, London; The Chem Soc, London; Am Chem Soc; Sigma Xi. *Res:* Radiation chemistry; combustion and fire protection; general physical chemistry; chemical education. *Mailing Add:* Dept of Chem San Jose State Univ San Jose CA 95192

LING, ALFRED SOY CHOU, b New York, NY, Mar 16, 28; m 54; c 3. PHARMACOLOGY. *Educ:* Princeton Univ, AB, 48; Univ Ill, MSc, 50; Univ Md, PhD(pharmacol), 60, MD, 62. *Prof Exp:* Asst endocrinol & mammal physiol, Univ Ill, 50-53, asst endocrinol, 53-54; asst pharmacol, Sch Med, Univ Md, 55-59; intern med, Pa Hosp, Philadelphia, 62-63; resident internal med, 63-65; res assoc, 65-67, asst prof, 67-70, ADJ ASSOC PROF BIOCHEM PHARMACOL, ROCKEFELLER UNIV, 70-; VPRES & DIR SCI AFFAIRS, IVES LABS, 80- *Concurrent Pos:* From asst physician to assoc physician, Rockefeller Univ, 65-70, physician, 70-80; assoc dir clin pharmacol, Ciba-Geigy Corp, 70-74; exec dir clin res, Wallace Labs, 74-77; sr assoc dir clin res, Squibb Inst Med Res, 77-78. *Mem:* Am Soc Pharmacol & Exp Therapeut; Sigma Xi; Am Soc Clin Pharmacol; Endocrine Soc; Am Fedn Clin Res. *Res:* Role of thyroid gland in brain metabolism; autoimmune aspects of thyroiditis; total body x-irradiation effect on blood volume of intact and adrenalectomized animals; effect of chemo-convulsant agents on brain metabolism; use of new convulsant agent, hexafluorodiethyl ether, in therapy of mentally ill patients. *Mailing Add:* Ives Labs 685 Third Ave New York NY 10017

LING, CHUNG-MEI, b Chekiang, China, May 5, 31; m 57; c 2. BIOCHEMISTRY. *Educ:* Nat Taiwan Univ, BS, 58; Ill Inst Technol, MS, 62, PhD(biochem), 65. *Prof Exp:* Teaching asst biochem & physiol, Ill Inst Technol, 60-64; res assoc biochem res, Michael Reese Res Found, Chicago, 64-65; asst prof biochem, Ill Inst Technol, 65-68; molecular biologist, 68-71, assoc res fel virol, 71-74, res fel, Dept Biochem, 74-76, head, Molecular Biol Lab, 74-77, HEAD, VIROL LAB, ABBOTT LABS, 77- *Concurrent Pos:* Adj asst prof, Ill Inst Technol, 68-69. *Mem:* AAAS; Sigma Xi; Am Soc Biol Chemists. *Res:* Molecular biology and immunodiagnostics of hepatitis viruses. *Mailing Add:* Diagnostic Div Abbott Labs North Chicago IL 60064

LING, DANIEL, b Wetherden, Eng, Mar 16, 26; Can citizen; m 58; c 2. AUDIOLOGY, COMMUNICATIONS. *Educ:* St John's Col, Univ York, dipl, 50; Victoria Univ, Manchester, dipl, 51; McGill Univ, MS, 66, PhD(human commun dis), 68. *Prof Exp:* Organizer educ deaf, Reading Educ Comt, 55-63; prin, Montreal Oral Sch Deaf, 63-66; DIR RES DEAF CHILDREN, McGill UNIV, 66-, ASSOC PROF & DIR ORAL REHAB, SCH HUMAN COMMUN DIS, 70-, PROF AURAL HABILITATION & EDUC, 74-; DIR, SPEECH & HEARING DIV, ROYAL VICTORIA HOSP, 70- *Concurrent Pos:* Can Fed Prov Health grants, McGill Univ, 66-; res assoc educ, Cambridge Univ, 55-58; asst prof audiol, Sch Human Commun Dis, McGill Univ, 68-70; hon dir, Coun Children's Audiol Rehab, Ctr Deaf Children, Mexico City, 66- *Mem:* Am Speech & Hearing Asn; Can Speech & Hearing Asn; Am Audiol Soc; Acoust Soc Am. *Res:* Communication development in deaf children; speech production among hearing impaired children; speech recognition using linear and coding amplifiers; diagnostic procedure relative to deafness. *Mailing Add:* McGill Univ Grad Studies & Res Montreal PQ H3A 2T5 Can

LING, DANIEL SETH, JR, b Chicago, Ill, Oct 22, 24; m 46; c 2. THEORETICAL PHYSICS. *Educ:* Univ Mich, BSE(physics) & BSE(math), 44, MS, 45, PhD(physics), 48. *Prof Exp:* Asst prof, 48-54, assoc prof PHYSICS, UNIV KANS, 54-, ASSOC PROF ASTRON, 73- *Mem:* AAAS; Am Phys Soc. *Res:* Nuclear physics. *Mailing Add:* Dept of Physics Univ of Kans Lawrence KS 66044

LING, DONALD PERCY, mathematics, deceased

LING, F(REDERICK) F(ONGSUN), b Tsingtao, China, Jan 2, 27; m 54; c 3. MECHANICAL ENGINEERING. *Educ:* St John's Univ, China, BS, 47; Bucknell Univ, BS, 49; Carnegie Inst Technol, MS, 51, DSc(mech eng), 54. *Prof Exp:* Proj mech engr, Carnegie Inst Technol, 52-54, asst prof math, 54-56; from asst prof to prof mech, 55-70, WILLIAM HOWARD HART PROF RATIONAL & TECH MECH, RENSSELAER POLYTECH INST, 70-, CHMN DEPT MECH ENG, AERONAUT ENG & MECH, 74- *Concurrent Pos:* Consult, Southwest Res Inst, 59-65, Gen Elec Co, 60-62, Mitre Corp, 61-63, Alco Prod, Inc, 61-62, Mech Tech, Inc, 62- 70 & Wear Sci Corp, 71-; NSF sr fel, 70; vis prof, Univ Leeds, 70-71. *Mem:* Nat Acad Eng; fel Am Soc Mech Engrs; fel Am Soc Lubrication Engrs; NY Acad Sci; fel Am Acad Mech; Am Phys Soc. *Res:* Surface mechanics and related phenomena; elastic stability. *Mailing Add:* Dept of Mech Eng & Aero Eng Rensselaer Polytech Inst Troy NY 12181

LING, GEORGE M, b Trinidad, WI, Apr 11, 23; Can citizen; m 55; c 2. PHARMACOLOGY. *Educ:* McGill Univ, BA, 43; Univ BC, MA, 57, PhD, 60. *Prof Exp:* Res asst pharmacol, Univ BC, 57-60, res assoc, 60-61, from asst prof to assoc prof, 61-65; prof pharmacol & chmn dept, Univ Ottawa, 65-75; external examr, Fac Med, 75-76, PROF PHARMACOL, UNIV WI, KINGSTON, JAMAICA, 76-; DIR, DIV NARCOTIC DRUGS, UN VIENNA INT CTR, AUSTRIA, 80- *Concurrent Pos:* Asst res anatomist, Brain Res Inst, Med Ctr, Univ Calif, Los Angeles, 62-63, assoc res pharmacologist, 63-64; head, Ment Health, Drug Dependence Unit, WHO, Geneva, 74-76. *Mem:* Am Soc Pharmacol & Exp Therapeut; Pharmacol Soc Can; Can Physiol Soc; Can Soc Chemother; Int Soc Chemother. *Res:* Pharmacology of central nervous system; neuro-humoral mediators and mechanisms of action of dependence producing substances and their antagonists behavior. *Mailing Add:* Div Narcotic Drugs UN Vienna Int Ctr PO Box 500 1400 Vienna Austria

LING, GILBERT NING, b Nanking, China, Dec 26, 19; m 51; c 3. PHYSIOLOGY. *Educ:* Nat Cent Univ, China, BSc, 43; Univ Chicago, PhD(physiol), 48. *Prof Exp:* Comen fel, Univ Chicago, 48-50; instr physiol optics, Sch Med, Johns Hopkins Univ, 50-53; from asst prof to assoc prof neurophysiol, Univ Ill, 53-57; sr staff scientist, Eastern Pa Psychiat Inst, 57-62; DIR DEPT MOLECULAR BIOL, PA HOSP, 62- *Concurrent Pos:* Mem, Woods Hole Marine Biol Corp. *Mem:* Am Physiol Soc. *Res:* Molecular mechanisms in cell function. *Mailing Add:* Dept Molecular Biol 8th & Spruce St Penn Hosp Philadelphia PA 19107

LING, HARRY WILSON, b Painesville, Ohio, Feb 14, 27; div. INORGANIC CHEMISTRY. *Educ:* Bowling Green State Univ, AB, 50; Ohio State Univ, PhD(inorg chem), 54. *Prof Exp:* Res chemist, Pigments Dept, Res Div, 54-64, tech serv chemist, Sales Div, 64-67, sr res chemist, 67-69, supvr, 69-72, prod mgr, 72-74, MGR TECH SERV, E I DU PONT DE NEMOURS AND CO, INC, 74- *Mem:* Am Chem Soc; Fedn Soc Paint Technol; Sigma Xi. *Res:* Inorganic nitrogen chemistry; elemental silicon; anodic oxidation of metal substrates; electrolytic capacitors; titanium dioxide pigments; pigment colors. *Mailing Add:* Pigments Dept Chestnut Run Lab E I du Pont de Nemours & Co Inc Wilmington DE 19898

LING, HSIN YI, b Taiwan, Dec 5, 30; m 58; c 2. MICROPALEONTOLOGY. *Educ:* Nat Taiwan Univ, BS, 53; Tohuku Univ, MS, 58; Wash Univ, PhD(geol), 63. *Prof Exp:* Instr geol, Nat Taiwan Univ, 54-55; res engr, Res Ctr, Pan Am Petrol Corp, Okla, 60-63; res instr geol oceanog, 63-64, from res asst prof to res assoc prof, 64-74, res prof, Dept Oceanog, Univ Wash, 74-78; PROF, GEOL DEPT, NORTHERN ILL UNIV, 78- *Mem:* Fel AAAS; Soc Econ Paleontologists & Mineralogists; Paleont Soc; Paleont Res Inst; Sigma Xi. *Res:* Geological oceanography and palynology. *Mailing Add:* Dept of Geol Northern Ill Univ De Kalb IL 60115

LING, HUBERT, b Chungking, China, Apr 28, 42; US citizen; m 67; c 2. PLANT TISSUE CULTURE, MYCOLOGY. *Educ:* Queens Col NY, BS, 63; Brown Univ, MS, 66; Wayne State Univ, PhD(biol), 69. *Prof Exp:* ASSOC PROF BIOL, UNIV DEL, 69- *Concurrent Pos:* Univ Res Found fel & Res Corp fel, Univ Del, 70-72, USPHS fel, 72-74. *Mem:* Bot Soc Am; Mycol Soc Am. *Res:* Somatic cell fusion, genetic and biochemical aspects; biology of the Myxomycetes; genetics of reproduction and heterokaryosis. *Mailing Add:* Samsen Lab 162 Heffernan St Staten Island NY 10312

LING, HUEI, b Fukien, China, Feb 24, 34; m 64. COMPUTER ARCHICTECTURE & LOGIC DESIGN. *Educ:* Nat Taiwan Univ, BSc, 57; Univ NB, MSc, 61; Univ Okla, PhD(elec eng), 65. *Prof Exp:* Method supvr, Bell Tel Can, 61; electronic engr, Sundstrand Aviation, 62-63; asst prof, Fla State Univ, 65; res staff mem, San Jose Res Lab, 65-77, mgr logic design & exp eng, 77-80, DEPT MGR COMPUTER ENG, IBM RES CTR, IBM CORP, 80- *Concurrent Pos:* Adj assoc prof, Fairleigh-Dickinson Univ, Teaneck Campus, 67-68, adj prof, 68. *Mem:* Asn Comput Mach; Inst Elec & Electronics Engrs. *Res:* Computer design. *Mailing Add:* Thomas J Watson Res Ctr IBM Corp Box 218 Yorktown Heights NY 10598

LING, HUNG CHI, b Wenchow, China; m 78. MATERIALS SCIENCE, ELECTRONIC CERAMICS. *Educ:* Mass Inst Technol, BS, 72, ScD, 78; State Univ NY, Stony Brook, MA, 74. *Prof Exp:* Res assoc mat sci, Dept Mat Sci & Eng, Mass Inst Technol, 78-81; RES STAFF, WESTERN ELEC ENG RES CTR, PRINCETON, NJ, 81- *Mem:* Am Soc Metals; Sigma Xi. *Res:* Solid state phase transformations; biomedical materials; electronics ceramics. *Mailing Add:* 200 Hendrickson Dr Princeton Junction NJ 08550

LING, JAMES GI-MING, b Wuhan, China, Oct 4, 30; m 61; c 3. SCIENCE POLICY, CHEMICAL ENGINEERING. *Educ:* Cornell Univ, BChemE, 53; Iowa State Univ, MS, 59; Stanford Univ, MS, 66, PhD(mgt sci), 67. *Prof Exp:* Chem engr, Chambers Works, DuPont Co, 53-54; transp navigator, Mil Airlift Command, 55-58; proj engr, Army Reactors, Atomic Energy Comn, 59-63; syst analyst, Joint Chiefs Staff, 67-70; chief opers, Anal Div, Hq 7th Air Force, 70-71; spec asst res & develop, Off Secy Defense, 71-72, asst plans & progs, Directorate Energy, 73-75; div dir, Off Energy Res, US Dept Energy, 78-81; SR POLICY ANALYST, OFF SCI & TECHNOL POLICY, EXEC OFF PRESIDENT, 81- *Concurrent Pos:* Chmn, Working Group Energy Resources, NATO, 75. *Mem:* Inst Mgt Sciences; Am Chem Soc; Am Inst Chem Engrs. *Res:* Planning models for resource allocation; evaluation of research and development management and institutions. *Mailing Add:* 9813 Brixton Lane Bethesda MD 20817

LING, JOSEPH TSO-TI, b Peking, China, June 10, 19; US citizen; m 44; c 4. ENVIRONMENTAL ENGINEERING, PUBLIC HEALTH. *Educ:* Hangchow Christian Col, Shanghai, BS, 44; Univ Minn, Minneapolis, MS, 50, PhD(sanit eng, pub health), 52. *Prof Exp:* Dist engr, Nanking-Shanghai RR Syst, 44-47; res asst sanit eng, Univ Minn, 48-52; sr staff engr, Gen Mills, Inc, 53-55; dir environ sci & Nat Res grant, Nat Res Inst Munic Eng, Peking, China, 56-57; prof civil eng, Baptist Univ, Hong Kong, 58-59; mgr water & sanit eng, 60-65, mgr sanit & civil eng, 66-69, DIR ENVIRON ENG & POLLUTION CONTROL, 3M CO, 70- *Concurrent Pos:* Adv, Ohio River Water Sanit Comn, 62-, Environ Pollution Panel, US Chamber of Com, 67- & Tech Contact, Nat Indust Pollution Control Coun, 71- *Mem:* Nat Acad Eng; Am Soc Civil Engrs; Air Pollution Control Asn; Water Pollution Control Fedn; Am Water Works Asn. *Res:* Water filtration and related purification processes; biological oxidation and advanced treatment technology for water pollution control; thermo-oxidation, recycling techniques in air pollution and solid waste disposal. *Mailing Add:* 3M Co Box 33331 St Paul MN 55133

LING, NICHOLAS CHI-KWAN, b Hong Kong, Aug 15, 40; m 71; c 1. PEPTIDE CHEMISTRY, PEPTIDE HORMONES. *Educ:* San Jose State Univ, BS, 64; Stanford Univ, PhD(org chem), 69. *Prof Exp:* Res assoc crystallog, Stanford Univ, 69-70; res assoc, 70-73, asst res prof, 74-78, ASSOC RES PROF BIOCHEM, SALK INST, 79- *Mem:* Am Chem Soc; AAAS; Am Soc Mass Spectrometry; Endocrine Soc. *Res:* Isolation and characterization of peptide hormones; synthesis of peptides by solid phase methodology; peptide sequence determination by mass spectrometry and Edman technique. *Mailing Add:* Salk Inst PO Box 85800 San Diego CA 92138

LING, ROBERT FRANCIS, b Hong Kong, Apr 21, 39; US citizen; m 63; c 1. STATISTICS. *Educ:* Berea Col, BA, 61; Univ Tenn, MA, 63; Yale Univ, MPhil, 68, PhD(statist), 71. *Prof Exp:* Asst prof math, E Tenn State Univ, 64-66; from instr to asst prof statist, Univ Chicago, 70-75; assoc prof, 75-76, PROF STATIST, CLEMSON UNIV, 77- *Mem:* Am Statist Asn; Am Math Asn; Inst Math Statist. *Res:* Cluster analysis; statistical computing; interactive data analysis; Bayesian statistics. *Mailing Add:* Dept of Math Sci Clemson Univ Clemson SC 29631

LING, SAMUEL CHEN-YING, b Canton, China, May 7, 29; US citizen; m 57; c 3. PHYSICS. *Educ:* Nat Taiwan Univ, BS, 51; Baylor Univ, MS, 53; Ohio State Univ, PhD(physics), 69. *Prof Exp:* Asst prof physics, Augustana Col, Ill, 59-64; asst prof, 69-74, ASSOC PROF PHYSICS, WRIGHT STATE UNIV, 74- *Mem:* Am Phys Soc. *Res:* Rutherford backing scattering studies of semiconducting thin films on the damage and recovery of crystallinity following ion implantation. *Mailing Add:* Dept of Physics Wright State Univ Dayton OH 45435

LING, SHIH-SHEN, b Taipei, Taiwan, Oct 9, 49; m 80; c 1. RADIATION PHYSICS, NUCLEAR PHYSICS. *Educ:* Fu-Jen Univ, Taiwan, BS, 72; Utah State Univ, MS, 76; Univ Calif, Los Angeles, PhD(med physics), 81. *Prof Exp:* Asst instr physics, Utah State Univ, 74-76; res assoc, Univ Calif, Los Angeles, 77-81; med physicist, Med Physics Serv, Inc, 80-81; STAFF MED PHYSICIST, HENRY FORD HOSP, 81- *Concurrent Pos:* Lectr, Sch Technol, Henry Ford Hosp, 81- *Mem:* Am Asn Physicists Med. *Res:* Measurement of the trabecular bone mineral density by coherent and compton scattering technique; clinically orientated research in medical physics. *Mailing Add:* 13149 LaSalle Huntington Woods MI 48070

LING, TING H(UNG), b Hwaiyuan, China, Nov 23, 19; US citizen; m 54; c 2. CHEMICAL ENGINEERING. *Educ:* Chekiang Univ, BS, 39; Ohio State Univ, MS, 49; Case Inst Technol, PhD(chem eng), 53. *Prof Exp:* Jr chem engr, 42nd arsenal, Ministry Nat Defense, China, 42-45; rubber compounder & troubleshooter, Dragon Rubber Co, China, 45-48; rubber chemist, Anaconda Wire & Cable Co, 53-55, sr res chemist, 55-63, supvr polymer res, 63-68, mgr, 68-78, SR TECH CONSULT, WIRE & CABLE DIV, ANACONDA CO, 78- *Mem:* Am Chem Soc; Inst Elec & Electronics Engrs. *Res:* Utilization and modification of high polymers in the insulation field, especially for the wire and cable industry; electric properties of high polymers; radiation effects on high polymers. *Mailing Add:* Wire & Cable Div E Eighth St Marion IN 46952

LINGAFELTER, EDWARD CLAY, JR, b Toledo, Ohio, Mar 28, 14; m 38; c 5. CHEMISTRY. *Educ:* Univ Calif, BS, 35, PhD(chem), 39. *Prof Exp:* Assoc phys chem, 39-41, from instr to assoc prof, 41-52, assoc dean, Grad Sch, 60-68, PROF CHEM, UNIV WASH, 52- *Mem:* AAAS; Am Chem Soc; Am Crystallog Asn (pres, 74). *Res:* Colloidal electrolytes; crystal structure of paraffin-chain compounds; structure of coordination compounds; hydrogen bond. *Mailing Add:* Dept of Chem BG-10 Univ of Wash Seattle WA 98195

LINGANE, JAMES JOSEPH, b St Paul, Minn, Sept 13, 09; m 38; c 4. ANALYTICAL CHEMISTRY. *Educ:* Univ Minn, ChB, 35, PhD(chem), 38. *Hon Degrees:* MA, Harvard Univ, 46. *Prof Exp:* Asst chem, Univ Minn, 35-37, instr & Baker fel, 38-39; instr, Univ Calif, 39-41; instr, 41-44, fac instr, 44-46, assoc prof, 46-50, PROF CHEM, HARVARD UNIV, 50- *Concurrent Pos:* Priestley lectr, Pa State Univ, 53. *Honors & Awards:* Gordon Res Conf Award, Am Asn Advan Sci, 52; Fisher Award, Am Chem Soc, 58; Medaile d'Hommage, Universite Libre de Bruxelles, 65. *Mem:* Am Chem Soc; Am Acad Arts & Sci; hon mem Brit Soc Anal Chem; hon fel Royal Soc Chem. *Res:* Electrochemistry; electroanalysis; instrumental methods of analysis; polarographic analysis; with the dropping-mercury electrode; physiochemical methods of chemical analysis. *Mailing Add:* 94 Adams St Lexington MA 02173

LINGANE, PETER JAMES, b Oakland, Calif, May 12, 40; m 67; c 2. ELECTROCHEMISTRY, HYDROMETALLURGY. *Educ:* Harvard Univ, AB, 62; Calif Inst Technol, PhD(chem), 66. *Prof Exp:* Asst prof chem, Univ Minn, Minneapolis, 66-70; sr chemist, Ledgemont Lab, Kennecott Copper Corp, 70-77; RES ASSOC, PROD RES DIV, CONOCO, 77- *Mem:* Am Chem Soc; Am Inst Mining, Metall & Petrol Eng. *Res:* Chemistry related to the solution mining of nonferrous ore minerals and to enhanced oil recovery, specifically carbon dioxide flooding; kinetics and mechanisms of solution reactions with particular emphasis upon the reactions which surround electrode processes. *Mailing Add:* 6 Hillcrest Ponca City OK 74601

LINGAPPA, BANADAKOPPA THIMMAPPA, b Mysore, India, Mar 19, 27; nat US; m 53; c 3. MICROBIOLOGY. *Educ:* Benaras Hindu Univ, BSc, 50, MSc, 52; Purdue Univ, PhD, 57. *Prof Exp:* Lectr mycol, Benaras Hindu Univ, 52-53; res asst, Purdue Univ, 53-57; res assoc, Univ Mich, 57-59; res assoc, Mich State Univ, 59-60, asst prof med mycol, 60; Nat Inst Sci India sr res fel, Bot Lab, Univ Madras, 61; asst prof, Mich State Univ, 61-62; from asst prof to assoc prof, 62-68, PROF BIOL, COL HOLY CROSS, 68- *Concurrent Pos:* Vis assoc prof, Mass Inst Technol, 68-; vis prof, Inst Gen Bot, Univ Geneva, 69-70. *Mem:* Mycol Soc Am; Bot Soc Am; Am Soc Microbiol. *Res:* Physiology of fungi; dormancy and germination of spores; self-inhibitors; morphogenesis; methane production by anaerobic fermentation of solid waste. *Mailing Add:* Dept of Biol Col of the Holy Cross Worcester MA 01610

LINGAPPA, YAMUNA, b Mysore, India, Dec 6, 29; nat US; m 53; c 3. MICROBIOLOGY. *Educ:* Mysore Univ, BSc, 49; Madras Univ, BT, 51; Purdue Univ, MS, 55, PhD, 58. *Prof Exp:* Res assoc, Univ Mich, 57-59 & Mich State Univ, 59-60; sci pool officer, Govt India, 61; RES ASSOC BIOL, COL HOLY CROSS, 63- *Concurrent Pos:* Vis scientist, Inst Bot, Univ Geneva, 69-70; instr human nutrit, Clark Univ & Worcester State Col, 74; res consult, Dept Pub Health, City Worcester; fac adv, Undergrad Res Partic Proj Methane Generation, Col Holy Cross, vis lectr nutrit & world hunger, 78; comnr, Gov's Comn on Status of Women, Mass, 77- *Mem:* Bot Soc Am; Mycol Soc Am; Int Soc Human & Animal Mycol; Am Pub Health Asn; Am Soc Microbiol. *Res:* Human nutrition; water quality; solid waste disposal; physiology of pathogenic fungi; microbial interactions. *Mailing Add:* 4 McGill St Worcester MA 01607

LINGELBACH, D(ANIEL) D(EE), b Wilkinsburg, Pa, Oct 4, 25; m 49; c 3. ELECTROMECHANICAL ENERGY CONVERSION. *Educ:* Kans State Col, BSEE, 47, MS, 48; Okla State Univ, PhD, 60. *Prof Exp:* From instr to asst prof elec eng, Univ Ark, 48-55; asst prof, 55-61, assoc prof, 61-79, PROF ELEC ENG, OKLA STATE UNIV, 79- *Mem:* Am Soc Eng Educ; Nat Soc Prof Engrs; Inst Elec & Electronics Engrs; Sigma Xi. *Res:* Electric power system modeling and optimization; wind turbine electric generation and energy conservation in the meat processing industry; power systems analysis. *Mailing Add:* Sch of Elec Eng ES 202 Okla State Univ Stillwater OK 74078

LINGENFELTER, RICHARD EMERY, b Farmington, NMex, Apr 5, 34; m 57; c 2. ASTROPHYSICS, COSMIC RAY PHYSICS. *Educ:* Univ Calif, Los Angeles, AB, 56. *Prof Exp:* Physicist, Lawrence Radiation Lab, Univ Calif, 57-62; assoc res geophysicist, Univ Calif, Los Angeles, 62-66, res geophysicist, Inst Geophys & Planetary Physics, 66-69, prof in residence, Dept Geophys & Space Physics, 69-79 & Dept Astron, 74-79; RES PHYSICIST, CTR ASTROPHYS & SPACE SCI, UNIV CALIF, SAN DIEGO, 79- *Concurrent Pos:* Fulbright res fel geophys & planetary physics, Tata Inst Fundamental Res, Bombay, India, 68-69. *Mem:* Am Phys Soc; Int Astron Union; Am Astron Soc. *Res:* Cosmic ray origins and interactions; gamma ray astronomy; solar flare particle interactions; planetology; radiocarbon variations. *Mailing Add:* Ctr Astrophys & Space Sci Univ Calif San Diego La Jolla CA 92093

LINGER, KEITH RADFORD, physics, materials science, see previous edition

LINGG, AL JOSEPH, b Mt Hope, Kans, Mar 26, 38; m 61; c 3. MICROBIOLOGY. *Educ:* Kans State Univ, BS, 64, MS, 66, PhD(microbiol), 69. *Prof Exp:* Instr, Kans State Univ, 66-68; PROF MICROBIOL, UNIV IDAHO, 69- *Concurrent Pos:* Fulbright lectr, Nepal, 79-80. *Mem:* Sigma Xi; Am Soc Microbiol. *Res:* Environmental microbiology; water quality; insect pathogens. *Mailing Add:* Dept Bact Univ Idaho Moscow ID 83843

LINGREL, JERRY B, b Byhalia, Ohio, July 13, 35; m 58; c 2. MOLECULAR GENETICS. *Educ:* Otterbein Col, BS, 57; Ohio State Univ, PhD(biochem), 60. *Prof Exp:* From asst prof to prof biol chem, 62-81, PROF & CHMN MICROBIOL & MOLECULAR GENETICS, UNIV CINCINNATI, 81- *Concurrent Pos:* Fel biol, Calif Inst Technol, 60-62. *Honors & Awards:* George Rieveschl Award. *Mem:* Am Chem Soc; Am Soc Biol Chemists; Am Soc Cell Biol; Sigma Xi. *Res:* Regulation of gene expression in animal cells; hemoglobin biosynthesis; messenger RNA; gene structure. *Mailing Add:* Dept of Biol Chem Univ of Cincinnati Col of Med Cincinnati OH 45267

LINGREN, WESLEY EARL, b Pasadena, Calif, Aug 27, 30; m 61; c 2. PHYSICAL CHEMISTRY, OCEANOGRAPHY. *Educ:* Seattle Pac Col, BS, 52; Univ Wash, MS, 54, PhD(electrochem), 62. *Prof Exp:* Instr phys sci, Pasadena Col, 56-58; from asst prof to assoc prof, 62-68, chmn dept, 68-73, PROF CHEM, SEATTLE PAC UNIV, 68-, DIR GEN HONORS, 70- *Concurrent Pos:* Res assoc, US Naval Radiol Defense Lab, 63-69; NSF fel, Yale Univ, 67-68. *Mem:* Am Chem Soc; Sigma Xi. *Res:* Rates of electrode reactions; electroanalytical chemistry; oxidation states of elements in seawater oceanography. *Mailing Add:* Sch of Natural & Math Sci Seattle Pac Univ Seattle WA 98119

LINHART, YAN BOHUMIL, b Prague, Czech, Oct 8, 39; US citizen. EVOLUTION, GENETICS. *Educ:* Rutgers Univ, New Brunswick, BS, 61; Yale Univ, MF, 63; Univ Calif, Berkeley, PhD(genetics), 72. Sinai Jr specialist forest genetics, Sch Forestry, Univ Calif, Berkeley, 63-65; asst specialist, 65-66; asst prof, 71-77, ASSOC PROF BIOL, UNIV COLO, BOULDER, 77-

Concurrent Pos: Res grant, Univ Colo, Boulder, 71-73; Colo Energy Res Inst grant, 75-76; NSF grants, 75-78, 78-80 & 81-84. *Mem:* AAAS; Genetics Soc Am; Brit Ecol Soc; Soc Study Evolution; Soc Am Foresters. *Res:* Adaptation; population biology; reproductive biology of plants; pollination biology; forest biology; plant biogeography. *Mailing Add:* Dept of Biol Univ of Colo Boulder CO 80309

LINIGER, WERNER, b Berne, Switz, Dec 22, 27; m 56; c 2. NUMERICAL ANALYSIS, ORDINARY DIFFERENTIAL EQUATIONS. *Educ:* Swiss Fed Inst Technol, Dipl, 51; Univ Lausanne, Dr es Sc(math), 56. *Prof Exp:* Asst numerical anal, Univ Lausanne, 52-55; mathematician, Swiss Nat Inst Accident Ins, 55-57; mem res staff, Remington Rand Univac Div, Sperry Rand Corp, 57-59; RES STAFF MEM, MATH SCI DEPT, T J WATSON RES CTR, IBM CORP, 59- *Concurrent Pos:* Invited prof, Swiss Fed Inst Technol, 72-73. *Mem:* Soc Indust & Appl Math. *Res:* Research in numerical analysis; ordinary differential equations; applied mathematics. *Mailing Add:* IBM Res Ctr PO Box 218 Yorktown Heights NY 10598

LININGER, LLOYD LESLEY, b Iowa City, Iowa, Mar 13, 39. MATHEMATICS. *Educ:* Univ Iowa, PhD(math), 64. *Prof Exp:* Asst prof math, Univ Mo, 64-65; asst to Prof Montgomery, Inst Advan Study, Princeton Univ, 65-67; res instr, Univ Mich, 67-70; ASSOC PROF MATH, STATE UNIV NY ALBANY, 70- *Concurrent Pos:* Statistician, Biometry Sect, NIH, Bethesda, 77-78. *Mem:* Am Math Soc; Am Statist Asn. *Res:* Applications of statistics; topology. *Mailing Add:* Dept of Math State Univ of NY Albany NY 12203

LINIS, VIKTORS, b Rostov, Russia, Sept 14, 16; m 52. MATHEMATICS. *Educ:* Univ Latvia, dipl, 40; McGill Univ, MSc, 51, PhD(math), 53. *Prof Exp:* Instr, Univ Sask, 52-54; from asst prof to assoc prof, 54-57, chmn dept, 57-72, PROF MATH, UNIV OTTAWA, 57- *Mem:* AAAS; Am Math Soc; Math Asn Am; Can Math Soc. *Res:* Univalent functions; history of mathematics; math education. *Mailing Add:* Dept of Math Fac of Sci & Eng Univ of Ottawa Ottawa ON K1N 9B4 Can

LINK, BERNARD ALVIN, b Columbus, Wis, Mar 23, 41. MEAT SCIENCE, FOOD SCIENCE. *Educ:* Univ Wis-Madison, BS, 62, MS, 64, PhD(meat & animal sci), 68. *Prof Exp:* Res asst meat sci, Univ Wis-Madison, 62-68; Welch Found fel, Tex A&M Univ, 68-72; res scientist meat chem, 70-72, res assoc biochem & biophys, 72-73; res biochemist, 73-77, MGR, PROTEIN RES, CARGILL INC, 77- *Mem:* Am Meat Sci Asn; Sigma Xi; Am Asn Cereal Chemists; Inst Food Technol. *Res:* Soy protein products. *Mailing Add:* Cargill Inc Res Dept PO Box 9300 Minneapolis MN 55440

LINK, CONRAD BARNETT, b Dunkirk, NY, Mar 5, 12; m 40; c 3. HORTICULTURE. *Educ:* Ohio State Univ, BS, 33, MS, 34, PhD(hort), 40. *Prof Exp:* Hybridist, Good & Reese Co, Ohio, 34-35; asst hort, Ohio State Univ, 35-38, exten specialist, 39-40; from instr to asst prof floricult, Pa State Univ, 38-45; horticulturist, Brooklyn Bot Garden, 45-48; PROF HORT, UNIV MD, COLLEGE PARK, 48- *Concurrent Pos:* Mem, Nat Coun Ther & Rehab Through Hort. *Mem:* Fel AAAS; fel Am Soc Hort Sci; Bot Soc Am; Am Hort Soc (secy, 48-49); Int Soc Hort Sci. *Res:* Photoperiodism; plant anatomy, nutrition and propagation. *Mailing Add:* Dept of Hort Holzapfel Hall Univ of Md College Park MD 20742

LINK, EDWIN ALBERT, aeronautics, deceased

LINK, GARNETT WILLIAM, JR, b Charlottesville, Va, May 7, 45; m 71; c 1. ICHTHYOLOGY. *Educ:* Univ Va, Charlottesville, BA, 67; Univ Richmond, MA, 71; Univ NC, Chapel Hill, PhD(zool), 80. *Prof Exp:* Teacher biol & phys sci, ECarteret High Sch, 75-81; res asst, 81, RES ASST ICHTHYOL, INST MARINE SCI, UNIV NC, 82- *Concurrent Pos:* Grad res asst, Inst Marine Sci, Univ NC, 72-80; consult, Marine Occup, ECarteret High Sch, 80- *Mem:* Am Soc Ichthyologists & Herpetologists; Asn Southeastern Biologists; Southeastern Fish Coun; Soc Systematic Zool. *Res:* Life-histories and systematics of fishes including Serranids and Percids. *Mailing Add:* Inst Marine Sci Univ NC 3407 Arendell St Morehead City NC 28557

LINK, GORDON LITTLEPAGE, b Charleston, WVa, Feb 9, 32; m 55; c 1. PHYSICAL CHEMISTRY. *Educ:* Col William & Mary, BS, 54; Univ Va, PhD(phys chem), 58. *Prof Exp:* MEM TECH STAFF, BELL LABS, INC, 58- *Mem:* Am Phys Soc; Am Chem Soc. *Res:* Dielectrics. *Mailing Add:* Bell Labs PO Box 261 Rm 1a332 Murray Hill NJ 07971

LINK, JOHN CLARENCE, b Iowa, Jan 5, 08; m 36; c 3. PHYSICS. *Educ:* Creighton Univ, AB, 28; Cath Univ Am, MA, 29. *Prof Exp:* Electronic scientist, US Dept Navy, 29-64, consult, Naval Res Lab, 55-64; mgr missile projs, Aerospace Corp, 64-66; mem staff, Avco Missile Systs Div, 66-68; independent consult electromagnetic reflectors, 68-81; RETIRED. *Res:* Countermeasures; electromagnetic reflectors; energy conversion. *Mailing Add:* 6413 Halleck St Forestville MD 20747

LINK, PETER K, b Batavia, Java, Nov 7, 30; US citizen; m 57; c 2. GEOLOGY, METEOROLOGY. *Educ:* Univ Wis, BS, 53, MS, 55, PhD(stratig geol), 65. *Prof Exp:* Geologist, Esso Standard Inc, Libya, 57-58, party chief, 58-59, subsurface geologist, 59-60, regional geologist, 60-61; regional geologist, Humble Oil & Refining Co, Okla, 62-63; res geologist, Atlantic Richfield Co, Dallas, 65-68, sr res geophysicist, 68-70; sr res scientist, Amoco Prod Co, 70-74; CONSULT, 74- *Concurrent Pos:* adj prof geol, Univ Tulsa, 74-77; found mem, Associated Resource Consult Inc, Tulsa, 79; staff instr, Oil & Gas Consult Int, Inc, Tulsa, 79- *Mem:* Am Asn Petrol Geologists; fel Geol Soc Am. *Res:* Stratigraphy; structure; tectonics; field, regional, well site, subsurface and petroleum geology; research operations; stratigraphic-seismic research exploration; exploration programs; sedimentation; photogeology; minerals and petroleum exploration. *Mailing Add:* 2151 S Norfolk Terr Tulsa OK 74114

LINK, RICHARD FOREST, b Eugene, Ore, July 3, 28; m 50, 82; c 3. MATHEMATICAL STATISTICS. *Educ:* Univ Ore, BS, 48, Princeton Univ, MA, 51, PhD(math), 53. *Prof Exp:* Asst, Univ Ore, 49-50; asst, Princeton Univ, 50-54; asst, Sandia Corp, 54-55; asst prof statist, Ore State Univ, 55-60, assoc prof, 60-63; mgr statist anal, Spec Comput Systs Projs, RCA Corp, 65-67; chief statistician, Louis Harris & Assocs, Inc, 67-69; vpres consult, Artronic Info Systs, Inc, 69-79; PRES, RICHARD F LINK & ASSOCS, INC, 79- *Concurrent Pos:* Vis lectr, Princeton Univ, 63-72. *Mem:* Fel AAAS; fel Am Statist Asn; Inst Math Statist; Opers Res Soc Am. *Res:* Sampling; geological statistics; operations research; systems analysis. *Mailing Add:* PO Box 236 Island Station NY 10044

LINK, ROGER PAUL, b Woodbine, Iowa, Jan 24, 10; m 38; c 1. VETERINARY PHARMACOLOGY. *Educ:* Iowa State Univ, DVM, 34; Kans State Univ, MS, 38; Univ Ill, PhD, 51. *Prof Exp:* Instr vet pharmacol, Mich State Univ, 34-35; from instr to asst prof vet physiol, Kans State Univ, 35-45; instr, Med Sch, Northwestern Univ, 46; from asst prof to assoc prof, 46-55, PROF VET PHYSIOL & PHARMACOL, COL VET MED, UNIV ILL, URBANA, 55-, HEAD DEPT, 61- *Concurrent Pos:* Vis prof, Chas Pfizer & Co, Inc, 55; panel mem antibact drugs, Nat Acad Sci-Nat Res Coun, 66; consult, Div Physician Manpower, Bur Health Manpower, Dept Health, Educ & Welfare, 67; mem revision comt, US Pharmacopoeia & Nat Formulary; adv bd, Morris Animal Found; mem, Coun Biologic & Therapeut Agents, Am Vet Med Asn, chmn, 61-62 & Coun Ed Commun Animal Technicians. *Mem:* Am Vet Med Asn (pres, 72); Am Chem Soc; Conf Res Workers Animal Dis; Am Soc Exp Pharm & Therapeut; Am Chem Soc. *Res:* Renal glucose threshold in the horse and pig; growth and reproduction in cats; steroid therapy; toxicology of agricultural chemicals. *Mailing Add:* 1708 Pleasant St Urbana IL 61801

LINK, WILLIAM B, b Darke, WVa, Mar 25, 28; m 56; c 3. ANALYTICAL CHEMISTRY, ORGANIC CHEMISTRY. *Educ:* Shepherd Col, BS, 53. *Prof Exp:* Med technician, Baker Vet Ctr, Martinsburg, WVa, 55; chemist, 55-57, anal chemist, 57-62, supvry chemist, 62-63, SUPVRY ANAL RES CHEMIST, US FOOD & DRUG ADMIN, 63- *Mem:* Asn Off Anal Chemists; Am Chem Soc. *Res:* Chemistry of all color additives used in foods, drugs and cosmetics. *Mailing Add:* Div of Colors Technol HFF-436 US Food & Drug Admin Washington DC 20204

LINK, WILLIAM EDWARD, b Ironwood, Mich, Jan 24, 21; m 47; c 2. ANALYTICAL CHEMISTRY. *Educ:* Northland Col, BA, 42; Univ Wis, MS, 51, PhD, 54. *Prof Exp:* Asst prof chem, Northland Col, 47-52; group leader, Res Lab, ADM Chem, 54-69, group leader, Res Ctr, Ashland Chem Co, 69-71, mgr, Anal Chem Res & Develop Div, Ashland Oil & Refining Co Ohio, 71-76, res mgr, Chem Prod Div, 76-78; DIR RES & DEVELOP, SHEREX CHEM CO, 79- *Concurrent Pos:* Ed, Off & Tentative Methods, Am Oil Chemists Soc, 71- *Mem:* Am Chem Soc; Am Oil Chemists Soc (pres, 75-76). *Res:* Organic analytical research; fats and oils chemistry; industrial fatty derivatives; specialty chemicals; fatty nitrogen chemicals; industrial fatty derivatives analysis; resin analysis. *Mailing Add:* 6039 Sedgwick Rd Worthington OH 43085

LINKE, CHARLES EUGENE, b Sioux City, Iowa, Dec 9, 20. SPEECH PATHOLOGY. *Educ:* Univ Iowa, BA, 49, MA, 52, PhD, 53. *Prof Exp:* Coordr speech & hearing serv, State Bd Health, Del, 53-55; speech therapist, Harlem Consol Schs, Ill, 55-56; ASSOC PROF OTOLARYNGOL, SCH MED, TULANE UNIV, 56-, ACTG HEAD SPEECH PATH & AUDIOL, 76- *Mem:* Fel Am Speech & Hearing Asn. *Res:* Audiology. *Mailing Add:* Speech & Hearing Ctr Sch of Med Tulane Univ New Orleans LA 70112

LINKE, HARALD ARTHUR BRUNO, b Bautzen, Ger, Aug 18, 36; m 71. MICROBIOLOGY. *Educ:* Univ Berlin, BSc, 61; Univ Gottingen, MSc, 63, PhD(biochem, microbiol), 67. *Prof Exp:* Res assoc enzym, Univ Gottingen, 66-67; fel biochem, Rutgers Univ New Brunswick, 67-69; res microbiologist, Allied Chem Corp, 69-72; res assoc, Inst Microbiol, Rutgers Univ, 72-73; asst prof, 73-77, ASSOC PROF, DEPT MICROBIOL, NY UNIV DENT CTR, 77- *Concurrent Pos:* Referee, Zentralblatt fuer Bakteriologie II. Abteilung, 66- *Mem:* Am Chem Soc; Am Soc Microbiol; Ger Chem Soc; Am Asn Dental Res. *Res:* Isolation and characterization of enzymes; utilizing isotope techniques in the study of microorganisms; biosynthesis and biodegradation of chemical and natural compounds; taxonomy of streptococci; etiology of dental caries; artificial sweeteners. *Mailing Add:* Dept Microbiol NY Univ Dent Ctr 421 First Ave New York NY 10010

LINKE, RICHARD ALAN, b Plainfield, NJ, Feb 15, 46; m 67; c 1. RADIO ASTRONOMY. *Educ:* Columbia Col, BA, 68, MS, 70, PhD(physics), 72. *Prof Exp:* MEM TECH STAFF RADIO PHYSICS RES, BELL TEL LABS, 72- *Mem:* Am Astron Soc. *Res:* Radio astronomical observations of interstellar matter; measurement of isotopic abundances and densities within molecular clouds; development of low noise millimeter wave receivers. *Mailing Add:* Bell Tel Labs Box 400 Holmdel NJ 07733

LINKE, SIMPSON, b Jellico, Tenn, Aug 10, 17; m 46; c 2. ELECTRICAL ENGINEERING EDUCATION. *Educ:* Univ Tenn, BS, 41; Cornell Univ, MEE, 49. *Prof Exp:* From instr to assoc prof, 46-63, asst dir lab plasma, 67-75, acting dir, 75-76, PROF ELEC ENG, CORNELL UNIV, 63-, COORDR ELEC ENG GRAD STUDIES, 81- *Concurrent Pos:* Consult, Philadelphia Elec Co, 56-57, Brookhaven Nat Labs, 76-80 & NMex Pub Serv Comn, 80-82; chief investr, NSF res grant, 61-64, prog mgr, NSF, 71-72; mem, US Nat Comt, Int Conf Large Elec Systs, 63- *Mem:* AAAS; Inst Elec & Electronics Engrs; Sigma Xi. *Res:* Transient stability of synchronous machines; energy conversion, electric energy systems; high voltage direct current transmission; electric power transmission. *Mailing Add:* Sch of Elec Eng Phillips Hall Cornell Univ Ithaca NY 14850

LINKE, WILLIAM FINAN, b Ravena, NY, Aug 5, 24; m 49; c 3. PHYSICAL CHEMISTRY. *Educ:* City Col New York, BS, 45; NY Univ, MS, 46, PhD(chem), 48. *Prof Exp:* Asst chem, NY Univ, 45-48, from instr to asst prof, 48-57; group leader phys chem, 57-59, group leader paper chem, 59-64, mgr res & develop paper & film chem, 65-67, tech dir paper chem dept, 67-70, dir res, Indust Chem & Plastics Div, 71, dir, Stamford Res Ctr, 72-79, DIR, TECHNOL ASSESSMENT & LICENSING, AM CYANAMID CO, 80- *Mem:* AAAS; Am Chem Soc; Tech Asn Pulp & Paper Indust; Soc Chem Indust. *Res:* Solubilities; phase equilibria; polyelectrolytes; stability of colloids; flocculation; adsorption; mining and paper chemicals; sizing; polymers; monomers; petrochemical processes; refinery catalysts; auto exhaust catalysts. *Mailing Add:* Stamford Res Ctr Am Cyanamid Co 1937 W Main St Stamford CT 06904

LINKENHEIMER, WAYNE HENRY, b Pittsburgh, Pa, May 23, 28; m 52; c 2. PHYSIOLOGY. *Educ:* Univ Pittsburgh, BS, 50, MS, 52, PhD, 54. *Prof Exp:* Res assoc, Sch Med, Univ Pittsburgh, 52-54; physiologist, Lederle Labs Div, Am Cyanamid Co, 54-59, group leader physiol, Agr Div, 59-64, mgr nutrit & physiol sect, 64-70; dir animal health labs, 70-80, MGR COMMERCIAL DEVELOP, E R SQUIBB & SONS, INC, 80- *Mem:* AAAS; Am Physiol Soc; Am Soc Animal Sci; NY Acad Sci. *Res:* Physiological relationships of sulfhydryl compounds in shock; erythropoietin and iron metabolism; radiotracer techniques; pharmacology of sulfonamides. *Mailing Add:* Diamond Shamrock Corp 1100 Superior Ave Cleveland OH 44114

LINKER, ALFRED, b Vienna, Austria, Nov 23, 19; US citizen; m 54; c 2. BIOCHEMISTRY, CARBOHYDRATE CHEMISTRY. *Educ:* City Col New York, BS, 49; Columbia Univ, PhD(biochem), 54. *Prof Exp:* Assoc biochem, Columbia Univ, 56-59; asst res prof biochem & path, 60-64, assoc res prof biochem, 64-72, ASSOC PROF PATH, COL MED, UNIV UTAH, 64-, RES PROF BIOCHEM, 72- *Concurrent Pos:* Res biochemist, Vet Admin Hosp, Salt Lake City, 60- *Mem:* Am Soc Biol Chemists; AAAS. *Res:* Structure, function and metabolism of the glycosaminoglycans of connective tissue, including studies of heparin, heparitin sulfate, the chondroitin sulfates, hyaluronic acid, and a variety of degradative enzymes isolated from mammalian and bacterial sources. *Mailing Add:* Vet Admin Hosp Salt Lake City UT 84148

LINKIE, DANIEL MICHAEL, b Utica, NY, Aug 12, 40; m 64; c 2. ENDOCRINOLOGY, PHYSIOLOGY. *Educ:* State Univ NY Albany, BS, 62, MS, 63; Univ Mich, PhD(zool), 71. *Prof Exp:* From res asst to res assoc obstet & gynec, Albany Med Col, Union Univ, 63-67; asst prof reproductive med & obstet & gynec, Univ Calif, San Diego, 73-75; ASST PROF ANAT, CELL BIOL & OBSTET & GYNEC, COL PHYSICIANS & SURGEONS, COLUMBIA UNIV, 75- *Concurrent Pos:* NIH fel, Univ Tex Health Sci Ctr, Dallas, 71-73. *Mem:* AAAS; Soc Study Reproduction; NY Acad Sci; Endocrine Soc; Soc Gynec Invest. *Res:* Mechanism of hormone action, specifically estradiol; interaction of steroids and gonadotropins; serum binding proteins; reproductive endocrinology. *Mailing Add:* Col of Phys & Surg Columbia Univ 630 W 168th St New York NY 10032

LINKINS, ARTHUR EDWARD, b Middletown, Ohio, Jan 13, 45; m 74; c 2. BIOLOGY. *Educ:* Dartmouth Col, AB, 67; Univ Mass, Amherst, PhD(bot), 73. *Prof Exp:* Fel plant physiol, Dept Plant Sci, Univ Calif, Riverside, 72-74; asst prof, 74-80, ASSOC PROF, DEPT BIOL, VA POLYTECH INST & STATE UNIV, 80- *Concurrent Pos:* Adj assoc prof, Inst Arctic Biol, Univ Alaska, 80- *Mem:* Am Soc Microbiol; Soil Sci Soc Am; Mycological Soc Am; AAAS; Am Inst Biol Sci. *Res:* Fungal physiological ecology: role of temperature in regulation of physiology and role of temperature, oxygen, and substrat quality in regualtion of fungal associated decomposition of organic matter. *Mailing Add:* Dept Biol Va Polytech Inst & State Univ Blacksburg VA 24061

LINKSZ, ARTHUR, b Hlohovec, Czech, June 23, 00; nat US; m 29, 78; c 2. OPHTHALMOLOGY. *Educ:* Univ Kiel, DMSc, 25; Univ Pecs, MD, 28. *Prof Exp:* Instr, Eye Inst, Dartmouth Med Sch, 39-43; instr, Postgrad Med Sch, NY Univ, 44-50, asst prof ophthal, 50-55, from assoc clin prof to clin prof, 55-68; CLIN PROF OPHTHAL, NY MED COL, 68- *Concurrent Pos:* Head aniseikonia dept, Manhattan Eye & Ear Hosp, 44-55, assoc attend surgeon, 50-55, attend surgeon, 55-; fac mem, Lancaster Basic Sci Course, 46-; vis lectr, Sch Med, Univ Colo, 53 & 57; Edward Jackson mem lectr, Am Acad Ophthal & Otolaryngol, 58; vis prof, Med Sch, Univ Pa, 67- & Med Sch, Tulane Univ, 68-; vis lectr, Inst Visual Sci, Presby Med Ctr, San Francisco, Calif. *Honors & Awards:* Medal of Honor, Am Acad Ophthal & Otolaryngol, 54; Semmelweis Medal, Am Hungarian Med Asn, 54 & 68; Arthur Linksz Medal & Prize, Int Strabismological Asn, 78. *Mem:* AAAS; Am Ophthal Soc; Asn Res Vision & Ophthal; NY Acad Med. *Res:* Physiology, refraction and motility of the eye; pharmacology of ophthalmic drugs. *Mailing Add:* 6 E 76th St New York NY 10021

LINLEY, JOHN ROGER, b Leeds, Eng, Aug 10, 38; m 68; c 3. ENTOMOLOGY, INSECT PHYSIOLOGY. *Educ:* Univ London, BSc, 59, MSc, 62, PhD(med entomol), 66, DSc(med entom), 78. *Prof Exp:* Entomologist, Sandfly Res Unit, Ministry Health, Jamaica, 59-64; lectr, London Sch Hyg & Trop Med, Univ London, 64-66; PROJ LEADER, ETHOLOGY SECT, FLA MED ENTOMOL LAB, INST FOOD & AGR SCI, UNIV FLA, 66- *Concurrent Pos:* NIH grant, Nat Inst Allergy & Infectious Dis, 69-; Off Naval res grant, 80- & US-Israel Binational Agr res & develop grant, 81- *Mem:* Royal Entom Soc; Am Mosquito Control Asn; AAAS; Am Soc Zoologists. *Res:* Medical entomology, especially biology of sandflies and mosquitoes, with special reference to behavior and physiology. *Mailing Add:* Fla Med Entomol Lab Inst Food & Agr Sci Univ Fla PO Box 520 Vero Beach FL 32960

LINMAN, JAMES WILLIAM, b Monmouth, Ill, July 20, 24; m 46; c 4. MEDICINE. *Educ:* Univ Ill, BS, 45, MD, 47; Am Bd Internal Med, dipl, 55, cert hemat, 74. *Prof Exp:* From intern to jr clin instr internal med, Univ Mich, 47-51, instr, 51-52 & 54-55, asst prof, 55-56; from asst prof to assoc prof med, Northwestern Univ, 56-65; from assoc prof to prof internal med, Mayo Grad Sch Med, Univ Minn, 65-72, consult, Div Hemat, Mayo Clin, 65-72; prof med & dir, Osgood Leukemia Ctr, Univ Ore Health Sci Ctr, 72-79, head Div Hemat, 74-78; PROF MED, JOHN A BURNS SCH MED, UNIV HAWAII, 79- *Mem:* Fel Am Col Physicians; Int Soc Hemat; Am Fedn Clin Res; Am Soc Clin Invest; Am Soc Hemat. *Res:* Hematology. *Mailing Add:* 2130 Pililani Pl Honolulu HI 96822

LINN, BRUCE OSCAR, b East Orange, NJ, Dec 12, 29; m 51; c 3. MEDICINAL CHEMISTRY, BIOCHEMISTRY. *Educ:* Duke Univ, BS, 52, PhD(org chem), 56. *Prof Exp:* Asst, Duke Univ, 52-54 & Off Naval Res, 53-54; sr chemist, 56-75, RES FEL, MERCK SHARP & DOHME RES LABS, 76- *Mem:* Am Chem Soc. *Res:* Medicinal and synthetic organic chemistry in human and animal health. *Mailing Add:* 743 Wingate Dr Bridgewater NJ 08807

LINN, CARL BARNES, b Auburn, Nebr, Feb 18, 07; m 32; c 3. ORGANIC CHEMISTRY. *Educ:* Univ Nebr, BS, 29, MSc, 30; Stanford Univ, PhD(chem), 34. *Prof Exp:* Asst, Univ Nebr, 34-35; from res chemist to group leader, Universal Oil Prod Co, 35-64; prin chemist, Midwest Res Inst, 64-68; sr res chemist, C J Patterson Co, 68-74; RETIRED. *Mem:* Fel AAAS; Am Chem Soc. *Res:* Grignard reagent; pyrolysis of hydrocarbons; homogeneous and heterogeneous catalytic reactions of hydrocarbons and derivatives; hydrogen fluoride technology; high pressure and high temperature technology; Friedel-Crafts reactions; carbohydrate chemistry, including catalytic condensation of sugars and derivatives with hydrocarbons and derivatives; chemistry of lactic acid. *Mailing Add:* 8125 Beverly Dr Prairie Village KS 66208

LINN, DEVON WAYNE, b Estherville, Iowa, Oct 9, 29; m 53; c 3. LIMNOLOGY. *Educ:* Mankato State Col, BA, 52; Ore State Univ, MS, 55; Utah State Univ, PhD(fishery biol, statist), 62. *Prof Exp:* Chemist, Mayo Clin, Minn, 52-53; res biologist, Fisheries Res Inst, Univ Wash, 55-58; asst prof biol, Dakota Wesleyan Univ, 62-64; from asst prof to assoc prof, 64-73, chmn dept, 69-73, PROF BIOL, SOUTHERN ORE STATE COL, 73- *Concurrent Pos:* Consult, Northwest Biol Consults, 62-; Peace Corps vol serving as Dep to Chief Fisheries Officer, Fisheries Dept Ministry Agr & Natural Resources, Lilongwe, Malawi, EAfrica, 73-75. *Mem:* Am Sci Affil. *Res:* Physiological effects of radiation and pesticides; water pollution and abatement; environmental quality and resource management. *Mailing Add:* Dept of Biol Southern Ore State Col Ashland OR 97520

LINN, JOHN CHARLES, b Bellingham, Wash. COMPUTER SCIENCE, SYSTEMS THEORY. *Educ:* Univ Wash, BS, 68; Stanford Univ, MS, 69, PhD(elec eng), 73. *Prof Exp:* Res engr laser commun, Honeywell Inc, 68; instr comput sci, Stanford Univ, 72; MEM TECH STAFF COMPUT SCI, TEX INSTRUMENTS INC, 73- *Mem:* Inst Elec & Electronics Engrs; Asn Comput Mach. *Res:* Computer architecture; algorithms, memory organization; human speech and language. *Mailing Add:* Texas Instruments 13588 N Central Expressway Dallas TX 75222

LINN, KURT O, b Denver, Colo, Mar 1, 30; m 56; c 4. GEOLOGY. *Educ:* Colo Sch Mines, GeolE, 52; Harvard Univ, MA, 58, PhD(geol), 64. *Prof Exp:* Geologist, Resurrection Mining Co, 55-57 & Int Minerals & Chem Corp, 60-65; GEOLOGIST, TEXASGULF, INC, 65- *Mem:* Soc Econ Geologists; Am Inst Mining, Metall & Petrol Engrs. *Res:* Geology of ore deposits. *Mailing Add:* Texasgulf Inc High Ridge Park Stamford CT 06904

LINN, MANSON BRUCE, b New Ross, Ind, June 15, 08; m 32; c 2. PLANT PATHOLOGY. *Educ:* Wabash Col, AB, 30, Cornell Univ, PhD(plant path), 40. *Prof Exp:* Lab asst bot, Wabash Col, 28-29, instr, 30-32; asst plant path, Cornell Univ, 41-42; asst prof veg dis, Veg Crop Exten, 42-45, from asst prof to prof plant path, 45-74, EMER PROF PLANT PATH, UNIV ILL, URBANA, 74- *Mem:* AAAS; Am Phytopath Soc. *Res:* Soil fungicides; vegetable and canning crop diseases. *Mailing Add:* 204 E Mumford Dr Urbana IL 61801

LINN, RICHARD HARRY, b Auburn, Nebr, July 23, 18; m 43; c 2. INTERNAL MEDICINE. *Educ:* Univ Nebr, BA, 40, MD, 43; Am Bd Internal Med, dipl, 52; Am Bd Pulmonary Dis, dipl, 55. *Prof Exp:* Resident internal med, USPHS Hosps, San Francisco, Calif, 47-49, resident chest dis, 49-50, dep chief med, Seattle, Wash, 50-53, chief med, New Orleans, La, 54-57, San Francisco, 57-62; chief clin res sect, Lab Med & Biol Sci Div Air Pollution, USPHS, 62-67, med officer-in-chg, USPHS Clin, Ohio, 67-69, AREA SUPVR, COLO, UTAH & IDAHO, FED EMPLOYEE HEALTH, USPHS, 69- *Concurrent Pos:* Asst clin prof, Sch Med, Tulane Univ, La, 54-57, Sch Med, Univ Calif, San Francisco, 61-62, Col Med, Univ Cincinnati, 64-69; vis physician, Charity Hosp, New Orleans, La, 54-57; mem, Cent Clin Invest Comt, Div Hosps, USPHS, 56-62; mem, Chronic Dis Subcomt, Nat Tuberc Asn, 62-64. *Mem:* Fel Am Col Physicians; fel Am Col Chest Physicians; Am Thoracic Soc. *Res:* Research administration; pulmonary diseases; clinical research; air pollution. *Mailing Add:* Bldg 40 Denver Fed Ctr Denver CO 80225

LINN, STUART MICHAEL, b Chicago, Ill, Dec 16, 40; m 67; c 2. BIOCHEMISTRY. *Educ:* Calif Inst Technol, BS, 62; Stanford Univ, PhD(biochem), 66. *Prof Exp:* Helen Hay Whitney fel, Univ Geneva, 66-68; asst prof, 68-73, assoc prof, 73-75, PROF BIOCHEM, UNIV CALIF, BERKELEY, 75- *Concurrent Pos:* Res grants, USPHS, Univ Calif, Berkeley, 68- & Dept Energy, 70-; Guggenheim fel, 74-75. *Mem:* AAAS; Am Soc Microbiol; Am Soc Biol Chemists. *Res:* Biochemistry of nucleic acids; nucleic acid enzymes. *Mailing Add:* Dept of Biochem Univ of Calif Berkeley CA 94720

LINN, THOMAS ARTHUR, JR, b Colorado Springs, Colo, Jan 9, 33; m 63. ANALYTICAL CHEMISTRY, RADIOCHEMISTRY. *Educ:* Colo Col, BSc, 55; Univ Ill, MSc, 57; Ariz State Univ, PhD(anal chem), 68. *Prof Exp:* Scientist, Westinghouse Elec Corp, Idaho, 58-61; engr, Gen Elec Co, 61-62; tech staff mem, Sandia Labs, NMex, 62-64; res assoc radiochem, Radiation Ctr, Ore State Univ, 67-69; ASSOC SCIENTIST, KENNECOTT RES CTR, METAL MINING DIV, KENNECOTT COPPER CORP, 69- *Concurrent Pos:* Adj asst prof nuclear sci, Univ Utah, 69- *Mem:* Soc Appl Spectros; Geochem Soc. *Res:* Methods development in chemical analysis; instrumental applications in trace element determinations; nuclear techniques applied to problems in geochemistry and analytical sciences. *Mailing Add:* Kennecott Minerals Co Copper Div 1121 E 3900 S Salt Lake City UT 84117

LINN, WILLIAM JOSEPH, b Crawfordsville, Ind, July 14, 27; m 56; c 2. ORGANIC CHEMISTRY. *Educ:* Wabash Col, AB, 50; Univ Rochester, PhD(chem), 53. *Prof Exp:* RES ASSOC, PETROCHEM DEPT, E I DU PONT DE NEMOURS & CO, INC, 53- *Concurrent Pos:* Res assoc, Northwestern Univ, 69-70. *Mem:* Am Chem Soc; AAAS. *Res:* Organometallic compounds; heterogeneous and homogeneous catalysis; catalytic oxidation. *Mailing Add:* Petrochem Dept Exp Sta E I du Pont de Nemours & Co Inc Wilmington DE 19898

LINNA, TIMO JUHANI, b Tavastkyro, Finland, Mar 16, 37; m 61; c 3. CANCER, IMMUNOLOGY. *Educ:* Univ Uppsala, BMed, 59, MD, 65, PhD(histol), 67. *Prof Exp:* Asst prof histol, Med Sch, Univ Uppsala, 67-71; asst prof, 70-71, assoc prof, 71-78, adv clin immunol, 72-80, prof, 78-80, RES PROF MICROBIOL & IMMUNOL, SCH MED, TEMPLE UNIV, 80-; GROUP LEADER, IMMUNOL CONTROL RES & DEVELOP DEPT, E I DU PONT DE NEMOURS & CO, INC, WILMINGTON, 80- *Concurrent Pos:* USPHS int res fel, Univ Minn, Minneapolis, 68-70, Univ Minn spec res fel, 70; consult immunol, UN Develop Prog/World Bank/WHO spec prog for res & training in tropical dis, WHO, Geneva, Switzerland, 78-79. *Mem:* Am Soc Exp Path; NY Acad Sci; Reticuloendothelial Soc; Swed Royal Lymphatic Soc; Am Asn Immunologists. *Res:* Immunobiology; experimental pathology; tumor immunology; cell kinetics. *Mailing Add:* Dept of Microbiol & Immunol Temple Univ Sch of Med Philadelphia PA 19140

LINNARTZ, NORWIN EUGENE, b Fischer, Tex, Apr 9, 26; m 57; c 2. FOREST SOILS, SILVICULTURE. *Educ:* Tex A&M Univ, BS, 53; La State Univ, MF, 59, PhD(soils), 61. *Prof Exp:* Range mgt asst soil conserv serv, USDA, 53-54, range conservationist, 54-57; res asst, Sch Forestry & Agr Exp Sta, 57-60, from asst prof to assoc prof, 61-70, asst dean, Grad Sch, 77-80, PROF FORESTRY, LA STATE UNIV, BATON ROUGE, 70- *Mem:* AAAS; Ecol Soc Am; Soc Range Mgt; Soc Am Foresters; Soil Sci Soc Am. *Res:* Site quality relationships of forest soils; forest soil-moisture-plant relationships; forest fertilization; forest range. *Mailing Add:* Sch Forestry & Wildlife Mgt La State Univ Baton Rouge LA 70803

LINNELL, ALBERT PAUL, b Canby, Minn, June 30, 22; m 44; c 5. ASTROPHYSICS. *Educ:* Col Wooster, AB, 44; Harvard Univ, PhD(astron), 50. *Hon Degrees:* MA, Amherst Col, 62. *Prof Exp:* From instr to prof astron, Amherst Col, 49-66; chmn, Astron Dept, 66-76, PROF PHYSICS & ASTRON, MICH STATE UNIV, 66- *Concurrent Pos:* Mem adv comt, Comput Ctr, Mass Inst Technol, 60-63; mem bd dirs, Asn Univs for Res Astron, 62-65. *Mem:* Int Astron Union; AAAS; Am Astron Soc; Sigma Xi. *Res:* Instrumentation for photoelectric photometry; photometry and theory of eclipsing binaries. *Mailing Add:* 1918 Yuma Trail Okemos MI 48864

LINNELL, RICHARD D(EAN), b Rapid River Twp, Mich, Sept 18, 20; m 58; c 1. AERODYNAMICS. *Educ:* Univ NH, BS, 46; Mass Inst Technol, SM, 48, ScD(aerodyn eng), 50. *Prof Exp:* Aerodyn engr, United Aircraft Corp, 48; aerodyn engr, Mass Inst Technol, 49, sr engr, 50-52; aerodyn engr, Convair Div, Gen Dynamics Corp, 52-55, staff scientist aerodyn, 56-60; actg mgr aerothermodyn, Gen Elec Co, 55-56; Chance Vought prof aeronaut eng, Sch Eng, Southern Methodist Univ, 60-62; analyst, Ctr Naval Anal, 62-79; ENGR, TRACOR INC, 81- *Mem:* Am Phys Soc; Am Inst Aeronaut & Astronaut. *Res:* Systems analysis; fluid mechanics; vehicle design. *Mailing Add:* Box 342 Rte 1 Northwood NH 03261

LINNELL, ROBERT HARTLEY, b Kalkaska, Mich, Aug 15, 22; m 50; c 4. ACADEMIC ADMINISTRATION, INSTITUTIONAL RESEARCH. *Educ:* Univ NH, BS, 44, MS, 47; Univ Rochester, PhD(chem), 50. *Prof Exp:* Instr chem, Univ NH, 47; asst prof, Am Univ Beirut, 50-52, assoc prof & chmn dept, 52-55; vpres, Tizon Chem Co, 55-58, dir, 55-62; assoc prof chem, Univ Vt, 58-61; lab dir, Scott Res Labs, 61-62; prog dir phys chem, NSF, 62-65, staff assoc planning, 65-67, staff assoc dept develop prog, 67-69; dean col letters, arts & sci, 69-70, PROF CHEM, UNIV SOUTHERN CALIF, 69-, DIR OFF INSTNL STUDIES, 70- *Concurrent Pos:* Grants, Res Corp, 50-54 & 58-60, NSF, 59-61, USPHS, 61-62 & Am Petrol Inst, 61-62; consult, Reheis Corp, 58-61, Tizon Chem Co, 58-62, Col Chem Consult Serv, Lake Erie Environ Studies Prog & Environ Protection Agency; grant, Exxon Educ Found, 74-76 & 78-80 & Carnegie Corp, 76-77 & 78-80. *Mem:* AAAS; Am Chem Soc; Asn Instnl Res; Am Asn Higher Educ; Am Asn Univ Adminr. *Res:* Hydrogen bonds; air pollution energy planning; science and public policy; science manpower; faculty and staff personnel research (salaries, fringe benefits, policies for consulting, intellectual properties and adult education); student and faculty surveys; higher education evaluation and planning. *Mailing Add:* Off of Instnl Studies Univ of Southern Calif Los Angeles CA 90007

LINNEMANN, ROGER E, b St Cloud, Minn, Jan 12, 31; m 51; c 5. RADIOLOGY, NUCLEAR MEDICINE. *Educ:* Univ Minn, Minneapolis, BA, 52, BS & MD, 56; Am Bd Radiol, cert, 64; Am Bd Nuclear Med, cert, 72. *Prof Exp:* Intern, Walter Reed Army Hosp, 56-57; physician, US Army, Europe, 57-61; res assoc radiobiol, Walter Reed Army Hosp, 61-62, resident radiol, 62-65; cmndg officer, Nuclear Med Res Detachment, US Army, Europe, 65-68; asst prof radiol, Univ Minn, Minneapolis, 68; radiologist, Hosp, 68-69, asst prof, 69-74, ASSOC PROF CLIN RADIOL, UNIV PA,

74-; PRES, RADIATION MGT CORP, 69- *Concurrent Pos:* US deleg radiation protection comt & panel experts med aspects nuclear biol & chem warfare, NATO, 65-68; Nat Res Coun James Picker Found res grant radiol, 68-69; nuclear med consult, Philadelphia Elec Co, 68-; mem ad hoc comt med aspects radiation accidents, AEC, 69-; vis assoc prof clin radiol, Northwestern Univ Sch Med, 77- *Mem:* AMA; Am Col Radiol; Am Nuclear Soc; Am Pub Health Asn; Indust Med Asn. *Res:* Medical aspects of nuclear industry accidents; kidney function studies using isotopes; radiological health. *Mailing Add:* Radiation Mgt Corp Sci Ctr Bldg 2 3508 Market St Philadelphia PA 19104

LINNERT, GEORGE EDWIN, b Chicago, Ill, Dec 8, 16; m 37; c 3. METALLURGY. *Prof Exp:* Metallurgist ferrous, Repub Steel Corp, 35-41; res metallurgist, Rustless Iron & Steel Corp, 41-46; res mgr, Armco, Inc, 46-73; HEAD, N AM OFF, WELDING INST, 73- *Honors & Awards:* Samuel Wylie Miller Mem Medal, Am Welding Soc, 72. *Mem:* Am Welding Soc (pres, 70-71); fel Am Soc Metals. *Res:* Metallurgy of joining metals by welding, brazing and soldering. *Mailing Add:* Welding Inst PO Box 5268 Hilton Head Island SC 29928

LINNERUD, ARDELL CHESTER, b Whitehall, Wis, Apr 9, 31; m 56. EXPERIMENTAL STATISTICS. *Educ:* Wis State Univ River Falls, BS, 53; Univ Minn, MS, 62, PhD(dairy husb), 64. *Prof Exp:* Res asst dairy husb, Univ Minn, 57-63, consult biomet, 64; fel biomath, 64-67, asst prof statist, 67-75, ASSOC PROF STATIST, NC STATE UNIV, 75- *Concurrent Pos:* Statist consult, Inst for Aerobics Res, 74- *Mem:* Am Dairy Sci Asn; Am Soc Animal Sci. *Res:* Design of experiments and mathematical model building; animal science and exercise physiology. *Mailing Add:* Dept of Statist NC State Univ Raleigh NC 27607

LINNSTAEDTER, JERRY LEROY, b Lindale, Tex, July 25, 37; m 62; c 3. MATHEMATICS. *Educ:* Tex A&M Univ, BA, 59, MS, 61; Vanderbilt Univ, PhD(math), 70. *Prof Exp:* Instr math, Northeastern La State Col, 61-63 & Vanderbilt Univ, 67-68; assoc prof, 68-71, PROF MATH, ARK STATE UNIV, 71-, CHMN DEPT MATH & PHYSICS, 68- *Concurrent Pos:* Prin investr NASA res grant, Ark State Univ, 69-71. *Mem:* Am Math Soc; Math Asn Am. *Res:* Multistage calculus of variations; classical analysis. *Mailing Add:* Dept of Math & Physics Ark State Univ Drawer F State University AR 72467

LINOWSKI, JOHN WALTER, b Boston, Mass, July 7, 45; m 72. PHYSICAL CHEMISTRY, ANALYTICAL CHEMISTRY. *Educ:* Boston Col, BS, 67; Canisius Col, MS, 70; Rutgers Univ, PhD(phys chem), 74. *Prof Exp:* Res assoc molecular dynamics, Univ Ill, 74-76; sr res chemist, 76-81, RES LEADER, DOW CHEM CO, 81- *Mem:* Am Chem Soc; Sci Res Soc NAm. *Res:* Dynamic nuclear polarization; molecular dynamics of liquids at high pressure and extreme temperatures; nuclear magnetic resonance; catalysis; process chemistry. *Mailing Add:* Dow Chem Co Ctr Chem Processes 1776 Bldg Midland MI 48640

LINS, THOMAS WESLEY, b Nov 24, 23; US citizen; m 69. MARINE GEOLOGY, STRUCTURAL GEOLOGY. *Educ:* Cornell Univ, BS, 48; Univ Kans, MS, 59, PhD(geol), 69. *Prof Exp:* Dist geologist, Sunray Oil Corp, 50-51; dist geologist, Monsanto Chem Co, 51-57, asst div geologist, 57-60, div geologist, 60-61, res geologist, 61-63; asst prof geol, Lamar Univ, 68-74; asst prof, 74-80, ASSOC PROF GEOL & GEOG, MISS STATE UNIV, 80- *Mem:* AAAS; Geol Soc Am. *Res:* Tectonics, structure of island arcs and trenches, recent sedimentation of the Gulf of Mexico. *Mailing Add:* Dept of Geol & Geog Miss State Univ State College MS 39762

LINSAY, ERNEST CHARLES, b Cleveland, Ohio, May 3, 42; m 66; c 3. ORGANIC CHEMISTRY. *Educ:* Yale Univ, BS, 63; Univ Wis-Madison, PhD(org chem), 68. *Prof Exp:* Res chemist, 68-78, SR RES CHEMIST, ORGANICS DEPT, HERCULES INC, 78- *Mem:* Am Chem Soc. *Res:* Physical organic chemistry; rosin and fatty acids; dispersions and emulsions; rosin-, terpene- and hydrocarbon-based resins. *Mailing Add:* Hercules Res Ctr Wilmington DE 19899

LINSCHEID, HAROLD WILBERT, b Goessel, Kans, Sept, 24, 06; m 33; c 3. MATHEMATICAL ANALYSIS. *Educ:* Bethel Col, Kans, BA, 29; Phillips Univ, MEd, 36; Univ Okla, MA, 40, PhD, 55. *Prof Exp:* Prin high sch, Okla, 29-36; instr, Okla Jr Col, 36-38; instr math, Univ Okla, 38-41; instr math & physics, Bluffton Col, 41-43; army specialized training prog, Univ Nebr, 43-44; asst prof math & physics, Eastern NMex Col, 44-46; assoc prof, Col Emporia, 51-58; from assoc prof to prof, 58-77, EMER PROF MATH, WICHITA STATE UNIV, 77- *Mem:* Am Math Soc; Math Asn Am. *Res:* Algebra; geometry; physics; electricity and magnetism. *Mailing Add:* 3701 E Funston Wichita KS 67218

LINSCHITZ, HENRY, b New York, NY, Aug 18, 19; m 64; c 1. PHYSICAL CHEMISTRY. *Educ:* City Col New York, BS, 40; Duke Univ, MA, 41, PhD(chem), 46. *Prof Exp:* Mem staff, Explosives Res Lab, Nat Defense Res Comt, 43; sect leader, Los Alamos Sci Lab, 43-45; fel, Inst Nuclear Studies, Univ Chicago, 46-48; from asst prof to assoc prof chem, Syracuse Univ, 48-57; assoc prof, 57-59, PROF CHEM, BRANDEIS UNIV, 59-, CHMN DEPT, 58- *Concurrent Pos:* Vis scientist, Brookhaven Nat Lab, 56-57; Fulbright vis prof, Hebrew Univ, Israel, 60; mem adv comt space biol, NASA, 60-61, study sect biophys & biophys chem, NIH, 62-66 & comt photobiol, Nat Res Coun, 64-69; Guggenheim fel, Weizmann Inst, 71-72. *Mem:* AAAS; Am Chem Soc; Am Acad Arts & Sci. *Res:* Photochemistry; spectroscopy and luminescence of complex molecules; photobiology. *Mailing Add:* Dept of Chem Brandeis Univ Waltham MA 02154

LINSCOTT, DEAN L, b Blue Springs, Nebr, Mar 31, 32; m 53; c 7. AGRONOMY. *Educ:* Univ Nebr, BSc, 53, MSc, 57, PhD(agron), 61. *Prof Exp:* Instr agron, Agr Res Serv, USDA, Univ Nebr, 57-61, RES AGRONOMIST, AGR RES SERV, USDA, & PROF FIELD CROPS, CORNELL UNIV, 61- *Mem:* AAAS; Weed Sci Soc Am; Soil Sci Soc Am; Am Soc Agron; Crop Sci Soc Am. *Res:* Absorption, translocation and degradation of herbicides; persistence of herbicides; vegetation management; plant protection. *Mailing Add:* Dept of Agron Cornell Univ Ithaca NY 14850

LINSCOTT, WILLIAM DEAN, b Bakersfield, Calif, Apr 23, 30; m 55; c 3. IMMUNOLOGY. *Educ:* Univ Calif, Los Angeles, BA, 51, PhD(infectious dis), 60. *Prof Exp:* Asst prof, 64-70, assoc prof, 70-80, PROF MICROBIOL, MED CTR, UNIV CALIF, SAN FRANCISCO, 80- *Concurrent Pos:* USPHS res fels, Labs Microbiol, Howard Hughes Med Inst, Fla, 60-62 & Div Exp Path, Scripps Clin & Res Found, Calif, 62-64. *Res:* Complement; immunologic unresponsiveness. *Mailing Add:* Dept of Microbiol Univ of Calif Med Ctr San Francisco CA 94143

LINSENMEYER, ROY F(OREST), b Braddock, Pa, May 9, 21; m 46; c 2. STRUCTURAL ENGINEERING. *Educ:* Univ Pittsburgh, BS, 43; Univ Mich, MS, 51. *Prof Exp:* Instr civil eng, Univ Pittsburgh, 46-48; assoc prof, Swarthmore Col, 48-59; sr opers res analyst, Hq Pac, US Air Force, 59-60; CHIEF OPERS ANALYST & SCI ADV TO COMDR IN CHIEF, PACIFIC, 60- *Mem:* Sigma Xi. *Res:* Operations research; principals of solid state science to engineering materials. *Mailing Add:* Comdr in Chief Pac J55 Box 15 Camp Smith HI 96861

LINSK, JACK, b New York, NY, May 20, 18; m 39; c 1. ORGANIC CHEMISTRY. *Educ:* City Col New York, BS, 40; Univ Iowa, MS, 41; Ohio State Univ, PhD(org chem), 48. *Prof Exp:* Chemist, Geo A Breon & Co, Mo, 41-45; asst chem, Ohio State Univ, 46-47; res chemist, Standard Oil Co, Ind, 48-63; tech specialist, Lockheed Propulsion Co, 63-71, RES SPECIALIST, LOCKHEED MISSILES & SPACE CO, 71- *Mem:* Am Chem Soc; Am Inst Aeronaut & Astronaut. *Res:* Steroids; polynuclear hydrocarbons; petroleum chemistry; organic synthesis; solid propellants. *Mailing Add:* 1324 Bobolink Circle Sunnyvale CA 94087

LINSKY, CARY BRUCE, b Chicago, Ill, June 9, 42; m 68; c 2. BIOLOGICAL CHEMISTRY. *Educ:* Univ Wis-Madison, BS, 64; Loyola Univ, PhD(biochem), 71. *Prof Exp:* RES ASSOC, JOHNSON & JOHNSON, 71-, ASST MGR, 80- *Mem:* Am Chem Soc; Sigma Xi; Am Burn Asn. *Res:* Role of inflammatory response and local environment in cutaneous wound healing; cellular components of inflammation; scar formation in surgical wounds; collagen biochemistry; hemostasis. *Mailing Add:* Dept of Skin Biol Johnson & Johnson North Brunswick NJ 08902

LINSKY, JEFFREY L, b Buffalo, NY, June 27, 41; m 67; c 2. SPACE PHYSICS, SOLAR PHYSICS. *Educ:* Mass Inst Technol, BS, 63; Harvard Univ, AM, 65, PhD(astron), 68. *Prof Exp:* Res assoc astrophys, 68-69, assoc prof adjoint, 74-79, LECTR, DEPT PHYSICS & ASTROPHYS, & DEPT ASTROGEOPHYS, UNIV COLO, 69-, PROF ADJOINT, DEPT ASTROGEOPHYS, 79-; ASTRONOMER, LAB ASTROPHYS, NAT BUR STANDARDS, 69- *Concurrent Pos:* Mem, Joint Inst Lab Astrophys, 68-71, fel, 71-; consult, NASA, 72- *Mem:* Am Astron Soc; Int Astron Union. *Res:* Radiative transfer; formation of spectral lines in the solar and stellar chromospheres; atmospheres of latetype stars; stellar coronae. *Mailing Add:* Joint Inst for Lab Astrophys Univ of Colo Boulder CO 80302

LINSLEY, EARLE GORTON, b Oakland, Calif, May 1, 10; m 35; c 2. ENTOMOLOGY. *Educ:* Univ Calif, BS, 32, MS, 33, PhD(entom), 38. *Prof Exp:* Asst entom, Univ Calif, 33-35; agr, Univ Calif, Los Angeles, 35-37; assoc quarantine entomologist, State Dept Agr, Calif, 38-39; instr entom & jr entomologist, 39-43, asst prof & asst entomologist, 43-49, assoc prof & assoc entomologist, 49-53, chmn dept entom & parasitol, 51-59, asst dir, Agr Exp Sta, 60-63, assoc dir, 63-73, dean, Col Agr Sci, 60-73, PROF ENTOM & ENTOMOLOGIST, AGR EXP STA, UNIV CALIF, BERKELEY, 53- *Concurrent Pos:* Instr, Yosemite Sch Field Nat Hist, 38-41; res assoc, Calif Acad Sci, 39-; secy, Am Comn Entom Nomenclature, 43-48; ed, Pan-Pac Entomologist, 43-50; Guggenheim fel, Am Mus Natural Hist, 47-48; collabr, US Dept Interior, 53-54; res prof, Miller Inst Basic Res in Sci, 60-; mem comt insect pests, Nat Res Coun-Nat Acad Sci, 63-69; partic, Galapagos Int Sci Proj, 64; mem Orgn Trop Studies, 68- *Mem:* AAAS; non mem Entom Soc Am (vpres, 46, 48, pres, 52); Ecol Soc Am; Am Soc Nat; Soc Syst Zool. *Res:* Systematic entomology; ecology and taxonomy of Coleoptera and Hymenoptera Apoidea; geographical distribution; mimicry and adaptive coloration; ethology of solitary bees; entomophagous Coleoptera; interrelations of flowers and insects; host specificity. *Mailing Add:* Div of Entom & Parasitol Univ of Calif Berkeley CA 94720

LINSLEY, JOHN, b Minneapolis, Minn, Mar 12, 25; m 66; c 3. PHYSICS, ASTRONOMY. *Educ:* Univ Minn, BPhys, 47, PhD(physics), 52. *Prof Exp:* Asst prof physics, Univ Va, 51-52; res fel, Univ Minn, 52-54; res assoc, Mass Inst Technol, 54-55, asst prof, 55-58, res assoc, 58-72; adj prof, 72-77, RES PROF PHYSICS, UNIV N MEX, 77- *Mem:* Fel Am Phys Soc; Sigma Xi; Am Astron Soc. *Res:* Origin and behavior of highest-energy cosmic rays by means of experimental and theoretical investigations of extensive air showers. *Mailing Add:* 1712 Old Town Rd NW Albuquerque NM 87104

LINSLEY, RAY K(EYES), JR, b Hartford, Conn, Jan 13, 17; m 37; c 4. CIVIL ENGINEERING. *Educ:* Worcester Polytech Inst, BS, 37. *Hon Degrees:* DSc, Univ Pac, 73; DEng, Worcester Polytech Inst, 79. *Prof Exp:* Engr, Tenn Valley Authority, 37-40; hydrologist, US Weather Bur, 40-50; from assoc prof to prof civil eng, 50-75, exec head dept, 56-58, dir prog eng-econ planning, 67-75, EMER PROF CIVIL ENG, STANFORD UNIV, 75- *Concurrent Pos:* Consult, World Meteorol Orgn, 57-58, State of Calif, 56-62, Govt of Israel, 61 & Govt of Venezuela, 64-; Sr Fulbright scholar, Imp Col, Univ London, 57-58; tech asst, Off Sci & Technol, 64-65; pres, Hydrocomp Int, 66-70, chmn, 70-78; mem, US Nat Water Comn, 68-73; pres, Linsley, Kraeger Assoc, 79- *Honors & Awards:* Julian Hinds Award, Am Soc Civil Engrs, 78. *Mem:* Nat Acad Eng; fel Am Soc Civil Engrs; fel Am Geophys Union; Am Meteorol Soc; Nat Soc Prof Engrs. *Res:* Surface water hydrology; public works planning; hydrological simulation techniques. *Mailing Add:* 280 Swanton Blvd Santa Cruz CA 95060

LINSLEY, ROBERT MARTIN, b Chicago, Ill, Feb 19, 30; m 54; c 3. INVERTEBRATE PALEONTOLOGY. *Educ:* Univ Mich, BS, 52, MS, 53, PhD(geol), 60. *Prof Exp:* Ford intern geol, 54-55, from instr to asst prof, 55-64, assoc prof & chmn dept, 64-71, dir natural sci course, 62-70, phys sci course, 59-64, prof, 71-78, HAROLD ORVILLE WHITNALL PROF GEOL, COLGATE UNIV, 78- *Concurrent Pos:* Mem Paleont Res Inst. *Mem:* AAAS; Geol Soc Am; Paleont Soc; Soc Study Evolution. *Res:* Evolution, functional morphology; behavior and taxonomy of Gastropoda. *Mailing Add:* Dept of Geol Colgate Univ Hamilton NY 13346

LINSTEDT, KERMIT DANIEL, b Portland, Ore, Nov 6, 40; m 64; c 3. SANITARY ENGINEERING. *Educ:* Ore State Univ, BS, 62; Stanford Univ, MS, 63, PhD(sanit eng), 68. *Prof Exp:* Sanit engr asst, Los Angeles Dept Water & Power, 61-62; from asst prof to prof sanit eng, Dept Civil & Environ Eng, Univ Colo, 67-81; PROJ MGR, BLACK & V EATCH, 81- *Concurrent Pos:* Consult, Denver Metro Dist, 69-71 & Environ Protection Agency, 78- *Honors & Awards:* Dow Award, Am Soc Eng Educrs, 72; Bedell Award, Water Pollution Control Fedn, 73; Res Div Award, Am Water Works Asn, 78. *Mem:* Water Pollution Control Fedn; Am Water Works Asn; Int Asn Water Pollution Res; Sigma Xi. *Res:* Treatment methods for water reuse; characterization and treatment of oil shale retort water. *Mailing Add:* Black & V Eatch Consult Engrs 12075 E 45th Ave Denver CO 80239

LINSTROMBERG, WALTER WILLIAM, b Beaufort, Mo, Oct 30, 12; m 43; c 2. ORGANIC CHEMISTRY. *Educ:* Univ Mo, AB, 37, MA, 50, PhD(chem), 55. *Prof Exp:* Instr chem, Univ Mo, 52-55; from asst prof to assoc prof, 55-60, PROF ORG CHEM, UNIV NEBR, OMAHA, 60- *Concurrent Pos:* Vis prof, Utah State Univ, 57; vis prof & res assoc, Univ Nebr, 60. *Mem:* Am Chem Soc. *Res:* Pharmaceutical chemistry. *Mailing Add:* Dept of Chem Univ of Nebr Omaha NE 68101

LINT, HAROLD L, b Lewiston, Idaho, Nov 27, 17; m 42; c 4. TAXONOMY. *Educ:* Univ Calif, Los Angeles, AB, 40, MA, 42; Ore State Univ, PhD, 77. *Prof Exp:* Inspector, US Food & Drug Admin, 42-47; instr bot, 47-52, assoc prof, 52-62, prof, 62-80, EMER PROF BIOL SCI, CALIF STATE POLYTECH UNIV, POMONA, 80- *Concurrent Pos:* Ranger-naturalist, US Nat Park Serv; NSF sci fac fel. *Mem:* AAAS; Sigma Xi; Int Asn Plant Taxon; Am Soc Plant Taxonomists. *Res:* Genera Agastache and Juncus. *Mailing Add:* Dept of Biol Sci Calif State Polytech Univ Pomona CA 91768

LINTNER, ANTHONY ETHELBERT, b Tolna, Hungary, Nov 27, 05; US citizen; m 40; c 2. CHEMISTRY. *Educ:* Inst Technol, Germany, Dipl, 30, DTech Sc, 33. *Prof Exp:* Chem engr, Filtex Co, Hungary, 33-38; tech dir, Teka Co, 39-45; res chemist, Sinnova Co, France, 47-48; chem consult, Argentina & Chile, 49-54; res chemist, E F Drew Co, Can, 55-56; res group leader, Calgon Corp, 57-70; CONSULT CHEMIST, 70- *Mem:* Am Chem Soc; fel Am Inst chem; Am Asn Textile Chem & Colorists; Soc Cosmetic Chem. *Res:* Surfactants and textile chemistry. *Mailing Add:* 920 Berkshire Ave Pittsburgh PA 15226

LINTNER, CARL JOHN, JR, b Louisville, Ky, July 15, 17; m 48; c 2. PHARMACEUTICAL CHEMISTRY. *Educ:* Univ Ky, BS, 40; Univ Wis, PhD(pharmaceut chem), 50. *Prof Exp:* Res chemist, 50-55, SECT HEAD, UPJOHN CO, 55- *Concurrent Pos:* Adj prof, Fla A&M Univ, Col Pharm, 75- *Mem:* AAAS; fel Acad Pharmaceut Sci; Am Pharmaceut Asn. *Res:* Organic synthesis; determination of functional groups; essential oil determination; kinetic studies; chromatography and ion exchange resins; phytochemistry; tablet coatings; ointment bases; chemistry of antibiotics; instrumentation tablet compression; pharmaceutical product stability. *Mailing Add:* 2125 Aberdeen Dr Kalamazoo MI 49008

LINTON, EVERETT PERCIVAL, b St John West, NB, Dec 30, 06; m 36; c 3. PHYSICAL CHEMISTRY. *Educ:* Mt Allison Univ, BSc, 28; McGill Univ, MSc, 30, PhD(chem), 32. *Hon Degrees:* DSc, Acadia Univ, 78. *Prof Exp:* Instr chem, Mt Allison Univ, 28-29; Royal Soc Can fel, Univ Munich, 32-33; chemist, Biol Bd Can, Halifax, NS, 34-36; instr chem, Acadia Univ, 36-41; asst phys chemist, Fisheries Res Bd, Halifax, 41-44; prof chem, Acadia Univ, 44-75, head dept, 66-75; RETIRED. *Mem:* Am Chem Soc. *Res:* Preparation of hydrogen peroxide; measurement of dielectric constants; interaction of neutral molecules; air-drying solids; smokes; colloidal chemistry; dipole moments of amine oxides; drying and smoke curing of fish. *Mailing Add:* PO Box 166 Wolfville NS B0P 1X0 Can

LINTON, FRED E J, b Italy, Apr 8, 38; US citizen; div. MATHEMATICS. *Educ:* Yale Univ BS, 58; Columbia Univ, MA, 59, PhD(math), 63. *Prof Exp:* From asst prof to assoc prof, 63-72, chmn dept, 75, PROF MATH, WESLEYAN UNIV, 72- *Concurrent Pos:* Res Coun res fel, Swiss Fed Inst Technol, 66-67; Izaak Walton Killam sr res fel, Dalhousie Univ, 69-70. *Mem:* Am Math Soc. *Res:* Categorical algebra, a branch of positive speculative philosophy. *Mailing Add:* Dept of Math Wesleyan Univ Middletown CT 06457

LINTON, HOWARD RICHARD, inorganic chemistry, see previous edition

LINTON, JOE R, b Carbondale, Ill, July 4, 31; m 54; c 3. ZOOLOGY. *Educ:* Univ Mo, BA, 57, MA, 59, PhD(zool), 62. *Prof Exp:* NIH fel, Marine Lab, Univ Miami, 62-63; asst prof zool, 63-74, ASSOC PROF BIOL, UNIV SOUTH FLA, 74- *Concurrent Pos:* NIH grant, 64-66. *Mem:* AAAS; Am Soc Zool. *Res:* Animal physiology; endocrinology. *Mailing Add:* Dept Biol Univ South Fla 4202 Fowler Ave Tampa FL 33620

LINTON, KENNETH JACK, aquatic ecology, biometry, see previous edition

LINTON, PATRICK HUGO, b Lineville, Ala, Sept 27, 25; m 52; c 4. PSYCHIATRY. *Educ:* Birmingham-Southern Col, AB, 49; Univ Ala, MD, 53. *Prof Exp:* Intern, US Naval Hosp, Jacksonville, Fla, 53-54; resident, Menninger Sch Psychiat, 54-56; staff psychiatrist, Vet Admin Hosp, Ft Lyon, Colo, 56-58; resident, Menninger Sch Psychiat, 58-59; actg chief neurol, Vet Admin Hosp, Topeka, Kans, 59-60; staff psychiatrist, Vet Admin Hosp, New Orleans, La, 60-61; from asst prof psychiat to assoc prof, Sch Med, Univ Ala, Birmingham, 61-69, dir psychiat res & head div behav sci, 64-68, actg chmn dept psychiat, 68-69, assoc prof dent, 68-76, PROF PSYCHIAT & CHMN DEPT, SCH MED, UNIV ALA, BIRMINGHAM, 69-, PROF PUB HEALTH, 76- *Concurrent Pos:* Actg chief psychiat serv, Vet Admin Hosp, Birmingham, Ala, 62-68; mem acad health affairs comt, Vet Admin Med Dist 14; mem, Jefferson, Blount, St Clair Ment Health Authority Bd. *Mem:* Am Med Asn; Am Psychiat Asn; Am Psychosom Soc. *Mailing Add:* Dept of Psychiatry Sch of Med Univ of Ala Birmingham AL 35294

LINTON, RICHARD WILLIAM, b Scranton, Pa, Apr 17, 51; m 76. SURFACE SPECTROSCOPY, MICROBEAM ANALYSIS. *Educ:* Univ Del, BS, 73; Univ Ill, MS, 75, PhD(chem), 77. *Prof Exp:* ASST PROF CHEM, UNIV NC, CHAPEL HILL, 77- *Mem:* Am Chem Soc; Microbeam Analysis Soc; Am Soc Testing Mat. *Res:* Surface and microprobe techniques for chemical analysis; surface chemistry of microparticulates (environmental pollutants, chromatographic supports, catalysts); biological microanalysis; ion beam-surface interactions. *Mailing Add:* Dept Chem Univ NC Chapel Hill NC 27514

LINTON, THOMAS LARUE, b Carlisle, Tex, July 25, 35; m 61; c 2. FISHERIES. *Educ:* Lamar State Col, BS, 59; Univ Okla, MS, 61; Univ Mich, PhD(fisheries), 66. *Prof Exp:* Res asst zool, Univ Ga, 63-65, res assoc, 65-67, asst prof, 67-70; mem staff, Div Com Sports Fisheries, NC Dept Conserv & Develop, 70-73, mem staff, NC Dept Natural & Econ Resources, 73-80. *Concurrent Pos:* Res grants, Ga Game & Fish Comn, 65-68 & US Dept Interior, 66-; Ga rep biol comt, Atlantic State Marine Fisheries Comn, 64-66. *Mem:* AAAS; Am Fisheries Soc. *Res:* Physiology; commercial and sport fisheries; pollution ecology. *Mailing Add:* 16821 Buccaneer Ln Houston TX 77058

LINTON, W(ILLIAM) HENRY, JR, b Upland, Pa, Dec 23, 22; m 45; c 4. CHEMICAL ENGINEERING. *Educ:* Drexel Inst, BS, 43; Mass Inst Technol, ScD(chem eng), 49. *Prof Exp:* Res engr, Polychem Dept, 49-53, res supvr, 53-58, prod mgr, 58-65, petrol chem res dir, 65-71, tech mgr, Nylon Intermediates, 71-79, PLAN MGR & ADMIN ASST, E I DU PONT DE NEMOURS & CO, INC, 79- *Mem:* Am Chem Soc; Am Inst Chem Engrs; Soc Chem Indust. *Res:* Mass transfer at liquid-solid boundaries; structure and properties of high polymers; automatic computation; petrochemicals; commercialization of chemical processes and manufacturing. *Mailing Add:* E I du Pont de Nemours & Co Inc 6498 Nemours Bldg Wilmington DE 19898

LINTVEDT, RICHARD LOWELL, b Edgerton, Wis, June 23, 37; m 59; c 3. PHYSICAL INORGANIC CHEMISTRY. *Educ:* Lawrence Univ, BA, 59; Univ Nebr, PhD(inorg chem), 66. *Prof Exp:* Res chemist, Chem Div, Morton Int, 59-62; asst prof inorg chem, 66-71, assoc prof, 71-76, PROF CHEM, WAYNE STATE UNIV, 76- *Concurrent Pos:* Petrol Res Fund grant, 66-68, 70-73, 76-78; Res Corp grant, 69-71; NSF grant, 76-; Dept of Energy grant, 78- *Mem:* Am Chem Soc. *Res:* Electronic structure and bonding in inorganic coordination and chelate compounds; inorganic photochemistry; physical inorganic chemistry; magnetochemistry of transition metal complexes. *Mailing Add:* Dept of Chem Wayne State Univ Detroit MI 48202

LINTZ, JOSEPH, JR, b New York, NY, June 15, 21; m 44; c 3. GEOLOGY. *Educ:* Williams Col, AB, 42; Univ Okla, MS, 47; Johns Hopkins Univ, PhD(geol), 56. *Prof Exp:* Jr geologist, Gen Petrol Corp, 47-48; geologist, Pure Oil Co, 49; from asst prof to assoc prof, 51-65, actg dean, 81-82, PROF GEOL, MACKAY SCH MINES, UNIV NEV, RENO, 65- *Concurrent Pos:* Instr, Mt Lake Biol Sta, Va, 51; asst geologist, Nev Bur Mines, 51-56, assoc geologist, 56-; vis prof, Bandung Tech Inst, 59-61; Nat Acad Sci-Nat Res Coun res assoc, Manned Spacecraft Ctr, Tex, 66-67; consult, Econ Comm Asia & Far East, UN, 71 & 74; consult, Atomic Energy Comn, 71-79. *Mem:* Paleont Soc; Am Asn Petrol Geol; AAAS. *Res:* Remote sensing of environment; petroleum possibilities and Pennsylvanian system of Nevada. *Mailing Add:* Mackay Sch of Mines Univ of Nev Reno NV 89557

LINVILL, JOHN G(RIMES), b Kansas City, Mo, Aug 8, 19; m 43; c 2. ELECTRICAL ENGINEERING, SOLID-STATE ELECTRONICS. *Educ:* William Jewell Col, AB, 41; Mass Inst Technol, SB, 43, SM, 45, ScD(elec eng), 49. *Hon Degrees:* DAppSc, Cath Univ Louvain, 66. *Prof Exp:* Asst prof elec eng, Mass Inst Technol, 49-51; mem tech staff, Bell Tel Labs, Inc, 51-55; assoc prof elec eng, 55-57, chmn dept, 64-80, assoc dean sch eng, 72-80, PROF ELEC ENG, STANFORD UNIV, 57-, PROF INTEGRATED SYSTS & DIR, CTR INTERGRATED SYSTS, 81- *Concurrent Pos:* Mem adv comt, Sensory Aids Eval & Develop Comt, Mass Inst Technol, 64-69; co-founder & dir, Telesensory Systs, Inc, 71-; dir, Spectra-Physics, Inc, 74-, Cromemco, Inc, 80- & Am Microsystics, Inc, 81- *Honors & Awards:* IR-100 Award, Indust Res, Inc, 71; John Scott Award, 80. *Mem:* Nat Acad Eng; fel Inst Elec & Electronics Engrs; fel AAAS; fel Am Acad Arts & Sci. *Res:* Custom integrated circuits and systems as sensory aids for the blind. *Mailing Add:* Dept of Elec Eng Stanford Univ Stanford CA 94305

LINVILL, WILLIAM K(IRBY), engineering, deceased

LINZ, ARTHUR, b Barcelona, Spain, Jan 30, 26; US citizen; m 55; c 1. SOLID STATE PHYSICS, MATERIALS SCIENCE. *Educ:* Brown Univ, BS, 46; Univ NC, MS, 50, PhD(physics), 52. *Prof Exp:* Res physicist, titanium div, Nat Lead Co, NJ, 52-58; res physicist, div sponsored res staff, lab insulation res, 58-63, res assoc elec eng, 63-70, SR RES ASSOC ELEC ENG, CRYSTAL PHYSICS LAB, MAT SCI CTR, MASS INST TECHNOL, 70- *Concurrent Pos:* Vis prof, Univ Nancy, 63; consult, Brookhaven Nat Lab, 69-79; vis sr reader, Univ Bath, 76. *Mem:* Am Phys Soc; Optical Soc Am; Am Asn Crystal Growth; Sigma Xi. *Res:* Materials engineering; single crystal growth; properties of crystals; laser crystals; photodetectors. *Mailing Add:* Rm 13-3154 Crystal Physics Lab Mat Sci Ctr Mass Inst of Technol Cambridge MA 02139

LINZ, PETER, b Apatin, Jugoslavia, July 19, 36; US citizen. COMPUTER SCIENCE. *Educ:* McGill Univ, BSc, 57; Univ Mich, MS, 60; Univ Wis, PhD(comput sci), 68. *Prof Exp:* Res engr, Dominion Eng Ltd, 57-59; assoc programmer, IBM Corp, 63-65; staff specialist numerical anal, Comput Ctr, Univ Wis, 65-68; asst prof comput sci, NY Univ, 68-70; from asst prof to assoc prof, 70-77, PROF MATH, UNIV CALIF, DAVIS, 77- *Res:* Numerical analysis; quadrature methods; solution and applications of integral equations. *Mailing Add:* Dept Math Univ Calif Davis CA 95616

LINZER, MELVIN, b New York, NY, Aug 5, 37; m 64; c 4. ULTRASOUND, PHYSICAL CHEMISTRY. *Educ:* Brooklyn Col, BS, 57; Princeton Univ, MA, 59, PhD(chem), 62. *Prof Exp:* Res assoc chem, Princeton Univ, 61; Nat Acad Sci-Nat Res Coun fel, 61-63, group leader signal processing & imaging, 78-81, PHYSICAL CHEMIST, NAT BUR STANDARDS, 63-, GROUP LEADER, FRACTURE & DEFORMATION DIV, 81- *Concurrent Pos:* Ed-in-Chief, Ultrasonic Imaging, 79-; cochairperson, Ultrasonic Tissue Signature Working Group, 76-78, chmn, Int Symp on Ultrasonic Imaging and Tissue Characterization, 75-; chmn, Int Symp on Ultrasonic Mat Characterization, 78- *Honors & Awards:* Ross Coffin Purdy Award, Am Ceramic Soc, 75; US Dept Commerce Gold Medal Award, 77; Nat Bur Standards Appl Res Award, 78. *Mem:* Am Phys Soc; Am Inst Ultrasound in Med; Sigma Xi. *Res:* Nondestructive evaluation; ultrasound medical diagnosis; acoustic emission; laser spectroscopy; combustion diagnostics; magnetic resonance spectroscopy; measurement techniques for spectroscopic and materials applications; shock wave structure. *Mailing Add:* Nat Bur Standards Washington DC 20234

LINZER, ROSEMARY, b Chicago, Ill, Feb 11, 44. ORAL MICROBIOLOGY. *Educ:* Alverno Col, BA, 66; Northwestern Univ, MS, 71, PhD(molecular biol & biochem), 73. *Prof Exp:* Res technician, Biochem Dept, Northwestern Univ, 66-69, res assoc, Dept Microbiol, Med Sch, 73-75; ASST PROF ORAL BIOL, STATE UNIV NY BUFFALO, 75- *Mem:* Int Asn Dent Res; Am Soc Microbiol. *Res:* Oral microorganisms, specifically the purification and characterization of the serotype antigens of Streptococcus mutans with emphasis on their immunogenicity and vaccine potential. *Mailing Add:* Dept of Oral Biol State Univ of NY 4510 Main St Buffalo NY 14226

LINZEY, DONALD WAYNE, b Baltimore, Md, Sept 4, 39; m 63; c 2. WILDLIFE BIOLOGY, MAMMALOGY. *Educ:* Western Md Col, AB, 61; Cornell Univ, MS, 63, PhD(vert zool, mammal), 66. *Prof Exp:* Instr biol, Cornell Univ, 66-67; from asst prof to assoc prof biol sci, Univ SAla, 67-77, cur zool natural hist collections, 70-77; RES BIOLOGIST, VA POLYTECH INST & STATE UNIV, 77- *Mem:* Am Soc Mammal; Wildlife Soc; Nat Audubon Soc; Am Inst Biol Sci; Soc Study Amphibians & Reptiles. *Res:* Life history; population dynamics; ecology; growth and development; systematics; state and regional surveys of mammal distribution. *Mailing Add:* Dept Biol Va Polytech Inst & State Univ Blacksburg VA 24061

LIONETTI, FABIAN JOSEPH, b Jersey City, NJ, Mar 3, 18; m 43; c 3. BIOCHEMISTRY. *Educ:* NY Univ, AB, 43, MS, 45; Rensselaer Polytech Inst, PhD(phys chem), 48. *Prof Exp:* From instr to assoc prof biochem, Sch Med, Boston Univ, 49-65; assoc mem, Inst Health Sci, Brown Univ, 65-68; SR INVESTR, CTR BLOOD RES, 68- *Honors & Awards:* Mathewson Medal, Am Inst Metals, 52. *Mem:* Am Soc Biol Chemists; Am Chem Soc; Cryobiol Soc. *Res:* Metabolism and preservation of human blood cells. *Mailing Add:* Ctr for Blood Res 800 Huntington Ave Boston MA 02115

LIOR, NOAM, b Mar 11, 40; US citizen. MECHANICAL ENGINEERING. *Educ:* Technion, Israel, BS, 62, MS, 66; Univ Calif, Berkeley, PhD(mech eng), 73; Univ Pa, MA, 78. *Prof Exp:* Instr, Dept Mech Eng, Technion, 65-66; res asst res eng water desalination, Seawater Conversion Lab, Univ Calif, Berkeley, 66-73; asst prof, 73-78, ASSOC PROF MECH ENG, DEPT MECH ENG & APPL ECH, UNIV PA, 78- *Concurrent Pos:* Prin investr, NSF grant, Pa Sci & Eng Found grant, US HUD grant, 75- & US Dept Energy grant, 75-; consult, US Energy Res & Develop Admin, 76-, Westinghouse Elec Corp, 77-78, Lawrence Livermore Labs & Solar Energy Res Inst; mem, Solar Collector Standards Comt, Am Soc Heating, Refrig & Air Conditioning Engrs, 75- *Mem:* Am Soc Mech Engrs; Int Solar Energy Soc; Instrument Soc Am; Am Soc Heating, Refrig & Air Conditioning Engrs. *Res:* Heat transfer, thermodynamics and fluid mechanics as related to solar energy applications, water desalination and combustion; thermo-fluid measurements. *Mailing Add:* Dept of ech Eng & Appl Mech Univ of Pa Philadelphia PA 19104

LIOU, JUHN G, b Taiwan, Dec 28, 39; m 64; c 2. METAMORPHIC PETROLOGY, GEOCHEMISTRY. *Educ:* Nat Twiwan Univ, BS, 62; Univ Calif, Los Angeles, PhD(geol), 70. *Prof Exp:* Teaching & res asst geol, Nat Taiwan Univ, 63-64; teaching asst, Univ Calif, Los Angeles, 65-69, NSF fel, 70; res fel geochem, Nat Res Coun, NASA, Houston, 70-72; asst prof geol, 72-76, ASSOC PROF GEOL, STANFORD UNIV, 76- *Concurrent Pos:* Guggenheim fel, John Simon Guggenheim Found, 78-79. *Honors & Awards:* Mineral Soc Am Award, 77. *Mem:* Geol Soc Am; Am Geophys Union; Mineral Soc Am. *Res:* To understand, through hydrothermal experiments and field observations, the parageneses and compositions of metamorphic minerals zeolites, prehnite, pumpellites and epidote; their imposed physical conditions for low-grade metabasites. *Mailing Add:* Dept of Geol Stanford Univ Stanford CA 94305

LIOY, FRANCO, b Gorizia, Italy, May 24, 32; m 66; c 1. PHYSIOLOGY. *Educ:* Univ Rome, MD, 56; Univ Minn, Minneapolis, PhD(physiol), 67. *Prof Exp:* Instr med, Univ Rome, 56-61; instr physiol, Univ Minn, Minneapolis, 66-67; from asst prof to assoc prof, 67-75, PROF PHYSIOL, UNIV BC, 75- *Concurrent Pos:* Mem, Sci Subcomt, Can Heart Found. *Mem:* Can Physiol Soc. *Res:* Cardiovascular physiology; coronary circulation; effect of hyperthermia on circulatory system; sympathetic control of circulation. *Mailing Add:* Dept of Physiol Univ of BC Vancouver BC V6T 1W5 Can

LIOY, PAUL JAMES, b Passaic, NJ, May 27, 47; m 71; c 1. ENVIRONMENTAL HEALTH, AIR POLLUTION. *Educ:* Montclair State Col, BA, 69; Auburn Univ, MS, 71; Rutgers Univ, MS, 73, PhD(environ sci), 75. *Prof Exp:* Sr air pollution engr, Interstate Sanit Comn, NY, 75-78; ASST PROF ENVIRON MED, INST ENVIRON MED, NY UNIV MED CTR, 78- *Concurrent Pos:* Lectr, Dept Civil & Environ Eng, Polytech Inst NY, 76-78; consult, State NJ, 78-, US Environ Protection Agency, 80 & indust organizations, 80-81; mem Am Conf Govt Indust Hygienists. *Mem:* Air Pollution Control Asn; fel NY Acad Sci. *Res:* Atmospheric transport of pollutants; chemical characteristics and distribution of inorganic trace elements and organic species; aerosol monitoring equipment and techniques; industrial and occupational hygiene; environmental health. *Mailing Add:* Inst Environ Med PO Box 817 Tuxedo NY 10987

LIPARI, NUNZIO OTTAVIO, b Ali' Terme, Italy, Jan 1, 45. SOLID STATE PHYSICS, MOLECULAR PHYSICS. *Educ:* Univ Messina, Laurea Physics, 67; Lehigh Univ, PhD(physics), 70. *Prof Exp:* Res asst solid state physics, Lehigh Univ, 67-70; res assoc, Univ Ill, 70-72; from asst scientist to scientist sr physics, Webster Res Lab, Xerox Corp, 75-77; MEM RES STAFF, IBM THOMAS J WATSON RES CTR, 77- *Mem:* Fel Am Phys Soc. *Res:* Optical properties of solids; electron-phonon interaction in molecular systems; excitation and impurity states in semiconductors. *Mailing Add:* PO Box 218 Yorktown Heights NY 10598

LIPE, JOHN ARTHUR, b Los Fresnos, Tex, Aug 28, 43; m 64; c 2. HORTICULTURE, PLANT PHYSIOLOGY. *Educ:* Tex A&M Univ, BS, 65, MS, 68, PhD(plant physiol), 71. *Prof Exp:* ASST PROF HORT, TEX A&M UNIV RES & EXTEN CTR, OVERTON, 71- *Honors & Awards:* Award, Am Soc Plant Physiol, 71. *Mem:* Am Soc Hort Sci. *Res:* Plant growth regulation, especially with fruits; role of ethylene in fruit dehiscence. *Mailing Add:* Tex A&M Univ Res & Exten Ctr PO Drawer E Overton TX 75684

LIPELES, MARTIN, b New York, NY, June 22, 38; m 68; c 2. DIGITAL TYPE, COMPUTER GRAPHICS. *Educ:* Columbia Univ, AB, 60, MA, 62, PhD(physics), 66. *Prof Exp:* Part-time res physicist, Radiation Lab, Columbia Univ, 62-66; mem tech staff, Sci Ctr, Rockwell Int, 66-76; pres, Med Microcomputers Inc, 77-78; DIR RES & DEVELOP, AUTOLOGIC INC, 78- *Mem:* AAAS; Am Phys Soc; Am Chem Soc; Sigma Xi. *Res:* Software for design of digital type and typesetter design; inelastic, ion-atom collisions at low energies; physics and chemistry of photochemical aerosol formation in the atmosphere. *Mailing Add:* 1476 Warwick Ave Thousand Oaks CA 91360

LIPETZ, LEO ELIJAH, b Lincoln, Nebr, Aug 10, 21; m 47; c 3. BIOPHYSICS, NEUROSCIENCES. *Educ:* Cornell Univ, BEE, 42; Univ Calif, PhD(biophys), 53. *Prof Exp:* Jr elec engr, Radar Lab, Signal Corps, 42-43; mem tech staff, Bell Tel Labs, 43-36; asst physics, Univ Southern Calif, 46-47; instr biophys, Exten Div, Univ Calif, 48; from instr to asst prof ophthal, 54-60, asst prof physiol, 56-61, assoc prof biophys, 60-61, actg chmn div, 65-67, assoc prof physiol, 61-65, chmn div, 67-71, chmn dept, 71-76, prof biophys & res assoc, Inst Res Vision, 65-81, PROF, DEPT ZOOL, OHIO STATE UNIV, 81- *Concurrent Pos:* Nat Found fel, Johns Hopkins Univ, 53-54; mem, Biophys Sci Training Comt, Nat Inst Gen Med Sci, 68-70. *Mem:* AAAS; Biophys Soc; fel Japan Soc Prom Sci; Asn Res Vision & Ophthal; Soc Neurosci. *Res:* Biophysics of the visual system; physical basis of behavior; local circuit neuronal networks; optics; information transfer; effect of high energy radiation. *Mailing Add:* Div of Sensory Biophys 1314 Kinnear Rd Columbus OH 43212

LIPICKY, RAYMOND JOHN, b Cleveland, Ohio, May 3, 33; m 58. INTERNAL MEDICINE, PHARMACOLOGY. *Educ:* Ohio Univ, AB, 55; Univ Cincinnati, MD, 60. *Prof Exp:* From intern to resident med, Barnes Hosp, St Louis, Mo, 60-62; resident, Strong Mem Hosp, Rochester, NY, 64-65; from asst prof to assoc prof pharmacol, Col Med, Univ Cincinnati, 66-72, from asst prof to assoc prof med, 66-73, prof pharmacol, 72-79, prof med & dir, Div Clin Pharmacol, 73-79; MED OFFICER, DIV CARDIORENAL DRUG PRODS, FOOD & DRUG ADMIN, 79- *Concurrent Pos:* Fel pharmacol, Univ Pa, 62-63 & Univ Cincinnati, 63-64; trainee cardiol, Strong Mem Hosp, Rochester, 65-66; mem corp, Marine Biol Lab, Woods Hole, Mass; guest worker, Lab Biophysics, NIH, 79- *Mem:* Soc Neurosci; Biophys Soc; Am Physiol Soc; Am Soc Pharmacol & Exp Therapeut. *Res:* Ion transport; clinical pharmacology; membrane permeability; bioelectric potentials; hemodynamics. *Mailing Add:* Div Cardiorenal Drug Prods Rm 16-B-45 Food & Drug Admin 5600 Fishers Lane Rockville MD 20857

LIPIN, BRUCE REED, b New York, NY, Nov 27, 47; m 71; c 1. PETROLOGY. *Educ:* City Col New York, BS, 70; Pa State Univ, PhD(mineral, petrol), 75. *Prof Exp:* Fel, Geophys Lab, Carnegie Inst Washington, 73-74; Nat Res Coun res assoc fel, 74-75, GEOLOGIST, US GEOL SURV, 75- *Mem:* Mineral Soc Am; Soc Econ Geol. Petrology of chromite deposits. *Res:* Economic geology of ultramafic rocks including chromite, platinum, asbestos and talc; petrology and origin of ultramafic rocks. *Mailing Add:* 2308 Archdale Rd Reston VA 22091

LIPINSKI, BOGUSLAW, b Sochaczew, Poland, July 21, 33; US citizen; m 57; c 1. BIOELECTRICITY. *Educ:* Inst Nuclear Res, Warsaw, PhD(biochem), 62; Univ Lodz, Poland, DSc, 71. *Prof Exp:* Vis prof, Vascular Lab, Lemnel Shattuck Hosp, Sch Med, Tufts Univ, 71-76; assoc dir, Vascular Lab, 76-81, DIR, BIOELEC LAB, ST ELIZABETH'S HOSP, TUFTS UNIV SCH MED, 81- *Concurrent Pos:* Asst ed, J Bioelec, 81- *Mem:* AAAS; Int Soc Thrombosis & Hemostosis; Fedn Am Scientists; Int Soc Bioelec (pres, 80-). *Res:* Mechamism of intravascular coagulation and fibrinolysis; effect of nutrition on thrombosis and atherosclerosis; effect of electricity on biological systems in relation to tissues regeneration and healing. *Mailing Add:* PO Box 82 Boston MA 02135

LIPINSKI, CHRISTOPHER ANDREW, b Dundee, Scotland, Feb 1, 44; US citizen; m 69; c 2. ORGANIC CHEMISTRY. *Educ:* San Francisco State Col, BS, 65; Univ Calif, Berkeley, PhD(org chem), 68. *Prof Exp:* Nat Inst Gen Med Sci fel, Calif Inst Technol, 69-70; sr res investr, 71-80, PRIN RES INVESTIGATOR, MED RES LABS, PFIZER CENT RES, 80- *Mem:* Am Chem Soc. *Res:* Medicinal chemistry. *Mailing Add:* Med Res Labs Pfizer Cent Res Groton CT 06340

LIPINSKI, WALTER C(HARLES), b Chicago, Ill, Jan 5, 27; m 51; c 1. ELECTRICAL ENGINEERING, NUCLEAR ENGINEERING. *Educ:* Univ Ill, BSc, 50; Ill Inst Technol, MSc, 63, PhD(elec eng), 69. *Prof Exp:* From asst elec engr to assoc elec engr, 50-74, SR ELEC ENGR, ARGONNE NAT LAB, 74- *Concurrent Pos:* US deleg, Int Electrotech Comn, 64-; consult, Adv Comt Reactor Safeguards, US Nuclear Regulatory Comn, 64- *Mem:* Am Nuclear Soc; Inst Elec & Electronics Engrs; Sigma Xi. *Res:* Control engineering; instrumentation; nuclear reactor control and instrumentation; nuclear power plant development; nuclear reactor safety. *Mailing Add:* Reactor Anal & Safety Div Argonne Nat Lab Argonne IL 60439

LIPINSKY, EDWARD SOLOMON, b Asheville, NC, Nov 15, 29; m 54; c 2. CHEMISTRY, ECONOMICS. *Educ:* Mass Inst Technol, BS, 52; Harvard Univ, AM, 54. *Prof Exp:* Res assoc, Ohio State Univ, 57-59; prin res scientist, 59-71, assoc div chief bus & tech planning, 71-74, res leader, 75-79, SR RES LEADER RES MGT, BATTELLE COLUMBUS DIV, 79- *Mem:* Am Chem Soc; fel AAAS; Sigma Xi; NY Acad Sci; Commercial Develop Asn. *Res:* Fuels from biomass; renewable resource technology and economics; microbiological processing; agricultural systems analysis. *Mailing Add:* Battelle Mem Inst 505 King Ave Columbus OH 43201

LIPKA, BENJAMIN, b New York, NY, Feb 5, 29; m 58; c 3. ORGANIC CHEMISTRY. *Educ:* NY Univ, BA, 49, PhD(org chem), 58. *Prof Exp:* Chemist, Geigy Chem Corp, 59-60; sr chemist, Allied Chem Corp, 60-67; SR DEVELOP CHEMIST, UPJOHN CO, 67- *Mem:* Am Chem Soc. *Res:* Laboratory synthesis and chemical plant production of organic compounds. *Mailing Add:* Upjohn Co 410 Sackett Point Rd North Haven CT 06473

LIPKA, JAMES J, b Highland Park, Mich, Aug 1, 54; m 80. BIOINORGANIC CHEMISTRY. *Educ:* Univ Mich, BS, 76; Columbia Univ, MA, 77, PhD(chem), 82. *Prof Exp:* FEL CHEM, BROOKHAVEN NAT LAB, 81- *Mem:* Am Chem Soc; Sigma Xi; AAAS; NY Acad Sci. *Res:* Methods for labelling biological polymers and assemblies with heavy atoms for the purpose of increasing contrast in high-resolution electron microscopy. *Mailing Add:* Biol Dept Brookhaven Nat Lab Upton NY 11973

LIPKE, HERBERT, b New York, NY, Jan 10, 23; m 48; c 4. BIOCHEMISTRY. *Educ:* Cornell Univ, BS, 47, MS, 48; Univ Ill, PhD(entom), 53. *Prof Exp:* Chemist, Calif Packing Corp, 48-50; asst entom, Univ Ill, 51-53, res assoc, 53-58; biochemist, Exp Zool Br, Physiol Div, Army Chem Ctr, 58-67; PROF BIOL, UNIV MASS, BOSTON, 67- *Concurrent Pos:* US Pub Health Serv fel, Univ Ill, 55; WHO fel, London Sch Hyg & Trop Med, 60-62. *Mem:* AAAS; Am Chem Soc; Entom Soc Am; Am Soc Biol Chem; Brit Biochem Soc. *Res:* Biochemistry and physiology of invertebrates. *Mailing Add:* Dept of Biol Univ of Mass Harbor Campus Boston MA 02125

LIPKE, PETER NATHAN, b San Francisco, Calif, June 18, 50; m 71; c 4. CELL-CELL ADHESION, CELL SURFACE DEVELOPMENT. *Educ:* Univ Chicago, BS, 71; Univ Calif, Berkeley, PhD(biochem), 76. *Prof Exp:* Fel, Dept Zool, Univ Wis-Madison, 76-78; ASST PROF MOLECULAR CELL BIOL, DEPT BIOL SCI, HUNTER COL, 78- *Mem:* Am Soc Microbiol; AAAS. *Res:* Molecular basis for cell-cell adhesion in eukaryotes, using mating in Saccharomyces cerevisiae as a model; developmental changes in cell surface structure. *Mailing Add:* Box 1008 Hunter Col 695 Park Ave New York NY 10021

LIPKE, WILLIAM G, b Chesterton, Ind, Dec 19, 36; m 57; c 4. PLANT PHYSIOLOGY, PLANT BIOCHEMISTRY. *Educ:* Purdue Univ, BS, 59; Univ Nebr, MS, 62; Tex A&M Univ, PhD(plant physiol), 66. *Prof Exp:* From asst prof to assoc prof plant physiol, 65-74, ASSOC PROF BIOL, NORTHERN ARIZ UNIV, 74-, PLANT PHYSIOLOGIST, 65- *Mem:* AAAS; Am Soc Plant Physiol. *Res:* Plant physiology, especially mineral nutrition; weed science, especially plant enzymes. *Mailing Add:* Box 5640 Biol Sci Northern Ariz Univ Flagstaff AZ 86001

LIPKIN, DAVID, b Philadelphia, Pa, Jan 30, 13; m 42; c 2. NUCLEIC ACID CHEMISTRY. *Educ:* Univ Pa, BS, 34; Univ Calif, PhD(org chem), 39. *Prof Exp:* Petrol res chemist, Res & Develop Dept, Atlantic Ref Co, Pa, 34-36; res fel chem, Univ Calif, 39-42, chemist, 42-43; chemist, Manhattan Dist, Los Alamos, NMex, 43-46; assoc prof, 46-48, chmn dept, 64-70, prof chem, 48-69, William Greenleaf Eliot prof chem, 69-81, WILLIAM GREENLEAF ELIOT EMER PROF CHEM, WASHINGTON UNIV, 81- *Concurrent Pos:* Guggenheim fel, 55; trustee, Argonne Univs Asn, 69-71; vis res scientist, John Innes Inst, Norwich, England, 71, spec consult, 78. *Honors & Awards:* St Louis Award, Am Chem Soc, 70. *Mem:* Am Chem Soc. *Res:* Free radicals; organic phosphorus compounds; nucleic acids; electrochemical synthesis. *Mailing Add:* Dept Chem Washington Univ St Louis MO 63130

LIPKIN, GEORGE, b New York, NY, Dec 31, 30; m 57; c 2. CELL BIOLOGY, DERMATOLOGY. *Educ:* Columbia Univ, AB, 52; State Univ NY Downstate Med Ctr, MD, 55. *Prof Exp:* From instr to assoc prof, 61-74, PROF DERMAT, MED SCH, NY UNIV, 74- *Concurrent Pos:* Nat Cancer Inst res grants, Dermat Found, Med Ctr, NY Univ, 61- *Mem:* Soc Invest Dermat; AAAS; Fed Am Sci; Am Acad Dermat; Harvey Soc. *Res:* Biology of malignant melanoma; biologic transformation of malignant cells. *Mailing Add:* Dept of Dermat NY Univ Med Ctr New York NY 10016

LIPKIN, HARRY JEANNOT, b New York, NY, June 16, 21; m 49; c 2. NUCLEAR PHYSICS, PARTICLE PHYSICS. *Educ:* Cornell Univ, BEE, 42; Princeton Univ, AM, 48, PhD(physics), 50. *Prof Exp:* Mem staff, Radiation Lab, Mass Inst Technol, 42-46; vis res fel reactor physics, AEC, France, 53-54; vis assoc prof physics, Univ Ill, 58-59; from assoc prof to prof, 59-71, HERBERT H LEHMAN CHAIR THEORET PHYSICS, WEIZMANN INST SCI, ISRAEL, 71- *Concurrent Pos:* Res physicist, Weizmann Inst Sci, 52-60, actg head dept physics, 60-61; consult, AEC, Israel, 55-58; vis lectr, Hebrew Univ, Israel, 56-58; vis prof, Univ Ill, 62-63 & Tel Aviv Univ, 65-66; vis prof, Princeton Univ, 67-68; vis scientist, Argonne Nat Lab & Nat Accelerator Lab, Ill, 71-72, 76-77 & 79-81. *Honors & Awards:* Rothschild Prize, Jerusalem, 80. *Mem:* Am Phys Soc; Ital Phys Soc; Phys Soc Israel; Europ Phys Soc; Israel Acad Sci & Humanities. *Res:* Elementary particle theory; theoretical and experimental nuclear structure; collective motion in many particle systems; Beta decay; Mossbauer effect; reactor and particle physics; theoretical physics. *Mailing Add:* Dept Nuclear Physics Weizmann Inst of Sci Rehovoth Israel

LIPKIN, LEWIS EDWARD, b New York, NY, Nov 2, 25; m 52; c 2. NEUROPATHOLOGY, COMPUTER SCIENCES. *Educ:* NY Univ, BA, 44; Long Island Col Med, MD, 49; Am Bd Path, dipl & cert anat path & neuropath, 52. *Prof Exp:* From intern med to resident path, Mt Sinai Hosp NY, 49-53; asst prof path & neuropath, State Univ NY Downstate Med Ctr, 56-62; head neuropath, Path Sect, Perinatal Res Br, Nat Inst Neurol Dis & Stroke, 62-72; dir, Div Cancer Biol & Diagnosis, head, Image Processing Unit Off, 72-80, CHIEF IMAGE PROCESSING SECT, LAB PATHOL, NAT CANCER INST, NIH, 80- *Concurrent Pos:* Asst pathologist, Kings County Hosp, 56-62; USPHS sr res fel neuropath, Mt Sinai Hosp NY, 55-56; USPHS res grant, 59-62; consult, Nat Inst Neurol Dis & Stroke, 61-62. *Mem:* Asn Res Nerv & Ment Dis; Int Acad Path; Am Asn Neuropath; Asn Comput Mach. *Res:* Computer analysis of microscopic images, especially neuropathologic material; automation of analysis of two dimensional gel electrophoresis; analysis and synthesis of nucleic acid secondary structure. *Mailing Add:* Div Cancer Treatment NIH Nat Cancer Inst Bethesda MD 20014

LIPKIN, MACK, b New York, NY, Mar 22, 07; m 36; c 3. INTERNAL MEDICINE, PSYCHIATRY. *Educ:* City Col New York, BS, 26, Cornell Univ, MD, 30; Am Bd Internal Med, dipl. *Prof Exp:* From intern to house physician, Univ Hosp, New York, 31-33; resident, Metrop Hosp, 33; resident, Rockland State Hosp, 33-34; from instr med to lectr psychiat, Columbia Univ, 36-52; clin asst prof med, 52-64, assoc prof med, Med Col, Cornell Univ, 64-72; prof psychiat med, 72-77, prof family pract, 74-77, EMER PROF PSYCHIAT MED & FAMILY PRACT, MED SCH, UNIV ORE, 77- *Concurrent Pos:* Asst attend physician, Univ Hosp, 34-46, chief div psychosomatic med, 39-46; dir, Group Health Ins, 38-68; asst vis physician, Goldwater Hosp, 44-46; med consult, Rehab Clin New York Hosp, 44-46; from asst attend physician to assoc attend physician, 52-; adj physician & dir, Psychosom Serv, Mt Sinai Hosp, 46-52; consult, Surgeon Gen, US Army, 48-55; sr consult, Vet Admin, 52-55; pres, Sergei Zlinkoff Found Med Educ Res, 56-; trustee, Riverside Res Inst, 67-75; vis prof, Dartmouth Med Sch, 68-69; vis prof, Med Sch, Univ Ore, 72-; trustee, NY Sch Psychiat, 74-76; pres, Ruth W Dolen Found Med Educ & Res, 74-; consult, Commonwealth Fund, 75-79; E & J Klingenstein Found, 78-79. *Mem:* Am Col Physicians; Am Psychosom Soc; Group Advan Psychiat; AMA; NY Acad Med. *Res:* Psychosomatic medicine; xiphoid syndrome; cardiovascular disease. *Mailing Add:* 450 Riverside Dr New York NY 10027

LIPKIN, MARTIN, b New York, NY, Apr 30, 26; m 58. GASTROENTEROLOGY, ONCOLOGY. *Educ:* NY Univ, AB, 46, MD, 50. *Prof Exp:* Instr physiol, Sch Med, Univ Pa, 53-54; from instr to assoc prof, 58-78, PROF MED, MED COL, CORNELL UNIV, 78-; PROF GRAD SCH MED SCI, MEM SLOAN KETTERING CANCER CTR, 78-, HEAD, LAB GASTROINTESTINAL CANCER RES, 72-; ASSOC MEM, SLOAN-KETTERING INST CANCER RES, 72- *Concurrent Pos:* Fel physiol, Med Col, Cornell Univ, 52-53; USPHS res fel, 55-56; fel med, Med Col, Cornell Univ, 55-58; NIH res career prog award, 61-71; res collabr, Brookhaven Nat Lab, 58-72; dir gastroenterol res unit, Cornell Med Div, Bellevue Hosp, 58-68; guest investr, Rockefeller Inst, 59-60; assoc attend physician, New York Hosp, 70- & Mem Hosp, 71-; assoc prof, Grad Sch Med Sci, Cornell Univ, 71-78; lectr, NY State Med Soc, 71, secy, Sect Gastroenterol & Colon & Rectal Surg, 71, vchmn, 72, chmn, 73; hon pres, Int Acad Pathol Conf colorectal cancer, 81; ann hon lectr, Israel Med Asn & Gastroenterol Soc, 82. *Mem:* Fel Am Col Physicians; Am Soc Clin Invest; Am Physiol Soc; Am Soc Exp Path; Am Asn Cancer Res. *Res:* Proliferation and differentiation of premalignant and malignant gastrointestinal cells in man. *Mailing Add:* Sloan Kettering Cancer Ctr 1275 York Ave New York NY 10021

LIPMAN, JOSEPH, b Toronto, Ont, Can, June 15, 38; m 62; c 2. MATHEMATICS. *Educ:* Univ Toronto, BA, 60; Harvard Univ, MA, 61, PhD(math), 65. *Prof Exp:* Asst prof math, Queen's Univ, Ont, 65 & Purdue Univ, 66-67; vis asst prof, Columbia Univ, 67-68; from asst prof to assoc prof, 68-72, PROF MATH, PURDUE UNIV, WEST LAFAYETTE, 72- *Mem:* Am Math Soc; Can Math Cong. *Res:* Algebraic geometry. *Mailing Add:* Dept of Math Purdue Univ West Lafayette IN 47907

LIPMAN, MARC JOSEPH, b Chicago, Ill, Mar 19, 50; m 81. GRAPH THEORY. *Educ:* Lake Forest Col, BA, 71; Dartmouth Col, AM, 73, PhD(math), 76. *Prof Exp:* Lectr math, Dartmouth Col, 73; ASST PROF MATH, IND UNIV-PURDUE UNIV, FT WAYNE, 76- *Concurrent Pos:* Assoc, Nat Res Coun, Naval Res Lab, 80. *Mem:* Am Math Soc; Math Asn Am. *Res:* Graph theory; representations of finite groups. *Mailing Add:* Ind Univ-Purdue Univ 2101 Coliseum Blvd Ft Wayne IN 46805

LIPMAN, PETER WALDMAN, b New York, NY, Apr 21, 35; m 62. GEOLOGY. *Educ:* Yale Univ, BS, 58; Stanford Univ, MS, 59, PhD(geol), 62. *Prof Exp:* GEOLOGIST, US GEOL SURV, 62- *Concurrent Pos:* NSF fel, Geol Inst, Tokyo, 64-65. *Mem:* Geol Soc Am; Mineral Soc Am. *Res:* Petrology and structural geology; volcanology, especially geology of calderas and related ash flows. *Mailing Add:* US Geol Surv Bldg 25 Denver Fed Ctr Denver CO 80225

LIPMAN, ROGER DAVID ARNOLD, b London, Eng, June 16, 38; US citizen; m 63, 81; c 4. PHYSICAL CHEMISTRY, POLYMER SCIENCE. *Educ:* London Univ, BSc, 59; Royal Col Sci, ARCS, 59; Cambridge Univ, PhD(phys chem), 62. *Prof Exp:* Res scientist polymer chem, Geigy Chem Corp, 64-67; group leader, CIBA-Geigy Corp, 67-73; sr res scientist plastics develop, Johnson & Johnson, 73-74, proj leader, 74-75, asst mgr adhesives, 75-78, mgr adhesive prods, 78-80; DIR RES & DEVELOP, CONVATEC DIV, E R SQUIBB, 81- *Concurrent Pos:* Fel, State Col Forestry, NY, 63-64. *Mem:* Am Chem Soc; Soc Plastics Engrs; Royal Soc Chem. *Res:* Polymerization kinetics; copolymerization plastics and adhesives development; health care products and medical device development. *Mailing Add:* Convatec Res & Develop 25 Cotters Lane East Brunswick NJ 08816

LIPMANN, FRITZ (ALBERT), b Koenigsberg, Ger, June 12, 99; nat US; m 31; c 1. BIOCHEMISTRY. *Educ:* Univ Berlin, MD, 24, PhD(chem), 27. *Hon Degrees:* MD, Univ Aix-Marseille, 47; ScD, Univ Chicago, 53; DHL, Sorbonne-Paris, Copenhagen, Brandeis Univ, 59 & Albert Einstein Col Med, 64; DSc, Univ Paris, 66, Harvard Univ, 67 & Rockefeller Univ, 71. *Prof Exp:* Asst intermediary metab, Kaiser Wilhelm Inst Biol, Berlin & Heidelberg, 27-31; res assoc tissue cult & intermediary metab, Biol Inst Carlsberg Found, Copenhagen, 32-39; res assoc biochem, Med Col, Cornell Univ, 39-41; head biochem res lab & prof biol chem, Harvard Univ & Mass Gen Hosp, 41-57; PROF BIOCHEM, ROCKEFELLER UNIV, 57- *Concurrent Pos:* Rockefeller Found fel, Rockefeller Inst, 31-32; assoc, Harvard Med Sch, 46-49, prof, 49-57. *Honors & Awards:* Nobel Prize in Med & Physiol, 53; Carl Neuberg Medal, 48; Mead Johnson & Co Award, 48; Nat Medal Sci, 66. *Mem:* Nat Acad Sci; Am Soc Biol Chemists (pres, 60-61); Harvey Soc; Am Philos Soc; fel Royal Danish Acad. *Res:* Energy metabolism; sulfate activation and protein synthesis; discovery and identification of coenzyme A. *Mailing Add:* Rockefeller Univ 1230 York Ave New York NY 10021

LIPNER, HARRY JOEL, b New York, NY, Aug 26, 22; m 49; c 4. REPRODUCTIVE ENDOCRINOLOGY. *Educ:* Long Island Univ, BS, 42; Univ Chicago, MS, 47; Univ Iowa, PhD(physiol), 52. *Prof Exp:* Res assoc thyroid iodine trap, Univ Iowa, 52; Nat Cancer Inst res fel thyroid physiol, 52-54; instr clin path, Chicago Med Sch, 54-55; from asst prof to assoc prof, 55-65, PROF PHYSIOL, FLA STATE UNIV, 65- *Concurrent Pos:* NIH fel & vis prof dept anat, Harvard Med Sch, 69-70; Fulbright vis prof, Ctr Advan Biochem, Indian Inst Sci, Bangalore, India, 74-75. *Mem:* AAAS; Endocrine Soc; Sigma Xi; Soc Study Reproduction; Am Physiol Soc. *Res:* Mechanism of ovulation; nonsteroidal gonadal feedback control of Gonadotropin secretion. *Mailing Add:* Dept of Biol Sci Fla State Univ Tallahassee FL 32306

LIPNER, STEVEN BARNETT, b Independence, Kans, Sept 30, 43; m 80. SOFTWARE SYSTEMS. *Educ:* Mass Inst Technol, SB, 65, SM, 66. *Prof Exp:* Assoc dept head, Intel & Info Syst, MITRE Corp, 77-80 & Command & Control Systs, 80-81; ENG MGR, CORP RES GROUP, DIGITAL EQUIP CORP, 81- *Concurrent Pos:* Hertz Found fel, Los Angeles, 65. *Mem:* Asn Comput Mach; Sigma Xi; Inst Elec & Electronics Engrs Comput Soc. *Res:* Security controls for computer systems; theoretical and practical advances in security models and secure operating systems. *Mailing Add:* 6 Midland Rd Wellesley MA 02181

LIPNICK, ROBERT LOUIS, b Baltimore, Md, Sept 9, 41; m 67; c 1. BIOORGANIC CHEMISTRY, NMR SPECTROSCOPY. *Educ:* Univ Md, College Park, BS, 63; Brandeis Univ, PhD(org chem), 69. *Prof Exp:* Fel chem, Univ Minn, Minneapolis, 68-72; vis scientist, var African univs, 73-74; res assoc, Sloan-Kettering Inst, 74-79; chemist, 79-80, LEADER STRUCTURE ACTIV GROUP, US ENVIRON PROTECTION AGENCY, 80- *Mem:* Am Chem Soc; AAAS. *Res:* Estimation of the conformational, physicochemical, and toxicological properties of molecules from molecular structure; conformation and interactions of biologically important molecules. *Mailing Add:* US Environ Protection Agency (TS-796) Washington DC 20460

LIPOVSKI, GERALD JOHN (JACK), b Coleman, Alta, Jan 28, 44; m 68; c 3. COMPUTER ENGINEERING, ELECTRICAL ENGINEERING. *Educ:* Univ Notre Dame, AB & BSEE, 66; Univ Ill, Urbana, MS, 67, PhD(elec eng), 69. *Prof Exp:* Res fel automata theory, Coordinated Sci Lab, Univ Ill, Urbana, 66-68, asst electronics, 67-68, asst comput archit, 68-69; asst prof elec eng, Univ Fla, 69-76; assoc prof, 76-82, PROF ELEC ENG & COMPUT SCI, UNIV TEX, AUSTIN, 82- *Concurrent Pos:* Consult, Harris Semiconductor, 73-74 & Sycor, 76-77. *Mem:* Asn Comput Mach; Comput Soc of Inst Elec & Electronics Engrs. *Res:* Computer architecture; parallel and distributed computer architectures; data base processor architectures; microcomputer architectures and applications; hardware design languages. *Mailing Add:* Dept of Elec Eng Univ of Tex Austin TX 78712

LIPOWITZ, JONATHAN, b Paterson, NJ, Apr 25, 37; m 60; c 2. ORGANOMETALLIC CHEMISTRY, POLYMER CHEMISTRY. *Educ:* Rutgers Univ, Newark, BS, 58; Univ Pittsburgh, PhD(chem), 64. *Prof Exp:* Fel, Pa State Univ, University Park, 64-65; res chemist, 65-74, res specialist, 74-75, sr res specialist, 75-79, ASSOC SCIENTIST, RES DEPT, DOW CORNING CORP, 79- *Mem:* Am Chem Soc. *Res:* Silicone flammability, mechanisms of; effects of silicones on flammability of organic polymers; silicone chemistry and physical properties. *Mailing Add:* Silicone Res Dept Dow Corning Corp Midland MI 48640

LIPOWSKI, STANLEY ARTHUR, b Warsaw, Poland, Sept 16, 05; US citizen; m 45; c 1. ORGANIC POLYMER CHEMISTRY. *Educ:* Warsaw Tech Univ, MS, 29; Danzig Tech Univ, PhD(chem), 31. *Prof Exp:* Chemist, M D Lipowski Tanning Co, Poland, 31-35; chief chemist, J B Rakower Tanning Co, 36-43; tech dir, State Tannery, 45-46; tech dir Thor Schriwer Co, Norway, 47-49; res chemist, Peter Moeller Chem Co, 50-52, div mgr, 53-54; res chemist, B D Eisendrath Co, Wis, 54-55; res chemist, Nopco Chem Co, 55-60, sr res chemist, 61-69, dir resin & polymer res & develop, Nopco Div, Diamond Shamrock Corp, 69-71; CONSULT CHEMIST & ENGR, 71- *Concurrent Pos:* Mem bd dirs, Nat Youth Sci Found, 65. *Mem:* Am Leather Chem Asn; sr mem Am Chem Soc. *Res:* Organic synthesis; synthetic tanning agents; surfactants; sulfanation processes; phenolic and aminoplast resins; oils and fats chemistry; complexing agents; chelation; water soluble organic polymers; emulsion polymerization. *Mailing Add:* 25 Ashwood Dr Livingston NJ 07039

LIPOWSKI, ZBIGNIEW J, b Warsaw, Poland, Oct 26, 24; Can citizen; m 46; c 2. PSYCHIATRY. *Educ:* Nat Univ Ireland, MB, BCh & BAO, 53; McGill Univ, dipl, 59. *Hon Degrees:* Dr Med, Helsinki; MA, Dartmouth Col. *Prof Exp:* Demonstr psychiat, McGill Univ, 59-62, lectr, 62-65, from asst prof to assoc prof, 65-71; PROF PSYCHIAT, DARTMOUTH MED SCH, 71- *Concurrent Pos:* Res fel psychophysiol, Allan Mem Inst Psychiat, 57-58; Mona Bronfman Shenkman teaching fel psychiat, Harvard Univ & Mass Gen Hosp, 58-59; clin asst, Allan Mem Inst Psychiat, 59-62, from asst psychiatrist to psychiatrist, 62-71; consult psychiat, Montreal Neurol Inst, 68-71; psychiatrist, Mary Hitchcock Mem Hosp, Hanover, NH, 71- *Mem:* Fel Am Psychiat Asn; Am Psychosom Soc; Acad Psychosom Med; Int Col Psychosom Med. Med Asn. *Res:* Psychosomatic medicine and psychopathology related to physical illness. *Mailing Add:* Dept of Psychiat Dartmouth Med Sch Hanover NH 03755

LIPP, JAMES P(ERSHING), b New York, NY, Apr 23, 19; m 42. ELECTRICAL ENGINEERING. *Educ:* Univ Okla, BS, 54. *Prof Exp:* Engr commun & opers anal, Advan Electronic Ctr, Gen Elec Co, NY, 54-58, supvr info theory & anal, 59, consult engr secure commun technol, 60-65, advan commun technol, Okla, 65-66, commun & comput oper, 66-67, comput memory coding, 67-76; CONSULT ENG, 76- *Mem:* Sigma Xi; Inst Elec & Electronics Engrs. *Res:* Coding and information theory; propagation and communications systems; reliability theory. *Mailing Add:* 1501 Oakhill Lane Oklahoma City OK 73127

LIPP, STEVEN ALAN, b Brooklyn, NY, Jan 25, 44. INORGANIC CHEMISTRY. *Educ:* Brooklyn Col, BS, 65; Univ Calif, Berkeley, PhD(inorg chem), 70. *Prof Exp:* MEM TECH STAFF, RCA LABS, DAVID SARNOFF RES CTR, 70- *Honors & Awards:* Achievement Award, RCA Labs, 74, David Sarnoff Award, RCA Corp, 75. *Mem:* Electrochem Soc. *Res:* Preparation and evaluation of new cathodoluminescent materials, as well as the design and testing of enhancements for chemical milling. *Mailing Add:* RCA Labs David Sarnoff Res Ctr Princeton NJ 08540

LIPPA, ERIK ALEXANDER, b Minneapolis, Minn, Nov 7, 45; m 74, 80; c 1. NUMBER THEORY. *Educ:* Calif Inst Technol, BS, 67; Univ Mich, MS, 68, PhD(math), 71; Albert Einstein Col Med, MD, 80. *Prof Exp:* NATO fel math, Oxford Univ, 71-72; asst prof math, Purdue Univ, West Lafayette, 72-76; med intern, NY Univ & Manhattan Vet Admin Hosp, 80-81; ophthal resident, Ill Eye & Ear Infirmary, 81-82. *Mem:* Math Asn Am; Sigma Xi; Am Med Asn. *Res:* Analytic number theory, specifically Siegel modular forms of several complex variables and their associated Dirichlet series; applications of mathematics to medicine and pharmaceutical sciences. *Mailing Add:* 1960 N Lincoln Park W Apt 1504 Chicago IL 60614

LIPPARD, STEPHEN J, b Pittsburgh, Pa, Oct 12, 40; m 64; c 2. INORGANIC CHEMISTRY, BIOCHEMISTRY. *Educ:* Haverford Col, BA, 62; Mass Inst Technol, PhD(chem), 65. *Prof Exp:* NSF fel, Mass Inst Technol, 65-66; from asst prof to assoc prof, 66-72, PROF CHEM, COLUMBIA UNIV, 72- *Concurrent Pos:* Consult, Esso Res & Eng Co, 67-73 & John Wiley & Sons, Inc, 81-; Alfred P Sloan Found fel, 68-70; John Simon Guggenheim Mem fel, Sweden, 72; ed, Progress in Inorganic Chem, John E Fogarty Sr Int fel, 78-79. *Honors & Awards:* Camille & Henry Dreyfus Teacher-Scholar Award, 72. *Mem:* Fel AAAS; Am Chem Soc; Am Crystallog Asn; Biophys Soc; Royal Soc Chem. *Res:* Inorganic and organometallic coordination chemistry, especially preparation, structural properties and reactions of transition metal complexes; lignad bridged bimetallic complexes and proteins; metal binding to nucleicacids; platinum antinmor drugs; high coordinate organo-metallic chemistry. *Mailing Add:* Dept of Chem Columbia Univ New York NY 10027

LIPPARD, VERNON WILLIAM, b Marlboro, Mass, Oct 4, 05; m 31; c 1. PEDIATRICS. *Educ:* Yale Univ, BS, 26, MD, 29. *Hon Degrees:* ScD, Univ Md, 55. *Prof Exp:* Intern pediat, New Haven Hosp, Conn, 29-30; asst res pediatrician, NY Nursery & Child's Hosp, New York, 30-31, res pediatrician, 31-32; res pediatrician, NY Hosp, 32-33; instr & assoc pediat, Med Col, Cornell Univ, 33-38; dir, Cmn Study Crippled Children, 38-39; assoc dean, Col Physicians & Surgeons, Columbia Univ, 39-46; prof pediat & dean, Sch Med, La State Univ, 46-49 & Sch Med, Univ Va, 49-52; prof, 52-71, dean 52-67, asst to pres med develop, 67-71, EMER PROF PEDIAT, SCH MED, YALE UNIV, 71-, EMER DEAN, 67- *Concurrent Pos:* Mem bd med consult, Oak Ridge Inst Nuclear Studies, 47-52, Brookhaven Nat Lab, 57-62 & Josiah Macy Jr Found, 67-75; mem bd dirs, Grant Found, 67-; Nat Fund Med Educ, 75- *Mem:* Soc Pediat Res; Asn Am Med Cols (pres, 54-55); Asn Am Physicians. *Res:* Acid-base balance and immunology in infancy; development of hypersensitiveness; medical education. *Mailing Add:* Sterling Hall of Med Yale Univ 333 Cedar St New Haven CT 06510

LIPPE, ROBERT LLOYD, b New York, NY, May 8, 23; m; c 2. CHEMISTRY. *Educ:* Yale Univ, BE, 42; Princeton Univ, MS, 47. *Prof Exp:* Eng trainee, Joseph E Seagram & Sons, Inc, Md, 43; jr scientist in charge radiographic res, Manhattan Dist, 45-46; chemist, Standard Varnish Works, 47-51; asst to vpres, Standard Tech Chems, Inc, 51-54; PRES, NOD HILL CHEM CORP, 53-; PRES, ARGUS PAINT & LACQUER CORP, 54- *Mem:* Am Chem Soc; Am Inst Chem Eng; Fedn Am Sci. *Res:* Radiography of explosives; organotitanium compounds; synthetic and natural resins for coatings; industrial organic coatings. *Mailing Add:* 2133 McCarter Hwy Newark NJ 07104

LIPPEL, KENNETH, b New York, NY, Feb 21, 29; m 61; c 1. BIOCHEMISTRY. *Educ:* City Col New York, BS, 49, MBA, 60; Univ Fla, PhD(biochem), 66. *Prof Exp:* NIH fel biochem, Univ Calif, Los Angeles, 66-68; asst prof dermat & biochem, Sch Med, Univ Miami, 68-70; res biochemist, Lipids Br, Human Nutrit Res Div, Agr Res Serv, USDA, 70-72; HEALTH SCI ADMINR, LIPID METAB BR, DIV HEART & VASCULAR DIS, NAT HEART, LUNG & BLOOD INST, NIH, 72- *Concurrent Pos:* Fel, Coun Arteriosclerosis, Am Heart Asn, 75- *Mem:* AAAS; Am Soc Biol Chem; Am Heart Asn; Am Chem Soc; Fedn Am Socs Exp Biol. *Res:* Regulation of fatty acid and lipid metabolism; relationship of lipoprotein metabolism to atherosclerosis; vitamin A metabolism. *Mailing Add:* 9604 Wis Ave Bethesda MD 20814

LIPPERT, BYRON E, b Los Angeles, Calif, July 1, 29; m 52; c 3. PHYCOLOGY. *Educ:* Univ Ore, BS, 54, MS, 57; Ind Univ, PhD(bot), 66. *Prof Exp:* Instr biol, Eastern Ore Col, 56-59; asst prof, 60-69, ASSOC PROF BIOL, PORTLAND STATE UNIV, 69- *Mem:* Phycol Soc Am; Brit Phycol Soc; Int Phycol Soc; Bot Soc Am. *Res:* Morphology, life cycles and sexual reproduction in desmids. *Mailing Add:* Dept of Biol Portland State Univ Portland OR 97207

LIPPERT, LAVERNE FRANCIS, b Deerlodge, Mont, Sept 21, 28; m 50; c 5. PLANT PATHOLOGY. *Educ:* State Col Wash, BS, 50; Univ Calif, Davis, PhD(plant path), 59. *Prof Exp:* Asst plant path, Univ Calif, Davis, 55-58; from asst olericulturist to assoc olericulturist, 58-72, PROF VEG CROPS & OLERICULTURIST, UNIV CALIF, RIVERSIDE, 72-, VCHMN DEPT PLANT SCI, 75- *Mem:* Am Genetic Soc; Am Hort Soc. *Res:* Vegetable crops breeding, especially peppers and melons. *Mailing Add:* Dept of Plant Sci Univ of Calif Riverside CA 92502

LIPPES, JACK, b Buffalo, NY, Feb 19, 24; m 47; c 3. REPRODUCTIVE PHYSIOLOGY, OBSTETRICS & GYNECOLOGY. *Educ:* Univ Buffalo, MD, 47. *Prof Exp:* Clin instr, 52-60, clin assoc, 60-66, assoc prof, 66-75, PROF OBSTET & GYNEC, SCH MED, STATE UNIV NY, BUFFALO & ATTEND ASST, CHILDREN'S HOSP, BUFFALO, 68- *Concurrent Pos:* Consult, World Neighbors Found, Okla, 66-78, Pop Coun, Rockefeller Univ, 59-75, Ortho Pharmaceut Corp, 66-78, Syntex Res, 78-79, WHO Comt Studying Human Reprod, 74-78 & Sterling-Winthrop Pharmaceut Corp grant, 77-78; investr, Upjohn Pharmaceut Co, 75-78 & Prog Appl Res Fertil Regulation, 75-78; chmn, Dept Obstet & Gynec, Deaconess Hosp, Buffalo, 75-81; vis prof obstet & gynec, Charing Cross Hosp, Med Sch, London, 81. *Mem:* Asn Planned Parenthood Physicians; Planned Parenthood Fedn; Am Fertil Soc; Am Col Obstet & Gynec. *Res:* Human oviductal fluid; contraception, especially intrauterine contraception; inventor and researcher of intrauterine contraceptive device known as the Loop; immunology of the genital tract. *Mailing Add:* 191 N St Buffalo NY 14201

LIPPINCOTT, BARBARA BARNES, b Raleigh, Ill, Oct 27, 34; m 56; c 3. MICROBIOLOGY, PLANT PHYSIOLOGY. *Educ:* Wash Univ, St Louis, AB, 55, MA, 57, PhD(zool & molecular biol), 59. *Prof Exp:* Jane Coffin Childs Mem Fund Med Res fel physiol genetics, Lab Physiol Genetics, Nat Ctr Sci Res, France, 59-60; res assoc, 60-80, SR RES ASSOC BIOL SCI, NORTHWESTERN UNIV, 80- *Concurrent Pos:* Vis scholar, Univ Calif, Berkeley, 70-71; vis scientist, Inst Bot, Univ Heidelberg, 74. *Mem:* Am Soc Microbiol; Sigma Xi. *Res:* Electron spin resonance in biological systems; crown-gall tumor formation; control mechanisms in replication, growth and development. *Mailing Add:* Dept Biochem Molecular & Cell Biol Northwestern Univ Evanston IL 60201

LIPPINCOTT, EZRA PARVIN, b Philadelphia, Pa, Sept 7, 39; m 63; c 3. NUCLEAR PHYSICS, NUCLEAR ENGINEERING. *Educ:* Mass Inst Technol, BS, 61, PhD(nuclear physics), 66. *Prof Exp:* Sr scientist, Battelle-Northwest Labs, 66-72; SR SCIENTIST, NUCLEAR ENG, WESTINGHOUSE-HANFORD CO, 72- *Mem:* Am Nuclear Soc; Am Phys Soc; AAAS. *Res:* Experimental and theoretical reactor physics; passive and active neutron and gamma-ray dosimetry; data analysis; methods development; nuclear cross section measurement and data file evaluation; standards preparation. *Mailing Add:* Westinghouse-Hanford Co PO Box 1970 Richland WA 99352

LIPPINCOTT, JAMES ANDREW, b Cumberland Co, Ill, Sept 13, 30; m 56; c 3. PLANT PHYSIOLOGY. *Educ:* Earlham Col, AB, 54; Wash Univ, AM, 56, PhD, 58. *Prof Exp:* Res assoc plant physiol & lectr bot, Wash Univ, 58-59; Jane Coffin Childs Mem Fund Med Res fel, Lab Phytotron, Nat Ctr Sci Res, France, 59-60; from asst prof to prof biol sci, 60-81, PROF BIOCHEM, MOLECULAR & CELL BIOL, NORTHWESTERN UNIV, 81-, ASSOC DEAN BIOL SCI, 80- *Concurrent Pos:* Vis assoc prof, Univ Calif, Berkeley, 70-71; vis prof, Univ Heidelberg, 74. *Mem:* AAAS; Am Soc Plant Physiol; Bot Soc Am; Am Soc Microbiol; Am Phytopath Soc. *Res:* Crown-gall tumor formation; control mechanisms in replication, growth and development; tumor induction in plants by Agrobacterium tumefaciens. *Mailing Add:* Dept Biochem Molecular & Cell Biol Northwestern Univ Evanston IL 60201

LIPPINCOTT, SARAH LEE, b Philadelphia, Pa, Oct 26, 20; m 80. ASTRONOMY. *Educ:* Univ Pa, BA, 42; Swarthmore Col, MA, 50. *Hon Degrees:* DSc, Villanova Univ, 73. *Prof Exp:* Res asst astron, 42-51, res assoc, 52-72, lectr, 61-76, dir, 72-81, prof, 77-81, EMER PROF & EMER DIR, SPROUL OBSERV, SWARTHMORE COL, 81- *Concurrent Pos:* Fulbright fel, France, 53-54; Mem Fr solar eclipse exped to Oland, Sweden, 54; partic vis prof prog, Am Astron Soc, 61-; vpres comn 26, Int Astron Union, 70-73, pres, 73-76. *Mem:* Am Astron Soc; Int Astron Union; Sigma Xi. *Res:* Parallaxes of nearby stars; double stars; search for planetary companions to nearby stars; stellar masses; chromosphere studies; spicules. *Mailing Add:* 507 Cedar Lane Swarthmore PA 19081

LIPPITT, LOUIS, b New York, NY, Mar 19, 24; m 48; c 4. GEOPHYSICS. *Educ:* City Col New York, BS, 47; Columbia Univ, MA, 53, PhD(geol), 59. *Prof Exp:* Physicist, Columbia Univ, 47-50 & NY Univ, 51-53; geologist, Standard Oil Co Calif, 54-58; GEOPHYSICIST & RES STAFF ENGR, LOCKHEED MISSILES & SPACE CO, 58- *Concurrent Pos:* Instr, Allan Hancock Col, 69- *Mem:* Geol Soc Am; Am Geophys Union; Soc Explor Geophys. *Res:* Satellite systems; geophysical exploration. *Mailing Add:* Lockheed Missiles & Space Co Box 1506 Vandenberg AFB CA 93437

LIPPKE, HAGEN, b Yorktown, Tex, Nov 4, 36; m 58; c 3. ANIMAL NUTRITION. *Educ:* Tex A&M Univ, BS, 59, MS, 61; Iowa State Univ, PhD(animal nutrit), 66. *Prof Exp:* From asst prof to assoc prof ruminant nutrit, 66-74, ASSOC PROF ANIMAL SCI, TEX A&M UNIV, 74- *Mem:* Am Dairy Sci Asn; Am Soc Animal Sci. *Res:* Ruminant nutrition; forage utilization by cattle; forage characteristics influencing intake and digestibility. *Mailing Add:* Dept of Animal Sci Tex A&M Univ College Station TX 77843

LIPPMAN, ALFRED, JR, b New Orleans, La, Mar 13, 08; m 34; c 3. CHEMICAL ENGINEERING. *Educ:* Tulane Univ, BE, 29. *Prof Exp:* Res chemist, Bay Chem Co, Inc, 29-31; sales rep, Chem Rubber Co, Ohio, 31-34; asst chief assayer, US Mint, La, 32-33; chief chemist, Bay Chem Div, Morton Salt Co, 34-37, from asst supt to mgr, 37-51; gen mgr, Commonwealth Eng Co, Ohio, 51-52; plant mgr, Godchaux Sugars, Inc, 53-56; staff asst to gen mgr, Alumina Div, Reynolds Metals Co, Ark, 56-58, gen dir, Alumina Res Div, 58-71; sr vpres & dir res & develop, Toth Aluminum Corp, New Orleans, 71-80. *Mem:* Fel Am Ceramic Soc; Am Chem Soc; Am Inst Chem Engrs; Am Inst Mining, Metall & Petrol Engrs; Nat Soc Prof Engrs. *Res:* New uses for hydrogen chloride and common salt; utilization of natural gas and agricultural residues as chemical raw material; manufacturing sugar from cane; refining raw sugar; manufacture of heavy and organic chemicals; products and processes for manufacture and use of aluminas and alumina hydrates. *Mailing Add:* 4613 Purdue Dr Metairie LA 70003

LIPPMAN, GARY EDWIN, b Little Rock, Ark. MATHEMATICAL ANALYSIS. *Educ:* San Jose State Col, BA, 63; Univ Calif, Riverside, MA, 65, PhD(math), 70; Univ San Francisco, JD, 78. *Prof Exp:* Asst prof math, Kenyon Col, 70-71; ASSOC PROF MATH, CALIF STATE UNIV, HAYWARD, 71- *Concurrent Pos:* Vis asst prof math, Univ Tenn, vis assoc prof comput sci & statist, Univ RI, 78-79. *Mem:* Am Math Soc; Math Asn Am; Comput Law Soc. *Res:* Fourier analysis. *Mailing Add:* Dept of Math Calif State Univ Hayward CA 94542

LIPPMAN, MARC ESTES, b New York, NY, Jan 15, 45; div; c 2. ONCOLOGY, ENDOCRINOLOGY. *Educ:* Cornell Univ, BA, 64; Yale Univ, MD, 68. *Prof Exp:* Resident & intern med, Osler Serv, Johns Hopkins Hosp, 68-70; clin assoc oncol, Leukemia Serv, Nat Cancer Inst, 70-71, clin assoc biochem, Biochem Lab, 71-73; fel endocrinol, Yale Med Sch, 73-74; SR INVESTR ONCOL, MED BR, NAT CANCER INST, 74-, HEAD, BREAST CANCER SECT, 76- *Concurrent Pos:* Mem, Breast Cancer Task Force, 76- & Vet Admin Med Res Serv Merit Review Bd, 78- *Honors & Awards:* Mallinkrodt Prize, Clin Radioassay Soc, 78. *Mem:* Fel Am Col Physicians; Am Soc Clin Oncol; Endocrine Soc; Am Asn Cancer Res; Am Soc Cell Biol. *Res:* Hormonal regulation of human neoplasia in clinical and laboratory studies. *Mailing Add:* Med Br 10/6B02 NIH Bethesda MD 20014

LIPPMANN, DAVID ZANGWILL, b Houston, Tex, July 6, 25; m 69. PHYSICAL CHEMISTRY. *Educ:* Univ Tex, BSc, 47, MA, 49; Univ Calif, Berkeley, PhD(phys chem), 53. *Prof Exp:* Chemist, Reaction Motors, Inc, 54-57, Fulton-Irgon Div, Lithium Corp Am, 57-61 & Proteus, Inc, 61-63; asst prof, 63-69, ASSOC PROF CHEM, SOUTHWEST TEX STATE UNIV, 69- *Mem:* Am Chem Soc. *Res:* Theoretical physical chemistry, especially thermodynamics and statistical mechanics; rocketry and ballistics; properties of gems. *Mailing Add:* Dept of Chem Southwest Tex State Univ San Marcos TX 78666

LIPPMANN, HEINZ ISRAEL, b Breslau, Ger, May 21, 08; nat US; m 36; c 3. MEDICINE. *Educ:* Univ Freiburg, BA, 26; Univ Berlin, MD, 31; Univ Genoa, MD, 33. *Prof Exp:* From asst prof to prof, 55-76, EMER PROF REHAB MED, ALBERT EINSTEIN COL MED, 76- *Concurrent Pos:* Assoc attend physician, Montefiore Hosp, Bronx, 44-; lectr, Columbia Univ, 46-62; chief phys med, Workman's Circle Home for Aged, 51-; chief peripheral vascular clin, Sydney Hillman Health Ctr, 51-67; chief peripheral vascular clin & vis physician, Bronx Munic Hosp Ctr, 56-; chief attend physician, Brace Clin, 57-67, chief peripheral vascular clin, 57-, dir amputee ctr, 61-76; consult peripheral vascular dis, Englewood Hosp, NJ & Vet Admin Hosp, East Orange, NJ, 67-; dir rehab med, Jewish Hosp & Rehab Ctr, Jersey City, 74-81; attend physician & chief, Rehab Med Dept, Barnert Mem Hosp, Paterson, NJ, 75- *Honors & Awards:* NAm Roentgen Soc Award, 58; Gold Medal Sci Exhibit, Am Cong Rehab Med, 59. *Mem:* Am Heart Asn; fel Am Col Physicians; Am Cong Rehab Med; NY Acad Sci; Am Acad Phys Med & Rehab. *Res:* Vascular physiology; peripheral vascular diseases; prosthetics; rheumatology. *Mailing Add:* Dept of Med Albert Einstein Col of Med New York NY 10461

LIPPMANN, IRWIN, b New York, NY, Dec 30, 30; m 56; c 3. PHARMACEUTICAL CHEMISTRY. *Educ:* Rutgers Univ, BS, 52, MS, 56; Univ Mich, PhD(pharmaceut chem), 60. *Prof Exp:* Instr anal chem, Rutgers Univ, 55-56; Am Found Pharmaceut Educ fel, 56-59; sr res pharmacist, Squibb Inst Med Res, 59-62; asst prof pharm, Med Col Va, 64-65; res assoc, 62-74, assoc dir, 74-79, DIR BIOPHARMACEUT RES, A H ROBINS CO, INC, 79- *Mem:* Am Pharmaceut Asn; Am Chem Soc. *Res:* Biopharmaceutics-pharmacokinetics; in vitro--in vivo correlations; sustained-action drugs; physical pharmacy. *Mailing Add:* A H Robins Co Inc 1211 Sherwood Ave Richmond VA 23220

LIPPMANN, MARCELO JULIO, b Buenos Aires, Arg, May 27, 39; m 65; c 1. GEOLOGICAL ENGINEERING, HYDROLOGY. *Educ:* Univ Buenos Aires, MS, 66; Univ Calif, Berkeley, MS, 69, PhD(eng sci), 74. *Prof Exp:* Asst geologist, Arg Geol Serv, 63-66, sedimentologist, 66-67; asst res eng, Dept Civil Eng, Univ Calif, Berkeley, 74-76; res eng geothermics, 76-80, STAFF SCIENTIST, EARTH SCI DIV, LAWRENCE BERKELEY LAB, 80- *Concurrent Pos:* Consult hydrogeologist, Hidrosud SA, Buenos Aires, 67; US tech coordr, Dept Energy, Comn Federal de Electricidad, 77-; Jane Lewis fel, Univ Calif, Berkeley, 69-71. *Mem:* Am Geophys Union. *Res:* Geothermal and groundwater resources; physics and numerical modeling of processes in porous media. *Mailing Add:* Lawrence Berkeley Lab Earth Sci Div Berkeley CA 94720

LIPPMANN, MORTON, b Brooklyn, NY, Sept 21, 32; m 56; c 3. ENVIRONMENTAL HEALTH. *Educ:* Cooper Union, BChE, 54; Harvard Univ, SM, 55; NY Univ, PhD(indust hyg), 67. *Prof Exp:* Indust hygienist, USPHS, Ohio, 55-57; indust hygienist, US AEC, NY, 57-62; sr res engr, Del Electronics Corp, 62-64; assoc res scientist aerosol physiol, 64-67, asst prof, 67-70, assoc prof, 70-77, PROF ENVIRON MED & DIR, AEROSOL & INHALATION RES LAB, INST ENVIRON MED, NY UNIV, 77- *Mem:* Am Conf Govt Indust Hygienists; Am Indust Hyg Asn; NY Acad Sci. *Res:* Environmental hygiene; regional deposition and clearance of inhaled particles; sampling and analysis of atmospheric particles; aerodynamic behavior of respirable aerosols. *Mailing Add:* NY Univ Inst of Environ Med 550 First Ave New York NY 10016

LIPPMANN, SEYMOUR A, b Brooklyn, NY, Nov 23, 19; m 45; c 3. APPLIED PHYSICS. *Educ:* Cooper Union, BChE, 42. *Prof Exp:* Group leader appl physics, Res Dept, US Rubber Co, 47-60, dept mgr phys res, 60-71, res assoc, 71-75, MGR TIRE-VEHICLE SYSTEMS LABS, UNIROYAL TIRE COMPANY, UNIROYAL INC, 75- *Mem:* Am Phys Soc; Fel Soc Automotive Eng; Inst Elec & Electronics Eng; Am Soc Testing & Mat; Sigma Xi. *Res:* Physics of polymeric materials; transmission of noise and vibrations; design of electronic instrumentation for the study of dynamic systems and properties; perception of sound in the presence of background noise; dynamics of the human as a link in control systems; mechanics of laminates and tires. *Mailing Add:* Tire Tech Ctr Uniroyal Inc 1305 Stephenson Hwy Troy MI 48084

LIPPMANN, WILBUR, b Galveston, Tex, Sept 6, 30. BIOCMEMICAL PHARMACOLOGY. *Educ:* Tex A&M Col, BS, 51; Univ Tex, MA, 56, PhD(biochem), 61. *Prof Exp:* Res biochemist, Biochem Inst, Univ Tex, 54-56, 58-62; res biochemist, Virus Inst, Univ Calif, Berkeley, 56-58; res biochemist, Univ Tex M D Anderson Hosp & Tumor Inst, 58; res biochemist, Lederle Labs, Am Cyanamid Co, NY, 62-66; head biogenic amine lab, 66-69, DIR DEPT BIOCHEM PHARMACOL, AYERST LABS, CAN, 69- *Concurrent Pos:* Fel, Univ Tex, 61-62. *Mem:* AAAS; Am Chem Soc; Am Soc Pharmacol & Exp Therapeut; Pharmacol Soc Can; NY Acad Sci. *Res:* Biosynthesis and mode of action of the biogenic amines; biochemical mechanisms of action of drugs with respect to cardiovascular, central nervous and gastrointestinal systems; biochemical mechanisms involved with gonadotrophin secretion. *Mailing Add:* Ayerst Labs 1025 Laurentien Blvd Montreal PQ H3C 3J1 Can

LIPPS, B(EN) J, chemical engineering, see previous edition

LIPPS, EMMA LEWIS, b Alexandria, Va, Feb 8, 19. PLANT ECOLOGY. *Educ:* Wesleyan Col, BA, 40; Emory Univ, MS, 49; Univ Tenn, Knoxville, PhD, 66. *Prof Exp:* Asst biol, Agnes Scott Col, 42-43; from asst to assoc prof, 43-62, dir NSF in-serv insts, 58-61, PROF LIFE & EARTH SCI, SHORTER COL, GA, 62-, CUR LIFE & EARTH SCI, MUS, 70- *Concurrent Pos:* Asst, Univ Tenn, 55-56; Southern Fel Fund fel, 61-62. *Mem:* AAAS; Sigma Xi; Ecol Soc Am; Nat Speleol Soc; Soc Vertebrate Paleont. *Res:* Relationship of present and primeval forests of northwest Georgia to geology and soils, especially the Marshall forest; northwestern Georgia's Pleistocene fossils. *Mailing Add:* Dept Life & Earth Sci Shorter Col Rome GA 30161

LIPPS, FREDERICK WIESSNER, b Baltimore, Md, Feb 18, 29; m 69; c 3. THEORETICAL PHYSICS, MATHEMATICS. *Educ:* Johns Hopkins Univ, AB, 50, PhD(theoret physics), 56. *Prof Exp:* Meson physics, Lorentz Inst, Holland, 56-57; physicst, cesium-clock, Nat Co, Mass, 57-59, cesium-rocket, Electro- Optical Systs, Calif, 60-63, fusion, Hughes Aircraft Co, DC, 63-64 & Apollo, TRW Syst Inc, 66-69; asst prof math, Tex Southern Univ, 71-73; RES SCIENTIST SOLAR ENERGY, ENERGY LAB, UNIV HOUSTON, 73- *Concurrent Pos:* Adj assoc prof, Physics Dept, Univ Houston, 77- *Mem:* Am Phys Soc; Am Math Soc; Int Solar Energy Soc; Math Asn Am; Sigma Xi. *Res:* Computer simulation of solar central receiver system optics; computer program development including innovations for shading and blocking, image formation and optimization. *Mailing Add:* Energy Lab Univ of Houston Houston TX 77004

LIPPS, JERE HENRY, b Los Angeles, Calif, Aug 28, 39; m 73; c 1. GEOLOGY, INVERTEBRATE PALEONTOLOGY. *Educ:* Univ Calif, Los Angeles, AB, 62, PhD(geol), 66. *Prof Exp:* Asst res geologist invert paleont, Calif Res Corp, 63-65; res geologist, Univ Calif, Los Angeles, 65-67; from asst prof to assoc prof, 67-75, PROF GEOL, UNIV CALIF, DAVIS & BODEGA MARINE LAB, 75-, RES GEOLOGIST, 67- *Concurrent Pos:* Res assoc, Los Angeles County Mus, 63-; guest prof, Aarhus Univ, Denmark, 77; prin invest, NSF grants, 68-79. *Mem:* Fel AAAS; Geol Soc Am; Paleont Soc; Am Naturalists; Soc Econ Paleont & Mineral. *Res:* Ecology of Cenozoic Foraminifera; evolutionary biology of protists; marine ecology. *Mailing Add:* Dept of Geol Univ of Calif Davis CA 95616

LIPPSON, ROBERT LLOYD, b Detroit, Mich, Apr 18, 31; m 72; c 7. MARINE BIOLOGY. *Educ:* Mich State Univ, BS, 63, MS, 64, PhD(zool), 75. *Prof Exp:* Res biologist, Chesapeake Biol Lab, Univ Md, 68-71; fisheries biologist, 71-73; asst coordr water resources, 73-75, res coordr, Environ Assessment Div, Oxford Lab, 75-81, res coordr, Habitat Protection Br, 81, LIAISON OFFFFICER, NORTHEAST REGION, OXFORD LAB, NAT MARINE FISHERIES SERV, 76- *Concurrent Pos:* Adj prof zool, Mich State Univ. *Mem:* Estuarine Res Fedn; Atlantic Estuarine Res Soc; Sigma Xi. *Res:* Population dynamics and physiological-ecology of crustacea. *Mailing Add:* Oxford Lab Nat Marine Fisheries Serv Oxford MA 21654

LIPS, HILAIRE JOHN, b Can, July 20, 18; m 46; c 5. CHEMISTRY. *Educ:* Univ BC, BA, 38, MA, 40; McGill Univ, PhD(agr chem), 44. *Prof Exp:* BIOCHEMIST & FOOD INFO OFFICER, NAT RES COUN CAN, 43- *Mem:* Am Oil Chem Soc. *Res:* Fats; oils; foods. *Mailing Add:* Nat Res Coun of Canada Ottawa ON K1N 6NS Can

LIPSCHULTZ, FREDERICK PHILLIP, b Los Angeles, Calif, Aug 27, 37. PHYSICS. *Educ:* Stanford Univ, BS, 59; Cornell Univ, PhD(physics), 66. *Prof Exp:* Res assoc physics, Cornell Univ, 62-65; fel, Brookhaven Nat Lab, 65-67; asst prof, 67-72, ASSOC PROF PHYSICS, UNIV CONN, 72- *Concurrent Pos:* Vis fel physics, Univ Nottingham, 76-77. *Mem:* AAAS; Am Phys Soc; Inst Elec & Electronic Engrs. *Res:* Thermal conductivity; low temperature physics; ultrasonics; use of thermal and acoustic properties of materials to investigate microscopic defects in solids. *Mailing Add:* Dept of Physics U-46 Univ of Conn Storrs CT 06268

LIPSCHUTZ, MICHAEL ELAZAR, b Philadelphia, Pa, May 24, 37; m 59; c 3. INORGANIC CHEMISTRY, COSMOCHEMISTRY. *Educ:* Pa State Univ, BS, 58; Univ Chicago, SM, 60, PhD(phys chem), 62. *Prof Exp:* NSF and NATO fel, Physics Inst, Berne, 64-65; asst prof chem, 65-68, asst prof geosci, 67-68, assoc prof chem, 68-73, prof chem & geosci, 73-78, PROF CHEM, PURDUE UNIV, 73- *Concurrent Pos:* Nininger meteorite res award, 62; Fulbright-Hays scholar, Tel Aviv Univ, 71-72; consult, NASA, 73- & Lunar Planeterium Inst, 81- *Mem:* AAAS; Am Geophys Union; Meteoritical Soc (treas, 79-); Geochem Soc; Am Chem Soc. *Res:* Neutron activation and atomic absorption methods for trace and ultratrace analysis; geochemistry; stable isotopes in lunar samples and meteorites; cosmogenic nuclear reactions; high pressure and temperature reactions. *Mailing Add:* Dept of Chem Purdue Univ West Lafayette IN 47907

LIPSCOMB, DAVID M, b Morrill, Nebr, Aug 4, 35; m 78; c 3. AUDIOLOGY. *Educ:* Univ Redlands, BA, 57, MA, 59; Univ Wash, PhD(audiol), 66. *Prof Exp:* Asst prof audiol, WTex State Univ, 60-62; asst prof, 62-64 & 66-69, assoc prof, 69-72, PROF AUDIOL & SPEECH PATH, UNIV TENN, KNOXVILLE, 72-, DIR, NOISE RES LAB, 71- *Concurrent Pos:* Consult, various industs & attorneys. *Mem:* Fel Am Speech & Hearing Asn; Acoust Soc Am. *Res:* Effect of high intensity noise upon the peripheral auditory mechanism. *Mailing Add:* Dept Audiol & Speech Path Univ Tenn Knoxville TN 37916

LIPSCOMB, ELIZABETH LOIS, b Hackensack, NJ, Nov 25, 27; m 49; c 1. BIOCHEMISTRY. *Educ:* Duke Univ, BS, 49; Univ Pittsburgh, MS, 51; NC State Univ, PhD(biochem), 73. *Prof Exp:* RES ASSOC BIOCHEM, NC STATE UNIV, 73- *Mem:* Sigma Xi; NY Acad Sci. *Res:* Catalytic and structural characteristics of the branched-chain amino acid aminotransferase of Salmonella typhimurium; creative application of techniques to elucidate the amino acid sequence is stressed. *Mailing Add:* Dept Biochem NC State Univ Raleigh NC 27607

LIPSCOMB, JOHN DEWALD, b Wilmington, Del, Apr 16, 47; m 72. BIOCHEMISTRY. *Educ:* Amherst Col, BA, 69; Univ Ill, MS, 71, PhD(biochem), 74. *Prof Exp:* Fel, Freshwater Biol Inst, 75-77, ASST PROF BIOCHEM, DEPT BIOCHEM, UNIV MINN, 77- *Concurrent Pos:* Prin investr, NIH res grant, 78- *Mem:* Am Chem Soc; Sigma Xi; Am Soc Biol Chemists. *Res:* Enzyme mechanisms, in particular metalloenzymes such as dioxygenases, cytochrome P450, iron-sulfur proteins; resonance spectroscopy; chemical modification reactions. *Mailing Add:* 4-225 Millard Hall Univ of Minn Minneapolis MN 55455

LIPSCOMB, NATHAN THORNTON, b Jan 16, 34; US citizen; m 62; c 2. POLYMER CHEMISTRY. *Educ:* Eastern Ky State Col, BS, 56; Univ Louisville, PhD(phys chem), 60. *Prof Exp:* From asst prof to assoc prof, 60-75, PROF CHEM, UNIV LOUISVILLE, 75- *Mem:* Am Chem Soc; Sigma Xi. *Res:* Kinetics of polymerization; radiation induced polymerization; polymer characterization; polymer properties. *Mailing Add:* Dept of Chem Univ of Louisville Louisville KY 40292

LIPSCOMB, PAUL ROGERS, b Clio, SC, Mar 23, 14; m 40; c 2. ORTHOPEDIC SURGERY. *Educ:* Univ SC, BS, 35; Med Col, SC, MD, 38; Univ Minn, MS, 42; Am Bd Orthop Surg, dipl. *Prof Exp:* Intern, Cooper Hosp, NJ, 38-39; resident orthop surg, Mayo Found, Univ Minn, 39-42, from asst prof to prof, 49-69; prof orthop, Surg & Chem Dept, Sch Med, Univ Calif, Davis, 69-81. *Concurrent Pos:* Consult, Mayo Clin, Minn, St Mary's Hosp Methodist Hosp, 42-69; David Grant US Air Force Med Ctr, Travis AFB, Calif, 70-, Letterman Gen Hosp, Presidio, San Francisco, 72- & Woodland Clinic, Woodland, Calif, 81-; secy, Am Bd Orthop Surg, 68, pres, 71-73. *Mem:* Clin Orthop Soc; AMA; Am Col Surg; Am Acad Orthop Surg; Am Orthop Asn (pres, 74-75). *Res:* Surgery of the hand. *Mailing Add:* Dept of Orthop Surg Univ of Calif Sch of Med Davis CA 95616

LIPSCOMB, ROBERT DEWALD, b Tulia, Tex, Dec 29, 17; m 43; c 2. ORGANIC CHEMISTRY. *Educ:* Univ Nebr, BS, 40, MS, 41; Univ Ill, PhD(org chem), 44. *Prof Exp:* Lab asst chem, Univ Nebr, 40-41; spec asst, Univ Ill, 41-42, investr, Off Sci Res & Develop & Nat Defense Res Comt, 42-44 & Univ Nebr, 44-45; RES CHEMIST, E I DU PONT DE NEMOURS & CO, 45- *Mem:* Am Chem Soc. *Res:* Chemistry of quinoline and benzoquinoline derivatives; amine bisulfites; organic polysulfides; free radicals; high temperature chemistry; polymerization. *Mailing Add:* Cent Res Dept E I du Pont de Nemours & Co Wilmington DE 19898

LIPSCOMB, WILLIAM NUNN, JR, b Cleveland, Ohio, Dec 9, 19; m 44; c 2. PHYSICAL CHEMISTRY. *Educ:* Univ Ky, BS, 41; Calif Inst Technol, PhD(phys chem), 46. *Hon Degrees:* DSc, Univ Ky, 63; MA, Harvard Univ, 59; Drhc, Munich, 75; DSc, Long Island Univ, 77, Rutgers Univ, 79, Gustavus Adolphus Col, 80, Marietta Col, 81. *Prof Exp:* Asst prof phys chem, Univ Minn, 46-50, assoc prof & actg chief div, 50-54, prof & chief, 54-59; prof, 59-71, chmn dept chem, 62-65, ABBOTT & JAMES LAWRENCE PROF CHEM, HARVARD UNIV, 71- *Concurrent Pos:* Guggenheim fel, Oxford, 54-55 & Cambridge, 72-73; NSF sr fel, 65-66; Mem nat comt crystallog, Nat Res Coun, 54-58, 60-63 & 65-67; mem rev comt, Chem Div, Argonne Nat Lab, 56-65; grants, Off Naval Res, 58-77, Off Ord Res, 54-56, NSF, 56-65 & 77-78, Air Force Off Sci Res, 58-64, NIH, 54-85, Upjohn Co, 58 & Adv Res Projs Agency, 61-73; distinguished lectr, Howard Univ & Welch Found lectr, Univ Tex, 66; Phillips lectr, Univ Okla, 67; Priestley lectr, Pa State Univ, 67;

William Pyle Phillips lectr, Haverford Col, 68; Baker lectr, Cornell Univ & Coover lectr, Iowa State Univ, 69; Nieuwland lectr, Univ Notre Dame & Am Cyanamid lectr, Univ Conn, 70; Mem nat comt crystallog, Nat Res Coun, 54-58, 60-63, 65-67; Harvard lectr, Yale, 72; Centenary lect, Chem Soc, 72; Weizmann lectr, Rehovoth Israel, 74; Van'tHoff Centenary commemoration lectr, Univ Leiden, 74; Gilbert Newton Lewis mem lectr, Berkeley, 74; Renaud lectr, Mich State Univ, 75; Dreyfus distinguished scholar, Univ Chicago, 80; Probst lectr, Southern Ill Univ at Edwardsville, 80; speaker/session chmn, Conf Quantum Chem in Biomed Sci, NY Acad Sci, 80; Dreyfus distinguished scholar-lectr, Univ Southern Calif, Los Angeles, 80; John Stauffer Mem lectr, Univ Southern Calif, Los Angeles, 80; invited lectr and speaker at many univs throughout the world. *Honors & Awards:* Nobel Prize in Chem, 76; Howe Award, Am Chem Soc, 58. Distinguished Serv Award, Am Chem Soc, 68; George Ledlie Prize, Harvard Univ, 71; Peter Debye Award, Phys Chem, Am Chem Soc, 73; Evans Award, Ohio State Univ, 74; Remsen Award, Maryland Sect, Am Chem Soc, 76. *Mem:* Nat Acad Sci; Am Phys Soc; Am Chem Soc; Am Crystallog Asn (pres, 55); fel Am Acad Arts & Sci. *Res:* Diffraction studies of crystals and molecules of biochemical interest. *Mailing Add:* Dept Chem Harvard Univ 12 Oxford St Cambridge MA 02138

LIPSETT, FREDERICK ROY, b Vancouver, BC, Can, Sept 26, 25; m 57; c 2. FORENSIC SCIENCE, CRYSTAL CROWTH. *Educ:* Univ BC, BApSc, 48, MApSc, 51; Univ London, PhD(physics), 54. *Prof Exp:* SR RES OFFICER ELEC ENG DIV, NAT RES COUN CAN, 54- *Concurrent Pos:* Part time lectr, Carleton Univ, Can, 62-64. *Mem:* Catgut Acoustical Soc; Am Asn Crystal Growth; AAAS. *Res:* Luminescence of organic solids; analysis and computer simulation of police patrol operations; floating zone crystal growth. *Mailing Add:* 37 Oriole Dr Ottawa ON K1J 7E8 Can

LIPSETT, MARIE NIEFT, b Chicago, Ill, Aug 10, 20; m 48; c 2. BIOLOGICAL CHEMISTRY. *Educ:* Northwestern Univ, BS, 41, MS, 43; Univ Southern Calif, PhD(biochem), 48. *Prof Exp:* Fel, US Pub Health Serv, Univ Calif, Los Angeles, 48-50; res assoc exp med, Univ Southern Calif, 50-53 & Sloan-Kettering Inst, 55-57; CHEMIST, NAT INST ARTHRITIS & METAB DIS, NAT INSTS HEALTH, 58- *Mem:* AAAS; Am Soc Biol Chem. *Res:* Interactions of polynucleotides and related compounds; immunochemistry of enzymes; natural thionucleotides. *Mailing Add:* Nat Inst of Arthritis & Metab Dis Nat Insts of Health Bethesda MD 20014

LIPSETT, MORTIMER BROADWIN, b New York, NY, Feb 20, 21; m 74; c 2. INTERNAL MEDICINE. *Educ:* Univ Calif, AB, 43; Univ Southern Calif, MS, 47, MD, 51; Am Bd Internal Med, dipl. *Prof Exp:* Res assoc, Univ Southern Calif, 46-47; intern, Los Angeles County Hosp, Calif, 51-52; resident internal med, Sawtelle Hosp, 52-54; USPHS fel & asst mem, Sloan-Kettering Inst, 54-57; mem staff endocrinol br, Nat Cancer Inst, 57-65, chief, 66-70; assoc sci dir reprod biol, Nat Inst Child Health & Human Develop, 70-74; prof med, Sch Med, Case Western Reserve Univ & dir, Cancer Ctr, Northeast Ohio, 74-76; ASSOC DIR CLIN CARE & DIR CLIN CTR, NIH, 76- *Concurrent Pos:* Instr, Sch Med, Cornell Univ, 56-57; sr assoc attend physician, Freedman's Hosp, 58-73; mem, Cleveland Clin; ed-in-chief, J Clin Endocrinol & Metab, 68-73. *Mem:* Endocrine Soc (pres, 78-79); Am Asn Cancer Res; Am Soc Clin Invest; Asn Am Physicians; fel Am Col Physicians. *Res:* Endocrinology; oncology; reproductive biology. *Mailing Add:* Bldg 10 Rm 1N-212 NIH Bethesda MD 20014

LIPSEY, SALLY IRENE, b Dec 31, 26; US citizen; m 48; c 3. MATHEMATICS EDUCATION. *Educ:* Hunter Col, AB, 47; Univ Wis, AM, 48; Columbia Univ, DEduc, 65. *Prof Exp:* Asst, Dept Math, Univ Wis, 47-48; high sch teacher, Bd Educ, New York, 48-49; lectr, Hunter Col, 49-53 & Barnard Col, 53-59; asst prof, Bronx Community Col, 59-65; asst prof educ, 65-71, asst prof, 71-78, ASSOC PROF MATH, BROOKLYN COL, 78- *Mem:* Nat Coun Teachers Math; Math Asn Am. *Mailing Add:* Dept of Math Brooklyn Col Brooklyn NY 11210

LIPSHITZ, STANLEY PAUL, b Cape Town, SAfrica, Nov 25, 43. APPLIED MATHEMATICS. *Educ:* Univ Natal, BSc, 64; Univ SAfrica, MSc, 65; Univ Witwatersrand, PhD(math), 70. *Prof Exp:* Vis lectr math, Univ Ariz, 67-68; ASST PROF APPL MATH, UNIV WATERLOO, 70- *Mem:* Am Math Soc; Audio Eng Soc. *Res:* Calculus of variations and applications to physical field theories; constrained variational problems; canonical formalisms; mathematical problems of audio and electroacoustics. *Mailing Add:* Dept of Appl Math Univ of Waterloo Waterloo ON N2L 3G1 Can

LIPSHULTZ, LARRY I, b Philadelphia, Pa, Apr 24, 42; m 66; c 2. UROLOGY. *Educ:* Franklin & Marshall Col, BS, 60; Univ Pa, MD, 68. *Prof Exp:* Asst instr urol, Univ Pa, 73-74, instr, 74-75; asst prof & clin fel reprod med, 75-77, assoc prof, 77-80, PROF UROL, UNIV TEX MED BR, HOUSTON, 80- *Concurrent Pos:* Res scholar, Am Urol Asn, 75-77; adj asst prof urol, Baylor Col Med, 76- *Mem:* Am Fertil Soc; Am Soc Andrology; Am Urol Asn; Soc Univ Urol. *Res:* The evaluation and diagnosis of reproductive disorders in the male, especially in the field of infertility; androgen binding protein in the human testis and epididymis and evaluation of androgen binding protein as a possible marker of sertoli cell function. *Mailing Add:* Univ of Tex Med Sch 6431 Fannin Suite 6018 MSMB Houston TX 77030

LIPSHUTZ, NELSON RICHARD, b Phila, Pa, July 14, 42; m 64; c 2. OPERATIONS RESEARCH, HIGH ENERGY PHYSICS. *Educ:* Univ Pa, AB, 62, MBA, 72; Univ Chicago, SM, 63, PhD(physics), 67. *Prof Exp:* Res assoc physics, Univ Chicago, 67; from instr to asst prof, Duke Univ, 67-70; mgt res analyst, Mgt & Behav Sci Ctr, Wharton Sch Finance & Commerce, Univ Pa, 70-72; MGT CONSULT, ARTHUR D LITTLE, INC, 72-; PRES, REGULATORY RES CORP, 77- *Mem:* Am Phys Soc; Inst Mgt Sci; AAAS; NY Acad Sci. *Res:* Theory of elementary particles; mathematical analysis of management decision problems; economic analysis of regulated industries. *Mailing Add:* 24 Radcliff Rd Regulatory Res Corp Waban MA 02168

LIPSICAS, MAX, b Tel-Aviv, Palestine, July 13, 25; m 64. CHEMISTRY, PHYSICS. *Educ:* Univ London, BSc, 50, BScEng, 51; Univ BC, PhD(physics), 60. *Prof Exp:* Physicist, Metrop-Vickers Elec Co, Eng, 51-57; asst res specialist, Dept Physics, Rutgers Univ, 61-63; assoc physicist, Brookhaven Nat Lab, 63-66; assoc prof chem, Yeshiva Univ, 66-69, actg chmn dept, 68-70, prof, Belfer Sch Sci, 69-78; MEM PROF STAFF, SCHLUMBERGER DOLL RES, 78- *Concurrent Pos:* Lectr & tutor, Postgrad Eng Course, Univ Manchester, 52-55; res collabr, Brookhaven Nat Lab. *Mem:* Am Phys Soc. *Res:* Nuclear magnetic resonance, including studies of gases and liquids; critical phenomena; electronic phase transitions; applications of spectroscopy to clay studies. *Mailing Add:* Schlumberger Doll Res PO Box 307 Ridgefield CT 06877

LIPSICH, H DAVID, b Pittsburgh, Pa, Feb 20, 20; m 46; c 2. MATHEMATICS. *Educ:* Univ Cincinnati, MA, 45, PhD(math), 49; Princeton Univ, MA, 46. *Prof Exp:* From instr to assoc prof, 46-61, vprovost, 67, head dept, 61-77, provost undergrad studies, 67-77, PROF MATH, UNIV CINCINNATI, 61-, DEAN, MCMICKEN COL ARTS & SCI, 77- *Concurrent Pos:* NSF fac fel, 59-60. *Mem:* Am Math Soc; Math Asn Am; Asn Symbolic Logic. *Res:* Mathematical logic; set theory. *Mailing Add:* Dept of Math Univ of Cincinnati Cincinnati OH 45221

LIPSIG, JOSEPH, b Brooklyn, NY, Dec 13, 30; m 60; c 1. PHYSICAL CHEMISTRY. *Educ:* Brooklyn Col, BA, 50; Polytech Inst Brooklyn, PhD(phys chem), 61. *Prof Exp:* Res assoc, Cornell Univ, 60-62; sr res chemist, Atlantic Ref Co, 62-66; asst prof, 66-68, ASSOC PROF CHEM, STATE UNIV NY COL OSWEGO, 68- *Mem:* Am Chem Soc. *Res:* Catalysis; geochemistry; chemical kinetics; electrochemistry. *Mailing Add:* Dept of Chem State Univ of NY Oswego NY 13126

LIPSITT, DON RICHARD, b Boston, Mass, Nov 24, 27; m 53; c 2. PSYCHIATRY, PSYCHOANALYSIS. *Educ:* NY Univ, BA, 49; Boston Univ, MA, 50; Univ Vt, MD, 56; Boston Psychoanal Soc & Inst, cert. 69. *Prof Exp:* Asst, 62-65, from instr to asst prof, 65-74, ASSOC PROF PSYCHIAT, HARVARD MED SCH, 74-; CHIEF PSYCHIAT, MT AUBURN HOSP, CAMBRIDGE, 69- *Concurrent Pos:* Teaching fel psychiat, Harvard Med Sch, 60-62; Dept Health, Educ & Welfare res grant, 66-68; head integration clin, Beth Israel Hosp, Boston, 62-69, asst psychiat, 62-64, assoc, 64-66, dir med psychol liaison serv, 66-69; consult behav sci, Lincoln Lab, Mass Inst Technol, 69-73; mem fac, Boston Psychoanal Soc & Inst, 71-72, 81-, adj prof, Sch Social Work, Simmons Col, 71-; consult, Dept Psychiat, Cambridge Hosp, 71-; consult psychiatrist, McLean Hosp, 71-; ed, Int J Psychiat Med, 70-79, Gen Hosp Psychiat, 79-; consult, NIMH, 74-80; fac div primary care & family med, Harvard Med Sch, 77- *Mem:* Am Psychiat Asn; Am Psychosom Soc; Asn Acad Psychiat; fel Am Col Psychiat; Am Asn Gen Hosp Psychiat. *Res:* Application of medical psychology to health problems in hospital and community; relationship of varieties of doctor-patient interaction to invalidism and chronicity; psychiatry and primary care; hypochondriasis; factitious illness. *Mailing Add:* 15 Griggs Rd Brookline MA 02238

LIPSITT, HARRY A(LLAN), b Detroit, Mich, June 7, 31; m 56; c 4. PHYSICAL METALLURGY. *Educ:* Mich State Univ, BS, 52; Carnegie Inst Technol, MS, 55, PhD(metall), 56. *Prof Exp:* Asst metall, Carnegie Inst Technol, 52-53; proj scientist, Aerospace Res Lab, 56-60, supvr metall res, 60-75, SR SCIENTIST, AIR FORCE MAT LAB, WRIGHT-PATTERSON AFB, 75- *Concurrent Pos:* Instr, Univ Dayton, 57-58; sabbatical, Cambridge Univ, 63-64; adj prof, Air Force Inst Technol, 65-71; liaison scientist, Off Naval Res, London, Eng, 67-69; adj prof Eng, Wright State Univ, 76- *Honors & Awards:* Award, Aerospace Ed Found, 64. *Mem:* Am Inst Mining, Metall & Petrol Engrs. *Res:* Mechanical metallurgy, especially fatigue, creep, tension and hardness and properties of ceramics; diffusion and strain aging; photomicrography of ceramics; elasticity, precipitation hardening and electron microscopy. *Mailing Add:* 1414 Birch St Yellow Springs OH 45387

LIPSITZ, PAUL, b York, Pa, Apr 23, 23; m 48; c 4. ORGANIC CHEMISTRY. *Educ:* Lebanon Valley Col, BS, 44; Univ Cincinnati, MS, 48, PhD(chem), 50. *Prof Exp:* Chemist, E I du Pont de Nemours & Co, 50-59; sr patent agent, Pennsalt Chems Corp, 59-69; SR PATENT AGT, PATENT & LICENCES DEPT, SUN VENTURES, INC, 69- *Mem:* Am Chem Soc; Am Inst Chem. *Mailing Add:* Sun Co Inc/Patents Dept 100 Matsonford Rd Bldg 2 Radnor PA 19087

• **LIPSITZ, PHILIP JOSEPH,** b Piketberg, SAfrica, May 17, 28; m 58; c 3. MEDICINE, PEDIATRICS. *Educ:* Univ Cape Town, MB, ChB, 52; Royal Col Physicians & Surgeons, dipl child health, 56; Am Bd Pediat, dipl, neonatal-perinatal med, cert. *Prof Exp:* House surgeon, Univ Cape Town, 52; house physician, Somerset Hosp, Cape Town, SAfrica, 53; resident surg house officer, Gen Hosp, Salisbury, SRhodesia, 53; Charles' house physician, St Hosp, London, Eng, 55; resident med officer, Banstead Br, Queen Elizabeth Hosp for Children, 56; house physician, Royal Hosp Sick Children, Edinburgh, Scotland, 56; registr, Prof Unit, Children's Hosp, Sheffield, Eng, 57-58; resident med officer, Red Cross War Mem Children's Hosp, Univ Cape Town, 58; consult Royal Col Physicians; with hosp appointments, Southwest Africa, 62-65; asst prof pediat, Med Col Ga, 65-67, assoc prof, 67-68; assoc prof, Beth Israel Med Ctr & Mt Sinai Sch Med, 68-73; prof pediat, Health Sci Ctr, State Univ NY Stony Brook, 73-75; dir pediat, South Shore Div, Long Island Jewish-Hillside Med Ctr, Far Rockaway, 73-74, PHYSICIAN-IN-CHG NEWBORN SERV, LONG ISLAND JEWISH-HILLSIDE MED CTR, NEW HYDE PARK, 74- *Concurrent Pos:* Fel pediat, Sch Med, Western Reserve Univ, 58-60; clin & res fel pediat & med, Children's Hosp Med Ctr, Harvard Med Sch, 60-61. *Mem:* Soc Pediat Res; NY Acad Sci; Am Acad Pediat. *Res:* Physiology of the newborn. *Mailing Add:* LI Jewish-Hillside Med Ctr 270-05 76th Ave New Hyde Park NY 11040

LIPSIUS, STEPHEN LLOYD, b NeW York, NY, Sept 25, 47. PHYSIOLOGY. *Educ:* State Univ NY, BA, 69, PhD(physiol), 75. *Prof Exp:* Teaching asst, Downstate Med Ctr, 70-75; res fel, 75-78; ASST PROF, DEPT PHYSIOL, LOYOLA UNIV, 78- *Concurrent Pos:* NIH fel, Univ Vt, 76-78. *Mem:* Int Study Group Res Cardiac Metab; Cardiac Electrophysiolic Soc. *Mailing Add:* Dept of Physiol 2160 S First Ave Maywood IL 60153

LIPSKY, JOSEPH ALBIN, b Glen Lyon, Pa, Mar 31, 30; m 57; c 2. PHYSIOLOGY. *Educ:* Pa State Univ, BSc, 51; Ohio State Univ, MSc, 59, PhD(physiol), 61. *Prof Exp:* From asst prof to assoc prof, 61-77, PROF PHYSIOL, COL MED, OHIO STATE UNIV, 77- *Concurrent Pos:* Consult to coun, Nat Bd Dent Exam, 67- *Mem:* AAAS; Fedn Am Socs Exp Biol; Am Physiol Soc. *Res:* Carbon dioxide transients and stores; hyperventilation. *Mailing Add:* Dept of Physiol Ohio State Univ Col of Med Columbus OH 43210

LIPSKY, SANFORD, b New York, NY, Jan 24, 30. PHYSICAL CHEMISTRY. *Educ:* Syracuse Univ, AB, 50; Univ Chicago, PhD(chem), 54. *Prof Exp:* Res assoc chem, Radiation Proj, Univ Notre Dame, 54-57; asst prof, NY Univ, 57-59; from asst prof to assoc prof, 59-67, PROF CHEM, UNIV MINN, MINNEAPOLIS, 67- *Mem:* Am Phys Soc; Am Chem Soc; Radiation Res Soc Am. *Res:* Photochemistry; photophysics; electron impact spectroscopy. *Mailing Add:* Dept of Chem Univ of Minn Minneapolis MN 55455

LIPSKY, SEYMOUR RICHARD, b New York, NY, Aug 5, 24; m 52; c 3. BIOCHEMISTRY, PHYSICAL CHEMISTRY. *Educ:* NY Univ, BA, 44; State Univ NY, MD, 49; Am Bd Internal Med, dipl, 56. *Prof Exp:* Fel, Univ Calif, 51-52; fel, 52-55, from instr to assoc prof, 55-68, PROF MED, SCH MED, YALE UNIV, 68-, DIR SECT PHYS SCI, 67- *Concurrent Pos:* Consult lunar sci subcomt & lunar & planetary prog comt, NASA, 61-62; biophys & biophys chem study sect, NIH, 64- & Nat Adv Heart Coun, Nat Heart Inst, 64-; mem postdoctoral fel comt, Nat Acad Sci, 65- *Honors & Awards:* Twsett Medal Chromatography, 82. *Mem:* Am Soc Biol Chem; Am Chem Soc; Am Soc Clin Invest. *Res:* Physical-chemical separation techniques; gas chromatography; mass spectrometry; ionization phenomena in gases; chemistry of membranes; analysis of planetary atmospheres; analysis of planetary surfaces for organic compounds; chemistry of macromolecules; nuclear magnetic resonance spectrometry; high performance liquid chromatography. *Mailing Add:* Sect of Phys Sci Yale Univ Sch of Med New Haven CT 06510

LIPSON, EDWARD DAVID, b Winnipeg, Man, Oct 27, 44; m 66; c 2. PHOTOBIOLOGY, SENSORY TRANSDUCTION. *Educ:* Univ Man, BSc, 66; Calif Inst Technol, PhD(physics), 71. *Prof Exp:* res fel biol, Calif Inst Technol, 71-74; sr res fel, 74-76; asst prof, 76-80, ASSOC PROF PHYSICS, SYRACUSE UNIV, 80- *Concurrent Pos:* Res fel, Alfred P Sloan Found, 79-83. *Mem:* Biophys Soc; Am Soc Phtobiol; Am Soc Photobiol; Am Phys Soc. *Res:* Light-growth responses of the microorganism, Phycomyces, with approaches from genetics, biochemistry and nonlinear systems theory, to elucidate the cellular and molecular mechanisms of sensory transduction and adaptation. *Mailing Add:* Dept Physics Syracuse Univ Syracuse NY 13210

LIPSON, HERBERT GEORGE, b Boston, Mass, July 4, 25; m 51; c 3. SOLID STATE PHYSICS. *Educ:* Mass Inst Technol, BS, 48; Northeastern Univ, MS, 64. *Prof Exp:* Jr physicist metall physics, Sylvania Elec Prods, Inc, 48-50; physicist, Brookhaven Nat Lab, 51; physicist, Naval Res Lab, 51-55; physicist, Lincoln Lab, Mass Inst Technol, 55-58; PHYSICIST, DEP ELECTRONIC TECHNOL, ROME AIR DEVELOP CTR, HANSCOM AFB, 58- *Mem:* Am Phys Soc; Sigma Xi; Am Soc Testing & Mat. *Res:* Optical properties of solids; lattice vibrations, impurities and plasma effects in semiconductors; laser and laser window material properties; infrared optical properties of impurities in quartz, radiation effects on quartz for radiation hardened oscillators. *Mailing Add:* 68 Aldrich Rd Wakefield MA 01880

LIPSON, JOSEPH, physics, see previous edition

LIPSON, MELVIN ALAN, b Providence, RI, June 1, 36; m 61; c 4. ORGANIC CHEMISTRY. *Educ:* Univ RI, BS, 57; Syracuse Univ, PhD(org chem), 63. *Prof Exp:* Res chemist, I C I (Organics) Inc, 63 & Eltex Res Corp, 63-64; res supvr org synthesis, Wayland Chem Div, Philip A Hunt Chem Corp, RI, 64-67; res mgr, 67-69; tech dir, 69-72, V PRES TECH OPERS, DYNACHEM CORP, 72- *Mem:* AAAS; Am Chem Soc; The Chem Soc. *Res:* Amino acids and peptides; chelating agents; photographic chemicals; surface active compounds; polymers; dyestuffs; carbohydrates; photopolymers; photoresists; electroless plating; corrosion inhibitors. *Mailing Add:* Dynachem Corp 2631 Michelle Dr Tustin CA 92680

LIPSON, RICHARD L, b Philadelphia, Pa, July 21, 31; c 2. RHEUMATOLOGY, INTERNAL MEDICINE. *Educ:* Lafayette Col, BA, 52; Jefferson Med Sch, MD, 56; Univ Minn, MSc, 60. *Prof Exp:* Res asst biophys, Mayo Clin & Mayo Found, 62-63; ASST PROF MED, COL MED, UNIV VT, 63- *Concurrent Pos:* Assoc dir rheumatism res unit, Univ Vt, 64-67. *Honors & Awards:* Arnold J Bergen Res Award, Mayo Found, 60. *Mem:* AMA; Am Fedn Clin Res; Am Rheumatism Asn; fel Am Col Physicians. *Res:* Biophysics and bionics of connective tissue, osmotic pressure, viscosity, electrogoniometry, biomechanics; fiber-optics instruments; cancer detection by fluorescence; fluorescent endoscopy; photosensitivity; rheumatology. *Mailing Add:* 233 Pearl St Burlington VT 05401

LIPSON, SAMUEL L(LOYD), b Odessa, Russia, July 30, 13; nat Can; m 44; c 3. STRUCTURAL ENGINEERING. *Educ:* Univ BC, BASc, 36; Calif Inst Technol, MS, 37. *Prof Exp:* Detailer, designer & estimator, Consol Steel Corp, 37-39, chief estimator, 40-46; designer, Mark Falk, Consult Engr, 39-40; assoc prof civil eng, 46-49, prof, 49-79, head dept, 70-79, EMER PROF CIVIL ENG, UNIV BC, 79- *Concurrent Pos:* Spec consult, Dominion Bridge Co, 51-67. *Mem:* Fel Am Soc Civil Engrs; Can Soc Civil Engrs; Eng Inst Can. *Res:* Composite construction of poured and precast concrete; plastic design; optimization of structural design. *Mailing Add:* 1420 W 45th Ave Vancouver BC V6M 2H1 Can

LIPSON, STEVEN MARK, b New York, NY, May 25, 45; m 71; c 2. LASER NEPHELOMETRY, CELL CULTURE. *Educ:* Long Island Univ, BS, 67; C W Post Col, MS, 72; NY Univ, PhD(biol), 82. *Prof Exp:* Teacher biol, Prospect Heights High Sch, 67-72; teaching fel biol, NY Univ, 74-75; technologist immunol, Mem Hosp, 75-76; teacher biol, Prospect Heights High Sch, 77-80; RES ASSOC, DEPT NEOPLASTIC DIS, MT SINAI MED CTR, 81- *Concurrent Pos:* Vis lectr microbiol, Adelphi Univ, 76; adj instr biol, Lincoln Ctr, Fordham Univ, 81-82. *Mem:* Am Soc Microbiol; Int Asn Water Pollution Res; Sigma Xi; AAAS. *Res:* Effect of polybrominated biphenyls on the in vitro synthesis of immunoglobulins; mechanisms involved in the adsorption of viruses to clay minerals. *Mailing Add:* 2364 E 74 St Brooklyn NY 11234

LIPTAI, ROBERT GEORGE, metallurgy, mechanics, see previous edition

LIPTAY, ALBERT, b Hampton, Ont, Nov 9, 41; m 67; c 3. HORTICULTURE, PLANT PHYSIOLOGY. *Educ:* Univ Guelph, BSA, 66, MSc, 67; McMaster Univ, PhD(biol), 72. *Prof Exp:* Lectr life sci, Conestoga Col, 72-73; asst prof biol, Camrose Lutheran Col, 73-74; RES SCIENTIST VEG MGT, AGR CAN, 74- *Mem:* Am Soc Hort Sci; Int Soc Hort Sci; Can Soc Hort Sci; Agr Inst Can. *Res:* Vegetable management and physiology; seed germination; seed vigour; plant establishment; growth factors. *Mailing Add:* Res Sta Agr Can Harrow ON N0R 1C0 Can

LIPTON, ALLAN, b New York, NY, Dec 29, 38; m 65; c 1. INTERNAL MEDICINE, ONCOLOGY. *Educ:* Amherst Col, BA, 59; NY Univ, MD, 63; Am Bd Internal Med, dipl, 70. *Prof Exp:* Intern med, Bellevue Hosp, New York, 63-64; resident, 64-65; asst prof, 71-74, assoc prof, 74-80, PROF MED, HERSHEY MED CTR, PA STATE UNIV, 80-, CHIEF, DIV ONCOL, DEPT MED, 74- *Concurrent Pos:* Fel hemat, Mem Hosp, New York, 67-68, fel oncol, 68-69; Dernham fel, Salk Inst Biol Studies, 69-71. *Mem:* AAAS; Am Asn Cancer Res; Am Fedn Clin Res. *Res:* Control of growth of normal and malignant cells by serum factors. *Mailing Add:* Dept of Med Hershey Med Ctr Pa State Univ Hershey PA 17033

LIPTON, JAMES MATTHEW, b Aug 10, 38; US citizen; m 59; c 2. NEUROSCIENCES. *Educ:* Univ Colo, PhD, 64. *Prof Exp:* Asst prof psychol, 66-73, asst prof physiol, 72-73, assoc prof, 73-77, assoc prof, 77-79, PROF PHYSIOL & NEUROL, UNIV TEX HEALTH SCI CTR, DALLAS, 79- *Concurrent Pos:* USPHS fel, Neuropath Lab, Med Sch, Univ Mich, 64-66; USPHS sr fel, Inst Animal Physiol, UK, 70-71; consult neurol, Vet Admin Hosp, Dallas, 74-80; mem staff, Pain Eval & Treatment Clin, Anesthesiol Dept, Southwestern Med Sch, Univ Tex Health Sci Ctr, Dallas, 81- *Mem:* AAAS; Soc Neurosci; Am Physiol Soc; Geront Soc; Soc Exp Biol & Med. *Res:* Central control of body temperature; central mechanisms in fever; pain mechanisms and control. *Mailing Add:* Dept Physiol Univ Tex Health Sci Ctr Dallas TX 75235

LIPTON, MORRIS ABRAHAM, b New York, NY, Dec 27, 15; m 40; c 3. EXPERIMENTAL PSYCHIATRY, MEDICINE. *Educ:* City Col New York, BS, 35; Univ Wis, PhM, 37, PhD(biochem), 39; Univ Chicago, MD, 44. *Prof Exp:* Asst physiol, Univ Chicago, 40-41, instr, 40-45, res assoc med, 45-46, instr med, 48-51, asst prof psychiat & med, 51-54; asst prof, Med Sch, Northwestern Univ, 54-59; from assoc prof to prof, 63-65, chmn dept, 70-73, SARAH GRAHAM KENAN DISTINGUISHED PROF PSYCHIAT, SCH MED, UNIV NC, CHAPEL HILL, 65-, PROF BIOCHEM & NEUROBIOL & HEAD DIV RES PSYCHIAT, DEPT PSYCHIAT, 63-, DIR, BIOL SCI RES CTR, CHILD DEVELOP INST & SCH MED, 65- *Concurrent Pos:* NIMH res career award, 62; chief psychosom serv, Vet Admin Hosp, Chicago & asst dir prof serv, Vet Admin Res Hosp, 54-59; chmn, Psychopharmacol Study Sect, NIMH, 64, consult preclin psychopharm, 72-; chmn, Comt Res Group Advan Psychiat, 66-; chmn, Task Force Megavitamin Ther Psychiat, Am Psychiat Asn, 69-74; Mem, Comp Studies Eval Comt, Vet Admin, 71-; consult, Bur Drugs, Food & Drug Admin, 72- *Mem:* AAAS; Am Soc Biol Chemists; Am Col Neuropsychopharmacol (pres-elect); Fedn Am Socs Exp Biol. *Res:* Neuropsychopharmacology; extra pituitary effects of the hypothalamic hormones. *Mailing Add:* Biol Sci Res Ctr Univ of NC Sch of Med Chapel Hill NC 27514

LIPTON, SAMUEL HARRY, b Burlington, Wis, Feb 6, 21. BIOCHEMISTRY, ORGANIC CHEMISTRY. *Educ:* Univ Wis, BS, 42, MS, 47; PhD(biochem, org chem), 48. *Prof Exp:* Asst, Univ Wis, 42, 46-48; res assoc, Univ Chicago, 49-50; res chemist, Lab, Pabst Brewing Co, Wis, 50-55; biochemist, Bioferm Corp, Calif, 56; proj assoc, Univ Wis, 57-67; RES CHEMIST, NUTRITION INSTITUTE, AGR RES SERV, USDA, 68- *Mem:* AAAS; Am Chem Soc. *Res:* Nucleotides and coenzymes; toxic nitriles and lathyrism; amino acids. *Mailing Add:* 7060 Hanover Pkwy Greenbelt MD 20770

LIPTON, WERNER JACOB, b Ger, Oct 16, 28; nat US; m 52; c 4. PLANT PHYSIOLOGY. *Educ:* Mich State Univ, BS, 51, MS, 53; Univ Calif, PhD(plant physiol), 57. *Prof Exp:* Asst, Univ Calif, 53-57; SR PLANT PHYSIOLOGIST, HORT FIELD STA, USDA, 57- *Concurrent Pos:* Assoc ed, Am Soc Hort Sci, 72-76, 78-, chmn, postharvest hort sect, 76-77, vpres, West Sect, 81-82. *Mem:* AAAS; Am Soc Hort Sci; Am Soc Plant Physiol; Am Meteorol Soc. *Res:* Postharvest physiology of vegetables; emphasis on effects of modified atmospheres and preharvest environmental factors. *Mailing Add:* US Dept of Agr PO Box 8143 Fresno CA 93747

LIRA, EMIL PATRICK, b Chicago, Ill, Mar 17, 34; m 58; c 4. ORGANIC CHEMISTRY. *Educ:* Elmhurst Col, BS, 56; Rutgers Univ, PhD(org chem), 63. *Prof Exp:* Chemist, Swift & Co, 56; chemist, Corn Prod Co, 58-59; res chemist, 63-69, Int Mineral & Chem Corp, 63-69, supvr org synthesis, 69-73, mgr org chem, 73-74; dir res, Velsicol Chem Corp, 74-76; DIR AGR-CHEM RES, NORTHWEST IND, INC, CHICAGO LAB, 76- *Mem:* Am Chem Soc. *Res:* Organic research and development with plasticizers, adhesives, polymer additives; plant growth regulators; pesticides; animal health products; synthetic sweeteners; organic processes. *Mailing Add:* Northwest Ind Inc 330 E Grand Ave Chicago IL 60611

LIS, ADAM W, b Przemysl, Poland, Jan 5, 25; US citizen. BIOCHEMISTRY. *Educ:* Univ Ark, BS, 49; Univ Calif, Berkeley, PhD(biochem), 60. *Prof Exp:* Res biochemist, Univ Calif, San Francisco, 60-62; res assoc, 63-65, asst prof, 65-67, assoc prof nucleic acids, Univ Ore Health Sci Ctr, 67-77, dir nucleic acids lab, 66-77; DIR, INTERMEDIARY METAB INST, 77-; PROF BIOCHEM, HUXLEY COL, WESTERN WASH UNIV, BELLINGHAM, WASH, 81- *Concurrent Pos:* Nat Cancer Inst fel, Univ Uppsala, 62-63; ed, Physiol Chem & Physics, 67- *Honors & Awards:* Copernicam Medal Med, 73. *Mem:* Brit Biochem Soc; Am Chem Soc; Am Soc Cell Biol; Radiation Res Soc Am; Biophys Soc. *Res:* Minor components in nucleic acids and their function; body fluids analysis in malignant and metabolic diseases. *Mailing Add:* 1117 SE Umatilla St Portland OR 97202

LIS, EDWARD FRANCIS, b Chicago, Ill, Apr 1, 18; m 44; c 2. PEDIATRICS. *Educ:* Univ Ill, BS, 39, MD, 43. *Prof Exp:* From asst prof to assoc prof, 52-65, PROF PEDIAT, UNIV ILL COL MED, 65-, MED DIR, CTR HANDICAPPED CHILDREN & DIR DIV SERV CRIPPLED CHILDREN, 59- *Res:* Handicapped children. *Mailing Add:* Dept of Pediat Univ of Ill Col of Med Chicago IL 60612

LIS, ELAINE WALKER, b Denver, Colo, Apr 25, 24; m 58; c 3. NUTRITION, BIOCHEMISTRY. *Educ:* Mills Col, AB, 45; Univ Calif, Berkeley, PhD(nutrit), 60. *Prof Exp:* Asst nutrit, Univ Calif, Berkeley, 56-60, USPHS fel, 60-62; lectr, Portland State Univ, 64-68; assoc prof, 68-81, PROF, CRIPPLED CHILDREN'S DIV, ORE HEALTH SCI UNIV, 81- *Concurrent Pos:* Consult, Crippled Children's Div, Med Sch, Univ Ore, 64-68. *Mem:* Am Asn Univ Prof; Am Asn Ment Deficiency; Soc Nutrit Educ; Am Home Econ Asn. *Res:* Metabolic approach to possible causes of retardation, emotional disturbances or other handicapping conditions with emphasis on inborn errors of metabolism such as phenylketonuria. *Mailing Add:* Crippled Children's Div Univ of Ore Health Sci Ctr Portland OR 97201

LIS, JOHN THOMAS, b Willimantic, Conn, June 15, 48; m 71. MOLECULAR GENETICS, CELL BIOLOGY. *Educ:* Fairfield Univ, BS, 70; Brandeis Univ, PhD(biochem), 75. *Prof Exp:* Fel, Dept Biochem, Stanford Univ, 75-78; ASST PROF, DEPT BIOCHEM, CORNELL UNIV, 78- *Res:* Relationship between genome structure and gene regulation using the heat shock genes of drosophila melanogaster as a model system. *Mailing Add:* Sect Biochem Molecular & Cell Biol Cornell Univ Ithaca NY 14853

LIS, MARTIN, b Praha, Czech, Jan 6, 35; Can citizen; m 60; c 2. EXPERIMENTAL MEDICINE. *Educ:* Sch Vet Med, Brno, Czech, DVM, 60; Czech Acad Sci, CSc(animal physiol), 67; McGill Univ, PhD(exp med), 72. *Prof Exp:* Fel animal physiol, Lab Animal Physiol, Czech Acad Sci, 60-68; fel exp med, Inst Exp Med & Surg, Univ Montreal, 68-69; fel exp med, 69-72, sr scientist, 72-75, DIR LAB COMP ENDOCRINOL, CLIN RES INST MONTREAL, 75-; ASST PROF MED, UNIV MONTREAL, 72- *Mem:* Can Soc Endocrinol & Metab. *Res:* Pituitary and hypothalamic peptides; hormone producing tumors; hormone responsive mammary tumors; morphine-like endogenous peptides; mechanism of action of peptide hormones. *Mailing Add:* Dept Med Univ Montreal Montreal PQ H3C 3J7 Can

LISA, JOSEPH DANIEL, b Jersey City, NJ, May 8, 28; div; c 1. PHYSIOLOGY, BIOMEDICAL ENGINEERING. *Educ:* St Peter's Col, NJ, BA, 51; Fordham Univ, MS, 54, PhD(physiol), 58. *Prof Exp:* Head bioastronaut, Advan Systs Dept, 63-68, RES SCIENTIST ENVIRON PHYSIOL, RES DEPT, GRUMMAN AEROSPACE CORP, 68- *Mem:* Aerospace Med Asn; NY Acad Sci. *Res:* Cytopathological investigation; holographic techniques; screening of cancer cells. *Mailing Add:* 12 Stonehenge Rd Rockville Centre NY 10020

LISAK, ROBERT PHILIP, b Brooklyn, NY, Mar 17, 41; m 64; c 2. NEUROLOGY, IMMUNOLOGY. *Educ:* NY Univ, BA, 61; Columbia Univ, MD, 65. *Prof Exp:* Intern med, Montefiore Hosp & Med Ctr, 65-66; res assoc immunol, Lab Clin Sci, NIMH, 66-68; jr resident med, Bronx Munic Med Ctr, Albert Einstein Col Med, 68-69; resident neurol, Hosp, 69-72, trainee allergy & immunol, 71-72, asst prof, 72-76, assoc prof, 76-80, PROF NEUROL, SCH MED, UNIV PA, 80-, MEM IMMUNOL GRAD GROUP, 75- *Concurrent Pos:* Consult neurol, Vet Admin Hosp, Philadelphia, 72-; spec consult, Nat Multiple Sclerosis Soc, 75 & Swiss Acad Med, 81; Fulbright-Hays sr res scholar, UK, 78-79. *Mem:* Am Asn Immunologists; Am Fedn Clin Res; Am Acad Neurol; AAAS; NY Acad Sci. *Res:* Humoral and cell-mediated immunologic mechanisms involved in clinical and experimental diseases of the central and peripheral nervous system and muscle. *Mailing Add:* Dept of Neurol Univ of Pa Hosp Philadelphia PA 19104

LISANKE, ROBERT JOHN, SR, b New York, NY, June 7, 32; m 57; c 4. ORGANIC POLYMER CHEMISTRY. *Educ:* Fordham Univ, BS, 54; Notre Dame Univ, MS, 56. *Prof Exp:* Control chemist, Chas Pfizer & Co, 50-54; chemist, Union Carbide Plastics Co, 55, chemist, Silicones Div, Union Carbide Corp, 56-59; chemist, Hooker Chem Corp, 59-60; res chemist, Mobil Oil Corp, NJ, 60-66; org chemist, Gen Elec Co, Syracuse, 66-71, process chemist, 71-73; SR CHEMIST, PRATT & WHITNEY AIRCRAFT DIV, UNITED TECHNOLOGIES CORP, WEST PALM BEACH, 74- *Mem:* Am Chem Soc; Am Inst Chem Eng; Inst Elec & Electronics Eng; Am Soc Mech Eng. *Res:* Thermogravimetry; ultra-high vacuum technology; chemical kinetics; materials science; computer programming. *Mailing Add:* PO Box 9101 Riviera Beach FL 33404

LISANO, MICHAEL EDWARD, b Houston, Tex, Oct 6, 42; c 2. REPRODUCTIVE PHYSIOLOGY, ENDOCRINOLOGY. *Educ:* Sam Houston State Univ, BS, 64, MS, 66; Tex A&M Univ, PhD(physiol), 70. *Prof Exp:* Instr biol, Hardin-Simmons Univ, 66-67; asst prof, 70-77, ASSOC PROF PHYSIOL, AUBURN UNIV, 77- *Mem:* Wildlife Soc; Southeastern Asn Fish & Wildlife Agencies. *Res:* Reproductive physiology and endocrinology of economically important game species. *Mailing Add:* Dept of Zool & Entom Auburn Univ Auburn AL 36830

LISCHER, LUDWIG F, b Mar 1, 15; US citizen. ENGINEERING. *Educ:* Purdue Univ, BSEE, 37. *Hon Degrees:* DEng, Purdue Univ, 76. *Prof Exp:* Mem staff, 37-64, vpres-in-chg eng & res, Commonwealth Edison Co, 64-80; RETIRED. *Concurrent Pos:* Dir, Chicago Eng & Sci Ctr, Proj Mgt Corp; chmn res adv comt, Elec Power Res Inst; mem var adv comts, NSF, Nat Acad Sci & Nat Acad Eng. *Mem:* Nat Acad Eng; fel Inst Elec & Electronics Engrs; Am Soc Mech Engrs; Am Nuclear Soc. *Res:* Electric utility systems for the development of government and industry energy policy. *Mailing Add:* 124 W Willow Lombard IL 60148

LI-SCHOLZ, ANGELA, b Hong Kong, Aug 15, 36; US citizen; m 66; c 2. ATOMIC PHYSICS, NUCLEAR PHYSICS. *Educ:* Manhattanville Col, BA, 56; NY Univ, MS, 57, PhD(physics), 63. *Prof Exp:* Jr res assoc nuclear physics, Brookhaven Nat Lab, 60-63; res assoc high energy physics, NY Univ, 63; res assoc nuclear physics, Yale Univ, 63-65; asst prof physics, City Col New York, 65-66; res assoc solid state physics, Univ Pa, 67-70; res assoc nuclear chem, Rensselaer Polytech Inst, 70-72; assoc prof, 72-77, PROF SCI, STATE UNIV NY, EMPIRE STATE COL, 77- *Concurrent Pos:* Res prof, State Univ NY, Albany, 78-; ed, Atomic Data & Nuclear Data Tables, 82- *Mem:* Am Phys Soc. *Res:* Atomic inner shell ionization; nuclei spectroscopy; interaction of nuclei with electromagnetic fields in solids. *Mailing Add:* Empire State Col 50 Wolf Rd Rm 200 Albany NY 12203

LISELLA, FRANK SCOTT, b Lancaster, Pa, Aug 11, 36; m 58. PUBLIC HEALTH. *Educ:* Pa State Teachers Col, Millersville, 57; Tulane Univ La, MPH, 61; Univ Iowa, PhD(prev med), 70. *Prof Exp:* Sanitarian, Pa Dept Health, 57-64; coordr, Commun Dis Control Proj, USPHS, Fla, 64-66, chief training & consultation, Pesticides Prog, Nat Commun Dis Ctr, 66-68; asst to dir div community studies, Food & Drug Admin, Ga, 69-70; asst dir div pesticide community studies, Environ Protection Agency, 70-72; health sci adv, Nat Med Audiovisual Ctr, 72-73; CHIEF, PROG DEVELOP BR, ENVIRON HEALTH SERVS DIV, CTR DIS CONTROL, GA, 73- *Concurrent Pos:* Adj prof, Dekalb Col, 70-75. *Honors & Awards:* USPHS Commendation Medal, 78. *Mem:* Nat Environ Health Asn; Am Pub Health Asn. *Res:* Epidemiology of acute intoxications involving chemical agents of various types; etiology of self-induced intoxications involving medicants, pesticides and other chemical compounds and measures for prevention of repetitive episodes. *Mailing Add:* 3042 Hathaway Ct Chamblee GA 30341

LISH, PAUL MERRILL, b Idaho, Feb 2, 21; m 41; c 4. PHARMACOLOGY. *Educ:* Idaho State Univ, BS, 49; Univ Nebr, MS, 51; St Louis Univ, PhD(pharmacol), 55. *Prof Exp:* Instr, Sch Med, St Louis Univ, 53-55; pharmacologist, group leader & sect leader, Mead Johnson Res Ctr, Ind, 55-62, dir pharmacol, 63-67, vpres biol sci, 67-69; dir res & develop, Pharmaceut Group, Chromalloy Am Corp, 69-78; SCI ADV LIFESCI, IIT RES INST, 78- *Mem:* AAAS; Am Chem Soc; Soc Exp Biol & Med; Am Soc Pharmacol & Exp Therapeut; NY Acad Sci. *Res:* Pharmacology of peripheral neuroeffector and cardiovascular systems; adrenergics and anti-adrenergics, anti-allergics, gastrointestinal drugs. *Mailing Add:* IIT Res Inst 10 W 35th St Chicago IL 60616

LISK, ROBERT DOUGLAS, b Pembroke, Ont, Nov 10, 34. PHYSIOLOGY, ENDOCRINOLOGY. *Educ:* Queen's Univ, Ont, BA, 57; Harvard Univ, AM, 59, PhD(biol), 60. *Prof Exp:* From instr to assoc prof, 60-70, PROF BIOL, PRINCETON UNIV, 70- *Concurrent Pos:* NSF grants, 60-66 & 73-82; vis asst prof, Sch Med, Univ Calif, Los Angeles, 65; NIH grants, 66-71; mem panel regulatory biol, Nat Sci Found, 72-75. *Mem:* Fel AAAS; Am Soc Zool; Am Asn Anat; Endocrine Soc; Am Physiol Soc. *Res:* Neuroendocrine mechanisms such as sites of action and interactions of hormones on central nervous system for regulation of hormone output by endocrine organs and hormone role in differentiation and triggering of behavioral sequences. *Mailing Add:* Dept of Biol Princeton Univ Princeton NJ 08540

LISKA, BERNARD JOSEPH, b Hillsboro, Wis, May 31, 31; m 52; c 2. FOOD TECHNOLOGY. *Educ:* Univ Wis, BS, 53, MS, 56, PhD(dairy & food technol), 57. *Prof Exp:* Asst prof, Univ Fla, 57-59; from asst prof to assoc prof animal sci, 59-65, dir, Food Sci Inst, 68-75, assoc dir, Agr Exp Sta, 72-75, dir & assoc dean, 75-80, PROF FOOD SCI, PURDUE UNIV, 65-, DEAN AGR, 80- *Concurrent Pos:* Sci ed, J Food Sci, 70-80; vchmn, Expert Panel on Food Safety & Nutrit, 71-77. *Honors & Awards:* Babcock Hart Award Jury, Inst Food Technologists, 69-73. *Mem:* Fel Inst Food Technologists; Am Dairy Sci Asn; Am Chem Soc. *Res:* Food bacteriology; lactic cultures; bulk handling of milk; milk quality and enzymes; food chemistry; food microbiology; chemical residues in food; pesticide residue analysis. *Mailing Add:* Purdue Univ Agr Admin West Lafayette IN 47907

LISKA, KENNETH J, b Hinsdale, Ill, June 4, 29; m 57; c 3. CHEMISTRY, PHARMACOLOGY. *Educ:* Univ Ill, BS, 51, MS, 53, PhD(med chem), 56. *Prof Exp:* Assoc prof pharmaceut chem, Duquesne Univ, 56-61 & Univ Pittsburgh, 61-69; assoc prof chem, US Int Univ, 69-75; INSTR CHEM, MESA COL, 75- *Mem:* Am Chem Soc; AAAS; Nutrit Today Soc. *Res:* Synthetic organic medicinal chemistry. *Mailing Add:* 2947 Honors Ct San Diego CA 92122

LISKEY, NATHAN EUGENE, b Live Oak, Calif, Apr 26, 37; m 57; c 3. HEALTH SCIENCE. *Educ:* La Verne Col, BA, 59; Ind Univ, Bloomington, MS, 61, HSD(health safety), 69. *Prof Exp:* Teacher pub schs, Calif, 59-65; asst prof health & phys educ, 65-68, assoc prof, 69-75, PROF HEALTH SCI, CALIF STATE UNIV, FRESNO, 75- *Concurrent Pos:* USPHS grant, HEW, 68-69; sex therapist, Ctr Coun & Ther, 73- *Mem:* Soc Sci Study Sex; Am Asn Sex Educ & Coun. *Res:* Physical and emotional aspects of behavior relating to accident prevention; human sexuality; sexual behavior of the aged. *Mailing Add:* Dept Health Sci Calif State Univ Fresno CA 93740

LISMAN, FREDERICK LOUIS, b Wilkes-Barre, Pa, Jan 14, 39; m 62; c 3. NUCLEAR CHEMISTRY. *Educ:* Fairfield Univ, BS, 60; Purdue Univ, PhD(nuclear chem), 65. *Prof Exp:* Sr res radiochemist, Idaho Nuclear Corp, 65-70; asst prof, 70-72, chmn dept, 75-79, ASSOC PROF CHEM,

FAIRFIELD UNIV, 72- *Mem:* AAAS; Am Chem Soc. *Res:* Fission yield determination; radiochemical separations; mass spectrometric techniques; measurement of fissionable material; mass and charge distribution in low Z fission; chemical separation techniques; energy resources. *Mailing Add:* 353 W Rutland Rd Milford CT 06460

LISMAN, HENRY, b Boston, Mass, July 3, 13; m 38; c 2. MATHEMATICS. *Educ:* Univ Boston, BS, 34, MS, 35, PhD(physics), 39. *Prof Exp:* Asst physics, Univ Boston, 34-35; instr, Northeastern Univ, 40-42; from assoc physicist to physicist, Sig Corps Eng Labs, NJ, 42-47; from instr to assoc prof, Yeshiva Univ, 47-57, prof math, 57-78; RETIRED. *Concurrent Pos:* Consult physicist, US Army Electronics Labs, 49-68. *Res:* Electromagnetic wave propagation. *Mailing Add:* 3777 Independence Ave Bronx NY 10463

LISMAN, PERRY HALL, b Sweetwater, Tex, July 21, 32; m 62. SYSTEMS DEVELOPMENT, ELECTRONICS SYSTEMS. *Educ:* Univ Tex, BA, 61. *Prof Exp:* Res scientist, Defense Res Lab, Univ Tex, Austin, 61-62, head, Missile Guid Sect, 62-64, head, Spec Projs Off, 64-67; sr staff mem, Appl Physics Lab, Johns Hopkins Univ, 67-74; asst dir, 74-80, DEP DIR, SRI INT, 80- *Mem:* Inst Elec & Electronics Engrs. *Res:* Foreign technology; electronics systems; countermeasures; research and development management; radar. *Mailing Add:* 6 Wood Lane Menlo Park CA 94025

LISONBEE, LORENZO KENNETH, b Mesa, Ariz, Nov 25, 14; m 38; c 8. BIOLOGY, SCIENCE EDUCATION. *Educ:* Ariz State Univ, BA, 37, MA, 40, EdD, 63. *Prof Exp:* Teacher sci & dept chmn high schs, Ariz, 40-58; SCI SUPVR, PHOENIX HIGH SCHS, 58-; FAC ASSOC, ARIZ STATE UNIV, 63- *Concurrent Pos:* Consult, Am Geol Inst & Am Inst Biol Sci & Biol Sci Curriculum Study; contribr, Encyclopedia Britannica, 62 & 74. *Mem:* Fel AAAS; Nat Asn Res Sci Teaching; Nat Sci Teachers Asn; Nat Asn Biol Teachers. *Res:* Research in science teaching; desert biology. *Mailing Add:* 1970 E Del Sur Dr Tempe AZ 85283

LISS, ALAN, b Pittsburgh, Pa, Sept 14, 47; m 71; c 3. MICROBIAL GENETICS, VIROLOGY. *Educ:* Univ Calif, Berkeley, BS, 69; Univ Rochester, PhD(microbiol), 73. *Prof Exp:* Fel microbiol, York Univ, 73-74; Nat Cancer Inst fel, Scripps Clin & Res Found, 74-75; asst prof biol, Univ Conn, 75-77; sr staff fel, 77-79, EXPERT-CONSULT, NAT INST ALLERGY & INFECTIOUS DIS, ROCKY MOUNTAIN LABS, NIH, 79- *Honors & Awards:* Sigrid Juselius Found Award, 75. *Mem:* AAAS; Am Soc Microbiol; Sigma Xi; NY Acad Sci. *Res:* Genetics and virology of members of the mycoplasmas; isolation of auxotrophic mutants; characterization of plasmid DNA; investigation of host-parasite interactions in mycoplasma-related infections. *Mailing Add:* Rocky Mountain Labs Nat Inst Allergy & Infectious Dis Hamilton MT 59840

LISS, IVAN BARRY, b Lebanon, Ky, June 21, 38; m 77; c 2. INORGANIC CHEMISTRY. *Educ:* Georgetown Col, BA, 60; Univ Ky, MA, 63; Univ Louisville, PhD(chem), 73. *Prof Exp:* Teacher chem, Shelby Co High Sch, Ky, 60-65; chemist, Reliance Universal, Inc, 65-67; fel, Univ Mo-Columbia, 73-74; MEM FAC CHEM, BLACKBURN COL, 74- *Mem:* Am Chem Soc; Sigma Xi. *Res:* Synthesis and characterization of chelates of the rare earth and transition metals. *Mailing Add:* Dept of Chem Blackburn Col Carlinville IL 62626

LISS, LEOPOLD, b Lwow, Poland, Nov 19, 23; nat US; m 48; c 2. NEUROPATHOLOGY. *Educ:* Lwow Gramar Sch, Poland, BA, 41; Univ Heidelberg, MD, 50; Univ Mich, MS, 55. *Prof Exp:* From instr to asst prof neuropath, Univ Mich, 51-60; assoc prof, 60-64, PROF NEUROPATH, OHIO STATE UNIV, 64-, CO-DIR OFF GERIAT MED, COL MED, 77- *Mem:* Am Asn Neuropath; Soc Neurosci; Int Acad Path; Am Geriat Soc; Asn Res Nerv & Ment Dis. *Res:* Clinical and experimental neuropathology; aging brain; Dementia; Alzheimer's disease; alcoholic encephalopathies; aluminum neurotoxicity. *Mailing Add:* Upham Hall Ohio State Univ Columbus OH 43210

LISS, MAURICE, b Boston, Mass, Dec 18, 26. BIOCHEMISTRY, BIOLOGY. *Educ:* Harvard Univ, AB, 49; Tufts Univ, PhD(biochem), 58. *Prof Exp:* Chemist, Peter Bent Brigham Hosp, 49-51; chemist, Mass Dept Pub Safety, 51-53; Am Cancer Soc res fel, enzymol, Brandeis Univ, 58-60; res assoc dermat, Sch Med, Tufts Univ, 61-63, from asst prof to assoc prof, 63-68; assoc prof, 68-73, PROF BIOL, BOSTON COL, 73- *Mem:* Am Chem Soc; Am Soc Biol Chem; AAAS; Am Asn Immunologists. *Res:* Proteins; immunology. *Mailing Add:* Dept of Biol Boston Col Chestnut Hill MA 02167

LISS, ROBERT H, b Boston, Mass, Nov 2, 36; m 61; c 2. CYTOLOGY, CYTOPATHOLOGY. *Educ:* Tufts Univ, BS, 59; Univ Mass, MA, 61, PhD(cytol, biochem), 64. *Prof Exp:* Head electron micros lab life sci div, 65-76, DIR EXP CELLULAR SCI, ARTHUR D LITTLE, INC, 76-; ASSOC SURG, HARVARD MED SCH, 70-; RES ASSOC CARDIOVASC SURG, CHILDREN'S MED CTR, BOSTON, 75- *Concurrent Pos:* Vis scientist, Tex Heart Inst, 72-; res assoc mat sci & eng, Mass Inst Technol, 77- *Mem:* Am Asn Cancer Res; AAAS; Am Soc Cell Biol; Electron Micros Soc Am; Soc Develop Biol. *Res:* Radioautography; electron microscopy. *Mailing Add:* Life Sci Div Arthur D Little Inc Acorn Park Cambridge MA 02140

LISS, WILLIAM JOHN, b Pittsburgh, Pa, June 18, 47. POPULATION & COMMUNITY ECOLOGY. *Educ:* Pa State Univ, BS, 69; Ore State Univ, MS, 74, PhD(fisheries), 77. *Prof Exp:* Res assoc, 77-78, ASST PROF FISHERIES, ORE STATE UNIV, 78- *Mem:* Sigma Xi. *Res:* Population and community ecology of aquatic and terrestrial organisms; fisheries exploitation theory; effects of toxic substances on aquatic communities. *Mailing Add:* Dept Fisheries & Wildlife Oak Creek Lab Biol Ore State Univ Corvallis OR 97331

LISSAMAN, PETER BARRY STUART, b Durban, SAfrica, Apr 10, 31; US citizen; m 55; c 3. AERODYNAMICS. *Educ:* Univ Natal, BS, 51; Cambridge Univ, MA, 54; Calif Inst Technol, MS, 55, PhD(aeronaut), 66. *Prof Exp:* Designer & struct analyst, Bristol Aircraft Co, Eng, 55-56; res aerodynamicist, Handley-Page Aircraft, Eng, 56-58; asst prof aeronaut, US Naval Postgrad Sch, 58-62, Calif Inst Technol, 62-69 & Jet Propulsion Lab, 68-69; dir continuum mech lab, Northrop Corp, 69-71; VPRES, AEROVIRONMENT INC, 72- *Concurrent Pos:* Consult, McDonnell Douglas Corp, 65-68; distinguished lectr, Am Inst Aeronaut & Astronaut, 72-79; prof, Art Ctr of Design, 76- *Honors & Awards:* Longstreth Medal, Franklin Inst, 79; Kremer Medal, Royal Aeronaut Soc, 79. *Mem:* Assoc fel Am Inst Aeronaut & Astronaut; Soc Exp Test Pilots. *Res:* Aerodynamics, hydrodynamics, structure and dynamics of aircraft; marine and ground vehicles; wind and marine turbines; automotive aerodynamics; wing, rotor theory; turbulence, diffusion, plume modelling; energy systems; bird flight. *Mailing Add:* AeroVironment Inc 145 N Vista Ave Pasadena CA 91107

LISSANT, ELLEN KERN, b St Louis, Mo, Nov 4, 22; m 47; c 3. PHYCOLOGY. *Educ:* Wash Univ, St Louis, AB, 44, AM, 46, PhD(bot), 68. *Prof Exp:* Lab instr bot, Wash Univ, St Louis, 43-45; teacher, Webster Groves High Sch, 45-46; asst bot, Wash Univ, St Louis, 46-47; asst herbarium, Stanford Univ, 47; from lectr to prof biol, Fontbonne Col, 60-78; RETIRED. *Concurrent Pos:* Fac assoc, Washington Univ, 79-81; instr, St Louis Community Col, Meramec, 81-82. *Mem:* Bot Soc Am; Phycol Soc Am. *Res:* Palaeobotany; genetics; morphogenetic studies in the genus Erythrocladia Rosenvinge. *Mailing Add:* 12804 Westledge Lane St Louis MO 63131

LISSANT, KENNETH JORDAN, b London, Eng, Aug 6, 20; nat US; m 47; c 3. COLLOID CHEMISTRY. *Educ:* Ottawa Univ, Kans, AB, 41; Wash Univ, St Louis, MS, 43; Stanford Univ, PhD(chem), 47. *Prof Exp:* Asst chem, Ottawa Univ, Kans, 39-41; asst chem, Wash Univ, St Louis, 41-44, instr physics, 43-44; res chemist, 44-65, advan res coordr, 65-68, DIR ADVAN RES, PETROLITE CORP, 68- *Concurrent Pos:* Bristol-Myers fel. *Mem:* AAAS; Am Chem Soc. *Res:* Vacuum-tube titrimeters; solubilization of liquids; polymerization of unsaturates; foams; surfactants; emulsions; information retrieval; pollution abatement. *Mailing Add:* Petrolite Corp 369 Marshall Ave Webster Groves MO 63119

LISSEY, ALLAN, hydrogeology, engineering geology, see previous edition

LISSNER, DAVID, b Rochester, NY, July 25, 31. MATHEMATICS. *Educ:* Mass Inst Technol, BS, 53; Cornell Univ, PhD(math), 59. *Prof Exp:* Design engr, NAm Aviation, Inc, 53-55; Off Naval Res fel math, Northwestern Univ, 59-60; instr, Yale Univ, 60-62; from asst prof to assoc prof, 62-77, PROF MATH, SYRACUSE UNIV, 77- *Mem:* Am Math Soc. *Res:* Ring theory; linear, commutative and homological algebra; algebraic geometry. *Mailing Add:* 38 Churchill Ct Fayetteville NY 13066

LIST, ALBERT, JR, b East Orange, NJ, Nov 5, 28; m 53; c 2. PLANT PHYSIOLOGY. *Educ:* Univ Mass, BS, 53; Cornell Univ, MS, 58, PhD(plant physiol), 61. *Prof Exp:* Instr bot, Douglass Col, Rutgers Univ, 61-62, asst prof bot & biol, 62-65; fel, Univ Pa, 65-66, lectr biomet & bot, 66-67; assoc prof biol, 67-74, ASSOC PROF BIOL SCI, DREXEL UNIV, 74- *Concurrent Pos:* NSF res grants, 63-65, 66-67 & 70-72; USPHS grant, 70-73. *Mem:* AAAS; Bot Soc Am; Am Soc Plant Physiol; Am Inst Biol Sci; Soc Develop Biol. *Res:* Developmental botany; control theory for plant root growth; relationships of relative elemental growth rates to bioelectric and membrane properties in roots; air pollution effects on growth. *Mailing Add:* Dept of Biol Sci Drexel Univ 32nd & Chestnut Sts Philadelphia PA 19104

LIST, HARVEY L(AWRENCE), b Brooklyn, NY, Sept 5, 24; m 46; c 2. CHEMICAL ENGINEERING. *Educ:* Polytech Inst Brooklyn, BChE, 50, DChE, 58; Univ Rochester, MS, 50. *Prof Exp:* Process engr chem eng, Esso Res & Eng Co, 50-55; assoc prof, 55-71, prof, 71-80, EMER PROF CHEM ENG, CITY COL NEW YORK, 80-; PRES, LIST ASSOCS, INC, 69- *Concurrent Pos:* Private consult, 55-69; Fulbright scholar, Tunghai Univ, 63-64; tech coordr, Adhesive & Sealant Coun, Ill; ed, Int Petrochem Develop. *Mem:* Am Chem Soc; Am Soc Eng Educ; Am Inst Chem Engrs. *Res:* Fluidization of solids; petroleum refining; chemical process economics; international relations; pollution control. *Mailing Add:* 56 Roundtree Rt 9W Piermont NJ 10968

LIST, JAMES CARL, b Paducah, Ky, July 6, 26; m 47; c 2. HERPETOLOGY. *Educ:* Notre Dame Univ, BS, 48, MS, 49; Univ Ill, PhD(zool), 56. *Prof Exp:* From instr to asst prof biol, Loyola Univ, Ill, 52-57; from instr to assoc prof, 57-66, PROF BIOL, BALL STATE UNIV, 66- *Mem:* Soc Syst Zool; Am Soc Ichthyol & Herpet; Soc Study Evolution; Herpetologists League; Soc Study Amphibians & Reptiles. *Res:* Anatomy and ecology of amphibians and reptiles. *Mailing Add:* Dept of Biol Ball State Univ Muncie IN 47306

LIST, ROLAND, b Frauenfeld, Switz, Feb 21, 29; m 56; c 2. ATMOSPHERIC PHYSICS. *Educ:* Swiss Fed Inst Technol, Dipl phys, 52, Dr sc nat(atmospheric physics), 60. *Prof Exp:* Sect head atmospheric ice formation, Swiss Fed Inst Snow & Avalanche Res, 52-63; assoc chmn dept physics, 69-73, adminr, Negotiated Develop Grant Atmospheric Dynamics, 74-79, PROF METEOROL, UNIV TORONTO, 63- *Concurrent Pos:* Chmn working group cloud physics & weather modification, World Meteorol Orgn, 70-, chmn panel experts in weather modification of exec comt, 72-, mem comn cloud physics, Int Asn Meteorol & Atmospheric Physics-Int Union Geod & Geophys, 71-80; trustee, Univ Corp Atmospheric Res, Colo, 74-77; chmn comt meteorol & atmospheric sci, Nat Res Coun, 72-74; mem adv comt cloud physics & weather modification, Atmospheric Environ Serv, 74-; vis prof, Swiss Fed Inst Technol, 74; mem adv comt convective storms div, Nat Ctr Atmospheric Res, 78-; mem sci coun, Univ Space Res Assoc, 78-81. *Honors & Awards:* Medal, Univ Leningrad, 70; Patterson Medal, 79. *Mem:* Fel Am Meteorol Soc; Am Geophys Union; Can Asn Physicists; Royal Meteorol Soc; Can Meteorol Soc. *Res:* Precipitation physics; hail formation; rain formation; cloud dynamics; atmospheric boundary layer studies with acoustic Doppler radar; weather modification; snow, avalanches; aerodynamics, heat and mass transfer. *Mailing Add:* Dept of Physics Univ of Toronto Toronto ON M5S 1A7 Can

LISTER, BRADFORD CARLTON, population biology, see previous edition

LISTER, CHARLES ALLAN, b Trenton, NJ, Nov 15, 18; m 46; c 3. ELECTRICAL ENGINEERING, ELECTRONICS ENGINEERING. *Educ:* Tufts Univ, BS, 40; Case Western Reserve Univ, MS, 51. *Prof Exp:* Test engr, Gen Elec Co, NY, 40-41, design engr, 41-43, appln engr, 46-47; asst prof elec eng, Swarthmore Col, 47-49; develop engr, Elec Controller & Mfg Div, Square D Co, Cleveland, 49-54, asst supvr, 54-56, supvr new prod develop, 56-62; design specialist, Lockheed Missiles & Space Co, Calif, 62-63, mgr test equip eng, 63-64; mgr spec devices eng, Lockheed Aircraft Serv Co, 64-65; dept head, Res & Develop, Otis Elevator Co, 65-67, mgr prod eng, 67-72, asst to vpres, 72-74, mgr proj admin, 74-75; MGR ENG SERV, SQUARE D CO, 76-. *Mem:* Inst Elec & Electronics Engrs; Sigma Xi. *Res:* Electromechanical and electronic systems and devices; high-voltage contactors; electric brakes; lifting magnets; elevator dispatching computer systems; elevator control systems; arc interruption; standards for industrial controls. *Mailing Add:* Square D Co PO Box 9247 Columbia SC 29290

LISTER, CLIVE R B, b Uxbridge, Eng, Feb 8, 36. HEAT FLOW, GEODYNAMICS. *Educ:* Cambridge Univ, BA, 59, PhD(geophys), 62. *Prof Exp:* Consult geophys, Saclant ASW Res Ctr, 62-63; chief geophysicist, Ocean Sci & Eng Co, 63-65; res asst prof oceanog, 65-68, asst prof, 68-73, assoc prof, 73-78, PROF OCEANOG & GEOPHYS, UNIV WASH, 78-. *Concurrent Pos:* Mem, Joides Heat Flow Comt, 67-74. *Mem:* Am Geophys Union; Brit Astron Asn. *Res:* Measurement of heat flow through the ocean floor; acoustic sub-bottom profiling; thermal theory applied to geodynamics; aspects of porous convection and water penetration applied to geothermal problems. *Mailing Add:* Dept of Oceanog WB-10 Univ of Washington Seattle WA 98195

LISTER, EARL EDWARD, b Harvey, NB, Apr 14, 34; m 56; c 3. RUMINANT NUTRITION. *Educ:* McGill Univ, BS, 55, MS, 57; Cornell Univ, PhD(nutrit), 60. *Prof Exp:* Feed nutritionist, Ogilvie Flour Mills Ltd, 60-65; res scientist, 65-75, dep dir, Animal Res Inst, 75-78, prog specialist, Cent Region, Ottawa, 78-80, DIR, CENT ATLANTIC REGION, RES BR, AGR CAN, HALIFAX, 80- *Concurrent Pos:* Assoc ed, Can J Animal Sci, 73-75, ed, 75-78. *Mem:* Can Soc Animal Sci; Am Dairy Sci Asn; Am Soc Animal Sci; Agr Inst Can. *Res:* Nutritional requirements of immature ruminants; feeding and management systems for beef cows and calves; production of beef from dairy breeds of cattle. *Mailing Add:* Dir Gen Atlantic Region Res Br Agr Can 1888 Brunswick St Halifax NS B3J 3J8 Can

LISTER, FREDERICK MONIE, b Trenton, NJ, May 9, 23; m 54; c 3. MATHEMATICS. *Educ:* Tufts Univ, BS, 47; Univ Mich, MA, 51; Univ Utah, PhD(math), 66. *Prof Exp:* Instr math, Phillips Acad, Mass, 47-49; instr, Western Wash Col Educ, 54-56, from asst prof to assoc prof, 58-67; asst prof, Chico State Col, 57-58; prof, Southern Ore Col, 67-68; assoc prof, 68-69, PROF MATH, CENT WASH STATE COL, 69- *Mem:* Am Math Soc; Math Asn Am. *Res:* Geometric topology; embeddings of 2-spheres in Euclidean 3-space. *Mailing Add:* Dept of Math Cent Wash Univ Ellensburg WA 98926

LISTER, MAURICE WOLFENDEN, b Tunbridge Wells, Eng, Mar 27, 14; nat Can; m 40; c 5. INORGANIC CHEMISTRY. *Educ:* Oxford Univ, PhD, 38, MA, 47. *Prof Exp:* Assoc prof, 53-62, PROF CHEM, UNIV TORONTO, 62- *Res:* Complex inorganic compounds; mechanisms of inorganic reactions; magnetic susceptibilities; thermodynamics of solids. *Mailing Add:* Dept of Chem Univ of Toronto Toronto ON M5S 1A1 Can

LISTER, RICHARD MALCOLM, b Sheffield, Eng, Nov 14, 28; m 53; c 4. PLANT VIROLOGY. *Educ:* Sheffield Univ, BSc, 49, dipl ed, 50; Cambridge Univ, dipl agr sci, 51; Imp Col Trop Agr, Trinidad, dipl, 52; St Andrews Univ, PhD, 63. *Prof Exp:* Plant pathologist, WAfrican Cocoa Res Inst, 52-56; plant pathologist, Scottish Hort Res Inst, 56-66; assoc prof, 66-72, PROF PLANT VIROL, PURDUE UNIV, WEST LAFAYETTE, 72- *Concurrent Pos:* Fel bot & plant path, Purdue Univ, 63-64; NSF res grants, 67-72; sr ed, Phytopath, 76; assoc ed, Virology, 71- *Mem:* Fel Am Phytopath Soc; Brit Asn Appl Biol. *Res:* Methods in plant virology; properties and interactions of virus-specific products of virus infections, with particular reference to functional specialization; serological techniques; transmission, purification, properties, and relationships of selected plant viruses and viruses of fungi. *Mailing Add:* Dept of Bot & Plant Path Life Sci Bldg Purdue Univ West Lafayette IN 47907

LISTERMAN, THOMAS WALTER, b Cincinnati, Ohio, Dec 21, 38; m 69; c 1. SOLID STATE SCIENCE. *Educ:* Xavier Univ, BS, 59; Ohio Univ, PhD(solid state physics), 65. *Prof Exp:* Sr res physicist, Mound Lab, Monsanto Res Corp, 65-67; asst prof, 67-72, asst provost, 71-73, asst dean sci & eng, 70-71, ASSOC PROF PHYSICS, WRIGHT STATE UNIV, 72- *Mem:* Am Asn Phys Teachers. *Res:* Electronic properties of materials; positron annihilation; cryogenics. *Mailing Add:* Dept of Physics Wright State Univ Dayton OH 45431

LISTGARTEN, MAX, b Paris, France, May 24, 35; Can citizen; m 63; c 3. DENTISTRY, PERIODONTOLOGY. *Educ:* Univ Toronto, DDS, 59; FRCD(C), 69. *Hon Degrees:* MA, Univ Pa, 71. *Prof Exp:* Intern dent, Hosp for Sick Children, Toronto, 59-60; res assoc periodont, Harvard Med Sch, 63-64; from asst prof to assoc prof, Fac Dent, Univ Toronto, 64-68; assoc prof, 68-71, PROF PERIODONT & DIR PERIODONT RES, UNIV PA, 71- *Concurrent Pos:* Nat Res Coun Can fel periodont, Harvard Med Sch, 60-63; US ed, J Biol Buccale, 72- *Honors & Awards:* Award Basic Res Periodont Dis, Int Asn Dent Res, 73; William J Gies Periodontol Award, Am Acad Periodontol, 81. *Mem:* Fel AAAS; Am Dent Asn; Am Acad Periodont; Int Asn Dent Res. *Res:* Ultrastructural investigations of the supporting structures of teeth and associated microbial flora in health and disease. *Mailing Add:* Ctr for Oral Health Res Univ of Pa Philadelphia PA 19104

LISTON, EDWARD MCLEOD, b Palo Alto, Calif, June 26, 30; m 60; c 2. CHEMICAL ENGINEERING. *Educ:* Univ Southern Calif, BE, 54, MS, 60, PhD(chem eng), 65. *Prof Exp:* Chem engr, Air Pollution Found, 55-56; sr res engr, N Am Aviation, Inc, 58-64; SR CHEM ENGR, STANFORD RES INST, 65- *Res:* High temperature chemistry; ablation research shock wave generation and chemistry; nonmetallic materials research including composite materials, nuclear quadrupole resonance and electronic instrumentation; air pollution measurement and test procedures. *Mailing Add:* Stanford Res Inst 333 Ravenswood Ave Menlo Park CA 94025

LISTON, RONALD ARGYLE, b Buffalo, NY, Apr 11, 26; m 81; c 6. MECHANICAL ENGINEERING, ENGINEERING MECHANICS. *Educ:* Univ Vt, BS, 49; Univ Mich, MS(mech eng), 58, MS(eng mech), 61; Mich Technol Univ, PhD(eng mech), 73. *Prof Exp:* Proof officer ballistics & automotive, US Army, 50-56, supvr automotive res engr, Tank-Automotive Command, 58-70, res mech engr, Cold Regions Res & Eng Lab, 70-74; res ctr dir, Mich Technol Univ, 74-75; SUPVR RES GEN ENGR, US ARMY COLD REGIONS RES & ENG LAB, 75- *Mem:* Int Soc Terrain-Vehicle Systs. *Res:* Off road vehicles; over snow vehicles. *Mailing Add:* US Army Cold Regions PO Box 282 Hanover NH 03775

LISTOWSKY, IRVING, b Vilna, Poland, Dec 21, 35; US citizen; m 63; c 3. BIOCHEMISTRY. *Educ:* Yeshiva Univ, BA, 57; Polytech Inst Brooklyn, PhD(org chem), 63. *Prof Exp:* From instr to asst prof, 65-73, assoc prof, 73-78, PROF BIOCHEM, ALBERT EINSTEIN COL MED, 79- *Concurrent Pos:* NIH career develop award, 71-76; sr investr, NY Heart Asn, 67-70. *Mem:* Am Soc Biol Chemists. *Res:* Structure-function relationships of various biological substances, especially protein chemistry assembly systems and interacting macromolecules. *Mailing Add:* Albert Einstein Col of Med Yeshiva Univ Bronx NY 10461

LISY, JAMES MICHAEL, b Cleveland, Ohio, Aug 5, 52; m 76. SPECTROSCOPY, MOLECULAR BEAMS. *Educ:* Iowa State Univ, BS, 74; Harvard Univ, MA, 77, PhD(chem physics), 79. *Prof Exp:* Res assoc, Lawrence Berkeley Lab, 79-81; ASST PROF CHEM, UNIV ILL, 81- *Mem:* Am Chem Soc; Am Phys Soc. *Res:* Structure, bonding and intramolecular energy transfer of small molecular clusters are studied using molecular beam techniques and laser spectroscopy. *Mailing Add:* Sch Chem Sci Univ Ill 175 NL-Box 64 505 S Mathews Urbana IL 61801

LISZT, HARVEY STEVEN, b Newark, NJ, Dec 5, 45; m 73; c 2. RADIO ASTRONOMY. *Educ:* Univ Mass, BS, 67; Princeton Univ, AM, 69, PhD(astron), 74. *Prof Exp:* Res assoc spectros, Princeton Univ Observ, 69-71; asst prof physics, Univ Pittsburgh, 75-76; res assoc, 73-75, assoc scientist, 76-79, SCIENTIST ASTRON, NAT RADIO ASTRON OBSERV, 79- *Res:* Structure and evolution of interstellar clouds; radiation transport in simple interstellar molecules; structure of the galactic nucleus, interstellar chemistry. *Mailing Add:* Nat Radio Astron Observ Edgemont Rd Charlottesville VA 22901

LIT, ALFRED, b New York, NY, Nov 24, 14; m 47. VISION, EXPERIMENTAL PSYCHOLOGY. *Educ:* Columbia Univ, BS, 38, AM, 43, PhD, 48. *Prof Exp:* Lectr optom, Columbia Univ, 46-48, assoc, 48-49, asst psychol, 49, asst prof optom, 49-52, assoc prof, 52-56; res psychologist, Univ Mich, 56-59; head, Human Factors Staff, Systs Div, Bendix Corp, 59-61; PROF PSYCHOL, SOUTHERN ILL UNIV, 61- *Concurrent Pos:* Res grant, Am Acad Optom, Columbia Univ, 49, mem psychol staff, Off Naval Res Contract, 49-56; lectr, Univ Mich, 57-58; res grants, Eye Inst, USPHS & NSF, 62; mem, Armed Forces-Nat Res Coun Comt Vision; mem, exec comt, Eng Biophysics Prog, Southern Ill Univ, 72-; mem exec comt, Molecular Sci Doctoral Prog, Southern Ill Univ, 73-80; sci referee, Am J Optom, 73. *Honors & Awards:* Sigma Xi-Kaplan Res Award, Southern Ill Univ Found, 71. *Mem:* Fel AAAS; fel Optical Soc Am; fel Am Psychol Asn; fel Am Acad Optom; NY Acad Sci. *Res:* Perception; systems research on human factors. *Mailing Add:* Dept of Psychol Southern Ill Univ Carbondale IL 62901

LIT, JOHN WAI-YU, b Canton, China, Aug 31, 37; Can citizen; c 2. OPTICS. *Educ:* Univ Hong Kong, BSc, 58, dipl ed, 61; Univ Laval, DSc(optics), 69. *Prof Exp:* Head physics, Diocesan Boys Sch, 61-64; teacher sci, Quebec High Sch, 64-65; fel optics, Univ Western Ont, 68-69; res assoc, 69-71, from asst prof to assoc prof optics, Univ Laval, 71-77; assoc prof, 77-80, PROF OPTICS, WILFRID LAURIER UNIV, 80-, CHMN, PHYSICS DEPT, 80- *Concurrent Pos:* Consult, Commun Res Ctr, Can, 73; Bell-Northern Res, Ottawa, 73-75; Gen-Tec Inc, Quebec, 74; Defence Res Estab Valcartier, Can, 75-76 & Can Wire & Cable, Montreal, 77-78; assoc ed, Optical Soc Am, 74-79; chmn div optical physics, Can Asn Physicists, 77-78. *Mem:* Can Asn Physicists; Optical Soc Am. *Res:* Diffraction and propagation of electromagnetic waves, fiber and integrated optics; optical instrumentation. *Mailing Add:* Dept of Physics Wilfrid Laurier Univ Waterloo ON N2L 3C5 Can

LITANT, IRVING, b Boston, Mass, July 29, 17; m 47; c 2. ORGANIC CHEMISTRY, MATERIALS SCIENCE. *Educ:* Boston Col, BS, 40; Univ Mass, MS, 42. *Prof Exp:* Res chemist, Allied Chem Corp, 50-55; chemist dielec mat, Transformer Div, Gen Elec Co, 55-60; sr research aerospace mat, Res & Advan Develop Div, AVCO Corp, 60-67; sr scientist electronic mat, Electronics Res Ctr, NASA, 67-70; MAT SCIENTIST HAZARDOUS MAT, TRANSP SYSTS CTR, US DEPT TRANSP, 70- *Concurrent Pos:* Mem ad hoc comt Fire Safety Aspects Polymeric Mat, Nat Acad Sci, 77-78. *Mem:* Sigma Xi; Am Chem Soc; Am Soc Testing & Mat; Soc Advan Mat & Processes; Nat Fire Protection Asn. *Res:* Engineering and fluorocarbon chemistry; dielectric properties; polymers and plastics; flammability; hazardous materials. *Mailing Add:* Dept of Transp Kendall Sq Cambridge MA 02142

LITCHFIELD, CAROL DARLINE, b Cincinnati, Ohio, Oct 10, 36; m 60. MARINE MICROBIOLOGY, MICROBIAL PHYSIOLOGY. *Educ:* Univ Cincinnati, BS, 58; Univ A&M Univ, PhD(biochem), 69. *Prof Exp:* Res scientist oceanog, Tex A&M Univ, 60-65; from instr to asst prof, 70-75, ASSOC PROF MICROBIOL, RUTGERS UNIV, NEW BRUNSWICK, 75- *Concurrent Pos:* Supvr, Aquatic & Microbiol Biol Sect, Haskell Lab, E I Du Pont de Nemours & Co. *Mem:* Am Soc Microbiol; Am Soc Limnol & Oceanog; Int Asn Theoret & Appl Limnol; Soc Gen Microbiol; Am Acad Microbiol. *Res:* Microbiol degradation processes; taxonomy of industrially important bacteria. *Mailing Add:* Dept of Microbiol Busch Campus Rutgers Univ New Brunswick NJ 08903

LITCHFIELD, CARTER, b Pasadena, Calif, Feb 18, 32; m 60. BIOCHEMISTRY. *Educ:* Rensselaer Polytech Inst, BS, 53; Am Inst Foreign Trade, BFT, 57; Tex A&M Univ, PhD(chem), 66. *Prof Exp:* Chemist, Procter & Gamble Co, 53-60; from asst prof to assoc prof lipid biochem, Tex A&M Univ, 60-69; assoc prof lipid biochem, Rutgers Univ, 69-73, from assoc prof to prof biochem, 73-79; WRITER & PUBL, OLEARIOS ED, 79- *Concurrent Pos:* Vis scientist, Fisheries Res Bd Can, 67 & Univ Trondheim, 75 & 79. *Honors & Awards:* Bond Award, Am Oil Chem Soc, 63, 66 & 78. *Mem:* Soc Hist Technol; Am Oil Chem Soc; Soc Indust Archeol. *Res:* Biochemistry of lipids of marine organisms; analysis of natural fat triglyceride mixtures; gas liquid chromatography of lipids; biochemical systematics of lipids; history of lipid biochemistry; history of fats & oils technology. *Mailing Add:* Olearius Editions PO Box H Kemblesville PA 19347

LITCHFIELD, JOHN HYLAND, b Scituate, Mass, Feb 13, 29; m 66; c 1. FOOD SCIENCE, INDUSTRIAL MICROBIOLOGY. *Educ:* Mass Inst Technol, SB, 50; Univ Ill, MS, 54, PhD(food technol), 56. *Prof Exp:* Chief chemist, Searle Food Corp, Fla, 50-51; res food technologist, Swift & Co, Ill, 56-57; asst prof food eng, Ill Inst Technol, 57-60; sr food technologist, 60-61, proj leader biosci, 61-62, asst chief biosci res, 62-64, chief biochem & microbiol res, 64-67 & microbiol & environ biol res, 67-68, assoc mgr life sci, Dept Chem & Chem Eng, 68-70, mgr biol & med sci sect, Columbus Labs, 70-72, sr tech adv, 73-76, mgr Bioeng & Health Sci Sect, 76-80, PROG MGR, BIOL SCI, COLUMBUS LABS, BATTELLE MEM INST, 80- *Concurrent Pos:* Consult to food indust, 57-60. *Mem:* Fel AAAS; fel Am Inst Chemists; fel Am Acad Microbiol; fel Am Indust Microbiol (pres, 70-71); fel Am Pub Health Asn. *Res:* Food processing and preservation; food, industrial, sanitary and public health microbiology; microbial biochemistry; mass cultivation of microorganisms; nutrional evaluation of food processing methods. *Mailing Add:* 255 Bryant Columbus OH 43085

LITCHFIELD, WILLIAM JOHN, b Waukegan, Ill, Feb 28, 50; m 72; c 1. BIOCHEMISTRY, CLINICAL CHEMISTRY. *Educ:* Univ Ill, BS, 72, MS, 73; Mich State Univ, PhD(biochem), 76. *Prof Exp:* Fel biophys, Johnson Res Found, Sch Med, Univ Pa, 76-77; RES BIOCHEMIST, INSTRUMENT PRODS DIV, E I DU PONT DE NEMOURS & CO, INC, 77- *Concurrent Pos:* NIH fel, 76-77. *Mem:* Am Chem Soc; Am Asn Clin Chem; Reticuloendothelial Soc; Biophys Soc. *Res:* Biophysics; solid state biochemical reactions; free- radical reactions in leukocytes, mitochondria and photosystems; immunology, enzymology, lipid chemistry. *Mailing Add:* Photo Prods Dept E I du Pont de Nemours & Co Inc Wilmington DE 19711

LITCHFORD, GEORGE B, b Long Beach, Calif, Aug 12, 18; m 42; c 2. ELECTRONICS. *Educ:* Reed Col, BA, 41. *Prof Exp:* Head eng sect, Aircraft Radio Dept, Sperry Gyroscope Co, 41-51; asst supvr navig dept, 51-55, head dept aviation systs res, 57-65, HEAD DEPT AVIATION SYSTS CONSULT BUS, AIRBORNE INSTRUMENTS LAB, 65- *Concurrent Pos:* Consult, Dept Transp, Dept Defense, NASA & indust. *Honors & Awards:* Wright Bros Lect Medal & Citation, Am Inst Aeronaut & Astronaut, 78; Lamme Medal, Inst Elec & Electronics Engrs, 81. *Mem:* Fel Inst Elec & Electronics Engrs; fel Am Inst Aeronaut & Astronaut. *Res:* Inventor of many systems including precision omniranges, allweather landing systems, distance measuring equipment, secondary radar systems; developed navigational and collision avoidance concepts; research into low visibility landing and air traffic control. *Mailing Add:* 32 Cherry Lawn Lane Northport NY 11768

LITCHFORD, ROBERT GARY, parasitology, see previous edition

LITHERLAND, ALBERT EDWARD, b Wallasey, Eng, Mar 12, 28; Can citizen; m 56; c 2. NUCLEAR PHYSICS. *Educ:* Univ Liverpool, BSc, 49, PhD(physics), 55. *Prof Exp:* Nat Res Coun Can fel nuclear physics, Atomic Energy Can, Ltd, 53-55, sci officer, 55-60; Atomic Energy Can Ltd vis scientist, Oxford Univ, 60-61, 72-73; sci officer, Atomic Energy Can, Ltd, 61-66; prof, 66-79, UNIV PROF PHYSICS, UNIV TORONTO, 79- *Honors & Awards:* Gold Medal, Can Asn Physicists, 71; Rutherford Medal, Brit Inst Physics, 74. *Mem:* Fel Am Phys Soc; Royal Soc; Can Asn Physicists; Royal Soc Can. *Res:* Electron induced fission of light elements, mass spectrometry of 14-C and 36-Cl; nuclear spectroscopy of light nuclei using charged particle accelerators; radiative capture of charged particles by nuclei; collective motion in light nuclei; fast neutron spectroscopy. *Mailing Add:* Dept of Physics Univ of Toronto Toronto ON M5S 1A7 Can

LITKE, JOHN DAVID, b Winchester, Mass, May 30, 44. COMPUTER SCIENCE, PHYSICS. *Educ:* Mass Inst Technol, BS, 65; Johns Hopkins Univ, PhD(physics), 76. *Prof Exp:* Instr physics, Johns Hopkins Univ, 67-75; mem tech staff comput sci, 76-80, MGR COMPUT ENG, BELL LABS, 81- *Mem:* Sigma Xi; Am Phys Soc; Inst Elec & Electronic Engrs; Asn Comput Mach. *Res:* Real-time command and control systems; artificial intelligence. *Mailing Add:* Kollmorgen C/Photo Circuits Div Bell Labs 31 Seacliff Ave Glen Cove NY 11542

LITKE, LARRY LAVOE, b Denver, Colo, June 1, 49; m 69; c 2. ELECTRON MICROSCOPY. *Educ:* Ottawa Univ, BA, 71; Kans State Teachers Col, MS, 73; Univ NDak, PhD(anat), 76. *Prof Exp:* Teaching asst anat, Univ NDak, 73-75, res asst, 75-76, instr, 76, asst prof, 77; instr, 77-78, ASST PROF ANAT, MED COL OHIO, 78- *Mem:* Sigma Xi; Electron Micros Soc Am;

Am Asn Anatomists. *Res:* Light and electron microscopy of normal and experimentally induced changes in cell morphology and behavior during early embryonic development; early germ layer formation and cardiovascular and nervous systmes of the chick embryo. *Mailing Add:* Dept Anat Med Col Ohio CS 10008 Toledo OH 43699

LITLE, WILLIAM A, civil engineering, see previous edition

LITMAN, BERNARD, b New York, NY, Oct 26, 20; m 49; c 2. ELECTRICAL ENGINEERING. *Educ:* Columbia Univ, BS, 41, PhD(elec eng), 49; Univ Pittsburgh, MS, 43. *Prof Exp:* Engr mach design, Westinghouse Elec Corp, 41-47; instr elec eng, Univ Pittsburgh, 47; engr fire control & guid, 48-53, mgr airborne equip, 56-58, res, 59-61, CHIEF ENGR, AMBAC INDUSTS, DIV UNITED TECHNOLOGIES CORP, 63- *Res:* Electromechanical control and computing equipment; weapon control and navigation; inertial guidance; data management systems for aircraft and scientific instruments. *Mailing Add:* 2857 Morgan Dr Wantagh NY 11794

LITMAN, BURTON JOSEPH, b Boston, Mass, May 8, 35; m 58; c 2. BIOCHEMISTRY. *Educ:* Boston Univ, BA, 58; Univ Ore, PhD(biophys chem), 66. *Prof Exp:* Asst prof, 68-76, assoc prof, 76-80, PROF BIOCHEM, SCH MED, UNIV VA, 80- *Concurrent Pos:* USPHS fel biochem, Sch Med, Univ Va, 66-68. *Mem:* AAAS; Biophys Soc; Am Soc Photobiol; Am Soc Biol Chemists; Asn Res Vision & Ophthal. *Res:* Structure-function relationships in biological membranes with particular emphasis on the molecular mechanism of vision. *Mailing Add:* Dept of Biochem Univ of Va Sch of Med Charlottesville VA 22908

LITMAN, DAVID JAY, b Philadelphia, Pa, Mar 30, 49. BIOCHEMISTRY, IMMUNOCHEMISTRY. *Educ:* Pa State Univ, BS, 70; Columbia Univ, MA, 72, PhD(chem), 75. *Prof Exp:* Fel membrane biochem, Yale Univ Med Sch, 75-77; sr chemist immuno diag, 77-81, RES MGR, SYVA RES INST, SYNTEX CORP, 81- *Mem:* AAAS. *Res:* Enzymology; membrane biochemistry; applying advanced concepts of biotechnology and bioengineering to clinical immunodiagnostic research; clinical chemistry. *Mailing Add:* Syva Res Inst 3221 Porter Dr Palo Alto CA 94304

LITMAN, GARY WILLIAM, b Shoemaker, Calif, June 26, 45; m 70. IMMUNOLOGY, BIOCHEMISTRY. *Educ:* Univ Minn, BA, 67, PhD(microbiol), 72. *Prof Exp:* Res asst microbiol, Univ Minn, 67-68, teaching specialist microbiol & pediat, 68-70, instr pediat & path, 70-72, asst prof path, 72; ASSOC MEM, DEPT MACROMOLECULAR BIOCHEM, SLOAN-KETTERING INST, 72-; ASSOC PROF BIOL, SLOAN-KETTERING DIV, GRAD SCH MED SCI, CORNELL UNIV, 73- *Concurrent Pos:* Assoc prof genetics, Sloan-Kettering Div, Grad Sch Med Sci, Cornell Univ, 76-, chmn biol unit, 78-80, assoc prof immunol, 80. *Mem:* AAAS; Am Asn Immunologists; Am Asn Biol Chemists; Am Soc Zoologists; Biophys Soc. *Res:* Evolution of immunoglobulin structure; a typical solubility characteristics of proteins; chemical carcinogenesis; chromosomal proteins. *Mailing Add:* Dept of Macromolec Biochem 145 Boston Post Rd Rye NY 10580

LITMAN, IRVING ISAAC, b Chelsea, Mass, Nov 16, 25. FOOD TECHNOLOGY. *Educ:* Univ Mass, BA, 49, MS, 51; Wash State Univ, PhD(food technol), 56. *Prof Exp:* Processed food inspector, Prod & Mkt Admin, USDA, 50-51; food technologist, Gen Prod Div, Qm Food & Container Inst, US Armed Forces, 51-53; asst dairy technologist, Wash State Univ, 53-55; jr res chemist, Univ Calif, 55-56; proj leader, Res Ctr, Gen Foods Corp, 56-62; flavor chemist, Givaudan Corp, 62-64; sect head, Durkee Famous Foods, 64-65; RES DIR, STEPAN FLAVORS & FRAGRANCES, INC, 66- *Mem:* Royal Soc Chem; Inst Food Technologists; AAAS; Sigma Xi; Flavor Chemists Soc. *Res:* Development of synthetic and natural flavorings for food, tobacco and pharmaceuticals. *Mailing Add:* Stepan Chem Co Flavor Fragrance Dept 500 Academy Dr Northbrook IL 60062

LITMAN, NATHAN, b New York, NY, Nov 22, 46; m 69; c 2. PEDIATRICS, INFECTIOUS DISEASES. *Educ:* Brooklyn Col, BS, 67; Albert Einstein Col Med, MD, 71. *Prof Exp:* Intern, resident & chief resident pediat, Montefiore Hosp & Med Ctr, 71-74; lieutenant comdr pediat, USPHS, 74-76; fel infectious dis, Albert Einstein Col Med, 76-78; ATTEND PEDIAT & INFECTIOUS DIS, MONTEFIORE HOSP & MED CTR, 78- *Mem:* Fel Am Acad Pediat. *Res:* Infectious etiologies of pediatric diarrhea. *Mailing Add:* Dept of Pediat NCent Bronx Hosp Bronx NY 10467

LITOSCH, IRENE, b New York, NY, June 7, 52. PHYSIOLOGICAL CHEMISTRY. *Educ:* New York Univ, Univ Arts & Sci, BA, 74; State Univ NY, Downstate Med Ctr, PhD(pharmacol), 79. *Prof Exp:* FEL RES, SECT PHYSIOL CHEM, BROWN UNIV, 79- *Mem:* NY Acad Sci. *Res:* Mechanism of regulation of intiacularlur calcium. *Mailing Add:* Sect Physiol Chem Box G Brown Univ Providence RI 02912

LITOVITZ, THEODORE AARON, b New York, NY, Oct 14, 23; m 46; c 2. PHYSICS. *Educ:* Cath Univ, AB, 46, PhD, 50. *Prof Exp:* From asst prof to assoc prof, 50-59, PROF PHYSICS, CATH UNIV AM, 59-, CO-DIR, VITREOUS STATE LAB, 68- *Concurrent Pos:* Consult, Univ Hosp, Georgetown, 50-57. *Mem:* Fel Am Phys Soc; fel Acoust Soc Am; Am Philos Soc. *Res:* Ultrasonic propagation and light scattering in studies of molecular motions in liquids and glasses; development of glasses with unique technical applications. *Mailing Add:* Dept of Physics Cath Univ of Am Washington DC 20064

LITSKY, BERTHA YANIS, b Chester, Pa, Jan 2, 20; m 65; c 2. MICROBIOLOGY, HOSPITAL ADMINISTRATION. *Educ:* Philadelphia Col Pharm, BSc, 42; NY Univ, MPA, 64; Walden Univ, PhD(educ), 74. *Prof Exp:* Head dept bact, Assoc Labs of Philadelphia, 42-44; asst supvr prod, Nat Drug Co, 44-45; res bacteriologist, Univ Pa, 45-50; self-employed, Pa & NY, 50-56; head dept bact, Staten Island Hosp, NY, 56-64; environ microbiol consult, 64-74; NURSE CONSULT, BINGHAM ASSOCS FUND, NEW

ENG MED CTR HOSP, 74- *Concurrent Pos:* Mem, Standards Comt, Asn Operating Room Nurses, 75- *Mem:* Am Hosp Asn; Am Soc Microbiol; Am Pub Health Asn; Inst Sanit Mgt; Royal Soc Health. *Res:* Environmental and clinical microbiology; control of cross-infection in hospitals; hospital sanitation, environmental microbiology and administration; antimicrobial agents, antiseptics, disinfectants and germicides; disinfection and sterilization; aseptic practices in the operating room. *Mailing Add:* Marshall Hall Univ of Mass Amherst MA 01002

LITSKY, WARREN, b Worcester, Mass, June 10, 24; m 65. BACTERIOLOGY. *Educ:* Clark Univ, AB, 45; Univ Mass, MS, 48; Mich State Univ, PhD(bact), 51. *Prof Exp:* Inst bact, Mich State Univ, 51; from asst res prof to res prof, 51-61, dir tech guid ctr, Environ Control, 68-73, COMMONWEALTH PROF BACT, UNIV MASS, AMHERST, 61-, DIR INST AGR & INDUST MICROBIOL, 63-, CHMN DEPT ENVIRON SCI, 72- *Concurrent Pos:* Ed, Newsletter, 62-66; NIH res fel marine microbiol, Oceanog Inst, Fla State Univ, 65-66; adv comt radiation preservation foods, Nat Acad Sci-Nat Res Coun, 65-67; consult, Div Water Supply & Pollution Control, Fed Water Pollution Control Admin, Environ Protection Agency & Sanit Prog, Health & Hosp Facil, Dept Health, Educ & Welfare; affiliate prof bact, Clark Univ, 66-72; mem task group microbiol aspects of raw shucked oysters, Nat Res Coun; pres, Environ Mgt Inc, 67-; mem adv coun, Mass Water Resource Res Ctr, 67-72; spec comn to study methods to reuse solid waste, Mass, 70-73; comt on environ impact statements, Lower Pioneer Valley Planning Comn, 71-; res grant study sect, Environ Protection Agency; consult, Shellfish Prog, Food & Drug Admin, 74-; mem, Mass Comn Nuclear Safety, 74-; mem, US Comt Israel Environ, 73-; Dir, Rush-Hampton Industs, 75- *Honors & Awards:* Sayer Prize, 51; dipl, Am Intersoc Acad Cert Sanit; Ed Award, Hosp Mgt Mag, 69. *Mem:* Fel AAAS; Soc Indust Microbiol; Am Soc Microbiol; fel Am Pub Health Asn; Brit Soc Appl Bact. *Res:* Water and sewage pollution; thermal death and vaccine production; fermentations; food and dairy bacteriology; disinfection; marine microbiology. *Mailing Add:* Dept Environ Sci Marshall Hall 9 Kettle Pond Rd Amherst MA 01002

LITSTER, JAMES DAVID, b Toronto, Ont, Can, June, 19, 38; m 65. SOLID STATE PHYSICS, OPTICS. *Educ:* McMaster Univ, BEng, 61; Mass Inst Tech, PhD(physics), 65. *Prof Exp:* From instr to assoc prof, 65-75, PROF PHYSICS, MASS INST TECHNOL, 75- *Concurrent Pos:* Fel, John Simon Guggenheim Mem Found, 71-72; lectr physics, Harvard Med Sch, 74- *Mem:* AAAS; Am Phys Soc. *Res:* Magnetism; light scattering; liquid crystals; x-ray scattering using synchrotron radiation. *Mailing Add:* Dept of Physics Mass Inst of Technol Cambridge MA 02139

LITT, BERTRAM D, b New York, NY, Oct 6, 25; m 60; c 2. BIOSTATISTICS. *Educ:* NY Univ, BA, 46; Univ Mo, MA, 52. *Prof Exp:* Assoc res scientist, Human Eng, Col Eng, Res Div, NY Univ, 54-60; assoc proj dir, Am Orthotic & Prosthetic Asn, 60-62; statistician, Bur Med & Surg, Vet Admin, 62-66 & Bur Med, Dept Navy, 66-69; math statistician, Bur Drugs, Food & Drug Admin, 69-79; STATISTICIAN, OFF PESTICIDE PROG, ENVIRON PROTECTION AGENCY, 79- *Concurrent Pos:* Consult, Clin Trials Comt, Rheumatoid Arthritis Found, 72-75, Food & Drug Admin, 79-, Fedn Am Socs Exp Biol, 78-81. *Mem:* Am Statist Asn; Biomet Soc. *Res:* Design and analysis of studies, particularly clinical and animal trials and design of medical information systems; assessment of risks. *Mailing Add:* 14502 Woodcrest Dr Rockville MD 20853

LITT, MICHAEL, b New York, NY, Apr 17, 33; m 56. BIOCHEMISTRY. *Educ:* Oberlin Col, BA, 54; Harvard Univ, PhD(chem), 58. *Prof Exp:* Instr chem, Reed Col, 58-62, asst prof, 64-67; assoc prof biochem, 67-71, PROF BIOCHEM & MED GENETICS, MED SCH, UNIV ORE, 71- *Concurrent Pos:* NIH spec fel, Mass Inst Technol, 62-63; NSF fel, Auckland Univ, 66-67. *Mem:* Am Chem Soc; Am Soc Biol Chemists. *Res:* Structure, function and metabolism of transfer RNA. *Mailing Add:* Dept of Biochem Univ of Ore Med Sch Portland OR 97201

LITT, MITCHELL, b Brooklyn, NY, Oct 11, 32; m 55; c 2. BIOENGINEERING, CHEMICAL ENGINEERING. *Educ:* Columbia Univ, AB, 53, BS, 54, MS 56, DEngSc(chem eng), 61. *Prof Exp:* Res engr, Esso Res & Eng Co, NJ, 58-61; from asst prof to assoc prof, 61-71, PROF CHEM ENG, UNIV PA, 71-, PROF BIOENG, 73- *Concurrent Pos:* Vis prof, Weizmann Inst, 79. *Mem:* Am Inst Chem Engrs; Am Soc Eng Educ; Biomed Eng Soc; Am Chem Soc; Int Soc Biorheology. *Res:* Application of chemical engineering techniques to biomedical problems; biorheology, with applications to blood and epithelial secretions. *Mailing Add:* Dept of Bioengineering Univ of Pa Philadelphia PA 19104

LITT, MORTIMER, b Brooklyn, NY, Sept 28, 25; m 54; c 3. IMMUNOLOGY. *Educ:* Columbia Univ, BA, 47; Univ Rochester, MD, 52. *Prof Exp:* Med house officer & asst resident physician, Peter Bent Brigham Hosp, 52-54; instr, 56-59, assoc, 60-65, asst prof, 65-71, asst dean teaching resources, 73-78, ASSOC PROF MICROBIOL & MOLECULAR GENETICS, HARVARD MED SCH, 71-, ASSOC DEAN EDUC PROGS, 79- *Concurrent Pos:* Res fel, Harvard Med Sch, 54-56 & 56-59; Helen Hay Whitney Found fel, 59-63; estab investr, Am Heart Asn, 63-68; asst dir dept bact, Boston City Hosp, 69-77. *Mem:* Am Asn Immunologists; Am Fedn Clin Res; NY Acad Sci. *Res:* Eosinophil leukocyte. *Mailing Add:* Harvard Med Sch Boston MA 02115

LITT, MORTON HERBERT, b Brooklyn, NY, Apr 10, 26; m 57; c 2. POLYMER CHEMISTRY. *Educ:* City Col New York, BS, 47; Polytech Inst Brooklyn, MS, 53, PhD(polymer chem), 56. *Prof Exp:* Turner & Newall res fel, Manchester Univ, 56-57; res assoc, State Univ NY Col Forestry, Syracuse, 58-60; sr scientist, Cent Res Lab, Allied Chem Corp, 60-64, assoc dir res, 65-67; assoc prof, 67-76, PROF POLYMER SCI, CASE WESTERN RESERVE UNIV, 76- *Mem:* AAAS; Am Chem Soc; NY Acad Sci; Am Phys Soc; The Chem Soc. *Res:* Ionic and free radical polymerization mechanisms; organo-fluorine chemistry; polymer mechanical properties; polymer electrical properties. *Mailing Add:* Dept Macromolecular Sci Case Western Reserve Univ Cleveland OH 44106

LITTAUER, ERNEST LUCIUS, b London, Eng, Mar 8, 36; US citizen; m 69. ELECTROCHEMISTRY, CORROSION. *Educ:* Univ London, BSc, 58, PhD(electrometall), 61. *Prof Exp:* Res scientist, Derby Luminescents Div, Derby Metals, LonLondon, 62-63; sr scientist, Lockheed Aircraft Serv Co, 63-69, mgr, Electrochem Dept, 69-72, MGR, CHEM DEPT, LOCKHEED MISSILES & SPACE CO, 72- *Concurrent Pos:* Fel corrosion, Battersea Col Technol, 61-62; lectr, Sir John Cass Col & Enfield Col, London, 62-63; chmn, Res Coun Corrosion Comt, Lockheed Aircraft Corp, 66-; lectr electrochem, Univ Santa Clara, 74-76. *Honors & Awards:* Recognition Award, Nat Asn Corrosion Engrs, 68. *Mem:* Electrochem Soc; Am Chem Soc. *Res:* Electrochemistry; energy conversion; process chemistry; analytical, inorganic and plasma chemistry; materials evaluation; chemical and chemical engineering development and design. *Mailing Add:* 27305 Deer Springs Way Los Altos Hills CA 94022

LITTAUER, RAPHAEL MAX, b Leipzig, Ger, Nov 28, 25; US citizen; m 50; c 2. EXPERIMENTAL HIGH ENERGY PHYSICS, ELECTRONICS. *Educ:* Cambridge Univ, MA & PhD(physics), 50. *Prof Exp:* Asst physics, Cambridge Univ, 47-50; res assoc nuclear physics, Cornell Univ, 50-54 & Synchrotron Lab, Gen Elec Co, 54-55; res assoc prof physics, 55-63, res prof, 63-65, chmn dept, 74-77, PROF PHYSICS & NUCLEAR STUDIES, CORNELL UNIV, 65- *Mem:* Am Phys Soc. *Mailing Add:* Newman Lab Cornell Univ Ithaca NY 14853

LITTELL, ARTHUR SIMPSON, b Washington, DC, Jan 18, 25; m 48, 71; c 5. BIOSTATISTICS. *Educ:* Harvard Univ, AB, 44; Johns Hopkins Univ, AM, 48, ScD(biostatist), 51. *Prof Exp:* From instr to assoc prof biostatist, Sch Med, Western Reserve Univ, dir dept, Biomet Comput Lab, 63-70; PROF BIOMET, UNIV TEX SCH PUB HEALTH, HOUSTON, 70- *Concurrent Pos:* Mem epidemiol & dis control study sect, Div Res Grants, NIH, 68-72. *Mem:* Biomet Soc; Am Statist Asn; Am Heart Asn; Am Pub Health Asn; Soc Epidemiol Res. *Res:* Actuarial and statistical methods in medicine and public health; applications of computers in public health; cooperative studies; cardiovascular research. *Mailing Add:* Univ of Tex Sch of Pub Health Box 20186 Houston TX 77025

LITTELL, RAMON CLARENCE, b Rolla, Kans, Nov 18, 42; m 66; c 1. AGRICULTURAL STATISTICS, MATHEMATICAL STATISTICS. *Educ:* Kans State Teachers Col, BS, 64; Okla State Univ, MS, 66, PhD(statist), 70. *Prof Exp:* Prof statist, 70-77, ASSOC PROF & ASSOC STATISTICIAN, UNIV FLA, 77- *Mem:* Am Statist Asn. *Res:* Determination of relative efficiencies of tests of hypothesis, nonparametric estimation, design of experiments and statistical computing. *Mailing Add:* 3840 NW 35th Pl Gainesville FL 32601

LITTERIA, MARILYN, b Cleveland, Ohio, Aug 9, 31. NEUROENDOCRINOLOGY. *Educ:* Case Western Reserve Univ, BS, 55; Univ Calif, Berkeley, PhD(physiol), 67. *Prof Exp:* Lab technician physiol, Case Western Reserve Univ, 55-59, lab technician anat, 59-60; teaching asst physiol, Univ Calif, Berkeley, 61-63; res fel endocrinol, Scripps Clin & Res Found & Develop Neuroendocrinol Lab, Vet Admin Hosp, San Fernando, 67-69; res assoc reproductive biol, Univ NC, 70-71; instr anat & Sloan fel, Northwestern Univ, 71-72; RES PHYSIOLOGIST & PRIN INVESTR, VET ADMIN HOSP, NORTH CHICAGO, ILL, 72- *Mem:* Endocrine Soc; Sigma Xi. *Res:* The role of sex steroids in central nervous system development. *Mailing Add:* Vet Admin Hosp North Chicago IL 60064

LITTERST, CHARLES LAWRENCE, b Cleveland, Ohio, 44. PHARMACOLOGY, TOXICOLOGY. *Educ:* Purdue Univ, BS, 66; Univ Wis, MS, 68, PhD(toxicol), 70. *Prof Exp:* Pharmacologist, Food & Drug Admin, Washington, DC, 70-72; PHARMACOLOGIST, LAB TOXICOL, NAT CANCER INST, BETHESDA, MD, 72- *Concurrent Pos:* Mem, Toxicol Info subcomt HEW comt to coord toxicol & related progs, 74- *Mem:* Am Soc Pharmacol & Exp Therapeut; Soc Toxicol. *Res:* Factors altering hepatic microsomal drug metabolism; toxicology and pharmacology of platinum; toxicology of antineoplastic drugs. *Mailing Add:* Lab Med Chem & Biol Rm 6028 Bldg 37 NIH Bethesda MD 20205

LITTLE, A BRIAN, b Montreal, Que, Mar 11, 25; US citizen; m 49; c 6. OBSTETRICS & GYNECOLOGY. *Educ:* McGill Univ, BA, 48, MD, CM, 50; Royal Col Physicians & Surgeons, Can, cert obstet & gynec, 55, FRCPS(C), 57; Am Bd Obstet & Gynec, dipl, 59. *Prof Exp:* Intern, Montreal Gen Hosp, 50-51; asst resident & resident, Boston Lying-in-Hosp & Free Hosp Women, Boston, 51-54; asst obstet, Harvard Med Sch, 55-56, instr obstet & gynec, 56-58, tutor med sci, 57-65, assoc obstet & gynec, 58-63, asst prof, 63-65; prof, 66-72, ARTHUR H BILL PROF OBSTET & GYNEC & DIR DEPT REPRODUCTIVE BIOL, SCH MED, CASE WESTERN RESERVE UNIV, 72- *Concurrent Pos:* Teaching fel obstet & gynec, Harvard Med Sch, 52-54; instr, Sch Nursing, Boston Univ, 51 & 55-57; asst obstetrician outpatients, Boston Lying-in-Hosp, 55-56, asst obstetrician, 56-58, assoc, 58-59, obstetrician & gynecologist, 59-65; sr obstetrician prenatal metab div, USPHS, 55-56; assoc vis surgeon, Boston City Hosp, 55-64, assoc dir dept obstet & gynec, 58-63, dir, 63-65, vis surgeon, 65; asst surgeon, Free Hosp Women, 58-64, mem courtesy staff, 64-65; mem consult staff, Sturdy Mem Hosp, Attleboro, 61-65; chief consult, Hunt Mem Hosp, Danvers, 62-65; mem consult staff, Elliott Community Hosp, Keene, NH, 63-65; dir dept obstet & gynec, Cleveland Metrop Hosp, Ohio, 66-72; assoc obstetrician & gynecologist, Univ Hosps, Cleveland, 66-72, dir dept obstet & gynec, 72- *Mem:* AMA; fel Am Col Obstet & Gynec; Am Gynec Soc; Soc Gynec Invest; fel Am Col Surgeons. *Res:* Steroid mechanism in vivo, in vitro, primarily in reproduction. *Mailing Add:* Univ Hosps 2065 Adelbert Rd Cleveland OH 44106

LITTLE, ANGELA C, b San Francisco, Calif, Jan 12, 20; m 47; c 1. FOOD SCIENCE. *Educ:* Univ Calif, AB, 40, MS, 54, PhD(agr chem), 69. *Prof Exp:* Res asst food sci, 53-56, jr specialist, 56-58, from asst specialist to assoc specialist, 58-69, asst food scientist, 69-71, assoc food scientist, 71-79, lectr food sci, 69-79, ASSOC PROF, UNIV CALIF, BERKELEY, 79- *Concurrent*

Pos: Vis scholar, Univ Wash, Seattle, 76-77. *Mem:* AAAS; Optical Soc Am; Inter-Soc Color Coun; Inst Food Technol. *Res:* Colorimetry; methodology and systems relating to objective measurements; color vision; taste perception related to changes in physiological state. *Mailing Add:* Dept of Nutrit Sci Univ of Calif Berkeley CA 94720

LITTLE, BARNEY HUGH, JR, aerodynamics, fluid mechanics, see previous edition

LITTLE, BRIAN WOODS, b Boston, Mass, Dec 15, 45. NEUROMUSCULAR PATHOLOGY, PEDIATRIC PATHOLOGY. *Educ:* Cornell Univ, BA, 67; Univ Vt, MD, 73, PhD(biochem), 77. *Prof Exp:* Resident pathologist, 73-75, ATTEND PATHOLOGIST, MED CTR HOSP VT, 76-; ASST PROF PATH, UNIV VT, 76-, ASST PROF BIOCHEM, 80-. *Mem:* Am Soc Clin Pathologists; Col Am Pathologists. *Res:* Mammalian nucleic acid metabolism; muscle disease; histochemistry; pulmonary smooth muscle biochemistry; pediatric, anatomic and clinical pathology. *Mailing Add:* Dept of Path Univ of Vt Burlington VT 05405

LITTLE, CHARLES DURWOOD, JR, b Denver, Colo, Dec 28, 46. ANATOMY, CELL BIOLOGY. *Educ:* Calif State Polytech Univ, Pomona, BS, 73; Univ Pittsburgh, PhD(anat & cell biol), 77. *Prof Exp:* Res fel, Develop Biol Lab, Mass Gen Hosp, Harvard Med Sch, 77-79; fel, Biol Dept, Univ Calif, San Diego, 79-81; ASST PROF ANAT, UNIV VA, 81- *Res:* Developmental biology of the extracellular matrix; cell surface matrix interactions; double immunolabeling techniques for use in florescence and electron microscopy. *Mailing Add:* Dept Anat Sch Med Univ Va Box 439 Charlottesville VA 22908

LITTLE, CHARLES EDWARD, b Kansas City, Kans, Apr 18, 26; m 47; c 3. MATHEMATICS. *Educ:* Univ Kans, AB, 48; Ft Hays Kans State Col, MS, 55; Colo State Col, EdD(math educ), 64. *Prof Exp:* Instr pub sch, Kans, 51-60, supt, 60-61; instr math, Colo State Col, 61-63; from asst prof to assoc prof, 64-68, chmn dept math, 67-70, PROF MATH EDUC, NORTHERN ARIZ UNIV, 68-, DEAN COL ARTS & SCI, 74- *Mem:* Math Asn Am. *Res:* Training of elementary and secondary mathematics teachers; methods of instruction in mathematics at college level, particularly educational media and techniques for handling large groups; mathematics for the social and behavioral sciences; linear models and statistics. *Mailing Add:* Off of the Dean Northern Ariz Univ Flagstaff AZ 86011

LITTLE, CHARLES GORDON, b Hunan, China, Nov 4, 24; m 54; c 5. ATMOSPHERIC PHYSICS, REMOTE SENSING. *Educ:* Univ Manchester, BSc, 48, PhD(radio astron), 52. *Prof Exp:* Jr engr, Cosmos Mfg Co, Eng, 44-46; jr physicist, Ferranti, Ltd, 46-47; asst lectr physics, Univ Manchester, 52-53; prof geophys res & dep dir geophys inst, Univ Alaska, 54-58; chief radio astron & arctic investigation sect, Nat Bur Standards, 58-60, upper atmosphere & space physics div, Boulder Labs, 60-62, dir cent radio propagation lab, 62-65; dir inst telecommun sci & aeronomy, Environ Sci Serv Admin, 65-67, DIR WAVE PROPAGATION LAB, ENVIRON RES LABS, NAT OCEANIC & ATMOSPHERIC ADMIN, 67- *Concurrent Pos:* Consult, US Nat Comt for Int Geophys Year, 57-59. *Mem:* Nat Acad Eng; AAAS; Inst Elec & Electronics Eng; Am Meterol Soc; Int Union Radio Sci. *Res:* Remote measurement of atmosphere and ocean, using electromagnetic and acoustic waves. *Mailing Add:* Wave Propagation Lab Nat Oceanic & Atmospheric Admin Boulder CO 80303

LITTLE, CHARLES HARRISON ANTHONY, b Toronto, Ont, May 4, 39; m 64; c 2. TREE PHYSIOLOGY. *Educ:* Univ NB, BScF, 61; Yale Univ, MF, 62, PhD(tree physiol), 66. *Prof Exp:* RES SCIENTIST, CAN FORESTRY SERV, 66- *Mem:* Can Soc Plant Physiol. *Res:* Production, movement and transformation of carbohydrate; growth substance regulation of bud and cambial activity. *Mailing Add:* Dept of Fisheries & Environ Can Forestry Serv PO Box 4000 Fredericton NB E3B 5P7 Can

LITTLE, CHARLES ORAN, b Schulenburg, Tex, July 21, 35; m 55; c 3. ANIMAL NUTRITION, AGRICULTURE. *Educ:* Univ Houston, BS, 57; Iowa State Univ, MS, 59, PhD(animal nutrit), 60. *Prof Exp:* Res asst animal nutrit, Iowa State Univ, 57-60; from asst prof to assoc prof, 60-67, indust res grants, 61-72, Agr Res Serv grant, 64-67, PROF ANIMAL SCI, UNIV KY, 67-, ASSOC DEAN RES, 69- *Concurrent Pos:* Assoc dir Ky Agr Exp Sta, 69-; mem & chmn, Southern Regional Res Comt, 72-75; mem, Southern Res Planning Comt, 73-75, chmn, Southern Asn Agr Exp Sta Dirs, 76-77, mem, Exp Sta Comt on Policy, 78- *Honors & Awards:* Distinguished Nutritionist Award, Nat Distillers Feed Res Coun, 64; Outstanding Res Awards, Thomas Poe Cooper & Ky Res Founds, 67. *Mem:* AAAS; Am Soc Animal Sci; Am Inst Nutrit. *Res:* Ruminant nutrition with emphasis on techniques and basic biochemical and physiological explanations of animal responses; general research administration. *Mailing Add:* -107 Agr Sci Ctr Univ of Ky Lexington KY 40506

LITTLE, EDWIN DEMETRIUS, b Orlando, Fla, July 2, 26. ORGANIC CHEMISTRY. *Educ:* Rollins Col, BS, 48; Duke Univ, AM, 53. *Prof Exp:* Sr res chemist, Nitrogen Div, Allied Chem Corp, 53-63, supvry res chemist, 63-66, res assoc, Plastics Div, 66-74, group leader, Specialty Chem Div, 74-79; RES ASSOC, VA CHEM INC, 79- *Mem:* Fel Am Inst Chem; Am Chem Soc; NY Acad Sci. *Res:* Heterocyclic nitrogen compounds; epoxide reactions; monomer synthesis. *Mailing Add:* Va Chem Inc 3340 W Norfolk Rd Portsmouth VA 23703

LITTLE, ELBERT LUTHER, JR, b Ft Smith, Ark, Oct 15, 07; m 43; c 3. BOTANY, DENDROLOGY. *Educ:* Univ Okla, BA, 27, BS, 32; Univ Chicago, MS & PhD(bot), 29. *Prof Exp:* Asst prof biol, Southwestern Okla State Univ, 30-33; from asst forest ecologist to assoc forest ecologist, Ariz, 34-42; dendrologist, US Forest Serv, Washington, DC, 42-76; collabr, 65-76, RES ASSOC, US NAT MUS NATURAL HIST, SMITHSONIAN INST, WASHINGTON, DC, 76- *Concurrent Pos:* Botanist, Econ Admin, Bogota, 43-45; prod specialist, US Com Co, Mexico City, 45; vis prof, Univ Andes,

Venezuela, 53-54 & 60; botanist from Univ Md, Guyana, 55; consult, UN mission, Costa Rica, 64-65 & 67, Ecuador, 65 & 75, Nicaragua, 71 & Okla Forestry Div 30, 77-; vis prof, Va Polytech Inst & State Univ, 66-67 & Univ DC, 79. *Mem:* Fel Explorers Club; fel Soc Am Foresters; Bot Soc Am; Am Soc Plant Taxon; Am Inst Biol Sci. *Res:* Trees of United States and tropical America, their identification, classification, nomenclature, and distribution; ecology. *Mailing Add:* 924 20th St S Arlington VA 22202

LITTLE, ERNEST LEWIS, JR, b Passaic, NJ, Aug 29, 19; m 46. CHEMISTRY. *Educ:* Mass Inst Technol, SB, 41, PhD(org chem), 47. *Prof Exp:* res chemist, E I du Pont de Nemours & Co, Inc, 47-77; RETIRED. *Res:* Organic chemistry; organometallic compounds; synthetic rubber; use of dienes and alkyl aromatic hydrocarbons in alfin catalysis; refractory metals; polymorphism. *Mailing Add:* 2116 The Hwy Wilmington DE 19810

LITTLE, GORDON RICE, optical physics, solid state physics, see previous edition

LITTLE, HAROLD FRANKLIN, b Williamsport, Pa, June 18, 32; m 59; c 1. ENTOMOLOGY, FUNCTIONAL MORPHOLOGY. *Educ:* Lycoming Col, AB, 54; Pa State Univ, MS, 56, PhD(zool), 59. *Prof Exp:* Asst prof biol, WVa Wesleyan Col, 59-63; from asst prof to assoc prof, 63-71, chmn, Div Nat Sci, 68-71 & 73-79, chmn, Biol Dept, 73-78, PROF BIOL, UNIV HAWAII, HILO, 71- *Mem:* AAAS; Am Inst Biol Sci; Am Soc Zool; Entom Soc Am. *Res:* Honey bee response to sounds and vibrations; effects of ionizing radiation on insect midgut epithelium; autoradio- graphy of insect midgut epithelial cell replacement; damage to Medfly pupal flight mucles. *Mailing Add:* Dept of Biol Univ of Hawaii PO Box 1357 Hilo HI 96720

LITTLE, HENRY NELSON, b Portland, Maine, Oct 17, 20; m 48; c 4. BIOCHEMISTRY. *Educ:* Cornell Univ, BS, 42; Univ Wis, MS, 46, PhD(biochem), 48. *Prof Exp:* Res assoc biochem, Univ Chicago, 48-49; asst prof biol, Johns Hopkins Univ, 49-51; from assoc prof chem to prof chem, 51-66, PROF BIOCHEM, UNIV MASS, AMHERST, 66- *Mem:* AAAS; Am Chem Soc; Am Soc Biol Chem. *Res:* Hemoproteins; porphyrins; biosynthesis of chlorophyll; oxidases. *Mailing Add:* Dept of Biochem Univ of Mass Amherst MA 01002

LITTLE, JAMES ALEXANDER, b Detroit, Mich, Dec 8, 22; Can citizen; m 53; c 2. MEDICINE, METABOLISM. *Educ:* Univ Toronto, MD, 46, MA, 50; FRCP(C), 52. *Prof Exp:* Res assoc med, 52-67, clin teacher, 54-63, dir diabetic clin, 54-70, assoc, 63-66, dir clin invest unit, 64-72, from asst prof to assoc prof, 66-74, PROF MED, ST MICHAEL'S HOSP, UNIV TORONTO, 74-, RES COORDR & SECY, RES SOC, 64-, DIR LIPID CLIN, 66-, PROJ DIR, UNIV TORONTO-McMASTER LIPID RES CLIN, 72- *Concurrent Pos:* Nat Res Coun Can fel biochem, Univ Toronto, 47-49, Can Red Cross fel arthritis, Sunnybrook Dept Vet Affairs Hosp, 51-52; mem, Can Nat Comn, Int Union Nutrit Sci, 71-75; dir div endocrinol, metab & nephrol, Lipid Clin, St Michael's Hosp, 70-73; mem, Exec Comt, Coun Atherosclerosis, Am Heart Asn, 74-; mem, Comt Nutrit & Cardiovasc Dis, Health Protection Br, Govt Can, 74- & Med Comt, Ont Heart Found, 65-75. *Mem:* Am Heart Asn; Can Cardiovasc Soc; Am Diabetes Asn; Nutrit Soc Can; Can Soc Clin Invest. *Res:* Relation between human atherosclerosis, plasma lipoproteins, nutrition and genetic factors; effect of insulin antibodies on diabetic complications. *Mailing Add:* Clin Invest Unit St Michael's Hosp Toronto ON M5B 1W8 Can

LITTLE, JAMES NOEL, b Kansas City, Mo, July 3, 40; m 64; c 3. ANALYTICAL CHEMISTRY. *Educ:* Univ Kans, BS, 62, Mass Inst Technol, PhD(anal chem), 66. *Prof Exp:* Res chemist, Hercules, Inc, Del, 66-67; sr res chemist, Waters Assocs, Inc, 68-69, mgr chromatography res, 69-71, vpres, 71-81; VPRES, ZYMARK CORP, 82- *Concurrent Pos:* Dir, Rheometrics Inc, 81- *Mem:* Am Chem Soc. *Res:* Separations; chromatography; polymer characterization; analytical methods development; spectroscopy; robotics. *Mailing Add:* Zymark Corp 102 South St Hopkinton MA 01748

LITTLE, JAMES W, oral pathology, see previous edition

LITTLE, JOHN BERTRAM, b Boston, Mass, Oct 5, 29; m 60; c 2. PHYSIOLOGY, RADIATION BIOLOGY. *Educ:* Harvard Univ, AB, 51; Boston Univ, MD, 55; Am Bd Radiol, dipl, 61, cert nuclear med, 61. *Prof Exp:* Intern med, Johns Hopkins Hosp, 55-56; resident radiol, Mass Gen Hosp, 58-61; USPHS res fel, 61-63, instr physiol, 63-65, asst prof, 65-69, assoc prof, 69-75, PROF RADIOBIOL, HARVARD SCH PUB HEALTH, 75-, CHMN, DEPT PHYSIOL, 80- *Concurrent Pos:* Consult Mass Gen Hosp, 65-; Peter Bent Brigham Hosp, 68-; Nat Cancer Inst & Am Cancer Soc fels, Sch Pub Health, Harvard, 68-78, lectr, Med Sch, 68- *Mem:* AAAS; Am Physiol Soc; Radiation Res Soc; Health Physics Soc; Am Asn Cancer Res. *Res:* Cellular radiation biology with emphasis on repair mechanisms; experimental carcinogenesis. *Mailing Add:* Dept of Physiol Harvard Sch of Pub Health Boston MA 02115

LITTLE, JOHN CLAYTON, b Battle Creek, Mich, Jan 1, 33; m 53; c 4. ORGANIC CHEMISTRY. *Educ:* Univ Calif, BS, 54; Univ Ill, PhD(org chem), 57. *Prof Exp:* Res chemist, 57-62, proj leader, 62-64, group leader, 64-71, res mgr, 71-81, MGR CHEM TECHNOL, DOW CHEM USA, 81- *Concurrent Pos:* Mem, Mich Found Advan Res. *Mem:* Am Chem Soc; Sigma Xi; The Chem Soc. *Res:* Pilot plant and process development studies; organic syntheses and structure-biological activity relationships; chemical manufacturing, environmental studies; petrochemical processing; chlorination; catalytic oxidation and reduction; Diels-Alder reactions and synthetic methods. *Mailing Add:* Agr Prod Dept Dow Chemical USA 2800 Mitchell Dr Walnut Creek CA 94598

LITTLE, JOHN DUTTON CONANT, b Boston, Mass, Feb 1, 28; m 53; c 4. OPERATIONS RESEARCH. *Educ:* Mass Inst Technol, SB, 48, PhD(physics), 55. *Prof Exp:* Engr tube develop, Gen Elec Co, 49-50; asst physics, Mass Inst Technol, 51-54; from asst prof to assoc prof opers res, Case Inst Technol, 57-62; assoc prof opers res, 62-67, dir opers res ctr, 69-75, prof opers res & mgt, 67-78, HEAD MGT SCI GROUP, SLOAN SCH, MASS INST TECHNOL, 72-, GEORGE M BUNKER PROF MGT, 78- *Concurrent Pos:* Chmn, Mgt Decision Systs, Inc, 67- *Honors & Awards:* Charles Coolidge Parlin Award in Mkt, 78. *Mem:* Am Mkt Asn; fel AAAS; Opers Res Soc Am (pres-elect, 78-79); Inst Mgt Sci (vpres, 76-79). *Res:* Applications in marketing and public systems. *Mailing Add:* E53-350 Mass Inst of Technol Cambridge MA 02139

LITTLE, JOHN LLEWELLYN, b Lakewood, Ohio, Feb 17, 19; m 49; c 1. COMPUTER STANDARDS, PHYSICS. *Educ:* Case Inst Technol, BS, 42. *Prof Exp:* Staff mem oper res, US Navy, Anti-Submarine Warfare Oper Res Group, 42-45; proj engr electronics, Reed Res, Inc, 47-48; staff mem oper res, Dept Defense, Res & Develop Bd, 49-51; chief planning dept res, Reed Res, Inc, 51-52; COMPUT SPECIALIST, NAT BUR STANDARDS, 53- *Concurrent Pos:* Task force coordr, Comput Network Protocol, Nat Comn Libr & Info Sci, 76-77. *Mem:* Asn Comput Mach; Inst Elec & Electronics Engrs. *Res:* Computer hardware standards; coded character sets; collating sequence; transferability of computer programs and data between dissimilar computer-based systems; network protocols. *Mailing Add:* Nat Bur of Standards Inst of Comput Sci Technol Washington DC 20234

LITTLE, JOHN RUSSELL, JR, b Cheyenne, Wyo, Oct 23, 30; m 55; c 3. IMMUNOLOGY. *Educ:* Cornell Univ, AB, 52; Univ Rochester, MD, 56. *Prof Exp:* Fel microbiol, 62-64; from asst prof to assoc prof med & microbiol, 69-73, PROF MED & MICROBIOL, SCH MED, WASHINGTON UNIV, 73- *Res:* Medicine and lymphocyte membrane structure and function. *Mailing Add:* Jewish Hosp Washington Univ Sch of Med St Louis MO 63110

LITTLE, JOHN STANLEY, b Fredericton, NB, July 27, 31; m 57; c 1. ORGANIC CHEMISTRY. *Educ:* Univ NB, BS, 52, PhD(org chem), 55. *Prof Exp:* Lord Beaverbrook Overseas Scholar, Univ London, 55-56; res chemist, Can Industs, Ltd, 56-62; group leader fiber res & develop, 62-65; sect leader all process & prod res, Celanese Corp, Can, 65-67; mgr appln res, 67-70, mgr indust prod develop, Celanese Fibers Mkt Co, 70-71; dir spec prod develop, 71-73; dir textile prod develop, 73-78, dir int indust markets, Celanese Corp, NY, 78-81; VPRES CORP TECHNOL, GREAT LAKES CHEM CORP, 81- *Mem:* Fel Chem Inst Can. *Res:* Synthetic fibers; alkaloids and steroids. *Mailing Add:* Great Lakes Chem Corp PO Box 2200 West Lafayette IN 47906

LITTLE, JOHN WESLEY, b Washington, DC, June 24, 41; m 69; c 2. BIOCHEMISTRY. *Educ:* Stanford Univ, BS, 61, PhD(biochem), 71. *Prof Exp:* Sr asst scientist, NIH, 67-69; sr staff fel, 69-72; res fel, Stanford Univ, 73-76, res assoc, 77-78; adj asst prof microbiol, 78-80, adj assoc prof molecular & med microbiol, 80-81, ASST PROF BIOCHEM, UNIV ARIZ, 82- *Mem:* AAAS. *Res:* Regulatory system which controls how E coli responds to conditions which damage DNA including the biochemistry of the proteins which control this response. *Mailing Add:* Dept Biochem Univ Ariz Tucson AZ 85721

LITTLE, JOSEPH ALEXANDER, b Bessemer, Ala, Mar 16, 18; m 41; c 3. MEDICINE. *Educ:* Vanderbilt Univ, BA, 40, MD, 43. *Prof Exp:* Intern, Vanderbilt Univ Hosp, 43 & 46-47; resident, Childrens Hosp, Univ Cincinnati, 47-48, instr pediat, Col Med, Univ, 48-49; from asst prof to prof, Sch Med, Univ Louisville, 49-62; assoc prof, Sch Med, Vanderbilt Univ, 62-70; PROF PEDIAT & HEAD DEPT, SCH MED, LA STATE UNIV, SHREVEPORT, 70- *Concurrent Pos:* Dir outpatient dept, Childrens Hosp, 48-49, physician in chief, 56-; med dir, State Crippled Children Comn, Ky, 51-54; consult, State Dept Health, Ky, 49-51. *Mem:* AAAS; Am Pediat Soc; Am Acad Pediat; NY Acad Sci. *Res:* Pediatric cardiology. *Mailing Add:* Dept of Pediat La State Univ Sch of Med Shreveport LA 71130

LITTLE, MAURICE DALE, b North Grove, Ind, Apr 13, 28; m 55; c 3. MEDICAL PARASITOLOGY. *Educ:* Purdue Univ, BS, 50; Tulane Univ, MS, 58, PhD(parasitol), 61. *Prof Exp:* Microbiologist, Ind State Bd Health, 53-56; from instr to asst prof, Sch Med, 63-68, assoc prof, 68-76, PROF PARASITOL, SCH PUB HEALTH & TROP MED, TULANE UNIV, 76- *Concurrent Pos:* NIH fel, Tulane Univ, 61-63. *Mem:* AAAS; Am Micros Soc; Am Soc Parasitol; Am Soc Trop Med & Hyg; Royal Soc Trop Med & Hyg. *Res:* Morphology, biology and epidemiology of Strongyloides species; zoonotic helminthiases; paragonimiasis; soil-transmitted helminths. *Mailing Add:* Dept of Trop Med Tulane Univ New Orleans LA 70112

LITTLE, MICHAEL ALAN, b Abington, Pa, Mar 24, 37; m 65; c 2. PHYSICAL ANTHROPOLOGY. *Educ:* Pa State Univ, BA, 62, MA, 65, PhD(anthrop), 68. *Prof Exp:* Asst prof anthrop, Ohio State Univ, 67-70; asst prof, 71-73, assoc prof, 73-81, PROF ANTHROP, STATE UNIV NY BINGHAMTON, 81- *Concurrent Pos:* Ohio State Univ res fel, Nunoa, Peru, 68; State Univ NY Binghamton res fel & grant, Nunoa, 72; vis assoc prof anthrop & sci coordr, US Int Biol Prog, Human Adaptability Component, Pa State Univ, 72-73; NSF sci equip grants, 74 & 80; NSF res grant, 78. *Mem:* Fel AAAS; Am Asn Phys Anthrop; Soc Study Human Biol; Human Biol Coun. *Res:* Biocultural adaptations; human biology; environmental stress; heat and cold adaptation; circadian rhythms; human populations at high altitude; child growth and development; ecology of savanna pastoralists. *Mailing Add:* Dept of Anthrop State Univ of NY Binghamton NY 13901

LITTLE, PERRY L, b Ball Ground, Ga, Aug 3, 28; m 51; c 1. NUTRITION, PHYSIOLOGY. *Educ:* Berry Col, BS, 50; Auburn Univ, MS, 57, PhD(path, nutrit, physiol), 66. *Prof Exp:* Teacher high sch Ala, 50-52 & 53-55; res asst poultry sci, Auburn Univ, 55-62; assoc prof, 62-80, PROF POULTRY SCI, SAM HOUSTON STATE UNIV, 80- *Mem:* Poultry Sci Asn; World Poultry Sci Asn. *Res:* Nutrition of parasites which involve poultry. *Mailing Add:* Dept of Agr Sam Houston State Univ Huntsville TX 77340

LITTLE, RANDEL QUINCY, JR, b Richmond, Va, Aug 14, 27; m 49; c 3. ORGANIC CHEMISTRY. *Educ:* Univ Richmond, BS, 48; Univ Mich, MS, 49; PhD(org chem), 54. *Prof Exp:* Res chemist, Am Oil Co, Stand Oil Co, Ind, 53-60, group leader motor oil additives, 60-62, res supvr, 62-68, asst dir lubricants res, 68-74, DIR LUBRICANTS & AGR PROD RES, AMOCO OIL CO, 74- *Mem:* Am Chem Soc; Sigma Xi; Am Soc Lubricating Engrs; Soc Automotive Engrs. *Res:* Organic reactions; motor oil additives; lubricants. *Mailing Add:* Amoco Oil Co PO Box 400 Naperville IL 60540

LITTLE, RAYMOND DANIEL, b Superior, Wis, Sept 12, 47; m 72. ORGANIC CHEMISTRY. *Educ:* Univ Wis-Superior, BS, 69; Univ Wis-Madison, PhD(org chem), 74. *Prof Exp:* Assoc chem, Yale Univ, 74-75; asst prof, 75-81, ASSOC PROF ORG CHEM, UNIV CALIF, SANTA BARBARA, 81- *Concurrent Pos:* Alfred P Sloan Found fel, 80-82. *Mem:* Am Chem Soc; Sigma Xi. *Res:* Development of new synthetic methods; total synthesis of pharmacologically active molecules and compounds of theoretical interest; mechanistic organic chemistry of thermal and phtochemical reactions; theoretical organic chemistry. *Mailing Add:* Dept of Chem Univ of Calif Santa Barbara CA 93106

LITTLE, ROBERT, b Jedburgh, Scotland, Mar 3, 39; m 62; c 3. PLASMA PHYSICS. *Educ:* Univ Glasgow, BSc, 61, PhD(physics), 64. *Prof Exp:* Res assoc physics, Cambridge Electron Accelerator, Harvard Univ, 64-73 & Mass Inst Technol, 73-75; PROF STAFF PHYSICS, PRINCETON PLASMA PHYSICS LAB, PRINCETON UNIV, 75- *Res:* Development of large tokomaks for controlled thermonuclear research. *Mailing Add:* Princeton Plasma Physics Lab Princeton Univ Princeton NJ 08544

LITTLE, ROBERT COLBY, b Norwalk, Ohio, June 2, 20; m 45; c 2. PHYSIOLOGY, MEDICINE. *Educ:* Denison Univ, AB, 42; Western Reserve Univ, MD, 44, MS, 48. *Prof Exp:* Intern, Grace Hosp, Detroit, Mich, 44-45; resident med, Crile Vet Hosp, Cleveland, 49-50; from asst prof to assoc prof physiol, Univ Tenn, 50-54, assoc prof med, 53-54; dir clin res, Mead Johnson & Co, 54-57; dir cardio-pulmonary labs, Scott & White Clin, Tex, 57-58; prof physiol, Seton Hall Col Med, 58-64, asst prof med, 59-64; prof physiol, chmn dept & asst prof med, Col Med, Ohio State Univ, 64-73; PROF PHYSIOL & MED & CHMN DEPT PHYSIOL, SCH MED, MED COL GA, 73- *Concurrent Pos:* USPHS res fel, Western Reserve Univ, 48-49. *Mem:* Am Physiol Soc; Soc Exp Biol & Med; Am Heart Asn; Am Fedn Clin Res. *Res:* Cardiovascular dynamics; heart sounds; clinical physiology; muscle dynamics. *Mailing Add:* Dept of Physiol Med Col of Ga Augusta GA 30912

LITTLE, ROBERT E(UGENE), b Enfield, Ill, May 24, 33; m 60; c 4. MECHANICAL ENGINEERING. *Educ:* BSE, 59; Ohio State Univ, MSME, 60; Univ Mich, PhD(mech eng), 63. *Prof Exp:* Asst prof mech eng, Okla State Univ, 63-65; assoc prof, 65-68, PROF MECH ENG, UNIV MICH-DEARBORN, 68- *Mem:* Am Soc Testing & Mat. *Res:* Modes of failure; fatigue; reliability; mechanical engineering reliability. *Mailing Add:* Dept Mech Eng Univ Mich 4901 Evergreen Rd Dearborn MI 48128

LITTLE, ROBERT GREENWOOD, b Evanston, Ill, Dec 26, 42. INORGANIC CHEMISTRY, X-RAY CRYSTALLOGRAPHY. *Educ:* Univ Calif, Davis, BS, 64; State Univ NY Buffalo, PhD(inorg reaction mechanisms), 70. *Prof Exp:* Fel crystallog, State Univ NY Buffalo, 69-70; fel crystallog & instr chem, Univ Calif, Irvine, 70-72; fel crystallog, Northwestern Univ, Evanston, 72-74; ASST PROF CHEM, UNIV MD, BALTIMORE COUNTY, 74- *Mem:* AAAS; Am Chem Soc. *Res:* Stereochemical requirements and mechanisms of inorganic reactions. *Mailing Add:* Dept of Chem Univ of Md Baltimore County Baltimore MD 21228

LITTLE, ROBERT LEWIS, b Monticello, Miss, July 1, 29; m 53; c 2. GEOLOGY. *Educ:* Univ Miss, BA, 51, MS, 59; Univ Tenn, Knoxville, PhD(geol), 69. *Prof Exp:* Instr geol, Univ Miss, 58-59 & Univ Tenn, Knoxville, 59-69; asst prof, 69-72, assoc prof, 72-81, head dept, 69-81, PROF GEOL & DEPT HEAD PHYSICS, ASTRON & GEOL, VALDOSTA STATE COL, 81- *Mem:* Geol Soc Am; Am Asn Univ Prof; Nat Asn Geol Teachers. *Res:* Areal geology; stratigraphy and structural geology. *Mailing Add:* Dept Physics Astron Geol Valdosta State Col Box 185 Valdosta GA 31698

LITTLE, ROBERT NARVAEZ, JR, b Houston, Tex, Mar 11, 13; m 42; c 2. NUCLEAR PHYSICS, SCIENCE EDUCATION. *Educ:* Rice Inst, BA, 35, MA, 42, PhD(physics), 43. *Prof Exp:* Asst seismologist, Shell Oil Co, Tex, 36-42, asst physics, Rice Inst, 43; asst prof, Univ Ore, 43-44; testing supvr, Mil Physics Res Lab, Univ Tex, 44-48, from asst prof to assoc prof physics, 46-55 & res scientist, Nuclear Physics Lab, 55-60, PROF PHYSICS & EDUC, UNIV TEX, 55- *Concurrent Pos:* Chief nuclear physics, Gen Dynamics Corp, 54; mem, Comn Col Physics, 62-66; physics educ asst proj, Nat Univ Cent Am, 65-71; vis prof, Univ Valle, Guatemala, 71; Catedratico Ad Honorem, Univ Nac de Edu a Distancia, Madrid, Spain, 81. *Mem:* Am Phys Soc; Am Asn Physics Teachers (pres, 70); Int Group Res on Educ Physics; Cent Am Soc Physics. *Res:* Neutron scattering; reactor physics; development and evaluation of physics teaching methods at all levels. *Mailing Add:* 3928 Balcones Dr Austin TX 78731

LITTLE, ROBERT WILLIAM, b Oklahoma City, Okla, Feb 25, 33; m 54, 75; c 5. ENGINEERING MECHANICS, APPLIED MATHEMATICS. *Educ:* Duke Univ, BSME, 55; Univ Wis, MS, 59, PhD(eng mech), 62. *Prof Exp:* Design engr, Steam Turbine Dept, Allis-Chalmers Mfg Co, 55-57; asst instr mech, Marquette Univ, 57-59; from instr to asst prof, Univ Wis, 59-63; asst prof, Okla State Univ, 63-65; from asst prof to assoc prof, 65-70, chmn dept mech eng, 72-77, PROF MECH, MICH STATE UNIV, 70- , CHMN DEPT BIOMECH, 77- *Concurrent Pos:* Consult, AC Spark Plug Div, Gen Motors Corp, 59-63, Lawrence Livermore Lab, Ford Motor Co, Goodridge, CBS Lab. *Mem:* Am Soc Eng Educ; Soc Eng Sci; Soc Natural Philos; Am Soc Mech Eng. *Res:* Linear elasticity; biomechanics; continuum mechanics; bioengineering. *Mailing Add:* Dept Biomech Mich State Univ East Lansing MI 48824

LITTLE, STEPHEN JAMES, b Akron, Ohio, July 5, 39; m 73; c 2. ASTRONOMY, ASTROPHYSICS. *Educ:* Univ Kans, BA, 61, MA, 63; UniV Calif, Los Angeles, PhD(astron), 71. *Prof Exp:* Fac assoc astron, Univ Tex, Austin, 68-70; asst prof, Ferris State Col, Big Rapids, Mich, 70-75; ASST PROF ASTRON, WELLESLEY COL, 75- *Concurrent Pos:* Consult scientist, Solar Physics Div, Am Sci & Eng, Cambridge, 76-77; lectr, Hayden Planetarium, Boston Mus Sci, 77-79, 81- *Mem:* Am Astron Soc; Sigma Xi. *Res:* Astronomical spectroscopy and photometry of red giant stars, Ap stars, and planets; solar x-ray physics. *Mailing Add:* Whitin Observ Wellesley Col Wellesley MA 02181

LITTLE, THOMAS MORTON, b Picture Rocks, Pa, July 25, 10; m 38; c 2. BIOMETRICS. *Educ:* Bucknell Univ, AB, 31; Univ Fla, MS, 33; Univ Md, PhD(genetics), 43. *Prof Exp:* Asst entom, Cornell Univ, 31; chief hybridist, W Atlee Burpee Co, Calif, 34-41; asst geneticist, USDA, Md, 41-44; dir crop res, Basic Veg Prod, Inc, 44-49; asst prof biol & hort, Univ Nev, 49-53; exten veg crops specialist, 53-64; exten biometrician, 64-72, EMER EXTEN BIOMETRICIAN, UNIV CALIF, RIVERSIDE, 72- *Concurrent Pos:* Fulbright lectr, Univ Zagreb, 67-68; biometrician, Int Inst Trop Agr, Ibadan, Nigeria, 72-74. *Mem:* Am Soc Hort Sci. *Res:* Design and analysis of agricultural experiments. *Mailing Add:* 1488 Argyle Lane Bishop CA 93514

LITTLE, WILLIAM ARTHUR, b Adelaide, SAfrica, Nov 17, 30; nat US; m 55; c 3. PHYSICS. *Educ:* Univ SAfrica, BSc, 50; Rhodes Univ, SAfrica, PhD, 55; Univ Glasgow, PhD, 57. *Prof Exp:* Nat Res Coun Can fel, Univ BC, 56-58; from asst prof to assoc prof, 58-65, PROF PHYSICS, STANFORD UNIV, 65- *Concurrent Pos:* Alfred P Sloan fel, 59-62; Guggenheim fel, 64-65; invited prof, Univ Geneva, 64-65; NSF sr fel, 71-72; chmn, MMR Technol Inc. *Mem:* Fel Am Phys Soc. *Res:* Organic fluorescence; magnetic resonance; low temperature physics; superconductivity; phase transition; chemical physics; neural network theory. *Mailing Add:* Dept of Physics Stanford Univ Stanford CA 94305

LITTLE, WILLIAM ASA, b Ellenville, NY, July 14, 31; m 52; c 2. OBSTETRICS & GYNECOLOGY. *Educ:* Johns Hopkins Univ, AB, 51; Univ Rochester, MD, 55. *Prof Exp:* Intern obstet & gynec, Barnes Hosp, Washington Univ, 55-56; resident, Columbia-Presby Med Ctr, 56-61; from asst prof to assoc prof, Univ Fla, 61-66; PROF OBSTET & GYNEC & CHMN DEPT, UNIV MIAMI, 66- *Concurrent Pos:* Josia Macy Jr fel, 57-60; Am Cancer Soc fel, 60-61; consult, US Navy, 61-65; asst chief perinatal res, Nat Inst Neurol Dis & Stroke, 62-64, consult, 64-; Nat Inst Child Health & Human Develop, 63-; Markle scholar, 62-; adv, US Food & Drug Admin, 64- *Mem:* AAAS; Am Col Obstet & Gynec; Am Fertil Soc; Am Pub Health Asn; AMA. *Res:* Placental pathology and transfer; enzymology; fetal pharmacology; teratology; mental retardation; cancer; reproductive biology. *Mailing Add:* Dept of Obstet & Gynec Univ of Miami Sch of Med Miami FL 33152

LITTLE, WILLIAM FREDERICK, b Morganton, NC, Nov 11, 29; m 58; c 1. ORGANIC CHEMISTRY, INORGANIC CHEMISTRY. *Educ:* Lenoir Rhyne Col, BS, 50; Univ NC, MA, 52, PhD(org chem), 55. *Prof Exp:* Instr chem, Reed Col, 55-56; from instr to asst prof, 56-65, asst to dean grad sch res admin, 59-62, prof chem & chmn dept, 65-70, vchancellor develop & pub serv, 73-78, UNIV DISTINGUISHED PROF, UNIV NC, CHAPEL HILL, 77- *Concurrent Pos:* Consult, Res Triangle Inst, 56-69, exec comt, Bd Gov, 69- *Honors & Awards:* Thomas Jefferson Award, 80. *Mem:* Am Chem Soc. *Res:* Organometallic compounds, especially metallocenes, and group VIII metals. *Mailing Add:* Dept of Chem Univ of NC Chapel Hill NC 27515

LITTLE, WINSTON WOODARD, JR, b Gainesville, Fla, Sept 4, 38. NUCLEAR ENGINEERING. *Educ:* Mass Inst Technol, BS, 60, MS, 62, ScD(nuclear eng), 64. *Prof Exp:* Mgr fast flux test facil, Nuclear Design & Anal Unit, Pac Northwest Labs, Battelle Mem Inst, 66-77; CONSULT SCIENTIST, WESTINGHOUSE HANFORD CO, 77- *Mem:* Am Nuclear Soc. *Res:* Nuclear design of the fast flux test facility. *Mailing Add:* Westinghouse Hanford Co PO Box 1970 Richland WA 99352

LITTLEDIKE, ERNEST TRAVIS, b Logan, Utah, Feb 25, 35; m 60; c 4. ENDOCRINOLOGY, MINERAL METABOLISM. *Educ:* Utah State Univ, BS, 58; Wash State Univ, DVM, 60; Univ Ill, PhD(physiol), 65. *Prof Exp:* Instr anat, Univ Ill, 60-62, NIH fel physiol, 62-64; fel endocrinol, Univ Wis, 64-65; VET MED OFFICER PHYSIOL, NAT ANIMAL DIS CTR, 65- *Concurrent Pos:* Vis scientist endocrinol, Mayo Clinic, 75-76; adj prof, Iowa State Univ, 69- *Mem:* Endocrine Soc; Am Soc Bone & Marine Res; World Vet Anatomists Asn; World Vet Physiologists & Pharmacologists Asn. *Res:* Mineral metabolism in domestic animals and the diseases that result from mineral imbalances; factors that effect mineral metabolism and the pathogenesis of diseases of mineral metabolism in domestic animals. *Mailing Add:* Dayton Rd Ames IA 50010

LITTLEFIELD, GAYLE, anatomy, cytogenetics, see previous edition

LITTLEFIELD, JOHN WALLEY, b Providence, RI, Dec 3, 25; m 50; c 3. PEDIATRICS. *Educ:* Harvard Med Sch, MD, 47. *Prof Exp:* From intern to resident med, Mass Gen Hosp, 47-50; from clin & res fel to asst prof med, Harvard Med Sch, 54-66, tutor, 59-65, asst prof pediat, 66-69, prof, 70-73; PROF PEDIAT & CHMN DEPT, JOHNS HOPKINS UNIV, 74- *Concurrent Pos:* USPHS fel, Inst Enzyme Res, Univ Wis, 51; Am Cancer Soc scholar, 56-59; Guggenheim fel, 65-66; asst physician, Mass Gen Hosp, 61-66, assoc pediatrician, 66-69. *Mem:* Nat Acad Sci; Am Soc Human Genetics; Am Acad Pediat; Am Pediat Soc; Am Soc Biol Chemists. *Res:* Human genetics; molecular biology. *Mailing Add:* Dept of Pediat Johns Hopkins Univ Baltimore MD 21205

LITTLEFIELD, LARRY JAMES, b Ft Smith, Ark, Feb 7, 38; m 63. PLANT PATHOLOGY. *Educ:* Cornell Univ, BS, 60; Univ Minn, MS, 62, PhD(plant path), 64. *Prof Exp:* Res asst plant path, Univ Minn, 60-64; NSF res fel, Uppsala, 64-65; from asst prof to assoc prof, 65-75, PROF PLANT PATH,

N DAK STATE UNIV, 75- *Concurrent Pos:* NIH fel, Purdue Univ, 69-70; res fel, Oxford Univ, 73-74. *Mem:* Mycol Soc Am; Brit Mycol Soc; Am Phytopath Soc. *Res:* Histology of host-parasite relations; fungus physiology; electron microscopy of fungi and diseased plants. *Mailing Add:* Plant Path Dept NDak State Univ Fargo ND 58105

LITTLEFIELD, NEIL ADAIR, b Santa Fe, NMex, Apr 25, 35; m 60; c 5. TOXICOLOGY. *Educ:* Brigham Young Univ, BS, 61; Utah State Univ, MS, 64, PhD(toxicol), 68. *Prof Exp:* Res assoc air pollution, Univ Utah, 66-67; staff scientist inhalation toxicol, Hazleton Lab, Inc, 67-70; pharmacologist pesticide regulation, Environ Protection Agency, 71-72; toxicologist, 72-79, DIR, DIV CHEM TOXICOL, NAT CTR TOXICOL RES, FOOD & DRUG ADMIN, 79- *Concurrent Pos:* Chmn, Interagency Task Force Inhalation Chronic Toxicity & Carcinogenesis, 74-75; mem, Food & Drug Admin Task Force Aerosol Prod, 75- *Mem:* Sigma Xi. *Res:* Investigations in concepts of long-term, low-dose exposures; extrapolation of animal toxicology data to risk-benefit in man; carcinogenesis. *Mailing Add:* Nat Ctr Toxicol Res Jefferson AR 72079

LITTLEJOHN, OLIVER MARSILIUS, b Cowpens, SC, Sept 29, 24; m 48; c 2. PHARMACY. *Educ:* Univ SC, BS, 48 & 49; Univ Fla, MS, 51, PhD(pharm), 53. *Prof Exp:* Asst prof pharm & head dept, Southern Col Pharm, 53-56; prof & head dept, Univ Ky, 56-57; DEAN, SOUTHERN SCH PHARM, MERCER UNIV, 57- *Mem:* Fel Am Found Pharmaceut Educ. *Res:* Pharmaceutical preservatives. *Mailing Add:* Mercer Univ Southern Sch Pharm 345 Blvd NE Atlanta GA 30312

LITTLE-MARENIN, IRENE RENATE, b Pilsen, Czech, May 4, 41; US citizen; m 73; c 1. ASTROPHYSICS. *Educ:* Vassar Col, AB, 64; Ind Univ, MA, 66, PhD(astrophys), 70. *Prof Exp:* Fel astron, Ohio State Univ, 70-72; asst prof, Univ Western Ont, 72-73; teaching fel, Ferris State Col, 74; res asst solar x-rays, Am Sci & Eng, 76-77; ASST PROF ASTRON, WELLESLEY COL, 77- *Concurrent Pos:* Sabbatical leave, vis asst prof, Dennison Univ & Ohio State, 80-81; vis scientist, Univ Colo, 80-81. *Mem:* Am Astron Soc; Sigma Xi. *Res:* A search for the radioactive element technetium in long-period variable stars; a determination of the isotopic ratio of carbon in carbon stars and in G and K giants and supergiants. *Mailing Add:* Whitin Observ Wellesley Col Wellesley MA 02181

LITTLEPAGE, JACK LEROY, b San Diego, Calif, Apr 14, 35; m 60. BIOLOGICAL OCEANOGRAPHY. *Educ:* San Diego State Col, BA, 57; Stanford Univ, PhD(biol), 66. *Prof Exp:* Asst prof, 65-71, ASSOC PROF BIOL, UNIV VICTORIA, 71- *Concurrent Pos:* Oceanographic consult to mining industies, 71- *Mem:* AAAS; Am Soc Limnol & Oceanog. *Res:* Physiology and ecology of marine zooplankton, especially copepods and euphausids; pollution monitoring. *Mailing Add:* Dept of Biol Univ of Victoria Victoria BC V8W 2Y2 Can

LITTLER, MARK MASTERTON, b Athens, Ohio, Sept 24, 39; m 66. ECOLOGY, PHYCOLOGY. *Educ:* Ohio Univ, BS, 61, MS, 66; Univ Hawaii, PhD(bot), 71. *Prof Exp:* Chemist, Testing Lab, Ohio State Hwy Dept, 61-64; asst prof, 70-74, ASSOC PROF, BIOL SCI, UNIV CALIF, IRVINE, 74- *Concurrent Pos:* US Dept Interior Off Water Resources & Technol grant, 74 & Bur Land Mgt res contract, 75. *Mem:* Int Phycol Soc; Phycol Soc Am; Japanese Phycol Soc; British Phycol Soc; Am Soc Limnol & Oceanog. *Res:* Man's effect on marine ecosystems; taxonomy, developmental morphology and seasonal cycles of marine benthos and phytoplankton; standing stock, productivity and the physiological ecology of temperate and reef-building benthic organisms. *Mailing Add:* Dept of Ecol & Evolutionary Biol Univ Calif Irvine CA 92717

LITTLETON, H(AROLD) T(HOMAS) J(ACKSON), b Parksley, Va, June 28, 21; m 48. CHEMICAL ENGINEERING. *Educ:* Univ Va, BChE, 43. *Prof Exp:* Chem engr, Naval Res Lab, 43-46; chem engr, Res Div, Polychem Dept, 46-53, res supvr, 53-62, sr res engr, Plastics Dept, Exp Sta, 62-69, res assoc, 69-73, LAB ADMINR, PLASTIC PROD & RESINS DEPT, EXP STA, E I DU PONT DE NEMOURS & CO, INC, 74- *Mem:* Am Chem Soc; Am Inst Chem Engrs. *Res:* Process development on nylon intermediates; high pressure processes; new plastics and plastics processing methods. *Mailing Add:* 320 Walden Rd Sharpley Wilmington DE 19803

LITTLETON, JOHN EDWARD, b Ballston Spa, NY, July 28, 43; m 76. STELLAR EVOLUTION, ASTROPHYSICAL PLASMA PHYSICS. *Educ:* Cornell Univ, BS, 65; Univ Rochester, PhD(astrophys), 72. *Prof Exp:* Res assoc astrophys, Belfer Grad Sch Sci, Yeshiva Univ, 72-73; res fel, Harvard Col Observ, 73-74, res assoc, 74-75; asst prof, 75-81, ASSOC PROF PHYSICS, WEST VA UNIV, 81- *Mem:* Am Astron Soc; AAAS; Am Asn Physics Teachers. *Res:* Plasma fluctuations in astrophysical media; structure of detonation waves in degenerate stellar cores; hydrodynamic properties of stellar atmospheres. *Mailing Add:* Dept Physics WVa Univ Morgantown WV 26506

LITTLEWOOD, BARBARA SHAFFER, b Buffalo, NY, Oct 8, 41; m 70. BIOCHEMISTRY, GENETICS. *Educ:* Univ Rochester, BA, 63; Univ Pa, PhD(biochem), 68. *Prof Exp:* NIH trainee, Cornell Univ, 68-70; res assoc biochem, 70-73, res assoc physiol chem, 73-76, RES ASSOC BIOCHEM, UNIV WIS-MADISON, 76- *Concurrent Pos:* Lectr, dept genetics, Cornell Univ, 70 & dept biochem, Univ Wis-Madison, 72. *Mem:* Genetics Soc Am; Am Soc Microbiol. *Res:* Yeast genetics and biochemistry. *Mailing Add:* 5102 Manor Cross Madison WI 53711

LITTLEWOOD, ROLAND KAY, b Mendota, Ill, Nov 26, 42. COMPUTER SCIENCE, MOLECULAR BIOLOGY. *Educ:* Univ Ill, Urbana, BS, 64; Cornell Univ, PhD(genetics), 70. *Prof Exp:* NIH fel, Lab Molecular Biol, 70-72, res assoc, 72-78, ASST SCIENTIST, BIOPHYS LAB, UNIV WIS-MADISON, 78- *Concurrent Pos:* Proprietor, Digital Comput Appl, 74- *Mem:* Inst Elec & Electronics Eng; Asn Comput Mach; Comput Soc. *Res:* Application of computers in the biological sciences. *Mailing Add:* Biophys Lab 1525 Linden Dr Univ Wis Madison WI 53706

LITTMAN, ARMAND, b Chicago, Ill, Apr 4, 21; m 52; c 3. MEDICINE. *Educ:* Univ Ill, Chicago, BS, 42, MD, 43, MS, 48, PhD(physiol), 51. *Prof Exp:* Intern, Cook County Hosp, Chicago, 44; from clin asst to assoc prof, 46-64, PROF MED, UNIV ILL COL MED, 64-; CHIEF MED SERV, HINES VET ADMIN HOSP, 59- *Concurrent Pos:* Raymond B Allen instructorship award, Univ Ill, 57; US AEC travel award, 58; resident, Cook County Hosp, Chicago, 48-50; pvt pract, 52-59; attend physician, Res & Educ Hosps, 55-; prof, Cook County Grad Sch Med, 58- *Mem:* AMA; Am Col Physicians; Am Fedn Clin Res; Am Gastroenterol Asn. *Res:* Gastroenterology; physiology. *Mailing Add:* Med Serv Vet Admin Hosp Hines IL 60141

LITTMAN, HOWARD, b Brooklyn, NY, Apr 22, 27; m 55; c 3. CHEMICAL ENGINEERING. *Educ:* Cornell Univ, BChE, 51; Yale Univ, PhD(chem eng), 56. *Prof Exp:* From asst prof to assoc prof chem eng, Syracuse Univ, 56-65; assoc prof, 65-67, PROF CHEM ENG, RENSSELAER POLYTECH INST, 67- *Concurrent Pos:* Resident res assoc, Argonne Nat Lab, 57-59; Fulbright-Hays lectr, Univ Belgrade, 72. *Mem:* Am Chem Soc; Am Inst Chem Engrs. *Res:* Fluidization and fluid-particle systems. *Mailing Add:* Dept of Chem & Environ Eng Rensselaer Polytech Inst Troy NY 12181

LITTMAN, WALTER, b Vienna, Austria, Sept 17, 29; US citizen; m 60; c 3. MATHEMATICAL ANALYSIS. *Educ:* Univ NY, BA, 52, PhD(math), 56. *Prof Exp:* Instr math, Univ Calif, Berkeley, 56-58, lectr, 58-59; asst prof, Univ Wis, 59-60; from asst prof to assoc prof, 60-66, PROF MATH, UNIV MINN, MINNEAPOLIS, 66- *Concurrent Pos:* Vis mem, Courant Inst Math Sci, NY Univ, 67-68; vis prof, Mittag-Leffler Inst, Djursholm, Sweden, 74, Chalmers Technol Univ, Gothenburg, Sweden, 75 & Hebrew Univ, Jerusalem, Israel, 81-82. *Mem:* Am Math Soc. *Res:* Partial differential equations; functional analysis; mathematical physics. *Mailing Add:* Dept of Math Univ of Minn Minneapolis MN 55455

LITTMANN, MARTIN F(REDERICK), b Brazil, Ind, Feb 9, 19; m 44; c 2. *Educ:* Univ Cincinnati, ChemE, 41, MS, 43. *Prof Exp:* From jr res engr to sr res engr, 43-68, prin res assoc, 68-75, PRIN RES ENGR, ARMCO INC, 75- *Mem:* Inst Elec & Electronics Engrs; Am Inst Mining, Metall & Petrol Engrs. *Res:* Deformation and recrystallization orientations in soft magnetic materials; studies of magnetic properties in relation to metallurgy of soft magnetic materials. *Mailing Add:* Res & Technol Armco Inc Middletown OH 45043

LITTON, GEORGE WASHINGTON, b Pennington Gap, Va, Feb 22, 10; m 38; c 2. ANIMAL HUSBANDRY. *Educ:* Va Polytech Inst, BS, 31, MS, 40. *Prof Exp:* County agr agent, Extension Serv, Va Polytech Inst & State Univ, 31-40, res & teaching beef & sheep mgt, 40-44, sheep specialist, 45-51, prof animal sci & head dept, 52-70, dir centennial progs, 70-73, EMER PROF ANIMAL SCI, VA POLYTECH INST & STATE UNIV, 73- *Mem:* Fel AAAS; Am Soc Animal Sci. *Res:* Animal breeding and management; beef, cattle and sheep. *Mailing Add:* Rt 3 Box 286 Blacksburg VA 24060

LITVAK, AUSTIN S, b Staten Island, NY, Dec 1, 33. UROLOGY. *Educ:* Wagner Col, BS, 54; Univ Va, MD, 58; Am Bd Urol, dipl. *Prof Exp:* Intern surg, Univ Va Hosp, 58-59; NIH fel, Surg Br, Nat Cancer Inst, 59-60; USPHS surgeon, Claremore Indian Hosp, Okla, 60-61; resident urol, Hosp Univ Pa, Jefferson Med Col Serv & Philadelphia Gen Hosp, 61-63; pvt pract, 63-73; asst in surg, Div Urol, Hahnemann Med Col, 70-73; asst prof, 73-75, ASSOC PROF SURG, DIV UROL, UNIV KY MED CTR, 76- *Concurrent Pos:* Asst attend urol, Monmouth Med Ctr & Riverview Hosp; assoc attend & div rep, Bayshore Hosp; courtesy staff, Jersey Shore Med Ctr; asst urol staff, Hahnemann Med Col; mem urol staff, Univ Ky Med Ctr 73-78; consult urol, Vet Admin Hosp, 73-75; active staff, St Josephs Hosp, Central Baptist Hosp & Claril County Hosp. *Honors & Awards:* First Prize, Nat Clin Soc, 68. *Mem:* Am Urol Asn; Am Fertil Soc; AMA; fel Am Col Surgeons; fel Int Col Surgeons. *Res:* Embryology of the kidney; acute and chronic prostatitis; lower urinary tract infections in children and adults; diseases of the kidney, urethra and bladder in children. *Mailing Add:* 1146 Lane Allen Rd Lexington KY 40504

LITVAK, MARVIN MARK, b Newark, NJ, Oct 20, 33; m 63; c 2. RADIATION-PLASMA INTERACTION, QUANTUM ELECTRONIC & OPTICS. *Educ:* Cornell Univ, BEngPhys, 56, PhD(theoret physics), 60. *Prof Exp:* Consult, Avco Corp, 55-60, sr staff mem, Avco-Everett Res Lab, 60-63; group leader, Lincoln Lab, Mass Inst Technol, 63-70; sr radio astronomer, Smithsonian Astrophys Observ, 70-78; MEM TECH STAFF, JET PROPULSION LAB, CALIF INST TECHNOL, 78- *Concurrent Pos:* Lectr, Harvard Col Observ, 70-78; consult, Lincoln Lab, Mass Inst Technol, 77-81. *Mem:* Int Astron Union; Am Phys Soc; Am Astron Soc. *Res:* Magnetohydrodynamic shock waves and power generation; current-carrying superconductors; laser-produced gas breakdown; gas laser characteristics; non-linear propagation effects of lasers; nonlinear properties of semiconductors; interstellar molecules and masers; millimeter-wave and submillimeter-wave radio astronomy and aeronomy. *Mailing Add:* MS T1166 Jet Propulsion Lab Calif Inst Technol 4800 Oak Grove Dr Pasadena CA 91125

LITVAN, GERARD GABRIEL, b Vienna, Austria, May 17, 27; Can citizen; m 64; c 1. SURFACE CHEMISTRY. *Educ:* Eotovos Univ, Budapest, Dipl, 52; Univ Toronto, PhD(surface chem), 62. *Prof Exp:* Asst prof phys chem, Inst Phys Chem, Eotovos Univ, 52-55; assoc phys chem, Cent Chem Res Inst, Hungarian Acad Sci, 55-56; res chemist phys polymer chem, Can Industs Ltd, 57-59; SR RES OFFICER, DIV BLDG RES, NAT RES COUN CAN, 62- *Concurrent Pos:* Lectr, Chem Dept, Carleton Univ, 66-67; First Int Conf Durability of Bldg Mat & Components; Can Stand Asn Subcomt chmn, 78. *Mem:* Fel Am Ceramic Soc; Am Concrete Inst; Am Chem Soc; fel Chem Inst Can. *Res:* Phase transitions of substances adsorbed in porous solids; mechanism of cyroinjury and cyroprotection in plant and animal tissue; mechanism of frost action in porous building materials. *Mailing Add:* Div Bldg Res Nat Res Coun Can Ottawa ON K1A 0R6 Can

LITWACK, GERALD, b Boston, Mass, Jan 11, 29; m 56, 73; c 2. BIOCHEMISTRY. *Educ:* Hobart Col, BA, 49; Univ Wis, MS, 51, PhD(biochem), 53. *Prof Exp:* From asst prof to assoc prof biochem, Rutgers Univ, 54-60; res assoc prof, Grad Sch Med, Univ Pa & dir biochem, Div Cardiol, Philadelphia Gen Hosp, 60-64; PROF BIOCHEM, SCH MED, TEMPLE UNIV, 64-, FELS RES INST, 64-, DEP DIR, 78- *Concurrent Pos:* Nat Found Infantile Paralysis fel, Biochem Lab, Univ Sorbonne, 53-54; trainee, Oak Ridge Inst Nuclear Studies, 55; Nat Inst Arthritis & Metab Dis res career develop award, 63-69; vis prof, Univ Calif, 56; hon prof, Rutgers Univ, 60-64; vis scientist, Univ London, 71 & Univ Calif, 72; assoc ed, Cancer Res, 77-; mem adv bd, Biochem & Chem Carcinogenesis, Am Cancer Soc, 77-80, chmn, 79, Anticancer Res, 82-; mem cell physiol panel, NSF, 80-83; assoc scientist, Wistar Inst, 77-78. *Honors & Awards:* Lalor Found Award, 56. *Mem:* Am Soc Biol Chemists; Am Asn Cancer Res; Am Soc Cell Biol; Endocrine Soc. *Res:* Ligandin; hormonal control of enzyme formation and activity; glucocorticoid receptor. *Mailing Add:* Fels Res Inst Temple Univ Sch of Med Philadelphia PA 19140

LITWAK, ROBERT SEYMOUR, b New York, NY, Nov 25, 24; m; c 3. SURGERY. *Educ:* Ursinus Col, BS, 45; Hahnemann Med Col, MD, 49; Am Bd Surg, dipl, 56; Am Bd Thoracic Surg, dipl, 58. *Prof Exp:* Asst surg, Sch Med, Boston Univ, 52; from instr to assoc prof surg, Med Sch, Univ Miami, 56-62; ATTEND SURGEON & CHIEF DIV CARDIOTHORACIC SURG, MT SINAI HOSP, 62-; PROF SURG, MT SINAI SCH MED, 71- *Concurrent Pos:* Consult, Vet Admin Hosp, Coral Gables, Fla, 57- & Variety Children's Hosp, 59-; chief div thoracic & cardiovascular surg, Jackson Mem Hosp, 59-62. *Mem:* Fel Am Col Surg; fel Am Col Chest Physicians; fel Am Col Cardiol; fel NY Acad Sci. *Res:* Cardiovascular physiology; cardiac surgery. *Mailing Add:* 1176 5th Ave New York NY 10029

LITWIN, MARTIN STANLEY, b Florence, Ala, Jan 8, 30; m 60; c 2. SURGERY. *Educ:* Univ Ala, BS, 51, MD, 55; Am Bd Surg, dipl, 63. *Prof Exp:* Instr med physiol, Sch Med, Univ Ala, 53; intern surg, Michael Reese Hosp, Chicago, 55-56; asst, Peter Bent Brigham Hosp, Boston, 56-58, jr asst resident, 57 & 58-59, sr asst resident, 60-61, sr resident, 61-62; instr, Harvard Med Sch, 66; from asst prof to assoc prof, 66-75, prof surg, 75-77, ASSOC DEAN, MED DIR FAC PRACT, ROBERT & VIOLA LOBRANO PROF SURG, SCH MED, TULANE UNIV, 77- *Concurrent Pos:* Surg res fel, Harvard Med Sch, 56-58; surg res fel, St Mary's Hosp & Med Sch, London, 59-60; George Gorham Peters fel, Peter Bent Brigham Hosp, Boston, 59-60, Am Cancer Soc clin fel, 61-62; teaching fel, Harvard Med Sch, 64-65; registr to prof teaching unit, St Mary's Hosp, London, 59-60; clin investr, Vet Admin Hosp, West Roxbury, 64-66, consult, 66-; adj prof biomed eng, Northeastern Univ, 64-67; mem, Surgeon-Gen Adv Comt Optical Lasers, Working Group Safety Stand Use Lasers, Armed Forces Nat Res Coun Comt Vision, Ad Hoc Initial Rev Group, Nat Ctr Radiol Health & Spec Study Sect Laser & NIH session chmn, Gordon Conf Lasers Biol Med, 65-67; chief surg, Peter Bent Brigham Hosp, 65 & jr assoc surg, 65-66; vis surgeon, Charity Hosp of La, mem active staff, Tulane Hosp; Nat Heart Inst investr career develop award, 68-72. *Mem:* Fel Am Col Surgeons; Am Surg Asn; Am Asn Surg Trauma; Soc Univ Surgeons; Soc Surg Alimentary Tract. *Res:* Blood rheology; vascular and gastrointestinal surgery; surgical metabolism; blood transfusion and treatment of skin cancer. *Mailing Add:* Dept of Surg Tulane Univ Med Sch New Orleans LA 70112

LITWIN, STEPHEN DAVID, b New York, NY, Apr 30, 34; m 61; c 3. GENETICS, IMMUNOLOGY. *Educ:* Brooklyn Col, BS, 55; New York Univ, MD, 59. *Prof Exp:* Intern & resident med, Montefiore Med Ctr, 59-64; investr immunol, Rockefeller Univ, 64-67; res hematologist, US Army, 67-69; asst prof, 65-71, assoc prof, 71-79, PROF MED, CORNEL MED COL, NEW YORK HOSP, 79- *Concurrent Pos:* USPHS career develop award, 70-72; mem various study sects, NIH, Ad Hoc Study Sect, Am Cancer Soc, 82. *Mem:* Am Soc Clin Investigation; Am Asn Human Genetics; Am Asn Immunologists. *Res:* Genetic control of human immunoglobulin synthesis including the genetic allotypes and subclasses of human immunoglobulin and inherited immunodeficiency diseases. *Mailing Add:* Cornell Med Col 1300 York Ave New York NY 10021

LITZ, LAWRENCE MARVIN, b Chicago, Ill, Oct 22, 21; m 42; c 4. CHEMICAL ENGINEERING, PHYSICAL CHEMISTRY. *Educ:* Univ Chicago, BS, 42; Ohio State Univ, PhD(phys chem), 48. *Prof Exp:* Res chemist, Tenn Valley Auth, 42-43; res metallurgist, Manhattan Proj, Los Alamos, 43-45; res chemist catalysis, Allied Chem Corp, 47-51; group leader chem metal, Standard Oil Calif, 51-53; group leader high temperature mat, Carbon Div, 53-62, develop mgr fuel cells, Advan Develop Dept, 62-66, sr group leader membrane technol, Corp Res, 66-72, gen mgr, Membrane Systs, 72-77, SR DEVELOP ASSOC GAS PRODS, LINDE DIV, UNION CARBIDE, 77- *Honors & Awards:* Kirkpatrick Award, Chem Eng J, 75. *Mem:* Am Inst Chem Engrs; Am Chem Soc; Electrochem Soc. *Res:* Membrane technology; high temperature materials and processes; electrochemical and process engineering; fuel cells, nuclear chemistry; chemical and physical metallurgy. *Mailing Add:* 16 Briarwood Lane Pleasantville NY 10570

LITZ, RICHARD EARLE, b Presque Isle, Maine, July 3, 44; m 69; c 2. PLANT PATHOLOGY, HORTICULTURE. *Educ:* Dalhousie Univ, BA, 66, MSc, 68; Univ Nottingham, PhD(plant virol), 71. *Prof Exp:* Fel mycol, Univ Durham, 71-73; res officer plant path, Twyford Labs Ltd, 73-76; fel, 76-77, res assoc plant path, 77-78, ASST PROF, FRUIT CROPS DEPT, UNIV FLA, 79- *Concurrent Pos:* Rare Fruits Coun Int grant, 78-; Rockefeller Found grants, 79-81 & 81- *Mem:* Int Asn Plant Tissue Cult. *Res:* Tissue culture of tropical fruits; disease resistance in tropical fruits. *Mailing Add:* Inst of Food & Agr Sci 18905 SW 280th St Homestead FL 83031

LITZENBERGER, SAMUEL CAMERON, b Calgary, AB, July 21, 14; nat US; m 41. AGRONOMY, FIELD CROPS. *Educ:* Colo State Univ, BS, 37; Mont State Univ, MS, 39; Iowa State Univ, PhD(plant path, crop breeding), 48. *Prof Exp:* From instr to assoc prof agron, Mont State Univ, 39-46, asst Exp

Sta, 39-43, agronomist, 43-46; assoc agronomist, Exp Sta, Fla, 48-49; agronomist, Ala Exp Sta, Agr Res Admin, USDA, 49-51; agriculturist, res adv agron & head dept, Agr Technol Serv, US Opers Mission, Int Coop Admin, Nicaragua, 51-57; agron adv, Cambodia, 58-63; agron adv, Food & Agr Off & Chief Div, USAID, Guinea, 64-67; agr res adv & chief prod and breeding, Tunisia, 67-68; chief regional cereals off, NAfrica, 68-69, Food & Agr Off, 69-70, agronomy res specialist & chief, Crops Prod Div, 70-75, SPEC CONSULT, OFF AGR, TECH ASSISTANCE BUR, AID, WASHINGTON, DC, 75- Concurrent Pos: Consult, Colo State Univ, 75- Honors & Awards: Superior Honor Award, AID, 75. Mem: Fel AAAS; fel Am Soc Agron; Am Phytopath Soc; Am Genetic Asn. Res: Inheritance and disease resistance of small grains; weed control; seed and soil improvement; crops production and improvement under tropical, sub-tropcial, temperate and sub-arctic environments; integrated programs for agricultural production and improvement of food crops for developing nations. Mailing Add: 1230 Tulip St Longmont CO 80501

LIU, ALICE YEE-CHANG, b Hunan, China, July 12, 48; US citizen; m 78. BIOCHEMICAL ENDOCRINOLOGY, CELLULAR PHYSIOLOGY. Educ: Chinese Univ Hong Kong, BSc Hons, 69; City Univ New York, PhD(pharmacol), 74. Prof Exp: Instr pharmacol, Mt Sinai Sch Med, 73; fel, Sch Med, Yale Univ, 73-77; ASST PROF PHARMACOL, MED SCH, HARVARD UNIV, 77- Concurrent Pos: Lectr med pharmacol, Med Sch, Harvard Univ, 78-, lectr endocrine pharmacol, 80 & lectr neuropharmacol, 81- Mem: Sigma Xi; NY Acad Sci. Res: Role of cyclic adenosine monophosphate dependent protein kinase in the control of growth and differentiation of eukaryotic cells; development of techniques to study the regulation and function of cyclic adenosine monophosphate dependent protein kinase in intact cells. Mailing Add: Dept Pharmacol Med Sch Harvard Univ 250 Longwood Ave Boston MA 02115

LIU, BEDE, b Shanghai, China, Sept 25, 34; US citizen; m 59; c 1. ELECTRICAL ENGINEERING. Educ: Nat Taiwan Univ, BSEE, 54; Polytech Inst Brooklyn, MEE, 56, DEE, 60. Prof Exp: Equipment engr, Western Elec Co, 54-56; mem tech staff commun systs, Bell Tel Labs, 59-62; from asst prof to assoc prof, 62-69, PROF ELEC ENG, PRINCETON UNIV, 69- Mem: Fel Inst Elec & Electronics Engrs; Inst Elec & Electronics Engrs Circuit Systs Soc. Res: Digital and optical signal processing; communication, circuit and system theory. Mailing Add: Dept of Elec Eng Princeton Univ Princeton NJ 08540

LIU, BENJAMIN Y H, b Shanghai, China, Aug 15, 34; m 58; c 1. MECHANICAL ENGINEERING. Educ: Univ Nebr, BSME, 56; Univ Minn, Minneapolis, PhD(mech eng), 60. Prof Exp: From asst prof to assoc prof, 60-69, PROF MECH ENG, UNIV MINN, MINNEAPOLIS, 69- Concurrent Pos: Guggenheim fel, 68-69, dir, Particle Technol Lab, 73- Mem: AAAS; Solar Energy Soc; Am Soc Heat, Refrig & Air-Conditioning Engrs; Air Pollution Control Asn; fel Am Soc Mech Engrs. Res: Terrestrial and space application of solar energy; aerosol science and technology; instrumentation and measurement. Mailing Add: Dept of Mech Eng Univ of Minn Minneapolis MN 55455

LIU, C(HANG) K(ENG), b Soochow, China, Mar 28, 21; nat US; m 51; c 2. MECHANICAL ENGINEERING. Educ: Nat Chiao-Tung Univ, China, BS, 43; Univ Ill, MS, 46, PhD(theoret & appl mech), 50. Prof Exp: Res assoc theoret & appl mech, Univ Ill, 50-52; ammunition design engr, Picatinny Arsenal, 52; res assoc appl math, Brown Univ, 52-54; from asst prof to assoc prof, 54-63, PROF MECH ENG, UNIV ALA, TUSCALOOSA, 63- Concurrent Pos: Consult, Marshall Space Flight Ctr, NASA, 60-68; fallout shelter analyst, 66- Mem: Am Soc Mech Engrs; Am Soc Eng Educ; Soc Eng Sci; Am Inst Aeronaut & Astronaut. Res: Radiation safety; fluid mechanics; viscous fluid flow; mechanics of social and human behavior; heat conduction in solids. Mailing Add: Dept of Aerospace & Mech Eng Univ of Ala at Tuscaloosa University AL 35486

LIU, C T, b Tai-Shin, Kiangsu, China, Oct 19, 31; m 70; c 3. PHYSIOLOGY, PHARMACOLOGY. Educ: Nat Taiwan Univ, BS, 56; Univ Tenn, MS, 59, PhD(physiol). Prof Exp: Assoc res biologist pharmacol, Sterling-Winthrop Res Inst, 65-66; asst prof physiol, Baylor Col Med, 66-73; RES PHYSIOLOGIST, US ARMY MED RES INST INFECTIOUS DIS, 73- Concurrent Pos: USPHS trainee, 63-65; adj prof physiol, Baylor Col Med, 80- Mem: Soc Pharmacol & Exp Therapeut; Am Physiol Soc; Soc Exp Biol & Med; Am Soc Nephrology. Res: Cardiovascular and renal physiology; water, electrolyte and lipid metabolism; mechanisms of infectious diseases and toxemias; effect of muscle trauma. Mailing Add: US Army Med Res Infect Dis Ft Detrick Frederick MD 21701

LIU, CHAMOND, b Waltham, Mass, Sept 28, 48. PERFORMANCE OF OPERATING SYSTEMS. Educ: Univ Calif, Berkeley, AB, 68; Cornell Univ, MS, 71, PhD(math), 73. Prof Exp: asst prof math, Fordham Univ, 73-79; sr assoc programmer, 79-81, STAFF PROGRAMMER, IBM, CORP, 81- Concurrent Pos: NSF grant, 75-76. Mem: Am Math Soc; Math Asn Am; Asn Comput Mach. Res: Performance and performance methodology of large operating systems including automatic work load characterization, automatic work load generation and architectural design. Mailing Add: Dept D86 IBM PO Box 390 Poughkeepsie NY 12602

LIU, CHAO-HAN, b Kwangsi, China, Jan 3, 39; m 63; c 2. PHYSICS, ELECTRICAL ENGINEERING. Educ: Nat Taiwan Univ, BS, 60; Brown Univ, PhD(elec sci), 65. Prof Exp: Res assoc, 65-66, from asst prof to assoc prof, 66-74, PROF ELEC ENG, UNIV ILL, URBANA-CHAMPAIGN, 74- Honors & Awards: Spec recognition award, Inst Elec & Electronics Engrs, 68. Mem: Am Phys Soc; Am Geophys Union; Inst Elec & Electronics Engrs. Res: Ionosphere, plasma and atmospheric physics; wave propagation in plasma and random media. Mailing Add: Dept of Elec Eng Univ of Ill at Urbana-Champaign Urbana IL 61801

LIU, CHEN YA, b Shanghsien, China, Sept 21, 24; US citizen; m 56; c 3. MECHANICAL ENGINEERING, APPLIED MATHEMATICS. Educ: Cent Univ, China, BS, 48; NY Univ, MME, 55, EngScD, 59. Prof Exp: Res engr, Ord Serv, China, 48-52, proj engr, 52-54; instr mech eng, NY Univ, 55-59; asst prof, Carnegie Inst Technol, 59-61; sr res engr, Res Ctr, B F Goodrich Co, 61-64; sr res engr, 65-69, assoc fel, Columbus Labs, 69-72, FEL, COLUMBUS LABS, BATTELLE MEM INST, 72- Concurrent Pos: Consult, Budd Electronics, Inc, 61; lectr, Univ Akron, 62-64. Mem: Am Inst Aeronaut & Astronaut; Am Soc Mech Engrs. Res: Fluid mechanics and heat transfer involving Newtonian or non-Newtonian fluids; elasticity of orthotropic materials. Mailing Add: 3007 Avalon St Upper Arlington OH 43221

LIU, CHIEN, b Canton, China, Mar 6, 21; m 47; c 4. INFECTIOUS DISEASES, VIROLOGY. Educ: Yenching Univ, BS, 42; WChina Union Univ, MD, 47; Am Bd Pediat, dipl, 64. Prof Exp: Intern, Ill Masonic Hosp, 46-47; med intern, Garfield Mem Hosp, Washington, DC, 47-48; asst med, Johns Hopkins Univ, 51-52, asst physician, Johns Hopkins Hosp, 49-52; res assoc bact & immunol, Harvard Med Sch, 52-55, assoc, 55-58, asst prof, 58; assoc prof pediat, 58-63, PROF MED & PEDIAT, SCH MED, UNIV KANS, 63- Concurrent Pos: Res fel med, Sch Med, Johns Hopkins Univ, 49-51; USPHS res career award, 63-; vis prof, Nat Defense Med Ctr, Taiwan, 66-67; med consult, US Naval Med Res Unit 2, 66-67. Mem: Am Soc Pediat Res; Am Soc Microbiol; Am Asn Immunologists; Am Acad Microbiol; Infectious Dis Soc Am. Mailing Add: Dept of Med Univ of Kans Sch of Med Kansas City KS 66103

LIU, CHING SHI, b Shanghai, China, July 23, 35. AERONAUTICS, FLUID DYNAMICS. Educ: SDak Sch Mines & Technol, BS, 57; Kans State Univ, MS, 58; Northwestern Univ, PhD(mech eng), 61. Prof Exp: Design engr, Int Harvester Co, 56-57; res engr, Bendix Corp, 59-60; asst prof gas dynamics, Northwestern Technol Inst, 61-68; ASSOC PROF ENG SCI, STATE UNIV NY BUFFALO, 68- Concurrent Pos: Consult, Cook Res Lab, Ill, 61-62; res assoc, Argonne Nat Lab, 63-64; sr res fel, Calif Inst Technol, 65- Mem: Am Inst Aeronaut & Astronaut; Am Soc Mech Engrs; Am Soc Eng Educ. Res: Gas dynamics; magneto gas dynamics; plasma physics. Mailing Add: Dept of Eng Sci State Univ of NY Buffalo NY 14214

LIU, CHI-SHENG, b Chinan, China, Nov 1, 34; US citizen; m 60; c 3. PHYSICAL ELECTRONICS, MATHEMATICS. Educ: Nat Taiwan Univ, BSEE, 57; WVa Univ, MSEE, 62; Univ Ill, Urbana, PhD(elec eng), 68. Prof Exp: Elec engr radio, Philco Corp, 60-61; mem eng staff TV, RCA Consumer Electronics Div, 62-69; SR RES SCIENTIST GASEOUS DISCHARGE, WESTINGHOUSE RES LABS, 69- Concurrent Pos: David Sarnoff fel, RCA, 65-68. Mem: Am Phys Soc. Res: Study of high pressure gas discharges; high efficiency arc lamps and gas lasers. Mailing Add: Westinghouse Res & Develop Ctr Pittsburgh PA 15235

LIU, CHONG TAN, b Shanghai, China, May 11, 36; US citizen; m 63; c 3. INORGANIC CHEMISTRY. Educ: Nat Taiwan Univ, BSc, 56; Univ Pittsburgh, PhD(inorg chem), 64. Prof Exp: Sr res chemist, Hooker Chem Corp, 64-71; sr res chemist, 72-78, GROUP SUPVR, STAUFFER CHEM CO, 79- Mem: Am Chem Soc. Res: Water treatment; industrial chemical processes; metal finishing; plating on plastics; corrosion controls; high temperature chemistry; coordination chemistry. Mailing Add: Stauffer Chem Co ERC Elmsford NY 10523

LIU, CHUAN SHENG, b Kwanhsi, China, Jan 9, 39; m 65; c 3. THEORETICAL ASTROPHYSICS, PLASMA PHYSICS. Educ: Tunghai Univ, BS, 60; Univ Calif, Berkeley, MA, 64, PhD(physics), 68. Prof Exp: Asst prof in residence physics, Univ Calif, Los Angeles, 68-70; vis scientist, Gulf Gen Atomic, Inc, 70-71; mem, Inst Advan Study, 71-74; prof physics, 74-81, PROF PHYSICS & ASTRON, UNIV MD, 81- Mem: Am Phys Soc. Mailing Add: Dept of Physics & Astron Univ of Md College Park MD 20740

LIU, CHUI FAN, b Chunking, China, Apr 5, 30; US citizen; m 59; c 3. INORGANIC CHEMISTRY. Educ: Univ Ill, AB, 52, PhD(chem), 56. Prof Exp: Res chemist, Dow Chem Co, 56-58; instr chem, Univ Conn, 58-60; asst prof, Univ Mich, 60-65; assoc prof, 65-70, PROF CHEM, UNIV ILL, CHICAGO CIRCLE, 70- Concurrent Pos: NSF & NIH res grants, 62- Res: Structure and chemistry of coordination compounds; asymmetric synthesis. Mailing Add: Dept of Chem Univ of Ill at Chicago Circle Chicago IL 60680

LIU, CHUI HSUN, b China, Nov 5, 31; US citizen; m 62. ANALYTICAL CHEMISTRY, INORGANIC CHEMISTRY. Educ: Univ Ill, BA, 52, PhD(chem), 57. Prof Exp: From asst prof to assoc prof chem, Polytech Inst Brooklyn, 57-65; PROF CHEM, ARIZ STATE UNIV, 65- Mem: Am Chem Soc. Res: Chemistry, electrochemistry and spectroscopy in molten salts and other nonaqueous solvents; chemistry of coordination compounds; chelating agents in chemical separations and analyses. Mailing Add: 949 E Libra Dr Tempe AZ 85253

LIU, CHUNG LAUNG, b Canton, China, Oct 25, 34; US citizen; m 60; c 1. COMPUTER SCIENCE. Educ: Cheng Kung Univ, Taiwan, BSc, 56; Mass Inst Technol, SM, 60, ScD(elec eng), 62. Prof Exp: From asst prof to assoc prof elec eng, Mass Inst Technol, 62-72; PROF COMPUT SCI, UNIV ILL, URBANA, 72- Mem: Inst Elec & Electronics Engrs; Asn Comput Mach; Math Asn Am; Opers Res Soc Am. Res: Theory of computation; combinatorial mathematics. Mailing Add: Dept of Comput Sci Univ of Ill Urbana IL 61801

LIU, CHUNG-CHIUN, b Canton, China, Oct 8, 36; m 67. CHEMICAL ENGINEERING. Educ: Cheng Kung Univ, Taiwan, BS, 59; Calif Inst Technol, MS, 62; Case Western Reserve Univ, PhD(chem eng), 68. Prof Exp: Res assoc, Eng Design Ctr, Case Western Reserve Univ, 68; asst prof chem eng, Univ Pittsburgh, 68-78; PROF CHEM ENG, CASE WESTERN RESERVE UNIV, 78- Mem: Am Inst Chem Engrs. Res: Electrochemistry; bio-medical engineering; material science. Mailing Add: Dept of Chem Eng Case Western Reserve Univ Cleveland OH 44106

LIU, CHUNG-YEN, b Canton, China. AERONAUTICAL ENGINEERING. *Educ:* Nat Taiwan Univ, BS, 56; Brown Univ, MS, 58; Calif Inst Technol, PhD(aeronaut), 62. *Prof Exp:* From asst prof to assoc prof, 62-76, PROF ENG, UNIV CALIF, LOS ANGELES, 76- *Mem:* Am Phys Soc; Am Inst Aeronaut & Astronaut. *Res:* Fluid mechanics. *Mailing Add:* Dept of Mech & Struct Univ of Calif Los Angeles CA 90024

LIU, DAVID H(O-FENG), b Chekiang, China, Feb 24, 28; m 56; c 2. CHEMICAL ENGINEERING. *Educ:* Jadavpur Univ, BSc, 51; Univ Pa, MSc, 54, PhD(chem eng), 56. *Prof Exp:* Sr chem engr, Monsanto Chem Co, 55-62; supvr chem eng res, Mobil Chem Co, Tex, 64-66; sr res assoc, Uniroyal Inc, 66-74; MGR PROCESS DEVELOP, RHONE-POULENC INC, 74- *Mem:* Am Chem Soc; Am Inst Chem Engrs. *Res:* Chemical thermodynamics; reaction kinetics; unit operations, engineering and economic analysis; pollution abatement; petrochemical processes; aroma chemicals; polymers; rubber and specialty chemicals. *Mailing Add:* 297 Jersey Ave Rhodia New Brunswick NJ 08903

LIU, DAVID H W, b Honolulu, Hawaii, Aug 5, 36; m 65; c 3. TOXICOLOGY. *Educ:* Univ Mich, BS, 58; Univ Ore, MA, 60; Ore State Univ, PhD(toxicol), 69. *Prof Exp:* Biologist, Hanford Atomic Prod Oper, Gen Elec Co, 62-65 & Pac Northwest Labs, Battelle Mem Inst, 65; NIH fel, Col Pharm, Wash State Univ, 69-71; sr aquatic biologist, Waste Mgt Syst Oper, Envirogenics Co, Aerojet Gen Corp, 71-73; dir, Aquatic Toxicol Prog, SRI Int, 73-80; SR PROJ SCIENTIST, WOODWARD-CLYDE CONSULTS, 80- *Concurrent Pos:* Mem, Aldehyde Comt, Nat Acad Sci, 79-80. *Res:* Toxicology of water pollutants. *Mailing Add:* Woodward-Clyde Consults 3 Embarcadero Ctr Suite 700 San Francisco CA 94111

LIU, DAVID SHIAO-KUNG, b Chung-King, China, Aug 27, 40; US citizen; m 66; c 3. FLUID MECHANICS, NUMERICAL METHODS. *Educ:* Cheng-Kung Univ, Taiwan, BS, 62; Univ Calif, Berkeley, MS, 65; New York Univ, PhD(appl math & hydraul), 73. *Prof Exp:* Phys scientist fluid mech, 72-76, SR PHYS SCIENTIST, RAND CORP, 76-; PROF HYDRAUL, NAT CHENG-KUNG UNIV, 77- *Concurrent Pos:* Sr consult, Va Inst Marine Sci, 77- *Mem:* Am Soc Civil Eng; Int Asn Water Resources. *Res:* Numerical modeling of three-dimensional non-homogeneous geophysical fluid systems; stochastic analysis and control theory of physical systems. *Mailing Add:* Rand Corp Santa Monica CA 90406

LIU, DICKSON LEE SHEN, b Shantung, China, Apr 6, 35; Can citizen; m 67; c 1. MICROBIOLOGY, WATER POLLUTION. *Educ:* Nat Taiwan Chung Hsin Univ, BSc, 62; Univ BC, MSc, 66, PhD(microbiol), 71. *Prof Exp:* Res scientist marine biochem, BC Res Coun, 66-68; res scientist eutrophication, Can Ctr Inland Waters, 71-72; res scientist wastewaters, Can Wastewater Technol Inst, 72-75; RES SCIENTIST TOXIC SUBSTANCES, NAT WATER RES INST, 75-; ASSOC PROF, DEPT ENVIRON HEALTH SCI, TULANE MED CTR, NEW ORLEANS, LA, 81- *Concurrent Pos:* Expert, Food Agr Orgn, UN, 68-; adv, Wastewater Technol Ctr, 75-; tech ed, Can Res, 77-; expert biodegradation, Can Nat Comt on Int Orgn Standards, 77-; mem, Assoc Comt on Sci Criteria Environ Qual, Nat Res Coun Can, 77-80. *Res:* Biodegradation of toxic substances; development of standard procedure for assessing the persistence of new substances in the natural environments; lake and river eutrophication; biological treatment of toxic industrial wastewaters; environmental toxicology. *Mailing Add:* Nat Water Res Inst PO Box 5050 Burlington ON L7R 4A6 Can

LIU, EDWIN CHIAP HENN, b Honolulu, Hawaii, Apr 11, 42; m 65. BIOCHEMISTRY. *Educ:* Johns Hopkins Univ, AB, 64; Mich State Univ, PhD(biochem), 71. *Prof Exp:* Res assoc biochem, AEC, Plant Res Lab, Mich State Univ, 71-72; ASST PROF BIOL, UNIV SC, 72- *Mem:* Am Chem Soc; Genetics Soc Am; Am Soc Plant Physiologists. *Res:* Biochemistry and developmental biology of isozymes. *Mailing Add:* Savannah River Ecol Lab PO Drawer E Aiken SC 29801

LIU, FOOK FAH, b Calcutta, India, Sept 30, 34; m 66; c 3. HIGH ENERGY PHYSICS. *Educ:* Presidency Col, Calcutta, India, BSc, 56; Purdue Univ, PhD(physics), 62. *Prof Exp:* Res assoc, High-Energy Physics Lab, Stanford Univ, 62-66; asst prof physics, Case Inst Technol, 66-68; staff physicist, Stanford Linear Accelerator Ctr, Stanford Univ, 68-70; asst prof, 70-74, assoc prof, 74-78, PROF PHYSICS, CALIF STATE COL, SAN BERNARDINO, 78- *Mem:* Am Phys Soc. *Res:* Photoinduced reactions at high energies; phenomenology of multibody final states; decay of unstable particles; microcomputer systems. *Mailing Add:* Dept of Physics Calif State Col San Bernardino CA 92407

LIU, FRANK C, b Shantung, China, Apr 15, 26; US citizen; m 54; c 3. MECHANICAL ENGINEERING. *Educ:* Chekiang Univ, BS, 49; Univ Wash, MS, 53; Univ Tex, PhD(mech eng), 58. *Prof Exp:* Teacher high sch, Formosa, 49-52; instr mech eng, Univ Tex, 55-57; res engr, Boeing Co, 57-62; tech consult, NASA, Marshall Space Flight Ctr, 62-64, sci asst appl math, 64-67; prof eng mech, Univ Ala, Huntsville, 67-80. *Mem:* Soc Indust & Appl Math. *Res:* Structures; structural dynamics and fluid mechanics; engineering mechanics and applied mathematics. *Mailing Add:* 8906 Valley View Dr SE Huntsville AL 35802

LIU, FRANK FU-WEN, b Taiwan. POMOLOGY, POSTHARVEST HORTICULTURE. *Educ:* Taiwan Univ, BS, 57; Cornell Univ, MS, 69, PhD(pomol), 74. *Prof Exp:* Horticulturist, Sino-Am Joint Comn Rural Reconstruct, 69-71; asst prof, 74-80, ASSOC PROF POMOL, CORNELL UNIV, 80- *Mem:* Am Soc Hort Sci; Sigma Xi. *Res:* Postharvest physiology with emphasis on the control mechanism of maturation and ripening of fruits and storage methods of fruits. *Mailing Add:* Dept of Pomol Cornell Univ Ithaca NY 14853

LIU, FRANK TSUNG YUAN, b Tongshan, China, Jan 2, 16; nat US; m 51; c 3. PHYSIOLOGY. *Educ:* Army Vet Col, China, DVM, 39; Univ Mo, MA, 47; Ohio State Univ, PhD(physiol), 54. *Prof Exp:* Asst prof physiol, Sch Dent, Temple Univ, 54-61; assoc prof, Sch Dent, Univ Pittsburgh, 61-67; assoc prof, 68-70, PROF PHYSIOL, SCH DENT, UNIV MO-KANSAS CITY, 70-, CHMN DEPT, 68-, LECTR MED, SCH MED, 73- *Mem:* NY Acad Sci; Soc Exp Biol & Med; Int Asn Dent Res; Am Inst Biol Sci; Am Physiol Soc. *Res:* Endocrinology; salivary glands; effects of hormones on oral structures; reproduction physiology; trace elements on dental caries; growth and development of mandible bone. *Mailing Add:* Sch Dent Med & Physiol Univ Missouri Kansas City MO 64108

LIU, FRED WEI JUI, b Canton, China, Jan 29, 26; nat US; m 61. PHYSICAL CHEMISTRY. *Educ:* St John's Univ, China, BS, 48; Temple Univ, MA, 50; Lehigh Univ, PhD(chem), 52. *Prof Exp:* Res assoc, Lehigh Leather Inst, Pa, 52-53; chief chemist, Lester Labs, Inc, 53-64; DIR, CONTINENTAL CONSULTS, INC, 64-; PRES, CONTINENTAL TRADING CO, 65- *Mem:* Am Chem Soc; Nat Asn Corrosion Engrs. *Res:* Colloid or surface chemistry; detergents; cleaning and maintenance chemicals formulation; corrosion; water treatment; foreign trade; industrial chemicals. *Mailing Add:* 157 Lake Forest Lane NE Atlanta GA 30305

LIU, FREDERICK F, b Chefoo, China, Apr 19, 19; US citizen; m 46; c 2. FUEL TECHNOLOGY, PHYSICS. *Educ:* Technische Hochschule, Berlin, dipl, 39; Carnegie Inst Technol, BS, 46; Princeton Univ, PhD(sci admin), 51. *Hon Degrees:* DSc, Polytech Univ Inst, China, various univ & insts, 54. *Prof Exp:* Res asst, Princeton Univ, 50-52, res assoc, 52-55; res eng specialist, Rockethyne & Atomics Int, NAm Aviation, Inc, 55-57; dir res, Dresser Dynamics, Inc, 57, exec vpres, 57-59; PRES & SCI DIR, QUANTUM DYNAMICS, INC, 59- *Concurrent Pos:* Vis lectr, Mass Inst Technol, 56 & Cambridge Univ, Eng, 64; vis scientist, Kyoto Univ, Japan, 67-; guest lectr, Technische Univ, Berlin, 70-; vis scientist & prof, Inst Mech, Chinese Acad Sci, 79- *Mem:* Sigma Xi; Am Phys Soc; Am Inst Aeronaut & Astronaut; assoc fel Int Inst Refrigeration; fel Am Inst Elec Eng. *Res:* Extremely fast, dynamic and transient phenomena relating to propulsion, weapon, nuclear, space and low temperature physical phenomena, together with the development of a range of modern instrumentation and computing technologies. *Mailing Add:* Quantum Dynamics Inc PO Box 865 Tarzana CA 91356

LIU, HAO-WEN, b China, Aug 20, 26; nat US; m 55; c 5. MECHANICS, MATERIALS SCIENCE. *Educ:* Univ Ill, BS, 54, MS, 56, PhD(appl mech), 59. *Prof Exp:* Asst prof appl mech, Univ Ill, 59-61; sr res fel, Calif Inst Technol, 61-63; assoc prof metall, 63-68, PROF MAT SCI, SYRACUSE UNIV, 68- *Mem:* Am Soc Mech Engrs; Am Inst Mech Engrs; Am Soc Testing & Mat; Sigma Xi. *Res:* Mechanical behavior and properties of materials and applied mechanics. *Mailing Add:* Dept of Chem Eng & Mat Sci Syracuse Univ Syracuse NY 13210

LIU, HENRY, b Peking, China, June 3, 36; m 64. FLUID MECHANICS. *Educ:* Nat Taiwan Univ, BS, 59; Colo State Univ, MS, 63, PhD(fluid mech), 66. *Prof Exp:* From asst prof to assoc prof, 65-77, PROF CIVIL ENG, UNIV MO-COLUMBIA, 77- *Concurrent Pos:* Prin investr water resources res grants, Dept Interior, 66-68; Capsule Pipeline res grants, US Dept Energy, 78-81 & NSF grant, 80-82; vis prof, Univ Melbourne, Australia, 80. *Mem:* Am Soc Civil Engrs; Int Asn Hydraul Res; Am Soc Eng Educ. *Res:* Electrokinetics; exploration of the physics of streaming potential fluctuations and the utilization of this phenomenon to study turbulence characteristics in liquid flows; dispersion of pollutants in river; hydraulic capsule pipeline; wind pressure inside buildings; flow measurement; cherepnov water lifter; hydropower. *Mailing Add:* Dept of Civil Eng Univ of Mo Columbia MO 65201

LIU, HOUNG-ZUNG, b China, Jan 23, 31; m 69; c 2. BIOCHEMICAL GENETICS, PLANT PROTOPLAST GENETICS. *Educ:* Taiwan Prov Col, BS, 53; NDak State Col, MS, 59; Cornell Univ, PhD(genetics, biochem, plant physiol), 64. *Prof Exp:* Asst cytol, Taiwan Agr Res Inst, Taipei, 54-56; asst gen genetics, Cornell Univ, 59-64; assoc prof genetics, 64-69, PROF GENETICS & CHMN, DEPT BIOL SCI, COL ARTS & SCI, STATE UNIV NY COL PLATTSBURGH, 69-, ACTG DEAN, FAC ARTS & SCI, 81- *Concurrent Pos:* NIH spec res fel, Marquette Univ, 67-68. *Mem:* AAAS; Am Chem Soc; Genetics Soc Am; Int Plant Tissue Asn. *Res:* Tryptophan operon mutants of Escherichia coli and indoleglycerol-phosphate synthetase; plant protoplast fusion and culture. *Mailing Add:* Dept of Biol Sci State Univ of NY Col Plattsburgh NY 12901

LIU, HSING-JANG, b Kiang-Su, China, Dec 2, 42; m 66; c 3. CHEMISTRY. *Educ:* Nat Taiwan Norm Univ, BSc, 64; Univ NB, Fredericton, PhD(chem), 68. *Prof Exp:* Fel chem, Univ NB, Fredericton, 68-69; res assoc, Columbia Univ, 69-70; teaching & res assoc, Univ NB, Fredericton, 70-71; asst prof, 71-77, ASSOC PROF CHEM, UNIV ALTA, 77- *Mem:* Am Chem Soc; Chem Inst Can. *Res:* Natural products, isolation, identification and synthesis; development of novel synthetic methods. *Mailing Add:* Dept of Chem Univ of Alberta Edmonton AB T6G 2G2 Can

LIU, HUA-KUANG, b Kueilin, China, Sept 2, 39; m 65; c 1. LASER OPTICS, ELECTROOPTICS. *Educ:* Nat Taiwan Univ, BS, 62; Univ Iowa, MS, 65; Johns Hopkins Univ, PhD(elec eng), 69. *Prof Exp:* Res asst, Univ Iowa, 63-64; instr elec eng, Va Mil Inst, 64-65; res asst, Johns Hopkins Univ & jr instr, Eve Col, 65-69; asst prof elec eng, 69-77, PROF ELEC ENG, UNIV ALA, 77- *Concurrent Pos:* Consult, Optimal Data Corp, Ala, 69-; res grants, Univ Ala, Tuscaloosa, 70-71 & NSF, 71-73 & 75-77 & NASA, 73-78; consult, NASA Marshall Space Flight Ctr, US Army Missile Command, 73; pres, Lumin, Inc, 75; vis assoc prof elec eng, Stanford Univ, 75-76. *Mem:* Inst Elec & Electronics Engrs; Optical Soc Am. *Res:* Solid-state electronics; optical image processing; holography and holographic nondestructive testing; halftone contact screens for printing. *Mailing Add:* 35 Woodland Forrest Sect 4 Tuscaloosa AL 35401

LIU, J(OSEPH) T(SU) C(HIEH), b Shanghai, China, Nov 9, 34; US citizen; m 64; c 3. FLUID MECHANICS. *Educ:* Univ Mich, BSE(math) & BSE(aeronaut eng), 57, MSE, 58; Calif Inst Technol, PhD(aeronaut), 64. *Prof Exp:* Propulsion engr aerothermodyn group, Gen Dynamics/Convair, 58-59; res assoc aerospace & mech sci, Gas Dynamics Lab, Princeton Univ, 64-66; from asst prof to assoc prof, 66-73, PROF ENG, BROWN UNIV, 73- *Concurrent Pos:* Consult, Space Systs Div, Avco Corp, Mass, 66-67; Systs Div, 69-70; vis, Dept Math, Imperial Col, Univ London, 72-73 & 79-80. *Honors & Awards:* Nat Award, Inst Aeronaut Sci, 58. *Mem:* Am Soc Mech Engrs; Am Phys Soc; Am Meteorol Soc. *Res:* Coherent structures in turbulent flows, nonlinear hydrodynamic stability; aeroacoustics; fluidized bed instabilities; bubble information. *Mailing Add:* Div Eng Brown Univ Providence RI 02912

LIU, JIH-HUA, b Chekiang, China, Oct 25, 41; m 74. INDUSTRIAL ORGANIC CHEMISTRY. *Educ:* Worcester Polytech Inst, BS, 65; Univ Wis-Mailwaukee, PhD(chem), 73. *Prof Exp:* Chemist, Pfizer Corp, 65-68; res asst chem, Univ Wis-Milwaukee, 68-73; ASSOC SR INVESTR CHEM, SMITH KLINE CORP, 73- *Mem:* Am Chem Soc; Sigma Xi. *Res:* Synthesis of decinine, homoprostanoids and cephalosporins. *Mailing Add:* Smith Kline Corp 1500 Spring Garden St Philadelphia PA 19101

LIU, JOHN K(UNGFU), b Hankow, China, Aug 22, 30; nat US; m 57. MECHANICS. *Educ:* Univ Pa, BSME, 52; Ill Inst Technol, MS, 57. *Prof Exp:* Struct engr, Shih & Assoc, 48-52; from design engr to proj engr, Int Harvester Co, 52-57; from sr proj engr to actg dir res & develop, Clearing Div, US Industs, 57-60; dir marine tech dept, Tech Ctr, 59-60; mgr marine tech lab, Stromberg Carlson Co Div, Gen Dynamics Co, 60-62; vpres, Force Control, Inc, 62-68; VPRES, CLUTCH DIV, PHILADELPHIA GEAR CORP, 68- *Mem:* Am Soc Mech Engrs; Sigma Xi; Am Soc Inventors. *Res:* Oceanographic instruments and devices; solid and fluid mechanics; marine propulsion equipment; pressure vessel design and development; fluid shear power transmission devices; industrial electronics and transducers. *Mailing Add:* 1763 Rockhill Lane Valley Forge PA 19481

LIU, JOHN MOYU, UK citizen. MATERIALS SCIENCE, APPLIED PHYSICS. *Educ:* St Vincent Col, BS, 66; Johns Hopkins Univ, MS, 69, PhD(mech & mat sci), 73. *Prof Exp:* Res assoc, 73-76, vis asst prof, 76-78, ASST PROF MAT SCI, STATE UNIV NY, STONY BROOK, 78- *Concurrent Pos:* Consult, NAm Philips Corp, 77- *Mem:* Am Soc Nondestructive Testing; Metall Soc; Am Inst Mining, Metall & Petrol Engrs. *Res:* Fracture mechanics; nondestructive testing; plastic deformation of metals. *Mailing Add:* Dept Mat Sci & Eng State Univ NY Stony Brook NY 11794

LIU, JOSEPH JENG-FU, b Chiangsi, China, Oct 24, 40; m 71. CELESTIAL MECHANICS, THEORETICAL MECHANICS. *Educ:* Cheng Kung Univ, Taiwan, BS, 62; Auburn Univ, MS, 66, PhD(celestial mech), 71. *Prof Exp:* Teaching asst appl mech, Cheng Kung Univ, 63-64 & Auburn Univ, 66-71; mem res staff astrodyn, Northrop Serv, Inc, Huntsville, Ala, 71-77; MEM TECH STAFF ASTRODYN, AEROSPACE DEFENSE COMMAND, 77- *Mem:* Am Inst Aeronaut & Astronaut; Am Astronaut Soc; Am Astron Soc. *Res:* General, special perturbation and semi-analytic theories, their applications for the orbital and attitude motions of an artificial satellite perturbed by conservative and nonconservative forces. *Mailing Add:* Directorate Astrodyn Applications Aerospace Defense Command Peterson AFB CO 80914

LIU, LIU, b Shanghai, China, Aug 12, 30; m 56; c 3. SOLID STATE PHYSICS. *Educ:* Univ Taiwan, BS, 54; Univ Chicago, MS, 57, PhD(physics), 61. *Prof Exp:* From asst prof to assoc prof, 61-74, PROF PHYSICS, NORTHWESTERN UNIV, ILL, 74- *Concurrent Pos:* Consult, Argonne Nat Lab, 61-64; Fulbright Sr Res Scholar to France, Presidential Bd Foreign Scholars, 75-76. *Mem:* Fel Am Phys Soc. *Res:* Band theory of semiconductors; theory of narrow-gap and zero-gap semiconductors. *Mailing Add:* Dept of Physics Northwestern Univ Evanston IL 60201

LIU, LON-CHANG, b China; US citizen. PHYSICS, NUCLEAR STRUCTURE. *Educ:* Univ Neuchatel, PhD(physics), 73. *Prof Exp:* Instr, City Univ New York, 73-75, asst prof physics, 75-79; STAFF MEM, LOS ALAMOS NAT LAB, 79- *Mem:* Am Phys Soc; Sigma Xi. *Res:* Theoretical intermediate energy nuclear physics; meson nucleus interaction. *Mailing Add:* Group CNC-11 MS H824 Los Alamos Nat Lab Los Alamos NM 87545

LIU, LUKE LOKIA, theoretical physics, exploration geophysics, see previous edition

LIU, MATTHEW J P, b Peking, China, July 19, 35; US citizen; m 61; c 2. MATHEMATICS. *Educ:* Lafayette Col, BS & BA, 58; Ill Inst Technol, MS, 61; Ind Univ, PhD(math), 75. *Prof Exp:* From instr to assoc prof, 61-76, PROF MATH, UNIV WIS, STEVENS POINT, 76- *Concurrent Pos:* NSF fel, Ind Univ, 67-68. *Mem:* Math Asn Am; Am Math Soc; Nat Coun Teachers Math. *Res:* Mathematics, summability. *Mailing Add:* Dept of Math Univ of Wis Stevens Point WI 54481

LIU, MAW-SHUNG, b Taiwan, Feb 2, 40; m 66; c 1. MEDICAL PHYSIOLOGY. *Educ:* Kaohsiung Med Col, Taiwan, DDS, 64; Univ Ky, MSc, 70; Univ Ottawa, PhD(physiol), 76. *Prof Exp:* Staff dentist & lectr oral surg, Chinese Army Hosp, Kaohsiung Med Col Hosp, Taiwan, 64-68; intern path, Med Ctr, Univ Ky, 68-69; Med Res Coun Can fel, 70-73; Alcoholism & Drug Addiction Res Found Ont res scholar, 73-74; instr physiol, 74-76, asst prof physiol, Sch Med, La State Univ Med Ctr, New Orleans, 76-78; assoc prof physiol, Bowman Gray Sch Med, Wake Forest Univ, Winston-Salem, NC, 78-82; PROF PHYSIOL, SCH MED, ST LOUIS UNIV, 82- *Mem:* Int Soc Heart Res; Shock Soc; Am Physiol Soc. *Res:* Myocardial and hepatic intermediary metabolism in endotoxic shock. *Mailing Add:* Dept Physiol Sch Med St Louis Univ St Louis MO 63104

LIU, MICHAEL T H, b Hong Kong, China, Mar 1, 39. Can citizen. PHYSICAL CHEMISTRY. *Educ:* St Dunstan's Univ, BSc, 61; St Francis Xavier, MA, 64; Univ Ottawa, PhD(phys chem), 67. *Prof Exp:* Technician, Can Celanese Ltd, 61-62; group leader qual control, Chemcell Ltd, 64; Nat Res Coun fel, Univ Reading, 67-68; asst prof, 68-73, assoc prof, 73-80, PROF CHEM, UNIV PRINCE EDWARD ISLAND, 80- *Concurrent Pos:* Nat Res Coun grant-in-aid, 68-; Def Res Bd of Can grant-in-aid, 74-76. *Mem:* Chem Inst Can. *Res:* Kinetics and mechanism of chain reaction; unimolecular reaction; carbene chemistry. *Mailing Add:* Dept of Chem Univ of Prince Edward Island Charlottetown PE C1A 4P3 Can

LIU, MING-BIANN, b Chang-Hua, Taiwan, June 22, 42; m 75; c 2. PHYSICAL CHEMISTRY, CHEMICAL ENGINEERING. *Educ:* Cheng-Kung Univ, Taiwan, BS, 68; Ill Inst Technol, PhD(chem), 74, MS, 80. *Prof Exp:* Res & teaching, Univ Kans, 74-75; res, Chem Div, Argonne Nat Lab, 76-78, asst chemist, Chem Eng Div, 78-81; ASST CHEMIST, DOW CHEM CO, 81- *Mem:* Am Chem Soc; Electrochem Soc. *Res:* High temperature materials and technology; plasma surface interaction; gas surface interaction; electrochemical processes and technology. *Mailing Add:* 709 Sylvan Lane Midland MI 48640

LIU, MING-TSAN, b Taiwan, China, Aug 30, 34; m 66. COMPUTER SCIENCE, COMPUTER ENGINEERING. *Educ:* Cheng Kung Univ, BS, 57; Univ Pa, MS, 61, PhD(elec eng), 64. *Prof Exp:* Asst elec eng, Cheng Kung Univ, 59-60; instr, Moore Sch Elec Eng, Univ Pa, 62-65, asst prof, 65-69; assoc prof, 69-78, PROF COMPUT & INFO SCI, OHIO STATE UNIV, 78- *Mem:* Inst Elec & Electronics Eng; Asn Comput Mach. *Res:* Computer architecture; computer networks; distributed processing; microcomputer systems; computer communication. *Mailing Add:* Dept of Comput & Info Sci 2036 Neil Ave Columbus OH 43210

LIU, PAN-TAI, b Taipei, Taiwan, Sept 22, 41; m 66; c 1. APPLIED MATHEMATICS. *Educ:* Nat Taiwan Univ, BS, 63; State Univ NY, Stony Brook, PhD(appl math), 68. *Prof Exp:* Asst prof, 68-74, assoc prof, 74-80, PROF MATH, UNIV RI, KINGSTON, 80- *Concurrent Pos:* Vis prof, Dept Elec Eng, Nat Taiwan Univ, Taipei, Taiwan, 74-75. *Mem:* Am Math Soc. *Res:* Optimal controls; differential games; stochastic processes. *Mailing Add:* Dept of Math Univ of RI Kingston RI 02881

LIU, PAUL CHI, b Chefoo, China, June 18, 35; m 65; c 1. PHYSICAL OCEANOGRAPHY, COASTAL ENGINEERING. *Educ:* Nat Taiwan Univ, BS, 56; Virginia Polytech Inst, MS, 61; Univ Mich, PhD(oceanic sci), 77. *Prof Exp:* Res phys scientist, US Lake Survey, Army Corps Engrs, 65-71; res phys scientist, Lake Surv Ctr, Nat Ocean Surv, 71-74, PHYS SCIENTIST, GREAT LAKES ENVIRON RES LAB, NAT OCEANIC & ATMOSPHERIC ADMIN, 74- *Concurrent Pos:* Vis scholar, Univ Mich, 78- *Mem:* Am Geophys Union; Am Meterol Soc; Am Soc Civil Engrs; Int Asn Great Lakes Res; Soc Indust & Applied Math. *Res:* Observational study hindcast and forecast of wind-generated waves on the Great Lakes; coastal engineering; air-sea interactions. *Mailing Add:* Great Lakes Environ Res Lab NOAA 2300 Washtenaw Ave Ann Arbor MI 48104

LIU, PAUL ISHEN, b Taiwan; US citizen. CLINICAL PATHOLOGY. *Educ:* Nat Taiwan Univ, MD, 60; St Louis Univ, PhD(path), 69. *Prof Exp:* Assoc prof path, Med Ctr, Univ Kans, 73-74; assoc dir lab med, Med Col Ga, 74-76; prof & vchmn, Med Univ SC, 76-80; PROF PATH & VCHMN DEPT, UNIV SOUTH ALA, 81- *Mem:* AMA; Col Am Path; Am Soc Clin Path; Asn Clin Sci; Am Soc Microbiol. *Res:* Leukemia; immunology. *Mailing Add:* Dept Path Col Med Univ South Ala Mobile AL 36617

LIU, PHILIP L-F, b Fu-Chu, China, Dec 11, 46. HYDRODYNAMICS, COASTAL ENGINEERING. *Educ:* Nat Taiwan Univ, BS, 68; Mass Inst Technol, SM, 71, ScD(hydrodyn), 74. *Prof Exp:* Res asst civil eng, Mass Inst Technol, 69-74; asst prof, 74-79, ASSOC PROF ENVIRON ENG, CORNELL UNIV, 79- *Concurrent Pos:* Justice asst prof, Justice Found, 78-79; Eng Found fel, 79; J S Guggenheim fel, 80; vis assoc, Calif Tech, 80-81. *Honors & Awards:* Walter L Huber Prize, Am Soc Civil Engrs, 78. *Mem:* Am Soc Civil Engrs; Am Geophys Union. *Res:* Wave hydrodynamics in coastal engineering; coastal currents and coastline processes; numerical methods for nonlinear free surface problems. *Mailing Add:* Sch Civil & Environ Eng Cornell Univ Ithaca NY 14853

LIU, PINGHUI VICTOR, b Formosa, China, Feb 9, 24; nat US; m 59; c 2. MEDICAL MICROBIOLOGY. *Educ:* Tokyo Jikel-kai Sch Med, MD, 47; Tokyo Med Sch, PhD(microbiol), 57; Am Bd Med Microbiol, dipl, 62. *Prof Exp:* Intern, Mercy Hosp, Cedar Rapids, Iowa, 54-55; intern internal med, Louisville Gen Hosp, 55-56; from instr to assoc prof, 57-69, prof microbiol, 69-81, PROF MICROBIOL & IMMUNOL, SCH MED, UNIV LOUISVILLE, 81- *Concurrent Pos:* Res fel microbiol, Sch Med, Univ Louisville, 56-57; USPHS sr res fel, 59-, res career develop award, 62-; mem, Subcomt Pseudomonas & Related Organisms, Int Comt Bact Nomenclature, 63- *Mem:* AAAS; Am Soc Microbiol; Infectious Dis Soc Am; NY Acad Sci. *Res:* Pathogenesis and taxonomy of pseudomonads and related organisms, such as aeromonads and vibrios; extracellular toxins, such as hemolysin, lecithinase and protease; immunities to infections. *Mailing Add:* Dept of Microbiol Univ Louisville Health Sci Ctr Louisville KY 40201

LIU, ROBERT SHING-HEI, b Shanghai, China, Aug 1, 38; m 67; c 2. ORGANIC CHEMISTRY. *Educ:* Howard Payne Col, BS, 61; Calif Inst Technol, PhD(chem), 65. *Prof Exp:* Res chemist, E I du Pont de Nemours & Co, Inc, 64-68; assoc prof, 68-72, PROF CHEM, UNIV HAWAII, 72- *Concurrent Pos:* Alfred P Sloan fel, 70-72; John Simon Guggenheim Found fel, 74-75. *Mem:* Inter-Am Photochem Soc; Am Chem Soc; Am Soc Photobiology; Royal Soc Chem London. *Res:* Photochemistry of polyenes; energy transfer processes in solution; reaction mechanism; new geometric isomers of vitamin A and carotenoids; visual pigment analogs. *Mailing Add:* Dept of Chem Univ of Hawaii Honolulu HI 96822

LIU, RUEY-WEN, b Kiangsu, China, Mar 18, 30; US citizen; m 57; c 2. ELECTRICAL ENGINEERING. *Educ:* Univ Ill, BS, 54, MS, 55, PhD(elec eng), 60. *Prof Exp:* From asst prof to assoc prof, 60-66; PROF ELEC ENG, UNIV NOTRE DAME, 66- *Concurrent Pos:* NSF grants 62-63, 64-66 & 71-73; vis assoc prof, Univ Calif, Berkeley, 65-66; vis prof, Nat Taiwan Univ, 69 & Univ Calif, Berkeley, 77-78. *Mem:* Am Math Soc; fel Inst Elec & Electronics Engrs. *Res:* System and network theory; large-scale dynamical systems. *Mailing Add:* Dept of Elec Eng Univ Notre Dame Notre Dame IN 46556

LIU, S(HING) G(ONG), b Soochow, China, Oct 24, 33; m 60; c 3. ELECTRICAL ENGINEERING, APPLIED PHYSICS. *Educ:* Univ Taiwan, BS, 54; NC State Col, MS 58; Stanford Univ, PhD(elec eng), 63. *Prof Exp:* Jr engr, Int Bus Mach Corp, 58-59, assoc engr, 59; asst microwave ferrites, Stanford Univ, 59-63; RES SCIENTIST, RCA LABS, 63- *Mem:* Am Phys Soc; Inst Elec & Electronics Engrs. *Res:* Spin waves in ferrites; microwave and optical frequency devices using semiconductors; ion implantation in gallium arsenide. *Mailing Add:* 48 Braeburn Dr Princeton NJ 08540

LIU, SAMUEL HSI-PEH, b Taiyuan, China, Apr 17, 34; m 61; c 2. THEORETICAL SOLID STATE PHYSICS. *Educ:* Taiwan Univ, BS, 54; Iowa State Univ, 58, PhD(physics), 60. *Prof Exp:* Assoc res mem, Res Lab, IBM Corp, 60-61, res staff mem, 61-64; from assoc prof to prof physics, Iowa State Univ, 64-81; SR RES STAFF MEM, OAK RIDGE NAT LAB, 81- *Concurrent Pos:* Vis prof, H C Oersted Inst, Copenhagen Univ, 71-72, Univ Calif, 75-76 & Free Univ, Berlin, WGer, 80. *Mem:* Fel Am Phys Soc. *Res:* Solid state theory; electronic and magnetic properties of metals and metallic compounds. *Mailing Add:* Oak Ridge Nat Lab Oak Ridge TN 37830

LIU, SHU-LEN HUANG, biochemistry, pharmacy, see previous edition

LIU, SI-KWANG, b Kwangsi, China, Dec 1, 25; m 60; c 4. VETERINARY PATHOLOGY. *Educ:* Vet Col Chinese Army, DVM, 49; Univ Calif, Davis, PhD(vet path), 64. *Prof Exp:* Sr vet res & diag, Provincial Taitung Agr Sta, China, 50-55; lectr vet path, Col Agr, Taiwan Univ, 56-59, chief path lab, Univ Vet Hosp, 56-59; res asst path & parasitol, Sch Vet Med, Univ Calif, Davis, 59-64; assoc pathologist, 64-66, cardiopulmonary pathologist, 66-69, asst head dept, 69-73, SR STAFF MEM, ANIMAL MED CTR, 73- *Concurrent Pos:* Clinical asst prof in comp path, NY Med Col, 69-; vis prof vet path, Nat Taiwan Univ & vis expert, Chinese Sci Coun, 76-77; consult path, NY Zool Soc Bronx Zoo & histopathologist, NY Cent Vet Lab, 79- *Mem:* Am Vet Med Asn; Am Soc Parasitol; Sigma Xi; NY Acad Sci; Int Acad Path. *Res:* Cardiovascular pathology in domestic animals as well as zoo animals; comparative pathology in cardiovascular and orthopedic diseases. *Mailing Add:* Animal Med Ctr 510 E 62nd St New York NY 10021

LIU, STEPHEN C Y, b Hunan, China, Feb 24, 27; m 54; c 4. MICROBIOLOGY, IMMUNOLOGY. *Educ:* Taiwan Univ, BSc, 51, MSc, 54; Univ Minn, PhD, 57. *Prof Exp:* Instr plant path, Taiwan Univ, 51-54; from res asst to res assoc, Univ Minn, 54-58; res plant pathologist, Nat Res Coun, 58-62, asst mgr Chas Pfizer & Co, Inc, 62-65; from asst prof to assoc prof, 65-74, PROF MICROBIOL, EASTERN MICH UNIV, 74- *Concurrent Pos:* Tech consult, People's Republic China, UN, 80-81. *Mem:* AAAS; Am Phytopath Soc; Am Soc Microbiol; NY Acad Sci. *Res:* Genetics of bacteria; immunology; virology. *Mailing Add:* Dept of Biol Eastern Mich Univ Ypsilanti MI 48197

LIU, SUNG-TSUEN, b Taiwan, Mar 11, 40; US citizen; m 66; c 3. PHYSICAL CHEMISTRY, INORGANIC CHEMISTRY. *Educ:* Taiwan Normal Univ, BS, 62; Nat Tsing-Hua Univ, MS, 66; State Univ NY, Buffalo, PhD(phys chem), 72. *Prof Exp:* Sr chemist, Ayerst Lab, 74-77; PROJ LEADER, PETROLITE CORP, 77- *Mem:* Am Chem Soc. *Res:* Kinetics and mechanism of crystallization and dissolution of minerals; metal complexation; salt solubility; micelle formation; surface and colloid chemistry; phase solubility; inorganic reaction mechanism. *Mailing Add:* 2100 SE Main St Irvine CA 92713

LIU, TAI-PING, b Taiwan, Repub of China, Nov 18, 45; m 73. MATHEMATICAL ANALYSIS. *Educ:* Nat Taiwan Univ, BS, 68; Ore State Univ, MS, 70; Univ Mich, PhD(math), 73. *Prof Exp:* Asst prof, 73-78, assoc prof, 78-81; PROF UNIV MD, COLLEGE PARK, 81- *Concurrent Pos:* Sloan fel. *Mem:* Am Math Soc. *Res:* Nonlinear conservation laws; shock waves theory; gas dynamics. *Mailing Add:* Dept of Math Univ of Md College Park MD 20742

LIU, TA-JO, b Taipei, Taiwan, Sept 16, 51. CHEMICAL ENGINEERING. *Educ:* Nat Taiwan Univ, BS, 73; Polytechnic Inst, NY, MS, 77, PhD(chem eng), 80. *Prof Exp:* Res scientist, 79-81, SR RES SCIENTIST, EASTMAN KODAK CO, 81- *Res:* Fundamental coating; optimal coating die design for newtonian and non-newtonian fluids; development of special coating techniques. *Mailing Add:* 325A Whitehall Dr Rochester NY 14616

LIU, TEH-YUNG, b Tainan, Formosa, May 24, 32; nat US; m 61; c 3. BIOCHEMISTRY. *Educ:* Taiwan Nat Univ, BS, 55; Univ Pittsburgh, PhD(biochem), 61. *Prof Exp:* Res assoc biochem, Rockefeller Univ, 61-65, asst prof, 65-67; biochemist, Biol Dept, Brookhaven Nat Lab, 67-73; sect head biochem microbial struct, Nat Inst Child Health & Human Develop, 73-74; dep dir, Div Bact Prod, 74-79, DIR, DIV BIOCHEM & BIOPHYS, BUR BIOLOGICS, FOOD & DRUG ADMIN, 80- *Concurrent Pos:* Adj prof, Chem Dept, Catholic Univ Am, Washington, DC. *Mem:* Am Soc Biol Chem. *Res:* Streptococcal proteinase; pneumococcal and meningococcal cell wall polysaccharides; human C-reactive protein; limulus lysate. *Mailing Add:* Bur of Biologics Bldg 29 Rm 425 8800 Rockville Pike Bethesda MD 20014

LIU, TING-TING Y, b Taipei, Taiwan, Aug 4, 49; m 75; c 1. STARCHBIOSYNTHESIS. *Educ:* Nat Taiwan Univ, BS, 71; Univ Hawaii, MS, 74; Pa State Univ, PhD(hort), 79. *Prof Exp:* Res asst, Dept Agron, Nat Taiwan Univ, 71-72; grad asst, Dept Hort, Pa State Univ, 74-78, res assoc, 79; TECH ASST, DEPT DAIRY SCI, OHIO AGR RES DEVELOP CTR, 79- *Mem:* Am Soc Plant Physiologists; Sigma Xi. *Res:* Isolate amyloplasts from corn endosperm to study sugar translocation and starch biosynthesis in plant, and the analysis of research data for animal toxicity studies statistically. *Mailing Add:* 640-C Station Dr Wooster OH 44691

LIU, TONY CHEN-YEH, b Fu-Chien, China, July 27, 43; US citizen; m 69; c 2. STRUCTURAL ENGINEERING, CIVIL ENGINEERING. *Educ:* Nat Chung-Hsing Univ, Taiwan, BS, 65; SDak Sch Mines & Technol, MS, 68; Cornell Univ, PhD(civil eng), 71. *Prof Exp:* Struct engr civil eng, Ammann & Whitney Inc, 71; group leader nuclear eng, Gen Atomic Co, 72-76; res engr, Waterways Exp Sta, 76-81, CIVIL ENGR, US ARMY CORPS ENGRS, 81- *Concurrent Pos:* Guide prof, World Open Univ, 75. *Honors & Awards:* Wason Res Medal, Am Concrete Inst, 74. *Mem:* Am Concrete Inst; Am Soc Civil Engrs; Sigma Xi. *Res:* Design of concrete hydraulic structures, precast concrete structures, repair and rehabilitation of deteriorated concrete structures and thermal stress analysis for mass concrete structures. *Mailing Add:* 1207 Wiesman Court Great Falls VA 22066

LIU, T(IEN)-S(HIH), b Hankow, China, Feb 19, 25; nat US; m 53; c 4. PHYSICAL METALLURGY. *Educ:* Nat Chiao Tung Univ, China, BS, 46; Univ Mo, MS, 49; Univ Notre Dame, PhD, 52. *Prof Exp:* Metallurgist, Puchen Locomotive Works, China, 46-48; proj supvr phys metall, Horizons, Inc, 52-57; sr res metallurgist, Titanium Metals Corp Am, 57-58; consult metallurgist, Southwest Res Inst, 58-61; STAFF SCIENTIST, HONEYWELL CORP CTR, 61- *Mem:* AAAS; Am Soc Metals; Metall Soc; Am Inst Mining, Metall & Petrol Engrs; Sigma Xi. *Res:* Plastic deformation, fracture; anisotropy; phase relationships; alloy design; joining techniques; mechanical-magnetic phenomena; thin films; magneto-optic materials; materials compatibility in electronic micropackaging; interconnections reliability. *Mailing Add:* Honeywell Corp Technol Ctr 10701 Lyndale Ave S Bloomington MN 55420

LIU, TUNG, b Peking, China, Mar 12, 26; nat US; m 58; c 3. CHEMICAL ENGINEERING. *Educ:* Nankai Univ, Tientsin, BS, 47; Univ Ill, MSc, 51, PhD(chem eng), 53. *Prof Exp:* Chem engr, Pittsburgh Consol Coal Co, 53-55; res chem engr, Monsanto Chem Co, 56-60; res mat engr, Air Force Mat Lab, 60-68; sr res engr, Occidental Petrol Corp, 68-77; RES ENGR, BENDIX RES LABS, 77- *Concurrent Pos:* Chem engr, Garrett Corp, 70-77. *Mem:* Am Chem Soc; Am Inst Chem Engrs. *Res:* Friction, lubrication and wear. *Mailing Add:* Bendix Ctr Bendix Res Labs Southfield MI 48037

LIU, VI-CHENG, b China, Sept 1, 17; nat US; m 47. AEROSPACE ENGINEERING. *Educ:* Chiao Tung Univ, BS, 40; Univ Mich, MS, 47, PhD(aeronaut eng), 51. *Prof Exp:* Res asst aerodyn, Aeronaut Res Inst, Tsing Hua Univ, China, 40-44, res instr, 44-46; res fel, Ministry Educ, 46-48; res assoc eng, Res Inst, 48-50, res engr, 50-59, PROF AEROSPACE ENG, UNIV MICH, ANN ARBOR, 59- *Mem:* Am Phys Soc; assoc fel Am Inst Aeronaut & Astronaut. *Res:* Upper atmosphere; rocket flight, rarefied gas and ionospheric gas dynamics; thermal diffusion; boundary layer flow; turbulent dispersion; plasma interaction; magnetospheric physics. *Mailing Add:* Dept Aerospace Eng Univ Mich Ann Arbor MI 48109

LIU, WEN CHIH, b Liao-Ning Province, China, Feb 19, 21; US citizen; m 60; c 3. BIOCHEMISTRY. *Educ:* Nat Hu-Nan Univ, BS, 44; Baylor Univ, MS, 53; Univ Wis-Madison, PhD(biochem), 58. *Prof Exp:* Res assoc biochem, Univ Wis, 58-59; res assoc, Univ Calif, Los Angeles, 59-60; sr res chemist, Pfizer, Inc, 60-69; SR RES INVESTR MICROBIOL, SQUIBB INST MED RES, 69- *Mem:* AAAS; Am Chem Soc. *Res:* Natural products; antibiotics; cancer chemotherapy; plant growth substances. *Mailing Add:* Squibb Inst for Med Res Princeton NJ 08540

LIU, WILLIAM SHIUN, gas dynamics, see previous edition

LIU, WINGYUEN TIMOTHY, US citizen. REMOTE SENSING, AIR-SEA INTERACTION. *Educ:* Ohio Univ, BS, 71; Univ Wash, MS, 74, PhD(atmospheric sci), 78. *Prof Exp:* Res assoc atmospheric sci, Univ Wash, 78-79; SR SCIENTIST SATELLITE OCEANOG, JET PROPULSION LAB, CALIF INST TECHNOL, 79- *Mem:* Am Meteorol Soc; Am Geophys Union. *Res:* Study of the planetary layer and transportation across the atmosphere-ocean interface. *Mailing Add:* Jet Propulsion Lab MS 183-501 4800 Oak Grove Dr Pasadena CA 91108

LIU, YOUNG KING, b Nanking, China, May 3, 34; US citizen; m 64; c 2. BIOMECHANICS, BIOMEDICAL ENGINEERING. *Educ:* Bradley Univ, BS, 56; Univ Wis-Madison, MS, 59; Wayne State Univ, PhD(mech), 63. *Prof Exp:* Instr mech, Wayne State Univ, 60-63; lectr, Univ Mich, Ann Arbor, 63-64, asst prof, 64-68; vis asst prof aeronaut & astronaut, Stanford Univ, 68-69; assoc prof, 69-72, prof biomech, Tulane Univ, 72-78; PROF & DIR, CTR FOR BIOMAT RES, UNIV IOWA, IOWA CITY, 78- *Concurrent Pos:* NIH spec res fel, Stanford Univ, 68-69; biophys consult, US Army Aeromed Res Lab, 72-; NIH res career develop award, 71. *Mem:* Am Soc Eng Educ; Orthop Res Soc; Am Asn Univ Profs; Sigma Xi; Am Acad Mech. *Res:* Biomechanics and physiologic basis of acupuncture. *Mailing Add:* Ctr for Biomat Res Univ of Iowa Iowa City IA 52242

LIU, YU, b China; US citizen; m 67; c 1. OPTICS, LASERS. *Educ:* Ga Inst Technol, PhD(physics), 74. *Prof Exp:* Res asst physics, Rice Univ, 62-69; instr physics, Tex Tech Univ, 66-69; teaching asst physics, Ga Inst Technol, 69-74; physicist optics & laser, US Army Missile Res & Develop Lab, 74-76; res physicist laser & optics, US Army Missile Res & Develop Command, 76-79; PHYSICIST LASER, INFRARED & OPTICS, US ARMY AVIATION RES & DEVELOP COMMAND, 79- *Mem:* Asn US Army. *Res:* Research, design and development of laser target guidance links; low temperature physics research. *Mailing Add:* US Army Aviation Res & Develop Command 4300 Goodfellow Blvd St Louis MO 63120

LIU, YUNG SHENG, b China, Sept 23, 44; m; c 2. PHYSICS, LASERS. *Educ:* Nat Taiwan Univ, BS, 66; Cornell Univ, PhD(physics), 73. *Prof Exp:* Teaching asst physics, Cornell Univ, 68-69, res asst, 70-73; PHYSICIST, GEN ELEC RES CTR, 72- *Concurrent Pos:* Vis scientist physics, Univ Calif, Los Angeles, 68-; fel, Cornell Univ, 69; Avco fel, 70. *Honors & Awards:* Outstanding Achievement Award, Gen Elec, 77. *Mem:* Optical Soc Am; Am Phys Soc; Sigma Xi; AAAS. *Res:* Laser physics; quantum electronics and optics; laser-matter interactions; semiconductor electronics; author or coauthor of over 30 publications. *Mailing Add:* Gen Elec Res & Develop Ctr PO Box 8 Schenectady NY 12301

LIU, YU-YING, b China, May 16, 44. SYNTHESIS LABELLED COMPOUND. *Educ:* Taiwan Normal Univ, BS, 67; Univ Minn, PhD(chem), 72. *Prof Exp:* Fel, Am Health Found, 71-73; SR SCIENTIST, HOFFMANN LAROCHE INC, 74- *Mem:* Am Chem Soc. *Res:* Natural product isolation; metabolism; quantitative analysis; synthesis of labelled compound of pharmaceutical interest. *Mailing Add:* 81 Lillian St Park Ridge NJ 07656

LIU-GER, TSU-HUEI, b Kwei-yang, Kwei-chow, Repub of China, Mar 10, 43; US citizen; m 71; c 2. THEORETICAL PHYSICS. *Educ:* Nat Taiwan Univ, BS, 64; Univ Ore, PhD(physics), 69. *Prof Exp:* Asst prof physics, Portland State Univ, 69-75; PHYSICIST, ELECTROMAGNETIC TRANSIENT PROG, BONNEVILLE POWER ADMIN, US DEPT ENERGY, 75- *Res:* Electromagnetic transient studies of the power systems. *Mailing Add:* Bonneville Power Admin Rte EOGB PO Box 3621 Portland OR 97208

LIUIMA, FRANCIS ALOYSIUS, b Utena, Lithuania, Mar 8, 19; nat US. PHYSICS. *Educ:* Boston Col, MS, 50; St Louis Univ, PhD(physics), 54. *Prof Exp:* ASST PROF PHYSICS, BOSTON COL, 54- *Mem:* Am Phys Soc; Am Asn Physics Teachers. *Res:* Microwave spectroscopy. *Mailing Add:* Dept of Physics Boston Col Chestnut Hill MA 02167

LIUKKONEN, JOHN ROBIE, b Oakland, Calif, Oct 23, 42. MATHEMATICAL ANALYSIS. *Educ:* Harvard Univ, BA, 65; Columbia Univ, PhD(math), 70. *Prof Exp:* Asst prof, 70-75, ASSOC PROF MATH, TULANE UNIV, 75- *Res:* Representations of locally compact groups; harmonic analysis on locally compact groups. *Mailing Add:* Dept Math Tulane Univ New Orleans LA 70118

LIUZZO, JOSEPH ANTHONY, b Tampa, Fla, Dec 16, 26; m 51; c 3. FOOD SCIENCE. *Educ:* Univ Fla, BS, 50, MSA, 55; Mich State Univ, PhD(nutrit, biochem), 58. *Prof Exp:* Res microbiologist, Univ Fla, 50-51, asst, 54-55; dir microbiol, Nutrilite Prod, Inc, Calif, 51-53, asst to dir biol res, 53-54; asst, Mich State Univ, 55-58; asst prof biochem, 58-62, assoc prof food sci & technol, 62-69, PROF FOOD SCI, LA STATE UNIV, BATON ROUGE, 69- *Mem:* AAAS; Am Inst Nutrit; Inst Food Technologists; Am Inst Chemists; Am Chem Soc. *Res:* Detection and isolation of growth factors and growth inhibitors from natural materials required by microorganisms and animals; radiation preservation of foods; development of protein supplements for deprived countries; utilization of by-products from agricultural commodities. *Mailing Add:* Dept of Food Sci La State Univ Baton Rouge LA 70803

LIVANT, PETER DAVID, b New York, NY, Sept 18, 48. PHYSICAL ORGANIC CHEMISTRY. *Educ:* City Col New York, BS, 69; Brown Univ, PhD(chem), 75. *Prof Exp:* Vis asst prof chem, Univ Ill, Urbana-Champaign, 74-75, res assoc, 75-76; res assoc, Univ Guelph, 76-77; ASST PROF CHEM, AUBURN UNIV, 77- *Mem:* Am Chem Soc. *Res:* Mechanisms of radical reactions; chemistry of hypervalent species; tetracoordinate tetracovalent sulfur compounds; chemically induced dynamic nuclear polarization dependence on magnetic field strength. *Mailing Add:* Dept of Chem Auburn Univ Auburn AL 36849

LIVDAHL, PHILIP V, b Bismarck, NDak, Feb 1, 23; m 44; c 3. PHYSICS. *Educ:* St Olaf Col, BA, 48; Univ Wash, MS, 52. *Prof Exp:* Assoc physicist, Calif Res & Develop Corp, 51-54; physicist, Lawrence Radiation Lab, Calif, 54-57; assoc physicist, Argonne Nat Lab, 57-67; actg dir, 78-79, PHYSICIST, FERMI NAT ACCELERATOR LAB, 67-, ASSOC DIR, 79- *Res:* High energy accelerators; linear accelerators and associated equipment for synchrotron injectors; experimental planning and operation for the zero gradient synchrotron. *Mailing Add:* Fermi Nat Accelerator Lab PO Box 500 Batavia IL 60510

LIVE, DAVID H, b Philadelphia, Pa, Apr 3, 46. BIOPHYSICS, PHYSICAL CHEMISTRY. *Educ:* Univ Pa, BA, 67; Calif Inst Technol, PhD(chem), 74. *Prof Exp:* Res assoc biophys, 74-78, ASST PROF PHYS BIOCHEM, ROCKEFELLER UNIV, 78- *Concurrent Pos:* Consult, Jet Propulsion Lab, Calif Inst Technol, 75- *Mem:* Am Chem Soc; AAAS; NY Acad Sci. *Res:* Biophysical applications of magnetic resonance to studying molecular conformation, particularly in peptides and proteins; geochemical investigations by magnetic resonance of terrestrial and lunar samples. *Mailing Add:* Dept of Phys Biochem 1230 York Ave New York NY 10021

LIVE, ISRAEL, b Austria, Apr 26, 07; nat US; m 36; c 2. VETERINARY SCIENCE. *Educ:* Univ Penn, VMD, 34, AM, 36, PhD(path), 40; Am Bd Microbiol, dipl. *Prof Exp:* Asst histopath & clin path, 34-37, from instr path to asst prof, 37-46, bact, 46-49, assoc prof, 49-53, PROF MICROBIOL, SCH VET MED, UNIV PA, 53- *Concurrent Pos:* Mem expert comt on brucellosis, WHO. *Mem:* Fel AAAS; fel Am Acad Microbiol; Am Vet Med Asn; Am Soc Microbiol; Asn; fel Am Col Vet Microbiol. *Res:* Diagnosis of filariasis in dogs; nature of Clostridium chauvoei aggressin; diagnosis, therapy and immunization in brucellosis; staphylococci in animals and man; serological characterization of staphylococci. *Mailing Add:* Dept of Microbiol Univ of Pa Sch of Vet Med Philadelphia PA 19104

LIVELY, DAVID HARRYMAN, b Indianapolis, Ind, Aug 17, 30; m 53; c 2. MICROBIOLOGY. *Educ:* Purdue Univ, BS, 52; Univ Tex, MA, 58, PhD, 62. *Prof Exp:* Mem water pollution serv team, State Bd Health, Ind, 52; bacteriologist, Biol Warfare Labs, US Army, 54-56; asst bacteriologist, Univ Tex, 56-57, res scientist, 57-60; sr microbiologist, 61-63, group leader microbiol, Chem Res Div, 63-66, asst mgr antibiotic develop, Antibiotic Mfg & Develop Div, 66-69, head microbiol res, 69-72, RES ASSOC, ELI LILLY & CO, 72- *Mem:* Fel AAAS; Am Chem Soc; Am Soc Microbiol; Brit Soc Gen Microbiol; Sigma Xi. *Res:* Bacterial endospore; production of biological active compounds by microorganisms; automation in microbiology. *Mailing Add:* Antibiotic Develop Div Eli Lilly & Co Indianapolis IN 46285

LIVENGOOD, DAVID ROBERT, b LaJunta, Colo, Mar 18, 37. BIOPHYSICS, ELECTROPHYSIOLOGY. *Educ:* Butler Univ, BS, 60; Ind Univ, PhD(physiol), 70. *Prof Exp:* Res assoc, Dept Biophysics, Sch Med, Univ Md, 71-73; res physiologist, Dept Neurobiol, 73-79, chief, Radiation Biophysics Div, 79-80, CHMN, DEPT PHYSIOL, ARMED FORCES RADIOBIOL RES INST, 80- *Concurrent Pos:* Grass Found fel, Woodshole Marine Biol Lab, 71; fel, Marine Biol Lab, STI, 76; res consult, Dept Physiol, George Washington Univ, 78-; adj staff, Dept Physiol, Uniformed Serv Univ Health Sci, 80- *Mem:* Biophys Soc; Soc Neurosci; Soc Gen Physiologists. *Res:* Biophysical properties of the membranes of nerve and muscle cells with particular reference to the electrogenecity of the sodium and potassium atpase. *Mailing Add:* Dept Physiol Nat Naval Med Ctr Armed Forces Radiobiol Res Inst Bethesda MD 20814

LIVENGOOD, SAMUEL MILLER, b Salisbury Pa, Nov 1, 17; m 41; c 3. ORGANIC CHEMISTRY. *Educ:* Juniata Col, BS, 38; Rutgers Univ, MS, 41, PhD(org chem), 43. *Prof Exp:* Instr chem, Rutgers Univ, 40-43; fel, Mellon Inst, 43-55, sr fel, 55-59; asst dir, 59-75, ASSOC DIR, RES & DEVELOP DEPT, CHEM DIV, UNION CARBIDE CORP, 59-, RES & DEVELOP DIR, ETHYLENE OXIDE DERIVATIVES DIV, 79- *Mem:* Am Chem Soc; Soc Chem Indust. *Res:* Detergents and cosmetics; textile intermediates; humectants; water soluble resins; hydraulic fluids; heat transfer fluids; metalworking fluids. *Mailing Add:* Res & Dev Union Carbide Tarrytown Tech Ctr Tarrytown NY 10591

LIVERMAN, JAMES LESLIE, b Brady, Tex, Aug 17, 21; m 43, 59; c 5. PLANT PHYSIOLOGY, BIOCHEMISTRY. *Educ:* Tex A&M Univ, BS, 49; Calif Inst Technol, PhD(plant physiol, bioorg chem), 52. *Prof Exp:* Fel plant physiol, Calif Inst Technol, 52-53; from asst prof to prof biochem, Agr & Mech Col, Univ Tex, 53-60; biochemist, AEC, 58-59, asst chief biol br, 59-60, chief 60-64; assoc dir biol div, Oak Ridge Nat Lab, 64-67, asst dir life sci, 67-69, assoc dir biomed & environ sci, 69-72; dir div biomed & environ res, US AEC, 72-75, asst gen mgr biomed & environ res & safety, 73-75, dir, Div Biomed & Environ Res & asst adminr environ safety, US Energy Res & Develop Admin, 75-77; actg asst secy environ, Dept Energy, 77-78, dep asst secy, 78-79; SR VPRES & GEN MGR, APPL SCI DIV, LITTON BIONETICS, INC, 79- *Concurrent Pos:* Consult agr chemist, 56-58; chmn, Gordon Conf Biochem & Agr, 61; Interim dir, Univ Tenn-Oak Ridge Grad Sch Biomed Sci, 65-66. *Mem:* Fel AAAS; Am Soc Plant Physiol; Am Chem Soc; Radiation Res Soc; Ecol Soc Am. *Res:* Cell physiology; photoperiodism; radiation in biological systems; immunology; bioengineering; policy science. *Mailing Add:* 5308 Manor Lake Court Rockville MD 20853

LIVERMAN, THOMAS PHILLIP GEORGE, b Salzburg, Austria, June 18, 23; US citizen; m 46; c 2. MATHEMATICS. *Educ:* Univ Pa, MA, 48, PhD(math), 56. *Prof Exp:* Instr math, Univ Del, 46-48; engr, C N R Co, France, 48-49; mathematician, Appl Physics Lab, Johns Hopkins Univ, 51-58; assoc prof, 58-60, chmn dept, 71-74, PROF MATH, GEORGE WASHINGTON UNIV, 71-, CHMN DEPT, 76- *Mem:* Soc Indust & Appl Math. *Res:* Functional analysis and applied mathematics; function theory; operational calculus; infinite dimensional generalized functions and fock spaces. *Mailing Add:* Dept of Math George Washington Univ Washington DC 20052

LIVERS, RONALD WILSON, plant breeding, deceased

LIVERSAGE, RICHARD ALBERT, b Fitchburg, Mass, July 8, 25; m 54; c 4. DEVELOPMENTAL BIOLOGY. *Educ:* Marlboro Col, BA, 51; Amherst, Col, AM, 53; Princeton Univ, AM, 57, PhD(biol), 58. *Prof Exp:* Lab instr biol, Amherst Col, 54-55; instr, Princeton Univ, 58-60; from asst prof to assoc prof, 60-69, grad secy dept, 75-77, assoc chmn grad affairs, 78-80, PROF ZOOL, UNIV TORONTO, 69-, ACTG CHMN, 81- *Concurrent Pos:* Vis investr, Huntsman Marine Lab, NB, Can, 68-71; res assoc, Dept Biophys, Strangeways Res Lab, Cambridge, Eng, 72. *Mem:* Can Soc Zool, Am Soc Zool; Soc Develop Biol; Royal Can Inst. *Res:* In vivo and in vitro studies on the role of nerves and endocrine secretions in amphibian appendage regeneration. *Mailing Add:* Ramsay Wright Zool Labs Univ of Toronto Toronto ON M5S 1A1 Can

LIVESAY, GEORGE ROGER, b Ashley, Ill, Dec 9, 24. MATHEMATICS. *Educ:* Univ Ill, BS & MS, 48, PhD, 52. *Prof Exp:* Instr math, Univ Mich, 50-56; res assoc, 56-58, from asst prof to assoc prof, 58-69, PROF MATH, CORNELL UNIV, 69- *Res:* Topology. *Mailing Add:* Dept of Math Cornell Univ Ithaca NY 14853

LIVETT, BRUCE G, b Melbourne, Australia, Aug 27, 43; m 76; c 2. NEUROSCIENCES, BIOCHEMICAL PHARMACOLOGY. *Educ:* Monash Univ, BSc, 65, PhD(biochem), 68. *Prof Exp:* Nuffield Dominions demonstr pharmacol, Oxford Univ, 69-71; jr res fel, Wolfson Col, 70-71; Queen Elizabeth II res fel biochem, Monash Univ, 71-73; asst prof, 73-77; ASSOC PROF MED & BIOCHEM, MONTREAL GEN HOSP, MCGILL UNIV, 77- *Concurrent Pos:* Med Res Coun fel neurosci, McMaster Univ, 75-76, prin investr, 77-; vis prof, Queen's Univ, 80; prin investr & mem adv bd, Muscular Dystrophy Asn Can, 78- *Mem:* Int Brain Res Orgn; Int Soc Neurochem; Soc Neurosci. *Res:* Investigation into the role of neuropeptides as neuromodulators of catecholamine secretion in the endocrine adrenal medulla and nervous system; role of the cellular immunity system in muscular dystrophy. *Mailing Add:* Div Neurol Montreal Gen Hosp 1650 Cedar Ave Montreal PQ H3G 1A4 Can

LIVEZEY, ROBERT LEE, biology, see previous edition

LIVIGNI, RUSSELL ANTHONY, b Akron, Ohio, July 20, 34. POLYMER CHEMISTRY. *Educ:* Univ Akron, BSc, 56, PhD(polymer chem), 60. *Prof Exp:* Res scientist polymer chem, Ford Sci Lab, 60-61; sr res chemist, 61-62, group leader polymer characterization & kinetics, 62-63, sect head, 63-69, sect head mat chem & polymer characterization, 69-75, dept mgr polymer & anal chem, 75-80, ASSOC DIR, RES DIV, GEN TIRE & RUBBER CO, 80-*Mem:* AAAS; Am Chem Soc. *Res:* Kinetics of free radical polymerization; kinetics and mechanism of anionic polymerization and copolymerization; determination of structure of block copolymers; characterization of polymer molecular weights and distribution; thermal analysis. *Mailing Add:* 2291 Manchester Rd Akron OH 44314

LIVINGOOD, CLARENCE SWINEHART, b Elverson, Pa, Aug 7, 11; m 47; c 5. DERMATOLOGY. *Educ:* Ursinus Col, BS, 32; Univ Pa, MD, 36; Am Bd Dermat, dipl, 61. *Prof Exp:* Asst prof dermat & syphil, Med Sch, Univ Pa, 46-48; prof dermat, Jefferson Med Col, 48-49; prof dermat & syphil, Sch Med, Univ Tex, 49-53; CHMN DEPT DERMAT, HENRY FORD HOSP, 53-*Concurrent Pos:* Consult, Vet Admin & Surg Gen, US Army; mem comn cutaneous dis, Armed Forces Epidemiol Bd; adv panel med sci, Dept Defense, 55-60; secy gen, Int Cong Dermat, 62; secy, Am Bd Dermat, 63- *Mem:* AAAS; Soc Invest Dermat (pres, 55); Am Dermat Asn; AMA; NY Acad Sci. *Res:* Epidemiology and treatment of cutaneous bacterial infections; topical corticosteroid therapy of cutaneous disease. *Mailing Add:* Dept of Dermat Henry Ford Hosp Detroit MI 48202

LIVINGOOD, JOHN JACOB, b Cincinnati, Ohio, Mar 7, 03; m 34; c 2. PHYSICS. *Educ:* Princeton Univ, AB, 25, MA, 27, PhD(physics), 29. *Prof Exp:* Instr physics, Palmer Phys Lab, Princeton Univ, 29-32; res assoc, Lawrence Radiation Lab, Univ Calif, 32-38; instr & tutor physics, Harvard Univ, 38-39, fac instr & tutor, 39-42, res assoc, Off Sci Res & Develop Proj, Radio Res Lab, 42-45; asst dir res div, Collins Radio Co, 45-52; assoc dir physics div, 52-56, dir particle accelerator div, 56-58, sr physicist, 58-68, CONSULT, ARGONNE NAT LAB, 68- *Mem:* Fel Am Phys Soc; fel Am Nuclear Soc. *Res:* Line spectroscopy; cyclotron design; high power oscillator tubes; artificial radioactivity. *Mailing Add:* 836 S County Line Rd Hinsdale IL 60521

LIVINGOOD, JOHN N B, b Birdsboro, Pa, June 8, 13; m 40; c 3. MATHEMATICS. *Educ:* Gettysburg Col, AB, 34; Univ Pa, AM, 36, PhD(math), 44. *Prof Exp:* Teacher high sch, 36-38; instr math, Gettysburg Col, 38-42; Rutgers Univ, 42-44; mathematician, Nat Adv Comt Aeronaut, 44-47; asst prof math, Rutgers Univ, 47-48; aeronaut res scientist, Nat Adv Comt Aeronaut 48-58 & NASA, 58-73; lectr math, Col Boca Raton, Fla, 73-81; RETIRED. *Mem:* Am Math Soc. *Res:* Theory of numbers; aeronautical research; turbine cooling; nuclear engineering. *Mailing Add:* 20 NW 24th St Delray Beach FL 33444

LIVINGOOD, MARVIN D(UANE), b Corning, Kans, Aug 15, 18; m 47; c 4. CHEMICAL ENGINEERING. *Educ:* Okla State Univ, BS, 38, MS, 40; Mich State Univ, PhD(chem eng), 52. *Prof Exp:* Chem engr, Arzone Prod Co, 41; instr chem eng, Mo Sch Mines, 41-46; asst prof, Mich State Univ, 46-49, res asst prof, Eng Exp Sta, 49-52; res chem engr, 52-74, environ control supvr, 74-79, SR ENGR, E I DU PONT DE NEMOURS & CO, INC, 79-*Concurrent Pos:* Chmn, Prof Develop Comt, Am Inst Chem Engrs, 80-82, Steering Comt, 80- *Mem:* Fel Am Inst Chem Engrs. *Res:* Chemical engineering design; economics; small scale pilot plant; pollution control; environmental compliance. *Mailing Add:* E I Du Pont de Nemours Co Camp Ground Rd Louisville KY 40211

LIVINGSTON, ALBERT EDWARD, b Hartford, Conn, Feb 28, 36. MATHEMATICAL ANALYSIS. *Educ:* Boston Col, BA, 58, MA, 60; Rutgers Univ, MS, 62, PhD(math), 63. *Prof Exp:* Asst prof math, Lafayette Col, 63-67; from asst prof to assoc prof, 67-75, PROF MATH, UNIV DEL, 75- *Mem:* Math Asn Am; Am Math Soc; Sigma Xi. *Res:* Univalent and multivalent fuctions, particularly the application of methods of extreme point theory and subordination chains to extremal problems in multivalent function theory. *Mailing Add:* Dept of Math Univ of Del Newark DE 19711

LIVINGSTON, CLARK HOLCOMB, b Eau Claire, Wis, Nov 25, 20; m 47; c 2. PLANT PATHOLOGY. *Educ:* Colo Agr & Mech Col, BS, 51, MS, 53; Univ Minn, PhD, 66. *Prof Exp:* ASSOC PROF BOT & PLANT PATH, COLO STATE UNIV, 55- *Mem:* Am Phytopath Soc; Potato Asn Am. *Res:* Potato diseases, particularly physiology of disease and viruses. *Mailing Add:* Dept of Bot & Plant Path Colo State Univ Ft Collins CO 80521

LIVINGSTON, DANIEL ISADORE, b New York City, NY, Oct 15, 19; m 56; c 2. PHYSICAL CHEMISTRY. *Educ:* City Col New York, BS, 41; Polytech Inst Brooklyn, PhD(phys chem), 50. *Prof Exp:* Dir polymer chem, Gen Latex & Chem Corp, 50-51; scientist, Polaroid Corp, 51-55; sr res engr, Ford Motor Co, 55-57; sr res chemist, Continental Can Co, Ill, 57-59; HEAD, POLYMER PHYSICS SECT, GOODYEAR TIRE & RUBBER CO, 59-*Concurrent Pos:* Assoc ed, Rubber Chem & Technol, 69-72; ed, Tire Sci & Technol, 72- *Mem:* Am Chem Soc; Am Phys Soc; Soc Rheology; Adhesion Soc; Am Soc Testing & Mat. *Res:* Physical chemistry of polymers; high polymer synthesis, research and development; radiation effects in polymer systems; polymer physics; tire physics. *Mailing Add:* 731 Frank Blvd Akron OH 44320

LIVINGSTON, G E, b Rotterdam, Netherlands, Feb 1, 27; m 48; c 3. FOOD SCIENCE. *Educ:* NY Univ, BA, 48; Univ Mass, MS, 51, PhD(food technol), 52. *Prof Exp:* Chemist, Bur Chem, NY Produce Exchange, 49; from asst prof to assoc prof food technol, Univ Mass, 51-59; dir, 56-80, PRES, FOOD SCI ASSOCS, INC, 56- *Concurrent Pos:* Vis prof, Laval Univ, 54; vis lectr, City Col New York, 59-60; res supvr, Continental Baking Co, 59-62; mem, Adv Bd Mil Personnel Supplies, Nat Acad Sci-Nat Res Coun, 61-64, chmn, Comt Food Serv Systs, 68-71; mgr, Instnl Prod Dept, Morton Frozen Foods Co,

62-65; adj prof, Columbia Univ, 66-72; invitee, White House Conf Food, Nutrit & Health, 69; chmn, Comt Food & Nutrit & mem, Bd Sci Consults, Am Health Found, 69-; chmn, Panel VII, Nat Conf Food Protection, 71; consult, US Army Natick Labs, 71-; mem, Bd Govs, Food Update, Food & Drug Law Inst, 71-75; adj prof, Pratt Inst, 73, NY Univ, 78-; mem, Food Stability Comn; co-ed, J Food Serv Systs, 80- *Mem:* Am Asn Cereal Chemists; Soc Food Serv Systs (pres, 81-); Inst Food Technologists; NY Acad Sci; Royal Soc Health. *Res:* Food colorimetry; prepared foods; food service systems; nutritive value. *Mailing Add:* Food Sci Assocs Inc 145 Palisade St Dobbs Ferry NY 10522

LIVINGSTON, HUGH DUNCAN, b Glasgow, Scotland, Nov 12, 40; US citizen; m 65. RADIOCHEMISTRY, OCEANOGRAPHY. *Educ:* Glasgow Univ, BSc, 62, PhD(chem), 66. *Prof Exp:* Res assoc chem, Woods Hole Oceanog Inst, 67-69; res fel, Bowman Gray Sch Med, 69-71; res assoc, 71-73, res specialist, 73-79, SR RES SPECIALIST CHEM, WOODS HOLE OCEANOG INST, 79- *Res:* Studies of artificial radioisotopes in the marine environment. *Mailing Add:* Dept Chem Woods Hole Oceanog Inst Woods Hole MA 02543

LIVINGSTON, JAMES D(UANE), b Brooklyn, NY, June 23, 30; m 53; c 3. PHYSICAL METALLURGY. *Educ:* Cornell Univ, BEngPhys, 52; Harvard Univ, MA, 53, PhD, 56. *Prof Exp:* PHYSICIST, RES LAB, GEN ELEC CO, 56- *Mem:* Fel Am Phys Soc; fel Am Soc Metals; Am Inst Mining, Metall & Petrol Eng; Magnetics Soc. *Res:* Superconducting, ferromagnetic and mechanical properties of metals and alloys and their relation to microstructure. *Mailing Add:* Res & Develop Ctr Gen Elec Co Schenectady NY 12301

LIVINGSTON, KNOX W, b Atlanta, Ga, Apr 24, 19; m 48; c 1. FORESTRY. *Educ:* Univ SC, BS, 40; Duke Univ, MF, 48. *Prof Exp:* Asst forestry, 48-49, asst forester, 49-63, from asst prof to assoc prof, 63-78, EMER ASSOC PROF FORESTRY, AUBURN UNIV, 78- *Mem:* Soc Am Foresters. *Res:* Density, site, growth relations, especially planted southern pine; soil, site relations. *Mailing Add:* 856 Cary Dr Auburn AL 36830

LIVINGSTON, MARILYN LAURENE, b High Prarie, Alta, Mar 3, 40. NUMBER THEORY. *Educ:* Univ Alta, BSc, 61, MSc, 63, PhD(math), 66. *Prof Exp:* Asst prof, Western Wash State Col, 66-67; vis asst prof, Ore State Univ, 67-69; from asst prof to assoc prof, 69-78, PROF MATH, SOUTHERN ILL UNIV, 78- *Concurrent Pos:* Mem, Sch Math, Inst Advan Study, Princeton, NJ, 74-75. *Mem:* Am Math Soc; Math Asn Am; Sigma Xi. *Res:* Combinatorics; analytic number theory. *Mailing Add:* Dept Math Statist & Comput Sci Southern Ill Univ Edwardsville IL 62026

LIVINGSTON, MILTON STANLEY, b Brodhead, Wis, May 25, 05; m 30; c 2. NUCLEAR PHYSICS. *Educ:* Pomona Col, AB, 26; Dartmouth Col, MA, 28; Univ Calif, PhD(physics), 31. *Prof Exp:* Instr physics, Dartmouth Col, 28-29; res assoc, Univ Calif, 32-34; asst prof, Cornell Univ, 34-38; from assoc prof to prof, 38-70, EMER PROF, MASS INST TECHNOL, 70- *Concurrent Pos:* Proj chmn, Brookhaven Nat Lab, 46-48; dir, Cambridge Electron Accelerator, Harvard Univ, 56-67; assoc dir, Nat Accelerator Lab, Univ Ill, 67-70; consult, Los Alamos, Oak Ridge, Argonne & Brookhaven Nat Labs. *Mem:* Nat Acad Sci; Am Phys Soc; Fedn Am Sci. *Res:* Design of high energy accelerators. *Mailing Add:* 1005 Calle Largo Santa Fe NM 87501

LIVINGSTON, RALPH, b Keene, NH, May 16, 19; div; c 4. CHEMICAL PHYSICS, MAGNETIC RESONANCE. *Educ:* Univ NH, BS, 40, MS, 41; Univ Cincinnati, DSc(chem), 43. *Prof Exp:* Chemist, metall lab, Univ Chicago, 43-45, assoc dir chem div, 65-75, CHEMIST, OAK RIDGE NAT LAB, 45-, GROUP LEADER, 75- *Concurrent Pos:* Guggenheim fel & Fulbright scholar, France, 60-61; vis prof chem, Cornell Univ, 61-62; prof, Univ Tenn, 64-76. *Mem:* Int Soc Magnetic Resonance; AAAS; Am Chem Soc; Am Phys Soc. *Res:* Radiation chemistry; chemical physics; pure quadrupole spectroscopy and electron spin resonance. *Mailing Add:* Chem Div Oak Ridge Nat Lab PO Box X Oak Ridge TN 37830

LIVINGSTON, ROBERT BURR, b Boston, Mass, Oct 9, 18; m 54; c 3. NEUROPHYSIOLOGY, NEUROANATOMY. *Educ:* Stanford Univ, AB, 40, MD, 44. *Prof Exp:* Intern, Stanford Hosp, 43, asst resident, 44; instr physiol, Sch Med, Yale Univ, 46-48; asst prof physiol, Sch Med & dir aeromed res unit, Yale Univ, 50-52; from assoc prof to prof physiol & anat, Univ Calif, Los Angeles, 52-56; dir basic res & sci dir, NIMH & Nat Inst Neurol Dis & Blindness, 56-60, chief lab neurobiol, NIMH, 60-63, chief gen res support br & assoc chief prog planning, Div Res Facil & Resources, NIH, 63-65; chmn dept neurosci, 65-71, PROF NEUROSCI, SCH MED, UNIV CALIF, SAN DIEGO, 65- *Concurrent Pos:* Nat Res Coun sr fel neurol, Inst Physiol, Switz, 48-49; Gruber fel neurophysiol, Switz, France & Eng, 49-50; NIMH sr fel, Gothenburg Univ, 56; res asst, Harvard Med Sch, 47-48; asst to pres, Nat Acad Sci, 51-52; prof lectr, Univ Calif, Los Angeles, 56-59; assoc, Neurosci Res Prog, 63-76, hon assoc, 76-; guest prof, Univ Zurich, 71-72. *Honors & Awards:* Matrix Midland Award, 81; Sachs Mem lectr, Dartmouth Med Sch, 81. *Mem:* AAAS; Am Physiol Soc; Asn Res Nerv & Ment Dis; Am Neurol Asn; Am Asn Anatomists. *Res:* Mechanisms relating to higher nervous processes, perception, learning and memory; plasticity of ultrastructure of nervous system; three-dimensional analysis and display of neuroanatomical structures. *Mailing Add:* Dept of Neurosci C-021 Univ of Calif at San Diego La Jolla CA 92093

LIVINGSTON, ROBERT LOUIS, b Ada, Ohio, Nov 15, 18; div; c 4. PHYSICAL CHEMISTRY. *Educ:* Ohio State Univ, BS, 39; Univ Mich, MS, 41, PhD(phys chem), 43. *Prof Exp:* Res assoc, Univ Mich, 42-44; assoc chemist, Naval Res Lab, Washington, DC, 44-46; from asst prof to assoc prof, 46-54, asst head dept, 60-68, PROF CHEM, PURDUE UNIV, 54-*Concurrent Pos:* Consult, Educ Testing Serv, Princeton, NJ, 73-74. *Mem:* Am Chem Soc; AAAS. *Res:* Molecular structure by electron diffraction; electron diffraction by surface films; chemical education. *Mailing Add:* Dept of Chem Purdue Univ West Lafayette IN 47907

LIVINGSTON, ROBERT SIMPSON, b Summerland, Calif, Sept 20, 14; m 55; c 5. PHYSICS, RESEARCH ADMINISTRATION. *Educ:* Pomona Col, BA, 35; Univ Calif, MA, 41, PhD(physics), 41. *Prof Exp:* Asst physics, Pomona Col, 35-36; asst, Univ Calif, 36-39, res fel, Lawrence Radiation Lab, 39-43; physicist, Tenn Eastman Corp, 43-47; res supt, Carbide & Carbon Corp, 47-50; dir, Electronuclear Div, Oak Ridge Nat Lab, 50-71, dir prog planning & anal, 71-81; CONSULT, 81- *Concurrent Pos:* Consult, Nuclear Physics Panel, Physics Surv Comt, Nat Acad Sci, 69-72; chmn, Ad Hoc Comt Heavy Ion Sources, Nuclear Sci Div, Nat Acad Sci, 72-74; chmn, NSF/Dept Energy study group on the role of electron accelerators in US medium energy nuclear sci, 77-78. *Mem:* Fel Inst Elec & Electronics Engrs; fel Am Phys Soc; fel AAAS; Am Nuclear Soc; Sigma Xi. *Res:* Long range planning of scientific research and development in energy; design of isochronous cyclotrons; heavy particle accelerators; new particle accelerator methods; high intensity ion sources. *Mailing Add:* 7204 Fairlane Dr Powell TN 37849

LIVINGSTON, WILLIAM CHARLES, b Santa Ana, Calif, Sept 13, 27; m 57; c 2. ASTRONOMY. *Educ:* Univ Calif, Los Angeles, AB, 53; Univ Calif, PhD(astron), 59. *Prof Exp:* Observer, Mt Wilson Observ, Carnegie Inst, 51-53; from jr astronr to assoc asstronr, 59-70, ASTRONR, KITT PEAK NAT OBSERV, 70- *Mem:* Am Astron Soc; Int Astron Union; Astron Soc India. *Res:* Solar spectroscopy; solar magnetism; solar cycle studies. *Mailing Add:* Kitt Peak Nat Observ 950 N Cherry Ave Tucson AZ 85726

LIVINGSTONE, DANIEL ARCHIBALD, b Detroit, Mich, Aug 3, 27; m 52; c 5. ECOLOGY. *Educ:* Dalhousie Univ, BSc, 48, MSc, 50; Yale Univ, PhD(zool), 53. *Prof Exp:* Field collector, NS Mus Sci, summers & demonstr biol, Dalhousie Univ, winters, 47-50; asst zool, Yale Univ, 50-53; Nat Res Coun Can fels, Cambridge Univ, 53-54 & Dalhousie Univ, 54-55; asst prof zool, Univ Md, 55-56; from asst prof to assoc prof, 56-66, PROF ZOOL, DUKE UNIV, 66- *Concurrent Pos:* Spec lectr biogeog, Dalhousie Univ, 54-55; limnologist, US Geol Surv, 56-63; Guggenheim fel, 60-61; mem environ biol panel, Nat Sci Found, 64-, consult Nat Sci Found Polar Prog, 74-76. *Mem:* Ecol Soc Am (ed, Ecol Monogr, 62-66); Am Soc Limnol & Oceanog; Am Soc Nat; Am Quaternary Asn; Sigma Xi; Am Soc Ichthyol & Herpet. *Res:* Pollen analysis; history of lakes; Pleistocene geology of Alaska, Nova Scotia, West, East and Central Africa; geochemistry of hydrosphere; sodium cycle; coring technology; paleoecology; limnology; biogeography of African fishes; distribution of grasses. *Mailing Add:* Dept of Zool Duke Univ Durham NC 22706

LIVINGSTONE, FRANK BROWN, b Winchester, Mass, Dec 8, 28; m 60; c 1. PHYSICAL ANTHROPOLOGY. *Educ:* Harvard Univ, AB, 50; Univ Mich, MA, 55, PhD(anthrop), 57. *Prof Exp:* Nat Sci Found fel, 57-59; from asst prof to assoc prof, 59-68, PROF ANTHROP, UNIV MICH, ANN ARBOR, 68- *Mem:* Am Asn Physical Anthropologists; Am Anthropol Asn. *Res:* Human and population genetics; abnormal hemoglobin; cultural determinants of human evolution. *Mailing Add:* Dept of Anthrop 204OF LSA Bldg Univ of Mich Ann Arbor MI 48109

LIZARDI, PAUL MODESTO, b San Juan, PR, Oct 13, 45; m 77. MOLECULAR BIOLOGY, BIOCHEMISTRY. *Educ:* Univ PR, BS, 66; Rockefeller Univ, PhD(cell biol), 71. *Prof Exp:* ASSOC PROF BIOCHEM, ROCKEFELLER UNIV, 73- *Concurrent Pos:* Jane Coffin Childs Mem Fund Med Res fel biochem, Carnegie Inst Dept Embryol, 71-73. *Mem:* Am Soc Cell Biol; AAAS. *Res:* Eukaryotic messenger RNA's; contol of RNA synthesis; gene cloning; structure of messenger RNA. *Mailing Add:* Rockefeller Univ New York NY 10021

LJUNG, HARVEY ALBERT, b Greensboro, NC, Oct 26, 05; m 35; c 3. ANALYTICAL CHEMISTRY. *Educ:* Univ NC, BS, 27, MS, 28, PhD(chem), 31. *Prof Exp:* Prof chem, Guilford Col, 31-69, acad dean, 46-62, Dana prof, 69-71, EMER DANA PROF, 71- *Concurrent Pos:* Nat Defense Res Comt, 41-42; mem gen chem & qual anal subcomt, Exam Comt, Div Chem Educ, 60-71; chem consult. *Mem:* Emer mem Am Chem Soc. *Res:* Chelation; electrochemistry. *Mailing Add:* 5314 W Friendly Ave Greensboro NC 27410

LJUNGDAHL, LARS GERHARD, b Stockholm, Sweden, Aug 5, 26; m 49; c 2. BIOCHEMISTRY, MICROBIOLOGY. *Educ:* Stockholm Tech Inst, BS, 45; Western Reserve Univ, PhD(biochem), 64. *Prof Exp:* Technician med chem, Karolinska Inst, Univ Sweden, 43-46; res chemist, Stockholm Brewery Co, 47-58; technician biochem, Case Western Reserve Univ, 58-59, sr instr, 64-66, asst prof, 66-67; from mem fac to assoc prof, 67-75, PROF BIOCHEM, UNIV GA, 75- *Concurrent Pos:* Alexander Von Humboldt Sr Scientist Award, 74- *Mem:* Am Soc Microbiol; Am Chem Soc; Brit Biochem Soc; Swedish Chem Soc; Am Soc Biol Chem. *Res:* Carbohydrate metabolism, carbon dioxide fixation, and one carbon metabolism inanaerobic microorganism; role of corrinoids, tetrahydrofolate derivatives and properties of enzymes in these processes. *Mailing Add:* Fermentation Plant Dept of Biochem Univ of Ga Athens GA 30602

LLAMAS, VICENTE JOSE, b Los Angeles, Calif, Feb 15, 44; m 66; c 1. SOLID STATE PHYSICS. *Educ:* Loyola Univ Los Angeles, BS, 66; Univ Mo-Rolla, MS, 68, PhD(physics), 70. *Prof Exp:* Asst physics, Univ Mo-Rolla, 66-68; asst prof, 70-75, ASSOC PROF PHYSICS & CHMN DEPT PHYSICS & MATH, N MEX HIGHLANDS UNIV, 75-, CO-DIR, SCI & MATH EDUC CTR, 74- *Concurrent Pos:* Consult, Fermi Nat Accelerater Lab, 70-, Minority Sci Educ Bibliog Proj, AAAS, 75- & NIH; assoc dir, Summer Sci Prog, Stanford Linear Accelerator Ctr, 74-77, dir, 78- *Mem:* Sigma Xi (secy-treas, 71-73, pres, 73-75); Am Phys Soc; Am Asn Physics Teachers; AAAS; Nat Sci Teachers Asn. *Res:* Surface studies of alkali halides in the infrared; atmospheric study of air pollutants. *Mailing Add:* Dept of Physics NMex Highlands Univ Las Vegas NM 87701

LLAURADO, JOSEP G, b Barcelona, Catalonia, Spain, Feb 6, 27; m 58, 66; c 6. NUCLEAR MEDICINE, BIOMEDICAL ENGINEERING. *Educ:* Balmes Inst, Barcelona, BA & BS, 44; Univ Barcelona, MD, 50, PhD, 60; Drexel Univ, MS, 63. *Prof Exp:* Inst med, Sch Med, Univ Barcelona, 50-52; asst med res, Postgrad Med Sch, Univ London, 52-54; asst prof exp surg, Med Sch, Univ Otago, NZ, 54-57; sr endocrinologist, Med Res Labs, Chas Pfizer & Co, Inc, Conn, 59-61; assoc prof physiol, Sch Med, Univ Pa, 63-67; PROF BIOMED ENG & PHYSIOL, MARQUETTE UNIV & MED COL WIS, 67- *Concurrent Pos:* Brit Coun scholar, Postgrad Med Sch, Univ London, 52-54; Hite Found fel exp med, Univ Tex M D Anderson Hosp & Tumor Inst, 57-58; USPHS fel steroid biochem, Col Med, Univ Utah, 58-59; fel, Coun Adv Sci Invests, Spain, 50-52; Rockefeller vis prof, Univ Valle, Colombia, 58; partic, Nat Colloquim Theoret Biol, NASA, Colo, 65; physician, Vet Admin Hosp, Wood, Wis, 67-; US rep, Int Atomic Energy Agency Symp Dynamic Studies Radioisotopes Med, Rotterdam, 70 & Knoxville, Tenn, 74; vis prof, Polytech Univ, Barcelona, Spain, 73 & 75; vis prof, Univ Zulia, Venezuela, 74 & 75 & Univ Padua, Italy, 75; sect ed, Int J Biomed Comput; consult, Good Samaritan Hosp, Milwaukee, Wis & St Joseph Mem Hosp, West Bend. *Honors & Awards:* Catalan Jocs Florals Prize, Amsterdam, 74 & Caracas, 75. *Mem:* Fel Am Col Nutrit; Am Soc Pharmacol & Exp Therapeut; Catalan Soc Biol; Soc Math Biol; sr mem Inst Elec & Electronics Engrs. *Res:* Radionuclides in cardiology (thallium-201 and analogs); compartmental analysis; sodium and potassium; computers in nuclear medicine; biomathematics. *Mailing Add:* VAC-115 Wood WI 53193

LLEWELLYN, CHARLES ELROY, JR, b Richmond, Va, Jan 16, 22; m 48; c 3. PSYCHIATRY. *Educ:* Hampden-Sydney Col, BS, 43; Med Col Va, MD, 46; Univ Colo, MSc, 53; Am Bd Psychiat & Neurol, dipl, 56. *Prof Exp:* Instr psychiat, Med Col Va, 46-47; assoc, 55-56, asst prof, 56-63, asst dir psychiat outpatient div, 55-56, head psychiat outpatient div, 56-76, head community & social psychiat div, 76-81, ASSOC PROF PSYCHIAT, SCH MED, DUKE UNIV, 63-, CHIEF TRAINING, DIV COMMUNITY & SOCIAL PSYCHIAT, 81- *Concurrent Pos:* Partic, NIMH vis fac sem community psychiat, Lab Community Psychiat, Harvard Med Sch, 65-67; prog dir Duke study group, Interuniv Forum Educr Community Psychiat, 67-71; consult, State Dept Social Serv, NC, 55-79; psychiat consult, NC Med Peer Rev Found, 75-79; chief psychiat consult for Peer Rev & Qual Assurance, NC Div Ment Health Serv, 75-78; Acad Relig & Ment Health. *Mem:* Am Group Psychother Asn; Pan-Am Med Asn; Am Med Asn; Am Asn Marital & Family Therapists; Am Psychiat Asn. *Res:* Community mental health; individual and group psychotherapy; marital and family therapy. *Mailing Add:* Dept of Psychiat Box 3173 Duke Univ Med Ctr Durham NC 27710

LLEWELLYN, GERALD CECIL, b Lonaconing, Md, Feb 8, 40; m 62; c 3. BIONUCLEONICS. *Educ:* Frostburg State Col, BS, 62; Purdue Univ, MS, 66, PhD(bionucleonics), 70. *Prof Exp:* Instr biol chem, Frederick County Bd Educ, Md, 62-66; lectr biol & microbiol, Frederick Community Col, 66-67; asst prof biol educ, 69-77, ASSOC BIOL EDUC, VA COMMONWEALTH UNIV, 77-, ASSOC PROF BIOL, 70- *Mem:* Nat Sci Teachers Asn. *Res:* Toxicological responses of hamsters to aflatoxin B. *Mailing Add:* Dept Biol Va Commonwealth Univ Acad Ctr 901 W Franklin St Richmond VA 23284

LLEWELLYN, J(OHN) ANTHONY, b Cardiff, Wales, Apr 22, 33; m 57; c 2. ENGINEERING SCIENCE, CHEMICAL PHYSICS. *Educ:* Univ Wales, BSc, 55, PhD(chem), 58. *Prof Exp:* Nat Res Coun Can fel, 58-60; res assoc chem, Fla State Univ, 60-61, res assoc chem, Inst Molecular Biophys, 61-62, asst prof chem, 62-64, assoc prof eng sci, Sch Eng Sci, 64-72; ASSOC PROF ENG, UNIV S FLA, 72- *Concurrent Pos:* Scientist astronaut, NASA, 67-68. *Mem:* Am Chem Soc; Am Inst Aeronaut & Astronaut; Royal Inst Chemists; Am Soc Mass Spectrometry; Am Vacuum Soc. *Res:* Chemical physics of high energy systems; collision processes for atoms, electrons and small molecules; mass spectroscopy; theories of reaction rates; bioengineering; deep diving and hyperbaric operations; computer applications in chemical engineering. *Mailing Add:* Dept of Energy Conversion Col Eng Univ of SFla Tampa FL 33620

LLEWELLYN, RALPH A, b Detroit, Mich, June 27, 33; m 55; c 4. NUCLEAR PHYSICS. *Educ:* Rose-Hulman Inst Technol, BS, 55; Purdue Univ, PhD(physics), 62. *Prof Exp:* Asst prof physics, Rose-Hulman Inst Technol, 61-64, assoc prof, 64-68, prof, 68-70, chmn dept, 69-70; prof & chmn dept, Ind State Univ, Terre Haute, 70-73; exec secy, Bd on Energy Studies, Nat Acad Sci, Nat Res Coun, 73-74; prof physics & chmn dept, Ind State Univ, Terre Haute, 74-80; DEAN, COL ARTS & SCI, UNIV CENT FLA, 80- *Concurrent Pos:* Mem, NSF Apparatus Develop Workshop, Rensselaer Polytech Inst, 64-65; prof physics & acting chmn dept, St Mary-of-the-Woods Col, 69-70; assoc ed, Phys Rev Lett, Am Inst Physics, 75- *Mem:* AAAS; Am Phys Soc; Am Asn Physics Teachers; NY Acad Sci; Fourm Physics & Soc (secy-treas). *Res:* Environmental physics, particularly beta and gamma decay; low level radiation in the environment; energy resources, energy and public policy; world - energy resources. *Mailing Add:* Col Arts & Sci Univ Cent Fla Orlando FL 32816

LLEWELLYN-THOMAS, EDWARD, b Salisbury, Eng, Dec 15, 17; Can citizen; m 47; c 3. MEDICINE, ENGINEERING. *Educ:* Univ London, BSc, 51; McGill Univ, MD, 55. *Prof Exp:* Res assoc, Cornell Univ, 57-59; sci officer psychophysiol, Defence Res Med Labs, Can, 58-61; med res assoc, Lakeshore Psychiat Hosp, 61-63; PROF PHARMACOL, UNIV TORONTO, 63-, ASSOC DEAN MED, 74- *Mem:* Inst Elec & Electronics Engrs; Brit Inst Elec Engrs; fel Royal Soc Can; fel Royal Soc Arts. *Res:* Biomedical engineering; psychopharmacology; human factors engineering. *Mailing Add:* Univ of Toronto Toronto ON M5S 1A1 Can

LLINAS, MIGUEL, b Cordoba, Argentina, Oct 16, 38; m 63; c 4. NUCLEAR MAGNETIC RESONANCE SPECTROSCOPY, MOLECULAR BIOPHYSICS. *Educ:* Cordoba Nat Univ, Argentina, Licentiate, 63; Univ Calif, Berkeley, PhD(biophysics), 71. *Prof Exp:* Fel assoc, Univ Calif, Berkeley, 71-74; asst, Swiss Fed Inst Technol, Zurich, 74-76; ASSOC PROF CHEM, CARNEGIE-MELLON UNIV, PA, 76- *Mem:* Biophys Soc; Am

Chem Soc; Int Soc Magnetic Resonance. *Res:* Applications of nuclear magnetic resonance spectroscopy to the study of biological polypeptides; structure and function of siderophores; protein structuure and dynamics; conformation of human plasminogen and its interaction with antifibrinolytics. *Mailing Add:* Dept Chem Carnegie-Mellon Univ 4400 Fifth Ave Pittsburgh PA 15213

LLINAS, RODOLFO, b Bogota, Colombia, Dec 16, 34; m 65; c 2. NEUROBIOLOGY, ELECTROPHYSIOLOGY. *Educ:* Pontificial Univ Javeriana, Colombia, MD, 59; Australian Nat Univ, PhD(neurophysiol), 65. *Prof Exp:* Instr neurophysiol, Nat Univ Colombia, 59; assoc prof, Univ Minn, 65-66; assoc mem neurobiol, Inst Biomed Res, AMA Educ & Res Found, 66-68, mem, 69-70; prof physiol & biophys & head div neurobiol, Univ Iowa, 70-76; PROF & CHMN PHYSIOL & BIOPHYS, NY UNIV MED CTR, 76- *Concurrent Pos:* Res fel psychiat & neurosurg, Mass Gen Hosp, 59-61; fel physiol, Univ Minn, 61-63; res scholar, Australian Nat Univ, 63-65; prof lectr, Col Med, Univ Ill, 67-68, clin prof, 68-71; guest prof, Wayne State Univ, 67-74; assoc prof, Med Sch, Northwestern Univ, 67-71; mem, Neurol Sci Res Training A Comt, NIH, 71-74 & Neurol A Study Sect, 74-, panel mem, NIH Task Force on Basic Sci, 78-; consult, US Air Force Sch Aerospace Med, 72-75; Bowditch lectr, 73; assoc, Neurosci Res Prog, Mass Inst Technol, 74-; chief ed, Neurosci Jour, 75-; mem, USA Nat Comt for IBRO, Nat Res Coun, 78-81. *Mem:* Am Physiol Soc; Am Soc Cell Biol; Soc Neurosci; Int Brain Res Orgn; Biophys Soc. *Res:* Structural and functional studies of neuronal systems; synaptic transmission in vertebrate and invertebrate forms; evolution and development of the central nervous system. *Mailing Add:* NY Univ Med Ctr 550 1st Ave New York NY 10016

LLOYD, CHARLES WAIT, b Catawba, Va, Jan 15, 14; m 43; c 2. ENDOCRINOLOGY. *Educ:* Princeton Univ, BA, 36; Univ Rochester, MD, 41; Am Bd Internal Med, dipl, 49. *Prof Exp:* Intern path, Med Col, Cornell Univ, 41-42; asst resident endocrinol, Med Sch, Duke Univ, 43-44; intern med, Med Sch, Yale Univ, 44-45; prof obstet & gynec & assoc prof med, State Univ NY Upstate Med Ctr, Syracuse, 46-62; dir training prog physiol reproduction, Clin Res Unit & sr scientist, Worcester Found Exp Biol, 62-72; prof obstet & gynec & chief div reproductive biol, Hershey Med Ctr, Pa State Univ, 72-74; prof clin psychiat & codir ctr study human sexual behav, Dept Psychiat, Univ Pittsburgh, 74-78; CLIN PROF OBSTET-GYNEC & MED, BOWMAN GRAY SCH MED, WAKE FOREST UNIV, 78- *Concurrent Pos:* Res fel endocrinol, Thorndike Lab, Harvard Med Sch & Boston City Hosp, 45-46. *Mem:* AAAS; Am Soc Clin Invest; Endocrine Soc; Am Physiol Soc; Soc Exp Biol & Med. *Res:* Endocrinology of reproduction; pituitary hormones and their control; hormones and behavior. *Mailing Add:* 1701 Queen St Winston-Salem NC 27103

LLOYD, CHRISTOPHER RAYMOND, b Bridgwater, Eng, Oct 16, 51; m 80. PALEOCLIMATES, TECTONICS. *Educ:* Cambridge Univ, BA, 73; Birmingham Univ, MSc, 74; Lancaster Univ, PhD(paleoclimatol), 77. *Prof Exp:* Ed geosci, Elsevier Sci Publ Co, 79-81; TECH ED ATMOSPHERIC SCI, AM METEOROL SOC, 81- *Mem:* Geol Soc Am; Am Meteorol Soc. *Res:* Mid-Cretaceous global tectonics, paleogeography, ocean circulation and temperature, atmospheric circulation and surface climate. *Mailing Add:* 108 Waverly St Arlington MA 02174

LLOYD, DAVID PIERCE CARADOC, b Auburn, Ala, Sept 22, 11; m 37, 57; c 3. PHYSIOLOGY. *Educ:* McGill Univ, BSc, 32; Oxford Univ, BA, 35, DPhil(physiol), 38; Rockefeller Univ, MA, 64, DSc, 68. *Prof Exp:* Demonstr physiol, Oxford Univ, 35-36; asst med res, Univ Toronto, 36-38, assoc, 38-39; from asst to assoc, Rockefeller Inst, 39-43; asst prof physiol, Sch Med, Yale Univ, 43-45; assoc mem, Rockefeller Univ, 46-49, mem, 49-70, prof physiol, 57-70; hon res fel, 70-80, HON RES ASSOC, UNIV COL, UNIV LONDON, 80- *Concurrent Pos:* Arthur lectr, Am Mus Natural Hist, 58; mem, Neurol Study Sect, NIH, 61-65, mem, Res & Training Grants Comt, Nat Inst Neurol Dis & Blindness, 66-70; mem, Med Adv Comts, Nat Found Infantile Paralysis & United Cerebral Palsy Found; trustee, Int Poliomyelitis Cong. *Mem:* Nat Acad Sci; AAAS; Am Physiol Soc. *Res:* Synaptic transmission in sympathetic ganglia; conduction and synaptic transmission in spinal cord; excitation and inhibition; physiology of sweat glands. *Mailing Add:* New Cottage Greatham Pulborough Sussex England United Kingdom

LLOYD, DOUGLAS ROY, b Kitchener, Ont, Sept 15, 48; m 74. MEMBRANE SCIENCE, POLYMER SCIENCE. *Educ:* Univ Waterloo, BASc, 73, MASc, 74, PhD(chem eng), 77. *Prof Exp:* asst prof chem eng, Va Polytech Inst & State Univ, 78-80; ASST PROF CHEM ENG, UNIV TEX, 80- *Concurrent Pos:* Res engr, Union Carbide Can, 69-70, Crane Can Ltd, 70-71; res assoc, Angelstone Ltd, 73; res assoc, Dept Chem Eng, Univ Waterloo, 72, fel, 77-78. *Mem:* Am Chem Soc; Am Inst Chem Engrs. *Res:* Synthetic polymeric membranes; membrane separation processes; polymer chemistry; polymer reaction engineering; enzyme engineering. *Mailing Add:* Univ Tex Austin TX 78712

LLOYD, DOUGLAS SEWARD, b Brooklyn, NY, Oct 16, 39. PUBLIC HEALTH. *Educ:* Duke Univ, AB, 61, MD, 71; Univ NC, MPH, 71. *Prof Exp:* COMNR, CONN STATE DEPT HEALTH, 73- *Concurrent Pos:* Mem courtesy staff, Hartford Hosp, 73-; lectr, Sch Med, Yale Univ, 73- & Univ Conn Health Ctr, 73- *Mailing Add:* Conn State Dept of Health 79 Elm St Hartford CT 06115

LLOYD, EDWARD C(HARLES), b Chicago, Ill, Jan 28, 15; m 38; c 2. ENGINEERING. *Educ:* Univ Calif, BS, 38; Univ Md, MS, 59. *Prof Exp:* Engr, Bur Ships, US Dept Navy, 39-47, head systs & auxiliary mach sect, Design Div, 47-51; asst to chief, Off Basic Instrumentation, Nat Bur Standards, 51-54, chief, Mech Instruments Sect, 54-60, consult, 61-64, chief, Mech Measurements Br, 64-70; CONSULT ENGR, 71- *Concurrent Pos:* Mem, Am Nat Standards Comt Pressure & Vacuum Gages & Comt Calibration Instruments. *Mem:* Fel Am Soc Mech Engrs; fel Instrument Soc Am. *Res:* Measurement, data handling and control; electromechanical devices; standards and measurements of pressure, vacuum, vibration and humidity. *Mailing Add:* 446 Santa Cecelia St Solana Beach CA 92075

LLOYD, EDWIN PHILLIPS, b San Antonio, Tex, Sept 18, 29; m 54; c 1. ENTOMOLOGY. *Educ:* Tex A&M Univ, BS, 51, MS, 52, PhD(entom), 58. *Prof Exp:* RES ENTOMOLOGIST, BOLL WEEVIL RES LAB, AGR RES SERV, USDA, 56-, DIR, 81- *Concurrent Pos:* Sci adv, pilot boll weevil eradication exp, 71-73; adj assoc prof, Miss State Univ, 71- *Honors & Awards:* Superior Serv Award, USDA, 74; Res Award, Miss Entom Asn, 74. *Mem:* Entom Soc Am. *Res:* Cotton insects, specifically the boll weevil. *Mailing Add:* Miss State Univ PO Box 5367 Mississippi State MS 39762

LLOYD, HARRIS HORTON, b Conway, Ark, Nov 14, 37; m 60; c 4. CANCER, CHEMOTHERAPY. *Educ:* Ouachita Baptist Univ, BA & BS, 59; Purdue Univ, PhD(phys chem), 68. *Prof Exp:* Chief dept chem, 406th Med Lab, US Army Med Command, Japan, 64-67; res chemist, 68-72, HEAD, MATH BIOL & DATA ANAL SECT, SOUTHERN RES INST, 72- *Mem:* Cell Kinetics Soc; Am Asn Cancer Res; Am Sci Affil. *Res:* Chemical kinetics; data analysis and mathematical simulation; Pharmacokinetics; kinetics of tumor growth and cell killing; design of computer-based information management systems. *Mailing Add:* Dept of Chemother Southern Res Inst PO Box 3700-A Birmingham AL 35255

LLOYD, JAMES ARMON, b Nanticoke, Pa, June 17, 33. ENDOCRINOLOGY, ETHOLOGY. *Educ:* Pa State Univ, BS, 55, MS, 57; Johns Hopkins Univ, ScD(behav endocrinol), 61. *Prof Exp:* Res asst endocrinol behav, Univ Pa, 61-63; asst mem, Albert Einstein Med Ctr, 63-71; ASSOC PROF DEPT REPRODUCTION MED & BIOL, UNIV TEX MED SCH HOUSTON, 71- *Concurrent Pos:* NIH res grants, Albert Einstein Med Ctr, 63-71. *Mem:* AAAS; Endocrine Soc; Am Soc Zoologists; Animal Behav Soc; NY Acad Sci. *Res:* Impact of increased population size on behavior and reproduction of populations of rodents, especially the integration of environmental stimuli--social pressure and endocrine reproductive physiology; behavior. *Mailing Add:* Dept Reproductive Med & Biol Univ Tex Med Sch PO Box 20708 Houston TX 77025

LLOYD, JAMES EDWARD, b Oneida, NY, Jan 17, 33; m 58; c 2. EVOLUTIONARY BIOLOGY, INSECT BEHAVIORAL ECOLOGY. *Educ:* State Univ NY Col Fredonia, BS, 60; Univ Mich, MA, 62; Cornell Univ, PhD(entom), 66. *Prof Exp:* Teacher high sch, 60; NSF res assoc syst & evolutionary biol, 66; from asst prof biol sci & entom to assoc profentom & nematol, 66-74, PROF ENTOM & NEMATOL, UNIV FLA, 74- *Concurrent Pos:* NSF res grant 68, 80; Nat Geog Soc res grant, 80. *Honors & Awards:* Res Award, Sigma Xi, 74. *Mem:* Am Soc Naturalists; AAAS; Asn for Trop Biol; Coleopterist's Soc. *Res:* Function of luminescence in insects; systematics in Lampyridae; animal behavior, ecology, evolution. *Mailing Add:* Dept of Entom & Nematol Univ of Fla Gainesville FL 32611

LLOYD, JAMES NEWELL, b Orange, NJ, Oct 20, 32; m 59; c 2. PHYSICS. *Educ:* Colgate Univ, BA, 54; Cornell Univ, PhD(physics), 63. *Prof Exp:* From instr to asst prof physics, 61-70, chmn, Dept Physics & Astron, 73-76, assoc prof physics, 70-79, PROF PHYS, COLGATE UNIV, 79- *Mem:* Am Phys Soc; Am Asn Physics Teachers. *Res:* Ferromagnetic resonance and transport properties in metals. *Mailing Add:* Dept of Physics & Astron Colgate Univ Hamilton NY 13346

LLOYD, JOHN EDWARD, b Munhall, Pa, Sept 28, 40; m 62; c 2. VETERINARY ENTOMOLOGY. *Educ:* Pa State Univ, BS, 62; Cornell Univ, PhD(entom), 67. *Prof Exp:* Asst prof entom, Pa State Univ, 67-68; from asst prof to assoc prof, 68-76, PROF ENTOM, UNIV WYO, 76- *Mem:* Entom Soc Am; Am Mosquito Control Asn. *Res:* Economic entomology; insects affecting livestock; insects affecting man. *Mailing Add:* Entom Sect Box 3354 Univ of Wyo Laramie WY 82071

LLOYD, JOHN WILLIE, III, b Winchester, Va, May 25, 43; m 65; c 2. ENDOCRINOLOGY, PHARMACOLOGY. *Educ:* Shepherd Col, BS, 66; WVa Univ, MS, 69, PhD(endocrinol), 73. *Prof Exp:* Asst prof pharmacol, WVa Univ, 73-74; asst prof endocrinol, Eastern Va Med Sch, 74-78; ASSOC PROF ENDOCRINOL, HOWARD UNIV, 78- *Concurrent Pos:* Dir, Endocrine Serv, Eastern Va Med Sch, 76-78. *Mem:* Sigma Xi; Soc Exp Biol & Med; Endocrine Soc; Am Physiol Soc. *Res:* Endocrinology; Reproductive physiology; hormonal regulation of the adrenal gland and accessory sex organs; prostatic cancer. *Mailing Add:* 518 N Loudoun St Winchester VA 22601

LLOYD, KENNETH OLIVER, b Denbigh, Wales, May 17, 36; US citizen; m 62; c 2. BIOCHEMISTRY, IMMUNOCHEMISTRY. *Educ:* Univ Wales, BSc, 57, PhD(chem), 60. *Prof Exp:* Res assoc microbiol, Columbia Univ, 63-68, asst prof biochem, 68-74; assoc prof, Sch Med, Tex Tech Univ, 74-75; assoc, 75-78, ASSOC MEM, SLOAN-KETTERING CANCER CTR, 78- *Concurrent Pos:* Fel, Washington Univ, 60-63; USPHS res career develop award, 68-73. *Mem:* AAAS; Am Chem Soc; Am Asn Immunologists; Soc Complex Carbohydrates. *Res:* Biochemistry, structure and immunochemistry of glycoproteins, particularly tumor antigens. *Mailing Add:* Assoc Mem Sloan Kettering Cancer Ctr 1275 York Ave New York NY 10021

LLOYD, LAURANCE H(ENRY), b Salem, Ore, Apr 24, 15; m 40; c 1. OPERATIONS RESEARCH, ELECTRICAL ENGINEERING. *Educ:* Ore State Univ, BS, 37; Ohio State Univ, MS, 51. *Prof Exp:* Engr, Idaho Power Co, 37-42; proj engr, Control Equip Br, Eng Div, Air Mat Command, Wright-Patterson AFB, 46-47, proj engr, Guided Missiles Br, Intel Dept, 48, chief, Nuclear Energy Br, 48, chief, Sci Br, 50, actg chief & chief engr, Signal Anal Sect, Air Technol Intel Ctr, 53; staff engr, Systs Eng Sect, Missile Test Proj, Radio Corp Am, Patrick AFB, 54; chief eval div, Dep Electronics Intel, Aerospace Technol Intel Ctr, Wright-Patterson AFB, 55-61, actg tech dir, 59-60, aerospace engr, Directorate of Synthesis, Systs Eng Group, 61-69 & Directorate of Opers Res, 69, opers res analyst, Simulation & Anal Div, 69-76; pres, Trident Marine Servs, 72-76; PRES, L-TECH SYSTS, 76- *Mem:* Fel AAAS; sr mem Inst Elec & Electronics Engrs; Opers Res Soc Am. *Res:* System effectiveness evaluation; computer simulation; electrical waveform analysis; electrical measurement theory. *Mailing Add:* 1000 Tarpon Ctr Dr Venice FL 33595

LLOYD, LEWIS EWAN, b Montreal, Que, Feb 3, 24; m 50; c 4. NUTRITION. *Educ:* Macdonald Col, McGill Univ, BSc, 48, MSc, 50, PhD(nutrit), 52. *Prof Exp:* Asst nutrit, Macdonald Col, McGill Univ, 48-52; res assoc, Cornell Univ, 52-53; from asst prof to assoc prof, Macdonald Col, McGill Univ, 53-60, prof animal sci & chmn dept, 60-67; dir sch home econ, Univ Man, 67-70, dean fac home econ, 70-77; DEAN FAC AGR, MACDONALD COL, McGILL UNIV, 77- *Concurrent Pos:* Underwood fel, Rowett Res Inst, Scotland, 58-59. *Mem:* Agr Inst Can; Can Inst Food Sci & Technol; Am Inst Nutrit; Nutrit Soc Can; Brit Nutrit Soc. *Res:* Utilization of food nutrients by the body. *Mailing Add:* Macdonald Campus McGill Univ 21111 Lakeshore Rd St Anne De Bellevue PQ H9X 1CO Can

LLOYD, MILTON HAROLD, b Des Moines, Iowa, Mar 27, 25; m 44; c 3. *Educ:* Creighton Univ, BS, 50, MS, 54. *Prof Exp:* Chemist prod develop, Tidy House Prod Co, 50-56; SECT MGR PROCESS RES & DEVELOP, OAK RIDGE NAT LAB, 56- *Mem:* Am Chem Soc; AAAS. *Res:* Transuranium element isolation and purification; plutonia sol-gel processes for preparation of advanced reactor fuels; chemical studies of plutonium behavior in reactor fuel reprocessing and waste solutions. *Mailing Add:* Oak Ridge Nat Lab PO Box X Oak Ridge TN 37830

LLOYD, MONTE, b Omaha, Nebr, July 6, 27; m 46, 69; c 4. ANIMAL ECOLOGY, TROPICAL FOREST CONSERVATION. *Educ:* Univ Calif, Los Angeles, AB, 52; Univ Chicago, PhD(zool), 57. *Prof Exp:* NSF fel, Bur Animal Pop, Oxford Univ, 57-59, Brit Nature Conserv res grant, 59-62; asst prof zool, Univ Calif, Los Angeles, 62-67; ASSOC PROF BIOL, UNIV CHICAGO, 67- *Concurrent Pos:* Ed, Ecology, 68-72. *Mem:* Soc Study Evolution; Am Soc Nat; Ecol Soc Am; Brit Ecol Soc. *Res:* Dynamics of animal populations and community ecology. *Mailing Add:* Dept of Biol Univ of Chicago 1101 E 57th St Chicago IL 60637

LLOYD, NELSON ALBERT, b Lorain, Ohio, Oct 12, 26; m 45; c 5. ANALYTICAL CHEMISTRY. *Educ:* Southern Methodist Univ, BS, 50, MS, 51; Okla State Univ, PhD(anal chem), 55. *Prof Exp:* Res chemist, Goodyear Atomic Corp, 54-56; assoc prof anal chem, Northeastern La State Col, 56-61 & Univ Ala, Tuscaloosa, 61-67; chmn Div Natural Sci, Mobile Col, Mobile, 67-70; CHIEF GEOCHEM DIV, GEOL SURV OF ALA, TUSCALOOSA, 70- *Concurrent Pos:* Consult, Tuscaloosa Metall Res Ctr, US Bur Mines, 63-67 & State Oil & Gas Bd, Ala, 66-67. *Mem:* Am Chem Soc. *Res:* Rock analysis, whole rock and trace metals in rock; trace substances in water, heavy metals, pesticides herbicides and various nitrogen species. *Mailing Add:* 209 32nd Ave E Tuscaloosa AL 35401

LLOYD, NORMAN EDWARD, b Oak Park, Ill, Feb 20, 29; m 51; c 8. BIOCHEMISTRY. *Educ:* Rockjurst Col, BS, 52; Kans State Col, MS, 53; Purdue Univ, PhD(biochem), 56. *Prof Exp:* Assoc chemist, Corn Prods Co, 56-58; cereal chemist, Int Milling Co, 58-59; supvr starch chem res, 60-64, dir sci develop, 64-69, asst res dir, 69-70, supvr chem res, 70-78, dir res & develop, 78-79, VPRES TECH, CLINTON CORN PROCESSING CO, 79- *Mem:* Am Chem Soc; Am Asn Cereal Chem. *Res:* Production and characterization of starches, sweeteners and enzymes; enzyme kinetics and immobilization; development of methods for separation of glucose and fructose on a large scale. *Mailing Add:* Res Dept Clinton Corn Processing Co Clinton IA 52732

LLOYD, RAY DIX, b March 10, 30; m 54; c 5. RADIATION PHYSICS, RADIOBIOLOGY. *Educ:* Univ Utah, PhD(biol), 74. *Prof Exp:* Res asst prof anat, Radiobiol Div, Dept Anat, Col Med, Univ Utah, 61-79; RES ASSOC PROF PHARMACOL, RADIOBIOL DIV, DEPT PHARMACOL, SCH MED, UNIV UTAH, 79- *Concurrent Pos:* Coun mem, Nat Coun Radiation Protection & Measurements, 80; adj asst prof, Dept Mech & Indust Eng, Univ Utah, 75- *Mem:* Radiation Res Soc; Health Physics Soc; Int Radiation Protection Asn. *Res:* Biological effects of ionizing radiation; internal emitters; sase-response models; risk assessment; risk modification by chelatica therapy; application of radioactivity to biomedical studies. *Mailing Add:* Radiobiol Div Bldg 351 Univ Utah Salt Lake City UT 84112

LLOYD, ROBERT, b Jackson, Miss, Mar 1, 16; m 49; c 1. CHEMICAL ENGINEERING. *Educ:* Purdue Univ, BS, 38; Temple Univ, MA, 46, PhD(phys chem), 54, Carnegie Mellon Univ, MS, 78. *Prof Exp:* Asst city engr, Gary, Ind, 38-41; chemist, Kingsbury Ord Plant, Ind, 41-42; chem engr, Graham Savage & Assocs, Inc, 45-55; CHEM ENGR, BETTIS ATOMIC POWER LAB, WESTINGHOUSE ELEC CORP, 55- *Mem:* Am Chem Soc; Am Inst Chem Engrs. *Res:* Metal complexes; electrochemistry; electroplating procedures; engineering design; nuclear atomic power engineering. *Mailing Add:* Westinghouse Elec Corp PO Box 79 West Mifflin PA 15122

LLOYD, ROBERT MICHAEL, b Los Angeles, Calif, Dec 26, 38; m 73; c 2. SYSTEMATIC BOTANY. *Educ:* Pomona Col, BA, 60; Claremont Grad Sch, MA, 62; Univ Calif, Berkeley, PhD(bot), 69. *Prof Exp:* Herbarium technician, Univ Calif, Los Angeles, 62-63; asst prof bot, Univ Hawaii, 68-71; asst prof, 71-75, assoc prof, 75-81, PROF BOT, OHIO UNIV, 81- *Concurrent Pos:* Prin invstr, NSF grants, 78-80 & 80-83. *Mem:* AAAS; Am Inst Biol Sci; Am Fern Soc (vpres, 78 & 79, pres 80 & 81); Am Soc Plant Taxon; Linnean Soc London. *Res:* Systematics and reproductive biology of ferns; systematics, morphology and evolution of the Pteridophyta; spore germination, breeding systems and genetics. *Mailing Add:* Dept Bot Ohio Univ Athens OH 45701

LLOYD, STUART PHINNEY, b Kansas City, Mo, Mar 23, 23. MATHEMATICS. *Educ:* Univ Chicago, SB, 43; Univ Ill, PhD(physics), 51. *Prof Exp:* Mem, Inst Advan Study, 51-52; MEM TECH STAFF, BELL LABS INC, 52- *Concurrent Pos:* Vis assoc prof, Univ Chicago, 62-63. *Mem:* AAAS; Am Math Soc; Math Asn Am; fel Inst Math Statist. *Res:* Probability theory; ocean acoustics. *Mailing Add:* Bell Labs Inc Whippany NJ 07981

LLOYD, THOMAS BLAIR, b Reedsville, WVa, Aug 29, 21; m 44; c 3. INDUSTRIAL CHEMISTRY, COLLOID CHEMISTRY. *Educ:* Washington & Jefferson Col, BS, 42; Western Res Univ, MS, 46, PhD(phys chem), 48. *Prof Exp:* Asst prof chem, Muhlenberg Co, 48-54; chem investr, 54-66, RES SUPVR, NJ ZINC CO, 66- *Mem:* Am Chem Soc; Sigma Xi. *Res:* Industrial process research, particularly pigments, hydrometallurgy and pollution control. *Mailing Add:* NJ Zinc Co One Highland Ave Bethlehem PA 18017

LLOYD, WALLIS A(LLEN), b Harrisburg, Pa, July 24, 26; m 55; c 4. CHEMICAL ENGINEERING. *Educ:* Pa State Univ, BS, 49; Univ Minn, PhD(chem eng), 54. *Prof Exp:* Res assoc chem eng, Univ Minn, 54-55; design engr, Calif Res Corp Div, Standard Oil Co Calif, 55-56; asst prof chem eng, Pa State Univ, 56-64; RES DIR, CANNON INSTRUMENT CO, 64- *Mem:* Assoc mem Am Inst Chem Engrs; Am Nuclear Soc; Am Soc Testing & Mat. *Res:* Heat transfer; chemonuclear research; separation processes; viscometry. *Mailing Add:* Cannon Instrument Co PO Box 16 State College PA 16801

LLOYD, WELDON S, b Miami, Fla, July 26, 39; m 60; c 2. CALCIUM & BONE METABOLISM. *Educ:* Boston Univ, BA, 66; Northeastern Univ, MS, 71. *Hon Degrees:* Boston Univ, DSc, 78. *Prof Exp:* Assoc, Harvard Univ, 63-68; Instr oral pharmacol, 68-71, assoc pharmacol res, 71-78, ASST PROF NUTRIT, BOSTON UNIV, 78- *Concurrent Pos:* Sr lectr, Roxbury Community Col, 80. *Mem:* AAAS. *Res:* Bone disease and hormone related studies; calcium and bone metabolism related studies in health and disease. *Mailing Add:* Sch Grad Dent Boston Univ 100 E Newton St Boston MA 02118

LLOYD, WILLIAM GILBERT, b New York, NY, July 10, 23; m 47; c 3. ORGANIC CHEMISTRY, APPLIED CHEMISTRY. *Educ:* Kalamazoo Col, AB, 47; Brown Univ, ScM, 50; Mich State Univ, PhD(org chem), 57. *Prof Exp:* Chemist, Dow Chem Co, 50-60, assoc scientist, 60-62; sr process res specialist, Lummus Co, NJ, 62-67; prof chem, Western Ky Univ, 67-74; sr res scientist, Inst Mining & Minerals Res, Univ Ky, 74-75, chief chemist, 75-77, assoc dir & mgr, Mat Div, 77-80; DEAN, OGDEN COL SCI, TECHNOL & HEALTH, WESTERN KY UNIV, 80- *Concurrent Pos:* Dir, Larox Res Corp, 72- *Mem:* AAAS; Am Chem Soc. *Res:* Catalysis of organic reactions; oxidations; free radical chemistry; chemistry of coal and coal-derived products; environmental chemistry. *Mailing Add:* Ogden Col Sci Technol & Health Western Ky Univ Bowling Green KY 42101

LLOYD, WILLIAM REESE, b Pueblo, Colo, Sept 26, 13; m 38. PHARMACY. *Educ:* Univ Colo, AB, 34, BS, 36; Univ NC, MS, 38; Univ Minn, PhD(pharmaceut chem), 41. *Prof Exp:* Asst chem, Univ NC, 36-38; asst pharm, Univ Minn, 38-41; asst prof, Univ Ga, 41-42; asst prof chem, Duquesne Univ, 42-44; biochemist, Armour Res Found, 44-45, supvr biochem res, 45-47, chemist, Int Div, 47-49; assoc prof pharm, Univ Tex, 49-60, asst dean, 52-60; TECH DIR, TEX PHARMACOL CO, 60- *Mem:* Am Chem Soc; Am Soc Oil Chem; Am Pharmaceut Asn. *Res:* Fats, oils and waxes; pharmaceutical formulation. *Mailing Add:* 2919 Larkwood Dr San Antonio TX 78209

LLOYD, WINSTON DALE, b Pensacola, Fla, Sept 9, 29; m 58; c 3. ORGANIC CHEMISTRY. *Educ:* Fla State Univ, BS, 51; Univ Washington, PhD(org chem), 56. *Prof Exp:* Org chemist, Dow Chem Co, 56-58 & USDA, 59-62; res prof, 65-66, ASSOC PROF CHEM, UNIV TEX, EL PASO, 62- *Mem:* Am Chem Soc; Sigma Xi; Phytochem Soc NAm. *Res:* Stereochemistry of cyclic dienes; mechanisms of organic chemical reactions; natural products; synthesis. *Mailing Add:* Dept of Chem Univ of Tex El Paso TX 79968

LNENICKA, WILLIAM J(OSEPH), b Hay Springs, Nebr, Oct 16, 22; m 47; c 2. STRUCTURAL ENGINEERING. *Educ:* Univ Nebr, BS, 49; Kansas State Univ, MS; Ga Inst Technol, PhD, 61. *Prof Exp:* Instr civil eng, Univ Nebr, 49-51 & Kans State Univ, 52-54; asst prof eng mech, Univ Okla, 54-57 & La State Univ, 57-58; from asst prof to assoc prof, 58-68, PROF ENG MECH, GA INST TECHNOL, 68-, ASSOC VPRES ACAD AFFAIRS, 78- *Concurrent Pos:* Consult, Aerial Tower Mfg Co, 54-59; mem bd dir, Vinings Chem Co, 64-73; Vinings Leasing Co, 68-73 & Wilroy & Assoc Consult Engrs, 70-78. *Mem:* Am Soc Eng Educ; Soc Am Mil Engrs; Soc Prof Engrs. *Res:* Chief field strength of materials. *Mailing Add:* Off Assoc Vpres Ga Inst Technol Atlanta GA 30332

LÖNNERDAL, BO L, b Linkoping, Sweden, Mar 5, 48; m 74; c 4. INFANT NUTRITION. *Educ:* Univ Uppsala, BSc, 69, MSc, 71, PhD(biochem), 73. *Prof Exp:* Res asst, Dept Biochem, Univ Uppsula, 69-74, res assoc, Inst Nutrit, 74-76; vis asst res nutritionist, 78-80, asst res nutritionist, 80-81, ASST PROF NUTRIT, UNIV CALIF, DAVIS, 81- *Concurrent Pos:* Res nutrit, Inst Nutrit, Univ Uppsula, 76- *Mem:* Am Inst Nutrit; Am Soc Clin Nutrit; Soc Exp Biol & Med; Soc Environ Geochem & Health. *Res:* Composition of breast milk, cow's milk and formulas; trace element metabolism in the perinatal period. *Mailing Add:* Dept Nutrit Univ Calif Davis CA 95616

LO, ARTHUR W(UNIEN), b Shanghai, China, May 21, 16; nat US; m 50; c 2. COMPUTER SCIENCE. *Educ:* Yenching Univ, China, BS, 38; Oberlin Col, MA, 46; Univ Ill, PhD(elec eng), 49. *Prof Exp:* Asst prof elec eng, Mich Col Mining & Technol, 49-50; lectr, City Col New York, 50-51; res & develop engr, Victor Div, Radio Corp Am, 51-52, sr mem tech staff, RCA Labs, 52-60; mgr adv tech develop, Data Systs Div, Int Bus Mach Corp, 60-64; PROF ELEC ENG, PRINCETON UNIV, 64- *Mem:* Fel Inst Elec & Electronics Engrs. *Res:* Digital electronics and computer organization. *Mailing Add:* 102 Maclean Circle Princeton NJ 08540

LO, CHENG FAN, b Taichung, Taiwan, Dec 14, 37; m 66; c 3. WOOD CHEMISTRY. *Educ:* Nat Taiwan Univ, BS, 62; Auburn Univ, MS, 66; Ore State Univ, PhD(wood chem), 70. *Prof Exp:* Res asst, Dept Forestry, Auburn Univ, 64-66; wood chemist, Forest Res Lab, Ore State Univ, 66-69; RES CHEMIST, BOISE CASCADE CHEM RES LAB, 69- *Mem:* Am Chem Soc;

Tech Asn Pulp & Paper Indust; Forest Prod Res Soc. *Res:* By-products development in wood cellulose and lignin material; technical assistance to paper production. *Mailing Add:* Boise Cascade Pulp & Paper 909 W Seventh St Vancouver WA 98660

LO, DAVID S(HIH-FANG), b China, Aug 27, 32; m 59; c 2. COMPUTER MEMORY TECHNOLOGY. *Educ:* Nat Taiwan Univ, BS, 54; Univ Minn, MS, 58, PhD(elec eng), 62. *Prof Exp:* Sr res scientist, Honeywell Res Ctr, 62-64; prin physicist, 64-71; staff physicist, 72-79, SR STAFF SCIENTIST, UNIVAC DIV, SPERRY CORP, 80- *Concurrent Pos:* Lectr, Univ Minn, 62- *Mem:* Inst Elec & Electronics Engrs; Soc Info Display. *Res:* Electrical properties and applications of ferric oxide semiconductors; ferromagnetic films; magnetic and optical memories; electroluminescent displays. *Mailing Add:* UNIVAC Sperry Corp PO Box 3525 St Paul MN 55165

LO, DONALD HUNG-TAK, b Loyang, China, Dec 3, 43; Can citizen; m 68; c 2. CLINICAL CHEMISTRY. *Educ:* McMaster Univ, BSc, 65; McGill Univ, PhD(quantum chem), 69. *Prof Exp:* Chemist, Can Indust Ltd, 65; res assoc chem with comput, Univ Tex, Austin, 69-73; trainee clin chem, Erie County Lab, 73-75; clin chemist, Union Carbide Corp, 75-80. *Concurrent Pos:* Nat Res Coun Can fel, McGill Univ, 68-69; Robert A Welch fel, Univ Tex, Austin, 71-73. *Mem:* Am Asn Clin Chemists; Clin Radioassay Soc. *Res:* Radioimmunoassay method development and optimization; systematic radioimmunoassay method comparison; computer simulation of kinetic antigen-antibody interaction; the teaching of clinical chemistry via flowcharts; a more efficient clinical chemistry laboratory organization. *Mailing Add:* 120 Ledgewood Circle Rochester NY 14615

LO, ELIZABETH SHEN, b Shanghai, China, Feb 24, 26; m 50; c 2. ORGANIC CHEMISTRY. *Educ:* St John's Univ, Shanghai, BS, 45; Univ Ill, MS, 47, PhD(chem), 49. *Prof Exp:* Univ Ill fel, 49-50; res chemist, Metalsalsts Corp, 51; J T Baker Chem Co Div, Vick Chem Co, 51-52; M W Kellogg Co, 53-57; Permacel Div, Johnson & Johnson, 57-60; staff chemist, IBM Corp, 60-63; sr res chemist, Thiokol Chem Corp, 65-70; vis fel, Princeton Univ, 71-73; MGR, MAT & CHEM PROCESS, FAIRCHILD-PMS PROD, 74- *Mem:* Am Chem Soc. *Res:* Polymer, rubber and resin chemistry; fluorocarbon polymers; liquid crystals. *Mailing Add:* 102 Maclean Circle Princeton NJ 08540

LO, GEORGE ALBERT, b Hong Kong, June 26, 34; US citizen; m 57; c 2. PHYSICAL CHEMISTRY, INORGANIC CHEMISTRY. *Educ:* Univ Ore, BA, 57, MA, 60; Wash State Univ, PhD(chem), 63. *Prof Exp:* Mem tech staff, Rocketdyne Div, Rockwell Int Corp, 63-77; STAFF SCIENTIST, LOCKHEED PALO ALTO RES LAB, 77- *Mem:* Am Chem Soc; Sigma Xi. *Res:* Chemical kinetics and propulsion; chemistry of inorganic complexes. *Mailing Add:* Lockheed Palo Alto Res Lab 3251 Hanover St Palo Alto CA 94304

LO, HOWARD H, b Hsinchu, Taiwan, Sept 3, 37; US citizen; m 65; c 2. GEOCHEMISTRY, PETROLOGY. *Educ:* Nat Taiwan Univ, BS, 60; Univ Minn, MSc, 64; Wash Univ, PhD(geochem), 70. *Prof Exp:* Jr geologist, Geol Surv Taiwan, 60-62; res & teaching asst, Univ Minn, 62-64; mine geologist, Opemiska Copper Mines, Ltd, Que, 64-65; instr sci & math, Ottawa Col Inst, Can, 65-67; res asst, Wash Univ, St Louis, 67-70; asst prof, 70-76, ASSOC PROF GEOL SCI, CLEVELAND STATE UNIV, 76- *Concurrent Pos:* Res Initiation Award, Cleveland State Univ, 71-72; NSF grant, 72-73. *Mem:* Am Geophys Union; Geol Soc Am; Geol Soc China. *Res:* Geochemical and petrological study of the volcanic rocks, igneous rocks and some metamorphic rocks, especially in the modern island arcs and Canadian shield. *Mailing Add:* Dept of Geol Sci Cleveland State Univ Cleveland OH 44115

LO, KWOK-YUNG, b Nanking, China, Oct 19, 47; US citizen; m 73. RADIO ASTRONOMY, ASTROPHYSICS. *Educ:* Mass Inst Technol, SB, 69, PhD(physics), 74. *Prof Exp:* Res fel radio astron, Owens Valley Radio Observ, Calif Inst Technol, 74-76; Miller fel basic res sci, Univ Calif, Berkeley, 76-78, asst res astronomer, Radio Astron Lab, 78; sr res fel, 78-80, ASST PROF RADIO ASTRON, CALIF INST TECHNOL, 80- *Concurrent Pos:* Miller fel, 76-79. *Mem:* Am Astron Soc; Int Astron Union. *Res:* Microwave spectroscopy studies of phenomena associated with star formation; studies of the intergalactic medium in nearby groups of galaxies; high angular resolution studies of galactic and extragalactic radio sources by interferometry and very long baseline interferometry techniques. *Mailing Add:* 105-24 Dept Astron Calif Inst of Technol Pasadena CA 91125

LO, MAN-WAI, b Hong Kong, Sept 9, 51; US citizen; m 76; c 1. DRUG DISPOSITION, DRUG ANALYSIS. *Educ:* San Francisco State Univ, BS, 74; Univ Calif, San Francisco, PhD(pharmaceut chem), 81. *Prof Exp:* RES BIOCHEMIST, BIOCHEM DEPT, PHARMACEUT DIV, STINE LAB, E I DU PONT DE NEMOURS & CO, INC, 81- *Res:* Biopharmaceutics and pharmacokinetics; analysis of drug metabolites in biological fluids; computer fitting; drug metabolism. *Mailing Add:* E I Du Pont de Nemours & Co Inc Stine Lab PO Box 30 Newark DE 19711

LO, MIKE MEI-KUO, b Formosa, China, Sept 21, 36; m 67. PHYSICAL CHEMISTRY. *Educ:* Nat Taiwan Univ, BS, 59; Univ Ill, MS, 65, PhD(chem), 67. *Prof Exp:* SR RES CHEMIST, S C JOHNSON & SON, INC, 67- *Concurrent Pos:* Res fel, Univ Ill. *Mem:* Am Chem Soc; Fine Particle Soc; Am Indust Hyg Asn; Am Soc Testing & Mat. *Res:* Microwave spectroscopy; ultrasonic impedometry; gas chromatography and mass spectroscopy; aerosol science and technology. *Mailing Add:* 4915 Vrana Lane Racine WI 53405

LO, PAK-KAN ALBERT, pharmaceutics, see previous edition

LO, ROBERT K, b Canton, China, Sept 15, 24; US citizen; m 53; c 1. MECHANICAL ENGINEERING. *Educ:* Nat Cent Univ, China, BS, 44; Stanford Univ, MS, 51; Ill Inst Technol, PhD(mech eng), 57. *Prof Exp:* Instr mech eng, Case Inst Technol, 51-53; asst res engr, Ill Inst Technol, 53-56;

specialist jet engines, Gen Elec Co, 56-57; res engr, Res Labs, Whirlpool Corp, 57-64, sr res engr, 64-66; STAFF MEM REACTOR ENG, ARGONNE NAT LAB, 66- *Concurrent Pos:* Lectr, Mich State Univ, 59-60, 62-63 & 65-66. *Mem:* Am Soc Mech Engrs; Sigma Xi. *Res:* Mechanical vibrations; fluid mechanics; heat transfer and nuclear reactor engineering. *Mailing Add:* Reactor Eng Div 9700 S Cass Ave Argonne IL 60439

LO, THEODORE CHING-YANG, b Shanghai, China, Dec 22, 43; Can citizen; m 74. MICROBIAL GENETICS, MEMBRANE FUNCTIONS. *Educ:* Univ Man, BSc, 69; Univ Toronto, PhD(med biophys), 73. *Prof Exp:* Res fel biochem, Harvard Univ, 73-75; asst prof, 75-80, ASSOC PROF BIOCHEM, UNIV WESTERN ONT, 80- *Mem:* Am Soc Microbiol; Am Soc Biol Chemists; Can Biochem Soc. *Res:* Molecular mechanisms for dicarboxylic acid transport in Escherichia coli K12; alterations of cell behavior by membrane perturbation. *Mailing Add:* Dept Biochem Univ Western Ont London ON N6A 5B7 Can

LO, W(ING) C(HEUK), b Macao, May 20, 24; US citizen; m 57; c 3. CERAMICS, METALLURGY. *Educ:* Lingnan Univ, BS, 47; Mo Sch Mines, BS, 54; Rutgers Univ, PhD(ceramic eng), 60. *Prof Exp:* Assoc ceramic engr, Crane Co, Ill, 54-55; res asst ceramics, Rutgers Univ, 55-59; MEM TECH STAFF, BELL TEL LABS, 59- *Mem:* Am Ceramic Soc; Am Soc Testing & Mat; Nat Inst Ceramic Engrs. *Res:* Evaluation and testing of components, materials and processes; material and process development; fabrication of optical components. *Mailing Add:* Div 523 Dept 52353 Discrete Bell Labs 555 Union Blvd Allentown PA 18103

LO, WAYNE, b Hupei, China; US citizen; m 78; c 3. SEMICONDUCTORS, ELECTRON PHYSICS. *Educ:* Taiwan Cheng Kung Univ, BS, 63; Univ RI, MS, 69; Columbia Univ, PhD(elec eng), 73. *Prof Exp:* Engr, Taiwan Electronics Corp, 64-66 & Gen Instrument Corp, 66-67; sr res scientist, 73-80, SR STAFF RES SCIENTIST, GEN MOTORS CORP, 80- *Mem:* Inst Elec & Electronics Engrs; AAAS. *Res:* Semiconductor materials and devices; lasers, quantum electronics and infrared spectroscopy. *Mailing Add:* Gen Motors Res Labs GM Tech Ctrs Warren MI 48090

LO, Y(UEN) T(ZE), b China, Jan 31, 20; US citizen; m 53; c 2. ELECTRICAL ENGINEERING. *Educ:* Nat Southwest Assoc Univ, BS, 42; Univ Ill, MS, 49, PhD(elec eng), 52. *Prof Exp:* Asst, Radio Res Inst, Tsinghua Univ, Peking, 42-46, instr, Tsinghua & Yenching Univs, 46-48; proj engr, Channel Master Corp, 52-56; from asst prof to assoc prof elec eng, 56-66, PROF ELEC ENG, UNIV ILL, URBANA, 66- *Concurrent Pos:* Consult, Westinghouse Elec Corp, 57-58, Andrew Corp, 63, Am Electronics Lab, 66, Emerson Elec, 68-69, IBM Corp, 69 & Raytheon, 69- *Honors & Awards:* John T Bolljahn Mem Award, Inst Elec & Electronics Engrs, 65. *Mem:* Inst Elec & Electronics Engrs; Int Union Radio Sci. *Res:* Antenna; electromagnetic theory; waves in plasma; radio astronomy. *Mailing Add:* Dept of Elec Eng Univ of Ill Urbana IL 61801

LOACH, KENNETH WILLIAM, b Portsmouth, Eng, Sept 5, 34; m 66; c 2. ANALYTICAL CHEMISTRY. *Educ:* Univ Auckland, BSc, 56, MSc, 58; Univ Wash, PhD(chem), 69. *Prof Exp:* Chemist, Ruakura Animal Res Sta, NZ, 58-60; div plant indust, Commonwealth Sci & Indust Res Orgn, Australia, 60-63; asst prof, 63-73, ASSOC PROF ANAL CHEM & COMPUT SCI, STATE UNIV NY COL PLATTSBURGH, 73- *Concurrent Pos:* NSF grants, Tufts Univ, 71, State Univ NY Col Plattsburgh, 72-73, State Univ NY Res Found fel & grant, 72-73 & 77-78. *Mem:* AAAS; Am Chem Soc; Asn Comput Mach. *Res:* Principles of analytical chemistry; trace analysis; chemical information systems and computing; chemical structure codes. *Mailing Add:* Dept of Chem State Univ of NY Col Plattsburgh NY 12901

LOACH, PAUL A, b Findlay, Ohio, July 18, 34; m 57; c 3. BIOCHEMISTRY, PHYSICAL BIOCHEMISTRY. *Educ:* Univ Akron, BS, 57; Yale Univ, PhD(biochem), 61. *Prof Exp:* Nat Acad Sci-Nat Res Coun fel photosynthesis, Univ Calif, Berkeley, 61-63; from asst prof to assoc prof, 63-73, PROF CHEM, NORTHWESTERN UNIV, 73-, PROF BIOCHEM & MOLECULAR BIOL, 74- *Concurrent Pos:* Res career develop award, NIH, 71-76. *Mem:* AAAS; Am Chem Soc; Am Soc Biol Chem; Biophys Soc; Am Soc for Photobiol. *Res:* Primary photochemistry of photosynthesis; chemistry of porphyrins and metalloporphyrins; biological oxidation and reduction; structure and function in bioenergetic membranes; photochemical models of photosynthesis. *Mailing Add:* Dept of Biochem & Molecular Biol Northwestern Univ Evanston IL 60201

LOADHOLT, CLAUDE BOYD, b Fairfax, SC, Mar 26, 40; m 63; c 2. BIOSTATISTICS. *Educ:* Clemson Univ, BS, 62, MS, 65; Va Polytech Inst, PhD(statist), 69. *Prof Exp:* Asst exp sta statistician, Clemson Univ, 65-66, asst prof exp statist, 68-70; div med univ, ASSOC PROF BIOMET, MED UNIV SC, 70- *Mem:* Biomet Soc. *Res:* Statistical consultation in biological and medical research; design of experiments; statistical data processing. *Mailing Add:* Dept of Biomet Med Univ of SC Charleston SC 29401

LOAN, CONRAD CHARLES, taxonomic entomology, biocontrol, see previous edition

LOAN, LEONARD DONALD, b London, Eng, Oct 6, 30; m 55; c 3. POLYMER CHEMISTRY. *Educ:* Univ Birmingham, BSc, 51, PhD(polymer chem), 54. *Prof Exp:* Sci off combustion chem, Royal Aircraft Estab, 54-57; chemist, Arthur D Little Res Inst, 57-59; prin sci off rubber chem, Rubber & Plastics Res Asn, 59-66; mem tech staff polymer chem, 66-74, HEAD PLASTICS CHEM, RES & DEVELOP, BELL TEL LABS, 74- *Mem:* Am Chem Soc. *Res:* Polymer crosslinking and aging. *Mailing Add:* Bell Tel Labs Mountain Ave Murray Hill NJ 07974

LOAN, RAYMOND WALLACE, b Ephrata, Wash, Apr 24, 31; m 52; c 4. IMMUNOBIOLOGY. *Educ:* Wash State Univ, BS, 52, DVM, 58; Purdue Univ, MS, 60, PhD(animal path), 61. *Prof Exp:* Instr vet microbiol, Purdue Univ, 58-61; from asst prof to prof vet microbiol, Univ Mo-Columbia, 61-80, chmn dept, 69-80; ASSOC DEAN RES & GRAD INSTR, COL VET MED & PROF VET MICROBIOL & PARASITOL, TEX A&M UNIV, 80- *Mem:* AM Vet Med Asn; Am Asn Immunol; Am Col Vet Microbiol; Am Soc Microbiol; Conf Res Workers Animal Diseases. *Res:* Cell mediated immunity; immunologic aspects of avian leukosis. *Mailing Add:* Col Vet Med Tex A&M Univ College Station TX 77843

LOAR, JAMES M, b Lancaster, Pa, Sept 10, 44. AQUATIC ECOLOGY, FISHERIES BIOLOGY. *Educ:* Gettysburg Col, BA, 66; Temple Univ, MEd, 69; Univ Wyo, PhD(zool), 75. *Prof Exp:* Teacher biol, Cherry Hill High Sch W, NJ, 66-70; RES ASSOC, ENVIRON SCI DIV, OAK RIDGE NAT LAB, 75- *Concurrent Pos:* Prin investr, Oak Ridge Nat Lab, 75- *Mem:* AAAS; Am Fisheries Soc; Ecol Soc Am; Sigma Xi. *Res:* Assessment of impact of nuclear, fossil and hydroelectric energy technologies; responses of aquatic biota to altered flow regimes below hydroelectric projects. *Mailing Add:* Oak Ridge Nat Lab Bldg 1505 PO Box X Oak Ridge TN 37830

LOBB, BARRY LEE, b Easton, Pa, Nov 25, 43; m 69; c 2. MATHEMATICS. *Educ:* Lafayette Col, BS, 65; Duke Univ, MA, 68, PhD(math), 69. *Prof Exp:* assoc prof, 69-80, FULL PROF MATH, BUTLER UNIV, 80- *Mem:* Math Asn Am. *Res:* Topology. *Mailing Add:* Dept of Math Butler Univ Indianapolis IN 46208

LOBB, DONALD EDWARD, b Saskatoon, Sask, Apr 25, 40. PHYSICS. *Educ:* Univ Sask, BE, 61, MSc, 63, PhD(physics), 66. *Prof Exp:* Nat Res Coun Can overseas fel, 66-67; asst prof, 67-74, ASSOC PROF PHYSICS, UNIV VICTORIA, BC, 74- *Mem:* Inst Elec & Electronics Engrs; Can Asn Physicists. *Res:* Beam optics. *Mailing Add:* Dept of Physics Univ of Victoria Victoria BC V8W 2Y2 Can

LOBB, R(ODMOND) KENNETH, b Can, Feb 10, 25; m 47; c 2. AERODYNAMICS. *Educ:* Univ Alta, BSc, 47; Univ Toronto, MASc, 48, PhD(aeronaut eng), 50. *Prof Exp:* Aeronaut engr, Naval Ord Lab, 48; res scientist, Can Defense Res Bd, 49; res assoc, Inst Fluid Dynamics, Univ Md, 50-51; aeronaut engr, Naval Ord Lab, 52-53, chief, Hypersonic Wind Tunnel Br, 54-55, Aerophys Div, 56 & Aerodyn Dept, 57-61, assoc head aeroballistics & hydroballistics, 61-74; tech dir, Naval Air Develop Ctr, Dept Defense, 74-81; RES PROG DIR, CTR NAVAL ANALYSES, 81- *Concurrent Pos:* Lectr, Cath Univ Am, 53-54 & Univ Md, 61-63. *Mem:* Am Inst Aeronaut & Astronaut. *Res:* Aircraft aerodynamics; structures; inertial navigation systems; boundary layers; hypersonic wind tunnel research and development; skin friction and heat transfer measurements in hypersonic flows; ballistics range studies; high temperature aerodynamics; underwater acoustics; underwater vehicles. *Mailing Add:* Ctr Naval Analyses 2000 N Beauregard St Alexandria VA 22311

LOBDELL, DAVID HILL, b Erie, Pa, July 9, 30. PATHOLOGY. *Educ:* Kenyon Col, AB, 52; Univ Mich, MD, 56. *Prof Exp:* From intern to resident path, Bellevue Hosp, New York, 56-59, asst pathologist, 59-60; assoc pathologist, 60-63, DIR LABS, ST VINCENT'S MED CTR, 63-, DIR SCH MED TECHNOL, 63- *Concurrent Pos:* Instr, Sch Med, NY Univ, 59-61, asst clin prof path, 61-69; lectr histol, Fairfield Univ, 64-73. *Mem:* AMA; fel Col Am Path; fel Am Soc Clin Path. *Res:* Osmometry; myeloproliferative disorders. *Mailing Add:* 2820 Main St Bridgeport CT 06606

LOBECK, CHARLES CHAMPLIN, b New Rochelle, NY, May 20, 26; m 54; c 4. PEDIATRICS. *Educ:* Hobart Col, AB, 48; Univ Rochester, MD, 52. *Prof Exp:* From instr to sr instr pediat, Sch Med & Dent, Univ Rochester, 55-58; from asst prof to prof, Sch Med, Univ Wis-Madison, 58-75, chmn dept, 64-74, assoc dean clin affairs, 74-75; DEAN, SCH MED, UNIV MO-COLUMBIA, 75- *Res:* Metabolic disease; membrane transport; cystic fibrosis. *Mailing Add:* Sch of Med Univ of Mo Med Ctr Columbia MO 65212

LOBENE, RALPH RUFINO, b Rochester, NY, Mar 30, 24; m 50. DENTISTRY, PERIODONTOLOGY. *Educ:* Univ Rochester, BS, 44; Univ Buffalo, DDS, 49; Tufts Univ, MS, 62; Am Bd Periodont, dipl, 65. *Prof Exp:* Res chemist, Manhattan Proj, Univ Rochester, 44-45; res chemist, Merck & Co, NJ, 45-46; intern periodont, Eastman Dent Dispensary, Rochester, NY, 4950; resident oral surg, Strong Mem Hosp, Rochester, 5051, asst dent surgeon, 53-62, instr dent & clin dent res, Sch Med & Dent, Univ Rochester, 53-62; asst prof periodont, Sch Dent, Univ Pac, 62-63; ASSOC PROF & ACAD ADMINR DENT ASST TRAINING PROG, NORTHEASTERN UNIV, 63-, DIR ADVAN EDUC, 70-, DEAN, FORSYTH SCH DENT HYGIENISTS, 75- *Concurrent Pos:* Res grants, Colgate Palmolive Co, 54-55 & 58-59; res grant, Sch Dent, Univ Pac, 62-63; res grant, Gen Elec Co, 62-65; staff dentist, Eastman Dent Dispensary, 53-54, res assoc, 58-62; pvt pract, 53-60; chief dent serv, State Indust & Agr Sch Boys, NY, 54-57; clin asst, Sch Dent Med, Tufts Univ, 61-62, lectr, 63-; asst mem staff, Forsyth Dent Ctr, Northeastern Univ, 63-66, lectr, 63-, head dept clin exp, Inst Res & Advan Study Dent, 66-, sr mem staff, 70-; consult, Dent Res Panel, Gen Elec Co, 63-; vis surgeon, Dept Dent, Boston City Hosp, 64-; grants, Robert Wood Johnson Found, 73-74 & 76-77, Nat Inst Dent Res, Off Collab Res, 73-75, Merril Richardson Co, 75-77 & Johnson & Johnson Co, 78; mem, Am Dent Asn Clin Cleansing Comt, 74-; mem, Mass Bd Dent Adv Comt, 78-; fel, Int Col Dent & Am Acad Dent Sci; lectr periodont, Harvard Sch Dent Med, 80. *Mem:* Fel AAAS; fel Am Col Dent; Am Dent Asn; Am Acad Oral Med; Am Acad Periodont. *Res:* Assessment of periodontal disease and evaluation of the effectiveness of therapeutic methods of treatment of periodontal disease; analytical methods for chemical analysis. *Mailing Add:* Forsyth Dent Ctr 140 Fenway Boston MA 02115

LOBER, PAUL HALLAM, b Minneapolis, Minn, Sept 25, 19. PATHOLOGY. *Educ:* Univ Minn, Minneapolis, BS, 42, MD, 44, PhD(path), 51; Am Bd Path, dipl, 52. *Prof Exp:* Mem fac, 51-60, surg pathologist, Univ Hosps, 51-74, PROF PATH, MED SCH, UNIV MINN, MINNEAPOLIS, 60-; SURG PATHOLOGIST, ABBOTT-NORTHWESTERN HOSP, 74- *Mem:* Am Soc Cytol; fel Am Col Path; Am Asn Pathologists; Int Acad Path; Am Soc Clin Path. *Res:* Coronary heart disease. *Mailing Add:* Abbott-Northwestern Hosp 800 E 28th St Minneapolis MN 55407

LOBKOWICZ, FREDERICK, b Prague, Czech, Nov 17, 32; US citizen; m 60; c 2. ELEMENTARY PARTICLE PHYSICS. *Educ:* Swiss Fed Inst Technol, 55, PhD(physics), 60. *Prof Exp:* Res assoc, 60-64, from asst prof to assoc prof, 64-73, PROF PHYSICS, UNIV ROCHESTER, 73- *Concurrent Pos:* Humboldt Found sr fel, 73-74; vis prof, Univ Munich, Ger, 73-74. *Mem:* Am Phys Soc; Swiss Phys Soc. *Res:* Muon and photon interactions. *Mailing Add:* Dept Physics & Astron Univ Rochester Rochester NY 14627

LOBL, RICHARD TOLSTOI, b Washington, DC, Sept 27, 42; m 63; c 2. ANATOMY, ENDOCRINE PHYSIOLOGY. *Educ:* George Washington Univ, AB, 64; Ind Univ, Indianapolis, MS, 66; Univ Calif, Los Angeles, PhD(anat), 70. *Prof Exp:* asst prof anat, Health Ctr, Univ Conn, 70-76; ASSOC PROF BIOMED SCI, UNIV CALIF, RIVERSIDE, 76- *Mem:* AAAS; Soc Study Reproduction; Int Soc Psychoneuroendocrinol; Am Asn Anatomists; Sigma Xi. *Res:* Neuroendocrinology of reproduction; sexual differentiation; uptake, intracellular transport and metabolic effects of steroid sex hormones. *Mailing Add:* Div of Biomed Sci Univ of Calif Riverside CA 92521

LOBL, THOMAS JAY, b Danville, Va, Oct 20, 44; m 68; c 2. PHARMACEUTICAL CHEMISTRY, REPRODUCTIVE PHYSIOLOGY. *Educ:* Univ NC, Chapel Hill, BS, 66; Johns Hopkins Univ, PhD(org chem), 70. *Prof Exp:* Res fel biochem, Calif Inst Technol, 70-73; RES ASSOC CHEM & BIOCHEM, UPJOHN CO, 73- *Mem:* Am Chem Soc; AAAS; Sigma Xi; Am Soc Andrology; Int Soc Andrology. *Res:* Regulation of male reproduction; spermatogenesis; epididymal function; hormone transport and receptor proteins; male contraception; chemical and biological deaminations; heterocyclic and steroid synthesis; reproductive physiology. *Mailing Add:* Fertil Res Upjohn Co Kalamazoo MI 49001

LOBO, ANGELO PETER, b Masindi, Uganda, May 19, 39; m 67; c 2. BIO-ORGANIC CHEMISTRY. *Educ:* Univ Bombay, BSc, 58; Univ Ind, Bloomington, PhD(org chem), 66. *Prof Exp:* Rockefeller Found spec lectr org chem, Makerere Univ Col, Univ Uganda, 66-68; res asst chem, Rensselaer Polytech Inst, 68-70; SR RES SCIENTIST, DIV LABS & RES, NY STATE DEPT HEALTH, 70- *Mem:* Am Chem Soc. *Res:* Active site studies of thrombin and other blood coagulation factors through the use of simple substrates and inhibitors. *Mailing Add:* Div of Labs & Res NY State Dept of Health Albany NY 12201

LOBO, CECIL T(HOMAS), b Mangalore, India, Sept 22, 34. CIVIL ENGINEERING. *Educ:* Gujarat Univ, India, BE, 55; Univ Notre Dame, MS, 60; Purdue Univ, PhD(civil eng), 66. *Prof Exp:* Asst engr, Shah Construct Co, Ltd, India, 56-57; from instr to asst prof, 63-67, assoc prof, 67-71, actg chmn dept, 71-72, PROF CIVIL ENG, ROSE-HULMAN INST TECHNOL, 71- *Concurrent Pos:* Consult, Universal Tank & Iron Works, Inc, Ind. *Mem:* Assoc Am Soc Civil Engrs; Am Soc Eng Educ. *Res:* Structural and soil mechanics. *Mailing Add:* Dept of Civil Eng Rose-Hulman Inst of Technol Terre Haute IN 47803

LOBO, FRANCIS X, b Aden, UAR, Oct 8, 25; US citizen; m 60; c 3. MICROBIOLOGY. *Educ:* Univ Bombay, BS, 47, MS, 50; Inst Divi Thomae, PhD(exp med, biol), 59; Nat Registry Microbiol, cert. *Prof Exp:* Technician, Path Dept, Worli Gen Hosp, India, 50; control & res microbiologist-chemist, Chemo Pharma Labs Ltd, Worli, Bombay, 50-57; assoc prof sci, 60-70, chmn dept biol, 70-74, PROF BIOL SCI, MARYWOOD COL, 70- *Concurrent Pos:* Consult, Radio Corp Am, 65-; NSF grant, Argonne Nat Lab, 66, resident res assoc, 68-69; fac res partic, Argonne Nat Lab, 67 & St Jude Children Res Hosp, Memphis, Tenn, 70; mem eval team, Pa Dept Educ, 71. *Mem:* Am Soc Microbiol; NY Acad Sci. *Res:* Intestinal microorganisms by enrichment culture techniques; citric acid from a cane-sugar molasses; beef brain extract in controlling staphylococcus infections; etiology of sludge formation in industrial wastes. *Mailing Add:* Dept of Biol Marywood Col Scranton PA 18509

LOBO, PAUL A(LLAN), b La Cumbre, Colombia, Oct 10, 28. CHEMICAL ENGINEERING. *Educ:* Mass Inst Technol, SB, 50, SM, 51; Univ Mich, PhD(chem eng), 55. *Prof Exp:* Supvr process develop sect, Petrochem Res Div, Continental Oil Co, Okla, 55-63, European rep, Res Dept, Holland, 63-64, petrolchem coord, Continental Oil Co, Ltd, Eng, 64-65, exec asst to pres, NY, 65-67, mgr develop, Petrochem Dept, 67-68; vpres & gen mgr, Pitt-Consol Chem Co, 68-70; dir bus develop & planning, Tenneco Chem Inc, Piscataway, 71-73, dir, Tech Group, 73-75, dir corp planning, Saddle Brook, NJ, 75-80, VPRES PLANNING, TENNECO CHEM INC, PISCATAWAY, NJ, 80- *Concurrent Pos:* Lectr, Univ Okla, 56-63. *Mem:* Am Chem Soc; Nat Soc Prof Engrs; Am Inst Chem Engrs. *Res:* High pressure; petrochemical process development; reaction kinetics. *Mailing Add:* 20 Woodcliff Lake Rd Saddle River NJ 07458

LOBO, WALTER E(DER), b Brooklyn, NY, Mar 29, 05; m 28; c 5. CHEMICAL ENGINEERING. *Educ:* Mass Inst Technol, BS, 26 & La State Univ, 26. *Prof Exp:* Chief chemist, Cent Agabama Formneto, Cuba, 27; chief chemist & factory supt, Ingenio Manuelita, Palmira, Colombia, 28-29; asst job engr, M W Kellogg Co Div, Pullman Inc NJ, 29-30, chem engr, NY, 30-33, process engr, 33-38, dir, Chem Eng Dept, 38-57; CONSULT CHEM ENGR, 57- *Concurrent Pos:* Lectr, Columbia Univ, 47-49; pres, United Eng Trustees, 65-67. *Honors & Awards:* Founders Award, Am Inst Chem Engrs, 70. *Mem:* AAAS; Am Soc Mech Engrs; Soc Chem Indust; Nat Soc Prof Engrs; Am Inst Chem Engrs. *Res:* Petroleum; petrochemical and chemical processing; furnace design; heat transfer; fluid flow. *Mailing Add:* 497 Lost District Dr New Canaan CT 06840

LOBSTEIN, OTTO ERVIN, b Czech, Apr 12, 22; nat US; m 52; c 3. CLINICAL BIOCHEMISTRY. *Educ:* Univ London, BSc, 45; Smae Inst, Eng, MSF, 45; Northwestern Univ, PhD(biochem), 52; Am Bd Clin Chem, dipl, 55. *Prof Exp:* Asst res chemist, Howards & Sons, Ltd, Eng, 42-46; biochemist, Elgin State Hosp, Ill, 47-48; instr chem, Wesley & Passavant Mem Hosps, Ill, 49-51; res assoc zool, Univ Southern Calif, 52-53; med dir res, Chemtech Labs, 52-62; biochemist-owner, Lobstein Biochem Lab, Calif, 62-64; asst prof chem, Loyola Univ, Calif, 64-65; head biochem dept, St Elizabeth Hosp Med Ctr, 65-76; DIR CLIN CHEM, MT SINAI HOSP MED CTR, 76- *Concurrent Pos:* Vis res prof, Univ Redlands, 59-65; secy-treas, Res Found Diseases Eye, 59-65; vis assoc prof, Purdue Univ, 68-73, adj prof, 65-76; prof biochem & path, Rush Presby St Lukes Med Ctr, Chicago, 76- *Mem:* Fel AAAS; Am Soc Microbiol; sr mem Am Chem Soc; fel Am Asn Clin Chem (secy, 81-83). *Res:* Biochemical investigation of the crystalline lens of the eye, protein structure and constitution in normal and in cataract lenses of the human and other species; changes in protein with a changed electrolyte environment; clinical investigation of lysozyme in carcinomatosis. *Mailing Add:* Dept of Path Mt Sinai Hosp Med Ctr Chicago IL 60608

LOBUE, JOSEPH, b Union City, NJ, Apr 19, 34; m 59; c 3. PHYSIOLOGY, HEMATOLOGY. *Educ:* St Peter's Col, NJ, BS, 55; Marquette Univ, MS, 57; NY Univ, PhD(physiol), 62. *Prof Exp:* From asst prof to assoc prof, 62-71, PROF BIOL, NY UNIV, 71-, CO-DIR, A S GORDON LAB EXP HEMAT, 67- *Concurrent Pos:* NIH fel, 62; Sigma Xi grant-in-aid, 64-65; Am Cancer Soc grant, 65-66; Nat Cancer Inst grant, 71-73, 75-78 & 79-81; Nat Leukemia Asn grant, 74-76; assoc, Danforth Found, 68-; co-dir, Hemat Training Prog, NIH, 65-75. *Honors & Awards:* Christian R & Mary F Lindback Found Award, NY Univ, 65. *Mem:* AAAS; Soc Exp Biol & Med; Am Asn Anat; Harvey Soc; Am Soc Hemat. *Res:* Mechanisms controlling leukocyte and erythrocyte production and release; pathophysiology and cytokinetics of rodent and avian leukemias. *Mailing Add:* A S Gordon Lab of Exp Hemat NY Univ New York NY 10003

LOBUGLIO, ALBERT FRANCIS, b Buffalo, NY, Feb 1, 38; m 62; c 5. HEMATOLOGY, IMMUNOLOGY. *Educ:* Georgetown Univ, MD, 62. *Prof Exp:* Intern med, Presby Univ Hosp, Pittsburgh, 62-63, resident, 63-65; instr, State Univ NY Buffalo, 67-68, asst prof, 68-69; assoc prof med, Ohio State Univ, 69-73, prof, 73-78; PROF MED, UNIV MICH, 78- *Concurrent Pos:* Hemat fel, Thorndike Mem Lab, Boston City Hosp, 65-67; hemat consult, Vet Admin Hosp, Buffalo, 67-69 & Dayton, Ohio, 69- *Mem:* Am Fedn Clin Res; Am Soc Hemat; Am Soc Clin Invest. *Res:* Tumor immunology; transplant immunology; human macrophage and lymphocyte functions. *Mailing Add:* 102 Observatory Rd Med Ctr Univ Mich Ann Arbor MI 48109

LOBUNEZ, WALTER, b Ukraine, Nov 22, 20; nat US; m 45; c 1. INDUSTRIAL CHEMISTRY. *Educ:* Univ Pa, MS, 52, PhD(chem), 54. *Prof Exp:* Res assoc immunol, Jefferson Med Col, 54-55; protein chem, Children's Hosp, Univ Penn, 55-59; sr scientist chem, Textile Res Inst, 59-60; res chemist, 60-67, sr res chemist 67-80, RES ASSOC, FMC CORP, 67- *Mem:* Am Chem Soc; Am Inst Chemists. *Res:* Chemistry of hydrocarbons; protein chemistry; chemistry of cellulose; soda ash processes; Ba and Sr processes. *Mailing Add:* 562 Ewing St Princeton NJ 08540

LOCALIO, S ARTHUR, b New York, NY, Oct 4, 11; m 45; c 4. SURGERY. *Educ:* Cornell Univ, AB, 33; Univ Rochester, MD, 36; Columbia Univ, DSc(med), 42; Am Bd Surg, dipl, 45. *Prof Exp:* From instr to assoc prof surg, 45-53, prof clin surg, 53-71, PROF SURG, MED SCH, NY UNIV, 71- *Concurrent Pos:* Consult, Riverview Hosp, Red Bank, NJ, 52, Monmouth Mem Hosp, Long Branch, NJ, 52 & St Barnabas Hosp, New York, 58; asst surgeon, Univ Hosp, 45-47, assoc attend surgeon, 47-49, assoc attend surgeon, 49-52, attend surgeon, 52-, clin asst vis surgeon, 49-52, vis surgeon, 52-; Johnson & Johnson distinguished prof surg, NY Univ, 72. *Mem:* AMA; Am Asn Surg of Trauma; Am Gastroenterol Asn; Am Col Surg; Am Surg Asn. *Res:* Wound healing; surgery of gastro-intestinal disease. *Mailing Add:* Dept of Surg New York Univ Sch of Med New York NY 10016

LOCASCIO, SALVADORE J, b Hammond, La, Oct 29, 33; m 54; c 3. HORTICULTURE. *Educ:* Southeastern La Col, BS, 55; La State Univ, MS, 56; Purdue Univ, PhD(plant physiol), 59. *Prof Exp:* Asst prof, 59-65, assoc horticulturist, 65-69, ASSOC PROF HORT, DEPT VEG CROPS, UNIV FLA, 65-, HORTICULTURIST, 69- *Mem:* AAAS; Weed Sci Soc Am; Sigma Xi; Am Soc Hort Sci. *Res:* Fertilizer and water requirements of vegetables; strawberry culture; chemical weed control for vegetables; teaching of commercial vegetable crops and vegetable crops nutrition. *Mailing Add:* Dept Veg Crops 1245 HS/PP Bldg Univ of Fla Gainesville FL 32611

LOCHHEAD, JOHN HUTCHISON, b Montreal, Que, Aug 7, 09; nat US; m 38; c 2. INVERTEBRATE ZOOLOGY. *Educ:* Univ St Andrew's, MA, 30; Cambridge Univ, BA, 32, Bachelor scholar, 33, PhD(zool), 37. *Prof Exp:* With Cambridge Univ Table, Marine Zool Sta, Naples, 34-35; sr cur, Mus Zool, Cambridge Univ, 35-38, instr zool, 36-38; fel by courtesy, Johns Hopkins Univ, 40; asst biologist, Va Fisheries Lab, 41-42; from instr to prof, 42-75, EMER PROF ZOOL, UNIV VT, 75- *Concurrent Pos:* Lectr, Col William & Mary, 41-42; instr, Woods Hole Marine Biol Lab, 43-55, mem corp, 44- *Mem:* Am Soc Zool. *Res:* Anatomy and physiology of Crustacea including their feeding mechanisms, locomotion, factors controlling swimming positions, responses to light, functions for the blood and related tissues, molting and reproduction. *Mailing Add:* 49 Woodlawn Rd London SW6 England United Kingdom

LOCHMAN-BALK, CHRISTINA, b Springfield, Ill, Oct 8, 07; m 47. INVERTEBRATE PALEONTOLOGY, STRATIGRAPHY. *Educ:* Smith Col, AB, 29, AM, 31; Johns Hopkins Univ, PhD(geol), 33. *Prof Exp:* Asst geol, Smith Col, 29-31; Nat Res Coun grant, 34; from instr to assoc prof, Mt Holyoke Col, 35-47; lectr phys sci, Univ Chicago, 47; lectr life sci, NMex Inst Min & Tech, 54; stratig geologist, State Bur Mines & Mineral Resources, 55-57; prof geol, 57-72, EMER PROF GEOL, NMEX INST MINING & TECHNOL, 72- *Concurrent Pos:* Am Geol Soc Am grants, 36 & 47; NSF grant, 59. *Mem:* Fel AAAS; Paleont Soc; fel Geol Soc Am; Nat Asn Geol Teachers. *Res:* Cambrian paleontology and stratigraphy of the United States. *Mailing Add:* PO Box 1421 Socorro NM 87801

LOCHMÜLLER, CHARLES HOWARD, b New York, NY, May 4, 40; m 63; c 3. ANALYTICAL CHEMISTRY. *Educ:* Manhattan Col, BS, 62; Fordham Univ, MS, 64, PhD(anal chem), 68. *Prof Exp:* Asst prof, 69-74, ASSOC PROF CHEM, DUKE UNIV, 74- *Concurrent Pos:* Assoc, Purdue Univ, 67-69. *Mem:* Am Chem Soc. *Res:* Factors effecting separation processes; nuclear magnetic resonance spectroscopy. *Mailing Add:* P M Gross Chem Lab Duke Univ Durham NC 27706

LOCHNER, JANIS ELIZABETH, b Bethesda, Md, Nov 27, 54. MEMBRANE BIOCHEMISTRY, CELLULAR COMMUNICATION. *Educ:* Allegheny Col, BS, 76; Univ Ore, PhD(biochem), 81. *Prof Exp:* RES FEL BIOCHEM, ORE HEALTH SCI UNIV, 81-; ASST PROF CHEM, LEWIS & CLARK COL, 81- *Mem:* AAAS. *Res:* Role of the plasma membrane in cellular communication; mechanisms of membrane transduction. *Mailing Add:* Dept Chem Lewis & Clark Col Portland OR 97219

LOCHNER, ROBERT HERMAN, b Madison, Wis, Apr 17, 39; m 62; c 4. STATISTICS. *Educ:* Univ Wis-Madison, BS, 61, MS, 62 & 66, PhD(statist), 69. *Prof Exp:* Math analyst, A C Electronics Div, Gen Motors Corp, 62-65; asst prof, 68-74, ASSOC PROF STATIST & MATH, MARQUETTE UNIV, 74- *Mem:* Am Statist Asn; Inst Math Statist. *Res:* Statistical methods in reliability and life testing; Bayesian inference. *Mailing Add:* Dept Math Statist & Comp Sci Marquette Univ Milwaukee WI 53233

LOCHSTET, WILLIAM A, b Port Jefferson, NY, Dec 5, 36; m 65; c 2. PHYSICS. *Educ:* Univ Rochester, BS, 57, MA, 60; Univ Pa, PhD(physics), 65. *Prof Exp:* Instr, 65-66, ASST PROF PHYSICS, PA STATE UNIV, 66- *Mem:* Am Phys Soc; AAAS. *Mailing Add:* Dept of Physics Pa State Univ University Park PA 16802

LOCICERO, JOSEPH CASTELLI, b Ontario Center, NY; m 37; c 2. ORGANIC CHEMISTRY. *Educ:* Univ Rochester, BA, 36; Pa State Univ, MS, 47, PhD(biochem), 48. *Prof Exp:* Chemist, Hooker Electrochem Co, NY, 37-43; sr res chemist, Nuodex Prods Co, NJ, 43-45; res chemist, Rohm and Haas Co, 48-52, sr scientist, 52-71; asst prof, 71-72, assoc prof, 72-77, PROF CHEM, CAMDEN COUNTY COL, 77- *Mem:* AAAS; Am Chem Soc. *Res:* Plasticizers, fungicides and insecticides; high pressure reactions; detergents; process development; ion exchange; sugar technology; halogenation; plastics. *Mailing Add:* 625 Devon Rd Moorestown NJ 08057

LOCK, BRIAN EDWARD, b Yeovil, Eng, Mar 21, 44; m 68; c 3. SEDIMENTOLOGY. *Educ:* Cambridge Univ, BA, 66, PhD(geol), 69. *Hon Degrees:* MA, Cambridge Univ, 70. *Prof Exp:* Consult, Fina Petrol Co, Belg, 69-70; lectr, Rhodes Univ, SAfrica, 70-74, sr lectr, 75-77; assoc prof, 77-80, PROF GEOL, UNIV SOUTHWESTERN LA, 80- *Concurrent Pos:* Sr res assoc, Exeter Univ, Eng, 75-76; overseas res burser, Coun Sci & Indust Res, Pretoria, 75-76; consult basic appl geol, Superior Oil Co. *Mem:* Am Asn Petrol Geologists; Soc Econ Paleontologists & Mineralogists; Geol Soc Am; Int Asn Volcanology & Chemistry of the Earth's Interior; Int Asn Sedimentologists. *Res:* Sedimentology of carbonate rocks; other aspects of sedimentology and stratigraphy; field work in South Africa, Ireland, Spitsbergen, Reunion Island, Canada and United States. *Mailing Add:* Dept of Geol Univ Southwestern La Lafayette LA 70504

LOCK, COLIN JAMES LYNE, b London, Eng, Oct 4, 33; m 60; c 2. PHYSICAL INORGANIC CHEMISTRY, CRYSTALLOGRAPHY. *Educ:* Univ London, BSc, 54, PhD(inorg chem) & DIC, 63. *Prof Exp:* Asst exp officer reactor chem, Atomic Energy Res Estab, Eng, 54-57, sci officer, 60; develop chem, Atomic Energy Can Lab, Chalk River, 57-60; asst lectr inorg chem, Imp Col, London, 61-63; from asst prof to assoc prof, 63-73, PROF CHEM, MCMASTER UNIV, 73- *Mem:* Fel Chem Inst Can; Royal Soc Chem. *Res:* physical methods of structure determination for heavy transition metal compounds; platinum anti-cancer drugs, technetium radiopharmaceuticals; gold anti-arthritic agents; structures of carbenium ions. *Mailing Add:* Inst for Mat Res McMaster Univ Hamilton ON L8S 4M1 Can

LOCK, G(ERALD) S(EYMOUR) H(UNTER), b London, Eng, June 30, 35; m 59; c 3. MECHANICAL ENGINEERING. *Educ:* Univ Durham, BSc, 59, PhD(mech eng), 62. *Prof Exp:* From asst prof to assoc prof, 62-70, PROF MECH ENG, UNIV ALBERTA, 70- *Concurrent Pos:* Chmn comt heat transfer, Nat Res Coun Can. *Honors & Awards:* Queen Elizabeth Silver Jubilee Medal. *Mem:* Am Soc Mech Engrs; fel Eng Inst Can; Can Soc Mech Engrs. *Res:* Biomedical engineering; heat transfer, especially ice engineering; technology assessment. *Mailing Add:* Dept of Mech Eng Univ of Alberta Edmonton AB T6G 2E8 Can

LOCK, JAMES ALBERT, b Cleveland, Ohio, Feb 12, 48; m 72. THEORETICAL NUCLEAR PHYSICS. *Educ:* Case Western Reserve Univ, BS, 70, MS, 73, PhD(physics), 74. *Prof Exp:* Lectr, Case Western Reserve Univ, 70-74, res assoc physics, 74-78; ASST PROF DEPT PHYSICS, CLEVELAND STATE UNIV, 78- *Mem:* Sigma Xi. *Res:* Meson exchange currents; three-pion systems; composite relativistic systems. *Mailing Add:* Dept of Physics Cleveland State Univ Cleveland OH 44115

LOCK, KENNETH, b Wushi, China, Mar 15, 32; m 54; c 4. ELECTRICAL ENGINEERING, COMPUTER SCIENCE. *Educ:* Battersea Polytech Inst, BSc, 55; Univ London, MSc, 57; Calif Inst Technol, PhD(elec eng, physics), 62. *Prof Exp:* From instr to asst prof elec eng, Calif Inst Technol, 59-65; advan programmer, Int Bus Mach Corp, 65-67, vis fel, 67-69; pres, Cyber Data, Inc, Calif, 69-71; mgr design automation, Burroughs Corp, 71-77, dept mgr, MCO div, 77-80; PRES, CYBERTEC, 80- *Concurrent Pos:* Consult, Jet Propulsion Lab, 62-65. *Mem:* Inst Elec & Electronics Engrs; Asn Comput Mach. *Res:* Physical systems on computers; network analysis; switching theory; programming system research; computer design; interactive use of computers in engineering, science and business. *Mailing Add:* Cybertec 367 Bird Rock Ave La Jolla CA 92037

LOCKARD, ISABEL, b Brandon, Man, June 27, 15. ANATOMY. *Educ:* Northwestern Univ, BS, 38; Univ Mich, MA, 42, PhD(anat), 46. *Prof Exp:* Asst anat, Univ Mich, 42-44 & 47; instr, Univ Pittsburgh, 44-45; instr, Sch Med Georgetown Univ, 47-49, asst prof, 49-52; from asst prof to assoc prof, 52-69, PROF ANAT, MED UNIV SC, 69- *Mem:* Am Asn Anatomists; Sigma Xi; Cajal Club. *Res:* Neuroanatomy; blood supply of central nervous system. *Mailing Add:* Dept of Anat Med Univ of SC Charleston SC 29425

LOCKARD, J DAVID, b Renovo, Pa, Dec 20, 29; m 51; c 4. BOTANY, SCIENCE EDUCATION. *Educ:* Pa State Univ, BS, 51, MEd, 55; PhD(bot), 62. *Prof Exp:* Dept chmn sci dept high sch, Pa, 53-56; consult sci teaching improvement prog, AAAS, 56-58; asst bot, Pa State Univ, 58-61; from asst prof to assoc prof, 61-70, PROF BOT & SCI EDUC, UNIV MD, COLLEGE PARK, 70-, DIR SCI TEACHING CTR, 62- *Concurrent Pos:* NSF-AAAS grant, Develop & Maintain Int Clearinghouse Sci & Math Curric Develops, 62-; dir off bio educ, Am Inst Biol Sci, 66-67; dir, NSF-AID Study Improvision Sci Teaching Mat Worldwide, 68-72; NSF grants, acad year inst sci supvrs, 69-73; dir NSF Impact Study, 74-75; rep, US Nat Comn to UNESCO, 75- *Honors & Awards:* Distinguished Serv to Sci Ed Award, Nat Sci Teacher's Asn, 74. *Mem:* AAAS (vpres, 71); Am Soc Plant Physiol; Int Coun Asn Sci Educ (pres, 73-76); Nat Asn Res Sci Teaching (pres, 72-73); Nat Sci Teachers Asn. *Res:* Investigating physiology of fungi and fruiting mechanism; improving science teaching techniques and equipment; studying science and math curriculum developments internationally; consulting in science education; science writing. *Mailing Add:* Sci Teaching Ctr Univ of Md College Park MD 20742

LOCKARD, RAYMOND G, b Patricia, Alta, Jan 1, 25; m 51; c 3. PLANT PHYSIOLOGY. *Educ:* Univ BC, BSA, 49; Univ Idaho, MSc, 51; Univ London, PhD, 56. *Prof Exp:* Plant physiologist, Can For Aid, Malaysia, 54-59, Ghana, 59-64; tech expert, Food & Agr Orgn, Philippines, 64-67; assoc prof hort, Univ Ky, 67-72, prof, 72-81; PROF CROP SCI, LA STATE UNIV, 81-; CROP SCI COORDR, USAID PROG, CENT AGR RES INST, LIBERIA, 81- *Mem:* Am Soc Plant Physiol; Am Soc Hort Sci; Can Soc Plant Physiol. *Res:* Dwarfing mechanisms in plants. *Mailing Add:* USAID PO Box 1445 Monrovia Liberia

LOCKARD, ROBERT BRUCE, ethology, deceased

LOCKART, ROYCE ZENO, JR, b Marshfield, Ore, Sept 7, 28; m 51; c 3. MICROBIOLOGY. *Educ:* Whitman Col, AB, 50; Univ Wash, MS, 53, PhD(microbiol), 57. *Prof Exp:* Res fel, Nat Inst Allergy & Infectious Dis, 57-58, bacteriologist, Radiation Br, Nat Cancer Inst, 58-60; from asst prof to assoc prof microbiol, Univ Tex, 60-66; res supvr, 66-80, BIOLOGIST, E I DU PONT DE NEMOURS & CO, INC, 80- *Mem:* Am Soc Microbiol; Brit Soc Gen Microbiol. *Res:* Virus cell interactions, particularly animal viruses and their control by natural means and by chemicals; image analysis of immunological cells. *Mailing Add:* E I du Pont de Nemours & Co Inc Wilmington DE 19898

LOCKE, BEN ZION, b New York, NY, Sept 8, 21; m 47; c 4. APPLIED STATISTICS, EPIDEMIOLOGY. *Educ:* Brooklyn Col, AB, 47; Columbia Univ, MS, 49. *Prof Exp:* Statistician, NY State Health Dept, 47-56; chief consult sect, Biomet Br, NIMH, 56-66; assoc prof eval & dir res & eval, Community Ment Health Ctr, Temple Univ, 66-67; asst chief, 67-75, CHIEF CTR EPIDEMIOL STUDIES, NIMH, 75- *Mem:* AAAS; Fel Am Pub Health Asn; Am Statist Asn; Soc Epidemiol Res. *Res:* Epidemiology of mental disorders; evaluation of programs designed to prevent and control mental disorders and promote mental health. *Mailing Add:* Ctr Epidemiol Studies NIMH Rm 18C05 5600 Fishers Lane Rockville MD 20857

LOCKE, CARL EDWIN, JR, b Palo Pinto Co, Tex, Jan 11, 36; m 56; c 2. CORROSION, POLYMER SCIENCE. *Educ:* Univ Tex, Austin, BS, 58, MS, 60, PhD(chem eng), 72. *Prof Exp:* Res engr, Continental Oil Co, 59-65; prod engr, R L Stone Co, 65-66; prog res engr, Tracor Inc, 66-68; instr & vis asst prof, Univ Tex, 71-73; asst prof, 73-76, assoc prof, 76-80, PROF & DIR CHEM ENG & MAT SCI, UNIV OKLA, 80- *Concurrent Pos:* Proj dir, & Okla Dept Transp, 75, 76-79. *Mem:* Am Inst Chem Engrs; Nat Asn Corrosion Engrs; Am Chem Soc; Electrochem Soc; Soc Plastics Engrs. *Res:* Polymers: polymer concrete, graft copolymers, polymer blends; corrosion; corrosion in concrete, passivity. *Mailing Add:* 202 W Boyd Rm 23 Univ Okla Norman OK 73019

LOCKE, CHARLES STEPHEN, b Murfreesboro, Tenn, Dec 6, 42; m 67. STATISTICS. *Educ:* David Lipscomb Col, BA, 64; Ohio State Univ, MS, 67, PhD(statist), 73. *Prof Exp:* Instr math, Mid Tenn State Univ, 67-69; asst prof math & comput sci, Univ SC, 73-77; SR BIOMETRICIAN, COMPUT & STATIST OPERS, PENNWALT PHARMACEUT DIV, 77- *Mem:* Inst Math Statist; Am Statist Asn. *Res:* Tests of goodness of fit for composite hypotheses, including tests of normality; nonparametric statistics; linear statistical models. *Mailing Add:* Comput & Statist Opers 755 Jefferson Rd Rochester NY 14623

LOCKE, DAVID CREIGHTON, b Garden City, NY, Mar 1, 39; m 62. CHEMISTRY. *Educ:* Lafayette Col, BS, 61; Kans State Univ, PhD(chem), 65. *Prof Exp:* Res chemist, Esso Res & Eng Co, 65-67; NSF fel, Univ Col Swansea, Univ Wales, 67-68; asst prof, 68-72, assoc prof, 72-76, PROF CHEM, QUEENS COL, NY, 76- *Mem:* AAAS; Am Chem Soc; Int Inst Conserv Hist & Artistic Works; NY Acad Sci. *Res:* Analytical chemistry; chemical separations; air pollution monitoring; chemistry of art conservation; organic compounds in water and wastewater. *Mailing Add:* Dept of Chem Queens Col Flushing NY 11367

LOCKE, HAROLD OGDEN, b Camden, NJ, Sept 14, 31; m 59; c 2. PHYSICAL CHEMISTRY, ANALYTICAL CHEMISTRY. *Educ:* Wesleyan Univ, BA, 53, MA, 56; Rutgers Univ, PhD(chem), 62. *Prof Exp:* Res chemist, Armstrong Cork Co, 61-65; ANAL CHEMIST, GAF CORP, 65- *Mem:* Am Chem Soc. *Res:* X-ray crystallography; polymer characterization; surfactants. *Mailing Add:* 816 Prince St Easton PA 18042

LOCKE, JACK LAMBOURNE, b Brantford, Ont, May 1, 21; m 46; c 2. PHYSICS. *Educ:* Univ Toronto, BA, 46, MA, 47, PhD(physics), 49. *Prof Exp:* Demonstr physics, Univ Toronto, 45-47; astrophysicist, Dom Observ, 49-59, chief, Stellar Physics Div, 59-66; radio astronr, 66-70, assoc dir, Radio & Elec Eng Div & chief astrophys br, 70-75, DIR, HERZBERG INST ASTROPHYSICS, NAT RES COUN CAN, 75- *Concurrent Pos:* Officer-in-chg, Dom Radio Astrophys Observ, 59-62. *Mem:* Am Astron Soc; Can Astron Soc; Int Astron Union. *Res:* Astrophysics; radio astronomy; solar physics; molecular spectra; infrared spectrum of the atmosphere. *Mailing Add:* Herzberg Inst of Astrophysics Nat Res Coun of Can Ottawa ON K1A 0R6 Can

LOCKE, JOHN LAUDERDALE, b Oak Park, Ill, Nov 16, 40; m 77. SPEECH PATHOLOGY, PSYCHOLINGUSITICS. *Educ:* Ripon Col, BA, 63; Ohio Univ, MA, 65; PhD(speech path). 68. *Prof Exp:* Speech pathologist, Vet Admin Ctr, 68-69; prof, Univ Ill, Champaign, 69-80; PROF, DEPT HEARING & SPEECH SCI, UNIV MD, COLLEGE PARK, 80- *Concurrent Pos:* Res fel, Yale Univ, 72-73 & Oxford Univ, 73-74; res consult, Vet Admin Hosp, Danville, Ill, 74-80 & Ft Howard, Md, 80- *Mem:* Am Speech & Hearing Asn; Ling Soc Am; Am Asn Appl Ling. *Res:* Language acquisition and impairment; child phonology; reading and cognition of the deaf; aphasia; speech perception. *Mailing Add:* Dept Hearing & Speech Sci Univ Md College Park MD 20742

LOCKE, KRYSTYNA KOPACZYK, b Warsaw, Poland, Dec 2, 26; m 70. BIOCHEMISTRY, ENZYMOLOGY. *Educ:* Wayne State Univ, BS, 53; Western Reserve Univ, MS, 56; Univ Ill, Champaign-Urbana, PhD(lipid chem), 62. *Prof Exp:* Res nutritionist, atherosclerosis res proj, VA Hosp, Downey, Ill, 56-58; Nat Inst Neurol Diseases & Blindness fel biochem, Ment Health Res Inst, Univ Mich, Ann Arbor, 62-64; trainee, Inst Enzyme Res, Univ Wis-Madison, 64-66; proj assoc, 66-69; res biochem, Biochem Toxicol Br, Div Toxicol, Food & Drug Admin, 69-77; BIOCHEMIST TOXICOL BR, HAZARD EVAL DIV, OFF TOXIC SUBSTANCES, ENVIRON PROTECTION AGENCY, 77- *Mem:* NY Acad Sci; Am Chem Soc. *Res:* Effects of environmental agents on biochemistry and ultrastructure of mitochondria. *Mailing Add:* 9200 Beachway Lane Springfield VA 22153

LOCKE, LOUIS NOAH, b Stockton, Calif, Mar 14, 28; m 53; c 1. ANIMAL PATHOLOGY. *Educ:* Univ Calif, AB, 50, DVM, 56. *Prof Exp:* Vet, USPHS, 56-58; wildlife res biologist, Patuxent Wildlife Res Ctr, US Dept Interior, 58-60; histopathologist, 61-75; WILDLIFE PATHOLOGIST, NAT WILDLIFE HEALTH LAB, US FED WILDLIFE SERV, 75- *Mem:* Wildlife Soc; Am Asn Avian Path; Am Vet Med Asn; Wildlife Disease Asn; Soc Toxicol. *Res:* Wildlife diseases, especially diseases and parasites of the mourning doves, waterfowl; effects of pollutants upon wild birds; lead poisoning in migratory birds. *Mailing Add:* Nat Wildlife Health Lab 1655 Linden Dr Madison WI 53706

LOCKE, MICHAEL, b Nottingham, Eng, Feb 14, 29. INSECT PHYSIOLOGY. *Educ:* Cambridge Univ, BA, 52, MA, 55, PhD, 56, DSc, 76. *Prof Exp:* Lectr zool, Univ WIndies, 56; assoc prof biol, Case Western Reserve Univ, 61-67; prof biol, 67-71; PROF ZOOL & CHMN DEPT, UNIV WESTERN ONT, 71- *Concurrent Pos:* Ed, Soc Develop Biol, 62-69; Raman prof, Univ Madras, 69. *Mem:* AAAS; Am Soc Cell Biol; fel Royal Soc Chem. *Res:* Coordination of growth in insects; insect cell development; insect morphogenesis. *Mailing Add:* Dept of Zool Univ of Western Ont London ON N6A 5B7 Can

LOCKE, PHILIP M, b Rockford, Ill, July 12, 37; m 61; c 2. MATHEMATICS. *Educ:* Bluffton Col, BS, 59; Univ NH, MS, 64, PhD(math), 67. *Prof Exp:* Asst prof math, Mont State Univ, 67-68; asst prof, 68-74, ASSOC PROF MATH, UNIV MAINE, ORONO, 74- *Mem:* Math Asn Am. *Res:* Ordinary differential equations. *Mailing Add:* Dept of Math Univ of Maine Orono ME 04473

LOCKE, RAYMOND KENNETH, b Terre Haute, Ind, July 2, 40; m 70. BIOCHEMISTRY, TOXICOLOGY. *Educ:* Wash Univ, BS, 65. *Prof Exp:* Res asst biochem, Univ Tex, Dallas, 66-67; res chemist, Div Nutrit, Food & Drug Admin, 68-69, Biochem & Metab Sect, Div Pesticides, 69-71 & Metab Br, Div Toxicol, 71-73, res chemist, Biochem Toxicol Br, 73-77, chemist, Contaminants & Natural Toxicants Eval Br, Div toxicol, 77-79; CHEMIST, OFF TOXIC SUBSTANCES, US ENVIRON PROTECTION AGENCY, 79- *Mem:* AAAS; Am Chem Soc; Tissue Cult Asn; NY Acad Sci. *Res:* Biochemical studies of the comparative in vivo and in vitro metabolism of foreign compounds by animals, plants and man. *Mailing Add:* 9200 Beachway Lane Springfield VA 22153

LOCKE, ROBERT F, b Washington, DC, July 16, 18; m 43; c 6. IMMUNOPATHOLOGY. *Educ:* Tex A&M Univ, DVM, 42; Univ Mich, MPH, 48; Univ Ill, PhD(immunol), 63; Am Col Lab Animal Med, dipl, 64. *Prof Exp:* Immunologist, USDA, 48-51; health officer, State Md, 51-60; NIH fel immunol, Univ Ill, 60-63; chief res lab animal med, sci & tech, Vet Admin Hosp, Hines, 63-67, part-time chief, 67; adminr, Med Res Lab, Univ Ill Med Ctr, 67-77, assoc prof environ health sci, Sch Pub Health, 71-77; RETIRED. *Concurrent Pos:* Consult & assoc prof, Col Med, Univ Ill, 64-; Grad Sch, Loyola Univ, Ill, 65-; assoc prof, Stritch Sch Med, 67-; vis prof, Rush-Presby-St Lukes Med Sch; chief, Res Lab Animal, Sci & Tech, West Side Vet Admin Hosp, 68- *Mem:* AAAS; Am Pub Health Asn; Am Asn Lab Animal Sci; Nat Soc Med Res. *Res:* Determinations of molecular parameters of immune globulins; intensive study of autoimmune diseases and developing concepts of antibody formation. *Mailing Add:* 1853 W Polk St Chicago IL 60612

LOCKE, STANLEY, b New York City, NY, June 18, 34; m 58; c 3. MATHEMATICS, PHYSICS. *Educ:* NY Univ, BME, 55, MS, 57, PhD(math), 60. *Prof Exp:* Res mathematician, Repub Aviation Corp, 59-60; sr res mathematician, 60-65, MEM SCIENTIFIC STAFF, SCHLUMBERGER-DOLL RES CTR, 65- *Mem:* Am Nuclear Soc; Am Phys Soc. *Res:* Oil field wire-line services. *Mailing Add:* 17 Deerwood Ct Norwalk CT 06851

LOCKE, WILLIAM, b Morden, Man, Mar 16, 16; m 45. INTERNAL MEDICINE. *Educ:* Univ Man, MD, 38; Univ Minn, MS, 47; McGill Univ, DTM, 45. *Prof Exp:* First asst med, Mayo Clin, 47-48; pres staff, 54-55, head, Sect Endocrinol & Metab, 69-76, MEM STAFF, OCHSNER CLIN & FOUND HOSP, 50-, PARTNER, OCHSNER CLIN, 57-, TRUSTEE, ALTON OCHSNER MED FOUND, NEW ORLEANS, 78- *Concurrent Pos:* Nat Res Coun & Commonwealth Fund fel, Harvard Univ, 48-50; clin prof med, Sch Med, Tulane Univ, 69-; sr vis physician, Charity Hosp, New Orleans. *Mem:* AAAS; Endocrine Soc; Am Diabetes Asn; fel Am Col Physicians. *Res:* Metabolic diseases. *Mailing Add:* Ochsner Clin 1514 Jefferson Hwy New Orleans LA 70121

LOCKER, JOHN L, b Florence, Ala, Oct 11, 30; m 59; c 8. MATHEMATICS. *Educ:* Auburn Univ, PhD(math), 60. *Prof Exp:* Instr math, Auburn Univ, 56-59; mathematician, Redstone Arsenal, 54; assoc prof, 60-70, PROF MATH, UNIV OF NORTHERN ALA, 70- *Concurrent Pos:* Lectr, NSF-Ala Acad Sci Vis Sci Prog, 61-65. *Mem:* Math Asn Am; Nat Coun Teachers Math. *Res:* Statistics; geometry. *Mailing Add:* Dept of Math Univ of Northern Ala Florence AL 35630

LOCKETT, M CLODOVIA, b Austin, Tex, Jan 23, 13. BIOLOGY. *Educ:* St Louis Univ, BS, 37, PhD, 52; De Paul Univ, MS, 47. *Prof Exp:* Asst prof biol, LeClerc Col, 47-49; from assoc prof to prof & dir dept, Notre Dame Col, 49-65; PROF BIOL, UNIV DALLAS, 65-, CHMN DEPT, 68- *Concurrent Pos:* Fel, Univ Okla, 61. *Mem:* AAAS. *Res:* Effects of drugs on iodine metabolism in the thyroid; the exchange and growth potential of phosphorus in algae cultures. *Mailing Add:* Dept of Biol Univ of Dallas Irving TX 75061

LOCKEY, RICHARD FUNK, b Lancaster, Pa, Jan 15, 40; div; c 2. ALLERGY, IMMUNOLOGY. *Educ:* Haverford Col, BS, 61; Univ Mich, Ann Arbor, MS, 72; Temple Univ, MD, 65. *Prof Exp:* Fel allergy & clin immunol, Univ Mich, 69-70; asst prof, 73-77, ASSOC PROF INT MED, COL MED, UNIV S FLA, 77- *Concurrent Pos:* Asst chief, Div Allergy & Clin Immunol, Col Med, Univ SFla, Vet Admin Hosp, Tampa, 73- *Mem:* Fel Am Acad Allergy; fel Am Col Physicians; fel Am Col Chest Physicians. *Res:* hymenoptera antigenic specificity in relationship to human hypersensitivity; effect of red tale toxin on canine smooth muscle and in asthma; imported fire ant and human hypersensitivity; asthma treatment with new pharmaceutical agents. *Mailing Add:* Vet Admin Hosp Div Allergy & Immunol 13000 N 30th St Tampa FL 33612

LOCKHART, BENHAM EDWARD, b St Vincent, WI, Jan 18, 45; US citizen; m 70; c 2. PLANT PATHOLOGY, AGRICULTURE. *Educ:* Univ WI, Trinidad, BSc, 65; Univ Calif, Riverside, PhD(plant path), 69. *Prof Exp:* Res fels plant path, Univ Nebr, 69-70 & Univ Calif, Berkeley, 70-71; asst prof, Minn Proj, US AID, Rabat, Morocco, 71-76; asst prof, 76-80, ASSOC PROF PLANT PATH, UNIV MINN, ST PAUL, 80- *Mem:* Am Phytopath Soc; Am Soc Hort Sci; Int Soc Hort Sci. *Res:* Identification properties and control of viruses of vegetable and ornamental crops. *Mailing Add:* Dept of Plant Path 1519 Gortner Ave St Paul MN 55108

LOCKHART, BROOKS JAVINS, b Sandyville, WVa, Feb 8, 20; m 40, 69; c 3. MATHEMATICS. *Educ:* Marshall Col, AB, 37; WVa Univ, MS, 40; Univ Ill, PhD(math), 43. *Prof Exp:* Asst instr math, Univ Ill, 40-43; instr, Univ Mich, 43-44 & 46-48; from asst prof to prof, 48-79, dean, 62-77, EMER PROF MATH, NAVAL POSTGRAD SCH, 79- *Mem:* Math Asn Am. *Res:* Classical algebraic geometry; numerical analysis; computer programming. *Mailing Add:* Dept of Math Naval Postgrad Sch Monterey CA 93940

LOCKHART, F(RANK) J(ONES), b Austin, Tex, Aug 10, 16; m 45; c 2. CHEMICAL ENGINEERING. *Educ:* Univ Tex, BS, 36, MS, 38; Univ Mich, PhD(chem eng), 43. *Prof Exp:* Jr engr, Humble Oil & Refining Co, Tex, 38-39; from asst to instr chem eng, Univ Mich, 40-43; process engr, Union Oil Co Calif, 43-46; process engr, Fluor Corp, Ltd, 46; from asst prof to assoc prof chem eng, Southern Calif, 46-52; head dept, 50-52; mgr prod eng dept, Fluor Corp, Ltd, 52-55; head dept, 55-68, PROF CHEM ENG, UNIV SOUTHERN CALIF, 55- *Concurrent Pos:* Consult, 46- *Mem:* Am Chem Soc; Am Inst Chem Engrs. *Res:* Fluid dynamics; petroleum refining operations; distillation; gas absorption and stripping; design and operation of water cooling towers; liquid-liquid extraction; effect of time and concentration on overall mass transfer coefficients. *Mailing Add:* 648 33rd St Manhattan Beach CA 90266

LOCKHART, HAINES BOOTS, b Crawfordsville, Ind, Oct 29, 20; m 44; c 2. NUTRITION, BIOCHEMISTRY. *Educ:* Wabash Col, AB, 42; Univ Ill, PhD(biochem), 45. *Prof Exp:* Asst, Wabash Col, 41-42; chemist, Univ Ill, 42-45; from res chemist to head baby foods res div, Swift & Co, 45-66, head new foods div, 66-71; sect mgr nutrit res, 71-80, STAFF NUTRITIONIST, JOHN STUART RES LABS, QUAKER OATS CO, 80- *Concurrent Pos:* Mem tech adv group, Comt on Nutrit, Am Acad Pediat. *Mem:* Am Chem Soc; Inst Food Technol. *Res:* Amino acids and proteins in nutrition; infant and geriatric nutrition. *Mailing Add:* John Stuart Res Labs Quaker Oats Co W Main St Barrington IL 60010

LOCKHART, HAINES BOOTS, JR, b Evergreen Park, Ill, Feb 4, 46; m 68; c 2. ENVIRONMENTAL CHEMISTRY, BIOCHEMISTRY. *Educ:* Wabash Col, AB, 67; Univ Nebr, Lincoln, MS, 69, PhD(chem), 73. *Prof Exp:* Sr res biochemist, 72-81, TECH ASSOC, HEALTH & SAFETY LAB, EASTMAN KODAK CO, 81- *Mem:* Am Chem Soc; Soc Environ Toxicol & Chem. *Res:* Environmental impact of synthetic chemicals, their biodegradation, photodegradation and bioconcentration in aquatic organisms. *Mailing Add:* Health & Safety Lab Bldg 320 Eastman Kodak Co Kodak Park Rochester NY 14650

LOCKHART, JAMES ARTHUR, b Grand Rapids, Mich, June 7, 26; m 72; c 1. PLANT PHYSIOLOGY, THEORETICAL ECOLOGY. *Educ:* Mich State Col, BS, 49, MS, 52; Univ Calif, Los Angeles, PhD(bot), 54. *Prof Exp:* Plant physiologist, Camp Detrick, Md, 51-52; NSF fel, Bot Lab, Univ Pa,

54-55; res fel biol, Calif Inst Technol, 55-60; assoc plant physiologist, Agr Exp Sta, Univ Hawaii, 60-65; assoc prof, 66-68, PROF BOT, UNIV MASS, AMHERST, 68- *Mem:* AAAS; Am Soc Plant Physiologists; Bot Soc Am. *Res:* Plant growth and development; mechanics of growth; theoretical analyses of plant growth, reproduction, dispersion. *Mailing Add:* Dept of Bot Univ of Mass Amherst MA 01003

LOCKHART, JAMES MARCUS, b Portsmouth, Ohio, June 11, 48. LOW TEMPERATURE PHYSICS, ACOUSTICS. *Educ:* Univ Mich, BS, 70; Stanford Univ, MS, 72, PhD(physics), 76. *Prof Exp:* Res affil, Stanford Univ, 76, actg instr physics, 76-77, actg asst prof, 77-80; MEM FAC, COLO SCH MINES, 80- *Concurrent Pos:* Fel, Dept Physics, Stanford Univ, 76-78. *Mem:* Am Phys Soc; Am Asn Physics Teachers; Audio Eng Soc. *Res:* Low temperature electrical properties of solids; electron beams; molecular beams; semiconductor device physics; musical acoustics; architectural acoustics; electroacoustics. *Mailing Add:* Colo Sch Mines Golden CO 80401

LOCKHART, JOAN CONWAY, b Berlin, NH, June 6, 43; m 72. PHYCOLOGY, MARINE BOTANY. *Educ:* Univ NH, BA, 67; UNIV MASS, MS, 72, PhD(bot), 76. *Prof Exp:* NATO fel marine bot, Biologische Anstalt Helgoland, 78-79; INSTR, CONT EDUC, UNIV MASS, 81-, CHEM TUTOR, 76- *Concurrent Pos:* consult algae, Mass Inst Technol, 81. *Mem:* Bot Soc Am; Phycological Soc Am; Int Phycological Soc; Brit Phycological Soc. *Res:* Development, morphogenesis and life histories of algae; photobiology and nutrition of algae; environmental control of algal development and morphology. *Mailing Add:* 294 Puffton Village Amherst MA 01002

LOCKHART, LILLIAN HOFFMAN, b Columbus, Tex, Oct, 23, 30; m 51; c 3. MEDICINE. *Educ:* Rice Univ, BA, 51; Univ Tex Med Br, Galveston, MA, 55, MD, 57. *Prof Exp:* Asst prof, 63-72, ASSOC PROF PEDIAT & GENETICS, UNIV TEX MED BR GALVESTON, 72- *Concurrent Pos:* Fel hemat, Univ Tex Med Br, Galveston, 62-63. *Mem:* Am Acad Pediat. *Res:* Genetics; chromosome disorders. *Mailing Add:* Dept of Pediat Univ of Tex Med Br Galveston TX 77550

LOCKHART, ROBERT KENNON, b Howard, Kans, Oct 19, 20; m 47; c 2. MATERIALS & ELECTRONIC ENGINEERING. *Educ:* Purdue Univ, BS, 47. *Prof Exp:* Elec engr, Radio Corp Am, NJ, 47-56, mgr adv prod develop, 56-59, mgr lightning develop eng, 59-63, mgr adv digital technol, 63-65, mgr new prod eng, 66-75, mgr circuits signal & packaging, Consumer Electronics Div, 75-76, mgr mat eng & develop, 76-81, SR ENGR PROJ TV RES & DEVELOP, RCA CORP, 81- *Honors & Awards:* RCA Victor Award of Merit, 53; David Sarnoff Outstanding Achievement Award, 69. *Res:* Color television; Gigahertz computer research; defining sociological factors describing consumer needs and filling those needs; holography; developing mechanical analysis tools for predicting plastics performance; creep, permanent set; high speed tensile/puncture analysis. *Mailing Add:* 5611 E Fall Creek Pkwy N Dr Indianapolis IN 46226

LOCKHART, WILLIAM LAFAYETTE, b Nashville, Tenn, Oct 15, 36; m 60; c 2. INORGANIC CHEMISTRY. *Educ:* Tenn Technol Univ, BS, 58; Univ Miss, MS, 61; Vanderbilt Univ, PhD(inorg chem), 67. *Prof Exp:* Res biochemist, US Food & Drug Admin, 60-63; asst prof, 67-71, assoc prof, 71-77, PROF CHEM, WEST GA COL, 71-, CHMN DEPT, 80- *Res:* Kinetics and mechanisms of inorganic reactions. *Mailing Add:* Dept of Chem WGa Col Carrollton GA 30118

LOCKHART, WILLIAM RAYMOND, b Carlisle, Ind, Nov 25, 25; m 47; c 4. BACTERIOLOGY. *Educ:* Ind State Teachers Col, AB, 49; Purdue Univ, MS, 51, PhD(bact), 54. *Prof Exp:* Asst bact, Purdue Univ, 50-51; from asst prof to assoc prof, 54-60, chmn dept, 60-74, PROF BACT, IOWA STATE UNIV, 60- *Mem:* Am Soc Microbiol; fel Am Acad Microbiol; Brit Soc Gen Microbiol. *Res:* Physiology of bacterial growth; numerical taxonomy. *Mailing Add:* Dept of Bact Iowa State Univ Ames IA 50011

LOCKNER, FREDERICK RUSSELL, animal behavior, see previous edition

LOCKRIDGE, OKSANA MASLIVEC, b Czech, Sept 4, 41; US citizen. BIOCHEMICAL PHARMACOLOGY, BIOCHEMICAL GENETICS. *Educ:* Smith Col, BA, 63; Northwestern Univ, Ill, PhD(chem), 71. *Prof Exp:* Fel human genetics, 72-74; res assoc pharmacol, 74-81, RES SCIENTIST, UNIV MICH, ANN ARBOR, 82- *Mem:* Am Chem Soc; Asn for Women in Sci; AAAS. *Res:* Pharmacogenetics; biochemical and structural studies on genetic variants of human pseudocholinesterase. *Mailing Add:* Dept of Pharmacol Univ Mich Ann Arbor MI 48109

LOCKSHIN, MICHAEL DAN, b Columbus, Ohio, Dec 9, 37; m 65; c 1. RHEUMATOLOGY, IMMUNOLOGY. *Educ:* Harvard Col, AB, 59; Harvard Med Sch, MD, 63. *Prof Exp:* Intern, Second (Cornell) Div Med, Bellevue & Mem Hosp, New York, 63-64; epidemic intel serv officer, Epidemic Intel Serv, Commun Dis Ctr, 64-66; resident, Second (Cornell) Div Med, Bellevue & Mem Hosp, New York, 66-68; fel rheumatol, Columbia Presby Med Ctr, 68-70; asst prof, 70-75, ASSOC PROF MED, COL MED, CORNELL UNIV, 75- *Concurrent Pos:* Adj asst prof epidemiol, Sch Pub Health, Univ Pittsburgh, 65-66; assoc scientist & assoc attend physician, Hosp Spec Surg, New York Hosp, 70-; consult rheumatol, Mem Hosp, New York, 70-; mem bd dirs, Arthritis Found. *Mem:* Am Rheumatism Asn; Am Col Physicians. *Res:* Cellular immunology; clinical rheumatology. *Mailing Add:* 535 E 70th St New York NY 10021

LOCKSHIN, RICHARD ANSEL, b Columbus, Ohio, Dec 9, 37; m 63; c 2. PHYSIOLOGY, DEVELOPMENTAL BIOLOGY. *Educ:* Harvard Univ, AB, 59, AM, 61, PhD(biol), 63. *Prof Exp:* Asst prof physiol, Sch Med, Univ Rochester, 65-75; assoc prof, 75-79, PROF PHYSIOL, ST JOHN'S UNIV, NY, 79- *Concurrent Pos:* NSF fel, Inst Animal Genetics, Univ Edinburgh, 63-64, NIH fel, 64-65. *Mem:* AAAS; Soc Cell Biol; Soc Develop Biol; Gerontol Soc; Am Soc Entom. *Res:* Destruction of tissues during metamorphosis of insects; early developmental events in insect embryogenesis; cellular differentiation. *Mailing Add:* Dept of Biol Sci St John's Univ Jamaica NY 11439

LOCKWOOD, ARTHUR H, b Jan 26, 47; US citizen. MOLECULAR BIOLOGY, CELL BIOLOGY. *Educ:* Carleton Col, BA, 68; Albert Einstein Col Med, PhD(molecular biol), 72. *Prof Exp:* Res fel molecular biol, Dept Biochem Sci, Princeton Univ, 73-74; res scientist cell biol, Sch Med, NY Univ, 75-80; PROF ANAT & CELL BIOL, MED SCH, UNIV NC, 80- *Concurrent Pos:* Arthritis Found fel, 74. *Mem:* AAAS; Am Soc Cell Biol; NY Acad Sci. *Res:* Biology of cytoplasmic microtubules; biochemistry of mitosis, cell senescence. *Mailing Add:* Dept Anat & Cell Biol Swing Bldg Med Sch Univ NC Chapel Hill NC 27514

LOCKWOOD, DAVID JOHN, b Christchurch, NZ, Jan 7, 42; m 79; c 1. SOLID STATE PHYSICS. *Educ:* Univ Canterbury, BSc, 64, MSc, 66, PhD(physics), 69; Univ Edinburgh, DSc, 78. *Prof Exp:* Teaching fel physics, Univ Canterbury, NZ, 65-69; fel chem, Univ Waterloo, Can, 70-71; res fel physics, Univ Edinburgh, 72-78; RES OFFICER PHYSICS, NAT RES COUN CAN, 78- *Concurrent Pos:* Univ bursaries, NZ Univ Grants Comt, 66-68; consult vis, Battelle Ctr de Res, Switz, 72-76; tutor, Open Univ, UK, 77-78; consult vis, Univ Paul Sabatier, Toulouse, France, 77-; vis prof, Essex Univ, England, 81-82. *Res:* Light scattering studies of structural and magnetic phase transitions, electronic exitations and phonons in solids. *Mailing Add:* Div of Physics Nat Res Coun Ottawa ON K1A 0R6 Can

LOCKWOOD, DEAN H, b Milford, Conn, June 17, 37; m 58; c 3. BIOCHEMISTRY, MEDICINE. *Educ:* Wesleyan Univ, AB, 59; Johns Hopkins Univ, MD, 63. *Prof Exp:* Intern & resident, Johns Hopkins Univ, 63-65, fel pharmacol, 67-69, asst & assoc prof med, 69-76; staff assoc, NIH, 65-67; PROF MED, UNIV ROCHESTER, 76- *Concurrent Pos:* NIH res develop award, 69-74 & res grant, 69-; mem endocrine merit rev bd, Vet Admin, 76-79; mem, NIH Metab Study Sect, 81- *Mem:* Am Soc Biol Chemists; Am Soc Clin Invest; Endocrine Soc; Am Fedn Clin Res; Am Diabetes Asn. *Res:* Mechanism of action of insulin and glucagon in normal and resistant states; plasma membrane receptors and biological responses emphasized. *Mailing Add:* 601 Elmwood Ave Rochester NY 14642

LOCKWOOD, GEORGE WESLEY, b Norfolk, Va, June 28, 41; m 65. ASTRONOMY, PLANETARY SCIENCES. *Educ:* Duke Univ, BS, 63; Univ Va, MA, 65, PhD(astron), 68. *Prof Exp:* Astronr, Kitt Peak Nat Observ, 68-73; ASTRONR, LOWELL OBSERV, 73- *Mem:* Am Astron Soc; Int Astron Union; Astron Soc Pac. *Res:* Planetary atmospheres; late-type stars; solar-planetary relations; variable stars. *Mailing Add:* Lowell Observ Box 1269 Flagstaff AZ 86002

LOCKWOOD, GRANT JOHN, b Byram, Conn, Oct 28, 31; m 56; c 4. EXPERIMENTAL ATOMIC PHYSICS, ELECTRON PHYSICS. *Educ:* Univ Conn, BA, 54, MS, 59, PhD(physics), 63. *Prof Exp:* Res asst physics, Univ Conn, 60-63; STAFF MEM, SANDIA LABS, 63- *Mem:* Am Phys Soc. *Res:* Electronic, atomic and molecular interactions to include ion-atom, ion-molecule, atom-atom and atom-molecule; interaction with surface and solids of ion beams. *Mailing Add:* Sandia Labs Div 4232 Albuquerque NM 87185

LOCKWOOD, JOHN ALEXANDER, b Easton, Pa, July 12, 19; m 42; c 3. PHYSICS. *Educ:* Dartmouth Col, AB, 41, Lafayette Col, MS, 43; Yale Univ, PhD(physics), 48. *Prof Exp:* From asst to instr physics, Lafayette Col, 41-44; tech supvr, Tenn Eastman Corp, 44-45; asst physics, Yale Univ, 45-46, asst instr, 46-47, asst, 47-48; from asst prof to assoc prof, 48-58, assoc prof res, 74-80, PROF PHYSICS, UNIV NH, 58-, DIR RES, 80- *Mem:* AAAS; Am Phys Soc; Am Asn Physics Teachers. *Res:* Development of linear electron accelerators; cosmic ray; nuclear physics. *Mailing Add:* Dept of Physics Univ of NH Durham NH 03824

LOCKWOOD, JOHN LEBARON, b Ann Arbor, Mich, May 28, 24; m 59; c 2. PLANT PATHOLOGY. *Educ:* Mich State Col, BA, 48, MS, 50; Univ Wis, PhD(plant path), 53. *Prof Exp:* Asst prof bot & plant path, Ohio Agr Exp Sta, 53-55; from asst prof to assoc prof, 55-67, PROF BOT & PLANT PATH, MICH STATE UNIV, 67- *Concurrent Pos:* NSF sr fel, Cambridge Univ, 70-71. *Mem:* Fel Am Phytopath Soc; Sigma Xi. *Res:* Ecology of root-infecting fungi; soybean diseases. *Mailing Add:* Dept Bot & Plant Path Mich State Univ East Lansing MI 48824

LOCKWOOD, JOHN PAUL, b Bridgeport, Conn, Oct 26, 39; m 63; c 2. GEOLOGY. *Educ:* Univ Calif, Riverside, AB, 61; Princeton Univ, PhD(geol), 66. *Prof Exp:* GEOLOGIST, US GEOL SURV, 66- *Concurrent Pos:* Partic, Nat Res Coun-Nat Acad Sci Sci Exchange Prog with USSR, res at Geol Inst Acad Sci, Moscow, 66, res at Dir Volcanologi, Bandung, Indonesia, 80-81. *Mem:* Geol Soc Am. *Res:* Petrology, mineralogy and structural features of serpentinites; general geology of the Sierra Nevada Mountains; circum-Pacific distribution of volcanic rocks; Caribbean geology; volcanic hazards; eruptive history and structure of Mauna Loa volcano, Hawaii. *Mailing Add:* US Geol Surv Hawaiian Volcano Observ Hawaii National Park HI 96718

LOCKWOOD, KARL LEE, organic chemistry, see previous edition

LOCKWOOD, LINDA GAIL, b New York, NY, May 25, 36. ENVIRONMENTAL BIOLOGY, SCIENCE EDUCATION. *Educ:* Columbia Univ, BS, 60, MA, 61 & 65, PhD(bot), 69. *Prof Exp:* Asst prof bot & ecol, Teachers Col, Columbia Univ, 69-73; ASSOC PROF ENVIRON SCI, UNIV MASS, AMHERST, 73- *Concurrent Pos:* Jessie Smith Noyes Found grant environ sci educ, Teachers Col, Columbia Univ, 71-73; prof plant & soil sci & Sch Educ, Univ Mass, Amherst, 73-; co-dir, US Off Educ grant, 74-75; Univ Mass fac res grant, 74-75 & Water Resources Res Ctr grant, 74-75; NSF grants, 75-79. *Mem:* Sigma Xi; AAAS; Scientist's Inst Pub Info; Nat Asn Biol Teachers; Audubon Soc. *Res:* Influence of photoperiod and exogenous nitrogen-containing compounds on the reproductive cycles of the liverwort Cephalozia media Lindb; experimental morphology and physiological ecology; environmental biology, especially physiological ecology, aquatic systems; environmental science education, especially teacher training, history and philosophy of science. *Mailing Add:* Dept of Environ Sci Marshall Hall Univ of Mass Amherst MA 01002

LOCKWOOD, ROBERT GREENING, b Faribault, Minn, Jan 12, 28; m 53; c 2. ORGANIC POLYMER CHEMISTRY, INDUSTRIAL ORGANIC CHEMISTRY. *Educ:* Carleton Col, BA, 49; Univ Minn, PhD(org chem), 53. *Prof Exp:* Lab instr inorg & org chem, Univ Minn, 49-53; res chemist, New Prod Develop Lab, Chem Div, Gen Elec Co, 53-54; sr chemist, 54-65, RES SPECIALIST, 3M CO, 65- *Mem:* Am Chem Soc. *Res:* Organic synthesis; carboxylic acids and derivatives; condensation polymers; manufacture of alkylated aromatic hydrocarbons and polycarboxylic acids. *Mailing Add:* 2 Hingham Circle St Paul MN 55118

LOCKWOOD, WILLIAM RUTLEDGE, b Memphis, Tenn, Apr 10, 29; m; c 5. INTERNAL MEDICINE, EXPERIMENTAL PATHOLOGY. *Educ:* Univ Miss, BA, 49, MA, 50; Univ Tenn, Memphis, MD, 57. *Prof Exp:* Intern, Charity Hosp La, New Orleans, 57-58; resident med, 59-61, from instr to asst prof, 62-70, ASST PROF MICROBIOL & PATH, MED CTR, UNIV MISS, 66-, ASSOC PROF MED, 70- *Concurrent Pos:* USPHS fel, Med Ctr, Univ Miss, 61-64, grant, 64-67; vis instr, Washington Univ, 64, attend physician, Univ Miss Hosp, 64-; asst dean res & assoc chief staff res, Vet Admin Ctr, 69-73. *Mem:* Infectious Dis Soc Am; fel Am Col Chest Physicians; Am Soc Trop Med & Hyg; Am Soc Microbiol; fel Am Col Physicians. *Res:* Pathogenesis of acute inflammation; pharmacology of antimicrobial agents; electron microscopy. *Mailing Add:* Dept Med Univ Miss Med Ctr Jackson MS 39216

LOCKYER, GEORGE DONALD, JR, b Los Angeles, Calif, Nov 17, 48; m 69. ORGANIC CHEMISTRY. *Educ:* Univ Calif, Irvine, BA, 70; Univ Calif, Riverside, PhD(org chem), 75. *Prof Exp:* Fel org chem, Tex Christian Univ, 75-76; res chemist, 76-80, GROUP LEADER, ALLIED CHEM, 80- *Mem:* Am Chem Soc; Inst Elec & Electronics Engrs. *Res:* Organic reactions mechanisms; free radical and carbene chemistry; photochemistry; organometallic reaction mechanisms; polymer chemistry; fluorine chemistry. *Mailing Add:* Allied Chem Corp 20 Peabody St Buffalo NY 14210

LOCOCK, ROBERT A, b Toronto, Ont, Aug 14, 35; m 61. PHARMACEUTICAL CHEMISTRY, PHARMACOGNOSY. *Educ:* Univ Toronto, BSc, 59, MSc, 61; Ohio State Univ, PhD(pharm), 65. *Prof Exp:* Lectr pharmaceut chem, Univ BC, 61-62; asst pharm, Ohio State Univ, 64-65; asst prof, 65-70, ASSOC PROF PHARM, UNIV ALTA, 70-, ASSOC PROF PHARMACEUT SCI, 74- *Mem:* AAAS; Am Chem Soc; Am Soc Pharmacog. *Res:* Chemistry of natural products; phytochemistry; chemotaxonomy; alkaloids and terpenoids. *Mailing Add:* 13943 107A Ave Edmonton AB T5M 2A8 Can

LOCY, ROBERT DONALD, b Defiance, Ohio, Jan 12, 47; m 69; c 3. PLANT BIOCHEMISTRY, PLANT CELL & TISSUE CULTURE. *Educ:* Defiance Col, AB, 69; Purdue Univ, PhD(plant biochem), 74. *Prof Exp:* Res assoc biochem, McMaster Univ, 74-76; res assoc plant physiol, DOE/MSU Plant Res Lab, Mich State Univ, 76-78; ASST PROF HORT SCI, NC STATE UNIV, 78- *Mem:* Am Soc Plant Physiologists. *Res:* Application of biochemistry and molecular biology to crop improvement using plant cell culture methods. *Mailing Add:* Dept of Hort Sci NC State Univ Raleigh NC 27650

LODA, RICHARD THOMAS, b Derby, Conn, May 19, 48. SPECTROSCOPY. *Educ:* Waterburg State Tech Col, AAS, 68; Univ Bridgeport, BA, 71; Wesleyan Univ, PhD(phys chem), 80. *Prof Exp:* NIH fel, Chem Dept, Univ Ore, 80-81; CHEM,IST RES DEPT, INSTRUMENTAL CHEM ANAL BR, NAVAL WEAPONS CTR, 81- *Mem:* Am Chem Soc; Am Phys Soc. *Res:* Application of lasers and spectroscopy to problems of physical and chemical interest; photochemistry; site selection and linewidth phenomena in condensed phase systems; coherent antistokes Raman scattering. *Mailing Add:* Naval Weapons Ctr Code 3851 China Lake CA 93555

LODATO, MICHAEL W, b Rochester, NY, June 17, 32; m 59; c 4. OPERATIONS RESEARCH. *Educ:* Colgate Univ, AB, 54; Univ Rochester, MS, 59; Rutgers Univ, PhD(math), 62. *Prof Exp:* Scientist, LFE Monterey Lab, 62-63; mem tech staff, Appl Math Dept, Mitre Corp, Mass, 63-65, head opers anal sub dept, 65-66; sr exec adv, Douglas Aircraft Corp, 66-67, mgr, Info Technol Dept, McDonnell Douglas Corp, 67-68; pres, Macro Systs Assocs, Inc, 68-70; prin bus planner, Xerox Data Systs, 70-71; vpres indust systs, Informatics, Inc, 71-78; exec vpres, Spectrum Int, Inc, 78-80; PRES, MWL INC, 80- *Mem:* Opers Res Am. *Res:* Topology; planning, scheduling and resource allocation; orbital mechanics; production and inventory control. *Mailing Add:* 32038 Watergate Ct Westlake Village CA 91361

LODEN, MICHAEL SIMPSON, b Fayette, Ala, Mar 30, 45; m 68; c 1. OLIGOCHAETA, WATER QUALITY. *Educ:* Auburn Univ, BS, 67, MS, 73; La State Univ, PhD(zool), 78. *Prof Exp:* Aquatic biologist, Aquatic Control, Inc, 73-75; asst prof zool, La State Univ, 78-81; ENVIRON QUALITY SUPVR, JEFFERSON PARISH, LA, 81- *Mem:* Sigma Xi; AAAS; Am Soc Zoologists; NAm Benthol Soc; Am Micros Soc. *Res:* Systematics, life histories, ecology and distribution of aquatic Oligochaeta. *Mailing Add:* 917 Trudeau Dr Metairie LA 70003

LODER, EDWIN ROBERT, b Irvington, NJ, Feb 24, 25; m 45; c 4. ANALYTICAL CHEMISTRY. *Educ:* Syracuse Univ, BA, 52; Mass Inst Technol, PhD, 55. *Prof Exp:* Asst chem, Mass Inst Technol, 52-53, asst org microanal, 53-55; chemist, Eastman Kodak Co, 55-59, chief anal chemist, Maumee Chem, 59-62, dir res serv, 62-65, sect mgr & tech assoc, Gen Aniline & Film Co, NY, 65-66; from dep dir res to dir res, Du Bois Chem Div, W R Grace & Co, 66-70, dir res & vpres, Du Bois Chem Div, Chemed Corp, 70-72, sr vpres corp affairs, 72-73, exec vpres, 73-74, GROUP EXEC VPRES, DU BOIS CHEM DIV, CHEMED CORP, 74- *Concurrent Pos:* Instr, Univ Toledo, 61-62. *Mem:* Fel AAAS; fel Am Inst Chem; Am Chem Soc; Soc Photog Sci & Eng; Am Soc Qual Control. *Res:* Electrochemistry; spectroscopy; research management; statistics. *Mailing Add:* Res Dept Du Bois Chem Div Chemed Corp Du Bois Tower Cincinnati OH 45202

LODEWIJK, ERIC, b The Hague, Neth, Nov 15, 40. SYNTHETIC ORGANIC CHEMISTRY. *Educ:* Univ Amsterdam, BSc, 65, PhD(org chem), 68. *Prof Exp:* Res chemist org chem, Bahamas, 69-70, group leader process develop, Chem Div, 70-73, sr res chemist, 73-77, group leader res org chem, 77-79, MGR, PROCESS RES, ARAPAHOE CHEM INC, SYNTEX CORP, 79- *Mem:* Am Chem Soc. *Res:* Process development and process research on fine organic chemicals and drugs; synthesis of fluorocorticosteroids and IG steroids. *Mailing Add:* Arapahoe Chem 2075 N 55 St Boulder CO 80301

LODGE, ARTHUR SCOTT, b Liverpool, Eng, Nov 20, 22; m 45; c 3. PHYSICS. *Educ:* Oxford Univ, BA, 45, MA, 48, DPhil(physics), 49. *Prof Exp:* Jr sci officer pile design, Atomic Energy, Montreal Anglo-Can Proj, 45-46 & rheology, Brit Rayon Res Asn, 49-60; lectr math, Inst Sci & Technol, Univ Manchester, 61-63, sr lectr rheology, 63-68; PROF RHEOLOGY, UNIV WIS-MADISON, 68-, CHMN DEPT, 69-, PROF ENG MECH, 77- *Concurrent Pos:* Vis prof chem eng, Univ Wis-Madison, 65-66. *Honors & Awards:* Bingham Medal, Soc Rheology, 71. *Mem:* Soc Rheology; Brit Soc Rheology; fel Brit Inst Physics & Phys Soc. *Res:* Rheological properties of concentrated polymer solutions; molecular theories of their constitutive equations and stress/optical properties; experimental methods. *Mailing Add:* Dept of Eng Univ of Wis-Madison Madison WI 53706

LODGE, CHESTER RAY, b McCausland, Iowa, Feb 19, 23; wid. ELECTRICAL ENGINEERING. *Educ:* Iowa State Univ, BS, 43, MS, 49, PhD(eng), 52. *Prof Exp:* Dean eng, Univ Peshawar, Pakistan, 52-53; asst prof, Iowa State Univ, 54; assoc prof, 54-58, PROF ENG, SAN DIEGO STATE UNIV, 58- *Concurrent Pos:* Fulbright lectr, Pakistan, 52-53. *Mem:* Am Soc Eng Educ; Inst Elec & Electronics Engrs. *Res:* Automatic control systems; symmetrical components and applications. *Mailing Add:* Dept of Eng San Diego State Univ San Diego CA 92115

LODGE, JAMES PIATT, JR, b Decatur, Ill, Feb 4, 26; m 48; c 5. ATMOSPHERIC CHEMISTRY, AIR POLLUTION. *Educ:* Univ Ill, BS, 47; Univ Rochester, PhD(chem), 51. *Prof Exp:* Asst prof chem, Keuka Col, 50-52; chemist, Cloud Physics Lab, Univ Chicago, 52-55; chief chem res & develop sect, Robert A Taft Sanit Eng Ctr, USPHS, Columbus, Ohio, 55-61; prog scientist, Nat Ctr Atmospheric Res, 61-74; CONSULT ATMOSPHERIC CHEM, 74- *Concurrent Pos:* Consult, Cook Res Labs, 51-53, ed, Atmospheric Environ, 59-; affil prof, La State Univ, 66-69; mem, State Air Pollution Variance Bd, Colo, 66-70; chmn, State Air Pollution Control Comn, Colo, 70-75. *Honors & Awards:* Distinguished Serv Award, Div Environ Chem, Am Chem Soc, 73; Frank A Chambers Award, Air Pollution Control Asn, 74. *Mem:* Fel AAAS; Am Chem Soc; Am Geophys Union; Am Meteorol Soc; Air Pollution Control Asn. *Res:* Air pollution and atmospheric chemistry; microchemical analysis; cloud physics; atmospheric electricity. *Mailing Add:* 385 Broadway Boulder CO 80303

LODGE, JAMES ROBERT, b Downey, Iowa, July 1, 25; m 47; c 2. REPRODUCTIVE PHYSIOLOGY. *Educ:* Iowa State Univ, BS, 52, MS, 54; Mich State Univ, PhD(dairy), 57. *Prof Exp:* Asst dairy, Mich State Univ, 54-57; res assoc dairy sci, 57-60, from asst prof to assoc prof, 60-69, PROF PHYSIOL, UNIV ILL, URBANA, 69- *Concurrent Pos:* Res fel, Nat Inst Child Health & Human Develop, 69-70. *Mem:* AAAS; Am Physiol Soc; Soc Study Reproduction; Am Soc Animal Sci; Am Dairy Sci Asn. *Res:* Physiology of reproduction and endocrinology. *Mailing Add:* Dept Dairy Sci 315 Animal Sci Lab Univ Ill 1207 W Gregory Dr Urbana IL 61801

LODGE, TIMOTHY PATRICK, b Sale, Eng, Apr, 11, 54. POLYMER SOLUTION DYNAMICS. *Educ:* Harvard Univ, BA, 75; Univ Wis, PhD(anal chem), 80. *Prof Exp:* Nat Res Coun assoc fel, Nat Bur Standards, 81-82; ASST PROF CHEM & CHEM ENG, UNIV MINN, 82- *Mem:* Am Chem Soc; Am Phys Soc; Soc Rheology; Sigma Xi. *Res:* Conformation and dynamics of macromolecules in solution studies by means of oscillatory flow birefringence quasi-elastic light scattering and small angle neutron scattering. *Mailing Add:* Dept Chem Kolthoff & Smith Halls Univ Minn Minneapolis MN 55455

LODHI, MOHAMMAD ARFIN KHAN, b Agra, India, Sept 17, 33; m 65; c 3. NUCLEAR PHYSICS. *Educ:* Univ Karachi, BSc, Hons, 52, MSc, 56; Univ London, DIC, 60, PhD(nuclear physics), 63. *Prof Exp:* Lectr math, S M Col, Karachi, 52-59; from asst prof to assoc prof, 63-73, PROF PHYSICS, TEX TECH UNIV, 73- *Concurrent Pos:* Vis prof, Univ Frankfurt & Darmstadt Tech Univ, 70-71. *Mem:* Brit Inst Physics. *Res:* High energy electron scattering by nuclei and electromagnetics transitions in nuclei and their role in elucidating nuclear structure; nuclear shell, cluster and resonating group models and their relationship; nuclear nonlocal potential and nuclear systematics; short-range nucleon-nucleon correlations. *Mailing Add:* Dept of Physics Tex Tech Univ Lubbock TX 79409

LODISH, HARVEY FRANKLIN, b Cleveland, Ohio, Nov 16, 41; m 63; c 3. BIOCHEMISTRY, MICROBIOLOGY. *Educ:* Kenyon Col, AB, 62; Rockefeller Univ, PhD(biol), 66. *Hon Degrees:* DSc, Kenyon Col, 82. *Prof Exp:* Am Cancer Soc fel biol, Med Res Coun Lab Molecular Biol, Eng, 66-68; from asst prof to assoc prof, 68-76, PROF BIOL, MASS INST TECHNOL, 76- *Concurrent Pos:* Res career develop award, Nat Inst Gen Med Sci, 71-75; mem panel develop biol, NSF, 72-; chmn, Gorder Conf on Animal Cells, 76; Guggenheim fel, 77-78. *Mem:* AAAS; Am Soc Microbiol; Am Chem Soc; Am Soc Biol Chemists; Am Soc Cell Biol. *Res:* Replication of ribonucleic acid viruses; mechanism and regulation of protein biosynthesis; synthesis of hemoglobin; differentiation of the slime mold dictyostelium discoideum; biosynthesis of cellular and viral membrane proteins. *Mailing Add:* Dept of Biol Mass Inst of Technol Cambridge MA 02139

LODMELL, DONALD LOUIS, b Polson, Mont, Aug 27, 39; m 63. VIROLOGY. *Educ:* Northwestern Univ, BA, 61; Univ Mont, MS, 63, PhD(microbiol), 67. *Prof Exp:* Scientist virol, Rocky Mountain Lab, NIH, 67-71; res assoc, Lab Oral Med, NIH, 71-72; sr scientist, 72-81, SCI DIR VIROL, ROCKY MOUNTAIN LAB, NIH, 81- *Concurrent Pos:* Assoc ed, J Immunol, 78-; fac affil, Dept Microbiol, Univ Mont, 78- *Mem:* Am Soc Microbiol; Am Asn Immunologists. *Res:* Immunological mechanisms of host defense against viral infections of the central nervous system; rabies. *Mailing Add:* Rocky Mountain Lab Hamilton MT 59840

LODOEN, GARY ARTHUR, b Camp Rucker, Ala, May 3, 43. POLYMER CHEMISTRY. *Educ:* Univ NDak, BS, 65; Cornell Univ, PhD(org chem), 69. *Prof Exp:* Fel, Univ Iowa, 69-70; res chemist, 70-73, sr res chemist, 73, res & develop supvr, 73-75, process supvr, 75-77, SR RES CHEMIST, TEXTILE FIBERS DEPT, E I DU PONT DE NEMOURS & CO, INC, 77- *Mem:* Am Chem Soc. *Res:* Spandex chemistry and structure; polyester glycol synthesis and properties; development of new and novel raw materials for spandex yarns. *Mailing Add:* DuPont Co DuPont Blvd Waynesboro VA 22980

LODWICK, GWILYM SAVAGE, b Mystic, Iowa, Aug 30, 17; m 47; c 4. RADIOLOGY, BIOENGINEERING. *Educ:* Univ Iowa, BA, 42, MD, 43. *Prof Exp:* Clin asst prof radiol, Univ Iowa, 52-55, assoc prof, Col Med, 55-56; acting dean, Sch Med, 59, assoc dean, 59-64, prof radiol & chmn dept, 56-78, interim chmn radiol, 80-81, RES PROF, DEPT RADIOL, SCH MED, UNIV MO-COLUMBIA, 78-, CHMN DEPT, 81- *Concurrent Pos:* Fel, Armed Forces Inst Path, 51; Nat Inst Gen Med Sci spec fel, 67-68; chief radiol serv, Vet Admin Hosp, Iowa City, 52-55; consult, Ellis Fischel State Cancer Hosp, 59-; mem radiol training comt, Nat Inst Gen Med Sci, 66-70; consult, Jet Propulsion Lab, Calif Inst Technol, 69-73; mem, Comt Radiol, Nat Acad Sci; mem, Comt Radiol, Div Med Sci, Nat Res Coun, 70-75; Sigma Xi res grant, Univ Mo-Columbia, 72; dir, Mid-Am Bone Diag Ctr & Registry; vis prof, Sch Med, Keio Univ, Tokyo, 74- & Univ Turku, Finland, 79; mem, Radiation Study Sect, Div Res Grants, NIH, 76-79, Study Sect Diag Radiol & Nuclear Med, 79-, chmn, 80-82. *Honors & Awards:* Bronze Medal Award, Roentgen Ray Soc, 51; Gold Medal, XIII Int Conf Radiol, Madrid, 73; Sakari Mustakallio medal, Finland, 79. *Mem:* Hon mem Portuguese Soc Radiol & Nuclear Med; AAAS; AMA; Radiol Soc NAm (3rd vpres, 74-75); fel Am Col Radiol. *Res:* Diagnostic radiology; diagnosis and prognosis of bone disease, computer-aided medical diagnosis; automated image analysis and pattern recognition; information systems. *Mailing Add:* 911 La Grange Columbia MO 65201

LOE, HARALD, b Steinkjer, Norway, July 19, 26; c 2. PERIODONTICS. *Educ:* Oslo Univ, DDS, 52, Dr Ondontol, 61. *Hon Degrees:* Dr Ondontol, Univ Gothenburg, Sweden, 73, Catholic Univ Leuven, Belg, 80, Univ Athens, Greece, Royal Dental Col, Aarhus, Denmark. *Prof Exp:* Instr oper dent, Sch Dent, Oslo, 52-55; res assoc, Norweg Inst Dent Res, 56-62; Fullbright res fel & res assoc oral path, Univ Ill, 57-58; univ res fel, Oslo Univ, 59-62; assoc prof periodont, Sch Dent, Oslo Univ, 60-61; vis prof, Hebrew Univ, Jerusalem, 66-67; prof & chmn periodont, Royal Dent Col, Aarhus, Denmark, 62-72, assoc dean & dean elect, 71-72; prof & dir, Dent Res Inst, Univ Mich, 72-74; DEAN & PROF PERIODONT, SCH DENT MED, UNIV CONN, 74- *Concurrent Pos:* Ed & founder J Periodont Res, 66-; mem, Danish Foreign Minstry Tech Aid Develop Countries Comt Dent, 69-72; mem, Nat Coun Med Res, Denmark, 71-72; mem, Nat Inst Dent Res Dent Caries Prog Adv Comt, 74-78; chmn, Dent Drugs Prod Adv Comt, US Food & Drug Admin, 74-78; mem, Senate Adv Comt, Univ Mich, 74-75; mem, Sci Panel Eval NIDR Periodont Dis Res, NIH, 75-76; consult, Coun Dent Therapeut, Am Dent, 77- *Honors & Awards:* Peridont Award, William J Gies Found, 78; Int Asn Dent Res Award, 69. *Mem:* Int Asn Dent Res (pres, 79-81); Am Acad Periodont; AAAS; Am Acad Dent Radiol; Scand Asn Dent Res. *Res:* Epidemiology, experimental pathology and prevention of peridontal disease; author or coauthor of over 200 scientific articles. *Mailing Add:* Univ Conn Sch Dent Med Farmington CT 06032

LOE, ROBERT WAYNE, b Larwill, Ind, Dec 2, 35; m 64; c 1. PLANT PHYSIOLOGY. *Educ:* Wabash Col, AB, 57; Columbia Univ, PhD(plant physiol), 64. *Prof Exp:* Instr gen biol & bot, Rutgers Univ, 61-64; NSF fel, Int Rice Res Inst, Los Banos, Phillipines, 65; sr physiologist, Res Dept, Honduras Div, Standard Fruit Co, 66-75, supt res, 76-80, sr plant physiologist, 74-80; DIR AGR RES, CASTLE & COOKE, INC, 80- *Mem:* Am Soc Plant Physiologists; Am Chem Soc; Am Inst Biol Sci. *Res:* Inhibition of nicotine by analogs of nicotinic acid in tobacco roots; absorption and translocation of radioactive iron in rice; physiological studies on bananas and pineapple. *Mailing Add:* Castle & Cooke Inc 50 Calif St San Francisco CA 94111

LOEB, ARTHUR LEE, b Amsterdam, Neth, July 13, 23; nat US; m 56. CHEMICAL PHYSICS, DESIGN SCIENCE. *Educ:* Univ Pa, BSCh, 43; Harvard Univ, AM, 45, PhD(chem physics), 49. *Prof Exp:* Mem staff, Bur Study Coun, Harvard Univ, 45-49; mem staff, Div Indust Coop & Lincoln Lab, Mass Inst Technol, 49-58, lectr, 56-58; from asst prof to assoc prof elec eng, Mass Inst Technol, 58-63; staff scientist, Ledgemont Lab, Kennecott Copper Corp, 63-73; SR LECTR VISUAL & ENVIRON STUDIES & CUR, CARPENTER CTR, HARVARD UNIV, 70- *Concurrent Pos:* Actg head, Dept Chem, Barlaeus Gym, Neth, 46; consult, Mass Inst Technol, 49-, Godfrey Lowell Cabot, Inc, 58 & IBM Corp, NY, 59; mem guest res staff, Univ Utrecht, 54-55. *Mem:* Acad Mgt; Am Soc Eng Educ; fel Royal Soc Arts; NY Acad Sci; fel Am Inst Chem. *Res:* Mathematical crystallography; educational technology; design science; communication of two-dimensional and three-dimensional concepts and patterns. *Mailing Add:* Dept of Visual & Environ Studies Harvard Univ Cambridge MA 02138

LOEB, GERALD ELI, b New Brunswick, NJ, June 26, 48; m 68; c 1. NEUROPHYSIOLOGY, BIOMEDICAL ENGINEERING. *Educ:* Johns Hopkins Univ, BA, 69, MD, 72. *Prof Exp:* Resident surg, Univ Ariz, 72-73; MED OFFICER NEUROPHYSIOL, NAT INST NEUROL & COMMUN DIS & STROKE, 73- *Concurrent Pos:* Fel, Seeing Eye, 69-72; NIH contract, Johns Hopkins Univ, 70-71; guest res assoc, Artificial Eye Proj, Univ Utah, 71; vis scientist, Univ Calif, San Francisco, 79- *Mem:* Soc Neurosci; Biomed Eng Soc. *Res:* Spinal control of locomotion, chronic unit recording techniques, neural prostheses, information processing by nerve networks. *Mailing Add:* Lab Neurol Control NIH Bldg 36 Rm 5A29 Bethesda MD 20205

LOEB, JEROD M, b Brooklyn, NY, Oct 21, 49. CARDIOVASCULAR PHYSIOLOGY. *Educ:* City Univ New York, BS, 71; State Univ NY, PhD(physiol), 76. *Prof Exp:* Teaching asst physiol, State Univ NY Downstate Med Ctr, 72-76; res fel med, Harvard Med Sch, 76-77; res assoc physiol, Stritch Sch Med, Loyola Univ, Chicago, 77-79; ASST PROF SURG & PHYSIOL, MED SCH, NORTHWESTERN UNIV, 79- *Concurrent Pos:* Mem Coun Basic Sci, Am Heart Asn; prin investr, Am Heart Asn Grant-in-Aid, 80-82; career develop award, Schweppe Found, Chicago, Ill, 80-83. *Mem:* Am Physiol Soc; Sigma Xi; NY Acad Sci; Soc Exp Biol & Med. *Res:* Electrophysiologic analysis of normal and abnormal cardiac pacemaker activity; autonomic control of cardiac pacemakers; electrophysiologic mapping of human cardiac arrhythmias. *Mailing Add:* Med Sch Northwestern Univ 303 E Chicago Ave Chicago IL 60611

LOEB, LAWRENCE ARTHUR, b Poughkeepsie, NY, Dec 25, 36; m 58; c 3. CANCER, BIOCHEMISTRY. *Educ:* City Col New York, BS, 57; NY Univ, MD, 61; Univ Calif, Berkeley, PhD(biochem), 67. *Prof Exp:* Intern, Med Ctr, Stanford Univ, 61-62; res assoc biochem, Nat Cancer Inst, 62-64; res assoc zool, Univ Calif, Berkeley, 64-67; asst mem biochem, Inst Cancer Res, 67-69, assoc mem 71-77, mem, 77-78; PROF DEPT PATH, SCH MED, UNIV WASH, 78-, DIR, GOTTSTEIN MEM CANCER RES LABS, 78-, ADJ PROF DEPT BIOCHEM, 78- *Concurrent Pos:* Res grants, Am Cancer Soc, 67-69, Stanley C Dordick Found, 67, NIH & NSF, 69-75; assoc prof, Dept Path, Sch Med & mem biol & molecular biol grad groups, Univ Pa, 67-68. *Mem:* Am Asn Cancer Res; Fedn Am Socs Exp Biol; Am Soc Cell Biol; fel Am Col Physicians. *Res:* Fidelity of DNA replication; environmental carcinogenesis; human leukemia; mechanism of catalysis by DNA polymerases; zinc metalloenzymes; lymphocyte transformation. *Mailing Add:* Dept of Path SM-30 Univ of Wash Sch of Med Seattle WA 98195

LOEB, LEOPOLD, b Franklin, La, July 22, 23; m 48; c 2. PHYSICAL CHEMISTRY. *Educ:* La State Univ, BS, 43; Tulane Univ, MS, 48. *Prof Exp:* Chemist, Southern Regional Res Lab, USDA, 48-55; chemist, Major Appliance Labs, Gen Elec Co, 56-64, mgr chem res, 64-71, MGR ADVAN TECHNOL PROGS, GEN ELEC CO, 71- *Mem:* Am Chem Soc; Inst Food Technol; Sigma Xi. *Res:* Textile detergent chemistry. *Mailing Add:* Major Appliance Labs Gen Elec Co Appliance Park Louisville KY 40225

LOEB, MARCIA JOAN, b New York, NY, Mar 26, 33; m 53; c 2. INVERTEBRATE PHYSIOLOGY. *Educ:* Brooklyn Col, BA, 53; Cornell Univ, MS, 57; Univ Md, PhD(physiol), 70. *Prof Exp:* Nat Res Coun res assoc physiol & endocrinol of coelenterate develop, Naval Res Lab, 70-72; instr biol & physiol, Northern Va Community Col, 73; res assoc marine biol, Marine Sci Lab, Univ Col N Wales, 74; prof lectr physiol, Am Univ, 75-77; PHYSIOLOGIST, USDA, 77- *Mem:* Am Soc Zoologists; Atlantic Estuarine Res Soc; Entom Soc Am; Int Soc Invert Reproduction. *Res:* Elucidation of the environmental, physiological and endocrine control of strobilation in the Chesapeake Bay sea nettle, Chrysaora quinquecirrha; associated physiological phenomena in Chrysaora quinquecirrha; physiology of settlement in some marine bryzoan larvae; endocrinology and physiology of spermatogenesis in lepidoptera. *Mailing Add:* 6920 Fairfax Rd Bethesda MD 20014

LOEB, MARILYN ROSENTHAL, b New York, NY, Feb 26, 30; m 49; c 3. BIOCHEMISTRY OF BACTERIAL CELL SURFACE. *Educ:* Barnard Col, Columbia Univ, BA, 51; Bryn Mawr Col, MA, 55; Univ Pa, PhD(biochem), 58. *Prof Exp:* Res assoc biochem, Univ Pa, 58-59; res assoc, Med Col Pa, 65-68; res assoc biochem, Inst Cancer Res, 68-75; asst res prof microbiol, Med Sch, George Washington Univ, 75-77; prog assoc cell biol prog, NSF, 77-78; ASST PROF PEDIAT, MED SCH, UNIV ROCHESTER, 78- *Mem:* AAAS; Am Soc Microbiol. *Res:* Role of outer membrane proteins in pathogenesis of gram negative bacteria; biochemistry of thyroxine interaction with cell envelope of Escherichia coli. *Mailing Add:* Dept of Pediat Box 690 Univ of Rochester Med Sch Rochester NY 14642

LOEB, MELVIN LESTER, b New York, NY, Jan 20, 43; m 67; c 2. RESEARCH MANAGEMENT, SURFACTANT SYNTHESIS. *Educ:* City Col New York, BS, 64; Mass Inst Technol, SM, 67, PhD(chem), 69; Univ Chicago, MBA, 77. *Prof Exp:* Res chemist & group leader, Kraft, Inc, 69-78; group leader, 78-79, MGR RES, STEPHAN CHEM CO, 79- *Mem:* Am Chem Soc; Am Oil Chemist Soc; Soc Indust Res Inst. *Res:* Amine oxide chemistry; dimer acid chemistry; synthetic lubricants, surfactants, fatty acids and derivatives. *Mailing Add:* Stepan Chem Co Edens & Winnetka Northfield IL 60093

LOEB, PETER ALBERT, b Berkeley, Calif, July 3, 37; m 58; c 3. MATHEMATICS. *Educ:* Harvey Mudd Col, BS, 59, Princeton Univ, MA, 61; Stanford Univ, PhD(math), 65. *Prof Exp:* Asst prof math, Univ Calif, Los Angeles, 64-68; from asst prof to assoc prof, 68-75, PROF MATH, UNIV ILL, URBANA, 75- *Concurrent Pos:* Grant, Ctr Advan Studies, 71. *Mem:* Am Math Soc. *Res:* Topology; potential theory; non-standard analysis. *Mailing Add:* Dept of Math Univ of Ill Urbana IL 61801

LOEB, VIRGIL, JR, b St Louis, Mo, Sept 21, 21; m 50; c 4. ONCOLOGY, HEMATOLOGY. *Educ:* Washington Univ, MD, 44. *Prof Exp:* From instr to asst prof med, 51-56, asst prof path, 55-78, asst prof clin med, 56-68, assoc prof, 68-78, PROF CLIN MED, SCH MED, WASHINGTON UNIV, 78- *Concurrent Pos:* Nat Cancer Inst trainee, Sch Med, Washington Univ, 49-50, Damon Runyan res fel hemat, 50-52; dir cent diag labs, Barnes Hosp, St Louis, 52-68; NIH grant prin investr, Southeastern Cancer Study Group, 56-77; chmn, Cancer Clin Invest Res Comt, Nat Cancer Inst, 66-69, consult, 66-, mem, Polycythemia Vera Study Group & Diag Res Adv Group; mem, Oncol Rev Group Vet Admin; mem, Inst Med, Nat Acad Sci, 78- *Mem:* Fel Am Col Physicians; Am Asn Cancer Res; Am Soc Clin Oncol; Am Soc Hemat; Int Soc Hemat. *Res:* Medical oncology. *Mailing Add:* 4989 Barnes Hosp Plaza St Louis MO 63110

LOEBBAKA, DAVID S, b Gary, Ind, Aug 18, 39; m 79; c 3. HIGH ENERGY PHYSICS. *Educ:* Calif Inst Technol, BS, 61; Univ Md, PhD(physics), 67. *Prof Exp:* Assoc res scientist, Univ Notre Dame, 66-68; asst prof high energy physics, Vanderbilt Univ, 68-72; assoc prof, 72-77, PROF PHYSICS, UNIV TENN, 77- *Mem:* Sigma Xi; Am Asn Physics Teachers. *Mailing Add:* Dept of Geosci & Physics Univ of Tenn Martin TN 38238

LOEBENSTEIN, WILLIAM VAILLE, b Providence, RI, Aug 9, 14; m 49; c 4. PHYSICAL CHEMISTRY, DENTAL RESEARCH. *Educ:* Brown Univ, ScB, 35, ScM, 36, PhD(phys chem), 40. *Prof Exp:* Lab glassblower, Eastern Sci Co, 38-40; res & control chemist, Corning Glass Works, RI, 41; res assoc phys chem, 46-51, CHEMIST, NAT BUR STANDARDS, 51- *Concurrent Pos:* Mem comt com stand, Commodity Stand Div, Off Tech Servs. *Honors & Awards:* Meritorious Serv Medal, US Dept Com, 58. *Mem:* AAAS; Am Chem Soc; Sigma Xi; Int Asn Dent Res. *Res:* Catalysis; glass technology; physical and chemical adsorption of gases on solid surfaces; kinetics of adsorption from solutions; simplified techniques for the improvement in precision of surface area determinations from adsorption measurements; ortho-para conversion of liquid hydrogen; surface chemistry of teeth and dental materials. *Mailing Add:* Nat Bur of Standards Washington DC 20234

LOEBER, ADOLPH PAUL, b Detroit, Mich, Feb 1, 20; m 45; c 4. PHYSICS. *Educ:* Wayne State Univ, BS, 41, MA, 49; Univ Chicago, cert, 43; Mich State Univ, PhD(physics), 54. *Prof Exp:* Technician, Metall Dept, Chrysler Corp, 41-42, engr, Truck Dept, 45-47; instr physics, Wayne State Univ, 47-50; asst, Mich State Univ, 50-54; proj engr, Chrysler Corp, 54-55, from asst mgr to mgr physics res, 55-61, mgr phys optics res, Missile Div, 61-64; assoc prof physics, Eastern Mich Univ, 64-66; mgr electrooptics, Missile Div, Chrysler Corp, 66-68; assoc prof, 68-71, PROF PHYSICS, EASTERN MICH UNIV, 71- *Concurrent Pos:* Consult, Missile Div, Chrysler Corp, 64-66. *Mem:* Acoust Soc Am; Indust Math Soc (secy, 57-58); Am Asn Physics Teachers; Optical Soc Am. *Res:* Ultrasonics; physical optics; polarized light. *Mailing Add:* Dept Physics Eastern Mich Univ Ypsilanti MI 48297

LOEBER, JOHN FREDERICK, b White Plains, NY, Oct 5, 42; m 62; c 7. MECHANICAL ENGINEERING, ENGINEERING MECHANICS. *Educ:* Lehigh Univ, BS, 64, MS, 65, PhD(appl mech), 68. *Prof Exp:* Engr, 67-71, lead engr, 71-73, mgr methods develop, 73-81, MGR AFC REACTOR EQUIP DESIGN, KNOLLS ATOMIC POWER LAB, GEN ELEC CO, 81- *Concurrent Pos:* NASA fel, Lehigh Univ, 64-67. *Mem:* Am Soc Mech Engrs. *Res:* Finite element methods of structural analysis including computer program development and graphics; theoretical fracture mechanics. *Mailing Add:* 45 Heritage Pkwy Scotia NY 12302

LOEBL, ERNEST MOSHE, b Vienna, Austria, July 30, 23; nat US; m 50; c 2. CHEMICAL PHYSICS, PHYSICAL CHEMISTRY. *Educ:* Hebrew Univ, MSc, 46; Columbia Univ, PhD(chem), 52. *Prof Exp:* Res chemist, Olamith Cement Co, 47; asst chemist, Columbia Univ, 48-50; instr, Rutgers Univ, 50-51; from instr to assoc prof, 52-63, PROF PHYS CHEM, POLYTECH INST NEW YORK, 63-, HEAD DIV, 65- *Concurrent Pos:* NSF fel, 63-64; lectr, Esso Res; vis prof, Uppsala Univ, Sweden, 63, Oxford Univ, Eng, 64, Sheffield Univ, Eng, 71 & Hebrew Univ, Jerusalem, 73; dean, Natural Sci & Math, Yeshiva Univ, New York, 80. *Mem:* AAAS; Am Chem Soc; Am Phys Soc; Sigma Xi; Am Asn Univ Professors. *Res:* Theoretical chemistry; quantum theory; polyelectrolytes; solid state; catalysis. *Mailing Add:* Dept Chem Polytech Inst NY 333 Jay St Brooklyn NY 11201

LOEBL, RICHARD IRA, b Battle Creek, Mich, Oct 18, 45; m 76. MATHEMATICS. *Educ:* Harvard Univ, AB, 67; Univ Calif, Berkeley, PhD(math), 73. *Prof Exp:* Teaching assoc, Univ Calif, Berkeley, 67-72; actg instr, Univ Calif, Santa Cruz, 72-73; asst prof, 73-79, ASSOC PROF MATH, WAYNE STATE UNIV, 79- *Concurrent Pos:* Res assoc, Univ Calif, Berkeley, 74; fac res award, Wayne State Univ, 75-76. *Mem:* Am Math Soc; Math Asn Am. *Res:* Functional analysis-operator theory. *Mailing Add:* Dept of Math Wayne State Univ Detroit MI 48202

LOEBLICH, ALFRED RICHARD, JR, b Birmingham, Ala, Aug 15, 14; m 39; c 4. MICROPALEONTOLOGY, PALYNOLOGY. *Educ:* Univ Okla, BS, 37, MS, 38; Univ Chicago, PhD(paleont), 41. *Prof Exp:* Instr geol, Tulane Univ, 40-42; assoc cur invert paleont & paleobot, US Nat Mus, 46-57; from sr res paleontologist to res assoc paleontologist, 57-61; sr res assoc, Chevron Res Co, Standard Oil Co Calif, 61-68, sr res assoc, Chevron Oil Field Res Co, 68-79. *Concurrent Pos:* Adj prof geol, Univ Calif, Los Angeles, 72- *Honors & Awards:* Elected Corresp Mem, Societe Geologique Belgique, 74; Joseph Cushman Award, 82. *Mem:* AAAS; Soc Syst Zool; Soc Econ Paleontologists & Mineralogists; Int Phycol Soc; Int Asn Plant Taxon. *Res:* Stratigraphy; micropaleontology; recent and fossil foraminifera and phytoplankton; lower Paleozoic phytoplankton systematics, paleoecology and biostratigraphy; morphology systematics and classification foraminifera. *Mailing Add:* Dept Earth & Space Sci Univ Calif Los Angeles CA 90024

LOEBLICH, ALFRED RICHARD, III, b New Orleans, La, Mar 2, 41; m 63; c 2. PHYCOLOGY, MARINE BIOLOGY. *Educ:* Univ Calif, Berkeley, AB, 63; Univ Calif, San Diego, PhD(marine biol), 71. *Prof Exp:* Lab helper, Herbarium, Univ Calif, Berkeley, 62-63; teaching asst, Dept Bot, 63-64; lab technician marine biol, Univ Calif, San Diego, 70-71; asst prof & asst cur, Harvard Univ, 71-76, assoc prof & assoc cur, 76-78; ASSOC PROF BIOL, UNIV HOUSTON, 78- *Concurrent Pos:* USPHS fel, Univ Calif, San Diego, 64-70; NIH grant, 72-78; NSF grant, 74-; Mass Sci & Technol Found grant, 75-77; mem, Nomenclature Comt Algae, Int Asn Plant Taxon, 75-; mem, Comt Systs & Evolution, Soc Protozoologists, 77-; mem, Darbaker Prize Comt, Bot Soc Am, 78- *Honors & Awards:* Darbaker Prize, Bot Soc Am, 77. *Mem:* Phycol Soc Am; Soc Protozoologists; Int Phycological Soc; Am Soc Limnol Oceanog; Marine Biol Asn UK. *Res:* Dinoflagellate genetics; characterization of DNA of primitive algae; ultrastructure and physiology of unicellular algae; algal evolution. *Mailing Add:* Univ Houston 305 4700 Ave U Galveston TX 77550

LOEBLICH, HELEN NINA (TAPPAN), b Norman, Okla, Oct 12, 17; m 39; c 4. MICROPALEONTOLOGY, PALEOECOLOGY. *Educ:* Univ Okla, BS, 37, MS, 39; Univ Chicago, PhD(geol), 42. *Prof Exp:* Asst geol, Univ Okla, 37-39; instr, Tulane Univ, 42-43; geologist US Geol Surv, 43-45 & 47-59; Guggenheim fel, 54; hon res assoc paleont, Smithsonian Inst, 54-57; lectr geol, 58-65, assoc res geologist, 61-63, sr lectr geol, 65-66, vchmn dept, 73-75, PROF GEOL, UNIV CALIF, LOS ANGELES, 66- *Honors & Awards:* Joseph Cushman Award, 82. *Mem:* Hon mem Soc Econ Paleontologists & Mineralogists; Am Micros Soc; fel Geol Soc Am; Phycol Soc Am; Soc Protozool. *Res:* Micropaleontology; living and fossil foraminiferans, tintinnids, thecamoebians and organic-walled, siliceous and calcareous phytoplankton; morphology, taxonomy, ecology, primary productivity and food chains, evolution and extinctions. *Mailing Add:* Dept Earth & Space Sci Univ Calif Los Angeles CA 90024

LOEBLICH, KAREN ELIZABETH, b Ft Sill, Okla, Oct 10, 44; m 75. ANIMAL BEHAVIOR, ENTOMOLOGY. *Educ:* Univ Calif, Los Angeles, AB, 66, MA, 67; Univ Calif, Davis, PhD(zool), 73. *Prof Exp:* Res assoc entomol, Univ Calif, Davis, 71-72; res assoc, Univ Calif, Riverside, 72-73; res assoc, Univ Hawaii, 74; lectr entomol & zool, San Francisco State Univ, 73-75; res scientist entomol, Agr Div, Upjohn Co, 75-76; lectr ecol & behav, San Diego State Univ, 77-78; MEM STAFF, DEPT ENTOM, UNIV CALIF, DAVIS, 78- UPJOHN CO, 75- *Mem:* Asn Study Animal Behav; Entomol Soc Am; Ecol Soc Am; Sigma Xi; AAAS. *Res:* Behavior and evolution of Diptera; Drosophilidae of Hawaii; insect grooming behavior; integrated pest management, especially of cotton. *Mailing Add:* Dept of Entom Univ of Calif Davis CA 95616

LOEBNER, EGON EZRIEL, b Plzen, Czech, Feb 24, 24; nat US; m 50; c 3. COMPUTER SCIENCE, SYSTEM INTELLIGENCE. *Educ:* Univ Buffalo, BA, 50, PhD(physics), 55. *Prof Exp:* Sr scientist, Sylvania Elec Prod, Inc, Gen Tel & Electronics Corp, 52-55; mem tech staff, RCA Labs, 55-61; mgr optoelectronics, HP Assocs, Hewlett-Packard Co, Calif, 61-65, head spec projs dept, Solid State Lab, 65-73, res adv, 73-74; counr sci & technol affairs, US Embassy, Moscow, 74-76; assoc, Solid State Lab, 76-77, head, Sect Data Base Mgt Systs, Comput Res Lab, Electronic Res Ctr, 77-81, HEAD, DEPT COGNITIVE INTERFACE COMPUT SCI LAB, COMPUT RES CTR, HEWLETT-PACKARD CO, 81- *Concurrent Pos:* Mem, State Comn Radiation Protection, NJ, 59-62 & IMD Electronic Mat Comt, 66-72; lectr, Stanford Univ, 68-74; dir, Compusec Corp, 71-73; interdisciplinary lectr, Univ Calif, Santa Cruz, 72-73. *Honors & Awards:* Radio Corp Am Award, 59. *Mem:* Nat Soc Prof Engrs; Sigma Xi; Cognitive Sci Soc; Inst Elec & Electronics Engrs; Am Asn Artificial Intel. *Res:* Solid state optoelectronic phenomena, materials, devices; image sensing, display and processing; medical, environmental instrumentation; neurophysiological networks; sensory perception, cognitive data processing; inventing, discovering, interdisciplinary transfer methodologies; cognitive science; psycholinguistics; computerized scientific research administration. *Mailing Add:* Comput Res Lab 3500 Deer Creek Rd Palo Alto CA 94304

LOECHELT, CECIL P(AUL), b Elfers, Fla, Nov 4, 35; m 56; c 3. CHEMICAL ENGINEERING. *Educ:* Vanderbilt Univ, BE, 56; La State Univ, MS, 62, PhD(adsorption), 64. *Prof Exp:* Instr chem eng, La State Univ, 63-64; sr process design engr, 64-70, SR ECON EVAL ENGR, ETHYL CORP, 70- *Mem:* Am Inst Chem Engrs. *Res:* Mathematical simulation of physical processes; evaluation and design of chemical processes. *Mailing Add:* 1904 Stanford Ave Baton Rouge LA 70808

LOEFER, JOHN B, b Forest Junction, Wis, June 14, 08; m 34; c 2. BIOLOGY. *Educ:* Lawrence Col, AB, 29; NY Univ, MS, 31, PhD(protozool), 33. *Prof Exp:* Asst zool, NY Univ, 33-35; assoc prof biol & chem, Berea Col, 35-43; instr biol, Brooklyn Col, 46; sr res biologist & head dept exp biol, Southwest Found Res & Ed, 46-53; coordr biol sci, Off Naval Res, 53-77; RETIRED. *Concurrent Pos:* Prof, Trinity Univ, 50-53; res zoologist, Univ Calif, Los Angeles, 53-; Hancock res scholar, Univ Southern California, 53; res fel, Calif Inst Technol, 54-62; partic, 4th Int Cancer Cong, St Louis; 2nd Int Cong, Biochem, Paris & Int Physiol Cong, Montreal; mem 3rd Int Cong Microbiol, New York & 7th Int Cong, Stockholm, partic, 6th Int Cong, Rome, 8th Int Cong Cell Biol, Leiden & 10th, Paris & 15th Int Cong Zool, London. *Mem:* AAAS; Soc Exp Biol & Med; Am Physiol Soc; Am Soc Zool; Soc Protozool. *Res:* Morphology, culture and nutrition of flagellates and ciliates; population studies; pH and growth; symbiosis; acclimatization and pattern formation; malarial and helminth incidence and control; chlorophyll inhibition and action of antibiotics on protozoa and fungi; bovine fetal fluid composition; tumor growth and host resistance phenomena; serology of Tetrahymena; scientific administration. *Mailing Add:* 1233 Sagemont Place Altadena CA 91001

LOEFFLER, ALBERT L, JR, b Mineola, NY, Oct 22, 27; m 57; c 3. TURBULENCE. *Educ:* Va Polytech Inst, BS, 49; Iowa State Univ, PhD(chem eng), 53. *Prof Exp:* Res engr, NASA, 54-59; res engr, 59-60, group leader, 60-74, STAFF SCIENTIST, RES DEPT, GRUMMAN AEROSPACE CORP, 74- *Mem:* Am Phys Soc; Am Inst Aeronaut & Astronaut. *Res:* Plasma physics; boundary layers; magnetohydrodynamics; heat transfer; potential flow problems. *Mailing Add:* Two Diamond Ct Huntington NY 11743

LOEFFLER, CHARLES EMIL, chemical engineering, see previous edition

LOEFFLER, FRANK JOSEPH, b Ballston Spa, NY, Sept 5, 28; m 51; c 4. PHYSICS. *Educ:* Cornell Univ, BS, 51, PhD(physics), 57. *Prof Exp:* Mem staff, Princeton Univ, 57-58; from asst prof to assoc prof, 58-67, PROF PHYSICS, PURDUE UNIV, 67- *Concurrent Pos:* Vis prof, Univ Hamburg, 63-64 & Univ Heidelberg, 71; Mem bd trustees & exec comt, chmn high energy physics comt, Argonne Univ Asn, 74-, fusion energy comt, 79- *Mem:* Fel Am Phys Soc; Sigma Xi. *Res:* Elementary particle physics; experimental study of elementary particle interactions at high energy using electronic detection systems; atmospheric physics; investigation of alternate energy sources. *Mailing Add:* Dept of Physics Purdue Univ Lafayette IN 47907

LOEFFLER, LARRY JAMES, b Beaver Falls, Pa, May 6, 32; m 57; c 2. ORGANIC CHEMISTRY. *Educ:* Princeton Univ, AB, 54, PhD(org chem), 61. *Prof Exp:* USPHS fel, Swiss Fed Inst Technol, 61-62; sr res chemist, Merck Sharp & Dohme Res Labs, Pa, 62-69; spec res fel, NIH, 69-71; asst prof, 71-74, assoc prof, 74-78, PROF MED CHEM, SCH PHARM, UNIV NC, CHAPEL HILL, 78- *Mem:* Am Chem Soc. *Res:* Medicinal chemistry; design and synthesis of compounds of interest as potential drugs; radioimmunoassay development. *Mailing Add:* 317 Wesley Dr Chapel Hill NC 27514

LOEFFLER, MARY CONSTANCE, b Pittsburgh, Pa, Oct 7, 22. PHYSICAL CHEMISTRY. *Educ:* Mt Mercy Col, Pa, BA, 44; Cath Univ Am, MS, 48; Carnegie Inst Technol, PhD(phys chem), 54. *Prof Exp:* Instr chem & physics, 45-54, asst prof chem, 55-56, ASSOC PROF CHEM, CARLOW COL, 56-, ASST TO PRES PLANNING, 71- *Mem:* Am Chem Soc; Am Asn Physics Teachers. *Res:* Biochemistry; chemical education. *Mailing Add:* 167 Southern Ave Pittsburgh PA 15211

LOEFFLER, ROBERT J, b Worcester, Mass, Oct 20, 22; m 56; c 4. BOTANY. *Educ:* Syracuse Univ, BA, 48; Univ Wis, MS, 50, PhD(bot, zool), 54. *Prof Exp:* From asst prof to prof, 54-73, EMER PROF BOT, CONCORDIA COL, MOORHEAD, MINN, 73- *Mem:* Bot Soc Am; Am Inst Biol Sci. *Res:* Pollen analysis of Spiritwood Lake, North Dakota; phytoplankton; plant anatomy and morphology. *Mailing Add:* 704 Eighth St So Moorhead MN 56560

LOEGERING, DANIEL JOHN, b Minn, Mar 11, 43; m 68; c 3. PHYSIOLOGY. *Educ:* St John's Univ, Minn, BS, 65; Univ SDak, Vermillion, MA, 67; Univ Western Ont, PhD(physiol), 70. *Prof Exp:* Instr physiol, Med Col Wis, 69-73; asst prof, 73-77, ASSOC PROF PHYSIOL, ALBANY MED COL, 77- *Concurrent Pos:* Wis Heart Asn fel, Med Col Wis, 70-72, NIH spec res fel, 72-73. *Mem:* Reticuloendothelial Soc; Am Physiol Soc. *Res:* Reticuloendothelial system function as related to systemic host defense during circulatory shock and serum enzyme changes during shock and exercise. *Mailing Add:* Dept of Physiol Albany Med Col Albany NY 12208

LOEHLIN, JAMES HERBERT, b Mussoorie, India, May 23, 34; US citizen; m 75; c 2. PHYSICAL CHEMISTRY, CRYSTALLOGRAPHY. *Educ:* Col Wooster, BA, 56; Mass Inst Technol, PhD(phys chem), 60. *Prof Exp:* Instr chem, Swarthmore Col, 60-61; from instr to asst prof, Col Wooster, 61-64; asst prof, Swarthmore Col, 64-66; from asst prof to assoc prof, 66-77, chmn dept, 71-74, PROF CHEM, WELLESLEY COL, 77-, CHMN DEPT, 81- *Concurrent Pos:* Res assoc, Univ Chicago, 69-70; vis mem fac, Inst Chem, Univ Uppsala, 76-77. *Mem:* Am Crystallog Asn; Am Phys Soc; AAAS; Sigma Xi; Int Solar Energy Soc. *Res:* Crystallography; molecular structure and solids; energy conversion; solid state phase behavior. *Mailing Add:* Dept of Chem Wellesley Col Wellesley MA 02181

LOEHMAN, RONALD ERNEST, b San Antonio, Tex, Feb 22, 43; m 65. CERAMICS, SOLID STATE CHEMISTRY. *Educ:* Rice Univ, BA, 64; Purdue Univ, PhD(chem), 69. *Prof Exp:* Res fel mat res, Thermophys Properties Res Ctr, Purdue Univ, 69-70; from asst prof to assoc prof mat eng, Univ Fla, 70-78; staff mem, Sandia Labs, Albuquerque, 77-78; STAFF SCIENTIST, SRI INT, 78- *Mem:* Am Ceramic Soc; AAAS; Nat Inst Ceramic Engrs. *Res:* Nitrogen ceramics; high temperature materials; electronic properties of materials; glass formation and crystallization; crystal growth. *Mailing Add:* SRI Int 333 Ravenswood Ave Menlo Park CA 94025

LOEHR, RAYMOND CHARLES, b Cleveland, Ohio, May 17, 31; m 53; c 8. CIVIL & SANITARY ENGINEERING. *Educ:* Case Inst Technol, BS, 53, MS 56; Univ Wis, PhD(sanit eng), 61. *Prof Exp:* From instr civil eng to asst prof, Case Inst Technol, 54-61; from assoc prof civil & sanit eng to prof, Univ Kans, 61-68; dir environ studies prog, 72-80, PROF AGR ENG & CIVIL ENG, CORNELL UNIV, 68-, LIBERTY HYDE BAILEY PROF ENG, 81- *Concurrent Pos:* US Pub Health Serv & Environ Protection Agency res grants, 63-; chmn technol assessment & pollution control adv comt, Sci Adv Bd, Environ Protection Agency, 78-80. *Honors & Awards:* Rudolph Hering Award, Am Soc Civil Engrs, 69. *Mem:* AAAS; Am Soc Civil Engrs; Water Pollution Control Fedn; Am Asn Prof Sanit Engrs (pres, 71). *Res:* Environmental health engineering; water and wastewater treatment; biological waste treatment; agricultural waste management; land treatment of wastes. *Mailing Add:* 207 Riley-Robb Cornell Univ Ithaca NY 14850

LOEHR, THOMAS MICHAEL, b Munich, Ger, Oct 2, 39; US citizen; m 65. CHEMISTRY. *Educ:* Univ Mich, Ann Arbor, BS, 63; Cornell Univ, PhD(chem), 67. *Prof Exp:* Asst prof chem, Cornell Univ, 67-68; asst prof chem, 68-74, assoc prof, 74-78, PROF CHEM, ORE GRAD CTR, 78- *Concurrent Pos:* NIH res grant, Ore Grad Ctr, 71-; vis lectr, Portland State Univ, 71-72; vis assoc chem, Calif Inst Technol, 78-79; res grant, NSF, 74-77; mem, NIH Metallobiochem Study Sect, 78- *Mem:* AAAS; Am Chem Soc; Soc Appl Spectros; Royal Soc Chem. *Res:* Structural inorganic chemistry; infrared and Raman spectroscopy; metal ion complexes; metallobiol chemistry; molecular and electronic structure of metalloproteins; solid state vibrational spectroscopy; analytical applications of Raman spectroscopy. *Mailing Add:* Ore Grad Ctr 19600 NW Walker Rd Beaverton OR 97005

LOEHRKE, HARRY F(REDERICK), b Toledo, Ohio, July 29, 21; m 43; c 3. ELECTRICAL ENGINEERING. *Educ:* Univ Toledo, BS, 47, MBA, 69. *Prof Exp:* Physicist, Kimble Glass Co Div Owens-Ill Glass Co, 47-53, physicist, Gen Res Div, 53-56, chief new develop sect, 56-60, mgr spec proj & dielectric lab, 60-62, personnel dir tech ctr, 62-66, facilities mgr, 66-73, mgr admin serv, 73-77, mgr craft serv, 77-78, MGR CRAFT SERV & TECH PROPERTIES, OWENS-ILL, INC, 78- *Res:* Electrical and dielectric properties of glass; stress development in glass bodies; monochrome and color television bulbs; low temperature sealing glasses; glass feeding; glass crystalline materials; management of research facilities. *Mailing Add:* Owens-Ill Inc One Sea Gate Toledo OH 43666

LOEHRKE, RICHARD IRWIN, b Milwaukee, Wis, May 11, 35; m 57; c 2. MECHANICAL ENGINEERING. *Educ:* Univ Wis, BS, 57; Univ Colo, MS, 65; Ill Inst Technol, PhD(mech eng), 70. *Prof Exp:* Tech engr aircraft nuclear propulsion dept, Gen Elec Co, 57-61; res engr, Sundstrand Corp, 61-65; asst prof mech eng, Ill Inst Technol, 70-71; asst prof, 71-76, ASSOC PROF MECH ENG, COLO STATE UNIV, 76- *Mem:* Am Soc Mech Engrs; Am Inst Aeronaut & Astronaut. *Res:* Heat transfer; fluid mechanics. *Mailing Add:* Dept of Mech Eng Colo State Univ Ft Collins CO 80523

LOELIGER, DAVID A, b Scranton, Pa, Mar 1, 39; m 60; c 4. COORDINATION CHEMISTRY. *Educ:* Col Wooster, BA, 61; Univ Chicago, MS, 62, PhD(chem), 65. *Prof Exp:* Asst prof chem, Purdue Univ, 64-67; sr res chemist, Eastman Kodak Co, 67-72; ASSOC PROF CHEM, INT CHRISTIAN UNIV, 72-, RES CONSULT, ARCHEOL RES CTR, 75- *Concurrent Pos:* Missionary, Am Lutheran Church, 72- *Mem:* Am Chem Soc. *Res:* Oxidation-reduction and subtitution reactions of transition metal ions and complexes; application of chemical techniques to problems of archaeological interest; chemical analysis of archaeological artifacts. *Mailing Add:* Dept of Chem Int Christian Univ Mitaka Tokyo Japan

LOENING, KURT L, b Berlin, Ger, Jan 18, 24; nat US; m 45; c 2. PHYSICAL CHEMISTRY, ORGANIC CHEMISTRY. *Educ:* Ohio State Univ, BS, 44, PhD(chem), 51. *Prof Exp:* From asst ed to sr assoc ed, Chem Abstracts, 51-63, assoc dir, Nomenclature, 63-64, DIR, NOMENCLATURE, CHEM ABSTRACTS, 64- *Concurrent Pos:* Chmn, Interdiv Comt, Nomenclatore & Symbols, Int Union Pure & Appl Chem, 76-, comt nomenclatore, Am Chem Soc, 64- *Mem:* AAAS; Am Chem Soc. *Res:* Acid-catalyzed esterification of organic acids; chemical nomenclature; literature. *Mailing Add:* 2064 Inchcliff Rd Columbus OH 43221

LOEPPERT, RICHARD HENRY, b Chicago, Ill, Mar 13, 14; m 40; c 1. ORGANIC CHEMISTRY. *Educ:* Northwestern Univ, BS, 35; Univ Minn, PhD(phys chem), 40. *Prof Exp:* Asst, Univ Minn, 35-39; res chemist, Richardson Co, Ill, 39-40; from instr to assoc prof, 40-59, prof, 59-79, EMER PROF CHEM, NC STATE UNIV, 79- *Mem:* AAAS; Am Chem Soc. *Mailing Add:* 1317 Rand Dr Raleigh NC 27608

LOEPPKY, RICHARD N, b Lewiston, Idaho, Aug 2, 37; m 65. PHYSICAL ORGANIC CHEMISTRY. *Educ:* Univ Idaho, BS, 59; Univ Mich, MS, 61, PhD(chem), 63. *Prof Exp:* Instr chem, Univ Mich, 63; NIH fel org chem, Univ Ill, 63-64; asst prof, 64-70, ASSOC PROF CHEM, UNIV MO-COLUMBIA, 70- *Concurrent Pos:* Resident vis, Bell Labs, 71-72. *Honors & Awards:* Kasimir Fajans Award, Univ Mich, 65. *Mem:* Am Chem Soc; AAAS. *Res:* Chemical carcinogenesis and physical organic chemistry; chemical and biochemical transformation of nitrosamines directed at understanding their environmental and biochemical formation, transformation and destruction. *Mailing Add:* Dept of Chem Univ of Mo Columbia MO 65201

LOESCH, HAROLD CARL, b Tex, Oct 3, 26; m 45; c 4. BIOLOGICAL OCEANOGRAPHY. *Educ:* Agr & Mech Col, Tex, BS, 51, MS, 54, PhD(biol oceanog), 62. *Prof Exp:* Asst, Agr & Mech Col, Tex, 50-52; prin marine biologist, State of Ala, 52-58; res scientist, Res Found, Agr & Mech Col, Tex, 59-60; expert fisheries biol, UN Food & Agr Orgn, Guatemala, 60, Honduras, 60-61, Ecuador, 61-66 & San Salvador, 66-68; prof marine sci & in off sea grants develop, La State Univ, 68-75; ESTUARINE ECOLOGIST, UNESCO, MEXICO, 76- *Mem:* Am Fisheries Soc; Am Soc Ichthyologists & Herpetologists; Am Soc Limnol & Oceanog; Nat Shellfisheries Asn; fel Int Acad Fishery Sci. *Res:* Estuarine hydrology and biology; shrimp, lobster and inshore fishes ecology; fisheries dynamics. *Mailing Add:* 1232 Dahlia St Baton Rouge LA 70808

LOESCH, JOSEPH G, b Middle Village, NY, May 5, 30; m; c 3. MARINE BIOLOGY. *Educ:* Univ RI, BS, 65; Univ Conn, MS, 68, PhD, 69. *Prof Exp:* Res asst bluefish migrations, Marine Lab, Univ Conn, Noank, 65-66, asst proj leader, Conn Rivers Study, 66-69; ASSOC PROF MARINE SCI, COL WILLIAM & MARY & UNIV VA, 69- *Concurrent Pos:* Assoc marine scientist, Va Inst Marine Sci. *Mem:* Am Fisheries Soc; Atlantic Estuarine Res Soc. *Res:* Marine fisheries; general life history study of anadromous fishes; biometrics and population dynamics of commercially important fishes. *Mailing Add:* Dept of Ichthyol Va Inst of Marine Sci Gloucester Point VA 23062

LOESCHER, WAYNE HAROLD, b Lima, Ohio, Nov 6, 42; m 67; c 1. PLANT PHYSIOLOGY. *Educ:* Miami Univ, BA, 64, MS, 66; Iowa State Univ, PhD(plant physiol), 72. *Prof Exp:* Res assoc plant physiol, Dept Agron, Iowa State Univ, 71-73; plant physiologist, Los Angeles Arboretum, Arcadia, Calif, 73-75; asst prof plant physiol & asst horticulturist, 75-80, ASSOC PROF & ASSOC HORTICULTURIST, WASH STATE UNIV, 80- *Res:* Plant growth and development; plant tissue culture. *Mailing Add:* Dept of Hort Wash State Univ Pullman WA 99163

LOESER, CHARLES NATHAN, cytology, neuroanatomy, deceased

LOESER, EUGENE WILLIAM, b Buffalo, NY, Nov 5, 26; m 55; c 1. MEDICINE. *Educ:* Univ Buffalo, MD, 52. *Prof Exp:* Asst neurol, Columbia Univ, 56-57; asst prof, Univ NC, 57-61; asst prof clin neurol, NY Univ, 64-71; clin assoc prof neurol, Rutgers Med Sch, 71-78; MEM STAFF, KIRKWOOD OUTPATIENT CTR, 78- *Mem:* AMA; Am Acad Neurol. *Res:* Medical neurology. *Mailing Add:* Outpatient Ctr Jupiter FL 33458

LOETTERLE, GERALD JOHN, b Edgar, Nebr, Sept 15, 06; m 37; c 3. GEOLOGY. *Educ:* Univ Nebr, AB, 31, MSc, 33; Columbia Univ, PhD(geol), 37. *Prof Exp:* Geologist, Shell Oil Co, Inc, Tex, 37-45; consult geologist, Hudnall, Pirtle & Loetterle, 45-75; GEOLOGIST, 75- *Mem:* Am Asn Petrol Geol. *Res:* Micropaleontology; exploration geology; estimation of petroleum reserves; micropaleontology of the Niobrara formation in Kansas, Nebraska and South Dakota. *Mailing Add:* Hudnall Pirtle & Loetterle 308 E Third St Tyler TX 75706

LOEV, BERNARD, b Philadelphia, Pa, Feb 26, 28; m 54; c 3. ORGANIC CHEMISTRY, MEDICINAL CHEMISTRY. *Educ:* Univ Pa, BSc, 49; Columbia Univ, MA, 50, PhD(org chem), 52. *Prof Exp:* Instr inorg & org chem, Columbia Univ, 49-51; proj leader, Pennsalt Chem Co, 52-58; group leader, Smith Kline & French Labs, Pa, 58-66, sr investr, 66-67, from asst dir to assoc dir chem, 67-75; dir, Chem Res & Develop Div, USV Pharmaceut Corp, 75-80, VPRES CHEM RES & DEVELOP, REVLON HEALTH CARE GROUP, 80- *Concurrent Pos:* Mem adv bd, Index Chemicus & Intra-Sci Res Found; mem bd dirs, Int Heterocyclic Cong; ed bd, Jour Heterocyclic Chem, 72- *Mem:* AAAS; Am Chem Soc; Am Inst Chem; NY Acad Sci. *Res:* Organic synthesis; organic sulfur compounds; medicinal chemistry; nitrogen and sulfur heterocycles; natural products; central nervous system, cardiovascular, asthma, anti-arthritic and anti-ulcer areas. *Mailing Add:* Revlon Health Care Group 1 Scarsdale Rd Tuckahoe NY 10707

LOEVINGER, ROBERT, b St Paul, Minn, Jan 31, 16; m 52; c 3. RADIOLOGICAL PHYSICS, METROLOGY. *Educ:* Univ Minn, BA, 36; Harvard Univ, MA, 41; Univ Calif, PhD(physics), 48. *Prof Exp:* Physicist, Radiation Lab, Univ Calif, 42-45, Los Alamos Sci Lab, 45-46, Radiation Lab, 46-48; asst physicist, Mt Sinai Hosp, 48-56; res assoc radiol, Sch Med, Stanford Univ, 57-60, asst prof, 60-65; mem staff, Div Isotopes, Int Atomic Energy Agency, 65-68; CHIEF DOSIMETRY SECT, CTR RADIATION RES, NAT BUR STANDARDS, 68- *Mem:* Fel Am Col Radiol; Am Asn Physicists in Med; Radiation Res Soc; Health Physics Soc; Radiol Soc NAm. *Res:* Radiation dosimetry and standards. *Mailing Add:* Radiation Physics C 210 Nat Bur Standards Washington DC 20234

LOEW, ELLIS ROGER, b Los Angeles, Calif, Jan 18, 47. VISUAL PHYSIOLOGY, SENSORY BIOPHYSICS. *Educ:* Univ Calif, Los Angeles, BA, 68, MA, 72, PhD(biol), 73. *Prof Exp:* Fel, Vision Unit, Med Res Coun, 73-74, vis fel, 74-75; res fel, 75-77, ASST PROF PHYSIOL, CORNELL UNIV, 77- *Mem:* AAAS; Marine Biol Asn UK; Brit Photobiol Asn; Inst Electronic & Elec Engrs. *Res:* Physiology and biochemistry of visual photoreceptors; biochemistry and biophysics of visual pigments; sensory ecology. *Mailing Add:* Physiol Sect Cornell Univ Ithaca NY 14853

LOEW, FRANKLIN MARTIN, b Syracuse, NY, Sept 8, 39; m 64; c 2. NUTRITIONAL TOXICOLOGY, ANIMAL MEDICINE. *Educ:* Cornell Univ, BS, 61, DVM, 65; Univ Sask, PhD(pharmacol, toxicol), 71. *Prof Exp:* Res scientist, R J Reynolds Tobacco Co, 65-66; res asst, Med Sch, Tulane Univ, 66-67; lectr vet med, Univ Sask, 67-69; MRC fel, Sch Med, Johns Hopkins Univ, 69-71, dir animal resources, 71-74, prof toxicol, 74-77, chief, Lab Animal Med, 77-82, dir, Div Comp Med, 79-82; DEAN, SCH VET MED, TUFTS UNIV, 82- *Concurrent Pos:* Consult, Am Asn Accreditation Lab Animal Care, 78-81, Human Nutrit Inst, USDA, 78-82 & Div Res Resources, NIH & Nat Inst Aging. *Mem:* Soc Toxicol; Am Inst Nutrit; Am Col Lab Animal Med; Am Asn Lab Animal Sci; Royal Soc Med. *Res:* Thiamin deficiency and metabolism; toxicology of long chain fatty acids; diseases of laboratory animals. *Mailing Add:* Div Comp Med Hopkins Univ Sch Med 720 Rutland Ave Baltimore MD 21205

LOEW, GILDA M HARRIS, b New York, NY; c 4. THEORETICAL BIOLOGY, BIOPHYSICS. *Educ:* NY Univ, BA, 51; Columbia Univ, MA, 52; Univ Calif, Berkeley, PhD(chem physics), 57. *Prof Exp:* Res physicist, Lawrence Radiation Lab, Univ Calif, Berkeley, 57-62 & Lockheed Missiles & Space Co, 62-64; assoc quantum biophys, Biophys Lab, Stanford Univ, 64-66; from asst prof to assoc prof physics, Pomona Col, 66-69; res biophysicist & instr biophys, Med Sch, Stanford Univ, 69-79, adj prof genetics, Med Ctr, 74-79; PRES, MOLECULAR RES INST, 79-; PROG DIR MOLECULAR THEORY, LIFE SCI DIV, SRI INT, 79- *Concurrent Pos:* Grants, NSF, 66-, NASA, 69- & NIH, 74-; adj prof, Rockefeller Univ, 79- *Mem:* Biophys Soc; fel Am Phys Soc; Int Soc Magnetic Resonance. *Res:* Molecular orbital and crystal field quantum chemical calculations; models for protein active sites; mechanisms and requirements for specific drug action; theoretical studies related to chemical evolution of life. *Mailing Add:* Life Sci Div SRI Int 333 Ravenswood Ave Menlo Park CA 94025

LOEW, LESLIE MAX, b New York, NY, Sept 2, 47; m 70; c 3. PHYSICAL ORGANIC CHEMISTRY, BIOPHYSICAL CHEMISTRY. *Educ:* City Col New York, BS, 69; Cornell Univ, MS, 72, PhD(chem), 74. *Prof Exp:* Res assoc chem, Harvard Univ, 73-74; asst prof, 74-79, ASSOC PROF CHEM, STATE UNIV NY BINGHAMTON, 79- *Concurrent Pos:* Vis scientist, Weizmann Inst Sci, 81-82. *Honors & Awards:* NIH Res Career Develop Award. *Mem:* Am Chem Soc; Biophys Soc; AAAS. *Res:* Organophosphorus chemistry; biomembranes; theoretical organic chemistry; electrical, adhesive and chemical properties of biomembranes using spectroscopic techniques. *Mailing Add:* Dept of Chem State Univ of NY Binghamton NY 13901

LOEWE, WILLIAM EDWARD, b Chicago, Ill, Apr 22, 32; m 53; c 3. APPLIED PHYSICS. *Educ:* Univ Chicago, AB, 52; Univ Ill, BS, 53; Ill Inst Technol, MS, 59, PhD(physics), 63. *Prof Exp:* Reactor physicist, Savannah River Lab, E I du Pont de Nemours & Co, 53-54, Savannah River Plant, 54-57; assoc physicist, IIT Res Inst, 57-59, res physicist, 59-62, res physicist group leader, 62-63, mgr nuclear physics, 63-66; adv scientist, Nerva, Astro-nuclear Lab, Westinghouse Elec Corp, 66-67; SR PHYSICIST, LAWRENCE LIVERMORE LAB, 67- *Mem:* Am Nuclear Soc; Am Phys Soc; AAAS. *Res:* Nuclear and atomic physics of ionized media and radiation transport, especially exploiting very high speed computers. *Mailing Add:* 1072 Xavier Way Livermore CA 94550

LOEWEN, ERWIN G, b Frankfurt am Maine, Ger, Apr 12, 21; m 52; c 2. MECHANICAL ENGINEERING. *Educ:* NY Univ, BME, 41; Mass Inst Technol, SM, 49, ME, 50, ScD, 52. *Prof Exp:* Tech dir, Taft-Peirce Mfg Co, 55-60; head, Dept Metrol, 60-67, DIR GRATING & METROL LABS, BAUSCH & LOMB CO, 67- *Mem:* AAAS; Am Soc Mech Engrs; Soc Mfg Engrs; Optical Soc Am; Soc Photo Instr Engrs. *Res:* Metal cutting; metrology; diffraction. *Mailing Add:* 56 Westwood Dr East Rochester NY 14445

LOEWEN, KENNETH LEROY, b Hillsboro, Kans, Mar 6, 27; m 79; c 4. MATHEMATICS. *Educ:* Tabor Col, AB, 48; Kans State Univ, MS, 50; Pa State Univ, PhD, 61. *Prof Exp:* Instr math, Kans State, 48-50; instr math & sci, Freeman Jr Col, 54-55; asst prof math, Tabor Col, 56-62, Westmont Col, 62-66 & Univ Okla, 66-71. *Mem:* Math Asn Am. *Res:* Mathematical logic; foundations of mathematics. *Mailing Add:* 1226 Barkley Norman OK 73071

LOEWENFELD, IRENE ELIZABETH, b Munich, Ger, June 2, 21; nat US. PHYSIOLOGY. *Educ:* Univ Bonn, PhD(zool), 56. *Prof Exp:* Asst ophthal, Columbia Univ, 58-61, instr, 61-62, res assoc, 62-68; from asst prof to assoc prof, 68-81, PROF OPHTHAL, SCH MED, WAYNE STATE UNIV, 81- *Mem:* Asn Res Vision & Ophthal. *Res:* Neurophysiology; neuroophthalmology; autonomic nervous system; pupil; visual physiology. *Mailing Add:* Kresge Eye Inst Wayne State Univ Detroit MI 48201

LOEWENSON, RUTH BRANDENBURGER, b Zurich, Switz; US citizen; c 2. BIOMETRICS. *Educ:* Univ Minn, Minneapolis, BA, 59, MS, 61, PhD(biomet), 68. *Prof Exp:* From instr to asst prof, 65-72, ASSOC PROF NEUROL & BIOMET, SCH MED, UNIV MINN, MINNEAPOLIS, 72- *Concurrent Pos:* Consult statistician, Vet Admin Hosp, Minneapolis, 71- *Mem:* Am Statist Asn; Biomet Soc; Am Pub Health Asn; Soc Epidemiol Res. *Res:* Epidemiology of cerebral vascular disease; clinical studies in neurology. *Mailing Add:* Dept of Neurol Univ of Minn Health Sci Ctr Minneapolis MN 55455

LOEWENSTEIN, ERNEST VICTOR, optics, spectroscopy, see previous edition

LOEWENSTEIN, HOWARD, b New York, NY, Jan 1, 24; m 58; c 2. FORESTRY. *Educ:* Colo State Univ, BS, 52; Univ Wis, PhD(soils), 55. *Prof Exp:* Instr soils, Univ Wis, 55-56; asst prof silvicult, State Univ NY, Col Forestry, Syracuse, 57-58; from asst prof to assoc prof, 58-68, PROF FOREST SOILS, UNIV IDAHO, 68- *Mem:* Soil Sci Soc Am. *Res:* Forest soil-site relationships; forest fertilization; problems of tree seedling establishment; soil microbiology. *Mailing Add:* Col of Forestry Univ of Idaho Moscow ID 83843

LOEWENSTEIN, JOSEPH EDWARD, b Crockett, Tex, Nov 25, 37; m 58; c 2. ENDOCRINOLOGY, INTERNAL MEDICINE. *Educ:* Univ Tex, Austin, BA, 59; Wash Univ, MD, 63. *Prof Exp:* Intern internal med, Barnes Hosp, St Louis, 63-64, resident, 67-69; res assoc, Nat Cancer Inst, 64-66, mem staff, 66-67; instr med, Wash Univ, 70; asst prof, 70-73, assoc prof, 73-78, PROF MED, SCH MED, LA STATE UNIV, SHREVEPORT, 78- CHIEF SECT ENDOCRINOL, 70- *Concurrent Pos:* Nat Inst Arthritis & Metab Dis fel metab, Wash Univ, 69-70; consult, US Vet Admin Hosp, Shreveport, 70- *Mem:* Endocrine Soc; fel Am Col Physicians. *Res:* Physiology of prolactin in humans; kinetics of iodine metabolism in thyroid; metabolic acidosis in diabetes. *Mailing Add:* Dept of Med La State Univ Med Ctr Shreveport LA 71130

LOEWENSTEIN, MATTHEW SAMUEL, b New York, NY, Dec 3, 41; m 65; c 3. GASTROENTEROLOGY. *Educ:* Union Col, BS, 62; Harvard Med Sch, MD, 67. *Prof Exp:* Intern, Harvard Med Unit, Boston City Hosp, 67-68, jr asst resident, 68-69, dep chief, Salmonella Unit, Ctr Disease Control, 69-70; chief, Enteric Dis Sect, Ctr Dis Control, USPHS, 70-72; sr resident, Harvard Med Unit, Boston City Hosp, 72-73, clin fel med, Harvard Med Sch, 72-73, instr & clin res assoc, 73-75, ASST PROF MED, HARVARD MED SCH, 75-, SR RES ASSOC, MALLORY GASTROENTEROL RES LAB, BOSTON CITY HOSP, 76- *Concurrent Pos:* Asst vis physician, Boston City Hosp, 75-; courtesy staff, Mt Auburn Hosp, 75-77, active staff, 78- *Mem:* Am Gastroenterol Asn; Am Asn Study Liver Dis; Am Fedn Clin Res. *Res:* Clinical use of tumor markers, particularly carcinoembryonic antigen and alpha-fetoprotein. *Mailing Add:* Gastroenterol Res Lab 784 Massachusetts Ave Boston MA 02118

LOEWENSTEIN, MORRISON, b Kearney, Nebr, Aug 21, 15; m 39; c 3. DAIRY CHEMISTRY, NUTRITION. *Educ:* Univ Nebr, BS, 38; Kans State Col, MS, 40; Ohio State Univ, PhD(dairy tech), 54. *Prof Exp:* Asst dairy, Kans State Col, 38-39; asst supt, Roberts Dairy Co, 39-40; instr dairy, NMex State Col, 40-41; from asst prof to assoc prof dairy, Okla Agr & Mech Col, 47-55; res dir, Crest Foods Co, Inc. 55-66, chmn bd, Sutton Crest Proteins Ltd, Can, 64-66; prof, 66-81, EMER PROF DAIRY SCI, UNIV GA, 81- *Mem:* Am Dairy Sci Asn; Inst Food Technol, AAAS. *Res:* Development, modification and compositional control of new and improved dairy products and milk protein concentrates. *Mailing Add:* Dairy Sci Bldg Univ of Ga Athens GA 30602

LOEWENSTEIN, WALTER B, b Gensungen, Ger, Dec 23, 26; US citizen; m 59; c 2. NUCLEAR SCIENCE. *Educ:* Univ Puget Sound, BS, 49; Ohio State Univ, PhD(physics), 54. *Prof Exp:* From asst physicist to sr physicist reactor physics, Argonne Nat Lab, 54-63, head, Fast Reactor Anal Sect, Reactor Physics Div, 63-66, mgr physics sect, Liquid Metal Fast Breeder Reactor, prog off, 66-68, assoc dir, EBR-II Proj, Argonne Nat Lab, 68-72, actg dir, 72, dir, 72-73; dir, Safety & Anal Dept, 73-81, DEP DIR, NUCLEAR POWER DIV, ELEC POWER RES INST, 81- *Concurrent Pos:* Tech adv, US del, Int Conf Peaceful Uses Atomic Energy, Geneva, 58; mem staff, UK Atomic Energy Authority, Dounreay, Scotland, 59; mem, Int Atomic Energy Agency Symp, Vienna, 61, Europ-Am adv comt reactor physics, Atomic Energy Comn, 66-73 & adv comt reactor physics, 66-73. *Mem:* Fel Am Phys Soc; fel Am Nuclear Soc; Sigma Xi. *Res:* Fast reactor physics and related technology, including fast reactor design, analysis and planning of fast critical experiments, fast flux irradiation facilities and conceptual studies; fast and water reactor safety and physics technology including reactor design and test programs supporting design; development of validated analytical methods for design and safety evaluation. *Mailing Add:* 3412 Hillview Palo Alto CA 94303

LOEWENSTEIN, WERNER RANDOLPH, b Spangenberg, Ger, Feb 14, 26; m 52; c 4. NEUROPHYSIOLOGY, BIOPHYSICS. *Educ:* Univ Chile, BSc(physics) & BSc(biol), 45, PhD(physiol), 50. *Prof Exp:* From instr to assoc prof physiol, Univ Chile, 49-57; res zoologist, Univ Calif, Los Angeles, 54-55; from asst prof to prof physiol, Col Physicians & Surgeons, Columbia Univ, 57-71; PROF PHYSIOL & BIOPHYS & CHMN DEPT, SCH MED, UNIV MIAMI, 71- *Concurrent Pos:* Fel neurophysiol, Sch Med & Hosp, Johns Hopkins Univ, 53-54, Kellogg Int fel physiol, 53-55; Block lectr, Univ Chicago, 60; ed, Biochem & Biophys 67-73; mem, Biochem, Molecular Genetics & Cell Biol Sect, President's Biomed Res Adv Panel, 77; ed-in-chief, J Membrane Biol, 69- *Mem:* AAAS; Biophys Soc; Am Physiol Soc; Harvey Soc; fel NY Acad Sci. *Res:* Mechanisms of nerve impulse production and energy conversion at sensory nerve endings; neuro-muscular and synaptic transmission in the nervous system; excitation of the nerve cells; biophysics of cellular membranes; intercellular communication. *Mailing Add:* Dept of Physiol & Biophys PO Box 016430 Miami FL 33101

LOEWENTHAL, LOIS ANNE, b Middletown, Conn, Oct 31, 26. BIOLOGY. *Educ:* Mt Holyoke Col, AB, 48; Brown Univ, AM, 50, PhD, 54. *Prof Exp:* Asst biol, Brown Univ, 48-53; res assoc zool, Mt Holyoke Col, 50-51; instr animal genetics, Univ Conn, 54-56; from instr to assoc prof zool, 57-74, ASSOC PROF EXP BIOL, UNIV MICH, ANN ARBOR, 74- *Mem:* AAAS; Am Soc Zool; Am Asn Anat; NY Acad Sci. *Res:* Histology and embryology; skin and hair growth. *Mailing Add:* Div Biol Sci Univ of Mich Ann Arbor MI 48109

LOEWUS, FRANK A, b Duluth, Minn, Oct 22, 19; m 47; c 3. BIOCHEMISTRY. *Educ:* Univ Minn, BSc, 42, MSc, 50, PhD(biochem), 52. *Prof Exp:* Asst agr biochem, Univ Minn, 47-51; res assoc biochem, Univ Chicago, 52-55; chemist, USDA, 55-64; prof cell & molecular biol, Dept Biol, State Univ NY Buffalo, 64-75; agr chemist, Dept Agr Chem, 75-80, PPROF BIOCHEM, INST BIOL CHEM, WASH STATE UNIV, 75-, FEL, 80- *Mem:* Phytochemical Soc NAm (pres, 75-76); AAAS; Am Chem Soc; Am Soc Biol Chem; Am Soc Plant Physiol. *Res:* Intermediary metabolism in plants, mechanisms of enzyme action; biochemistry of natural products. *Mailing Add:* Inst Biol Chem Wash State Univ Pullman WA 99164

LOEWY, ARIEL GIDEON, b Bucharest, Roumania, Mar 12, 25; US citizen; m 51; c 5. PHYSIOLOGY. *Educ:* McGill Univ, BSc, 45, MSc, 47; Univ Pa, PhD, 51. *Prof Exp:* Asst instr, Univ Pa, 47-49; NIH fel & univ res fel phys chem, Harvard Univ, 50-52; Nat Res Coun fel, Cambridge Univ, 52-53; from instr to assoc prof, 53-65, PROF BIOL, HAVERFORD COL, 65-, CHMN DEPT, 57- *Mem:* Am Soc Biol Chem; Am Soc Cell Biol. *Res:* Photosynthesis; protoplasmic streaming and contract; fibrin formation; structural proteins in cellular physiology. *Mailing Add:* Dept of Biol Haverford Col Haverford PA 19041

LOEWY, ARTHUR DECOSTA, b Chicago, Ill, Jan 9, 43; m 71. NEUROANATOMY. *Educ:* Lawrence Univ, BA, 64; Univ Wis-Madison, PhD(anat), 69. *Prof Exp:* Res assoc & instr neuroanat, Univ Chicago, 69-71; res assoc, 71-74, sr res fel neuroanat, Mayo Grad Sch Med, Univ Minn, 74-75; asst prof, 75-79, ASSOC PROF ANAT & NEUROBIOL, SCH MED, WASHINGTON UNIV, 80- *Concurrent Pos:* Res assoc neuroanat, Mayo Found, 71-75. *Mem:* Am Asn Anat; Soc Neurosci. *Res:* Organization of central autonomic pathways; neural control of cardiovascular system. *Mailing Add:* Dept of Anat & Neurobiol Sch of Med Washington Univ St Louis MO 63110

LOEWY, ROBERT G(USTAV), b Philadelphia, Pa, Feb 12, 26; m 55; c 3. AERONAUTICAL & MECHANICAL ENGINEERING. *Educ:* Rensselaer Polytech Inst, BAE, 47; Mass Inst Technol, MS, 48; Univ Pa, PhD(eng mech), 62. *Prof Exp:* Res asst, Mass Inst Technol, 48; sr vibration engr, Martin Co, Md, 48-49; assoc res engr, Cornell Aero Lab, Buffalo, 49-52, prin engr, 53-55; staff stress engr, Piasecki Helicopter Corp, Pa, 52-53; chief dynamics engr, Vertol Aircraft Corp, Pa, 55-58, chief tech engr, 58-62; from assoc prof to prof mech & aerospace sci, Univ Rochester, 62-74, dean, Col Eng & Appl Sci, 67-74; PROF MECH & AEROSPACE SCI, RENSSELAER POLYTECH INST, 74- *Concurrent Pos:* Consult various govt agencies & pvt industs, 59-; chief scientist, Dept Air Force, 65-66, dir, Space Sci Ctr, Univ Rochester, 66-71; mem res & eng adv coun, US Post Off Dept, 66-68; mem aviation sci adv group, US Army Aviation Mat Command, 67-71; mem div adv group, Aeronaut Systs Div, US Air Force, 67-69 & Sci Adv Bd, 67-, vchmn, 71-73, chmn, 73-76; mem mil aircraft panel, President's Sci Adv Coun, 68-72; mem, NASA Aeronaut Comt, Res & Technol Adv Coun, 71- *Honors & Awards:* Lawrence Sperry Award, Am Inst Aeronaut & Astronaut, 58; Except Civilian Serv Award, US Air Force, 66 & 76. *Mem:* Nat Acad Eng; fel Am Inst Aeronaut & Astronaut; hon fel Am Helicopter Soc; Am Soc Eng Educ. *Res:* Structural dynamics and aeroelasticity; unsteady aerodynamics; magnetohydrodynamics; servomechanisms and systems stability. *Mailing Add:* Rensselaer Polytech Inst Troy NY 12181

LOF, JOHN L(ARS) C(OLE), b Denver, Colo, Dec 11, 15; m 48; c 1. ELECTRICAL ENGINEERING. *Educ:* Univ Denver, BS, 38; Mass Inst Technol, SM, 41, EE, 51. *Prof Exp:* Asst elec eng, Mass Inst Technol, 38-45, res assoc, 45-49, instr, 49-52; from asst prof to prof, 52-76, dir, Comput Ctr, 61-76, EMER PROF ELEC ENG, UNIV CONN, 76- *Honors & Awards:* Inst Elec Eng Prize, Inst Elec & Electronics Engrs, 58. *Mem:* Am Soc Eng Educ; Inst Elec & Electronics Engrs. *Res:* Electronic computing systems; analog and digital computers; digital differential analyzers. *Mailing Add:* Univ Comput Ctr Univ of Conn Storrs CT 06268

LOFERSKI, JOSEPH J, b Hudson, Pa, Aug 7, 25; m 49; c 6. SEMICONDUCTORS, ENERGY CONVERSION. *Educ:* Univ Scranton, BS, 48; Univ Pa, MS, 49, PhD(physics), 53. *Prof Exp:* Res assoc physics, Univ Pa, 52-53; res physicist, RCA Labs, 53-60; assoc prof, 61-66, chmn, Div Eng, 68-74, PROF ELEC ENG, BROWN UNIV, 66-, ASSOC DEAN, GRAD SCH, 80- *Concurrent Pos:* Chmn exec comt, Div Eng, Brown Univ, 68-74; vis sr scientist Europ Space Res Orgn, Holland, 67-68; mem res & technol adv comt space power & elec propulsion, NASA, 69-71; mem solar energy panel, comt energy res & develop goals, US Off Sci & Technol, 71-72; consult, Exxon Labs, 73-, Honeywell Inc, 77- & Jet Propulsion Labs, 78-; exchange fel, US-Poland Acad of Sci, 74-75; pres, Solamat Inc, 77- *Honors & Awards:* Freeman Medal, Providence Eng Soc, 74; Wm E Cherry Award, Inst Elec & Electronics Engrs, 81. *Mem:* Fel AAAS; fel Inst Elec & Electronics Engrs; Am Phys Soc; Sigma Xi. *Res:* Semiconductor physics; photovoltaic effect; radiation effects in semiconductors and semiconductor devices; large scale utilization of solar energy; author or coauthor of over 100 publications. *Mailing Add:* 33 Slater Ave Providence RI 02906

LOFFELMAN, FRANK FRED, b St. Louis, Mo, Nov 29, 25; m 45; c 1. ORGANIC CHEMISTRY. *Educ:* Loyola Univ (Ill), BS, 49; Notre Dame Univ, PhD(chem), 54. *Prof Exp:* Res chemist, 54-65, group leader, 65-76, proj leader, 76-81, MGR, PLASTICS ADDITIVES & FINE CHEM RES & DEVELOP, CHEM RES DIV, AM CYANAMID CO, 81- *Mem:* Am Chem Soc; Sigma Xi; Soc Plastics Engrs. *Res:* Organic synthesis; dyestuffs; optical bleaches; light stabilizers for thermoplastics; medicinals; fine chemicals; antioxidants; flame retardants. *Mailing Add:* Chem Res Div Am Cyanamid Co Bound Brook NJ 08805

LOFGREEN, GLEN PEHR, b St David, Ariz, Sept 28, 19; m 45; c 7. ANIMAL NUTRITION. *Educ:* Univ Ariz, BS, 44; Cornell Univ, MS, 46, PhD(animal nutrit), 48. *Prof Exp:* Asst prof animal husb, Mont State Col, 48; from asst prof to assoc prof, 48-61, prof, 61-81, EMER PROF ANIMAL HUSB, UNIV CALIF, DAVIS, 81- *Concurrent Pos:* Grant, Univ Hawaii, 58-59; consult, USDA; mem subcomt beef cattle nutrit, Nat Res Coun. *Honors & Awards:* Am Feed Mfrs Nutrit Award, 63. *Mem:* Am Soc Animal Sci (vpres, 60); Am Dairy Sci Asn. *Res:* Nutrient requirements and feed evaluation on large domestic animals; calcium and phosphorus metabolism. *Mailing Add:* Dept of Animal Sci Univ of Calif Davis CA 95616

LOFGREN, CLIFFORD SWANSON, b St James, Minn, July 29, 25; m 54; c 3. ENTOMOLOGY. *Educ:* Gustavus Adolphus Col, BA, 50; Univ Minn, MS, 54; Univ Fla, PhD(entom), 68. *Prof Exp:* Entomologist, Entom Res Div, Agr Res Serv, 55-57 & Plant Pest Control Div, 57-63, ENTOMOLOGIST. INSECTS AFFECTING MAN RES LAB, USDA, 63-; PROF ENTOM, INST FOOD & AGR SCI, UNIV FLA, 80- *Mem:* Entom Soc Am; Am Mosquito Control Asn; Int Union Study Social Insects. *Res:* Methods of controlling mosquitoes, imported fire ants and other insects of medical importance, particularly insecticides and equipment evaluation; studies on resistance, chemosterilants, pheromones and biology. *Mailing Add:* 1321 NW 31st Dr Gainesville FL 32605

LOFGREN, EDWARD JOSEPH, b Chicago, Ill, Jan 18, 14; m 38, 68; c 3. PHYSICS, ACCELERATORS. *Educ:* Univ Calif, AB, 38, PhD(physics), 46. *Prof Exp:* Asst, Univ Calif, 38-40, physicist, Lawrence Radiation Lab, 40-44 & 45-46, group leader, Los Alamos Sci Lab, 44-45; asst prof physics, Univ Minn, 46-48; group leader, 48-73, assoc dir, 73-79, SR STAFF SCIENTIST, LAWRENCE BERKELEY LAB, UNIV CALIF, 79- *Concurrent Pos:* With European Orgn Nuclear Res, 59; mem, High Energy Physics Adv panel, 67-70. *Mem:* AAAS; Am Phys Soc. *Res:* Elementary particle physics; accelerators for particle and heavy-ion physics and for biomedical applications; separation of uranium isotopes; discovery of heavy component of cosmic rays. *Mailing Add:* Lawrence Berkeley Lab Berkeley CA 94720

LOFGREN, JAMES R, b West Point, Nebr, May 18, 31; m 62; c 3. PLANT BREEDING, GENETICS. *Educ:* Univ Nebr, BS, 60; NDak State Univ, MS, 62; Kans State Univ, PhD(plant breeding, genetics), 68. *Prof Exp:* Asst agron, NDak State Univ, 60-62; res asst, Kans State Univ, 62-67; asst prof, Northwest Exp Sta, Univ Minn, 67-71; AGRONOMIST-PLANT BREEDER, DAHLGREN & CO, INC, 71- *Mem:* Am Soc Agron. *Res:* Breeding and genetics of sunflowers to improve productivity and quality. *Mailing Add:* Dahlgren & Co Inc 1220 Sunflower St Crookston MN 56716

LOFGREN, KARL ADOLPH, b Killeberg, Sweden, Apr 1, 15; US citizen; m 42; c 2. SURGERY. *Educ:* Harvard Med Sch, MD, 41; Univ Minn, MS, 47; Am Bd Surg, dipl, 53. *Prof Exp:* Intern, Univ Minn Hosp, 41-42; resident surg, Mayo Grad Sch Med, Univ Minn, 42-44 & 46-48; resident, Royal Acad Hosp, Univ Uppsala, 49; asst to staff, Mayo Clin, 49-50; from instr to asst prof, Mayo Grad Sch Med, 51-74, assoc prof, 74-79, PROF SURG, MAYO MED SCH, UNIV MINN, 79-; MEM SURG STAFF, MAYO CLIN, 50- *Mem:* Fel Am Col Surgeons; Int Cardiovasc Soc; Soc Vascular Surg; Swed Surg Soc; Sigma Xi. *Res:* Peripheral venous disorders. *Mailing Add:* 1001 Seventh Ave NE Rochester MN 55901

LOFGREN, NORMAN LOWELL, b Oroville, Calif, Dec 26, 21; m 47. CHEMISTRY. *Educ:* Univ Calif, BS, 43, PhD(phys chem), 49. *Prof Exp:* Res chemist, Radiation Lab, Univ Calif, 43-49; from asst prof to assoc prof, 49-59, PROF CHEM, CALIF STATE UNIV, CHICO, 59- *Mem:* Am Chem Soc. *Res:* Thermodynamic properties of metal halides; preparation and properties of refractories; solid state galvanic cells; microprocessor applications in chemical instrumentation. *Mailing Add:* Dept of Chem Calif State Univ Chico CA 95926

LOFGREN, PHILIP ALLEN, b Iowa, July 30, 44; m 77. NUTRITION. *Educ:* Iowa State Univ, BS, 66; Cornell Univ, MS, 69, PhD(nutrit), 71. *Prof Exp:* Res asst animal nutrit, Cornell Univ, 66-71; fel nutrit, Univ Calif, Berkeley, 72-73; ASST DIR NUTRIT RES, NAT DAIRY COUN, 73- *Mem:* Am Dairy Sci Asn; Inst Food Technologists; Am Oil Chemists Soc; Am Inst Nutrit. *Res:* Human and animal nutrition; unidentified growth factors; nutrient interactions; nutritional physiology of food intake regulation. *Mailing Add:* Nat Dairy Coun 6300 N River Rd Rosemont IL 60018

LOFQUIST, GEORGE W, b Brookhaven, Miss, Oct 6, 30; m 55; c 2. MATHEMATICS. *Educ:* Univ NC, BS, 52, MEd, 59; La State Univ, Baton Rouge, MS, 63, PhD(math), 67. *Prof Exp:* Instr math, La State Univ, New Orleans, 59-64 & Baton Rouge, 66-67; from asst prof to assoc prof, 67-73, PROF MATH, ECKERD COL, 73- *Mem:* Am Math Soc; Math Asn Am; Opers Res Soc Am. *Res:* Algebra; number theory. *Mailing Add:* Dept of Math Eckerd Col St Petersburg FL 33733

LOFQUIST, MARVIN JOHN, b Chicago, Ill, Oct 19, 43; m 65; c 2. INORGANIC CHEMISTRY. *Educ:* Augustana Col, BA, 65; Northwestern Univ, PhD(inorg chem), 70. *Prof Exp:* Asst prof chem, Camrose Lutheran Col, 69-73; mem fac, 73-81, ASSOC PROF, DEPT CHEM, FERRIS STATE COL, 81- *Mem:* Am Chem Soc. *Res:* Kinetics and mechanisms of organometallic transition metal complexes. *Mailing Add:* Dept of Chem Ferris State Col Big Rapids MI 49307

LOFSTROM, JOHN GUSTAVE, b Mason, Wis, June 4, 27; m 52; c 3. ANALYTICAL CHEMISTRY. *Educ:* Northwestern Univ, BS, 50; Univ Wis, PhD(chem), 54. *Prof Exp:* Asst chem, Univ Wis, 50-52; res chemist, 53-66, SR RES CHEMIST, PHOTO PROD DEPT, E I DU PONT DE NEMOURS & CO, INC, 66- *Res:* Instrumental analyses. *Mailing Add:* 58 McGuire St Metuchen NJ 08840

LOFTFIELD, ROBERT BERNER, b Detroit, Mich, Dec 15, 19; m 46; c 10. ORGANIC CHEMISTRY, BIOCHEMISTRY. *Educ:* Harvard Univ, BS, 41, MA, 42, PhD(org chem), 46. *Prof Exp:* Asst chem, Harvard Univ, 42-44, res assoc, 44-46; res assoc, Mass Inst Technol, 46-48; res assoc, Mass Gen Hosp, 48-56, assoc biochemist, 56-64; assoc, Harvard Med Sch, 56-60, asst prof org chem, 60-64; chmn dept, 64-71, PROF BIOCHEM, MED SCH, UNIV N MEX, 64-, CHMN DEPT, 78- *Concurrent Pos:* Fel, Brookhaven Nat Lab, 50; Runyon fel, Medinska Nobel Inst, Stockholm, 52-53; Guggenheim fel, Med Res Coun, Cambridge, Eng, 61-62; USPHS sr res fel, Dunn Sch Path, Oxford Univ, 71-72; chief spec assistance div, Off Strategic Serv, 46-47; tutor, Harvard Univ, 48-64; instr, Marine Biol Lab, Woods Hole, 59-62; mem biochem study sect, USPHS, 64-68; mem adv comn pathogenesis of cancer, Am Cancer Soc, 64-67, mem adv comn proteins & nucleic acids, 71-74; Fulbright prof, Abo Akademi, Turku, Finland, 77; mem, Fulbright Adv Comn, 78- *Mem:* Am Chem Soc; Am Soc Biol Chem; Am Asn Cancer Res; Biophys Soc; Am Pub Health Asn. *Res:* Radioactive carbon 14 techniques; organic synthesis; organic reaction mechanisms; protein synthesis. *Mailing Add:* Univ of NMex Med Sch Albuquerque NM 87131

LOFTIN, HORACE (GREELEY), ecology, see previous edition

LOFTNESS, ROBERT L(ELAND), b Devils Lake, NDak, Feb 14, 22; m 46; c 3. NUCLEAR ENGINEERING. *Educ:* Univ Puget Sound, BS, 43; Univ Wash, MS, 47; Swiss Fed Inst Technol, DSc, 49. *Prof Exp:* Res chemist radiation lab, Univ Calif, 43-45; res engr, US Naval Ord Testing Sta, 45; NAm Aviation, Inc, 49-51; sci attache, Am Embassy, Sweden, 51-53; mgr applns eng, Atomics Int Div, NAm Aviation, Inc, 53-60; com dir, Dynatom, France, 60-61; div dir Atomics Int Div, NAm Aviation, Inc, 61-70; dep dir, Off Atomic Energy Affairs, Bur Int Sci & Tech Affairs, Dept of State, 70-73; DIR WASHINGTON OFF, ELEC POWER RES INST, 73- *Mem:* AAAS; Am Nuclear Soc. *Res:* Radiation and nuclear chemistry; dielectric properties of chemical systems; nuclear engineering. *Mailing Add:* 5805 Bent Branch Rd Bethesda MD 20816

LOFTSGAARDEN, DON OWEN, b Big Timber, Mont, July 7, 39; m 62; c 3. MATHEMATICAL STATISTICS. *Educ:* Mont State Univ, BS, 61, MS, 63, PhD(math statist), 64. *Prof Exp:* Res engr, Autonetics Div, NAm Aviation, Inc, 62; statistician, Battelle Mem Inst, 63; instr statist, Mont State Univ, 64-65; asst prof, Western Mich Univ, 65-67; from asst prof to assoc prof, 67-75, chmn dept, 78-79, PROF MATH, UNIV MONT, 75- *Mem:* Am Statist Asn; Inst Math Statist; Math Asn Am. *Res:* Statistical inference. *Mailing Add:* Dept of Math Univ of Mont Missoula MT 59801

LOGAN, ALAN, b Newcastle-on-Tyne, Eng, Sept 20, 37; m 62; c 2. PALEOECOLOGY. *Educ:* Univ Durham, BSc, 59, PhD(paleont), 62. *Prof Exp:* Lectr paleont, Univ Leeds, 64-67; asst prof, 67-70, assoc prof, 70-76, PROF GEOL, UNIV NB, ST JOHN, 76- *Concurrent Pos:* Nat Res Coun fel, McMaster Univ, 62-64; vis fel, Univ Calgary. *Mem:* Brit Palaeontograph Soc. *Res:* Paleontology, paleoecology and ecology of Permian, Triassic and Holocene bivalves and brachiopods; ecology of Holocene coral reefs. *Mailing Add:* Dept of Geol Univ of NB Tucker Park St John NB E2B 4L5 Can

LOGAN, BRIAN ANTHONY, b Newcastle-upon-Tyne, Eng, Dec 22, 38; m 69. NUCLEAR PHYSICS. *Educ:* Univ Birmingham, BSc, 60, PhD(physics), 64. *Prof Exp:* Res assoc physics, Univ Birmingham, 64-65; lectr, 65-66. from asst prof to assoc prof, 66-81, PROF PHYSICS, UNIV OTTAWA, 81- *Mem:* Can Asn Physicists; Am Phys Soc. *Res:* Nuclear physics. *Mailing Add:* Dept of Physics Univ of Ottawa Ottawa ON K1H 5T1 Can

LOGAN, CHARLES DONALD, b St John, NB, May 15, 24; wid; c 3. WOOD CHEMISTRY. *Educ:* Mt Allison Univ, BSc, 45; McGill Univ, PhD(org chem), 49. *Prof Exp:* From res chemist to sr res chemist, 49-65, asst dir, 65-74, DIR CHEM RES, ONT PAPER CO, LTD, 74- *Mem:* Am Chem Soc; Am Pulp & Paper Assoc; Brit Paper & Board Makers Asn; Can Res Mgt Asn; Chem Inst Can. *Res:* Vanillin and lignin chemistry; ion exchange chemical recovery; pulp and paper by-product utilization; chemimech pulping. *Mailing Add:* Ontario Paper Co Thorold ON L2V 3Z5 Can

LOGAN, CHERYL ANN, b Syracuse, NY, Apr 1, 45. ANIMAL BEHAVIOR, NEUROPSYCHOLOGY. *Educ:* Southern Methodist Univ, BA, 67; Univ Calif, San Diego, PhD, 74. *Prof Exp:* asst prof, 74-79, ASSOC PROF PSYCHOL, UNIV NC, GREENSBORO, 80- *Mem:* Animal Behav Soc; Am Ornith Union. *Res:* animal communication; ecology and evolution of learning; structure and function of birdsong; territorial and reproductive function of mockingbird song. *Mailing Add:* Dept of Psychol Univ of NC Greensboro NC 27412

LOGAN, DAVID MACKENZIE, b Toronto, Ont, July 23, 37; m 60; c 3. MOLECULAR BIOLOGY, BIOCHEMISTRY. *Educ:* Univ Toronto, BA, 60, MA, 63, PhD(med biophys), 65. *Prof Exp:* Res assoc biochem, NIH, 65-67; Nat Res Coun Can fel, McMaster Univ, 67-68; asst prof, 68-74, ASSOC PROF MOLECULAR BIOL, YORK UNIV, 68- *Concurrent Pos:* Jane Coffin Childs Mem Fund fel med res, 65-67. *Mem:* AAAS; Biophys Soc;

Can Biochem Soc; NY Acad Sci. *Res:* Biochemical and biophysical aspects of nerve-muscle interactions, particularly neurotrophic effects in regeneration and acetylcholine esterases and receptors in normal and dystrophic animals. *Mailing Add:* Dept Biol York Univ 4700 Keele St Downsview ON M3J 1P3 Can

LOGAN, GEORGE BRYAN, b Pittsburgh, Pa, Aug 1, 09; m 39; c 2. PEDIATRICS. *Educ:* Washington & Jefferson Col, BS, 30; Harvard Univ, MD, 34; Univ Minn, MS, 40; Am Bd Pediat, dipl, 41. *Prof Exp:* From instr to prof pediat, Mayo Grad Sch Med, Univ Minn, 40-73, prof pediat, Mayo Med Sch, 73-75, EMER STAFF, MAYO CLIN, 75- *Concurrent Pos:* Consult, Sect Pediat, Mayo Clin, 40-68, sr consult, 68-75; chmn sub-bd allergy, Am Bd Pediat, 63-66. *Mem:* AAAS; Am Pediat Soc; AMA; Am Acad Allergy; Am Acad Pediat (pres, 67-68). *Res:* Allergic and liver diseases in children. *Mailing Add:* 200 First St SW Rochester MN 55902

LOGAN, H(ENRY) L(EON), b New York, NY, Mar 15, 96; m 21; c 1. ENGINEERING. *Hon Degrees:* LLD, Iona Col, 61. *Prof Exp:* Designer, Cram, Goodhue & Ferguson, NY, 16 & Thomas W Lamb, 16-17; tech dir, L Sonneborn & Sons, 19; asst to chief engr, Holophane Co, Ohio, 19-21, dist mgr, 21-27, eng consult, New York, 27-39, mgr controlens div, 39-46, dir & mgr, Dept Appl Res, 46-50, vpres in charge res, 50-71, chmn bd, 69-71; dir & vpres, Charles Franck Found, 62-72; RES & WRITING, 72- *Concurrent Pos:* Mem exped, Mex, 44; bd consult, Marymount Col, 48-70; dir, Found Sci Relaxation, 52-70; mem, US Nat Comt, Int Comn Illum, 53-; vchmn bd, Holophane Co, 62-69; trustee, Iona Col, 63; mem, Div Eng, Nat Res Coun. *Honors & Awards:* Silver Plate Award, Mex Inst Elec Engrs, 44; Bldg Res Inst Gold Seal Award, 65; Knight, Sovereign Mil Order of Malta, 65; Gold Medal Award, Illum Eng Soc, 65; Knight, Equestrian Order of Holy Sepulchre, 67. *Mem:* Fel Illum Eng Soc; fel Inst Elec & Electronics Engrs; hon mem Mex Inst Illum; fel Brit Illum Eng Soc. *Res:* Effects of natural solar electromagnetic radiation on people and effects of the artificial radiation which replaced it under modern urban living conditions. *Mailing Add:* 5 Hewitt Ave Bronxville NY 10708

LOGAN, JAMES EDWARD, b Thorndale, Ont, Jan 14, 20; wid; c 2. CLINICAL CHEMISTRY, HEMATOLOGY. *Educ:* Univ Western Ontario, BSc, 49, PhD(biochem), 52. *Prof Exp:* Sr res asst biochem, Univ Western Ontario, 52-54; chemist, Biol Control Labs, 54-59, sr biochemist, Clin Labs, 59-73, chief clin chem, 73-77, actg dir, Bur Med Biochem, 77-79, CHIEF CLIN CHEM, LAB CTR DIS CONTROL, CAN DEPT NAT HEALTH & WELFARE, 79- *Concurrent Pos:* Chmn, Int Fedn Clin Chem Expert Panal, Evaluation Diag Reagent Sets, 79- *Honors & Awards:* Ames Award, Can Soc Clin Chem, 81. *Mem:* Can Biochem Soc; Can Soc Clin Chem; Am Asn Clin Chem. *Res:* Chemistry of peripheral nervous system; radioisotope tracer studies; quality control and methodology; hemoglobin; evaluation of diagnostic kits and clinical laboratory instruments; radioimmunoassay; reference methods; trace element analyses. *Mailing Add:* Bur Med Biochem Lab Ctr Dis Control Tunney's Pasture Ottawa ON K1A 0L2 Can

LOGAN, JENNIFER ANN, b Scotland, Feb 5, 49. TROPOSPHERIC CHEMISTRY, STRATOSPHERIC CHEMISTRY. *Educ:* Univ Edinburgh, BSc, 71; Mass Inst Technol, PhD(phys chem), 75. *Prof Exp:* Res fel, Ctr Earth & Planetary Physics, 75-79, RES ASSOC ATMOSPHERIC CHEM, HARVARD UNIV, 79- *Concurrent Pos:* Rockefeller fel environ affairs, Harvard Univ, 77. *Mem:* AAAS; Am Geophys Union. *Res:* Theoretical analysis of the photochemistry of the Earth's troposphere and stratosphere; assessment of the effects of man's activities on atmospheric composition. *Mailing Add:* Harvard Univ 108 Pierce Hall Cambridge MA 02138

LOGAN, JESSE ALAN, b Pueblo, Colo, June 11, 44; m 70; c 1. POPULATION ECOLOGY, ENTOMOLOGY. *Educ:* Colo State Univ, BS, 67, MS, 69; Wash State Univ, PhD(entom), 77. *Prof Exp:* Res assoc entom, Colo State Univ, 71-72; comput programmer, Wash State Univ, 72-73, res asst, 73-76; res fel, NC State Univ, 76-78; ASST PROF ZOOL/ENTOM, COLO STATE UNIV, 78- *Mem:* AAAS; Sigma Xi; Entom Soc Am; Am Inst Biol Sci. *Res:* Systems analysis and population dynamics of invertebrate populations; relationship of these organisms to the efficient utilization of renewable natural resources. *Mailing Add:* Dept of Zool/Entom Colo State Univ Ft Collins CO 80523

LOGAN, JOHN A(LEXANDER), b Yorkton, Sask, Sept 26, 08; nat US; m 36; c 3. CIVIL ENGINEERING. *Educ:* Univ Sask, BSc, 29, BCE, 34; Harvard Univ, MSc, 35, DSc, 42; Wabash Col, LLD, 70. *Hon Degrees:* DSc, Ind State Univ, 65. *Prof Exp:* Instr civil eng, Iowa State Univ, 35-36; design engr, Greeley & Hansen, 36-37; asst prof civil eng, Univ Mo, 37-41; chief engr, Russel & Axon, 42-44; mem staff, Int Health Div, Rockefeller Found, France, Italy, UK & Africa, 46-54; prof civil eng & chmn dept, Northwestern Univ, 54-56 & 58-62, assoc dir, Transp Ctr, 56-57; pres, Rose-Hulman Inst Technol, 62-77; mem staff, Wabash Valley Interstate Comn, 77-80. *Concurrent Pos:* Consult, WHO, 48-, Health Div, Int Coop Admin, 54-62 & Arctic Aeromed Lab, 56-62; Chadwick lectr, Univ London, 54; mem experts comts environ sanit & marlaria eradication, WHO; dep dir environ sanit comn, Armed Forces Epidemiol Bd, 56-62; mem comt metrop health, USPHS, 63-66; chmn environ health panel, White House Conf Health, 65. *Honors & Awards:* Erlaas Medal, Govt Sardinia, 54. *Mem:* Nat Acad Eng; fel Am Soc Civil Engrs; fel Nat Soc Prof Engrs; fel Am Pub Health Asn; fel Royal Inst Pub Health. *Res:* Engineering education; malaria eradication; economics of civil engineering; environmental health. *Mailing Add:* 63 Longridge Rd Terre Haute IN 47802

LOGAN, JOHN MERLE, b Pittsburgh, Pa, July 7, 34. STRUCTURAL GEOLOGY, TECTONOPHYSICS. *Educ:* Mich State Univ, BS, 56; Univ Okla, MS, 62, PhD(geol), 65. *Prof Exp:* Geologist, Shell Develop Co, 65-67; from asst prof to assoc prof geol & geophys, 67-78, PROF, EXP ROCK DEFORMATION, DEPT GEOPHYS & GEOL, TEX A&M UNIV, 78- *Concurrent Pos:* Advan Projs Res Agency, US Dept Defense res grant, 71-78; consult, Amoco Prod Co, 67-81 & Los Alamos Nat Lab, 78-81. *Mem:* Assoc Geol Soc Am; assoc Am Geophys Union. *Res:* Experimental rock deformation as applied to structural geological problems. *Mailing Add:* Ctr for Tectonophys Tex A&M Univ College Station TX 77843

LOGAN, JOSEPH GRANVILLE, JR, b Washington, DC, June 8, 20; m 44; c 2. PHYSICS. *Educ:* DC Teachers Col, BS, 41; Univ Buffalo, PhD(physics), 55. *Prof Exp:* Physicist aerodyn, Nat Bur Standards, 43-47; physicist aerodyn propulsion, Cornell Aeronaut Lab, Inc, 47-57; head aerophys lab, Space Technol Labs, Inc, 57-59, mgr propulsion res dept, 59-60; dir aerodyn & propulsion lab, Aerospace Corp, 60-67; spec asst to dir res & develop, Western Div, McDonnell Douglas Astronaut Co, 67-69, mgr vulnerability & hardening develop eng, 69-72, chief engr nuclear weapons effects, Western Div, 72-74; pres, Appl Energy Sci, Inc, 74-78; VPRES RES & DEVELOP, WEST COAST RES CORP, 78- *Mem:* Am Phys Soc. *Res:* New energy systems. *Mailing Add:* West Coast Res Corp PO Box 25061 Los Angeles CA 90025

LOGAN, JOSEPH SKINNER, b New York, NY, June 4, 32; m 52; c 4. ELECTRICAL ENGINEERING. *Educ:* Cornell Univ, BEE, 55, MS, 56; Stanford Univ, PhD(elec eng), 61. *Prof Exp:* Adv engr, Int Bus Mach Corp, 60-71, SR ENGR, E FISHKILL FACIL, IBM CORP, FISHKILL, 71- *Mem:* Inst Elec & Electronics Engrs; Electrochem Soc; Am Vacuum Soc. *Res:* Semiconductor surface physics and device development; radio frequency sputtering of thin insulator films. *Mailing Add:* E Fishkill Facil IBM Corp Dept 206 Bldg 300-48A Fishkill NY 12524

LOGAN, KATHRYN VANCE, b Atlanta, Ga, June 12, 46; m 67; c 2. MATERIALS RESEARCH & DEVELOPMENT. *Educ:* Ga Inst Technol, BCerE, 70, MSCerE, 80. *Prof Exp:* Res engr I, 70-76, RES ENGR II, GA INST TECHNOL, 76- *Concurrent Pos:* Consult, 81- *Honors & Awards:* Monie A Ferst Award, 70. *Mem:* Am Ceramic Soc; Nat Inst Ceramic Engrs; Ceramic Educ Coun; Am Soc Metals; Mat Res Soc. *Res:* Materials characterization via analytical instrumentation, advanced materials development, microwave ferrites, directionally solidified composites; crystal growth by directional solidification; clay mineralogy. *Mailing Add:* Eng Exp Sta Rm 271 Ga Inst Technol Atlanta GA 30332

LOGAN, LOWELL ALVIN, b Langley, Ark, Oct 29, 21; m 44. ECOLOGY, PLANT TAXONOMY. *Educ:* Henderson State Col, BS, 43; Univ Ark, MS, 47; Univ Mo, PhD(bot), 59. *Prof Exp:* Instr biol, Ark Polytech Col, 46-49, head dept, 49-60; assoc prof bot, La Polytech Inst, 60-62 & La State Univ, 62-65; prof, Memphis State Univ, 65-67; V PRES ACAD AFFAIRS, SOUTHERN ARK UNIV, ARK, 67- *Mem:* AAAS; Ecol Soc Am; Bot Soc Am. *Res:* Ecology and distribution of American Beech; local floras; ecological factors affecting vegetation in restricted habitats. *Mailing Add:* 504 Alice St Magnolia AR 71753

LOGAN, R(ICHARD) S(UTTON), b Carthage, Mo, Oct 8, 18; m 48; c 1. CHEMICAL ENGINEERING. *Educ:* Univ Mo, BS, 47; Okla Agr & Mech Col, MS, 53. *Prof Exp:* Mem staff lubricant & lubricant additives group, Res & Develop Dept, 48-57, group leader uranium milling processes, 57-58 & lubricant additives, 58-60, mgr process develop sect, 60-62, mgr catalytic reactions sect, 62-66, mgr refining & separating, 66-80, dir petrol res, 80, MGR, PETROL, CHEM & ENERGY PROCESSES DIV, PHILLIPS PETROL CO, 80- *Mem:* Am Inst Chem Engrs; Am Petrol Inst; Nat Soc Prof Engrs; Independent Petrol Asn Am. *Res:* Petroleum processing; uranium milling; lubricant oils and additives; sulfonation; halogenation; alkylation; catalytic cracking. *Mailing Add:* 1808 Skyline Place Bartlesville OK 74003

LOGAN, RALPH ANDRE, b Cornwall, Ont, Sept 22, 26; nat US; m 50; c 9. SOLID STATE PHYSICS. *Educ:* McGill Univ, BSc, 47, MSc, 48; Columbia Univ, PhD(physics), 52. *Prof Exp:* Asst physics, Columbia Univ, 49-52; MEM TECH STAFF, BELL LABS, 52- *Mem:* Fel Am Phys Soc; sr mem Inst Elec & Electronic Engrs. *Res:* Semiconductor research. *Mailing Add:* 179 Mills St Morristown NJ 07960

LOGAN, ROBERT KALMAN, b New York, NY, Aug 31, 39. PHYSICS, FUTUROLOGY. *Educ:* Mass Inst Technol, BS, 61, PhD(physics), 65. *Prof Exp:* Res asst physics, Univ Ill, 65-67; res asst prof, 67-68, asst prof, 68-75, ASSOC PROF PHYSICS, UNIV TORONTO, 75- *Res:* Strong interactions of elementary particles; high energy and elementary particle physics; futures research into the planning and designing of the future; impact and effect of communication media on science and society. *Mailing Add:* Dept Physics Fac Arts & Sci Univ Toronto St George Campus Toronto ON M5S 1A7 Can

LOGAN, ROWLAND ELIZABETH, b Los Angeles, Calif, Aug 1, 23. PHYSIOLOGY. *Educ:* Univ Calif, AB, 45; Northwestern Univ, MS, 51, PhD(physiol), 54. *Prof Exp:* Instr physiol, Sch Med, WVa Univ, 54-55; instr biol, Bard Col, 56-58; ASST PROF BIOL, GETTYSBURG COL, 58- *Mem:* AAAS. *Res:* Cell metabolism; arthropod behavior. *Mailing Add:* Dept of Biol Gettysburg Col Gettysburg PA 17325

LOGAN, TED JOE, b Ft. Wayne, Ind, June 22, 31; m 54; c 2. INDUSTRIAL CHEMISTRY. *Educ:* Ind Univ, AB, 53; Purdue Univ, MS, 56, PhD(chem), 58. *Prof Exp:* Res chemist, 58-63, sect head, 63-78, MGR RECRUITING, PROCTER & GAMBLE CO, 78- *Mem:* Am Chem Soc. *Res:* Product development & research. *Mailing Add:* Proctor & Gamble Co PO Box 39175 Cincinnati OH 45247

LOGAN, TERRY JAMES, b Georgetown, Guyana, Feb 6, 43; US citizen; m 73; c 2. SOIL CHEMISTRY. *Educ:* Calif Polytech State Univ, BS, 66; Ohio State Univ, MS, 69, PhD(soil sci), 71. *Prof Exp:* Asst prof soil chem, Ohio Agr Res & Develop Ctr, 71-72; asst prof, 72-76, ASSOC PROF SOIL CHEM, OHIO STATE UNIV, 76- *Mem:* Soil Sci Soc Am; Am Soc Agron; Int Soil Sci Soc; Soil Conserv Soc Am. *Res:* Non-point sources of pollution; phosphate chemistry of soil and sediments; land disposal of sewage sludge; erosion and sedimentation of agricultural soils. *Mailing Add:* Dept Agron Studies Ohio State Univ Columbus OH 43210

LOGCHER, ROBERT DANIEL, b The Hague, Neth, Dec 27, 35; US citizen; m 63; c 3. CIVIL ENGINEERING, COMPUTER SCIENCE. *Educ:* Mass Inst Technol, SB, 58, SM, 60, ScD(civil eng), 62. *Prof Exp:* From asst prof to assoc prof, 62-76, PROF CIVIL ENG, MASS INST TECHNOL, 76-

Concurrent Pos: Ford Found fel, 62-64; dir & sr consult, Eng Comput Int, Inc, Mass. *Mem:* Am Soc Civil Engrs; Asn Comput Mach. *Res:* Application of digital computer to structural design; development of computer-aided design techniques; design process; management of constructed facility projects; information systems. *Mailing Add:* Rm 1-253 Mass Inst Technol Cambridge MA 02139

LOGEMANN, JERILYN ANN, b Berwyn, Ill, May 21, 42. SPEECH PATHOLOGY. *Educ:* Northwestern Univ, Chicago, BA, 63, MS, 64, PhD(speech path), 68. *Prof Exp:* Res assoc, 70-74, asst prof, 74-78, ASSOC PROF NEUROL & OTOLARYNGOL, NORTHWESTERN UNIV, CHICAGO, 78- *Concurrent Pos:* NIH fel, Northwestern Univ, Chicago, 68-70; consult, Downey Vet Admin Hosp, 73-76; assoc attend staff, Northwestern Mem Hosp, 73- *Mem:* Fel Am Speech & Hearing Asn; Linguistic Soc Am. *Res:* Speech science; laryngeal physiology; voice disorders; language disorders; language development. *Mailing Add:* Dept of Neurol Northwestern Univ Chicago IL 60611

LOGERFO, JOHN J, b New York, NY, Feb 12, 18; m 55. ZOOLOGY, MEDICAL TECHNOLOGY. *Educ:* NY Univ, BA, 42; Columbia Univ, MA, 52, EdD, 61. *Prof Exp:* Lab supvr med tech, Lenox Hill Hosp, New York, 41-57; chief biochemist, Clin Lab, S Shore Anal Labs, 57-58; instr biol & gen sci, 58-60, from asst prof to assoc prof, 60-69, PROF BIOL, C W POST COL, LI UNIV, 69-, DIR MED TECHNOL, 63-, CHMN DEPT HEALTH SCI & CHMN PREMED COMT, 71- *Concurrent Pos:* Consult biochemist, St Claires Hosp, New York, 55-58; res assoc, Community Hosp, Glen Cove, NY, 58-64; USPHS res grant, 62-64; prog dir allied health sci traineeship dept, USPHS, 67- *Mem:* AAAS; NY Acad Sci; Am Soc Med Technol; Am Soc Microbiol; Asn Schs Allied Health Professions. *Res:* Hematology; parasitology; comparative anatomy, embryology; chordate vertebrate morphology; experimental embryology. *Mailing Add:* Dept of Health Sci CW Post Col L I Univ Greenvale NY 11548

LOGGINS, DONALD ANTHONY, b Brooklyn, NY, June 13, 51. HEAVY METAL DYNAMICS. *Educ:* City Univ New York, BA, 74; C W Post Col, NY, MPA, 76. *Prof Exp:* Consult urban design, Coun Environ NY, 76-77; vpres, G G Inc, 77-79; STAFF ANALYST ENVIRON PROTECTION & ENG, TASKFORCE NEW YORK, 79- *Concurrent Pos:* Consult, NY Consult Group, 76- *Mem:* Nat Audubon Soc; Am Mgt Asn; Am Planning Asn. *Res:* Effects of lead and cadmium in urban soils and flora; urban soil science; environmental design of urban spaces. *Mailing Add:* 723 E 10th St Brooklyn NY 11230

LOGGINS, PHILLIP EDWARDS, b Yorkville, Tenn, Feb 12, 21; m 42; c 2. ANIMAL NUTRITION. *Educ:* Okla State Univ, BS, 52, MS, 53. *Prof Exp:* Instr animal husb, Univ Fla, 53-55, from asst prof to assoc prof, 55-74, PROF ANIMAL HUSB, UNIV FLA, 74-, ANIMAL HUSBANDMAN, AGR EXP STA, 55- *Mem:* Am Soc Animal Sci. *Res:* Animal nutrition; parasitic effect on nutritional requirements; feeding requirements of animals during reproduction. *Mailing Add:* Dept of Animal Sci Univ of Fla Gainesville FL 32611

LOGIC, JOSEPH RICHARD, b Iron Mountain, Mich, Apr 23, 35; m 64. CARDIOVASCULAR PHYSIOLOGY, NUCLEAR MEDICINE. *Educ:* Marquette Univ, MD, 60, MS, 63, PhD(physiol), 64. *Prof Exp:* Intern med, C T Miller Hosp, St Paul, Minn, 60-61; instr physiol, Sch Med, Marquette Univ, 61-64 & 65-66; resident med, Mayo Clin, Rochester, Minn, 64-65; asst prof med, Col Med, Univ Ky, 66-69; assoc prof med & physiol, Univ Tenn, Memphis, 69-73; resident nuclear med, 74, ASSOC PROF NUCLEAR MED & MED, MED CTR, UNIV ALA, BIRMINGHAM, 74- *Res:* Peripheral circulatory failure; adrenergic blockade; electrolyte role in cardiac electrophysiology and contractility; myocardial nuclear medicine. *Mailing Add:* Div of Nuclear Med Univ of Ala Med Ctr Birmingham AL 35294

LOGIN, ROBERT BERNARD, b Brooklyn, NY, Nov 15, 42; m 71; c 2. ORGANIC CHEMISTRY, POLYMER CHEMISTRY. *Educ:* Brooklyn Col, BA, 66; Purdue Univ, PhD(org chem), 70. *Prof Exp:* Chemist paper specialties, Spring House Lab, Rohm and Haas Co, 70-73; sr chemist, BASF-Wyandotte Corp, 73-74, sect head, 74-75, supvr fiber specialities, 75-80. *Mem:* Am Chem Soc; Am Asn Textile Chemists & Colorists. *Res:* Design of new and improved fiber processing auxiliaries and additives such as warp sizes, spin finish components and internal antistats. *Mailing Add:* 611 W Rose Tree Rd Media PA 19063

LOGOTHETIS, ANESTIS LEONIDAS, b Thessaloniki, Greece, June 29, 34. POLYMER CHEMISTRY. *Educ:* Grinnell Col, BA, 55; Mass Inst Technol, PhD(org chem), 58. *Prof Exp:* Res chemist, Cent Res Dept, 58-66, Elastomers Dept, 66-72, supvr develop, 72-76, DIV HEAD FLUOROELASTOMER RES, E I DU PONT DE NEMOURS & CO, INC, 76- *Mem:* Am Chem Soc. *Res:* Synthetic organic chemistry; development of new products. *Mailing Add:* Elastomers Dept Exp Sta E I du Pont de Nemours & Co Inc Wilmington DE 19899

LOGOTHETIS, ELEFTHERIOS MILTIADIS, b Almyros, Greece; US citizen. SOLID STATE DEVICES, ELECTRONIC PROPERTIES OF MATERIALS. *Educ:* Univ Athens, BS, 59; Cornell Univ, MS, 65, PhD(physics), 67. *Prof Exp:* PRIN SR SCIENTIST, DEPT PHYSICS, ENG & RES STAFF, FORD MOTOR CO, 67- *Mem:* Am Phys Soc; Am Ceramic Soc. *Res:* Electrical and optical properties of semiconductors, metal oxides, layered compounds and ionic materials; defect chemistry and gas/solid interactions; solid state devices such as gas, optical and general automotive sensors. *Mailing Add:* Dept Physics Eng & Res Staff Rm S-3053 PO Box 2053 Ford Motor Co Dearborn MI 48121

LOGOTHETOPOULOS, J, b Athens, Greece, Mar 12, 18; Can citizen; m 53; c 1. MEDICINE, PHYSIOLOGY. *Educ:* Nat Univ Athens, MD, 41; Univ Toronto, PhD(physiol), 62. *Prof Exp:* From asst prof to assoc prof, 59-64, PROF MED RES, BANTING & BEST DEPT MED RES & DEPT PHYSIOL, UNIV TORONTO, 64- *Concurrent Pos:* Res fel, Postgrad Med Sch, Univ London, 52-56; fel med res, Banting & Best Dept Med Res, Univ Toronto, 56-59. *Mem:* Am Diabetes Asn; Am Soc Exp Path; Can Physiol Soc. *Res:* Structure and function of the thyroid and the pituitary gland; experimental diabetes; structure and function of the islets of Langerhans. *Mailing Add:* Banting & Best Dept Med Res Univ of Toronto Toronto ON M5S 2R8 Can

LOGSDON, CHARLES ELDON, b Mo, May 8, 21; m 48; c 3. PLANT PATHOLOGY. *Educ:* Univ Kansas City, AB, 42; Univ Minn, PhD, 54. *Prof Exp:* Res prof plant path, 53-68, plant pathologist, 53-71, assoc dir, Inst Agr Sci, 71-78, prof, 68-78, EMER PROF PLANT PATH, UNIV ALASKA, 78-; PRES, AGRESOURCES CO, 78- *Mem:* AAAS; Am Phytopath Soc; Potato Asn Am. *Res:* Potato and vegetable diseases. *Mailing Add:* PO Box 387 Palmer AK 99645

LOGSDON, DONALD FRANCIS, JR, b Chicago, Ill, Mar 7, 40; m 63; c 4. BIOLOGY, MEDICAL TECHNOLOGY. *Educ:* Northwestern Univ, BA, 61; Trinity Univ, MS, 70; LaSalle Exten Univ, LLB, 72; Colo State Univ, PhD(zool), 75. *Prof Exp:* Chief clin lab, 4510th US Air Force Hosp, Luke AFB, Ariz, 66-67; chief radioisotope lab, US Air Force Sch Aerospace Med, 67-70; assoc prof, Dept Life Sci, US Air Force Acad, 70-75; from asst chief to chief & staff biomed scientist, US Air Force Occup Environ Health Lab, 75-78; health sci coordr & asst prof, 78-81, dir, Sacramento Area Residence Educ Ctr, Chapman Col, 81- *Concurrent Pos:* Instr life sci, Am River Col, Sacramento, Calif, 75-79 & Sierra Col, Rocklin, Calif, 77-78. *Mem:* AAAS; Sigma Xi; Am Indust Hyg Asn; Asn Off Anal Chemists; Am Soc Radiol Technologists. *Res:* Effects of radiation on living methods for radiation detection; action of radioprotective drugs; comparison of routine plating versus fluorescent antibody methods for the detection of Beta Streptococcus; medical technology. *Mailing Add:* 7341 Spicer Dr Citrus Heights CA 95610

LOGUE, J(OSEPH) C(ARL), b Philadelphia, Pa, Dec 20, 20; m 43; c 3. ENGINEERING. *Educ:* Cornell Univ, BEE, 44, MEE, 49. *Prof Exp:* Instr elec eng, Cornell Univ, 44-49, asst prof spec assignment, Brookhaven Nat Lab, 49-51; tech engr, 51-53, proj engr, 53-55, develop engr, 55-56, mgr mach develop, 56-57, mgr solid state circuit develop, 57-58, mgr equip eng, 58-59, mgr tech develop, 59-63, mgr adv tech systs, 63-64, mgr adv logic tech develop, 64-67, dir corp tech comt, 67-77, MGR TECHNOL & DESIGN SYSTS, IBM CORP, 77- *Concurrent Pos:* Secy, Int Solid State Circuits Conf, 57; IBM fel, 71- *Honors & Awards:* Invention Achievement Award, IBM Corp, 61, Outstanding Invention Award, 64. *Mem:* AAAS; fel Inst Elec & Electronics Engrs; Sigma Xi. *Res:* Development and application of new discoveries to advanced digital computers and systems; solid state devices and their applications; electronic aids to aircraft navigation. *Mailing Add:* 52 Boardman Rd Poughkeepsie NY 12603

LOGUE, JAMES NICHOLAS, b Pittston, Pa, June 18, 46; m 72; c 2. EPIDEMIOLOGY. *Educ:* King's Col, BS, 68; Univ Mich, MPH, 71; Columbia Univ, DrPH(epidemiol 78. *Prof Exp:* Statistician pharmaceut res, Warner-Lambert Res Inst, 69-70, 71-73; sr med biostatistician, Ciba-Geigy Pharmaceut Co, 73-78; sr environ epidemiologist mgt consult, Geomet, Inc, 78-80; CHIEF, EPIDEMIOL SECT, EPIDEMIOL STUDIES BR, US FOOD & DRUG ADMIN BUR RADIOL HEALTH, 80- *Mem:* Soc Epidemiol Res; Int Epidemiol Asn; Am Pub Health Asn; AAAS. *Res:* Chronic disease; epidemiology; environmental and occupational epidemiology; clinical trials research; mental health research; disaster research. *Mailing Add:* 10374 Eclipse Way Columbia MD 21044

LOGUE, MARSHALL WOFORD, b Danville, Ky, June 4, 42. CHEMICAL SYNTHESIS. *Educ:* Centre Col Ky, AB, 64; Ohio State Univ, PhD(chem), 69. *Prof Exp:* Res assoc chem, Univ Ill, 69-71; asst prof chem, Univ Md, Baltimore County, 71-77; asst prof chem, NDak State Univ, 77-81; ASSOC PROF CHEM, MICH TECH UNIV, 81- *Mem:* NY Acad Sci; AAAS; Am Chem Soc; Royal Soc Chem. *Res:* Synthetic organic chemistry; bio-organic chemistry; pyrimidines; nucleosides; synthesis of carbohydrates and nucleosides. *Mailing Add:* Dept Chem & Chem Eng Mich Tech Univ Houghton MI 49931

LOGULLO, FRANCIS MARK, b Wilmington, Del, Dec 19, 39; m 62; c 3. ORGANIC POLYMER CHEMISTRY. *Educ:* Univ Del, BS, 61; Case Inst Technol, PhD(org chem), 65. *Prof Exp:* Res chemist, 65-70, sr res chemist, 70-77, RES ASSOC, E I DU PONT DE NEMOURS & CO, INC, 77- *Mem:* Am Chem Soc. *Res:* Polymer chemistry; synthetic fibers; chemistry of arynes. *Mailing Add:* Fibers Dept Exp Sta 302 E I du Pont de Nemours & Co Wilmington DE 19898

LOH, EDWIN DIN, b Suchow, China, Jan 21, 48; US citizen. PHYSICS. *Educ:* Calif Inst Technol, BS, 69; Princeton Univ, PhD(physics), 77. *Prof Exp:* Physicist, US Army Missile Command, 69-71; instr, 76-78, ASST PROF PHYSICS, PRINCETON UNIV, 78- *Res:* Astrophysics. *Mailing Add:* Dept of Physics Princeton Univ Princeton NJ 08540

LOH, EUGENE C, b Soochow, China, Oct 1, 33; US citizen; c 3. COSMIC RAY, HIGH ENERGY. *Educ:* Va Polytech Inst, BS, 55; Mass Inst Technol, PhD, 61. *Prof Exp:* Res assoc physics, Mass Inst Technol, 61-64, asst prof, 64-65; sr res assoc nuclear studies, Cornell Univ, 65-75; assoc prof, 75-77, PROF PHYSICS & DEPT CHMN, DEPT PHYSICS, UNIV UTAH, 77- *Concurrent Pos:* Vis scientist, Stanford Linear Accelerator Ctr, 80-81. *Mem:* Am Phys Soc; Sigma Xi. *Mailing Add:* Dept Physics Univ Utah Salt Lake City UT 84112

LOH, HORACE H, b Canton, China, May 28, 36; m 62; c 1. BIOCHEMISTRY, BIOCHEMICAL PHARMACOLOGY. *Educ:* Nat Taiwan Univ, BS, 58; Univ Iowa, PhD(biochem), 65. *Prof Exp:* Lectr biochem pharmacol, Univ Calif, San Francisco, 67, asst res pharmacologist, 67-68; assoc prof biochem pharmacol, Wayne State Univ, 68-70; chief, Drug Dependence Res Ctr, Mendocino State Hosp, Talmage, Calif, 71-72; RES

SPECIALIST, LANGLEY PORTER NEUROPYSCHIAT INST, 72-; PROF PHARMACOL, SCH MED, UNIV CALIF, SAN FRANCISCO, 72- *Concurrent Pos:* Fel biochem, Univ Calif, San Francisco, 65-66. *Mem:* Am Chem Soc; Am Soc Pharm Exp Therapeut. *Res:* Opiate receptors; mechanisms of drug tolerance. *Mailing Add:* Dept of Pharmacol Univ of Calif Med Ctr San Francisco CA 94122

LOH, PHILIP CHOO-SENG, b Singapore, Sept 14, 25; nat US; m 55; c 2. VIROLOGY. *Educ:* Morningside Col, BS, 50; Univ Iowa, MS, 53; Univ Mich, MPH, 54, PhD, 58; Am Bd Microbiol, dipl, 63. *Prof Exp:* Res assoc, Virus Lab, Univ Mich, 58-61; assoc prof, 61-66, PROF VIROL, UNIV HAWAII, 66- *Concurrent Pos:* USPH spec res fel, NIH, 67-68; Eleanor Roosevelt int cancer fel, Int Union Against Cancer, Geneva, 75. *Mem:* Fel AAAS; Am Asn Immunol; Am Soc Microbiol; Tissue Cult Asn; Soc Exp Biol & Med. *Res:* Biosynthesis and pathobiology of animal viruses at the cellular level and environmental virology. *Mailing Add:* 2552 Peter St Honolulu HI 96816

LOHER, WERNER J, b Landshut, Ger, June 27, 29; m 61; c 1. ZOOLOGY. *Educ:* Univ Munich, PhD(zool), 55; Univ London, PhD(entom) & DIC, 59. *Prof Exp:* Asst prof zoophysiol, Univ Tubingen, 60-65, privat docent, 65-67; assoc prof, 67-70, PROF ENTOM, UNIV CALIF, BERKELEY, 70- *Concurrent Pos:* Sr res award, Antilocust Res Ctr, Eng, 56-59; vis lectr, Glasgow Univ, 67. *Mem:* AAAS; Animal Behav Soc; Brit Soc Exp Biol; Ger Zool Soc. *Res:* Circadian rhythms and sexual behavior in insects. *Mailing Add:* Dept of Entom Univ of Calif Berkeley CA 94720

LOHMAN, KENNETH ELMO, b Los Angeles, Calif, Sept 11, 97; m 31. GEOLOGY. *Educ:* Calif Inst Technol, BS, 29, MS, 31, PhD(paleont & geol), 57. *Prof Exp:* Chemist, Cert Lab Prod, Inc, Calif, 24-31; geologist, US Geol Surv, 31-67; RES ASSOC, US NAT MUS, SMITHSONIAN INST, 67- *Concurrent Pos:* Chmn Am Comn Stratig Nomenclature, 59-61. *Honors & Awards:* Distinguished Serv Award, US Dept Interior, 67. *Mem:* AAAS; fel Geol Soc Am; hon mem Soc Econ Paleont & Mineral (vpres, 61-62); Am Asn Petrol Geol; fel Royal Micros Soc. *Res:* Diatoms; paleontology and stratigraphy; stratigraphic nomenclature; paleoecology; petroleum geology; photomicrography. *Mailing Add:* Smithsonian Inst Nat Mus of Natural History Washington DC 20560

LOHMAN, STANLEY WILLIAM, b Los Angeles, Calif, May 19, 07; m 33; c 3. GEOLOGY. *Educ:* Calif Inst Technol, BS, 29, MS, 38. *Prof Exp:* Asst mineral, Calif Inst Technol, 29-30; from jr geologist to prin geologist, Br Ground Water, Water Resources Div, US Geol Surv, 30-74, dist geologist chg ground water invests, Kans, 37-45 & Colo, 45-51, staff geologist, States in Ark-White-Red Basins, 51-56, br area chief, Rocky Mountain area, 56-59, res geologist, 59-62, STAFF GEOLOGIST, US GEOL SURV, 62- *Honors & Awards:* Distinguished Serv Award, US Dept Interior, 74. *Mem:* Fel Geol Soc Am; Am Asn Petrol Geologists; Sigma Xi; fel Am Geophys Union. *Res:* Ground water geology and hydrology. *Mailing Add:* 2060 S Madison Denver CO 80210

LOHMAN, TIMOTHY GEORGE, b Park Ridge, NJ, Dec 10, 40; m 61; c 4. ANIMAL NUTRITION. *Educ:* Univ Ill, Urbana, BS, 62, MS, 64, PhD(body compos), 67. *Prof Exp:* Res assoc whole-body counting, 67-69, asst prof body compos animals & man, Dept Animal Sci, 69-77, ASST PROF PHYS EDUC, UNIV ILL, URBANA, 77- *Mem:* AAAS; Am Soc Animal Sci. *Res:* Exercise physiology; animal body composition; atherosclerosis in relation to nutrition and genetics; physical exercise and body composition. *Mailing Add:* Dept of Phys Educ 212 Huff Gym Univ of Ill Urbana IL 61801

LOHMAN, TIMOTHY MICHAEL, b Rockville Ctr, NY, June 2, 51; m 78. BIOPHYSICAL CHEMISTRY, MOLECULAR BIOLOGY. *Educ:* Cornell Univ, Ithaca, AB, 73; Univ Wis, Madison, PhD(phys chem), 77. *Prof Exp:* res asst biophys chem, Univ Calif, San Diego, 77-79; NIH fel, Univ Ore, 79-81; ASST PROF BIOCHEM & BIOPHYSICS, TEXAS A&M UNIV, 81- *Mem:* Biophys Soc; Am Phys Soc; AAAS. *Res:* Thermodynamics and kinetics of macromolecular interactions; protein-nucleic acid interactions involved in DNA replication, recombination and control of gene expression. *Mailing Add:* Dept Biochem & Biophysics Tex A&M Univ College Station TX 77843

LOHMANN, KARL H, b Berlin, Ger, May 30, 24; US citizen; m 61; c 3. ORGANIC CHEMISTRY. *Educ:* Mass Inst Technol, BS, 50, PhD(org chem), 59. *Prof Exp:* Mgr textile finishing, Tintorex, Colombia, 50-55; res chemist, E I du Pont de Nemours & Co, Inc, Del, 59-61; res chemist, 61-71, GROUP LEADER DYES APPLN, TOMS RIVER PLANT, 71-, GROUP LEADER DYES DISPERSIONS, 74- *Mem:* Am Chem Soc; Asn Textile Chemists & Colorists. *Res:* Dye and fiber research and application. *Mailing Add:* Toms River Plant CIBA-GEIGY Box 71 Toms River NJ 08753

LOHNER, DONALD J, b Brooklyn, NY, Mar 10, 39. ORGANIC CHEMISTRY. *Educ:* Queens Col, BS, 61; Adelphi Univ, PhD(org chem), 66. *Prof Exp:* Instr chem, Adelphi Univ, 64-66; res chemist, 66-76, RES ASSOC, E I DU PONT DE NEMOURS & CO, INC, 76- *Mem:* Am Chem Soc. *Mailing Add:* E I du Pont de Nemours & Co Photo Prod Dept Parlin NJ 08859

LOHNES, ROBERT ALAN, b Springfield, Ohio, Feb 5, 37; m 60; c 2. SOIL ENGINEERING, GEOLOGY. *Educ:* Ohio State Univ, BSc, 59; Iowa State Univ, MS, 61, PhD(soil eng, geol), 64. *Prof Exp:* Asst geol, Iowa State Univ, 59-62, instr, 62-64; asst prof, Wis State Univ, River Falls, 64-65; from asst prof to assoc prof, 65-74, PROF CIVIL ENG, IOWA STATE UNIV, 74- *Concurrent Pos:* Vis assoc prof civil eng, Middle East Tech Univ, Ankara, Turkey, 73-74. *Mem:* Am Soc Civil Engrs; Am Geophys Union; Geol Soc Am. *Res:* Applied geomorphology, soil fabric as related to mechanical behavior; soil creep and shear strength; engineering properties of tropical soils; quantitative geomorphology; alluvial geology. *Mailing Add:* Dept of Civil Eng Iowa State Univ Ames IA 50011

LOHR, DELMAR FREDERICK, JR, b Madison Co, Va, Sept 9, 34. POLYMER CHEMISTRY. *Educ:* Va Polytech Inst, BS, 62; Duke Univ, MA, 63; PhD(chem), 65. *Prof Exp:* Res org chemist, 65-70, sr res scientist, 70-77, ASSOC SCIENTIST, FIRESTONE TIRE & RUBBER CO, 78- *Mem:* Am Chem Soc; Sigma Xi. *Res:* Synthesis and reactions of aromatic heterocycles, particularly those containing both nitrogen and sulfur; polymer synthesis and characterization. *Mailing Add:* 200 Casterton Ave Akron OH 44303

LOHR, DENNIS EVAN, b Waukegan, Ill, Jan 12, 44. PHYSICAL BIOCHEMISTRY. *Educ:* Beloit Col, BA, 65; Univ NC, Chapel Hill, PhD(biochem), 69. *Prof Exp:* Teacher chem, Peace Corps, Kenya, EAfrica, 70-71; res assoc biochem, Ore State Univ, 72-79; ASST PROF BIOCHEM, ARIZ STATE UNIV, 79- *Res:* Enzymatic investigation of the subunit structure of yeast chromatin and physical characterization of the subunits. *Mailing Add:* Dept of Biochem & Biophys Ariz State Univ Tempe AZ 85281

LOHR, JOHN MICHAEL, b Chicago, Ill, June 21, 44. PLASMA PHYSICS. *Educ:* Univ Tex, Austin, BS, 66; Univ Wis-Madison, MS, 67, PhD(nuclear physics), 72. *Prof Exp:* Res assoc plasma physics, Fusion Res Ctr, Univ Tex, Austin, 72-76; STAFF PHYSICIST, GEN ATOMIC CO, SAN DIEGO, 76- *Mem:* Am Phys Soc. *Res:* Tokamak and plasma physics research. *Mailing Add:* Gen Atomic Co PO Box 81608 San Diego CA 92138

LOHR, LAWRENCE LUTHER, JR, b Charlotte, NC, May 29, 37; m 63; c 1. THEORETICAL CHEMISTRY. *Educ:* Univ NC, BS, 59; Harvard Univ, AM, 62, PhD(chem), 64. *Prof Exp:* Res assoc chem, Univ Chicago, 63-65; res scientist, Sci Lab, Ford Motor Co, 65-68; assoc prof, 68-73, PROF CHEM, UNIV MICH, ANN ARBOR, 73- *Concurrent Pos:* Consult, Ford Motor Co, 68-71 & Bell Tel Labs, 69 & 72; Alfred P Sloan res fel, 69-71; vis prof & scholar, Univ Calif, Berkeley, 74-75; vis scientist, Inst Molecular Sci, Okazaki, Japan, 81. *Mem:* Am Phys Soc; Am Chem Soc; AAAS. *Res:* Theories of chemical bonding; interpretation of electronic spectra of molecules and solids with emphasis on properties of transition metal complexes; relativistic quantum chemistry; reaction mechanisms. *Mailing Add:* Dept Chem 1040 Chem Bldg Univ Mich Ann Arbor MI 48109

LOHRDING, RONALD KEITH, b Coldwater, Kans, Jan 1, 41; m 62; c 2. ENERGY POLICY, INTERNATIONAL TECHNOLOGY COOPERATION. *Educ:* Southwestern Col, Kans, BA, 63; Kans State Univ, MA, 66, PhD(statist), 68. *Prof Exp:* Inst math, St John's Col Prep Sch, PR, 63-64; consult statistician, 68-74; group leader statist & energy assessment, 74-75, energy systs & statist, 75-78, energy systs & econ anal, 78-79, alt div leader, Systs Anal & Assessment, 78-80, dep assoc dir environ & biosci, 80-81, DEP ASSOC DIR INT AFFAIRS & ENERGY POLICY, LOS ALAMOS NAT LAB, 81- *Concurrent Pos:* Adj prof, Univ NMex, 69-70; vis prof oper res, Univ Hawaii; res fel, Resource Systs Inst, East-West Ctr, 79. *Mem:* Am Statist Asn; AAAS. *Res:* International technology cooperation and foreign policy; energy policy analysis; energy model evaluation and sensitivity analysis; comparative analysis of energy futures; large data set analysis; computer graphic data displays. *Mailing Add:* Los Alamos Nat Lab Los Alamos NM 87545

LOHRENGEL, CARL FREDERICK, II, b Kansas City, Mo, Nov 24, 39; m 71. GEOLOGY. *Educ:* Univ Kansas City, BS, 62; Univ Mo-Columbia, MA, 64; Brigham Young Univ, PhD(geol), 68. *Prof Exp:* Res assoc, Marine Inst, Univ Ga, 68-69; asst prof geol, 69-77, ASSOC PROF GEOL & MATH, SNOW COL, 77- *Mem:* Am Asn Petrol Geol; Paleont Soc. *Res:* Palynology of the Upper Cretaceous of Utah; Upper Cenozoic and modern dinoflagellates of the Georgia coastal plain; Cretaceous stratigraphy of Utah; upper cretaceous stratigraphy of Wyoming. *Mailing Add:* Dept of Geol Snow Col Ephraim UT 84627

LOHRMANN, ROLF, b Bissingen-Enz, Ger, Mar 2, 30; m 60. BIO-ORGANIC CHEMISTRY. *Educ:* Stuttgart Tech Univ, dipl(chem), 58, Dr rer nat(chem), 60. *Prof Exp:* Proj assoc, Inst Enzyme Res, Univ Wis, 62-65; sr res assoc, 65-74, ASSOC RES PROF, SALK INST BIOL STUDIES, 74- *Mem:* Ger Chem Soc. *Res:* Prebiotic chemistry; molecular evolution. *Mailing Add:* Salk Inst for Biol Studies PO Box 1809 San Diego CA 92112

LOHSE, CARLETON LESLIE, b Minot, NDak, Nov 10, 36; m 68; c 2. ANATOMIC PATHOLOGY. *Educ:* Iowa State Univ, DVM, 60; Univ Sydney, PhD(anat), 71. *Prof Exp:* Lectr vet anat, Univ Sydney, 66-68; vet practr, Boise Animal Hosps, Inc, 71-72; lectr, 72-73, asst prof, 73-76, ASSOC PROF ANAT, SCH VET MED, UNIV CALIF, DAVIS, 76- *Concurrent Pos:* Res consult, Gaines Nutrit Ctr, Gen Foods Corp, 74- *Mem:* Sigma Xi; World Asn Vet Anatomists; Am Asn Vet Anatomists; Am Vet Med Asn. *Res:* Gross and microscopic anatomy of the parotid gland and duct in relation to surgery on these structures; muscle growth and pathoanatomic studies of animal organs and tissues. *Mailing Add:* Dept of Anat Univ of Calif Sch of Vet Med Davis CA 95616

LOHSE, E(DGAR) ALAN, b Boonville, Mo, July 11, 22; m 46, 65; c 5. GEOLOGY, ENVIRONMENTAL SCIENCES. *Educ:* Univ Houston, BS, 48; Univ Tex, PhD, 52. *Prof Exp:* Geologist, Shell Oil Co, 52-58; consult petrol & eng geol, 58-62; staff geologist, Monsanto Co, 62-66; assoc prof geol, Univ Houston, 66-71; sr scientist, Gulf Univ Res Consortium, 71-76; exec vpres, Gruy Fed Inc, 76-81; CONSULT, 81- *Concurrent Pos:* Instr, Univ Corpus Christi, 52 & Del Mar Jr Col, 56-60; lectr, Univ Houston, 62-66; mem house of rep, Am Geol Inst, 66-69; lectr, Univ Mass, 68. *Mem:* AAAS; Am Asn Petrol Geologists; Soc Petrol Engrs. *Res:* Environmental research and development for petroleum, coasts and harbors; economic development of coastal resources; energy resources and management. *Mailing Add:* 69 Litchfield Lane Houston TX 77024

LOHUIS, DELMONT JOHN, b Oostburg, Wis, Jan 24, 14; m 37; c 3. CHEMISTRY. *Educ:* Carroll Col, Wis, BA, 34; Univ Wis, MS, 36. *Prof Exp:* Mgr, assoc dir & dir res, Milk Container Div, Am Can Co, Greenwich, Conn, 35-60, asst to corp vpres res & develop, 60-61 & 64-70, dir & vpres res &

develop, 61-64, dir corp res & develop staff, 70-75; asst to pres, Tech Air Corp, Am Can Co, 75-78; CONSULT ON PYROLYSIS & RESOURCE RECOVERY FROM SOLID WASTES, 78- *Mem:* Am Chem Soc; fel Am Inst Chem. *Res:* Container construction materials; pyrolysis and gasification of ligno cellulosic materials; resource recovery from solid wastes; paper based consumer products; specialty chemicals. *Mailing Add:* 9450 River Lake Dr Roswell GA 30075

LOHWATER, A J, b Rochester, NY, Oct 20, 22; m 49; c 3. MATHEMATICS. *Educ:* Univ Rochester, PhD(math), 51. *Prof Exp:* Instr math, Univ Rochester, 43-44 & 46-47; from instr to assoc prof, Univ Mich, 49-59; prof, Rice Univ, 59-65; vprovost, 69-70, chmn dept, 68-74, PROF MATH, CASE WESTERN RESERVE UNIV, 65- *Concurrent Pos:* Fulbright res grant, Finland, 55-56; Guggenheim fel, 55-; vis prof, Univ Helsinki, 56; res assoc, Brown Univ, 61-65; exec ed, Math Rev, Am Math Soc, 61-65. *Mem:* NY Acad Sci; London Math Soc; Finnish Math Soc; Swiss Math Soc. *Res:* Conformal mapping; meromorphic and harmonic functions. *Mailing Add:* Dept of Math Case Western Reserve Univ Cleveland OH 44106

LOIRE, NORMAN PAUL, b St Louis, Mo, May 7, 27; m 53; c 3. ORGANIC CHEMISTRY. *Educ:* Shurtleff Col, BS, 51; NY Univ, PhD(chem), 60. *Prof Exp:* Chemist, Ciba Pharmaceut Prod Co, 52-54; res chemist, Benger Res Lab, Textile Fibers Dept, E I du Pont de Nemours & Co, 58-62; sr res chemist, Narmco Res & Develop Div, Whittaker Corp, 62-67; sr res chemist, Chemplex Co, 67-71; lab mgr, Saber Labs, Wheeling, 71-77; SR RES CHEMIST, MORTON CHEM CO, WOODSTOCK, ILL, 77- *Mem:* Am Chem Soc. *Res:* Development of new products based on water-borne polymer systems. *Mailing Add:* 471 Killarney Pass Circle Mundelein IL 60060

LOISELLE, ROLAND, b Montreal, Que, Can, July 30, 28. PLANT BREEDING. *Educ:* McGill Univ, BSc, 49, MSc, 51; Univ Wis, PhD(plant breeding, genetics), 55. *Prof Exp:* Cerealist, Cereal Crops Div, Can Dept Agr, 55-59, geneticist, Genetics & Plant Breeding Res Inst, 59-64, res sta, 64-70, HEAD, CENT OFF PLANT GENE RESOURCES CAN, RES BR, CAN DEPT AGR, 70- *Concurrent Pos:* Secy, Can Comt Plant Gene Resources, 70-; ed, Can J Plant Sci, 72-74. *Mem:* Genetics Soc Can; Can Soc Agron; Agr Inst Can. *Res:* Development of a national computerized system for the recording, storage and retrieval of informational data on more than 86,000 plant cultivars or genetic stocks maintained in the country; international and national exchange of plant genetic material. *Mailing Add:* Cent Off Plant Gene Resources Can Dept of Agr Ottawa ON K1A 0C6 Can

LOIZZI, ROBERT FRANCIS, b Oak Park, Ill, Oct 18, 35; m 60; c 4. PHYSIOLOGY, CELL BIOLOGY. *Educ:* Loyola Univ, Ill, BS, 57; Marquette Univ, MS, 60; Iowa State Univ, PhD(cell biol), 66. *Prof Exp:* Instr physiol, Iowa State Univ, 65-66; asst prof, 66-71, ASSOC PROF PHYSIOL, UNIV ILL COL MED, 71- *Mem:* AAAS; Am Soc Zoologists; Am Soc Cell Biol; Am Physiol Soc. *Res:* Cyclic nucleotides and regulation of cell proliferation and lactation in normal and neoplastic mammary gland; fine structure, cytochemistry, and physiology of crustacean hepatopancreas; gill; transepithelial transport. *Mailing Add:* Dept of Physiol Univ of Ill Chicago IL 60680

LOK, ROGER, b Macao, Oct 19, 43; US citizen; m 70; c 2. ORGANIC CHEMISTRY. *Educ:* Univ Calif, Berkeley, BS, 66; Univ Washington, PhD(org chem), 71. *Prof Exp:* Fel, Dept Pharmacol, Yale Univ, 71-74; RES CHEMIST, EASTMAN KODAK CO, 74- *Mem:* Am Chem Soc. *Res:* Organic synthesis; preparation of dyes; enzyme immobilization; affinity chromatography; synthesis of photographically active compounds. *Mailing Add:* Kodak Park Eastman Kodak Res Labs Rochester NY 14650

LOKAY, JOSEPH DONALD, b Chicago, Ill, Dec 17, 29; m 54; c 4. CHEMICAL ENGINEERING. *Educ:* Ill Inst Technol, BS, 52, MS, 53, PhD(chem eng), 55. *Prof Exp:* Engr, Westinghouse Elec Corp, 55-59 & Argonne Nat Lab, 59-62; mgr res & develop, Continental Can Co, 62-66; STAFF ENGR RES & DEVELOP, GULF OIL CORP, 66- *Mem:* Am Inst Chem Engrs. *Res:* Research and development planning; the commercial evaluation of research and development projects related to petroleum processes and products including synthetic fuels and minerals. *Mailing Add:* Gulf Oil Co PO Box 2038 Pittsburgh PA 15230

LOKEN, HALVAR YOUNG, b Oslo, Norway, June 18, 44; US citizen; m 81; c 2. ORGANIC & POLYMER CHEMISTRY. *Educ:* Clark Univ, AB, 66; Brown Univ, PhD(chem), 71. *Prof Exp:* Nat Inst Allergy & Infectious Diseases fel trace org anal, Baker Lab, Cornell Univ, 70-72; res chemist, 72-76, sr res chemist, 76-80, carpet tech supvr, 80-81, MKT REP, E I DU PONT DE NEMOURS & CO, INC, 81- *Mem:* AAAS; Am Chem Soc; Soc Advan Mat & Process Eng. *Res:* Fiber chemistry and physics composites. *Mailing Add:* Textile Fibers Dept Chestnut Run Bldg 701 Wilmington DE 19898

LOKEN, KEITH I, b Sandstone, Minn, Oct 3, 29; m 57; c 3. VETERINARY MICROBIOLOGY. *Educ:* Univ Minn, St Paul, BS, 51, DVM, 53, PhD(vet med), 59. *Prof Exp:* Res fel vet med, 55-58, from instr to assoc prof, 58-71, prof vet microbiol, 71-74, PROF VET BIOL, UNIV MINN, ST PAUL, 74- *Concurrent Pos:* Fulbright res fel, NZ Dept Agr, Ruakura Agr Res Ctr, 65-66. *Mem:* Am Vet Med Asn; Wildlife Dis Asn; Am Soc Microbiol. *Res:* Teaching veterinary microbiology; host-parasite relationships; epidemiology of infectious diseases of animals. *Mailing Add:* Dept of Vet Biol Col of Vet Med Univ of Minn St Paul MN 55101

LOKEN, MERLE KENNETH, b Hudson, SDak, Jan 21, 24; m 47; c 5. NUCLEAR MEDICINE, BIOPHYSICS. *Educ:* Augustana Col, BA, 46; Mass Inst Technol, BS, 48, MS, 49; Univ Minn, PhD(biophys), 56, MD, 62; Am Bd Nuclear Med, cert, 72. *Prof Exp:* Asst physics, Mass Inst Technol, 48-49; asst prof, Augustana Col, 49-51; instr biophys, 53-56, from asst prof to assoc prof, 56-68, PROF RADIOL, UNIV MINN, MINNEAPOLIS, 68-, DIR DIV NUCLEAR MED, 64- *Mem:* Fel Am Col Radiol; Soc Nuclear Med; Radiol Soc NAm. *Res:* Clinical uses of radioisotopes; radiation dosimetry and hazards; effects of radiation on biological systems; applications of radioisotopes as tracer elements in metabolic studies of normal and cancer cells. *Mailing Add:* Dept of Radiol Univ of Minn Hosp Minneapolis MN 55455

LOKEN, STEWART CHRISTIAN, b Montreal, Que, Feb 16, 43; m 70; c 2. EXPERIMENTAL HIGH ENERGY PHYSICS. *Educ:* McMaster Univ, BSc, 66; Calif Inst Technol, PhD(physics), 71. *Prof Exp:* Res assoc physics lab nuclear studies, Cornell Univ, 71-74; PHYSICIST, LAWRENCE BERKELEY LAB, UNIV CALIF, 74- *Res:* Measurement of high energy muon-nucleon scattering and experimental studies of rare muon-induced processes at high energies; study of high energy electron-positron interactions. *Mailing Add:* Bldg 50-137 Lawrence Berkeley Lab Univ of Calif Berkeley CA 94720

LOKENSGARD, JERROLD PAUL, b Saskatoon, Sask, July 30, 40; US citizen; m 65; c 2. ORGANIC CHEMISTRY. *Educ:* Luther Col, Iowa, BA, 62; Univ Wis, Madison, MA, 64, PhD(org chem), 67. *Prof Exp:* NIH fel, 67; res assoc chem, Iowa State Univ, 67; asst prof, 67-76, chmn dept, 76-79, ASSOC PROF CHEM, LAWRENCE UNIV, 76- *Concurrent Pos:* Vis assoc prof chem, Cornell Univ, 80-81. *Mem:* AAAS; Am Chem Soc. *Res:* Natural products synthesis, especially insect defensive compounds; diazo ketones; small strained hydrocarbons; novel organic compounds. *Mailing Add:* Dept Chem Lawrence Univ PO Box 599 Appleton WI 54912

LOKKEN, DONALD ARTHUR, b Tomahawk, Wis, Sept 27, 37; c 2. INORGANIC CHEMISTRY, SOLID STATE CHEMISTRY. *Educ:* Univ Wis-Madison, BA, 63; Iowa State Univ, PhD(inorg chem), 70. *Prof Exp:* Chemist, Enzyme Inst, Univ Wis-Madison, 57-59, pesticide chem, Wis Alumni Res Found, 59-63; teaching & res asst, Iowa State Univ, 63-70; ASSOC PROF CHEM, UNIV ALASKA, FAIRBANKS, 70- *Mem:* Am Chem Soc; Am Crystallog Asn; Sigma Xi. *Res:* Inorganic and solid state chemistry; x-ray crystallography; mineralogy; unusual oxidation states. *Mailing Add:* Dept of Chem Univ of Alaska Fairbanks AK 99701

LOKKEN, JOHN ERWIN, b Canwood, Sask, Can, Oct 22, 24; m 47; c 2. GEOPHYSICS. *Educ:* Univ Western Ont, BSc, 51, MSc, 52; Univ BC, PhD(physics), 56. *Prof Exp:* Physicist, Pac Naval Lab, Defence Res Bd Can, 55-66 & Saclant Anti Submarine Warfare Res Centre, La Spezia, Italy, 66-69; HEAD ELECTROMAGNETICS SECT, DEFENSE RES ESTAB PAC, CAN, 69- *Mem:* Can Asn Physicists; Can Geophys Union. *Res:* Underwater acoustics, geomagnetics and data reduction. *Mailing Add:* Defense Res Estab Pac FMO Victoria BC V0S 1B0 Can

LOKKEN, STANLEY JEROME, b Fargo, NDak, Sept 22, 31; m 65. PHYSICAL CHEMISTRY. *Educ:* NDak State Univ, BS, 53; Univ Calif, Berkeley, MS, 54; Iowa State Univ, PhD(phys chem), 62. *Prof Exp:* Res chemist, Glidden Co, 62-65 & Continental Oil Co, 65-68; asst prof chem, Univ Wis-Platteville, 68-75; ASST PROF CHEM, BRUNSWICK JR COL, 77- *Concurrent Pos:* Vis asst prof chem, Ill Inst Technol, 75-77. *Mem:* Am Chem Soc. *Res:* Ion exchange theory and techniques; radiochemistry; solution kinetics and mechanisms of reactions; titanium chemistry; phosphate chemistry. *Mailing Add:* Nat Sci Div Brunswick Jr Col Brunswick GA 31523

LOLLAR, ROBERT MILLER, b Lebanon, Ohio, May 17, 15; m 41; c 2. LEATHER CHEMISTRY, ENVIRONMENTAL CHEMISTRY. *Educ:* Univ Cincinnati, ChE, 37, MS, 38, PhD(leather chem), 40. *Prof Exp:* Develop chemist, Best Foods Corp, Ind, 40-41; assoc prof tanning res & assoc dir, Tanners' Coun Res Lab, 41-58; tech dir, Armour Leather Co Div, Armour & Co, 58-64, dir tech eval, 65-73; TECH DIR, TANNERS' COUN AM, UNIV CINCINNATI, 75- *Concurrent Pos:* Pres, Lollar & Assocs, Consults, 73- *Honors & Awards:* Alsop Medal, Am Leather Chemists Asn, 54. *Mem:* Am Chem Soc; Am Soc Qual Control; Am Leather Chemists Asn (pres, 66-68); Inst Food Technol; mem World Mariculture Soc. *Res:* Research administration; statistical quality control; collagen chemistry; industrial biochemistry; marine biology. *Mailing Add:* Tanners' Coun of Am Univ of Cincinnati Location 14 Cincinnati OH 45221

LOLLEY, RICHARD NEWTON, b Blaine, Kans, May 25, 33; m 59; c 3. PHYSIOLOGY, BIOCHEMISTRY. *Educ:* Univ Kans, BS, 55, PhD(physiol), 61. *Prof Exp:* Pharmacist, Hawk Pharm, Inc, 55-56; asst prof, 66-70, assoc prof, 70-76, assoc mem, Jules Stein Eye Inst, 78-81, PROF ANAT, UNIV CALIF, LOS ANGELES, 76-, MEM, JULES STEIN EYE INST, 81- *Concurrent Pos:* USPHS res fel biochem, Maudsley Hosp, Univ London, 61-62; fel neuropath, McLean Hosp & Harvard Med Sch, 62-65; res pharmacologist, Vet Admin Hosp, 65-71, chief, Lab Develop Neurol, 71-, actg assoc chief staff res, 78-80; Vet Admin res career scientist, 79- *Mem:* Int Soc Neurochem; Am Soc Neurochem; Soc Neurosci; Am Asn Anat; Asn Res Vision & Ophthal. *Res:* Chemical and physiological investigation of retina and regions of the developing brain; quantitative histochemical studies of normal tissues and of regions of the central nervous system afflicted by inherited diseases; animal models of human blindness; role of cyclic nucleotides in photoreceptor cell function and disease. *Mailing Add:* Lab Develop Neurol Vet Admin Med Ctr Sepulveda CA 91343

LOLY, PETER DOUGLAS, b Edmonton, Eng, Mar 7, 41; Can citizen; m 68; c 2. THEORETICAL PHYSICS, SOLID STATE PHYSICS. *Educ:* Univ London, BSc, 63, PhD(physics) & DIC, 66. *Prof Exp:* Fel, Theoret Physics Inst, Alberta, 66-68; asst prof, 68-75, assoc prof, 75-80, PROF PHYSICS, UNIV MAN, 80- *Concurrent Pos:* Travel fel, Nat Res Coun Can, 75; sabbatical leave, Lab Solid State Physics, Univ Paris-Sud, 75-76 & Physigne, Univ Sherbrooke, 81-82. *Mem:* Am Phys Soc; Can Asn Physicists; Brit Inst Physics & Phys Soc. *Res:* Spin waves in ferromagnets and anti-ferromagnets; density of states; Fermi surface instabilities; Brillouin zone sums; lattice green functions; spin-peierls and XY systems; real space rescaling; many-body problems; band structure modelling. *Mailing Add:* Dept Physics Univ Man Winnipeg MB R3T 2N2 Can

LOMAN, JAMES MARK, b Waterbury, Conn, Nov 14, 54; m 75; c 1. RADIATION EFFECTS. *Educ:* Villanova Univ, BS, 75; Univ Notre Dame, MS, 77; Univ Del, PhD(physics), 80. *Prof Exp:* Res assoc, Brookhaven Nat Lab, 80-81; ENG SPECIALIST, FORD AEROSPACE & COMMUN CORP, 81- *Mem:* Am Phys Soc. *Res:* Experimental radiation effects in electronic devices and insulators; spacecraft charging; ion implantation; computer modeling; radiation effects in geological material for nuclear waste disposal applications. *Mailing Add:* Ford Aerospace & Commun Corp 3939 Fabian Way Palo Alto CA 94303

LOMAN, M LAVERNE, b Stratford, Okla, June 10, 28; m 44; c 1. MATHEMATICS. *Educ:* Univ Okla, BS, 56, MA, 57, PhD(math educ), 61. *Prof Exp:* From asst to instr math, Univ Okla, 56-61; from asst prof to assoc prof, 61-65, PROF MATH, CENT STATE UNIV, OKLA, 66- *Mem:* Math Asn Am; Nat Coun Teachers Math. *Res:* Mathematics education. *Mailing Add:* Dept of Math Cent State Univ Edmond OK 73034

LOMANITZ, ROSS, b Bryan, Tex, Oct 10, 21; m 47. THEORETICAL PHYSICS. *Educ:* Univ Okla, BS, 40; Cornell Univ, PhD(theoret physics), 51. *Prof Exp:* Teaching asst physics, Univ Calif, Berkeley, 40-42, physicist, Lawrence Radiation Lab, 42-43, teaching asst physics, 46-47; teaching asst, Cornell Univ, 47-49; assoc prof, Fisk Univ, 49; laborer, Okla, 49-54; tutor physics & math, Okla, 54-60; assoc prof physics, Whitman Col, 60-62; asst prof, 62-66, assoc prof, 66-80, PROF PHYSICS, NMEX INST MINING & TECHNOL, 80-, ASSOC PHYSICIST, 62- *Concurrent Pos:* NSF res grant, 63- *Mem:* Am Phys Soc; Am Geophys Union; Math Asn Am. *Res:* Electromagnetic isotope separator; quantum electrodynamics; superconductivity; theoretical plasma physics; theoretical ground water hydrology. *Mailing Add:* Dept of Physics NMex Inst of Mining & Technol Socorro NM 87801

LOMAX, EDDIE, b Atlanta, Ga, Aug 12, 23; m 48. ORGANIC CHEMISTRY. *Educ:* Morehouse Col, BS, 48; Atlanta Univ, MS, 51. *Prof Exp:* Control chemist, 51-53, res chemist, 53-57, lab mgr, 57-71, asst tech dir, 71-73, TECH DIR, PURITAN CHEM CO, 73- *Concurrent Pos:* Sci consult, Atlanta Bd Educ. *Mem:* Am Chem Soc. *Res:* Free radical mechanism in solutions; surfactants, insecticides and disinfectants; floor polishes; cyclobutadiene series. *Mailing Add:* 495 Harlan Rd SW Atlanta GA 30311

LOMAX, MARGARET IRENE, b Roanoke, Va, Nov 13, 38; m 64; c 2. MOLECULAR GENETICS, GENOME ORGANIZATION OF ORGANELUES. *Educ:* Western Reserve Univ, BA, 60; Univ Mich, PhD(biol chem), 64. *Prof Exp:* Res assoc biol chem, Univ Mich, Ann Arbor, 64-67, instr, 67-68, ASST RES SCI, DIV BIOL SCI, UNIV MICH, ANN ARBOR, 74- *Concurrent Pos:* Am Cancer Soc fel, 64-66. *Mem:* AAAS; Am Soc Microbiol. *Res:* Genome organization of mitochondria and chloroplasts; molecular evolution of cytochromec oxidase in primates; genetic engineering. *Mailing Add:* Div Biol Sci Univ Mich Ann Arbor MI 48104

LOMAX, PETER, b Eng, May 12, 28; m 57; c 3. PHARMACOLOGY. *Educ:* Univ Manchester, MB & ChB, 54, MD, 64, DSc, 71. *Prof Exp:* Resident surgeon neurosurg, Univ Manchester, 54-57, lectr physiol, 57-61, asst prof, 61-69; assoc prof, 69-75, PROF PHARMACOL, SCH MED, UNIV CALIF, LOS ANGELES, 75- *Mem:* AAAS; Am Physiol Soc; Am Soc Pharmacol & Exp Therapeut; Brit Med Asn. *Res:* Pharmacological and immunological studies of drug abuse; role of the central nervous system in cold acclimation; effect of drugs on temperature regulation; experimental epilepsy. *Mailing Add:* Dept of Pharmacol Univ of Calif Sch of Med Los Angeles CA 90024

LOMAX, RONALD J(AMES), b Stockport, Eng, July 18, 34; m 64; c 2. SOLID STATE DEVICES, COMPUTER SIMULATION. *Educ:* Cambridge Univ, BA, 56, MA & PhD(appl math), 60. *Prof Exp:* From vis asst prof to assoc prof, 61-73, PROF ELEC ENG, UNIV MICH, ANN ARBOR, 73- *Concurrent Pos:* Vis prof, Stanford Univ, 77-78. *Mem:* Inst Elec & Electronics Engrs; Soc Indust & Appl Math; Cambridge Philos Soc. *Res:* Solid-state devices; electron device modeling; finite element method; very large scale integration design. *Mailing Add:* Dept of Elec & Comput Eng Univ of Mich Ann Arbor MI 48109

LOMBARD, DAVID BISHOP, b Lexington, Mass, June 10, 30; m 52; c 5. EXPERIMENTAL PHYSICS. *Educ:* Northeastern Univ, BS, 53; Pa State Univ, MS, 55, PhD(physics), 59. *Prof Exp:* Physicist, Lawrence Livermore Lab, Univ Calif, 59-70; mgr, Atcor, Inc, 70-71; pres, Geo-Resource Assocs, 71-72; vpres, Subcom, Inc, 72-74; prog mgr, NSF, 74; br chief, geothermal energy div, Energy Res Develop Admin, 75-77; BR CHIEF, BIOMASS ENERGY TECHNOL DIV, DEPT ENERGY, 77- *Mem:* Am Phys Soc; Am Inst Mining, Metall & Petrol Engrs. *Res:* Geopressured geothermal energy; neutron physics, fission-to-indium age of neutrons in water; strong shocks in solids; applications of nuclear explosions to natural gas stimulation; oil shale; mining and leaching; disposal of radioactive wastes. *Mailing Add:* Div of Geothermal Energy Dept of Energy Washington DC 20585

LOMBARD, JULIAN H, b El Paso, Tex, Oct 31, 47. PHYSIOLOGY, ZOOLOGY. *Educ:* Univ Tex, El Paso, BA, 69; Ariz State Univ, MS, 71; Med Col Wis, PhD(physiol), 75. *Prof Exp:* Asst prof, 77-80, ASSOC PROF PHYSIOL, MED COL WIS, 80- *Concurrent Pos:* Nat Res Serv award, NIH, 75-77; Young Investr res grant, Nat Heart, Lung & Blood Inst, 78-81. *Mem:* Am Physiol Soc; Soc Exp Biol & Med; Sigma Xi; Microcirculatory Soc. *Res:* Vascular smooth muscle physiology; physiology of the microcirculation; local regulation of blood flow and nervous control of small blood vessels during hemorrhage, low flow states, and hypertension. *Mailing Add:* Dept Physiol Med Col Wis PO Box 26509 Milwaukee WI 53226

LOMBARD, LOUISE SCHERGER, b Wichita, Kans, Nov 20, 21; m 48; c 4. PATHOLOGY. *Educ:* Kans State Univ, DVM, 44; Univ Wis, MS, 47, PhD(path), 50. *Prof Exp:* Vet asst, Morgan's Animal Hosp, 44-45; diagnostician, Corn States Serum Co, 45-46; instr path, Univ Wis, 46-50; instr, Woman's Med Col Pa, 50-51; res assoc virol, Univ Pa, 51-53, asst prof path, 53-55; biologist, Nat Cancer Inst, 55-57; assoc pathologist, Argonne Nat Labs, Ill, 57-64; assoc prof path, Stritch Sch Med, Loyola Univ Chicago, 64-69; res scientist, Univ Chicago, 69-70, assoc prof path & pharmacol, 70-73; sect head path, Abbott Labs, Abbott Park, Ill, 73-75; assoc path, 75-77, VET PATHOLOGIST, ARGONNE NAT LABS, ILL, 77- *Concurrent Pos:* Consult pathologist, Chicago Zool Park, 60- & Argonne Nat Lab, 64-75. *Mem:* AAAS; Am Soc Exp Path; Wildlife Dis Asn; Am Vet Med Asn. *Res:* Neoplasms in animals; chemical carcinogenesis; viral oncology; radiobiology. *Mailing Add:* D202 Argonne Nat Lab Argonne IL 60439

LOMBARD, PORTER BRONSON, b Yakima, Wash, Feb 6, 30; m 55; c 3. HORTICULTURE. *Educ:* Pomona Col, BA, 52; Wash State Univ, MS, 55; Mich State Univ, PhD(hort), 58. *Prof Exp:* Asst horticulturist, Citrus Exp Sta, Calif, 58-63; assoc prof, 63-70, PROF HORT, ORE STATE UNIV, 70-, SUPT, SOUTHERN ORE EXP STA, 63- *Mem:* AAAS; Am Soc Hort Sci. *Res:* Pear varieties; rootstocks; nutrition, pear fruit bud hardiness and water requirements. *Mailing Add:* Dept of Hort Ore State Univ Corvallis OR 97331

LOMBARD, RICHARD ERIC, b Brooklyn, NY, May 16, 43; m 67; c 2. MORPHOLOGY. *Educ:* Hanover Col, AB, 65; Univ Chicago, PhD(anat), 71. *Prof Exp:* Res assoc, Mus Vert Zool, Univ Calif, Berkeley, 71; res assoc, Univ Southern Calif, 71-72; asst prof, 72-78, ASSOC PROF ANAT & EVOLUTIONARY BIOL, UNIV CHICAGO, 78-; RES ASSOC, FIELD MUSEUM NATURAL HIST, 81- *Mem:* AAAS; Am Soc Ichthyologists & Herpetologists; Am Soc Zoologists; Soc Study Amphibians & Reptiles; Soc Study Evolution. *Res:* The evolutionary and functional morphology of major adaptive features of lower vertebrates including auditory periphery in frogs, feeding apparatus of frogs and salamanders and the vestibular system in salamanders. *Mailing Add:* Dept of Anat Univ of Chicago Chicago IL 60637

LOMBARDI, JOHN ROCCO, b June 10, 41; US citizen; c 1. PHYSICAL CHEMISTRY. *Educ:* Cornell Univ, AB, 63; Harvard Univ, AM, 66, PhD(chem), 67. *Prof Exp:* Asst prof chem, Univ Ill, 67-72; vis scientist physics, Univ Leiden, Neth, 72-73; vis scientist chem, Mass Inst Technol, 73-75; ASSOC PROF CHEM, CITY COL, CITY UNIV NY, 75- *Mem:* Int Photochem Soc. *Res:* Laser spectroscopy; molecular structure; scattering. *Mailing Add:* Dept of Chem City Col New York NY 10031

LOMBARDI, MAX H, b Huanuco City, Peru, Apr 25, 32; m 61; c 3. RADIATION BIOLOGY, NUCLEAR MEDICINE. *Educ:* Univ Lima, BSc & DVM, 58; Cornell Univ, MSc, 61. *Prof Exp:* From asst prof to assoc prof biochem & nutrit, Vet Col Peru, 60-64; scientist biomed appln & consult, lectr & overall coord progs Latin Am, Oak Ridge Assoc Univs, 64-68, sr scientist & coordr, Radiation Biol & Med Radioisotope Training Progs, Oak Ridge Assoc Univs, 68-77; PROF NUCLEAR MED, HILLSBOROUGH COMMUNITY COL, 77- *Concurrent Pos:* Asst dir in vitro div, Tampa Gen Hosp, 77- *Mailing Add:* Hillsborough Community Col PO Box 22127 Tampa FL 33622

LOMBARDI, PAUL SCHOENFELD, b Salt Lake City, Utah, Nov 13, 40; m 68; c 2. MICROBIOLOGY, VIROLOGY. *Educ:* Univ Utah, BA, 63, MA, 65; Univ Rochester, PhD(microbiol), 69. *Prof Exp:* Instr, 71-73, ASST PROF MICROBIOL, COL MED, UNIV UTAH, 73- *Concurrent Pos:* Damon Runyon Mem Fund fel, Swiss Inst Exp Cancer Res, 69-70; Am Cancer Soc fel, Univ Utah, 71-73; NIH grant, 74-76. *Mem:* Am Soc Microbiol. *Res:* Cell-virus interactions of polyoma virus in permissive cells; structural proteins of polyoma virions; mycoplasma viruses and their interactions with mammalian cells. *Mailing Add:* 1026 N Oakridge Rd Centerville UT 80414

LOMBARDINI, JOHN BARRY, b San Francisco, Calif, July 2, 41; m 68; c 2. PHARMACOLOGY. *Educ:* St Mary's Col Calif, BS, 63; Univ Calif, San Francisco, PhD(biochem), 68. *Prof Exp:* Fel, Sch Med, Johns Hopkins Univ, 68-72, res assoc pharmacol, 72-73; asst prof, 73-77, ASSOC PROF PHARMACOL, TEX TECH UNIV, HEALTH SCI CTR, 77- *Mem:* Am Soc Pharmacol & Exp Therapeut. *Res:* Function of taurine as a possible neurotransmitter or modulator of nerve impulses; role of taurine in cardiac and retinal tissues; formation, function and regulatory properties of S-adenosylmethionine synthetase. *Mailing Add:* Dept Pharmacol & Therapeut Sch Med Tex Tech Univ Lubbock TX 79430

LOMBARDINO, JOSEPH GEORGE, b Brooklyn, NY, July 1, 33; m 60; c 3. ORGANIC CHEMISTRY. *Educ:* Brooklyn Col, BS, 54; Polytech Inst Brooklyn, PhD, 58. *Prof Exp:* sr res investr, 57-59, RES ADV, PFIZER, INC, 79- *Mem:* Am Chem Soc; Int Soc Heterocyclic Chem; Inflammation Res Asn. *Res:* Synthetic organic medicinals; nitrogen heterocycles; anti-inflammatory drugs; immunoregulatory drugs. *Mailing Add:* Charles Pfizer Co Chem Res Groton CT 06340

LOMBARDO, ANTHONY, b Brooklyn, NY, Jan 4, 39. ORGANIC CHEMISTRY. *Educ:* Queens Col, NY, BS, 61; Syracuse Univ, PhD(org chem), 67. *Prof Exp:* Fel, Univ Calif, Santa Barbara, 67-68; asst prof, 68-77, ASSOC PROF CHEM, FLA ATLANTIC UNIV, 77- *Res:* Coenzyme models; donor-acceptor complexes; kinetics; spectroscopy. *Mailing Add:* Dept of Chem Fla Atlantic Univ Boca Raton FL 33432

LOMBARDO, MICHAEL E, biochemistry, see previous edition

LOMBARDO, PASQUALE, b Brooklyn, NY, Nov 2, 30; m 57; c 4. ANALYTICAL CHEMISTRY. *Educ:* City Col New York, BS, 52; Columbia Univ, MA, 53. *Prof Exp:* Sr res chemist pesticide chem, Allied Chem Corp, 55-66; res chemist pesticide chem, 66-73, supvry chemist indust pollutants, 73-80, DEP DIV DIR, DIV CHEM TECH, FOOD & DRUG ADMIN, 80- *Mem:* Am Chem Soc. *Res:* Investigation of industrial chemicals, pesticides and toxic elements which are contaminants of foods. *Mailing Add:* 9210 Twin Hill Lane Laurel MD 20708

LOMBARDO, R(OSARIO) J(OSEPH), b Pawcatuck, Conn, Oct 17, 21; m; c 3. CHEMICAL ENGINEERING. *Educ:* Univ RI, BS, 43, MS, 47; Pa State Univ, PhD(chem eng), 51. *Prof Exp:* Engr, Hamilton Standard Div, United Aircraft Corp, 43-46; chem engr, 51-56, tech supvr, 56-59, tech supt, 59-60, asst plant mgr, 61, asst dir tech serv lab, 61-64, mgr plants tech sect, Pigments Dept, 65-68, prod mgr, Chem & Pigments Dept, 68-79, MGR MFT SERV, CHEM & PIGMENTS DEPT, E I DU PONT DE NEMOURS & CO, INC, 79- *Mem:* Am Chem Soc; Am Inst Chem Engrs; Sigma Xi. *Res:* Engineering administration; production administration. *Mailing Add:* Chem & Pigments Dept E I du Pont de Nemours & Co Inc Wilmington DE 19898

LOMBOS, BELA ANTHONY, b Apr 22, 31; Can citizen; m 56. MATERIALS SCIENCE, MICROELECTRONICS. *Educ:* Univ Szeged, BSc, MSc, 55; Univ Montreal, PhD(spectros), 67. *Prof Exp:* Sci staff, Cent Labs Construct Mat, 55-56, Battelle Mem Inst, 56-59 & Res & Develop, Northern Elec Co, 59-64; fel Nat Ctr Sci Res, France, 67-69; assoc prof, Sir Georges Williams Univ, 69-74; PROF ENG, CONCORDIA UNIV, 74- *Concurrent Pos:* Consult, Northern Elec Co, Ltd, 64-67. *Mem:* Electrochem Soc. *Res:* Electronic materials sciences; low energy gap semiconductors for photovoltaic infrared detectors; technology of gallium arsenide: semi-insulating gallium arsenide for CO2 laser modulator and windows. *Mailing Add:* Dept Elec Eng 1455 de Maisonneuve Blvd Montreal PQ H3G 1M8 Can

LOMEN, DAVID ORLANDO, b Decorah, Iowa, May 11, 37; m 61; c 1. APPLIED MATHEMATICS. *Educ:* Luther Col, Iowa, BA, 59; Iowa State Univ, MS, 62, PhD, 64. *Prof Exp:* Design specialist, Gen Dynamics/ Astronaut, 63-66; from asst prof to assoc prof, 69-74, PROF MATH, UNIV ARIZ, 74- *Concurrent Pos:* Consult var industs. *Mem:* Soc Indust & Appl Math; Am Math Soc. *Res:* Diffusion processes in soils and physiology. *Mailing Add:* Dept of Math Univ of Ariz Tucson AZ 85721

LOMMEL, J(AMES) M(YLES), b Evanston, Ill, Feb 7, 32; m 59; c 2. INFORMATION SCIENCE, METALLURGY. *Educ:* Ill Inst Technol, BS, 53, MS, 54; Harvard Univ, PhD(appl physics), 58. *Prof Exp:* Metallurgist, H M Harper Co, 54-56; metallurgist, 57-69, mgr personnel & tech admin, Electronics Sci & Eng, 69-77, MGR INFO RESOURCES OPER, GEN ELEC RES & DEVELOP CTR, 77- *Concurrent Pos:* Asst, Tufts Univ, 55 & Harvard Univ, 55-56; instr, Rensselaer Polytech Inst, 58. *Mem:* Inst Elec & Electronics Engrs; Am Inst Mining, Metall & Petrol Engrs. *Res:* Physical metallurgy; magnetic materials and recording; computer systems service; information retrieval. *Mailing Add:* Gen Elec Res & Develop Ctr PO Box 8 Schenectady NY 12301

LOMNITZ, CINNA, b Cologne, Ger, May 4, 25; m 51; c 4. SEISMOLOGY. *Educ:* Univ Chile, CE, 48; Harvard Univ, MS, 50; Calif Inst Technol, PhD(geophys), 55. *Prof Exp:* Res fel seismol, Calif Inst Technol, 55-57; prof geophys, Univ Chile, 57-64, dir inst geophys & seismol, 58-64; assoc res seismologist, Seismog Sta, Univ Calif, Berkeley, 64-68; PROF SEISMOL, INST APPL MATH & SYST ANAL, NAT UNIV MEX, 68- *Concurrent Pos:* Consult, Geol Surv, Chile, 58-; vis assoc, Calif Inst Technol & Univ Calif, San Diego, 69- *Mem:* Seismol Soc Am; Am Geophys Union. *Res:* Geophysics of the solid earth; creep properties of rocks; viscoelasticity and internal friction in solids; seismicity; structure of the Andes; origin of earthquakes and tsunamis. *Mailing Add:* Aptdo 20-726 Univ of Mex 01000 Mexico DF Mexico

LOMON, EARLE LEONARD, b Montreal, Que, Nov 15, 30; nat US; m 51; c 3. PARTICLE & NUCLEAR THEORY. *Educ:* McGill Univ, BSc, 51; Mass Inst Technol, PhD(theoret physics), 54. *Prof Exp:* Res physicist, Can Defence Res Bd, 50-51 & Baird Assocs, Mass, 52-53; Nat Res Coun Can overseas res fel, Inst Theoret Physics, Denmark, 54-55; fel, Weizmann Inst, 55-56; res assoc, Lab Nuclear Studies, Cornell Univ, 56-57; assoc prof theoret physics, McGill Univ, 57-60; assoc prof physics, 60-70, PROF PHYSICS, MASS INST TECHNOL, 70- *Concurrent Pos:* Guggenheim Mem Found fel, 65-66; vis scientist, Los Alamos Sci Lab, 68-; proj dir, Unified Sci & Math for Elem Sch, 71-77; vis prof, Univ Paris, 79-80; adj prof, Louvain-la-Neuve, Belgium, 80; res fel, Univ Col, London, 80. *Mem:* Am Phys Soc; Can Asn Physicists. *Res:* Nuclear and high energy physics; field theory. *Mailing Add:* Dept of Physics Mass Inst of Technol Cambridge MA 02139

LOMONACO, SAMUEL JAMES, JR, b Dallas, Tex, Sept 23, 39; m 68; c 1. MATHEMATICS, COMPUTER SCIENCE. *Educ:* St Louis Univ, BS, 61; Princeton Univ, PhD(math), 64. *Prof Exp:* Asst prof math, St Louis Univ, 64-65 & Fla State Univ, 65-69; res mathematician & comput scientist, Tex Instruments, Inc, 69-71; assoc prof comput sci & math, State Univ NY Albany, 71-80. *Concurrent Pos:* Indust prof, Southern Methodist Univ, 69-71; actg chmn, Dept Comput Sci, State Univ NY, Albany, 73-74; vis, Inst Defense Anal, Princeton, NJ, 74-76; vis lectr, Dept Math, Princeton Univ, 75-76. *Mem:* Am Math Soc; Asn Comput Mach; Math Asn Am; Soc Indust & Appl Math. *Res:* Algebraic topology, higher dimensional knot theory; algebraic coding theory; complexity theory. *Mailing Add:* 7004 S Ridge Dr Dallas TX 75214

LOMONT, JOHN S, b Ft Wayne, Ind, Aug 26, 24. MATHEMATICAL PHYSICS. *Educ:* Purdue Univ, MS, 47, PhD(physics), 51. *Prof Exp:* Physicist theoret solid state physics, NAm Aviation, Inc, 51-52; physicist, Res Dept, Michelson Lab, Naval Ord Test Sta, 52-54; physicist, NY Univ, 54-57 & Int Bus Mach Corp, 57-60; prof math, Polytech Inst Brooklyn, 62-65; PROF MATH, UNIV ARIZ, 65- *Concurrent Pos:* Sabbatical, Courant Inst Math Sci, NY Univ, 71-72. *Mem:* Am Phys Soc; Am Math Soc. *Res:* Applied group theory; quantum field theory; functional analysis. *Mailing Add:* Dept of Math Univ of Ariz Tucson AZ 85721

LONADIER, FRANK DALTON, b Clarence, La, May 6, 32; m 59; c 3. PHYSICAL CHEMISTRY, INORGANIC CHEMISTRY. *Educ:* Northwestern State Col, La, BS, 54; Univ Tex, PhD(phys chem), 59. *Prof Exp:* Res asst, Los Alamos Sci Lab, Univ Calif, 57-58; sr res chemist, 59-61, group leader inorg & nuclear chem, 61-64, sect mgr mat eval, 64-65, sect mgr nuclear develop, 65-67, mgr nuclear prod, 67-69, mgr explosive technol, 69-76, MGR ADVAN DEVICES PROD, MOUND LAB, MONSANTO RES CORP, 76- *Mem:* Am Chem Soc. *Res:* Actinide elements, particularly uranium and plutonium; inorganic chemistry of polonium; behavior of secondary explosives; environmental pollutant abatement. *Mailing Add:* Mound Lab Monsanto Res Corp Miamisburg OH 45342

LONARD, ROBERT (IRVIN), b Valley Falls, Kans, June 5, 42; m 65; c 1. PLANT TAXONOMY. *Educ:* Kans State Teachers Col, BSE, 64, MS, 66; Tex A&M Univ, PhD(plant taxon), 70. *Prof Exp:* ASST PROF BIOL, PAN AM UNIV, 70- *Mem:* AAAS; Am Soc Plant Taxonomists; Int Asn Plant Taxonomists. *Res:* Flora of south Texas; grass systematics. *Mailing Add:* Dept of Biol Pan Am Univ Edinburg TX 78539

LONBERG-HOLM, KNUD KARL, b New York, NY, Sept 22, 31; m 52, 61; c 3. BIOCHEMISTRY. *Educ:* Harvard Univ, BA, 53; Univ Calif, Berkeley, PhD(biochem), 62. *Prof Exp:* Chemist, Hyman Labs, Fundamental Res, Inc, 59-60; BIOCHEMIST, CENT RES DEPT, E I DU PONT DE NEMOURS & CO, INC, 62- *Concurrent Pos:* USPHS fel, Univ Uppsala, 67-69; assoc prof microbiol & immunol, Sch Med, Temple Univ, 76-77. *Res:* Biochemistry of plasma proteins; virus-cell interaction; biochemical virology. *Mailing Add:* Cent Res Dept E I du Pont de Nemours & Co Inc Wilmington DE 19898

LONCAREVIC, BOSKO (D), marine geophysics, see previous edition

LONCRINI, DONALD FRANCIS, b Springfield, Mass, Mar 24, 30; m 56; c 3. ORGANIC CHEMISTRY. *Educ:* Siena Col, BS, 51; Fla State Univ, PhD(org chem), 56. *Prof Exp:* Chemist, Gen Elec Co, 51-56, develop chemist, 56-60, advan develop chemist, Insulating Mat Dept, 60-62, specialist, NY, 63-68; dir res & develop, P D George Co, Mo, 68-72; MGR RES, MALLINCKRODT CHEM WORKS, 72- *Mem:* Am Chem Soc; Royal Soc Chem; Sigma Xi. *Res:* Organosilicon compounds; fluorinated amino acids; chemistry of bicylic compounds; carbonates; polycarbonates; polymers; high temperature polymers; organic synthesis and processes. *Mailing Add:* Res & Develop Labs Mallinckrodt Chem Works St Louis MO 63160

LONDERGAN, JOHN TIMOTHY, b Niagara Falls, NY, Mar 13, 43; c 3. MEDIUM-ENERGY NUCLEAR THEORY. *Educ:* Univ Rochester, BS, 65; Oxford Univ, DPhil, 69. *Prof Exp:* Res assoc physics, Case Western Reserve Univ, 69-71, Univ Wis, 71-73; asst prof, 73-77, ASSOC PROF PHYSICS, IND UNIV, 77- *Mem:* Am Phys Soc; AAAS. *Res:* Intermediate-energy nuclear theory; photonuclear reactions; scattering theory at medium energies. *Mailing Add:* Physic Dept Ind Univ Bloomington IN 47405

LONDON, A(LEXANDER) L(OUIS), b Nairobi, Kenya, Aug 31, 13; US citizen; m 38; c 3. MECHANICAL ENGINEERING. *Educ:* Univ Calif, BS, 35, MS, 38. *Prof Exp:* Engr, Standard Oil Co Calif, 36-37; instr, Univ Santa Clara, 37-38; from instr to assoc prof, 38-48, PROF MECH ENG, STANFORD UNIV, 48- *Concurrent Pos:* Res assoc, Argonne Nat Lab, 55-56. *Mem:* Am Soc Mech Engrs; Am Soc Eng Educ. *Res:* Heat transfer; thermodynamics; fluid mechanics. *Mailing Add:* Dept of Mech Eng Stanford Univ Stanford CA 94305

LONDON, EDYTHE D, b Rome, Italy, Sept 14, 48; US citizen; m 69; c 2. NEUROCHEMISTRY, NEUROPHARMACOLOGY. *Educ:* George Wash Univ, BS, 69; Towson State Univ, MS, 73; Univ Md, PhD(pharmacol), 76. *Prof Exp:* Fel psychopharmacol, Sch Med, Johns Hopkins Univ, 76-78; staff fel, 79-80, SR STAFF FEL, LAB NEUROSCI, NAT INST ON AGING, 80- *Mem:* Soc Neurosci; AAAS; Am Soc Pharmacol Exp Therapeut; Am Aging Asn. *Res:* Regional cerebral metabolism and changes in neurotransmitter balance in the aging brain. *Mailing Add:* Lab of Neurosci Geront Res Ctr Baltimore City Hosps Baltimore MD 21224

LONDON, GILBERT J(ULIUS), b Philadelphia, Pa, May 30, 31; m 52; c 4. METALLURGICAL ENGINEERING. *Educ:* Drexel Inst Technol, BS, 53; Univ Pa, MS, 55, PhD(metall eng), 59. *Prof Exp:* Metallurgist, Aerosci Lab, Gen Elec Co, 56-59; sr res metallurgist & mgr, Mech Metall Lab, Franklin Inst, Pa, 59-70; mgr metall res & develop, Kawecki Berylco Industs, 70-75; BR HEAD STRUCT MAT, NAVAL AIR DEVELOP CTR, 75- *Concurrent Pos:* Adj assoc prof, Eve Col, Drexel Univ. *Mem:* Am Soc Metals; Am Inst Mining, Metall & Petrol Engrs; Am Inst Aeronaut & Astronaut; Sigma Xi. *Res:* Flow and fracture of iron; dispersed hard particle strengthening of metals; beryllium; purification; high purity alloys; micro-strain properties; slip analysis; coextruded composites; beryllium alloys. *Mailing Add:* Naval Air Develop Ctr Code 6063 Warminster PA 18974

LONDON, IRVING MYER, b Malden, Mass, July 24, 18; m 55; c 2. MEDICINE. *Educ:* Harvard Univ, AB, 39, MD, 43. *Hon Degrees:* ScD, Univ Chicago, 66. *Prof Exp:* From instr to assoc prof med, Columbia Univ, 47-55; prof & chmn dept, Albert Einstein Col Med, 55-70; PROF MED, HARVARD UNIV & PROF MED & BIOL, MASS INST TECHNOL, 70-, GROVER M HERMANN PROF HEALTH SCI & TECHNOL, 77- *Concurrent Pos:* Asst physician, Presby Hosp, NY, 46-52, from asst attend physician to assoc attend physician, 52-55; dir, Harvard-Mass Inst Technol prog in health sci & technol, 69-77, dir, Div Health Sci & Technol, 77-, dir, Whitaker Col Health Sci Technol & Mgt, 78; vis prof, Albert Einstein Col Med, 70-; physician, Peter Bent Brigham Hosp; mem med fel bd & subcomt blood & related probs, Nat Acad Sci-Nat Res Coun, 55-63; res coun mem, Pub Health Res Inst, NY, 58-63; mem exec comt, Health Res Adv Coun, 58-63; bd sci consult, Sloan-Kettering Inst Cancer Res, 60-72; metab study sect mem, USPHS, 60-63, chmn, 61-63, mem bd sci coun, Nat Heart Inst, 64-68; mem panel biol sci & advan med, Nat Acad Sci, 66-67, bd med, 67-70 & exec comt, Inst Med, 70-73; mem adv comt to dir, NIH, 66-70; mem, Nat Cancer Adv Bd, 72-76; mem, bd sci coun, Nat Inst Arthritis, Metab & Digestive Dis, 79- *Honors & Awards:* Smith Award, AAAS, 53. *Mem:* Nat Acad Sci; Am Acad Arts & Sci; Asn Am Physicians; Am Soc Clin Invest; Am Soc Biol Chem. *Res:* Hemoglobin metabolism; metabolism of erythrocytes; eukaryotic protein synthesis. *Mailing Add:* Harvard-MIT Div & Whitaker Col Health Sci Tech 77 Massachusetts Ave Cambridge MA 02139

LONDON, JACK P, bacteriology, biochemistry, see previous edition

LONDON, JULIUS, b Newark, NJ, Mar 26, 17; m 46; c 2. METEOROLOGY. *Educ:* Brooklyn Col, BA, 41; NY Univ, MS, 48, PhD, 51. *Prof Exp:* Meteorologist, US Weather Bur, 42; instr meteorol, US Air Force, 42-47; res assoc meteorol, NY Univ, 48-52, asst prof, 52-56, res assoc prof, 56-59, assoc prof, 59-61; chmn dept astro-geophys, 66-69, PROF ASTRO-GEOPHYS, UNIV COLO, BOULDER, 61- *Concurrent Pos:* Lectr, Columbia Univ, 54-55; vis prof, Pa State Univ, 55; vis scientist, High Altitude Observ, Univ Colo, 56-57 & 59-61; Max Planck Inst Physics, Gottingen, 58; vis res scientist, Nat Ctr Atmospheric Res, 61-66; mem, Int Ozone Comn, Int Asn Meteorol & Atmospheric Physics, 60-, secy, Int Radiation Comn, 63-71, pres, 71-79; chmn panel ozone, Nat Res Coun, Nat Acad Sci, 64-65, mem, Comt Human Resources, 78-81; vis prof, Swiss Fed Inst Technol, 67, 74-76; ed, Contrib Atmospheric Physics, 72-; rep, Exec Coun Comt Space Res, Int Union Geod & Geophys, 75-79; chief US deleg, XVII Gen Assembly, Int Asn Meteorol & Atmospheric Physics, 79; lectr, Chinese Acad Sci, Inst Atmospheric Physics, 80. *Mem:* AAAS; Am Asn Univ Prof; fel Am Meteorol Soc; Royal Meteorol Soc; Am Geophys Union. *Res:* Atmospheric radiation; physics of the atmosphere; ozone. *Mailing Add:* Dept of Astro-Geophys Univ of Colo Boulder CO 80302

LONDON, RALPH L, b Johnstown, Pa, Apr 17, 36; m 60; c 2. PROGRAM UNDERSTANDING, PROGRAMMING ENVIRONMENTS. *Educ:* Washington & Jefferson Col, BA, 58; Carnegie-Mellon Univ, MS, 60, PhD(math, systs & commun sci), 64. *Prof Exp:* Asst res scientist, Carnegie-Mellon Univ, 63-64; from asst prof to assoc prof comput sci, Univ Wis-Madison, 64-72; assoc prof comput sci & proj leader & res staff mem, Info Sci Inst, Univ Southern Calif, 72-81. *Concurrent Pos:* Res assoc, Stanford Univ, 71-72. *Mem:* Asn Comput Mach; Inst Elec & Electronics Engrs; Int Fedn Info Processing. *Res:* Personal programming environments; program understanding systems; specification techniques for designs and programs; analyzing properties of specifications and programs; design and construction of modifiable programs; formal definition of programming. *Mailing Add:* Info Comput Sci Dept Univ Calif Irvine CA 92717

LONDON, ROBERT ELLIOT, b Brooklyn, NY, Oct 25, 46; m 69; c 2. BIOPHYSICAL CHEMISTRY. *Educ:* Brooklyn Col, BS, 67; Univ Ill, MS, 69, PhD(physics), 73. *Prof Exp:* Fel, 73-75, STAFF MEM BIOPHYS CHEM, LOS ALAMOS NAT LAB, 75- *Mem:* NY Acad Sci; Am Chem Soc; AAAS. *Res:* Nuclear magnetic resonance studies of biologically important molecules. *Mailing Add:* Group CNC-4 MS-346 Los Alamos Nat Lab Los Alamos NM 87545

LONDON, S J, b New York, NY, Oct 15, 17; m 43; c 2. MEDICINE, CLINICAL PHARMACOLOGY. *Educ:* Univ Louisville, BA, 37, MD, 41; Am Bd Internal Med, dipl, 51. *Prof Exp:* Resident med, Sea View Hosp, Staten Island, NY, 46-47; resident, Halloran Vet Admin Hosp, 47-48; staff physician, Manhattan Beach Vet Admin Hosp, Brooklyn, 48-50; pvt pract internal med, Brooklyn & Detroit, 50-58; med dir, Purdue Frederick Co, NY, 58-59, vpres, 59-61, vpres & med dir, M R Thompson, Inc, 61-64; from assoc dir to dir clin res, 64-70, dir biomed sci, 70-73, med dir, 73-81, ASST MED AFFAIRS TO THE VPRES, VICK DIV RES & DEVELOP, RICHARDSON-MERRELL, INC, 81- *Mem:* Fel Am Med Writers' Asn; Am Soc Clin Pharmacol & Therapeut; Am Acad Clin Toxicol; Am Thoracic Soc. *Res:* Clinical pharmacology of subjective responses; respiratory pharmacology; diabetes; atherosclerosis; thyroid diseases; hepatobiliary and pancreatic diseases. *Mailing Add:* Vick Div Res & Develop Richardson-Merrell Inc Mt Vernon NY 10551

LONDON, WILLIAM THOMAS, b New York, NY, Mar 11, 32; m 57; c 4. INTERNAL MEDICINE, ENDOCRINOLOGY. *Educ:* Oberlin Col, BA, 53; Cornell Univ, MD, 57. *Prof Exp:* Intern med, Bellevue Hosp, 57-58, resident, Med Ctr, 58-60; res epidemiologist, Nat Inst Arthritis & Metab Dis, 62-66; res physician, Inst Cancer Res, 66-78; assoc, 66-71, asst prof med, 71-76, assoc prof, 76-78, ADJ PROF MED, SCH MED, UNIV PA, 78-; SR RES PHYSICIAN, INST CANCER RES, 78- *Concurrent Pos:* Fel endocrinol, Sloan-Kettering Inst, NY, 60-62; asst, Med Col, Cornell Univ, 60-62; instr, Sch Med, George Washington Univ, 64- *Mem:* Am Thyroid Asn; Am Asn Cancer Res. *Res:* Susceptibility factors to cancer; variations in host response to hepatitis B infection. *Mailing Add:* Inst for Cancer Res 7701 Burholme Ave Philadelphia PA 19111

LONE, MUHAMMAD ASLAM, b East Punjab, India, Jan 28, 37; m 70; c 3. EXPERIMENTAL NUCLEAR PHYSICS. *Educ:* Punjab Univ, West Pakistan, BSc, 58, MSc, 60; State Univ NY Stony Brook, PhD(physics), 67. *Prof Exp:* Lectr physics, Govt Col, Lahore, Pakistan, 60-62; fel, Ind Univ, Bloomington, 67-68; Nat Res Coun Can fel, 68-70, asst res officer physics, 70-73, ASSOC RES OFFICER PHYSICS, CHALK RIVER NUCLEAR LABS, ATOMIC ENERGY CAN LTD, 73- *Mem:* Can Asn Physicists; Am Phys Soc. *Res:* Nuclear spectroscopy by gamma ray, neutron, and charged particle induced reactions; investigation of nuclear reaction mechanism. *Mailing Add:* Chalk River Nuclear Labs Atomic Energy of Can Ltd Chalk River ON K0J 1J0 Can

LONERGAN, DENNIS ARTHUR, b West Bend, Ind, May 30, 49; m 80. FOOD SCIENCE, FOOD TECHNOLOGY. *Educ:* Univ Wis-Madison, BS, 71, MS, 75, PhD(food sci), 78. *Prof Exp:* Scientist res, Pillsbury Co, 78-80; ASST PROF FOOD ANAL, PURDUE UNIV, 80- *Mem:* Inst Food Technologists. *Res:* Functionality of casein as a food ingredient; methods of determining water mobility in food; membrane processing of foods. *Mailing Add:* Food Sci Inst 127A Smith Hall Purdue Univ West Lafayette IN 47907

LONEY, ROBERT AHLBERG, b Odebolt, Iowa, June 16, 22; wid; c 3. STRUCTURAL GEOLOGY, PETROLOGY. *Educ:* Univ Wash, BS, 49, MS, 51; Univ Calif, Berkeley, PhD(geol), 61. *Prof Exp:* Geologist, Superior Oil Co, Tex, 51-52 & Wyo, 52-54; GEOLOGIST, US GEOL SURV, 56- *Mem:* Am Geophys Union; Geol Soc Am; Mineral Soc Am; Ger Geol Asn. *Res:* Structural petrology and petrology of mafic-ultramafic complexes and associated terranes; Pacific coastal region. *Mailing Add:* US Geol Surv 345 Middlefield Rd Menlo Park CA 94025

LONG, ALAN JACK, b Baton Rouge, La, Oct 17, 44; m 66; c 2. FOREST ECOLOGY, FOREST GENETICS. *Educ:* Univ Calif, Berkeley, BS, 67, MS, 71; NC State Univ, PhD(forestry, genetics), 73. *Prof Exp:* Asst prof forest genetics, Pa State Univ, 73-74; res scientist regeneration ecol, Weyerhaeuser Co, 74-79; field sta mgr tropical forestry res, Indonesia, 79-80; FORESTRY RES FIELD STA MGR, WEYERHAEUSER CO, 80- *Res:* Technology requisite for plantation establishment and early growth of western conifers; use of clonal material in tree improvement and regeneration programs; root growth of conifer seedlings. *Mailing Add:* Weyerhauser Co Box 275 Springfield OR 97477

LONG, ALEXANDER B, b New York, NY, Jan 16, 43; m 66. NUCLEAR ENGINEERING. *Educ:* Williams Col, BA, 64; Univ Ill, Urbana, MS, 66, PhD(nuclear eng), 69. *Prof Exp:* Asst nuclear engr, Argonne Nat Lab, 69-78; MEM STAFF ELEC POWER RES, NUCLEAR SAFETY ANAL, 78- *Mem:* Am Nuclear Soc. *Res:* Reactor physics, especially experimental techniques for on line determination of reactor physics parameters; fission physics. *Mailing Add:* Elec Power Res PO Box 10412 Palo Alto CA 94304

LONG, ALEXIS BORIS, b New York, NY, Sept 9, 44; m 74. CLOUD PHYSICS. *Educ:* Reed Col, BA, 65; Syracuse Univ, MS, 66; Univ Ariz, PhD(atmospheric sci), 72. *Prof Exp:* Res asst cloud physics, Inst Atmospheric Physics, Univ Ariz, 69-72; NSF fel & vis scientist, Div Cloud Physics, Commonwealth Sci & Indust Res Orgn, 72-73; res assoc cloud physics, Coop Inst Res Environ Sci, Univ Colo, 73-75; scientist & head hail suppression group, Nat Hail Res Exp, Nat Ctr Atmospheric Res, 75-80; MEM STAFF, DEPT METEOROL, TEX A&M UNIV, COLLEGE STATION, 80- *Mem:* Am Meteorol Soc; Am Geophys Union; Royal Meteorol Soc. *Res:* Weather modification; hail suppression; rain augmentation; hail measuring systems and networks; ice crystal and hail growth; stochastic coalescence growth of cloud droplets; cloud droplet collision efficiencies; nucleation theory. *Mailing Add:* Dept Meteorol Tex A&M Univ College Station TX 77843

LONG, ALTON LOS, JR, b Liberty, Tex, Sept 25, 32; m 55; c 4. ELECTRONICS, MATERIALS TECHNOLOGY. *Educ:* Carnegie Inst Technol, BS, 53, MS, 55. *Prof Exp:* Jr res chemist radiochem, Carnegie Inst Technol, 53-54; unit chief radiation effects, US Army Signal Res & Develop Labs, Ft Monmouth, 57-60, nuclear scientist, 60; develop engr, lab, 60-61, supvr testing & eval sect, 61-65, staff engr, Adv Develop Dept, 65-70, prog mgr, Comput Microfilm Systs, 70-72, prog mgr, Illiac IV Syst, 72-73, dept mgr, Components Eval, 73-77, PROG MGR, ADVAN TECHNOL, BURROUGHS CORP, 77- *Concurrent Pos:* Instr, Monmouth Col, 58-59. *Mem:* Am Chem Soc; Inst Elec & Electronics Engrs; Sigma Xi; Nat Mgt Asn. *Res:* Microelectronics; information science; radiation effects on materials; electronic materials; environmental science; physics of failure; radiocarbon dating; applied radiation technology; interconnection and packaging technology. *Mailing Add:* 558 Willis Lane Wayne PA 19087

LONG, ANDREW FLEMING, JR, b Amboy, WVa, Dec 20, 38. MATHEMATICS. *Educ:* WVa Univ, BS, 60, MS, 61; Duke Univ, PhD(math), 65. *Prof Exp:* Asst prof math, St Andrews Presby Col, 65-67; asst prof, 67-75, ASSOC PROF MATH, UNIV NC, GREENSBORO, 75- *Mem:* Math Asn Am; Am Math Soc; Sigma Xi. *Res:* Irreducible factorable polynomials over a finite field; number theory. *Mailing Add:* Dept of Math Univ of NC Greensboro NC 27412

LONG, ARTHUR OWEN, b Danbury, Conn, May 12, 21; m 44; c 5. PHYSICAL CHEMISTRY. *Educ:* Brown Univ, AB, 42; Univ Wis, PhD(chem), 50. *Prof Exp:* Asst prof chem, Univ Vt, 49-51; res assoc, US Naval Ord Lab, 51-53; ASSOC PROF CHEM, STATE UNIV NY ALBANY, 53- *Mem:* Am Chem Soc. *Res:* Reactions of glass surfaces with ions in aqueous solution; exchange of nitrogen-15 between nitrogen dioxide and nitrogen monoxide. *Mailing Add:* Dept of Chem State Univ of NY Albany NY 12222

LONG, AUSTIN, b Olney, Tex, Dec 12, 36; m 61; c 2. GEOCHEMISTRY. *Educ:* Midwestern Univ, BS, 57; Columbia Univ, MA, 59; Univ Ariz, PhD(geochem), 66. *Prof Exp:* Res asst geochem, Geochronol Labs, Univ Ariz, 59-63; geochemist, Smithsonian Inst, 63-68; ASSOC PROF GEOSCI, LAB ISOTOPE GEOCHEM, UNIV ARIZ, 68- *Mem:* Geochem Soc. *Res:* Pleistocene paleoclimatology; radiocarbon dating; stable isotope geochemistry. *Mailing Add:* Lab of Isotope Geochem Dept of Geosci Univ of Ariz Tucson AZ 85721

LONG, CALVIN H, b Myerstown, Pa, Feb 16, 27; m 54; c 2. ANALYTICAL CHEMISTRY. *Educ:* Univ Miami, BS, 50; Franklin & Marshall Col, MS, 56; Stanford Univ, PhD(chem), 63. *Prof Exp:* Chemist, Armstrong Cork Co, 50-58; res chemist, Chevron Res Co, 63-64; res group leader anal chem, 64-68, sect mgr, 69-78, MGR, KERR-MCGEE CORP, 79- *Mem:* Am Chem Soc. *Res:* Chemical equilibria; mineral benefication. *Mailing Add:* 8105 NW 114th Oklahoma City OK 73132

LONG, CALVIN LEE, b NC, Jan 27, 28; m 51; c 3. BIOCHEMISTRY. *Educ:* Wake Forest Col, BS, 48; NC State Col, MS, 51; Univ Ill, PhD, 54. *Prof Exp:* Assoc chemist biochem, Gen Food Corp, 54-57, proj leader, 57-62; res assoc, Harvard Univ, 63 & Col Physicians & Surgeons, Columbia Univ, 64-74; assoc prof, 75-80, PROF BIOCHEM & SURG, MED COL OHIO, 80- *Mem:* AAAS; Am Inst Nutrit; Am Chem Soc; NY Acad Sci; Am Soc Parenteral & Enteral Nutrit. *Res:* Intermediary metabolism and nutritional biochemistry. *Mailing Add:* CS10008 Dept of Surg Med Col of Ohio Toledo OH 43699

LONG, CALVIN THOMAS, b Rupert, Idaho, Oct 10, 27; m 52; c 2. ELEMENTARY NUMBER THEORY, COMBINATORIAL NUMBER THEORY. *Educ:* Univ Idaho, BS, 50; Univ Ore, MS, 52, PhD(math), 55. *Prof Exp:* Analyst, Nat Security Agency, 55-56; from asst prof to assoc prof, 56-65, chmn dept, 70-78, PROF MATH, WASH STATE UNIV, 65- *Concurrent Pos:* Educ consult, Wash State Dept Educ, 61-67 & NSF, 63-64 & 72; assoc ed, Fibonacci Quarterly, 63-; assoc ed, Math Mag, 64-69; vis prof, Univ

Jabalpur, India, 65; vis prof, Univ BC, 72; consult, Educ Comn States, Nat Assessment Educ Progress, 75; adj prof, Clemson Univ, 78-79. *Mem:* Math Asn Am; Nat Coun Teachers Math; Asn Teachers Math; Fibonacci Asn; Am Math Soc. *Res:* Probabilistic and combinatorial number theory and other combinatorial problems. *Mailing Add:* Dept of Math Wash State Univ Pullman WA 99164

LONG, CARL F(ERDINAND), b New York, NY, Aug 6, 28; m 55; c 2. CIVIL ENGINEERING, ENGINEERING MECHANICS. *Educ:* Mass Inst Technol, SB, 50, SM, 52; Yale Univ, DEng, 64. *Hon Degrees:* MA, Dartmouth Col, 71. *Prof Exp:* Asst civil eng, Mass Inst Technol, 52-54, res engr, 54; from instr civil eng to assoc prof, 54-70; assoc dean, 72, DEAN, THAYER SCH ENG, DARTMOUTH COL, 72-, PROF CIVIL ENG, 70- *Concurrent Pos:* Consult, NH State Water Pollution Comn, 58- & Small Arms Systs Agency, US Army; trustee, Mt Washington Observ, 75-; mem corp, Mary Hitchcock Mem Hosp, 73-; dir, Controlled Environ Corp, Grantham, NH, 76-, vpres opers, 77-; pres & dir, OS-Oxygen Processes, Portland, Maine, 79- *Mem:* AAAS; Am Soc Civil Engrs; Am Soc Eng Educ. *Res:* Analytical and experimental investigations of structures and structural elements; planning and decision making for small towns and cities with time-sharing computers. *Mailing Add:* Thayer Sch of Eng Dartmouth Col Hanover NH 03755

LONG, CARL LEE, applied physics, nuclear physics, see previous edition

LONG, CARLETON C(URTIS), b Boulder, Colo, June 3, 09; m 35; c 3. CHEMICAL & METALLURGICAL ENGINEERING. *Educ:* Univ Colo, BS, 31, PhD(chem), 35; Stanford Univ, MA, 32. *Prof Exp:* Res chemist, Zinc Smelting Div, St Joseph Lead Co, 35-37, dir plant res dept, 37-55, dir res, St Joe Minerals Corp, 55-74; RETIRED. *Mem:* Fel AAAS; fel Am Soc Metals; Am Inst Chem Engrs; hon mem Am Inst Mining, Metall & Petrol Engrs (vpres, 61-63); fel Metall Soc (pres, 60). *Res:* Electrothermic winning of zinc and allied operations; research management. *Mailing Add:* 1100 Linden Ave Boulder CO 80302

LONG, CEDRIC WILLIAM, b Minneapolis, Minn, Mar 4, 37. BIOCHEMISTRY, VIROLOGY. *Educ:* Univ Calif, Los Angeles, BA, 60, MA, 62; Princeton Univ, PhD(biochem), 66. *Prof Exp:* Am Cancer Soc fel biochem, Univ Calif, Berkeley, 66-68; Nat Cancer Inst fel path, Med Sch, NY Univ, 68-69; instr cell biol, 69-70; sr scientist, Flow Labs, Inc, 70-72, head cell biol sect, 72-76; head cell biol sect, Frederick Cancer Res Ctr, 76-80; CHIEF, PRECLIN TRIALS SECT, BIOL RESPONSE MODIFIERS PROG, NAT CANCER INST, 80- *Mem:* AAAS; Am Soc Microbiol; Am Soc Biol Chem. *Res:* Genetic and biochemical aspects of mammalian cell growth; interaction of tumor viruses with cells in culture; functional aspects of viral proteins; modification of host reponse to tumor cells. *Mailing Add:* Frederick Cancer Res Facil Bldg 426 PO Box B Frederick MD 21701

LONG, CHARLES ALAN, b Pittsburg, Kans, Jan 19, 36; m 60; c 2. ZOOLOGY. *Educ:* Pittsburg State Univ, BS, 57, MS, 58; Univ Kans, PhD(zool), 63. *Prof Exp:* Asst zool, Univ Kans, 59-63; instr, Univ Ill, Urbana, 63-65, asst prof zool & life sci, 65-66; from asst prof to assoc prof biol, 68-71, CUR MAMMALS, MUS NATURAL HIST, 66-, DIR, 69-, PROF BIOL, UNIV WIS-STEVENS POINT, 71- *Concurrent Pos:* Fac fel, Univ Ill, 64; consult, Lake Mich Proj, Argonne Nat Lab, 74-; Univ Adv Minor Mus Tech, 74- *Mem:* Am Inst Biol Sci; Am Soc Mammal; Am Asn Sci. *Res:* Vertebrate zoology, particularly systematics and zoogeography of mammals and their evolution; morphology and ecology; variability of mammals; Wyoming and Wisconsin mammals; badgers of the world. *Mailing Add:* Dept of Biol Univ of Wis Stevens Point WI 54481

LONG, CHARLES ANTHONY, b San Antonio, Tex, Feb 22, 45. CHEMICAL PHYSICS. *Educ:* Carleton Col, BA, 67; Ind Univ, PhD(chem physics), 72. *Prof Exp:* Fel chem physics, Univ Calif, Riverside, 72-73; asst prof chem, Lake Forest Col, 73-77; res assoc, Brookhaven Nat Lab, 77-79; INSTRUMENTATION SUPVR, JOHNS HOPKINS UNIV, 79- *Concurrent Pos:* NSF res grant, 74. *Mem:* Am Phys Soc; Am Chem Soc. *Res:* Applications of lasers to problems of the chemistry and physics of small molecules. *Mailing Add:* Dept of Chem Johns Hopkins Univ Baltimore MD 21218

LONG, CHARLES H, b Batesville, Ark, Dec 20, 35; m 61. ANIMAL NUTRITION. *Educ:* Ark State Col, BSA, 60; Mich State Univ, PhD(animal nutrit), 64. *Prof Exp:* Asst prof animal husb, Univ Mo, 64-67; mgr livestock nutrit res, Western Grain Co, 67-69; mgr animal nutrit, ConAgra, Inc, Ala, 69-74; ANIMAL NUTRITIONIST, SOUTHERN FARMERS ASN, 74- *Mem:* Am Soc Animal Sci; Am Dairy Sci Asn; assoc mem Am Soc Agr Consult. *Res:* Protein nutrition of neonatales; antibody absorption and production; feed composition; milk secretion and composition. *Mailing Add:* Southern Farmers Asn 824 N Palm North Little Rock AR 72114

LONG, CLARENCE SUMNER, JR, b Adairsville, Ga, June 5, 29; m 56; c 4. GEOLOGY. *Educ:* Tulane Univ, BS, 51; Univ Colo, PhD(geol), 66. *Prof Exp:* Geologist, Gulf Oil Corp, 54-57; asst geol, Univ Colo, 57-64; explor geologist, Pan Am Petrol Corp, 64-66; asst prof geol, Univ Ga, 66-69; assoc prof, 69-74, PROF GEOL, WGA COL, 74-, CHMN DEPT, 69- *Concurrent Pos:* Chattahoochee-Flint Planning Comn proj dir, Mineral Study Chattahoochee-Flint Area, 77-69. *Mem:* AAAS; Geol Soc Am; Am Asn Petrol Geol. *Mailing Add:* Dept of Geol WGa Col Carrollton GA 30117

LONG, CLIFFORD A, b Chicago, Ill, Apr 10, 31; m 57; c 4. MATHEMATICS. *Educ:* Univ Ill, BS, 54, MS, 55, PhD(math), 60. *Prof Exp:* From instr to assoc prof, 59-71, PROF MATH, BOWLING GREEN STATE UNIV, 71- *Mem:* Math Asn Am. *Res:* Computer graphics; numerical analysis. *Mailing Add:* Dept of Math Bowling Green State Univ Bowling Green OH 43403

LONG, DALE DONALD, b Louisa, Va, Jan 30, 35; m 65; c 2. EXPERIMENTAL PHYSICS. *Educ:* Va Polytech Inst, BS, 58, MS, 62; Fla State Univ, PhD(physics), 66. *Prof Exp:* Instr physics, Va Polytech Inst, 60; instr, Samford Univ, 60-62; asst prof, 67-79, ASSOC PROF PHYSICS, VA POLYTECH INST & STATE UNIV, 79- *Mem:* Am Phys Soc; Am Asn Physics Teachers. *Res:* Experimental nuclear physics. *Mailing Add:* Dept of Physics Va Polytech Inst & State Univ Blacksburg VA 24061

LONG, DANIEL R, b Redding, Calif, June 9, 38; m 61; c 2. PHYSICS. *Educ:* Univ Wash, PhD(physics), 67. *Prof Exp:* Asst prof, 67-71, assoc prof, 71-81, PROF PHYSICS, EASTERN WASH STATE COL, 81- *Concurrent Pos:* Sloan Found fel, 77. *Mem:* Am Phys Soc. *Res:* Electron impact ionization of metastable helium; experimental examination of the mass separation dependence of the gravitational constant. *Mailing Add:* Dept of Physics Eastern Wash State Col Cheney WA 99004

LONG, DARREL GRAHAM FRANCIS, b Yorkshire, Eng, Sept 6, 47; m 73; c 2. CLASTIC SEDIMENTOLOGY, COAL GEOLOGY. *Educ:* Univ Leicester, Eng, BSc, 69; Univ Western Ont, MSc, 73, PhD(geol), 76. *Prof Exp:* Fel geol, Geol Surv Can, 76-77, res scientist coal geol, 77-81; ASST PROF SEDIMENTOL, LAURENTIAN UNIV, SUDBURY, 81- *Mem:* Geol Asn Can; Geol Soc Am; Int Asn Sedimentologists; Soc Econ Paneontologists & Mineralogists. *Res:* Clastic sedimentology of precambrian sequences in Ontario, Yukon and Northwest Territory Canada; sedimentology and coal bearing sequences in British Columbia, Yukon, Northwest Territory and Ontario. *Mailing Add:* Dept Geol Laurentian Univ Sudbur ON P3E 2C6 Can

LONG, DARYL CLYDE, b Mason City, Iowa, Aug 19, 39; m 60; c 3. SOIL SCIENCE. *Educ:* Iowa State Univ, BS, 62, MS, 64; Univ Nebr, Lincoln, PhD, 67. *Prof Exp:* Instr soils, Univ Nebr, Lincoln, 64-67; asst prof, 67-77, ASSOC PROF SCI & MATH, PERU STATE COL, 77- *Mem:* Am Soc Agron; Soil Sci Soc Am; Nat Coun Teachers Math. *Res:* Mechanics of soil erosion and plant removal of nutrients from soil aggregates. *Mailing Add:* Dept of Sci & Math Peru State Col Peru NE 68421

LONG, DAVID MICHAEL, b Shamokin, Pa, Feb 26, 29; c 6. CARDIOVASCULAR SURGERY, THORACIC SURGERY. *Educ:* Muhlenberg Col, BS, 51; Hahnemann Med Col, MS, 54, MD, 56; Univ Minn, PhD(physiol), 65; Am Bd Surg, dipl, 66; Bd Thoracic Surg, dipl, 67. *Prof Exp:* Instr surg, Univ Minn, 65; from asst prof to assoc prof, Chicago Med Sch, 65-67; from assoc prof to prof surg, Abraham Lincoln Sch Med, Univ Ill Med Ctr, 69-73, attend staff & head div cardiovasc & thoracic surg, Hosp, 67-73; CLIN ASSOC PROF RADIOL, UNIV CALIF, SAN DIEGO, 73- *Concurrent Pos:* Assoc prof, Cook County Grad Sch Med, 65-73; assoc attend staff, Cook County Hosp, 65-73; asst dir dept surg res, Hektoen Inst Med Res, 65-68, dir, 68-73; attend staff, W Side Vet Admin Hosp, 66-73; consult, Chicago State Tuberc Sanitarium, 67-72; pvt pract, 73- *Honors & Awards:* First Prize Res, Am Urol Asn, 66. *Mem:* AAAS; Am Asn Thoracic Surg; fel Am Col Cardiol; fel Am Col Chest Physicians; fel Am Col Surg. *Res:* Surgical research; physiology and morphology; cancer chemotherapy; development of the radiopaque compound perfluorocarbon. *Mailing Add:* Suite 221 5565 Grossmont Ctr Dr La Mesa CA 92041

LONG, DONLIN MARTIN, b Rolla, Mo, Apr 14, 34; m 59; c 3. NEUROSURGERY, ELECTRON MICROSCOPY. *Educ:* Univ Mo, MD, 59; Univ Minn, PhD(anat), 64. *Prof Exp:* Clin assoc, Surg Neurol Bd, NIH, 65-67; assoc prof neurosurg, Univ Minn Hosps, 67-73; PROF NEUROL SURG & DIR DEPT, SCH MED, JOHNS HOPKINS UNIV, 73- *Concurrent Pos:* Consult neurosurgeon, Vet Admin Hosp, Minneapolis, 67- *Mem:* AAAS; Am Asn Neurol Surg; Cong Neurol Surg; Am Asn Neuropath; Soc Neurosci. *Res:* Electron microscopy of normal and abnormal control nervous system. *Mailing Add:* Dept of Neurol Surg Johns Hopkins Univ Sch of Med Baltimore MD 21205

LONG, EARL ELLSWORTH, b Akron, Ohio, Mar 27, 19; m 41; c 4. PUBLIC HEALTH LABORATORY ADMINISTRATION. *Educ:* Univ Akron, BSc, 42; Univ Pa, MSc, 47. *Prof Exp:* Asst instr med bact, Sch Med, Univ Pa, 45-48; asst prof bact, Univ Akron, 48-49; dir labs, Akron Health Dept, 49-61; DIR LABS, GA DEPT PUB HEALTH, 61-63 & 63- *Mem:* Am Soc Microbiol; fel Am Pub Health Asn; Asn State & Territorial Pub Health Labs Dirs (pres, 80); Sigma Xi. *Res:* State public health laboratory administration with emphasis on implementation of rapidly changing concepts in service and research. *Mailing Add:* Div of Labs Ga Dept Pub Health 47 Trinity Ave SW Atlanta GA 30334

LONG, EDWARD B, b White Plains, NY, Dec 5, 27; m 52, 70; c 3. AQUATIC ECOLOGY. *Educ:* Hamilton Col, BA, 52; Kent State Univ, MS, 71, PhD(biol), 75. *Prof Exp:* Mem staff mkt, Carbon Prod Div, Union Carbide Corp, 6-52-64, proj mgr, New Prod Mkt Develop, 64-69; tech mgr environ prog, Northeast Ohio Areawide Coord Agency, 75-81; ENVIRONMENTAL CONSULT, 81- *Mem:* Am Soc Limnol & Oceanog; Ecol Soc Am; AAAS. *Res:* Envrionmental quality of Northeast Ohio. *Mailing Add:* 200 Granger Rd # 50 Medina OH 44256

LONG, EDWARD RICHARDSON, JR, b Annapolis, Md, Sept 1, 41; m 68. MOLECULAR PHYSICS, MATERIAL SCIENCE. *Educ:* Col William & Mary, BS, 63, MS, 67; NC State Univ, PhD(molecular physics, nuclear magnetic resonance), 74. *Prof Exp:* Res scientist human factors, Aeronaut & Space Mech Div, Guid & Control Br, 63-67, res scientist solid state physics, Appl Math & Physics Div, Chem & Physics Br, 69-72, res scientist org pollution, Environ & Space Sci Div, Laser & Molecular Physics Br, 72-76, res scientist mat sci, Mat Div, Mat Res Br, 76-80, RES SCIENTIST MAT SCI, MAT DIV, ENVIRON EFFECTS BR, LANGLEY RES CTR, NASA, 80- *Concurrent Pos:* Assoc prof, George Wash Univ, 76- *Honors & Awards:* Spec Achievement Award & Innovation Award, NASA, 78. *Mem:* Am Phys Soc. *Res:* Solid state physics and organic chemical physics as applied to pollution spectroscopy and materials science. *Mailing Add:* MS/396 Environ Effects Br NASA Hampton VA 23665

LONG, ERNEST M, forest genetics, see previous edition

LONG, F(RANCIS) M(ARK), b Iowa City, Iowa, Nov 10, 29; m 64; c 4. ELECTRICAL ENGINEERING, BIOENGINEERING. *Educ:* Univ Iowa, BS, 53, MS, 56; Iowa State Univ, PhD(elec eng, biomed electronics), 61. *Prof Exp:* Asst elec eng, Univ Iowa, 55-56; instr, Univ Wyo, 56-58; instr, Iowa State Univ, 58-60; from asst prof to prof, Univ Wyo, 60-74, dir bioeng, 65-74, HEAD DEPT ELEC ENG, UNIV WYO, 77- *Concurrent Pos:* Engr, Collins Radio Co, 55; US Naval Air Missile Testing Ctr, Calif, 56; Good-All Elec Co, 57; spec fel NIH, 72-73; Engr, Globe-Union Co, 75. *Mem:* Sr mem, Inst Elec & Electronics Engrs; Am Soc Eng Educ (vpres, 77-79); Alliance for Eng in Med & Biol (vpres, 80-). *Res:* Circuit theory and biomedical engineering; instrumentation and system design; system modelling; microcircuit technology; animal biotelemetry. *Mailing Add:* Dept of Elec Eng Box 3295 Univ Sta Laramie WY 82071

LONG, FRANKLIN A, b Great Falls, Mont, July 27, 10; m 37; c 2. PHYSICAL CHEMISTRY, SCIENCE POLICY. *Educ:* Univ Mont, AB, 31, MA, 32; Univ Calif, PhD(phys chem), 35. *Prof Exp:* Instr chem, Univ Calif, 35-36; instr, Univ Chicago, 36-37; from instr to assoc prof chem, 37-42, chmn dept, 50-60, dir prog sci, technol & soc, 69-73, prof chem, 46-79, Luce prof sci & soc, 69-79, dir, Peace Studies Prog, 75-77, EMER PROF, CORNELL UNIV, 79- *Concurrent Pos:* Res supvr, Explosives Res Lab, Nat Defense Res Comt, 42-45; consult, Ballistics Res Lab, Dept Army, 53-59; mem sci adv bd, Air Force Off Sci Res, 59-63; mem, Pres Sci Adv Comt, 61 & 64-67; asst dir, US Arms Control & Disarmament Agency, 62-63; mem bd sci & technol for int develop, Nat Acad Sci, 74-77; mem, US-India Comn Educ & Cult Affairs, 74-, co-chmn, 77-; mem adv panel, Policy Res & Anal Div, NSF, 77-80; mem bd & consult, Carrier Corp & Exxon Corp; mem bd, Alfred P Sloan Found, Arms Control Asn & Assoc Univs, Inc. *Mem:* Nat Acad Sci; AAAS; Am Chem Soc; Am Acad Arts & Sci. *Res:* Kinetics of solution reactions; isotopic chemistry; arms control; science and public policy. *Mailing Add:* 632 Clark Hall Cornell Univ Ithaca NY 14853

LONG, FRANKLIN LESLIE, b Hinesville, Ga, July 22, 18; m 43. SOIL CHEMISTRY, SOIL FERTILITY. *Educ:* Univ Ga, BS, 57, MS, 58; Univ Fla, PhD(soils), 60. *Prof Exp:* RES SOIL SCIENTIST, AGR RES SERV, USDA, 60- *Mem:* Am Soc Agron; Soil Sci Soc Am; Int Soc Soil Sci. *Res:* Soils in the Coastal Plains and Piedmont areas of United States. *Mailing Add:* Agr Res Serv USDA 252 Funchess Hall Auburn AL 36830

LONG, G(EORGE) DONALD, b Elizabeth, NJ, Nov 12, 29; m 52; c 2. PHYSICS. *Educ:* Lehigh Univ, BS, 51; Univ Pa, PhD(physics), 56. *Prof Exp:* Res scientist, Res Ctr, Minneapolis-Honeywell Regulator Co, 55-60, mgr res dept, Corp Res Ctr, 60-77, mgr corp mat sci, 77-80, CHIEF SCIENTIST PHYSICAL SCI, CORP TECHNOL CTR, HONEYWELL INC, 80- *Mem:* Fel Am Phys Soc. *Res:* Semiconductors, especially basic properties determining performance of solid state devices. *Mailing Add:* Honeywell Inc Corp Technol Ctr 10701 Lyndale Ave S Bloomington MN 55420

LONG, GARY JOHN, b Binghamton, NY, Dec 3, 41; m 63; c 1. PHYSICAL INORGANIC CHEMISTRY. *Educ:* Carnegie-Mellon Univ, BS, 64; Syracuse Univ, PhD(chem), 68. *Prof Exp:* Asst prof, 68-74, assoc prof, 74-82, PROF CHEM, UNIV MO-ROLLA, 82- *Concurrent Pos:* Res assoc, Inorg Chem Lab & St John's Col, Oxford Univ, 74-75; res assoc, Atomic Energy Res Estab, Harwell, 75-81. *Mem:* Am Chem Soc; Am Phys Soc; fel Royal Soc Chem; Sigma Xi. *Res:* Transition metal inorganic coordination chemistry; Mossbauer and electronic spectroscopy; high-pressure optical and infrared spectroscopy; magnetic studies of coupled systems; x-ray and neutron diffraction studies. *Mailing Add:* Dept of Chem Univ of Mo Rolla MO 65401

LONG, GEORGE, b Greenville, Miss, Jan 17, 22; m 51; c 1. CHEMICAL ENGINEERING. *Educ:* Univ Tulane, BE, 44. *Prof Exp:* Res chemist, Div 8, Nat Defense Res Comt, Ohio, 44-45; chief chemist, USAAF, 45-46; res engr, Aluminum Co Am, 46-62; gen coordr res & develop, 62-67, dir, 67-77, MGR DIR RES & DEVELOP, NORTHERN ILL GAS CO, 77- *Mem:* Am Gas Asn; Sigma Xi; fel Am Inst Chem; Chem Mkt Res Asn; Am Chem Soc. *Res:* Process metallurgy of aluminum melting and smelting; aluminum-water explosions; high temperature refractory materials; natural gas utilization, materials and devices for distribution systems, substitute natural gas processes and natural gas combustion; synthetic fuel processes. *Mailing Add:* 24 Sylvia Lane Naperville IL 60540

LONG, GEORGE GILBERT, b Cincinnati, Ohio, July 12, 29; m 52; c 3. INORGANIC CHEMISTRY. *Educ:* Ind Univ, AB, 51; NC State Univ, MS, 53; Univ Fla, PhD(chem), 57. *Prof Exp:* Chemist, Ethyl Corp, 57-58; from asst prof to assoc prof, 58-70, chmn anal inorg chem, 69-77, PROF CHEM, NC STATE UNIV, 70- *Mem:* Am Chem Soc. *Res:* Chemistry of group V metalloids-organometalloid compounds; 121-Sb Mossbauer spectroscopy, structure and syntheses; vibrational spectroscopy. *Mailing Add:* Dept of Chem NC State Univ Raleigh NC 27607

LONG, GEORGE LOUIS, b Atkin, Minn, Dec 20, 43; m 67; c 2. BIOCHEMISTRY, ENZYMOLOGY. *Educ:* Pac Lutheran Univ, BA, 66; Brandeis Univ, PhD(biochem), 71. *Prof Exp:* NIH trainee molecular endocrinol sch med, Univ Calif, San Diego, 71-73; asst prof chem, Pomona Col, 73-80; NIH SR FEL BIOCHEM, UNIV WASH, 80- *Mem:* Am Soc Biol Chem; Sigma Xi; Am Chem Soc; AAAS. *Res:* Comparative enzymology of glycolytic enzymes; molecular mechanism of hemostasis. *Mailing Add:* Dept Biochem Univ Wash Seattle WA 98195

LONG, H(UGH) M(ONTGOMERY), b Montgomery, Ala, June 28, 24; m 49; c 2. ENHANCED OIL RECOVERY, ELECTRICAL LOAD MANAGEMENT. *Educ:* Ala Polytech Inst, BS, 47, MS, 49; Oxford Univ, DPhil(physics), 53. *Prof Exp:* Instr math, Auburn Univ, 47-48, res asst, 47-49; res physicist, Linde Div, Oak Ridge Nat Lab, Union Carbide Corp, 54-61, cryogenics consult, 61-71, group leader eng sci, Thermonuclear Div, 71-76, mgr elec energy systs prog, Energy Div, 76-80; assoc prof elec eng, Univ Tenn, Knoxville, 71-80; vpres mkt develop, Vedelt Energy Res Inc, 80-81; STAFF EXEC, ENHANCED ENERGY SYSTS, INC, 81- *Concurrent Pos:* Mem, Nat Acad Sci-Nat Res Coun adv panel to Nat Bur Standards Cryogenic Eng Lab, 61-65; US rep, Comt I, Int Inst Refrig, 64-; mem & chmn, US Delegation USSR Scientific & Technol Exchange Superconductivity Power Transmission, 73-79. *Honors & Awards:* Ben S Gilmer Award, Auburn Univ, 78. *Mem:* AAAS; Am Phys Soc; sr mem Inst Elec & Electronics Engrs; NY Acad Sci; Soc Petrol Engrs. *Res:* Low temperature physics; cryogenic engineering; gas liquefaction; low temperature phase equilibria; mechanical properties of materials at low temperatures; superconductivity; power system engineering; energy management. *Mailing Add:* Enhanced Energy Systs Inc 3537 Old Conejo Rd Suite 107 Newbury Park CA 91320

LONG, HOWARD CHARLES, b Seizholtzville, Pa, Dec 12, 18; m 45; c 3. PHYSICS. *Educ:* Northwestern Univ, BS, 41; Ohio State Univ, PhD(physics), 48. *Prof Exp:* Physicist, Naval Ord Lab, 42-45; instr physics, Ohio State Univ, 47-48; asst prof, Washington & Jefferson Col, 48-51; physicist, Naval Ord Lab, 51-52; assoc prof physics & chmn dept, Am Univ, 52-53; prof & chmn dept, Gettysburg Col, 53-59; chmn dept, 63-74, prof, 59-81, EMER PROF PHYSICS, DICKINSON COL, 81- *Concurrent Pos:* Consult, Naval Ord Lab, 54-73. *Mem:* Am Phys Soc; Am Asn Physics Teachers; Audio Eng Soc. *Res:* Low period fluctuations in earth's magnetism; environmental noise reduction; air pollution by solid particulates; molecualr structure and infrared spectroscopy; electromagnetism. *Mailing Add:* Dept of Physics & Astron Dickinson Col Carlisle PA 17013

LONG, JAMES ALVIN, b Porto Alegre, Brazil, July 13, 17; US citizen; wid; c 4. EXPLORATION GEOPHYSICS. *Educ:* Univ Okla, BA, 37. *Prof Exp:* Computer & party chief, Stanolind Oil & Gas Co, 37-46; party chief, United Geophys Corp, 46-48, supvr, Venezuela, Brazil & Chile, 48-54, area mgr, Southern SAm, 54-59, regional opers mgr, South & Cent Am, 59-62, sr geophysicist, 62-65, coordr digital tech, 65-66, asst chief geophysicist, 66-67, regional mgr, Latin Am, 67-72; sr geophysicist, Tetra Tech, Inc, 73-74; geophys adv, Bolivian Govt Oil Co, Santa Cruz, 74- 77; INT CONSULT GEOPHYSICIST, 73- *Honors & Awards:* Best Paper Award, Soc Explor Geophys, 66. *Mem:* Soc Explor Geophysicist; fel Explorers Club. *Res:* Seismic of surface sources; special seismic interpretation problems, particularly in South America, Australia and China. *Mailing Add:* 3951 Gulf Shore Blvd N Naples FL 33940

LONG, JAMES DELBERT, b Dover, Okla, Dec 18, 39. HORTICULTURE, PLANT PHYSIOLOGY. *Educ:* Okla State Univ, BS, 62; Univ Md, College Park, MS, 67, PhD(hort), 69. *Prof Exp:* Res asst weed control, Univ Md, College Park, 64-67, instr hort, 67-68; res biologist agr chem, 68-79, PROD DEVELOP MGR, E I DU PONT DE NEMOURS & CO, INC, WILMINGTON, DEL, 79- *Mem:* Weed Sci Soc Am. *Res:* Control and modification of plant growth through the use of chemicals; new herbicide development. *Mailing Add:* E I du Pont de Nemours & Co 213 Blake Rd Elkton MD 21921

LONG, JAMES DUNCAN, b Rusk, Tex, Sept 23, 25. ZOOLOGY. *Educ:* Sam Houston State Col, BS, 48, MA, 51; Univ Tex, PhD, 57. *Prof Exp:* Teacher, High Sch, Tex, 48-49 & Pub Schs, 51-52; instr biol, Lamar State Col Technol, 52-53; asst, Univ Tex, 53-56; assoc prof biol & head dept, Ill Col, 56-59; assoc prof, 59-63, dir dept, 63-72, PROF BIOL, SAM HOUSTON STATE UNIV, 63- *Mem:* AAAS; Soc Syst Zool; Entom Soc Am; Am Mosquito Control Asn. *Res:* Mosquito biology. *Mailing Add:* Dept of Biol Sam Houston State Univ Huntsville TX 77341

LONG, JAMES EARL, b Steelton, Pa, Jan 28, 28; m 53; c 2. TOXICOLOGY, INDUSTRIAL HYGIENE. *Educ:* Gettysburg Col, BA, 50; Univ Pittsburgh, MS, 55, ScD(indust health), 59. *Prof Exp:* Toxicologist, Med Res Labs, Army Chem Ctr, Md, 50-53, aerosol chemist, Chem & Radiol Labs, 53-54; res assoc respiratory physiol, Toxicol & Indust Hyg, Grad Sch Pub Health, Univ Pittsburgh, 55-58, instr indust hyg, 58-60; res indust hygienist, Environ Health Lab, Am Cyanamid Co, 60-62, sr res environ health scientist, 62-64; indust toxicologist & hygienist, M&T Chem, Inc, NJ, 64-68; dir environ toxicol, Int Res & Develop Corp Mich, 68-69; MGR TOXICOL, MINN MINING & MFG CO, 69- *Concurrent Pos:* AEC fel indust hyg, Grad Sch Pub Health, Univ Pittsburgh, 54-55; adj assoc prof, Grad Sch Pub Health, Univ Minn, 69- *Mem:* AAAS; Am Indust Hyg Asn; Water Pollution Control Fedn; Am Chem Soc; Soc Toxicol. *Res:* Industrial hygiene sampling and instrumentation; assessment of physiological impairment by pulmonary irritants; synergistic effects of aerosols and vapors; inhalation toxicology. *Mailing Add:* 2044 Oakdale Ave West St Paul MN 55118

LONG, JAMES FRANTZ, b Center Valley, Pa, Sept 17, 31; m 56; c 3. PHYSIOLOGY. *Educ:* Mich State Univ, BS, 57, MS, 59; Univ Pa, PhD(physiol), 64. *Prof Exp:* From instr to assoc prof physiol, Albany Med Col, 64-69; prin scientist, 69-75, RES FEL, DEPT PHARMACOL, SCHERING CORP, 75- *Mem:* Am Physiol Soc; Am Gastroenterol Asn. *Res:* Gastrointestinal physiology and pharmacology. *Mailing Add:* Dept of Pharmacol Schering Corp Bloomfield NJ 07003

LONG, JAMES HARVEY, JR, b Johnson City, Tenn, Sept 14, 44; m 65; c 1. CHEMISTRY, CHEMICAL ENGINEERING. *Educ:* Univ Tenn, BS, 65, PhD(chem), 68. *Prof Exp:* Chemist, Shell Chem Co, 68-71, sr chemist, Shell Develop Co, 72-73, process mgr, 73-77, STAFF ENGR & PROJ COORDR, SHELL CHEM CO, 77- *Mailing Add:* 755 International Houston TX 77024

LONG, JAMES WILLIAM, b Boise, Idaho, Aug 26, 43; m 65; c 1. BIOCHEMISTRY. *Educ:* Univ Wash, BS, 65; Univ Calif, Berkeley, PhD(biochem), 69. *Prof Exp:* Res assoc biochem, Purdue Univ, West Lafayette, 70-71, NIH res fel, 71-72, res assoc, 72-73; res assoc, Univ Ore, 73-74; asst prof, 74-77, ASSOC PROF CHEM, COL GREAT FALLS, 77- *Concurrent Pos:* Assoc prof chem, Univ Ore, Eugene, 78-79. *Mem:* Am Chem Soc. *Res:* Nuclear magnetic resonance in biological studies; structure-function relationships in enzymes; mechanisms of enzyme action; enzyme model systems; role of metal ions in enzyme catalysis. *Mailing Add:* Dept of Chem Col of Great Falls Great Falls MT 59405

LONG, JEROME R, b Lafayette, La, May 17, 35; m 62; c 2. PHYSICS. *Educ:* Univ Southwestern La, BS, 56; La State Univ, MS, 58, PhD(physics), 65. *Prof Exp:* Res engr, Gen Dynamics/Pomona, 58-59; fel metall, Univ Pa, 65-67; asst prof physics, 67-71, ASSOC PROF PHYSICS, VA POLYTECH INST & STATE UNIV, 71- *Concurrent Pos:* Vis prof, Simon Fraser Univ, 78-79. *Mem:* Am Phys Soc. *Res:* Transport and magnetic properties of metallic materials; cryophysics. *Mailing Add:* Dept of Physics Va Polytech Inst & State Univ Blacksburg VA 24061

LONG, JIM T(HOMAS), b Central, SC, Oct 5, 23; m 46; c 1. ELECTRICAL ENGINEERING. *Educ:* Clemson Col, BEE, 43; Ga Inst Technol, MSEE, 49, PhD(elec eng), 64. *Prof Exp:* From instr to assoc prof, 43-67, PROF ELEC ENG & COORDR UNDERGRAD PROG, CLEMSON UNIV, 67- *Concurrent Pos:* Asst, Ga Inst Technol, 48-49, asst prof, 57-64. *Mem:* Am Soc Eng Educ; Inst Elec & Electronics Engrs. *Res:* Electronics; network theory; solid state electronics. *Mailing Add:* Dept of Elec & Comput Eng Clemson Univ Clemson SC 29631

LONG, JOHN A, b Lewistown, Mont, Sept 1, 27; m 49; c 4. AGRONOMY, BIOCHEMISTRY. *Educ:* Univ Idaho, BS, 52; Wash State Univ, MS, 54; Tex A&M Univ, PhD(agron), 61. *Prof Exp:* Asst in agron, NMex State Univ, 54-56; instr, Tex A&M Univ, 56-61; proj leader agron, 61-63, DIR BIOCHEM RES, O M SCOTT & SONS CO, 63- *Concurrent Pos:* Chmn student interest com, Southern Weed Control Asn, 59-60, turf sect, Weed Sci Soc Am, 63-64; chmn mem comt, Agr Res Inst, 72-73, mem prog comt, 73-74; dir, Nat Coun Com Plant Breeders, 76-78, second vpres, 77-78, first vpres, 78-79, pres, 79-80. *Res:* Plant physiology; horticulture; phytopathology. *Mailing Add:* Biochem Res O M Scott & Sons Co Marysville OH 43041

LONG, JOHN ARTHUR, b Kingman, Kans, July 30, 34. CYTOLOGY, ANATOMY. *Educ:* Univ Kans, AB, 56; Univ Wash, PhD(zool), 64. *Prof Exp:* Res assoc anat, Harvard Med Sch, 66-67; asst prof, 67-74, ASSOC PROF ANAT, MED CTR, UNIV CALIF, SAN FRANCISCO, 74- *Mem:* AAAS; Am Soc Zool. *Res:* Fine structure of steroid secreting cells in ovary and adrenal glands. *Mailing Add:* Dept of Anat Univ of Calif Med Ctr San Francisco CA 94143

LONG, JOHN FREDERICK, b Napoleon, Ohio, May 30, 24; m 48; c 5. VETERINARY PATHOLOGY. *Educ:* Ohio State Univ, BA, 47, MSc, 48, DVM, 55, PhD(comp neuropath), 66. *Prof Exp:* Res asst animal sci, Ohio Agr Exp Sta, 49-50; diag vet pathologist, Vet Diag Lab, State of Ohio, 55-63; res assoc comp neuropath, 63-64, NIH res fel, 64-66, instr vet path, 66-67, NIH spec res fel comp neuropath, 67-68, asst prof vet path, 68-71, ASSOC PROF VET PATH, OHIO STATE UNIV, 71- *Mem:* Am Vet Med Asn; Am Asn Avian Path. *Res:* Comparative neuropathology; viral encephalomyelitides; use of brain explant culture and germ-free animals in the study of the effects of encephalitogenic agents; demyelinating encephalomyelitides of animals. *Mailing Add:* 2765 Bexley Park Rd Columbus OH 43209

LONG, JOHN KELLEY, b NY, Dec 12, 21; m 48; c 3. NUCLEAR PHYSICS, NUCLEAR ENGINEERING. *Educ:* Columbia Univ, BS, 42; Ohio State Univ, PhD(physics), 53. *Prof Exp:* Chemist plastics, Hercules Powder Co, 42-45; engr, Wright Field, 47-50; physicist, Battelle Mem Inst, 52-55; physicist, Idaho Div, Argonne Nat Lab, 55-74; REACTOR ENGR, US NUCLEAR REGULATORY COMN, 74- *Res:* Fast reactor physics; critical experiments; reactor licensing; fast reactor safety test facilities; plutonium toxicity. *Mailing Add:* US Nuclear Regulatory Comn Washington DC 20555

LONG, JOHN PAUL, b Albia, Iowa, Oct 4, 26; m 50; c 3. PHARMACOLOGY. *Educ:* Univ Iowa, BS, 50, MS, 52, PhD(pharmacol), 54. *Prof Exp:* From asst to instr pharmacol, Univ Iowa, 50-54; res assoc, Sterling-Winthrop Res Inst, 54-56; from asst prof to assoc prof, 56-62, PROF PHARMACOL, COL MED, UNIV IOWA, 62-, HEAD DEPT, 70- *Mem:* Am Soc Pharmacol & Exp Therapeut; Soc Exp Biol & Med. *Res:* Structure-activity relationships of autonomic and anesthetic agents. *Mailing Add:* Dept of Pharmacol Univ of Iowa Col of Med Iowa City IA 52240

LONG, JOHN REED, b Chicago, Ill, Oct 2, 22; m 48; c 2. INDUSTRIAL ENGINEERING, MANUFACTURINIG ENGINEERING. *Educ:* Northwestern Univ, BS, 47; Iowa State Univ, MS, 48, PhD(chem eng), 51. *Prof Exp:* Asst, AEC, Ames Lab, Iowa State Univ, 48-51; sr engr, 51-60, process engr, 61-66, sr process engr, 66-80, SUPVR PROCESS ENGR, HERCULES, INC, 80- *Mem:* Am Chem Soc; Am Inst Chem Engrs. *Res:* Process design of chemical plants. *Mailing Add:* Hercules Inc 910 Market St Wilmington DE 19899

LONG, JOHN VINCENT, b San Diego, Calif, Feb 18, 10; m 38; c 4. PHYSICS. *Educ:* Univ Calif, Los Angeles, AB, 37. *Prof Exp:* Lab asst physics, San Diego State Col, 32-35; serv demonstr, Ford Motor Co, Calif, 35-36; res engr, Douglas Aircraft Co, 36-37; geophysicist, Continental Oil Co, Okla, 37-40; res engr, Int Harvester Co, 40; res physicist & asst dir res, 46-51, dir res, Solar Div, 51-80; MEM STAFF, MGL DEVELOP, 80- *Mem:* Soc Explor Geophys; Acoust Soc Am; Soc Exp Stress Anal; assoc Inst Elec & Electronics Engrs. *Res:* Ceramics; metallurgy; vibration and sound; high altitude research; ceramic coatings for high temperature corrosion and oxidation protection of iron, stainless steel; super alloys and refractory metals. *Mailing Add:* 1756 E Lexington Ave El Cajon CA 92021

LONG, JOSEPH POTE, b Baker Summit, Pa, Feb 26, 13; m 42; c 4. OBSTETRICS & GYNECOLOGY. *Educ:* Juniata Col, BS, 34; Jefferson Med Col, MD, 39; Univ Pa, MS, 48. *Prof Exp:* From demonstr to assoc prof, 48-75, clin prof, 75-78, HON CLIN PROF OBSTET & GYNEC, JEFFERSON MED COL, THOMAS JEFFERSON UNIV, 78- *Mem:* AMA; Am Col Surg; Am Col Obstet & Gynec; Am Fertil Soc; NY Acad Sci. *Mailing Add:* 2209 Douglas Dr Carlisle PA 17013

LONG, KEITH ROYCE, b Lincoln, Kans, Mar 17, 22; m 45; c 5. ENVIRONMENTAL HEALTH. *Educ:* Univ Kans, AB, 51, MA, 53; Univ Iowa, PhD, 60. *Prof Exp:* Asst instr bact, Univ Kans, 52-53, instr bact res, Med Ctr, 53-56; sr bacteriologist & virologist, State Hyg Lab, 56-57, instr, Inst Agr Med, 57-58, asst bact, 58-60, assoc prof hyg & prev med, Inst Agr Med, Col Med, 60-69, PROF PREV MED & ENVIRON HEALTH SCI, INSTR AGR MED & ENVIRON HEALTH, COL MED, UNIV IOWA, 69-, DIR, INST, 74-, PROF CIVIL ENG, UNIV, 70- *Mem:* Soc Occup & Environ Health; NY Acad Sci. *Res:* Environmental toxicology; epidemiology; pesticides. *Mailing Add:* Inst Agr Med & Environ Health Univ Iowa Col Med Iowa City IA 52240

LONG, KENNETH MAYNARD, b Nappanee, Ind, July 10, 32; m 52; c 5. INORGANIC CHEMISTRY, SPELEOLOGY. *Educ:* Goshen Col, BS, 54; Mich State Univ, MA, 60; Ohio State Univ, PhD(chem), 67. *Prof Exp:* Instr, Parochial Sch, Ark, 54-56; instr, High Sch, Mich, 56-61; from instr to asst prof chem, 62-70, asst dean, 71-75, assoc prof, 70-79, PROF CHEM, WESTMINSTER COL, PA, 79- *Concurrent Pos:* Fel, Kent State Univ, 79. *Mem:* Am Chem Soc; Nat Asn Geol Teachers; Nat Speleol Soc. *Res:* Macrocyclic complexes of transition metals; catalytic properties of transition metal complexes; kinetics; hydrology; geology and mapping of caves. *Mailing Add:* Dept Chem Westminster Col New Wilmington PA 16142

LONG, LAWRENCE WILLIAM, b Akron, Ohio, Nov 6, 42; m 69. BIOCHEMISTRY. *Educ:* Franklin & Marshall Col, AB, 65; Villanova Univ, PhD(chem), 71. *Prof Exp:* Instr biochem, Thomas Jefferson Univ, 71-73; res scientist, Stevens Inst Technol, 73-74; proj leader chem, 74-77, MGR ALLIED PROD, ANHEUSER-BUSCH INC, 78- *Mem:* Am Chem Soc; Am Soc Brewing Chemists. *Res:* Utilization of brewing residuals. *Mailing Add:* Anheuser-Busch Inc One Busch Pl St Louis MO 63118

LONG, LELAND TIMOTHY, b Auburn, NY, Sept 6, 40; m 70; c 3. GEOPHYSICS, SEISMOLOGY. *Educ:* Univ Rochester, BS, 62; NMex Inst Mining & Technol, MS, 64; Ore State Univ, PhD(geophys), 68. *Prof Exp:* From asst prof to assoc prof, 68-80, PROF GEOPHYS, GA INST TECHNOL, 81- *Mem:* Am Geophys Union; Seismol Soc Am; Soc Explor Geophys; Sigma Xi. *Res:* Earthquake seismology; regional gravity studies. *Mailing Add:* Sch of Geophys Sci Ga Inst Technol Atlanta GA 30332

LONG, LEON EUGENE, b Wanatah, Ind, May 4, 33; m 56; c 2. GEOCHEMISTRY. *Educ:* Wheaton Col, BS, 54; Columbia Univ, MA, 58, PhD(geochem), 59. *Prof Exp:* Geochemist, Lamont Geol Observ, Columbia Univ, 59-60; NSF fel, Oxford Univ, 60-62; from asst prof to assoc prof, 62-75, PROF GEOL, UNIV TEX, AUSTIN, 75- *Mem:* Fel Geol Soc Am; Geochem Soc; Sigma Xi. *Res:* Isotopic age methods. *Mailing Add:* Dept of Geol Sci Univ of Tex Austin TX 78712

LONG, MAURICE W(AYNE), b Madisonville, Ky, Apr 20, 25; m 50, 63; c 4. ELECTRONICS, PHYSICS. *Educ:* Ga Inst Technol, BEE, 46, MS, 57, PhD(physics), 59; Univ Ky, MSEE, 48. *Prof Exp:* Asst, Eng Exp Sta, Ga Inst Technol, 46-47; instr elec eng, Univ Ky, 47-49; res engr, Eng Exp Sta, Ga Inst Technol, 50-51, asst prof, 51-53, spec res engr, 53-65, head, Radar Br, 55-60, chief, Electronics Div, 59-68, prin res physicist, 65-68, prof elec eng, 68-74, dir, Exp Sta, 68-75; CONSULT, 75- *Concurrent Pos:* Liaison scientist, Off Naval Res, London, 66-67; mem comt remote sensing prog for earth resources surv, Nat Acad Sci, 77. *Mem:* Fel Inst Elec & Electronics Engrs; Am Phys Soc. *Res:* Antennas and propagation; radar; electromagnetic scattering from rough surfaces; research management. *Mailing Add:* 1036 Somerset Dr NW Atlanta GA 30327

LONG, MICHAEL EDGAR, b CZ, June 22, 46; m 68. PHYSICAL CHEMISTRY. *Educ:* Univ Toledo, BEd, 68; Wayne State Univ, PhD(chem), 73. *Prof Exp:* Fel chem, Cornell Univ, 73-75; RES CHEMIST, EASTMAN KODAK CO, 75- *Concurrent Pos:* NIH fel, Cornell Univ, 74-75. *Mem:* Am Chem Soc; Am Phys Soc; Sigma Xi. *Res:* Molecular electronic spectroscopy and photophysical processes in organic molecules. *Mailing Add:* Eastman Kodak Co Res Labs Bldg 81 Rochester NY 14650

LONG, PAUL EASTWOOD, JR, b Philadelphia, Pa, Oct 9, 42; m 69; c 1. METEOROLOGY, NUMERICAL ANALYSIS. *Educ:* Drexel Univ, BS, 65, MS, 68, PhD(physics), 70. *Prof Exp:* Mathematician, Philco-Ford Corp, 64-65; fel, Drexel Univ, 70-71; assoc, Nat Weather Serv, 71-73, res meteorologist, 73-74; res meteorologist, Savannah River Lab, E I du Pont de Nemours & Co, Inc, 74-76; METEOROLOGIST, NAT WEATHER SERV, 76- *Mem:* Am Meteorol Soc; Am Inst Physics. *Res:* Numerical planetary boundary layer modeling. *Mailing Add:* 6 Hilltop Rd Silver Spring MD 20910

LONG, R(OBERT) B(YRON), b Annville, Pa, Feb 18, 23; m 44; c 6. CHEMICAL ENGINEERING. *Educ:* Pa State Col, BS, 44, MS, 47, PhD(chem eng), 51. *Prof Exp:* Res engr, Standard Oil Develop Co, 50-53, proj leader, 53-57, res assoc, 57-64, sr res assoc, 64-69, SCI ADV, EXXON RES & ENG CO, 69- *Mem:* Am Chem Soc; Am Inst Chem Engrs. *Res:* Separation processes; solvent extraction; petroleum processing; synthetic fuels. *Mailing Add:* 12 Keystone Dr Atlantic Highlands NJ 07716

LONG, RAYMOND CARL, b Shattuck, Okla, June 17, 39; m 59; c 4. PLANT PHYSIOLOGY. *Educ:* Kans State Univ, BS, 61, MS, 62; Univ Ill, Urbana, PhD(plant physiol), 66. *Prof Exp:* Asst prof, 66-73, ASSOC PROF CROP SCI, NC STATE UNIV, 73- *Mem:* Am Soc Plant Physiol; Am Soc Agron. *Res:* Biochemistry of growth and senescence of higher plants; diurnal variations in metabolism; nitrogen metabolism; environmental stress and plant growth. *Mailing Add:* Dept of Crop Sci NC State Univ Raleigh NC 27650

LONG, ROBERT ALLEN, b Kingman, Ariz, Aug 17, 41; m 63; c 3. PHARMACEUTICAL CHEMISTRY, MEDICAL SCIENCES. *Educ:* Portland State Univ, BA, 64; Univ Utah, PhD(org chem), 70. *Prof Exp:* Res chemist, ICN Pharmaceut Inc, Calif, 70-77; CLIN RES SCIENTIST,

CARDIOVASC SECT, MED DIV, BURROUGHS WELLCOME CO, 77- *Mem:* Am Chem Soc; Am Pharmaceut Asn; Acad Pharmaceut Sci. *Res:* Heterocyclic chemistry; nucleic acid chemistry; antiviral and antitumor research; cardiovascular research, clinical trials of new drugs; continued medical support for marketed products; project leader for new product development. *Mailing Add:* Burroughs Wellcome Co 3030 Cornwallis Rd Research Triangle Park NC 27709

LONG, ROBERT LEROY, b Renovo, Pa, Sept 9, 36; m 57; c 3. NUCLEAR ENGINEERING. *Educ:* Bucknell Univ, BS, 58; Purdue Univ, MSE, 59, PhD(nuclear eng), 62. *Prof Exp:* Res assoc exp reactor physics, Argonne Nat Lab, 60-62; reactor specialist nuclear effects br, White Sands Missile Range, NMex, 62-65; from asst prof to prof nuclear eng, Univ NMex, 65-78, asst dean, 72-74, chmn chem & nuclear eng dept, 74-78; mgr, Generation Productivity Dept, 78-79, dir, Generation Productivity Dept, Gen Pub Utilities Serv Corp, 79-80, DIR TRAINING & EDUC, GEN PUB UTILITIES NUCLEAR CORP, 80- *Concurrent Pos:* Res partic, Sandia Corp, 65-; consult, White Sands Missile Range Fast Burst Reactor Facil, 65-; res assoc nuclear res div, Atomic Weapons Res Estab, Eng, 66-67; assoc reactor engr, Con Edison, NY, 70-71; proj mgr nuclear eng & opers, Elec Power Res Inst, 76-77. *Mem:* AAAS; Atomic Indust Forum; Am Nuclear Soc; Am Inst Chem Engrs. *Res:* Reliability engineering data and applications; experimental reactor physics; fast burst reactors; power reactor technology; engineering teaching methods. *Mailing Add:* Gen Pub Utilities Serv Corp 260 Cherry Hill Rd Parsippany NJ 07054

LONG, ROBERT RADCLIFFE, b Glen Ridge, NJ, Oct 24, 19; m 63; c 2. METEOROLOGY. *Educ:* Princeton Univ, AB, 41; Univ Chicago, MS, 49, PhD, 50. *Prof Exp:* Meteorologist, US Weather Bur, 46-47; sr investr, hydrodyn lab, Univ Chicago, 49-51; from asst prof to assoc prof meteorol, 51-59, PROF FLUID MECH, JOHNS HOPKINS UNIV, 59- *Concurrent Pos:* Mem adv panel gen sci, US Secy Defense Res & Eng. *Mem:* Am Meteorol Soc. *Res:* Geophysical fluid mechanics; theoretical studies and laboratory models of geophysical phenomena; general circulation of the atmosphere; atmospheric and oceanic flow over barriers. *Mailing Add:* Dept of Earth & Planetary Sci Johns Hopkins Univ Baltimore MD 21218

LONG, ROBERT WILLIAM, b New Albany, Ind, Mar 14, 17; m 46; c 2. PHYSICAL CHEMISTRY. *Educ:* Ind State Univ, AB, 38; Univ Calif, Berkeley, PhD(chem), 41. *Prof Exp:* Res chemist, Union Oil Co Calif, 41-50; PROF CHEM, EL CAMINO COL, 50- *Concurrent Pos:* NSF sci fac fel, Calif Inst Technol, 61-62. *Res:* Gas phase association of hydrogen and deuterium fluorides; shale oil chemistry and utilization; nitrocycloalkanes. *Mailing Add:* Dept of Chem El Camino Col Torrance CA 90506

LONG, RONALD K(ILLWORTH), b Steubenville, Ohio, Dec 5, 32; m 59. ELECTRICAL ENGINEERING. *Educ:* Ohio Wesleyan Univ, BA, 54; Harvard Univ, MS, 56; Ohio State Univ, PhD, 63. *Prof Exp:* Res engr labs, Radio Corp Am, 55; asst, Harvard Univ, 55-56; res engr, NAm Aviation, Inc, 56-57; asst supvr, Antenna Lab, Ohio State Univ, 58-63, from asst prof to assoc prof, 63-69, prof elec eng, 69-80. *Res:* Lasers; atmospheric propagation; infrared techniques; computer data acquisition. *Mailing Add:* 1516 Essex Rd Columbus OH 43221

LONG, RUSSELL E(DWIN), b Perth Amboy, NJ, July 10, 21; m 43; c 3. CERAMICS ENGINEERING. *Educ:* Ohio State Univ, BS, 43. *Prof Exp:* Ceramic engr, Stupakoff Ceramic & Mfg Co, 43-46, Battelle Mem Inst, 46-52 & Brush Beryllium Co, 52-57; sr res engr, 57-67, DIR CERAMIC RES, AM OLEAN TILE CO, INC, 67- *Mem:* Fel AAAS; Am Ceramic Soc; Nat Inst Ceramic Engrs; Brit Ceramic Soc; Am Soc Testing & Mat. *Res:* Non-plastic refractory ceramics; control of raw material for steatite manufacture; refractory metals; ceramic wall tile; polymer strengthening of ceramic tile. *Mailing Add:* Am Olean Tile Co Inc 1000 N Cannon Ave Lansdale PA 19446

LONG, SALLY YATES, b Moyock, NC, Nov 8, 41; m 73; c 2. EMBRYOLOGY, TERATOLOGY. *Educ:* Col William & Mary, BS, 63; Univ Fla, PhD(anat), 67. *Prof Exp:* Lectr genetics, McGill Univ, 68-70; res assoc teratology, Karolinska Inst, Sweden, 70-71; asst prof, 71-76, asst dean student affairs, 78-81, ASSOC PROF ANAT, MED COL WIS, 76-, ASSOC DEAN STUDENT AFFAIRS, 81- *Concurrent Pos:* NIH fel, McGill Univ, 68-70. *Mem:* Teratology Soc (secy, 77-); Am Asn Anat; Europ Teratology Soc. *Res:* Interactions of genetic and environmental factors in causing malformations, especially cleft palate and limb defects. *Mailing Add:* Dept Anat Med Col Wis 8701 Watertown Plank Rd Milwaukee WI 53226

LONG, SHARON RUGEL, b San Marcos, Tex, Mar 2, 51; m 79. DEVELOPMENTAL BIOLOGY. *Educ:* Calif Inst Technol, BS, 73; Yale Univ PhD(biol), 79. *Prof Exp:* Res fel, dept biol, Harvard Univ, 78-81; ASST PROF, DEPT BIOL SCI, STANFORD UNIV, 82- *Mem:* Am Soc Plant Physiologists; Genetics Soc Am; Soc Develop Biol. *Res:* Genetics and developmental biology of symbiotic nitrogen fixation in legumes; role of plasmids in symbiosis; embryo development and seed germination in higher plants. *Mailing Add:* Dept Biol Sci Stanford Univ Stanford CA 94305

LONG, STERLING K(RUEGER), b Petersburg, Va, Mar 11, 27; m 48, 73; c 2. BACTERIOLOGY. *Educ:* Univ Fla, BS, 49, MS, 51; Univ Tex, PhD(bact), 58. *Prof Exp:* Asst instr bot, Univ Miami, 49-50; asst bact & sanit eng, Univ Fla, 50-51; instr bact, Dent Br, Univ Tex, 57-58; assoc indust bacteriologist, Agr Res & Educ Ctr, Univ Fla, 58-74; RES MICROBIOLOGIST, NAT DISTILLERS & CHEM CORP, 74- *Mem:* Am Soc Microbiol. *Res:* Industrial fermentations; clinical and sanitary bacteriology; thermophilic spore forming bacteria; biochemistry. *Mailing Add:* Cent Res Lab 1275 Section Rd Cincinnati OH 45237

LONG, STUART A, b Philadelphia, Pa, Mar 6, 45; m 69; c 2. APPLIED ELECTROMAGNETICS, ANTENNAS. *Educ:* Rice Univ, BA, 67, MEE, 68; Harvard Univ, PhD(appl physics), 74. *Prof Exp:* Asst prof, 74-79, ASSOC PROF ELEC ENG, UNIV HOUSTON, 79-, CHMN DEPT, 81- *Mem:* Inst Elec & Electronics Engrs; Antennas & Propagation Soc; Int Union Radio Sci. *Res:* Applied electromagnetics: antennas; electromagentic methods of nondestructive evaluation; well-logging; subsurface communications; millimeter waveguiding and radiating structures. *Mailing Add:* Dept Elec Eng Univ Houston Houston TX 77004

LONG, TERRILL JEWETT, b Newark, Ohio, Mar 19, 32; m 55; c 4. BOTANY. *Educ:* Ohio Univ, BSAg, 56; Ohio State Univ, MSc, 59, PhD(bot), 61. *Prof Exp:* NIH fel, Oak Ridge Nat Lab, 61-63, res assoc bot, 63-64; asst prof biol, Vanderbilt Univ, 64-65; res assoc biochem, Ohio State Univ, 65-67; asst prof, 67-70, ASSOC PROF BIOL, CAPITAL UNIV, 70- *Concurrent Pos:* Consult, C S Fred Mushroom Co, 66-70. *Mem:* Am Soc Plant Physiol; Bot Soc Am; Mycol Soc Am. *Res:* Physiology and biochemistry of irradiated wheat and mushrooms and related fungi. *Mailing Add:* Dept of Biol Capital Univ 2199 E Main St Columbus OH 43209

LONG, THOMAS CARLYLE, genetics, see previous edition

LONG, THOMAS ROSS, b Lexington, Ky, Nov 6, 29; m 52; c 3. SOLID STATE PHYSICS. *Educ:* Ohio Wesleyan Univ, BA, 51; Case Inst Technol, MS, 53, PhD(physics), 56. *Prof Exp:* Mem tech staff, Bell Tel Labs, Inc, NJ, 56-67, head fundamental studies dept, Bell Labs, Ohio, 67-77; HEAD MAT ENG & CHEM DEPT, BELL LABS, GA, 77- *Mem:* AAAS; Inst Elec & Electronics Engrs; Am Phys Soc. *Res:* Communications device and techniques; memory and logic devices; contact physics; material science. *Mailing Add:* Bell Labs 2000 Northeast Expressway Norcross GA 30071

LONG, WALTER K, b Austin, Tex, Jan 26, 19; m 50; c 1. HUMAN GENETICS. *Educ:* Univ Tex, BA, 40; Harvard Univ, MD, 43. *Prof Exp:* Res asst cardiol, Thorndike Mem Lab, Boston City Hosp, Mass, 45-48; RES SCIENTIST HUMAN GENETICS, UNIV TEX, AUSTIN, 59-, LECTR ZOOL, 70- *Concurrent Pos:* Life Ins med res fel, 47-48; chief cardiovasc sect, William Beaumont Army Hosp, Ft Bliss, Tex, 51-53. *Mem:* Am Soc Human Genetics. *Res:* Relation between sulfhydryl compounds and pharmacology of organic mercurial diuretics; pentose phosphate metabolic pathway in relation to certain human diseases. *Mailing Add:* Dept of Zool Univ of Tex Austin TX 78712

LONG, WALTER KYLE, JR, b Montgomery, Ala, Dec 5, 44. VIROLOGY. *Educ:* Univ Ga, BS, 66; Univ Ill, PhD(microbiol), 72. *Prof Exp:* Fel, Dept Microbiol & Pediat, Univ Ala, Birmingham, 72-75; res assoc, 75-76; asst prof, 76-82, ASSOC PROF MICROBIOL, SCH DENT, TEMPLE UNIV, 82- *Mem:* AAAS; Am Soc Microbiol; NY Acad Sci; Sigma Xi. *Res:* Effects of antiviral drugs on herpe viruses; oncogenicity of herpes viruses; role of genetic factors in the development of malignancy; nature of the DNA repair defects in certain genetic disorders. *Mailing Add:* Sch Dent Temple Univ 3223 N Broad St Philadelphia PA 19140

LONG, WILLIAM ELLIS, b Minot, NDak, Aug 18, 30; m 55, 71; c 6. HYDROLOGY, GEOMORPHOLOGY. *Educ:* Univ Nev, BS, 57; Ohio State Univ, MSc, 61, PhD(geol), 64. *Prof Exp:* Instr geol, Ohio State Univ, 63-64; explor geologist, Tenneco Oil Co, La, 64-65; from asst prof to assoc prof, 65-72, PROF GEOL, ALASKA METHODIST UNIV, 72-; CHIEF, WATER RESOURCES SECT, ALASKA STATE GEOL SURV, 78- *Concurrent Pos:* Mem, US Antarctic Res Prog, NSF Geol Invest, 63-64; mem discharge prediction glacial melt-water, Off Water Res, 68-70; consult, Shelf Explor Co, 71 & Forest Oil Co, 74-75; investr potential natural landmarks in Alaska, Nat Park Serv, 71; vis lectr, Univ Canterbury, 72. *Mem:* Am Groundwater Asn; Am Asn Petrol Geol; Am Inst Prof Geol; Geol Soc Am; Glaciol Soc. *Res:* Stratigraphic, geologic and glaciological exploration of Gondwana sequences of Antarctica during International Geophysical Year and following years; stratigraphic and glacial geology; water resources of Alaska. *Mailing Add:* Alaska State Geol Surv PO Box 1831 Palmer AK 99645

LONG, WILLIAM HENRY, b Decatur, Ala, Sept 20, 28; m 53; c 3. ENTOMOLOGY. *Educ:* Univ Tenn, BA, 52; NC State Col, MS, 54; Iowa State Col, PhD, 57. *Prof Exp:* From asst prof to prof entom, La State Univ, 57-65; PROF BIOL SCI, NICHOLLS STATE UNIV, 65- *Concurrent Pos:* Pres, Long Pest Mgt, Inc, 72-; consult entom, UN Food & Agr Orgn, United Arab Republic, 73-74; entom expert, Int Atomic Energy Agency, 75-76; mem staff, Nuclear Ctr, Agr Col, Univ Sao Paulo, 75-76. *Mem:* Entom Soc Am; Am Soc Sugarcane Technologists. *Res:* Development of sugar cane pest management programs; entomology. *Mailing Add:* PO Box 1193 Thibodaux LA 70301

LONG, WILLIS FRANKLIN, b Lima, Ohio, Jan 30, 34; m 59; c 3. ELECTRICAL ENGINEERING. *Educ:* Univ Toledo, BS, 57, MS, 62; Univ Wis-Madison, PhD(elec eng), 70. *Prof Exp:* Proj engr, Doehler Jarvis, Nat Lead Co, 57, 59-60; asst, Univ Toledo, 60-62, instr elec eng, 62-66; NSF fel, Univ Wis-Madison, 67-68, lectr, 69; mem tech staff, Hughes Res Labs, 69-73; asst prof, 73-75, assoc prof, 75-80, PROF & CHMN, ELEC ENG & EXTEN ENG, UNIV WIS, 80- *Concurrent Pos:* Consult, Hughes Aircraft Co, Los Angeles Dept Power & Water, 73-; Spec Adv Comt, Wis Dept Indust, Labor & Human Rels, 76-77. *Mem:* Inst Elec & Electronics Engrs; Int Conf Large High Voltage Elec Systs. *Res:* Analysis, simulation and testing of interconnected AC/DC electric power systems; active filtering concepts for power system harmonic currents; power switching techniques; continuing education, electric power systems. *Mailing Add:* Dept of Eng & Appl Sci 432 N Lake St Madison WI 53706

LONG, WILMER NEWTON, JR, b Hagerstown, Md, Apr 24, 18; m 42; c 2. MEDICINE, OBSTETRICS & GYNECOLOGY. *Educ:* Juniata Col, BS, 40; Johns Hopkins Univ, MD, 43. *Prof Exp:* Instr gynec & obstet, Sch Med, Johns Hopkins Univ, 48-65; assoc prof, 65-67, PROF GYNEC & OBSTET, SCH MED, EMORY UNIV, 67- *Concurrent Pos:* Pvt pract obstet, 48-65; med officer in chg obstet & gynec, Navajo Med Ctr, Ft Defiance, Ariz, 53-55. *Mem:* Am Col Obstet & Gynec; AMA. *Res:* Diabetes in pregnancy. *Mailing Add:* 80 Butler St SE Atlanta GA 30303

LONGACRE, RONALD SHELLEY, b Lindsay, Calif, Aug 15, 41; m 71; c 4. PARTICLE PHYSICS. *Educ:* Calif Polytech State Univ, BS, 64; Univ Calif, Berkeley, MA, 68, PhD(physics), 74. *Prof Exp:* Res asst, Dept Physics Elem Particles, Comn L'Etude des Nuages-SACLAY, 74-75; res asst, Northeastern Univ, Boston, 75-78; asst physicist, 78-80, PHYSICIST, BROOKHAVEN NAT LAB, 80- *Res:* Determine Hadronic particle spectrum using three particle decay models; chief tool is the use of partial wave analyses via the Isobar model. *Mailing Add:* Dept of Physics Brookhaven Nat Lab Upton NY 11973

LONGACRE, SUSAN ANN BURTON, b Los Angeles, Calif, May 26, 41; m 64; c 2. SEDIMENTARY PETROLOGY, PETROLEUM GEOLOGY. *Educ:* Univ Tex, Austin, BS, 64, PhD(geol), 68. *Prof Exp:* Res assoc III, Getty Oil Co, 69-72, res assoc IV, 72-75, res scientist I geol, Explor & Prod Res Lab, 75-76, geol specialist II, Offshore Dist, 76-78, res scientist III explor & prod res, 78-80. *Mem:* Am Asn Petrol Geologists; Geol Soc Am; Soc Econ Paleontologists & Mineralogists. *Res:* Petrology and petrography of carbonate and clastic sediments, particularly those Permian, Jurassic and Cretaceous sediments that accumulated in shallow marine to continental depositional environments. *Mailing Add:* PO Box 42214 Houston TX 77042

LONGAKER, PERRY R, physics, see previous edition

LONGANBACH, JAMES ROBERT, b Akron, Ohio, July 4, 42; m 66; c 2. CHEMISTRY. *Educ:* Univ Akron, BS, 64; Yale Univ, MS, 66, MPh, 67, PhD(chem), 69. *Prof Exp:* Chemist, E I du Pont de Nemours & Co, Inc, 69-71; sr chemist, Res Div, Occidental Petrol Corp, 71-76; PRIN RES CHEMIST, COLUMBUS LABS, BATTELLE MEM INST, 76- *Mem:* Am Chem Soc. *Res:* Physical-organic coal conversion and process develop chemistry. *Mailing Add:* Columbus Labs Battelle Mem Inst 505 King Ave Columbus OH 43201

LONGCOPE, CHRISTOPHER, b Lee, Mass, Aug 5, 28; m 61; c 3. ENDOCRINOLOGY, REPRODUCTIVE BIOLOGY. *Educ:* Harvard Univ, AB, 49; Johns Hopkins Univ, MD, 53. *Prof Exp:* Intern, Presby Hosp, NY, 53-54, asst resident, 54-55, fel endocrinol, 59-60; asst resident, Johns Hopkins Hosp, 55-56; fel endocrinol, Univ Wash, Seattle, 60-62 & Univ Calif, San Francisco, 62-63; steroid training prog, Worcester Found Exp Biol, 65-66, staff scientist, 66-70, sr scientist, 70-80; PROF OBSTET, GYNEC & MED, MED SCH, UNIV MASS, 80- *Concurrent Pos:* Asst med, Johns Hopkins Univ, 63-64, instr med, 64-65; consult endocrinol, Perry Point Vet Admin Hosp, Md, 63-65; from asst prof med to assoc prof and dir Endocrine Outpatients Clin, Boston Univ, 68-; mem, Aging Review Comt, Nat Inst Aging, NIH, 73-77 & Breast Cancer Task Force, 80- *Mem:* Endocrine Soc; Am Physiol Soc; Soc Exp Biol & Med; Soc Study Reproduction; Am Diabetes Asn. *Res:* Steroid dynamics, their production and mode of action. *Mailing Add:* Dept Obstet & Gynec Med Sch Univ Mass 55 Lake Ave N Worcester MA 01605

LONGENECKER, BRYAN MICHAEL, b Dover, Del, Sept 1, 42; m 63; c 2. IMMUNOLOGY, CELL BIOLOGY. *Educ:* Univ Mo, AB, 64, PhD(zool), 68. *Prof Exp:* Med Res Coun Can fel, 68-71, Nat Cancer Inst Can res grant, 71-73, Nat Cancer Inst Can res scholar immunol, 71-77, ASST PROF IMMUNOL & MEM NAT CANCER INST, UNIV ALTA, 77- *Mem:* AAAS. *Res:* Genetic control of allo-immunocompetence and resistance to virally induced neoplasms. *Mailing Add:* Dept of Immunol Univ of Alta Edmonton AB T6G 2E1 Can

LONGENECKER, HERBERT EUGENE, b Lititz, Pa, May 6, 12; m 36; c 4. BIOLOGICAL CHEMISTRY. *Educ:* Pa State Col, BS, 33, MS, 34, PhD(agr biol chem), 36. *Hon Degrees:* ScD, Duquesne Univ, 51; LLD, Loyola Univ, 63; LittD, Univ Miami, 72; DSc, Loyola Univ, 76; DSc, Univ Ill, 76. *Prof Exp:* Asst agr & biochem, Pa State Col, 33-35, instr, 35-36; Nat Res Coun fel, Univ Liverpool, 36-37, Univ Cologne, 37-38 & Queen's Univ, Ont, 38; fac mem, Univ Pittsburgh, 38-55, from asst prof to prof, 38-55, dean res natural scis, 44-55, dean grad sch, 46-55; vpres in charge Univ Ill Med Ctr, 55-60; pres, 60-75, EMER PRES, TULANE UNIV, 75-; MGR DIR, INT TRADE MART, 76- *Concurrent Pos:* Mem food & nutrit bd, Nat Res Coun, 43-53, chmn comt food protection, 48-53; mem res coun, Chem Corps Adv Bd, 49-65; mem adv panel biol & chem warfare, Off Asst Secy Defense, 53-61; mem nat selection comn Fulbright student awards, 53-55, chmn, Western Europe Sect, 54-55; mem bd gov, Inst Med Chicago, 57-60; trustee, Coun Southern Univs, 60-75, Inst Defense Anal, 60-, Am Univs Field Staff, 60-74, Southwestern Res Inst, 60-69, Nat Med Fels, Inc, 65-71 & Alfred P Sloan Found, 71-; trustee, Nutrit Found, 61-, chmn, 65-72; mem, Coun Financial Aid to Educ, 64-71; chmn acad bd adv, US Naval Acad, 66-72; dir, A G Bush Found, 69-; mem panel sci & technol, US House of Rep Comt Sci & Astronaut, 70-73; dir, CPC Int, 66-, Equitable Life Assurance Soc US, 68-, United Student Aid Funds, 71- & Fed Home Loan Bank Little Rock, 76-79. *Mem:* AAAS; Am Oil Chem Soc (vpres, 46); fel Am Pub Health Soc; fel Am Inst Chem; fel NY Acad Sci. *Res:* Nutrition; fat metabolism; research administration. *Mailing Add:* Tulane Univ New Orleans LA 70118

LONGENECKER, JOHN BENDER, b Salunga, Pa, July 8, 30; m 54; c 2. NUTRITION, BIOCHEMISTRY. *Educ:* Franklin & Marshall Col, BS, 52; Univ Tex, MS, 54, PhD(biochem), 56. *Prof Exp:* Res biochemist, E I du Pont de Nemours & Co, Inc, Del, 56-61; group leader, Mead Johnson & Co, Ind, 61-64; PROF NUTRIT & HEAD DIV, UNIV TEX, AUSTIN, 64- *Concurrent Pos:* USPHS grant, 64-71; Allied Health Fel grant, 69-74. *Mem:* Am Chem Soc; Am Inst Nutrit; NY Acad Sci. *Res:* In vivo plasma amino acid studies to evaluate protein and amino acid nutrition; interrelationships among nutrients; nutritional status studies. *Mailing Add:* Nutrit Div Univ of Tex Austin TX 78712

LONGENECKER, WILLIAM HILTON, b Cambridge, Md, Mar 28, 18; m 44. ORGANIC CHEMISTRY. *Educ:* Ohio State Univ, BA, 41; Georgetown Univ, MS, 49. *Prof Exp:* Chemist, Kankakee Ord Works, 42, Universal Oil Prod Co, 43, Armour & Co, 43-44, Toxicity Lab, Univ Chicago, 44, NIH, 46-49, Exp Sta, E I du Pont de Nemours & Co, Inc, 49-62, Am Petrol Inst, 62-63 & Tech Info Div, Ft Detrick, 63-70; CHEMIST, NAT AGR LIBR, USDA, 70- *Mem:* AAAS; Am Chem Soc; Sigma Xi; fel Am Inst Chem. *Res:* Systematic chemical nomenclature; chemical notation systems and machine methods of chemical documentation; bibliography compilations. *Mailing Add:* 11311 Cedar Lane Beltsville MD 20705

LONGERBEAM, JERROLD KAY, b Downey, Iowa, Nov 10, 22; m 47; c 3. SURGERY, PHYSIOLOGY. *Educ:* Univ Louisville, MD, 48. *Prof Exp:* From instr to assoc prof, 58-68, PROF SURG, LOMA LINDA UNIV, 68-; CHIEF SURG, RIVERSIDE COUNTY GEN HOSP, 63- *Concurrent Pos:* Bank of Am Giannini fel, 58-61; fel surg physiol, Grad Sch, Univ Minn, 59-63; USPHS spec fel, 61-63; asst head physician, Los Angeles County Gen Hosp, 58-59. *Mem:* Am Col Surg; Soc Cryobiol. *Res:* Total body irradiation; pathophysiology and treatment of hemorrhagic and septic shock; renal, gastric and lung homotransplantation; renal physiology. *Mailing Add:* Riverside Co Gen Hosp 9851 Magnolia Ave Riverside CA 92503

LONGERICH, HENRY PERRY, b Du Quoin, Ill, June 20, 40; m 64; c 1. ANALYTICAL CHEMISTRY, COMPUTER SCIENCE. *Educ:* Millikin Univ, BS, 63; Ind Univ, PhD(chem), 67. *Prof Exp:* Asst prof chem, Univ Alaska, 67-72; fel, Dalhousie Univ, 72-74; res assoc, 74-75, res fel, 75-78, ASST PROF GEOL, MEM UNIV, ST JOHN'S, 78- *Concurrent Pos:* Sessional, comput sci, Mem Univ, 79- *Mem:* Am Chem Soc. *Res:* Real-time on-line computer control and data acquisiton at analytical instrumentation. *Mailing Add:* Geol Dept Mem Univ St John's NF A1B 3X5 Can

LONGEST, WILLIAM DOUGLAS, b Pontotoc, Miss, Jan 22, 29; m 60. INVERTEBRATE ZOOLOGY. *Educ:* Baylor Univ, BSc, 54, MSc, 56; La State Univ, PhD(invert zool, ecol), 66. *Prof Exp:* Teacher, Parma High Sch, 55-56; instr biol, Northwest Jr Col, 56-59; prof natural sci, Blue Mountain Col, 59-62; instr biol, Memphis State Univ, 62-63; teaching asst zool, La State Univ, 63-65, instr, 65-66; from asst prof to assoc prof biol, 66-73, PROF BIOL, UNIV MISS, 73- *Mem:* Bot Soc Am; Ecol Soc Am; Am Soc Zool. *Res:* Botanical research; foliar embryos of Kalanchoe studied in an explant medium; taxonomy of freshwater Tricladida; study of freshwater triclads in the Florida Parishes of Louisiana. *Mailing Add:* Dept of Biol Univ of Miss University MS 38677

LONGFELLOW, DAVID G(ODWIN), b Akron, Ohio, Nov 16, 42; m 65; c 2. MOLECULAR CARCINOGENESIS, BIOCHEMISTRY. *Educ:* Lynchburg Col, BS, 64; Johns Hopkins Univ, PhD(biol), 72. *Prof Exp:* Damon Runyon res fel breast cancer, Biol Lab, Div Cancer Biol, 72-74, res fel, 74-75, res staff, 75-76, sect head, Molecular Carcinogenesis Sect, 76-79, ASST CHIEF, CHEM & PHYS BR, DIV CANCER CAUSE & PREV, NAT CANCER INST, NIH, 79- *Mem:* Am Asn Cancer Res. *Res:* Assistant Chief of an extramural program awarding contracts and grants for research and resource support in the cause and prevention of chemical and physical carcinogenesis; DNA Repair and Chemical Resources programs. *Mailing Add:* Chem & Phys Carcinogenesis Br Nat Cancer Inst Landow Bldg 8C-29 Bethesda MD 20014

LONGFIELD, JAMES EDGAR, b Mt Brydges, Ont, Mar 12, 25; nat US; m 47; c 3. PHYSICAL CHEMISTRY. *Educ:* Univ Western Ont, BSc, 47, MSc, 48; Univ Rochester, PhD(phys chem), 51. *Prof Exp:* Asst, Univ Rochester, 48-50; res chemist, Res Div, 51-57, group leader eng res, 57-62, mgr eng res, 62-72, dir process eng dept, Chem Res Div, 72-74, DIR BOUND BROOK LABS, CHEM RES DIV, AM CYANAMID CO, 74- *Mem:* Am Chem Soc; Am Inst Chem Eng. *Res:* Vapor phase reactions of organic compounds; reaction kinetics; catalysis; reactor design and mechanism studies. *Mailing Add:* Chem Res Div Am Cyanamid Co Bound Brook NJ 08805

LONGHI, JOHN, b White Plains, NY, Oct 12, 46; m 70; c 1. IGNEOUS PETROLOGY, PHYSICAL CHEMISTRY. *Educ:* Univ Notre Dame, BS, 68; Harvard Univ, PhD(geol), 76. *Prof Exp:* Res assoc, Mass Inst Technol, 76-77; res assoc lunar petrol, Univ Ore, 77-80; ASST PROF, YALE UNIV, 80- *Mem:* Am Geophys Union; Mineral Soc Am; Sigma Xi. *Res:* Origin and evolution of the moon; experimental petrology; physical chemistry of silicates. *Mailing Add:* Dept Geol & Geophys Yale Univ PO Box 6666 Newhaven CT 06511

LONGHI, RAYMOND, b Plymouth, Mass, Nov 14, 35; m 61; c 3. INORGANIC CHEMISTRY, ORGANIC CHEMISTRY. *Educ:* Univ Mass, BS, 57; Dartmouth Col, MA, 59; Univ Ill, PhD(inorg chem), 62. *Prof Exp:* Res chemist, 62-64, sr res chemist, 64-65, res supvr, 65-69, sr supvr tech, 69-71, sr supvr res & develop, 71-74, TECH SUPT, E I DU PONT DE NEMOURS & CO, INC, 74- *Mem:* Am Asn Textile Chemists & Colorists; Am Chem Soc; Royal Soc Chem; Sigma Xi. *Res:* Structures of transition metal complexes; reactions of nitrogen oxide; characterization of organic compounds; textile fibers. *Mailing Add:* E I du Pont de Nemours & Co Inc Seaford DE 19973

LONGHOUSE, ALFRED DELBERT, b Dunkirk, NY, Feb 17, 12; m 36; c 2. AGRICULTURAL ENGINEERING. *Educ:* Cornell Univ, BS, 37, MS, 38, PhD(agr eng), 47. *Prof Exp:* Asst agr eng, Cornell Univ, 37-38; instr, WVa Univ, 38-41; spec rep agr educ serv, US Off Educ, DC, 40-41; from asst prof to prof, 41-77, head dept, 45-76, EMER PROF AGR ENG, WEST VA UNIV, 76- *Mem:* Fel Am Soc Agr Engrs; AAAS; Am Soc Eng Educ. *Res:* Developing undergraduate and graduate education and research programs in forest engineering; poultry waste management, utilization, housing and environmental requirements; pollution control and/or elimination for poultry houses. *Mailing Add:* 378 Elmhurst St Morgantown WV 26505

LONGHURST, ALAN R, b Plymouth, Eng, May 3, 25; Can citizen; m 63; c 2. BIOLOGICAL OCEANOGRAPHY, MARINE ECOLOGY. *Educ:* Univ London, BSc, 52, PhD(zool), 62, DSc, 69. *Prof Exp:* Sci officer, WAfrican Fisheries Res Inst, Freetown, Sierra Leone, 54-57; marine biologist, Fisheries Lab, Wellington, NZ, 57-58; sr sci officer, Fishery Develop & Res Unit, Sierra

Leone, 58-60; prin sci officer, Fed Fisheries Serv, Lagos, Nigeria, 60-63; assoc res biologist, Scripps Inst Oceanog, 63-67; dir, Fishery-Oceanog Ctr, Nat Oceanic Atmospheric Admin, 67-71; dep dir, Inst Marine Environ Res, Nat Environ Res Coun, Eng, 71-77; dir, Marine Ecol Lab, NS, 77-79, DIR GEOL, OCEAN SCI & SURV, ATLANTIC, CAN DEPT FISHERIES & OCEANS, BEDFORD INST OCEANOG, 79- Concurrent Pos: Coordr, Eastern Trop Pac Oceanog Expeditions, 67-70; mem, Group Experts Ocean Variability Intergovt Oceanog Comn/Integrated Global Ocean Sta Syst, 69-71, Food & Agr Orgn Adv Comt Marine Res, 69-74, Dartmoor Nat Park Comt, Devon County Coun, 74-76, UK Delegation UN Conf Law Sea, 74-77; chmn, Continuous Monitoring Biol Oceanog, Sci Comt Oceanic Res/Adv Comt Marine Resources Res, 69-72; secy, Sci Coun Oceanic Res, 79- Res: Ecology of tropical benthos; population dynamics of tropical demersal fish; descriptive tropical physical oceanography; response to climate changes of marine biota; production and grazing relation in zooplanton in tropical, temperate and artic oceans; formulation of large scale numerical ecological models. Mailing Add: Bedford Inst Oceanog PO Box 1006 Dartmouth NS B2Y 4A2 Can

LONGHURST, JOHN CHARLES, b Napa, Calif, March 18, 47; m 69; c 3. CARDIOVASCULAR PHYSIOLOGY, INTERNAL MEDICINE. Educ: Univ Calif, Davis, BS, 69, MD, 73, PhD(physiol), 74; Am Bd Internal Med, dipl, 77. Prof Exp: Fac assoc internal med, 78-79, instr internal med & physiol, 79-80, ASST PROF INTERNAL MED, HEALTH SCI CTR, UNIV TEX, DALLAS, 80-, ASST PROF PHYSIOL, 81- Concurrent Pos: Estab investr, Am Heart Asn, 81-86; mem, Coun Clin Cardiol & Coun Circulation, Am Heart Asn. Mem: Am Fedn Clin Res; Am Physiol Soc; fel Am Col Cardiol. Res: Neural control of the circulation; exercise physiology; physiology of the coronary circulation. Mailing Add: Dept Internal Med Univ Tex Health Sci Ctr 5323 Harry Hines Blvd Dallas TX 75235

LONGINI, IRA MANN, JR, b Cincinnati, Ohio, Oct 2, 48. EPIDEMIOLOGY. Educ: Univ Fla, BS, 71, MS, 73; Univ Minn, PhD(biomet), 77. Prof Exp: Assoc fel biomath, Int Ctr Med Res, 77-79; SCHOLAR BIOMET & LECTR EPIDEMIOL, DEPT EPIDEMIOL, UNIV MICH, 80- Concurrent Pos: Vis prof biomath, Univ Del Valle, 77-79. Mem: Biomet Soc; Soc Math Biol. Res: Development of mathmatical and statistical methods in epidemiology; genetics and biology. Mailing Add: Dept Epidemiol Univ Mich 109 Observ St Ann Arbor MI 48109

LONGINI, RICHARD LEON, b US, Mar 11, 13; m 37; c 2. PHYSICS, BIOENGINEERING. Educ: Univ Chicago, BS, 40; Univ Pittsburgh, MS, 44, PhD(physics), 48. Prof Exp: Physicist, Chicago TV & Res Labs, Inc, 34-35; Akay Electron Co, 35-38 & Wheelco Instruments Co, 38-41; physicist, Westinghouse Elec Corp, 41-51, sect mgr solid state electronics, 51-56, adv physicist, 56-58, sect mgr semiconductors, 58-60, consult physicist, 60-62; prof solid state electronics, 62-75, prof elec eng & urban affairs, 76-78, EMER PROF ELECT ENG & URBAN AFFAIRS, CARNEGIE-MELLON UNIV, 78-, SUPVR, SYSTS ENG LAB, 64- Mem: Fel Am Phys Soc; fel Inst Elec & Electronics Engr. Res: Solid state and medical electronics; data analysis and automated aids for diagnoses; application of engineering principles to solution of social problems. Mailing Add: 6731 Forest Glen Rd Pittsburgh PA 15217

LONGLEY, B JACK, b Dousman, Wis, July 19, 13; m 48; c 3. SURGERY. Educ: Univ Wis, BS, 34, PhD(pharmacol), 40, MD, 42. Prof Exp: Instr, 47-49, ASSOC PROF SURG, SCH MED & ASST DIR TUMOR CLIN UNIV WIS, MADISON, 49-; ASST CHIEF SURG SERV, VET ADMIN HOSP, 50- Res: Cardiovascular research. Mailing Add: 14 Merlham Dr Madison WI 53705

LONGLEY, GLENN, JR, b Del Rio, Tex, June 2, 42; m 61; c 4. LIMNOLOGY. Educ: Southwest Tex State Univ, BS, 64; Univ Utah, MS, 66, PhD(environ biol), 69. Prof Exp: asst prof, 69-77, assoc prof, 77-80, PROF AQUATIC BIOL, SOUTHWEST TEX STATE UNIV, 80- Concurrent Pos: Res grant, Southwest Tex State Univ, 71; dir environ consult firm, 80- Mem: AAAS; Am Fisheries Soc; Am Soc Limnol & Oceanog; Entom Soc Am; Water Pollution Control Fedn. Res: Use of subterranean fauna as indicators of ground water quality; Edwards Aquifer study; water pollution; heavy metals; organic wastes; pesticides; population dynamics; plankton; groundwater studies. Mailing Add: Aquatic Sta Southwest Tex State Univ San Marcos TX 78666

LONGLEY, H(ERBERT) JERRY, b Tahoka, Tex, Jan 3, 26; m 52, 62; c 5. THEORETICAL PHYSICS. Educ: Univ Tex, BS, 46, PhD(physics), 52; Tex Tech Col, BS, 48. Prof Exp: Asst prof & res assoc physics, NMex Inst Mining & Technol, 52-54; staff mem, Los Alamos Sci Lab, Univ Calif, 54-71; staff mem, Mission Res Corp, 71-78; CONSULT, 78- Concurrent Pos: Mem staff, Los Alamos Nuclear Corp, 70-71. Mem: Am Phys Soc. Res: Nuclear weapons and weapons testing; hydrodynamics, numerical solutions; radioactive waste storage; nuclear weapons effects; electromagnetic pulse; nuclear physics; linec design; fundamental particles. Mailing Add: 1944 Gibralter Rd Santa Barbara CA 93105

LONGLEY, JAMES BAIRD, b Baltimore, Md, June 27, 20; m 44; c 4. HISTOCHEMISTRY. Educ: Haverford Col, BSc, 41; Cambridge Univ, PhD(zool), 50. Prof Exp: From asst scientist to scientist, Nat Inst Arthritis & Metab Dis, 50-60; assoc prof anat, Sch Med, Georgetown Univ, 60-62; PROF ANAT & CHMN DEPT, SCH MED, UNIV LOUISVILLE, 62- Concurrent Pos: USPHS sr res fel, 60-62; instr, Sch Med, Johns Hopkins Univ, 51-52; asst ed, J Histochem & Cytochem, Histochem Soc, 57-64, actg ed, 64-65; ed, Stain Technol, Biol Stain Comn, 73- Mem: Histochem Soc; Am Asn Anat; Am Soc Cell Biol; Biol Stain Comn. Res: Renal histochemistry, morphology and physiology. Mailing Add: Dept of Anat Univ Louisville Health Sci Ctr Louisville KY 40292

LONGLEY, RICHMOND WILBERFORCE, meteorology, climatology, deceased

LONGLEY, ROBERT W(ILLIAM), b Baltimore, Md, July 7, 25; m 50; c 5. NUTRITION, BIOCHEMISTRY. Educ: Loyola Col, Md, BS, 45; George Washington Univ, MS, 55, PhD(biochem), 57. Prof Exp: Res asst, Res Lab, Brady Urol Inst, 47-53; technician biochem, George Washington Univ, 53-55, instr biochem, 56; investr, Dorn Lab Med Res, 56-58; asst prof, Med Col Ala, 58-60; biochemist, Cent Res Labs, Gen Mills, Inc, 60-62, res assoc, James F Bell Res Ctr, 62-67; dir food res, Nutrit Div, Mead Johnson Subsidiary, Bristol Myers Co, Ind, 67-68 & Drackett Co, 68-70, dir food prod res, Mead Johnson Res Ctr, 70-71; consult food indust, 71-72; pres, Grist Mill Co, Minn, 72-73; DIR RES, DELMARK CO, MINNEAPOLIS, 73- Concurrent Pos: Mgr res & develop, Camargo Foods Div, Drackett Co, Bristol Myers Co, Ohio, 69-71; mgr spec proj corp res & develop, Joseph Schlitz Brewing Co, Wis, 71. Mem: Am Asn Cereal Chemists; Inst Food Technologists; Am Soc Parenteral & Enteral Nutrit. Res: Carbohydrate metabolism; diabetes; clinical nutrition. Mailing Add: 100 Sweetwater Dr Apple Valley MN 55124

LONGLEY, WILLIAM JOSEPH, b Middleton, NS, May 25, 38; m 63; c 2. REPRODUCTIVE PHYSIOLOGY, ENDOCRINOLOGY. Educ: Univ Toronto, BSA, 61, MSA, 63; Univ Mass, PhD(vet animal sci), 67. Prof Exp: Lectr physiol, Med Sch, Dalhousie Univ, 67-68, asst prof, 68-73, assoc prof path, 73-80; qual control tech prod mgr, 80-81, PROD DEVELOP MGR, CORNING MED & SCI, CORNING GLASS WORKS, 81- Concurrent Pos: Endocrinologist, NS Dept Pub Health, 73- Mem: Can Soc Clin Chem; Soc Study Reproduction. Res: Endocrinology of the female, particularly fetal-placental function as related to steroid synthesis; clinical chemistry of various hormones including thyroid and adrenal. Mailing Add: Corning Med & Sci Corning Glass Works East Walpole MA 02032

LONGLEY, WILLIAM WARREN, b Paradise, NS, Apr 8, 09; US citizen; m 35, 57; c 3. GEOLOGY. Educ: Acadia Univ, BS, 31; Univ Minn, MS & PhD(geol), 37. Prof Exp: Instr geol, Dartmouth Col, 35-40; from asst prof to assoc prof geol & geophys, 40-52, prof, 52-77, EMER PROF GEOL, UNIV COLO, BOULDER, 77- Concurrent Pos: Consult, Que Dept Mines, 36-50, Kennecott Copper Corp, 45- & Kennco Explor Ltd, 46- Mem: Fel Geol Asn Can; fel Geol Soc Am; Soc Econ Geol; Am Asn Petrol Geol; Soc Explor Geophys. Res: Photogeology; mineral deposits in pre-Cambrian shield of Canada. Mailing Add: 821 Spring Dr Boulder CO 80303

LONGLEY, WILLIAM WARREN, JR, b Hanover, NH, Aug 30, 37; m 60; c 2. COMPUTER SCIENCES, PHYSICS. Educ: Univ Colo, BA, 58, PhD(physics), 63. Prof Exp: Physicist, Boulder Labs, Nat Bur Standards, 56-59; engr, Denver Div, Martin Co, 59-60, sr engr, 60-63; assoc physicist, Midwest Res Inst, 64-68; asst prof, Upper Iowa Col, Fayette, 68-70, assoc prof physics, 70-81, dir, Comput-Data Processing Ctr & actg head, Dept Bus Admin, 77-81; ASSOC PROF MATH & COMPUT SCI, ST CLOUD STATE UNIV, 81- Concurrent Pos: Fel, Theoret Physics Inst, Univ Alta, 63-64. Mem: Fel AAAS; Am Phys Soc; Sigma Xi. Res: Computer applications; economic statistics. Mailing Add: Math & Comput Sci Dept St Cloud State Univ St Cloud MN 56301

LONGLEY-COOK, MARK T, b Tonbridge, Eng, June 29, 43; US citizen; m 67; c 1. ENVIRONMENTAL ENGINEERING, TRAFFIC ENGINEERING. Educ: Cornell Univ, BS, 65, MEng, 66; Univ Ariz, MS, 70, PhD(physics), 72. Prof Exp: Physicist, Brookhaven Nat Lab, 66 & Univ Ariz, 66-72, fel physics, Inst Atmospheric Physics, 72; physicist, Aircraft Environ Support Off, Naval Air Rework Facil, North Island, 72-76, energy engr, Western Div, Naval Facil Eng Command, 76-79, supvry mech engr, 79-80; PRINCIPAL, LONGLEY-COOK ENG, 80- Concurrent Pos: Consult, 71- Mem: Inst Transp Engrs; Am Soc Heating, Refrigerating & Airconditioning Engrs. Res: Community noise; aircraft noise; liquid crystals; instrumentation; analysis; thermal conductivity; programming; atmospheric electricity; diffusion in the atmosphere. Mailing Add: Longley-Cook Eng 312 F Ave Coronado CA 92118

LONGMAN, MARK WALTER, sedimentary petrology, paleontology, see previous edition

LONGMAN, RICHARD WINSTON, b Iowa City, Iowa, Sept 2, 43. MECHANICAL ENGINEERING, AEROSPACE ENGINEERING. Educ: Univ Calif, Riverside, BA, 65; Univ Calif, San Diego, MS, 67, MA & PhD(aerospace eng), 69. Prof Exp: Mem tech staff, Control Systs Res Dept, Bell Tel Labs, NJ, 69-70; asst prof, 70-74, assoc prof, 74-79, PROF MECH ENG, COLUMBIA UNIV, 79-; AEROSPACE ENGR, SPACE SYSTS DIV, NAVAL RES LAB, 78- Concurrent Pos: Consult, Rand Corp, 66-69; NASA-Am Soc Eng Educ fac fel, Goddard Space Flight Ctr, 73-74; NSF fac res partic, Martin Marietta Corp, 75; consult, Xerox Corp, 75; managing ed, J Astronaut Sci, 76-; Alexander von Humboldt res fel, Technische Hochschule Darmstadt, WGer, 77 & 80; vis assoc prof mech eng, Mass Inst Technol, 78; consult, Europ Space Opers Ctr, Darmstadt, WGer, 77- Mem: Fel Am Astronaut Soc; assoc fel Am Inst Aeronaut & Astronaut; fel Brit Interplanetary Soc; Am Soc Mech Engrs. Res: System dynamics and control: control of large flexible spacecraft, satellite attitude dynamics and control; optimal control theory and applications; stability of nonlinear mechanical systems. Mailing Add: Dept of Mech Eng Columbia Univ New York NY 10027

LONGMIRE, CONRAD LEE, b Loyston, Tenn, Aug 23, 21; m 43; c 7. PHYSICS. Educ: Univ Ill, BS, 43; Rochester Univ, PhD(theoret physics), 48. Hon Degrees: DSc, New Eng Col Pharm, 61. Prof Exp: Mem staff, Radiation Lab, Mass Inst Technol, 43-46; instr physics, Columbia Univ, 48-49; mem staff, Los Alamos Sci Lab, 49-57, alternate leader, Theoret Div, 57-68; PRES, LOS ALAMOS NUCLEAR CORP, 68- Concurrent Pos: Vis prof, Cornell Univ, 53-54; chmn bd, Mission Res Corp, 70- Honors & Awards: E O Lawrence Award, AEC, 61; Air Force Commendation Meritorious Civilian Serv, 65. Mem: Am Phys Soc; fel Am Acad Arts & Sci. Res: Nuclear physics; energy sources weapons and rockets; plasma physics. Mailing Add: Mission Res Corp PO Drawer 719 Santa Barbara CA 93102

LONGMIRE, DENNIS B, b Dayton, Ohio, June 4, 44. RUMINANT NUTRITION. *Educ:* Univ Tenn, BS, 66, MS, 69, PhD(animal sci), 73. *Prof Exp:* Dairy res specialist, 73-74, sr ruminant nutritionist, 74-75, ruminant feeds dir, 76-77, DIR INT FEED RES, CENT SOYA CO INC, 78- *Mem:* Am Dairy Sci Asn. *Res:* Management with emphasis on feed processing and production systems. *Mailing Add:* Cent Soya Co Inc 1200 N Second St Decatur IN 46733

LONGMIRE, MARTIN SHELLING, b Morristown, Tenn, Mar 6, 31. ENGINEERING PHYSICS, GENERAL PHYSICS. *Educ:* Univ Cincinnati, BS, 53; Mass Inst Technol, PhD(phys chem), 61. *Prof Exp:* Res assoc phys chem, Ohio State Univ, 61-62; res fel, Mellon Inst, 62-64; res assoc, Mass Inst Technol, 64-65, physicist, Electronics Res Ctr, NASA, Mass, 65-70; ASSOC PROF PHYSICS, WESTERN KY UNIV, 70- *Concurrent Pos:* Res physicist, Nat Oceanic & Atmospheric Admin, 72 & Naval Res Lab, 71 & 73- *Mem:* AAAS; Am Phys Soc; Am Inst Chem. *Res:* Processing of signals from infrared sensors; development of infrared surveillance systems; absorption of solar ultraviolet light by atmospheric contaminants and minor constituents. *Mailing Add:* Dept of Physics & Astron Western Ky Univ Bowling Green KY 42101

LONGMIRE, RICHARD M, b Columbus, Ohio, Aug 19, 29; m 54; c 3. ELECTRICAL ENGINEERING, OPERATIONS RESEARCH. *Educ:* Ohio State Univ, BS, 52; Univ Southern Calif, MS, 60. *Prof Exp:* Analyst, Columbia Res & Develop Corp, 55-56; proj engr electronic countermeasures, Battelle Mem Inst, 56-57; scientist, Hughes Aircraft Co, 57-59; group leader functional anal & scientist, Syst Develop Corp, 60-65; sr analyst, Res Anal Corp, 65-66, proj chmn info systs, 66-68, dept mgr pub commun & safety, 68-70; assoc adminr planning, res & training, Social & Rehab Serv, HEW, 70-73; vpres, PRC Systs Sci Co, 73-77; mgr new prog develop, ABT Assocs, 77; head prog develop & eval, Community Rels Serv, US Dept Justice, 78-79; HEAD, PESTICIDE PROG DEVELOP & EVAL, ENVIRON PROTECTION AGENCY, 79- *Honors & Awards:* Bronze Medal, Environ Protection Agency, 81. *Mem:* Inst Elec & Electronics Engrs; Opers Res Soc Am; Am Soc Pub Admin. *Res:* Electronic countermeasures; nuclear weapon effects; fire control, command control and crime control systems; radar; computers. *Mailing Add:* Environ Protection Agency 401 M St Southwest Washington DC 20537

LONGMIRE, WILLIAM POLK, JR, b Sapulpa, Okla, Sept 14, 13; m 39; c 3. SURGERY. *Educ:* Univ Okla, AB, 34; Johns Hopkins Univ, MD, 38; Am Bd Surg, dipl. *Prof Exp:* Mem vis staff, Sapulpa City Hosp, Okla, 40-42; asst surg, Sch Med, Johns Hopkins Univ, 42-43, from instr to assoc prof, 43-48; chmn, Dept Surg, 48-76, PROF SURG, SCH MED, UNIV CALIF, LOS ANGELES, 48- *Concurrent Pos:* Cushing fel exp surg, Sch Med, Johns Hopkins Univ, 39-40, Halsted fel surg path, 40; asst res, Johns Hopkins Hosp, 42-44, res, 44, surgeon, 47-48; guest prof, Univ Berlin, 52-54; consult, Air Surgeon, US Air Force, 55-75, Vet Admin Hosp, Wadsworth & Harbor County Gen Hosp, 60- & Med Corps, US Army, 60- *Honors & Awards:* William F Rienhoff jr lectr, Johns Hopkins Hosp, 76. *Mem:* Soc Clin Surg; Am Surg Asn; AMA; Am Col Surg (pres); hon mem Asn Surg Gt Brit & Ireland. *Res:* Tissue transplantation; cancer of the stomach; reconstructions of the biliary system. *Mailing Add:* Dept of Surg Univ of Calif Sch of Med Los Angeles CA 90024

LONGMORE, WILLIAM JOSEPH, b La Jolla, Calif, Oct 7, 31; m 53; c 4. BIOCHEMISTRY. *Educ:* Univ Calif, Berkeley, AB, 57; Univ Kans, PhD(biochem), 61. *Prof Exp:* Nat Heart Inst fel metab res, Scripps Clin & Res Found, 61-63, res assoc biochem, 63-66; from asst prof to assoc prof, 66-73, PROF BIOCHEM, SCH MED, ST LOUIS UNIV, 73- *Concurrent Pos:* USPHS res career develop award, 66-76; Fogarty int sr fel, State Univ Utrecht, Neth, 77-78. *Mem:* AAAS; Am Chem Soc; Am Soc Biol Chemists. *Res:* Phospholipid metabolism; control mechanisms for regulation of carbohydrate and lipid metabolism, especially in lung tissue. *Mailing Add:* Dept of Biochem St Louis Univ Sch of Med St Louis MO 63104

LONGMUIR, ALAN GORDON, b Vancouver, BC, Mar 1, 41; m 62; c 2. CONTROL ENGINEERING. *Educ:* Univ BC, BASc, 64, PhD(elec eng), 68. *Prof Exp:* Control engr, 68-78, MGR METALS AUTOMATION, KAISER ALUMINUM & CHEM CORP, 78- *Concurrent Pos:* Assoc ed, Automatica, 76- *Mem:* Inst Elec & Electronics Engrs. *Res:* Control systems engineering; application of computers to industrial process control. *Mailing Add:* Kaiser Aluminum & Chem Corp 300 Lakeside Dr Oakland CA 94643

LONGMUIR, IAN STEWART, b Glasgow, Scotland, Mar 12, 22; m 49; c 4. BIOCHEMISTRY, PHYSIOLOGY. *Educ:* Cambridge Univ, BA, 43, MA & MB, BChir, 48. *Prof Exp:* Res assoc colloid sci, Cambridge Univ, 48-51; prin sci officer, Ministry Supply, Eng, 51-54; sr lectr biochem, Univ London, 54-65; PROF CHEM & BIOCHEM, NC STATE UNIV, 65- *Concurrent Pos:* Ed jour, Brit Polarographic Soc, 57-62; Isaac Ott fel, Univ Pa, 62-63. *Mem:* AAAS; Am Physiol Soc; Am Chem Soc; Am Soc Biol Chem; Aerospace Med Asn. *Res:* Oxygen transport in blood and tissue; inert gas metabolism. *Mailing Add:* Dept of Biochem NC State Univ Raleigh NC 27607

LONGNECKER, DANIEL SIDNEY, b Omaha, Nebr, June 8, 31; m 52; c 4. PATHOLOGY. *Educ:* State Univ Iowa, AB, 54, MD, 56, MS, 62. *Prof Exp:* From asst to assoc prof path, Univ Iowa, 61-69; assoc prof Sch Med, St Louis Univ, 69-72; PROF PATH, DARTMOUTH MED SCH, 72- *Concurrent Pos:* NIH spec fel, Dept Path, Univ Pittsburgh, 65-67; USPHS res grants, Univ Iowa, 67-69, St Louis Univ, 69-71 & Dartmouth Col, 75-; vis asst prof, Dept Path, Univ Pittsburgh, 65-67. *Mem:* Am Soc Clin Path; Int Acad Path; Soc Exp Biol & Med; Am Asn Pathologists; Am Asn Cancer Res. *Res:* Biochemical mechanisms of cell injury; experimental pancreatitis; chemical carcinogenesis. *Mailing Add:* Dept of Path Dartmouth Med Sch Hanover NH 03755

LONGNECKER, DAVID EUGENE, b Kendallville, Ind, May 29, 39; m 63; c 3. ANESTHESIOLOGY. *Educ:* Ind Univ, AB, 61, MD, 64. *Prof Exp:* Intern, Blodgett Mem Hosp, Grand Rapids, 64-65; resident anesthesiol, Ind Univ, Indianapolis, 65-68; clin assoc, NIH, 68-70; asst prof, Univ Mo-Columbia, 70-73; assoc prof, 74-78, PROF ANESTHESIOL, UNIV VA, 78- *Concurrent Pos:* NIH spec res fel, Ind Univ, 67-68; contrib ed, Anesthesia & Analgesia, Int Anesthesia Res Soc J, 74-; res career develop award, Nat Heart & Lung Inst, 75. *Mem:* Am Soc Anesthesiologists; Inst Anesthesia Res Soc; Am Physiol Soc; Asn Univ Anesthetists. *Res:* Microcirculatory mechanisms during hemorrhagic shock; effect of anesthetics on the microcirculation during normovolemia and hypovolemia. *Mailing Add:* Dept of Anesthesiol Univ of Va Charlottesville VA 22908

LONGO, FRANK JOSEPH, b Cleveland, Ohio, Nov 16, 39; m 62; c 6. CELL BIOLOGY. *Educ:* Loyola Univ, BS, 62; Ore State Univ, MS, 65, PhD(cell biol), 67. *Prof Exp:* Asst prof, 70-75, ASSOC PROF ANAT, COL OF MED, UNIV IOWA, 75- *Mem:* AAAS; Am Soc Cell Biol; Am Asn Anat; Soc Study Reproduction. *Res:* Cellular and developmental biology at the fine structural and biochemical levels; comparative pronuclear development and fusion; gametogenesis and fertilization; cell division and differentiation. *Mailing Add:* Dept of Anat Univ of Iowa Iowa City IA 52442

LONGO, FREDERICK R, b Trenton, NJ, May 4, 30; m ; c 6. PHYSICAL CHEMISTRY. *Educ:* Villanova Col, BA, 53; Drexel Inst, MS, 58; Univ Pa, PhD(phys chem), 62. *Prof Exp:* Chemist, Am Biltrite Rubber Co, 55-57; assoc prof, 57-68, head dept chem & chem eng, Evening Col, 73-76, PROF CHEM, DREXEL UNIV, 68- *Mem:* Am Chem Soc; Sigma Xi. *Res:* Synthesis and spectral properties of porphyrins; emphasis on conversion of solar energy into chemical potential energy. *Mailing Add:* Dept of Chem Drexel Univ Philadelphia PA 19104

LONGO, JOHN M, b Hartford, Conn, Nov 6, 39; m 64; c 3. INORGANIC CHEMISTRY. *Educ:* Univ Conn, BA, 61, PhD(inorg chem), 64. *Prof Exp:* Fel, Univ Stockholm, 64-65; chemist, Lincoln Lab, Mass Inst Technol, 65-70; CHEMIST, CORP RES LABS, EXXON RES & ENG CO, 70- *Mem:* Electrochem Soc; Am Chem Soc. *Res:* Preparation and characterization of solid state inorganic materials. *Mailing Add:* Corp Res Labs Exxon Res & Eng Co Linden NJ 07036

LONGO, JOSEPH THOMAS, b Ferndale, Mich, Jan 13, 42; m 64; c 2. SOLID STATE PHYSICS. *Educ:* Univ Detroit, BS, 64; Mich State Univ, MS, 66, PhD(solid state physics), 68. *Prof Exp:* Asst, Mich State Univ, 64-68; fel, 68-69, mem tech staff, 69-72, mgr, 72-77, asst dir, 77-78, DIR, NORTH AM ROCKWELL SCI CTR, 78- *Mem:* Am Phys Soc. *Res:* High field magnetoresistance and Hall effect in intermetallic compounds; crystal growth, optical and device properties of narrow gap semiconductors. *Mailing Add:* 1049 Comino Dos Rios Rockwell Int Sci Ctr Thousand Oaks CA 91320

LONGO, LAWRENCE DANIEL, b Los Angeles, Calif, Oct 11, 26; m 48; c 4. PHYSIOLOGY. *Educ:* Pac Union Col, BA, 49; Loma Linda Univ, MD, 54. *Prof Exp:* Asst prof obstet & gynec, Univ Ibadan, 59-62; asst prof, Univ Calif, Los Angeles, 62-64; lectr physiol, Univ Pa, 64-66, asst prof physiol, 66-68; PROF PHYSIOL, OBSTET & GYNEC, LOMA LINDA UNIV, 68- *Concurrent Pos:* USPHS fel obstet & gynec, Univ Calif, Los Angeles, 59, spec fel physiol, Univ Pa, 64-66 & res career develop award, 66-68, res career develop award & grant, Loma Linda Univ, 68- & grant, 69-; consult, Nat Inst Child Health & Human Develop, 71. *Mem:* AAAS; NY Acad Sci; Am Physiol Soc; Soc Gynec Invest (secy-treas, pres-elect); Perinatal Res Soc. *Res:* Fetal and placental physiology; kinetics of placental transfer of respiratory gases; fetal oxygenation; fetal cerebral blood flow. *Mailing Add:* Div Perinatal Biol Loma Linda Univ Loma Linda CA 92350

LONGO, MICHAEL JOSEPH, b Philadelphia, Pa, Apr 7, 35; m 58; c 3. HIGH ENERGY PHYSICS, SCIENCE EDUCATION. *Educ:* La Salle Col, BA, 56; Univ Calif, Berkeley, PhD(physics), 61. *Prof Exp:* NSF fel physics, Saclay Nuclear Res Ctr, France, 61-62; from asst prof to assoc prof, 62-68, PROF PHYSICS, UNIV MICH, ANN ARBOR, 68- *Mem:* Am Phys Soc; Sigma Xi. *Res:* Nucleon-nucleon interaction at high energies; K-meson decays; proportional chambers and scintillation counters; neutrino interactions; magnetic monopoles; science communications; software systems. *Mailing Add:* Dept of Physics Univ of Mich Ann Arbor MI 48104

LONGOBARDO, GUY S, b New York, NY, Oct 23, 28; m 52; c 2. MECHANICAL ENGINEERING, BIOENGINEERING. *Educ:* Columbia Univ, BS, 49, MS, 50, EngScD, 61. *Prof Exp:* Develop engr, E I du Pont de Nemours & Co, 50-52; instr mech eng, Sch Eng, Columbia Univ, 52-61, asst prof mech eng & bioeng, 61-65, dir, Fluid Mech Lab, 63-65; adv eng med info systs, IBM Corp, 65-77, mem corp staff, 77-81; SR FORECASTER, WORLD TRADE CORP, 81- *Concurrent Pos:* Consult, Am Mach & Foundry Co, 61-65 & Case Western Dept Med, 75- *Mem:* Assoc Am Soc Mech Engrs. *Res:* Medical information systems, clinical application of computer technology, operation of the respiratory control system and its unstable modes; medical information systems. *Mailing Add:* IBM Corp 360 Hamilton Ave White Plains NY 10601

LONGONE, DANIEL THOMAS, b Worcester, Mass, Sept 16, 32; m 54. ORGANIC CHEMISTRY. *Educ:* Worcester Polytech Inst, BS, 54; Cornell Univ, PhD(org chem), 58. *Prof Exp:* Res assoc org chem, Univ Ill, 58-59; from instr to assoc prof, 59-71, PROF ORG CHEM, UNIV MICH, ANN ARBOR, 71- *Concurrent Pos:* Am Chem Soc-Petrol Res Fund int fel, 67-68; Fulbright scholar, 70-71; vis prof, Univ Cologne, 70-71. *Mem:* Am Chem Soc. *Res:* Synthetic and mechanistic organic chemistry; bridged aromatic compounds; cyclophane chemistry; monomer synthesis and polymerization. *Mailing Add:* 2307 Chemistry Bldg Univ of Mich Ann Arbor MI 48109

LONGPRE, EDWIN KEITH, b Detroit, Mich, Mar 7, 33; m 65; c 1. SYSTEMATIC BOTANY. *Educ:* Univ Mich, BS, 55, MS, 56; Mich State Univ, PhD(bot), 67. *Prof Exp:* Instr bot, Tex Tech Col, 56-57; assoc prof bot & biol, 65-80, PROF BOT, WESTERN STATE COL COLO, 80- *Mem:* Am Soc Plant Taxon; Am Inst Biol Sci; Int Asn Plant Taxon. *Res:* Systematical studies in the tribe Heliantheae of the family Compositae; general cytotaxonomical and floristic studies. *Mailing Add:* Dept of Bot Western State Col of Colo Gunnison CO 81230

LONGROY, ALLAN LEROY, b Flint, Mich, May 28, 36; m 55; c 3. ORGANIC CHEMISTRY. *Educ:* Univ Mich, AB, 58, MS, 61, PhD(chem), 63. *Prof Exp:* Res fel chem, Brandeis Univ, 62-64; asst prof, Ind Univ, 64-67; asst prof, 67-69, ASSOC PROF CHEM, PURDUE UNIV, 69- *Mem:* Am Chem Soc. *Res:* organic reaction mechanisms and kinetics; demonstrations in chemistry. *Mailing Add:* Dept Chem Ind Univ Purdue Univ Fort Wayne IN 46805

LONGSHORE, JOHN DAVID, b Birmingham, Ala, Mar 8, 36; m 64; c 2. PETROLOGY. *Educ:* Emory Univ, BA, 57; Rice Univ, MA, 59, PhD(geol), 65. *Prof Exp:* Teacher, Westminster Schs, Ga, 60-62; PROF GEOL, HUMBOLDT STATE UNIV, 65- *Concurrent Pos:* NASA res grant chem invest Medicine Lake Area, 67-69. *Res:* Chemistry and petrology of igneous rocks. *Mailing Add:* Dept of Geol Humboldt State Univ Arcata CA 95521

LONGSTRETH, DAVID J, b Phoenix, Ariz, Mar 22, 48. PLANT ECOPHYSIOLOGY. *Educ:* Ariz State Univ, BS 70, MS, 72; Duke Univ, PhD(bot), 76. *Prof Exp:* Fel, Duke Univ & Univ Calif, Los Angeles, 77-79; ASST PROF BOT, LA STATE UNIV, 79- *Mem:* Am Soc Plant Physiologists; Ecol Soc Am; Sigma Xi. *Res:* The interaction between environmental extreme and plant photosynthetic response; salinity effects on plant water relations and photosynthetic response. *Mailing Add:* Dept Bot La State Univ Baton Rouge LA 70803

LONGSWORTH, LEWIS GIBSON, physical chemistry, deceased

LONGTIN, BRUCE, b North Fork, Calif, Aug 23, 13; m 53; c 6. THERMODYNAMICS. *Educ:* Univ Calif, BS, 35, MS, 37, PhD(chem), 38. *Prof Exp:* Asst chem, Univ Calif, 35-38, Shell Oil Co fel, 38-39; from instr to assoc prof, Ill Inst Technol, 39-51; from chemist to staff chemist, E I du Pont de Nemours & Co, Inc, 51-78; teaching assoc, Univ SC, Salkehotochie Campus, 78-81. *Concurrent Pos:* Assoc chemist, Argonne Nat Labs, 48-49. *Mem:* Am Chem Soc. *Res:* Thermodynamics of industrial processes; thermodynamic properties of solutions; reactor water and water wastes; chemistry, radiolysis and control of impurities in water coolant and moderator of nuclear reactors. *Mailing Add:* 1209 Summerhill Rd North Augusta SC 29841

LONGWELL, ARLENE CROSBY (MAZZONE), genetics, cytogenetics, see previous edition

LONGWELL, JOHN PLOEGER, b Denver, Colo, Apr 27, 18; m 45; c 3. CHEMICAL ENGINEERING, COMBUSTION. *Educ:* Univ Calif, Berkeley, BS, 40; Mass Inst Technol, ScD(chem eng), 43. *Prof Exp:* Asst nat defense res comt, Mass Inst Technol, 42-43; chem engr, Esso Res & Eng Co, 43-55, asst dir, Exxon Res & Eng Co, 55-58, head, Spec Proj Unit, 58-73, dir, Cent Basic Res Lab, 59-68, mgr corp res staff, 68-73; E R GILLILAND PROF CHEM ENG, MASS INST TECHNOL, 77- *Concurrent Pos:* Mem subcomt combustion, Nat Adv Comt Aeronaut; res adv comt aeronaut propulsion, NASA; tech adv panel ord, Asst Secy Defense Res & Eng; mem aeronaut adv comt, Nat Aeronaut & Space Admin, 78-; chmn comt advan energy storage, Nat Res Coun, 78- *Honors & Awards:* Sir Alfred Egerton Medal, Combustion Inst, 74. *Mem:* Nat Acad Eng; Am Inst Chem Engrs; Am Inst Aeronaut & Astronaut; Am Chem Soc; Combustion Inst (pres). *Res:* Combustion; chemistry; propulsion and propellants; energy technology; coal conversion processes. *Mailing Add:* Mass Inst of Technol 77 Massachusetts Ave Cambridge MA 02139

LONGWELL, P(AUL) A(LAN), b Santa Maria, Calif, Aug 4, 19; m 40; c 2. CHEMICAL ENGINEERING. *Educ:* Calif Inst Technol, BS, 40, MS, 41, PhD(chem eng), 57. *Prof Exp:* Chemist, Shell Oil Co, Calif, 41; instr chem eng, Calif Inst Technol, 41-45; chem engr, US Naval Ord Test Sta, 45-50, head ord processing, 50-51, head, Explosives Dept, 51-54; from instr to assoc prof chem eng, Calif Inst Technol, 55-64; sr staff scientist, Aerojet-Gen Corp, 64-70, CHIEF SCIENTIST, ENVIROGENICS CO, AEROJET-GEN CORP, 70- *Concurrent Pos:* Consult, Aerojet-Gen Corp, 61-64. *Mem:* Am Chem Soc; Am Inst Chem Engrs. *Res:* Applied mathematics in engineering problems; heat, mass and momentum transfer; cryogenic plant processes; desalting plant processes. *Mailing Add:* Aerojet Gen Corp 10300 N Torrey Pines Rd La Jolla CA 92037

LONGWORTH, JAMES W, b Stockton Heath, Eng, Sept 16, 38; m 65; c 2. BIOPHYSICS, CHEMICAL PHYSICS. *Educ:* Univ Sheffield, BSc, 59, PhD(biochem). 62. *Prof Exp:* USPHS fel phys chem, Univ Minn, 62-63; mem staff, Bell Tel Labs, 63-65; MEM STAFF, BIOL DIV, OAK RIDGE NAT LAB, 65- *Concurrent Pos:* Mem, US Nat Comt Photobiol, 72-76, chmn, 76-78; prog comt, Int Congr Photobiol, 80; assoc ed, Biophysical J, 79-81, ed, Comments Molecular & Cellular Biophysics, 80- *Mem:* Am Soc Photobiol (pres, 78-79); Biophys Soc; Brit Biochem Soc; Brit Biophys Soc; Am Soc Biol Chem. *Res:* Photophysics and excited state chemistry of proteins, nucleic acids and their synthetic analogues, particularly their luminescent behavior; use of optical methods to study conformation and function of proteins and nucleic acids and their complexes. *Mailing Add:* Oak Ridge Nat Lab Biol Div PO Box Y Oak Ridge TN 38730

LONGWORTH, RUSKIN, b Oldham, Eng, Aug 13, 27; m 57; c 4. POLYMER CHEMISTRY, POLYMER PHYSICS. *Educ:* Univ London, BSc, 50, PhD(chem), 56. *Prof Exp:* Asst, Polytech Inst Brooklyn, 52-55; chemist, Vauxhall Motors Ltd, Eng, 56-57; SR RES CHEMIST, PLASTICS

PROD & RESINS DEPT, EXP STA, E I DU PONT DE NEMOURS & CO, INC, 57- *Mem:* Am Chem Soc; NY Acad Sci; fel Royal Inst Chem. *Res:* Physical chemistry of polymers, especially rheology, solution properties and ionicpolymers. *Mailing Add:* Plastics Prod & Resins Dept E I du Pont de Nemours & Co Inc Wilmington DE 19898

LONGYEAR, JUDITH QUERIDA, b Harrisburg, Pa, Sept 20, 38; c 2. PURE MATHEMATICS. *Educ:* Pa State Univ, BA, 62, MS, 64, PhD(math), 72. *Prof Exp:* Atmospheric physicist, White Sands Missile Range, 66-67; consult, Auerbach Corp, 67-68; asst prof math, Community Col Philadelphia, 68-70; John Wesley Young res assoc, Dartmouth Col, 72-74; asst prof, 74-76, ASSOC PROF MATH, WAYNE STATE UNIV, 76- *Mem:* Am Math Soc; Math Asn Am; Am Women in Math; Soc Indust & Appl Math; NY Acad Sci. *Res:* Combinatorial mathematics; block designs; Hadamard matrices; transversal theory; tactical configurations. *Mailing Add:* 605 MacKenzie Hall Wayne State Univ Detroit MI 48202

LONIGRO, ANDREW JOSEPH, b St Louis, Mo, July 22, 36; m 68; c 3. INTERNAL MEDICINE, PHARMACOLOGY. *Educ:* St Louis Univ, BS, 58, MD, 66. *Prof Exp:* Intern-resident, St Louis Univ Hosps, 66-69, fel cardiol, 69-71; from instr to asst prof pharmacol & internal med, Med Col Wis, 71-76; ASSOC PROF INTERNAL MED & PHARMACOL, ST LOUIS UNIV, 76- *Concurrent Pos:* Spec res fel, USPHS, 69-71; res & educ assoc, Vet Admin, 72-74; clin investr, 74-76, prog specialist clin pharmacol, 76-; dir div clin pharmacol, Sch Med, St Louis Univ, 76-; chief clin pharmacol, Vet Admin Hosp, St Louis, 76- *Mem:* Am Fedn Clin Res; Am Soc Nephrology; Am Physiol Soc; Am Soc Pharmacol & Exp Therapeut. *Res:* Circulatory control mechanisms; protaglandins, hypertension; renal function. *Mailing Add:* Vet Admin Hosp St Louis MO 63125

LONKY, MARTIN LEONARD, b New York, NY, Jan 5, 44; m 66. ELECTRONIC PHYSICS, SOLID STATE PHYSICS. *Educ:* Rensselaer Polytech Inst, BS, 64; Univ Del, MS, 67, PhD(physics), 72. *Prof Exp:* Teaching asst physics, Univ Del, 64-67, res fel, 67-72; Presidential intern chem, US Army Land Warfare Lab, 72, res analyst, 72-73; sr engr electronics, Westinghouse Elec Corp, 73-75, fel engr physics, 76-79; MGR SOLID STATE TECHNOL, QUESTRON CORP, 79- *Mem:* Electrochem Soc; Inst Elec & Electronics Engrs. *Res:* Electron device physics, with emphasis on memory field effect transistors and transparent gate metal-oxide-silicon technology; device fabrication technologies. *Mailing Add:* Questron Corp 101 Continental Blvd, Suite 500 El Segundo CA 90245

LONNES, PERRY BERT, b St Paul, Minn, Feb 22, 40; m 65; c 1. ENVIRONMENTAL SCIENCE, ANALYTICAL CHEMISTRY. *Educ:* Univ Minn, St Paul, BS, 63, MS, 65, PhD(environ sci), 72. *Prof Exp:* Instr air anal, Univ Minn, St Paul, 68-70; mgr anal serv & contract res, Environ Res Corp, 70-73; MGR ENVIRON MEASUREMENTS, INTERPOLL INC, 73- *Mem:* Am Chem Soc; Air Pollution Control Asn. *Res:* Characterization of adsorbents to predict gas sampling potentials; gas sampling methodology; gas chromatography; air pollution analytical instrumentation. *Mailing Add:* 1996 W County Rd C St Paul MN 55113

LONNGREN, KARL E(RIK), b Milwaukee, Wis, Aug 8, 38; m 63; c 2. PLASMA PHYSICS, ELECTRICAL ENGINEERING. *Educ:* Univ Wis-Madison, BS, 60, MS, 62, PhD(elec eng), 64. *Prof Exp:* Alumni Res Found res asst, Univ Wis, 64; grant, Royal Inst Technol, Sweden, 64-65; from asst prof to assoc prof, 65-72, PROF ELEC ENG, UNIV IOWA, 72- *Concurrent Pos:* Vis prof, Inst Plasma Physics, Japan, 72, Math Res Ctr, Univ Wis-Madison, 76-77 & Inst Space & Astronaut Sci, Japan, 81. *Mem:* Fel Am Phys Soc; sr mem Inst Elec & Electronics Engrs. *Res:* Nonlinear plasma physics; interaction of electromagnetic waves and plasmas. *Mailing Add:* Dept of Elec & Comput Eng Univ of Iowa Iowa City IA 52242

LONSDALE, CAROL JEAN, b Stockport, Eng, Mar 9, 55; m 81. INFRARED ASTRONOMY, STAR FORMATION. *Educ:* Univ St Andrews, BSc, 76; Univ Edinburgh, PhD(astron), 80. *Prof Exp:* NATO res fel astron, Univ Hawaii, 80-82; ADJ ASST PROF ASTRON, UNIV CALIF, LOS ANGELES, 82- *Mem:* Fel Royal Astron Soc; Am Astron Soc. *Res:* The study of star formation in our galaxy and external galaxies using the techniques of infrared astronomy. *Mailing Add:* Dept Astron Univ Calif Los Angeles 405 Hilgard Ave Los Angeles CA 90024

LONSDALE, EDWARD MIDDLEBROOK, b Kansas City, Mo, July 21, 15; m 41; c 2. ELECTRICAL ENGINEERING. *Educ:* Univ Kans, BS, 36; Univ Iowa, MS, 41, PhD, 52. *Prof Exp:* Dial telephone engr, Southwest Bell Telephone Co, 36-38; TV engr, Midland TV Co, 39-40; radar countermeasures engr, Naval Res Lab, 42-46; prof elec eng, Univ Iowa, 46-56; prof elec eng, Univ Wyo, 56-72; clin engr, 72-80, HEAD BIOMED ENG, ST JOSEPH'S HOSP, 80- *Mem:* Am Soc Eng Educ; Am Inst Elec & Electronics Engrs; Asn Advan Med Instrumentation. *Res:* Biomedical instrumentation; radio telemetry from fresh water fish. *Mailing Add:* St Joseph's Hosp 350 N Wilmont Tucson AZ 85711

LONSDALE, HAROLD KENNETH, b Westfield, NJ, Jan 19, 32; m 53; c 2. PHYSICAL CHEMISTRY. *Educ:* Rutgers Univ, BS, 53; Pa State Univ, PhD(chem), 57. *Prof Exp:* Staff mem, Gen Atomic Co, 59-70; prin scientist, Alza Corp, 70-72; vis scientist, Max Planck Inst Biophys, 73; vis prof, Weizmann Inst, 74; PRES, BEND RES, INC, 75- *Concurrent Pos:* Ed, J Membrane Sci, 75- *Mem:* Am Chem Soc. *Res:* Transport in synthetic membranes, desalination by reverse osmosis; controlled release of biologically active agents. *Mailing Add:* Bend Res Inc 64550 Research Rd Bend OR 97701

LONSETH, ARVID T, b Berkeley, Calif, Feb 9, 36. PHYSICS, ATOMIC SPECTROSCOPY. *Educ:* Univ Ore, BS, 61, MS, 63, PhD(physics), 70. *Prof Exp:* ASST PROF PHYSICS, SOUTHERN ORE STATE COL, 69- *Mem:* Am Asn Physics Teachers; Optical Soc Am. *Res:* Pressure effects in atomic absorption spectroscopy. *Mailing Add:* Dept of Physics Southern Ore State Col Ashland OR 97520

LONSKI, JOSEPH, b Port Jefferson, NY, 43; c 2. DEVELOPMENTAL BIOLOGY. *Educ:* Cornell Univ, BS, 64; Univ Calif, Los Angeles, MA, 66; Princeton Univ, PhD(biol), 73. *Prof Exp:* Instr biol, Southampton Col, 66 & Princeton Univ, 71-72; asst prof, 72-80, ASSOC PROF BIOL, BUCKNELL UNIV, 80- *Mem:* Sigma Xi; Am Soc Plant Physiol; Soc Develop Biol. *Res:* Chemotaxis in the myxobacteria and cellular slime molds. *Mailing Add:* Dept of Biol Bucknell Univ Lewisburg PA 17837

LONTZ, ROBERT JAN, b Wilmington, Del, Oct 19, 36; m 62; c 2. PHYSICS. *Educ:* Yale Univ, BSc, 58; Duke Univ, PhD(physics), 62. *Prof Exp:* Asst, Physics Div, 62-64, chief, Gen Physics Br, 64-67, assoc dir, 67-73, DIR, PHYSICS DIV, US ARMY RES OFF, 73-; DIR, PHYSICS DIV, US ARMY RES OFF. *Concurrent Pos:* Dep asst res, Off Undersecy Defense Res & Eng, 78-79. *Res:* Paramagnetic resonance spectroscopy; lasers. *Mailing Add:* US Army Res Off PO Box 12211 Research Triangle Park NC 27709

LONZETTA, CHARLES MICHAEL, b Hazleton, Pa, Jan 28, 50; m 71; c 1. ORGANIC CHEMISTRY, PHYSICAL-ORGANIC CHEMISTRY. *Educ:* Pa State Univ, BS, 71; Harvard Univ, AM, 74, PhD(org chem), 77. *Prof Exp:* Fel phys-org chem, Brandeis Univ, 76-78; RES CHEMIST, ROHM & HAAS CO, 78- *Concurrent Pos:* Head teaching fel, Harvard Exten Sch, 74-78. *Mem:* Am Chem Soc. *Res:* Mechanistic organic chemistry: singlet oxygen formation and reactions; organophosphorus reaction kinetics; free radical reactions; pulsed megawatt infrared laser reaction kinetics; monomer process technology. *Mailing Add:* Rohm & Haas Co Norristown & McKean Rds Spring House PA 19477

LOO, BILLY WEI-YU, b Chungking, China, Oct 26, 39; US citizen; m 65; c 2. FOSSIL ENERGY INSTRUMENTATION, ENVIRONMENTAL SCIENCES. *Educ:* Univ Mich, Ann Arbor, BSE, 63, MS, 65, PhD(physics & nuclear eng), 72. *Prof Exp:* Asst res physicist high energy physics, Univ Mich, 65-69; ENG PHYSICIST, LAWRENCE BERKELEY LAB, UNIV CALIF, 72- *Mem:* Am Phys Soc; Am Chem Soc; AAAS; Air Pollution Control Asn; Nat Space Inst. *Res:* Research and development in fossil fuel instrumentation; sampling and analysis of atmospheric aerosols. *Mailing Add:* M/S 7OA Lawrence Berkeley Lab Univ of Calif Berkeley CA 94720

LOO, C(HING) C(HEE), b Canton, China, Sept 29, 23; nat US; m 50; c 3. AGRICULTURAL ENGINEERING. *Educ:* St John's Univ, China, BS, 46; Ohio State Univ, MS, 49; Mich State Univ, PhD(agr eng), 52. *Prof Exp:* Res engr, Pilot Plant, Carnation Co, Calif, 52-53, group leader food res, 53-63, group leader process develop, 63-66; regional food technologist southern Asia, Food & Agr Orgn, UN, 66-69; mgr prod develop, Carnation Int, 69-75, DIR PROD DEVELOP, CARNATION CO, ASIA/PAC, 75- *Concurrent Pos:* UN tech adv, Govt Iraq, 62-63. *Mem:* Am Soc Agr Engrs; Am Dairy Sci Asn; Inst Food Technologists. *Res:* Veterinary medicine; dairy technology; spray drying and ion exchange of dairy products; hydraulics of milk pumps; fluidized bed drying; aseptic packaging; adhesives; starch preparation; protein foods; consumer research. *Mailing Add:* Carnation Co 1602 Marina House Shenton Way 2 Singapore

LOO, FRANCIS T C, b Tongshan, Hopei, China, July 25, 27; m 58; c 2. SOLID MECHANICS. *Educ:* Nat Taiwan Univ, BS, 52; Syracuse Univ, MS, 59, PhD(mech & aerospace eng), 64. *Prof Exp:* Res assoc mech & aerospace eng, Syracuse Univ, 59-63, asst prof, 63-66; ASSOC PROF MECH ENG, CLARKSON COL TECHNOL, 66- *Concurrent Pos:* Summer fac res fel, NASA, NSF & US Air Force; assoc ed, J Mech Design, Am Soc Mech Engrs. *Mem:* Am Soc Mech Engrs; Am Acad Mech. *Res:* Thermal stresses; stability of shells subjected to concentrated loads and uniform pressure; fracture mechanics; vibration of structures; experimental stress analysis; structural mechanics; finite element method. *Mailing Add:* Dept Mech & Indust Eng Clarkson Col Technol Potsdam NY 13676

LOO, MELANIE WAI SUE, b Honolulu, Hawaii, Nov 24, 48. GENETICS. *Educ:* Univ Calif, BA, BS, 70; Univ Wash, PhD(genetics), 74. *Prof Exp:* Proj res assoc genetics, Dept Physiol Chem, Univ Wis, 75-77; ASST PROF BIOL & GENETICS, DEPT BIOL SCI, CALIF STATE UNIV, SACRAMENTO, 77- *Mem:* AAAS. *Res:* Genetic regulation. *Mailing Add:* Dept Biol Sci Calif State Univ Sacramento CA 95819

LOO, TI LI, b Changsha, China, Jan 7, 18; nat US; m 51; c 3. CLINICAL PHARMACOLOGY, CANCER CHEMOTHERAPY. *Educ:* Tsing Hua Univ, China, BSc, 40; Oxford Univ, DPhil, 47. *Prof Exp:* Asst pharmacol, Oxford Univ, 46-47; fel org chem, Univ Md, 47-51; res assoc, Christ Hosp Inst Med Res, 51-54; supvry chemist, NIH, 55-65; PHARMACOLOGIST & PROF, DEPT DEVELOP THERAPEUT, UNIV TEX M D ANDERSON HOSP & TUMOR INST & PROF PHARMACOL, UNIV TEX MED SCH & GRAD BIOMED SCI, 65-, ASHBEL SMITH PROF THER, 81- *Concurrent Pos:* Adj prof pharmacol, Univ Houston, 77- *Mem:* Am Chem Soc; Am Asn Cancer Res; The Chem Soc; Am Soc Clin Oncol; Am Soc Clin Pharmacol & Therapeut. *Res:* Pharmacology of anticancer drugs; cancer chemotherapy; metabolism of drugs; chemical structure and biological activities; pharmacokinetics. *Mailing Add:* M D Anderson Hosp & Tumor Inst 6723 Bertner Dr Houston TX 77030

LOO, YEN HOONG, b Honolulu, Hawaii, Dec 19, 14. BIOCHEMISTRY. *Educ:* Columbia Univ, BA, 37; Univ Mich, PhD(biochem), 43. *Prof Exp:* Res asst biochem, Univ Ill, 44-51; biochemist, Nat Heart Inst, 51-52; res biochemist, Labs, Eli Lilly & Co, 52-68; assoc res scientist, 68-79, RES SCIENTIST VII, NY STATE INST BASIC RES MENT RETARDATION, 80- *Concurrent Pos:* Fel, Univ Tex, 43-44; fel, Inst Animal Physiol & Cambridge Univ, Eng, NIH, 66-67; prin investr, NIH, 75- *Mem:* AAAS; Am Soc Biol Chem; Am Soc Neurochem; NY Acad Sci. *Res:* Antibiotics, vitamin B6, biochemistry of the developing brain, mechanism of brain damage in experimental phenylketonuria. *Mailing Add:* Inst Basic Res Ment Retardation 1050 Forest Hill Rd Staten Island NY 10314

LOOFBOURROW, ALAN G, b Columbus, Ohio, June 9, 12; m 64. MECHANICAL ENGINEERING. *Educ:* Ohio State Univ, BS, 34; Univ Mich, MS, 35; Chrysler Inst Eng, MAutomotive Eng, 37. *Hon Degrees:* DSc, Ohio State Univ, 72. *Prof Exp:* Mem staff, 35-44, chief engr, Chrysler Atomic Prog, 44-45, vpres, Marine-Indust Engine Div, 51-52, dir eng div, 58, vpres, 61, vpres group exec power train, 63, vpres qual & reliability, 67, vpres vehicle safety, qual & serv, 69, vpres eng & res, 70-73, VPRES ENG, CHRYSLER CORP, 73- *Honors & Awards:* Centennial Achievement Award & Benjamin G Lamme Medal, Ohio State Univ. *Mem:* Nat Acad Eng; Soc Automotive Engrs. *Mailing Add:* 183 E Long Lake Rd Bloomfield Hills MI 48013

LOOK, DAVID C, b St Paul, Minn, Dec 19, 38; m 68; c 2. SOLID STATE PHYSICS. *Educ:* Univ Minn, BPhys, 60, MS, 62; Univ Pittsburgh, PhD(physics), 65. *Prof Exp:* Res physicist, Aerospace Res Labs, 66-69; sr res physicist, Univ Dayton, 69-80; SR RES PHYSICIST, WRIGHT STATE UNIV, 80- *Mem:* Am Phys Soc; Am Sci Affil. *Res:* Transport properties; nuclear magnetic resonance; ion implantation; radiation damage in semiconductors. *Mailing Add:* Univ Res Ctr Wright State Univ Dayton OH 45435

LOOKER, JAMES HOWARD, b Bloomingburg, Ohio, Nov 24, 22; m 46; c 2. ORGANIC CHEMISTRY. *Educ:* Ohio State Univ, BS, 43, PhD(chem), 49. *Prof Exp:* From instr to assoc prof, 50-60, PROF CHEM, UNIV NEBR, LINCOLN, 60- *Concurrent Pos:* NIH spec fel guest prof, Univ Vienna, 63-64. *Res:* Flavonoid substances; diazoesters; arylserines; sulfonic esters. *Mailing Add:* Dept of Chem Univ of Nebr Lincoln NE 68588

LOOKER, JEROME J, b Columbus, Ohio, July 7, 35; m 57; c 3. ORGANIC CHEMISTRY. *Educ:* Kenyon Col, AB, 58; Univ Ill, MS, 60, PhD(org chem), 61. *Prof Exp:* Nat Sci Found fel, Cornell Univ, 61-62; RES CHEMIST, EASTMAN KODAK CO, 62- *Res:* Synthetic organic chemistry. *Mailing Add:* 333 Panorama Trail Rochester NY 14625

LOOKHART, GEORGE LEROY, b North Platte, Nebr, Aug 25, 43; m 63; c 3. ANALYTICAL CHEMISTRY, PHYSICAL BIOCHEMISTRY. *Educ:* Kearney State Col, BS, 68; Univ Wyo, PhD(phys chem), 73. *Prof Exp:* RES ANAL CHEMIST, USDA, US GRAIN MKT RES LAB, 76- *Concurrent Pos:* Teaching internship fel, Chem Dept, Univ Ky, 73-74; fel biochem dept, Univ Mo, Columbia, 74-76. *Mem:* Am Chem Soc; Am Asn Cereal Chemists. *Res:* Develop high pressure liquid chromatographic methods of analysis for protein, estrogens, amino acids and vitamins; develop new electrophoretic methods to fingerprint protein. *Mailing Add:* US Grain Mkt Res Lab 1515 College Ave Manhattan KS 66502

LOOMAN, JAN, b Apeldoorn, Netherlands, Oct 18, 19; Can citizen; m 58; c 2. BOTANY. *Educ:* Univ Wis, MSc, 60, PhD(bot, soils), 62. *Prof Exp:* Technician pasture res, Cent Inst Agr Res, Wageningen, Netherlands, 52-54; technician pasture res, 54-58, RES SCIENTIST, RES STA, CAN DEPT AGR, 62- *Mem:* Agr Inst Can; Int Soc Veg Sci. *Res:* Pasture research; classification of plant communities, including lichens and bryophytes, particularly classification in relation to practical application. *Mailing Add:* Res Sta Can Dept of Agr Swift Current SK S9H 3X2 Can

LOOMANS, MAURICE EDWARD, b Wisconsin Rapids, Wis, Aug 10, 33; m 57; c 3. DERMATOLOGY. *Educ:* Hope Col, BA, 57; Univ Wis, MS, 59, PhD(biochem), 62. *Prof Exp:* RES CHEMIST, MIAMI VALLEY LABS, PROCTER & GAMBLE CO, 62- *Mem:* Soc Invest Dermat. *Res:* Keratinization; epidermal cellular control; acne; percutaneous absorption. *Mailing Add:* Miami Valley Labs Procter & Gamble Co Cincinnati OH 45247

LOOMBA, RAJINDER PAL, electrical engineering, computer science, see previous edition

LOOMIS, ALBERT GEYER, b Lexington, Mo, Feb 17, 93; m 19, 32; c 3. CHEMISTRY. *Educ:* Univ Mo, AB, 14, AM, 15; Univ Calif, PhD(chem), 19. *Prof Exp:* Instr chem, Univ Ill, 19-20; asst prof, Univ Mo, 20; Nat Res Coun fel, Cryogenic Lab, US Bur Mines, 21-22, phys chemist, 21-28, chemist, Explosives Div, Exp Sta, Pa, 28-29; chief chemist, Gulf Res & Develop Co, 29-35; asst dir, Shell Develop Co, 35-42, assoc dir, 42-45; consult chemist & petrol engr, 45-48; petrol engr, US Bur Mines, 48-63; consult chemist, Loomis Labs, 63-76; GUEST SCIENTIST, CHEM DEPT, UNIV CALIF, BERKELEY, 76- *Concurrent Pos:* Lectr, George Washington Univ, 23-25; coop expert, Int Critical Tables, 25-27; sr indust fel, Mellon Inst, 29-35. *Honors & Awards:* Distinguished Serv Hon Award, US Dept Interior, 63; Anthony F Lucas Gold Medal Award, Am Inst Mining, Metall & Petrol Eng, 72. *Mem:* Am Chem Soc; Am Inst Mining, Metall & Petrol Eng. *Res:* Extraction of radium, vanadium and uranium from carnotite ore; liquid ammonia systems; thermodynamic properties of hydrocarbon systems at low temperatures; recovery of helium from natural gas; flame temperatures and explosives; colloid physics of clay dispersions; utilization of redwood products; petroleum production. *Mailing Add:* 85 Parnassus Rd Berkeley CA 94708

LOOMIS, ALDEN ALBERT, b Pittsburgh, Pa, July 22, 34; m 57; c 3. GEOLOGY, OCEANOGRAPHY. *Educ:* Stanford Univ, AB, 56, PhD(petrol, geol), 61. *Prof Exp:* Asst prof geol, San Jose State Col, 60-61; SR SCIENTIST, JET PROPULSION LAB, CALIF INST TECHNOL, 61- *Concurrent Pos:* Assoc prof, Calif State Col Los Angeles, 65-66; consult geoscientist, 69-; eng geologist, State of Calif, 72- *Res:* Space applications to oceanography and geology; igneous petrology, volcanology; metamorphic petrology; gravity and crustal structure; geology of moon and Mars; development of experiments for lunar and planetary exploration; engineering and environmental geology; mineral exploration. *Mailing Add:* Jet Propulsion Lab Calif Inst of Technol 4800 Oak Grove Dr Pasadena CA 91103

LOOMIS, EDMOND CHARLES, b San Francisco, Calif, June 25, 21; m 48; c 4. PARASITOLOGY, ACAROLOGY. *Educ:* Univ Calif, Berkeley, BS, 47, PhD(parasitol), 59. *Prof Exp:* Sr vector control specialist, State Dept Pub Health, Calif, 52-59; malaria adv, USAID, Indonesia, 59-61; PARASITOLOGIST & LECTR, AGR EXTEN SERV, UNIV CALIF, DAVIS, 62- *Concurrent Pos:* Parasitologist, Long Pocket Labs, Commonwealth Sci & Indust Res Orgn, Queensland, Australia, 69-70; parasitologist, Waireka Res Sta, Ivon Watkins Dow Ltd, 74-75. *Honors & Awards:* Exten Educ Aids Blue Ribbon Award, Am Soc Agr Engr, 81. *Mem:* Am Soc Parasitol; Entom Soc Am; Am Mosquito Control Asn. *Res:* Epizootiology; epidemiology; parasitic and arthropod borne diseases of animals and man; acarology; statewide agricultural sanitation program coordination. *Mailing Add:* Vet Med Unit Surge IV Complex Univ of Calif Davis CA 95616

LOOMIS, GARY LEE, b Baltimore, Md, March 3, 43; m 81. POLYMER SYNTHESIS, FUNCTIONALIZED POLYMERS. *Educ:* Johns Hopkins Univ, MA, 74, PhD(org chem), 75. *Prof Exp:* Res fel org chem, Inst Chem, London, 75-76 & Ecol Normale Superieure, Paris, 76-77; RES CHEMIST ORG POLYMER CHEM, EXP STA, E I DU PONT, CO, 78- *Mem:* Am Chem Soc; Chem Soc London; Sigma Xi. *Res:* Polymer networks; high pressure and free radical polymerization of novel vinyl monomers; design of novel crosslinking systems for elastomeric polymers; thermoplastic elastomer compositions. *Mailing Add:* 3201 Highland Ave Drexel Hill PA 19026

LOOMIS, HAROLD GEORGE, b Erie, Pa, Aug 22, 25; m 47; c 4. MATHEMATICS. *Educ:* Stanford Univ, BS, 50; Pa State Univ, MA, 52, PhD(math), 57. *Prof Exp:* Sr mathematician, Haller, Raymond & Brown, Inc, 52-55; instr math, Pa State Univ, 55-57; asst prof, Amherst Col, 57-62; mem staff, Res Corp, Syracuse Univ, 62-63; asst prof, Univ Hawaii, 63-66; mathematician, Pac Marine & Environ Lab, Nat Oceanic & Atmospheric Admin, 66-81; PROF OCEAN ENG, UNIV HAWAII, 81- *Mem:* Soc Indust & Appl Math; Math Asn Am. *Res:* Tsunamis; numerical analysis; oceanography. *Mailing Add:* 250 Kawaihae St Honolulu HI 96825

LOOMIS, HERSCHEL HARE, JR, b Wilmington, Del, May 31, 34; m 57; c 2. ELECTRICAL ENGINEERING, COMPUTER ENGINEERING. *Educ:* Cornell Univ, BEE, 57; Univ Md, MS, 59; Mass Inst Technol, PhD(elec eng), 63. *Prof Exp:* Staff engr, Lincoln Lab, Mass Inst Technol, 60-61; from asst prof to assoc prof, 62-74, chmn dept, 70-75, PROF ELEC ENG, UNIV CALIF, DAVIS, 74- *Concurrent Pos:* Consult, Lawrence Livermore Lab, Univ Calif, 63-; NSF grants, 64 & 67-69. *Mem:* Inst Elec & Electronics Engrs; Asn Comput Mach. *Res:* Theory, design and applications of digital computers; digital design automation. *Mailing Add:* Dept of Elec Eng Univ of Calif Davis CA 95616

LOOMIS, LYNN H, b Afton, NY, Apr 25, 15; m 39; c 2. MATHEMATICS. *Educ:* Rensselaer Polytech Inst, BS, 37; Harvard Univ, AM, 38, PhD(math), 42. *Prof Exp:* Fac instr math, 41-46, assoc prof, 46-56, DWIGHT PARKER ROBINSON PROF MATH, HARVARD UNIV, 56- *Mem:* Am Math Soc; Math Asn Am; Am Acad Arts & Sci. *Res:* Abstract analysis. *Mailing Add:* Dept of Math Harvard Univ Cambridge MA 02138

LOOMIS, RICHARD BIGGAR, b Lincoln, Nebr, June 18, 25; m 47; c 3. ACAROLOGY, HERPETOLOGY. *Educ:* Univ Nebr, BSc, 48; Univ Kans, PhD(zool), 55. *Prof Exp:* Lab asst biol & vert zool, Univ Nebr, 47-48; asst, US Navy Chigger Proj, Univ Kans, 48-53, asst instr biol & comp anat, 53, asst, Sch Med, 53-55; PROF BIOL, CALIF STATE UNIV, LONG BEACH, 55- *Concurrent Pos:* Prin investr, USPHS Grant, 60-74; res assoc, Los Angeles County Mus Natural Hist; mem bd govs, Calif Desert Studies Consortium; NSF grant, 80-82. *Mem:* Am Soc Mammal; Am Soc Ichthyol & Herpet; Am Soc Parasitol; Am Soc Acarologists. *Res:* Systematics, life histories and ecology of parasitic acarines, especially trombiculid mites and their vertebrate hosts in North America; medical acarology. *Mailing Add:* Dept of Biol Calif State Univ Long Beach CA 90840

LOOMIS, ROBERT HENRY, b Atlanta, Ga, Nov 9, 23; m 45; c 4. ZOOLOGY, LIMNOLOGY. *Educ:* Univ Ga, BS, 47; Okla State Univ, MS, 51, PhD(zool), 56. *Prof Exp:* Instr biol, Piedmont Col, 48, Cent State Col, Okla, 51-52 & Jimma Agr Sch, Ethiopia, 52-54; asst prof, Cent State Col, Okla, 54-55; from asst prof to prof, Northeastern State Col, 55-63; prof, Parsons Col, 63-68; prof & chmn div sci, Pikeville Col, 68-75; prof life sci, Sacramento City Col, 75-78; MEM FAC, DEPT BIOL, CALIF STATE UNIV, 78- *Mem:* AAAS; Am Inst Biol Sci. *Res:* Watershed conditions on fish populations; food habits of mesopelagic fishes; identification of photosynthetic active components of phytoplankton communities; temperature acclimation in crayfish populations. *Mailing Add:* Dept of Biol Calif State Univ Long Beach CA 90840

LOOMIS, ROBERT MORGAN, b Mauston, Wis, Aug 31, 22; m 48; c 6. FORESTRY. *Educ:* Univ Mich, BS; Univ Mo, MS, 65. *Prof Exp:* Forester, Ochoco Nat Forest, Ore, 48-51; adminr, Ottawa Nat Forest, Mich, 51-56 & Mo Nat Forests, 56-57; fire researcher, Cent States Forest Exp Sta, Columbia Forest Res Ctr, Mo, 57-66; res forester, 66-71; res forester, NCent Forest Exp Sta, Mich State Univ, 71-80; RETIRED. *Mem:* Soc Am Foresters. *Res:* Forest fire effects, fuels and danger rating. *Mailing Add:* 750 Pebblebrook East Lansing MI 48823

LOOMIS, ROBERT SIMPSON, b Ames, Iowa, Oct 11, 28; m 51; c 2. PLANT PHYSIOLOGY. *Educ:* Iowa State Univ, BS, 49; Univ Wis, MS, 51, PhD(bot), 56. *Prof Exp:* Instr agron & jr agronomist, 56-58, asst prof & asst agronomist, 58-64, assoc prof & assoc agronomist, 64-68, dir, Inst Ecol, 69-72, assoc dean environ studies, 70-72, PROF AGRON & AGRONOMIST, UNIV CALIF, DAVIS, 68- *Concurrent Pos:* NIH spec fel, Harvard Univ, 63-64; NZ Nat Res Adv Coun res fel, 71. *Mem:* AAAS; Am Soc Plant Physiol (secy, 65-67); Am Soc Sugar Beet Technol; Am Soc Agron; Scand Soc Plant Physiol. *Res:* Physiology of field crops including growth and development; crop ecology with emphasis on productivity and system simulation; sugar beet production. *Mailing Add:* Dept of Agron & Range Sci Univ of Calif Davis CA 95616

LOOMIS, STEPHEN HENRY, b Flint, Mich, Oct 3, 52; m 80. PHYSIOLOGICAL ECOLOGY. *Educ:* Univ Calif, Davis, BS, 74, PhD(zool), 79. *Prof Exp:* Res assoc, Rice Univ, 79-80; ASST PROF COMPARATIVE PHYSIOL & INVERTEBRATE ZOOL, CONN COL, 80- *Mem:* Am Soc Zoologists; AAAS. *Res:* Mechanisms of the control of carbohydrate synthesis in nematodes during the induction of anhydrobiosis and factors influencing the distribution of Crepidula Fornicata in the Pattagansett Marsh. *Mailing Add:* Dept Zool Conn Col Box 1496 New London CT 06320

LOOMIS, TED ALBERT, b Spokane, Wash, Apr 24, 17; m; c 2. PHARMACOLOGY, TOXICOLOGY. *Educ:* Univ Wash, BS, 39; Univ Buffalo, MS, 41, PhD(pharmacol), 43; Yale Univ, MD, 46. *Prof Exp:* Intern, US Marine Hosp, 46-47; assoc prof, 47-59, PROF PHARMACOL & TOXICOL, SCH MED, UNIV WASH, 59- *Concurrent Pos:* State toxicologist, Wash, 55-77. *Res:* Pesticide and insecticide toxicology; anticoagulant agents; alcohol research; toxicological methods; mechanisms of drug action and action of toxic chemicals. *Mailing Add:* Dept of Pharmacol Univ of Wash Sch of Med Seattle WA 98195

LOOMIS, THOMAS CLEMENT, b Pekin, Ill, Sept 15, 24; m 51; c 8. ANALYTICAL CHEMISTRY. *Educ:* Bradley Univ, BS, 48; Iowa State Univ, PhD(chem), 53. *Prof Exp:* MEM TECH STAFF, CHEM RES DEPT, BELL LABS, INC DIV, AM TEL & TEL CO, 53- *Mem:* Soc Appl Spectros. *Res:* X-ray spectrochemical analysis; trace and micro analysis. *Mailing Add:* MH 1A 216 Bell Labs Inc Murray Hill NJ 07974

LOOMIS, TIMOTHY PATRICK, b Alhambra, Calif, May 25, 46. PETROLOGY, REACTION KINETICS. *Educ:* Univ Calif, Davis, BS, 67; Princeton Univ, PhD(geol), 71. *Prof Exp:* J W Gibbs instr geol, Yale Univ, 71-73; adj asst prof, Univ Calif, Los Angeles, 73-74; asst prof, 74-76, ASSOC PROF GEOL, UNIV ARIZ, 76- *Mem:* Geol Soc Am; Am Geophys Union. *Res:* Heat and mass transfer and reaction kinetics in chemical processes. *Mailing Add:* Dept of Geosci Univ of Ariz Tucson AZ 85721

LOOMIS, WALTER DAVID, b Fayetteville, Ark, Mar 2, 26; m 52. BIOCHEMISTRY. *Educ:* Iowa State Univ, BS, 48; Univ Calif, PhD(comp biochem), 53. *Prof Exp:* Instr biochem, 53-54, from asst prof to assoc prof, 54-68, PROF BIOCHEM, ORE STATE UNIV, 68- *Concurrent Pos:* USPHS res career develop award, 61-67; vis researcher, Univ Col Wales, 65-66. *Mem:* Am Chem Soc; Am Soc Plant Physiol; Am Soc Biol Chem; Phytochem Soc NAm; Can Soc Plant Physiol. *Res:* Plant enzymes and proteins; terpene metabolism. *Mailing Add:* Dept of Biochem & Biophysics Ore State Univ Corvallis OR 97331

LOOMIS, WILLIAM FARNSWORTH, JR, b Boston, Mass, Sept 17, 40; m 62; c 2. DEVELOPMENTAL BIOLOGY. *Educ:* Harvard Univ, BS, 62; Mass Inst Technol, PhD(microbiol), 65. *Prof Exp:* NIH fel, Brandeis Univ, 65-66; asst prof, 66-73, assoc prof, 73-79, PROF BIOL, UNIV CALIF, SAN DIEGO, 79- *Mem:* Soc Develop Biol; Am Soc Biol Chemists. *Res:* Cellular interactions involved in the biochemical differentiation in Dictyostelium discoideum; genetics of slime molds. *Mailing Add:* Univ Calif San Diego Dept Biol PO Box 109 La Jolla CA 92037

LOONEY, CHARLES THOMAS GEORGE, structural engineering, see previous edition

LOONEY, DUNCAN HUTCHINGS, b Muskogee, Okla, July 26, 23; m 51; c 3. PHYSICS. *Educ:* Purdue Univ, BS, 48; Mass Inst Technol, PhD(physics), 53. *Prof Exp:* Develop engr, 53-58, head dept solid state devices, 58-63, dir, Power Systs Lab, 63-74, DIR, LOOP PLANT INSTALLATION & ELEC PROTECTION LAB, BELL LABS, INC, 74- *Mem:* Inst Elec & Electronics Eng. *Res:* Solid state physics; magnetic devices; power systems. *Mailing Add:* Bell Labs Inc Whippany Rd Whippany NJ 07981

LOONEY, NORMAN E, b Adrian, Ore, May 31, 38; m 57; c 3. POMOLOGY, PLANT PHYSIOLOGY. *Educ:* Wash State Univ, BS, 60, PhD(hort), 66. *Prof Exp:* Sr exp aid hort, Wash State Univ, 60-62, res asst post-harvest hort, 62-66; pomologist, 66-74, HEAD POMOLOGY SECT, AGR CAN, 75- *Mem:* Am Soc Hort Sci; Am Soc Plant Physiol; Can Soc Hort Sci; Int Soc Hort Sci; Can Soc Plant Physiol. *Res:* Physiology of growth, development and ripening of fruits; investigations of agroclimatology and plant growth regulators. *Mailing Add:* Pomology Sect Agr Can Res Sta Summerland BC V0H 1Z0 Can

LOONEY, RALPH WILLIAM, b Spencer, WVa, June 30, 31; m 61; c 3. PHYSICAL CHEMISTRY, POLYMER CHEMISTRY. *Educ:* WVa Univ, BS, 53, MS, 54; Univ Wis, PhD(phys chem), 60. *Prof Exp:* Res chemist, Esso Res & Eng Co, 60-63, sr chemist, 63-66, sect head new chem intermediates, 66-72, res assoc chem intermediates, Elastomers Tech Div, 72-76, res assoc chem intermediates, Tech Div, 76-78, RES ASSOC, SPECIALTIES TECH DIV, EXXON CHEM CO, 78- *Mem:* Am Chem Soc. *Res:* Polymerization catalysts; kinetics of polymerization; polymer physics and oxonation of olefins. *Mailing Add:* Exxon Chem Co PO Box 241 Baton Rouge LA 70821

LOONEY, WILLIAM BOYD, b South Clinchfield, Va, Mar 18, 22; m 55; c 2. RADIOBIOLOGY, BIOPHYSICS. *Educ:* Emory & Henry Col, BS, 44; Med Col Va, MD, 48; Cambridge Univ, PhD(radiobiol, biophys), 60. *Hon Degrees:* DSc, Emory & Henry Col, 78. *Prof Exp:* Intern, Presby Hosp, Chicago, 48-49; asst resident, 49-50; asst prof radiol, Johns Hopkins Univ, 59-60; from asst prof to assoc prof, 61-68, PROF RADIOBIOL & BIOPHYS & DIR DIV, UNIV VA, 68- *Concurrent Pos:* Mem interdisciplinary prog biophys, Univ Va, 66-; vis fel med oncol, Mem Sloan-Kettering Cancer Ctr, 78. *Mem:* AAAS; Am Asn Cancer Res; Am Soc Cell Biol; Biophys Soc; Radiation Res Soc. *Res:* Cancer; mathematical evaluation of tumor growth curves; cell cycle and cell kinetics studies in experimental tumors; modification of tumor growth rates and cell kinetics by radiation, alone or in combination with different chemotherapeutic agents; host-tumor interaction. *Mailing Add:* Div of Radiobiol & Biophys Univ of Va Hosp Charlottesville VA 22908

LOOP, JOHN WICKWIRE, b Belvidere, Ill, July 23, 24; m 57; c 5. RADIOLOGY, MEDICINE. *Educ:* Univ Wyo, BS, 48; Harvard Med Sch, MD, 52. *Prof Exp:* Intern med & surg, King County Hosps, Seattle, Wash, 52-53; asst resident radiol, Univ Chicago, 53-56, instr, 57-58; assoc radiologist, Mass Inst Technol, 58-59; from instr to assoc prof, 59-74, PROF RADIOL, UNIV WASH, 74-, ACTG CHMN RADIOL, 78-; RADIOLOGIST-IN-CHIEF, HARBORVIEW MED CTR, SEATTLE, 71- *Concurrent Pos:* Swedish Govt fel, Univ Lund, 56-57; mem med radiation adv comt, US Dept Health, Educ & Welfare, 71-75. *Mem:* Am Soc Neuroradiol; Asn Univ Radiol; Am Col Radiol. *Res:* Radiological diagnosis. *Mailing Add:* Dept of Radiol Harborview Med Ctr Seattle WA 98104

LOOP, MICHAEL STUART, b Pittsburgh, Pa, Feb 28, 46; c 1. VISION, HERPETOLOGY. *Educ:* Fla State Univ, BS, 68, MS, 71, PhD(psychobiol), 72. *Prof Exp:* NIH fel neurol surg, Univ Va, 72-74, Sloane Found fel physiol, 74-75; vis asst prof physiol & biophys, Univ Ill, 75-78; asst prof, 78-81, ASSOC PROF PHYSIOL OPTICS, UNIV ALA, BIRMINGHAM, 81- *Mem:* Asn Res Vision & Ophthalmol. *Res:* Vertebrate visual system psychophysiology; comparative animal behavior. *Mailing Add:* Med Ctr/Sch of Optom Univ Sta Birmingham AL 35294

LOOR, RUEYMING, b Taiwan, Repub China, Aug 16, 48; US citizen; m 76. STEROID HORMONE ACTION, TUMOR IMMUNOLOGY. *Educ:* Nat Chungshing Univ, Taiwan, BS, 70; Univ Wis, MS, 74; State Univ NY, Buffalo, PhD(cell & molecular biol), 78. *Prof Exp:* Asst res genetics, Inst Zool, Taiwan Acad Sinica, 71-73; teaching asst biol, State Univ NY, Buffalo, 74-76; res assoc biochem, Ben May Lab, Univ Chicago, 78-79; sr scientist immunol & biochem, Roswell Park Mem Inst, Buffalo, 80-82; SR CHEMIST IMMUNOL, BIO-RAD LAB, RICHMOND, CALIF, 82- *Mem:* Am Soc Cell Biol. *Res:* Molecular mechanism of androgen action; tumor immunology and immunodiagnosis of cancer; expression of cancer-associated antigen in cancer. *Mailing Add:* Clin Div, Bio-Rad Lab 2200 Wright Ave Richmond CA 94804

LOOS, HENDRICUS G, b Amsterdam, Neth, Dec 18, 25; nat US; m 52; c 2. ENVIRONMENTAL PHYSICS. *Educ:* Univ Amsterdam, Drs(math), 51; Univ Delft, ScD, 52. *Prof Exp:* Res engr, Nat Aeronaut Res Inst, Neth, 46-52; res fel, Calif Inst Technol, 52-55; sr engr, Propulsion Res Corp, 55-57; sr physicist, Giannini Sci Corp, 57-66; mem staff, Douglas Advan Res Lab, 66-70, sr staff scientist, McDonnell-Douglas Astronaut Co, 70-71; prof math, Cleveland State Univ, 71-74; DIR, LAGUNA RES LAB, 74- *Concurrent Pos:* Lectr, Univ Calif, Riverside, 63-64, assoc prof in residence, 64-70, adj prof, 70-76. *Mem:* Am Phys Soc; Soc Photo-Optical Instrumentation Engrs. *Res:* Gauge theory; atmospheric physics; fluid mechanics; general relativity. *Mailing Add:* Laguna Res Lab 21421 Stans Lane Laguna Beach CA 92651

LOOS, JAMES STAVERT, b Grafton, NDak, May 24, 40; m 61; c 2. PHYSICS. *Educ:* Univ NDak, BS, 62; Univ Ill, MS, 63, PhD(physics), 68. *Prof Exp:* Res assoc high energy physics, Stanford Linear Accelerator Ctr, 68-72; asst prof physics, Duke Univ, 72-77; RES PHYSICIST HIGH ENERGY PHYSICS, ARGONNE NAT LAB, 77- *Mem:* Am Phys Soc. *Res:* Experimental high energy physics; electron-positron collisions at high energies; high energy particle detectors and techniques. *Mailing Add:* Bldg 362 Argonne Nat Lab Argonne IL 60439

LOOS, KARL RUDOLF, b New York, NY, July 10, 39; m 65; c 3. PHYSICAL CHEMISTRY, ENVIRONMENTAL ANALYSIS. *Educ:* Rensselaer Polytech Inst, BS, 60; Mass Inst Technol, PhD(phys chem), 65. *Prof Exp:* Res assoc, Inst Phys Chem, Swiss Fed Inst Technol, 65-66; SR RES CHEMIST, SHELL DEVELOP CO, 67- *Mem:* Am Chem Soc. *Res:* Environmental air analysis; source emissions; ambient air; trace organic determinations; vibrational spectroscopy. *Mailing Add:* Shell Develop Co PO Box 1380 Houston TX 77001

LOOSANOFF, VICTOR L, b Kiev, Russia, Oct 3, 99; nat US; m 28. FISHERIES. *Educ:* Univ Wash, BS, 27; Yale Univ, PhD(biol), 36. *Prof Exp:* Aquatic biologist, State Dept Fisheries, Wash, 27-30; chief marine biologist, Comn Fisheries, Va, 31; dir marine biol lab, 35-62, AQUATIC BIOLOGIST, US FISH & WILDLIFE SERV, 32- *Concurrent Pos:* Sci consult, Bingham Oceanog Lab, Yale Univ; hon prof, Rutgers Univ, 53-59; dir, Taylor Libr; adj prof, Univ of the Pac, 63-; lectr, Univ Wash, 63-; NSF grant, 66-68; consult, US Nat Marine Fisheries Serv, 66-; mem, Nat Tech Adv Comt Water Qual Criteria, 67-68; consult maricult, Lummi Indian Tribe, Wash, 68- *Honors & Awards:* Dept Interior Distinguished Serv Award, 65. *Mem:* AAAS; hon mem Nat Shellfisheries Asn (vpres, 45, pres, 47-49). *Res:* Marine biology in relation to ecology and physiology of oysters and other pelecypods. *Mailing Add:* 17 Los Cerros Dr Greenbrae CA 94904

LOOSE, LELAND DAVID, b Reading, Pa, Jan 25, 40; m 71. PHYSIOLOGY, IMMUNOLOGY. *Educ:* Tenn Wesleyan Col, BS, 63; ETenn State Univ, MA, 65; Univ Mo, Columbia, PhD(physiol), 70. *Prof Exp:* Instr physiol, Lees-McRae Col, 65-67; asst prof, Sch Med, Tulane Univ, 70-74; asst prof physiol, Dept Physiol & Inst Exp Path & Toxicol, Albany Med Col, 74-75, assoc prof, 75-80; PROJ LEADER IMMUNOTHER, PFIZER INC, 80- *Mem:* Am Physiol Soc; Am Soc Trop Med & Hyg; NY Acad Sci; Am Soc Zool; Sigma Xi. *Res:* Physiological control mechanisms of immune responses; influence of environmental chemicals on immune responses; differentiation of lymphoid tissue with special reference to hormonal effects; macrophage antigen processing; calcium alterations in shock. *Mailing Add:* Pfizer Inc Eastern Point Rd Groton CT 06340

LOOSLI, JOHN KASPER, b Clarkston, Utah, May 16, 09; m 36; c 3. ANIMAL NUTRITION. *Educ:* Utah State Univ, BS, 31; Colo State Univ, MS, 32; Cornell Univ, PhD(animal nutrit), 38. *Prof Exp:* Instr agr, Col Southern Utah, 33-35; asst animal nutrit, Cornell Univ, 35-38; agent, Bur Biol Surv, USDA, 38-39; from asst prof to prof animal nutrit, 39-74, head dept animal sci, 63-71, EMER PROF ANIMAL NUTRIT, CORNELL UNIV, 74- *Concurrent Pos:* Collabr, US Fish & Wildlife Serv, 39-56; vis prof, Univ Philippines, 53-54 & 66 & Univ Ibadan, 72-74; consult, US Army Vet Grad Sch, 54 & USAID, Nigeria, 61; ed, J Animal Sci, 55-58; Fulbright lectr, Univ Queensland, 60; mem comt animal nutrit, Agr Bd, Nat Res Coun; vis prof, Univ Fla, 74-, actg chmn dept animal sci, 75-76, actg dean for res, 77. *Honors & Awards:* Am Feed Mfrs Award Nutrit, 50; Borden Award Dairy Prod, 51; Morrison Award, 56. *Mem:* Am Soc Animal Sci (vpres, 59, pres, 60); Am Dairy Sci Asn (pres, 70-71); Am Inst Nutrit; Brit Soc Animal Prod. *Res:* Fat metabolism and requirements; vitamin requirements; lactation; mineral requirements; feed composition. *Mailing Add:* 406 SW 40th St Gainesville FL 32607

LOOV, ROBERT EDMUND, b Wetaskiwin, Alta, Oct 29, 33; m 79; c 2. STRUCTURAL ENGINEERING. *Educ:* Univ Alta, BSc, 58; Stanford Univ, MS, 59; Univ Cambridge, PhD(struct eng), 73. *Prof Exp:* Sales engr, Con-Force Prod Ltd, 59-61, chief engr, 61-63; from asst prof to assoc prof civil eng, 63-74, asst to vpres, 70-73, actg head civil eng, 80-81, PROF CIVIL ENG, UNIV CALGARY, 74- *Concurrent Pos:* Nat Res Coun Can res grants, 64-67 & 69-; on leave, Churchill Col, Eng, 67-69. *Mem:* Am Concrete Inst; Eng Inst Can; Can Soc Civil Engrs; Prestressed Concrete Inst. *Res:* Strength and behavior of precast connections; optimum design of reinforced and prestressed concrete, sulfur concrete and composite materials. *Mailing Add:* Dept of Civil Eng Univ of Calgary Calgary AB T2N 1N4 Can

LOOYENGA, ROBERT WILLIAM, b NDak, Oct 21, 39; m 63; c 4. ANALYTICAL CHEMISTRY. *Educ:* Hope Col, AB, 61; Wayne State Univ, PhD(anal chem), 69. *Prof Exp:* Fel chem, Univ Wis-Milwaukee, 70; res chemist, Printing Develop Inc, 70-72; asst prof, 72-78, ASSOC PROF CHEM, SDAK SCH MINES & TECHNOL, 78- *Concurrent Pos:* Chemist, SDak Racing Comn, 75-78; consult, SDak Law Enforcement Agencies. *Mem:* Am Chem Soc; Sigma Xi. *Res:* Analytical research and analysis of trace metals and organics in municipal and natural waters, of selenium and tellurium, and of abused drugs; analytical separations and methods development. *Mailing Add:* Dept of Chem SDak Sch of Mines & Technol Rapid City SD 57701

LOPARDO, VINCENT JOSEPH, b Pittsburgh, Pa, Dec 1, 25; m 50; c 4. MECHANICAL ENGINEERING. *Educ:* Univ Pittsburgh, BSME, 48, MSME, 51; Cath Univ Am, PhD(mech eng), 68. *Prof Exp:* Design engr, Peth & Reed Engrs, 48-49 & Hunting, Larsen & Dunnells Engrs, 51; from instr to asst prof mech eng, Univ Pittsburgh, 51-60; assoc prof, 60-68, chmn dept, 76-80, PROF MECH ENG, US NAVAL ACAD, 68- *Concurrent Pos:* Design engr, Hunting, Larsen & Dunnells Engrs, 55; consult, Charles M Wellons Consult Engrs, 55-60; res prof eng res div, Univ Pittsburgh, 51-53; sr assoc, Trident Eng Assocs, 61-; Naval Acad Res Coun grant, US Naval Acad, 68-69; Nat Bur Standards grant, Naval Ship Res & Develop Ctr, 81. *Mem:* Soc Exp Stress Anal; Am Soc Eng Educ; Am Soc Mech Engr. *Res:* Stress analysis; stress and strains in large deformations of polyurethanes using photoelasticity and moire; energy and the second law analyses of power systems. *Mailing Add:* 40 Redwood Rd Severna Park MD 21146

LOPATIN, WILLIAM, b Brooklyn, NY, July 20, 46; m 67; c 2. BIOCHEMISTRY, BIO-ORGANIC CHEMISTRY. *Educ:* Univ Fla, BS, 67; Univ SFla, MA, 71, PhD(chem), 77. *Prof Exp:* Teacher chem, Hillsborough Co, Fla Bd Pub Instr, 69-73; res assoc biochem, Univ Tex, 77-80. *Concurrent Pos:* Chmn sci dept, Blake High Sch, Tampa, 70-71. *Mem:* Sigma Xi; AAAS; Am Chem Soc. *Res:* Application of physical organic techniques to the study of enzyme reaction mechanisms. *Mailing Add:* 50900 Mercury Dr Granger IL 46530

LOPER, CARL R(ICHARD), JR, b Wauwatosa, Wis, July 3, 32; m 56; c 2. METALLURGICAL ENGINEERING, ENVIRONMENTAL SCIENCE. *Educ:* Univ Wis, BS, 55, MS, 58, PhD(metall eng), 61. *Prof Exp:* Metall engr, Pelton Steel Castings Co, 55-56; instr metall eng, 56-58, res proj asst, 58-60, from asst prof to assoc prof, 61-69, PROF METALL ENG & ENVIRON STUDIES, UNIV WIS-MADISON, 69- *Concurrent Pos:* Consult, Gray & Ductile Iron Founders Soc, 62-, Gen Motors Corp & Brillion Iron Works, 66-, Oil City iron Works, 73- & Sperry-New Holland, 74- *Honors & Awards:* Adams Mem Award, Am Welding Soc, 64; H F Taylor Award, Am Foundrymen's Soc, 67, John A Penton Gold Medal, 72. *Mem:* Am Foundrymen's Soc; Am Welding Soc; fel Am Soc Metals; Clay Minerals Soc; Am Soc Eng Educ. *Res:* Solidification and process control of cast irons; solidification and property relationships in aluminum and copper base alloys; fracture toughness of cast components; welding metallurgy; failure analysis; recycling of metallic solid wastes. *Mailing Add:* Dept of Metall & Mineral Eng 1509 University Ave Madison WI 53706

LOPER, DAVID ERIC, b Oswego, NY, Feb 14, 40; m 66; c 4. MAGNETOHYDRODYNAMICS, APPLIED MATHEMATICS. *Educ:* Carnegie Inst Technol, BS, 61; Case Inst Technol, MS, 64, PhD(mech eng), 65. *Prof Exp:* Sr scientist, Douglas Aircraft Corp, 65-68; from asst prof to assoc prof, 68-77, PROF MATH, FLA STATE UNIV, 77- *Concurrent Pos:* Nat Ctr Atmospheric Res fel, 67-68; sr vis fel, Univ Newcastle-upon-Tyne, Eng, 74-75. *Mem:* Am Phys Soc; Am Geophys Union; Soc Indust & Appl Math. *Res:* Boundary layers in rotating, stably stratified, electrically conducting fluids; evolution of the earth's core including stratification, heat transfer, solidification and particle precipitation. *Mailing Add:* 18 Keen Bldg Fla State Univ Tallahassee FL 32306

LOPER, GERALD D, b Brooklyn, NY, May 4, 37; m 60; c 1. NUCLEAR PHYSICS. *Educ:* Univ Wichita, AB, 59; Okla State Univ, MS, 62, PhD(physics), 64. *Prof Exp:* Asst prof, 64-67, chmn dept, 66-78, ASSOC PROF PHYSICS, WICHITA STATE UNIV, 67- *Mem:* Am Phys Soc; Sigma Xi. *Res:* Measurement of positron lifetimes in solids; nuclear spectroscopy; internal conversion. *Mailing Add:* Dept of Physics Wichita State Univ Wichita KS 67208

LOPER, GERALD MILTON, b Sykesville, Md, Jan 7, 36; m 62; c 2. AGRONOMY, BIOCHEMISTRY. *Educ:* Univ Md, Bsc, 58; Univ Wis, MSc, 60, PhD(agron), 61. *Prof Exp:* Res agronomist, USDA, SDak, 62-67; assoc prof, 69-74, PROF AGRON & PLANT GENETICS, UNIV ARIZ, 74-; RES PLANT PHYSIOLOGIST, FED HONEY BEE LAB, 67- *Mem:* Bot Soc Am; Am Soc Agron. *Res:* Effect of environment and infective organisms on the chemical composition of forages in relation to animal nutrition; attractiveness of forage legumes to honey bees; pollination physiology; seed production and crop physiology investigations. *Mailing Add:* Fed Honey Bee Lab 2000 E Allen Rd Tucson AZ 85719

LOPER, JOHN C, b Hadley, Pa, June 21, 31; m 56; c 3. MICROBIOLOGY, GENETICS. *Educ:* Western Md Col, BA, 52; Emory Univ, MS, 53; Johns Hopkins Univ, PhD(biol), 60. *Prof Exp:* From instr to asst prof pharmacol, Sch Med, St Louis Univ, 60-63; from asst prof to assoc prof, 63-74, PROF MICROBIOL, COL MED, UNIV CINCINNATI, 74-, PROF ENVIRON HEALTH, 79- *Concurrent Pos:* NIH res grants, 62-78; NIH spec vis fel genetics, Res Sch Biol Sci, Australian Nat Univ, 70-71; Environ Protection Agency grants, 76-; mem biol comt, Argonne Nat Lab-Argonne Univ Asn, 70-73; mem subcomt toxicol, Safe Drinking Water Comt, Nat Res Coun, 78-79. *Mem:* Am Soc Microbiol; Genetics Soc Am; NY Acad Sci; Environ Mutagen Soc. *Res:* Bacterial genetics; resistance plasmids in pseudomonas; characterization of complex organic mixtures; mutagenesis. *Mailing Add:* Dept of Microbiol Univ of Cincinnati Col of Med Cincinnati OH 45219

LOPER, WILLARD H(EWITT), b Alden, NY, Apr 30, 26; m 50; c 4. AGRICULTURAL ENGINEERING. *Educ:* Cornell Univ, BSA, 53. *Prof Exp:* Sales & serv rep, Holz Col, 53-54; design & prod engr, Cochran Equip Co, 54-55; asst prof, 55-63, ASSOC PROF AGR ENG, CALIF POLYTECH STATE UNIV, SAN LUIS OBISPO, 63- *Concurrent Pos:* Civil engr, Bur Reclamation, US Dept Interior & State Div Hwys, 57 & 58; tech leader, Foreign Agr Serv, USDA, 59. *Mem:* Am Soc Agr Engrs. *Res:* Agricultural crop harvest mechanization. *Mailing Add:* Dept of Agr Eng Calif Polytech State Univ San Luis Obispo CA 93407

LOPEZ, ANTHONY, b Chile, SAm, May 13, 19; US citizen; m 47; c 3. FOOD SCIENCE. *Educ:* Catholic Univ, Chile, BS, 42; Univ Mass, PhD(food tech), 47. *Prof Exp:* Chemist, SA Organa, Chile, 42-45; tech dir, Indust de Productos Alimenticios, 48-52; assoc res prof food technol, Univ Mass, 52-53; assoc prof, Univ Ga, 53-54; PROF FOOD SCI & TECHNOL, VA POLYTECH INST & STATE UNIV, 54- *Concurrent Pos:* Instr, UN Latin Am Fisheries Training Ctr, Chile, 52; lectr, Ministry Commerce, Spain, 60; consult food processing, Govt Spain, 62, 63; consult food technol, UN Food & Agr Orgn, Chile, 66 & Brazil, 69, 72 & 75; Orgn Am States in Mex, 70-74; tech ed, Food Prod Mgt, 71- *Mem:* Am Chem Soc; Inst Food Technol; Chilean Soc Nutrit. *Res:* Processing and nutritive value of fish; composition of fresh fruits and vegetables; processing of fruits and vegetables; chemical changes in processed foods during storage; food packaging; microwave irradiation of foods; effect of processing on nutritive value of foods. *Mailing Add:* Dept of Food Sci & Technol Va Polytech Inst & State Univ Blacksburg VA 24061

LOPEZ, ANTONIO VINCENT, b Montgomery, Ala, Apr 24, 38. PHARMACEUTICAL CHEMISTRY, PHARMACOGNOSY. *Educ:* Auburn Univ, BS, 59, MS, 61; Univ Miss, PhD(pharm chem), 66. *Prof Exp:* chmn, Dept Pharmaceut Chem, 66-76, asst dean, 78-80, CHMN, DIV NATURAL SCI, SOUTHERN SCH PHARM, MERCER UNIV, 76-, ASSOC DEAN, 80- *Mem:* AAAS; Am Pharmaceut Asn. *Res:* Central nervous system drugs. *Mailing Add:* Southern Sch of Pharm Mercer Univ 345 Boulevard NE Atlanta GA 30312

LOPEZ, CARLOS, b Ponce, PR, Jan 15, 42; m 70; c 1. IMMUNOLOGY, VIROLOGY. *Educ:* Univ Minn, BS, 65, MS, 66, PhD(pub health), 70. *Prof Exp:* Res fel, Univ Minn, 70-72, asst prof path, 72-73; ASSOC MEM SLOAN-KETTERING CANCER CTR & ASST PROF BIOL, SLOAN-KETTERING DIV, SCH MED, CORNELL UNIV, 73- *Concurrent Pos:* NIH fel, 70-71; fel, Nat Thoracic & Respiratory Dis Asn, 71-73. *Mem:* Am Asn Immunologists; Am Asn Exp Pathologists; Am Soc Microbiol; AAAS. *Res:* Immunological resistance to virus infections; immunologic response to virus induced tumors. *Mailing Add:* Sloan-Kettering Cancer Ctr 425 E 68th St New York NY 10021

LOPEZ, DIANA MONTES DE OCA, b Havana, Cuba, Aug 26, 37; US citizen; m 58; c 3. MICROBIOLOGY. *Educ:* Univ Havana, BS, 60; Univ Miami, MS, 68, PhD(microbiol), 70. *Prof Exp:* Res assoc, 70-71, from instr to asst prof microbiol, 71-77, ASSOC PROF MICROBIOL, SCH MED, UNIV MIAMI, 77- *Concurrent Pos:* Sect leader tumor virol & immunol, Comprehensive Cancer Ctr, State Fla, 80- *Mem:* Am Soc Microbiol; Tissue Cult Asn; Sigma Xi; Am Asn Immunologists; NY Acad Sci. *Res:* Tumor immunology; viral oncogenesis; cell kinetics. *Mailing Add:* Dept Microbiol D4-4 Sch Med Univ Miami PO Box 016960 Miami FL 33101

LOPEZ, GENARO, b Brownsville, Tex, Jan 24, 47; m 72. ECONOMIC ENTOMOLOGY. *Educ:* Tex Tech Univ, BS, 70; Cornell Univ, PhD(econ entom), 75. *Prof Exp:* Res asst entom, Cornell Univ, 70-75; entomologist, Tex Agr Exten Serv, Tex A&M Univ, 75-76; ASST PROF BIOL, TEX SOUTHMOST COL, 76-; INSTR BIOL, PAN AM UNIV, BROWNSVILLE, 76- *Mem:* Entom Soc Am; Acaralogical Soc Am. *Res:* Bionomics, ecology and control of insects affecting man's home environment; teaching biology to the bicultural/bilingual student at the college level. *Mailing Add:* Dept of Biol Tex Southmost Col Brownsville TX 78520

LOPEZ, JOSE MANUEL, b San Juan, PR, Jan 7, 50; m 73; c 2. ENVIRONMENTAL CHEMISTRY, CHEMICAL OCEANOGRAPHY. *Educ:* Univ PR, BS, 71; Univ Wis-Madison, MS, 73; Univ Tex, PhD(environ chem), 76. *Prof Exp:* Res scientist marine chem, 76-81, HEAD, MARINE ECOL DIV, CTR ENERGY & ENVIRON RES, 81- *Concurrent Pos:* Pres Sci Teachers Asn, 79-80; consult, indust & govt; asst prof marine chem, Univ PR. *Mem:* AAAS; Am Chem Soc; Am Soc Limnol & Oceanog; Am Bot Soc; Water Pollution Control Fedn. *Res:* Sources, fate and significance of chemicals in aquatic ecosystems; biological availability of contaminants to aquatic organisms; nutrient dynamics; response of mangroves to hydrocarbons, trace metals and other pollution. *Mailing Add:* Ctr Energy & Environ Res College Station Mayaguez PR 00708

LOPEZ, LEONARD ANTHONY, b Waltham, Mass, Dec 27, 40; m 61; c 3. CIVIL ENGINEERING. *Educ:* Tufts Univ, BS, 62; Univ Ill, MS, 63, PhD(civil eng), 66. *Prof Exp:* Asst prof civil eng, Lehigh Univ, 66-67; PROF CIVIL ENG, UNIV ILL, URBANA, 67- *Mem:* Am Soc Civil Engrs. *Res:* Digital simulation; numerical methods; mechanics of nonlinear solids; computer system; earthquakes. *Mailing Add:* Dept of Civil Eng Univ of Ill Urbana IL 61801

LOPEZ, RAFAEL, b Dominican Republic, Dec 15, 29; m 56; c 2. PEDIATRICS, HEMATOLOGY. *Educ:* Seton Hall Univ, BSc, 52; Univ PR, MD, 56. *Prof Exp:* assoc prof pediat, New York Med Col, Flower & Fifth Ave Hosp, 65-80, ASSOC PROF PEDIAT, NEW YORK MED COL, MISERICORDIA HOSP MED CTR, 80- *Mem:* Soc Study Blood; Int Soc Hemat; Am Soc Hemat; NY Acad Sci. *Res:* Glutathione reductase as a tool for diagnosis of riboflavin deficiency in infants, children, adolescents; malabsorption syndromes and the effect of phototherapy upon this vitamin in the newborn. *Mailing Add:* Apt 2E 4489 Broadway New York NY 10040

LOPEZ-SANTOLINO, ALFREDO, b Salamanca, Spain, July 23, 31; m 62; c 2. MEDICINE, BIOCHEMISTRY. *Educ:* Inst Ensenanza Media, Salamanca, BS, 49; Lit Univ Salamanca, MD, 55, PhD(med sci), 58; Tulane Univ, PhD(biochem), 63. *Prof Exp:* Asst prof physiol med, Sch Med, Lit Univ Salamanca, 56-58; instr biochem, Cali Univ Sch Med, 58-59; asst prof internal med, Col Med & biochemist, Clin Res Ctr, Univ Iowa, 64-67; assoc prof, 67-74, PROF INTERNAL MED, MED SCH, LA STATE UNIV MED CTR, NEW ORLEANS, 74- *Concurrent Pos:* Mem coun atherosclerosis, Am Heart Asn. *Mem:* AAAS; Am Oil Chem Soc; Soc Nutrit Educ; Am Inst Nutrit; Am Soc Clin Nutrit. *Res:* Nutrition and metabolic diseases; metabolism of lipids and steroid hormones. *Mailing Add:* Dept of Med La State Univ Med Ctr New Orleans LA 70112

LOPINA, ROBERT F(ERGUSON), b Jamestown, NY, May 13, 36; m 58; c 3. AERONAUTICAL ENGINEERING, AVIONICS. *Educ:* Purdue Univ, Lafayette, BS, 57; Mass Inst Technol, MSc, 65, ME, 66, PhD(mech eng), 67. *Prof Exp:* US Air Force, 57-, assoc prof aeronaut, US Air Force Acad, 67-74, chief scientist, Europ Off Aerospace Res & Develop, 74-76, chief, Flight Control Div, Air Force Flight Dynamics Lab, 77-78, Comdr & dir, Air Force Avionics Lab, 78-80, DEP, AERONAUT ENG SYSTS DIV, WRIGHT-PATTERSON AFB, OHIO, 80- *Mem:* Am Inst Aeronaut & Astronaut; Am Soc Mech Engrs; Am Soc Eng Educ; Sigma Xi. *Res:* Swirl flow heat transfer; computer applications in aeronautical education; night attack systems development. *Mailing Add:* Aeronaut Systs Div Wright-Patterson AFB OH 45433

LO PINTO, RICHARD WILLIAM, b New York, NY, Nov 7, 42; m 70; c 2. PHYSIOLOGICAL ECOLOGY, MARINE BIOLOGY. *Educ:* Iona Col, BS, 63; Fordham Univ, MS, 65, PhD(microbiol ecol), 72. *Prof Exp:* Res asst water pollution, Osborne Lab Marine Sci, 67-68; ASSOC PROF BIOL, FAIRLEIGH DICKINSON UNIV, RUTHERFORD, 70- *Concurrent Pos:* Consult, Hackensack Meadowlands Develop Comn, 71-, Hartz Mountain Indust Inc, 76-77, Sierra Club, New York, 76; dir, Marine Biol Prog, Fairleigh Dickinson Univ, Rutherford, NJ, 72-; asst dir, Meadowlands Regional Study Ctr, 74-75; assoc, Seminar Pollution & Water Resources, Columbia Univ, 75; chmn tech adv comt, N NJ Water Quality Prog, 77-; assoc ed, Bulletin of the NJ Acad Sci, 78. *Mem:* Sigma Xi; AAAS; Soc Protozoologists; Am Inst Biol Sci; Phycol Soc Am. *Res:* Bioassay development for marine and fresh water organisms; aquatic toxicology; phytoplankton physiology; microbial ecology; mariculture of plankton feeders. *Mailing Add:* Dept of Biol Fairleigh Dickinson Univ Rutherford NJ 07070

LOPREST, FRANK JAMES, b New York, NY, Jan 8, 29; m 60; c 5. PHYSICAL CHEMISTRY. *Educ:* St John's Univ, NY, BS, 50; NY Univ, MS, 52, PhD, 54. *Prof Exp:* Res chemist, Oak Ridge Nat Lab, 54-56; sr res chemist & supvr adv res, Reaction Motors Div, Thiokol Chem Corp, 56-65; tech assoc, Res & Develop Div, GAF Corp, 65-67, sect mgr new imaging processes res, 67-69, mgr appl chem, Res & Develop & Res Serv, Indust Photo Div, 69-77; DIR BASIC SCI, PRINCETON RES CTR, AM CAN CO, 77- *Mem:* AAAS; Am Chem Soc; Soc Photog Scientists & Engr; Sigma Xi; Tech Asn Pulp & Paper Indust. *Res:* Heterogeneous equilibria; kinetics of liquid solid reactions; high temperature materials; physical chemistry of liquid and solid propellants; adhesion phenomena; cellulose and paper science; photochemistry and photoconductors, imaging systems. *Mailing Add:* 838 Winthrop Dr Yardley PA 19067

LOPRESTI, PHILIP V(INCENT), b Johnstown, Pa, Sept 27, 32; m 59; c 3. ELECTRICAL ENGINEERING. *Educ:* Univ Notre Dame, BSEE, 54, MSEE, 58; Purdue Univ, Lafayette, PhD(elec eng), 63. *Prof Exp:* Asst prof elec eng, Ill Inst Technol, 64-67 & Northwestern Univ, 67-70; MEM RES STAFF, ENG RES CTR, WESTERN ELEC CO, 70- *Concurrent Pos:* Instr, Univ Notre Dame, 58-60 & Purdue Univ, Lafayette, 60-63; consult, Ill Inst Technol, 64-70. *Honors & Awards:* Darlington Prize, Inst Elec & Electronics Engrs Circuits & Systs Soc, 78. *Mem:* Inst Elec & Electronics Engrs; Sigma Xi. *Res:* Automatic control theory; digital signal processing. *Mailing Add:* Eng Res Ctr Western Elec Co PO Box 900 Princeton NJ 08540

LOPUSHINSKY, THEODORE, b Brooklyn, NY, Oct 25, 37. ECOLOGY, PATHOLOGY. *Educ:* Pa State Univ, BS, 59; Univ Tenn, Knoxville, MS, 61; Mich State Univ, PhD(ecol, path), 69. *Prof Exp:* Asst prof natural sci, Mich State Univ, 69-70; prog rep, Mich Asn Regional Med Progs, 70-71, actg dir, 72, dir prog develop, 72-73; asst prof proj develop, Col Human Med, 73-75, asst prof, 75-82, ASSOC PROF, DEPT NATURAL SCI, MICH STATE UNIV, 82- *Concurrent Pos:* Archivist, Soc Col Sci Teachers, 81. *Mem:* Sigma Xi; Nat Sci Teachers Asn. *Res:* Parasitism and disease pathologies in wildlife populations; general education science; science-humanities relationships. *Mailing Add:* Dept of Natural Sci Mich State Univ East Lansing MI 48840

LOPUSHINSKY, WILLIAM, b Rome, NY, July 25, 30; m 60; c 3. PLANT PHYSIOLOGY. *Educ:* State Univ NY, BS, 53, MS, 54; Duke Univ, PhD(plant physiol), 60. *Prof Exp:* Asst plant physiol, Duke Univ, 57-60, res assoc bot, 60-61; PLANT PHYSIOLOGIST, FORESTRY SCI LAB, USDA, 62- *Mem:* Am Soc Plant Physiol; Soc Am Foresters. *Res:* Plant water relations. *Mailing Add:* Forestry Sci Lab 1133 N Western Ave Wenatchee WA 98801

LORAND, JOHN PETER, b Wilmington, Del, Dec 6, 36; m 64; c 3. PHYSICAL ORGANIC CHEMISTRY. *Educ:* Brown Univ, ScB, 58; Harvard Univ, PhD(org chem), 64. *Prof Exp:* NSF scientist, Univ Calif, Los Angeles, 64-65; asst prof org chem, Boston Univ, 65-71; from asst prof to assoc prof, 71-77, PROF ORG CHEM, CENT MICH UNIV, 77- *Concurrent Pos:* Vis prof, Univ Groningen, Neth, 77-78. *Mem:* Am Chem Soc. *Res:* Free radicals; C-H hydrogen bonding; charge-transfer complexes. *Mailing Add:* Dept of Chem Cent Mich Univ Mt Pleasant MI 48859

LORAND, JOYCE BRUNER, b Omaha, Nebr, Feb 3, 23; m 53; c 1. ZOOLOGY. *Educ:* Creighton Univ, BS, 44; Univ Iowa, MS, 45, PhD(zool), 50. *Prof Exp:* Asst zool, Univ Iowa, 46-50, res assoc urol, 50-52, res assoc zool, 52-53; independent investr, Marine Biol Lab, Woods Hole, 53-54; RES ASSOC CHEM, NORTHWESTERN UNIV, EVANSTON, 55- *Concurrent Pos:* Asst, Max Planck Inst Biol, 49; independent investr, Marine Biol Lab, Woods Hole, 56-80. *Mem:* AAAS; Am Soc Zool. *Res:* Embryology; endocrinology; sex differentiation in vertebrates; blood clotting. *Mailing Add:* Dept Biochem & Molecular Biol Northwestern Univ Evanston IL 60201

LORAND, LASZLO, b Gyor, Hungary, Mar 23, 23; nat US; m 53; c 1. BIOCHEMISTRY, PHYSIOLOGY. *Educ:* Leeds Univ, PhD(biomolecular struct), 51; Budapest Univ, absolutorium med, 48. *Prof Exp:* Demonstr biochem, Budapest Univ, 46-48; asst biomolecular struct, Leeds Univ, 48-52; res assoc physiol & pharmacol, Wayne State Univ, 52-53, asst prof, 53-55; from asst prof to prof chem, 55-74, prof biochem & molec biol, 74-81, PROF BIOCHEM, MOLEC & CELL BIOLOGY, NORTHWESTERN UNIV, 81- *Concurrent Pos:* Beit Mem fel, Eng, 52; Lalor fac award, 57; USPHS career award, 62; mem corp, Marine Biol Lab, Woods Hole, Mass. *Honors & Awards:* James F Mitchell Found Award, heart & vascular res, 73. *Mem:* AAAS; Am Soc Biol Chem; Soc Exp Biol & Med; Am Physiol Soc; Brit Biochem Soc. *Res:* Blood proteins; coagulation of blood; muscle chemistry; protein and enzyme chemistry. *Mailing Add:* Dept of Biochem & Molec Biol Northwestern Univ Evanston IL 60201

LORANGER, WILLIAM FARRAND, b Detroit, Mich, Nov 6, 25. XERORADIOGRAPHY. *Educ:* Denison Univ, BA, 47; Univ Ill, MS, 50, PhD(chem & x-ray diffraction), 52. *Prof Exp:* Asst, Anal Div, Ill State Geol Surv, 47-49; proj scientist, Wright Air Develop Div, US Air Force, Ohio, 51-54, instr physics & chem, US Mil Acad, 54-56; sales engr, X-Ray Dept, Gen Elec Co, 56-57; asst prof, Univ Fla, 57-58; tech adv indust sales, X-Ray Dept, Gen Elec Co, 58-61; prod mgr x-ray & electron optics, Picker X-Ray Corp, NY, 62-70, mkt mgr, Indust Div, Picker Corp, 70-72; new mkt res mgr, 72-73, DIR EDUC, XERORADIOGRAPHY, XEROX CORP, 73- *Mem:* AAAS; Am Chem Soc; Sigma Xi; Am Crystallog Asn. *Res:* X-ray diffraction and emission; optical methods of instrumental analysis; instrumental chemical analysis; radiography; diseases of the breast; diagnostic ultrasound; applied x-rays. *Mailing Add:* Spec Prod & Systs Div Xerox Corp 125 N Vinedo Ave Pasadena CA 91107

LORBEER, JAMES W, b Oxnard, Calif, Oct 30, 31; m 64. PLANT PATHOLOGY, MYCOLOGY. *Educ:* Pomona Col, BA, 53; Univ Wash, MS, 55; Univ Calif, Berkeley, PhD(plant path), 60. *Prof Exp:* Asst bot, Univ Wash, 53-55; asst plant path, Univ Calif, Berkeley, 55-60; from asst prof to assoc prof, 60-72, PROF PLANT PATH, CORNELL UNIV, 72- *Mem:* Mycol Soc Am; Am Phytopath Soc; NY Acad Sci; Brit Mycol Soc. *Res:* Diseases of vegetable crops; epidemiology; plant disease control; biology of Botrytis; fungal genetics. *Mailing Add:* Dept of Plant Path Cornell Univ Ithaca NY 14853

LORBER, ARTHUR, internal medicine, rheumatology, see previous edition

LORBER, HERBERT WILLIAM, b Indianapolis, Ind, July 12, 29; m 62; c 2. ELECTRONIC WARFARE, DECISION ANALYSIS. *Educ:* Purdue Univ, BS, 51; Rutgers Univ, MSc, 55; Univ Pa, PhD(elec eng), 62. *Prof Exp:* Engr, Signal Corp Eng Labs, 51 & 53-54; mem tech staff, RCA Labs, 55-62; sr sci specialist, Edgerton Germeshausen & Grier, Inc, 62-71; electron res specialist, Teledyne Ryan Aeronaut, 72-76; mem staff, Los Alamos Nat Lab, 76-82; SR RES SPECIALIST, LOCKHEED CALIF CO, 82- *Concurrent Pos:* Consult, N J Damaskos, Inc, Los Alamos Tech Assocs, Inc & Convair Div Gen Dynamics, 82. *Mem:* Inst Elec & Electronics Engrs; Oper Res Soc Am; Soc Comput Simulation; AAAS; Sigma Xi. *Res:* Interaction of spacecraft and military vehicles with radar systems; quantitative space-system concept assessment; applications of utility theory to management decision-making; analysis of military and business operations. *Mailing Add:* Lockheed Calif Co 2555 Hollywood Way Burbank CA 91520

LORBER, MORTIMER, b New York, NY, Aug 30, 26; m 56; c 2. PHYSIOLOGY, HEMATOLOGY. *Educ:* NY Univ, BS, 45; Harvard Univ, DMD, 50, MD, 52. *Prof Exp:* Rotating intern, Univ Chicago Clins, 52-53; resident hemat, Mt Sinai Hosp, NY, 53-54, asst resident med, 57; med officer hemat res, Naval Med Res Inst, 55-56; sr asst resident med, Univ Hosp, 58, from instr to asst prof, 59-68, ASSOC PROF PHYSIOL, SCH MED & DENT, GEORGETOWN UNIV, 68- *Concurrent Pos:* Lederle Med Fac Award, Georgetown Univ, 60-63, USPHS res career develop award, 63-70. *Mem:* Am Soc Hemat; Int Soc Hemat; Am Soc Cell Biol; Int Asn Dent Res; Am Physiol Soc. *Res:* Splenic function; iron metabolism in Gaucher's disease; organ regeneration, particularly of mammalian submandibular salivary glands following removal of parenchyma. *Mailing Add:* Dept Physiol & Biophys Georgetown Univ Sch Med & Dent Washington DC 20007

LORBER, VICTOR, b Cleveland, Ohio, Apr 22, 12; m 37; c 3. PHYSIOLOGY. *Educ:* Univ Chicago, BS, 33; Univ Ill, MD, 37; Univ Minn, PhD(physiol), 43. *Prof Exp:* From instr to asst prof, Med Sch, Univ Minn, 41-46; from assoc prof biochem to prof, Case Western Reserve Univ, 46-51; prof, 52-80; EMER PROF PHYSIOL, SCH MED, UNIV MINN, MINNEAPOLIS, 80- *Concurrent Pos:* Career investr, Am Heart Asn, 51. *Mem:* Am Physiol Soc; Soc Exp Biol & Med. *Res:* Cardiac metabolism; ionic fluxes in heart muscle. *Mailing Add:* 3707 Modena Way Santa Barbara CA 93105

LORCH, EDGAR RAYMOND, b Nyon, Switz, July 22, 07; nat US; m 37, 56; c 5. MATHEMATICS. *Educ:* Columbia Univ, AB, 28, PhD(math), 33. *Prof Exp:* Asst math, Columbia Univ, 28-30, instr, 31-33; Nat Res Coun fel, Harvard Univ, 33-34; Cutting traveling fel, Univ Szeged, 34-35; instr math, Columbia Uni, 35-41, from asst prof to assoc prof, 41-48, prof, 48-74, chmn dept, 68-72, Adrain prof, 74-76. *Concurrent Pos:* Ed, Am Math Soc Bull, 41-46 & Ind Univ Math J, 66-75; res mathematician, Nat Defense Res Coun, 43-45; sci adv to chief of staff, US Army, 48-49; vis prof, Carnegie Inst Technol, 49, Univ Rome, 53-54, 66 & 82, Col of France, 58, Stanford Univ, 63, Mid East Tech Univ, Ankara, 65 & Univ Florence, 75; Fulbright lectr, Italy, 53-54 & France, 58; mem, Sec Sch Math Curric Improvement Study, 66-72; vis lectr, Fordham Univ, 66-73; ed, La Qualita, Sem de Venezia, 74; Fulbright lectr, Colombia, 77. *Mem:* Am Math Soc; Math Asn Am; Math Soc France; Austrian Math Soc; Math Union Italy. *Res:* Linear spaces; Banach algebras; theory of convex bodies and integration; point set topology. *Mailing Add:* 445 Riverside Dr New York NY 10027

LORCH, JOAN, b Offenbach, Ger, June 13, 23; m 52; c 2. CELL BIOLOGY, PROTOZOOLOGY. *Educ:* Univ Birmingham, BSc, 45; Univ London, PhD(physiol), 48. *Prof Exp:* Nuffield fel, King's Col, Univ London, 49-52; res assoc cell biol, Ctr Theoret Biol, State Univ NY Buffalo, 63-68, res asst prof, 68-72; lectr, 71-72, asst prof, 72-79, ASSOC PROF BIOL, CANISIUS COL, 79-, CHAIR, BIOL DEPT, 81- *Mem:* AAAS; Am Soc Cell Biol; Inst Soc, Ethics & Life Sci. *Res:* Nuclear-cytoplasmic relationships; species specificity; protozoa; bio-ethics; symbiosis. *Mailing Add:* Dept of Biol Canisius Col Buffalo NY 14208

LORCH, LEE (ALEXANDER), b New York, NY, Sept 20, 15; m 43; c 1. MATHEMATICS. *Educ:* Cornell Univ, BA, 35; Univ Cincinnati, MA, 36, PhD(math), 41. *Prof Exp:* Asst mathematician, Nat Adv Comt Aeronaut, 42-43; instr math, City Col New York, 46-49; asst prof, Pa State Univ, 49-50; assoc prof & chmn dept, Fisk Univ, 50-53, prof & chmn dept, 53-55; prof & chmn dept, Philander Smith Col, 55-58; vis lectr, Wesleyan Univ, 58-69; from assoc prof to prof, Univ Alta, 59-68; PROF MATH, YORK UNIV, 68- *Mem:* Am Math Soc; Can Math Soc; Asn Women Math; Nat Asn Mathematicians; fel Royal Soc Can. *Res:* Fourier series; special functions; summability; ordinary differential equations. *Mailing Add:* Dept of Math York Univ Downsview ON M3J 1P3 Can

LORCH, STEVEN KALMAN, b New York, NY, Aug 21, 44; m 67; c 3. FORENSIC SCIENCE, MANAGEMENT. *Educ:* City Col New York, BS, 66; State Univ NY Binghamton, MA, 70; Univ Md, PhD(plant physiol), 72. *Prof Exp:* Res assoc, Mich State Univ-AEC Plant Res Lab, 72-73; crime lab scientist, Div Crime Detection, Mich Dept Pub Health, 73-75, chief drug identification unit, 75-77; supvr, narcotics & dangerous drug unit, East Lansing Sci Lab, 77-78, SUPVR NARCOTICS & DANGEROUS DRUGS UNIT, MADISON HEIGHTS LAB, FORENSIC SCI DIV, MICH STATE POLICE, 78- *Mem:* Am Soc Plant Physiologists; Am Chem Soc; Bot Soc Am; Am Soc Mass Spectrom; Am Acad Forensic Sci. *Res:* Identification of controlled and prescription drugs; gas chromatographic-mass spectrometry; forensic plant identification; crime scene investigation, clandestine laboratories; development of latent fingerprints. *Mailing Add:* 30303 Stephenson Hwy Madison Heights Lab Mich State Police Madison Heights MI 48071

LORD, ARTHUR E, JR, b Buffalo, NY, Apr 7, 35; m 62; c 2. PHYSICS, MATERIALS SCIENCE. *Educ:* Purdue Univ, BSc, 57, MSc, 59; PhD(metall), Columbia Univ, 64. *Prof Exp:* Res assoc appl math, Brown Univ, 64-66, asst res prof physics, 66-68; assoc prof, 68-75, PROF PHYSICS, DREXEL UNIV, 75- *Concurrent Pos:* Fel, Columbia Univ, 64. *Honors & Awards:* IR-100 Award, 77; Drexel Res Achievement Award, 78. *Mem:* Am Phys Soc; Acoustic Emission Working Group. *Res:* Acoustic emission studies in soils and magnetic materials; viscous properties of metallic glasses; nondestructive testing techniques in geotechnical problems; use of electron spin resonance techniques to study mechanical effects in soils. *Mailing Add:* Drexel Univ 32nd & Chestnut St Philadelphia PA 19104

LORD, ARTHUR N(ELSON), b Los Angeles, Calif, May 7, 32; m 61; c 2. PHYSICAL METALLURGY. *Educ:* Stanford Univ, BS, 53, MS, 55, PhD(creep of aluminum), 60. *Prof Exp:* Physical metallurgist, Adv Tech Labs, 58-65, METALLURGIST, KNOLLS ATOMIC POWER LAB, GEN ELEC CO, 65- *Mem:* Am Inst Mining, Metall & Petrol Engrs; Am Phys Soc; Am Soc Metals; Brit Inst Metals. *Res:* Transport properties of solids; effects of radiation damage in metals. *Mailing Add:* Knolls Atomic Power Lab Gen Elec Co PO Box 1072 Schenectady NY 12301

LORD, EDITH M, b Kingman, Kans. IMMUNOLOGY. *Educ:* Univ Kans, BA, 70; Univ Calif, PhD(biol), 75. *Prof Exp:* Res immunologist, Univ Calif, San Francisco, 75-76; sr instr, 76-77, ASST PROF ONCOL, UNIV ROCHESTER, 77- *Mem:* Am Asn Immunologists; Radiation Res Soc. *Res:* Interaction between host immune cells and tumor cells; modulation of these interactions for therapeutic advantage. *Mailing Add:* Univ Rochester Cancer Ctr 601 Elmwood Ave Rochester NY 14642

LORD, GARY EVANS, b Portland, Ore, Feb 15, 35; m 56; c 4. APPLIED MATHEMATICS. *Educ:* Univ Wash, BS, 58, PhD(chem eng), 63, MS, 78. *Prof Exp:* Sr res assoc, Fisheries Res Inst, Univ Wash, 70-76; engr, 62-70, engr, 76-80, SR MATHEMATICIAN, APPL PHYSICS LAB, UNIV WASH, 81- *Concurrent Pos:* Affil assoc prof, Col Fisheries, Univ Wash, 76- *Res:* Applied analysis; underwater acoustics; biomath. *Mailing Add:* Appl Physics Lab Univ Wash Seattle WA 98195

LORD, GEOFFREY HAVERTON, b Georgetown, Guyana, May 17, 23; nat US; m 52; c 3. PATHOLOGY. *Educ:* Univ Toronto, DVM, 49; Univ Wis, MS, 50, PhD, 53. *Prof Exp:* Asst vet sci, Univ Wis, 49-53; sr pathologist, Dept Pharmacol, 53-57, asst dir, 57-60, DIR, JOHNSON & JOHNSON RES FOUND, 60- *Concurrent Pos:* Actg state wildlife pathologist, Wis, 52-53; consult, Middlesex Gen Hosp, New Brunswick. *Honors & Awards:* Johnson Medal, 76. *Mem:* Am Col Lab Animal Med; Am Vet Med Asn; Am Asn Accreditation Lab Animal Care. *Res:* Experimental vascular surgery; laboratory animal pathology; drug safety evaluation; wound healing; safety evaluation of devices; experimental vascular and orthopedic surgery. *Mailing Add:* Res & Develop Dept Domestic Oper Co 501 George St New Brunswick NJ 08903

LORD, HAROLD WESLEY, b Clayton, Mich, July 12, 31; m 60; c 3. ENGINEERING MECHANICS, MECHANICAL ENGINEERING. *Educ:* Univ Mich, BSE, 60, MSE, 61; Northwestern Univ, PhD(mech eng, astronaut sci), 66. *Prof Exp:* Test engr systs div, Bendix Corp, 60; instr mech eng, Univ Maine, 61-63; assoc engr res div, Gen Am Transp Corp, 65-66; asst prof eng sci, Univ Western Ont, 66-67; assoc prof, 67-74, PROF ENG MECH, MICH TECHNOL UNIV, 74-, CHMN DEPT, 80- *Concurrent Pos:* Lectr, Univ Western Ont, 67-68; NSF initiation grant, 68-69; vis fel, Inst Sound & Vibration Res, 76-77. *Mem:* Inst Noise Control Eng; Am Soc Eng Educ; Am Acad Mech; Acoust Soc Am. *Res:* Transient thermoelastic phenomena; vibration and stress analysis; noise control. *Mailing Add:* Dept of Mech Eng/Eng Mech Mich Technol Univ Houghton MI 49931

LORD, HARRY CHESTER, III, b Utica, NY, May 28, 39; m 61, 72; c 5. PHYSICAL CHEMISTRY, ANALYTICAL CHEMISTRY. *Educ:* Tufts Univ, BS, 61; Univ Calif, San Diego, PhD(chem), 67. *Prof Exp:* Sr scientist, Jet Propulsion Lab, 67-69, vpres, 69-77; pres, Envviron Data Corp, 77-81; PRES, SYCONEX CORP, 80- *Honors & Awards:* Gold Medal, Am Inst Chemists, 61. *Mem:* Am Chem Soc; Instr Soc Am; Air Pollution Control Asn; Combustion Inst; Sigma Xi. *Res:* Modification of combustion, improved control techniques; hardware to increase efficiency and to reduce pollutant emissions. *Mailing Add:* 1504 Highland Ave Duarte CA 91010

LORD, JERE JOHNS, b Portland, Ore, Jan 3, 22; m 47; c 3. PHYSICS. *Educ:* Reed Col, AB, 43; Univ Chicago, MS, 48, PhD(physics), 50. *Prof Exp:* Civilian with Radiation Lab, Univ Calif, 42-46; res assoc physics, Univ Chicago, 50-52; instr, 52-62, PROF PHYSICS, UNIV WASH, 62- *Mem:* Am Phys Soc. *Res:* Cosmic ray and high energy physics. *Mailing Add:* Dept of Physics Univ of Wash Seattle WA 98195

LORD, JERE WILLIAMS, JR, b Baltimore, Md, Oct 12, 10; m 41, 71; c 3. SURGERY. *Educ:* Princeton Univ, AB, 33; Johns Hopkins Univ, MD, 37; Am Bd Surg, dipl. *Prof Exp:* From intern to resident surgeon, NY Hosp, 37-44; PROF CLIN SURG, POSTGRAD SCH MED, MED CTR, NY UNIV, 53- *Concurrent Pos:* Consult surgeon, Univ Hosp, Bellevue Hosp, Fourth Div Med Bd & Doctors Hosp & Hackensack Hosp, NJ, St Luke's Hosp, Newburgh, NY, Norwalk Hosp, Conn, 50-, Cent Suffolk Hosp, Riverhead, NY, 51-, Elizabeth Horton Mem Hosp, Middletown, NY, 54-, St Agnes Hosp, White Plains, NY, 55-, Paterson Gen Hosp, NJ, 58 & Univ Hosp; chief, Vascular Surg, Columbus Hosp, NY, 66- *Mem:* Am Col Surg; Am Surg Asn; James IV Asn Surg (secy, 67-75); Am Heart Asn (secy, 53-55); Int Cardiovasc Soc (treas, 53-60, vpres, 61-63). *Res:* Cardiovascular surgery, especially atherosclerosis; gastrointestinal surgery, particularly portal hypertension and intestinal obstruction. *Mailing Add:* 50 Sutton Pl S New York NY 10022

LORD, PETER REEVES, b Ruckinge, Eng, Feb 10, 23; m 47; c 3. ENGINEERING, TEXTILE TECHNOLOGY. *Educ:* Battersea Polytech, Eng, BSc, 50; Univ London, PhD(eng), 66, DSc(eng), 76. *Prof Exp:* Res asst heat transfer, Delaney-Gallay Ltd, Eng, 45-46; draughtsman, Fairey Aviation Co Ltd, 46-47; sect leader eng, Vacuum Oil Co Ltd, 47-51; sr test engr, Vickers Armstrongs Ltd, 51-58; lectr textile technol, Univ Manchester, 58-69; from assoc prof to prof, 69-75, ABEL C LINEBERGER PROF TEXTILES, NC STATE UNIV, 75- *Concurrent Pos:* Alexander von Humboldt US sr scientist award, 80. *Honors & Awards:* Harold DeWitt Smith Award, Am Soc Testing & Mat, 79. *Mem:* Fel Brit Inst Mech Eng; fel Brit Textile Inst; Am Soc Mech Engrs; Am Fiber Soc; Sigma Xi. *Res:* Modern methods of yarn formation; open-end spinning; fabric forming systems; design of textile machinery; physics of fibrous assemblies. *Mailing Add:* 3116 Monticello Dr Raleigh NC 27612

LORD, SAMUEL SMITH, JR, b Rockland, Maine, Apr 10, 27; m 48; c 5. ANALYTICAL CHEMISTRY. *Educ:* Tufts Col, BS, 47; Mass Inst Technol, PhD(anal chem), 52. *Prof Exp:* Res chemist, Fabrics & Finishes Dept, E I du Pont de Nemours & Co, Inc, 47-49, res chemist, Org Chem Dept, 52-57, res supvr, Elastomer Chem Dept, 57-59, div head, 59-65, supt qual control, 65-67, supt monomer area, 67-70, gen prod supt, 70-71, asst works dir, Maydown Works, Du Pont Co (UK) Ltd, 71-75, WORKS MGR, BEAUMONT WORKS, E I DU PONT DE NEMOURS & CO, INC, 75- *Mem:* AAAS; Am Chem Soc. *Res:* Polarography; coulometry; infrared and ultraviolet spectrophotometry; urethane chemistry. *Mailing Add:* Beaumont Works PO Box 3269 E I du Pont de Nemours & Co Inc Beaumont TX 77704

LORD, WILLIAM JOHN, b Farmington, NH, Nov 3, 21; m 47; c 1. POMOLOGY. *Educ:* Univ NH, BS, 43, MS, 53; Pa State Univ, PhD(hort), 55. *Prof Exp:* EXTEN PROF POMOL, AGR EXTEN SERV, UNIV MASS, AMHERST, 55- *Mem:* Am Soc Hort Sci. *Res:* Weed control; nutrition; growth regulators. *Mailing Add:* French Hall Univ of Mass Amherst MA 01002

LORDI, NICHOLAS GEORGE, b Orange, NJ, Mar 25, 30; m 61; c 3. PHARMACY. *Educ:* Rutgers Univ, BSc, 52 & MSc, 53; Purdue Univ, PhD(pharmaceut chem), 55. *Prof Exp:* From asst prof to assoc prof, 57-64, chmn dept, 77-82, PROF PHARM, RUTGERS UNIV, 64-, ASST DEAN, 81- *Mem:* Am Chem Soc; AAAS; Am Pharmaceut Asn; NY Acad Sci. *Res:* Physical stability pharmaceutical systems; pharmaceutical technology. *Mailing Add:* Col of Pharm Rutgers Univ PO Box 789 Piscataway NJ 08854

LORDS, JAMES LAFAYETTE, b Salt Lake City, Utah, Apr 5, 28; m 55; c 2. PLANT PHYSIOLOGY. *Educ:* Univ Utah, BS, 50, MS, 51, PhD(plant physiol), 60. *Prof Exp:* Asst bot, Univ Utah, 56-58, instr biol, 58-59; proj assoc plant path, Univ Wis, 60-62; from asst prof to assoc prof, 62-75, PROF MOLECULAR & GENETIC BIOL, UNIV UTAH, 75-, PROF BIOL, 75- *Res:* Microwave interactions with biological systems. *Mailing Add:* Dept of Biol Univ of Utah Salt Lake City UT 84112

LORE, JOHN M, JR, b New York, NY, July 26, 21; m; c 4. OTOLARYNGOLOGY, SURGERY. *Educ:* Col of Holy Cross, BS, 44; NY Univ, MD, 45; Am Bd Otolaryngol, dipl, 54; Am Bd Surg, dipl, 56. *Prof Exp:* Intern, St Vincent's Hosp, New York, 45-46, resident otolaryngol & head & neck surg, 48-50; asst resident gen surg, St Clare's Hosp, 50-52, sr resident, 54-55; asst resident surg & radiation, Mem Cancer Ctr, 52-53; asst clin prof surg & asst attend surgeon, NY Med Col, Flower & Fifth Ave Hosps, 64-66; PROF OTOLARYNGOL & CHMN DEPT, SCH MED, STATE UNIV NY BUFFALO, 66- *Concurrent Pos:* Fel exp surg, St Clare's Hosp, 53-54; asst vis surgeon, Metrop Hosp Ctr, New York, 64-66; dir surg, Good Samaritan Hosp, Suffern, attend surgeon, St Clare's Hosp, New York & consult surgeon, Tuxedo Mem Hosp, 65-66; head dept otolaryngol & chief combined head & neck serv, Buffalo Gen Hosp & Buffalo Children's Hosp, 66-; head dept otolaryngol & chief combined head & neck serv, E J Meyer Mem Hosp, 66-; consult, Buffalo Vet Admin Hosp, 66-; chmn dept otolaryngol, Sisters of Charity Hosp, 75-; vis prof, Col Med, Baylor Univ, 67; consult, Roswell Park Mem Inst, 68-; clin consult, NY State Dept Health, 68-; consult, Deaconess Hosp, Buffalo, NY, 69; vis prof, Denver Med Ctr, 69 & Dept Otolaryngol, Bethesda Naval Med Ctr, Md, 71. *Honors & Awards:* Hektoen Gold Medal, AMA, 52. *Mem:* Fel Am Col Surg; Am Cancer Soc; fel Am Acad Ophthal & Otolaryngol; AMA; James Ewing Soc. *Res:* General surgery, including maxillofacial surgery and plastic surgery of the head and neck. *Mailing Add:* Suite 208 Seton Prof Bldg 2121 Main St Buffalo NY 14214

LOREE, THOMAS ROBERT, b Seattle, Wash, Feb 1, 36; m 58; c 3. LASERS, SOLID STATE PHYSICS. *Educ:* Willamette Univ, BA, 57; Univ Wis, MS, 60, PhD(solid state physics), 62. *Prof Exp:* MEM RES STAFF, LOS ALAMOS NAT LABS, 62- *Concurrent Pos:* Consult, Particle Technol, Inc, 73-76. *Mem:* Am Phys Soc; Optical Soc Am. *Res:* Electronic properties of metals and semiconductors; shock waves in metals; excimer laser research; laser system design; non-linear optics research and design; photochemistry and spectroscopy. *Mailing Add:* Los Alamos Nat Labs Box 1663 MS 564 Los Alamos NM 87545

LORENSEN, LYMAN EDWARD, b Lincoln, Nebr, Sept, 26, 23; m 50; c 3. ORGANIC POLYMER CHEMISTRY. *Educ:* Univ Nebr, BS, 47; Cornell Univ, PhD(chem), 52. *Prof Exp:* Jr chemist, Bristol Labs, 47-48; asst org chem, Cornell Univ, 50-52; chemist, Shell Develop Co, 52-64, mem staff, Mfg Res Dept, 58-60; MEM STAFF POLYMERS & PLASTICS, LAWRENCE LIVERMORE LAB, UNIV CALIF, 64- *Mem:* Am Chem Soc; Sigma Xi. *Res:* High temperature polymers; polymers for geothermal applications; unsaturated glycols; possible precursors in biosynthesis of rubber; lubricating oil additives; silicone and epoxy polymers; filled polymers. *Mailing Add:* 9 Broadview Terr Orinda CA 94563

LORENTE DE NO, RAFAEL, b Zaragoza, Spain, Apr 8, 02; nat US; m 31; c 1. PHYSIOLOGY. *Educ:* Univ Madrid, MD, 23. *Hon Degrees:* MD, Univ Uppsala, 53; DSc, Clark Univ, 64, Rockefeller Univ, 78. *Prof Exp:* Asst, Inst Cajal, Madrid, 21-29; head dept otolaryngol, Valdecilla Hosp, Santander, 29-31; neuroanatomist, Cent Inst for Deaf, St Louis, Mo, 31-36; assoc, 36-38, assoc mem, 38-41, mem & prof, 41-74, EMER PROF PHYSIOL, ROCKEFELLER UNIV, 74- *Concurrent Pos:* Lectr, Med Sch, Wash Univ, 35-36; vis prof, Dept Surg, Univ Calif, Los Angeles. *Mem:* Nat Acad Sci; Am Physiol Soc; Am Asn Anat; Am Neurol Asn; Am Acad Arts & Sci. *Res:* Anatomy of the central nervous system; neurophysiology. *Mailing Add:* 31-24 Rehab Ctr 1000 Veteran Ave Los Angeles CA 90024

LORENTS, DONALD C, b Minn, Mar 26, 29; m 52; c 2. ATOMIC PHYSICS. *Educ:* Concordia Col, Moorhead, Minn, BA, 51; Univ Nebr, MA, 54, PhD(physics), 58. *Prof Exp:* Res physicist, Westinghouse Res Labs, 58-59; physicist, 59-63, chmn, Dept Molecular Physics, 63-67, head, Atomic & Molecular Collisions Sect, 67-68, physicist, 69-70, sr physicist, 70-75, assoc dir, 75-79, DIR, MOLECULAR PHYSICS LAB, SRI INT, 80- *Concurrent Pos:* Vis res physicist, Inst Physics, Aarhus Univ, 68-69. *Mem:* AAAS; fel Am Phys Soc. *Res:* Atomic and molecular collision processes with emphasis on scattering, charge transfer and excitation in ion-atom or ion-molecule collisions; kinetic processes in electronically excited dense gases. *Mailing Add:* Dept of Molecular Physics 333 Ravenswood Menlo Park CA 94025

LORENTZ, GEORGE G, b St Petersburg, Russia, Feb 25, 10; m 42; c 5. MATHEMATICAL ANALYSIS. *Educ:* Univ Leningrad, Cand, 35; Univ T06bingen, Dr rer nat(math), 44. *Hon Degrees:* Dr, Univ Tübingen. *Prof Exp:* Lectr math, Univ Leningrad, 36-42 & Univ Frankfurt, 46-48; prof, Univ Tübingen, 48-49; from asst to asst prof, Univ Toronto, 49-53; prof, Wayne State Univ, 53-58; prof, Syracuse Univ, 58-69; PROF MATH, UNIV TEX, AUSTIN, 69- *Concurrent Pos:* Res grants, NSF & Off Sci Res. *Mem:* Am Math Soc; Math Asn Am; Ger Math Soc. *Res:* Mathematical analysis, especially approximations and expansions; summability; Birkhoff interpolation; functional analysis, especially Banach function spaces; interpolation theorems for operators. *Mailing Add:* Dept Math RLM 8-100 Univ Tex Austin TX 78712o

LORENTZEN, KEITH EDEN, b Heber City, Utah, Apr 13, 21; m 47, 80; c 6. PHYSICAL ORGANIC CHEMISTRY. *Educ:* Univ Utah, BA, 42, MS, 47; Pa State Univ, PhD(chem), 51. *Prof Exp:* Chemist, Standard Oil Co (Ind), 51-62; asst prof, 63-69, asst chmn dept, 66-70, ASSOC PROF CHEM, IND UNIV NORTHWEST, 69-, CHMN CHEM DEPT, 70-, CHMN DEPT, PHYSICS & ASTRON, 77- *Mem:* Am Chem Soc; fel Am Inst Chemists; Am Asn Univ Professors. *Res:* Conductivity measurements; chemistry of lubricating oils and additives; organic analytical chemistry; chromatography; polarography; Friedel-Crafts acylation of xylenes. *Mailing Add:* Dept of Chem Ind Univ Northwest Gary IN 46408

LORENZ, CARL EDWARD, b New York, NY, Aug 22, 33; m 56; c 3. ORGANIC CHEMISTRY. *Educ:* NY Univ, BA, 53, PhD(chem), 57. *Prof Exp:* Asst chem, NY Univ, 53-57; chemist, Plastics Dept, Exp Sta, 57-63, sr res chemist, 63-68, supvr, 68, sr supvr, 68-69, lab supt, 69-70, res lab mgr, Sabine River Works, 70-72, res mgr, Wilmington, 72-74, asst dir, Int Dept, 74-76, prod mgr, 76-78, dir, Feedstocks Div, 78-79, dir Res Div, Cent Res & Develop, 79-81, DIR RES & DEVELOP, POLYMER PROD DEPT, E I DU PONT DE NEMOURS & CO, INC, 81- *Honors & Awards:* Award, Am Inst Chem, 53. *Mem:* Am Chem Soc; Am Inst Chem; The Chem Soc. *Res:* Fluorocarbon monomer syntheses and polymerizations; high pressure hydrocarbon syntheses; heterogeneous catalysis; chemistry of anionic and radical polymerizations. *Mailing Add:* Polymer Prod Dept E I du Pont de Nemours & Co Inc Wilmington DE 19898

LORENZ, DONALD H, b Brooklyn, NY, Oct 18, 36; m 62. ORGANIC CHEMISTRY, POLYMER CHEMISTRY. *Educ:* Polytech Inst Brooklyn, BS, 58, PhD(org chem), 63. *Prof Exp:* Asst org chem, Polytech Inst Brooklyn, 58-59, organometallics, 59-62, asst scientist chem eng res div, NY Univ, 62-63; sr polymer chemist, Tex-US Chem Co, 63-65; explor polymer chemist, Gen Aniline & Film Co, 65-70, group leader polymer synthesis, GAF Corp, 70-74, mgr vinyl polymer res, 74-80; DIR RES & DEVELOP, HYDROMER INC, 80- *Mem:* Am Chem Soc. *Res:* Organometallic chemistry; elastomers; resins; adhesives; polymers of vinyl ethers and vinyl amides; polyurethanes; fire retardants; ultraviolet and ethylene dibromide curable resins; coatings for medical devices. *Mailing Add:* 12 Radel Pl Basking Ridge NJ 07920

LORENZ, DOUGLAS, b Dubuque, Iowa, July 12, 28; m 68; c 2. MICROBIOLOGY, VIROLOGY. *Educ:* Univ Calif, Los Angeles, BA, 53, PhD(microbiol), 63. *Prof Exp:* Res fel virol, Med Sch, Univ Minn, 63-64; asst prof, Sch Med, Univ NMex, 64-65; sr scientist, Life Sci Div, Melpar, Inc, Va, 65-67; res microbiologist, Div Biol Standards, NIH, 67-72, RES MICROBIOLOGIST, BUR BIOLOGICS, FOOD & DRUG ADMIN, 72- *Mem:* Am Soc Microbiol. *Res:* Animal models for human hepatitis; herpesvirus tumors; animal testing of human vaccines; effectiveness of various commercial disinfectants on Newcastle disease virus by usedilution test; adsorption rates of Rous sarcoma virus on susceptible and non-susceptible cells. *Mailing Add:* 5515 Alta Vista Rd Bethesda MD 20814

LORENZ, EDWARD NORTON, b West Hartford, Conn, May 23, 17; m 48; c 3. METEOROLOGY. *Educ:* Dartmouth Col, AB, 38; Harvard Univ, AM, 40; Mass Inst Technol, SM, 43, ScD(meteorol), 48. *Prof Exp:* Asst meteorol, Mass Inst Technol, 46-48, mem staff, 48-54; vis assoc prof, Univ Calif, Los Angeles, 54-55; from asst prof to assoc prof, 55-62, PROF METEOROL, MASS INST TECHNOL, 62-, HEAD DEPT, 76- *Mem:* Nat Acad Sci; Am Math Soc; Am Meteorol Soc. *Res:* General circulation of the atmosphere; dynamical and statistical weather prediction. *Mailing Add:* Dept of Meteorol Mass Inst of Technol Cambridge MA 02139

LORENZ, JOHN CLARK, b Coshocton, Ohio, June 11, 23; m 53; c 4. ORGANIC CHEMISTRY. *Educ:* Carnegie Inst Technol, BS, 48; Univ Ill, PhD, 51. *Prof Exp:* RES CHEMIST, E I DU PONT DE NEMOURS & CO INC, 51- *Mem:* Am Chem Soc. *Res:* Fluorocarbon elastomers; polyurethanes and other elastomer polymers. *Mailing Add:* RD 2 Box 354 Berkeley Ridge Hockessin DE 19707

LORENZ, KLAUS J, b Berlin, Ger, June 22, 36; US citizen; m 60; c 2. CEREAL CHEMISTRY. *Educ:* Northwestern Univ, Ill, PhB, 68; Kans State Univ, MS, 69, PhD(food sci), 70. *Prof Exp:* Baking technologist, Am Inst Baking, 61-65; food technologist, Nat Dairy Prod Corp, 65-68; asst prof, 70-74, assoc prof, 74-78, PROF FOOD SCI & NUTRIT, COLO STATE UNIV, 78- *Mem:* Am Asn Cereal Chem; Inst Food Technologists; Swiss Soc Food Sci & Technol. *Res:* Development of high-protein foods; evaluation of new cereal grain varieties. *Mailing Add:* Dept Food Sci & Nutrit Colo State Univ Ft Collins CO 80521

LORENZ, MAX RUDOLPH, b Detroit, Mich, June 25, 30; m 55; c 3. PHYSICAL CHEMISTRY, PHYSICS. *Educ:* Rensselaer Polytech Inst, BChE, 57, PhD(phys chem), 60. *Prof Exp:* Res assoc, Gen Elec Res Lab, 60-63; res staff mem, Thomas J Watson Res Ctr, NY, 63-73, HEAD DEPT INORG MAT, IBM RES DIV, IBM CORP, 73- *Mem:* Am Phys Soc; Electrochem Soc; NY Acad Sci; fel Am Inst Chem; sr mem Inst Elec & Electronics Engrs. *Res:* Physics and chemistry of semiconductors, especially the role and control of defects and electrical and optical properties; magnetic dish coating technology and recording physics. *Mailing Add:* IBM Res Lab K64/281 5600 Cottle Rd San Jose CA 95193

LORENZ, OSCAR ANTHONY, b Colorado Springs, Colo, Dec 5, 14; m 47. VEGETABLE CROPS, PLANT NUTRITION. *Educ:* Colo State Col, BS, 36; Cornell Univ, PhD(veg crops), 41. *Prof Exp:* Asst hort, Colo State Col, 36-37; asst veg crops, Cornell Univ, 37-41; from instr to assoc prof, 41-55, vchmn dept, 55-64, PROF VEG CROPS, COL AGR, UNIV CALIF, DAVIS, 55-, CHMN DEPT, 64- *Concurrent Pos:* Mem, Agr Comn to Bermuda, 39. *Honors & Awards:* Vaughn Award, 42. *Mem:* Fel Am Soc Hort Sci; fel Am Soc Plant Physiol; fel Am Soc Agron; fel Am Potato Asn. *Res:* Mineral nutrition of vegetable crops; boron deficiency in table beets; soils and plant nutrient relationships; environmental factors affecting vegetable production. *Mailing Add:* Dept of Veg Crops Col of Agr Univ of Calif Davis CA 95616

LORENZ, PATRICIA ANN, b New York, NY, Jan 31, 38; m 62; c 2. INFORMATION SCIENCE, ANALYTICAL CHEMISTRY. *Educ:* Marymount Manhattan Col, BS, 59; Polytech Inst Brooklyn, PhD(anal chem), 65. *Prof Exp:* Info chemist, Exxon Res & Eng Co, 65-67; consult info sci, 67-77; GROUP HEAD, ANAL & INFO DIV, EXXON RES & ENG CO, 78- *Mem:* Am Chem Soc; Am Soc Info Sci. *Res:* Mechanism of acid-base reactions in benzene. *Mailing Add:* Exxon Res & Eng Co PO Box 101 Florham Park NJ 07932

LORENZ, PHILIP BOALT, b Dayton, Ohio, Aug 14, 20; m 46; c 3. PHYSICAL CHEMISTRY. *Educ:* Swarthmore Col, AB, 41; Harvard Univ, MA, 46, PhD(chem), 49. *Prof Exp:* Asst biol, Princeton Univ, 42-43; asst, Phys Chem, SAM Labs, Columbia Univ, 44-45; phys chemist surface chem, Petrol Res Ctr, US Bur Mines, 49-71, res chemist, Petrol Prod & Environ Res, 71-75, RES CHEMIST, BARTLESVILLE ENERGY TECHNOL CTR, US DEPT ENERGY, 75- *Mem:* Am Chem Soc; Sigma Xi; Soc Petrol Engrs; Am Inst Mining & Metall Engrs. *Res:* Surface chemistry; electrochemistry; petroleum engineering. *Mailing Add:* Bartlesville Energy Technol Ctr PO Box 1398 Bartlesville OK 74005

LORENZ, PHILIP JACK, JR, b Atlanta, Ga, Apr 15, 24; m 70; c 2. ATMOSPHERIC PHYSICS. *Educ:* Oglethorpe Univ, BS, 49; Vanderbilt Univ, MS, 52. *Prof Exp:* Lab asst, Oglethorpe Univ, 48; qual control tech, Transparent Package Co, 50-51; asst prof physics, Lemoyne Col, 52-54, Ky Wesleyan Col, 54-56 & Upper Iowa Univ, 56-61; res assoc, Syracuse Univ, 63-65, vis instr, 65-66; chmn dept, 66-74, ASSOC PROF PHYSICS, UNIV OF THE SOUTH, 66- *Concurrent Pos:* Lab asst, Vanderbilt Univ, 52; consult physicist, Empirical Explor Co, Ky, 56; univ fel, Syracuse Univ, 58-59, Nat Sci Found fac fel, 61-63; textbook consult, J B Lippincott Co, 71-72. *Mem:* Sigma Xi; Am Phys Soc; Am Asn Physics Teachers; Hist Sci Soc. *Res:* Atmospheric electricity in fair and foggy weather; geophysics of environmental radioactivity at sandstone sinkhole sites; history of medieval Persian and Arabic science; history of astronomy; designing laboratory experiments for premedical physics, optics and thermodynamics. *Mailing Add:* Dept of Physics Univ of the South Sewanee TN 37375

LORENZ, RALPH WILLIAM, b Waseca, Minn, Aug 19, 07; m 39; c 2. FORESTRY. *Educ:* Univ Minn, BS, 30, PhD(plant Physiol), 38. *Prof Exp:* Asst plant physiol, Univ Minn, 30-33; jr forester, US Forest Serv, 33-35; instr forestry, Univ Farm, Univ Minn, 35-38; assoc, 38-41, asst chief, 41-44, assoc chief, 44-47, assoc prof forest res, 47-55, prof, 55-73, actg head dept, 65-66, EMER PROF FORESTRY, UNIV ILL, URBANA, 73- *Mem:* Soc Am Foresters. *Res:* Forest research in planting; silviculture; dendrology; regeneration and forest management. *Mailing Add:* 1707 S Pleasant Urbana IL 61801

LORENZ, RICHARD ARNOLD, b Fond du Lac, Wis, Mar 7, 42; m 65; c 4. SHOCK DYNAMICS. *Educ:* Marquette Univ, BS, 65, MS, 68. *Prof Exp:* Physicist, Naval Ord Lab, 67-70, res physicist, 70-74; RES PHYSICIST APPL PHYSICS, NAVAL SURFACE WEAPONS CTR, 74- *Concurrent Pos:* Consult, Advan Reactors Br, Nuclear Regulatory Comn, 75-78. *Mem:* Am Phys Soc. *Res:* Explosion effects; shock waves; atmospheric sound focusing; data reduction techniques; hydrodynamics; computer simulations. *Mailing Add:* Code R15 Naval Surface Weapons Ctr White Oak Lab Silver Spring MD 20910

LORENZ, ROMAN R, b Breslau, Ger, July 15, 35; US citizen; m 60; c 3. ORGANIC CHEMISTRY. *Educ:* Rensselaer Polytech Inst, BS, 58; Univ Mich, MS, 60, PhD(med chem), 62. *Prof Exp:* Res org chemist, 62-69, sr res chemist & sect head, 69-74, sr res assoc & sect head, 74-76, DIR CHEM DEVELOP, STERLING-WINTHROP RES INST, 77- *Mem:* Am Chem Soc. *Res:* Synthesis of organic and medicinal compounds. *Mailing Add:* Sterling-Winthrop Res Inst Rensselaer NY 12144

LORENZEN, CARL JULIUS, b Toftum, Ger, Feb 12, 38; m 60; c 3. BIOLOGICAL OCEANOGRAPHY, FOOD CHAIN DYNAMICS. *Educ:* Cornell Univ, BS, 59, MS, 62, PhD(oceanog), 64. *Prof Exp:* Fel res biol, Scripps Inst Oceanog, 64-65, asst res biol, 65-67; asst scientist, Woods Hole Oceanog Inst, 67-71; staff assoc, Oceanog Sect, Nat Sci Found, 71-73; RES ASSOC PROF, DEPT OCEANOG, UNIV WASH, 73- *Mem:* Am Soc Limnol & Oceanog; AAAS; Sigma Xi. *Res:* Food chain ecology and carbon cycling in the marine environment. *Mailing Add:* Sch Oceanog Univ Wash Seattle WA 98195

LORENZEN, HOWARD O(TTO), b Atlantic, Iowa, June 24, 12; m 36; c 1. ELECTRONICS. *Educ:* Iowa State Col, BSEE, 35. *Prof Exp:* Develop engr electronics, Colonial Radio Corp, 35-39 & Zenith Radio Corp, 39-40; head, Electronic Countermeasures Br, Naval Res Lab, 40-66, supt, Electronic Warfare Div, 66-70, supt, Space Systs Div, 70-80; RETIRED. *Concurrent Pos:* Tech adv, Chief Naval Opers Off, Off Secy Defense, Joint Chiefs Staff, Dir Naval Intel & to Dir Naval Labs. *Honors & Awards:* Meritorious Civilian Sci Award, US Navy, 48; Distinguished Civilian Serv Award, 60. *Mem:* Fel Inst Elec & Electronics Engrs. *Res:* Signal indication and analysis; direction finding; propagation; electronic countermeasures; satellite design; space data reduction. *Mailing Add:* 9000 Lake Washington Blvd NE Bellevue WA 98004

LORENZEN, JERRY ALAN, b Grand Island, Nebr, Oct 3, 44; m 67; c 2. SURFACE CHEMISTRY, DISPLAY DEVELOPMENT. *Educ:* Midland Lutheran Col, BS, 66; Okla State Univ, PhD(chem), 70. *Prof Exp:* Instr chem, Okla State Univ, 69-70; staff chemist, Mat Lab, 70-73, mgr environ technol, 73-75, adv chemist display develop, 75-80, SR CHEMIST, IBM CORP, 80- *Mem:* Am Chem Soc. *Res:* Environmental chemistry; corrosion; gas-solid interaction; plasma display panels; engineering statistics. *Mailing Add:* IBM Corp Neighborhood Rd Kingston NY 13760

LORENZETTI, OLE J, b Chicago, Ill, Oct 25, 36; m 62; c 3. PHARMACOLOGY, BIOCHEMISTRY. *Educ:* Univ Ill, Chicago, BS, 58; Ohio State Univ, MS, 62, PhD(pharmacol & toxicol), 65. *Prof Exp:* Asst chief pharmacist, WSuburban Hosp, 58; instr pharm, Univ Ill, Chicago, 58-59; asst instr pharmacol, Ohio State Univ, 59-62; from res pharmacologist to sr res pharmacologist, Therapeut Res Labs, Dome Chem Inc Div, Miles Labs, Ind, 64-69; sr res, scientist, Alcon Labs Inc, 69-71; dir immunol & biochem mgr biol res, 72-74; vpres, 71-72, res 67-70, PRES PHARMACEUT CONSULT, INC, 70-; DIR DERMATOL RES & DEVELOP, ALCON LABS INC, 79- *Concurrent Pos:* Assoc prof pharmacol, Univ Tex Health Sci Ctr, Dallas, 70-; adj prof, Tex

Christian Univ, 72- *Mem:* AAAS; Am Chem Soc; Soc Cosmetic Chem; Am Acad Clin Toxicol; Soc Invest Dermat. *Res:* Pharmacodynamics; evaluations of analgesic, anti-inflammatory agents and antiglaucoma agents; development of drug screening programs; autonomic and biochemical pharmacology; topical pharmacology and toxicology of eye and skin; ophthalmology; dermatology; toxicology; immunology; drug metabolism; pharmacokinetics. *Mailing Add:* Alcon Labs Inc 6201 S Freeway Ft Worth TX 76101

LORENZO, ANTONIO V, b Vigo, Spain, July 23, 28; US citizen; m 58; c 2. NEUROPHARMACOLOGY, NEUROCHEMISTRY. *Educ:* Univ Chicago, BA, 56, BS, 58, PhD(pharmacol), 66. *Prof Exp:* From asst to assoc neurol, Children's Hosp Med Ctr, 64-68, instr pharmacol, 66-68; asst prof, 69-71, ASSOC PROF PHARMACOL, HARVARD MED SCH, 71-; DIR NEUROSURG, CHILDREN'S HOSP MED CTR, 68- *Concurrent Pos:* Epilepsy Found Am fel, Children's Hosp Med Ctr, 65 & dir neurol res, 69-78; Nat Inst Neurol Dis & Stroke proj grant, 71-73; NIH career develop award, Harvard Med Sch, 70-75. *Mem:* AAAS; Am Soc Pharmacol & Exp Therapeut; NY Acad Sci; Am Soc Neurochem; Am Acad Neurol. *Res:* Pathophysiology of the blood, role of brain barrier, putative transmitter seizures; cerebrospinal fluid transport phenomena; cerebrospinal fluid dynamics. *Mailing Add:* Neurosurg Children's Hosp Med Ctr Boston MA 02115

LORETZ, CHRISTOPHER ALAN, b Santa Monica, Calif, Apr 28, 51. ENDOCRINOLOGY. *Educ:* Univ Wash, BS, 72; Univ Calif, Los Angeles, MA, 74, PhD(comp physiol), 78. *Prof Exp:* Fel, Dept Zool & Cancer Res Lab, Univ Calif, Berkeley, 78-81; ASST PROF, DEPT BIOL SCI, STATE UNIV NY BUFFALO, 81- *Mem:* Am Soc Zoologists. *Res:* Osmoregulation in aquatic vertebrates; hormonal control of epithelial ion transport. *Mailing Add:* Dept Biol Sci 109 Cooke Hall State Univ NY Buffalo NY 14260

LOREY, FRANK WILLIAM, b Staten Island, NY, May 7, 29; m 51; c 3. PAPER CHEMISTRY. *Educ:* State Univ New York Col Forestry, Syracuse, BS, 51, MS, 52. *Prof Exp:* Res engr, Mead Corp, Ohio, 52-54; assoc prof pulp & paper chem & pilot plant group leader, State Univ New York Col Forestry, Syracuse, 54-66; asst to gen mgr, 66-67, corp tech dir, 67-75, VPRES RES, GARDEN STATE PAPER CO, GARFIELD, 75- *Concurrent Pos:* Develop consult, AB Kamyr, Sweden, 65. *Mem:* Tech Asn Pulp & Paper Indust. *Res:* Improved methods in pulping of wood and use of chemicals for influencing paper properties; development of processes and design of systems for deinking of waste papers. *Mailing Add:* 82 Dogwood Terr Ramsey NJ 07446

LOREY, FREDERICK D(AVID), b Portsmouth, Ohio, Dec 4, 24; m 48; c 4. CERAMICS. *Educ:* Ohio State Univ, BCerE & MS, 50. *Prof Exp:* Technician, Fed Glass Co, 48; res assoc, Res Found, Ohio State Univ, 49-50; glass technologist, 50-54, process engr, 54-56, supvr melting, 56-58, mgr plant melting servs, 58-59, melting opers, 59-60, DIR MELTING TECHNOL, CORNING GLASS WORKS, 60- *Mem:* Am Ceramic Soc; Nat Inst Ceramic Engrs; Nat Soc Prof Engrs. *Res:* Infrared transmission of glasses. *Mailing Add:* Corning Glass Works HP-ME-2 Corning NY 14830

LORHAN, PAUL HERMAN, b Mont Clare, Pa, Apr 7, 08; m 42; c 5. ANESTHESIOLOGY. *Educ:* Ohio State Univ, AB, 31; Creighton Univ, MD, 35; Am Bd Anesthesiol, dipl, 41. *Prof Exp:* From instr to prof anesthesiol, Univ Kans, 38-58, dir anesthesia, 38-39; PROF ANESTHESIOL, UNIV CALIF, LOS ANGELES, 58-; DIR ANESTHESIOL, HARBOR GEN HOSP, TORRANCE, CALIF, 58- *Concurrent Pos:* Consult, US Army Hosp, Ft McArthur, 58-; del, White House Conf Aging, 71; consult, US Naval Hosp, Long Beach, Calif. *Mem:* Am Soc Anesthesiol (vpres, 54); Int Anesthesia Res Soc; fel AMA; fel Am Col Anesthesiol; Acad Anesthesiol. *Res:* Anoxia in anesthesia; vasopressor drugs in anesthesia; circulatory dynamics during anesthesia; effects of methoxyflurane on renal and hepatic function; massive blood transfusions; anesthesia for the aged; evaluation of antiemetics. *Mailing Add:* 913 Via Mirola Palos Verdes Estates CA 90274

LORIA, JOHN C(ECIL), b Boston, Mass, Jan 17, 24; m 47; c 7. SYSTEMS & AERONAUTICAL ENGINEERING. *Educ:* Mass Inst Technol, SB, 50, SM, 52. *Prof Exp:* Res engr aeronaut dept, Mass Inst Technol, 50-57; staff engr eng div, Arthur D Little, Inc, 57-63; tech prog mgr systs eng, NASA Electronics Res Ctr, Mass, 63-70; dir safety & oper systs off, Off Aero & Space Technol, 70-77, PROG MGR PHOTOVOLTAICS, NASA HQ, 77- *Mem:* Am Inst Aeronaut & Astronaut. *Res:* Systems safety. *Mailing Add:* 11042 Ring Rd Reston VA 22070

LORIA, ROGER MOSHE, b Antwerpen, Belgium, Apr 19, 40; US citizen; m 78; c 1. VIROLOGY. *Educ:* Bar-Ilan Univ, Israel, BS, 65; State Univ NY, Buffalo, MS, 68; Boston Univ, PhD(microvirol), 72. *Prof Exp:* Asst prof biochem, Mass Col Optom, 69-70; asst virol, Sch Med, Boston Univ, 68-72, instr microbiol, 72-74; asst prof, 74-78, ASSOC PROF MICROBIOL, MED COL VA, 78-, ADJ ASST PROF ACAD PATH, 78- *Concurrent Pos:* Mass Heart Asn fel, 72-74; res assoc, Sch Med, Boston Univ, 74; NIH res grants, Arthritis & Metab Dis, 74 & 78, 79, Heart & Lung Div, 75; Young investr develop award, Am Diabetes Asn, 75-77; instr pediat, Harvard Sch Med, 80- *Mem:* Am Soc Microbiol; AAAS; Am Fedn Clin Res; Reticuloendothelial Syst Soc; Am Diebetes Asn. *Res:* Investigation on the role of group B coxsackieviruses in diabetes, atherosclerosis and cardiovascular disease in experimental animal models; general aspects of host-virus interaction; viral infection by the oral route; nutritional hypercholesteremia; effects on host resistance; rapid viral diagnosis. *Mailing Add:* Dept of Microbiol & Immunol Med Col Va Box 678 Richmond VA 23298

LORIMER, JOHN WILLIAM, b Oshawa, Ont, Apr 16, 29; m 54; c 3. PHYSICAL CHEMISTRY. *Educ:* Univ Toronto, BA, 51, MA, 52, PhD(phys chem), 54. *Prof Exp:* Asst phys chem, Univ Leiden, Netherlands, 54-56; asst res officer, Atlantic Regional Lab, Nat Res Coun Can, 56-61, assoc res officer, 61; asst prof, 61-65, assoc prof, 65-79, PROF PHYS CHEM, UNIV WESTERN ONT, 79- *Mem:* Royal Soc Chem; fel Chem Inst Can; Int Union Pure & Appl Chem (co-secy). *Res:* Thermodynamics of liquids; transport in membranes; irreversible thermodynamics; electrochemistry. *Mailing Add:* Dept Chem Univ Western Ont London ON N6A 5B7 Can

LORIMER, NANCY L, b Mishawaka, Ind, Feb 8, 47; m 72; c 3. INSECT GENETICS. *Educ:* Ind Univ, AB, 69; Univ Notre Dame, PhD(biol), 75. *Prof Exp:* Fel genetic control, Int Centre Insect Ecol & Physiol, 74-75; RES ENTOMOLOGIST, NCENT FOREST EXP STA, FOREST SERV, USDA, 75-; ADJ ASST PROF, DEPT ENTOMOL, FISH WILDLIFE, UNIV MINN, 79- *Concurrent Pos:* Consult, WHO, 73; assoc ed, Am Midland Nat, 80- *Mem:* Entom Soc Am; Asn Women Sci; AAAS; Genetics Soc Am; Sigma Xi. *Res:* Assessment of genetic variation in forest insect populations and how these variations interact with other factors to influence population dynamics. *Mailing Add:* USDA Forest Serv NCent Forest Exp Sta Folwell Ave St Paul MN 55108

LORINCZ, ALLAN LEVENTE, b Chicago, Ill, Oct 31, 24; m 52; c 3. DERMATOLOGY. *Educ:* Univ Chicago, SB, 45, MD, 47. *Prof Exp:* Res fel dermat, Cancer Clin, 50-51, from instr to assoc prof, 51-67, PROF DERMAT, UNIV CHICAGO, 67- *Concurrent Pos:* Mem dermat training grants comt, USPHS, 61-64; mem comt cutaneous syst, Div Med Sci, Nat Res Coun, 62-65; nat consult to Surgeon Gen, US Air Force, 62-; mem dermat adv comt, Food & Drug Admin, 71-72. *Mem:* Soc Invest Dermat; Soc Exp Biol & Med; Am Soc Dermatopath; Am Dermat Asn; Am Fedn Clin Res. *Res:* Psoriasis; cutaneous fungus infections; biochemistry and physiology of the skin, especially melanin chemistry and sebaceous gland control by endocrine factors; immunology. *Mailing Add:* Dept of Med Univ of Chicago Chicago IL 60637

LORINCZ, ANDREW ENDRE, b Chicago, Ill, May 17, 26; m 65. PEDIATRICS, BIOCHEMISTRY. *Educ:* Univ Chicago, PhB, 48, BS, 50, MD, 52. *Prof Exp:* From intern to jr asst resident pediat, Univ Chicago Clin, 52-54, jr asst resident fel, Rosenthal Clin, 54-55, instr, Sch Med, 56-59; from asst prof to assoc prof, Sch Med, Univ Fla, 59-68; PROF PEDIAT, ASSOC PROF BIOCHEM & DIR CTR DEVELOP & LEARNING DISORDERS, MED CTR, UNIV ALA, BIRMINGHAM, 68-, PROF DENT & ASSOC PROF PEDIAT OPTICS, 70-, ASSOC PROF SCH NURSING & ENG BIOPHYS, 71- *Concurrent Pos:* Res fel, Univ Chicago, 54-55 & Arthritis & Rheumatism Found res fel, 55-58; instr, La Rabida Inst, 57-59; consult ed, Am J Dis of Children, 71-; med consult, Headstart, 71- *Mem:* Am Chem Soc; Am Soc Pediat Res; fel Am Acad Pediat; Soc Invest Dermat; Orthop Res Soc. *Res:* Heritable disorders of connective tissue acid mucopolysaccharides; inborn errors of metabolism; mental retardation; biochemistry. *Mailing Add:* Ctr for Develop & Learning Dis Univ of Ala Birmingham AL 35233

LORING, ARTHUR PAUL, b New York, NY, May 22, 36; m 63; c 3. GEOLOGY, ENVIRONMENTAL GEOLOGY. *Educ:* Columbia Univ, AB, 58; Pa State Univ, MS, 61; NY Univ, PhD(geol), 66. *Prof Exp:* Lectr geol, Brooklyn Col, 62-65; instr, 66-67; asst prof, Upsala Col, 67; asst prof, 67-73, ASSOC PROF GEOL, YORK COL, NY, 73- *Mem:* AAAS; fel Geol Soc Am; Am Soc Photogram; Asn Eng Geol; Sigma Xi. *Res:* Distribution and stratigraphy of planktonic foraminifera and general geologic field mapping in areas of folded and faulted sediments. *Mailing Add:* Dept of Geol York Col 150-14 Jamaica Ave Jamaica NY 11432

LORING, BLAKE M(ARSHALL), b Belmont, NH, Mar 21, 14; m 42; c 3. PHYSICAL METALLURGY. *Educ:* Mass Inst Technol, SB, 37, ScD(metall), 40; George Washington Univ, MA, 45. *Prof Exp:* Asst x-ray metallog, Mass Inst Technol, 37-40; chief nonferrous br, US Naval Res Lab, 40-50; tech officer, US Naval Ord Lab, 51-53; CONSULT METALL ENGR, 53- *Concurrent Pos:* From instr to assoc prof, Univ Md, 47-53; US tech adv, Geneva Conf Peaceful Uses Atomic Energy, 55. *Mem:* Am Soc Metals; Sigma Xi; Am Inst Mining, Metall & Petrol Engrs. *Res:* Metal processing; alloy and copper steels. *Mailing Add:* Rte 2 Laconia NH 03246

LORING, DOUGLAS HOWARD, b Concord, NH, July 25, 34; Can citizen; m 61; c 3. MARINE GEOCHEMISTRY. *Educ:* Acadia Univ, BSc, 54, MSc, 56; Univ Manchester, PhD(geochem), 60. *Prof Exp:* Tech officer, Geol Surv Can, 54-55; res fel geochem, Univ Manchester, 57-60; RES SCIENTIST, BEDFORD INST, 60- *Concurrent Pos:* Spec lectr, Dalhousie Univ, 62-68. *Mem:* Mineral Asn Can; fel Geol Asn Can; Geochem Soc. *Res:* Geochemistry of ancient and modern marine sediments; marine geology of the Gulf of St Lawrence. *Mailing Add:* Atlantic Oceanog Lab Bedford Inst Box 1006 Dartmouth NS B2Y 4A2 Can

LORING, WILLIAM BACHELLER, b Haileybury, Ont, Mar 4, 15; m 45; c 2. ECONOMIC GEOLOGY. *Educ:* Mich Col Min, BS, 40; Univ Ariz, MS, 47, PhD, 59. *Prof Exp:* Field geologist, Noranda Mines Co, Can, 41-42; inspector, US Dept Eng, 42-43; field engr, US Bur Mines, Mich, 43-44; party chief, Nfld Geol Surv, 44; party chief, Mining Geophys Co, Can, 44-45; mine mgr, Discovery Yellowknife Gold Mine, 46; geologist, Great Northern Explor Co, Ariz, 46-48; geologist, Eagle-Picher Mining & Smelting Co, 49-55; chief geologist, Big Indian Dist, Hidden Splendor Mining Co, 55-62; staff geologist, Atlas Minerals, 62-66; mine geologist, US Smelting, Ref & Mining Co, NMex, 66-67; dist geologist, Cities Serv Minerals Corp, Wyo, 67-71, staff geologist, 71-78; CONSULT, 78- *Mem:* Am Inst Mining, Metall & Petrol Eng; Soc Econ Geol; Can Inst Mining & Metall; Int Asn Genesis Ore Deposits. *Res:* Ore deposits, especially controlling structures and surface indications. *Mailing Add:* 2058 11th St Douglas AZ 85607

LORING, WILLIAM ELLSWORTH, b Portland, Maine, Nov 6, 20; m 47; c 3. PATHOLOGY. *Educ:* Bowdoin Col, BS, 43; Columbia Univ, MD, 46; Am Bd Path, dipl, 54. *Prof Exp:* Res asst, Sch Med, Yale Univ, 51-52, instr, 52-53; asst prof, Sch Med, Univ NC, 53-56; assoc prof, Sch Med, NY Univ, 56-66; dir labs, Mercy Hosp, 66-72; CONSULT PATH & FORENSIC MED, 72- *Concurrent Pos:* Teaching fel path, Col Med, State Univ NY, 49-51; John Polachek Fund fel, 58-61; lectr, Columbia Univ, 56-66; investr, Health Res Coun, NY, 60-65; consult, St Vincent's Hosp, Bridgeport, Conn. *Mem:* Am Soc Exp Path; Am Soc Clin Path; Am Thoracic Soc; Am Soc Cytol; Am Asn Path & Bact. *Res:* Chest pathology. *Mailing Add:* 7 Riverside Dr Falmouth ME 04105

LORIO, PETER LEONCE, JR, b New Orleans, La, Apr 10, 27; m 57; c 6. FOREST SOILS, FOREST ECOLOGY. *Educ:* La State Univ, BS, 53; Duke Univ, MF, 54; Iowa State Univ, PhD(forestry-soils), 62. *Prof Exp:* Soil scientist, Standard Fruit & Steamship Co, 54-58, chief soil scientist, 58-59; soil scientist, 62-68, prin soil scientist, 68-76, SUPVRY SOIL SCIENTIST, FOREST INSECT RES PROJ, SOUTHERN FOREST EXP STA, US FOREST SERV, 76- *Mem:* Am Soc Agron; Int Soc Trop Foresters; Sigma Xi; Soil Sci Soc Am; Int Soc Soil Sci. *Res:* Soil, tree, and stand factors affecting pine susceptibility to bark beetles; soil water; tree rooting; rootlet pathogens; tree physiology; stand composition, age, density. *Mailing Add:* 2500 Shreeveport Hwy Pineville LA 71360

LORKOVIC, HRVOJE RADOSLAV, muscular physiology, see previous edition

LORRAIN, PAUL, b Montreal, Que, Sept 8, 16; m 44; c 4. ELECTROMAGNETISM. *Educ:* Univ Ottawa, BA, 37; McGill Univ, BSc, 40, MSc, 41, PhD(physics), 47. *Prof Exp:* Lectr physics, Sir George Williams Col, 42-43, Univ Laval, 43-46 & Inst Physics Univ Montreal, 46; res assoc, Lab Nuclear Studies, Cornell Univ, 47-49; head dept, 57-66, PROF PHYSICS, UNIV MONTREAL, 49- *Concurrent Pos:* Vis prof fac sci, Univ Grenoble, France, 61-62 & Univ Madrid, 68-69; mem, Nat Res Coun, 60-66; vis fel, Oxford Univ, 81. *Mem:* Royal Soc Can; Am Phys Soc; Can Asn Physicists (pres, 64-65). *Res:* Electromagnetism and geophysics. *Mailing Add:* Dept Physics Univ Montreal Case Postale 6128 Montreal PQ H3C 3J7 Can

LORSCHEIDER, FRITZ LOUIS, b Rochester, NY, Aug 27, 39; m 67; c 4. PHYSIOLOGY, ENDOCRINOLOGY. *Educ:* Univ Wis, BSc, 63; Mich State Univ, MSc, 67, PhD(physiol, endocrinol), 70. *Prof Exp:* Res asst endocrinol, Radioisotope Unit, Med Col Wis, 63-64; from asst prof to assoc prof, 70-80, PROF MED PHYSIOL, FAC MED, UNIV CALGARY, 80- *Concurrent Pos:* NIH fel, Mich State Univ, 70. *Mem:* Am Physiol Soc; Can Physiol Soc; Can Soc Clin Invest; AAAS; Int Soc Oncodevelopmental Biol & Med. *Res:* Reproductive and fetal physiology; chemistry and physiology of onco-fetal proteins; fetal steroid metabolism. *Mailing Add:* Dept Med Physiol Univ of Calgary Fac of Med Calgary AB T2N 1N4 Can

LORTIE, MARCEL, forest protection, forest policy, see previous edition

LORY, HENRY JAMES, b Baltimore, Md, Mar 3, 36; m 60; c 3. ELECTRICAL ENGINEERING. *Educ:* Johns Hopkins Univ, BES, 58, PhD(elec eng), 63. *Prof Exp:* Asst, Air Res & Develop Command Contract Proj, Johns Hopkins Univ, 57-58, mem res staff, Radiation Lab, 61-63; MEM TECH STAFF, BELL TEL LABS, 63- *Mem:* Sigma Xi. *Res:* Development of Schottky barrier devices, especially analysis of high temperature failure mechanisms; design of linear integrated circuits. *Mailing Add:* 3221 Stoudts Ferry Bridge Rd Riverview Park PA 19605

LOS, MARINUS, b Ridderkerk, Netherlands, Sept 18, 33; m 57; c 4. CHEMISTRY. *Educ:* Univ Edinburgh, BSc, 55, PhD(chem), 57. *Prof Exp:* Res fel, Nat Res Coun Can, 58-60; res chemist, 60-71, GROUP LEADER, ORGANIC SYNTHESIS, AM CYANAMID CO, 71- *Concurrent Pos:* Sr res fel, Dept Pharmacol, Univ Edinburgh, 69-70. *Mem:* Am Chem Soc. *Res:* Aliphatic and aromatic chemistry, especially nitrogen heterocycles; natural products, especially alkaloids and terpenes. *Mailing Add:* Agr Div Am Cyanamid Co PO Box 400 Princeton NJ 08540

LOSCALZO, ANNE GRACE, b New York, NY, Sept 2, 17; m 40; c 1. MICROCHEMISTRY, ANALYTICAL CHEMISTRY. *Educ:* NY Univ, BA, 37, MS, 41, PhD(chem), 43. *Prof Exp:* Asst instr chem, Wash Square Col, NY Univ, 41-43, instr, 43-46; lectr, City Col New York, 53-58; from asst prof to assoc prof, 58-71, PROF CHEM, LONG ISLAND UNIV, 71- *Mem:* Am Chem Soc. *Res:* Educational projects to improve learning abilities of students in chemistry. *Mailing Add:* Dept of Chem Conolly Col Long Island Univ Brooklyn NY 11201

LOSCHIAVO, SAMUEL RALPH, b Transcona, Man, June 28, 24; m 50; c 2. INSECT PHYSIOLOGY. *Educ:* Univ Man, BSc, 46, MSc, 50, PhD, 64. *Prof Exp:* Chemist, Man Sugar Co, 48; RES SCIENTIST, CAN DEPT AGR, 49- *Concurrent Pos:* Hon prof, Univ Man. *Mem:* Entom Soc Am; fel Entom Soc Can (pres, 80-81); Sigma Xi. *Res:* Biology, behavior and control of insects associated with stored grain and milled cereal products. *Mailing Add:* Agr Can Res Sta 195 Dafoe Rd Winnipeg MB R3T 2M9 Can

LOSCUTOFF, SUSAN MARIE, b Corvallis, Ore, Feb 5, 48; m 74; c 2. PULMONARY PHYSIOLOGY. *Educ:* Univ Calif, Davis, BS, 70; Johns Hopkins Univ, PhD(physiol), 74. *Prof Exp:* RES SCIENTIST, PAC NORTHWEST DIV, BATTELLE MEM INST, 74- *Concurrent Pos:* Adj asst prof, Joint Ctr Grad Study, 76- *Mem:* Assoc Am Physiol Soc; Am Thoracic Soc; AAAS. *Res:* Pulmonary effects of inhaled pollutant compounds. *Mailing Add:* Pac Northwest Div PO Box 999 Richland WA 99352

LOSECCO, JOHN M, b New York, NY, Oct 21, 50. ELEMENTARY PARTICLE PHYSICS. *Educ:* Cooper Union, BS, 72; Harvard Univ, AM, 73, PhD(physics), 76. *Prof Exp:* Res asst, Albert Einstein Col Med, 68-72; res assoc, Harvard Univ, 76-79; asst res scientist, Univ Mich, 79-81; ASST PROF PHYSICS, CALIF INST TECHNOL, 81- *Concurrent Pos:* Res asst, Harvard Univ, 73, 74; res assoc, Albert Einstein Col Med, 75; fel, Harvard Univ, 73-76, res asst, 75-76; systs programmer, Int Systs Assoc Ltd, 69. *Mem:* Am Phys Soc. *Res:* Study of particle interactions leading to a better understanding of the unification of the strong, weak and electromagnetic forces. *Mailing Add:* Lauritsen Lab 256-48 Calif Inst Technol Pasadena CA 91125

LOSEE, DAVID LAWRENCE, b Mineola, NY, July 19, 39; m 63; c 2. SOLID STATE PHYSICS, SEMICONDUCTORS. *Educ:* Cornell Univ, BEng, 62, MS, 63; Univ Ill, PhD(solid state physics), 67. *Prof Exp:* RES ASSOC, EASTMAN KODAK CO, 67- *Mem:* Am Phys Soc; Electrochem Soc. *Res:* Physics of the noble gas solids; physics of semiconductors and semiconductor devices. *Mailing Add:* 100 W Church St Fairport NY 14450

LOSEE, FERRIL A, b Lehi, Utah, June 5, 28; m 53; c 9. ELECTRICAL ENGINEERING. *Educ:* Univ Utah, BSEE, 53; Univ Southern Calif, MSEE, 57. *Prof Exp:* Elec engr, Hughes Aircraft Co, 53-59 & Aeronutronic Div, Philco Corp, 59-65; PROF ELEC ENG & CHMN DEPT, BRIGHAM YOUNG UNIV, 65- *Res:* Communication; electronic countermeasures; systems engineering. *Mailing Add:* Dept of Elec Eng Brigham Young Univ Provo UT 84602

LOSEKAMP, BERNARD FRANCIS, b Cincinnati, Ohio, July 16, 36; m 58; c 4. POLYMER CHEMISTRY, ORGANIC CHEMISTRY. *Educ:* Xavier Univ, Ohio, BS, 58, MS, 61; Univ Akron, PhD(polymer chem), 66. *Prof Exp:* Res asst, Wm S Merrell Co, Ohio, 61; res chemist, Inst Polymer Sci, Univ Akron, 61-64; asst ed, 64-67, assoc ed, 67-69, sr indexer, 69-71, group leader, 71-72, SR ED, CHEM ABSTR SERV, COLUMBUS, OHIO, 72- *Mem:* Am Chem Soc-Rubber Div. *Res:* Acenaphthene arsenicals; synthesis and characterization of polymers; polymer nomenclature; thermal polymerization; information science. *Mailing Add:* Chem Abstr Serv PO Box 3012 Columbus OH 43210

LOSEY, GEORGE SPAHR, JR, b Louisville, Ky, June 30, 42; m 67; c 2. MARINE ZOOLOGY, ETHOLOGY. *Educ:* Miami Univ, BS, 64; Scripps Inst Oceanog, Univ Calif, PhD(marine biol), 68. *Prof Exp:* NIH res fel fish behav, Hawaii Inst Marine Biol, 68-70; from asst prof to assoc prof, 70-80, PROF ZOOL, HAWAII INST MARINE BIOL, UNIV HAWAII, 80- *Honors & Awards:* Stoye Award, Am Soc Ichthyol & Herpet, 67. *Mem:* Animal Behav Soc; Am Soc Ichthyol & Herpet. *Res:* Ethology and ecology of fish; symbiotic cleaner fish and mimicry in Blenniidae fish; behavioral ecology of herbivorous fish. *Mailing Add:* Dept Zool Univ Hawaii Honolulu HI 96822

LOSEY, GERALD OTIS, b Detroit, Mich, Nov 13, 30; m 63. ALGEBRA. *Educ:* Univ Mich, BS, 52, MS, 53, PhD(math), 58. *Prof Exp:* Res instr math, Princeton Univ, 57-58; instr, Univ Wis, 58-61; asst prof, 61-64; assoc prof, 64-67, PROF MATH, UNIV MAN, 67- *Mem:* Am Math Soc; Can Math Cong. *Res:* Group theory; ring theory. *Mailing Add:* 50 Sandra Ft Garry MB R3T 1C0 Can

LOSICK, RICHARD MARC, b Jersey City, NJ, July 27, 43; m 70. MOLECULAR BIOLOGY. *Educ:* Princeton Univ, AB, 65; Mass Inst Technol, PhD(biochem), 69. *Prof Exp:* Harvard Soc fels jr fel biochem, 68-71, asst prof, 71-74, assoc prof biochem, 74-77, PROF BIOL, HARVARD UNIV, 77- *Honors & Awards:* Camille & Henry Dreyfus Award, Camille & Henry Dreyfus Found, 73. *Mem:* Am Soc Biol Chemists; Am Soc Microbiol. *Res:* Bacterial sporulation; regulatory subunits of RNA polymers. *Mailing Add:* Biol Labs Harvard Univ Cambridge MA 02138

LOSIN, EDWARD THOMAS, b Racine, Wis, July 9, 23; m 50; c 2. PHYSICAL ORGANIC CHEMISTRY, ENERGY CONVERSION. *Educ:* Univ Ill, BS, 48; Columbia Univ, AM, 50, PhD(chem), 54. *Prof Exp:* Res assoc, Eng Res Inst, Univ Mich, 54-57; res chemist, Union Carbide Corp, 57-61; chem dept mgr, Isomet Corp, 61-63; sr res scientist, 63-71, mgr nonmetallic mat, 71-73, SR RES SCIENTIST, ALLIS-CHALMERS CORP, 73- *Mem:* Am Chem Soc; The Chem Soc; NY Acad Sci; AAAS. *Res:* Reaction mechanisms of organic, stereospecific and free radical gas-phase reactions; electrical insulation materials and systems for various applications; epoxy technology; high temperature fuel gas cleanup; coal combustion of pulverized fuel in entrained-bed combustors; coal-fired cement and iron ore pelletizing systems. *Mailing Add:* Allis-Chalmers Corp Adv Tech Ctr PO Box 512 Milwaukee WI 53201

LOSPALLUTO, JOSEPH JOHN, b New York, NY, Nov 8, 25. BIOCHEMISTRY. *Educ:* City Col New York, BS, 45; NY Univ, PhD, 53. *Prof Exp:* Chemist, Fleischman Labs, Stand Brands, Inc, 45-47; instr biochem, NY Univ, 53-58; from asst prof to assoc prof, 58-72, PROF BIOCHEM, UNIV TEX HEALTH SCI CTR, DALLAS, 72- *Concurrent Pos:* Res fel, Arthritis & Rheumatism Found, 56-58; res fel, Whitney Found, 58-61; sr investr, Arthritis Found, 61-66. *Mem:* Fel AAAS; Am Asn Immunol; Am Rheumatism Asn; Am Soc Biol Chemists. *Res:* Proteins, especially chemistry and immunology; antibodies and connective tissue chemistry. *Mailing Add:* Dept of Biochem Univ of Tex Health Sci Ctr Dallas TX 75235

LOSSING, FREDERICK PETTIT, b Norwich, Ont, Aug 4, 15; m 38; c 3. CHEMICAL PHYSICS. *Educ:* Univ Western Ont, BA, 38, MA, 40; McGill Univ, PhD(phys chem), 42. *Prof Exp:* Res chemist, Shawinigan Chem, Ltd, 42-46; prin res officer, Div Chem, Nat Res Coun Can, 46-49 & 77-80, asst dir, 69-77; HON SR SCIENTIST, DEPT CHEM, UNIV OTTAWA, 80- *Mem:* Fel Royal Soc Can; Royal Astron Soc Can; Am Soc Mass Spectrometry. *Res:* Mass spectrometry; chemical kinetics; photochemistry; properties of free radicals; ionization processes. *Mailing Add:* Div of Chem Nat Res Coun Ottawa ON K1A 0R6 Can

LOSURDO, ANTONIO, b Spadafora, Italy, Jan 1, 43; US citizen. PHYSICAL CHEMISTRY. *Educ:* Syracuse Univ, BA, 65, PhD(chem), 70. *Prof Exp:* Res asst chem, Syracuse Univ, 65-69; NIH fel, Rutgers Univ, New Brunswick, 69-70, instr, 70-71; mem vis fac chem, Syracuse Univ, 71-72; res assoc, Ohio State Univ, 72-73; lectr chem, 73-74; res assoc chem, Clark Univ, 74-75; chief chemist, Cambridge Instrument Co, 75-76; res asst prof, 77-79, RES ASSOC PROF CHEM OCEANOG, UNIV MIAMI, 79- *Mem:* Am Chem Soc; NY Acad Sci; Sigma Xi; AAAS. *Res:* Physical chemistry of multicomponent electrolyte solutions and seawater; thermochemistry and thermodynamics of solutions; solute-solvent and solute-solute interactions; transport properties of hydrophobic electrolytes; electroanalytical chemistry; author or coauthor of over 50 publications. *Mailing Add:* 312 Swansea Ave Syracuse NY 13206

LOTAN, JAMES E, b Mich, Mar 20, 31; m 51; c 5. SILVICULTURE, FIRE MANAGEMENT. *Educ:* La State Univ, BSF, 59; Univ Mich, MF, 61, PhD, 70. *Prof Exp:* Forestry technician, Southern Forest & Range Exp Sta, US Forest Serv, La, 57-59, fire control, Deerlodge Nat Forest, Mont, 59; asst forest res, Univ Mich, 60; res forester, 61-65, proj leader forest sci res, 65-74, prog mgr, multifunctional Res & Develop Prog, 74-79, PROG MGR, FIRE EFFECTS RES & DEVELOP PROG, NORTHERN FOREST FIRE LAB, INTERMOUNTAIN FOREST & RANGE EXP STA, US FOREST SERV, 79- *Mem:* AAAS; Am Forestry Asn; Soc Am Foresters; Ecol Soc Am. *Res:* Silviculture and ecology of pinus contorta; effects of fire on forests and rangelands of the intermountain west and northern Rocky Mountains; multifunctional RD&A Program integrating fire management into multiple-use planning process. *Mailing Add:* Intermountain Forest Exp Sta North Forest Fire Lab Drawer G Missoula MT 59801

LOTH, JOHN LODEWYK, b Hague, Neth, Sept 14, 33; c 3. AERODYNAMICS. *Educ:* Univ Toronto, BASc, 57, MASc, 58, PhD(mech eng), 62. *Prof Exp:* French Govt fel aeronaut eng, Nat Ctr Sci Res, Ministry Ed, France, 58-59; lectr mech eng, Univ Toronto, 60-62; asst prof aeronaut eng, Univ Ill, Urbana, 62-67; assoc prof, 67-71, PROF AEROSPACE ENG, WEST VA UNIV, 71- *Concurrent Pos:* Consult, Ellard Wilson Assocs, Ont, 57-61; Air Force & ARO Inc, 63-66, Off Naval Res, 68-72 & Dept Energy, 73-; pres, Dynamic Flow Inc, 72- *Mem:* Am Inst Aeronaut & Astronaut; Sigma Xi; Am Soc Engr Educ. *Res:* Low speed aerodynamics; aerodynamic mixing and supersonics; combustion; solar and wind energy utilization. *Mailing Add:* Dept of Aerospace Eng Eng Sci Bldg WVa Univ Morgantown WV 26506

LOTHERS, JOHN EDMOND, JR, b Wichita, Kans, Nov 25, 31; m 62; c 2. GENETICS. *Educ:* Okla State Univ, BS, 54; Kans State Univ, MS, 56; Univ Kans, PhD(zool, genetics), 66. *Prof Exp:* Teaching asst chem, Kans State Univ, 54-56; lab technologist, St Francis Hosp, Wichita, Kans, 57-58; instr chem & biol, King's Col, NY, 58-61; from asst prof to assoc prof, 66-75, PROF BIOL, COVENANT COL, TENN, 75- *Mem:* Am Inst Biol Sci. *Res:* Physiology of reproduction in mammals and mammalian genetics. *Mailing Add:* 201 Hardy Rd Lookout Mountain TN 37350

LOTKER, MICHAEL, b New York, NY, May 28, 48; m 71; c 2. ENERGY SYSTEMS ANALYSIS. *Educ:* Queens Col, City Univ NY, BA, 70; Univ Ill, MS, 72. *Prof Exp:* Sr assoc, Northeast Utilities, 72-77 & Booz, Allen & Hamilton Inc, 77-78; prin, Advan Energy Systs, Donovan, Hamester & Rattien Inc, 78-79; EXEC VPRES, SYNECTICS GROUP, INC, 79- *Concurrent Pos:* Consult, Off Technol Assessment & Nat Acad Sci-CONAES, 78- *Mem:* AAAS. *Res:* Technical, economic and institutional analyses of the field of advanced energy technologies; long-term planning and commercialization problems. *Mailing Add:* 1009 Broadmore Circle Silver Springs MD 20904

LOTLIKAR, PRABHAKAR DATTARAM, b Shirali, India, May 21, 28; US citizen; m 60; c 1. BIOCHEMISTRY, PHARMACOLOGY. *Educ:* Univ Bombay, BS, 50, MS, 54; Ore State Univ, PhD(biochem, pharmacol, bact), 60. *Prof Exp:* Asst chemist, Raptakos Brett & Co, Ltd, India, 50-55; proj assoc, McArdle Lab Cancer Res, Univ Wis, 63-65, instr, 65-66; res instr, 67-68, asst prof, 68-75, ASSOC PROF BIOCHEM, FELS RES INST, SCH MED, TEMPLE UNIV, 75-, INVESTR, 67- *Concurrent Pos:* Res fel oncol, McArdle Lab Cancer Res, Univ Wis, 60-63. *Mem:* AAAS; Am Chem Soc; Am Asn Cancer Res; Am Soc Biol Chem; NY Acad Sci. *Res:* Mechanisms of chemical carcinogenesis. *Mailing Add:* Fels Res Inst Temple Univ Sch of Med Philadelphia PA 19140

LOTRICH, VICTOR ARTHUR, b Pueblo, Colo, July 10, 34; m 55; c 3. POPULATION ECOLOGY. *Educ:* Northern Colo Univ, BA, 56, MA, 60; Univ Ky, PhD(biol), 69. *Prof Exp:* ASSOC PROF ECOL, UNIV DEL, 69- *Res:* Population dynamics of tide marsh fish and tide marsh estuarine interactions. *Mailing Add:* Sch Life & Health Sci Univ Del Newark DE 19711

LOTSPEICH, FREDERICK JACKSON, b Keyser, WVa, Mar 12, 25; m 48; c 1. BIO-ORGANIC CHEMISTRY. *Educ:* WVa Univ, BS, 48, MS, 51; Purdue Univ, PhD(chem), 55. *Prof Exp:* Res chemist, E I du Pont de Nemours & Co, 48-50; asst org chem, WVa Univ, 50-52; asst, Purdue Univ, 52-53; asst prof chem, Simpson Col, 54-56; from asst prof to prof biochem, Med Ctr, WVa Univ, 66-78; PROF BIOCHEM, MED SCH, MARSHALL UNIV, 78- *Mem:* Am Chem Soc. *Res:* Chemistry and biochemistry of S-adenosyl methionine and derivatives. *Mailing Add:* Dept of Biochem Marshall Univ Med Sch Huntington WV 25701

LOTSPEICH, JAMES FULTON, b Cincinnati, Ohio, Oct 22, 22; m 60. PHYSICS. *Educ:* Princeton Univ, BA, 43; Univ Cincinnati, MS, 49; Columbia Univ, PhD(physics), 58. *Prof Exp:* Lab instr gen physics, Univ Cincinnati, 47-48; asst, Columbia Univ, 51-56; RES PHYSICIST, LABS, HUGHES AIRCRAFT CO, 56- *Mem:* Am Phys Soc; Sigma Xi; NY Acad Sci; Optical Soc Am. *Res:* Microwave spectroscopy and molecular structure; electrooptic techniques; applied laser technology; photodetection techniques. *Mailing Add:* Optical Physics Dept Hughes Res Labs 3011 Malibu Canyon Rd Malibu CA 90265

LOTT, FRED WILBUR, JR, b Ohio, Oct 8, 17; m 41; c 3. MATHEMATICS, MATHEMATICAL STATISTICS. *Educ:* Cedarville Col, AB, 39; Univ Mich, MA, 46, PhD(math), 55. *Prof Exp:* From asst prof to assoc prof, 49-61, PROF MATH, UNIV NORTHERN IOWA, 61-, ASST VPRES ACAD AFFAIRS, 71- *Concurrent Pos:* Opers analyst, US Air Force, 55-64. *Mem:* Am Math Soc; Math Asn Am; Am Statist Asn; Inst Math Statist. *Mailing Add:* Dept Math Univ Northern Iowa Cedar Falls IA 50613

LOTT, JAMES ROBERT, b Houston, Tex, Jan 16, 24; m 42; c 4. PHYSIOLOGY, BIOPHYSICS. *Educ:* Univ Tex, BA, 49, MA, 51, PhD(physiol, bact), 56. *Prof Exp:* Med bacteriologist, Brackenridge Hosp, Austin, Tex, 55; lectr zool, Univ Tex, 55-56, res scientist, Radiobiol Lab, Balcones Res Inst, 56; instr physiol, Sch Med, Emory Univ, 56-57; from asst prof to assoc prof, 57-64, PROF BIOL, N TEX STATE UNIV, 64- *Concurrent Pos:* Sr res investr, AEC, 58-; NSF grant, 63-64. *Mem:* Am Physiol Soc; Soc Gen Physiol; Radiation Res Soc; Int Soc Biometeorol. *Res:*

Neurophysiology; effects of x-irradiation, microwaves, and electric fields on the nervous system; effects of electric fields on cancer growth; effects of stress on heart action; endocrinology; effects of x-irradiation on the adrenal-pituitary axis; ion and water flux in root systems. *Mailing Add:* 1907 Locksley Lane Denton TX 76201

LOTT, JAMES STEWART, b Sarnia, Ont, Apr 10, 20; m 50; c 4. MEDICINE, RADIOLOGY. *Educ:* Univ Western Ont, BA, 43, MD, 46; Royal Col Physicians & Surgeons, dipl med radiother, 52 & specialist therapeut radiol, 54. *Prof Exp:* Instr radiol, Univ Western Ont, 52-62, assoc prof radiother & actg head dept, 62-63; assoc prof radiol, Sch Med, Johns Hopkins Univ & head div radiother, Hosp, 64-71; PROF THERAPEUT RADIOL & CHMN DEPT, QUEEN'S UNIV, ONT, 71-; DIR ONT CANCER FOUND, KINGSTON CLIN, 71- *Concurrent Pos:* Fel histol, Univ Western Ont, 46-47, fel path, 47-48, fel radiol, 48-49; Can Cancer Soc fel radiother, 50-51; Brit Empire Cancer Campaign exchange fel, 51-52; consult, Westminster Vet Hosp, 56-63 & St Joseph's Hosp, London, Can, 56-63; consult & radiologist in chg ther, Hackley Hosp, Muskegon, Mich, 63-64. *Mem:* AMA; Can Med Asn; Can Asn Radiol. *Res:* Radiobiology applied to radiotherapy; clinical radiotherapy applied to cancer. *Mailing Add:* Ont Cancer Found Kingston Clin Kingston Gen Hosp Kingston ON K7L 2V7 Can

LOTT, JOHN ALFRED, b Ger, Oct 30, 36; US citizen; m 63; c 1. ANALYTICAL CHEMISTRY. *Educ:* Rutgers Univ, BS, 59, MS, 61, PhD(anal chem), 65. *Prof Exp:* Instr chem, Rutgers Univ, 64-65; asst prof, Flint Col, Univ Mich, 65-68; asst prof, 68-72, assoc prof 72-79, PROF PATHOL, OHIO STATE UNIV, 79- & DIR, OUTPATIENT CLINIC LAB, OHIO STATE HOSP. *Honors & Awards:* Katchman Award, Am Asn Clin Chem, 79. *Mem:* Am Assoc Clin Chem; Nat Acad Clin Biochemits, (treas, 78-79, pres, 81-82); Am Chem Soc. *Res:* Instrumentation; methodology development; enzymology; specific-ion electrodes. *Mailing Add:* Rm 342 Univ Hosp Ohio State Univ 410 W Tenth Ave Columbus OH 43210

LOTT, JOHN NORMAN ARTHUR, b Summerland, BC, Jan 20, 43; m 66. PLANT ANATOMY, PLANT PHYSIOLOGY. *Educ:* Univ BC, BSc, 65; Univ Calif, Davis, MSc, 67, PhD(bot), 69. *Prof Exp:* Res asst bot, Univ Calif, Davis, 65-69; asst prof, 69-75, assoc prof, 75-81, PROF BIOL, MCMASTER UNIV, 81- *Concurrent Pos:* Natural Sci & Eng Res Coun Can res grant, 70- *Mem:* Can Bot Asn; Am Soc Plant Physiol; Bot Soc Am; Can Soc Cell Biol. *Res:* Ultrastructure and physiological studies of developing and germinating seeds, with special emphasis on protein bodies; mineral nutrient storage in seeds. *Mailing Add:* Dept of Biol McMaster Univ Hamilton ON L8S 4K1 Can

LOTT, LAYMAN AUSTIN, b Ft Collins, Colo, Sept 21, 37; m 58; c 4. PHYSICS. *Educ:* Colo State Univ, BS, 59, MS, 61; Iowa State Univ, PhD(physics), 65. *Prof Exp:* Res physicist, Rocky Flats Div, Dow Chem USA, 65-71; sr res physicist, 71-73; SR ENG SPECIALIST, IDAHO NAT ENG LAB, 73- *Mem:* Am Phys Soc; Am Soc Nondestructive Test; Sigma Xi. *Res:* Solid state physics; physical properties of materials; nondestructive testing; development of advanced nondestructive testing methods. *Mailing Add:* 701 9th St Idaho Falls ID 83401

LOTT, PETER F, b Berlin, Ger, Mar 26, 27; nat US; m 56; c 2. PHYSICAL CHEMISTRY, ANALYTICAL CHEMISTRY. *Educ:* St Lawrence Univ, BS, 49, MS, 50; Univ Conn, PhD(chem), 56. *Prof Exp:* Asst instr chem, Univ Conn, 54-56; res chemist, E I du Pont de Nemours & Co, 56; assoc prof, Univ Mo, 56-59; chemist, Pure Carbon Co, 59-60; assoc prof chem, St John's Univ, NY, 60-64; PROF CHEM, UNIV MO-KANSAS CITY, 64- *Mem:* Am Chem Soc; Am Microchem Soc; Royal Soc Chem. *Res:* Analytical methods development; trace and instrumental analysis; chemical kinetics; radiochemistry; physical measurements; organic reagents; forensic chemistry. *Mailing Add:* Dept Chem Univ Mo Kansas City MO 64110

LOTT, RICHARD VINCENT, pomology, deceased

LOTT, SAM HOUSTON, JR, b New Orleans, La, Sept 22, 36; m 59. PHYSICS, HEALTH PHYSICS. *Educ:* La State Univ, BS, 58; Vanderbilt Univ, MS, 60, PhD(physics), 65. *Prof Exp:* Res assoc physics, 65-66, dir radiation safety off, Vanderbilt Univ, 66-76; consult, Nat Cancer Inst, 73-76; HEAD, HEALTH PHYSICS DEPT, KING FAISAL SPECIALIST HOSP & RES CTR, 76- *Concurrent Pos:* Consult, 66-76. *Mem:* Am Phys Soc; Health Phys Soc; Am Asn Physicists in Med. *Res:* Three-color photometric study of variable stars; Zeeman & Faraday effects in high pulsed magnetic fields; calibration techniques for diagnostic and therapeutic machines. *Mailing Add:* Box 3354 King Faisal Specialist Hospt & Res Ctr Riyadh Saudi Arabia

LOTTES, P(AUL) A(LBERT), b Wilkinsburg, Pa, Aug 2, 26; m 47; c 3. MECHANICAL ENGINEERING. *Educ:* Purdue Univ, PhD(mech eng), 50. *Prof Exp:* Assoc mech engr, 50-60, SR MECH ENGR, ARGONNE NAT LAB, 60- *Mem:* Fel Am Soc Mech Engrs; fel Am Nuclear Soc. *Res:* Heat transfer and pressure drop in boiling; nuclear reactor safety. *Mailing Add:* Argonne Nat Lab 9700 S Cass Ave Argonne IL 60439

LOTTMAN, ROBERT P(OWELL), b Brooklyn, NY, Sept 24, 33; m 56. CIVIL ENGINEERING. *Educ:* Polytech Inst Brooklyn, BCE, 54; Purdue Univ, MSCE, 56; Ohio State Univ, PhD, 65. *Prof Exp:* Proj engr, Struct Appln Sect, Grumman Aircraft Eng Corp, 56-57; supvr, Asphalt Tech Serv Lab, Standard Oil Co, Ohio, 57-59; res supvr hwy mat, Transp Eng Ctr, Ohio State Univ, 59-65, asst prof civil eng, 65-66; PROF CIVIL ENG, UNIV IDAHO, 66- *Concurrent Pos:* Instnl & comt mem, Hwy Res Bd, Nat Acad Sci-Nat Res Coun, 60- *Mem:* Asn Asphalt Paving Technol; Am Soc Testing & Mat. *Res:* Study and evaluation of physical and chemical properties of construction materials to determine mechanical behavior under various loading and environmental conditions. *Mailing Add:* Dept Civil Eng Univ Idaho Moscow ID 83843

LOTTS, ADOLPHUS LLOYD, b Buchanan, Va, June 10, 34; m 54; c 4. NUCLEAR SAFETY, WASTE MANAGEMENT. *Educ:* Va Polytech Inst, BS, 55, MS, 57. *Prof Exp:* Instr metall eng, Va Polytech Inst, 56-57; assoc mat scientist, Atomic Energy Div, Babcock & Wilcox Co, 58-59; assoc metallurgist, Metals & Ceramics Div, 59-61, group leader fuel cycle technol, 61-66, head fuel cycle technol oper, Metals & Ceramics Div, 66-70, assoc dir gas-cooled reactor & thorium utilization progs, 70-78, assoc dir nuclear waste prog, 78-81, CHMN, LONG RANGE PLANNING GROUP, OAK RIDGE NAT LAB, 69-, DIR, NUCLEAR REGULATORY COMN PROG, 81- *Honors & Awards:* E O Lawrence Mem Award, US Dept Energy, 76. *Mem:* Fel Am Nuclear Soc; Am Soc Metals. *Res:* Nuclear fuel processing technology; economics and properties of nuclear fuel; materials for reactor systems; radioactive and toxic waste management; nuclear reactor and safety technology. *Mailing Add:* Metals & Ceramics Div Oak Ridge Nat Lab PO Box X Oak Ridge TN 37830

LOTZ, FREDERICK, b Hrastovac, Yugoslavia, July 16, 23; Can citizen; m 52; c 5. PHARMACOLOGY, PHYSIOLOGY. *Educ:* Univ Western Ont, BA, 49, MSc, 53, PhD(physiol), 57. *Prof Exp:* Asst prof cancer res, Cancer Res Inst, Univ Sask, 58-60; asst prof, Cancer Res Ctr, Univ BC, 60-62; assoc prof physiol, Ont Vet Col, 62-65; ASSOC PROF PHYSIOL, UNIV GUELPH, 65- *Concurrent Pos:* Nat Cancer Inst Can res fel, Chester Beatty Inst Cancer Res, Royal Cancer Hosp, London, Eng, 57-58. *Mem:* AAAS; NY Acad Sci; Can Physiol Soc; Can Soc Immunol; Int Atherosclerosis Soc. *Res:* Cardiovascular research; coagulation platelets; congenital disorders of atherosclerosis; lipid metabolism; lipid transport pharmacology. *Mailing Add:* Dept of Biomed Sci Univ of Guelph Guelph ON N1G 2W1 Can

LOU, ALEX YIH-CHUNG, b Chungking, China, Nov 10, 38; US citizen; m 69; c 2. ENGINEERING MATERIALS, MECHANICS. *Educ:* Nat Taiwan Univ, BS, 60; Purdue Univ MS, 65, PhD(solid mech), 69. *Prof Exp:* Sr engr composites, The Boeing Co, 69-70; res scientist, 70-76, SR RES SCIENTIST MAT, FIRESTONE TIRE & RUBBER CO, 76- *Mem:* Am Soc Mech Engr. *Res:* Characterization and evolution of composite; polymer materials for engineering applications; tire mechanics such as rolling resistance. *Mailing Add:* Firestone Tire & Rubber Co Cent Res Lab Akron OH 44317

LOU, DAVID YEONG-SUEI, b Yuncom, China, Nov 12, 37; m 64; c 2. MECHANICAL ENGINEERING. *Educ:* Taiwan Univ, BS, 59; Mass Inst Technol, MS, 63, MechE, 66, ScD(mech eng), 67. *Prof Exp:* Res asst mech eng, Mass Inst Technol, 61-63; thermodyn engr, Jackson & Moreland Consult Co, 63; asst thermionic energy conversion, Mass Inst Technol, 63-64, asst mech eng, 64-65, asst molecular beams, 65-67; from asst prof to prof mech eng, Univ Del, 67-79; PROF MECH ENG & CHMN DEPT, UNIV TEX, ARLINGTON, 79- *Mem:* Am Phys Soc; Am Inst Aeronaut & Astronaut; Am Soc Mech Engrs. *Res:* Solar energy; kinetic theory of gases; molecular beams; thermodynamics; fluid mechanics; heat transfer; direct energy conversion devices; biomedical engineering. *Mailing Add:* Dept Mech Eng Univ Tex Arlington TX 76019

LOU, KINGDON, b Stockton, Calif, Aug 3, 22; m 45; c 2. IMMUNOLOGY. *Educ:* Stanford Univ, AB, 52, AM, 56; Am Bd Bioanal, dipl. *Prof Exp:* From res asst to res assoc, Hyland Labs, Baxter Labs, 57-64, dir immunol dept, Res Div, 64-67; sr immunochemist, Res Div, Hoffmann-La Roche, 67-68; dir immunol, Kallestad Labs, 68-69; DIR IMMUNOL RES, ICL SCI, 70- *Mem:* Am Soc Microbiol; Am Asn Clin Chemists; NY Acad Sci. *Res:* Immunochemical diagnostic reagents; isolation and purification of serum protein constituents. *Mailing Add:* 21866 Michigan Lane El Toro CA 92630

LOU, MARJORIE FENG, biochemistry, see previous edition

LOU, PETER LOUIS, b Shanghai, China, Dec 9, 45; Can citizen. MOLECULAR BIOLOGY, OPHTHALMOLOGY. *Educ:* McMaster Univ, Can MSc, 70; Univ Ottawa, BSc, 67, MD, 74; Univ Toronto, dipl ophthal, 77. *Prof Exp:* Instr biol, McMaster Univ, 67-70; resident ophthal, Univ Toronto, 74-77; INSTR OPHTHAL, HARVARD MED SCH, 79- *Concurrent Pos:* Retina fel, Retina Assoc, Mass Eye & Ear Infirmary, Boston, 77-78. *Mem:* Asn Res Vision & Ophthal; fel, Am Acad Ophthal & Otolaryngol. *Res:* Effect of near ultraviolet light on aphakic retina metabolism; diabetic retinopathy; pathophysiology of vitreous and retina. *Mailing Add:* Retina Serv Mass Eye & Ear Infirmary 243 Charles St Boston MA 02114

LOUCH, CHARLES DUKES, b Kanpor, India, Dec 24, 25; m 56; c 1. ZOOLOGY. *Educ:* Col Wooster, BA, 50; Univ Wis, MS, 52, PhD(zool), 55. *Prof Exp:* Asst prof biol, Hope Col, 55-57; from asst prof to assoc prof, 57-68, PROF BIOL, LAKE FOREST COL, 68- *Concurrent Pos:* USPHS res fel, Johns Hopkins Univ, 59-60. *Mem:* Ecol Soc Am. *Res:* Vertebrate ecology, particularly relationship between population density and physiological activities of members of population. *Mailing Add:* 905 Central Ave Deerfield IL 60015

LOUCK, JAMES DONALD, b Grand Rapids, Mich, Dec 13, 28; m 60; c 3. MATHEMATICAL PHYSICS. *Educ:* Ala Polytech Inst, BS, 50; Ohio State Univ, MS, 52, PhD(physics), 58. *Prof Exp:* Staff mem, Los Alamos Nat Lab, 58-60; assoc res prof physics, Auburn Univ, 60-63; STAFF MEM, LOS ALAMOS NAT LAB, UNIV CALIF, 63- *Mem:* Am Phys Soc; AAAS; Int Asn Math Physicists. *Res:* Application and development of group theoretical methods in physics. *Mailing Add:* Los Alamos Sci Lab Univ of Calif Los Alamos NM 87545

LOUCKS, CHARLES M(ALCOLM), b Russell, NY, Jan 20, 06; m 44. CHEMISTRY. *Educ:* St Lawrence Univ, BS, 26; Univ Ill, MS, 31; NY Univ, PhD(chem), 37. *Prof Exp:* Maintenance engr, NY Tel Co, 26-27; chemist, Gen Elec Co, 27-29; instr chem, Univ Ill, 29-31 & Univ Tulsa, 31-32; asst, NY Univ, 35-37; assoc prof, Univ Tulsa, 37-43; dist chemist, Dowell Div, Dow Chem Co, 43-59, consult chemist, 60-65, mem staff, Tech Serv & Develop Dept, 65-66; consult chemist chem indust plant maintenance, 66-67; chem consult, Harza Eng Co, WPakistan & Iran, 67-71; indust consult, 71-81; RETIRED. *Mem:* Am Chem Soc; Nat Asn Corrosion Engrs. *Res:* Phase rule studies of reciprocal salt systems; industrial chemical cleaning and related maintenance problems. *Mailing Add:* Kimberling City MO 65686

LOUCKS, DANIEL PETER, b Chambersburg, Pa, June 4, 32; m 67; c 2. ENVIRONMENTAL ENGINEERING, SYSTEMS ANALYSIS. *Educ:* Pa State Univ, BS, 54; Yale Univ, MS, 55; Cornell Univ, PhD(systs eng, econ), 65. *Prof Exp:* Asst prof water resources eng, 65-70, assoc prof environ eng, 70-75, prof environ eng & chmn dept, 76-80, ASSOC DEAN RES & GRAD STUDY, COL ENG, CORNELL UNIV, 80- *Concurrent Pos:* Prin investr, NSF, Environ Protection Agency, Resources for the Future & US Dept Interior Res Grants, 67-; sem assoc, Columbia Univ, 67-; res fel, Harvard Univ, 68; consult, UN Develop Prog, WHO, Food & Agr Orgn, UN & IRBD; economist, World Bank, 72-73; vis prof, Mass Inst Technol, 77-78; res scholar, Int Inst Appl Systs Anal, Austria, 81-82. *Honors & Awards:* Res Award, Am Soc Civil Engrs, 70. *Mem:* Water Pollution Control Fedn; Am Water Works Asn; Opers Res Soc Am; Int Mgt Sci; Am Geophys Union. *Res:* Applications of operations research to problems in environmental and water resources engineering; public policy analysis. *Mailing Add:* Hollister Hall Cornell Univ Ithaca NY 14850

LOUCKS, ORIE LIPTON, b Minden, Ont, Oct 2, 31; m 55; c 3. BOTANY, ECOLOGY. *Educ:* Univ Toronto, BSc, 53, MSc, 55; Univ Wis, PhD(bot), 60. *Prof Exp:* Forest ecologist, Dept Forestry, Can Govt, 55-62; from asst prof to prof bot, Univ Wis-Madison, 62-78; SCI DIR, INST ECOL, 78- *Concurrent Pos:* Univ Wis rep, State Bd Preserv Sci Areas, 64-78; consult, Can Land Inventory, 65; coordr environ mgt progs, US/Int Biol Prog, Univ Tex, 73. *Honors & Awards:* George Mercer Award, Ecol Soc Am, 64. *Mem:* AAAS; Soc Am Foresters; Ecol Soc Am; Am Inst Biol Sci; Soc Gen Systs Res. *Res:* Forest ecology and stand dynamics; micrometeorology and forest hydrology; forest and lake ecosystem modeling and analysis; watershed and water quality systems studies; computer simulation of land use change. *Mailing Add:* Inst of Ecol Butler Univ Indianapolis IN 46208

LOUD, ALDEN VICKERY, b Boston, Mass, Apr 6, 25; m 50; c 4. CELL BIOLOGY, BIOPHYSICS. *Educ:* Mass Inst Technol, BS & MS, 51, PhD(biophys), 55. *Prof Exp:* Res assoc, Detroit Inst Cancer Res & asst prof biophys, Col Med, Wayne State Univ, 57-65; asst prof path, Col Physicians & Surgeons, Columbia Univ, 65-68; assoc prof, 68-80, PROF PATH, NY MED COL, 80- *Concurrent Pos:* Res fel med, Mass Gen Hosp, 51-57. *Mem:* Electron Micros Soc Am; Am Soc Cell Biol; Int Soc Stereology; Royal Micros Soc. *Res:* Stereologic morphometry; quantitative electron microscopy and methods of ultrastructure research; correlation of cellular ultrastructure with metabolic function. *Mailing Add:* Dept of Path NY Med Col Valhalla NY 10595

LOUD, OLIVER SCHULE, b Vernal, Utah, Jan 16, 11; m 35; c 2. HISTORY & PHILOSOPHY OF SCIENCE. *Educ:* Harvard Univ, AB, 29; Columbia Univ, AM, 40, EdD, 43. *Prof Exp:* Master, Nichols Sch, NY, 29-32; instr high sch, Ohio, 32-36; teacher gen sci, Sarah Lawrence Col, 36-40; res assoc, Bur Educ Res Sci, Columbia, 39-43; asst prof physics, Antioch Col, 43-44; instr, Ohio State Univ, 44; tech supvr, Tenn Eastman Corp, Tenn, 44-45; from assoc prof to prof phys sci, Antioch Col, 45-78, distinguished univ prof, 78-81; CONSULT, 81- *Concurrent Pos:* Ford Found fel, Harvard Univ, 52-53; mem staff fac develop prog, Great Lakes Cols Asn, Ann Arbor, Mich; mem staff, Wilmington Col, Ohio & Proj Talents, Lebanon Correctional Inst, Lebanon, Ohio. *Mem:* AAAS; Soc Social Responsibility Sci. *Res:* Science in general education; suggestions for teaching problems of good land use. *Mailing Add:* 1430 Meadow Lane Yellow Springs OH 45387

LOUD, WARREN SIMMS, b Boston, Mass, Sept 13, 21; m 47; c 3. MATHEMATICS. *Educ:* Mass Inst Technol, SB, 42, PhD(math), 46. *Prof Exp:* Instr math, Mass Inst Technol, 43-47; from asst prof to assoc prof, 47-59, PROF MATH, UNIV MINN, MINNEAPOLIS, 59- *Concurrent Pos:* Res engr, Mass Inst Technol, 45-47, vis fel, 55-56; guest prof, Darmstadt Tech Univ, 64-65; vis prof, Kyoto Univ, Japan, 74-75 & Univ Florence & Univ Trento, Italy, 81-82. *Mem:* AAAS; Am Math Soc; Soc Indust & Appl Math (ed, 61-); Math Asn Am. *Res:* Theory of differential equations; numerical methods of solution of differential equations; stationary solutions of Van der Pol's equation with a forcing term; nonlinear mechanics. *Mailing Add:* Dept Math Univ Minn Minneapolis MN 55455

LOUDEN, L RICHARD, b Monroe, Wash, July 8, 33; m 63. GEOCHEMISTRY, SATELLITE COMMUNICATIONS. *Educ:* Univ Würzburg, PhD(geochem), 63. *Prof Exp:* Assoc prof geochem, Univ Houston, 63-64; geologist, Magnet Cove Barium Corp, 64-65, supvr, X-ray Dept, 65-67, mgr anal sect, 67-69, tech adv, 69-71, spec proj engr, 71-72, develop mgr, Dresser Pollution, Dresser Oilfield Prod Div, 72-73, prod mgr, 73-76, mkt mgr, Dresser-Swaco, 76-78; exec vpres res, eng, construct & mfg, The Analysts Inc, 78-80; PRES, LOUDEN-REHM RESOURCE DEVELOP CORP, 80-; VPRES, SATELLITE COMMUN, DRILLING INFO SERV CO, 81- *Concurrent Pos:* Co-worker, NASA grant, Univ Houston, 63-64. *Mem:* AAAS; Marine Tech Soc; Clay Minerals Soc; Ger Geol Asn; Nat Oilfield Equip Mfrs & Distribr Soc. *Res:* Organic geochemistry, oceanography, clay mineralogy, and x-ray analysis; new and novel equipment and chemicals for oilwell and other drilling practices. *Mailing Add:* 8011 Highmeadow Houston TX 77063

LOUDON, GORDON MARCUS, b Baton Rouge, La, Oct 10, 42; m 64; c 2. BIOCHEMISTRY, ORGANIC CHEMISTRY. *Educ:* La State Univ, Baton Rouge, BS, 64; Univ Calif, Berkeley, PhD(org chem), 68. *Prof Exp:* USPHS fel, Univ Calif, Berkeley, 69-70, lectr biochem, 70; from asst prof to assoc prof chem, Cornell Univ, 70-77; ASSOC PROF MED CHEM, PURDUE UNIV, 77- *Mem:* Am Soc Biol Chemists; Am Chem Soc; AAAS. *Res:* Mechanisms of enzyme catalysis; enzyme model systems; synthetic methods; bioanalytical methods. *Mailing Add:* Dept of Med Chem & Pharmacog Purdue Univ Sch of Pharm West Lafayette IN 47907

LOUDON, ROBERT G, b Edinburgh, Scotland, June 27, 25; US citizen; m 55; c 3. INTERNAL MEDICINE. *Educ:* Univ Edinburgh, MB & ChB, 47. *Prof Exp:* House physician gen med, Western Gen Hosp, Edinburgh, Scotland, 47-48; sr house physician tuberc wards, City Hosp, 49-50; asst med officer,

Tor-na-Dee Sanatorium, Aberdeen, 50-51; house physician, Chest Hosp, Brompton Hosp, London, Eng, 51-52; clin tutor gen med, Royal Infirmary, Edinburgh, 53-54; staff physician, South-East Kans Tuberc Hosp, Chanute, 56-60, supt, 60-61; from asst prof to assoc prof internal med, Univ Tex Southwestern Med Sch Dallas, 61-69; assoc prof med, Sch Med, George Washington Univ, 69-71; PROF INTERNAL MED, MED CTR & DIR PULMONARY DIS DIV, COL MED, UNIV CINCINNATI, 71- Concurrent Pos: Assoc med, Univ Kans, 57-61; staff physician, Woodlawn Hosp, Dallas, 61-69; chief res in respiratory dis, Vet Admin Cent Off, Washington, DC, 69-71. Mem: Am Thoracic Soc; AMA. Res: Chest diseases; tuberculosis; aerobiology. Mailing Add: Pulmonary Dis Div Univ Cincinnati Med Ctr Cincinnati OH 45267

LOUGEAY, RAY LEONARD, b Medford, Ore, Feb 9, 44; m 68. PHYSICAL GEOGRAPHY, REMOTE SENSING. Educ: Rutgers Univ, AB, 66; Univ Mich, MS, 69, PhD(phys geog), 71. Prof Exp: Lectr phys geog, Univ Mich, 69-70; asst prof, 71-79, ASSOC PROF GEOG & DIR ENVIRON STUDIES, STATE UNIV NY COL GENESEO, 79- Mem: Asn Am Geogr; AAAS; Am Meteorol Soc; Am Soc Photogram. Res: Remote sensing; applied climatology and environmental modification as a function of radiative energy balances and hydrologic water balances; Alpine periglacial environments. Mailing Add: Dept of Geog State Univ of NY Col Geneseo NY 14454

LOUGH, JOHN WILLIAM, JR, b St Louis, Mo, Apr 2, 43; m 68; c 3. ANATOMY, CELL BIOLOGY. Educ: St Louis Univ, BS, 65, MS, 68; Wash Univ, St Louis, PhD(cell biol & anat), 75. Prof Exp: Res assoc biol, Mass Inst Technol, 75-77; ASST PROF ANAT, MED COL WIS, 77- Mem: Am Soc Cell Biol; Am Asn Anatomists. Res: Muscle differentiation in cell culture; changes in chromosomal proteins during myoblast differentiation. Mailing Add: Dept of Anat Med Col Wis Milwaukee WI 53226

LOUGHER, EDWIN HENRY, b Greenfield, Ind, May 30, 20; m 48; c 2. PHYSICAL CHEMISTRY, RESEARCH ADMINISTRATION. Educ: Purdue Univ, BSChE, 42; Ohio State Univ, PhD(phys chem), 52. Prof Exp: Chem engr, Sinclair Ref Co, 42-43; prin chemist, 51-57, assoc chief phys chem div, 57-71, contracts adminr, 71-73, SUPVR, BUS REP, BATTELLE MEM INST, COLUMBUS LABS, 73- Mailing Add: Battelle Mem Inst 505 King Ave Columbus OH 43201

LOUGHHEED, THOMAS CROSSLEY, b Sherbrooke, Que, Oct 22, 29; m 53; c 3. FOOD SCIENCE. Educ: Bishop's Univ, BSc, 49; McGill Univ, MSc, 54; Univ London, PhD(microbiol), &dipl, Imp Col, 58. Prof Exp: Res officer biochem, Can Dept Agr, 53-63; RES OFFICER, ANAL BIOCHEM, JOHN LABATT LTD, 63- Mem: Am Chem Soc; Micros Soc Can; Royal Micros Soc. Res: Applications of microscopy to research in food science. Mailing Add: Cent Res & Develop Dept John Labatt Ltd PO Box 5050 London ON N6A 4M3 Can

LOUGHLIN, THOMAS RICHARD, b Santa Monica, Calif, July 19, 43; m 71; c 2. MARINE MAMMALOGY, BEHAVIORAL ECOLOGY. Educ: Univ Calif, Santa Barbara, BA, 72; Humboldt State Univ, MA, 74; Univ Calif, Los Angeles, PhD(biol), 77. Prof Exp: MARINE MAMMAL RES SPECIALIST, NAT MARINE FISHERIES SERV, 77- Concurrent Pos: Biol consult, TerraScan, Inc, Environ Consults, 72-74; recipient res funds, Univ Calif, 75 & US Marine Mammal Comn, 75-77; vis scientist, Smithsonian Inst & US Dept Com alt mem, US Endangered Species Sci Authority, 77-80. Honors & Awards: Cert Recognition Outstanding Performance, US Dept Com, 78. Mem: AAAS; Am Asn Biol Sci; Am Soc Mammalogists; Animal Behav Soc. Res: Natural history, including physiological and behavioral ecology of marine mammals and the impact of man caused perturbations on them; recovery of endangered species; phylogenetic relationship between marine mammals; general oceanography. Mailing Add: Nat Marine Mammals Lab Fisheries Serv 7600 Sand Point Way NE Seattle WA 98115

LOUGHLIN, TIMOTHY ARTHUR, b Bay Shore, NY, Nov 16, 42; m 65; c 4. APPLIED MATHEMATICS. Educ: State Univ NY Stony Brook, BS, 64; Rensselaer Polytech Inst, MS, 66, PhD(math), 69. Prof Exp: asst prof math, Union Col, NY, 69-76; ASSOC PROF MATH, NEW YORK INST TECHNOL, 76- Mem: Math Asn Am. Res: Network theory; realization of matrices as impedance and admittance matrices. Mailing Add: Dept of Math NY Inst of Technol Old Westbury NY 11568

LOUGHMAN, BARBARA ELLEN EVERS, b Frankford, Ind, Oct 26, 40; m 62; c 2. IMMUNOBIOLOGY. Educ: Univ Ill, BS, 62; Univ Notre Dame, PhD(microbiol & immunol), 72. Prof Exp: From asst res microbiologist to assoc res microbiologist, Ames Res Lab, Miles Labs Inc, 62-71, res scientist immunol, 71-72; staff fel immunol, Nat Inst Child Health & Human Develop, 72-74; res scientist, 74-79, RES HEAD IMMUNOL, HYPERSENSITIVITY DIS RES, UPJOHN CO, 79- Mem: AAAS; Asn Gnotobiotics; Am Asn Immunologists. Res: Cellular immunology; regulatory mechanisms in cells using controlled in vitro and in vivo systems as models for specific intervention in an immune response; clinical research immunobiology of transplantation and blood dyscrasia; management. Mailing Add: Hypersensitivity Dis Res Upjohn Co Kalamazoo MI 49001

LOUGHRAN, EDWARD DAN, b Canton, Ohio, June 2, 28; m 59; c 3. ANALYTICAL CHEMISTRY. Educ: Ohio State Univ, BS, 50; MS, 53, PhD(chem), 55. Prof Exp: Asst chem, Res Found, Ohio State Univ, 53-55; MEM STAFF, LOS ALAMOS NAT LAB, 55-, ASSOC GROUP LEADER, 81- Mem: Fel Am Inst Chem; Am Soc Mass Spectrometry. Res: Analytical mass spectrometry; surveillance and compatibility studies of plastic-bonded explosives; physical properties, modes of decomposition and radiation chemistry of organic explosives. Mailing Add: Box 1663 MS 920 Los Alamos NM 87545

LOUGHRAN, GERARD ANDREW, SR, b Mt Vernon, NY, Sept 10, 18; m 45; c 4. ORGANIC CHEMISTRY. Educ: Fordham Univ, BS, 41; NY Univ, MS, 48. Prof Exp: Anal chemist, NY Quinine & Chem Works, 41-43; asst chem, Fordham Univ, 43-44; chemist, Am Cyanamid Co, 46-56; chemist, R T Vanderbilt Co, 56-59; chemist, 60-73, PROJ SCIENTIST, MAT LAB, US AIR FORCE, WRIGHT AERONAUTICAL LABS, 73- Mem: fel Am Inst Chem; Am Chem Soc. Res: Petroleum and rubber chemicals; polymer chemistry; high temperature materials. Mailing Add: US Air Force Wright Aeronautical Labs MLBT Wright Patterson AFB OH 45433

LOUGHRIDGE, MICHAEL SAMUEL, b Jacksonville, Tex, Aug 27, 36; m 61; c 1. MARINE GEOLOGY. Educ: Rice Univ, BA, 58; Harvard Univ, MA, 61, PhD(geol), 67. Prof Exp: Grad res geologist II, Marine Phys Lab, Scripps Inst, Calif, 61-63, postgrad res geologist II, 63-64, postgrad res geologist III, 64-67, asst res geologist, 67-68; sci staff asst, Oceanog Surv Dept, US Naval Oceanog Off, 68-78; SUPVRY OCEANOGR, NAT GEOPHYS & SOLAR TERRESTRIAL DATA CTR, 78- Mem: AAAS; Geol Soc Am; Am Geophys Union; assoc mem Soc Explor Geophys. Res: Studies of specialized techniques of echo sounding and the micro-topography of the sea floor; studies of fine scale magnetics of the sea floor; instrumentation for marine geology; seismic profiling; quantitative geomorphology; stream hydraulics; relationships between archaeology and geology. Mailing Add: Nat Geophys & Solar 3100 Marine Boulder CO 80302

LOUGHRY, FRANK GLADE, b Marion Center, Pa, Apr 16, 10; m 44. SOIL CONSERVATION. Educ: Pa State Univ, BS, 31, PhD(agron, soils), 60; Ohio State Univ, MS, 34. Prof Exp: Asst agron, Ohio Agr Exp Sta, 31-33; soil scientist, USDA Soil Conserv Serv, 34-35, asst regional soil scientist, Northeastern US, 36-45, state soil scientist, Pa, 45-66; soil scientist, Pa Dept Health, 66-70; chief, Soil Sci Unit, 71-77, CONSULT SOIL SCIENTIST, PA DEPT ENVIRON RESOURCES, 77- Mem: Fel AAAS; Am Soc Agron; Int Soc Soil Sci; fel Soil Conserv Soc Am. Res: Relation of soil morphology to aeration; soil factors affecting renovation of waste; interpretation of soil data for environmental protection; use of soil surveys in environmental programs. Mailing Add: Brethern Village Box 5093 Lancaster PA 17601

LOUGHTON, ARTHUR, b Wisbech, Eng, May 25, 31; Can citizen; m 55; c 2. HORTICULTURE. Educ: Univ Nottingham, Eng, BSc, 54, MSc, 60. Prof Exp: Hort officer res, Stockbridge House Exp Hort Sta, Ministry Agr, Fisheries & Food, Eng, 54-62, dep dir, 62-67; res scientist veg res, 67-75, DIR HORT RES, HORT EXP STA, ONT MINISTRY AGR & FOOD, SIMCOE, ONT, 75- Mem: Can Soc Hort Sci; Int Soc Hort Sci; Agr Inst Can. Res: Field vegetables: production and management of asparagus, carrots, cole crops and potatoes; evaluation of various horticultural crops as alternatives for tobacco growers; administration of total station program in fruit and vegetable research. Mailing Add: Ont Ministry of Agr & Food Hort Exp Sta Box 587 Simcoe ON N3Y 4N5 Can

LOUGHTON, BARRY G, biology, see previous edition

LOUI, MICHAEL CONRAD, b Philadelphia, Pa, June 1, 55. COMPUTER SCIENCE. Educ: Yale Univ, BS, 75; Mass Inst Technol, MS, 77, PhD(comput sci), 80. Prof Exp: Vis res asst prof & vis asst prof elec eng, 81-82, RES ASST PROF, COORD SCI LAB & ASST PROF ELEC ENG, UNIV ILL, URBANA, 82- Mem: Asn Comput Mach; Inst Elec & Electronics Engrs; Math Asn Am; Soc Indust & Appl Math. Res: Theory of computation; algebraic and combinatorial algorithms, automata, computational complexity and data structures. Mailing Add: Coord Sci Lab Univ Ill 1101 W Springfield Ave Urbana IL 61801

LOUIE, RAYMOND, plant pathology, see previous edition

LOUIE, ROBERT EUGENE, b Oakland, Calif, Aug 2, 29; m 62; c 1. VIROLOGY. Educ: Univ Calif, Berkeley, BA, 51, MA, 53, PhD(bacteriol), 63. Prof Exp: Res asst virol, Ft Detrick, Md, 54-55; res microbiologist virol, 61-77, MGR VIROL RES DEPT, CUTTER LABS, 77- Mem: Am Soc Microbiol; Sigma Xi. Res: Development of viral vaccines for human use; viral chemotherapy; virus-cell relationships. Mailing Add: Microbial Res Dept Cutter Labs Fourth & Parker Sts Berkeley CA 94710

LOUIE, STEVEN GWON SHENG, b Canton, China, Mar 26, 49; US citizen; m 75; c 1. THEORETICAL SOLID STATE PHYSICS. Educ: Univ Calif, AB, 72, PhD(physics), 76. Prof Exp: NSF fel, Dept Physics, Univ Calif, Berkeley, 76-77; fel theoret solid state physics, T J Watson Res Ctr, IBM Corp, 77-80; ASSOC PROF PHYSICS, UNIV CALIF, BERKELEY, 80- Mem: Am Phys Soc. Res: Theoretical solid state physics; electronic properties of solids and of solid surfaces and interfaces; theory of lattice dynamics; theory of superconductivity. Mailing Add: Dept Physics Univ Calif Berkeley CA 94720

LOUIS, BRIAN GREGORY, b Edmonton, Alta, Sept 21, 46; m 69; c 2. BIOCHEMISTRY, ENDOCRINOLOGY. Educ: McGill Univ, BSc, 68; Univ Ottawa, PhD(biochem), 72. Prof Exp: Sci asst, Max Planck Inst Biochem, 72-74; fel, Banting & Best Dept Med Res, Univ Toronto, 74-76, res assoc, 76-78; RES SCIENTIST, DEPT OBSTET & GYNEC, ST MICHAEL'S HOSP, 78- Concurrent Pos: Asst prof, Dept Obstet & Gynec, Univ Toronto, 78- Mem: Biochem Soc; Can Biochem Soc; Biometric Soc; Endocrine Soc; Soc Study Fertil. Res: Hormonal control of gonadal function; mechanism of action of glycoprotein hormones. Mailing Add: Dept of Obstet & Gynec 30 Bond St Toronto ON M5B 1W8 Can

LOUIS, JEAN FRANCOIS, b Ixelles, Belg, Mar 31, 32; m 58; c 3. FLUID MECHANICS. Educ: Univ Brussels, Ingenieur, 54; Cambridge Univ, PhD(mech eng), 57. Prof Exp: Scientist, SHAPE Air Defense Tech Ctr, 59-60; prin res scientist, Avco Everett Res Lab, Mass, 60-69, consult, 69; assoc prof aeronaut & astronaut, Mass Inst Technol, 69-76, assoc dir, Energy Lab, 75, dir, Energy Conversion Prog, 76-81; ASSOC DIR, CTR HEALTH EFFECTS OF FOSSIL FUEL UTILIZATION, NAT INST ENVIRON

HEALTH SCI, 81- *Concurrent Pos:* Vis prof, Stanford Univ, 68-69. *Mem:* Assoc fel Am Inst Aeronaut & Astronaut. *Res:* Magnetohydrodynamics; turbomachinery; plasma physics. *Mailing Add:* Nat Inst Environ Health Sci PO Box 12233 Research Triangle Park NC 27709

LOUIS, JOHN, b Chicago, Ill, June 21, 24; m 67. HEMATOLOGY, CLINICAL PHARMACOLOGY. *Educ:* Univ Ill, BS, 48, MS & MD, 50. *Prof Exp:* Instr med, Col Med, Univ Ill, 51-65; asst prof, Stritch Sch Med, Loyola Univ, Chicago, 65-70; Prof med, Chicago Med Sch, 75; chief hematol sect, Vet Admin Hosp, Downey, Ill, 75; assoc dir, Div Hematol & Oncol, Chicago Med Sch, 75; CONSULT HEMAT & ONCOL, 70- *Concurrent Pos:* Consult to various hosps & Chicago State TB Sanatorium, 58-; chmn leukemia criteria comt, NIH, 61-65, leukemia task force, 62-65. *Res:* Clinical pharmacology of drugs relating to hematology and cancer. *Mailing Add:* 347 Circle Lane Lake Forest IL 60045

LOUIS, KWOK TOY, b Shanghai, China, Jan 22, 27; m 54; c 3. TEXTILE CHEMISTRY. *Educ:* Tex Tech Col, BS, 51. *Prof Exp:* Lab dir, Otto Goedecke, Inc, Tex, 53-54; develop chemist, Burlington Indust, Inc, NC, 55-56; chief chemist, United Piece Dye Works, SC, 57-61; applns chems, Ciba Chem & Dye Co, 61-62, group leader appln res & qual control, 63-64, admin mgr res & appln, Tech Appln Prod, 64-68, mgr cent lab, 68-71; dir tech dept, Dyes & Chem Div, Crompton & Knowles Corp, NJ, 71-76; tech dir, 76-77, VPRES, APEX CHEM CO, INC, 78- *Mem:* Am Asn Textile Chemists & Colorists; AAAS; NY Acad Sci. *Mailing Add:* 442 Ellis Place Wyckoff NJ 07481

LOUIS, LAWRENCE HUA-HSIEN, b Canton, China, Apr 23, 08; nat US; m 42; c 4. BIOCHEMISTRY. *Educ:* Univ Mich, BS, 32, MS, 33, ScD, 37. *Prof Exp:* Fel physiol, Univ Pa, 40-41; asst internal med, 41-46, instr biochem, 46-48, from asst prof to assoc prof, 48-69, prof biochem, Univ Mich, Ann Arbor, 70-78; RETIRED. *Mem:* AAAS; Am Chem Soc; Am Soc Biol Chem. *Res:* Endocrinology and metabolism. *Mailing Add:* 2302 Manchester Rd Ann Arbor MI 48104

LOUIS, THOMAS MICHAEL, b Pensacola, Fla, Dec 27, 44; m 69; c 2. REPRODUCTIVE ENDOCRINOLOGY. *Educ:* Va Polytech Inst & State Univ, BS, 68, MS, 71; Mich State Univ, PhD(sci), 75. *Prof Exp:* Lalor res fel reproductive endocrinol, Univ Oxford, 75-76; asst prof, 76-78, ASSOC PROF ANAT, SCH MED, EAST CAROLINA UNIV, 78- *Honors & Awards:* Richard Hoyte Res Prize, Am Dairy Sci Asn, 75. *Mem:* AAAS; Am Soc Animal Sci; Sigma Xi; Soc Study Endocrinol; Am Asn Anatomists. *Res:* Chronic effects of alcohol, nicotine, and the nervous system on pregnancy and parturition; studies include endocrinology of parturition, fetal endocrinology, endocrinology of the estrous and menstrual cycle and endocrine control of the hypothalamus and pituitary; effects of fetal asphyxia on the neonate. *Mailing Add:* Dept of Anat Sch of Med East Carolina Univ Greenville NC 27834

LOUISELL, WILLIAM HENRY, b Mobile, Ala, Aug 22, 24; m 51; c 5. PHYSICS. *Educ:* Univ Mich, BS, 48, MS, 49, PhD(physics), 53. *Prof Exp:* Mem tech staff, Bell Tel Labs, NJ, 53-66; chmn dept physics, 67-69, PROF PHYSICS & ELEC ENG, UNIV SOUTHERN CALIF, 66- *Concurrent Pos:* Consult, US Army Missile Command, Ala, 70-78, App Math & Sci Lab, Aberdeen Proving Ground, 74-76 & Los Alamos Nat Lab, 75-; Alexander von Humboldt US sr scientist award, 79-80. *Mem:* Fel Am Phys Soc; fel Inst Elec & Electronics Eng. *Res:* Microwave and quantum electronics; nonlinear optics. *Mailing Add:* Dept Physics SSC 329 Univ of Southern Calif Los Angeles CA 90007

LOULLIS, COSTAS CHRISTOU, b Nicosia, Cyprus, Jan 5, 50. NEUROBIOLOGY, NEUROCHEMISTRY. *Educ:* Fairfield Univ, BS, 74; Syracuse Univ, MA, 75, PhD(biopsychol), 78. *Prof Exp:* Teaching asst biopsychol, Dept Psychol, Syracuse Univ, 74-78; NIMH fel neurochem & behavior, Dept Psychiat, Sch Med, Ind Univ, 78-80; SCIENTIST, MED RES DIV, AM CYANAMID CO, 80- *Mem:* Soc Neurosci; NY Acad Sci. *Res:* Psychopharmacology; CNS lesions; limbic system; schedule induced polydipsia; taste aversion; operant behavior; eating and drinking behaviors; neurotransmitters; aging. *Mailing Add:* 56A/116 Med Res Div Am Cyanamid Co Pearl River NY 10965

LOULOU, RICHARD JACQUES, b Relizane, Algeria, Apr 19, 44; Can citizen; m 67; c 2. OPERATIONS RESEARCH, PROBABILITY. *Educ:* Sch Polytech, Paris, BSc, 66; Univ Calif, Berkeley, MSc, 68, PhD(opers res), 71. *Prof Exp:* Asst prof, 70-73, ASSOC PROF OPERS RES, McGILL UNIV, 73- *Concurrent Pos:* Consult, Archer, Seaden & Assocs, 72-73. *Mem:* Inst Mgt Sci; Opers Res Soc Am; Can Opers Res Soc. *Res:* Queueing theory; congested service systems; stochastic processes simulation; heuristics in optimization. *Mailing Add:* McGill Univ 1001 Sherbrooke W Montreal PQ H3A 1G5 Can

LOULOUDES, SPIRO JAMES, b Stratford, Conn, Mar 22, 28; m 54; c 4. ENTOMOLOGY. *Educ:* DePauw Univ, BA, 52; Kans State Col, MS, 55, PhD(entom), 58. *Prof Exp:* Asst entom, Kans State Col, 56-57, instr, 57-58; ENTOMOLOGIST INSECT PHYSIOL, INSECT PATH LAB, AGR RES CTR, SCI & EDUC ADMIN-AGR RES, USDA, 58- *Mem:* NY Acad Sci; Entom Soc Am; Am Chem Soc. *Res:* Insect physiology, pathology and biochemistry; dynamic aspects of cuticular hydrocarbon synthesis and the exotoxins of insect pathogens; lipid metabolism in insect cell cultures. *Mailing Add:* US Dept Agr SEA Insect Path Lab Agr Res Ctr-W Beltsville MD 20705

LOUNIBOS, LEON PHILIP, b Petaluma, Calif, Aug 19, 47. INSECT ECOLOGY, INSECT BEHAVIOR. *Educ:* Univ Notre Dame, BS, 69; Harvard Univ MS, 70, PhD(biol), 74. *Prof Exp:* Res scientist & head, Int Ctr Insect Physiol & Ecol, Coastal Res Sta, 74-77; ENTOMOLOGIST III, FLA MED ENTOM LAB, 77- *Concurrent Pos:* NIH fel, 74-77. *Mem:* AAAS; Sigma Xi; Entom Soc Am; Am Soc Zoologists; Ecol Soc Am. *Res:* Insect ecology: seasonality, diapause strategies, predator-prey relationships, community organization; insect behavior: building, predatory, oviposition behaviors. *Mailing Add:* Fla Med Entom Lab PO Box 520 Vero Beach FL 32960

LOUNSBURY, FRANKLIN, b Chicago, Ill, May 6, 12; m 41; c 3. MEDICINE. *Educ:* Univ Wis, AB, 34; Northwestern Univ, MD, 39, MS, 48. *Prof Exp:* Asst prof, 54-65, ASSOC PROF SURG, NORTHWESTERN UNIV, CHICAGO, 65- *Concurrent Pos:* Attend physician, Northwestern Mem Hosp, 46-80, emer physician, 80- *Mem:* Am Col Surg; Cent Surg Asn; Soc Surgery Alimentary Tract. *Res:* Abdominal surgery, especially of the biliary tract. *Mailing Add:* 165 N Kenilworth Oak Park IL 60301

LOURENCO, RUY VALENTIM, b Lisbon, Portugal, Mar 25, 29; US citizen; m 60; c 2. MEDICINE, PHYSIOLOGY. *Educ:* Univ Lisbon, BSc, 46, MD, 51. *Prof Exp:* Intern, Lisbon City Hosps, 52, resident internal med, 53-55; asst med, Sch Med, Lisbon, 56-59; from asst prof to assoc prof, NJ Col Med, 63-67; assoc prof med, 67-69, dir pulmonary sect, Dept Med, 70-77, PROF MED & PHYSIOL, ABRAHAM LINCOLN SCH MED, UNIV ILL COL MED, 69-, CHMN DEPT MED, 77-, FOLEY PROF MED, 78-, PHYSICIAN IN CHIEF, UNIV ILL HOSP, 77- *Concurrent Pos:* Fel med, Cologne Univ, 57 & Columbia-Presby Med Ctr, 59-63; Lederle int fel, 59-60; Polachek Found fel, 61-63; attend physician, Newark City Hosp, 65-67; consult physician, Vet Admin Hosps, 65-; dir respiratory res, Hektoen Inst Med Res, Chicago, 67-70; attend physician, Univ Ill Hosp, 67-, dir pulmonary serv & labs, 70-; dir respiratory physiol lab, Cook County Hosp, Chicago, 67-69, dir dept pulmonary med, 69-70; mem cardio-pulmonary coun, Am Heart Asn; mem task force sci basis respiratory therapeut, Nat Heart & Lung Inst, 71-72; mem study sect, NIH, 72-76; chmn sci assembly, Am Thoracic Soc, 74-75. *Mem:* Am Physiol Soc; Am Fedn Clin Res; Am Thoracic Soc; Am Soc Clin Invest; Soc Exp Biol & Med. *Res:* Internal medicine; chest diseases; respiratory physiology and biochemistry; regulation of ventilation; muscles of breathing; pulmonary defense mechanisms. *Mailing Add:* Abraham Lincoln Sch of Med Univ of Ill Col of Med Chicago IL 60680

LOURIA, DONALD BRUCE, b New York, NY, July 11, 28; m 55; c 3. INTERNAL MEDICINE, MICROBIOLOGY. *Educ:* Harvard Univ, BS, 49, MD, 53. *Prof Exp:* From instr to assoc prof med, Col Med, Cornell Univ, 58-69; PROF PREV MED & COMMUNITY HEALTH & CHMN DEPT, NJ MED SCH, COL MED & DENT NJ, 69- *Concurrent Pos:* Pres, NY State Coun Drug Addiction, 65-73. *Mem:* Am Soc Clin Invest; Am Fedn Clin Res; Am Soc Microbiol; Am Col Physicians. *Res:* Mycology, especially fungal toxins and the pathogenesis of Candida infections; prevention programs for adults; health education; health manpower; cancer epidemiology; health problems of the aging. *Mailing Add:* Dept Prev Med & Community Health NJ Med Sch Newark NJ 07103

LOURIE, ALAN DAVID, b Boston, Mass, Jan 13, 35; m 59; c 2. ORGANIC CHEMISTRY. *Educ:* Harvard Univ, AB, 56; Univ Wis, MS, 58; Univ Pa, PhD(org chem), 65; Temple Univ, JD, 70. *Prof Exp:* Res chemist, Monsanto Co, 57-59; res chemist, Wyeth Labs, 59-60, lit chemist, 60-62, patent chemist, 62-64; patent agent chem, Smith Kline & French Labs, 64-70, patent attorney, 70-71, assoc patent counsel, 71-74, asst dir, patent dept, 74-76, VPRES CORP PATENTS, SMITHKLINE CORP, 76- *Mem:* Am Chem Soc. *Res:* Synthesis of heterocyclic compounds; medicinal chemistry. *Mailing Add:* 1500 Spring Garden St Philadelphia PA 19101

LOURIE, HERBERT, b St George, SC, Mar 6, 29; m 48; c 4. NEUROSURGERY. *Educ:* Univ SC, BS, 48; Duke Univ, MD, 52. *Prof Exp:* From instr to assoc prof, 60-68, PROF NEUROSURG, STATE UNIV NY UPSTATE MED CTR, 68- *Concurrent Pos:* Fel clin neurosurg, Wash Univ, 54, fel neurophysiol, 59; Am Heart Asn res grant, 66-67. *Mem:* Cong Neurol Surg; Am Asn Neurol Surg; Am Col Surg; Am Acad Neurol Surg; Neurosurg Soc Am (pres, 81-82). *Res:* Hypertensive vascular disease in experimental animals; neurophysiologic investigation of coma and arousal in cat; intracranial hemorrhage of newborns. *Mailing Add:* 725 Irving Ave Suite 504 Syracuse NY 13210

LOURIE, REGINALD SPENCER, b Brooklyn, NY, Sept 10, 88; m 31; c 3. PSYCHIATRY. *Educ:* Cornell Univ, BS, 30; Long Island Col Med, MD, 36; Columbia Univ, ScD(psychiat), 42. *Prof Exp:* Asst bact, Res Labs, New York Dept Health, 30-31; intern & resident pediat & psychiat, Long Island Col Hosp, 36-38, NY State Psychiat Inst, 38-39 & Bellevue Psychiat Hosp, 39-40; assoc res psychiat, Col Physicians & Surgeons, Columbia Univ, 42-46; instr pediat & psychiat, Sch Med, Rochester Univ, 46-48; asst prof, Col Med, George Wash Univ, 48-53, assoc clin prof pediat psychiat, 54-65, prof, 65-71, Prof, 71-74, EMER PROF CHILD HEALTH & DEVELOP & PSYCHIAT, COL MED, GEORGE WASH UNIV, 74- *Concurrent Pos:* Scottish Rite Fund & Markle Found fel, NY State Psychiat Inst & Hosp, 40-43; asst pediatrician, Vanderbilt Clin, 41-46; civilian with off Sci Res & Develop, 42; assoc pediatrician, Univ Hosp, George Wash Univ, 48-; dir dept psychiat, Children's Hosp & Hillcrest Children's Ctr, Washington, DC, 48-74; consult, Walter Reed Army Med Ctr, 49- & President's Panel Ment Retardation, 59-61; mem, Nat Adv Ment Health Coun, 64-68; pres, Joint Coun Ment Health Children, 65-75; lectr, Howard Univ, Am Univ & Cath Univ Am; sr res scientist, Nat Inst Ment Health, 75-; chmn, Human Serv Inst Children & Families, 73-74; sr consult, Psychiat Inst Wash, DC, 74- *Honors & Awards:* Comdr, Royal Order of Phoenix, Greece; McGAvin Award, Am Psychiat Asn; Dickinson Medal, State Univ NY, Downstate Med Sch, 64. *Mem:* Am Psychiat Asn; Am Orthopsychiat Asn (pres, 57-58); Am Psychoanal Asn; Am Acad Child Psychiat (secy, 61-63, pres, 63-65); Int Asn Child Psychiat (treas, 70-74). *Res:* Infant psychiatry, psychopathology and psychophysiology; autonomic nervous system function in children. *Mailing Add:* 4305 Thornapple St Chevy Chase MD 20015

LOUSTAUNAU, JOAQUIN, b San Louis Potosi, Mex, Sept 17, 36; m 66. MATHEMATICS. *Educ:* Okla State Univ, BS, 58, MS, 60; Univ Ill, PhD(math), 65. *Prof Exp:* Instr math, Inst Tech & Higher Educ, Monterrey, Mex, 60-61; ASST PROF MATH, NMEX STATE UNIV, 65- *Mem:* Math Asn Am; Am Math Soc. *Res:* Functional analysis. *Mailing Add:* Dept of Math NMex State Univ Las Cruces NM 88003

LOUTFY, RAFIK OMAR, b Cairo, Egypt, Nov, 43, Can citizen; m 65; c 2. PHOTOCHEMISTRY, PHYSICAL CHEMISTRY. *Educ:* Ain Shams Univ, Cairo, BSc, 64, MSc, 67; Univ Western Ont, PhD(photochem), 72. *Prof Exp:* Fel laser flash photolysis, Nat Res Coun Can, 72-74; fel photochem, Univ Toronto, 74; mem sci staff, 74-80, AREA MGR, XEROX RES CTR CAN, 80- *Concurrent Pos:* Adj assoc prof, Univ Western Ont, 79- *Mem:* Am Chem Soc; Chem Inst Can; Inter-Am Photochem Soc; Europ Photochem Soc. *Res:* Photophysics of small molecules and polymers; solar energy conversion using organic semiconductors; dye sensitization of semiconductors; electrochemistry and spectroscopy of organic molecules and dyes. *Mailing Add:* Xerox Res Ctr Can 2480 Dunwin Dr Mississauga ON L5L 1J9 Can

LOUTTIT, ROBERT IRVING, b Honolulu, Hawaii, July 23, 29; m 54; c 3. EXPERIMENTAL HIGH ENERGY PHYSICS. *Educ:* Univ NH, BS, 52; Wash Univ, PhD(physics), 58. *Prof Exp:* From asst physicist to assoc physicist, 58-64, PHYSICIST, BROOKHAVEN NAT LAB, 64- *Concurrent Pos:* Physicist, Nuclear Res Ctr, Saclay, France, 63-64. *Mem:* AAAS; Am Phys Soc; Sigma Xi. *Res:* Bubble chamber development; neutrino interactions. *Mailing Add:* Accelerator Dept Brookhaven Nat Lab Upton NY 11973

LOVAGLIA, ANTHONY RICHARD, b San Jose, Calif, Jan 25, 23; m 44; c 3. MATHEMATICS. *Educ:* Univ Calif, Los Angeles, AB, 45, PhD(math), 51; Stanford Univ, MS, 48; Univ Calif, Berkeley, PhD(math), 51. *Prof Exp:* From asst prof to assoc prof, 51-60, PROF MATH, SAN JOSE STATE UNIV, 60- *Mem:* Math Asn Am. *Res:* Analysis. *Mailing Add:* Dept of Math San Jose State Univ San Jose CA 95114

LOVALD, ROGER ALLEN, b Marshall, Minn, Aug 8, 38; m 57; c 2. ORGANIC POLYMER CHEMISTRY. *Educ:* Univ Minn, BChem, 60; Univ Wis, PhD(org chem), 65. *Prof Exp:* Chemist, Spring Res Lab, Rohm & Haas Co, 65-67; cent res, 67-71, sect leader, Resin Develop, 71-75, TECH DIR RESINS, GEN MILLS CHEM, INC, 75- *Res:* Heteroaliphatic and organic chemistry; addition and condensation polymerization; acrylics; polyamides; polyesters; polyurethanes. *Mailing Add:* Gen Mills Chem Inc 2010 E Hennepin Ave Minneapolis MN 55413

LOVAS, FRANCIS JOHN, b Cleveland, Ohio, July 29, 41; m 70. MOLECULAR SPECTROSCOPY, RADIO ASTRONOMY. *Educ:* Univ Detroit, BS, 63; Univ Calif, Berkeley, PhD(phys chem), 67. *Prof Exp:* Res grant, Lawrence Radiation Lab, Univ Calif, Berkeley, 67-68; NATO fel, Phys Inst, Free Univ Berlin, 68-70; Nat Res Coun-Nat Bur Standards, Assoc, 70-72, DIR MOLECULAR SPECTRA DATA CTR, NAT BUR STANDARDS, 72- *Mem:* AAAS; Am Phys Soc. *Res:* Properties of diatomic molecules by high temperature microwave adsorption and molecular beam electric resonance techniques; microwave spectroscopy of transient molecules and molecular radio astronomy; critical evaluation of microwave spectroscopic data. *Mailing Add:* Molecular Spectros Div 545 Nat Bur Standards Washington DC 20234

LOVASS-NAGY, VICTOR, b Debrecen, Hungary, Apr 25, 23; m 51; c 2. APPLIED MATHEMATICS. *Educ:* Budapest Tech Univ, dipl, 47, PhD(math), 49. *Prof Exp:* Instr math, Budapest Tech Univ, 47-49, from asst prof to assoc prof, 49-58; consult engr, Ganz Elec Works, Hungary, 60-64; reader eng math, Univ Khartoum, 64-66; PROF MATH, CLARKSON COL TECHNOL, 66-, PROF COMPUT SCI, 77- *Mem:* Soc Indust & Appl Math; Am Math Soc; Math Asn Am; Tensor Soc; sr mem Inst Elec & Electronics Eng. *Res:* Matrix theory; numerical analysis; network theory. *Mailing Add:* 8 Division Potsdam NY 13676

LOVATT, CAROL JEAN, b Kansas City, Mo, May 14, 47; div; c 2. METABOLIC REGULATION. *Educ:* Univ Mass, BA, 73; Univ RI, MS, 76, PhD(bot), 80. *Prof Exp:* Res assoc, 80, ASST PROF PLANT PHYSIOL & ASST PLANT PHYSIOLOGIST, DEPT BOT & PLANT SCI, UNIV CALIF, RIVERSIDE, 80- *Mem:* Am Soc Plant Physiologists; AAAS; Am Women Sci; Sigma Xi. *Res:* Metabolic regulation of nucleotide metabolism and arginine biosyntesis/urea cycle; citrus physiology: regulation of flowering, fruit set, and fruit growth; role of boron in plant metabolism. *Mailing Add:* Dept Bot & Plant Sci Univ Calif Riverside CA 92521

LOVE, ALLAN WALTER, b Toronto, Ont, May 28, 16; US citizen; m 46; c 3. ELECTROMAGNETISM. *Educ:* Univ Toronto, BA, 38, MA, 39, PhD(microwave physics), 51. *Prof Exp:* Res officer, Radiophysics Lab, Commonwealth Sci & Indust Res Orgn, Australia, 46-48; demonstr asst, Physics Lab, Univ Toronto, 48-51; chief instrumentation, Newmont Explor Ltd, Conn & Ariz, 51-57; staff scientist, Giannini Res Lab, Wiley Electronics Co, Ariz, 57-62, mgr, Physics Lab, Calif, 62-63; group scientist, Antenna Lab, Autonetics Div, NAm Aviation, Inc, 63; area mgr, Nat Eng Sci Co, 63-65; group scientist theoret anal, Autonetics Div, NAm Aviation, Inc, 65-71, mem tech staff, Space Div, NAm Rockwell Corp, 71-73, PROG MGR, SPACE DIV, ROCKWELL INT, 73- *Mem:* fel Inst Elec & Electronics Engrs. *Res:* Microwave and millimeter wave physics; antenna theory and design; development of spacecraft antenna systems. *Mailing Add:* 518 Rockford Pl Corona Del Mar CA 92625

LOVE, CALVIN MILES, b Chicago, Ill, Mar 2, 37; m 60; c 3. INORGANIC CHEMISTRY, RADIOCHEMISTRY. *Educ:* Ill Inst Technol, BS, 59; Mich State Univ, PhD(inorg chem), 64. *Prof Exp:* res specialist, 64-80, SR RES SPECIALIST, MOUND FACIL, MONSANTO RES CORP, 80- *Mem:* AAAS; Am Chem Soc. *Res:* Kinetics and mechanisms of inorganic oxidation-reduction reactions; plutonium separation and recovery; polonium process development; metal distillation; metal hydrides; radiation damage; thermal analysis; hydrides for hydrogen storage; chemistry of pyrotechnics. *Mailing Add:* Mound Facil Monsanto Res Corp Miamisburg OH 45342

LOVE, CARL G(EORGE), b Warsaw, NY, Sept 20, 40; m 71; c 2. SYSTEMS ANALYSIS. *Educ:* Rochester Inst Technol, BS, 63; Carnegie Inst Technol, MS, 65, PhD(elec eng). 67. *Prof Exp:* Coop student, Rochester Gas & Elec Corp, 58-60; coop student, Delco Appl Div, Gen Motors Corp, 60-63, proj engr, 63; sr engr, 67-71, fel engr, 72, MGR SYST PLANNING & TECH ASSESSMENT, WESTINGHOUSE RES & DEVELOP CTR, 72- *Mem:* Inst Elec & Electronics Engrs; Inst Mgt Sci; Opers Res Soc Am. *Res:* Technology forecasting; business analysis; energy analysis. *Mailing Add:* Westinghouse Res & Develop Ctr 1310 Beulah Rd Pittsburgh PA 15235

LOVE, DANIEL LINDSLEY, b Portland, Ore, May 26, 28; m 50; c 2. RADIOCHEMISTRY. *Educ:* Reed Col, BA, 50; Univ Portland, MS, 51; Pa State Univ, PhD(fuel tech), 55. *Prof Exp:* Asst phys chem, Univ Tex, 51-52 & Pa State Univ, 52-55; head radiochem anal sect, US Naval Radiol Defense Labs, 55-64, appl res br, Calif, 64-69, chief nuclear chem div, Naval Ord Lab, 69-75, head, nuclear br, 75-79, HEAD, ELECTRO-OPTICS BR, NAVAL SURFACE WEAPONS CTR, 79- *Concurrent Pos:* Part-time mem fac, Montgomery Col; consult, State of Md Dept of Natural Resources, 71- *Res:* Analytical chemistry; polarography; radioavtive tracers; fuel chemistry; separation and decay schemes of short-lived radionuclides; oceanography; radiation chemistry; Mossbauer spectrometry; mechanisms of carcinogenesis; lasers; fluorine chemistry; power plant siting; electro-optics. *Mailing Add:* 4416 Norbeck Rd Rockville MD 20853

LOVE, DAVID VAUGHAN, b St John, NB, Aug 25, 19; m 43; c 3. FOREST MANAGEMENT. *Educ:* Univ NB, BSc, 41; Univ Mich, MF, 46. *Prof Exp:* From lectr to prof, 46-72, asst dean, 72-76, ASSOC DEAN FORESTRY, UNIV TORONTO, 77- *Concurrent Pos:* Vpres, Conservation Coun Ont, 59-64, pres, 74-75; vchmn, Can Coun on Rural Develop, 75-79; rep, Can Forestry Asn, 73. *Mem:* Soc Am Foresters; Can Pulp & Paper Asn; Can Inst Forestry (secy-mgr, 48-54, pres, 65-66); Ont Forestry Asn (vpres, 70-71, pres, 72-73); Can Forestry Asn (vpres, 74, 75 & 81, pres, 75). *Res:* Land use. *Mailing Add:* Fac of Forestry Univ of Toronto 203 College St Toronto ON M5S 1A1 Can

LOVE, DAVID WAXHAM, b Laramie, Wyo, Nov 1, 46. QUATERNARY STRATIGRAPHY. *Educ:* Beloit Col, BA, 69; Univ NMex, MS, 71, PhD(geol), 80. *Prof Exp:* Asst prof geol, Wash State Univ, 76-78; ENVIRON GEOLOGIST, NMEX BUR MINES & MINERAL RESOURCES, 80- *Mem:* Geol Soc Am; Sigma Xi; Soc Archeol Sci. *Res:* Geomorphic processes and stratigraphy of surficial deposits in New Mexico and adjacent areas for assessing natural hazards and for determining stability of land forms for siting industrial plants or for storing hazardous materials. *Mailing Add:* N Mex Bur Mines & Mineral Resources Socorro NM 87801

LOVE, GEORGE M, b Lima, Ohio, Oct 5, 44; m 72. ORGANIC CHEMISTRY. *Educ:* DePauw Univ, BA, 66; Wake Forest Univ, MA, 68; Mich State Univ, PhD(org chem), 72. *Prof Exp:* Fel org chem, Rutgers Univ, 72-73; sr res chemist, 73-80, RES FEL, MERCK INC, 80- *Mem:* Sigma Xi; Am Chem Soc. *Res:* Process research in organic chemistry. *Mailing Add:* Merck Inc Rahway NJ 07065

LOVE, GORDON ROSS, b Cleveland, Ohio, July 31, 37; m 62; c 1. MATERIALS SCIENCE. *Educ:* Case Inst Technol, BS, 58; Carnegie Inst Technol, MS, 61, PhD(metall), 63. *Prof Exp:* Metallurgist, Oak Ridge Nat Lab, 62-64, group leader superconducting mat, 64-70; asst mgr technol, Mat Syst Div, Union Carbide Corp, 70-80; WITH SPRAGUE ELEC, 80- *Concurrent Pos:* Lectr, Univ Tenn, 66-67. *Mem:* Am Inst Mining, Metall & Petrol Engrs; Am Phys Soc. *Res:* Diffusion; superconductivity; statistical process control; powder technology; surface and interface properties; ceramic dielectric materials. *Mailing Add:* Sprague Elec Marshall St North Adams MA 01247

LOVE, HARRY SCHROEDER, JR, b Idabel, Okla, Aug 20, 27; m 52; c 2. BOTANY, ECOLOGY. *Educ:* Okla State Univ, BS, 52, MS, 58, PhD(bot), 71. *Prof Exp:* assoc prof, 67-80, PROF BIOL, EAST CENT OKLA STATE UNIV, 80- *Mem:* AAAS; Am Inst Biol Sci; Nat Asn Biol Teachers. *Res:* Terrestrial plant ecology, especially clonal and root-graft relationships. *Mailing Add:* Dept of Biol E Cent State Univ Ada OK 74820

LOVE, HUGH MORRISON, b Northern Ireland, Aug 21, 26. PHYSICS. *Educ:* Queen's Univ, Belfast, BSc & PhD(physics), 50. *Prof Exp:* Asst lectr, Queen's Univ, Belfast, 46-50; lectr, Univ Toronto, 50-52; from asst prof to assoc prof, 52-65, PROF PHYSICS, QUEEN'S UNIV, ONT, 65-, VPRIN, 76- *Mem:* Am Phys Soc. *Res:* Solid state physics; surface physics. *Mailing Add:* 119 Queen's Circle Kingston ON K7L 2S9 Can

LOVE, JAMES ALLAN, b Johnstone, Scotland, Nov 7, 42; m 67; c 2. POLYMER CHEMISTRY. *Educ:* Univ Strathclyde, BSc, 64, PhD(chem), 68. *Prof Exp:* Res chemist, Int Cellulose Res, Int Paper Co, 68-71; res dir, Fabricated Plastics Ltd, 71-72; res chemist, Com Alcohols Ltd, Int Paper Co, 72-73, res assoc chem, 73-77, mgr wood prod, 77, mgr primary processing res, 78-80. *Mem:* Chem Inst Can; Tech Asn Pulp & Paper Indust; The Chem Soc; Forest Prod Res Soc; Plastics Inst. *Res:* Cellulose polymer combinations; composite wood structures; properties of fiber reinforced plastics. *Mailing Add:* 8138 Maxfield Lane Cincinnati OH 45243

LOVE, JIM, b Bathgate, Scotland, Oct 21, 38; m 62; c 2. ORGANIC CHEMISTRY. *Educ:* Univ Edingurgh, BSc, 60, PhD(carbohydrate chem), 63. *Prof Exp:* Fel, Scripps Inst, Univ Calif, 63-64 & Ohio State Univ, 64-65; res chemist, Mich, 65-67 & Western Div, 67-74, res specialist, 74-77, group leader, 77-79, RES MGR, WESTERN DIV, DOW CHEM CO, PITTSBURG, CALIF, 79- *Mem:* Am Chem Soc; The Chem Soc. *Res:* Carbohydrate chemistry, particularly polysaccharide and mucopolysaccharide structural determination and biological activity; synthesis and biological activity of heterocyclic compounds. *Mailing Add:* 3378 Whitehaven Dr Walnut Creek CA 94598

LOVE, JOHN DAVID, b Riverton, Wyo, Apr 17, 13; m 40; c 4. GEOLOGY. *Educ:* Univ Wyo, BA, 33, MA, 34; Yale Univ, PhD(geol), 38. *Hon Degrees:* LLD, Univ Wyo, 61. *Prof Exp:* Asst geologist, Geol Surv Wyo, 33-37; field asst, US Geol Surv, 38; asst geologist, Shell Oil Co, Inc, 38-40, geologist, 40-42; asst geologist, 42-43, from assoc geologist to prin geologist, 43-56, supvr heavy metals, Jackson Proj, 66-68, Northern Rocky Mts Br, 64-66, 67-69, in charge Wyo basins fuels proj, 43-56, STAFF GEOLOGIST, US GEOL SURV, 56-, SUPVR, LARAMIE OFF, REGIONAL GEOL BR, 69- *Concurrent Pos:* Adj prof, Univ Wyo, 69-; affil prof geol, Univ Idaho, 74-; exten instr geol, Univ Calif, Davis, 77-; grad res adv, Univ Wash & Univ Minn. *Mem:* AAAS; fel Geol Soc Am; Am Asn Petrol Geol; Sigma Xi. *Res:* Geology of fuels; uranium, vanadium and gold investigations; stratigraphic and structural geology; author or coauthor of about 190 scientific publications. *Mailing Add:* US Geol Surv Box 3007 Univ Sta Laramie WY 82071

LOVE, JOSEPH E(UGENE), JR, b Chicago, Ill, Apr 9, 20; m 42; c 2. CIVIL ENGINEERING. *Educ:* Northwestern Univ, BS, 42, MS, 48, PhD(civil eng), 51. *Prof Exp:* Struct analyst, Curtiss-Wright Corp, 42-43; instr math & eng, Ripon Col, 43-45; from instr to asst prof civil eng, Northwestern Univ, 46-51; struct engr, Hanford Atomic Prod Oper, 52-55, struct engr, Atomic Power Equip Dept, 55-66, mgr arrangements & struct design, 66-72, mgr advan eng, 72-75, MGR PLANT STRUCT SYSTS, NUCLEAR ENERGY DIV, GEN ELEC CO, 75- *Concurrent Pos:* Contribr, 1st Int Conf Peaceful Uses of Atomic Energy; chmn working group on containment, Int Orgn Standardization, Technol Comt 85, subcomt 3, 76- *Mem:* AAAS; Am Soc Civil Engrs. *Res:* Plasticity effects in flexure; nuclear power plant design. *Mailing Add:* 15605 On Orbit Dr Saratoga CA 95070

LOVE, L J CLINE, b Richmond, Mo, Oct 1, 40; m 72; c 2. LUMINESCENCE, MICELLAR CHEMISTRY. *Educ:* Univ Mo-Columbia, BS, 62, MA, 65; Univ Ill, Urbana, PhD(chem), 69. *Prof Exp:* Fel chem, Univ Fla, 69-70; asst prof anal chem, Mich State Univ, 70-72; asst prof, 72-77, assoc prof, 77-82, PROF ANAL CHEM, SETON HALL UNIV, 82- *Concurrent Pos:* Prin investr, NIH, 81-83. *Mem:* Am Chem Soc; Soc Appl Spectros; Am Microchem Soc; Sigma Xi. *Res:* Development of new instrumentation and methodology in luminescence; analytical applications of micellar systems, atomic, absorption-emission-fluorescence spectroscopy ; automation of chemical instrumentation; high performance liquid chromatography; computer factor analysis of data. *Mailing Add:* Dept of Chem Seton Hall Univ South Orange NJ 07079

LOVE, LEON, b New York, NY, Sept 7, 23; m 56; c 3. RADIOLOGY. *Educ:* City Col New York, BS, 43; Chicago Med Sch, MD, 46; Am Bd Radiol, dipl, 51. *Prof Exp:* Radiologist, Cook County Hosp, Chicago, 56-61; assoc prof radiol, Chicago Med Sch, 58-67, clin prof, 67-69; PROF RADIOL & CHMN DEPT, MED CTR, LOYOLA UNIV CHICAGO, 69- *Concurrent Pos:* Consult, Dwight Vet Admin Hosp, 56-62; dir diag radiol, Cook County Hosp, Chicago, 61-69; consult, House of Correction, Chicago, 61- & WSide Vet Admin Hosp, 62- *Mem:* Am Col Radiol; Radiol Soc NAm. *Res:* Renal radiology; radiology of the gastro-intestinal tract. *Mailing Add:* Dept of Radiol Loyola Univ Med Ctr Maywood IL 60153

LOVE, NORMAN DUANE, b Howell, Mich, Jan 1, 39; m 62; c 3. LOW TEMPERATURE PHYSICS. *Educ:* Albion Col, AB, 60; Western Mich Univ, MA, 62; Mich State Univ, PhD(physics), 67. *Prof Exp:* From asst prof to assoc prof, Maryville Col, 67-77, dir comput serv, 71-77; SOFTWARE SPECIALIST, DIGITAL EQUIP CORP, 77- *Concurrent Pos:* Nat Sci Found comput grant, 68-73. *Mem:* Am Phys Soc; Am Asn Physics Teachers. *Res:* Effect of magnons on transport of phonons; phase boundaries in an antiferro magnetic material using calorimetric techniques. *Mailing Add:* Digital Equip Corp 9041 Executive Park Dr Knoxville TN 37919

LOVE, RAYMOND CHARLES, b Washington, DC, July 30, 53; m 76. CLINICAL PHARMACY. *Educ:* Univ Md, Baltimore, DrPharm, 77. *Prof Exp:* Dir, Area Health Educ Ctr, Cumberland, 77-78, ASST PROF CLIN PHARM, SCH PHARM, UNIV MD, 77- *Concurrent Pos:* Consult, Mem Hosp, Cumberland, Md, Sacred Heart Hosp, Thomas B Finan Ctr, & Memt Health Clin, Allegany Health Ctr, 77-; lectr, Squibb Pharmaceut, E R Squibb & Son, 78-; mem adv coun, Md High Blood Pressure Coord Coun, 78- *Mem:* Am Soc Hosp Pharmacists; Am Asn Cols Pharm. *Res:* Tardive dyskinesia; psychotherapeutic agents; hypertension; geriatric health care. *Mailing Add:* Area Health Educ Ctr Algonquin Hotel Cumberland MD 21502

LOVE, RICHARD HARRISON, b Brooklyn, NY, Aug 23, 39; m 63; c 2. UNDERWATER ACOUSTICS. *Educ:* Univ Md, BS, 61, MS, 63; Cath Univ Am, PhD(mech eng), 76. *Prof Exp:* Res scientist fluid mech, Hydronautics, Inc, 63-65; mech engr, Naval Res Lab, 65-67; oceanographer acoustics, Naval Oceanog Off, 67-76; OCEANOGRAPHER ACOUSTICS, NAVAL OCEAN RES & DEVELOP ACTIV, NAT SPACE TECH LABS, 76- *Mem:* Acoust Soc Am. *Res:* Scattering and reflection of underwater acoustic energy from marine organisms. *Mailing Add:* Naval Ocean Res & Develop Activ NSTL Station MS 39529

LOVE, ROBERT LYMAN, b Oswego, NY, July 28, 25; m 50; c 4. HEALTH SCIENCES. *Educ:* Syracuse Univ, AB, 47, MSEd, 49. *Prof Exp:* Teacher, Middlesex Valley Cent Sch, 49-53; from instr to assoc prof physiol & biochem, State Univ NY Agr & Tech Col at Alfred, 53-61, prof, 61-81, dean, Sch Allied Health Technol, 64-81; RETIRED. *Concurrent Pos:* Adv comt Allied Health Proj, Am Asn Community & Jr Col, 73; consult, Steering Comt, Am Med Asn, 75-77; pres, Educ Consult Serv, 81- *Mem:* Asn Schs Allied Health Professions; Am Soc Med Technol; Am Med Record Asn. *Mailing Add:* Rte 1 Box 164 Alfred Station NY 14803

LOVE, ROBERT MERTON, b Tantallon, Sask, Can, Jan 29, 09; nat US; m 36; c 3. RANGE SCIENCE, ECOLOGY. *Educ:* Univ Sask, BSc, 32, MSc, 33; McGill Univ, PhD(genetics), 35. *Prof Exp:* Instr, Univ Sask, 30-32, asst, 32-33; asst, McGill Univ, 33-34; asst agr scientist, Cereal Div, Cent Exp Farm, Can Dept Agr, 35-40; instr agron & jr agronomist, 40-41, asst prof &

asst agronomist, 41-45, assoc prof & assoc agronomist, 45-51, chmn dept agron, 59-70, PROF AGRON & AGRONOMIST, EXP STA, UNIV CALIF, DAVIS, 51-, CHMN GRAD PROG ECOL, 71- *Concurrent Pos:* Spec lectr, McGill Univ, 38; Can Dept Agr del, Int Genetics Cong, Scotland, 39; organizer, Cytogenetic Lab, Brazilian Ministry Agr, Rio Grande do Sul, 48-49; Fulbright res scholar, NZ & Australia, 56-57, Greece, 67; chmn range improvement adv comt, State Bd Forestry, Calif, 54-67; Rockefeller Found travel grant, 64; vis prof, Univ Ghana, 70-71 & Univ BC & Univ Guelph, 71; consult, Int Coop Admin, Govt Spain, 60, Food & Agr Orgn, Greece, 70, Kenya Meat Comn, 71, Spain, 75, AID, Ivory Coast, Univ Chile, 80 & Ctr Arg Engrs Agron, 81; mem panel resource technol, Nat Acad Sci-Nat Res Coun; mem ecol adv comt, Sci Adv Bd, US Environ Protection Agency, 74- *Honors & Awards:* Calouste Gulbenakian Award, Portugal, 67; Stevenson Award, Am Soc Agron, 52, Agronomic Serv Award, 66; Medallion Award, Am Forage & Grassland Coun, 66. *Mem:* Fel AAAS; Bot Soc Am; fel Am Soc Agron; hon mem Biol Soc; Can Soc Agron. *Res:* Cytogenetics of range forage crops and species; effect of grazing treatment on range species; interspecific hybridization of grasses; range plant improvement; ecology of grasslands. *Mailing Add:* 740 Miller Dr Davis CA 95616

LOVE, RUSSELL JACQUES, b Chicago, Ill, Jan 11, 31; m 61; c 2. SPEECH PATHOLOGY. *Educ:* Northwestern Univ, Ill, BS, 53, MA, 54, PhD(speech path), 62. *Prof Exp:* Speech & hearing therapist, Moody State Sch Cerebral Palsied Children, Tex, 54-56; staff clinician, Cerebral Palsy Speech Clin, Northwestern Univ, Ill, 58-61; audiologist, WSide Vet Admin Hosp, Chicago, Ill, 61-62; res speech pathologist, Vet Admin Hosp, Coral Gables, Fla, 62-64; assoc prof speech path, DePaul Univ, 64-67; from asst prof to assoc prof, 67-78, PROF SPEECH & LANG PATH, SCH MED, VANDERBILT UNIV, 78- *Concurrent Pos:* Consult speech pathologist, Michael Reese Hosp & Med Ctr, Chicago, Ill, 64-67; chief speech pathologist, Bill Wilkerson Hearing & Speech Ctr, Tenn, 67-71, consult & res speech pathologist, 71-; fel, Am Speech Found, Sci & Handicapped. *Mem:* Am Speech, Lang & Hearing Asn; Am Cleft Palate Asn. *Res:* Aphasia; Dyspraxia of speech; Dysarthria; speech and language development and disorders; rights of the handicapped; cerebral palsy. *Mailing Add:* Hearing & Speech Sci Vanderbilt Univ Med Sch Nashville TN 37232

LOVE, SAMUEL HARRIS, b South Hill, Va, July 28, 27; m 53; c 3. MICROBIOLOGY. *Educ:* Univ Va, BA, 50; Miami Univ, MS, 51; Univ Pa, PhD(microbiol), 54. *Prof Exp:* Res assoc biochem, Mass Inst Technol, 54, fel, Nat Found Infantile Paralysis, 54-55; from instr to asst prof, 55-66, ASSOC PROF MICROBIOL & IMMUNOL, BOWMAN GRAY SCH MED, 66-, DIR BIOCHEM CORE LAB, 74- *Concurrent Pos:* USPHS sr res fel, 56-61; res assoc, Univ Pa, 59. *Mem:* Am Soc Microbiol. *Res:* Purification and characterization of biologically active macromolecules; hyaluronic acid accumulation during delayed hypersensitivity; hyaluronic acid/fibronectin interactions as related to the delayed hypersensity response. *Mailing Add:* Dept Microbiol Brown Gray Sch Med Winston-Salem NC 27103

LOVE, SYDNEY FRANCIS, b Winnipeg, Man, June 20, 23. MANAGEMENT SCIENCE, ELECTRONICS. *Educ:* Univ Toronto, BASc, 47, MA, 48; Univ Waterloo, MASc(systs design), 70. *Prof Exp:* Supvr appln, Can Gen Elec Co Ltd, 52-59; mgr TV & organ eng, Electrohome Ltd, 59-66; consult electronics, Sparton of Can, 66-68; PRES MGT SCI, DESIGNECTICS INT INC, 70-, PRES, ADVAN PROF DEVELOP INST, 74- *Concurrent Pos:* Fel, Imp Oil Ltd, 67-68 & Cent Mortgage & Housing Corp, 68-70; consult, Xerox Corp, 72-74 & Govt of Can, 74-77. *Mem:* Sr mem Inst Elec & Electronics Engrs; Proj Mgt Inst. *Res:* The application of engineering principles and models to the practice of management, especially to engineering design management and to project management. *Mailing Add:* 5519 Carpenter Ave N Hollywood CA 91607

LOVE, TOM JAY, JR, b Jonesboro, Ark, Oct 2, 23; m 45; c 3. HEAT TRANSFER, BIOMEDICAL ENGINEERING. *Educ:* Univ Okla, BS, 48; Univ Kans, MS, 56; Purdue Univ, PhD(mech eng), 63. *Prof Exp:* Proj engr, Colgate Palmolive Co, 47-52; sr res engr, Midwest Res Inst, 52-56; from asst prof to assoc prof mech eng, 56-65, dir sch, 63-72, prof aerospace & mech eng, 65-72, HALLIBURTON PROF ENG, UNIV OKLA, 72- *Concurrent Pos:* Mem bd dirs, Sverdrup-ARO, Inc, 77-81. *Mem:* AAAS; Am Inst Aeronaut & Astronaut; Am Soc Mech Engrs; Am Optical Soc; Am Soc Eng Educ. *Res:* Physiological heat transfer; radiative heat transfer; thermography. *Mailing Add:* 865 ASP Rm 200 Sch Aerospace Mech & Nuclear Eng Univ Okla Norman OK 73069

LOVE, WARNER EDWARDS, b Philadelphia, Pa, Dec 1, 22; m 45; c 2. BIOPHYSICS. *Educ:* Swarthmore Col, BA, 46; Univ Pa, PhD(physiol), 51. *Prof Exp:* Asst instr physiol, Univ Pa, 48-49, fel biophys, Johnson Found, 51-53, assoc, 53-55; res asst physics, Inst Cancer Res, 55-56, res assoc, 56-57; from asst prof to assoc prof, 57-65, chmn dept, 72-75, PROF BIOPHYS, JOHNS HOPKINS UNIV, 65-, CHMN DEPT, 80- *Concurrent Pos:* Phillips lectr, Haverford Col, 55. *Mem:* Am Physiol Soc; Biophys Soc; Am Crystallog Asn; Am Soc Biol Chemists. *Res:* Biological ultrastructural basis of functions; x-ray crystallography of macromolecules, hemoglobins and hemocyamins. *Mailing Add:* Thomas C Jenkins Dept Biophys Johns Hopkins Univ Baltimore MD 21218

LOVE, WILLIAM ALFRED, b Pittsburgh, Pa, Aug 4, 32; m 57. PHYSICS, ELEMENTARY PARTICLES. *Educ:* Carnegie Inst Technol, BS, 54, MS, 55, PhD(physics), 58. *Prof Exp:* Res physicist, Carnegie Inst Technol, 58-59; fel, Nat Sci Found, European Orgn Nuclear Res, Switzerland, 59-60; from asst physicist to assoc physicist, 60-66, PHYSICIST, BROOKHAVEN NAT LAB, 66- *Mem:* Fel Am Phys Soc. *Res:* Particle physics. *Mailing Add:* Brookhaven Nat Lab Upton NY 11973

LOVE, WILLIAM F, b Houston, Tex, July 3, 25; m 51; c 3. SOLID STATE PHYSICS. *Educ:* Rice Inst, BS, 45, MA, 47, PhD, 49. *Prof Exp:* Instr physics, Randal Morgan Lab, Univ Pa, 49-52, asst prof, 52-54; from asst prof to assoc prof, 54-63, PROF PHYSICS, UNIV COLO, BOULDER, 63- *Mem:* Am

Phys Soc; Am Asn Physics Teachers; AAAS; Sigma Xi. *Res:* Symmetry properties of crystals; galvanomagnetic properties of metals and semiconductors in high magnetic fields; electrical noise in semiconductors. *Mailing Add:* Dept of Physics Univ of Colo Boulder CO 80309

LOVE, WILLIAM GARY, b Meridian, Miss, Aug 16, 41; m 66; c 2. NUCLEAR PHYSICS. *Educ:* Univ Tenn, BS, 63, PhD(physics), 68. *Prof Exp:* Res assoc physics, Fla State Univ, 68-70; asst prof, 70-77, ASSOC PROF PHYSICS, UNIV GA, 77- *Mem:* Am Phys Soc. *Res:* Study of the properties of the nucleon-nucleon interaction as they are manifested in multi-nucleon systems, for example, in scattering. *Mailing Add:* Dept of Physics & Astron Univ of Ga Athens GA 30602

LOVECCHIO, FRANK VITO, b Syracuse, NY, Apr 30, 43. ANALYTICAL CHEMISTRY. *Educ:* Syracuse Univ, AB, 65, PhD(chem), 70. *Prof Exp:* Fel, Ohio State Univ, 70-73; RES CHEMIST, EASTMAN KODAK CO, 73- *Mem:* Am Chem Soc; Soc Photog Scientists & Engrs. *Res:* Reactions and mechanisms of coordination compounds, including electron transfer reactions. *Mailing Add:* 20 North Point Terr Rochester NY 14617

LOVECCHIO, KAREN K, b Peekskill, NY, June 23, 42; m 68. ELECTROCHEMISTRY. *Educ:* State Univ NY Binghamton, BA, 64; Syracuse Univ, PhD(electrochem), 69. *Prof Exp:* Chemist, Syracuse Univ Res Corp, 69-70; ed, Chem Abstr Serv, 70-73; CHEMIST, EASTMAN KODAK CO, 74- *Mem:* Am Chem Soc; Soc Photog Scientists & Engrs. *Res:* Polarography; coulometry; non-aqueous titrations. *Mailing Add:* 1185 Hidden Valley Trail Rochester NY 14680

LOVEJOY, DAVID ARNOLD, b Nashua, NH, Dec 12, 43; m 69, 80; c 1. MAMMALIAN ECOLOGY. *Educ:* Univ Conn, BA, 65, PhD(zool, ecol), 70. *Prof Exp:* Asst prof, 70-75, ASSOC PROF BIOL, WESTFIELD STATE COL, 75- *Mem:* Am Soc Mammal; Ecol Soc Am. *Res:* Ecology of small mammals; Siphonapteran parasites of mammals. *Mailing Add:* Dept of Biol Westfield State Col Westfield MA 01086

LOVEJOY, DEREK R, b London, Eng, Jan 19, 28; Can citizen; m 53; c 3. ENERGY PHYSICS. *Educ:* Univ London, BS, 50; Univ Toronto, MA, 52, PhD(physics), 54. *Prof Exp:* Assoc res officer, Appl Physics Div, Nat Res Coun Can, 54-66; proj officer, Res Div, 66-72; sr tech adv, Tech Adv Div, UN Develop Prog, 72-78; SR TECH ADV NEW SOURCES OF ENERGY, UN, 78- *Concurrent Pos:* Expert thermal metrol, Nat Phys Lab Metrol Proj, Cairo, United Arab Repub, UNESCO, 64-65. *Mem:* AAAS; US/Int Solar Energy Soc. *Res:* Liquid helium physics; temperature scales and measurements from very low to very high temperatures. *Mailing Add:* United Nations New York NY 10017

LOVEJOY, EARL MARK PAUL, structural geology, geomorphology, deceased

LOVEJOY, ELWYN RAYMOND, b Nashua, NH, Aug 7, 27; m 62; c 2. POLYMER CHEMISTRY. *Educ:* Boston Univ, AB, 49; Univ Ill, MS, 50, PhD(chem), 53. *Prof Exp:* RES CHEMIST, E I DU PONT DE NEMOURS & CO, INC, 53- *Res:* Polymers; fluorocarbon and high temperature resins. *Mailing Add:* E I du Pont de Nemours Co Inc 1007 Market St Wilmington DE 19898

LOVEJOY, OWEN, b Paducah, Ky, Feb 11, 43; m 69. HUMAN BIOLOGY, BIOMECHANICS. *Educ:* Western Reserve Univ, BA, 65; Case Inst Technol, MA, 67; Univ Mass, Amherst, PhD(human biol), 70. *Prof Exp:* Assoc prof phys anthrop, 69-77, PROF SOCIOL & ANTHROP, KENT STATE UNIV, 77-; ASST CLIN PROF, DIV ORTHOP SURG, SCH MED, CASE WESTERN RESERVE UNIV, 70- *Mem:* Brit Soc Study Human Biol; Am Asn Phys Anthrop; Am Eugenics Soc. *Res:* Primate anatomy, biomechanics and taxonomy; human palaeontology and palaeodemography; skeletal biology. *Mailing Add:* Dept of Sociol & Anthrop Kent State Univ Kent OH 44242

LOVEJOY, ROLAND WILLIAM, b Portland, Ore, June 18, 31; m 59; c 2. PHYSICAL CHEMISTRY. *Educ:* Reed Col, BA, 55; Wash State Univ, PhD(chem), 60. *Prof Exp:* Fel chem, Univ Wash, 59-62; from asst prof to assoc prof, 62-76, PROF CHEM, LEHIGH UNIV, 76- *Mem:* Am Phys Soc. *Res:* Analysis of vibration-rotation spectra of inorganic and organic molecules using infrared and Raman spectroscopy; applications of far-infrared interferometry. *Mailing Add:* Dept of Chem Lehigh Univ Bethlehem PA 18015

LOVEJOY, THOMAS E, b New York, NY, Aug 22, 41; m 66; c 3. ECOLOGY. *Educ:* Yale Col, BS, 64; Yale Univ, PhD(biol), 71. *Prof Exp:* Res assoc, biol, Univ Pa, 71-74; exec asst to sci dir & asst to vpres resources & planning, Acad Natural Sci, 72-73; VPRES SCI, WORLD WILDLIFE FUND-US, 73- *Concurrent Pos:* Vis lectr, trop ecol, Yale Sch Forestry & Environ Studies, 82; chmn, Wildlife Preservtion Trust Int, 74-; treas, Int Coun Bird Preservation, 73-; res assoc ornithol, Acad Natural Sci, 71- *Mem:* AAAS; Am Inst Biol Sci; Am Ornithologists Union. *Res:* Tropical ecology; ornithology; problems of ecology theory relating to conservation and natural resource management. *Mailing Add:* World Wildlife Fund-US 800 1601 Connecticut Ave NW Washington DC 20009

LOVELACE, ALAN MATHIESON, b St Petersburg, Fla, Sept 4, 29; m 52; c 2. CHEMISTRY. *Educ:* Univ Fla, BA, 51, MA, 52, PhD(chem), 54. *Prof Exp:* mem staff, Air Force Mat Lab, Wright Patterson AFB, 54-72; dir sci & technol, Andrews AFB, Washington, DC, 72-73; prin dep asst secy, Air Force Res & Develop, 73-74; assoc admin, Aerospace Technol Off Aeronaut & Space Technol, 74-76; dep admin, Aerospace Technol, NASA, 76-81; VPRES SCI & ENG, GEN DYNAMICS CORP, 81- *Concurrent Pos:* Chmn, Adv Group Aerospace Res & Develop, NATO, 79- *Mem:* Nat Acad Eng; fel Am Inst Aeronaut & Astronaut; Am Astronaut Soc. *Res:* High performance macromolecular materials. *Mailing Add:* Gen Dynamics Corp 7733 Forsyth St Louis MO

LOVELACE, C JAMES, b Holdenville, Okla, Sept 26, 34; m 72; c 2. PLANT PHYSIOLOGY, BIOCHEMISTRY. *Educ:* Harding Col, BS, 61; Utah State Univ, MS, 64, PhD(plant physiol), 66. *Prof Exp:* PROF BOT, HUMBOLDT STATE UNIV, 65- *Mem:* Am Soc Plant Physiol; Int Soc Fluoride Res. *Res:* Air pollution; fluoride research in relation to enzyme reactions within plants; heavy metal toxicants; organic fluoride biosynthesis in plants; chlorophyl biosynthesis. *Mailing Add:* Dept of Biol Humboldt State Univ Arcata CA 95521

LOVELACE, CLAUD WILLIAM VENTON, b London, Eng, Jan 16, 34. THEORETICAL PHYSICS. *Educ:* Univ Capetown, BS, 54. *Prof Exp:* Dept Sci & Indust Res res fel, Imp Col, Univ London, 61-62, lectr physics, 62-65; sr physicist, Europ Orgn Nuclear Res, Geneva, 65-71; PROF PHYSICS, RUTGERS UNIV, NEW BRUNSWICK, 70- *Res:* Theoretical particle physics; strong interactions; high energy phenomenology. *Mailing Add:* Dept of Physics Rutgers Univ New Brunswick NJ 08903

LOVELACE, RICHARD VAN EVERA, b St Louis, Mo, Oct 16, 41; m 73; c 2. PLASMA PHYSICS, ASTROPHYSICS. *Educ:* Wash Univ, BS, 64; Cornell Univ, PhD(physics), 70. *Prof Exp:* Res assoc, Lab Plasma Studies, Cornell Univ, 70-73 & Plasma Physics Lab, Princeton Univ, 73-74; asst prof, 75-77, ASSOC PROF APPL PHYSICS, CORNELL UNIV, 78- *Concurrent Pos:* Vis res assoc, US Naval Res Lab, 70-71; consult, Lawrence Livermore Lab, 71- & Plasma Physics Lab, Princeton Univ, 74-75. *Mem:* Am Astron Soc; Am Phys Soc. *Res:* Plasma physics of controlled fusion systems; collective phenomena of galaxies and quasars; wave propagation through random media; electrokinetic properties of lymphocytes. *Mailing Add:* Dept of Appl Physics Cornell Univ Ithaca NY 14853

LOVELAND, DONALD WILLIAM, b Rochester, NY, Dec 26, 34. MATHEMATICS, COMPUTER SCIENCE. *Educ:* Oberlin Col, AB, 56; Mass Inst Technol, SM, 58; NY Univ, PhD(math), 64. *Prof Exp:* Mathematician & programmer, Int Bus Mach Corp, 58-59; instr math, NY Univ, 63-64; asst prof, 64-67; from asst prof to assoc prof, Carnegie-Mellon Univ, 67-73; PROF COMPUT SCI, DUKE UNIV, 73- *Mem:* Asn Comput Mach; Asn Symbolic Logic; AAAS. *Res:* Artificial intelligence; theorem proving by computer; foundational study of the notion of random sequence; fast approximation algorithms for computationally hard problems. *Mailing Add:* Dept of Comput Sci Duke Univ Durham NC 27706

LOVELAND, ROBERT EDWARD, b Camden, NJ, May 3, 38; m 62; c 3. BIOLOGY. *Educ:* Rutgers Univ, Camden, AB, 59; Harvard Univ, MA, 61, PhD(biol), 63. *Prof Exp:* Asst prof biol, Long Beach State Col, 63-64; asst prof zool, 64-70, ASSOC PROF ZOOL, RUTGERS UNIV, NEW BRUNSWICK, 70- *Concurrent Pos:* NSF sci fac fel, Univ BC, 71-72. *Mem:* AAAS; Atlantic Estuarine Res Soc. *Res:* Distribution of marine invertebrates; behavioral modelling; population models of biological systems. *Mailing Add:* Dept of Zool Rutgers Univ New Brunswick NJ 08904

LOVELAND, WALTER (DAVID), b Chicago, Ill, Dec 23, 39; m 62. NUCLEAR CHEMISTRY. *Educ:* Mass Inst Technol, SB, 61; Univ Wash, PhD(chem), 66. *Prof Exp:* Res assoc chem, Argonne Nat Lab, 66-67; res asst prof, 67-68, asst prof, 68-74, assoc prof, 74-81, PROF CHEM, ORE STATE UNIV, 81- *Concurrent Pos:* US Dept Energy res grant, Ore State Univ, 68-; vis scientist, Lawrence Berkeley Lab, 76, 77 & 80; Tarter fel, Ore State Univ, 77. *Mem:* AAAS; Am Phys Soc; Am Chem Soc. *Res:* Nuclear reactions, especially heavy ion reactions and fission; activation analysis; use of computers for data acquisition; environmental chemistry. *Mailing Add:* Radiation Ctr Ore State Univ Corvallis OR 97331

LOVELL, BERNARD WENTZEL, b Greenfield, Mass. COMPUTER SCIENCE, ELECTRICAL ENGINEERING. *Educ:* Mass Inst Technol, BS, 58, MS, 58, EE, 63; Univ Conn, PhD(comput sci), 69. *Prof Exp:* Electronic engr, US Naval Ord Lab, 54-59; instr elec eng, Mass Inst Technol, 59-63; asst prof, Univ Mass, 63-67; ASSOC PROF ELEC ENG, UNIV CONN, 69- *Mem:* Inst Elec & Electronics Engrs; Am Phys Soc; Asn Comput Mach. *Res:* Automata theory; operating systems. *Mailing Add:* Comput Ctr Univ of Conn Storrs CT 06268

LOVELL, CHARLES W(ILLIAM), JR, b Louisville, Ky, Nov 16, 22; m 48; c 2. CIVIL ENGINEERING, SOIL MECHANICS. *Educ:* Univ Louisville, BCE, 44; Purdue Univ, MSCE, 51, PhD(civil eng), 57. *Prof Exp:* Instr civil eng, Univ Louisville, 46-48; from res asst to res engr & instr, 48-57, from asst prof to assoc prof, 57-76, PROF CIVIL ENG, PURDUE UNIV, 76- *Concurrent Pos:* Vis assoc prof, Mass Inst Technol, 62-63; mem, Hwy Res Bd, Nat Acad Sci-Nat Res Coun. *Mem:* Nat Soc Prof Engrs; Am Soc Civil Engrs; Am Soc Eng Educ; Am Soc Testing & Mat. *Res:* Frost action; load-deformation characteristics of soils; subsurface exploration. *Mailing Add:* Sch of Civil Eng Purdue Univ West Lafayette IN 47907

LOVELL, DONALD JOSEPH, b Racine, Wis, June 8, 22; m 53; c 1. OPTICS. *Educ:* Univ Wis, PhB & MS, 47. *Prof Exp:* Asst math & physics, Univ Wis, 46-47; instr physics, Norwich Univ, 47-48; physicist, Naval Res Lab, 49-52; engr, Air Arm Div, Westinghouse Elec Corp, 52-53; proj engr, Photoswitch, Inc, 54-56; head res group, Barnes Eng Co, 56-58; prin engr optics, Prod Div, Bendix Corp, 59-61; res physicist, Univ Mich, 61-68; sr res physicist, Astron Res Facility, Univ Mass, Amherst, 68-69; prof optics, Mass Col Optom, 69-73; OPTICAL CONSULT, 71- *Concurrent Pos:* Lectr, Univ Conn, 57-58; consult, Inst Defense Anal, 63-69. *Mem:* Optical Soc Am; Soc of Photo-Optical Instrumentation Engr. *Res:* Infrared physics; optical instruments; history of optics. *Mailing Add:* Barton Road Stow MA 01775

LOVELL, EDWARD GEORGE, b Windsor, Ont, May 25, 39; US citizen; m 64; c 2. ENGINEERING, STRUCTURAL MECHANICS. *Educ:* Wayne State Univ, BSAE, 60, MSEM, 61; Univ Mich, Ann Arbor, PhD(eng mech), 67. *Prof Exp:* Instr eng mech, Univ Mich, Ann Arbor, 63-67; Nat Acad Sci-Nat Res Coun res associateship, Langley Res Ctr, NASA, 67-68; ASSOC PROF ENG MECH, UNIV WIS-MADISON, 68- *Concurrent Pos:* Proj engr,

Boeing Co, Wash, 62; design engr, Pratt & Whitney Aircraft, Conn, 70; NATO sr sci fel, Univ Manchester, Eng, 73. *Mem:* Sigma Xi. *Res:* Nonlinear vibrations of structures; structural instability; stress analysis; nuclear reactor structural mechanics. *Mailing Add:* Dept of Eng Mech Univ of Wis Madison WI 53706

LOVELL, FREDERICK MAURICE, b Maesteg, SWales, Jan 6, 30; US citizen; m 57; c 3. X-RAY CRYSTALLOGRAPHY. *Educ:* Univ Wales, BSc, 52, PhD(physics, crystallog), 60. *Prof Exp:* Res fel chem, Univ Leeds, Eng, 59-60; res fel, Univ Sydney, Australia, 60-63; res assoc, Colo Univ, Boulder, 63-64; asst prof biochem, Columbia Univ, 64-69; asst prof physics, Trinity Univ, San Antonio, 69-70; SR X-RAY CRYSTALLOGR, LEDERLE LABS, DIV AM CYANAMID CO, 70- *Mem:* Am Crystallog Asn. *Res:* X-ray crystal structure analysis of compounds of pharmaceutical interest. *Mailing Add:* Lederle Labs Pearl River NY 10965

LOVELL, HAROLD LEMUEL, b Bellwood, Pa, July 13, 22; m 44; c 2. FUEL SCIENCE, MINERAL ENGINEERING. *Educ:* Pa State Univ, BS, 43, MS, 45, PhD(fuel tech), 52. *Prof Exp:* Asst chem micros, Pa State Univ, 43-44, microchem, 44-45; res chemist, Mallinckrodt Chem Works, 45-47; asst fuel technol, 47-51, res assoc spectros, 51-52, asst prof, 52-58, mineral prep, 58-64, assoc prof, 64-71, actg head dept mineral prep, 64-68, assoc prof, 71-76, PROF MINERAL ENG, PA STATE UNIV, 77-, DIR MINE DRAINAGE RES SECT, 68- *Concurrent Pos:* Consult, US Dept Com-Com Tech Adv Bd, 74-75. *Mem:* Am Chem Soc; Am Inst Mining, Metall & Petrol Eng; Am Soc Test Mat. *Res:* Mineral preparation; analytical chemistry; absorption and emission; microchemistry; coal constitution chemistry; chemical utilization of coal; mine water pollution-treatment; coal preparation; physical processing of coal for synfuel feed stock management. *Mailing Add:* 109 Mineral Industry Bldg Pa State Univ University Park PA 16802

LOVELL, JAMES BYRON, b Fallentimber, Pa, Mar 19, 27; m; c 2. ENTOMOLOGY. *Educ:* Pa State Univ, BS, 50; Univ Ill, MS, 55, PhD(entom), 56. *Prof Exp:* Entomologist, US Army Chem Ctr, Md, 50-53; asst, Univ Ill, 53-56; RES ENTOMOLOGIST, AGR DIV, AM CYANAMID CO, 56- *Mem:* AAAS; Entom Soc Am. *Res:* Insect physiology and toxicology; mode of action of insecticides; mechanism of resistance in insects. *Mailing Add:* Agr Div Am Cyanamid Co Princeton NJ 08540

LOVELL, JAMES F, environmental biology, science administration, see previous edition

LOVELL, PAUL FRANCIS, chemical engineering, see previous edition

LOVELL, RICHARD ARLINGTON, b Kentland, Ind, Aug 4, 30; m 65; c 6. NEUROCHEMISTRY. *Educ:* Xavier Univ, Ohio, BS, 52, MS, 53; St Louis Univ, Lic Philos, 59; McGill Univ, PhD(biochem), 63. *Prof Exp:* Proj assoc physiol, Epilepsy Res Ctr, Univ Wis, 64-65; USPHS Psychopharmacol Res Training Prog fel psychiat, Yale Univ, 65-66; from instr to asst prof neurochem in psychiat, Univ Chicago, 69-75; MGR BIOCHEM PHARMACOL, CIBA-GEIGY CORP, SUMMIT, NJ, 75- *Concurrent Pos:* Res fel, Schweppe Found, 68-71. *Mem:* AAAS; Am Chem Soc; Am Soc Neurochem; Am Epilepsy Soc; Soc Neurosci. *Res:* Neurochemistry; neuropharmacology; biochemical control mechanisms in the nervous system. *Mailing Add:* Ciba-Geigy Corp 556 Morris Ave Summit NJ 07901

LOVELL, RICHARD THOMAS, b Lockesburg, Ark, Feb 21, 34; m 63; c 2. FISHERIES. *Educ:* Okla State Univ, BS, 56, MS, 58; La State Univ, PhD(nutrit, biochem), 63. *Prof Exp:* From asst prof to assoc prof food sci, La State Univ, 63-69; assoc prof, 69-75, PROF FISHERIES & ALLIED AQUACULT, AUBURN UNIV, 75- *Concurrent Pos:* Consult fish cult, US AID, 72-74; columnist, Com Fish Farmer & World Aquacult, 74-; mem, Comt Animal Nutrit, Nat Res Coun-Nat Acad Sci, 74-; assoc ed, Trans Am Fisheries Soc, 75- *Mem:* Fel Am Inst Chemists; Am Fisheries Soc; Am Chem Soc; Inst Food Technologists. *Res:* Fish nutrition, especially vitamin C requirements and energy metabolism of warm water fish cultured for food; environment-related off-flavors in intensively-cultured food fishes. *Mailing Add:* Dept of Fisheries & Allied Aquacult Auburn Univ Auburn AL 36830

LOVELL, ROBERT EDMUND, b Ann Arbor, Mich, Aug 12, 21; m 47. SYSTEMS ENGINEERING, ELECTRICAL ENGINEERING. *Educ:* Univ Mich, BSE, 43; Univ Ariz, MS, 71, PhD(systems eng), 75. *Prof Exp:* Navigator & electronics officer, US Navy, 43-46; engr, Pacific Gas & Elec Co, Calif, 46-48; res engr, NAm Aviation Inc, NMex, 48-49; engr & mgr, Dynalectron Corp, 49-69; assoc prof indust eng, Ariz State Univ, 72-76; systs eng, Univ Petroleum & Minerals, Saudi Arabia, 76-77; ASSOC PROF INDUST ENG, ARIZ STATE UNIV, 77- *Mem:* Inst Elec & Electronics Engrs; Am Soc Eng Educ; Am Inst Indust Engrs. *Res:* Computer simulation of large scale systems. *Mailing Add:* Dept of Indust & Mgt Systs Eng Ariz State Univ Tempe AZ 85281

LOVELL, ROBERT GIBSON, b Ann Arbor, Mich, May 13, 20; m 48; c 5. INTERNAL MEDICINE, ALLERGY. *Educ:* Univ Mich, MD, 44, AB, 57. *Prof Exp:* From instr to asst prof, 50-73, fac secy, 54-56, asst dean sch med, 57-59, CLIN PROF INTERNAL MED, SCH MED, UNIV MICH, ANN ARBOR, 73- *Concurrent Pos:* Consult physician, US Vet Admin Hosp, 54-55; consult, President's Comn Vet Pensions, US Air Force, 55; consult, Wayne County Gen Hosp, Mich, 59-; chmn med ed comt, St Joseph Mercy Hosp, 63- *Mem:* AMA; assoc Am Col Chest Physicians; fel Am Acad Allergy. *Res:* Use of medications and aerosol preparations in treatment of bronchial asthma. *Mailing Add:* 3000 Geddes Ave Ann Arbor MI 48104

LOVELL, STUART ESTES, b Seattle, Wash, Oct 8, 28; m 55; c 2. COMPUTER SCIENCE. *Educ:* Univ Wash, BS, 53; Brown Univ, PhD(chem), 58. *Prof Exp:* Proj assoc chem, Univ Wis, 58-63, asst prof comput sci, 63-67; mgr computer serv, 65-75, SYSTEM ANALYST, KITT PEAK OBSERV, 75- *Mem:* Asn Comput Mach. *Res:* Systems programming; computer based systems. *Mailing Add:* 950 N Cherry Ave Kitt Peak Nat Observ Tucson AZ 85719

LOVELOCK, DAVID, b Bromley, Eng. MATHEMATICS, THEORETICAL PHYSICS. *Educ:* Univ Natal, BSc, 59, Hons, 60, PhD(math), 62, DSc, 74. *Prof Exp:* Res asst math, Univ Natal, 60-61; jr fel, Bristol Univ, 62-63, lectr, 63-69; assoc prof, 69-74, prof appl math, Univ Waterloo, Ont, 74; PROF MATH, UNIV ARIZ, 74- *Concurrent Pos:* Nat Res Coun Can grant, Univ Waterloo, 69-, adj prof appl math, 74- *Mem:* Am Math Soc; Tensor Soc. *Res:* General relativity; calculus of variations; differential geometry. *Mailing Add:* Dept of Math Univ Ariz Tucson AZ 85721

LOVELY, RICHARD HERBERT, b Santa Monica, Calif, Sept 20, 41; div. BEHAVIORAL TOXICOLOGY, NEUROSCIENCES. *Educ:* Calif State Univ, Northridge, BA, 65; Cent Wash Univ, MS, 67; Univ Wash, Seattle, PhD(psychol), 74. *Prof Exp:* Instr psychol, Yakima Valley Col, 67-68; lectr psychol, Univ Wash, 70-72, psychol & rehab med, 73-75, asst prof, 75-79; SR RES SCIENTIST NEUROSCI, DEPT BIOL, BATTELLE MEM INST, 79- *Concurrent Pos:* Vis prof, Calif State Univ, Chico, 72-73; Consult, Nat Inst Environ Health Sci, 76-, Nat Coun Radiation Protection & Measurements, 78- *Mem:* Soc Neurosci; Psychonomic Soc; Behav Teratol Soc; Bioelectromagnetic Soc; Fedn Am Soc Exp Biol. *Res:* Biopsychological effects of electromagnetic radiation exposure; in utero determinants of adult behavior; neurobehavioral toxicology; neural substrates of learning and memory, limbic system functions and constraints on animal behavior. *Mailing Add:* Neurosci Group Biol Dept Battelle Mem Inst Richland WA 99352

LOVENBERG, WALTER MCKAY, b Trenton, NJ, Aug 9, 34; m 58; c 2. BIOCHEMISTRY. *Educ:* Rutgers Univ, BS, 56, MS, 58; George Washington Univ, PhD(biochem), 62. *Prof Exp:* Biochemist, 59-72, trainee, 62-63, HEAD SECT BIOCHEM PHARMACOL, HYPERTENSION-ENDOCRINE BR, NAT HEART, LUNG & BLOOD INST, 72- *Mem:* Am Soc Biol Chem; Am Soc Pharmacol & Exp Therapeut; Biochem Soc; Am Soc Neurochem; Am Col Neuropsychopharmacol. *Res:* Enzymatic mechanisms and the chemistry of proteins involved in neurohumoral amine biosynthesis. *Mailing Add:* Rm 7N262 Clin Ctr Nat Inst Health Bethesda MD 20205

LO VERDE, PHILIP THOMAS, b Benton Harbor, MI, Oct 5, 46; m 65; c 3. PARASITOLOGY, MEDICAL MALACOLOGY. *Educ:* Univ Mich, BS, 68, MS, 71, MS, PhD(epidemiol sci), 76. *Prof Exp:* Mus asst, Zool Mus, Univ Mich, 68-69, NIH fel, 70-75, curatorial asst, 73-75, teaching fel, Dept Zool, 72-73; res assoc med malacol, Ain Shams Univ, Cairo, 74-75; asst prof parasitol, dept biol sci, Purdue Univ, 76-81; ASST PROF PARASITOL, DEPT MICRO, SCH MED, STATE UNIV NY, BUFFALO, 81- *Concurrent Pos:* Guest scientist, Naval Med Res Unit No 3, Cairo, Egypt, 74-75. *Honors & Awards:* Chester A Herrick Award, Eli Lilly & Co, 74. *Mem:* Am Soc Parasitologists; Am Micros Soc; Soc Exp Descriptive Malacol; AAAS; NY Acad Sci. *Res:* Host-parasite interrelationships; invertebrate defense mechanisms; parasite immunology and molecular biology; parasitology; malacology; schistosomiasis. *Mailing Add:* Dept of Biol Sci Purdue Univ West Lafayette IN 47907

LOVERING, EDWARD GILBERT, b Winnipeg, Man, Oct 15, 34; m 58; c 3. PHARMACEUTICAL CHEMISTRY. *Educ:* Univ Man, BSc, 57, MSc, 58; Univ Ottawa, PhD(chem), 61. *Prof Exp:* Sci officer radiation chem, Defense Res Bd, 58-59; Nat Res Coun Can fel, Oxford Univ, 61-63; res chemist, Polymer Corp Ltd, 63-69, assoc scientist, Polymer Corp, 69-71; RES SCIENTIST HEALTH & WELFARE OF CAN, 71- *Mem:* Am Chem Soc; Chem Inst Can; Acad Pharmaceut Sci; Sigma Xi. *Res:* contaminants in drugs and cosmetics; drug raw material characteriation; drug stability; pharmaceutical and cosmetic analysis. *Mailing Add:* Drug Res Labs Tunney's Pasture Ottawa ON K1A 0L2 Can

LOVERING, THOMAS SEWARD, b St Paul, Minn, May 12, 96; m 19; c 1. ECONOMIC GEOLOGY. *Educ:* Univ Minn, EM, 22, MS, 23, PhD(econ geol), 24. *Prof Exp:* Instr geol, Univ Minn, 22-24; instr, Univ Ariz, 24-25; jr geologist, US Geol Surv, 25-26, from asst geologist to geologist, 26-46, br res geologist, 47-54, chief geochem explor sect, 54-58, div res scientist, 58-65; prof geol & consult sci & eng, Univ Ariz, 66-76; RETIRED. *Concurrent Pos:* Mem, Yale Exped, Nfld & Labrador, 20; prof, Univ Mich, 34-42, 46-47; consult remote sensors, NASA; AID tech adv & consult, Govt Mex, 62; UN consult, Mineral Explor Seminar, Mex City, 64; geologist, US Geol Surv, Colo; mem comt terrestrial resources & future man, Nat Acad Sci; lectr, Am Inst Mining, Metall & Petrol Eng, 65; US del, Int Geol Cong, Algiers, 52, Centenary Cong Mineral Sci & Indust, France, Paris, 55, Inst Geol Cong, Mex City, 56, Pakistan Sci Cong, West Pakistan, 57, US rep mineral resources, Econ Comn Asia & Far East, Bangkok, 54, Japanese-Am energy panel, Joint US-Japan Coop Develop & Utilization Nat Resources, 65. *Honors & Awards:* US Dept Interior Distinguished Serv Gold Medal, 59; Penrose Gold Medal, Soc Econ Geol, 65; Jackling Award, Am Inst Mining, Metall & Petrol Eng, 65. *Mem:* Nat Acad Sci; fel Geol Soc Am (past pres); fel Mineral Soc Am; Soc Econ Geol; Soc Environ Geochem & Health. *Res:* Mathematics of heat conduction and model experiments; petrology of rock alteration; geochemical exploration; structures; geology of Precambrian; mining geology; rock failure; physiography; biochemistry and geochemistry of weathering; mineral economics; stable isotopes in altered rocks; biological history. *Mailing Add:* 2663 Tallant Rd Apt 186N Santa Barbara CA 93105

LOVESTEDT, STANLEY ALMER, b Iliff, Colo, June 7, 13; m 40; c 3. ORAL SURGERY. *Educ:* Univ Southern Calif, BS & DDS, 38; Univ Minn, MS, 45; Am Bd Oral Surg, dipl. *Prof Exp:* Asst, Mayo Grad Sch Med, Univ Minn, 41-43, consult, 43-46, from instr to assoc prof oral surg, 60-69; consult, 43-62, head dept, 55-62, sr consult, Dept Dent & Oral Surg, Mayo Clin, 62-78; clin prof oral surg, 69-78, EMER CLIN PROF ORAL SURG, MAYO MED SCH, UNIV MINN, 78- *Mem:* AAAS; Am Soc Oral Surg; Am Dent Asn; Am Acad Dent Radiol; fel Am Col Dent (pres, 69). *Res:* Radiology; oral medicine. *Mailing Add:* Mayo Clin 200 First St SW Rochester MN 55901

LOVETT, EVA G, b Orange, NJ, Aug 17, 40; m 63. ORGANIC CHEMISTRY. *Educ:* Douglass Col, Rutgers Univ, BA, 62; Univ Rochester, PhD(chem), 66. *Prof Exp:* Sr chemist, Merck, Sharp & Dohme Res Lab, 66-67; res assoc chem, Washington Univ, St Louis, 69-76; RES CHEMIST, TRETOLITE DIV/PETROLITE CORP, ST LOUIS, 76- *Res:* Synthesis, degradation and mass spectroscopy of natural products, particularly purines, pyrimidines and related heterocyclic compounds; polymer synthesis and characterization. *Mailing Add:* Tretolite Div/Petrolite Corp 369 Marshall Ave St Louis MO 63119

LOVETT, JACK R, b Logan, Utah, Nov 29, 32; m 60; c 4. ACOUSTICS, PHYSICAL OCEANOGRAPHY. *Educ:* Brigham Young Univ, BA, 58. *Prof Exp:* Physicist, US Naval Ord Test Sta, 58-67, physicist, Naval Undersea Ctr, 67-77, PHYSICIST, NAVAL OCEAN SYSTS CTR, 77- *Mem:* Acoust Soc Am; Sigma Xi; Sci Res Soc NAm. *Res:* Underwater sound propogation and attenuation; turbulence theory and effect on propogation; instrumentation; salinity; temperature; pressure; sound velocity. *Mailing Add:* Naval Ocean Systs Ctr Code 5313 B San Diego CA 92152

LOVETT, JAMES SATTERTHWAITE, b Fallsington, Pa, Aug 22, 25; m 46; c 1. BOTANY, BIOCHEMISTRY. *Educ:* Earlham Col, AB, 53; Mich State Univ, PhD, 59. *Prof Exp:* Fel bot, Mich State Univ, 59-60; from asst prof to assoc prof, 60-69, assoc head, Dept Biol Sci, 75-79, PROF MYCOL, PURDUE UNIV, 69- *Concurrent Pos:* Nat Sci Found sr fel, 66-67; Europ Molecular Biol Orgn fel, 71; assoc ed, Exp Mycol, 76-79; mem, Microbial Physiol Study Sect, NIH, 79-81. *Mem:* AAAS; Am Soc Microbiol; Soc Develop Biol; Mycol Soc Am. *Res:* Physiology of fungi; genetic and metabolic control of development in the lower fungi, principally the aquatic Phycomycetes. *Mailing Add:* Dept Biol Sci Purdue Univ West Lafayette IN 47907

LOVETT, JOHN ROBERT, b Norristown, Pa, June 17, 31; m 56; c 3. ORGANIC CHEMISTRY. *Educ:* Ursinus Col, BS, 53; Univ Del, MS, 55, PhD(chem), 57. *Prof Exp:* Res chemist polymer processes, Esso Res & Eng Co, 57-59, prof leader high energy propellants, 59-60, sr chemist, 60-61, sect head, 61-64, dir govt res lab, 65-68, dir petrol additives lab, 68-70, vpres paramins dept, Exxon Chem Co, 70-73, worldwide tech mgr, 73-76; vpres res, Air Prod & Chem Inc, 76-81, mem bd dir, 77-81; PRES & MEM BD DIR, AIR PROD EUROPE, INC, 81- *Concurrent Pos:* Bd trustees, Cedar Crest Col, 77-81; adv bd, US Dept Energy, 78- *Mem:* Am Chem Soc; Indust Res Inst; Mfg Chemists Asn; AAAS. *Res:* Polymers; chemical additives; industrial gases; catalysts; fossil energy technology. *Mailing Add:* Air Prod & Chem Inc PO Box 538 Allentown PA 18105

LOVETT, JOSEPH, b Columbus Co, NC, Feb 24, 33; m 57; c 2. ENVIRONMENTAL HEALTH, PUBLIC HEALTH. *Educ:* Wake Forest Univ, BS, 56; Univ NC, Chapel Hill, MSPH, 60; Univ Minn, Minneapolis, MS, 65, PhD(environ health, microbiol), 71. *Prof Exp:* Asst supt water treat, City of Raleigh, NC, 57-58; regional consult, Interstate Carrier Prog Environ Eng & Food Protection, USPHS, 60-64, chief mycol sect, Food Microbiol Br, 66-77, ASST BR CHIEF, BACT PHYSIOL BR, DIV MICROBIOL, BUR FOODS, FOOD & DRUG ADMIN, USPHS, 77- *Mem:* Int Asn Milk, Food & Environ Sanitarians; Am Soc Microbiol; Am Dairy Sci Asn; Sigma Xi; Inst Food Technologists. *Res:* Toxic microbial metabolites in foods and the ecology of toxigenic and pathogenic microorganisms. *Mailing Add:* Bact Physiol Br Food & Drug Admin Cincinnati OH 45226

LOVETT, PAUL SCOTT, b Philadelphia, Pa, Dec 14, 40; m 64; c 1. MICROBIOLOGY. *Educ:* Delaware Valley Col, BS, 64; Temple Univ, PhD(microbiol), 68. *Prof Exp:* USPHS fel microbiol, Scripps Clin & Res Found, Calif, 68-70; from asst prof to assoc prof, 70-78, PROF BIOL SCI, UNIV MD, BALTIMORE COUNTY, 78- *Concurrent Pos:* USPHS career develop award, 76-81; mem gen biol study sect, NSF, 78-81. *Mem:* Am Soc Microbiol. *Res:* Microbial genetics; mechanisms of bacteriophage infection; bacillus plasmids. *Mailing Add:* Dept of Biol Sci Univ of Md Baltimore County Catonsville MD 21228

LOVETT-DOUST, JOHN WILLIAM, psychiatry, deceased

LOVICK, ROBERT CLYDE, b Atchison, Kans, Aug 25, 21; m 45; c 2. ELECTRICAL ENGINEERING. *Educ:* Univ Nebr, BSc, 44. *Prof Exp:* Sr tech adv, Eastman Kodak Co, 44-78; PRES, IDEAS FOR INDUST, 78- *Concurrent Pos:* Soc Motion Picture & TV Eng fel, 63; mem S-1 comt sound recording, Am Nat Standards Inst, High Definition TV Study Group. *Mem:* Brit Kine, Sound & TV Soc; Soc Motion Picture & TV Eng; Int Studies Orgn; Int Electrotech Comn. *Res:* Development of proximity fuses for naval ordnance; systems for silver sound records on reversal color films; development of magnetic prestriping on removable backing color films; co-inventor multi-layer digital magnetic recording media; establishment of electronic-optical image evaluation center. *Mailing Add:* Ideas for Indust 88 Hillhurst Lane Rochester NY 14617

LOVING, BEN A, b Edgewood, Tex, Dec 29, 33; m 56; c 3. CHEMISTRY. *Educ:* E Tex State Univ, BS, 56; Univ Tex, Austin, MA, 59; Univ Utah, PhD(chem), 68. *Prof Exp:* Cereal chemist, Int Milling Co, Greenville, Tex, 56; teaching asst, Univ Tex, Austin, 56-58; assoc prof chem, Carroll Col, Wis, 59-60; NSF res assoc, Inst Paper Chem, Wis, 60; proj engr, Explosives Eval & Test Div, US Air Force, Hill AFB, Utah, 60-62, chief, Tech Br, Aerospace Fuels Field Off, Tokyo, 62-65, res mat engr, Fluids & Lubricants Mat Br, Nonmetallic Mat Div, Mat Lab, 68-71, chief, Chem Physics Br, Mat Lab, Ohio, 71-72, res mgr chem & weaponry, Dir Sci, Dir Sci & Technol, Hq Air Force Systs Command, Andrews AFB, Washington, DC, 72-75, dir, chem Chem Sci, 75-78, chief scientist, F J Seiler Res Lab, 78-80. *Concurrent Pos:* Res consult, Nicholas-Glidden Pharmaceut Co, Wis, 59-60; instr chem, Univ Va, Arlington, 74-75. *Mem:* Am Chem Soc; Sigma Xi. *Res:* Explosives, propellants, thermal batteries, laser chemistry (kinetics and spectroscopy of exited states). *Mailing Add:* 6743 Doolittle Dr Edwards CA 93523

LOVING, FRANK A(BRAHAM), b Sherman, Tex, Mar 15, 20; m 45; c 3. CHEMICAL ENGINEERING. *Educ:* Tex A&M Univ, BS, 41. *Prof Exp:* Chemist, Eastern Lab, 41-46, sr engr, 46-48, sr res engr, 58-64, res supt, Potomac River Develop Lab, 64-67, dir, 67-75, SR RES ASSOC, POTOMAC RIVER DEVELOP LAB, E I DU PONT DE NEMOURS & CO, INC, 75- *Concurrent Pos:* Mem adv comt explosives tagging, Bur Alcohol, Tobacco & Firearms, Dept Treas, 75- *Mem:* AAAS; Am Ord Asn; Am Chem Soc; Inst Makers Explosives. *Res:* Formulation, fabrication, experimental design and safety of high explosives. *Mailing Add:* River Develop Lab E I Du Pont de Nemours Inc Martinsburg WV 25401

LOVINGER, ANDREW JOSEPH, b Athens, Greece, May 15, 48; m 76. POLYMER SCIENCE, CHEMICAL ENGINEERING. *Educ:* Columbia Univ, BS, 70, MS, 71, ScD(polymer sci), 77. *Prof Exp:* MEM TECH STAFF POLYMER RES, BELL TEL LABS INC, 77- *Concurrent Pos:* Adj asst prof, Dept Chem Eng & Appl Chem, Columbia Univ, NY, 81-82, adj assoc prof, 82- *Mem:* Am Phys Soc; Am Chem Soc; Sigma Xi; Electron Micros Soc Am. *Res:* Structure and properties of polymeric materials; biomedical engineering. *Mailing Add:* Bell Labs Murray Hill NJ 07974

LOVINGOOD, JUDSON ALLISON, b Birmingham, Ala, July 18, 36; m 55; c 4. MATHEMATICS, ELECTRICAL ENGINEERING. *Educ:* Univ Ala, BSEE, 58, PhD(math), 68; Univ Minn, MS, 63. *Prof Exp:* Assoc engr, Martin Co, 58-59; res engr, Honeywell Inc, 59-62; aerospace engr, 62-64, dep chief astrodyn guid theory div, 64-69, chief dynamics & control div, Aero-Astrodyn Lab, 69-74, DIR SYSTS DYNAMICS LAB, MARSHALL SPACE FLIGHT CTR, NASA, 74- *Concurrent Pos:* Asst prof, Univ Ala, Huntsville, 68- *Mem:* Am Inst Aeronaut & Astronaut. *Res:* Optimal and adaptive control theory research applications to launch and space vehicles; mathematical research in guidance theory, control theory and celestial mechanics. *Mailing Add:* Systs Dynamics Lab NASA-Marshall Space Flight Ctr Huntsville AL 35812

LOVINS, ROBERT E, b Ashgrove, Mo, Sept 25, 35; m 56; c 1. MASS SPECTROMETRY, PROTEIN BIOCHEMISTRY. *Educ:* Univ Calif, Riverside, AB, 58; San Jose State Col, MS, 61; Univ Calif, Davis, PhD(chem), 63. *Prof Exp:* Lectr, chem & res chemist, Univ Calif, 63-65; res assoc chem, Mass Inst Technol, 65-66, asst dir, Mass Spectrometry Lab, 66-69; assoc prof biochem & dir, High Resolution Mass Spectrometry Ctr, Univ Ga, 69-76; ASSOC PROF BASIC & CLIN IMMUNOL & MICROBIOL, MED UNIV SC, 76- *Concurrent Pos:* NIH Res Career Develop Award, 71- *Mem:* Am Soc Biol Chem; Am Asn Immunologists; Am Soc Mass Spectrometry. *Res:* Application of mass spectrometry to the sequence analysis of heterogeneous proteins; structural heterogeneity of antibody proteins; tumor antigen structures. *Mailing Add:* Dept of Immunol & Microbiol Med Univ of SC Charleston SC 29403

LOVRIEN, REX EUGENE, b Eagle Grove, Iowa, Jan 25, 28; m 56; c 2. PHYSICAL BIOCHEMISTRY. *Educ:* Univ Minn, BS, 53; Univ Iowa, PhD, 58. *Prof Exp:* Res assoc phys chem, Yale Univ, 58-61; asst prof, 65-69, assoc prof, 69-76, PROF BIOCHEM, UNIV MINN, 76- *Mem:* Am Chem Soc; Biophys Soc. *Res:* Macromolecular biochemistry; solution physical chemistry; light energy utilization. *Mailing Add:* Dept of Biochem Gortner Lab Col of Biol Sci Univ of Minn St Paul MN 55101

LOVSHIN, LEONARD LOUIS, JR, b Rochester, Minn, Mar 21, 42; m 73; c 1. FISHERIES MANAGEMENT. *Educ:* Miami Univ, BA, 64; Univ Wis, MS, 66; Auburn Univ, PhD(fisheries), 72. *Prof Exp:* Asst prof, 72-78, ASSOC PROF FISHERIES, AUBURN UNIV, 78- *Concurrent Pos:* USAID-Auburn Univ proj coordr, Tech Assistance Prog Fisheries Develop, Ctr Ichthyol Res, Fortaleza, Brazil, 72- *Mem:* Am Fisheries Soc. *Res:* Fish culture research dealing with Tilapias, all male hybrid tilapias, native species indigenous to Brazil, and the extension of research results to local fish farmers. *Mailing Add:* Dept of Fisheries Auburn Univ Auburn AL 36830

LOW, BARBARA WHARTON, b Lancaster, Eng, Mar 23, 20; nat US; m 50. PROTEIN STRUCTURE & FUNCTION. *Educ:* Oxford Univ, BA, 42, MA, 46, DPhil(chem), 48. *Prof Exp:* Res assoc, Harvard Med Sch, 48, assoc phys chem, 48-50, asst prof, 50-56; assoc prof, 56-66, PROF BIOCHEM, COL PHYSICIANS & SURGEONS, COLUMBIA UNIV, 66- *Concurrent Pos:* Assoc mem, Lab Phys Chem, Harvard Univ, 50-54; vis prof, Univ Strasbourg, 65; mem biophys & biophys chem study sect, USPHS, 66-69; vis prof, Tohoku Univ, 75. *Mem:* AAAS; Am Chem Soc; Am Soc Biol Chem; Am Crystallog Asn; Am Acad Arts & Sci. *Res:* X-ray crystal structure of non-enzyme proteins and peptides, particularly snake venom post-synaptic neurotoxins, cytotoxins and membrane proteins; protein-protein interactions and initiation of quasi-ordered arrays; prediction of protein conformation; role of bile acids and their degradation products in colon carcinogenesis; choleic acids. *Mailing Add:* Columbia Univ Col Physicians & Surgeons 630 W 168th St New York NY 10032

LOW, BOBBI STIERS, b Louisville, Ky, Dec 4, 42. EVOLUTIONARY BIOLOGY, ECOLOGY. *Educ:* Univ Louisville, BA, 62; Univ Tex, Austin, MA, 64, PhD(evolutionary zool), 67. *Prof Exp:* Can Med Res Coun fel physiol, Univ BC, 67-69; Commonwealth Sci & Res Orgn res assoc ecol, Univ Melbourne & Univ S Australia, 69-72; asst prof, 72-75, ASSOC PROF RESOURCE ECOL, SCH NATURAL RESOURCES, UNIV MICH, ANN ARBOR, 75- *Mem:* AAAS; Am Soc Naturalists; Sigma Xi; Soc Study Evolution. *Res:* Evolution of life history strategies; herbivorous competition; reproductive ecology in arid environments. *Mailing Add:* Sch of Natural Resources Univ of Mich Ann Arbor MI 48104

LOW, CHOW-ENG, b Selama, Malaysia, May 31, 38; m 66; c 3. IMMUNOPATHOLOGY, ORGANIC ANALYTICAL CHEMISTRY. *Educ:* Chung Chi Col, Chinese Univ, BS, 62; Tex Southern Univ, MS, 66; Univ Tex, Austin, PhD(org chem), 70. *Prof Exp:* Vis asst prof, Dept Chem, La State Univ, 70-71; res fel, Ind Univ, Bloomington, 72-75; res assoc, Dept Human Biol Genetics, Univ Tex Med Br, 76-78; ASST PROF BIOCHEM,

GEORGE WASHINGTON UNIV MED CTR, 78- *Mem:* Am Chem Soc; AAAS; Chem Soc London; Sigma Xi. *Res:* Autoxidation of polyunsaturated fatty acids; lipoxygenase metabolities of arachidonic acid as cytokines. *Mailing Add:* Dept Biochem George Washington Med Ctr 2300 Eye St NW Washington DC 20037

LOW, EMMET FRANCIS, JR, b Peoria, Ill, June 10, 22; m 74. APPLIED MATHEMATICS. *Educ:* Stetson Univ, BS, 48; Univ Fla, MS, 50, PhD(math), 53. *Prof Exp:* Instr phys sci, Univ Fla, 50-51, physics, 51-54; aeronaut res scientist, Nat Adv Comt Aeronaut, 54-55; asst prof math, Univ Miami, 55-59; vis res scientist, Courant Inst Math Sci, NY Univ, 59-60; assoc prof math & chmn dept, Univ Miami, 60-66, actg dean col arts & sci, 66-67, prof math & assoc dean faculties, 68-72; DEAN OF COL & PROF MATH, CLINCH VALLEY COL, UNIV VA, 72- *Mem:* AAAS; Am Math Soc; Soc Indust & Appl Math; Sigma Xi; Nat Coun Teachers Math. *Res:* Stress and functional analysis. *Mailing Add:* Clinch Valley Col Univ of Va Wise VA 24293

LOW, FRANCIS EUGENE, b New York, NY, Oct 27, 21; m 48; c 3. THEORETICAL PHYSICS. *Educ:* Harvard Univ, BS, 42; Columbia Univ, AM, 47, PhD(physics), 49. *Prof Exp:* Instr physics, Columbia Univ, 49-50; mem, Inst Advan Study, 50-52; from asst prof to assoc prof physics, Univ Ill, 52-56; prof, 57-68, KARL COMPTON PROF PHYSICS, MASS INST TECHNOL, 68-, DIR CTR THEORETICAL PHYSICS, 74- *Concurrent Pos:* Consult, AEC, 55-; Loeb lectr, Harvard Univ, 59; Fulbright fel, 61-62; Guggenheim fel, 61-62. *Mem:* Nat Acad Sci; Am Acad Arts & Sci; fel Am Phys Soc. *Res:* Theoretical, atomic and nuclear physics; field theory. *Mailing Add:* Dept of Physics Mass Inst of Technol Cambridge MA 02139

LOW, FRANK JAMES, b Mobile, Ala, Nov 23, 33; m 56; c 3. SOLID STATE PHYSICS. *Educ:* Yale Univ, BS, 55; Rice Univ, MA, 57, PhD(physics), 59. *Prof Exp:* Mem tech staff, Tex Instruments, Inc, 59-62; assoc scientist, Nat Radio Astron Observ, WVa, 62-65; prof physics, Univ Ariz, 65-66, res assoc, Lunar & Planetary Lab, 64-65, RES PROF, LUNAR & PLANETARY LAB, UNIV ARIZ, 66- *Concurrent Pos:* Prof space sci, Rice Univ, 66-71; adj prof, 71-; pres, Infrared Labs, Inc, Ariz, 67- *Honors & Awards:* H A Wilson Award, Rice Univ, 59; Helen B Warner Prize, Am Astron Soc, 68; Tex Instruments Corp Award, 76. *Mem:* Nat Acad Sci; Am Phys Soc; Am Astron Soc. *Res:* Infrared astronomy; infrared physics; cryogenic engineering. *Mailing Add:* Steward Observ Univ of Ariz Tucson AZ 85721

LOW, FRANK NORMAN, b Brooklyn, NY, Feb 9, 11. ANATOMY. *Educ:* Cornell Univ, AB, 32, PhD(micros anat), 36. *Prof Exp:* From instr to asst prof, Univ NC, 37-45; assoc, Sch Med, Univ Md, 45; assoc prof, Sch Med, WVa Univ, 46; asst prof, Sch Med, Johns Hopkins Univ, 46-49; from assoc prof to prof, Sch Med, La State Univ, 49-64; Hill res prof, Sch Med, Univ NDak, 64-73, Chester Fritz distinguished prof, 75-77, res prof, 73-81. *Concurrent Pos:* Charlton fel anat, Med Sch, Tufts Univ, 36-37; mem, Great Plains Regional Res Rev & Adv Comt, Am Heart Asn, 72-74; assoc ed, Am J Anat, 75-81; vis prof anat, Sch Med, La State Univ, New Orleans. *Mem:* Electron Micros Soc Am; Am Asn Anat; Am Asn Hist Med; Am Soc Cell Biol. *Res:* Transmission and scanning electron microscopy; fine structure of lung; subarachnoid space development of connective tissues. *Mailing Add:* 1901 Peroido St La State Med Ctr New Orleans LA 70112

LOW, GARY LOH-LEE, b Kuala Lumpur, Malaysia, Jan 15, 48; m 73. FISHERIES. *Educ:* Univ Wash, BS, 70, MS, 72, PhD(fisheries), 74. *Prof Exp:* Fishery biologist, Univ Wash, 74; FISHERY BIOLOGIST & OPERS RES ANALYST, NORTHWEST FISHERIES CTR, NAT MARINE FISHERIES SERV, 74- *Concurrent Pos:* Consult, Food & Agr Orgn, UN, 75. *Res:* Fisheries population dynamics; computer modelling of fisheries systems; international fisheries management. *Mailing Add:* NW Fish Ctr Nat Marine Fish Serv 2725 Montlake Blvd E Seattle WA 98112

LOW, GEORGE M(ICHAEL), b Vienna, Austria, June 10, 26; US citizen; m 49; c 5. AERONAUTICAL ENGINEERING. *Educ:* Rensselaer Polytech Inst, BS, 48, MS, 50. *Hon Degrees:* DEng, Rensselaer Polytech Inst, 69; DSc, Univ Fla, 69. *Prof Exp:* Aeronaut res scientist, Nat Adv Comt Aeronaut, Lewis Res Ctr, Ohio, 49-54, head fluid mech sect, 54-56, chief spec proj br, 56-58, chief manned space flight progs, NASA, Washington, DC, 58-60, dir spacecraft flight missions, 61-62, dep assoc adminr manned space flight, 63-64, dep dir, Manned Spacecraft Ctr, Tex, 64-67, prog mgr, Apollo Spacecraft, 67-69, dep adminr, NASA, 69-76; PRES, RENSSELAER POLYTECH INST, 76- *Concurrent Pos:* Consult, NASA, 76-; dir, Gen Elec Co, 77- *Honors & Awards:* Outstanding Leadership Award, NASA, 62, Distinguished Serv Medals for Contrib to Apollo 8 & Contrib to Success of Apollo Prog, 69; Arthur S Flemming Award, 63; Space Flight Award, Am Astronaut Soc, 68; Paul T Jones Trophy, Arnold Air Soc, 69; Louis W Hill Space Transp Award, Am Inst Aeronaut & Astronaut, 69; Rockefeller Pub Serv Award, 75; Founders Medal, Nat Acad Eng, 78. *Mem:* Nat Acad Eng; hon fel Am Inst Aeronaut & Astronaut; fel Am Astronaut Soc; hon mem Aerospace Med Asn. *Res:* Experimental and theoretical research in aerodynamic heating, boundary layer transition, internal aerodynamics and space technology; management of manned spaceflight programs, including Mercury, Gemini and Apollo. *Mailing Add:* Off of the Pres Rensselaer Polytech Inst Troy NY 12181

LOW, HANS, b Vienna, Austria, Oct 22, 21; nat US; m 49; c 3. ORGANIC CHEMISTRY. *Educ:* Marietta Col, BS, 50; Purdue Univ, MS, 52; St Louis Univ, PhD(chem), 59; Univ Tex, MPH, 76. *Prof Exp:* Instr German & Latin, Marietta Col, 47-50; res chemist, 52-67, group leader lubricant additives, 67-72, staff technologist, 72-78, SR STAFF TECHNOLOGIST, HEALTH, SAFETY & ENVIRON, SHELL OIL CO, 78- *Mem:* Am Chem Soc, NY Acad Sci. *Res:* Petroleum solvents and lubricants; synthetic lubricants; lubricant additives; industrial toxicology; public health. *Mailing Add:* 10719 Creedtree Dr Houston TX 77070

LOW, JAMES ALEXANDER, b Toronto, Ont, Sept 22, 25; m 52; c 3. MEDICINE. *Educ:* Univ Toronto, MD, 49; FRCS(C). *Prof Exp:* Clin teacher obstet & gynec, Univ Toronto, 55-65; PROF OBSTET & GYNEC & HEAD DEPT, QUEEN'S UNIV, ONT, 65- *Mem:* Soc Gynec Invest; Can Soc Clin Invest; Soc Obstet & Gynec Can; Am Asn Obstetricians & Gynecologists; Am Gynecol Soc. *Res:* Perinatal medicine; bladder function and control. *Mailing Add:* Dept of Obstet & Gynec Queen's Univ Kingston ON K7L 3N6 Can

LOW, JOHN R(OUTH), JR, b Washington, Pa, Feb 19, 09; m 37; c 3. METALLURGY. *Educ:* Purdue Univ, BS, 31; Carnegie Inst Technol, DSc, 43. *Prof Exp:* Metallurgist, Keystone Steel & Wire Co, Ill, 31-33 & Repub Steel Corp, 33-38; asst prof metall, Pa State Univ, 42-44, prof & head div, 45-48; develop engr, Carnegie-Ill Steel Corp, 44-45, head metall res sect, Knolls Atomic Power Lab, Gen Elec Co, 48-53, res assoc, Res & Develop Ctr, 53-67; prof, 67-77, EMER PROF METALL & MAT SCI, CARNEGIE-MELLON UNIV, 77- *Honors & Awards:* Vincent Bendix Award, Am Soc Eng Educ, 73; Gold Medal, Am Soc Metals, 78. *Mem:* Nat Acad Eng; fel Am Soc Metals; fel Am Inst Mining, Metall & Petrol Engrs; fel Am Soc Testing & Mat. *Res:* Physical and mechanical metallurgy; deformation and fracture of metals. *Mailing Add:* 7609 Marilea Rd Richmond VA 23225

LOW, KENNETH BROOKS, JR, b New Rochelle, NY, Jan 19, 36; m 60; c 2. GENETICS, DNA RECOMBINATION. *Educ:* Amherst Col, BA, 58; Univ Pa, MS, 60, PhD(molecular biol), 65. *Prof Exp:* Asst prof radiobiol, 68-71, asst prof radiobiol & microbiol, 71-73, assoc prof, 73-78, sr scientist radiobiol, 78-81, SR SCIENTIST RADIOBIOL & BIOL, YALE UNIV, 81- *Concurrent Pos:* USPHS fel, Med Ctr, NY Univ, 66-68; mem, Microbiol Genetics Study Sect, NIH, 78-; consult comn to study antibiotic use in animal feeds, Nat Acad Sci, 79. *Mem:* Am Soc Microbiol. *Res:* Molecular genetics; genetic recombination and control. *Mailing Add:* Radiobiol Labs Yale Univ Med Sch New Haven CT 06510

LOW, LAWRENCE J(ACOB), b New York, NY, June 22, 21; m 51; c 1. MECHANICAL ENGINEERING, OPERATIONS RESEARCH. *Educ:* Stevens Inst Technol, ME, 42. *Prof Exp:* Aerodynamicist, Curtiss Wright Airplane Div, NY, 42-43; res aerodynamicist, Cornell Aeronaut Lab, 46-50; sr res engr, Stanford Res Inst, 55-65, dir, Naval Warfare Res Ctr, 65-76, DIR, SRI INT, 76- *Concurrent Pos:* Mem US Marine air defense eval group, Off Naval Res, DC, 57-58; chmn opers anal sect, Advan Surface Missile Assessment Group, 65. *Mem:* AAAS; Sigma Xi; Am Inst Aeronaut & Astronaut; Opers Res Soc Am; Am Ord Asn. *Res:* Aerodynamics; fluid mechanics; weapon systems analysis and evaluation. *Mailing Add:* SRI Int 333 Ravenswood Ave Menlo Park CA 94025

LOW, LEONE YARBOROUGH, b Cushing, Okla, Aug 27, 35; div; c 2. MATHEMATICAL STATISTICS, APPLIED STATISTICS. *Educ:* Okla State Univ, BS, 56, MS, 58, PhD(math), 61. *Prof Exp:* Instr math, Univ Ill, 60-64; asst prof, 64-68, ASSOC PROF MATH, WRIGHT STATE UNIV, 68- *Concurrent Pos:* Nat Res Coun res assoc, Wright-Patterson AFB, 67-68; consult, Systs Res Lab, 71-; vis assoc prof, Iowa State Univ, 80-81. *Mem:* AAAS; Inst Math Statist; Am Statist Asn; Sigma Xi; fel Royal Statist Soc. *Res:* Variance component models in the analysis of variance; bootstrapping; laws of large numbers; modeling. *Mailing Add:* Dept of Math Wright State Univ Dayton OH 45435

LOW, MANFRED JOSEF DOMINIK, b Karlsbad, Bohemia, June 18, 28; nat US; m 65. PHYSICAL CHEMISTRY. *Educ:* NY Univ, BA, 52, MS, 54, PhD(phys chem), 56. *Prof Exp:* Asst chem, NY Univ, 52-55; res chemist, Davison Chem Co Div, W R Grace & Co, 56-58; sr chemist, Texaco, Inc, 58-61; asst prof chem, Rutgers Univ, 61-67; assoc prof, 67-72, PROF CHEM, NY UNIV, 72- *Mem:* Am Chem Soc; Soc Appl Spectros; NY Acad Sci. *Res:* Chemisorption; heterogeneous catalysis; infrared spectra of surfaces; infrared emission spectroscopy; surface chemistry and physics; Fourier transform spectroscopy; photoacoustic spectroscopy. *Mailing Add:* Dept of Chem NY Univ 4 Washington Place New York NY 10003

LOW, MARC E, b Ada, Okla, Sept 25, 35; m 57; c 2. MATHEMATICS. *Educ:* Okla State Univ, BS, 58, MS, 60; Univ Ill, PhD(math), 65. *Prof Exp:* Instr math, 64-65, asst prof, 65-71, ASSOC PROF MATH, WRIGHT STATE UNIV, 71-, ASST DEAN, COL SCI & ENG, 73- *Mem:* Math Asn Am; Am Math Soc. *Res:* Elementary and analytic number theory. *Mailing Add:* Dept of Math Wright State Univ Colonel Glenn Hwy Dayton OH 45435

LOW, MORTON DAVID, b Lethbridge, Alta, Mar 25, 35; div; c 3. NEUROPHYSIOLOGY. *Educ:* Queen's Univ, Ont, MD & CM, 60, MSc, 62; Baylor Univ, PhD(physiol), 66; FRCP(C), 73. *Prof Exp:* From instr to asst prof physiol, Baylor Univ Col Med, 65-68; assoc prof, 68-78, PROF MED, UNIV BC, 78-, DIR DIAG NEUROPHYSIOL, VANCOUVER GEN HOSP, 68- & SHAUGNESSEY HOSP, 71- *Concurrent Pos:* Fel anat, Queen's Univ, Ont, 61-62; fel physiol, Baylor Univ Col Med, 63-65; Med Res Coun Can grants, Univ BC, 68-; Mr & Mrs P A Woodward's Found grants, Vancouver Gen Hosp, 69-; MRC-INSERM Can-France exchange scientist, 78-79. *Mem:* AAAS; Am EEG Soc; Can Soc EEG (secy, 70-72, pres, 72-74); Am Epilepsy Soc; Int Fedn Socs (secy, 81-85). *Res:* Neural basis of perception and performance; brain mechanisms in maintenance and disorders of consciousness; sleep; epilepsy. *Mailing Add:* Dept of Diag Neurophysiol Vancouver Gen Hosp Vancouver BC V5Z 1M9 Can

LOW, NIELS LEO, b Copenhagen, Denmark, Dec 16, 16; nat US; m 43; c 2. MEDICINE. *Educ:* Med Col SC, MD, 40. *Prof Exp:* Clin instr pediat, Marquette Univ, 46-53; res assoc neurol, Univ Ill, 54; assoc res prof pediat, Univ Utah, 56-58; asst prof neurol, 60-67, assoc prof clin neurol, 67-75, PROF CLIN NEUROL & CLIN PEDIAT, COL PHYSICIANS & SURGEONS, COLUMBIA UNIV, 75-; DIR PEDIAT, BLYTHEDALE CHILDREN'S HOSP, VALHALLA, NY, 67- *Concurrent Pos:* Fel, Columbia Univ, 55 & 58-59; consult, NIH. *Mem:* Am EEG Soc; fel Am Acad Neurol; fel Am Acad Pediat; Am Epilepsy Soc; Int Child Neurol Asn (pres, 75-). *Res:* Pediatric neurology; metabolic disease affecting brain of children. *Mailing Add:* Columbia Univ Col Physicians & Surgeons New York NY 10032

LOW, PHILIP FUNK, b Carmangay, Alta, Oct 15, 21; nat US; m 42; c 6. SOIL CHEMISTRY. *Educ:* Brigham Young Univ, BS, 43; Calif Inst Technol, MS, 44; Iowa State Univ, PhD(soil chem), 49. *Prof Exp:* Soil scientist, USDA, 49; asst prof soil chem, 49-52, assoc prof, 52-55, PROF SOIL CHEM, PURDUE UNIV, 55- *Concurrent Pos:* Sigma Xi res award, Purdue Univ, 60; distinguished vis award to Australia, 68; consult, Exxon Prod Res Lab & Pac Northwest Labs, Battelle Mem Inst. *Mem:* Soil Sci Soc Am (pres-elect, 71-72, pres, 72-73); fel Am Soc Agron; Clay Minerals Soc. *Res:* Physical and colloidal chemistry of soils. *Mailing Add:* Dept of Agron Purdue Univ West Lafayette IN 47906

LOW, PHILIP STEWART, b Ames, Iowa, Aug 8, 47; m 69; c 4. BIOCHEMISTRY. *Educ:* Brigham Young Univ, BS, 71; Univ Calif, San Diego, PhD(biochem), 75. *Prof Exp:* Res assoc, Dept Chem, Univ Mass, 75-76; ASST PROF BIOCHEM, DEPT CHEM, PURDUE UNIV, 76- *Mem:* Am Chem Soc; Sigma Xi; Am Soc Biol Chem. *Res:* Biochemistry and physical chemistry of biological membranes. *Mailing Add:* Dept of Chem Purdue Univ West Lafayette IN 47907

LOW, ROBERT BURNHAM, b Greenfield, Mass, Sept 19, 40; m 67; c 1. PHYSIOLOGY. *Educ:* Princeton Univ, AB, 63; Univ Chicago, PhD(physiol), 68. *Prof Exp:* NIH fel biol, Mass Inst Technol, 68-70; asst prof physiol, 70-74, ASSOC PROF PHYSIOL & BIOPHYS, UNIV VT, 74- *Concurrent Pos:* NIH & Muscular Dystrophy res grants, Univ Vt. *Mem:* Am Soc Cell Biol. *Res:* Mammalian protein turnover; physiology and biochemistry of muscle; plasma membrane turnover; macrophage response to environment. *Mailing Add:* Dept of Physiol & Biophys Given Bldg E-211 Univ of Vt Burlington VT 05401

LOW, SETHA M, b Los Angeles, Calif, Mar 14, 48; m 80. MEDICAL ANTHROPOLOGY, HEALTH PLANNING. *Educ:* Pitzer Col, BA, 69; Univ Calif, Berkeley, MA, 71, PhD(anthrop), 76. *Prof Exp:* ASST PROF HEALTH PLANNING ANTHROP, UNIV PA, 76- *Concurrent Pos:* Prin investr, Urban Health Care, San Jose, Costa Rica, NIMH, 72-74; guest lectr, Sch Pub Health, Univ Tex, Houston, 77 & Sci & Pub Policy Panel, Am Anthrop Asn, 79; corresponding ed, Soc Med Anthrop, 77- & Soc Appl Anthrop, 78- *Mem:* Am Anthrop Asn; Soc Med Anthrop; Soc Appl Anthrop; Soc Psychol Anthrop; World Union Urban Anthropologists. *Res:* Cultural aspects of public health and environmental problems; community social structure as it influences health behavior and disease incidence; symbolic aspects of psychosomatic illness; health planning and policy in developing countries. *Mailing Add:* 305 Leverington Ave Philadelphia PA 19128

LOW, TERESA LINGCHUN KAO, b Hankow, China, Feb 17, 41; US citizen; m 66; c 3. PROTEIN CHEMISTRY, THYMIC HORMONES. *Educ:* Tunghai Univ, Taiwan, BS, 62; Tex Woman's Univ, MSc, 66; Univ Tex, Austin, PhD(biochem), 70. *Prof Exp:* Sci res specialist, Dept Biochem, La State Univ, 70-71; res assoc, Dept Zool, Ind Univ, 72-75; fel, Dept Human Biol Chem & Genetics, Univ Tex Med Br, 76-77; instr protein chem, 77-78; asst prof, 78-81, ASSOC PROF PROTEIN CHEM & IMMUNOL, DEPT BIOCHEM, MED SCH, GEORGE WASHINGTON UNIV, 81- *Mem:* Sigma Xi; NY Acad Sci; Chinese Med & Health Asn. *Res:* Chemical and biological characterization of thymosin, a family of hormones derived from the thymus gland and demonstrated to have potent immunomodulating properties. *Mailing Add:* Dept Biochem George Washington Univ Med Ctr 2300 Eye St NW Washington DC 20037

LOW, WALTER CHENEY, b Madera, Calif, May 11, 50. NEUROPHYSIOLOGY. *Educ:* Univ Calif, Santa Barbara, BS, 72; Univ Mich, MS, 74, PhD(bioeng), 79. *Prof Exp:* NIH-Nat Inst Gen Med Sci fel bioeng, Univ Mich, 75-78, res assoc neurophysiol, 78-79; res fel neurophysiol, Cambridge Univ, 79-80; RES FEL NEUROPHYSIOL, UNIV VT, 80- *Concurrent Pos:* NIH-Nat Neurol & Commun Disorders & Stroke fel, Univ Mich, 79; NSF/NATO fel, Cambridge Univ, 79-80; fel, Univ VT, 80-81, NIH-Nat Heart, Lung & Blood Inst, 81-82. *Mem:* AAAS; Soc Neurosci; Sigma Xi; NY Acad Sci. *Res:* Central nervous system physiology; neural transplantation and the recovery of function. *Mailing Add:* Dept Physiol & Biophysics Given Med Bldg Univ Vt Burlington VT 05405

LOW, WILLIAM, b Vienna, Austria, Apr 25, 22; nat Can; m 48, 70; c 9. PHYSICS. *Educ:* Queen's Univ, Ont, BA, 46; Columbia Univ, MA, 47, PhD, 50. *Prof Exp:* Tutor physics, Queen's Univ, Ont, 45-46; asst, Columbia Univ, 46-50; lectr, Hebrew Univ, Israel, 50-55, sr lectr, 55-59; res assoc, Univ Chicago, 55-56; assoc prof, 59-61, PROF PHYSICS, HEBREW UNIV, ISRAEL, 61- *Concurrent Pos:* Guggenheim fel, 63-64; ed, Physics Letters; chmn Israel comt, Int Union Radio Sci; pres & rector, Jerusalem Col Technol, Israel. *Honors & Awards:* Morrison Award, NY Acad Sci, 56; Israel Prize Exact Sci, 61; Rothschild Prize Physics, 64. *Mem:* Am Phys Soc; NY Acad Sci; Phys Soc Israel (vpres, 58-60, pres, 60-61 & 70-72); Europ Phys Soc; Int Union Pure & Appl Physics. *Res:* Paramagnetic resonance in solids; microwave spectroscopy in gases; quantum electronics; electron density behind shock waves; light scattering from macromolecules. *Mailing Add:* Microwave Div Dept Physics Hebrew Univ Jerusalem Israel

LOWANCE, FRANKLIN ELTA, b Monroe Co, WVa, Dec 29, 07; m 31; c 1. PHYSICS. *Educ:* Roanoke Col, BS, 27; Duke Univ, MA, 31, PhD(physics), 35. *Prof Exp:* Prof eng & physics, Edinburg Col, 33-35; assoc prof math & astron, Wofford Col, 35-38; head dept physics & eng, Centenary Col, 38-42; assoc prof physics, Ga Inst Tech, 41-43, prof, 45-49; res assoc, Harvard Univ, 44; mem staff, Radiation Lab, Mass Inst Technol, 45; tech dir, Naval Civil Eng Lab, 49-53; assoc tech dir, Naval Ord Test Sta, 53-54; dir res & vpres, Westinghouse Air Brake Co, 55-58; vpres eng, Crosley Div, Avco Corp, 58-60; pres, Adv Tech Corp, 60-62; CONSULT & VPRES, MERCO CORP, 62- *Mem:* Am Phys Soc; Nat Soc Prof Eng; Am Asn Physics Teachers. *Res:* Microwave propagation and beacons; acoustics; ferromagnetism; magnetothermoelectricity. *Mailing Add:* 41 Tierra Cielo Santa Barbara CA 93105

LOWDEN, J ALEXANDER, b Toronto, Ont, Feb 21, 33; m 56; c 4. NEUROCHEMISTRY. *Educ:* Univ Toronto, MD, 57; McGill Univ, PhD(biochem), 64. *Prof Exp:* Resident pediat, Hosp Sick Children, 58-60; res assoc, Univ Toronto, 65-67; assoc scientist, 64-74, ASSOC DIR, RES INST, HOSP SICK CHILDREN, 75-; assoc prof pediat, 67-80, PROF PEDIAT & CLIN BIOCHEM, UNIV TORONTO, 80- *Concurrent Pos:* Fel neurochem, Montreal Neurol Inst, 61-64; Helen Hay Whitney Found fel, 63-66. *Mem:* AAAS; Can Biochem Soc; Int Soc Neurochem; Am Soc Neurochem; Soc Pediat Res. *Res:* Inborn errors of metabolism, especially lysosomal storage disease. *Mailing Add:* Res Inst Hosp Sick Children 555 University Ave Toronto ON M5G 1X8 Can

LOWDEN, RICHARD MAX, b Columbus, Ohio, Sept 27, 43; m 70; c 2. PLANT SYSTEMATICS. *Prof Exp:* Asst prof bot, Ohio State Univ, 71; asst prof, 71-75, ASSOC PROF BIOL & BOT, CATH UNIV, SANTIAGO, 75-, DIR, MOSCOSO HERBARIUM, 73- *Mem:* Sigma Xi; Int Asn Plant Taxon; Asn Trop Biol; Asn Aquatic Vascular Plant Biologists; Acad Ciencias Republica Dominicana. *Res:* Aquatic freshwater vascular flora of Hispaniola; Latin American botany; botanical collectors; international index compiler. *Mailing Add:* Univ Cath Madre y Maestra Moscoso Herbarium Santiago de los Caballeros Dominican Republic

LOWDER, J ELBERT, b Pinedale, Wyo, Mar 18, 40; m 64; c 3. APPLIED PHYSICS. *Educ:* Univ Calif, Berkeley, BS, 63, MS, 65; Univ Calif, San Diego, PhD(eng physics), 71. *Prof Exp:* Flight test engr, Northrop Aircraft Corp, 63-64; proj engr, Aeronutronic Div, Philco-Ford Corp, 65-68; mem staff, Lincoln Lab, Mass Inst Technol, 71-75, assoc group leader appl physics, 75-80; VPRES, SPARTA INC, 80- *Mem:* Optical Soc Am; Am Inst Aeronaut & Astronaut; Soc Photo-Optical Instrumentation Engrs. *Res:* Effects of atmospheric aerosols on propagation of laser radiation; interaction of high power laser radiation with solid surfaces; laser radar applications; passive infrared detection systems. *Mailing Add:* Sparta Inc 1844B Mass Ave Lexington MA 02173

LOWDER, WAYNE MORRIS, b Chicago, Ill, Jan 6, 33; div; c 2. PHYSICS, RADIATION PHYSICS. *Educ:* Harvard Univ, AB, 54; Int Sch Nuclear Sci & Eng, Argonne Nat Lab, cert, 55. *Prof Exp:* PHYSICIST, ENVIRON MEASUREMENTS LAB, US DEPT ENERGY, 55-, PROG MGR, OFF HEALTH & ENVIRON RES, 77- *Concurrent Pos:* Mem Sci Comt, Nat Coun Radiation Protection & Measurement, 73-; consult, UN Sci Comt, Effects Atomic Radiation, 77- *Mem:* Am Phys Soc. *Res:* Measurement of ionizing radiation from natural and manmade radionuclides in the environment and the assessment of dose to man from these sources. *Mailing Add:* US Dept of Energy 376 Hudson St New York NY 10014

LOWDIN, PER-OLOV, b Uppsala, Sweden, Oct 28, 16; m 60; c 4. THEORETICAL PHYSICS, QUANTUM BIOLOGY. *Educ:* Univ Uppsala, Fil Kand, 37, Fil Mag, 39, Fil Lic, 42, Fil Dr(theoret physics), 48. *Prof Exp:* Lectr math & physics, 42-48, asst prof theoret physics, 48-55, assoc prof quantum chem, 55-60, head dept, 60-74, PROF QUANTUM CHEM, UNIV UPPSALA, 60-; GRAD RES PROF CHEM & PHYSICS & DIR QUANTUM THEORY PROJ, UNIV FLA, 60- *Concurrent Pos:* Fel, Swiss Fed Inst Technol, 46; H H Wells Phys Lab, Univ Bristol, 49; vis prof & consult, Duke Univ, Univ Chicago, Mass Inst Technol & Calif Inst Technol, 50-60; ed-in-chief, Advances in Quantum Chem, Int J Quantum Chem. *Mem:* Swed Royal Soc Arts & Sci; Swed Royal Soc Sci; Norweg Acad Sci & Letters; Int Soc Quantum Biol (pres, 71-72); Int Acad Quantum Molecular Sci (vpres, (vpres, 68-). *Res:* Theoretical physics and chemistry; quantum theory of atoms, molecules and solid state; quantum genetics and pharmacology. *Mailing Add:* Dept of Chem Univ of Fla Gainesville FL 32601

LOWE, A(RTHUR) L(EE), JR, b Boyce, Va, Jan 25, 27; m 53; c 3. METALLURGICAL & MATERIALS ENGINEERING. *Educ:* Va Polytech Inst, BS, 51; Lehigh Univ, MS, 55; Lynchburg Col, MBA, 73. *Prof Exp:* Proj engr, Richmond Eng Co, 51-53; res asst, Lehigh Univ, 53-54; welding engr, Metals Joining Div, Battelle Mem Inst, 54-57; group supvr liquid metal fuel reactor exp mat, 57-59, adv reactor concepts mat, 59-63, supvr metall eng group, Nuclear Develop Ctr, 63-65, staff specialist, Mat Processes Sect, 65-67, sr mat engr, Nuclear Power Generation Dept, 67-72, prin mat engr, 72-81, ADV ENGR MAT, NUCLEAR POWER GENERATION DIV, BABCOCK & WILCOX CO, 81- *Concurrent Pos:* Pvt consult engr, 63- *Mem:* Am Soc Metals; Am Inst Mining, Metall & Petrol Engrs; Brit Inst Metals; Am Soc Testing & Mat. *Res:* Nuclear materials applications; metal corrosion and fabrication problems; general materials application problems; forensic engineering-failure analysis and accident reconstruction; technical problems. *Mailing Add:* PO Box 1396 Lynchburg VA 24505

LOWE, CARL CLIFFORD, b West Salem, Ohio, Jan 1, 19; m 42; c 3. PLANT BREEDING. *Educ:* Colo Agr & Mech Col, BS, 48; Cornell Univ, MS, 50, PhD(plant breeding), 52. *Prof Exp:* From asst prof to assoc prof, 52-62, PROF PLANT BREEDING, NY STATE COL AGR & LIFE SCI, CORNELL UNIV, 62-, PROF BIOMETRY, 70- *Mem:* Am Soc Agron. *Res:* Forage crops breeding. *Mailing Add:* NY State Col of Agr & Life Sci Cornell Univ Plant Breeding Dept Ithaca NY 14853

LOWE, CHARLES HERBERT, JR, b Los Angeles, Calif, Apr 16, 20; m 44; c 2. ZOOLOGY. *Educ:* Univ Calif, Los Angeles, AB, 43, PhD(zool), 50. *Prof Exp:* Consult, AEC, 47-50; instr, 50-53, from asst prof to assoc prof, 53-64, prof zool, 64-80, PROF ECOL & EVOLUTION, UNIV ARIZ, 80-, CUR AMPHIBIANS & REPTILES, 77- *Mem:* AAAS; Am Soc Ichthyol & Herpet; Ecol Soc Am; Soc Study Evolution; Soc Syst Zool. *Res:* Animal and plant ecology; systematics; evolution; vertebrate zoology. *Mailing Add:* Dept of Zool Univ of Ariz Tucson AZ 85721

LOWE, CHARLES UPTON, b Pelham, NY, Aug 24, 21; m 55; c 4. PEDIATRICS. *Educ:* Harvard Univ, BS, 42; Yale Univ, MD, 45. *Prof Exp:* From intern to asst resident pediat, Children's Hosp, Boston, 45-46; resident, Mass Gen Hosp, 47; assoc prof pediat, Sch Med, State Univ NY Buffalo, 51-55, res prof, 55-65; prof, Col Med, Univ Fla, 65-68, dir human develop ctr, 66-68; sci dir, Nat Inst Child Health & Human Develop, 68-74; exec dir, Nat Comn Protection Human Subjects Biomed & Behav Res, HEW, 74-77, spec asst child health affair, Off of Asst Secy Health, 74-79; ACTG ASSOC DIR, MED APPLN RES, NIH, 80- *Concurrent Pos:* Nat Res Coun fel, Med Sch, Univ Minn, 48-51; Buswell fel, Sch Med, State Univ NY Buffalo, 55; ed-in-chief, Pediat Res, 66-74; John F Kennedy Mem Lectr, 66; Grover Powers Mem Lectr, 69; exec dir, President's Biomed Res Panel, 74-76, mem, President's Reorgn Proj Food & Nutrit Study, 78. *Honors & Awards:* Super Serv Award, NIH, 71; Clifford G Grulee Award, Am Acad Pediat, 71. *Mem:* Soc Pediat Res; Soc Exp Biol & Med; Am Soc Exp Path; Am Pediat Soc; Am Soc Clin Invest. *Res:* Clinical and laboratory study of nutritional disease, including celiac and cystic fibrosis of the pancreas; relationship between adrenocortical steroids and nucleic acid metabolism; inborn errors of metabolism and parenteral fluid therapy. *Mailing Add:* Nat Insts Health Bethesda MD 20205

LOWE, DONALD RAY, b Sacramento, Calif, Sept 22, 42; m 64; c 2. SEDIMENTOLOGY. *Educ:* Stanford Univ, BS, 64; Univ Ill, Urbana, PhD(geol), 67. *Prof Exp:* Instr geol, Univ Ill, Urbana, 67-68; res assoc, US Geol Surv, Calif, 68-70; asst prof, 70-73, assoc prof, 73-78, PROF GEOL, LA STATE UNIV, BATON ROUGE, 78- *Mem:* Soc Econ Paleont & Mineral; Int Asn Sedimentologists. *Res:* Sediment transport systems; deep-sea sedimentation; Archean sedimentology. *Mailing Add:* Dept Geol La State Univ Baton Rouge LA 70803

LOWE, HARRY J, b Nogales, Ariz, Dec 21, 19; m 47; c 5. ANESTHESIOLOGY. *Educ:* Univ Ariz, BS, 44; Johns Hopkins Univ, SM, 45, MD, 49. *Prof Exp:* Assoc prof biochem, Univ Tex, Southwest Med Sch, 53-56; prin res scientist, Roswell Park Mem Inst, NY, 58-62; resident anesthesiol & dir hyperbaric med, Millard Fillmore Buffalo, 62-66; prof anesthesiol & chmn dept, Pritzker Sch Med, Univ Chicago, 66-73; prof anesthesiol, Univ Southern Calif, 73-78; prof anesthesiol, Univ Ala, Birmingham, 79-80; DIR, DEPT ANESTHESIOL, CITY OF HOPE MED CTR, 80- *Concurrent Pos:* Am Cancer Soc fel, Johns Hopkins Univ, 49-52. *Mem:* AAAS; AMA; Am Chem Soc; Am Anesthesiol Soc. *Res:* Quantitative automated administration of volatile anesthetics in closed circuit systems; acid-base regulation of physiological ventilation during anesthesia. *Mailing Add:* City of Hope Med Ctr 1500 Duarte Rd Duarte CA 91010

LOWE, IRVING J, b Woonsocket, RI, Jan 4, 29; m 53; c 2. SOLID STATE PHYSICS. *Educ:* Cooper Union, BEE, 51; Washington Univ, St Louis, PhD(physics), 57. *Prof Exp:* Fel, Sloan Found & res assoc physics, Washington Univ, St Louis, 56-58; asst prof, Univ Minn, 58-62; assoc prof, 62-66, PROF PHYSICS, UNIV PITTSBURGH, 66- *Mem:* Am Phys Soc. *Res:* Experimental and theoretical studies of the structure and behavior of solids using nuclear magnetic resonance techniques. *Mailing Add:* Dept of Physics Univ of Pittsburgh Pittsburgh PA 15260

LOWE, JACK IRA, b Fairmount, Ga, Dec 8, 27; m 57. MARINE ECOLOGY, TOXICOLOGY. *Educ:* Berea Col, AB, 50; Univ Ga, MS, 55. *Prof Exp:* Biologist, US Fish & Wildlife Serv, 57-61 & US Bur Com Fisheries, 61-70; aquatic biologist, 70-71, dep lab dir, 71-75, assoc dir tech assistance, 75-76, CHIEF EXP ENVIRON BR, ENVIRON RES LAB, ENVIRON PROTECTION AGENCY, 76- *Mem:* Am Fisheries Soc; Nat Shellfisheries Asn; Gulf Estuarine Res Soc. *Res:* Estuarine and coastal ecology; effects of organic pollutants on marine organisms and their environment. *Mailing Add:* Environ Res Lab Environ Protection Agency Gulf Breeze FL 32561

LOWE, JAMES HARRY, JR, b Vonore, Tenn, Mar 15, 31; m 55; c 3. ENTOMOLOGY. *Educ:* Univ Tenn, BA, 55; Ohio State Univ, MSc, 57; Yale Univ, PhD(forest entom), 66. *Prof Exp:* Res entomologist, Northeastern Forest Exp Sta, USDA, Conn, 59-62, insect res ecologist, 63-65; ASSOC PROF FORESTRY & ZOOL, UNIV MONT, 65- *Mem:* Entom Soc Am; Entom Soc Can. *Res:* Ecology of insects in forest communities; insect dispersal and distribution; alpine entomology; behavioral and meteorological aspects of flight of insects. *Mailing Add:* Sch of Forestry Univ of Mont Missoula MT 59812

LOWE, JAMES N, b Grand Forks, NDak, May 3, 36; m 61; c 3. ORGANIC CHEMISTRY. *Educ:* Antioch Col, BS, 59; Stanford Univ, PhD(chem), 64. *Prof Exp:* Asst prof chem, Smith Col, 63-65; from asst prof to assoc prof, 71-78, PROF CHEM, UNIV OF THE SOUTH, 78- *Concurrent Pos:* Am Chem Soc Petrol Res Fund grant, 64-66 & 67-69; fel, Univ Calif, Davis, 70-71; fel Univ Ill, 77-78; res corp grant, 80. *Mem:* Am Chem Soc; AAAS. *Res:* Coenzyme mechanisms. *Mailing Add:* Box 1225 Sewanee TN 37375

LOWE, JAMES URBAN, JR, b Durham, NC, June 30, 21. PHYSICAL ORGANIC CHEMISTRY. *Educ:* Va State Col, BS, 42, MS, 46; Howard Univ, PhD, 63; Tenn State Univ, MPA, 82. *Prof Exp:* Asst prof chem, Tenn State Col, 47-52 & Ft Valley State Col, 52-56; fel, Howard Univ, 56-59, instr, 59-60; res chemist, US Govt, Md, 60-68; assoc dean admin, 69-81, ASSOC PROF BIOCHEM, SCH MED, MEHARRY MED COL, 68-, ASST DEAN ADMIN, 81- *Mem:* Am Chem Soc; Sigma Xi. *Res:* Synthesis of 0-nitrobenzoates; aryloxyaliphatic acids; nitroguanidines; physical studies of beta diketones; nuclear magnetic resonance, ultraviolet, infrared spectroscopy of guanidines and perfluoroaromatics; longitudinal study of scholastic performance of Meharry medical students. *Mailing Add:* 4230 Eatons Creek Rd Nashville TN 37218

LOWE, JANET MARIE, b Ellensburg, Wash, Jan 13, 24. MICROBIOLOGY, EMBRYOLOGY. *Educ:* Univ Wash, BS, 45; Univ Chicago, SM, 47. *Prof Exp:* Res assoc bact, Univ Chicago, 47-49; instr biol, 49-54, asst prof, 54-58, assoc prof zool, 58-74, PROF BIOL & DIR ALLIED HEALTH SCI PROG, CENT WASH STATE COL, 74- *Concurrent Pos:* NSF res grant, 58-60. *Mem:* AAAS; Am Soc Microbiol; Am Inst Biol Sci. *Res:* Chick embryology; bacteriology. *Mailing Add:* Dept of Biol Cent Wash State Col Ellensburg WA 98926

LOWE, JOHN, III, soil engineering, see previous edition

LOWE, JOHN EDWARD, b Newark, NJ, May 20, 35; m 57; c 2. VETERINARY SURGERY. *Educ:* Cornell Univ, DVM, 59, MS, 63. *Prof Exp:* Intern vet surg, 59-60, resident, 60-61, instr vet path, 61-63, asst prof vet surg, 63-68, ASSOC PROF VET SURG, NY STATE COL VET MED, CORNELL UNIV, 68-, COORD MGR, EQUINE RES PARK, 74-, ASSOC PROF, NY STATE COL AGR & LIFE SCI, 68- *Mem:* Am Vet Med Asn; Am Asn Equine Practitioners. *Res:* Endocrine control of the equine skeletal system; effect of nutrition on equine bone and joint disease; equine gastrointestinal surgery. *Mailing Add:* NY State Col of Vet Med Cornell Univ Ithaca NY 14853

LOWE, JOHN PHILIP, b Rochester, NY, Aug 28, 36; m 59; c 2. QUANTUM CHEMISTRY. *Educ:* Univ Rochester, BS, 58; Johns Hopkins Univ, MAT, 59; Northwestern Univ, PhD(quantum chem), 64. *Prof Exp:* Teacher high sch, NJ, 59-60; NIH fel theoret chem, Johns Hopkins Univ, 64-66; asst prof chem, 66-70, ASSOC PROF CHEM, PA STATE UNIV, UNIVERSITY PARK, 70- *Concurrent Pos:* Petrol Res Fund starter grant, 66-68; type AC grant, 69-71. *Mem:* AAAS; Am Chem Soc; Am Phys Soc. *Res:* Chemical carcinogenicity; chemical reactivities; relations between Huckel and ab initio calculations; quantum chemistry of solids. *Mailing Add:* Dept of Chem Pa State Univ University Park PA 16802

LOWE, JOHN RAYMOND, physical biochemistry, computer science, see previous edition

LOWE, KURT EMIL, b Munich, Ger, Nov 21, 05; nat US; m 40; c 1. PETROLOGY. *Educ:* City Col New York, BS, 33; Columbia Univ, MA, 37, PhD(petrol), 47; Asn Prof Geol Scientists, cert. *Hon Degrees:* DSc, Jersey City State Col, 81. *Prof Exp:* Lab asst & tutor geol, Eve Session, 33-42, tutor, 46-47, instr, 47-50, from asst to assoc prof, 50-64, chmn dept, 57-68, prof, 65-72, EMER PROF GEOL, CITY COL NEW YORK, 72- *Concurrent Pos:* Asst, Columbia Univ, 40-42; consult, NY, 36-42 & 47-; consult, NY Trap Rock Corp, 53-73. *Honors & Awards:* Neil Miner Award, Nat Asn Geol Teachers, 68. *Mem:* Fel AAAS; fel Am Geol Soc; fel Mineral Soc Am; fel NY Acad Sci; Nat Asn Geol Teachers (pres, 51-52). *Res:* Mineragraphy; optical mineralogy; structural petrology of granites; Storm King granite at Bear Mountain, New York; structure of the Palisades of Rockland County, New York. *Mailing Add:* 49-01 Francis Lewis Blvd Bayside NY 11364

LOWE, LAWRENCE E, b Toronto, Ont, Mar 29, 33; m 57; c 3. SOIL CHEMISTRY. *Educ:* Oxford Univ, BA, 54, MA, 61; McGill Univ, MSc, 60, PhD(agr chem), 63. *Prof Exp:* Soil chemist, Res Coun Alta, 63-66; from asst to assoc prof, 66-75, PROF SOILS, UNIV BC, 75- *Mem:* Can Soc Soil Sci; Int Soc Soil Sci; Soil Sci Soc Am. *Res:* Soil organic matter; sulphur in soil. *Mailing Add:* Dept of Soils Univ of BC Vancouver BC V6T 2A2 Can

LOWE, REX LOREN, b Marshalltown, Iowa, Dec 28, 43; m 64; c 2. PHYCOLOGY. *Educ:* Iowa State Univ, BS, 66, PhD(phycol), 70. *Prof Exp:* Asst bot, Iowa State Univ, 66-69; ASST PROF BIOL, BOWLING GREEN STATE UNIV, 70- *Concurrent Pos:* Consult, Icthyol Assocs, 71-; collabr, US Nat Park Serv, 75-76. *Mem:* Phycol Soc Am; Int Phycol Soc; Am Inst Biol Sci; Brit Phycol Soc. *Res:* Diatom taxonomy and ecology. *Mailing Add:* Dept of Biol Bowling Green State Univ Bowling Green OH 43403

LOWE, RICHIE HOWARD, b Huff, Ky, Apr 9, 35; m 58; c 2. PLANT PHYSIOLOGY, BIOCHEMISTRY. *Educ:* Univ Ky, BS, 58, MS, 59; Ore State Univ, PhD(plant physiol), 63. *Prof Exp:* Res plant physiologist, 63-74, PLANT PHYSIOLOGIST, AGR RES SERV, USDA, 74- *Mem:* Am Soc Plant Physiol. *Res:* Enzymatic activity and biochemical changes associated with plant senescence and post harvest physiology; inorganic nitrogen and phosphorous metabolism. *Mailing Add:* Agr Res Ctr Univ of Ky Lexington KY 40506

LOWE, ROBERT FRANKLIN, JR, b Chicago, Ill, Nov 14, 41. CARDIOVASCULAR PHYSIOLOGY. *Educ:* Univ Wis, BS, 64, PhD(physiol), 69. *Prof Exp:* ASST PROF PHYSIOL, SCH MED, TULANE UNIV, 70- *Concurrent Pos:* NIH fel, Univ Wis-Madison, 69-70. *Mem:* Am Physiol Soc; Am Heart Asn; Am Fedn Clin Res. *Res:* Autonomic pharmacology. *Mailing Add:* Tulane Univ Dept Physiol 1430 Tulane Ave New Orleans LA 70116

LOWE, ROBERT PETER, b Cambridge, Eng, July 8, 35; Can citizen. AERONOMY, INFRARED ASTRONOMY. *Educ:* Univ Western Ont, BSc, 57, PhD(atomic physics), 67. *Prof Exp:* Sci officer, Defense Res Bd, Can, 56-68; asst prof, 68-71, assoc prof, 71-80, PROF PHYSICS, UNIV WESTERN ONT, 80- *Mem:* Am Geophys Union; Can Asn Physicists. *Res:* Infrared airglow; stratospheric composition; infrared spectroscopy of HII regions and planetary nebulae; electronic, vibrational and rotational excitation in ion-molecular collisions. *Mailing Add:* Dept Physics Univ Western Ont London ON N6A 5B8 Can

LOWE, RONALD EDSEL, b Terre Haute, Ind, Jan 8, 35; m 55; c 6. ECOLOGY, ENVIRONMENTAL SCIENCES. *Educ:* Ohio State Univ, BSc, 62; Purdue Univ, PhD(entom), 67. *Prof Exp:* Res asst entom, Purdue Univ, 62-66; res entomologist, Cent Am Res, Int Progs Div, Sci & Educ Admin, USDA, 66-75, proj leader, 75-79; DIR, PLANT OPERATIONS, ANIMAL & PLANT HEALTH INSPECTION SERV, VET SERV, USDA, TUXTLA GUTIERREZ, MEX, 79- *Concurrent Pos:* Courtesy prof, Univ Fla, 66- *Mem:* AAAS; Entom Soc Am; Am Mosquito Control Asn; Soc Invert Path; Sigma Xi. *Res:* Population dynamics of sterile-male release programs; growth regulation compounds for control of medically important insects; pathogenic microorganisms for biological control programs; ecology and epidemiology; agricultural research administration. *Mailing Add:* USDA Apartado Postal 544 Tuxtla Gutierrez Chiapas Mexico

LOWE, WARREN, b San Francisco, Calif, June 4, 22; m 56. ORGANIC CHEMISTRY. *Educ:* Univ Calif, Berkeley, BS, 45. *Prof Exp:* Res asst, Manhattan Proj, US AEC, Univ Calif Radiation Lab, 43-45; from res chemist to sr res chemist, 45-74, SR RES ASSOC CHEM, CHEVRON RES CO, 74- *Mem:* AAAS; Am Chem Soc; Sigma Xi; fel Am Inst Chem. *Res:* Exploratory research of petroleum products and chemicals. *Mailing Add:* 5619 Jordan Ave El Cerrito CA 94530

LOWE, WILLIAM WEBB, b Bartlesville, Okla, Dec 18, 20. CHEMICAL ENGINEERING. *Educ:* Purdue Univ, BS, 47. *Prof Exp:* Staff mem radiochem, Los Alamos Sci Lab, 44-48; chief nuclear eng sect, USAEC, 48-54; nuclear engr, Bath Iron Works, Maine, 54-56; PARTNER, PICKARD, LOWE & GARRICK INC, 56- *Concurrent Pos:* Co-ed, Power Reactor Technol, AEC, 60. *Mem:* Am Chem Soc; Am Nuclear Soc. *Res:* Nuclear engineering; engineering economics. *Mailing Add:* 300 N Pitt Alexandria VA 22314

LOWELL, A(RTHUR) I(RWIN), b New York, NY, Nov 9, 25; m 54; c 3. POLYMER CHEMISTRY. *Educ:* Brooklyn Col, AB, 45; Univ Pa, MS, 48, PhD(chem), 51. *Prof Exp:* Res chemist, Air Reduction Co, Inc, 51-57, sect head, 57-58; res assoc, Lucidol Div, Wallace & Tiernan, Inc, 59-60, supvr appln res, 61-62; res assoc, Berkeley Chem Corp, 62 & Heyden Newport Chem Co, 63; sr res chemist, Mobil Chem Co, 64-66, group leader, 66-68, sect leader, 69-73; sci teacher pub schs, Edison, NJ, 73-76; group leader, Norton & Son, 77-78; SR RES CHEMIST, SUN CHEM CORP, 78- *Mem:* Am Chem Soc. *Res:* Polymerization kinetics; organic peroxide initiators; polymer process and product development; emulsion polymerization; coatings; inks. *Mailing Add:* Sun Chem Corp 631 Cent Ave Carlstadt NJ 07072

LOWELL, ANTHONY M, b Western Ukraine, July 22, 08; US citizen. PUBLIC HEALTH. *Educ:* Alfred Univ, NY, BS, 32; Mass Inst Technol, MPH, CPH, 35. *Prof Exp:* Supvr, USPHS, 36-37; statistician, Philadelphia Health Coun, 37-39; dir Statist Div, NY Tuberc & Health Asn, 39-62; chief, Statist & Anal Sect, Tuberc Control Div, Ctr Dis Control, Atlanta, 62-78; FREE-LANCE CONSULT, 78- *Mem:* Am Med Writers Asn; fel, Am Public Health Asn; Epidemiol Res Soc; Int Health Soc; Int Union Against Tuberc. *Res:* International tuberculosis statistics; epidemiology of tuberculosis. *Mailing Add:* 3645 Peachtree Rd NE Atlanta GA 30319

LOWELL, FRANCIS CABOT, b Boston, Mass, Aug 6, 09; m 38; c 3. MEDICINE. *Educ:* Harvard Univ, BS, 32; Harvard Med Sch, MD, 36; Am Bd Internal Med, dipl, 43; Am Bd Allergy, dipl, 46. *Prof Exp:* Intern, Boston City Hosp, 37-38; asst resident, Thorndike Mem Hosp, Boston, 38-40; from instr to assoc prof med, Sch Med, Univ, 40-58; asst prof, 58-69, ASSOC PROF, HARVARD MED SCH, 69- *Concurrent Pos:* Asst dean, Sch Med, Boston Univ, 48-51; mem staff, Robert Dawson Evans Mem Hosp, 44-58; mem staff, Mass Mem Hosp, 44-58; physician & chief allergy unit, Mass Gen Hosp, 58-76, sr staff, 77-; mem study sect, Admin Hosp, 63-; ed, J Allergy, Am Acad Allergy, 57-63. *Mem:* AAAS; Am Soc Clin Invest; Am Asn Immunol; fel Am Col Physicians; Am Acad Allergy (secy, 54-58, pres, 58-59). *Res:* Applied immunology and allergy. *Mailing Add:* Longfellow Med Assoc, PC 1 Longfellow Pl Boston MA 02114

LOWELL, GARY RICHARD, b Modesto, Calif, Sept 26, 42; m 68; c 2. GEOLOGY. *Educ:* San Jose State Col, BS, 65; N Mex Inst Mining & Technol, PhD(geol), 69. *Prof Exp:* Asst prof, 69-77, assoc prof, 77-81, PROF GEOL, SOUTHEAST MO STATE UNIV, 81- *Concurrent Pos:* Vis prof geol, Univ Fed do Para, Brazil, 78-80; consult, Houston Int Minerals Corp, Alaska, 80 & 81. *Mem:* Geol Soc Am; Mineral Asn Can. *Res:* Igneous and metamorphic petrology; metallic ore deposits. *Mailing Add:* Dept of Earth Sci Southeast Mo State Univ Cape Girardeau MO 63701

LOWELL, JAMES DILLER, b Lincoln, Nebr, Aug 17, 33; m 57; c 4. PETROLEUM GEOLOGY, STRUCTURAL GEOLOGY. *Educ:* Univ Nebr, BSc, 55; Columbia Univ, MA, 57, PhD(geol), 58. *Prof Exp:* Geologist, Am Overseas Petrol Ltd, 58-65; asst prof geol, Washington & Lee Univ, 65-66; sr res specialist, Esso Prod Res Co, 66-73; explor geologist, Exxon Co, USA, 73-74; mgr geol, Northwest Explor Co, 74-76; CONSULT GEOLOGIST, 76- *Concurrent Pos:* Assoc, Oil & Gas Consults Int Inc, 76- *Mem:* Fel Geol Soc Am; Am Asn Petrol Geologists; Am Geophys Union. *Res:* Structural geology of sedimentary rocks. *Mailing Add:* 5836 S Colorow Dr Morrison CO 80465

LOWELL, PHILIP S(IVERLY), b Manila, Philippines, July 9, 31; US citizen; m 59, 74; c 3. CHEMICAL ENGINEERING. *Educ:* Univ Tex, BS, 54, MS, 63, PhD, 66. *Prof Exp:* Process engr, Jefferson Chem Co, Inc, 54-55; process engr, C F Braun & Co, 55-59, sr process engr, 59-60; sr engr, Tex Res Assocs, Inc, 60-64; asst dir chem res, Tracor, Inc, 64-69; vpres, Radian Corp, 69-77; PRES, P S LOWELL & CO, INC, 77- *Concurrent Pos:* Adj prof, Univ Tex, Austin, 74; proj group mem, Environ Protection Coop Effort, US/USSR, 74- *Mem:* Am Inst Chem Engrs; Am Chem Soc; Air Pollution Control Asn. *Res:* Process engineering of chemical plants and refineries; application of thermodynamics to practical problems; research in chemical process dynamics and thermodynamics. *Mailing Add:* P S Lowell & Co Inc 4107 Pkwy Suite 214 Austin TX 78756

LOWELL, ROBERT PAUL, b Chicago, Ill, Apr 10, 43; thermal convection; c 2. GEOPHYSICS. *Educ:* Loyola Univ Chicago, BS, 65; Ore State Univ, MS, 67, PhD(geophys), 72. *Prof Exp:* Asst prof, 71-78, ASSOC PROF GEOPHYS, GA INST TECHNOL, 78- *Mem:* Am Geophys Union; Sigma Xi. *Res:* Thermal geophysics; heat transfer processes on ocean ridges; geothermal energy; mantle convection; thermoelastic phenomena. *Mailing Add:* Sch of Geophys Sci Ga Inst of Technol Atlanta GA 30332

LOWELL, SHERMAN CABOT, b Olean, NY, Aug 15, 18; m 41; c 2. PHYSICS, THEORETICAL NUMERICAL ANALYSIS. *Educ:* Univ Chicago, BS, 40; NY Univ, PhD(math), 49. *Prof Exp:* Sci liaison officer math sci, Office Naval Res, London, Eng, 49-51; from asst to assoc prof math, NY Univ, 51-57; prof math, head dept & dir grad progs math & appl sci, Adelphi Univ, 57-62; prof math & info sci, 62-66, PROF PHYSICS & COMPUT SCI, WASH STATE UNIV, 66-, MATHEMATICIAN, COMPUT CTR, 62- *Concurrent Pos:* Asst to sci dir, Inst Math Sci, NY Univ, 53-57; vis scientist, Lab Physics of Solids, Paris, 68 & Nat Ctr Very Low Temp, Grenoble, France, 69; consult serv bur, Int Bus Mach Corp, 59-62 & Lawrence Livermore Lab, Univ Calif, 63- *Mem:* AAAS; Am Meteorol Soc; Soc Indust & Appl Math; Am Phys Soc. *Res:* Lattice dynamics; wave propagation; numerical analysis. *Mailing Add:* NE 1610 Upper Dr Pullman WA 99163

LOWEN, GERARD G, b Munich, Ger, Oct 52; 21; US citizen; m; c 3. MECHANICAL ENGINEERING. *Educ:* City Col New York, BME, 54; Columbia Univ, MSME, 58; Munich Tech Univ, Dr Ing, 63. *Prof Exp:* PROF MECH ENG, CITY COL NEW YORK, 54- *Concurrent Pos:* Consult, var indust, 63-; NSF grants, Army Res Off; expert witness, Army Armament Res & Develop Command res grants. *Mem:* AAAS; fel Am Soc Mech Engrs; Am Soc Eng Educ; NY Acad Sci; Soc Mfg Engrs. *Res:* Dynamics of high speed machinery; rigid and elastic body behavior of linkages and mechanisms; kinematic synthesis and analysis; stress and vibration analysis. *Mailing Add:* Dept of Mech Eng Sch Eng Convent Ave at 138th St New York NY 10031

LOWEN, W(ALTER), b Cologne, Ger, May 17, 21; nat US; m 43; c 2. SYSTEMS SCIENCES, MECHANICAL ENGINEERING. *Educ:* NC State Univ, BME, 43, MS, 47; Swiss Fed Inst Technol, DrSc(nuclear eng), 62. *Prof Exp:* Instr mech eng, NC State Col, 43-47; prof, Union Col, NY, 47-67, actg chmn dept, 59 & 67, chmn div eng, 56-59 & 66-67; dir sch advan technol, 67-68, dean, 68-77, PROF SCH ADVAN TECHNOL, STATE UNIV NY BINGHAMTON, 67- *Concurrent Pos:* Consult, Alco Prod, Inc, 52-54, 56, Oak Ridge Nat Lab, 54-57 & Gen Elec Co, 60; consult inst appl technol, Nat Bur Standards, 65-66; vis prof, Swiss Fed Inst Technol, 65-66; dir, Vols for Int Tech Assistance, Inc, 66-69; mem charter bd, 69-; guest sabbatical, IBM Systs Res Inst, 78 & 79; acad guest, Sarss Fed Inst Technol, Zurich, Switz, 82. *Mem:* Am Soc Mech Engrs; Am Nuclear Soc; Am Soc Eng Educ; NY Acad Sci; World Acad Arts & Sci. *Res:* Dichotomous models; nuclear reactor shielding; internal combustion engines. *Mailing Add:* Sch of Advan Technol State Univ NY Binghamton NY 13901

LOWEN, WARREN KEALOHA, analytical chemistry, see previous edition

LOWENBACH, HANS, b Duisburg, Ger, Jan 31, 05; nat US; m 41; c 3. PSYCHIATRY. *Educ:* Univ Hamburg, MD, 29; Am Bd Psychiat & Neurol, dipl. *Prof Exp:* Asst, Physiol Inst, Univ Freiburg, 30-32; asst med clin, Univ Cologne, 32-33; asst, Neurophysiol Div, Kaiser Wilhelm Inst Hirnforschung, Berlin-Dahlem, 33-35; ship's surgeon, Whaling Expeds, 36-38; asst psychiat, Johns Hopkins Hosp, 39 & 40; from assoc prof to prof, 40-74, EMER PROF PSYCHIAT, SCH MED, DUKE UNIV, 74- *Concurrent Pos:* Nansen Found fel, Univ Oslo, 35-36; consult, Vet Admin, US Army & Off Health, Educ & Welfare, civilian with Off Sci Res & Develop & Field Info Agencies Technol, 46. *Mem:* AAAS; Am EEG Soc; AMA; Am Psychiat Asn; Asn Res Nerv & Ment Dis. *Res:* Therapy of psychiatric disorders. *Mailing Add:* Rt 3 Box 273 Durham NC 27713

LOWENBERG, E(DWIN) C(ARL), b Donnellson, Iowa, Oct 2, 20; m 40; c 3. ELECTRICAL ENGINEERING. *Educ:* Univ Iowa, BSEE, 51, MS, 53, PhD(elec eng), 57. *Prof Exp:* Engr, Collins Radio Co, 41-50; res assoc elec eng, Univ Iowa, 50-56, from instr to asst prof, 56-59; from asst prof to assoc prof, Univ Tex, 59-64; PROF ELEC ENG, UNIV NEBR, LINCOLN, 64- *Mem:* AAAS; Inst Elec & Electronics Engrs; Am Soc Eng Educ; NY Acad Sci. *Res:* Bioengineering; statistical decision theory. *Mailing Add:* Univ Nebraska Lincoln NE 68508

LOWENGRUB, MORTON, b Newark, NJ, Mar 31, 35; m 61; c 1. MATHEMATICS. *Educ:* NY Univ, BA, 56; Calif Inst Technol, MS, 58; Duke Univ, PhD(math), 61. *Prof Exp:* Instr math, Duke Univ, 60-61; asst prof, NC State Col, 61-62; Leverhulme res fel, Glasgow Univ, 62-63; asst prof, Wesleyan Univ, 63-66; NSF fel, Glasgow Univ, 66-67; assoc prof, 67-72, chmn dept, 77-80, PROF MATH, IND UNIV, BLOOMINGTON, 72- *Concurrent Pos:* Sr res fel, Sci Res Coun, Gt Brit, 73-74; ed, Ind Math J, 77-81 & Math Reviews, 81- *Mem:* Math Asn Am; Am Math Soc; Soc Indust & Appl Math; Am Math Soc. *Res:* Mathematical theory of elasticity. *Mailing Add:* Dept of Math Ind Univ Bloomington IN 47401

LOWENHAUPT, BENJAMIN, b St Louis, Mo, July 15, 18; m 50; c 3. BIOPHYSICS, PLANT PHYSIOLOGY. *Educ:* Iowa State Col, BS, 40; Univ Chicago, MS, 41; Univ Calif, Berkeley, PhD(plant physiol), 54. *Prof Exp:* Res assoc, Univ Calif, Berkeley, 54-55; res assoc, Rockefeller Inst, 56-60, NIH fel, 60-62; sr res assoc physiol, Col Med, Univ Cincinnati, 62-67; PROF BIOL, EDINBORO STATE COL, 67- *Concurrent Pos:* Sabbatical, Flinders Univ S Australia, 74-75. *Mem:* AAAS; Am Chem Soc; Am Soc Plant Physiol. *Res:* Biochemistry; role of inorganic ions in biology; ion transport and excitation. *Mailing Add:* RD #1 Henry Rd Cambridge Springs PA 16403

LOWENSCHUSS, OSCAR, b Vienna, Austria, Apr 6, 25; US citizen; m 45; c 2. ELECTRICAL ENGINEERING. *Educ:* City Col New York, BS, 48; NY Univ, MS, 52; Columbia Univ, ScD(eng), 58. *Prof Exp:* Sr proj engr, Radio Receptor Co Div, Gen Industs Inc, 54-56; res engr, Sperry Gyroscope Co, 56-58; res dir, Budd Electronics Inc, 58-60; CONSULT SCIENTIST DIGITAL SYSTS, ELECTROMAGNETIC SYSTS DIV, RAYTHEON CO, 60- *Concurrent Pos:* Instr, Columbia Univ, 58-59; lectr, Polytech Inst Brooklyn, 59-60; mem, Nike-Zeus Adv Comt Polarization, 61; res adv comt commun, instrumentation & data processing, NASA, 62- *Mem:* Sr mem Inst Elec & Electronics Engrs. *Res:* Digital computers; radar; signal processing; digital logic, phased array antennas; redundancy in computer design; radar backscatter; target recognition. *Mailing Add:* Electromagnetic Systs Div Raytheon Co Goleta CA 93017

LOWENSOHN, HOWARD STANLEY, b Columbus, Ohio, Jan 23, 31; m 53; c 1. CORONARY PHYSIOLOGY, EXERCISE. *Educ:* Franklin & Marshall Col, BS, 56; Univ Southern Calif, MS, 62; Univ Md, PhD(physiol), 72. *Prof Exp:* RES PHYSIOLOGIST, WALTER REED ARMY INST RES, 63-; ASSOC PROF PHYSIOL, UNIFORMED SERV UNIV HEALTH SCI, 80- *Concurrent Pos:* Consult, Johns Hopkins Univ, 77-; res adv, Nat Res Coun, 80- *Mem:* Am Physiol Soc; NY Acad Sci; AAAS. *Res:* Hemodynamics of coronary blood flow in chronic conscious dogs at rest, during exercise and with varying degrees of ischemia; hypertrophied hearts, including the initial chronic studies of phasic coronary artery blood flow in the right heart in normal and hypertrophied and dilated hearts. *Mailing Add:* Dept Pharmacol Div Exp Therapeut Med Ctr Walter Reed Army Inst Res Washington DC 20012

LOWENSTAM, HEINZ ADOLF, b Siemianowita, Ger, Oct 9, 12; nat US; m 37; c 3. ECOLOGY. *Educ:* Univ Chicago, PhD(paleont), 39. *Prof Exp:* Cur paleont, Ill State Mus, 40-43; assoc geologist, State Geol Surv, Ill, 43-49, geologist, 49-50; res assoc, Univ Chicago, 48-50, assoc prof, 50-52; PROF PALEOECOL, CALIF INST TECHNOL, 52- *Concurrent Pos:* Spec staff to aid war effort, Coal & Oil Develop, State Geol Surv, Ill, 43-45. *Mem:* AAAS; fel Geol Soc Am; Paleont Soc; Soc Study Evolution; assoc Soc Econ Paleont & Mineral. *Res:* Paleoecology; biogeochemistry; paleo-temperatures; evolution of reef ecology; impact of the evolution of life on chemical and physical processes in the oceans; minerals in hard tissue precipitates of marine invertebrates. *Mailing Add:* Div of Geol & Planetary Sci Calif Inst of Technol Pasadena CA 91109

LOWENSTEIN, CARL DAVID, b New York, NY, Sept 3, 34; m 65; c 1. APPLIED PHYSICS. *Educ:* Kent State Univ, BA, 55; Harvard Univ, SM, 56, PhD(physics), 63. *Prof Exp:* Res fel, Harvard Univ, 63-64; asst res physicist, 64-69, ASSOC PROF PHYSICS LAB, UNIV CALIF, SAN DIEGO, 69- *Concurrent Pos:* Mem sensors comt, US Navy Deep Submergence Syst Prog, 64- *Mem:* Acoust Soc Am; Audio Eng Soc; Inst Elec & Electronics Engrs. *Res:* Synthesis of directive arrays; signal processing; underwater acoustics; computer applications. *Mailing Add:* Marine Physics Lab Univ of Calif San Diego CA 92132

LOWENSTEIN, DEREK IRVING, b Hampton Court, Eng, Apr 26, 43; US citizen; m 68; c 2. HIGH ENERGY PHYSICS. *Educ:* City Col New York, BS, 64; Univ Pa, MS, 65, PhD(physics), 69. *Prof Exp:* Res assoc, Univ Pa, 69-70 & Univ Pittsburgh, 70-73; asst physicist, 73-75, assoc physicist, 75-77, PHYSICIST & HEAD, EXP PLANNING & SUPPORT DIV, BROOKHAVEN NAT LAB, 77-, DEP CHMN, ACCELERATOR DEPT, 81- *Mem:* Am Phys Soc; AAAS. *Res:* Experimental high energy physics. *Mailing Add:* Accelerator Dept Brookhaven Nat Lab Upton NY 11973

LOWENSTEIN, EDWARD, b Duisburg, Ger, May 29, 34; US citizen; m 59; c 3. ANESTHESIOLOGY, CARDIOPULMONARY PHYSIOLOGY. *Educ:* Univ Mich, MS, 59; Am Bd Anesthesiol, dipl. *Prof Exp:* Assoc anesthesia, 68-70, asst prof, 70-72, assoc prof, 72-81, PROF ANESTHESIA, HARVARD MED SCH, 81- *Concurrent Pos:* Assoc anesthetist, Mass Gen Hosp, 68-71, anesthetist, 71- *Mem:* Am Soc Anesthesiol. *Res:* Physiological effects of cardiac disease, cardiopulmonary bypass and cardiac surgery; cardiac anesthesia. *Mailing Add:* Dept of Anesthesia Mass Gen Hosp Boston MA 02114

LOWENSTEIN, J(ACK) G(ERT), b Frankfurt, Ger, Mar 19, 27; US citizen; m 50; c 3. CHEMICAL ENGINEERING. *Educ:* Pratt Inst, BChE, 50; Univ Md, MSChE, 58. *Prof Exp:* Asst prod mgr, Gen Gummed Prod, Inc, 50-51; chem engr, Army Chem Ctr, US Army, 53-56; res engr, Org Div, 56-60, eng supvr, 60-64, process evaluator, Inorg Div, 64-66, asst dir res & develop, 66-72, asst dir res & develop, Niagara Chem Div, 72-76, tech dir mfg, Agr Chem Group, 76-80, VENTURE MGR, CHEM TECHNOL DEPT, FMC CORP, 80- *Concurrent Pos:* Lectr, Sch Continuing Educ, NY Univ, 68- *Mem:* Am Inst Chem Engrs; Am Chem Soc; Nat Soc Prof Engrs; Am Mgt Asn; Am Inst Chemists. *Res:* Study of research management and management science; chemical engineering research, particularly in the chemical separation unit operations; technical aspects of manufacturing, including quality assurance. *Mailing Add:* FMC Corp PO Box 8 Princeton NJ 08540

LOWENSTEIN, JEROLD MARVIN, b Danville, Va, Feb 11, 26; m 49; c 3. NUCLEAR MEDICINE. *Educ:* Columbia Univ, BS, 46, MD, 53. *Prof Exp:* Physicist, Los Alamos Sci Lab, 46-48; instr med & radiol, Sch Med, Stanford Univ, 57-58; asst clin prof, 63-68, assoc clin prof, 68-81, CLIN PROF MED THYROID RES, UNIV CALIF, SAN FRANCISCO, 81- *Concurrent Pos:* Nat Found fel radiobiol, 55-56; NIH res grant thyroid & cellular changes in pregnancy, 60-66, etiology of nontoxic nodular goiter, 61-66, measurement of blood digitalis levels, 62-66; dir nuclear med, Presby Med Ctr, San Francisco, 59-; partic, Galapagos Int Sci Proj, 64; dir nuclear med, Children's Hosp, 64- *Mem:* AMA; Soc Nuclear Med; Am Fedn Clin Res. *Res:* Applications of physics to medicine, especially medical uses of radioactive isotopes. *Mailing Add:* 2203 Scott San Francisco CA 94115

LOWENSTEIN, JEROME F(RANKLIN), electronic engineering, see previous edition

LOWENSTEIN, JOHN HOOD, b Newark, NJ, Mar 15, 41; m 67; c 2. THEORETICAL PHYSICS. *Educ:* Harvard Univ, AB, 62; Univ Ill, Urbana, BS, 63, PhD(physics), 66. *Prof Exp:* Res assoc physics, Univ Minn, 66-68; vis asst prof, Univ Sao Paulo, 68-70; res assoc, Univ Pittsburgh, 70-72; res asst prof, 72-74, ASSOC PROF PHYSICS, NY UNIV, 74- *Mem:* Am Phys Soc. *Res:* Quantum field theory, with emphasis on renormalized perturbation theory and soluble two-dimensional models. *Mailing Add:* Dept of Physics 4 Washington Place New York NY 10003

LOWENSTEIN, JOHN MARTIN, b Berlin, Ger, Oct 28, 26; m 54. BIOCHEMISTRY. *Educ:* Univ Edinburgh, BSc, 50; Univ London, PhD, 53. *Prof Exp:* Demonstr chem & biochem, Med Sch, St Thomas' Hosp, Eng, 50-53; res assoc biochem, Med Sch, Univ Wis, 53-55; Beit mem fel med res, Oxford Univ, 55-58; prof, 59-77, HELENA RUBINSTEIN PROF BIOCHEM, BRANDEIS UNIV, 77- *Concurrent Pos:* Ed, Methods in Enzymol, Archives Biochem & Biophysics, 67-72, J Lipid Res, 79-, J Biol Chem, 79-; mem adv comt, Med Found Res Comt, 74-77, Biochem Study Sect, 77-81; lectr, Indian Dept Sci & Indust Res, 80. *Mem:* AAAS; Am Chem Soc; Am Soc Biol Chem; Brit Biochem Soc. *Res:* Regulated enzymes; integration and control of metabolism pathways. *Mailing Add:* Dept Biochem Brandeis Univ Waltham MA 02254

LOWENSTEIN, LEAH MIRIAM, b June 17, 30; US citizen; m 54; c 3. MEDICINE, BIOCHEMISTRY. *Educ:* Univ Wis, BS, 50, MD, 54; Oxford Univ, DPhil, 58; Am Bd Internal Med, dipl, 63. *Prof Exp:* Instr med, Sch Med, Tufts Univ, 61-64; res assoc, Harvard Med Sch, 64-65, assoc, 65-68; asst prof med, 68-71, PROF MED & BIOCHEM, SCH MED, BOSTON UNIV, 76-, ASST DEAN, 78- *Concurrent Pos:* Assoc med, Thorndike Mem Lab, 65-68; vis scientist, Med Sch, Univ Pa, 66-67; trustee Hampstead Mem Found, 67-; assoc med, Harvard Med Sch, 69-70; mem, Nat Kidney Found; mem coun kidney in cardiovasc dis, Am Heart Asn; mem first-level rev comt, Artificial Kidney-Chronic Uremia Prog, NIH, 72-; mem-at-large, Sect N (Med Sci) Comt, AAAS, 73-; mem, Exp Models Aging Comt, Nat Inst Aging, 74-; comt animals in aging, Nat Res Coun; med adv, Off of Dep Asst Secy for Health Policy, Res & Statist. *Mem:* AAAS; Am Fedn Clin Res; Am Asn Study Liver Dis; Am Soc Nephrology; Am Med Soc Alcoholism. *Res:* Renal and hepatic metabolism; alcoholism. *Mailing Add:* Sch of Med Boston Univ Boston MA 02118

LOWENSTEIN, MICHAEL ZIMMER, b Hornell, NY, Oct 4, 38; m 62; c 2. SOLAR ENERGY. *Educ:* Oberlin Col, AB, 60; Ariz State Univ, MS, 62, PhD(x-ray crystallog), 65. *Prof Exp:* Asst prof chem, 64-71, prof chem, Adams State Col, 71-78; EDUC PROJ MGR, JOINT US-SAUDI PROG, SOLAR ENERGY RES INST, 78- *Concurrent Pos:* AEC fac res assoc, Ariz State Univ, 70-71; consult, Citizen's Workshop, Energy Res & Develop Agency, 74-76; Dept Energy, 76-78; vis prof, Solar Energy Appln Lab, Colo State Univ, Ft Collins, 75-76; prof chem, Adams State Col, Alamosa, 71-77; dir, Solar Energy Div, Navarro Col, Tex, 77-78. *Mem:* Int Solar Energy Soc. *Res:* Instrumentation; energy problems; applications of solar energy to heating and cooling; solar energy education; solar thermal storage. *Mailing Add:* SERI 1536 Cole Blvd Golden CO 80401

LOWENTHAL, DENNIS DAVID, b Yakima, Wash, Nov 10, 42; m 66; c 2. PLASMA PHYSICS, ELEMENTARY PARTICLE PHYSICS. *Educ:* Calif State Univ, Northridge, BS, 65; Univ Calif, Los Angeles, MS, 66; Univ Calif, Irvine, PhD(physics), 75. *Prof Exp:* Res & develop engr, Aeronutronic Div, Philco-Ford Corp, 66-75; physicist, Math Sci Northwest, 75-80. *Mem:* Am Phys Soc; Optical Soc Am; AAAS. *Res:* Experimental search for the double beta decay of selenium 82; geometrical and wave optics; plasma physics diagnostics. *Mailing Add:* 2755 Northup Way Bellevue WA 98004

LOWENTHAL, FRANKLIN, mathematics, see previous edition

LOWENTHAL, JOSEPH PHILIP, b New York, NY, July 21, 19; m 54; c 2. MICROBIOLOGY, IMMUNOLOGY. *Educ:* Brooklyn Col, AB, 39; Johns Hopkins Univ, ScD(microbiol), 52; Am Bd Med Microbiol, dipl. *Prof Exp:* Lab asst, City Dept Health, New York, 40-44; bacteriologist, Vet Admin Hosp, Ft Harrison, Ind, 47-48 & Army Med Serv Grad Sch, 52-56; chief, Microbiol Sect, Dept Biologics Res, 56-62, WITH DEPT BIOL RES, WALTER REED ARMY INST RES, 62- *Concurrent Pos:* Mem comn rickettsial dis, Armed Forces Epidemiol Bd, 66- *Honors & Awards:* Award, Off Surgeon Gen, Dept Army, 57. *Mem:* AAAS; Am Soc Microbiol; NY Acad Sci. *Res:* Botulinal hemagglutination; bacterial enzymes; bacterial, viral and rickettsial vaccines. *Mailing Add:* 3812 48th NW Washington DC 20016

LOWENTHAL, WERNER, b Krefeld, Ger, Dec 20, 30; US citizen; m 61; c 2. PHARMACY. *Educ:* Albany Col Pharm, Union Univ, NY, BS, 53; Univ Mich, PhD(pharmaceut chem), 58. *Prof Exp:* Asst, Univ Mich, 53-55; res pharmacist, Abbott Labs, 57-61; asst prof pharm, 61-66, assoc prof, 66-71, PROF PHARM, SCH PHARM, MED COL VA, VA COMMONWEALTH UNIV, 71-, PROF EDUC PLANNING & DEVELOP, 74-, DIR CONTINUING EDUC, 80- *Concurrent Pos:* Mem US Pharmacopoeia Rev Comt, 75-80. *Mem:* AAAS; Am Pharmaceut Asn; Am Asn Cols Pharm. *Res:* Pharmaceutical product development; drug absorption; programmed instruction; continuing education; curriculum development. *Mailing Add:* Sch of Pharm Med Col of Va Va Commonwealth Univ Richmond VA 23298

LOWER, GERALD MALCOLM, JR, oncology, biochemistry, see previous edition

LOWER, RICHARD ROWLAND, b Detroit, Mich, Aug 15, 29; m 53; c 5. THORACIC SURGERY, CARDIOVASCULAR SURGERY. *Educ:* Amherst Col, AB, 51; Cornell Univ, MD, 55; Am Bd Surg, dipl, 63, cert thoracic surg, 64. *Prof Exp:* Intern, King County Hosp, 55-56; asst prof surg, Stanford Univ, 62-65; PROF SURG & CHMN DIV THORACIC & CARDIAC SURG, MED COL VA, 65- *Concurrent Pos:* Res asst, Stanford Univ Hosps, 58-63; chief thoracic & cardiovasc surg, Palo Alto Vet Admin Hosp, 64-65. *Res:* Cardiac transplantation. *Mailing Add:* Div of Thoracic & Cardiac Surg Med Col of Va Richmond VA 23298

LOWER, STEPHEN K, b Oakland, Calif, Sept 8, 33; m 63. PHYSICAL CHEMISTRY. *Educ:* Univ Calif, Berkeley, BA, 55; Ore State Univ, MS, 58; Univ BC, MSc, 60, PhD(phys chem), 63. *Prof Exp:* Fel phys chem, Polytech Inst Brooklyn, 63-64 & Univ Calif, Los Angeles, 64-65; ASST PROF PHYS CHEM, SIMON FRASER UNIV, 65- *Concurrent Pos:* Nat Res Coun Can grants, 65-71, mem panel on comput assisted instruction lang, 70- *Mem:* AAAS; Am Chem Soc; Asn Develop Instructional Systs. *Res:* Electronic spectra and physical chemistry of organic solids and charge-transfer complexes, fluorescence spectroscopy; instructional systems design; computer-assisted instruction and instructional technology applied to college teaching. *Mailing Add:* Dept of Chem Simon Fraser Univ Burnaby ON V5A 1S6 Can

LOWER, WILLIAM RUSSELL, b La Junta, Colo, Oct 28, 30; m 71; c 2. GENETICS, ENVIRONMENTAL HEALTH. *Educ:* Univ Calif, Los Angeles, BA, 53; Univ Calif, Berkeley, PhD(genetics), 65. *Prof Exp:* Res assoc genetics of nematodes, Kaiser Found Res Inst, 64-66; res assoc, Clin Pharmacol Res Inst, 67-69; res assoc biol monitoring, Environ Health Surveillance Ctr, 70-72, ASSOC PROF COMMUNITY HEALTH & MED PRACT & BIOL, UNIV MO-COLUMBIA, 72-, GROUP LEADER, ENVIRON TRACE SUBSTANCES RES CTR, 72- *Concurrent Pos:* Fel, Univ Mo, 69-70. *Mem:* Genetics Soc Am; Environ Mutagen Soc; AAAS; Soc Environ Geochem & Health; Soc Study Evolution. *Res:* Genetic, biochemical, and physiological effects of airborne, terrestrial and fresh water environmental pollutants in situ in the real world as well as under controlled laboratory conditions; mutagenesis of environmental contaminants. *Mailing Add:* Environ Trace Substances Res Ctr Univ Mo Rt 3 Columbia MO 65201

LOWERY, CHARLES E, JR, b Austin, Tex, Sept 1, 31; m 53; c 1. MICROBIOLOGY. *Educ:* Univ Tex, BA, 56, MA, 58, PhD(microbiol), 65. *Prof Exp:* RES MICROBIOLOGIST, CHEM DIV, MILES LABS, INC, 65- *Mem:* Am Soc Microbiol. *Res:* Antibiotics; petroleum microbiology; fermentation chemistry. *Mailing Add:* Chem Div 1127 Myrtle Elkhart IN 46514

LOWERY, LEE LEON, JR, b Corpus Christi, Tex, Dec 26, 38; m 60; c 2. STRUCTURAL ENGINEERING. *Educ:* Tex A&M Univ, BS, 60, MS, 61, PhD(struct eng), 67. *Prof Exp:* From asst prof to assoc prof, 61-71, PROF ENG, TEX A&M UNIV, 71- *Concurrent Pos:* Res engr, Albritton Eng Corp, 63-66, Tex Transp Inst, 67- & Interface Eng Assocs, 77-78; consult engr, Esso Prod Res Corp, 66-68, Shell Oil Corp, 76-78 & Marathon Oil Corp, 77-78; prof construct, Sch Archit, Tex A&M Univ, 65-69, prof struct, Dept Aerospace Eng, 67-70; failure analyst, Eng Consult, Inc, 70-76, prod failure analyst, 76-77. *Mem:* Am Soc Exp Stress Anal; Am Soc Civil Engrs; Soc Marine Technol; Am Soc Eng Educ; Nat Soc Prof Engrs. *Res:* Basic research, engineering structures and products; applied research in areas of design and analysis of coastal, offshore structures; product failure analysis, consumer protection; engineering applications of computer analysis. *Mailing Add:* Dept of Civil Eng Tex A&M Univ College Station TX 77843

LOWERY, R(ICHARD) L, b Haven, Kans, July 25, 35; m 59; c 2. MECHANICAL ENGINEERING. *Educ:* Tex Tech Col, BS, 56; Okla State Univ, MS, 57; Purdue Univ, PhD(mech eng), 61. *Prof Exp:* Instr mech eng, Tex Tech Col, 57-58; from asst prof to prof, 61-72, HALLIBURTON PROF MECH ENG & DIR CTR TEACHING, OKLA STATE UNIV, 72- *Concurrent Pos:* Consult, Fed Aviation Agency, 64-65. *Mem:* Acoust Soc Am; Am Soc Eng Educ. *Res:* Acoustics; sonic boom research; ultrasonics; vibrations; instrumentation. *Mailing Add:* Sch of Mech Eng Okla State Univ Stillwater OK 74174

LOWERY, THOMAS J, b Brooklyn, NY, Jan 21, 22; m 50; c 9. CYTOLOGY, PHYSIOLOGY. *Educ:* St Francis Col, NY, BS, 46; Fordham Univ, MS, 49, PhD(cytol & physiol), 55. *Prof Exp:* Instr zool & genetics, Stonehill Col, 50-51; instr zool, physiol & anat, Duquesne Univ, 51-53; instr biol, Fordham Univ, 53-55; assoc prof cytol & physiol, Villanova Univ, 55-62; ASSOC PROF BIOL, LA SALLE COL, 62- *Mem:* Am Micros Soc; Torrey Bot Club. *Res:* Cytological implications of relationship between the chromosome number of maternal tissue, embryo, and endosperm and its effect on producing various aberrancies such as somatoplastic sterility and neoplasm of plants. *Mailing Add:* Dept of Biol La Salle Col Philadelphia PA 19141

LOWES, BRIAN EDWARD, b Harrow, Eng, Sept 21, 35; Can citizen; m 66; c 2. GEOLOGY. *Educ:* Imperial Col, London Univ, BSc, 57; Queen's Univ, Ont, MSc, 63; Univ Wash, Seattle, PhD(geol), 72. *Prof Exp:* Mine geologist asst, Opemiska Copper Ventures Ltd, 57-59; explor geologist, Hollinger Consol Gold Mines, 61-62; tech asst, Can Geol Surv, 63-64; asst prof, 68-75, ASSOC PROF EARTH SCI, PAC LUTHERAN UNIV, 75-, CHMN DEPT, 77- *Mem:* Geol Soc Am; Geol Asn Can; Mineral Asn Can. *Res:* Structural geology and metamorphic petrology of crustal basement rocks in Pacific Northwest. *Mailing Add:* Dept of Earth Sci Pac Lutheran Univ Tacoma WA 98447

LOWEY, SUSAN, b Vienna, Austria, Jan 22, 33; nat US. PROTEIN CHEMISTRY, PHYSICAL CHEMISTRY. *Educ:* Columbia Univ, BA, 54; Yale Univ, PhD(chem), 58. *Prof Exp:* Res fel biol, Harvard Univ, 57-59; assoc prof biochem, 72-74, PROF BIOCHEM, BRANDEIS UNIV, 74-, MEM STAFF, ROSENSTIEL BASIC MED SCI RES CTR, 72- *Concurrent Pos:* Res assoc, Children's Cancer Res Found, 59-72. *Mem:* Am Chem Soc. *Res:* Physical chemistry of muscle proteins. *Mailing Add:* Dept of Biochem Brandeis Univ Waltham MA 02154

LOWIG, HENRY FRANCIS JOSEPH, b Prague, Czech, Oct 29, 04; m 49; c 2. PURE MATHEMATICS. *Educ:* Ger Univ, Prague, Dr rer nat, 28; Univ Tasmania, DSc, 51. *Prof Exp:* Privatdozent math, Ger Univ, Prague, 35-38; lectr, Univ Tasmania, 48-51, sr lectr, 51-57; from assoc prof to prof, 57-70, EMER PROF MATH, UNIV ALTA, 70- *Concurrent Pos:* Vis fel, Res Sch Phys Sci, Australian Nat Univ, 66-67. *Mem:* Am Math Soc; Can Math Soc. *Res:* Functional analysis; lattice theory; universal algebra. *Mailing Add:* 15212 81st Ave Edmonton AB T5R 3P1 Can

LOWITZ, DAVID AARON, b Newark, NJ, Dec 18, 28; m 53; c 4. CHEMICAL PHYSICS. *Educ:* Rutgers Univ, BA, 50; Pa State Univ, MS, 53, PhD(physics), 55. *Prof Exp:* Asst physics, Pa State Univ, 50-53, res asst, 55-56; physicist, Gulf Res & Develop Co, 56-64; res assoc & head cent res physics sect, Lord Corp, 64-67; mgr, Physics Div, 67-79, TECHNOL

PLANNING COORDR APPL RES, PHILIP MORRIS RES CTR, 79- *Concurrent Pos:* Am Petrol Inst fel, 52-56. *Honors & Awards:* IR 100 Award, 72. *Mem:* Am Phys Soc; Int Soc Quantum Biol; Sigma Xi. *Res:* Tobacco technology; charge transport in solids; quantum mechanics; liquid pressure-volume-temperature and pressure-temperature-viscosity; electromagnetic wave propagation; dielectrics; electron optics; color centers in solids. *Mailing Add:* Philip Morris Res Ctr PO Box 26583 Richmond VA 23261

LOWMAN, BERTHA PAULINE, b Newton, NC, Mar 17, 29. MATHEMATICS. *Educ:* Lenoir-Rhyne Col, BS, 51; Univ Ala, MA, 52; George Peabody Col, PhD(math), 76. *Prof Exp:* Instr math, Campbell Col, 52-53; instr sci & math, Anderson Col, 53-54; asst, Univ NC, 55; asst prof math, Hardin-Simmons Univ, 55-59, ECarolina Col, 59-60 & Elon Col, 60-62; asst prof, 62-78, PROF MATH, WESTERN KY UNIV, 78- *Mem:* Math Asn Am; Nat Coun Teachers Math. *Res:* Number theory and algebra; geometry and history of mathematics. *Mailing Add:* Dept Math Western Ky Univ Bowling Green KY 42101

LOWMAN, PAUL DANIEL, JR, b Elizabeth, NJ, Sept 26, 31; m 58. ASTROGEOLOGY, PHOTOGEOLOGY. *Educ:* Rutgers Univ, BS, 53; Univ Colo, PhD(geol), 63. *Prof Exp:* AEROSPACE TECHNOLOGIST, GODDARD SPACE FLIGHT CTR, NASA, 59- *Concurrent Pos:* Vis lectr, US Air Force Inst Technol, 63-64; lectr, Cath Univ, 63-66; lectr, Univ Calif, Santa Barbara, 70. *Honors & Awards:* John C Lindsay Mem Award, Goddard Space Flight Ctr, 74. *Mem:* Geol Soc Am; AAAS; Am Geophys Union. *Res:* Planetology; lunar geology; geologic application of orbital photography; remote sensing; comparative planetology. *Mailing Add:* RR1 Box 300 Bowie MD 20715

LOWMAN, ROBERT MORRIS, b Baltimore, Md, Dec 31, 12; m 37; c 2. RADIOLOGY. *Educ:* Harvard Univ, AB, 32; Univ Md, MD, 36. *Hon Degrees:* MA, Yale Univ, 65. *Prof Exp:* Instr radiol, Grad Sch Med, Univ Pa, 36-38, asst dir dept radiol, Grad Hosp, 40-45; asst, Sch Med, Boston Univ, 38-40; assoc prof, 55-62, actg chmn dept, 73, PROF RADIOL, MED SCH, YALE UNIV, 62-; DIR MEM UNIT, YALE-NEW HAVEN HOSP, 62- *Concurrent Pos:* Angiol Res Found honors achievement award, 64-65; attend physician, Grace-New Haven Community Hosp, 45-, dir dept radiol, Mem Unit, 45-; consult, W Haven Vet Hosp, 62-; pres, New Eng Roentgen Ray Soc, 71-72, mem exec comt & chmn exec bd, 72-74; fel, Davenport Col, Yale Univ. *Mem:* Fel Am Col Radiol; Radiol Soc NAm; Sigma Xi. *Res:* Thoracic lymphatics; embryology of the bladder; cardiac kymography; experimental coronary arteriography. *Mailing Add:* Mem Unit Box 1001 Yale-New Haven Med Ctr New Haven CT 06504

LOWN, JAMES WILLIAM, b Blyth, Eng, Dec 19, 34; m 62. PHYSICAL ORGANIC CHEMISTRY. *Educ:* Univ London, BSc, 56, PhD(org chem) & dipl, Impt Col, 59. *Prof Exp:* Asst lectr chem, Imp Col, Univ London, 59-61; fel, Univ Alta, 61-62, asst prof, 62-63; res chemist, Walter Reed Army Inst Res, DC, 62-63; from asst to assoc prof, 64-74, PROF CHEM, UNIV ALTA, 74-; MEM, NAT CANCER INST CAN, 77- *Mem:* Am Chem Soc; The Chem Soc; Sigma Xi. *Res:* Organic reaction mechanisms; heterocyclic synthesis; antibiotics. *Mailing Add:* Dept of Chem Univ of Alta Edmonton AB T6G 2G2 Can

LOWNDES, DOUGLAS H, JR, b Pasadena, Calif, Jan 3, 40; m 61; c 2. SEMICONDUCTORS, PHOTOVOLTAIC CELL RESEARCH. *Educ:* Stanford Univ, BS, 61; Univ Colo, PhD(physics), 69. *Prof Exp:* Res asst solid state physics, Hewlett-Packard Assocs, Calif, 62-63; NSF fel physics, Sch Math & Phys Sci, Univ Sussex, 68-70; asst prof, 70-74, PROF PHYSICS, UNIV ORE, & ASSOC, SOLAR ENERGY CTR, 74- *Concurrent Pos:* Guest prof phys, Univ Nijmegen, 76-77. *Mem:* Am Phys Soc; Int Solar Energy Soc. *Res:* Experimental techniques; pulsed and continious wave laser annealing; solar cells; nanosecond and picosecond laser measurements; de Haas-van Alphen and Fermi surface studies; superconductivity and magnetism; transition metal carbides; laser interactions with semiconductors. *Mailing Add:* Solid State Div Bldg 2000 Oak Ridge Nat Lab Oak Ridge TN 37830

LOWNDES, HERBERT EDWARD, b Barrie, Ont, July 12, 43; m 66; c 3. NEUROTOXICOLOGY, NEUROPHARMACOLOGY. *Educ:* Univ Sask, BA, 64, MSc, 70; Cornell Univ, PhD(pharmacol), 72. *Prof Exp:* Fel pharmacol, Univ Western Ont, 72-73; asst prof, 73-77, assoc prof, 77-81, PROF PHARMACOL, COL MED & DENTISTRY, NJ MED SCH, 81- *Concurrent Pos:* Vis prof, Univ Paul Sabatier, Toulouse, France, 66-; consult, Toxicology Study Section, NIH, 80- & Toxicology Data Bank, Nat Libr Med, 81-. *Mem:* Am Soc Pharmacol & Exp Therapeut; NY Acad Sci; Soc Toxicol; Soc Neurosci. *Res:* Neurotoxicology and neuropharmacology of central and peripheral nervous sytem, particularly electrophysiological and morphological correlates. *Mailing Add:* Dept Pharmacol Col Med & Dentistry NJ Med Sch 100 Bergen St Newark NJ 07103

LOWNDES, ROBERT P, b Derby, Eng, Dec 11, 39. PHYSICS. *Educ:* Univ London, BSc, 62, Queen Mary Col, PhD(exp solid state physics), 67; Northeastern Univ, MBA, 76. *Prof Exp:* Res assoc physics, Mass Inst Technol, 67-68; asst prof, 68-72, assoc prof, 72-78, PROF PHYSICS, NORTHEASTERN UNIV, 78-, CHMN DEPT, 81- *Mem:* Am Inst Physics; Brit Inst Physics; fel Sci Res Coun; fel Am Coun Educ. *Res:* High pressure dielectric and far infrared spectroscopic studies of solids. *Mailing Add:* Dept Physics Northeastern Univ Boston MA 02115

LOWNEY, EDMUND DILLAHUNTY, b Port Arthur, Tex, Nov 8, 31; m 58; c 2. DERMATOLOGY. *Educ:* Univ Tex, BA, 53; Yale Univ, PhD(psychol), 57; Univ Pa, MD, 60. *Prof Exp:* From instr to asst prof dermat, Univ Mich, Ann Arbor, 64-67; assoc prof, Med Col Va, 67-69; PROF DERMAT, UNIV HOSP, COL MED, OHIO STATE UNIV, 69- *Mem:* Soc Invest Dermat; Am Dermatol Asn. *Res:* Immunology. *Mailing Add:* Dept of Dermat Univ Hosp Ohio State Univ Col of Med Columbus OH 43210

LOWNIE, H(AROLD) W(ILLIAM), JR, b Buffalo, NY, July 11, 18; m 76; c 2. METALLURGY, ENGINEERING, ECONOMIC FEASIBILITY. *Educ:* Purdue Univ, BS, 39; Univ Pittsburgh, MS, 44; Ohio State Univ, MBA, 72. *Prof Exp:* Foundry engr, Westinghouse Elec Corp, Pa, 39-45; asst supvr, 45-50, chief process metall, 50-81, RES LEADER, COLUMBUS DIV, BATTELLE MEM INST, 71- *Honors & Awards:* Whiting Gold Medal, Foundrymens Soc, 59; Merit Award, Am Soc Testing & Mat, 66. *Mem:* Fel AAAS; Am Soc Metals; Foundrymens Soc; Am Inst Mining, Metall & Petrol Engrs; fel Am Soc Testing & Mat; Asn Iron & Steel Engrs. *Res:* Metallurgy and inoculation of gray cast iron; use of foundry coke; cupola operation; blast-furnace practice; general foundry practice; research administration; direct reduction of iron ore; chemical metallurgy; economics of metallurgy processes. *Mailing Add:* Columbus Div Battelle Mem Inst 505 King Ave Columbus OH 43201

LOWNSBERY, BENJAMIN FERRIS, b Wilmington, Del, July 28, 20; m 50; c 1. PLANT NEMATOLOGY. *Educ:* Univ Del, BA, 42; Cornell Univ, PhD(plant path), 50. *Prof Exp:* Chemist explosives div, E I du Pont de Nemours & Co, 42-45; asst plant path, Cornell Univ, 45-50; asst plant pathologist, Conn Agr Exp Sta, 51-53; from asst to assoc nematologist, 54-67, lectr nematol, 60-70, PROF NEMATOL, UNIV CALIF, DAVIS, 70-, NEMATOLOGIST, EXP STA, 67- *Concurrent Pos:* Mem subcomt nematodes, Agr Bd, Nat Acad Sci-Nat Res Coun, 66-68; sr ed, J Nematol, 77-78, ed-in-chief, 78-81. *Honors & Awards:* Stark Award, Am Soc Hort Sci, 70. *Mem:* Soc Nematol; Am Phytopath Soc. *Res:* Forest and agricultural nematology. *Mailing Add:* Div Nematol Univ of Calif Davis CA 95616

LOWRANCE, EDWARD WALTON, b Ogden, Utah, June 17, 08; m 35; c 2. ANATOMY. *Educ:* Univ Utah, AB, 30, AM, 32; Stanford Univ, PhD(biol), 37. *Prof Exp:* Asst zool, Stanford Univ, 32-34, Rockefeller asst exp embryol, 34-36 & 37-38; from instr to assoc prof zool, Univ Nev, 38-49; asst prof anat, Sch Med, Univ SDak, 49-50; assoc prof, 50-55, prof, 55-78, EMER PROF ANAT, SCH MED, UNIV MO-COLUMBIA, 78- *Concurrent Pos:* Actg assoc prof, Sch Med, Univ Kans, 44-46; State secy, Mo State Anat Bd, 69-78. *Mem:* AAAS; Am Asn Anat; Am Micros Soc; NY Acad Sci. *Res:* Comparative and experimental embryology; quantitative and statistical anatomy. *Mailing Add:* Dept Anat Univ Mo Med Ctr Columbia MO 65212

LOWRANCE, WILLIAM WILSON, JR, b El Paso, Tex, May 8, 43. SCIENCE POLICY, RISK ASSESSMENT. *Educ:* Univ NC, Chapel Hill, AB, 65; Rockefeller Univ, PhD(biochem), 70. *Prof Exp:* Res chemist, Tenn Eastman Co, Kingsport, 70-71; res consult, NC Dept Educ, Raleigh, 71-72; asst exec ed, J Cell Biol, New York, 72-73; resident fel, Nat Acad Sci, Washington, DC, 73-75; res fel, Prog Sci & Int Affairs, Harvard Univ, 75-76; spec asst to US Secy State, Washington, DC, 77-78; vis assoc prof human biol, Stanford Univ, 78-80; SR FEL & DIR, LIFE SCI & PUB POLICY PROG, ROCKEFELLER UNIV, NEW YORK, 80- *Mem:* AAAS. *Res:* National and international science policy; decisions regarding public health risks; ethical responsibilities of technical people; nuclear proliferation; synthetic and mechanistic organic photochemistry. *Mailing Add:* Life Sci & Pub Policy Prog Rockefeller Univ 1230 York Ave New York NY 10021

LOWREY, CHARLES BOYCE, b New Orleans, La, Mar 15, 41; m 61; c 3. PHYSICAL ORGANIC CHEMISTRY. *Educ:* Centenary Col, BS, 63; Univ Houston, PhD(heterocyclic chem), 68. *Prof Exp:* Teaching asst chem, Univ Houston, 63-66; from asst prof to assoc prof chem, Centenary Col La, 73-77, asst dean col, 74-77; gen mgr opers & prod, Petrol Assocs of Lafayette, Inc, 77-79; asst gen mgr & tech mgr, Port Arthur, Tex Facil, Chem Water Mgt, Inc, 79-81; CONSULT HAZARDOUS WASTE DISPOSAL, PRICE-CURTIS & ASSOC, INC, 81- *Concurrent Pos:* Consult, Baifield Industs, La, 66-70; water pollution consult, Ford Battery Plant, Shreveport, 68-73 & Gould Battery Plant, Shreveport, 73-75. *Mem:* Am Chem Soc; Soc Petrol Engrs. *Res:* Synthesis and study of electronic effects in substituted benzo(b) furans and benzo(b) thiophenes. *Mailing Add:* Price-Curtis & Assoc Inc 4100 Southwest Freeway Suite 510 Houston TX 77027

LOWREY, GEORGE HARRISON, b Mansfield, Ohio, Nov 14, 17; m 43; c 3. PEDIATRICS. *Educ:* Univ Mich, Ann Arbor, AB, 40, MD, 43. *Prof Exp:* Rockefeller Found fel, Med Ctr, Univ Mich, Ann Arbor, 46-47, from asst prof to prof pediat, 49-70; assoc dean student affairs, 70-76, prof pediat, 70-79, EMER PROF PEDIAT, SCH MED, UNIV CALIF, DAVIS, 79- *Concurrent Pos:* From assoc prof to prof postgrad med, Univ Mich, Ann Arbor, 56-70; sci ed, Mich Med, 66-70; adv continuing educ, Calif Med Asn, 70-73; Earl H Baxter vis prof, Ohio State Univ, 71- *Mem:* AMA; Am Pediat Soc; Am Acad Pediat; Am Diabetic Asn; Asn Am Med Cols. *Res:* Growth and development of children; endocrinology in children. *Mailing Add:* Dept of Pediat Univ of Calif Sch of Med Davis CA 95616

LOWREY, ROBERT S, animal nutrition, biochemistry, see previous edition

LOWRIE, ALLEN, b Washington, DC, Dec 30, 37; div; c 1. MARINE GEOLOGY, CONTINENTAL MARGINS. *Educ:* Columbia Univ, BA, 62. *Prof Exp:* Res asst marine geol, Lamont Geol Observ, 63-68; oceanogr marine geol, Naval Oceanog Off, 68-76 & 78-81 & Naval Ocean Res & Develop Act, 76-78; EXPLORATIONIST, MOBIL OIL CORP, 81- *Concurrent Pos:* Consult geologist, Seagull Int Explor, Houston, Tex & Int Inc, Kenner, La; invited lectr, Catholic Univ Am, Washington, DC, 72-73 & Universidad de Los Andes, Bogota, Colombia, 78-; guest lectr oceanog & ecol, Calverton Sch, Huntington, Md, 74-76; consult, St Stanislaus Col, Bay St Louis, Miss, 76-; instr, Tulane Univ, New Orleans, La. *Mem:* Soc Econ Paleont & Mineral; Am Asn Petrol Geologists; NY Acad Sci; Am Inst Prof Geologists; Sigma Xi. *Res:* Interaction along subduction zones of Western North and South America, i.e., Chile, Isthmus of Panama, and Western Colombia; sediment type and thickness and acoustic response in ocean basins; evolution of passive margins. *Mailing Add:* Explor Dept Rm 1366 Mobil Oil Corp 1250 Poydras New Orleans LA 70113

LOWRIE, HARMAN SMITH, b Soochow, China, June 30, 26; m 51; c 4. ORGANIC CHEMISTRY. *Educ:* Ohio State Univ, BSc, 48, PhD(chem), 52. *Prof Exp:* Res chemist med dept, Ohio State Univ, 52-54; CHEMIST, G D SEARLE & CO, 54- *Mem:* Am Chem Soc. *Res:* Organic synthesis; heterocyclics; medicinal chemistry. *Mailing Add:* G D Searle & Co Box 5110 Chicago IL 60680

LOWRIGHT, RICHARD HENRY, b Bethlehem, Pa, Aug 31, 40; m 66. SEDIMENTOLOGY. *Educ:* Franklin & Marshall Col, AB, 62; Pa State Univ, PhD(geol), 71. *Prof Exp:* Teacher pub sch, NY, 64-66; asst prof, 71-78, ASSOC PROF GEOL, SUSQUEHANNA UNIV, 78- *Concurrent Pos:* Consult geol, 73- *Mem:* Nat Water Well Asn; Soc Econ Paleontologists & Mineralogists. *Res:* Stratigraphy and depositional environments of Lower Devonian rocks in Snyder County, Pennsylvania. *Mailing Add:* Dept Geol Susquehanna Univ Selinsgrove PA 17870

LOWRY, EDWARD MACLEAN, b Dallas, Tex, Apr 9, 14; m 44; c 2. BIOLOGY. *Educ:* Ripon Col, AB, 36; Univ Mo, PhD(zool), 53. *Prof Exp:* Assoc biologist fisheries, State Conserv Comn, Mo, 47-54; asst prof biol, Meredith Col, 54-56; res asst prof zool, NC State Col, 56-59; assoc prof sci & math, 59-64, chmn dept, 71-76, PROF BIOL, UNIV WIS-STOUT, 64- *Mem:* Am Fisheries Soc. *Res:* Farm pond fish culture; fish growth; limnology; aquatic ecology. *Mailing Add:* Dept of Biol Univ of Wis-Stout Menomonie WI 54751

LOWRY, ERIC G, b Berlin, Ger, Nov 23, 16; US citizen; m 54; c 1. PHYSICAL CHEMISTRY. *Educ:* Univ Geneva, PhD(phys chem), 43. *Prof Exp:* Res chemist fluorochem, Gen Chem Div, Allied Chem Corp, 47-49; res chemist photog, Remington-Rand Div, Sperry Rand Corp, 51-58; res chemist lithography, Polychrome Corp, 59; res chemist, Addressograph-Multigraph Corp, 59-65, chief chemist reprography, 65-77, sect supvr, Charles Bruning Co Div, 77-81; RETIRED. *Mem:* AAAS; Am Chem Soc; Soc Photog Sci & Eng; Tech Asn Pulp & Paper Indust. *Res:* Reprography. *Mailing Add:* 73 Lewis St Middleton CT 06457

LOWRY, GEORGE GORDON, b Chico, Calif, Jan 12, 29; m 53; c 4. PHYSICAL CHEMISTRY. *Educ:* Chico State Col, AB, 50; Stanford Univ, MS, 52; Mich State Univ, PhD(phys chem), 63. *Prof Exp:* Res asst, Stanford Res Inst, 51; res chemist, Dow Chem Co, 51-62; NSF fel, 62-63; from asst prof to assoc prof chem, Claremont Men's Col, 63-68; assoc prof, 68-75, PROF CHEM, WESTERN MICH UNIV, 75- *Mem:* Am Chem Soc; Sigma Xi. *Res:* Polymerization kinetics and processes; copolymerization; statistical theory of kinetic chain processes; physical properties of liquids and non-ionic solutions. *Mailing Add:* Dept of Chem Western Mich Univ Kalamazoo MI 49008

LOWRY, GERALD LAFAYETTE, b Harrisburg, Pa, Sept 12, 28; m 49; c 3. FORESTRY, SOIL SCIENCE. *Educ:* Pa State Univ, BS, 53; Ore State Univ, MS, 55; Mich State Univ, PhD(forestry), 61. *Prof Exp:* Asst, Ore State Univ, 53-55; instr stripmine reclamation, Ohio Agr Exp Sta, Wooster, 55-61; res forester, Pulp & Paper Res Inst Can, 61-72; assoc prof, 72-76, PROF, STEPHEN F AUSTIN STATE UNIV, 76- *Concurrent Pos:* Asst prof, Ohio State Univ, 57-58; spec res asst, Mich State Univ, 58-59; vchmn forestry comt, Coun Fertilizer Appln, 61-63, chmn, 63-65. *Mem:* Soc Am Foresters; Soil Sci Soc Am; Can Land Reclamation Asn. *Res:* Forest soil-site relationships; rehabilitation of burned and cutover lands; coal stripmine reclamation; soil chemistry, physics and fertility; tree physiology and silviculture. *Mailing Add:* Sch of Forestry Stephen F Austin State Univ Nacogdoches TX 75961

LOWRY, JAMES LEE, b Birmingham, Ala, Feb 19, 31; m 56; c 3. ELECTRICAL ENGINEERING. *Educ:* Auburn Univ, BEE, 55, MS, 57; Univ Fla, PhD(elec eng), 63. *Prof Exp:* From instr to asst prof elec eng, Auburn Univ, 55-59; teaching assoc, Univ Fla, 62-63; assoc prof, 63-65, PROF ELEC ENG, AUBURN UNIV, 65- *Concurrent Pos:* Consult, Ala Power Co. *Mem:* Sr mem Inst Elec & Electronics Engrs; Am Soc Eng Educ; Nat Soc Prof Engrs. *Res:* Circuit analysis and synthesis; power systems. *Mailing Add:* Dept of Elec Eng Auburn Univ Auburn AL 36830

LOWRY, JEAN, b Indianapolis, Ind, Feb 7, 21. GEOLOGY. *Educ:* Pa State Univ, BS, 42; Yale Univ, PhD(geol), 51. *Prof Exp:* Jr economist, Off Price Admin, 42-43; jr geologist, US Geol Surv, 43-46, asst geologist, 46-49; dist geologist, State Geol Surv, Va, 49-57; from asst to assoc prof geol, 58-68, PROF GEOL, E CAROLINA UNIV, 68- *Concurrent Pos:* Vis prof, Concepcion Univ, 62-63. *Mem:* Geol Soc Am; Nat Asn Geol Teachers. *Res:* Stratigraphy and structure of southern Appalachians; caves. *Mailing Add:* 211 S Eastern St Greenville NC 27834

LOWRY, JERALD FRANK, b Listie, Pa, Oct 22, 39; m 61; c 4. EXPERIMENTAL PHYSICS. *Educ:* Univ Pittsburgh, BS, 61; Cornell Univ, MS, 63. *Prof Exp:* Jr engr, Testing Reactor, Westinghouse Elec Corp, 61; teaching asst physics, Cornell Univ, 61-63; SR ENGR APPL PHYSICS, WESTINGHOUSE RES & DEVELOP CTR, 63- *Mem:* Am Phys Soc; AAAS. *Res:* Low pressure plasmas; fluorescent lamp discharges; generation of high power electron beams; measurement of power density distribution and beam radiance. *Mailing Add:* 1730 Yorktown Pl Pittsburgh PA 15235

LOWRY, JOHN ALLEN, b Fort Lauderdale, Fla, June 1, 49; m 71; c 2. REACTION KINETICS. *Educ:* Univ Fla, BS, 71; Univ Ariz, MS, 73. *Prof Exp:* Chemist, E I DuPont De Nemours & Co, 73-77; develop assoc, Celanese Corp, 77-81; GROUP LEADER, SHEREX CHEM CO, 81- *Res:* Development of new and improved processes for a wide variety of polymer and specialty chemical products. *Mailing Add:* 105 Timberlane Dr Morton IL 61550

LOWRY, LEWIS ROY, JR, b Little Falls, NY, Dec 3, 28; m 50; c 4. PHYSICS, ELECTRICAL ENGINEERING. *Educ:* Miami Univ, AB, 49, MS, 54; Ohio State Univ, PhD(physics), 67. *Prof Exp:* Design engr, Aerospace Elec Div, 51-63, fel engr, 63-68, mgr appl res, 68-72, mgr device technol, 72-81, MGR SEMICONDUCTOR RES, RES & DEVELOP CTR, WESTINGHOUSE ELEC CORP, 81- *Mem:* Am Phys Soc; AAAS; Inst Elec & Electronics Engrs. *Mailing Add:* Westinghouse Res & Develop Ctr 1310 Beulah Rd Pittsburgh PA 15235

LOWRY, NANCY, b Newburgh, NY, Sept 4, 38; m 61; c 3. PHYSICAL ORGANIC CHEMISTRY. *Educ:* Smith Col, AB, 60; Mass Inst Technol, PhD(chem), 65. *Prof Exp:* Res assoc chem, Mass Inst Technol, 65-66 & Amherst Col, 66-67; lectr, Smith Col, 67-69, res assoc, 69-70; asst prof, 70-74, ASSOC PROF CHEM, HAMPSHIRE COL, 74- *Mem:* AAAS; NY Acad Sci; Inst Soc, Ethics, & Life Sci. *Res:* Free radical mechanisms and stereochemistry. *Mailing Add:* Sch of Nat Sci & Math Hampshire Col Amherst MA 01002

LOWRY, OLIVER HOWE, b Chicago, Ill, July 18, 10; m 35; c 5. PHARMACOLOGY, BIOCHEMISTRY. *Educ:* Northwestern Univ, BS, 32; Univ Chicago, MD & PhD(biochem), 37. *Prof Exp:* Instr biochem, Harvard Med Sch, 37-42; mem staff, Pub Health Res Inst, NY, 42-44, assoc chief, Div Physiol & Nutrit, 44-47; prof pharmacol, 47-79, head dept, 47-76, dean, 55-58, EMER PROF PHARMACOL, SCH MED, WASH UNIV, 79- *Concurrent Pos:* Commonwealth Found fel, Carlsberg Lab, Copenhagen Univ, 39. *Honors & Awards:* Midwest Award, Am Chem Soc, 62, Scott Award, 63; Borden Award, Asn Am Med Cols, 66. *Mem:* Nat Acad Sci; Am Soc Pharmacol & Exp Therapeut; Am Soc Biol Chem; Am Chem Soc; Histochem Soc. *Res:* Tissue electrolytes; chemistry of aging; nutrition and detection of nutritional deficiency; histochemistry; neurochemistry. *Mailing Add:* Dept of Pharmacol Sch of Med Wash Univ St Louis MO 63110

LOWRY, PHILIP HOLT, b New York, NY, Feb 20, 18; m 45; c 2. OPERATIONS RESEARCH. *Educ:* Princeton Univ, AB, 39; Yale Univ, MA, 42, PhD(int rels), 49. *Prof Exp:* Meteorologist, Brookhaven Nat Lab, 47-51; opers analyst, Opers Res Off, Johns Hopkins Univ, 51-61; opers analyst, Res Anal Corp, 61-72; opers analyst, Gen Res Corp, 72-80; CONSULT, 80- *Mem:* Opers Res Soc Am; Am Meteorol Soc; Am Astron Soc. *Res:* Military operations research; impact of technology on international relations; nuclear policy and strategy. *Mailing Add:* 8701 Georgetown Pike McLean VA 22102

LOWRY, RALPH A(DDISON), b Clay County, Mo, Aug 9, 26; m 47; c 4. ENGINEERING, PHYSICS. *Educ:* Iowa State Univ, BS, 49, PhD(physics), 55. *Prof Exp:* Sr scientist, Res Labs Eng Sci, 55-62, from assoc prof to prof aerospace eng, 62-77, chmn dept aerospace eng & eng physics, 65-72, prof nuclear eng & eng physics, 77-78, JOHN LLOYD NEWCOMB PROF ENG & APPL SCI, UNIV VA, 78- *Mem:* Am Phys Soc; Am Inst Aeronaut & Astronaut. *Res:* Atomic and molecular physics; isotope separation; gas centrifuges; fluid mechanics. *Mailing Add:* Rte 6 Box 302 Charlottesville VA 22901

LOWRY, ROBERT JAMES, b Chelsea, Mich, Aug 26, 12; m 34; c 1. BOTANY. *Educ:* Univ Mich, BS, 40, MS, 41, PhD(bot), 47. *Prof Exp:* Res assoc, Univ Mich, 42-45; asst prof bot, Mich State Univ, 46-48; from asst prof to prof, 48-81, EMER PROF BOT, UNIV MICH, ANN ARBOR, 81- *Mem:* AAAS; Am Bryol & Lichenological Soc; Bot Soc Am; Am Genetic Asn; Torrey Bot Club. *Res:* Cytotaxonomy; electron microscopy. *Mailing Add:* Dept of Bot Univ of Mich Ann Arbor MI 48104

LOWRY, ROBERT KIMBALL, b Ft Lauderdale, Fla, May 12, 44; m 76; c 1. ANALYTICAL CHEMISTRY, MATERIALS SCIENCE. *Educ:* Stetson Univ, BS, 66; Fla Atlantic Univ, MS, 69. *Prof Exp:* assoc prin engr, 69-80, SECT HEAD ANALYTICAL LAB, HARRIS SEMICONDUCTOR, 80- *Concurrent Pos:* Adj instr chem, Fla Inst Technol, 78- *Mem:* Am Chem Soc; Soc Appl Spectros; Am Soc Testing & Mat; Am Inst Chemists. *Res:* Methods development in analytical chemistry; characterization of semiconductor materials. *Mailing Add:* 510 Ave B Melbourne Beach FL 32951

LOWRY, THOMAS HASTINGS, b New York, NY, June 16, 38; m 61; c 3. ORGANIC CHEMISTRY. *Educ:* Princeton Univ, AB, 60; Harvard Univ, PhD(chem), 65. *Prof Exp:* NIH fel chem, Mass Inst Technol, 64-65, res assoc, 65-66; asst prof, 66-74, assoc prof, 74-81, PROF CHEM, SMITH COL, 81- *Mem:* Am Chem Soc. *Res:* Physical organic chemistry. *Mailing Add:* Dept of Chem Smith Col Northampton MA 01063

LOWRY, WALLACE DEAN, b Medford, Ore, Oct 5, 17; m 42. GEOLOGY. *Educ:* Ore State Univ, BS, 39, MS, 40; Univ Rochester, PhD(geol), 43. *Prof Exp:* Geologist, Ore Dept Geol & Mineral Indust, 42-47; geologist, Texaco, Inc, 47-49; assoc prof, 49-58, PROF GEOL, VA POLYTECH INST & STATE UNIV, 58- *Mem:* Fel Geol Soc Am; Am Asn Petrol Geol. *Res:* Late Cenozoic stratigraphy of the lower Columbia River basin; ferruginous bauxite deposits of Northwestern Oregon; silica sands of Western Virginia; porosity of sandstone reservoir rocks; role of Tertiary volcanism in tectonism; relation of silicification and dolomitization; geology of the Blue Mountains, Oregon; mechanics of Appalachian thrusting; North American geosynclines. *Mailing Add:* Dept of Geol Sci Va Polytech Inst & State Univ Blacksburg VA 24061

LOWRY, WILLIAM THOMAS, b Hobbs, NMex, Dec 11, 42; m 65; c 2. OCCUPATIONAL SAFETY & HEALTH. *Educ:* E Tex State Univ, BS, 65, MS, 67; Colo State Univ, PhD(natural prod chem), 71; Am Inst Chemists, cert, 75; Am Bd Forensic Toxicol, cert, 76. *Prof Exp:* Chemist, Fed Bur Invest, 65; res assoc biochem, Va Polytech Inst & State Univ, 71-72; spec agent, Fed Bur Invest, 72-73; TOXICOLOGIST, SOUTHWESTERN INST FORENSIC SCI, 73-; ASST PROF TOXICOL, GRAD SCH BIOMED SCI, UNIV TEX HEALTH SCI CTR, 77- *Concurrent Pos:* Assoc consult attend staff toxicol, Parkland Mem Hosp, 73-; instr path, Univ Tex Southwestern Med Sch, 73-75, instr path & forensic sci, 75-77, asst prof path, 77-; adj asst prof chem, East Tex State Univ, 76-77, adj assoc prof, 77-80; adj asst prof civil eng, Univ Tex, Arlington, 82- *Mem:* Am Acad Clin Toxicol; Am Acad Forensic Sci; Am Chem Soc; Am Inst Chemists; Am Soc Pharmacog. *Res:* Environmental toxicology; biodegradation of toxic substances; utilizing bacteria. *Mailing Add:* Southwestern Inst Forensic Sci PO Box 35728 Dallas TX 75235

LOWTHER, FRANK EUGENE, b Orrville, Ohio, Feb 3, 29; m 51; c 4. ENGINEERING PHYSICS. *Educ:* Ohio State Univ, BS, 52. *Prof Exp:* Sr engr, Raytheon Mfg Co, 52-57; consult, Gen Elec Co, 57-65; founder dir & vpres, Purification Sci, Inc, 65-75; sr eng assoc, Union Carbide, 75-79; SR RES SCIENTIST, ATLANTIC RICHFIELD CO, 80- *Mem:* Am Inst Aeronaut & Astronaut; Inst Elec & Electronics Engrs. *Res:* Ozone chemistry; plasma generators; solid state power devices; internal combustion engines; electrodesorption; thermoelectrics; virus and bacteria disinfection systems. *Mailing Add:* 5145 N Douglas Fir Rd Calabasas CA 91302

LOWTHER, JAMES DAVID, b Jackson, Miss, June 22, 39; m 61; c 3. MECHANICAL ENGINEERING. *Educ:* Miss State Univ, BS, 61, MS, 62; Univ Tex, Austin, PhD(mech eng), 68. *Prof Exp:* Mech engr, Baton Rouge refinery, Humble Oil & Refining Co, 62-63; asst prof, 63-68, ASSOC PROF MECH ENG, LA TECH UNIV, 68- *Concurrent Pos:* NSF res grant, 70-71. *Mem:* Am Soc Mech Engrs; Am Soc Eng Educ; Instrument Soc Am. *Res:* Heat transfer and two-phase flow. *Mailing Add:* Dept of Mech Eng La Tech Univ Ruston LA 71270

LOWTHER, JOHN LINCOLN, b Burlington, Iowa, Sept 5, 43. COMPUTER SCIENCE. *Educ:* Univ Iowa, BA, 65, MS, 67, PhD(comput sci), 75. *Prof Exp:* Instr math, Southwest Minn State Col, 67-71; instr, 74-75, asst prof, 75-77, ASSOC PROF COMPUT SCI, MICH TECHNOL UNIV, 77- *Mem:* Asn Comput Mach; Math Asn Am; Sigma Xi; Inst Elec & Electronics Engrs. *Res:* Compiler writing; programming languages; computer graphics; microprogramming. *Mailing Add:* Dept of Math & Comput Sci Mich Technol Univ Houghton MI 49931

LOWTHER, JOHN STEWART, b Cochrane, Ont, July 31, 25; m 53. PALEONTOLOGY, PALEOBOTANY. *Educ:* McGill Univ, BSc, 49, MSc, 50; Univ Mich, PhD(geol), 57. *Prof Exp:* From instr to asst prof, 56-72, assoc prof, 72-80, PROF GEOL, UNIV PUGET SOUND, 80- *Mem:* Paleont Soc; Bot Soc Am; Am Asn Petrol Geologists; Nat Asn Geol Teachers; Brit Paleont Asn. *Res:* Sedimentology; economic geology; Mesozoic paleobotany and stratigraphy; arctic paleobotany; geology education. *Mailing Add:* Dept of Geol Univ of Puget Sound Tacoma WA 98416

LOWY, BERNARD, b New York, NY, Feb 29, 16; m 50; c 2. MYCOLOGY. *Educ:* Univ Long Island, BS, 38; Univ Iowa, MS, 49, PhD(bot), 51. *Prof Exp:* Tech asst biol, Univ Long Island, 38-42, instr, 46-48; instr bot, Univ Iowa, 49-51; from asst to assoc prof, 51-62, prof, 62-80, EMER PROF BOT & CUR MYCOL HERBARIUM, LA STATE UNIV, BATON ROUGE, 80- *Concurrent Pos:* Fulbright scholar, Peru, 58-59 & 72 & Brazil, 65-66; vis prof, Univ Tucuman, Argentina, 59; Am Philos Soc grant, Mex, 62; Sigma Xi grant, Guatemala, 63; res partic, Orgn Trop Studies, Costa Rica, 64; mem numerous mycol expeds, Mex, Cent Am, SAm & West Indies, 50-78; consult ed, Revista Interam, Interam Univ, PR, 71-; chmn, Ethnomycol Sect, Int Mycol Cong, 75-77; mem, Proj Flora Amazonica, Brazil, 80. *Mem:* Mycol Soc Am; Bot Soc Am; Am Bryol & Lichenological Soc; hon mem Mex Soc Mycol; Int Asn Plant Taxon. *Res:* Taxonomy and phylogeny of neotropical tremellaceous fungi; ethnomycology of Central America. *Mailing Add:* Dept Bot La State Univ Baton Rouge LA 70803

LOWY, BERTRAM ALAN, biochemistry, deceased

LOWY, PETER HERMAN, b Vienna, Jan 3, 14; nat US; m 40; c 3. ORGANIC CHEMISTRY. *Educ:* Univ Vienna, Dr(chem), 36. *Prof Exp:* Food chemist, Rochester, NY, 40-45; res asst, 46-49, from res fel chem to sr res fel, 49-72, res assoc, 72-81, SR RES ASSOC BIOL, CALIF INST TECHNOL, 81- *Mem:* AAAS; Am Chem Soc; Fedn Am Socs Exp Biol; Am Soc Hemat. *Res:* Organic chemical synthesis, particularly of radioactive compounds; isolation and structure determination of bio-organic substances. *Mailing Add:* Dept of Biol Calif Inst of Technol Pasadena CA 91109

LOWY, STANLEY H(OWARD), b New York, NY, Mar 10, 22; m 45; c 2. AEROSPACE ENGINEERING. *Educ:* Purdue Univ, BS, 43; Univ Minn, MS, 47. *Prof Exp:* Test engr, Allison Div, Gen Motors Corp, 47; instr mech eng, Ore State Col, 47-50; struct design engr, Willamette Iron & Steel Co, 50-51; standards engr, Hughes Aircraft Co, 52; chief engr, Peters Co, 52-53; chief engr, A Young & Son Iron Works, 53-56; consult struct engr, Stan H Lowy & Assocs, 56-58; assoc prof aerospace eng, Univ Okla, 58-64; assoc prof, 64-69, ASSOC DIR, PROJ THEMIS, RES FOUND, TEX A&M UNIV, 69-, PROF AEROSPACE ENG, 77-, ASST DEAN ENG, 80- *Concurrent Pos:* Proj dir space shuttle wind tunnel tests & anals, Manned Spacecraft Ctr, NASA, 69. *Mem:* Am Soc Eng Educr; Am Inst Aeronaut & Astronaut; Am Helicopter Soc. *Res:* Aircraft design; aircraft power plants; orbital mechanics. *Mailing Add:* Col Eng Tex A&M Univ College Station TX 77843

LOY, JAMES BRENT, b Borger, Tex, Feb 28, 41; div. PLANT SCIENCE, DEVELOPMENTAL GENETICS. *Educ:* Okla State Univ, BS, 63; Colo State Univ, MS, 65, PhD(genetics), 67. *Prof Exp:* Asst prof, 67-73, assoc prof, 73-81, PROF PLANT SCI, UNIV NH, 81- *Concurrent Pos:* Vis scholar bot, Univ Calif, Berkeley, 74-75. *Mem:* Am Soc Hort Sci; Soc Econ Bot; Am Soc Plant Physiol. *Res:* Cucurbit breeding; hormonal and genetic regulation of sex expression in Cucumis melo cell division and elongation in shoots of Citrullus lanatus; biochemical genetics of testa development in cucubit pepo. *Mailing Add:* Dept of Plant Sci Univ of NH Durham NH 03824

LOY, REBEKAH, b Berkeley, Calif, Dec 30, 47; m 78; c 2. NEUROANATOMY, NEURAL DEVELOPMENT & PLASTICITY. *Educ:* Univ Calif, Irvine, BS, 71, PhD(psychobiol), 75. *Prof Exp:* Fel, 75-78, ASST PROF NEUROSCI, UNIV CALIF, SAN DIEGO, 78- *Concurrent Pos:* Prin investr, Nat Inst Neurol & Commun Dis & Stroke, 78-; panel mem, Neurobiol Prog, Subpanel Integrative & Motor Processes, NSF, 82- *Mem:* AAAS; Soc Neurosci; Int Soc Develop Neurosci; Am Asn Anatomists. *Res:* Neuronal reorganization in response to brain injury; sex differences in brain function, development and repair; control of synaptic specificity and plasticity in development, after injury and in response to chronic drug treatment. *Mailing Add:* Dept Neurosci M-024 Univ Calif La Jolla CA 92093

LOY, ROBERT GRAVES, b Prescott, Ariz, Feb 7, 24; m 51; c 5. ANIMAL PHYSIOLOGY. *Educ:* Ariz State Univ, BS, 55; Univ Wis, MS, 56, PhD(physiol of reprod), 59. *Prof Exp:* Instr genetics, Univ Wis, 56-59; asst prof animal husb, Univ Calif, Davis, 59-66; from asst to assoc prof vet sci, Univ Ky, 66-71; agr consult, 71-74; ASSOC PROF VET SCI, UNIV KY, 74- *Mem:* Am Soc Animal Sci. *Res:* Physiology and endocrinology of reproduction in horses. *Mailing Add:* Dept of Vet Sci Univ of Ky Lexington KY 40506

LOY, WAYNE RICHARD, b Macomb, Ill, Sept 7, 21; m 47; c 1. WATER CHEMISTRY. *Educ:* Western Ill Univ, BS, 43, MS, 47. *Prof Exp:* Instr chem, Wis State Univ, Oshkosh, 47-49; assoc prof, Wis State Col & Inst Technol, 49-59; ASSOC PROF CHEM, UNIV WIS-PLATTEVILLE, 59- *Mem:* Am Chem Soc; Am Soc Eng Educ. *Res:* Radioisotope techniques in water analysis and sanitary sciences. *Mailing Add:* Dept of Chem Univ of Wis Platteville WI 53818

LOYALKA, SUDARSHAN KUMAR, b Pilani, India, Apr 11, 43. NUCLEAR & MECHANICAL ENGINEERING. *Educ:* Univ Rajasthan, BEMech, 64; Stanford Univ, MS, 65, PhD(nuclear eng), 67. *Prof Exp:* From asst prof to assoc prof, 67-77, PROF NUCLEAR ENG, UNIV MO-COLUMBIA, 77-, JAMES C DOWELL CHAIR ENG, 80- *Concurrent Pos:* Vis scientist, Max Planck Inst Aerodyn, Gottingen, 69-71. *Res:* Kinetic theory of gases; neutron transport theory and reactor physics; nuclear reactor safety analysis; mechanics of aerosols. *Mailing Add:* Dept of Nuclear Eng Univ of Mo Columbia MO 65202

LOYD, DAVID HERON, b Shreveport, La, July 3, 41; m 60; c 2. ATOMIC PHYSICS, NUCLEAR PHYSICS. *Educ:* Univ Tex, Austin, BS, 63, MA, 64; Univ Wis-Madison, PhD(physics), 70. *Prof Exp:* ASST PROF PHYSICS, ANGELO STATE UNIV, 69- *Mem:* Am Phys Soc. *Res:* Atomic collisions. *Mailing Add:* Dept of Physics Angelo State Univ San Angelo TX 76901

LOYNACHAN, THOMAS EUGENE, b Oskaloosa, Iowa, Nov 18, 45; m 67; c 3. SOIL MICROBIOLOGY, SOIL FERTILITY. *Educ:* Iowa State Univ, BS, 68, MS, 72; NC State Univ, PhD(soil sci), 75. *Prof Exp:* Asst prof agron, Univ Alaska, 75-78; MEM TEACHING STAFF SOIL SCI, IOWA STATE UNIV, 78-, MEM RES STAFF FIXATION & SOIL ECOL, 78- *Mem:* AAAS; Soil Sci Soc Am; Am Soc Agron; Coun Agr Sci & Technol. *Res:* Nitrification inhibitors; oil degradation in Arctic soils; nitrogen fixation of legumes. *Mailing Add:* Dept of Agron Iowa State Univ Ames IA 50011

LOZANO, EDGARDO A, b Tampico, Mex, Nov 20, 24; m 49; c 3. BACTERIOLOGY. *Educ:* Univ Tex, BA, 48; Univ Wis, MS, 54; Mont State Univ, PhD(microbiol), 65. *Prof Exp:* Bacteriologist vaccine prod, Agr Res Serv, 48-50; res, Am Sci Labs, 54-55; dept head prod & develop, Corn States Labs, 55-59; dir bio-prod, Philips Roxane Inc, 63-64; asst prof bact, 65-68, ASSOC PROF BACT, VET RES LAB, MONT STATE UNIV, 68-, ASSOC PROF MICROBIOL, 80- *Res:* Bacteriological antigens and their purification; bacterial toxins; electrophoresis; telemetry of domestic animals. *Mailing Add:* Vet Res Lab Mont State Univ Bozeman MT 59715

LOZERON, HOMER A, b Grande Prairie, Alta, July 24, 34; m 67; c 2. BIOCHEMISTRY. *Educ:* Univ Alta, BSc, 56, MSc, 59; Univ Wash, PhD(biochem), 64. *Prof Exp:* Proj assoc, McArdle Lab Cancer Res, 65-67, instr, 67-72; asst prof, 72-77, ASSOC PROF BIOCHEM, SCH MED, ST LOUIS UNIV, 77- *Mem:* Am Soc Biol Chemists; Am Soc Microbiol. *Res:* RNA processing pathways and regulation of gene expression in bacterial virus systems. *Mailing Add:* St Louis Univ Med Ctr 1402 S Grand Blvd St Louis MO 63104

LOZIER, DANIEL WILLIAM, b Portland, Ore, Apr 10, 41; m 66; c 1. NUMERICAL ANALYSIS, SPECIAL FUNCTIONS. *Educ:* Ore State Univ, BA, 62; Am Univ, MA, 69; Univ Md, PhD(appl math), 79. *Prof Exp:* Mathematician, US Army Eng Res & Develop Lab, Ft Belvoir, Va, 63-69; MATHEMATICIAN, NAT BUR STANDARDS, US DEPT COM, 69- *Mem:* Soc Indust Appl Math; Math Asn Am; Asn Comput Mach; Inst Elec & Electronics Engrs; Sigma Xi. *Res:* Numerical analysis and computer science; computation of special functions; forward and backward recurrence methods; floating-point computer arithmetic; rounding error analysis; interval analysis; numerical aspects of programming languages. *Mailing Add:* Math Anal Div Ctr Appl Math Nat Bur Standards Washington DC 20234

LOZIER, JOHN C(HAPIN), b New York, NY, Feb 5, 12; m 36; c 4. ELECTRONIC ENGINEERING. *Educ:* Columbia Univ, AB, 34. *Prof Exp:* MEM TECH STAFF, BELL TEL LABS, 36- *Concurrent Pos:* MacKay vis prof, Univ Calif, Berkeley; mem tech adv comt bd governors, Argonne Nat Labs, 62-64; pres, Am Automatic Control Coun, 60. *Honors & Awards:* Chevalier, Legion Merite Postale, French Govt, 62. *Mem:* Fel Inst Elec & Electronics Engrs; Int Fedn Automatic Control (vpres, 66, pres, 72). *Res:* Feedback control systems. *Mailing Add:* 21 Park Rd Short Hills NJ 07078

LOZO, FRANK EDGAR, geology, deceased

LOZZIO, BISMARCK BERTO, b Patagones, Arg, Jan 27, 31; m 55; c 1. HEMATOLOGY, ONCOLOGY. *Educ:* Bernardino Rivadavia Col, Arg, BS & BA, 49; Univ Buenos Aires, MD, 55. *Prof Exp:* Instr internal med & assoc gastroenterologist, Clin Univ Hosp & Inst Med Invest, Univ Buenos Aires, 55-58; assoc gastroenterologist, NIH, Buenos Aires, Arg, 58-65; res assoc, 65-67, from asst prof to assoc prof res, 68-75, res prof, 75-78, PROF MED BIOL, MEM RES CTR, UNIV TENN, KNOXVILLE, 78- *Concurrent Pos:* Arg Nat Coun Sci & Technol res grant, NIH, Buenos Aires, 58-64; NSF grant, Univ Tenn, Knoxville, 67-69, NIH grant, 68-, Am Cancer Soc grant, 70-78. *Mem:* Am Soc Hemat; Am Asn Immunol; Am Asn Cancer Res; Soc Exp Biol & Med. *Res:* Differentiation of hematopoietic cells; cell homeostasis; leukemia; dissemination of heterotransplanted human malignant blood cells; mechanisms of metastasis. *Mailing Add:* Dept of Med Biol 1924 Alcoa Hwy Knoxville TN 37920

LOZZIO, CARMEN BERTUCCI, b Buenos Aires, Arg, Dec 20, 31; US citizen; m 55; c 1. MEDICAL GENETICS, CELL BIOLOGY. *Educ:* Univ Buenos Aires, physician, 55, MD, 60. *Prof Exp:* Physician in chg cytol, Rivadavia Hosp, Buenos Aires, 56-60; instr genetics, Univ Buenos Aires, 60-65; from res assoc to asst res prof, 65-72, assoc res prof med genetics, 72-78, DIR, BIRTH DEFECTS CTR, MEM RES CTR & HOSP, UNIV TENN, KNOXVILLE, 66-, PROF MED BIOL, CTR HEALTH SCI, UNIV TENN, KNOXVILLE, 78- *Concurrent Pos:* Arg Asn Prog Sci Millet fel & Arg Nat Res Coun fel radiation res, Rivadavia Hosp & Arg AEC, 57-60; grants, Arg Nat Res Coun, Univ Buenos Aires, 61-65, Pan Am Union, Biol Div, Oak Ridge Nat Lab, 64, Am Cancer Soc, Univ Tenn, Knoxville, 66-71, Nat Found-March of Dimes, 66-80, Physicians Med Educ & Res Found, 69-70, NIH, 69-71 & 75-81, US Dept Health, Educ & Welfare, 70-74, Tenn Dept Human Serv, 74-, Tenn Dept Ment Health, 74- & Tenn Dept Pub Health, 78- *Honors & Awards:* Honor Cert, World Cong Obstet & Gynec & Int Cong Internal Med, 64. *Mem:* Genetics Soc Am; Genetics Soc Can; Am Asn Ment Deficiency; Am Soc Human Genetics; NY Acad Sci. *Res:* Studies on human genetics and cytogenetics; genetic counseling and prenatal diagnosis of hereditary disorders; experimental studies on cell culture of human diploid strains with genetic markers and the effect of antimetabolites on mammalian cell cultures. *Mailing Add:* Birth Defects Ctr Univ of Tenn Mem Res Ctr & Hosp Knoxville TN 37920

LU, ADOLPH, b Chengtu, China, Feb 19, 42; Can citizen. HIGH ENERGY PHYSICS. *Educ:* Queen's Univ, BSc, 64; Univ Toronto, MA, 65; Univ Calif, Berkeley, PhD(physics), 73. *Prof Exp:* Researcher, Univ D'Orsay, Paris, 73-75; ASSOC RES PHYSICIST HIGH ENERGY PHYSICS, UNIV CALIF, SANTA BARBARA, 76- *Mem:* Am Phys Soc. *Res:* Bubble chamber physics; proton storage ring studies: high point events; photon cross sections; two-photon physics. *Mailing Add:* Physics Dept Univ Calif Santa Barbara CA 93106

LU, ANTHONY Y H, b Hupei, China, Jan 12, 37; m 65; c 1. BIOCHEMISTRY. *Educ:* Nat Taiwan Univ, BS, 58; Univ NC, Chapel Hill, PhD(biochem), 66. *Prof Exp:* Fel inst sci & technol, Univ Mich, Ann Arbor, 66-70; sr biochemist, Res Div, Hoffmann-La Roche Inc, 70-74, res fel, 74-78; SR INVESTR, RES LABS, MERCK SHARP & DOHME LABS, 78- *Mem:* AAAS; Am Chem Soc; Am Soc Pharmacol & Exp Therapeut; Am Soc Biol Chemists; NY Acad Sci. *Res:* Basic research in biochemistry and biochemical pharmacology. *Mailing Add:* Res Labs Merck Sharp & Dohme Rahway NJ 07065

LU, BENJAMIN C(HIH) Y(EU), b Peking, China, Oct 20, 26; m 52; c 3. CHEMICAL ENGINEERING. *Educ:* Nat Cent Univ, China, BASc, 47; Univ Toronto, MASc, 51, PhD(chem eng), 54. *Prof Exp:* Asst engr, Chinese Petrol Corp, China, 47-50; res assoc, Ont Res Found, Can, 54-55; lectr chem eng, Univ Toronto, 55-56; from asst prof to assoc prof, 56-62, actg chmn dept, 60, chmn dept, 61-76, vdean eng, Fac Sci & Eng, 69-76, PROF CHEM ENG, UNIV OTTAWA, 62- *Concurrent Pos:* Mem, Grant Selection Comt, Nat Res Coun Can, 69-72 & Nat Comt Deans Eng & Appl Sci, 69-76; exchange scientist, Inst Chem Process Fundamentals, Czech Acad Sci, 75; vis prof, Univ Pittsburgh, 76; exchange scientist, Japan Soc for Promotion Sci, 77; UNESCO consult, Univ Zulia, Venezuela, 78; mem, Hazardous Prod Bd Review, Can Govt, 80-81. *Mem:* Fel Chem Inst Can; Am Inst Chem Engrs; Am Chem Soc; Can Soc Chem Engrs; Sigma Xi. *Res:* Phase equilibria; thermodynamic properties of solutions; cryogenic research; energy engineering. *Mailing Add:* Dept of Chem Eng Univ of Ottawa Ottawa ON K1N 9B4 Can

LU, BENJAMIN CHI-KO, b Changchow, China, Mar 9, 32; m 62; c 2. GENETICS, CELL BIOLOGY. *Educ:* Taiwan Univ, BS, 55; Univ Alta, MS, 62, PhD(bot, genetics), 65. *Prof Exp:* Instr bot, Taiwan Univ, 58-60; fel fungal genetics, Cambridge Univ, 65-67; vis fel, Copenhagen Univ, 66; asst prof, 67-70, assoc prof, 70-79, PROF GENETICS, UNIV GUELPH, 79- *Concurrent Pos:* Nat Res Coun Can overseas fel, 65-67, res grant, Rask-Orsted Found fel & Carlsberg Found grant, 66-67; Nat Res Coun grant, 68-78; Natural Sci & Eng Res Coun, Can grant, 79- *Mem:* Genetics Soc Am; Am Soc Microbiol; Genetics Soc Can. *Res:* Fungal genetics; meiotic systems and fine structure of meiotic chromosomes in fungi; genetic recombination. *Mailing Add:* Dept of Bot & Genetics Univ of Guelph Guelph ON N1G 2W1 Can

LU, CHUNG-CHENG, invertebrate zoology, marine biology, see previous edition

LU, FRANK CHAO, b Hupeh, China, Mar 9, 15; nat US; m 39; c 3. PHARMACOLOGY, TOXICOLOGY. *Educ:* Cheeloo Univ, MD, 39. *Prof Exp:* Assoc ed, Coun on Pub, Chinese Med Asn, 40-42; sr asst pharmacol, Cheeloo Univ, 42-44, lectr, 45-47; lectr, WChina Union Univ, 44-45; pharmacologist, Food & Drug Labs, Can Dept Nat Health & Welfare, 51-60, actg head pharmacol & toxicol sect, 60-63, head, 63-65; chief food additives, WHO, 65-76; clin prof pharmacol, Sch Med, Univ Miami, 77-79; CONSULT TOXICOL, 79- *Concurrent Pos:* Res fel exp surg, McGill Univ, 47-48, med res fel pharmacol, 48-51. *Mem:* Am Col Toxicol; Am Soc Pharmacol & Exp Therapeut; Soc Toxicol; Europ Soc Toxicol; Can Pharmacol Soc. *Res:* Animal parasites in West China; distribution of sulfonamides in body fluids; physiology and pharmacology of coronary circulation; bioassay of drugs; cardiac glycosides; blood dyscrasias; toxicology of drugs, food additives, pesticides and contaminants. *Mailing Add:* 7452 SW 143rd Ave Miami FL 33183

LU, JING JONG, b Taiwan, China, Feb 27, 46; m 73; c 1. ANIMAL RESEARCH. *Educ:* Nat Normal Taiwan Univ, BS, 68, MS, 72; Purdue Univ, PhD(org chem), 80. *Prof Exp:* Assoc res scientist, Food Indust & Develop Inst, 72-74; RES SCIENTIST, INST MINERAL & CHEM CORP, 80- *Mem:* Am Chem Soc. *Res:* Syntheses of biologically active substances for use as anthelmintics, coccidiostats, antimicrobials or improved feed efficiency. *Mailing Add:* PO Box 207 Terre Haute IN 47808

LU, KUO CHIN, b Singapore, Dec 26, 17; US citizen; m 58; c 1. SOIL MICROBIOLOGY, PLANT PATHOLOGY. *Educ:* Nanking Univ, BS, 37; Ore State Univ, PhD(microbiol), 53. *Prof Exp:* Jr bacteriologist, Ore State Univ, 53-57; asst soil microbiologist, Cornell Univ, 57-59; res scientist, US Army Biol Warfare Lab, Md, 59-60; soil microbiologist, 60-67, PRIN MICROBIOLOGIST, FORESTRY SCI LAB, USDA, 67-; ASSOC PROF SOIL MICROBIOL, ORE STATE UNIV, 67- *Mem:* AAAS; Am Soc Microbiol; Am Phytopath Soc; Mycol Soc Am; Soil Sci Soc Am. *Res:* Antagonistic organisms against root-rot pathogens; biological control of forest diseases; rhizosphere association of mycorrhizal roots; influence of characteristic carbon-nitrogen ratio in decomposition of forest litters; biochemistry. *Mailing Add:* Forestry Sci Lab USDA 3200 Jefferson Way Corvallis OR 97331

LU, KUO HWA, b Antung, China, Jan 7, 23; US citizen; m 56; c 4. BIOSTATISTICS, GENETICS. *Educ:* Nat Cent Univ, China, BS, 45; Univ Minn, MS, 48, PhD(genetics), 51. *Prof Exp:* Agr adv, Continental Develop Found, 52-53; assoc prof appl statist, Utah State Univ, 56-60; assoc prof, 60-63, PROF BIOSTATIST, DENT SCH, ORE HEALTH SCI UNIV, 63-, PROF MED PSYCHOL, MED SCH, 71-, ADJ PROF MED GENETICS, 79- *Concurrent Pos:* Eli Lilly fel, Univ Minn, 53-56; sta statistician, Utah Agr Exp Sta, 56-60; consult, Lab Nuclear Med & Radiation Biol, Univ Calif, Los Angeles, 63-, NIH fel, vis prof, 66-67; consult, Appl Math Assoc, Inc, 63-; adj prof, Portland State Univ, 67-; consult, Tempo, Gen Elec, 78-80 & Procter & Gamble Co. *Mem:* AAAS; Biomet Soc; Am Math Soc; Am Statist Asn; Int Asn Dent Res. *Res:* Development and application of statistical methodology in biomedical research; statistical methods; dental public health; actuarial investigations in medical and dental insurance programs; simulation of oral diseases. *Mailing Add:* Ore Health Sci Univ Portland OR 97210

LU, KWANG-TZU, b China. ATOMIC SPECTROSCOPY. *Educ:* Nat Taiwan Univ, BS, 63; Univ Chicago, PhD(physics), 71. *Prof Exp:* Res assoc physics, Univ Ariz, 71-72; consult, Univ Chicago, 72-73; res assoc, Imp Col London, 73-75; res assoc physics, 76-78, asst physicist, 78-79, PHYSICIST, ARGONNE NAT LAB, 79- *Mem:* Am Phys Soc; Optical Soc Am. *Res:* Non-linear optical spectroscopy; rydberg atoms. *Mailing Add:* Chem Div Argonne Nat Lab Argonne IL 60439

LU, LE-WU, b Shanghai, China, June 5, 33; m 63; c 2. STRUCTURAL ENGINEERING. *Educ:* Nat Taiwan Univ, BS, 54; Iowa State Univ, MS, 56; Lehigh Univ, PhD(civil eng), 60. *Prof Exp:* Res asst civil eng, 58-59, res assoc, 59-61, res asst prof, 61-65, res assoc prof, 65-67, assoc prof, 67-69, PROF CIVIL ENG & DIR BLDG SYSTS DIV, FRITZ ENG LAB, LEHIGH UNIV, 69- *Concurrent Pos:* USSR Fulbright-Hays lectureship, Int Coun Exchange Scholars, 75; hon prof, Harbin Civil Eng Inst, 80. *Honors & Awards:* Leon Moisseiff Award, Am Soc Civil Engrs, 67. *Mem:* Assoc Am Soc Civil Engrs; Am Concrete Inst; Int Asn Bridge & Struct Engrs; Am Soc Eng Educ; Earthquake Eng Res Inst. *Res:* Behavior of building frames and their components in the elastic and inelastic range; planning and design of tall buildings; response of reinforced concrete building structures to earthquake ground motion. *Mailing Add:* Fritz Eng Lab No 13 Lehigh Univ Bethlehem PA 18015

LU, MARY KWANG-RUEY CHAO, b Liao-ning, China, Sept 6, 35; US citizen; m 61; c 2. ORGANIC CHEMISTRY, MATHEMATICS. *Educ:* Notre Dame Col, Ohio, BS, 59; Univ Detroit, MS, 61; Univ Tenn, Knoxville, PhD(org chem), 68. *Prof Exp:* Technician, Chem Lab, NY Hosp, New York, 59; chemist, US Testing Co, Inc, 61-63; asst prof chem, Morris Col, SC, 63-64; prof chem & math, Lincoln Mem Univ, 68-78; ASSOC PROF CHEM, WALTERS STATE COMMUNITY COL, MORRISTOWN, TENN, 78- *Concurrent Pos:* US Dept Energy res grant. *Mem:* AAAS; Am Chem Soc. *Res:* Organometallic chemistry; silicon solar cells. *Mailing Add:* Rte 7 Box 356 Morristown TN 37814

LU, MATTHIAS CHI-HWA, b Fukien, China, Jan 3, 40; m; c 2. PHARMACY, MEDICINAL CHEMISTRY. *Educ:* Kaohsiung Med Col, Taiwan, BSc, 63; Ohio State Univ, PhD(med chem), 69. *Prof Exp:* Res asst med chem, Univ Iowa, 64-67 & Ohio State Univ, 67-69; res assoc, Col Pharm, Univ Mich, Ann Arbor, 69-71, instr, 71-72, asst prof, 72-73; asst prof, 73-78, ASSOC PROF MED CHEM, COL PHARM, UNIV ILL MED CTR, 78- *Mem:* Am Chem Soc. *Res:* Steroidogenesis and metabolisms; enzyme inhibitors, synthesis and bioassay; agents for insect growth inhibition, mechanism of actions of neurotransmitters; synthesis of antitumor agents; biological oxidations and reductions. *Mailing Add:* Dept of Med Chem Col of Pharm Univ of Ill Med Ctr 833 S Wood Chicago IL 60680

LU, PAU-CHANG, b Kiangsu, China, Apr 11, 30; m 63. MECHANICAL ENGINEERING, AEROSPACE SCIENCE. *Educ:* Nat Taiwan Univ, BS, 54; Kans State Univ, MS, 59; Case Western Reserve Univ, PhD, 63. *Prof Exp:* Mech engr, Taiwan Power Co, 54-56; asst eng, Cheng Kung Univ, Taiwan, 56-57, asst eng, Kans State Univ, 57-59 & Case Western Reserve Univ, 59-62, res assoc, 62-63, asst prof, 63-68; assoc prof, 68-72, PROF MECH ENG, UNIV NEBR, LINCOLN, 72- *Mem:* Am Soc Mech Engrs; Am Inst Aeronaut & Astronaut; Am Acad Mech; Am Soc Eng Educ; Am Asn Physics Teachers. *Res:* Viscous flow; magneto-fluid-mechanics; heat exchangers; free convection; integral transforms and other branches of applied mathematics. *Mailing Add:* 2021 Pacific Dr Lincoln NE 68506

LU, PHILLIP KEHWA, b Anhui, China, Oct 11, 32; m 59; c 3. ASTRONOMY, PHYSICS. *Educ:* Maritime Col, Taiwan, BS, 60; Wesleyan Univ, MA, 65, DSc, 69; Columbia Univ, PhD(astron & sci educ), 70. *Prof Exp:* Math analyst inst math, Chinese Acad Sci, 60-63; instr comput sci, Jefferson Prof Inst, 65-67; res assoc astron observ, Yale Univ, 67-70; chmn earth & space sci dept, 73-74, asst prof, 70-77, ASSOC PROF ASTRON, OBSERV, WESTERN CONN STATE COL, 77- *Concurrent Pos:* Consult, Bd Educ, New York, 74-75; sci educ scholar, NSF, 74-75. *Mem:* Fel Royal Astron Soc; Am Astron Soc; Am Phys Soc; Sigma Xi. *Res:* Quasistellar sources; galaxies; photometry and astrometry. *Mailing Add:* Western Conn State Col Observ Danbury CT 06810

LU, PONZY, b Shanghai, China, Oct 7, 42; US citizen. MOLECULAR BIOLOGY. *Educ:* Calif Inst Technol, BS, 64; Mass Inst Technol, PhD(biophys), 70. *Prof Exp:* Arthritis Found fel biophys, Max Planck Inst Biophys Chem, 70-73; Europ Molecular Biol Orgn fel genetics, Univ Geneva, 73; ASSOC PROF CHEM, UNIV PA, 73- *Concurrent Pos:* NIH career award, 77-82. *Mem:* AAAS; Biophys Soc; Sigma Xi; Am Soc Biol Chemists. *Res:* Molecular compoents involved in the regulation of gene expression. *Mailing Add:* Dept of Chem Univ of Pa Philadelphia PA 19174

LU, SHIH-LAI, b Fukien, China, Nov 1, 46; m 71; c 2. ORGANIC CHEMISTRY, POLYMER CHEMISTRY. *Educ:* Fu Jen Univ, BS, 68; Wright State Univ, MS, 71; Iowa State Univ, PhD(org chem), 75. *Prof Exp:* Res assoc acad res, Iowa State Univ, 75-76 & Univ Chicago, 77-78; SR CHEMIST RES & DEVELOP, 3M CO, 78- *Mem:* Am Chem Soc. *Res:* Synthesis and thermoxidative degradation studies of polymers; mechanistic studies of organic reactions involving carbonium, radical and carbanion intermediates; process research; total synthesis of natural products; new products developments; polymer characterization. *Mailing Add:* 3M Ctr 230-2E 3M Co St Paul MN 55144

LU, WEI-KAO, b Kiangsu, China, Apr 6, 33; m 64. METALLURGY, PHYSICAL CHEMISTRY. *Educ:* Cheng Kung Univ, Taiwan, BS, 57; Univ Minn, PhD(metall), 64. *Prof Exp:* Fel, Univ Minn, 64-65; from asst prof to assoc prof metall, 65-73, STELCO PROF METALL, MCMASTER UNIV, 73- *Mem:* Am Inst Mining, Metall & Petrol Engrs; Iron & Steel Inst Japan; Can Inst Mining & Metall. *Res:* Theoretical and experimental study of chemical kinetics of gas-solid and slag-metal reactions; heterogeneous kinetics of iron and steelmaking reactions; iron ore agglomeration; coke and carbonization. *Mailing Add:* Dept of Metall McMaster Univ Hamilton ON L8S 4L8 Can

LU, YEH-PEI, US citizen. MECHANICAL ENGINEERING. *Educ:* Nat Taiwan Univ, BS, 58; Univ Houston, MS, 64, PhD(mech eng), 67. *Prof Exp:* Second Lieutenant eng, Chinese Air Force, 58-60; customer engr, IBM Corp, Taiwan, 61; teaching & res fel, Univ Houston, 62-67; mech engr, 68-72, SR PROJ ENGR, DAVID W TAYLOR NAVAL SHIP RES & DEVELOP CTR, 72- *Mem:* Am Soc Mech Engrs; Acoust Soc Am; Sigma Xi. *Res:* Vibration and acoustics; structural dynamics; fluid-structural interaction; numerical analyses. *Mailing Add:* David W Taylor Naval Ship Res & Develop Ctr Annapolis MD 21402

LUBAHN, J(ACK) D(OUGLAS), b Cleveland, Ohio, May 4, 17; m 42; c 4. PHYSICAL METALLURGY. *Educ:* Case Inst Technol, BS, 39, MS, 41, PhD(metall), 60. *Prof Exp:* Res engr, Case Inst Technol, 41-46 & res lab, Gen Elec Co, 46-56, mat engr gen eng lab, 56-58, consult engr, Knolls Atomic Power Lab, 58-60; vis prof mech, Univ Wis, 60-61; prof metall eng & dir mat res lab, 61-77, PROF BASIC ENG, COLO SCH MINES, 77- *Mem:* Am Soc Mech Engrs. *Res:* Heat treated steels; metal working operations; welding; impact; plasticity; creep; brittle fracture; fatigue. *Mailing Add:* Dept of Metall Eng Colo Sch of Mines Golden CO 80401

LUBAN, MARSHALL, b Seattle, Wash, May 29, 36; m 59; c 4. PHYSICS. *Educ:* Yeshiva Univ, AB, 57; Univ Chicago, SM, 58, PhD(theoret physics), 62. *Prof Exp:* Mem, Inst Advan Study, 62-63; asst prof physics, Univ Pa, 63-66; Guggenheim Mem Found fel, 66-67, chmn dept, 67-70, dean fac natural sci, 69-71, assoc prof, 67-74, PROF PHYSICS, BAR-ILAN UNIV, ISRAEL, 74- *Concurrent Pos:* Mem, Israel Coun Res & Develop, 70-73; mem bd trustees & exec coun, Bar-Ilan Univ, 71-74 & 79-81; mem bd trustees, Jerusalem Inst Technol, 79-81; vis prof, Washington Univ, Mo, 81-82. *Mem:* Israel Phys Soc (vpres, 78-79 & pres, 79-82); Am Phys Soc. *Res:* Statistical mechanics and the many-body problem. *Mailing Add:* Dept Physics Bar-Ilan Univ Ramat-Gan Israel

LUBAR, JOEL F, b Washington, DC, Nov 16, 38; m 61; c 2. NEUROSCIENCES, PSYCHOPHYSIOLOGY. *Educ:* Univ Chicago, BS, 60, PhD(biopsychol), 63. *Prof Exp:* Asst prof psychol, Univ Rochester, 63-67; assoc prof, 67-71, PROF PSYCHOL, UNIV TENN, 71- *Concurrent Pos:* NIH grant, 65-73, prog dir, 70-75; vis lectr, Inst Physiol, Univ Bergen, Norway, 72; NSF fel, Sch Med, Univ Calif, Los Angeles, 75-76; regional ed, Physiol & Behav J, 70-; psychol consult, Vet Admin Hosp, 72-; co-dir, Southeastern Biofeedback Inst, 76-80, dir, 80- *Mem:* Am Psychol Asn; Sigma Xi; Soc Neurosci; Biofeedback Soc Am; NY Acad Sci. *Res:* Operant control of electroencephalographic and electrophysiological responses with special emphasis on epilepsy, hyperkinesis, learning disabilities and psychophysiological disorders; neuroanatomical substrates of emotional and motivational behavior. *Mailing Add:* Dept of Psychol 310 AP Knoxville TN 37916

LUBAROFF, DAVID MARTIN, b Philadelphia, Pa, Feb 1, 38; m 61; c 3. IMMUNOLOGY. *Educ:* Philadelphia Col Pharm & Sci, BS, 61; Georgetown Univ, MS, 64; Yale Univ, PhD(microbiol), 67. *Prof Exp:* Assoc, Univ Pa, 69-70, asst prof, 70-73; asst prof urol & microbiol, 73-77, ASSOC PROF UROL & MICROBIOL, UNIV IOWA, 77- *Concurrent Pos:* USPHS fel, Univ Pa, 67-69. *Mem:* Am Asn Immunologists; Transplant Soc; AAAS; Int Soc Prev Oncol. *Res:* Delayed hypersensitivity reactions; transplantation immunology; tumor immunology; lymphocyte membrane antigens. *Mailing Add:* Dept of Urol Univ of Iowa Iowa City IA 52242

LUBARSKY, BERNARD, mechanical engineering, see previous edition

LUBATTI, HENRY JOSEPH, b Oakland, Calif, Mar 16, 37; m 68; c 3. PHYSICS. *Educ:* Univ Calif, Berkeley, AB, 60, PhD(physics), 66; Univ Ill, Urbana, MS, 63. *Prof Exp:* Physicist, Boeing Co, Wash, 60-61; res assoc physics, Linear Accelerator Lab, Univ Paris, 66-68; asst prof, Mass Inst Technol, 68-69; assoc prof, 69-74, PROF PHYSICS, UNIV WASH, 74-, SCI DIR VISUAL TECH LAB, 69- *Concurrent Pos:* Vis lectr, Int Sch Physics, Erice, Sicily 68 & Herceg-Novi Int Sch, Yugoslavia, 69; Alfred P Sloan fel, 71-75. *Mem:* AAAS; fel Am Phys Soc. *Res:* Elementary particle physics, experimentalist; phenomenology of elementary particles. *Mailing Add:* Visual Tech Lab Dept of Physics FM-15 Univ of Wash Seattle WA 98195

LUBAWY, WILLIAM CHARLES, b South Bend, Ind, Nov 30, 44; m 71; c 3. PHARMACOLOGY. *Educ:* Butler Univ, BS, 67; Ohio State Univ, MS, 69, PhD(pharmacol), 72. *Prof Exp:* Asst prof, 72-77, ASSOC PROF PHARMACOL & GRAD CTR TOXICOL, COL PHARM, UNIV KY, 77- *Mem:* Am Asn Col Pharm. *Res:* Metabolism of tobacco smoke components by isolated organ systems; isolated lung synthesis of prostaglandins. *Mailing Add:* Col of Pharm Univ of Ky Lexington KY 40506

LUBBERTS, GERRIT, b Oldemarkt, The Netherlands, Sept 15, 35; US citizen; m 59; c 2. SOLID STATE ELECTRONICS. *Educ:* Univ Rochester, 62, MS, 67, PhD, 71. *Prof Exp:* Technician, Case-Hoyt Corp, 56-58; technician, 58-62, res physicist, 62-71, sr res physicist, 71-78, RES ASSOC, EASTMAN KODAK CO, 78- *Mem:* Inst Elec & Electronics Engrs; Am Phys Soc. *Res:* Semiconductor physcis; surface barrier photodetectors, charge coupled devices. *Mailing Add:* Eastman Kodak Co Res Lab 1669 Lake Ave Rochester NY 14650

LUBCHENCO, JANE, b Denver, Colo, Dec 4, 47; m 71; c 2. ECOLOGY, MARINE BIOLOGY. *Educ:* Colo Col, BA, 69; Univ Wash, MS, 71; Harvard Univ, PhD(ecol), 75. *Prof Exp:* Asst prof ecol, Harvard Univ, 75-77; ASST PROF ECOL, ORE STATE UNIV, 78- *Concurrent Pos:* Prin investr, NSF, 76-; res assoc, Smithsonian Inst, 77-; sci adv, Ocean Trust Found, 78- & West Quoddy Marine Sta, 81- *Mem:* Ecol Soc Am; Phycol Soc Am; Am Soc Naturalists. *Res:* Population and community ecology; plant-herbivore and predator-prey interactions; competition; marine ecology; algal ecology. *Mailing Add:* Dept of Zool Ore State Univ Corvallis OR 97331

LUBEGA, SETH GASUZA, b Mubende, Uganda, Dec 24, 36; m 71; c 2. EMBRYOLOGY, GENETICS. *Educ:* Oakwood Col, BA, 67; Howard Univ, MS, 69, PhD(zool), 75. *Prof Exp:* Instr biol, Oakwood Col, 71-72; asst prof, Ft Valley State Col, 75-76; ASSOC PROF BIOL, OAKWOOD COL, 76- *Mem:* Genetic Soc Am; Nat Inst Sci. *Res:* Isoenzymes of octanol dehydrogenase in populations of Drosophila species, developmental stages, and specific organs. *Mailing Add:* Box 165 Oakwood Col Huntsville AL 35806

LUBELL, DAVID, b Brooklyn, NY, Apr 1, 32; m 60; c 3. MATHEMATICS. *Educ:* Columbia Univ, BS, 56; NY Univ, PhD(math), 60. *Prof Exp:* Benjamin Peirce instr math, Harvard Univ, 60-61; res instr, NY Univ, 61-62; sr mathematician, Systs Res Group Inc, 62-66; asst prof math, NY Univ, 66-70; assoc prof, 70-74, PROF MATH, ADELPHI UNIV, 75- *Concurrent Pos:* Consult, Systs Res Group Inc, 66-67 & US Air Force, 67-68; math adv, Nassau County Med Ctr, 69-72. *Mem:* Am Math Soc. *Res:* Combinatorics; biomathematics. *Mailing Add:* Dept of Math Adelphi Univ Garden City NY 11530

LUBELL, JERRY IRA, b New York, NY, Oct 19, 43; m 66; c 2. ELECTRONICS, NUCLEAR ENGINEERING. *Educ:* Univ Wash, BS, 66, MS, 68. *Prof Exp:* Mem tech staff, TRW Systs Group, 69-73, head, Response Anal Sect, 73-75, asst mgr, Electronic Syst & Technol Dept, 75-77; res scientist, Kaman Sci Corp, 77-78, mgr radiation & electromagnetics, 78-80; ASST TO PRES, SYSTS HARDENING, MISSION RES CORP, 80- *Concurrent Pos:* Prof nuclear engr, State Calif, 77- *Mem:* Am Nuclear Soc. *Res:* Nuclear weapon effects on electronic systems, subsystems and piece parts; electromagnetic pulse, system generated electromagnetic pulse and transient radiation effects causing both temporary and permanent damage. *Mailing Add:* 525 Wintery Cr S Colorado Springs CO 80919

LUBELL, MARTIN S, b New York, NY, June 5, 32; m 62. SOLID STATE PHYSICS. *Educ:* Mass Inst Technol, SB, 54; Univ Calif, Berkeley, MA, 56. *Prof Exp:* Asst, Univ Calif, 55-56; res physicist, Res Labs, Westinghouse Elec Corp, 56-67; res physicist, 67-73, asst dept mgr, 74-76, SECT HEAD, OAK RIDGE NAT LAB, 76- *Mem:* Am Phys Soc. *Res:* Low temperature physics; superconductivity; fusion reactor technology. *Mailing Add:* Oak Ridge Nat Lab Bldg 9204-1 Fusion Energy Div PO Box Y Oak Ridge TN 38730

LUBENSKY, TOM C, b Kansas City, Mo, May 7, 43; m 68; c 1. THEORETICAL SOLID STATE PHYSICS. *Educ:* Calif Inst Technol, BS, 64; Harvard Univ, MA, 65, PhD(physics), 69. *Prof Exp:* NSF fel physics, Fac Sci, Orsay, France, 69-70; res asst, Brown Univ, 70-71; asst prof, 71-75, assoc prof, 75-80, PROF PHYSICS, UNIV PA, 80- *Concurrent Pos:* Sloan Found fel, 75; Guggenheim fel, 81-82; assoc prof, Univ de Paris VI, 81-82. *Res:* Liquid crystals, phase transitions, cooperative phenomena in random systems and applications of the Wilson renormalization group. *Mailing Add:* Dept of Physics Univ of Pa Philadelphia PA 19104

LUBEROFF, BENJAMIN JOSEPH, b Philadelphia, Pa, Apr 17, 25; m 44; c 3. INDUSTRIAL CHEMISTRY. *Educ:* Cooper Union, BChE, 49; Columbia Univ, AM, 50, PhD(phys org chem), 53. *Prof Exp:* Statutory asst chem, Columbia Univ, 49-51; inst, Cooper Union, 51-53; chemist high pressure lab, Am Cyanamid Co, 53-57; head gen chem res sect, Stauffer Chem Co, 57-62; mgr process res dept, Lummus Co, 62-70; CONSULT & ED, CHEMTECH, AM CHEM SOC, 70- *Concurrent Pos:* Actg dir, Continuing Sci Educ, Rutgers Univ, 76-78. *Honors & Awards:* Cooper Medal, 49. *Mem:* Am Chem Soc; Am Inst Chem; Am Inst Chem Eng; Am Soc Magazine Ed. *Res:* Research and development management; applied physical chemistry; high temperature and pressure processes; petrochemicals; catalysis; pesticides; analytical chemistry; technical journalism. *Mailing Add:* 19 Brantwood Dr Summit NJ 07901

LUBIC, RUTH WATSON, b Bucks County, Pa, Jan 18, 27; m 55. NURSE-MIDWIFERY. *Educ:* Sch Nursing Hosp Univ Pa, Dipl, 55; Teachers Col, Columbia Univ, BS, 59, MA, 61, EdD, 79. *Prof Exp:* From staff nurse to head nurse, Mem Ctr Cancer & Allied Dis, 55-58; instr maternal nursing, Sch Nursing, Flower & Fifth Ave Hosp, 61; instr clin nurse-midwifery, Downstate Med Ctr, 62, parent educ & consult, 63-67, GEN DIR, MATERNITY CTR ASN, 70- *Mem:* Inst Med-Nat Acad Sci; AAAS; fel Am Nurses Asn; Am Col Nurse-Midwives; Am Public Health Asn. *Mailing Add:* 48 E 92nd St New York NY 10028

LUBIN, ARTHUR RICHARD, b Newark, NJ, Mar 24, 47. MATHEMATICAL ANALYSIS. *Educ:* Mich State Univ, BS, 67; Univ Wis, MA, 68, PhD(math), 72. *Prof Exp:* Asst prof math, Tulane Univ, 72-73 & Northwestern Univ, 73-75; ASST PROF MATH, ILL INST TECHNOL, 75- *Mem:* Am Math Soc. *Res:* Operator theory; functional analysis; Hardy spaces. *Mailing Add:* Dept of Math Ill Inst of Technol Chicago IL 60616

LUBIN, CLARENCE ISAAC, b Albany, Ga, Oct 15, 00; m 54. MATHEMATICAL ANALYSIS. *Educ:* Univ Cincinnati, ChemE, 23; Harvard Univ, PhD(math), 29. *Prof Exp:* Instr math, 23-26, from asst to assoc prof, 29-56, prof, 56-71, EMER PROF MATH, UNIV CINCINNATI, 71-; RES & WRITING, 71- *Mem:* Am Math Soc; Math Asn Am. *Res:* Differential equations; analysis. *Mailing Add:* 838 Clifton Hills Terr Cincinnati OH 45220

LUBIN, GERALD I, child psychiatry, see previous edition

LUBIN, JONATHAN DARBY, b Staten Island, NY, Aug 10, 36. MATHEMATICS. *Educ:* Columbia Univ, AB, 57; Harvard Univ, AM, 58, PhD(math), 63. *Prof Exp:* Instr math, Bowdoin Col, 62-63, from asst to assoc prof, 63-67; assoc prof, 67-70, PROF MATH, BROWN UNIV, 70- *Concurrent Pos:* Assoc prof, Inst Henri Poincare, Univ Paris, 68-69; lectr, Math Inst, Copenhagen Inst, 74-75. *Mem:* Am Math Soc. *Res:* Algebraic geometry; number theory. *Mailing Add:* Dept of Math Brown Univ Providence RI 02912

LUBIN, MARTIN, b NY, Mar 30, 23; m 42; c 4. CELL BIOLOGY. *Educ:* Harvard Univ, AB, 42, MD, 45; Mass Inst Technol, PhD(biophys), 54. *Prof Exp:* Res assoc biol, Mass Inst Technol, 53-54; assoc pharmacol, Harvard Med Sch, 54-57, asst prof, 57-68; PROF MICROBIOL & HEAD DIV CELL BIOL, DARTMOUTH MED SCH, 68- *Concurrent Pos:* USPHS sr res fel, 56-61; Lalor Found fel, 57-59; Guggenheim fel, Lab Molecular Biol, Cambridge Univ, 65-66, Commonwealth Fund fel, 66-67. *Mem:* Am Soc Biol Chem; Am Soc Microbiol; Biophys Soc; Am Soc Cell Biol; Soc Gen Physiol. *Res:* Active transport; regulation of synthesis of macromolecules; ribosome structure and function; animal cells and viruses. *Mailing Add:* Dept of Microbiol Dartmouth Med Sch Hanover NH 03755

LUBIN, MOSHE J, b Tel Aviv, Israel, May 24, 38; US citizen; m 61; c 2. PLASMA PHYSICS, AERODYNAMICS. *Educ:* Israel Inst Technol, BSc, 61; Cornell Univ, PhD(aeronaut eng & eng physics), 65. *Prof Exp:* Asst prof plasma physics, Univ Rochester, 65-68, assoc prof, 68-74, assoc prof optics, 70-74, dir, Lab Laser Energetics, 70-81, prof optics, mech eng & aerospace eng, 74-81; VPRES RES, DEVELOP, PATENT & LICENSE, STANDARD OIL CO, OHIO, 81- *Concurrent Pos:* Consult, NY State Sci & Technol Found, Off Technol Assessment, Cong US, Los Alamos Nat Lab & Argonne Univs Asn. *Mem:* Am Phys Soc; Am Inst Aeronaut & Astronaut; NY Acad Sci; Inst Elec & Electronics Eng; Optical Soc Am. *Res:* Nonlinear wave propagation in plasma media; magnetoaerodynamics; electromagnetic plasma interactions; thermonuclear fusion; laser fusion; x-ray laser development; fundamental interaction of radiation with matter; development of energy resources; energy policy. *Mailing Add:* Standard Oil Co Res Ctr 4440 Warrensville Rd Cleveland OH 44128

LUBINIECKI, ANTHONY STANLEY, b Greensburg, Pa, Oct 4, 46; m 68; c 1. IMMUNOLOGY, VIROLOGY. *Educ:* Carnegie Inst Technol, BS, 68; Univ Pittsburgh, ScD, 72. *Prof Exp:* Res asst microbiol, Grad Sch Pub Health, Univ Pittsburgh, 71-72, asst res prof, 72-74; prin scientist immunol & virol, 74-80, MANAGING DIR, SPECIAL REAGENTS, LIFE SCI DIV, MELOY LABS INC, 80- *Concurrent Pos:* Mem, Dengue Task Force, US Army Med Res & Develop Command, 71-74; prin investr contract, 73-74; prin investr, Nat Inst Allergy & Infectious Dis grant, 73-74; prin investr contract, Nat Cancer Inst, 74- & Nat Inst Child Health & Human Develop, 75-77. *Mem:* Am Soc Microbiol; Soc Gen Microbiol; Soc Exp Biol & Med. *Res:* Cell biology models of human genetic diseases and cancer; antigenic composition of cells; autoimmune diseases; interferon; genetic mutants of mammalian cells and their viruses; infectious disease models; carcinogenesis. *Mailing Add:* Meloy Labs Ins 6715 Electronic Dr Springfield VA 22151

LUBINSKI, ARTHUR, b Antwerp, Belg, Mar 30, 10; nat US; m 35; c 3. MECHANICS. *Educ:* Univ Brussels, Cand Ing, 31, Ing CM & E, 34. *Prof Exp:* Res engr, Barnsdall Res Corp, 47-50; spec res assoc, Marine & Arctic Opers Group, Res Ctr, Amoco Prod Co, 50-75; PVT TECH CONSULT, TULSA, OKLA, 75- *Concurrent Pos:* Mem panel drill tech, Mohole Proj Phase I, AMSOC Comt, Nat Acad Sci; consult, Mohole Proj Phase II, Brown & Root; lectr, Univ Tex, 60 & 67; mem panel energy & resources, Comt Ocean Eng, Nat Acad Eng, 67-; tech eval bd & tech assistance bd, Deep Sea Drilling Proj, Scripps Inst Oceanog, 67-70. *Honors & Awards:* Distinguished Achievement Award, Offshore Technol Conf, 76. *Mem:* Am Soc Mech Engrs; Am Inst Mining Metall & Petrol Engrs; Am Petrol Inst; Belg Eng Asn; Belg Fedn Eng Asns. *Res:* Elastic stability of strings of pipe subjected to distributed weight and pressures; elasticity of porous bodies; hydraulics; shocks; wave propagation; applied mechanics; offshore structures; marine and arctic technology. *Mailing Add:* 4469 S Gary Ave Tulsa OK 74105

LUBITZ, BETTY BAUM, b New York, NY, Oct 14, 25; m 46; c 3. ANALYTICAL CHEMISTRY, ORGANIC CHEMISTRY. *Educ:* Brooklyn Col, BA, 45; Univ Mich, MS, 49, PhD(org chem), 57. *Prof Exp:* Technician, Rockefeller Inst, 45-46; instr chem, Univ Mich, 51, res assoc radiation lab, Res Inst, 56-57, assoc res chemist, 57-60; asst prof chem, Skidmore Col, 65-66; chemist, Behr-Manning Co, 66-67; assoc res chemist, 68-77, RES CHEMIST, STERLING-WINTHROP RES INST, 77- *Mem:* Am Chem Soc. *Res:* Dielectric relaxation; oxime equilibria; gel filtration; chromatography. *Mailing Add:* 1237 Glenwood Blvd Rensselaer NY 12308

LUBITZ, CECIL ROBERT, b Brooklyn, NY, Mar 18, 25; m 46; c 3. NUCLEAR PHYSICS, NEUTRON CROSS SECTIONS. *Educ:* US Naval Acad, BS, 45; Univ Mich, MSEE, 49, PhD(physics), 60. *Prof Exp:* Res assoc elec eng, Res Inst, Univ Mich, 49-54; PHYSICIST, KNOLLS ATOMIC POWER LAB, GEN ELEC CO, 60- *Mem:* Am Nuclear Soc. *Res:* Neutron cross sections for technological applications. *Mailing Add:* Knolls Atomic Power Lab Gen Elec Co Schenectady NY 12301

LUBKER, ROBERT A(LFRED), b Puyallup, Wash, May 19, 20; m 45; c 2. METALLURGICAL ENGINEERING. *Educ:* Univ Wash, BS, 42; Carnegie Inst Technol, MS, 46. *Prof Exp:* Metall engr, Westinghouse Elec Corp, Pa, 42-46; supvr nonferrous metals, Metals Res Dept, Armour Res Found, Ill Inst Technol, 46-47, asst chmn, 47-51, assoc mgr, 51-53, mgr, 53-58; dir res & develop, Alan Wood Steel Co, 58-61, vpres res & develop, 61-67; dir res & develop, CF&I Steel Corp, 67-70 & Gen Cable Corp, 70-72; vpres technol, Assoc Metals & Minerals Corp, 72-74; vpres, AVA Steel Prod Int, Inc, 74-80; PRES, M&R REFRACTORY METALS INC, WINSLOW, NJ, 80- *Concurrent Pos:* Exec vpres, AVA-Toshin Corp, 76- *Mem:* Am Inst Mining, Metall & Petrol Engrs; Am Soc Metals; Am Iron & Steel Inst. *Res:* General physical metallurgy; welding; foundry; powder metallurgy; extractive metallurgy; mechanical metallurgy; copper, aluminum, titanium, molybdenum, tungsten and alloy steels; supervision and direction of research; engineering problems; wire and cable; steelmaking research and development. *Mailing Add:* PO Box 497 New Vernon NJ 07976

LUBKIN, ELIHU, b Brooklyn, NY, Oct 25, 33; m 62; c 2. THEORETICAL PHYSICS. *Educ:* Columbia Univ, AB, 54, AM, 57, PhD(physics), 60. *Prof Exp:* Asst theoret physics radiation lab, Univ Calif, Berkeley, 59-61; res assoc high energy group, Brown Univ, 61-63, res asst prof theoret physics, 63-66; ASSOC PROF PHYSICS, UNIV WIS-MILWAUKEE, 66- *Mem:* Am Phys Soc. *Res:* Differential geometry used to interpret the old and for new constructions in physics; interpretation of quantum mechanics; quantum measurement theory; quantum psychology; thermodynamics. *Mailing Add:* Dept of Physics Univ of Wis Milwaukee WI 53211

LUBKIN, GLORIA BECKER, b Philadelphia, Pa, May 16, 33; div; c 2. PHYSICS. *Educ:* Temple Univ, AB, 53; Boston Univ, MA, 57. *Prof Exp:* Mathematician aircraft div, Fairchild Stratos Corp, 54 & Letterkenny Ord Depot, US Defense Dept, 55-56; physicist tech res group, Control Data Corp, 56-58; actg chmn dept physics, Sarah Lawrence Col, 61-62; vpres, Lubkin Assocs, 62-63; assoc ed, 63-69, SR ED, PHYSICS TODAY, AM INST PHYSICS, 70- *Concurrent Pos:* Consult ctr for hist & philos of physics, Am Inst Physics, 66-67; Nieman fel, Harvard Univ, 74-75; mem exec comt Forum Physics & Soc, Am Phys Soc, 77-79; mem, Nieman Adv Comt, Harvard Univ, 78- *Mem:* NY Acad Sci; Fel Am Phys Soc; Nat Asn Sci Writers. *Res:* Nuclear physics; science policy; physics reporting, writing and editing. *Mailing Add:* Am Inst of Phys 335 E 45th St New York NY 10017

LUBKIN, JAMES LEIGH, b New York, NY, Mar 5, 25; m 48; c 2. STRUCTURAL ENGINEERING, ENGINEERING EDUCATION. *Educ:* Columbia Univ, BS, 44, MS, 47, PhD(appl mech), 50. *Prof Exp:* Consult, Appl Mech & Eng Probs, Mergenthaler Linotype Co, 49-50; sr proj analyst, Appl Physics Div, Midwest Res Inst, 50-56; sr res engr & head theoret anal group, Cent Res Lab, Am Mach & Foundry Co, Conn, 56-63; PROF CIVIL & SANIT ENG, MICH STATE UNIV, 63- *Mem:* Am Soc Mech Engrs; Soc Exp Stress Anal; Am Soc Eng Educ. *Res:* Computer-assisted testing and homework; individualized instruction; computer-aided design in engineering; computer applications in engineering education; vibration of vehicles. *Mailing Add:* Dept of Civil Eng Mich State Univ East Lansing MI 48824

LUBLIN, PAUL, b New York, NY, Sept 8, 24; m 52; c 3. PHYSICAL CHEMISTRY. *Educ:* NY Univ, BA, 48; Purdue Univ, MS, 49. *Prof Exp:* Res chemist, Pigment Div, Am Cyanamid Co, 51-53; asst res staff mem, Res Div, Raytheon Mfg Co, 53-54; appln engr, Instrument Div, Philips Electronics, 54-56; sr engr, 56-59, res engr, 59-61, adv res engr, 61-63, eng specialist, 63-67, MEM TECH STAFF, GEN TEL & ELECTRONICS LABS, INC, WALTHAM, 67-, MGR MAT EVAL, 78- *Mem:* Am Crystallog Asn; Soc Appl Spectros; Sigma Xi; Microbeam Anal Soc; fel Am Inst Chem. *Res:* Materials analysis, applications of x-ray diffraction and spectroscopy to structure and chemical identification of materials; electron probe and scanning electron microscopy as applied to electronic materials. *Mailing Add:* Gen Tel & Electronics Labs Inc 40 Sylvan Rd Waltham MA 02154

LUBLINER, J(ACOB), b Lodz, Poland, May 5, 35; US citizen; m 60; c 3. MECHANICS, BIOPHYSICS. *Educ:* Calif Inst Technol, BS, 57; Columbia Univ, MS, 58, PhD(eng mech), 60. *Prof Exp:* Mem tech staff appl mech, Bell Tel Labs, 60; NSF fel, Polytech Sch, Paris, 60-61; preceptor civil eng, Columbia Univ, 61-62, asst prof, 62-63; from asst prof to assoc prof, 63-68, assoc prof eng sci, 68-73, PROF ENG SCI, UNIV CALIF, BERKELEY, 73- *Concurrent Pos:* NIH spec fel, Weizmann Inst Sci, Israel, 69-70; vis prof, Univ Andes, Bogota, Colombia, 77. *Res:* Thermomechanics of viscoelastic and viscoplastic materials; wave propagation in solids; thermodynamics; mechanochemistry; wave propagation in biological systems; high frequency structural dynamics; segmented telescope design. *Mailing Add:* Dept of Civil Eng Univ of Calif Berkeley CA 94720

LUBMAN, DAVID, b Chicago, Ill, Aug 3, 34; m 56; c 1. ACOUSTICS, ELECTRICAL ENGINEERING. *Educ:* Ill Inst Technol, BS, 60; Univ Southern Calif, MS, 62. *Prof Exp:* Sr scientist, LTV Corp Res Ctr, Anaheim, 67-68 & Bolt Beranek & Newman Inc, Van Nuys, 68-69; staff engr underwater acoust, 60-67, SR SYSTS ENGR, GROUND SYSTS GROUP, HUGHES AIRCRAFT CO, 76- *Concurrent Pos:* Vis prof math, Chapman Col, Orange, 63-68; consult, D Lubman & Assocs, 69-; mem working group, Am Nat Standards Inst, 70-74; consult, Off Naval Res, Washington, DC, 69-76, Aircraft Engine Group, Gen Elec Co, 71-73, Nat Bur Standards, Washington, DC, 73-74 & Dept Archit & Construct, State of Calif, 76-; vis prof acoust, Calif State Univ, Los Angeles, 76-; vis lectr, Univ Calif, Santa Barbara, 76- *Mem:* Fel Acoust Soc Am; Inst Noise Control Eng; Am Soc Testing & Mat. *Res:* Architectural and underwater acoustics; characterization and measurement of the statistics of sound fields over space, time and frequency; reverberation chambers; measurement of sound power, sound particle velocity and nearfield radiation. *Mailing Add:* 2217 Vista Del Sol Fullerton CA 92634

LUBORSKY, FRED EVERETT, b Philadelphia, Pa, May 14, 23; m 46; c 3. PHYSICAL CHEMISTRY. *Educ:* Univ Pa, BS, 47; Ill Inst Technol, PhD(phys chem), 52. *Prof Exp:* Asst chemist, Ill Inst Technol, 47-51; res assoc res lab, 51-52, phys chemist instrument dept, 52-55, physicist appl physics unit, 55-58, PHYS CHEMIST, RES & DEVELOP CTR, GEN ELEC CO, 58- *Concurrent Pos:* Mem div eng & indust res, Nat Acad Sci, 52-55; pres, Magnetics Soc, Inst Elec & Electronics Eng, 75-77; ed-in-chief, Inst Elec & Electronics Eng Transactions Magnetics, 72-75. *Mem:* AAAS; Am Chem Soc; Am Phys Soc; fel Inst Elec & Electronics Engrs; NY Acad Sci. *Res:* Nucleation and growth of sub-micron size particles; development of single domain particle permanent magnetic materials; electrochemistry; magnetism; magnetic thin films; amorphous magnetic materials; magnetic separation. *Mailing Add:* Res & Develop Ctr Gen Elec Co Box 8 Schenectady NY 12301

LUBORSKY, SAMUEL WILLIAM, b Philadelphia, Pa, Jan 18, 31; m 53; c 3. MOLECULAR BIOLOGY. *Educ:* Univ Mich, BS, 52; Northwestern Univ, PhD, 57. *Prof Exp:* Fel, 57-58, BIOCHEMIST, NIH, 58- *Mem:* Am Chem Soc. *Res:* Molecular biology; biochemistry. *Mailing Add:* Nat Inst of Health Bldg 8 Rm 107 Bethesda MD 20205

LUBOWE, ANTHONY G(ARNER), b New York, NY, Dec 21, 37; m 59; c 2. ELECTRONIC PACKAGING, ENGINEERING MECHANICS. *Educ:* Columbia Univ, AB, 57, BS, 58, MS, 59, EngScD(eng mech), 61. *Prof Exp:* Res asst, Sch Eng, Columbia Univ, 60-61; mem tech staff, 61-73, SUPVR, INTERCONNECTION TECHNOL LAB, BELL LABS, INC, 73- *Mem:* Am Soc Mech Engrs; Int Electronics Packaging Soc. *Res:* Elasticity; orbit prediction; electronic assembly; electronic packaging. *Mailing Add:* Interconnection Design Dept Bell Labs Inc Whippany NJ 07981

LUBOWSKY, JACK, b Brooklyn, NY, July 11, 40. BIOMATHEMATICS. *Educ:* City Col New York, BEE, 62; Polytech Inst Brooklyn, MSEE, 66, PhD(elec eng), 73. *Prof Exp:* Engr, Brookhaven Nat Labs, 61-62; proj engr, Airborne Instruments Lab, 62-66; res assoc, 66-67, instr med comput sci, 67-70, asst proc comput sci, 70-72, Dept Neurol, 72-73, DIR, SCI COMPUT CTR, STATE UNIV NY DOWNSTATE MED CTR, 73- *Concurrent Pos:* Co-investr, Spec Res Resources Div Biomath Comput Ctr, NIH, 72-73, prin investr, 73-75; asst prof, Dept Neurol, Down State Med Ctr, 73-78, assoc prof, Dept Neurol, 78-, Dept Biohysics, 80- *Mem:* Inst Elec & Electronics Engrs; AAAS; Sigma Xi. *Res:* Application of computers to biomedical research; investigation of adaptive and optimal search techniques to the determination of recognition properties of visual system neurons. *Mailing Add:* Sci Comput Ctr Box #7 State Univ NY Down State Med Ctr 450 Clarkson Ave Brooklyn NY 11203

LUBRAN, MYER MICHAEL, b London, Eng, Mar 9, 15; m 44; c 3. CLINICAL PATHOLOGY. *Educ:* Univ London, MB, BS, 38, BSc, 43, PhD(chem), 55; FRCPath. *Prof Exp:* Lectr physiol, biochem & clin chem, Guy's Med Sch, London, 38-43; lectr physiol & biochem, Med Sch, Univ Birmingham, 43-44; asst clin pathologist, Emergency Health Serv, Eng, 46-48; consult pathologist, Nat Health Serv, WMiddlesex Hosp, 48-64; prof path & dir clin chem, Sch Med, Univ Chicago, 64-70; PROF PATH, UNIV CALIF, LOS ANGELES, 70-; CHIEF CLIN PATH, HARBOR GEN HOSP, 70- *Concurrent Pos:* Mem hosp mgt comt & chmn med staff comt, WMiddlesex Hosp, 56-58, dir cent sterile supply dept & chmn cross-infection comt, 58-64; mem exam bd, Int Med Lab Technol, Eng; examr, Royal Col Path. *Mem:* AAAS; Am Soc Clin Path; Asn Clin Sci (pres, 74-75); Am Asn Clin Chem; NY Acad Sci. *Res:* Clinical pathology; trace metals. *Mailing Add:* Harbor Gen Hosp 1000 W Carson St Torrance CA 90509

LUBY, ELLIOT DONALD, b Detroit, Mich, Apr 3, 24; m 50; c 3. PSYCHIATRY, LAW. *Educ:* Univ Mo-Columbia, BS, 47; Wash Univ, MD, 49; Am Bd Psychiat & Neurol, dipl, 57. *Prof Exp:* Resident psychiat, Menninger Found, 50-51; sr asst surgeon, USPHS, 51-52; resident psychiat, Yale Univ, 52-54; chief adult inpatient sect, Lafayette Clin, Detroit, 57-62, assoc dir in chg clin serv, 62; prof law, 62-76, PROF PSYCHIAT, WAYNE STATE UNIV, 65-, PROF LAW, 80- *Honors & Awards:* Gold Medal Award, Am Acad Psychosom Med, 62. *Mem:* NY Acad Sci; AMA; Am Psychiat Asn; Am Psychosom Soc; fel Am Col Psychiat. *Res:* Psychopharmacology; model psychoses, drug induced sleep deprivation; law and psychiatry; schizophrenia. *Mailing Add:* Dept of Psychiat Wayne State Univ Detroit MI 48202

LUBY, PATRICK JOSEPH, b Zanesville, Ohio, May 20, 30; m 56; c 4. AGRICULTURAL ECONOMICS. *Educ:* Univ Dayton, BA, 52; Purdue Univ, MS, 54, PhD(agr econ), 56. *Prof Exp:* Instr agr econ, Purdue Univ, 54-56, asst prof, 56-58; economist, 58-66, gen mgr provisions, 66-71, GEN MGR PROVISIONS & PROCUREMENT, OSCAR MAYER & CO, 71-, VPRES, 72-, CORP ECONOMIST, 74- *Mem:* Am Agr Econ Asn. *Res:* Use of statistical methods to analyze and forecast meat and livestock supplies and prices; efficient marketing of livestock and meats. *Mailing Add:* Oscar Mayer & Co PO Box 7188 Madison WI 53707

LUBY, ROBERT JAMES, b Kansas City, Mo, Apr 13, 28; m 51; c 8. OBSTETRICS & GYNECOLOGY. *Educ:* Rockhurst Col, BS, 48; Creighton Univ, MD, 52, MS, 59. *Prof Exp:* Intern obstet & gynec, Creighton Mem St Joseph Hosp, Omaha, 52-53, resident, 55-58; assoc prof, Col Med, Univ Nebr, 68-69; assoc dir obstet & gynec, 69-72, chmn dept, 72-77, PROF OBSTET & GYNEC, CREIGHTON UNIV, 69- *Mem:* AMA; Am Col Obstet & Gynec; Am Col Surg. *Res:* Nutritional aspects of infectious perinatal morbidity and mortality. *Mailing Add:* Dept of Obstet & Gynec Creighton Univ Omaha NE 68108

LUCAL, HAROLD M(ARTIN), b Washington, DC, Dec 6, 22; m 50; c 3. ELECTRICAL ENGINEERING. *Educ:* Ohio State Univ, BSc, 44, MSc, 47; Mass Inst Technol, ScD(elec eng), 53. *Prof Exp:* Asst elec eng, Mass Inst Technol, 47-49, instr, 49-53; asst prof, 53-58, ASSOC PROF ELEC ENG, UNIV CONN, STORRS, 58- *Mem:* Am Soc Eng Educ; Inst Elec & Electronics Engrs. *Res:* Communication theory; network synthesis. *Mailing Add:* Dept of Elec Eng Univ of Conn Storrs CT 06268

LUCANSKY, TERRY WAYNE, b Massillon, Ohio, Aug 21, 42; m 66. BOTANY. *Educ:* Univ SC, BS, 64, MS, 67; Duke Univ, PhD(bot), 71. *Prof Exp:* ASSOC PROF BOT, UNIV FLA, 71- *Mem:* Bot Soc Am; Am Fern Soc; Am Inst Biol Sci; Sigma Xi. *Res:* Comparative anatomical and morphological studies of tropical pteridophytes; anatomical studies of aquatic plants and vines in relation to their habit and habitat. *Mailing Add:* Dept Bot Rm 3175 McCarty Hall Univ of Fla Gainesville FL 32611

LUCANTONI, DAVID MICHAEL, b Baltimore Md, Aug 31, 54. COMPUTATIONAL PROBABILITY. *Educ:* Towson State Univ, BS, 76; Univ Del, MS, 78, PhD(opers res), 82. *Prof Exp:* MEM TECH STAFF, BELL LABS, 81- *Mem:* Opers Res Soc Am; Math Asn Am; Am Math Soc. *Res:* Computationally stable algorithms for the solution of complex stochastic models such as those arising in the theory of queues. *Mailing Add:* Rm 2D424 Bell Labs Holmdel NJ 07733

LUCAS, ALEXANDER RALPH, b Vienna, Austria, July 30, 31; US citizen; m 56; c 4. CHILD PSYCHIATRY. *Educ:* Mich State Univ, BS, 53; Univ Mich, MD, 57. *Prof Exp:* Rotating intern, Univ Mich Hosp, 57-58; resident child psychiat, Hawthorn Ctr, 58-59; resident psychiat, Lafayette Clin, Detroit, 59-61; resident child psychiat, Hawthorn Ctr, 61-62; from staff child psychiatrist to sr psychiatrist, Hawthorn Ctr, Northville, Mich, 62-67; from asst prof to assoc prof psychiat, Wayne State Univ, 67-71; assoc prof, 73-76, PROF PSYCHIAT, MAYO MED SCH, 76-; head, 71-81, CONSULT SECT CHILD & ADOLESCENT PSYCHIAT, MAYO CLIN, 81- *Concurrent Pos:* Res child psychiatrist & res coordr, Lafayette Clin, Detroit, 67-71; consult, State of Minn Dept Pub Welfare, 72-80 & NIMH, 74-77. *Mem:* Am Orthop Asn; Am Psychiat Asn; Am Acad Child Psychiat; Soc Prof Child Psychiat; Soc Biol Psychiat. *Res:* Biologic aspects of child psychiatry; eating disorders. *Mailing Add:* Mayo Clin Rochester MN 55901

LUCAS, CAROL LEE, b Aberdeen, SDak, Feb 13, 40; m 61; c 2. BIOMEDICAL MATHEMATICS. *Educ:* Dakota Wesleyan Univ, BA, 61; Univ Ariz, MS, 67; Univ NC, Chapel Hill, PhD(biomed math, eng), 73. *Prof Exp:* Jr systs analyst, Cargill, Inc, Minneapolis, 62-65; res asst biomed math & eng, 67-68, res assoc, Div Cardiothoracic Surg, 72, lectr biomed math & eng, 76-77, ASST PROF BIOMED MATH & ENG, UNIV NC, CHAPEL HILL, 77- *Concurrent Pos:* High sch teacher, US Army Educ Ctr, Furth, Ger, 61-62; teaching asst, Dept Math & Eng, Univ Ariz, 65-67, comput lab asst, 66-67. *Mem:* Am Heart Asn; Sigma Xi; Biomed Eng Soc. *Res:* Mathematical modelling and computer simulation of physiological systems; digital processing of dynamic physiological data. *Mailing Add:* Dept Surg Univ NC Chapel Hill NC 27514

LUCAS, COLIN ROBERT, b Toronto, Can, Oct 11, 43; m 69; c 3. ORGANOMETALLIC CHEMISTRY. *Educ:* Acadia Univ, BSc, 68, MSc, 69; Oxford Univ, PhD(organometallic chem), 72. *Prof Exp:* Res fel, Univ Alberta, 73-74; asst prof chem, 74-79, ASSOC PROF CHEM, MEM UNIV, NFLD, 79- *Mem:* Chem Inst Can. *Res:* Synthesis and properties of organometallic compounds containing sulfur; which sulfur d-orbitals transmit electronic effects in a molecule and thus affect its properties. *Mailing Add:* Dept Chem Mem Univ St Johns NF A1B 3X7 Can

LUCAS, DAVID OWEN, b Orange, Calif, Oct 19, 42; div; c 2. IMMUNOLOGY. *Educ:* Duke Univ, BA, 64, PhD(microbiol, immunol), 69. *Prof Exp:* Asst prof, 70-76, ASSOC PROF MICROBIOL, COL MED, UNIV ARIZ, 76- *Concurrent Pos:* Res fel immunol, Children's Hosp Med Ctr, Harvard Med Sch, 68-70, actg dept head, 77-79. *Mem:* AAAS; Am Asn Immunologists; Am Soc Microbiol; Reticuloendothelial Soc. *Res:* Cellular immunology; lymphocyte metabolism; interferon; hybridomas. *Mailing Add:* Dept Microbiol & Med Ariz Health Sci Ctr Univ of Ariz Tucson AZ 85724

LUCAS, EDGAR ARTHUR, b Franklin, Ind, Oct 28, 33; m 60; c 2. ANATOMY, NEUROPHYSIOLOGY. *Educ:* Ball State Univ, BA, 61, MS, 65; Univ Calif, PhD(anat), 72. *Prof Exp:* Teacher, Sch, Town of Griffith, 61-62; planner admin, Rocketdyne Div, NAm Rockwell Corp, 62-63, assoc res engr, 64-65; instr, 72-74, asst prof, 74-79, ASSOC PROF ANAT, UNIV ARK MED CTR, LITTLE ROCK, 79- *Concurrent Pos:* mem comt Polysomnography Asn Sleep Disorder Ctrs. *Mem:* Inc Soc Chronobiol; Asn Psychophysiol Study Sleep; Am Asn Anat. *Res:* Biological rhythms; sleep; neuroanatomy. *Mailing Add:* Dept Anat Univ Ark Med Ctr Little Rock AR 72205

LUCAS, FRED VANCE, b Grand Junction, Colo, Feb 7, 22; m 48; c 2. PATHOLOGY. *Educ:* Univ Calif, AB, 42; Univ Rochester, MD, 50. *Prof Exp:* From asst to asst prof path, Med Sch, Univ Rochester, 51-55; assoc prof, Col Physicians & Surgeons, Columbia Univ, 55-60; prof & chmn dept, Sch Med, Univ Mo-Columbia, 60-77, res assoc, Space Sci Res Ctr, 64-77; dir med serv, Univ Hosp & assoc dean & prof path, 77-79, ASSOC VPRES MED AFFAIRS, SCH MED, VANDERBILT UNIV, 79- *Concurrent Pos:* Vet fel path, Med Sch, Univ Rochester, 50-51, Gleeson fel, 51-52, Lilly fel, 52-53; Lederle med fac award, 54; from asst resident to chief resident, Strong Mem Hosp, Rochester, 51-54; consult, Highland Hosp, Rochester, 54-55; assoc attend pathologist, Presby Hosp, New York, 55-; consult, NIH, 66- & Vietnam med educ proj, US AID-AMA, 67- *Mem:* Am Soc Exp Path; Harvey Soc; Am Asn Path & Bact; Am Soc Clin Path; Col Am Path. *Res:* Oxidative enzymes in proliferating tissue; plasma proteins studies employing C-14; hemoglobin; activation and inactivation of human chromosomes; ultrastructure of normal and abnormal human endometrium. *Mailing Add:* Sch of Med Vanderbilt Univ Nashville TN 37232

LUCAS, GENE ALLAN, b Des Moines, Iowa, Oct 15, 28; m 48; c 3. GENETICS. *Educ:* Drake Univ, BA, 54, MA, 58; Iowa State Univ, PhD(genetics), 68. *Prof Exp:* Lab instr biol, Drake Univ, 54-59, instr, 60-67; asst genetics, Iowa State Univ, 61-66; asst prof biol, 68-74, ASSOC PROF BIOL, DRAKE UNIV, 74- *Mem:* AAAS; Genetics Soc Am; Int Oceanog Found. *Res:* Pigmentation, especially of aquarium fish; pigment genetics of Siamese fighting fish; application of biological principles to world problems; race and population problems; teaching; biology and behavior of Siamese fighting fish. *Mailing Add:* Dept of Biol Drake Univ Des Moines IA 50311

LUCAS, GEORGE BLANCHARD, b Philipsburg, Pa, Mar 8, 15; m 40, 55; c 7. PLANT PATHOLOGY. *Educ:* Pa State Col, BS, 40; La State Univ, MS, 42, PhD(plant path), 46. *Prof Exp:* From asst prof to assoc prof, 46-63, PROF PLANT PATH, NC STATE UNIV, 63- *Mem:* Bot Soc Am; Mycol Soc Am; Am Phytopath Soc. *Res:* Tobacco diseases; genetics of fungi. *Mailing Add:* Dept of Plant Path NC State Univ Raleigh NC 27607

LUCAS, GEORGE BOND, b New Orleans, La, Dec 21, 24; m 62; c 2. ORGANIC GEOCHEMISTRY. *Educ:* Tulane Univ, BS, 48; Iowa State Col, PhD(phys & org chem), 52. *Prof Exp:* Res fel, Northwestern Univ, 52-53; sr res chemist res div, Redstone Arsenal, Rohm and Haas Co, 53-56; from asst to assoc prof phys chem, 56-67, PROF PHYS CHEM, COLO SCH MINES, 67- *Mem:* Am Chem Soc; Geochem Soc. *Res:* Solution kinetics; organic mechanisms; origin of petroleum. *Mailing Add:* Dept of Chem Colo Sch of Mines Golden CO 80401

LUCAS, GLENNARD RALPH, b Marissa, Ill, Feb 22, 16; m 41; c 2. ORGANIC POLYMER CHEMISTRY. *Educ:* Monmouth Col, BS, 38; Columbia Univ, PhD(phys org chem), 42. *Prof Exp:* Asst chem, Monmouth Col, 36-38 & Columbia Univ, 38-41; res chemist, Gen Elec Co, Mass, 42-52, process engr, NY, 52-54, supvr process eng, 54-56, mgr adv proj develop, Mass, 56-58; RES DIR, SIGNODE CORP, 58- *Mem:* AAAS; Am Chem Soc; Am Mgt Asn; Soc Plastics Eng. *Res:* Mechanisms of organic reactions; polymer studies of styrene and silicone resins; plastic and steel strapping materials; high speed paint cure. *Mailing Add:* 1011 Hunter Rd Glenview IL 60025

LUCAS, J RICHARD, b Scottdale, Pa, May 3, 29; m 52; c 2. MINING & MINERAL ENGINEERING. *Educ:* Waynesburg Col, BS, 51; WVa Univ, BS, 52; Univ Pittsburgh, MS, 54; Columbia Univ, PhD(mining eng), 65. *Prof Exp:* Miner, Crucible Steel Co Am, 48-52; field engr, Joy Mfg Co, 52-54; mem fac mining eng, Ohio State Univ, 54-56, head div, 57-61; head dept, 61-71, head div minerals eng, 71-76, HEAD, DEPT MINING & MINERALS ENG, VA POLYTECH INST & STATE UNIV, 76- *Concurrent Pos:* Dir, US Off Coal Res Proj, Va Polytech Inst & State Univ, 62-; actg asst dir, Va Eng Exp Sta, 63-64; mem secy's res adv coun coal miner's health, HEW, 70-73; consult & reviewer, Prog Comn, Mining Safety & Health Admin, Dept Labor, 69-, NSF, 73-74, 76-77 & Ad-Hoc Panel Coal Mining Technol, Nat Res Coun, 75-78; mem, Joint Comt Coal Mining Health, Safety & Res, Mining Safety & Health Admin, US Dept Labor & Bur Mines, US Dept Interior, 70-, rev comt, Fel Prog Mining & Minerals Eng & Conserv, Off Educ, HEW, Washington, DC, 79, prog comt, State Mine Recovery Competition, Div Mines, Va Mining Inst, 78-, ad hoc comt coal mine safety, Dept Indust & Resources, 79, Coal Conversion Fac, 79, exec comt, Va Mining & Mineral Resources Res Inst, 79-; coordr, Va Ctr Coal & Energy Res, Coal Inst, 77- *Mem:* Am Inst Mining, Metall & Petrol Engrs; Am Soc Eng Educ; Am Mining Cong; Nat Soc Prof Engrs; AAAS. *Res:* Mining systems engineering; mineral property evaluation; mining design and layout; computer applications in underground coal mining systems; coal mining safety research; methane from coal seams; underground coal-mining research. *Mailing Add:* Dept Mining & Minerals Eng Va Polytech Inst & State Univ Blacksburg VA 24061

LUCAS, JAMES M, b Philipsburg, Pa, July 21, 41. STATISTICAL METHODOLOGY. *Educ:* Pa State Univ, BS, 63; Yale Univ, MS, 65; Tex A&M Univ, PhD(statist), 72. *Prof Exp:* CONSULT STATIST, E I DU PONT DE NEMOURS & CO, INC, 65- *Concurrent Pos:* Adj assoc prof, Univ Del, 72- *Honors & Awards:* Brumbaugh Award, Am Soc Qual Control, 76. *Mem:* Am Statist Asn; Am Soc Qual Control. *Res:* Control and improvement of industrial processes using cumulative sum techniques. *Mailing Add:* Louviers 3170 E I Du pont de Nemours & Co Inc Wilmington DE 19898

LUCAS, JAMES ROBERT, b Mankato, Minn, Apr 26, 47. GEOLOGY. *Educ:* Mankato State Univ, BA, 69; Univ Iowa, MA, 73, PhD(geol), 77. *Prof Exp:* Instr earth sci, Providence Sch, South St Paul, Minn, 69-70; res geologist, Iowa Geol Surv, 75-76; appln scientist water resources, Earth Resources Observ Systs Data Ctr, SDak, 76-80. *Concurrent Pos:* Adj instr geol, Univ Iowa, 75-76; prin investr, NASA contract, 75-76. *Mem:* Geol Soc Am; Am Quaternary Asn; Am Soc Photogrammetry; Sigma Xi; Am Water Resources Asn. *Res:* Remoteley sensed data as applied to water resources; land classification of southeastern Iowa from computer enhanced LANDSAT images; glacial geomorphology of northwestern Iowa; mapping via rock stratigraphy and remote sensing techniques; semi-quantitative analysis of clay minerals by x-ray diffraction. *Mailing Add:* 4501 Mountain Ash Dr Sioux Falls SD 57103

LUCAS, JOHN PAUL, b Youngstown, Ohio, Nov 16, 45; m 68. MICROBIOLOGY. *Educ:* Univ Pittsburgh, BS, 67, MS, 69, ScD(microbiol), 73. *Prof Exp:* Res assoc virol, Grad Sch Pub Health, Univ Pittsburgh, 74; MICROBIOLOGIST, FOOD & DRUG ADMIN, 74- *Mem:* Am Soc Microbiol; Sigma Xi. *Res:* Develop growing area standards for shellfish. *Mailing Add:* 18908 Bluewillow Ln Gaithersburg MD 20760

LUCAS, JOHN W, b Pomona, Calif, Mar 14, 23; m 53; c 3. MECHANICAL ENGINEERING, HEAT TRANSFER. *Educ:* Univ Calif, Berkeley, BS, 48; Univ Calif, Los Angeles, MS, 49, PhD(mech eng), 53. *Prof Exp:* NSF fel, Fritz Haber Inst, Max Planck Soc Adv Sci, WBerlin, Ger, 53-54; sr res engr, 54-59, group supvr, 59-65, res rep eng mech, 66-70, mgr res & planetary quarantine, 70-74, exec asst to dir, 74-76, MGR POINT FOCUS DISTRIBUTED RECEIVER SOLAR ENERGY TECHNOL PROJ, JET PROPULSION LAB, CALIF INST TECHNOL, 76- *Mem:* Am Inst Aeronaut & Astronaut. *Res:* Ice nucleation in lemons; spacecraft advanced propulsion; radiation, conduction and convection heat transfer as related to spacecraft thermal control in space, on the moon and planets, and in solar thermal energy. *Mailing Add:* Jet Propulsion Lab MS 180-700 4800 Oak Grove Dr Pasadena CA 91103

LUCAS, KENNETH ROSS, b Bradford, Pa, June 4, 39; m 61; c 4. ANALYTICAL CHEMISTRY, POLYMER PHYSICS. *Educ:* Univ Pittsburgh, BS, 61; Univ Ill, MS, 64, PhD(anal chem), 66. *Prof Exp:* Res chemist, 66-71, sr res chemist, 71-81, ASSOC SCIENTIST, FIRESTONE TIRE & RUBBER CO, 81- *Mem:* Am Chem Soc; Electrochem Soc. *Res:* Molten salt and organic electrochemistry; x-ray diffraction; polymer physics; electro-organic synthesis; polymer morphology analysis; radiothermoluminescence. *Mailing Add:* Firestone Tire & Rubber Co 1200 Firestone Pkwy Akron OH 44317

LUCAS, LEON THOMAS, b Halifax, NC, July 30, 42; m 64; c 1. PLANT PATHOLOGY, MICROBIOLOGY. *Educ:* NC State Univ, BS, 64; Univ Calif, Davis, PhD(plant path), 68. *Prof Exp:* Res asst plant path, Univ Calif, Davis, 64-68; asst prof, 68-76, assoc prof, 76-80, PROF PLANT PATH, NC STATE UNIV, 80- *Mem:* Am Phytopath Soc. *Res:* Diseases of turfgrasses and forage crops in North Carolina; bacterial diseases of plants. *Mailing Add:* Dept of Plant Path NC State Univ Raleigh NC 27607

LUCAS, MYRON CRAN, b Cincinnati, Ohio, Nov 15, 46 BIOCHEMICAL GENETICS. *Educ:* Lewis & Clark Col, BS, 69; Wash State Univ, PhD(genetics), 74. *Prof Exp:* Res assoc bot, Univ Ill, Urbana, 73-75; res assoc genetics, Univ Ga, 75-77; res assoc biochem, Univ Idaho, 77-78; ASST PROF BIOL, LA STATE UNIV, SHREVEPORT, 78- *Concurrent Pos:* Adj asst prof biol, Fla State Univ, 77. *Mem:* Genetics Soc Am; Am Soc Microbiol; NY Acad Sci; AAAS. *Res:* Biochemical genetics of Neurospora crassa; structure and function of low molecular weight RNA; gene regulation and synthesis of messenger RNA; biosynthesis of membrane proteins and assembly of membranes. *Mailing Add:* Dept Biol Sci La State Univ Shreveport LA 71115

LUCAS, OSCAR NESTOR, b Resistencia, Arg, Aug 6, 32. HEMATOLOGY, PHYSIOLOGY. *Educ:* Univ Buenos Aires, Dentist, 58, DDS, 59; Univ Sask, PhD(physiol), 65. *Prof Exp:* Res assoc physiol, Med Sch, Univ Sask, 63-64; from asst prof to assoc prof, Med & Dent Sch, Univ Alta, 65-68; assoc prof, 68-70, PROF ORAL BIOL, DENT SCH, UNIV ORE, 70-, PROF DENT, MED SCH, 70- *Concurrent Pos:* Univ Buenos Aires fel, Jefferson Med Hosp, Philadelphia, Pa, 59-60; Cardeza Found fel, 60-63; affil, Div Hemat, Med Sch, Univ Ore, 71- *Mem:* Int Soc Hemat; Int Asn Dent Res. *Res:* Fibrinolysis; mast cell and connective tissue reparative process. *Mailing Add:* Dept of Oral Biol Univ of Ore Dent Sch Portland OR 97201

LUCAS, ROBERT ALAN, b Allentown, Pa, June 13, 35; m 57; c 4. MECHANICAL ENGINEERING. *Educ:* Lehigh Univ, BS, 57, MS, 59, PhD(mech eng), 64. *Prof Exp:* Design engr, Air Prod & Chem, Inc, Pa, 57-58; from asst to asst prof, 58-69, ASSOC PROF MECH ENG, LEHIGH UNIV, 69- *Concurrent Pos:* Nat Res Coun-Naval Res Lab resident res assoc, Naval Res Lab, DC, 65-66. *Res:* Design; applied elasticity; thermal stresses; applied mathematics; fracture; computer aided design; computer aided instruction. *Mailing Add:* Dept of Mech Eng & Mech Lehigh Univ Bethlehem PA 18015

LUCAS, ROBERT ELMER, b Malolos, Philippines, June 27, 16; m 41; c 5. SOIL SCIENCE. *Educ:* Purdue Univ, BSA, 39, MS, 41; Mich State Col, PhD(soil sci), 47. *Prof Exp:* Asst soils, Va Truck Exp Sta, 41-43 & Mich State Col, 45-46; agronomist, Wm Gehring, Inc, Ind, 46-51, 77-78; from assoc prof to prof, 51-76, exten specialist, 53-77, EMER PROF SOIL SCI, MICH STATE UNIV, 77- *Concurrent Pos:* Vis prof, Univ Fla, 79-80. *Mem:* Fel Soil Sci Soc Am; fel Am Soc Agron; Int Peat Soc. *Res:* Micronutrients in crop production; phosphite fertilizer injury to corn; soil organic matter dynamics and models; physical and chemical properties of organic soils (histosols); energy requirements for agricultural crops; plant nutrient requirements. *Mailing Add:* Dept of Crop & Soil Sci Mich State Univ East Lansing MI 48824

LUCAS, ROBERT GILLEM, b Springfield, Ohio, Sept 7, 46; m 72; c 3. NUCLEAR ENGINEERING, MECHANICAL ENGINEERING. *Educ:* US Naval Acad, BS, 68; Stanford Grad Sch Bus, MBA, 81. *Prof Exp:* Nuclear div officer nuclear submarines, USS James K Polk, US Navy, 69-71, USS Permit, 71-73, eng officer, USS Barb, 75-78; proj mgr, Nuclear Div, Elec Power Res Inst, 78-81; ASSOC, IDANTA PARTNERS, VENTURE CAPITAL, 81- *Res:* Development of high and low temperature filters for power plants; improving condenser integrity; testing new nuclear steam generator designs; improving oxygen control measures in power plants; evaluating steam generator operating parameters. *Mailing Add:* 4703 Murat Pl San Diego CA 92117

LUCAS, RUSSELL VAIL, JR, b Des Moines, Iowa, Nov 2, 28; m 51; c 4. PEDIATRIC CARDIOLOGY. *Educ:* Macalester Col, BA, 50; Wash Univ, MD, 54. *Prof Exp:* From intern to resident pediat, Univ Hosp, Univ Minn, Minneapolis, 54-56, resident, 58-59; from asst prof to assoc prof pediat, Med Ctr, WVa Univ, 61-66; assoc prof, 66-69, PROF PEDIAT, UNIV MINN, MINNEAPOLIS, 69- *Concurrent Pos:* NIH fel pediat cardiol, Univ Hosps, Univ Minn, Minneapolis, 59-61; NIH res career develop award, WVa Univ, 63-66. *Honors & Awards:* Distinguished Achievement Award, Am Heart Asn, 66. *Mem:* Soc Pediat Res; Am Acad Pediat; Asn Am Med Cols; Am Fedn Clin Res; AMA. *Res:* Physiology of ventricular function; pathology, physiology and natural history of congenital cardiac defects. *Mailing Add:* Pediat Cardiol Univ of Minn Hosps Minneapolis MN 55455

LUCAS, THOMAS RAMSEY, b Tampa, Fla, June 9, 39; m 70. MATHEMATICS. *Educ:* Univ Fla, BS, 61; Univ Mich, Ann Arbor, MS, 62; Ga Inst Technol, PhD(math), 70. *Prof Exp:* Sr engr, Martin Co, 62-65; asst prof math, 69-75, ASSOC PROF MATH, UNIV NC, CHARLOTTE, 75- *Mem:* Am Math Soc; Soc Indust & Appl Math. *Res:* Numerical analysis; approximation theory; spline theory. *Mailing Add:* Dept of Math Univ of NC Box 20428 Charlotte NC 28223

LUCAS, WILLIAM FRANKLIN, b Detroit, Mich, Apr 21, 33; m 57; c 4. OPERATIONS RESEARCH, APPLIED MATHEMATICS. *Educ:* Univ Detroit, BS, 54, MA, 56, MS, 58; Univ Mich, PhD(math), 63. *Prof Exp:* Instr math, Univ Detroit, 56-58 & 61-62, asst prof, 62-63; res instr, Princeton Univ, 63-65; Fulbright fel & vis asst prof econ & statist, Mid East Tech Univ, Ankara, 65-66; vis assoc prof, Math Res Ctr, Univ Wis-Madison, 66-67; mathematician, Rand Corp, 67-69; assoc prof opers res & appl math, 69-70, dir ctr appl math, 71-74, PROF OPERS RES & APPL MATH, CORNELL UNIV, 70- *Concurrent Pos:* Consult, Rand Corp, 69-77 & Educ Develop Ctr, 75-; sci exchange with USSR, US Nat Acad Sci, 76; Chautauqua lectr, AAAS, 75-79. *Mem:* Am Math Soc; Math Asn Am; Soc Indust & Appl Math; Opers Res Soc Am; Asn Women Math. *Res:* Elasticity; applied mathematics; game theory. *Mailing Add:* Dept of Opers Res 334 Upson Hall Cornell Univ Ithaca NY 14853

LUCAS, WILLIAM JOHN, b Adelaide, S Australia, Feb 23, 45; m 67; c 2. PLANT PHYSIOLOGY, PLANT BIOPHYSICS. *Educ:* Univ Adelaide, BSc, 71, PhD(plant physiol), 75. *Prof Exp:* Res assoc, Dept Bot, Univ Toronto, 75-77; asst prof plant physiol, 77-80, ASSOC PROF BOT, UNIV CALIF, DAVIS, 80- *Mem:* Am Soc Plant Physiologists; Australian Soc Plant Physiologists; Australian Soc Biophysicists; Bot Soc Am. *Res:* Biophysical and physiological aspects of ion transport across plant membranes, in particular the plasmalemma. *Mailing Add:* Dept of Bot Univ of Calif Davis CA 95616

LUCAS, WILLIAM R(AY), b Newbern, Tenn, Mar 1, 22; m 48; c 3. CHEMISTRY, METALLURGY. *Educ:* Memphis State Univ, BS, 43; Vanderbilt Univ, MS, 50, PhD(chem, metall), 52. *Hon Degrees:* DHL, Mobile Col, 77; DSc, Southeastern Inst Technol, 80; Univ Ala, Huntsville, 81. *Prof Exp:* Instr chem, Memphis State Univ, 46-48; chemist, guided missile develop div, Redstone Arsenal, 52-54, chief chem sect, 54-55; chief eng mat sect, Army Ballistic Missile Agency, 55-56, chief eng mat br, 56-60; chief eng mat br, Marshall Space Flight Ctr, 60-63, chief mat div, 63-66, dir propulsion & vehicle eng lab, 66-68, dir prog develop, 68-71, dep dir, 71-74, DIR, MARSHALL SPACE FLIGHT CTR, NASA, 74- *Honors & Awards:* Except Sci Achievement Medal, NASA, 64, Except Serv Medal, 69, Distinguished Serv Medal, 72; Oberth Award, Am Inst Aeronaut & Astronaut, 65, Holger N Toftoy Award, 76. *Mem:* Nat Acad Eng; fel Am Inst Aeronaut & Astronaut; fel Am Astronaut Soc; fel Am Soc Metals; Sigma Xi. *Res:* Materials engineering, metallurgy and inorganic chemistry; environmental effects on materials, especially space environmental effects. *Mailing Add:* 6805 Criner Rd Huntsville AL 35802

LUCAS-LENARD, JEAN MARIAN, b Bridgeport, Conn, July 17, 37; m 64. MOLECULAR BIOLOGY. *Educ:* Bryn Mawr Col, AB, 59; Yale Univ, PhD(protein synthesis), 63. *Prof Exp:* USPHS fel enzymol, Inst Physiochem Biol, Paris, 63-64; guest investr protein synthesis, Rockefeller Univ, 64-65, res assoc, 65-68, asst prof, 68-70; assoc prof, 70-76, PROF BIOL, UNIV CONN, 76- *Concurrent Pos:* Estab investr, Am Heart Asn, 70-71; NIH career develop award, 71-76. *Res:* Mechanism of protein biosynthesis in eukaryotes and prokaryotes; translational control mechanisms in virus infected cells. *Mailing Add:* Dept of Biochem & Biophys Univ of Conn Storrs CT 06268

LUCAST, DONALD HURRELL, b Minneapolis, Minn, July 11, 46; m 75; c 2. ORGANIC CHEMISTRY. *Educ:* Univ Minn, BS, 68, PhD(org chem), 76. *Prof Exp:* RES CHEMIST, ETHYL CORP, 77- *Concurrent Pos:* Fel, Univ Detroit, 75-76 & Wayne State Univ, 77. *Mem:* Am Chem Soc. *Res:* Organic synthesis; reaction mechanisms. *Mailing Add:* Ethyl Corp 1600 W Eight-Mile Rd Ferndale MI 48220

LUCATORTO, THOMAS B, b New York, NY, May 9, 37; c 2. LASERS. *Educ:* City Univ NY, BS, 60; Columbia Univ, MA, 64, PhD(physics), 68. *Prof Exp:* Res assoc physics, Columbia Univ, 68-69; RES PHYSICIST, NAT BUR STANDARDS, 69- *Honors & Awards:* IR-100 Award, Nat Bur Standards, 80; Silver Medal, Dept Com, 80. *Mem:* Am Phys Soc. *Res:* Atomic photoabsorption in the vacuum ultraviolet; laser-excitation of plasmas and laser ionization. *Mailing Add:* 3600 Van Ness St NW Washington DC 20008

LUCCA, JOHN J, b Brooklyn, NY, July 12, 21; m 46; c 6. DENTISTRY. *Educ:* NY Univ, AB, 41; Columbia Univ, DDS, 47; Am Bd Prosthodontics, dipl. *Prof Exp:* From instr to assoc prof dent, 47-64, PROF PROSTHODONTICS & DIR DIV, SCH DENT & ORAL SURG, COLUMBIA UNIV, 64- *Concurrent Pos:* Consult, Vet Admin & USPHS; hon police surgeon & consult, New York Police Dept, 64-; consult, US Naval Dent Sch; attend, Presby Hosp & Grasslands Hosp; consult ed prosthodont, Progreso-Odonto-Stomatologique. *Honors & Awards:* Ewell Medal, 47. *Mem:* Fel Am Col Dent; fel Am Col Prosthodont; fel Int Col Dent. *Res:* Precision attachment; partial dentures. *Mailing Add:* Div of Prosthodontics Columbia Univ New York NY 10032

LUCCHESI, CLAUDE A, b Chicago, Ill, Apr 20, 29; m 54; c 2. ANALYTICAL CHEMISTRY, PHYSICAL CHEMISTRY. *Educ:* Univ Ill, BS, 50; Northwestern Univ, PhD, 54. *Prof Exp:* Asst, Northwestern Univ, 50-54; spectros group leader, Shell Develop Co, Tex, 54-56; dir anal res dept, Sherwin-Williams Co, 56-61; mgr anal & phys chem dept, Mobil Chem Co, 61-67, mgr cent coatings lab, 67-68; LECTR CHEM & DIR ANAL SERV, NORTHWESTERN UNIV, 68- *Mem:* Am Chem Soc; Soc Appl Spectros; Instrument Soc Am; Fedn Soc Paint Technol; Brit Soc Anal Chem. *Res:* General applied spectroscopy; x-ray spectroscopy; chelate chemistry; differential thermal analysis; plastics and coating characterization and analysis; trace analysis. *Mailing Add:* Dept Chem Northwestern Univ Evanston IL 60201

LUCCHESI, JOHN CHARLES, b Cairo, Egypt, Sept 3, 34; US citizen; m 55; c 2. GENETICS. *Educ:* La Grange Col, AB, 55; Univ Ga, MS, 58; Univ Calif, Berkeley, PhD(zool), 63. *Prof Exp:* NIH res assoc biol, Univ Ore, 63-65; from asst prof to assoc prof, 65-72, PROF ZOOL & GENETICS, UNIV NC, CHAPEL HILL, 72- *Concurrent Pos:* Vis investr, Max Planck Inst Biol,

Tübingen, Ger, 69; NIH res career develop award, 70-75; vis Kenan prof, Dept Genetics, Univ Calif, Berkeley, 78. *Mem:* Genetics Soc Am; Am Soc Cell Biol; Soc Develop Biol. *Res:* Molecular cytogenetics; biochemistry of development. *Mailing Add:* Dept of Zool Univ of NC Chapel Hill NC 27514

LUCCHESI, PETER J, b New York, NY, Sept 23, 26; m 49; c 2. PHYSICAL CHEMISTRY. *Educ:* NY Univ, AB, 49, MS, 53, PhD(chem), 54. *Prof Exp:* Instr chem, Adelphi Col, 52, NY Univ, 53-54 & Ill Inst Technol, 54-55; res chemist, 55-68, dir corp res lab, 68-75, VPRES CORP RES, EXXON RES & ENG CO, 75- *Mem:* Am Chem Soc. *Res:* Radiation chemistry; heterogeneous catalysis; crystal growth and dissolution. *Mailing Add:* Exxon Res & Eng Co PO Box 45 Linden NJ 07036

LUCCHITTA, BAERBEL KOESTERS, b Muenster, Ger, Oct 2, 38; US citizen; m 64; c 1. PLANETARY GEOLOGY, GEOMORPHOLOGY. *Educ:* Kent State Univ, BS, 61; Pa State Univ, MS, 63, PhD(geol), 66. *Prof Exp:* GEOLOGIST, BR ASTROGEOL, US GEOL SURV, 68- *Concurrent Pos:* Prin investr, three lunar projs, NASA, 74-78, guest investr, Viking Lander Imaging Team, 76, prin investr, three martian projs, 78-, mem, Planetary Geol Rev Panel, 80-82, coordr, Galilean Satellite Geol Mapping Prog, 80-; assoc ed, J Geophys Res, 80- *Mem:* Asn Women Geoscientists; Asn Women Sci. *Res:* Dark mantles, secondary craters, basin formation, plains formation, scarps and ridges, northside and Apollo 17-site geological map of the moon; erosion, landform development, map of Ismenius Lacus, canyons and scarps, landslides, channels, glacial and periglacial features of Mars; geomorphology and structural geology of earth; geologic map of Jupiter Satellite Europa; structure of Ganymede. *Mailing Add:* Br Astrogeol US Geol Surv 2255 N Gemini Dr Flagstaff AZ 86001

LUCCHITTA, IVO, b Budweis, Czech, June 17, 37; US citizen; m 64; c 1. GEOLOGY. *Educ:* Calif Inst Technol, BSc, 61; Pa State Univ, PhD(geol), 67. *Prof Exp:* Geologist, proj chief & coordr Apollo geol methods, US Geol Surv, 66-70, geologist & proj chief earth resources technol satellite appln & anal, 70-73, geologist nat landslide overview map, 73-74, geologist & proj chief West Ariz Tectonics, US geol surv, 73-; GEOLOGIST, SHIVWITS-GRAND WASH WILDERNESS AREA, 80- *Concurrent Pos:* Adj prof, Northern Ariz Univ, 74- *Mem:* Fel Geol Soc Am. *Res:* Tectonic history of southwestern Colorado plateau and of plateau basin and range transition; basement control of structure; tectonic heredity; history of Colorado River and Grand Canyon; cenozoic continental rocks. *Mailing Add:* US Geol Surv 2255 N Gemini Dr Flagstaff AZ 86001

LUCCI, ROBERT DOMINICK, b Norwalk, Conn, July 11, 50; m 71; c 2. ANALYTICAL CHEMISTRY. *Educ:* Univ Conn, BA, 72; Cornell Univ, PhD(org chem), 77. *Prof Exp:* SR SCIENTIST, HOFFMANN-LAROCHE, INC, 77- *Mem:* Am Chem Soc; Sigma Xi. *Res:* Safe, economic and environmentally sound industrial chemical processes from research synthesis. *Mailing Add:* Tech Develop Dept Hoffmann-LaRoche, Inc Nutley NJ 07110

LUCE, JAMES EDWARD, b Toronto, Ont, Aug 24, 35. PAPER CHEMISTRY, PHYSICS. *Educ:* Univ Toronto, BASc, 56; McGill Univ, PhD(chem), 60; NY Inst Tech, MBA, 80. *Prof Exp:* Asst mgr basic res, CIP Res Ltd, 60-71; sci admin officer, Atomic Energy Can, Ltd, 71; sr mgr oper systs develop, 72-81, ASSOC DIR ADVANCED DEVELOP, INT PAPER CO, 81- *Mem:* Tech Asn Pulp & Paper Indust; Can Pulp & Paper Asn; Chem Inst Can; Brit Paper & Board Indust Fedn. *Res:* Application of modern instrumental techniques to control of pulp and paper processes; development of paperworking processes. *Mailing Add:* Int Paper Co PO Box 797 Tuxedo Park NY 10987

LUCE, R(OBERT) DUNCAN, b Scranton, Pa, May 16, 25; div; c 1. MATHEMATICAL PSYCHOLOGY, THEORY MEASUREMENT. *Educ:* Mass Inst Technol, BS, 45, PhD(math), 50. *Hon Degrees:* MS, Harvard Univ, 76. *Prof Exp:* Mem staff, Res Lab Electronics, Mass Inst Technol, 50-53; asst prof sociol & math statist, Columbia Univ, 54-57; prof psychol, Univ Pa, 59-67, Benjamin Franklin prof, 67-68; vis prof social sci, Inst Advan Study, Princeton, 69-72; prof soc sci, Univ Calif, Irvine, 72-75; ALFRED NORTH WHITEHEAD PROF PSYCHOL & MATH PSYCHOL, HARVARD UNIV, 76- *Concurrent Pos:* Lectr social rels, Harvard Univ, 57-59; vis prof psychol, Catholic Univ Rio de Janeiro, 68-69; managing dir, Behav Models Proj, Columbia Univ, 53-57, fel, Ctr Advan Study Behav Sci, 54-55 & 66-67; Guggenheim Found fel, 80-81. *Mem:* Nat Acad Sci; Am Acad Arts & Sci; Soc Math Psychol (pres, 79); Psychometric Soc (pres, 76-77); AAAS. *Res:* Theoretical work on measurement and structures, especially conjoint and utility ones; theoretical and experimental work in psychophysics, including absolute identification, detection and recognition, magnitude estimation and reaction time. *Mailing Add:* Dept Psychol & Social Rels Harvard Univ Cambridge MA 02138

LUCE, ROBERT JAMES, b Boston, Mass, Aug 7, 29; m 81. ROCK MAGNETISM. *Educ:* Drexel Univ, BS, 73; Univ Pittsburgh, MS, 75, PhD(geophysics), 80. *Prof Exp:* ASST PROF PHYSICS & GEOL, WASHINGTON & JEFFERSON COL, 80- *Mem:* Am Phys Soc; Am Asn Physics Teachers. *Res:* Theoretical models of single-domain thermoremanent magnetization processes and interactions, especially with reference to the stable magnetic memory of magnetite grains in rocks. *Mailing Add:* Dept Physics Wahsington & Jefferson Col Washington PA 15301

LUCE, ROBERT WILLIAM, b Teaneck, NJ, July 27, 38. GEOCHEMISTRY. *Educ:* Dartmouth Col, BA, 60; Univ Ill, MS, 62; Stanford Univ, PhD(geochem), 69. *Prof Exp:* GEOLOGIST, US GEOL SURV, 68- *Mem:* Soc Econ Geol; Am Inst Mech Engrs; Geochem Soc; Mineral Soc Am; Clay Minerals Soc. *Res:* Geochemistry of mineral weathering, including kinetics, surface chemistry and clay mineral formation; studies of ore deposits and rock alteration in Arizona, Saudi Arabia and South Carolina. *Mailing Add:* US Geol Surv 954 Nat Ctr Reston VA 22092

LUCE, WILLIAM GLENN, b Beaver Dam, Ky, Mar 21, 36; m 70; c 2. ANIMAL NUTRITION. *Educ:* Univ Ky, BS, 58; Univ Nebr, MS, 64, PhD(animal nutrit), 65. *Prof Exp:* Mgt trainee grocery & meat merchandising, Kroger Co, Ky, 58-60, co-mgr grocery & meat merchanidising, 60-62; asst nutrit res, Univ Nebr, 62-65; asst prof swine exten, Univ Ga, 65-68; PROF SWINE EXTEN, OKLA STATE UNIV, 68- *Mem:* Sigma Xi; Am Soc Animal Sci. *Res:* Swine nutrition; cereal grain utilization and amino acid requirements. *Mailing Add:* Dept Animal Sci Okla State Univ Stillwater OK 74078

LUCEY, CAROL ANN, b Johnstown, NY, Sept 16, 43; m 64; c 1. THEORETICAL PHYSICS, PHILOSOPHY OF SCIENCE. *Educ:* Harpur Col, BA, 65; State Univ NY Binghamton, MA, 68; Brown Univ, PhD(physics), 72. *Prof Exp:* Actg assoc dean instr, 76-78, ASSOC PROF PHYSICS, JAMESTOWN COMMUNITY COL, 73- *Mem:* Am Phys Soc; Philos Sci Asn. *Res:* Study of cosmological implication for elementary particle physics; consequences of the hot model and possible neutrino degeneracy in CP violations; scientific methodology. *Mailing Add:* Dept of Physics Jamestown Community Col Jamestown NY 14701

LUCEY, JEROLD FRANCIS, b Holyoke, Mass, Mar 26, 26; m 50; c 3. PEDIATRICS. *Educ:* Dartmouth Col, AB, 48; NY Univ, MD, 52. *Prof Exp:* Intern pediat, Bellevue Hosp, New York, 52-53; asst resident, Columbia-Presby Med Ctr, 53-55; from instr to assoc prof, 56-66, PROF PEDIAT, COL MED, UNIV VT, 66- *Concurrent Pos:* Bowen Brooks scholar, NY Acad Med, Bellevue Hosp, New York, 54; Mead Johnson fel, Columbia-Presby Med Ctr, 54-55; Nat Found Infantile Paralysis res fel, Harvard Med Sch, 55-56; Markle scholar, 59-64; res fel biochem, Harvard Med Sch, 60-61; consult, Vt State Health Dept, 56-81; chmn, Nat Bd Pediat Exam, 68-72; mem, Am Bd Pediat Exam, 70; ed-in-chief, Pediatrics, 73-; Humboldt Found fel, 78; Litchfield lectr, Oxford Univ, 78. *Mem:* Soc Pediat Res; fel Am Acad Pediat; Am Pediat Soc; Am Soc Photobiol; Royal Soc Med. *Res:* Neonatal physiology; transcutaneous oxygen. bilirubin metabolism. *Mailing Add:* Med Ctr Hosp of Vt 52 Overlake Park Burlington VT 05401

LUCEY, JOHN WILLIAM, b Winthrop, Mass, Aug 21, 35; m 57; c 4. NUCLEAR ENGINEERING. *Educ:* Univ Notre Dame, BS, 57; Mass Inst Technol, SM, 63, PhD(nuclear eng), 65. *Prof Exp:* Asst prof, 65-68, ASSOC PROF NUCLEAR ENG, UNIV NOTRE DAME, 68- *Concurrent Pos:* Dir, Ind Civil Defense Prof Adv Serv, 69-73. *Mem:* AAAS; Am Nuclear Soc; Am Soc Eng Educ; Health Physics Soc; Sigma Xi. *Res:* Numerical methods for nuclear reactor calculations; radiation shielding; transport calculations. *Mailing Add:* Dept of Aerospace & Mech Eng Univ of Notre Dame Notre Dame IN 46556

LUCEY, JULIANA MARGARET, b Santa Monica, Calif. NUMERICAL ANALYSIS. *Educ:* Univ Wash, AM, 62; Univ Ariz, MS, 72; St Louis Univ, PhD(math), 75. *Prof Exp:* Teacher high sch math & chmn dept, Sisters of the Holy Names of Jesus & Mary, 65; asst prof math, Holy Names Col, 65-69; teaching asst, Univ Ariz, 69-71; teaching fel, St Louis Univ, 73-74; asst prof, Holy Names Col, 74-75; instr math, Wayne State Univ, 75-76; asst prof math, Marquette Univ, 76-80; VIS ASST PROF MATH, UNIV ALASKA, 80- *Mem:* Am Math Soc; Am Statist Asn. *Res:* Solutions of stiff ordinary differential equations by a fifth order composite multistep method; index and Lefschetz number in the structure of gratings. *Mailing Add:* Dept Math Univ Alaska Fairbanks AK 99701

LUCEY, ROBERT FRANCIS, b Worcester, Mass, Mar 13, 26; m 52; c 7. AGRONOMY. *Educ:* Univ Mass, BVA, 50; Univ Md, MS, 54; Mich State Univ, PhD(field crops), 59. *Prof Exp:* Asst prof agron, Univ NH, 57-61; from asst to assoc prof field crops, 61-70, PROF FIELD CROPS, NY STATE COL AGR & LIFE SCI, CORNELL UNIV, 70-, CHMN DEPT AGRON, 75- *Mem:* Am Soc Agron. *Res:* Production of field crops, especially crop-climate relationships; adaptability; plant competition. *Mailing Add:* NY State Col Agr & Life Sci Dept Agron Cornell Univ Ithaca NY 14850

LUCHINS, EDITH HIRSCH, b Poland, Dec 21, 21; nat US; m 42; c 5. MATHEMATICS. *Educ:* Brooklyn Col, BA, 42; NY Univ, MS, 44; Univ Ore, PhD(math), 57. *Prof Exp:* Govt inspector anti-aircraft dirs, Sperry Gyroscope Co, NY, 42-44; instr math, Brooklyn Col, 44-46 & 48-49; asst appl math lab, NY Univ, 46; Am Asn Univ Women res fel & res assoc math, Univ Ore, 57-58; from res assoc to assoc prof math, Univ Miami, 59-62; assoc prof, 62-70, PROF MATH, RENSSELAER POLYTECH INST, 70- *Mem:* Math Asn Am; Am Math Soc; Soc Indust & Appl Math. *Res:* Banach algebras; functional analysis; mathematical psychology. *Mailing Add:* Dept of Math Sci Rensselaer Polytech Inst Troy NY 12181

LUCHSINGER, WAYNE WESLEY, b Milaca, Minn, May 8, 24; m 43; c 4. BIOCHEMISTRY. *Educ:* Univ Minn, BS, 51, MS, 54, PhD(biochem), 56. *Prof Exp:* Asst biochem, Univ Minn, 51-55; sr chemist, Kurth Malting Co, 56-58, asst dir res, 58-60; assoc prof biochem, WVa Univ, 60-66; assoc prof chem, 66-68, PROF CHEM, ARIZ STATE UNIV, 68- *Mem:* AAAS; Am Chem Soc; Am Soc Brewing Chem; Am Asn Cereal Chem. *Res:* Enzymes; barley carbohydrates; chemistry and mechanism of action of carbohydrates; carbohydrate structure. *Mailing Add:* Dept of Chem Ariz State Univ Tempe AZ 85287

LUCHTEL, DANIEL LEE, b Carroll, Iowa, Jan 13, 42; m 73; c 1. MICROSCOPIC ANATOMY, CELL BIOLOGY. *Educ:* St Benedict's Col, Kans, BS, 63; Univ Wash, PhD(zool), 69. *Prof Exp:* NIH fel, 69-71; res assoc biol struct, 71-73, res assoc, 73, environ health, 74, ASST PROF ENVIRON HEALTH, UNIV WASH, 75- *Concurrent Pos:* Res fel, Hubrecht Lab, Utrecht, Neth, 72. *Mem:* AAAS; Sigma Xi; Am Soc Cell Biol; Am Inst Biol Sci; Electron Microscipy Soc Am. *Res:* Lung ultrastructure and effects of gaseous and particulate air pollutants; respiratory tract mucus; lung development; mechanisms of pulmonary edema; tracheal organ cultures. *Mailing Add:* Dept of Environ Health Univ of Wash Seattle WA 98195

LUCID, MICHAEL FRANCIS, b Indianapolis, Ind, Feb 23, 37; m 67; c 3. INORGANIC CHEMISTRY. *Educ:* Ind Univ, Bloomington, BS, 61; Purdue Univ, Lafayette, MS, 65. *Prof Exp:* Res chemist, Kerr McGee Corp, 65-67, sr res chemist, 67-75, res proj chemist, 75-78; staff engr, 78-80, STAFF MINING ENGR, SHELL OIL CO, 80- *Mem:* Am Chem Soc. *Res:* Hydrometallurgy; solvent extraction; ion exchange; solution chemistry; geochemistry; solution mining, uranium, vanadium, copper; oil shale. *Mailing Add:* Shell Oil Co Mining PO Box 2906 Houston TX 77001

LUCIER, JOHN J, b Detroit, Mich, Aug 10, 17. ORGANIC CHEMISTRY. *Educ:* Univ Dayton, BS, 37; Western Reserve Univ, MS, 50, PhD(org chem), 51. *Prof Exp:* Instr chem, 45-47 & 51-52, from asst to assoc prof, 52-63, chmn dept, 64-79, PROF CHEM, UNIV DAYTON, 63- *Mem:* AAAS; Am Chem Soc; Soc Appl Spectros; NY Acad Sci; The Chem Soc. *Res:* Organic synthesis; infrared spectroscopy. *Mailing Add:* Dept of Chem Univ of Dayton Dayton OH 45409

LUCIS, OJARS JANIS, b Latvia, Apr 2, 24; Can citizen; m 49; c 2. ENDOCRINOLOGY, CLINICAL PHARMACOLOGY. *Educ:* Sir George Williams Univ, BSc, 54; McGill Univ, MSc, 57, PhD(invest med), 59, MD, CM, 61, cert clin chem, 74. *Prof Exp:* Res asst invest med, McGill Univ, 56-60; asst prof endocrinol, Dalhousie Univ, 65-71; MED OFFICER, HEALTH & WELFARE CAN, 71-, DIV CHIEF ENDOCRINOL & METAB, 74- *Concurrent Pos:* Med Res Coun Can fel, McGill Univ, 62-63, res scholar, 63-65; Med Res Coun Can scholar steroid biochem, Dalhousie Univ, 65-68; asst pathologist, Prov NS Dept Pub Health, 66-68, assoc pathologist, 68-71. *Mem:* Can Soc Clin Chem; Endocrine Soc. *Res:* Biosynthesis and metabolism of hormones; immunochemical assays of hormones; interaction of trace elements with the cells and the mammalian organism; biosynthesis and isolation of cadmium binding proteins; pharmacology and toxicology of drugs. *Mailing Add:* Health & Welfare Can Health Protection Br Bur Drugs Ottawa ON K1A 0L2 Can

LUCIS, RUTA, b Rujiena, Latvia, Apr 9, 25; Can citizen; m 49; c 2. COMPARATIVE ENDOCRINOLOGY. *Educ:* Sir George Williams Univ, BSc, 57; McGill Univ, MS, 64, PhD(invest med), 66. *Prof Exp:* Res asst endocrinol, McGill Univ, 62-65; res asst, Path Inst, 66-71; clin chemist, Coop Labs, Ottawa, 72-73; CLIN CHEMIST, ANIMAL RES INST, OTTAWA, 73- *Mem:* NY Acad Sci. *Res:* Biochemistry of steroids; immunochemical assays and metabolism of hormones; environmental health. *Mailing Add:* 1512 Caverley St Ottawa ON K1G 0Y1 Can

LUCK, CLARENCE FREDERICK, JR, b Buffalo, NY, Oct 4, 25; m 51, 69; c 5. PHYSICS. *Educ:* Univ Buffalo, BA, 49; Duke Univ, PhD(physics), 56. *Prof Exp:* Tool designer, Bell Aircraft Corp, 43-44; supvr microwave tube res, Polarad Electronics Corp, 56-60; sr staff physicist, Res Div, 60-62, mgr laser advan develop ctr, Spec Microwave Devices Oper, 62-66, PRIN ENGR, LASER ADVAN DEVELOP CTR, SPEC MICROWAVE DEVICES OPER, RAYTHEON CO, 66- *Mem:* Am Phys Soc; Optical Soc Am. *Res:* Spectroscopy; optics; photography; optical maser; laser and laser machining equipment. *Mailing Add:* 45 Weir Rd Waltham MA 02154

LUCK, DAVID GEORGE CROFT, b Whittier, Calif, July 26, 06; m 30; c 1. PHYSICS. *Educ:* Mass Inst Technol, SB, 27, PhD(physics), 32. *Prof Exp:* Res engr, Thomas A Edison, Inc, 29; asst physics, Mass Inst Technol, 29-32; res engr, Victor Div, Radio Corp Am, NJ, 32-42, labs div, 42-53, aviation staff engr, Eng Prod Div, 54-64; mem tech staff, Defense Res Corp, 64-69, Strategic Systs Div, Gen Res Corp, 69-74; CONSULT, 74- *Honors & Awards:* Ballantine Medal, Franklin Inst, 53; Achievement Awards, RCA Labs; Pioneer Award, Nat Airborne Electronics Conf. *Mem:* Fel Inst Elec & Electronics Eng; Am Inst Navig. *Res:* Magnetic materials; resistors; electronic systems for communications and specialized communication systems; fire control; air traffic control; color television; radar, especially FM radar; radio navigation; radio direction finding; navigation aides; omni-range system of air navigation. *Mailing Add:* 4756 Calle Camarada Santa Barbara CA 93110

LUCK, DAVID JONATHAN LEWIS, b Milwaukee, Wis, Jan 7, 29. CYTOLOGY. *Educ:* Univ Chicago, SB, 49; Harvard Med Sch, MD, 53; Rockefeller Univ, PhD, 62. *Prof Exp:* From asst prof to assoc prof, 64-68, PROF CELL BIOL, ROCKEFELLER UNIV, 68- *Concurrent Pos:* Teaching fel, Harvard Med Sch, 57-59; fel, Rockefeller Univ, 59-64; res physician, Mass Gen Hosp, Boston, 57-59. *Res:* Biochemical cytology; cell structure; biochemical function. *Mailing Add:* Rockefeller Univ New York NY 10021

LUCK, DENNIS NOEL, b Durban, SAfrica, Dec 8, 39; m 69; c 1. MOLECULAR BIOLOGY. *Educ:* Univ Natal, BSc, 61, MSc, 63; Oxford Univ, DPhil(molecular biol), 66. *Prof Exp:* Lectr biochem, Univ Natal, 66-68; vis asst prof pharmacol, Baylor Col Med, 69; asst prof zool, Univ Tex, Austin, 70-72; asst prof, 72-75, ASSOC PROF BIOL, OBERLIN COL, 75- *Concurrent Pos:* Eleanor Roosevelt Int Cancer fel, Univ Oxford, 78-79. *Mem:* Brit Biochem Soc; Am Soc Develop Biol; Am Soc Cell Biol; Sigma Xi. *Res:* Regulation of genetic transcription and translation; control mechanisms in endocrinology; effects of sex steroid hormones on metabolism of reproductive organs. *Mailing Add:* Dept of Biol Oberlin Col Oberlin OH 44074

LUCK, ETTA ROBENA, b Danville, Va, Dec 24, 19; div. MYCOLOGY. *Educ:* Howard Univ, SB, 41; Univ Iowa, MS, 42; Univ Toronto, MA, 56, PhD(bot), 58. *Prof Exp:* Instr biol, Fla Agr & Mech Col, 48-49; assoc prof, Tex Southern Univ, 49-54; asst, 56-59, lectr, 59-63, asst prof, 63-69, assoc prof mycol, Univ Toronto, 69-76; assoc prof, Inst Geront, Univ DC, 77-80; ADJ PROF, HOWARD UNIV, 80- *Concurrent Pos:* Res grant, Nat Res Coun Can, 75- *Mem:* Mycol Soc Am; Brit Mycol Soc; Bot Soc Am; Can Bot Asn. *Res:* Mycology; pathology; cultural and taxonomic studies of tremellaceous fungi; coprophilous ascomycetes; Tremellales of Ontario. *Mailing Add:* 201 11559 Rolling Green Reston VA 22091

LUCK, JOHN VIRGIL, b Chalmers, Ind, Jan 20, 26; m 45; c 3. MICROBIOLOGY. *Educ:* Purdue Univ, BS, 49, MS, 51, PhD(microbiol, biochem), 54. *Prof Exp:* Dir beer fermentation res, Pabst Brewing Co, 53-55; proj leader chem res, Gen Foods Corp, NY, 55-58; head biol chem dept, Armour & Co, 58-60; dir res & develop, Durkee Famous Foods, Glidden Co, Ill, 60-70; VPRES & TECH DIR, GEN MILLS, INC, MINNEAPOLIS, 70- *Concurrent Pos:* Mem, Res & Develop Assocs. *Mem:* AAAS; Am Chem Soc; Am Oil Chem Soc; Inst Food Technol; Soc Indust Microbiol. *Res:* Food chemistry; fats; starch; proteins emulsifiers; enzymology. *Mailing Add:* Gen Mills Inc 9000 Plymouth Ave N Minneapolis MN 55425

LUCK, LEON D(AN), b Spokane, Wash, Apr 25, 21; m 41; c 2. CIVIL ENGINEERING. *Educ:* Wash State Univ, BS, 43; Univ Minn, MS, 51; Stanford Univ, CE, 60. *Prof Exp:* Mine engr, Pend Oreille Mines & Metals Co, 43 & 46-47; from instr to assoc prof civil eng, Wash State Univ, 47-57; lectr, Stanford Univ, 57-59; assoc prof, 59-62, chmn dept civil & environ eng, 72-76, PROF CIVIL ENG, WASH STATE UNIV, 62- *Concurrent Pos:* Consult engr, Potlatch Forests, Inc, 56-60; vis prof, Univ Leeds, 69-70. *Mem:* Am Soc Civil Engrs; Am Soc Eng Educ; Nat Soc Prof Engrs. *Res:* Shear characteristics of Palouse clay; seepage flow through porous soil media; rigid frame analysis by matrix methods with the aid of a digital computer. *Mailing Add:* Dept of Civil & Environ Eng Wash State Univ Pullman WA 99164

LUCK, RICHARD EARLE, b Roanoke, Va, Mar 9, 50; m 78. ASTROPHYSICS, ASTRONOMY. *Educ:* Univ Va, BA, 72; Univ Tex, MA, 75, PhD(astron), 77. *Prof Exp:* RES ASSOC, DEPT PHYSICS & ASTRON, LA STATE UNIV, 77- *Mem:* Am Astron Soc; Royal Astron Soc. *Res:* Chemical composition of late-type stars to determine the effects of stellar and galactic chemical evolution on such objects. *Mailing Add:* 453 Baird Dr Baton Rouge LA 70808

LUCK, RUSSELL M, b Reading, Pa, May 11, 26; m 63; c 2. POLYMER CHEMISTRY, ORGANIC CHEMISTRY. *Educ:* Albright Col, BSc, 47; Bucknell Univ, MSc, 48. *Prof Exp:* Asst chem, Bucknell Univ, 47-48; asst prod mgr, Wyomissing Glazed Papers, Inc, 48-51; engr, Mat Eng Dept, 53-60, sr engr, Res & Develop Ctr, 60-71, FEL SCIENTIST, RES & DEVELOP CTR, WESTINGHOUSE ELEC CORP, 71- *Mem:* Am Chem Soc. *Res:* Organic and inorganic polymers for application as lubricants and electrical insulations with high temperature capabilities. *Mailing Add:* Westinghouse Elec Res & Develop Ctr Insul & Appl Chem Res Dept Pittsburgh PA 15235

LUCKE, JOHN BECKER, b New York, NY, Feb 26, 08; m 37; c 3. GEOLOGY. *Educ:* Princeton Univ, BS, 29, AM, 32, PhD(geol), 33. *Prof Exp:* Geologist, Torrey, Fralich & Simmons, Pa, 29; asst geol, Princeton Univ, 30-32; prof, John Marshall Col, 33-34; asst dist geologist, Tex Co, 34-35; asst soil surv, Soil Conserv Serv, USDA, 35-36; asst prof geol, Univ WVa, 36-40; assoc prof geol & head dept geol & geog, Univ Conn, 40-48, prof geol & head dept, 48-63; prof & chmn dept, 64-73, EMER PROF GEOL & CONSULT, GRAND VALLEY STATE COL, 73-, LECTR, 75- *Concurrent Pos:* Asst geologist, Sloan & Zook Co, Pa, 30 & State Geol Surv, WVa, 36-38; mem, Conn Geol & Natural Hist Surv Comn, 46-63, dir, 54-60; mem, Nat Geog-Woods Hole Oceanog Atlantis Exped, Mid-Atlantic Ridge, 48 & Nat Park Serv Katmai exped, 53; del, Int Geol Cong, Copenhagen, 60, Prague, 68, Montreal, 72, Sydney, 76 & Int Asn Quaternary Res Cong, Colo, 65. *Mem:* AAAS; fel Geol Soc Am; Am Asn Petrol Geol; Nat Asn Geol Teachers (vpres, 53). *Res:* Geomorphology and oceanography, especially marine shorelines; photogeology. *Mailing Add:* The Anchorage E-24 15 Pleasant St Harwich Port MA 02646

LUCKE, ROBERT LANCASTER, b Norfolk, Va, July 22, 45. ASTROPHYSICS. *Educ:* Johns Hopkins Univ, BA, 68, MA, 72, PhD(physics), 75. *Prof Exp:* Assoc res scientist physics, Johns Hopkins Univ, 75-76; Nat Res Coun fel, Goddard Space Flight Ctr, NASA, 76-78; ASST PROF PHYSICS & ASTRON, UNIV TOLEDO, OHIO, 79- *Res:* Far ultraviolet albedo of the moon; coronal line emission in supernova remnants; x-ray astronomy; astronomical instrumentation. *Mailing Add:* 10608 Ridge Dr Clinton MD 20735

LUCKE, WILLIAM E, b Grand Island, Nebr, July 31, 36; m 59; c 5. ANALYTICAL CHEMISTRY. *Educ:* Univ Nebr, BS, 58; Ohio State Univ, PhD(chem), 63. *Prof Exp:* Res chemist, Olympic Res Div, Rayonier Inc, 63-69; res assoc, Cincinnati Milling Mach Co, 69-71, supvr, Cimcool Customer Lab Serv, Cincinnati Milacron Inc, 71-74, SR ANAL CHEMIST, CIMCOOL DIV, CINCINNATI, MILACRON INC, 74- *Mem:* AAAS; Am Chem Soc. *Res:* Carbohydrate, cellulose and wood chemistry; analytical chemistry of industrial metal working products. *Mailing Add:* Cincinnati Milacron Inc PO Box 9013 Cincinnati OH 45209

LUCKEN, KARL ALLEN, b Portland, NDak, Apr 7, 37; m 60; c 3. CROP BREEDING. *Educ:* Concordia Col, Minn, BA, 59; Iowa State Univ, PhD(plant breeding), 64. *Prof Exp:* From asst prof to assoc prof, 64-74, PROF AGRON, NDAK STATE UNIV, 74- *Mem:* Am Soc Agron. *Res:* Breeding and development of hybrid wheat; genetics of extrachromosomal variability in wheat. *Mailing Add:* Dept of Agron NDak State Univ Fargo ND 58102

LUCKENBACH, THOMAS ALEXANDER, b Plains, Pa, Feb 26, 33; m 59; c 6. TIRE CORD TECHNOLOGY. *Educ:* Kings Col, Pa, BS, 54; Catholic Univ, PhD(phys chem), 58. *Prof Exp:* Sr chemist, Harris Res Labs, Inc, DC, 58-61; group leader, Toni Co Div, Gillette Corp, Ill, 61-64; res assoc, Huyck Felt Co, 64-65, asst mgr res, 65-66, res assoc, Huyck Res Ctr, 66-68, mgr chem & phys res, 68-73, mgr formex prods, Res & Develop, 73-74; tech mgr, 74-76, GROUP MGR, TIRE TEXTILE DEVELOP, B F GOODRICH TIRE CO, 76- *Mem:* Am Chem Soc; Int Soc Indust Fabric Mfrs; Sigma Xi. *Res:* Chemistry of human hair; synthetic fibers; chemical and physical testing of fibers and fabrics; paper making fabrics; textile resin treatments; textile adhesives; textile technology; plastics; fiberglass; tire cords and adhesives; rubber compounding; tire technology. *Mailing Add:* B F Goodrich Tire Co 500 S Main St Akron OH 44318

LUCKENBAUGH, RAYMOND WILSON, b Hanover, Pa, Dec 29, 21; m 47; c 2. AGRICULTURAL CHEMISTRY. *Educ:* Gettysburg Col, AB, 43; Univ Md, PhD(chem), 52. *Prof Exp:* Jr chemist org synthesis, Rohm and Hass Co, 47-48; agr chemist, 52-58, res scientist, 58-62, res assoc, 62-64, RES SUPVR, E I DU PONT DE NEMOURS & CO, INC, 64- *Mem:* Am Chem Soc; Weed Sci Soc Am. *Res:* Herbicidal ureas, carbamates, and uracils; diphenylethylene and uretidinedione fungicides; toxicity of agrichemicals. *Mailing Add:* Biochem Dept Exp Sta Bldg 324 E I du Pont de Nemours & Co Inc Wilmington DE 19898

LUCKENS, MARK MANFRED, b Kiev, Russia, Apr 7, 12; US citizen; m 43; c 2. PHARMACOLOGY, TOXICOLOGY. *Educ:* Columbia Univ, BS, 35; NY Univ, MS, 50; Univ Conn, PhD(pharmacol, toxicol), 63; Polytech Inst New York, MSES, 72; Am Bd Indust Hyg, dipl. *Prof Exp:* Jr chemist, Wilkow Food Prod, 28-33, chemist, 33-36; chief chemist, Technichem Labs, 37-41; inspector, Chem Warfare Serv, 41-43; dir, Emmet Tech Assocs, 48-54; toxicologist, Conn State Dept Health, 54-61; from asst prof to assoc prof toxicol & pharmacol, Col Pharm, Univ Ky, 61-77, dir, Inst Environ Toxicol & Occup Hyg, 62-77, mem fac & co-dir interdisciplinary grad prog toxicol, 73-77; RETIRED. *Concurrent Pos:* Consult, Ky State Dept Human Resources, 61-, Lexington-Fayette County Dept of Health, Ky Poison Info & Environ Health Control Prog, 61-, Lab Serv, Childrens's Hosp, Louisville, Ky, 63-, Spindletop Res Ctr, 65- & Nat Inst Occup Health & Safety, 77; Fulbright travel grant, 65-66; award, Partners- in-the-Americas, 65-66; mem, adv comt pesticides, Ky Dept Agr, 65-; mem exec bd, Am Asn Poison Control Ctrs; vis prof, Polytech Inst of Guayaquil; vis dir, Oceanog Inst Ecuador & Environ Protection Inst Ecuador; mem nat comt occup health & safety, Am Inst Chemists; dir, Hemispheric Prog Poison Info & Control; pvt pract, 77- *Mem:* Fel AAAS; fel Am Inst Chem; fel Am Acad Indust Hyg; fel Am Acad Forensic Sci; Am Chem Soc. *Res:* Toxicodynamics; comparative toxicology and pharmacology; environmental, occupational, clinical, analytical, food and forensic toxicology; chemical pathology; drug action in hibernation; biorhythms; effects of psychosocial parameters on toxicity and pharmacologic action. *Mailing Add:* 664 Sheridan Dr Lexington KY 40503

LUCKERT, H(ANS) J(OACHIM), b Ger, Aug 26, 05; nat Can; m 53; c 1. AERODYNAMICS, APPLIED MATHEMATICS. *Educ:* Harvard Univ, AM, 29; Univ Berlin, Dr Phil, 33. *Prof Exp:* Asst to prof math, Mining Acad Freiberg, Ger, 29-34; aerodynamicist, Henschel Aircraft Co, 35-37; sr group leader aerodyn, Arado Aircraft Co, 37-45; scientist transl & aero res, Brit Ministry Supply, 45-47; consult aerodyn, Control Comn for Ger, 47-52; engr, Canadair, Ltd, 52-54, design specialist, 54-57, chief tech sect, Missiles & Systs Div, 57-63, sect chief missiles & space res, 63-64, staff scientist res & develop, 64-65; chief aerodynamicist, Space Res Inst, McGill Univ, 65-68; chief aerodynamicist, Space Res Inst, Inc, 68-69, chief aerodynamicist, Space Res Corp, 69-80; CONSULT, POTTON TECH INDUST INC, 80- *Concurrent Pos:* Chmn, Nat Res Coun Res Coord Group, Upper Atmosphere Res Vehicles, 64-65, mem assoc comt aerodyn, 63-66, mem assoc comt space res, 64-67; hon res assoc, McGill Univ, 67- *Mem:* Assoc fel Am Inst Aeronaut & Astronaut; fel Can Aeronaut & Space Inst; Ger Soc Aeronaut & Astronaut. *Res:* Aerodynamics and physics; astronautics; aircraft and missiles. *Mailing Add:* 197 - 58th Ave Laval des Rapides PQ H7V 2A5 Can

LUCKETT, WINTER PATRICK, b Atlanta, Ga, Mar 23, 37. ANATOMY, EMBRYOLOGY. *Educ:* Univ Mo, AB, 61, MA, 63; Univ Wis-Madison, PhD(anat), 67. *Prof Exp:* Instr, Col Physicians & Surgeons, Columbia Univ, 68-69, asst prof anat, 69-75; ASSOC PROF ANAT, SCH MED, CREIGHTON UNIV, 75- *Mem:* AAAS; Am Asn Anat; Soc Study Reproduction; Int Primatol Soc. *Res:* Comparative morphogenesis of the placenta and fetal membranes; comparative structure of the ovary; endocrinology of reproduction; evolution of primates. *Mailing Add:* Dept of Anat Sch Med Creighton Univ Omaha NE 68178

LUCKEY, EGBERT HUGH, b Jackson, Tenn, Jan 1, 20; m 42, 70; c 4. INTERNAL MEDICINE. *Educ:* Union Univ, Tenn, BS, 41; Vanderbilt Univ, MD, 44. *Hon Degrees:* ScD, Union Univ, Tenn, 54. *Prof Exp:* Intern med, New York Hosp, 44-45, asst resident, 45-46, asst resident cardiol, 48-49; from instr to assoc prof med, Med Col, 49-57, chmn dept, 57-66, dean med col & assoc dean grad sch, 54-57, vpres med affairs, 66-77, PROF MED, CORNELL UNIV, 57-, PRES, NEW YORK HOSP-CORNELL MED CTR, 66- *Concurrent Pos:* Asst vis physician & asst dir, Second Med Div, Bellevue Hosp Ctr, Cornell Univ, 49-50, dir, 50-54, vis physician, 50-54, vpres med bd, 52-54, secy-treas exec comt med bd, 53-54; from asst attend physician to attend physician, New York Hosp, 52-57, physician-in-chief, 57-66; consult, US Vet Admin, New York, 54, mem dean's comt, 54-57, mem spec adv group, 64-69; sci consult, Sloan-Kettering Inst, 54-57; mem comt med, W K Kellogg Found, 55-61; trustee, Cornell Univ, 57-62 & Vanderbilt Univ, 62-; med dir, Russell Sage Inst Path, 58-67, mem bd dirs, 58-; mem bd dirs, Josiah Mach Jr Found, 58-; mem heart spec proj comt, NIH, 63-67; vpres Soc New York Hosp, 66- *Mem:* Asn Acad Health Ctrs; Harvey Soc; master Am Col Physicians; Asn Am Physicians; Am Heart Asn. *Mailing Add:* 449 E 68th St New York NY 10021

LUCKEY, GEORGE WILLIAM, b Dayton, Ohio, Apr 17, 25; m 58; c 3. PHYSICAL CHEMISTRY. *Educ:* Oberlin Col, BA, 47; Rochester Univ, PhD(chem), 50. *Prof Exp:* Mem staff, Photog Theory Dept, 50-56, Appl Photog Div, 56-60 & Spec Res Dept, 61-77, RES FEL & LAB HEAD, SPEC RES LAB, EASTMAN KODAK CO, 77- *Mem:* Am Chem Soc; Am Phys Soc; Royal Soc Chem; Soc Photog Scientists & Engrs; Electrochem Soc. *Res:* Photochemistry; photographic theory; luminescence; processing chemistry; photographic and radiographic systems. *Mailing Add:* 240 Weymouth Dr Rochester NY 14625

LUCKEY, PAUL DAVID, JR, b Pittsburgh, Pa, May 18, 28; m 55; c 1. PHYSICS. *Educ:* Carnegie Inst Technol, BS, 49; Cornell Univ, PhD(physics), 54. *Prof Exp:* Res assoc physics, Cornell Univ, 53-56; mem sci res staff, 56-70, SR RES SCIENTIST PHYSICS, MASS INST TECHNOL, 70- *Mem:* Am Phys Soc. *Res:* Meson physics; photoproduction of Pi mesons; electron synchrotrons. *Mailing Add:* Dept of Physics Mass Inst of Technol Cambridge MA 02139

LUCKEY, THOMAS DONNELL, b Casper, Wyo, May 15, 19; m 43; c 3. BIOCHEMISTRY, NUTRITION. *Educ:* Colo Agr Col, BS, 41; Univ Wis, MS, 44, PhD(biochem), 46. *Prof Exp:* Asst, Agr & Mech Col, Tex, 41-42 & Univ Wis, 42-46; asst res prof biochem, Univ Notre Dame, 46-54; PROF BIOCHEM, SCH MED, UNIV MO-COLUMBIA, 54- *Concurrent Pos:* NSF traveling fel, Paris Nutrit Cong, 57; Univ Mo fel, Stockholm Microbiol Cong, 58; Commonwealth res fel, 61-62; Am Inst Nutrit traveling fel, Cong, 63; dir, WCent States Biochem Conf, 64-; moderator symp gnotobiol, Int Meeting Microbiol, Moscow, 66; mem subcomt interaction of infection & nutrit, Nat Acad Sci, 72-74; nutrit consult, NASA Johnson Space Ctr, Houston; consult, McDonnell Aircraft Corp, Mygrodol Prod Inc & Gen Elec Co. *Mem:* AAAS; Am Chem Soc; Soc Exp Biol & Med; Am Soc Microbiol; Am Inst Nutrit. *Res:* Nutrition and metabolism of germ-free vertebrates; folic acid and related compounds in chick nutrition; comparative nutrition; modes of action of antibiotics; gnotobiology; thymic hormones. *Mailing Add:* Dept of Biochem Univ of Mo Sch of Med Columbia MO 65201

LUCKHAM, DAVID COMPTOM, b Kingston, Jamaica, Sept 7, 36. COMPUTER SCIENCE. *Educ:* Univ London, BSc, 56, MSc, 57; Mass Inst Technol, PhD(math logic), 63. *Prof Exp:* Res assoc comput sci, Mass Inst Technol, 63-65; lectr math, Univ Manchester, 65-68; res assoc comput sci, Stanford Univ, 68-70; from asst prof to assoc prof, Univ Calif, Los Angeles, 70-72; res comput scientist, 72-76, sr res assoc, 76-78, ADJ PROF ELEC ENG, STANFORD UNIV, 78- *Concurrent Pos:* Consult, Bolt, Beranek & Newman Inc, 63-65, Jet Propulsion Lab, 71- & Systs Control Inc, 78-; Sci Coun res grant, Univ Manchester, 65-68; lectr, Ctr Comput & Automation, Imp Col, Univ London, 67-68; Hayes sr fel, Harvard Univ, 76-77. *Mem:* Am Math Soc; Asn Comput Mach; Asn Symbolic Logic. *Res:* Theory of computation; automated proof procedures and applications to computer-aided programming, verification of programs; semantics of programming languages; parallel programs; microprocessor systems; artificial intelligence. *Mailing Add:* Dept of Comput Sci Stanford Univ Stanford CA 94305

LUCKMANN, WILLIAM HENRY, b Cape Girardeau, Mo, Jan 15, 26; m 49; c 5. ENTOMOLOGY. *Educ:* Univ Mo, BS, 49; Univ Ill, MS, 51, PhD, 56. *Prof Exp:* Asst entomologist, State Natural Hist Surv, Ill, 51-53 & tech develop, Shell Chem Corp, Colo, 53-54; assoc entomologist, 54-59, entomologist, 59-65, ENTOMOLOGIST & HEAD SECT ECON ENTOM, STATE NATURAL HIST SURV, ILL, 65-; PROF & HEAD, OFF AGR ENTOM, COL AGR, UNIV ILL, 65- *Mem:* Entom Soc Am. *Res:* Ecology; biology; applied control. *Mailing Add:* 172 Natural Resources Bldg State Natural Hist Surv Urbana IL 61803

LUCKOCK, ARLENE SUZANNE, b Oakland, Calif, Nov 23, 48; m 76; c 2. NEUROPHYSIOLOGY, ENDOCRINOLOGY. *Educ:* Univ Calif, Berkeley, BA, 69, PhD(physiol), 74. *Prof Exp:* Fel, Dept Psychiat, Med Sch, Stanford Univ, 74-76 & Dept Genetics, 76-78; instr physiol, West Valley Col, Saratoga, Calif, 78-79; ASST PROF PHYSIOL, PALMER COL CHIROPRACTIC-W, 79- *Res:* Effects of thyroid hormones on mammalian brain development; genetic differences in testosterone synthesis in two strains of mice; genetic polymorphhisms in testosterone-estradiol binding globulin in human populations. *Mailing Add:* Palmer Col Chiropractic W 1095 Dunford Way Sunnyvale CA 94080

LUCKRING, R(ICHARD) M(ICHAEL), b Canton, Ohio, Feb 3, 17; m 54; c 6. TECHNICAL MANAGEMENT. *Educ:* Heidelberg Col, BS, 40; Lehigh Univ, BSChE, 42. *Prof Exp:* Field engr, Eng Dept, 42-52, res engr, Pigments Dept, 52-53, res supvr, 53-55, res mgr, 55-71, tech mgr inorg fibers, 71-75, environ mgr, 75-78, PLANNING ASSOC, CHEM, DYES, & PIGMENTS DEPT, E I DU PONT DE NEMOURS & CO, 78- *Mem:* Am Chem Soc; Am Inst Chem Engrs. *Res:* Process development; extractive metallurgy; refractory metals; titanate and titanium dioxide products and processes. *Mailing Add:* 108 Meriden Dr Canterbury Hills Hockessin DE 19707

LUCKY, GEORGE W(ILLIAM), b Dallas, Tex, Nov 7, 23; m 48; c 1. ELECTRICAL ENGINEERING. *Educ:* Okla State Univ, BSEE, 44, MS, 60, PhD(eng), 65. *Prof Exp:* Asst engr, Southwestern Bell Tel Co, 46-52, sr engr, 52-56; asst prof, Okla State Univ, 56-64; from asst prof to assoc prof, 64-69, PROF ELEC ENG, N MEX STATE UNIV, 69- *Concurrent Pos:* Consult, J B Payne Assocs, Inc, 60- *Mem:* Am Soc Eng Educ; Inst Elec & Electronics Engrs. *Res:* Computer characterization of electric networks; network synthesis. *Mailing Add:* Dept of Elec Eng NMex State Univ Las Cruces NM 88003

LUCKY, ROBERT W, b Pittsburgh, Pa, Jan 9, 36; m 61; c 2. ELECTRICAL ENGINEERING. *Educ:* Purdue Univ, BSEE, 57, MSEE, 59, PhD(elec eng), 61. *Prof Exp:* Mem tech staff, Holmdel, NJ, 61-64, supvr signal theory group, 64-65, head data theory dept, 65-78, asst dir, 78-80, DIR ELECTRONIC & COMPUT SYSTS RES LAB, BELL LABS, 78- *Mem:* Nat Acad Eng; Inst Elec & Electronics Engrs (vpres, 78, exec vpres, 81). *Res:* Communication theory; information theory; data transmission. *Mailing Add:* Rm 7B-202 Bell Labs Murray Hill NJ 07974

LUCOVSKY, GERALD, b New York, NY, Feb 28, 35; m 57; c 5. SOLID STATE PHYSICS. *Educ:* Univ Rochester, BS, 56, MA, 58; Temple Univ, PhD(physics), 60. *Prof Exp:* Mem staff solid state physics, Philco Corp, Pa, 58-65; sr scientist, Xerox Corp, 65-67; assoc prof eng, Case Western Reserve Univ, 67-68; mgr, Photoconductor Res Br, Xerox Corp, 68-69, solid state res br, 69-70, solid state sci br, Palo Alto Res Ctr, 70-73, assoc lab mgr, Gen Sci Lab, 73-74, sr res fel, Gen Sci Lab, Palo Alto Res Ctr, 74-80; UNIV PROF PHYSICS, NC STATE UNIV, RALEIGH, 80- *Mem:* Fel Am Phys Soc. *Res:* Optical properties of solids; lattice dynamics; amorphous semiconductors. *Mailing Add:* Dept Physics 104 Cox Hall NC State Univ Raleigh NC 27650

LUCY, ROBERT F(REDERICK), physics, see previous edition

LUDDEN, GERALD D, b Quincy, Ill, Sept 6, 37; m 61; c 3. MATHEMATICS. *Educ:* St Ambrose Col, BA, 59; Univ Notre Dame, MS, 61, PhD(math), 66. *Prof Exp:* Lectr math, Ind Univ, 65-66; from asst prof to assoc prof, 66-77, PROF MATH, MICH STATE UNIV, 77- *Mem:* Math Asn Am; Am Math Soc; Tensor Soc. *Res:* Hypersurfaces of manifolds with an f-structure; submanifolds of real and complex space forms. *Mailing Add:* Dept of Math Mich State Univ East Lansing MI 48824

LUDDEN, PAUL W, b Omaha, Nebr, Nov 7, 50; m 74. BIOCHEMISTRY. *Educ:* Univ Nebr, Lincoln, BS, 72; Univ Wis-Madison, PhD(biochem), 77. *Prof Exp:* Res asst, Univ Wis-Madison, 72-77; res assoc, Mich State Univ, 77-78; asst prof biochem & asst biochemist, Univ Calif, Riverside, 78-81; ASST PROF BIOCHEM, UNIV WIS-MADISON, 81- *Concurrent Pos:* Fel, Rockefeller Found, 77-78. *Mem:* Am Chem Soc; Am Soc Plant Physiol; Am Soc Microbiol. *Res:* Plant biochemistry; nitrogen metabolism in plants and bacteria; carbon monoxide oxidation. *Mailing Add:* Dept Biochem Univ Wis Madison WI 53706

LUDDEN, THOMAS MARCELLUS, b Kansas City, Mo, Jan 16, 46; m 67; c 2. BIOPHARMACEUTICS, DRUG METABOLISM. *Educ:* Univ Mo-Kansas City, BS, 69, PhD(pharmacol), 73. *Prof Exp:* Vis res assoc pharmaceut, Ohio State Univ, 74-75; asst prof, 75-80, ASSOC PROF PHARMACOL, UNIV TEX, AUSTIN, 80-; ASSOC PROF PHARMACOL, UNIV TEX HEALTH SCI CTR, SAN ANTONIO, 81- *Concurrent Pos:* Tech consult, Audie Murphy Vet Hosp, San Antonio, 77-; asst prof pharmacol, Univ Tex Health Sci Ctr, San Antonio, 76-81. *Mem:* Am Pharmaceut Asn; Acad Pharmaceut Sci; Am Asn Cols Pharm; Sigma Xi; NY Acad Sci. *Res:* Applied pharmacokinetics and new drug development. *Mailing Add:* 7703 Floyd Curl Dr San Antonio TX 78284

LUDEKE, CARL ARTHUR, b Cincinnati, Ohio, Sept 26, 14. PHYSICS, OCEANOGRAPHY. *Educ:* Univ Cincinnati, AB, 35, PhD(physics), 38. *Prof Exp:* Instr math, John Carroll Univ, 38-40; instr, Univ Cincinnati, 40-43, from asst prof to assoc prof mech, 42-54, prof physics, 54-72; prof, Phys Oceanog Lab, NY Inst Technol at Nova Univ, 72-75, sr scientist, 75-79; RETIRED. *Concurrent Pos:* Consult, Gen Elec Co, 56-70. *Mem:* Int Asn Analog Comput. *Res:* Nonlinear mechanics; vibration analysis; shock mounts; mathematical physics; energy from the sun, sea and atmosphere. *Mailing Add:* PO Box 21682 Ft Lauderdale FL 33335

LUDEKE, RUDOLF, b Hannover, Ger, May 6, 37; m 64; c 2. SOLID STATE PHYSICS, MATERIAL SCIENCE. *Educ:* Univ Cincinnati, BS, 61; Harvard Univ, MA, 62, PhD(appl physics), 68. *Prof Exp:* RES STAFF MEM, T J WATSON RES CTR, IBM CORP, 68- *Concurrent Pos:* Vis scientist, Max Planck Inst, Stuttgart, Ger, 77-78; Alexander Von Humboldt Found fel, 77. *Mem:* Am Phys Soc; Sigma Xi. *Res:* Semiconductor physics; surface and interface physics; thin film technology. *Mailing Add:* T J Watson Res Ctr PO Box 218 Yorktown Heights NY 10598

LUDEL, JACQUELINE, b Boston, Mass, Mar 17, 45. BIOPSYCHOLOGY. *Educ:* Queens Col, NY, BA, 66; Ind Univ, PhD(psychol), 71. *Prof Exp:* Asst prof psychol, Jacksonville Univ, 71-73 & Stockton State Col, 73-76; ASSOC PROF BIOL & PSYCHOL, GUILFORD COL, 76- *Concurrent Pos:* Assoc instr, Ind Univ, 67-71; Kenan grant, Guilford Col, 77-; Danforth Assoc; trustee, Marine Mammal Stranding Ctr. *Mem:* AAAS. *Res:* Sensory anatomy and physiology; stranded and beached cetaceans. *Mailing Add:* Depts of Biol & Psychol Guilford Col Greensboro NC 27410

LUDEMA, KENNETH C, b Dorr, Mich, Apr 30, 28; m 55; c 5. MECHANICAL ENGINEERING, SURFACE PHYSICS. *Educ:* Calvin Col, BS, 55; Univ Mich, BS, 55, MS, 56, PhD(mech eng), 63; Cambridge Univ, PhD(physics), 65. *Prof Exp:* Instr mech eng, Univ Mich, 55-62; Ford Found & Univ Mich Inst Sci & Technol fac develop grant, Cambridge Univ, 62-64; from asst prof to assoc prof, 64-72, PROF MECH ENG, UNIV MICH, ANN ARBOR, 72- *Mem:* Am Soc Mech Engrs; Am Soc Testing & Mat. *Res:* Sliding friction and wear behavior of solids, steels, plastics and rubbers; fundamental adhesion mechanisms between dissimilar materials; skid resistance properties of tires and roads. *Mailing Add:* Dept of Mech Eng Univ of Mich Ann Arbor MI 48109

LUDEMANN, CARL ARNOLD, b Brooklyn, NY, June 21, 34; m 56; c 2. NUCLEAR PHYSICS. *Educ:* Brooklyn Col, BS, 56; Univ Md, PhD(nuclear physics, elec eng), 64. *Prof Exp:* Res assoc physics, Univ Md, 64-65; vis scientist, 64-65, PHYSICIST, ELECTRONUCLEAR DIV, OAK RIDGE NAT LAB, 65- *Mem:* Am Phys Soc; Am Asn Physics Teachers. *Res:* Neutron threshold measurements; gamma ray spectroscopy; angular correlation and nuclear reaction mechanism; nuclear structure studies. *Mailing Add:* Physics Div Oak Ridge Nat Lab Bldg 6000 X10 Nuclear Lab Oak Ridge TN 37830

LUDEMANN, WESLEY DALE, b Mt Pleasant, Iowa, Aug 14, 26. METALLURGY. *Educ:* Univ Calif, Berkeley, AB, 49, BS, 57, MS, 59, PhD(metall), 69. *Prof Exp:* Metallurgist, US Bur Mines, Reno, Nev, 63-64; METALLURGIST, LAWRENCE LIVERMORE LAB, 64- *Res:* Investigating metallic corrosion in ground waters; developing a model to predict corrosion rates of metals in geologic media; consulting on selection of materials to use for radioactive waste storage canisters. *Mailing Add:* Lawrence Livermore Lab PO Box 808 Livermore CA 94550

LUDERS, RICHARD CHRISTIAN, b Staten Island, NY, July 23, 34; m 57; c 2. ANALYTICAL CHEMISTRY. *Educ:* Wagner Col, BS, 56. *Prof Exp:* Chemist, S B Penick & Co, 56-57; chemist, Ciba Pharmaceut Co, 58-66, group supvr anal res, 66-67, supvr, 67-70, head bioanal studies, Drug Metab Sect, 70-72, SR CHEMIST, DRUG METAB DIV, CIBA-GEIGY CORP, 72- *Mem:* Am Chem Soc. *Res:* Gas liquid chromatographic analysis and methods development for pharmaceutical compounds, preparations and raw materials; blood level determinations of pharmaceutical compounds. *Mailing Add:* RD 2 Katonah NY 10536

LUDFORD, GEOFFREY STUART STEPHEN, b London, Eng, Feb 2, 28; nat US; m 50; c 2. APPLIED MATHEMATICS. *Educ:* Cambridge Univ, BA, 48, MA & PhD(math), 52, ScD(math), 62. *Prof Exp:* Asst appl math, Harvard Univ, 50-51; from asst prof to assoc prof math, Univ Md, 51-59, prof aeronaut engr, 59-60; prof appl math, Brown Univ, 60-61; PROF APPL MATH, CORNELL UNIV, 61- *Concurrent Pos:* Guggenheim fel, Harvard Univ, 57-58; NSF sr fel, Univ Paris, 68-69; Fulbright-Hays sr scholar & vis prof, Univ Queensland, 76; vis prof, Math Res Ctr, Wis, 77; sr vis fel, UK Sci Res Coun, Cambridge Univ & fel, Churchill Col, 81; Alexander von Humboldt US sr scientist award, 81-82. *Mem:* Am Math Soc; Soc Indust & Appl Math; Ger Soc Appl Math & Mech; Soc Eng Sci; Soc Natural Philos. *Res:* Fluid mechanics; magneto-hydrodynamics; differential equations; mathematical theory of combustion. *Mailing Add:* Dept of Theoret & Appl Math Cornell Univ Ithaca NY 14853

LUDIN, ROGER LOUIS, b Jersey City, NJ, June 13, 44; m 66; c 2. NUCLEAR PHYSICS. *Educ:* Brown Univ, ScB, 66; Worcester Polytech Inst, MS, 68, PhD(physics), 69. *Prof Exp:* Fel, Worcester Polytech Inst, 69-71; PROF PHYSICS, BURLINGTON COUNTY COL, 71- *Mem:* AAAS; Am Phys Soc; Am Asn Physics Teachers. *Res:* Neutron-deuteron scattering. *Mailing Add:* Dept of Physics Burlington County Col Pemberton NJ 08068

LUDINGTON, ELWYN WHIT, astronomy, see previous edition

LUDINGTON, MARTIN A, b Detroit, Mich, Mar 7, 43; m 64; c 2. NUCLEAR PHYSICS. *Educ:* Albion Col, AB, 64; Univ Mich, MS, 65, PhD(physics), 69. *Prof Exp:* ASSOC PROF PHYSICS, ALBION COL, 69-, CHMN DEPT, 80- *Mem:* Am Phys Soc; Am Asn Physics Teachers. *Res:* Nuclear spectroscopy; prompt-gamma activation analysis. *Mailing Add:* Dept of Physics Albion Col Albion MI 49224

LUDINGTON, STEPHEN DEAN, b Omaha, Nebr, Apr 13, 44. GEOCHEMISTRY. *Educ:* Stanford Univ, BS, 67; Univ Colo, MS, 69, PhD(geol), 74. *Prof Exp:* Res assoc geochem, 74-75, GEOLOGIST, US GEOL SURV, 75- *Mem:* Mineral Soc Am; Am Geophys Union. *Res:* Role of fluorine and chlorine in petrology, with emphasis on micas; thermodynamics of magmas. *Mailing Add:* Mail Stop 930 US Geol Surv Denver CO 80225

LUDKE, JAMES LARRY, b Vicksburg, Miss, Jan 11, 42; m 65. ENVIRONMENTAL BIOLOGY. *Educ:* Millsaps Col, 64; Miss State Univ, MS, 67, PhD(physiol), 70. *Prof Exp:* Res asst physiol, Miss State Univ, 70-71; RES PHYSIOLOGIST, PATUXENT WILDLIFE RES CTR, US FISH & WILDLIFE SERV, 71- *Mem:* Am Soc Zoologists; Sigma Xi; AAAS. *Res:* Study of the chronic or lethal effects of pollutants on nontarget species; emphasis on fate of chemicals, diagnostic methods and chemical interactions. *Mailing Add:* Patuxent Wildlife Res Ctr US Fish & Wildlife Serv Laurel MD 20811

LUDLAM, WILLIAM MYRTON, b Teaneck, NJ, Mar 31, 31; m 54; c 3. OPTOMETRY, PHYSIOLOGICAL OPTICS. *Educ:* Columbia Univ, BS, 53, MS, 54; Mass Col Optom, OD, 63. *Prof Exp:* Dir, Vision Res Lab, Optom Ctr NY, 61-73; assoc prof physiol optics & optom, Col Optom, State Univ NY, 71-73; assoc prof, 74-80, PROF PHYSIOL OPTICS & OPTOM, COL OPTOM, PAC UNIV, 80- *Concurrent Pos:* Res grants, Am Optom Found, 55-56, NY Acad Optom, 57, Optom Ctr Res Fund, 60-61 & NIH, 63-74. *Mem:* Fel AAAS; fel Am Acad Optom; Optical Soc Am; fel NY Acad Sci. *Res:* Ocular dioptric components; pathophysiology of strabismus and its remediation; ametropia and its etiology; vision and learning. *Mailing Add:* Col of Optom Pac Univ Forest Grove OR 97116

LUDLOW, CHRISTY L, b Montreal, Que, June 7, 44; m 68. SPEECH PATHOLOGY, AUDIOLOGY. *Educ:* McGill Univ, BSc, 65, MSc, 67; NY Univ, PhD(psycholing, speech path), 73. *Prof Exp:* Res asst, McGill Univ, 66-67; res speech pathologist, Med Ctr, NY Univ, 67-70, W A Anderson fel, 70-72; vis lectr speech & hearing sci, Univ Md, 73-74; proj mgr, Am Speech & Hearing Asn, 73-74; RES SPEECH PATHOLOGIST, NAT INST NEUROL & COMMUN DIS & STROKE, 74- *Concurrent Pos:* Liason rep, AAAS, 77-81; ed consult, J Speech & Hearing Dis, 77- & J Speech & Hearing Res, 77- *Honors & Awards:* Dir Award, NIH, 77. *Mem:* Int Neuropsychol Soc; Acoust Soc Am; Soc Neurosci; AAAS; Asn Res Otolaryngol. *Res:* Speech science; neurolinguistics; aphasia; developmental language disorders; neuropharmacology; vocal pathologies; neurological disorders affecting speech and language functioning. *Mailing Add:* Commun Dis Prog Fed Bldg Rm 1C-13 Bethesda MD 20014

LUDLUM, DAVID BLODGETT, b Brooklyn, NY, Sept 30, 29; m 52; c 2. PHARMACOLOGY. *Educ:* Cornell Univ, BA, 51; Univ Wis-Madison, PhD(chem), 54; NY Univ, MD, 62. *Prof Exp:* Res chemist, E I du Pont de Nemours & Co, Inc, Del, 54-58; intern, 3rd & 4th Med Divs, Bellevue Hosp, 62-63; asst prof pharmacol & Am Cancer Soc fac res assoc, Sch Med, Yale Univ, 63-68; from assoc prof to prof pharmacol, Sch Med, Univ Md, Baltimore City, 70-76; chmn dept, 76-80, PROF PHARMACOL, ALBANY MED COL, 76-, PROF MED, 80- *Concurrent Pos:* Markle scholar acad med, Yale Univ & Univ Md, 67-72; Nat Inst Gen Med Sci career develop award, Yale Univ, 68; assoc ed, Cancer Res, 80- *Mem:* Am Chem Soc; Am Soc Pharmacol & Exp Therapeut; Am Soc Biol Chem; Am Asn Cancer Res; Am Soc Clin Pharmacol & Therapeut. *Res:* Pharmacology of untineoplastic agents; cancer chemotherapy; mutagenesis and carcinogenesis; molecular and clinical pharmacology. *Mailing Add:* Dept Med Albany Med Col Albany NY 12208

LUDLUM, JOHN CHARLES, b Chevy Chase, Md, Feb 2, 13; m 40. GEOLOGY. *Educ:* Lafayette Col, BS, 35; Cornell Univ, MS, 39, PhD(struct geol), 42. *Prof Exp:* Mem staff, Socony Vacuum Oil Co, 35-37 & Amerada Petrol Corp, 37; from asst instr to instr geol, Cornell Univ, 37-42; from asst prof to prof, 46-72, dir ctr resource develop, 62-63, dir off res & develop, Appalachian Ctr, 63-66, from asst dean to dean grad sch, 66-72, EMER

PROF GEOL, WVA UNIV, 72- *Concurrent Pos:* Consult, 46-62; coop econ geologist, State Geol Surv, 46- *Mem:* Fel Geol Soc Am; Soc Econ Geol; Am Asn Petrol Geol; Am Inst Mining, Metall & Petrol Eng. *Res:* Structural and economic geology of West Virginia; natural and human resources research applied toward improvement of the economy and life in West Virginia and the Appalachian highlands. *Mailing Add:* 612 Callen Ave Morgantown WV 26505

LUDLUM, KENNETH HILLS, b Albany, NY, Nov 16, 29; m 53; c 4. PHYSICAL CHEMISTRY. *Educ:* Col Educ Albany, BA, 51, MA, 52; Rensselaer Polytech Inst, PhD(phys chem), 61. *Prof Exp:* Chemist, Beacon Res Lab, 61-62, sr chemist, 62-65, res chemist, 65-73, sr res chemist, 73-80, RES ASSOC, TEXACO INC, 80- *Mem:* Am Chem Soc; Catalysis Soc. *Res:* Reaction kinetics; air pollution studies and related environmental science; catalysis and surface chemistry. *Mailing Add:* Texaco Res Ctr PO Box 509 Beacon NY 12508

LUDMAN, ALLAN, b Brooklyn, NY, Mar 7, 43. GEOLOGY, PETROLOGY. *Educ:* Brooklyn Col, BS, 63; Ind Univ, Bloomington, AM, 65; Univ Pa, PhD(geol), 69. *Prof Exp:* Asst prof geol, Smith Col, 69-75; ASST PROF EARTH & ENVIRON SCI, QUEENS COL, NY, 75- *Concurrent Pos:* Field geologist, Maine Geol Surv, 66- *Mem:* Geol Soc Am; Mineral Soc Am. *Res:* Regional geologic mapping in central and eastern Maine; low-temperature metamorphism of pelitic and calcareous rocks; tectonic evolution of northeastern New England. *Mailing Add:* Dept of Earth & Environ Sci Queens Col Flushing NY 11300

LUDMAN, JACQUES ERNEST, b Chicago, Ill, Nov 26, 34; m 70; c 1. SOLID STATE PHYSICS. *Educ:* Middlebury Col, BA, 56; Northeastern Univ, PhD(solid state physics), 73. *Prof Exp:* Res physicist, 59-75, CHIEF, OPTICAL PROCESSING SECT, AIR FORCE CAMBRIDGE RES LAB, 75- *Res:* Injection laser development; radiation damage effects on semiconductor devices; infrared sensor physics. *Mailing Add:* Hanscom AFB RADC ESD Bedford MA 01731

LUDOVICI, PETER PAUL, b Pittsburgh, Pa, Aug 9, 20; m 45; c 5. BACTERIOLOGY. *Educ:* Washington & Jefferson Col, BS, 42; Univ Pittsburgh, MS, 49, PhD(bact), 51. *Prof Exp:* Res bacteriologist immunol, West Penn Hosp, 49-51; res assoc, Univ Pittsburgh, 51; res assoc obstet & gynec, Univ Mich, 51-54; instr, 54-56, asst prof, 56-63, microbiol, obstet & gynec, 63-64, microbiol & cent tissue cult facilities, 64-65; assoc prof, 65-69, PROF MICROBIOL, UNIV ARIZ, 69- *Mem:* AAAS; Am Soc Microbiol; Tissue Cult Asn; Soc Exp Biol & Med. *Res:* Tissue culture; cancer; virology; cell transformations. *Mailing Add:* 5425 E Rosewood Ave Tucson AZ 85721

LUDOWIEG, JULIO, b Trujillo, Peru, Feb 10, 24; US citizen; m 53; c 2. BIOCHEMISTRY. *Educ:* San Marcos Univ, Lima, BS, 49; Univ Chicago, PhD(biochem), 60. *Prof Exp:* Asst biochem, Univ Chicago, 51-60; res biochemist, 60-77, RES ASSOC MED CTR, UNIV CALIF, SAN FRANCISCO, 77- *Concurrent Pos:* Res grants, Sch Med, Univ Calif, San Francisco, 61-65; Arthritis Found grants, 63 & 64; prin investr, USPHS Grants, 65-72. *Mem:* AAAS; Am Chem Soc; Fedn Am Soc Exp Biol. *Res:* Biochemical research in connective tissue involving acid mucopolysaccharides and proteins; asymmetric behavior of enzymes, their specificity and mechanism of action. *Mailing Add:* Dept of Orthop Surg Univ of Calif Med Ctr San Francisco CA 94122

LUDUENA, RICHARD FROILAN, b San Francisco, Calif, Feb 9, 46; m 81. BIOCHEMISTRY. *Educ:* Harvard Univ, BA, 67; Stanford Univ, PhD(biol), 73. *Prof Exp:* Fel pharmacol, Sch Med, Stanford Univ, 73-75, fel genetics, 75-76; ASST PROF BIOCHEM, UNIV TEX HEALTH SCI CTR, SAN ANTONIO, 76- *Concurrent Pos:* Jane Coffin Childs Mem Fund Med Res fel, 73-75. *Mem:* Am Soc Cell Biol; Int Soc Neurochem. *Res:* Regulation of microtubule assembly; structure and evolution of tubulin; pharmacology of microtubule proteins. *Mailing Add:* Dept of Biochem Univ of Tex Health Sci Ctr San Antonio TX 78284

LUDVIK, GEORGE FRANKLIN, entomology, pesticide benefits, see previous edition

LUDWICK, ADRIANE GURAK, b Passaic, NJ, June 16, 41; m 68; c 2. ORGANIC CHEMISTRY. *Educ:* Rutgers Univ, New Brunswick, AB, 63; Univ Ill, Urbana, MS, 65, PhD(chem), 67. *Prof Exp:* Asst prof chem, Tuskegee Inst, 67-68; vis asst prof & res assoc, Univ Ill, Urbana, 68-69; from asst prof to assoc prof, 69-77, PROF CHEM, TUSKEGEE INST, 77- *Concurrent Pos:* Res assoc, Environ Sci Div, Oak Ridge Nat Lab, 74 & Chem Div, Lawrence Livermore Lab, 78; NIH fac fel, Macromolecular Res Ctr, Univ Mich, 78-79. *Mem:* AAAS; Am Chem Soc; Sigma Xi. *Res:* Synthetic macromolecules and simpler organic molecules with potential biological activity. *Mailing Add:* Dept Chem Tuskegee Inst AL 36088

LUDWICK, ALBERT EARL, b San Diego, Calif, Feb 27, 40; m 61; c 2. SOIL FERTILITY. *Educ:* Calif State Polytech Col, BS, 62; Univ Wis, MS, 64, PhD(soil fertil), 67. *Prof Exp:* Instr soil fertil, Univ Wis, 66-68, asst prof, 68-70; from asst prof to prof soil fertil, Colo State Univ, 70-80, WESTERN DIR, POTASH & PHOSPHATE INST, 80- *Mem:* Am Soc Agron; Soil Sci Soc Am; Coun Soil Testing & Plant Anal. *Res:* Management of plant nutrients with emphasis on nitrogen; development of soil testing for fertilizer recommendations; calibration of testing procedures for fertilizer recommendations. *Mailing Add:* Dept Agron Plant Sci Bldg Colo State Univ Ft Collins CO 80523

LUDWICK, JOHN CALVIN, JR, b Berkeley, Calif, Apr 25, 22; m 50, 57. MARINE GEOLOGY. *Educ:* Univ Calif, Los Angeles, AB, 47; Scripps Inst Oceanog, MS, 49, PhD(oceanog), 51. *Prof Exp:* Res asst, Scripps Inst Oceanog, 49-50; sedimentation, Gulf Res & Develop Co, Tex, 50, group leader, 51-52, party chief, 53-59, Pa, 59-61, sr res geologist, 61-63, sect suvpr,

63-68; SLOVER PROF OCEANOG, OLD DOMINION UNIV, 68- *Concurrent Pos:* Old Dominion Univ eminent scholar, 74- *Mem:* Soc Econ Paleont & Mineral; fel Geol Soc Am; Am Geol Inst; AAAS. *Res:* Marine sedimentation; mechanics of marine sediment transport; physical oceanography; environmental interpretation of ancient sediments; shoal construction; tidal current analysis; beach processes. *Mailing Add:* Inst of Oceanog Old Dom Univ Norfolk VA 23508

LUDWICK, LARRY MARTIN, b Jamestown, NY, Oct 15, 41; m 68; c 2. INORGANIC CHEMISTRY. *Educ:* Mt Union Col, BS, 63; Univ Melbourne, BSc, 65; Univ Ill, Urbana, MS, 67, PhD(inorg chem), 69. *Prof Exp:* Res chemist, PPG Industs, 65; asst prof, 69-73, assoc prof, 74-76, PROF CHEM, TUSKEGEE INST, 76- *Concurrent Pos:* NIH fel, Biophys Res Div, Univ Mich, 78-80. *Mem:* AAAS; Am Chem Soc; Sigma Xi; Nat Sci Teachers Asn. *Res:* Metal binding studies; copper and zinc binding constants using superoxide dismutase. *Mailing Add:* Dept of Chem Tuskegee Inst Tuskegee Institute AL 36088

LUDWICK, THOMAS MURRELL, b Cox's Creek, Ky, Aug 2, 15. DAIRY HUSBANDRY. *Educ:* Eastern Ky Teachers Col, BS, 36; Univ Ky, MS, 39; Univ Minn, PhD(dairy sci, animal genetics), 42; Univ Chicago, dipl, 43; Univ Va, dipl, 43. *Prof Exp:* Dairy & tobacco farmer, Ky, 25-39; asst cattle breeding & physiol, Univ Minn, 39-42; asst prof dairy sci, Univ Ky, 46-48; assoc prof, 48-55, PROF DAIRY SCI, OHIO STATE UNIV, 55- *Concurrent Pos:* Teacher high sch, Ky, 37-38; dir, Ohio Regional Dairy Cattle Breeding Proj, 48- *Mem:* Am Soc Animal Sci. *Res:* Physiology of reproduction and milk secretion; artificial insemination; animal breeding. *Mailing Add:* 8071 Sawmill Rd Dublin OH 43017

LUDWIG, BERNARD JOHN, b Burlington, Vt, Nov 2, 12; m 33; c 5. ORGANIC CHEMISTRY. *Educ:* Univ Vt, BS, 35, MS, 36; Columbia Univ, PhD(org chem), 40. *Prof Exp:* Asst chemist, Exp Sta, Univ Vt, 35-37; asst instr chem, Columbia Univ, 36-38; chemist res & develop, Wallace & Tiernan, Inc, 39-47; tech dir, Dabney Pharmacol Co, Inc, 47-48; asst dir res & develop, Carter Prod Inc, 48-64, vpres chem res, 64-73, vpres res & develop, Wallace Labs Div, Carter-Wallace Inc, 73-76; CONSULT, 76- *Mem:* AAAS; Am Chem Soc; Am Pharmaceut Asn; fel Am Inst Chemists; NY Acad Sci. *Res:* Ethical pharmaceuticals; muscle relaxing drugs; tranquilizing drugs; antiatherosclerosis agents; psychopharmacological agents; bacterial endotoxins; immunological agents. *Mailing Add:* 2051 NE Ocean Blvd Stuart FL 33494

LUDWIG, CHARLES HEBERLE, b Minneapolis, Minn, May 1, 20; m 56; c 2. WOOD CHEMISTRY. *Educ:* Macalester Col, BA, 42; Univ Wash, PhD(chem), 61. *Prof Exp:* Chemist, D A Dodd, Mfg Chemist, 47-55 & Univ Wash, 56-61; mem res staff, Ga Pac Corp, 61-82; RETIRED. *Mem:* Am Chem Soc; Sigma Xi. *Res:* Nuclear magnetic resonance spectroscopy of lignins and lignin models; chemistry of lignosulfonates and other lignins. *Mailing Add:* Waldron WA 98297

LUDWIG, CLAUS BERTHOLD, b Berlin, Ger, Nov 18, 24; m 54; c 2. MOLECULAR SPECTROSCOPY, ENVIRONMENTAL PHYSICS. *Educ:* Aachen Tech Univ, MS, 51, PhD(physics), 53. *Prof Exp:* Design analyst, Eng Dept, Int Harvester Corp, 53-58; sr staff scientist, Space Sci Lab, Gen Dynamics-Convair, 58-72; scientist, Sci Appln, Inc, 72-77; SR SCIENTIST & VPRES, PHOTON RES ASSOCS, 77- *Mem:* Am Phys Soc; Optical Soc Am; Air Pollution Control Asn; assoc fel Am Inst Aeronaut & Astronaut Engrs. *Res:* Molecular physics; high temperature molecular spectroscopy; infrared phenomena; radiative energy transfer; optical properties of small solid particles; guiding research and development in remote sensing of air pollution; development of air pollution monitors based on optical methods. *Mailing Add:* 5218 Cassandra Lane San Diego CA 92109

LUDWIG, DONALD A, b New York, NY, Nov 14, 33; m 53; c 2. MATHEMATICS. *Educ:* NY Univ, BA, 54, MS, 57, PhD(math), 59. *Prof Exp:* Res assoc math, Inst Math Sci, NY Univ, 59-60; Fine instr, Princeton Univ, 60-61; asst prof, Univ Calif, Berkeley, 61-64; from assoc prof to prof, NY Univ, 64-74; PROF MATH, UNIV BC, 74- *Concurrent Pos:* Guggenheim fel, Tel Aviv, Rehovot, Dundee, 70-71. *Mem:* Am Math Soc; Soc Indust & Appl Math. *Res:* Partial differential equations; mathematical methods for population biology. *Mailing Add:* Dept Math Univ BC Vancouver BC V6T 1W5 Can

LUDWIG, EDWARD JAMES, b New York, NY, Apr 13, 37; m 58; c 4. NUCLEAR PHYSICS. *Educ:* Fordham Univ, BS, 58; Ind Univ, MS, 60, PhD(physics), 63. *Prof Exp:* Res fel physics, Rutgers Univ, 63-66; from asst prof to assoc prof, 66-76, PROF PHYSICS, UNIV NC, CHAPEL HILL, 76- *Mem:* Am Phys Soc. *Res:* Solid state detectors; nuclear reactions and scattering cross sections and polarization effects; reaction mechanisms. *Mailing Add:* Dept of Physics Univ of NC Chapel Hill NC 27514

LUDWIG, FRANK ARNO, b West Reading, Pa, Jan 17, 31. ELECTROCHEMISTRY, CORROSION RESISTANT MATERIALS. *Educ:* Calif Inst Technol, BS, 53; Case Western Reserve Univ, MS, 65, PhD(phys chem), 68. *Prof Exp:* Proj engr, Carter Labs, Inc, 53-56; res engr, Hughes Aircraft Co, 56-57; vpres, Tech Commun, Inc, 55-58; dept mgr fuel cells, thermogalvanics, Electro-Optical Systs, Inc, 58-62; dept mgr org electrolyte batteries, electrochem trace gas sensors, Whittaker Corp, 68-69; supvr, Res Lab, Ford Motor Co, 69-78; mgr, Near-Term Elec Vehicle Battery Contracts, Argonne Nat Lab, 78-79; PRIN ENGR, CORROSION, MAT DEVELOP FOR AEROSPACE & COMMUN CORP, 79- *Mem:* Electrochem Soc; Am Chem Soc; Sigma Xi. *Res:* Materials, corrosion, chemicals and electrochemical kinetics; development of new sodium-sulfur battery electrodes; electroanalytical chemistry, surface chemistry; improvements in lead-acid, nickel/zinc and nickel/iron batteries for electric vehicles; energy storage and conversion devices; electrochemical instruments; thermodynamics. *Mailing Add:* 41 Brena Irvine CA 92714

LUDWIG, FREDERIC C, b Bad Nauheim, WGer, Jan 22, 24; US citizen; m 58; c 4. EXPERIMENTAL PATHOLOGY. *Educ:* Univ Tübingen, MD, 49; Univ Paris, ScD(radiobiol), 58. *Prof Exp:* Sect chief radiation path, AEC, France, 55-59; assoc res pathologist, Med Ctr, Univ Calif, San Francisco, 58-62, lectr path, 62-65, assoc prof in residence, 65-71; PROF PATH & RADIOL SCI, COL MED, UNIV CALIF, IRVINE, 71- *Concurrent Pos:* Consult, Stanford Res Inst, 65- *Honors & Awards:* Award, Nat Inst Hyg, France, 59. *Mem:* Radiation Res Soc Am; Am Soc Exp Path; NY Acad Sci; Fr Asn Anat; Ger Path Soc. *Res:* Abscopal effects of radiation; radiation injury in blood forming organs; pathogenesis of radiation leukemia; homeostasis of white blood cells; gerontology. *Mailing Add:* Dept of Path & Radiol Sci Univ of Calif Col of Med Irvine CA 92664

LUDWIG, FREDERICK JOHN, SR, b St Louis, Mo, June 20, 28; m 56; c 2. ANALYTICAL CHEMISTRY, ORGANIC CHEMISTRY. *Educ:* Washington Univ, AB, 50; St Louis Univ, PhD(chem), 53. *Prof Exp:* Lab asst chem, St Louis Univ, 50-53; res chemist, Uranium Div, Mallinckrodt Chem Corp, 55-59; group leader, Petrolite Corp, 59-73, RES SCIENTIST, TRETOLITE DIV, PETROLITE CORP, 73- *Mem:* Am Chem Soc; Sigma Xi. *Res:* Gas-liquid and liquid-solid chromatography; infrared spectroscopy; wax-polymers; water-treatment chemicals; nuclear magnetic resonance spectroscopy. *Mailing Add:* Res Lab Petrolite Corp 369 Marshall Ave St Louis MO 63119

LUDWIG, GARRY (GERHARD ADOLF), b Mannheim, Ger, Sept 4, 40; Can & German citizen. GENERAL RELATIVITY. *Educ:* Univ Toronto, BSc, 62; Brown Univ, PhD(physics), 66. *Prof Exp:* Asst prof, 66-72, assoc prof, 72-82, PROF MATH, UNIV ALTA, 82- *Concurrent Pos:* Nat Res Coun grants, 67-82. *Mem:* Am Math Soc; Am Phys Soc; Can Math Soc. *Res:* General relativity and gravitation; asymptotically flat spacetimes, H-space, exact solutions, spin-coefficient formalism. *Mailing Add:* Dept of Math Univ of Alta Edmonton AB T6G 2G1 Can

LUDWIG, GEORGE H, b Johnson Co, Iowa, Nov 13, 27; m 50; c 4. ENVIRONMENTAL SCIENCES, SPACE SCIENCES. *Educ:* Univ Iowa, BA, 56, MS, 59, PhD(elec eng), 60. *Prof Exp:* Res assoc space res, Univ Iowa, 60; head instrumentation sect, Goddard Space Flight Ctr, NASA, 60-65, chief info processing div, 65-71, assoc dir data opers, 71-72; dir systs integration, Nat Earth Satellite Serv, 72-75, dir opers, 75-80, tech dir, 80, sr scientist, 80-81, DIR, ENVIRON RES LABS, NAT OCEANIC & ATMOSPHERIC ADMIN, 81- *Honors & Awards:* Golden Plate Award, Acad Achievement, 62; Except Serv Medal, NASA, 69; NOAA Prog & Mgt Award, Nat Oceanic & Atmospheric Admin, 77. *Mem:* Am Meteorol Soc; Am Geophys Union; Inst Elec & Electronics Engrs. *Res:* Cosmic rays; development of space instrumentation; on board and ground data processing; co-discovery and investigation of Van Allen radiation belts; atmospheric, oceanic, hydrologic remote sensing and forecasting; direction of space, atmospheric and oceanic environmental research. *Mailing Add:* 880 Crescent Dr Boulder CO 80303

LUDWIG, GERALD W, b New York, NY, Jan 7, 30; m 51; c 3. SEMICONDUCTORS, SOLID STATE PHYSICS. *Educ:* Harvard Univ, AB, 50, AM, 51, PhD(chem physics), 55. *Prof Exp:* Physicist, 55-63, liaison scientist, 63-65, physicist, 65-71, MGR, INTEGRATED CIRCUITS BR, RES & DEVELOP CTR, GEN ELEC CORP, 71- *Mem:* Fel Am Phys Soc; sr mem, Inst Elec & Electronics Engrs; Electrochem Soc. *Res:* Integrated circuits; charge transfer devices; semiconductor materials and processing; x-ray and cathode ray phosphors; Gunn effect; electron paramagnetic resonance; transport properties of semiconductors. *Mailing Add:* Res & Develop Ctr Gen Elec Co PO Box 8 Schenectady NY 12301

LUDWIG, HOWARD C, b Beaver Falls, Pa, July 31, 16; m 41; c 1. CHEMICAL PHYSICS, PLASMA PHYSICS. *Educ:* Geneva Col, BS, 41. *Prof Exp:* Chem analyst, Armstrong Cork Co, 41-42; spectroscopist, Propeller Div, Curtiss-Wright Corp, 42-46; res engr, Res Labs, Westinghouse Elec Corp, 46-59, fel scientist, Res & Develop Ctr, 59-76; consult plasma physics, 76-80; RETIRED. *Honors & Awards:* IR 100 Award, 63; Lincoln Gold Medal, Am Welding Soc, 56. *Res:* Research and development of high pressure plasmas. *Mailing Add:* 159 Roberta Dr Pittsburgh PA 15221

LUDWIG, HUBERT JOSEPH, b Lincoln, Ill, July 27, 34; m 65; c 2. MATHEMATICS. *Educ:* Univ Ill, Urbana, BS, 56; St Louis Univ, MS, 64, PhD(math), 68. *Prof Exp:* Instr math, chem & eng mech, Springfield Col, Ill, 56-65; teaching asst math, St Louis Univ, 65-68; asst prof, 68-75, ASSOC PROF MATH, BALL STATE UNIV, 75- *Mem:* Math Asn Am; Am Math Soc. *Res:* Autometrized spaces; 2-metric spaces. *Mailing Add:* Dept of Math Sci Ball State Univ Muncie IN 47306

LUDWIG, J(OHN) T(RUMAN), b Portland, Ore, Aug 11, 26; div; c 5. ELECTRICAL ENGINEERING. *Educ:* Univ Minn, BEE, 48, MS, 52, PhD(elec eng), 54. *Prof Exp:* Elec engr, Minn Mining & Mfg Co, 51; sr res scientist, Res Ctr, Honeywell, Inc, 54-58, sr res engr, Aeronaut Div, 58-59; prin eng specialist, Electronic Commun, Inc, 60-62; mgr microwaves, antennas & propagation, IIT Res Inst, 62-63; assoc electronics engr, Argonne Nat Lab, 63-66; consult, 66-71; ENGR, STATE OF FLA BUR HEALTH FACIL, 71- *Concurrent Pos:* Hon fel, Univ Minn, 59-60; spec exten instr, Univ Fla, 60-62; tech phase evaluator, McGraw-Hill Publ Co, 60-63. *Honors & Awards:* Patron Award, Inst Elec & Electronics Engrs, 62. *Mem:* AAAS; Am Phys Soc; Inst Elec & Electronics Engrs; Am Vacuum Soc; Nat Soc Prof Engrs. *Res:* Microwave circuitry; reflex keystron oscillators; magnetic recording and devices; communication and information theory; antennas; scanning electron microscopy; health care delivery systems. *Mailing Add:* PO Box 52026 Jacksonville FL 32201

LUDWIG, JEROME HOWARD, organic chemistry, see previous edition

LUDWIG, JOHN HOWARD, b Burlington, Vt, Mar 7, 13; m 46; c 2. ENVIRONMENTAL SCIENCES. *Educ:* Univ Calif, Berkeley, BS, 34; Univ Colo, MS, 41; Harvard Univ, MS, 56, ScD(indust hyg), 58; Environ Eng Intersoc Bd, dipl. *Prof Exp:* Design engr, US Bur Reclamation, Colo, 36-39; design engr, Corps Engrs, Ore, 39-43, chief dams design sect, Calif, 46-48; consult engr, Ludwig Bros, Engrs, 48-51; chief tech opers br, Div Civilian Health Requirements, USPHS, 51-53, spec asst to chief, Div Water Supply & Pollution Control, 53-55 & Div Air Pollution, 55-62, chief lab eng & phys sci, 62-67; assoc dir control tech res & develop, Nat Ctr Air Pollution Control, 67-68; assoc comnr, Nat Air Pollution Control Admin, 68-70; dir tech coordr, Off Air Progs, Environ Protection Agency, 70-72; CONSULT, 72- *Concurrent Pos:* Vis lectr, Harvard Univ, 64-; mem expert adv panel air pollution, WHO, 65-; US deleg, Orgn Econ Coop & Develop & Econ Comn Europe, 68- *Mem:* Nat Acad Eng; AAAS; fel Am Pub Health Asn; Am Soc Civil Engrs; Am Meteorol Soc. *Res:* Air pollution in physical sciences and engineering controls. *Mailing Add:* 43 Alston Pl Santa Barbara CA 93108

LUDWIG, MARTHA LOUISE, b Pittsburgh, Pa, Aug 16, 31; m 61. BIOCHEMISTRY. *Educ:* Cornell Univ, BA, 52, PhD(biochem), 56; Univ Calif, Berkeley, MA, 55. *Prof Exp:* Res fel biochem, Harvard Med Sch, 56-59; res assoc biol, Mass Inst Technol, 59-62; res fel chem, Harvard Univ, 62-67; from asst prof to assoc prof, 67-75, PROF BIOL CHEM, UNIV MICH, ANN ARBOR, & RES BIOPHYSICIST, BIOPHYS RES DIV, 75- *Mem:* Am Chem Soc; Am Soc Biol Chemists; Biophys Soc; Am Crystallog Asn. *Res:* Protein crystallography; protein structure and function. *Mailing Add:* Dept of Biol Chem Univ of Mich Ann Arbor MI 48104

LUDWIG, OLIVER GEORGE, b Philadelphia, Pa, Nov 15, 35. PHYSICAL CHEMISTRY. *Educ:* Villanova Univ, BS, 57; Carnegie Inst Technol, MS, 60, PhD(quantum chem), 61. *Prof Exp:* Mem math lab & sr res worker theoret chem, Cambridge Univ, 61-63; asst prof chem & fac assoc, Comput Ctr, Univ Notre Dame, 63-68; ASSOC PROF CHEM, VILLANOVA UNIV, 68- *Concurrent Pos:* NSF fel, 61-63; actg chmn, Dept Chem, Villanova Univ, 69-70. *Mem:* Am Chem Soc; Am Phys Soc; Asn Comput Mach. *Res:* Quantum chemistry; chemical applications of digital computers; development of methods for scientific computing. *Mailing Add:* Dept of Chem Villanova Univ Villanova PA 19805

LUDWIG, RICHARD ELI, b Pottstown, Pa, Oct 16, 29; m 55; c 2. ORGANIC CHEMISTRY. *Educ:* Ursinus Col, BS, 52; Univ Del, MS, 54, PhD, 56. *Prof Exp:* SR RES CHEMIST, CHRISTINA LAB, E I DU PONT DE NEMOURS & CO, 55- *Mem:* Am Chem Soc; Tech Asn Pulp & Paper Indust. *Res:* Catalytic air oxidation of aromatic hydrocarbons; synthesis of trialkyl-pyrrolidine triones; epoxy resin chemistry; powder compaction; new product development of nonwoven materials; printing technology. *Mailing Add:* Christina Lab E I du Pont de Nemours & Co Wilmington DE 19898

LUDWIG, THEODORE FREDERICK, b Castlewood, SDak, July 8, 24; m 45; c 1. PROSTHODONTICS. *Educ:* Cent Col, Iowa, AB, 45; Ohio State DDS, 59, MSc, 63. *Prof Exp:* Asst prof dent, Sch Dent, WVa Univ, 63-67; asst prof, Sch Dent, Univ Iowa, 67-69; ASSOC PROF PROSTHODONTICS, COL DENT MED, MED UNIV SC, 69- *Concurrent Pos:* NIH grant, 62-63; mem, Carl O Boucher Prosthodontic Conf, 66- *Mem:* Am Dent Asn. *Res:* Esthetics in complete dentures; design and metals in removable partial dentures. *Mailing Add:* Dept of Prosthodontics Med Univ of SC Charleston SC 29403

LUDWIG, WILLIAM JACKSON, b New York, NY, May 25, 32; m 60; c 2. MARINE GEOPHYSICS. *Educ:* Univ Houston, BS, 56; Hokkaido Univ, PhD, 69. *Prof Exp:* Res asst geophys, 56-60, res scientist, 60-65, res assoc geophys, 65-69, SR RES ASSOC GEOPHYS, LAMONT-DOHERTY GEOL OBSERV, COLUMBIA UNIV, 69-, HEAD MARINE SEISMOL GROUP, 76- *Mem:* Am Geophys Union; Soc Explor Geophys; fel Geol Soc Am; Am Asn Petrol Geologists. *Res:* Structure and development of continental margins and ocean basins. *Mailing Add:* Lamont-Doherty Geol Observ Columbia Univ Palisades NY 10964

LUDWIN, ISADORE, b Malden, Mass, Feb 23, 15; m 49; c 5. ANIMAL GENETICS, PHYSIOLOGY. *Educ:* Univ Mass, BS, 37; Univ Wis, MS, 39; Harvard Univ, PhD(genetics), 48. *Prof Exp:* Statist analyst, US Dept Navy, DC, 41-42; asst prof biol, Univ Mass, 46-48; fel, Tufts Col, 48; assoc cancer biologist, Roswell Park Mem Inst, 49-51; prof sci, Calvin Coolidge Col, 57-62; prof biol, Cambridge Jr Col, 57-67; lectr, Northeastern Univ, 67-68; PVT RES & DEVELOP, 68- *Mem:* AAAS; Asn Advan Med Instrumentation. *Mailing Add:* 1073 Centre St Newton MA 02159

LUEBBE, RAY HENRY, JR, b Schenectady, NY, Mar 31, 31; m 59; c 3. PHYSICAL CHEMISTRY. *Educ:* Dartmouth Col, AB, 53; Univ Wis, PhD(phys chem), 58. *Prof Exp:* Asst phys chem, Univ Wis, 53-55; chemist, Photo Prod Dept, E I du Pont de Nemours & Co, 58-64; scientist, Xerox Corp, 64-79; UNIT MGR, QWIP SYSTS, EXXON ENTERPRISES, 79- *Res:* Hot atom and photo chemistry; photographic science; photopolymerization; electrophotography. *Mailing Add:* 165 Lake Destiny Trail Maitland FL 32757

LUEBBERS, RALPH H(ENRY), b Burlington, Iowa, Mar 24, 06; m 35; c 3. CHEMICAL ENGINEERING. *Educ:* Iowa State Col, BS, 27, MS, 32, PhD(chem eng, sanit bact), 35. *Prof Exp:* Plant chemist, Universal Gypsum Co, Iowa, 27; plant chemist & chem engr, Des Moines Water Works, 28; jr engr, Int Combustion Eng Corp, NY, 28-29; develop engr, Dorr Co, Inc, 29-31; chem & sanit engr, US Army Dept, Kans, 35-37; from instr to prof, 38-72, EMER PROF CHEM ENG, UNIV MO-COLUMBIA, 72- *Concurrent Pos:* Eng consult. *Mem:* Am Chem Soc; Am Soc Eng Educ; Am Water Works Asn; Am Inst Chem Eng; Nat Soc Prof Engrs. *Res:* Mixing of dry powders and liquids; heat transfer in packed columns; biological oxidation processes; fluid flow of suspensions. *Mailing Add:* Dept of Chem Eng Univ of Mo Columbia MO 65201

LUEBKE, EMMETH AUGUST, b Manitowoc, Wis, Aug 1, 15; c 2. PHYSICS. *Educ:* Ripon Col, BA, 36; Univ Ill, PhD(physics), 41. *Prof Exp:* Asst physics, Univ Ill, 36-41; group leader, Radiation Lab, Mass Inst Technol, 41-45; res assoc, Res Lab, Gen Elec Co, 45-50, mgr reactor eval, Knolls Atomic Power Lab, 50-55, gen physicist, Missile & Space Vehicle Dept, 55-58 & Gen Eng Lab, 58-63, physicist, Tempo, 63-72; ADMIN JUDGE, US NUCLEAR REGULATORY COMN, 72- *Concurrent Pos:* Mem, Joint Liquid Metals Comt, US Navy AEC, 50-55; presiding tech mem, Atomic Safety & Licensing Bd. *Mem:* Fel Am Phys Soc; Am Nuclear Soc. *Res:* Linear accelerator; velocity spectrometer measurement of neutron cross section; microwave radar components; system design; liquid metal heat transfer; design and evaluation of reactor power plants; breeder; submarine propulsion; central station types; environmental controls. *Mailing Add:* 5500 Friendship Blvd Apt 1923 N Chevy Chase MD 20815

LUEBS, RALPH EDWARD, b Wood River, Nebr, Mar 21, 22; m 51; c 4. SOILS. *Educ:* Univ Nebr, BS, 48, MS, 52; Iowa State Univ, PhD(soil fertil), 54. *Prof Exp:* Asst agron, Univ Nebr, 48-49; soil scientist, Agr Res Serv, Univ Nebr, USDA, 55-56, Ft Hays Exp Sta, Kans, 56-59 & Univ Calif, Riverside, 59-75; chief, Agron Div, 75-81, SR PROJ SCIENTIST, ENVIRON SYSTEMS DIV, WOODWARD-CLYDE CONSULTS, 81- *Mem:* Am Soc Agron; Soil Sci Soc Am; Sigma Xi; Soil Conserv Soc Am; Soc Range Mgt. *Res:* Nitrogen availability and rainfall use efficiency for dryland crops; mined land reclamation. *Mailing Add:* 13347 W Exposition Dr Denver CO 80204

LUECK, CHARLES HENRY, b St Paul, Minn, Oct 1, 28; m 55; c 6. ANALYTICAL CHEMISTRY. *Educ:* Col St Thomas, BS, 50; Univ Detroit, MS, 53; Wayne State Univ, PhD, 56. *Prof Exp:* Res chemist, E I du Pont de Nemours & Co, 56-66, anal res supvr, Textile Fibers Dept, 66-80. *Mem:* Am Chem Soc. *Res:* Spectrophotometric analysis; chemical degradation studies. *Mailing Add:* 216 Pineview Dr Greenville NC 27834

LUECK, ROGER HAWKS, b Fox Lake, Wis, Dec 17, 96; m 24; c 2. RESEARCH ADMINISTRATION, CORROSION. *Educ:* Carroll Col, BS, 19; Univ Wis, MS, 21. *Hon Degrees:* DSc, Carroll Col, 43. *Prof Exp:* Instr chem, Univ Wis, 19-22; chemist, Am Can Co, Ill, 22-26, dist mgr, Res Dept, Calif, 26-34, mgr, Hawaiian Div, 34-35, admin mgr, Res Dept, Ill, 35-41, dir res, 41-44, mgr sales, Pac Div, 44-50, gen mgr, Res & Tech Dept, NY, 50-54, vpres res & develop, 55-62, consult res admin & packaging technol, 62-78. *Concurrent Pos:* Consult, Off Qm Gen, US Army, 42-44; dir, James Dole Corp, 61-78; trustee, Midwest Res Inst; mem, Vis Comt, Dept Food Technol, Mass Inst Technol & Adv Coun, Col Eng, NY Univ. *Mem:* Am Chem Soc; AAAS; Am Mgt Asn (vpres); fel Am Inst Chemists; Inst Food Technologists (vpres, 44). *Res:* Kinetics of chemical reaction; corrosion of tinplate; organic coatings on metal; canning technology; metal complexes with flavones; frothy fermentation of saccharine foods; administration of industrial research. *Mailing Add:* 20016 Winter Lane Saratoga CA 95070

LUECKE, GLENN RICHARD, b Bryan, Tex, May 19, 44; m 67; c 2. MATHEMATICAL ANALYSIS. *Educ:* Mich State Univ, BS, 66; Calif Inst Technol, PhD(math), 70. *Prof Exp:* Asst prof, 69-74, assoc prof, 74-80, PROF MATH, IOWA STATE UNIV, 80- *Mem:* Am Math Soc; Soc Indust & Appl Math. *Res:* Study of continuous linear transformations in Hilbert space. *Mailing Add:* Dept of Math Iowa State Univ Ames IA 50011

LUECKE, RICHARD H, b Cincinnati, Ohio, Mar 27, 30; m 53; c 5. CHEMICAL ENGINEERING. *Educ:* Univ Cincinnati, BChE, 53; Univ Okla, MChE, 63, PhD(chem eng), 66. *Prof Exp:* Engr, E I du Pont de Nemours & Co, Inc, 53-62; res engr, Monsanto Co, 66-67; assoc prof, 67-80, PROF CHEM ENG, UNIV MO-COLUMBIA, 80- *Concurrent Pos:* Consult, Chemshare Corp, Okla, 69- *Mem:* Am Inst Chem Eng. *Res:* Process control; optimization; mathematical methods; bioengineering. *Mailing Add:* 408 Spring Valley Rd Columbia MO 65201

LUECKE, RICHARD WILLIAM, b St Paul, Minn, July 12, 17; m 41; c 3. BIOCHEMISTRY, NUTRITION. *Educ:* Macalester Col, BA, 39; Univ Minn, MS, 41, PhD(biochem), 43. *Prof Exp:* PROF BIOCHEM, MICH STATE UNIV, 45- *Concurrent Pos:* Assoc prof biochem, Tex A&M Univ, 43-45; consult, Armour Res Labs, Chicago, 55-66; mem comt on animal nutrit, Nat Res Coun, 55-65; mem food & nutrit bd, Food & Agr Orgn, UN, 60-65; consult, Merck Sharp & Dohme Res Labs, 62-69. *Honors & Awards:* Award, Am Soc Animal Sci, 56. *Mem:* Am Chem Soc; Am Inst Nutrit; Brit Nutrit Soc; Am Soc Biol Chemists; Soc Exp Biol & Med. *Res:* Trace element metabolism in animals. *Mailing Add:* Dept of Biochem Mich State Univ East Lansing MI 48824

LUEDECKE, LLOYD O, b Hamilton, Mont, July 28, 34; m 57; c 2. DAIRY BACTERIOLOGY. *Educ:* Mont State Col, BS, 56; Mich State Univ, MS, 58, PhD(food sci), 62. *Prof Exp:* Asst prof dairy sci, 62-70, assoc prof & assoc dairy scientist, 70-73, assoc prof, 73-77, PROF FOOD SCI, WASH STATE UNIV, 77- *Mem:* Am Dairy Sci Asn; Inst Food Technol. *Res:* Heat resistance of psychrophiles; bacteriological aspects of mastitis. *Mailing Add:* Dept of Food Sci & Technol Clark Hall Wash State Univ Pullman WA 99163

LUEDEKING, ROBERT, b York, Pa, July 5, 24; m 52; c 5. CHEMICAL ENGINEERING. *Educ:* Purdue Univ, BS, 46; Univ Minn, PhD(chem eng), 56. *Prof Exp:* Asst prof, 56-63, ASSOC PROF CHEM ENG, WASH STATE UNIV, 63- *Mem:* Am Chem Soc; Am Inst Chem Engrs; Am Soc Eng Educ. *Res:* Fermentation kinetics and technology; unit operations. *Mailing Add:* Dept Chem Eng Wash State Univ Pullman WA 99163

LUEDEMAN, JOHN KEITH, b Ft Wayne, Ind, Apr 27, 41; m 63; c 4. ALGEBRA. *Educ:* Valparaiso Univ, BA, 63; Southern Ill Univ, Carbondale, MA, 65; State Univ NY, Buffalo, PhD(math), 69. *Prof Exp:* Instr math, State Univ NY, Buffalo, 67-68; from asst prof to assoc prof, 68-80, PROF MATH, CLEMSON UNIV, 80- *Concurrent Pos:* Consult math, Oconee County Sch Syst, SC, 74- *Mem:* Am Math Soc; Math Asn Am; Sigma Xi. *Res:* Ring and module theory; mathematical biology; semigroups; graph theory; computing on graphs. *Mailing Add:* Dept of Math Clemson Univ Clemson SC 29631

LUEDEMANN, LOIS W, b Chicago, Ill, Mar 22, 31; m 54; c 1. GEOCHEMISTRY, MATERIALS SCIENCE. *Educ:* Hunter Col, BA, 51; Syracuse Univ, MS, 53; Pa State Univ, PhD(mineral), 56. *Prof Exp:* Asst mineral, Pa State Univ, 52-56; res assoc chem, Syracuse Univ, 56-59; instr mat sci, assoc prof, 60-77, PROF GEOL & CHEM, FAIRLEIGH DICKINSON UNIV, 77- *Mem:* Nat Asn Geol Teachers; Am Chem Soc; Am Ceramic Soc; Am Mineral Soc; Am Soc Metals. *Res:* Petrography and x-ray analysis of uranium bearing shales; crystal chemical study of hydrous vanadates; preparation and characterization of boron-hydrides; phase equilibria in alkalimetal-alkaline earth metal systems. *Mailing Add:* Dept of Chem Fairleigh Dickinson Univ Rutherford NJ 07070

LUEG, RUSSELL E, b Chicago, Ill, Nov 24, 29; m 56; c 5. ELECTRICAL ENGINEERING. *Educ:* Univ Ark, BS, 51; Univ Tex, MS, 56, PhD(elec eng), 61. *Prof Exp:* Prog engr, Gen Elec Co, NY, 53-54; radio engr & instr elec eng, Univ Tex, 54-60; assoc prof, 60-64, actg head dept, 66-68, PROF ELEC ENG, UNIV ALA, 64- *Concurrent Pos:* Consult, Army Missile Command, Ala, 64-65. *Mem:* Inst Elec & Electronics Engrs; Am Soc Eng Educ. *Res:* Nonlinear control systems. *Mailing Add:* Dept of Elec Eng Univ of Ala University AL 35486

LUE-HING, CECIL, b Jamaica, WI, Nov 3, 30; m 52; c 2. CIVIL & ENVIRONMENTAL ENGINEERING. *Educ:* Marquette Univ, BCE, 61; Case Inst Technol, MS, 63; Washington Univ, St Louis, DSc(sanit eng), 66. *Prof Exp:* Chief technician, Col Med, Univ WI, 50-55; instr histol & cytol chem & lab supvr, Sch Med Technol, Mt Sinai Hosp, Wis, 55-61; res assoc clin biochem, Huron Rd Hosp, Ohio, 61-63; res assoc environ eng, Washington Univ, St Louis, 63-65, asst prof, 65-66; assoc, Ryckman, Edgerley, Tomlinson & Assocs, 66-68, sr assoc, 68-77; DIR RES & DEVELOP, METROP SANIT DIST, CHICAGO, 77- *Concurrent Pos:* Fel, Washington Univ, Mo. *Mem:* AAAS; Am Soc Civil Engrs; Am Pub Health Asn; Water Pollution Control Fedn; Am Water Works Asn. *Res:* Pesticide pollution of water supplies; significance of enzyme response in pesticide detection in water supplies; phosphorus and nutrient removal from water supplies; industrial wastes detoxification and biodegradation. *Mailing Add:* Metrop Sanit Dist 100 E Erie St Chicago IL 60611

LUEHR, CHARLES POLING, b Plentywood, Mont, Sept 27, 30. APPLIED MATHEMATICS. *Educ:* Ore State Col, BS, 53, MS, 56; Univ Calif, Berkeley, PhD(appl math), 62. *Prof Exp:* Mem prof staff, Gen Elec Co, Calif, 62-68; fel, 68-70, asst prof, 70-75, ASSOC PROF MATH, UNIV FLA, 75- *Mem:* Math Asn Am; Am Math Soc; Am Phys Soc; Am Chem Soc; Soc Indust & Appl Math. *Res:* Methods of mathematical physics; tensor analysis with applications in physics; theory of spinors with applications in quantum mechanics and relativity theory; applications of modern differential geometry to general relativity. *Mailing Add:* Dept of Math Univ of Fla Gainesville FL 32611

LUEHRMANN, ARTHUR WILLETT, JR, b New Orleans, La, Mar 8, 31; m 61; c 2. COMPUTER SCIENCE, SCIENCE EDUCATION. *Educ:* Univ Chicago, AB, 55, SB, 57, SM, 61, PhD(physics), 66. *Prof Exp:* From instr to asst prof, 65-70, adj assoc prof physics & dir, Off Acad Comput, Dartmouth Col, 70-77; assoc dir, Lawrence Hall Sci, Univ Calif, Berkeley, 77-80; PARTNER, COMPUTER LITERACY, 80- *Concurrent Pos:* Consult, NSF Off Comput Activities, 68-, res grant, 69-78; Fulbright lectr, Fulbright Comn, Colombia, SAm, 69. *Honors & Awards:* Distinguished Serv Citation, Am Asn Physics Teachers, 71. *Mem:* Am Asn Physics Teachers; Am Phys Soc; Asn Computing Machines; Inst Elec & Electronics Engrs. *Res:* Solid state theory; band structure; computational physics; computer graphics; computer-based instruction; solid state physics. *Mailing Add:* Computer Literacy 1466 Grizzly Peak Blvd Berkeley CA 94708

LUEHRS, DEAN C, b Fremont, Nebr, Aug 20, 39; m 69. INORGANIC CHEMISTRY. *Educ:* Mich State Univ, BS, 61; Univ Kans, PhD(chem), 65. *Prof Exp:* Asst prof, 65-69, ASSOC PROF CHEM, MICH STATE TECHNOL UNIV, 69- *Mem:* Am Chem Soc. *Res:* Nonaqueous solvents; electrochemistry. *Mailing Add:* Dept Chem & Chem Eng Mich Technol Univ Houghton MI 49931

LUEKING, DONALD ROBERT, b Cincinnati, Ohio, Nov 24, 46; m 73. MICROBIAL BIOCHEMISTRY. *Educ:* Ind Univ, Bloomington, BS, 69, PhD(microbiol), 73. *Prof Exp:* Trainee microbiol, Univ Pa, 73-74, fel, 74-75; fel microbiol, Univ Ill, Urbana, 75-78; ASST PROF MICROBIOL, TEX A&M UNIV, 78- *Mem:* Am Soc Microbiol; AAAS; Sigma Xi. *Res:* The use of the photosynthetic bacteria as a model system for the study of the factors involved in the regulation of membrane biosynthesis and differentiation. *Mailing Add:* Dept Biol Tex A&M Univ College Station TX 77843

LUENBERGER, DAVID GILBERT, b Los Angeles, Calif, Sept 16, 37; m 62; c 4. SYSTEMS ENGINEERING. *Educ:* Calif Inst Technol, BS, 59; Stanford Univ, MS, 61, PhD(elec eng), 63. *Prof Exp:* Engr, Westinghouse Elec Corp, 61-63; asst prof elec eng, 63-67, assoc prof eng-econ systs & elec eng, 67-71, PROF ENG-ECON SYSTS & ELEC ENG, STANFORD UNIV, 71-, CHMN, ENG-ECON SYSTS, 80- *Concurrent Pos:* Consult, Stanford Res Inst, 66-, Wolf Mgr Systs, 69-70, Intasa, Inc, 70-72, Systs Control Inc, 74- & Time & Space Processing, 81; tech asst to dir, Off Sci & Technol, Exec Off of the President, 71-72; vis prof, Mass Inst Technol, 76. *Mem:* Inst Mgt Sci; Oper Res Soc Am; Inst Elec & Electronics Engrs; Econometric Soc; Am Soc Eng Educ. *Res:* Control systems, particularly multivariable systems; optimization, including control, operations research and estimation; economic systems. *Mailing Add:* Dept Eng-Econ Systs Terman Eng Ctr 306 Stanford Univ Stanford CA 94305

LUEPSCHEN, NORMAN SIEGFRIED, b Buffalo, NY, Jan 6, 33; m 53; c 4. PLANT PATHOLOGY. *Educ:* Wheaton Col, Ill, BS, 54; Cornell Univ, PhD(plant path), 60. *Prof Exp:* Asst plant path, Cornell Univ, 54-59, exten specialist, 59-60; assoc pathologist, Mkt Qual Serv, USDA, 60-61; asst plant pathologist, Colo State Univ, 62-65, assoc plant pathologist, 65-75, prof plant path, 75-81; PLANT PATH CONSULT, TREE DISEASES, 81- *Mem:* Am Phytopath Soc; Am Soc Hort Sci; Am Pomol Soc; Mycol Soc Am. *Res:* Tree fruit diseases; storage, transit and market diseases; antibiotics. *Mailing Add:* 73179 Hwy 64 Meeker CO 81641

LUERSSEN, FRANK W, b Reading, Pa, Aug 14, 27; m 50; c 5. METALLURGY, PHYSICAL CHEMISTRY. *Educ:* Pa State Univ, BS, 50; Lehigh Univ, MS, 51. *Prof Exp:* Jr res engr, Bethlehem Steel Corp, 51-52; metallurgist, 52-54, chief reduction & ref, 54-57, chief res engr, 57-61, asst mgr, Res Dept, 62-63 assoc mgr, 63-64, mgr, 64-68, vpres res, 68-77, vpres steel mfg, 77-78, exec vpres, 78, PRES, INLAND STEEL CO, 78- *Mem:* Nat Acad Eng; Brit Inst Metals; Am Iron & Steel Inst; fel Am Soc Metals; Am Inst Mining, Metall & Petrol Engrs. *Res:* Physical chemistry of slag metal systems and steel refining; process research in ironmaking and steelmaking; physical metallurgy of iron base alloy systems. *Mailing Add:* Inland Steel Co 30 W Monroe St Chicago IL 60603

LUESCHEN, WILLIAM EVERETT, b Springfield, Ill, Jan 29, 42; m 65; c 2. AGRONOMY. *Educ:* Southern Ill Univ, BS, 64; Univ Ill, MS, 66, PhD(agron), 68. *Prof Exp:* PROF AGRON & AGRONOMIST, SOUTHERN EXP STA, UNIV MINN, 68- *Mem:* Am Soc Agron; Crop Sci Soc Am; Weed Sci Soc Am. *Res:* Crop production, management and weed science. *Mailing Add:* Southern Exp Sta Univ of Minn Waseca MN 56093

LUESSENHOP, ALFRED JOHN, b Chicago, Ill, Feb 6, 26; m 52; c 4. MEDICINE, NEUROSURGERY. *Educ:* Yale Univ, BS, 49; Harvard Med Sch, MD, 52. *Prof Exp:* Intern surg, Univ Chicago, 52-53; resident neurosurg, Mass Gen Hosp, 53-58; vis scientist, Nat Inst Neurol Dis & Blindness, 59-60; from instr to assoc prof neurosurg, 60-73, PROF SURG, SCH MED, GEORGETOWN UNIV, 73-, CHIEF DIV NEUROSURG, 65- *Concurrent Pos:* Teaching fel, Harvard Med Sch, 57-58; res fel neurosurg, Harvard Med Sch, 53-54; res consult, Nat Inst Neurol Dis & Stroke, 60-65, clin consult, 65-; clin consult, Vet Admin Hosp, 65-; consult, Fed Aviation Agency, 67 & Nat Naval Med Ctr, 67- *Mem:* Cong Neurol Surg; Am Asn Neurol Surg. *Res:* Cerebrovascular disease. *Mailing Add:* Georgetown Univ Hosp 3800 Riserview Rd Washington DC 20007

LUETZELSCHWAB, JOHN WILLIAM, b Hammond, Ind, Sept 8, 40; m 63; c 2. HEALTH PHYSICS. *Educ:* Earlham Col, AB, 62; Washington Univ, MA & PhD(physics), 68. *Prof Exp:* Asst prof, 68-73, ASSOC PROF PHYSICS, DICKINSON COL, 73- *Mem:* Am Asn Physics Teachers; Health Physics Soc. *Res:* Environmental radioactivity; effects of nuclear power plants on the environment. *Mailing Add:* Dept of Physics & Astron Dickinson Col Carlisle PA 17013

LUFBURROW, ROBERT ALLEN, b New Brunswick, NJ, July 8, 22; m 56; c 3. PHYSICS. *Educ:* Berea Col, BA, 48; Purdue Univ, MS, 50; Washington Univ, MA, 64. *Prof Exp:* Res assoc physics, Oceanog Inst, Woods Hole, 52-58; asst prof, 58-67, ASSOC PROF PHYSICS, ST LAWRENCE UNIV, 67- *Mem:* Am Asn Physics Teachers. *Res:* Optical physics; solar energy. *Mailing Add:* Dept of Physics St Lawrence Univ Canton NY 13617

LUFKIN, DANIEL HARLOW, b Philadelphia, Pa, Sept 26, 30; m 51; c 3. SOLAR PHYSICS. *Educ:* Mass Inst Technol, BS, 52, MS, 58; Univ Stockholm, Fil lic meteorol, 64. *Prof Exp:* Meteorol officer, Air Weather Serv, US Air Force, DC, 53-69, dir solar forecast facility, 69-73; CONSULT, SOLAR ENERGY SCI SERV, 74-; ASST PROF ASTRON, HOOD COL, 75- *Concurrent Pos:* Dir, Off Systs & Advan Technol, Nat Oceanic & Atmospheric Admin, 76- *Mem:* Am Meteorol Soc; Optical Soc Am; Pattern recognition Soc; Int Solar Energy Soc; Am Soc Heating Refrig & Air Conditioning Engrs. *Res:* Application of solar energy to heating and cooling and generation of power. *Mailing Add:* 303 W College Terr Frederick MD 21701

LUFKIN, EDWARD GWYNNE, b Northfield, Minn, Oct 15, 35; m 61; c 2. ENDOCRINOLOGY, INTERNAL MEDICINE. *Educ:* Carleton Col, Minn, BA, 57; Med Sch, Northwestern Univ, Chicago, MD, 61. *Prof Exp:* Resident physician internal med, Vet Admin Res Hosp, Chicago, 62-65; fel endocrinol & renal dis, Med Ctr, Univ Colo, Denver, 65-66; internist, 98th Gen Hosp, APO New York, 66-69; res internist metab, US Army Med Res & Nutrit Lab, Fitzsimons Army Med Ctr, Denver, 69-74; CONSULT ENDOCRINOL & INTERNAL MED, MAYO CLIN, MAYO GRAD SCH MED, ROCHESTER, MINN, 74- *Mem:* Am Col Physicians; Am Fedn Clin Res; Endocrine Soc; Cent Soc Clin Res. *Res:* Platelet function in diabetes; development of radioimmunoassay. *Mailing Add:* Mayo Clin Rochester MN 55901

LUFKIN, JAMES E, b Gloucester, Mass, Mar 11, 20; m 44; c 3. ORGANIC CHEMISTRY. *Educ:* Univ NH, BS, 41. *Prof Exp:* Chemist, Explosives Dept, Eastern Lab, E I du Pont de Nemours & Co, 41-52; asst supt, Repauno Works, 52-53, spec asst, Process Sect, 53-54, dir, Carney's Point Process Lab, 54-60 & Carney's Point Develop Lab, 60-70, tech progs mgr, 71-72, prod sales mgr, Polymer Intermediates Dept, Explosives Dept, 72-77, spec accts mgr, Petrochem Dept, 77-80. *Mem:* Inst Food Technologists. *Res:* Explosives; polymer intermediates; plasticizers; dye intermediates; cellulose derivatives; smokeless powder; explosion hazards; food additives. *Mailing Add:* Wilmington DE 19898

LUFT, JOHN HERMAN, b Portland, Ore, Feb 6, 27; m 49; c 3. HISTOLOGY. *Educ:* Univ Wash, BS, 49, MD, 53. *Prof Exp:* Intern, Peter Bent Brigham Hosp, Boston, Mass, 53-54; from asst prof anat to assoc prof biol struct, 56-67, PROF BIOL STRUCT, MED SCH, UNIV WASH, 67- *Concurrent Pos:* Nat Res Coun Rockefeller fel, Harvard Med Sch, 54-56; USPHS sr fel, 57-65. *Mem:* AAAS; Am Asn Anat; Electron Micros Soc Am; Am Soc Cell Biol. *Res:* Microscopy and electron microscopy; fixatives; basic cellular structure and function; external cell coats; ultrastructure. *Mailing Add:* Dept of Biol Struct Univ of Wash Med Sch Seattle WA 98195

LUFT, LUDWIG, b Lvov, Poland, Nov 9, 26; nat US; m 52; c 2. PHYSICAL CHEMISTRY. *Educ:* Univ Frankfurt, Dipl, 51; Univ Kans, PhD(phys chem), 56. *Prof Exp:* Asst, Univ Kans, 52-55; asst prof chem, Univ Miami, 55-57; res supvr, MSA Res Corp, 57-58; tech & managerial mem staff, Gen Elec Co, 58-62; sr scientist, Allied Res Assocs, 62-63; dir res, Instrumentation Lab Inc, 63; PRES, LUFT INSTRUMENTS, INC, 63- *Mem:* AAAS; Am Chem Soc; Instrument Soc Am. *Res:* Chemical engineering; automatic controls; methods development; electrochemistry. *Mailing Add:* Hillside Rd Lincoln MA 01773

LUFT, STANLEY JEREMIE, b Turin, Italy, Sept 26, 27; US citizen; m 55; c 4. GEOLOGY. *Educ:* Syracuse Univ, AB, 49; Pa State Col, MS, 51. *Prof Exp:* Asst geol, Pa State Col, 49-51; explor geologist, NJ Zinc Co, 51-54; geologist mineral deposits, US Geol Surv, 54-56; geologist, Northern Pac Rwy Co, 56-58; prof geol & Mineral & head dept, Oriente Univ, 59-60; proj geologist, Callahan Mining Corp, 61; GEOLOGIST, US GEOL SURV, 61- *Mem:* Geol Soc Am; Soc Econ Geol; AAAS; Am Inst Mining, Metall & Petrol Eng. *Res:* Petrography and petrology of volcanic rocks; geology of metallic and nonmetallic deposits; stratigraphy; Pleistocene of northern Kentucky; geology of uranium in Tertiary intermontaine basins. *Mailing Add:* US Geol Surv Mail Stop 913 Box 25046 Fed Ctr Denver CO 80225

LUFT, ULRICH CAMERON, b Berlin, Ger, Apr 25, 10; nat US; m 41; c 1. HUMAN PHYSIOLOGY. *Educ:* Univ Berlin, MD, 37. *Prof Exp:* Chief high altitude physiol, Aeromed Res Inst, Univ Berlin, 37-45, actg dir dept physiol, Univ, 46-47; res physiologist & assoc prof physiol, Sch Aviation Med, Air Univ, Randolph AFB, Tex, 47-54; head, Dept Physiol, Lovelace Found, 54-80; RETIRED. *Concurrent Pos:* Consult human factors group, Comt Space Technol, Nat Adv Comt Aeronaut, 58; consult, Nat Acad Sci, 58 & Air Res & Develop Command, 58; mem adv bd, Off Manned Space Flight, NASA, 65-; assoc physiol, Univ NMex. *Mem:* AAAS; Soc Exp Biol & Med; Am Physiol Soc; Aerospace Med Asn; fel Am Col Chest Physicians. *Res:* Physiology of respiration and circulation; aviation medicine; acclimatization to high altitudes; cold and hot climates; physical exercise; clinical physiology. *Mailing Add:* 1900 Ridgecrest Dr SE Albuquerque NM 87108

LUFTIG, RONALD BERNARD, b Brooklyn, NY, Dec 8, 39; m 61; c 3. MICROBIOLOGY, BIOPHYSICS. *Educ:* City Col New York, BS, 60; NY Univ, MS, 62; Univ Chicago, PhD(biophys), 67. *Prof Exp:* Asst prof microbiol, Med Ctr, Duke Univ, 69-73; sr scientist, Worcester Found Exp Biol, 74-79; PROF MICROBIOL, MED SCH, UNIV SC, 79- *Concurrent Pos:* NSF fel, Calif Inst Technol, 67-69; NIH res grant, Med Ctr, Duke Univ, 70-73; res grants, Worcester Found, 74-79 & Univ SC Med Sch, 79- *Mem:* AAAS; Am Soc Biol Chem; Am Soc Microbiol; Am Soc Cell Biol. *Res:* Viral and membrane ultrastructure; leukemia virus morphogenesis; microtubule function. *Mailing Add:* Dept Microbiol & Immunol Med Sch Univ SC Columbia SC 29208

LUGAR, RICHARD CHARLES, b Philadelphia, Pa. CHEMISTRY. *Educ:* Univ Pa, BS, 62, PhD(chem), 69. *Prof Exp:* ASSOC PROF ORG CHEM, DELAWARE VALLEY COL, 67- mem: Am Chem Soc. *Res:* Conformational analysis of alicyclic systems. *Mailing Add:* Dept of Chem Delaware Valley Col Doylestown PA 18901

LUGASSY, ARMAND AMRAM, b Kenitra, Morocco, July 23, 33; m 66; c 2. MATERIALS SCIENCE, PROSTHODONTICS. *Educ:* Toulouse Fac Med & Pharm, France, Chirurgien-Dentiste, 59; Univ Pa, DDS, 62, PhD(metall, mat sci), 68. *Prof Exp:* Monitor oper dent, Toulouse Fac Med & Pharm, France, 58-59; instr, Sch Dent Med, Univ Pa, 62-63; asst prof biol mat, Dent-Med Sch, Northwestern Univ, 68-71; assoc prof, 71-77, PROF FIXED PROSTHODONTICS, SCH DENT, UNIV OF THE PAC, 77- *Concurrent Pos:* Nat Inst Dent Res traineeship, Sch Metall & Mat Sci, Univ Pa, 63-68; consult, USPHS Hosp, San Francisco, Calif, 71- *Mem:* Am Soc Metals; Int Asn Dent Res. *Res:* Physical properties of calcified tissues; behavior of materials and devices in clinical applications. *Mailing Add:* Dept of Fixed Prosthodontics Univ of the Pac Sch of Dent San Francisco CA 94115

LUGAY, JOAQUIN CASTRO, b Manila, Philippines, Apr 3, 38; US citizen; m 62; c 3. BIOCHEMISTRY, FOOD SCIENCE. *Educ:* Univ Santo Thomas, Manila, BS, 60; State Univ NY, PhD(chem), 69. *Prof Exp:* Chemist brewing, San Miguel Brewey Inc, 60-62; chemist rice lipids, Int Rice Res Inst, 62-63; sr chemist biotechnol, 69-71, res specialist, 71-73, sr res specialist protein, 73-77, SR LAB MGR PROTEIN BIOTECHNOL COFFEE, GEN FOODS CORP, 78- *Mem:* AAAS; Am Chem Soc; Sigma Xi. *Res:* Isolation and characterization of enzymes; utilization of enzymes in foods; protein texturization; meat analogs; pet food palatability; functional properties of proteins; protein modification; alternate sources of proteins. *Mailing Add:* Gen Foods Corp West North St Dover NY 19901

LUGINBUHL, GERALDINE HOBSON, b Los Angeles, Calif, Feb 27, 44; m 65; c 1. MICROBIOLOGY. *Educ:* Stanford Univ, BA, 65; Univ NC, Chapel Hill, PhD(bact, immunol), 71. *Prof Exp:* NIH fel bact, Duke Univ, 71-74; asst prof, 74-80, ASSOC PROF MICROBIOL, NC STATE UNIV, 80- *Mem:* Am Soc Microbiol; Sigma Xi. *Res:* Genetics and physiology of virulence; alcaligenes. *Mailing Add:* Dept of Microbiol NC State Univ Raleigh NC 27650

LUGINBUHL, WILLIAM HOSSFELD, b Des Moines, Iowa, Mar 11, 29; m 55; c 5. PATHOLOGY. *Educ:* Iowa State Univ, BS, 49; Northwestern Univ, MD, 53. *Prof Exp:* Intern, Wesley Mem Hosp, Chicago, Ill, 53-54; resident path, Children's Mem Hosp, 54-55; resident, Univ Hosps Cleveland, Ohio, 55-57; from asst prof to assoc prof, 60-67, assoc dean col, 67-70, DEAN HEALTH SCI & COL, COL MED, UNIV VT, 70-, PROF PATH, 67- *Concurrent Pos:* Fel, Col Med, Univ Vt, 59-60. *Mem:* Col Am Path; Am Soc Clin Path. *Res:* Gynecologic and obstetrical pathology; endometrial anatomy and physiology. *Mailing Add:* Off of the Dean Univ of Vt Col of Med Burlington VT 05401

LUGMAIR, GUENTER WILHELM, b Wels, Austria, Feb 5, 40; m 65; c 2. COSMOCHEMISTRY, GEOCHRONOLOGY. *Educ:* Univ Vienna, Austria, PhD(physics), 68. *Prof Exp:* Fel nuclear physics, Max Plank Inst, Mainz, Ger, 65-68; chemist, 68-71, asst res chemist, 71-77, ASSOC RES CHEM, UNIV CALIF, SAN DIEGO, 77-, ASSOC RES GEOCHEM, SCRIPPS INST OCEANOG, 79- *Concurrent Pos:* Consult, Jet Propulsion Lab, Calif Inst Technol, 69-71; co-investr, Lunar & Planetary Sci Prog, NASA, 69-, mem-consult, Rev Panel, 78-80. *Mem:* Am Geophys Union; fel Meteoritical Soc. *Res:* Origin and history of the solar system; nucleosynthesis; extinct radioactivities; geo dating of terrestial and extraterrestial materials; cosmic ray effects. *Mailing Add:* Dept of Chem Code B-107 Univ of Calif San Diego La Jolla CA 92093

LUGO, ARIEL EMILIO, ecology, see previous edition

LUGO, HERMINIO LUGO, b San German, PR, June 6, 18; m 41; c 2. PLANT PHYSIOLOGY. *Educ:* Polytech Inst, PR, BA, 39; Cornell Univ, MS, 48, PhD, 54. *Prof Exp:* Teacher pub sch, PR, 41-46; instr biol & bot, Polytech Inst PR, 46-47; from asst prof to prof biol, bot & plant physiol, Col Agr, Mayaguez, 48-60; prof biol, 60-69, asst dean studies, 60-66, acad coord, Rio Piedras Campus, 66-69, PROF ECOL, UNIV PR, 69-, DIR PREMED STUDIES, 71-, DIR CAYEY UNIV COL, 78- *Concurrent Pos:* Fel, Inst Ecol, Univ Ga, 68-69. *Mem:* Bot Soc Am; Am Soc Agr Sci. *Res:* Germination of vanilla seeds. *Mailing Add:* Off of Dir Cayey Univ Col Cayey PR 00633

LUGO-LOPEZ, MIGUEL ANGEL, b Mayaguez, PR, July 21, 21; m 45; c 2. SOIL SCIENCE. *Educ:* Univ PR, BSA, 43; Cornell Univ, MS, 45, PhD(soil sci), 50. *Prof Exp:* Asst, Fed Exp Sta, PR, 43-44; asst prof agron, Univ PR, 46-48, asst scientist & assoc soil scientist, Agr Exp Sta, 48-57, assoc soil scientist & soil scientist chg, Gurabo Substa, 57-60; asst dir chg, Univ PR, Mayaguez, 60-61, asst dir, Agr Exp Sta, 61-64, actg dir, 64-66, assoc dir, 66-69, dir off progs & plans & assoc dean, Col Agr Sci, 69-72, dean students, 72-74, prof soil sci & soil scientist, 74-76. *Concurrent Pos:* Consult, Cornell Univ-AID, 74-78. *Mem:* Soil Sci Soc Am; Am Soc Agron; Am Soc Agr Sci; Int Soc Soils. *Res:* Tropical soils, fertility, management; physical properties of tropical soils. *Mailing Add:* Box 506 Isabela Agr Exp Sta Isabela PR 00662

LUGT, HANS JOSEF, b Bonn, Ger, Sept 12, 30; US citizen; m 57; c 2. FLUID DYNAMICS. *Educ:* Univ Bonn, Vordiplom, 52; Aachen Tech Univ, Diplom, 54; Stuttgart Tech Univ, PhD(eng), 60. *Prof Exp:* Asst hydraul, Ruhrgas AG, Essen, Ger, 54-57, head physics lab, 57-60; res physicist hydrodyn, US Naval Weapons Lab, Va, 60-66; head, Numerical Mech Div, 74-78, SR RES SCIENTIST, DAVID W TAYLOR NAVAL SHIP RES & DEVELOP CTR, 67- *Concurrent Pos:* Lectr, Am Univ, 62-66; prof lectr, 68-69; Alexander von Humboldt US sr scientist award, Ger Govt, 81. *Honors & Awards:* David W Taylor Award 1974, US Navy, 75. *Mem:* Am Phys Soc; Sigma Xi; Asn Appl Math & Mech Ger. *Res:* Mathematical fluid dynamics; vortex motion; rotating fluids; numerical solution of Navier-Stokes equations; flow simulation with computer. *Mailing Add:* Naval Ship Res & Develop Ctr Bethesda MD 20084

LUGTHART, GARRIT JOHN, JR, b Los Angeles, Calif, Feb 11, 23; m 55; c 3. ENTOMOLOGY, GENETICS. *Educ:* Mich State Univ, BS, 50, MS, 51; Univ Wis, PhD(entom), 59. *Prof Exp:* Asst prof biol, Adrian Col, 56-61; ASSOC PROF BIOL, LE MOYNE COL, NY, 61-, CHMN DEPT, 79- *Mem:* AAAS; Entom Soc Am. *Res:* Biology and control of insects injurious to man. *Mailing Add:* Dept of Biol Le Moyne Col Syracuse NY 13214

LUH, BOR SHIUN, b Shanghai, China, Jan 13, 16; m 40; c 1. FOOD SCIENCE. *Educ:* Chiao Tung Univ, BS, 38; Univ Calif, MS, 48, PhD(agr chem), 52. *Prof Exp:* Instr, Chiao Tung Univ, 38-41; chemist, Ma Ling Canned Foods Co, Ltd, 41-46; asst, 48-51, jr specialist, Dept Food Technol, 52-56, from jr food technologist to assoc food technologist, 56-69, FOOD TECHNOLOGIST, UNIV CALIF, DAVIS, 69-, LECTR FOOD TECHNOL, 57- *Concurrent Pos:* Consult. *Mem:* AAAS; Am Chem Soc; Inst Food Technol; Am Oil Chem Soc; Am Asn Cereal Chemists. *Res:* Chemistry of foods; food processing; biochemistry. *Mailing Add:* Dept of Food Sci Univ of Calif Davis CA 95616

LUH, JIANG, b Haining, Chekiang, China, June 24, 32; m 56; c 3. ALGEBRA. *Educ:* Taiwan Normal Univ, BS, 56; Univ Nebr, MS, 59; Univ Mich, PhD(math), 63. *Prof Exp:* Assoc prof math, Ind State Univ, 63-66 & Wright State Campus, Miami-Ohio State Univ, 66-68; assoc prof, 68-71, PROF MATH, NC STATE UNIV, 71- *Mem:* Am Math Soc; Math Asn Am. *Res:* Ring theory; semi-group theory; linear algebra. *Mailing Add:* 5613 Deblyn Ave Deblyn Park Raleigh NC 27612

LUH, JOHNSON YANG-SENG, b Shanghai, China, Apr 9, 25; US citizen; m 57; c 2. ELECTRICAL ENGINEERING, APPLIED MATHEMATICS. *Educ:* Utopia Univ, China, BS, 47; Harvard Univ, MS, 50; Univ Minn, PhD(elec eng), 63. *Prof Exp:* Teaching fel elec eng, Harvard Univ, 50-51; engr, Nat Pneumatic Co, 51-56 & Curtiss-Wright Corp, 56-57; assoc engr, Int Bus Mach Corp, 57-58, staff engr, 62-63; instr elec eng, Univ Minn, 58-60; sr res scientist, Honeywell, Inc, 63-65; assoc prof, 65-71, PROF ELEC ENG, PURDUE UNIV, 71- *Concurrent Pos:* Lectr, Univ Minn, 63-65; prin investr, NASA res grant, Jet Propulsion Lab, 65- *Mem:* Soc Indust & Appl Math; sr mem Inst Elec & Electronics Engrs; sr mem Am Astronaut Soc. *Res:* Control and information systems and computer aided engineering design, especially bounded-state, stochastic control, learning and communication, and data reduction systems. *Mailing Add:* Sch of Elec Eng Purdue Univ West Lafayette IN 47907

LUHAN, JOSEPH ANTON, b Chicago, Ill, Feb 6, 01; m 44. NEUROLOGY. *Educ:* Northwestern Univ, BS, 27, MD, 28, MS, 31, PhD(neurol), 34; Am Bd Psychiat & Neurol, dipl, 38. *Prof Exp:* Clin asst neurol, Northwestern Univ, 28-34, instr, 34-35, assoc, 35-41; from assoc clin prof to clin prof neurol & psychiat, 41-54, prof, 54-73, EMER PROF NEUROL & PSYCHIAT, STRITCH SCH MED, LOYOLA UNIV CHICAGO, 73- *Concurrent Pos:* Practicing physician, 28-; asst dir, Psychiat Inst, Munic Court, Ill, 35-40; attend neurologist, Cook County Hosp, 39-59; dir neuropath lab, 40-61; sr attend neurologist & psychiatrist, Loretto Hosp, 41-73, dept chmn, 62-69; expert civilian consult to Surgeon Gen, US Dept Army, Percy Jones Gen Hosp, Mich, 47-50; former consult neuropsychiatrist, St Anthony's Hosp, Chicago & McNeal Mem Hosp, Berwyn, Ill; attend neurologist, Loyola Univ Hosp, Maywood, Ill, 69-73; attend psychiatrist, Mem Hosp, Hollywood, Fla, 73- *Mem:* Fel AAAS; AMA; fel Am Psychiat Asn; Am Neurol Asn; fel Am Acad Neurol. *Res:* Neuropathology; clinical neurology and psychiatry. *Mailing Add:* 4016 Grant St Hollywood FL 33021

LUHBY, ADRIAN LEONARD, b New York, NY, Dec 21, 16; m 67; c 1. HEMATOLOGY, PEDIATRICS. *Educ:* Columbia Univ, AB, 38; NY Univ, MD, 43. *Prof Exp:* Intern path & bact, Mt Sinai Hosp, New York, 44-45, intern med & surg, 45-46; res assoc immunol, Children's Hosp, Ohio State Univ, 48-49, asst resident pediat, Hosp & instr, Univ, 49-50; from instr to assoc prof, 50-59, PROF PEDIAT, NEW YORK MED COL, 59- *Concurrent Pos:* Fel hemat, Children's Hosp, Boston, Mass, 46-48; pres, Am Bd Nutrit, 76- *Honors & Awards:* Distinguished Serv Award, Cooley's Anemia Found, 63. *Mem:* Am Asn Cancer Res; Am Physiol Soc; Am Inst Nutrit; Am Soc Clin Nutrit; Am Hemat Soc. *Res:* Morphologic hematology; oncology; nutrition; megaloblastic anemias; physiology, metabolism, biochemistry and nutrition of folic acid, vitamin B-12 and vitamin B-6. *Mailing Add:* Dept of Pediat Bird S Coler Hosp New York NY 10044

LUI, YIU-KWAN, b Hong Kong, Mar 24, 37; US citizen; m 67; c 1. PHYSICAL CHEMISTRY. *Educ:* Chung Chi Col, Hong Kong, BS, 59; Lehigh Univ, MS, 61, PhD(phys chem), 66. *Prof Exp:* Res chemist, Titanium Pigment Div, NL Indust, 65-74, Indust Chem Div, 75; res chemist, 76-78, sr res chemist, 78-81, RES ASSOC, ENGELHARD INDUST DIV, ENGELHARD CORP, 81- *Mem:* Am Chem Soc. *Res:* Heterogeneous catalysis; preparation and characterization of precious metal catalysts; colloid and surface properties of silica and alumina; physical properties of rheological additives; dispersion stability; physical and surface properties of titanium dioxide pigments. *Mailing Add:* Engelhard Indust Div Engelhard Corp Edison NJ 08817

LUIBRAND, RICHARD THOMAS, b Detroit, Mich, Apr 13, 45. ORGANIC CHEMISTRY. *Educ:* Wayne State Univ, BS, 66; Univ Wis, PhD(org chem), 71. *Prof Exp:* Fel, Alexander von Humboldt Found, WGer, 71-72; from asst prof to assoc prof, 72-81, PROF ORG CHEM, CALIF STATE UNIV, HAYWARD, 81- *Concurrent Pos:* Cottrell res grant, Res Corp, 73. *Mem:* Am Chem Soc; AAAS. *Res:* Reaction mechanisms in organic chemistry; natural products chemistry. *Mailing Add:* Dept of Chem Calif State Univ Hayward CA 94542

LUICK, JACK ROGER, b Niagara Falls, NY, Jan 2, 21; m 48; c 8. PHYSIOLOGY, NUTRITION. *Educ:* Univ Calif, BS, 50, PhD(nutrit), 56. *Prof Exp:* Assoc specialist radiobiol, Univ Calif, 56-58, assoc res physiologist, 58-64; UN expert nutrit, Inst Appl Nuclear Energy in Agr, Yugoslavia, 64-65; assoc prof physiol, 65-67, PROF NUTRIT, UNIV ALASKA, 67- *Concurrent Pos:* Fulbright res scholar nutrit, NEng, Australia, 65-66. *Mem:* AAAS; Am Dairy Sci Asn; Am Soc Animal Sci; Am Physiol Soc. *Res:* Metabolism of intact animals; environmental and nutritional physiology of arctic ungulates, especially reindeer, caribou, and moose; quantitative aspects of intermediary metabolism with interspecies comparisons; mineral and water metabolism. *Mailing Add:* Inst of Arctic Biol Univ of Alaska Fairbanks AK 99701

LUINE, VICTORIA NALL, b Pine Bluff, Ark, Apr 22, 45. NEUROCHEMISTRY. *Educ:* Allegheny Col, BS, 67; State Univ NY, Buffalo, PhD(pharmacol), 71. *Prof Exp:* Res assoc, 72-75, asst prof neurochem, 75-77, MEM FAC, DEPT PHYSIOL PSYCHOL, ROCKEFELLER UNIV, 77- *Mem:* AAAS; Soc Neurosci. *Res:* Effect of hormones and drugs on enzymes and metabolites in the developing central nervous system. *Mailing Add:* Dept of Neurochem Rockefeller Univ New York NY 10021

LUISADA, ALDO AUGUSTO, b Florence, Italy, June 26, 01; nat US; m 31; c 1. MEDICINE, PHYSIOLOGY. *Educ:* Univ Florence, MD, 24. *Prof Exp:* Pvt docent med & clin med, Univ Padua, 29-32; asst prof med, Univ Naples, 31-35; prof, Univs Sassari & Ferrara, 35-38; instr physiol & pharmacol & lectr med, Med Sch, Tufts Univ, 43-49; from asst prof to assoc prof med, 49-60, dir div cardiol, 52-71, prof cardiovasc res & dir div, 61-72, prof med, 60-71, prof physiol & biophys, 69-71, DISTINGUISHED PROF PHYSIOL & MED, CHICAGO MED SCH, 71- *Concurrent Pos:* Assoc, Beth Israel Hosp, Boston, Mass, 43-49; chief cardiac clin, Mt Sinai Hosp, Chicago, 49-60, from assoc attend cardiologist to attend cardiologist, 55-71; consult, La Rabida Sanitarium, 53-57 & Hines Vet Admin Hosp, 54-; sr med officer, Oak Forest Hosp, 71-, chmn cardiol, 72- *Mem:* AAAS; fel Am Physiol Soc; Soc Exp Biol & Med; fel AMA; Am Heart Asn. *Res:* Electrokymography; phonocardiography; echocardiography; pulmonary circulation, intracardiac pressures; experimental and clinical studies of pulmonary edema; digitalis; heart failure. *Mailing Add:* 5000 S Cornell Ave Chicago IL 60615

LUISADA-OPPER, ANITA VICTORIA, biochemistry, clinical chemistry, see previous edition

LUK, GORDON DAVID, b Shangai, China, Nov 15, 50; US citizen; m 73; c 2. POLYAMINES, GASTROENTEROLOGY. *Educ:* Univ Pa, BA, 71; Harvard Med Sch, MD, 75; Am Bd Internal Med, cert med, 78, cert gastroenterol, 79. *Prof Exp:* Resident med, 75-77, fel gastroenterol, 77-79, instr med, 79-80, ASST PROF MED & ONCOL, JOHNS HOPKINS UNIV, 80- *Concurrent Pos:* Physician, Johns Hopkins Hosp, 79- *Mem:* Am Fedn Clin Res; Am Col Physician; Am Gastroenterol Asn; Am Soc Gastrointestinal Endoscopy; Am Asn Study Liver Dis. *Res:* Cell proliferation and differentiation with special emphasis on the potential regulatory role of polyamines; diseases of gastrointestinal epithelia and neoplastic diseases. *Mailing Add:* Johns Hopkins Hosp Baltimore MD 21205

LUK, KING SING, b Canton, China, Sept 1, 32; US citizen; m 57; c 4. STRUCTURAL ENGINEERING. *Educ:* Los Angeles State Col, BS, 57; Univ Southern Calif, MSCE, 60; Univ Calif, Los Angeles, PhD(dynamics, soils & struct eng), 71. *Prof Exp:* Chief engr, R E Rule, Inc, Calif, 58-60; from asst prof to assoc prof, 60-65, from assoc chmn to chmn dept, 66-72, PROF CIVIL ENG, CALIF STATE UNIV, LOS ANGELES, 70- *Concurrent Pos:* Consult, King S Luk & Assoc, Calif, 60-; comnr, Calif Seismic Safety Comn, 80- *Mem:* Fel Am Soc Civil Engrs. *Res:* Engineering education; structural engineering in design and practice of reinforced concrete and steel structures; foundations; time dependent soil and foundation engineering; reinforced concretes. *Mailing Add:* Dept of Civil Eng 5151 University Dr Los Angeles CA 90032

LUKACH, CARL ANDREW, b Wilkes-Barre, Pa, Dec 18, 30; m 53; c 3. ORGANIC CHEMISTRY, POLYMER CHEMISTRY. *Educ:* Lehigh Univ, BS, 52, MS, 53; Univ Notre Dame, PhD(org chem), 57. *Prof Exp:* Res chemist, Hercules Inc, 56-69, res supvr, 69-73, res mgr, Org Div, 73-78, mgr, Chem Sci Div, 78-79, proj mgr cellulose derivaties, 80-81. *Mem:* Am Chem Soc; Sigma Xi. *Res:* Polymerization and copolymerization of olefins and olefin oxides; polymerization kinetics; conformational analysis; reverse osmosis; cross-linking agents; paper chemistry; cellulose chemistry. *Mailing Add:* 4807 Lancaster Pike Wilmington DE 19807

LUKACS, EUGENE, b Szombathely, Hungary, Aug 14, 06; US citizen; m 35. MATHEMATICS. *Educ:* Univ Vienna, PhD(math), 30. *Prof Exp:* Mathematicianm US Naval Ord Test Sta, Calif, 48-50 & Nat Bur Standards, 50-53; head statist br, Off Naval Res, 53-55; prof math & dir statist lab, Cath Univ, 55-72; prof math, Bowling Green State Univ, 72-75; vis prof, Tech Univ Vienna, 75-77; RETIRED. *Concurrent Pos:* From lectr to adj prof, Am Univ, 54-56; vis prof, Sorbonne, 61, 66, Swiss Fed Inst Technol, 62, Inst Technol Austria, 70 & Univ Hull, 71. *Mem:* Fel AAAS; fel Inst Math Statist; Am Math Soc; fel Am Statist Asn; Biomet Soc. *Res:* Probability theory; mathematical statistics. *Mailing Add:* 3727 Van Ness St NW Washington DC 20016

LUKAS, GEORGE, b Budapest, Hungary, Mar 16, 31; m 56; c 2. INDUSTRIAL PHARMACY. *Educ:* Univ Budapest, BS, 54; Polytech Inst Brooklyn, MS, 60; Mass Inst Technol, PhD(org chem), 63; NY Univ, MBA, 72. *Prof Exp:* Develop engr, United Pharmaceut Works, Hungary, 54-56; chemist, Avery Industs, Calif, 57; develop engr, Chas Pfizer & Co, 57-59; NIH fel, Inst Chem Natural Substances, Gif-Sur-Yvette, France, 63-64; res chemist, 64-65, res biochemist, 65-67, group leader, Biochem Dept, 67-71, mgr drug metabol, 71-80, assoc dir drug metabol, 80-81, DIR PHARMACEUT & PHARM TECHNOL, CIBA-GEIGY CORP, 81- *Concurrent Pos:* adj assoc prof, Dept Pharmacol, NY Med Col, 80- *Mem:* Am Soc Pharmacol & Exp Therapeut; Am Chem Soc; NY Acad Sci; Am Pharmaceut Asn. *Res:* Chemistry of natural products; pharmacodynamics; absorption and disposition of drugs. *Mailing Add:* 6 Devoe Rd Armonk NY 10504

LUKAS, JOAN DONALDSON, b New Haven, Conn, June 19, 42; m 63; c 2. MATHEMATICS. *Educ:* Columbia Univ, AB, 63; Mass Inst Technol, PhD(math), 67. *Prof Exp:* Asst prof, 67-74, ASSOC PROF MATH, UNIV MASS,BOSTON, 74- *Concurrent Pos:* Vis lectr, Brandeis Univ, 71. *Mem:* Am Math Soc; Math Asn Am; Asn Symbolic Logic. *Res:* Mathematical logic; recursive function theory. *Mailing Add:* Dept of Math Univ of Mass Boston MA 02116

LUKAS, KAREN JEANNE, b Jersey City, NJ, Apr 14, 41. MARINE GEOLOGY. *Educ:* Syracuse Univ, BS, 63; Harvard Univ, AM, 65; Univ RI, PhD(oceanog), 73. *Prof Exp:* Asst scientist, NY State Geol Surv, 65-66; lectr biol, Boston Univ, 70-71, res asst, 71-72, res assoc, 72-73; scientist, Harbor Br Found, Inc, 73-76; asst prof, 76-82, ASSOC PROF GEOL, VASSAR COL, 82- *Mem:* Soc Econ Paleontologists & Mineralogists; Sigma Xi. *Res:* Taxonomy and ecology of endolithic marine mycrophyta; organism-sediment interrelationships; coral reef ecology. *Mailing Add:* Vassar Col Box 316 Poughkeepsie NY 12601

LUKAS, RONALD JOHN, b Syracuse, NY, Aug 22, 49. NEUROCHEMISTRY. *Educ:* State Univ NY, Cortland, BS, 71; State Univ NY Downstate Med Ctr, PhD(biophysics), 76. *Prof Exp:* Fel, Univ Calif, Berkeley, 76-78; res assoc, Lab Chem Biodynamics, 78-79; fel neurobiol, Stanford Univ, 79-80; NEUROCHEMIST NEUROPHARMACOL, BARROW NEUROL INST, PHOENIX, ARIZ, 80- *Concurrent Pos:* Adj asst prof pharmacol, Univ Ariz, Tucson, 79-80. *Mem:* Soc Neurosci; Am Soc Neurochem; Biophys Soc; Sigma Xi. *Res:* Neurotransmitters, neurotoxins and synaptic receptors, nervous system hormone, tropic factors and molecular aspects of developmental neurobiology. *Mailing Add:* Div Neurobiol Barrow Neurol Inst 350 W Thomas Rd Phoenix AZ 85013

LUKASEWYCZ, OMELAN ALEXANDER, m 68; c 2. IMMUNOBIOLOGY, ACADEMIC ADMINISTRATION. *Educ:* St Joseph's Col, Pa, AB, 64; Villanova Univ, MS, 68; Bryn Mawr Col, PhD(microbiol), 72. *Prof Exp:* Res asst microbiol, Univ Tex, Austin, 70-72; lectr microbiol, Med Sch, Univ Mich, Ann Arbor, 73-75; asst prof, 75-78, ASSOC PROF MED MICROBIOL & IMMUNOL, SCH MED, UNIV MINN, DULUTH, 78-, ASST DEAN CURRICULAR AFFAIRS, 77- *Concurrent Pos:* Res scholar tumor immunol, Med Sch, Univ Mich, Ann Arbor, 73-75. *Mem:* Am Soc Microbiol; AAAS; Am Asn Immunologists; Fedn Am Socs Exp Med; Sigma Xi. *Res:* Evaluation of immunocompetent cell populations in immune mechanisms of leukemia; contribution of B and T cell subsets; role of macrophage; role of histocompatibility antigens; role of copper in the immune response; effects of copper deficiency on tumor immunity. *Mailing Add:* Dept Med Microbiol & Immunol Univ of Minn Med Sch Duluth MN 55812

LUKASIEWICZ, JULIUS, b Warsaw, Poland, Nov 7, 19; US citizen; m 41; c 2. AEROSPACE ENGINEERING. *Educ:* Univ London, BSc, 43, DIC, 45, DSc(eng), 66; Polish Tech Univ, Eng, dipl, 44. *Prof Exp:* Sr sci officer, Aerodyn Dept, Royal Aircraft Estab, Eng, 45-48; head high speed aerodyn lab, Nat Res Coun Can, 49-57; chief Von Karman Gas Dynamics Facil, Arnold Eng Develop Ctr, ARO, Inc, Tenn, 58-68; prof aerospace eng & assoc dean grad studies & res, Col Eng, Va Polytech Inst & State Univ, 68-70, Whittemore prof eng, 70-71; PROF ENG, CARLETON UNIV, 71- *Concurrent Pos:* Chmn, Aeroballistic Range Asn, 61-62; mem, Adv Group Aeronaut Res & Develop, NATO, 62-68; consult adv comt, US Air Force Systs Command, Nat Acad Sci, 69-71; mgr transp study, Sci Coun Can, 77-78. *Mem:* Fel Am Inst Aeronaut & Astronaut; fel Can Aeronaut & Space Inst; fel Brit Inst Mech Engrs; NY Acad Sci; Supersonic Tunnel Asn. *Res:* High speed aerodynamics; test facilities; energy and transportation; technology-society interaction. *Mailing Add:* 46 Whippoorwill Dr Ottawa ON K1J 7H9 Can

LUKASIK, STEPHEN JOSEPH, b Staten Island, NY, Mar 19, 31; m 53; c 4. PHYSICS. *Educ:* Rensselaer Polytech Inst, BS, 51; Mass Inst Technol, SM, 53, PhD(physics), 56. *Prof Exp:* Asst physics, Mass Inst Technol, 51-55; scientist, Westinghouse Elec Corp, 55-57; chief, Fluid Physics Div, Davidson Lab, Stevens Inst Technol, 57-66, assoc res prof physics, 59-66; dir nuclear test detection, Advan Res Projs Agency, 66-68, dept dir, 68-71, dir, 71-74; vpres, Systs Develop Div, Xerox Corp, 75-76; vpres nat security res, Rand Corp, 77-78, chief scientist, 78-79; CHIEF SCIENTIST, FED COMMUN COMN, 79- *Concurrent Pos:* Acoust engr, Bolt, Beranek & Newman Co, 52-55; consult, Vitro labs, Vitro Corp Am, 59-66; mem, Bd Trustees, Stevens Inst Technol, 75- & Bd Overseers, Ctr Naval Anal, Univ Rochester, 75-77; mem, Comput Sci Adv Comt, Stanford Univ, 76- *Honors & Awards:* Ottens Res Award, 63. *Mem:* AAAS; Am Phys Soc; Sigma Xi. *Res:* Relaxation processes in gases and liquids; viscous boundary layer phenomena; energy dissipation processes in water waves; interaction of explosives with magnetic fields. *Mailing Add:* 9301 Kentsdale Dr Potomac MD 20854

LUKE, HERBERT HODGES, b Pavo, Ga, Feb 2, 23; m 46; c 2. PLANT PATHOLOGY. *Educ:* Univ Ga, BS, 50; La State Univ, MS, 52, PhD, 54. *Prof Exp:* Plant pathologist, Delta Br Exp Sta, USDA, Miss, 54-55, PLANT PATHOLOGIST, AGR EXP STA, UNIV FLA, USDA, 55-, PROF PLANT PATH, 70- *Mem:* Am Phytopath Soc. *Res:* Chemical nature of disease resistance in plants, particularly isolation and identification of host metabolites that inhibit pathogenesis of pathogen; chemical and genetic control of small grain diseases. *Mailing Add:* Agr Exp Sta Univ of Fla Gainesville FL 32611

LUKE, JAMES LINDSAY, b Cleveland, Ohio, Aug 29, 32; m 57; c 3. PATHOLOGY. *Educ:* Columbia Univ, BS, 56; Western Reserve Univ, MD, 60. *Prof Exp:* Intern Path, Yale-New Haven Hosp, 60-61; chief resident, Inst Path, Western Reserve Univ, 61-63; staff researcher, Lab Exp Path, Nat Inst Arthritis & Metab Dis, 63-65; assoc med examr forensic path, Off Chief Med Examr, New York, 65-67; prof forensic path, Sch Med, Univ Okla, 67-71; CHIEF MED EXAMR, WASHINGTON, DC, 71- *Concurrent Pos:* State med examr, Okla, 67-71; clin prof path, Georgetown Univ, George Washington Univ & Howard Univ, 71- *Mem:* Fel Am Acad Forensic Sci. *Res:* Epidemiological research in legal medicine; pathology of strangulation, hanging and sudden natural death; aspects of forensic pathology as related to pediatrics; experimental pathology of quantitated blunt force injury. *Mailing Add:* 5240 Loughboro Rd NW Washington DC 20016

LUKE, JON CHRISTIAN, b Minneapolis, Minn, Aug 10, 40. APPLIED MATHEMATICS. *Educ:* Mass Inst Technol, SB, 62, SM, 63; Calif Inst Technol, PhD(appl math), 66. *Prof Exp:* NSF fel, 66-68; asst prof math, Univ Calif, San Diego, 68-73; postdoctoral assoc, Univ Minn, 73-74; vis assoc, Calif Inst Technol, 74-75; ASST PROF MATH SCI, IND UNIV-PURDUE UNIV, INDIANAPOLIS, 75- *Mem:* Sigma Xi; Am Math Soc. *Res:* Nonlinear methods in applied mathematics; applications in nonlinear wave problems, geomorphology, economics biophysics, and acoustics. *Mailing Add:* Dept of Math Ind Univ-Purdue Univ 1201 E 38 St Indianapolis IN 46205

LUKE, ROBERT A, b Rigby, Idaho, Jan 5, 38; m 64; c 6. PARTICLE PHYSICS. *Educ:* Utah State Univ, BS, 62, MS, 66, PhD(physics), 68. *Prof Exp:* Asst prof, 68-72, assoc prof, 72-77, PROF PHYSICS, BOISE STATE UNIV, 77- *Mem:* Am Asn Physics Teachers; Am Nuclear Soc. *Res:* X-ray investigation of clay mixtures; multi-pion production in pion proton interactions. *Mailing Add:* 9121 Pattie Dr Boise ID 83704

LUKE, STANLEY D, b Sialkot, WPakistan, Jan 1, 28; m 52; c 5. MATHEMATICS. *Educ:* Univ Panjab, WPakistan, BA, 47, MA, 49; Carnegie-Mellon Univ, MS, 54; Univ Pittsburgh, PhD(math), 68. *Prof Exp:* Prof math, Gordon Col, WPakistan, 49-64; instr, Univ Pittsburgh, 67-68; PROF MATH, NEBR WESLEYAN UNIV, 68- *Mem:* Math Asn Am. *Res:* Mathematical analysis with special interest in summability. *Mailing Add:* Dept of Math Nebr Wesleyan Univ Lincoln NE 68504

LUKE, YUDELL LEO, b Kansas City, Mo, June 26, 18; m 42; c 4. MATHEMATICS. *Educ:* Univ Ill, BS, 39, MS, 40. *Prof Exp:* Asst math, Univ Ill, 40-42; res mathematician, Midwest Res Inst, 46-48, engr chg anal, 48-50, head math anal sect, 50-67, prin adv math, 67-71; prof, 71-78, CURATORS' PROF MATH, UNIV MO-KANSAS CITY, 78- *Mem:* Am Math Soc; Soc Indust & Appl Math; Math Asn Am. *Res:* Numerical analysis and applied mathematics. *Mailing Add:* Dept of Math Univ of Mo Kansas City MO 64110

LUKEHART, CHARLES MARTIN, b DuBois, Pa, Dec 21, 46; m 73. ORGANOMETALLIC CHEMISTRY. *Educ:* Pa State Univ, BS, 68; Mass Inst Technol, PhD(inorg chem), 72. *Prof Exp:* Res assoc chem, Tex A&M Univ, 72-73; asst prof, 73-77, ASSOC PROF INORG CHEM, VANDERBILT UNIV, 77- *Concurrent Pos:* Alfred P Sloan res fel, 79-83. *Mem:* Am Chem Soc; Sigma Xi. *Res:* Synthesis, characterization and chemical reactivity of organometallic and coordination complexes containing transition metals. *Mailing Add:* Dept of Chem Vanderbilt Univ Nashville TN 37235

LUKEN, WILLIAM LOUIS, b Dayton, Ohio, Feb 15, 47; m 73. THEORETICAL CHEMISTRY. *Educ:* Mass Inst of Technol, BS, 69; Yale Univ, PhD(chem), 74. *Prof Exp:* Fel chem, Yale Univ, 74-76; ASST PROF CHEM, DUKE UNIV, 76- *Res:* Theory of the electronic structure of atoms and molecules; electron correlation effects; energies of electronic states of atoms and molecules; electron correlation effects; energies of electronic states of atoms and molecules; radiative transition probabilities; molecular potential energy surfaces. *Mailing Add:* Paul M Gross Chem Lab Duke Univ Durham NC 27706

LUKENS, FRANCIS DRING WETHERILL, b Philadelphia, Pa, Oct 5, 99; m 33; c 2. MEDICINE. *Educ:* Yale Univ, AB, 21; Univ Pa, MD, 25. *Prof Exp:* Intern, Pa Hosp, 25-27, resident med, 27-28; from instr to prof, Univ Pa, 30-66, dir, George S Cox Med Res Inst, 36-66; PROF MED, UNIV PITTSBURGH, 66- *Concurrent Pos:* Jacques Loeb fel med, Johns Hopkins Univ, 28-30; chief staff, Vet Admin Hosp, 66-70, staff physician, 70- *Mem:* Am Physiol Soc; Soc Exp Biol & Med; Am Soc Clin Invest; Endocrine Soc (pres, 65); fel AMA. *Res:* Diabetes mellitus; endocrine control of metabolism. *Mailing Add:* Dept Med Univ Pittsburgh 4200 Fifth Ave Pittsburgh PA 15260

LUKENS, HERBERT RICHARD, JR, b Coquille, Ore, May 19, 21; m 45; c 2. CHEMISTRY, PSYCHOPHYSIOLOGY. *Educ:* Univ Calif, Berkeley, BA, 45; US Int Univ, San Diego, MA, 75, PhD(human behav), 78. *Prof Exp:* Chemist, Albers Milling Co, 45-46, Consumers Yeast Co, 46-48, Tracerlab Inc, 48-55, Shell Develop Co, 55-62 & Gen Atomic, 62-73; CHEMIST, IRT CORP, 73- *Concurrent Pos:* Family counsr, San Diego Youth Serv, 75-77, consult, 77- *Mem:* Am Asn Marriage & Family Therapists; Am Chem Soc. *Res:* Anxiety, its psychophysiology and existential aspects; biochemistry, immunochemical applications; nucleonics, nuclear fuel cycle. *Mailing Add:* 5616 Abalone Pl La Jolla CA 92037

LUKENS, LEWIS NELSON, b Philadelphia, Pa, Jan 21, 27; m 64; c 4. BIOCHEMISTRY. *Educ:* Harvard Univ, AB, 49; Univ Pa, PhD(biochem), 58. *Prof Exp:* Instr biochem, Mass Inst Technol, 56-58; Nat Res Coun res fel chem, Columbia Univ, 58-59, USPHS res fel, 59-60; asst prof biochem, Yale Univ, 64-66; assoc prof, 66-73, chmn biol dept, 78-81, PROF BIOCHEM, WESLEYAN UNIV, 73- *Mem:* Am Soc Biol Chem. *Res:* Protein synthesis and its control in eukaryotes, especially collagen. *Mailing Add:* Dept of Biol Wesleyan Univ Middletown CT 06457

LUKENS, PAUL W, JR, b Hibbing, Minn, Apr 24, 28; m 60; c 2. MAMMALOGY. *Educ:* Univ Minn, BS, 52, PhD(zool), 63; Tex A&M Univ, MS, 56. *Prof Exp:* From instr to assoc prof, 61-70, PROF ZOOL, UNIV WIS-SUPERIOR, 70- *Concurrent Pos:* Bd regents res grant, Univ Wis, 65-66. *Mem:* Am Soc Mammal. *Res:* Identification, interpretation and paleoecology of vertebrate faunas from archaeological sites; paleozoology; environmental conservation. *Mailing Add:* Dept of Biol Univ of Wis-Superior Superior WI 54880

LUKENS, RAYMOND JAMES, b Beverly, NJ, Feb 25, 30; m 54; c 5. PLANT PATHOLOGY. *Educ:* Rutgers Univ, BS, 54, MS, 55; Univ Md, PhD(bot), 58. *Prof Exp:* Asst plant pathologist, Conn Agr Exp Sta, 57-60, assoc plant pathologist, 60-69, plant pathologist, 70-75; SR PLANT PATHOLOGIST, ORTHO DIV, CHEVRON CHEM CO, 75- *Concurrent Pos:* Lectr plant path, Univ Calif, Berkeley, 77-78. *Mem:* Soc Indust Microbiol; Am Phytopath Soc; Bot Soc Am. *Res:* Chemistry of fungicides; correlation between structure and activity of fungicides; fungicide screening and plant disease control. *Mailing Add:* Agr Res Lab Chevron Chem Co Richmond CA 94804

LUKER, JAMES A(LLISON), b Yazoo City, Miss, Feb 5, 23; m 48; c 4. CHEMICAL ENGINEERING. *Educ:* La State Univ, BS, 44; Mass Inst Technol, MS, 46, PhD(chem eng), 50. *Prof Exp:* Res engr, Shell Oil Co, 50; asst prof chem eng & assoc res engr, Univ Denver, 50-52; prof, Univ Miss, 52-53; Assoc prof chem eng, Syracuse Univ, 53-59, prof, 59-81, actg chmn, Dept Chem & Metall, 54-55, chmn, 60-69, assoc dean eng, 69-71, actg dean, 70-71, dean, 71-81; RETIRED. *Mem:* Fel Am Inst Chem Engrs. *Res:* Mathematical modeling; analog simulation; detonation of gaseous mixtures; programmed instruction. *Mailing Add:* 1304 Via Rubles Santa Fe NM 87501

LUKER, WILLIAM DEAN, b Yazoo City, Miss, Sept 21, 20. ANALYTICAL CHEMISTRY, CHEMICAL ENGINEERING. *Educ:* La State Univ, BS, 41; Univ Wis, PhD(chem), 55. *Prof Exp:* Process engr, Union-Camp Corp, Ga, 41-52; technologist, E I du Pont de Nemours & Co, Inc, 55-58; res chemist, State Chem Lab, 58-65, asst state chemist, 65-67, assoc prof chem eng, 58-65, ASSOC STATE CHEMIST, MISS STATE CHEM LAB, MISS STATE UNIV, 67-, ASSOC PROF CHEM, UNIV, 65- *Mem:* Am Chem Soc; assoc mem Am Inst Chem Eng. *Res:* Fats and oils, including studies of unsaponifiable matter. *Mailing Add:* Dept of Chem Miss State Univ State College MS 39762

LUKERT, MICHAEL T, b Kansas City, Mo, June 28, 37; m 61; c 3. GEOLOGY, GEOCHEMISTRY. *Educ:* Univ Ill, BS, 60; Northern Ill Univ, MS, 62; Case Western Reserve Univ, PhD(geol), 73. *Prof Exp:* Instr geol, Northern Ill Univ, 62-64; from asst prof to assoc prof, 67-74, PROF GEOL, EDINBORO STATE COL, 74- *Concurrent Pos:* Consult, Pa Geol Surv, 75; adj prof, Thiel Col, 75-76 & Mercyhurst Col, 79 & 81; geologist C, Va Div Mineral Resources, 76-77. *Mem:* Geol Soc Am; Geochem Soc. *Res:* Geochronology; igneous and metamorphic petrology; Precambrian geology; geostatistics. *Mailing Add:* Dept of Earth Sci Edinboro State Col Edinboro PA 16444

LUKERT, PHIL DEAN, b Topeka, Kans, Nov 1, 31; m 56; c 4. MICROBIOLOGY. *Educ:* Kans State Univ, BS, 53, DVM, 60, MS, 61; Iowa State Univ, PhD(microbiol), 67. *Prof Exp:* Res assoc microbiol, Kans State Univ, 60-61; res vet, Nat Animal Dis Lab, Agr Res Serv, USDA, Iowa, 61-67; MEM STAFF, COL VET MED, UNIV GA, 67- *Mem:* Am Vet Med Asn; Am Soc Microbiol; Am Asn Avian Path. *Res:* Animal virology, particularly pathogenesis of viral infections, identification of new pathogenic viruses and the development of new diagnostic methods for viral diseases. *Mailing Add:* Dept of Med Microbiol Col of Vet Med Univ of Ga Athens GA 30602

LUKES, ROBERT MICHAEL, b San Francisco, Calif, Mar 27, 23; m 49; c 6. ORGANIC CHEMISTRY. *Educ:* Univ San Francisco, BS, 43; Univ Calif, MS, 47; Univ Notre Dame, PhD(org chem), 49. *Prof Exp:* Res chemist, Merck & Co, Inc, 49-53; res assoc, Res Labs, Gen Elec Co, 54-58, supvr, Insulation Lab, Locomotive & Car Equip Dept, 58-64, MGR FINISH SYSTS LAB, MAJOR APPLIANCE LABS, GEN ELEC CO, 64- *Mem:* Am Chem Soc; Am Electroplaters Soc; fel Am Inst Chemists; Fedn Socs Paint Technol. *Res:* Hydrogenation; steroid synthesis; plastics; resins; electrical insulation; surface coatings; paint; surface chemistry; electroless plating. *Mailing Add:* Gen Elec Co Appliance Park 35-1117 Louisville KY 40225

LUKES, THOMAS MARK, b San Jose, Calif, Mar 28, 20; m 52; c 4. FOOD SCIENCE. *Educ:* San Jose State Col, BS, 47; Univ Calif, Berkeley, MS, 49. *Prof Exp:* Microbiologist, Real Gold Citrus, Mutual Orange Distributor, 49-51; head lab qual control, Gentry Div, Consol Food Corp, 51-62; assoc prof, 62-73, PROF FOOD PROCESSING & HEAD DEPT FOOD INDUST, CALIF POLYTECH STATE UNIV, SAN LUIS OBISPO, 73- *Mem:* AAAS; Am Chem Soc; Inst Food Technol. *Res:* Application of evolutionary operations to the food processing industry; development of chemical methods of flavor evaluation and application of new developments in food dehydration to the industrial scale. *Mailing Add:* Dept of Food Indust Calif Polytech State Univ San Luis Obispo CA 93407

LUKEZIC, FELIX LEE, b Florence, Colo, May 27, 33; m 55; c 2. PLANT PATHOLOGY. *Educ:* Colo State Univ, BS, 56, MS, 58; Univ Calif, PhD(plant path), 63. *Prof Exp:* Asst plant path, Colo State Univ, 56-58; lab technician, Univ Calif, 58-63; plant pathologist, Div Trop Res, United Fruit Co, Honduras, 63-65; from asst prof to assoc prof, 65-75, PROF PLANT PATH, PA STATE UNIV, 75- *Mem:* Am Phytopath Soc; Am Soc Plant Physiol. *Res:* Physiology of plant parasitism, especially bacterial caused diseases. *Mailing Add:* 211 Buckhout Labs Pa State Univ University Park PA 16802

LUKIN, LARISSA SKVORTSOV, b Lvov, Poland, Aug 30, 25; nat US; m 45; c 1. PHYSIOLOGY. *Educ:* Col Women, Poland, BA, 44; Univ Heidelberg, Cand med, 49; Columbia Univ, PhD, 55; Univ of the Pacific, MS, 79. *Prof Exp:* Asst physiol, Columbia Univ, 51-55, instr, 55-56; asst prof, Ohio State Univ, 56-63; sr scientist, Hamilton Standard, 63-64; asst res physiologist, Biomech Lab, Med Ctr, Univ Calif, San Francisco, 64-66, assoc res physiologist, 66-70; ASSOC PROF PHYSIOL, SCH DENT, UNIV OF THE PAC, 70- *Concurrent Pos:* Lectr physiol, Sch Med, Univ Calif, San Francisco, 74- *Mem:* Am Physiol Soc. *Res:* Cardiovascular physiology; blood volumes; cardiac outputs; energy metabolism in exercise; cardiopulmonary physiology. *Mailing Add:* Univ of the Pac Sch of Dent San Francisco CA 94115

LUKIN, MARVIN, b Cleveland, Ohio, Feb 12, 28; m 62; c 2. ORGANIC CHEMISTRY, BIOCHEMISTRY. *Educ:* Ohio Univ, BS, 49; Case Western Reserve Univ, MS, 54, PhD(org chem), 56. *Prof Exp:* Fel org synthesis, Mellon Inst, 56-57; fel protein chem, Albert Einstein Col Med, 57-61; res assoc immunochem, St Lukes Hosp, 61-63; staff asst, Cleveland Clin, 63-65; fel antibiotics, Case Western Reserve Univ, 66-67; asst prof, 67-75, ASSOC PROF CHEM, YOUNGSTOWN STATE UNIV, 75- *Mem:* Am Chem Soc; The Chem Soc. *Res:* Organic synthesis; peptide synthesis. *Mailing Add:* Dept of Chem Youngstown State Univ Youngstown OH 44503

LUKOFF, HERMAN, electrical engineering, deceased

LUKOWIAK, KENNETH DANIEL, b Newark, NJ, Jan 10, 47. NEUROPHYSIOLOGY, DEVELOPMENTAL NEUROBIOLOGY. *Educ:* Iona Col, BSc, 69; State Univ NY, Albany, PhD(neurophysiol), 73. *Prof Exp:* Fel neurophysiol, Univ Ky, 73-75; asst prof physiol, McGill Univ, 75-78; asst prof, 78-80, ASSOC PROF MED PHYSIOL, UNIV CALGARY, 80- *Concurrent Pos:* NIH fel, 73-75; Med Res Coun Can grant, 75-77 & 75-78. *Mem:* Am Physiol Soc; Am Soc Zoologists; Can Physiol Soc; Sigma Xi; AAAS. *Res:* Nueral and peptidergic mechanisms of adaptive behavior including associative learning in invertebrates; interactions between the central and peripheral nervous systems in the mediation of habituation, sensitization and dishabituation. *Mailing Add:* Div Med Physiol Fac Med Univ Calgary Calgary AB T2N 1N4 Can

LULAY, ARTHUR, b Garfield, NJ, Apr 27, 26; m 47; c 4. CHEMICAL ENGINEERING, MATHEMATICS. *Educ:* Bucknell Univ, BS, 49. *Prof Exp:* Engr, Res Div, Textile Fibers Dept, 49-52, specialist, Mkt Div, 52-57, res engr, Tech Div, 57-63, sr res engr, 63-68, DEVELOP ASSOC, TEXTILE FIBERS DEPT, E I DU PONT DE NEMOURS & CO, INC, 68- *Res:* Cellulosic chemistry; preparation and development of synthetic fibers; fundamental studies of converting textile fibers into fabrics and garments. *Mailing Add:* 2406 Lori Lane S Wilmington DE 19810

LULL, DAVID B, b Rochester, NY, Feb 21, 23; m 49; c 4. CHEMICAL ENGINEERING. *Educ:* Mass Inst Technol, BS, 47, Univ Mich, MS, 49. *Prof Exp:* Res engr, Arthur D Little Inc, 49-62; prin scientist, Appl Sci Lab, GCA Tech Div, 62-71; gen engr, US Naval Weapons Lab, 71-76, gen engr, 76-80, CHEM ENGR, NAVAL SURFACE WEAPONS CTR, 80- *Res:* Generation and assessment of aerosols; propagation and suppression of dust explosions; fracture and propulsion of solids and liquids by high explosives; effectiveness of spaced armor. *Mailing Add:* Naval Surface Weapons Ctr White Oak Silver Springs MD 20910

LULLA, KOTUSINGH, b Shikarpur, WPakistan, Sept 19, 35; m 61. ATOMIC PHYSICS. *Educ:* Univ Bombay, BSc, 57; NY Univ, MS, 60, PhD(physics), 64. *Prof Exp:* NASA fel physics, Univ Pittsburgh, 63-65, res assoc, 65-66, asst prof, 66-69; asst prof, Howard Univ, 69-71; chmn dept, 71-76, ASSOC PROF

PHYSICS, NY INST TECHNOL, 71- *Mem:* Am Phys Soc. *Res:* Experimental research in the field of inter-atomic forces; plasma physics and physics of upper atmosphere. *Mailing Add:* Dept of Physics NY Inst of Technol Old Westbury NY 11568

LUM, BERT KWAN BUCK, b Honolulu, Hawaii, May 9, 29; m 52; c 4. PHARMACOLOGY. *Educ:* Univ Mich, BS, 51, PhD(pharmacol), 56; Univ Kans, MD, 60. *Prof Exp:* From instr to asst prof pharmacol, Med Ctr, Univ Kans, 56-62; from asst prof to prof, Sch Med, Marquette Univ, 62-69, asst chmn dept, 64-69; PROF PHARMACOL & CHMN DEPT, SCH MED, UNIV HAWAII, MANOA, 69- *Mem:* Am Soc Pharmacol & Exp Therapeut; Cardiac Muscle Soc. *Res:* Cardiovascular and autonomic pharmacology. *Mailing Add:* Dept of Pharmacol Univ of Hawaii Sch of Med Honolulu HI 96822

LUM, KIN K, b Ipoh, Malaya, Sept 4, 40; US citizen; m 65; c 2. PHOTOGRAPHIC CHEMISTRY. *Educ:* Hong Kong Baptist Col, BSc, 62; Baylor Univ, PhD(org chem), 66. *Prof Exp:* Res fel, Utah State Univ, 66-68; RES ASSOC, EASTMAN KODAK CO RES LABS, 68- *Mem:* Am Chem Soc; Soc Photog Sci & Eng. *Res:* Application of novel imaging chemistry into color image transfer systems. *Mailing Add:* 633 Chalelaine Dr Webster NY 14580

LUM, PATRICK TUNG MOON, b Honolulu, Hawaii, Nov 6, 28; div; c 2. ENTOMOLOGY. *Educ:* Earlham Col, BA, 50; Univ Ill, MS, 52, PhD(entom), 56. *Prof Exp:* Asst entom, Univ Ill, 54-56, res assoc, 56, USPHS res fel, 57; res biologist, Entom Res Ctr, Fla State Bd Health, 57-65; RES ENTOMOLOGIST, STORED PROD INSECT RES & DEVELOP, USDA, 65- *Mem:* AAAS; Int Mgt Coun; Entom Soc Am; Am Mosquito Control Asn. *Res:* Physiology of egg hatching and reproduction in mosquitoes; pathogenecity of micro-organisms to insects; photoperiodism and circadian rhythms in insects; physiology of growth and reproduction in moths. *Mailing Add:* Stored Prod Insect Res & Develop US Dept of Agr PO Box 22909 Savannah GA 31403

LUM, VINCENT YU-SUN, b China, Sept 26, 33; US citizen; m 60; c 3. COMPUTER SCIENCE, ELECTRICAL ENGINEERING. *Educ:* Univ Toronto, BAS, 60; Univ Wash, MS, 61; Univ Ill, Urbana, PhD(elec eng), 66. *Prof Exp:* Assoc engr, IBM Develop Lab, 62-63, RES STAFF MEM, IBM RES LAB, 66-, PROJ MGR, 74- *Concurrent Pos:* Adj asst prof, Loyola Col, Fordham Univ, 67-68. *Mem:* Inst Elec & Electronics Engrs; Asn Comput Mach; Comput Soc. *Res:* Data base application and research; office automation; information and data organization and management; computer system application, analysis and design. *Mailing Add:* 15248 Janor Ct Los Gatos CA 95030

LUMB, GEORGE DENNETT, b London, Eng, Jan 26, 17; nat US; m 45; c 1. PATHOLOGY. *Educ:* Univ London, MB & BS, 39, MD, 46. *Prof Exp:* Assoc prof path, Univ London, 53-57; prof, Univ Tenn, 57-59; dir clin labs & pathologist, James Walker Mem Hosp, 59-65; dir, Warner-Lambert Res Inst Can, 65-69, vpres & dir, Pharmaceut Co, Fla, 69-71, dir med serv & res & develop, 71-73; vpres med affairs, Synapse Commun Serv Inc, 73-77; vpres prod safety assessment, Searle Labs, 77-80; PROF PATH, HAHNEMANN MED COL & HOSP, 80- *Concurrent Pos:* Traveling res fel, Westminster Hosp, London, consult pathologist, 48-57; vis assoc prof health affairs, Sch Med, Univ NC, 60-; assoc prof, Univ Toronto, 66-71. *Mem:* Am Soc Exp Path; Am Asn Path & Bact; Col Am Path; Int Acad Path; Path Soc Gt Brit & Ireland. *Res:* Cardiac research; conduction of specialized muscle pathways in hogs; experimental production of infarcts in canine hearts. *Mailing Add:* Hahnemann Med Col & Hosp 230 N Broad St Philadelphia PA 19107

LUMB, JUDITH RAE H, b Bridgeport, Conn, Mar 19, 43; m 64; c 2. IMMUNOLOGY. *Educ:* Univ Kans, BA, 65, MA, 66; Stanford Univ, PhD(med microbiol), 69. *Prof Exp:* Asst prof, 69-75, ASSOC PROF BIOL, ATLANTA UNIV, 75- *Concurrent Pos:* NIH career develop award, 75-80. *Mem:* AAAS; Reticuloendothelial Soc; Am Soc Microbiol. *Res:* Biochemistry of alkaline phosphatase of C57BL lymphomas; derepression of embryo functions in C57BL lymphomas; computer simulation of the development of the thymus. *Mailing Add:* Dept of Biol Atlanta Univ Atlanta GA 30314

LUMB, RALPH F, b Worcester, Mass, May 27, 21; m 41; c 7. PHYSICAL CHEMISTRY, NUCLEAR SCIENCES. *Educ:* Clark Univ, AB, 47, PhD(phys chem), 51. *Prof Exp:* Instr chem, Assumption Col, 47-48 & Northeastern Univ, 49-51; chief, Chem-Physics Br, Div Nuclear Mat Mgt, US AEC, 51-56; proj leader, Quantum Inc, 56-59, vpres, 59-60; dir, Western NY Nuclear Res Ctr, Inc, 60-68; pres, Advan Technol Consult Corp, 68-71; PRES, NUSAC INC, 71- *Concurrent Pos:* Secy, Adv Comt Uranium Standards, AEC, 53-56; mem, Adv Comt Safeguarding Spec Nuclear Mat, 67-69 & Safeguards Steering Group, Atomic Indust Forum, 66-; consult, Univ Buffalo Nuclear Reactor Proj, 56-60 & Safeguards Br, Int Atomic Energy Agency, 63- *Mem:* Fel AAAS; fel Am Inst Chemists; Am Nuclear Soc. *Res:* Applications of nuclear energy; nuclear research; reactor design, operation and utilization. *Mailing Add:* 1850 Samuel Morse Dr Reston VA 22090

LUMB, ROGER H, b Union, NJ, June 29, 40; m 62. BIOCHEMISTRY. *Educ:* Alfred Univ, AB, 62; Univ SC, MS, 65, PhD(biol), 67. *Prof Exp:* Instr biol, Univ SC, 65-67; from asst prof to assoc prof, 67-74, PROF BIOL, WESTERN CAROLINA UNIV, 74- *Concurrent Pos:* Damon Runyon fel, 71-73; researcher, Utrecht, Neth, 75-76. *Res:* Lipid metabolism in lung; lipid metabolism in cancer cells; membrane biochemistry. *Mailing Add:* Dept of Biol Western Carolina Univ Cullowhee NC 28723

LUMB, WILLIAM VALJEAN, b Sioux City, Iowa, Nov 26, 21; m 49; c 1. VETERINARY MEDICINE. *Educ:* Kans State Univ, DVM, 43; Tex A&M Univ, MS, 53; Univ Minn, PhD(vet med), 57; Am Col Vet Anethesiologists, Dipl. *Prof Exp:* From intern to resident, Angell Mem Animal Hosp, Boston, 46-48; from instr to assoc prof med & surg, Tex A&M Univ, 49-52; assoc prof clin & surg, Colo State Univ, 54-58 & surg & med, Mich State Univ, 58-60;

assoc prof med, 60-63, dir surg lab, 63- 79, PROF SURG, COL VET MED, COLO STATE UNIV, 63- *Concurrent Pos:* Ralston-Purina res award, 80. *Honors & Awards:* Gaines Award, 65. *Mem:* Fel AAAS; Am Vet Med Asn; Am Asn Vet Clinicians; Am Col Vet Surg; NY Acad Sci. *Res:* Experimental surgery and anesthesiology. *Mailing Add:* Surg Lab Colo State Univ Ft Collins CO 80521

LUMBERS, SYDNEY BLAKE, b Toronto, Ont, Aug 6, 33. GEOLOGY, PETROLOGY. *Educ:* McMaster Univ, BSc, 58; Univ BC, MSc, 60; Princeton Univ, PhD(geol), 67. *Prof Exp:* Geologist, Ont Div Mines, Ministry Natural Resources, 62-73; CUR GEOL, ROYAL ONT MUS, 73- *Concurrent Pos:* Mem comt study of solid earth sci Can, Sci Coun Can, 68-69; corresp, Subcomt Precambrian Stratig, Int Union Geol Sci, 72- *Mem:* Geol Soc Am; Mineral Asn Can; Geol Asn Can; Sigma Xi. *Res:* Precambrian geology; evolution of Grenville Province of Canadian Precambrian Shield; metamorphism; petrogenesis of anorthosite suite rocks and alkalic rocks; geochronology; relationship of mineral deposits to stratigraphy, metamorphism and plutonism. *Mailing Add:* Dept of Mineral & Geol Royal Ont Mus 100 Queen's Park Toronto ON M5S 2C6 Can

LUMENG, LAWRENCE, b Manila, Philippines, Aug 10, 39; US citizen; m 66; c 2. MEDICINE, BIOCHEMISTRY. *Educ:* Ind Univ, Bloomington, BS, 60; Ind Univ, Indianapolis, MD, 64, MS, 69; Am Bd Internal Med, dipl, 70. *Prof Exp:* asst prof, 71-74, assoc prof, 74-79, PROF MED BIOCHEM, SCH MED, IND UNIV, INDIANAPOLIS, 79- *Concurrent Pos:* Res & educ associateship, Vet Admin Hosp, Indianapolis, 71-73; clin investr, 73-76, chief in gastroenterol, 77- *Mem:* Am Soc Clin Investr; Am Col Phys; Am Soc Biol Chemists; Am Gastroenterol Asn; Am Asn Study Liver Dis. *Res:* Regulation of metabolic pathways; ethanol metabolism; pyridoxine and thiamine metabolism; clinical liver diseases. *Mailing Add:* Dept Med Ind Univ Med Ctr Indianapolis IN 46202

LUMING, HENRY, mechanical engineering, applied mechanics, see previous edition

LUMLEY, JOHN L(EASK), b Detroit, Mich, Nov 4, 30; m 53; c 3. FLUID MECHANICS. *Educ:* Harvard Univ, AB, 52; Johns Hopkins Univ, MSE, 54, PhD(aeronaut), 57. *Prof Exp:* Asst & jr instr mech eng, Johns Hopkins Univ, 53-54, asst aeronaut, 54-57, res assoc mech eng, 57-59; from asst prof to assoc prof eng res, Pa State Univ, 59-61, from assoc prof to prof aerospace eng, 61-74, Evan Pugh prof, 74-77; WILLIS H CARRIER PROF ENG, SIBLEY SCH MECH & AEROSPACE ENG, CORNELL UNIV, 77- *Concurrent Pos:* Instr, McCoy Col, 56-59; courtesy fel, Johns Hopkins Univ, 57-58, fel, 58-59; exchange prof, Univ Aix-Marseille, 66-67; vis prof, Univ Louvain-la-Neuve, Belg & Fulbright sr lectr, Univ Liege, 73-74; consult, David Taylor Naval Ship Res & Develop Ctr, 76- & Appl Res Lab, Pa State Univ, 77-; Guggenheim fels, Mech Fluids Lab, Sch Cent Lyon & Inst Mech Statist Turbulence, Univ d'Aix-Marseille II, France. *Honors & Awards:* Medallion, Univ Liege, 71. *Mem:* Fel Am Phys Soc; Soc Natural Philos; NY Acad Sci; fel Am Acad Mech; Am Inst Aeronaut & Astronaut. *Res:* Turbulence; stochastic processes; electronic instrumentation. *Mailing Add:* 238 Upson Hall Cornell Univ Ithaca NY 14853

LUMMA, WILLIAM CARL, JR, b Detroit, Mich, Apr 21, 41; m 75; c 2. ORGANIC CHEMISTRY, MEDICINAL CHEMISTRY. *Educ:* Wayne State Univ, BS, 63; Mass Inst Technol, PhD(org chem), 66. *Prof Exp:* Asst prof chem, St Louis Univ, 66-70; sr res chemist process develop, Rahway, NJ, 70-72, res fel med chem, 72-81, SR RES FEL MED CHEM, MERCK, SHARP & DOHME RES LABS, WEST POINT, PA, 81- *Mem:* Am Chem Soc. *Res:* Heterocyclic and organic synthetic chemistry. *Mailing Add:* Merck Sharpe & Dohme Res Labs Merck & Co Inc West Point PA 19486

LUMPKIN, LEE ROY, b Oklahoma City, Okla, Sept 6, 25; m 53; c 5. DERMATOLOGY, PATHOLOGY. *Educ:* Univ Okla, BA, 49, MD, 53; Am Bd Dermat, dipl. *Prof Exp:* Intern, Tripler Gen Hosp, US Air Force, Honolulu, Hawaii, 53-54, resident dermat, Walter Reed Gen Hosp, Washington, DC, 58-61, chief dermat serv & clins, 3070th Air Force Hosp, Torrejon AFB, Spain, 61-64, chief dermat & clins, Air Force Hosp, Carswell AFB, Tex, 65-67, chief dermat serv, Wilford Hall Air Force Med Ctr, Lackland AFB, 67-72, dir residency training, 69-72; prof, 72-80, CLIN PROF DERMAT, ALBANY MED COL, 80-, DIV HEAD, 72- *Concurrent Pos:* Fel dermal-path, Armed Forces Inst Path, 64-65; vis lectr, US Air Force Sch Aerospace Med; clin assoc prof, Univ Tex Med Sch, San Antonio; assoc mem comn of cutaneous dis, Armed Forces Epidemiol Bd; US Air Force rep, Nat Prog Dermat. *Honors & Awards:* Cert of Appreciation, Strategic Air Command, 64 & Surgeon Gen Air Force, 69; James Clarke White Award, 71. *Mem:* Fel Am Col Physicians; fel Am Acad Dermat; Soc Air Force Physician (pres-elect, 71); AMA; fel Am Soc Dermatopath. *Mailing Add:* Div of Dermat Albany Med Col Albany NY 12208

LUMPKIN, MICHAEL DIRKSEN, b Dallas, Tex, Feb 2, 53. NEUROENDOCRINOLOGY, REPRODUCTION. *Educ:* Univ Tex, Austin, BA, 75; Univ Tex Health Sci Ctr, Dallas, PhD(physiol), 81. *Prof Exp:* Teaching asst physiol, 75-76, NIH fel, 76-81, RES ASSOC NEUROENDOCRINOL, UNIV TEX HEALTH SCI CTR, DALLAS, 81- *Concurrent Pos:* Lectr, Univ Tex Health Sci Ctr, Dallas, 78-82. *Res:* Elucidation of the role of hypothalamic and gastrointestinal peptides in the control of anterior pituitary gland function; role of hypothalamic and pituitary hormones in the regulation of male and female gonadal function. *Mailing Add:* Dept Physiol Univ Tex Health Sci Ctr 5323 Harry Hines Blvd Dallas TX 75235

LUMRY, RUFUS WORTH, b Bismarck, NDak, Nov 3, 20; m 43; c 3. PHYSICAL CHEMISTRY. *Educ:* Harvard Univ, AB, 42, MS, 48, PhD(chem physics), 49. *Prof Exp:* Res assoc, Div Eight, Nat Defense Res Comt, 42-45; Merck fel, Univ Utah, 48-50, asst prof phys chem, 50-53, asst res prof biochem, 51-53; assoc prof, 53-57, PROF PHYS CHEM, UNIV MINN, MINNEAPOLIS, 57-, DIR LAB BIOPHYS CHEM, 63- *Concurrent Pos:*

NSF sr fel & vis prof, Lab Carlsberg, Copenhagen, 59-60; vis prof, Inst Protein Res, Osaka, Japan, 61, Inst Biol Chem Rome, 63 & Univ Calif, San Diego, 77-78. *Mem:* Am Chem Soc; Soc Biol Chem; Sigma Xi; Biophys Soc; Photobiol Soc. *Res:* Bophysical chemistry; enzymes, proteins; fast reactions. *Mailing Add:* Sch of Chem Univ of Minn Minneapolis MN 55455

LUMSDAINE, EDWARD, b Hong Kong, Sept 30, 37; US citizen; m 59; c 4. SOLAR ENERGY, MECHANICAL ENGINEERING. *Educ:* NMex State Univ, BSME, 63, MSME, 64, DSc(mech eng), 66. *Prof Exp:* Res engr, Boeing Co, Wash, 66-67; assoc prof mech eng, SDak State Univ, 67-72; prof mech & aerospace eng, Univ Tenn, Knoxville, 72-77; prof mech eng & res engr, Phys Sci Lab, 77-78; DIR, N MEX SOLAR ENERGY INST & PROF MECH ENG, N MEX STATE UNIV, 78- *Concurrent Pos:* Lectr, Seattle Univ, 66-67; consult, Tenn Valley Authority, 78- & Phys Sci Lab, NMex State Univ, 78-; prin investr of many res grants, NSF & US Dept Energy. *Mem:* Am Soc Mech Engrs; Am Soc Eng Educ; Int Solar Energy Soc; Am Soc Heating, Refrig & Air-Conditioning Engrs. *Res:* Compressor noise; unsteady transonic flow; boundary layer; solar energy applications in photovoltaics, desalination and irrigation; collector testing; passive solar building design; high-temperature solar industrial applications; development of Egyptian village with renewable resources. *Mailing Add:* NMex Solar Energy Inst Box 3 SOL Las Cruces NM 88003

LUMSDEN, CHARLES JOHN, b Hamilton, Ont, Apr 9, 49. HUMAN SOCIOBIOLOGY, EVOLUTIONARY THEORY. *Educ:* Univ Toronto, BSc, 72, MSc, 74, PhD(theoret physics), 77. *Prof Exp:* Res fel biol, Harvard Univ, 79-81; ASSOC PROF MED, BIOPHYS DEPT, SCH MED, UNIV TORONTO, 82- *Mem:* Biophys Soc; Soc Math Biol. *Res:* Theoretical biology, cognitive science and sociobiology; theoretical medicine and physical theory in biology. *Mailing Add:* Dept Med Univ Toronto Sch Med Toronto ON M5S 1A1 Can

LUMSDEN, DAVID NORMAN, b Buffalo, NY, Aug 29, 35; m 63; c 2. GEOLOGY. *Educ:* State Univ NY, Buffalo, BA, 58, MA, 60; Univ Ill, PhD(geol), 65. *Prof Exp:* Res engr, Carborundum Co, 60-62; sr geologist, Pan Am Petrol Corp, 65-67; from asst prof to assoc prof, 67-77, PROF GEOL, MEMPHIS STATE UNIV, 77- *Mem:* Geol Soc Am; Am Asn Petrol Geol; Soc Econ Paleont & Mineral. *Res:* Study of carbonate and quartzose sedimentary rocks. *Mailing Add:* Dept of Geol Memphis State Univ Memphis TN 38111

LUMSDEN, RICHARD, b New Orleans, La, Apr 6, 38; m 59. CELL BIOLOGY, PARASITOLOGY. *Educ:* Tulane Univ, BSc, 60, MSc, 62; Rice Univ, PhD(biol), 65. *Prof Exp:* From asst prof to assoc prof, 65-73, PROF BIOL, TULANE UNIV, 73-, TROP MED, 74-, ANAT, 75- *Concurrent Pos:* Am Cancer Soc res grant, 65-66; NIH res grants, 65-68, 69-73 & 72-77, career develop award, 69-74; NSF res grant, 68-72; ed consult, J Parasitol, 75-; res contract, US Food & Drug Admin, 74-76. *Mem:* AAAS; Am Soc Parasitol; Am Soc Zoologists; Am Soc Trop Med & Hyg; Am Soc Cell Biol. *Res:* Cytology and biochemistry of parasitic helminths and host-parasite relationships. *Mailing Add:* Dept of Biol Tulane Univ New Orleans LA 70118

LUMSDEN, ROBERT DOUGLAS, b Washington, DC, June 21, 38; m 60; c 2. PLANT PATHOLOGY. *Educ:* NC State Univ, BS, 61, MS, 63; Cornell Univ, PhD(plant path), 67. *Prof Exp:* RES PLANT PATHOLOGIST, SOILBORNE DIS LAB, PLANT PROTECTION INST, AGR RES CTR W, BELTSVILLE AGR RES CTR, USDA, 66- *Mem:* Am Phytopath Soc. *Res:* Physiology of plant diseases, including the physiology of pathogenesis and disease resistance; pathology and biological control of plant pathogens, especially soilborne plant pathogens; soil ecology. *Mailing Add:* 262 Biosci Bldg Agr Res Ctr W USDA Beltsville MD 20705

LUMSDEN, WILLIAM WATT, JR, b Dallas, Tex, Dec 21, 20; m 45; c 2. GEOLOGY, PALEONTOLOGY. *Educ:* Univ Calif, Los Angeles, AB, 55, PhD, 64. *Prof Exp:* Asst prof, Univ Calif, Los Angeles, 55-58; from asst prof to assoc prof, 58-70, chmn dept, 58-74, PROF GEOL, CALIF STATE UNIV, LONG BEACH, 70- *Concurrent Pos:* Leverhulme fel for Gt Brit, Aberdeen Univ. *Mem:* AAAS; Paleont Soc; Soc Econ Paleont & Mineral; Am Asn Petrol Geol. *Res:* Invertebrate paleontology; field geology; stratigraphy. *Mailing Add:* Dept of Geol Calif State Univ Long Beach CA 90840

LUNAN, KENNETH DALE, b Detroit, Mich, Nov 24, 30. ENGINEERING. *Educ:* Calif Inst Technol, BS, 53; Iowa State Univ, MS, 55; Univ Calif, Los Angeles, PhD(biochem), 62. *Prof Exp:* USPHS fel, Calif Inst Technol, 62-65; asst prof path, Univ Southern Calif, 65-66; res scientist, SRI Int, 66-74, sr res scientist, 74-80; ENGR, LOCKHEED MISSILES & SPACE CORP, 80- *Mailing Add:* 3553 Alma Palo Alto CA 94306

LUNARDINI, VIRGIL J(OSEPH), JR, b Holyoke, Mass, May 10, 35; m 60; c 3. MECHANICAL ENGINEERING, HEAT TRANSFER. *Educ:* Univ Notre Dame, BS, 57; Ohio State Univ, MS, 60, PhD(mech eng), 63. *Prof Exp:* Instr eng, Ohio State Univ, 58-63; asst prof, Clarkson Col Technol, 63-66; assoc prof, State Univ NY Buffalo, 66-69; assoc prof mech eng, 69-79, PROF MECH ENG, UNIV OTTAWA, 79-; RES ENGR, US COLD REGIONS LAB, 79- *Concurrent Pos:* Consult, NASA Lewis Labs, Ohio, 64, Pratt & Whitney Aircraft Div, United Aircraft Corp, 66-67, Chisolm-Ryder, NY, 68- & Govt Can, 78-; State Univ NY Buffalo fac fel, 67; adj prof Thayer Sch, Dartmouth, 79- *Honors & Awards:* Eugune Jacob Award, Petroleum Div, Am Soc Mech Engrs, 81. *Mem:* Am Soc Mech Engrs; Am Soc Heating, Refrig & Air-Conditioning Engrs; Can Soc Mech Eng; Eng Inst Can; Sigma Xi. *Res:* Permafrost heat transfer; cold regions engineering; energy conservation; radiative heat transfer. *Mailing Add:* US Cold Regions Lab Lyme Rd Hanover NH 03705

LUND, ANDERS EDWARD, b Luverne, Minn, Sept 26, 28. WOOD SCIENCE. *Educ:* Colo State Univ, BS, 55; Duke Univ, MF, 56, DF(wood sci, bus mgt), 64. *Prof Exp:* Forest prod technician, US Forest Prod Lab, 56-58; sr scientist, Koppers Co, Inc, 58-66; assoc prof wood sci, Clemson Univ, 66-67; head admin, Tex Forest Prod Lab, Tex A&M Univ, 67-73; DIR, INST WOOD RES, MICH TECHNOL UNIV, 74- *Concurrent Pos:* Consult, Forest Prod Co, 66-; prof, Tex A&M Univ, 67-73; consult, Cent States Energy Res Comn, 77, Sci & Educ Admin, USDA, 78 & Mich Energy Admin, 78- *Mem:* Int Asn Wood Anatomists; Int Res Group Wood Preservation; Am Wood Preservers Asn; Forest Prod Res Soc; Soc Wood Sci & TEchnol. *Res:* Wood deterioration and prevention; composite wood products; research administration. *Mailing Add:* Inst Wood Res Mich Technol Univ Houghton MI 49931

LUND, ARNOLD JEROME, b Clarissa, Minn, July 9, 16; m 43; c 4. BACTERIOLOGY. *Educ:* St Olaf Col, BA, 38; Univ Minn, PhD(bact), 49. *Prof Exp:* Teacher high sch, Minn, 38-40; res fel, Hormel Inst, Univ Minn, 49-52, asst prof bact, 52-64; assoc prof, 64-67, PROF MICROBIOL, MANKATO STATE UNIV, 67- *Mem:* Am Soc Microbiol. *Res:* Physiology of bacterial spores; effects of low temperature on microorganisms; food microbiology. *Mailing Add:* Dept of Biol Mankato State Col Mankat MN 56001

LUND, CURTIS JOSEPH, obstetrics & gynecology, deceased

LUND, DARYL B, b San Bernardino, Calif, Nov 4, 41; m 63; c 2. FOOD ENGINEERING, FOOD PROCESSING. *Educ:* Univ Wis, Madison, BS, 63, MS, 65, PhD(food sci, chem eng), 68. *Prof Exp:* From instr to assoc prof food sci, 67-77, PROF FOOD SCI & AGR ENG, UNIV WIS-MADISON, 77- *Concurrent Pos:* invited vis prof, Agr Univ, Wageningen, Holland, 79. *Mem:* Fel Inst Food Technol; Am Soc Agr Eng; Am Inst Chem Engrs. *Res:* Food engineering; fouling of heat exchangers; nutrient retention in processing; starch gelatinization; water movement in foods. *Mailing Add:* Dept of Food Sci Univ of Wis 110 Babcock Hall Madison WI 53706

LUND, DONALD S, b Evanston, Ill, Sept 23, 32. PHYSICS. *Educ:* Northwestern Univ, BS, 54; Univ NMex, MA, 61. *Prof Exp:* Res asst, Univ NMex, 59-61; physicist, Nat Bur Standards, 61-62; res asst, High Altitude Observ, 62-65; physicist, Wave Propagation Lab, Nat Oceanic & Atmospheric Admin, 65-77; SR STAFF ENGR, MARTIN-MARIETTA AEROSPACE DIV, 77- *Mem:* Am Phys Soc; Am Geophys Union. *Res:* Aeronomy; radio physics and astronomy. *Mailing Add:* PO Box 1664 Boulder CO 80302

LUND, DOUGLAS E, b Newcastle, Nebr, Dec 12, 33; m 58; c 2. GENETICS. EMBRYOLOGY. *Educ:* Nebr Wesleyan Univ, BA, 58; Univ Nebr, MS, 60, PhD(zool), 62. *Prof Exp:* Asst prof zool, 62-68, PROF BIOL, KEARNEY STATE COL, 68- *Mem:* AAAS. *Res:* Temperature effects on early developmental stages of mammalian embryos; carbon dioxide sensitivity in Drosophila. *Mailing Add:* Dept of Biol Kearney State Col Kearney NE 68847

LUND, FREDERICK H(ENRY), b Seattle, Wash, June 2, 29; m 50; c 4. AEROSPACE & ELECTRONICS ENGINEERING. *Educ:* Univ Wash, BSEE, 51; Mass Inst Technol, SM, 57. *Prof Exp:* Proj engr, US Naval Air Missile Test Ctr, Calif, 53-57, sr proj engr, 57-58, head system employ br, 58-61, plans & anal group officer, 61-65; sr res engr, Stanford Res Inst, 65-69; sr staff engr, 69-78, MEM PROF STAFF, MARTIN MARIETTA CORP, ORLANDO, 78- *Concurrent Pos:* Mem exec comt, Mil Opers Res Symp, Off Naval Res, 62-66. *Mem:* Inst Elec & Electronics Engrs; Sigma Xi; Asn Old Crows. *Res:* Conduct of system analyses; operations research studies; analysis of electronic and optical countermeasures systems; development, test and evaluation of missile weapon systems; development of electronic instrumentation for guided missile systems; military requirements analyses; ballistic missile defense studies. *Mailing Add:* Sand Lake Rd Box 5837 Orlando FL 32805

LUND, HARTVIG ROALD, b Fargo, NDak, May 15, 33; m 57; c 4. AGRONOMY. *Educ:* NDak State Univ, BS, 55, MS, 58; Purdue Univ, PhD(agron, plant breeding), 65. *Prof Exp:* Res asst agron, NDak State Univ, 55-58, asst prof, 59-62; res asst, Purdue Univ, 62-65; assoc prof, 65-74, assoc dean, Col Agr & assoc dir, Agr Exp Sta, 74-79, PROF AGRON, NDAK STATE UNIV, 74-, DEAN, COL AGR & DIR, AGR EXP STA, 79- *Concurrent Pos:* Asst dean, Col Agr & asst dir, Agr Exp Sta, NDak State Iniv, 71-74. *Mem:* Am Soc Agron; Crop Sci Soc Am. *Res:* Rust genetics of durum wheat; chemical mutagenesis in corn; corn breeding and corn endosperm genetics. *Mailing Add:* Col of Agr Morrill Hall NDak State Univ Fargo ND 58102

LUND, J KENNETH, b Brooklyn, NY, Feb 11, 33; m 60; c 2. CHEMICAL ENGINEERING. *Educ:* Polytech Inst Brooklyn, BChE, 55; Princeton Univ, MSE, 58, PhD(chem eng), 63. *Prof Exp:* Sr res engr, Plastics Div, Monsanto Co, Mass, 61-65, res group leader, Hydrocarbons & Polymers Div, Tex, 65-69, prod develop mgr, NJ, 69-71; dir res & develop, Polyester Div, Olin Corp, 71-73; asst to pres, Occidental Res Corp, 74-78; SR VPRES, EXEC TECH RES, VARO CORP, 78- *Mem:* Am Chem Soc; Soc Plastics Engrs; Am Inst Chem Engrs. *Res:* Polymer melt rheology; shear degradation of polymer melts; polymer fatigue failure; high speed tensile studies; extrusion processing of polyolefins and foamed polystyrene polyolefins. *Mailing Add:* Varo Corp 1800 N Highland Ave Los Angeles CA 90028

LUND, JOHN EDWARD, b Detroit, Mich, Mar 16, 39; m 59; c 2. VETERINARY PATHOLOGY. *Educ:* Mich State Univ, BS, 62, MS & DVM, 64; Wash State Univ, PhD(vet sci), 69; Am Cl Vet Pathologists, dipl. *Prof Exp:* Instr path, Med Sch, Stanford Univ, 68-70; from asst prof to assoc prof, Sch Vet Sci & Med, Purdue Univ, 70-73; sr scientist, Battelle Northwest Labs, Wash, 73-74, mgr & res assoc, Exp Path Sect, Biol Dept, 74-77; sr res scientist, 77-80, RES HEAD, UPJOHN CO, 80- *Concurrent Pos:* Consult & vet pathologist, Inst Chem Biol, Univ San Francisco, 69-72. *Mem:* Am Vet Med Asn; AAAS; Am Soc Vet Clin Path; Int Acad Path. *Res:* Hematologic diseases of animals; neutrophil kinetics in blood and bone marrow; chemical carcinogenesis. *Mailing Add:* 3721 Arbutus Trail Kalamazoo MI 49002

LUND, JOHN TURNER, b Brooklyn, NY, Nov 3, 29; m 55; c 2. PHYSICAL CHEMISTRY. *Educ:* Brown Univ, AB, 51; Univ Wash, PhD(phys chem), 54. *Prof Exp:* Fel, Univ Wash, 54-55; res chemist, 55-69, TECH MGR, TEXTILE FIBERS DEPT, E I DU PONT DE NEMOURS & CO, INC, 69- *Mem:* Am Chem Soc; Am Phys Soc. *Res:* Industrial research on textile fibers. *Mailing Add:* Textile Fibers Dept E I du Pont de Nemours & Co Inc Wilmington DE 19898

LUND, LANNY JACK, b Dalton, Nebr, May 1, 43; m 64; c 2. SOIL MORPHOLOGY. *Educ:* Univ Nebr, BS, 65, MS, 68; Purdue Univ, PhD, 71. *Prof Exp:* Asst prof & asst soil scientist, 71-77, ASSOC PROF SOIL SCI & ASSOC SOIL SCIENTIST, UNIV CALIF, RIVERSIDE, 77- *Mem:* Am Soc Agron; Soil Sci Soc Am. *Res:* Soil morphology, genesis and classification; soil and the environment. *Mailing Add:* Dept of Soil & Environ Sci Univ of Calif Riverside CA 92502

LUND, LOUIS HAROLD, b Jefferson City, Mo, Mar 17, 19; m 42; c 2. CHEMICAL PHYSICS. *Educ:* Kans Wesleyan Univ, AB, 40; Univ Mo, AM, 43, PhD(physics), 48. *Prof Exp:* Instr physics, Univ Mo, 43-44; physicist, Lucas-Harold Corp, 44-45; instr math, 45-47, physics, 47-48, asst, 48-52, assoc prof, 52-55, PROF PHYSICS, UNIV MO-ROLLA, 55- *Mem:* Am Phys Soc. *Res:* Liquid structure, x-ray scattering by liquids. *Mailing Add:* Dept of Physics Univ of Mo Rolla MO 65401

LUND, MELVIN ROBERT, b Siren, Wis, Oct 17, 22; m 46; c 3. DENTISTRY. *Educ:* Univ Ore, DMD, 46; Univ Mich, MS, 54. *Prof Exp:* From instr to prof restorative dent, Loma Linda Univ, 53-71; PROF OPER DENT & CHMN DEPT, IND UNIV-PURDUE UNIV, INDIANAPOLIS, 71- *Concurrent Pos:* Fel, Claremont Grad Sch, 69-70. *Mem:* Int Asn Dent Res; Acad Oper Dent; Am Acad Gold Foil Opers (pres, 79-80). *Res:* Physical research in dental materials; biologic research in dental procedures. *Mailing Add:* Dept of Oper Dent Ind Univ-Purdue Univ Sch of Dent Indianapolis IN 46202

LUND, PAULINE KAY, b Golborne, Lancashire, April 20, 55; m 80. GASTROENTEROLOGY, ENDOCRINOLOGY. *Educ:* Univ Newcastle, UK, BSc Hons, 75, PhD(gastrointestinal endocrinol), 79. *Prof Exp:* Demonstr physiol, Univ Newcastle, UK, 77-79; RES FEL, LAB MOLECULAR ENDOCRINOL, HARVARD MED SCH, MASS GEN HOSP, 79. *Res:* Biosynthesis of gastrointestinal hormones and neuropeptides, particularly glucagon utilizing recombinant DNA techniques to investigate genomic organilation and regulation. *Mailing Add:* 294 Marginal St East Boston MA 02114

LUND, RICHARD, b New York, NY, Sept 17, 39; m 65, 78; c 3. VERTEBRATE PALEONTOLOGY. *Educ:* Univ Mich, Ann Arbor, BS, 61, MS, 63; Columbia Univ, PhD(zool), 68. *Prof Exp:* Asst cur fossil fish, Sect Vert Fossils, Carnegie Mus, 66-69; asst prof earth & plant sci, Univ Pittsburgh, 69-74; asst prof, 74-75, assoc prof, 75-81, PROF BIOL, ADELPHI UNIV, 81- *Concurrent Pos:* Pittsburgh Found fel, Carnegie Mus, 67-69, res assoc, 69-; Pittsburgh Found fel, Univ Pittsburgh, 71-74; res assoc, WVa Geol Surv, 74. *Mem:* AAAS; Soc Vert Paleont; Am Soc Icthyol & Herpet; Am Soc Zoologists; Paleont Soc. *Res:* Fossil fish; late Paleozoic biostratigraphy. *Mailing Add:* Dept of Biol Adelphi Univ Garden City NY 11530

LUND, STEVE, b Wis, Dec 3, 23; m 46; c 5. AGRONOMY. *Educ:* Clemson Col, BS, 49; Univ Wis, MS, 51, PhD(agron), 53. *Prof Exp:* Exten agronomist, Clemson Col, 53-54; from asst res specialist to assoc res specialist farm crops, Rutgers Univ, New Brunswick, 54-62, res prof, 62-75; SUPT & PROF, COLUMBIA BASIN AGR RES CTR, ORE STATE UNIV, 75-; EMER PROF, RUTGERS UNIV, 75- *Concurrent Pos:* Chmn dept soils & crops, Rutgers Univ, New Brunswick, 71-75. *Mem:* Am Soc Agron; Crop Sci Soc Am. *Res:* Cereal breeding. *Mailing Add:* 1201 SW 23rd St Pendleton OR 97801

LUND, WILLIAM ALBERT, JR, b Worcester, Mass, July 14, 30; m 58. ICHTHYOLOGY. *Educ:* Univ Mass, BS, 53, Cornell Univ, MS, 56, PhD(ichthyol), 60. *Prof Exp:* Fishery biologist, State Conserv Dept, Mass, 53; asst ichthyol, Cornell Univ, 55; from asst prof to assoc prof biol, 64-74, ASSOC PROF BIOL SCI, UNIV CONN, 74- *Mem:* AAAS; Am Soc Ichthyol & Herpet; Am Fisheries Soc; Am Soc Limnol & Oceanog; Biomet Soc. *Res:* Taxonomy; ecology and life history of fishes; dynamics of fish populations. *Mailing Add:* Dept of Biol Sci Univ of Conn Storrs CT 06268

LUNDBERG, CHARLES ANDREW, JR, b Boston, Mass, June 12, 42; m 71; c 1. SYNTHETIC ORGANIC CHEMISTRY. *Educ:* Harvard Univ, AB, 63, AM, 65, PhD(chem), 70. *Prof Exp:* Res chemist, Esso Res & Eng Co, 69-70; res chemist, Merrell-Nat Labs, 70-77, res chemist, Univ Cincinnati Med Ctr, 78-80. *Concurrent Pos:* Referee, J Org Chem, 73-; instr, Xavier Univ, 74- *Mem:* Am Chem Soc; NY Acad Sci. *Res:* Design and synthesis of novel substances as potential therapeutic agents. *Mailing Add:* 4707 Williamsburg Rd Northwest Cincinnati OH 45215

LUNDBERG, GEORGE DAVID, b Pensacola, Fla, Mar 21, 33; m 56; c 3. PATHOLOGY. *Educ:* Univ Ala, BS, 52; Med Col Ala, MD, 57; Am Bd Path, dipl anat & clin path, 62; Baylor Univ, MS, 64. *Prof Exp:* Intern, Tripler Gen Hosp, Honolulu, Hawaii, 57-58; resident path, Brooke Gen Hosp, San Antonio, Tex, 58-62; chief anat path, Letterman Gen Hosp, San Francisco, Calif, 62-63, res officer, 63-64; chief path, William Beaumont Gen Hosp, El Paso, Tex, 64-67; from assoc prof to prof path, Sch Med, Univ Southern Calif, 67-77; asst dir labs, Los Angeles County/Univ Southern Calif Med Ctr, 68-73, assoc dir, 73-77; prof path, Sch Med, Univ Calif, Davis & dir path & labs, Med Ctr, Sacramento, 77-82. *Concurrent Pos:* US Army Med Res & Develop Command res grants, 63-64 & 65-67; vis prof forensic med, Lund Univ, Sweden, 76 & Univ London, 76-77; vpres sci info & ed-in-chief jour, AMA, 82- *Mem:* Col Am Path; Am Soc Clin Path; Am Asn Path & Bact; Int Acad Path; Am Acad Forensic Sci. *Res:* Laboratory computer applications; diseases produced by drugs; toxicology; drug abuse; laboratory management. *Mailing Add:* Dept of Path Sch of Med Univ of Calif Davis CA 95616

LUNDBERG, GUSTAVE HAROLD, b Fremont, Nebr, Sept 5, 01; m 35. APPLIED MATHEMATICS. *Educ:* Midland Col, BS, 24; Colo State Col, MA, 37; Vanderbilt Univ, MA, 32; George Peabody Col, PhD(math), 51. *Prof Exp:* Prof math & sci, Dana Col, 24-29; teacher high sch, Colo, 29-34; instr, Allen Acad, 34-41; prof appl math, Vanderbilt Univ, 42-67; prof, 67-72, EMER PROF MATH, AUSTIN PEAY STATE UNIV, 72-; EMER PROF APPL MATH, VANDERBILT UNIV, 67- *Concurrent Pos:* Res partic, Oak Ridge Nat Lab, 57; vis prof, George Peabody Col, 60 & 61; ed, J Tenn Acad Sci, 63-66, pres, Tenn Acad Sci, 69. *Mem:* Sigma Xi; Math Asn Am. *Res:* Engineering mathematics. *Mailing Add:* 2001 21st Ave S Nashville TN 37212

LUNDBERG, JOHN L(AUREN), b St Paul, Minn, Oct 8, 24; m 55; c 4. POLYMER SCIENCE, TEXTILE ENGINEERING. *Educ:* Univ Minn, BChE, 48; Univ Calif, PhD(chem), 52. *Prof Exp:* Mem tech staff, Bell Tel Labs, Inc, 52-68; assoc prof textile chem, Clemson Univ, 68-71, chmn dept, 70-71; CALLAWAY PROF TEXTILE CHEM, GA INST TECHNOL, 72- *Concurrent Pos:* Vis assoc prof, Polytech Inst Brooklyn, 61-62, lectr, 63, adj prof, 64-68. *Mem:* AAAS; Am Asn Textile Chem & Colorists; Am Asn Textile Technol; Am Chem Soc; Am Inst Chem. *Res:* Physical chemistry and physics of polymers, fibers and textiles; solution chemistry, diffusion and physical properties of polymer solutions; light scattering by fibers, liquids and solutions. *Mailing Add:* A French Sch of Textiles Ga Inst of Technol Atlanta GA 30332

LUNDBERG, ROBERT DEAN, b Valley City, NDak, May 30, 28; m 53; c 2. POLYMER CHEMISTRY. *Educ:* Harvard Univ, BA, 52, MA & PhD(phys chem), 57. *Prof Exp:* Chemist, Eastman Kodak Co, 52-53; chemist, Union Carbide Corp, 57-62, group leader, Res & Develop Dept, Union Carbide Chem & Plastic Co, 62-69; vpres res, Inter-Polymer Res Corp, 69-70; res assoc, 70-71, sr res assoc, 71-76, SCI ADV, EXXON RES & ENG RES LAB, 76- *Mem:* Am Chem Soc; NY Acad Sci. *Res:* Synthesis of synthetic polypeptides; polymer interactions; ionic polymers; block copolymers; thermoplastic elastomers; polymer blends; dilute polymer solution behavior. *Mailing Add:* Corp Res Lab Exxon Res & Eng Co Linden NJ 07036

LUNDBLAD, ROGER LAUREN, b San Francisco, Calif, Oct 31, 39; m 66. BIOCHEMISTRY, HEMATOLOGY. *Educ:* Pac Lutheran Univ, BS, 61; Univ Wash, PhD(biochem), 65. *Prof Exp:* Res assoc biochem, Univ Wash, 65-66; res assoc, Rockefeller Univ, 66-68; asst prof, 68-71, assoc prof, 71-77, PROF PATH & BIOCHEM, DENT RES CTR, UNIV NC, CHAPEL HILL, 77- *Concurrent Pos:* Mem coun basic sci & coun thrombosis, Am Heart Asn. *Mem:* AAAS; Am Chem Soc; Am Soc Biol Chem; Int Soc Thrombosis & Haemostasis. *Res:* Mechanism of blood coagulation; protein chemistry; secretory proteins of the parotid gland. *Mailing Add:* Dept of Path & Biochem Dent Res Ctr Univ of NC Chapel Hill NC 27514

LUNDE, BARBARA KEGERREIS, b Oak Park, Ill, Aug 10, 37; div; c 2. ELECTRICAL ENGINEERING, RADIO ENGINEERING. *Educ:* Northwestern Univ, Ill, BA, 57, MS, 59; Iowa State Univ, PhD(solid state physics), 70. *Prof Exp:* Res engr, Charles Stark Draper Lab, Mass Inst Technol, 59-61; aerospace engr, Goddard Space Flight Ctr, NASA, 61-65; vpres & chief engr, Radio Sta KLFM, 67-75; asst prof food & nutrit, Iowa State Univ, 70-71, assoc biophys, 71-72, asst prof aerospace eng, 71-76; assoc engr, Ames Lab, 74-76, assoc prof civil eng, 80-81; prof solar & elec engr, Brooks Borg & Skiles, Engrs-Architects, 76-80; vpres & chief engr, Radio Sta KANY, 76-80; TECH CONSULT ENERGY SYSTS, NORTHWESTERN BELL, 81- *Concurrent Pos:* Mem, Nat Adv Comn on Foods, Food & Drug Admin, 71-72. *Mem:* Asn Energy Engrs; Am Soc Heating, Refrig & Air Conditioning Engrs; Am Inst Aeronaut & Astronaut; Nat Soc Prof Engrs. *Res:* Nuclear magnetic resonance of metals; solar energy for heating and cooling; electrical design of buildings; energy management in buildings. *Mailing Add:* 2209 SW Park Ave Des Moines IA 50321

LUNDE, KENNETH E(VAN), b Great Falls, Mont, Mar 6, 18; m 43; c 3. CHEMICAL ENGINEERING. *Educ:* Mont State Col, BS, 40; Univ Wash, MS, 41. *Prof Exp:* Process engr, Permanente Metals Corp, 41-42, chem engr, 43-44; chem engr, Henry J Kaiser Co, 42-43; sr engr, Kaiser Aluminum & Chem Corp, 46-47; mech engr, Ralph M Parsons Co, 47-48; head chem eng, Stanford Res Inst, 48-55, mgr indust air res, 55-59; sr engr, Yuba Consol Industs, 59; mgr, Carad Chem Corp, 59-60, vpres, 60-62; mgr process econ, Stanford Res Inst, 62-69, dir chem indust econ, 69-77, DIR SPEC PROJS, SRI INT, 77- *Concurrent Pos:* Lectr, Stanford Univ, 53. *Mem:* Am Chem Soc; Am Inst Chem Engrs. *Res:* Dust collection; gas absorption; drying; heat transfer; cost estimation. *Mailing Add:* 1101 Noel Dr Menlo Park CA 94025

LUNDE, MILFORD NORMAN, b Dodgeville, Wis, Apr 17, 24; m 50; c 2. PARASITOLOGY. *Educ:* Luther Col, AB, 47; Univ NC, MPH, 48. *Prof Exp:* Bacteriologist, WVa State Hyg Lab, 48-51; parasitologist, Inst Trop Med, Bowman-Gray Sch Med, 51-52 & Am Found Trop Med, 52-53; bacteriologist, Army Med Ctr, Ft Detrick, Md, 53-55; RES PARASITOLOGIST, LAB PARASITIC DIS, NAT INST ALLERGY & INFECTIOUS DIS, NIH, 55- *Mem:* Am Soc Parasitologists; Am Soc Trop Med & Hyg. *Res:* Immunodiagnosis of parasitic diseases; application of enzyme immunoassay for detection of antigens and characterization of antibodies; toxoplasmosis; amebiasis and schistosomiasis. *Mailing Add:* Lab Parasitic Dis NIH Bethesda MD 20014

LUNDE, PETER J, b New York, NY, June 8, 31; m 57; c 3. CHEMICAL & SOLAR ENGINEERING. *Educ:* Pa State Univ, BS, 53, MS, 60, PhD(chem eng), 62. *Prof Exp:* Instrument engr, Union Carbide Plastics Co, 56-57; chem engr process design, Chevron Res Corp, 61-63; sr chem engr, Res Div, Carrier Corp, 63-67; sr chem engr, Hamilton Standard Div, United Aircraft Corp, 67-69, head advan design & develop, Space Life Support Systs, 69-73, head chem process anal, 71-73; sr res scientist, Ctr Environ & Man, Inc, 73-77; solar eng colsult, 77-81; PRES, NEW ENERGY RESOURCES, INC, 81- *Concurrent Pos:* Vis prof, Univ Conn, 74-75 & 77; adj prof, Hartford Grad Ctr, 75- *Mem:* Am Inst Chem Engrs; Am Chem Soc; Am Soc Heating, Refrig & Air Conditioning Engrs; Int Solar Energy Soc; Sigma Xi. *Res:* Solar engineering; solar system performance prediction; solar air-conditioning. *Mailing Add:* Hartford Grad Ctr 275 Windsor St Hartford CT 06120

LUNDEEN, ALLAN JAY, b New York, NY, Aug 24, 32; m 54; c 4. ORGANIC CHEMISTRY. *Educ:* Southwestern Col, Kans, AB, 54; Rice Univ, PhD(chem), 57. *Prof Exp:* Res chemist org chem, 57-60, sr res chemist, 60-62, res group leader, 62-70, dir explor res, 70-78, DIR PLASTICS RES, CONTINENTAL OIL CO, 78- *Mem:* Am Chem Soc. *Res:* Chemistry of mustard oil glucosides; reactions of carbonium ions; heterogenous catalysis; chemistry of organoaluminum compounds; hydrocarbon oxidation; polymer chemistry. *Mailing Add:* 2108 El Camino Ponca City OK 74601

LUNDEEN, CARL VICTOR, JR, b Baltimore, Md, Jan 20, 43; m 65; c 2. BIOCHEMISTRY. *Educ:* Univ NC, Chapel Hill, AB, 65; Rockefeller Univ, PhD(life sci), 72. *Prof Exp:* Res assoc plant biol, Rockefeller Univ, 71-72; asst prof chem, 72-74, asst prof biol, 74-77, ASSOC PROF BIOL, UNIV NC, WILMINGTON, 77- *Mem:* Sigma Xi. *Res:* Attempting to elucidate the mechanisms by which autonomous cells attain the capability for rapid growth. *Mailing Add:* Dept of Biol Univ of NC Wilmington NC 28406

LUNDEEN, GLEN ALFRED, b Sterling, Colo, June 7, 22; m 48; c 6. FOOD SCIENCE, AGRICULTURE & FOOD CHEMISTRY. *Educ:* Univ Calif, BS, 47; Ore State Univ, MS, 49, PhD(food technol), 52. *Prof Exp:* In chg qual control, Smith Canning & Freezing Co, Ore, 50; asst prof hort & asst horticulturist, Univ Ariz, 51-52; prof subtrop hort, Am Univ, Beirut, 52-54, prof & head dept food technol, 54-57; asst prof hort, Mich State Univ, 57-60 & food sci, 60-64; res chemist, Nutrit Div, Wyeth Lab, Inc, 64; assoc prof, Fresno State Col, 64-68; DIR FOOD SCI RES CTR, 68- *Mem:* AAAS; Am Chem Soc; Am Soc Hort Sci; Inst Food Technol. *Res:* Food antioxidants; oxidation-reduction potentials in food products; enzymes in fruits and vegetables; compounding nutrition foods; milk chemistry; preservation of fruit and vegetable products; world food problems; human nutrition problems. *Mailing Add:* 3451 E Bellaire Way Fresno CA 93726

LUNDEGARD, ROBERT JAMES, b Youngstown, Ohio, Feb 22, 27; m 51; c 1. TECHNICAL MANAGEMENT, RESEARCH ADMINISTRATION. *Educ:* Univ Ohio, BS, 50; Purdue Univ, MS, 52, PhD(math, statist), 57. *Prof Exp:* Asst prof math, Syracuse Univ, 56-60; head, Logistics & Math Statist Br, 60-69, dir, Math & Info Sci Div, 69-79, actg chief scientist, 77-78, dep tech dir, 79-81, MEM STAFF, OFF NAVAL RES, 60- *Mem:* Am Statist Asn; Math Asn Am; Inst Math Statist; Soc Indust & Appl Math; Asn Comput Mach. *Res:* Models for problems in engineering and research management. *Mailing Add:* Off Naval Res Arlington VA 22217

LUNDELIUS, ERNEST LUTHER, JR, b Austin, Tex, Dec 2, 27; m 53; c 2. VERTEBRATE PALEONTOLOGY. *Educ:* Univ Tex, BS, 50; Univ Chicago, PhD(paleozool), 54. *Prof Exp:* Fulbright scholar vert paleont, Univ Western Australia, 54-55 & 76; res fel paleoecol, Calif Inst Technol, 56-57; from asst prof to assoc prof, 57-69, PROF GEOL, UNIV TEX, AUSTIN, 69-, JOHN A WILSON PROF VERT PALEONT, 78- *Mem:* Soc Vert Paleont (secy-treas, 75-, pres, 81); Soc Study Evolution; Am Soc Mammalogists; Geol Soc Am; Am Soc Naturalists. *Res:* Pleistocene vertebrates; paleoecology; adaptive morphology; Australian marsupials. *Mailing Add:* Dept of Geol Sci Univ of Tex Austin TX 78712

LUNDELL, ALBERT THOMAS, b Riverside, Calif, Dec 23, 31; m 52; c 3. MATHEMATICS. *Educ:* Univ Utah, AB, 52, AM, 55; Brown Univ, PhD(math), 60. *Prof Exp:* Instr math, Brown Univ, 59-60; lectr, Univ Calif, Berkeley, 60-62; asst prof, Purdue Univ, 62-66; assoc prof, 66-69, chmn dept, 70-72, PROF MATH, UNIV COLO, BOULDER, 70- *Mem:* Am Math Soc. *Res:* Algebraic topology. *Mailing Add:* Dept of Math Univ of Colo Boulder CO 80302

LUNDELL, O ROBERT, b Revelstoke, BC, Nov 7, 31; m 56; c 2. PHYSICAL CHEMISTRY. *Educ:* Queen's Univ, Ont, BA, 54; Mass Inst Technol, PhD(phys chem), 58. *Prof Exp:* Lectr chem, Royal Mil Col, Ont, 58-61; from asst prof to assoc prof, 61-71, actg chmn dept biol, 67-68, assoc dean, 68-74, PROF CHEM, YORK UNIV, 71-, DEAN, FAC SCI, 74- *Concurrent Pos:* Res assoc, Mass Inst Technol, 60-62. *Mem:* Chem Inst Can. *Res:* Calorimetry and kinetics of gas phase reactions. *Mailing Add:* Dept of Chem York Univ 4700 Keele St Downsview ON M3J 2R3 Can

LUNDEN, ALLYN OSCAR, b Toronto, SDak, Feb 5, 31; m 55; c 3. PLANT BREEDING, PLANT GENETICS. *Educ:* SDak State Col, BS, 52, MS, 56; Univ Fla, PhD(plant genetics), 60. *Prof Exp:* Asst agronomist, SDak State Col, 55-56; asst scientist plant genetics, Univ Tenn-AEC Agr Res Lab, 59-62, assoc prof agron, 62-64; assoc prof agron, 64-76, head, Seed Lab, 76-80, SEED RESEARCHER, SDAK STATE UNIV, 81- *Mem:* Am Soc Agron; Asn Off Seed Anal. *Res:* Irradiation sensitivity of plant tissues; genetic effects of ionizing and ultraviolet irradiation of plant tissues; seed testing techniques; seed vigor testing; seed germination; seed technology; seed storage research. *Mailing Add:* Dept of Plant Sci SDak State Univ Brookings SD 57007

LUNDERGAN, C(HARLES) DONALD, b Washington, Ind, Sept 24, 23. SYSTEMS RESEARCH. *Educ:* Univ Notre Dame, BSc, 47, MSc, 51. *Prof Exp:* Instr math, St Louis Univ, 51-54, acting dir aeronaut eng, 52-54; instr physics, Agr & Mech Col, Tex, 54-56; physicist mat sci, 56-61, sect supvr, 61-62, div supvr, 62-67, mem staff, Mat Res, 67-73, Reactor Safety Res, 73-75 & Mgt Staff, 75-78, MEM STAFF, SYSTS RES, SANDIA LAB, 78- *Concurrent Pos:* Res consult George Mallinckrodt Res, 53-54 & Ohio State, Wright-Patterson AFB, 62-63. *Res:* Equations of state of solids, propagation of shock waves in solids, dynamic stress-strain relations of metals; dynamic behavior of composites; effects of nuclear explosions; remote detection of nuclear effects. *Mailing Add:* Systs Res Sandia Lab Albuquerque NM 87185

LUNDGREN, CARL W(ILLIAM), JR, b Columbus, Ohio, Sept 17, 33; m 63; c 2. PHYSICS, ELECTRICAL ENGINEERING. *Educ:* Univ Cincinnati, EE, 57, MS, 59, PhD(instrumentation), 61. *Prof Exp:* Mem tech staff, Bell Tel Labs, 61-80; RETIRED. *Mem:* AAAS; Inst Elec & Electronics Engrs; NY Acad Sci; Am Inst Aeronaut & Astronaut. *Res:* Impact of selective (multipath) fading on high-speed digital microwave radio transmission--experiments and analyses; microwave transmission, interference and circuit outage problems associated with communication satellite and high speed digital radio systems; electrodynamics; gyro-mechanics. *Mailing Add:* 100 S Ash St Hobart IN 46342

LUNDGREN, DALE A(LLEN), b Duluth, Minn, Apr 26, 32; m 54; c 6. AIR POLLUTION, INDUSTRIAL HYGIENE. *Educ:* Univ Minn, BS, 58, MS, 62, PhD(environ health), 73. *Prof Exp:* Engr, Link-Belt Co, Minn, 55-58; asst mech eng, Univ Minn, 58-61; scientist, Electronics Div, Gen Mills, Inc, 61-63; prin scientist, Appl Sci Div, Litton Industs, Inc, 63-65; head air & particle anal lab, Ctr Air Environ Studies & instr mech eng & air pollution, Pa State Univ, 65-67; specialist & head aerosol lab, Statewide Air Pollution Res Ctr, Univ Calif, Riverside, 67-69; chief engr-dir, Air Pollution Control Equipment Sect, Environ Res Corp, St Paul, Minn, 69-72; PROF, ENVIRON ENG DEPT, UNIV FLA, 72- *Concurrent Pos:* Consult, Dale A Lundgren Assoc, 72- & various indust. *Mem:* Air Pollution Control Asn; Am Indust Hyg Asn; Am Soc Mech Engrs. *Res:* Aerosol physics; air pollution; industrial hygiene; air sampling instrumentation; air pollution control equipment. *Mailing Add:* Environ Eng Dept Univ of Fla Gainesville FL 32611

LUNDGREN, DAVID LEE, b Aberdeen, Wash, Sept 28, 31; wid; c 5. MICROBIOLOGY, INHALATION TOXICOLOGY. *Educ:* Ore State Univ, BS, 54; Univ Utah, MS, 61, PhD(microbiol), 68. *Prof Exp:* Bacteriologist, Univ Utah, 54-59, chief epizool diag lab, 59-62, chief infectious disease lab, 61-64, microbiologist, Biol Div, Dugway Proving Ground, 64-66; res virologist, 66-80, BIOLOGIST, LOVELACE INHALATION TOXICOL RES INST, 80- *Concurrent Pos:* Adj prof biol, Univ NMex, 72- *Mem:* Radiation Res Soc; Am Soc Microbiol; Health Physics Soc; Soc Exp Biol & Med; NY Acad Sci. *Res:* Toxicity of inhaled radionuclides from nuclear energy generation and fossil fuel effluents; biological effects studies in experimental animals. *Mailing Add:* Inhalation Toxicol Res Inst Lovelace Found PO Box 5890 Albuquerque NM 87115

LUNDGREN, DONALD GEORGE, b Manchester, NH, Aug 29, 24; m 49; c 2. MICROBIOLOGY. *Educ:* St Anselm Col, BA, 49; Stetson Univ, MA, 50; Syracuse Univ, PhD(bact), 54. *Prof Exp:* Asst instr, 52-54, instr plant sci, 54-58, from asst prof bact to assoc prof microbiol, 58-65, PROF BIOL, SYRACUSE UNIV, 65-, CHMN DEPT BIOL, 71- *Mem:* AAAS; Am Soc Microbiol; Brit Soc Gen Microbiol; NY Acad Sci. *Res:* Bacterial physiology; ecological microbiology; microbial leaching of metals. *Mailing Add:* Dept of Biol Syracuse Univ Biol Res Labs Syracuse NY 13210

LUNDGREN, HAROLD PALMER, b Minneapolis, Minn, Mar 22, 11; m 39; c2. TEXTILE CHEMISTRY. *Educ:* NDak Agr Col, BS, 32; Univ Minn, PhD(physiol chem), 35. *Prof Exp:* Asst, NDak Agr Col, 31-32; res fel, Phys Chem Inst, Univ Uppsala, 35-37; res assoc colloid chem, Univ Wis, 37-41; from assoc chemist to sr chemist, Western Regional Res Lab, Agr Res Serv, USDA, 41-53, head protein sect, 53-57, chief wool & mohair lab, 57-74; actg chmn div textiles & clothing, Univ Calif, Davis, 74-78; RETIRED. *Honors & Awards:* H D Smith Mem Award, Am Soc Testing & Mat, 65; Olney Gold Medal Award, Am Asn Textile Chemists & Colorists, 68; Norman E Borlaug Award, World Farm Found, 75. *Mem:* Am Chem Soc; Am Soc Biol Chemists; Fiber Soc; Am Asn Textile Chemists & Colorists; fel Brit Textile Inst. *Res:* Physical chemistry of proteins and protein derivatives; synthetic and natural protein fibers. *Mailing Add:* 92 Kingston Rd Kensington CA 94707

LUNDGREN, HARRY RICHARD, b Chicago, Ill, May 2, 28; m 55. STRUCTURAL ENGINEERING. *Educ:* Purdue Univ, BSCE, 50; Ariz State Univ, MSE, 62; Okla State Univ, Phd(struct eng), 67. *Prof Exp:* Proj engr, Kawneer Co, Mich, 53-58; vpres eng, R B Feffer & Sons, Ariz, 58-59; sr civil engr, Salt River Proj, 59-61; from instr to assoc prof struct eng, 62-73, PROF STRUCT ENG, ARIZ STATE UNIV, 73- *Mem:* Am Soc Civil Engrs; Nat Soc Prof Engrs. *Res:* Finite element applications to structural engineering problems; structural stability; light gauge steel structures; wind engineering. *Mailing Add:* Eng Ctr Ariz State Univ Tempe AZ 85281

LUNDGREN, J RICHARD, b Springfield, Mass, Oct 1, 42; m 64; c 2. APPLICAITONS OF GRAPH THEORY. *Educ:* Worcester Polytech Inst, BS, 64; Ohio State Univ, MS, 69, PhD(math), 71. *Prof Exp:* Proj engr, New Eng Tel, 64-67; asst prof math, Allegheny Col, 71-77, assoc prof math, 77-81; ASSOC PROF MATH, UNIV COLO, DENVER, 81- *Mem:* Am Math Soc; Math Asn Am; Soc Indust & Appl Math. *Res:* Applications of graphs and metrics, mathematical; modeling. *Mailing Add:* 1413 S Ward St Lakewood CO 80228

LUNDGREN, LAWRENCE WILLIAM, JR, b Attleboro, Mass, Mar 17, 32; div; c 2. ENVIRONMENTAL GEOLOGY. *Educ:* Brown Univ, AB, 53; Yale Univ, PhD(geol), 58. *Prof Exp:* From instr to assoc prof geol, 56-67, chmn dept geol sci, 71-74, PROF GEOL, UNIV ROCHESTER, 67-, CHMN DEPT GEOL SCI, 76- *Concurrent Pos:* Fulbright lectr, Finland, 67-68; NSF fac fel geog & environ eng, Johns Hopkins Univ, 76; mem staff, US Geol Surv, Menlo Park, 77. *Mem:* AAAS; Geol Soc Am. *Res:* Structure of metamorphic rocks; geology and public policy. *Mailing Add:* Dept of Geol Univ of Rochester Rochester NY 14627

LUNDHOLM, J(OSEPH) G(IDEON), JR, b Emporia, Kans, Feb 19, 25; m 56; c 2. APPLIED PHYSICS, ENGINEERING PHYSICS. *Educ:* Kans State Univ, BS, 46, MS, 48; NC State Univ, PhD(eng physics), 56. *Prof Exp:* Instr math, Kans State Univ, 47-48; instrumentation develop engr, Oak Ridge Nat Lab, 48-52; res assoc physics, NC State Univ, 52-56, supvr, Raleigh Res Reactor, 52-57; staff res specialist, Reactor Develop Dept, Atomics Int Div, NAm Aviation, Inc, 57-59, supvr syst control & safety, Compact Power Plants, 59-60; mem tech staff, Res & Adv Develop Div, Avco Co, Mass, 60-62, proj mgr, Adv Space Systs, 62-64; dir adv res & tech, Space Systs Div, Fairchild-Hiller Corp, 64-65; mgr exp prog, Skylab Prog, Hq, 65-74, res prog mgr, Off Aeronaut & Space Technol Res Div, 74-81, ADV TECHNOL MGR, ADV LAND OBSERVATIONS SYSTS OFF, GODDARD SPACE FLIGHT CTR, NASA, 81- *Concurrent Pos:* Mem, Comt on Radioactive

Waste Mgt, Nat Acad Sci, 76-78; res assoc, Mat Sci Dept, Univ Md, 78-79. *Mem:* Assoc fel Am Inst Aeronaut & Astronaut; sr mem Am Astronaut Soc. *Res:* Space research and technology, especially space payloads, laser systems, advance energy conversion methods, ultra low temperature coolers; nuclear systems technology and safety; ultra high pressure research; instrumentation and control systems; earth remote sensing technology. *Mailing Add:* 8106 Post Oak Rd Rockville MD 20854

LUNDIN, BRUCE T(HEODORE), b Alameda, Calif, Dec 28, 19; m 46; c 3. MECHANICAL ENGINEERING. *Educ:* Univ Calif, BS, 42. *Prof Exp:* Design engr, Standard Oil Co, Calif, 42-43; res engr aircraft engine res lab, NASA, 44-45, head jet propulsion res sect, Lewis Flight Propulsion Lab, 46-49, chief engine res div, 50-58, asst dir, Lewis Res Ctr, Ohio, 58-61, assoc dir, 61-68, dep assoc adminstr, Off Advan Res & Technol, Washington, DC, 68-69, DIR, LEWIS RES CTR, NASA, 69- *Honors & Awards:* Outstanding Leadership Award, NASA, 65, Pub Serv Award & Distinguished Serv Medal, 71. *Mem:* Nat Acad Eng; AAAS; Am Inst Aeronaut & Astronaut. *Res:* High energy chemical, nuclear and electric propulsion systems; direct and indirect energy conversion systems for space vehicles, including processes, components and systems research; launch vehicle development and operation. *Mailing Add:* Lewis Res Ctr NASA 21000 Brookpark Rd Cleveland OH 44135

LUNDIN, CARL D, b Yonkers, NY, Dec 16, 34; m 57; c 3. PHYSICAL METALLURGY. *Educ:* Rensselaer Polytech Inst, BMetEng, 57, PhD(mat sci), 66. *Prof Exp:* Res asst metall, Rensselaer Polytech Inst, 60-62, from instr to asst prof, 62-68; from assoc prof to prof metall & dir welding res, Univ Tenn, 68-75; welding sect mgr, Babcock & Wilcox Co, 75-77; MAGNOVOX PROF ENG, TENN TOMORROW PROF & DIR WELDING RES, UNIV TENN, KNOXVILLE, 77- *Concurrent Pos:* Supvr welding res mat div, Rensselaer Polytech Inst, 60-68; consult, Oak Ridge Nat Labs, 67-; NSF res initiation grant, 67-68; mem, Welding Res Coun & Pressure Vessel Res Comt. *Honors & Awards:* Adams Mem Award, Am Welding Soc, 68 & 73, Sparager Award, 78; McKay-Helm Award, 81; Adams Mem lectr, Am Welding Soc, 81. *Mem:* Am Welding Soc; Am Soc Metals. *Res:* Physical metallurgy associated with welding and joining--solid state transformations, solidification, diffusion, fissuring, arc physics; process development in welding industry. *Mailing Add:* Dept Chem & Metall Eng Univ Tenn Knoxville TN 37916

LUNDIN, FRANK E, JR, b Chicago, Ill, Aug 25, 28; m 49, 79; c 4. EPIDEMIOLOGY. *Educ:* Manchester Col, BA, 49; Ind Univ, MD, 53; Johns Hopkins Univ, MPH, 59, DrPH, 62. *Prof Exp:* USPHS, 53-, intern, Hosp, Norfolk, Va, 53-54, staff physician, Hosp, Carville, La, 54-56, epidemiologist, Cancer Invest, Nat Cancer Inst, Univ Tenn, 56-58, instr, Johns Hopkins Univ, 60-61, res assoc, 61-62, head special studies section, Epidemiol Br, Nat Cancer Inst, 62-67, sr epidemiologist, Occup Studies, Nat Inst Environ Health Sci, NIH, 67-71, sr epidemiologist, Epidemiol Br, Epidemiol & Biomet Div, Nat Inst Child Health & Human Develop, 71-74, dep chief, 74-75, chief, 75-80, SR EPIDEMIOLOGIST, EPIDEMIOL STUDIES BR, BUR RADIOL HEALTH, FOOD & DRUGS ADMIN, USPHS, 80- *Mem:* Soc Epidemiol Res; Am Pub Health Asn; Soc Occup & Environ Health; Am Med Asn. *Res:* Epidemiology of cancer, especially of the cervix; lung cancer; leukemia and lymphoma; occupational cancer, infant and fetal mortality and parental smoking; health effects of radiation. *Mailing Add:* 7212 Maple Ave Takoma Park MD 20912

LUNDIN, ROBERT ENOR, b Boston, Mass, Mar 19, 27; m 52; c 2. NUCLEAR MAGNETIC RESONANCE. *Educ:* Harvard Univ, AB, 50; Univ Calif, Berkeley, PhD(chem), 55. *Prof Exp:* Res chemist, San Ctr, Texaco, Inc, 55-58; RES CHEMIST, WESTERN REGIONAL RES CTR, USDA, 58- *Mem:* AAAS; Am Chem Soc; Soc Appl Spectros. *Res:* High resolution nuclear magnetic resonance spectroscopy; catalysis; radiation chemistry; gaseous thermodynamics. *Mailing Add:* Western Regional Res Ctr USDA Berkeley CA 94710

LUNDIN, ROBERT FOLKE, b Rockford, Ill, July 20, 36; m 58. GEOLOGY, PALEONTOLOGY. *Educ:* Augustana Col, Ill, AB, 58; Univ Ill, MS, 61, PhD(geol), 62. *Prof Exp:* From asst prof to assoc prof, 62-74, res comt res grants, 66-67, 70-74 & 76, PROF GEOL, ARIZ STATE UNIV, 74-, ASSOC CHMN DEPT, 78- *Concurrent Pos:* Petrol Res Fund res grants, 63-65, 66-68 & 70-72; Res Corp res grant, 70; guest scientist, Univ Uppsala, 70, distinguished vis prof, 73-74 & 81; Swedist Natural Sci Res Coun res grant, 73-74 & 81; co-ed, J Paleont, 74-80. *Mem:* Soc Econ Paleont & Mineral; Am Asn Petrol Geol; Geol Soc Am; Paleont Soc; Int Paleont Asn. *Res:* Siluro, Devonian and Mississippi ostracodes, conodonts and stratigraphy; Cenozoic stratigraphy; freshwater ostracodes. *Mailing Add:* Dept of Geol Ariz State Univ Tempe AZ 85281

LUNDQUIST, BURTON RUSSELL, b Chicago, Ill, June 29, 27; m 50; c 4. FOOD SCIENCE, FOOD CHEMISTRY. *Educ:* Univ Ill, Urbana, BS, 50. *Prof Exp:* Chemist & bacteriologist, Dairy Div, Borden Co, 50-53; anal chemist, Res & Develop Ctr, Swift & Co, 53-54; packaging engr, 54-63, mgr packaging develop, 63-67; dir mkt, Champion Packaging Co, Champion Int, 67-71; MGR PACKAGING RES & DEVELOP, RES CTR, ARMOUR & CO, 71- *Concurrent Pos:* Mem packaging coun, Am Mgt Asn, 76- *Mem:* Am Soc Testing & Methods; Tech Asn Pulp & Paper Indust. *Res:* Food preservation using package designing and systems as primary tool to maintain quality throughout merchandising cycle and until consumed; food science bacteriology. *Mailing Add:* Armour & Co 15101 N Scottsdale Rd Scottsdale AZ 85260

LUNDQUIST, CHARLES ARTHUR, b Webster, SDak, Mar 26, 28; m 51; c 5. SPACE SCIENCES. *Educ:* SDak State Univ, BS, 49; Univ Kans, PhD(physics), 53. *Prof Exp:* Asst prof eng res, Pa State Univ, 53-54; physicist, Tech Feasibility Study Off, Redstone Arsenal, 54-56, chief physics & astrophys sect, Army Ballistic Missile Agency, 56-60; chief physics & astrophys br, Marshall Space Flight Ctr, NASA, 60-62; asst dir sci,

Smithsonian Astrophys Observ, 62-73; DIR SPACE SCI LAB, MARSHALL SPACE FLIGHT CTR, NASA, 73- *Concurrent Pos:* Assoc, Harvard Col Observ, 62-73. *Mem:* AAAS; Int Astron Union; Am Astron Soc; Am Geophys Union; Am Phys Soc. *Res:* Spacecraft orbital mechanics and orbit determination; space technology; classical mechanics; radiative transfer. *Mailing Add:* Space Sci Lab NASA Marshall Space Flight Ctr Huntsville AL 35812

LUNDQUIST, MARJORIE ANN, b Newport News, Va, Aug 17, 38. INDUSTRIAL HYGIENE. *Educ:* Randolph-Macon Woman's Col, AB, 59; Univ Va, MS, 62, PhD(physics), 65. *Prof Exp:* Res fel, Dept Phys & Inorg Chem, Univ Adelaide, 65-66; physicist mat sci, 67, tech prog planner lead-acid battery eng, 67-72, supvr monitoring, anal & compliance occup safety & health, 72-74, MGR INDUST HYG, GLOBE-UNION, INC, 74- *Concurrent Pos:* Adj asst prof, Dept Energetics, Col Eng & Appl Sci, Univ Wis-Milwaukee, 74-75, mem bd dirs, Occup Health Inst, 79-81. *Mem:* Am Indust Hyg Asn; Soc Occup & Environ Health; Air Pollution Control Asn; Am Soc Testing & Mat. *Res:* Cigarette smoking as a source of occupational exposure to lead and other metals; biological monitoring of lead-exposed employees; correlation between airborne lead exposure and lead absorption of employee populations. *Mailing Add:* Globe-Union Inc 5757 N Green Bay Ave Milwaukee WI 53201

LUNDSAGER, C(HRISTIAN) BENT, b Denmark, Feb 27, 25; nat US; m 47; c 4. ENGINEERING, PLASTICS. *Educ:* Tech Univ Denmark, MSc, 50. *Prof Exp:* Engr, Tech Univ Denmark, 47-52 & E I du Pont de Nemours & Co, Inc, 52-62; RES ASSOC, RES DIV, W R GRACE & CO, COLUMBIA, MD, 62- *Mem:* Soc Plastics Engrs. *Res:* Thermoplastics processing; concept development of novel products and processes including ceramics. *Mailing Add:* 1308 Patuxent Dr Ashton MD 20702

LUNDSTROM, JERRY EUGENE, b Waupun, Wis, Aug 23, 37; m 69; c 1. PHYSICAL CHEMISTRY. *Educ:* Univ Wis-Madison, BS, 60; Stanford Univ, MS, 65; Univ Kans, PhD(phys chem), 70; Babson Col, MBA, 78. *Prof Exp:* Instr chem, Univ Wis, 60-62; sr res asst, Exobiol Lab, Stanford Univ, 62-63; develop engr med devices & mat, Gen Elec Co, 69-72; proj leader & mgr separation processes, Brunswick Corp, 72-76; MGR CONTRACT RES & NEW BUS DEVELOP, IONICS, INC, 76- *Honors & Awards:* Louis & Bert Freedman Found Award, NY Acad Sci, 72. *Mem:* Am Chem Soc; NY Acad Sci. *Res:* Membrane transport, diffusion, separation processes, electrochemical and thermal processes; water treatment and purification processes. *Mailing Add:* Blueberry Circle Pelham NH 03076

LUNDSTROM, LOUIS C, b Tekamah, Nebr, June 7, 15; m 40; c 4. AUTOMOTIVE ENGINEERING, HIGHWAY SAFETY. *Educ:* Univ Nebr, BS & MS, 39, PhD(eng), 62. *Prof Exp:* Dir proving ground, Gen Motors Corp, 56-65, dir auto safety, 65-73, exec dir environ activ, 73-80. *Concurrent Pos:* Chmn, Dept Transp Motor Vehicle Safety Adv Coun. *Mem:* Nat Acad Eng; fel Soc Automotive Engrs. *Res:* Vehicle and highway safety; vehicle and highway noise. *Mailing Add:* 14390 E Marina Dr C-104 Aurora CO 80014

LUNDVALL, RICHARD, b Boxholm, Iowa, Dec 10, 20; m 41; c 3. VETERINARY MEDICINE. *Educ:* Iowa State Univ, DVM, 44, MS, 56. *Prof Exp:* From instr to assoc prof, 44-71, PROF VET MED & SURG, IOWA STATE UNIV, 71- *Res:* Large animal surgery; ophthalmology. *Mailing Add:* Vet Med Clin Iowa State Univ Ames IA 50010

LUNDY, TALMAGE E, b Andalusia, Ala, Feb 17, 17; m 48. BIOLOGY. *Educ:* Livingston State Col, BS, 48; Univ Ala, MA, 49, MEd, 53, PhD(biol), 62. *Prof Exp:* Teacher high sch, Ala, 49-50; mgr drug store, 50-51; teaching prin pub sch, 51-52, teacher & prin, 52-55, supv prin 55-57, guid counsr & teacher, 57-58 & 59-61; assoc prof biol, ECarolina Univ, 62-69; assoc prof, 69-74, PROF BIOL, PENSACOLA COL, 74- *Concurrent Pos:* Consult, Green-Thumb Nursery, Fla, 50-60; assoc dir, NSF Inst Jr High Sch Teachers, 62-65; curriculum consult, 64-71. *Mem:* Nat Audubon Soc. *Res:* Bird banding and migratory studies; avian ecology; transfer of viruses in genus Camelia; endoparasitism of domesticated dog; ectoparasitism and endoparasitism of common house sparrow; helminthology of swine; sterile techniques of camillia seed germination and meristem tissue propagation. *Mailing Add:* Dept of Biol Pensacola Col Pensacola FL 32503

LUNDY, TED SADLER, b Sumner Co, Tenn, Apr 24, 33; m 55; c 1. METALLURGY, MATHEMATICS. *Educ:* Univ Tenn, BS, 54, MS, 57, PhD(metall), 64; Oak Ridge Sch Reactor Technol, Dr Pile Eng, 58. *Prof Exp:* Instr eng drawing, 55-57; metallurgist, Metals & Ceramics Div, 57-59, group leader diffusion studies, 59-71, supvr corrosion res, 71-76, RES STAFF MEM, OAK RIDGE NAT LAB, 76- *Concurrent Pos:* Lectr, Univ Tenn, 66-; mem, Knox County Ct; mem bd dirs, Knoxville Urban League. *Mem:* Sigma Xi; Am Inst Mining, Metall & Petrol Engrs; Am Soc Metals. *Res:* Solid state reactions; diffusion in metals and ceramics. *Mailing Add:* Metals & Ceramics Div Oak Ridge Nat Lab Box X Oak Ridge TN 37830

LUNER, CHARLES, physical chemistry, see previous edition

LUNER, PHILIP, b Vilno, Poland, June 1, 25; US citizen; m 51; c 2. PHYSICAL CHEMISTRY. *Educ:* Loyola Col, BSc, 47; McGill Univ, PhD(phys chem), 51. *Prof Exp:* Res chemist, Pulp & Paper Res Inst Can, 51-54; group leader, Sulfite Pulp Mfrs League, 54-57; from res assoc to assoc prof, 57-64, PROF PULP & PAPER RES, STATE UNIV NY COL ENVIRON SCI & FORESTRY, 64-, SR RES ASSOC, EMPIRE STATE PAPER RES INST, 77- *Mem:* Am Chem Soc; Tech Asn Pulp & Paper Indust; Can Pulp & Paper Asn. *Res:* Diffusion and penetration studies of pulping; chromophores in model lignin compounds; mechanical properties of fibers and paper; surface chemical properties of wood polymers. *Mailing Add:* State Univ NY Col Environ Sci & Forestry Syracuse NY 13210

LUNER, STEPHEN JAY, b New York, NY, Oct 2, 40; m 65; c 3. BIOPHYSICS. *Educ:* Calif Inst Technol, BS, 61; Univ Calif, Los Angeles, PhD(biophys), 69. *Prof Exp:* Res biophysicist, Univ Calif, Los Angeles, 68-71, asst res biophysicist, Biophys Lab, 71, asst prof in residence pediat, 72-77; ASST PROF PATH, DALHOUSIE UNIV, 77- *Concurrent Pos:* NIMH trainee, Univ Calif, Los Angeles, 69-71. *Mem:* Biophys Soc; Sigma Xi; Am Soc Cell Biol; Am Soc Hemat. *Res:* Biophysics of the cell surface; electrophoresis; cell surface antigens; effects of enzymes on cell interactions; immunohematology. *Mailing Add:* Dept of Path Dalhousie Univ Halifax NS B3H 4H7 Can

LUNG, BEN, b Porterville, Calif, Jan 27, 39. CELL BIOLOGY, HISTOLOGY. *Educ:* San Jose State Col, BA, 64; Univ Calif, Davis, MA, 66; Univ Md, PhD(histol), 72. *Prof Exp:* Asst histol, Univ Md, 70-71, actg asst prof histol, 73; fel develop biol, 74-75, res affil develop biol, Dept Anat, Sch Med, Stanford Univ, 75-77; RES ASSOC DEVELOP BIOL, DEPT ANAT, SCH MED, UNIV COLO, 77- *Res:* Ultrastructure and biology of mammalian sperm chromosomes and nuclei; somatic chromosomes and nuclei; reproductive biology. *Mailing Add:* Dept of Anat Univ Colo Sch of Med Denver CO 80262

LUNGSTROM, LEON, b Lindsborg, Kans, July 22, 15; m 65; c 2. MEDICAL ENTOMOLOGY. *Educ:* Bethany Col, Kans, BS, 40; Kans State Univ, MS, 46, PhD(med entom), 50. *Prof Exp:* Entomologist, USPHS, Commun Dis Ctr, 49-52; biologist, 52-73, prof biol & head dept, 52-80, EMER PROF, BETHANY COL, KANS, 81- *Concurrent Pos:* NSF fac fel, Stanford Univ, 59-60 & Univ Okla, 65; co dir, McPherson County Old Mill Mus & Park, 81- *Mem:* Am Mosquito Control Asn. *Res:* Mosquitoes. *Mailing Add:* Dept of Biol Bethany Col Lindsborg KS 67456

LUNIN, MARTIN, b New York, NY, Aug 31, 17; m 47. PATHOLOGY. *Educ:* Okla Agr & Mech Col, BS, 38; Wash Univ, DDS, 50; Columbia Univ, MPH, 52. *Prof Exp:* Assoc prof path, Univ Tex Dent Br, 59-64; asst dean curriculum affairs, 69-71, assoc dean acad affairs, 71-74, PROF PATH & HEAD SCH DENT, UNIV MD, BALTIMORE, 64- *Concurrent Pos:* Sr consult, Univ Tex M D Anderson Hosp & Tumor Inst, 60-64; consult, Vet Admin Hosp, 62- & Children's & Lutheran Hosps, Baltimore, Md, 64- *Mem:* AAAS; Am Dent Asn; Am Acad Oral Path; Int Asn Dent Res. *Res:* Diseases of the soft and hard tissues of the head and neck. *Mailing Add:* 28 Olmstead Green Baltimore MD 21201

LUNK, WILLIAM ALLAN, b Johnstown, Pa, May 6, 19; m 47; c 4. ORNITHOLOGY. *Educ:* Univ WVa, AB, 41, MS, 46; Univ Mich, PhD(zool), 55. *Prof Exp:* Instr biol, Univ WVa, 46-47; preparator, 49-59, assoc cur exhibits & lectr zool, Univ, 59-64; CUR EXHIBITS, EXHIBIT MUS, UNIV MICH, ANN ARBOR, 64- *Concurrent Pos:* Consult, Kalamazoo Nature Ctr, 63-77. *Mem:* Cooper Ornith Soc; Wilson Ornith Soc; assoc Am Ornith Union. *Res:* Ornithological life history; taxonomy and distribution; fossil birds; exhibit techniques. *Mailing Add:* Exhibit Mus Univ of Mich Ann Arbor MI 48109

LUNNEY, DAVID CLYDE, b Charleston, SC. CHEMICAL INSTRUMENTATION. *Educ:* Univ SC, BS, 59, PhD(phys chem), 65. *Prof Exp:* NIH fel, Duke Univ, 66-68; asst prof, 68-73, ASSOC PROF CHEM, E CAROLINA UNIV, 73- *Concurrent Pos:* Pres, Serendipity Systs, Inc, 75- *Mem:* Instrument Soc Am; Audio Eng Soc; Am Chem Soc. *Res:* Chemical instrumentation and computerization. *Mailing Add:* Dept of Chem E Carolina Univ Greenville NC 27834

LUNSFORD, CARL DALTON, b Richmond, Va, Feb 11, 27; m 47; c 3. PHARMACEUTICAL CHEMISTRY. *Educ:* Univ Richmond, BS, 49, MS, 50; Univ Va, PhD(chem), 53. *Prof Exp:* Instr chem, Univ Va, 52-53; res chemist, 53-57, assoc dir chem res, 58, dir, 59-64, dir labs, 62-64, dir res, 64-66, asst vpres, 66-74, vpres, 73-80, SR VPRES, A H ROBINS CO, INC, 80- *Mem:* AAAS; Am Chem Soc; Am Inst Chemists. *Res:* Medicinal and organic chemistry and development. *Mailing Add:* PO Box 26609 1211 Sherwood Ave Richmond VA 23261

LUNSFORD, JACK HORNER, b Houston, Tex, Feb 6, 36; m 60; c 7. PHYSICAL CHEMISTRY. *Educ:* Tex A&M Univ, BS, 57; Rice Univ, PhD(chem eng), 62. *Prof Exp:* Asst prof chem eng, Univ Idaho, 61-62; asst prof chem, Sam Houston State Col, 65-66; from asst prof to assoc prof, 66-71, PROF CHEM, TEX A&M UNIV, 71- *Honors & Awards:* Paul H Emmett Award, Catalysis Soc, 75. *Mem:* Am Chem Soc. *Res:* Surface chemistry and heterogeneous catalysis, using modern spectroscopic techniques. *Mailing Add:* Dept of Chem Tex A&M Univ College Station TX 77843

LUNSFORD, JESSE V(ERNON), b Ninnekah, Okla, Sept 4, 23; m 48; c 5. CIVIL & SANITARY ENGINEERING. *Educ:* Univ NMex, BS, 53; Univ Calif, MS, 54. *Prof Exp:* Asst prof & asst res engr, Wash State Univ, 54-57; assoc prof, Rensselaer Polytech Inst, 57-58; PROF CIVIL ENG, N MEX STATE UNIV, 58- *Mem:* Am Soc Civil Engrs; Nat Soc Prof Engrs; Am Soc Eng Educ; Am Pub Health Asn; Am Water Works Asn. *Res:* Anaerobic digestion; stream sanitation; algae production; water reclamation and utilization. *Mailing Add:* Dept of Civil Eng Box 3CE NMex State Univ Las Cruces NM 88003

LUNSFORD, WILLIE B, biochemistry, organic chemistry, deceased

LUNT, OWEN RAYNAL, b El Paso, Tex, Apr 8, 21; m 53; c 3. SOIL FERTILITY. *Educ:* Brigham Young Univ, AB, 47; NC State Univ, PhD(agron), 51. *Prof Exp:* Lectr soil chem, NC State Univ, 50; from instr to assoc prof soil sci, 51-63, actg dir lab nuclear med & radiation biol, 65-68, actg chmn dept biophys, 65-70, PROF BIOL, UNIV CALIF, LOS ANGELES, 63-, DIR LAB NUCLEAR MED & RADIATION BIOL, 68- *Mem:* Fel Soil Sci Soc Am; fel Am Soc Agron; Am Soc Hort Sci; Am Nuclear Soc. *Res:* Soil chemistry; environmental pollution. *Mailing Add:* 1200 Roberto Lane Los Angeles CA 90077

LUNT, STEELE RAY, b Mammoth, Utah, Jan 5, 35; m 59; c 5. ENTOMOLOGY, GENETICS. *Educ:* Univ Utah, BS, 57, MS, 59, PhD(entom), 64. *Prof Exp:* From asst prof to assoc prof, 64-74, PROF BIOL, UNIV NEBR AT OMAHA, 74- *Mem:* Am Inst Biol Sci; Am Mosquito Control Asn; Entom Soc Am. *Res:* Control, systematics, ecology, and medical importance of mosquitoes; ecology. *Mailing Add:* 3853 N 100th Ave Omaha NE 68134

LUNTZ, MYRON, b New York, NY, Jan 16, 40; m 64; c 2. RADIATION PHYSICS. *Educ:* City Col New York, BS, 62; Univ Conn, MS, 64, PhD(physics), 68. *Prof Exp:* Res asst physics, Univ Conn, 64-68, fel, 68; vis scientist, Inst Physics, Univ Aarhus, 68-69; asst prof, 69-74, ASSOC PROF PHYSICS, STATE UNIV NY COL FREDONIA, 74-, CHMN DEPT, 78- *Concurrent Pos:* Vis assoc prof physics, Univ Del, 75- *Mem:* Am Phys Soc; Am Asn Physics Teachers; Sigma Xi; Soc Physics Students. *Res:* Theoretical study of the penetration of matter by energetic charged particles, with emphasis on effects associated with the spatial distribution of energy desposition about particle tracks; experimental study of surface alteration of metal substrates by ion beam irradiation. *Mailing Add:* Dept of Physics State Univ of NY Col Fredonia NY 14063

LUOMA, ERNIE VICTOR, b Sault Ste Marie, Mich, Sept 1, 32; m 54; c 5. INDUSTRIAL CHEMISTRY. *Educ:* Mich Technol Univ, BS, 54; Univ Calif, Berkeley, MS, 56; Mich State Univ, PhD(phys inorg chem), 66. *Prof Exp:* Instr chem, Mich Technol Univ, 56-57; chemist, 57-62, group leader, 62-70, res mgr, 70-77, tech dir, 77-78, dir, Anal Labs, 78-80, DIR ANAL SCI, CORP RES & DEVELOP, DOW CHEM CO, 80- *Mem:* Am Chem Soc; Am Inst Chem Engrs. *Res:* Industrial research. *Mailing Add:* Corp Res Develop Dow Chem Co 2020 Dow Ctr Midland MI 48640

LUOMA, JOHN ROBERT VINCENT, b Huntingdon, Pa, June 3, 38; m 61; c 2. PHYSICAL CHEMISTRY. *Educ:* Ohio Univ, BA & BS, 61; Purdue Univ, Lafayette, PhD(phys chem), 66. *Prof Exp:* Asst prof chem, NDak State Univ, 66-69; asst prof, 69-74, ASSOC PROF CHEM, CLEVELAND STATE UNIV, 74- *Res:* Mossbauer spectroscopy; molecular beam computations. *Mailing Add:* Dept of Chem Cleveland State Univ Cleveland OH 44115

LUPAN, DAVID MARTIN, b Cleveland, Ohio, Oct 23, 45; m 68; c 2. MEDICAL MYCOLOGY. *Educ:* Univ Ariz, BS, 67; Univ Iowa, MS, 70, PhD(microbiol), 73. *Prof Exp:* asst prof, 73-78, ASSOC PROF MICROBIOL, SCH MED SCI, UNIV NEV, RENO, 78- *Mem:* Sigma Xi; Am Soc Microbiol; Int Soc Human & Animal Mycol; Med Mycol Soc of the Americas. *Res:* The mechanism of pathogenesis of fungi. *Mailing Add:* Sch Med Sci Univ of Nev Reno NV 89557

LUPINSKI, JOHN HENRY, b Schenectady, NY, Feb 28, 27; m 54; c 3. POLYMER CHEMISTRY. *Educ:* State Univ Leyden, BS, 49, MS, 53, PhD(chem), 59. *Prof Exp:* Res chemist, Res & Develop Ctr, 60-72, proj mgr, Corp Res & Develop Ctr, 72-79, UNIT MGR CORP RES & DEVELOP, GEN ELEC CO, 79- *Mem:* AAAS; Am Chem Soc; Fedn Am Scientist. *Res:* Organic conductors; polymer electro-chemistry; electrical insulation and polymer application processes; electrostatics. *Mailing Add:* 26 Country Fair Lane Scotia NY 12302

LUPIS, CLAUDE HENRI PAUL, metallurgy, physical chemistry, see previous edition

LUPTON, CHARLES HAMILTON, JR, b Norfolk, Va, July 17, 19; m 45; c 3. MEDICINE, PATHOLOGY. *Educ:* Univ Va, BA, 42, MD, 44; Am Bd Path, dipl, 51. *Prof Exp:* Asst prof path, Sch Med, Univ Va, 51-53; assoc prof, 55-60, chmn dept, 61-74, PROF PATH, MED CTR, UNIV ALA, BIRMINGHAM, 60- *Concurrent Pos:* Consult, Vet Admin, Birmingham. *Mem:* AAAS; Am Asn Path; Int Acad Path; AMA; Col Am Path. *Res:* Cardiovascular-renal diseases, especially the kidney as studied by simpler histochemical techniques. *Mailing Add:* Dept of Path Univ of Ala Birmingham AL 35294

LUPTON, JOHN EDWARD, b Bakersfield, Calif, July 30, 44. CHEMICAL OCEANOGRAPHY, ISOTOPE GEOLOGY. *Educ:* Princeton Univ, BA, 66; Calif Inst Technol, PhD(physics), 72. *Prof Exp:* Asst res physicist, Scripps Inst Oceanog, 73-81; ASSOC RES OCEANOGRAPHER, MARINE SCI INST, UNIV CALIF, SANTA BARBARA, 81- *Concurrent Pos:* Cruise coordr res vessel, Melville Vulcan Exped, Scripps Inst Oceanog, 80-81; adj assoc prof geol, Univ Calif, Santa Barbara, 81- *Mem:* Am Geophys Union. *Res:* Application of helium and rare gas isotopes to ocean circulation studies; geothermal and volcanic gases; outgassing of mantle volatiles; numerical modeling of ocean tracer distributions. *Mailing Add:* Marine Sci Inst Univ Calif Santa Barbara CA 93106

LUPTON, WILLIAM HAMILTON, b Charlottesville, Va, July 25, 30. PLASMA PHYSICS. *Educ:* Univ Va, BA, 50; Univ Md, PhD(physics), 60. *Prof Exp:* Physicist, Radio Div, Nat Bur Stand, 52-55; PHYSICIST, PLASMA PHYSICS DIV, US NAVAL RES LAB, 60- *Mem:* AAAS; Am Phys Soc; Inst Elec & Electronics Engrs. *Res:* Plasma spectroscopy; high voltage and high current pulse technology; high power laser development. *Mailing Add:* Naval Res Lab Code 6770 4555 Overlook Ave Washington DC 20375

LURA, RICHARD DEAN, b Kenosha, Wis, Aug 21, 45; m 68. PHYSICAL ORGANIC CHEMISTRY. *Educ:* Univ Wis, BS, 67; Iowa State Univ, PhD(chem), 71. *Prof Exp:* asst prof, 71-80, ASSOC PROF CHEM, MILLIGAN COL, 80- *Concurrent Pos:* Consult, R I Schattner Co, 72-79. *Res:* Research and devleopment of germicidal and sporicidal solutions for hospital and home use. *Mailing Add:* 1903 Eastwood Dr Johnson City TN 37601

LURCH, E(DWARD) NORMAN, b Morristown, NJ, Dec 23, 19; m 41; c 4. ELECTRICAL ENGINEERING. *Educ:* NY Univ, BEE, 40, MEE, 43. *Prof Exp:* Tutor elec eng, City Col New York, 41-43; instr, Manhattan Col, 43-47; asst prof, Univ Fla, 47; asst prof, Clarkson Col Technol, 48-49; assoc prof electronics, State Univ NY Agr & Tech Col, Farmingdale, 49-60; chief engr, Chemtronics, Inc, 60-61; aerospace technologist, Goddard Space Flight Ctr, NASA, 62-65; assoc prof, 65-66, PROF ELECTRONICS, STATE UNIV NY AGR & TECH COL, FARMINGDALE, 66- *Concurrent Pos:* Lectr grad div, State Univ NY Col, New Paltz, 58-61; consult engr, Oil Heat Inst, Long Island, 57-59. *Res:* Fundamentals of electronics; electric circuits. *Mailing Add:* 11 Black Duck Dr Stony Brook NY 11790

LURIA, S(AUL) M(ARTIN), b Athol, Mass, Dec 24, 29; m 63; c 2. PHYSIOLOGICAL PSYCHOLOGY. *Educ:* Univ Richmond, BS, 49; Univ Pa, MA, 51, PhD(psychol), 55. *Prof Exp:* RES PSYCHOLOGIST, US NAVAL SUBMARINE MED CTR, 57- *Concurrent Pos:* Lectr, Univ RI, 66-, Univ Conn, 68-70 & Univ New Haven, 71- *Mem:* Fel AAAS; fel Am Psychol Asn; fel Optical Soc Am; Psychonomic Soc; fel NY Acad Sci. *Res:* Vision. *Mailing Add:* 35 Beacon Hill Dr Waterford CT 06385

LURIA, SALVADOR EDWARD, b Turin, Italy, Aug 13, 12; nat US; m 45; c 1. BACTERIOLOGY. *Educ:* Turin Univ, MD, 35. *Prof Exp:* Res fel, Curie Lab, Inst Radium, Paris, 38-40; res asst surg bact, Columbia Univ, 40-42; Guggenheim fel, Vanderbilt & Princeton Univs, 42-43; from instr to assoc prof bact, Univ Ind, 43-50; prof, Univ Ill, 50-59; prof microbiol & chmn microbiol comt, 59-64, SEDGWICK PROF BIOL, MASS INST TECHNOL, 64-, INST PROF, 70-, DIR, CTR CANCER RES, 74- *Concurrent Pos:* Investr, Off Sci Res & Develop, Carnegie Inst, 45-46; Jesup lectr, Columbia Univ, 50; lectr, Univ Colo, 50; Nieuwland fel, Univ Notre Dame, 59; non-resident fel, Salk Inst, 65-; ed, Virol, 55-; sect ed, Biol Abstr, 58- *Honors & Awards:* Nobel Prize in Med, 69. *Mem:* Nat Acad Sci; Nat Inst Med; AAAS; Am Soc Nat; Am Soc Microbiol. *Res:* Bacterial viruses; microbial genetics; biological effects of radiation. *Mailing Add:* Dept of Microbiol Mass Inst of Technol Cambridge MA 02139

LURIE, ALAN GORDON, b Los Angeles, Calif, Apr 23, 46; m 69; c 2. RADIATION BIOLOGY, CARCINOGENESIS. *Educ:* Univ Calif, Los Angeles, DDS, 70; Univ Rochester, PhD(radiation biol, biophys), 74. *Prof Exp:* Asst prof oral radiol, 73-77, asst prof oral diag, 77, ASSOC PROF ORAL DIAG, UNIV CONN HEALTH CTR, 77- *Concurrent Pos:* Consult oral radiol, Newington Vet Admin Hosp, 75-; HEW/NIH grants, Am Cancer Soc, 75- *Honors & Awards:* E H Hatton Award, Int Asn Dent Res, 69. *Mem:* Am Asn Cancer Res; Radiation Res Soc; Int Asn Dent Res. *Res:* Radiation pathophysiology; radiation carcinogenesis and cocarcinogenesis at low doses; chemical carcinogenesis; mechanistic roles of vascular changes during carcinogenesis. *Mailing Add:* Univ Conn Health Ctr Div of Oral Radiol Farmington CT 06032

LURIE, ARNOLD PAUL, b Brooklyn, NY, July 22, 32; m 54; c 3. ORGANIC CHEMISTRY. *Educ:* NY Univ, BA, 54; Purdue Univ, PhD(org chem), 58. *Prof Exp:* Lab asst org chem, Purdue Univ, 54-56, fel, 58; res chemist, 58-61, sr res chemist, 61-66, INFO SCIENTIST, RES LAB, EASTMAN KODAK CO, 65-, RES ASSOC, 66- *Mem:* Am Chem Soc. *Res:* Synthetic and theoretical organic chemistry related to photographic systems; computerized handling of information. *Mailing Add:* 489 Eastbrooke Lane Rochester NY 14618

LURIE, ARON OSHER, b Johannesburg, SAfrica, Sept 9, 25; US citizen; m 52; c 2. INTERNAL MEDICINE, BIOCHEMISTRY. *Educ:* Univ Witwatersrand, BSc, 46, MB, BCh, 51; Univ Cape Town, PhD(endocrinol), 61; Am Bd Internal Med, dipl, 74. *Prof Exp:* Registr internal med, King Edward VIII Hosp, Univ Natal, 56-58; sr bursar endocrinol, Groote Schuur Hosp, Univ Cape Town, 58-60; registr, North Middlesex Hosp, London, Eng, 61-62; registr, Guys Hosp, 63-64; res assoc biol chem, Harvard Univ, 64-68; ASSOC PROF MED, SCH MED, TUFTS UNIV, 68-; DIR, CONTINUING MED EDUC & STAFF PHYSICIAN, NEWTON-WELLESLEY HOSP, 74- *Concurrent Pos:* Dir, Steroid Hormone Res Univ, Boston City Hosp, 66-68, dir, Dept Clin Biochem, 68-81, assoc vis physician; med consult, Div Disability Serv, Mass Rehab Comn, 73- *Mem:* AMA; Endocrine Soc; Brit Med Asn. *Res:* Clinical biochemistry; reproductive endocrinology; gas liquid chromatography of steroid hormones; endocrinological disturbances of malnutrition. *Mailing Add:* 21 Salisbury Rd Brookline MA 02146

LURIE, DAN, biostatistics, see previous edition

LURIE, FRED MARCUS, b Boston, Mass, Nov 16, 30. PHYSICS. *Educ:* Univ NC, Chapel Hill, BS, 52; Univ Ill, Urbana, MS, 57, PhD, 63. *Prof Exp:* Teaching asst physics, Univ Ill, Urbana, 57-59; from instr to asst prof, Univ Pa, 63-67; asst prof, 67-70, ASSOC PROF PHYSICS, IND UNIV, BLOOMINGTON, 70- *Mem:* Am Phys Soc. *Mailing Add:* Dept of Physics Ind Univ Bloomington IN 47401

LURIE, HAROLD, b Durban, SAfrica, Mar 28, 24; nat US; m 59; c 2. ENGINEERING. *Educ:* Univ Natal, BSc, 45, MSc, 46; Calif Inst Technol, PhD(aeronaut, math), 50. *Prof Exp:* Lectr aeronaut, Calif Inst Technol, 48-50; head weapons effectiveness group, Rand Corp, 50-52; from asst prof appl mech to prof eng sci & assoc dean grad studies, Calif Inst Technol, 53-71; dir res & develop, New Eng Elec Syst, 71-78; consult, 78-80; PROF ENG & DEAN COL, POLYTECH INST NY, 80- *Concurrent Pos:* Sr develop engr, Oak Ridge Nat Lab, 56-57; consult, Yankee Atomic Elec Co, 70-71. *Mem:* Am Nuclear Soc; Am Soc Eng Educ; assoc fel Am Inst Aeronaut & Astronaut; assoc fel Royal Aeronaut Soc. *Res:* Energy conversion; nuclear and aerospace engineering; structural mechanics. *Mailing Add:* Polytech Inst of NY 333 Jay St Brooklyn NY 11201

LURIE, JOAN B, b New York, NY, Jan 21, 41; m 61; c 2. THEORETICAL SOLID STATE PHYSICS. *Educ:* Brooklyn Col, BS, 61; Rutgers Univ, MS, 62, PhD(physics), 67. *Prof Exp:* Mem tech staff physics res, RCA Labs, 62-66; fel appl math, Univ Col, Univ London, 67-68; syst programmer comput sci, Appl Data Res, 69-70; fel solid state physics, Rutgers Univ, 70-72; asst prof, 72-76, ASSOC PROF PHYSICS, RIDER COL, 76- *Concurrent Pos:* Am Phys Soc indust fel, Colgate Palmolive Res Lab. *Mem:* Am Phys Soc; Am Asn Univ Prof. *Res:* Theoretical research in lattice dynamics of solid state of rare gases; computer assisted instruction, particularly in physics and mathematics; image analysis. *Mailing Add:* Dept of Math & Physics Rider Col Lawrenceville NJ 08648

LURIE, NORMAN A(LAN), b Detroit, Mich, Dec 2, 40; m 67; c 2. NUCLEAR PHYSICS & ENGINEERING. *Educ:* Univ Mich, BSE, 63, MSE, 65, PhD(nuclear eng), 69. *Prof Exp:* Fel physics, Univ Mo-Columbia, 69-71; sr res assoc, Brandeis Univ, 71-74; sr physicist, 74-75, staff physicist, 75-76, prog mgr res, Nuclear Systs Div, 78-81, PRIN PHYSICIST, IRT CORP, 76-, MGR TECH OPERS, 81- *Concurrent Pos:* Res collabr, Brookhaven Nat Lab, 71-74. *Mem:* Am Nuclear Soc; Am Phys Soc; Am Soc Testing & Mat. *Res:* Applied nuclear physics. *Mailing Add:* IRT Corp PO Box 80817 San Diego CA 92138

LURIE, ROBERT M(ANDEL), b Boston, Mass, Feb 24, 31; m 53; c 3. CHEMICAL ENGINEERING, COLLOIDAL CHEMISTRY. *Educ:* Mass Inst Technol, SB, 52, ScD(chem eng), 55. *Prof Exp:* Chem engr & prod res mgr, Dewey & Almy Chem Co Div, W R Grace & Co, 55-60; sr chem engr, Ionics, Inc, 60-63; mgr mat develop, Res & Adv Develop Div, Avco Corp, 63-65; dir mats, Systs Div, 65-70; PRES, NYACOL PROD INC, 70- *Mem:* Soc Plastics Engrs; Am Inst Aeronaut & Astronaut; Am Chem Soc; Am Inst Chem Engrs; Fire Retardant Chem Asn. *Res:* Polymer synthesis; adhesion of polymers; unit operations of polymer manufacture and polymer fabrications; electrochemistry; fuel cells; ablation phenomena; physics of reinforced plastics; reentry vehicle design; organic dyes; colloidal chemicals. *Mailing Add:* 4 Tufts Rd Lexington MA 02173

LURIO, ALLEN, b Rockville Center, NY, July 11, 29. PHYSICS. *Educ:* Mass Inst Technol, BS, 50; Columbia Univ, MS, 52, PhD, 56. *Prof Exp:* Asst, Columbia Univ, 51-55; instr physics, Yale Univ, 55-57; RES PHYSICIST, IBM CORP, 57- *Concurrent Pos:* Adj asst prof, Columbia Univ, 64-67, adj assoc prof, 67-, mem exec comt, Div Electron & Atomic Physics, 66-69. *Mem:* Fel Am Phys Soc. *Res:* Atomic beam and optical double resonance spectroscopy; far infrared spectroscopy; ion solid interac interactions. *Mailing Add:* IBM Watson Res Ctr PO Box 218 Yorktown Heights NY 10598

LUSAS, EDMUND W, b Woodbury, Conn, Nov 25, 31; m 57; c 3. FOOD SCIENCE, FOOD TECHNOLOGY. *Educ:* Univ Conn, BS, 54; Iowa State Univ, MS, 55; Univ Wis, PhD(food technol), 58; Univ Chicago, MBA, 72. *Prof Exp:* Proj leader, Res Labs, Quaker Oats Co, 58-64, mgr canned foods res, 64-66, mgr pet foods res, 66-72, mgr sci serv, 72-77; DIR, FOOD PROTEIN RES & DEVELOP CTR, 78- *Mem:* Sigma Xi; Inst Food Technol; Am Chem Soc; Am Oil Chemists Soc; Am Cereal Chem Asn. *Res:* Protein and oil utilization from cottonseed, peanuts, soy, sunflower and sesame; criteria for ingredient selection and stability factors in foods; human and pet food development; research and development administration; technical staff services management. *Mailing Add:* Food Protein Res & Develop Ctr FM 183 Tex A&M Univ College Station TX 77843

LUSCHER, ULRICH, b Oftringen, Switz, July 18, 32; m 62; c 2. CIVIL ENGINEERING. *Educ:* Swiss Fed Inst Technol, BS, 56; Mass Inst Technol, SM, 59, ScD(civil eng & soil mech), 63. *Prof Exp:* Designer, Vevey Metal Works, Switz, 57 & Stone & Webster Eng Corp, 58-59; res engr, Mass Inst Technol, 59-60, asst prof civil eng, 63-67; MEM STAFF, WOODWARD-CLYDE CONSULTS, 67- *Mem:* Am Soc Civil Engrs; Int Soc Soil Mech & Found Eng; Sigma Xi. *Res:* Soil mechanics and foundation engineering; research in soil mechanics; underground structures; permafrost and arctic engineering. *Mailing Add:* Woodward-Clyde Consults 3 Embarcadero Ctr San Francisco CA 94111

LUSCOMBE, HERBERT ALFRED, b Johnstown, Pa, Aug 9, 16; m 42; c 3. DERMATOLOGY. *Educ:* St Vincent Col, BSc, 36; Jefferson Med Col, MD, 40. *Prof Exp:* PROF DERMAT & HEAD DEPT, JEFFERSON MED COL, 59- *Mailing Add:* Dept of Dermat Jefferson Med Col Philadelphia PA 19107

LUSENA, CHARLES V, b Palermo, Italy, Feb 15, 19; Can citizen; m 47; c 2. MOLECULAR BIOLOGY. *Educ:* McGill Univ, BScA, 42, MSc, 44, PhD(biochem), 47. *Prof Exp:* SR RES OFFICER, DIV BIOL SCI, NAT RES COUN CAN, 47- *Res:* Yeast mitochondrial DNA; synthesis and transport of extracellular enzymes; fermentation of biomass by various organisms. *Mailing Add:* 35 Kilbarry Crescent Ottawa ON K1N 8X6 Can

LUSHBAUGH, CLARENCE CHANCELUM, b Covington, Ky, Mar 15, 16; m 42, 63; c 3. PATHOLOGY. *Educ:* Univ Chicago, BS, 38, PhD(path), 42, MD, 48. *Prof Exp:* Asst path, Univ Chicago, 39-42, from instr to asst prof, 42-49, pathologist, Toxicity Lab, 41-49; mem staff, Los Alamos Sci Lab, Univ Calif, 49-63; chief scientist appl radiobiol, 63-75, NASA Total Body Irradiation Proj, 64-75, CHIEF SCIENTIST EXP & HISTOCHEM PATH, MARMOSET RES COLONY, OAK RIDGE ASSOC UNIVS, 64-, DIR, RADIATION EMERGENCY ASSISTANCE CTR/TRAINING SITE, 74-, CHMN, MED & HEALTH SCI DIV, 75- *Concurrent Pos:* Pathologist, Los Alamos Med Ctr, NMex, 49-63; mem path study sect, NIH, 61-64; mem radiobiol adv panel, Space Sci Bd, Nat Acad Sci-Nat Res Coun, 66-72; mem adv comt space radiation effects lab, Col William & Mary, 68- *Mem:* Am Soc Exp Path; Soc Exp Biol & Med; Health Physics Soc; Radiation Res Soc. *Res:* Pathology of obstetric shock; chemotherapy of cancer; mitotic poisons; radiation damage; diagnostic radioisotopology; human radiobiology; electronic clinical pathology; primate pathology. *Mailing Add:* 109 Darwin Lane Oak Ridge TN 37830

LUSHBOUGH, CHANNING HARDEN, b Watertown, SDak, Aug 11, 29; m 52; c 4. NUTRITION, RESOURCE MANAGEMENT. *Educ:* Univ Chicago, AB, 48, AM, 52, PhD(nutrit, biochem), 56. *Prof Exp:* Res chemist, Res Lab, Carnation Co, Wis, 50-51; assoc biochemist & actg chief, Div Biochem & Nutrit, Am Meat Inst Found, Ill, 56-59; dir prod info, Res Ctr, Mead Johnson & Co, Ind, 59-67; vpres planning & develop, Blue Cross, NY, 67-71; assoc dir, Consumers Union US, 71-73; dir & exec secy, Citizens Comn on Science, Law & Food Supply, Rockefeller Univ, 73-75; vpres qual assurance, Kraft, Inc, 76-81; MGR PARTNER, 200 PARTNERS, LTD, 81- *Concurrent Pos:* Instr grad nutrit, Ill Inst Technol, 56; lectr, Univ Chicago, 57-59 & Northwestern Univ, 58-59. *Mem:* Am Inst Nutrit; AAAS; Am Soc Qual Control; Inst Food Technologists; NY Acad Sci. *Res:* Nutritional quality of natural proteins; effects of processing on vitamin retention; relations of dietary fat, protein and carbohydrate to atherosclerosis. *Mailing Add:* 420 Elm St Glenview IL 60025

LUSIGNAN, BRUCE B(URR), b San Francisco, Calif, Dec 22, 36; m 58; c 2. ELECTRICAL ENGINEERING. *Educ:* Stanford Univ, BS, 58, MS, 59, PhD(elec eng), 63. *Prof Exp:* Instr, 62-63, res asst, 62-64, actg asst prof, 63-65, asst prof, 65-68, ASSOC PROF ELEC ENG, STANFORD UNIV, 68-, DIR, COMMUN SATELLITE PLANNING CTR, 68- *Res:* Applications of satellite, radio and digital technology to communications; transfer of planning and manufacturing knowledge to developing countries. *Mailing Add:* Radiosci Lab Stanford Univ Stanford CA 94305

LUSIS, ALDONS JEKABS, b Esslingen, Ger, June 22, 47; US citizen. MOLECULAR BIOLOGY. *Educ:* Wash State Univ, BS, 69; Ore State Univ, PhD(biochem), 73. *Prof Exp:* Res assoc molecular biol, Roswell Park Mem Inst, 73-80. *Concurrent Pos:* NIH fel, 74- *Mem:* Sigma Xi. *Res:* Mechanisms controlling developmental expression of enzymes in mammals; processing of mouse lysosomal enzymes. *Mailing Add:* 4381 Jasmine Ave Culver City CA 90230

LUSK, GRAHAM, b New York, NY, May 14, 35; m 64; c 2. FOOD SCIENCE. *Educ:* Mass Inst Technol, SB, 57, SM, 60, PhD(food sci), 63. *Prof Exp:* Res food engr, Gen Mills Inc, 63-65, res assoc, 65-68, head frozen food res, 68-69, lab mgr, Gorton Corp, 69-74; dir corp qual assurance, 74-79, DIR CORP COMPLIANCE, PEAVEY CO, 79- *Mem:* Inst Food Technologists; Am Asn Cereal Chemists; Asn Off Analytical Chemists. *Res:* Food safety; employee safety and health; energy and environmental matters. *Mailing Add:* Peavey Co 730 Second Ave S Minneapolis MN 55402

LUSK, JOAN EDITH, b Teaneck, NJ, July 29, 42. BIOCHEMISTRY. *Educ:* Radcliffe Col, BA, 64; Harvard Univ, PhD(biol chem), 70. *Prof Exp:* Nat Cystic Fibrosis Res Found fel biol, Mass Inst Technol, 70-71, NIH fel biol, 71-72; asst prof, 72-77, ASSOC PROF CHEM, BROWN UNIV, 77- *Concurrent Pos:* Prin investr, NIH res grant, 73- & NSF grant, 74-; NIH career develop award, 76. *Mem:* Am Soc Microbiol; AAAS. *Res:* Membrane structure and function; colicin action; transport. *Mailing Add:* Dept of Chem Brown Univ Providence RI 02912

LUSK, JOHN WILLIAM, b Lowden, Wash, Sept 10, 17; m 45; c 3. DAIRY SCIENCE. *Educ:* Wash State Univ, BSc, 41, MSc, 47; Miss State Univ, PhD(animal nutrit), 67. *Prof Exp:* Supvr, Dairy Herd Improv Asn, Walla Walla County, Wash, 41-43; dairy herdsman, Wash State Univ, 43-46, supt testing purebred dairy cattle, 46-47; instr dairy prod, Tenn Jr Col, 47-48; from instr to assoc prof, 48-75, PROF DAIRY SCI, MISS STATE UNIV, 75- *Mem:* Am Dairy Sci Asn; Am Soc Animal Sci. *Res:* Forage evaluation; ruminant nutrition. *Mailing Add:* 410 White Dr Starkville MS 39759

LUSKIN, LEO SAMUEL, b Buffalo, NY, Feb 1, 14; m 39; c 3. ORGANIC CHEMISTRY, POLYMER CHEMISTRY. *Educ:* Univ Mich, BSc, 36, MSc, 42. *Prof Exp:* Chemist coal tar prod, Barrett Div, Allied Chem Corp, 43-44; chemist org chem & polymers, 44-62, head tech writing sect, Spec Prod Dept, 62-68, promotion mgr, indust chem, plastics intermediates, 68-76, SR TECH WRITER, ADVERT DEPT, ROHM AND HAAS CO, 76- *Mem:* Am Chem Soc. *Res:* Synthesis of organic chemicals; polymers; monomers. *Mailing Add:* Rohm and Haas Co Independence Mall West Philadelphia PA 19105

LUSS, DAN, b Tel Aviv, Israel, May 5, 38; m 66; c 3. CHEMICAL ENGINEERING. *Educ:* Israel Inst Technol, BSc, 60, MSc, 63; Univ Minn, Minneapolis, PhD(chem eng), 66. *Prof Exp:* Asst prof chem eng, Univ Minn, 66-67; from asst prof to assoc prof, 67-72, PROF CHEM ENG, UNIV HOUSTON, 72-, CHMN DEPT, 75- *Honors & Awards:* Honor Scroll, Indust & Eng Div, Am Chem Soc, 68; Best Paper Awards, Am Inst Chem Engrs, 68, 70 & 75, A P Colburn Award, 72; Curtis W McGraw Award, Am Soc Eng Educ, 77. *Mem:* Am Inst Chem Engrs; Am Chem Soc. *Res:* Stability of chemical reactors; diffusional effects in catalysts; lumping of complex reactions networks. *Mailing Add:* Dept of Chem Eng Univ of Houston Houston TX 77004

LUSSIER, JEAN PAUL, b Montreal, Que, Sept 17, 17; m 43; c 7. DENTISTRY. *Educ:* Univ Montreal, BA, 38, DDS, 42, MS, 52; Univ Calif, PhD(endocrinol), 59; FRCD(C). *Hon Degrees:* DSc, McGill Univ, 72. *Prof Exp:* Lectr mat med, Fac Dent, Univ Montreal, 44-46, lectr physiol, Fac Med, 46-48, asst prof, 48-52; asst endocrinol, Grad Sch, Univ Calif, 52-54; assoc prof physiol & fac med, 54-58, secy, 56-58, assoc dean & dir studies, 58-62, prof dent, dean & dir studies, Fac Dent, 62-79, CHMN, HEALTH SCI COORDR COMT, UNIV MONTREAL, 79- *Concurrent Pos:* Mem exec assoc comt dent res, Nat Res Coun Can, 54-59, chmn, 64-67; mem exec comt, Med Res Coun Can, 67-70; mem coun higher educ, Minister Educ, 68-71; consult, Minister Nat Defence, Can Royal Dent Corps, 70-73, Int Dent Fedn & WHO; past pres, Asn Can Faculties Dent. *Honors & Awards:* Award, Am Acad Oral Med, 58. *Mem:* Fel AAAS; fel Am Col Dent; fel Int Col Dent. *Res:* Nutrition; endocrinology; bone physiology; dental education; preventative dentistry. *Mailing Add:* Comn Coordr Sci Sante Univ Montreal PO Box 6128 Montreal PQ H3C 3J7 Can

LUSSIER, ROGER JEAN, b Newport, RI, Apr 29, 43; m 66; c 2. INORGANIC CHEMISTRY. *Educ:* Univ Mass, Amherst, BS, 65; Brown Univ, PhD(inorg chem), 69; Johns Hopkins Univ, MA, 75. *Prof Exp:* NSF grant, Cath Univ Am, 69-70; res chemist, 70-80, SR RES CHEMIST, DAVISON DIV, W R GRACE & CO, 80- *Mem:* Am Chem Soc. *Res:* Heterogeneous catalysis; reaction mechanisms; homogeneous catalysis; transition metal chemistry; surface chemistry; mineral synthesis and chemistry. *Mailing Add:* Dept 911 Washington Res Ctr W R Grace & Co 7399 Rte 32 Columbia MO 21044

LUSSKIN, ROBERT MILLER, b Dec 14, 21; m 47; c 2. ORGANIC CHEMISTRY. *Educ:* Harvard Univ, AB, 43; NY Univ, MS, 46, PhD(chem), 50. *Prof Exp:* Chemist, Spencer Kellogg & Sons, 43 & Grosvenor Labs, 45-46; with Trubek Labs, 47-55, res dir, 56-60; dir chem res, UOP Chem Co, Universal Oil Prod Co, 60-67; supt nonwoven lab, Kimberly-Clark Corp, Wis, 67-68, mgr basic & explor res, 68-72, mgr new concepts res, 72-75; tech dir, Resource Planning Assocs, 75-77; dir tech serv, Raltech Sci Serv, 77-82; DIR CENT RES SERV, RALSTON PURINA CO, 82- *Mem:* AAAS; Am Chem Soc. *Res:* Business strategy development; consumer new products; polymer and fiber research; chemical intermediates; energy and materials management; analytical and environmental chemistry. *Mailing Add:* 12856 Hawthicker Des Peres MO 63131

LUSTBADER, EDWARD DAVID, b Baltimore, Md, June 15, 46; m 69; c 2. BIOSTATISTICS. *Educ:* Case Inst Technol, BS, 67; Univ Pa, PhD(statist), 72. *Prof Exp:* Systs analyst, Gen Elec Co, 67-70; STATISTICIAN, FOX CHASE CANCER CTR, 72- *Concurrent Pos:* Res assoc, Mgt Sci Ctr, Univ Pa, 70-72. *Mem:* Am Statist Asn; Biometric Soc; AAAS. *Res:* Model building for survival studies; statistical computing; relation of diet and growth to cancer. *Mailing Add:* Div Clin Res 7701 Burholme Ave Philadelphia PA 19111

LUSTED, LEE BROWNING, b Mason City, Iowa, May 22, 22; m 43; c 2. RADIOLOGY. *Educ:* Cornell Col, BA, 43; Harvard Med Sch, MD, 50; Am Bd Radiol, dipl. *Hon Degrees:* DSc, Cornell Col, 63. *Prof Exp:* Spec res assoc, Radio Res Lab, Harvard Univ, 43-46; from instr to asst prof radiol, Med Sch, Univ Calif, San Francisco, 55-57; asst radiologist, NIH, 57-58; from asst prof to assoc prof radiol, Sch Med, Univ Rochester, 58-60, prof biomed eng, 60-62; prof radiol, Med Sch, Univ Ore & sr scientist, Ore Primate Res Ctr, 62-68; prof radiol & chmn dept, Stritch Sch Med, Loyola Univ Chicago, 68-69; prof radiol & vchmn dept, Univ Chicago, 69-78; RADIOLOGIST, SOUTHERN CALIF PERMANENTE MED GROUP, 78- *Concurrent Pos:* Chmn comt comput biol & med, Nat Acad Sci-Nat Res Coun, 58-59; consult, Strong Mem Hosp, 58-62; chmn adv comt comput res, NIH, 60-64; assoc dean prof affairs & chief of staff, Loyola Univ Hosp, Chicago, 68-69; clin prof radiol, Univ Calif, San Diego, 78-; ed-in-chief, Int J Med Decision Making, 78-; adj distinguished clin mem, Scripps Clin & Res Found, La Jolla, 78- *Mem:* Fel AAAS; fel Am Col Radiol; fel Inst Elec & Electronics Engrs; Roentgen Ray Soc; Radiol Soc NAm. *Res:* Study of medical decision making; application of signal detection theory to assess system and observer performance in radiographic diagnosis. *Mailing Add:* PO Box 2209 Rancho Sante Fe CA 92067

LUSTGARTEN, RONALD KRISSES, b New York, NY, Feb 24, 42. CHEMISTRY. *Educ:* Columbia Univ, AB, 62; Pa State Univ, PhD(chem), 66. *Prof Exp:* NIH fel, Univ Calif, Los Angeles, 66-68; res assoc & Mellon fel chem, Carnegie-Mellon Univ, 68-74; STAFF MEM, UPJOHN CO, 75- *Mem:* AAAS; Am Chem Soc; Fedn Am Scientists. *Res:* Organic mechanisms; reactive intermediates; kinetics. *Mailing Add:* Upjohn Co Kalamazoo MI 49001

LUSTICK, SHELDON IRVING, b Syracuse, NY, Aug 16, 34; m 70. ENVIRONMENTAL PHYSIOLOGY, VERTEBRATE ZOOLOGY. *Educ:* San Fernando Valley State Col, BA, 63; Syracuse Univ, MS, 65; Univ Calif, Los Angeles, PhD(zool), 68. *Prof Exp:* From asst prof to assoc prof, 68-76, PROF ZOOL OHIO STATE UNIV, 76- *Concurrent Pos:* Dept of Interior res grant, 69-72 & 73-75; NSF grant, 76-78; Air Force Off Sci Res grant, 78-80. *Mem:* AAAS; Cooper Ornith Soc; Am Ornith Soc; Ecol Soc Am; Sigma Xi. *Res:* How animals adapt physiologically to environmental stress. *Mailing Add:* Dept of Zool Ohio State Univ Columbus OH 43210

LUSTIG, BERNARD, b Kolomea, Austria, Dec 21, 02; nat US; m 38; c 2. BIOCHEMISTRY. *Educ:* Univ Vienna, PhD(chem), 25. *Prof Exp:* Chemist, Rudolf Hosp, Vienna, 26-32; chief biochemist, Pearson Cancer Found, 33-38 & West London Hosp, 38-40; biochemist, Lawrence R Bruce Inc, 40-44, dir res, 45-58; vpres chg res, Clairol Inc, 58-68, vpres & dir basic res, 68-70; RETIRED. *Honors & Awards:* Prize, Asn Chocolate Mfrs, 30. *Mem:* AAAS; Am Chem Soc; Soc Exp Biol & Med; Am Asn Textile Chemists & Colorists; NY Acad Sci. *Res:* Chemistry and biochemistry of proteins and lipids; biochemistry of cancer; chemistry and technology of keratin fibers. *Mailing Add:* 38 Chester St Stamford CT 06905

LUSTIG, CLAUDE DAVID, b Berlin, Ger, June 21, 33; m 67; c 2. PHYSICS. *Educ:* Oxford Univ, BA, 55, MA, 58, DPhil(physics), 58. *Prof Exp:* Res officer, Clarendon Lab, Oxford Univ, 58-59; res assoc plasma physics, Princeton Univ, 59-60; sr sci officer, Serv Electronics Res Lab, Eng, 61-62; res staff mem, 62-68, head systs tech dept, 68-70, mgr electron & ion physics dept, 70-73, MGR ELECTRONIC DEVICES DEPT, SPERRY RES CTR, 73- *Mem:* Am Phys Soc; sr mem Inst Elec & Electronics Eng. *Res:* Gas discharge displays; plasma physics, interaction of microwaves with plasmas; magnetic disk recording technology. *Mailing Add:* Sperry Res Ctr Sudbury MA 01776

LUSTIG, HARRY, b Vienna, Austria, Sept 23, 25; nat US; wid; c 2. PHYSICS. *Educ:* City Col New York, BS, 48; Univ Ill, MS, 49, PhD(physics), 53. *Prof Exp:* Asst physics, Univ Ill, 49-53; from instr to assoc prof, 53-67, chmn dept, 65-70, exec officer PhD prog physics, 68-70, assoc dean sci, 72-75, dean col lib arts & sci, 73-74, PROF PHYSICS, CITY COL NEW YORK, 67-, DEAN

SCI, 75- *Concurrent Pos:* Prin scientist, Nuclear Develop Corp Am, 56-61; vis res asst prof, Univ Ill, 59-60; fel, Colo Inst Theoret Physics, 60; Fulbright lectr, Univ Dublin, 64-65; vis prof, Univ Colo, 66 & Univ Wash, 67 & 69; sr officer, UNESCO, Paris, 70-72, consult, 72-75. *Mem:* Am Phys Soc; Fedn Am Scientists; fel NY Acad Sci. *Res:* Theoretical nuclear physics; Mossbauer effect; solar energy. *Mailing Add:* Off of the Dean of Sci City Col of New York New York NY 10031

LUSTIG, HOWARD E(RIC), b Vienna, Austria, Oct 23, 25; US citizen; m 50; c 3. ELECTRONICS, SYSTEMS ENGINEERING. *Educ:* Columbia Univ, BS, 49, MSEE, 51, EE, 56. *Prof Exp:* Instr electronics, Sch Eng, Cooper Union, 49-51; proj supvr electronic eng, Ford Instrument Co, Sperry Rand Corp, 51-59; prod area mgr eng mgt, Radio Receptor Div, Gen Instrument Corp, 59-67; corp dir eng, Superior Mfg & Instrument Corp, 67-70; vpres eng, Am Comput Commun Co, Inc, 70-71 & Phonplex Corp, 71-74; asst vpres, Citibank, 74-76; prog mgr, 76-80, VPRES, MGT INFO SYSTS TELEPHONICS CORP, 80- *Mem:* Sr mem Inst Elec & Electronics Engrs; Am Soc Photogram; Marine Technol Soc. *Res:* Military reconnaissance systems; digital interface and processing systems; oceanographic sensors; engineering management. *Mailing Add:* Mgt Info Systs Telephonics Corp 770 Park Ave Huntington NY 11743

LUSTIG, MAX, b Chicago, Ill, Apr 9, 32; m 54; c 1. INORGANIC CHEMISTRY, AIR POLLUTION. *Educ:* Univ Calif, Los Angeles, BS, 57; Univ Wash, PhD(inorg chem), 62. *Prof Exp:* Chemist, Olin Mathieson Chem Corp, 57-58; res chemist, Redstone Arsenal Res Div, Rohm and Haas Co, Ala, 62-68; asst prof chem, Memphis State Univ, 68-73; res chemist, IIT Res Inst, 73-78, consult environ effects & chem hazards, 78-80. *Concurrent Pos:* Eve instr, Univ Ala, 63-68. *Mem:* Am Chem Soc; fel Am Inst Chemists. *Res:* Physical and chemical studies of boron hydrides; chemistry of non-metal compounds with oxygen and fluorine, especially peroxides and hypofluorites; free radical chemistry; organometallic compounds; air pollution studies; high vacuum techniques; reaction kinetics involving air pollutants in the troposphere and stratosphere. *Mailing Add:* 8303 Steven Lane Canoga Park CA 91304

LUSTIG, STANLEY, b Brooklyn, NY, Feb 23, 33; m 60; c 2. PHYSICAL CHEMISTRY. *Educ:* Univ Toledo, BS, 58. *Prof Exp:* Chemist, Save Elec Corp, 58-59; res chemist, 59-65, res proj leader, 65-70, group leader, 70-73, TECH MGR, FILMS-PKG DIV, UNION CARBIDE CORP, 73- *Mem:* Am Chem Soc; Soc Plastics Engrs; Packaging Inst Am. *Res:* Plastic products and processes. *Mailing Add:* 561 Lakewood Blvd Park Forest IL 60466

LUSTMAN, BENJAMIN, b Pittsburgh, Pa, Oct 31, 14; m 46; c 3. METALLURGY, NUCLEAR MATERIALS. *Educ:* Carnegie-Mellon Univ, BS, 36, MS, 38, DSc(metall), 40. *Prof Exp:* Metallurgist, Standard Steel Spring Co, 39-41, Metals Res Lab, 41-43 & Int Minerals & Chem Corp, 43-44; metallurgist res lab, 44-49, METALLURGIST, BETTIS ATOMIC POWER LAB, WESTINGHOUSE ELEC CORP, 49- *Honors & Awards:* Order of Merit, Westinghouse Elec Corp, 56; Achievement Award, Am Nuclear Soc, 68; Kroll Mem Award, Colo Sch Mines, 78. *Mem:* Nat Acad Eng; Am Soc Metals; Am Nuclear Soc; Am Inst Mining Engrs. *Res:* Metallic corrosion; surface reactions; nuclear metallurgy; fuel element development. *Mailing Add:* Westinghouse Elec Corp PO Box 79 West Mifflin PA 15122

LUSTY, CAROL JEAN, b Chicago, Ill, Sept 25, 36. RECOMBINANT DNA. *Educ:* Univ Mich, BS, 58; Wayne State Univ, PhD(biochem), 63. *Prof Exp:* Assoc, 68-78, ASSOC MEM, DEPT BIOCHEM, PUB HEALTH RES INST, 78- *Mem:* Am Chem Soc; Am Soc Biol Chemists; AAAS; NY Acad Sci. *Res:* Gene structure and evolution of carbamyl phosphate synthetases; regulatory mechanisms of mammalian arginine biosynthesis; protein structure and function. *Mailing Add:* Pub Health Res Inst 455 1st Ave New York NY 10016

LUTES, CHARLENE MCCLANAHAN, b Grundy, Va, Feb 4, 38; m 62; c 1. GENETICS, DEVELOPMENTAL BIOLOGY. *Educ:* Radford Col, BS, 59; Ohio State Univ, MSc, 62, PhD(genetics), 68. *Prof Exp:* From instr to prof, Radford Col, 64-80, PROF BIOL, RADFORD UNIV, 80-, CHMN DEPT BIOL, 81- *Mem:* AAAS; Am Soc Zoologists; Am Inst Biol Sci. *Res:* Developmental genetics of wing venation patterns in drosophila melanogaster. *Mailing Add:* Dept Biol Radford Univ Radford VA 24141

LUTES, DALLAS D, b St Louis, Mo, July 12, 25; m 45; c 2. PLANT PATHOLOGY. *Educ:* La Polytech Inst, BS, 49; Univ Mo, PhD(bot), 54. *Prof Exp:* Instr bot, ETex State Col, 54-55; from assoc prof to prof bot, 55-74, head dept, 63-73, PROF BOT & BACT, LA TECH UNIV, 74- *Mem:* AAAS. *Res:* Disease resistance by breeding; virus transmission; seed germination affected by light; mistletoe seed germination; fern taxonomy and distribution. *Mailing Add:* Dept of Bot & Bact La Tech Univ Ruston LA 71270

LUTES, LOREN DANIEL, b Stapleton, Nebr, Dec 1, 39; div; c 4. ENGINEERING MECHANICS. *Educ:* Univ Nebr, BSc, 60, MSc, 61; Calif Inst Technol, PhD(appl mech), 67. *Prof Exp:* Res engr, Jet Propulsion Lab, 67; asst prof civil eng, 67-72, assoc prof, 72-80, assoc prof math, 75-80, PROF CIVIL ENG, RICE UNIV, 80- *Concurrent Pos:* Vis prof, Univ Chile, 71; vis adj prof civil eng, Univ Waterloo, 74-75. *Honors & Awards:* Wason Res Medal, Am Concrete Inst, 64. *Mem:* Am Soc Civil Engrs. *Res:* Response of nonlinear systems to random excitations; first-passage probabilities for stochastic processes; fatigue damage caused by stochastic loadings. *Mailing Add:* Dept of Civil Eng Rice Univ Houston TX 77001

LUTES, OLIN SILAS, b Faribault, Minn, Apr 29, 22; m 48, 71; c 3. ELECTROMAGNETISM. *Educ:* Carnegie Tech Univ, BS, 44; Columbia Univ, MA, 50; Univ Md, PhD(physics), 56. *Prof Exp:* Physicist, Sinclair Ref Co, 46-48 & Nat Bur Stand, 51-56; SR PRIN SCIENTIST, RES CTR, HONEYWELL, INC, 56- *Mem:* Am Phys Soc; Inst Elec & Electronics Engrs. *Res:* Magnetic thin flim physics; integrated sensors. *Mailing Add:* Honeywell Corp Technol Ctr 10701 Lyndale Ave S Bloomington MN 55420

LUTEYN, JAMES LEONARD, b Kalamazoo, Mich, June 23, 48. SYSTEMATIC BOTANY. *Educ:* Western Mich Univ, BA, 70; Duke Univ, MA, 72, PhD(bot), 75. *Prof Exp:* Assoc cur, 75-81, CUR BOT, NEW YORK BOT GARDENS, 81- *Concurrent Pos:* Assoc ed, BRITTONIA, 76-; ed, Proceedings Int Rhododendron Conf, 78; assoc ed, Flora Neotropica 80- *Mem:* Sigma Xi; Am Soc Plant Taxonomists; Ecol Soc Am; Int Asn Plant Taxon; Bot Soc Am. *Res:* Evolution and systematics of the neotropical Ericaceae-Vacciniceae. *Mailing Add:* New York Bot Gardens Bronx NY 10458

LUTH, WILLIAM CLAIR, b Winterset, Iowa, June 28, 34; m 53; c 3. GEOLOGY, GEOCHEMISTRY. *Educ:* Univ Iowa, BA, 58, MS, 60; Pa State Univ, PhD(geochem), 63. *Prof Exp:* Res assoc geochem, Pa State Univ, 63-65; asst prof, Mass Inst Technol, 65-68; from assoc prof to prof geol, Stanford Univ, 68-79; SUPVR, GEOPHYS RES DIV, SANDIA NAT LABS, 79- *Concurrent Pos:* Alfred P Sloan Found res fel, Mass Inst Technol, 66-67; geoscientist, Off Basic Energy Sci, Dept Energy, Washington, DC, 76-78; vis staff mem, Los Alamos Nat Lab, 78. *Mem:* Am Geophys Union; Geol Soc Am; Mineral Soc Am; Geochem Soc. *Res:* Experimental petrology; physical chemistry of the igneous and metamorphic rocks; phase equilibria in silicate-volatile systems at high pressure and temperature; disposal radioactive wastes. *Mailing Add:* Geophys Res Div Sandia Nat Labs Albuquerque NM 87185

LUTHE, JOHN CHARLES, theoretical high energy physics, see previous edition

LUTHER, EDWARD TURNER, b Nashville, Tenn, Feb 11, 28; m 55; c 2. GEOLOGY. *Educ:* Vanderbilt Univ, BA, 50, MS, 51. *Prof Exp:* From geologist to chief geologist, 51-77, ASST STATE GEOLOGIST, TENN DIV GEOL, 67- *Concurrent Pos:* Instr, Univ Tenn, Nashville, 55-57 & 76-78; fuels engr, Tenn Valley Authority, 57. *Mem:* Fel Geol Soc Am. *Res:* Areal and economic geology of various areas in Tennessee, particularly the stratigraphy and structural geology of the Cumberland Plateau; coal resources, particularly in Eastern United States. *Mailing Add:* Tenn Div of Geol G5 State Off Bldg Nashville TN 37219

LUTHER, GEORGE WILLIAM, III, b Philadelphia, Pa, Feb 17, 47; m 71. INORGANIC & MARINE CHEMISTRY. *Educ:* LaSalle Col, BA, 68; Univ Pittsburgh, PhD(chem), 72. *Prof Exp:* Asst prof, 72-76, ASSOC PROF CHEM, KEAN COL NJ, 76-, CHMN DEPT PHYSICS, 76- *Concurrent Pos:* Investr, Nat Oceanic & Atmospheric Admin grant, 76- *Mem:* Am Chem Soc; AAAS; Electrochem Soc; Sigma Xi. *Res:* Fate of inorganic pollutants in estuarine environments; analysis of metals in sea water samples by atomic absorption spectrophotometry and differential pulse anodic stripping voltammetry. *Mailing Add:* Dept of Chem & Physics Kean Col of NJ Union NJ 07083

LUTHER, HERBERT GEORGE, b Brooklyn, NY, Oct 1, 14; m 38; c 4. CHEMISTRY. *Educ:* Cooper Union, New York, BChE, 40; NY Univ, MS, 44; Polytech Inst Brooklyn, DChE, 57. *Prof Exp:* With Sunshine Biscuit Co, 34-41, dir biochem labs, 41-44; asst dir tech serv, Chas Pfizer & Co, 45-52, dir agr res & develop, 52-59, sci dir agr, 59-69; pres, Luther Assocs, 69-74; DIR ANIMAL HEALTH RES, HOFFMAN-LA ROCHE INC, NUTLEY, NJ, 74- *Concurrent Pos:* Expert, Comn Food Additives, WHO/Food Agr Orgn; consult res & develop. *Mem:* Am Chem Soc; Am Inst Chem Engrs; Am Asn Animal Sci; Poultry Sci Asn. *Res:* Antibiotics; antibacterials; vitamins; steroids; tranquilizers; unidentified growth factors; enzymes; antioxidants; nutrition; animal health; pharmacokinetics; operations research; food and feed technology. *Mailing Add:* Head of the River Smithtown NY 11787

LUTHER, HOLGER MARTIN, b Gdynia, Poland, Feb 4, 40; US citizen; M 69. MASS SPECTROMETRY, ELECTRON OPTICS. *Educ:* Marietta Col, BScL, 63; Pa State Univ, MS, 66, PhD(physics), 70. *Prof Exp:* Sr res physicist, CBS Labs, 69-75, EPSCO Labs, 75-76 & Electron Sci & Tech Ctr, Div Carson Alexiou Corp, 76-77; staff mem, Avco Everett Corp, 77-80; STAFF MEM, C S DRAPER LABS, 80- *Concurrent Pos:* Fac mem, Bridgeport Eng Inst, 71-77. *Res:* Electron-optical and elctro-optical instrumentation; compact radio frequency mass spectrometers; electron beam recorders and storage tubes; high speed tracking cameras for charged particle beams. *Mailing Add:* 294 Perkins Row Topsfield MA 01983

LUTHER, LESTER CHARLES, b Joliet, Ill, Apr 19, 31; m 54; c 4. INDUSTRIAL ENGINEERING. *Educ:* Univ Ill, Urbana, BS, 53 & 58; Univ Nebr, Lincoln, MS, 60; Ariz State Univ, PhD(indust eng), 68. *Prof Exp:* Instr mech eng, Univ Nebr, 58-61; indust engr, Reynolds Metals Co, Ariz, 61-62; qual assurance engr, Motorola, Inc, 62-68; assoc prof mech engr, 68-72, PROF MECH ENG, CALIF STATE UNIV, SACRAMENTO, 72- *Concurrent Pos:* Indust engr, Cushman Motor Works, Nebr, 59-61 & McClellan AFB, Calif, 69-70; Nat Sci Found fel, Sacramento State Col, 71-72. *Mem:* Am Inst Indust Engr; Am Soc Eng Educ. *Res:* Economic interactions between quality assurance and inventory control. *Mailing Add:* Dept Mech Eng Calif State Univ Sacramento CA 95819

LUTHER, MARVIN L, b Waterloo, Iowa, Nov 16, 34; m 59; c 4. ATOMIC PHYSICS, NUCLEAR PHYSICS. *Educ:* Macalester Col, BA, 57; Univ Fla, MS, 60; Va Polytech Inst, PhD(physics), 67. *Prof Exp:* Asst prof physics, Randolph-Macon Men's Col, 60-63; asst prof, 66-67, ASSOC PROF PHYSICS, ILL STATE UNIV, 67- *Mem:* Am Asn Physics Teachers. *Res:* Atomic spectroscopy using collisionally excited beams provided by an accelerator. *Mailing Add:* Dept of Physics Ill State Univ Normal IL 61761

LUTHER, NORMAN Y, b Palo Alto, Calif, June 3, 36; m 58; c 4. PURE MATHEMATICS. *Educ:* Stanford Univ, BS, 58; Univ Iowa, MS, 60, PhD(math), 63. *Prof Exp:* Instr math, Univ Iowa, 63; NSF fel, 63-64; asst prof, 64-69, ASSOC PROF MATH, WASH STATE UNIV, 69- *Concurrent Pos:* Assoc prof, Albany State Col, Ga, 71-72; mem staff, East-West Ctr & Univ Hawaii, 78- *Mem:* Inst Math Statist; Am Math Soc; Math Asn Am. *Res:* Probability and statistics; measure theory. *Mailing Add:* Dept of Math Wash State Univ Pullman WA 99164

LUTHEY, JOE LEE, b Winslow, Ariz, Sept 21, 43. SPACE PHYSICS. *Educ:* Univ Calif, Berkeley, AB, 65; Univ Kans, Lawrence, PhD(physics), 70. *Prof Exp:* Res assoc space physics, Univ Iowa, Iowa City, 70-73; resident res assoc space physics, 73-75, consult radiation physics, 75-77, MEM TECH STAFF, NEW EARTH PROBE, JET PROPULSION LAB, CALIF INST TECHNOL, 77- *Concurrent Pos:* Consult, Physics Dept, Univ Iowa, 73-74; resident res assoc, Nat Res Coun, Jet Propulsion Lab. 73-75. *Mem:* Am Geophys Union. *Res:* Test/create Jovian radiation belt models; determine x-ray and gamma-ray emission from natural and artificial satellites in the Jovian trapped electron proton belts. *Mailing Add:* 350 E Del Mar Blvd #223 Pasadena CA 91101

LUTHIN, JAMES NICHOLAS, b Berkeley, Calif, Dec 4, 15; m 46; c 2. SOIL SCIENCE, DRAINAGE ENGINEERING. *Educ:* Univ Calif, Berkeley, BS, 38; Mich State Col, MS, 47; Iowa State Col, PhD(soils), 49. *Prof Exp:* Soil scientist, Soil Conserv Serv, 38-46; PROF DRAINAGE, UNIV CALIF, DAVIS, 49- *Concurrent Pos:* Fulbright scholar, Commonwealth Sci & Indust Res Orgn, Waite Inst, Australia, 57-58; vis prof, Swiss Forest Res Inst, Zurich, 62-63 & Univ Alaska, Fairbanks, 71; consult, Leeds, Hill, Bechtel, Turkey, 67-69 & Bechtel Corp, 76- *Honors & Awards:* Hancor Soil & Water Eng Award, Am Soc Agr Engrs, 69. *Mem:* Fel Am Soc Agr Engrs; fel Am Soc Agron; fel Soil Sci Soc Am; Am Geophys Union; Am Soc Civil Engrs. *Res:* Coupled heat and moisture transfer through soils. *Mailing Add:* Rte 1 Box 21D Winters CA 95694

LUTHRA, KRISHAN LAL, b Jaipur, India, Sept 28, 49. HIGH TEMPERATURE CHEMISTRY, CHEMICAL METALLURGY. *Educ:* Univ Rajasthan, BEng, 70; Indian Inst Technol, Kanpur, MTech, 72; Univ Pa, PhD(metall & mat sci), 76. *Prof Exp:* METALLURGIST, CORP RES & DEVELOP, GEN ELEC CO, 76- *Concurrent Pos:* Sr res asst, Dept Metall Eng, Indian Inst Technol, Kanpur, 71-72; res fel, Dept Metall & Mat Sci, Univ Pa, 72-76. *Mem:* Electrochem Soc; Metall Soc; Am Inst Mining, Metall & Petrol Engrs. *Res:* Thermodynamic and kinetics of high temperature reactions; corrosion at elevated temperatures; gas-liquid-solid reactions; high temperature materials. *Mailing Add:* Corp Res & Develop Gen Elec Co Schenectady NY 12301

LUTHY, JAKOB WILHELM, b Staefa, Switz, Jan 31, 19; nat US; m 48; c 3. CHEMISTRY. *Educ:* Swiss Fed Inst Technol, MS, 44, DSc(org chem), 47. *Prof Exp:* Asst prof org technol, Swiss Fed Inst Technol, 46-47; chemist, Gen Aniline & Film Corp, NJ, 47-48; chemist, Sandoz Chem Works, 48-51; head appln lab, Chem Div, 51-54, dir appln & promotion, 54-58, TECH MGR, DYESTUFF DIV, SANDOZ, INC, 58-, EXEC V PRES, 64-, PRES COLORS & CHEM DIV & DIR, 67- *Concurrent Pos:* Dir, Toms River Chem Corp, 58-81. *Mem:* Fel Am Chem Soc; Am Asn Textile Chemists & Colorists; fel Swiss Chem Soc. *Res:* Dyestuffs. *Mailing Add:* Sandoz Inc 59 Rte 10 Hanover NJ 07936

LUTHY, RICHARD GODFREY, b Buffalo, NY, June 11, 45; m 69; c 3. ENVIRONMENTAL & CIVIL ENGINEERING. *Educ:* Univ Calif, Berkeley, BS, 67, MS, 74, PhD(civil eng), 76; Univ Hawaii, MS, 69. *Prof Exp:* Res asst, Dept Civil Eng, Univ Hawaii, 68-69; res proj officer, Naval Civil Eng Lab, Civil Eng Corps, US Navy, 70-71, asst officer-in-chg underwater construct team, 71-72; res asst, Div Sanit Eng, Univ Calif, Berkeley, 73-75; ASST PROF DEPT CIVIL ENG, CARNEGIE-MELLON UNIV, 75- *Concurrent Pos:* Consult, Environ Res & Technol Inc, Lancy Div, Dart Environ Serv Co. *Honors & Awards:* G Tallman Ladd Award, Carnegie Inst Technol, 77; Nalco Award, Asn Environ Eng Prof, 78. *Mem:* Water Pollution Control Fedn; Am Soc Civil Engrs; Int Asn Water Pollution Res; Asn Environ Eng Prof. *Res:* Wastewater treatment and industrial wastewater treatment; chemistry of dilute aqueous systems; treatment of wastewaters from petroleum refining, coal coking and conversion, and iron and steel making. *Mailing Add:* Dept of Civil Eng Schenley Park Pittsburgh PA 15213

LUTON, EDGAR FRANK, b Memphis, Tenn, Mar 3, 21; m 44; c 3. INTERNAL MEDICINE. *Educ:* Univ Tenn, Memphis, MD, 44; Am Bd Internal Med, dipl & cert nephrol, 74. *Prof Exp:* Staff physician neuropsychiat serv med teaching group, Vet Admin Hosp, Memphis, 48-49, resident internal med, 49-51, staff physician med serv, 51-59, sect chief internal med & allergy, 59-67, sect chief allergy & nephrology, 67-77; from asst to assoc prof, 61-74, PROF MED, CTR HEALTH SCI, UNIV TENN, MEMPHIS, 74- *Mem:* Fel Am Col Physicians; Am Soc Nephrology; Int Soc Nephrology. *Res:* Nephrology. *Mailing Add:* Ctr for Health Sci 800 Madison Ave Memphis TN 38104

LUTRICK, MONROE CORNELIUS, b Grayson, La, July 22, 27; m 52; c 4. AGRONOMY, SOIL CHEMISTRY. *Educ:* La State Univ, BS, 51, MS, 53; Ohio State Univ, PhD(agron), 56. *Prof Exp:* Asst agron, La State Univ, 51-53; asst agronomist, 56-67, assoc soil chemist, 67-77, SOIL CHEMIST, AGR RES CTR, UNIV FLA, 77- *Mem:* Am Soc Agron; Soil Sci Soc Am. *Res:* Soil chemistry and maximum production of field crops; utilization of liquid digested sludge on agricultural lands; micronutrient status of field crops grown in North Florida. *Mailing Add:* Agr Res Ctr Univ of Fla Jay FL 32565

LUTS, HEINO ALFRED, b Torva, Estonia, Dec 18, 19; nat US; m 54; c 4. MEDICINAL CHEMISTRY. *Educ:* Upsala Col, BA, 52; Univ Miss, MS, 58, PhD, 66. *Prof Exp:* Asst chem, Inst Therapeut Res, Warner-Hudnut, Inc, 49-52; res chemist, Wallace Labs Div, Carter Prod, Inc, 53-55, C D Smith Pharmacal Co, 55-56 & Ciba Pharmaceut Prod, Inc, 56-57; NSF asst, Univ Miss, 57-58; dir, Southern Vitamin Prod, 58-67; PROF CHEM, EASTERN KY UNIV, 67- *Concurrent Pos:* Proj leader, Horizons, Inc, 58-61; pres, Struct-Activity Res, Inc, 60-67; Fulbright-Hays sr lectr, Finland, 75, Oak Ridge, 79. *Mem:* AAAS; Am Chem Soc; Int Pharmaceut Fedn; Am Pharmaceut Asn. *Res:* Analgetics; antispasmatics; tranquilizers; sedatives; metabolites; diuretics; synthetic antibiotics; vitamins. *Mailing Add:* Dept of Chem Eastern Ky Univ Richmond KY 40475

LUTSCH, EDWARD F, b Chicago, Ill, Nov 23, 30; m 65. ZOOLOGY. *Educ:* Northern Ill Univ, BS, 52; Northwestern Univ, MS, 57, PhD(biol), 62. *Prof Exp:* Asst prof zool, Univ Ill, Chicago, 62-68; from asst prof to assoc prof, 68-74, PROF BIOL, NORTHEASTERN ILL UNIV, 74- *Mem:* AAAS; Am Inst Biol Sci; Am Soc Zoologists. *Res:* Biological rhythms and clocks; rhythmic response of animals to pharmacological drugs; comparative physiology; animal behavior. *Mailing Add:* Dept of Biol Northeastern Ill Univ Chicago IL 60625

LUTSKY, IRVING, b Paterson, NJ, June 12, 26; m 48; c 4. LABORATORY ANIMAL MEDICINE, OCCUPATIONAL HYPERSENSITIVITY. *Educ:* Rutgers Univ, BS, 48; Purdue Univ, MS, 51; Univ Pa, VMD, 55; Am Col Lab Animal Med, dipl, 65. *Prof Exp:* Res asst poultry diseases, Purdue Univ, 49-51; staff vet, Fromm Labs, 55-58; asst prof vet sci, Med Col Wis, 60-66, assoc prof comp med, 66-72, adminr surg res lab, Allen Bradley Med Sci Lab, 60-72; ASSOC PROF & CHMN, DEPT COMP MED, SCH MED, HEBREW UNIV, 72- *Concurrent Pos:* Vis prof comp med, Sch Med, Hebrew Univ, 71-72; Am Asn Lab Animal Sci res award, 77. *Mem:* Am Soc Microbiol; Am Asn Lab Animal Sci; Am Vet Med Asn; Asn Gnotobiotics; Am Soc Animal Pract. *Res:* Infectious diseases; natural disease resistance; applied gnotobiology; occupational allergies; occupationally related hypersensitivity lung disease in laboratory animal workers, veterinarians, and poultry workers. *Mailing Add:* Dept Comp Med Sch Med Hebrew Univ POB 1172 91010 Jerusalem Israel

LUTT, CARL J, b Guthrie Co, Iowa, Feb 10, 21; m 45; c 2. ANATOMY, PHYSIOLOGY. *Educ:* Creighton Univ, BSM, 42, MD, 45. *Prof Exp:* Dir, Student Health Serv, 60-65, PROF BIOL, HEALTH SCI & KINESBIOL, CALIF STATE UNIV, HAYWARD, 60-, ASST DIR, STUDENT HEALTH SERV, 73-, DIR SPORTS MED, 75- *Mem:* Am Col Sports Med. *Mailing Add:* Student Health Serv Calif State Univ Hayward CA 94542

LUTTGES, MARVIN WAYNE, b Chico, Calif, Feb 3, 41; m 69. NEUROBIOLOGY, BIOENGINEERING. *Educ:* Univ Ore, Eugene, BSc, 62; Univ Calif, Irvine, PhD(biol sci), 68. *Prof Exp:* Res asst dept psychol, Univ Ore, 62-64; teaching asst psychobiol, Univ Calif, Irvine, 64-68; USPHS fel neurochem, Med Sch, Northwestern Univ, 68-69; asst prof to assoc prof, 69-79, PROF BIOENG, AEROSPACE ENG SCI, UNIV COLO, 80- *Concurrent Pos:* Noise consult, City of Boulder, Colo, 76-78; Am Eng Soc res award, 79. *Mem:* Soc Neurosci; AAAS; Sigma Xi; Biophys Soc. *Res:* Neurobiological basis of learning and memory; nervous system degeneration and regeneration; biological and physical acoustics; comparative studies of brain structure and function. *Mailing Add:* Aerospace Eng Sci Univ of Colo Boulder CO 80309

LUTTINGER, JOAQUIN MAZDAK, b New York, NY, Dec 2, 23. THEORETICAL PHYSICS. *Educ:* Mass Inst Technol, BS, 44, PhD(physics), 47. *Prof Exp:* Swiss-Am exchange fel, 47-48; Nat Res Coun fel, 48-49; Jewett fel, Inst Advan Study, 49-50; from asst prof to assoc prof physics, Univ Wis, 50-53; assoc prof, Univ Mich, 53-57 & Ecole Normale Superieure, Paris, 57-58; prof, Univ Pa, 58-60; PROF PHYSICS, COLUMBIA UNIV, 60-, CHMN DEPT, 77- *Mem:* Nat Acad Sci; Fel Am Phys Soc. *Res:* Theoretical magnetism; quantum field theory; statistical mechanics; theory of solids. *Mailing Add:* Dept Physics 814 Pupin Lab Columbia Univ New York NY 10027

LUTTINGER, LIONEL, physical chemistry, colloid chemistry, see previous edition

LUTTMANN, FREDERICK WILLIAM, b New Brunswick, NJ, Aug 9, 40; m 66. MATHEMATICS. *Educ:* Amherst Col, AB, 61; Stanford Univ, MS, 64; Univ Ariz, PhD(math), 67. *Prof Exp:* Assoc, Univ Ariz, 63-67; assoc prof math, Alaska Methodist Univ, 67-70; asst prof, 70-74, assoc prof, 74-81, PROF MATH, SONOMA STATE UNIV, 81- *Mem:* Am Math Soc; Math Asn Am. *Res:* Steiner symmetrization of convex bodies; polynomial interpolation. *Mailing Add:* Dept of Math Sonoma State Univ Rohnert Park CA 94928

LUTTON, JOHN D, b Sioux City, Iowa, Feb 3, 37; c 2. EXPERIMENTAL HEMATOLOGY. *Educ:* Univ Nebr, BS, 61, MS, 63; NY Univ, PhD(cell biol & physiol), 69. *Prof Exp:* Instr gen physiol, Dept Biol, NY Univ, 66-68, asst prof, 70-71, instr & res scientist, Dept Cell Biol, Med Sch, 71-73; asst prof physiol & hemat, Dept Physiol, Mt Sinai Sch Med, 73-77; asst prof hemat, Downstate Med Ctr, State Univ NY, 77; ASST PROF MED & ANAT, NY MED COL, 77- *Concurrent Pos:* Adj asst prof, Dept Biol, City Col, City Univ New York, 71-73; Mercy Col, Dobbs Ferry, NY, 81 & Baruuch Col, City Univ New York, 81- *Mem:* Am Soc Hemat; Int Soc Exp Hemat; Reticulo Endothelial Soc; AAAS. *Res:* Regulation of hematopoiesis: in vitro aspects on the regulation of erythropoiesis including regulatory aspects of hemebiosynthesis and degradation; in vitro characteristics of disorders of erythropoiesis such as anemia, polycythemins, neoplastic states and disorders of iron metabolism; granulopoiesis. *Mailing Add:* Dept Met NY Med Col Valhalla NY 10595

LUTTON, JOHN KAZUO, b Tokyo, Japan, July 11, 49; US citizen; m 71; c 1. NEUROPHARMACOLOGY, ENZYMOLOGY. *Educ:* Pac Lutheran Univ, BS, 71; Purdue Univ, PhD(biochem), 76. *Prof Exp:* Grad student, Dept Biochem, Purdue Univ, 71-76 & chem anal, Ind State Chem Off, 72-73; res assoc pharmacol, Med Sch, Univ Colo, 76-77 & Univ NC, 77-80; ASST PROF, CHEM DEPT, KENYON COL, 80- *Mem:* Am Chem Soc; AAAS; Sigma Xi. *Res:* Molecular mechanisms of hormone action especially the role of cyclic nucleotides in brain function and cell growth; enzymatic mechanisms of redox enzymes especially flavin-containing dehydrogenases. *Mailing Add:* Dept Chem Kenyon Col Gambier OH 43022

LUTTON, LEWIS MONTFORT, vertebrate zoology, see previous edition

LUTTRELL, ERIC MARTIN, b Wheeling, WVa, May 12, 41; m 63; c 2. PETROLEUM GEOLOGY. *Educ:* Univ Wis-Madison, BS, 62, MS, 65; Princeton Univ, PhD(geol), 68. *Prof Exp:* Geologist, Producing Dept, Texaco Inc, 68-69, sr geologist, 69-73, res geologist, Res & Tech Dept, 73-76, asst supvr geol res, 76-79, consult explor geologist, 79-80; regional geologist, Sohio Petrol Co, 80-82. *Mem:* Geol Soc Am; Soc Econ Paleontologists & Mineralogists; Am Asn Petrol Geologists. *Res:* Applications of clastic sedimentology; organic geochemistry and geologic thermometry to petroleum exploration. *Mailing Add:* Sohio Petrol Co 5400 Lyndon B Johnson Freeway Dallas TX 75240

LUTTRELL, GEORGE HOWARD, b Glendale, Calif, Dec 23, 41; m 64. ANALYTICAL CHEMISTRY. *Educ:* Univ Tex, BS, 65; Southern Methodist Univ, MS, 69; Univ Ga, PhD(chem), 75. *Prof Exp:* Res chemist anal, Alcon Labs, 69-72, res chemist anal, Ctr Labs, 75-77, MEM STAFF, ALCON LABS PR, 77- *Mem:* Am Chem Soc. *Res:* Preconcentration of trace metal cations and oxyanions for analysis by x-ray fluorescence using immobilized complexing and chelating reagents. *Mailing Add:* Alcon Labs PR PO Box 3000 Humacao PR 00661

LUTTS, JOHN A, b Baltimore, Md, Feb 26, 32; m 67; c 6. MATHEMATICS. *Educ:* Spring Hill Col, BS, 57; Univ Pa, MA, 59, PhD(math), 61; Woodstock Col, Md, STL, 65. *Prof Exp:* From instr to asst prof math, Loyola Col, Md, 65-66; asst prof, 66-70, fac growth fel, 67, fac res grant, 70-71, ASSOC PROF MATH, UNIV MASS, HARBOR CAMPUS, 70- *Mem:* Math Asn Am. *Res:* Cultural history of mathematics; discrete mathematics. *Mailing Add:* Dept of Math Univ of Mass Harbor Campus Boston MA 02125

LUTWAK, ERWIN, b USSR, Feb 9, 46; US citizen; m 68. MATHEMATICS. *Educ:* Polytech Inst Brooklyn, BS, 68, MS, 72; Polytech Inst NY, PhD(math), 74. *Prof Exp:* Asst prof math, Col Pharmaceut Sci, Columbia Univ, 70-75; asst prof, 75-80, ASSOC PROF MATH, POLYTECH INST NY, 80- *Mem:* Am Math Soc; London Math Soc; Math Asn Am; Sigma Xi. *Res:* Convexity; integral geometry; analytic and geometric inequalities. *Mailing Add:* Polytech Inst NY 333 Jay St Brooklyn NY 11201

LUTWAK, LEO, b New York, NY, Mar 27, 28; m 50, 78; c 7. ENDOCRINOLOGY, NUTRITION. *Educ:* City Col New York, BS, 45; Univ Wis, MS, 46; Univ Mich, PhD(biochem), 50; Yale Univ, MD, 56. *Prof Exp:* Biochemist med, Brookhaven Nat Lab, 50-52; clin assoc metab, Metab Dis Br, Nat Inst Arthritis & Metab Dis, 57-59, sr investr, 60-63; Jameson prof clin nutrit, Grad Sch Nutrit, Cornell Univ, 63-72; prof med, Univ Calif, Los Angeles, 72-76, prof nutrit, Sch Pub Health, 73-76; sect chief metab, Vet Admin Hosp, Sepulveda, 72-76; PROF MED, NORTHEAST OHIO UNIV, 76-, PROF NUTRIT & PROG CHIEF, 76- *Concurrent Pos:* NSF sr NASA fel, Ames Res Lab, Moffett Field, Calif, 70-71; prin investr, NASA, 63-; consult, Div Res Grants, NIH, 64-69; consult, Tompkins County Hosp, Ithaca, NY, 64-69; vis prof, Sch Med, Stanford Univ, 70-71; chmn dept med, Akron City Hosp, Ohio, 76-78; mem, Am Bd Clin Nutrit, pres, 81-82. *Mem:* AAAS; Am Physiol Soc; Am Inst Nutrit; fel Am Col Physicians; fel Am Col Nutrit. *Res:* Isotope kinetics in metabolic bone disease; calcium, phosphorus and magnesium in human nutrition; effect of space flight on bone and muscle metabolism; obesity control; diabetes and electrolyte metabolism; hospital malnutrition. *Mailing Add:* 1211 Oak Knoll Dr Akron OH 44313

LUTY, FRITZ, b Essen, Ger, Apr 12, 28; m 60; c 2. SOLID STATE PHYSICS. *Educ:* Univ Gottingen, dipl physics, 53; Stuttgart Univ, Dr rer nat(physics), 55. *Prof Exp:* Asst physics, Stuttgart Univ, 53-62, dozent, Physics Inst, 64-65; vis assoc prof, Univ Ill, Urbana, 63; PROF PHYSICS, UNIV UTAH, 65- *Concurrent Pos:* Vis prof, Soc Advan Sci, Japan, 73. *Mem:* Fel Am Phys Soc; Ger Phys Soc. *Res:* Defects in ionic crystals; radiation damage; absorption and emission spectroscopy; field emission; magneto-optics, paraelectric and paraelastic effects; low temperature dielectric and electro-caloric studies; Raman-scattering; phase transitions. *Mailing Add:* Dept of Physics Univ of Utah Salt Lake City UT 84112

LUTZ, ALBERT WILLIAM, b Baltimore, Md, Sept 26, 24; m 51; c 2. AGRICULTURAL CHEMISTRY. *Educ:* Johns Hopkins Univ, AB, 49, MA, 50, PhD(chem), 53. *Prof Exp:* Assoc prof chem, Col William & Mary, 53-56; res chemist, Chemagro Corp, 56-57; res chemist, 57-59, sr res chemist, 59-69, GROUP LEADER HERBICIDES, AGR DIV, AM CYANAMID CO, 69- *Honors & Awards:* J Shelton Horsley Award. *Mem:* AAAS; Am Chem Soc. *Res:* Pesticides, particularly growth regulants and herbicides. *Mailing Add:* Agr Div Am Cyanamid Co PO Box 400 Princeton NJ 08540

LUTZ, ARTHUR LEROY, b Louisville, Ohio, Oct 22, 08; m 37; c 2. NUCLEAR PHYSICS. *Educ:* Capital Univ, BS, 31; Ohio State Univ, MS, 36, PhD(physics), 43. *Prof Exp:* High sch teacher, Ohio, 31-40; asst physics, Ohio State Univ, 40-43; prof, 43-75, EMER PROF PHYSICS, WITTENBERG UNIV, 75- *Concurrent Pos:* Fac fel, NSF, 60-61. *Mem:* AAAS; Am Phys Soc; Am Asn Physics Teachers. *Res:* Radioactive isotopes; internal conversion and K-capture in the radioactive isotopes of lead and bismuth. *Mailing Add:* 1605 Shelby Dr Wittenberg Univ Springfield OH 45504

LUTZ, BARRY LAFEAN, b Windsor, Pa, Jan 2, 44. ASTROPHYSICS, MOLECULAR SPECTROSCOPY. *Educ:* Lebanon Valley Col, BS, 65; Princeton Univ, AM, 67, PhD(astrophys sci), 68. *Prof Exp:* Fel physics, Nat Res Coun Can, 68-70; res astronr, Lick Observ, Univ Calif, 70-71; from adj asst prof to adj assoc prof, State Univ NY Stony Brook, 73-77; sr res assoc, 71-87; ASTRONOMER, LOWELL OBSERV, 77- *Concurrent Pos:* Vis astron, Observ Paris, 79 & Univ Dijon, 80; adj assoc prof, Ariz State Univ, 81- *Mem:* Int Astron Union; Am Astron Soc; Sigma Xi. *Res:* High resolution spectroscopy of the interstellar medium and of stellar and planetary atmospheres; laboratory astrophysics; intensity measurements and long path length planetary atmospheres simulations. *Mailing Add:* Lowell Observ PO Box 1269 Flagstaff AZ 86002

LUTZ, BRUCE CHARLES, b London, Ont, May 16, 20; m 45; c 3. PHYSICS. *Educ:* Western Ont Univ, BA, 42, MA, 44; Johns Hopkins Univ, PhD, 54. *Prof Exp:* Instr electronics & radio, Western Ont Univ, 41-44; lectr electronics & physics, Univ Man, 45-47; instr electronics, 47-57, assoc prof elec eng, 57-62, PROF ELEC ENG, UNIV DEL, 62-, ACTG CHMN DEPT, 73- *Mem:* Am Inst Aeronaut & Astronaut (treas, Rocket Soc, 59-60); Inst Elec & Electronics Eng. *Res:* Nuclear reactor physics and engineering; plasma-microwave interaction; signal analysis. *Mailing Add:* Dept of Elec Eng Univ of Del Col of Eng Newark DE 19711

LUTZ, CHARLES WILLIAM, b Philadelphia, Pa, Nov 10, 29; m 53; c 2. PHYSICAL CHEMISTRY, INORGANIC CHEMISTRY. *Educ:* Temple Univ, AB, 53, MA, 58; Bryn Mawr Col, PhD(phys chem), 61. *Prof Exp:* Res chemist, 61-67, SR RES CHEMIST RES & DEVELOP, INDUST CHEM DIV, FMC CORP, 67- *Mem:* Sigma Xi; Am Soc Testing & Mat; fel Am Inst Chem. *Res:* Heterogeneous equilibria; non-stoichiometric tungsten compounds; crystal-field spectra; thermodynamics, kinetics and physical properties of polyphosphates and polyphosphoric acids; phosphate glasses and coatings; corrosion inhibition; peroxygen compounds; crystal chemistry. *Mailing Add:* Indust Chem Div FMC Corp Res & Develop Box 8 Princeton NJ 08540

LUTZ, DONALD ALEXANDER, b Syracuse, NY, Apr 2, 40. MATHEMATICS. *Educ:* Syracuse Univ, BS, 61, MS, 63, PhD(math), 65. *Prof Exp:* Instr math, Syracuse Univ, 65; from asst prof to assoc prof, 65-78, PROF MATH, UNIV WIS-MILWAUKEE, 78- *Concurrent Pos:* Lectr, Univ Md, 67-69; vis asst prof, Math Res Ctr, Univ Wis-Madison, 69-70; vis assoc prof math, Univ Southern Calif, 73; Humboldt fel, Univ Ulm, W Ger, 75-76. *Mem:* Am Math Soc; German Math Union. *Res:* Systems of linear ordinary differential equations with meromorphic coefficients; systems of linear difference equations. *Mailing Add:* Dept of Math Univ of Wis Milwaukee WI 53201

LUTZ, GEORGE JOHN, b New England, NDak, May 9, 33; m 65; c 2. PHYSICAL CHEMISTRY. *Educ:* Augustana Col, BA, 53; Iowa State Univ, PhD(phys chem), 62. *Prof Exp:* Jr chemist, Ames Lab, Univ Iowa, 55-58; resident res assoc, Argonne Nat Lab, 62-64; CHEMIST, NAT BUR STANDARDS, 64- *Concurrent Pos:* Sr US Scientist award, Alexander von Humboldt Found, Bonn, WGer, 74-75. *Mem:* Am Chem Soc; Am Nuclear Soc; Am Soc Metals. *Res:* Activation analysis; applications of radioactive isotopes. *Mailing Add:* Nat Bur of Standards Washington DC 20234

LUTZ, HAROLD JOHN, b Saline, Mich, Aug 11, 00; m 26; c 2. FORESTRY. *Educ:* Mich State Col, BS, 24; Yale Univ, MF, 27, PhD(forestry), 33. *Prof Exp:* Tech asst, US Forest Serv, 24-26, assoc silviculturist, Allegheny Forest Exp Sta, 28-29; asst forester, Conn Exp Sta, 27-28; asst prof forestry, Pa State Col, 29-31; from asst prof to prof, 33-48, Morris K Jesup prof silvicult, 48-65, Oastler prof forest ecol, 65-68, OASTLER EMER PROF FOREST ECOL, YALE UNIV, 68- *Concurrent Pos:* Walker-Ames prof, Univ Wash, 59; H R MacMillan lectr, Univ BC, 49; summers, US Forest Serv, 49-52 & 57 & vis prof, Univ Colo, 64-69. *Honors & Awards:* Soc Am Foresters Award, 57. *Mem:* Fel Soc Am Foresters. *Res:* Forest ecology and soils. *Mailing Add:* Rte 6 Box 346 Thomas St Allegan MI 49010

LUTZ, HARRY FRANK, b Philadelphia, Pa, Jan 30, 36; m 60; c 2. NUCLEAR PHYSICS. *Educ:* Univ Pa, AB, 57; Mass Inst Technol, PhD(physics), 61. *Prof Exp:* PHYSICIST, LAWRENCE LIVERMORE LAB, 61- *Mem:* Am Phys Soc. *Res:* Nuclear reactions and nuclear spectroscopy. *Mailing Add:* Lawrence Livermore Lab PO Box 808-L531 Livermore CA 94550

LUTZ, JOHN EWALD, b Benton Harbor, Mich, Sept 16, 27; m 51; c 4. ZOOLOGY. *Educ:* Yale Univ, BS, 50; Univ Mich, AM, 51, PhD(zool, mammal), 64. *Prof Exp:* Biol aide, US Fish & Wildlife Serv, Alaska, summers, 48-51, wildlife mgt biologist, 52-53; instr zool, Univ Mich, 56-57; from asst prof to assoc prof biol, Eastern Mich Univ, 57-65; from asst prof to assoc prof, 65-72, PROF BIOL, BELOIT COL, 72- *Concurrent Pos:* Sabbatical, Tulane Univ, 72. *Mem:* Am Soc Zool; Am Soc Mammal; Animal Behav Soc; Ecol Soc Am. *Res:* Mammalogy; ecology; animal behavior; developmental biology. *Mailing Add:* Dept of Biol Beloit Col Beloit WI 53511

LUTZ, JULIE HAYNES, b Mt Vernon, Ohio, Dec 17, 44; m 66; c 2. ASTRONOMY. *Educ:* San Diego State Univ, BA, 65; Univ Ill, MS, 68, PhD(astron), 72. *Prof Exp:* Asst prof, 72-78, ASSOC PROF ASTRON, WASH STATE UNIV, 78- *Mem:* Int Astron Union; Royal Astron Soc; Am Astron Soc. *Res:* Planetary nebulae; stellar evolution. *Mailing Add:* Prog Astron Wash State Univ Pullman WA 99164

LUTZ, PAUL E, b Hickory, NC, June 25, 34; m 78; c 1. INVERTEBRATE ZOOLOGY, ECOLOGY. *Educ:* Lenoir-Rhyne Col, AB, 56; Univ Miami, MS, 58; Univ NC, PhD(zool), 62. *Prof Exp:* Asst zool, Univ Miami, 56-58 & Univ NC, 58-61; from instr to assoc prof, 61-70, PROF BIOL, UNIV NC, GREENSBORO, 70- *Concurrent Pos:* Am Philos Soc grant, 64; NSF grants, 65-67 & 69-71. *Mem:* AAAS; Ecol Soc Am. *Res:* Ecology and physiology of aquatic insects, especially effects of temperature and photoperiod as they affect seasonal regulation of developmental patterns. *Mailing Add:* Dept Biol Univ NC Greensboro NC 27412

LUTZ, PETER LOUIS, b Glasgow, Scotland, Sept 29, 39. RESPIRATION, OSMOREGULATION. *Educ:* Glasgow Univ, Scotland, BSc, 64, PhD(zool), 70. *Prof Exp:* Lectr physiol, Univ Ife, Nigeria, 64-66, asst Univ Glasgow, Scotland, 69-70; asst prof biol, Duke Univ, NC, 70-72; lectr biol, Bath Univ, Eng, 72-76; assoc prof, 76-82, PROF PHYSIOL, MARINE SCH, MIAMI UNIV, FLA, 82- *Mem:* Soc Exp Biol; Am Soc Zoologists. *Res:* Animal physiology, particularly respiration and osmoregulation; anaerobic metabolism; applied physiology of aquaculture of crustaceans; pollution. *Mailing Add:* Sch Marine & Atmospheric Sci Univ Miami Miami FL 33149

LUTZ, RAYMOND, b Oak Park, Ill, Feb 27, 35; m 58. INDUSTRIAL ENGINEERING, ENGINEERING ECONOMICS. *Educ:* Univ NMex, BS, 58, MBA, 62; Iowa State Univ, PhD(eng valuation), 64. *Prof Exp:* Instr mech eng, Univ NMex, 58-61; asst indust eng, Iowa State Univ, 61-64; asst prof mech eng, NMex State Univ, 64-67; from assoc prof to prof indust eng, Univ Okla, 68-72; dean, Sch Mgt, 73-78, PROF, UNIV TEX, DALLAS, 73-, EXECUTIVE DEAN GRAD STUDIES & RES, 79- *Concurrent Pos:* Ed, Eng Economist, 72-77. *Honors & Awards:* E L Grant Award, Am Soc Eng Educ, 72. *Mem:* Fel AAAS; fel Am Inst Indust Engrs; Opers Res Soc Am; Inst Sci; Am Inst Decision Sci. *Res:* Operations research; industrial management. *Mailing Add:* 10275 Hollow Way Dallas TX 75229

LUTZ, RAYMOND PAUL, b Cleveland, Ohio, May 31, 32. PHYSICAL ORGANIC CHEMISTRY. *Educ:* Univ Fla, BS, 53, MS, 55; Calif Inst Technol, PhD(org chem), 62. *Prof Exp:* Res chemist, E I du Pont de Nemours & Co, Ky & Mich, 55-57; instr chem, Harvard Univ, 61-64, lectr, 64-65; asst prof, Univ Ill, Chicago, 65-68; asst prof, 68-69, ASSOC PROF CHEM, PORTLAND STATE UNIV, 69- *Mem:* Am Chem Soc. *Res:* Reaction mechanisms, including displacement reactions and thermal isomerizations. *Mailing Add:* Dept of Chem Portland State Univ Portland OR 97207

LUTZ, RICHARD ARTHUR, b New York, NY, June 8, 49; m 81. BIOLOGICAL OCEANOGRAPHY, MARINE ECOLOGY. *Educ:* Univ Va, BA, 71; Univ Maine, PhD(oceanog), 75. *Prof Exp:* Res asst, Dept Oceanog, Univ Maine, 71-75; res assoc, Darling Ctr, 75-78; res assoc dept geol & geophys, Yale Univ, 77-79; ASST PROF, DEPT OYSTER CULT, RUTGERS UNIV, 79- *Concurrent Pos:* Nat Oceanic & Atmospheric Admin sea grant, prin investr, 75-78; biol consult, Blue Gold Sea Farms, 76-; assoc investr, Nat Oceanic & Atmospheric Admin sea grant, Yale Univ, 78-; co-prin investr, NSF grant, Univ Calif, Santa Barbara, 78-; prin investr, NSF grant, Rutgers Univ, 81- *Honors & Awards:* Thurlow C Nelson Award, Nat Shellfisheries Asn, 73. *Mem:* World Mariculture Soc; Nat Shellfisheries Asn (vpres, 81-); Am Soc Zoologists; Esturaine Res Fedn; AAAS. *Res:* Shellfish biology; molluscan shell structure and mineralogy; shellfish aquaculture; bivalve larval ecology; marine ecology and paleoecology; malacology; waste heat, especially power plant effluent, utilization; paleoclimatology; deep-sea hydrothermal vents, ecology. *Mailing Add:* Dept Oyster Cult Nelson Biol Labs Rutgers Univ PO Box 1059 Piscataway NJ 08854

LUTZ, ROBERT WILLIAM, b Mason City, Iowa, Sept 14, 37; m 56; c 4. CHEMICAL PHYSICS, COMPUTER SCIENCE. *Educ:* Drake Univ, BA, 62; Univ NMex, MS, 66; Ill Inst Technol, PhD(physics), 69. *Prof Exp:* Res asst physics, Los Alamos Sci Lab, 62-64, staff mem, 64-66; asst prof, 69-73, ASSOC PROF PHYSICS, DRAKE UNIV, 73-, DIR COMPUT SERV, 74- *Mem:* Am Phys Soc; Am Asn Physics Teachers; Combustion Inst; Sigma Xi; Asn Comput Mach. *Res:* Computer assisted instruction; computers in undergraduate curriculum. *Mailing Add:* Comput Ctr Drake Univ Des Moines IA 50311

LUTZ, THOMAS EDWARD, b Teaneck, NJ, Nov 20, 40; m 66; c 2. ASTRONOMY. *Educ:* Manhattan Col, BME, 62; Univ Ill, MS, 65, PhD(astron), 69. *Prof Exp:* asst prof astron, 69-75, assoc prof, 75-81, DIR PROG ASTRON, WASH STATE UNIV, 80- *Concurrent Pos:* Vis astronomer, Royal Greenwich Observ, 76-77. *Mem:* Am Astron Soc; Int Astron Union; Royal Astron Soc; AAAS. *Res:* Calibration of luminosity criteria; observational astrophysics; application of statistical techniques to astronomy. *Mailing Add:* Prog Astron Wash State Univ Pullman WA 99164

LUTZ, WILSON BOYD, b Mogadore, Ohio, May 12, 27; m 50; c 2. BIOCHEMISTRY, ORGANIC CHEMISTRY. *Educ:* Manchester Col, BA, 50; Ohio State Univ, PhD(org chem), 55. *Prof Exp:* Fel biochem, Med Col, Cornell Univ, 55-57; scientist, Warner-Lambert Res Inst, 57-60, sr scientist, 60-62; from asst prof to assoc prof, 62-72, PROF CHEM, MANCHESTER COL, 72- *Concurrent Pos:* Consult, Warner-Lambert Res Inst, 63-66; guest worker, NIH, 71; res assoc & dir, Inst Biomed Res, Univ Tex, Austin, 81; consult, Miles Lab, Elkhart, Ind, 82. *Mem:* Am Chem Soc. *Res:* Synthesis of new derivatives of hydroxylamine and substances of biological interest including melanogenic indoles. *Mailing Add:* Dept of Chem Manchester Col North Manchester IN 46962

LUTZE, FREDERICK HENRY, JR, b Brooklyn, NY, Nov 27, 37; m 65. AEROSPACE ENGINEERING. *Educ:* Worcester Polytech Inst, BS, 59; Univ Ariz, MS, 64, PhD(aerospace eng), 67. *Prof Exp:* Mech engr, Eclipse Pioneer Div, Bendix Corp, 59-60; instr aerospace eng, Univ Ariz, 65-66; asst prof, 66-69, assoc prof, 69-81, PROF AEROSPACE ENG, VA POLYTECH INST & STATE UNIV, 81- *Concurrent Pos:* Mem staff, Boeing Corp NAm. *Mem:* Am Inst Aeronaut & Astronaut. *Res:* Trajectory optimization; flight mechanics; aircraft stability and control. *Mailing Add:* Dept of Aerospace Eng Va Polytech Inst & State Univ Blacksburg VA 24061

LUTZKER, EDYTHE, b Berlin, Ger, June 25, 04; c 3. HISTORY OF SCIENCE, HISTORY OF MEDICINE. *Educ:* City Col New York, BA, 54; Columbia Univ, MA, 59. *Prof Exp:* Res asst hist of sci, City Col New York, 52-55; RES & WRITING, 55- *Honors & Awards:* Am Philos Soc Johnson Fund Grant, 64 & Penrose Fund Grant, 65; NIH grant, 66 & 68-74. *Mem:* AAAS; Am Asn Hist Med; Am Soc Microbiol; Int Soc Hist Med; Royal Soc Med. *Res:* Social history; participation by women in science and medicine; pioneers of 19th century medicine in British Empire and India. *Mailing Add:* 201 W 89th St New York NY 10024

LUUS, R(EIN), b Tartu, Estonia, Mar 8, 39; Can citizen; m 73. CHEMICAL ENGINEERING. *Educ:* Univ Toronto, BASc, 61, MASc, 62; Princeton Univ, AM, 63, PhD(chem eng), 64. *Prof Exp:* Fel optimal control, Princeton Univ, 64-65; from asst prof to assoc prof, 65-74, PROF CHEM ENG, UNIV TORONTO, 74- *Concurrent Pos:* Consult, Can Gen Elec Co, Ltd, 65-66; Shell Oil Co Can, 66-70 & 78-79, Milltronics Ltd, 67-71 & Imperial Oil Ltd, 74-77; dir, Chem Eng Res Consults Ltd, 66-; Nat Res Coun Can sr indust fel, 72-73; vis assoc, Calif Inst Technol, 79-80. *Honors & Awards:* ERCO Award,

Can Soc Chem Eng, 80. *Mem:* Can Soc Chem Eng (secy, 67-68, vchmn, 68-69, chmn 69-70, past chmn, 70-71); fel Chem Inst Can. *Res:* Development of optimization procedures suitable for optimal and suboptimal control of nonlinear systems; nonlinear analysis; optimal control of distributed parameter systems; parameter estimation and mathematical modeling ; model reduction. *Mailing Add:* Dept of Chem Eng Univ of Toronto Toronto ON M5S 1A4 Can

LUVALLE, JAMES ELLIS, b San Antonio, Tex, Nov 10, 12; m 46; c 3. PHYSICAL CHEMISTRY, PHOTOGRAPHIC CHEMISTRY. *Educ:* Univ Calif, Los Angeles, AB, 36, AM, 37; Calif Inst Technol, PhD(chem), 40. *Prof Exp:* Instr chem, Fisk Univ, 40-41; res chemist, Res Labs, Eastman Kodak Co, 41-42, phys chemist, Kodak Res Labs, 43-53; phys chemist, Nat Defense Res Comt, Chicago, 42 & Calif Inst Technol, 42; proj dir, Tech Opers, Inc, 53-59; dir basic res, Fairchild Camera & Instrument Corp, NY, 59-63, dir res, Ill, 63-68; tech dir microstatics lab, SCM Corp, 68-69; dir physics & chem res, Smith Corona Marchant Labs, 69-70; sci coordr, Res & Develop Labs, SCM Bus Equip Div, Calif, 70-75; LAB ADMINR, CHEM DEPT, STANFORD UNIV, 75- *Concurrent Pos:* Vis lectr, Brandeis Univ, 57-59; vis scholar, Stanford Univ, 71-75; independent consult, 75- *Mem:* AAAS; Am Chem Soc; Am Phys Soc; Soc Photog Scientists & Engrs; fel Royal Soc Chem. *Res:* Photochemistry; electron diffraction; magnetic susceptibility; reaction kinetics and mechanisms; photographic theory; magnetic resonance; solid state physics; neurochemistry, chemistry of memory and learning. *Mailing Add:* 3580 Evergreen Dr Palo Alto CA 94303

LUX, CARL RAY, nuclear chemistry, see previous edition

LUX, RICHARD ALAN, b Lawrence, Mass, Nov 25, 50; m 77. GEOPHYSICAL FLUID DYNAMICS. *Educ:* Univ Rochester, BS, 74, MS, 75, PhD(mech & aerospace sci), 79. *Prof Exp:* FEL GEOPHYS, DEPT TERRESTRIAL MAGNETISM, CARNEGIE INST WASHINGTON, 78- *Mem:* Am Geophys Union. *Res:* Mantle convection; computational fluid dynamics. *Mailing Add:* Dept of Terrestrial Magnetism 5241 Broad Branch Rd NW Washington DC 20015

LUXEMBURG, WILHELMUS ANTHONIUS JOSEPHUS, b Delft, Neth, Apr 11, 29; m 55; c 2. MATHEMATICAL ANALYSIS. *Educ:* State Univ Leiden, BSc, 50, MSc, 53; Delft Univ Technol, PhD, 55. *Prof Exp:* Fel math, Queen's Univ, Can, 55-56; asst prof, Univ Toronto, 56-58; from asst prof to assoc prof, 58-62, PROF MATH, CALIF INST TECHNOL, 62-, EXEC OFFICER MATH, 70- *Concurrent Pos:* Humboldt award, 80. *Mem:* Am Math Soc; Can Math Cong; Neth Math Soc; corresp mem Royal Acad Sci Amsterdam. *Res:* Functional analysis, particularly measure and integration theory, Banach function space theory and theory of locally convex spaces; Riesz spaces; nonstandard analysis. *Mailing Add:* Dept of Math Calif Inst of Technol Pasadena CA 91125

LUXENBERG, HAROLD RICHARD, b Chicago, Ill, Feb 2, 21; m 42; c 3. APPLIED MATHEMATICS. *Educ:* Univ Calif, Los Angeles, BA, 42, MA, 48, PhD(math), 50. *Prof Exp:* Mathematician, Nat Bur Stand, 50-51; res physicist, Hughes Res & Develop Labs, 51-53; consult engr, Remington Rand, Inc, 53-55; proj consult, Litton Industs, 56-58; mgr display dept, Thompson-Ramo-Wooldridge Corp, 59-60; vpres eng & asst gen mgr, Houston Fearless Corp, 61-63; consult, Lux Assocs, 64-70; PROF COMPUT SCI, CALIF STATE UNIV, CHICO, 70- *Concurrent Pos:* Lectr & instr, Univ Calif, Los Angeles, 52-69. *Mem:* Sr mem Inst Elec & Electronics Engrs; Sigma Xi. *Res:* Data display; document storage and retrieval; photo-optical systems; digital computers in command and control applications. *Mailing Add:* 20 Sunland Dr Chico CA 95926

LUXMOORE, ROBERT JOHN, b Adelaide, Australia, Nov 7, 40; m 75. SOIL PHYSICS, WHOLE PLANT PHYSIOLOGY. *Educ:* Univ Adelaide, BAgSc, 62, BAgSc Hons, 63; Univ Calif, Riverside, PhD(soil physics), 69. *Prof Exp:* Agronomist, Dept Agr, SAustralia, 63-66; res asst, Univ Calif, Riverside, 66-69; res assoc, Univ Ill, 69-70; fel, Univ Calif, Riverside, 70-71; res assoc, Univ Wis, Madison, 71-72; SOIL & PLANT SCIENTIST, OAK RIDGE NAT LAB, 73- *Concurrent Pos:* Vis scientist, Commonwealth Sci & Indust Res Orgn, Australia, 76; consult, Ctr Law & Social Policy, Washington, DC, 79; mem, Rural Abandoned Mines Prog, Tenn, 80-81. *Mem:* Am Soc Agron; Soil Sci Soc Am; Crop Sci Soc Am. *Res:* Experimental and computer modeling research on the relationships between environmental variables and whole plant physiological processes including disruptions induced by pollutant stress. *Mailing Add:* Environ Sci Div Oak Ridge Nat Lab PO Box X Oak Ridge TN 37830

LUYBEN, WILLIAM LANDES, b Omaha, Nebr, Oct 17, 33; m 63; c 2. CHEMICAL ENGINEERING. *Educ:* Pa State Univ, BS, 55; Rutgers Univ, MBA, 58; Univ Del, MSChE, 62, PhD(chem eng), 63. *Prof Exp:* Process engr, Humble Oil & Refining Co, 55-58 & Iranian Oil & Refining Co, 58-60; tech serv engr, E I du Pont de Nemours & Co, Inc, 63-67; assoc prof, 67-73, PROF CHEM ENG, LEHIGH UNIV, 73- *Concurrent Pos:* Lectr, Univ Del, 63-66; consult, E I du Pont de Nemours & Co, Inc & Sun Oil Co, 67- *Mem:* Am Inst Chem Eng. *Res:* Process dynamics, control and simulation, particularly in distillation columns and chemical reactors. *Mailing Add:* Dept of Chem Eng Lehigh Univ Bethlehem PA 18015

LUYENDYK, BRUCE PETER, b Freeport, NY, Feb 23, 43; m 67. MARINE GEOPHYSICS. *Educ:* San Diego State Col, BS, 65; Scripps Inst Oceanog, Univ Calif, San Diego, PhD(oceanog), 69. *Prof Exp:* Geophysicist, US Navy Electronics Lab, 65-66; res asst oceanog, Scripps Inst Oceanog, Univ Calif, San Diego, 65-69; fel, Woods Hole Oceanog Inst, 69-70, asst scientist, 70-73; asst prof, 73-75, assoc prof, 75-81, PROF GEOL SCI, UNIV CALIF, SANTA BARBARA, 81- *Concurrent Pos:* Mem working group marine geophys data, Comn Oceanog, Nat Acad Sci, 71; mem working group Mid-Atlantic Ridge, US Geodyn Comn, 71; ed adv, Geol Mag, 74- *Mem:* AAAS; Am Geophys Union; fel Geol Soc Am. *Res:* Geotectonics; paleomagnetism; paleoceanography. *Mailing Add:* Dept of Geol Sci Univ of Calif Santa Barbara CA 93106

LUYKX, PETER (VAN OOSTERZEE), b Detroit, Mich, Dec 14, 37; m 60; c 2. CYTOGENETICS. *Educ:* Harvard Univ, AB, 59; Univ Calif, Berkeley, PhD(zool), 64. *Prof Exp:* Asst prof cytol, Univ Minn, Minneapolis, 64-67; asst prof, 67-74, ASSOC PROF BIOL, UNIV MIAMI, 67- *Concurrent Pos:* NIH res grants, 65-73, NSF res grants, 78-80. *Mem:* AAAS; Genetics Soc Am; Am Soc Cell Biol. *Res:* Meiosis and mitosis; cytogenetics of social insects. *Mailing Add:* Dept of Biol Univ of Miami Coral Gables FL 33124

LUYTEN, JAMES REINDERT, b Minneapolis, Minn, Dec 26, 41; m 67; c 3. PHYSICAL OCEANOGRAPHY. *Educ:* Reed Col, AB, 63; Harvard Univ, AM, 65, PhD(chem physics), 69. *Prof Exp:* Res fel geophys fluid dynamics, Harvard Univ, 69-71; asst scientist, 71-75, ASSOC SCIENTIST, WOODS HOLE OCEANOG INST, 75- *Mem:* Am Geophys Union. *Res:* Theoretical and observational study of the dynamics of low frequency variability of ocean circulation; moored current meter arrays; observations of the Gulf Stream system; equatorial current systems in Pacific and Indian Oceans. *Mailing Add:* Woods Hole Oceanog Inst Woods Hole MA 02543

LUYTEN, WILLEM JACOB, b Semarang, Dutch E Indies, Mar 7, 99; nat US; m 30; c 3. ASTRONOMY. *Educ:* Univ Amsterdam, BA, 18; State Univ Leiden, PhD(astron), 21. *Hon Degrees:* DSc, Case Western Reserve Univ & Univ St Andrews, 71. *Prof Exp:* Asst, Observ, State Univ Leiden, 20-21; fel, Lick Observ, Univ Calif, 21-22, Kellogg fel, 22-23; astronr, Harvard Observ, 23-27, asst prof astron, Univ, 27-30; from asst prof to prof, 31-75, EMER PROF ASTRON, UNIV MINN, MINNEAPOLIS, 75- *Concurrent Pos:* Mem, Lick Observ Calif Eclipse Exped, Ensenada, Baja, Calif, 23 & Hamburg Observ Eclipse Exped, Jokkmokk, Lapland, 27; Guggenheim fel, 28-30 & 37-38. *Honors & Awards:* Watson Medal, Nat Acad Sci, 64; Bruce Medal, Astron Soc of Pac, 68. *Mem:* Nat Acad Sci; AAAS; Am Astron Soc; Am Asn Variable Star Observers; Int Astron Union. *Res:* Stellar motions; nearby stars; white dwarfs; origin of the solar system. *Mailing Add:* Space Sci Ctr Univ of Minn Minneapolis MN 55455

LUZZI, THEODORE E, JR, b Floral Park, NY, June 15, 27; m 55; c 2. ENGINEERING SCIENCE. *Educ:* Stevens Inst Technol, ME, 51; Mass Inst Technol, MS, 53; Columbia Univ, Eng ScD, 63. *Prof Exp:* Engr, M W Kellogg Co, NY, 53-58; res engr, 58-61, res scientist plasma physics, 63-73, staff scientist, 73-82, SR STAFF SCIENTIST, GRUMMAN AEROSPACE CORP, 82- *Mem:* Am Phys Soc; Am Inst Aeronaut & Astronaut; Am Soc Mech Eng. *Res:* Gas dynamics; plasma physics; heat transfer. *Mailing Add:* S Oyster Bay Rd Grumman Aerospace Corp Bethpage NY 11714

LUZZIO, ANTHONY JOSEPH, b Lawrence, Mass, Oct 13, 24; m 52; c 4. IMMUNOLOGY. *Educ:* Univ Mass, BS, 47; Kans State Col, MS, 50, PhD(microbiol), 55. *Prof Exp:* Bacteriologist, Wyo State Vet Lab, 47-49; asst, Univ Kans, 50-52; chemist, Hercules Powder Co, 52-54; chief, Immunol Br, US Army Med Res Lab, 55-71, res immunologist, Blood Transfusion Res Div, 71-74, immunologist, Letterman Army Inst Res, 74-80. *Concurrent Pos:* Lectr, Univ Louisville, 55-74. *Mem:* AAAS; Am Soc Microbiol; Am Asn Immunol; Radiation Res Soc. *Res:* Effects of ionizing radiation on immune mechanisms; effects of arctic climates on immunity; protein degradation and alterations in antigenic specificity by exposure to ionizing rays; immune mechanisms in leishmaniasis. *Mailing Add:* 2167 Bay St San Francisco CA 94129

LWOWSKI, WALTER WILHELM GUSTAV, b Garmisch, Ger, Dec 28, 28; US citizen. ORGANIC CHEMISTRY. *Educ:* Univ Heidelberg, dipl, 54, Dr rer nat, 55. *Prof Exp:* Fel, Univ Calif, Los Angeles, 55-57; asst, Univ Heidelberg, 57-59; res fel chem, Harvard Univ, 59-60; asst prof, Yale Univ, 60-66; RES PROF CHEM, NMEX STATE UNIV, 66- *Concurrent Pos:* mem bd dirs, Boehringer-Mannheim Corp, Indianapolis. *Mem:* Fel AAAS; Am Chem Soc; fel NY Acad Sci; Ger Chem Soc; Royal Soc Chem. *Res:* Reactions mechanisms; electron-deficient nitrogen intermediates; photochemistry; heterocyclic chemistry; heteroatom rearrangements. *Mailing Add:* Dept of Chem NMex State Univ PO Box 3-C Las Cruces NM 88003

LYCETTE, RICHARD MILTON, b Houlton, Maine, Sept 20, 26; m 52; c 5. PHYSIOLOGY, MICROBIOLOGY. *Educ:* Univ Maine, Orono, BS, 50; Ill Inst Technol, MS, 63, PhD(physiol), 68. *Prof Exp:* Food technologist bacteriol & foods chem, Gen Foods Corp, Albion, NY, 50-52; res scientist, Continental Can Co, Chicago, 52-62; res assoc blood physiol, Presby St Luke's Hosp & Med Sch, Univ Ill, Chicago, 62-69; dir blood prod res & develop, Parke-Davis Co, Detroit, 73-74; sr chemist polymers, Fuller/OBrien Corp, South Bend, Ind, 74-76; res assoc physiol, Med Sch, Wayne State Univ, 76-79; LAB DIR, WORLD WIDE CHEM CORP, 80- *Concurrent Pos:* NIH fels, Nat Heart Inst & Off Surgeon Gen, US Army, 68-69; consult, Ind Biomed Systs Co, Mich, 69-; vis lectr, Univ Maine Augusta, 69-73; sci adv to gov, Off Res & Develop, Maine, 70-73; consult biochemist, Togus Vet Admin Hosp, Maine, 71-72; dir white cell res sect, Blood Res Ctr, Am Nat Red Cross, Bethesda, Md, 72-73. *Mem:* Am Soc Microbiol; Am Chem Soc; Inst Food Technologists; fel Royal Microbiol Soc. *Res:* Cell physiology and microbiology; influence of cell membranes and lipids on aggregation; bioenergetics in cancer; degradation polymers; blood coagulation process. *Mailing Add:* 18171 Cambridge Blvd Lathrup Village MI 48076

LYDA, STUART D, b Bridger, Mont, June 6, 30; m 53; c 5. PLANT PATHOLOGY. *Educ:* Mont State Col, BS, 56, MS, 58; Univ Calif, PhD(plant path), 63. *Prof Exp:* Lab technician, Univ Calif, 59-62; assoc prof plant path, Univ Nev, Reno, 62-67; assoc prof, 67-77, PROF PLANT PATH, TEX A&M UNIV, 77- *Mem:* AAAS; Mycol Soc Am; Am Phytopath Soc. *Res:* Fungus and plant physiology; mycology. *Mailing Add:* Dept of Plant Sci Tex A&M Univ College Station TX 77843

LYDING, ARTHUR R, b New York, NY, May 12, 25; m 57; c 1. POLYMER CHEMISTRY, ORGANIC CHEMISTRY. *Educ:* Cornell Univ, BA, 45; Univ Pa, MS, 48, PhD(chem), 51. *Prof Exp:* Instr, Cornell Univ, 44-45; control chemist, Gen Baking Co, 46; res chemist, Heyden Chem Corp, 50-52; sr res chemist, Olin Industs, 52-56, group leader polymers div, Olin Mathieson Chem Corp, Conn, 57-64, tech asst to vpres res & develop, Pkg Div, 64-69; sr res scientist, FMC Corp, 69-75; SECT LEADER NL CHEM, NL INDUSTS, INC, HIGHTSTOWN, 75- *Concurrent Pos:* Asst prof, Southern Conn State Col, 64-69; sci Ger translr, 79- *Mem:* Am Chem Soc; Sigma Xi. *Res:* Agricultural chemicals; vinyl monomers and polymers; plastics and plastics additives; oil additives; cellulose chemistry; textile stain repellents and flame retardants; fluorochemicals; emulsion polymerization; synthesis of polymers and plastics additives; coatings; rheological additives. *Mailing Add:* 24 Broadripple Dr Princeton NJ 08540

LYDY, DAVID LEE, b Elwood, Ind, Apr 27, 36; m 59; c 3. SKIN RESEARCH, DENTAL RESEARCH. *Educ:* Ind Univ, AB, 58; Univ Ill, PhD(inorg chem), 63. *Prof Exp:* Res chemist, 63-68, SECT HEAD, MIAMI VALLEY LABS, PROCTER & GAMBLE CO, 68- *Mem:* Am Chem Soc. *Res:* new opportunities research. *Mailing Add:* Miami Valley Labs Procter & Gamble Co Cincinnati OH 45247

LYE, ROBERT GLEN, b Kimberley, BC, Sept 21, 26; m 51; c 3. SOLID STATE PHYSICS. *Educ:* Univ BC, BASc, 50, MASc, 52; Univ Minn, PhD(elec eng), 57. *Prof Exp:* Jr develop engr, Consol Mining & Smelting Co, Can, 51-53; res physicist, Res Labs, Nat Carbon Co Div, Union Carbide Corp, 57-65; mem staff, Res Inst Advan Studies, Martin Co, 65-69; head physics dept & assoc dir, Res Inst Advan Studies, 69-74, CORP SCIENTIST, MARTIN MARIETTA CORP, 74- *Mem:* AAAS; Am Phys Soc; Can Asn Physicists. *Res:* Physical electronics; electronic, thermal and optical properties of crystals. *Mailing Add:* 123 Edgewood Town Baltimore MD 21204

LYERLA, JO ANN HARDING, b Long Beach, Calif, Sept 28, 40; m 64; c 1. BIOLOGY, ECOLOGICAL GENETICS. *Educ:* Univ Calif, Davis, BS, 62; San Diego State Univ, MA, 67; Clark Univ, PhD(biol), 78. *Prof Exp:* Lab technician, Univ Calif, Davis, 62-63, Gen Atomics Div, Gen Dynamics Corp, 63-64, Rockefeller Univ, 66-67 & Pa State Univ, 67-70; ASSOC PROF BIOL, BECKER JR COL, LEICESTER, 76- *Mem:* Genetics Soc; Am Soc Zoologists. *Res:* Ecological genetics of terrestial isopods; isozyme studies in animal population. *Mailing Add:* Davidson Rd Charlton MA 01507

LYERLA, TIMOTHY ARDEN, b Long Beach, Calif, Mar 5, 40; m 64; c 1. DEVELOPMENTAL GENETICS. *Educ:* Univ Calif, Davis, BA, 63; San Diego State Col, MA, 67; Pa State Univ, University Park, PhD(zool), 70. *Prof Exp:* NIH fel, Northwestern Univ, Ill, 70-71; asst prof, 71-77, ASSOC PROF DEVELOP GENETICS, CLARK UNIV, 77- *Concurrent Pos:* NSF sci fac fel, 78-79; assoc biochem, Shriver Ctr Mental Retardation, Waltham, Mass, 80- *Mem:* AAAS; Am Soc Zoologists; Soc Develop Biol. *Res:* Isozymes in vertebrate embryogenesis; cell and tissue differentiation in amphibian development; lysosomal storage diseases in humans. *Mailing Add:* Dept of Biol Clark Univ Worcester MA 01610

LYFORD, JOHN H, JR, b Chicago, Ill, July 10, 28; m 51; c 6. ECOLOGY. *Educ:* Carleton Col, BA, 50; Ore State Univ, MS, 62, PhD(bot), 66. *Prof Exp:* Pub sch teacher, Wash, 55-62; res biologist, Ore State Game Comn, 63-65; asst prof, 65-72, ASSOC PROF BIOL, ORE STATE UNIV, 72- *Mem:* AAAS; Ecol Soc Am; Am Bryol Soc. *Res:* Trophic structure of aquatic communities; ecology and distribution of mosses. *Mailing Add:* Dept of Gen Sci Ore State Univ Corvallis OR 97331

LYFORD, SIDNEY JOHN, JR, b Exeter, NJ, Jan 20, 37; m 61; c 3. ANIMAL NUTRITION, BIOCHEMISTRY. *Educ:* Univ NH, BS, 58; NC State Univ, MS, 60, PhD(animal nutrit), 64. *Prof Exp:* ASSOC PROF ANIMAL NUTRIT, UNIV MASS, AMHERST, 63- *Mem:* Am Dairy Sci Asn; Am Soc Animal Sci; Sigma Xi. *Res:* Mechanism of action of certain natural inhibitors and of volatile fatty acid absorption from the ruminant stomach; pectin degradation; nutritive evaluation of byproduct materials as animal feedstuffs. *Mailing Add:* Dept of Vet & Animal Sci Stockbridge Hall Univ of Mass Amherst MA 01003

LYGRE, DAVID GERALD, b Minot, NDak, Aug 10, 42; m 66. BIOCHEMISTRY. *Educ:* Concordia Col, Moorhead, Minn, BA, 64; Univ NDak, PhD(biochem), 68. *Prof Exp:* Am Cancer Soc fel, Case Western Reserve Univ, 68-70; asst prof chem & res corp grant, 70-73, assoc prof, 73-79, PROF CHEM, CENT WASH UNIV, 79-, ASST DEAN, 80- *Concurrent Pos:* Lectr, Am Inst Chem Engrs. *Mem:* Am Chem Soc; Sigma Xi; AAAS. *Res:* Enzymology of carbohydrate metabolism; development of experiments for instructional use; techniques for manipulating life and their implications. *Mailing Add:* Dept of Chem Cent Wash Univ Ellensburg WA 98926

LYJAK, ROBERT FRED, b Detroit, Mich. MATHEMATICS. *Educ:* Wayne State Univ, BS, 51; Univ Mich, Ann Arbor, MA, 53, PhD(math), 60. *Prof Exp:* Assoc mathematician, Res Inst, Univ Mich, 53-56, instr math, Univ, 56-58, mathematician, Res Inst, 59-62; res mathematician, Conduction Corp, 62-63 & Res Inst, Univ Mich, 63-66; assoc prof, 66-69, chmn dept, 67-70, PROF MATH, UNIV MICH-DEARBORN, 69- *Mem:* Am Math Soc. *Res:* Transformation groups; mathematical models of stochastic systems. *Mailing Add:* Dept of Math Univ of Mich Dearborn MI 48128

LYKE, EDWARD BONSTEEL, b Boston, Mass, Nov 9, 37; m 62; c 2. CYTOLOGY, INVERTEBRATE ZOOLOGY. *Educ:* Miami Univ, BA, 59; Univ Wis-Madison, MS, 62, PhD(zool), 65. *Prof Exp:* From asst prof to assoc prof, 65-73, PROF BIOL SCI, CALIF STATE UNIV, HAYWARD, 73- *Mem:* AAAS; Am Soc Zoologists; Am Inst Biol Sci; Marine Biol Asn UK. *Res:* Invertebrate cytology and histology; spermatogenesis and oogenesis; ecology of estuarine invertebrates. *Mailing Add:* Dept of Biol Sci Calif State Univ Hayward CA 94542

LYKKEN, GLENN IRVEN, b Grafton, NDak, Jan 27, 39; m 64; c 2. PHYSICS. *Educ:* Univ NDak, BS, 61; Univ NC, MS, 64, PhD(physics), 66. *Prof Exp:* Asst physics, Univ NDak, 61-62 & Univ NC, 62-65; from asst prof to assoc prof, 65-76, PROF PHYSICS, UNIV NDAK, 76- *Concurrent Pos:*

Vis prof, Univ NC, 69-70; res physicist, Human Nutrit Lab, USDA, Grand Forks, NDak, 77- *Res:* Thin films; superconducting tunneling; whole body counting. *Mailing Add:* Dept of Physics Univ of NDak Grand Forks ND 58201

LYKOS, PETER GEORGE, b Chicago, Ill, Jan 22, 27; m 50; c 3. PHYSICAL CHEMISTRY. *Educ:* Northwestern Univ, BS, 50; Carnegie Inst Technol, PhD(chem), 55. *Prof Exp:* Instr chem, Carnegie Inst Technol, 54-55; from instr to assoc prof chem, 55-64, dir comput ctr & comput sci dept, 64-71, PROF CHEM, ILL INST TECHNOL, 64- *Concurrent Pos:* Consult, Solid State Sci Div, Argonne Nat Lab, 58-67; consult, Dept Radiation Ther, Michael Reese Hosp, 66-70; pres, Four Pi, Inc, 66-; mem-at-large & chmn comt comput in chem, Nat Acad Sci-Nat Res Coun, 68-74; prog dir, Off Comput Activities, NSF, 71-73; originator series int conferences comput in chem res & educ, Ill, 71, Yugoslavia, 73, Venezuela, 76, USSR, 78 & Japan, 80; co-chmn, Nat Resource Comput in Chem Proposal Develop Team, Argonne Univs Asn-Argonne Nat Lab, 74-77; chmn comput in chem div, Am Chem Soc, 73-77, mem comt prof training, 77- & adv comt, Chem & Eng News, 77-80; dir, Interactive Instr TV Network, 76-78; mem bd, Asn Media-based Continuing Eng Educ, 76-78. *Mem:* Asn Comput Mach; Am Chem Soc; Sigma Xi. *Res:* Quantum chemistry; computational chemistry; computers in chemical education. *Mailing Add:* 316 N Ridgeland Ave Oak Park IL 60302

LYKOUDIS, PAUL S, b Preveza, Greece, Dec 3, 26; nat US; m 53; c 1. AERONAUTICAL ENGINEERING. *Educ:* Nat Tech Univ, Greece, Mech & Elec Engr, 50; Purdue Univ, MS, 54, PhD, 56. *Prof Exp:* From asst prof to assoc prof, 56-60, dir aerospace sci lab, 68-73, PROF AEROSPACE, ASTRONAUTICS & ENG SCI, PURDUE UNIV, 60-, HEAD DEPT NUCLEAR ENG, 73- *Concurrent Pos:* Vis prof aeronaut eng, Cornell Univ, 60-61; consult, Rand Corp, 60-; Nat Sci Found grant, 60- *Mem:* Assoc fel Am Inst Aeronaut & Astronaut; Am Phys Soc; Am Astron Soc; Am Nuclear Soc; Sigma Xi. *Res:* Contributor of numerous papers in field of fluid mechanics, magneto-fluid-mechanics, astrophysics, and fluid mechanics of physiological systems. *Mailing Add:* Sch of Nuclear Eng Purdue Univ Lafayette IN 47907

LYLE, BENJAMIN FRANKLIN, b Johnson City, Tenn, Aug 14, 33; m 57; c 3. INDUSTRIAL ENGINEERING, SYSTEMS ANALYSIS. *Educ:* Univ Tenn, Knoxville, BS, 55, MS, 56; E Tenn State Univ, MA, 62; NMex State Univ, ScD(indust eng), 69. *Prof Exp:* Engr artist, Fisher Body Div, Gen Motors Corp, Mich, 55; pres, Lyle Furniture Co, Tenn, 55-61; instr math, E Tenn State Univ, 61-66; from instr to asst prof indust eng, NMex State Univ, 66-70; assoc prof, 70-76, PROF MATH, E TENN STATE UNIV, 76- *Mem:* Am Inst Indust Eng; Am Soc Eng Educ; Nat Soc Prof Engrs. *Res:* Decision theory; economic evaluation; mathematical modeling. *Mailing Add:* Dept of Math East Tenn State Univ Johnson City TN 37601

LYLE, EVERETT SAMUEL, JR, b Dyersburg, Tenn, Mar 17, 27; m 47; c 2. FORESTRY, SOIL SCIENCE. *Educ:* Univ Ga, BSF, 51; Duke Univ, MF, 52; Auburn Univ, PhD(soil sci), 69. *Prof Exp:* Staff asst, Union Camp Corp, 52-57; RESEARCHER, AUBURN UNIV, 57- *Concurrent Pos:* Researcher, Ala Surface Mine Reclamation Coun, 73-77; state comnr, Ala Surface Mining Reclamation Comn, 76-80. *Mem:* Soc Am Foresters; Am Soc Agron; Soil Sci Soc Am; Can Land Reclamation Asn. *Res:* Coal surface mine reclamation; tree nutrition; forest soils. *Mailing Add:* Dept of Forestry Auburn Univ Auburn AL 36830

LYLE, GLORIA GILBERT, b Atlanta, Ga, Aug 7, 23; m 47. ORGANIC CHEMISTRY. *Educ:* Vanderbilt Univ, BA, 44; Emory Univ, MS, 46; Univ NH, PhD, 58. *Prof Exp:* Instr chem, Hollins Col, 46-47; res assoc, McArdle Lab Cancer Res, Univ Wis, 47-49; from instr to prof chem, Univ NH, 51-77; asst prof pharmacol, Tex Col Osteopathic Med, 77-80. *Concurrent Pos:* USPHS res fel, 58-59; vis assoc prof, Univ Va, 73-74. *Mem:* Am Chem Soc; NY Acad Sci; The Chem Soc; Sigma Xi. *Res:* Organic synthesis; natural products; optical rotatory dispersion and circular dichroism; stereochemistry. *Mailing Add:* 12814 Kings Forest San Antonio TX 78230

LYLE, JAMES ALBERT, b Lexington, Ky, Sept 19, 16; m 48; c 1. BOTANY. *Educ:* Univ Ky, BS, 40; NC State Col, MS, 46; Univ Minn, PhD(plant path), 53. *Prof Exp:* Jr plant pathologist, Exp Sta, Univ Hawaii, 46-47; from asst plant pathologist to assoc plant pathologist, 47-54, prof bot & microbiol & head dept, 54-79, EMER PROF, BOT, PLANT PATH & MICROBIOL DEPT, AUBURN UNIV, 79- *Mem:* Am Phytopath Soc; Am Asn Adranament Sci; Coun Agr Sci & Technol; Am Inst Biol Sci. *Res:* Fungus ecology and plant disease control, especially peanuts. *Mailing Add:* Dept Bot Plant Path & Microbiol Auburn Univ Auburn AL 36830

LYLE, ROBERT EDWARD, organic chemistry, see previous edition

LYLE, WILLIAM MONTGOMERY, b Summerside, PEI, Oct 4, 13; m 56; c 3. OPTOMETRY. *Educ:* Col Optom Ont, dipl, 38, OD, 58; Ind Univ, Bloomington, MS, 63, PhD(physiol optics), 65. *Prof Exp:* Pvt pract optom, 38-60; res assoc physiol optics, Ind Univ, 60-62; lectr, 62-65; asst prof optom, Col Optom Ont, 65-67; chief path sect, 67-74, assoc prof, 67-70, dir clins, 74-77, PROF OPTOM, UNIV WATERLOO, 70- *Concurrent Pos:* Pres, Asn Schs Optom Can, 71-73; ed, Am J Optom & Physiol Optics, 79- *Mem:* Can Asn Optom (pres, 55-57); AAAS; Am Acad Optom; Am Soc Human Genetics; Am Optom Asn. *Res:* Side effects of drugs; inheritance of astigmatism; intraracial differences in refraction. *Mailing Add:* Sch Optom Univ Waterloo Waterloo ON N2L 3G1 Can

LYLES, SANDERS TRUMAN, b Reeves, La, May 24, 07; m 46; c 4. BACTERIOLOGY. *Educ:* Rice Univ, BA, 30, MA, 31; Southwestern Baptist Sem, ThM, 36, ThD, 49; Univ Tex, PhD(bact, biochem), 55. *Prof Exp:* From instr to prof biol, Tex Christian Univ, 46-77; res scientist, 52-54; CONSULT ECOL & ENVIRON, 70- *Mem:* Am Soc Microbiol; Sigma Xi. *Res:* Epidemiology and antibiotic resistance of staphylococcus; biochemical studies of blood serum. *Mailing Add:* 3901 Stadium Dr Ft Worth TX 76109

LYMAN, CHARLES PEIRSON, b Brookline, Mass, Sept 23, 12; m 41; c 5. BIOLOGY. *Educ:* Harvard Univ, AB, 36, MA, 39, PhD(biol), 42. *Prof Exp:* Asst physiol, 42, asst cur, Mus Comp Zool, 45-50, fel anat, Med Sch, 46-48, res assoc, 48-62, assoc cur, Mus Comp Zool, 50-57, res assoc, 58-62, from asst prof to assoc prof anat, Med Sch, 62-76, cur mammal, Mus Comp Zool, 68-81, prof, 76-81, EMER PROF BIOL, HARVARD UNIV, 81- *Mem:* AAAS; Am Physiol Soc; Am Soc Mammal; Am Soc Zoologists; Am Acad Arts & Sci. *Res:* Hibernation and temperature regulation in mammals; physiological ecology. *Mailing Add:* Mus Comp Zool Harvard Univ Cambridge MA 02138

LYMAN, DONALD JOSEPH, b Chicago, Ill, Nov 5, 26; m 48; c 2. POLYMER CHEMISTRY, BIOMATERIALS. *Educ:* Univ Nev, BS, 49; Univ Del, MS, 51, PhD(chem), 52. *Prof Exp:* Asst chem, Univ Del, 50-52; res chemist high polymers, E I du Pont de Nemours & Co, 52-61; sr polymer chemist, Stanford Res Int, 61-64, head biomed polymer res, 64-69; prof mat sci, 69-74, RES ASSOC PROF SURG, UNIV UTAH, 69-, PROF BIOENG, 74- *Concurrent Pos:* Lectr, Dept Mat Sci, Stanford Univ, 64-68; chmn, Gordon Conf Sci & Technol Biomat; mem comt surv mat sci & eng, Nat Acad Sci; mem eval panel polymer div, Nat Bur Standards, 73-76. *Honors & Awards:* Am Soc Artificial Internal Organs Award, 69. *Mem:* AAAS; Am Chem Soc; Am Soc Artificial Internal Organs; NY Acad Sci; Soc Biomat. *Res:* Synthetic polymers and polymer intermediates; mechanisms of polymerization; structure-property relationships of polymers; biomedical polymers; implants for artificial organs and reconstruction surgery. *Mailing Add:* Dept of Bioeng 2086 Merrill Eng Bd Univ of Utah Salt Lake City UT 84112

LYMAN, ERNEST MCINTOSH, b Berlin, Ger, Sept 23, 10; m 34; c 5. PHYSICS. *Educ:* Pomona Col, BA, 31; Dartmouth Col, MA, 33; Univ Calif, PhD(physics), 38. *Prof Exp:* Assoc physics, Univ Ill, 38-40; mem staff, Radiation Lab, Mass Inst Technol, 40-45; from assoc prof to prof physics, 45-74, assoc head dept, 70-73, EMER PROF PHYSICS, UNIV ILL, URBANA, 74- *Mem:* Fel Am Phys Soc; Am Asn Physics Teachers. *Res:* Nuclear physics; beta-ray spectra; cyclotron design; betatron design problems; electronics; high energy physics; electrical breakdown in high vacuum. *Mailing Add:* Dept of Physics Univ of Ill Urbana IL 61801

LYMAN, FRANK LEWIS, b Springfield, Ill, Nov 6, 21; m 47; c 6. TOXICOLOGY. *Educ:* Swarthmore Col, AB, 43; Hahnemann Med Col, MD, 46. *Prof Exp:* Intern, WJersey Hosp, Camden, NJ, 47; physician, coach & instr biol, William Penn Col, 47-48; pvt pract, Iowa, 48-55; staff pediatrician, US Naval Hosp, Beaufort, SC, 55-57; assoc med dir, Mead Johnson & Co, 57-60; assoc dir, Med Dept, Geigy Chem Corp, 60-61; asst to med dir, 61-63; dir indust med, Ciba-Geigy Corp, 63-76; CONSULT TOXICOL, 76- *Concurrent Pos:* Instr, Seton Hall Col, 60-62; assoc prof, Sch Med, Temple Univ, 77-; mem various comts, Nat Acad Sci, 78- *Mem:* AAAS; Am Col Toxicol; Soc Toxicol; Am Acad Clin Toxicol; Am Asn Poison Control Ctrs. *Res:* Dietary management of phenylketonuria; toxicology of fluorescent whitening agents; pesticide toxicology. *Mailing Add:* 68F Long Beach Blvd North Beach NJ 08008

LYMAN, FREDERIC A, b Syracuse, NY, Sept 4, 34; m 54; c 3. MECHANICAL ENGINEERING, ENGINEERING MECHANICS. *Educ:* Syracuse Univ, BME, 55, MME, 57; Rensselaer Polytech Inst, PhD(eng mech), 61. *Prof Exp:* Preceptor eng mech, Columbia Univ, 61-62; aerospace res engr, Lewis Res Ctr, NASA, 62-66, head plasma flow sect, 66-67; assoc prof eng, Case Western Reserve Univ, 67-70; assoc prof mech & aerospace eng, 70-78, PROF MECH & AEROSPACE ENG, SYRACUSE UNIV, 78- *Concurrent Pos:* Vis res engr, Princeton Univ, 77-78. *Mem:* AAAS; Am Phys Soc; Am Inst Aeronaut & Astronaut; Am Soc Mech Engrs. *Res:* Fluid mechanics; heat transfer; plasma dynamics; acoustics; combustion. *Mailing Add:* 323 Scott Ave Syracuse NY 13224

LYMAN, HARVARD, b San Francisco, Calif, Sept 25, 31. PLANT PHYSIOLOGY, MOLECULAR BIOLOGY. *Educ:* Univ Calif, Berkeley, BA, 53; Univ Wash, MS, 57; Brandeis Univ, PhD(biol), 60. *Prof Exp:* Asst biol, Univ Wash, 55-57; instr, Brooklyn Col, 60-62; vis scientist biochem, Brookhaven Nat Lab, 62-63; asst prof biol, Brooklyn Col, 63-65; asst scientist microbiol, Brookhaven Nat Lab, NY, 65-67, assoc scientist, Med Dept, 67-68; ASSOC PROF BIOL, STATE UNIV NY STONY BROOK, 68- *Concurrent Pos:* NIH res grant, 63-65; NSF travel grant, 64, grant, 70-72. *Mem:* AAAS; Am Soc Plant Physiologists; Soc Protozoologists; Am Soc Cell Biologists; Biophys Soc. *Res:* Biosynthesis and inheritance of cellular organelles; development, physiology and differentiation of algae and fleshy and unicellular fungi. *Mailing Add:* Dept of Biol State Univ of NY Stony Brook NY 11794

LYMAN, JOHN L, b Delta, Utah, June 16, 44; m 68; c 5. LASER PHOTOCHEMISTRY. *Educ:* Brigham Young Univ, BS, 68, PhD(phys chem), 73. *Prof Exp:* Phys scientist asst, US Army Dugway Proving Ground, 69-70; mem staff, 73-81, ASST GROUP LEADER, LOS ALAMOS NAT LAB, 81- *Concurrent Pos:* Guest prof, Ctr Interdisciplinary Res, Univ Bielefeld, WGer, 80. *Mem:* Am Chem Soc; Optical Soc Am. *Res:* Interaction of laser radiation with polyatomic molecules, including laser photochemistry, laser istope separation, infrared excitation of polyatomic molecules, and vibrational energy dynamics. *Mailing Add:* Los Alamos Nat Lab MSJ567 PO Box 1663 Los Alamos NM 87545

LYMAN, JOHN TOMPKINS, b Berkeley, Calif, May 25, 32; m 80; c 3. BIOPHYSICS. *Educ:* Univ Calif, AB, 54 & 58, PhD(biophys), 65. *Prof Exp:* Res asst, 59-65, biophysicist, 65-79, STAFF SR SCIENTIST, LAWRENCE BERKELEY LAB, 79- *Mem:* Am Asn Physicists in Med; AAAS; Sigma Xi. *Res:* Radiation physics; radiation therapy; radiobiology; heavy charged-particle radiation dosimetry; radiobiology and radiotherapy. *Mailing Add:* Lawrence Berkeley Lab Univ of Calif MS 55-121 Berkeley CA 94720

LYMAN, ONA RUFUS, b Jamaica, Vt, Nov 18, 30; m 54; 3. PHYSICS. *Educ:* Univ Vt, BA, 52. *Prof Exp:* Jr engr, Sprague Elec Co, 52-54; PHYSICIST, TERMINAL BALLISTICS LAB, BALLISTICS RES LAB, ABERDEEN PROVING GROUND, 56- *Res:* Neutron shielding; combustion; interaction of laser beams with materials; blast and fragment protection for industrial workers; initiation mechanisms of explosives. *Mailing Add:* 303 Carter St Aberdeen MD 21001

LYMAN, W(ILKES) STUART, b Mt Vernon, SDak, Apr 13, 24; m 48; c 3. PHYSICAL METALLURGY. *Educ:* Univ Notre Dame, BS, 44; Univ Calif, MS, 52. *Prof Exp:* Jr metallurgist, Nat Adv Comt Aeronaut, Ohio, 44; head adv planning unit, Off Chief Engr, US Forces Frankfurt, Ger, 46-47, engr, Spec Assignment, Heidelberg, 48-49; asst, Univ Calif, 49-50, res engr, Inst Eng Res, 50-51; staff metallurgist, Mat Adv Bd, Nat Res Coun, 51-54; asst dept consult, Battelle Mem Inst, 55-57, div consult ferrous metall, 57-62, div chief, 62-64; mgr tech serv & mkt res, 64-79, vpres, 79-81, SR VPRES, COPPER DEVELOP ASN INC, 81- *Mem:* Am Soc Metals; Am Inst Mining, Metall & Petrol Engrs; Am Soc Mech Engrs; Am Soc Testing & Mat; Soc Automotive Engrs. *Res:* Metal fabrication; materials application; alloy selection. *Mailing Add:* Copper Develop Asn Inc 405 Lexington Ave New York NY 10017

LYMAN, WILLIAM CHESTER, JR, b Hilton, NY, Aug 28, 21; m 47; c 4. ORGANIC CHEMISTRY. *Educ:* Univ Mich, BS, 48. *Prof Exp:* Res chemist, Nat Aniline Div, Allied Chem Corp, 49-51; res chemist, Distillation Prod Industs Div, 51-60, res admin, 60-67, tech asst to vpres mkt, 67-69, COORDR ORG CHEM, EASTMAN KODAK CO, 69- *Mem:* Am Chem Soc. *Res:* Fats and oils; dye intermediates; vitamins; amino acids. *Mailing Add:* Eastman Kodak Co 343 State St Rochester NY 14650

LYMAN, WILLIAM RAY, b Stratton, Vt, May 30, 20; m 44; c 4. CHEMISTRY, RADIOISOTOPES IN RESEARCH. *Educ:* Univ Vt, BS, 41; Mass Inst Technol, PhD(org chem), 47; Columbia Univ, AM, 47. *Prof Exp:* Asst chem, Columbia Univ, 41-44; jr chemist, Tenn Eastman Corp Div, Eastman Kodak Co, 44-46; res chemist, Resinous Prod & Chem Co, 47-48; res chemist, 48-66, lab head, 66-73, proj leader, 73-81, RES SECT MGR, ROHM AND HAAS CO, 81- *Mem:* Am Chem Soc. *Res:* Pesticide residue analysis; fate of pesticides in plant and animal systems and in the environment. *Mailing Add:* Rohm & Haas Co Springhouse PA 19477

LYMANGROVER, JOHN R, b Ft Wayne, Ind, July 24, 44. ENDOCRINOLOGY, ELECTROPHYISOLOGY. *Educ:* Xavier Univ, BS, 66; Univ Ky, MS, 68; Univ Cincinnati, PhD(physiol), 72. *Prof Exp:* Fel res, Dept Biochem, Med Col Ohio, 72-75; asst prof, Dept Physiol, Tulane Univ, 75-80; ASST PROF, DEPT PHYSIOL & PHARMACOL & DIR MED PHYSIOL TEACHING, BOWMAN-GRAY MED SCH, 80- *Concurrent Pos:* Adj assoc prof, Dept Elec Eng, Tulane Univ, 80-; consult, grants reviewer, NIH, 79-81; mem, Basic Sci & High Blood Pressure Coun, Am Heart Asn. *Mem:* AAAS; Sigma Xi; Bioelectromagnetics Soc. *Res:* Neruoendocrinology; extrahypothalamic regulation of anterior pituitary hormone release; mechanism of peptide hormone action on adrenal cortical hormone release; role of endogenous opioids on adrenal steroid secretion and regulation of blood pressure. *Mailing Add:* Dept Physiol & Pharmacol Bowman Gray Med Sch Winston-Salem NC 27103

LYMN, RICHARD WESLEY, b Flushing, NY, July 26, 44; m 70; c 2. BIOPHYSICS, BIOCHEMISTRY. *Educ:* Johns Hopkins Univ, BA, 64; Univ Chicago, PhD(biophys), 70. *Prof Exp:* USPHS fel biophys, Univ Chicago, 70-71; Brit-Am fel, Am Heart Asn, MRC Lab Molecular Biol, Cambridge, Eng, 71-74; sr staff fel biophys, Phys Biol Lab, Nat Inst Arthritis Metab & Digestive Dis, 74-78, grants assoc, Div Res Grants, 78-79, ASST ASSOC DIR, ARTHRITIS, MUSCULOSKELETAL & SKIN DIS, NAT INST ARTHRITIS, DIABETES, DIGESTIVE AND KIDNEY DISEASES, NIH, 79- . *Mem:* Biophys Soc; Am Soc Biol Chemists; AAAS. *Res:* Enzyme kinetics; cellular and morphological movement; mathematical modelling; molecular mechanism of muscle contraction and tension development; science administration. *Mailing Add:* NIH Westwood Bldg Rm 403 Bethesda MD 20205

LYNCH, BENJAMIN LEO, b Omaha, Nebr, Dec 29, 23; m 56; c 6. ORAL SURGERY. *Educ:* Creighton Univ, BS, 45, DDS, 47, MA, 53; Northwestern Univ, MSD, 54; Am Bd Oral Surg, dipl. *Prof Exp:* From asst instr to assoc prof oral surg, 48-53, dir dept, 54-55 & 60-67, dean sch dent, 54-61, assoc prof oral surg, 54-55, PROF ORAL SURG, SCH DENT, CREIGHTON UNIV, 57-, COORDR GRAD & POSTGRAD STUDIES, 80- *Concurrent Pos:* Pres dent staff, Children's Mem Hosp, 52 & 59; pvt pract, 65-; mem, Omaha-Douglas County Health Bd, 66-68, vpres, 67, pres, 68; mem bd dir, Nebr Blue Cross, 68-; bd mem, Nebr Dent Serv Corp, 71-, pres, 74-75; guest lectr, Walter Reed Army Inst Res, DC; consult, Vet Hosp & Strategic Air Command Hq, Omaha, Nebr & Jenny Edmundson Hosp, Council Bluffs, Iowa. *Mem:* Am Soc Oral Surg; Am Dent Asn; fel Am Col Dent. *Res:* Dental education. *Mailing Add:* 128 Swanson Prof Bldg 8601 W Dodge Rd Omaha NE 68114

LYNCH, BRIAN MAURICE, b Melbourne, Australia, Jan 20, 30; m 56; c 2. PHYSICAL ORGANIC CHEMISTRY. *Educ:* Univ Melbourne, BSc, 52, MSc, 54, PhD(chem), 56. *Prof Exp:* Fel & vis prof cancer chemother, NMex Highlands Univ, 56-57; asst prof org chem, St Francis Xavier Univ, Can, 57-58; res officer chem, Div Coal Res, Commonwealth Sci & Indust Res Orgn, Australia, 58-59; asst prof phys chem, Mem Univ Nfld, 59-62; assoc prof, 62-68, chmn dept, 72-79, PROF ORG CHEM, ST FRANCIS XAVIER UNIV, 68-, CHMN DEPT, 80- *Concurrent Pos:* Nat Res Coun Can sr res fel, Australian Nat Univ, 68-69; Natural Sci & Eng Res Coun sr indust fel, NS Res Found, 81-82. *Mem:* Am Chem Soc; fel Chem Inst Can; fel Royal Soc Chem London. *Res:* Nuclear magnetic resonance; infrared spectra by Fourier transform techniques. *Mailing Add:* NS St Francis Xavier Univ Antigonish NS B2G 1C0 Can

LYNCH, CAROL BECKER, b New York, NY, Dec 3, 42; m 67. BEHAVIORAL GENETICS, EVOLUTIONARY GENETICS. *Educ:* Mt Holyoke Col, AB, 64; Univ Mich, MA, 65; Univ Iowa, PhD(zool), 71. *Prof Exp:* NSF fel, Inst Behav Genetics, Univ Colo, 72-73; asst prof, 73-79, ASSOC PROF BIOL, WESLEYAN UNIV, 79- *Mem:* Behave Genetics Asn; Genetics Soc Am; Animal Behav Soc; Soc Study Evolution; Am Soc Naturalists. *Res:* Genetic and environmental influences on behavioral and physiological thermoregulation mice; the role of dominance in genetic correlations; interrelations of maternal behavior and temperature regulation; geographic variation in thermoregulation. *Mailing Add:* Dept of Biol Wesleyan Univ Middletown CT 06457

LYNCH, DAN K, b San Francisco, Calif, Aug 6, 20; m 53; c 1. INDUSTRIAL CHEMISTRY. *Educ:* Principia Col, BS, 42; Stanford Univ, MA, 44. *Prof Exp:* Instr, Principia Col, 44-48; anal chemist, Monsanto Co, Mo, 48-53, res chemist, Org Chem Div, 53-63, res specialist, 63-71; SR GROUP LEADER PLANT PROCESS TECHNOL, WM G KRUMMRICH PLANT, MONSANTO CHEM INTERMEDIATES CO, 71- *Mem:* Am Chem Soc; fel Am Inst Chemists; AAAS. *Res:* Plant process improvement and maintenance research. *Mailing Add:* Wm G Krummrich Plant Monsanto Chem Intermediation Co Sauget IL 62201

LYNCH, DANIEL MATTHEW, b Detroit, Mich, June 28, 21. PLANT ECOLOGY. *Educ:* Univ Detroit, AB, 43; Mich State Univ, MS, 48; Wash State Univ, PhD(bot), 52. *Prof Exp:* Asst bot, Mich State Univ, 47-48 & Wash State Univ, 48-52; from instr to assoc prof, 54-65, PROF BIOL, ST EDWARD'S UNIV, 65- *Mem:* AAAS; Ecol Soc Am; Bot Soc Am. *Res:* Ecology of the southwestern grasslands and woodlands. *Mailing Add:* Div of Phys & Biol Sci St Edward's Univ Austin TX 78704

LYNCH, DARREL LUVENE, b Dewey, Okla, Feb 6, 21; m 49; c 4. ORGANIC CHEMISTRY, SOIL MICROBIOLOGY. *Educ:* Univ Ill, PhD(agron), 53; Univ Del, MS, 57. *Prof Exp:* Instr & asst soil biol, Univ Ill, 48-52; asst prof agron, Univ Del, 52-58; asst prof soil sci, Univ Alta, 58-60; assoc prof chem, Ga Southern Col, 60-62; assoc prof, 62-66, PROF BIOL SCI, NORTHERN ILL UNIV, 66- *Mem:* Am Soc Microbiol. *Res:* Nitrogen fixation of Rhizobia and nodulation; soil organic matter; soil polysaccharides; morphology and nutrition studies with algae; ultrastructure studies with the Actinoplanaceae; pigment production in bacteria. *Mailing Add:* 306 Dresser Rd DeKalb IL 60115

LYNCH, DAVID WILLIAM, b Rochester, NY, July 14, 32; m 54; c 3. SOLID STATE PHYSICS. *Educ:* Rensselaer Polytech Inst, BS, 54; Univ Ill, MS, 55, PhD(physics), 58. *Prof Exp:* Fulbright fel, Pavia, Italy, 58-59; from asst prof to assoc prof, 59-66, PROF PHYSICS, IOWA STATE UNIV, 66- *Concurrent Pos:* Sr physicist, Ames Lab, US Dept Energy, 66-; vis prof, Univ Hamburg, 74. *Mem:* AAAS; fel Am Phys Soc; Optical Soc Am. *Res:* Optical properties of solids, including use of synchrotron radiation and modulation-spectroscopy. *Mailing Add:* Dept of Physics Iowa State Univ Ames IA 50011

LYNCH, DERMOT ROBORG, b Johannesburg, SAfrica, Feb 9, 40; Can citizen; m 65; c 2. PLANT BREEDING, PLANT PHYSIOLOGY. *Educ:* Univ Natal, SAfrica, BSc, 63, MSc, 69; Univ Guelph, Can, PhD(plant physiol), 74. *Prof Exp:* Crop specialist, Tech Servs, Dept Agr, 65-66, res scientist potato mgt & physiol, 68-71; res scientist, McCain Foods Ltd, 74-75; asst prof potato and vegetable crops, NS Agr Col, RES SCIENTIST POTATO BREEDING, LETHBRIDGE RES STA, AGR CAN, 78- *Mem:* Agr Inst Can; Potato Asn Am. *Res:* Potato breeding; physiology of the potato and development of superior management options. *Mailing Add:* Agr Can Res Sta Lethbridge AB T1J 4B1 Can

LYNCH, DON MURL, b Delano, Calif, Feb 19, 34. ORGANIC CHEMISTRY. *Educ:* Fresno State Col, AB, 60; Univ Calif, Berkeley, PhD(org chem), 64. *Prof Exp:* Sr res chemist, Abbott Labs, 64-67; sr res chemist, Cutter Labs, 67-68; sr res chemist, 68-78, sr clin res assoc, 78-81, CLIN MONITOR, ABBOTT LABS, 81- *Mem:* Am Chem Soc. *Res:* Synthesis of potential pharmaceuticals and agricultural chemicals; isolation, structure and synthesis of natural products; preparation of clinical protocols and monitoring clinical investigations. *Mailing Add:* Abbott Labs North Chicago IL 60064

LYNCH, EDWARD CONOVER, b Fayette, Mo, Feb 24, 33; m 55; c 4. INTERNAL MEDICINE, HEMATOLOGY. *Educ:* Wash Univ, BA, 53, MD, 56. *Prof Exp:* From intern to asst resident med, Barnes Hosp, St Louis, Mo, 56-58; from assoc resident to chief resident, Strong Mem Hosp, Rochester, NY, 58-60; from instr to assoc prof, 62-72, assoc dean, Med Sch, 71-74, dean student affairs, 74-76, PROF MED, BAYLOR COL MED, 72-, ASSOC CHMN DEPT, 77- *Concurrent Pos:* Adj assoc prof biomed eng, Rice Univ, 71-73; adj prof, 73- *Mem:* Am Col Physicians; Am Fedn Clin Res; Southern Soc Clin Invest; Am Soc Hemat; Am Soc Artificial Internal Organs. *Res:* Effects of physical forces on erythrocytes and blood rheology; internal distribution of iron in various anemias. *Mailing Add:* 311 Wilchester Houston TX 77079

LYNCH, EUGENE DARREL, b Danville, Ill, Sept 4, 21; m 43; c 3. CERAMICS. *Educ:* Univ Ill, BS, 43, MS, 45, PhD, 55. *Prof Exp:* Spec asst, Univ Ill, 43-45; ceramic engr & gen mgr, Kentuckiana Pottery Co, Ky, 45; asst develop mineral, Univ Tex, 45-46; asst high temperature ceramics, Air Materiel Command proj, Univ Ill, 46-47, from asst prof to prof ceramic eng, 47-58; assoc ceramist, Argonne Nat Lab, 58-66; mgr, Mat Lab, 66-72, MGR, MAT & CHEM LAB, LYNCHBURG RES CTR, BABCOCK & WILCOX CO, 72- *Mem:* Fel Am Ceramic Soc; Am Nuclear Soc. *Res:* High temperature materials; ceramic nuclear fuels. *Mailing Add:* Mat & Chem Lab Lynchburg Res Ctr Babcock & Wilcox Co PO Box 239 Lynchburg VA 24505

LYNCH, EUGENE JOSEPH MICHAEL, b New York, NY, July 1, 27; m 50; c 3. PHYSICS. *Educ:* Cornell Univ, BA, 50; Duke Univ, PhD(physics), 59. *Prof Exp:* Asst physics, Duke Univ, 53-54, instr, 58-59; res physicist, Tonawanda Labs, Linde Div, Union Carbide Corp, 59-69; proj leader, New Ventures Div, 69-73, SR SCIENTIST, XEROX CORP, 73- *Mem:* Am Phys Soc; Asn Comput Mach. *Res:* Theoretical physics; cryogenics; liquid helium; superconductivity; heat transfer; solid state physics; statistics; inertial guidance; color science; computer graphics; computer interfacing; systems design. *Mailing Add:* W129 Xerox Corp Xerox Sq Rochester NY 14644

LYNCH, FRANCIS WATSON, b Winona, Minn, June 21, 06; m 31; c 3. DERMATOLOGY. *Educ:* Univ Minn, BS, 28, MB, 29, MD, 30, MS, 33; Am Bd Dermat, dipl, 36. *Prof Exp:* Mem fac, 33-57, head dept dermat, 57-71, prof, 57-74, EMER PROF DERMAT, MED SCH, UNIV MINN, MINNEAPOLIS, 74- *Concurrent Pos:* Pvt pract, 33-76. chief dermat, Ancker City & County Hosps, 55-57, chief staff, 57, hon consult staff, 58-; chief staff, St Joseph's Hosp, 59; vpres, Am Bd Dermat, 57, pres, 58, adv, 60- *Honors & Awards:* Finnerud Award, Dermat Found, 72. *Mem:* Soc Invest Dermat (vpres, 52); Am Cancer Soc; hon mem Am Dermat Asn (pres, 64); hon mem Am Acad Dermat (vpres, 50, pres, 60); fel AMA. *Mailing Add:* 6272 Cerrada Moreno Tucson AZ 85718

LYNCH, FRANK W, b San Francisco, Calif, Nov 26, 21; m 50; c 2. ENGINEERING, ELECTRONICS. *Prof Exp:* Res lab analyst, Boeing Airplane Co, Seattle, 48-50; res engr, Northrop Aircraft, Inc, 50, supvr dynamic anal, 50-51, gen supvr component develop, 51-52, asst chief guid & controls, 52-54 & 55-57, chief flight controls, 54-55; vpres eng, Hallamore Electronics, 57-59; vpres & mgr, Electro-Mech Div, 69-75, sr vpres opers, 76-79, SR VPRES, TACTICAL & ELECTRONIC SYSTS GROUP, NORTHROP CORP, 79- *Mem:* Aerospace Indust Asn Am; sr mem Inst Elec & Electronics Engrs; Am Ord Asn. *Res:* Analog computers and flight simulators; autopilots; guidance sensor systems; astroinertial guidance systems. *Mailing Add:* Northrup Corp 1800 Century Pike E Century City CA 90067

LYNCH, G PAUL, b Leominster, Mass, Sept 17, 25; m 62; c 2. PHYSIOLOGY. *Educ:* Univ Mass, BS, 50; Univ Idaho, MS, 56; Cornell Univ, PhD(animal physiol, biochem), 62. *Prof Exp:* Asst prof animal sci, Univ WVa, 56-59; res asst, Cornell Univ, 59-62; ANIMAL PHYSIOLOGIST, SCI & EDUC ADMIN-AGR RES, USDA, 62- *Mem:* Fel AAAS; Am Dairy Sci Asn; Am Soc Animal Sci; Sigma Xi. *Res:* Methods of determining the body composition of live animals; Pb and Cl toxicity in livestock; nitrogen and protein metabolism in young ruminants. *Mailing Add:* Ruminant Nutrition Lab Nutrit Inst Bldg 200 ARC East Beltsville MD 20705

LYNCH, GEORGE ROBERT, b Pittsburgh, Pa, Oct 5, 41; m 67. PHYSIOLOGICAL ECOLOGY, COMPARATIVE PHYSIOLOGY. *Educ:* Grove City Col, BS, 64; Univ Mich, MS, 66; Univ Iowa, PhD(zool), 72. *Prof Exp:* Instr zool, Ohio Wesleyan Univ, 66-67; instr biol, Augustana Col, Ill, 67-69; asst prof zool, Univ Maine, Orono, 73-74; ASST PROF BIOL, WESLEYAN UNIV, 74- *Concurrent Pos:* NIH fel, Inst Behav Genetics, Univ Colo, 72-73. *Mem:* Am Soc Zoologists; Ecol Soc Am. *Res:* Role of photoperiod in behavioral and physiological temperature regulation in small mammals. *Mailing Add:* Dept of Biol Wesleyan Univ Middletown CT 06457

LYNCH, GERARD FRANCIS, b Glascow, Scotland, Oct 10, 45; Can citizen; m 67; c 2. PHYSICS, ENGINEERING PHYSICS. *Educ:* Glasgow Univ, BSc, 67; Queen's Univ, Can, PhD(physics), 71. *Prof Exp:* Lectr physics, Queen's Univ, 71-73; scientist, 73-81, HEAD, ELECTRONICS BR, CHALK RIVER NUCLEAR LABS, ATOMIC ENERGY CAN LTD, 81- *Concurrent Pos:* Fel, Queen's Univ, 71, spec lectr, 79-; mem working group, Int Electrotech Comn, 76- *Mem:* Instrument Soc Am. *Res:* Instrumentation development for nuclear reactor applications; infrared spectroscopy; radiation detection and measurement, and analytical techniques. *Mailing Add:* Chalk River Nuclear Labs Atomic Energy Can Ltd Chalk River ON K0J 1J0 Can

LYNCH, HARRY JAMES, b Glenfield, Pa, Jan 18, 29; m 63. NEUROENDOCRINOLOGY. *Educ:* Geneva Col, BS, 57; Univ Pittsburgh, PhD(biol), 71. *Prof Exp:* Clin chemist, Western Pa Hosp, Pittsburgh, 55-66; sr tech fel res asst, Univ Pittsburgh, 66-71; NIH fel, 71-73, res assoc, Lab Richard Wurtman, 74-75, RES SCIENTIST, LAB NEUROENDOCRINE REGULATION, DEPT NUTRIT & FOOD SCI, MASS INST TECHNOL, 81- *Mem:* Endocrine Soc; Am Asn Clin Chemists; AAAS; Am Soc Zoologists. *Res:* Neuroendocrine regulation exemplified by the pineal gland of vertebrate animals; pineal gland function as evidenced by melatonin biosynthesis and excretion; physiological, pharmacological, and environmental factors that influence pineal function. *Mailing Add:* 37-307 Lab Neuroendocrine Reg Dept of Nutrit & Food Sci MIT Cambridge MA 02139

LYNCH, HENRY T, b Lawrence, Mass, Jan 4, 28; m 51; c 3. MEDICAL GENETICS, INTERNAL MEDICINE. *Educ:* Univ Okla, BS, 51; Univ Denver, MA, 52; Univ Tex, MD, 60. *Prof Exp:* Intern, St Mary's Hosp, Evansville, Ind, 60-61; resident internal med, Col Med, Univ Nebr, 61-64; asst prof biol & asst internist, M D Anderson Hosp & Tumor Inst, Tex, 66-67; assoc prof, 67-71, PROF PREV MED & PUB HEALTH, SCH MED, CREIGHTON UNIV, 71-, CHMN DEPT, 67- *Concurrent Pos:* USPHS sr clin cancer trainee, Eppley Cancer Inst, Nebr, 64-66. *Mem:* Am Soc Human Genetics; Am Soc Clin Oncol; Am Asn Cancer Res. *Res:* Cancer genetics. *Mailing Add:* Dept of Prev Med & Pub Health Creighton Univ Sch of Med Omaha NE 68178

LYNCH, JAMES CARLYLE, b Clifton Hill, Mo, Mar 1, 42; m 65; c 2. NEUROPHYSIOLOGY. *Educ:* Univ Mo, AB, 64; Stanford Univ, MA & PhD(neurol sci), 71. *Prof Exp:* Instr physiol, Sch Med, Johns Hopkins Univ, 74-76; asst prof anat, Med Sch, 76-81; ASST PROF ANAT, UNIV MISSISSIPPI MED CTR, 81- *Concurrent Pos:* Nat Inst Neurol Dis & Stroke neurophysiol training grant, Dept Physiol, Sch Med, Johns Hopkins Univ, 71-73; assoc consult physiol, Mayo Found, 76-81. *Mem:* Am Physiol Soc; Soc Neurosci. *Res:* Central neural mechanisms of sensation, perception and motor control. *Mailing Add:* Dept Anat Univ Mississippi Med Ctr Jackson MS 39216

LYNCH, JOHN AUGUST, b Jan 29, 47; US citizen; m 71. ANALYTICAL CHEMISTRY. *Educ:* St Peter's Col, NJ, BS, 70; Pa State Univ, PhD(chem), 76. *Prof Exp:* NSF teaching asst chem, Pa State Univ, 70-71, PHS res fel, 71-75; ASST PROF CHEM, UNIV TENN, CHATTANOOGA, 75- *Concurrent Pos:* Univ Chattanooga Found grant, 76-78; Res Corp grant, 77- *Mem:* Am Chem Soc. *Res:* Thermometric methods of analysis used in conjunction with computer interpretation of data; chlorine addition reactions and formation of the phosphate-molybdate complex. *Mailing Add:* Dept of Chem Univ of Tenn Chattanooga TN 37401

LYNCH, JOHN BROWN, b Akron, Ohio, Feb 5, 29; m 50; c 2. PLASTIC SURGERY. *Educ:* Vanderbilt Univ, BS, 49; Univ Tenn, MD, 52; Am Bd Surg & Am Bd Plastic Surg, dipl. *Prof Exp:* Internship, John Gaston Hosp, Tenn, 53-54; resident surg, Univ Tex Med Br, Galveston, 56-59, res plastic surg, 59-62; from instr to assoc prof, 62-73; PROF PLASTIC SURG, VANDERBILT UNIV SCH MED, 73-, CHMN DEPT, 73- *Concurrent Pos:* Nat consult plastic surg to Surgeon Gen, USAF, 74-; mem, Food & Drug Admin Adv Panel, HHS, Gen Surg & Plastic Surg Devices, 74- *Mem:* AMA; Am Soc Plastic & Reconstructive Surgeons; Am Asn Plastic Surg; fel Am Col Surg; Plastic Surg Res Coun. *Res:* Pathophysiological aspects of burns and laboratory projects related to congenital anomalies. *Mailing Add:* Vanderbilt Univ Hosp Rm S-2221 Nashville TN 37232

LYNCH, JOHN DOUGLAS, b Collins, Iowa, July 30, 42; m 64; c 2. ZOOLOGY, HERPETOLOGY. *Educ:* Univ Ill, Urbana, BA, 64, MS, 65; Univ Kans, PhD(zool), 69. *Prof Exp:* Asst prof, 69-73, assoc prof zool, 73-80, PROF LIFE SCI, UNIV NEBR, LINCOLN, 80- *Mem:* Am Soc Ichthyol & Herpet; Soc Systs Zool; Soc Study Evolution; Soc Study Amphibians & Reptiles; Herpetologists' League. *Res:* Systematics and zoogeography of leptodactyloid frogs especially of neotropical genus Eleutherodactylus; evolution in tropical ecosystems. *Mailing Add:* Sch of Life Sci Univ of Nebr Lincoln NE 68588

LYNCH, JOHN EDWARD, b Taunton, Mass, Feb 3, 23; m 46; c 2. BACTERIOLOGY, PARASITOLOGY. *Educ:* Providence Col, BS, 49; Mich State Univ, MS, 50, PhD(bact), 52; Am Bd Med Microbiol, dipl. *Prof Exp:* Res bacteriologist, Chas Pfizer & Co, Inc, 52-56, head parasitol lab, 57-60; res microbiologist, Hoffmann-La Roche, Inc, 60-61; res virologist, Chas Pfizer & Co, Inc, 61-63, mgr dept bact & parasitol, 63-70, asst dir dept pharmacol, 71-76, DIR, BACT & PARASITOL RES, PFIZER, INC, 76- *Mem:* Am Soc Microbiol; Soc Exp Biol & Med; fel Am Acad Microbiol; fel Royal Soc Trop Med & Hyg. *Res:* Chemotherapy of infectious diseases; parasitology. *Mailing Add:* Cent Res Div Pfizer Inc Groton CT 06340

LYNCH, MAURICE PATRICK, b Boston, Mass, Feb 24, 36; m 65; c 2. BIOLOGICAL OCEANOGRAPHY. *Educ:* Harvard Col, AB, 57; Col William & Mary, MA, 65, PhD(marine sci), 72. *Prof Exp:* Assoc marine scientist, 71-73, sr marine scientist & head dept spec progs, 73-75, asst dir & head div biol oceanog, 75-77, DIR SCI & EDUC ADMIN, ASST DIR & HEAD, DIV SPECIAL PROGS & SCI SERV, VA INST MARINE SCI, 77-. *Concurrent Pos:* Asst prof marine sci, Col William & Mary & Univ Va, 71-75; adj prof earth sci, Va State Col, 74-; assoc prof marine sci, Col William & Mary & Univ Va, 76-81. *Mem:* Am Inst Biol Sci; Marine Technol Soc; Am Soc Zoologists; Am Fisheries Soc; Am Soc Limnol & Oceanog. *Res:* Management of marine and estuarine resources with special emphasis on management-research interactions and communications; physiology of marine and estuarine organisms with special emphasis on development of physiological conditions indices. *Mailing Add:* Va Inst of Marine Sci Gloucester Point VA 23062

LYNCH, PETER JOHN, b Minneapolis, Minn, Oct 22, 36; m 64; c 2. DERMATOLOGY. *Educ:* Univ Minn, Minneapolis, BS, 59, MD, 61. *Prof Exp:* Clin instr dermat, Univ Minn, 65-66; from asst prof to assoc prof, Univ Mich, Ann Arbor, 70-73; assoc prof, 73-75, PROF DERMAT & CHIEF DIV, UNIV ARIZ, 75-, ASSOC HEAD, DEPT INTERNAL MED, 77- *Concurrent Pos:* Consult, Wayne County Gen Hosp, Eloise, Mich, 68-73, Vet Admin Hosp, Ann Arbor, Mich, 71-73, Vet Admin Hosp, Tucson, Ariz & Kino Community Hosp, Tucson, Ariz, 74- *Mem:* AAAS; Am Acad Dermat; Soc Invest Dermat; Am Dermat Asn; Asn Am Med Cols. *Res:* Clinical subjects in diseases of the skin. *Mailing Add:* Div of Dermat Univ Ariz Health Sci Ctr Tucson AZ 85724

LYNCH, PETER ROBIN, b Philadelphia, Pa, July 18, 27; m 53; c 3. PHYSIOLOGY. *Educ:* Univ Miami, BS, 50; Temple Univ, MS, 54, PhD, 58. *Prof Exp:* From instr to assoc prof physiol, 58-70, PROF PHYSIOL & RADIOL, TEMPLE UNIV, 70- *Mem:* Am Physiol Soc. *Res:* Cardiovascular and radiologic physiology; rheology. *Mailing Add:* Dept of Physiol Temple Univ Med Sch Philadelphia PA 19140

LYNCH, RICHARD VANCE, III, b Philadelphia, Pa, Feb 24, 44; m 68; c 2. MARINE BIOLOGY, BIOPHYSICS. *Educ:* Yale Univ, BS, 66; Univ Pittsburgh, PhD(biophys), 71. *Prof Exp:* Fel org chem, Tokyo Kyoiku Univ, 72-73; RES BIOLOGIST MARINE BIOL, NAVAL RES LAB, DEPT DEFENSE US, 73- *Mem:* Am Soc Photobiol. *Res:* Bioluminescence. *Mailing Add:* Code 4351 Naval Res Lab Washington DC 20375

LYNCH, RICHARD WALLACE, b Ft Leavenworth, Kans, June 17, 39; m 62; c 3. CHEMICAL PHYSICS, CHEMICAL ENGINEERING. *Educ:* Univ Calif, Berkeley, BS, 62; Univ Ill, MS, 64, PhD(chem eng), 66. *Prof Exp:* Tech staff mem chem physics, 66 & 68-71, supvr appl mat sci div, 71-73, supvr chem technol div, 73-76, MGR, WASTE MGT & ENVIRON PROGS, SANDIA LABS, 76- *Mem:* AAAS; Am Inst Chem Engrs; Am Phys Soc. *Res:* Nuclear waste solidification; geologic isolation of nuclear wastes. *Mailing Add:* Orgn 4530 Sandia Labs Albuquerque NM 87115

LYNCH, ROBERT EARL, b Luxora, Ark, Oct 4, 43; m 61; c 2. ENTOMOLOGY. *Educ:* Ark State Univ, BSE, 65; Iowa State Univ, MS, 69, PhD(entom), 74. *Prof Exp:* Agr res technician, 66-68, entomologist, 68-69, RES ENTOMOLOGIST, USDA, 69- *Mem:* Entom Soc Am; Am Peanut Res & Educ Asn. *Res:* Population distributions and economic thresholds of insects on forage grasses and peanuts; resistance in peanuts to insects. *Mailing Add:* Coastal Plain Exp Sta USDA AR Tifton GA 31794

LYNCH, ROBERT EMMETT, b Chicago, Ill, Feb 5, 32; m 55; c 3. APPLIED MATHEMATICS. *Educ:* Cornell Univ, BEngPhys, 54; Harvard Univ, MA, 59, PhD(appl math), 63. *Prof Exp:* Sr res mathematician, Res Labs, Gen Motors Corp, 61-64; asst prof math & res mathematician, Univ Tex, Austin, 64-66, assoc prof, 66-67; ASSOC PROF MATH, PURDUE UNIV, 67- *Mem:* Am Math Soc; Math Asn Am; Soc Indust & Appl Math. *Res:* Numerical analysis, particularly numerical solution of partial differential equations and applied mathematics. *Mailing Add:* 105 E Navajo West Lafayette IN 47906

LYNCH, ROBERT MICHAEL, b Brooklyn, NY, May 30, 44; m 69; c 2. STATISTICS, COMPUTER SCIENCE. *Educ:* State Univ NY, Brockport, BSc, 66; Univ Northern Colo, PhD(statist), 71. *Prof Exp:* Asst prof mgt, Eastern Ill Univ, 71-73; PROF STATIST, UNIV NORTHERN COLO, 73- *Concurrent Pos:* Fel WIE, Inst Educ Leadership, George Washington Univ, 72-73; consult, Far West Lab, Berkeley, Calif, 73, Weld Co District Attorney's Off, 76-; lectr, Ctr Spec & Advan Progs, 73-; reviewer, J Computing Reviews, 73-; consult ed, J Exp Educ, 78-; Fulbright prof, Thammasat Univ, Bangkok, 78-79; vis prof, Col Virgin Islands, 81-82. *Mem:* Royal Statist Soc; Am Statist Asn; Asn Comput Mach. *Res:* Linear models; nonparametric statistics; social science research questions. *Mailing Add:* Dept Statist Univ Northern Colo Greeley CO 80639

LYNCH, STEVEN PAUL, b Los Angeles, Calif, Aug 19, 46; m 67; c 1. SYSTEMATIC BOTANY, POLLINATION ECOLOGY. *Educ:* Calif Polytech State Univ, San Luis Obispo, BS, 69, MA, 71; Univ Calif, Davis, PhD(bot), 77. *Prof Exp:* ASST PROF BIOL, LA STATE UNIV, 77- *Concurrent Pos:* Researcher, Univ Calif, Davis, 77; environ consult, Demopulos & Ferguson Inc Assoc Engrs, 78- *Mem:* Bot Soc Am; Am Soc Plant Taxonomists; Int Soc Plant Taxonomists; Sigma Xi. *Res:* Plant-animal coevolution; floral biology of Asclepias; Monarch Butterfly migratory and feeding behavior; systematics of the Asclepiadaceae and Euphorbiaceae; pollen morphology and Angiosperm Phylogeny; scanning electron microscopy techniques. *Mailing Add:* Dept of Biol 8515 Youree Dr Shreveport LA 71115

LYNCH, T(HOMAS) E(LWIN), b Mexico, Maine, Aug 7, 14; m 44. ENGINEERING. *Educ:* Univ Maine, BS, 38. *Prof Exp:* Engr, Brush Develop Co, 39-43, head, Dept Electronics Eng, 43-52 & Clevite Corp, 52-57, gen mgt, Ord Prod Div, 57-59, vpres, 65-69; vpres, Gould Inc, 69-75; PRES, ELWIN ASSOC, 75- *Concurrent Pos:* Chmn, Cleveland Crystals Inc & Design & Mfg Co, Inc. *Mem:* Audio Eng Soc; Am Defense Prep Asn; Nat Security Indust Asn; Inst Elec & Electronics Engrs (vpres). *Res:* Underwater sound; disc and magnetic recording; underwater ordnance; government contracting; energy technology. *Mailing Add:* Old Mill Rd Gates Mills OH 44040

LYNCH, THOMAS JOHN, b Quincy, Mass, Mar 3, 41; m 69. POLYMER CHEMISTRY. *Educ:* Boston Col, BS, 62; Mass Inst Tech, PhD(org chem), 66. *Prof Exp:* Res chemist, 66-71, sr res chemist, Gulf Res & Develop Co, 71-75 & Gulf Oil Chem Co, 75-78, res assoc, 78, MGR POLYSTYRENE PRODUCT RES, GULF OIL CHEM CO, 78- *Mem:* AAAS; Am Chem Soc; The Chem Soc. *Res:* Properties and synthesis of specialty polymers for lubricants, flow modifiers and surface active agents; synthesis and degradation of functional fluids; polymer process development; polymer catalyst research and development. *Mailing Add:* PO Box 79070 Houston TX 77279

LYNCH, VINCENT DE PAUL, b Niagara Falls, NY, May 27, 27; m 54; c 4. PHARMACOLOGY. *Educ:* Niagara Univ, BS, 50; St John's Univ, NY, BS, 54; Univ Conn, MS, 56, PhD(pharmacol), 59. *Prof Exp:* Asst pharmacol, Univ Conn, 56-58; from asst prof to assoc prof, 58-66, chmn dept pharmacog, pharmacol & allied sci, 61-73; PROF PHARMACOL, ST JOHN'S UNIV, NY, 66-, DIR DIV TOXICOL, 69-, CHMN DEPT PHARMACEUT SCI, 73- *Concurrent Pos:* Res fel pharmacol, Univ Conn, 54-56; consult, NY State Off Drug Abuse Serv & NY State Assembly Ment Health Comt Drug Abuse Adv Coun. *Mem:* Soc Forensic Toxicol; Int Soc Psychoneuroendocrinol; Int Narcotic Enforcement Off Asn; Sigma Xi. *Res:* Neuropharmacology; toxicology; drug abuse. *Mailing Add:* Dept of Pharmaceut Sci St John's Univ Jamaica NY 11439

LYNCH, WESLEY CLYDE, b Vancouver, Wash, Feb 28, 44; m 65. NEUROPSYCHOLOGY. *Educ:* Univ Hawaii, BA, 67; Hollins Col, MA, 68; Univ NMex, PhD(exp psychol), 72. *Prof Exp:* Fel physiol psychol, Rockefeller Univ, 71-73, asst prof, 73-75; vis asst fel physiol psychol, John B Pierce Found Lab, 75-80; ASST PROF PSYCHOL, MONT STATE UNIV, 80- *Concurrent Pos:* Adj asst prof, Rockefeller Univ, 75-; res assoc psychol, Yale Univ, 75- *Mem:* Am Psychol Asn; AAAS; Sigma Xi. *Res:* Psychological and physiological bases of motivation, reward and learning. *Mailing Add:* Dept Psychol Mont State Univ Bozeman MT 59717

LYNCH, WILLIAM C, b Cleveland, Ohio, Apr 27, 37; div; c 4. MATHEMATICS, COMPUTER SCIENCE. *Educ:* Case Univ, BS, 59; Univ Wis, MS, 60, PhD(math), 63. *Prof Exp:* Actg instr numerical anal, Univ Wis, 62-63, asst prof, 63; from asst prof to prof comput eng, Case Western Reserve Univ, 63-76; PRIN SCIENTIST, XEROX CORP, 76- *Concurrent Pos:* Vis prof, Comput Lab, Univ Newcastle, 70-71; vis prof, Univ Fed Rio de Janeiro, 75. *Mem:* AAAS; Asn Comput Mach; Am Math Soc. *Res:* Mathematical linguistics; design, construction, measurement and modelling of operating systems. *Mailing Add:* Xerox Corp 3408 Hillview Ave Palo Alto CA 94304

LYND, JULIAN QUENTIN, b Joplin, Mo, Feb 11, 22; m 43; c 2. SOIL SCIENCE. *Educ:* Univ Ark, BS, 43; Mich State Univ, MS, 47, PhD(soil sci), 48. *Prof Exp:* Asst prof soil sci, Mich State Univ, 48-51; assoc prof, 52-57, PROF AGRON, OKLA STATE UNIV, 57- *Mem:* Fel Am Soc Agron; Soil Sci Soc Am; Int Soc Soil Sci; Am Soc Microbiol; Mycol Soc Am. *Res:* Soil microbiology; induced antibiosis to carcinogenic mycotoxins and biopathway of biotoxin degradation. *Mailing Add:* Dept of Agron Okla State Univ Stillwater OK 74074

LYND, LANGTRY EMMETT, b Can, Feb 8, 19; nat US; m 42; c 2. CHEMICAL METALLURGY, ECONOMIC GEOLOGY. *Educ:* Univ Man, BSc, 41; Rutgers Univ, MS, 55, PhD(geol), 57. *Prof Exp:* Mgr raw mat sect, Res & Develop Dept, Titanium Pigment Div, Sayreville, 48-72, sr res scientist, Cent Res Lab, N L Industs, Inc, Hightstown, NJ, 72-75; PHYS SCIENTIST & TITANIUM SPECIALIST, BUR MINES, US DEPT INTERIOR, 77- *Mem:* Geol Soc Am; Am Inst Mining, Metall & Petrol Eng. *Res:* Preparation and evaluation of concentrates for titanium dioxide pigment processes; utilization of titaniferous magnetite; treatment of industrial plant wastes; titanium geology and mineralogy; petrography and mineragraphy; commodity specialist, titanium and zirconium; supply/demand analysis. *Mailing Add:* 10213 Raider Lane Fairfax VA 22030

LYNDE, RICHARD ARTHUR, b Orange, NJ, Apr 12, 42; m 61; c 2. INORGANIC CHEMISTRY. *Educ:* Hamilton Col, AB, 64; Iowa State Univ, PhD(inorg chem), 70. *Prof Exp:* Asst prof, 70-75, chmn, Dept Chem, 73-76, assoc prof, 75-80, actg dean, 76-80, PROF & DEAN, SCH MATH & NATURAL SCI, MONTCLAIR STATE COL, 80- *Mem:* Am Chem Soc; AAAS. *Res:* Elucidation of the stoichiometry, structure and bonding of compounds formed by the post-transition and transition metals in unusual oxidation states. *Mailing Add:* Sch Math & Sci Montclair State Col Upper Montclair NJ 07043

LYNDON, ROGER CONANT, b Calais, Maine, Dec 18, 17. MATHEMATICS. *Educ:* Harvard Univ, AB, 39, MA, 41, PhD(math), 46. *Prof Exp:* Sci liaison officer, US Off Naval Res, Eng, 46-48; from instr to asst prof math, Princeton Univ, 48-53; from asst prof to assoc prof, 53-58, PROF MATH, UNIV MICH, ANN ARBOR, 58- *Concurrent Pos:* Vis assoc prof, Univ Calif, 56-57; mathematician, Inst Defense Anal, Princeton Univ, 59-60; vis prof, Queen Mary Col, Univ London, 60-61 & 64-65, Morehouse Col, Atlanta Univ, 69 , Univ Montpellier, France, 74-75 & Univ Picardie, France, 80-81. *Mem:* Am Math Soc; Math Asn Am; Asn Symbolic Logic; London Math Soc. *Res:* Abstract algebra; group theory; mathematical logic. *Mailing Add:* Dept of Math Angell Hall Univ of Mich Ann Arbor MI 48109

LYNDRUP, MARK LEROY, b Traverse City, Mich, Aug 29, 39; m 63; c 2. PHYSICAL BIOCHEMISTRY. *Educ:* Trinity Col, Conn, BS, 61; Northwestern Univ, PhD(chem), 66. *Prof Exp:* Res fel, Inst Phys Chem, Sweden, 66-68; res chemist, Western Utilization Res & Develop Div, Agr Res Serv, USDA, 68-69; asst prof chem, Trinity Col, 69-70; asst prof chem, Lebanon Valley Col, 70-73; ASST PROF CHEM, MONTCLAIR STATE COL, 73- *Mem:* Am Chem Soc. *Res:* Macromolecular chemistry; solution properties of water soluble polymers; characterization of egg white proteins; computers interfacing. *Mailing Add:* Dept of Chem Montclair State Col Montclair NJ 07043

LYNDS, BEVERLY T, b Shreveport, La, Aug 19, 29; m 54; c 1. ASTRONOMY. *Educ:* Centenary Col, BS, 49; Univ Calif, PhD(astron), 55. *Prof Exp:* Res assoc astron, Nat Radio Astron Observ, Green Bank, WVa, 60-62; asst prof astron, Univ Ariz & asst astronomer, Steward Observ, 62-65, assoc prof astron Univ Ariz & assoc astronomer, Steward Observ, 65-71; asst dir, 71-78, ASTRONOMER, KITT PEAK NAT OBSERV, 74- *Concurrent Pos:* Consult, Astron Adv Panel, NSF, 75-77 & NSF Sci & Technol Policy Off, Adv Group Sci Progs, 75-77; councilor, Am Astron Soc, 74-77. *Mem:* Am Astron Soc; Int Astron Union. *Res:* Interstellar medium; galactic structure; composition of galaxies. *Mailing Add:* Kitt Peak Nat Observ PO Box 26732 Tucson AZ 85726

LYNDS, CLARENCE ROGER, b Kirkwood, Mo, July 28, 28; m 54; c 1. ASTRONOMY. *Educ:* Univ Calif, AB, 52, PhD(astron), 55. *Prof Exp:* Asst, Lick Observ, 52; astron, Univ Calif, 53-54; jr res astronr & assoc astron, 55-58; Nat Res Coun Can fel, Dom Astrophys Observ, Can, 58-59; asst astronr, Nat Radio Astron Observ, 59-61; from asst to assoc astronr, 61-68, ASTRONR, KITT PEAK NAT OBSERV, 68- *Mem:* Nat Acad Sci; Am Astron Soc; Royal Astron Soc; Int Astron Union. *Res:* Photometry & spectroscopy of quasi-stellar objects and galaxies; observational cosmology; optical interferometry. *Mailing Add:* Kitt Peak Nat Observ PO Box 26732 Tucson AZ 85726

LYNE, LEONARD MURRAY, SR, b Riverhurst, Sask, Aug 20, 19; m 46; c 2. PAPER CHEMISTRY. *Educ:* Queen's Univ Ont, BSc, 42, MSc, 46. *Prof Exp:* Chemist, Int Nickel Co, 42-43; res chemist, Dom Plywoods, Ltd, 45-46; res chemist, E B Eddy Co, 46-56, res mgr, 56-62; head printability, Pulp & Paper Res Inst, 62-65; asst res dir pulp & paper, 65-67, DIR QUAL ASSURANCE, ONT PAPER CO, 67- *Mem:* Tech Asn Pulp & Paper Indust; Can Pulp & Paper Asn. *Res:* Fundamental and applied research of pulp and paper. *Mailing Add:* Ontario Paper Co Allanburg Rd Thorold ON L2V 3Z5 Can

LYNK, EDGAR THOMAS, b Kansas City, Mo, Aug 26, 41. LASERS. *Educ:* Yale Univ, BS, 63, MS, 65, PhD(physics), 70. *Prof Exp:* Assoc prof physics, Southern Univ, 69-74; STAFF PHYSICIST, RES & DEVELOP CTR, GEN ELEC CO, 74- *Mem:* AAAS; Am Phys Soc. *Res:* Atomic excitation cross sections; computerized tomography; ultrasound for medical imaging. *Mailing Add:* Res & Develop Ctr Gen Elec Co PO Box 8 Schenectady NY 12301

LYNN, DENIS HEWARD, b Kingston, Ontario, Apr 20, 47; m 73; c 2. PROTOZOOLOGY, EVOLUTIONARY BIOLOGY. *Educ:* Univ Guelph, BSc, 69; Univ Toronto, PhD(zool), 75. *Prof Exp:* Res assoc protozool, Dept Zool Univ Md, College Park, 72-73; fel cell biol, Dept Zool, Univ St Andrews,

Scotland, 75-77; ASST PROF ZOOL & PROTOZOOL, UNIV GUELPH, 77- *Mem:* Am Micros Soc; Soc Protozoologists; Can Soc Cell Biologists; Soc Evolutionary Protistology. *Res:* Form and function of ciliated protozoa as unicellular organisms using techniques of light and electron microscopy; evolution and taxonomy of protists, especially ciliated protozoa; using techniques cytology, of molecular biology (Electrophoresis, DNA) and numerical taxonomy. *Mailing Add:* Dept Zool Univ Guelph Guelph ON N1G 2W1 Can

LYNN, DONALD JAMES, image processing, see previous edition

LYNN, EDWARD JOSEPH, psychiatry, see previous edition

LYNN, HUGH BAILEY, b Verona, NJ, Aug 13, 14; m 40; c 3. SURGERY. *Educ:* Princeton Univ, AB, 36; Columbia Univ, MD, 40. *Prof Exp:* Assoc surg, Newark Babies Hosp, 52-53; assoc prof surg & chief sect pediat surg, Sch Med, Univ Louisville, 53-60; head sect pediat surg, Mayo Clin, 61-78, prof surg, Mayo Grad Sch Med, Univ Minn, 71-78; PROF SURG, UNIV ALA, BIRMINGHAM, 78- *Concurrent Pos:* Teaching fel, Harvard Univ, 51-52; surgeon-in-chief, Children's Hosp, Louisville, Ky, 53-60. *Mem:* Fel Am Col Surg; Am Acad Pediat. *Mailing Add:* 1601 Sixth Ave S Birmingham AL 35233

LYNN, JEFFREY WHIDDEN, b Hackensack, NJ, Mar 2, 47; m 64; c 2. SOLID STATE PHYSICS. *Educ:* Ga Inst Technol, BS, 69, MS, 70, PhD(physics), 74. *Prof Exp:* Res asst physics, Oak Ridge Nat Lab, 72-74; res assoc, Brookhaven Nat Lab, 74-76; asst prof, 76-79, ASSOC PROF PHYSICS, UNIV MD, 79- *Concurrent Pos:* Nat Res Coun fel, 74; Brookhaven Nat Lab fel, 74-76; NSF grant, 76-; consult, Nat Bur Standards, 76-; guest scientist, Brookhaven Nat Lab, 76-; guest scientist, Argonne Nat Lab, 77-; Res Corp grant, 77-80. *Mem:* Am Phys Soc; Am Inst Physics; AAAS. *Res:* Neutron scattering-solid state research; magnetic properties of solids; spin dynamics; magnetic and structural phase transitions; structurally amorphous solids; magnetic superconductors; fundamental physics of neutrons. *Mailing Add:* Dept of Physics Univ of Md College Park MD 20742

LYNN, JOHN R, b Dallas, Tex, Mar 8, 30; m 54; c 5. OPHTHALMOLOGY. *Educ:* Rice Univ, BA, 51; Univ Tex, MD, 55. *Prof Exp:* Res assoc, Univ Iowa Hosps, 61-63; from asst prof to assoc prof, 63-70, PROF SURG, UNIV TEX HEALTH SCI CTR DALLAS, 70-, CHMN DEPT OPHTHAL, 63- *Concurrent Pos:* Nat Inst Neurol Dis & Blindness spec fel, Univ Iowa Hosps, 61-63 & Eye Clin, Univ Tübingen, 62-63. *Mem:* AMA; Am Acad Ophthal & Otolaryngol; Asn Res Vision & Ophthal. *Res:* Methods of clinical perimetry; acute visual function effects by raising the intraocular pressure; threshold, summation and visual acuity of accentric scotomatous areas during phototopic, mesopic and scotopic adaptations. *Mailing Add:* Dept of Opthal 5323 Harry Hines Blvd Dallas TX 75235

LYNN, JOHN WENDELL, b New York, NY, Mar 23, 25; m 46; c 3. ORGANIC CHEMISTRY. *Educ:* Yale Univ, BS, 48, PhD(chem), 51. *Prof Exp:* Res chemist & proj leader, Org Chem Res Dept, 51-55, group leader, 55-60, res assoc, 60-61, asst dir res & develop, 61-69, mgr new mkt develop, 69-70, dir technol, Fibers & Fabrics, 69-72, new venture mgr, Chem & Plastics, 72-73, ASSOC DIR RES & DEVELOP, CHEM & PLASTICS, UNION CARBIDE CORP, 73- *Mem:* Am Chem Soc; Electrochem Soc. *Res:* Nitrogenous substances; vinyl monomers; organic synthesis; synthetic fibers; vinyl fabrics; nonwovens; thermoplastic M & E resins; phenolic resins. *Mailing Add:* 209 Lynn Lane Westfield NJ 07090

LYNN, KELVIN G, b Rapid City, SD, Feb 2, 48. SOLID STATE PHYSICS, MATERIALS SCIENCE. *Educ:* Univ Utah, BS, 71, BS, 72, PhD(mat sci), 74. *Prof Exp:* Res assoc, Dept Mat Sci, Univ Utah, 73-74; PHYSICIST, BROOKHAVEN NAT LAB, 74- *Concurrent Pos:* Res vis, Bell Labs, 74-77; vis prof, State Univ NY, Stony Brook, 77-; adj prof, Univ Guelph, Ont. *Mem:* Am Phys Soc; Am Inst Metall Engrs; Am Soc Metals. *Mailing Add:* 510B Brookhaven Nat Lab Upton NY 11973

LYNN, LOUIS BERNARD, agriculture, horticulture, see previous edition

LYNN, MELVYN, b Brooklyn, NY, May 7, 46; m 71; c 2. MICROBIOLOGY, IMMUNOLOGY. *Educ:* City Univ NY, BA, 68; Rutgers Univ, MS, 73, PhD(microbiol), 75. *Prof Exp:* Lab technician, NY Med Col, 68-69, Ft Gordon Army Hosp, US Army, 70-71; res fel, Col Med NJ-NJ Med Sch, 75-77; ASST PROF MICROBIOL, COL MED DENT NJ-SCH OSTEOP MED, 77- *Concurrent Pos:* Chief lab technician, Sera-Tec Biologicals, 71-72; adj asst prof, Seton Hall Univ, 75-77; co-investr, NIH grant, 78-81. *Mem:* Am Soc Microbiol. *Res:* Ribosomal vaccines; Haemophilus influenzae infections; pathogenesis of infectious diseases. *Mailing Add:* Dept of Microbiol-NJSOM University Heights Piscataway NJ 08854

LYNN, MELVYN STUART, b London, Eng, July 7, 37; m 60; c 3. MATHEMATICS. *Educ:* Oxford Univ, BA, 58, MA, 65; Univ Calif, Los Angeles, MA, 60, PhD(math), 62. *Prof Exp:* Res asst numerical anal, Univ Calif, Los Angeles, 59-60, res mathematician, 60-62; res mathematician, Calif Res Corp, 62; jr fel math, Nat Phys Labs, Eng, 62-63, sr sci off, 63-64; staff mem, IBM Sci Ctr, Calif, 64-65, mgr res dept, Tex, 65-68, mgr ctr, 68-71; prof math sci & dir inst comput serv & appln, Rice Univ, 71-77; PROF ELEC ENG COMPUT SCI & DIR COMPUT AFFAIRS, UNIV CALIF, BERKELEY, 77- *Mem:* Inst Elec & Electronics Engrs; Soc Indust & Appl Math; Asn Comput Mach. *Res:* Numerical solution of systems of linear and integral equations; biomathematics; computer science. *Mailing Add:* Off of Comput Affairs Univ Calif Berkeley CA 94705

LYNN, MERRILL, b New Columbia, Pa, Nov 20, 30; m 57. POLYMER CHEMISTRY. *Educ:* Bucknell Univ, BS, 56; Univ Fla, PhD(chem), 61. *Prof Exp:* Res chemist, Esso Res & Eng Co, 61-69; SR RES CHEMIST, CORNING GLASS WORKS, 70- *Mem:* AAAS; Am Chem Soc; Am Inst Chem; NY Acad Sci. *Res:* Bonding to glass surfaces; glass reinforced plastics; polymer modifications; coating resins; immobilized enzymes; ceramic binders. *Mailing Add:* 2920 Olcott Rd Big Flats NY 14814

LYNN, R(ALPH) EMERSON, JR, b Elkhart, Ind, Mar 17, 20; m 46. CHEMICAL ENGINEERING. *Educ:* Purdue Univ, BS, 42; Univ Tex, MS, 49, PhD(chem eng), 53. *Prof Exp:* Tech serv supvr, US Rubber Co, 43-46; sr res engr, B F Goodrich Co, 52-56, res scientist, 56, mgr chem eng res, 56-60, prog planning, B F Goodrich Chem Co Div, 60-66, mgr, E P Rubber Develop, B F Goodrich Chem Co, Ohio, 66-67; ALCOA PROF CHEM ENG, OHIO STATE UNIV, 67- *Mem:* AAAS; Am Chem Soc; fel Am Inst Chem Engrs; Soc Plastics Engrs; Am Soc Eng Educ. *Res:* Economics; thermodynamics; kinetics; polymerization and polymer processing. *Mailing Add:* Dept of Chem Eng Ohio State Univ 140 W 19th Ave Columbus OH 43210

LYNN, RALPH BEVERLEY, b Penetanguishene, Ont, Aug 24, 21; m 44; c 4. SURGERY. *Educ:* Queen's Univ, Ont, MD, CM, 45; FRCS(E), 48; FRCS, 49; Royal Col Physicians & Surgeons Can, cert, 57; FRCS(C), 65. *Prof Exp:* Jr intern, Kingston Gen Hosp, 44-46; sr intern surg, Royal Victoria Hosp, Montreal, Que, 46-47; sr registr, Post-Grad Med Sch, Univ London, 47-48; clin tutor, Royal Infirmary, Edinburgh, Scotland, 48-49; asst lectr surg, Post-Grad Med Sch, Univ London, 49-50 & 52-54; sr registr, Southampton Chest Hosp, Eng, 54-55; from asst prof to assoc prof surg, Univ Sask, 55-58; assoc prof, 58-62, PROF SURG, SCH MED, QUEEN'S UNIV, ONT, 62-; HEAD CARDIOTHORACIC UNIT, KINGSTON GEN HOSP, 58- *Concurrent Pos:* Nat Res Coun Can scholar, Western Reserve Univ, 50-51; traveling fel, Post-Grad Med Fedn, Johns Hopkins Univ, 51-52; Markle scholar, Univ Sask, 55-57; surgeon, Cleveland City Hosp, Ohio, 50-51; consult, Hotel Dieu & Can Forces Hosp, 58- & Dept Vet Affairs, 58-; fel coun clin cardiol, Am Heart Asn, 65. *Mem:* Asn Thoracic Surg; fel Am Col Surg; fel Am Col Chest Physicians; NY Acad Sci; Can Thoracic Soc. *Res:* Thoracic, cardiovascular and peripheral vascular surgery. *Mailing Add:* Dept of Surg Queen's Univ Sch of Med Kingston ON K7L 3N6 Can

LYNN, RAYMOND J, b Bitner, Pa, Oct 23, 28; m 58; c 3. MEDICAL MICROBIOLOGY, HOST-PARASITE INTERACTION. *Educ:* Univ Pittsburgh, BS, 52, MS, 53; Univ Pa, PhD(med microbiol), 56. *Prof Exp:* Asst biol, Univ Pittsburgh, 52-53; res investr microbiol, Univ Pa, 53-56, res microbiologist, 56-57; res assoc microbiol, Sch Med, Univ Pittsburgh, 58-60, instr, 60-61; from asst prof to assoc prof, 61-70, PROF MICROBIOL, SCH MED, UNIV SDAK, VERMILLION, 70- *Concurrent Pos:* Secy-treas, SDak Bd Examr in Basic Sci, 71-79; rep Dak Affil, regional rev comt, Am Heart Asn, 75-78. *Mem:* AAAS; Am Pub Health Asn; Am Soc Microbiol; Soc Exp Biol & Med; NY Acad Sci. *Res:* Immunology of the Mycoplasmataceae; role of L-forms in sequelae disease states; immunochemistry of streptococcal L-forms and relation of such antigens to rheumatic fever and acute glomerular nephritis; cell-wall defective microorganisms as agents of immunoregulation. *Mailing Add:* Dept of Microbiol Univ of SDak Sch of Med Vermillion SD 57069

LYNN, ROBERT THOMAS, b Coleman, Tex, Jan 15, 31; m 54; c 2. ANIMAL BEHAVIOR, ECOLOGY. *Educ:* Fla State Univ, BA, 56, MA, 57; Univ Okla, PhD(zool), 63. *Prof Exp:* Instr biol, Austin Col, 57-59; asst prof, Emory & Henry Col, 63-64; assoc prof, Presby Col, SC, 64-67; ASSOC PROF BIOL SCI, SOUTHWESTERN OKLA STATE UNIV, 67- *Mem:* AAAS; Ecol Soc Am; Am Inst Biol Sci; Am Ornith Union; Wilson Ornith Soc. *Res:* Ecology and behavior of birds and lizards. *Mailing Add:* 1208 N Indiana Weatherford OK 73096

LYNN, ROGER YEN SHEN, b Shanghai, China, Jan 18, 41. APPLIED MATHEMATICS. *Educ:* Cheng Kung Univ, Taiwan, BS, 61; Brown Univ, MS, 64; NY Univ, PhD(math), 68. *Prof Exp:* Lectr math, Univ Ind, Bloomington, 68-69, asst prof, 69-71; ASST PROF MATH, VILLANOVA UNIV, 71- *Mem:* Am Math Soc; Soc Indust & Appl Math; NY Acad Sci. *Res:* Asymptotic solutions of differential equations; operations research; computer graphics. *Mailing Add:* Dept of Math Villanova Univ Villanova PA 19085

LYNN, SCOTT, b Iola, Kans, June 18, 28; m 54; c 4. CHEMICAL ENGINEERING. *Educ:* Calif Inst Technol, BS, 50, MS, 51, PhD(chem eng), 54. *Prof Exp:* Asst, Tech Hogesch, Holland, 53-54; res engr, Dow Chem Co, Calif, 54-67; actg prof, 67-69, PROF CHEM ENG, UNIV CALIF, BERKELEY, 69- *Concurrent Pos:* Ed, Indust Electrolytic Div, J Electrochem Soc. *Mem:* Am Chem Soc; fel Am Inst Chem Engrs; Electrochem Soc. *Res:* Viscous and turbulent fluid flow; gas absorption; electrochemistry and electrochemical engineering; process synthesis and development. *Mailing Add:* 2646 San Antonio Dr Walnut Creek CA 94598

LYNN, THOMAS NEIL, JR, b Ft Worth, Tex, Feb 14, 30; m 52; c 3. MEDICINE, PREVENTIVE MEDICINE. *Educ:* Univ Okla, BS, 51, MD, 55. *Prof Exp:* From intern to asst resident med, Barnes Hosp, St Louis, 55-57; clin assoc, Nat Heart Inst, Md, 57-59; chief res, Med Ctr, Univ Okla, 59-61, instr, 61-63, asst prof prev med, 61-64, asst prof med, 63-69, assoc prof prev med & pub health, 64-69, vchmn dept, 63-69, prof family pract, community med & dent & chmn dept, 69-80, actg dean, Col Med, 74-76, dean, 76-80; VPRES, BAPTIST MED CTR, OKLAHOMA CITY, 80- *Mem:* AAAS; Asn Teachers Prev Med; AMA; Am Fedn Clin Res; Asn Am Med Cols. *Res:* Epidemiology of coronary artery disease; psycho-social aspects of dependence and rehabilitation; ballistocardiography and electrocardiography. *Mailing Add:* 3300 Northwest Exp Oklahoma City OK 75112

LYNN, WALTER R(OYAL), b New York, NY, Oct 1, 28; m 60; c 1. CIVIL & ENVIRONMENTAL ENGINEERING. *Educ:* Univ Miami, Fla, BSCE, 50; Univ NC, MSSE, 54; Northwestern Univ, PhD, 63. *Prof Exp:* Asst prof civil eng, Univ Miami, 54-58, assoc prof, 58-61; assoc prof, 61-67, dir, Sch Civil & Environ Eng, 70-78, dir, Ctr Environ Qual Mgt, 66-76, PROF ENVIRON ENG, CORNELL UNIV, 67- *Concurrent Pos:* Dir res, Ralph B Carter Co, 55-57; lectr nat high sch inst, Northwestern Univ, 60; consult, Reeder & Lynn, Consult Engrs, 57-61, Rockefeller Fdn, 76-80 & WHO, 69-; adj prof pub health, Med Col, Cornell Univ, 71-, dir, Prog Sci, Tech & Soc, 80-; mem mem bd dir, Cornell Res Found, 78-, bd trustees, Cornell Univ, 80-; assoc ed, J Oper Res, 68-76, J Environ Econs & Mgt, 78- *Mem:* AAAS; Opers Res Soc Am; Am Soc Civil Engrs; Inst Mgt Sci. *Res:* Systems analysis and operations research applications in civil and environmental engineering and public health; environmental control; science, technology policy, science and technology for development. *Mailing Add:* Sch of Civil & Environ Eng Cornell Univ Ithaca NY 14853

LYNN, WARREN CLARK, b Satanta, Kans, Dec 4, 35; m 60; c 3. SOIL SCIENCE. *Educ:* Kans State Univ, BS, 57, MS, 58; Univ Calif, PhD(soil sci), 64. *Prof Exp:* SOIL SCIENTIST, NAT SOIL SURV LAB, USDA, 63- *Mem:* Int Soc Soil Sci; Soil Sci Soc Am; Clay Minerals Soc; Int Peat Soc. *Res:* Properties of cat clays or acid sulfate soils; clay minerals in relation to soil properties; organic soils. *Mailing Add:* Nat Soil Surv Lab US Dept of Agr Fed Bldg Lincoln NE 68508

LYNN, WILLIAM GARDNER, b Washington, DC, Dec 26, 05; m 33; c 2. ZOOLOGY. *Educ:* Johns Hopkins Univ, AB, 28, PhD(zool), 31. *Prof Exp:* From asst to instr to assoc zool, Johns Hopkins Univ, 28-42; from assoc prof to prof biol, 42-74, head dept, 58-63, EMER PROF BIOL, CATH UNIV AM, 74- *Concurrent Pos:* Fel Rockefeller Found, Yale Univ, 39-40; Fulbright scholar, Univ Col, WIndies, 52-53. *Mem:* Am Soc Naturalists. *Res:* Anatomy of reptiles; amphibian metamorphosis. *Mailing Add:* Dept of Biol Cath Univ of Am Washington DC 20017

LYNN, WILLIAM SANFORD, b Clarendon, Va, June 14, 22; m 49; c 4. MEDICINE. *Educ:* Ala Polytech Inst, BS, 43; Columbia Univ, MD, 46. *Prof Exp:* Instr biochem, Univ Pa, 52-55; from asst prof to assoc prof, 56-64, PROF MED & BIOCHEM, DUKE UNIV, 64- *Concurrent Pos:* Markle scholar, 55-59. *Mem:* Am Soc Biol Chem; Am Soc Clin Invest. *Res:* Biochemistry; pulmonary secretions and hormone action. *Mailing Add:* Dept of Biochem Sch Med Duke Univ Durham NC 27710

LYNN, YEN-MOW, b Shanghai, China, Jan 17, 35; m 64; c 3. APPLIED MATHEMATICS. *Educ:* Nat Taiwan Univ, BS, 55; Calif Inst Technol, MS, 57, PhD, 61. *Prof Exp:* From asst res scientist to assoc res scientist, Courant Inst Math Sci, NY Univ, 60-64; assoc prof, Ill Inst Technol, 64-67; assoc prof, 67-72, PROF MATH, UNIV MD, BALTIMORE COUNTY, 72-, CHMN DEPT, 76- *Concurrent Pos:* Consult, Ames Res Ctr, NASA, 66; consult, Ballistic Res Lab, US Army, 69-75. *Mem:* AAAS; Am Math Soc; Soc Indust & Appl Math; Math Asn Am; Am Phys Soc. *Res:* Magneto-gas dynamics; plasma physics; partial differential equations; rotating fluids. *Mailing Add:* Dept of Math Univ of Md Baltimore County Baltimore MD 21228

LYNTON, ERNEST ALBERT, b Berlin, Ger, July 17, 26; nat US; m 53; c 2. ACADEMIC ADMINISTRATION, LOW TEMPERATURE PHYSICS. *Educ:* Carnegie Inst Technol, BS, 47, MS, 48; Yale Univ, PhD(physics), 51. *Prof Exp:* Asst, Off Naval Res, Yale Univ, 48-50; AEC fel, Univ Leiden, 51-52; from asst prof to prof physics, Rutgers Univ, 52-74, dean Livingston Col, 65-74; sr vpres acad affairs, 74-80, COMMONWEALTH PROF PHYSICS, UNIV MASS, 75- *Concurrent Pos:* Vis prof, Univ Grenoble, 59-60; mem, Comn Higher Educ, Mid States Asn, 70-75. *Mem:* Fel Am Phys Soc. *Res:* Low temperature physics helium 3 and helium 4 mixtures; superconductors; dilute metallic alloys; thermal conductivity. *Mailing Add:* Univ of Mass Harbor Campus Boston MA 02125

LYNTS, GEORGE WILLARD, b Edgerton, Wis, July 26, 36; m 59; c 2. GEOLOGY, PALEONTOLOGY. *Educ:* Univ Wis, BS, 59, MS, 61, PhD(geol), 64. *Prof Exp:* USPHS fel, Columbia Univ, 64-65; asst prof, 65-71, ASSOC PROF GEOL, DUKE UNIV, 71- *Concurrent Pos:* Mem, Cushman Found Foraminifera Res. *Mem:* AAAS; Soc Econ Paleont & Mineral; Paleont Soc; Protozool Soc. *Res:* Biology and ecology of the Foraminifera; application of quantitative techniques to the solution of geological and biological problems; micropaleontology and paleoecology of the oceans. *Mailing Add:* Dept of Geol Duke Univ Box 6665 Col Sta Durham NC 27708

LYON, CAMERON KIRBY, b Islampur, India, July 23, 23; US citizen; m 48; c 3. ORGANIC CHEMISTRY. *Educ:* Col Wooster, BA, 47; Northwestern Univ, PhD(chem), 52. *Prof Exp:* Chemist, Jackson Lab, E I du Pont de Nemours & Co, 51-59; CHEMIST, WESTERN REGIONAL RES LAB, USDA, ALBANY, 59- *Mem:* Am Chem Soc; Am Oil Chem Soc. *Res:* Polymers; urethanes; fats and oils; oilseed and leaf proteins. *Mailing Add:* 5 North Lane Orinda CA 94563

LYON, DAVID LOUIS, b Oshkosh, Wis, Jan 20, 35; m 57; c 3. ECOLOGY, ORNITHOLOGY. *Educ:* Beloit Col, BA, 56; Univ Mo, MA, 59; Iowa State Univ, PhD(wildlife ecol), 65. *Prof Exp:* Wildlife biologist, Nebr Game & Parks Comn, 59-61; asst prof, 65-73, ASSOC PROF BIOL, CORNELL COL, 73- *Mem:* AAAS; Ecol Soc Am; Am Ornithologists' Union. *Res:* Competition ecology, particularly territoriality and its relation to resource utilization; pollination ecology. *Mailing Add:* Dept of Biol Cornell Col Mt Vernon IA 52314

LYON, DAVID N, b Altoona, Kans, Apr 15, 19; m 42; c 2. PHYSICAL CHEMISTRY. *Educ:* Univ Mo, MA, 42; Univ Calif, PhD(chem), 48. *Prof Exp:* Res assoc, 48-51, asst res chemist, 51-53, assoc res chemist, 53-59, res chem engr, 59-65, lectr chem eng, 57-65, asst dean, Col Chem, 69-72, PROF CHEM ENG, COL CHEM, UNIV CALIF, BERKELEY, 65- *Mem:* NY Acad Sci; AAAS; Am Chem Soc; Am Inst Chem Eng; Sigma Xi. *Res:* Chemical thermodynamics; cryogenic engineering; chemical process design. *Mailing Add:* Col of Chem Univ of Calif Berkeley CA 94720

LYON, DONALD WILKINSON, b Manchester, Eng, Aug 6, 16; nat US; m 42; c 3. INORGANIC CHEMISTRY. *Educ:* Ohio Wesleyan Univ, BA, 37; Ohio State Univ, PhD(inorg chem), 41. *Prof Exp:* Res chemist, E I du Pont de Nemours & Co, Inc, 41-54, tech supvr, 54-62, admin supvr, Pigments Dept, 62-77, personnel coordr, Chem Dyes & Pigments Dept, 77-81; RETIRED. *Honors & Awards:* Borman Award, Am Soc Eng Educ, 81. *Mem:* Am Chem Soc. *Res:* Titanium dioxide. *Mailing Add:* 110 Banbury Dr Windsor Hills Wilmington DE 19803

LYON, DUANE EDGAR, b Muskegon, Mich, Mar 12, 39; m 61; c 2. FOREST PRODUCTS. *Educ:* Univ Mich, BS, 62, MS, 63; Univ Calif, Berkeley, PhD(forest prod), 75. *Prof Exp:* Asst technologist, Dept Wood Technol, Wash State Univ, 63-66; asst specialist, Forest Prod Lab, Univ Calif, 66-73; asst prof, 73-78, ASSOC PROF FOREST PROD, MISS FOREST PROD LAB, MISS STATE UNIV, 78- *Mem:* Forest Prod Res Soc; Soc Wood Sci & Technol. *Res:* Development and characterization of composite engineering materials made wholly or in part from wood. *Mailing Add:* Miss Forest Prod Lab PO Drawer FP Mississippi State MS 39762

LYON, EDWARD SPAFFORD, b Chicago, Ill, Feb 26, 26; m 51; c 12. GENITOURINARY SURGERY. *Educ:* Univ Chicago, PhB, 48, SB, 50, MD, 53. *Prof Exp:* Intern, Univ Hosps, 53-54, resident surg, 54-56, resident urol, 56-59, asst prof, Univ, 59-65, ASSOC PROF UROL, UNIV CHICAGO, 65- *Res:* Urolithiasis. *Mailing Add:* 950 E 59th St Chicago IL 60637

LYON, GORDON EDWARD, b New London, Wis, June 8, 42; m 71; c 1. COMPUTER SCIENCE. *Educ:* Mich Technol Univ, BS, 64; Univ Mich, MS, 66 & 67, PhD(comput sci), 72. *Prof Exp:* Mathematician, Comput Sci Dept, Gen Motors Res Labs, 67-68; res assoc, Ment Health Res Inst, Dept Psychiat, Univ Mich, 70-72; COMPUT SCIENTIST, NAT BUR STANDARDS, 72- *Concurrent Pos:* Assoc prof lectr, Dept Elec Eng & Comput Sci, George Washington Univ, 78-79. *Honors & Awards:* Silver Medal Award, US Dept Com, 78. *Mem:* Asn Comput Mach; Soc Indust Appl Math. *Res:* Algorithm design; programming techniques; programming languages. *Mailing Add:* 16705 Frontenac Terrace Derwood MD 20855

LYON, GORDON FREDERICK, b London, Eng, May 10, 22; Can citizen; m 43; c 1. PHYSICS. *Educ:* Univ Sask, BA, 56, MA, 58, PhD(physics), 61. *Prof Exp:* Instr physics, Univ Sask, 56-62; from asst prof to assoc prof, 62-69, PROF PHYSICS, UNIV WESTERN ONT, 69- *Concurrent Pos:* Mem comn 6, Int Union Geod & Geophys-Int Asn Geomag & Aeronomy, 63-; mem subcomt aeronomy, Nat Res Coun Can, 66- *Mem:* Am Geophys Union; Am Asn Physics Teachers; Can Asn Physicists. *Res:* Radio physics of the upper atmosphere; scattering of radio waves by ionospheric inhomogeneities; ionospheric absorption; travelling ionospheric disturbances; ionospheric electron content utilizing beacon satellites; associated geophysical phenomena; aurora. *Mailing Add:* Dept of Physics Univ of Western Ont London ON N6A 5B8 Can

LYON, HARVEY WILLIAM, b Chicago, Ill, May 20, 20; m 46; c 3. DENTAL RESEARCH. *Educ:* Marquette Univ, BS, 42, DDS, 45; Georgetown Univ, MS, 51, PhD(anat), 56. *Prof Exp:* Head dept periodontia, Naval Dent Sch, Md, 51-52, consult, 55-59, res officer, Naval Med Res Inst, 52-53, 54-59, dent officer, 62, Head dent res dept, 62-64, head res br, Dent Div, Bur Med & Surg, 64-65, dent proj officer, Off Naval Res, 64-65; sr res assoc, Am Dent Asn, 65-69, secy, Coun Dent Res & dir, Dent Res Info Ctr, 68-70, head, Electron Optics Facil, 70, dir clin studies, 69-74, secy, Coun Dent Res, 74-79; RES CONSULT, 79- *Concurrent Pos:* Guest scientist, Nat Bur Stand, 49-51; Navy rep dent study sect, NIH, 58-59; res collabr, Brookhaven Nat Lab, 59; consult, Naval Dent Res Inst, Ill, 67-; res assoc, Col Dent, Northwestern Univ, Ill, 69-75, mem exec comt, Div Med Sci, Nat Res Coun, 69-74. *Mem:* fel AAAS; fel Am Col Dent; Int Asn Dent Res (asst secy-treas, 69-70); Electron Probe Anal Soc Am; Int Dent Fedn. *Res:* Dental pathology, physiology and anatomy; dental materials; electron microprobe analysis; scanning electron microscopy. *Mailing Add:* 788 Taylor Lane Stoughton WI 53589

LYON, JOHN B(ENNETT), b Washington, DC, Mar 13, 27; m 57; c 1. CHEMICAL ENGINEERING. *Educ:* Catholic Univ, BChE, 50; Univ Del, PhD(chem eng), 53. *Prof Exp:* Res engr, Polychem Dept, 53-57, tech investr, Film Dept, 57-58, res engr, 58-59, engr res supvr, Yerkes Res Lab, 60-62, process develop supvr, Clinton Film Plant, Iowa, 62-65 & Spruance Film Plant, Richmond, Va, 65-76, sr engr, 76-80, STAFF ENGR, SABINE RIVER WORKS, E I DU PONT DE NEMOURS & CO, INC, 80- *Mem:* Am Chem Soc; Am Inst Chem Engrs. *Res:* Heat and mass transfer; application of reaction kinetics. *Mailing Add:* Sabine River Works E I du Pont de Nemours & Co Inc Orange TX 77630

LYON, JOHN BLAKESLEE, JR, b Auburn, NY, Mar 17, 25; m 48; c 2. BIOCHEMISTRY. *Educ:* Hamilton Col, AB, 50; Brown Univ, ScM, 52, PhD(biol), 54. *Prof Exp:* Asst biol, Brown Univ, 50-52; Life Ins Med Res Fund fel biochem, 54-56, from instr to assoc prof, 56-70, PROF BIOCHEM, EMORY UNIV, 70- *Concurrent Pos:* Lederle Med Fac award, Emory Univ, 56-59, USPHS sr res fel, 59. *Mem:* Am Soc Biol Chem. *Res:* Regulatory mechanisms of metabolism; glycogen metabolism; vitamin B-six. *Mailing Add:* Dept of Biochem Emory Univ Atlanta GA 30322

LYON, K(ENNETH) C(ASSINGHAM), b La Harpe, Ill, Jan 22, 08; m 33; c 3. CERAMICS ENGINEERING. *Educ:* Univ Ill, BS, 31, MS, 33, PhD(ceramic eng), 36. *Prof Exp:* Asst, Eng Exp Sta, Univ Ill, 31-33; ceramic engr, Glass Tech Lab, Gen Elec Co, 35-40; asst chief chemist, Armstrong Cork Co, NJ, 40-42, chief chemist, 42-46, asst mgr glass res, 46-54; tech mgr, Ind Glass Co, 54-55; mgr glass res, Ball Bros Res Corp, 55-67, mgr glass process develop, Ball Bros Co, 67-71; res assoc & glass container mfgrs inst fel, Nat Bur Standards, Md, 72-73. *Concurrent Pos:* Mem div chem & technol, Nat Res Coun, 53-56. *Mem:* Fel Am Ceramic Soc (vpres, 55-56); fel Am Inst Chem. *Res:* Quantitative relationship composition to physical and chemical properties of soda-lima glasses; surface tension of glass; electric melting of glass. *Mailing Add:* 317 E Washington St Dunkirk IN 47336

LYON, LEONARD JACK, b Sterling, Colo, Oct 31, 29; m 56; c 2. WILDLIFE ECOLOGY, FOREST ECOLOGY. *Educ:* Colo State Univ, BS, 51, MS, 53; Univ Mich, PhD(wildlife mgt), 60. *Prof Exp:* Res biologist & proj leader pheasant habitat, Colo Game & Fish Dept, 55-62; WILDLIFE BIOLOGIST & PROJ LEADER FOREST WILDLIFE HABITAT, FORESTRY SCI LAB, INTERMT FOREST & RANGE EXP STA, US FOREST SERV, 62- *Concurrent Pos:* Res assoc, Univ Mont, 65- *Mem:* Wildlife Soc; Am Inst Biol Sci; Ecol Soc Am. *Res:* Forest seral ecology; wildlife habitat. *Mailing Add:* Forestry Sci Lab US Forest Serv Intermt Forest & Range Exp Sta Missoula MT 59806

LYON, LUTHER LAWRENCE, JR, b Greensburg, Kans, Oct 28, 18; m 42. PHYSICAL INORGANIC CHEMISTRY. *Educ:* Southwestern Col AB, 39; Univ Kans, MS, 41; Univ Southern Cal, PhD(chem), 44. *Prof Exp:* Asst lab instr, Univ Kans, 39-41; assoc prof chem, Univ Wichita, 46-58, prof, 58-60; alternate group leader, Los Alamos Sci Lab, 60-73; RETIRED. *Concurrent Pos:* Dir, Res Found, Univ Wichita, 51-54; consult, 73- *Mem:* Am Chem Soc. *Res:* Inorganic carbon chemistry; surface area and adsorption measurements; diffusion of gases. *Mailing Add:* 3007 Woodland Ave Los Alamos NM 87544

LYON, RICHARD HALE, b Marquette, Mich, Nov 15, 20; c 3. MICROBIOLOGY, BIOCHEMISTRY. *Educ:* Univ Minn, BA, 47, MS, 62, PhD(microbiol, biochem), 65. *Prof Exp:* City bacteriologist, Sioux City Dept Health, Iowa, 48-49; bacteriologist, Vet Admin Ctr, Sioux Falls, SDak, 49-54; res microbiologist, Bact Res Lab, Vet Admin Hosp, Minneapolis, 54-77; res microbiologist, Mastitis Res, Col Vet Med, Univ Minn, 77-79; DIR QUAL CONTROL, PABST MEAT SUPPLY INC, INVER GROVE HEIGHTS, MINN, 79- *Mem:* Am Soc Microbiol; fel Am Inst Chem; Am Thoracic Soc; Inst Food Technologists; Sigma Xi. *Res:* Microbial physiology, specifically as it pertains to metabolic differences in the mycobacteria and to the relationship of these differences to drug susceptibility, taxonomy and virulence. *Mailing Add:* 1301 Valley High Dr Minneapolis MN 55431

LYON, RICHARD KENNETH, b Cleveland, Ohio, Dec 22, 33; m 68. PHYSICAL CHEMISTRY. *Educ:* Col William & Mary, BS, 55; Harvard Univ, PhD(phys chem), 60. *Prof Exp:* Chemist, 60-64, sr chemist, Cent Basic Res Lab, 64-67, res assoc, 67-75, sr res assoc, 75-80, SCI ADV, EXXON RES & ENG CO, 80- *Honors & Awards:* Indust Res 100 Award. *Mem:* Am Chem Soc; Combustion Inst. *Res:* Chemical reaction kinetics; combustion science; cage effect in solution and gas phase; gas phase detonations and shock waves; radiation and high pressure chemistry; laser isotope separation. *Mailing Add:* Exxon Res & Eng Co Linden NJ 07036

LYON, RICHARD NORTON, b Joliet, Ill, July 10, 16; m 39; c 2. NUCLEAR ENGINEERING. *Educ:* Univ Chicago, BS, 38; Univ Mich, MS, 42, PhD(chem eng), 49. *Prof Exp:* Mem staff, Nat Bur Stand, 34; group leader metall lab, Univ Chicago, 42-45; group leader Clinton Lab, Oak Ridge, 45-46, sect chief, 46-58, assoc div dir, 58-71, TECH DIR REACTOR DIV, OAK RIDGE NAT LAB, 71- *Concurrent Pos:* Lectr, Univ Tenn, 50- *Mem:* Fel AAAS; Am Chem Soc; Am Nuclear Soc; Sigma Xi; Am Inst Chem Eng. *Res:* Design and development of chain reaction piles; heat transfer to gases and liquids. *Mailing Add:* 348 East Dr Oak Ridge TN 37830

LYON, ROBERT LYNDON, b Dolgeville, NY, Apr 17, 27; div; c 3. FOREST ENTOMOLOGY, INSECT TOXICOLOGY. *Educ:* Syracuse Univ, BS, 53, MS, 54; Univ Calif, Berkeley, PhD(insect toxicol), 61. *Prof Exp:* Res entomologist, 53-72, supvry res entomologist & proj leader, Insecticide Eval Proj, Pac Southwest Forest & Range Exp Sta, 72-76, MEM STAFF, FOREST INSECT & DIS RES, US FOREST SERV, WASHINGTON, DC, 76- *Mem:* Entom Soc Am; Entom Soc Can. *Res:* Development of safe, selective, nonpersistent and effective chemical insecticides and techniques to manage forest insect populations and protect forest resource values with minimal adverse effects on the environment. *Mailing Add:* Forest Insect & Dis Res US Forest Serv USDA Washington DC 20250

LYON, RONALD JAMES PEARSON, b Northam, WAustralia, Jan 15, 28; US citizen; m 61; c 4. GEOLOGY, MINERALOGY. *Educ:* Univ Western Australia, BS, 48, Hons, 49; Univ Calif, Berkeley, PhD(geol), 54. *Prof Exp:* Geologist, Lake George Mines, Captains Flat, NSW, 49-51; Goewey res fel geol, Univ Calif, Berkeley, 51-54; res off mining, Commonwealth Sci Res Orgn, Australia, 54-56; geochemist, Kennecott Res Ctr, Utah, 56-59; sr geochemist, Stanford Res Inst, 59-63; Nat Acad Sci sr fel geol, Ames Res Ctr, NASA, 63-65; assoc prof, 65-71 PROF MINERAL EXPLOR, STANFORD UNIV, 72- *Concurrent Pos:* Fulbright travel grant, 51-54 & 78-79; chmn geol panel, Nat Acad Sci, Woods Hole, Mass, 67-69; consult planetary atmospheres, NASA, 68-70; consult & prin assoc, Earth Satellite Corp, 70-; mem remote sensing group, Int Hydrol Decade, Nat Acad Sci, 72- *Honors & Awards:* Photog Interpretation Award, Am Soc Photogram, 72. *Mem:* AAAS; Soc Econ Geol; Am Soc Photogram. *Res:* Use of airborne geophysical techniques and remote sensing in exploration for mineral deposits; recognition of rock and soil materials using land satellite and Skylab spectral data; airborne scanners. *Mailing Add:* Dept of Appl Earth Sci Stanford Univ Stanford CA 94305

LYON, WALDO (KAMPMEIER), b Los Angeles, Calif, May 19, 14; m 37; c 2. PHYSICS. *Educ:* Univ Calif, Los Angeles, AB, 36, MA, 37, PhD(physics), 41. *Prof Exp:* Asst physics, Univ Calif, Los Angeles, 40-41; chief scientist, Arctic Submarine Res, US Navy Electronics Lab, 41-66, DIR, ARCTIC SUBMARINE LAB, NAVAL OCEAN SYSTS CTR, 66- *Concurrent Pos:* Sr scientist, Wave Measurement Group, Bikini atom bomb tests, 46; lectr, Univ Calif, Los Angeles, 48-49; physicist, Submarine Opers, US Navy-Byrd Antarctic exped, 46-47; chief scientist, US-Can Aleutian exped, 49, Beauford Sea expeds, 51-54; sr scientist, Transpolar Submarine Exped, 57-78. *Honors & Awards:* Distinguished Civilian Serv Award, US Navy, 55 & 58; US Dept Defense, 56; Am Soc Naval Engrs Gold Medal Award, 59; President's Distinguished Fed Civilian Serv Award, 62. *Mem:* Fel AAAS; fel Am Phys Soc; fel Acoust Soc Am; fel Arctic Inst NAm; Am Soc Naval Eng. *Res:* Ocean-cryology and physics of sea ice; underwater acoustics. *Mailing Add:* 1330 Alexandria Dr San Diego CA 92107

LYON, WARD L(EWIS), b New Hampton, Iowa, Nov 17, 20; m 44; c 4. CHEMICAL ENGINEERING. *Educ:* Iowa State Col, BS, 47. *Prof Exp:* Asst metall, Manhattan Proj, Iowa State Col, 42-47; chem engr, Gen Elec Co, Wash, 47-60, Vallecitos Atomic Lab, Calif, 60-67; mgr chem process develop, Nuclear Fuel Div, 67-77, adv engr, syst syst div, Westinghouse Nuclear Energy, 77-80, FEL ENGR, WESTINGHOUSE ADV REACTOR, WESTINGHOUSE ELEC CORP, 80- *Mem:* Am Inst Chem Engrs; Am Chem Soc; Am Nuclear Soc; Am Soc Testing & Mat. *Res:* Metallurgy of actinides; chemistry; physics; solvent extraction; pyrochemistry; plutonium fuels. *Mailing Add:* Westinghouse Elec Corp PO Box 355 Pittsburgh PA 15230

LYON, WILLIAM D, b Chicago, Ill, Sept 3, 36; m 58; c 3. THEORETICAL CHEMISTRY. *Educ:* Univ Ill, BS, 58; Univ Wis, PhD(phys chem), 67. *Prof Exp:* Asst chem, Univ Wis, 61-66; res assoc, Univ Minn, 66-67; ASST PROF CHEM, UNIV AKRON, 67- *Mem:* Am Chem Soc. *Res:* Molecular quantum mechanics and x-ray cystallography. *Mailing Add:* Dept of Chem Univ of Akron Akron OH 44325

LYON, WILLIAM FRANCIS, b Mt Gilead, Ohio, Jan 24, 37; m 62; c 5. ECONOMIC ENTOMOLOGY. *Educ:* Ohio State Univ, BSc, 59, MSc, 62, PhD(entom), 69. *Prof Exp:* County exten agent, Ohio Coop Exten Serv, 59-61; surv entomologist, Ohio Agr Res & Develop Ctr, 62-64; exten entomologist, Ohio Coop Exten Serv, 66-72; Plant protection entomologist, Makerere Univ, Uganda, 72-73; pest mgt entomologist, Univ Nairobi, Kenya, 73-74; EXTEN ENTOMOLOGIST, OHIO COOP EXTEN SERV, 74- *Concurrent Pos:* Crop res entomologist, Afgoi Res Sta Magadiscio, Somalia, 76-78. *Mem:* Entom Soc Am; Am Inst Biol Sci; E African Acad. *Res:* Identification and control of livestock, poultry and mosquito insects. *Mailing Add:* 1735 Neil Ave Ohio State Univ Columbus OH 43210

LYON, WILLIAM GRAHAM, b Chelsea, Mass, Apr 29, 44; m 65; c 2. PHYSICAL CHEMISTRY. *Educ:* Univ Mich, BS, 66, MS, 68, PhD(chem), 73. *Prof Exp:* Fel phys chem, Univ Mich, 73-74; fel phys chem, Argonne Nat Lab, 74-76; FEL PHYS CHEM, PHILLIPS PETROLEUM CO, 76- *Mem:* Am Chem Soc Sigma Xi; Sigma Xi. *Res:* Geochemistry and thermodynamics of the solid state. *Mailing Add:* Phillips Petroleum Co Res and Develop Bartlesville OK 74004

LYON, WILLIAM SOUTHERN, JR, b Pulaski, Va, Jan 25, 22; m 46; c 2. RADIOCHEMISTRY. *Educ:* Univ Va, BS, 43; Univ Tenn, MS, 68. *Prof Exp:* Chemist, E I du Pont de Nemours & Co, WVa, 43-44 & Wash, 44-45; lab foreman, Tenn Eastman Corp, 45-47; chemist, 47-62, group leader radiochem, 62-77, SECT HEAD, ANAL METHODOL, OAK RIDGE NAT LAB, 77- *Concurrent Pos:* Consult, Thai Atomic Energy for Peace Lab, Bangkok, 66-; mem sci comt 25, Nat Coun Radiation Protection, 67-; assoc ed, Radiochem-Radioanal Lett, 70-; regional ed, J Radioanal Chem, 71- *Honors & Awards:* Radiation Indust Award, Am Nuclear Soc, 80; Hevesy Medal, 81. *Mem:* Am Chem Soc; Am Nuclear Soc. *Res:* Trace element analysis; new energy sources; nuclear decay schemes; specialized radioactivity measurements; scientometrics. *Mailing Add:* Anal Chem Div Oak Ridge Nat Lab PO Box X Oak Ridge TN 37830

LYONS, CARL J(OHN), b Chicago, Ill, Apr 20, 24; m 47; c 3. CHEMICAL ENGINEERING. *Educ:* Pa State Univ, BSc, 47; Ohio State Univ, MSc, 50. *Prof Exp:* From asst div chief fuels & phys chem to mgr biol, environ & chem dept, 47-73, assoc dir, Res Opers, 73-76, ASSOC DIR, PROJ MGT & PROG DEVELOP, BATTELLE COLUMBUS LABS, 76- *Mem:* AAAS; Am Chem Soc; Am Ord Asn. *Res:* Physical chemistry of fuel reactions; surface chemistry; environmental effects of combustion; solid waste technology; application of physical sciences to medical sciences. *Mailing Add:* Proj Mgt & Prog Develop Battelle-Columbus 505 King Ave Columbus OH 43201

LYONS, DON CHALMERS, b Jackson, Mich, May 5, 99; m 23; c 3. BACTERIOLOGY. *Educ:* Univ Mich, DDS, 21, MS, 32; Mich State Univ, PhD(bact), 35; Am Bd Oral Med, dipl. *Prof Exp:* Instr oral surg, Univ Mich, 21, asst, Univ Hosp, 23-25; DIR, LYONS RES LAB, 37- *Concurrent Pos:* Practicing oral surgeon, 35-; res assoc, Mich State Univ & Univ Mich, 23-26; Fulbright prof, Univ Lima, 62, Univ Guenca, 64, Cent Univ Ecuador, 64 & Univ Tehran, 67; mem staff, Mercy, Sheldon, Cedar Knoll, Marlin Community Hosps, Faith Haven & Highland Exten Care Hosps; consult & mem exec bd, W A Foote Hosp; chmn, Am Bd Oral Med; Am Acad Oral Med acad fel; Miller Mem lectr. *Mem:* Fel Am Col Dentists; fel Int Col Dentists; Am Dent Asn; fel Am Pub Health Asn; fel Am Acad Oral Med . *Res:* Antibiosis associated with biochemical activities of bacteria; oral surgery. *Mailing Add:* 420 W Michigan Ave Jackson MI 49201

LYONS, DONALD HERBERT, b Buffalo, NY, Feb 28, 29; m 51; c 3. PHYSICS. *Educ:* Univ Buffalo, BA, 49; Univ Pa, MA, 51, PhD(physics), 54. *Prof Exp:* Staff scientist, Lincoln Lab, Mass Inst Technol, 56-61 & Sperry Rand Res Ctr, 61-63; res prof physics, Inst Solid State Physics, Univ Tokyo, 63-64; staff scientist, Sperry Rand Res Ctr, Mass, 64-66; assoc prof, 66-68, chmn dept, 67-68 & 70-72, PROF PHYSICS, UNIV MASS, BOSTON, 68- *Concurrent Pos:* Fulbright grant, 63-64. *Mem:* Am Phys Soc. *Res:* Theoretical magnetism; communication theory; theoretical nuclear physics. *Mailing Add:* Dept of Physics Univ of Mass 100 Arlington St Boston MA 02116

LYONS, EDWARD ARTHUR, b Halifax, NS, Mar 15, 43; m 67; c 1. RADIOLOGY, ULTRASOUND. *Educ:* Univ Man, BSc, 63, MD, 68; FRCP(C), 73. *Prof Exp:* DIR, ULTRASOUND SECT, HEALTH SCI CTR, WINNIPEG, 73-, ST BONIFACE HOSP, 73-; ASSOC PROF MED, UNIV MAN, 76- *Mem:* Am Inst Ultrasound in Med; Can Asn Radiologists. *Res:* Long term effects of ultrasound; immunological effects of ultrasound. *Mailing Add:* Ultrasound Sect 700 William Ave Winnipeg MB R3E OZ3 Can

LYONS, EUGENE T, b Yankton, SDak, May 6, 31. PARASITOLOGY. *Educ:* SDak State Univ, BS, 56; Kans State Univ, MS, 58; Colo State Univ, PhD(parasitol), 63. *Prof Exp:* Asst prof, 58-60 & 63-70, assoc prof, 70-77, PROF PARASITOL, UNIV KY, 77- *Mem:* Am Soc Parasitol; Wildlife Dis Asn. *Res:* Parasites of jackrabbits, fur seals, horses, sheep and cattle. *Mailing Add:* Dept Vet Sci Animal Path Bldg Univ Ky Lexington KY 40546

LYONS, GEORGE D, b New Orleans, La, Jan 19, 28; m 54; c 5. OTOLARYNGOLOGY. *Educ:* Southeastern La Col, BS, 50; La State Univ, New Orleans, MD, 54. *Prof Exp:* From clin instr to clin assoc prof, 58-70, assoc prof, 70-71, PROF OTOLARYNGOL & HEAD DEPT, SCH MED, LA STATE UNIV, NEW ORLEANS, 71-, PROF BIOCOMMUN, 77- *Concurrent Pos:* Mem, Soc Acad Chmn Otolaryngol, 72- *Honors & Awards:* Recognition Award, AMA. *Mem:* Fel Am Laryngol, Rhinol & Otol Soc; fel Am Acad Facial Plastic & Reconstruct Surg; fel Am Col Surg; fel Pan-Am Soc Otolaryngol. *Res:* Regional plastic surgery; otology. *Mailing Add:* Dept of Otolaryngol 1542 Tulane Ave New Orleans LA 70112

LYONS, HAROLD, b New York, NY, Mar 27, 19; m 41; c 3. ANALYTICAL CHEMISTRY, MOLECULAR PATHOLOGY. *Educ:* City Col New York, BS, 45; Okla State Univ, MS, 49, PhD(chem), 51. *Prof Exp:* Chemist, Climax Rubber Co, 37-41; res chemist, Ruberoid Co, 45-48; sr res chemist, Gen Elec Co, 51-52 & Pa Salt Mfg Co, 52-55; lab mgr, Koppers Co, Inc, 55-58; assoc prof, 58-60, PROF CHEM, SOUTHWESTERN AT MEMPHIS, 60-; PROF PATH, MED UNITS, UNIV TENN, MEMPHIS, 63- *Mem:* AAAS; Am Chem Soc. *Res:* Instrumental analysis; forensic toxicology; analytical biochemistry; biophysical chemistry. *Mailing Add:* Dept of Chem Southwestern at Memphis Memphis TN 38112

LYONS, HAROLD ALOYSIUS, b Brooklyn, NY, Sept 14, 31; m 40; c 8. MEDICINE. *Educ:* St Johns Univ, NY, BS, 35; Long Island Col Med, MD, 40; Am Bd Internal Med, dipl, 50. *Prof Exp:* Intern, Brooklyn Hosp, 40-41; asst clin prof med, Long Island Col Med, 46-50; asst prof, Col Med, Georgetown Univ, 50-52; clin asst prof, 52-53, assoc prof, 53-56, dir pulmonary dis div & cardiovasc lab, 70-76, PROF MED, COL MED, STATE UNIV NY DOWNSTATE MED CTR, 56- *Concurrent Pos:* Consult, Hosps, 52; dir, Pulmonary Dis Div, Kings County Hosp Ctr, 53-; med adv, Security Serv Admin, USPHS, 62-; mem exec comt cardiopulmonary coun, Am Heart Asn. *Mem:* AAAS; Am Thoracic Soc; Harvey Soc; fel AMA; Am Heart Asn. *Res:* Internal medicine; cardiopulmonary physiology; pulmonary diseases; biomedical engineering; mechanics of respiration; ventilation-perfusion relationships. *Mailing Add:* Dept of Med Pulmonary Div State Univ NY Downstate Med Ctr Brooklyn NY 11203

LYONS, HAROLD DWIGHT, synthetic organic chemistry, see previous edition

LYONS, JAMES EDWARD, b Montpelier, Vt, Oct 20, 37; m 63; c 2. ORGANIC CHEMISTRY, ORGANOMETALLIC CHEMISTRY. *Educ:* Boston Col, BS, 59; Purdue Univ, MS, 61; Univ Calif, Davis, PhD(org chem), 68. *Prof Exp:* Chemist, Res & Develop Ctr, Gen Elec Co, 62-64; res chemist, 68-74, sr res chemist, 74-77, GROUP LEADER, SUN CO, 77- *Mem:* AAAS; Am Chem Soc; NY Acad Sci. *Res:* Mechanisms and synthetic applications of transition metal catalyzed reactions in organic and organometallic systems. *Mailing Add:* Res & Eng Div Sun Co Marcus Hook PA 19061

LYONS, JAMES MARTIN, b Livermore, Calif, Oct 9, 29; m 52; c 2. PLANT PHYSIOLOGY. *Educ:* Univ Calif, Berkeley, BS, 51; Univ Calif, Davis, MS, 58, PhD(plant physiol), 62. *Prof Exp:* Asst plant physiologist, Univ Calif, Riverside, 62-66, vchmn dept veg crops, 64-66, asst prof, 65-66, assoc prof, chmn dept & assoc plant physiologist, 66-70; chmn, Dept Veg Crops, 70-73, assoc dean, Col Biol & Agr Sci, 73-81, PROF VEG CROPS & PLANT PHYSIOLOGIST, UNIV CALIF, DAVIS, 70-, ASST DIR, EXP STA, 81- *Mem:* AAAS; Am Soc Hort Sci; Am Soc Plant Physiol; Int Soc Hort Sci. *Res:* Biochemistry and physiology of fruit ripening; low temperature biology and chilling injury in vegetable crops. *Mailing Add:* Col of Biol & Agr Sci Univ of Calif Davis CA 95616

LYONS, JOHN BARTHOLOMEW, b Quincy, Mass, Nov 22, 16; m 45; c 5. GEOLOGY. *Educ:* Harvard Univ, AB, 38, AM, 39, PhD(geol), 42. *Prof Exp:* Geologist, US Geol Surv, 41-45; asst prof, 46-52, PROF GEOL, DARTMOUTH COL, 52- *Mem:* Fel Geol Soc Am; Mineral Soc Am. *Res:* Petrology; structural geology; glaciology. *Mailing Add:* Dept of Earth Sci Dartmouth Col Hanover NH 03755

LYONS, JOHN WINSHIP, b Reading, Mass, Nov 5, 30; m 53; c 4. PHYSICAL CHEMISTRY. *Educ:* Harvard Univ, AB, 52; Washington Univ, AM, 63, PhD(phys chem), 64. *Prof Exp:* Prof chemist, Monsanto Co, 55-73; dir, Ctr Fire Res, Nat Bur Standards, 73-77; DIR, NAT ENG LAB, 77- *Concurrent Pos:* Chmn, Prod Res Comt, 74-; mem adv comt eng, NSF & adv coun, Col Eng, Univ Md. *Honors & Awards:* Gold Medal Award, US Dept Com, 77; Presidential Mgt Improv Award, President, US, 78. *Mem:* Fel AAAS; Am Chem Soc (pres, 73); Sigma Xi. *Res:* Phosphorus compounds; rheology; fire and fire retardants; surface chemistry; polyelectrolytes; solution behavior of DNA. *Mailing Add:* Nat Eng Lab Tech Bldg B-100 Washington DC 20234

LYONS, JOSEPH F, b Wappingers Falls, NY, Nov 27, 20; m 46; c 6. PETROLEUM CHEMISTRY, ALTERNATE FEEDSTOCKS. *Educ:* Fordham Univ, BS, 41; Purdue Univ, MS, 48, PhD(chem), 50. *Prof Exp:* Chemist, 41-46, 50-53, group leader, 53-60, res supvr, 60-73, ASST MGR, TEXACO, INC, 73- *Mem:* Am Chem Soc; Sigma Xi. *Mailing Add:* Texaco Res Ctr Box 509 Beacon NY 12508

LYONS, JOSEPH PAUL, b Ardmore, Pa, Dec 9, 47; m 70; c 1. OPERATIONS RESEARCH, PUBLIC HEALTH ADMINISTRATION. *Educ:* Bloomsburg State Col, BA, 70; Johns Hopkins Univ, ScD, 75. *Prof Exp:* Syst analyst ment health, Pa Off Ment Health, 70-71; SCIENTIST ALCOHOLISM, RES INST ALCOHOLISM, 75- *Concurrent Pos:* Nat Inst Ment Health trainee, Johns Hopkins Univ, 71-75; assoc consult, Elliott Assocs, 71-74; admin consult, Md Dept Ment Hyg, 73; asst clin prof, Dept Psychiat, Sch Med & adj asst prof, Dept Indust Eng, Sch Eng, State Univ NY Buffalo, 75- *Mem:* Oper Res Soc Am; AAAS; Asn Ment Health Admin. *Res:* Problem oriented record and its application to alcoholism service delivery; treatment planning in both in-patient and out-patient settings and systems design for delivery of alcoholism services. *Mailing Add:* 357 W 11th St New York NY 10014

LYONS, KENNETH BRENT, b St Louis, Mo, Aug 31, 46; m 68; c 2. SOLID STATE PHYSICS. *Educ:* Univ Okla, BS, 68; Univ Colo, MS, 69, PhD(physics), 73. *Prof Exp:* MEM RES STAFF, BELL TEL LABS, 73- *Mem:* Am Phys Soc. *Res:* Raman and Brillouin light scattering in solids, with emphasis on non-equilibrium phenomena phase transitions and surface effects. *Mailing Add:* 1A126 Bell Tel Labs 600 Mountain Ave Murray Hill NJ 07974

LYONS, LAWRENCE RUBERT, b Culver City, Calif, Oct 31, 46. SPACE PHYSICS. *Educ:* Univ Calif, Los Angeles, BA, 68, MS, 69, PhD(meteorol), 72. *Prof Exp:* Res asst space physics, Dept Meteorol, Univ Calif, Los Angeles, 68-72; resident res assoc, 72-74, PHYSICIST, SPACE ENVIRON LAB, ENVIRON RES LAB, NAT OCEANIC & ATMOSPHERIC ADMIN, 74- *Mem:* Am Geophys Union. *Res:* Magnetospheric physics. *Mailing Add:* Space Environ Lab R43 Nat Oceanic & Atmospheric Admin Boulder CO 80303

LYONS, NANCY I, b Akron, Ohio, Sept 17, 46. ECOLOGICAL STATISTICS. *Educ:* Kent State Univ, BS, 68, MA, 70; NC State Univ, PhD(statist), 75. *Prof Exp:* Statistician, Res Triangle Inst, 74-75; asst prof, 75-81, ASSOC PROF STATIST, UNIV GA, 81- *Mem:* Am Statist Asn. *Res:* Development of statistical methods for comparing ecological species diversity indices based on importance values. *Mailing Add:* Dept Statist & Comput Sci Univ Ga Athens GA 30602

LYONS, PAUL CHRISTOPHER, b Cambridge, Mass, Oct 1, 38; m 63; c 4. MINERALOGY, PETROLOGY. *Educ:* Boston Univ, AB, 63, AM, 64, PhD(geol), 69. *Prof Exp:* Pub sch teacher, Mass, 64-68; instr, Boston Univ, 68-69, asst prof phys sci, Boston Univ, 69-75. *Concurrent Pos:* Res grants, Boston Univ, 71-72 & Mineral Soc Gt Brit; lectr, Lowell Technol Inst, 72 & Boston Univ Metrop Col, 72-73. *Mem:* AAAS; Geol Soc Am; Am Asn Petrol Geologist. *Res:* Geology of granites, eastern Massachusetts and Rhode Island; Pennsylvanian stratigraphy plant megafossils of New England. *Mailing Add:* 2060 Royal Fern Ct #2A Reston VA 22091

LYONS, PETER BRUCE, b Hammond, Ind, Feb 23, 43; m 63; c 3. PLASMA PHYSICS. *Educ:* Univ Ariz, BS, 64; Calif Inst Technol, PhD(physics), 69. *Prof Exp:* Staff mem, 69-76, assoc group leader, 76-77, alt group leader, 77-79, GROUP LEADER, LOS ALAMOS NAT LAB, 79- *Mem:* Am Phys Soc; Optical Soc Am; Laser Inst Am; Inst Elec & Electronics Eng. *Res:* X-ray interactions and dosimetry; high intensity monoenergetic x-ray generation; x-ray and nuclear detectors and instrumentation; low energy nuclear physics; fiber optic technology; plasma diagnostics; accelerator technology; plastic scintillators. *Mailing Add:* Group P-14 MS-410 Los Alamos Nat Lab Los Alamos NM 87545

LYONS, PETER FRANCIS, b Philadelphia, Pa, Nov 29, 42; m 68; c 3. PHYSICAL CHEMISTRY, POLYMER SCIENCE. *Educ:* Villanova Univ, BS, 64; Princeton Univ, MA, 67, PhD(chem), 70. *Prof Exp:* res chemist, 68-71, sr res chemist, 71-73, mkt rep, 73-78, mkt supvr, 78-80, BUS STRATEGIST, TEXTILE FIBERS DEPT, E I DU PONT DE NEMOURS & CO, INC, 80- *Mem:* Am Chem Soc. *Res:* Physical chemistry of polymeric systems including work on degradation, strength mechanisms and viscosity theory. *Mailing Add:* Textile Fibers Dept E I du Pont de Nemours & Co Inc Wilmington DE 19898

LYONS, PHILIP AUGUSTINE, b Lancashire, Eng, May 26, 16; US citizen; m 49; c 4. PHYSICAL CHEMISTRY. *Educ:* La Salle Col, BA, 37; Univ Wis, PhD(chem), 48. *Prof Exp:* From instr to assoc prof, 48-65, PROF CHEM, YALE UNIV, 65- *Concurrent Pos:* Consult, Audiotape Corp; vis prof, Univ Islamabad, WPakistan, 71. *Res:* Raman spectra; nonaqueous solutions; diffusion in liquids; Soret effect; critical solution phenomena. *Mailing Add:* Dept of Chem Yale Univ New Haven CT 06520

LYONS, W(ILLIS) CARSON, mechanical & aeronautical engineering, see previous edition

LYONS, WALTER ANDREW, b Brooklyn, NY, June 14, 43. METEOROLOGY, AIR POLLUTION. *Educ:* St Louis Univ, BS, 64; Univ Chicago, MS, 65, PhD(meteorol), 70. *Prof Exp:* Prof meteorol, Univ Wis-Milwaukee, 69-76; PRES, MESOMET INC, 78- *Concurrent Pos:* Mem energy budget panel, Int Field Year for Great Lakes, 68-73; chmn comn on meterol aspects of air pollution, Am Meteorol Soc, 73-75; adj prof dept mech eng, Univ Minn, Minneapolis, 76- mem, NASA sci adv coun, 78- *Mem:* Am Meteorol Soc; Am Geophys Union; Air Pollution Control Asn; Int Asn Gt Lakes Res. *Res:* Air pollution meteorology, especially the effect of small scale features, such as cities and lakes, on the regional transport of pollutants; study using aircraft, balloons, ground networks, photography and satellites. *Mailing Add:* Mesomet Inc 35 E Wacker Suite 3330 Chicago IL 60601

LYRENE, PAUL MAGNUS, b Ala, Apr 16, 46. PLANT BREEDING. *Educ:* Auburn Univ, BS, 68; Univ Wis, MS, 70, PhD(plant breeding), 74. *Prof Exp:* asst prof agron, 74-77, ASST PROF HORT, UNIV FLA EXP STA, 77- *Mem:* Am Soc Hort Sci. *Res:* Blueberry variety improvement; blueberry interspecific hybridization; blueberry cytogenetics and polyploidy; Zizyphus (Chinese date) investigations. *Mailing Add:* Dept of Fruit Crops Univ of Fla Gainesville FL 32611

LYS, JEREMY EION ALLEYNE, b Dannevirke, NZ, Apr 17, 38; m 68; c 2. HIGH ENERGY PHYSICS. *Educ:* Univ Canterbury, BSc, 58, MSc, 60; Oxford Univ, PhD:physics), 64; Mitchell Col, New South Wales, DipEd, 74. *Prof Exp:* Res fel physics, Univ Liverpool, 63-65; res assoc physics, Univ Mich, 66-72; sch teacher sci, De la Salle Col, New South Wales, 72-74; res assoc physics, Fermi Nat Accelerator Lab, 75-77; PHYSICIST, LAWRENCE BERKELEY LAB, 77- *Res:* High energy physics. *Mailing Add:* Bldg 50B-5239 Lawrence Berkeley Lab Berkeley CA 94720

LYSEN, JOHN C, b Benson, Minn, Sept 2, 31; m 58; c 2. MECHANICAL ENGINEERING. *Educ:* St Olaf Col, BA, 53; Iowa State Univ, BS, 58, PhD(mech & aerospace eng), 62. *Prof Exp:* Instr mech eng, Iowa State Univ, 58-60, asst prof, 60-63; assoc prof, 63-66, res coord, Col Eng, 66-68, prof mech & aerospace eng, 68-76, DIR ENG EXP STA, UNIV MO-COLUMBIA, 76- *Mem:* AAAS; Am Soc Mech Eng; Am Soc Eng Educ. *Res:* Flow characteristics in converging passages, particularly axially-symmetric annular passages with rotating center bodies. *Mailing Add:* Eng Exp Sta Univ of Mo Columbia MO 65201

LYSER, KATHERINE MAY, b Berkeley, Calif, May 11, 33; m 65. NEUROEMBRYOLOGY; ONCOLOGY. *Educ:* Oberlin Col, AB, 55, Radcliffe Col, MA, 57, PhD(biol), 60. *Prof Exp:* Instr zool, Oberlin Col, 57-58; NSF fel exp embryol, Col France, 60-61; res fel, Med Col, Cornell Univ, 61-62, instr anat, 62-64; asst prof, Sch Med & Dent, Georgetwon Univ, 64-65; from asst prof to assoc prof, 65-76, PROF BIOL SCI, HUNTER COL CITY UNIV NY, 76- *Concurrent Pos:* Part-time fac mem, Sarah Lawrence Col, 61-62; USPHS res grants, Med Col, Cornell Univ, 63 & Hunter Col, 65-70; United Cerebral Palsy Res & Educ Found grant, Cornell Univ & Georgetown Univ, 64-65; guest investr, P A Weiss Lab, Rockefeller Univ, 67-70; fac res award, City Univ New York, 76-82. *Mem:* Int Soc Develop Neurosci; Am Soc Zool; Am Asn Anat; Soc Neurosci; Soc Develop Biol. *Res:* Factors controlling differentiation in the embryonic nervous system and in human neuroblastomas; cytology of normal nervous system and neural tumors. *Mailing Add:* Box 1030 Dept of Biol Sci Hunter Col 695 Park Ave New York NY 10021

LYSIAK, RICHARD JOHN, b Chicago, Ill, Dec 29, 28; m 53; c 2. PHYSICS. *Educ:* Aeronaut Univ, Chicago, BSAE, 50; Tex Christian Univ, BA, 59, MA, 60, PhD(physics), 63. *Prof Exp:* Sr aerosyst engr, Gen Dynamics/Ft Worth, 54-61; teaching fel, 61-63, asst prof, 63-67, ASSOC PROF PHYSICS, TEX CHRISTIAN UNIV, 67-, CHMN DEPT, 69-, DIR PRE-ENG PROG, 77- *Res:* Quantum electronics; optics; random noise theory. *Mailing Add:* Dept of Physics Tex Christian Univ Fort Worth TX 76129

LYSMER, JOHN, b Copenhagen, Denmark, Aug 18, 31; US citizen. EARTHQUAKE ENGINEERING, SOIL DYNAMICS. *Educ:* Tech Univ Denmark, MSc, 54; Univ Mich, PhD(civil eng), 65. *Prof Exp:* Civil engr, Ove Arup & Partners, London, 55-61; PROF SOIL MECH, UNIV CALIF, BERKELEY, 65- *Concurrent Pos:* Eng consult, 65-; Thomas Middlebrooks Award, Am Soc Civil Engrs, 67, Walter Huber Civil Eng Prize, 76. *Mem:* Am Soc Civil Engrs; Seismol Soc Am; Earthquake Eng Res Inst. *Res:* Theoretical soil mechanics and dynamics; developed computer codes for seismic response analysis of earth dams and soil-structure interaction analysis. *Mailing Add:* 440 Davis Hall Univ Calif Berkeley CA 94720

LYSNE, PETER C, b Milwaukee, Wis, July 20, 39; m 62; c 2. APPLIED PHYSICS. *Educ:* Grinnell Col, BA, 61; Ariz State Univ, PhD(physics), 66. *Prof Exp:* STAFF MEM, SHOCK PHYSICS RES, SANDIA LABS, 66- *Mem:* Am Phys Soc. *Res:* Thermodynamics and its relation to shock physics; shock propagation in solid, liquid and porous media; shock-wave induced depolarization of ferroelectrics. *Mailing Add:* Sandia Labs Albuquerque NM 87115

LYSTER, MARK ALLAN, b Kalamazoo, Mich, Jan 5, 53; m 75; c 2. ORGANIC CHEMISTRY. *Educ:* Albion Col, BA, 75; Univ Calif, Los Angeles, PhD(org chem), 79. *Prof Exp:* RES CHEMIST, UPJOHN CO, 79- *Mem:* Am Chem Soc. *Res:* Developing processes to produce bulk quantities of prospective new drugs. *Mailing Add:* Upjohn Co Unit 7965 Bldg 91 7171 Portage Rd Kalamazoo MI 49001

LYSYJ, IHOR, b Tarnow, Poland, Apr 13, 29; nat US; m 57; c 2. ANALYTICAL CHEMISTRY, ENVIRONMENTAL TECHNOLOGY. *Educ:* Ukrainian Tech Inst, Ger, MS, 50. *Prof Exp:* Anal chemist, Ex-Lax, Inc, NY, 52-54; dir res, Gaston Johnston Corp, 54-56; anal chemist, Cent Res Lab, Food Mach & Chem Corp, 56-60; res scientist, Ethicon, Inc, 60-61; PRIN SCIENTIST, ROCKETDYNE DIV, ROCKWELL INT CORP, 61- *Mem:* Am Chem Soc. *Res:* Microchemistry; chemical detection and sensing technology; environmental quality monitoring systems and networks. *Mailing Add:* 8485 Carla Lane Canoga Park CA 91304

LYTLE, CARL DAVID, b Millersburg, Ohio, Jan 28, 41; c 2. BIOPHYSICS. *Educ:* Kent State Univ, BS, 63; Cornell Univ, MS, 65; Pa State Univ, PhD(biophys), 68. *Prof Exp:* Res biophysicist, Bur Radiol Health, USPHS, 68-70, chief path studies sect, 70, chief path studies sect, Environ Protection Agency, 70-71, chief mult environ stresses br, 71-74, MEM STAFF, BUR RADIOL HEALTH, FOOD & DRUG ADMIN, 74- *Concurrent Pos:* Adj prof, George Washington Univ, 71- *Mem:* AAAS; Am Soc Photobiol; Bioelectromagnetics Soc. *Res:* Radiation virology, oncology; host cell reactivation; induced repair induced mutagenesis; ultraviolet carcinogenesis. *Mailing Add:* Bur of Radiol Health 5600 Fishers Lane Rockville MD 20852

LYTLE, CHARLES FRANKLIN, b Crawfordsville, Ind, May 13, 32; m 55; c 5. ZOOLOGY. *Educ:* Wabash Col, AB, 53; Ind Univ, MA, 58, PhD(zool), 59. *Prof Exp:* Asst zool, Ind Univ, 53-55, 57-58, res assoc, 59-60; asst prof, Tulane Univ, 60-62; res analyst, US Govt, 63-64; from asst prof to assoc prof zool, Pa State Univ, 64-69; assoc prof, 69-72, PROF ZOOL, NC STATE UNIV, 72-, COORDR BIOL SCI PROG, 69- *Concurrent Pos:* Fel embryol, Ind Univ, 59; consult, US Dept Army, 62-63 & Educ Testing Serv, 69-; res assoc, NC Mus of Natural Hist, 77- *Mem:* Fel AAAS; Am Soc Zool; Am Inst Biol Sci; Sigma Xi; Asn Southeastern Biologists. *Res:* Invertebrate zoology; cell biology; cellular structure and function in invertebrate development; differentiation and regulation of cellular organelles; systematics and ecology of Hydrozoa; biological education; instructional television. *Mailing Add:* Dept Biol Sci N C State Univ PO Box 50328 Raleigh NC 27650

LYTLE, DEAN WINTON, b Long Beach, Calif, May 23, 27; m 55; c 4. ELECTRICAL ENGINEERING. *Educ:* Univ Calif, BS, 50; Stanford Univ, MS, 54, PhD(elec eng), 57. *Prof Exp:* Electronic scientist, US Navy Electronics Lab, Calif, 50-53; asst elec eng, Stanford Univ, 53-57; asst prof, Robert Col, Turkey, 57-58; assoc prof, 58-69, PROF ELEC ENG, UNIV WASH, 69- *Concurrent Pos:* Consult, Aerospace Div, Boeing Co, 59- & Seattle Develop Lab, Honeywell, Inc, 63- *Mem:* Inst Elec & Electronics Engrs. *Res:* Information and communication theory. *Mailing Add:* Col of Eng Univ of Wash Seattle WA 98195

LYTLE, FARREL WAYNE, b Cedar City, Utah, Nov 10, 34; m 54; c 4. SOLID STATE PHYSICS. *Educ:* Univ Nev, BS, 56, MS, 58. *Prof Exp:* Chemist, US Bur Mines, 55-58; sr basic res scientist, Boeing Sci Res Labs, 60-74, PRIN RES SCIENTIST, BOEING CO, 74-; PRES, EXAFS CO, 74- *Honors & Awards:* Warren Diffractrition Physics Award, Am Crystallog Asn, 79. *Mem:* AAAS; Am Phys Soc; fel Am Inst Chem. *Res:* X-ray physics, x-ray absorbtion fine structure spectroscopy and diffraction; x-ray astronomy; radiation chemistry; cryogenics; structural inorganic chemistry; amorphous structures; structure of catalysts. *Mailing Add:* 10815 24th Ave S Seattle WA 98168

LYTLE, FRED EDWARD, b Lewisburg, Pa, Jan 13, 43; m 67; c 1. CHEMISTRY. *Educ:* Juniata Col, BS, 64; Mass Inst Technol, PhD(chem), 68. *Prof Exp:* From asst prof to assoc prof, 68-74, PROF CHEM, PURDUE UNIV, WEST LAFAYETTE, 79- *Honors & Awards:* Merck Co Found Fac Develop Award, 69. *Mem:* Am Chem Soc; Soc Appl Spectros. *Res:* Time resolved spectroscopy; trace analysis; use of lasers in applied spectroscopy. *Mailing Add:* Dept of Chem Purdue Univ West Lafayette IN 47907

LYTLE, IVAN M, physiology, deceased

LYTLE, LOY DENHAM, b Glendale, Calif, Apr 8, 43; m 74; c 2. PSYCHOPHARMACOLOGY, NEUROSCIENCES. *Educ:* Univ Calif, Santa Barbara, BA, 66; Princeton Univ, PhD(psychoi), 70. *Prof Exp:* NIMH fel neuropharmacol, Mass Inst Technol, 70-72, asst prof psychopharmacol, 72-77; ASSOC PROF PSYCHOPHARMACOL, UNIV CALIF, SANTA BARBARA, 77- *Concurrent Pos:* Alfred P Sloan fel neurosci, 75. *Mem:* Am Soc Pharmacol & Exp Therapeut; Nutrit Soc; Int Soc Develop Psychobiol; Neurosci Soc; AAAS. *Res:* Effects of drugs on physiological and behavioral development; diet and drug induced changes in behavior; effects of drugs on brain and peripheral neurotransmitters. *Mailing Add:* Dept of Psychol Univ of Calif Santa Barbara CA 93106

LYTLE, RAYMOND ALFRED, b Spartanburg, SC, Sept 23, 19; m 44; c 4. MATHEMATICS. *Educ:* Wofford Col, BS, 40; Univ Va, MA, 46; Univ Ga, PhD, 55. *Prof Exp:* Instr math, Univ Va, 42-46; adj prof, 46-56, ASSOC PROF MATH, UNIV SC, 56- *Concurrent Pos:* Researcher, Univ Ga, 52- *Mem:* Am Math Soc; Math Asn Am. *Res:* Topology. *Mailing Add:* Dept of Math Univ of SC Columbia SC 29208

LYTTON, BERNARD, b London, Eng, June 28, 26; m; c 4. UROLOGY. *Educ:* Univ London, MB, BS, 48; FRCS, 55. *Prof Exp:* House officer med & surg, London Hosp, 55-61; from asst prof to assoc prof urol, 62-71, PROF UROL, SCH MED, YALE UNIV, 71-, CHIEF SECT UROL, 67- *Concurrent Pos:* Brit Empire Cancer res fel surg, Univ Hosp, King's Col, Univ London, 61-62; USPHS grant; resident surg, Royal Victoria Hosp, McGill Univ, 57-58; attend, Yale-New Haven Hosp, 62-; consult, West Haven Vet Admin Hosp, 62- & Hartford Hosp & Hosp of St Raphael, 68- *Mem:* AAAS; fel Am Col Surg; Soc Pelvic Surg; Am Asn Genito-Urinary Surg; Asn Univ Urol. *Res:* Immunologic aspects of cancer; delayed hypersensitivity response to autogenous tumor extracts; effects of pressure on infections; renal responses to alterations in bladder pressure; compensatory renal growth in parabiotic animals and effects of hemodialysis. *Mailing Add:* 789 Howard Ave New Haven CT 06510

LYTTON, JACK L(ESTER), b Los Angeles, Calif, Aug 4, 33; m 54; c 4. MATERIALS SCIENCE, METALLURGY. *Educ:* Univ Calif, Berkeley, BS, 56, MS, 57; Stanford Univ, PhD(mat sci), 62. *Prof Exp:* Res engr, Inst Eng Res, Univ Calif, Berkeley, 56-57; res scientist, Lockheed Missiles & Space Co, 60-65; PROF METALL ENG, VA POLYTECH INST & STATE UNIV, 65- *Mem:* Am Soc Metals; Am Inst Mining, Metall & Petrol Engrs. *Res:* Mechanical behavior of solids, recovery and creep at high temperatures; plastic flow and fracture; failure analysis; structure-property relationships; electronmicroscopy. *Mailing Add:* Dept of Mat Eng Col of Eng Va Polytech Inst & State Univ Blacksburg VA 24061

LYZNICKI, EDWARD PETER, JR, organic chemistry, see previous edition